...ISING

The **2020 Harris Directories** provides you with the most up-to-date information on the region's most prominent companies. Through offering you multiple ways to look up any specific business within the area, important data can easily be located.
. For reliability and assurance, Harris directories are the source for all pertinent information for all companies in there state.

To **Highlight** your company and get the most exposure necessary you can now get full page color advertisements inserted in the front of the book. This gives your company a step up showing all your company's information while remaining competitive with the larger companies. These ad pages are supplied by you and can showcase your company logo's, shareholder letters or any other information you would like the thousands of readers who use the Harris Directories to see.

You also get **complimentary** books highlighting your company's information and you can also purchase extra books at a 40% discount.

Plan 1

$1,500

1 full page 4 color ad. (Supplied by you)

DISCARD

3 free books (Additional books can be purchased at a 40% discount of regular price)

Plan 2

$2,100

2 full page 4 color ads. (Supplied by you)

5 free books (Additional books can be purchased at a 40% discount of regular price)

Plan 3

$4,000

4 full page color ads. (Supplied by you)

10 Free Book (Additional books can be purchased at 40% discount off original costs)

For additional information or to order please contact

Thomas Wecera at 212-413-7726 thomas.wecera@mergent.com

2021

Harris

Texas

Manufacturers Directory

MERGENT

Exclusive Provider of
Dun & Bradstreet Library Solutions

dun & bradstreet

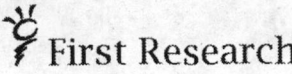

Published May 2021 next update May 2022

Publisher

Mergent Inc.
444 Madison Ave
New York, NY 10022

©Mergent Inc All Rights Reserved
2021 Mergent Business Press
ISSN 1080-2614
ISBN 978-1-64972-087-8

TABLE OF CONTENTS

SUMMARY OF CONTENTS

Number of Companies 20,985
Number of Decision Makers 52,425
Minimum Number of Employees 9

EXPLANATORY NOTES

How to Cross-Reference in This Directory

Sequential Entry Numbers. Each establishment in the Geographic Section is numbered sequentially (G-0000). The number assigned to each establishment is referred to as its "entry number." To make cross-referencing easier, each listing in the Geographic, SIC, Alphabetic and Product Sections includes the establishment's entry number. To facilitate locating an entry in the Geographic Section, the entry numbers for the first listing on the left page and the last listing on the right page are printed at the top of the page next to the city name.

Source Suggestions Welcome

Although all known sources were used to compile this directory, it is possible that companies were inadvertently omitted. Your assistance in calling attention to such omissions would be greatly appreciated. A special form on the facing page will help you in the reporting process.

Analysis

Every effort has been made to contact all firms to verify their information. The one exception to this rule is the annual sales figure, which is considered by many companies to be confidential information. Therefore, estimated sales have been calculated by multiplying the nationwide average sales per employee for the firm's major SIC/NAICS code by the firm's number of employees. Nationwide averages for sales per employee by SIC/NAICS codes are provided by the U.S. Department of Commerce and are updated annually. All sales—sales (est)—have been estimated by this method. The exceptions are parent companies (PA), division headquarters (DH) and headquarter locations (HQ) which may include an actual corporate sales figure—sales (corporate-wide) if available.

Types of Companies

Descriptive and statistical data are included for companies in the entire state. These comprise manufacturers, machine shops, fabricators, assemblers and printers. Also identified are corporate offices in the state.

Employment Data

This directory contains companies with 9 or more employees in the manufacturing industry. The employment figure shown in the Geographic Section includes male and female employees and embraces all levels of the company: administrative, clerical, sales and maintenance. This figure is for the facility listed and does not include other plants or offices. It should be recognized that these figures represent an approximate year-round average. These employment figures are broken into codes A through G and used in the Product and SIC Sections to further help you in qualifying a company. Be sure to check the footnotes on the bottom of pages for the code breakdowns.

Standard Industrial Classification (SIC)

The Standard Industrial Classification (SIC) system used in this directory was developed by the federal government for use in classifying establishments by the type of activity they are engaged in. The SIC classifications used in this directory are from the 1987 edition published by the U.S. Government's Office of Management and Budget. The SIC system separates all activities into broad industrial divisions (e.g., manufacturing, mining, retail trade). It further subdivides each division. The range of manufacturing industry classes extends from two-digit codes (major industry group) to four-digit codes (product).

For example:

Industry Breakdown	Code	Industry, Product, etc.
*Major industry group	20	Food and kindred products
Industry group	203	Canned and frozen foods
*Industry	2033	Fruits and vegetables, etc.

*Classifications used in this directory

Only two-digit and four-digit codes are used in this directory.

Arrangement

1. The **Geographic Section** contains complete in-depth corporate data. This section is sorted by cities listed in alphabetical order and companies listed alphabetically within each city. A County/City Index for referencing cities within counties precedes this section.

IMPORTANT NOTICE: It is a violation of both federal and state law to transmit an unsolicited advertisement to a facsimile machine. Any user of this product that violates such laws may be subject to civil and criminal penalties, which may exceed $500 for each transmission of an unsolicited facsimile. Mergent Inc. provides fax numbers for lawful purposes only and expressly forbids the use of these numbers in any unlawful manner.

2. The **Standard Industrial Classification (SIC) Section** lists companies under approximately 500 four-digit SIC codes. An alphabetical and a numerical index precedes this section. A company can be listed under several codes. The codes are in numerical order with companies listed alphabetically under each code.

3. The **Alphabetic Section** lists all companies with their full physical or mailing addresses and telephone number.

4. The **Product Section** lists companies under unique Harris categories. An index preceding this section lists all product categories in alphabetical order. Companies can be listed under several categories.

USER'S GUIDE TO LISTINGS

GEOGRAPHIC SECTION

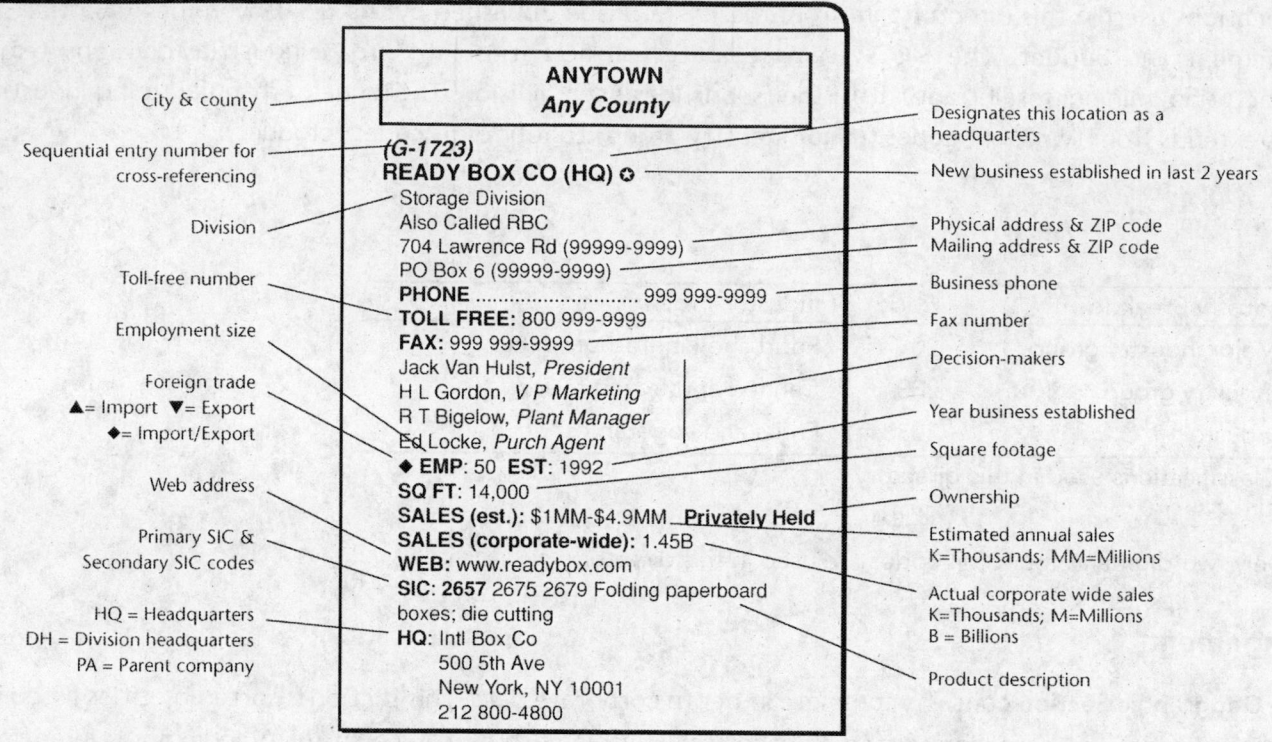

City & county

Sequential entry number for cross-referencing

Division

Toll-free number

Employment size

Foreign trade
▲= Import ▼= Export
◆= Import/Export

Web address

Primary SIC & Secondary SIC codes

HQ = Headquarters
DH = Division headquarters
PA = Parent company

ANYTOWN
Any County

(G-1723)
READY BOX CO (HQ) ✪
Storage Division
Also Called RBC
704 Lawrence Rd (99999-9999)
PO Box 6 (99999-9999)
PHONE 999 999-9999
TOLL FREE: 800 999-9999
FAX: 999 999-9999
Jack Van Hulst, *President*
H L Gordon, *V P Marketing*
R T Bigelow, *Plant Manager*
Ed Locke, *Purch Agent*
◆ **EMP:** 50 **EST:** 1992
SQ FT: 14,000
SALES (est.): $1MM-$4.9MM **Privately Held**
SALES (corporate-wide): 1.45B
WEB: www.readybox.com
SIC: 2657 2675 2679 Folding paperboard boxes; die cutting
HQ: Intl Box Co
500 5th Ave
New York, NY 10001
212 800-4800

Designates this location as a headquarters

New business established in last 2 years

Physical address & ZIP code
Mailing address & ZIP code

Business phone

Fax number

Decision-makers

Year business established

Square footage

Ownership

Estimated annual sales
K=Thousands; MM=Millions

Actual corporate wide sales
K=Thousands; M=Millions
B = Billions

Product description

SIC SECTION

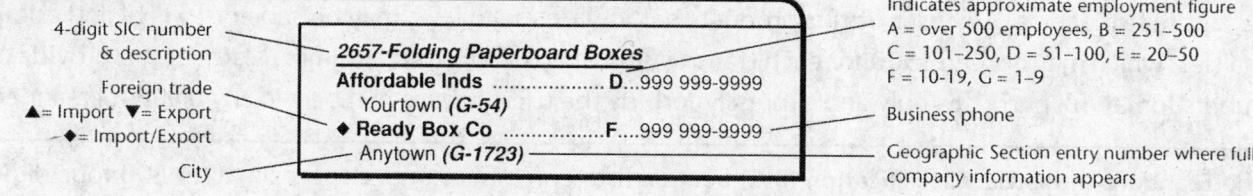

4-digit SIC number & description

Foreign trade
▲= Import ▼= Export
◆= Import/Export

City

2657-Folding Paperboard Boxes
Affordable Inds .... **D**...999 999-9999
Yourtown *(G-54)*
◆ **Ready Box Co** .... **F**....999 999-9999
Anytown *(G-1723)*

Indicates approximate employment figure
A = over 500 employees, B = 251–500
C = 101–250, D = 51–100, E = 20–50
F = 10-19, G = 1–9

Business phone

Geographic Section entry number where full company information appears

ALPHABETIC SECTION

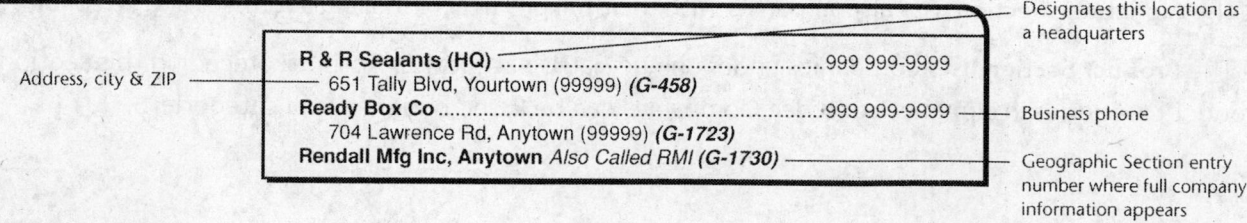

Address, city & ZIP

R & R Sealants (HQ) 999 999-9999
651 Tally Blvd, Yourtown (99999) *(G-458)*
Ready Box Co 999 999-9999
704 Lawrence Rd, Anytown (99999) *(G-1723)*
Rendall Mfg Inc, Anytown *Also Called RMI (G-1730)*

Designates this location as a headquarters

Business phone

Geographic Section entry number where full company information appears

PRODUCT SECTION

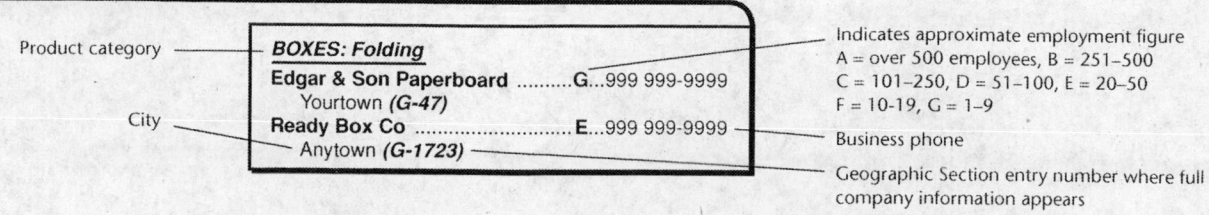

Product category

City

BOXES: Folding
Edgar & Son Paperboard ....**G**...999 999-9999
Yourtown *(G-47)*
Ready Box Co ....**E**...999 999-9999
Anytown *(G-1723)*

Indicates approximate employment figure
A = over 500 employees, B = 251–500
C = 101–250, D = 51–100, E = 20–50
F = 10-19, G = 1–9

Business phone

Geographic Section entry number where full company information appears

GEOGRAPHIC SECTION

Companies sorted by city in alphabetical order

In-depth company data listed

STANDARD INDUSTRIAL CLASSIFICATIONS

Alphabetical index of classifcation descriptions

Numerical index of classifcation descriptions

Companies sorted by SIC product groupings

ALPHABETIC SECTION

Company listings in alphabetical order

PRODUCT INDEX

Product categories listed in alphabetical order

PRODUCT SECTION

Companies sorted by product and manufacturing service classifications

GEOGRAPHIC

SIC

ALPHABETIC

PRDT INDEX

PRODUCT

Texas
County Map

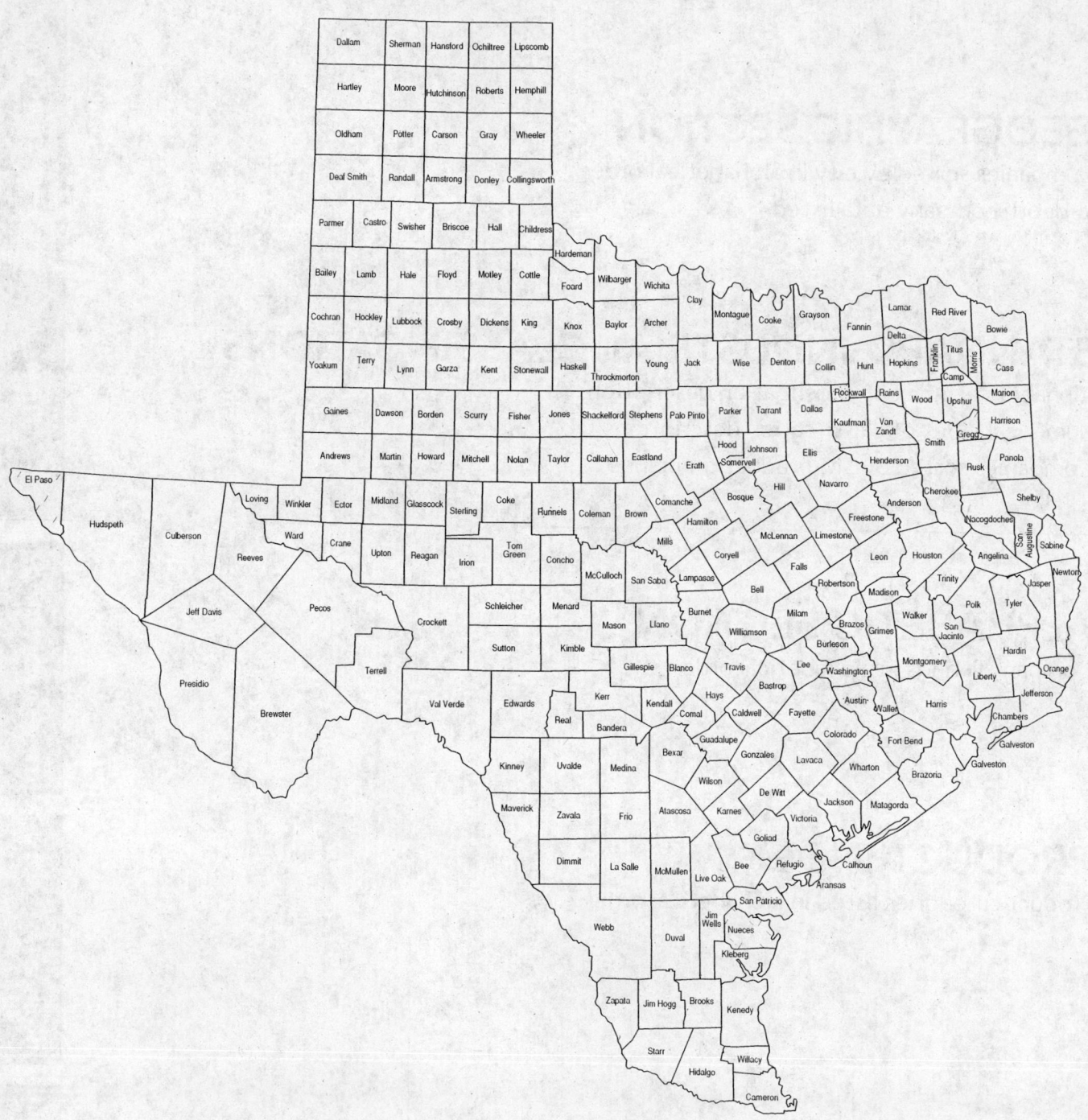

COUNTY/CITY CROSS-REFERENCE INDEX

	ENTRY #		ENTRY #		ENTRY #		ENTRY #		ENTRY #

Dimmit
Asherton .... (G-814)
Big Wells .... (G-2104)
Carrizo Springs........ (G-2683)
Catarina .... (G-2933)

Donley
Clarendon .... (G-3070)

Duval
Benavides .... (G-2035)
Freer .... (G-7222)
San Diego .... (G-18669)

Eastland
Carbon .... (G-2682)
Cisco .... (G-3066)
Eastland .... (G-5561)
Gorman .... (G-7771)
Olden .... (G-16219)
Ranger .... (G-17231)
Rising Star .... (G-17478)

Ector
Gardendale .... (G-7420)
Goldsmith .... (G-7741)
Odessa .... (G-15897)

Edwards
Rocksprings............. (G-17533)

El Paso
Anthony .... (G-588)
Canutillo .... (G-2662)
Clint .... (G-3147)
El Paso .... (G-5630)
Fort Bliss................. (G-6317)
Horizon City .... (G-8361)
Socorro .... (G-19016)
Vinton .... (G-20340)

Ellis
Ennis .... (G-6087)
Ferris .... (G-6229)
Italy .... (G-13213)
Midlothian .... (G-15475)
Milford .... (G-15500)
Red Oak .... (G-17236)
Waxahachie............. (G-20526)

Erath
Dublin .... (G-5514)
Stephenville............. (G-19406)

Falls
Marlin...................... (G-14759)

Fannin
Bonham .... (G-2152)
Honey Grove .... (G-8357)
Leonard .... (G-14001)
Randolph .... (G-17230)
Ravenna .... (G-17234)
Savoy .... (G-18741)
Telephone .... (G-19665)
Trenton .... (G-20016)

Fayette
Ellinger .... (G-6062)
Flatonia .... (G-6233)
La Grange .... (G-13693)
Schulenburg .... (G-18770)
Warda .... (G-20513)

Fisher
Rotan...................... (G-17618)

Floyd
Floydada .... (G-6292)

Fort Bend
Beasley.................... (G-1840)
Fresno .... (G-7236)
Fulshear .... (G-7327)
Houston .... (G-8369)
Katy .... (G-13347)
Missouri City .... (G-15575)
Needville .... (G-15762)
Orchard .... (G-16272)
Richmond .... (G-17449)
Rosenberg .... (G-17575)
Stafford .... (G-19279)
Sugar Land .... (G-19436)

Franklin
Mount Vernon .... (G-15666)

Freestone
Fairfield .... (G-6168)
Streetman .... (G-19434)
Teague.................... (G-19664)
Wortham .... (G-20922)

Frio
Dilley .... (G-5480)
Pearsall .... (G-16612)

Gaines
Loop .... (G-14340)
Seagraves .... (G-18803)
Seminole .... (G-18880)

Galveston
Bacliff...................... (G-1732)
Dickinson .... (G-5468)
Friendswood .... (G-7241)
Galveston .... (G-7387)
Hitchcock .... (G-8333)
Kemah .... (G-13471)
La Marque .... (G-13704)
League City .... (G-13944)
Port Bolivar .... (G-17134)
Santa Fe................. (G-18733)
Texas City .... (G-19785)

Garza
Post .... (G-17190)

Gillespie
Fredericksburg.......... (G-7168)
Harper .... (G-8209)
Stonewall .... (G-19430)
Willow City .... (G-20870)

Glasscock
Garden City .... (G-7417)

Goliad
Goliad .... (G-7746)

Gonzales
Gonzales .... (G-7748)
Harwood .... (G-8212)
Nixon .... (G-15866)
Waelder .... (G-20482)

Gray
Pampa .... (G-16314)

Grayson
Bells .... (G-2005)
Denison .... (G-5334)
Gordonville .... (G-7770)
Gunter .... (G-8115)

Howe .... (G-12734)
Pottsboro .... (G-17197)
Sherman .... (G-18904)
Tom Bean .... (G-19951)
Van Alstyne .... (G-20211)
Whitesboro .... (G-20727)
Whitewright............. (G-20728)

Gregg
Gladewater .... (G-7716)
Kilgore .... (G-13529)
Longview .... (G-14186)
White Oak .... (G-20712)

Grimes
Anderson .... (G-529)
Bedias .... (G-1981)
Iola .... (G-12900)
Navasota .... (G-15725)
Plantersville .... (G-17058)

Guadalupe
Cibolo .... (G-3060)
Kingsbury .... (G-13620)
Marion .... (G-14755)
Mc Queeney .... (G-14828)
Schertz .... (G-18742)
Seguin .... (G-18822)
Selma .... (G-18876)

Hale
Abernathy .... (G-2)
Hale Center .... (G-8118)
Petersburg .... (G-16652)
Plainview .... (G-16751)

Hall
Memphis .... (G-14999)

Hamilton
Hamilton .... (G-8164)
Hico .... (G-8302)

Hansford
Spearman .... (G-19085)

Hardeman
Quanah .... (G-17217)

Hardin
Batson .... (G-1766)
Kountze .... (G-13668)
Lumberton .... (G-14566)
Saratoga .... (G-18740)
Silsbee .... (G-18949)
Sour Lake .... (G-19033)
Village Mills .... (G-20337)

Harris
Barker .... (G-1745)
Baytown .... (G-1806)
Bellaire .... (G-1990)
Channelview .... (G-3012)
Crosby .... (G-3725)
Cypress .... (G-3769)
Deer Park .... (G-5258)
Galena Park .... (G-7376)
Highlands .... (G-8311)
Hockley .... (G-8341)
Houston .... (G-8398)
Humble .... (G-12742)
Jersey Village .... (G-13291)
Katy .... (G-13386)
Kingwood .... (G-13637)
La Porte .... (G-13715)
Mont Belvieu .... (G-15620)

Pasadena .... (G-16375)
Seabrook .... (G-18784)
South Houston........ (G-19036)
Spring .... (G-19097)
The Woodlands .... (G-19819)
Tomball .... (G-19952)
Waller .... (G-20489)
Webster .... (G-20632)

Harrison
Hallsville .... (G-8126)
Marshall .... (G-14760)
Scottsville .... (G-18781)
Waskom .... (G-20514)

Hartley
Channing .... (G-3045)
Hartley .... (G-8211)

Haskell
Haskell .... (G-8213)
O Brien .... (G-15888)
Rule .... (G-17728)

Hays
Austin .... (G-856)
Buda .... (G-2519)
Creedmoor.............. (G-3705)
Driftwood .... (G-5498)
Dripping Springs ... (G-5501)
Kyle .... (G-13677)
San Marcos .... (G-18676)
Wimberley............... (G-20881)

Hemphill
Canadian .... (G-2647)

Henderson
Athens .... (G-818)
Brownsboro .... (G-2333)
Gun Barrel City .... (G-8114)
Malakoff .... (G-14634)
Murchison .... (G-15680)
Poynor .... (G-17201)

Hidalgo
Alamo .... (G-177)
Alton .... (G-321)
Donna .... (G-5486)
Edinburg .... (G-5573)
Elsa .... (G-6079)
Hargill .... (G-8171)
Hidalgo .... (G-8304)
McAllen.................. (G-14831)
Mercedes .... (G-15001)
Mission .... (G-15547)
Palmview .... (G-16310)
Penitas .... (G-16629)
Pharr .... (G-16694)
San Juan .... (G-18670)
Sullivan City .... (G-19577)
Weslaco .... (G-20659)

Hill
Abbott .... (G-1)
Covington .... (G-3694)
Hillsboro................. (G-8320)
Hubbard .... (G-12737)
Itasca .... (G-13215)
Malone .... (G-14638)
Whitney .... (G-20730)

Hockley
Levelland .... (G-14003)
Sundown .... (G-19610)

Hood
Cresson .... (G-3706)
Granbury .... (G-7791)

Hopkins
Como .... (G-3247)
Saltillo .... (G-17766)
Sulphur Springs........ (G-19578)

Houston
Crockett .... (G-3716)
Grapeland .... (G-8005)
Kennard .... (G-13494)
Latexo .... (G-13941)
Lovelady .... (G-14355)

Howard
Big Spring .... (G-2067)
Coahoma .... (G-3164)

Hudspeth
Fort Hancock .... (G-6321)

Hunt
Caddo Mills............. (G-2623)
Campbell .... (G-2645)
Commerce .... (G-3241)
Greenville .... (G-8061)
Lone Oak .... (G-14179)
McKinney .... (G-14993)
Quinlan .... (G-17223)
Wolfe City .... (G-20906)

Hutchinson
Borger .... (G-2161)
Stinnett .... (G-19427)

Irion
Mertzon .... (G-15019)

Jack
Jacksboro .... (G-13217)
Jermyn .... (G-13290)

Jackson
Edna .... (G-5606)
Ganado .... (G-7415)
Lolita .... (G-14173)

Jasper
Brookeland .... (G-2308)
Buna .... (G-2559)
Evadale .... (G-6167)
Jasper .... (G-13275)

Jeff Davis
Fort Davis .... (G-6318)

Jefferson
Beaumont .... (G-1846)
Groves .... (G-8109)
Nederland .... (G-15746)
Port Arthur .... (G-17101)
Port Neches............. (G-17157)

Jim Hogg
Hebbronville............. (G-8234)

Jim Wells
Alice .... (G-203)
Orange Grove......... (G-16268)
Premont .... (G-17203)

Johnson
Alvarado .... (G-323)
Burleson .... (G-2565)
Cleburne .... (G-3079)
Godley .... (G-7734)

	ENTRY #
Grandview	(G-8001)
Joshua	(G-13316)
Keene	(G-13465)
Rio Vista	(G-17477)
Venus	(G-20217)

Jones

Anson	(G-587)
Hamlin	(G-8170)
Hawley	(G-8230)
Lueders	(G-14517)
Stamford	(G-19402)

Karnes

Falls City	(G-6182)
Karnes City	(G-13346)
Kenedy	(G-13488)
Runge	(G-17729)

Kaufman

Crandall	(G-3696)
Forney	(G-6301)
Kaufman	(G-13456)
Kemp	(G-13483)
Mabank	(G-14575)
Scurry	(G-18782)
Terrell	(G-19728)

Kendall

Bergheim	(G-2049)
Boerne	(G-2113)
Comfort	(G-3238)

Kerr

Kerrville	(G-13516)

Kimble

Junction	(G-13337)

Kleberg

Kingsville	(G-13623)

Knox

Knox City	(G-13662)

La Salle

Cotulla	(G-3689)
Encinal	(G-6086)
Fowlerton	(G-7161)

Lamar

Blossom	(G-2112)
Brookston	(G-2328)
Paris	(G-16357)
Powderly	(G-17198)
Reno	(G-17251)
Sumner	(G-19606)

Lamb

Littlefield	(G-14144)
Olton	(G-16226)

Lampasas

Kempner	(G-13486)
Lampasas	(G-13832)
Lometa	(G-14178)

Lavaca

Hallettsville	(G-8119)
Shiner	(G-18939)
Yoakum	(G-20957)

Lee

Dime Box	(G-5484)
Giddings	(G-7690)

Leon

Buffalo	(G-2542)
Centerville	(G-3011)
Jewett	(G-13307)
Oakwood	(G-15892)

Liberty

Cleveland	(G-3118)
Daisetta	(G-3832)
Dayton	(G-5220)
Hull	(G-12741)
Liberty	(G-14114)
Mont Belvieu	(G-15622)
Old River Winfree	(G-16218)
Raywood	(G-17235)

Limestone

Coolidge	(G-3407)
Groesbeck	(G-8107)
Kosse	(G-13666)
Mexia	(G-15086)
Thornton	(G-19943)

Lipscomb

Booker	(G-2157)
Darrouzett	(G-5214)

Live Oak

George West	(G-7623)
Three Rivers	(G-19944)

Llano

Buchanan Dam	(G-2517)
Horseshoe Bay	(G-8366)
Kingsland	(G-13621)

Lubbock

Idalou	(G-12889)
Lubbock	(G-14356)
Shallowater	(G-18890)
Slaton	(G-18968)
Wolfforth	(G-20907)

Lynn

Tahoka	(G-19641)

Madison

Madisonville	(G-14584)
Midway	(G-15499)
North Zulch	(G-15884)

Marion

Jefferson	(G-13283)

Martin

Stanton	(G-19403)

Mason

Mason	(G-14812)
Pontotoc	(G-17098)

Matagorda

Bay City	(G-1767)
Palacios	(G-16292)

Maverick

Eagle Pass	(G-5547)
Quemado	(G-17222)

Mcculloch

Brady	(G-2211)
Rochelle	(G-17522)
Voca	(G-20344)

Mclennan

Axtell	(G-1718)
Crawford	(G-3704)
Elm Mott	(G-6063)
Hewitt	(G-8299)
Lorena	(G-14341)
Mc Gregor	(G-14820)
Riesel	(G-17470)
Robinson	(G-17500)
Ross	(G-17617)
Waco	(G-20353)
West	(G-20672)
Woodway	(G-20921)

Mcmullen

Tilden	(G-19947)

Medina

Castroville	(G-2926)
D Hanis	(G-3828)
Devine	(G-5449)
Hondo	(G-8353)
La Coste	(G-13690)
Mico	(G-15094)

Menard

Menard	(G-15000)

Midland

Midland	(G-15099)

Milam

Cameron	(G-2639)
Rockdale	(G-17523)

Mills

Goldthwaite	(G-7744)

Mitchell

Colorado City	(G-3223)

Montague

Bowie	(G-2189)
Forestburg	(G-6299)
Nocona	(G-15868)
Saint Jo	(G-17762)
Sunset	(G-19624)

Montgomery

Conroe	(G-3251)
Cut and Shoot	(G-3768)
Magnolia	(G-14591)
Montgomery	(G-15624)
New Caney	(G-15834)
Oak Ridge North	(G-15889)
Pinehurst	(G-16733)
Porter	(G-17170)
Shenandoah	(G-18895)
Splendora	(G-19096)
Spring	(G-19190)
Stagecoach	(G-19401)
The Woodlands	(G-19822)
Willis	(G-20841)

Moore

Cactus	(G-2622)
Dumas	(G-5519)
Sunray	(G-19616)

Morris

Daingerfield	(G-3830)
Lone Star	(G-14180)
Naples	(G-15719)

Motley

Matador	(G-14816)
Roaring Springs	(G-17497)

Nacogdoches

Cushing	(G-3767)
Garrison	(G-7611)
Nacogdoches	(G-15684)

Navarro

Corsicana	(G-3660)
Rice	(G-17265)

Newton

Bon Wier	(G-2149)
Newton	(G-15864)
Wiergate	(G-20840)

Nolan

Maryneal	(G-14811)
Sweetwater	(G-19629)

Nueces

Bishop	(G-2105)
Corpus Christi	(G-3462)
Port Aransas	(G-17100)
Robstown	(G-17503)

Ochiltree

Farnsworth	(G-6227)
Perryton	(G-16631)

Oldham

Vega	(G-20216)

Orange

Bridge City	(G-2280)
Orange	(G-16229)
Orangefield	(G-16271)
Vidor	(G-20324)
West Orange	(G-20692)

Palo Pinto

Gordon	(G-7769)
Graford	(G-7773)
Mineral Wells	(G-15517)
Santo	(G-18738)
Strawn	(G-19432)

Panola

Beckville	(G-1971)
Carthage	(G-2898)
De Berry	(G-5235)
Gary	(G-7616)
Panola	(G-16349)

Parker

Aledo	(G-196)
Millsap	(G-15501)
Poolville	(G-17099)
Springtown	(G-19271)
Weatherford	(G-20571)
Willow Park	(G-20872)

Parmer

Friona	(G-7251)

Pecos

Coyanosa	(G-3695)
Fort Stockton	(G-6326)
Iraan	(G-12916)

Polk

Camden	(G-2638)
Corrigan	(G-3659)
Goodrich	(G-7768)
Livingston	(G-14150)
Onalaska	(G-16228)

Potter

Amarillo	(G-391)
Bushland	(G-2621)

Presidio

Marfa	(G-14753)

Rains

Emory	(G-6081)
Point	(G-17079)

Randall

Amarillo	(G-476)
Canyon	(G-2669)

Reagan

Big Lake	(G-2054)

Real

Leakey	(G-13983)

Red River

Bagwell	(G-1735)
Bogata	(G-2145)
Clarksville	(G-3072)
Detroit	(G-5448)

Reeves

Pecos	(G-16616)

Refugio

Refugio	(G-17239)

Robertson

Franklin	(G-7163)
Hearne	(G-8231)

Rockwall

Fate	(G-6228)
Rockwall	(G-17534)
Royse City	(G-17714)

Runnels

Ballinger	(G-1739)
Winters	(G-20904)

Rusk

Henderson	(G-8257)
Mount Enterprise	(G-15645)
New London	(G-15849)
Overton	(G-16275)
Tatum	(G-19644)

Sabine

Hemphill	(G-8245)
Pineland	(G-16738)

San Augustine

San Augustine	(G-18650)

San Jacinto

Coldspring	(G-3166)
Oakhurst	(G-15891)
Shepherd	(G-18899)

San Patricio

Aransas Pass	(G-592)
Gregory	(G-8098)
Ingleside	(G-12891)
Mathis	(G-14817)
Odem	(G-15894)
Portland	(G-17185)
Sinton	(G-18960)
Taft	(G-19640)

San Saba

San Saba	(G-18717)

Schleicher

Eldorado	(G-6044)

Scurry

Ira	(G-12912)
Snyder	(G-18982)

Shackelford

Albany	(G-184)

	ENTRY #		ENTRY #		ENTRY #		ENTRY #		ENTRY #
Shelby		Hurst	(G-12831)	**Trinity**		Hempstead	(G-8248)	Jarrell	(G-13268)
Center	(G-2995)	Keller	(G-13466)	Apple Springs	(G-591)	Pattison	(G-16531)	Leander	(G-13984)
Joaquin	(G-13310)	Kennedale	(G-13495)	Groveton	(G-8112)	**Ward**		Liberty Hill	(G-14128)
Shelbyville	(G-18894)	Lake Worth	(G-13812)	Trinity	(G-20019)	Grandfalls	(G-8000)	Round Rock	(G-17620)
Tenaha	(G-19723)	Lakeside	(G-13813)	**Tyler**		Monahans	(G-15599)	Taylor	(G-19646)
Timpson	(G-19948)	Mansfield	(G-14652)	Colmesneil	(G-3222)	Wickett	(G-20839)	Walburg	(G-20488)
Smith		North Richland Hills	(G-15873)	Hillister	(G-8318)	**Washington**		**Wilson**	
Arp	(G-812)	Pantego	(G-16350)	Spurger	(G-19278)	Brenham	(G-2242)	Floresville	(G-6246)
Bullard	(G-2551)	Richland Hills	(G-17434)	Woodville	(G-20914)	Burton	(G-2619)	La Vernia	(G-13800)
Flint	(G-6236)	River Oaks	(G-17479)	**Upshur**		Chappell Hill	(G-3046)	Poth	(G-17195)
Lindale	(G-14132)	Saginaw	(G-17735)	Big Sandy	(G-2064)	**Webb**		Stockdale	(G-19429)
Troup	(G-20022)	Southlake	(G-19057)	Diana	(G-5459)	Bruni	(G-2450)	**Winkler**	
Tyler	(G-20042)	**Taylor**		Gilmer	(G-7705)	Laredo	(G-13852)	Kermit	(G-13508)
Whitehouse	(G-20725)	Abilene	(G-3)	Ore City	(G-16274)	**Wharton**		Wink	(G-20887)
Winona	(G-20903)	Buffalo Gap	(G-2550)	**Upton**		Boling	(G-2146)	**Wise**	
Somervell		Merkel	(G-15014)	Mc Camey	(G-14819)	East Bernard	(G-5557)	Alvord	(G-388)
Glen Rose	(G-7731)	Tye	(G-20041)	Midkiff	(G-15095)	El Campo	(G-5610)	Aurora	(G-853)
Rainbow	(G-17229)	**Terry**		Rankin	(G-17232)	Lane City	(G-13851)	Boyd	(G-2203)
Starr		Brownfield	(G-2329)	**Uvalde**		Louise	(G-14351)	Bridgeport	(G-2288)
Rio Grande City	(G-17471)	**Throckmorton**		Knippa	(G-13661)	Wharton	(G-20698)	Chico	(G-3050)
Stephens		Throckmorton	(G-19946)	Utopia	(G-20187)	**Wheeler**		Decatur	(G-5240)
Breckenridge	(G-2219)	**Titus**		Uvalde	(G-20188)	Shamrock	(G-18891)	Newark	(G-15862)
Stonewall		Cookville	(G-3404)	**Val Verde**		Wheeler	(G-20708)	Paradise	(G-16354)
Aspermont	(G-815)	Mount Pleasant	(G-15646)	Del Rio	(G-5304)	**Wichita**		Rhome	(G-17253)
Sutton		Mt Pleasant	(G-15667)	**Van Zandt**		Burkburnett	(G-2563)	**Wood**	
Sonora	(G-19024)	**Tom Green**		Ben Wheeler	(G-2030)	Electra	(G-6048)	Alba	(G-181)
Swisher		San Angelo	(G-17767)	Canton	(G-2657)	Iowa Park	(G-12902)	Hawkins	(G-8228)
Tulia	(G-20034)	**Travis**		Edgewood	(G-5572)	Sheppard Afb	(G-18902)	Mineola	(G-15506)
Tarrant		Austin	(G-868)	Grand Saline	(G-7997)	Wichita Falls	(G-20734)	Quitman	(G-17228)
Arlington	(G-605)	Del Valle	(G-5329)	Van	(G-20205)	**Wilbarger**		Winnsboro	(G-20895)
Azle	(G-1719)	Jonestown	(G-13314)	Wills Point	(G-20873)	Vernon	(G-20227)	**Yoakum**	
Bedford	(G-1973)	Lago Vista	(G-13804)	**Victoria**		**Willacy**		Denver City	(G-5414)
Benbrook	(G-2036)	Lakeway	(G-13814)	Bloomington	(G-2111)	Lyford	(G-14571)	Tokio	(G-19950)
Colleyville	(G-3210)	Manchaca	(G-14639)	Victoria	(G-20233)	**Williamson**		**Young**	
Crowley	(G-3751)	Manor	(G-14642)	**Walker**		Austin	(G-1689)	Graham	(G-7774)
Euless	(G-6125)	Pflugerville	(G-16655)	Huntsville	(G-12811)	Cedar Park	(G-2957)	Newcastle	(G-15863)
Forest Hill	(G-6294)	Spicewood	(G-19090)	New Waverly	(G-15852)	Coupland	(G-3693)	Olney	(G-16220)
Fort Worth	(G-6333)	Sunset Valley	(G-19626)	Riverside	(G-17480)	Florence	(G-6238)	**Zapata**	
Grapevine	(G-8009)	The Hills	(G-19818)	**Waller**		Georgetown	(G-7631)	Zapata	(G-20979)
Haltom City	(G-8131)	West Lake Hills	(G-20676)	Brookshire	(G-2309)	Hutto	(G-12874)	**Zavala**	
Haslet	(G-8215)							Crystal City	(G-3756)

GEOGRAPHIC SECTION

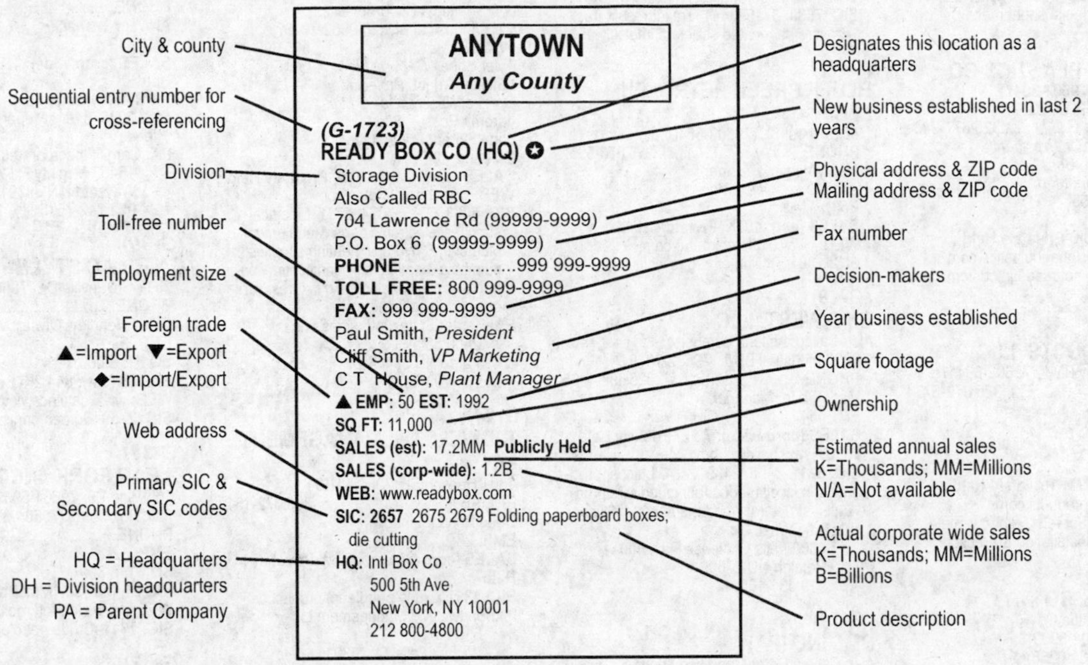

City & county
Sequential entry number for cross-referencing
Division
Toll-free number
Employment size
Foreign trade ▲=Import ▼=Export ◆=Import/Export
Web address
Primary SIC & Secondary SIC codes
HQ = Headquarters
DH = Division headquarters
PA = Parent Company
ANYTOWN
Any County
(G-1723)
READY BOX CO (HQ) ✪
Storage Division
Also Called RBC
704 Lawrence Rd (99999-9999)
P.O. Box 6 (99999-9999)
PHONE.....................999 999-9999
TOLL FREE: 800 999-9999
FAX: 999 999-9999
Paul Smith, President
Cliff Smith, VP Marketing
C T House, Plant Manager
▲ EMP: 50 EST: 1992
SQ FT: 11,000
SALES (est): 17.2MM Publicly Held
SALES (corp-wide): 1.2B
WEB: www.readybox.com
SIC: 2657 2675 2679 Folding paperboard boxes; die cutting
HQ: Intl Box Co
500 5th Ave
New York, NY 10001
212 800-4800
Designates this location as a headquarters
New business established in last 2 years
Physical address & ZIP code
Mailing address & ZIP code
Fax number
Decision-makers
Year business established
Square footage
Ownership
Estimated annual sales K=Thousands; MM=Millions N/A=Not available
Actual corporate wide sales K=Thousands; MM=Millions B=Billions
Product description

See footnotes for symbols and codes identification.

- This section is in alphabetical order by city.
- Companies are sorted alphabetically under their respective cities.
- To locate cities within a county refer to the County/City Cross Reference Index.

IMPORTANT NOTICE: It is a violation of both federal and state law to transmit an unsolicited advertisement to a facsimile machine. Any user of this product that violates such laws may be subject to civil and criminal penalties which may exceed $500 for each transmission of an unsolicited facsimile. Harris InfoSource provides fax numbers for lawful purposes only and expressly forbids the use of these numbers in any unlawful manner.

Abbott
Hill County

(G-1)
WARREN LABORATIES LLC
1656 Ih 35 S (76621-3014)
PHONE.....................................254 580-9990
EMP: 14
SQ FT: 21,000
SALES (est): 5.5MM **Privately Held**
WEB: www.warrenlabsaloe.com
SIC: 2844 Cosmetic preparations; shampoos, rinses, conditioners: hair

Abernathy
Hale County

(G-2)
BURRIS CUSTOM SMOKERS & GRILLS
1480 County Road 315 (79311-6006)
PHONE.....................................806 893-3360
Donney Burris, *Co-Owner*
Jeff Hamilton, *Co-Owner*
EMP: 12
SQ FT: 5,000
SALES (est): 100K **Privately Held**
SIC: 3631 Barbecues, grills & braziers (outdoor cooking)

Abilene
Taylor County

(G-3)
AB-TEX BEVERAGE LTD (DH)
650 Colonial Dr (79603-3104)
P.O. Box 6639 (79608-6639)
PHONE.....................................325 673-7171
Cleber Massey, *CEO*
Kirk Massey, *President*
Russell Smith, *General Mgr*
David Lawrence, *Vice Pres*
EMP: 250
SQ FT: 150,000
SALES (est): 69.6MM
SALES (corp-wide): 67.1B **Publicly Held**
WEB: www.pepsico.com
SIC: 2086 Soft drinks: packaged in cans, bottles, etc.; water, pasteurized: packaged in cans, bottles, etc.
HQ: Pepsi-Cola Metropolitan Bottling Company, Inc.
1111 Westchester Ave
White Plains NY 10604
914 767-6000

(G-4)
ABILENE AG SERVICE & SUP INC (PA)
303 S 14th St (79602-3917)
PHONE.....................................325 677-4371
J W Vinson, *President*
Lanny Ross Vinson, *Vice Pres*
Randell Don Vinson, *Vice Pres*
Monteva Vinson, *Treasurer*
Hope Rowe, *Office Mgr*
EMP: 52
SQ FT: 9,000
SALES (est): 16.8MM **Privately Held**
WEB: www.abileneag.com
SIC: 5191 2874 2048 Fertilizer & fertilizer materials; feed; seeds: field, garden & flower; phosphatic fertilizers; prepared feeds

(G-5)
ABILENE MILL WORK
533 Plum St (79601-5203)
PHONE.....................................325 677-8856
Jeff Luther, *President*
Andrew Valdez, *General Mgr*
Melinda Luther, *Vice Pres*
Eddie Schneider, *Asst Mgr*
Brenna Murray, *Assistant*
EMP: 11
SALES (est): 1.7MM **Privately Held**
WEB: www.abilenemillwork.com
SIC: 2431 Millwork

(G-6)
ABILENE PRINTING & STY CO
1274 N 2nd St (79601-5706)
P.O. Box 1560 (79604-1560)
PHONE.....................................325 677-2673
Patsy F Lacy, *CEO*
Harlan Owen, *President*
Karla Bailey, *Vice Pres*
Sandra Lowe, *Officer*
EMP: 15 **EST:** 1882
SQ FT: 7,800
SALES (est): 7.4MM **Privately Held**
WEB: www.abileneprinting.com
SIC: 5021 2759 Office furniture; commercial printing

(G-7)
ABILENE SHEET METAL INC
1025 Walnut St (79601-4222)
P.O. Box 1318 (79604-1318)
PHONE.....................................325 677-2654
Ronald Mc Millon, *President*
EMP: 10 **EST:** 1934
SQ FT: 13,000
SALES (est): 1.6MM **Privately Held**
WEB: www.mcmillonmechanical.com
SIC: 1711 1761 3444 Warm air heating & air conditioning contractor; plumbing contractors; sheet metalwork; sheet metalwork

(G-8)
ABIMAR FOODS INC
Also Called: Lil' Dutch Maid Cookies
5425 N 1st St (79603-6424)
PHONE.....................................325 691-5425
Miguel Moreno, *President*
Steve Fehr, *President*
Gerardo Duarte, *CFO*
Timea Wichner, *Manager*
◆ **EMP:** 560
SQ FT: 500,000
SALES (est): 147.9MM **Privately Held**
WEB: www.abimarfoods.com
SIC: 2099 Food preparations
PA: Grupo Nutresa S A
Carrera 43 A 1 A Sur 143
Medellin

(G-9)
ACCURATE AIR SOLUTIONS LLC
6737 E I 20 Abilene (79601)
P.O. Box 5817 (79608-5817)
PHONE.....................................325 672-2966
Tony Phelps, *Owner*

EMP: 22 **EST:** 2013
SALES (est): 3.5MM **Privately Held**
SIC: 1711 1731 3444 Warm air heating & air conditioning contractor; general electrical contractor; ducts, sheet metal

(G-10)
ACME SIGN & PLASTICS CO
1225 Walnut St (79601-3647)
P.O. Box 2977 (79604-2977)
PHONE..................................325 677-9469
David Mc Meekan Jr, *President*
Linda Mc Meekan, *Corp Secy*
Robert Kern, *Opers Mgr*
EMP: 11 **EST:** 1955
SQ FT: 9,000
SALES (est): 950K **Privately Held**
WEB: www.acmesignandplastics.com
SIC: 3993 Signs, not made in custom sign painting shops

(G-11)
AIRTITE PRODUCTS LLC
4008 S Treadaway Blvd (79602-6941)
PHONE..................................325 672-5774
Robert Hoemke,
Paulley Howmke,
EMP: 10 **EST:** 1975
SQ FT: 14,000
SALES (est): 1.4MM **Privately Held**
WEB: www.airtiteproducts.com
SIC: 3442 1751 Screens, window, metal; window & door installation & erection

(G-12)
ALEXANDER & CO
Also Called: Jma Cattle Co
155 Pine St (79601-5909)
P.O. Box 58 (79604-0058)
PHONE..................................325 677-1309
James Alexander, *Owner*
EMP: 20
SQ FT: 7,500
SALES (est): 1.7MM **Privately Held**
SIC: 1382 0211 Oil & gas exploration services; beef cattle feedlots

(G-13)
APANI SOUTHWEST INC
5401 N 1st St (79603-6424)
P.O. Box 12031, Lubbock (79452-2031)
PHONE..................................325 690-1550
Arden Hawkins, *President*
Jay Pickens, *President*
EMP: 20
SALES (est): 3.4MM **Privately Held**
WEB: www.apanisw.com
SIC: 2086 Water, pasteurized: packaged in cans, bottles, etc.

(G-14)
ATLAS OILFIELD CNSTR CO LLC (PA)
2 Village Dr Ste 207 (79606-8237)
PHONE..................................325 428-0552
Gary Morrison,
Jody Finley,
EMP: 12
SALES (est): 78.1MM **Privately Held**
SIC: 1382 Oil & gas exploration services

(G-15)
BANYAN INTERNATIONAL CORP
2118 E I 20 (79601)
PHONE..................................888 782-8548
Jim Breckenridge, *President*
Michael Breckenridge, *Vice Pres*
Mike Breckenridge, *Vice Pres*
John W Michener Jr, *CFO*
Eric Morgan, *Representative*
▼ **EMP:** 25
SQ FT: 20,000
SALES (est): 4.1MM **Privately Held**
WEB: www.healthfirst.com
SIC: 3841 2834 Surgical & medical instruments; pharmaceutical preparations

(G-16)
BEALL CONSTRUCTION COMPANY INC
Also Called: Tiger Manufacturing
2631 Fm 3034 (79601-8301)
PHONE..................................325 677-2112
Joe Allen Beall, *President*
Marilyn Beall, *Vice Pres*
Cade Wilkerson, *Manager*

EMP: 85
SQ FT: 10,000
SALES (est): 8.3MM **Privately Held**
WEB: www.tigermfgco.com
SIC: 7539 3715 3441 Trailer repair; truck trailers; fabricated structural metal

(G-17)
BLUFF CREEK PETROLEUM LLC
4625 N 1st St (79603-6540)
PHONE..................................325 676-5557
Monty Vogler, *President*
Alice Grice, *Office Mgr*
EMP: 11
SALES (est): 400K **Privately Held**
WEB: www.bluffcreekpetro.com
SIC: 1381 Drilling oil & gas wells

(G-18)
BMC WEST LLC
Also Called: Abilene Lumber
2025 Industrial Blvd (79602-7839)
PHONE..................................325 698-4465
Mark White, *Manager*
EMP: 54
SALES (corp-wide): 7.2B **Publicly Held**
WEB: www.buildwithbmc.com
SIC: 5211 3496 2439 2431 Lumber products; miscellaneous fabricated wire products; structural wood members; millwork
HQ: Bmc West, Llc
  4800 Falls Of Neuse Rd # 400
  Raleigh NC 27609
  919 431-1000

(G-19)
BML INC (PA)
Also Called: Berry Marketing Logistics
4841 Hill St (79602-7854)
P.O. Box 5061 (79608-5061)
PHONE..................................325 676-3355
Dean Berry, *Vice Pres*
Greg Berry, *Vice Pres*
Ray Berry, *Vice Pres*
Mike Wilcox, *Opers Mgr*
Chuck Holloway, *Buyer*
EMP: 27
SALES (est): 98.4MM **Privately Held**
WEB: www.bmloil.com
SIC: 5172 1389 Crude oil; construction, repair & dismantling services

(G-20)
BMLCRUDE INC
4841 Hill St (79602-7854)
P.O. Box 5061 (79608-5061)
PHONE..................................325 676-3355
Berry Powel, *President*
David Lynn, *CFO*
Greg Berry, *VP Mktg*
EMP: 11
SALES (est): 1.2MM **Privately Held**
WEB: www.bmloil.com
SIC: 1381 Drilling oil & gas wells

(G-21)
BOEING COMPANY
426 3rd St Bldg 7008 (79607-1526)
P.O. Box 9577 (79607-0577)
PHONE..................................325 696-5771
EMP: 14
SALES (corp-wide): 58.1B **Publicly Held**
WEB: www.boeing.com
SIC: 3721 Aircraft
PA: The Boeing Company
  100 N Riverside Plz
  Chicago IL 60606
  312 544-2000

(G-22)
BOOKSTORE MANAGER SOFTWARE
201 Fannin St (79603-7118)
PHONE..................................325 673-2826
Randy Voorhees, *President*
Trudy Box, *Vice Pres*
Brent Casey, *Vice Pres*
Shane Price, *Vice Pres*
Brent Cassey, *VP Opers*
EMP: 30
SQ FT: 14,000
SALES (est): 3.1MM **Privately Held**
WEB: www.bsmgr.com
SIC: 7372 5942 Business oriented computer software; book stores

(G-23)
BORDER STATES INDUSTRIES INC
Nunn Elc Sup A Div Brder Sttes
2250 Industrial Blvd (79602-7846)
PHONE..................................325 698-4595
Tyler Soper, *General Mgr*
Lindsay Wright, *Project Mgr*
Sondra Walters, *Opers Mgr*
Jeremy Rosser, *Site Mgr*
John Floren, *Purch Agent*
EMP: 11
SALES (corp-wide): 2.4B **Privately Held**
WEB: www.borderstates.com
SIC: 5063 5065 5074 1711 Electrical supplies; electronic parts & equipment; plumbing & hydronic heating supplies; plumbing, heating, air-conditioning contractors; plastics plumbing fixtures; vitreous plumbing fixtures
PA: Border States Industries, Inc.
  2400 38th St S
  Fargo ND 58104
  701 293-5834

(G-24)
BRIDWELL OIL MANAGEMENT LLC
1801 Henson St (79603-1107)
PHONE..................................325 672-1512
Doug Bond, *Manager*
EMP: 25
SALES (corp-wide): 5.5MM **Privately Held**
SIC: 1311 Crude petroleum production
PA: Bridwell Oil Management Llc
  810 8th St
  Wichita Falls TX 76301
  940 723-4351

(G-25)
BROADWIND HVY FABRICATIONS INC
Also Called: Abilene Heavy Industries
1126 N Arnold Blvd (79603-5224)
PHONE..................................325 437-5950
Don Fran, *Branch Mgr*
Carlos Kernz, *Maintence Staff*
EMP: 15 **Publicly Held**
WEB: www.bwen.com
SIC: 3621 Motors & generators
HQ: Broadwind Heavy Fabrications, Inc.
  101 S 16th St
  Manitowoc WI 54220
  920 482-3529

(G-26)
BWJ METALWORKS LLC
3125 E Us Highway 80 (79601-6409)
P.O. Box 3853 (79604-3853)
PHONE..................................325 672-4909
Bob W Johnson, *Mng Member*
EMP: 56
SALES (est): 141.1K **Privately Held**
WEB: www.bwjmetalworks.com
SIC: 3441 Fabricated structural metal

(G-27)
BYRD OILFIELD SERVICES LLC (PA)
4725 Loop 322 (79602-8057)
PHONE..................................325 690-0053
Clint Concord, *Sales Staff*
Teddy Jordan, *Sales Staff*
Justin Paredez, *Sales Staff*
Robert Rodriguez, *Sales Staff*
Mike Byrd, *Mng Member*
▲ **EMP:** 21
SALES (est): 22MM **Privately Held**
WEB: www.byrdoilfield.com
SIC: 1389 Perforating well casings

(G-28)
CABINETTECH INC
3557 E Us Highway 80 (79601-6417)
PHONE..................................325 670-0414
Joey Newman, *President*
EMP: 10
SQ FT: 18,300
SALES (est): 710K **Privately Held**
SIC: 2599 2511 2434 Factory furniture & fixtures; wood household furniture; wood kitchen cabinets

(G-29)
CARGILL INCORPORATED
1025 China St (79602-2723)
PHONE..................................325 672-3271
Al Ward, *Manager*
EMP: 39
SALES (corp-wide): 113.4B **Privately Held**
WEB: www.cargill.com
SIC: 2048 5191 Prepared feeds; animal feeds
PA: Cargill, Incorporated
  15407 Mcginty Rd W
  Wayzata MN 55391
  952 742-7575

(G-30)
CATTILAC STYLE
2317 S Danville Dr (79605-6412)
PHONE..................................325 695-6263
Cindy Hendley, *Owner*
EMP: 9
SQ FT: 8,000
SALES (est): 844.2K **Privately Held**
WEB: www.cattilacstyle.com
SIC: 2759 Screen printing

(G-31)
CLEAR FORK INCORPORATED
155 Pine St (79601-5909)
P.O. Box 3095 (79604-3095)
PHONE..................................325 677-1309
EMP: 12
SQ FT: 5,800
SALES (est): 8.1MM **Privately Held**
WEB: www.clearforkroofing.com
SIC: 1311 Crude petroleum production

(G-32)
CLOUD PRINTING CO OF ABILENE
858 N 1st St (79601-5902)
P.O. Box 3777 (79604-3777)
PHONE..................................325 676-9396
Lyndon Cloud, *President*
EMP: 9
SQ FT: 20,000
SALES (est): 1.3MM **Privately Held**
WEB: www.cloudprinting.com
SIC: 2752 2759 5943 2791 Commercial printing, offset; letterpress printing; office forms & supplies; typesetting; bookbinding & related work

(G-33)
COCA-COLA REFRESHMENTS USA INC
2074 N 1st St (79603-7301)
P.O. Box 1441 (79604-1441)
PHONE..................................325 672-3232
Kelly Knight, *Branch Mgr*
EMP: 65
SALES (corp-wide): 37.2B **Publicly Held**
WEB: www.coca-colacompany.com
SIC: 2086 Bottled & canned soft drinks
HQ: Coca-Cola Refreshments Usa, Inc.
  2500 Windy Ridge Pkwy Se
  Atlanta GA 30339
  770 989-3000

(G-34)
COCA-COLA REFRESHMENTS USA INC
1849 Albany Hwy (79603)
PHONE..................................325 437-5000
Troy Cummins, *Branch Mgr*
EMP: 90
SALES (corp-wide): 37.2B **Publicly Held**
WEB: www.us.coca-cola.com
SIC: 2086 Bottled & canned soft drinks
HQ: Coca-Cola Refreshments Usa, Inc.
  2500 Windy Ridge Pkwy Se
  Atlanta GA 30339
  770 989-3000

(G-35)
CONLEY PRINTING CO INC
2401 Industrial Blvd (79605-7206)
P.O. Box 6606 (79608-6606)
PHONE..................................325 675-5500
James Conley, *President*
Dean Conley, *Vice Pres*
EMP: 14
SQ FT: 8,400

▲ = Import ▼=Export
◆ =Import/Export

SALES (est): 2.2MM **Privately Held**
WEB: www.conleyprinting.com
SIC: **2752** Commercial printing, offset

(G-36)
CONTRACTORS SERVICE LTD (PA)
967 S 25th St (79602-5921)
P.O. Box 5284 (79608-5284)
PHONE.................................325 692-4317
Herman Lloyd, *Owner*
Doris Lloyd, *Vice Pres*
Randy Lloyd, *Vice Pres*
EMP: **10 EST:** 1966
SQ FT: 14,000
SALES (est): 786.5K **Privately Held**
SIC: **3993 2439** Signs, not made in custom sign painting shops; structural wood members

(G-37)
DESERT NDT LLC
6849 E Hwy 80 (79601-7643)
PHONE.................................325 864-6547
Bryan Adams, *Manager*
EMP: 20
SALES (corp-wide): 1.1B **Privately Held**
WEB: www.shawcor.com
SIC: **1389** Oil field services
HQ: Desert Ndt, Llc
   4250 N Sam Houston Pkwy E # 180
   Houston TX 77032
   713 568-3513

(G-38)
DRINK A PAK INC
Also Called: Apani Southwest
5401 N 1st St (79603-6424)
P.O. Box 5282 (79608-5282)
PHONE.................................325 690-1550
James Q Pickens, *President*
Glenda Pickens, *Admin Sec*
EMP: 12
SQ FT: 5,600
SALES (est): 1.5MM **Privately Held**
WEB: www.apanisw.com
SIC: **2899 2086** Distilled water; pasteurized & mineral waters, bottled & canned

(G-39)
DUFFCO OIL TOOLS INC
810 Anson Ave (79601-1657)
P.O. Box 2360 (79604-2360)
PHONE.................................325 672-2446
EMP: **60 EST:** 2001
SALES (est): 2.7MM **Privately Held**
WEB: www.sojodrilling.com
SIC: **1381** Drilling oil & gas wells

(G-40)
EVANS ENTERPRISES INC
1650 Vision Dr Ste 100 (79602-7866)
PHONE.................................325 235-1776
Justin Guinn, *Division Mgr*
Baugh Dylan, *Branch Mgr*
EMP: 55
SALES (corp-wide): 132.7MM **Privately Held**
WEB: www.goevans.com
SIC: **3625 7629 7699 5084** Relays & industrial controls; electrical repair shops; industrial equipment services; industrial machinery & equipment; motors & generators
PA: Evans Enterprises, Inc.
   6707 N Interstate Dr
   Norman OK 73069
   405 631-1344

(G-41)
FOX NDE (PA)
1102 Energy Dr (79602-7949)
PHONE.................................325 690-1633
Billy Lackay, *Owner*
EMP: 11
SALES (est): 12MM **Privately Held**
WEB: www.iiafieldservices.com
SIC: **1381** Drilling oil & gas wells

(G-42)
FRONTIER CHEMICAL LLC
7551 Us Highway 277 S (79606-6105)
P.O. Box 3234 (79604-3234)
PHONE.................................325 672-0072
Kent Sojouner, *Mng Member*
EMP: 15

SALES (est): 2MM **Privately Held**
WEB: www.frontierchemical.com
SIC: **2819** Industrial inorganic chemicals

(G-43)
GENERAL ELECTRIC COMPANY
162 Caddo Dr Ste 100 (79602-8043)
PHONE.................................325 794-5100
Beth Comstock, *Branch Mgr*
EMP: 9
SALES (corp-wide): 95.2B **Publicly Held**
WEB: www.ge.com
SIC: **6159 3511 3724** Equipment & vehicle finance leasing companies; turbines & turbine generator sets; aircraft engines & engine parts
PA: General Electric Company
   5 Necco St
   Boston MA 02210
   617 443-3000

(G-44)
GOOCH INVESTMENTS INC
Also Called: Absolutely World Class
1250 Canterbury Dr (79602-4258)
P.O. Box 300 (79604-0300)
PHONE.................................325 677-5904
Robert C Gooch, *President*
Lana Zullo, *Treasurer*
Janelle Gooch, *Admin Sec*
EMP: **14 EST:** 1971
SALES (est): 1MM **Privately Held**
WEB: www.absolutelyworldclass.com
SIC: **2033 6726** Barbecue sauce: packaged in cans, jars, etc.; investment offices

(G-45)
H AND L CRIMP INC
8001 Us Highway 277 (79601-0915)
P.O. Box 1091 (79604-1091)
PHONE.................................325 672-9282
Troy Limbaugh, *President*
C W Hunter, *Principal*
Jones Jennifer H, *Director*
EMP: **10 EST:** 1975
SALES (est): 409.6K **Privately Held**
SIC: **1389 3494** Oil field services; valves & pipe fittings

(G-46)
HARTMANNS INC
1221 Fulwiler Rd (79603-5213)
P.O. Box 2154 (79604-2154)
PHONE.................................325 695-7641
Pat Hartmann, *President*
Ronnie Hartmann, *Vice Pres*
Alan Hartmann, *VP Mfg*
EMP: **17 EST:** 1954
SALES (est): 4.9MM **Privately Held**
WEB: www.hartmannsinc.com
SIC: **5013 5084 3533** Automotive engines & engine parts; engines & parts, diesel; oil & gas field machinery

(G-47)
HAYHURST BROS DRILLING CO
12906 County Road 218 (79602-9134)
PHONE.................................325 340-1865
Jay Hayhurst, *President*
Betty Hayhurst, *Shareholder*
EMP: 19
SALES (est): 1.6MM **Privately Held**
WEB: www.hayhurstdrilling.com
SIC: **1381** Directional drilling oil & gas wells

(G-48)
HEART LAND PETROLEUM CORP
Also Called: Heart Land Trucking
1213 E South 11th St A (79602-4282)
P.O. Box 3714 (79604-3714)
PHONE.................................325 437-8430
Terry Goodman, *President*
Becky Goodman, *Admin Sec*
EMP: 90
SQ FT: 500
SALES (est): 14.1MM **Privately Held**
SIC: **1381** Drilling oil & gas wells

(G-49)
HERALD OF TRUTH MINISTRIES
Also Called: Herald Truth Rdo & TV Programs
3444 N 1st St Ste 400 (79603-6940)
P.O. Box 2439 (79604-2439)
PHONE.................................325 698-4370

EMP: **10 EST:** 1952
SALES: 928.4K **Privately Held**
WEB: www.heraldoftruth.org
SIC: **4833 4832 2721 7812** Television broadcasting stations; radio broadcasting stations; magazines: publishing only, not printed on site; motion picture & video production

(G-50)
HIPPLE ICE COMPANY
Also Called: Abilene Ice Company
5513 N 1st St (79603-6426)
PHONE.................................325 692-0101
Marianne Pool, *President*
Randy Pool, *Vice Pres*
EMP: 10
SQ FT: 10,000
SALES (est): 1.1MM **Privately Held**
WEB: www.reddyice.com
SIC: **2097** Manufactured ice

(G-51)
INCOUNTERS INC
2364 Butternut St (79602-5832)
PHONE.................................325 675-5909
Ed Wright, *President*
Rebel Taylor, *Vice Pres*
Susie Stock, *Manager*
EMP: 30
SALES (est): 5.4MM **Privately Held**
WEB: www.incounters.com
SIC: **2542 1751 1799 3281** Counters or counter display cases: except wood; cabinet & finish carpentry; counter top installation; cut stone & stone products; plastics materials & resins; wood partitions & fixtures

(G-52)
INGRAM CONCRETE LLC
Also Called: Morris Ready-Mix Concrete
1801 N Danville Dr (79603-2444)
P.O. Box 1477 (79604-1477)
PHONE.................................325 677-2001
Jeff Roberts, *Partner*
Jerry Roberts, *Partner*
Kyle Ramon, *Site Mgr*
EMP: 28
SQ FT: 5,000
SALES (est): 3.2MM
SALES (corp-wide): 1.4B **Publicly Held**
WEB: www.ingramconcrete.com
SIC: **3273** Ready-mixed concrete
HQ: Childs Ready-Mix Concrete Company
   4301 Danhil Dr
   Brownwood TX 76801
   325 646-6518

(G-53)
J P C PLASTICS INC
Also Called: Hunter Texas Stone
8001 Us Highway 277 (79601-0915)
P.O. Box 3879 (79604-3879)
PHONE.................................325 672-2895
Troy Limbaugh, *President*
Pam Tippen, *Vice Pres*
Carla Limbaugh, *Treasurer*
EMP: 12
SQ FT: 9,600
SALES (est): 1MM **Privately Held**
SIC: **3084 2824** Plastics pipe; organic fibers, noncellulosic

(G-54)
JAMES PURYEAR WELDNG FABRCTN
350 T And P Ln (79602-1826)
PHONE.................................325 672-2009
James Puryear,
Ashley Puryear,
EMP: 12
SQ FT: 5,000
SALES (est): 1.3MM **Privately Held**
WEB: www.jamespuryearwelding.net
SIC: **7692** Welding repair

(G-55)
L C S PRODUCTION COMPANY
74 35 Hwy 277 S (79606)
P.O. Box 6663 (79608-6663)
PHONE.................................325 692-3903
Larry C Smith, *President*
Robert W Cockrell, *Corp Secy*
EMP: 75
SQ FT: 5,000

SALES (est): 6.1MM **Privately Held**
SIC: **1311** Crude petroleum production

(G-56)
LEE DILL INC
Also Called: Tiger Manufacturing
2631 Fm 3034 (79601-8301)
PHONE.................................325 677-0474
H Lee Dill, *President*
Lee Dill, *Principal*
Blake Dill, *Vice Pres*
Debbie Dill, *Vice Pres*
EMP: 80
SQ FT: 60,000
SALES (est): 17.8MM **Privately Held**
WEB: www.tigermfgco.com
SIC: **3715** Truck trailers

(G-57)
LEGACY VULCAN LLC
6301 E Hwy 80 (79601-7637)
PHONE.................................325 676-0001
Tye Bradshaw, *Manager*
EMP: 30 **Publicly Held**
WEB: www.vulcanmaterials.com
SIC: **3273** Ready-mixed concrete
HQ: Legacy Vulcan, Llc
   1200 Urban Center Dr
   Vestavia AL 35242
   205 298-3000

(G-58)
LEGACY VULCAN LLC
Also Called: Southwest Division
14500 County Road 224 (79602-9148)
PHONE.................................325 529-3785
Ron Kelley, *Manager*
EMP: 25 **Publicly Held**
WEB: www.vulcanmaterials.com
SIC: **1442 2951** Construction sand & gravel; asphalt paving mixtures & blocks
HQ: Legacy Vulcan, Llc
   1200 Urban Center Dr
   Vestavia AL 35242
   205 298-3000

(G-59)
MARTIN SPROCKET & GEAR INC
4300 Fm 18 (79602-2018)
P.O. Box 3062 (79604-3062)
PHONE.................................325 677-3591
Jon Patty, *Engineer*
Jim Gibson, *Manager*
EMP: 62
SALES (corp-wide): 539MM **Privately Held**
WEB: www.martinsprocket.com
SIC: **3566 3462 3568** Gears, power transmission, except automotive; iron & steel forgings; sprockets (power transmission equipment)
PA: Martin Sprocket & Gear, Inc.
   3100 Sprocket Dr
   Arlington TX 76015
   817 258-3000

(G-60)
MUELLER SUPPLY COMPANY INC
4625 Fm 18 (79602-2009)
PHONE.................................325 690-7700
Keith Fields, *Principal*
EMP: 60
SALES (corp-wide): 180.3MM **Privately Held**
WEB: www.muellerinc.com
SIC: **3448** Prefabricated metal components
PA: Mueller Supply Company, Inc.
   1913 Hutchins Ave
   Ballinger TX 76821
   325 365-3555

(G-61)
OKELLEY OFFICE SUPPLY INC
290 Cypress St (79601-5892)
PHONE.................................325 673-6422
Carroll E O'Kelley Sr, *President*
Carroll E O'Kelley Jr, *Vice Pres*
Susan O'Kelley, *Vice Pres*
Marilyn Chittum, *Treasurer*
Carolyn Donaldson, *Admin Sec*
EMP: **10 EST:** 1955
SQ FT: 50,000

G E O G R A P H I C

SALES (est): 2.2MM **Privately Held**
WEB: www.okelleyos.com
SIC: **5943** 5021 5044 2752 Office forms & supplies; office furniture; office equipment; commercial printing, offset; office supplies

(G-62)
OWENS MACH & MANUFACTURING
Also Called: Owens Machine & Manufacturing
917 Oil Center Dr (79601-6703)
PHONE...............................325 672-4161
Ginger Owens, *Owner*
Benny Owens, *Co-Owner*
Lanny Owens, *Opers Mgr*
EMP: 15
SQ FT: 17,000
SALES (est): 2MM **Privately Held**
SIC: **3599** 7699 Machine shop, jobbing & repair; welding equipment repair

(G-63)
PASSARE INC
6550 Directors Pkwy (79606-5854)
PHONE...............................325 695-3412
Jay Thomas, *CEO*
Annie Bailey, *Opers Staff*
Kelly Gilgenbach, *Sales Staff*
Kaley Turner, *Sales Staff*
Gilyn Abordo, *Manager*
EMP: 20
SALES (est): 463.1K **Privately Held**
WEB: www.passare.com
SIC: **7372** Business oriented computer software

(G-64)
PERCOMONLINE INCORPORATED
149 N Willis St Ste 10 (79603-6924)
P.O. Box 3744 (79604-3744)
PHONE...............................325 480-2617
Jerry Dinsmore, *General Mgr*
Jane Dinsmore, *Director*
EMP: 18
SALES (est): 827K **Privately Held**
WEB: www.percomonline.com
SIC: **8049** 7372 7389 Paramedic; educational computer software;

(G-65)
PINE STREET SALVAGE CO (PA)
3833 Pine St (79601-1113)
P.O. Box 3543 (79604-3543)
PHONE...............................325 677-8831
Dan Dankworth, *President*
Gregory Dankworth, *Vice Pres*
Caleb Allen, *Opers Mgr*
Sheila Dankworth, *Treasurer*
EMP: 25
SQ FT: 2,500
SALES (est): 7.5MM **Privately Held**
WEB: www.scrapabilene.com
SIC: **5093** 4953 3341 Ferrous metal scrap & waste; recycling, waste materials; secondary nonferrous metals

(G-66)
PRIDE REFINING INC
1209 N 4th St (79601-5729)
PHONE...............................325 677-5444
Brad Stephens, *CEO*
E Peter Cercarian, *Ch of Bd*
EMP: 350
SALES (est): 25.6MM **Privately Held**
SIC: **2911** Petroleum refining

(G-67)
QUAIL WELL SERVICE INC
110 Caddo Dr (79602-8035)
P.O. Box 2557 (79604-2557)
PHONE...............................325 677-0323
EMP: 20 EST: 1973
SALES (est): 3.1MM **Privately Held**
SIC: **1389** 1382 Servicing oil & gas wells; oil & gas exploration services

(G-68)
QUIKRETE COMPANIES LLC
794 Fm 2404 (79601-9208)
PHONE...............................325 672-4634
EMP: 46 **Privately Held**
WEB: www.quikrete.com
SIC: **3272** Dry mixture concrete

HQ: The Quikrete Companies Llc
5 Concourse Pkwy Ste 1900
Atlanta GA 30328
404 634-9100

(G-69)
RED DIAMOND ENERGY SVCS INC (PA)
Also Called: Mustang Tubing Testers
402 S 7th St (79602-1756)
P.O. Box 7269 (79608-7269)
PHONE...............................325 690-0053
Brett Hight, *President*
Randy Davis, *President*
EMP: 30
SALES (est): 7.9MM **Privately Held**
WEB: www.reddiamondenergy.net
SIC: **1389** Oil field services

(G-70)
RENTECH BOILER SERVICES INC (PA)
5025 C East Business 20 (79601)
P.O. Box 3295 (79604-3295)
PHONE...............................325 672-2900
David Hunter, *President*
Mark Colman, *Vice Pres*
Jack Rentz, *Vice Pres*
Lee King, *Sales Mgr*
Phyllis Jaques, *Office Mgr*
EMP: 133
SQ FT: 10,000
SALES (est): 18.3MM **Privately Held**
WEB: www.rentechboilers.com
SIC: **3443** 7699 Boilers: industrial, power, or marine; boiler repair shop

(G-71)
REYNOLDS MFG CORP INC
5489 N 3rd St (79603-6409)
P.O. Box 6058 (79608-6058)
PHONE...............................325 698-7300
Vicki Reynolds, *President*
Danny K Reynolds, *Corp Secy*
Reynolds Harvey, *Vice Pres*
EMP: 20
SQ FT: 20,000
SALES (est): 2.2MM **Privately Held**
WEB: www.reynoldstx.com
SIC: **2511** 5712 5999 Children's wood furniture; customized furniture & cabinets; children's furniture

(G-72)
RIG TESTERS INC (PA)
5333 N 3rd St (79603-6407)
P.O. Box 172 (79604-0172)
PHONE...............................325 673-2771
Randy Myers, *President*
Frances F Myers, *Vice Pres*
EMP: 9 EST: 1963
SQ FT: 5,000
SALES (est): 2.1MM **Privately Held**
WEB: www.rigtesters.com
SIC: **1389** Oil field services

(G-73)
RITA BARBER INC
133 Wall St (79603-6430)
P.O. Box 880 (79604-0880)
PHONE...............................325 698-0111
Harwell Barber, *Ch of Bd*
Lee A Hampton, *President*
Joy Tichenor, *Vice Pres*
Carolyn Barber, *Admin Sec*
EMP: 17 EST: 1928
SQ FT: 30,000
SALES (est): 1MM **Privately Held**
WEB: www.veralee.com
SIC: **2389** 5087 Burial garments; funeral directors' equipment & supplies

(G-74)
ROBINSON FANS INC
2424 Oak St (79602-5938)
P.O. Box 100, Zelienople PA (16063-0100)
PHONE...............................325 437-3267
Roger Walker, *Prdtn Mgr*
Doug Bollinger, *CFO*
Richard Humphrey, *Branch Mgr*
EMP: 21
SQ FT: 22,764 **Privately Held**
WEB: www.robinsonfans.com
SIC: **3564** Blowers & fans

HQ: Robinson Fans, Inc.
400 Robinson Dr
Zelienople PA 16063
863 646-5270

(G-75)
ROCKWELL COLLINS INC
7318 Dafb (79607)
P.O. Box 9596, Dyess Afb (79607-0596)
PHONE...............................325 695-0308
Frank McKnight, *Manager*
EMP: 151
SALES (corp-wide): 56.5B **Publicly Held**
WEB: www.rockwellcollins.com
SIC: **3812** Search & navigation equipment
HQ: Rockwell Collins, Inc.
400 Collins Rd Ne
Cedar Rapids IA 52498

(G-76)
ROVER OILFIELD SERVICES LLC
118 Alex Way (79602-1193)
PHONE...............................979 533-7195
Jonathan Brooke,
EMP: 50
SALES (est): 631.6K **Privately Held**
SIC: **1389** Oil field services

(G-77)
RSI INSPECTION LLC
402 S Treadaway Blvd (79602-1751)
PHONE...............................325 673-9800
Patricia N Robinson, *Mng Member*
EMP: 20
SALES (est): 1MM **Privately Held**
WEB: www.rsiinspection.com
SIC: **7389** 7692 Inspection & testing services; cracked casting repair

(G-78)
SCHLUMBERGER TECHNOLOGY CORP
Also Called: Schlumberger Well Services
5445 N 3rd St (79603-6409)
PHONE...............................325 692-1930
Gaylan Dillewyn, *Manager*
EMP: 17
SQ FT: 9,925 **Publicly Held**
SIC: **1389** Oil field services
HQ: Schlumberger Technology Corp
300 Schlumberger Dr
Sugar Land TX 77478
281 285-8500

(G-79)
SCRIPPS TEXAS NEWSPAPERS LP
Also Called: Abilene Reporter-News
100 Cypress St (79601)
P.O. Box 30 (79604-0030)
PHONE...............................325 673-4271
Susan Elgin, *CFO*
EMP: 200
SALES (est): 1,000K **Privately Held**
SIC: **2711** Newspapers, publishing & printing

(G-80)
SMI-CARR INC
2573 Pine St (79601-1529)
P.O. Box 3436 (79604-3436)
PHONE...............................325 677-0491
Willard D Carroll Jr, *President*
Patricia Carroll, *Vice Pres*
Pat Carroll, *Manager*
Jami Parraresh, *Info Tech Mgr*
EMP: 15 EST: 1965
SQ FT: 6,000
SALES (est): 1.3MM **Privately Held**
WEB: www.smicarr.com
SIC: **3082** 3531 Unsupported plastics profile shapes; construction machinery

(G-81)
SOJOURNER DRILLING CORPORATION
810 Anson Ave (79601-1657)
P.O. Box 3234 (79604-3234)
PHONE...............................325 672-2832
William C Sojourner Jr, *President*
Jana B Sojourner, *Vice Pres*
Dale Dixon, *Opers Mgr*
Gene Brady, *CFO*
Elma Bernal, *Manager*

EMP: 30 EST: 1946
SQ FT: 11,000
SALES (est): 8.5MM **Privately Held**
WEB: www.sojodrilling.com
SIC: **1311** Crude petroleum production; natural gas production

(G-82)
SQUARES DISTRIBUTING INC
Also Called: Square's Gourmet Meat
4801 Buffalo Gap Rd (79606-3306)
PHONE...............................325 692-4797
Al Callaway, *President*
EMP: 16
SQ FT: 40,000
SALES (est): 594.3K **Privately Held**
WEB: www.alsmesquitegrill.com
SIC: **5812** 2013 Barbecue restaurant; smoked meats from purchased meat

(G-83)
STONE-CMPBELL REST MVMENT PUBG
Also Called: Hillcresc Publishing
1626 Campus Ct (79601-3701)
PHONE...............................325 674-2720
Leonard Allen, *Director*
EMP: 9 EST: 1985
SALES (est): 680.1K **Privately Held**
WEB: www.leafwoodpublishers.com
SIC: **2731** 8661 Book clubs: publishing & printing; religious organizations

(G-84)
STRONG READY MIX LTD
108 County Road 583 (79606-4712)
PHONE...............................325 260-6935
EMP: 10 EST: 2015
SALES (est): 1.5MM **Privately Held**
WEB: www.strongreadymix.com
SIC: **3273** Ready-mixed concrete

(G-85)
SUMMIT ELECTRIC SUPPLY CO INC
3202 S Treadaway Blvd (79602-6734)
PHONE...............................325 691-9600
Scott Ashlock, *Accounts Mgr*
Brian Luckenbach, *Branch Mgr*
EMP: 20
SALES (corp-wide): 494.6MM **Privately Held**
WEB: www.summit.com
SIC: **5063** 3699 Electrical supplies; electrical equipment & supplies
PA: Summit Electric Supply Co., Inc.
2900 Stanford Dr Ne
Albuquerque NM 87107
505 346-2900

(G-86)
TEJON EXPLORATION CO
400 Pine St Ste 900 (79601-5141)
P.O. Box 176 (79604-0176)
PHONE...............................325 673-6429
Julia Jones Matthews, *President*
EMP: 9
SALES (est): 482.2K **Privately Held**
SIC: **1389** Gas field services; oil field services

(G-87)
TIGE BOATS INC
1801 State Highway 36 (79602-4284)
PHONE...............................325 676-7777
Charlie Pigeon, *CEO*
Daniel Gutierrez, *President*
Marcia Jerner, *Opers Mgr*
Jennifer King, *Buyer*
Jack Smith, *Buyer*
◆ EMP: 110
SQ FT: 63,000
SALES (est): 29.9MM **Privately Held**
WEB: www.tige.com
SIC: **3732** Motorboats, inboard or outboard: building & repairing

(G-88)
TOM JAMES COMPANY
2401 S Willis St Ste 117 (79605-6248)
PHONE...............................325 695-0190
Roger Harris, *Sales Staff*
EMP: 11

▲ = Import ▼=Export
◆ =Import/Export

SALES (corp-wide): 574.6MM **Privately Held**
WEB: www.tomjames.com
SIC: 2311 Suits, men's & boys': made from purchased materials
PA: Tom James Company
263 Seaboard Ln
Franklin TN 37067
615 771-1122

(G-89)
TORO COMPANY
Also Called: Integrated Ctrl Systems & Svcs
500 Chestnut St Ste 400 (79602-1468)
P.O. Box 3339 (79604-3339)
PHONE....................................325 673-8762
Jeff Stewart, *Manager*
Faith Gage, *Technical Staff*
EMP: 80
SALES (corp-wide): 3.3B **Publicly Held**
WEB: www.thetorocompany.com
SIC: 3523 3524 Fertilizing, spraying, dusting & irrigation machinery; lawn & garden equipment
PA: The Toro Company
8111 Lyndale Ave S
Bloomington MN 55420
952 888-8801

(G-90)
VOLUME FEED & SEED INC
Also Called: Acco Feeds Division
249 S 11th St (79602-3927)
PHONE....................................325 676-3302
Kevin Jackson, *Manager*
EMP: 9
SQ FT: 9,240
SALES (corp-wide): 3MM **Privately Held**
WEB: www.jacksonbrosfeed.com
SIC: 2048 Prepared feeds
PA: Volume Feed & Seed Inc
3818 S Treadaway Blvd
Abilene TX 79602
325 691-1110

(G-91)
VULCAN MATERIALS COMPANY
14500 County Road 224 (79602-9148)
PHONE....................................325 529-3785
Tye Bradshaw, *President*
Billy Rucker, *Director*
EMP: 22 **Publicly Held**
WEB: www.vulcanmaterials.com
SIC: 3273 Ready-mixed concrete
PA: Vulcan Materials Company
1200 Urban Center Dr
Vestavia AL 35242

(G-92)
W&W-AFCO STEEL LLC
Also Called: Hirschfeld Steel
771 Virgil St (79602-1865)
P.O. Box 3695 (79604-3695)
PHONE....................................325 676-1422
Mike McDonald, *Manager*
EMP: 85
SALES (corp-wide): 9B **Publicly Held**
WEB: www.wwafcosteel.com
SIC: 3441 Fabricated structural metal
HQ: W&W-Afco Steel Llc
1730 W Reno Ave
Oklahoma City OK 73106
405 235-3621

(G-93)
WES TEX DRILLING COMPANY LLC
Also Called: Westec Sterling Co
400 Pine St Ste 700 (79601-5197)
P.O. Box 3739 (79604-3739)
PHONE....................................325 677-9121
David Morris, *Partner*
Dwayne Chitwood, *Mng Member*
EMP: 10 EST: 1954
SALES (est): 1.7MM **Privately Held**
WEB: www.wtdc.us
SIC: 1311 Crude petroleum production

(G-94)
WEST TEXAS WANT ADS INC (PA)
Also Called: Thrifty Nickel Want ADS
1634 N 1st St (79601-5603)
PHONE....................................325 673-4521
Karla Hutchinson, *President*
Christianson Robert L, *Vice Pres*

EMP: 13
SQ FT: 2,200 **Privately Held**
WEB: www.wacoamericanclassifieds.com
SIC: 2741 2711 Shopping news: publishing & printing; newspapers

(G-95)
WYLIE & SON INC
Also Called: Wylie Implement
3542 S Treadaway Blvd (79602-6748)
PHONE....................................325 695-0000
Shane Buchanan, *Store Mgr*
Joe Gaither, *Parts Mgr*
EMP: 12
SALES (corp-wide): 27MM **Privately Held**
WEB: www.wyliesprayers.com
SIC: 3523 3089 Sprayers & spraying machines, agricultural; plastic hardware & building products
PA: Wylie & Son, Inc.
101 N Main St
Petersburg TX 79250
806 667-3566

(G-96)
YOUR IDEAS INC
825 Oak St (79602-2634)
PHONE....................................325 673-5860
Mike Davis, *President*
Trampas Cox, *Manager*
EMP: 11
SQ FT: 4,000
SALES (est): 842.8K **Privately Held**
WEB: www.yourideasinc.net
SIC: 7336 2396 Silk screen design; automotive & apparel trimmings

(G-97)
ZACHRY ASSOCIATES INC
3457 Curry Ln (79606-8217)
P.O. Box 1739 (79604-1739)
PHONE....................................325 677-1342
EMP: 20
SALES (est): 4.3MM **Privately Held**
WEB: www.zachryinc.com
SIC: 7311 8732 7389 2752 Advertising consultant; commercial nonphysical research; fund raising organizations; commercial printing, lithographic

---

Addison
Dallas County

(G-98)
ACC-KP LLC
Also Called: Meggitt Control Systems
4554 Claire Chennault St (75001-5321)
PHONE....................................972 407-1234
James Simpkins, *President*
Greg Dewitt, *President*
Rick Steiner, *Exec VP*
Robert W Soukup, *Vice Pres*
Chad Rhoades, *Opers Staff*
▲ EMP: 55
SQ FT: 20,000
SALES (est): 11.1MM
SALES (corp-wide): 16.9MM **Privately Held**
WEB: www.keithproducts.com
SIC: 3728 3585 Oxygen systems, aircraft; refrigeration & heating equipment
PA: Air Comm Corporation Llc
1575 W 124th Ave Ste 210
Westminster CO 80234
303 440-4075

(G-99)
ADDISON JET MAINTENANCE INC
4553 Glenn Curtiss Dr (75001-3244)
P.O. Box 2646 (75001-2646)
PHONE....................................972 559-1000
Stephen M Wilson, *President*
EMP: 10
SALES (est): 831.9K **Privately Held**
WEB: www.myelitejet.com
SIC: 3724 Aircraft engines & engine parts

(G-100)
ADDISON OIL LLC (PA)
15851 Dallas Pkwy Ste 401 (75001-3369)
PHONE....................................972 239-2400
Mikel Parker, *Mng Member*

Mike L Parker, *Mng Member*
EMP: 15
SALES (est): 17.7MM **Privately Held**
WEB: www.enduranceresourcesllc.com
SIC: 1382 Oil & gas exploration services

(G-101)
AER MANUFACTURING LP
4040 Lindbergh Dr (75001-4342)
PHONE....................................972 392-4130
David Walker, *Sales Mgr*
Brant Schlotfelt, *Manager*
EMP: 10
SALES (corp-wide): 139MM **Privately Held**
WEB: www.aermanufacturing.com
SIC: 3089 Automotive parts, plastic
PA: Aer Manufacturing, Inc.
1605 Surveyor Blvd
Carrollton TX 75006
972 418-6499

(G-102)
ALL-PLASTICS LLC
Also Called: A P M
15700 Midway Rd (75001-4272)
PHONE....................................972 239-2686
Thomas Houdeshell, *CEO*
David Batey, *Manager*
▲ EMP: 75 EST: 1964
SQ FT: 40,000
SALES (est): 18MM **Privately Held**
WEB: www.all-plastics.com
SIC: 3089 Injection molding of plastics

(G-103)
ALVIN J BART & SONS INC
4130 Lindbergh Dr (75001-4344)
PHONE....................................718 417-1300
Richard Bart, *Ch of Bd*
Alvin J Bart, *President*
Ira Bart, *Vice Pres*
Rich Bart, *Vice Pres*
David Rosen, *CFO*
▲ EMP: 150 EST: 1956
SQ FT: 170,000
SALES (est): 19.2MM **Privately Held**
WEB: www.lpcink.com
SIC: 2759 Bank notes: engraved

(G-104)
ANDAX CORP
Also Called: Signgrafx
4213 Wiley Post Rd (75001-4266)
PHONE....................................972 392-3999
Richard Wischkowsky, *President*
EMP: 15
SQ FT: 17,000
SALES (est): 1.7MM **Privately Held**
WEB: www.signgrafx.com
SIC: 3993 7319 Signs & advertising specialties; display advertising service

(G-105)
BALLISTIC GL ARMOR SLTIONS LLC
15504 Wright Brothers Dr (75001-4273)
PHONE....................................214 382-4100
Monna Blackmore,
EMP: 16
SALES (est): 526.5K **Privately Held**
WEB: www.ballisticglassandarmor.com
SIC: 3231 Products of purchased glass

(G-106)
BASIS TECHNOLOGIES INC
16301 Quorum Dr Ste 100b (75001-6867)
PHONE....................................888 623-0220
Karl Pringle, *President*
Tess Cliff, *Marketing Mgr*
Duncan Williamson, *Risk Mgmt Dir*
EMP: 40
SALES (est): 2.7MM **Privately Held**
WEB: www.basistechnologies.com
SIC: 7372 Business oriented computer software

(G-107)
BEST PRESS INC
4201 Airborn Dr (75001-5183)
PHONE....................................972 930-1000
Wendy Kalisher, *President*
Joe Bessonette, *Accounts Exec*
Larry Cannon, *Accounts Exec*
Rosendo Ferrer, *Marketing Staff*
Wayne Barron, *Manager*

EMP: 70
SQ FT: 98,000
SALES (est): 16.3MM **Privately Held**
WEB:
SIC: 2752 Commercial printing, offset

(G-108)
BRUCEMARK PETROLEUM INC (PA)
14275 Midway Rd Ste 220 (75001-3652)
PHONE....................................630 339-5490
Bruce Rafael, *President*
EMP: 10
SQ FT: 5,500
SALES (est): 5MM **Privately Held**
WEB: www.brucemarkpetroleum.com
SIC: 5172 1381 Petroleum brokers; drilling oil & gas wells

(G-109)
CHILDRESS FURNITURE & FABR INC
15201 Midway Rd (75001-4523)
PHONE....................................214 565-0900
Barbara Childress, *Branch Mgr*
EMP: 69 **Privately Held**
WEB: www.childressfabrics.com
SIC: 7641 2392 Reupholstery & furniture repair; blankets, comforters & beddings
PA: Childress Furniture & Fabric, Inc.
2512 Ferris St
Dallas TX 75226

(G-110)
COHORT ENERGY COMPANY
15508 Wright Brothers Dr (75001-4273)
PHONE....................................972 233-8191
Hg Westerman Jr, *Ch of Bd*
Laura Westerman, *Corp Secy*
C D Mc Daniels, *Vice Pres*
EMP: 50
SQ FT: 10,000
SALES (est): 3.7MM **Privately Held**
WEB: www.jwpower.net
SIC: 1311 1382 Natural gas production; oil & gas exploration services
HQ: J-W Operating Company
15505 Wright Brothers Dr
Addison TX 75001
972 233-8191

(G-111)
COLLINS GOLD LABEL INC
4115 Lindbergh Dr (75001-4345)
PHONE....................................972 960-7346
James D Collins, *Ch of Bd*
James M Collins, *President*
Patricia A Collins, *Vice Pres*
EMP: 9
SQ FT: 15,000
SALES (est): 1.1MM **Privately Held**
SIC: 2087 Beverage bases, concentrates, syrups, powders & mixes; cocktail mixes, nonalcoholic; concentrates, drink; syrups, drink

(G-112)
COMPOSITE PANL TCHNLGY-SUTH IN
4125 Billy Mitchell Dr # 100 (75001-4351)
PHONE....................................972 720-0477
Skip Kennedy, *President*
EMP: 50
SALES (est): 5MM **Privately Held**
SIC: 3444 Siding, sheet metal

(G-113)
CONSOLIDATED ARMOR PDTS LLC (PA)
Also Called: Cap Architectural Products
15504 Wright Brothers Dr (75001-4273)
PHONE....................................214 382-4100
Dale Caudle, *Ch of Bd*
Paul R Sivertson, *President*
Patrick Curry, *Exec VP*
EMP: 31
SQ FT: 25,000
SALES (est): 750K **Privately Held**
WEB: www.caparmor.com
SIC: 3083 3089 3211 Laminated plastics plate & sheet; windows, plastic; flat glass

(G-114)
CTL MEDICAL CORPORATION
4550 Excel Pkwy Ste 300 (75001-5714)
PHONE..................................214 545-5830
Tim Bertone, *Engineer*
Patrick Doran, *Engineer*
Adam Ferreira, *Engineer*
Rose Moore, *VP Bus Dvlpt*
Fiona Lazarow, *CFO*
EMP: 10
SALES (est): 224.8K **Privately Held**
WEB: www.ctlmed.com
SIC: 3841 Surgical & medical instruments

(G-115)
DEAN TECHNOLOGY INC (PA)
Also Called: Hvca
4117 Billy Mitchell Dr (75001-4351)
PHONE..................................972 248-7691
Craig S Dean, *President*
Jawanza Hall, *Engineer*
Chris McBurney, *Sales Staff*
◆ **EMP:** 15
SALES (est): 26MM **Privately Held**
WEB: www.deantechnology.com
SIC: 3674 Diodes, solid state (germanium, silicon, etc.); rectifiers, solid state

(G-116)
DFW INSTRUMENT LLC
Also Called: Dfw Instruments
4570 Westgrove Dr Ste 270 (75001-5397)
PHONE..................................214 217-7600
James A Zollo, *President*
Nina Zollo, *Vice Pres*
Zach Troegle, *Manager*
EMP: 15
SALES (est): 3.3MM **Privately Held**
WEB: www.dfwinstrument.com
SIC: 7699 3829 Aircraft flight instrument repair; measuring & controlling devices

(G-117)
DIAGEO NORTH AMERICA INC
Also Called: Gunness Udv
5080 Spectrum Dr 1200e (75001-4648)
PHONE..................................972 716-7700
Brittney Noonan, *Partner*
Christian Gray, *Vice Pres*
Tanja Edenfield, *Sales Dir*
Colleen Davis, *Marketing Mgr*
Dave Ensler, *Marketing Mgr*
EMP: 31
SALES (corp-wide): 14.3B **Privately Held**
WEB: www.malts.com
SIC: 2085 Distilled & blended liquors
HQ: Diageo North America Inc.
3 World Trade Ctr
New York NY 10007
212 202-1800

(G-118)
EIGHT EIGHTY-EIGHT INC
Also Called: Allegra Print & Imaging
14131 Midway Rd Ste 119 (75001-3638)
PHONE..................................972 404-0155
James F Larue Jr, *President*
Hillary Huens, *Accounts Mgr*
EMP: 10
SQ FT: 5,500
SALES (est): 900K **Privately Held**
WEB: www.allegramarketingprint.com
SIC: 2752 7334 Commercial printing, offset; photocopying & duplicating services

(G-119)
ELTAMD INC (PA)
15601 Dallas Pkwy # 1000 (75001-6682)
PHONE..................................972 385-2900
William O Kling, *President*
Penne Thornet, *General Mgr*
Ede Payne, *COO*
Himalaya Gunasekaran, *Vice Pres*
Darius McDonald, *Purch Mgr*
▲ **EMP:** 60
SQ FT: 75,000
SALES (est): 8.6MM **Privately Held**
WEB: www.eltamd.com
SIC: 2834 2844 Pharmaceutical preparations; toilet preparations

(G-120)
ENCOMPASS GROUP LLC
Also Called: Encompass Medical
16415 Addison Rd Ste 660 (75001-5434)
PHONE..................................972 732-7694
Ed Howard, *President*
Robin Holmes, *Sales Staff*
Kaye Louk, *Executive*
EMP: 13
SALES (corp-wide): 110.2MM **Privately Held**
WEB: www.encompassgroup.com
SIC: 2389 2392 Hospital gowns; blankets, comforters & beddings; napkins, fabric & nonwoven: made from purchased materials; dishcloths, nonwoven textile: made from purchased materials
HQ: Encompass Group, L.L.C.
615 Macon St
Mcdonough GA 30253
800 284-4540

(G-121)
ENDURANCE RESOURCES LLC
15455 Dallas Pkwy # 1050 (75001-6721)
PHONE..................................214 996-0900
Donald G Ritter, *President*
Tom Gingerich, *Treasurer*
EMP: 30 **EST:** 2009
SALES (est): 3.2MM **Privately Held**
WEB: www.enduranceresourcesllc.com
SIC: 1382 Oil & gas exploration services

(G-122)
EWB INTERNATIONAL INC
16220 Midway Rd (75001-4214)
PHONE..................................972 764-5252
Mervyn Price, *President*
CJ Comu, *Chairman*
Buddy Barnes, *CFO*
Harley Barnes, *CFO*
EMP: 10
SQ FT: 3,000
SALES (est): 1.4MM **Privately Held**
WEB: www.earthwater.com
SIC: 2086 Bottled & canned soft drinks

(G-123)
FINANCIAL INDUSTRY COM
Also Called: Fics
14285 Midway Rd Ste 200 (75001-3620)
PHONE..................................972 458-8583
L Dawn Gibbs, *Ch of Bd*
Susan Graham, *President*
Johnny Gibbs, *Exec VP*
Scott Gambrel, *Engineer*
Shalecia Stewart, *Manager*
EMP: 65
SALES (est): 11.1MM **Privately Held**
WEB: www.fics.com
SIC: 7372 Prepackaged software

(G-124)
FMC TECHNOLOGIES INC
15851 Dallas Pkwy # 1103 (75001-3369)
PHONE..................................214 363-8000
Tyler Schnell, *Branch Mgr*
EMP: 29
SALES (corp-wide): 13.4B **Privately Held**
WEB: www.technipfmc.com
SIC: 3533 Oil & gas field machinery
HQ: Fmc Technologies, Inc.
11740 Katy Fwy Enrgy Twr
Houston TX 77079
281 591-4000

(G-125)
FORECLOSURE LISTING SERVICE
Also Called: Roddy Information Services
4851 Keller Springs Rd # 219 (75001-6259)
P.O. Box 1007 (75001-1007)
PHONE..................................972 250-0993
George Roddy, *President*
EMP: 10
SALES (est): 1.2MM **Privately Held**
WEB: www.4closure.info
SIC: 2731 6531 Pamphlets: publishing only, not printed on site; real estate agents & managers

(G-126)
FORNEY CORPORATION (HQ)
Also Called: Forney International
16479 Dallas Pkwy Ste 600 (75001-6876)
PHONE..................................972 458-6100
John Conroy, *President*
Matt Lenzi, *COO*
Eric Fournier, *Vice Pres*
Bob Parent, *Vice Pres*
Jose Berrones, *Buyer*
▲ **EMP:** 47 **EST:** 1994
SQ FT: 20,000
SALES (est): 21.8MM
SALES (corp-wide): 2.9B **Publicly Held**
WEB: www.forneycorp.com
SIC: 3822 5084 3823 3812 Ignition controls for gas appliances & furnaces, automatic; industrial machinery & equipment; industrial instrmnts msrmnt display/control process variable; search & navigation equipment; switchgear & switchboard apparatus
PA: Graham Holdings Company
1300 17th St N Fl 17
Arlington VA 22209
703 345-6300

(G-127)
FOUNDATION ENERGY MGT LLC (PA)
5057 Keller Springs Rd # 650 (75001-6583)
P.O. Box 1085 (75001-1085)
PHONE..................................972 707-2500
Eddie W Reha, *President*
Jeff Stark, *Counsel*
Richard Payne, *Exec VP*
Joel Sauer, *Exec VP*
John G Wetzel, *Vice Pres*
EMP: 45
SALES (est): 24.3MM **Privately Held**
WEB: www.foundationenergy.com
SIC: 1382 Oil & gas exploration services

(G-128)
FROM HERE INC
Also Called: Three Leaf Studio
4901 Keller Springs Rd 106a (75001-6250)
PHONE..................................805 368-3363
Troy Radloff, *CEO*
Jesse Hancox, *President*
Courtney Radloff, *Vice Pres*
EMP: 10 **EST:** 2017
SALES (est): 163.6K **Privately Held**
SIC: 3999 Candles

(G-129)
GENERAL MILLS INC
15305 Dallas Pkwy Ste 710 (75001-4637)
PHONE..................................972 892-4100
Patricia Bellows, *Manager*
EMP: 50
SALES (corp-wide): 17.6B **Publicly Held**
WEB: www.generalmills.com
SIC: 5149 2041 Breakfast cereals; flour mixes
PA: General Mills, Inc.
1 General Mills Blvd
Minneapolis MN 55426
763 764-7600

(G-130)
GEO MESA ANALYSIS LLC
Also Called: King Capital
4287 Belt Line Rd Pmb 155 (75001-4510)
PHONE..................................443 637-2436
Stephen D Kaiser,
Zachary Kaiser,
EMP: 23 **EST:** 2009
SALES (est): 1MM **Privately Held**
SIC: 1382 Oil & gas exploration services

(G-131)
GOLDEN BLOUNT INC (PA)
4301 Westgrove Dr (75001-3221)
PHONE..................................972 250-3113
Golden Blount, *Ch of Bd*
James G Blount, *President*
Julia Blount, *Corp Secy*
R Steve Blount, *Vice Pres*
◆ **EMP:** 20
SQ FT: 60,000
SALES (est): 7.5MM **Privately Held**
WEB: www.goldenblountinc.com
SIC: 3429 3433 5023 5719 Fireplace equipment, hardware: andirons, grates, screens; logs, gas fireplace; fireplace equipment & accessories; fireplace equipment & accessories

(G-132)
GRAND ENERGY INC (PA)
15303 Dallas Pkwy # 1010 (75001-4651)
PHONE..................................972 788-2080
James Harris, *President*
Terry Mackey, *Opers Mgr*
EMP: 20
SQ FT: 9,407
SALES (est): 7.9MM **Privately Held**
WEB: www.grandenergy.com
SIC: 1382 Oil & gas exploration services

(G-133)
GRAND OPERATING INC
Also Called: Grand Financial
15303 Dallas Pkwy # 1010 (75001-4677)
PHONE..................................972 788-2080
James L Harris, *President*
EMP: 9
SQ FT: 9,407
SALES (est): 4.8MM
SALES (corp-wide): 7.9MM **Privately Held**
WEB: www.grandenergy.com
SIC: 1389 Oil field services
PA: Grand Energy, Inc.
15303 Dallas Pkwy # 1010
Addison TX 75001
972 788-2080

(G-134)
HOLCIM (US) INC
Also Called: Lafargeholcim US
15900 Dooley Rd Ste 200 (75001-4243)
PHONE..................................214 596-9760
Chuck Counts, *Superintendent*
Jim Addams, *Principal*
Tony Sorcic, *Principal*
EMP: 10
SALES (corp-wide): 1.7B **Privately Held**
WEB: www.lafargeholcim.us
SIC: 3241 3272 Portland cement; concrete products
HQ: Holcim (Us) Inc.
8700 W Bryn Mawr Ave
Chicago IL 60631

(G-135)
HOLLY FABRICATION INC
4143 Billy Mitchell Dr (75001-4351)
PHONE..................................972 233-5362
R W Canterbury, *President*
Stephen White, *Vice Pres*
Eric Willard, *Engineer*
EMP: 32
SALES (est): 6.5MM **Privately Held**
WEB: www.hollyfab.com
SIC: 3444 Sheet metalwork

(G-136)
IMPORT MDSG CONCEPTS GP LLC
15565 Wright Brothers Dr (75001-4274)
PHONE..................................214 572-2000
Brad Smith, *President*
Bryan Youngbood, *Vice Pres*
▲ **EMP:** 14
SALES (est): 3.9MM **Privately Held**
WEB: www.imcimports.com
SIC: 5032 3281 Granite building stone; building stone products

(G-137)
J-W ENERGY COMPANY (PA)
16479 Dallas Pkwy Ste 850 (75001-6906)
P.O. Box 226406, Dallas (75222-6406)
PHONE..................................972 233-8191
Howard G Westerman, *CEO*
Perry A Harris, *President*
David A Miller, *President*
Celeste Ahern, *Chief*
Dean Gutzwiller, *District Mgr*
EMP: 70
SALES (est): 766.9MM **Privately Held**
WEB: www.jwenergy.com
SIC: 1311 7353 3533 1381 Crude petroleum production; natural gas production; oil field equipment, rental or leasing; oil & gas field machinery; drilling oil & gas wells

(G-138)
J-W OPERATING COMPANY (HQ)
Also Called: Cohort Energy Company
15505 Wright Brothers Dr (75001-4274)
P.O. Box 226406, Dallas (75222-6406)
PHONE..................................972 233-8191
Howard G Westerman, *CEO*
Tony Meyer, *President*
Gary Hale, *District Mgr*
John A Daniels, *Business Mgr*

C D McDaniels, *Exec VP*
▲ EMP: 70 EST: 1960
SQ FT: 10,000
SALES (est): 713MM **Privately Held**
WEB: www.jwpower.net
SIC: 1311 Crude petroleum production

(G-139)
J-W POWER COMPANY (HQ)
Also Called: Midessa Compression
16479 Dallas Pkwy Ste 850 (75001-6906)
P.O. Box 226406, Dallas (75222-6406)
PHONE.................................972 233-8191
Don Bizzell, *President*
Bryan Domingue, *Superintendent*
Lindon Leners, *Vice Pres*
Patrick Skinner, *Engineer*
Dave Thompson, *Manager*
EMP: 160
SALES (est): 51.1MM **Privately Held**
WEB: www.jwpower.net
SIC: 3563 Air & gas compressors including vacuum pumps

(G-140)
JEG HOLDINGS LLC
5080 Spectrum Dr Ste 510e (75001-6581)
PHONE.................................972 532-6419
Dennis Irby, *Mng Member*
EMP: 250
SALES (est): 75MM **Privately Held**
SIC: 2865 Cyclic organic crudes

(G-141)
JJ OF DALLAS MANUFACTURING INC
4124 Billy Mitchell Dr (75001-4350)
PHONE.................................972 866-9866
John B Greeley, *President*
Lana Greeley, *Vice Pres*
EMP: 27
SQ FT: 7,500
SALES (est): 1.3MM **Privately Held**
WEB: www.jjofdallas.com
SIC: 5136 2759 2396 2395 Caps, men's & boys'; screen printing; automotive & apparel trimmings; pleating & stitching

(G-142)
KUSTER SIGN LLC
4305 Lindbergh Dr (75001-4539)
PHONE.................................972 991-5841
Nick Kuster, *Manager*
Kevin G Kuster,
Chris M Kuster,
Kevin Kuster,
Nicholas Kuster,
EMP: 9
SQ FT: 14,000
SALES (est): 1.2MM **Privately Held**
WEB: www.kustersignco.com
SIC: 3993 Signs, not made in custom sign painting shops

(G-143)
LATTIMORE MATERIALS CORP (DH)
Also Called: Lattimore Ready Mix
15900 Dooley Rd (75001-4243)
P.O. Box 2469 (75001-2469)
PHONE.................................972 221-4646
Scott Chrimes, *President*
Steve Coiro, *Manager*
Yakelia Clemmons, *Director*
▲ EMP: 121
SQ FT: 22,000
SALES (est): 286.5MM
SALES (corp-wide): 1.7B **Privately Held**
WEB: www.lafargeholcim.us
SIC: 3273 1422 1442 Ready-mixed concrete; limestones, ground; sand mining
HQ: Aggregate Industries Management, Inc.
8700 W Bryn Mawr Ave # 300
Chicago IL 60631
773 372-1000

(G-144)
LAUREN PUBLICATIONS INC
Also Called: Dallas Child Magazine
4275 Kellway Cir Ste 146 (75001-5731)
PHONE.................................214 628-9720
Joylyn Niebes, *President*
EMP: 16
SQ FT: 6,000

SALES (est): 1.9MM **Privately Held**
WEB: www.dfwchild.com
SIC: 2721 Magazines: publishing only, not printed on site

(G-145)
LINK WORLD TRADE INC
Also Called: Link World Technologies
3801 Arapaho Rd (75001-4314)
PHONE.................................972 713-8000
Paul Calixto, *President*
Edson Calixto, *Exec VP*
Roger Mourao, *Exec VP*
EMP: 120
SQ FT: 60,000
SALES (est): 15.4MM **Privately Held**
SIC: 3699 5045 4731 5084 Electrical equipment & supplies; computers, peripherals & software; freight transportation arrangement; industrial machinery & equipment; electronic parts & equipment; electronic computers

(G-146)
LONGFELLOW ENERGY LP
16803 Dallas Pkwy (75001-5212)
P.O. Box 1989 (75001-1989)
PHONE.................................972 590-9900
Todd C Dutton, *President*
James R Huling, *COO*
Pat Garrard, *Senior VP*
John Albert, *Vice Pres*
David Mitchell, *Engineer*
EMP: 50
SQ FT: 60,000
SALES (est): 10.7MM **Privately Held**
WEB: www.longfellowenergy.com
SIC: 1382 Oil & gas exploration services

(G-147)
M ALVAREZ ENTERPRISES INC
Also Called: Fulfillment Resource
4287 Belt Line Rd Ste 360 (75001-4510)
PHONE.................................972 514-2255
Miguel Alvarez, *President*
EMP: 12
SQ FT: 680
SALES (est): 780K **Privately Held**
WEB: www.fulfillmentresource.com
SIC: 2754 Envelopes: gravure printing

(G-148)
MEERA ENTERPRISES INC
Also Called: AlphaGraphics 391
15404 Midway Rd (75001-4251)
PHONE.................................972 385-3900
Sam Patel, *President*
Kelly Patel, *Treasurer*
EMP: 11
SALES (est): 1.4MM **Privately Held**
WEB: www.alphagraphics.com
SIC: 2752 5065 Commercial printing, lithographic; facsimile equipment

(G-149)
MEI MICRO INC
4555 Excel Pkwy Ste 500 (75001-5691)
PHONE.................................972 690-9494
Louis Ross, *CEO*
EMP: 50
SQ FT: 54,150
SALES (est): 138.3K **Privately Held**
SIC: 3674 7371 Microcircuits, integrated (semiconductor); monolithic integrated circuits (solid state); computer software development

(G-150)
NEXLUBE OPERATING LLC
16803 Dallas Pkwy Ste 30 (75001-5212)
P.O. Box 1989 (75001-1989)
PHONE.................................972 590-9908
Malone Mitchell, *Ch of Bd*
Monte Bell, *President*
Michael Burnett, *CFO*
EMP: 10
SALES (est): 896.8K **Privately Held**
WEB: www.nexlube.com
SIC: 2911 Petroleum refining

(G-151)
OCCIDENTAL CHEMICAL CORP
16300 Ledgemont Ln # 1403 (75001-5998)
P.O. Box 809050, Dallas (75380-9050)
PHONE.................................800 699-5123
EMP: 133

SALES (corp-wide): 21.2B **Publicly Held**
WEB: www.oxy.com
SIC: 2874 2812 Phosphatic fertilizers; alkalies & chlorine
HQ: Occidental Chemical Corporation
14555 Dallas Pkwy Ste 400
Dallas TX 75254
972 404-3800

(G-152)
ONE BOOK AT A TIME PUBG LLC
4680 Belt Line Rd (75001-4517)
PHONE.................................972 392-2679
Jack Granoff,
EMP: 10
SALES (est): 962.6K **Privately Held**
WEB: www.onebookpub.com
SIC: 2741 Miscellaneous publishing

(G-153)
OPEN OPTIONS LLC
16650 Westgrove Dr # 150 (75001-5601)
P.O. Box 703822, Dallas (75370-3822)
PHONE.................................972 818-7001
Roscoe Coffman, *Vice Pres*
Stacy Molenda, *Prdtn Mgr*
Anthony Shea, *Purch Mgr*
Gary Bell, *Engineer*
John Hubbard, *Engineer*
EMP: 32
SQ FT: 10,616
SALES (est): 4.9MM **Privately Held**
WEB: www.ooaccess.com
SIC: 3669 Signaling apparatus, electric

(G-154)
OSTEOMED LLC
3885 Arapaho Rd (75001-4314)
PHONE.................................972 677-4600
Walter J Humann, *President*
Joshua Joseph, *QC Mgr*
EMP: 250
SQ FT: 60,000
SALES (est): 74.2MM
SALES (corp-wide): 254.6B **Publicly Held**
WEB: www.osteomed.com
SIC: 3841 Surgical instruments & apparatus
HQ: Colson Associates, Inc.
225 W Washington St # 2200
Chicago IL 60606
312 980-1100

(G-155)
PINNACLE GRAPHICS INC
4098 Lindbergh Dr Ste A (75001-4342)
PHONE.................................972 418-1202
Christopher F Hill, *President*
Bob Tamura, *Creative Dir*
EMP: 18
SQ FT: 20,000
SALES (est): 2.4MM **Privately Held**
WEB: www.pinnaclegraphics.com
SIC: 2759 Commercial printing

(G-156)
PLASTECH CORPORATION
15606 Wright Brothers Dr (75001-4275)
PHONE.................................972 490-1155
Rex Rayfield Sr, *President*
Mark Chapman, *Prdtn Mgr*
Pat Wilson, *Natl Sales Mgr*
ARA Rayfield, *Executive*
▲ EMP: 40
SQ FT: 60,000
SALES (est): 10.7MM **Privately Held**
WEB: www.plastechcorp.com
SIC: 3089 Injection molding of plastics; plastic processing

(G-157)
Q-WEST ENERGY COMPANY
15505 Wright Brothers Dr (75001-4274)
P.O. Box 226406, Dallas (75222-6406)
PHONE.................................972 233-8191
Howard G Westerman Jr, *President*
Laura J Westerman, *Corp Secy*
C D Mc Daniels, *Exec VP*
EMP: 9
SQ FT: 10,000
SALES (est): 1MM **Privately Held**
WEB: www.jwpower.net
SIC: 1311 Crude petroleum & natural gas

HQ: J-W Operating Company
15505 Wright Brothers Dr
Addison TX 75001
972 233-8191

(G-158)
RECON EXPLORATION INC
15506 Wright Brothers Dr # 100 (75001-4273)
P.O. Box 870 (75001-0870)
PHONE.................................972 960-8600
C Keith Thompson, *President*
Cecelia K Reed, *Corp Secy*
K Ray Burson, *Vice Pres*
EMP: 10 EST: 1974
SALES (est): 775.8K **Privately Held**
SIC: 1382 Oil & gas exploration services

(G-159)
RMG NETWORKS HOLDING CORP (HQ)
15301 Dallas Pkwy Ste 500 (75001-6707)
PHONE.................................800 827-9666
Robert Michelson, *President*
George Clopp, *Senior VP*
Jerry Rosen, *Senior VP*
Jana Ahlfinger Bell, *CFO*
Jennifer Park, *Marketing Staff*
EMP: 21
SQ FT: 31,255
SALES: 37MM
SALES (corp-wide): 9.8MM **Privately Held**
WEB: www.rmgnetworks.com
SIC: 3993 7372 Signs & advertising specialties; prepackaged software

(G-160)
ROI TELEPHONY LLC
4951 Airport Pkwy Ste 660 (75001-6615)
PHONE.................................214 364-2425
Tom McCrary, *President*
Robert Dubek, *COO*
◆ EMP: 12
SALES (est): 1.9MM **Privately Held**
WEB: www.roitechnology-solutions.com
SIC: 3661 Telephone dialing devices, automatic

(G-161)
SCENTSIBLE LLC
Also Called: Poo-Pourri
4901 Keller Springs Rd (75001-5930)
PHONE.................................972 818-8200
Suzanne Batiz, *CEO*
Sarah Mosely, *Business Mgr*
Nicole Hofmann, *Vice Pres*
Delana Veres, *Vice Pres*
Jamie Guenther, *Purchasing*
EMP: 75
SQ FT: 20,000
SALES (est): 17.8MM **Privately Held**
WEB: www.poopourri.com
SIC: 2844 2842 5999 Toilet preparations; sanitation preparations, disinfectants & deodorants; toiletries, cosmetics & perfumes

(G-162)
SENTRY ENERGY PRODUCTION LLC
4570 Westgrove Dr Ste 220 (75001-5441)
PHONE.................................972 380-1600
Antoinette Rand, *Mng Member*
EMP: 10
SALES (est): 817.1K **Privately Held**
WEB: www.sentryenergyproduction.com
SIC: 1381 Directional drilling oil & gas wells

(G-163)
SIMS AVIATION INC
4390 Sunbelt Dr (75001-5611)
PHONE.................................972 733-3828
Minh Nyugen, *President*
Jeff Hodgson, *Vice Pres*
Traci Lynch, *Sales Mgr*
EMP: 11
SQ FT: 2,500
SALES (est): 1.2MM **Privately Held**
WEB: www.simsaviation.net
SIC: 7699 3829 Aircraft flight instrument repair; aircraft & motor vehicle measurement equipment

(G-164)
SKELETAL KINETICS LLC
3885 Arapaho Rd (75001-4314)
PHONE....................................408 366-5000
EMP: 22
SALES (est): 3.7MM Privately Held
SIC: 3841 Mfg Surgical/Medical Instruments

(G-165)
STINGRAY WORLDWIDE LLC
Also Called: Stingray Import
4300 Wiley Post Rd (75001-4267)
PHONE....................................972 818-6025
Philip Baird, Business Mgr
Bradford Stoot, Opers Mgr
Lily Garcia, Accounts Mgr
Kevin Gardner,
▲ EMP: 20
SQ FT: 16,000
SALES (est): 4MM Privately Held
WEB: www.stingrayworldwide.com
SIC: 2759 Screen printing

(G-166)
STRYKER CORPORATION
Also Called: Stryker Orthopaedics
15160 Marsh Ln (75001-8047)
PHONE....................................214 461-4663
Jim Webber, Sales Mgr
Nick Talbott, Sales Staff
Donna Long, Branch Mgr
EMP: 103
SALES (corp-wide): 14.3B Publicly Held
WEB: www.stryker.com
SIC: 3841 Surgical & medical instruments
PA: Stryker Corporation
    2825 Airview Blvd
    Portage MI 49002
    269 385-2600

(G-167)
TECHSTYLES INC
16415 Addison Rd Ste 660 (75001-5434)
PHONE....................................972 732-7694
Edward Howard, President
Carey Howard, Exec VP
Kaye Louk, Manager
▲ EMP: 35
SALES (est): 3.7MM Privately Held
WEB: www.encompassgroup.com
SIC: 2389 2392 Hospital gowns; blankets, comforters & beddings

(G-168)
TESTFORCE USA INC
15020 Beltway Dr (75001-3709)
PHONE....................................925 281-3501
Sami Stephan, President
Tony Tirelli, Vice Pres
EMP: 10
SALES (est): 371K Privately Held
WEB: www.entestinc.com
SIC: 5049 3825 Scientific instruments; test equipment for electronic & electric measurement

(G-169)
TRANSATLANTIC PETRO USA CORP (HQ)
16803 Dallas Pkwy (75001-5212)
P.O. Box 246 (75001-0246)
PHONE....................................214 220-4323
Malone Mitchell III, CEO
Gary Mize, President
Scott C Larsen, Vice Pres
Jeffrey S Mecom, Vice Pres
Mel Riggs, Director
EMP: 10
SQ FT: 3,600
SALES (est): 4.3MM Privately Held
WEB: www.transatlanticpetroleum.com
SIC: 1382 Oil & gas exploration services

(G-170)
TRANSATLANTIC PETROLEUM LTD (PA)
16803 Dallas Pkwy (75001-5212)
P.O. Box 246 (75001-0246)
PHONE....................................214 220-4323
N Malone Mitchell 3rd, Ch of Bd
Todd C Dutton, President
Chad D Burkhardt, Vice Pres
Harold Muncy, Vice Pres
G Fabian Anda, CFO

EMP: 24
SALES: 67.3MM Privately Held
WEB: www.transatlanticpetroleum.com
SIC: 1311 1382 Crude petroleum production; oil & gas exploration services

(G-171)
TRONICS MEMS INC
15050 E Beltwood Pkwy (75001-3715)
PHONE....................................469 872-0300
Julien Bon, CEO
Stephane Renard, Founder
Brian Stephenson, COO
Matthieu Cousson, CFO
EMP: 100
SALES (est): 2.7MM Privately Held
WEB: www.tronicsgroup.com
SIC: 3674 Semiconductors & related devices
PA: Tdk Corporation
    2-5-1, Nihombashi
    Chuo-Ku TKY 103-0

(G-172)
TURBINE AIRCRAFT MARKETING INC
4550 Jimmy Doolittle Dr (75001-3270)
PHONE....................................972 248-3108
Patrick Cannon, President
David Finley, Vice Pres
Richard Wheldon, Vice Pres
EMP: 15
SQ FT: 26,000
SALES (est): 1.6MM Privately Held
WEB: www.turbineairmarketing.com
SIC: 3728 Aircraft parts & equipment

(G-173)
USA SECURGLASS CORPORATION
15504 Wright Brothers Dr (75001-4273)
PHONE....................................214 907-9445
Paul Sivertson, CEO
EMP: 40
SQ FT: 25,000
SALES (est): 5MM Privately Held
WEB: www.secureglassarmor.com
SIC: 3211 Strengthened or reinforced glass

(G-174)
USSERY PRINTING COMPANY INC
4201 Airborn Dr (75001-5183)
PHONE....................................972 438-8344
Fran Ussery, CEO
Joe Trizza, President
Mike Lamb, COO
John Henry Lawrimore, Vice Pres
Carl Ussery, Vice Pres
EMP: 61
SALES (est): 13.7MM Privately Held
WEB: www.propegon.com
SIC: 2752 Commercial printing, offset

(G-175)
YJ USA CORP (PA)
Also Called: Lifesells USA
3970 Lindbergh Dr (75001-4340)
PHONE....................................877 927-8777
Craig Adams, President
Orson Lin, Admin Sec
▲ EMP: 10
SQ FT: 2,500
SALES (est): 3MM Privately Held
WEB: www.jumpking.com
SIC: 3949 2399 3792 Trampolines & equipment; sleeping bags; tent-type camping trailers

Adkins
Bexar County

(G-176)
AW INSTALLERS INC
4514 Billy Sames (78101-9470)
PHONE....................................210 649-1618
Carl E Coleman Jr, President
Carl Coleman Jr, President
Will Haston, Superintendent
Cynthia Coleman, Vice Pres
Bob Lee, Project Mgr
EMP: 50

SQ FT: 2,000
SALES (est): 4.3MM Privately Held
WEB: www.awinstallers.com
SIC: 1751 2431 Finish & trim carpentry; millwork

Alamo
Hidalgo County

(G-177)
BRAVO CONCEALMENT LLC
1012 N Alamo Rd (78516-6800)
P.O. Box 1871, Edinburg (78540-1871)
PHONE....................................956 783-7682
Angelica Aguirre, General Mgr
Mark Lopez, Branch Mgr
Rene Aguirre, Mng Member
EMP: 11 EST: 2012
SALES (est): 200K Privately Held
WEB: www.bravoconcealment.com
SIC: 5399 2821 Army-Navy goods; polyvinyl chloride resins (PVC)

(G-178)
CONNER INDUSTRIES INC
Also Called: Conner Distributors
700 N Tower Rd (78516-9740)
PHONE....................................956 781-0215
EMP: 23
SALES (corp-wide): 125MM Privately Held
SIC: 5031 2426 2421 Whol Lumber/Plywood/Millwork Hardwood Dimension/Floor Mill Sawmill/Planing Mill
PA: Conner Industries, Inc.
    3800 Sandshell Dr Ste 235
    Fort Worth TX 76137
    800 413-8006

(G-179)
H E BUTT GROCERY COMPANY
Also Called: H-E-B Food Store 421
1211 W Frontage Rd (78516-2315)
PHONE....................................956 702-2289
Sergio Davila, Branch Mgr
EMP: 150
SALES (corp-wide): 14.8B Privately Held
WEB: www.heb.com
SIC: 5411 5912 5461 2051 Supermarkets, chain; drug stores; bakeries; bread, cake & related products
PA: H. E. Butt Grocery Company
    646 S Flores St
    San Antonio TX 78204
    210 938-8000

(G-180)
MEDEK L L C
315 E Business Highway 83 (78516-9627)
PHONE....................................956 800-4366
Dennis Garcia,
EMP: 10
SALES (est): 929K Privately Held
WEB: www.medekllc.com
SIC: 2679 Paper products, converted

Alba
Wood County

(G-181)
CRH AMERICAS INC
650 W Greenville St 69n (75410-6494)
P.O. Box 336 (75410-0336)
PHONE....................................903 765-2212
Danny Butler, General Mgr
George Hand, Treasurer
EMP: 25
SALES (corp-wide): 30.6B Privately Held
WEB: www.crhamericas.com
SIC: 3354 3449 Aluminum extruded products; miscellaneous metalwork
HQ: Crh Americas, Inc.
    900 Ashwood Pkwy Ste 600
    Atlanta GA 30338
    770 804-3363

(G-182)
DIMENSION IN STONE & GLASS
Also Called: Central Marble
205 N Hopkins St (75410)
P.O. Box 302 (75410-0302)
PHONE....................................214 651-7230

Wendell Williams, President
Sharon Williams, Corp Secy
EMP: 11
SALES (est): 1MM Privately Held
WEB: www.dimensionscentralmarble.com
SIC: 3281 1743 Marble, building: cut & shaped; terrazzo, tile, marble, mosaic work

(G-183)
VALERO ENERGY CORPORATION
Also Called: Pay-N-Save
182 S Fm 17 (75410-4986)
P.O. Box 319 (75410-0319)
PHONE....................................903 765-2900
Clay Hass, Branch Mgr
EMP: 30
SALES (corp-wide): 108.3B Publicly Held
WEB: www.valero.com
SIC: 2911 Petroleum refining
PA: Valero Energy Corporation
    1 Valero Way
    San Antonio TX 78249
    210 345-2000

Albany
Shackelford County

(G-184)
BASIC ENERGY SERVICES INC
5690 E Us Highway 180 (76430-4162)
PHONE....................................325 762-2239
Ronnie Anderson, Manager
EMP: 26
SALES (corp-wide): 567.2MM Publicly Held
WEB: www.basices.com
SIC: 1389 Oil field services
PA: Basic Energy Services, Inc.
    801 Cherry St Unit 2
    Fort Worth TX 76102
    817 334-4100

(G-185)
BILL SMALLEY DRILLING & TRCKG
Also Called: Smalley Bill Drilling & Trckg
160 Fm 1084 (76430)
PHONE....................................325 762-3409
Bill Terrelle Jr, President
Bill Smalley Jr, President
Douglas Terrelle, Chairman
EMP: 50
SALES (est): 1.8MM Privately Held
SIC: 1381 Service well drilling

(G-186)
CONCHO OILFIELD SERVICES LLC
9555 S Us Highway 283 (76430-4706)
PHONE....................................325 762-3300
Randy Hudson, President
Andrew Hudson, Vice Pres
EMP: 25 EST: 2012
SQ FT: 12,000
SALES (est): 6.2MM Privately Held
WEB: www.conchooilfield.com
SIC: 1389 Cementing oil & gas well casings

(G-187)
EBAA IRON INC
5 Miles S Hwy 6 (76430)
P.O. Box 3157 (76430-8056)
PHONE....................................325 762-3084
Danny Husmann, Manager
EMP: 25
SALES (corp-wide): 91.8MM Privately Held
WEB: www.ebaa.com
SIC: 3321 Gray & ductile iron foundries
PA: Ebaa Iron, Inc.
    County Rd 442 Fm 570 S 1
    Eastland TX 76448
    254 629-1737

(G-188)

FLYING A PUMPING SERVICES LLC
9555 S Us Highway 283 (76430-4706)
P.O. Box 2123 (76430-8005)
PHONE.....................................325 794-1667
Justin Anderson,
EMP: 45
SALES (est): 840.2K **Privately Held**
WEB: www.flyingapumps.com
SIC: 1382 Oil & gas exploration services

(G-189)

H R STASNEY & SONS LTD
441 S 2nd St (76430-2501)
P.O. Box 3190 (76430-8057)
PHONE.....................................325 762-3311
Charles R Stasney, *Partner*
Lance Thomas, *General Mgr*
Charles R Stansney, *Principal*
Emma Hudman, *Administration*
Cindy Parsons, *Clerk*
EMP: 13 **EST:** 1930
SALES (est): 1.7MM **Privately Held**
WEB: www.stasneyscookranch.com
SIC: 1311 0212 5172 Crude petroleum
  production; natural gas production; beef
  cattle except feedlots; petroleum products

(G-190)

LAVERTON OILFIELD SERVICES LLC
124 Hill St (76430)
PHONE.....................................325 899-3556
EMP: 14
SALES: 2.5MM **Privately Held**
SIC: 1389 Oil/Gas Field Services

(G-191)

MOMENTUM OPERATING CO INC
224 S Main St (76430)
P.O. Box 2439 (76430-8020)
PHONE.....................................325 762-3331
Michael J Parsons, *President*
Don Tidwell, *Vice Pres*
Lynn Ness, *Treasurer*
Bob Tidwell, *Admin Sec*
EMP: 27
SQ FT: 7,000
SALES (est): 7.6MM **Privately Held**
WEB: www.momentumoperating.com
SIC: 1382 1389 Oil & gas exploration
  services; oil field services

(G-192)

SHEKINAH OILFIELD SERVICES INC
140 Hill St (76430-3158)
P.O. Box 2411 (76430-8018)
PHONE.....................................325 762-2205
Shawna L Knight, *Principal*
EMP: 12 **EST:** 2009
SALES (est): 1.8MM **Privately Held**
WEB: www.shekinahoilfield.com
SIC: 1389 Oil field services

(G-193)

SMALLEY DRILLING & TRCKG CORP
160 Fm 1084 (76430)
P.O. Box 2155 (76430-8007)
PHONE.....................................325 762-3409
John William Smalley Jr, *President*
Doug Terrell, *Superintendent*
J William Smalley Jr, *Vice Pres*
Janelle Raymond, *Admin Sec*
EMP: 50
SQ FT: 1,000
SALES (est): 3.9MM **Privately Held**
SIC: 1381 1311 Drilling oil & gas wells;
  crude petroleum production

(G-194)

SNYDER DRILLING CORP
Also Called: Bob's Well Service
  Throckmorton Hwy Aka (76430)
P.O. Box 2798 (76430-8039)
PHONE.....................................325 762-2389
Jackie Snyder, *President*
Dan Neff, *Treasurer*
EMP: 15
SQ FT: 2,000

SALES (est): 1.2MM **Privately Held**
SIC: 1389 1381 Oil field services; drilling
  oil & gas wells

(G-195)

VAN OPERATING LTD
216 Hill St (76430-3159)
P.O. Box 2530 (76430-8025)
PHONE.....................................325 762-3353
A V Jones Jr, *Owner*
A D J Experation Corp, *General Ptnr*
Don Fitzgibbons, *CFO*
Randy Walker, *Controller*
Charlotte Taggart, *Admin Asst*
EMP: 33 **EST:** 1932
SQ FT: 12,000
SALES (est): 3.1MM **Privately Held**
WEB: www.vanoperating.com
SIC: 1311 0212 Crude petroleum produc-
  tion; beef cattle except feedlots

Aledo
Parker County

(G-196)

BRYANT GRAIN CO
300 N Front St (76008-6426)
P.O. Box 596 (76008-0596)
PHONE.....................................817 441-9782
James C Bryant Jr, *President*
EMP: 49
SQ FT: 4,000
SALES (est): 13.8MM **Privately Held**
WEB: www.bryantgrainco.com
SIC: 2048 Prepared feeds

(G-197)

C & A CONTRACTORS INC (PA)
1217 Gerry Dr (76008-2621)
PHONE.....................................817 441-4178
Connie Oliver, *President*
Arlie Oliver, *Vice Pres*
EMP: 11
SALES (est): 1MM **Privately Held**
SIC: 1389 Construction, repair & disman-
  tling services

(G-198)

FTS INTERNATIONAL SERVICES LLC
119 Nu Energy Rd (76008-3127)
P.O. Box 1416 (76008-1416)
PHONE.....................................817 862-2000
Mark Grissom, *Opers Spvr*
Bill Barker, *Branch Mgr*
Johnny Martinez, *Supervisor*
Kevin Roycroft, *Supervisor*
EMP: 35 **Publicly Held**
WEB: www.ftsi.com
SIC: 1382 Oil & gas exploration services
HQ: Fts International Services, Llc
  777 Main St Ste 2900
  Fort Worth TX 76102
  817 862-2000

(G-199)

GLOBALOGIX INC
701 Bear Cat Rd Unit B (76008-3163)
PHONE.....................................817 441-5570
EMP: 15
SALES (corp-wide): 28.9MM **Privately
  Held**
SIC: 1389 Oil/Gas Field Services
PA: Globalogix, Inc.
  13831 Nw Fwy Ste 600
  Houston TX 77064
  713 987-7630

(G-200)

NU ENERGY SERVICES LP
225 Jakes Trl (76008-4848)
P.O. Box 26807, Fort Worth (76126-0807)
PHONE.....................................817 832-0724
Burns Joe, *VP Opers*
Eddy Longley, *Mng Member*
EMP: 12
SALES (est): 3MM **Privately Held**
WEB: www.nuenergyservices.com
SIC: 3533 7389 Oil field machinery &
  equipment; business services

(G-201)

PMI PUMP PARTS LLC
178 Bear Cat Rd (76008-3154)
PHONE.....................................817 441-7787
Danny Paterson, *President*
Eli Guardiola, *Info Tech Mgr*
EMP: 18
SALES (est): 2.1MM **Privately Held**
WEB: www.pmipumpparts.com
SIC: 3599 Whale oil production, crude

(G-202)

SPECIALTY RESEARCH ASSOCIATES
426 Circle Dr (76008-4376)
P.O. Box 397 (76008-0397)
PHONE.....................................817 441-6044
David Barton, *President*
EMP: 20
SALES (est): 1.9MM **Privately Held**
SIC: 2741 8732 Miscellaneous publishing;
  educational research

Alice
Jim Wells County

(G-203)

ALICE NEWSPAPERS INC
Also Called: Nueces County Record Star
405 E Main St (78332-4968)
P.O. Box 1610 (78333-1610)
PHONE.....................................361 664-6588
Tony Morris, *President*
EMP: 27 **EST:** 1975
SQ FT: 6,500
SALES (est): 1.7MM
SALES (corp): 1.8B **Publicly Held**
WEB: www.alicetx.com
SIC: 2711 2752 Newspapers: publishing
  only, not printed on site; commercial print-
  ing, lithographic
HQ: Gatehouse Media, Llc
  175 Sullys Trl Fl 3
  Pittsford NY 14534
  585 598-0030

(G-204)

ALLIED WELL SERVICE INC
2681 W Front St (78332)
P.O. Box 8 (78333-0008)
PHONE.....................................361 664-6122
Charles L Galindo, *President*
Jennifer Rosado, *Purch Mgr*
EMP: 17
SALES (est): 744.6K **Privately Held**
WEB: www.weatherford.com
SIC: 1389 Servicing oil & gas wells

(G-205)

CHACHOS LEASE SERVICE INC
4933 S Us Highway 281 (78332-3070)
P.O. Box 3324 (78333-3324)
PHONE.....................................361 661-1143
Humberton Jasso, *President*
Lance Pusley, *Admin Sec*
EMP: 12
SALES (est): 1.1MM **Privately Held**
SIC: 1389 Lease tanks, oil field: erecting,
  cleaning & repairing

(G-206)

COIL SOLUTIONS INC
1465 S Flournoy Rd (78332-4271)
PHONE.....................................361 444-0058
Cecil Hassard, *CEO*
Michael Herrera, *Partner*
Bryan Hassard, *Principal*
Robert Kletzel, *Principal*
Roland Garcia, *District Mgr*
EMP: 45
SQ FT: 5,000
SALES (est): 10.3MM
SALES (corp-wide): 7.9MM **Privately
  Held**
WEB: www.coilsolutions.com
SIC: 3533 3317 Drilling tools for gas, oil or
  water wells; steel pipe & tubes
PA: Coil Solutions Inc
  3111 Shepard Pl Se
  Calgary AB T2C 4
  403 252-2124

(G-207)

COPANO/OPERATIONS INC
Also Called: Copano Field Svcs Agua Dulce
3943 N Hwy281 (78332)
PHONE.....................................361 668-8580
Robert Ellis, *Manager*
EMP: 14 **Privately Held**
WEB: www.kindermorgan.com
SIC: 1389 Oil field services
PA: Copano/Operations, Inc
  1200 Smith St Ste 2300
  Houston TX 77002

(G-208)

DE LAUNE DRILLING SERVICE LTD
200 Hub (78332-3058)
P.O. Box 1469 (78333-1469)
PHONE.....................................361 664-0106
Mark Delaune, *Principal*
Brenda Timmons, *Corp Secy*
Lee Delaune, *Vice Pres*
EMP: 10
SQ FT: 2,000
SALES (est): 2.1MM **Privately Held**
SIC: 1389 Pipe testing, oil field service

(G-209)

DORSAL SERVICES INC (PA)
6052 E Highway 44 (78332-8056)
P.O. Box L, Freer (78357-2012)
PHONE.....................................361 394-6300
EMP: 24
SALES (est): 14.9MM **Privately Held**
SIC: 1389 Pipe testing, oil field service

(G-210)

DS OILFIELD CONSTRUCTION LLC
186 Fm 2507 (78332-7763)
P.O. Box 3368 (78333-3368)
PHONE.....................................361 396-0089
Donald Sutton,
EMP: 18
SALES (est): 2.5MM **Privately Held**
SIC: 1389 Roustabout service

(G-211)

EDGE SPECIALTY SERVICES INC
3784 W Highway 44 (78332-3800)
P.O. Box 4126 (78333-4126)
PHONE.....................................361 668-3343
EMP: 38
SQ FT: 9,000
SALES (est): 8MM **Privately Held**
SIC: 1389 Oil field services

(G-212)

ENERGY FISHING & RENTAL SVC
2101 Energy Ave (78332-9650)
P.O. Box 1430 (78333-1430)
PHONE.....................................361 668-8000
Robert Whiley, *Owner*
EMP: 12
SALES (est): 929.8K **Privately Held**
WEB: www.energyfrs.com
SIC: 1389 Oil field services

(G-213)

FESCO LTD
1400 E Main St (78332-3929)
PHONE.....................................361 661-1538
Ryan McWilliams, *Production*
David Tyler, *Production*
Casey Vanetti, *Production*
Joshua Wagner, *Production*
Gloria Varte, *Branch Mgr*
EMP: 55
SALES (corp-wide): 201MM **Privately
  Held**
WEB: www.fescoinc.com
SIC: 1389 Oil field services
PA: Fesco, Ltd.
  1000 Fesco Dr
  Alice TX 78332
  361 664-3479

(G-214)

FMC TECHNOLOGIES INC
1266 N Hwy 281 Byp (78332)
PHONE.....................................361 668-0886
EMP: 29

SALES (corp-wide): 6.1B **Publicly Held**
SIC: 3533 Mfg Oil/Gas Field Machinery
PA: Fmc Technologies, Inc.
　5875 N Sam Houston Pkwy W
　Houston TX 77079
　281 591-4000

(G-215)
FORBES ENERGY SERVICES LTD (PA)
3000 S Business Hwy 281 (78332)
PHONE.................................361 664-0549
John E Crisp, *Ch of Bd*
Steve Macek, *COO*
Jerry Woodall, *Safety Mgr*
Delfino Escalante, *Opers Staff*
L Melvin Cooper, *CFO*
EMP: 18
SALES: 188.4MM **Publicly Held**
WEB: www.forbesenergyservices.com
SIC: 1389 Haulage, oil field; oil field services; processing service, gas

(G-216)
FRONTIER SERVICES INC
2404 N Us Highway 281 (78332-2967)
PHONE.................................361 668-1188
EMP: 41 **Privately Held**
WEB: www.frontierservicesinc.com
SIC: 1389 Testing, measuring, surveying & analysis services
PA: Frontier Services, Inc.
　21222 Gathering Oak # 102
　San Antonio TX 78260

(G-217)
J-III CONCRETE CO
6765 S Us Highway 281 (78332-3019)
PHONE.................................361 396-1951
AC Cuellar, *Owner*
EMP: 9
SALES (corp-wide): 9.8MM **Privately Held**
WEB: www.j3concrete.com
SIC: 3273 Ready-mixed concrete
PA: J-Iii Concrete Co
　1700 E 28th St
　Weslaco TX 78596
　956 968-1371

(G-218)
JE OILFIELD SERVICES LLC
183 County Road 162 (78332-7992)
PHONE.................................361 701-1324
EMP: 12
SALES (est): 272.2K **Privately Held**
SIC: 1389 Oil field services

(G-219)
JMI MACHINE LLC
600 S Johnson St (78332-5656)
P.O. Box 68 (78333-0068)
PHONE.................................361 664-2848
Julian Ortiz, *President*
Michelle M Ortiz, *Vice Pres*
EMP: 14
SQ FT: 5,000
SALES (est): 1.4MM **Privately Held**
SIC: 1389 7699 Oil & gas wells: building, repairing & dismantling; industrial machinery & equipment repair

(G-220)
KEY ENERGY SERVICES INC
511 Commerce St (78332-2964)
PHONE.................................361 668-1526
John Dworazyk, *Manager*
EMP: 20
SALES (corp-wide): 413.8MM **Publicly Held**
WEB: www.keyenergy.com
SIC: 1389 Oil field services
PA: Key Energy Services, Inc.
　1301 Mckinney St Ste 1800
　Houston TX 77010
　713 651-4300

(G-221)
KEY ENERGY SERVICES INC
4309 S Us Highway 281 (78332-3055)
P.O. Box 1789 (78333-1789)
PHONE.................................361 668-1818
Richard Moore, *Manager*
EMP: 80

SALES (corp-wide): 413.8MM **Publicly Held**
WEB: www.keyenergy.com
SIC: 1389 Construction, repair & dismantling services
PA: Key Energy Services, Inc.
　1301 Mckinney St Ste 1800
　Houston TX 77010
　713 651-4300

(G-222)
KEY ENERGY SERVICES INC
135 County Road 336 (78332-7009)
PHONE.................................361 661-0488
Roy Dallegos, *Branch Mgr*
EMP: 46
SALES (corp-wide): 413.8MM **Publicly Held**
WEB: www.keyenergy.com
SIC: 1389 Construction, repair & dismantling services
PA: Key Energy Services, Inc.
　1301 Mckinney St Ste 1800
　Houston TX 77010
　713 651-4300

(G-223)
KNIGHT OIL TOOLS LLC
1270 Airport Rd (78332-7334)
PHONE.................................361 668-8065
Jerry Smith, *Manager*
EMP: 12
SALES (corp-wide): 66.3MM **Privately Held**
WEB: www.knightoiltools.com
SIC: 1389 Oil field services
HQ: Knight Oil Tools, Llc
　2727 Se Evangeline Trwy
　Lafayette LA 70508
　337 233-0464

(G-224)
LIGHTNING FLUID SERVICES INC
1310 Southwood St (78332-3923)
P.O. Box 4165 (78333-4165)
PHONE.................................361 396-0801
William Starns, *President*
EMP: 12
SALES (est): 334.3MM **Privately Held**
SIC: 1389 7389 Oil field services; business services

(G-225)
LUERAS WELDING SERVICE INC
3869 W State Highway 44 (78332-9167)
P.O. Box 4108 (78333-4108)
PHONE.................................361 668-4572
Mateo Luera, *President*
EMP: 20
SALES (est): 4.2MM **Privately Held**
WEB: www.lueraswelding.com
SIC: 3533 1799 Oil & gas drilling rigs & equipment; welding on site

(G-226)
M & G DEVELOPMENT LP
2681 W Front St (78332)
P.O. Box 8 (78333-0008)
PHONE.................................361 664-6122
Charles Galindo, *Partner*
EMP: 12
SALES (est): 898.6K **Privately Held**
SIC: 1389 Pipe testing, oil field service

(G-227)
MANUFACTURING GLOBAL RESOURCES
3707 S Us Highway 281 (78332-2915)
P.O. Box 3490 (78333-3490)
PHONE.................................361 668-0111
EMP: 10
SALES (est): 1.2MM **Privately Held**
SIC: 1389 Oil/Gas Field Services

(G-228)
MEASUREMENT SERVICES INC
196 Arena Trl (78332-7569)
PHONE.................................361 227-4998
Albert Perez Jr, *President*
Gilbert Inocencio, *Vice Pres*
EMP: 10

SALES (est): 671.1K **Privately Held**
SIC: 1389 7389 Measurement of well flow rates, oil & gas;

(G-229)
MO VAC SERVICE CO OF ALICE
2 N Johnson St 31 (78332-4518)
P.O. Box 247 (78333-0247)
PHONE.................................361 668-8203
Tom Mendiola, *Manager*
EMP: 13 **Privately Held**
WEB: www.mo-vac.com
SIC: 1389 Oil field services
PA: Mo Vac Service Co Of Alice
　5 Onehalf Mi N Mccoll Rd
　Mcallen TX 78501

(G-230)
R & R LEASE SERVICE INC
1791 Martin L King Blvd (78332)
P.O. Box 644 (78333-0644)
PHONE.................................361 562-8379
Rudy Silva, *President*
EMP: 20 **EST:** 1973
SALES (est): 1.4MM **Privately Held**
SIC: 1389 Oil field services

(G-231)
RAM-GEAR MANUFACTURING INC
6150 E Highway 44 (78332-7384)
P.O. Box 537, Agua Dulce (78330-0537)
PHONE.................................361 668-0235
Ramiro Tagle, *President*
Gary Gillham, *General Mgr*
Aaron Tagle, *Opers Mgr*
Roy Tagle, *CFO*
Andrea Jones, *Office Mgr*
▼ **EMP:** 18
SQ FT: 14,500
SALES (est): 5.3MM **Privately Held**
WEB: www.ram-gear.com
SIC: 5082 3566 3462 Oil field equipment; reduction gears & gear units for turbines, except automotive; iron & steel forgings

(G-232)
RATHOLE DRILLING INC (PA)
2427 N Us Highway 281 (78332-2937)
P.O. Box 389 (78333-0389)
PHONE.................................361 664-9995
Gary Mills, *President*
Mills Gary L, *President*
Christopher Graees, *Vice Pres*
Chris Graves, *Vice Pres*
EMP: 48
SQ FT: 2,240
SALES (est): 19.2MM **Privately Held**
WEB: www.ratholedrillinginc.com
SIC: 1389 Construction, repair & dismantling services; building oil & gas well foundations on site

(G-233)
SCHLUMBERGER TECHNOLOGY CORP
2725 County Road 342 (78332-6854)
P.O. Box 451 (78333-0451)
PHONE.................................361 210-6200
Rene Bilano, *Manager*
EMP: 65 **Publicly Held**
WEB: www.coiltubingpartners.com
SIC: 1389 Oil field services
HQ: Schlumberger Technology Corp
　300 Schlumberger Dr
　Sugar Land TX 77478
　281 285-8500

(G-234)
SCHLUMBERGER TECHNOLOGY CORP
Also Called: Dowell Schlumberger
1126 Airport Rd (78332-9628)
PHONE.................................361 664-3458
Fax: 361 668-5166
EMP: 200 **Publicly Held**
SIC: 1389 Oil/Gas Field Services
HQ: Schlumberger Technology Corp
　100 Gillingham Ln
　Sugar Land TX 77478
　281 285-8500

(G-235)
SMITH SERVICES RED BARON
2225 Energy Ave (78332-9623)
PHONE.................................361 396-0521
Elas Smith, *General Mgr*
EMP: 10
SALES (est): 387.4K **Privately Held**
SIC: 1389 Oil consultants

(G-236)
SOUTH TEXAS MACHINE SHOP INC
1714 S Us Highway 281 (78332-5716)
P.O. Box 547 (78333-0547)
PHONE.................................361 664-8902
Carlos Leal, *President*
Victor Herrera, *Vice Pres*
Stephanie Leal, *Treasurer*
Angeles Herrera, *Admin Sec*
EMP: 10 **EST:** 1979
SQ FT: 5,400
SALES (est): 1.9MM **Privately Held**
WEB: www.stxmachine.com
SIC: 3599 Machine shop, jobbing & repair

(G-237)
SOUTH TXAS OLFLD SOLUTIONS LLC
411 Flournoy Rd 102 (78332-4084)
P.O. Box 3320 (78333-3320)
PHONE.................................361 396-1777
Clinton James Carpenter, *President*
Orlando Espinoza, *Vice Pres*
EMP: 59
SQ FT: 1,500
SALES (est): 10MM **Privately Held**
WEB: www.stxofs.com
SIC: 1389 5084 Oil field services; oil well machinery, equipment & supplies

(G-238)
SUPERIOR TUBING TESTER
4783 S Us Highway 281 (78332-2944)
P.O. Box 250 (78333-0250)
PHONE.................................361 668-4611
Robert E Jenkins,
John Crisp,
Charles Forbes,
EMP: 10
SALES (est): 897K **Privately Held**
SIC: 1389 Servicing oil & gas wells; oil field services

(G-239)
TCCA INC (PA)
Also Called: The Copy Center
1023 E Main St (78332-5044)
PHONE.................................361 668-9636
Loren Fine, *President*
Debra Fine, *Admin Sec*
EMP: 13
SALES (est): 1.3MM **Privately Held**
WEB: www.tccaconference.com
SIC: 5044 2752 Photocopy machines; commercial printing, offset

(G-240)
TEXAS ENERGY SERVICES LP (PA)
4932 N Us Hwy 281 (78332)
P.O. Box 2108 (78333-2108)
PHONE.................................361 664-5020
John Crisp, *General Ptnr*
Charles C Forbes, *General Ptnr*
EMP: 415
SQ FT: 1,700
SALES (est): 57.6MM **Privately Held**
SIC: 1389 Oil field services

(G-241)
TREND SERVICES INC
3230 W Highway 44 (78332-7358)
PHONE.................................361 396-0048
James Bahn, *Branch Mgr*
EMP: 9
SALES (corp-wide): 16.7MM **Privately Held**
WEB: www.trendservicesinc.com
SIC: 1389 Construction, repair & dismantling services
PA: Trend Services, Inc.
　2825 Se Evangeline Trwy
　Lafayette LA 70508
　337 234-7990

(G-242)
TRI ELEMENT INCORPORATED
1216 Airport Rd (78332-7334)
PHONE..............................361 664-5000
Baldemar Alaniz, *President*
Jennifer Alaniz, *Vice Pres*
EMP: 17
SALES (est): 3.5MM **Privately Held**
SIC: 2819 3589 Industrial inorganic chemicals; sandblasting equipment

(G-243)
V P SALES & COMPANY LP
2733 San Diego Hwy 44 W (78332)
P.O. Box 408 (78333-0408)
PHONE..............................361 664-2999
Victor Perez, *Managing Prtnr*
Erik Perez, *Partner*
Pam C Perez, *Partner*
Jesse Guerra, *Sales Staff*
EMP: 22
SQ FT: 5,000
SALES (est): 6.7MM **Privately Held**
WEB: www.stronglinkpumps.com
SIC: 1389 Oil field services

(G-244)
W L FLOWERS MCH WLDG CO INC
Also Called: Flowers Ranch
2585 S Us Highway 281 (78332-3036)
PHONE..............................361 664-6527
Aj Flowers, *President*
Gary Flowers, *Vice Pres*
Ross Flowers, *Vice Pres*
Nancy Haskett, *Admin Sec*
EMP: 60 EST: 1945
SQ FT: 50,000
SALES (est): 9.3MM **Privately Held**
WEB: www.wlflowersmachineshop.com
SIC: 1389 Oil field services

(G-245)
WARRIOR ENERGY SERVICES CORP
Also Called: Spc Rentals
908 Cecilia St (78332-6569)
P.O. Box 137269, Fort Worth (76136-1269)
PHONE..............................817 237-9223
EMP: 15 **Publicly Held**
WEB: www.superiorenergy.com
SIC: 1389 Oil field services
HQ: Warrior Energy Services Corporation
5801 Highway 90 E
Broussard LA 70518
337 714-2400

(G-246)
WEATHERFORD INTERNATIONAL LLC
2650 Old Airport Rd (78332)
PHONE..............................361 815-2104
Byron Sprawls, *Branch Mgr*
EMP: 25 **Privately Held**
WEB: www.weatherford.com
SIC: 3533 Oil field machinery & equipment
HQ: Weatherford International, Llc
2000 Saint James Pl
Houston TX 77056
713 693-4000

Allen
Collin County

(G-247)
ACER AMERICA CORPORATION
900 Guardians Way (75013-1197)
PHONE..............................214 383-3194
EMP: 123 **Privately Held**
WEB: www.acer.com
SIC: 3577 Computer peripheral equipment
HQ: Acer America Corporation
1730 N 1st St Ste 400
San Jose CA 95112
408 533-7700

(G-248)
AIR QUALITY SYSTEMS LLC
207 W Main St Ste 202 (75013-2780)
PHONE..............................214 495-9991
Chris Foster, *Sales Staff*
Laura Mora, *Sales Staff*
Matt Morgan, *Sales Staff*

Paul Parkinson, *Sales Staff*
Jeannie Wertz, *Office Mgr*
EMP: 13
SALES (est): 3.3MM **Privately Held**
WEB: www.airqualitysys.com
SIC: 3564 Air purification equipment

(G-249)
ALYTA INTERNATIONAL CORP (PA)
1511 Bethlehem Rd (75002-5315)
PHONE..............................972 978-1980
Alejandro Garcia, *President*
EMP: 19
SALES (est): 3.6MM **Privately Held**
WEB: www.alytainternational.com
SIC: 3545 Precision measuring tools

(G-250)
AMERICAN PERMANENT WARE CO
Also Called: Apw/Wyott Foodservice Eqp Co
1307 N Watters Rd Ste 180 (75013-5538)
P.O. Box 71 (75013-0002)
PHONE..............................972 908-6100
Hylton Jonas, *President*
Howard Kraines, *Vice Pres*
Brian Rosenbloom, *Vice Pres*
Lawrence Rosenbloom, *Vice Pres*
Don Wall, *Vice Pres*
▲ EMP: 175
SQ FT: 70,000
SALES (est): 31.7MM
SALES (corp-wide): 604.5MM **Publicly Held**
WEB: www.apwwyott.com
SIC: 3914 3634 Stainless steel ware; electric household cooking appliances; toasters, electric: household; teakettles, electric; heating units, for electric appliances
HQ: Associated American Industries, Inc.
1307 N Watters Rd
Allen TX 75013

(G-251)
AMPHENOL CORPORATION
Also Called: Amphenol Fiber Systems
1300 Cntl Expy N Ste 100 (75013)
PHONE..............................214 547-2400
EMP: 345
SALES (corp-wide): 8.6B **Publicly Held**
WEB: www.amphenol.com
SIC: 3678 Electronic connectors
PA: Amphenol Corporation
358 Hall Ave
Wallingford CT 06492
203 265-8900

(G-252)
ASICS AMERICA CORPORATION
820 W Stacy Rd Ste 218 (75013-4841)
PHONE..............................972 678-0200
EMP: 47 **Privately Held**
WEB: www.asics.com
SIC: 5139 5136 5137 2369 Footwear, athletic; sportswear, men's & boys'; men's & boys' furnishings; sportswear, women's & children's; women's & children's accessories; girls' & children's outerwear; women's & misses' outerwear; men's & boys' furnishings
HQ: Asics America Corporation
7755 Irvine Center Dr # 40
Irvine CA 92618
949 453-8888

(G-253)
ATRION CORPORATION (PA)
1 Allentown Pkwy (75002-4206)
PHONE..............................972 390-9800
Emile A Battat, *Ch of Bd*
David A Battat, *President*
Jeff Summers, *Vice Pres*
Stanley Herington, *Facilities Mgr*
Chris Harton, *Engineer*
▲ EMP: 31
SALES (est): 155MM **Publicly Held**
WEB: www.atrioncorp.com
SIC: 3841 Surgical & medical instruments

(G-254)
AUDIOTEL CORPORATION
1021 Central Expy S (75013-2790)
PHONE..............................972 359-5500
Scott Doores, *President*

Sutomu Arifan, *Vice Pres*
EMP: 75
SQ FT: 4,300
SALES (est): 3.5MM
SALES (corp-wide): 1.7B **Publicly Held**
SIC: 7372 Prepackaged software
PA: Jack Henry & Associates, Inc.
663 W Highway 60
Monett MO 65708
417 235-6652

(G-255)
B I PRODUCTS LLC
Also Called: Brooks Instrument
915 Enterprise Blvd (75013-8003)
PHONE..............................972 359-4000
Jim Dale, *CEO*
EMP: 100
SALES (est): 9.6MM **Privately Held**
WEB: www.brooksinstrument.com
SIC: 3677 3823 3643 3625 Electronic coils, transformers & other inductors; industrial instrmnts msrmnt display/control process variable; current-carrying wiring devices; relays & industrial controls
PA: Aip, Llc
450 Lexington Ave Fl 40
New York NY 10017

(G-256)
BAKERS PRIDE OVEN CO INC
Also Called: Baker's Pride
1307 N Watters Rd Ste 180 (75013-5538)
P.O. Box 71 (75013-0002)
PHONE..............................800 431-2745
John Abbott, *Principal*
EMP: 14
SALES (est): 3.6MM **Privately Held**
WEB: www.bakerspride.com
SIC: 3556 Food products machinery

(G-257)
BASWOOD INC (HQ)
825 Watters Creek Blvd # 200 (75013-3779)
P.O. Box 91427, Santa Barbara CA (93190-1427)
PHONE..............................888 560-5517
Dan Simon, *CEO*
Kendall Yorn, *Senior VP*
Phani Peddi, *Engineer*
Kai Zhang, *Engineer*
Jaimi Klein, *Marketing Staff*
EMP: 25
SQ FT: 3,000
SALES (est): 3.1MM **Privately Held**
WEB: www.baswood.com
SIC: 3589 Water treatment equipment, industrial

(G-258)
BRICK DUDES LLC
2347 Timberlake Cir (75013-5835)
PHONE..............................214 592-7904
Edward Padol, *Principal*
EMP: 19 EST: 2014
SALES (est): 3.1MM **Privately Held**
SIC: 3271 Concrete block & brick

(G-259)
COLORDYNAMICS INC
200 E Bethany Dr (75002-3804)
PHONE..............................972 390-6500
Rosemary Leach, *Ch of Bd*
Charles Chalifoux, *President*
Chuck Chalifoux, *President*
Aaron Fitzgerald, *General Mgr*
Joseph Leach, *Vice Pres*
EMP: 340
SQ FT: 70,000
SALES (est): 84.1MM **Privately Held**
WEB: www.colordynamics.com
SIC: 2759 7389 Commercial printing; printing broker

(G-260)
CONCUR TECHNOLOGIES INC
700 Central Expy S # 230 (75013-8098)
PHONE..............................972 612-7121
Steve Stingh, *Branch Mgr*
Kevin Bird, *Manager*
Nathan Novelli, *Technical Staff*
EMP: 11

SALES (corp-wide): 30.4B **Publicly Held**
WEB: www.concur.com
SIC: 7372 Business oriented computer software
HQ: Concur Technologies, Inc.
601 108th Ave Ne Ste 1000
Bellevue WA 98004

(G-261)
CYTRACOM LLC
450 Century Pkwy Ste 100 (75013-8135)
PHONE..............................877 411-2987
Mary Signorelli, *Vice Pres*
Meredith Caram, *VP Sales*
Dave Goldie, *VP Sales*
Steve Conkle,
Ben Booth,
EMP: 12
SALES (est): 1.8MM **Privately Held**
WEB: www.cytracom.com
SIC: 3661 Telephones & telephone apparatus

(G-262)
DIGITAL SPEECH SYSTEMS INC
901 Kilgore Ct (75013-1115)
PHONE..............................972 235-2999
Kevin Smith, *President*
Mike Marshall, *Engineer*
Jane Hatton, *Director*
EMP: 20
SALES (est): 1.5MM **Privately Held**
WEB: www.digitalspeech.com
SIC: 5065 7371 3823 3661 Tapes, audio & video recording; custom computer programming services; industrial instrmnts msrmnt display/control process variable; telephone & telegraph apparatus; computer peripheral equipment

(G-263)
EASTERN STAR GROUP LLC
1512 Harvest Run Dr (75002-4588)
PHONE..............................972 729-9955
Chawanat Penaree, *Manager*
EMP: 13
SALES (est): 2.4MM **Privately Held**
SIC: 3564 1711 7623 Filters, air: furnaces, air conditioning equipment, etc.; heating & air conditioning contractors; air conditioning repair

(G-264)
ELECTION SYSTEMS & SFTWR LLC
1253 Allen Station Pkwy (75002)
PHONE..............................469 675-8990
Hank Foster, *Branch Mgr*
EMP: 60
SALES (corp-wide): 120.4MM **Privately Held**
WEB: www.essvote.com
SIC: 2754 7371 7372 Commercial printing, gravure; computer software systems analysis & design, custom; prepackaged software
PA: Election Systems & Software Llc
11208 John Galt Blvd
Omaha NE 68137
402 593-0101

(G-265)
EPIROC DRILLING SOLUTIONS LLC
Also Called: Allen Distribution Center
815 Enterprise Blvd (75013-2771)
PHONE..............................214 547-7800
Ian Hale, *General Mgr*
EMP: 100
SALES (corp-wide): 4.2B **Privately Held**
WEB: www.us.atlascopco.com
SIC: 3541 5251 Drilling & boring machines; tools
HQ: Epiroc Drilling Solutions Llc
2100 N 1st St
Garland TX 75040
972 496-7400

(G-266)
EWING ELECTRONICS INC
Also Called: Ewing Engineered Solutions
1022 S Grnvlle Ave Ste 30 (75002)
PHONE..............................469 519-2900
Phil Hawley, *President*
Mary K Hawley, *Corp Secy*
Kimberly Felix, *Sr Corp Ofcr*

Frank Felix, *Vice Pres*
Paul Galan, *Vice Pres*
EMP: 11
SQ FT: 3,500
SALES (est): 547.3K **Privately Held**
WEB: www.ewinges.com
SIC: 7629 3663 Electronic equipment repair; carrier equipment, radio communications

(G-267)
FIBER SYSTEMS INTL INC (HQ)
Also Called: Amphenol Fiber Systems Intl
1300 Central Expy N # 100 (75013-6108)
PHONE..................214 547-2400
Martin H Loeffler, *President*
Bill Waite, *VP Opers*
William Waite, *VP Opers*
Michael Cox, *Plant Mgr*
Stacy Usery, *Purch Agent*
▲ **EMP:** 133
SQ FT: 50,000
SALES (est): 19.4MM
SALES (corp-wide): 8.6B **Publicly Held**
WEB: www.fibersystems.com
SIC: 3357 Nonferrous wiredrawing & insulating
PA: Amphenol Corporation
358 Hall Ave
Wallingford CT 06492
203 265-8900

(G-268)
FINISAR CORPORATION
Also Called: AOC
600 Millenium Dr (75013-2791)
PHONE..................214 509-2700
Jeff Brown, *Vice Pres*
Ed Franco, *Purch Mgr*
Jeff Salisbury, *Manager*
Jim Francis, *Director*
Piyush Desai, *Analyst*
EMP: 250
SALES (corp-wide): 2.3B **Publicly Held**
WEB: www.optical.communications.ii-vi.com
SIC: 3674 Semiconductors & related devices
HQ: Finisar Corporation
1389 Moffett Park Dr
Sunnyvale CA 94089
408 548-1000

(G-269)
FORMULIFE INC
1253 Andrews Pkwy (75002-2692)
PHONE..................214 221-4911
Brandon Mark Smith, *President*
Scott Fuhrman, *COO*
Chuck Letchman, *CFO*
Mayra Gonzalez, *Office Mgr*
EMP: 110 **EST:** 2008
SQ FT: 45,000
SALES (est): 12.2MM **Privately Held**
WEB: www.formulifesupplements.com
SIC: 2023 Dietary supplements, dairy & non-dairy based

(G-270)
GC PACKAGING LLC (PA)
204 E Bethany Dr (75002-3804)
PHONE..................214 383-7700
Michael Tinnon, *President*
John Tinnon, *Chairman*
Steve Skalski, *Exec VP*
John Jones, *Maint Spvr*
Joe Yaney, *CFO*
▲ **EMP:** 55
SQ FT: 37,540
SALES (est): 63MM **Privately Held**
WEB: www.gcpackaging.com
SIC: 2754 7389 Cards, except greeting: gravure printing; packaging & labeling services

(G-271)
GTL SUPPLY SOLUTIONS LLC
101 N Greenville Ave C (75002-2200)
PHONE..................214 644-2402
Terry Lacy-Little, *General Mgr*
Rosetta Bullock,
EMP: 10
SQ FT: 1,000

SALES (est): 3.5MM **Privately Held**
WEB: www.gtlsolutions.com
SIC: 5047 1611 3829 Medical & hospital equipment; highway & street construction; thermometers, including digital: clinical

(G-272)
GWM PRODUCTS LLC
Also Called: Keneric Healthcare
825 Watters Creek Blvd # 250 (75013-3770)
PHONE..................855 872-2013
Al Henry, *VP Sales*
Bob Gavranch,
Phil Sheridan,
Harvey Svetlik,
EMP: 10
SALES (est): 1.1MM **Privately Held**
WEB: www.kenerichealthcare.com
SIC: 3842 Bandages & dressings

(G-273)
HEITMAN LABORATORIES INC
4711 Sycamore Ln (75002-5705)
P.O. Box 941390, Plano (75094-1390)
PHONE..................972 982-2224
Lynn Heitman, *CEO*
D L Heitman, *Corp Secy*
EMP: 15
SQ FT: 1,750
SALES (est): 2.5MM **Privately Held**
WEB: www.heitmanlabs.com
SIC: 3829 Liquid leak detection equipment

(G-274)
HI TECH OIL BLENDS INC
Also Called: Champion HI Tech
1005 Hanover Dr (75002-4777)
PHONE..................972 231-5464
▼ **EMP:** 12
SALES: 1MM **Privately Held**
SIC: 2992 5172 Mfg Lubricating Oils/Greases Whol Petroleum Products

(G-275)
HILLTOP TEXAS INC
1420 W Mcdermott Dr # 11 (75013-2846)
PHONE..................214 430-1311
Hussam Almahdwai, *CEO*
EMP: 20
SALES (est): 821.2K **Privately Held**
SIC: 3556 1541 5084 2522 Food products machinery; food products manufacturing or packing plant construction; food product manufacturing machinery; office furniture, except wood; office furniture

(G-276)
HOLLOWAY WELDING & PIPING CO
820 W Forest Grove Rd (75002-8446)
PHONE..................972 562-5033
Stuart Holloway, *President*
David Holloway, *Vice Pres*
Miriam Gomez, *Office Mgr*
Carol Borden, *Manager*
Kevin Holloway, *Admin Sec*
EMP: 15
SQ FT: 6,800
SALES (est): 3.7MM **Privately Held**
WEB: www.hollowaywp.com
SIC: 3441 Fabricated structural metal

(G-277)
HURLEY INTERNATIONAL LLC
820 W Stacy Rd Ste 201 (75013-4800)
PHONE..................972 912-3040
Hurley Npalmer, *Branch Mgr*
EMP: 105
SALES (corp-wide): 118.4MM **Privately Held**
WEB: www.hurley.com
SIC: 2329 Men's & boys' sportswear & athletic clothing
PA: Hurley International Llc
1945 Placentia Ste G
Costa Mesa CA 92627
949 548-9375

(G-278)
IPDISPLAYS LLC
817 S Greenville Ave (75002-3312)
PHONE..................214 453-3570
Kevin Hook, *CEO*
Anna Black, *CFO*
Matt Pope, *Officer*

EMP: 16
SQ FT: 5,000
SALES (est): 1.3MM **Privately Held**
WEB: www.ipdisplays.com
SIC: 3677 Inductors, electronic

(G-279)
J SUZETTE & COMPANY INC (PA)
1293 Allen Station Pkwy (75002)
PHONE..................972 359-0001
Suzette Hohensee, *President*
John P Villarreal, *Vice Pres*
▲ **EMP:** 11
SQ FT: 40,000
SALES (est): 1.3MM **Privately Held**
WEB: www.jsuzette.com
SIC: 2339 Sportswear, women's

(G-280)
JOURNEYEDCOM INC
80 E Mcdermott Dr (75002-2802)
P.O. Box 732357, Dallas (75373-2357)
PHONE..................800 876-3507
Gregory Lamkin, *CEO*
Timothy Lilly, *President*
Shelly Poole, *Accounts Mgr*
Ryan Rodriguez, *Accounts Mgr*
Patee Franks, *Marketing Staff*
EMP: 95
SALES (est): 15.8MM **Privately Held**
WEB: www.journeyed.com
SIC: 8222 7372 8211 5734 Technical institute; educational computer software; specialty education; personal computers; computers, peripherals & software

(G-281)
JW NUTRITIONAL LLC (PA)
601 Century Pkwy Ste 300 (75013-8037)
P.O. Box 258 (75013-0005)
PHONE..................214 221-0404
Jesse D Windrix, *President*
Nick Klugiewicz, *Vice Pres*
Dean Marks, *Warehouse Mgr*
Nate Hewitt, *Opers Staff*
Dra Dragos, *QC Mgr*
▲ **EMP:** 85 **EST:** 2004
SQ FT: 56,000
SALES (est): 35.6MM **Privately Held**
WEB: www.jwnutritional.com
SIC: 2023 Dietary supplements, dairy & non-dairy based

(G-282)
KEYNOTE TECHNOLOGIES LLC
Also Called: Keynote Photonics
400 W Bethany Dr Ste 110 (75013-3714)
PHONE..................877 528-4747
Keith Elliott, *Project Mgr*
Gloria Stringer, *CFO*
Adam Kunzman, *Mng Member*
Amanda Kunzman,
▼ **EMP:** 12
SALES (est): 2.5MM **Privately Held**
WEB: www.keynotephotonics.com
SIC: 7371 3861 8711 Computer software development; projectors, still or motion picture, silent or sound; electrical or electronic engineering

(G-283)
KONE INC
450 Century Pkwy Ste 300 (75013-8136)
PHONE..................469 854-8861
Stefano Socci, *Principal*
EMP: 150
SALES (corp-wide): 11B **Privately Held**
WEB: www.kone.us
SIC: 7699 1796 3534 Elevators: inspection, service & repair; elevator installation & conversion; escalators, passenger & freight
HQ: Kone Inc.
4225 Naperville Rd # 400
Lisle IL 60532
630 577-1650

(G-284)
LANGES LEGACY HOME LTD
23 Prestige Cir (75002-3419)
P.O. Box 2476, Frisco (75034-0045)
PHONE..................972 712-3949
David Lange, *CEO*
Peter Lange, *President*
◆ **EMP:** 10

SALES (est): 1.1MM **Privately Held**
SIC: 2392 Household furnishings

(G-285)
METTLER-TOLEDO LLC
101 N Greenville Ave C (75002-2200)
PHONE..................972 727-8669
Bob Neff, *Manager*
EMP: 19
SALES (corp-wide): 3B **Publicly Held**
WEB: www.mt.com
SIC: 3596 Scales & balances, except laboratory
HQ: Mettler-Toledo, Llc
1900 Polaris Pkwy Fl 6
Columbus OH 43240
614 438-4511

(G-286)
MICRON TECHNOLOGY INC
805 Central Expy S # 100 (75013-8019)
PHONE..................972 521-5200
Noman Qadri, *Engineer*
Dean Walker, *Sales Staff*
Greg Armstrong, *Manager*
Suzaen Jones, *Manager*
A Hawey, *Supervisor*
EMP: 115
SALES (corp-wide): 21.4B **Publicly Held**
WEB: www.micron.com
SIC: 3674 Random access memory (RAM)
PA: Micron Technology, Inc.
8000 S Federal Way
Boise ID 83716
208 368-4000

(G-287)
MICRON TECHNOLOGY TEXAS LLC
805 Central Expy S # 100 (75013-8019)
PHONE..................972 521-5200
Greg Armstrong, *Principal*
Randy Hancock, *Regl Sales Mgr*
Dean Walker, *Sales Staff*
Roger Norwood, *Executive*
EMP: 90
SALES (est): 7.4MM
SALES (corp-wide): 21.4B **Publicly Held**
WEB: www.micron.com
SIC: 3674 Semiconductors & related devices
PA: Micron Technology, Inc.
8000 S Federal Way
Boise ID 83716
208 368-4000

(G-288)
NETSCOUT SYSTEMS TEXAS LLC
915 Guardians Way (75013-1143)
PHONE..................469 330-4000
Doug Barnes, *Vice Pres*
Susan Downing, *Production*
Karl Hansen, *Production*
Jerome Frazier, *Engineer*
John Gerst, *Engineer*
EMP: 300
SALES (corp-wide): 891.8MM **Publicly Held**
WEB: www.kavokerr.com
SIC: 7372 Prepackaged software
HQ: Netscout Systems Texas, Llc
2200 Penn Ave Nw Ste 800w
Washington DC 20037
202 828-0850

(G-289)
NORTH TEXAS EPITAXY LLC
Also Called: Ntxepi
301 Ridgemont Dr (75002-4203)
PHONE..................972 747-8603
Mikko Murto, *Vice Pres*
Sami Simula, *Mng Member*
Todd Bounds,
Dennis Storey,
EMP: 36
SALES (est): 1.6MM **Privately Held**
WEB: www.ntxepi.com
SIC: 3674 Silicon wafers, chemically doped

(G-290)
PEGASUS AUTOMATION INC
130 Danbury Ct (75002-8474)
PHONE..................972 390-9548
Scott Bensmiller, *President*

▲ = Import ▼=Export
◆ =Import/Export

Dewesa Bensmiller, *Admin Sec*
▲ **EMP:** 10 **EST:** 1997
SQ FT: 5,000
SALES (est): 1.3MM **Privately Held**
WEB: www.pegasusautomation.com
SIC: 3625 Relays & industrial controls

(G-291)
PERDURE PETROLEUM LLC
1101 Central Expy S # 150 (75013-8131)
PHONE..................................281 668-8488
Tracy Evans, *CEO*
Russell Martin, *CFO*
EMP: 15
SALES (est): 119.9K **Privately Held**
WEB: www.perdurepetro.com
SIC: 1311 1382 Crude petroleum production; natural gas production; oil & gas exploration services

(G-292)
PHAZR INC
8 Prestige Cir Ste 104 (75002-3425)
PHONE..................................972 693-7829
Farooq Khan, *CEO*
Robert Daniels, *Engrg Dir*
Andrew Thornburg, *Senior Engr*
EMP: 487 **EST:** 2016
SALES (est): 2MM
SALES (corp-wide): 484.2K **Privately Held**
WEB: www.jmawireless.com
SIC: 3663 Radio & TV communications equipment
HQ: John Mezzalingua Associates, Llc
7645 Henry Clay Blvd
Liverpool NY 13088
315 431-7100

(G-293)
PHOENIX MFG INC
2880 Country Club Rd (75002-8717)
PHONE..................................214 544-7507
Joe Powell, *Principal*
EMP: 15 **EST:** 1975
SQ FT: 23,000
SALES (est): 4.3MM **Privately Held**
WEB: www.phoenix-tx.com
SIC: 3444 3599 Sheet metal specialties, not stamped; machine shop, jobbing & repair

(G-294)
PHOTRONICS INC
601 Millenium Dr (75013-2792)
PHONE..................................469 675-8520
Charlie Croke, *General Mgr*
Lucas Gray, *Mfg Spvr*
Wendy Ambrose, *Engineer*
Chris Cooke, *Engineer*
Scott Gallagher, *Engineer*
EMP: 130
SALES (corp-wide): 609.6MM **Publicly Held**
WEB: www.photronics.com
SIC: 3559 Semiconductor manufacturing machinery
PA: Photronics, Inc.
15 Secor Rd
Brookfield CT 06804
203 775-9000

(G-295)
PHOTRONICS TEXAS ALLEN INC
601 Millenium Dr (75013-2792)
PHONE..................................972 889-6275
Charlie Burns, *President*
Donna Bovee, *Vice Pres*
Richelle Burr, *Vice Pres*
Dave Moffett, *Vice Pres*
Sean Smith, *Director*
EMP: 180
SQ FT: 62,000
SALES (est): 15.2MM
SALES (corp-wide): 609.6MM **Publicly Held**
WEB: www.photronics.com
SIC: 3861 Photographic equipment & supplies
PA: Photronics, Inc.
15 Secor Rd
Brookfield CT 06804
203 775-9000

(G-296)
PREMIER ELECTION SOLUTIONS INC (HQ)
1253 Allen Station Pkwy (75002)
PHONE..................................469 675-8990
Robert J Urosevich, *President*
Dave Bird, *CFO*
▲ **EMP:** 40
SALES (est): 10.4MM
SALES (corp-wide): 120.4MM **Privately Held**
WEB: www.essvote.com
SIC: 3579 5087 Voting machines; voting machines
PA: Election Systems & Software Llc
11208 John Galt Blvd
Omaha NE 68137
402 593-0101

(G-297)
QUEST MEDICAL INC
1 Allentown Pkwy (75002-4206)
PHONE..................................800 627-0226
Emile Battat, *President*
Kenneth Jones, *President*
Alfredo Najera, *Purchasing*
Jeff Albertsen, *Research*
Thomas Couch, *Engineer*
▲ **EMP:** 156 **EST:** 1997
SQ FT: 107,000
SALES (est): 33.8MM
SALES (corp-wide): 155MM **Publicly Held**
WEB: www.questmedical.com
SIC: 3841 3845 Surgical & medical instruments; electromedical equipment
PA: Atrion Corporation
1 Allentown Pkwy
Allen TX 75002
972 390-9800

(G-298)
SOFTWARE CONSTRUCTION CO INC (PA)
Also Called: Advanced Data Spectrum
1024 S Greenville Ave # 160 (75002-3348)
PHONE..................................214 495-7387
EMP: 16 **EST:** 1996
SQ FT: 6,000
SALES (est): 1.4MM **Privately Held**
WEB: www.advanceddataspectrum.com
SIC: 7372 Prepackaged software

(G-299)
SRJ HOLDINGS LLC
Also Called: Epitek Silicon
301 Ridgemont Dr (75002-4203)
PHONE..................................972 747-8613
Namraj Johal,
Johnny Ng,
Subba Pinamandni,
EMP: 38
SQ FT: 33,000
SALES (est): 16MM **Privately Held**
SIC: 3674 Integrated circuits, semiconductor networks, etc.

(G-300)
STANDEX INTERNATIONAL CORP
1307 N Watters Rd (75013-5537)
PHONE..................................972 908-6100
EMP: 255
SALES (corp-wide): 604.5MM **Publicly Held**
WEB: www.standex.com
SIC: 3585 Refrigeration & heating equipment
PA: Standex International Corporation
23 Keewaydin Dr Ste 300
Salem NH 03079
603 893-9701

(G-301)
TEL MNFACTURING ENGRG AMER INC
600 Millenium Dr (75013-2791)
PHONE..................................972 643-2000
John Walker, *Manager*
EMP: 120
SQ FT: 178,029 **Privately Held**
SIC: 3559 3821 Semiconductor manufacturing machinery; laboratory apparatus & furniture

HQ: Tel Manufacturing And Engineering Of America, Inc.
3455 Lyman Blvd
Chaska MN 55318
952 448-5440

(G-302)
THRAILKILL ALL METALS FABG INC
Also Called: K-Flex Systems
200 Allentown Pkwy (75002-4210)
PHONE..................................972 747-1230
William B Thrailkill Jr, *CEO*
Eleanor Thrailkill, *Corp Secy*
Tammie Thrailkill Cunningham, *Vice Pres*
Debra Lankin, *Vice Pres*
Will Rushing, *Vice Pres*
EMP: 51
SQ FT: 86,000
SALES (est): 15.6MM **Privately Held**
WEB: www.ametals.com
SIC: 3444 3443 Sheet metalwork; fabricated plate work (boiler shop)

(G-303)
TOPS SOFTWARE CORPORATION
1301 Central Expy S # 200 (75013-8083)
PHONE..................................972 739-8677
William J Rehring, *Owner*
Reet Randhawa, *Engineer*
Trey Carson, *Accounts Mgr*
Logan Sharkey, *Accounts Mgr*
Sarah Kramer, *Manager*
EMP: 20
SALES (est): 4MM **Privately Held**
WEB: www.topseng.com
SIC: 7372 Prepackaged software

(G-304)
TRITECH SOFTWARE DEVELOPMENT
1205 S Greenville Ave (75002-4162)
PHONE..................................972 680-2223
Robert McCollom, *CEO*
Robert Llewellyn, *President*
Mary Caputo, *Vice Pres*
Jennifer Harris, *Vice Pres*
Robbie Mc Collum, *Treasurer*
EMP: 33
SQ FT: 12,599
SALES (est): 644.8K **Privately Held**
WEB: www.tritechsoft.com
SIC: 7371 7372 Computer software development; prepackaged software

(G-305)
UPRIGHT LIGHTING LLC
1513 Jamison Dr (75013-5874)
P.O. Box 1804 (75013-0031)
PHONE..................................408 472-6379
Liang Chen, *Mng Member*
▲ **EMP:** 10
SQ FT: 2,000
SALES (est): 1.1MM **Privately Held**
WEB: www.uprlt.com
SIC: 3641 Health lamps, infrared or ultraviolet

(G-306)
WATCHGUARD INC
Also Called: Watchguard Video
415 E Exchange Pkwy (75002-2616)
PHONE..................................972 423-9777
Robert Vanman, *CEO*
Stephen Coffman, *President*
Ted Hajec, *Vice Pres*
Brian Kirkham, *Vice Pres*
Stuart Mallory, *Vice Pres*
▼ **EMP:** 330
SQ FT: 1,440,000
SALES (est): 59.9MM
SALES (corp-wide): 7.8B **Publicly Held**
WEB: www.watchguardvideo.com
SIC: 3695 Video recording tape, blank
PA: Motorola Solutions, Inc.
500 W Monroe St Ste 4400
Chicago IL 60661
847 576-5000

(G-307)
XTERA INC
Also Called: Xtera Subsea
500 W Bethany Dr Ste 100 (75013-3727)
PHONE..................................972 649-5000

Keith Henderson, *CEO*
Leigh Frame, *COO*
Bill McCutcheon, *Vice Pres*
John McLaughlin, *Engineer*
Stuart Barnes, *Director*
EMP: 30
SALES (est): 3MM **Privately Held**
WEB: www.xtera.com
SIC: 3661 Carrier equipment, telephone or telegraph; multiplex equipment, telephone & telegraph; fiber optics communications equipment

Alleyton
Colorado County

(G-308)
HEADWATERS CNSTR MTLS LLC
Also Called: Southwest Concrete Products
2088 Fm 949 (78935-2124)
PHONE..................................713 393-3300
Kirk A Benson, *CEO*
Bobby L Whishant, *President*
Harlan M Hatfield, *Vice Pres*
Donald P Newman, *CFO*
Scott Jackson, *Treasurer*
EMP: 250
SALES (est): 38.6MM **Privately Held**
WEB: www.headwaterscm.com
SIC: 3271 Concrete block & brick
HQ: Headwaters Incorporated
10701 S River Front Pkwy # 300
South Jordan UT 84095

(G-309)
HEADWATERS INCORPORATED
2088 Fm 949 (78935-2124)
PHONE..................................713 393-3328
Kelli Clogston, *Sales Staff*
Phil Holbrook, *Sales Staff*
Cheryl Kincheloe, *Sales Staff*
Jeff Parker, *Sales Staff*
EMP: 15 **Privately Held**
WEB: www.flyash.com
SIC: 3271 Concrete block & brick
HQ: Headwaters Incorporated
10701 S River Front Pkwy # 300
South Jordan UT 84095

(G-310)
LAUSON DRILLING SERVICES INC
4861 Highway 90 (78935-2051)
P.O. Box 820, Columbus (78934-0820)
PHONE..................................979 733-0345
Raymond Bubak, *President*
EMP: 50
SALES (est): 2MM **Privately Held**
SIC: 1381 Drilling oil & gas wells

Alpine
Brewster County

(G-311)
BIG BEND SADDLERY INC
2701 E Highway 90 (79830-4114)
P.O. Box 38 (79831-0038)
PHONE..................................432 837-5551
Gary Dunshee, *President*
Bret Collier, *Vice Pres*
Carla Spencer, *CFO*
EMP: 10 **EST:** 1977
SQ FT: 4,000
SALES (est): 1.2MM **Privately Held**
WEB: www.bigbendsaddlery.com
SIC: 5941 3199 5699 5611 Saddlery & equestrian equipment; saddles or parts; belts, apparel: custom; hats, men's & boys'; men's boots

(G-312)
TEXAS RAPID LLC
10 Los Ranchos Dr (79830-8000)
PHONE..................................432 837-1049
Charles Weinacht, *President*
Ray Kesey, *Corp Secy*
Alexander Nadvorsky, *Vice Pres*
EMP: 20
SALES (est): 1.6MM **Privately Held**
SIC: 1481 Nonmetallic mineral services

(G-313)
WTG FUELS INC
3001 N State Highway 118 (79830-2500)
P.O. Box 1398 (79831-1398)
PHONE....................................432 837-2518
Buddy Cavness, *Branch Mgr*
EMP: 16
SALES (corp-wide): 96.1MM **Privately Held**
WEB: www.wtgfuels.com
SIC: 5989 2992 Coal; lubricating oils
HQ: Wtg Fuels, Inc.
    211 N Colorado St
    Midland TX 79701

Alto
Cherokee County

(G-314)
ATHLETIC HLMET RCNDTIONING LLC
17548 Us Highway 69 S (75925-4006)
PHONE....................................936 858-9990
EMP: 40 EST: 2010
SALES (est): 2.5MM **Privately Held**
WEB: www.helmetrecon.com
SIC: 3949 Helmets, athletic

(G-315)
FORREST HODGES OPERATIONS
10922 State Highway 21 (75925-5030)
PHONE....................................936 867-4910
Forrest K Hodges, *President*
EMP: 43
SALES (est): 15MM **Privately Held**
SIC: 2411 Logging

(G-316)
HICKS POST CO INC
10690 Us Highway 69 S (75925-5962)
PHONE....................................936 858-4228
Alton J Hicks, *President*
Juanita Hicks, *Vice Pres*
EMP: 20
SQ FT: 1,280
SALES (est): 2.6MM **Privately Held**
WEB: www.hickspost.com
SIC: 2411 2421 Posts, wood: hewn, round or split; cants, resawed (lumber)

(G-317)
LEO HICKS CREOSOTING CO INC
11840 Us Highway 69 S (75925-6046)
P.O. Box 498 (75925-0498)
PHONE....................................936 858-4419
Frances Hicks, *President*
Anne McLinden, *Vice Pres*
Kim Hopper, *Treasurer*
Pam Johnson, *Admin Sec*
EMP: 16
SQ FT: 2,320
SALES (est): 2.9MM **Privately Held**
WEB: www.hickspost.com
SIC: 2491 Wood preserving

(G-318)
WARNER BAILEY INC
Also Called: Boss Tiedowns & Strapping
4736 Us Highway 69 S (75925-6631)
P.O. Box 769, Wells (75976-9007)
PHONE....................................936 867-4801
Blake Bailey, *CEO*
Nona Bailey, *CFO*
EMP: 18
SALES (est): 1.3MM **Privately Held**
WEB: www.bossstraps.com
SIC: 2299 2421 Batting, wadding, padding & fillings; lumber: rough, sawed or planed

(G-319)
WEST CRAFT MANUFACTURING INC
506 Palestine Rd (75925-2145)
P.O. Box 596 (75925-0596)
PHONE....................................936 858-4426
Gerald West, *President*
Josh West, *Vice Pres*
▲ EMP: 94
SQ FT: 40,000

SALES (est): 24.5MM **Privately Held**
WEB: www.westcraftmfg.com
SIC: 3593 Fluid power cylinders, hydraulic or pneumatic

(G-320)
XTO ENERGY INC
12642 Us Highway 69 S (75925-6024)
PHONE....................................936 858-3533
EMP: 44
SALES (corp-wide): 264.9B **Publicly Held**
WEB: www.xtoenergy.com
SIC: 1311 Crude petroleum production
HQ: Xto Energy Inc.
    22777 Sprngwoods Vlg Pkwy
    Spring TX 77389

Alton
Hidalgo County

(G-321)
ALOE VERA OF AMERICA INC
1401 N Inspiration Blvd (78573-1479)
PHONE....................................956 585-9704
Xavier Resendez, *Manager*
EMP: 125
SALES (corp-wide): 76.3MM **Privately Held**
SIC: 2844 7231 5261 2833 Cosmetic preparations; facial salons; nurseries; medicinals & botanicals
PA: Aloe Vera Of America, Inc.
    13745 Jupiter Rd
    Dallas TX 75238
    214 355-5400

(G-322)
CAST SHEET METAL LLC
715 N Bryan Blvd (78573-1433)
P.O. Box 5926, McAllen (78502-5926)
PHONE....................................956 580-9960
Oscar D Castaneda, *Mng Member*
EMP: 49
SQ FT: 600
SALES (est): 1.9MM **Privately Held**
WEB: www.castsheetmetalllc.business.site
SIC: 1711 3441 Plumbing, heating, air-conditioning contractors; fabricated structural metal

Alvarado
Johnson County

(G-323)
AMERICAN FILM & PRINTING LTD
502 E Shelton St (76009-3902)
PHONE....................................817 783-7600
Blake Hanna, *President*
▲ EMP: 60
SALES (est): 5.4MM **Privately Held**
WEB: www.americanfilmandprinting.com
SIC: 2759 2673 Commercial printing; plastic bags: made from purchased materials

(G-324)
BEAKLEY ENTERPRISES INC (PA)
Also Called: C & W Manufacturing & Sales Co
6933 Shelmor Rd (76009-5876)
P.O. Box 908, Crowley (76036-0908)
PHONE....................................817 783-5000
Deryl Beakley, *President*
April Day, *Traffic Mgr*
Leslie McWhorter, *Purch Mgr*
Jon Haines, *Engineer*
Robert Smith, *Engineer*
EMP: 32
SQ FT: 34,000
SALES (est): 6.4MM **Privately Held**
WEB: www.cwdusttech.com
SIC: 3564 Dust or fume collecting equipment, industrial

(G-325)
BHC INDUSTRIES OF TEXAS INC
486 County Road St 318 (76009)
PHONE....................................817 556-2306

Gary Barken, *Owner*
EMP: 16
SALES (est): 3MM **Privately Held**
WEB: www.barkenshardchrome.com
SIC: 3999 3471 3356 Barber & beauty shop equipment; plating of metals or formed products; nickel

(G-326)
BRANCH IRONWORKS LLC
7733 E Fm 917 (76009-8504)
P.O. Box 1449, Burleson (76097-1449)
PHONE....................................817 783-5183
Rick Motley, *Project Mgr*
Cindy Fincher, *Office Mgr*
Eddy Branch, *Mng Member*
EMP: 15
SALES (est): 4.3MM **Privately Held**
WEB: www.branchironworks.com
SIC: 3446 Architectural metalwork

(G-327)
COLOR FAST INDUSTRIES INC
Also Called: Colorfast
912 W Highway 67 (76009-3251)
PHONE....................................817 546-4910
Dexter Tuttle, *President*
Bob Pugh, *Sales Staff*
Zack Tuttle, *Sales Staff*
EMP: 22
SQ FT: 10,000
SALES (est): 5.4MM **Privately Held**
WEB: www.colorfastind.com
SIC: 2842 Specialty cleaning, polishes & sanitation goods

(G-328)
DFW INFRASTRUCTURE INC
809 Fm 2738 (76009-6728)
P.O. Box 7347, Fort Worth (76111-0347)
PHONE....................................888 739-9070
Donna Brown, *President*
EMP: 13
SALES (est): 1.7MM **Privately Held**
WEB: www.dfwinfrastructure.com
SIC: 4959 3271 1623 Sanitary services; sewer & manhole block, concrete; water & sewer line construction

(G-329)
ELITE COATING SERVICES
10616 County Road 604 (76009-8595)
PHONE....................................469 431-3353
EMP: 16
SALES (est): 1.8MM **Privately Held**
SIC: 3479 Metal coating & allied service

(G-330)
EOG RESOURCES INC
4449 S Interstate 35 W (76009-6397)
PHONE....................................817 212-3100
Ronald Oden, *Opers Staff*
EMP: 42
SALES (corp-wide): 17.3B **Publicly Held**
WEB: www.eogresources.com
SIC: 1382 Oil & gas exploration services
PA: Eog Resources, Inc.
    1111 Bagby Sky Lbby 2
    Houston TX 77002
    713 651-7000

(G-331)
F & F INDUSTRIES INC
Also Called: Centramatic
5345 S Interstate 35 W (76009-6382)
P.O. Box 310 (76009-0310)
PHONE....................................800 523-8473
Robert Coolidge, *President*
Floyd Allred, *Vice Pres*
Christopher Harris, *Vice Pres*
EMP: 15
SQ FT: 25,600
SALES (est): 9.1MM **Privately Held**
WEB: www.centramatic.com
SIC: 3559 Wheel balancing equipment, automotive

(G-332)
FILTRATION AUTOMATION INC
Also Called: Micron-Pro, The
4541 J D Mouser Pkwy (76009-5158)
PHONE....................................817 999-8190
Gary H Haddock, *President*
Stephen Haddock, *Vice Pres*
EMP: 32
SQ FT: 12,000

SALES (est): 1MM **Privately Held**
WEB: www.micronpro.com
SIC: 3677 3589 3556 5084 Filtration devices, electronic; commercial cooking & foodwarming equipment; food products machinery; food product manufacturing machinery

(G-333)
HALLIBURTON COMPANY
Also Called: Jet Research Center
8432 S I 35 W S (76009-8214)
P.O. Box 327 (76009-0327)
PHONE....................................817 783-5111
Anton Schweitzer, *Manager*
Victor Fuchs, *Technical Staff*
EMP: 200 **Publicly Held**
WEB: www.halliburton.com
SIC: 1629 2892 3533 Power plant construction; explosives; oil & gas field machinery
PA: Halliburton Company
    3000 N Sam Houston Pkwy E
    Houston TX 77032

(G-334)
HERITAGE STL ERCTION FBRCATION
4639 S Interstate 35 W (76009-6399)
P.O. Box 112, Cleburne (76033-0112)
PHONE....................................817 790-5170
Fax: 817 783-2864
EMP: 14
SALES (est): 1MM **Privately Held**
SIC: 1791 3441 Structural Steel Erection Structural Metal Fabrication

(G-335)
I 35 SANDPIT INC
4531 S Interstate 35 W (76009-6398)
P.O. Box 611 (76009-0611)
PHONE....................................817 790-2772
Finis L Shipman Jr, *President*
EMP: 35
SQ FT: 15,000
SALES (est): 5.5MM **Privately Held**
SIC: 1442 4212 Sand mining; local trucking, without storage

(G-336)
JOHNSON COUNTY PIPE INC
800 County Road 209 (76009-8028)
PHONE....................................817 783-3444
Kevin Thompson, *President*
Lane Chamblee, *Regl Sales Mgr*
▲ EMP: 100
SALES (est): 36.8MM **Privately Held**
WEB: www.uscompositepipe.com
SIC: 3498 Fabricated pipe & fittings

(G-337)
PKS DESIGNS INC
9329 County Road 519 (76009-6046)
PHONE....................................817 429-5174
Philip Shoults, *President*
EMP: 16
SALES (est): 1MM **Privately Held**
SIC: 3281 1743 Granite, cut & shaped; marble installation, interior

(G-338)
QUALITY ROLLER SUPPLY INC
9620 E Fm Hwy 917 (76009)
P.O. Box 509, Lillian (76061-0509)
PHONE....................................817 783-5100
Darin Debaun, *President*
EMP: 13
SQ FT: 12,000
SALES (est): 2.6MM **Privately Held**
SIC: 3555 Printing trades machinery

(G-339)
QUIKRETE COMPANIES LLC
1008 E Highway 67 (76009-3302)
PHONE....................................817 783-3010
Cary Gaskell, *Plant Mgr*
Joe Kerlee, *Sales Staff*
EMP: 80 **Privately Held**
WEB: www.quikrete.com
SIC: 5032 3241 Cement; cement, hydraulic
HQ: The Quikrete Companies Llc
    5 Concourse Pkwy Ste 1900
    Atlanta GA 30328
    404 634-9100

(G-340)
RISK MANAGEMENT ARMORED SEC
8909 County Road 109 (76009-6971)
PHONE................................817 932-5923
Irma Rebecca Sanchez, *Principal*
Joseph Kelley, *Principal*
EMP: 15
SALES (est): 769.9K **Privately Held**
SIC: 6289 1731 3699 7381 Security transfer agents; safety & security specialization; security devices; detective & armored car services; security guard service

(G-341)
RIVAL PRCSION MNFCTRNG RPM LLC
4545 J D Mouser Pkwy (76009-5158)
PHONE................................817 487-9694
Steton Gilley, *President*
EMP: 15
SALES (est): 233.5K **Privately Held**
SIC: 3999 Manufacturing industries

(G-342)
RLRA INC
3813 Easy St (76009-6005)
PHONE................................817 783-3335
EMP: 11
SQ FT: 2,000
SALES (est): 693.8K **Privately Held**
SIC: 7374 7372 Data Processing/Preparation Prepackaged Software Services

(G-343)
SABRE INDUSTRIES INC (HQ)
Also Called: Sabre Communications
8653 E Highway 67 (76009-4012)
P.O. Box 658, Sioux City IA (51102-0658)
PHONE................................817 852-1700
Peter Sandore, *President*
Ray McRae, *General Mgr*
Andres Franzese, *Exec VP*
Carroll Baynard, *Vice Pres*
Richard Guipe, *Vice Pres*
▼ EMP: 500
SALES (est): 638.9MM
SALES (corp-wide): 5.6B **Privately Held**
WEB: www.sabreindustriesinc.com
SIC: 3441 Tower sections, radio & television transmission
PA: Kohlberg & Co., L.L.C.
111 Radio Circle Dr
Mount Kisco NY 10549
914 241-7430

(G-344)
SABRE INDUSTRIES INC
Sabre Galvanizing Services
8669 E Highway 67 (76009-4012)
PHONE................................817 852-1950
Carroll Baynard, *General Mgr*
Darin Gilligan, *Buyer*
Sandy Meredith, *Buyer*
Lisa Nairn, *Office Mgr*
Michael Del Giudice, *Director*
EMP: 12
SALES (corp-wide): 5.6B **Privately Held**
WEB: www.sabreindustriesinc.com
SIC: 3441 Fabricated structural metal
HQ: Sabre Industries, Inc.
8653 E Highway 67
Alvarado TX 76009
817 852-1700

(G-345)
SEIDLER OIL & GAS LP
7140 E Fm 917 (76009-6025)
PHONE................................817 259-1777
Frank Seidler, *President*
Candace Seidler, *Exec VP*
Hampo Hekimian, *Vice Pres*
Matthew Wilde, *VP Opers*
Mary Dvorak, *VP Finance*
EMP: 9
SALES (est): 1MM **Privately Held**
WEB: www.soglp.com
SIC: 1382 Oil & gas exploration services

(G-346)
TERVITA LLC
7912 S Ih 35 W (76009)
PHONE................................817 783-2777
Steve Wood, *Manager*

EMP: 10
SALES (corp-wide): 10.3B **Publicly Held**
WEB: www.tervita.com
SIC: 1389 Oil field services
HQ: Tervita, Llc
10613 W Sam Houston Pkwy
Houston TX 77064
832 399-4500

(G-347)
TOTAL PALLET SOLUTIONS LLC
Also Called: T P S
3532 S Burleson Blvd (76009-6364)
P.O. Box 12446, Fort Worth (76110-8446)
PHONE................................817 783-5565
Kyle Lane, *President*
Jody Goldsberry, *Opers Staff*
Alexis Lane Lane, *Treasurer*
EMP: 23
SALES (est): 4.5MM **Privately Held**
WEB: www.totalpalletsolutions.com
SIC: 2448 Pallets, wood

(G-348)
US COMPOSITE PIPE INC
800 County Rd Ste 209 (76009)
PHONE................................817 783-3444
Kenneth M Thompson, *President*
Eric H Davidson, *Vice Pres*
Rafael Deloera, *Vice Pres*
EMP: 50
SALES (est): 4.9MM **Privately Held**
WEB: www.uscompositepipe.com
SIC: 3498 Fabricated pipe & fittings

Alvin
Brazoria County

(G-349)
ADVANCED MAT SYSTEMS LLC
1030 1/2 County Road 129 (77511-8730)
PHONE................................281 839-4258
Kendall Kinchen,
EMP: 9
SALES (est): 1.2MM **Privately Held**
WEB: www.advancedmatsystems.com
SIC: 3061 Mechanical rubber goods

(G-350)
AHI SUPPLY INC (PA)
Also Called: A H I
2800 N Gordon St (77511-9581)
P.O. Box 2789 (77512-2789)
PHONE................................281 331-0088
Robert N Allen, *Ch of Bd*
William M Hill, *President*
Christopher Sellers, *Vice Pres*
Annette Widmer, *Production*
Mike Hill, *Personnel*
EMP: 55
SQ FT: 3,000
SALES (est): 25.2MM **Privately Held**
WEB: www.ahi-supply.com
SIC: 3241 3441 3271 5032 Masonry cement; fabricated structural metal; architectural concrete: block, split, fluted, screen, etc.; building stone

(G-351)
ALVIN SUN & ADVERTISER INC
Also Called: Alvin Sun, The
570 Dula St (77511-2942)
PHONE................................281 331-4421
Fred Hartman, *President*
Jim Schwind, *Principal*
Don F Jones, *Corp Secy*
EMP: 20 EST: 1956
SALES (est): 1.3MM **Privately Held**
WEB: www.alvinsun.net
SIC: 2711 Newspapers: publishing only, not printed on site

(G-352)
ASCEND PRFMCE MTLS OPRTONS LLC
Fm Rd 2917 (77512)
P.O. Box 711 (77512-0711)
PHONE................................281 228-4000
Paul Cartlidge, *Plant Mgr*
Lou Gerona, *Human Res Dir*
Shay Johnson, *Technician*
EMP: 373

SALES (corp-wide): 992.8MM **Privately Held**
WEB: www.ascendmaterials.com
SIC: 2821 Plastics materials & resins
HQ: Ascend Performance Materials Operations Llc
1010 Travis St Ste 900
Houston TX 77002

(G-353)
AXXAIRUSA INC
2201 Highway 35 Byp N D (77511-8887)
P.O. Box 867 (77512-0867)
PHONE................................281 968-7138
Jonathan Forte, *General Mgr*
▲ EMP: 9
SALES (est): 1MM **Privately Held**
WEB: www.axxairusa.com
SIC: 3317 Steel pipe & tubes

(G-354)
BEAED LP (PA)
Also Called: Communikay Graphics
1850 Highway 35 Byp N (77511-4785)
P.O. Box 1760 (77512-1760)
PHONE................................281 331-2035
Lawrence Mann, *General Mgr*
William Hartman, *General Ptnr*
Mike Hebert, *Accounting Mgr*
Joe Crowley, *VP Sales*
Joseph Crowley, *VP Sales*
▼ EMP: 77 EST: 1978
SQ FT: 45,000
SALES (est): 12.7MM **Privately Held**
WEB: www.beaed.com
SIC: 3993 3999 Signs, not made in custom sign painting shops; identification tags, except paper

(G-355)
BEAED LP
Also Called: Communikay Graphics
1900 Highway 35 Byp N (77511-4786)
P.O. Box 2347 (77512-2347)
PHONE................................281 968-7249
Lany Corral, *Sales Staff*
Jody Douce, *Manager*
EMP: 40
SALES (corp-wide): 12.7MM **Privately Held**
WEB: www.beaed.com
SIC: 3993 Signs, not made in custom sign painting shops
PA: Beaed, L.P.
1850 Highway 35 Byp N
Alvin TX 77511
281 331-2035

(G-356)
COASTAL PLASTIC MOLDING INC
735 County Road 281 (77511-1431)
PHONE................................281 331-7909
Robert C Wall, *President*
Carolyn S Wall, *Treasurer*
EMP: 12
SQ FT: 7,600
SALES (est): 1.5MM **Privately Held**
WEB: www.coastalplastics.com
SIC: 3089 Injection molding of plastics

(G-357)
DAPCO SERVICES INC
18854 Avitts Acres (77511-4582)
PHONE................................281 482-1479
EMP: 13 EST: 2013
SALES (est): 2MM **Privately Held**
WEB: www.dapcoservices.com
SIC: 1389 Oil field services

(G-358)
DENBURY ONSHORE LLC
Also Called: Denbury Management
19315 N Highway 35 (77511-8711)
PHONE................................281 482-7581
Jeff Marcel, *Branch Mgr*
EMP: 17
SALES (corp-wide): 1.2B **Publicly Held**
WEB: www.denbury.com
SIC: 1311 1381 Crude petroleum & natural gas; drilling oil & gas wells
HQ: Denbury Onshore, Llc
5320 Legacy Dr
Plano TX 75024
972 673-2000

(G-359)
DIPPER INC
1107 W Highway 6 (77511-7655)
P.O. Box 400 (77512-0400)
PHONE................................281 585-8400
Charles Dunn, *President*
Karen Nash, *Vice Pres*
◆ EMP: 9
SALES (est): 1.8MM **Privately Held**
WEB: www.thedipper.com
SIC: 2899 5199 5331 Incense; general merchandise, non-durable; variety stores

(G-360)
DIRECT PRCHASE QICK CPLNGS INC
Also Called: Dnp Industrial
860 Fm 517 Rd (77511-7478)
PHONE................................281 388-0253
Charles Pate, *President*
EMP: 20
SALES (est): 1.4MM **Privately Held**
WEB: www.dnpamericas.com
SIC: 3492 Hose & tube couplings, hydraulic/pneumatic

(G-361)
E J REYNOLDS COMPANY INC
4252 Fm 528 Rd (77511-7522)
PHONE................................281 331-4556
Eddy Reynolds, *CEO*
Amy Reynolds, *President*
Brandon Crain, *General Mgr*
Slinda Knape, *Admin Sec*
EMP: 15
SQ FT: 6,000
SALES (est): 4.8MM **Privately Held**
WEB: www.ejreynolds.com
SIC: 2891 7699 0291 Sealants; compressor repair; animal specialty farm, general

(G-362)
FRANKS INTERNATIONAL LLC
3735 E Hwy 6 (77511)
P.O. Box 1324 (77512-1324)
PHONE................................281 331-1501
Terry Bartusk, *Manager*
EMP: 70
SQ FT: 1,400
SALES (corp-wide): 581MM **Privately Held**
WEB: www.franksinternational.com
SIC: 1382 Oil & gas exploration services
HQ: Frank's International, Llc
10260 Westheimer Rd
Houston TX 77042
281 966-7300

(G-363)
GAS TURBINE ENGINES INC (PA)
Also Called: G T Enterprises
1001 Highway 35 Byp N (77511-2593)
P.O. Box 1787 (77512-1787)
PHONE................................281 824-9200
George Tobon, *President*
Ginger Denos, *Vice Pres*
▲ EMP: 15
SQ FT: 300,000
SALES (est): 2.5MM **Privately Held**
WEB: www.gtein.com
SIC: 3728 Aircraft parts & equipment

(G-364)
GLOBAL AM-TX, INC.
210 S Hood St (77511-2353)
P.O. Box 1287 (77512-1287)
PHONE................................281 331-0200
▲ EMP: 17
SALES (est): 5.8MM **Privately Held**
WEB: www.globalam-tx.com
SIC: 1389 Oil field services

(G-365)
HAWKINS LEASE SERVICE INC (PA)
3205 Fm 2403 Rd (77511-1448)
P.O. Box 1699 (77512-1699)
PHONE................................281 331-2739
Richard J Hawkins, *President*
Eugenio Garza, *Superintendent*
James Bendele, *Manager*
Monika Stefanini, *Manager*
Christy Villalobos, *Manager*

G E O G R A P H I C

EMP: 70
SQ FT: 4,250
SALES (est): 31MM Privately Held
WEB: www.hawkinsleaseservice.com
SIC: 1389 Oil field services

(G-366)
INEOS OLIGOMERS USA LLC
2 Miles S Of Fm 2917 Fm 2 (77512)
PHONE.............................281 581-3203
EMP: 28
SALES (corp-wide): 4.8MM Privately Held
SIC: 2869 Ethylene
PA: Ineos Oligomers Usa Llc
    2600 S Shore Blvd Ste 400
    League City TX 77573
    281 535-4266

(G-367)
INTERNATIONAL COMMODITIES
301 N Highway 6 (77511-5621)
P.O. Box 141 (77512-0141)
PHONE.............................281 331-1252
Herbert J Zieben, Ch of Bd
David Vlasek, President
Jerrel E Sullivan, Principal
EMP: 12
SQ FT: 14,000
SALES (est): 2.2MM Privately Held
SIC: 3549 Screw driving machines

(G-368)
J W HALL ENTERPRISES INC
17731 Elizabeth Rd (77511-8431)
P.O. Box 68, Santa Fe (77517-0068)
PHONE.............................409 925-7712
John Kantowski, President
Delia Hall, Treasurer
EMP: 10
SQ FT: 1,000
SALES (est): 1.7MM Privately Held
WEB: www.jwhall.com
SIC: 3441 3599 Fabricated structural
    metal; machine shop, jobbing & repair

(G-369)
J W HALL LTD LIABILITY CO
Also Called: Gulf Runner Yatchs
17731 Elizabeth Rd (77511-8431)
PHONE.............................281 337-6311
Patricia K Kantowski,
EMP: 10
SALES (est): 1.2MM Privately Held
WEB: www.jwhall.com
SIC: 3599 Machine & other job shop work

(G-370)
K-3 RESOURCES LP (PA)
Also Called: K3 Bmi
850 County Road 149 (77511-1316)
P.O. Box 2236 (77512-2236)
PHONE.............................281 585-2817
Karlis Ercums III, General Ptnr
Kerry Ercums, VP Sales
Scott Womack, Sales Staff
James Morris, Manager
Donna Taylor, Technology
EMP: 74
SQ FT: 1,200
SALES (est): 112.5MM Privately Held
WEB: www.k3bmi.us
SIC: 1389 Oil field services

(G-371)
LARRY GRIMES INTEREST INC
1006 Fm 517 Rd (77511-6608)
P.O. Box 2807 (77512-2807)
PHONE.............................281 331-3273
Larry Grimes, CEO
Marie Grimes, President
Brian Grimes, Vice Pres
EMP: 13
SQ FT: 5,000
SALES (est): 2MM Privately Held
SIC: 3599 Machine shop, jobbing & repair

(G-372)
LUMADYNE LLC
1600 E Highway 6 Ste 425 (77511-2575)
P.O. Box 20425, Houston (77225-0425)
PHONE.............................281 220-2409
Cristopher L Harris, Owner
Purvez Captain, Principal
Cristopher Harris,
EMP: 9 EST: 2012

SALES (est): 1MM Privately Held
WEB: www.lumadyne.com
SIC: 3821 Physics laboratory apparatus

(G-373)
MARVIN DACE COMPANY
Also Called: Dace Manufacturing
18315 W Clover Ln (77511-1213)
PHONE.............................281 482-1450
EMP: 10
SALES (est): 1.4MM Privately Held
SIC: 3585 5999 7389 Air conditioning
    condensers & condensing units; flags;

(G-374)
NORAK INC
44 County Road 249 (77511-1585)
PHONE.............................281 585-4091
Karon Winwood, President
EMP: 9
SALES (est): 1.3MM Privately Held
WEB: www.norakinc.com
SIC: 3823 Industrial instrmnts msrmnt dis-
    play/control process variable

(G-375)
OGBURN TRUCK PARTS LP
19511 Highway 35 (77511-1402)
PHONE.............................281 331-0005
Gilbert Perez, Branch Mgr
EMP: 11
SALES (corp-wide): 34.5MM Privately Held
WEB: www.ogburns.com
SIC: 5531 5013 3069 Truck equipment &
    parts; automotive servicing equipment;
    brake linings, rubber
PA: Ogburns Truck Parts L.P
    900 E Northside Dr
    Fort Worth TX 76102
    817 332-1511

(G-376)
OIL STATES ENERGY SERVICES LLC
1131 Fm 517 Rd (77511-1876)
PHONE.............................281 331-1800
Robert Hollier, Branch Mgr
EMP: 30
SALES (corp-wide): 1B Publicly Held
WEB: www.oses.com
SIC: 1389 Oil field services
HQ: Oil States Energy Services, L.L.C.
    333 Clay St Ste 2100
    Houston TX 77002
    713 425-2400

(G-377)
PHOENIX MILLWORK LLC
Also Called: Phoenix Construction Services
1901 E House St (77511-4109)
P.O. Box 2788 (77512-2788)
PHONE.............................281 388-2211
Mark Hamilton, President
Les Hansen, CFO
EMP: 60
SQ FT: 25,000
SALES (est): 13.6MM Privately Held
WEB: www.phoenixmillwork.net
SIC: 2431 1742 Millwork; drywall

(G-378)
REACTOR SERVICES INTERNATIONAL
Also Called: RSI
200 Avenue I Bldg G (77511-5523)
PHONE.............................281 824-0841
Merlin Hoiseth, Ch of Bd
EMP: 11
SALES (est): 2.1MM Privately Held
WEB: www.reactorservices.com
SIC: 3559 Petroleum refinery equipment

(G-379)
RICETEC INC (PA)
1925 Fm 2917 Rd (77511-1755)
P.O. Box 1305 (77512-1305)
PHONE.............................281 756-3300
Mike Gumina, CEO
Kevin Segers, Area Mgr
Federico Cuevas, Exec VP
Robert Grant, Vice Pres
Larry Haugen, Vice Pres
◆ EMP: 140

SALES (est): 75MM Privately Held
WEB: www.ricetec.com
SIC: 2044 Rice milling

(G-380)
SOUTHWEST REFRACTORY TEXAS LP
Also Called: Southwest Companies
2443 N Gordon St Ste A (77511-4590)
P.O. Box 1308 (77512-1308)
PHONE.............................979 285-7219
Rodney Rudell, Partner
Bryan Culwell, Manager
Andee Hasty, Office Admin
▲ EMP: 50
SALES (est): 11.7MM Privately Held
WEB: www.swrrefractory.com
SIC: 3297 1741 Nonclay refractories; re-
    fractory or acid brick masonry

(G-381)
T & L LEASE SERVICE LTD
Also Called: T and L Environmental
427 E South St (77511-3557)
P.O. Box 760 (77512-0760)
PHONE.............................281 331-8221
EMP: 130
SQ FT: 15,000
SALES (est): 29.5MM Privately Held
SIC: 1389 Construction, repair & disman-
    tling services

(G-382)
TOTAL GROW HOLDINGS LLC
Also Called: Total Grow Control
2190 Washington Ave (77511-6522)
PHONE.............................281 585-9500
Derek Oxford, Mng Member
Allan Waldhim,
EMP: 15
SALES (est): 1.3MM Privately Held
WEB: www.totalgrowcontrol.com
SIC: 3625 Control equipment, electric

(G-383)
U S WEATHERFORD L P
2548 E Highway 6 (77511)
PHONE.............................281 331-5505
Andy Hickman, Manager
EMP: 35
SQ FT: 10,000 Privately Held
WEB: www.weatherford.com
SIC: 1389 Oil field services
HQ: U S Weatherford L P
    179 Weatherford Dr
    Schriever LA 70395
    985 493-6100

(G-384)
UNICAT CATALYST TECH LLC
5918 S Highway 35 (77511-8208)
P.O. Box 1516 (77512-1516)
PHONE.............................281 331-2231
Mani Erfan, CEO
Larry Foley, COO
Eric Steens, Vice Pres
Xavier Llorente, Engineer
Kathy McKimmy, CFO
▲ EMP: 15
SALES (est): 26MM Privately Held
WEB: www.unicatcatalyst.com
SIC: 2819 Catalysts, chemical

(G-385)
UV COUNTRY INC
Also Called: Uvc Pwersports Trctrs Outdoors
2616 Tx 35 (77511)
P.O. Box 2729 (77512-2729)
PHONE.............................713 649-0556
Scott M Tracy, Dir Ops-Prd-Mfg
Shannon Tracy, Director
EMP: 27
SQ FT: 5,400
SALES (est): 1.9MM Privately Held
WEB: www.uvcountry.com
SIC: 3799 7532 All terrain vehicles (ATV);
    customizing services, non-factory basis

(G-386)
WOVEN METAL PRODUCTS INC (PA)
1201 Fm 517 (77511)
P.O. Box 1384 (77512-1384)
PHONE.............................281 331-4466
Russell Hillenburg, President
Heather Bennett, Business Mgr

Roy Hillenburg, Vice Pres
Heather Allen, Vice Pres
Gene Eberhardt, Vice Pres
◆ EMP: 35
SQ FT: 2,000
SALES (est): 9.8MM Privately Held
WEB: www.wovenmetal.com
SIC: 3441 3446 3444 3443 Fabricated
    structural metal; architectural metalwork;
    sheet metalwork; fabricated plate work
    (boiler shop)

(G-387)
X-ANALOG COMMUNICATIONS INC
1835 Algoa Friendswood Rd (77511-8479)
PHONE.............................409 925-4702
▲ EMP: 20
SALES (est): 3.9MM Privately Held
SIC: 3663 Mfg Radio/Tv Communication
    Equipment

Alvord
Wise County

(G-388)
M R FABRICATION
3640 County Road 2690 (76225-4313)
PHONE.............................940 427-4701
Russell Stephens, Owner
Cindy Stevens, Owner
Cindy Stephens, Co-Owner
EMP: 9 EST: 1997
SALES (est): 1MM Privately Held
WEB: www.mr-fabrication.com
SIC: 7692 Welding repair

(G-389)
MIRAMAR WF LLC
3858 N Us Highway 287 (76225-7915)
PHONE.............................940 626-4309
Gary Shell, Manager
EMP: 11 Privately Held
WEB: www.midwesternmud.com
SIC: 1381 Drilling oil & gas wells
PA: Miramar Wf, Llc
    811 6th St Ste 205
    Wichita Falls TX

(G-390)
RECON COATING SOLUTIONS LLC
3984 N Us Highway 287 (76225-7912)
PHONE.............................979 277-8455
Aden Martin, Principal
EMP: 12
SQ FT: 9,000
SALES (est): 1.3MM Privately Held
WEB: www.reconcoat.com
SIC: 3479 Etching & engraving

Amarillo
Potter County

(G-391)
ADVANCED LIMB & BRACE
4 Medical Dr Ste B (79106-4166)
P.O. Box 50130 (79159-0130)
PHONE.............................806 351-1775
Jeffrey Peterman,
EMP: 12
SALES (est): 1.5MM Privately Held
WEB: www.advancedlimbandbrace.com
SIC: 3842 Limbs, artificial

(G-392)
ALLIANCE ENTERTAINMENT LLC
6900 W I 40 Ste 200 (79106-2525)
PHONE.............................806 381-3945
Tim McRight, Vice Pres
EMP: 22
SALES (corp-wide): 219.2MM Privately Held
WEB: www.aent.com
SIC: 5199 3651 General merchandise,
    non-durable; home entertainment equip-
    ment, electronic
HQ: Alliance Entertainment, Llc
    1401 Nw 136th Ave Ste 100
    Sunrise FL 33323

(G-393)
AMARILLO CUSTOM BOX CO (HQ)
Also Called: Acbc
1501 S Johnson St (79101-4413)
P.O. Box 1361 (79105-1361)
PHONE....................................806 371-9111
Rodney Turnipseed, *President*
Michael A Hale, *Vice Pres*
EMP: 30
SQ FT: 43,500
SALES (est): 11.4MM
SALES (corp-wide): 16.2MM **Privately Held**
WEB: www.dallascontainer.com
SIC: 2653 Boxes, corrugated: made from purchased materials
PA: Dallas Container Corporation
8330 Endicott Ln
Dallas TX 75227
214 381-7148

(G-394)
AMARILLO ELC SPECIALISTS INC
2620 Tee Anchor Blvd (79104-2412)
P.O. Box 9048 (79105-9048)
PHONE....................................806 372-3798
Pam Montgomery, *President*
Shirley Gibbs, *Vice Pres*
Dana Sandavol, *Vice Pres*
Dana Sandoval, *Vice Pres*
Frank W Gibbs, *Engineer*
EMP: 16
SQ FT: 7,500
SALES (est): 3.8MM **Privately Held**
WEB: www.amarilloelectric.com
SIC: 1731 7694 5063 General electrical contractor; electric motor repair; motors, electric; electrical fittings & construction materials

(G-395)
AMARILLO LITHO INC
2400 Sw 7th Ave (79106-6604)
PHONE....................................806 372-2245
Dennis Clounch, *President*
Ronald Dickey, *Vice Pres*
Jerry Blackwell, *Treasurer*
EMP: 10
SQ FT: 8,518
SALES (est): 1.2MM **Privately Held**
WEB: www.amarillolitho.com
SIC: 2752 Commercial printing, offset

(G-396)
AMARILLO MOP & BROOM CO INC
1712 Se 27th Ave (79103-2510)
P.O. Box 30098 (79120-0098)
PHONE....................................806 372-8596
E W Bryan, *President*
Sue Ann Bryan, *Vice Pres*
EMP: 21 **EST:** 1947
SQ FT: 20,800 **Privately Held**
WEB: www.amarilloroofer.com
SIC: 3751 Mopeds & parts

(G-397)
AMARILLO PLSTIC FBRICATORS LTD
305 S Jefferson St (79101-1225)
PHONE....................................806 372-1207
Richard B Rogowski Jr, *Partner*
Gary Benson, *Sales Mgr*
EMP: 13
SQ FT: 35,000
SALES (est): 2.4MM **Privately Held**
WEB: www.amarilloplasticfabricators.com
SIC: 2541 Cabinets, except refrigerated: show, display, etc.: wood; table or counter tops, plastic laminated

(G-398)
AMARILLO SPERIOR IRONWORKS INC
1203 Sw 5th Ave (79101-1111)
PHONE....................................806 331-9353
Patrick Hand, *President*
Marci Hand, *Admin Sec*
EMP: 9
SALES (est): 1.2MM **Privately Held**
SIC: 3446 Architectural metalwork

(G-399)
AMERICAN WEST WINDMILL CO
1701 Se 3rd Ave (79102-3401)
PHONE....................................806 373-0478
Mark Durham, *President*
EMP: 12 **EST:** 2001
SALES (est): 704.2K **Privately Held**
SIC: 3523 Windmills for pumping water, agricultural

(G-400)
ARDEN COMPANIES INC
10901 Airport Blvd (79111-1236)
PHONE....................................806 335-1147
Carrie Belcher, *Marketing Staff*
Johnny Coker, *Manager*
Gary Furlow, *Executive*
EMP: 180
SALES (corp-wide): 2.7B **Publicly Held**
WEB: www.ardencompanies.com
SIC: 2842 2392 3999 Specialty cleaning, polishes & sanitation goods; household furnishings; garden umbrellas
HQ: Arden Companies, Llc
30400 Telg Rd Ste 200
Bingham Farms MI 48025
248 415-8500

(G-401)
ASARCO LLC
Also Called: Amarillo Plant
8 Miles Ne Cy On Hwy 136 (79120)
P.O. Box 30200 (79120-0200)
PHONE....................................806 468-4000
Larry Caster, *Branch Mgr*
EMP: 576 **Publicly Held**
WEB: www.asarcoreorg.com
SIC: 3341 3356 3339 3331 Copper smelting & refining (secondary); nonferrous rolling & drawing; primary nonferrous metals; primary copper; industrial inorganic chemicals
HQ: Asarco Llc
5285 E Williams Cir # 2000
Tucson AZ 85711

(G-402)
BECK COWBOY BOOTS INC
723 S Georgia St (79106-8913)
PHONE....................................806 373-1600
Harry Carl Beck, *President*
Carolyn Beck, *Vice Pres*
Jeremy Pool, *Vice Pres*
▲ **EMP:** 9
SQ FT: 3,500
SALES (est): 906.1K **Privately Held**
WEB: www.beckboots.com
SIC: 5661 3199 Men's boots; boots, horse

(G-403)
BELL BOEING JOINT PROJECT OFF
401 Tiltrotor Dr (79111-1200)
PHONE....................................301 866-6835
Eugene Cunningham, *Manager*
Elizabeth Louis, *Manager*
EMP: 20
SALES (est): 5.3MM **Privately Held**
WEB: www.bellflight.com
SIC: 3728 Aircraft parts & equipment

(G-404)
BELL HELICOPTER TEXTRON INC
401 Tiltrotor Dr (79111-1200)
PHONE....................................806 341-3400
EMP: 11
SALES (corp-wide): 14.2B **Publicly Held**
SIC: 3728 Mfg Aircraft Parts/Equipment
HQ: Bell Helicopter Textron Inc.
3255 Bell Flight Blvd
Fort Worth TX 76118
817 280-2011

(G-405)
BELL HELICOPTER TEXTRON INC
401 Tiltrotor Dr (79111-1200)
PHONE....................................817 280-4700
EMP: 12
SALES (est): 1.3MM
SALES (corp-wide): 14.2B **Publicly Held**
SIC: 3728 Mfg Aircraft Parts/Equipment

PA: Textron Inc.
40 Westminster St
Providence RI 02903
401 421-2800

(G-406)
BELL TEXTRON INC
Also Called: Military Aircraft Assmbly & De
401 Tiltrotor Dr (79111-1200)
PHONE....................................806 341-3400
April Fowler, *Mfg Staff*
Roger Williams, *Branch Mgr*
Jenna Tyler, *Manager*
Monty Wolfe, *Manager*
Emily Pfeiffer, *Administration*
EMP: 131
SALES (corp-wide): 13.6B **Publicly Held**
WEB: www.bellflight.com
SIC: 3728 Aircraft parts & equipment
HQ: Bell Textron Inc.
3255 Bell Flight Blvd
Fort Worth TX 76118
817 280-2011

(G-407)
BELL TEXTRON INC
10901 Airport Blvd Bldg 9 (79111-1236)
P.O. Box 482, Fort Worth (76101-0482)
PHONE....................................806 341-3400
Eric Diss, *Branch Mgr*
Jason Alvis, *Manager*
John Doyle, *Manager*
EMP: 131
SALES (corp-wide): 13.6B **Publicly Held**
WEB: www.bellflight.com
SIC: 3728 Aircraft parts & equipment
HQ: Bell Textron Inc.
3255 Bell Flight Blvd
Fort Worth TX 76118
817 280-2011

(G-408)
BERNADETTE DEBRANGO
Also Called: Sir Speedy
416 Sw 8th Ave (79101-2216)
PHONE....................................806 342-0606
Bernadette Debrango, *Principal*
Chris Blanchard, *Accounts Exec*
Peter Piland, *Marketing Staff*
Mike Sleese, *Manager*
EMP: 12
SQ FT: 6,000
SALES (est): 2MM **Privately Held**
WEB: www.sirspeedy.com
SIC: 2752 2741 Commercial printing, lithographic; art copy & poster publishing

(G-409)
BORDER STATES INDUSTRIES INC
Nunn Elc Sup A Div Brder Sttes
700 S Adams St (79101-2128)
PHONE....................................806 457-4100
Shawn Brown, *Accounts Mgr*
Justin Jeter, *Accounts Mgr*
Arthur Ybarra, *Branch Mgr*
Timothy Baker, *Branch Mgr*
Kelly Renken, *Administration*
EMP: 20
SALES (corp-wide): 2.4B **Privately Held**
WEB: www.borderstates.com
SIC: 5063 5065 5074 1711 Electrical supplies; electronic parts & equipment; plumbing & hydronic heating supplies; plumbing, heating, air-conditioning contractors; plastics plumbing fixtures; vitreous plumbing fixtures
PA: Border States Industries, Inc.
2400 38th St S
Fargo ND 58104
701 293-5834

(G-410)
C & B PRINTING CO
Also Called: C & B Marketing
2400 Sw 6th Ave (79106-6641)
PHONE....................................806 374-6262
Mike Pryer, *President*
Shrese Tanner, *Office Mgr*
Shane Warden, *Graphic Designe*
Gaye Wilson, *Graphic Designe*
EMP: 12 **EST:** 1973
SQ FT: 4,000

SALES (est): 1MM **Privately Held**
WEB: www.candbmarketing.com
SIC: 2752 7336 7311 Commercial printing, offset; commercial art & graphic design; advertising consultant

(G-411)
CACTUS VARIED INDUSTRIES LLC
2005 Ave B Hngr 7000 (79107)
PHONE....................................806 335-9470
Scott Atwood, *Mng Member*
EMP: 500
SALES (est): 19.7MM
SALES (corp-wide): 113.5MM **Privately Held**
SIC: 3549 7389 5999 Wiredrawing & fabricating machinery & equipment, ex. die; design services; welding supplies
HQ: Cactus Operating, Llc
2209 Sw 7th Ave
Amarillo TX 79106

(G-412)
CAVINESS BEEF PACKERS LTD
4206 E Amarillo Blvd (79107-5704)
P.O. Box 31117 (79120-1117)
PHONE....................................806 372-5781
Trevor Caviness, *President*
Jorge Aleman, *QC Mgr*
Jim Hargis, *Human Res Mgr*
Heather Hughes, *Human Res Mgr*
Brian McGee, *Sales Staff*
EMP: 312
SALES (corp-wide): 180MM **Privately Held**
WEB: www.cavinessbeefpackers.com
SIC: 2011 Beef products from beef slaughtered on site
PA: Caviness Beef Packers, Ltd.
3255 W Hwy 60
Hereford TX 79045
806 357-2443

(G-413)
CAVINESS BEEF PACKERS LTD
4206 E Amarillo Blvd (79107-5704)
PHONE....................................806 372-5781
Trevor Caviness, *Branch Mgr*
EMP: 80
SALES (corp-wide): 180MM **Privately Held**
WEB: www.cavinessbeefpackers.com
SIC: 2011 Meat packing plants
PA: Caviness Beef Packers, Ltd.
3255 W Hwy 60
Hereford TX 79045
806 357-2443

(G-414)
CENVEO WORLDWIDE LIMITED
109 S Fillmore St (79101-1530)
P.O. Box 9068 (79105-9068)
PHONE....................................806 376-4347
Douglas Holeman, *President*
Paul Ortega, *Chief Mktg Ofcr*
Steve Trafton, *Branch Mgr*
Barry Homfeld, *Maintence Staff*
EMP: 82
SALES (corp-wide): 1B **Privately Held**
WEB: www.cenveo.com
SIC: 2752 2791 2789 2759 Commercial printing, offset; typesetting; bookbinding & related work; commercial printing
HQ: Cenveo Worldwide Limited
200 First Stamford Pl # 2
Stamford CT 06902
203 595-3000

(G-415)
CHEP (USA) INC
13001 Ne 29th Ave (79111-1361)
PHONE....................................806 553-5655
Butch Palmer, *Branch Mgr*
EMP: 30 **Privately Held**
WEB: www.chep.com
SIC: 2448 Pallets, wood
HQ: Chep (U.S.A.) Inc.
5897 Windward Pkwy
Alpharetta GA 30005
770 668-8100

G E O G R A P H I C

(G-416)
CITY MACHINE & WELDING INC
9701 Business I 40 W 40 I (79124)
P.O. Box 51018 (79159-1018)
PHONE..................................806 358-7293
Lawrence A Oeschger, *President*
Sharon Oeschger, *Corp Secy*
Greg Hudspeth, *Vice Pres*
Kent Carroll, *Info Tech Mgr*
▲ EMP: 43 EST: 1949
SQ FT: 40,000
SALES (est): 5.9MM **Privately Held**
WEB: www.cmwelding.com
SIC: 8734 7692 7539 Hydrostatic testing
laboratory; welding repair; trailer repair

(G-417)
COCA-COLA REFRESHMENTS USA INC
8700 Centerport Blvd (79108-5732)
PHONE..................................806 324-5300
Bill Pevehluse, *Manager*
EMP: 78
SALES (corp-wide): 37.2B **Publicly Held**
WEB: www.coca-colacompany.com
SIC: 2086 Bottled & canned soft drinks
HQ: Coca-Cola Refreshments Usa, Inc.
2500 Windy Ridge Pkwy Se
Atlanta GA 30339
770 989-3000

(G-418)
COMAC FIXTURES INC
205 S Philadelphia St (79104-1024)
P.O. Box 31237 (79120-1237)
PHONE..................................806 376-4511
Ruby Weiss, *President*
Cristin Betven, *Vice Pres*
Casey Weiss, *Vice Pres*
Cristin Weiss, *Treasurer*
EMP: 17
SQ FT: 42,000
SALES (est): 1.9MM **Privately Held**
WEB: www.comacfixtures.com
SIC: 2499 5046 Laundry products, wood;
shelving, commercial & industrial

(G-419)
CUMMINS SOUTHERN PLAINS LLC
Also Called: Southeran Plains Power
5224 I 40 E (79103-7411)
P.O. Box 31570 (79120-1570)
PHONE..................................806 373-3793
Wayne Pearson, *Branch Mgr*
EMP: 27
SQ FT: 25,000
SALES (corp-wide): 19.8B **Publicly Held**
WEB: www.cummins.com
SIC: 5084 3519 Engines & parts, diesel;
internal combustion engines
HQ: Cummins Southern Plains Llc
600 N Watson Rd
Arlington TX 76011
817 640-6801

(G-420)
DATA PRINT LTD
509 S Johnson St (79101-2529)
P.O. Box 9613 (79105-9613)
PHONE..................................806 324-4350
Jim Austin, *Ch of Bd*
Charles Graham, *President*
David Dudding, *Vice Pres*
Lacie Burnett, *Admin Sec*
EMP: 36 EST: 1980
SQ FT: 38,000
SALES (est): 4.1MM **Privately Held**
WEB: www.grahamdata.com
SIC: 2782 2752 2761 Blankbooks &
looseleaf binders; commercial printing,
lithographic; computer forms, manifold or
continuous

(G-421)
EASY PRINT INC (PA)
Also Called: Zip Print
501 S Jackson St (79101-2219)
PHONE..................................806 374-7711
Drew Bergen, *President*
Thomas Drew Bergen, *Vice Pres*
Marilynn Bergen, *Treasurer*
EMP: 23
SQ FT: 16,000
SALES: 1.5MM **Privately Held**
WEB: www.zip-print.com
SIC: 7334 2752 2789 2759 Photocopying
& duplicating services; commercial print-
ing, lithographic; bookbinding & related
work; commercial printing

(G-422)
ENERGY PRECISION TSTG LAB LLC (PA)
905 S Polk St (79101-3405)
P.O. Box 7687 (79114-7687)
PHONE..................................806 665-0750
C Lloyd Brown, *Mng Member*
Victoria Watts, *Technician*
Jeff Snyder,
EMP: 10
SQ FT: 6,000
SALES (est): 1.7MM **Privately Held**
WEB: www.energyptl.com
SIC: 1382 Geological exploration, oil & gas
field

(G-423)
FC TRAFFIC CONTROL INC
1100 S Fillmore St 105a (79101-4309)
P.O. Box 15603 (79105-5603)
PHONE..................................806 570-5633
Fernando Chairez, *President*
EMP: 10
SALES (est): 561.9K **Privately Held**
WEB: www.fc-traffic.com
SIC: 3669 Traffic signals, electric

(G-424)
FOUST INCORPORATED (PA)
Also Called: Whit-Co Checks
1500 S Polk St (79101-4229)
P.O. Box 664 (79105-0664)
PHONE..................................806 374-7005
J W Foust, *President*
EMP: 20
SQ FT: 25,000
SALES (est): 7MM **Privately Held**
WEB: www.whitcochecks.com
SIC: 2759 3953 3993 2752 Screen print-
ing; embossing seals & hand stamps; em-
bossing seals, corporate & official;
stencils, painting & marking; name plates:
except engraved, etched, etc.: metal;
commercial printing, lithographic

(G-425)
FREEZE TECHNOLOGY INTL (HQ)
500 S Taylor St Unit 1010 (79101-2442)
P.O. Box 2329 (79105-2329)
PHONE..................................806 371-8854
Mike R Brister, *Ch of Bd*
Harry Janzen, *Corp Secy*
Paul Mooney, *Vice Pres*
G H Riffe, *Vice Pres*
EMP: 20
SQ FT: 2,500
SALES (est): 2.9MM
SALES (corp-wide): 46.1MM **Privately Held**
WEB: www.freezetechnology.com
SIC: 1389 Oil field services
PA: Enerpipe, Ltd.
500 S Taylor St Ste 1010
Amarillo TX 79101
806 371-8851

(G-426)
G E JONES ELECTRIC CO INC
200 N Polk St 16 (79107-5230)
P.O. Box 2049 (79105-2049)
PHONE..................................806 372-5505
George Stratton, *President*
Noel Moore, *General Mgr*
Linda Stratton, *Corp Secy*
Norma Stratton, *Vice Pres*
EMP: 30
SQ FT: 33,600
SALES (est): 4.9MM **Privately Held**
WEB: www.gejones.com
SIC: 7694 5063 Electric motor repair; mo-
tors, electric; generators; transformers,
electric; motor controls, starters & relays:
electric

(G-427)
G TACOS INC
Also Called: Taco Garcia Mexican Cafe
1100 Ross St (79102-4400)
PHONE..................................806 371-0411
George Veloz, *President*
Reyna Trejo, *Bookkeeper*
EMP: 56
SQ FT: 2,300
SALES (est): 650K **Privately Held**
SIC: 5812 2099 Mexican restaurant; tor-
tillas, fresh or refrigerated

(G-428)
GICON PUMPS & EQUIPMENT LTD
Also Called: Apsco
1701 Se 3rd Ave (79102-3401)
P.O. Box 30310 (79120-0310)
PHONE..................................806 373-0478
Roy Harris, *Opers Mgr*
EMP: 9
SQ FT: 10,596
SALES (corp-wide): 1.3B **Publicly Held**
WEB: www.giconpumps.com
SIC: 5084 5074 5039 5051 Water pumps
(industrial); pipes & fittings, plastic; septic
tanks; pipe & tubing, steel; windmills for
pumping water, agricultural; septic system
construction
HQ: Gicon Pumps & Equipment, Llc
1001 Texas Ave
Lubbock TX 79401
806 401-8287

(G-429)
GRACE SHURSEN MOORE ASSOC INC
Also Called: G S M
221 Grace Ln (79124-1773)
PHONE..................................806 358-6894
Robert D Grace, *President*
K A Selinger, *Vice Pres*
Robert A Stewart, *Vice Pres*
EMP: 9
SQ FT: 10,000
SALES (est): 1MM
SALES (corp-wide): 1.8MM **Privately Held**
WEB: www.gsm-inc.com
SIC: 1389 8748 Oil consultants; business
consulting
PA: Gsm Enterprises Inc
221 Grace Ln
Amarillo TX 79124
806 358-6894

(G-430)
GSM ENTERPRISES INC (PA)
221 Grace Ln (79124-1773)
P.O. Box 50790 (79159-0790)
PHONE..................................806 358-6894
Robert D Grace, *President*
Richard Carden, *Vice Pres*
Jerry Shursen, *Vice Pres*
Max Mefford, *VP Opers*
Bill Beakley, *CFO*
EMP: 28
SALES (est): 1.8MM **Privately Held**
WEB: www.gsm-inc.com
SIC: 8711 1311 Petroleum engineering;
crude petroleum production; natural gas
production

(G-431)
GTM MANUFACTURING LLC
2100 Spruce St (79103-1128)
P.O. Box 31598 (79120-1598)
PHONE..................................806 373-9473
Ken Kelley,
▼ EMP: 50
SQ FT: 8,600
SALES (est): 9.8MM **Privately Held**
WEB: www.kelleygtm.com
SIC: 3443 Industrial vessels, tanks & con-
tainers

(G-432)
HANSON AGGREGATES LLC
2001 W Amarillo Blvd (79107-5067)
P.O. Box 3669 (79116-3669)
PHONE..................................806 372-8114
Brett Hargrove, *Manager*
EMP: 40
SALES (corp-wide): 20.8B **Privately Held**
WEB: www.heidelbergcement.com
SIC: 3273 Ready-mixed concrete
HQ: Hanson Aggregates Llc
8505 Freport Pkwy Ste 500
Irving TX 75063
469 417-1200

(G-433)
HARD ROCK CRUSHING
2300 E Hastings Ave (79108-5410)
PHONE..................................806 383-1721
Mike Morgan, *Partner*
Richard Howell, *Partner*
EMP: 10
SALES (est): 750K **Privately Held**
SIC: 1429 Boulder, crushed & broken-
quarrying

(G-434)
HOAREL SIGN CO
819 Ne 7th Ave (79107-5417)
P.O. Box 1832 (79105-1832)
PHONE..................................806 373-2175
Gary Cox, *President*
Ray Cox, *Vice Pres*
Linda Cox, *Treasurer*
Lisa Cox Orosco, *Admin Sec*
Lisa Orosco, *Admin Sec*
EMP: 14 EST: 1927
SQ FT: 18,800
SALES (est): 2.4MM **Privately Held**
WEB: www.hoarelsign.com
SIC: 3993 1799 Electric signs; neon signs;
sign installation & maintenance

(G-435)
HOLMES CONSTRUCTION CO LP
10221 Climer Cir (79124-2404)
PHONE..................................806 376-8629
Ray Evans, *Manager*
EMP: 100
SALES (corp-wide): 28MM **Privately Held**
WEB: www.holmes-farrar.com
SIC: 1611 3444 1771 Surfacing & paving;
culverts, sheet metal; concrete work
PA: Holmes Construction Co., L.P.
7901 Sw 34th Ave
Amarillo TX 79121
806 376-8629

(G-436)
HOWELL SAND COMPANY INC
2300 E Hastings Ave (79108-5410)
PHONE..................................806 383-1721
James R Howell Jr, *President*
Josh Howell, *Vice Pres*
EMP: 60
SQ FT: 6,000
SALES (est): 22.1MM **Privately Held**
WEB: www.howellsand.com
SIC: 1442 Sand mining

(G-437)
IFCO SYSTEMS NORTH AMERICA INC
9531 Whse Rd 1 Bldg 9531 (79111)
P.O. Box 31943 (79120-1943)
PHONE..................................806 335-1746
EMP: 35
SQ FT: 23,602 **Privately Held**
SIC: 2448 Mfg Wood Pallets/Skids

(G-438)
IMMUNOTEK BIO CENTERS LLC
1813 E Amarillo Blvd (79107-5552)
PHONE..................................806 310-2859
Lindsay Rehling, *Manager*
EMP: 27
SALES (corp-wide): 27MM **Privately Held**
WEB: www.immunotek.com
SIC: 2836 Blood derivatives
PA: Immunotek Bio Centers, L.L.C.
3900 N Causeway Blvd # 1200
Metairie LA 70002
337 500-1175

(G-439)
INTERNATIONAL PAPER COMPANY
4715 Ne 24th Ave (79107-5801)
PHONE..................................806 381-0121

Layne Van Winkle, *Engineer*
Doug Mitchem, *Manager*
EMP: 83
SQ FT: 190,511
SALES (corp-wide): 22.3B **Publicly Held**
WEB: www.internationalpaper.com
SIC: 2653 2631 5113 Boxes, corrugated: made from purchased materials; paperboard mills; corrugated & solid fiber boxes
PA: International Paper Company
6400 Poplar Ave
Memphis TN 38197
901 419-9000

(G-440)
INTERNTNAL AROSPC COATINGS INC
10801 Baker St (79111-1235)
PHONE..............................806 335-2616
Niall Cunningham, *CEO*
Rod Friese, *President*
EMP: 10 **Privately Held**
WEB: www.associatedpaintersinc.com
SIC: 4581 3721 Aircraft servicing & repairing; motorized aircraft
PA: International Aerospace Coatings, Inc.
5709 W Sunset Hwy Ste 205
Spokane WA 99224

(G-441)
J LEE MILLIGAN INC
9200 Triangle Dr (79108-7531)
P.O. Box 30188 (79120-0188)
PHONE..............................806 373-5352
Douglas Walterscheid, *President*
Swanson Hagerman, *Vice Pres*
Tammy Brannon, *Admin Sec*
EMP: 240
SQ FT: 6,000
SALES (est): 75.4MM **Privately Held**
WEB: www.jleemilligan.com
SIC: 2951 Asphalt paving mixtures & blocks

(G-442)
JAYVIC INC (PA)
Also Called: Perdue Acoustic
4210 Hester Dr (79124-7825)
PHONE..............................806 374-9402
Joab Perdue, *CEO*
Jay Perdue, *President*
Vicki Perdue, *Vice Pres*
Melissa Perdue, *CFO*
EMP: 17
SQ FT: 4,152
SALES (est): 3.4MM **Privately Held**
WEB: www.perdueacoustics.com
SIC: 3296 Acoustical board & tile, mineral wool

(G-443)
JENKINS FABCO INC (PA)
820 Sw 6th Ave (79101-2106)
P.O. Box 1108 (79105-1108)
PHONE..............................806 372-4336
Anthony Ledwig, *President*
Ledwig Robert A, *Vice Pres*
EMP: 10
SQ FT: 10,000
SALES (est): 1.3MM **Privately Held**
WEB: www.jenkinsdoorsandwindows.com
SIC: 2431 Doors, wood

(G-444)
JOHNSON FILTRATION PDTS INC
601 Ross St (79102-3427)
P.O. Box 30010 (79120-0010)
PHONE..............................806 371-8033
Charles W Johnson, *President*
EMP: 35
SQ FT: 38,000
SALES (est): 6.6MM **Privately Held**
WEB: www.johnsonfiltration.com
SIC: 3569 Filters, general line: industrial

(G-445)
KIRBY - SMITH MACHINERY INC
3922 I 40 E (79103-6123)
PHONE..............................806 373-1229
Tim Carothers, *Branch Mgr*
Susan Young, *Admin Asst*
EMP: 15

SALES (corp-wide): 575.9MM **Privately Held**
WEB: www.kirby-smith.com
SIC: 3559 5082 7389 Assembly machines, non-metalworking; cranes, construction; crane & aerial lift service
PA: Kirby - Smith Machinery, Inc.
6715 W Reno Ave
Oklahoma City OK 73127
888 861-0219

(G-446)
MIDWEST FAB & CONSTRUCTION INC
10720 E Amarillo Blvd (79108-7540)
P.O. Box 3957 (79116-3957)
PHONE..............................806 335-9126
Robert Urteaga, *President*
EMP: 10
SALES (est): 2.3MM **Privately Held**
WEB: www.midwestfab-construction.com
SIC: 7692 Welding repair

(G-447)
MORRIS COMMUNICATIONS CO LLC
Also Called: Amarillo Globe Times
600 S Tyler St Ste 600 # 600 (79101-2304)
PHONE..............................806 376-4488
Garet Von Netzer, *Publisher*
Belinda W Mills, *General Mgr*
Jaime Pipkin, *Sales Staff*
Les Simpson, *Manager*
Kendall Holman, *Supervisor*
EMP: 155 **Privately Held**
WEB: www.morris.com
SIC: 2711 Newspapers, publishing & printing
HQ: Morris Communications Company Llc
725 Broad St
Augusta GA 30901
706 724-0851

(G-448)
MOSES ENVMTL & CNSTR SVCS LLC
Also Called: Mec Services
3433 Plains Blvd (79102-1019)
PHONE..............................806 418-8525
Billy Moses, *Mng Member*
EMP: 25
SALES (est): 2MM **Privately Held**
SIC: 1389 8744 1771 1795 Construction, repair & dismantling services; ; patio construction, concrete; wrecking & demolition work

(G-449)
MULTIPLE SYSTEMS INC (PA)
2716 Tee Anchor Blvd (79104-2534)
P.O. Box 15025 (79105-5025)
PHONE..............................806 373-7073
Preston Montgomery, *President*
D D Montgomery, *Vice Pres*
Joe Montgomery, *Vice Pres*
Doye Montgomery, *CFO*
EMP: 32
SQ FT: 8,000
SALES (est): 7MM **Privately Held**
WEB: www.multiplesystems.com
SIC: 3559 3599 7699 5085 Leather working machinery; machine shop, jobbing & repair; industrial equipment services; bearings; power transmission equipment & apparatus

(G-450)
MULTIPLE SYSTEMS INC
2700 Tee Anchor Blvd (79104-2534)
P.O. Box 15025 (79105-5025)
PHONE..............................806 373-7073
Dede Montgomery, *Manager*
EMP: 40
SALES (corp-wide): 7MM **Privately Held**
WEB: www.multiplesystems.com
SIC: 3559 3599 7699 5085 Leather working machinery; machine shop, jobbing & repair; industrial equipment services; bearings
PA: Multiple Systems, Inc.
2716 Tee Anchor Blvd
Amarillo TX 79104
806 373-7073

(G-451)
PANTERA ENERGY COMPANY
817 S Polk St Ste 201 (79101-3433)
PHONE..............................806 376-6625
Jason Herrick, *President*
Scott D Herrick, *Vice Pres*
EMP: 57
SQ FT: 5,000
SALES (est): 5.5MM **Privately Held**
WEB: www.panteraenergy.com
SIC: 1311 Crude petroleum production; natural gas production

(G-452)
PEPSI-COLA METRO BTLG CO INC
8115 E Amarillo Blvd (79107-7849)
P.O. Box 2248 (79105-2248)
PHONE..............................806 372-8717
Jim Earl, *Manager*
EMP: 30
SQ FT: 23,210
SALES (corp-wide): 67.1B **Publicly Held**
WEB: www.pepsico.com
SIC: 2086 Carbonated soft drinks, bottled & canned
HQ: Pepsi-Cola Metropolitan Bottling Company, Inc.
1111 Westchester Ave
White Plains NY 10604
914 767-6000

(G-453)
PETERSON DRILLING AND TSTG INC (PA)
1700 Se 22nd Ave (79103-2100)
P.O. Box 30699 (79120-0699)
PHONE..............................806 342-4911
Dalana Peterson, *Ch of Bd*
Lee Peterson, *Vice Pres*
EMP: 37
SQ FT: 18,500
SALES (est): 6.3MM **Privately Held**
WEB: www.peterson-drilling.com
SIC: 1389 Testing, measuring, surveying & analysis services

(G-454)
PINE STREET SALVAGE CO
Scrap Processing
95 Browning St (79104-1000)
P.O. Box 30262 (79120-0262)
PHONE..............................806 372-5678
Greg Dankworth, *Manager*
Bobby Stewart, *Asst Mgr*
EMP: 10
SQ FT: 45,260
SALES (corp-wide): 7.5MM **Privately Held**
WEB: www.scrapabilene.com
SIC: 5093 5051 4953 3444 Ferrous metal scrap & waste; steel; recycling, waste materials; culverts, sheet metal
PA: Pine Street Salvage Co.
3833 Pine St
Abilene TX 79601
325 677-8831

(G-455)
PLAINS DAIRY LLC
300 N Taylor St (79107-5238)
PHONE..............................806 374-0385
Paul Harpole, *Mayor*
George Lankford, *Vice Pres*
Tim Zinn, *Chief Engr*
Bobby Flick, *Manager*
Walter Garlington,
▲ **EMP:** 1010 **EST:** 1934
SQ FT: 50,000
SALES (est): 153MM
SALES (corp-wide): 1.4B **Privately Held**
WEB: www.plainsdairy.com
SIC: 2026 2086 2033 Milk processing (pasteurizing, homogenizing, bottling); water, pasteurized: packaged in cans, bottles, etc.; fruit juices: packaged in cans, jars, etc.
PA: Affiliated Foods, Inc.
1401 W Farmers Ave
Amarillo TX 79118
806 372-3851

(G-456)
PROFESSIONAL REBUILD & OPTIMAL
14115 Indian Hill Rd (79124-2638)
PHONE..............................806 358-3636
Mark Fitte, *Branch Mgr*
EMP: 25 **Privately Held**
WEB: www.theprosco.com
SIC: 3599 Machine shop, jobbing & repair
PA: Professional Rebuild & Optimal Service, Llc
2523 86th St
Lubbock TX 79423

(G-457)
PUBLIC STEEL INC
1012 Sw 4th Ave (79101-1106)
P.O. Box 2444 (79105-2444)
PHONE..............................806 376-8221
James N Gleason, *Vice Pres*
Roy E Duck, *Vice Pres*
Chris Gleason, *CFO*
EMP: 27
SQ FT: 14,000
SALES (est): 6.6MM **Privately Held**
WEB: www.publicsteel.com
SIC: 3599 5051 1791 Machine & other job shop work; bars, metal; plates, metal; wire screening; reinforcement mesh, wire; structural steel erection

(G-458)
RIO PETROLEUM
2805 Sw 15th Ave (79102-2244)
PHONE..............................806 356-8033
Barrett W Pierce, *Owner*
Barbara Wilbanks, *Office Mgr*
John W Walker Jr, *Director*
Leslie Reneau, *Analyst*
EMP: 15
SQ FT: 1,000
SALES (est): 1.5MM **Privately Held**
WEB: www.riopetroleum.com
SIC: 1382 Oil & gas exploration services

(G-459)
ROCLA CONCRETE TIE INC
1601 Holly St (79108-7733)
PHONE..............................806 383-7071
Fax: 806 383-7360
EMP: 23
SQ FT: 29,836
SALES (corp-wide): 1B **Privately Held**
SIC: 3272 5211 2421 Mfg Concrete Products Ret Lumber/Building Materials Sawmill/Planing Mill
HQ: Rocla Concrete Tie, Inc
1819 Denver West Dr # 450
Lakewood CO 80401
303 296-3500

(G-460)
RUSH EYE ASSOCIATES PLLC
7308 Fleming Ave Ste A (79106-1810)
PHONE..............................806 353-0125
Paula Morris, *Office Mgr*
J Avery Rush, *Mng Member*
Sloan W Rush,
EMP: 30
SALES (est): 139.5K **Privately Held**
WEB: www.rushlasik.com
SIC: 3841 8011 Ophthalmic lasers; ophthalmologist

(G-461)
SAVAGE COMPANIES
8400 N Lakeside Dr (79108-5712)
PHONE..............................806 381-0261
Abe Elizondo, *Maint Spvr*
Reed Barlow, *Sr Project Mgr*
John Walters, *Manager*
Justin Ackerman, *Manager*
Shawn Daniel, *Manager*
EMP: 35
SALES (corp-wide): 1.1B **Privately Held**
WEB: www.railcartracking.com
SIC: 5052 1241 Coal; coal mining services
HQ: Savage Companies
901 W Legacy Center Way
Midvale UT 84047
801 944-6600

(G-462)
SCICRON TECHNOLOGIES LLC
501 W Amarillo Blvd (79107-5179)
PHONE..............................806 372-8300

Greg Lines, *General Mgr*
Heather Davis, *Marketing Mgr*
EMP: 27 **Privately Held**
WEB: www.sctech.com
SIC: 2821 Plastics materials & resins
PA: Scidron Technologies, Llc
　　8547 E Arapahoe Rd Unit J
　　Greenwood Village CO 80112

(G-463)
**SIDWELL OPERATING
COMPANY LP**
712 Sw 9th Ave (79101-3204)
P.O. Box 9298 (79105-9298)
PHONE..................................806 371-7513
Eugene R Sidwell, *Ch of Bd*
Reid Sidwell, *President*
Cliff Sanders, *Vice Pres*
Donna Sidwell, *Vice Pres*
EMP: 9
SQ FT: 4,110 **Privately Held**
SIC: 1311 Crude petroleum production;
　　natural gas production

(G-464)
STONEFAB INTL LLC
4005 W Amarillo Blvd (79106-7033)
PHONE..................................806 352-3416
Nagarjun Samala, *Mng Member*
▲ **EMP:** 9
SALES (est): 1.1MM **Privately Held**
WEB: www.stonefab.net
SIC: 2541 Counter & sink tops

(G-465)
TALON/LPE LTD
301 S Polk St (79101-1403)
PHONE..................................806 372-6600
EMP: 12
SALES (corp-wide): 29.5MM **Privately
Held**
SIC: 8748 8742 1522 1389 Business
　　Consulting Svcs Mgmt Consulting Svcs
　　Residential Construction Oil/Gas Field
　　Services
PA: Talon/Lpe, Ltd.
　　921 N Bivins St
　　Amarillo TX 79107
　　806 467-0607

(G-466)
TALON/LPE LTD (PA)
921 N Bivins St (79107-6806)
PHONE..................................806 467-0607
W David Prescott II, *Partner*
Jason Lincoln, *General Mgr*
Jason Shubert, *District Mgr*
Lindsay Currie, *Vice Pres*
Shane Currie, *Vice Pres*
EMP: 93
SQ FT: 27,000
SALES (est): 24.7MM **Privately Held**
WEB: www.talonlpe.com
SIC: 8748 8711 1781 1381 Environmen-
　　tal consultant; engineering services; water
　　well servicing; drilling water intake wells

(G-467)
**THOMAS REDI-MIX COMPANY
INC**
N Western & Loop 335 (79108)
P.O. Box 5664 (79117-5664)
PHONE..................................806 381-8485
John Thomas, *President*
Becky Thomas, *Admin Sec*
EMP: 50
SALES (est): 9.7MM **Privately Held**
WEB: www.thomasredimix.com
SIC: 3273 Ready-mixed concrete

(G-468)
TIERNAN AERATION INC
Also Called: Tiernan Outdoor Products
1722 Ne 3rd Ave (79107-5546)
P.O. Box 7588 (79114-7588)
PHONE..................................806 372-4051
Michael G Tierman, *President*
Kim Steinkoenig, *Finance Mgr*
Sue Stockton, *Admin Sec*
EMP: 22
SQ FT: 34,000
SALES (est): 4.4MM **Privately Held**
WEB: www.icookout.com
SIC: 3564 Ventilating fans: industrial or
　　commercial

(G-469)
TYSON FRESH MEATS INC
Also Called: Trans Continental Cold Storage
1912 E Fm Rd Hwy 60 (79187)
PHONE..................................806 335-7492
Paul McCord, *Warehouse Mgr*
Dan Flanigan, *Production*
Tim Read, *Manager*
Ronnie Terry, *Maintence Staff*
EMP: 25
SALES (corp-wide): 43.1B **Publicly Held**
WEB: www.tysonfreshmeats.com
SIC: 2011 Meat packing plants
HQ: Tyson Fresh Meats, Inc.
　　800 Stevens Port Dr
　　Dakota Dunes SD 57049
　　479 290-6397

(G-470)
TYSON FRESH MEATS INC
Also Called: Iowa Beef Processors
5000 N Sm 1912 (79187)
P.O. Box 30500 (79120-0500)
PHONE..................................806 335-7322
Ernesto Sanchez, *Branch Mgr*
EMP: 4000
SALES (corp-wide): 43.1B **Publicly Held**
WEB: www.tysonfreshmeats.com
SIC: 2011 2013 Beef products from beef
　　slaughtered on site; sausages & other
　　prepared meats
HQ: Tyson Fresh Meats, Inc.
　　800 Stevens Port Dr
　　Dakota Dunes SD 57049
　　479 290-6397

(G-471)
TYSON FRESH MEATS INC
Tasco
2201 B Ave (79111)
P.O. Box 32350 (79120-2350)
PHONE..................................806 335-2301
Gene Leman, *Branch Mgr*
EMP: 31
SQ FT: 31,000
SALES (corp-wide): 43.1B **Publicly Held**
WEB: www.tysonfoods.com
SIC: 2011 Meat packing plants
HQ: Tyson Fresh Meats, Inc.
　　800 Stevens Port Dr
　　Dakota Dunes SD 57049
　　479 290-6397

(G-472)
US CONCRETE INC
Also Called: Golden Spread
100 S Van Buren St (79101-1348)
PHONE..................................806 373-4951
Jeff Roberts, *Branch Mgr*
EMP: 48
SALES (corp-wide): 1.4B **Publicly Held**
WEB: www.us-concrete.com
SIC: 3273 Ready-mixed concrete
PA: U.S. Concrete, Inc.
　　331 N Main St
　　Euless TX 76039
　　817 835-4105

(G-473)
WCSA INC
Also Called: Whiteside Cnstr Svcs Amarillo
2349 E Loop 335 N (79108-5686)
P.O. Box 20634 (79114-2634)
PHONE..................................806 383-1060
Joe Whiteside, *President*
Jeffery Whiteside, *President*
Carolyn Whiteside, *Corp Secy*
EMP: 15
SQ FT: 2,800
SALES (est): 1.6MM **Privately Held**
WEB: www.wcsainc.com
SIC: 1794 1795 7349 3563 Excavation
　　work; excavation & grading, building con-
　　struction; demolition, buildings & other
　　structures; cleaning service, industrial or
　　commercial; vacuum (air extraction) sys-
　　tems, industrial

(G-474)
WELLBORN SIGN INC (PA)
700 Se 10th Ave (79101-3614)
PHONE..................................806 331-3563
Michael Wellborn, *President*
Patti Garza, *Office Mgr*
Scott Nix, *Graphic Designe*
EMP: 18

SQ FT: 12,500
SALES (est): 2.4MM **Privately Held**
WEB: www.wsignco.com
SIC: 3993 Signs, not made in custom sign
　　painting shops

(G-475)
WILLBORN BROS CO LLC
105 S Houston St (79102-3301)
P.O. Box 2089 (79105-2089)
PHONE..................................806 372-4311
Chan Davidson, *CEO*
Tim Boeckman Boeckman, *General Mgr*
Chris Barrett, *Manager*
Aaron Kubitscheck, *Director*
EMP: 26 **EST:** 1911
SQ FT: 21,000
SALES (est): 14.6MM **Privately Held**
WEB: www.willbornco.com
SIC: 5084 3443 1791 Pumps & pumping
　　equipment; tanks, standard or custom
　　fabricated: metal plate; storage tanks,
　　metal: erection

Amarillo
Randall County

(G-476)
AFFILIATED FOODS INC (PA)
Also Called: A F
1401 W Farmers Ave (79118-6134)
P.O. Box 30300 (79120-0300)
PHONE..................................806 372-3851
Randy Arceneaux, *CEO*
Roger Lowe, *Ch of Bd*
Dennis Porter Jr, *Vice Ch Bd*
Dave Rudder, *Managing Dir*
Jeff Robinson, *COO*
▲ **EMP:** 149
SQ FT: 780,000
SALES: 1.4B **Privately Held**
WEB: www.afiama.com
SIC: 4225 2026 2051 5149 General
　　warehousing & storage; fluid milk; bread,
　　cake & related products; groceries & re-
　　lated products; mercantile financing

(G-477)
AIR OASIS LLC
3401 Airway Blvd (79118-7742)
PHONE..................................806 373-7788
Jon Bennert, *CEO*
John Bennert, *President*
Brad Baxter, *Vice Pres*
Jeremiah Dorsett, *Engineer*
Charles Robinson, *Accounts Mgr*
EMP: 28
SALES (est): 1.6MM **Privately Held**
WEB: www.airoasis.com
SIC: 3564 Air purification equipment

(G-478)
**AMARILLO GEAR COMPANY
LLC (DH)**
2401 W Sundown Ln (79118-6004)
P.O. Box 1789 (79105-1789)
PHONE..................................806 622-1273
Steve Chaloupka, *President*
Jake Richards, *Vice Pres*
Robert Webb, *Admin Sec*
▲ **EMP:** 142
SQ FT: 123,000
SALES (est): 26.5MM
SALES (corp-wide): 254.6B **Publicly
Held**
WEB: www.amarillogear.com
SIC: 3566 5084 3462 Drives, high speed
　　industrial, except hydrostatic; industrial
　　machinery & equipment; gear & chain
　　forgings
HQ: Union Tank Car Company
　　175 W Jackson Blvd # 2100
　　Chicago IL 60604
　　312 431-3111

(G-479)
**AMARILLO WATERBLASTERS
INC**
4614 Mccarty Blvd (79110-2212)
P.O. Box 7010 (79114-7010)
PHONE..................................806 352-2765
George Cumming Jr, *President*
Eddey Hankins, *Treasurer*
EMP: 18

SQ FT: 4,100
SALES (est): 1.1MM **Privately Held**
SIC: 3312 Blast furnaces & steel mills

(G-480)
AMERICAN CLASSIFIEDS
Also Called: Thrifty Nickel Want ADS
15097 S Dowell Rd (79119-2614)
PHONE..................................806 376-8663
Robert Christensen, *President*
Ryan Putman, *Manager*
Debbie Burnette, *Admin Sec*
EMP: 12
SQ FT: 3,826
SALES (est): 924.7K **Privately Held**
WEB: www.wacoamericanclassifieds.com
SIC: 2711 Newspapers: publishing only,
　　not printed on site

(G-481)
**BISON DEVELOPMENT
COMPANY**
5744 Canyon Dr (79109-6356)
P.O. Box 7446 (79114-7446)
PHONE..................................806 355-8253
William H Attebury, *President*
Edward Attebury, *Vice Pres*
Joyce K Attebury, *Admin Sec*
EMP: 10 **EST:** 1961
SQ FT: 1,000
SALES (est): 3MM **Privately Held**
WEB: www.bisondevelopment.com
SIC: 0212 6512 1311 Beef cattle except
　　feedlots; commercial & industrial building
　　operation; crude petroleum production;
　　natural gas production

(G-482)
BLUNCK STUDIOS INC
3303 Wimberly Rd (79109-3444)
PHONE..................................806 358-7064
Brad Lee, *Manager*
EMP: 9
SALES (corp-wide): 2.9MM **Privately
Held**
WEB: www.lifetouch.com
SIC: 7221 2759 Photographer, still or
　　video; invitation & stationery printing &
　　engraving
PA: Blunck Studios Inc
　　614 Frisco Ave
　　Clinton OK 73601
　　580 323-0383

(G-483)
CLASSIC FENCE
15005 Mescalero Trl (79118-3425)
P.O. Box 21143 (79114-3143)
PHONE..................................806 517-0708
Norman Roger Cape Jr, *Owner*
Roger Cape, *Owner*
EMP: 10
SALES (est): 635.1K **Privately Held**
SIC: 3315 Fence gates posts & fittings:
　　steel

(G-484)
COOPER CROUSE-HINDS LLC
Also Called: Eaton Cooper Crouse-Hinds
1901 W Farmers Ave (79118-6102)
PHONE..................................806 358-4585
Ronald Riley, *Principal*
Terry Henderson, *Foreman/Supr*
EMP: 20 **Privately Held**
WEB: www.coopercrouse-hinds.com
SIC: 3699 Electrical equipment & supplies
HQ: Cooper Crouse-Hinds, Llc
　　1201 Wolf St
　　Syracuse NY 13208
　　315 477-7000

(G-485)
**CRAMER COMPUTER SUPPLIES
LTD**
Also Called: Data Flow
3221 Church St (79109-1541)
P.O. Box 32566 (79120-2566)
PHONE..................................806 371-7310
Josette Cramer, *President*
James F Cramer, *Principal*
Tammy Lard, *Manager*
Mitch Khoury, *Creative Dir*
Angelica Darnell, *Admin Sec*
EMP: 20
SQ FT: 800

SALES (est): 2.2MM **Privately Held**
WEB: www.dataflow.us
SIC: 5112 5065 2752 2281 Computer paper; business forms; diskettes, computer; commercial printing, offset; embroidery yarn, spun

(G-486)
EXCEL MACHINERY LTD (PA)
12100 E Interstate 40 (79118-6953)
P.O. Box 31118 (79120-1118)
PHONE...................................806 335-1553
Gilbert Gonzalez, *Partner*
Stanley Holloway, *Partner*
Rene Vidaurri, *Partner*
Kirk Andrews, *Vice Pres*
Wade Johnson, *Purch Mgr*
◆ EMP: 15
SQ FT: 32,000
SALES (est): 22.4MM **Privately Held**
WEB: www.excelmach.com
SIC: 3531 3559 5084 5082 Rock crushing machinery, portable; scrapers, graders, rollers & similar equipment; recycling machinery; crushing machinery & equipment; construction & mining machinery

(G-487)
EXPLORATION CENTER BUILDING
Also Called: O'Connell, James F
5402 Meadowgreen Dr (79110-4646)
P.O. Box 7006 (79114-7006)
PHONE...................................806 353-9123
Dudley Stanley, *Partner*
Bob Callan,
Jim O Connell,
EMP: 20
SQ FT: 7,326
SALES (est): 968.2K **Privately Held**
SIC: 1382 6512 8999 Geological exploration, oil & gas field; commercial & industrial building operation; geological consultant

(G-488)
FEDEX OFFICE & PRINT SVCS INC
3801 Olsen Blvd Unit 2 (79109-3070)
PHONE...................................806 359-9684
EMP: 18
SALES (corp-wide): 69.2B **Publicly Held**
WEB: www.fedex.com
SIC: 7334 2789 2759 2675 Photocopying & duplicating services; bookbinding & related work; commercial printing; die-cut paper & board
HQ: Fedex Office And Print Services, Inc.
7900 Legacy Dr
Plano TX 75024
800 463-3339

(G-489)
GLOBAL ANIMAL PRODUCTS INC
3701 Airway Blvd (79118-7746)
PHONE...................................806 622-9600
Ken Ridenour, *President*
Randy Maclin, *Regional Mgr*
Cindy Scarborough, *Corp Secy*
Gary Culp, *Vice Pres*
Tracy Thompson, *Manager*
◆ EMP: 27
SQ FT: 3,000
SALES (est): 8MM **Privately Held**
WEB: www.globalanimalproducts.com
SIC: 2048 Feed supplements

(G-490)
GROOMS & GROOMS INC
Also Called: Amarillo Transmission
4410 Canyon Dr (79109-5612)
PHONE...................................806 358-8119
Thomas J Grooms, *President*
Geneva Grooms, *Vice Pres*
EMP: 9
SQ FT: 6,500
SALES (est): 850.8K **Privately Held**
WEB: www.gandmtransmissions.com
SIC: 3714 7537 Transmissions, motor vehicle; automotive transmission repair shops

(G-491)
GTX TECHNOLOGIES LLC
13636 S Fm 1541 (79118-3696)
PHONE...................................806 367-7074
Norbert Chirase,
John Doyle,
Ken Ridenour,
▼ EMP: 14
SALES (est): 1.2MM **Privately Held**
WEB: www.gtxag.com
SIC: 3999 Barber & beauty shop equipment

(G-492)
HI-PLAINS CANVAS PRODUCTS INC
Also Called: AAA Signs of Amarillo
6337 Canyon Dr (79110-4020)
P.O. Box 7714 (79114-7714)
PHONE...................................806 352-5345
Gene Bural, *President*
Kevin Bural, *Vice Pres*
Dale Bural, *Sales Executive*
Sam Warren, *Manager*
Charity Jones, *IT/INT Sup*
EMP: 28 EST: 1957
SQ FT: 15,000
SALES (est): 2.5MM **Privately Held**
WEB: www.hiplainscanvas.com
SIC: 3993 2394 Signs & advertising specialties; canvas & related products

(G-493)
INTEGRATED ADVANTAGE GROUP LP (PA)
Also Called: Iag Energy Services, LP
5700 Sw 45th Ave (79109-5204)
P.O. Box 7687 (79114-7687)
PHONE...................................806 367-8031
Lloyd Brown, *General Ptnr*
Grayson Oheim, *Opers Staff*
Monte Green, *CFO*
Dana Rodriguez, *Asst Controller*
Craig Hartman, *Accounts Mgr*
EMP: 17
SALES (est): 18.5MM **Privately Held**
WEB: www.iag-1.com
SIC: 1389 Gas field services; oil field services

(G-494)
JOHNSON BURNS CO
Also Called: Johnson Ranches
1310 Se 46th Ave (79118-7707)
P.O. Box 32365 (79120-2365)
PHONE...................................806 372-5869
Montford T Johnson III, *Owner*
Linda Eastlake, *Manager*
EMP: 13
SALES (est): 420K **Privately Held**
SIC: 0212 1381 Beef cattle except feedlots; drilling oil & gas wells

(G-495)
K C FAB INC
5601 S Washington St (79110-3508)
P.O. Box 30535 (79120-0535)
PHONE...................................806 372-9281
Mark D Johnston, *Vice Pres*
EMP: 19 **Privately Held**
SIC: 3569 Sprinkler systems, fire: automatic
PA: K C Fab Inc
2836 Delafield St
Houston TX 77023

(G-496)
KRUCKEBERG CORPORATION
Also Called: Inline Technology
3229 Commerce St (79109-3275)
PHONE...................................806 352-9262
Ken Kruckeberg, *President*
Lloyd Kruckeberg, *Sales Mgr*
EMP: 9
SQ FT: 26,000
SALES (est): 1.1MM **Privately Held**
WEB: www.inlinetechnologies.com
SIC: 5699 5084 2759 T-shirts, custom printed; printing trades machinery, equipment & supplies; screen printing

(G-497)
L & L PALLET SUPPLY INC
2795 E Fm 1151 (79118-4304)
PHONE...................................806 272-5041

Thomas Landry, *President*
EMP: 10
SALES (corp-wide): 2MM **Privately Held**
WEB: www.llpallet.com
SIC: 2448 Pallets, wood
PA: L & L Pallet Supply, Inc.
1230 Us Highway 84
Muleshoe TX 79347
806 272-5041

(G-498)
LOCO SOLUTIONS LLC
5700 Sw 45th Ave (79109-5204)
P.O. Box 7667 (79114-7667)
PHONE...................................817 437-6438
Greg Swindle, *President*
EMP: 86
SALES (est): 18.5MM **Privately Held**
SIC: 2899 8711 Chemical preparations; chemical engineering
PA: Integrated Advantage Group, Lp
5700 Sw 45th Ave
Amarillo TX 79109
806 367-8031

(G-499)
LONE STAR MACHINE AND TOOL CO
10501 S Fm 1541 (79118-6014)
P.O. Box 7296 (79114-7296)
PHONE...................................806 622-5106
David W Baker, *President*
Tracy Baker, *Admin Sec*
EMP: 10
SALES (est): 1.4MM **Privately Held**
SIC: 3599 Machine shop, jobbing & repair

(G-500)
MAXI VOLT CORPORATION INC
Also Called: Mvc
9350 S Georgia St (79118-5065)
P.O. Box 8171 (79114-8171)
PHONE...................................806 371-0722
Mark Wingate, *President*
Jeanette Wingate, *Treasurer*
Jack Klaus, *Consultant*
John Wingate, *Consultant*
EMP: 11
SALES (est): 1.9MM **Privately Held**
WEB: www.maxivolt.com
SIC: 3613 3612 Regulators, power; transformers, except electric

(G-501)
MIDWEST MACHINE LLC
6601 S Fm 1541 (79118-6138)
P.O. Box 50314 (79159-0314)
PHONE...................................806 355-9400
Matt Kiefer, *Production*
Ethan Long, *Engineer*
Ed Paden, *Supervisor*
Steve Dunivan,
EMP: 20
SQ FT: 24,000
SALES (est): 2MM **Privately Held**
WEB: www.midwestmachinellc.com
SIC: 7692 3599 3535 Welding repair; custom machinery; machine shop, jobbing & repair; conveyors & conveying equipment

(G-502)
MILLER PAPER COMPANY
Also Called: Miller Paper & Packaging
6511 S Washington St (79118-8347)
PHONE...................................806 353-0317
Joseph Earl Schmidt, *President*
Corby Bleckert, *Vice Pres*
Beth Furgerson, *Vice Pres*
Charles Furgerson, *Vice Pres*
Cindy Schmidt, *Vice Pres*
EMP: 42
SQ FT: 50,000
SALES (est): 23.3MM **Privately Held**
WEB: www.millerpaper.com
SIC: 5113 5087 2621 5199 Paper & products, wrapping or coarse; janitors' supplies; packaging paper; packaging materials

(G-503)
NUCO2 SUPPLY LLC
Also Called: Amarillo Depot
3970 Business Park Dr (79110-4232)
PHONE...................................817 676-7580
EMP: 20

SALES (corp-wide): 274.4K **Privately Held**
SIC: 2813 Industrial gases
PA: Nuco2 Supply Llc
321 Commerce Way Unit 3
Pembroke NH 03275
770 280-5605

(G-504)
OWENS CORNING SALES LLC
1701 Hollywood Rd (79118-6017)
P.O. Box 8000 (79114-8000)
PHONE...................................806 622-1582
John Campbell, *Branch Mgr*
Rafael Mendiola,
EMP: 350 **Publicly Held**
WEB: www.owenscorning.com
SIC: 3296 Fiberglass insulation
HQ: Owens Corning Sales, Llc
1 Owens Corning Pkwy
Toledo OH 43659
419 248-8000

(G-505)
PIONEER MILL WORKS INC
Also Called: Pioneer Millworks
3850 Mack Rd (79118-3601)
P.O. Box 7968 (79114-7968)
PHONE...................................806 622-3201
David Thompson, *President*
EMP: 12
SALES (est): 1.3MM **Privately Held**
WEB: www.pioneermillworks.com
SIC: 2431 Millwork

(G-506)
PIONEER MILLWORK INC
3850 Mack Rd (79118-3601)
P.O. Box 7968 (79114-7968)
PHONE...................................806 622-3100
Tom Walters, *President*
Karen H Walters, *Vice Pres*
EMP: 16
SALES (est): 2MM
SALES (corp-wide): 13.4MM **Privately Held**
WEB: www.pioneermillworks.com
SIC: 2431 Millwork
PA: Pioneer General Contractors, Inc.
3850 Mack Rd
Amarillo TX 79118
806 622-3100

(G-507)
PORTERSVILLE SALES & TESTING
114 Se 46th Ave (79118-7803)
P.O. Box 2446 (79105-2446)
PHONE...................................806 373-6811
Bill Piehl, *President*
Helen Piehl, *Vice Pres*
EMP: 20
SQ FT: 2,400
SALES (est): 2.5MM **Privately Held**
WEB: www.westernsalesinc.com
SIC: 3715 7539 3537 3443 Trailer bodies; trailer repair; industrial trucks & tractors; fabricated plate work (boiler shop)

(G-508)
POWER PIPE AND TANK LLC
511 Sw 48th Ave (79110-2701)
P.O. Box 31240 (79120-1240)
PHONE...................................417 447-4508
Marcie Fisher, *General Mgr*
Gerald Dickens, *Principal*
Lupe Vasquez, *Prdtn Mgr*
EMP: 30
SQ FT: 70,000
SALES (est): 3MM **Privately Held**
WEB: www.powerpipeandtank.com
SIC: 3795 1799 2679 Tanks & tank components; insulation of pipes & boilers; pipes & fittings, fiber: made from purchased material

(G-509)
PPG INDUSTRIES INC
Also Called: PPG 8329
2511 Paramount Blvd B2 (79109-1749)
PHONE...................................806 467-9707
Joe Truesdell, *Branch Mgr*
EMP: 24
SALES (corp-wide): 15.3B **Publicly Held**
WEB: www.ppg.com
SIC: 2851 Paints & paint additives

PA: Ppg Industries, Inc.
1 Ppg Pl
Pittsburgh PA 15272
412 434-3131

(G-510)
PROGRESS RAIL SERVICES CORP
12100 Walls Rd (79118-6965)
PHONE..................................806 335-3900
Charles Hanna, *Prdtn Mgr*
John Clark, *Manager*
David Brecheen, *Manager*
Hugo Benavides, *Executive*
Karen Yates, *Executive*
EMP: 100
SALES (corp-wide): 53.8B **Publicly Held**
WEB: www.progressrail.com
SIC: 3743 Railroad equipment
HQ: Progress Rail Services Corporation
1600 Progress Dr
Albertville AL 35950
256 505-6421

(G-511)
SCHRY-WAY CASES
10525 S Washington St (79118-6014)
P.O. Box 8580 (79114-8580)
PHONE..................................806 622-0066
Philip Herring, *President*
EMP: 10 **EST:** 1953
SQ FT: 10,000
SALES (est): 1MM **Privately Held**
WEB: www.schryway.com
SIC: 2441 Cases, wood

(G-512)
TASMAN INDUSTRIES INC
Also Called: Tasman Amarillo
102 Beefco Rd (79118-7300)
PHONE..................................806 372-3850
Steve Fausey, *Plant Mgr*
EMP: 30
SQ FT: 50,448
SALES (corp-wide): 62.5MM **Privately Held**
WEB: www.tasmanusa.com
SIC: 3111 2011 Hides: tanning, currying & finishing; meat packing plants
PA: Tasman Industries, Inc.
930 Geiger St
Louisville KY 40206
502 785-7477

(G-513)
TEEMS RIG MANUFACTURING LLC
14290 S Us Highway 287 (79118-7035)
P.O. Box 50970 (79159-0970)
PHONE..................................806 379-6904
Ed Podzemny, *Mng Member*
Eddie C Podzemny Jr,
EMP: 18
SALES (est): 1.3MM **Privately Held**
WEB: www.teemsmfg.com
SIC: 1389 Oil field services

(G-514)
THOMAS LEASE SERVICE
2602 S Hayden St (79109-2306)
P.O. Box 1088, Perryton (79070-1088)
PHONE..................................806 202-1800
Ray Thomas, *Owner*
EMP: 14
SALES (est): 1MM **Privately Held**
SIC: 1389 Oil & gas wells: building, repairing & dismantling

(G-515)
TRINITY FELLOWSHIP (PA)
Also Called: Arbor Christian Academy
5000 Hollywood Rd (79118-5000)
PHONE..................................806 355-8955
Sr Pastor Jimmy Evans, *Pastor*
Ralph Vasquez, *Pastor*
Teel Merrick, *Director*
Tamara Hubbard, *Admin Asst*
Rita Wilkinson, *Admin Asst*
EMP: 180
SQ FT: 110,000
SALES (est): 6.8MM **Privately Held**
WEB: www.tfc.org
SIC: 8661 8299 5942 2731 Non-denominational church; bible school; books, religious; book publishing

(G-516)
UGLYPRESS L L C
3608 Mockingbird Ln (79109-3294)
PHONE..................................806 322-1050
Roberto Acevedo, *Owner*
EMP: 10
SALES (est): 220.7K **Privately Held**
WEB: www.uglypress.com
SIC: 2741 Miscellaneous publishing

(G-517)
VALERO MARKETING AND SUPPLY CO
7201 Canyon Dr (79110-4339)
P.O. Box 631 (79105-0631)
PHONE..................................877 882-5376
Jeff Stout, *Engineer*
Dane Williams, *Director*
David Neeley, *Admin Sec*
EMP: 120
SALES (corp-wide): 108.3B **Publicly Held**
WEB: www.valero.com
SIC: 2911 Petroleum refining
HQ: Valero Marketing And Supply Company
1 Valero Way
San Antonio TX 78249

(G-518)
VALLEY PROTEINS (DE) INC
8415 Se 1st Ave (79118-7302)
PHONE..................................540 247-2798
Jason Evans, *General Mgr*
EMP: 53
SALES (corp-wide): 473.5MM **Privately Held**
WEB: www.valleyproteins.com
SIC: 2077 Animal & marine fats & oils
PA: Valley Proteins (De), Inc.
151 Valpro Dr
Winchester VA 22603
540 877-2533

(G-519)
VALLEY PROTEINS (DE) INC
80 N Lakeside Dr (79118-7308)
PHONE..................................806 379-6001
Armando Pena, *Safety Mgr*
Allen Morgan, *Engineer*
EMP: 45
SALES (corp-wide): 473.5MM **Privately Held**
WEB: www.valleyproteins.com
SIC: 2047 5172 2077 2048 Dog & cat food; lubricating oils & greases; rendering; prepared feeds
PA: Valley Proteins (De), Inc.
151 Valpro Dr
Winchester VA 22603
540 877-2533

(G-520)
VENABLES CONSTRUCTION INC (PA)
Also Called: Venable's Welding & Roustabout
7410 Continental Pkwy (79119-6740)
PHONE..................................806 381-2121
Scott Venable, *President*
Ronnie Green, *Superintendent*
John Hendrix, *Superintendent*
Robert Kirkpatrick, *Superintendent*
Charlie Kiser, *Superintendent*
EMP: 151
SQ FT: 5,000
SALES (est): 102.8MM **Privately Held**
WEB: www.venablesconstruction.com
SIC: 1623 1794 1389 4922 Oil & gas pipeline construction; excavation work; roustabout service; natural gas transmission; crude petroleum pipelines; welding on site

(G-521)
WESTERN BOWL
5120 Canyon Dr (79109-6153)
P.O. Box 7445 (79114-7445)
PHONE..................................806 359-5211
Marty Fenberg, *Owner*
Randy Webb, *General Mgr*
EMP: 32 **EST:** 1956
SQ FT: 46,000

SALES (est): 2.6MM **Privately Held**
WEB: www.westernbowlama.com
SIC: 3949 5812 5813 Bowling alleys & accessories; American restaurant; cocktail lounge

(G-522)
WESTERN SLS TSTG AMARILLO INC
114 Se 46th Ave 16 (79118-7803)
P.O. Box 2446 (79105-2446)
PHONE..................................806 373-6811
Bill Piehl, *President*
Mark Griffin, *Exec VP*
Steve Aderholt, *Vice Pres*
Helen Piehl, *Vice Pres*
Geryl Hurst, *Prdtn Mgr*
EMP: 40
SALES (est): 6.8MM **Privately Held**
WEB: www.westernsalesinc.com
SIC: 8734 3715 Hydrostatic testing laboratory; trailer bodies

(G-523)
WESTERN VALVE INC (PA)
114 Se 46th Ave (79118-7803)
P.O. Box 2446 (79105-2446)
PHONE..................................806 373-6811
Bill Piehl, *President*
Steve Aderholt, *Vice Pres*
Helen Piehl, *Vice Pres*
Kevin Reynolds, *Sales Staff*
▲ **EMP:** 14
SQ FT: 2,000
SALES (est): 2.5MM **Privately Held**
WEB: www.westernvalveinc.com
SIC: 3494 Valves & pipe fittings

(G-524)
WESTERN VALVE INC
6701 Mccormick (79118)
P.O. Box 2446 (79105-2446)
PHONE..................................806 373-6811
Dennis Hatfield, *Manager*
EMP: 11
SALES (corp-wide): 2.5MM **Privately Held**
WEB: www.westernvalveinc.com
SIC: 3494 Valves & pipe fittings
PA: Western Valve, Inc.
114 Se 46th Ave
Amarillo TX 79118
806 373-6811

(G-525)
ZACHRY HOLDINGS INC
6440 S Fm 1541 (79118-7856)
P.O. Box 30608 (79120-0608)
PHONE..................................806 322-4100
EMP: 13 **Privately Held**
WEB: www.zachrygroup.com
SIC: 2499 Cooling towers, wood or wood & sheet metal combination
PA: Zachry Holdings, Inc.
527 Logwood Ave
San Antonio TX 78221

Anahuac
Chambers County

(G-526)
KIVA CONSTRUCTION & ENGRG INC
600 Shipyard Rd (77514)
PHONE..................................409 252-3211
Joseph B McDermott, *President*
EMP: 40
SALES (est): 3.5MM **Privately Held**
SIC: 8711 1389 Petroleum engineering; oil & gas wells: building, repairing & dismantling

(G-527)
PRIMED UP NITROGEN SVCS LLC
230 Barrow White Rd (77514-2127)
P.O. Box 1803 (77514-1803)
PHONE..................................361 543-0747
Nathan Thompson, *President*
Amanda Satterwhite, *Vice Pres*
Gabriel Martinez,
EMP: 10

SALES (est): 348.4K **Privately Held**
WEB: www.primedupnitrogen.com
SIC: 1389 Servicing oil & gas wells

(G-528)
SYSTEMS INTERNATIONAL INC
4318 Fm 1985 (77514)
P.O. Box J, Highlands (77562-0336)
PHONE..................................281 424-2700
Steve Clark, *President*
EMP: 12
SQ FT: 500
SALES (est): 500K **Privately Held**
WEB: www.systemsinternational.com
SIC: 1389 Oil field services

Anderson
Grimes County

(G-529)
ENERFLOW INDUSTRIES INC
6740 Highway 30 (77830-9035)
PHONE..................................918 355-6300
Mark Williamson, *Principal*
Larry Lindholm, *Principal*
EMP: 79
SALES (est): 39.1MM **Privately Held**
SIC: 3533 Oil field machinery & equipment

(G-530)
NATIONAL OILWELL VARCO INC
Also Called: Nov Rolligon
6740 Highway 30 (77830-9035)
PHONE..................................936 873-2600
Scott Toler, *General Mgr*
Tiffany Matthews, *Engineer*
Matt Mueller, *Engineer*
Don Huelsebusch, *Accountant*
Tina Vanhorn, *Branch Mgr*
EMP: 102
SALES (corp-wide): 8.4B **Publicly Held**
WEB: www.nov.com
SIC: 3533 Oil & gas field machinery
PA: National Oilwell Varco, Inc.
7909 Parkwood Circle Dr
Houston TX 77036
713 346-7500

(G-531)
ROLLIGON NOV LP
6740 Highway 30 (77830-9035)
PHONE..................................936 873-2600
Fax: 936 873-9994
▼ **EMP:** 115
SALES (est): 62.8MM **Privately Held**
SIC: 3799 7353 Mfg Transportation Equipment Heavy Construction Equipment Rental

Andrews
Andrews County

(G-532)
A AND M SERVICES INC
3255 Se 2000 (79714)
P.O. Box 867 (79714-0867)
PHONE..................................432 290-5536
Alonso Soto, *President*
EMP: 19 **EST:** 2017
SALES (est): 1.2MM **Privately Held**
SIC: 1389 Servicing oil & gas wells

(G-533)
ANDREWS COUNTY NEWS
210 E Broadway St (79714-6586)
PHONE..................................432 523-2085
Don Ingram, *Owner*
EMP: 13
SALES (est): 1MM **Privately Held**
WEB: www.andrewscountynews.com
SIC: 2711 Newspapers: publishing only, not printed on site

(G-534)
ANDREWS PUMP & SUPPLY INC (PA)
507 Nw Mustang Dr (79714-4500)
P.O. Box 1378 (79714-1378)
PHONE..................................432 523-2166
Bill C Sommers, *President*

Billy L Sommers, *Principal*
Torreya S Bryan, *Corp Secy*
Travis E Bryan, *Vice Pres*
Dorothy Sommers, *Admin Sec*
EMP: 25 **EST:** 1973
SQ FT: 12,509
SALES (est): 8MM **Privately Held**
WEB: www.andrewspump.com
SIC: 3561 7699 3547 Pumps, oil well & field; pumps & pumping equipment repair; rod mills (rolling mill equipment)

(G-535)
ANDREWS SAFETY ANCHORS INC
1200 Se Mustang Dr (79714-7427)
P.O. Box 316 (79714-0316)
PHONE..................................432 524-6659
Mike Reid, *President*
Sherie Reid, *Treasurer*
Reid Roy, *Director*
◆ **EMP:** 12
SQ FT: 3,000
SALES (est): 400K **Privately Held**
WEB: www.andrewssafetyanchors.com
SIC: 3533 3462 Oil field machinery & equipment; anchors, forged

(G-536)
APACHE CORPORATION
209 Nw 12th St (79714-6006)
P.O. Box 1247 (79714-1247)
PHONE..................................432 524-2277
Brad Follis, *Manager*
EMP: 17
SALES (corp-wide): 6.4B **Publicly Held**
WEB: www.apachecorp.com
SIC: 1311 Crude petroleum production; natural gas production
PA: Apache Corporation
      2000 Post Oak Blvd Ste 10
      Houston TX 77056
      713 296-6000

(G-537)
BASIC ENERGY SERVICES INC
G & L Tool
510 Nw Mustang Dr (79714-4512)
P.O. Box 2027 (79714-2027)
PHONE..................................432 523-4251
Asher Branner, *Manager*
EMP: 15
SALES (corp-wide): 567.2MM **Publicly Held**
WEB: www.basices.com
SIC: 1389 Oil field services
PA: Basic Energy Services, Inc.
      801 Cherry St Unit 2
      Fort Worth TX 76102
      817 334-4100

(G-538)
BIG C RENTALS LLC
203 Se 1000 (79714-5723)
P.O. Box 1228 (79714-1228)
PHONE..................................432 266-8834
Ralph Carruth, *Mng Member*
EMP: 9
SALES (est): 220.6K **Privately Held**
SIC: 1389 Lease tanks, oil field: erecting, cleaning & repairing; oil & gas wells: building, repairing & dismantling; oil field services; servicing oil & gas wells

(G-539)
BILLY R COATS INC
Also Called: Coats Construction Company
1805 Sw Mustang Dr (79714-7537)
P.O. Box 1949 (79714-1949)
PHONE..................................432 523-3861
Billy Rex Coats, *President*
Coats Randy, *Vice Pres*
Randall R Coats, *Treasurer*
EMP: 10 **EST:** 1959
SALES (est): 230K **Privately Held**
SIC: 1389 Construction, repair & dismantling services; servicing oil & gas wells

(G-540)
BOF SERVICES INC
1300 S Us Highway 385 (79714-6023)
PHONE..................................432 523-2110
Wesley Morgan, *Branch Mgr*
EMP: 60

SALES (corp-wide): 16.2MM **Privately Held**
SIC: 1389 Oil field services
PA: B.O.F. Services, Inc.
      2416 Erskine St
      Lubbock TX 79415
      806 741-1080

(G-541)
BRAVE SERVICES INCORPORATED
109 Sw Mustang Dr (79714-6725)
PHONE..................................432 355-4001
Ashley Newbrough, *President*
Frank Couch, *Opers Mgr*
EMP: 30
SALES (est): 2.8MM **Privately Held**
WEB: www.braveservices-inc.com
SIC: 7692 Welding repair

(G-542)
CHEMICAL SERVICE COMPANY
401 Ne 3100 (79714-9239)
P.O. Box 1149 (79714-1149)
PHONE..................................432 523-5290
Joe Dan, *Owner*
EMP: 30 **EST:** 1967
SQ FT: 2,000
SALES (est): 2.4MM **Privately Held**
WEB: www.chemicalserviceco.com
SIC: 4212 1389 Local trucking, without storage; chemically treating wells

(G-543)
CHEVRON CORPORATION
Also Called: Unocal
21 M Sw Of Andrews (79714)
PHONE..................................432 523-7950
Dana Thomas, *Opers-Prdtn-Mfg*
Craig Schneider, *Branch Mgr*
Sergio Martinez, *Manager*
EMP: 40
SALES (corp-wide): 146.5B **Publicly Held**
WEB: www.chevron.com
SIC: 1321 Natural gas liquids
PA: Chevron Corporation
      6001 Bollinger Canyon Rd
      San Ramon CA 94583
      925 842-1000

(G-544)
HLC CUSTOM PROCESSING LLC
820 Sw 3001 (79714-9030)
PHONE..................................432 556-2443
EMP: 13
SALES (est): 985K **Privately Held**
SIC: 2011 Meat Packing Plant

(G-545)
JGT SERVICES
401 W Broadway St (79714-6215)
P.O. Box 1134 (79714-1134)
PHONE..................................432 553-5167
Jose Truvino, *Owner*
EMP: 30
SALES (est): 2.3MM **Privately Held**
SIC: 1389 Construction, repair & dismantling services

(G-546)
JODYS OILFIELD SERVICE INC
110 Sw Mustang Dr (79714-6700)
PHONE..................................432 523-6866
Jody Grinslade, *President*
EMP: 15
SQ FT: 8,400
SALES (est): 2.8MM **Privately Held**
WEB: www.jodysoilfieldserviceinc.com
SIC: 1389 Oil field services

(G-547)
KEY ENERGY SERVICES INC
100 Taylor Rd (79714)
PHONE..................................432 523-5155
Doug Young, *Opers Mgr*
Steve Southern, *Manager*
Terry McBeth, *Supervisor*
EMP: 80
SALES (corp-wide): 413.8MM **Publicly Held**
WEB: www.keyenergy.com
SIC: 1389 Oil field services

PA: Key Energy Services, Inc.
      1301 Mckinney St Ste 1800
      Houston TX 77010
      713 651-4300

(G-548)
KEY ENERGY SERVICES INC
1203 Sw Mustang Dr (79714-7533)
PHONE..................................432 523-5155
Claude Horton, *Manager*
EMP: 18
SALES (corp-wide): 413.8MM **Publicly Held**
WEB: www.keyenergy.com
SIC: 1389 Servicing oil & gas wells
PA: Key Energy Services, Inc.
      1301 Mckinney St Ste 1800
      Houston TX 77010
      713 651-4300

(G-549)
LEGEND ENERGY SERVICES LLC
212 Nw 2000 (79714-9122)
PHONE..................................432 523-6585
Clay Loughridge, *Branch Mgr*
EMP: 47
SALES (corp-wide): 150MM **Privately Held**
WEB: www.legendenergyservices.com
SIC: 1389 Oil field services
PA: Legend Energy Services, Llc
      5801 Broadway Ext Ste 210
      Oklahoma City OK 73118
      405 600-1264

(G-550)
MARTINS FISHING TLS & RENTALS
Also Called: Martin's Gas Testers & Rental
5110 Se 2000 (79714-5973)
PHONE..................................432 524-7456
Linda Martin, *Managing Prtnr*
EMP: 18
SQ FT: 144
SALES (est): 6MM **Privately Held**
SIC: 1389 5082 Fishing for tools, oil & gas field; oil field equipment

(G-551)
MARTINS FISHING TOOLS
5110 Se 2000 (79714-5973)
P.O. Box 307 (79714-0307)
PHONE..................................432 524-7456
EMP: 22
SALES (est): 1.1MM **Privately Held**
SIC: 1389 Oil/Gas Field Services

(G-552)
MID-WEST TRUCK CENTER INC
801 N Main St Ste Q (79714-4030)
PHONE..................................432 523-3451
Doyle Weishuhn, *President*
Max Mainord, *Vice Pres*
EMP: 100
SALES (est): 20.3MM **Privately Held**
WEB: www.midwesttruckcenter.com
SIC: 1389 Oil field services

(G-553)
MUSTANG WELL SERVICE LLC
2681 Se 1000 (79714-5837)
P.O. Box 77 (79714-0077)
PHONE..................................432 524-6112
Jose D Bustamante, *Mng Member*
EMP: 11
SALES (est): 1.7MM **Privately Held**
SIC: 1381 Service well drilling

(G-554)
NABORS WELL SERVICES LTD
701 Nw Mustang Dr (79714-3015)
P.O. Box 2033 (79714-2033)
PHONE..................................432 523-4420
Hazel Florist, *Safety Mgr*
Chad Amen, *Manager*
EMP: 100 **Privately Held**
WEB: www.nabors.com
SIC: 1389 Oil field services
HQ: Nabors Well Services Ltd.
      515 W Greens Rd Ste 1200
      Houston TX 77067
      281 874-0035

(G-555)
OCCIDENTAL PERMIAN LTD
711 Sw 7th Pl (79714-7821)
PHONE..................................432 523-7556
Vain Findley, *Manager*
Norma Gonzales, *Associate*
EMP: 14
SALES (corp-wide): 21.2B **Publicly Held**
WEB: www.oxy.com
SIC: 1311 Crude petroleum production
HQ: Occidental Permian Ltd.
      5 Greenway Plz Ste 110
      Houston TX 77046

(G-556)
PALMER OF TEXAS TANKS INC
Also Called: Palmer Industrial Products
1701 N Us Highway 385 (79714-9035)
P.O. Box 1069 (79714-1069)
PHONE..................................432 523-5904
Jim Lee, *Ch of Bd*
Rick Talley, *Manager*
▲ **EMP:** 55
SQ FT: 40,000
SALES (est): 19.3MM
SALES (corp-wide): 305.1MM **Publicly Held**
WEB: www.palmeroftexas.com
SIC: 3443 5084 3088 Industrial vessels, tanks & containers; tanks, storage; plastics plumbing fixtures
PA: Synalloy Corporation
      4510 Cox Rd Ste 201
      Glen Allen VA 23060
      804 822-3260

(G-557)
QUAIL ENERGY SERVICES LP (PA)
Also Called: Quail Construction
2495 N Us Highway 385 (79714-9210)
PHONE..................................432 523-3742
Tim Allen, *President*
Nelda Couch, *Manager*
Melissa Allen, *Shareholder*
EMP: 33
SQ FT: 9,500
SALES (est): 23.5MM **Privately Held**
WEB: www.quailenergy.com
SIC: 1389 Oil field services

(G-558)
SCOTT FETZER COMPANY
Kirby West, The
Seminole Hwy N (79714)
P.O. Box 749 (79714-0749)
PHONE..................................432 523-5511
Bob Alexander, *General Mgr*
EMP: 250
SALES (corp-wide): 254.6B **Publicly Held**
WEB: www.scottfetzer.com
SIC: 3635 Household vacuum cleaners
HQ: The Scott Fetzer Company
      28800 Clemens Rd
      Westlake OH 44145
      440 892-3000

(G-559)
SUPERIOR WELDING INC
Also Called: Andrews Anchors & Service
1010 S Us Highway 385 (79714-5744)
P.O. Box 425 (79714-0425)
PHONE..................................432 523-2038
Roy Reid, *President*
Patricia Reid, *Corp Secy*
Cathey Reid, *Vice Pres*
Mike Reid, *Vice Pres*
EMP: 25
SQ FT: 12,000
SALES (est): 3MM **Privately Held**
WEB: www.andrewstx.com
SIC: 7692 1799 Welding repair; building site preparation

(G-560)
TEJAS TRUCKING INC
2185 E State Highway 176 (79714-9431)
P.O. Box 1767 (79714-1767)
PHONE..................................432 523-5786
Kenny Thompson, *President*
Carruth Billy, *Vice Pres*
EMP: 9
SQ FT: 420

SALES (est): 1.1MM **Privately Held**
SIC: 4212 1389 Local trucking, without storage; oil field services

(G-561)
VIVA WELL SERVICING II L P
Also Called: Viva Support Services
1501 W Broadway St (79714-6001)
P.O. Box 4437, Odessa (79760-4437)
PHONE..............................432 524-2781
EMP: 10
SALES (est): 950.6K **Privately Held**
WEB: www.vivawsc.com
SIC: 1389 Oil field services

(G-562)
XTO ENERGY INC
1584 Sw 5900 (79714)
P.O. Box 1007 (79714-1007)
PHONE..............................432 524-6545
Garry Oknesski, *Branch Mgr*
Yari Egger, *Admin Asst*
EMP: 10
SALES (corp-wide): 264.9B **Publicly Held**
WEB: www.xtoenergy.com
SIC: 1311 Crude petroleum production
HQ: Xto Energy Inc.
22777 Sprngwoods Vlg Pkwy
Spring TX 77389

(G-563)
YELLOWJACKET OILFIELD SVCS LLC
300 Nw Mustang Dr (79714-4511)
PHONE..............................432 523-3692
EMP: 11
SALES (corp-wide): 25.4MM **Privately Held**
WEB: www.yjoslllc.com
SIC: 1389 Oil field services
PA: Yellowjacket Oilfield Services, L.L.C.
200 N Loraine St Ste 1150
Midland TX 79701
432 242-7570

Angleton
Brazoria County

(G-564)
3M COMPANY
1508 E Cedar St (77515-4141)
PHONE..............................979 848-8489
EMP: 13
SALES (corp-wide): 32.1B **Publicly Held**
WEB: www.3m.com
SIC: 3479 Coating of metals & formed products
PA: 3m Company
3m Center
Saint Paul MN 55144
651 733-1110

(G-565)
BENCHMARK ELECTRONICS INC
Also Called: BEI Angleton
3000 Technology Rd (77515-2599)
PHONE..............................979 849-6550
Mark Troutman, *Vice Pres*
Al Faupel, *Prdtn Mgr*
Timothy Valley, *Receiver*
Elvis Ramirez, *Mfg Spvr*
Charlie Goh, *Opers Staff*
EMP: 180
SALES (corp-wide): 2.2B **Publicly Held**
WEB: www.bench.com
SIC: 3672 Printed circuit boards
PA: Benchmark Electronics, Inc.
56 S Rockford Dr
Tempe AZ 85281
623 300-7000

(G-566)
BRAZOSPORT PLASTICS INC
2015 County Road 220 (77515-8656)
P.O. Box 509 (77516-0509)
PHONE..............................979 849-5422
Joseph P Rybak, *President*
Frank Spillers, *VP Finance*
Georgia Lewis, *Manager*
Jaime Simon, *Admin Sec*
EMP: 9 **EST:** 1969

SQ FT: 10,000
SALES (est): 2MM **Privately Held**
WEB: www.brazosportplastics.com
SIC: 3089 Plastic & fiberglass tanks; injection molded finished plastic products

(G-567)
COASTAL MACHINE & MECH LLC
14004 S Highway 288b (77515-9656)
PHONE..............................979 849-9323
Terry Edwards, *General Mgr*
Terry D Edwards, *Principal*
EMP: 27 **EST:** 2010
SALES (est): 1MM **Privately Held**
WEB: www.coastalmandm.com
SIC: 3599 Machine shop, jobbing & repair

(G-568)
COLLEGE PORT ENTERPRISES INC (PA)
Also Called: Baystar Printing
200 S Velasco St (77515-6033)
PHONE..............................979 848-3070
Kaye Starustka, *President*
Thomas Starustka, *Treasurer*
Tom Starustka, *Sales Staff*
Cheryl Peterson, *Marketing Staff*
Tina Schobel, *Admin Sec*
EMP: 10
SQ FT: 5,500 **Privately Held**
WEB: www.baystargroup.net
SIC: 7331 2741 Direct mail advertising services; miscellaneous publishing

(G-569)
COLLINS INSTRUMENT COMPANY
1520 Gifford Ln (77515-3176)
P.O. Box 938 (77516-0938)
PHONE..............................979 849-8266
Roger D Collins, *President*
James Collins, *Vice Pres*
EMP: 27 **EST:** 1946
SQ FT: 19,000
SALES (est): 5.2MM **Privately Held**
WEB: www.collinsinst.com
SIC: 3491 3599 Industrial valves; machine shop, jobbing & repair

(G-570)
DIVERSIFIED PLANT SVCS L L C
14004 S Highway 288b (77515-9656)
PHONE..............................979 848-8900
Lloyd G Murrell,
T R Richardson,
EMP: 70
SQ FT: 20,000
SALES (est): 9.3MM **Privately Held**
SIC: 3498 3441 Fabricated pipe & fittings; fabricated structural metal

(G-571)
ENCORE WELLHEAD SYSTEMS LLC
28024 N Highway 288b C (77515-2530)
PHONE..............................832 742-1325
Kenneth Bean, *President*
EMP: 29
SALES (corp-wide): 37.9MM **Privately Held**
WEB: www.encorewellhead.com
SIC: 1389 Bailing, cleaning, swabbing & treating of wells
PA: Encore Wellhead Systems, Llc
3403 Marquart St
Houston TX 77027
832 742-1350

(G-572)
EPD INC
1407 E Cedar St (77515-4121)
PHONE..............................979 239-1917
Paula Saleem, *Manager*
Troy L Calvert, *Exec Dir*
Troy Calvert, *Exec Dir*
Melissa Largent, *Planning*
Heather Kinard,
EMP: 30
SQ FT: 38,000
SALES (est): 2.4MM **Privately Held**
WEB: www.epdinc.org
SIC: 2099 Food preparations

(G-573)
HYDROCUT INC
2015 County Road 220 (77515-8656)
P.O. Box 509 (77516-0509)
PHONE..............................979 849-5422
Joe Rybak, *Principal*
Joseph Rybak, *Principal*
EMP: 14
SALES (est): 1.2MM **Privately Held**
WEB: www.texashydrocut.com
SIC: 3634 Electric housewares & fans

(G-574)
J S MCKINNEY INC
571 Jimmy Phillips Blvd (77515-7405)
PHONE..............................979 849-7283
J S Mc Kinney Jr, *President*
Carol Mc Kinney, *Vice Pres*
Therson Dossey, *Treasurer*
EMP: 70 **EST:** 1957
SQ FT: 3,200
SALES (est): 7.3MM **Privately Held**
SIC: 3498 3443 3441 Fabricated pipe & fittings; industrial vessels, tanks & containers; fabricated structural metal

(G-575)
OVERNITE SOFTWARE INC
1212 N Velasco St Ste 110 (77515-3064)
PHONE..............................979 319-8371
Armando Caceres Jr, *President*
Tina Hoskins, *President*
Gwen Follett, *Vice Pres*
Jim Wadd, *Vice Pres*
Amber Caceres, *QC Mgr*
EMP: 40
SALES (est): 4.2MM **Privately Held**
WEB: www.overnitecbt.com
SIC: 7372 8299 Educational computer software; ceramic school

(G-576)
R R RAMSOWER INC
1413 S Hwy 288b (77515)
P.O. Box 819 (77516-0819)
PHONE..............................979 849-6441
EMP: 40
SQ FT: 10,000
SALES (est): 10.1MM **Privately Held**
SIC: 3441 7692 7699 Fabricated structural metal; welding repair; knife, saw & tool sharpening & repair

(G-577)
REACTIVE METALS CORP
2115 County Road 233 (77515-8944)
P.O. Box 148 (77516-0148)
PHONE..............................979 849-7197
John Rouse, *President*
EMP: 10
SQ FT: 7,000
SALES (est): 1.2MM **Privately Held**
SIC: 3599 Machine shop, jobbing & repair

(G-578)
SCHLUMBERGER TECHNOLOGY CORP
Also Called: Coil Tubing Services
22535 N Highway 288b (77515-4882)
PHONE..............................281 369-3800
Ed Burchfield, *Branch Mgr*
EMP: 50 **Publicly Held**
SIC: 1389 Oil field services
HQ: Schlumberger Technology Corp
300 Schlumberger Dr
Sugar Land TX 77478
281 285-8500

(G-579)
SYNEO LLC
3601 Galaznik Rd (77515-6096)
PHONE..............................979 849-8700
John Solheim, *Principal*
EMP: 9
SALES (corp-wide): 7.2MM **Privately Held**
WEB: www.syneoco.com
SIC: 3599 Custom machinery
PA: Syneo, Llc
3875 Fiscal Ct Ste 300
West Palm Beach FL 33404
561 848-6684

(G-580)
TECHNICAL INNOVATIONS LLC
Also Called: Syneo
3601 Galaznik Rd (77515-6096)
PHONE..............................979 849-8700
C Garrison Cordell, *CEO*
Chelsea Strickland,
EMP: 25
SQ FT: 8,500
SALES (est): 3.9MM **Privately Held**
WEB: www.syneoco.com
SIC: 3841 Surgical & medical instruments

(G-581)
UNIVERSAL MANAGEMENT SVCS LLC
Also Called: Universal Wldg & Fabrication
201 N Walker St (77515-4215)
P.O. Box 400 (77516-0400)
PHONE..............................979 481-5711
Jason Barker, *Mng Member*
EMP: 24
SQ FT: 1,500
SALES (est): 500K **Privately Held**
WEB: www.umsservice.com
SIC: 1629 7692 8742 Land clearing contractor; welding repair; construction project management consultant

(G-582)
WILBUR-ELLIS NUTRITION LLC
1500 E Cedar St (77515-4141)
PHONE..............................979 849-6757
Ed Brauer, *Manager*
EMP: 24
SALES (corp-wide): 3.1B **Privately Held**
WEB: www.wilburellisnutrition.com
SIC: 2048 5191 Fish food; animal feeds
HQ: Wilbur-Ellis Nutrition, Llc
2001 Se Clmbia Rver Dr St
Vancouver WA 98661
360 892-2677

Anna
Collin County

(G-583)
BRONCO MANUFACTURING INC
500 W White St (75409-2556)
P.O. Box 8 (75409-0008)
PHONE..............................972 924-4576
Johnny Bradley, *President*
Carolyn Bradley, *Vice Pres*
John M Ellis, *VP Sales*
John Ellis, *Manager*
Danny Pingleton, *Manager*
▲ **EMP:** 55 **EST:** 1979
SQ FT: 32,800
SALES (est): 9.6MM **Privately Held**
WEB: www.broncomfg.net
SIC: 3599 Machine shop, jobbing & repair

(G-584)
LIBERTY SAND & GRAVEL INC
500 Highview Ln (75409-4244)
P.O. Box 270149, Flower Mound (75027-0149)
PHONE..............................972 924-8065
Amanda Meador, *President*
Allan Meador, *Treasurer*
EMP: 15 **EST:** 1999
SQ FT: 5,000
SALES (est): 3.1MM **Privately Held**
WEB: www.needrock.com
SIC: 1442 Construction sand & gravel

(G-585)
SELECTOUCH CORPORATION
105 Fourth St (75409)
P.O. Box 38 (75409-0038)
PHONE..............................972 924-3289
Raymond Stone, *President*
Allan Stone, *Vice Pres*
EMP: 22
SALES (est): 3.1MM **Privately Held**
WEB: www.selectouch.com
SIC: 3625 3993 3643 3081 Switches, electronic applications; signs & advertising specialties; current-carrying wiring devices; unsupported plastics film & sheet; commercial printing, lithographic

▲ = Import ▼ =Export
◆ =Import/Export

(G-586)
SOUTHWESTERN NAMEPLATE MFG CO
4th St (75409)
P.O. Box 35 (75409-0035)
PHONE..................................972 924-3289
Raymond E Stone, *President*
Betty Stone, *Treasurer*
Allen Stone, *Admin Sec*
EMP: 14
SQ FT: 6,800
SALES (est): 1MM **Privately Held**
SIC: 3993 Name plates: except engraved, etched, etc.: metal

Anson
Jones County

(G-587)
WCC ENERGY LLC (PA)
11848 County Road 372 (79501-5708)
P.O. Box 741, Wink (79789-0741)
PHONE..................................432 208-2839
Ronald K Worden, *President*
Jalaine Worden, *Vice Pres*
EMP: 35
SQ FT: 1,100
SALES (est): 2.2MM **Privately Held**
WEB: www.wccenergy.com
SIC: 1389 Gas field services

Anthony
El Paso County

(G-588)
MUELLER SUPPLY COMPANY INC
8810 S Desert Blvd (79821-7348)
PHONE..................................915 886-3383
Rudy Fuentes Jr, *Manager*
EMP: 39
SALES (corp-wide): 180.3MM **Privately Held**
WEB: www.muellerinc.com
SIC: 3444 Nonresidential construction
PA: Mueller Supply Company, Inc.
1913 Hutchins Ave
Ballinger TX 76821
325 365-3555

(G-589)
P ROCKIN ENTERPRISES INC
Also Called: Custom Equipment Fabricators
310 Valley Chili Rd (79821-7296)
PHONE..................................915 886-4912
Dena Parkey, *President*
R Brett Parkey, *Vice Pres*
EMP: 9
SQ FT: 16,000
SALES (est): 1.4MM **Privately Held**
SIC: 3469 Kitchen fixtures & equipment: metal, except cast aluminum

(G-590)
STARRFOAM MANUFACTURING INC
1004 Omar St (79821-9345)
PHONE..................................915 886-4636
John Elkins, *Manager*
EMP: 27 **Privately Held**
WEB: www.starrfoam.com
SIC: 2821 Polystyrene resins
HQ: Starrfoam Manufacturing, Inc.
3220 Avenue F
Arlington TX 76011
817 654-4688

Apple Springs
Trinity County

(G-591)
DEWAYNE ROGERS LOGGING INC
3451 Bwo Rd (75926)
PHONE..................................936 831-2060
Dewayne Rogers, *President*
EMP: 18

SALES (est): 1.7MM **Privately Held**
SIC: 2411 Logging camps & contractors

Aransas Pass
San Patricio County

(G-592)
J M DAVIDSON INC (PA)
Also Called: J M D
2564 County Road 1960 (78336-8960)
P.O. Box 4639, Corpus Christi (78469-4639)
PHONE..................................361 883-0983
John M Davidson, *President*
Nzilani Barry, *General Mgr*
Justin Davidson, *General Mgr*
Joe R Wallace, *Vice Pres*
Misty Tucker, *Accounting Mgr*
EMP: 250
SQ FT: 3,000
SALES (est): 66.6MM **Privately Held**
WEB: www.industrial-construction-solutions.com
SIC: 1541 1731 3441 Industrial buildings, new construction; general electrical contractor; fabricated structural metal

(G-593)
KELLOGG BROWN ROOT
Also Called: Production Services
224 State Hwy 361 (78335)
PHONE..................................361 758-2554
John Allen, *General Mgr*
EMP: 40
SALES (est): 1.4MM **Privately Held**
SIC: 1389 Oil field services

(G-594)
MILE 533 MARINE WAYS INC
748 E Goodnight Ave (78336-5800)
P.O. Box 2269, Rockport (78381-2269)
PHONE..................................361 758-5379
Raymond Duggat, *Manager*
Mark Wolfe, *Manager*
Chad S Chapman, *Director*
Manning B Chapman, *Director*
EMP: 15 EST: 1997
SQ FT: 6,000 **Privately Held**
WEB: www.mile533.com
SIC: 7699 3732 Boat repair; boat building & repairing
PA: Brown Water Marine Service, Inc.
843 Cr 4714
Ingleside TX 78362

Archer City
Archer County

(G-595)
DEEN DRILLING COMPANY
501 E South St (76351)
P.O. Box 845 (76351-0845)
PHONE..................................940 574-2561
Darlton D Deen, *President*
Chad W Deen, *Vice Pres*
EMP: 10 EST: 1960
SQ FT: 5,000
SALES (est): 1.8MM **Privately Held**
SIC: 1381 Drilling oil & gas wells

(G-596)
LINDEMANN DRILLING CO INC
518 N Center St (76351)
P.O. Box 1086 (76351-1086)
PHONE..................................940 691-1344
James D Lindemann, *President*
Brenda Goldsmith, *Senior Engr*
EMP: 15
SALES (est): 1MM **Privately Held**
WEB: www.edi-nola.com
SIC: 1381 Drilling oil & gas wells

(G-597)
TUBING TESTERS INC
801 N Center (76351-1585)
P.O. Box 655 (76351-0655)
PHONE..................................940 574-2177
Kevin Reneau, *President*
Lacey Foster, *Sales Staff*
EMP: 20

SALES (est): 1.3MM **Privately Held**
WEB: www.tubingtestersinc.com
SIC: 1389 Pipe testing, oil field service

(G-598)
USA ROCK BIT INC (PA)
507 N Center (76351-1567)
P.O. Box 1067 (76351-1067)
PHONE..................................940 574-2238
Ronnie Williams, *President*
Rocky Glasscock, *Vice Pres*
Matt Williams, *Sales Staff*
Melissa Hale, *Admin Asst*
▲ EMP: 9
SQ FT: 3,800
SALES (est): 2MM **Privately Held**
WEB: www.usarockbit.com
SIC: 1389 Servicing oil & gas wells

Argyle
Denton County

(G-599)
ADVANCED LIGHTNING TECH LTD (PA)
Also Called: A L T
122 Leesley Ln (76226-6324)
PHONE..................................940 455-7300
David Riley, *President*
▲ EMP: 66
SQ FT: 5,000
SALES (est): 21.3MM **Privately Held**
WEB: www.altfab.com
SIC: 5063 3643 Electrical supplies; lightning protection equipment

(G-600)
FASTERRA GROUP LP
200 Highland Cir (76226-3959)
PHONE..................................940 240-5800
Jim Haltom, *Partner*
EMP: 250
SALES (est): 29.4MM
SALES (corp-wide): 250MM **Privately Held**
SIC: 1522 1541 1389 Residential construction; industrial buildings & warehouses; factory construction; pipe testing, oil field service; gas compressing (natural gas) at the fields; oil field services
PA: Us Trinity Energy Services, Llc
200 Highland Cir
Argyle TX 76226
940 240-5800

(G-601)
FORUM ENERGY TECHNOLOGIES INC
6335 Fm 1830 (76226-5065)
PHONE..................................817 602-1174
Graham Chenault, *Branch Mgr*
EMP: 10 **Publicly Held**
WEB: www.f-e-t.com
SIC: 1389 Removal of condensate gasoline from field (gathering) lines
PA: Forum Energy Technologies, Inc.
10344 Sam Houston Park Dr # 300
Houston TX 77064

(G-602)
ONLINE TRAINING SOLUTIONS INC
Also Called: Otsi
315 Wooded Ct (76226-4234)
P.O. Box 2224, Redmond WA (98073-2224)
PHONE..................................888 308-6874
Joan Lambert, *CEO*
Gale Nelson, *Vice Pres*
Joan Preppernau, *Vice Pres*
EMP: 20
SQ FT: 5,000
SALES (est): 1.6MM **Privately Held**
WEB: www.otsi.com
SIC: 2731 7372 2741 Textbooks: publishing only, not printed on site; prepackaged software; miscellaneous publishing

(G-603)
TEXAS SCIENTIFIC PRODUCTS
11941 Hilltop Rd (76226-3149)
PHONE..................................972 757-2304
Doug Keene, *Managing Prtnr*

Bruce K Moulton, *Principal*
EMP: 11
SALES (est): 897.1K **Privately Held**
WEB: www.txscientific.com
SIC: 3999 Manufacturing industries

(G-604)
TRITON PRODUCTS LLC
Also Called: Omni Lubricants,
4014 Brooks Ct Ste 200 (76226-4508)
P.O. Box 51080, Denton (76206-1080)
PHONE..................................940 455-2800
Spence Mackenzie, *Mng Member*
M Alex Mackenzie,
EMP: 10
SQ FT: 2,400
SALES (est): 1.1MM **Privately Held**
WEB: www.tritonproducts.com
SIC: 2077 3586 Grease rendering, inedible; grease guns (lubricators)

Arlington
Tarrant County

(G-605)
4 OVER LLC
Also Called: ASAP Printing
3200 Avenue E E (76011-5231)
PHONE..................................801 263-2727
Patricia L Aharonov, *Branch Mgr*
EMP: 10
SALES (corp-wide): 190.6MM **Privately Held**
WEB: www.4over.com
SIC: 2759 Commercial printing
HQ: 4 Over, Llc
5900 San Fernando Rd D
Glendale CA 91202
818 246-1170

(G-606)
AC ELECTRONICS
3401 Avenue D (76011-7607)
PHONE..................................817 701-1400
Dwayne Hillman, *Owner*
Michael Throckmorton, *Sales Mgr*
Lisa Chen, *Sales Staff*
Cynthia Wice, *Manager*
▲ EMP: 10
SALES (est): 1.4MM **Privately Held**
WEB: www.aceleds.com
SIC: 5999 3645 Electronic parts & equipment; residential lighting fixtures

(G-607)
AC GLOBAL SYSTEMS INC
Also Called: AC Global Gps
301 W Abram St (76010-7124)
P.O. Box 150295 (76015-6295)
PHONE..................................214 497-0280
Shaun Ashman, *Vice Pres*
EMP: 9
SALES (est): 800K **Privately Held**
WEB: www.acglobalsystems.com
SIC: 3663

(G-608)
ACP INTERNATIONAL INC
Also Called: Stonehouse Signs
521 N Great Sw Pkwy (76011-5422)
P.O. Box 1212, Arvada CO (80001-1212)
PHONE..................................817 640-0992
Joseph Nussbaum, *President*
Jeffrey L Barhoover, *President*
Jeffry G Stone, *Vice Pres*
Christina Townsend, *Sales Staff*
Jeff Stone, *Executive*
▲ EMP: 58 EST: 1984
SQ FT: 30,000
SALES (est): 5.2MM **Privately Held**
WEB: www.stonehousesigns.com
SIC: 3993 Signs, not made in custom sign painting shops

(G-609)
ACRYLIC SOURCE
401 Exchange Dr (76011-7809)
PHONE..................................800 275-0316
Jayson Fulks, *Owner*
Sean Clowe, *Senior Mgr*
EMP: 45
SQ FT: 25,000

SALES (est): 6.7MM **Privately Held**
WEB: www.acrylicsource.com
SIC: 3089 Tops: dispenser, shaker, etc.:
plastic

(G-610)
ADTEC COLORANT CORPORATION
514 N Great Sw Pkwy (76011-5423)
PHONE..................................817 633-3004
Mahesh Parikh, *President*
Pam Conroy, *Opers Mgr*
Terry Halper, *Engineer*
Jeff Genualdi, *Sales Dir*
▲ EMP: 18
SQ FT: 30,000
SALES (est): 2.2MM
SALES (corp-wide): 1.1MM **Privately Held**
SIC: 2816 Color pigments
HQ: Tosaf, Inc.
330 Southridge Pkwy
Bessemer City NC 28016
980 533-3000

(G-611)
AF TECHNOLOGIES INC
2801 E Randol Mill Rd (76011-6723)
PHONE..................................817 649-2500
Al Akhtar, *President*
Joe Baligh, *Vice Pres*
Stephanie Redman, *Opers Mgr*
Melissa Hall, *Purchasing*
Jamie Reitman, *Purchasing*
EMP: 155
SQ FT: 85,000
SALES (est): 18.7MM **Privately Held**
WEB: www.aftechno.com
SIC: 3643 3699 Connectors & terminals
for electrical devices; electrical equipment
& supplies

(G-612)
AG DEVELOPMENT INC
801 Avenue H E Ste 100 (76011-7701)
P.O. Box 210354, Bedford (76095-7354)
PHONE..................................817 472-7260
Jon Ayres, *President*
EMP: 12
SALES (est): 1.6MM **Privately Held**
SIC: 2752 Commercial printing, lithographic

(G-613)
AIR POWER INC
Also Called: Air Power Inc Engines
4900 S Collins St (76018-1135)
PHONE..................................817 557-5855
Howard Van Bortel, *President*
Jose Gloria, *Partner*
Michael Dickson, *Supervisor*
Darla Birkes, *Administration*
◆ EMP: 24
SQ FT: 26,000
SALES (est): 3.8MM
SALES (corp-wide): 16.2MM **Privately Held**
WEB: www.airpowerinc.com
SIC: 3728 Aircraft parts & equipment
PA: Van Bortel Aircraft, Inc.
4900 S Collins St
Arlington TX 76018
817 468-7788

(G-614)
ALL-PRO THREADED PRODUCTS
191 Peyco Dr N (76001)
P.O. Box 151222 (76015-7222)
PHONE..................................817 467-5700
Rudy Covington, *General Mgr*
Jerry Dunsmore, *Principal*
▲ EMP: 15
SALES (est): 5.3MM **Privately Held**
WEB: www.aptp.com
SIC: 3452 3599 5072 Bolts, metal; machine shop, jobbing & repair; hardware

(G-615)
AMERICAN CAST-STONE INC
3500 Avenue E E (76011-5237)
PHONE..................................817 695-1800
Cindy Crawford, *President*
Sam Shipley, *Vice Pres*
EMP: 50
SQ FT: 49,000

SALES (est): 4.2MM **Privately Held**
WEB: www.ams-cs.com
SIC: 3272 Cast stone, concrete

(G-616)
AMERICAN EXCELSIOR COMPANY
900 Avenue H E (76011-7722)
PHONE..................................817 385-4300
Terry A Sadowski, *Branch Mgr*
EMP: 40
SALES (corp-wide): 56.7MM **Privately Held**
WEB: www.americanexcelsior.com
SIC: 3086 2429 5023 5199 Packaging &
shipping materials, foamed plastic; wood
wool, excelsior; floor coverings; packaging materials; plastics materials & resins;
packaging paper & plastics film, coated &
laminated
PA: American Excelsior Company Inc
850 Avenue H E
Arlington TX 76011
817 385-3500

(G-617)
AMERICAN MASONRY SUPPLY INC
3500 Avenue E E (76011-5237)
PHONE..................................817 695-1800
Sam L Shipley, *President*
William M Welwood, *Vice Pres*
Cindy C Shipley, *Admin Sec*
▼ EMP: 200
SQ FT: 49,000
SALES (est): 34.9MM **Privately Held**
WEB: www.ams-cs.com
SIC: 3272 Silo staves, cast stone or concrete

(G-618)
ANDROID INDUSTRIES LLC
3408 E Randol Mill Rd (76011-6842)
PHONE..................................972 343-3300
Jerry Elson, *Manager*
EMP: 75
SALES (corp-wide): 474.4MM **Privately Held**
WEB: www.android-ind.com
SIC: 3694 Engine electrical equipment
PA: Android Industries, L.L.C.
2155 Executive Hills Dr
Auburn Hills MI 48326
248 454-0500

(G-619)
APS INDUSTRIAL SERVICES INC
3430 Dalworth St (76011-6816)
PHONE..................................817 385-5500
Roy Marin Jr, *President*
Les Strickland, *Principal*
Sean R Petras, *Vice Pres*
Rebecca Marin, *Office Mgr*
EMP: 27
SALES (est): 6.4MM **Privately Held**
WEB: www.aps-ind.com
SIC: 3441 7382 Fabricated structural
metal; security systems services

(G-620)
APX PLASTICS INC
621 109th St (76011-7601)
PHONE..................................817 275-3883
Cathey Hunter, *President*
EMP: 10
SQ FT: 5,000
SALES (est): 1.7MM **Privately Held**
WEB: www.apxplastics.com
SIC: 3679 5065 5072 Electronic circuits;
electronic parts; hardware

(G-621)
AQUATIC CO
1521 N Cooper St Ste 500 (76011-5533)
PHONE..................................817 801-8300
Martin Joines, *Vice Pres*
Steve Dowler, *Opers Mgr*
EMP: 10
SALES (corp-wide): 463.9MM **Privately Held**
WEB: www.aquaticbath.com
SIC: 3088 Plastics plumbing fixtures

HQ: Aquatic Co.
665 Industrial Rd
Savannah TN 38372

(G-622)
ARCOSA MATERIALS INC (HQ)
1112 E Cpeland Rd Ste 500 (76011)
PHONE..................................817 635-8500
Carl W Campbell, *President*
Gail M Peck, *Treasurer*
Bryan Gay, *Sales Staff*
Jared S Richardson, *Admin Sec*
EMP: 369
SALES (est): 263.5MM
SALES (corp-wide): 1.7B **Publicly Held**
WEB: www.arcosalightweight.com
SIC: 3295 3532 Shale, expanded; washers, aggregate & sand
PA: Arcosa, Inc.
500 N Akard St Ste 400
Dallas TX 75201
972 942-6500

(G-623)
ARGOS USA LLC
640 New York Ave (76010-7610)
PHONE..................................817 468-1333
Ness N Comerford, *Manager*
EMP: 70
SQ FT: 903 **Privately Held**
WEB: www.argos-us.com
SIC: 3273 Ready-mixed concrete
HQ: Argos Usa Llc
3015 Windward Plz Ste 300
Alpharetta GA 30005
678 368-4300

(G-624)
ARLINGTON BRICK AND SUPPLY INC
9 Nora Ct (76013-3169)
PHONE..................................817 460-5511
EMP: 18 EST: 1979
SQ FT: 9,000
SALES (est): 3MM **Privately Held**
SIC: 5084 3559 Whol Industrial Equipment Mfg Misc Industry Machinery

(G-625)
ARLINGTON INTL AVI PDTS LLC
Also Called: Aiap
7321 Commercial Blvd E (76001-7149)
PHONE..................................817 465-9880
Bill Ganss, *President*
Rick Ferguson, *Vice Pres*
Lorraine Torres, *Accounts Mgr*
EMP: 50
SQ FT: 12,000
SALES (est): 14.3MM
SALES (corp-wide): 45.5MM **Privately Held**
WEB: www.aiapinc.com
SIC: 3728 Aircraft parts & equipment
PA: Fastener Distribution Holdings, Llc
400 Continental Blvd # 280
El Segundo CA 90245
213 620-9950

(G-626)
AUTO-CHLOR SERVICES LLC
701 107th St (76011-5310)
PHONE..................................817 525-1021
EMP: 20
SALES (est): 2.5MM **Privately Held**
WEB: www.autochlor.com
SIC: 3589 Dishwashing machines, commercial

(G-627)
B AND D BINDER AND INDEX INC
2621 S Cooper St (76015-2414)
P.O. Box 150388 (76015-6388)
PHONE..................................817 261-8227
John Steffens, *President*
Durwin Overall, *Owner*
James Foster, *Vice Pres*
Brent Johnson, *Vice Pres*
EMP: 29
SQ FT: 30,000
SALES (est): 3.6MM **Privately Held**
WEB: www.bdbinderindex.com
SIC: 2782 Blankbooks & looseleaf binders

(G-628)
B AND D INDEX INC
Also Called: Simpro
2621 S Cooper St (76015-2414)
P.O. Box 150388 (76015-6388)
PHONE..................................817 261-8227
John Steffens, *President*
James Foster, *Vice Pres*
EMP: 12
SALES (est): 2.1MM **Privately Held**
WEB: www.bdbinderindex.com
SIC: 2678 Stationery products

(G-629)
BADMOON ENTERPRISES LLC
Also Called: 3di Sign & Design
1133 W Main St (76013-1872)
PHONE..................................817 548-0561
Paul David Fulks, *President*
EMP: 23 EST: 2011
SQ FT: 4,046
SALES (est): 1.7MM **Privately Held**
WEB: www.3di-signanddesign.com
SIC: 1799 3993 Sign installation & maintenance; signs & advertising specialties

(G-630)
BELLA DESIGN GROUP LLC
Also Called: Bella Group
709 109th St (76011-7603)
PHONE..................................972 304-4100
Jeffrey Gern, *President*
Blake Decarlo, *Accounts Exec*
Joyce Nicholson, *Sales Staff*
Mark Lieberenz,
Kathy Donnelly, *Admin Asst*
EMP: 10
SALES (est): 1.1MM **Privately Held**
WEB: www.bellagroupdesign.com
SIC: 3949 Bags, golf

(G-631)
BETA ENGINEERING INC
468 Dodson Lake Dr (76012-3441)
PHONE..................................817 265-3367
Steve Austin, *President*
Billy Bob Austin, *President*
John Dashner, *QC Mgr*
Shirley Austin, *Treasurer*
Patti George, *Chief Acct*
EMP: 15
SQ FT: 23,000
SALES (est): 3MM **Privately Held**
WEB: www.betaeng.com
SIC: 3728 3533 3714 Aircraft parts &
equipment; oil field machinery & equipment; motor vehicle parts & accessories

(G-632)
BLUMBERGEXCELSIOR INC
2300 Ashcroft Ln Apt 620 (76006-5409)
PHONE..................................817 462-1530
Bill Honer, *Branch Mgr*
EMP: 40 **Privately Held**
WEB: www.blumberg.com
SIC: 2678 2796 2761 2759 Stationery
products; platemaking services; manifold
business forms; commercial printing; envelopes
PA: Blumbergexcelsior, Inc.
16 Court St Fl 14
Brooklyn NY 11241

(G-633)
BODYCOTE THERMAL PROC INC
428 Dodson Lake Dr (76012-3441)
PHONE..................................817 265-5878
Lewis Lance, *President*
Joe Turner, *Safety Mgr*
EMP: 50
SALES (corp-wide): 929.6MM **Privately Held**
WEB: www.bodycote.com
SIC: 3398 Brazing (hardening) of metal
HQ: Bodycote Thermal Processing, Inc.
12750 Merit Dr Ste 1400
Dallas TX 75251
214 904-2420

(G-634)
BUILDERS FRSTSRC-TXAS GROUP LP
3403 E Abram St (76010-1415)
PHONE..................................817 640-1234

Jeff Tatman, *Branch Mgr*
EMP: 274
SALES (corp-wide): 7.2B **Publicly Held**
WEB: www.bldr.com
SIC: 5031 3231 Lumber: rough, dressed & finished; insulating glass: made from purchased glass
HQ: Builders Firstsource-Texas Group, L.P.
3403 E Abram St
Arlington TX 76010

(G-635)
C-SQUARE INTL TRDG LLC (PA)
3703 Avenue E E (76011-5418)
PHONE..................................817 633-9000
Yin Chua, *Managing Prtnr*
Choon Boon Ng, *General Mgr*
Boone Ng, *Opers Mgr*
Yin Hwee Chua, *Mng Member*
▼ **EMP:** 11
SQ FT: 60,000
SALES (est): 3.8MM **Privately Held**
WEB: www.csquareusa.com
SIC: 2821 5093 4953 Plastics materials & resins; plastics scrap; recycling, waste materials

(G-636)
CA INC
624 Six Flags Dr Ste 250 (76011-6370)
PHONE..................................402 494-2411
Richard Vance, *Branch Mgr*
EMP: 12
SALES (corp-wide): 23.8B **Publicly Held**
WEB: www.broadcom.com
SIC: 3674 Application computer software
HQ: Ca, Inc.
520 Madison Ave
New York NY 10022
800 225-5224

(G-637)
CACTUS COIN
1112 111th St (76011-7706)
PHONE..................................817 640-1791
Perry Scott, *Manager*
EMP: 15
SALES (corp-wide): 19.8MM **Privately Held**
SIC: 5812 3581 7389 Eating places; automatic vending machines; coffee service
PA: Cactus Coin
120 Precision
Buda TX 78610
512 295-2248

(G-638)
CALYAN WAX COMPANY LLC
7901 Valcasi Dr Ste 300 (76001-7751)
PHONE..................................817 455-0895
Jacob Johnson,
Troy Cruthers,
EMP: 10
SALES (est): 1MM **Privately Held**
WEB: www.calyanwaxco.com
SIC: 3999 Candles

(G-639)
CARBON CARBN ADVANCED TECH INC
Also Called: C-Cat
4704 Eden Rd (76001-3300)
PHONE..................................817 985-2500
Francis A Schwind, *CEO*
Patrick Schwind, *President*
James Thompson, *Vice Pres*
Aaron Brown, *Engineer*
Edward C Schwind, *Admin Sec*
EMP: 30
SQ FT: 48,000
SALES (est): 4.7MM **Privately Held**
WEB: www.c-cat.net
SIC: 3624 Carbon & graphite products

(G-640)
CENIKOR FOUNDATION
Also Called: Screen Visions
6801 Paces Trl Apt 321 (76017-0857)
PHONE..................................817 921-2771
Martin Deichert, *Business Mgr*
Mark Bartee, *Manager*
Kris Karain, *Admin Asst*
EMP: 12

SALES (corp-wide): 47.1MM **Privately Held**
WEB: www.cenikor.org
SIC: 2396 8093 8069 Screen printing on fabric articles; drug clinic, outpatient; drug addiction rehabilitation hospital
PA: Cenikor Foundation
11931 Wickchester Ln # 300
Houston TX 77043
713 266-9944

(G-641)
CHOICE EXPLORATION INC
2221 Avenue J (76006-5867)
P.O. Box 167626, Irving (75016-7626)
PHONE..................................817 633-7777
Jon Martin, *President*
Jon Griffin, *Vice Pres*
Tina Sbriglia, *Mktg Coord*
EMP: 25
SQ FT: 2,500
SALES (est): 9.4MM **Privately Held**
WEB: www.choiceexploration.com
SIC: 1382 Oil & gas exploration services

(G-642)
CIRCUIT SYSTEMS COMPANY INC
5301 W Pioneer Pkwy (76013-2829)
P.O. Box 171322 (76003-1322)
PHONE..................................817 861-6575
Grady King, *CEO*
Patrick Kaler, *COO*
Michelle Blessing, *Purch Agent*
Michelle Flores, *Sales Mgr*
Ahmed Biyabani, *Sales Staff*
EMP: 38
SQ FT: 11,880
SALES (est): 4.5MM **Privately Held**
WEB: www.cirsysco.com
SIC: 3679 Harness assemblies for electronic use: wire or cable; electronic circuits

(G-643)
CITRONIX INC
2241 S Watson Rd Ste 111 (76010-8181)
PHONE..................................817 633-3200
Nigel Bond, *President*
Debbie Darling, *Corp Secy*
Robert Bison, *Vice Pres*
Michael Embree, *Engineer*
Trevor Benson, *Director*
▲ **EMP:** 27
SALES (est): 6.6MM **Privately Held**
WEB: www.citronix.com
SIC: 3555 Printing trades machinery

(G-644)
CITY OF ARLINGTON
Also Called: Arlington Police Department
620 W Division St (76011-7421)
PHONE..................................817 459-5700
Kevin Kolbye, *Chief*
Leland Strickland, *Chief*
Alex Radke, *Opers Staff*
Martha Woody, *Manager*
Jose Alvarez, *Officer*
EMP: 900
SALES (est): 17.8MM **Privately Held**
WEB: www.arlingtontx.gov
SIC: 3669 7371 Pedestrian traffic control equipment; computer software development & applications

(G-645)
CONSTRUCT CAPITAL LLC (PA)
Also Called: Perma-Pier Fndation Repr Texas
2821 E Randol Mill Rd (76011-6723)
P.O. Box 202383 (76006-8383)
PHONE..................................214 637-1444
Philip Sears, *Business Mgr*
Wanda Lawson, *COO*
Robby Brown, *Opers Staff*
Allan Lee, *Controller*
Caitlin Brown, *Hum Res Coord*
▲ **EMP:** 150
SALES (est): 64.4MM **Privately Held**
WEB: www.permapier.com
SIC: 1629 1741 1381 Drainage system construction; foundation & retaining wall construction; service well drilling

(G-646)
CONTEMPORARY DESIGN PLASTICS
Also Called: Metroplex Plastics
412 113th St (76011-5402)
PHONE..................................817 640-7539
EMP: 25
SQ FT: 40,000
SALES (est): 2.2MM **Privately Held**
WEB: www.metrocustomplastics.com
SIC: 3089 Injection molding of plastics

(G-647)
CORPORATE BUS SOLUTIONS INC
401 Exchange Dr (76011-7809)
P.O. Box 201686 (76006-1686)
PHONE..................................817 701-1390
Kim Gama, *President*
EMP: 25
SALES (est): 1.9MM **Privately Held**
WEB: www.1cbs.com
SIC: 7336 2752 7331 Commercial art & graphic design; commercial printing, offset; direct mail advertising services

(G-648)
CORR-WOOD MFG INC
1912 Peyco Dr S (76001-6714)
PHONE..................................817 467-5525
Al Spradlin, *President*
Barbara Spradlin, *Admin Sec*
EMP: 65
SQ FT: 18,000
SALES (est): 7.3MM **Privately Held**
SIC: 2448 Pallets, wood

(G-649)
COVERS ETC INC
925 W Harris Rd (76001-6807)
PHONE..................................817 467-5030
Joe Zanti Jr, *President*
Brad Zanti, *Vice Pres*
Jim Laleman, *Sales Staff*
▲ **EMP:** 50
SQ FT: 20,000
SALES (est): 5.7MM **Privately Held**
WEB: www.coversetc.com
SIC: 3949 Sporting & athletic goods

(G-650)
CREATIVE HANDWORKS INC
2400 E Randol Mill Rd (76011-6335)
PHONE..................................214 682-2090
Alicia Lanford, *President*
David Lanford, *Vice Pres*
EMP: 30 **EST:** 2008
SQ FT: 7,000
SALES (est): 1.2MM **Privately Held**
WEB: www.creativehandworks.net
SIC: 2732 Books: printing & binding

(G-651)
CROWN EQUIPMENT CORPORATION
Also Called: Crown Lift Trucks
4000 Scientific Dr (76014-4513)
PHONE..................................972 988-9000
Katherine Rickels, *Marketing Staff*
Kevin Poling, *Manager*
EMP: 123
SALES (corp-wide): 3.7B **Privately Held**
WEB: www.crown.com
SIC: 3537 Lift trucks, industrial: fork, platform, straddle, etc.
PA: Crown Equipment Corporation
44 S Washington St
New Bremen OH 45869
419 629-2311

(G-652)
CUMMINS INC (PA)
Also Called: Cummins Engine Company
600 N Watson Rd (76011-5377)
P.O. Box 842316, Dallas (75284-2316)
PHONE..................................615 986-2596
Richard Moussalli, *Vice Pres*
Chris Johns, *Engineer*
Matt Weston, *Engineer*
Bob Davis, *Technician*
EMP: 9
SALES (est): 2MM **Privately Held**
WEB: www.cummins.com
SIC: 3714 Motor vehicle parts & accessories

(G-653)
CUMMINS SOUTHERN PLAINS LLC (HQ)
600 N Watson Rd (76011-5377)
P.O. Box 90027 (76004-3027)
PHONE..................................817 640-6801
Raj Menon, *President*
Kelly Gorham, *General Mgr*
Peter Anderson, *Vice Pres*
Boye Omotoye, *Plant Mgr*
Jeremy Tennery, *Purch Mgr*
◆ **EMP:** 100
SQ FT: 130,000
SALES (est): 263MM
SALES (corp-wide): 19.8B **Publicly Held**
WEB: www.cummins.com
SIC: 5084 3519 Engines & parts, diesel; internal combustion engines
PA: Cummins Inc.
500 Jackson St
Columbus IN 47201
812 377-5000

(G-654)
CURBELL PLASTICS INC
Also Called: Nationwide Plastics
2001 Timberlake Dr (76010-5321)
PHONE..................................214 239-3870
Chris Jones, *Manager*
EMP: 25
SALES (corp-wide): 226.9MM **Privately Held**
WEB: www.curbellplastics.com
SIC: 5162 3081 Plastics film; plastics materials; plastics products; plastics sheets & rods; plastic film & sheet
HQ: Curbell Plastics, Inc.
7 Cobham Dr
Orchard Park NY 14127

(G-655)
CURRENTECH
1810 Lakeside Dr (76013-3320)
P.O. Box 2297, Azle (76098-2297)
PHONE..................................214 693-6751
Ron Bracy, *Owner*
EMP: 10 **EST:** 2011
SALES (est): 399.3K **Privately Held**
SIC: 3812 7699 Aircraft control systems, electronic; aircraft & heavy equipment repair services

(G-656)
CUSTOM PPR TUBE SOUTHWEST INC
925 111th St (76011-5226)
PHONE..................................817 385-5367
Jack Cox, *Owner*
Malcolm Faulkenberry, *Owner*
▲ **EMP:** 17
SALES (est): 4.1MM **Privately Held**
WEB: www.papertubesnow.com
SIC: 2655 5113 Fiber cans, drums & similar products; industrial & personal service paper

(G-657)
D & S CYCLE OF ARLINGTON INC
3636 S Cooper St (76015-3411)
PHONE..................................817 465-5454
Rex L Mansell, *President*
Robert Busbey, *General Mgr*
Randy Mansell, *Vice Pres*
Richard Mansell, *Vice Pres*
Caleb Barnett, *Sales Associate*
EMP: 12
SQ FT: 7,500
SALES (est): 3.1MM **Privately Held**
WEB: www.dscycle.com
SIC: 5571 7699 5551 3751 Motorcycles; motorcycle repair service; jet skis; motorcycles, bicycles & parts

(G-658)
DELL INC
3811 S Cooper St Ste 2056 (76015-4146)
PHONE..................................817 408-5725
Jimmy Combs, *Manager*
EMP: 9 **Publicly Held**
WEB: www.dell.com
SIC: 3571 Electronic computers

HQ: Dell Inc.
1 Dell Way
Round Rock TX 78682
800 289-3355

(G-659)
DELTA TEE INTERNATIONAL INC
1000 Commercial Blvd S # 100
(76001-7154)
P.O. Box 172212 (76003-2212)
PHONE...................................817 466-9991
Essa Firooz, *President*
Alex Kovachev, *Vice Pres*
Munir Hyder, *Engineer*
Rachmat Sofian, *Design Engr*
Juan Rivera, *Sales Staff*
▲ EMP: 26
SQ FT: 22,000
SALES (est): 7.1MM **Privately Held**
WEB: www.delta-tee.com
SIC: 3585 Refrigeration equipment, complete

(G-660)
DEMILEC INTERNATIONAL INC
3315 E Division St (76011-6832)
PHONE...................................817 640-4900
Jacques Lariviere, *President*
▲ EMP: 20
SALES (est): 3.8MM
SALES (corp-wide): 6.8B **Publicly Held**
WEB: www.demilec.com
SIC: 2821 0782 Polyurethane resins;
epoxy resins; molding compounds, plastics; spraying services, lawn
HQ: Huntsman Building Solutions (Canada) Inc
870 Boul Du Cure-Boivin
Boisbriand QC J7G 2
866 345-3916

(G-661)
DIECO INC (PA)
3321 Dalworth St Ste B (76011-6867)
P.O. Box 6331 (76005-6331)
PHONE...................................817 822-4292
▲ EMP: 30 EST: 1974
SQ FT: 10,000
SALES (est): 6.4MM **Privately Held**
WEB: www.dieco.net
SIC: 3544 Special dies & tools

(G-662)
DIGITAL CORP COMPANIES INC
801 Station Dr Ste 109 (76015-1650)
PHONE...................................817 801-8000
Sandra K Matiner, *Vice Pres*
Kenneth A Mattner, *Director*
EMP: 15
SALES (est): 1.9MM **Privately Held**
WEB: www.digitalcpinc.com
SIC: 2759 Financial note & certificate printing & engraving

(G-663)
DIRT ROAD MUSIC GROUP LLC
2608 Southern Hills Blvd (76006-3488)
PHONE...................................678 525-3982
EMP: 10
SALES (est): 86.9K **Privately Held**
SIC: 7389 2741 Artists' agents & brokers;
music & broadcasting services; music distribution systems; music books: publishing only, not printed on site

(G-664)
DIVERSFIED LBLING SLUTIONS INC
900 N Great Sw Pkwy (76011-5413)
PHONE...................................817 471-1310
Dalton Gladden, *General Mgr*
EMP: 20 **Privately Held**
WEB: www.teamdls.com
SIC: 2679 2672 Labels, paper: made from purchased material; labels (unprinted), gummed: made from purchased materials
HQ: Diversified Labeling Solutions, Inc.
1285 Hamilton Pkwy
Itasca IL 60143
630 625-1225

(G-665)
DOT IT REST FULFILLMENT LLC
Also Called: Dynamic Color Graphics
2001 E Randol Mill Rd (76011-8287)
PHONE...................................817 275-7714
Gary Cooper, *CEO*
Cindy Gibson, *Controller*
Adriane Baumgardner, *Accounts Exec*
Jarod Joyce, *Marketing Staff*
Adriane Arnold, *Manager*
EMP: 55
SALES (est): 7.6MM
SALES (corp-wide): 34.2MM **Privately Held**
WEB: www.dotit.com
SIC: 5963 2759 Home related products, direct sales; labels & seals: printing
PA: National Checking Company
899 Montreal Way
Saint Paul MN 55102
651 251-1500

(G-666)
DSI SOLUTIONS LLC
701 Highlander Blvd # 250 (76015-4600)
PHONE...................................817 633-1772
Gail Bellon, *Vice Pres*
Rod Nunley, *Supervisor*
Victor Watson,
Christopher Scogin, *Administration*
EMP: 22
SALES (est): 2.3MM **Privately Held**
WEB: www.dsisolutions.biz
SIC: 7372 Business oriented computer software

(G-667)
DYNAMIC ATTRACTIONS INC (PA)
1601 E Lamar Blvd Ste 214 (76011-4464)
PHONE...................................817 652-1212
Guy Nelson, *CEO*
Peter Schnable, *President*
Cindy Whiton, *General Mgr*
Campbell McIntyre, *Treasurer*
Karen Atkins, *Sales Staff*
▲ EMP: 10
SALES (est): 8.3MM **Privately Held**
WEB: www.dynamicattractions.com
SIC: 3599 Amusement park equipment

(G-668)
EMERSON CLIMATE TECH INC
3100 W Arkansas Ln # 102 (76016-5895)
PHONE...................................817 277-7764
Scott Moreland, *Manager*
EMP: 112
SALES (corp-wide): 16.7B **Publicly Held**
WEB: www.climate.emerson.com
SIC: 3585 3564 Condensers, refrigeration;
filters, air: furnaces, air conditioning equipment, etc.
HQ: Emerson Climate Technologies, Inc.
1675 Campbell Rd
Sidney OH 45365
937 498-3011

(G-669)
EMI INDUSTRIES LLC
1110 Eden Rd (76001-7913)
PHONE...................................817 987-1516
Alan Harvill, *Branch Mgr*
EMP: 39
SALES (corp-wide): 56.5MM **Privately Held**
WEB: www.emiindustries.com
SIC: 3556 Food products machinery
PA: Emi Industries, Llc
1316 Tech Blvd
Tampa FL 33619
813 626-3166

(G-670)
ENDURO PRODUCTS INC
728 111th St (76011-7617)
PHONE...................................817 704-7346
Michie White, *President*
EMP: 20
SQ FT: 24,000
SALES (est): 1.5MM **Privately Held**
SIC: 3519 3714 Parts & accessories, internal combustion engines; motor vehicle parts & accessories

(G-671)
EOH INDUSTRIES INC
1901 Southeast Pkwy (76018-3605)
PHONE...................................817 468-3181
Emmett Hickey, *President*
Jim Plog, *COO*
EMP: 51 EST: 1981
SQ FT: 15,000
SALES (est): 4.7MM **Privately Held**
WEB: www.eohind.com
SIC: 2844 5999 Manicure preparations;
hair care products

(G-672)
EPCS ENVIRONMENTAL LLC
5409 S Collins St Ste 111 (76018-9800)
PHONE...................................817 975-5790
Dale Anderson,
EMP: 10
SALES (est): 1.2MM **Privately Held**
SIC: 8748 8744 1795 3531 Environmental consultant; ; wrecking & demolition work; rock crushing machinery, portable

(G-673)
ETKON USA INC
916 113th St Ste A (76011-5416)
PHONE...................................817 701-1181
Peter H Parsinen, *President*
Scott G Parsinen, *Vice Pres*
▲ EMP: 9
SQ FT: 14,000
SALES (est): 1.3MM **Privately Held**
SIC: 3356 Zirconium

(G-674)
EVANS FOODS INC
Also Called: Mac's Snacks
615 N Great Sw Pkwy (76011-5424)
PHONE...................................817 640-5626
Jim Speake, *General Mgr*
Ann Crowe, *Regional Mgr*
Brad Booth, *Opers Mgr*
David Sparesus, *Engineer*
Mike Rusk, *Maintence Staff*
EMP: 15
SQ FT: 40,000
SALES (corp-wide): 116.2MM **Privately Held**
WEB: www.evansfood.com
SIC: 2096 2099 Pork rinds; food preparations
HQ: Evans Foods, Inc.
4118 S Halsted St
Chicago IL 60609
773 254-7400

(G-675)
FARMER BROS CO
Also Called: Farmers Brothers Coffee
744 Avenue H E (76011-3187)
PHONE...................................817 640-8111
Janie Page, *Marketing Staff*
Bobby Morrison, *Manager*
EMP: 20
SALES (corp-wide): 501.3MM **Publicly Held**
WEB: www.farmerbros.com
SIC: 2095 5499 5046 Coffee roasting (except by wholesale grocers); beverage stores; coffee brewing equipment & supplies
PA: Farmer Bros. Co.
1912 Farmer Brothers Dr
Northlake TX 76262
682 549-6767

(G-676)
FARROW MACHINE & MFG CO INC
1030 Commercial Blvd N (76001-7119)
PHONE...................................817 633-4686
Sid Farrow, *President*
Betty Farrow, *Vice Pres*
EMP: 22
SQ FT: 8,000
SALES (est): 2.2MM **Privately Held**
WEB: www.argmanufacturing.com
SIC: 3599 Machine shop, jobbing & repair

(G-677)
FAURECIA EXHAUST SYSTEMS INC
2100 Design Rd Ste 110 (76014-4593)
PHONE...................................812 314-5995
Eric Bailey, *Branch Mgr*
EMP: 182
SALES (corp-wide): 33.3MM **Privately Held**
SIC: 3714 5013 Mufflers (exhaust), motor vehicle; motor vehicle supplies & new parts
HQ: Faurecia Emissions Control Systems Na, Llc
543 Matzinger Rd
Toledo OH 43612
812 341-2000

(G-678)
FEDEX OFFICE & PRINT SVCS INC
1400 E Copeland Rd (76011-4954)
PHONE...................................817 543-0833
EMP: 20
SALES (corp-wide): 69.2B **Publicly Held**
WEB: www.fedex.com
SIC: 7334 3993 2789 Photocopying & duplicating services; signs & advertising specialties; bookbinding & related work
HQ: Fedex Office And Print Services, Inc.
7900 Legacy Dr
Plano TX 75024
800 463-3339

(G-679)
FIRESTICK PRODUCTIONS
420 Lillard Rd Ste 101 (76012-3613)
PHONE...................................817 360-7740
EMP: 25
SALES (est): 1MM **Privately Held**
SIC: 2395 7219 Embroidery & art needlework; garment making, alteration & repair

(G-680)
FOUNDERS OIL & GAS OPER LLC
1341 Horton Cir (76011-4310)
PHONE...................................817 390-1800
Donald R Horton, *Ch of Bd*
David V Auld, *President*
Michael J Murray, *Exec VP*
Ted I Harbour, *Senior VP*
Cade C Anderson, *Vice Pres*
EMP: 13
SALES (est): 1.1MM
SALES (corp-wide): 20.3B **Publicly Held**
WEB: www.foundersoil.com
SIC: 1311 Crude petroleum & natural gas production
PA: D.R. Horton, Inc.
1341 Horton Cir
Arlington TX 76011
817 390-8200

(G-681)
FRITO-LAY NORTH AMERICA INC
948 Avenue H E (76011-7786)
PHONE...................................817 649-3266
Charles Mora, *Project Mgr*
Keith Massa, *Opers-Prdtn-Mfg*
Jeanne Murphy, *Manager*
EMP: 100
SQ FT: 63,476
SALES (corp-wide): 67.1B **Publicly Held**
WEB: www.fritolay.com
SIC: 2096 5145 2099 2035 Potato chips & similar snacks; potato chips; food preparations; pickles, sauces & salad dressings; dehydrated fruits, vegetables, soups
HQ: Frito-Lay North America, Inc.
7701 Legacy Dr
Plano TX 75024

(G-682)
FTC INDUSTRIES INC
728 111th St (76011-7617)
PHONE...................................817 431-1511
Rick Flores, *President*
Dianna S Flores, *Admin Sec*
EMP: 50
SQ FT: 8,500
SALES (est): 650K **Privately Held**
WEB: www.ftcindustries.com
SIC: 3599 Machine shop, jobbing & repair

(G-683)
FUTURE HORIZONS INC
107 W Randol Mill Rd # 100 (76011-5889)
PHONE.................................817 277-0727
Wayne R Gilpin, *President*
Rose Heredia, *Manager*
▲ EMP: 22
SALES (est): 2.7MM **Privately Held**
WEB: www.fhautism.com
SIC: 2731 Books: publishing only

(G-684)
G & H TRUCK EQUIPMENT INC
1015 Commercial Blvd S (76001-7125)
PHONE.................................817 467-9883
Ray Jean Hankey, *President*
Juan Briseno, *Engineer*
Scott Wright, *CFO*
Dale McInnis, *Manager*
Scott Ratty, *Manager*
EMP: 35
SQ FT: 14,000
SALES (est): 7.3MM **Privately Held**
WEB: www.ghmfg.com
SIC: 3537 Industrial trucks & tractors

(G-685)
GAMMA2 LLC (DH)
2300 E Randol Mill Rd (76011-6333)
PHONE.................................760 734-4003
Alice Tillet, *Mng Member*
▲ EMP: 50
SQ FT: 8,000
SALES (est): 8.7MM
SALES (corp-wide): 493.3MM **Privately Held**
WEB: www.vittlesvault.com
SIC: 3089 5149 Injection molding of plastics; dog food
HQ: Doskocil Manufacturing Company, Inc.
2300 E Randol Mill Rd
Arlington TX 76011
877 738-6283

(G-686)
GAVSTAR SERVICES
8160lla Frontera (76002)
PHONE.................................817 657-4020
Gilbert Sanchez, *CEO*
EMP: 25
SALES (est): 501.1K **Privately Held**
SIC: 1382 Oil & gas exploration services

(G-687)
GENERAL MAGNAPLATE CORPORATION (PA)
801 Avenue G (76011-7709)
PHONE.................................817 640-1761
Candida C Aversenti, *CEO*
Edmund V Aversenti Jr, *President*
Larry Campbell, *Vice Pres*
EMP: 58 EST: 1959
SALES (est): 20.4MM **Privately Held**
WEB: www.magnaplate.com
SIC: 3479 3471 Coating of metals & formed products; coating, rust preventive; electroplating of metals or formed products

(G-688)
GENERAL MAGNAPLATE TEXAS INC
801 Avenue G (76011-7796)
PHONE.................................817 649-8989
Candida Aversenti, *President*
EMP: 30
SQ FT: 67,500
SALES (est): 11.1MM
SALES (corp-wide): 20.4MM **Privately Held**
WEB: www.magnaplate.com
SIC: 3479 Coating of metals & formed products; coating, rust preventive
PA: General Magnaplate Corporation
801 Avenue G
Arlington TX 76011
817 640-1761

(G-689)
GENERAL MAGNAPLATE WISCONSIN
801 Avenue G (76011-7709)
PHONE.................................800 441-6173
Candida C Aversenti, *CEO*
Edmund V Aversenti, *COO*

EMP: 15 EST: 1973
SALES (est): 1.2MM
SALES (corp-wide): 20.4MM **Privately Held**
WEB: www.magnaplate.com
SIC: 3479 Coating of metals & formed products
PA: General Magnaplate Corporation
801 Avenue G
Arlington TX 76011
817 640-1761

(G-690)
GENERAL MOTORS LLC
2525 E Abram St (76010-1346)
PHONE.................................817 652-2200
Juan C Jimenec, *General Mgr*
Peter Foster, *Production*
Ira Fuller, *Production*
Diane Woods, *QC Mgr*
Atif Mahmood, *Engineer*
EMP: 64 **Publicly Held**
WEB: www.gm.com
SIC: 3469 Metal stampings
HQ: General Motors Llc
300 Renaissance Ctr L1
Detroit MI 48243

(G-691)
GENERAL MOTORS LLC
2919 E Division St (76011-6710)
PHONE.................................817 652-2182
Juan Jimenez, *Branch Mgr*
EMP: 2000 **Publicly Held**
WEB: www.gm.com
SIC: 5511 3714 Automobiles, new & used; motor vehicle parts & accessories
HQ: General Motors Llc
300 Renaissance Ctr L1
Detroit MI 48243

(G-692)
GLIDEPATH LLC
Also Called: Beumer Glidepath
2241 S Watson Rd Ste 151 (76010-8183)
PHONE.................................972 641-4200
Kenneth Stevens, *Ch of Bd*
Finn Lyng Pedersen, *President*
Thomas Dalstein, *President*
David Mead, *Vice Pres*
Hayden Stoddart, *Engineer*
◆ EMP: 69
SQ FT: 20,000
SALES (est): 49.6MM
SALES (corp-wide): 1B **Privately Held**
WEB: www.glidepathgroup.com
SIC: 3535 Conveyors & conveying equipment
PA: Beumer Group Gmbh & Co. Kg
Oelder Str. 40
Beckum 59269
252 124-0

(G-693)
GRIFFITH POLYMERS INC
432 W Fork Dr Ste A (76012-3473)
PHONE.................................503 612-0999
Corey Barge, *President*
Erika Filippi, *President*
Donald G Barge, *Principal*
Barbara Barge, *Treasurer*
Stacey Holcombe, *Accounts Mgr*
▲ EMP: 37
SALES (est): 7.2MM **Privately Held**
WEB: www.indian-companies.com
SIC: 2821 Thermosetting materials

(G-694)
H2O GREENWORKS LLC
405 Lemon Dr (76018-1672)
PHONE.................................817 884-7788
Ronald Johnson,
EMP: 10
SALES (est): 216.3K **Privately Held**
SIC: 1389 Construction, repair & dismantling services

(G-695)
HEARTLAND FURNITURE INC
7900 Valcasi Dr (76001-7769)
PHONE.................................817 483-6161
Marilyn Jones, *President*
EMP: 20
SQ FT: 40,000

SALES (est): 1.4MM **Privately Held**
SIC: 2434 5712 Wood kitchen cabinets; cabinet work, custom

(G-696)
HELDOORN MANUFACTURING INC
419 W Fork Dr (76012-3450)
PHONE.................................817 275-0835
Fred Heldoorn, *President*
Jason Ditez, *Manager*
EMP: 15
SQ FT: 10,000
SALES (est): 2.6MM **Privately Held**
WEB: www.heldoornmfg.com
SIC: 3728 Aircraft assemblies, subassemblies & parts

(G-697)
HONEYCOMB ONE LLP
2800 E Randol Mill Rd (76011-6724)
PHONE.................................817 649-7056
David Wagner, *Managing Prtnr*
Anthony Vaughn, *Opers Mgr*
EMP: 60
SALES (est): 3.9MM **Privately Held**
WEB: www.texasalmet.com
SIC: 3365 Aerospace castings, aluminum

(G-698)
HORMEL FOODS CORP SVCS LLC
4601 Hollow Tree Dr # 10 (76018-1287)
PHONE.................................817 465-4735
Robert Joyner, *Manager*
EMP: 10
SALES (corp-wide): 9.6B **Publicly Held**
WEB: www.hormelfoods.com
SIC: 2011 Meat packing plants
HQ: Hormel Foods Corporate Services, Llc
1 Hormel Pl
Austin MN 55912

(G-699)
HORNBEEK ENTERPRISES INC
Also Called: Chips Custom Cabinets
7503 Us 287 Hwy (76001-6959)
PHONE.................................817 478-2447
Howard Hornbeek Jr, *President*
EMP: 18
SQ FT: 14,000
SALES (est): 1.5MM **Privately Held**
WEB: www.chipskitchens.com
SIC: 2434 Wood kitchen cabinets

(G-700)
HOSKIN & MUIR INC
Also Called: Cardinal Showers
825 Avenue H E Ste 115 (76011-7729)
PHONE.................................817 640-7220
Mike Petitpas, *Manager*
EMP: 10
SALES (corp-wide): 92.9MM **Privately Held**
WEB: www.hmicardinal.com
SIC: 3088 Shower stalls, fiberglass & plastic
PA: Hoskin & Muir, Inc.
4795 Shepherdsville Rd
Louisville KY 40218
502 969-4059

(G-701)
HUNTSMAN BLDG SLUTIONS USA LLC (HQ)
3315 E Division St (76011-6832)
PHONE.................................817 640-4900
Robert D Massaro, *CEO*
Jacques Lariviere, *President*
Jim Upton, *General Mgr*
Michele Dacus, *Corp Secy*
Doug Brady, *Vice Pres*
▲ EMP: 90
SQ FT: 30,000
SALES (est): 28.8MM
SALES (corp-wide): 6.8B **Publicly Held**
WEB: www.demilec.com
SIC: 2821 Polyurethane resins; epoxy resins; molding compounds, plastics
PA: Huntsman Corporation
10003 Woodloch Forest Dr # 260
The Woodlands TX 77380
281 719-6000

(G-702)
INCAB AMERICA LLC
640 107th St (76011-5309)
PHONE.................................833 344-6222
Alexander Smilgevich, *President*
Mike Riddle, *Exec VP*
Mike Page, *Plant Mgr*
Dan L Berg, *Sales Staff*
Jacob Manske, *Sales Staff*
EMP: 22 EST: 2017
SQ FT: 36,500
SALES (est): 5.6MM **Privately Held**
WEB: www.incabamerica.com
SIC: 3357 Fiber optic cable (insulated)

(G-703)
INDIAN AEROSPACE INC
427a W Fork Dr (76012-3450)
PHONE.................................817 265-5137
Roger L Crudup, *President*
Bradley Crudup, *Sales Staff*
Wanda Kitchens, *Administration*
EMP: 15
SQ FT: 7,000
SALES (est): 3.2MM **Privately Held**
WEB:
SIC: 3452 3429 5088 Bolts, nuts, rivets & washers; manufactured hardware (general); aircraft & parts

(G-704)
INDIAN INDUSTRIES LP (PA)
Also Called: Indian Rubber
432 W Fork Dr Ste A (76012-3473)
PHONE.................................817 265-6731
▲ EMP: 17 EST: 1973
SALES (est): 9.7MM **Privately Held**
WEB: www.indian-companies.com
SIC: 5085 3053 Rubber goods, mechanical; packing, rubber

(G-705)
INDIAN RUBBER COMPANY INC
440 W Fork Dr (76012-3488)
PHONE.................................817 265-6732
Steven Crudup, *President*
Rodney Reynolds, *QC Mgr*
▲ EMP: 45
SALES (est): 8.1MM **Privately Held**
WEB: www.indian-companies.com
SIC: 3069 3061 Molded rubber products; mechanical rubber goods

(G-706)
INTEGRATED PRODUCTION SYSTEMS
419 Duncan Perry Rd # 101 (76011-5438)
PHONE.................................817 385-0700
Donald Jackson, *CEO*
Anthony J Rowley, *President*
Lana Jackson, *Admin Sec*
EMP: 13
SQ FT: 10,200
SALES (est): 4MM **Privately Held**
WEB: www.ipstx.com
SIC: 3599 Custom machinery

(G-707)
INX INTERNATIONAL INK CO
3701 New York Ave Ste 130 (76014-4403)
PHONE.................................817 375-0075
Daivd Corona, *Manager*
Mike Burton, *Manager*
EMP: 31
SQ FT: 7,500 **Privately Held**
WEB: www.inxinternational.com
SIC: 2893 5085 Printing ink; ink, printers'
HQ: Inx International Ink Co.
150 N Martingale Rd # 700
Schaumburg IL 60173
630 382-1800

(G-708)
ISOTHERM INC
7401 Commercial Blvd E (76001-7142)
P.O. Box 172379 (76003-2379)
PHONE.................................817 472-9922
Zahid Ayub, *President*
Daniel Garay, *Manager*
Huang Liang, *Manager*
Salman Khalid, *Admin Mgr*
◆ EMP: 25 EST: 1999
SQ FT: 16,000

SALES (est): 8.4MM **Privately Held**
WEB: www.iso-therm.com
SIC: 3449 1711 Lath, expanded metal;
plumbing, heating, air-conditioning contractors

(G-709)
**J M FABRICATION COMPANY
LLC**
415 Duncan Perry Rd (76011-5412)
PHONE..................................817 652-0526
Stephanie Matheus, *President*
Mario Belloti, *QC Mgr*
Michael Chesko, *QC Mgr*
Joseph Matheus,
Jonas Matheus,
▲ EMP: 15 EST: 1981
SQ FT: 30,000
SALES (est): 3.4MM **Privately Held**
WEB: www.jmfab.com
SIC: 3451 3679 3545 3444 Screw ma-
chine products; harness assemblies for
electronic use: wire or cable; precision
tools, machinists'; sheet metalwork;
guided missile & space vehicle parts &
auxiliary equipment

(G-710)
JAEGER PRODUCTS INC (HQ)
2201 E Lamar Blvd Ste 240 (76006-7440)
PHONE..................................817 695-5680
Philip E Kamins, *CEO*
Gary E Kamins, *President*
Thian C Cheong, *Exec VP*
Cecil Ellison, *Vice Pres*
John Halbirt, *Vice Pres*
◆ EMP: 25
SQ FT: 13,500
SALES (est): 3.2MM
SALES (corp-wide): 1.7B **Privately Held**
WEB: www.jaeger.com
SIC: 3053 Packing materials
PA: Pmc Global, Inc.
12243 Branford St
Sun Valley CA 91352
818 896-1101

(G-711)
JM GRAPHICS LLC
Also Called: Swifty Printing & Graphics
2407 S Cooper St (76015-1605)
PHONE..................................817 460-7562
Jerry Mechell, *President*
Janie Mechell, *Vice Pres*
EMP: 19
SQ FT: 9,000
SALES: 1.9MM **Privately Held**
WEB: www.swiftysolutions.com
SIC: 2752 7334 Commercial printing, off-
set; photocopying & duplicating services

(G-712)
**KINRO TEXAS LTD
PARTNERSHIP**
4381 W Green Oaks Blvd # 200
(76016-4477)
PHONE..................................817 483-7791
David L Webster, *Partner*
Devin McChristian, *Engineer*
EMP: 304
SALES (est): 31.1MM **Privately Held**
SIC: 3442 Metal doors, sash & trim

(G-713)
L3 TECHNOLOGIES INC
2200 Arlington Downs Rd (76011-6320)
P.O. Box 5328 (76005-5328)
PHONE..................................817 619-4756
Ashok Sisodia, *President*
Kathy Contino-Schlarb, *Vice Pres*
David Duggan, *VP Bus Dvlpt*
Jim Dunn, *Manager*
Erin Pfarner, *Director*
EMP: 1600
SALES (corp-wide): 11.3B **Publicly Held**
WEB: www.l3t.com
SIC: 3663 8299 3699 Telemetering equip-
ment, electronic; airline training; elec-
tronic training devices
HQ: L3 Technologies, Inc.
600 3rd Ave Fl 34
New York NY 10016
212 805-5234

(G-714)
L3 TECHNOLOGIES INC
Also Called: Link Training & Simulation
2200 Arlington Downs Rd (76011-6320)
P.O. Box 5328 (76005-5328)
PHONE..................................817 619-2000
Leonard Genna, *President*
William Frain, *Exec VP*
Vinod Chitkara, *Vice Pres*
Richard A Cody, *Vice Pres*
Paul De Lia, *Vice Pres*
EMP: 1700
SALES (corp-wide): 11.3B **Publicly Held**
WEB: www.l3t.com
SIC: 3663 Telemetering equipment, elec-
tronic
HQ: L3 Technologies, Inc.
600 3rd Ave Fl 34
New York NY 10016
212 805-5234

(G-715)
L3 TECHNOLOGIES INC
Also Called: Link Training & Simulation
2116 Arlington Downs Rd (76011-8209)
P.O. Box 5328 (76005-5328)
PHONE..................................817 619-2000
Larry Muenzberg, *Opers Mgr*
Christopher Fontenot, *Engineer*
Jonathan Gabel, *Engineer*
John McNellis, *Branch Mgr*
EMP: 700
SALES (corp-wide): 11.3B **Publicly Held**
WEB: www.l3t.com
SIC: 3663 3669 3679 3769 Telemetering
equipment, electronic; receiver-transmit-
ter units (transceiver); amplifiers, RF
power & IF; signaling apparatus, electric;
intercommunication systems, electric; mi-
crowave components; guided missile &
space vehicle parts & auxiliary equip-
ment; aircraft control systems, electronic
HQ: L3 Technologies, Inc.
600 3rd Ave Fl 34
New York NY 10016
212 805-5234

(G-716)
**LAKELAND PAPER
CORPORATION**
Also Called: Lakland Paper
600 109th St (76011-7602)
PHONE..................................817 840-5470
Curtis Haack, *Manager*
EMP: 20
SALES (corp-wide): 3.3MM **Privately
Held**
WEB: www.lakelandpaper.com
SIC: 2679 Paperboard products, converted
PA: Lakeland Paper Corporation
68345 Edgewater Beach Rd
White Pigeon MI 49099
269 651-5474

(G-717)
LANE SUPPLY INC (PA)
120 Fairview St (76010-7221)
PHONE..................................817 261-9116
Ronnie Jones, *CEO*
Billy Carnahan, *Chairman*
Richard Drouillard, *Project Mgr*
Sherry Jones, *Purch Agent*
Cari Golovich, *Plant Engr*
EMP: 90
SQ FT: 100,000
SALES (est): 20.9MM **Privately Held**
WEB: www.lanesupplyinc.com
SIC: 3446 3448 3443 3444 Architectural
metalwork; prefabricated metal buildings;
miscellaneous metalwork; sheet metal-
work

(G-718)
**LANGFORD CONSTRUCTION
INC**
Also Called: Real Log Com
5919 Woodmeadow Dr (76016-4419)
PHONE..................................817 478-0218
David Langford, *President*
David Bishop, *President*
EMP: 13
SALES (est): 1.3MM **Privately Held**
SIC: 1521 2452 New construction, single-
family houses; log cabins, prefabricated,
wood

(G-719)
LASER CARE INC
Also Called: Alliance Laser Technologies
1222 W Corporate Dr Ste A (76006-6106)
P.O. Box 121086 (76012-1086)
PHONE..................................817 640-6665
Bill Tapp, *President*
EMP: 12
SQ FT: 8,000
SALES (est): 1.6MM **Privately Held**
WEB: www.lciofficesolutions.com
SIC: 3555 Printing trade parts & attach-
ments

(G-720)
LEXUS GROUP INC
6407 S Cooper St Ste 137b (76001-5813)
PHONE..................................682 323-5942
EMP: 10
SALES (est): 726K **Privately Held**
WEB: www.lexus.com
SIC: 5511 5012 3711 Automobiles, new &
used; automobile auction; motor vehicles
& car bodies

(G-721)
LFC INDUSTRIES INC
1221 W Corporate Dr (76006-6103)
P.O. Box 5982 (76005-5982)
PHONE..................................817 640-1322
B Kelly Koons, *President*
Mark G Gramlich, *General Mgr*
Bob Reece, *Corp Secy*
Matt Bolton, *Vice Pres*
Charles Ramsey, *Vice Pres*
EMP: 60
SQ FT: 28,000
SALES (est): 9.5MM **Privately Held**
WEB: www.lfc-ind.com
SIC: 3429 3452 Metal fasteners; bolts,
nuts, rivets & washers

(G-722)
LIGHT GAUGE SOLUTIONS INC
1100 Eden Rd (76001-7913)
PHONE..................................682 564-0378
Elizabeth A Zatopek, *President*
Vickie Jones, *Purch Agent*
Michale Zatopek, *Manager*
EMP: 12
SQ FT: 55,000
SALES (est): 1.8MM **Privately Held**
WEB: www.lightgaugesolutions.com
SIC: 3448 Trusses & framing: prefabri-
cated metal

(G-723)
LIMA USA INC
2001 Ne Green Oaks Blvd (76006-2601)
PHONE..................................817 385-0777
Luigi Ferrari, *CEO*
Paolo Ricardi, *Director*
EMP: 26 EST: 2011
SQ FT: 12,100
SALES (est): 23MM **Privately Held**
WEB: www.limacorporate.com
SIC: 3842 Implants, surgical

(G-724)
LSC COMMUNICATIONS US LLC
401 N Great Sw Pkwy (76011-5420)
PHONE..................................817 640-9987
Doug Willie, *Manager*
EMP: 156
SALES (corp-wide): 3B **Publicly Held**
WEB: www.lsccom.com
SIC: 2759 Commercial printing
HQ: Lsc Communications Us, Llc
191 N Wacker Dr Ste 1400
Chicago IL 60606
844 572-5720

(G-725)
LURACO INC
Also Called: Luraco Technologies
1132 107th St (76011-3109)
PHONE..................................817 633-1080
Tom Le, *CEO*
Tracy Le, *President*
Caitlyn Nguyen, *Vice Pres*
Khoa Nguyen, *Vice Pres*
▲ EMP: 40
SQ FT: 38,000
SALES: 6.9MM **Privately Held**
WEB: www.luraco.com
SIC: 3999 Barber & beauty shop equip-
ment

(G-726)
M C R OIL TOOLS LLC
7315 Business Pl (76001-7135)
P.O. Box 151748 (76015-7748)
PHONE..................................817 701-5100
Michael Robertson, *President*
Shane Brumback, *Pastor*
Monica Barlow, *Vice Pres*
Aaron Robertson, *Vice Pres*
Sherry Robertson, *Vice Pres*
▲ EMP: 10
SQ FT: 7,000
SALES (est): 2.1MM **Privately Held**
WEB: www.mcroiltools.com
SIC: 3532 3533 Bits, except oil & gas field
tools, rock; bits, oil & gas field tools: rock;
drilling tools for gas, oil or water wells

(G-727)
MAIN STREET INSTALLERS LLC
Also Called: Marketing and Service Assoc
1133 W Main St (76013-1872)
PHONE..................................817 459-2001
John Wright, *President*
EMP: 10 EST: 2008
SALES (est): 1.1MM **Privately Held**
WEB:
www.mainstreetsignsandgraphics.com
SIC: 3993 Signs & advertising specialties

(G-728)
MARKING SERVICES INC
5905 Polo Club Dr (76017-4546)
P.O. Box 173128 (76003-3128)
PHONE..................................817 419-0061
Jeff Dicketson, *President*
EMP: 30 EST: 1988
SALES (est): 1.6MM **Privately Held**
SIC: 3999 Identification plates

(G-729)
MATERIAL CONTROL INC
918 A 113th St (76011)
PHONE..................................817 695-1400
Neil Mullins, *Branch Mgr*
EMP: 52
SALES (corp-wide): 82.6MM **Privately
Held**
WEB: www.materialcontrolinc.com
SIC: 3499 3953 Ladders, portable: metal;
letters (marking devices), metal
PA: Material Control Inc.
130 Seltzer Rd
Croswell MI 48422
630 892-4274

(G-730)
MCR OIL TOOLS LLC
7327 Business Pl (76001-7135)
P.O. Box 151748 (76015-7748)
PHONE..................................817 704-6677
David Gorrell, *Mfg Mgr*
Mike Ward, *Mfg Staff*
Long Nguyen, *Info Tech Dir*
Michael Robertson,
Sherry Robertson,
EMP: 50
SQ FT: 41,000
SALES (est): 9.4MM **Privately Held**
WEB: www.mcroiltools.com
SIC: 1389 3292 3533 Oil field services;
tubing & piping, asbestos & asbestos ce-
ment; bits, oil & gas field tools: rock

(G-731)
METRO CUSTOM PLASTICS INC
615 109th St (76011-7601)
PHONE..................................817 640-5646
EMP: 24 EST: 1972
SQ FT: 115,000
SALES (est): 6.3MM **Privately Held**
WEB: www.metrocustomplastics.com
SIC: 3089 Injection molding of plastics

(G-732)
METRO MATS
412 113th St (76011-5402)
PHONE..................................817 640-6287
Robert Brown, *Owner*
EMP: 20

2021 Harris Texas
Manufacturers Directory

▲ = Import ▼=Export
◆ =Import/Export

SALES (est): 852.3K **Privately Held**
SIC: 2273 Carpets & rugs

(G-733)
MOZAIC COMPANY
1101 Avenue G (76011-7715)
PHONE..................................972 386-3332
John Patrick A Lane, *Exec Dir*
EMP: 40
SALES (est): 1.4MM **Privately Held**
WEB: www.mozaicco.com
SIC: 8611 2511 2392 Chamber of Commerce; headboards: wood; cushions & pillows

(G-734)
MULTITECH GROUP INC
3705 W Green Oaks Blvd A (76016-3327)
PHONE..................................817 496-5500
Ora Joiner, *President*
Keith Gross, *Vice Pres*
EMP: 10
SALES (est): 2.1MM **Privately Held**
WEB: www.multitechgroupinc.com
SIC: 3535 1796 Conveyors & conveying equipment; installing building equipment

(G-735)
MYGIS EMPIRE LLC
Also Called: Pudding On Smiles
1807 Lost Crossing Trl (76002-3637)
P.O. Box 1678, Rockwall (75087-1678)
PHONE..................................972 674-9758
Kendra McFarlane, *CEO*
EMP: 15
SALES (est): 138.4K **Privately Held**
SIC: 2051 Bakery: wholesale or wholesale/retail combined

(G-736)
NATHAN FAULK
Also Called: Get Low Transportation
735 Polk Dr Apt A (76011-3424)
PHONE..................................432 634-9223
Nathan Faulk, *Owner*
EMP: 10
SALES (est): 120K **Privately Held**
SIC: 3711 Truck & tractor truck assembly

(G-737)
ND INDUSTRIES INC
3611 Dalworth St (76011-5408)
PHONE..................................817 633-2788
Andrew Bryers, *Prdtn Mgr*
Jim Counts, *Office Mgr*
Daniel Conner, *Manager*
EMP: 79
SQ FT: 14,167
SALES (corp-wide): 59.9MM **Privately Held**
WEB: www.ndindustries.com
SIC: 3479 Coating of metals & formed products
PA: Nd Industries Inc
1000 N Crooks Rd
Clawson MI 48017
248 288-0000

(G-738)
NEWS PRINTING INC
1007 Paula Dr (76012-3218)
PHONE..................................817 275-5601
Ghazi Shah-Hosseini, *President*
EMP: 21
SQ FT: 9,000
SALES (est): 1MM **Privately Held**
SIC: 2759 Newspapers: printing

(G-739)
NOIRCROXX BIOLOGICALS LLC
4706 Oak Valley Dr (76016-1738)
PHONE..................................406 471-0671
Melinda Roach, *CFO*
Duane Johnson, *Mng Member*
EMP: 36
SALES (est): 2MM **Privately Held**
WEB: www.insurancelafayettega.com
SIC: 2076 Vegetable oil mills

(G-740)
NORTHSTAR GRAPHIX INC
305 W Fork Dr (76012-3448)
PHONE..................................817 385-1902
Alvin Halford, *President*
Joan Halford, *CFO*
EMP: 17

SQ FT: 7,500
SALES (est): 2.3MM **Privately Held**
WEB: www.northstargraphix.com
SIC: 2759 Screen printing

(G-741)
OIL STATES INDUSTRIES INC
Special Products Div
1031 Commercial Blvd N (76001-7124)
P.O. Box 670 (76004-0670)
PHONE..................................817 468-1400
Charles Moses, *Vice Pres*
Kevin Barrett, *Network Enginr*
EMP: 96
SQ FT: 40,000
SALES (corp-wide): 1B **Publicly Held**
WEB: www.oilstates.com
SIC: 1389 Oil field services
HQ: Oil States Industries, Inc.
7701 S Cooper St
Arlington TX 76001

(G-742)
OIL STATES INDUSTRIES INC
Aerospace Products Division
1115 Commercial Blvd S (76001-7126)
PHONE..................................817 468-1400
Ernie White, *Manager*
EMP: 30
SALES (corp-wide): 1B **Publicly Held**
WEB: www.oilstates.com
SIC: 3731 Marine rigging
HQ: Oil States Industries, Inc.
7701 S Cooper St
Arlington TX 76001

(G-743)
OIL STATES INDUSTRIES INC (HQ)
7701 S Cooper St (76001-7015)
P.O. Box 670 (76004-0670)
PHONE..................................817 548-4200
Scott Moses, *President*
Tama D Lucas, *Vice Pres*
Mat Moody, *Vice Pres*
Melba Carter, *Buyer*
Tom Clay, *Engineer*
◆ EMP: 190
SQ FT: 11,000
SALES (est): 362.7MM
SALES (corp-wide): 1B **Publicly Held**
WEB: www.oilstates.com
SIC: 1389 3061 3561 3533 Oil & gas wells: building, repairing & dismantling; oil field services; oil & gas field machinery rubber goods (mechanical); pumps & pumping equipment; drilling tools for gas, oil or water wells
PA: Oil States International, Inc.
333 Clay St Ste 4620
Houston TX 77002
713 652-0582

(G-744)
OIL STATES SYSTEMS INC
Also Called: Innco
7701 S Cooper St (76001-7015)
P.O. Box 670 (76004-0670)
PHONE..................................713 445-2210
Charles Fahrmeier, *President*
Patrick McKeever, *District Mgr*
Bill Maxwell, *Counsel*
Christopher Cragg, *Vice Pres*
Ricky Simic, *Vice Pres*
◆ EMP: 100
SALES (est): 9.5MM
SALES (corp-wide): 1B **Publicly Held**
WEB: www.oilstates.com
SIC: 1389 Oil field services
HQ: Oil States Industries, Inc.
7701 S Cooper St
Arlington TX 76001

(G-745)
P&H SALES LTD
Also Called: P & H Casters
1016 W Harris Rd (76001-6806)
PHONE..................................817 468-3850
David Hicks, *CEO*
▲ EMP: 25
SALES (est): 3.1MM **Privately Held**
WEB: www.phcasters.com
SIC: 3714 3562 5085 Wheels, motor vehicle; casters; bearings

(G-746)
PACKAGING CORPORATION AMERICA
Also Called: PCA
1001 113th St (76011-7707)
PHONE..................................817 640-1888
Michael Rooney, *Business Mgr*
Tom Hassfurther, *Exec VP*
Danny Summerville, *Purchasing*
Jason Scott, *Engineer*
Dana Alvarez, *Controller*
EMP: 31
SALES (corp-wide): 6.9B **Publicly Held**
WEB: www.packagingcorp.com
SIC: 2653 Boxes, corrugated: made from purchased materials
PA: Packaging Corporation Of America
1 N Field Ct
Lake Forest IL 60045
847 482-3000

(G-747)
PACTIV LLC
500 113th St (76011-5404)
PHONE..................................817 608-9009
Roger Schultz, *Sales Executive*
Bob Widman, *Manager*
EMP: 45 **Publicly Held**
WEB: www.pactiv.com
SIC: 5113 2671 Corrugated & solid fiber boxes; packaging paper & plastics film, coated & laminated
HQ: Pactiv Llc
1900 W Field Ct
Lake Forest IL 60045
847 482-2000

(G-748)
PARADIGM TRAFFIC SYSTEMS INC (PA)
2201 E Div St (76011)
P.O. Box 5508 (76005-5508)
PHONE..................................817 831-9406
Jerry Priester, *President*
Michael Fiske, *President*
Larry Laske, *Vice Pres*
Jeff Bryan, *Treasurer*
Matt Hendricks, *Sales Staff*
EMP: 13
SQ FT: 3,500
SALES (est): 3.2MM **Privately Held**
WEB: www.paradigmtraffic.com
SIC: 5088 3669 Transportation equipment & supplies; transportation signaling devices

(G-749)
PARAGON FURNITURE INC
Also Called: Inc, Paragon Furniture
2224 E Randol Mill Rd (76011-6331)
PHONE..................................817 633-3242
Richard L Kassanoff, *Partner*
Mark P Hubbard, *Partner*
Gregory S Kassanoff, *Partner*
Steve Pryor, *Partner*
James Battley, *Engineer*
▲ EMP: 73
SQ FT: 88,000
SALES (est): 19.5MM **Privately Held**
WEB: www.paragoninc.com
SIC: 2522 2493 2521 3821 Desks, office: except wood; particleboard, plastic laminated; desks, office: wood; laboratory apparatus & furniture

(G-750)
PEPSI-COLA METRO BTLG CO INC
1000 113th St (76011-7781)
PHONE..................................817 640-4445
Chris Bailey, *Opers Staff*
Ron Williams, *Opers Staff*
Mary Heidenreich, *QC Mgr*
Josue Cruz, *Engineer*
Derek Mowery, *Engineer*
EMP: 100
SALES (corp-wide): 67.1B **Publicly Held**
WEB: www.pepsico.com
SIC: 2086 Carbonated soft drinks, bottled & canned
HQ: Pepsi-Cola Metropolitan Bottling Company, Inc.
1111 Westchester Ave
White Plains NY 10604
914 767-6000

(G-751)
PEPSI-COLA SALES AND DIST INC
1000 113th St (76011-7781)
PHONE..................................817 640-4445
EMP: 60
SALES (corp-wide): 67.1B **Publicly Held**
WEB: www.pepsico.com
SIC: 2086 Carbonated soft drinks, bottled & canned
HQ: Pepsi-Cola Sales And Distribution, Inc.
700 Anderson Hill Rd
Purchase NY 10577

(G-752)
PERFECT WINDOWS INC
2400c Roosevelt Dr Ste C (76016-5805)
PHONE..................................817 277-0014
Fax: 817 277-0042
EMP: 17
SQ FT: 7,500
SALES: 700K
SALES (corp-wide): 988.5K **Privately Held**
SIC: 2391 Mfg Curtains/Draperies
HQ: Ssp Gmbh
Bilche 1
Amriswil TG

(G-753)
PETMATE HOLDINGS CO (PA)
2300 E Randol Mill Rd (76011-6333)
P.O. Box 1246 (76004-1246)
PHONE..................................817 467-5116
Alice Tillett, *CEO*
Iris Ho-Palmer, *Admin Sec*
◆ EMP: 1000
SQ FT: 50,888
SALES (est): 493.3MM **Privately Held**
SIC: 5999 3999 Pet supplies; pet supplies

(G-754)
PMC INC
Also Called: Raschig Jaeger Technologies
2201 E Lamar Blvd Ste 240 (76006-7440)
PHONE..................................817 695-5680
Brad Fleming, *Branch Mgr*
EMP: 159
SALES (corp-wide): 1.7B **Privately Held**
WEB: www.pmcglobalinc.com
SIC: 3086 Plastics foam products
HQ: Pmc, Inc.
12243 Branford St
Sun Valley CA 91352
818 896-1101

(G-755)
POLY U MOLDING & MFG LP
1016 W Harris Rd (76001-6806)
PHONE..................................817 701-0779
David Hicks, *President*
EMP: 15 EST: 2006
SALES (est): 2.8MM **Privately Held**
SIC: 3089 Molding primary plastic

(G-756)
POLYMER PRODUCTS LP
432 W Fork Dr Ste A (76012-3473)
PHONE..................................972 647-1000
Steven Crudup, *President*
EMP: 10
SQ FT: 22,000
SALES (est): 2.3MM
SALES (corp-wide): 9.7MM **Privately Held**
WEB: www.indian-companies.com
SIC: 3089 Synthetic resin finished products
PA: Indian Industries, L.P.
432 W Fork Dr Ste A
Arlington TX 76012
817 265-6731

(G-757)
PP EXIT LLC (PA)
Also Called: Print Place
1130 Avenue H E (76011-7726)
PHONE..................................817 701-3555
Shawn Petersen, *President*
Mark Deloach, *CFO*
▼ EMP: 35
SALES (est): 10.1MM **Privately Held**
WEB: www.printplace.com
SIC: 2759 Commercial printing

GEOGRAPHIC

(G-758)
PRECISION TURNING
6301 Calender Rd (76001-5441)
PHONE................................817 472-7999
Bernie Piatt, *Owner*
EMP: 9
SALES (est): 480K **Privately Held**
WEB: www.atprecision.com
SIC: 3312 Forgings, iron & steel

(G-759)
PRINTEGRA CORP
3301 Avenue E E (76011-5232)
PHONE................................800 972-1175
Wade Brewer, *General Mgr*
Tommy Gillis, *Branch Mgr*
EMP: 40
SALES (corp-wide): 438.4MM **Publicly Held**
WEB: www.printegra.com
SIC: 2761 2782 Continuous forms, office & business; blankbooks & looseleaf binders
HQ: Printegra Corp
5040 Highlands Pkwy Se
Smyrna GA 30082
770 487-5151

(G-760)
PRIVILEGED CULTURE LLC
3700 Trailwood Ct Apt 832 (76014-4228)
PHONE................................682 252-5173
Stephen Hunt,
EMP: 11
SALES (est): 300K **Privately Held**
SIC: 2389 Apparel & accessories

(G-761)
PRO-CHEM OF DFW INC
Also Called: Pro Chem Cleaning Systems
609 112th St (76011-7620)
P.O. Box 26835, Fort Worth (76126-0835)
PHONE................................817 695-1660
Debbie Davis, *President*
Marty Davis, *Vice Pres*
EMP: 11
SQ FT: 17,000
SALES (est): 3.2MM **Privately Held**
WEB: www.prochemofdfw.com
SIC: 2842 5084 Specialty cleaning preparations; industrial machinery & equipment

(G-762)
PROGRESSIVE INCORPORATED
Also Called: Pccfasteners
1030 Commercial Blvd N (76001-7119)
PHONE................................817 465-3221
Guinn D Crousen, *President*
William Michalski, *Vice Pres*
◆ EMP: 275
SALES (est): 83.3MM
SALES (corp-wide): 254.6B **Publicly Held**
WEB: www.progressive-llc.com
SIC: 3812 3429 3728 Search & navigation equipment; aircraft hardware; aircraft body & wing assemblies & parts
HQ: Precision Castparts Corp.
4650 Sw Mcdam Ave Ste 300
Portland OR 97239
503 946-4800

(G-763)
QFC INDUSTRIES INC (PA)
3201 E Arkansas Ln 111 (76010-7002)
P.O. Box 5231 (76005-5231)
PHONE................................817 640-2151
▲ EMP: 12
SQ FT: 33,000
SALES (est): 5MM **Privately Held**
WEB: www.qfcindustries.com
SIC: 3545 5085 Cutting tools for machine tools; diamond cutting tools for turning, boring, burnishing, etc.; industrial supplies; fasteners & fastening equipment

(G-764)
QFC PLASTICS INC
4304 Larry Ln (76017-5811)
P.O. Box 152196 (76015-8196)
PHONE................................817 375-5774
Jeff Kelly, *CEO*
Chris Poe, *President*
Shane Pearson, *Vice Pres*
Stephen Kirkpatrick, *Project Mgr*
Karla Molina, *Purchasing*

▲ EMP: 120 EST: 1994
SQ FT: 150,000
SALES (est): 34.8MM **Privately Held**
WEB: www.qfcplastics.com
SIC: 3089 Injection molding of plastics

(G-765)
QUALITY HONEYCOMB LP
624 107th St (76011-5309)
PHONE................................817 640-1190
Michelle Wagner, *President*
David Wagner, *Partner*
Lance Lawless, *General Mgr*
Dan McArthur, *COO*
Rodger McCurdy, *QC Mgr*
EMP: 50
SQ FT: 1,000
SALES (est): 9.5MM **Privately Held**
WEB: www.qualityhoneycomb.com
SIC: 3724 Aircraft engines & engine parts

(G-766)
RACK TECHNOLOGY INC
1001 Enterprise Pl (76001-7141)
PHONE................................817 468-2233
Bennie Jeter, *President*
Terri Jeter, *Corp Secy*
Joe Anderson, *Vice Pres*
EMP: 20
SQ FT: 12,000
SALES (est): 3.6MM **Privately Held**
SIC: 3559 3443 Anodizing equipment; ladles, metal plate

(G-767)
RANGER PLASTIC EXTRUSIONS INC
Also Called: Rpe
801 N Great Sw Pkwy (76011-5428)
P.O. Box 5443 (76005-5443)
PHONE................................817 640-6067
John M Earnest, *President*
Gordon Jacobson, *Treasurer*
Susan Laney, *Sales Mgr*
Bob Hestes, *Admin Sec*
Robert Hestes, *Admin Sec*
EMP: 35
SQ FT: 30,000
SALES (est): 7.3MM **Privately Held**
WEB: www.rangerplastics.com
SIC: 3089 Injection molding of plastics

(G-768)
RAVAGO AMERICAS LLC
Enplast Americas
616 111th St (76011-7615)
PHONE................................817 635-4770
Kyle Davis, *Branch Mgr*
EMP: 13
SALES (corp-wide): 1.9MM **Privately Held**
WEB: www.amcopolymers.com
SIC: 2821 Plastics materials & resins
HQ: Ravago Americas Llc
1900 Smmit Twr Blvd Ste 9
Orlando FL 32810
407 875-9595

(G-769)
RAYTHEON COMPANY
621 Six Flags Dr Ste 100 (76011-6305)
PHONE................................703 525-1550
Pat Siegling, *Principal*
EMP: 500
SALES (corp-wide): 56.5B **Publicly Held**
WEB: www.rtx.com
SIC: 3812 Sonar systems & equipment
HQ: Raytheon Company
870 Winter St
Waltham MA 02451
781 522-3000

(G-770)
REHER-MORRISON RACING ENGINES
1120 Enterprise Pl (76001-7138)
PHONE................................817 467-7171
David P Reher, *President*
Linda Cooper, *Treasurer*
Fernando Franco, *Manager*
Bruce Allen, *Director*
▼ EMP: 26
SALES (est): 3.8MM **Privately Held**
WEB: www.rehermorrison.com
SIC: 3714 Motor vehicle parts & accessories

(G-771)
RKR TECHNOLOGIES LTD
Also Called: Rocket Air Supply Division
724 111th St (76011-7617)
P.O. Box 5368 (76005-5368)
PHONE................................817 640-5340
B Kelly Koons, *Partner*
John Hill, *Partner*
Charles Ramsey, *Partner*
Bob Reece, *Partner*
Gary Erickson, *General Mgr*
EMP: 75 EST: 1963
SQ FT: 15,000
SALES (est): 18.8MM **Privately Held**
WEB: www.rocketairsupply.com
SIC: 3728 Aircraft parts & equipment

(G-772)
ROLAND CURTAINS INC
Also Called: Roltrans Group America
3212 Pinewood Dr (76010-5305)
PHONE................................817 607-0080
Erwin Van Uytvanck, *President*
Pete Johnson, *Vice Pres*
Hermann Acker, *Manager*
▲ EMP: 15 EST: 1984
SQ FT: 24,000
SALES (est): 2.3MM
SALES (corp-wide): 66.7MM **Privately Held**
WEB: www.rolandcurtains.com
SIC: 2391 Curtains & draperies
HQ: Roland - Loadlok Nederland B.V.
Oudewei 4
Tiel 4004
773 769-292

(G-773)
ROY JOHNSON INCORPORATED
Also Called: Mid South Roller
1108 Enterprise Pl (76001-7138)
PHONE................................817 468-2939
Amanda Blaty, *Finance Mgr*
Bryan Acton, *Sales Staff*
Roy Johnson, *Branch Mgr*
EMP: 38
SALES (corp-wide): 18.3MM **Privately Held**
WEB: www.midsouthroller.com
SIC: 3069 7629 3312 2822 Rubber rolls & roll coverings; electrical repair shops; blast furnaces & steel mills; synthetic rubber; platemaking services
PA: Roy Johnson, Incorporated
200 Porter Industrial Rd
Clarksville AR 72830
479 754-6993

(G-774)
ROYAL BUSINESS FORMS INC
Also Called: Royal Natnwde PRNtng&bus
2801 Avenue E E (76011-5207)
PHONE................................817 640-5253
James Hervey, *Manager*
EMP: 500
SQ FT: 25,128
SALES (corp-wide): 438.4MM **Publicly Held**
WEB: www.royalbf.com
SIC: 2761 Manifold business forms
HQ: Royal Business Forms Inc.
3301 Avenue E E
Arlington TX
817 640-5248

(G-775)
ROYAL CUP INC
Also Called: Royal Cup of Coffee
2112 E Randol Mill Rd (76011-8217)
PHONE................................817 261-7527
Jason Carter, *Manager*
EMP: 12
SQ FT: 39,940
SALES (corp-wide): 266.9MM **Privately Held**
WEB: www.royalcupcoffee.com
SIC: 2095 5812 5499 Roasted coffee; coffee shop; beverage stores
PA: Royal Cup Inc.
160 Cleage Dr
Birmingham AL 35217
205 849-5836

(G-776)
RS LOGISTICS LLC
512 Kingscote Ct (76010-7438)
PHONE................................318 347-5915
Tyqoreya Sterling,
EMP: 10
SALES (est): 360.4K **Privately Held**
SIC: 3799 Transportation equipment

(G-777)
RSI PARTNERS LLC
Also Called: Restaurant Services
2901 E Randol Mill Rd (76011-6725)
PHONE................................817 640-5415
Gerald L Durr, *President*
Kerry Singh, *Purchasing*
Steve Turknett, *Controller*
Ronald D Bassett,
Sidney L Tassin,
EMP: 70
SQ FT: 60,000
SALES (est): 24.8MM **Privately Held**
WEB: www.rsidrivesroi.com
SIC: 5046 3589 1799 Restaurant equipment & supplies; commercial cooking & foodwarming equipment; food service equipment installation

(G-778)
RTC MANUFACTURING INC
1016 Enterprise Pl (76001-7140)
P.O. Box 150189 (76015-6189)
PHONE................................817 860-1217
Dale Thomson, *President*
Ron Featherston, *Vice Pres*
Mark Sampson, *Electrical Engi*
Marty Bowen, *Sales Staff*
Kyle Edelmann, *Internal Med*
▲ EMP: 17
SQ FT: 20,000
SALES (est): 3.6MM **Privately Held**
WEB: www.rtc-traffic.com
SIC: 3621 Timing motors, synchronous, electric

(G-779)
SCHAEFER ART BRONZE LP
132 S Collins St Ste 132 # 132 (76010-1224)
PHONE................................817 460-1102
Robert C Hunt, *Partner*
EMP: 13
SALES (est): 1.8MM **Privately Held**
WEB: www.reynoldsam.com
SIC: 3366 Castings (except die): bronze

(G-780)
SHIOLENO INDUSTRIES INC (PA)
1715 Peyco Dr N (76001-6701)
PHONE................................817 465-9361
Anthony Shioleno, *President*
A J Shioleno, *President*
Chris Shioleno, *Exec VP*
EMP: 16
SQ FT: 200,000
SALES (est): 15.2MM **Privately Held**
WEB: www.shiolenoindustries.com
SIC: 2542 3441 2541 2599 Fixtures: display, office or store: except wood; fabricated structural metal; store fixtures, wood; hotel furniture

(G-781)
SI PRINTING LP
7316 Business Pl (76001-7134)
P.O. Box 150114 (76015-6114)
PHONE................................817 375-9016
Bernard Fritz, *Principal*
EMP: 10
SALES (est): 1.2MM **Privately Held**
SIC: 2752 Commercial printing, lithographic

(G-782)
SKL PRIME SERVICES LLC
Also Called: Prime Equipment Services
1121 108th St (76011-3110)
PHONE................................469 733-1540
Mitch R Long, *President*
Sam Long, *Vice Pres*
Melissa Long, *Treasurer*
Hil Davis,
Veeral Rathod,
▼ EMP: 100

SALES (est): 24.5MM **Privately Held**
WEB: www.pesfab.com
SIC: 3585 Cabinets, show & display, refrigerated

(G-783)
SORITA ENTERPRISES INC
Also Called: AlphaGraphics
2407 S Cooper St (76015-1605)
PHONE.............................817 860-2679
Mark S Lee, *President*
A Gabriela Lee, *Vice Pres*
EMP: 14 EST: 2012
SALES (est): 2.4MM **Privately Held**
WEB: www.alphagraphics.com
SIC: 2752 Commercial printing, lithographic

(G-784)
SPARTAN PRINTING INC (PA)
320 109th St (76011-6800)
PHONE.............................817 640-6341
Jim Trebilcock, *President*
Tim Englehart, *Prdtn Mgr*
Diana Jones, *Associate*
EMP: 30 EST: 1963
SQ FT: 22,000
SALES (est): 4.5MM **Privately Held**
WEB: www.spartanprinting.com
SIC: 2752 2791 2789 Commercial printing, offset; typesetting; bookbinding & related work

(G-785)
SPARTECH POLYCOM (TEXAS) INC
1121 108th St (76011-3110)
PHONE.............................817 640-5600
EMP: 50 EST: 1989
SALES (est): 6.2MM
SALES (corp-wide): 2.9B **Publicly Held**
SIC: 2821 Mfg Plastic Materials/Resins
HQ: Polyone Designed Structures And Solutions, Llc
120 S Central Ave # 1700
Saint Louis MO 63146
314 721-4242

(G-786)
SPS TECHNOLOGIES LLC
Also Called: Progressive
1030 Commercial Blvd N (76001-7119)
PHONE.............................817 467-0031
Mark Donegan, *Mng Member*
EMP: 683
SALES (corp-wide): 254.6B **Publicly Held**
WEB: www.pccfasteners.com
SIC: 3452 Bolts, nuts, rivets & washers
HQ: Sps Technologies, Llc
301 Highland Ave
Jenkintown PA 19046
215 572-3000

(G-787)
STARRFOAM MANUFACTURING INC (DH)
3220 Avenue F (76011-5220)
PHONE.............................817 654-4688
Michael Stanley, *President*
Joan Stanley, *Corp Secy*
Joseph Adamowicz, *VP Opers*
Joe Danowicz, *CFO*
Travis Montgomery, *Sales Staff*
▲ EMP: 40
SALES (est): 20MM **Privately Held**
WEB: www.starrfoam.com
SIC: 3999 Bleaching & dyeing of sponges
HQ: Atlas Roofing Corporation
802 Highway 19 N Ste 190
Meridian MS 39307
601 484-8900

(G-788)
STATIONARY POWER SYSTEMS INC (PA)
1115 Sturgeon Ct Ste 119 (76001-7172)
PHONE.............................877 924-4949
Matthew Campbell, *CEO*
▼ EMP: 18
SQ FT: 900
SALES (est): 2.5MM **Privately Held**
WEB: www.spsystems.net
SIC: 3594 Fluid power pumps

(G-789)
SYNERGY ENVIRONMENTAL SVCS LLC
2500 E Randol Mill Rd (76011-6350)
P.O. Box 1217, Hurst (76053-1217)
PHONE.............................972 513-1118
Stacey Moore, *President*
Kevin Johnson,
Stacy Moore,
EMP: 22
SQ FT: 1,430
SALES: 5.7MM **Privately Held**
WEB: www.synergyhvac.net
SIC: 7623 3585 1711 Air conditioning repair; heating & air conditioning combination units; heating systems repair & maintenance; heating & air conditioning contractors

(G-790)
SYSTEMS INTEGRATION INC
7316 Business Pl (76001-7134)
P.O. Box 150287 (76015-6287)
PHONE.............................817 468-1494
Bernhard Fritz, *President*
Randy Mears, *Manager*
▲ EMP: 30
SQ FT: 20,000
SALES (est): 8.9MM **Privately Held**
WEB: www.sitexas.com
SIC: 3535 1799 1731 8711 Bulk handling conveyor systems; food service equipment installation; electrical work; engineering services; plumbing, heating, air-conditioning contractors; structural steel erection

(G-791)
TEXAS ALMET LP
2800 E Randol Mill Rd (76011-6724)
PHONE.............................817 649-7056
Alan Wagner, *Partner*
Anthony Vaughn, *COO*
Tony Vaughn, *Opers Mgr*
Stan Maples, *QC Mgr*
Chip Bay, *VP Sales*
EMP: 64
SQ FT: 25,000
SALES (est): 15.5MM **Privately Held**
WEB: www.texasalmet.com
SIC: 3999 3724 3728 Airplane models, except toy; aircraft engines & engine parts; aircraft parts & equipment

(G-792)
TEXAS PNEUMATIC SYSTEMS INC
Also Called: Turbine Fuel Systems
1001 Commercial Blvd N (76001-7124)
PHONE.............................817 794-0068
Bernard E Rookey, *Branch Mgr*
EMP: 10 **Privately Held**
WEB: www.txps.com
SIC: 7699 4581 3494 Aircraft & heavy equipment repair services; aircraft servicing & repairing; valves & pipe fittings
PA: Texas Pneumatic Systems, Inc.
2404 Superior Dr
Pantego TX 76013

(G-793)
TEXAS SADDLEBAGS INC
3600 E Randol Mill Rd (76011-5433)
PHONE.............................817 649-2626
John Ehlert, *President*
Curtis Boozer, *CFO*
EMP: 75
SQ FT: 100,000
SALES (est): 15.8MM **Privately Held**
SIC: 3714 Motor vehicle parts & accessories

(G-794)
TEXAS SEAL SUPPLY CO INC
330 Westway Pl Ste 446 (76018-1025)
PHONE.............................817 640-1193
Jeffrey L Hamilton, *CEO*
Jeffrey S Albright, *President*
Melissa A Jones, *Vice Pres*
EMP: 10

SALES (est): 6.6MM
SALES (corp-wide): 100MM **Privately Held**
WEB: www.texasseal.com
SIC: 5085 3053 Seals, industrial; gaskets, packing & sealing devices
PA: Engineered Seal Products, Inc.
5920 Dry Creek Ln Ne
Cedar Rapids IA 52402
319 393-4310

(G-795)
TEXAS STONE DESIGNS INC
2001 W Mayfield Rd (76015-2839)
P.O. Box 13514 (76094-0514)
PHONE.............................817 265-4011
Dan Grant, *CEO*
EMP: 20
SQ FT: 30,000
SALES (est): 4.6MM **Privately Held**
WEB: www.texasstonedesigns.com
SIC: 3446 3272 Architectural metalwork; stone, cast concrete

(G-796)
TEXSTARS LLC
Also Called: PPG Aerospace
925 Avenue H E (76011-7721)
PHONE.............................972 647-1366
Daniel Korte, *President*
Dave Greer, *Branch Mgr*
Odaliza Corniell, *Planning Mgr*
EMP: 120
SQ FT: 189,000
SALES (corp-wide): 15.3B **Publicly Held**
WEB: www.texstars.com
SIC: 3089 3728 3211 Toilets, portable chemical: plastic; aircraft parts & equipment; laminated glass
HQ: Texstars, Llc
802 E Avenue J
Grand Prairie TX 75050
972 647-1366

(G-797)
THEAG NORTH ARLINGTON LLC
Also Called: Fastsigns
803 E Lamar Blvd (76011-3504)
PHONE.............................817 261-3027
Lance Tucker, *Prdtn Mgr*
Chris Allen,
Sean Allen,
EMP: 11
SQ FT: 4,100
SALES (est): 1.9MM **Privately Held**
WEB: www.fastsigns.com
SIC: 3993 Signs & advertising specialties

(G-798)
THURSBY SOFTWARE SYSTEMS LLC
4901 S Collins St (76018-1106)
PHONE.............................817 478-5070
William Thursby, *CEO*
Kenneth Bobu, *Vice Pres*
Debbie Buck, *Purch Mgr*
Paul Nelson, *VP Engrg*
Carolyn Stewart, *QC Mgr*
EMP: 28
SQ FT: 6,000
SALES (est): 8.1MM **Publicly Held**
WEB: www.thursby.com
SIC: 7372 Prepackaged software
PA: Identiv, Inc.
2201 Walnut Ave Ste 100
Fremont CA 94538

(G-799)
TIDELINE DESIGNS INC
623 107th St (76011-5308)
PHONE.............................214 275-3958
Armando Garcia, *Director*
EMP: 13
SALES (est): 59.9K **Privately Held**
SIC: 7389 3231 Design services; aquariums & reflectors, glass

(G-800)
TOMDAO LLC
Also Called: Petroleum Network Solutions
4401 Little Rd 550-324 (76016-5624)
PHONE.............................817 888-6167
EMP: 18

SALES (est): 4.5MM **Privately Held**
SIC: 1389 Construction, repair & dismantling services

(G-801)
TPE SOLUTIONS INC
616 111th St (76011-7615)
PHONE.............................978 425-3033
EMP: 17
SALES (corp-wide): 50MM **Privately Held**
WEB: www.tpesinc.com
SIC: 2821 Plastics materials & resins
PA: Tpe Solutions, Inc.
3 Patterson Rd Ste 2
Shirley MA 01464
978 425-3033

(G-802)
TRANSNORM SYSTEM INC
2810 Avenue E E (76011-5208)
PHONE.............................972 606-0303
Gary Cline, *CEO*
Kay Lynn Wolfe, *CFO*
Kay Lynn Wolf, *Auditor*
▲ EMP: 80
SQ FT: 50,000
SALES (est): 24.3MM
SALES (corp-wide): 36.7B **Publicly Held**
WEB: www.transnorm.com
SIC: 3535 5084 Conveyors & conveying equipment; conveyor systems
HQ: Transnorm System Gmbh
Forster Str. 2
Harsum 31177
512 740-20

(G-803)
TRINITY SLING AUTHORITY INC
3508 Avenue F (76011-5225)
PHONE.............................817 589-2404
Bruce R Hartin II, *President*
William Bill Bieterich, *Sales Mgr*
Blesson George, *Sales Engr*
Bill Bethel, *Sales Staff*
Glenn Sims, *Sales Staff*
▲ EMP: 17
SQ FT: 15,000
SALES (est): 4.5MM **Privately Held**
WEB: www.trinitysling.com
SIC: 3496 Slings, lifting: made from purchased wire

(G-804)
TRIUMPH GROUP INC
1401 Nolan Ryan Expy (76011-4907)
P.O. Box 160433, Clearfield UT (84016-0433)
PHONE.............................817 804-9400
Peter Wick, *Exec VP*
Gary Constantine, *Controller*
Nolan Porter, *Human Res Mgr*
Ash Sampath, *Consultant*
Rupesh Patel, *Director*
EMP: 20 **Publicly Held**
WEB: www.triumphgroup.com
SIC: 3728 3724 3812 Aircraft body & wing assemblies & parts; aircraft engines & engine parts; aircraft control instruments
PA: Triumph Group, Inc.
899 Cassatt Rd Ste 210
Berwyn PA 19312

(G-805)
TRNLWB LLC (PA)
Also Called: Trinity Esc
1112 E Cpeland Rd Ste 500 (76011)
PHONE.............................800 581-3117
Carl Campbell, *President*
Steven Rowe, *Vice Pres*
EMP: 200
SALES (est): 15.1MM **Privately Held**
WEB: www.arcosalightweight.com
SIC: 3271 Concrete block & brick

(G-806)
TSI PRODUCTS INC
Also Called: Tsi Aquisitions
809 110th St (76011-7612)
PHONE.............................817 649-2626
John H Ehlert, *President*
William Quest, *Vice Pres*
◆ EMP: 32 EST: 2008

G
E
O
G
R
A
P
H
I
C

SALES (est): 10.3MM **Privately Held**
WEB: www.tsiproducts.com
SIC: 3089 2821 Plastic containers, except foam; molding compounds, plastics

(G-807)
U S ENERGY DEVELOPMENT CORP
Also Called: U.S. Energy Development
1521 N Cooper St Ste 700 (76011-5598)
PHONE.................................682 305-2868
Greg Brown, *Manager*
EMP: 10
SALES (corp-wide): 50.2MM **Privately Held**
WEB: www.usedc.com
SIC: 1382 Oil & gas exploration services
PA: U. S. Energy Development Corporation
1400 Sweet Home Rd Ste 5
Buffalo NY 14228
716 636-0401

(G-808)
VBI GROUP LLC (PA)
Also Called: Ikongps
1161 W Corp Dr Ste 130 (76006)
PHONE.................................817 533-3180
Sam Husein Mahrouk, *President*
Amber Barger, *General Counsel*
EMP: 25
SALES (est): 2.9MM **Privately Held**
WEB: www.ikontechnologies.com
SIC: 3699 Electronic training devices

(G-809)
WILLIAMS PRODUCTS INC
2127 Exchange Dr (76011-7823)
PHONE.................................214 630-3131
Cindy Van Sickle, *President*
Cindy Vansicle, *President*
EMP: 10
SALES (est): 1.4MM **Privately Held**
WEB: www.williamsproducts.com
SIC: 3086 5199 Plastics foam products; packaging materials

(G-810)
WOODS TOOL AND MACHINE CO INC (PA)
Also Called: Woods Tool Company
423 Dodson Lake Dr (76012-3442)
P.O. Box 120696 (76012-0696)
PHONE.................................817 275-4541
Glenda Hickey, *President*
Carl Hickey, *Vice Pres*
EMP: 10
SQ FT: 6,000
SALES (est): 914.6K **Privately Held**
SIC: 3599 Machine shop, jobbing & repair

(G-811)
WRAPS GORILLA
615 Six Flags Dr (76011-6305)
PHONE.................................817 652-2882
Kevin Richards, *Principal*
EMP: 10
SALES (est): 740.2K **Privately Held**
WEB: www.gorillawraps.com
SIC: 3993 Signs & advertising specialties

Arp
Smith County

(G-812)
JUSTISS OIL COMPANY INC
Altech Industries
100 State Highway 64 E (75750-9696)
P.O. Box 40 (75750-0040)
PHONE.................................903 859-2111
Angela Ritchey, *President*
Ernest Maddox, *Vice Pres*
Ray Manley, *Project Mgr*
Larry Patterson, *Opers Mgr*
Logan Raborn, *Production*
EMP: 100
SQ FT: 7,000

SALES (corp-wide): 20.6MM **Privately Held**
WEB: www.justissoil.com
SIC: 3443 1791 1799 3441 Tanks, lined: metal plate; storage tanks, metal: erection; welding on site; fabricated structural metal; aluminum extruded products; gaskets, packing & sealing devices
PA: Justiss Oil Company, Inc.
1120 E Oak St
Jena LA 71342
318 992-4111

(G-813)
TYSON FOODS INC
15131 E Ridge Rd (75750-9780)
PHONE.................................903 859-4030
EMP: 277
SALES (corp-wide): 43.1B **Publicly Held**
WEB: www.tysonfoods.com
SIC: 2011 Meat packing plants
PA: Tyson Foods, Inc.
2200 W Don Tyson Pkwy
Springdale AR 72762
479 290-4000

Asherton
Dimmit County

(G-814)
TIMS SOUTH TEXAS LLC
Also Called: Asherton Store
6627 S Us Highway 83 (78827-7102)
PHONE.................................830 468-3860
Arnulfo Gonzales, *Manager*
EMP: 14
SALES (corp-wide): 1MM **Privately Held**
WEB: www.timssouthtexas.com
SIC: 5999 3799 Welding supplies; trailers & trailer equipment
PA: Tims South Texas, Llc
4055 E Main St
Uvalde TX 78801
830 278-3368

Aspermont
Stonewall County

(G-815)
DOUBLE MOUNTAIN INC
Also Called: Ellison Insulation
305 E Swenson Ave (79502-2065)
P.O. Box 783 (79502-0783)
PHONE.................................940 988-4491
Patti A Ellison, *President*
Kathy Castaneda, *Vice Pres*
EMP: 50 EST: 2000
SQ FT: 2,000
SALES (est): 2.1MM **Privately Held**
WEB: www.doublemountainservices.com
SIC: 5033 3823 Insulation materials; thermal conductivity instruments, industrial process type

(G-816)
DUNAGIN TRANSPORT COMPANY
1215 S Broadway St (79502)
PHONE.................................325 928-5253
Bradley Dunagin, *Branch Mgr*
EMP: 10
SALES (corp-wide): 17MM **Privately Held**
WEB: www.dunagintransport.com
SIC: 1382 Oil & gas exploration services
PA: Dunagin Transport Company
10179 S Access Rd I 20 20 I
Merkel TX 79536
325 928-5253

Atascosa
Bexar County

(G-817)
QUANTUM CORPORATION
Also Called: Innovate Quantum Group
12081 Barker Rd (78002-4900)
PHONE.................................210 622-9235
Souksavanh Escobar, *Branch Mgr*

EMP: 110
SALES (corp-wide): 402.9MM **Publicly Held**
WEB: www.quantum.com
SIC: 3572 Computer storage devices
PA: Quantum Corporation
224 Airport Pkwy Ste 550
San Jose CA 95110
408 944-4000

Athens
Henderson County

(G-818)
AAGAPE FIRST INVESTMENTS LLC
Also Called: Aagape Drywall Systems
1322 S Palestine St (75751-3621)
PHONE.................................903 675-7876
Bruce Lawrence, *Mng Member*
EMP: 32
SQ FT: 2,000
SALES (est): 1.4MM **Privately Held**
WEB: www.aagapedrywallsystems.com
SIC: 3296 1742 Mineral wool insulation products; plastering, drywall & insulation

(G-819)
ARGON MEDICAL DEVICES INC
1445 Flat Creek Rd (75751-5002)
PHONE.................................903 675-9321
Greg Quickel, *Marketing Staff*
George Leondis, *Branch Mgr*
EMP: 274
SALES (corp-wide): 240.9MM **Privately Held**
WEB: www.argonmedical.com
SIC: 3845 3842 3841 Electromedical equipment; surgical appliances & supplies; surgical & medical instruments
HQ: Argon Medical Devices, Inc.
2600 Dallas Pkwy Ste 440
Frisco TX 75034
903 675-9321

(G-820)
ATHENS STEEL BUILDING CORP
900 Ne Loop 7 (75752-5201)
P.O. Box 1427 (75751-1427)
PHONE.................................903 675-5733
John H Brown, *President*
Keno Brown, *Vice Pres*
Tommy Clark, *Vice Pres*
Jimmy Hudson, *Vice Pres*
Rory Mills, *Vice Pres*
EMP: 45 EST: 1975
SQ FT: 34,000
SALES (est): 9.7MM **Privately Held**
WEB: www.athenssteelbuilding.com
SIC: 3448 3444 Prefabricated metal buildings; sheet metalwork

(G-821)
BIOMERICS LLC
1605 Enterprise St (75751-8839)
PHONE.................................903 677-9166
EMP: 400 **Privately Held**
WEB: www.biomerics.com
SIC: 3841 Catheters; biopsy instruments & equipment
HQ: Biomerics, Llc
6030 W Harold Gatty Dr
Salt Lake City UT 84116

(G-822)
CHERRY CONSTRUCTION SYSTEMS
11293 State Highway 19 N (75752-3926)
P.O. Box 1174 (75751-1174)
PHONE.................................903 675-5901
Ron Cherry, *President*
Angie Brown, *Corp Secy*
EMP: 30
SALES (est): 1.9MM **Privately Held**
SIC: 3444 3531 3441 Concrete forms, sheet metal; construction machinery; fabricated structural metal

(G-823)
COMMERCIAL FORMS INC
11293 State Highway 19 N (75752-3926)
P.O. Box 1174 (75751-1174)
PHONE.................................903 675-2511

Ron Cherry, *President*
Angie Brown, *Treasurer*
David Heith, *Manager*
EMP: 25
SQ FT: 15,000
SALES (est): 4.9MM **Privately Held**
WEB: www.commercialforms.net
SIC: 3444 3443 Concrete forms, sheet metal; fabricated plate work (boiler shop)

(G-824)
CONTRACTORS SUPPLIES INC
1400 N Palestine St (75751-4145)
PHONE.................................903 670-1085
Chris Sonnalaker, *Manager*
EMP: 14
SALES (corp-wide): 30.6MM **Privately Held**
WEB: www.csiconcrete.com
SIC: 3273 Ready-mixed concrete
PA: Contractor's Supplies, Inc.
304 Webber St
Lufkin TX 75904
936 634-3341

(G-825)
COSMEC INC
Also Called: Dynamic Rubber Div
1501 Rocky Ridge Rd (75751-5413)
P.O. Box 2159 (75751-7159)
PHONE.................................903 677-2871
Donald Vose, *Sales Executive*
Robert L Burhoe, *Branch Mgr*
EMP: 25
SALES (corp-wide): 14.1MM **Privately Held**
WEB: www.cosmecinc.com
SIC: 2822 3568 Synthetic rubber; power transmission equipment
PA: Cosmec, Inc.
1501 Rocky Ridge Rd
Athens TX 75751
903 677-2871

(G-826)
FLOWERS BAKING CO TYLER LLC
1601 Rocky Ridge Rd (75751)
PHONE.................................903 677-2455
EMP: 160
SALES (corp-wide): 4.1B **Publicly Held**
WEB: www.flowersfoods.com
SIC: 2051 Bread, cake & related products
HQ: Flowers Baking Company Of Tyler, Llc
1200 W Erwin St
Tyler TX 75702
903 595-2421

(G-827)
HOWARD MEASUREMENT CO INC (PA)
Also Called: Howard Field Services
1637 Enterprise St (75751-8839)
PHONE.................................903 677-0700
Pam Hobgood, *President*
Thompson Dan L, *Vice Pres*
Peter Douglas, *Manager*
Christopher Hobgood, *Manager*
Brittni James, *Analyst*
EMP: 20 EST: 1981
SQ FT: 5,000
SALES (est): 4.1MM **Privately Held**
WEB: www.howardmeasurement.com
SIC: 1389 Gas field services

(G-828)
HP CAR ACCESSORIES & ATV SALES
414 E Tyler St (75751-2050)
PHONE.................................903 675-0032
Satinderjit S Avaira, *Owner*
EMP: 11
SALES (est): 1.5MM **Privately Held**
SIC: 3465 3715 Body parts, automobile: stamped metal; truck trailers

(G-829)
HVAC MANUFACTURING INC
1010 W Corsicana St (75751-2218)
PHONE.................................408 254-5420
Stella Karamanos, *CEO*
John Karamanos, *COO*
Abhay Chauhan, *Project Mgr*
Tarkan Cuneyit, *Sales Mgr*
EMP: 16

SQ FT: 20,000
SALES (est): 6.7MM **Privately Held**
SIC: 3585 Air conditioning equipment, complete

(G-830)
MED LOGICS INC
1627 Enterprise St (75751-8839)
PHONE....................949 582-3891
EMP: 9
SALES (est): 1.6MM **Privately Held**
WEB: www.mlogics.com
SIC: 3851 Frames, lenses & parts, eyeglass & spectacle

(G-831)
MEDICAL DEVICE TECH INC (DH)
Also Called: Angiotech
1445 Flat Creek Rd (75751-5002)
PHONE....................800 338-0440
Jason Armstrong, *Manager*
EMP: 21
SALES (est): 8.3MM
SALES (corp-wide): 240.9MM **Privately Held**
WEB: www.argonmedical.com
SIC: 8731 3841 3842 Commercial physical research; surgical & medical instruments; surgical appliances & supplies
HQ: Argon Medical Devices, Inc.
2600 Dallas Pkwy Ste 440
Frisco TX 75034
903 675-9321

(G-832)
MEDTEX CONVERTERS INC
1653 Enterprise St (75751-8839)
PHONE....................903 670-3270
Lynn Kitchens, *President*
EMP: 15
SALES (est): 1.6MM **Privately Held**
WEB: www.medtexconverters.com
SIC: 3842 First aid, snake bite & burn kits

(G-833)
MERIDIAN BRICK LLC
200 Athens Brick Rd (75751-6302)
P.O. Box 70 (75751-0070)
PHONE....................903 675-2256
Wayne Turnage, *Manager*
EMP: 44
SALES (corp-wide): 441MM **Privately Held**
WEB: www.meridianbrick.com
SIC: 3251 Brick clay: common face, glazed, vitrified or hollow
PA: Meridian Brick Llc
6455 Shiloh Rd D
Alpharetta GA 30005
770 645-4500

(G-834)
MUD TECHNOLOGY INTL INC
2610 State Highway 31 W (75751-6402)
PHONE....................903 675-3240
John Miller, *CEO*
John Ike Miller Jr, *President*
◆ EMP: 35
SALES (est): 3.1MM **Privately Held**
WEB: www.mud-tech.com
SIC: 3532 Cleaning machinery, mineral

(G-835)
NEWSPAPER HOLDING INC
Also Called: Athens Daily Review
201 S Prairieville St (75751-2541)
P.O. Box 32 (75751-0032)
PHONE....................903 675-5626
Lange Svehlak, *CEO*
EMP: 20
SALES (corp-wide): 23.7B **Privately Held**
WEB: www.oskaloosa.com
SIC: 2711 Newspapers, publishing & printing
HQ: Newspaper Holding, Inc.
425 Locust St
Johnstown PA 15901
814 532-5102

(G-836)
NINE ENERGY SERVICE INC
29119 State Highway 19 N (75752-6975)
PHONE....................903 479-3155
EMP: 18

SALES (corp-wide): 832.9MM **Publicly Held**
WEB: www.nineenergyservice.com
SIC: 1389 Oil field services
PA: Nine Energy Service, Inc.
2001 Kirby Dr Ste 200
Houston TX 77019
281 730-5100

(G-837)
OTE INTERNATIONAL HOLDINGS LLC
6695 County Road 4628 (75752-6371)
PHONE....................888 666-9361
Mark Kitchens,
▲ EMP: 12
SALES (est): 1.8MM **Privately Held**
WEB: www.oteinternational.com
SIC: 3699 5063 Laser systems & equipment; apparatus wire & cordage

(G-838)
SCHNEIDER-BANKS INC
Also Called: S B I Fine Fabric Finishing
1108 Commercial St (75751-8801)
PHONE....................903 675-1440
Gene Banks, *President*
EMP: 15
SALES (est): 1.7MM **Privately Held**
WEB: www.sbifinishing.com
SIC: 2262 2261 Chemical coating or treating: manmade broadwoven fabrics; finishing plants, cotton

(G-839)
SEISMIC PRODUCTS INC (PA)
518 Progress Way (75751-5924)
PHONE....................903 675-8571
Lesliel A Jasper, *President*
C Richard Vermillion, *Principal*
Steve Bate, *Vice Pres*
Stephen Lack, *Vice Pres*
Richard Bishop, *Maint Spvr*
▲ EMP: 49
SQ FT: 50,000
SALES (est): 11.2MM **Privately Held**
WEB: www.dsbrown.com
SIC: 3441 Bridge sections, prefabricated highway

(G-840)
THRILLWORKS INC (PA)
Also Called: Extreme Engineering
1391 Flat Creek Rd (75751-5006)
PHONE....................916 663-1749
Jeff Wilson, *President*
Richard Hinnant, *Buyer*
Shari Sanford, *Accountant*
Marsha Benson, *Manager*
Joana Wilson, *Shareholder*
◆ EMP: 20
SQ FT: 12,000
SALES (est): 3.1MM **Privately Held**
WEB: www.extremeengineering.com
SIC: 2899 Plastic wood

Atlanta
Cass County

(G-841)
CARAUSTAR INDUSTRIES INC
Also Called: Newark Paperboard Products
902 S William St (75551-2890)
P.O. Box 970 (75551-0970)
PHONE....................903 799-5100
Carl De Palma, *Manager*
EMP: 35
SALES (corp-wide): 4.5B **Publicly Held**
WEB: www.greif.com
SIC: 2631 2679 5093 2675 Paperboard mills; book covers, paper; paperboard products, converted; waste paper; die-cut paper & board; fiber cans, drums & similar products
HQ: Caraustar Industries, Inc.
5000 Austell Powder Sprin
Austell GA 30106
770 948-3101

(G-842)
DOUGLASSVILLE TIMBER CO
307 N Louise St Ste B (75551-2285)
PHONE....................903 796-7691
E Don Crutcher, *Owner*

EMP: 9
SQ FT: 600
SALES (est): 865.3K **Privately Held**
SIC: 2411 Logging camps & contractors

(G-843)
GUARD-LINE INC
1001 Progress Dr (75551-7052)
P.O. Box 1030 (75551-1030)
PHONE....................903 796-4111
Dennis J Stanley, *President*
H Lee Stanley, *Vice Pres*
Larry Mills, *Finance*
J Michael Stanley, *Shareholder*
▲ EMP: 220
SQ FT: 65,000
SALES (est): 27.4MM **Privately Held**
WEB: www.guardline.com
SIC: 3151 3842 2394 2381 Gloves, leather: work; welders' gloves; personal safety equipment; clothing, fire resistant & protective; gloves, safety; canvas & related products; fabric dress & work gloves; hats, caps & millinery; men's & boys' work clothing

(G-844)
GUARD-LINE INC
1001 Progress Dr (75551-7052)
P.O. Box 1030 (75551-1030)
PHONE....................903 796-4111
EMP: 100
SQ FT: 40,000
SALES (corp-wide): 21.6MM **Privately Held**
SIC: 3842 3151 Mfg Surgical Appliances/Supplies Mfg Leather Gloves/Mittens
PA: Guard-Line, Inc.
215 S Louise St
Atlanta TX 75551
903 796-4111

(G-845)
STANCO MANUFACTURING INC
2004 W Main St (75551-3052)
P.O. Box 1148 (75551-1148)
PHONE....................903 796-7936
Edward Stanley, *President*
Don H Simmons, *Exec VP*
Tony King, *Regl Sales Mgr*
Kristen Pickney, *Cust Mgr*
Dianna M Reed, *Shareholder*
▲ EMP: 75
SQ FT: 45,000
SALES (est): 9.9MM **Privately Held**
WEB: www.stancomfg.com
SIC: 3548 3842 2381 2326 Welding apparatus; personal safety equipment; clothing, fire resistant & protective; gloves, safety; fabric dress & work gloves; men's & boys' work clothing

Aubrey
Denton County

(G-846)
ARC PRESSURE DATA INC (PA)
3718 Warschun Rd (76227-4083)
P.O. Box 979, Denton (76202-0979)
PHONE....................432 563-2371
Amy Turner, *President*
Craig Turner, *Vice Pres*
Michael Woods, *Info Tech Dir*
Glena Turner, *Director*
Rebecca Jung, *Executive*
EMP: 11
SQ FT: 7,700
SALES (est): 25.4MM **Privately Held**
WEB: www.arcpressure.com
SIC: 1389 3826 Servicing oil & gas wells; analytical instruments

(G-847)
BLUE DIAMOND INDUSTRIES LLC
917 S Highway 377 Ste 240 (76227-5536)
PHONE....................859 224-0415
Sherri R Simpson,
EMP: 30
SALES (est): 987.1K **Privately Held**
SIC: 3084 Plastics pipe

(G-848)
BLUE STREAK LLC
14565 Industrial Park (76227-6200)
P.O. Box 560 (76227-0560)
PHONE....................940 440-2105
Jeff Prescott, *Mng Member*
▲ EMP: 9
SQ FT: 14,000
SALES (est): 1.1MM **Privately Held**
WEB: www.bluestreakchem.com
SIC: 2431 Doors, wood; door trim, wood

(G-849)
COLEMAN WOOD PRODUCTS INC
5650 Us Highway 377 S (76227-6213)
P.O. Box 190 (76227-0190)
PHONE....................940 440-2300
Russell D Coleman, *Ch of Bd*
James C Garner, *President*
EMP: 30
SALES (est): 1.7MM **Privately Held**
WEB: www.sunrisewooddesigns.com
SIC: 2434 2431 4212 1751 Wood kitchen cabinets; millwork; lumber & timber trucking; cabinet & finish carpentry; wood household furniture

(G-850)
LAURAS CAROUSEL INC
Also Called: Rocking Horse Designs
10459 Redfearn Rd (76227-5965)
PHONE....................940 365-1875
Sheree McCabe, *President*
Laura Perish, *Vice Pres*
EMP: 13
SQ FT: 1,500
SALES (est): 450K **Privately Held**
SIC: 2211 5712 Bed sheeting, cotton; bedspreads, cotton; juvenile furniture

(G-851)
NORTEX REDIMIX LLC
5191 Fm 2931 (76227-7460)
PHONE....................214 681-5200
Zachary Weir, *Mng Member*
EMP: 50
SALES (corp-wide): 10.2MM **Privately Held**
SIC: 3273 Ready-mixed concrete
PA: Nortex Redimix, Llc
2010 Valley View Ln
Farmers Branch TX 75234
214 681-5200

(G-852)
WEIR BROTHERS CONTRACTING LLC
Also Called: Weir Bros Pit
4523 Fm 2931 (76227-7479)
PHONE....................940 440-2931
Lee Weir, *Owner*
EMP: 11 **Privately Held**
SIC: 5032 4212 1442 Brick, stone & related material; local trucking, without storage; construction sand & gravel
PA: Weir Brothers Contracting, Llc
2010 Valley View Ln # 300
Farmers Branch TX 75234

Aurora
Wise County

(G-853)
ALPHA DOOR AND RAIL INC
Also Called: Alpha Waterjet Machining
110 Aurora Vista Trl (76078-4511)
PHONE....................817 358-8687
Fred C Beagles Jr, *President*
Barbara Beagles, *Corp Secy*
Janet Beagles, *Vice Pres*
EMP: 10
SQ FT: 15,000
SALES (est): 1.3MM **Privately Held**
WEB: www.alphacommercialblinds.com
SIC: 2591 3231 Window blinds; doors, glass: made from purchased glass

GEOGRAPHIC

(G-854)
T L TEDFORD ENTERPRISES INC
206 S Madison St (76078-4620)
P.O. Box 664, Justin (76247-0664)
PHONE....................................817 808-8052
EMP: 20 EST: 2011
SALES (est): 1.2MM Privately Held
SIC: 3629 Electronic generation equipment

(G-855)
TUBE PRODUCTS INC
1471 Fm 718 (76078-5292)
P.O. Box 419, Newark (76071-0419)
PHONE....................................817 489-2264
Barker Bounds, President
David Worthey, President
Sharleen Worthey, Treasurer
▲ EMP: 13
SQ FT: 30,000
SALES (est): 2.2MM Privately Held
WEB: www.tubeproductstexas.com
SIC: 3498 Tube fabricating (contract bending & shaping)

Austin
Hays County

(G-856)
AMPTEC RESEARCH CORPORATION
13231 Rooster Springs Rd (78737-9235)
PHONE....................................512 858-4045
Sarah Clark, President
▼ EMP: 14
SALES (est): 2MM Privately Held
WEB: www.amptec.com
SIC: 3825 Instruments to measure electricity

(G-857)
AUSTIN INDUSTRIES INC
8302 La Plata Loop (78737-3125)
PHONE....................................512 288-1831
Randy Miller, Principal
EMP: 382
SALES (corp-wide): 2.3B Privately Held
WEB: www.austin-ind.com
SIC: 3999 Barber & beauty shop equipment
PA: Austin Industries, Inc.
　　3535 Travis St Ste 300
　　Dallas TX 75204
　　214 443-5500

(G-858)
BLACK DIAMOND STRUCTURES LLC
12310 Trail Dr (78737)
PHONE....................................512 900-3822
John Hacskaylo, CEO
Andrew Kodis, CEO
Kurt Swogger, Ch of Bd
Elly Burghout, Director
Ernesto Occhiello, Director
EMP: 15
SALES (est): 975.5K Privately Held
WEB: www.blackdiamond-structures.com
SIC: 2869 Industrial organic chemicals

(G-859)
CYCLONE CONSTRUCTION LLC
12117 W Highway 290 Apt 3 (78737-9608)
PHONE....................................512 288-0430
Bradley P Ledwik,
EMP: 14
SALES (est): 4.6MM Privately Held
SIC: 1389 Construction, repair & dismantling services

(G-860)
ENERGETIC SOLUTIONS LLC
11101 W Highway 290 (78737-2806)
PHONE....................................512 382-6864
Melissa Rogers, Mng Member
▼ EMP: 10
SQ FT: 2,500
SALES (est): 1.2MM Privately Held
WEB: www.0bugzone.com
SIC: 2879 Insecticides & pesticides

(G-861)
ESPY CORPORATION
13033 Trautwein Rd (78737-9364)
PHONE....................................512 261-1016
Mark E Smith, President
Whitney E Harris, Vice Pres
Thomas W Potthast Jr, Vice Pres
Jared McGehee, Engineer
Jeromy Smith, Engineer
EMP: 24 EST: 1999
SQ FT: 11,000
SALES (est): 9.5MM Privately Held
WEB: www.espy.com
SIC: 7371 3663 3812 7379 Computer software development; receivers, radio communications; search & navigation equipment; antennas, radar or communications; search & detection systems & instruments; computer related consulting services

(G-862)
GUNVISION SYSTEMS LLC
14101 W Hwy 290 Ste 2000a (78737-9331)
P.O. Box 92827 (78709-2827)
PHONE....................................512 858-4045
Kerry Clark,
David Hightower,
EMP: 10
SQ FT: 2,500
SALES (est): 648.5K Privately Held
SIC: 3825 Ignition testing instruments

(G-863)
HILLER MEASUREMENTS INC
14141 W Hwy 290 Ste 100 (78737-9345)
P.O. Box 244, Driftwood (78619-0244)
PHONE....................................512 394-8356
EMP: 128 EST: 2011
SALES (est): 21.3MM Privately Held
WEB: www.hillermeas.com
SIC: 8711 7371 3699 Electrical or electronic engineering; mechanical engineering; computer software systems analysis & design, custom; electrical equipment & supplies

(G-864)
LUMINATED LIVING LLC
13247 Mesa Verde Dr (78737-4682)
PHONE....................................512 523-5550
Ken Miyamoto,
EMP: 10
SALES (est): 557.8K Privately Held
SIC: 3646 Commercial indusl & institutional electric lighting fixtures

(G-865)
MYRAMID ANALYTICAL INC
Also Called: Calcon Analytical
12345 Pauls Valley Rd # 7 (78737-9633)
P.O. Box 91417 (78709-1417)
PHONE....................................512 288-5093
Bobby C Manley, President
Carol Manley, CFO
Reed Killion, Director
EMP: 10
SQ FT: 9,800
SALES (est): 2MM Privately Held
WEB: www.myramid.com
SIC: 8731 8734 3829 Environmental research; testing laboratories; gas detectors

(G-866)
ROADWAY SPECIALTIES INC
14152 Fm 1826 (78737-9635)
P.O. Box 90309 (78709-0309)
PHONE....................................512 280-6666
Danette Shelton, President
Jim Brummer, Superintendent
Stacey Reinhart, Project Mgr
EMP: 75
SQ FT: 4,000
SALES (est): 14.4MM Privately Held
WEB: www.roadwayspecialties.com
SIC: 0781 3531 0721 Landscape services; pavers; crop seeding services

(G-867)
WORLDWIDE J R WOOD LLC
Also Called: John Christian Company
14101 W Hwy 290 Ste 900 (78737-9375)
PHONE....................................512 858-2556
Ken Owens, CFO
Kenneth Owens, CFO

Alice Ferrick-Mauer, Manager
John T Waugh,
Turner C Waugh,
▲ EMP: 20
SQ FT: 5,700
SALES (est): 4.9MM Privately Held
WEB: www.john-christian.com
SIC: 3911 3961 Jewelry, precious metal; jewelry apparel, non-precious metals

Austin
Travis County

(G-868)
1 STARVIEW SOLUTIONS LP
9433 Fm 2244 Rd (78733-6135)
PHONE....................................512 366-3939
Chris Griffin, President
Robert W Fay, CFO
EMP: 16 EST: 2009
SQ FT: 3,300
SALES (est): 2.4MM Privately Held
SIC: 7372 Prepackaged software

(G-869)
3M COMPANY
11705 Rsrch Blvd Bldg 137 (78759-2419)
PHONE....................................512 984-1800
Keith Moe, Principal
Philip Domb, Mfg Spvr
Robert Jennings, Research
David Wilson, Manager
Veronica Vasquez, Supervisor
EMP: 500
SALES (corp-wide): 32.1B Publicly Held
WEB: www.3m.com
SIC: 3825 3423 Test equipment for electronic & electrical circuits; hand & edge tools
PA: 3m Company
　　3m Center
　　Saint Paul MN 55144
　　651 733-1110

(G-870)
3M COMPANY
11705 Res Blvd Bldg 1 (78759)
PHONE....................................512 984-2370
Michael Moerbe, Principal
Roger MD Lacey, Division VP
Ed Povalish, Manager
EMP: 300
SALES (corp-wide): 32.1B Publicly Held
WEB: www.3m.com
SIC: 3829 Geophysical or meteorological electronic equipment
PA: 3m Company
　　3m Center
　　Saint Paul MN 55144
　　651 733-1110

(G-871)
3M COMPANY
11705 Research Blvd (78759-2419)
PHONE....................................512 984-2708
Steve Phillips, Branch Mgr
EMP: 25
SALES (corp-wide): 32.1B Publicly Held
WEB: www.3m.com
SIC: 2672 3661 Tape, pressure sensitive: made from purchased materials; telephone & telegraph apparatus
PA: 3m Company
　　3m Center
　　Saint Paul MN 55144
　　651 733-1110

(G-872)
A J L ADVERTISING SPECIALTIES
2101 Airport Blvd Ste 100 (78722-1403)
PHONE....................................512 320-0070
Lee Lundin, President
EMP: 20
SQ FT: 4,700
SALES (est): 3MM Privately Held
WEB: www.ajladvertising.com
SIC: 5199 5699 2759 Advertising specialties; caps & gowns (academic vestments); screen printing

(G-873)
A T D AUSTIN
Also Called: Golden Gulf Coast Directory
7225 W Highway 71 Ste A (78735-8351)
P.O. Box 92052 (78709-2052)
PHONE....................................512 288-6215
Fax: 512 288-6217
EMP: 17
SQ FT: 1,100
SALES (est): 680K Privately Held
SIC: 2741 Misc Publishing

(G-874)
A-1 SMF LLC
9409 Highway 290 W (78736-7819)
PHONE....................................512 288-9900
Glenn Kritch, Mng Member
Karen Domel, Manager
Kevin Johnson,
EMP: 25 EST: 2012
SALES (est): 1MM Privately Held
SIC: 3444 3585 Sheet metalwork; air conditioning equipment, complete

(G-875)
AAC GROUP HOLDING CORP (DH)
Also Called: American Achvement Group Holdg
7211 Circle S Rd (78745-6603)
PHONE....................................512 444-0571
Jerry Ellis, Principal
Sherice P Bench, Exec VP
Norman C Smith, Vice Pres
Steve Arnold, Engineer
Kris G Radhakrishnan, CFO
EMP: 12
SQ FT: 23,000
SALES (est): 659.7MM Privately Held
WEB: www.balfour.com
SIC: 3911 Jewelry, precious metal

(G-876)
ABIIE LLC
Plz 7000 7000 N Mop (78731)
P.O. Box 90116 (78709-0116)
PHONE....................................512 514-6325
Kenneth Chuah, Mktg Dir
Jane Khor,
▲ EMP: 15
SQ FT: 700
SALES (est): 1MM Privately Held
WEB: www.abiie.com
SIC: 2676 Infant & baby paper products

(G-877)
ABNEY GROUP INC
Also Called: Hightech Signs
1707 Hydro Dr (78728-7726)
PHONE....................................512 832-0000
Vicky L Abney, President
Paul Abney, Treasurer
Michael D Miller, Sales Mgr
Michael Miller, Sales Mgr
EMP: 10
SQ FT: 6,000
SALES (est): 1.3MM Privately Held
WEB: www.signsaustin.com
SIC: 3993 Signs, not made in custom sign painting shops

(G-878)
ABRAMS & COMPANY PUBLS INC
Also Called: Abrams Learning Trends
4503 E Rapid Springs Cv (78746-1632)
PHONE....................................800 227-9120
Aaron Mayers, CEO
William Thomas, President
▲ EMP: 25
SALES (est): 2.3MM Privately Held
WEB: www.abramsandcompany.com
SIC: 2741 2731 Miscellaneous publishing; book publishing

(G-879)
ABSOLUTE MULTIMEDIA INC
8868 Res Blvd Ste 108 (78758)
PHONE....................................512 892-8682
Thomas B Martin, President
Mark Fisher, Vice Pres
Harry Pearson, Vice Pres
Sally Renolds, Director
EMP: 35
SQ FT: 3,594

SALES (est): 2.6MM **Privately Held**
WEB: www.tas-ipad.com
SIC: 5731 2721 Radio, television & electronic stores; magazines: publishing only, not printed on site

(G-880)
ABSOLUTE SOFTWARE INC (HQ)
11401 Century Oaks Ter (78758-8699)
PHONE..............................512 600-7455
Geoff Haydon, *CEO*
Anuj Bhalla, *Partner*
Derek Prieto, *Partner*
Deirdre Rushing, *Partner*
Phil Gardner, *Principal*
EMP: 31 EST: 1998
SALES (est): 17.2MM
SALES (corp-wide): 104.6MM **Privately Held**
WEB: www.absolute.com
SIC: 7372 Prepackaged software
PA: Absolute Software Corporation
1055 Dunsmuir St Suite 1400
Vancouver BC
604 730-9851

(G-881)
ABUTEC LLC
16310 Bratton Ln Ste 350 (78728-2402)
PHONE..............................512 836-9473
Andy Smith, *Principal*
EMP: 71 EST: 2014
SALES (est): 2MM
SALES (corp-wide): 126.9MM **Privately Held**
WEB: www.cimarron.com
SIC: 3433 Heating equipment, except electric
PA: Flare Industries, Llc
16310 Bratton Ln Ste 350
Austin TX 78728
512 836-9473

(G-882)
ABUYO INC
611 S Congress Ave # 130 (78704-8706)
PHONE..............................855 850-3850
Samarra Davis, *Principal*
EMP: 30 **Privately Held**
WEB: www.selecthub.com
SIC: 7372 7389 Business oriented computer software; purchasing service
PA: Abuyo, Inc.
216 16th St Ste 1280
Denver CO 80202

(G-883)
ACCEPT SOFTWARE CORPORATION
401 Congress Ave Ste 2650 (78701-3708)
PHONE..............................512 201-8222
EMP: 50
SALES (est): 2.9MM **Privately Held**
SIC: 7372 Prepackaged Software Services

(G-884)
ACT GLOBAL SPORTS TECH INC (HQ)
4201 W Parmer Ln Ste B175 (78727-4158)
PHONE..............................512 733-5300
John Baize, *CEO*
Robert Baumgardner, *Opers Mgr*
Mark Weightman, *Opers Staff*
Mark West, *Regl Sales Mgr*
Stan Nix, *Sales Staff*
◆ EMP: 30
SALES (est): 7.7MM
SALES (corp-wide): 9.9MM **Privately Held**
WEB: www.actglobal.com
SIC: 3999 3949 Grasses, artificial & preserved; sporting & athletic goods
PA: Act Global Usa Inc
4201 W Parmer Ln Ste B175
Austin TX 78727
512 733-5300

(G-885)
ACTION RIGGING AND PUMP SVC LP
13807 Dragline Dr Ste B (78728-7631)
PHONE..............................512 670-9567
EMP: 12 EST: 1997
SQ FT: 2,000

SALES (est): 2.2MM **Privately Held**
WEB: www.actioncu.com
SIC: 3535 3599 1796 Conveyors & conveying equipment; custom machinery; machinery installation

(G-886)
ACTION SCREEN GRAPHICS
Also Called: John Schexnayder
1406 Smith Rd Ste F (78721-3562)
PHONE..............................512 478-6248
John Schexnayder, *Owner*
EMP: 12
SQ FT: 6,000
SALES (est): 1.1MM **Privately Held**
WEB: www.actionscreengraphics.com
SIC: 7336 2759 2395 Silk screen design; screen printing; embroidery products, except schiffli machine

(G-887)
ACTIVE POWER INC
2128 W Braker Ln Ste Bk12 (78758-4163)
PHONE..............................512 836-6464
Charlotte Langley, *CEO*
Debbie Canales, *Buyer*
Randal McLoud, *Buyer*
Rich Buccieri, *Engineer*
Richard Greer, *Engineer*
EMP: 88
SALES (est): 2.8MM
SALES (corp-wide): 907.4MM **Privately Held**
WEB: www.activepower.com
SIC: 3699 3612 Electrical equipment & supplies; transformers, except electric
HQ: Piller Power Systems Inc.
45 Wes Warren Dr
Middletown NY 10941

(G-888)
ACUMEN PM LLC
7320 N Mo Pac Expy # 301 (78731-2338)
PHONE..............................512 291-6259
Dan Patterson, *President*
EMP: 20
SALES (est): 1.3MM
SALES (corp-wide): 200MM **Privately Held**
WEB: www.deltek.com
SIC: 7372 Prepackaged software
HQ: Deltek, Inc.
2291 Wood Oak Dr Ste 100
Herndon VA 20171
703 734-8606

(G-889)
ADVANCED ENERGY INDUSTRIES INC
Also Called: Aera Products
8601 Cross Park Dr # 100 (78754-4578)
PHONE..............................512 339-7100
Douglas S Schatz, *Ch of Bd*
EMP: 110
SALES (corp-wide): 788.9MM **Publicly Held**
WEB: www.advancedenergy.com
SIC: 3829 Measuring & controlling devices
PA: Advanced Energy Industries, Inc.
1595 Wynkoop St Ste 800
Denver CO 80202
970 407-6626

(G-890)
ADVANCED GEOSCIENCES INC
Also Called: Agi
2121 Geoscience Dr (78726-1013)
PHONE..............................512 335-3338
Mats Lagmanson, *President*
Lk Lagmanson, *Vice Pres*
Ray Stroud, *Prdtn Mgr*
Jason Ciranna, *Electrical Engi*
Jennifer Martin, *CFO*
EMP: 21
SQ FT: 5,000
SALES (est): 4.5MM **Privately Held**
WEB: www.agiusa.com
SIC: 3829 Geophysical or meteorological electronic equipment

(G-891)
ADVANCED MICRO DEVICES INC
5204 E Ben White Blvd (78741-7306)
PHONE..............................512 602-1000
Nick George, *General Mgr*

Robert Gama, *Senior VP*
Keivan Keshvari, *Senior VP*
Beth Apperley, *Vice Pres*
Forrest Norrod, *Vice Pres*
EMP: 275
SALES (corp-wide): 9.7B **Publicly Held**
WEB: www.amd.com
SIC: 3674 Integrated circuits, semiconductor networks, etc.
PA: Advanced Micro Devices, Inc.
2485 Augustine Dr
Santa Clara CA 95054
408 749-4000

(G-892)
ADVANCED MICRO DEVICES INC
7171 Southwest Pkwy (78735-6139)
PHONE..............................512 602-1000
Rose Jennings, *Counsel*
Shantnu Sharma, *Vice Pres*
Gary Dean, *Export Mgr*
David Longenecker, *Opers Staff*
Laura Smith, *Chief Engr*
EMP: 143
SALES (corp-wide): 9.7B **Publicly Held**
WEB: www.amd.com
SIC: 3674 Integrated circuits, semiconductor networks, etc.; microprocessors; memories, solid state; microcircuits, integrated (semiconductor)
PA: Advanced Micro Devices, Inc.
2485 Augustine Dr
Santa Clara CA 95054
408 749-4000

(G-893)
ADVANCED MICRO DEVICES INC
5900 E Ben White Blvd (78741-7502)
PHONE..............................512 602-5204
John Yi, *Engineer*
Dudley Pannell, *Manager*
EMP: 12
SALES (corp-wide): 9.7B **Publicly Held**
WEB: www.amd.com
SIC: 3674 Integrated circuits, semiconductor networks, etc.
PA: Advanced Micro Devices, Inc.
2485 Augustine Dr
Santa Clara CA 95054
408 749-4000

(G-894)
ADVANCED RFURBISHMENT TECH LLC
Also Called: Art Semi
9208 Wtrford Cntre Blvd S (78758-7501)
PHONE..............................512 377-1016
Mike Catanzaro, *COO*
David Rabago, *Purchasing*
Tim Ickes, *Engineer*
Polly Bell, *Sales Mgr*
Chris Lewis, *Mng Member*
▲ EMP: 20
SQ FT: 20,000
SALES (est): 4.4MM **Privately Held**
WEB: www.artsemi.com
SIC: 3674 Semiconductors & related devices

(G-895)
ADVANCED TELESENSORS INC
6203 Sotol Cv (78759-7757)
PHONE..............................888 292-2208
Sajol Ghoshal, *Principal*
Stephanie Probasco, *Business Mgr*
Philippe Adam, *COO*
Mike Gargano, *Sales Staff*
Cindy Chalfant, *Manager*
EMP: 10
SALES (est): 940.5K **Privately Held**
WEB: www.cardio.io
SIC: 8711 3999 Engineering services; atomizers, toiletry

(G-896)
AEGLEA BIOTHERAPEUTICS INC (PA)
805 Las Cimas Pkwy # 100 (78746-5472)
PHONE..............................512 942-2935
Anthony G Quinn, *CEO*
Armen Shanafelt, *Ch of Bd*
Leslie Sloan, *COO*
Henry L Hebel, *Vice Pres*

Scott W Rowlinson, *Vice Pres*
EMP: 30
SQ FT: 10,100
SALES (est): 4.9MM **Publicly Held**
WEB: www.aegleabio.com
SIC: 2834 Pharmaceutical preparations

(G-897)
AEGLEA DEVELOPMENT COMPANY INC
Also Called: Aeglea Biotherapeutic Holdings
805 Las Cimas Pkwy # 100 (78746-5493)
PHONE..............................512 942-2935
David Lowe, *CEO*
Ann M Lowe, *Vice Pres*
Scott W Rowlinson, *Vice Pres*
Joseph E Tyler, *Vice Pres*
Charles N York, *Vice Pres*
EMP: 14
SALES (est): 1.7MM **Privately Held**
WEB: www.aegleabio.com
SIC: 2836 Biological products, except diagnostic

(G-898)
AERO CAPITAL SOLUTIONS INC
3700 N Cpitl Of Txas Hwy (78746-3453)
PHONE..............................737 717-0624
Jason Barany, *President*
Penny Curtis, *Vice Pres*
Phillip Grant, *Vice Pres*
Peter Siaw, *Vice Pres*
John Walker, *Vice Pres*
EMP: 40 EST: 2010
SALES (est): 9.8MM **Privately Held**
WEB: www.aerocapitalsolutions.com
SIC: 3724 Aircraft engines & engine parts

(G-899)
AESTHETIC MEDICAL EDUCATORS
7606 Hawkeye Dr (78749-2814)
P.O. Box 1794, Manchaca (78652-1794)
PHONE..............................512 301-2125
Julie A Lopez, *Principal*
Penny Bailey, *VP Opers*
EMP: 14
SALES (est): 2MM **Privately Held**
WEB: www.aestheticmedicaltraining.com
SIC: 2834 Dermatologicals

(G-900)
AFAM CAPITAL INC
Also Called: Prudent Speculator, The
221 W 6th St 5 (78701-3400)
PHONE..............................512 354-7041
Jeff Montgomery, *CEO*
Cynthia Mendoza, *Vice Pres*
Christophera Quigley, *Research*
Diane Peck, *CFO*
Jackie Baumann, *Office Mgr*
EMP: 20
SQ FT: 2,000
SALES (est): 4.2MM **Privately Held**
WEB: www.afamcapital.com
SIC: 6211 6282 2741 Investment firm, general brokerage; manager of mutual funds, contract or fee basis; newsletter publishing

(G-901)
AIRBOX LLC
2213 Ranch Road 620 N # 10 (78734-2672)
PHONE..............................512 968-5496
Timothy Self,
EMP: 9
SALES (est): 348K **Privately Held**
WEB: www.airboxairpurifier.com
SIC: 3564 3634 Air purification equipment; air purifiers, portable

(G-902)
AIRGAS USA LLC
11111 N Lamar Blvd (78753-3058)
PHONE..............................512 835-0202
Gary Underwood, *Manager*
EMP: 15
SQ FT: 16,200
SALES (corp-wide): 129.8MM **Privately Held**
WEB: www.airgas.com
SIC: 5169 5999 3599 7359 Industrial gases; welding supplies; machine & other job shop work; equipment rental & leasing; welding machinery & equipment

HQ: Airgas Usa, Llc
259 N Radnor Chester Rd
Radnor PA 19087
216 642-6600

(G-903)
ALAFAIR BIOSCIENCES INC
6101 W Courtyard Dr 2-2 (78730-5115)
PHONE.................................512 739-9510
Greg Brophy, *CEO*
John Joyoprayitno, *COO*
Bhushan Holay, *Vice Pres*
Sarah Mayes, *Research*
Scott Zawko, *Research*
EMP: 13
SQ FT: 1,800
SALES (est): 374.8K **Privately Held**
WEB: www.alafairbiosciences.com
SIC: 3842 5999 Surgical appliances &
supplies; implants, surgical; medical ap-
paratus & supplies

(G-904)
ALAMO CONCRETE PRODUCTS
LTD
4200 Todd Ln (78744-1113)
PHONE.................................512 444-2464
Bryan Pennington, *President*
EMP: 45 **Privately Held**
SIC: 3273 Ready-mixed concrete
PA: Alamo Concrete Products, Ltd.
6055 W Green Mountain Rd
Austin TX 78744

(G-905)
ALAMO CONCRETE PRODUCTS
LTD (PA)
6055 W Green Mountain Rd (78744)
P.O. Box 34210, San Antonio (78265-4210)
PHONE.................................512 444-2464
Allen Walsh, *Principal*
Kirk Taylor, *COO*
Robert Wells, *Vice Pres*
Alan Leitko, *CFO*
EMP: 100
SQ FT: 66,123
SALES (est): 169.4MM **Privately Held**
SIC: 3273 Ready-mixed concrete

(G-906)
ALEREON INC
10800 Pecan Park Blvd # 100
(78750-1232)
PHONE.................................512 345-4200
Eric Brockman, *CEO*
Dave Shoemaker, *Vice Pres*
Greg McClendon, *Engineer*
Dirk Luthro, *CFO*
Jim Lansford, *CTO*
EMP: 79
SQ FT: 26,600
SALES (est): 18.1MM **Privately Held**
WEB: www.alereon.com
SIC: 3674 Semiconductors & related de-
vices

(G-907)
ALEX ESOLUTIONS INC
Also Called: Sheshunoff Information Svcs
807 Las Cimas Pkwy # 300 (78746-6191)
PHONE.................................512 305-6500
Phil Gabel, *CEO*
Timothy B Smith, *CFO*
EMP: 150
SALES (est): 11.1MM
SALES (corp-wide): 10.6B **Publicly Held**
WEB: www.store.lexisnexis.com
SIC: 2741 Miscellaneous publishing
HQ: Woodbridge Company Limited, The
65 Queen St W Suite 2400
Toronto ON M5H 2
416 364-8700

(G-908)
ALL WASHED UP INC
15106 W Hwy 71 (78738-2800)
P.O. Box 92109 (78709-2109)
PHONE.................................512 288-5522
Daniel Bauerle, *President*
EMP: 11
SALES (est): 724.1K **Privately Held**
SIC: 4959 3991 Sweeping service: road,
airport, parking lot, etc.; street sweeping
brooms, hand or machine

(G-909)
ALLERGAN INC
12331 Riata Trace Pkwy (78727-6419)
PHONE.................................512 527-6649
Jose Vazquez, *Manager*
EMP: 9 **Privately Held**
WEB: www.allergan.com
SIC: 2834 Solutions, pharmaceutical; der-
matologicals; drugs acting on the central
nervous system & sense organs; propri-
etary drug products
HQ: Allergan, Inc.
5 Giralda Farms
Madison NJ 07940
862 261-7000

(G-910)
AMBIENTE OPCO LLC (PA)
Also Called: Ambiente Wine
2314 Rutland Dr Ste 205 (78758-5274)
PHONE.................................512 835-2299
David Gundelach, *Vice Pres*
Jeremy Stiles, *Vice Pres*
Melanie Forehand, *VP Sales*
Elizabeth Esquivel, *Sales Staff*
David Means, *Director*
EMP: 11
SALES (est): 2MM **Privately Held**
WEB: www.ambientewine.com
SIC: 2084 Wines

(G-911)
AMBION INC (DH)
Also Called: Ambion Austin Finished Gds DC
2130 Woodward St Ste 200 (78744-1038)
PHONE.................................512 651-0200
Bruce Leander, *President*
Fred Rhoads, *Vice Pres*
Rigo Vallejo, *Vice Pres*
John Dahler, *CFO*
Dan Andrade, *Supervisor*
▲ EMP: 215
SQ FT: 72,000
SALES (est): 29.9MM
SALES (corp-wide): 25.5B **Publicly Held**
SIC: 2836 2835 5049 Biological products,
except diagnostic; in vitro & in vivo diag-
nostic substances; laboratory equipment,
except medical or dental

(G-912)
AMBION DIAGNOSTICS INC
Also Called: Life Technologies
2150 Woodward St Ste 100 (78744-1038)
PHONE.................................512 651-0200
Bernard Andruss, *Manager*
EMP: 115
SALES (est): 15.8MM
SALES (corp-wide): 25.5B **Publicly Held**
WEB: www.thermofisher.com
SIC: 3826 Analytical instruments
HQ: Ambion, Inc.
2130 Woodward St Ste 200
Austin TX 78744
512 651-0200

(G-913)
AMBIQ MICRO INC
6500 Rver Pl Blvd Bldg 7 (78730)
PHONE.................................512 879-2850
Fumihide Esaka, *CEO*
Aaron Grassian, *Vice Pres*
Dale Hancock, *Vice Pres*
Mike Salas, *Vice Pres*
Jaye Parker, *Accounting Mgr*
EMP: 30
SALES (est): 6.3MM **Privately Held**
WEB: www.ambiqmicro.com
SIC: 3674 Fuel cells, solid state

(G-914)
AMC PUBLISHING LLC
Also Called: Opulence Magazine
5114 Balcones Woods Dr (78759-5273)
PHONE.................................512 380-1611
Anita Roberts,
EMP: 20
SQ FT: 2,000
SALES (est): 1.4MM **Privately Held**
WEB: www.amcpublishing.net
SIC: 2721 Periodicals

(G-915)
AMERICAN BOTTLING
COMPANY
Also Called: 7up/Rc/Big Red of Austin
2120 Grand Avenue Pkwy # 20
(78728-3900)
PHONE.................................512 385-4477
Ken Timms, *Manager*
EMP: 90 **Publicly Held**
WEB: www.keurigdrpepper.com
SIC: 2086 5149 Soft drinks: packaged in
cans, bottles, etc.; groceries & related
products
HQ: The American Bottling Company
5301 Legacy Dr
Plano TX 75024

(G-916)
AMERICAN INNOVATIONS LTD
(PA)
12211 Technology Blvd (78727-6102)
PHONE.................................512 249-3400
Rich Smalling, *President*
Randall Chance, *Partner*
Brenda Travis, *Purchasing*
Donald Hayden, *Business Anlyst*
Leslie Lyon-House, *Marketing Staff*
EMP: 40
SQ FT: 25,000
SALES (est): 15.4MM **Privately Held**
WEB: www.aiworldwide.com
SIC: 3825 3824 3674 Electrical energy
measuring equipment; gas meters, do-
mestic & large capacity: industrial; water
meters; semiconductors & related devices

(G-917)
AMERICAN PRINTERS
EXCHANGE INC
Also Called: American Printing and Mailing
1606 Headway Cir Ste 100 (78754-5152)
PHONE.................................512 452-5058
Daniel J Brannon, *President*
Larry Conchola, *Sales Staff*
Linda Skinner, *Office Mgr*
Chris Urias, *Manager*
EMP: 12
SALES (est): 1.2MM **Privately Held**
WEB: www.americanprinters.com
SIC: 2752 Commercial printing, offset

(G-918)
AMERICAN TIRE DISTRIBUTORS
INC
810 W Howard Ln (78753-9708)
PHONE.................................704 992-2000
EMP: 19
SALES (corp-wide): 170.8MM **Privately
Held**
WEB: www.atd-us.com
SIC: 5531 5099 5014 3011 Automotive
tires; firearms & ammunition, except
sporting; tires & tubes; tires & inner tubes
HQ: American Tire Distributors Inc.
12200 Herbert Wayne Ct # 150
Huntersville NC 28078
704 992-2000

(G-919)
AMKOR TECHNOLOGY INC
8140 N Mopac Expy Ste 150 (78759-8837)
PHONE.................................512 953-0701
Fred Farris, *Vice Pres*
EMP: 61
SALES (corp-wide): 4B **Publicly Held**
WEB: www.amkor.com
SIC: 3674 Semiconductors & related de-
vices
PA: Amkor Technology, Inc.
2045 E Innovation Cir
Tempe AZ 85284
480 821-5000

(G-920)
AMPLIFY SNACK BRANDS INC
(HQ)
500 W 5th St Ste 1350 (78701-3836)
PHONE.................................512 600-9893
Thomas C Ennis, *President*
Craig Shiesley, *President*
Jason Shiver, *President*
Greg Christenson, *CFO*
Brian Goldberg, *CFO*
EMP: 24
SQ FT: 11,000
SALES: 270.8MM
SALES (corp-wide): 7.9B **Publicly Held**
WEB: www.amplifysnackbrands.com
SIC: 2099 2064 2096 Food preparations;
popcorn balls or other treated popcorn
products; tortilla chips
PA: Hershey Company
19 E Chocolate Ave
Hershey PA 17033
717 534-4200

(G-921)
AMS ACQUISITION CORP (PA)
Also Called: 3 Axis Technologies
4616 W Howard Ln 5-550 (78728-6324)
P.O. Box 80249 (78708-0249)
PHONE.................................512 491-7411
Brad Scoggins, *President*
Joseph C Morgan, *CFO*
▲ EMP: 26
SQ FT: 30,000
SALES (est): 19.7MM **Privately Held**
WEB: www.austinmfg.com
SIC: 3672 Printed circuit boards

(G-922)
ANALOG DEVICES INC
6500 River Place Blvd # 1 (78730-1119)
PHONE.................................512 427-1000
Damon Clary, *Engineer*
Matt Prewett, *Engineer*
Alan McGrath, *Marketing Staff*
Elie Ahddad, *Manager*
EMP: 90
SALES (corp-wide): 5.6B **Publicly Held**
WEB: www.analog.com
SIC: 3674 Integrated circuits, semiconduc-
tor networks, etc.
PA: Analog Devices, Inc.
1 Analog Way
Wilmington MA 01887
781 329-4700

(G-923)
ANUE SYSTEMS INC
Also Called: Ixia
8310 N Cptl Tx Hwy # 300 (78731-1011)
PHONE.................................512 600-5400
Himanshu Thaker, *CEO*
Alex Pepe, *President*
Keith E Cheney, *Senior VP*
Kevin Przybocki, *Senior VP*
Yuanqing Hu, *Engineer*
▼ EMP: 58
SQ FT: 16,600
SALES (est): 10MM
SALES (corp-wide): 4.3B **Publicly Held**
WEB: www.ixiacom.com
SIC: 3829 Testing equipment: abrasion,
shearing strength, etc.
HQ: Ixia
26601 Agoura Rd
Calabasas CA 91302
818 871-1800

(G-924)
APPLIED MATERIALS INC
8505 Cross Park Dr # 300 (78754-4577)
PHONE.................................512 272-7075
Melissa Hernandez, *President*
Ray Devreugd, *Engineer*
Dave Lischka, *Engineer*
James Reed, *Project Engr*
Mike Forbes, *Manager*
EMP: 48
SQ FT: 151,862
SALES (corp-wide): 17.2B **Publicly Held**
SIC: 3674 Semiconductors & related de-
vices
PA: Applied Materials, Inc.
3050 Bowers Ave Bldg 1
Santa Clara CA 95054
408 727-5555

(G-925)
APPLIED MATERIALS INC
9700 E Highway 290 (78724-1102)
P.O. Box 210067, Dallas (75211-0067)
PHONE.................................512 272-1000
Nick Parisi, *Managing Dir*
Scott Watson, *Managing Dir*
Lior Engel, *Vice Pres*
Hari Ponnekanti, *Vice Pres*
John White, *Vice Pres*
EMP: 2000

▲ = Import ▼=Export
◆ =Import/Export

SQ FT: 1,719,000
SALES (corp-wide): 17.2B Publicly Held
WEB: www.appliedmaterials.com
SIC: 3674 Semiconductors & related devices
PA: Applied Materials, Inc.
3050 Bowers Ave Bldg 1
Santa Clara CA 95054
408 727-5555

(G-926)
AQUILAN TECHNOLOGIES INC
901 S Mo Pac Expy (78746-5776)
PHONE.................................512 751-4226
Clifford Hagler, CEO
Brian Hagler, Project Mgr
EMP: 14 EST: 2012
SALES (est): 933.4K Privately Held
WEB: www.aquilan.com
SIC: 7372 Application computer software

(G-927)
ARAMARK SERVICES INC
7171 Southwest Pkwy (78735-6139)
PHONE.................................512 602-1000
EMP: 110 Publicly Held
WEB: www.aramark.com
SIC: 3674 Integrated circuits, semiconductor networks, etc.
HQ: Aramark Services, Inc.
2400 Market St Ste 600
Philadelphia PA 19103
215 238-3000

(G-928)
ARAVAS INC (HQ)
6836 Bee Caves Rd Bldg 3s (78746-5059)
PHONE.................................512 614-1848
Taneli Jouhikainen, COO
David Lowrance, CFO
Danielle Brown, Controller
Mike Ciesla, VP Finance
Jessica Jackson, Director
EMP: 14
SALES (est): 1.5MM Publicly Held
WEB: www.savarapharma.com
SIC: 2834 Solutions, pharmaceutical

(G-929)
ARBOL PUBLISHING LP
Also Called: El Mundo Newspaper
2519 E 5th Street Austin (78702)
P.O. Box 6519 (78762-6519)
PHONE.................................512 476-8636
Angela Angulo, Managing Prtnr
Alba Angulo, Partner
John Linares, Pub Rel Mgr
Betty Portuondo, Sales Executive
Carmen Sosa, Sales Executive
EMP: 12
SQ FT: 2,500
SALES (est): 710.1K Privately Held
WEB: www.elmundonewspaper.com
SIC: 2711 7313 Newspapers: publishing only, not printed on site; newspaper advertising representative

(G-930)
ARCHITERRA INC
Also Called: Architerra Austin
1701 Evergreen Ave Unit 2 (78704-2953)
PHONE.................................512 441-8062
George Barber, President
Dolores Spontak, Principal
EMP: 15
SALES (est): 1.6MM Privately Held
WEB: www.architerrashowroom.com
SIC: 3259 5211 3253 Architectural terra cotta; tile, ceramic; ceramic wall & floor tile

(G-931)
ARCTOS ASSEMBLY GROUP LTD
12317 Technology Blvd (78727-6133)
PHONE.................................512 682-4801
Matthew Ache, President
John E Bosch Jr, Partner
EMP: 18
SALES (est): 102.3K Privately Held
WEB: www.irexmfg.com
SIC: 3672 Printed circuit boards
PA: Tyrex Group, Ltd.
12317 Tech Blvd Ste 100
Austin TX 78727

(G-932)
ARM INC
5707 Sw Pkwy Ste 1-100 (78735-6214)
PHONE.................................408 576-1500
Fares Bagh, Vice Pres
Aashish Chaddha, Engineer
Amit Gurung, Engineer
Lingchuan Meng, Engineer
Aditya Rathi, Engineer
EMP: 12
SALES (est): 1.6MM Privately Held
WEB: www.arm.com
SIC: 3674 Semiconductors & related devices

(G-933)
ARM INC
Encino Trace 5707 Sw Park (78735)
PHONE.................................512 327-9249
Simon Segars, CEO
Doug Maas, Partner
Kathy Simmons, General Mgr
Eric Van Hensbergen, General Mgr
Joe Frisby, Business Mgr
EMP: 100 Privately Held
WEB: www.arminc.us
SIC: 3674 Integrated circuits, semiconductor networks, etc.
HQ: Arm, Inc.
150 Rose Orchard Way
San Jose CA 95134

(G-934)
AROMA ALTERNATIVES LTD CO (PA)
11110 Metric Blvd Ste D (78758-4097)
PHONE.................................512 535-3646
Kevin Bales, General Mgr
Deborah Bales,
EMP: 11
SALES (est): 4MM Privately Held
WEB: www.aromaalternatives.com
SIC: 2844 Cosmetic preparations

(G-935)
ARTE SANO LLC
6110 Trade Center Dr (78744-1301)
PHONE.................................512 400-8743
EMP: 95
SALES (est): 1.5MM Privately Held
WEB: www.arte-sano-llc.business.site
SIC: 2096 Tortilla chips

(G-936)
ARTEMIS INTL SOLUTIONS CORP (DH)
401 Congress Ave Ste 2650 (78701-3708)
PHONE.................................512 201-8222
Scott Brighton, President
Randall Jacops, President
Sean Fallon, Vice Pres
Christopher Smith, Vice Pres
Chris Tower, Vice Pres
▲ EMP: 67 EST: 1976
SALES (est): 29MM Privately Held
WEB: www.aurea.com
SIC: 7372 Prepackaged software

(G-937)
ARTHROCARE CORPORATION (DH)
7000 W William Cannon Dr # 1 (78735-8509)
PHONE.................................512 391-3900
David Fitzgerald, President
Todd Newton, COO
Richard Rew, Senior VP
Jean Woloszko, Senior VP
Brian Simmons, Vice Pres
EMP: 140
SALES (est): 174.8MM
SALES (corp-wide): 5.1B Privately Held
WEB: www.smith-nephew.com
SIC: 3841 Surgical & medical instruments
HQ: Smith & Nephew, Inc.
7135 Goodlett Farms Pkwy
Cordova TN 38016
901 396-2121

(G-938)
ARX FIT
9715a Burnet Rd (78758-5215)
PHONE.................................512 633-3768
EMP: 10 EST: 2011

SALES (est): 1.5MM Privately Held
WEB: www.arxfit.com
SIC: 3949 Exercise equipment

(G-939)
ASPHALT INC LLC
11675 Jllyvlle Rd Ste 205 (78759)
PHONE.................................512 428-5739
EMP: 25
SALES (est): 14.2MM Privately Held
WEB: www.lonestarpavingtx.com
SIC: 2951 5032 Asphalt paving mixtures & blocks; asphalt mixture

(G-940)
ASPIRA WOMENS HEALTH INC (PA)
Also Called: Vermillion
12117 Bee Cves Rd Bldg 3 (78738)
PHONE.................................512 519-0400
James T Lafrance, Ch of Bd
Valerie B Palmieri, President
David Jansen, Vice Pres
Jon Thomas, Vice Pres
Rowan Bullock, Research
EMP: 44
SQ FT: 4,218
SALES: 4.5MM Publicly Held
WEB: www.aspirawh.com
SIC: 2835 In vitro diagnostics

(G-941)
ASPIRE FOOD GROUP USA INC
6231 E Stassney Ln 12-105 (78744-3088)
PHONE.................................512 645-0700
Mohammed Ashour, Director
EMP: 20 EST: 2015
SALES (est): 3.9MM Privately Held
SIC: 2099 3523 Food preparations; farm machinery & equipment

(G-942)
ASURAGEN INC
2150 Woodward St Ste 100 (78744-1038)
PHONE.................................512 681-5200
Matthew M Winkler, Ch of Bd
Matthew McManus, President
Tom Copa, Senior VP
Colin Hill, Senior VP
Jenny Manuel, Vice Pres
EMP: 100
SALES (est): 25.5MM Privately Held
WEB: www.asuragen.com
SIC: 3841 8731 2835 Surgical & medical instruments; biological research; in vitro & in vivo diagnostic substances

(G-943)
ASURE SOFTWARE INC (PA)
3700 N Capital Of Texas H (78746-3454)
PHONE.................................512 437-2700
Patrick Goepel, Ch of Bd
Eyal Goldstein, President
Rhonda Parouty, COO
Kelyn Brannon, CFO
EMP: 24
SQ FT: 15,000
SALES: 73.1MM Publicly Held
WEB: www.asuresoftware.com
SIC: 7372 Prepackaged software

(G-944)
ATHENA MANUFACTURING LP
15900 Bratton Ln (78728-3003)
PHONE.................................512 928-2693
Bill Johnson, President
Shaun Bunting, Partner
William Johnson, Partner
John Newman, Partner
Gilbert Robertson, Partner
▲ EMP: 100
SQ FT: 44,000
SALES (est): 29.2MM Privately Held
WEB: www.athenamfg.com
SIC: 3599 Machine shop, jobbing & repair

(G-945)
ATHENS GROUP HOLDINGS LLC (PA)
3301 Northland Dr Ste 500 (78731-4954)
PHONE.................................512 345-0600
Michael J Haney, Mng Member
Donald F Shafer,
EMP: 9
SALES (est): 5.3MM Privately Held
SIC: 1381 Drilling oil & gas wells

(G-946)
ATLAS SAND COMPANY LLC (PA)
5918 W Courtyard Dr # 500 (78730-5102)
PHONE.................................432 276-3990
Bud Brigham, CEO
Hunter Wallace, COO
Fritz Feltner, Vice Pres
Chris Scholla, Vice Pres
Brian Vinson, Plant Mgr
EMP: 23 EST: 2017
SALES (est): 5.3MM Privately Held
WEB: www.atlassand.com
SIC: 3272 1442 Covers, catch basin: concrete; sand mining

(G-947)
ATX OIL AND MORE LLC
9311 N Fm 620 Rd (78726-4129)
PHONE.................................512 660-0696
Ketan Pandya,
EMP: 20
SALES (est): 327.3K Privately Held
SIC: 1389 Oil field services

(G-948)
AUGMENTIX CORPORATION
4030 W Braker Ln Ste 100 (78759-5353)
PHONE.................................512 334-0111
Stephan Godevais, President
Kirk Patterson, CFO
Todd Grabbe, Director
▲ EMP: 65
SQ FT: 9,000
SALES (est): 10.2MM
SALES (corp-wide): 146.7MM Privately Held
SIC: 3577 Computer peripheral equipment
HQ: Entorian Technologies Inc.
4030 W Braker Ln 2-100
Austin TX

(G-949)
AUS-TEX DUPLICATORS INC
Also Called: Aus-Tex Printing & Mailing
2431 Forbes Dr (78754-5148)
P.O. Box 141157 (78714-1157)
PHONE.................................512 476-7581
John Eastty, President
Marie Eastty, Vice Pres
Ben Ornelas, Manager
EMP: 47
SQ FT: 31,000
SALES (est): 9.9MM Privately Held
WEB: www.austex.com
SIC: 7331 2752 Mailing service; lithographing on metal

(G-950)
AUSTEX DUMPSTERS LLC
9608 Swansons Ranch Rd (78748-1446)
PHONE.................................512 292-3867
Michael P Christophe II, Mng Member
EMP: 9
SALES (est): 841K Privately Held
WEB: www.austexdumpsters.com
SIC: 3443 Dumpsters, garbage

(G-951)
AUSTIN BRAKE & CLUTCH SUPPLY
8151 N Lamar Blvd (78753-6299)
PHONE.................................512 836-0482
Fax: 512 836-0957
EMP: 12
SQ FT: 12,000
SALES (est): 2.8MM Privately Held
SIC: 3714 5013 Mfg Motor Vehicle Parts/Accessories Whol Auto Parts/Supplies

(G-952)
AUSTIN CHRONICLE CORPORATION
4000 N Intrstate 35 Frnta (78751)
P.O. Box 49066 (78765-9066)
PHONE.................................512 454-5766
Nick Barbaro, President
Marjorie Baumgarten, Editor
Cassidy N Frazier, Editor
Leeann Atherton, Sales Staff
Willis Gates, Sales Staff
EMP: 55
SQ FT: 8,000

SALES (est): 4.3MM **Privately Held**
WEB: www.austinchronicle.com
SIC: 2711 Newspapers, publishing & printing

(G-953)
AUSTIN COCA-COLA BOTTLING CO
9600 Burnet Rd (78758-5214)
PHONE.................................512 832-2652
Lee Lockard, *Manager*
Wendell Kang, *Manager*
EMP: 48
SQ FT: 20,000
SALES (corp-wide): 309.5MM **Privately Held**
SIC: 2086 Bottled & canned soft drinks
PA: Austin Coca-Cola Bottling Company
1 Coca Cola Pl
San Antonio TX 78219
210 225-2601

(G-954)
AUSTIN COCA-COLA BOTTLING CO
2311 Denton Dr (78758-4509)
PHONE.................................512 836-0870
Jim Slater, *Manager*
EMP: 35
SQ FT: 31,920
SALES (corp-wide): 309.5MM **Privately Held**
SIC: 2086 Bottled & canned soft drinks
PA: Austin Coca-Cola Bottling Company
1 Coca Cola Pl
San Antonio TX 78219
210 225-2601

(G-955)
AUSTIN FIT MAGAZINE LP
2499 S Cpitl Of Txas Hwy (78746-7762)
PHONE.................................512 407-8383
Lou Earle, *Managing Prtnr*
Alex Ecenia, *COO*
Lynne Earle, *VP Sales*
Kat Barclay, *Manager*
Carley Beyer, *Creative Dir*
EMP: 10
SALES (est): 923.1K **Privately Held**
WEB: www.austinfitmagazine.com
SIC: 2721 Magazines: publishing only, not printed on site

(G-956)
AUSTIN MFG SVCS I INC
Also Called: AMS
Na4616 W Howard Ln Bldg Na (78728)
P.O. Box 80249 (78708-0249)
PHONE.................................512 491-7411
Brad Scoggins, *President*
Iain Hurn, *Exec VP*
Joe Morgan, *CFO*
Joseph C Morgan, *CFO*
Renee Brown, *Treasurer*
▲ **EMP:** 90
SALES (est): 19.7MM **Privately Held**
WEB: www.austinmfg.com
SIC: 3672 Printed circuit boards
PA: Ams Acquisition Corp.
4616 W Howard Ln 5-550
Austin TX 78728

(G-957)
AUSTIN NORTH TAXI SERVICE
3314 W Parmer Ln (78727)
PHONE.................................512 704-9999
Joseph Cekren,
EMP: 17
SALES (est): 550K **Privately Held**
WEB: www.taxisvc.com
SIC: 4121 3532 Taxicabs; shuttle cars, underground

(G-958)
AUSTIN READY-MIX LLC
4005 Banister Ln Ste 225c (78704-8077)
P.O. Box 579, Del Valle (78617-0579)
PHONE.................................512 386-7187
Les Juliano Sr, *Owner*
EMP: 10
SALES (est): 1.8MM **Privately Held**
WEB: www.armtexas.net
SIC: 3273 Ready-mixed concrete

(G-959)
AUSTIN RUBBER COMPANY LLC
506 W 14th St Ste C (78701-1736)
PHONE.................................512 904-0152
W A Fitzhugh Lee, *President*
Donald Drew, *Vice Pres*
Shahram Shafie, *Vice Pres*
Paul Gefrovich, *Manager*
EMP: 9
SALES (est): 123.6K **Privately Held**
WEB: www.austinrubber.com
SIC: 3011 Automobile tires, pneumatic; industrial tires, pneumatic
PA: Green Source Holdings Llc
13413 Galleria Cir # 140
Austin TX 78738

(G-960)
AUSTIN SAMSUNG SEMICDTR LLC
12100 Samsung Blvd (78754-1903)
PHONE.................................512 672-1000
Sung Whan Lee, *President*
Ahmed Ali, *Engineer*
Valentine Constancio, *Engineer*
Conner Morrow, *Engineer*
Sean Pedersen, *Engineer*
◆ **EMP:** 950
SQ FT: 550,000
SALES (est): 228.8MM **Privately Held**
WEB: www.austintexas.gov
SIC: 3674 Microprocessors; microcircuits, integrated (semiconductor); computer logic modules; memories, solid state
HQ: Samsung Semiconductor, Inc.
3655 N 1st St
San Jose CA 95134
408 544-4000

(G-961)
AUSTIN SCREEN PRINTING INC
Also Called: A S P
4204 Medical Pkwy (78756-3310)
PHONE.................................512 454-6249
Virgil E Hargett Jr, *President*
Ed Hargett, *President*
Ron Habitzreiter, *Corp Secy*
Jenna Cox, *Mktg Dir*
EMP: 50
SQ FT: 4,000
SALES (est): 6.8MM **Privately Held**
WEB: www.austinsscreenprinting.net
SIC: 7336 3993 2396 Silk screen design; signs & advertising specialties; automotive & apparel trimmings

(G-962)
AUSTIN SEMICONDUCTOR INC
Also Called: Micross Components
8701 Crotx Pk Dr Ste 105 (78754)
PHONE.................................512 339-1188
Richard Kingeon, *CEO*
Allen Wares, *QC Mgr*
▲ **EMP:** 140
SQ FT: 26,600
SALES (est): 9.8MM
SALES (corp-wide): 77.3MM **Privately Held**
WEB: www.micross.com
SIC: 3674 Semiconductors & related devices
PA: Micross Components, Inc.
7725 N Orange Blossom Trl
Orlando FL 32810
407 298-7100

(G-963)
AUSTIN VENTURES LP (PA)
835 W 6th St Ste 1500 (78703-5472)
PHONE.................................512 485-1900
Joseph C Aragona, *Partner*
Michael Bennet, *Partner*
Mike Bennett, *Partner*
Shelby H Carter Jr, *Partner*
Jim Clardy, *Partner*
EMP: 31
SALES (est): 146.7MM **Privately Held**
WEB: www.austinventures.com
SIC: 6799 2038 Venture capital companies; frozen specialties

(G-964)
AUSTIN WATERJET INC
8510 Lava Hill Rd (78744-7803)
PHONE.................................512 243-9000
James D Miller, *President*

Janet Miller, *Corp Secy*
Yessica Martinez, *Manager*
EMP: 11
SQ FT: 14,800
SALES (est): 2.7MM **Privately Held**
WEB: www.waterjetcutting.com
SIC: 3599 Machine shop, jobbing & repair

(G-965)
AUSTIN WESTERN RAILROAD LLC
14205 N Mo Pac Expy # 130 (78728-6532)
P.O. Box 95, Mc Neil (78651-0095)
PHONE.................................512 388-6350
John Anderson, *General Mgr*
Audie Cavazos, *Manager*
EMP: 25
SQ FT: 1,200
SALES (est): 2.7MM
SALES (corp-wide): 997.9MM **Privately Held**
SIC: 3441 Railroad car racks, for transporting vehicles: steel
PA: Watco Companies, L.L.C.
315 W 3rd St
Pittsburg KS 66762
620 231-2230

(G-966)
AUSTIN WHITE LIME COMPANY (PA)
14001 Mcneil Rd (78728-6310)
P.O. Box 9556 (78766-9556)
PHONE.................................512 255-3646
Patricia M Robinson, *Partner*
Charlotte D Allen, *Partner*
Florence L Cosper, *Partner*
George E Robinson Jr, *Partner*
James E Robinson, *Partner*
EMP: 13 **EST:** 1888
SQ FT: 8,500
SALES (est): 29MM **Privately Held**
WEB: www.austinwhitelime.com
SIC: 3274 2819 Building lime; industrial inorganic chemicals

(G-967)
AUSTIN WINDOW FASHION INC (PA)
10321 Burnet Rd Ste A (78758-4426)
PHONE.................................512 836-3388
Thomas Thom, *President*
Mason Thom, *Engineer*
EMP: 18
SQ FT: 10,000
SALES (est): 3MM **Privately Held**
WEB: www.austinwindowfashions.com
SIC: 1751 2391 5719 5714 Window & door (prefabricated) installation; curtains, window: made from purchased materials; window shades; draperies; vertical blinds

(G-968)
AVASTAR BRANDS LLC
Also Called: Autosol
13219 N Highway 183 Ste I (78750-3245)
P.O. Box 340358 (78734-0006)
PHONE.................................512 804-9337
Lisa Valleau, *Mng Member*
Edwin Mallory,
▲ **EMP:** 21
SQ FT: 2,500
SALES (est): 3.3MM **Privately Held**
WEB: www.autosol.com
SIC: 5169 2819 Industrial chemicals; hypophosphites

(G-969)
AVIAT US INC (HQ)
200 Parker Dr Ste C100a (78728-1206)
PHONE.................................408 941-7100
John Mutch, *Ch of Bd*
Meena L Elliott, *Senior VP*
John J Madigan, *Vice Pres*
Ralph Marimon, *CFO*
Shaun McFall, *Chief Mktg Ofcr*
▼ **EMP:** 450
SQ FT: 60,000
SALES (est): 144.6MM **Publicly Held**
WEB: www.aviatnetworks.com
SIC: 3663 3661 Radio broadcasting & communications equipment; transmitter-receivers, radio; mobile communication equipment; fiber optics communications equipment

(G-970)
AVOLIN LLC
401 Congress Ave Ste 2650 (78701-3708)
PHONE.................................512 524-6149
Michael Speranza, *CEO*
EMP: 201
SALES (est): 3.9MM
SALES (corp-wide): 7.5MM **Privately Held**
SIC: 7371 7372 Software programming applications; business oriented computer software
PA: Avolin, Inc.
401 Congress Ave Ste 2650
Austin TX 78701
512 524-6149

(G-971)
AZTEC CUSTOM SCREENPRINTING (PA)
2815 Manor Rd (78722-1717)
PHONE.................................512 744-0195
Alejandro Vasquez, *Owner*
Fontaine Schibi, *Sales Mgr*
▲ **EMP:** 17
SQ FT: 3,000
SALES (est): 980K **Privately Held**
WEB: www.aztecworld.com
SIC: 2759 Screen printing

(G-972)
BAE SYSTEMS INC
6500 Tracor Ln (78725-2000)
PHONE.................................512 276-3100
J D Bennett, *Principal*
Srinivasa Madala, *General Ptnr*
Ken Berry, *Engineer*
Mark Dube, *Engineer*
Keith Kunz, *Engineer*
EMP: 55
SALES (est): 10.9MM
SALES (corp-wide): 23.6B **Privately Held**
WEB: www.geospatialexploitationproducts.com
SIC: 3728 Aircraft parts & equipment
PA: Bae Systems Plc
6 Carlton Gardens Stirling Square
London
125 237-3232

(G-973)
BAE SYSTEMS INFO & ELEC SYS
6500 Tracor Ln (78725-2000)
PHONE.................................512 276-3100
Greg Zito, *Prgrmr*
EMP: 606
SALES (corp-wide): 23.6B **Privately Held**
WEB: www.baesystems.com
SIC: 3812 Search & navigation equipment
HQ: Bae Systems Information And Electronic Systems Integration Inc.
65 Spit Brook Rd
Nashua NH 03060
603 885-4321

(G-974)
BANKS PETROLEUM INC
Also Called: Banks Group, The
1601 Rio Grande St # 331 (78701-1137)
P.O. Box 12851 (78711-2851)
PHONE.................................512 478-0059
James E Bleckly, *President*
James E Bleckley, *President*
Joe Gonzalez, *Vice Pres*
Carissa Ries, *Vice Pres*
EMP: 20
SQ FT: 5,000
SALES (est): 5MM **Privately Held**
WEB: www.banksinfo.com
SIC: 1389 8748 7374 8731 Oil consultants; environmental consultant; data processing & preparation; environmental research; electronic research

(G-975)
BARTON SPRNGS E AQUIFER CNSRVT
1124 Regal Row (78748-3701)
PHONE.................................512 282-8441
Robert Larsen, *President*
Bill E Couch, *General Mgr*
Craig Smith, *Director*
EMP: 15
SQ FT: 3,321

SALES (est): 3.1MM **Privately Held**
WEB: www.bseacd.org
SIC: 3823 8734 Water quality monitoring
& control systems; product certification,
safety or performance

(G-976)
BARTON TABLE LLC
1626 Palma Plz Apt 6 (78703-3452)
PHONE..................................512 791-2260
EMP: 9 EST: 2014
SALES (est): 211.6K **Privately Held**
WEB: www.thebartontable.com
SIC: 5812 2099 Eating places; desserts,
ready-to-mix

(G-977)
BAXTER PLANNING SYSTEMS INC
7801 N Capital Of Texas H (78731-1193)
PHONE..................................512 323-5959
Greg Baxter, *President*
Rob Cunningham, *Vice Pres*
Phillip Kennedy, *Vice Pres*
Naresh RAO, *Vice Pres*
Tinka Saxena, *Vice Pres*
EMP: 44
SQ FT: 5,000
SALES (est): 5.7MM **Privately Held**
WEB: www.baxterplanning.com
SIC: 7371 7379 7374 7372 Computer
software systems analysis & design, cus-
tom; computer related consulting serv-
ices; data processing & preparation;
prepackaged software

(G-978)
BAXTER PLG SYSTEMS OPCO LLC
7801 N Capital Of Tx Ste (78731-1169)
PHONE..................................512 323-5959
Greg Baxter,
EMP: 60
SALES (est): 999.5K **Privately Held**
WEB: www.baxterplanning.com
SIC: 7372 Prepackaged software

(G-979)
BAY ADVANCED TECHNOLOGIES LLC
Also Called: Bay Advanced Tech 0054
8200 Cross Park Dr Ste 2a (78754-5227)
PHONE..................................512 929-5400
Matt Shea, *General Mgr*
Kensey Davidson, *Buyer*
Bob Rogers, *Accounts Mgr*
Roy Blankenship, *Branch Mgr*
EMP: 39
SALES (corp-wide): 3.2B **Publicly Held**
WEB: www.bayat.com
SIC: 5084 3494 Pneumatic tools & equip-
ment; valves & pipe fittings
HQ: Bay Advanced Technologies, Llc
8100 Central Ave
Newark CA 94560
510 857-0900

(G-980)
BAZAARVOICE INC (HQ)
10901 Stonelake Blvd (78759-5749)
PHONE..................................512 551-6000
Keith Nealon, *CEO*
Gene Austin, *President*
Julie Laplante, *Partner*
Michael Paulson, *Exec VP*
Kelly Trammell, *Exec VP*
▲ EMP: 141
SQ FT: 137,615
SALES (est): 157.7MM
SALES (corp-wide): 140.8MM **Privately Held**
WEB: www.bazaarvoice.com
SIC: 7372 Business oriented computer
software; application computer software
PA: Bv Parent, Llc
10901 Stonelake Blvd
Austin TX 78759
512 551-6000

(G-981)
BBS TELECOM LC
2499 S Cpitl Of Texas Hwy (78746-7762)
PHONE..................................512 328-9500
Fax: 512 328-9600
EMP: 9

SQ FT: 5,000
SALES: 1.5MM **Privately Held**
SIC: 3661 8748 5065 Mfg
Telephone/Telegraph Apparatus Business
Consulting Services Whol Electronic
Parts/Equipment

(G-982)
BC WIND-DOWN INC
Also Called: Briggo
11000 N Mopac Expy # 150 (78759-5428)
PHONE..................................512 799-2075
Kevin Nater, *CEO*
Scott Snyder, *Vice Pres*
Melisa Blahnik, *Engineer*
Jonathan Benjamin, *VP Business*
EMP: 13
SALES (est): 2.3MM **Privately Held**
WEB: www.briggo.com
SIC: 3549 Assembly machines, including
robotic

(G-983)
BEARDED BROTHERS LLC
1321 Rutherford Ln # 170 (78753-6720)
PHONE..................................940 367-8256
Caleb Simpson, *Principal*
Nick Meyer, *Vice Pres*
EMP: 10 EST: 2016
SALES (est): 1.4MM **Privately Held**
WEB: www.beardedbros.com
SIC: 2064 Granola & muesli, bars & clus-
ters

(G-984)
BEE DELIGHTFUL LLC
2105 W 10th St (78703-3840)
PHONE..................................253 722-3018
Skyler Johnston, *Mng Member*
EMP: 25
SQ FT: 2,000
SALES (est): 700K **Privately Held**
WEB: www.beedelightful.com
SIC: 2099 Honey, strained & bottled

(G-985)
BEEHIVE SPECIALTY CO
9101 Wall St Ste 1080 (78754-4554)
PHONE..................................512 912-7940
EMP: 15 EST: 1998
SALES (est): 4.1MM **Privately Held**
WEB: www.beehivespecialty.com
SIC: 7311 3993 7319 Advertising consult-
ant; signs & advertising specialties; ad-
vertising novelties; distribution of
advertising material or sample services

(G-986)
BEETNIK FOODS LLC
2407 S Congress Ave E212 (78704-5506)
PHONE..................................512 584-8228
David Perkins, *CEO*
Rhonda Millan, *Controller*
Nikki Magee, *Finance Dir*
Michael Perkins, *Sales Mgr*
Meaghan Perkins, *Director*
EMP: 10
SALES (est): 900K **Privately Held**
WEB: www.beetnikfoods.com
SIC: 2038 Frozen specialties

(G-987)
BELL TEXTRON INC
9801 Metric Blvd Bldg 10 (78758-5508)
PHONE..................................817 280-2011
Alan Adamson, *Associate*
EMP: 131
SALES (corp-wide): 13.6B **Publicly Held**
WEB: www.bellflight.com
SIC: 3728 Aircraft parts & equipment; air-
craft body assemblies & parts
HQ: Bell Textron Inc.
3255 Bell Flight Blvd
Fort Worth TX 76118
817 280-2011

(G-988)
BELLAGIO MENSWEAR LLC
Also Called: Gatsby Mens Ware
12701 Hill Country Blvd (78738-6357)
PHONE..................................512 496-8322
Larry Claybough, *Mng Member*
EMP: 9
SALES (est): 1.6MM **Privately Held**
SIC: 2325 Men's & boys' trousers & slacks

(G-989)
BELLS ADVERTISING INC (HQ)
Also Called: Bells Collegiate Products
109 Denson Dr Ste D (78752-4153)
PHONE..................................512 454-9663
Terrence R Wilt, *CEO*
Randolph R Wilt, *President*
Marvin R Wilt, *Chairman*
EMP: 12
SQ FT: 3,000
SALES (est): 5.6MM **Privately Held**
WEB: www.bells.com
SIC: 5199 2759 Advertising specialties;
commercial printing

(G-990)
BIGCOMMERCE INC (HQ)
11305 Four Points Dr I (78726-2204)
PHONE..................................512 865-4500
Brent Bellm, *Ch of Bd*
Kasey Durbin, *Partner*
Nicole Forbes, *Partner*
Nell Kennedy, *Partner*
Derek Rosenzweig, *Partner*
EMP: 165 EST: 2009
SALES (est): 61MM
SALES (corp-wide): 112.1MM **Publicly Held**
WEB: www.bigcommerce.com
SIC: 7372 Business oriented computer
software
PA: Bigcommerce Holdings, Inc.
11305 Four Points Dr I
Austin TX 78726
512 865-4500

(G-991)
BIRCH GROVE SOFTWARE INC
Also Called: Activtrak
1301 S Mo Pac Expy Ste LI (78746-6916)
PHONE..................................888 907-0301
EMP: 60 EST: 1995
SQ FT: 3,800
SALES (est): 275K **Privately Held**
WEB: www.activtrak.com
SIC: 7372 7371 Prepackaged software;
custom computer programming services

(G-992)
BISI INC
Also Called: Speedway Copying & Printing
8708 S Congress Ave A180 (78745-7379)
PHONE..................................512 478-3334
Samuel Odunsi, *President*
EMP: 9
SALES (est): 1.2MM **Privately Held**
WEB: www.speedwayyearbooks.com
SIC: 2759 5192 Commercial printing;
books

(G-993)
BIZNESS APPS INC
401 Congress Ave Ste 2650 (78701-3708)
PHONE..................................415 655-9496
Nick Misewicz, *Partner*
Andrew Gazdecki, *Principal*
Stephen Heisserer, *Vice Pres*
Sam Schnaible, *Vice Pres*
Brian Cross, *CFO*
EMP: 17
SALES (est): 1.3MM **Privately Held**
WEB: www.biznessapps.com
SIC: 7372 Prepackaged software

(G-994)
BLACK SAND TECHNOLOGIES INC
9600 N Mopac Expy Ste 900 (78759-6555)
PHONE..................................512 329-9400
John Diehl, *CEO*
David Pietruszynski, *President*
EMP: 17
SALES (est): 2.4MM
SALES (corp-wide): 23.5B **Publicly Held**
SIC: 3674 Semiconductors & related de-
vices
PA: Qualcomm Incorporated
5775 Morehouse Dr
San Diego CA 92121
858 587-1121

(G-995)
BLACKBAUD INC
11501 Domain Dr Ste 200 (78758-3599)
PHONE..................................512 652-7969
Caroline Hall, *Counsel*

Kevin Mooney, *Exec VP*
Jared Harbour, *Engineer*
Nelson Judan, *Engineer*
Dale Leonard, *Engineer*
EMP: 12
SALES (corp-wide): 900.4MM **Publicly Held**
WEB: www.blackbaud.com
SIC: 7372 8748 Prepackaged software;
business consulting
PA: Blackbaud, Inc.
65 Fairchild St
Daniel Island SC 29492
843 216-6200

(G-996)
BLOOMFIRE INC
1717 W 6th St Ste 100 (78703-4776)
PHONE..................................512 485-0910
Bob Zukis, *CEO*
David Mc Cann, *Principal*
William R Paape, *Principal*
Kyle Rutter, *Sales Dir*
Nish Sheth, *Sales Dir*
EMP: 39
SALES (est): 7.5MM **Privately Held**
WEB: www.bloomfire.com
SIC: 7372 Business oriented computer
software

(G-997)
BLUE GOJI LLC
4201 S Congress Ave # 32 (78745-1198)
PHONE..................................512 270-4747
Coleman Fung, *CEO*
Franklin Huang, *COO*
Kyra Constam, *Marketing Staff*
Luyi Huang, *Analyst*
EMP: 25 EST: 2010
SALES (est): 6MM **Privately Held**
WEB: www.bluegoji.com
SIC: 3944 Electronic games & toys

(G-998)
BLUE MOON SOFTWARE
500 W 16th St Ste 100 (78701-1536)
P.O. Box 684926 (78768-4926)
PHONE..................................512 322-0460
Javier Gonzalez, *Principal*
Tim Rogers, *COO*
Eric Clark, *Exec VP*
Michael Esposito, *Vice Pres*
Ankit Anchlia, *Sr Software Eng*
EMP: 10
SALES (est): 1.9MM **Privately Held**
WEB: www.bluemoonforms.com
SIC: 7372 Prepackaged software

(G-999)
BMC SOFTWARE INC
10431 Morado Cir Ste 1 (78759-6247)
PHONE..................................512 343-1961
Cory Bleuer, *Senior VP*
John McKenny, *Senior VP*
Jason Andrew, *Vice Pres*
John Barnard, *Vice Pres*
Hannah Cho, *Vice Pres*
EMP: 32
SALES (corp-wide): 1.4B **Privately Held**
WEB: www.bmc.com
SIC: 7372 7371 Utility computer software;
custom computer programming services
PA: Bmc Software, Inc.
2103 Citywest Blvd # 2100
Houston TX 77042
713 918-8800

(G-1000)
BOARDWALK TECHNOLOGY LLC
Also Called: Ewm Enterprises
11100 Metric Blvd 200c (78758-4000)
PHONE..................................512 258-2303
EMP: 33 EST: 2016
SQ FT: 10,000
SALES (est): 7MM **Privately Held**
WEB: www.ewme.com
SIC: 3672 Printed circuit boards

(G-1001)
BORDER STATES INDUSTRIES INC
Nunn Elc Sup A Div Brder Sttes
622 Morrow St (78752-1336)
PHONE..................................512 458-6313
Phil Settles, *Manager*

EMP: 15
SQ FT: 23,754
SALES (corp-wide): 2.4B **Privately Held**
WEB: www.borderstates.com
SIC: 5063 5065 5074 1711 Electrical supplies; electronic parts & equipment; plumbing & hydronic heating supplies; plumbing, heating, air-conditioning contractors; plastics plumbing fixtures; vitreous plumbing fixtures
PA: Border States Industries, Inc.
    2400 38th St S
    Fargo ND 58104
    701 293-5834

(G-1002)
BORLAND SOFTWARE CORPORATION (DH)
8310 N Cpitl Of Texas Hwy (78731-1011)
PHONE....................512 340-2200
Erik E Prusch, *President*
Pragati Day, *Partner*
Chuck Maples, *Senior VP*
Peter J Morowski, *Senior VP*
Richard Novak, *Senior VP*
EMP: 27
SQ FT: 47,309
SALES (est): 40.3MM **Privately Held**
WEB: www.microfocus.com
SIC: 7372 Business oriented computer software
HQ: Micro Focus (Us), Inc.
    700 King Farm Blvd # 125
    Rockville MD 20850
    301 838-5000

(G-1003)
BOTTOM LINE FD PROCESSORS INC
Also Called: Michael Angelo's Gourmet Foods
200 Michael Angelo Way (78728-1200)
PHONE....................512 218-3500
Michael Angelo Renna, *Ch of Bd*
Anthony Renna, *Vice Pres*
Elsie Mejias, *Production*
Lori C Ewell, *Research*
Joe Keip, *VP Sales*
▲ **EMP:** 30
SQ FT: 133,000
SALES (est): 140.6MM
SALES (corp-wide): 2.7MM **Privately Held**
WEB: www.michaelangelos.com
SIC: 2038 Dinners, frozen & packaged; lunches, frozen & packaged
HQ: Sovos Brands Intermediate, Inc.
    75 State St
    Boston MA 02109
    617 951-9400

(G-1004)
BPL PLASMA INC (PA)
2801 Via Fortuna Ste 400 (78746-7909)
PHONE....................512 582-7525
Rob Jardeleza, *President*
Wayne Sharp, *COO*
Katherine Pacpaco, *Opers Dir*
Nicole Slowman, *Opers Mgr*
Julia Owens, *Opers Staff*
EMP: 195
SALES (est): 1B **Privately Held**
WEB: www.bplplasma.com
SIC: 2836 8099 Plasmas; plasmapherous center

(G-1005)
BRANDT PRECISION MACHINING
11116 N Lamar Blvd Unit D (78753-3047)
PHONE....................512 339-7251
Duane Brandt, *Owner*
Stephanie Thompson, *Office Mgr*
Elsie Merritt, *Manager*
EMP: 10
SQ FT: 4,000
SALES (est): 1.3MM **Privately Held**
WEB: www.brandtprecision.com
SIC: 3469 3599 7699 Machine parts, stamped or pressed metal; machine shop, jobbing & repair; industrial machinery & equipment repair

(G-1006)
BRAZOS FOREST PRODUCTS LP
600 Industrial Blvd (78745-1299)
PHONE....................512 443-0777
Johnny Joyner, *Sales Staff*
Jose Mosqueda, *Sales Staff*
Shane Robinson, *Branch Mgr*
EMP: 30
SALES (corp-wide): 263MM **Privately Held**
WEB: www.brazosfp.com
SIC: 5031 2426 Lumber: rough, dressed & finished; lumber, hardwood dimension
HQ: Forest Brazos Products L P
    2760 N Great Sw Pkwy
    Grand Prairie TX 75050

(G-1007)
BRIGHAM MINERALS INC
5914 W Courtyard Dr # 100 (78730-4918)
PHONE....................512 220-6350
Robert M Roosa, *CEO*
Ben M Brigham, *Ch of Bd*
Geoff Boyd, *Vice Pres*
S Bradley Burris, *Vice Pres*
Hamilton W Hogsett, *Vice Pres*
EMP: 30
SALES: 101.5MM **Privately Held**
WEB: www.brighamminerals.net
SIC: 1311 Crude petroleum & natural gas

(G-1008)
BRIGHT INITIATIVES LLC
11308 Pickard Ln (78748-3444)
PHONE....................512 466-4734
Quinn E Holub, *Principal*
EMP: 13 **EST:** 2010
SALES (est): 855.2K **Privately Held**
SIC: 4953 7699 2079 Refuse collection & disposal services; recycling, waste materials; cleaning services; edible fats & oils

(G-1009)
BRIGHT MACHINES INC
12455 Res Blvd D Dock (78759)
PHONE....................512 750-5266
EMP: 355
SALES (corp-wide): 76MM **Privately Held**
SIC: 3549 Mfg Metalworking Machinery
PA: Bright Machines, Inc.
    585 Howard St Fl 1
    San Francisco CA 94105
    415 867-4402

(G-1010)
BRIGHTLEAF GROUP INC
7000 N Mo Pac Expy Ste 20 (78731-3027)
PHONE....................512 795-8900
Jane Scott, *President*
Cathi Biagi, *Project Mgr*
EMP: 16
SALES (est): 1MM **Privately Held**
WEB: www.brightleafgroup.com
SIC: 2741 2731 Technical manuals: publishing only, not printed on site; book publishing

(G-1011)
BROADLEAF COMMERCE LLC
807 Brazos St Ste 401 (78701-2774)
PHONE....................800 282-7443
Kelly Tisdell, *Branch Mgr*
EMP: 10
SALES (corp-wide): 5MM **Privately Held**
WEB: www.broadleafcommerce.com
SIC: 7372 Application computer software
PA: Broadleaf Commerce, Llc
    5550 Granite Pkwy Ste 155
    Plano TX 75024
    800 282-7443

(G-1012)
BROOKS INDUSTRIAL COATINGS INC
1902 Bench Mark Dr (78728-7621)
P.O. Box 2365, Round Rock (78680-2365)
PHONE....................512 990-5333
Connie Brooks, *President*
Bob Munzer, *Manager*
EMP: 14
SQ FT: 16,000

SALES (est): 1.1MM **Privately Held**
WEB: www.bic-texas.com
SIC: 3471 3569 2759 2396 Finishing, metals or formed products; assembly machines, non-metalworking; screen printing; automotive & apparel trimmings

(G-1013)
BSU INC
1611 Hdway Cir Bldg 1ste (78754)
PHONE....................607 272-8100
Catalina Chamseddine, *CEO*
Ahmad Chamseddine, *COO*
Sean Plumlee, *Controller*
Dorothy Slocum, *Controller*
Dottie Highfield, *Human Res Mgr*
EMP: 29
SQ FT: 17,000
SALES (est): 3.5MM **Privately Held**
WEB: www.bsuinc.com
SIC: 3672 5065 8711 Printed circuit boards; electronic parts & equipment; engineering services

(G-1014)
BUCKEYE INTERNATIONAL INC
720 Bastrop Hwy S (78741-3647)
PHONE....................512 870-8555
Mike Harrison, *Branch Mgr*
Victor Gutierrez, *Branch Mgr*
EMP: 16
SALES (corp-wide): 158.4MM **Privately Held**
WEB: www.buckeyeinternational.com
SIC: 2842 Specialty cleaning preparations
PA: Buckeye International, Inc.
    2700 Wagner Pl
    Maryland Heights MO 63043
    314 291-1900

(G-1015)
BUILD A SIGN LLC (DH)
Also Called: Buildasign.com
11525 Stonehollow Dr A100 (78758-3269)
PHONE....................512 374-9850
Bryan Kranik, *CEO*
Kirk Bergeron, *Business Mgr*
Matt Cathey, *Opers Mgr*
Steven Spriggs, *Opers Mgr*
Jason Walker, *Finance Dir*
▼ **EMP:** 188
SQ FT: 15,000
SALES (est): 43.7MM **Privately Held**
WEB: www.buildasign.com
SIC: 3993 2621 Signs & advertising specialties; wallpaper (hanging paper)
HQ: Cimpress Usa Incorporated
    275 Wyman St Ste 100
    Waltham MA 02451
    866 614-8002

(G-1016)
BUILD A SIGN LLC
Carwrap.com
11550 Stonehollow Dr # 140 (78758-3103)
PHONE....................512 339-4447
Daniel J Lowe, *VP Sales*
Darren Nelson, *Cust Mgr*
Emily Lew, *Marketing Staff*
Hailee Marcinek, *Marketing Staff*
Jami Moubry, *Software Engr*
EMP: 13 **Privately Held**
WEB: www.buildasign.com
SIC: 3993 Signs & advertising specialties
HQ: Build A Sign Llc
    11525 Stonehollow Dr A100
    Austin TX 78758

(G-1017)
BVSN LLC (DH)
401 Congress Ave Ste 2650 (78701-3708)
PHONE....................512 524-6149
Scott Brighton, *CEO*
EMP: 59
SALES (est): 5MM **Privately Held**
WEB: www.broadvision.com
SIC: 7372 Prepackaged software

(G-1018)
C&D BOBCAT AND BACKHOE LLC
15121 Spillman Ranch Loop (78738-6580)
PHONE....................512 358-0163
Tiffany Alaniz, *Mng Member*
David Rumgay,
EMP: 10

SALES (est): 2.4MM **Privately Held**
SIC: 1381 7389 Drilling oil & gas wells;

(G-1019)
CADENCE DESIGN SYSTEMS INC
12515 Res Blvd Ste 7-250 (78759)
PHONE....................512 349-1100
Sam Chitwood, *Engineer*
Roger Giles, *Engineer*
Craig Hamilton, *Engineer*
Keyuan Huang, *Engineer*
Zhiyu Zeng, *Engineer*
EMP: 75
SALES (corp-wide): 2.3B **Publicly Held**
WEB: www.cadence.com
SIC: 7372 Application computer software
PA: Cadence Design Systems, Inc.
    2655 Seely Ave Bldg 5
    San Jose CA 95134
    408 943-1234

(G-1020)
CALXEDA INC
7000 N Mo Pac Expy # 250 (78731-3073)
PHONE....................512 582-5100
Barry Evans, *President*
Gopal Hegde, *COO*
David Borland, *Vice Pres*
Larry Wikelius, *Vice Pres*
Tim Semones, *CFO*
EMP: 100
SALES (est): 13.1MM **Privately Held**
WEB: www.calxeda.com
SIC: 3674 Integrated circuits, semiconductor networks, etc.

(G-1021)
CALYTERA US INC
804 Las Cimas Pkwy # 100 (78746-5150)
PHONE....................512 623-9786
Zeynep Young, *CEO*
Pete Freeland, *President*
Christian Foster, *Vice Pres*
Brian Thomson, *CFO*
EMP: 62
SALES (est): 2.8MM
SALES (corp-wide): 63.9MM **Privately Held**
WEB: www.calytera.com
SIC: 7372 5045 Application computer software; computers, peripherals & software
PA: Granicus, Inc.
    1999 Broadway Ste 3600
    Denver CO 80202
    415 357-3618

(G-1022)
CANDEN RESOURCES LTD
101 6th Avenue Sw (73301-0001)
PHONE....................403 473-8786
Temple Tobins, *CEO*
EMP: 25
SALES (est): 448.8K **Privately Held**
SIC: 1389 Oil & gas field services

(G-1023)
CANNON ENGINEERING INC
Also Called: Drive Shafts By Cannon
1611 Linscomb Ave (78704-1438)
PHONE....................818 508-0123
EMP: 10 **EST:** 1945
SQ FT: 10,000
SALES: 1MM **Privately Held**
SIC: 3714 7538 Mfg Motor Vehicle Parts/Accessories General Auto Repair

(G-1024)
CANON NANOTECHNOLOGIES INC
1807 W Braker Ln Bldg C30 (78758-3607)
P.O. Box 81485 (78708-1485)
PHONE....................512 339-7760
C Mark Melliar Smith, *President*
David Gino, *COO*
Doug Resnick, *Vice Pres*
Anshuman Cherala, *Research*
Laurie Hahn, *Human Res Mgr*
▲ **EMP:** 80
SQ FT: 38,000
SALES (est): 27.6MM **Privately Held**
WEB: www.cnt.canon.com
SIC: 3559 3674 Semiconductor manufacturing machinery; semiconductors & related devices

PA: Canon Inc.
3-30-2, Shimomaruko
Ota-Ku TKY 146-0

(G-1025)
CAPITAL ASSET EXCH & TRDG LLC (PA)
Also Called: Cae Online
401 Congress Ave (78701-4071)
PHONE..................................650 326-3313
Ryan Jacob, *CEO*
Jeffrey Robbins, *President*
Brett Pearson, *Chief*
Jim O'Reilly, *Sales Staff*
EMP: 13
SALES (est): 15.4MM **Privately Held**
WEB: www.caeonline.com
SIC: 6282 3559 Investment advice; semiconductor manufacturing machinery

(G-1026)
CAPITAL CITY APPLIANCE LLC
2209b Rutland Dr 100 (78758-5233)
PHONE..................................512 491-7600
Jeff Jenkins, *Managing Prtnr*
Gabriel Sutton,
Michael Walker,
EMP: 15
SALES (est): 11.1MM **Privately Held**
SIC: 3678 Electronic connectors

(G-1027)
CAPITAL PRINTING LLC
4001 Caven Rd (78744-1194)
P.O. Box 17548 (78760-7548)
PHONE..................................512 442-1415
Sib Deliberato, *Vice Pres*
Billy Seidel, *Vice Pres*
Kristi Breland, *Production*
Kay Bristow, *Production*
Eric Griffis, *Production*
EMP: 75
SQ FT: 32,500
SALES (est): 14.8MM
SALES (corp-wide): 17MM **Privately Held**
WEB: www.capitalprintingco.com
SIC: 2752 2789 2732 Commercial printing, offset; bookbinding & related work; books: printing & binding
PA: Slate Group
6024 45th St
Lubbock TX 79407
806 794-7752

(G-1028)
CARDINAL SOFTWARE INC (DH)
6850 Austin Center Blvd (78731-3201)
PHONE..................................512 275-0072
Jace Day, *CEO*
Angela Moore, *CFO*
EMP: 10
SQ FT: 12,000
SALES (est): 71.7K
SALES (corp-wide): 93.1MM **Privately Held**
WEB: www.cardinal400.com
SIC: 7372 Utility computer software
HQ: Its, Inc.
6700 Pioneer Pkwy
Johnston IA 50131
515 288-2828

(G-1029)
CARGO SYSTEMS INC
2120 Denton Dr Ste 108 (78758-4554)
P.O. Box 81098 (78708-1098)
PHONE..................................512 837-1300
Harold Mc Elfish, *President*
Jim Dennis, *Technical Staff*
▲ EMP: 10
SQ FT: 5,500
SALES (est): 1.6MM **Privately Held**
WEB: www.cargosystems.com
SIC: 2298 Cargo nets

(G-1030)
CARROLL SYSTEMS LP
4603 Commercial Park Dr (78724-2632)
PHONE..................................512 927-1200
EMP: 35
SQ FT: 8,316

SALES (est): 6MM **Privately Held**
WEB: www.carrollsystems.com
SIC: 3429 1731 Security cable locking system; voice, data & video wiring contractor
PA: Britt Rice Construction Company, Lp
3002 Longmire Dr Ste D
College Station TX 77845

(G-1031)
CASSAVA SCIENCES INC
7801 N Cpitl Of Txas Hwy (78731-1169)
PHONE..................................512 501-2444
Remi Barbier, *Ch of Bd*
George Thornton, *Vice Pres*
Ruth Araya, *Opers Staff*
Lindsay Burns, *Research*
Eric Schoen, *CFO*
EMP: 9
SQ FT: 6,000
SALES (est): 1.6MM **Privately Held**
WEB: www.paintrials.com
SIC: 2834 Pharmaceutical preparations

(G-1032)
CBG CORPORATION
2601 Mchale Ct Ste 45 (78758-4461)
PHONE..................................512 491-7541
Paul L Sinclair, *President*
EMP: 21
SALES (est): 1MM **Privately Held**
WEB: www.cbgcorp.com
SIC: 1389 Oil field services

(G-1033)
CBG CORPORATION
Also Called: C B G
4616 W Howard Ln Ste 900 (78728-6300)
PHONE..................................512 491-7541
Chris Schnoor, *CEO*
Paul Sinclair, *President*
James F Harber, *Vice Pres*
Douglas G Wilson, *Vice Pres*
EMP: 23
SQ FT: 1,250
SALES (est): 3.8MM **Privately Held**
WEB: www.cbgcorp.com
SIC: 3674 Semiconductors & related devices

(G-1034)
CD3 INC
15505 Long Vista Dr Ste 2 (78728-3831)
PHONE..................................512 252-2592
William Moore, *President*
Gene Whitehead, *President*
Tod A Barrett, *Chairman*
Ronald E Hunt, *Senior VP*
V Eugene Whitehead, *Vice Pres*
▲ EMP: 20
SQ FT: 20,000
SALES (est): 50.1K **Privately Held**
WEB: www.cd3.com
SIC: 3572 Computer storage devices

(G-1035)
CE SOIR LINGERIE CO INC
Also Called: Fashion Forms
12317 Tech Blvd Ste 300 (78727)
PHONE..................................512 953-4500
Beverly Ann Deall, *President*
◆ EMP: 77
SQ FT: 90
SALES (est): 50MM **Privately Held**
SIC: 5632 2342 Lingerie (outerwear); bras, girdles & allied garments

(G-1036)
CEDRONE OBRIEN INC
Also Called: AlphaGraphics
2227 W Braker Ln (78758-4031)
PHONE..................................512 426-5200
William O'Brien Sr, *President*
Alfredo Cedrone, *Vice Pres*
EMP: 14
SQ FT: 2,400
SALES (est): 1.7MM **Privately Held**
WEB: www.agnortheast.com
SIC: 2752 7334 Commercial printing, lithographic; photocopying & duplicating services

(G-1037)
CENTAUR TECHNOLOGY INC
9111 Jollyville Rd # 206 (78759-7411)
PHONE..................................512 418-5700

G Glenn Henry, *President*
Nikhil Patil, *Engineer*
Taylor Jerry, *Director*
Chad Murrah, *Technician*
EMP: 85
SQ FT: 35,000
SALES (est): 9.1MM **Privately Held**
WEB: www.centtech.com
SIC: 8731 3674 7371 Computer (hardware) development; microprocessors; computer software systems analysis & design, custom
PA: Via Technologies, Inc.
8f, 535, Zhongzheng Rd.,
New Taipei City TAP 23148

(G-1038)
CENTEX MATERIALS LLC
16438 N Ih 35 (78728-1907)
PHONE..................................512 251-5106
Rodney McGowen,
EMP: 45
SALES (corp-wide): 1.4B **Publicly Held**
WEB: www.centexmaterials.com
SIC: 3273 1442 Ready-mixed concrete; construction sand mining
HQ: Centex Materials Llc
3019 Alvin Devane Blvd # 100
Austin TX 78741
512 460-3003

(G-1039)
CENTEX MATERIALS LLC
817 E Saint Elmo Rd (78745-1229)
PHONE..................................512 444-9591
Gary Johnson, *Manager*
EMP: 45
SQ FT: 4,648
SALES (corp-wide): 1.4B **Publicly Held**
WEB: www.centexmaterials.com
SIC: 3273 1442 Ready-mixed concrete; construction sand mining
HQ: Centex Materials Llc
3019 Alvin Devane Blvd # 100
Austin TX 78741
512 460-3003

(G-1040)
CENTEX MATERIALS LLC (HQ)
3019 Alvin Devane Blvd # 100 (78741-7419)
PHONE..................................512 460-3003
David Loftis, *President*
Jake Seay, *Vice Pres*
Beth Pieprzica, *VP Finance*
Carl Maynes, *Executive Asst*
Rodney E Cummickel,
▲ EMP: 16 EST: 1980
SALES (est): 25.2MM
SALES (corp-wide): 1.4B **Publicly Held**
WEB: www.centexmaterials.com
SIC: 3273 1442 Ready-mixed concrete; construction sand mining; gravel mining
PA: Eagle Materials Inc.
5960 Berkshire Ln Ste 900
Dallas TX 75225
214 432-2000

(G-1041)
CENTRAL TXAS MET ROOFG SUP INC (PA)
830 Sagebrush Dr (78758-4823)
PHONE..................................512 452-1515
Ben Garza III, *President*
Peter Jancik, *Vice Pres*
Richard Finney, *Opers Mgr*
Danelle Wilhite, *Med Doctor*
EMP: 10
SQ FT: 15,000
SALES (est): 11.9MM **Privately Held**
WEB: www.ctmrs.com
SIC: 3444 Metal roofing & roof drainage equipment

(G-1042)
CHAMELEON COLD BREW LLC
6205 Burnet Rd (78757-3227)
P.O. Box 841933, Dallas (75284-1933)
PHONE..................................512 323-0345
Matthew Swenson, *President*
Bradley W Crawford,
Steven J Williams,
EMP: 23
SQ FT: 1,600

SALES (est): 1.5MM
SALES (corp-wide): 93.5B **Privately Held**
WEB: www.chameleoncoldbrew.com
SIC: 2095 2087 Coffee extracts; concentrates, drink
HQ: Nestle Usa, Inc.
1812 N Moore St Ste 118
Rosslyn VA 22209
440 264-7249

(G-1043)
CHAMPION OILFIELD SERVICES LLC
401 Congress Ave Fl 33 (78701-3792)
PHONE..................................512 327-3300
Natin Paul, *Principal*
EMP: 50 EST: 2012
SALES (est): 1.3MM **Privately Held**
SIC: 1389 Oil field services

(G-1044)
CHARTA GROUP INC
Permalite
301 W Howard Ln Ste 300 (78753-9790)
PHONE..................................310 327-0244
Oliver Choron, *Partner*
Tony Sary, *Branch Mgr*
EMP: 50
SALES (corp-wide): 47.3MM **Privately Held**
WEB: www.permalite.com
SIC: 2671 Paper coated or laminated for packaging
PA: Charta Group, Inc.
301 W Howard Ln
Austin TX 78753
310 327-0244

(G-1045)
CHEM ELEVEN PRODUCTS INC
6300 Bridge Point Pkwy (78730-5073)
PHONE..................................512 278-8800
Stacy Barton, *President*
EMP: 50
SALES (est): 3.1MM **Privately Held**
SIC: 3999 Artificial flower arrangements

(G-1046)
CHEN GRNER STVENS PRTNERS LLC
Also Called: Eureka Water Probes
2113 Wlls Br Pkwy Ste 440 (78728)
PHONE..................................512 302-4333
Stuart Garner, *Managing Prtnr*
Doug Michalsky, *Engineer*
Colin Kirk, *Sales Staff*
EMP: 12
SALES (est): 10MM **Privately Held**
WEB: www.waterprobes.com
SIC: 3823 Water quality monitoring & control systems

(G-1047)
CHEROKEE WELDING INC (PA)
6312 Us Highway 183 S (78744-5424)
PHONE..................................512 243-0002
Ernesto Camacho, *Principal*
EMP: 18 EST: 2010
SALES (est): 1.8MM **Privately Held**
SIC: 7692 Welding repair

(G-1048)
CHIPHONG INC
Also Called: Advance Machining Tech.
8115 Altoga Dr (78724-2613)
PHONE..................................512 933-9292
Kevin Nguyen, *President*
Sarah Nguyen, *Admin Sec*
EMP: 30
SQ FT: 11,000
SALES (est): 2MM **Privately Held**
WEB: www.fabcor.net
SIC: 3679 Quartz crystals, for electronic application

(G-1049)
CHIRON HEALTH HOLDINGS LLC
2350 Wilson St (78704-5504)
PHONE..................................319 400-3772
Andrew O Hara, *CEO*
EMP: 18 EST: 2013

SALES (est): 387.5K
SALES (corp-wide): 4.6MM **Privately Held**
WEB: www.chironhealth.com
SIC: 7372 Business oriented computer software
PA: Ch Resolution, Inc.
　　3000 E Cesar Chavez St
　　Austin TX

(G-1050)
CIRRUS LOGIC INC (PA)
800 W 6th St (78701-2722)
PHONE............................512 851-4000
Jason P Rhode, *CEO*
Alan R Schuele, *Ch of Bd*
John Forsyth, *President*
Rosa Guerra, *Principal*
Lynn Mason, *Business Mgr*
▲ **EMP:** 261
SQ FT: 155,000
SALES: 1.2B **Publicly Held**
WEB: www.cirrus.com
SIC: 3674 Microcircuits, integrated (semiconductor)

(G-1051)
CISCO SYSTEMS INC
12515 Res Blvd Bldg 3 (78759)
PHONE............................512 378-1112
Kurt Sell, *Regional Mgr*
Mike Grammer, *Opers Mgr*
Naveen Burra, *Engineer*
Ed Danford, *Engineer*
Jeffrey George, *Engineer*
EMP: 600
SALES (corp-wide): 49.3B **Publicly Held**
WEB: www.cisco.com
SIC: 3577 8731 7372 Computer peripheral equipment; commercial physical research; prepackaged software
PA: Cisco Systems, Inc.
　　170 W Tasman Dr
　　San Jose CA 95134
　　408 526-4000

(G-1052)
CLEANPLANET CHEMICAL INC
6207 Fm 2244 Rd Ste 165 (78746-5078)
PHONE............................855 256-7568
Alexander Richert, *CEO*
Trent Staats, *President*
Rebecca Ruwaldt, *Business Mgr*
Rory Griffin, *Controller*
Joe Brassaw, *VP Sales*
EMP: 10
SQ FT: 500
SALES (est): 2.1MM **Privately Held**
WEB: www.cleanplanetchemical.com
SIC: 3559 Recycling machinery

(G-1053)
CML EXPLORATION LLC (PA)
Barton Oaks Plz 1 Ste 430 (78746)
PHONE............................512 328-8085
Kenneth Nelson, *General Mgr*
Casey Satterfield, *Opers Mgr*
Kenneth C Nelson, *Mng Member*
Cindy Cannon, *Manager*
Lee Staiger, *Manager*
EMP: 20
SQ FT: 7,000
SALES (est): 9.4MM **Privately Held**
WEB: www.cmlexploration.com
SIC: 1382 Oil & gas exploration services

(G-1054)
COBALT GROUP INC
7004 Bee Caves Rd Ste 100 (78746-5004)
PHONE............................206 269-6363
EMP: 30
SALES (corp-wide): 14.5B **Publicly Held**
WEB: www.cdkglobal.com
SIC: 7372 Business oriented computer software
HQ: The Cobalt Group Inc
　　605 5th Ave S Ste 800
　　Seattle WA 98104

(G-1055)
CODY BUILDERS SUPPLY INC
12002 N Lamar Blvd (78753-1801)
PHONE............................512 339-9834
Stacy Sass, *President*
Tracy Springer, *Project Mgr*
Koto Szombathy, *Prdtn Mgr*

▲ **EMP:** 50
SQ FT: 15,000
SALES (est): 17.6MM **Privately Held**
WEB: www.codybuilderssupply.com
SIC: 3441 Building components, structural steel

(G-1056)
COFFEE TRADERS INC
Also Called: Texas Coffee Traders
1400 E 4th St (78702-3808)
PHONE............................512 476-2279
Beth Beall, *President*
Alli Beall, *General Mgr*
R C Beall, *Vice Pres*
Ron Deyoung, *Opers Staff*
Brent Armstrong, *Purch Mgr*
EMP: 25
SQ FT: 14,000
SALES (est): 4.9MM **Privately Held**
WEB: www.texascoffeetraders.com
SIC: 2095 5499 Coffee roasting (except by wholesale grocers); coffee

(G-1057)
COLVIN PAINOVICH LP
Also Called: Republic Print & Mail
8905 Mccann Dr (78757-6932)
PHONE............................512 459-4139
Sam Painovich, *Partner*
Barrett Colvin, *Partner*
Corey Elrod, *Accounts Mgr*
EMP: 18
SQ FT: 7,700
SALES (est): 4.4MM **Privately Held**
WEB: www.republicprint.com
SIC: 5112 2752 Business forms; stationery; commercial printing, offset

(G-1058)
COMMAND MANUFACTURING LLC
8116 Ferguson Cut Off (78724-2611)
PHONE............................512 927-0033
Julie Headrick,
Michael Borg,
Doug Bournazian,
Robert Herrera,
EMP: 28
SQ FT: 8,300
SALES (est): 6.2MM **Privately Held**
WEB: www.command-mfg.com
SIC: 3469 Machine parts, stamped or pressed metal

(G-1059)
COMPASS ALPHA LLC
1701 Dirs Blvd Ste 110 (78744)
PHONE............................512 557-9138
Alexander Candelario, *Mng Member*
EMP: 25
SALES (est): 809.2K
SALES (corp-wide): 3.4MM **Privately Held**
WEB: www.compass.com
SIC: 2023 Dietary supplements, dairy & non-dairy based
PA: Practice Interactive, Inc.
　　1701 Dirs Blvd Ste 110
　　Austin TX 78744
　　844 413-2602

(G-1060)
CONDUSIV TECHNOLOGIES CORP (PA)
3600 Kellywood Dr (78739-4403)
PHONE............................818 252-5538
Craig Jensen, *CEO*
Brian Olson, *President*
Gary Quan, *Senior VP*
Nick Tidd, *Senior VP*
Frederic T Boyer, *CFO*
EMP: 20
SQ FT: 72,000
SALES (est): 7MM **Privately Held**
WEB: www.condusiv.com
SIC: 7372 Prepackaged software

(G-1061)
CONFERENCE TECHNOLOGIES INC
11525 Stonehollow Dr (78758-3352)
PHONE............................512 584-8275
EMP: 110 **Privately Held**
WEB: www.conferencetech.com

SIC: 3651 7359 Household audio & video equipment; audio-visual equipment & supply rental
PA: Conference Technologies, Inc.
　　11653 Adie Rd
　　Maryland Heights MO 63043

(G-1062)
CONTINNTAL CON MXER SLTONS LLC
105 Riley Rd (78746-5715)
PHONE............................859 234-1100
EMP: 25
SALES (corp-wide): 9.4MM **Privately Held**
WEB: www.continentalmixers.com
SIC: 3273 Ready-mixed concrete
PA: Continental Concrete Mixer Solutions Llc
　　200 Ladish Rd
　　Cynthiana KY 41031
　　859 234-1100

(G-1063)
CONTROL PANELS USA INC
16310 Bratton Ln Ste 100 (78728-2405)
PHONE............................512 852-8280
Martin Salyer, *President*
David Morgan, *Vice Pres*
Brain Wetherholt, *Vice Pres*
Fernando Arvizo, *Project Mgr*
William Burdick, *Project Mgr*
▲ **EMP:** 45
SQ FT: 7,500
SALES (est): 13.1MM **Privately Held**
WEB: www.controlpanelsusa.net
SIC: 3613 Control panels, electric

(G-1064)
CONVIO INC (HQ)
11501 Domain Dr Ste 200 (78758-3599)
PHONE............................512 652-2600
Gene Austin, *Ch of Bd*
Beth Goldstein, *Principal*
Shirley Sexton, *Principal*
Richard Sokolov, *Vice Chairman*
Gary Allison, *Vice Pres*
EMP: 200
SALES (est): 31.9MM
SALES (corp-wide): 900.4MM **Publicly Held**
WEB: www.convio.com
SIC: 7372 Prepackaged software
PA: Blackbaud, Inc.
　　65 Fairchild St
　　Daniel Island SC 29492
　　843 216-6200

(G-1065)
COOPER CONSULTING COMPANY
1705 Crossing Pl Apt 101a (78741-3229)
P.O. Box 81651 (78708-1651)
PHONE............................512 527-1000
Melynda Caudle, *President*
Robin Schwab, *General Mgr*
Kellye Prosise, *COO*
Constantin Radu, *Vice Pres*
Melissa Caudle, *Finance Dir*
EMP: 21
SQ FT: 3,100
SALES (est): 4MM **Privately Held**
WEB: www.cooperconsulting.com
SIC: 7373 7372 7371 3661 Systems software development services; prepackaged software; custom computer programming services; telephone sets, all types except cellular radio

(G-1066)
CORETRAC INC
6101 W Courtyard Dr 2-100 (78730-5030)
PHONE............................512 236-9120
Dan Martin, *President*
Patrick McClain, *CFO*
EMP: 20
SQ FT: 6,000
SALES (est): 2MM
SALES (corp-wide): 356.1MM **Privately Held**
WEB: www.avolin.com
SIC: 7372 Business oriented computer software

PA: Aptean, Inc.
　　4325 Alexander Dr Ste 100
　　Alpharetta GA 30022
　　770 351-9600

(G-1067)
CORONA LABS INC
Also Called: Ansca Mobile
720 Brazos St Ste 1100 (78701-2516)
PHONE............................312 953-7586
Roj Niyogi, *CEO*
EMP: 15
SALES (est): 1.3MM **Privately Held**
WEB: www.coronalabs.com
SIC: 5999 7372 Mobile telephones & equipment; prepackaged software

(G-1068)
COSTELLO DOAB ENTERPRISES LLC
Also Called: Crushing Tigers
411 W Saint Elmo Rd # 22 (78745-3374)
P.O. Box 41405 (78704-0024)
PHONE............................512 364-1708
EMP: 11 **EST:** 2015
SALES (est): 305.3K **Privately Held**
WEB: www.crushingtigers.com
SIC: 1442 Construction sand & gravel

(G-1069)
COX TEXAS NEWSPAPERS LP
305 S Congress Ave (78704-1200)
P.O. Box 670 (78767-0670)
PHONE............................512 445-3500
Michael Vivio, *Principal*
EMP: 99 **Privately Held**
WEB: www.statesman.com
SIC: 2711 Newspapers, publishing & printing
HQ: Cox Texas Newspapers, Lp
　　305 S Congress Ave
　　Austin TX 78704
　　512 445-3500

(G-1070)
COX TEXAS NEWSPAPERS LP (DH)
305 S Congress Ave (78704-1200)
P.O. Box 670 (78767-0670)
PHONE............................512 445-3500
Jane Williams, *Publisher*
Susie Ellwood, *Principal*
Kristin Finan, *Editor*
Eddie Burns, *Vice Pres*
Patrick Dorsey, *Vice Pres*
▲ **EMP:** 60
SQ FT: 10,000
SALES (est): 227.5MM **Privately Held**
WEB: www.statesman.com
SIC: 2711 Newspapers, publishing & printing

(G-1071)
CRAY INC
6011 W Courtyard Dr # 200 (78730-5113)
PHONE............................512 651-7020
Dave Bass, *Senior VP*
Chris McBride, *Engineer*
Mike Lance, *Manager*
Joe Sekel, *Director*
EMP: 50
SALES (corp-wide): 26.9B **Publicly Held**
WEB: www.cray.com
SIC: 3571 Electronic computers
HQ: Cray Inc.
　　901 5th Ave Ste 1000
　　Seattle WA 98164
　　206 701-2000

(G-1072)
CREATIVE COMPUTING WEST INC
Also Called: CC West
3636 Dime Cir Ste 301 (78744-2332)
P.O. Box 19047 (78760-9047)
PHONE............................512 804-2299
Donna Couch, *President*
Rex Couch, *Vice Pres*
James Diorio, *Vice Pres*
Sara Momberg, *Prdtn Mgr*
Jeff Thurman, *Sales Mgr*
EMP: 17
SQ FT: 5,000

SALES (est): 3.3MM **Privately Held**
WEB: www.ccwestprinting.com
SIC: 2752 Commercial printing, offset

(G-1073)
CRITERIA LABS INC (PA)
706 Brentwood St (78752-4042)
PHONE..................................512 637-4500
Doug Myron, *CEO*
Kevin Hammel, *General Mgr*
Melissa Clearwater, *Purchasing*
Tracy Fuller, *CFO*
Nate Woodard, *Finance Dir*
EMP: 50
SQ FT: 80,000
SALES (est): 9.6MM **Privately Held**
WEB: www.criterialabs.com
SIC: 3674 8711 Semiconductors & related
devices; engineering services

(G-1074)
**CROSSROADS SYSTEMS
(TEXAS)**
11000 N Mopac Expy # 100 (78759-5428)
PHONE..................................512 349-0300
EMP: 127
SALES (est): 1.8MM
SALES (corp-wide): 674K **Publicly Held**
SIC: 3577 5045 Mfg Computer Peripheral
Equipment Whol Computers/Peripherals
PA: Crossroads Systems, Inc.
11000 N Mopac Expy # 100
Austin TX 75225
512 349-0300

(G-1075)
**CRUSADER ENERGY GROUP
LLC**
807 Las Cimas Pkwy # 350 (78746-6193)
PHONE..................................512 328-2953
Roy Fletcher, *Vice Pres*
Charles Paulson, *Vice Pres*
David Le Norman, *Mng Member*
EMP: 35
SALES (est): 2.6MM
SALES (corp-wide): 236.3MM **Publicly
Held**
WEB: www.jonesenergy.com
SIC: 1382 Oil & gas exploration services
HQ: Jones Energy Holdings, Llc
14301 Caliber Dr Ste 110
Oklahoma City OK 73134
512 328-2953

(G-1076)
CSG SYSTEMS INC
15404 Long Vista Dr (78728-3814)
PHONE..................................512 949-2200
EMP: 100 **Publicly Held**
WEB: www.csgi.com
SIC: 2752 Commercial printing, litho-
graphic
HQ: Csg Systems, Inc.
18020 Burt St
Elkhorn NE 68022

(G-1077)
**CUMMINS SOUTHERN PLAINS
LLC**
1700 Smith Rd (78721-3543)
PHONE..................................512 389-2276
Daniel Holbrook, *Manager*
EMP: 43
SALES (corp-wide): 19.8B **Publicly Held**
WEB: www.cummins.com
SIC: 5084 3519 Engines & parts, diesel;
internal combustion engines
HQ: Cummins Southern Plains Llc
600 N Watson Rd
Arlington TX 76011
817 640-6801

(G-1078)
CURSE OF GOOD TASTE INC
Also Called: Authentic Presence
3016 Guadalupe St Ste 200 (78705-2863)
P.O. Box 160365 (78716-0365)
PHONE..................................512 327-9660
Joan Griffith, *President*
EMP: 12
SALES (est): 900K **Privately Held**
WEB: www.wildwoodbakehouse.com
SIC: 2273 5461 Rugs, hand & machine
made; bakeries

(G-1079)
CUSTOM CRETE INC
4433 Terry O Ln (78745-2039)
PHONE..................................512 443-5787
Bill Heath, *Branch Mgr*
EMP: 30
SQ FT: 1,976
SALES (corp-wide): 1.4B **Publicly Held**
WEB: www.custom-crete.com
SIC: 5032 3273 Building stone; ready-
mixed concrete
HQ: Custom Crete, Inc.
2624 Joe Field Rd
Dallas TX 75229
972 243-4466

(G-1080)
CUSTOM SIGN CREATIONS LLC
1130 Rutherford Ln # 180 (78753-6742)
PHONE..................................512 374-9300
William R Lehman, *Director*
Christopher Brazell, *Director*
Andrew J Leffler, *Director*
James S Mitol, *Director*
EMP: 24
SALES (est): 2.1MM **Privately Held**
WEB: www.customsigncreations.com
SIC: 3993 Electric signs

(G-1081)
CYBERNANCE CORPORATION
5805 Davenport Divide Rd (78738-2102)
P.O. Box 340758 (78734-0013)
PHONE..................................512 850-5909
Michael Shultz, *CEO*
Gary Seeger, *Principal*
Charlie Leonard, *COO*
Ralph Hasson, *Exec VP*
Alicia Thrasher, *Opers Staff*
EMP: 15
SALES (est): 369.3K **Privately Held**
WEB: www.cybernance.com
SIC: 7372 Business oriented computer
software

(G-1082)
**CYPRESS SEMICONDUCTOR
CORP**
5204 E Ben White Blvd (78741-7306)
PHONE..................................512 934-6699
Casey Barber, *Engineer*
Steven Anderson, *Manager*
Tony Baker, *Manager*
Kendall Holt, *Manager*
Michael Kriger, *Manager*
EMP: 14
SALES (corp-wide): 10.1B **Privately Held**
WEB: www.cypress.com
SIC: 3674 Integrated circuits, semiconduc-
tor networks, etc.
HQ: Cypress Semiconductor Corporation
198 Champion Ct
San Jose CA 95134
408 943-2600

(G-1083)
D R & J INC
Also Called: Texas Printing Company
1209 E Cesar Chavez St (78702-4332)
P.O. Box 6280 (78762-6280)
PHONE..................................512 474-4331
Fax: 512 474-6040
EMP: 10
SQ FT: 6,000
SALES (est): 880K **Privately Held**
SIC: 2752 2759 2754 Commerical Print-
ers

(G-1084)
DAILY DOT LLC
3112 Windsor Rd Ste A391 (78703-2350)
PHONE..................................512 420-9403
Nicholas White, *CEO*
Josh Katzowitz, *Editor*
Robert Mohundro, *COO*
Austin Powell, *Manager*
Ronald Petty, *Executive*
EMP: 15 EST: 2010
SALES (est): 1.1MM **Privately Held**
WEB: www.dailydot.com
SIC: 2711 5192 Newspapers, publishing &
printing; newspapers

(G-1085)
DBA SOFTWARE INC
9111 Jollyville Rd # 204 (78759-7471)
PHONE..................................512 342-1769
Michael Hart, *President*
Warren Hart, *Vice Pres*
EMP: 13
SQ FT: 1,200
SALES (est): 1.7MM **Privately Held**
WEB: www.dbamanufacturing.com
SIC: 7372 Business oriented computer
software

(G-1086)
**DCI BIOLOGICALS AUSTIN II
LLC**
1807 W Slaughter Ln # 4 (78748-6230)
PHONE..................................512 865-4200
EMP: 10
SALES (est): 703.1K
SALES (corp-wide): 1B **Privately Held**
SIC: 2836 8099 Plasmas; plasmapherous
center
PA: Bpl Plasma, Inc.
2801 Via Fortuna Ste 400
Austin TX 78746
512 582-7525

(G-1087)
DECORUM TILE & STONE INC
Also Called: Decorum Architectural Stone
4308 Terry O Ln (78745-1242)
PHONE..................................512 344-9235
Candelaria D Garay, *President*
EMP: 15
SQ FT: 2,000
SALES (est): 2MM **Privately Held**
WEB: www.decorumstone.com
SIC: 3281 5032 Stone, quarrying & pro-
cessing of own stone products; brick,
stone & related material

(G-1088)
DELL USA LP
2214 W Braker Ln Ste D (78758-4143)
PHONE..................................512 728-3366
Beth Summers, *Principal*
EMP: 17 **Publicly Held**
WEB: www.dell.com
SIC: 3571 Electronic computers
HQ: Dell Usa L.P.
401 Dell Way
Round Rock TX 78664

(G-1089)
DFA DAIRY BRANDS FLUID LLC
1819 Rutland Dr (78758-5423)
PHONE..................................512 755-6015
EMP: 45
SALES (corp-wide): 15.8B **Privately Held**
SIC: 2026 Fluid milk
HQ: Dfa Dairy Brands Fluid, Llc
1405 N 98th St
Kansas City KS 66111
816 801-6455

(G-1090)
DIESELGREEN FUELS LLC
2823 E M L Kng Jr Blvd (78702)
PHONE..................................512 247-3835
Jason Burroughs, *Mng Member*
EMP: 15
SALES (est): 2.3MM **Privately Held**
WEB: www.dieselgreenfuels.com
SIC: 2869 Fuels

(G-1091)
**DIETZ MEMORIAL COMPANY
INC**
4522 Burnet Rd (78756-3025)
PHONE..................................512 451-1983
Kevin Golliher, *Vice Pres*
EMP: 30
SALES (est): 2.1MM **Privately Held**
WEB: www.dietzmemorial.com
SIC: 1411 6553 Granite dimension stone;
mausoleum operation

(G-1092)
DIGERATI DIST & MKTG LLC
2000 Kinney Ave (78704-4008)
PHONE..................................512 569-1772
Nicholas Alfieri,
EMP: 9

SALES (est): 224.6K **Privately Held**
WEB: www.digerati.games
SIC: 7372 Home entertainment computer
software

(G-1093)
DIGITAL MARKETER LABS LLC
4330 Gaines Ranch Loop (78735-6733)
PHONE..................................512 892-3022
Ryan Deiss, *CEO*
Garrett D'Entremont, *Partner*
Michael Meola, *Partner*
Jason Burkle, *COO*
John Grimshaw, *Opers Staff*
EMP: 40
SQ FT: 5,000
SALES (est): 3.3MM **Privately Held**
WEB: www.digitalmarketer.com
SIC: 2741 8742 Miscellaneous publishing;
marketing consulting services

(G-1094)
DIGITAL VIDEO CAMERA CO
Also Called: DVC Company
4120 Freidrich Ln Ste 500 (78744-1025)
PHONE..................................512 301-9564
Ash Prabala, *President*
Dr Douglas Benson, *Director*
Martin A Parker, *Director*
Paul L Thomas, *Director*
EMP: 16
SQ FT: 4,600
SALES (est): 3MM **Privately Held**
WEB: www.dvcco.com
SIC: 3827 Optical instruments & lenses

(G-1095)
DILOGR LLC
43 Rainey St Apt 3201 (78701-4456)
PHONE..................................800 455-9632
Gary Spirer, *CEO*
Alexandra Spirer, *Technology*
EMP: 12
SALES (est): 728.6K **Privately Held**
WEB: www.dilogr.com
SIC: 7372 Application computer software

(G-1096)
**DISTINCTIVE INDS TEXAS INC
(PA)**
4516 Seton Center Pkwy # 13
(78759-5370)
P.O. Box 140949 (78714-0949)
PHONE..................................512 491-3500
Dwight Forrester, *President*
Linda Forrister, *Admin Sec*
EMP: 29
SALES (est): 37.5MM **Privately Held**
WEB: www.distinctiveindustries.com
SIC: 2386 Leather & sheep-lined clothing

(G-1097)
DJO GLOBAL INC
9800 Metric Blvd (78758-5445)
PHONE..................................512 832-9500
Leslie H Cross, *CEO*
Denise Cruz, *Vice Pres*
Kevin Runte, *Project Mgr*
Aaron Zimmel, *Manager*
Delta Lane, *Senior Mgr*
EMP: 10
SALES (corp-wide): 3.3B **Publicly Held**
WEB: www.djoglobal.com
SIC: 3842 Surgical appliances & supplies
HQ: Djo Global, Inc.
2900 Lake Vista Dr
Lewisville TX 75067

(G-1098)
DOBIE SUPPLY LLC (PA)
3809 S 2nd St Ste D200 (78704-7191)
PHONE..................................512 437-6499
Robin Pope,
Kennon Calvert Beasley,
Richard Kemp,
EMP: 9 EST: 2012
SALES (est): 1.8MM **Privately Held**
WEB: www.dobiesupply.com
SIC: 3824 5084 Integrating & totalizing
meters for gas & liquids; safety equipment

(G-1099)
DOCUMENT SOLUTIONS
2706 Montopolis Dr (78741-6408)
PHONE..................................512 471-5464
Richard Beto, *Director*

**G
E
O
G
R
A
P
H
I
C**

EMP: 50
SALES (est): 538.3K **Privately Held**
WEB: www.austin.utexas.edu
SIC: 2752 Commercial printing, litho-
graphic

(G-1100)
DRAKE INDUSTRIES INC
1916 Hydro Dr (78728-7626)
PHONE.............................512 251-2231
Timothy Merrfield, *President*
Clay Boykin, *Vice Pres*
EMP: 13
SQ FT: 5,000
SALES (est): 2.4MM
SALES (corp-wide): 7.6MM **Privately
Held**
WEB: www.drake.com
SIC: 2759 Screen printing
PA: The Cubbison Company
     380 Victoria Rd
     Youngstown OH 44515
     330 793-2481

(G-1101)
DRILLING INFO INC (PA)
Also Called: Enverus
2901 Via Fortuna Ste 200 (78746-0007)
P.O. Box 5545 (78763-5545)
PHONE.............................512 477-9200
Jeff Hughes, *President*
Silas Martin, *General Mgr*
Allen Gilmer, *Chairman*
Scott Stewart, *Regional Mgr*
Jimmy Fortuna, *Senior VP*
EMP: 100
SALES (est): 359.6MM **Privately Held**
WEB: www.enverus.com
SIC: 1382 Oil & gas exploration services

(G-1102)
**DRILLING SUPPLY AND MFG
INC**
Also Called: DSM Mayhew
7301 Hwy 183 S (78744-7899)
PHONE.............................512 243-1986
Stanley Martin, *President*
Randy Young, *Corp Secy*
Dick Hughes, *Finance*
▼ **EMP:** 32
SQ FT: 4,000
SALES (est): 8.8MM **Privately Held**
WEB: www.dsm-mayhew.com
SIC: 3532 7699 Drills & drilling equipment,
mining (except oil & gas); industrial equip-
ment services

(G-1103)
DRONESENSE INC
2600 Via Fortuna Ste 340 (78746-8038)
PHONE.............................512 582-0444
Christopher Eyhorn, *CEO*
Eric Schank, *VP Engrg*
Arnab Biswas, *CFO*
Eric Thompson, *Technical Staff*
EMP: 17
SALES (est): 260.9K **Privately Held**
WEB: www.dronesense.com
SIC: 7372 Application computer software

(G-1104)
DSM FLUID POWER INC
7301 Us Highway 183 S (78744-7831)
PHONE.............................512 243-1986
Palmer Martin, *President*
Stanley Martin, *Corp Secy*
Ken Young, *Vice Pres*
Kathryn Peace, *Controller*
EMP: 30
SQ FT: 4,000
SALES (est): 2MM **Privately Held**
WEB: www.dsm-mayhew.com
SIC: 1799 3492 5084 Hydraulic equip-
ment, installation & service; hose & tube
fittings & assemblies, hydraulic/pneu-
matic; hydraulic systems equipment &
supplies

(G-1105)
DUNAN MICROSTAQ INC
4120 Freidrich Ln Ste 225 (78744-1085)
PHONE.............................512 628-2890
Parthiban Arunasalam, *CEO*
Gene Yao, *President*
Nelson Fuller, *Principal*
Mark Luckevich, *Principal*

Dhaman Besarla, *Engineer*
▲ **EMP:** 16
SALES (est): 2.7MM **Privately Held**
WEB: www.dmq-us.com
SIC: 3699 Accelerating waveguide struc-
tures
PA: Zhejiang Dunan Artificial Environment
     Co., Ltd.
     Dun'an Development Mansion,
     No.239, Taian Road, Binjiang Distric
     Hangzhou 31005

(G-1106)
E I PRODUCTS INC
Also Called: Egress Technology
3000 S Interstate 35 # 375 (78704-6513)
PHONE.............................512 357-2776
George Kasee, *President*
▲ **EMP:** 15
SQ FT: 10,000
SALES (est): 2.7MM **Privately Held**
WEB: www.limelite.com
SIC: 2833 Drugs & herbs: grading, grinding
& milling

(G-1107)
E-MDS INC (PA)
10901 Stonelake Blvd (78759-5749)
P.O. Box 2889, Cedar Park (78630-2889)
PHONE.............................512 257-5200
Jim Brady, *CEO*
Ted Pakes, *COO*
Patrick Hall, *Exec VP*
Bret Bandi, *Vice Pres*
Abhinav Awasthi, *Opers Staff*
EMP: 107
SQ FT: 50,000
SALES (est): 60.6MM **Privately Held**
WEB: www.e-mds.com
SIC: 7372 Business oriented computer
software

(G-1108)
E2OPEN LLC (PA)
9600 Great Hills Trl 300e (78759-5681)
PHONE.............................866 432-6736
Michael Farlekas, *President*
Ziao Liu, *Principal*
Peter Hantman, *COO*
Bert Chen, *Exec VP*
Paul Carmody, *Senior VP*
EMP: 80
SQ FT: 24,606
SALES (est): 148MM **Privately Held**
WEB: www.e2open.com
SIC: 7372 Prepackaged software

(G-1109)
E2OPEN LLC
Also Called: Steelwedge Software
9600 Great Hills Trl 300e (78759-5681)
PHONE.............................925 460-1700
Michael Farlekas, *CEO*
EMP: 70
SALES (corp-wide): 148MM **Privately
Held**
WEB: www.e2open.com
SIC: 7372 Prepackaged software
PA: E2open, Llc
     9600 Great Hills Trl 300e
     Austin TX 78759
     866 432-6736

(G-1110)
**EAGLE VLY ENRGY PARTNERS
LLC**
13413 Galleria Cir # 100 (78738-7111)
PHONE.............................512 413-7140
Matthew Telfer, *CEO*
EMP: 14
SALES (est): 5MM **Privately Held**
WEB: www.bbxllc.com
SIC: 1382 Oil & gas exploration services

(G-1111)
**EAST SIDE COMPOST
PEDALLERS**
1000 Brazos St Ste C (78701-2351)
PHONE.............................512 436-3884
Dustin Fedako, *Owner*
Eric Goff, *CFO*
EMP: 11
SALES (est): 809.7K **Privately Held**
SIC: 2875 4953 Compost; recycling,
waste materials

(G-1112)
EBIZSOFT INC
2028 E Ben White Blvd (78741-6966)
PHONE.............................954 272-0500
Aris Ahmad, *Manager*
EMP: 20
SALES (corp-wide): 6MM **Privately Held**
WEB: www.e-bizsoft.com
SIC: 7372 Prepackaged software
PA: Ebizsoft, Inc
     12525 Orange Dr Ste 711
     Davie FL 33330
     954 272-0500

(G-1113)
**EDEN EQUIPMENT COMPANY
INC (PA)**
6231 E Stassney Ln 12-100 (78744-3086)
PHONE.............................909 629-2217
Joe Kovach, *President*
◆ **EMP:** 15 **EST:** 1982
SQ FT: 10,000
SALES (est): 1.6MM **Privately Held**
WEB: www.edenequipment.com
SIC: 3569 Filters, general line: industrial;
filters

(G-1114)
EDGE SOFTWARE INC
15101 Kevin Ln (78734-2345)
PHONE.............................512 345-7793
John C Davidson, *President*
EMP: 11
SALES (est): 846K **Privately Held**
WEB: www.edge.ws
SIC: 7372 Prepackaged software

(G-1115)
EDGENUITY INC
11501 Domain Dr Ste 160 (78758-3598)
PHONE.............................512 478-9600
Nicole Wells, *Human Resources*
Aimee Burley, *Accounts Exec*
Billy McCrary, *Accounts Exec*
Amanda Bennett, *Sales Staff*
Jennifer Goss, *Technology*
EMP: 230 **Publicly Held**
WEB: www.edgenuity.com
SIC: 7372 Educational computer software
HQ: Edgenuity Inc.
     8860 E Chaparral Rd # 100
     Scottsdale AZ 85250
     480 423-0118

(G-1116)
EDUSPARK INC
2028 E Ben White Blvd (78741-6966)
PHONE.............................512 535-6139
Laura Machuca, *President*
Teresa Aldrete, *President*
EMP: 10
SALES (est): 484.3K **Privately Held**
WEB: www.eduspark.com
SIC: 7372 7389 Prepackaged software;

(G-1117)
EIXSYS LLC
501 W Powell Ln Ste 219 (78753-5947)
PHONE.............................512 666-3574
Scott Buchanan, *Senior VP*
Amin Salahuddin, *EMP:* 9
SALES (est): 159.2K **Privately Held**
WEB: www.eixsys.com
SIC: 7371 7372 Custom computer pro-
gramming services; application computer
software

(G-1118)
EL CHILITO FOODS INC
2209 Manor Rd (78722-2133)
PHONE.............................512 391-0550
Carlos Rivero, *President*
EMP: 10
SQ FT: 780
SALES (est): 1.3MM **Privately Held**
WEB: www.elchilito.com
SIC: 2673 Food storage & frozen food
bags, plastic

(G-1119)
**ELECTRONINKS
INCORPORATED**
7901 E Riverside Dr # 150 (78744-1663)
PHONE.............................512 766-5555

Steven Walker, *CEO*
Spencer Violette, *Finance*
Hagan Huffaker, *Manager*
Anali Diaz, *Administration*
▲ **EMP:** 30
SALES (est): 117.9K **Privately Held**
WEB: www.circuitscribe.com
SIC: 2893 Printing ink

(G-1120)
**ELECTRONINKS WRITEABLES
INC**
7901 E Riverside Dr # 150 (78744-1663)
PHONE.............................512 766-7555
Steven Brett Walker, *CEO*
Melburne Lemieux, *President*
Ana Diaz, *Principal*
Zack Tidwell, *Prdtn Mgr*
Spencer Violette, *Director*
EMP: 10
SALES (est): 482.3K **Privately Held**
WEB: www.electroninks.com
SIC: 2899 3672 Ink or writing fluids;
printed circuit boards

(G-1121)
**EMBARCADERO
TECHNOLOGIES INC (HQ)**
10801 N Mopac Expy 1-100 (78759-5460)
PHONE.............................512 226-8080
Wayne Williams, *CEO*
Wayne D Williams, *CEO*
Atanas Popov, *General Mgr*
Nigel Brown, *Senior VP*
Tony De La Lama, *Senior VP*
EMP: 142
SQ FT: 24,300
SALES (est): 46.1MM
SALES (corp-wide): 137.5MM **Privately
Held**
WEB: www.embarcadero.com
SIC: 7371 7372 Computer software devel-
opment; software programming applica-
tions; business oriented computer
software
PA: Idera, Inc.
     2950 North Loop W Ste 700
     Houston TX 77092
     713 523-4433

(G-1122)
EMC CORPORATION
11044 Res Blvd Ste B500 (78759)
PHONE.............................512 343-3332
EMP: 10
SALES (corp-wide): 78.6B **Publicly Held**
SIC: 3572 5734 Mfg Computer Storage
Devices Ret Computers/Software
HQ: Emc Corporation
     176 South St
     Hopkinton MA 01748
     508 435-1000

(G-1123)
**EMERALD PT MARINA
PARTNERS LTD**
5973 Hiline Rd (78734)
PHONE.............................512 266-1535
Marina Ventures, *General Ptnr*
EMP: 150
SALES (est): 6.7MM **Privately Held**
WEB: www.shmarinas.com
SIC: 4493 5813 3536 Marine
basins; bar (drinking places); grills (eating
places); boat lifts

(G-1124)
**EMERGENCY TECHNOLOGIES
INC**
Also Called: Eti
9020 N Capital Of Texas H (78759-7279)
PHONE.............................919 676-6200
Gar Keaton, *Ch of Bd*
Kyle Breischaft, *President*
EMP: 25
SQ FT: 5,700
SALES (est): 2.9MM **Privately Held**
SIC: 7372 Prepackaged software

(G-1125)
ENCORE MEDICAL LP
Also Called: Djo Surgical
9800 Metric Blvd (78758-5445)
PHONE.............................512 832-9500
Toby Bost, *President*

Steven Ingel, *President*
Susan Crawford, *Exec VP*
Jeanine Kestler, *Exec VP*
Craig Smith, *Exec VP*
▲ **EMP:** 900
SQ FT: 66,000
SALES (est): 223.2MM
SALES (corp-wide): 3.3B **Publicly Held**
WEB: www.djoglobal.com
SIC: 3842 5047 Surgical appliances &
supplies; implants, surgical; medical
equipment & supplies
HQ: Djo, Llc
1430 Decision St
Vista CA 92081
760 727-1283

(G-1126)
ENERGY XTREME LLC
2215 Westlake Dr Fl 2 (78746-2966)
PHONE..................................512 617-7902
Devin Scott, *Mng Member*
EMP: 11
SQ FT: 1,500
SALES (est): 1.1MM **Privately Held**
WEB: www.energyxtreme.net
SIC: 3674 Solar cells

(G-1127)
**ENVIROCON TECHNOLOGIES
INC**
3601 S Congress Ave G600 (78704-7483)
P.O. Box 3547 (78764-3547)
PHONE..................................512 382-9842
Curtis Eggemeyer, *CEO*
Jim Eggemeyer, *President*
Joe Harvey, *COO*
Travis Cassedy, *Opers Mgr*
Gary Barbieri, *Regl Sales Mgr*
EMP: 28
SQ FT: 35,000
SALES (est): 10.3MM **Privately Held**
WEB: www.lemishine.com
SIC: 2842 Cleaning or polishing prepara-
tions

(G-1128)
EPAK INTERNATIONAL INC
4926 Spicewood Springs Rd # 200
(78759-8434)
PHONE..................................512 231-8083
Steve Dezso, *President*
Mao Shi Khoo, *COO*
Ben Krause, *Accounts Mgr*
Rich Westfall, *Sales Staff*
James R Thomas, *CTO*
▲ **EMP:** 1160
SQ FT: 10,000
SALES (est): 3.7MM **Privately Held**
WEB: www.epak.com
SIC: 3089 Plastic containers, except foam

(G-1129)
EPIC PROVISIONS LLC (DH)
1902 S Congress Ave D (78704-3503)
P.O. Box 684581 (78768-4581)
PHONE..................................512 944-8502
EMP: 14 **EST:** 2010
SALES (est): 4.6MM
SALES (corp-wide): 17.6B **Publicly Held**
WEB: www.epicprovisions.com
SIC: 2034 7389 Fruits, dried or dehy-
drated, except freeze-dried; business
services

(G-1130)
**EPICOR SOFTWARE
CORPORATION**
Also Called: CCI-Triad
804 Las Cimas Pkwy # 200 (78746-5179)
PHONE..................................512 328-2300
Cathy Crusco, *Manager*
EMP: 63 **Privately Held**
WEB: www.epicor.com
SIC: 7372 Business oriented computer
software
PA: Epicor Software Corporation
804 Las Cimas Pkwy # 200
Austin TX 78746

(G-1131)
**EPICOR SOFTWARE
CORPORATION**
804 Las Cimas Pkwy # 200 (78746-5179)
PHONE..................................949 585-4000

Omar Guzman, *Opers Staff*
Omar E Garcia, *Manager*
Kevin Torbett, *Sr Software Eng*
Mark Nyquist, *Director*
Bettina Dee, *Administration*
EMP: 100 **Privately Held**
WEB: www.epicor.com
SIC: 3577 5045 Computer peripheral
equipment; computers, peripherals & soft-
ware
PA: Epicor Software Corporation
804 Las Cimas Pkwy # 200
Austin TX 78746

(G-1132)
**EPICOR SOFTWARE
CORPORATION (PA)**
804 Las Cimas Pkwy # 200 (78746-5179)
PHONE..................................512 328-2300
Steve Murphy, *CEO*
Stephanie Reese, *Principal*
Andy Coussins, *Senior VP*
Jason Taylor, *Senior VP*
John Berg, *Vice Pres*
EMP: 148
SQ FT: 75,000
SALES (est): 648MM **Privately Held**
WEB: www.epicor.com
SIC: 7372 Prepackaged software

(G-1133)
EPM LIVE INC
401 Congress Ave Ste 1850 (78701-3788)
PHONE..................................425 452-1111
John McDonald, *President*
EMP: 120 **EST:** 2000
SQ FT: 13,550
SALES (est): 19.4MM **Publicly Held**
WEB: www.ignitetech.com
SIC: 7372 7812 7311 Business oriented
computer software; audio-visual program
production; advertising agencies
PA: Upland Software, Inc.
401 Congress Ave Ste 1850
Austin TX 78701

(G-1134)
EQUINOR ENERGY LP
6300 Bridge Point Pkwy # 2 (78730-5073)
PHONE..................................512 427-3300
Andrea Kubik, *CEO*
Malcom Brown, *Controller*
Christine Wigand, *Comms Mgr*
EMP: 85
SQ FT: 3,400
SALES (est): 21.1MM **Privately Held**
WEB: www.brighamresources.net
SIC: 1382 Oil & gas exploration services
HQ: Equinor Exploration Company
6300 Bridge Point Pkwy
Austin TX 78730

(G-1135)
**EQUINOR EXPLORATION
COMPANY (DH)**
Also Called: Statoil Exploration Company
6300 Bridge Point Pkwy (78730-5073)
PHONE..................................512 427-3300
Andrea Kubik, *CEO*
Stephen C Hurley, *Principal*
Stephen P Reynolds, *Principal*
Hobart A Smith, *Principal*
Scott W Tinker PHD, *Principal*
EMP: 19
SALES (est): 264.7MM **Privately Held**
WEB: www.brighamdevelopment.net
SIC: 1311 Crude petroleum & natural gas
HQ: Equinor Usa Properties, Inc.
6300 Bridge Point Pkwy
Austin TX 78730
713 918-8200

(G-1136)
**EQUINOR USA PROPERTIES
INC (DH)**
6300 Bridge Point Pkwy (78730-5073)
PHONE..................................713 918-8200
Andrea Kubik, *CEO*
Charlotte Tjlsen, *Vice Pres*
Michael Miller, *Manager*
EMP: 9
SALES (est): 71.7MM **Privately Held**
WEB: www.equinor.com
SIC: 1382 Oil & gas exploration services

HQ: Equinor Us Holdings Inc.
120 Long Ridge Rd 3eo1
Stamford CT 06902
203 978-6900

(G-1137)
ERNIES WELDING SHOP INC
6511 Burnet Ln (78757-2835)
PHONE..................................512 459-6346
Clarence Kuehner Jr, *President*
Mary Sue Kuehner, *Corp Secy*
Ernie Kuehner, *Opers Mgr*
EMP: 14
SQ FT: 8,000
SALES (est): 190K **Privately Held**
SIC: 7692 Welding repair

(G-1138)
ESI TECHNOLOGIES LLC
6705 Lakewood Point Cv (78750-8140)
PHONE..................................512 633-2897
Rham Sriram,
Steve Bankhead,
EMP: 9
SALES (est): 750K **Privately Held**
WEB: www.esitechnologies.com
SIC: 7371 7372 Software programming
applications; application computer soft-
ware; business oriented computer soft-
ware

(G-1139)
ESTOVEL INC
6203 Shadow Mountain Cv (78731-4110)
PHONE..................................512 345-6997
Philip Stovall, *Principal*
EMP: 9
SALES (est): 1.1MM **Privately Held**
SIC: 3567 Industrial furnaces & ovens

(G-1140)
ESW HOLDINGS INC (HQ)
401 Congress Ave Ste 2650 (78701-3708)
PHONE..................................512 524-6149
Leela Kaza, *President*
Andrew Price, *CFO*
Michael Luebbert, *Officer*
EMP: 13
SQ FT: 13,000
SALES (est): 209.1MM **Privately Held**
WEB: www.wavesys.com
SIC: 7371 7372 Computer software devel-
opment; application computer software

(G-1141)
EVERGREEN SOLUTIONS INC
3500 Dime Cir 109 (78744-2338)
PHONE..................................512 389-0625
Roger Sikes, *President*
EMP: 25
SALES (est): 2.2MM **Privately Held**
SIC: 8748 3559 Environmental consultant;
semiconductor manufacturing machinery

(G-1142)
EVERI GAMES INC
4616 W Howard Ln Ste 500 (78728-6300)
PHONE..................................512 439-3100
Derek Sisemore, *Area Mgr*
David Lucchese, *Exec VP*
Douglas Fenn, *Vice Pres*
Matthew Chapman, *Engineer*
Brad Gianulis, *Engineer*
EMP: 70
SALES (corp-wide): 533.2MM **Publicly
Held**
WEB: www.everi.com
SIC: 3999 7993 Slot machines; mechani-
cal games, coin-operated
HQ: Everi Games Inc.
206 Wild Basin Rd Bldg B
West Lake Hills TX 78746
512 334-7500

(G-1143)
EVERLY WELL INC
Also Called: Everywell
823 Congress Ave Ste 1200 (78701-2402)
PHONE..................................512 309-5588
Julia Cheek, *CEO*
Andy Page, *President*
Joshua Stanley, *CFO*
Joe Maragoni, *Sales Staff*
Matthew Carroll, *Marketing Staff*
EMP: 20

SALES (est): 3MM **Privately Held**
WEB: www.everlywell.com
SIC: 3841 Diagnostic apparatus, medical

(G-1144)
**EXCEED DRILLING TECH LLC
(PA)**
3112 Windsor Rd Ste 519 (78703-2350)
PHONE..................................512 656-9669
EMP: 15 **EST:** 2011
SQ FT: 20,000
SALES (est): 1MM **Privately Held**
WEB: www.exceeddrilling.com
SIC: 1381 7353 8711 7389 Directional
drilling oil & gas wells; oil well drilling
equipment, rental or leasing; engineering
services; design services

(G-1145)
EXIT PLAN LLC
Also Called: Gomo
1102 Kinney Ave (78704-2140)
PHONE..................................213 444-6106
Jason Nichol, *Owner*
EMP: 20
SALES (est): 421K **Privately Held**
SIC: 7372 Prepackaged software

(G-1146)
**FALCONSTOR SOFTWARE INC
(PA)**
701 Brazos St Ste 400 (78701-3273)
PHONE..................................631 777-5188
Todd Brooks, *CEO*
John Yang, *General Mgr*
Mark Delsman, *Vice Pres*
Frank Wu, *Vice Pres*
Diana Popa, *Opers Staff*
EMP: 48
SQ FT: 3,711
SALES: 17.8MM **Publicly Held**
WEB: www.falconstor.com
SIC: 7372 7371 Application computer soft-
ware; computer software development;
computer software systems analysis &
design, custom

(G-1147)
**FEATHERLITE BUILDING PDTS
CORP**
Also Called: Acme Building Brands
2824 Real St (78722-1715)
P.O. Box 425, Round Rock (78680-0425)
PHONE..................................512 472-2424
H V Moss, *President*
John J Justin Jr, *Chairman*
Wade Allbritton, *Vice Pres*
Richard J Savitz, *Vice Pres*
Emmett Trussell, *Vice Pres*
EMP: 300
SALES (est): 20.7MM
SALES (corp-wide): 254.6B **Publicly
Held**
WEB: www.featherlitetexas.com
SIC: 3281 3271 Stone, quarrying & pro-
cessing of own stone products; blocks,
concrete or cinder: standard
HQ: Justin Industries, Inc.
3024 Acme Brick Plz
Fort Worth TX 76109
817 332-4101

(G-1148)
**FEDEX OFFICE & PRINT SVCS
INC**
13729 N Hwy 183 Ste 820 (78750-2267)
PHONE..................................512 331-0800
EMP: 9
SALES (corp-wide): 69.2B **Publicly Held**
WEB: www.fedex.com
SIC: 7334 3993 2759 2752 Photocopying
& duplicating services; signs & advertising
specialties; commercial printing; commer-
cial printing, lithographic
HQ: Fedex Office And Print Services, Inc.
7900 Legacy Dr
Plano TX 75024
800 463-3339

(G-1149)
**FEDEX OFFICE & PRINT SVCS
INC**
9222 Burnet Rd Ste 101 (78758-5251)
PHONE..................................512 339-1191
EMP: 42

SQ FT: 1,504
SALES (corp-wide): 69.2B **Publicly Held**
WEB: www.fedex.com
SIC: 7334 2759 2752 Photocopying & duplicating services; commercial printing; commercial printing, lithographic
HQ: Fedex Office And Print Services, Inc.
7900 Legacy Dr
Plano TX 75024
800 463-3339

(G-1150)
FEDEX OFFICE & PRINT SVCS INC
2711 Guadalupe St (78705-3701)
PHONE..................................512 476-3242
EMP: 33
SALES (corp-wide): 69.2B **Publicly Held**
WEB: www.fedex.com
SIC: 7334 2789 Photocopying & duplicating services; bookbinding & related work
HQ: Fedex Office And Print Services, Inc.
7900 Legacy Dr
Plano TX 75024
800 463-3339

(G-1151)
FEDEX OFFICE & PRINT SVCS INC
327 Congress Ave Ste 100 (78701-3691)
PHONE..................................512 472-4448
EMP: 20
SALES (corp-wide): 69.2B **Publicly Held**
WEB: www.fedex.com
SIC: 7334 3861 2759 Photocopying & duplicating services; photographic equipment & supplies; commercial printing
HQ: Fedex Office And Print Services, Inc.
7900 Legacy Dr
Plano TX 75024
800 463-3339

(G-1152)
FEDEX OFFICE & PRINT SVCS INC
6406 N Ih 35 Ste 1210 (78752-4343)
PHONE..................................512 452-3600
EMP: 20
SALES (corp-wide): 69.2B **Publicly Held**
WEB: www.fedex.com
SIC: 7334 7338 2789 Photocopying & duplicating services; secretarial & court reporting; bookbinding & related work
HQ: Fedex Office And Print Services, Inc.
7900 Legacy Dr
Plano TX 75024
800 463-3339

(G-1153)
FEINKIND INC
1000 E 5th St Apt 656 (78702-0015)
PHONE..................................914 591-5868
Josh Feinkind, CEO
▲ EMP: 16
SALES (est): 2.1MM **Privately Held**
SIC: 2511 Wood household furniture

(G-1154)
FENIEX INDUSTRIES INC
6320 E Stassney Ln Bldg 1 (78744-3134)
PHONE..................................800 615-8350
Hanza Deyaf, President
Eman Kallash, Vice Pres
Muna Marawi, Vice Pres
Yemilyn Ortiz-Flores, Vice Pres
Nick Mazzanti, Engineer
▲ EMP: 23 EST: 2009
SALES (est): 3.8MM **Privately Held**
WEB: www.feniex.com
SIC: 3647 Motor vehicle lighting equipment

(G-1155)
FILETRAIL INC
2505 E 6th St Ste D (78702-3981)
PHONE..................................408 289-1300
Darrell Mervau, President
Tom Permberton, Vice Pres
Jamie Richgels, Vice Pres
Nick Brazsal, Project Mgr
Austin Pettyjohn, Sales Engr
EMP: 25
SQ FT: 2,000
SALES: 4.7MM **Privately Held**
WEB: www.filetrail.com
SIC: 7372 Utility computer software

(G-1156)
FINELINE SPORTSWEAR INC
8407 N Lamar Blvd A (78753-5922)
PHONE..................................512 832-1441
Scott O'Glee, President
Teri O'Glee, Vice Pres
EMP: 16
SQ FT: 3,500
SALES (est): 1.8MM **Privately Held**
WEB: www.finelinesportswear.com
SIC: 7336 2396 Silk screen design; automotive & apparel trimmings

(G-1157)
FLAGSHIP MANUFACTURING CORP
2101 Donley Dr (78758-4511)
PHONE..................................512 382-6410
Brian Dailey, President
Jack Fuller, Vice Pres
EMP: 10
SALES (est): 483.1K **Privately Held**
WEB: www.fs-mfg.com
SIC: 3672 Printed circuit boards

(G-1158)
FLEXTRONICS AMERICA LLC
12455 Research Blvd (78759-2314)
PHONE..................................512 425-4129
Corey Ingra, Manager
EMP: 2200 **Privately Held**
WEB: www.flex.com
SIC: 3672 Printed circuit boards
HQ: Flextronics America, Llc
6201 America Center Dr
San Jose CA 95002
408 576-7000

(G-1159)
FLEXTRONICS AMERICA LLC
Also Called: Solectron USA
9500 Metric Blvd (78758-5430)
PHONE..................................512 698-1407
Michael McNamara, President
David Bennett, Vice Pres
Tom Linton, Vice Pres
Timothy Stewart, Vice Pres
Douglas Watson, Engineer
EMP: 10
SALES (est): 1MM **Privately Held**
WEB: www.flex.com
SIC: 3672 Printed circuit boards
PA: Flex Ltd.
2 Changi South Lane
Singapore 48612

(G-1160)
FLEXTRONICS INTL PA INC
12455 Research Blvd (78759-2314)
PHONE..................................512 425-4100
Gilbert Botello, Production
Kirk Rich, Production
Charles Ji, Engineer
Jimmy Smith, Engineer
Monica Wilson, Engineer
EMP: 34 **Privately Held**
WEB: www.flex.com
SIC: 3672 Printed circuit boards
HQ: Flextronics International Pa, Inc.
847 Gibraltar Dr
Milpitas CA 95035
408 576-7000

(G-1161)
FLEXTRONICS INTL USA INC
12455 Research Blvd (78759-2314)
PHONE..................................512 425-4100
Concepcion Perez, Facilities Mgr
Jim Esch, Engineer
Misael Saucedo, Engineer
Mark Canales, Branch Mgr
Denise Fondren, Planning
EMP: 505 **Privately Held**
WEB: www.flex.com
SIC: 3672 Printed circuit boards
HQ: Flextronics International Usa, Inc.
6201 America Center Dr
San Jose CA 95002

(G-1162)
FLEXTRONICS INTL USA INC
9500 Metric Blvd (78758-5430)
PHONE..................................512 740-1904
Steven Dyer, Buyer
Rudy Salinas, Technician
EMP: 535 **Privately Held**

WEB: www.flex.com
SIC: 3672 Printed circuit boards
HQ: Flextronics International Usa, Inc.
6201 America Center Dr
San Jose CA 95002

(G-1163)
FLUENCE BIOENGINEERING INC
4129 Coml Ctr Dr Ste 450 (78744)
PHONE..................................512 212-4544
David Cohen, CEO
Scott Gardner, CFO
Clay Brewer, Manager
Marc Miller, Manager
Russell Paik, CTO
◆ EMP: 70
SQ FT: 36,000
SALES (est): 17.2MM
SALES (corp-wide): 2B **Privately Held**
WEB: www.fluence.science
SIC: 3646 Commercial indusl & institutional electric lighting fixtures
HQ: Osram Sylvania Inc
200 Ballardvale St # 305
Wilmington MA 01887
978 570-3000

(G-1164)
FORCEPOINT LLC (PA)
10900 A Stnlake Blvd Quar (78759)
PHONE..................................858 320-8000
Manny Rivelo, CEO
Sean D Berg, Senior VP
Ray Gallagher, Vice Pres
Galen Jackman, Vice Pres
John Sorensen, Vice Pres
EMP: 41
SALES (est): 424.4MM **Privately Held**
WEB: www.forcepoint.com
SIC: 7372 Prepackaged software

(G-1165)
FORMASPACE LP
1100 E Howard Ln Ste 400 (78753-9721)
PHONE..................................512 279-2576
Jeff Turk, CEO
Brett Gray, Project Mgr
EMP: 49
SQ FT: 60,000
SALES (est): 12.6MM **Privately Held**
WEB: www.formaspace.com
SIC: 2599 Factory furniture & fixtures

(G-1166)
FORMATION BIOLOGICS CORP (HQ)
Also Called: Forbius
701 Brazos St Ste 930 (78701-2583)
PHONE..................................713 357-1062
Ilia Tikhomirov, CEO
EMP: 10
SALES (est): 774.7K
SALES (corp-wide): 42.5B **Publicly Held**
WEB: www.forbius.com
SIC: 2834 Drugs affecting neoplasms & endocrine systems
PA: Bristol-Myers Squibb Company
430 E 29th St Fl 14
New York NY 10016
212 546-4000

(G-1167)
FORMULARY PRODUCTIONS LLC
301 Cedar Hurst Ln (78734-3975)
P.O. Box 171178, Memphis TN (38187-1178)
PHONE..................................901 767-3000
Laura Paxton, President
J Fred Wimmer, Chairman
EMP: 12
SALES (est): 1MM **Privately Held**
SIC: 2731 Book publishing

(G-1168)
FORTERRA PIPE & PRECAST LLC
801 Airport Blvd (78702-4105)
P.O. Box 6010 (78762-6010)
PHONE..................................512 385-3950
Olaf Schmidt, District Mgr
Jessica Gilbertson, Clerk
EMP: 50

WEB: www.flex.com
SIC: 3672 Printed circuit boards
HQ: Flextronics International Usa, Inc.
6201 America Center Dr
San Jose CA 95002

SALES (corp-wide): 1.5B **Publicly Held**
WEB: www.forterrabp.com
SIC: 3272 5211 Pipe, concrete or lined with concrete; masonry materials & supplies
HQ: Forterra Pipe & Precast, Llc
511 E John Carpenter Fwy
Irving TX 75062
469 458-7973

(G-1169)
FORTIS SOLUTIONS GROUP LLC
1610a Dungan Ln (78754-4064)
PHONE..................................512 302-0204
Mike Arispe, Branch Mgr
EMP: 17 **Privately Held**
WEB: www.fortissolutionsgroup.com
SIC: 2679 2759 Labels, paper: made from purchased material; flexographic printing
PA: Fortis Solutions Group, Llc
2505 Hawkeye Ct
Virginia Beach VA 23452

(G-1170)
FOUR RIVERS SFTWR SYSTEMS INC
11500 Alterra Pkwy # 110 (78758-3191)
PHONE..................................412 256-9020
Henry Wilde, President
Samantha Rouse, Senior VP
Barry Skirble, CTO
EMP: 33
SALES (est): 2.4MM
SALES (corp-wide): 6.4B **Publicly Held**
WEB: www.frsoft.com
SIC: 7372 Business oriented computer software
HQ: Accruent, Llc
11500 Alterra Pkwy # 110
Austin TX 78758

(G-1171)
FREESCALE SMCDTR HLDINGS V INC (HQ)
6501 W William Cannon Dr (78735-8523)
PHONE..................................512 895-2000
Gregg A Lowe, President
Robert Gleason, Project Mgr
Kenneth Benko, Opers Staff
Rodolfo Guillen, Engineer
Fareed Mohammed, Manager
EMP: 12
SALES (est): 3.7B
SALES (corp-wide): 8.8B **Privately Held**
WEB: www.freescale.com
SIC: 3674 Semiconductors & related devices
PA: Nxp Semiconductors N.V.
High Tech Campus 60
Eindhoven 5656
402 729-999

(G-1172)
FRH CONSUMER SERVICES INC
Also Called: One Logos Education Solution
7801 N Capital Of Texas H (78731-1187)
PHONE..................................512 657-8945
Richard E Haines, CEO
EMP: 9
SQ FT: 1,500 **Privately Held**
WEB: www.onelogos.com
SIC: 7373 7372 Systems software development services; educational computer software

(G-1173)
FUSION SERVICES INC
Also Called: Compound Security Specialists
440 Industrial Blvd (78745-1209)
PHONE..................................512 444-4283
Brenda Reese, President
Adolfo R Ridrieuez, Vice Pres
Rosendo Lopez, Purchasing
Robbie Cook, Sales Staff
EMP: 36
SALES (est): 10.6MM **Privately Held**
WEB: www.compoundsecure.com
SIC: 7629 1799 3315 3446 Electronic equipment repair; welding on site; chain link fencing; fences or posts, ornamental iron or steel; fences, gates, posts & flagpoles; gates, ornamental metal

(G-1174)
FUTURE PROOF BRANDS LLC
1023 Springdale Rd Ste 1j (78721-2465)
P.O. Box 150397 (78715-0397)
PHONE..................................512 790-9967
Justin D Fenchel, *CEO*
Amy Steadman, *COO*
Nicholas Greeninger, *Mktg Dir*
Chance Dingman, *Marketing Staff*
Aimy Steadman, *Mng Member*
EMP: 25 **EST:** 2011
SALES (est): 53K **Privately Held**
WEB: www.beatboxbeverages.com
SIC: 2084 Wines

(G-1175)
**FUTURSARCH TRIALS
NEUROLOGY LP**
5508 Parkcrest Dr Ste 300 (78731-4915)
PHONE..................................512 380-9925
John Morrison, *Partner*
EMP: 10
SQ FT: 2,500
SALES (est): 409.5K **Privately Held**
WEB: www.fstrials.com
SIC: 2836 Veterinary biological products

(G-1176)
**G4 SPATIAL TECHNOLOGIES
LLC (DH)**
4111 Todd Ln (78744-1149)
P.O. Box 19014 (78760-9014)
PHONE..................................512 447-9879
Wayne Rodriguez, *President*
Virginia Rodriguez, *Treasurer*
EMP: 26 **EST:** 1950
SQ FT: 10,600
SALES (est): 3.2MM
SALES (corp-wide): 4.5MM **Privately
Held**
WEB: www.easydrivestake.com
SIC: 2499 5999 3829 Surveyors' stakes,
wood; architectural supplies; surveying &
drafting equipment

(G-1177)
GABHEN INC
9200 Waterfrd Ctr Blvd (78758-7502)
PHONE..................................512 832-7902
EMP: 13
SQ FT: 5,000
SALES (corp-wide): 70MM **Privately
Held**
SIC: 3089 Mfg Plastic Products
PA: Gabhen, Inc.
1 Maltese Dr
Totowa NJ 07512
800 631-3572

(G-1178)
GARDEN STATE SALSA INC
828 W 6th St (78703-5468)
PHONE..................................512 242-4534
Stephen Dean, *President*
EMP: 10
SALES (est): 561.2K **Privately Held**
SIC: 2099 Sauces: gravy, dressing & dip
mixes

(G-1179)
**GE FLIGHT EFFICIENCY SVCS
INC**
400 W 15th St Ste 1000 (78701-1696)
P.O. Box 303365 (78703-0057)
PHONE..................................512 270-2701
Michael Thompson, *Manager*
EMP: 35
SQ FT: 4,000
SALES (est): 5.4MM
SALES (corp-wide): 95.2B **Publicly Held**
WEB: www.geaviation.com
SIC: 3812 8731 Flight recorders; elec-
tronic research
HQ: Ge Aviation Systems Llc
1 Neumann Way
Cincinnati OH 45215
937 898-9600

(G-1180)
GEM-CAP INC
Also Called: Hayes Software Systems
12007 Res Blvd Ste 103 (78759)
PHONE..................................512 219-7610
Matt Winebright, *CEO*
Anna Maxin, *COO*

Debbie Hartman, *Vice Pres*
Laura Sager, *Vice Pres*
Becky Child, *Opers Staff*
EMP: 39
SQ FT: 1,600
SALES (est): 5.7MM **Privately Held**
WEB: www.hayessoft.com
SIC: 7372 Prepackaged software
PA: Transition Capital Partners Lp
2100 Mckinney Ave # 1501
Dallas TX 75201

(G-1181)
GENERAL MOTORS LLC
13201 Mccallen Pass (78753-5382)
PHONE..................................512 470-4730
Qiana Greene, *Marketing Mgr*
Kathleen Carmody, *Manager*
Randy Mott, *CIO*
Cave Wetterau, *IT/INT Sup*
EMP: 1000 **Publicly Held**
WEB: www.gm.com
SIC: 5511 3711 Automobiles, new & used;
motor vehicles & car bodies
HQ: General Motors Llc
300 Renaissance Ctr L1
Detroit MI 48243

(G-1182)
GENSYM CORPORATION (DH)
401 Congress Ave Ste 2600 (78701-3744)
PHONE..................................512 377-9700
David A Smith, *Ch of Bd*
Robert B Ashton, *President*
Philippe C Printz, *Vice Pres*
Stephen D Allison, *CFO*
EMP: 54
SQ FT: 16,928
SALES (est): 4.7MM **Privately Held**
WEB: www.ignitetech.com
SIC: 7372 Business oriented computer
software

(G-1183)
GINCOP INC (DH)
Also Called: Ginny's Printing
8410 Tuscany Way Ste B (78754-4824)
PHONE..................................512 454-6874
Michael Martin, *CEO*
Bart Spanjersberg, *Vice Pres*
Cheryl Degan, *CFO*
Larry Bolden, *VP Sales*
Gary Cole, *Accounts Mgr*
EMP: 34
SQ FT: 108,000
SALES (est): 37.1MM
SALES (corp-wide): 31.4MM **Privately
Held**
WEB: www. 1touchpoint.com
SIC: 2752 7334 2759 Commercial print-
ing, offset; photocopying & duplicating
services; commercial printing

(G-1184)
GLOBALFOUNDRIES US INC
5113 Sw Pkwy (78735-8915)
PHONE..................................512 457-3407
Bruce McDougall, *CFO*
John Volkmann, *VP Mktg*
Dick Thielen, *Manager*
Daniel Shamlian, *Technical Staff*
Jason Stephens, *Technical Staff*
EMP: 10 **Privately Held**
WEB: www.globalfoundries.com
SIC: 3369 Nonferrous foundries
HQ: Globalfoundries U.S. Inc.
2600 Great America Way
Santa Clara CA 95054

(G-1185)
GOBBATO BUILDERS LLC
Also Called: Construction Contractors
11601 Anderson Mill Rd (78750-1354)
PHONE..................................737 843-4327
Eunice Gobbato, *Mng Member*
EMP: 15
SALES (est): 240K **Privately Held**
SIC: 1522 1389 1611 1531 Hotel/motel &
multi-family home renovation & remodel-
ing

(G-1186)
**GOLD STAR MARBLE
CORPORATION**
Also Called: Gold Star Cabinets
16240 N Interstate 35 (78728-2502)
PHONE..................................512 251-9279
Trojan Tidwell, *President*
Josephine Tidwell, *Corp Secy*
EMP: 20 **EST:** 1976
SQ FT: 20,000
SALES (est): 2.6MM **Privately Held**
WEB: www.goldstarcabinets.com
SIC: 3281 5211 Bathroom fixtures, cut
stone; cabinets, kitchen

(G-1187)
GOOD FAT CO LTD
Also Called: Love Good Fat
8641 Old Bee Caves Rd (78735-8148)
PHONE..................................512 300-8391
Susan Yorke, *President*
EMP: 30
SALES (est): 3MM **Privately Held**
WEB: www.lovegoodfats.com
SIC: 2066 2038 Chocolate bars, solid;
snacks, including onion rings, cheese
sticks, etc.

(G-1188)
**GOOD FLOW HONEY & JUICE
CO**
Also Called: Crowfut Honey Company
6001 Techni Center Dr # 3 (78721-2375)
PHONE..................................512 472-6714
Tom Crofut, *CEO*
Daniel Crofut, *President*
Judy Crofut, *CFO*
EMP: 18
SQ FT: 1,200
SALES (est): 4.8MM **Privately Held**
WEB: www.goodflowhoney.com
SIC: 2033 2099 Fruit juices: fresh; honey,
strained & bottled

(G-1189)
**GOOD FLOW JUICE COMPANY
LLC**
6001 Tehnictr Dr 3 (78721)
PHONE..................................512 472-6714
Tom Crofut, *CEO*
Daniel Crofut, *President*
Mark McDaniel, *COO*
Judy Crofut, *CFO*
EMP: 15
SALES (est): 1.3MM **Privately Held**
WEB: www.goodflowhoney.com
SIC: 2033 Fruit juices: fresh

(G-1190)
GP TM ACQUISITION LLC (PA)
Also Called: Texas Monthly Magazine
816 Congress Ave Ste 1700 (78701-2643)
P.O. Box 1569 (78767-1569)
PHONE..................................512 320-6900
Michael R Levy, *CEO*
David B Dunham, *Publisher*
Tom Foster, *Editor*
Tim Taliaferro, *Chief*
Marsha Cook, *Exec VP*
EMP: 95
SQ FT: 20,000
SALES (est): 11.7MM **Privately Held**
WEB: www.texasmonthly.com
SIC: 2721 Magazines: publishing only, not
printed on site

(G-1191)
GPD MARINE INC
Also Called: Eriksen Marine
5975 Hiline Rd (78734-1150)
PHONE..................................512 266-1834
Peter Clark, *Director*
Grant Eriksen, *Director*
EMP: 10
SALES (est): 1.3MM **Privately Held**
WEB: www.platinummarineatx.com
SIC: 3732 5551 Boat building & repairing;
boat dealers

(G-1192)
GREEN OCEAN SCIENCES INC
Also Called: 3144 Labs
3636 Dime Cir Ste A (78744-2337)
PHONE..................................512 200-4505
Alex Andrawes, *CEO*

David Crawford, *President*
David Cree Crawford, *President*
EMP: 20
SALES (est): 185.9K **Privately Held**
WEB: www.greenoceansciences.com
SIC: 3826 8731 Analytical instruments;
commercial physical research; agricultural
research; environmental research

(G-1193)
**GREENLEAF BOOK GROUP
LLC**
Also Called: Greenleaf Enterprises
4005 Banister Ln Ste B (78704-8079)
P.O. Box 91689 (78709-1869)
PHONE..................................512 891-6100
◆ **EMP:** 35 **EST:** 1997
SALES (est): 10.2MM **Privately Held**
WEB: www.greenleafbookgroup.com
SIC: 2731 Books: publishing only

(G-1194)
**GRESHAM ENTERPRISE
STORAGE INC**
10205 Brimfield Dr (78726-1892)
PHONE..................................512 250-0916
Paul Harris, *CEO*
Steve Purchase, *Director*
Andrew Waltongreen, *Director*
EMP: 30
SQ FT: 10,000
SALES (est): 2.7MM
SALES (corp-wide): 32.2MM **Privately
Held**
WEB: www.greshamtech.com
SIC: 7379 7371 7372 Data processing
consultant; computer software develop-
ment; business oriented computer soft-
ware
PA: Gresham Technologies Plc
Aldermary House
London EC4N
207 653-0200

(G-1195)
**HAAS GROUP INTERNATIONAL
LLC**
Also Called: Hass Tcm
10801 N Mopac Expy 3-150 (78759-5459)
PHONE..................................512 519-3989
Michael Faist, *Manager*
EMP: 45
SALES (corp-wide): 1.7B **Privately Held**
WEB: www.wescoair.com
SIC: 8741 2899 Management services;
metal treating compounds
HQ: Haas Group International, Llc
1475 Phnxvlle Pike Ste 10
West Chester PA 19380
484 564-4500

(G-1196)
HABITEK INTERNATIONAL INC
Also Called: Medical Polymers
8121 Fm 2244 Rd Ste 100 (78746-4938)
P.O. Box 50442 (78763-0442)
PHONE..................................512 347-8800
Carlton Lee Cooke, *President*
Kimberly Cooke Lyon, *Treasurer*
Julie Stark, *Marketing Staff*
Tom Gerding PHD, *CIO*
EMP: 110
SQ FT: 1,200
SALES (est): 11MM **Privately Held**
SIC: 2822 Ethylene-propylene rubbers,
EPDM polymers

(G-1197)
HANGER INC (PA)
10910 Domain Dr Ste 300 (78758-7807)
PHONE..................................512 777-3800
Christopher B Begley, *Ch of Bd*
Vinit K Asar, *President*
Samuel M Liang, *President*
Regina Weger, *President*
Dyan Cassady, *Partner*
EMP: 250
SALES: 1.1B **Publicly Held**
WEB: www.hanger.com
SIC: 8093 5047 3842 Specialty outpatient
clinics; artificial limbs; orthopedic equip-
ment & supplies; prosthetic appliances;
braces, orthopedic; abdominal support-
ers, braces & trusses

(G-1198)
HARTE HANKS INC (PA)
2800 Wells Branch Pkwy (78728-6762)
PHONE......................................512 343-1100
Andrew Benett, *Ch of Bd*
Elizabeth Spang, *Partner*
Brian Linscott, *COO*
Charlie Carlisle, *Vice Pres*
Jan Hogan, *Vice Pres*
◆ EMP: 20
SALES: 217.5MM **Privately Held**
WEB: www.hartehanks.com
SIC: 7331 7372 Direct mail advertising
services; prepackaged software

(G-1199)
HASSE ENTERPRISES INC
Also Called: Safequip
10201b Mckalla Pl Unit D (78758-4407)
PHONE......................................512 835-7697
Judy J Hasse, *President*
Jim Hasse, *Vice Pres*
John J Hasse Sr, *Vice Pres*
David Esquivel, *Supervisor*
James Hasse, *Shareholder*
EMP: 11
SQ FT: 3,000
SALES (est): 850K **Privately Held**
SIC: 5099 7389 5999 5087 Safety equip-
ment & supplies; fire extinguisher servic-
ing; fire extinguishers; firefighting
equipment; contractors' materials; hose,
pneumatic: rubber or rubberized fabric

(G-1200)
**HEALTH MANAGEMENT
SYSTEMS INC**
505 E Huntland Dr Ste 380 (78752-3757)
PHONE......................................512 407-9680
Annette Wolf, *Principal*
EMP: 37
SALES (corp-wide): 626.4MM **Publicly
Held**
WEB: www.hms.com
SIC: 7374 7372 Data processing & prepa-
ration; application computer software
HQ: Health Management Systems Inc
5615 High Point Dr # 100
Irving TX 75038
214 453-3000

(G-1201)
**HEYDAY BEVERAGE COMPANY
LLC**
701 E 6th St (78701-3717)
P.O. Box 1269 (78767-1269)
PHONE......................................512 387-2399
Kelly Driscoll Smith, *President*
Bart Smith, *Vice Pres*
EMP: 15
SQ FT: 1,500
SALES (est): 300K **Privately Held**
WEB: www.drinkheyday.com
SIC: 2086 Bottled & canned soft drinks

(G-1202)
**HID GLOBAL CORPORATION
(DH)**
611 Center Ridge Dr (78753-1013)
PHONE......................................800 237-7769
Bjorn Lidefelt, *President*
Audrey Hansen, *Principal*
Doug Cubell, *Business Mgr*
Samuel Asarnoj, *Senior VP*
Tim Moxon, *Vice Pres*
▲ EMP: 200
SQ FT: 12,800
SALES (est): 558.9MM
SALES (corp-wide): 9.7B **Privately Held**
WEB: www.hidglobal.com
SIC: 3825 1731 8741 Radio frequency
measuring equipment; access control
systems specialization; management
services

(G-1203)
HIGH END SYSTEMS INC (HQ)
2105 Gracy Farms Ln (78758-2963)
PHONE......................................512 836-2242
Dic K Titus, *CEO*
H David Scott, *President*
Lowell R Fowler, *Chairman*
Kelly A Elliott, *Corp Secy*
Julie Cymbalak, *COO*
◆ EMP: 77

SQ FT: 105,000
SALES (est): 24.2MM
SALES (corp-wide): 302.9MM **Privately
Held**
WEB: www.highend.com
SIC: 3648 5063 Lighting equipment; light-
ing fixtures
PA: Electronic Theatre Controls, Inc.
3031 Pleasant View Rd
Middleton WI 53562
608 831-4116

(G-1204)
**HILL COUNTRY PROVISIONS
LLC (PA)**
Also Called: Hudson Meat Market
1800 S Congress Ave (78704-3502)
PHONE......................................512 564-3013
Thomas Gardner,
EMP: 15 EST: 2017
SALES (est): 1.1MM **Privately Held**
WEB: www.hudsonsmeatmarket.com
SIC: 2013 5147 5421 Canned meats (ex-
cept baby food) from purchased meat;
meats & meat products; food & freezer
plans, meat

(G-1205)
HIPRO TECHNOLOGIES INC
13915 Burnet Rd Ste 308 (78728-6538)
PHONE......................................512 833-6600
Ming Hui Chuang, *President*
Frank Jih Chyang, *Treasurer*
Brett Brewer, *Admin Sec*
▲ EMP: 21
SALES (est): 1.9MM **Privately Held**
SIC: 3677 Transformers power supply,
electronic type

(G-1206)
**HMH SUPPLEMENTAL
PUBLISHERS**
Also Called: Harcourt Achieve, Inc
10801 N Mopac Expy 3-150 (78759-5459)
PHONE......................................512 721-7000
Linda Zecher, *CEO*
Rick Morgan, *Business Mgr*
William Bayers, *Exec VP*
Eric Shuman, *Exec VP*
Mott Nolley, *Director*
EMP: 200
SQ FT: 48,000
SALES (est): 19.4MM
SALES (corp-wide): 1.3B **Publicly Held**
WEB: www.hmhco.com
SIC: 2731 Book publishing
HQ: Houghton Mifflin Harcourt Publishing
Company
125 High St Ste 900
Boston MA 02110
617 351-5000

(G-1207)
HOLLIS BAKER SIGN CO INC
9711 Beck Cir (78758-5403)
PHONE......................................512 835-5782
Greg Baker, *President*
Viickie Baker, *Vice Pres*
EMP: 11 EST: 1955
SQ FT: 4,000
SALES (est): 600K **Privately Held**
WEB: www.custom-signs-banners.com
SIC: 7389 2759 Sign painting & lettering
shop; screen printing

(G-1208)
**HONEYWELL INTERNATIONAL
INC**
5307 Industrial Oaks Blvd # 430
(78735-8821)
PHONE......................................512 301-8414
Ujjwal Kumar, *Vice Pres*
Ric Sauer, *Branch Mgr*
EMP: 147
SALES (corp-wide): 36.7B **Publicly Held**
WEB: www.honeywell.com
SIC: 3724 Aircraft engines & engine parts
PA: Honeywell International Inc.
300 S Tryon St
Charlotte NC 28202
704 627-6200

(G-1209)
HORIBA INSTRUMENTS INC
Also Called: Horiba Stec
9701 Dessau Rd Ste 605 (78754-3941)
PHONE......................................408 730-4772
Yvette Fisher, *Accounts Mgr*
EMP: 30 **Privately Held**
WEB: www.horiba.com
SIC: 3829 5065 3825 Measuring & con-
trolling devices; semiconductor devices;
instruments to measure electricity
HQ: Horiba Instruments Incorporated
9755 Research Dr
Irvine CA 92618
949 250-4811

(G-1210)
HOTSCHEDULESCOM INC
6504 Bridge Point Pkwy # 42 (78730-5011)
PHONE......................................512 904-4299
Anthony Lye, *President*
Ray Pawlikowski, *COO*
Carl Benefiel, *Vice Pres*
Justin Buckley, *Vice Pres*
Casey Clinkenbeard, *Vice Pres*
EMP: 35 EST: 2000
SALES (est): 9.4MM **Privately Held**
WEB: www.hotschedules.com
SIC: 7372 Application computer software

(G-1211)
HOWMEDICA OSTEONICS CORP
Also Called: Stryker Orthopaedics
11500 Metric Blvd Ste 495 (78758-4145)
PHONE......................................512 491-0222
Richard Segina, *General Mgr*
Vicky Hunter, *Opers Mgr*
James David, *Sales Mgr*
Robert Long, *Manager*
EMP: 9
SALES (corp-wide): 14.3B **Publicly Held**
SIC: 3842 Surgical appliances & supplies
HQ: Howmedica Osteonics Corp.
325 Corporate Dr
Mahwah NJ 07430
201 831-5000

(G-1212)
**HUBBELL BUILDING AUTOMTN
INC**
Also Called: H B A
1812 Centre Creek Dr # 240 (78754-5145)
PHONE......................................512 450-1100
T H Powers, *President*
J H Biggart, *Vice Pres*
W A Cable, *Vice Pres*
R W Davies, *Vice Pres*
M C Preneta, *Vice Pres*
▲ EMP: 33
SQ FT: 15,000
SALES (est): 7MM
SALES (corp-wide): 4.1B **Publicly Held**
WEB: www.hubbell.com
SIC: 3648 3643 Lighting equipment; cur-
rent-carrying wiring devices
HQ: Hubbell Lighting, Inc.
701 Millennium Blvd
Greenville SC 29607

(G-1213)
HULL SUPPLY COMPANY INC
Also Called: Lamrite
5117 E Cesar Chavez St (78702-5142)
PHONE......................................512 385-1262
Rick Hull, *Branch Mgr*
EMP: 50
SALES (corp-wide): 18.4MM **Privately
Held**
WEB: www.hullsupply.com
SIC: 3083 2542 Laminated plastics plate
& sheet; partitions for floor attachment,
prefabricated: except wood
PA: Hull Supply Company, Inc.
5117 E Cesar Chavez St
Austin TX 78702
512 385-1262

(G-1214)
HUMAN POWER OF N COMPANY
1120 S Cap Of Tx Hwy (78746)
PHONE......................................855 636-4040
EMP: 9
SALES (est): 1.2MM **Privately Held**
SIC: 2834 Mfg Pharmaceutical Prepara-
tions

(G-1215)
HYPER9 INC
9015 Mt Ridge Dr Ste 140 (78759)
PHONE......................................800 748-0685
Bill Kennedy, *CEO*
Anthony Mariotti, *CFO*
EMP: 20
SALES (est): 1MM
SALES (corp-wide): 932.5MM **Publicly
Held**
WEB: www.solarwinds.com
SIC: 7372 Prepackaged software
HQ: Solarwinds North America, Inc.
7171 Southwest Pkwy
Austin TX 78735
512 682-9300

(G-1216)
ICHOR SYSTEMS INC
200 Parker Dr Ste C600 (78728-1231)
PHONE......................................512 246-9092
Henry Moreno, *Buyer*
Greg Hartenstein, *Engineer*
Amy Ybarra, *Human Res Mgr*
Charles Temple, *Branch Mgr*
Rudy Caudillo, *Program Mgr*
EMP: 95
SALES (corp-wide): 620.8MM **Publicly
Held**
WEB: www.ichorsystems.com
SIC: 3674 Semiconductors & related de-
vices
HQ: Ichor Systems, Inc.
3185 Laurelview Ct
Fremont CA 94538

(G-1217)
ICU MEDICAL INC
3900 Howard Ln (78728-6515)
PHONE......................................512 255-2000
Richard Alexander, *Engineer*
Renee Blaha, *Engineer*
Khurram Qazi, *Plant Engr*
Ruben Suarez, *Plant Engr*
Vivek Jain, *Manager*
EMP: 100
SALES (corp-wide): 1.2B **Publicly Held**
WEB: www.icumed.com
SIC: 2834 Pharmaceutical preparations
PA: Icu Medical, Inc.
951 Calle Amanecer
San Clemente CA 92673
949 366-2183

(G-1218)
IDEA INCUBATOR LP
4330 Gaines Ranch Loop (78735-6733)
PHONE......................................512 892-3022
Jason Burkle, *Partner*
Ryan Deiss, *Partner*
▲ EMP: 50
SALES (est): 3MM **Privately Held**
WEB: www.breakingnewsalerts.com
SIC: 2741

(G-1219)
IDEAL POWER INC
4120 Freidrich Ln Ste 100 (78744-1085)
PHONE......................................512 264-1542
Lon E Bell, *Ch of Bd*
Dan Brdar, *President*
Uwe Uhmeyer, *Vice Pres*
Andrew Young, *Engineer*
Timothy W Burns, *CFO*
EMP: 19
SQ FT: 14,782 **Privately Held**
WEB: www.idealpower.com
SIC: 3691 3621 Storage batteries; motors
& generators

(G-1220)
IGLEHART ENTERPRISES INC
4219 Iriona Bnd (78749-4914)
PHONE......................................512 282-2559
Martha Iglehart, *President*
EMP: 9
SALES (est): 535.9K **Privately Held**
SIC: 2741 Miscellaneous publishing

(G-1221)
IGT GLOBAL SOLUTIONS CORP
5301 Riata Park Ct Ste E (78727-3438)
PHONE......................................512 908-4310
John Graham, *Principal*
Cindy Hutchens, *Administration*
EMP: 50

SALES (corp-wide): 4.7B **Privately Held**
WEB: www.igt.com
SIC: 7372 Prepackaged software
HQ: Igt Global Solutions Corporation
10 Memorial Blvd
Providence RI 02903
401 392-1000

(G-1222)
IIAT SERVICES COMPANY (HQ)
Also Called: Indepndent Insur Agnts Assn Tx
1115 San Jacinto Blvd # 100 (78701-1902)
P.O. Box 684487 (78768-4487)
PHONE................................512 476-6281
Marit Peters, *President*
Watt Will E, *Vice Chairman*
Joe Vincent, *Manager*
David Vandelinder, *Exec Dir*
Landon O Gilvie, *Bd of Directors*
EMP: 30
SQ FT: 10,000
SALES: 4.4MM
SALES (corp-wide): 4.3MM **Privately Held**
WEB: www.iiat.org
SIC: 2721 Trade journals: publishing & printing
PA: Independent Insurance Agents
1115 San Jacinto Blvd # 100
Austin TX 78701
512 476-6281

(G-1223)
IKEY LTD
2621 Ridgepoint Dr # 235 (78754-5232)
P.O. Box 142443 (78714-2443)
PHONE................................512 837-0283
Steve Meyer, *CEO*
Courtney Schmierer-Davis, *General Mgr*
Nancy Ebe, *COO*
Dan Dixon, *Finance*
Ashley Mittag, *Sales Staff*
▲ EMP: 23 EST: 2001
SQ FT: 24,000
SALES (est): 7.3MM **Privately Held**
WEB: www.ikey.com
SIC: 3575 Keyboards, computer, office machine

(G-1224)
ILLUMITEX INC
6301 E Stassney Ln 6-400 (78744-3091)
PHONE................................512 279-5020
Jeff Bisberg, *CEO*
Eric Helwig, *Vice Pres*
Yvonne Reinke, *Vice Pres*
Dennis Riling, *Vice Pres*
John Spencer, *Vice Pres*
▲ EMP: 70
SQ FT: 24,000
SALES (est): 13.1MM **Privately Held**
WEB: www.illumitex.com
SIC: 3646 Commercial indusl & institutional electric lighting fixtures

(G-1225)
IMPACT FIRE SERVICES LLC
14000 Summit Dr Ste 700 (78728-7109)
PHONE................................512 243-7788
Benjamin Fowler, *Branch Mgr*
EMP: 23
SALES (corp-wide): 39.8MM **Privately Held**
WEB: www.impactfireservices.com
SIC: 3669 Fire alarm apparatus, electric
HQ: Impact Fire Services, Llc
103 12th St Ste 200
Pflugerville TX 78660

(G-1226)
INCENERGY LLC
12012 Tech Blvd Ste 101 (78727)
P.O. Box 92682 (78709-2682)
PHONE................................512 327-2020
Shane Mericle, *COO*
Barry McConachie,
Liz Cunningham,
EMP: 12
SALES (est): 2.3MM **Privately Held**
WEB: www.incenergy.com
SIC: 3822 Auto controls regulating residntl & coml environmt & applncs

(G-1227)
INCHBUG LLC
Also Called: Inchbug.com
9421 Neils Thompson Dr (78758-7652)
PHONE................................512 837-1010
Brenda Feldman, *Mng Member*
▲ EMP: 10
SQ FT: 9,000
SALES (est): 2MM **Privately Held**
WEB: www.inchbug.com
SIC: 2679 Tags & labels, paper

(G-1228)
INFOCYTE INC
Also Called: Infocyte Security
3801 N Capital Of Texas H (78746-1473)
PHONE................................844 463-6298
Chris Gerritz, *President*
Virginia Satrom, *VP Mktg*
Nick Leasure, *Manager*
Ryan Morris, *CTO*
EMP: 25 EST: 2014
SALES (est): 321.3K **Privately Held**
WEB: www.infocyte.com
SIC: 7372 Prepackaged software

(G-1229)
INSIGHT EQUITY HOLDINGS LLC
5910 Courtyard Dr Ste 210 (78731-3334)
PHONE................................512 372-9063
EMP: 239 **Privately Held**
WEB: www.insightequity.com
SIC: 3999 Atomizers, toiletry
PA: Insight Equity Holdings Llc
1400 Civic Pl Ste 250
Southlake TX 76092

(G-1230)
INSURGICAL INC
Also Called: Insurgical Powered Instruments
11002 Metric Blvd Ste C (78758-4191)
PHONE................................512 318-2980
Peter Aman, *CEO*
Dave Martinez, *Vice Pres*
Frederick Matthews, *Vice Pres*
Matt Jones, *Opers Staff*
Rich Acevedo, *Engineer*
EMP: 13 EST: 2012
SQ FT: 3,500
SALES (est): 1.3MM **Privately Held**
WEB: www.insurgical.com
SIC: 3841 Surgical & medical instruments

(G-1231)
INTEGRATED MGT CONCEPTS INC
3800 N Lamar Blvd Ste 200 (78756-0003)
PHONE................................805 778-1629
Mark Tillema, *President*
Bela Mikofalvy, *Vice Pres*
Karen Rose, *Treasurer*
Mark Tilema, *Manager*
EMP: 25
SALES (est): 2.7MM **Privately Held**
WEB: www.decisionedge.com
SIC: 7372 Application computer software

(G-1232)
INTEL CORPORATION
1300 S Mo Pac Expy (78746-1203)
PHONE................................512 362-1000
Hui Fu, *General Mgr*
Neil Rosenberg, *Chief*
Timothy Brodnax, *Engineer*
Ben Byron, *Engineer*
Alexander Groszewski, *Engineer*
EMP: 60
SALES (corp-wide): 77.8B **Publicly Held**
WEB: www.intel.com
SIC: 3577 Computer peripheral equipment
PA: Intel Corporation
2200 Mission College Blvd
Santa Clara CA 95054
408 765-8080

(G-1233)
INTERACT INC
Also Called: Interact Software Systems
9390 Res Blvd Ste Ii100 (78759)
PHONE................................512 501-2680
Lynn McKee, *President*
Greg Gissler, *Vice Pres*
EMP: 50
SALES (est): 2.5MM **Privately Held**
SIC: 7372 Prepackaged software

(G-1234)
INTERACTIVE LIFE FORMS LLC
Also Called: Fleshlight
7000 Burleson Rd Ste C (78744-3213)
PHONE................................888 804-4453
Todd Porter, *Opers Mgr*
Richard Millan, *CFO*
Daniel Pacheco, *Marketing Staff*
Roger Reyes, *Marketing Staff*
Wayne Washington, *Manager*
◆ EMP: 100
SQ FT: 12,000
SALES (est): 34.7MM **Privately Held**
WEB: www.interactivelifeforms.com
SIC: 2821 Plastics materials & resins

(G-1235)
INTERLINE TRAVEL & TOUR INC (PA)
Also Called: Interline Vacations
12708 Riata Vst Cira 125 (78727)
PHONE................................512 691-4500
Lawrence K Fleischman, *CEO*
Paddy Mark, *Vice Pres*
Becky Ortiz, *Opers Staff*
Deana Wilson, *Controller*
Lori Ploch, *Manager*
EMP: 50 EST: 2001
SQ FT: 6,543
SALES (est): 5.3MM **Privately Held**
WEB: www.perx.com
SIC: 4724 4725 2741 Tourist agency arranging transport, lodging & car rental; tour operators; miscellaneous publishing

(G-1236)
INTERNATIONAL BIOMEDICAL LTD (PA)
Also Called: Airborne Life Support System
8206 Cross Park Dr (78754-5252)
P.O. Box 143449 (78714-3449)
PHONE................................512 873-0033
◆ EMP: 60 EST: 1974
SQ FT: 30,000
SALES (est): 14.3MM **Privately Held**
WEB: www.int-bio.com
SIC: 3842 Radiation shielding aprons, gloves, sheeting, etc.; infant incubators

(G-1237)
INTERNATIONAL BIOPHYSICS CORP
2101-2 E St Elmo Rd Ste 2 (78744)
P.O. Box 18238 (78760-8238)
PHONE................................512 326-3244
David Shockley, *President*
William Wilkinson, *Vice Pres*
Ray Ayala, *Manager*
▲ EMP: 20
SQ FT: 6,500
SALES (est): 3.9MM **Privately Held**
WEB: www.biophysicscorp.com
SIC: 3841 5047 Surgical & medical instruments; medical equipment & supplies

(G-1238)
INTERNATIONAL INNOVATIONS INC
Also Called: International Hanger
3933 Spicewood Springs Rd (78759-8761)
PHONE................................512 600-4517
Kurt Lemke, *President*
Edward Hite, *Vice Pres*
Jacquelyn George, *Treasurer*
Aric Pearson, *Sales Staff*
Vannesa Moore, *Office Mgr*
◆ EMP: 65
SALES (est): 13.3MM **Privately Held**
WEB: www.hangersdirect.com
SIC: 5199 2499 Clothes hangers; garment hangers, wood

(G-1239)
INTESOLV INC
8303 N Mopac Expy 127b (78759-8363)
PHONE................................512 681-7272
Thomas Keith, *President*
Sergio Angulo, *Software Dev*
Justin Luther, *Software Dev*
EMP: 12 EST: 1989
SALES (est): 847.8K **Privately Held**
WEB: www.intesolv.com
SIC: 7372 Application computer software; business oriented computer software

(G-1240)
INTROGEN THERAPEUTICS INC
301 Congress Ave Ste 1850 (78701-2996)
PHONE................................512 708-9310
J David Enloe Jr, *President*
David L Parker PHD, *Vice Pres*
Robert E Sobol MD, *Vice Pres*
James W Albrecht Jr, *CFO*
David G Nance, *Director*
EMP: 80
SQ FT: 8,000
SALES (est): 12.3MM **Privately Held**
WEB: www.viahope.org
SIC: 2834 Pharmaceutical preparations

(G-1241)
INVIEW TECHNOLOGY CORPORATION (PA)
6201 E Oltorf St Ste 400 (78741-7509)
PHONE................................512 243-8751
Robert Bridge, *CEO*
Lenore McMackin, *President*
Bill Chatterjee, *Vice Pres*
Sujoy Chatterjee, *Vice Pres*
EMP: 9
SALES (est): 680.6K **Privately Held**
WEB: www.inviewcorp.com
SIC: 3861 Photographic equipment & supplies

(G-1242)
ION ART INC
407 Radam Ln Ste A100 (78745-1253)
PHONE................................512 326-9333
Sharon Gaisford, *President*
Gregory Keshishian, *Vice Pres*
Thomas Staats, *Project Mgr*
Carrie Wood, *Project Mgr*
Ion Art, *Opers Mgr*
EMP: 14
SQ FT: 2,400
SALES (est): 1MM **Privately Held**
WEB: www.ionart.com
SIC: 3993 Neon signs

(G-1243)
IREX GROUP LTD
12317 Tech Blvd Ste 150 (78727)
PHONE................................512 835-1200
Matthew Ache, *Partner*
▲ EMP: 23
SALES: 9.5MM **Privately Held**
WEB: www.irexmfg.com
SIC: 3651 Electronic kits for home assembly: radio, TV, phonograph
PA: Tyrex Group, Ltd.
12317 Tech Blvd Ste 100
Austin TX 78727

(G-1244)
IRIS BIOTECH LLC (HQ)
212 Technology Blvd (78727)
PHONE................................512 219-8020
Homi Shamir, *President*
EMP: 30 **Publicly Held**
SIC: 6719 3826 Investment holding companies, except banks; analytical instruments

(G-1245)
IXPALIA INC
Also Called: Fiesta Tortilla Factory
3800 Promontory Point Dr (78744-1100)
P.O. Box 17563 (78760-7563)
PHONE................................512 389-0389
Jaime Picos, *President*
Peter Alvaro, *Human Res Mgr*
Javier Picos, *Maintence Staff*
EMP: 30
SQ FT: 10,000
SALES (est): 6.6MM **Privately Held**
WEB: www.fiestatortillas.com
SIC: 2096 2099 5812 Tortilla chips; tortillas, fresh or refrigerated; Mexican restaurant

(G-1246)
IXRF INC
10421 Old Manchaca Rd (78748-1441)
PHONE................................512 386-6100
William Snider, *CEO*
Mandi Hellested, *General Mgr*
Michael Caspani, *Bd of Directors*
EMP: 10

SALES (est): 542.6K **Privately Held**
WEB: www.ixrfsystems.com
SIC: **3826** Analytical instruments

(G-1247)
IXRF SYSTEMS INC
10421 Old Manchaca Rd # 620
(78748-1441)
PHONE....................................512 386-6100
Kenneth C Witherspoon, *President*
Kenneth Witherspoon, *President*
Travis Witherspoon, *Opers Staff*
EMP: 15
SQ FT: 6,000
SALES (est): 4.5MM **Privately Held**
WEB: www.ixrfsystems.com
SIC: **3826** Analytical instruments

(G-1248)
JACKAL MERGER SUB A LLC
303 Colorado St Ste 3000 (78701-4654)
PHONE....................................737 704-2300
Matthew Gallagher, *President*
EMP: 94
SALES: 581.6MM
SALES (corp-wide): 9.3B **Publicly Held**
WEB: www.jaggedpeakenergy.com
SIC: **1311** Crude petroleum & natural gas
HQ: Parsley Energy, Inc.
303 Colorado St Ste 3000
Austin TX 78701
737 704-2300

(G-1249)
JAGGED PEAK ENERGY MGT LLC
303 Colorado St Ste 3000 (78701-4654)
PHONE....................................720 215-3700
Joe Jaggers, *CEO*
EMP: 30 EST: 2013
SALES (est): 212.5K
SALES (corp-wide): 47.8MM **Privately Held**
SIC: **1382** Oil & gas exploration services
PA: Jagged Peak Energy Llc
1401 Lawrence St Ste 1800
Denver CO 80202
720 215-3700

(G-1250)
JAMES AVERY CRAFTSMAN INC
9600 Interstate Hwy (78748)
PHONE....................................512 541-3823
EMP: 17
SALES (corp-wide): 180.9MM **Privately Held**
WEB: www.jamesavery.com
SIC: **5944 3915** Jewelry, precious stones & precious metals; jewelers' castings
PA: James Avery Craftsman, Inc.
145 Avery Rd
Kerrville TX 78028
830 353-4001

(G-1251)
JANIS LITCHFIELD
Also Called: Rapid Filter
4330 Gaines Ranch Loop # 120
(78735-6733)
PHONE....................................325 625-1001
Janis Litchfield, *Principal*
Michael Otto, *Principal*
EMP: 12
SALES (est): 1.5MM **Privately Held**
WEB: www.rapidfilter.com
SIC: **3589** Water filters & softeners, household type

(G-1252)
JD ABRAMS LP (HQ)
Also Called: Trans-Mountain Equipment
5811 Trade Center Dr # 1 (78744-1309)
PHONE....................................512 322-4000
Brad Everett, *Ch of Bd*
James D Abrams Sr, *Partner*
J Kelly Gallagher, *Partner*
Bob Underwood, *Partner*
Steven Zbranek, *Principal*
EMP: 30 EST: 1966
SQ FT: 11,000

SALES (est): 155.1MM **Privately Held**
WEB: www.jdabrams.com
SIC: **1611 1622 1629 3272** General contractor, highway & street construction; bridge construction; dam construction; prestressed concrete products
PA: Abrams International Incorporated
111 Congress Ave Ste 2400
Austin TX 78701
512 322-4000

(G-1253)
JD ABRAMS LP
Also Called: Austin Pre-Stressed
7300 Us Highway 183 S (78744-8700)
PHONE....................................512 243-1090
James D Abrams Jr, *Manager*
EMP: 32
SQ FT: 8,796
SALES (corp-wide): 155.1MM **Privately Held**
WEB: www.jdabrams.com
SIC: **3272 1611** Prestressed concrete products; general contractor, highway & street construction
HQ: J.D. Abrams, L.P.
5811 Trade Center Dr # 1
Austin TX 78744
512 322-4000

(G-1254)
JEEVES INFORMATION SYSTEMS INC
7500 Rialto Blvd Ste 230 (78735-8531)
PHONE....................................512 333-4418
Nicolas Tognoni, *President*
Gothenburg Gotheen, *Partner*
EMP: 14
SALES (est): 1.1MM **Privately Held**
WEB: www.jeeveserp.com
SIC: **7372** Business oriented computer software

(G-1255)
JI COMMUNICATIONS INC
9229 Wterford Ctr Ste 100 (78758-7686)
P.O. Box 26655 (78755-0655)
PHONE....................................512 346-6921
Herman Juarez, *Principal*
William Martin, *Principal*
EMP: 62
SALES (est): 334.4K **Privately Held**
SIC: **2741 6411** Directories: publishing & printing; insurance agents, brokers & service
HQ: York Risk Services Group
10535 Boyer Blvd Ste 100
Austin TX
512 427-2300

(G-1256)
JIVE SOFTWARE INC (DH)
401 Congress Ave Ste 2650 (78701-3708)
PHONE....................................877 495-3700
Elisa A Steele, *CEO*
Scott F Brighton, *President*
Jeff Lautenbach, *President*
Ofer Ben-David, *Exec VP*
Falak Ravani, *Engineer*
EMP: 57 EST: 2001
SQ FT: 12,500
SALES (est): 204MM **Privately Held**
WEB: www.jivesoftware.com
SIC: **4899 7372** Data communication services; prepackaged software

(G-1257)
JOHN COLE CHEMICAL CORPORATION
Also Called: Josco Products
6110 Trade Center Dr # 102 (78744-1301)
P.O. Box 17545 (78760-7545)
PHONE....................................512 443-1037
Colleen Halbrook, *President*
Colleen Cole, *President*
Joan Cole, *Corp Secy*
Barbie Thomas, *COO*
John Cole, *Vice Pres*
▲ EMP: 28
SQ FT: 18,000
SALES (est): 5.7MM **Privately Held**
WEB: www.joscoproducts.com
SIC: **2299 5162 5099** Recovering textile fibers from clippings & rags; resins; containers: glass, metal or plastic

(G-1258)
JOHNSON CABINETS & WOODWORKING
15401 Storm Dr (78734-2772)
PHONE....................................512 266-7099
William D Johnson, *President*
Julie Johnson, *Vice Pres*
EMP: 12
SQ FT: 6,700
SALES (est): 1.2MM **Privately Held**
WEB: www.johnsoncabinet.com
SIC: **2434** Cabinet building & installation

(G-1259)
JOHNSON CONTROLS INC
401 Center Ridge Dr # 400 (78753-1397)
PHONE....................................512 973-3555
Mike Blankenship, *Manager*
EMP: 40 **Privately Held**
WEB: www.johnsoncontrols.com
SIC: **1711 7623 3822** Warm air heating & air conditioning contractor; air conditioning repair; auto controls regulating residntl & coml environmt & applncs
HQ: Johnson Controls, Inc.
5757 N Green Bay Ave
Glendale WI 53209
800 382-2804

(G-1260)
JOLLYRHINO INC
5100 Cuesta Verde (78746-1560)
PHONE....................................909 732-8507
Ben Murphy, *President*
John Osborne, *Principal*
Dennis Jackson, *CFO*
EMP: 12 EST: 2016
SALES (est): 248.5K **Privately Held**
SIC: **8742 7372** Financial consultant; business oriented computer software

(G-1261)
JORDAN TECHNOLOGIES LLC (PA)
16310 Bratton Ln Ste 350 (78728-2402)
PHONE....................................502 267-8344
Mark A Jordan, *President*
Michael Browne, *Vice Pres*
John F Jordan, *Vice Pres*
Paul D Jordan, *Vice Pres*
Gene Sparkman, *Vice Pres*
◆ EMP: 63
SALES (est): 14.9MM **Privately Held**
WEB: www.aereon.com
SIC: **3671** Gas or vapor tubes

(G-1262)
JP3 MEASUREMENT LLC
4109 Todd Ln Ste 200 (78744-1033)
PHONE....................................512 537-8450
Matt Thomas, *President*
Gregg Williams, *Senior VP*
William Howard, *Vice Pres*
Grant Kerkman, *Project Mgr*
Charles De Tarr, *CFO*
EMP: 22
SQ FT: 3,000
SALES (est): 9.6MM
SALES (corp-wide): 119.3MM **Publicly Held**
WEB: www.jp3measurement.com
SIC: **1381 1389** Drilling oil & gas wells; testing, measuring, surveying & analysis services
PA: Flotek Industries, Inc.
8846 N Sam Houston Pkwy W # 150
Houston TX 77064
713 849-9911

(G-1263)
K & K LANGHAM LTD
Also Called: Austin Counter Tops
11209 Metric Blvd Ste B (78758-4184)
PHONE....................................512 835-5100
Mark Raby, *Partner*
EMP: 80
SQ FT: 35,000
SALES (est): 10.1MM **Privately Held**
SIC: **3281 2541** Marble, building: cut & shaped; table or counter tops, plastic laminated

(G-1264)
KAMMOK GEAR LLC
7301 Burnet Rd 101-161 (78757-2250)
PHONE....................................512 947-7344
Jeffrey Scott McEvilly,
Ty Clark,
Grant Hickman,
EMP: 9
SALES (est): 147.8K **Privately Held**
WEB: www.kammok.com
SIC: **2399** Hammocks & other net products

(G-1265)
KAY ROCK BIT COMPANY (PA)
2928 Manor Rd (78722-1411)
P.O. Box 684865 (78768-4865)
PHONE....................................512 478-2900
Jim Mattox, *President*
EMP: 15
SALES (est): 1.4MM **Privately Held**
WEB: www.kayrockbitcompany.com
SIC: **3532** Bits, except oil & gas field tools, rock

(G-1266)
KEGSPEED LLC
12500 Pluto Ln (78727-5127)
PHONE....................................267 714-8854
Timothy Jones, *President*
EMP: 10
SALES (est): 548.8K **Privately Held**
WEB: www.kegspeed.com
SIC: **3411 3585 3663** Metal cans; beer dispensing equipment; radio broadcasting & communications equipment

(G-1267)
KERIO TECHNOLOGIES INC
401 Congress Ave Ste 2650 (78701-3708)
PHONE....................................408 496-4500
Mirek Kren, *CEO*
Martin Viktora, *CEO*
Scott Schrieman, *President*
Alan Hughes, *CFO*
EMP: 107
SALES (est): 8.9MM **Privately Held**
WEB: www.gfi.com
SIC: **7372** Business oriented computer software

(G-1268)
KHOROS LLC (PA)
7300 Ranch Road 2222 # 1 (78730-3255)
PHONE....................................415 757-3100
Sandy Dorman, *Project Mgr*
Sam Monti, *CFO*
Katherine Calvert, *Chief Mktg Ofcr*
Jack Blaha, *Mng Member*
Chanh Dinh, *Software Engr*
EMP: 400
SALES (est): 109.4MM **Privately Held**
WEB: www.khoros.com
SIC: **7372** Business oriented computer software

(G-1269)
KIDASA SOFTWARE INC
1114 Lost Creek Blvd # 300 (78746-6318)
PHONE....................................512 368-2326
Susan Butler, *President*
Donald Elder, *Vice Pres*
EMP: 10
SQ FT: 1,800
SALES (est): 1.3MM **Privately Held**
WEB: www.kidasa.com
SIC: **7372** Prepackaged software

(G-1270)
KLA CORPORATION
8834 N Capital Of Texas H (78759-6396)
PHONE....................................512 231-4200
Dave Price, *Marketing Staff*
Patrick Lee, *Branch Mgr*
Alan Davila, *Software Engr*
EMP: 50
SALES (corp-wide): 5.8B **Publicly Held**
WEB: www.kla-tencor.com
SIC: **3674** Semiconductors & related devices
PA: Kla Corporation
1 Technology Dr
Milpitas CA 95035
408 875-3000

(G-1271)
KODIAK ASSEMBLY SOLUTIONS LLC
2400 Grand Avenue Pkwy # 10
(78728-3952)
PHONE................................512 275-1700
Susan Wandell, *Principal*
EMP: 46
SQ FT: 30,000
SALES (est): 15.8MM **Privately Held**
WEB: www.kodiakassembly.com
SIC: 3672 Printed circuit boards

(G-1272)
KONY INC (HQ)
9225 Bee Cave Rd Bldg As (78733-6203)
PHONE................................512 792-2900
Thomas Hogan, *President*
Eunice Bergin, *President*
Guilherme Bujes, *President*
Jim Lambert, *President*
Ken Leonard, *Partner*
EMP: 120
SQ FT: 10,000
SALES (est): 88.5MM
SALES (corp-wide): 588.3MM **Privately Held**
WEB: www.kony.com
SIC: 7372 Application computer software
PA: Temenos Ag
  Rue De L'Ecole-De-Chimie 2
  GenCve GE 1205
  227 081-150

(G-1273)
KOVACH ENCLOSURE SYSTEMS LLC
2415 Kramer Ln Ste D (78758-4066)
PHONE................................480 926-9292
EMP: 70
SALES (est): 1.4MM
SALES (corp-wide): 66.4MM **Privately Held**
SIC: 1761 1793 3211 Roofing, siding & sheet metal work; glass & glazing work; flat glass
PA: Kovach Enclosure Systems, Llc
  3195 W Armstrong Pl
  Chandler AZ 85286
  480 926-9292

(G-1274)
KUDZOOKINECT INC
Also Called: Liveo
1145 W 5th St Ste 200 (78703-5358)
PHONE................................512 363-0704
EMP: 27 EST: 2012
SQ FT: 10,000
SALES (est): 1.9MM **Privately Held**
SIC: 7372 Prepackaged Software Services

(G-1275)
KUHLMAN CELLARS LLC
1602 Sharon Ln (78703-3234)
PHONE................................512 920-2675
EMP: 20 EST: 2014
SALES (est): 1MM **Privately Held**
WEB: www.kuhlmancellars.com
SIC: 2084 Wines

(G-1276)
KWEST RV LLC
Also Called: American Dream Vction Rv Rentl
10777 Us Highway 183 S (78747-2247)
PHONE................................512 294-2634
Kurt West, *President*
EMP: 14
SALES (est): 1.5MM **Privately Held**
WEB: www.americandreamvacations.net
SIC: 3799 7519 5561 Recreational vehicles; recreational vehicle rental; recreational vehicle dealers

(G-1277)
KYLE BUNTING HOLDINGS INC
1340 Arprt Commrce Dr (78741-6831)
PHONE................................512 264-1148
Kyle Bunting, *President*
EMP: 14
SALES (est): 1.7MM **Privately Held**
WEB: www.kylebunting.com
SIC: 3999 Furniture, barber & beauty shop

(G-1278)
KYOCERA MEDICAL TECH INC
10415 Morado Cir I350 (78759-5696)
PHONE................................909 557-2360
Takahiro Kobayashi, *President*
EMP: 57
SALES (est): 1.6MM **Privately Held**
WEB: www.kyocera-medical.com
SIC: 3841 Surgical & medical instruments

(G-1279)
L3 TECHNOLOGIES INC
817 W Howard Ln (78753-1052)
PHONE................................512 251-3441
Scott Morehead, *Manager*
EMP: 140
SALES (corp-wide): 11.3B **Publicly Held**
WEB: www.l3t.com
SIC: 3728 3724 7699 5088 Aircraft parts & equipment; aircraft engines & engine parts; aircraft & heavy equipment repair services; aircraft & parts; testing laboratories
HQ: L3 Technologies, Inc.
  600 3rd Ave Fl 34
  New York NY 10016
  212 805-5234

(G-1280)
LAMMES CANDIES SINCE 1885 INC (PA)
Also Called: Lamme's Candies
200b Parker Dr Ste B500 (78728-1228)
PHONE................................512 310-1885
Pam Teich, *President*
Bryan Teich, *Vice Pres*
Lana K Schmidt, *Treasurer*
Lana Schmidt, *Admin Sec*
EMP: 15
SQ FT: 16,000
SALES (est): 20.3MM **Privately Held**
WEB: www.lammes.com
SIC: 5441 2064 Candy; chocolate candy, except solid chocolate

(G-1281)
LAMRITE
5117 E Cesar Chavez St (78702-5142)
PHONE................................512 385-4455
Richard Hull, *Principal*
EMP: 11
SQ FT: 41,999
SALES (est): 887.9K **Privately Held**
WEB: www.hullsupply.com
SIC: 2542 3083 Partitions for floor attachment, prefabricated: except wood; laminated plastics plate & sheet

(G-1282)
LAP KING LLC
2802 Flintrock Trce # 101 (78738-1744)
PHONE................................512 415-3034
Jospeh Jarke, *CEO*
Michael Swett,
EMP: 10
SALES (est): 1.1MM **Privately Held**
WEB: www.lap-king.com
SIC: 3577 Computer peripheral equipment

(G-1283)
LAUREN CONCRETE INC
4501 Shaw Ln Plant 2/9 29 Plant (78744)
P.O. Box 3737, Pflugerville (78691-3737)
PHONE................................512 389-2113
Ronald W Klatt, *President*
Melvin Klatt, *Vice Pres*
EMP: 80
SQ FT: 1,260
SALES (est): 18.8MM **Privately Held**
WEB: www.laurenconcrete.com
SIC: 3273 Ready-mixed concrete

(G-1284)
LDIA HOLDINGS LLC
Also Called: Prometheus SEC Group Globl
3019 Alvin Devane Blvd (78741-7422)
PHONE................................512 247-3700
Richard Gross, *President*
James Braden, *Mfg Spvr*
Kevin Bray, *Sales Mgr*
EMP: 50 EST: 2016
SQ FT: 10,000

SALES (est): 8MM **Privately Held**
WEB: www.psgglobal.net
SIC: 3315 3663 3669 3822 Steel wire & related products; radio & TV communications equipment; emergency alarms; auto controls regulating residntl & coml environmt & applncs; custom computer programming services; security systems services

(G-1285)
LDR HOLDING CORPORATION (HQ)
13785 Res Blvd Ste 200 (78750)
PHONE................................512 344-3333
Christophe Lavigne, *President*
Scott Way, *Exec VP*
Robert McNamara, *CFO*
Denise Cruz, *Controller*
Rashad Hodge, *Regl Sales Mgr*
EMP: 27
SQ FT: 67,410
SALES: 164.4MM
SALES (corp-wide): 7.9B **Publicly Held**
WEB: www.ir.ldr.com
SIC: 3841 Surgical & medical instruments
PA: Zimmer Biomet Holdings, Inc.
  345 E Main St
  Warsaw IN 46580
  574 267-6131

(G-1286)
LEE QUIGLEY COMPANY
700 Rockmead Dr Ste 216 (78745)
PHONE................................512 762-4046
Tom Stoub, *Branch Mgr*
EMP: 11
SALES (corp-wide): 6.1MM **Privately Held**
WEB: www.leequigley.com
SIC: 3341 Recovery & refining of nonferrous metals
PA: The Lee Quigley Company
  21013 Old Sorters Rd A
  Porter TX 77365
  281 358-9608

(G-1287)
LEFT RIGHT MEDIA LLC
7910 Ceberry Dr (78759-8914)
PHONE................................972 897-6578
Thomas Christopher Perez,
EMP: 9
SALES (est): 687.5K **Privately Held**
WEB: www.chrisleftright.com
SIC: 2721 Magazines: publishing only, not printed on site

(G-1288)
LEGERITY HOLDINGS INC
4509 Freidrich Ln Ste 200 (78744-1866)
PHONE................................512 228-5400
EMP: 180
SQ FT: 70,000
SALES (est): 15MM **Privately Held**
SIC: 3674 8711 7373 Semiconductors And Related Devices, Nsk

(G-1289)
LETS GEL INC (PA)
Also Called: Gel Pro
11525b Stnholw Dr 200 (78758-3213)
PHONE................................512 628-1700
Robert McMahan, *CEO*
Joel Kocher, *President*
Scott Robertson, *COO*
Zac Fellabaum, *CFO*
Lisa McMahan, *Relations*
◆ EMP: 23
SQ FT: 10,000
SALES (est): 11MM **Privately Held**
WEB: www.gelpro.com
SIC: 2273 Mats & matting

(G-1290)
LEVELFIELDCOM INC
Also Called: On Line Agency
8705 Shoal Creek Blvd # 205
(78757-6848)
PHONE................................512 401-9200
Jude Samson, *President*
George A Thompson, *Vice Pres*
EMP: 15 EST: 2001
SALES (est): 1.5MM **Privately Held**
WEB: www.levelfield.com
SIC: 7372 Prepackaged software

(G-1291)
LIBREDIGITAL INC (DH)
Also Called: Newsstand.com
1835 Kramer Ln Ste B150 (78758-4230)
PHONE................................512 334-5100
Russell P Reeder, *President*
Myles Fuchs, *Senior VP*
Tyler Ruse, *Vice Pres*
Thad Swiderski, *VP Opers*
Kelly Bates, *Project Mgr*
EMP: 13
SQ FT: 22,000
SALES: 11.1MM
SALES (corp-wide): 3B **Publicly Held**
WEB: www.libredigital.com
SIC: 2711 7375 2741 Newspapers: publishing only, not printed on site; on-line data base information retrieval; miscellaneous publishing
HQ: Lsc Communications, Inc.
  4101 Winfield Rd
  Warrenville IL 60555
  773 272-9200

(G-1292)
LICENSE PLATES OF TEXAS LLC
Also Called: My Plates
7301 N Fm 620 Rd Ste 155 (78726-4537)
PHONE................................512 583-8585
Matt Rocco,
James Humrichouse,
Ashok Kumar,
Nina X Vaca-Humrichouse,
EMP: 15
SALES (est): 2.2MM **Privately Held**
WEB: www.myplates.com
SIC: 2796 Platemaking services

(G-1293)
LIFE TECHNOLOGIES CORPORATION
Also Called: Thermo Fisher Scientific
2130 Woodward St (78744-1038)
PHONE................................512 721-4857
Matt Winkler, *CEO*
Ricky Liu, *Business Mgr*
EMP: 13
SALES (corp-wide): 25.5B **Publicly Held**
WEB: www.thermofisher.com
SIC: 3826 Analytical instruments
HQ: Life Technologies Corporation
  5781 Van Allen Way
  Carlsbad CA 92008
  760 603-7200

(G-1294)
LIQUID LITIGATION MGT INC
Also Called: Llm
1300 Guadalupe St Ste 100 (78701-1643)
P.O. Box 1527 (78767-1527)
PHONE................................210 757-4881
Cas Campaigne, *President*
Lindsay Stevens, *President*
Jason Hetherington, *Project Mgr*
Jeroen Vanagtmael, *CFO*
Scott Pittman, *Admin Sec*
EMP: 10
SALES (est): 1.9MM **Privately Held**
WEB: www.liquidlitigation.com
SIC: 7373 7372 Systems software development services; application computer software

(G-1295)
LIVE SODA LLC
Also Called: Live Soda Kombucha
4020 S Industrial Dr # 133 (78744-1155)
PHONE................................512 888-9959
Laura Fleetwood, *Vice Pres*
Joel Skurnik, *Vice Pres*
Taryn Block, *CFO*
Jon Hill, *Sales Staff*
Trevor Ross, *Mng Member*
EMP: 15 EST: 2012
SALES (est): 2.6MM **Privately Held**
WEB: www.livesoda.com
SIC: 2086 5149 Tea, iced: packaged in cans, bottles, etc.; tea

(G-1296)
LMS ACQUISITIONS LLC
Also Called: LMS Fulfillment
2032 Centimeter Cir (78758-4956)
PHONE................................512 371-7028

Terri Lynn Whaley, *Principal*
Stephen Teter,
Jennifer Horton,
▲ **EMP:** 10
SALES (est): 993.6K **Privately Held**
WEB: www.lmsfulfillment.com
SIC: 7336 7389 4225 7372 Graphic arts
& related design; printing broker; general
warehousing & storage; prepackaged
software

(G-1297)
LOBATO STUDIO LLC
1300 W Anderson Ln (78757-1450)
PHONE..............................512 483-1327
Nancy Lira, *Vice Pres*
Ariel Lovato, *Vice Pres*
EMP: 10
SALES (est): 1.3MM **Privately Held**
WEB: www.porteusa.com
SIC: 3442 Metal doors

(G-1298)
LOGITECH INC
Lifesize Communications
1601 S Mopac Expy Ste 100 (78746)
PHONE..............................512 347-9300
Colin Buechler, *Division Mgr*
Michael Helmbrecht, *Vice Pres*
Clayton Reed, *Vice Pres*
Shyam Thirumalaisamy, *Opers Staff*
Robert Wallis, *Opers Staff*
EMP: 80
SALES (corp-wide): 3B **Privately Held**
WEB: www.logitech.com
SIC: 5065 3663 Video equipment, elec-
tronic; television broadcasting & commu-
nications equipment
HQ: Logitech Inc.
7700 Gateway Blvd
Newark CA 94560
510 795-8500

(G-1299)
LONE STAR INDUSTRIES INC
2320 Tom Miller St (78723-5382)
PHONE..............................512 917-8394
EMP: 10
SALES (corp-wide): 395.5MM **Privately
Held**
WEB: www.buzziunicemusa.com
SIC: 3241 Portland cement
HQ: Lone Star Industries Inc
10401 N Meridian St # 120
Indianapolis IN 46290
317 706-3314

(G-1300)
LONE STAR READY-MIX LP
7900 Old Manor Rd (78724-2600)
PHONE..............................512 260-3629
Ana Rodriguez, *Branch Mgr*
EMP: 28
SALES (corp-wide): 3MM **Privately Held**
SIC: 3273 Ready-mixed concrete
PA: Lone Star Ready-Mix, Lp
9210 Fm 2243
Leander TX 78641
512 260-0300

(G-1301)
LOREDO TRUSS COMPANY INC
2506 Ferguson Ln (78754-4603)
P.O. Box 140006 (78714-0006)
PHONE..............................512 926-1782
Eleuterio Loredo Jr, *President*
Judy Loredo, *Corp Secy*
Virginia Gonzalez, *Vice Pres*
Virginia Loredo, *Vice Pres*
EMP: 21
SQ FT: 2,000
SALES (est): 3.6MM **Privately Held**
WEB: www.loredotruss.com
SIC: 2439 Trusses, wooden roof

(G-1302)
**LOS ANGLES TMES
CMMNCTIONS LLC**
119 E 10th St (78701-2419)
PHONE..............................512 476-7777
Jack Harrison, *Branch Mgr*
EMP: 160

SALES (corp-wide): 930.8MM **Privately
Held**
WEB: www.latimes.com
SIC: 2711 Newspapers, publishing & print-
ing
PA: Los Angeles Times Communications,
Llc
2300 E Imperial Hwy
El Segundo CA 90245
213 237-5000

(G-1303)
LOST FALLS LLC
Also Called: St Elmo Brewing Company
2310 La Casa Dr (78704-3823)
PHONE..............................737 300-1965
Timothy Bullock, *President*
EMP: 14
SALES (corp-wide): 1.6MM **Privately
Held**
WEB: www.stelmobrewing.com
SIC: 2082 Beer (alcoholic beverage)
PA: Lost Falls Llc
440 E Saint Elmo Rd G-2
Austin TX 78745
737 300-1965

(G-1304)
LOUISIANA WILD LLC
13359 N Hwy 183 Ste 406b (78750-7154)
PHONE..............................512 799-2537
Jason Hohenberger, *Mng Member*
EMP: 9
SALES (est): 228.9K **Privately Held**
WEB: www.louisianawild.com
SIC: 5812 3433 Caterers; burners, fur-
naces, boilers & stokers

(G-1305)
**LOWER COLORADO RIVER
AUTHORITY (PA)**
Also Called: Lcra
3700 Lake Austin Blvd (78703-3504)
P.O. Box 220 (78767-0220)
PHONE..............................512 473-3200
Amanda Esquibel, *Partner*
Brandon Mathis, *Superintendent*
Timothy Timmerman, *Chairman*
Dawn Reed, *Dean*
Mary King, *Counsel*
EMP: 600
SQ FT: 150,000
SALES (est): 1.3B **Privately Held**
WEB: www.lcra.org
SIC: 4911 1629 4941 3613 Distribution,
electric power; waste water & sewage
treatment plant construction; water sup-
ply; control panels, electric

(G-1306)
LTD MATERIAL LLC
8115 Altoga Dr Ste A (78724-2613)
PHONE..............................512 933-9292
Sara Nguyen, *Office Mgr*
Kevin Nguyen, *Mng Member*
Stuart Featherston, *Manager*
◆ **EMP:** 50
SQ FT: 38,400
SALES (est): 5MM **Privately Held**
WEB: www.ltdmaterial.com
SIC: 3674 Semiconductors & related de-
vices

(G-1307)
LUA BR LLC
606 W 17th St Apt 307 (78701-1152)
PHONE..............................404 610-0118
Christiano P Prado, *Principal*
EMP: 9
SALES (est): 621.5K **Privately Held**
SIC: 2051 Doughnuts, except frozen

(G-1308)
LUMINEX CORPORATION
12201 Technology Blvd (78727-6130)
PHONE..............................512 219-8020
Diana Eckert, *Production*
Brian Schrader, *Branch Mgr*
Ruben Campos, *Manager*
Christoph Cordes, *Manager*
Sachin Sah, *Manager*
EMP: 16 **Publicly Held**
WEB: www.luminexcorp.com
SIC: 3841 Surgical & medical instruments

PA: Luminex Corporation
12212 Technology Blvd
Austin TX 78727

(G-1309)
LUMINEX CORPORATION (PA)
12212 Technology Blvd (78727-6100)
PHONE..............................512 219-8020
Nachum Shamir, *President*
Melissa Hennig, *Partner*
Todd Bennett, *General Mgr*
Ron Borden, *Business Mgr*
Liz Combs, *Business Mgr*
EMP: 242
SQ FT: 184,000
SALES (est): 334.6MM **Publicly Held**
WEB: www.luminexcorp.com
SIC: 3841 8731 Diagnostic apparatus,
medical; commercial physical research;
biological research

(G-1310)
LUMOS PHARMA SUB INC
4200 Marathon Blvd # 200 (78756-3433)
PHONE..............................512 215-2630
EMP: 9 EST: 2014
SALES (est): 110.8K
SALES (corp-wide): 936K **Publicly Held**
WEB: www.lumos-pharma.com
SIC: 2834 Pharmaceutical preparations
PA: Lumos Pharma, Inc.
4200 Marathon Blvd # 200
Austin TX 78756
512 215-2630

(G-1311)
LUNA PIENA INC
Also Called: Tableaux
8212 Bagby Dr (78724-5150)
PHONE..............................512 926-6346
Christian Garces, *CEO*
Thomas Schimonsky, *President*
Diane Belvin, *Director*
EMP: 20
SQ FT: 17,500
SALES (est): 3.1MM **Privately Held**
WEB: www.tableaux.com
SIC: 2431 Window shutters, wood

(G-1312)
**LUNAR LIGHTING SOLUTIONS
LLC**
100 Congress Ave Ste 2000 (78701-2745)
PHONE..............................866 434-0732
George Ossolinski, *CEO*
EMP: 9
SALES (est): 555.8K **Privately Held**
WEB: www.lunarlighting.com
SIC: 3646 Commercial indusl & institu-
tional electric lighting fixtures

(G-1313)
LUXOTTICA OF AMERICA INC
Also Called: Lenscrafters
2206 Highland Mall (78752)
PHONE..............................512 450-1234
Michael Villareal, *General Mgr*
Teresa Garza, *Branch Mgr*
Eric Stewart, *Director*
EMP: 20
SALES (corp-wide): 1.7MM **Privately
Held**
WEB: www.luxottica.com
SIC: 5995 3851 Eyeglasses, prescription;
ophthalmic goods
HQ: Luxottica Of America Inc.
4000 Luxottica Pl
Mason OH 45040

(G-1314)
LYRIS TECHNOLOGIES INC (DH)
Also Called: Sparklist
401 Congress Ave Ste 2650 (78701-3708)
PHONE..............................510 844-1600
Wolfgang Maasberg, *CEO*
EMP: 14
SALES (est): 5.3MM **Privately Held**
WEB: www.aurea.com
SIC: 7372 Prepackaged software

(G-1315)
M S I CORPORATION
Also Called: Manufacturing Systems
8704 Lava Hill Rd Ste B (78744-7813)
PHONE..............................512 243-9000
Jim Miller, *President*

Janet D Miller, *General Mgr*
EMP: 15
SQ FT: 2,300
SALES (est): 1.6MM **Privately Held**
WEB: www.msicorp.com
SIC: 3541 Machine tools, metal cutting
type

(G-1316)
MADE IN AMERICA MFG LLC
8704 Lava Hill Rd Ste G (78744-7813)
PHONE..............................512 435-9952
James B Eudy, *Mng Member*
EMP: 9
SALES (est): 370.1K **Privately Held**
WEB: www.madeinamericamfg.com
SIC: 3541 3291 Machine tools, metal cut-
ting type; steel wool

(G-1317)
MAGDATA INC
515 Congress Ave Ste 1510 (78701-3515)
PHONE..............................425 372-2699
S Christopher Ney, *CEO*
Timothy Skansi, *Corp Secy*
EMP: 120
SQ FT: 3,749
SALES (est): 2.3MM **Privately Held**
SIC: 7372 Business oriented computer
software

(G-1318)
**MAGNUM CUSTOM TRLR MFG
CO INC (PA)**
Also Called: Magnum Custom Trailers
10806 N Fm 620 Rd (78726-1709)
PHONE..............................512 258-4101
Charles McLemore, *President*
Mike McLemore, *General Mgr*
Vangie McLemore, *Vice Pres*
Todd McLemore, *Purchasing*
James Waters, *Sales Staff*
▲ **EMP:** 75
SQ FT: 91,000
SALES (est): 15MM **Privately Held**
WEB: www.magnumtrailers.com
SIC: 3715 5531 Truck trailers; truck equip-
ment & parts; trailer hitches, automotive

(G-1319)
MAISON DE NAVAR
Also Called: Navajo Skin Care
7301 N Fm 620 Rd (78726-4539)
PHONE..............................512 266-6100
Fermin Navar, *Owner*
EMP: 9
SALES (est): 1.3MM **Privately Held**
WEB: www.navajoskincare.com
SIC: 2844 Toilet preparations

(G-1320)
MAM LLC
404 W Powell Ln Ste 104 (78753-6256)
PHONE..............................512 407-9940
EMP: 19 **Privately Held**
WEB: www.midamericametals.com
SIC: 3471 Finishing, metals or formed
products
PA: Mam Llc
1567 W Diane St Ste A
Ozark MO 65721
800 544-4576

(G-1321)
MANCOMM INC
Also Called: American Safety Training
300 Bowie St Apt 2705 (78703-4667)
PHONE..............................563 323-6245
Benjamin W Mangan, *President*
EMP: 50
SALES (est): 4.6MM **Privately Held**
WEB: www.mancomm.com
SIC: 2731 Books: publishing & printing

(G-1322)
MANGSTOR INC
4201 W Parmer Ln Ste A200 (78727-4157)
PHONE..............................512 779-6999
Craig Gilmore, *President*
John Archambeault, *Vice Pres*
Paul Prince, *CTO*
Trevor Smith, *Director*
EMP: 18
SQ FT: 7,000

SALES (est): 5.1MM **Privately Held**
WEB: www.exten.io
SIC: 3572 Computer storage devices

(G-1323)
MANGSTOR LLC
4201 W Parmer Ln Ste A200 (78727-4157)
PHONE.................................512 879-9241
Trevor Smith, *CEO*
Ashwin Kamath, *Principal*
John Archambeault, *Vice Pres*
Stu Sorensen, *CFO*
Stuart Sorensen, *CFO*
EMP: 19
SALES (est): 4.2MM **Privately Held**
WEB: www.exten.io
SIC: 3572 Disk drives, computer

(G-1324)
MANNING NAVCOMP INC
12741 Res Blvd Ste 500 (78750)
PHONE.................................877 680-1188
Jeff Manning, *President*
Michael Feeley, *Natl Sales Mgr*
Javier Ortiz, *Sales Staff*
Lee Simmonds, *CTO*
Josh Rox, *Software Engr*
◆ EMP: 20
SQ FT: 2,500
SALES (est): 2.3MM **Privately Held**
WEB: www.rastrac.com
SIC: 7371 3694 Computer software development; breaker point sets, internal combustion engine

(G-1325)
MAPSPEOPLE INC
3205 Industrial Ter # 100 (78758-7615)
PHONE.................................512 368-0038
Jonas Berntsen, *CEO*
Jonas Nedegaard-Berntsen, *CEO*
Michael Gram, *Director*
EMP: 50
SQ FT: 4,000
SALES (est): 1.1MM **Privately Held**
WEB: www.mapspeople.com
SIC: 7372 Business oriented computer software

(G-1326)
MARALO LLC
1717 W 6th St Ste 470 (78703-5082)
PHONE.................................512 322-0041
Clayton Maybius, *Manager*
EMP: 13
SALES (corp-wide): 3.6MM **Privately Held**
WEB: www.maralo.com
SIC: 1311 Natural gas production
PA: Maralo, Llc
4400 Post Oak Pkwy # 2550
Houston TX 77027
713 622-5420

(G-1327)
MARKETMAP INC
Also Called: Conclusive Strategies
9433 Fm 2244 Rd Bldg 1 (78733-6105)
PHONE.................................512 576-6403
Lawrence Daniel, *President*
Gary Novosel, *Vice Pres*
EMP: 12
SQ FT: 7,726
SALES (est): 800.1K
SALES (corp-wide): 37.5MM **Privately Held**
SIC: 2741 Maps: publishing & printing
HQ: Magnify Ii, Inc.
300 W Summit Ave Ste 300 # 300
Charlotte NC 28203

(G-1328)
MATERIAL HANDLING CONCEPTS
16515 Bratton Ln (78728-1902)
P.O. Box 1629, Round Rock (78680-1629)
PHONE.................................512 836-6598
William Carl Young, *President*
Stefanie Young, *Info Tech Dir*
EMP: 10
SQ FT: 5,000

SALES (est): 3.5MM **Privately Held**
WEB: www.emhci.com
SIC: 5084 3441 3531 Materials handling machinery; conveyor systems; hoists; fabricated structural metal; backhoes, tractors, cranes, plows & similar equipment

(G-1329)
MATERIALS PRODUCTS INC (PA)
Also Called: M P I
835 Kramer Ln (78758-4302)
P.O. Box 141156 (78714-1156)
PHONE.................................512 821-3303
Jessie G Candelas, *President*
EMP: 12
SQ FT: 10,500
SALES (est): 3.5MM **Privately Held**
SIC: 5039 5211 5082 3446 Prefabricated structures; lumber & other building materials; contractors' materials; stairs, staircases, stair treads: prefabricated metal; stone, cast concrete; retaining wall construction

(G-1330)
MATHESON TRI-GAS INC
3519 E 5th St (78702-4913)
P.O. Box 6478 (78762-6478)
PHONE.................................512 385-0611
Joe Colton, *Manager*
EMP: 22 **Privately Held**
WEB: www.mathesongas.com
SIC: 2813 5084 5169 5984 Industrial gases; welding machinery & equipment; oxygen; liquefied petroleum gas dealers
HQ: Matheson Tri-Gas, Inc.
3 Mountainview Rd Ste 3 # 3
Warren NJ 07059
908 991-9200

(G-1331)
MAXMILE TECHNOLOGIES LLC
10623 Winchelsea Dr (78750-4033)
PHONE.................................512 961-1187
Max MA,
EMP: 10
SALES (est): 660K **Privately Held**
WEB: www.maxmiletech.com
SIC: 8731 3825 Biotechnical research, commercial; electronic research; semiconductor test equipment; measuring instruments & meters, electric

(G-1332)
MCCARTHY PRINT INC
1804 Chicon St Ste 106 (78702-1226)
PHONE.................................512 479-8938
Teri McCarthy, *President*
Sarah Schenk, *Partner*
EMP: 11 EST: 1997
SQ FT: 4,200
SALES (est): 1.4MM **Privately Held**
WEB: www.mccarthyprint.com
SIC: 2752 Commercial printing, offset

(G-1333)
MEDAPOINT INC
3005 S Lamar Blvd D109 (78704-8864)
PHONE.................................512 659-1117
EMP: 9 EST: 2012
SALES (est): 745.5K **Privately Held**
WEB: www.mptechnologies.com
SIC: 7372 Prepackaged software

(G-1334)
MEDICAL PRESENT VALUE INC
5000 Plaza On The Lk # 265 (78746-1069)
PHONE.................................512 795-0015
Felipe Jimenez, *General Mgr*
Jennifer Zimmerman, *Controller*
T J Harais, *Manager*
Merideth Wilson, *Manager*
Chris Kirby, *Technology*
EMP: 12 **Privately Held**
WEB: www.experianplc.com
SIC: 8742 7372 Hospital & health services consultant; prepackaged software
PA: Medical Present Value, Inc.
601 Nw Loop 410 Ste 450
San Antonio TX 78216

(G-1335)
MEDICI TECHNOLOGIES LLC
Also Called: Chiron Health
7500 Rialto Blvd 2-100 (78735-8531)
PHONE.................................800 768-8131
Karl Nicholas, *Sales Staff*
EMP: 19
SALES (corp-wide): 5MM **Privately Held**
WEB: www.medici.md
SIC: 7372 Application computer software
PA: Medici Technologies, Llc
7500 Rialto Blvd Bldg Ii
Austin TX 78735
970 948-0886

(G-1336)
MEGLADON MFG GROUP LTD
12317 Tech Blvd Ste 100 (78727)
PHONE.................................512 491-0006
Andrew Cooper, *CEO*
Daniel Hogberg, *President*
John E Bosch Jr, *Partner*
Reina Wantt, *General Mgr*
Cynthia Ferrell, *Buyer*
▲ EMP: 26
SALES (est): 5.3MM **Privately Held**
WEB: www.megladonmfg.com
SIC: 3357 Fiber optic cable (insulated)
PA: Tyrex Group, Ltd.
12317 Tech Blvd Ste 100
Austin TX 78727

(G-1337)
MHC SEMICONDUCTOR PROCESSING
Also Called: Micro Hybrid Components
7801 N Lamar Blvd B155 (78752-1016)
PHONE.................................512 331-6632
Dorothy Casteel, *CEO*
Marc Casteel, *President*
Marc Yeates, *General Mgr*
Scarbrough Gary, *Vice Pres*
Marc Yeates - Sales, *Vice Pres*
EMP: 12
SQ FT: 2,800
SALES (est): 1.5MM **Privately Held**
WEB: www.mhcsemi.com
SIC: 3674 5065 Integrated circuits, semiconductor networks, etc.; semiconductor devices

(G-1338)
MICROCHIP TECHNOLOGY INC
10900b Stonelake Blvd (78759-5748)
PHONE.................................512 334-1931
David Gammie, *Engineer*
Sonia Carbajal, *Manager*
Mike Catherwood, *Technical Staff*
EMP: 9
SALES (est): 1.2MM **Privately Held**
WEB: www.microchip.com
SIC: 3674 Semiconductors & related devices

(G-1339)
MICRON SEMICONDUCTOR PDTS INC
101 W Louis Henna Blvd # 210 (78728-1235)
PHONE.................................512 248-8283
John Groves, *Research*
Joshua Lee, *Design Engr*
Tom Pratt, *Senior Mgr*
EMP: 88
SALES (corp-wide): 21.4B **Publicly Held**
WEB: www.micron.com
SIC: 3674 Semiconductors & related devices
HQ: Micron Semiconductor Products, Inc.
8000 S Federal Way
Boise ID 83716
208 368-4000

(G-1340)
MICROSEMI SEMICONDUCTOR (US)
4509 Freidrich Ln Ste 200 (78744-1866)
PHONE.................................512 228-5400
David Boikess, *Vice Pres*
Robert Wilcox, *Opers Mgr*
Daren Allee, *Design Engr*
Mike Willingham, *Technical Staff*
EMP: 100

SALES (corp-wide): 5.2B **Publicly Held**
WEB: www.microsemi.com
SIC: 3674 Semiconductors & related devices
HQ: Microsemi Semiconductor (U.S.) Inc
1 Enterprise
Aliso Viejo CA 92656
949 380-6100

(G-1341)
MICROSTAQ INC
4120 Freidrich Ln Ste 225 (78744-1085)
PHONE.................................512 628-2890
Sandeep Kumar, *CEO*
Wayne Long, *Engineer*
Nelson Fuller, *Info Tech Dir*
Arvind RAO, *Sr Software Eng*
EMP: 23
SQ FT: 5,700
SALES (est): 4.4MM **Privately Held**
WEB: www.dmq-us.com
SIC: 3491 Industrial valves

(G-1342)
MICROTRANSPONDER
2802 Flintrock Trce Ste 2 (78738-1743)
PHONE.................................214 280-9677
Frank McEachern, *CEO*
Will Rosellini, *Ch of Bd*
Jordan Curnes, *President*
Reema Casavan, *Vice Pres*
Cecilia Prudente, *Research*
EMP: 10
SALES (est): 801.2K **Privately Held**
WEB: www.microtransponder.com
SIC: 3845 Electrotherapeutic apparatus

(G-1343)
MIKE DAVIS AND ASSOCIATES INC (PA)
Also Called: Imagecraft Exhibits
15505 Long Vista Dr # 200 (78728-3832)
P.O. Box 216, Salado (76571-0216)
PHONE.................................512 836-8442
Tom Blair, *CEO*
Mike Davis, *President*
Kenny Moore, *Vice Pres*
Doug Davis, *Opers Staff*
Gaylon Edwards, *Executive*
EMP: 40
SQ FT: 38,000
SALES (est): 13.3MM **Privately Held**
SIC: 7389 2541 6531 Convention & show services; display fixtures, wood; appraiser, real estate

(G-1344)
MILLER IMGING DGITAL SOLUTIONS
1000 E 7th St (78702-3261)
PHONE.................................512 381-5266
EMP: 10
SALES (est): 1.7MM **Privately Held**
SIC: 2759 Commercial Printing

(G-1345)
MILLER UNIFORMS & EMBLEMS INC
Also Called: K & D Caps
826 Rutland Dr (78758-5817)
PHONE.................................512 302-5541
Bob Miller, *President*
Mark Miller, *Vice Pres*
Keith Miller, *Treasurer*
Paulette Cox, *Administration*
Marc Miller, *Representative*
▲ EMP: 24
SQ FT: 3,200
SALES (est): 2MM **Privately Held**
WEB: www.milleruniforms.com
SIC: 5699 2395 Uniforms; emblems, embroidered

(G-1346)
MLC CAD SYSTEMS LLC (PA)
4625 W William Cannon Dr (78749-2320)
PHONE.................................512 288-8511
Charlotte O Hill, *CEO*
Joel Hill, *President*
Kevin Schreiner, *Principal*
Tugay Angay, *Engineer*
James Frick, *Engineer*
EMP: 12
SQ FT: 3,000

SALES (est): 20.8MM **Privately Held**
WEB: www.mlc-cad.com
SIC: 7372 7373 Prepackaged software; computer-aided design (CAD) systems service

(G-1347)
MOBILE MINI INC
2851 S A W Grimes Blvd (73301-0001)
PHONE..........................512 251-2461
Larry Spears, *Branch Mgr*
Chris Macabuhay, *Manager*
EMP: 19
SALES (corp-wide): 1B **Publicly Held**
WEB: www.mobilemini.com
SIC: 3448 Buildings, portable: prefabricated metal
HQ: Mobile Mini, Inc.
4646 E Van Buren St # 400
Phoenix AZ 85008
480 894-6311

(G-1348)
MOBOTREX INC
301 W Howard Ln Ste 200 (78753-9754)
PHONE..........................512 521-3060
Joel Wright, *President*
Mihaela Pologescu, *Purchasing*
EMP: 125
SALES (corp-wide): 32MM **Privately Held**
WEB: www.mobotrex.com
SIC: 3669 Transportation signaling devices
PA: Mobotrex, Inc.
109 W 55th St
Davenport IA 52806
563 323-0009

(G-1349)
MODERN SHADE LLC
4213 Felter Ln (78744-3221)
P.O. Box 150069 (78715-0069)
PHONE..........................512 385-4100
Thomas F Harper, *President*
Clay Birdwell, *Vice Pres*
Hilda Avila, *Admin Sec*
EMP: 20
SQ FT: 50,000
SALES (est): 2.8MM **Privately Held**
WEB: www.modernshadellc.com
SIC: 2394 Canvas awnings & canopies

(G-1350)
MOLECULA CORP
4200 N Lamar Blvd Ste 225 (78756-3411)
PHONE..........................512 649-9113
EMP: 9
SALES (est): 669K **Privately Held**
SIC: 3652 Pre-recorded records & tapes

(G-1351)
MOLEX LLC
Also Called: Molex Connector
9111 Jollyville Rd # 105 (78759-7406)
PHONE..........................512 345-1092
Paul Patterson, *Manager*
EMP: 10
SALES (corp-wide): 36.8B **Privately Held**
WEB: www.molex.com
SIC: 3678 Electronic connectors
HQ: Molex, Llc
2222 Wellington Ct
Lisle IL 60532
630 969-4550

(G-1352)
MONOGRAM ORTHOPAEDICS INC
3913 Todd Ln Ste 307 (78744-1057)
PHONE..........................512 399-2656
Benjamin John Sexson, *CEO*
Douglas Unis, *CEO*
EMP: 11 **EST:** 2015
SALES (est): 153.5K **Privately Held**
SIC: 3842 Implants, surgical

(G-1353)
MOTION COMPUTING INC
8601 Rr 2222 Bldg Ii (78730-2304)
PHONE..........................512 637-1100
Philip S Sassower, *CEO*
Mark Holleran, *President*
Ralph Mitchell, *Vice Pres*
Michael J Rapisand, *CFO*
Jason Hamilton, *Sales Staff*
EMP: 200

SQ FT: 11,000
SALES (est): 19.8MM
SALES (corp-wide): 4.4B **Publicly Held**
WEB: www.xploretech.com
SIC: 3577 Computer peripheral equipment
HQ: Xplore Technologies Corporation Of America
14000 Summit Dr Ste 900
Austin TX 78728
512 336-7797

(G-1354)
MOTOROLA SOLUTIONS INC
2120 W Braker Ln Ste P (78758-4064)
PHONE..........................512 422-9028
Clay Cassard, *Sales Staff*
EMP: 141
SALES (corp-wide): 7.8B **Publicly Held**
WEB: www.motorolasolutions.com
SIC: 3663 Radio & TV communications equipment
PA: Motorola Solutions, Inc.
500 W Monroe St Ste 4400
Chicago IL 60661
847 576-5000

(G-1355)
MOTOROLA SOLUTIONS INC
6501 W William Cannon Dr (78735-8523)
PHONE..........................512 895-2000
EMP: 24
SALES (corp-wide): 6.3B **Publicly Held**
SIC: 3661 Mfg Telephone/Telegraph Apparatus
PA: Motorola Solutions, Inc.
500 W Monroe St Ste 4400
Chicago IL 60661
847 576-5000

(G-1356)
MOTOROLA SOLUTIONS INC
4515 Seton Center Pkwy # 330 (78759-5290)
PHONE..........................512 821-1560
EMP: 25
SALES (corp-wide): 5.7B **Publicly Held**
SIC: 3663 Wireless Manufacture
PA: Motorola Solutions, Inc.
1303 E Algonquin Rd
Schaumburg IL 60661
847 576-5000

(G-1357)
MURPHY CONNECTED ENTPS INC
Also Called: Paragon Printing & Mailing
10423 Mckalla Pl (78758-4448)
PHONE..........................512 821-0222
Donald Murphy, *President*
Shelly Murphy, *Vice Pres*
Robert Romero, *Prdtn Mgr*
Ken Moyer, *Accounts Exec*
Andrew Murphy, *Marketing Staff*
EMP: 25
SQ FT: 10,000
SALES (est): 3.1MM
SALES (corp-wide): 2.6MM **Privately Held**
WEB: www.paragonprinting.solutions
SIC: 7331 2759 Mailing service; commercial printing
PA: Murphy Connected Consulting, Llc
10423 Mckalla Pl
Austin TX 78758
512 821-0222

(G-1358)
MUTO TECHNOLOGY INC
2121 Grand Avenue Pkwy (78728-3938)
PHONE..........................512 251-2211
Rosario Muto, *President*
David Muto, *Vice Pres*
Eddie Garcia, *Opers Mgr*
Marisa Hoover, *Controller*
Eric Hoover, *Manager*
EMP: 24
SQ FT: 10,000
SALES (est): 6.3MM **Privately Held**
WEB: www.mutotech.com
SIC: 3674 Integrated circuits, semiconductor networks, etc.

(G-1359)
MYEDU CORPORATION
Also Called: Pick-A-Prof
1301 S Mo Pac Expy # 250 (78746-6916)
PHONE..........................512 469-9777
EMP: 20 **EST:** 2001
SQ FT: 1,200
SALES (est): 1.6MM **Privately Held**
SIC: 7372 Prepackaged Software Services
HQ: Blackboard Inc.
1111 19th St Nw
Washington DC 20190
202 463-4860

(G-1360)
NATIONAL INSTRUMENTS CORP (PA)
11500 N Mopac Expy (78759-3563)
PHONE..........................512 683-0100
▲ **EMP:** 674 **EST:** 1976
SQ FT: 232,000
SALES: 1.3B **Publicly Held**
WEB: www.ni.com
SIC: 7372 3577 Prepackaged software; application computer software; computer peripheral equipment; input/output equipment, computer

(G-1361)
NAVITAIRE
1501 S Mo Pac Expy # 300 (78746-7543)
PHONE..........................512 617-2121
Thomas Cook, *Principal*
Melanie Jones, *Project Mgr*
EMP: 50
SALES (est): 1.9MM **Privately Held**
SIC: 7372 Operating systems computer software

(G-1362)
NCC NANO LLC
Also Called: Novacentrix
400 Parker Dr Ste 1110 (78728-1252)
PHONE..........................512 491-9500
Charles C Munson, *CEO*
Karl Martin, *Vice Pres*
John Entralgo, *Engineer*
Deb Dalton, *Marketing Staff*
Melissa Devorsky, *Manager*
EMP: 30
SALES (est): 8.5MM **Privately Held**
WEB: www.novacentrix.com
SIC: 2893 3567 3399 Printing ink; industrial furnaces & ovens; metal powders, pastes & flakes

(G-1363)
NETEFFECT INC
9211 Waterford Ctr Blvd (78758-7679)
PHONE..........................512 302-0002
EMP: 30
SQ FT: 23,000
SALES (est): 2.9MM
SALES (corp-wide): 62.7B **Publicly Held**
SIC: 3674 Mfg Semiconductors/Related Devices
PA: Intel Corporation
2200 Mission College Blvd
Santa Clara CA 95054
408 765-8080

(G-1364)
NEU SECURITY SERVICES LLC
Also Called: N S S
8206 Cross Park Dr # 300 (78754-5252)
PHONE..........................512 469-9980
Stephen Neusch, *CEO*
EMP: 55
SQ FT: 5,000
SALES (est): 9.1MM **Privately Held**
WEB: www.neusecurity.com
SIC: 1799 3446 7382 1531 Fence construction; architectural metalwork; protective devices, security;

(G-1365)
NEWPOINT MEDIA GROUP LLC
12912 Hill Country Blvd F-245 (78738-6484)
PHONE..........................770 962-7220
Pamela Bruesewitz, *Production*
Robert Hardy, *CFO*
Chris Fitzpatrick, *Accounts Mgr*
Bobby Orr, *Accounts Mgr*
Rebecca Chandler, *VP Mktg*
EMP: 100

SALES (est): 40MM **Privately Held**
WEB: www.newpoint.media
SIC: 2731 Books: publishing & printing

(G-1366)
NICOLE DIONNE
Also Called: Primalscream Music
500 N Capitl Of Texas Hwy (78746-3302)
PHONE..........................310 699-7556
Nicole Dionne, *Owner*
EMP: 12
SALES (est): 958.2K **Privately Held**
WEB: www.primalscream.audio
SIC: 3652 7389 Master records or tapes, preparation of; business services

(G-1367)
NIELSEN & BAINBRIDGE LLC (HQ)
Also Called: Pinnacle Frames & Accents
12303 Tech Blvd Ste 950 (78727)
PHONE..........................512 506-3900
Scott Slater, *CEO*
Randall Daltesek, *VP Mktg*
◆ **EMP:** 50 **EST:** 1999
SQ FT: 5,000
SALES (est): 285.8MM **Privately Held**
WEB: www.nielsenbainbridgegroup.com
SIC: 2499 2392 5021 Picture frame molding, finished; cushions & pillows; furniture; household furniture

(G-1368)
NORTH AMERICAN BEVERAGES LTD (PA)
Also Called: Big Red
6500 River Place Blvd (78730-1119)
PHONE..........................512 501-3890
Gary Smith, *President*
James Bradley, *CFO*
EMP: 16
SQ FT: 20,000
SALES (est): 3.7MM **Privately Held**
WEB: www.bigred.com
SIC: 2087 Flavoring extracts & syrups

(G-1369)
NORTHROP GRUMMAN SYSTEMS CORP
7745 Chevy Chase Dr # 100 (78752-1508)
PHONE..........................512 374-4100
Alma Garcia, *Buyer*
Justine Molina, *Engineer*
Stu Dickey, *Accountant*
Linda Jackson, *Accountant*
Pennie Jackson, *Accountant*
EMP: 65 **Publicly Held**
WEB: www.northropgrumman.com
SIC: 7373 7372 Computer integrated systems design; prepackaged software
HQ: Northrop Grumman Systems Corporation
2980 Fairview Park Dr
Falls Church VA 22042
703 280-2900

(G-1370)
NORTHROP GRUMMAN SYSTEMS CORP
4000 S Ih 35 (78704-7420)
PHONE..........................512 804-2153
Michael Cole, *Branch Mgr*
EMP: 137 **Publicly Held**
WEB: www.northropgrumman.com
SIC: 3812 Search & navigation equipment
HQ: Northrop Grumman Systems Corporation
2980 Fairview Park Dr
Falls Church VA 22042
703 280-2900

(G-1371)
NPPI INTERMEDIATE INC
106 E 6th St Ste 300 (78701-3661)
PHONE..........................512 476-7100
Michael Stakias, *Ch of Bd*
David Rogalski, *Vice Pres*
Gary Kofnovec, *CFO*
Mike Derrick, *Treasurer*
EMP: 35
SALES (est): 361.8MM **Privately Held**
SIC: 3086 Insulation or cushioning material, foamed plastic

(G-1372)
NUVIEW SYSTEMS INC (PA)
401 Congress Ave Ste 2650 (78701-3708)
PHONE..................................978 296-6600
Shafiq Lokhandwala, *CEO*
Randall Ratsch, *Principal*
Ken Bero, *COO*
Steve Manning, *Vice Pres*
Srinath Narasimhan, *Vice Pres*
EMP: 70
SQ FT: 13,000
SALES (est): 11MM **Privately Held**
WEB: www.ignitetech.com
SIC: 7372 Business oriented computer
  software

(G-1373)
NXP USA INC
Also Called: Nxp Semiconductors
3501 Ed Bluestein Blvd (78721-2903)
P.O. Box 6000 (78762-6000)
PHONE..................................512 933-6000
EMP: 1000
SALES (corp-wide): 8.8B **Privately Held**
WEB: www.nxp.com
SIC: 3674 Semiconductors & related de-
  vices
  HQ: Nxp Usa, Inc.
    6501 W William Cannon Dr
    Austin TX 78735
    512 933-8214

(G-1374)
NXP USA INC (DH)
Also Called: Nxp Semiconductors USA
6501 W William Cannon Dr (78735-8523)
PHONE..................................512 933-8214
Jennifer Wuamett, *President*
Darrell Block, *Business Mgr*
Glenn Daves, *Vice Pres*
Jorge Salhuana, *Vice Pres*
Alasdair Smith, *Vice Pres*
▲ **EMP:** 2400
SALES (est): 3.3B
SALES (corp-wide): 8.8B **Privately Held**
WEB: www.nxp.com
SIC: 3674 Semiconductor diodes & recti-
  fiers

(G-1375)
OCCIDENTAL CHEMICAL CORP
604 W 14th St (78701-1726)
P.O. Box 809050, Dallas (75380-9050)
PHONE..................................512 476-2245
John Webster, *Opers Staff*
Jacob Lopez, *Production*
Julie Moore, *Director*
Aaron Gatzki, *Analyst*
EMP: 35
SALES (corp-wide): 21.2B **Publicly Held**
WEB: www.oxy.com
SIC: 2812 Alkalies & chlorine
  HQ: Occidental Chemical Corporation
    14555 Dallas Pkwy Ste 400
    Dallas TX 75254
    972 404-3800

(G-1376)
OCEANUS AUTOMOTIVE LLC
Also Called: Square Root
508 Oakland Ave (78703-5152)
PHONE..................................512 551-9726
Chris Taylor, *Principal*
Paul Devere, *Vice Pres*
Qiong Zeng, *Sales Staff*
Sarah Gerichten, *Mktg Dir*
Mary Feild, *Marketing Staff*
EMP: 25 **EST:** 2009
SALES (est): 3.8MM **Privately Held**
WEB: www.square-root.com
SIC: 7372 Business oriented computer
  software

(G-1377)
OFFICE PRINTING & SUPPLY INC
408 W 17th St (78701-1242)
PHONE..................................512 474-2036
Marylin Hershman, *Manager*
EMP: 20
SALES (est): 1MM **Privately Held**
SIC: 2752 Commercial printing, offset

(G-1378)
OMEGA OPTICS INC
8500 Shoal Creek Blvd 4-200
(78757-7598)
PHONE..................................512 996-8833
Ray Chen, *President*
Gloria Chen, *Marketing Mgr*
EMP: 11
SALES (est): 1.5MM **Privately Held**
WEB: www.omegaoptics.com
SIC: 3827 Optical test & inspection equip-
  ment

(G-1379)
OMGANICS INC
1821 Waterston Ave Unit B (78703-3938)
PHONE..................................512 560-3262
Carissa Hoop, *CEO*
EMP: 2014
SALES (est): 61.1MM **Privately Held**
WEB: www.omganics.com
SIC: 2676 Infant & baby paper products

(G-1380)
OMNI SURGICAL LP
Also Called: Spine 360
5000 Plaza On The Lk # 305 (78746-1094)
PHONE..................................512 327-6400
EMP: 10
SALES (est): 1.9MM **Privately Held**
SIC: 3845 Mfg Electromedical Equipment

(G-1381)
OMNI WATER SOLUTIONS INC
4007 Coml Ctr Dr Ste 700 (78744)
P.O. Box 40250 (78704-0005)
PHONE..................................512 275-0804
Warren Sumner, *CEO*
Steve Braccini, *COO*
Kirk Patterson, *CFO*
Wayne Wolf, *CTO*
▲ **EMP:** 31
SALES (est): 7.5MM **Privately Held**
WEB: www.omniwatersolutions.com
SIC: 3589 Water treatment equipment, in-
  dustrial

(G-1382)
OMNIBASE SERVICES OF TEXAS (PA)
7320 N Mo Pac Expy # 310 (78731-2338)
PHONE..................................512 346-6511
Charles Brothers, *Partner*
Michael Nall, *Partner*
Charles Tracy, *Partner*
Charles Cannon, *Opers Mgr*
Donetta Jenkins, *Human Res Dir*
EMP: 11
SALES (est): 1.1MM **Privately Held**
WEB: www.omnibase.com
SIC: 7372 Business oriented computer
  software

(G-1383)
ON SHORE QLTY CTRL SPCLIST LLC
111 Congress Ave Ste 600 (78701-4075)
P.O. Box 911 (78767-0911)
PHONE..................................512 443-3582
Savannah Prinz, *Manager*
Eddie E Hooks Jr,
EMP: 100 **EST:** 1964
SALES (est): 16.8MM **Privately Held**
WEB: www.onshoreqcs.com
SIC: 1389 Pipe testing, oil field service

(G-1384)
ON-X LIFE TECHNOLOGIES INC (HQ)
1300 E Anderson Ln Ste B (78752-1739)
PHONE..................................512 832-8548
Clyde Baker, *President*
Sam T Shee, *Business Mgr*
Jon Wells, *Business Mgr*
Derek Southard, *COO*
John Ely, *Exec VP*
EMP: 100
SQ FT: 40,000
SALES (est): 17.4MM
SALES (corp-wide): 276.2MM **Publicly Held**
WEB: www.onxlti.com
SIC: 3829 Medical diagnostic systems, nu-
  clear

  PA: Cryolife, Inc.
    1655 Roberts Blvd Nw
    Kennesaw GA 30144
    770 419-3355

(G-1385)
ONE SEMICONDUCTOR LLC
3105 Scott Dr Unit 1 (78734-2127)
PHONE..................................512 785-4456
EMP: 17 **EST:** 2011
SALES (est): 2.7MM **Privately Held**
WEB: www.onesemiconductor.com
SIC: 3674 Semiconductors & related de-
  vices

(G-1386)
ONE SOURCE RECYCLING INC
7400 Fm 969 (78724-6101)
P.O. Box 92852 (78709-2852)
PHONE..................................512 549-2812
EMP: 60
SQ FT: 40,000
SALES (corp-wide): 34.9MM **Privately Held**
SIC: 5093 2611 3089 Whol Scrap/Waste
  Mat Pulp Mill Mfg Plastic Products
  PA: One Source Recycling, Inc.
    7500 W Highway 71 Ste 200
    Austin TX 78735
    512 468-8817

(G-1387)
ONE WORLD FOODS INC
Also Called: Stubbs Legendary Kitchen
1219 W 6th St (78703-5208)
P.O. Box 40220 (78704-0004)
PHONE..................................512 480-0203
Kurt Koegler, *CEO*
▼ **EMP:** 17
SQ FT: 4,000
SALES (est): 4.2MM
SALES (corp-wide): 5.6B **Publicly Held**
WEB: www.stubbsbbq.com
SIC: 2033 Barbecue sauce: packaged in
  cans, jars, etc.; spaghetti & other pasta
  sauce: packaged in cans, jars, etc.
  PA: Mccormick & Company Incorporated
    24 Schilling Rd Ste 1
    Hunt Valley MD 21031
    410 771-7301

(G-1388)
OPEN SKY MEDIA INC
Also Called: Austin Monthly
1712 Rio Grande St Ste A (78701-1177)
PHONE..................................512 263-9133
Jefferey R Brady, *President*
Scott Dickes, *Vice Pres*
Todd P Paul, *CFO*
Peter Thomas, *Info Tech Mgr*
Kerri Nolan, *Director*
EMP: 87
SALES (est): 2.2MM **Privately Held**
WEB: www.sanantoniomag.com
SIC: 2721 Magazines: publishing only, not
  printed on site

(G-1389)
ORACLE AMERICA INC
Also Called: Sun Microsystems
5300 Riata Park Ct (78727-6430)
PHONE..................................512 401-1000
Kurt Kreutzer, *Engineer*
Chase Leinberger, *Sales Staff*
Stephen Spess, *Sales Staff*
Margaret Harrist, *Marketing Staff*
Melissa Segal, *Manager*
EMP: 21
SALES (corp-wide): 39B **Publicly Held**
WEB: www.ea.com
SIC: 7372 Prepackaged software
  HQ: Oracle America, Inc.
    500 Oracle Pkwy
    Redwood City CA 94065
    650 506-7000

(G-1390)
ORACLE CORPORATION
9600 N Mopac Expy Ste 700 (78759-6502)
PHONE..................................512 372-8207
Jean-Simon Roy, *Regl Sales Mgr*
Aron J Donatiello, *Sales Staff*
Tony Olesen, *Sales Staff*
Desmond Ng, *Branch Mgr*
Ehtesham Hoq, *Manager*
EMP: 302

SALES (corp-wide): 39B **Publicly Held**
WEB: www.oracle.com
SIC: 7372 Business oriented computer
  software
  PA: Oracle Corporation
    2300 Oracle Way
    Austin TX 78741
    737 867-1000

(G-1391)
ORACLE CORPORATION (PA)
2300 Oracle Way (78741-1400)
PHONE..................................737 867-1000
Safra A Catz, *CEO*
Lawrence J Ellison, *Ch of Bd*
Jeffrey O Henley, *Vice Ch Bd*
Dorian E Daley, *Exec VP*
Edward Screven, *Exec VP*
EMP: 2300
SQ FT: 2,100,000
SALES: 39B **Publicly Held**
WEB: www.oracle.com
SIC: 7379 8243 3571 3674 Computer re-
  lated consulting services; software train-
  ing, computer; minicomputers;
  microprocessors; business oriented com-
  puter software

(G-1392)
ORACLE CORPORATION
11400 N Lamar Blvd (78753-2663)
PHONE..................................512 832-1599
Gilbert Martinez, *Chief*
Mike Miezio, *Regional Mgr*
Curtis Angell, *Manager*
Matthew Riley, *Marketing Staff*
Saurabh Singhvi, *Program Mgr*
EMP: 14
SALES (est): 2.4MM
SALES (corp-wide): 39B **Publicly Held**
WEB: www.cbsaustin.com
SIC: 7372 Prepackaged software
  PA: Oracle Corporation
    2300 Oracle Way
    Austin TX 78741
    737 867-1000

(G-1393)
ORIGEN BIOMEDICAL INC
7000 Burleson Rd Bldg D (78744-3213)
PHONE..................................512 474-7278
Richard Martin, *President*
Rachel Cossum, *QC Mgr*
Greg Sansom, *CFO*
Diann Fisk, *Manager*
Raymundo Rendon, *Manager*
EMP: 47
SQ FT: 42,000
SALES (est): 12.1MM **Privately Held**
WEB: www.origen.com
SIC: 3841 Surgical & medical instruments

(G-1394)
OSTEOCENTRIC TECHNOLOGIES INC
11000 N Mopac Expy # 600 (78759-5384)
PHONE..................................800 969-0639
Eric Brown, *President*
EMP: 14 **EST:** 2013
SALES (est): 1.4MM **Privately Held**
WEB: www.osteocentric.com
SIC: 3842 Surgical appliances & supplies

(G-1395)
OVERTON ENTERPRISES LLC
Also Called: SPI Brand
8201 E Riverside Dr # 125 (78744-1610)
PHONE..................................512 394-6089
Kim Overton, *President*
Ashley Berd, *Manager*
▲ **EMP:** 12
SALES (est): 1.6MM **Privately Held**
WEB: www.spibelt.com
SIC: 2389 5131 Suspenders; piece goods
  & notions

(G-1396)
PARADIGM BKS LECTURE NOTES LTD (PA)
Also Called: Notes-N-Quotes
407 W 24th St (78705-5209)
P.O. Box 5215 (78763-5215)
PHONE..................................217 344-4433
Robert E Pyeatt, *Partner*
Sarah Lyford, *Vice Pres*
Kathy Flynn, *Admin Sec*

(PA)=Parent Co (HQ)=Headquarters (DH)=Div Headquarters
✿ = New Business established in last 2 years
                        2021 Harris Texas
                    Manufacturers Directory   69

GEOGRAPHIC (side tab)

EMP: 15
SQ FT: 750
SALES (est): 350K **Privately Held**
WEB: www.paradigmbooks.com
SIC: 5999 2731 5942 Education aids, devices & supplies; textbooks: publishing only, not printed on site; book stores

(G-1397)
PARROT INC
7000 N Mopac Fl 2 Flr 2 (78731)
PHONE...................................512 514-6840
Edward Valdez, *President*
Scott Chauvette, *Manager*
EMP: 25
SQ FT: 1,600
SALES (est): 256.1K
SALES (corp-wide): 6MM **Privately Held**
WEB: www.parrotdm.com
SIC: 3647 Headlights (fixtures), vehicular
PA: Parrot
　　Zone Industrielle Gray
　　Dole 39100
　　384 826-151

(G-1398)
PARSLEY ENERGY INC (HQ)
303 Colorado St Ste 3000 (78701-4654)
PHONE...............................737 704-2300
Bryan Sheffield, *Ch of Bd*
Matthew Gallagher, *President*
David Brandenburg, *Superintendent*
Sam Bright, *Superintendent*
Robert Holley, *Superintendent*
EMP: 68
SALES: 1.9B
SALES (corp-wide): 9.3B **Publicly Held**
WEB: www.parsleyenergy.com
SIC: 1311 Crude petroleum production
PA: Pioneer Natural Resources Company
　　777 Hidden Rdg
　　Irving TX 75038
　　972 444-9001

(G-1399)
PATIENT CONVERSATION MEDIA INC (PA)
4315 Guadalupe St Ste 200 (78751-3644)
PHONE...................................512 522-0966
Donald Hackett, *CEO*
EMP: 35 EST: 2012
SALES (est): 3MM **Privately Held**
WEB: www.patientconversation.com
SIC: 7372 Application computer software

(G-1400)
PATTERN BIOSCIENCE INC
9600 Great Hills Trl 160e (78759-6309)
PHONE...................................512 905-9527
Nicolas Arab, *President*
David Bussian, *Vice Pres*
Kyle Fieleke, *Vice Pres*
Ross Johnson, *Chief Engr*
Cindy Lopez, *Director*
EMP: 20
SALES (est): 137.8K **Privately Held**
WEB: www.klarisdx.com
SIC: 2835 In vitro & in vivo diagnostic substances

(G-1401)
PATTON MANUFACTURED PDTS LP
Also Called: Patton Cabinet Doors
10206b N Interstate 35 (78753-3708)
PHONE...................................512 918-3737
David Patton, *General Mgr*
Char Goodmanson, *Accountant*
Jim Shramek, *Mktg Dir*
EMP: 45
SQ FT: 16,500
SALES (est): 3.4MM **Privately Held**
WEB: www.pattoncabinetdoors.com
SIC: 2511 5211 5712 2431 Wood household furniture; cabinets, kitchen; cabinet work, custom; millwork

(G-1402)
PC LEGAL TOOLS INC
Also Called: Tracker
5001 Plz On The Lk Ste 11 (78746-1070)
PHONE...................................415 808-8800
Fred Colman, *CEO*
David Ziegler, *President*
Cecilia Johnson, *Human Res Mgr*
Julie Pearl, *Director*

Victor Neeley, *Officer*
EMP: 40
SALES (est): 6.4MM **Privately Held**
WEB: www.trackercorp.com
SIC: 7373 7372 Systems software development services; prepackaged software

(G-1403)
PEACHED TORTILLA MOBILE LLC
5350 Burnet Rd Apt 425 (78756-2048)
PHONE...................................512 297-8635
Sarafina Riskind, *Opers Mgr*
Kevin Kok, *Manager*
EMP: 12 EST: 2010
SALES (est): 1.5MM **Privately Held**
WEB: www.thepeachedtortilla.com
SIC: 2099 Tortillas, fresh or refrigerated

(G-1404)
PEARSON EDUCATION INC
400 Center Ridge Dr Ste F (78753-1034)
PHONE...................................512 989-5300
Jeffrey Walker Martin, *Branch Mgr*
EMP: 27
SALES (corp-wide): 5B **Privately Held**
SIC: 2731 Book publishing
HQ: Pearson Education, Inc.
　　221 River St
　　Hoboken NJ 07030
　　201 236-7000

(G-1405)
PEARSON EDUCATION INC
Also Called: Thea Test
2535 Ridgepoint Dr (78754-5257)
P.O. Box 140347 (78714-0347)
PHONE...................................866 565-4879
Ben Dehoyon, *Branch Mgr*
EMP: 15
SALES (corp-wide): 5B **Privately Held**
SIC: 2721 Periodicals
HQ: Pearson Education, Inc.
　　221 River St
　　Hoboken NJ 07030
　　201 236-7000

(G-1406)
PEGICORN ENTERPRISES LLC
Also Called: Friendly Car Care
9110 Burnet Rd (78758-5204)
PHONE...................................512 821-3300
Greg Murphy,
Jone Bott,
EMP: 12
SQ FT: 10,000
SALES (est): 1.6MM **Privately Held**
WEB: www.friendlycarcare.com
SIC: 7538 3559 General automotive repair shops; automotive maintenance equipment

(G-1407)
PEN TECH ASSEMBLY LLC
2400 Grand Avenue Pkwy # 103 (78728-3952)
PHONE...................................512 275-0590
Susan M Wandell, *Mng Member*
Raymond Wandell,
EMP: 27
SQ FT: 30,100
SALES (est): 3.1MM **Privately Held**
WEB: www.kodiakassembly.com
SIC: 3672 Printed circuit boards

(G-1408)
PEOPLEADMIN INC (DH)
805 Las Cimas Pkwy # 400 (78746-5493)
PHONE...................................877 637-5800
Jack Blaha, *CEO*
Kenneth Hunter, *Partner*
Joanna Sullivan, *Partner*
Jimmy Kelly, *COO*
Jonathan Cottrell, *Research*
EMP: 25
SALES (est): 29.9MM
SALES (corp-wide): 3.1B **Privately Held**
WEB: www.peopleadmin.com
SIC: 7372 Business oriented computer software
HQ: Powerschool Group Llc
　　150 Parkshore Dr
　　Folsom CA 95630
　　916 288-1588

(G-1409)
PERCEPTION SOFTWARE INC
8310 N Capital Of Tx Hwy (78731-1011)
P.O. Box 458 (78767-0458)
PHONE...................................512 593-6996
EMP: 11
SALES (est): 905.2K **Privately Held**
SIC: 7372 Prepackaged Software
HQ: Altium, Inc.
　　4225 Executive Sq Ste 800
　　La Jolla CA 92037
　　858 864-1661

(G-1410)
PERENNIAL DESIGN LLC
2105 Donley Dr Ste 100 (78758-4510)
PHONE...................................512 387-1582
Darryl Kelinske, *Mng Member*
EMP: 15
SQ FT: 6,000
SALES (est): 945K **Privately Held**
SIC: 2653 Corrugated & solid fiber boxes

(G-1411)
PERFECT SURFACE OF AUSTIN (PA)
Also Called: Heart of Texas Perfect Surface
6800 West Gate Blvd # 132 (78745-4883)
PHONE...................................512 339-9937
James Barrentine, *President*
EMP: 10
SALES (est): 1.6MM **Privately Held**
WEB: www.paragonaustin.com
SIC: 3088 Tubs (bath, shower & laundry), plastic

(G-1412)
PERISCOPE INTERMEDIATE CORP
Also Called: Periscope Holdings
5000 Plz On The Lk # 100 (78746-1022)
PHONE...................................512 717-0684
Brian Utley, *CEO*
David English, *CFO*
Rose Canas, *Controller*
EMP: 87
SQ FT: 10,527
SALES (est): 152.8K **Privately Held**
SIC: 7372 Prepackaged software

(G-1413)
PETHONESTY LLC
600 Congress Ave Fl 14 (78701-3263)
PHONE...................................909 435-6574
Benjamin Arneberg, *Mng Member*
Daniel Kiuttu,
Scott Patterson,
EMP: 15
SALES (est): 528.5K **Privately Held**
SIC: 2047 Dog & cat food

(G-1414)
PETROLEGACY ENERGY II LLC
6101 W Courtyard Dr # 212 (78730-5115)
PHONE...................................512 735-9000
Paul C Lee Jr, *President*
EMP: 50
SALES (est): 203.4K **Privately Held**
WEB: www.plellc.com
SIC: 1382 Oil & gas exploration services

(G-1415)
PHLUR INC (PA)
2400 E Cesar Chavez St (78702-4607)
PHONE...................................888 771-9434
Eric Korman, *President*
Shawn Freeman, *COO*
EMP: 14
SALES (est): 2.7MM **Privately Held**
WEB: www.phlur.com
SIC: 2844 5122 5999 Toilet preparations; cosmetics, perfumes & hair products; toiletries, cosmetics & perfumes

(G-1416)
PHUNWARE INC
7800 Shoal Creek Blvd 230s (78757-1052)
PHONE...................................512 693-4199
Alan S Knitowski, *CEO*
Blythe Masters, *Ch of Bd*
Randall Crowder, *COO*
Matt Aune, *CFO*
Luan Dang, *CTO*
EMP: 93
SQ FT: 10,600

SALES: 19.1MM **Privately Held**
SIC: 7372 Prepackaged software

(G-1417)
PINNERGY LTD (PA)
111 Congress Ave Ste 2020 (78701-4080)
PHONE...................................512 343-8880
Randy Taylor, *President*
Tommy Mouser, *President*
Steve Nations, *President*
Wade Webster, *COO*
Justin Taylor, *Exec VP*
EMP: 63
SQ FT: 5,000
SALES (est): 862.2MM **Privately Held**
WEB: www.pinnergy.com
SIC: 1389 Oil field services

(G-1418)
PITNEY BOWES INC
11400 Burnet Rd Bldg 7 (78758-3406)
PHONE...................................512 823-0833
EMP: 37
SALES (corp-wide): 3.5B **Publicly Held**
SIC: 3579 7359 Mfg Office Machines
　Equipment Rental/Leasing
PA: Pitney Bowes Inc.
　　3001 Summer St
　　Stamford CT 06905
　　203 356-5000

(G-1419)
PIXELS & POWERTOOLS LLC
4201 S Congress Ave # 316 (78745-1198)
PHONE...................................844 458-1847
Royston Guidry, *Mng Member*
EMP: 15
SALES (est): 628.8K **Privately Held**
WEB: www.accpl.co
SIC: 3449 Miscellaneous metalwork

(G-1420)
PLASTIC SPECIALTIES INC
Also Called: P S I Urethanes
10503 Metropolitan Dr (78758-4950)
PHONE...................................512 835-5873
George L Manson, *President*
Richard E Manson, *Vice Pres*
Nancy Bell, *Sales Staff*
Arthur J Manson III, *Admin Sec*
Jean Becerra, *Graphic Designe*
◆ EMP: 35 EST: 1966
SQ FT: 45,000
SALES (est): 8.9MM **Privately Held**
WEB: www.psiurethanes.com
SIC: 2821 Plastics materials & resins

(G-1421)
PLAYWOOD OUTDOOR FUN
10208 N Fm 620 Rd Ste 1a (78726-2200)
PHONE...................................512 250-8819
Richard G Wood, *Owner*
EMP: 25
SQ FT: 16,000
SALES (est): 1.5MM **Privately Held**
SIC: 3949 Playground equipment

(G-1422)
PLUGGED IN LLC
8701 Shoal Creek Blvd # 101 (78757-6864)
PHONE...................................512 380-0900
Ray Cole, *Mng Member*
Nora Fernandez, *Consultant*
EMP: 13
SQ FT: 2,000
SALES (est): 808.4K **Privately Held**
SIC: 7372 Prepackaged software

(G-1423)
PLUS THERAPEUTICS INC (PA)
4200 Marathon Blvd # 200 (78756-3435)
PHONE...................................737 255-7194
Richard J Hawkins, *Ch of Bd*
Marc H Hedrick, *President*
Gregory Stein, *Senior VP*
Christina Lawton, *Associate*
▼ EMP: 37
SQ FT: 17,535
SALES: 7MM **Publicly Held**
WEB: www.cytori.com
SIC: 2834 Pharmaceutical preparations

(G-1424)
POOL & ELECTRICAL PRODUCTS INC
407 Radam Ln (78745-1121)
PHONE.....................512 707-0109
Oscar Silva, *Director*
EMP: 11 **Privately Held**
WEB: www.poolelectrical.com
SIC: 3648 Swimming pool lighting fixtures
PA: Pool & Electrical Products Inc.
1595 E 6th St
Corona CA 92879

(G-1425)
POOL ENERGY CORPORATION
Also Called: Richman Oil
12885 N Hwy 183 Ste 104 (78750-3223)
PHONE.....................512 249-9252
Keith H Adams, *President*
Dale McNeill, *Senior VP*
Ron Risringer, *Vice Pres*
Salina Simons, *Assoc VP*
EMP: 12
SALES (est): 1.5MM **Privately Held**
WEB: www.richmanoil.com
SIC: 1382 Oil & gas exploration services

(G-1426)
PPG INDUSTRIES INC
Also Called: PPG 8358
7401 W Highway 71 Ste 115 (78735-8261)
PHONE.....................512 288-5505
Steve Powell, *Branch Mgr*
EMP: 24
SALES (corp-wide): 15.3B **Publicly Held**
WEB: www.ppg.com
SIC: 2851 Paints & allied products
PA: Ppg Industries, Inc.
1 Ppg Pl
Pittsburgh PA 15272
412 434-3131

(G-1427)
PRACTICE INTERACTIVE INC (PA)
Also Called: Procial
1701 Dirs Blvd Ste 110 (78744)
PHONE.....................844 413-2602
Alexander Candelario, *President*
Robb Duke, *Mktg Dir*
Megan Monk, *Mktg Coord*
Jerry Hsiang, *Director*
EMP: 11 **EST:** 2012
SQ FT: 2,700
SALES (est): 3.4MM **Privately Held**
WEB: www.intivahealth.com
SIC: 7372 Application computer software

(G-1428)
PRE MANAGEMENT INC
7600 Burnet Rd Ste 160 (78757-1267)
PHONE.....................512 891-0300
Sebastian Stadler, *Principal*
EMP: 9
SALES (est): 976.2K **Privately Held**
WEB: www.premgmt.com
SIC: 2741 Miscellaneous publishing

(G-1429)
PRECISION JOINT SOLUTION INC
3903 S Congress Ave # 42108
(78704-0201)
P.O. Box 42108 (78704-0036)
PHONE.....................972 351-0470
Cherie Hecht, *CEO*
Brad Schafer, *CFO*
Kelley Hulihen, *Admin Sec*
EMP: 11 **EST:** 2011
SALES (est): 2.4MM **Privately Held**
WEB: www.precisionjointsolution.com
SIC: 5191 7389 2048 Animal feeds; ; feed supplements

(G-1430)
PRECISION PEARL INLAY INC
7208 Cooper Ln (78745-6304)
PHONE.....................512 442-4941
Tom Ellis, *Owner*
EMP: 12
SALES (est): 800K **Privately Held**
WEB: www.precisionpearl.com
SIC: 3931 Musical instruments

(G-1431)
PRESTIGE TANK & PUMP SVCS INC
Also Called: Idcastings
1600 S 8th St (78718)
P.O. Box 170398 (78717-0025)
PHONE.....................512 698-9645
Anthony Lewis, *President*
Vanessa Frix,
EMP: 30
SALES (est): 8.4MM **Privately Held**
SIC: 3321 Ductile iron castings

(G-1432)
PRINTEDD PRODUCTS & SVCS LTD
Also Called: Printed Products
2400 Forbes Dr Ste 100 (78754-5213)
PHONE.....................512 835-2253
Darrel Stracner, *General Mgr*
Patty Hiles, *Regl Sales Mgr*
EMP: 35
SALES (corp-wide): 12.2MM **Privately Held**
WEB: www.printedd.com
SIC: 2759 5943 2752 Commercial printing; office forms & supplies; commercial printing, lithographic
PA: Printedd Products & Services, Ltd.
2641 N Forum Dr
Grand Prairie TX 75052
972 660-3800

(G-1433)
PRINTMPRO LTD
Also Called: Printmailpro.com
9011 Tuscany Way Ste 200 (78754-4794)
PHONE.....................512 821-9000
Keith Daboub, *Partner*
Daniel Thompson, *Opers Staff*
Eric Governale, *Software Dev*
EMP: 40
SALES (est): 7MM **Privately Held**
WEB: www.printmailpro.com
SIC: 7389 7336 2752 2759 Mailing & messenger services; graphic arts & related design; commercial printing, offset; business form & card printing, lithographic; calendar & card printing, lithographic; promotional printing

(G-1434)
PROCESS INDUSTRY PRACTICES
Also Called: PIP Printing
3925 W Braker Ln R4500 (78759-5316)
PHONE.....................512 232-3041
Mina Chau, *Vice Pres*
Austin Reynolds, *Vice Pres*
Ken Hamilton, *Project Mgr*
Kathy Brooks, *Facilities Mgr*
Julia Lopez, *Purch Mgr*
EMP: 9
SALES (est): 1.4MM **Privately Held**
WEB: www.pip.org
SIC: 2752 1541 Commercial printing, offset; industrial buildings, new construction

(G-1435)
PROGRESSIVE MFG TECH INC
Also Called: Pe Ceramics
5507 Honey Dew Ter (78749-1222)
PHONE.....................512 380-1991
George Fuller, *President*
Jeff Simpson, *Sales Staff*
Deepak Burman, *Director*
Dan Christiano, *Director*
Jerry Gilliam, *Director*
EMP: 17
SALES (est): 3.1MM **Privately Held**
WEB: www.promtinc.com
SIC: 3674 Wafers (semiconductor devices)

(G-1436)
PROGRESSIVE MILLWORKS INC
11118 N Lamar Blvd Ste A (78753-3047)
PHONE.....................512 832-0551
Robert Nagelhout, *President*
EMP: 57
SQ FT: 20,000
SALES (est): 8.6MM **Privately Held**
SIC: 2431 1751 2434 Millwork; carpentry work; wood kitchen cabinets

(G-1437)
PUBLICTIONS COMMUNICATIONS INC
Also Called: PCI
13552 N Hwy 183 Ste A (78750-2251)
PHONE.....................512 250-9023
Gary Pittman, *President*
Bill Liflind, *Vice Pres*
Eugene Morgan, *Manager*
EMP: 20
SQ FT: 5,000
SALES (est): 2.2MM **Privately Held**
WEB: www.pcinews.com
SIC: 2721 Magazines: publishing only, not printed on site

(G-1438)
PUSHNAMI LLC (PA)
6600 N Lamar Blvd (78752-3502)
PHONE.....................512 961-7042
Kacey Meguin, *Accounts Mgr*
Emerson Smith,
EMP: 11
SALES (est): 2.1MM **Privately Held**
WEB: www.pushnami.com
SIC: 7372 Application computer software

(G-1439)
Q2 HOLDINGS INC (PA)
13785 Res Blvd Ste 150 (78750)
PHONE.....................512 275-0072
Robert Hank Seale III, *Ch of Bd*
Matthew P Flake, *President*
Adam D Blue, *Exec VP*
John E Breeden, *Exec VP*
Rekha D Garapati, *Exec VP*
EMP: 39
SQ FT: 196,000
SALES (est): 315.4MM **Publicly Held**
WEB: www.q2.com
SIC: 7372 Prepackaged software; application computer software

(G-1440)
QSI CUSTOM CABINETS LP
3800 Drossett Dr Ste B (78744-1131)
P.O. Box 19383 (78760-9383)
PHONE.....................512 443-3303
EMP: 35
SQ FT: 47,000
SALES (est): 4.3MM **Privately Held**
SIC: 2434 Mfg Wood Kitchen Cabinets

(G-1441)
QUADRABYTE LLC
700 Lavaca St Ste 1401 (78701-3135)
PHONE.....................469 619-0749
Ronald Steelman, *CEO*
EMP: 10
SALES (est): 419K **Privately Held**
WEB: www.quadrabyte.net
SIC: 3652 7379 Pre-recorded records & tapes; computer related consulting services

(G-1442)
QUALCOMM TECHNOLOGIES INC
9600 Mo Pac Dr (78731)
PHONE.....................512 623-3700
Choh F Yeap, *Vice Pres*
Victor Andrade, *Engineer*
Bailey Chris, *Engineer*
Michael Hobbs, *Engineer*
Chris Koob, *Engineer*
EMP: 125
SALES (corp-wide): 23.5B **Publicly Held**
WEB: www.qualcomm.com
SIC: 3663 Space satellite communications equipment
HQ: Qualcomm Technologies, Inc.
5775 Morehouse Dr
San Diego CA 92121
858 587-1121

(G-1443)
QUALITY FOUNDATION REPAIR INC
Also Called: Wallace Foundation, The
9906 Gray Blvd Ste A (78758-5429)
PHONE.....................512 363-7769
Simon Wallace, *Owner*
Melisa Taylor, *Office Mgr*
EMP: 18
SQ FT: 30,000
SALES (est): 2MM **Privately Held**
WEB: www.qualityfoundationrepairaustin.com
SIC: 1389 Construction, repair & dismantling services

(G-1444)
QUIK PRINT OF AUSTIN INC (PA)
Also Called: Quik Print Prtg & Copying Ctr
8508 Cross Park Dr (78754-4532)
PHONE.....................512 467-9382
Gil P Gravley, *President*
Theresa A Gravley, *Corp Secy*
Michael Gravley, *Vice Pres*
EMP: 60
SQ FT: 6,000
SALES (est): 9.4MM **Privately Held**
WEB: www.qpaustin.com
SIC: 2752 7334 Commercial printing, offset; photocopying & duplicating services

(G-1445)
QUINSTAR CORPORATION
Also Called: Specter Instruments
2024 E Saint Elmo Rd (78744-1018)
P.O. Box 19229 (78760-9229)
PHONE.....................512 326-1011
▼ **EMP:** 14 **EST:** 1974
SQ FT: 5,600
SALES: 2.5MM **Privately Held**
WEB: www.win911.com
SIC: 7372 3699 Application computer software; electrical equipment & supplies

(G-1446)
QVINCI SOFTWARE
1601 S Mo Pac Expy (78746-7009)
PHONE.....................512 637-7337
Adam Nance, *Manager*
Aaron Bartlett, *Consultant*
Joseph Pelletier, *Consultant*
Charles B Nagel,
EMP: 14 **EST:** 2007
SALES (est): 1.4MM **Privately Held**
WEB: www.qvinci.com
SIC: 7372 Prepackaged software

(G-1447)
R F HIGGINBOTHAM INC
Also Called: Capitol Company
8723 N Lamar Blvd (78753-5423)
PHONE.....................512 836-8985
Robert Higginbotham Sr, *President*
Doris A Higginbotham, *Vice Pres*
▲ **EMP:** 20
SQ FT: 10,000
SALES (est): 3MM **Privately Held**
WEB: www.capitolcompany.com
SIC: 3444 5051 Cornices, sheet metal; gutters, sheet metal; hoods, range: sheet metal; metals service centers & offices

(G-1448)
R W GONZALEZ OFFICE PDTS INC (PA)
Also Called: Gonzalez Solutions For Bus
600 Congress Ave Ste 1400 (78701-3234)
PHONE.....................512 300-2300
Wayne R Gonzalez, *President*
Dale Gonzalez, *COO*
Pamela Gonzalez, *Vice Pres*
Roy Gonzalez, *Bd of Directors*
EMP: 15
SQ FT: 7,500
SALES (est): 2.5MM **Privately Held**
WEB: www.rwgop.com
SIC: 5712 3993 2621 Office furniture; signs & advertising specialties; printing paper

(G-1449)
R2SONIC LLC
5307 Industrial Oaks Blvd (78735-8821)
PHONE.....................512 891-0000
Charles Brennan, *Engineer*
Cris Sabo, *VP Sales*
Mike Brissette, *Sales Staff*
Emma Vas, *Director*
Jens R Steenstrup,
EMP: 12
SQ FT: 2,000
SALES (est): 2.7MM **Privately Held**
WEB: www.r2sonic.com
SIC: 3812 5731 Sonar systems & equipment; marine radios & radar equipment

G E O G R A P H I C

(G-1450)
RADTKE JENNA
Also Called: Lucy In Disguise With Diamonds
1506 S Congress Ave (78704-2437)
PHONE...................................512 444-2002
Jenna Radtke, *Owner*
EMP: 25
SQ FT: 5,000
SALES (est): 990.6K **Privately Held**
WEB: www.lucyindisguise.com
SIC: 5932 2389 7299 Clothing, second-
hand; masquerade costumes; costume
rental

(G-1451)
RAMAN SYSTEMS INC
7301 N Fm 620 Rd Ste 155 (78726-4537)
PHONE...................................512 673-7364
▲ EMP: 20
SQ FT: 25,000
SALES (est): 1.9MM **Privately Held**
SIC: 3826 Mfg Analytical Instruments

(G-1452)
RANCH HOUSE JERKY LLC
4201 Hidden Canyon Cv (78746-1256)
PHONE...................................512 347-8999
Henry Green, *Manager*
EMP: 30
SALES (est): 1.2MM **Privately Held**
SIC: 2013 Snack sticks, including jerky:
from purchased meat
PA: Vsm Brands, Inc.
12647 Alcosta Blvd # 165
San Ramon CA 94583

(G-1453)
RBT INDUSTRIES LLC (PA)
Also Called: Hardwood Bargains
800 Interchange Blvd # 101 (78721-3652)
PHONE...................................512 600-5994
Ben Thompson, *CEO*
Charles Mercer, *Marketing Mgr*
Ross Bayley, *Mng Member*
Dave Armstrong, *Manager*
▲ EMP: 18 EST: 2008
SQ FT: 30,000
SALES (est): 5.5MM **Privately Held**
WEB: www.hardwoodbargains.com
SIC: 5211 2426 Flooring, wood; flooring,
hardwood

(G-1454)
**REAGAN OUTDOOR
ADVERTISING**
Also Called: Reagan National Advertising
7301 N Burleson Rd (78744-3207)
PHONE...................................512 926-7740
William K Reagan II, *Exec VP*
EMP: 35 **Privately Held**
WEB: www.reaganoutdoor.com
SIC: 7312 3993 Billboard advertising;
signs & advertising specialties
PA: Reagan Outdoor Advertising
1775 N Warm Springs Rd
Salt Lake City UT 84116

(G-1455)
RED BOOK CONNECT LLC
Also Called: Hotschedules
6504 Bridge Point Pkwy # 42 (78730-5011)
PHONE...................................877 741-9610
Anthony Lye, *CEO*
Larry Abramson, *Principal*
John W Chidsey, *Chairman*
Ray Pawlikowski,
EMP: 459
SALES (est): 64.4MM **Privately Held**
WEB: www.fourth.com
SIC: 7372 Prepackaged software

(G-1456)
REFUGE INDUSTRIES LLC
Also Called: Bold Mfg & Supply
4310 Willow Springs Rd (78745-1244)
PHONE...................................512 961-4907
EMP: 10 EST: 2016
SALES (est): 1MM **Privately Held**
WEB: www.boldmfg.com
SIC: 3993 Advertising novelties

(G-1457)
**REGAL PLASTIC SUPPLY CO
INC**
9311 Metric Blvd (78758-5994)
PHONE...................................512 836-3629
Chris Pisculli, *Opers Mgr*
Chris Zubko, *Purchasing*
Ronnie Stockton, *Manager*
EMP: 11
SQ FT: 21,840
SALES (corp-wide): 69.3MM **Privately
Held**
WEB: www.regal-plastics.com
SIC: 5162 5999 5169 3089 Plastics prod-
ucts; safety supplies & equipment; silicon
lubricants; molding primary plastic
PA: Regal Plastic Supply Company, Inc.
9200 N Royal Ln Ste 120
Irving TX 75063
800 441-1553

(G-1458)
REMORA ROYALTIES INC
807 Las Cimas Pkwy Ii (78746-6191)
PHONE...................................512 579-3590
George B Peyton V, *Ch of Bd*
Grant W Livesay, *President*
Corwin Y Ames, *Vice Pres*
Aaron T Brack, *Vice Pres*
Christopher J Manuel, *Vice Pres*
EMP: 22
SALES (est): 519.6K **Privately Held**
SIC: 1311 Crude petroleum & natural gas
production

(G-1459)
**RESIDEO TECHNOLOGIES INC
(PA)**
901 E 6th St (78702-3206)
PHONE...................................512 726-3500
Roger B Fradin, *Ch of Bd*
Jay Geldmacher, *President*
Robert Aarnes, *President*
Sach Sankpal, *President*
Jeannine J Lane, *Exec VP*
EMP: 19
SALES: 4.9B **Publicly Held**
WEB: www.resideo.com
SIC: 5065 3699 Security control equip-
ment & systems; security control equip-
ment & systems

(G-1460)
RESONANT INC (PA)
10900 Stnlake Blvd Ste 10 (78759)
PHONE...................................805 308-9803
George B Holmes, *CEO*
John E Major, *Ch of Bd*
Dylan J Kelly, *COO*
Neal Fenzi, *Exec VP*
Greg Hey-Shipton, *Vice Pres*
EMP: 53
SALES: 735K **Publicly Held**
WEB: www.resonant.com
SIC: 3674 Semiconductors & related de-
vices

(G-1461)
RESTAURANT DEPOT LLC
820 Blackson Ave (78752-2710)
PHONE...................................512 454-5600
James Mercer, *Owner*
EMP: 50
SALES (corp-wide): 24.5B **Privately Held**
WEB: www.restaurantdepot.com
SIC: 5046 3589 Restaurant equipment &
supplies; commercial cooking & food-
warming equipment
HQ: Restaurant Depot, Llc
1710 Whitestone Expy
Whitestone NY 11357

(G-1462)
RETAIL CONCEPTS INC
Also Called: Sun & Ski Sports Expo
2438 W Anderson Ln B1a (78757-1149)
PHONE...................................512 467-2782
Brandon Bromley, *Manager*
EMP: 14

SALES (corp-wide): 96.2MM **Privately
Held**
WEB: www.sunandski.com
SIC: 5941 3949 Tennis goods & equipment; skiing equipment; bicycle & bicycle
parts; water sport equipment; exercising
cycles
PA: Retail Concepts, Inc.
10225 Mula Rd Ste 120
Stafford TX 77477
281 340-5000

(G-1463)
RETRONIX GLOBAL INC
Also Called: Retronix Inc
11221 Blairview Ln (78748-3911)
PHONE...................................512 808-5659
Dennis Rooney, *President*
Jeffrey Barranti, *Regional Mgr*
Kathleen Boswell, *Vice Pres*
Katie Venters, *Opers Staff*
Phil Myers, *Sales Staff*
EMP: 107 EST: 2010
SALES: 12.3MM **Privately Held**
WEB: www.retronixsemiconductor.com
SIC: 3674 Semiconductors & related de-
vices
PA: Retronix Ltd.
North Caldeen Road
Coatbridge ML5 4

(G-1464)
RF CODE INC
9229 Waterford Centre Blv (78758-7511)
PHONE...................................512 439-2200
Dale Quayle, *CEO*
Christal Hood-Mcdonald, *General Mgr*
Connie Brigham, *Business Mgr*
Tom Bishop, *Vice Pres*
Richard Jenkins, *Vice Pres*
▼ EMP: 49
SQ FT: 11,413
SALES (est): 13.9MM **Privately Held**
WEB: www.rfcode.com
SIC: 3663 Radio & TV communications
equipment

(G-1465)
RFMICRON INC
Also Called: Axzon
6101 W Courtyard Dr # 1 (78730-5115)
PHONE...................................512 535-4647
Shahriar Rokhsaz, *CEO*
Brian Young, *General Mgr*
Hal Steele, *Vice Pres*
Tanmay Zargar, *Marketing Staff*
Debora Kyser, *Office Mgr*
EMP: 21 EST: 2006
SALES (est): 501.9K **Privately Held**
WEB: www.axzon.com
SIC: 3571 Electronic computers

(G-1466)
**RILEY EXPLORATION GROUP
LLC**
111 Congress Ave (78701-4050)
PHONE...................................512 481-7676
EMP: 79
SALES (corp-wide): 70.6MM **Privately
Held**
WEB: www.rileyexplorationgroup.com
SIC: 1382 Oil & gas exploration services
PA: Riley Exploration Group, Llc
29 E Reno Ave Ste 5
Oklahoma City OK 73104
405 485-8200

(G-1467)
RIVER CITY CABINETS INC
115 E Saint Elmo Rd Ste D (78745-1266)
PHONE...................................512 442-9990
Duane Eller, *President*
EMP: 17
SALES (est): 2.9MM **Privately Held**
WEB: www.rivercitycabinets.com
SIC: 2434 Wood kitchen cabinets

(G-1468)
ROC SOFTWARE LP (PA)
Also Called: ROC Software Systems
3305 Northland Dr Ste 105 (78731-4940)
PHONE...................................512 336-4200
Wendy Compton, *Managing Prtnr*
O'Gara Business Trust, *Managing Prtnr*
Paul Scripko, *Vice Pres*
Brian Wharton, *Controller*

Cristi Hurdle, *Manager*
EMP: 20
SALES (est): 2.4MM **Privately Held**
WEB: www.rocsoftware.com
SIC: 7371 7372 Computer software devel-
opment; prepackaged software

(G-1469)
**ROCHE ROUGE COMPANY L L
C**
Also Called: Austin American Awnings
600 E Saint Elmo Rd (78745-1226)
PHONE...................................512 326-1670
Roger C Solomon, *Mng Member*
Maria Solomon,
EMP: 11
SQ FT: 6,000
SALES (est): 1MM **Privately Held**
WEB: www.austinawning.com
SIC: 2394 Canvas awnings & canopies

(G-1470)
ROKA SPORTS INC
2214 W Braker Ln Ste A (78758-4146)
PHONE...................................877 985-7652
Robert Canales, *CEO*
Jamie Oman, *General Mgr*
Diana Swope, *Vice Pres*
Jessica Lester, *Opers Staff*
Michael O'Neil, *Opers Staff*
▲ EMP: 46
SQ FT: 3,026
SALES (est): 12.9MM **Privately Held**
WEB: www.rokasports.com
SIC: 5136 5137 2329 2339 Sportswear,
men's & boys'; swimsuits: women's, chil-
dren's & infants'; bathing suits &
swimwear: men's & boys'; bathing suits:
women's, misses' & juniors'

(G-1471)
RON T FELT (PA)
Also Called: Fastsigns
8820 Burnet Rd Ste 504 (78757-7050)
PHONE...................................512 258-5523
Ron T Felt, *Owner*
EMP: 15 EST: 1991
SALES (est): 1,000K **Privately Held**
WEB: www.fastsigns.com
SIC: 3993 Signs & advertising specialties

(G-1472)
RON T FELT
Also Called: Fastsigns
13497 N Hwy 183 Ste 301 (78750-2306)
PHONE...................................512 335-7446
Ron Feld, *Branch Mgr*
EMP: 15
SALES (corp-wide): 1,000K **Privately
Held**
WEB: www.fastsigns.com
SIC: 3993 Signs & advertising specialties
PA: Ron T Felt
8820 Burnet Rd Ste 504
Austin TX 78757
512 258-5523

(G-1473)
ROOTS ROCKS INC
Also Called: Kirk Root Designs
10000 Res Blvd Ste 126 (78759)
PHONE...................................512 346-1780
Fax: 512 346-4113
EMP: 11
SQ FT: 1,300
SALES (est): 1.9MM **Privately Held**
SIC: 5944 3911 Ret Jewelry Mfg Precious
Metal Jewelry

(G-1474)
**ROYALTY CLEARINGHOUSE
LTD**
201 W 5th St Ste 1350 (78701-3090)
PHONE...................................800 877-5122
Shane McCaig, *Managing Prtnr*
Al Koehler, *Mng Member*
EMP: 15
SALES (est): 1.7MM **Privately Held**
WEB: www.royaltyclearinghouse.com
SIC: 1382 Oil & gas exploration services

(G-1475)
RUBEN ARISPE JR
Also Called: Jwacs Commercial Group
8300 Thaxton Rd (78747-4038)
PHONE...................................512 543-3444

▲ = Import ▼=Export
◆ =Import/Export

Ruben Arispe Jr, *Owner*
EMP: 12
SALES (est): 486K **Privately Held**
SIC: 1389 Construction, repair & dismantling services

(G-1476)
RUBICON COMMUNICATIONS LLC
Also Called: Netgate
4616 W Howard Ln Ste 900 (78728-6300)
PHONE................512 646-4100
Chad Leedy, *Vice Pres*
Sean Henry, *Sales Staff*
Angela Rodriguez, *Sales Staff*
Jamie Thompson, *Mng Member*
Nathan Pintar, *Technical Staff*
▲ **EMP:** 42
SQ FT: 15,000
SALES (est): 2.2MM **Privately Held**
WEB: www.netgate.com
SIC: 7372 7373 Prepackaged software; business oriented computer software; turnkey vendors, computer systems

(G-1477)
RUSSELLS BAKERY AND COFFEE BAR
3339 Hancock Dr (78731-5430)
PHONE................512 419-7877
Russell Millner, *Owner*
Jemma Millner, *Co-Owner*
EMP: 14
SALES (est): 1.4MM **Privately Held**
WEB: www.russellsbakery.com
SIC: 2051 5812 Bakery: wholesale or wholesale/retail combined; coffee shop

(G-1478)
SABEREX GROUP LTD
12317 Tech Blvd Ste 100 (78727)
PHONE................512 623-4694
Andrew Cooper, *CEO*
John Bosch Jr, *Partner*
Robert Zawadzki, *Engineer*
Angela Roush, *Asst Controller*
Larry Krupicka, *Manager*
◆ **EMP:** 41
SQ FT: 149,067
SALES (est): 7.8MM **Privately Held**
WEB: www.saberex.com
SIC: 3672 Printed circuit boards
PA: Tyrex Group, Ltd.
12317 Tech Blvd Ste 100
Austin TX 78727

(G-1479)
SACHEM INC (PA)
821 Woodward St (78704-7418)
PHONE................512 421-4900
John Mooney, *President*
Richard Goodin, *Vice Pres*
Louis Hunt, *Vice Pres*
ARI Kar, *Vice Pres*
Eric Riden, *Vice Pres*
◆ **EMP:** 50 **EST:** 1950
SQ FT: 20,000
SALES (est): 91.2MM **Privately Held**
WEB: www.sacheminc.com
SIC: 2869 Industrial organic chemicals

(G-1480)
SACHEM INC
5700 S Mopac Bldg B (78749)
PHONE................512 421-4946
Tanya Hunter, *Accountant*
Rosemary Hoffman, *Manager*
Denise Watkins, *Executive Asst*
EMP: 55
SALES (corp-wide): 91.2MM **Privately Held**
WEB: www.sacheminc.com
SIC: 2869 Industrial organic chemicals
PA: Sachem, Inc.
821 Woodward St
Austin TX 78704
512 421-4900

(G-1481)
SAGE SOFTWARE INC
Also Called: Best Software Non Profit
10800 Pecan Park Blvd # 400
(78750-1224)
PHONE................512 331-0723
Krista Ensley, *Manager*
EMP: 125

SALES (corp-wide): 2.4B **Privately Held**
WEB: www.na.sage.com
SIC: 7372 Business oriented computer software
HQ: Sage Software, Inc.
271 17th St Nw Ste 1100
Atlanta GA 30363
866 996-7243

(G-1482)
SAILPOINT TECH HOLDINGS INC (PA)
11120 Four Points Dr # 10 (78726-2118)
PHONE................512 346-2000
Mark D McClain, *CEO*
Mary Berg, *Partner*
Berk Bucukoglu, *Partner*
Sarah Granger, *Partner*
Vlad Khazanovich, *Partner*
EMP: 1003 **EST:** 2004
SQ FT: 164,818
SALES: 288.5MM **Publicly Held**
WEB: www.sailpoint.com
SIC: 7372 Prepackaged software

(G-1483)
SAILPOINT TECHNOLOGIES INC (HQ)
11120 Four Points Dr # 100 (78726-2118)
PHONE................512 346-2000
Mark McClain, *CEO*
Dave Hendrix, *Partner*
Christine Kungl, *Partner*
Grady Summers, *Exec VP*
Joe Gottlieb, *Senior VP*
EMP: 148
SQ FT: 164,818
SALES (est): 185.9MM
SALES (corp-wide): 288.5MM **Publicly Held**
WEB: www.sailpoint.com
SIC: 7372 Prepackaged software
PA: Sailpoint Technologies Holdings, Inc.
11120 Four Points Dr # 10
Austin TX 78726
512 346-2000

(G-1484)
SALIENT SYSTEMS CORPORATION
4616 W Howard Ln 1-100 (78728-6300)
PHONE................512 617-4800
Per Hanssen, *CEO*
Chris Meiter, *President*
Robert C Wilbur, *Principal*
Robert O Williams, *Principal*
Bob Wilber, *Vice Pres*
EMP: 16
SQ FT: 5,862
SALES (est): 4MM **Privately Held**
WEB: www.salientsys.com
SIC: 7374 3577 Computer graphics service; computer peripheral equipment

(G-1485)
SANMINA CORPORATION
Also Called: Sanmina-Sci
9100 Cameron Rd (78754-3916)
PHONE................512 997-1100
Denni Sims, *Business Mgr*
Brittany Bowles, *Purch Mgr*
Tim Trandai, *Engineer*
Malcolm Bounds, *Sales Mgr*
Rusty Zunker, *Planning Mgr*
EMP: 10 **Publicly Held**
WEB: www.sanmina.com
SIC: 3672 Circuit boards, television & radio printed
PA: Sanmina Corporation
2700 N 1st St
San Jose CA 95134

(G-1486)
SAPLING SYSTEMS INC
2815 Exposition Blvd (78703-1207)
PHONE................512 323-6565
Darren Trumeter, *CEO*
James W Caras, *President*
Paige Caras, *Vice Pres*
EMP: 20
SALES (est): 2.1MM **Privately Held**
WEB: www.sciencetechnologies.com
SIC: 7372 Educational computer software

(G-1487)
SAS INSTITUTE INC
1801 E 6th St Fl 5 (78702-2791)
PHONE................512 258-5171
William Baylor, *Engr R&D*
Jeff Jones, *Executive*
EMP: 85
SALES (corp-wide): 2.1B **Privately Held**
WEB: www.sas.com
SIC: 7372 Application computer software
PA: Sas Institute Inc.
100 Sas Campus Dr
Cary NC 27513
919 677-8000

(G-1488)
SAVARA INC (PA)
6836 Bee Caves Rd 3-200 (78746-5879)
PHONE................512 614-1848
Matthew Pauls, *Ch of Bd*
David Lowrance, *CFO*
Badrul Chowdhury, *Chief Mktg Ofcr*
Anne Erickson, *Officer*
EMP: 31
SQ FT: 6,151
SALES (est): 2MM **Publicly Held**
WEB: www.savarapharma.com
SIC: 2834 Pharmaceutical preparations

(G-1489)
SCALABLE SOFTWARE INC
600 Congress Ave Ste C100 (78701-2989)
P.O. Box 2335, Cornelius NC (28031-2335)
PHONE................512 501-2828
Chris Gomersall, *President*
Mark Cresswell, *Chairman*
Lou Meyer, *Controller*
Tyler Schlief, *Consultant*
EMP: 19
SALES (est): 2.8MM
SALES (corp-wide): 351.1K **Privately Held**
WEB: www.scalable.com
SIC: 7372 Application computer software
HQ: Scalable Software Ltd
Gainsborough House
Richmond
203 695-4632

(G-1490)
SCIENTIFIC MACHINE & WLDG INC
3404 Duke Rd (78724-2512)
PHONE................512 926-8400
Alan J Basta, *President*
EMP: 23
SQ FT: 15,000
SALES (est): 2.6MM **Privately Held**
WEB: www.sm-w.com
SIC: 7692 3599 3499 Welding repair; machine shop, jobbing & repair; tablets, bronze or other metal

(G-1491)
SEMICONDUCTOR SUPPORT SVCS CO
Also Called: SSS Co.
4715 Steiner Ranch Blvd (78732-2317)
PHONE................512 267-7087
Robert Basnett, *President*
Sherri Basnett, *Vice Pres*
Dawn Bellemare, *Sales Staff*
◆ **EMP:** 27
SQ FT: 45,741
SALES (est): 5.4MM **Privately Held**
WEB: www.semiconservice.com
SIC: 3674 Semiconductors & related devices

(G-1492)
SENOX CORPORATION (PA)
Also Called: Spruce Creek Company
15409 Long Vista Dr (78728-3815)
PHONE................512 251-3333
A B Walters, *President*
Nicole Walters Budworth, *Exec VP*
Bill Budworth, *Vice Pres*
Chris Chandler, *Vice Pres*
John Ellis, *Vice Pres*
◆ **EMP:** 33
SQ FT: 84,000

SALES (est): 48.9MM **Privately Held**
WEB: www.senox.com
SIC: 1761 3089 Gutter & downspout contractor; gutters (glass fiber reinforced), fiberglass or plastic

(G-1493)
SENSORTRAN INC
10110-C W Samhouston Pkwy (78744)
PHONE................281 876-2323
Phil Longorio, *Ch of Bd*
Marc Edwards, *President*
David Adams, *Vice Pres*
Paul Ruiz, *CFO*
John Angel, *VP Sales*
▲ **EMP:** 25
SALES (est): 2.3MM **Publicly Held**
SIC: 3229 Fiber optics strands
PA: Halliburton Company
3000 N Sam Houston Pkwy E
Houston TX 77032

(G-1494)
SENTECH ARCHTCTRAL SYSTEMS LLC
4421 Supply Ct Ste 100 (78744-3663)
PHONE................512 266-7045
Alfonso Lopez, *CEO*
Donald R Brown, *President*
Brian Bartz, *Project Mgr*
Oscar Lopez, *Project Mgr*
Rick Bradfute, *Prdtn Mgr*
▲ **EMP:** 20
SQ FT: 20,846
SALES (est): 5.7MM **Privately Held**
WEB: www.sentechas.com
SIC: 3446 8711 8712 Architectural metalwork; structural engineering; pollution control engineering; architectural services

(G-1495)
SERETTI DENTAL LAB INC
1820 W 35th St (78703-1323)
PHONE................512 452-8989
Julio Seretti, *CEO*
EMP: 24
SQ FT: 780
SALES (est): 2.9MM **Privately Held**
WEB: www.serettidentallab.com
SIC: 3843 8072 Dental equipment & supplies; dental laboratories

(G-1496)
SEVCO SECURITY INC
6302 Lost Horizon Dr (78759-6154)
PHONE................512 413-2211
Jeffrey Guy, *Principal*
Greg Fitzgerald, *Principal*
EMP: 10
SALES (est): 221.8K **Privately Held**
SIC: 7372 Prepackaged software

(G-1497)
SHATTUCK LABS INC (PA)
1018 W 11th St Ste 100 (78703-4987)
PHONE................919 864-2700
Taylor Schreiber, *CEO*
Josiah Hornblower, *Ch of Bd*
Suresh De Silva, *Vice Pres*
George Fromm, *Vice Pres*
Thomas Lampkin, *Vice Pres*
EMP: 45
SQ FT: 4,550
SALES: 9.8MM **Publicly Held**
WEB: www.shattucklabs.com
SIC: 2834 Pharmaceutical preparations

(G-1498)
SHI/GOVERNMENT SOLUTIONS INC
3828 Pecana Trl (78749-3559)
P.O. Box 847434, Dallas (75284-7434)
PHONE................512 634-8100
Koguan Leo, *Ch of Bd*
Thai-HI T Lee, *President*
Craig Bailey, *Accounts Exec*
Lindsay Claussen, *Accounts Exec*
Elizabeth Gonzalez, *Accounts Exec*
EMP: 34
SALES: 289.6MM **Privately Held**
WEB: www.shi.com
SIC: 5045 7372 Computer software; prepackaged software; business oriented computer software

(G-1499)
SIEMENS INDUSTRY INC
1826 Kramer Ln Ste D (78758-4239)
PHONE..................................512 339-6991
Janet Smith, *Human Res Mgr*
Mike Dhar, *Branch Mgr*
EMP: 9
SALES (corp-wide): 67.4B **Privately Held**
WEB: www.new.siemens.com
SIC: 3661 Telephones & telephone apparatus
HQ: Siemens Industry, Inc.
   1000 Deerfield Pkwy
   Buffalo Grove IL 60089
   847 215-1000

(G-1500)
SIEMENS INDUSTRY INC
9225 Bee Cave Rd Bldg B (78733-6204)
PHONE..................................512 837-8300
Gunther Emmel, *CFO*
EMP: 24
SALES (corp-wide): 67.4B **Privately Held**
WEB: www.new.siemens.com
SIC: 3999 Barber & beauty shop equipment
HQ: Siemens Industry, Inc.
   1000 Deerfield Pkwy
   Buffalo Grove IL 60089
   847 215-1000

(G-1501)
SIGNACERT INC
12912 Hill Country Blvd (78738-6328)
PHONE..................................512 577-4894
Toney Jennings, *CEO*
EMP: 12
SALES (est): 888K **Privately Held**
SIC: 7372 Business oriented computer software

(G-1502)
SIGNS WEST INC
11926 Wirth Rd (78748-3704)
PHONE..................................512 282-5001
James Ashley, *President*
EMP: 12
SQ FT: 5,000
SALES (est): 250K **Privately Held**
WEB: www.signswestaustin.com
SIC: 3993 Signs & advertising specialties

(G-1503)
SILENT PARTNERS INC
8727 Shoal Creek Blvd A (78757-6905)
PHONE..................................512 458-1191
Lori S Brix, *President*
EMP: 10
SQ FT: 2,024
SALES (est): 1.1MM **Privately Held**
WEB: www.silentpartners.com
SIC: 2721 Magazines: publishing only, not printed on site

(G-1504)
SILICON HILLS DESIGN INC
8504 Cross Park Dr (78754-4532)
PHONE..................................512 836-1088
Harold Pantaze, *President*
Theo Painter, *President*
Shaikh Ahmad, *General Mgr*
Cathy Cook, *Project Mgr*
EMP: 35
SQ FT: 15,000
SALES (est): 6.9MM **Privately Held**
WEB: www.siliconhills.com
SIC: 3672 Circuit boards, television & radio printed

(G-1505)
SILICON LABORATORIES INC (PA)
400 W Cesar Chavez St (78701-3883)
PHONE..................................512 416-8500
Navdeep S Sooch, *Ch of Bd*
G Tyson Tuttle, *President*
Daniel Cooley, *Senior VP*
Matt Johnson, *Senior VP*
Sandeep Kumar, *Senior VP*
EMP: 277
SQ FT: 441,000
SALES: 886.6MM **Publicly Held**
WEB: www.silabs.com
SIC: 3674 Integrated circuits, semiconductor networks, etc.

(G-1506)
SILICON SPACE TECHNOLOGY CORP
Also Called: Vorago Technologies
1501 S Mopac Expy Ste 350 (78746)
PHONE..................................512 347-1814
Bernd Leinhard, *CEO*
Garry Nash, *Senior VP*
David Gifford, *Vice Pres*
Kevin Klein, *Vice Pres*
Anne Joubert, *VP Sales*
EMP: 14
SQ FT: 3,000
SALES (est): 666.6K **Privately Held**
WEB: www.siliconspacetech.com
SIC: 3674 Integrated circuits, semiconductor networks, etc.

(G-1507)
SIPS BY LLC
2215 W Braker Ln (78758-4031)
PHONE..................................214 208-0184
Staci Brinkman, *Mng Member*
EMP: 9
SALES (est): 173.7K **Privately Held**
WEB: www.sipsby.com
SIC: 2741

(G-1508)
SIR SPEEDY 4092
3818 Far West Blvd # 105 (78731-3050)
PHONE..................................512 338-9818
Connie Johns, *President*
EMP: 10
SALES (est): 1.9MM **Privately Held**
WEB: www.sirspeedy.com
SIC: 2752 Commercial printing, lithographic

(G-1509)
SKORPIOS TECHNOLOGIES INC
2706 Montopolis Dr (78741-6408)
PHONE..................................512 356-2000
John Hamma, *Vice Pres*
Michael Morgan, *Opers Mgr*
Mike Morgan, *Opers Mgr*
Paul Lloyd, *Engineer*
Mike Zimmermann, *Manager*
EMP: 110
SALES (corp-wide): 28MM **Privately Held**
WEB: www.skorpiosinc.com
SIC: 3674 Semiconductors & related devices
PA: Skorpios Technologies, Inc.
   7401 Snaproll Ne
   Albuquerque NM 87109
   505 369-1542

(G-1510)
SKYGRID LLC
4030 W Braker Ln Ste 400 (78759-5332)
PHONE..................................844 205-7173
Amir Husain,
EMP: 15
SALES (est): 609.2K **Privately Held**
WEB: www.skygrid.com
SIC: 3812 Acceleration indicators & systems components, aerospace

(G-1511)
SMART PACKAGER INC
600 Congress Ave Ste C100 (78701-2989)
PHONE..................................713 316-4903
Paul Pieske, *President*
Jeff Woeber, *Vice Pres*
EMP: 30
SALES (est): 1MM **Privately Held**
WEB: www.scalable.com
SIC: 7372 Utility computer software

(G-1512)
SMITH & NEPHEW INC
Also Called: Smith and Nephew
7000 W William Cannon Dr (78735-8509)
PHONE..................................512 358-5975
Todd Newton, *COO*
Mack Morgan, *Project Mgr*
Susan Rush, *Project Mgr*
Karl Corser, *Opers Mgr*
Roberto Rodriguez, *Opers Mgr*
EMP: 14
SALES (corp-wide): 5.1B **Privately Held**
WEB: www.smith-nephew.com
SIC: 3842 Surgical appliances & supplies

HQ: Smith & Nephew, Inc.
   7135 Goodlett Farms Pkwy
   Cordova TN 38016
   901 396-2121

(G-1513)
SMPL INC
Also Called: Simple Booth
902 E 5th St Ste 202 (78702-3853)
PHONE..................................402 525-5078
Mark Hennings, *CEO*
Jeremy Cox, *COO*
EMP: 23 **EST:** 2013
SQ FT: 950
SALES (est): 1.8MM **Privately Held**
WEB: www.simplebooth.com
SIC: 7372 3448 Application computer software; screen enclosures

(G-1514)
SNEAKY CHEF FOODS LLC
6610 Lancret Hill Dr (78745-4715)
PHONE..................................203 768-5654
Paul Greenberg, *CEO*
Helen Spanjer, *COO*
Laurence Chase, *Vice Pres*
▲ **EMP:** 10
SALES (est): 1MM **Privately Held**
WEB: www.thesneakychef.com
SIC: 2033 2099 Spaghetti & other pasta sauce: packaged in cans, jars, etc.; peanut butter

(G-1515)
SOCK CLUB ENTERPRISES LLC
2200 Tillery St B (78723-5744)
PHONE..................................919 619-4981
Hallie Toor, *Accounts Mgr*
Noah Drewlee, *Exec Dir*
Dane Jensen,
EMP: 9
SALES (est): 1.2MM **Privately Held**
WEB: www.sockclub.com
SIC: 2252 Socks

(G-1516)
SOFTWARE GLOBAL LTD
2000 S Interstate 35 A (78704-4434)
P.O. Box 970, Del Valle (78617-0970)
PHONE..................................832 274-0478
Seenapppa Poola, *President*
Stephanie Dowd, *Analyst*
EMP: 15 **EST:** 2001
SALES (est): 3.3MM **Privately Held**
WEB: www.softwareglobalusa.com
SIC: 7372 7371 7379 Prepackaged software; computer software development; computer related maintenance services

(G-1517)
SOLARWINDS CORPORATION (PA)
7171 Sw Pkwy Bldg 400 (78735-0002)
PHONE..................................512 682-9300
Kevin B Thompson, *President*
Jason W Bliss, *Exec VP*
Woong Joseph Kim, *Exec VP*
Christoph Pfister, *Exec VP*
Andrew Beyer, *Vice Pres*
EMP: 17
SQ FT: 348,000
SALES: 932.5MM **Publicly Held**
WEB: www.solarwinds.com
SIC: 7372 Prepackaged software

(G-1518)
SOLARWINDS HOLDINGS INC (HQ)
7171 Sw Pkwy Bldg 400 (78735-0002)
PHONE..................................512 682-9300
Kevin B Thompson, *President*
Andrew Beyer, *Vice Pres*
Justin Clem, *Vice Pres*
Lenka Lagova, *Vice Pres*
Chris Lapoint, *Vice Pres*
EMP: 17 **EST:** 2015
SALES (est): 428.7MM
SALES (corp-wide): 932.5MM **Publicly Held**
WEB: www.solarwinds.com
SIC: 7372 Prepackaged software
PA: Solarwinds Corporation
   7171 Sw Pkwy Bldg 400
   Austin TX 78735
   512 682-9300

(G-1519)
SOLARWINDS NORTH AMERICA INC (DH)
7171 Southwest Pkwy (78735-6139)
PHONE..................................512 682-9300
Kevin B Thompson, *President*
Douglas G Hibberd, *Exec VP*
J Barton Kalsu, *Exec VP*
John Pagliuca, *Exec VP*
John Rizzo, *Exec VP*
EMP: 120 **EST:** 1999
SQ FT: 172,000
SALES: 428.7MM
SALES (corp-wide): 932.5MM **Publicly Held**
WEB: www.solarwinds.com
SIC: 7372 Prepackaged software
HQ: Solarwinds Holdings, Inc.
   7171 Sw Pkwy Bldg 400
   Austin TX 78735
   512 682-9300

(G-1520)
SOLARWINDS WORLDWIDE LLC
7171 Southwest Pkwy (78735-6139)
PHONE..................................512 682-9300
Kevin B Thompson, *CEO*
Michael Bennett, *Vice Pres*
Brian Cantrell, *COO*
J Barton Kalsu, *Senior VP*
Joseph Kim, *Senior VP*
EMP: 28
SALES (est): 3.4MM
SALES (corp-wide): 932.5MM **Publicly Held**
WEB: www.solarwinds.com
SIC: 7373 7372 Systems software development services; prepackaged software
HQ: Solarwinds North America, Inc.
   7171 Southwest Pkwy
   Austin TX 78735
   512 682-9300

(G-1521)
SOURCEDAY INC
9737 Great Hills Trl # 100 (78759-6449)
PHONE..................................512 361-7029
Tom Kieley, *CEO*
Clint McRee, *COO*
Emeka Obianwu, *Senior VP*
Erica Lanyon, *Vice Pres*
Mark Garcia, *Engineer*
EMP: 31 **EST:** 2013
SALES (est): 4.8MM **Privately Held**
WEB: www.sourceday.com
SIC: 7372 Business oriented computer software

(G-1522)
SOUTHERN CHAMPION TRAY LP
4140 S Congress Ave (78745-1102)
PHONE..................................512 442-2337
EMP: 28 **Privately Held**
WEB: www.sctray.com
SIC: 2679 Building, insulating & packaging paperboard
PA: Southern Champion Tray, L.P.
   220 Compress St
   Chattanooga TN 37405

(G-1523)
SPANSION LLC
5204 E Ben White Blvd (78741-7306)
PHONE..................................512 934-6427
James Doran, *COO*
Tom Moon, *Opers Staff*
Claudine Gonzales, *Production*
Mark Lozano, *Technical Mgr*
Ray Glay, *Engineer*
EMP: 126
SALES (corp-wide): 10.1B **Privately Held**
WEB: www.spansion.com
SIC: 3674 Computer logic modules
HQ: Spansion Llc
   198 Champion Ct
   San Jose CA 95134
   408 691-8500

(G-1524)
SPECTER INSTRUMENTS INC
Also Called: Win-911 Software
4020 S Industrial Dr # 120 (78744-1078)
PHONE..................................512 326-1011

Greg Jackson, *CEO*
Amanda Dubose, *Finance*
Jeremy Meegan, *Sales Staff*
EMP: 16
SALES (est): 2.3MM Privately Held
WEB: www.win911.com
SIC: 7372 Application computer software

(G-1525)
SPICEWORKS INC
3700 N Capital Of Texas (78746-3453)
PHONE...................................512 346-7743
Jay Hallberg, *CEO*
J Scott Di Valerio, *COO*
Manish Dixit, *Vice Pres*
Greg Kattawar, *Vice Pres*
Kevin McKeown, *Vice Pres*
EMP: 350
SALES (est): 62.1MM
SALES (corp-wide): 1.3B Publicly Held
WEB: www.spiceworks.com
SIC: 8742 7372 Management information
systems consultant; application computer
software
HQ: Ziff Davis B2b Focus, Inc.
625 2nd St
San Francisco CA 94107
415 696-5453

(G-1526)
SPIGIT INC
12301 Res Blvd Ste 5-101 (78759)
PHONE...................................855 774-4480
Scott Raskin, *CEO*
Rami Vij, *Vice Pres*
Stephen Anderson, *CFO*
Mario Tarantino, *Finance Mgr*
Michael Walker, *Sales Staff*
EMP: 99
SALES (est): 13.7MM Privately Held
WEB: www.spigit.com
SIC: 7372 Business oriented computer
software
HQ: Spigit Holdings Corporation
12301 Res Blvd Ste 5-101
Austin TX 78759

(G-1527)
SPINESMITH HOLDINGS LLC (PA)
Also Called: Celling Biosciences
4719 S Congress Ave # 100 (78745-2354)
PHONE...................................512 637-2073
Steve Melchiode, *President*
Mike Smedes, *Vice Pres*
Richard Kana, *Research*
Wilson Davis, *Accountant*
Brenda Annette Campos, *Administration*
EMP: 50
SALES (est): 14.8MM Privately Held
WEB: www.spinesmithusa.com
SIC: 3841 Surgical & medical instruments

(G-1528)
SPIRITED COCKTAILS CORPORATION
Also Called: Canteen Spirits
8201 Carranzo Dr (78735-1820)
PHONE...................................512 256-0150
Brandon Cason, *President*
Daniel Barnes, *Principal*
EMP: 10
SALES (est): 1.5MM Privately Held
WEB: www.spiritedcocktailclasses.com
SIC: 2085 Vodka (alcoholic beverage)

(G-1529)
ST GEORGE SOFTWARE L L C
5003 Tahoe Trl (78745-1586)
PHONE...................................512 442-6794
Therel Moore, *President*
EMP: 14
SALES (est): 757.5K Privately Held
SIC: 7372 Prepackaged software

(G-1530)
ST JUDE MEDICAL LLC
6300 Bee Caves Rd # 210 (78746-5832)
PHONE...................................512 732-7400
Joel Becker, *President*
Philip Adamson, *Vice Pres*
Jeff Dallager, *Finance*
Ezekiel Lee, *Manager*
Raul Garcia, *Director*
EMP: 32

SALES (corp-wide): 31.9B Publicly Held
WEB: www.cardiovascular.abbott
SIC: 2834 Pharmaceutical preparations
HQ: St. Jude Medical, Llc
1 Saint Jude Medical Dr
Saint Paul MN 55117
651 756-2000

(G-1531)
STARK HOLDINGS INC
Also Called: Austin Technical Branch
1705 S Capital Of Texas H (78746-6578)
PHONE...................................512 329-8109
EMP: 10
SALES (corp-wide): 14.5MM Privately
Held
SIC: 3695 7372 7371 7361 Mfg Magnetic
Disks/Tapes Prepackaged Software Svc
Computer Programming Svc Employment
Agency
PA: Stark Holdings Inc.
1705 S Texas Hwy
Austin TX 78746
512 329-8100

(G-1532)
STATE HOUSE PRINTING INC
2117 E Cesar Chavez St (78702-4513)
P.O. Box 6177 (78762-6177)
PHONE...................................512 472-5331
Richard Moreno, *President*
Pete Moreno, *Vice Pres*
Johnny Moreno, *Production*
EMP: 12
SQ FT: 6,000
SALES (est): 1.6MM Privately Held
WEB: www.statehouseprinting.com
SIC: 2752 Commercial printing, offset

(G-1533)
STATOIL OIL & GAS SERVICES INC
6300 Bridge Point Pkwy 2-500
(78730-5027)
PHONE...................................512 427-3300
Torstein Hole, *President*
Malcom O Brown, *Treasurer*
Kari A Potts, *Admin Sec*
EMP: 60
SQ FT: 10,000
SALES (est): 3.6MM Privately Held
WEB: www.brighamresources.net
SIC: 1311 Crude petroleum & natural gas
HQ: Equinor Exploration Company
6300 Bridge Point Pkwy
Austin TX 78730

(G-1534)
STEALTH POWER LLC (PA)
1201 Old Bastrop Hwy (78742-2600)
PHONE...................................512 306-0088
Devin Scott, *CEO*
Jordan Schroeder, *Office Mgr*
EMP: 13
SALES (est): 2.3MM Privately Held
WEB: www.idlereduction.com
SIC: 3694 Generators, automotive & air-
craft

(G-1535)
STELLAR MICRO DEVICES INC
9210 Cameron Rd Ste 300 (78754-3971)
PHONE...................................512 997-7781
Mark Eaton, *President*
EMP: 12
SQ FT: 7,200
SALES (est): 1.5MM Privately Held
WEB: www.stellar-micro.com
SIC: 3671 Electron tubes

(G-1536)
STEVE JACKSON GAMES INC (PA)
3735 Promontory Point Dr (78744-1109)
P.O. Box 18957 (78760-8957)
PHONE...................................512 447-7866
Steven G Jackson, *President*
Steven Marsh, *Editor*
Loren K Wiseman, *Editor*
Susan Bueno, *COO*
Stephen Sopko, *COO*
▲ EMP: 25
SQ FT: 2,000

SALES (est): 3.4MM Privately Held
WEB: www.sjgames.com
SIC: 3944 Board games, children's &
adults'

(G-1537)
STOCK BUILDING SUP TEXAS LLC (DH)
Also Called: Calcasieu Lumber Company
4501 Burleson Rd (78744-1203)
PHONE...................................512 444-3172
Paul Bauer, *Sales Mgr*
Dixie Fromberg,
EMP: 457
SQ FT: 250,000
SALES (est): 116.9MM
SALES (corp-wide): 7.2B Publicly Held
SIC: 5031 5211 2491 2439 Lumber:
rough, dressed & finished; lumber & other
building materials; millwork, treated wood;
structural wood members

(G-1538)
STONE CLIFF TECHNOLOGY LLC (PA)
Also Called: Kortivity
500 N Capital Hwy Bldg 2 (78746)
PHONE...................................512 640-0650
Jason Burns, *CEO*
Ben Fuller, *Sales Staff*
EMP: 10
SALES (est): 485.8K Privately Held
WEB: www.kortivity.com
SIC: 7372 7371 Application computer soft-
ware; computer software development &
applications

(G-1539)
STONE PRODUCTION INC
Also Called: Austin Stone Works
13810 N Interstate 35 (78728-7706)
P.O. Box 144621 (78714-4621)
PHONE...................................512 990-9800
James Pair, *President*
Karen D Pair, *Vice Pres*
Chryel Coker, *Office Mgr*
EMP: 19
SQ FT: 2,000
SALES (est): 2.3MM Privately Held
WEB: www.austinstoneworks.com
SIC: 1743 3281 5999 5211 Marble instal-
lation, interior; tile installation, ceramic;
marble, building: cut & shaped; granite,
cut & shaped; monuments & tombstones;
tile, ceramic; counter top installation

(G-1540)
STONE SYSTEMS CENTL TEXAS LLC
4101 Smith School Rd # 2 (78744-3206)
PHONE...................................512 295-2950
Roberto Contreras, *President*
EMP: 50
SALES (est): 6.6MM
SALES (corp-wide): 2.6MM Privately
Held
SIC: 3281 1799 Granite, cut & shaped;
counter top installation
HQ: Stone Suppliers, Inc.
13124 Trinity Dr
Stafford TX

(G-1541)
STRATASYS DIRECT INC
9715 Burnet Rd Ste A500 (78758-5382)
PHONE...................................512 821-1112
Jill Bojorquez, *Production*
Heather Schenian, *Production*
Jonathan Allison, *Engineer*
Ken Rather, *Project Engr*
Colleen Bitner, *Human Resources*
EMP: 11
SALES (corp-wide): 620.5MM Privately
Held
WEB: www.stratasysdirect.com
SIC: 2791 Photocomposition, for the print-
ing trade
HQ: Stratasys Direct, Inc.
28309 Avenue Crocker
Valencia CA 91355

(G-1542)
STRATFOR ENTERPRISES LLC
7708 Rialto Blvd Unit 200 (78735-8578)
P.O. Box 92529 (78709-2529)
PHONE...................................512 744-4300
Dave Sikora, *CEO*
George Friedman, *Ch of Bd*
Maverick Fisher, *Editor*
Reva Goujon, *Vice Pres*
Ted Obenchain, *Vice Pres*
EMP: 100
SQ FT: 15,000
SALES (est): 11.6MM Privately Held
WEB: www.stratfor.com
SIC: 2741

(G-1543)
STUARTS SHEET METAL INC
9623 Beck Cir (78758-5401)
PHONE...................................512 491-0112
Eric Stuart, *President*
EMP: 22
SQ FT: 3,200
SALES (est): 4.2MM Privately Held
WEB: www.stuartssheetmetal.com
SIC: 3444 Sheet metal specialties, not
stamped

(G-1544)
SULLYS LONE STAR OFFICE PDTS (PA)
Also Called: Wall-Tech
10200 Mckalla Pl Ste 400 (78758-4492)
P.O. Box 14583 (78761-4583)
PHONE...................................512 835-9506
Kevin W Kliefoth, *President*
Kevin Kliefoth, *President*
Robert Arnold, *Business Mgr*
Barbara Kliefoth, *Treasurer*
Bobby Sullivan, *Sales Mgr*
EMP: 16
SQ FT: 75,000
SALES (est): 2.4MM Privately Held
WEB: www.walltechtx.com
SIC: 7641 2542 Office furniture repair &
maintenance; partitions for floor attach-
ment, prefabricated: except wood

(G-1545)
SUNPOWER CORPORATION
Also Called: Solarbridge Technologies
9229 Wtrford Cntre Blvd S (78758-7504)
PHONE...................................512 294-3859
Tom Werner, *Principal*
Jeffrey Blose, *Vice Pres*
Joshua Kossman, *Regl Sales Mgr*
Peter Braun, *Sales Staff*
Sarah Zhu, *Manager*
EMP: 60
SALES (corp-wide): 7B Publicly Held
WEB: www.us.sunpower.com
SIC: 3621 Power generators; inverters, ro-
tating: electrical
HQ: Sunpower Corporation
51 Rio Robles
San Jose CA 95134
408 240-5500

(G-1546)
SUNPOWER CORPORATION
2900 Esprnza Crssing 2nd Flr 2 (78758)
PHONE...................................512 735-0119
Stephen Harrington, *Counsel*
Jack Semrani, *Counsel*
Sally Derrick, *Project Mgr*
Trey Barr, *Accounting Mgr*
Holly Tuccio, *Sr Project Mgr*
EMP: 10
SALES (corp-wide): 7B Publicly Held
WEB: www.us.sunpower.com
SIC: 3674 Solar cells
HQ: Sunpower Corporation
51 Rio Robles
San Jose CA 95134
408 240-5500

(G-1547)
SUPER SEED FOODS LLC
Also Called: Good Seed
3005 S Lamar Blvd (78704-8864)
PHONE...................................512 698-7907
Mike Eyerly, *Sales Mgr*
Erin Shotwell, *Mng Member*
Oliver Ponce, *Mng Member*
EMP: 9 EST: 2013

SALES (est): 121.5K **Privately Held**
WEB: www.goodseedburger.com
SIC: **2038** Breakfasts, frozen & packaged

(G-1548)
SUPERCIRCUITS INC (DH)
Also Called: Security Cameras Direct
15505 Long Vista Dr # 250 (78728-3833)
PHONE................................877 995-2288
Brian Wood, *CEO*
Tabatha Vanwagner, *Buyer*
Victoria Richardson, *CFO*
Carol Cates, *Accounting Mgr*
Lisa Raulston, *Human Res Mgr*
◆ EMP: 100
SALES (est): 13.4MM
SALES (corp-wide): 3.3B **Publicly Held**
WEB: www.supercircuits.com
SIC: **3699** 5065 5999 Security control
  equipment & systems; security control
  equipment & systems; electronic parts &
  equipment
HQ: Observint Technologies, Inc.
  15505 Long Vista Dr # 250
  Austin TX 78728
  877 995-2288

(G-1549)
SUPERCONDUCTOR TECH INC (PA)
Also Called: STI
15511 W State Highway 71 (78738-2824)
PHONE................................512 650-7775
Jeffrey A Quiram, *President*
Robert L Johnson, *Senior VP*
Adam L Shelton, *Vice Pres*
Clay Sakewitz, *Engineer*
William J Buchanan, *CFO*
EMP: 21
SQ FT: 94,000
SALES: 545K **Publicly Held**
WEB: www.suptech.com
SIC: **3674** Integrated circuits, semiconduc-
  tor networks, etc.

(G-1550)
SUPERIOR STONE INC (PA)
7011 Fm 2244 Rd (78746-5011)
PHONE................................512 327-4509
Fred Tillman, *President*
EMP: 20
SQ FT: 1,500
SALES (est): 1.1MM **Privately Held**
WEB: www.superiorstoneinc.com
SIC: **1422** Crushed & broken limestone

(G-1551)
SWAY WATER INC
6500 Cannonleague Dr (78745-4918)
PHONE................................512 693-7588
Albert Swantner, *President*
▲ EMP: 10
SALES (est): 500K **Privately Held**
WEB: www.swaywater.com
SIC: **2082** 5149 Beer (alcoholic bever-
  age); beverages, except coffee & tea

(G-1552)
SWEET RITUAL LLC
8711 Burnet Rd Ste H100 (78757-7072)
PHONE................................512 923-1930
Valerie Ward, *Principal*
EMP: 9
SALES (est): 675K **Privately Held**
WEB: www.sweetritual.com
SIC: **2024** Ice cream & frozen desserts

(G-1553)
SWIM SWAM PARTNERS LLC
Also Called: Swimswam.com
7308 Seneca Falls Loop (78739-2216)
PHONE................................512 827-9040
Tiffany Stewart, *Principal*
EMP: 40
SALES (est): 1.7MM **Privately Held**
WEB: www.swimswam.com
SIC: **2741**

(G-1554)
T&V OPTIMUM LLC
Also Called: Optimum Steel Industries
10202 Spicewood Mesa (78759-6851)
PHONE................................512 398-5271
Valerie L Erickson, *Mng Member*
Thomas S Erickson,
EMP: 26

SQ FT: 20,000
SALES (est): 6MM **Privately Held**
SIC: **3496** Miscellaneous fabricated wire
  products

(G-1555)
TANK TOWN LLC
Also Called: Richard's Rainwater
1621 E 6th St Apt 1149 (78702-3347)
PHONE................................512 894-0861
Richard A Heinichen, *Mng Member*
EMP: 20
SALES (est): 1.2MM **Privately Held**
WEB: www.rainwatercollection.com
SIC: **5499** 1711 3589 Water: distilled min-
  eral or spring; irrigation sprinkler system
  installation; water purification equipment,
  household type

(G-1556)
TECHCOMP (USA) INC
4801 Southwest Pkwy # 125 (78735-8957)
PHONE................................512 215-8335
Octavio Cruz-Aedo, *President*
EMP: 17
SALES (est): 3.7MM **Privately Held**
WEB: www.scioninstruments.com
SIC: **3826** Analytical instruments

(G-1557)
TECHLINE SPORTS LIGHTING LLC
15303 Storm Dr (78734-2743)
PHONE................................512 977-8880
Marco A Barros, *President*
Rodney M Hawthorne, *Principal*
Susan Schiller, *Opers-Prdtn-Mfg*
Lewis Rhoden, *CFO*
Ryan Buchanan, *Regl Sales Mgr*
EMP: 10
SALES (est): 1.9MM **Privately Held**
WEB: www.sportlighting.com
SIC: **3643** Lightning protection equipment

(G-1558)
TECHWORKS INC
11100 Metric Blvd Ste 750 (78758-4072)
PHONE................................512 349-1300
Hajime Nakai, *Principal*
EMP: 15
SALES (est): 3.1MM **Privately Held**
WEB: www.buftek.com
SIC: **3577** Computer peripheral equipment
PA: Melco Ltd.
  2-2-11, Shinsenjidori, Chuo-Ku
  Kobe HYO 651-0

(G-1559)
TEKMOS INC
7901 E Riverside Dr # 150 (78744-1661)
PHONE................................512 342-9871
Lynn Reed, *President*
Bob Abrams, *Vice Pres*
James Betts, *Vice Pres*
John Hoenig, *Vice Pres*
Holman Rick, *Design Engr*
◆ EMP: 9
SQ FT: 5,500 **Privately Held**
WEB: www.tekmos.com
SIC: **3674** Integrated circuits, semiconduc-
  tor networks, etc.

(G-1560)
TEKTRONIX INC
2324 Ridgepoint Dr Ste D (78754-5214)
PHONE................................512 926-7625
Michelle Lopez, *Sales Staff*
April Bell, *Manager*
EMP: 11
SALES (corp-wide): 6.4B **Publicly Held**
WEB: www.tek.com
SIC: **3825** Instruments to measure electric-
  ity
HQ: Tektronix, Inc.
  14150 Sw Karl Braun Dr
  Beaverton OR 97005
  800 833-9200

(G-1561)
TELEPRIME ADVANCED COMMUNICATI
7500 Rialto Blvd Ste 250 (78735-8556)
PHONE................................512 271-9503
William Dawson, *President*
EMP: 9

SALES (est): 277.8K **Privately Held**
WEB: www.teleprimeacd.com
SIC: **8748** 3663 3661 7629 Telecommunications consultant; light communications equipment; multiplex equipment,
  telephone & telegraph; telecommunication equipment repair (except telephones)

(G-1562)
TEMPO SEMICONDUCTOR INC
8627 N Mopac Expy Ste 130 (78759-8362)
PHONE................................512 827-3440
Kenneth Gozie, *President*
Jeff Rozmus, *Vice Pres*
David Grant, *Marketing Staff*
EMP: 16
SQ FT: 3,500
SALES (est): 2.2MM **Privately Held**
WEB: www.temposemi.com
SIC: **3674** Semiconductors & related de-
  vices

(G-1563)
TERADYNE INC
5700 S Mo Pac Expy # 400 (78749-1458)
PHONE................................512 891-9600
Phil Wendall, *Manager*
EMP: 65
SALES (corp-wide): 2.3B **Publicly Held**
WEB: www.teradyne.com
SIC: **3643** 3825 Connectors & terminals
  for electrical devices; test equipment for
  electronic & electric measurement
PA: Teradyne, Inc.
  600 Riverpark Dr
  North Reading MA 01864
  978 370-2700

(G-1564)
TEST SPECTRUM INC
9701 Brodie Ln Ste 101 (78748-6283)
PHONE................................512 472-6750
Todd Turner, *President*
Keith Remlinger, *Exec VP*
Paul Salazar, *Exec VP*
Bob Scott, *Exec VP*
Darcy Laveau, *Vice Pres*
◆ EMP: 19
SQ FT: 5,000
SALES (est): 3MM **Privately Held**
WEB: www.testspectrum.com
SIC: **3672** 7371 7372 8711 Printed circuit
  boards; custom computer programming
  services; application computer software;
  engineering services

(G-1565)
TEXAS DENTAL ASSOCIATION INC
1946 S Interstate 35 # 400 (78704-3644)
PHONE................................512 443-3675
Mary Kay Linn, *Director*
EMP: 29
SQ FT: 18,000
SALES (est): 895.8K **Privately Held**
WEB: www.tdaperks.com
SIC: **8621** 8299 2721 Dental association;
  educational services; trade journals: pub-
  lishing only, not printed on site

(G-1566)
TEXAS DEPARTMENT TRNSP
Also Called: Texas Highways Magazine
1101 W Anderson Ln (78757-1446)
P.O. Box 141009 (78714-1009)
PHONE................................512 486-5887
Oz Lopez, *Publisher*
Jack Lowry, *Principal*
Kimya Kavehkar, *Editor*
Ana Perez, *Warehouse Mgr*
Karen Garza, *Publications*
EMP: 29
SALES (corp-wide): 128.4B **Privately
Held**
WEB: www.txdot.gov
SIC: **2721** 9621 Periodicals: publishing
  only;
HQ: Texas Department Of Transportation
  150 E Riverside Dr
  Austin TX 78704

(G-1567)
TEXAS ELECTRIC COOPS INC (PA)
1122 Colorado St Ste 2400 (78701-2167)
PHONE................................512 454-0311

Mike Williams, *President*
Jason Kearney, *COO*
Martin Bevins, *Vice Pres*
Eric Craven, *Vice Pres*
Carlton Penney, *Mfg Dir*
EMP: 50 EST: 1940
SQ FT: 42,000
SALES (est): 200MM **Privately Held**
WEB: www.texas-ec.org
SIC: **2491** 8621 3612 Poles & pole
  crossarms, treated wood; professional
  membership organizations; transformers,
  except electric; power & distribution trans-
  formers

(G-1568)
TEXAS LIGHTSMITH INC
3410 Andtree Blvd (78724-2502)
PHONE................................512 264-2266
John Worsham, *President*
Harold Jones, *Vice Pres*
Robin Rieck, *Bookkeeper*
Dave McLaughlin, *Technology*
EMP: 11
SQ FT: 4,500
SALES (est): 1.9MM **Privately Held**
WEB: www.texaslightsmith.com
SIC: **3646** Commercial indusl & institu-
  tional electric lighting fixtures

(G-1569)
TEXAS OFFICE PDTS & SUP INC
Also Called: Props By Tops
1300 E 5th St (78702-3800)
PHONE................................512 472-1340
Karen D Richards, *Owner*
Matthew Hahn, *Vice Pres*
Valdemar Barrera, *Sales Staff*
Gary Bergvall, *Sales Staff*
Alex Lindsey, *Sales Staff*
EMP: 10
SALES (est): 1.2MM **Privately Held**
WEB: www.topstexas.com
SIC: **2512** 5072 5021 Upholstered house-
  hold furniture; furniture hardware; office
  furniture

(G-1570)
TEXAS STATE HISTORICAL ASSN (PA)
Also Called: Tsha
3001 Lake Austin Blvd # 3116
  (78703-4217)
P.O. Box 5428 (78763-5428)
PHONE................................512 471-2600
Brian Bolinger, *CEO*
Ron Tyler, *Principal*
Elizabeth Alvarez, *Editor*
Terri Killen, *Editor*
Nathan Herron, *Marketing Staff*
▲ EMP: 17
SQ FT: 6,500
SALES: 1.7MM **Privately Held**
WEB: www.tshaonline.org
SIC: **2731** Book publishing

(G-1571)
TEXTRUSS COMPONENT BLDG INC
12201 Dorsett Rd (78727-5817)
P.O. Box 9735 (78766-9735)
PHONE................................512 836-4830
Mike Shelton, *CEO*
EMP: 40 EST: 1970
SQ FT: 27,000
SALES: 4.5MM **Privately Held**
WEB: www.textruss.com
SIC: **2439** Trusses, wooden roof; trusses,
  except roof: laminated lumber

(G-1572)
THERMO FINNIGAN LLC
Also Called: Tremetrics
2215 Grand Avenue Pkwy (78728-3812)
PHONE................................512 251-1400
Eric Johnson, *General Mgr*
Theo Melas Kyriazi, *CFO*
EMP: 70
SALES (corp-wide): 25.5B **Publicly Held**
SIC: **3823** 3824 3829 3825 Industrial in-
  strmnts msrmnt display/control process
  variable; odometers; measuring & control-
  ling devices; instruments to measure
  electricity

▲ = Import ▼=Export
◆ =Import/Export

HQ: Thermo Finnigan Llc
355 River Oaks Pkwy
San Jose CA 95134
408 965-6000

(G-1573)
THERMO FISHER SCIENTIFIC INC
2215 Grand Avenue Pkwy (78728-3812)
PHONE..................................512 251-1525
Gary Phinney, *Engineer*
Michael Crowley, *Regl Sales Mgr*
Andy Walder, *Branch Mgr*
Nicholas Mollison, *Manager*
Bob Stevens, *Info Tech Dir*
EMP: 75
SALES (corp-wide): 25.5B **Publicly Held**
WEB: www.thermofisher.com
SIC: 3826 Analytical instruments
PA: Thermo Fisher Scientific Inc.
168 3rd Ave
Waltham MA 02451
781 622-1000

(G-1574)
THINKSMART LLC
5001 Plz On The Lk Ste 11 (78746-1070)
PHONE..................................888 489-4284
Paul Hirner, *CEO*
Dillon Knowlton, *Production*
Dani Dayan, *Accountant*
Kelli Negro, *Marketing Staff*
Michael Concannon, *Mng Member*
EMP: 12 EST: 2013
SALES (est): 747.4K
SALES (corp-wide): 45.4MM **Privately Held**
WEB: www.thinksmartsoft.com
SIC: 7372 Business oriented computer software
PA: Mitratech Holdings, Inc.
5001 Plz On The Lk Ste 11
Austin TX 78746
512 382-7322

(G-1575)
THINKWELL CORPORATION
505 E Huntland Dr Ste 150 (78752-3750)
PHONE..................................888 416-8880
Carl Tyson, *CEO*
Amy Bryant, *Vice Pres*
Pavol Chalupka, *Vice Pres*
Mark Schnug, *Vice Pres*
Andrea Palmer, *Office Mgr*
▼ EMP: 17
SQ FT: 10,000
SALES (est): 2.7MM **Privately Held**
WEB: www.thinkwell.com
SIC: 2731 7372 Textbooks: publishing & printing; educational computer software

(G-1576)
THOMAS GRAPHICS INC
9501 N Interstate 35 (78753-3821)
P.O. Box 142226 (78714-2226)
PHONE..................................512 719-3535
Robert E Thomas, *President*
Scott Pond, *Chairman*
James Price, *Vice Pres*
Ben Thomas, *Vice Pres*
Mike Yancey, *Manager*
EMP: 53
SQ FT: 26,000
SALES (est): 9.6MM **Privately Held**
WEB: www.thomasgraphicsinc.com
SIC: 2752 7336 2796 2791 Commercial printing, offset; commercial art & graphic design; platemaking services; typesetting

(G-1577)
THREE RIVERS OPERATING CO LLC
5301 Sw Pkwy Ste 400 (78735-8986)
PHONE..................................512 600-3190
John Oberg, *President*
Michael Poynter, *Financial Analy*
Gabe Ellisor,
Mike Wichterich,
EMP: 15
SALES (est): 8.5MM **Privately Held**
WEB: www.3roc.com
SIC: 1382 Oil & gas exploration services

(G-1578)
THYSSENKRUPP ELEVATOR CORP
3615 Willow Springs Rd F (78704-7225)
PHONE..................................512 486-1000
Lee Gravell, *Superintendent*
Rolly Burke, *Manager*
EMP: 15
SALES (corp-wide): 918MM **Privately Held**
WEB: www.thyssenkruppelevator.com
SIC: 5084 1796 7699 3999 Elevators; elevator installation & conversion; elevators: inspection, service & repair; wheelchair lifts
HQ: Thyssenkrupp Elevator Corporation
11605 Haynes Bridge Rd
Alpharetta GA 30009
678 319-3240

(G-1579)
TIFFS TREATS RBD INC
8900 Shoal Creek Blvd (78757-6810)
PHONE..................................512 614-3200
Leon Chen, *CEO*
Tiffany Taylor, *President*
EMP: 40
SQ FT: 5,000
SALES (est): 8MM **Privately Held**
WEB: www.cookiedelivery.com
SIC: 2052 Cookies & crackers

(G-1580)
TIFS TREATS
1806 Nueces St (78701-1141)
PHONE..................................512 473-2600
Tiffany Taylor, *President*
Jeffrey Sartor, *Exec VP*
Wendy Keffer, *Human Res Dir*
Skye Bond, *Hum Res Coord*
Jessica Isfalt, *Mktg Coord*
EMP: 30
SQ FT: 1,232 **Privately Held**
WEB: www.cookiedelivery.com
SIC: 2052 Cookies & crackers

(G-1581)
TIPS IRON & STEEL CO INC
300 Baylor St (78703-5321)
P.O. Box 2003 (78768-2003)
PHONE..................................512 478-8511
Steve Wimberly, *President*
EMP: 25 EST: 1999
SQ FT: 34,311
SALES (est): 3.5MM **Privately Held**
WEB: www.atx-steel.com
SIC: 3441 Fabricated structural metal

(G-1582)
TLMI CORPORATION
2111 W Braker Ln Ste 500 (78758-4126)
PHONE..................................512 833-7075
Don Prusha, *President*
Mark Rowe, *CFO*
Kyle Baldwin, *VP Mktg*
Djohan Sutedja, *Director*
EMP: 13
SQ FT: 16,000
SALES: 2.2MM **Privately Held**
WEB: www.tlmicorp.com
SIC: 3471 Electroplating of metals or formed products

(G-1583)
TOKYO ELECTRON AMERICA INC (DH)
2400 Grove Blvd (78741-6500)
PHONE..................................512 424-1000
Barry Mayer, *CEO*
Tetsuo Tsuneishi, *Ch of Bd*
Larry Smith, *President*
Julie Bannister, *General Mgr*
Kurt Williams, *General Mgr*
EMP: 300 EST: 1972
SQ FT: 150,000
SALES (est): 373.8MM **Privately Held**
WEB: www.tel.com
SIC: 3559 8711 Semiconductor manufacturing machinery; engineering services
HQ: Tokyo Electron U.S. Holdings, Inc.
2400 Grove Blvd
Austin TX 78741
512 424-1000

(G-1584)
TOKYO ELECTRON AMERICA INC
3910 S Industrial Dr (78744-1156)
PHONE..................................512 424-1000
Barry Mayer, *CEO*
EMP: 19 **Privately Held**
WEB: www.tel.com
SIC: 8711 3559 Engineering services; semiconductor manufacturing machinery
HQ: Tokyo Electron America, Inc.
2400 Grove Blvd
Austin TX 78741
512 424-1000

(G-1585)
TOKYO ELECTRON US HOLDINGS INC (HQ)
2400 Grove Blvd (78741-6500)
P.O. Box 270448, Saint Louis MO (63127-0448)
PHONE..................................512 424-1000
Tetsuro Higashi, *President*
Cheryl G Rose, *Principal*
Rick Perras, *Vice Pres*
Scott Sechovec, *Vice Pres*
Larry Nunnery, *Opers Staff*
▲ EMP: 450
SQ FT: 100,000
SALES (est): 461.6MM **Privately Held**
WEB: www.tel.com
SIC: 3674 Semiconductors & related devices

(G-1586)
TOUCH INTERNATIONAL INC
2222 W Rundberg Ln # 200 (78758-5469)
PHONE..................................512 832-8292
Michael Woolstrum, *President*
Suzanne Koenig, *Controller*
Gary Barrett, *CTO*
◆ EMP: 90
SQ FT: 5,000
SALES: 36MM **Privately Held**
WEB: www.touchinternational.com
SIC: 3577 Computer peripheral equipment

(G-1587)
TOUCHMATE INC
7703 N Lamar Blvd Ste 100 (78752-1003)
PHONE..................................512 949-3330
Ben Williams, *President*
David Ellsworth, *Vice Pres*
Erica Goldman, *Technology*
EMP: 30
SALES (est): 5.2MM **Privately Held**
WEB: www.touchmateusa.com
SIC: 3571 7371 5045 Electronic computers; computer software development; computers, peripherals & software

(G-1588)
TPV INTERNATIONAL (USA) INC (PA)
3737 Executive Center Dr # 261 (78731-1647)
PHONE..................................512 241-1508
Hao Lung Chen, *President*
Sidney Lin, *CFO*
Scott Lu, *Manager*
Jack Chao, *Exec Dir*
◆ EMP: 10
SQ FT: 1,200
SALES (est): 20.9MM **Privately Held**
SIC: 3577 Computer peripheral equipment

(G-1589)
TRADESORG LLC
3605 Menchaca Rd (78704-5947)
PHONE..................................512 729-3544
Christian Rodriguez, *CEO*
EMP: 25
SALES (est): 100K **Privately Held**
SIC: 1522 1799 7372 7299 Single-family housing construction; single-family home remodeling, additions & repairs; general remodeling, single-family houses; hotel/motel & multi-family home renovation & remodeling; remodeling, multi-family dwellings; kitchen & bathroom remodeling

(G-1590)
TRAVIS ASSN FOR THE BLIND (PA)
Also Called: Lighthouse For The Blind
2307 Business Center Dr (78744-1090)
P.O. Box 3297 (78764-3297)
PHONE..................................512 442-2329
William O Cromwell, *President*
Benny Wayne Galloway, *CFO*
Benny Galloway, *CFO*
Donald Harcum, *CFO*
Nonie Knight, *Manager*
▲ EMP: 113
SQ FT: 67,000
SALES (est): 50.6MM **Privately Held**
WEB: www.austinlighthouse.org
SIC: 2387 2782 8243 3172 Apparel belts; blankbooks & looseleaf binders; operator training, computer; key cases; packaging & labeling services; sheltered workshop; vocational training agency

(G-1591)
TRAXIS MANUFACTURING LLC
Also Called: Traxis Machining & Fabrication
511 E Saint Elmo Rd (78745-1223)
PHONE..................................512 383-0089
Thomas Buerkle, *President*
August Buerkle, *President*
Gus Buerkle, *Principal*
EMP: 10
SALES: 798.2K **Privately Held**
WEB: www.traxismfg.com
SIC: 3999 Manufacturing industries

(G-1592)
TRIAZ DIGITAL PRINTING LLC
Also Called: Commercial Printing
2013 Wlls Br Pkwy Ste 307 (78728)
PHONE..................................512 491-7000
Bharat Mahta, *CEO*
Krisha Mehta, *President*
Carol Doughty, *Marketing Staff*
Bharat Mahta,
EMP: 12
SALES (est): 1.2MM **Privately Held**
WEB: www.triazprinting.com
SIC: 2759 5736 Commercial printing; musical instrument stores

(G-1593)
TRILLIUM US INC
Also Called: Austin Scientific
1340 Arprt Commrce Dr # 175 (78741-6823)
P.O. Box 18863 (78760-8863)
PHONE..................................512 441-6893
James Beatty, *CEO*
EMP: 60
SALES (corp-wide): 41.7MM **Privately Held**
WEB: www.trilliumus.com
SIC: 3563 Air & gas compressors
PA: Trillium Us Inc.
13011 Se Jennifer St # 20
Clackamas OR 97015
503 607-0393

(G-1594)
TRINITY ENVIRONMENTAL SVCS LLC (PA)
Also Called: Trinity Storage Services
6300 Bridge Point Pkwy 2-210 (78730-5084)
PHONE..................................512 582-8050
Daniel B Porter, *CEO*
Jay Klein, *Managing Dir*
Raymond A Welch, *Exec VP*
Andrew Kilgore, *Vice Pres*
Lonnie Allen, *Opers Mgr*
EMP: 14
SALES (est): 13.7MM **Privately Held**
WEB: www.trinityenv.com
SIC: 1389 Oil field services

(G-1595)
TRINITY ENVMTL CTARINA SWD LLC
113443 Hwy 71 W (78738)
PHONE..................................512 524-7281
Daniel B Porter, *CEO*
Diego Rubio, *President*
John Turner, *CFO*
EMP: 43

SALES (est): 1.2MM **Privately Held**
SIC: 1389 Oil consultants

(G-1596)
TROUX TECHNOLOGIES INC (HQ)
12301 Res Blvd Bldg Vste (78759)
PHONE..................................512 346-8600
Greg Gilmore, *Principal*
Bryan Urioste, *Exec VP*
Amy Adams, *Opers Mgr*
Vic Chynoweth, *CFO*
Matthew Laakso, *Sales Staff*
EMP: 85
SALES (est): 12.5MM **Privately Held**
WEB: www.troux.com
SIC: 7371 7372 Computer software development; prepackaged software; business oriented computer software

(G-1597)
TRUCKPRO LLC
Also Called: Austin Brake & Clutch Supply
8151 N Lamar Blvd (78753-6232)
PHONE..................................512 836-0482
Melinda Sanchez, *Branch Mgr*
EMP: 12
SALES (corp-wide): 477.8MM **Privately Held**
WEB: www.truckpro.com
SIC: 3714 5013 Motor vehicle brake systems & parts; automotive brakes
HQ: Truckpro, Llc
1900 Charles Bryan Rd
Cordova TN 38016
901 252-4200

(G-1598)
TRUSOURCE LABS LLC (DH)
Also Called: Everise Px
13011 Mccallen Pass A (78753-5380)
PHONE..................................512 487-7103
Thomas Lloyd, *Manager*
Alton Martin,
Roger Meador,
EMP: 27
SALES (est): 11MM **Privately Held**
WEB: www.trusourcelabs.com
SIC: 3695 5045 Computer software tape & disks: blank, rigid & floppy; computer software

(G-1599)
TSUNAMI RIG WASH LLC
Also Called: Westlake Power Washing
9313 Circle Dr (78736-7916)
PHONE..................................512 280-1649
James Hasty, *President*
Howard Florence, *Vice Pres*
EMP: 21 **EST:** 2012
SALES (est): 2.6MM **Privately Held**
WEB: www.westlakepowerwashing.com
SIC: 1389 Cleaning wells

(G-1600)
TWC PRINT SHOP
4405 Springdale Rd (78723-6050)
PHONE..................................512 927-0002
EMP: 18
SALES (est): 1.3MM **Privately Held**
SIC: 2759 Commercial Printing

(G-1601)
TWG SOLUTIONS LLC (PA)
Also Called: Whelan Group, The
4129 Coml Ctr Dr Ste 400 (78744)
PHONE..................................512 472-8972
Kim Kasee, *CEO*
Melissa Walker, *Exec VP*
Michael Rogles, *Sales Staff*
Shawn Kelly,
Ed Olkkola,
EMP: 49 **EST:** 1950
SQ FT: 38,000
SALES (est): 49.1MM **Privately Held**
WEB: www.thewhelangroup.com
SIC: 2759 7389 Screen printing; document storage service

(G-1602)
TWO HILLS STUDIO INC
2706 S Lamar Blvd (78704-4708)
PHONE..................................512 707-7571
Britt Medford, *President*
Cydney Medford, *Vice Pres*
EMP: 23

SALES (est): 1.6MM **Privately Held**
WEB: www.twohillsstudio.com
SIC: 3499 3444 Metal household articles; sheet metalwork

(G-1603)
TYREX GROUP LTD (PA)
12317 Tech Blvd Ste 100 (78727)
PHONE..................................512 623-4694
Andrew Cooper, *CEO*
John Bosch Jr, *Partner*
Matthew Ache, *Partner*
Kevin B Alwell, *Vice Pres*
Martin Johnson, *VP Bus Dvlpt*
▲ **EMP:** 18
SQ FT: 89,000
SALES (est): 26.9MM **Privately Held**
WEB: www.tyrexmfg.com
SIC: 3643 3644 3669 3672 Current-carrying wiring devices; noncurrent-carrying wiring services; intercommunication systems, electric; printed circuit boards; optical instruments & lenses

(G-1604)
UDUNDI LLC
101 Colorado St (78701-4103)
PHONE..................................917 727-4220
EMP: 10 **EST:** 2012
SALES (est): 283.6K **Privately Held**
WEB: www.udundi.com
SIC: 3652 Pre-recorded records & tapes

(G-1605)
UHNDER INC (PA)
3409 Executive Center Dr # 205 (78731-1641)
PHONE..................................512 722-6353
Manju Hegde, *CEO*
Curtis Davis, *President*
Otto Schmid, *Vice Pres*
Sonal Banka, *Controller*
Lindsay Fengel, *Office Mgr*
EMP: 39
SQ FT: 7,412
SALES (est): 5.3MM **Privately Held**
WEB: www.uhnder.com
SIC: 3674 Semiconductors & related devices

(G-1606)
ULTRA CLEAN TECHNOLOGY SYSTEMS
500 Center Ridge Dr # 400 (78753-1024)
PHONE..................................512 252-6100
Iordan Iordanov, *Research*
Jordan Barr, *Engineer*
Connie Canino-Romeo, *Credit Staff*
Brad Chasney, *Sales Staff*
Shelley Prihoda, *Marketing Staff*
EMP: 130
SALES (corp-wide): 1B **Publicly Held**
WEB: www.uct.com
SIC: 7361 3674 4924 Employment agencies; semiconductors & related devices; natural gas distribution
HQ: Ultra Clean Technology Systems And Service, Inc.
26462 Corporate Ave
Hayward CA 94545

(G-1607)
UNIFORM CONCEPTS INC
5206 Backtrail Dr (78731-2603)
PHONE..................................512 345-5793
Dawn N South, *President*
William P South, *General Mgr*
EMP: 12
SQ FT: 3,800
SALES (est): 1MM **Privately Held**
SIC: 5136 5137 7213 2395 Uniforms, men's & boys'; caps, men's & boys'; men's & boys' outerwear; shirts, men's & boys'; uniforms, women's & children's; caps & gowns; coats: women's, children's & infants'; skirts; uniform supply; embroidery products, except schiffli machine

(G-1608)
UNITED OIL CORPORATION
6300 Fm 2244 Rd Bldg 500 (78746-5833)
PHONE..................................303 856-6444
James T Huffman, *President*
William F Skewes, *Corp Secy*
David Vreemam, *Vice Pres*
Kreager Charles W, *Vice Pres*

EMP: 10
SALES (est): 689.4K
SALES (corp-wide): 20.3B **Publicly Held**
SIC: 1311 Crude petroleum production; natural gas production
HQ: Forestar Petroleum Corporation
6300 Fm 2244 Rd Bldg 2
Austin TX 78746
512 433-5200

(G-1609)
UNIVERSITY OF TEXAS AT AUSTIN
University of Texas Press
3001 Lake Austin Blvd (78703-4206)
P.O. Box 7819 (78713-7819)
PHONE..................................800 252-3206
Lynne Ferguson, *Editor*
Leonard Moore, *Vice Pres*
Lance Owen, *Project Mgr*
Cynthia Juniper, *Research*
Lizbeth Lynch, *CFO*
EMP: 44
SALES (corp-wide): 16.3B **Privately Held**
WEB: www.utexas.edu
SIC: 8221 2731 University; book publishing
HQ: University Of Texas At Austin
110 Inner Campus Dr
Austin TX 78712
512 471-3434

(G-1610)
UNIVERSITY OF TEXAS AT AUSTIN
Also Called: Daily Texan Publications
2500 Whitis Ave Rm 3200 (78712-1502)
P.O. Box De 4100 (78705)
PHONE..................................512 471-1865
Gerald Johnson, *Principal*
EMP: 50
SALES (corp-wide): 16.3B **Privately Held**
WEB: www.utexas.edu
SIC: 7313 2752 2711 8221 Newspaper advertising representative; commercial printing, lithographic; newspapers; university
HQ: University Of Texas At Austin
110 Inner Campus Dr
Austin TX 78712
512 471-3434

(G-1611)
UPLAND SOFTWARE INC (PA)
401 Congress Ave Ste 1850 (78701-3788)
PHONE..................................833 875-2631
John T McDonald, *CEO*
Rodney C Favaron, *President*
Timothy W Mattox, *President*
Sandra Cartwright, *Partner*
Timothy Mattox, *COO*
EMP: 107
SQ FT: 9,900
SALES: 222.6MM **Publicly Held**
WEB: www.uplandsoftware.com
SIC: 7372 Business oriented computer software

(G-1612)
UPLAND SOFTWARE I INC
Also Called: Powersteering Software
401 Congress Ave Ste 1850 (78701-3788)
PHONE..................................617 494-5515
John McDonald, *President*
Amber Bennett, *Vice Pres*
Austin Woody, *Vice Pres*
Michael Hill, *CFO*
Reginald Kenon, *Accounts Exec*
EMP: 75
SQ FT: 9,000
SALES (est): 6MM **Publicly Held**
WEB: www.uplandsoftware.com
SIC: 7372 7371 7379 Business oriented computer software; custom computer programming services; computer related maintenance services
PA: Upland Software, Inc.
401 Congress Ave Ste 1850
Austin TX 78701

(G-1613)
UPLOGIX INC
7600b N Cpitl Of Txas Hwy (78731-1168)
PHONE..................................512 857-7000
Tom Goldman, *CEO*
Michael Luther, *President*

Ken Rock, *Business Mgr*
Daniel Verastiqui, *Opers Staff*
Martta Howard, *Technical Mgr*
EMP: 60
SQ FT: 11,000
SALES (est): 11MM **Privately Held**
WEB: www.uplogix.com
SIC: 7372 Prepackaged software

(G-1614)
UPPER CRUST BAKERY INC
4508 Burnet Rd (78756-3025)
PHONE..................................512 467-0102
Stiefine Shuster, *President*
Stiefine Shuster, *President*
Stephanie Schuster, *Finance*
EMP: 40
SQ FT: 4,200
SALES (est): 1.4MM **Privately Held**
WEB: www.uppercrustbakery.com
SIC: 2051 5461 Bakery: wholesale or wholesale/retail combined; bakeries

(G-1615)
UPTIME DEVICES INC
11724 Dunfries Ln (78754-5820)
PHONE..................................512 328-1800
EMP: 10 **EST:** 2001
SQ FT: 3,000
SALES (est): 1.6MM **Privately Held**
SIC: 3577 Mfg Computer Peripheral Equipment

(G-1616)
US FARATHANE HOLDINGS CORP
820 W Howard Ln (78753-9708)
PHONE..................................734 656-9000
David Howard, *General Mgr*
Preston Miller, *Principal*
Tom Snyder, *Maint Spvr*
Paola Lopez, *Human Resources*
Tom Frederick, *Manager*
EMP: 122
SALES (corp-wide): 852.8MM **Privately Held**
WEB: www.usfarathane.com
SIC: 3089 Injection molding of plastics
PA: U.S. Farathane Holdings Corp.
11650 Park Ct
Shelby Township MI 48315
586 726-1200

(G-1617)
US SURFACE WAREHOUSE
Also Called: Livingstone
4601 Spicewood Springs Rd 1-100 (78759-7848)
PHONE..................................866 433-2229
EMP: 20
SALES (est): 829K **Privately Held**
SIC: 2541 Mfg Wood Partitions/Fixtures

(G-1618)
USA COMPRESSION PARTNERS LLC (HQ)
111 Congress Ave Ste 2400 (78701-4083)
PHONE..................................512 369-1380
Eric D Long, *President*
Pete Alspaugh, *Area Mgr*
Case McDonald, *Area Mgr*
Clint Rogers, *Area Mgr*
Kevin M Bourbonnais, *COO*
EMP: 10
SALES (est): 158.9MM
SALES (corp-wide): 698.3MM **Publicly Held**
WEB: www.usacompression.com
SIC: 1389 Gas compressing (natural gas) at the fields
PA: Usa Compression Partners, Lp
111 Congress Ave Ste 2400
Austin TX 78701
512 473-2662

(G-1619)
USA COMPRESSION PARTNERS LP (PA)
111 Congress Ave Ste 2400 (78701-4083)
PHONE..................................512 473-2662
EMP: 30 **EST:** 1998
SQ FT: 19,297

SALES: 698.3MM Publicly Held
WEB: www.investors.usacpartners.com
SIC: 1389 7699 Gas compressing (natural gas) at the fields; gas field services; compressor repair

(G-1620)
USAC LEASING 2 LLC
100 Congress Ave Ste 450 (78701-2747)
PHONE..................................512 473-2662
Eric Long, *Principal*
EMP: 187 EST: 2014
SALES (est): 148.5MM
SALES (corp-wide): 698.3MM Publicly Held
WEB: www.usacompression.com
SIC: 1389 Oil & gas field services
PA: Usa Compression Partners, Lp
111 Congress Ave Ste 2400
Austin TX 78701
512 473-2662

(G-1621)
VALEN LIGHT LLC
Also Called: Solar Streetscapes
2101 E Saint Elmo Rd # 3 (78744-1171)
PHONE..................................512 222-5550
Daniel Giblett,
▲ EMP: 24 EST: 2010
SALES (est): 5.1MM Privately Held
WEB: www.valenenergy.com
SIC: 3648 Lighting equipment

(G-1622)
VALLEY ORTHOPEDIC INC
10910 Domain Dr Ste 300 (78758-7807)
PHONE..................................512 771-1970
Vinit K Asar, *CEO*
Dave McCalmont, *Business Mgr*
Aaron Flores, *Vice Pres*
Rodolfo Szoke, *Vice Pres*
Drew Morton, *VP Human Res*
EMP: 39
SALES (est): 4.2MM Privately Held
SIC: 3842 Surgical appliances & supplies

(G-1623)
VAPOR IO INC
6200 Brdgpint Pkwy Bldg F (78730)
PHONE..................................512 600-1123
Colton M Crawford, *CEO*
Don Duet, *President*
Steven White, *Chief*
Jacques Greyling, *COO*
Alan Bock, *VP Business*
▲ EMP: 30 EST: 2015
SALES (est): 200K Privately Held
WEB: www.vapor.io
SIC: 7372 Application computer software

(G-1624)
VARIOUS FIELDS LLC
Also Called: Mmmpanadas
1301 Broadmoor Dr (78723-3121)
PHONE..................................512 788-2228
Kristen Studer, *Principal*
Fields Cody, *Opers Mgr*
EMP: 12
SALES (est): 2MM Privately Held
WEB: www.mmmpanadas.com
SIC: 2656 Frozen food & ice cream containers

(G-1625)
VAULT 55
710 Colorado St Ste 150 (78701-3063)
PHONE..................................512 482-8810
Doug Myron, *Owner*
Debbie Bishop, *Manager*
EMP: 18 Privately Held
WEB: www.vault55.com
SIC: 3272 Burial vaults, concrete or precast terrazzo

(G-1626)
VEGGIE NOODLE CO LLC
Also Called: Cece's Veggie Co.
3714 Bluestein Dr Ste 631 (78721-2921)
PHONE..................................512 200-3337
Chris Self, *Project Mgr*
Lane Forsander, *Director*
Jessica Kezar, *Director*
Chris Romano, *Officer*
Mason Arnold,
EMP: 70

SALES (est): 1.8MM Privately Held
WEB: www.cecesveggieco.com
SIC: 2099 Vegetables, peeled for the trade

(G-1627)
VENABLE CORPORATION
Also Called: Venable Instruments
8656 W Highway 71 Bldg E (78735-8001)
PHONE..................................512 949-3144
Donald Woodard, *President*
Michael Gray, *Info Tech Dir*
EMP: 10
SQ FT: 4,500
SALES (est): 2.1MM Privately Held
WEB: www.venableinstruments.com
SIC: 3825 Analyzers for testing electrical characteristics

(G-1628)
VENADO OIL & GAS LLC (PA)
13301 Galleria Cir # 300 (78738-6435)
PHONE..................................512 518-2900
Mark Jaeger, *Prdtn Mgr*
Jonathan Woods, *Manager*
Russell Scott Garrick,
Sally Allen, *Administration*
EMP: 12
SALES (est): 15.6MM Privately Held
WEB: www.vogllc.com
SIC: 1382 Oil & gas exploration services

(G-1629)
VENKEL LTD (PA)
5900 Shepherd Mountain Cv (78730-5074)
PHONE..................................512 794-0081
Anil Venkatrao, *Managing Prtnr*
Hena Venkatrao, *Partner*
Ravi Venkatrao, *Partner*
Weston Butler, *General Mgr*
Steve Cornell, *Purchasing*
▲ EMP: 36
SQ FT: 35,000
SALES (est): 25MM Privately Held
WEB: www.venkel.com
SIC: 5065 3676 3675 Electronic parts; electronic resistors; electronic capacitors

(G-1630)
VERGE LABS INC
Also Called: Nitro AV
209 E Ben White Blvd # 114 (78704-7309)
PHONE..................................512 707-0001
Michael A Broadway, *President*
EMP: 10
SALES (est): 2.5MM Privately Held
WEB: www.vergelabs.net
SIC: 3572 Computer storage devices

(G-1631)
VERSATA INC (DH)
401 Congress Ave Ste 2600 (78701-3744)
PHONE..................................512 524-6149
Davin Cushman, *President*
William Frederick, *President*
Brett Adam, *Vice Pres*
Andrew Price, *CFO*
Jay Kamm, *Technical Staff*
EMP: 73
SQ FT: 25,000
SALES (est): 95.3MM Privately Held
WEB: www.versata.com
SIC: 7372 Business oriented computer software

(G-1632)
VIATRAN INC
404 W Powell Ln Ste 408 (78753-6265)
PHONE..................................512 832-8400
Thomas Erb, *President*
Michael Erb, *Vice Pres*
Mike Erb, *Sales Staff*
Erica Nelson, *Graphic Designe*
Roger Borowicz, *Maintence Staff*
EMP: 33
SQ FT: 20,000
SALES (est): 3.9MM Privately Held
WEB: www.viatraninc.com
SIC: 2759 Screen printing

(G-1633)
VIC WEST IMPORTERS LTD CO
512 E Rverside Dr Ste 200 (78704)
PHONE..................................888 698-6463
Nicholas P Olynyk, *President*
◆ EMP: 12 EST: 2017
SQ FT: 175

SALES (est): 2.2MM Privately Held
WEB: www.vicwestimporters.com
SIC: 2879 Pesticides, agricultural or household

(G-1634)
VIKAY GROUP LLC
Also Called: Stitch Texas
321 W Ben White Blvd # 112 (78704-7086)
PHONE..................................512 291-8234
Kristopher Stevens, *Mng Member*
EMP: 15
SALES (est): 739.6K Privately Held
WEB: www.stitchtexas.com
SIC: 2389 Apparel for handicapped

(G-1635)
VIRTEX ASSEMBLY SERVICES INC
12234 N Interstate 35 A (78753-1725)
PHONE..................................512 835-6772
Brad Heath, *President*
Mike Montano, *General Mgr*
Sareta Heath, *Vice Pres*
Cathy Chamseddine, *VP Opers*
Chad Hohenberger, *Project Mgr*
▲ EMP: 70
SQ FT: 62,000
SALES (est): 34.6MM Privately Held
WEB: www.virtexassembly.com
SIC: 3672 3699 8711 Printed circuit boards; electrical equipment & supplies; electrical or electronic engineering

(G-1636)
VIRTEX ENTERPRISES LP (PA)
12234 N Interstate 35 (78753-1725)
PHONE..................................512 835-6772
Brad Heath, *CEO*
Eugene Watkins, *Engineer*
Jeff Wanago, *CFO*
Clayton Ridesel, *Sales Staff*
Lara Tietz, *Manager*
EMP: 41
SALES (est): 59MM Privately Held
WEB: www.virtexassembly.com
SIC: 3672 Printed circuit boards

(G-1637)
VISERV INC
Also Called: Personal Advisor, The
2211 S Interstate 35 # 205 (78741-3865)
P.O. Box 27616 (78755-2616)
PHONE..................................512 454-7403
Robert Moeser, *President*
Heather Moeser, *Treasurer*
EMP: 20
SALES (est): 2.3MM Privately Held
WEB: www.thepersonneladvisor.com
SIC: 2731 Books: publishing only

(G-1638)
VISION CENTERS PA (PA)
Also Called: McCormick Vision Centers
12701 Research Blvd (78759-4386)
PHONE..................................512 258-2020
John McCormick, *President*
Michael McCormick, *Vice Pres*
EMP: 21
SQ FT: 3,800
SALES (est): 4.7MM Privately Held
WEB: www.mccormickvision.com
SIC: 5995 8042 3827 Contact lenses, prescription; offices & clinics of optometrists; optical instruments & lenses

(G-1639)
VISIONAEL CORPORATION
401 Congress Ave Ste 2950 (78701-4424)
PHONE..................................650 963-0960
Chris Ney, *CEO*
John McDonald, *President*
Tony Fox, *Consultant*
Ian Urquhart, *Consultant*
John Hinners, *Info Tech Mgr*
EMP: 10
SQ FT: 1,000
SALES (est): 899.9K Privately Held
WEB: www.visionael.com
SIC: 7372 Business oriented computer software

(G-1640)
VISUAL CLICK SOFTWARE INC
3267 Bee Caves Rd (78746-6700)
P.O. Box 161657 (78716-1657)
PHONE..................................512 231-9990
John McCann, *President*
Steve Garms, *Exec VP*
Michael Fabry, *VP Sales*
Lacy Hecker, *Sales Associate*
Mark Green, *Business Dir*
EMP: 21
SQ FT: 8,000
SALES (est): 3.2MM Privately Held
WEB: www.visualclick.com
SIC: 7372 Business oriented computer software

(G-1641)
VITAL FARMS INC
3601 S Congress Ave C1 (78704-7250)
P.O. Box 17395 (78760-7395)
PHONE..................................877 455-3063
Matthew O'Hayer, *Ch of Bd*
Russell Diez-Canseco, *President*
Jason Dale, *COO*
Jonathan Skaare, *VP Sales*
Scott Marcus, *Chief Mktg Ofcr*
▲ EMP: 161
SQ FT: 9,000
SALES: 140.7MM Privately Held
WEB: www.vitalfarms.com
SIC: 0252 2026 Chicken eggs; buttermilk, cultured

(G-1642)
VIXEN CREATIONS INC
4803 Commercial Park Dr (78724-2636)
PHONE..................................512 928-4933
Marilyn Bishara, *President*
EMP: 9 EST: 1993
SQ FT: 7,000
SALES (est): 1MM Privately Held
WEB: www.vixencreations.com
SIC: 3499 Novelties & specialties, metal

(G-1643)
VOG PALO VERDE LP
13301 Galleria Cir # 300 (78738-6434)
PHONE..................................512 518-2900
Steven Mickey, *Business Mgr*
Alexia Little, *Controller*
Russell Scott Garrick,
EMP: 22
SALES (est): 457.2K Privately Held
WEB: www.vogllc.com
SIC: 1382 Oil & gas exploration services

(G-1644)
VOIP TEL LP
Also Called: Grand Signs
7801 N Lamar Blvd B168 (78752-1031)
PHONE..................................512 543-9556
Amin Hemani, *Partner*
Mahmood Ali, *Partner*
Mubarak Maknojia, *Partner*
Muhammad Hanif Khatri, *Analyst*
EMP: 11
SQ FT: 4,200
SALES (est): 1.3MM Privately Held
WEB: www.voiptelusa.com
SIC: 4813 3993 ; signs & advertising specialties

(G-1645)
VOLUSION LLC (HQ)
Also Called: Mozu
1835 Kramer Ln Ste 100 (78758-4233)
PHONE..................................800 646-3517
Liz Downs, *Vice Pres*
David Campbell, *Engineer*
Jordan Knight, *Engineer*
Adam Drullinger, *Accountant*
Frank Farias, *Finance*
EMP: 19
SALES (est): 15.7MM
SALES (corp-wide): 57.2MM Privately Held
WEB: www.volusion.com
SIC: 7372 Prepackaged software
PA: Kibo Software, Inc.
717 N Harwood St Ste 1800
Dallas TX 75201
707 780-1600

GEOGRAPHIC

(G-1646)
WARGAMING AMERICA INC (DH)
10415 Morado Cir 3-110 (78759-5631)
PHONE..................................510 962-6747
Evgueni Kislyi, *CEO*
Andrei Yarantsau, *Vice Pres*
EMP: 38
SQ FT: 1,000
SALES (est): 22MM **Privately Held**
WEB: www.wargaming.com
SIC: 7372 Application computer software
HQ: Wargaming (Usa), Inc.
    651 W Washington Blvd # 600
    Chicago IL 60661
    312 258-0500

(G-1647)
WASTE REPURPOSING INTL INC
Also Called: Smarter Sorting
4901 E Cesar Chavez St (78702-5139)
PHONE..................................760 525-7180
Chris Ripley, *CEO*
EMP: 33
SALES (est): 108.4K **Privately Held**
WEB: www.smartersorting.com
SIC: 3429 Manufactured hardware (general)

(G-1648)
WATERFALL INTERNATIONAL INC
401 Congress Ave Ste 1850 (78701-3788)
P.O. Box 77408, San Francisco CA (94107-0408)
PHONE..................................844 627-2438
Matthew Sechrest, *CEO*
John McLane, *COO*
Michael Ahearn, *Development*
Elsbeth Cloninger, *Development*
Matt Close, *Development*
EMP: 40
SALES (est): 2.1MM **Publicly Held**
WEB: www.uplandsoftware.com
SIC: 7372 Prepackaged software
PA: Upland Software, Inc.
    401 Congress Ave Ste 1850
    Austin TX 78701

(G-1649)
WATERLOO SPARKLING WATER CORP
2612 E Cesar Chavez St # 200
(78702-4704)
PHONE..................................512 910-8990
Jason Shiver, *CEO*
Adam Price, *Vice Pres*
Daniel Barnes, *Director*
Brandon Cason, *Director*
Sean Cusack, *Director*
EMP: 13
SALES (est): 166.5K **Privately Held**
WEB: www.drinkwaterloo.com
SIC: 2086 Mineral water, carbonated:
packaged in cans, bottles, etc.; pasteurized & mineral waters, bottled & canned; water, pasteurized: packaged in cans, bottles, etc.

(G-1650)
WAVE QUANTUM DEF & TECH LLC
11701 Fm 2244 Ste 124 (78738-6907)
PHONE..................................512 505-2339
Chris Mashburn,
EMP: 10
SALES (est): 471.5K **Privately Held**
SIC: 3812 7389 Defense systems & equipment; personal service agents, brokers & bureaus

(G-1651)
WAYNE FUELING SYSTEMS LLC
Also Called: Wayne Services Group
401 Parker Dr Ste A (78728-1262)
PHONE..................................512 388-8446
EMP: 12
SALES (corp-wide): 7.1B **Publicly Held**
WEB: www.wayne.com
SIC: 3586 Gasoline pumps, measuring or dispensing
HQ: Wayne Fueling Systems Llc
    3814 Jarrett Way
    Austin TX 78728
    512 388-8311

(G-1652)
WAYNE FUELING SYSTEMS LLC (HQ)
Also Called: Wayne Services Group
3814 Jarrett Way (78728-1212)
P.O. Box 660367, Dallas (75266-0367)
PHONE..................................512 388-8311
Neil Thomas, *CEO*
Jeffrey Lass, *CFO*
John Hall, *Treasurer*
Zaid Swadi, *Regional*
EMP: 11
SALES (est): 3.1MM
SALES (corp-wide): 7.1B **Publicly Held**
WEB: www.wayne.com
SIC: 1389 Pipe testing, oil field service
PA: Dover Corporation
    3005 Highland Pkwy # 200
    Downers Grove IL 60515
    630 541-1540

(G-1653)
WEBSENSE LLC (HQ)
10900 Stonelake Blvd (78759-5795)
PHONE..................................858 320-8000
John McCormack, *CEO*
Mark Gooderum, *Principal*
Shannon Shankman, *Regional Mgr*
Mark Arnold, *Vice Pres*
Eric Jackson, *Vice Pres*
EMP: 398
SQ FT: 122,000
SALES (est): 379.5MM
SALES (corp-wide): 424.4MM **Privately Held**
WEB: www.support.forcepoint.com
SIC: 7372 Prepackaged software
PA: Forcepoint Llc
    10900 A Stnlake Blvd Quar
    Austin TX 78759
    858 320-8000

(G-1654)
WELLSMITH INC
2901 Via Fortuna Ste 600 (78746-7710)
PHONE..................................866 266-7793
Jeanne Teshler, *CEO*
Dan Bitman, *CTO*
Jen Chaney, *Director*
EMP: 17
SALES (est): 746.2K **Privately Held**
WEB: www.wellsmith.com
SIC: 7372 Business oriented computer software

(G-1655)
WENZEL ASSOCIATES INC (DH)
2215 Kramer Ln (78758-4002)
PHONE..................................512 835-2038
Mark Mirelez, *President*
Greg Peacock, *Vice Pres*
Liz Ronchetti, *Vice Pres*
Kathleen Wenzel, *Vice Pres*
Beverly Schwartz, *Purch Mgr*
EMP: 77
SQ FT: 26,000
SALES (est): 21.3MM
SALES (corp-wide): 12.4MM **Privately Held**
WEB: www.wenzel.com
SIC: 3825 Oscillators, audio & radio frequency (instrument types); electrical power measuring equipment

(G-1656)
WENZEL SPINE INC
1130 Rutherford Ln # 200 (78753-6746)
PHONE..................................512 469-0600
Chad Neely, *CEO*
William Wilson, *COO*
Garland Abernathy, *Opers Mgr*
Andi Cragen, *Design Engr*
John Krause, *Design Engr*
▼ EMP: 10
SALES (est): 2.3MM **Privately Held**
WEB: www.wenzelspine.com
SIC: 3841 Surgical & medical instruments

(G-1657)
WESTCAVE PRINTING CORPORATION
Also Called: Horizon Printing
2111 Grand Avenue Pkwy (78728-3938)
PHONE..................................512 989-0006
Mike Spann, *President*

Justin Snyder, *President*
Gerardo Calderon, *Production*
Kevin Waybourn, *Production*
Gary Motal, *Sales Executive*
▲ EMP: 46
SQ FT: 22,000
SALES (est): 10MM **Privately Held**
WEB: www.horizonprinting.net
SIC: 2752 Commercial printing, offset

(G-1658)
WESTERN INDUSTRIES CORPORATION
4616 W Howard Ln 7-750 (78728-6327)
PHONE..................................512 837-0240
Mirthala Montelongo, *General Mgr*
Don Peterson, *Branch Mgr*
Claudia Robertson, *Officer*
EMP: 20
SALES (corp-wide): 27.5MM **Privately Held**
WEB: www.wicpack.com
SIC: 7389 3086 Packaging & labeling services; plastics foam products
PA: Western Industries Corporation
    5500 S Hattie Ave
    Oklahoma City OK 73129
    405 419-3100

(G-1659)
WESTLAKE ENES SCENCE TECH ASSN
Also Called: WESTA
304 N Laurelwood Dr (78733-3130)
P.O. Box 162202 (78716-2202)
PHONE..................................512 751-5049
Joyce Witowski, *President*
Nicole David, *Treasurer*
Norman Morgan, *Director*
Sally Brainard, *Representative*
EMP: 9
SALES: 169K **Privately Held**
WEB: www.westaaustin.org
SIC: 3999 Education aids, devices & supplies

(G-1660)
WHEEL INNOVATIONZ INC
5905 Sir Ivor Cv (78746-2126)
PHONE..................................408 390-2871
Srni Gurrapu, *CEO*
EMP: 10
SALES (est): 658.7K **Privately Held**
WEB: www.wheelinnovationz.com
SIC: 7372 Application computer software

(G-1661)
WHITEWATER MIDSTREAM LLC (PA)
100 Congress Ave Ste 2200 (78701-2747)
PHONE..................................512 953-2100
Matthew Calhun, *Senior VP*
Steven Nelson, *Vice Pres*
Caleb Ryan, *Vice Pres*
Scott Simmons, *Vice Pres*
Travis Allison, *Opers Staff*
EMP: 21 EST: 2016
SALES (est): 25.2MM **Privately Held**
WEB: www.whitewatermidstream.com
SIC: 1389 Haulage, oil field

(G-1662)
WHITLEY & SIDDONS (PA)
Also Called: Whitley Siddons Hwy Cnstr Info
11612 Fm 2244 Rd 1-230 (78738-5409)
P.O. Box 164047 (78716-4047)
PHONE..................................512 477-9491
Robert C Siddons, *President*
Bettye Ann Rodgers, *Vice Pres*
Steven B Siddons, *Vice Pres*
Eric Buescher, *Opers Mgr*
Brandi Wilson, *Sales Mgr*
EMP: 10
SALES (est): 1MM **Privately Held**
WEB: www.whitleysiddons.com
SIC: 2731 Books: publishing only

(G-1663)
WHITLEY GROUP LLC
Also Called: Twg
4129 Coml Ctr Dr Ste 400 (78744)
PHONE..................................512 476-7101
Kevin B Cassis, *President*
Kevin Burgess, *Vice Pres*
Setoria Taylor, *Project Mgr*

▲ EMP: 25
SALES (est): 4.3MM **Privately Held**
SIC: 2752 Letters, circular or form: lithographed

(G-1664)
WHOLE TOMATO SOFTWARE INC
10801-1 N Mpac Expy Bldg (78759)
PHONE..................................512 226-8080
Randy Jacops, *CEO*
Jeffrey Straathof, *President*
Sean Echevarria, *Vice Pres*
EMP: 250
SALES (est): 1.1MM **Privately Held**
WEB: www.wholetomato.com
SIC: 7372 Application computer software

(G-1665)
WIGWAG LLC
5707 Southwest Pkwy 1-100 (78735-6214)
PHONE..................................512 814-6459
Ed Hemphill, *CEO*
Travis McCollum, *COO*
Qiao Hu, *CFO*
Tiffany Tesinsky, *Sales Staff*
Conrad Hametner, *Chief Mktg Ofcr*
EMP: 10
SALES (est): 988.5K **Privately Held**
WEB: www.arm.com
SIC: 3679 Video triggers, except remote control TV devices

(G-1666)
WILDER SYSTEMS LLC
5811 Techni Center Dr # 5 (78721-2352)
PHONE..................................713 825-7348
William Wilder, *CEO*
EMP: 10 EST: 2015
SALES (est): 2MM **Privately Held**
SIC: 3728 Research & dev by manuf., aircraft parts & auxiliary equip

(G-1667)
WILLIAM B SIDES
Also Called: Rainbow Lake Aquaculture Co
8908 Ramirez Ln (78742-1428)
PHONE..................................512 385-3826
William Ssides, *Owner*
David Sides, *Manager*
EMP: 10
SQ FT: 4,500
SALES (est): 700K **Privately Held**
SIC: 2092 7999 5146 Fish, fresh: prepared; fishing lakes & piers, operation; fish, fresh

(G-1668)
WILLIAM TOTAH PRINTING LLC
Also Called: Ultimate Imaging
10024 Austral Cv (78739-1719)
PHONE..................................512 916-9780
Bill Totah,
EMP: 10
SQ FT: 3,900 **Privately Held**
SIC: 2752 Commercial printing, offset

(G-1669)
WILSON COUNTY HOLDINGS LLC (DH)
111 Congress Ave Ste 400 (78701-4143)
PHONE..................................512 402-7273
Mark See, *CEO*
Brad Sparks, *CFO*
EMP: 13
SALES (est): 3.6MM **Publicly Held**
WEB: www.laredo-oil.com
SIC: 1382 Oil & gas exploration services
HQ: Stranded Oil Resources Corporation
    110 Rubey Dr Ste 120
    Golden CO 80403
    512 279-7870

(G-1670)
WILSONART JORDAN HOLDINGS INC
13413 Galleria Cir # 200 (78738-6344)
PHONE..................................512 302-6500
Maryann Spiegel, *Administration*
EMP: 16
SALES (est): 3.2MM **Privately Held**
WEB: www.wilsonart.com
SIC: 2821 Plastics materials & resins

(G-1671)
WIN-911 SOFTWARE
2024 E Saint Elmo Rd (78744-1018)
P.O. Box 19229 (78760-9229)
PHONE..................................512 326-1011
Craig Jackson, *CEO*
Robert Brooker, *Ch of Bd*
EMP: 26
SALES (est): 5MM **Privately Held**
WEB: www.win911.com
SIC: 7372 Prepackaged software

(G-1672)
WINCOR NIXDORF INC (DH)
12345 N Lamar Blvd # 200 (78753-1337)
PHONE..................................512 676-5000
Stan Holcomb, *CEO*
Javier Lopez Bartolome, *Senior VP*
Patrick Leonard, *Vice Pres*
Gina Miller, *CFO*
Sonja Bennefield, *Manager*
▲ EMP: 96
SQ FT: 65,000
SALES (est): 45.7MM
SALES (corp-wide): 4.4B **Publicly Held**
WEB: www.dieboldnixdorf.com
SIC: 7379 5734 3577 Computer related
    consulting services; computer & software
    stores; computer peripheral equipment
HQ: Wincor Nixdorf International Gmbh
    Heinz-Nixdorf-Ring 1
    Paderborn 33106
    525 169-330

(G-1673)
WINDY HILL SPIRITS INC
4301 W William Cannon Dr (78749-1473)
PHONE..................................615 678-4785
Patrick Dillingham, *Principal*
EMP: 14
SALES (est): 2.4MM **Privately Held**
SIC: 2085 Distillers' dried grains & solubles
    & alcohol

(G-1674)
WINTEGRA INC
6850 Austin Center Blvd # 215
(78731-3131)
PHONE..................................512 345-3808
Jacob Ben Zvi, *President*
Robert O Dell, *Exec VP*
Ricardo Berger, *Vice Pres*
Arnon Mordoh, *Vice Pres*
Michael Phillip, *Vice Pres*
EMP: 165
SALES (est): 17.2MM
SALES (corp-wide): 5.2B **Publicly Held**
SIC: 3674 Semiconductors & related de-
    vices
HQ: Microsemi Storage Solutions, Inc.
    1380 Bordeaux Dr
    Sunnyvale CA 94089
    408 239-8000

(G-1675)
**WOLFSON
MICROELECTRONICS INC**
800 W 6th St (78701-2722)
PHONE..................................408 329-9800
Jason P Rhode, *President*
EMP: 415 EST: 2000
SALES (est): 18.3MM
SALES (corp-wide): 1.2B **Publicly Held**
WEB: www.cirrus.com
SIC: 3679 5065 Electronic circuits; elec-
    tronic parts & equipment
HQ: Cirrus Logic International (Uk) Ltd
    7b Nightingale Way
    Edinburgh EH3 9
    131 272-7000

(G-1676)
WONDERCIDE LLC
9415 Neils Thompson Dr (78758-7652)
PHONE..................................877 896-7426
Stephanie Boone, *CEO*
Steven Owen, *President*
Ross Scarbro, *Sales Staff*
EMP: 19
SALES (est): 6.4MM **Privately Held**
WEB: www.wondercide.com
SIC: 2836 Veterinary biological products

(G-1677)
**XPLORE TECHNOLOGIES CORP
(HQ)**
8601 Rr 2222 Ste 1 (78730-2304)
PHONE..................................512 637-1100
Michael Cho, *President*
Jim Kaput, *Vice Pres*
Olivier Leonetti, *Treasurer*
Robert Boback, *Sales Staff*
Rick Jones, *Sales Staff*
EMP: 12
SQ FT: 16,228
SALES: 86.8MM
SALES (corp-wide): 4.4B **Publicly Held**
WEB: www.xploretech.com
SIC: 3571 3663 Computers, digital, analog
    or hybrid; mobile communication equip-
    ment
PA: Zebra Technologies Corporation
    3 Overlook Pt
    Lincolnshire IL 60069
    847 634-6700

(G-1678)
**YARRINGTON ROAD
MATERIALS LP**
2705 Bee Caves Rd Ste 130 (78746-5808)
P.O. Box 50324 (78763-0324)
PHONE..................................512 306-7800
Edward R Coleman, *Managing Prtnr*
EMP: 10
SALES (est): 1.7MM **Privately Held**
WEB: www.yrmaterials.com
SIC: 1442 5032 3273 Construction sand
    & gravel; stone, crushed or broken;
    ready-mixed concrete

(G-1679)
**YASH & LUJAN CONSULTING
INC**
100 Congress Ave Ste 2000 (78701-2745)
PHONE..................................800 519-5221
David Gawlik, *Branch Mgr*
EMP: 307
SALES (corp-wide): 40.4MM **Privately
Held**
WEB: www.mypmware.com
SIC: 7372 Business oriented computer
    software
PA: Yash & Lujan Consulting, Inc
    5750 Epsilon
    San Antonio TX 78249
    210 340-0098

(G-1680)
YETI COOLERS LLC (HQ)
7601 Southwest Pkwy (78735-8989)
P.O. Box 163686 (78716-3686)
PHONE..................................512 394-9384
Matthew J Reintjes, *CEO*
Ryan Seiders, *Founder*
Andrew Hollon, *COO*
Bryan Barksdale, *Vice Pres*
Paul Carbone, *Vice Pres*
◆ EMP: 213
SALES (est): 46.2MM
SALES (corp-wide): 913.7MM **Publicly
Held**
WEB: www.yeti.com
SIC: 3086 Ice chests or coolers (portable),
    foamed plastic
PA: Yeti Holdings, Inc.
    7601 Southwest Pkwy
    Austin TX 78735
    512 394-8220

(G-1681)
YETI HOLDINGS INC (PA)
7601 Southwest Pkwy (78735-8989)
PHONE..................................512 394-8220
EMP: 31
SALES: 913.7MM **Publicly Held**
WEB: www.yeti.com
SIC: 3086 3949 5941 Ice chests or cool-
    ers (portable), foamed plastic; camping
    equipment & supplies; camping & back-
    packing equipment; camping equipment

(G-1682)
YOTTA SOLAR INC
3512 Montopolis Dr B (78744-1418)
PHONE..................................512 856-7788
Omeed Badkoobeh, *CEO*
Phil Gilchrist, *COO*
EMP: 12

SALES (est): 334.5K **Privately Held**
WEB: www.yottaenergy.com
SIC: 3699 Electrical equipment & supplies

(G-1683)
YOUNICOS INC
3100 Alvin Devane Blvd (78741-7425)
PHONE..................................512 268-8191
Stephen L Prince, *CEO*
Jayesh Goyal, *COO*
Chuck McLemore, *Exec VP*
Dean Tuel, *Vice Pres*
Asem Ahmed, *Project Mgr*
EMP: 145 EST: 2010
SALES (est): 38.2MM
SALES (corp-wide): 2B **Privately Held**
WEB: www.aggreko.com
SIC: 3612 Transformers, except electric
HQ: Aggreko Deutschland Gmbh
    Barbarastr. 62
    Dorsten 46282

(G-1684)
YOYO MANAGEMENT INC
Also Called: Blues Crawlers, The
2113 Cimarron Trl (78745-1602)
PHONE..................................512 447-1455
Gil Jenkins, *President*
EMP: 9
SALES (est): 520K **Privately Held**
WEB: www.thebluescrawlers.com
SIC: 2741 7929 Music, sheet: publishing &
    printing; entertainers & entertainment
    groups

(G-1685)
ZEVEX CORPORATION
510 Hearn St Ste 300 (78703-4516)
PHONE..................................512 322-9039
Justin Lynch, *President*
Gerald S Lindenmuth, *Vice Pres*
Paul Buller, *Admin Sec*
EMP: 10
SALES (est): 694.7K **Privately Held**
SIC: 1311 Crude petroleum production

(G-1686)
ZIFTEN TECHNOLOGIES INC
801 Barton Springs Rd 9 (78704-1146)
PHONE..................................512 298-5501
Mike Hamilton, *CEO*
Mark Obrecht, *President*
Michael W Little, *Principal*
Mickey Dipietro, *VP Sales*
EMP: 32
SALES (est): 6.5MM **Privately Held**
WEB: www.ziften.com
SIC: 8742 7372 Management consulting
    services; application computer software

(G-1687)
ZILKS FOODS LLC
1807 W Slaughter Ln # 495 (78748-6230)
P.O. Box 152289 (78715-2289)
PHONE..................................512 633-8904
John Anderson, *CEO*
Tom Valvo, *Plant Mgr*
Jason Ray, *Opers Staff*
Lani Holmes, *Marketing Mgr*
EMP: 18
SQ FT: 16,000
SALES (est): 3.4MM **Privately Held**
WEB: www.zilksfoods.com
SIC: 2099 Food preparations

(G-1688)
ZINEPAK LLC
1902 Forest Trl (78703-2928)
PHONE..................................212 706-8621
EMP: 10
SALES (est): 2.9MM **Privately Held**
WEB: www.thesuperfancompany.com
SIC: 2731 Book publishing

Austin
Williamson County

(G-1689)
ALWAYS PRINTING INC
13200 Pond Springs Rd A101
(78729-7128)
PHONE..................................512 250-5056
Arlene M O'Brien, *President*
Pat O'Brien, *Manager*

EMP: 9
SQ FT: 1,500
SALES (est): 1.1MM **Privately Held**
WEB: www.alwaysprinting.com
SIC: 2752 Commercial printing, offset

(G-1690)
APPLIED MATERIALS INC
10000 Spectrum Dr (78717-4557)
PHONE..................................512 845-1126
Sujoy Sur, *Managing Dir*
Douglas Morse, *Opers Staff*
Mark Norcia, *Opers Staff*
Reginald Rongero, *Engineer*
Bala Subramaniam, *Engineer*
EMP: 12
SALES (corp-wide): 17.2B **Publicly Held**
WEB: www.appliedmaterials.com
SIC: 3674 Semiconductors & related de-
    vices
PA: Applied Materials, Inc.
    3050 Bowers Ave Bldg 1
    Santa Clara CA 95054
    408 727-5555

(G-1691)
APPLIED RIGAKU TECH INC
Also Called: A R T
9825 Spectrum Dr Bldg 4 (78717-4931)
PHONE..................................512 225-1796
Robert P Bartek, *President*
Jennifer Lynch, *Mktg Dir*
Arlene Pollock, *Executive Asst*
EMP: 30
SQ FT: 20,000
SALES (est): 12MM **Privately Held**
WEB: www.rigakuedxrf.com
SIC: 3826 Analytical instruments
PA: Rigaku Corporation
    3-9-12, Matsubaracho
    Akishima TKY 196-0

(G-1692)
ENDOCARE INC (HQ)
9825 Spectrum Dr Bldg 2 (78717-4929)
PHONE..................................512 328-2892
Dow Wilson, *CEO*
EMP: 28
SQ FT: 28,000
SALES (est): 13.4MM
SALES (corp-wide): 3.1B **Publicly Held**
WEB: www.endocare.com
SIC: 3845 Electromedical equipment
PA: Varian Medical Systems, Inc.
    3100 Hansen Way
    Palo Alto CA 94304
    650 493-4000

(G-1693)
GULF COAST II LITHOTRIPSY LP
9825 Spectrum Dr Bldg 3 (78717-4930)
PHONE..................................866 598-2734
Russell Newman, *Principal*
EMP: 457
SALES (est): 14.9MM **Privately Held**
SIC: 3845 Electromedical apparatus

(G-1694)
HEALTHTECH SOLUTIONS INC
9825 Spectrum Dr Bldg 3 (78717-4930)
PHONE..................................763 559-7082
Russell Newman, *President*
EMP: 14
SALES (est): 1.6MM
SALES (corp-wide): 176.3MM **Privately
Held**
SIC: 8062 3841 3845 General medical &
    surgical hospitals; surgical & medical in-
    struments; laser systems & equipment,
    medical
HQ: Healthtronics, Inc.
    9825 Spectrum Dr Bldg 3
    Austin TX 78717

(G-1695)
**HEALTHTRNICS MBL
SOLUTIONS LLC**
9825 Spectrum Dr Bldg 3 (78717-4930)
PHONE..................................866 598-2734
Russell Newman, *President*
Clint Davis, *Vice Pres*
EMP: 99
SALES (est): 2.8MM **Privately Held**
WEB: www.healthtronics.com
SIC: 3845 Electromedical equipment

G
E
O
G
R
A
P
H
I
C

(G-1696)
HEALTHTRONICS INC (HQ)
9825 Spectrum Dr Bldg 3　(78717-4930)
PHONE..................................512 328-2892
Russel Newman, *CEO*
Russell Newman, *CEO*
Bruce Cohen, *COO*
Clint Davis, *Senior VP*
Gary Kozen, *Vice Pres*
▲ EMP: 11
SALES (est): 176.3MM　**Privately Held**
WEB: www.healthtronics.com
SIC: 3845　Lithotripters
PA: Ht Intermediate Company, Llc
　　9825 Spectrum Dr Bldg 3
　　Austin TX 78717
　　512 328-2892

(G-1697)
HEALTHTRONICS SERVICE CTR LLC
9825 Spectrum Dr Bldg 3　(78717-4930)
PHONE..................................512 328-2892
EMP: 400 EST: 1992
SALES: 165.9MM　**Privately Held**
SIC: 1389　Oil/Gas Field Services

(G-1698)
HP INC
13620 Ranch Road 620 N B　(78717-1116)
PHONE..................................512 432-8000
Molly Moulthrop, *Marketing Staff*
Gail Hamilton, *Manager*
Lakienya Williams, *Technology*
Dennis Yao, *Technology*
EMP: 500
SALES (corp-wide): 56.6B　**Publicly Held**
WEB: www.hp.com
SIC: 5045　8711　8731　3577　Computer peripheral equipment; consulting engineer; commercial physical research; computer peripheral equipment
PA: Hp Inc.
　　1501 Page Mill Rd
　　Palo Alto CA 94304
　　650 857-1501

(G-1699)
HT INTERMEDIATE COMPANY LLC (PA)
9825 Spectrum Dr Bldg 3　(78717-4930)
PHONE..................................512 328-2892
Jeanne Pickersgill, *Office Mgr*
Carl Bricker, *Technology*
Chris Mattison, *Technician*
▲ EMP: 9
SALES (est): 176.3MM　**Privately Held**
WEB: www.healthtronics.com
SIC: 3845　Lithotripters

(G-1700)
HUSSY MEDIA LLC
9900 Spectrum Dr　(78717-4555)
PHONE..................................832 906-5816
Eoles Whitaker II,
Terrance Bolton,
Malik Wheeler,
EMP: 22
SALES (est): 686.4K　**Privately Held**
SIC: 2721　Periodicals

(G-1701)
LASER VENTURES INC (DH)
9825 Spectrum Dr Bldg 3　(78717-4930)
PHONE..................................770 516-4600
Russell Newman, *President*
Gary Kozen, *Vice Pres*
Matthew McIntyre, *Vice Pres*
EMP: 10
SALES (est): 2MM
SALES (corp-wide): 176.3MM　**Privately Held**
WEB: www.laserventures.com
SIC: 3845　Laser systems & equipment, medical

(G-1702)
LITHOTRIPTERS INC
9825 Spectrum Dr Bldg 3　(78717-4930)
PHONE..................................888 252-6575
Russell Newman, *President*
Joseph Jenkins, *President*
Alan Terry, *COO*
EMP: 100
SQ FT: 6,000

SALES (est): 7MM
SALES (corp-wide): 176.3MM　**Privately Held**
SIC: 3699　Electric sound equipment
HQ: Healthtronics, Inc.
　　9825 Spectrum Dr Bldg 3
　　Austin TX 78717

(G-1703)
MAXIM INTEGRATED PRODUCTS INC
8516 Anderson Mill Rd # 200　(78729-4705)
PHONE..................................512 249-0307
Jason Green, *Manager*
EMP: 10
SALES (corp-wide): 2.1B　**Publicly Held**
WEB: www.maximintegrated.com
SIC: 3674　Semiconductors & related devices
PA: Maxim Integrated Products, Inc.
　　160 Rio Robles
　　San Jose CA 95134
　　408 601-1000

(G-1704)
MEDSTONE INTERNATIONAL INC
9825 Spectrum Dr Bldg 3　(78717-4930)
PHONE..................................512 328-2892
Brad Hummel, *President*
Christopher Schneider, *Group VP*
Steve Debrock, *Vice Pres*
Richard A Rusk, *Vice Pres*
John Q Barnidge, *CFO*
EMP: 40
SQ FT: 20,600
SALES (est): 3.4MM
SALES (corp-wide): 176.3MM　**Privately Held**
WEB: www.medstone.nl
SIC: 3845　Lithotripters
HQ: Healthtronics, Inc.
　　9825 Spectrum Dr Bldg 3
　　Austin TX 78717

(G-1705)
MOLECULAR TEMPLATES INC (PA)
9301 Amberglen Blvd # 100　(78729-1153)
PHONE..................................512 869-1555
Eric E Poma, *CEO*
Harold E Selick, *Ch of Bd*
Jason S Kim, *President*
Jack Higgins, *COO*
Ryan Hawkins, *Vice Pres*
EMP: 38
SQ FT: 33,000
SALES: 22.2MM　**Publicly Held**
WEB: www.mtem.com
SIC: 2834　Pharmaceutical preparations

(G-1706)
NEOSEM TECHNOLOGY INC
11001 Lakeline Blvd　(78717-5997)
PHONE..................................512 257-5000
DH Yeom, *President*
EMP: 17　**Privately Held**
WEB: www.neosem.com
SIC: 3825　Test equipment for electronic & electrical circuits
HQ: Neosem Technology, Inc.
　　1965 Concourse Dr
　　San Jose CA 95131

(G-1707)
NVIDIA CORPORATION
11001 Lakeline Blvd # 100　(78717-5997)
PHONE..................................512 401-4762
Peter Lillian, *Business Mgr*
Jason Clemons, *Research*
Neil Gabriel, *Engineer*
Tom Putnam, *Engineer*
Drew Walker, *Engineer*
EMP: 17　**Publicly Held**
WEB: www.nvidia.com
SIC: 3674　Semiconductors & related devices
PA: Nvidia Corporation
　　2788 San Tomas Expy
　　Santa Clara CA 95051

(G-1708)
NXP USA INC
7700 W Parmer Ln　(78729-8101)
PHONE..................................512 996-4000

Fawzi Behmann, *Director*
EMP: 1600
SALES (corp-wide): 8.8B　**Privately Held**
WEB: www.nxp.com
SIC: 3674　Semiconductors & related devices
HQ: Nxp Usa, Inc.
　　6501 W William Cannon Dr
　　Austin TX 78735
　　512 933-8214

(G-1709)
POLYCOM INC
Also Called: Polycom of Austin
7700 W Parmer Ln　(78729-8101)
PHONE..................................512 372-7000
Jeff Astill, *Business Mgr*
Jeremy Keefe, *Vice Pres*
Leila Lewis, *Vice Pres*
Denise Markham, *Vice Pres*
Briana Miller, *Senior Buyer*
EMP: 15
SALES (corp-wide): 1.6B　**Publicly Held**
WEB: www.poly.com
SIC: 3661　Telephones & telephone apparatus
HQ: Polycom, Inc.
　　6001 America Center Dr
　　San Jose CA 95002

(G-1710)
SANTANNA NATURAL GAS CORP (PA)
Also Called: Santanna Energy Services
7701 San Felipe Blvd # 2　(78729-7615)
PHONE..................................512 346-2500
T W Gatlin, *President*
Douglas Cueller, *Vice Pres*
Greg Rabaey, *Vice Pres*
Chris Tessler, *Vice Pres*
Richard McDonald, *CFO*
EMP: 28
SQ FT: 8,500
SALES: 60.6MM　**Privately Held**
WEB: www.santannaenergyservices.com
SIC: 5172　3699　Gases; electrical equipment & supplies

(G-1711)
SENSATRONICS LLC
13091 Pond Springs Rd　(78729-7149)
P.O. Box 679, Manor　(78653-0679)
PHONE..................................800 633-1033
Keith Wright, *President*
EMP: 13
SALES (est): 3.1MM　**Privately Held**
WEB: www.sensatronics.com
SIC: 3829　Meteorological instruments

(G-1712)
SOUTHWEST MARBLE & GRANITE INC
Also Called: Stasswender's
13240 Pond Springs Rd　(78729-7103)
P.O. Box 203123　(78720-3123)
PHONE..................................512 918-0135
Robert Stasswender, *President*
Todd P Wojtowecz, *Vice Pres*
Lee Smeltzer, *Admin Sec*
▲ EMP: 9
SQ FT: 8,500
SALES (est): 1.5MM　**Privately Held**
WEB: www.southwestmarble.com
SIC: 3281　5999　Marble, building: cut & shaped; granite, cut & shaped; limestone, cut & shaped; slate products; monuments & tombstones

(G-1713)
TAN BOOTS LLC
10904 Casitas Dr　(78717-3874)
PHONE..................................512 921-0720
John Green, *CEO*
EMP: 15
SALES (est): 183.8K　**Privately Held**
WEB: www.tan-boots.com
SIC: 8999　8111　7382　1389　Lecturing services; specialized legal services; security systems services; confinement surveillance systems maintenance & monitoring; oil & gas wells: building, repairing & dismantling; oil field services

(G-1714)
TARPS LLC
12910 Broadmeade Ave　(78729-4617)
PHONE..................................833 469-8277
David Urban,
EMP: 12
SALES (est): 338.7K　**Privately Held**
SIC: 2394　Canvas & related products

(G-1715)
TRUFORM METALSERVICE INC
13496 Pond Springs Rd B　(78729-4412)
P.O. Box 202410　(78720-2410)
PHONE..................................512 258-1675
Mike Mc Carty, *CEO*
EMP: 70
SQ FT: 28,000
SALES (est): 10.9MM
SALES (corp-wide): 70.9MM　**Privately Held**
WEB: www.agcaustin.org
SIC: 1711　3441　Warm air heating & air conditioning contractor; building components, structural steel
PA: The Mc Carty Corporation
　　13494 Pond Springs Rd
　　Austin TX 78729
　　512 331-1344

(G-1716)
WENO HEALTHCARE INC
9403 Longvale Dr　(78729-3504)
PHONE..................................210 912-8143
Tina L Johnson, *President*
EMP: 34
SALES (est): 1.9MM　**Privately Held**
WEB: www.wenohealthcare.com
SIC: 2741　Miscellaneous publishing

(G-1717)
ZIMMER (DH)
Also Called: Sulzermedica USA
9900 Spectrum Dr　(78717-4555)
PHONE..................................800 613-6131
Coleman Lannum, *Vice Pres*
Jeff Frizell, *VP Finance*
Barbara Goslee, *Director*
EMP: 797
SQ FT: 210,000
SALES (est): 68.5MM
SALES (corp-wide): 2.6MM　**Privately Held**
WEB: www.zimmerbiomet.com
SIC: 3841　5047　3842　Surgical & medical instruments; surgical equipment & supplies; medical equipment & supplies; surgical appliances & supplies

Axtell
Mclennan County

(G-1718)
PETERSON CONSTRUCTION
2682 Highway 31　(76624-1207)
PHONE..................................254 227-0738
Marshall Peterson, *CEO*
EMP: 15
SALES (est): 922.4K　**Privately Held**
SIC: 3448　Carports: prefabricated metal

Azle
Tarrant County

(G-1719)
ALLEN PRFMCE RESOURCES INC
Also Called: PSC
11468 S Fm 730　(76020-3040)
P.O. Box 926　(76098-0926)
PHONE..................................817 270-0102
Tom Allen, *President*
Kimberly Allen, *CFO*
EMP: 10
SALES (est): 3MM　**Privately Held**
WEB: www.pscmotorsports.com
SIC: 3714　Motor vehicle parts & accessories

▲ = Import ▼ =Export
◆ =Import/Export

(G-1720)
AZLE TRI-COUNTY ADVERTISER (PA)
Also Called: Azle News
321 W Main St (76020-2903)
P.O. Box 1409 (76098-1409)
PHONE..................................817 270-3340
Kim Ware, *Principal*
Walter Buckel, *Corp Secy*
Larry Crabtree, *Vice Pres*
Sarah Biondolillo, *Manager*
EMP: 10 **EST:** 1974
SQ FT: 5,120
SALES (est): 1MM **Privately Held**
WEB: www.azle-news.com
SIC: 2711 Commercial printing & newspaper publishing combined

(G-1721)
CLARKS PRECISION MACHINE & TL
Also Called: Clarks Precision Machine & Tl
636 Profit St (76020-2422)
PHONE..................................817 444-2533
Ann Clark-Hengstler, *CEO*
Juile Groomer, *Purch Mgr*
Diane Spooner, *CFO*
Dwane Cargill, *Program Mgr*
Michael Groomer, *Manager*
EMP: 44 **EST:** 1968
SQ FT: 54,000
SALES (est): 10MM **Privately Held**
WEB: www.clarksmachine.com
SIC: 3599 Machine shop, jobbing & repair

(G-1722)
COYOTE ELECTRONICS INC
525 Logan Dr (76020-4859)
PHONE..................................817 485-3336
Paul Dewey Boggs, *CEO*
Richard Bibb, *Vice Pres*
Susan J Boggs, *Shareholder*
▲ **EMP:** 14
SQ FT: 5,000
SALES (est): 2.1MM **Privately Held**
SIC: 3613 3566 Control panels, electric; speed changers, drives & gears

(G-1723)
DEXTER BRAHMA LLC
Also Called: Kodiak Trailer Components
604 W Main St (76020-2910)
PHONE..................................817 284-5141
William Glidewell, *President*
Chuck Deegear, *General Mgr*
▲ **EMP:** 17
SALES (est): 2.9MM
SALES (corp-wide): 2.6B **Privately Held**
WEB: www.kodiaktrailer.com
HQ: Dexter Axle Company
2900 Industrial Pkwy
Elkhart IN 46516

(G-1724)
GMS STEEL MANUFACTURE LLC
230 S Cardinal Rd (76020)
PHONE..................................817 270-0447
Gustavo Salas, *President*
EMP: 9
SALES (corp-wide): 2MM **Privately Held**
WEB: www.gmssteel.com
SIC: 3441 Fabricated structural metal
PA: Gms Steel Manufacture, Llc
1250 E Highway 199 # 101
Springtown TX 76082
817 270-0447

(G-1725)
INTEGRATED MCHY SOLUTIONS LLC
Also Called: Team IMS
1500 Northwest Pkwy (76020-2706)
P.O. Box 2129 (76098-2129)
PHONE..................................877 693-7467
Rick Reeves, *Vice Pres*
Natasha Houston, *Human Resources*
Stephen Bond Jr, *Mng Member*
EMP: 55
SQ FT: 30,000
SALES (est): 18.8MM **Privately Held**
WEB: www.team-ims.com
SIC: 3536 Hoists, cranes & monorails

(G-1726)
LOCKHEED MARTIN CORPORATION
2109 Amon Ct (76020-5001)
PHONE..................................817 777-4242
Jeffrey Moore, *Manager*
Margie McInroe, *Admin Asst*
EMP: 430 **Publicly Held**
WEB: www.lockheedmartin.com
SIC: 3812 Search & navigation equipment
PA: Lockheed Martin Corporation
6801 Rockledge Dr
Bethesda MD 20817

(G-1727)
NORTH TEXAS INGREDIENTS INC
308 Commerce St Ste C (76020-2437)
PHONE..................................817 270-2397
Phillip Rodriguez, *President*
EMP: 14
SQ FT: 15,000
SALES (est): 1.7MM **Privately Held**
SIC: 2099 Seasonings & spices

(G-1728)
QUALITY TRAILER PRODUCTS LP (DH)
Also Called: Century Wheel & Rim
604 W Main St (76020-2910)
P.O. Box 1349 (76098-1349)
PHONE..................................817 444-4518
Chris Dietemann, *Partner*
Donald Stover, *Partner*
Brent Pope, *Vice Pres*
Van Massey, *Purch Mgr*
Jim Clagett, *Buyer*
◆ **EMP:** 100 **EST:** 1969
SQ FT: 52,000
SALES (est): 214MM
SALES (corp-wide): 2.6B **Privately Held**
WEB: www.rockwellamerican.com
SIC: 3714 5013 Motor vehicle parts & accessories; trailer parts & accessories

(G-1729)
SILVER CREEK MACHINE LTD
6216 Frank Christian Rd (76020-7303)
PHONE..................................817 238-0131
Greg Christian,
EMP: 15 **EST:** 2005
SQ FT: 10,000
SALES (est): 2.7MM **Privately Held**
WEB: www.silvercreekmachine.com
SIC: 3599 Machine shop, jobbing & repair

(G-1730)
TEXAS TURBINE INC
Also Called: TTI
624 Profit St (76020-2422)
P.O. Box 651 (76098-0651)
PHONE..................................817 444-5528
Claude Giroux, *President*
Ken Vega, *Vice Pres*
Mike Cantwell, *Engineer*
Victor Trinh, *Engineer*
Jan Giroux, *Treasurer*
▲ **EMP:** 31
SQ FT: 13,000
SALES (est): 7.3MM **Privately Held**
WEB: www.txturbine.com
SIC: 3569 3563 7699 Gas producers, generators & other gas related equipment; air & gas compressors; compressor repair

(G-1731)
TJ MACHINE & TOOL LTD
11220 S Fm 730 (76020-3054)
PHONE..................................817 444-5540
Michael Wright, *President*
Billie Wells, *Safety Mgr*
Ginger Moeller, *Controller*
David Wright, *Manager*
Shawn Tamjidi, *Info Tech Mgr*
▲ **EMP:** 68
SQ FT: 88,000
SALES (est): 13.5MM **Privately Held**
WEB: www.tjmachine.com
SIC: 3599 Machine shop, jobbing & repair

Bacliff
Galveston County

(G-1732)
HOFFMAN VENTURES INC
Also Called: Al's Millwork
4403 15th St (77518-2622)
PHONE..................................281 339-2812
Doug Hoffman, *President*
EMP: 12
SQ FT: 10,000
SALES (est): 1.8MM **Privately Held**
WEB: www.alsmillworks.com
SIC: 2431 Exterior & ornamental woodwork & trim

(G-1733)
INOUII ALLOY FABRICATION INC
1127 Jackson Ave (77518-2762)
P.O. Box 417, Texas City (77592-0417)
PHONE..................................713 894-6662
Vilma Giovanna Hutchison, *CEO*
Gary David Hutchison, *President*
EMP: 11
SQ FT: 2,400
SALES (est): 1.3MM **Privately Held**
WEB: www.inouiialloy.com
SIC: 3599 Machine shop, jobbing & repair

(G-1734)
LIBERTY TOWER & FLARE INC
4815 6th St (77518-1708)
PHONE..................................281 339-1410
Gary Alexander, *Branch Mgr*
EMP: 16
SALES (corp-wide): 4.7MM **Privately Held**
WEB: www.libertytower.net
SIC: 2899 Flares
HQ: Liberty Tower & Flare Inc.
4433 3rd St
Bacliff TX 77518
281 339-3743

Bagwell
Red River County

(G-1735)
FOWLER POST CO INC
309 Farm Road 2118 (75412-4013)
PHONE..................................903 966-2417
Wade Fowler, *President*
Erma F Fowler, *Corp Secy*
EMP: 9
SQ FT: 6,000
SALES (est): 1.4MM **Privately Held**
SIC: 2491 Preserving (creosoting) of wood

Baird
Callahan County

(G-1736)
TANK AND VESSEL BUILDERS LP
100 E Tp Ln (79504)
P.O. Box 1177 (79504-1177)
PHONE..................................325 854-8450
Bruce Kromer, *Partner*
Darryl Harris, *Partner*
Steve Ward, *QC Mgr*
EMP: 23
SQ FT: 25,000
SALES (est): 5.5MM **Privately Held**
WEB: www.tankandvesselbuilders.com
SIC: 3441 Fabricated structural metal

Balch Springs
Dallas County

(G-1737)
BINFORD FENCE SUPPLY LTD (PA)
2815 Hickory Tree Rd (75180-1619)
P.O. Box 800607 (75180-0607)
PHONE..................................972 286-2881
Steven B Stanley, *CEO*
Rick Istre, *Principal*
Glenn Petroff, *Opers Mgr*
Staci Bodiford, *Credit Mgr*
Scott Boyd, *Sales Staff*
EMP: 19
SQ FT: 2,160
SALES (est): 18.9MM **Privately Held**
WEB: www.binfordsupply.com
SIC: 5039 3446 Wire fence, gates & accessories; fences or posts, ornamental iron or steel

(G-1738)
PAL-SERV OF DALLAS LLC
2150 S Peachtree Rd (75180-1230)
PHONE..................................214 631-4600
Randy Foster, *Mng Member*
Steve Fraser,
EMP: 15
SQ FT: 100,000
SALES (est): 3.5MM **Privately Held**
WEB: www.pal-serv.com
SIC: 2448 Pallets, wood

Ballinger
Runnels County

(G-1739)
3D STEEL BUILDING SYSTEMS LLC
45 Pr 4592 (76821)
PHONE..................................325 365-5494
Juston Dankworth,
John Dankworth,
EMP: 20
SQ FT: 14,000
SALES (est): 4.7MM **Privately Held**
WEB: www.3dsteelbuildings.com
SIC: 3441 Fabricated structural metal

(G-1740)
DANKWORTH PACKING CO INC
Also Called: Texas Smoked Meats
1609 Eubank Ave (76821-2635)
P.O. Box 7265, San Antonio (78207-0265)
PHONE..................................325 365-3552
Mike Dankworth, *President*
Duane Geistmann, *Treasurer*
EMP: 48
SQ FT: 30,000
SALES (est): 6.4MM **Privately Held**
SIC: 2013 Sausages from purchased meat

(G-1741)
MUELLER SUPPLY COMPANY INC (PA)
1913 Hutchins Ave (76821-4401)
PHONE..................................325 365-3555
Morris B Davenport, *President*
Kay Browning, *COO*
Nyle T Davenport, *Vice Pres*
Justin Meyer, *Project Mgr*
Jessie Campolla, *Warehouse Mgr*
▲ **EMP:** 162 **EST:** 1936
SQ FT: 500,000
SALES (est): 180.3MM **Privately Held**
WEB: www.muellerinc.com
SIC: 3448 3496 5039 Prefabricated metal components; miscellaneous fabricated wire products; metal buildings

(G-1742)
ROUGH COUNTRY ACCESSORIES
1408 N 8th St (76821-3820)
PHONE..................................325 365-5258
Donald R Bowman, *Owner*
EMP: 15
SALES (est): 1.2MM **Privately Held**
SIC: 3714 Pickup truck bed liners

Bandera
Bandera County

(G-1743)
CITY OF BANDERA
548 State Highway 16 S (78003-3808)
PHONE..................................830 796-3401
John Clark, *Branch Mgr*
EMP: 9

SALES (corp-wide): 1.7MM **Privately Held**
WEB: www.cityofbandera.org
SIC: **3589** Water treatment equipment, industrial
PA: City Of Bandera
511 Main St
Bandera TX 78003
830 460-7170

(G-1744)
ROGER D STEVENS CONTRACTOR
Also Called: Bandera Rock and Road
587 Fm 3240 (78003-5219)
P.O. Box 2869 (78003-2869)
PHONE..........................830 796-3714
Evert H Mc Dougal Jr, *President*
Stevens Michael, *Vice Pres*
EMP: 18 EST: 1956
SQ FT: 3,600
SALES (est): 2.2MM
SALES (corp-wide): 8.8MM **Privately Held**
WEB: www.banderacounty.org
SIC: **3273 1794** Ready-mixed concrete; excavation & grading, building construction
PA: M & P Construction Co.
554 Se 6th St
Crane TX
432 558-3564

Barker
Harris County

(G-1745)
CRAIG BAKER MARBLE CO INC
Also Called: C B M B I
1918 Baker Rd (77413)
P.O. Box 104 (77413-0104)
PHONE..........................281 492-2365
Craig Baker, *President*
D Bruce Baker, *Vice Pres*
▲ EMP: 60
SALES (est): 6.9MM **Privately Held**
WEB: www.iwantgranite.com
SIC: **3281** Marble, building: cut & shaped

(G-1746)
DIAMOND OFFSHORE FINANCE CO (DH)
15415 Katy Fwy Ste 100 (77413)
P.O. Box 4558, Houston (77210-4558)
PHONE..........................281 492-5300
Lawrence Dickerson, *President*
EMP: 300
SALES (est): 586.8MM
SALES (corp-wide): 12.5B **Publicly Held**
WEB: www.diamondoffshore.com
SIC: **1381** Drilling oil & gas wells

Bartonville
Denton County

(G-1747)
TRACK WHAT MATTERS LLC
2652 Fm 407 E Ste 215 (76226-7024)
PHONE..........................817 430-9201
Holyn Bradford, *Mng Member*
Steven Van O' Oyen, *Mng Member*
EMP: 12
SQ FT: 3,000
SALES (est): 150K **Privately Held**
WEB: www.trackwhatmatters.com
SIC: **3949** Track & field athletic equipment

Bastrop
Bastrop County

(G-1748)
ACCURATE ELASTOMER PDTS INC (PA)
Also Called: Manufacturer
769 N State Highway 95 (78602-7654)
PHONE..........................512 285-4585
Doug Wade, *President*
Joe Martinez, *Opers Mgr*
Marcel Smith, *Manager*

Marybeth Prete, *Executive*
EMP: 52
SQ FT: 80,000
SALES (est): 5.2MM **Privately Held**
WEB: www.accurateelastomer.com
SIC: **3069** Molded rubber products; brake linings, rubber

(G-1749)
BASTROP SCALE COMPANY INC (PA)
192 Harmon Rd (78602-5697)
P.O. Box 2100 (78602-9100)
PHONE..........................512 321-3443
Brian Darilek, *President*
EMP: 18
SQ FT: 3,400
SALES (est): 450K **Privately Held**
WEB: www.bastropscale.com
SIC: **3545 5046** Scales, measuring (machinists' precision tools); scales, except laboratory

(G-1750)
CHILL KING
115 Modock Dr (78602-6858)
PHONE..........................512 303-1529
Pat King, *Owner*
EMP: 20 EST: 2008
SALES (est): 3.3MM **Privately Held**
WEB: www.chillking.com
SIC: **3632** Household refrigerators & freezers

(G-1751)
COOK SALES INC
Also Called: Cook Portable Warehouse
1398 State Highway 95 (78602-2631)
PHONE..........................512 321-2888
William Mugno, *Principal*
EMP: 30
SALES (corp-wide): 17.4MM **Privately Held**
WEB: www.cookstuff.com
SIC: **2452** Prefabricated wood buildings
PA: Cook Sales, Inc.
3455 Old Highway 51 N
Cobden IL 62920
618 893-2114

(G-1752)
CREATIVE STONE INC
140 Watterson Rd (78602-3449)
PHONE..........................512 303-7866
Scott Halbert, *President*
Chuck Halbert, *Vice Pres*
Glenda Halbert, *Admin Sec*
EMP: 22
SALES (est): 2.5MM **Privately Held**
WEB: www.creativestoneinc.com
SIC: **3272** Concrete products, precast

(G-1753)
DARLING INGREDIENTS INC
Also Called: Darling International
264 Fm 2336 (78602-3618)
PHONE..........................512 303-2571
EMP: 11
SALES (corp-wide): 3.3B **Publicly Held**
WEB: www.darlingii.com
SIC: **2077** Animal & marine fats & oils
PA: Darling Ingredients Inc.
5601 N Macarthur Blvd
Irving TX 75038
972 717-0300

(G-1754)
DAVID BACON INCORPORATED
445 Fm 20 (78602-3776)
PHONE..........................512 321-2323
David Backon, *President*
EMP: 12
SALES (est): 2.2MM **Privately Held**
WEB: www.dbiequipment.com
SIC: **2899** Flares

(G-1755)
DEEP IN HEART ART FOUNDRY
405 S Jackson St (78602-4303)
PHONE..........................512 321-7868
Clint Howard, *CEO*
Liz Nelson, *Purchasing*
Mike Zingleman, *CFO*
EMP: 40
SQ FT: 6,000

SALES (est): 9.3MM **Privately Held**
WEB: www.deepintheheart.net
SIC: **3366** Castings (except die): bronze

(G-1756)
DESIGNED SECURITY INC
Also Called: DSI
1402 Hawthorne St (78602-2654)
PHONE..........................512 321-4426
Philip N Haselton, *Ch of Bd*
John H Blodgett, *President*
Matt Hamborsky, *Buyer*
Virginia Morales, *Controller*
EMP: 30
SQ FT: 12,000
SALES (est): 5.1MM
SALES (corp-wide): 16.1MM **Privately Held**
WEB: www.dsigo.com
SIC: **3699 1731** Security control equipment & systems; electrical work
PA: Detex Corporation
302 Detex Dr
New Braunfels TX 78130
800 729-3839

(G-1757)
FEDERAL PRISON INDUSTRIES
Also Called: Unicor
1341 State Highway 95 (78602-2630)
P.O. Box 730 (78602-0730)
PHONE..........................512 321-3903
Brad Beus, *Superintendent*
EMP: 300 **Publicly Held**
WEB: www.bop.gov
SIC: **2353 9223** Hats, caps & millinery; correctional institutions
HQ: Federal Prison Industries, Inc
320 1st St Nw
Washington DC 20534

(G-1758)
HUNTINGTON FOAM LLC
Also Called: Huntington Solutions
1278 Highway 71 W (78602-3118)
PHONE..........................512 581-7500
Thomas Forrest, *Manager*
EMP: 22
SALES (corp-wide): 9MM **Privately Held**
WEB: www.hunt-sol.com
SIC: **3086** Packaging & shipping materials, foamed plastic
HQ: Huntington Foam, Llc
125 Caliber Ridge Dr # 200
Greer SC 29651

(G-1759)
MUELLER SUPPLY COMPANY INC
1455 Highway 71 W (78602-3116)
PHONE..........................512 308-9173
Greg Morris, *Branch Mgr*
EMP: 60
SALES (corp-wide): 180.3MM **Privately Held**
WEB: www.muellerinc.com
SIC: **3448** Prefabricated metal components
PA: Mueller Supply Company, Inc.
1913 Hutchins Ave
Ballinger TX 76821
325 365-3555

(G-1760)
MURPHY USA INC
490 Agnes St (78602-3739)
PHONE..........................512 332-0622
EMP: 11 **Publicly Held**
WEB: www.murphyusa.com
SIC: **5541 2911** Filling stations, gasoline; petroleum refining
PA: Murphy Usa Inc.
200 E Peach St
El Dorado AR 71730

(G-1761)
SWIFTEX MANUFACTURING CORP
Hwy 71 (78602)
P.O. Box Bb (78602-1963)
PHONE..........................512 321-2574
Sharon Warfield Wilkes, *President*
EMP: 10 EST: 1957
SALES (est): 1.3MM **Privately Held**
WEB: www.swiftexfurniture.com
SIC: **2512** Living room furniture: upholstered on wood frames

(G-1762)
TEXAS AGGREGATES LP
420 Old Perkins Rd (78602)
P.O. Box Mm (78602-1984)
PHONE..........................512 303-4215
Ken Meyer, *Partner*
Melvin R Klatt, *Partner*
Ronnie Klatt, *Partner*
Jack Wheeler, *Partner*
EMP: 19
SALES (est): 4.8MM **Privately Held**
WEB: www.laurenconcrete.com
SIC: **3273** Ready-mixed concrete

(G-1763)
TEXAS FOAM INC
1278 Highway 71 W (78602-3118)
PHONE..........................512 581-7500
Thomas Forrest, *President*
Kirt Groat, *Vice Pres*
Darcia Boyd, *Info Tech Mgr*
Cindi Boyd, *Admin Asst*
▲ EMP: 22
SQ FT: 20,000
SALES (est): 4MM **Privately Held**
WEB: www.texasfoam.com
SIC: **3086** Packaging & shipping materials, foamed plastic

(G-1764)
TRIPP RESEARCH INC
529 Kelley Rd (78602-5696)
P.O. Box 2240 (78602-9240)
PHONE..........................512 321-9445
Virgil P Tripp, *President*
Sherida G Tripp, *Corp Secy*
EMP: 12
SQ FT: 7,000
SALES (est): 1.1MM **Privately Held**
WEB: www.trippresearchinc.com
SIC: **2389** Men's miscellaneous accessories

(G-1765)
WATER STREET MILLWORKS INC
910 Water St B (78602-3834)
PHONE..........................512 321-5741
Robert Hunt, *President*
Jane Hunt, *Admin Sec*
EMP: 9 EST: 1973
SQ FT: 7,000
SALES (est): 1.2MM **Privately Held**
SIC: **5712 2431** Cabinet work, custom; millwork

Batson
Hardin County

(G-1766)
BATSON LUMBER COMPANY LLC
25960 Hwy 770 S (77519)
P.O. Box 444 (77519-0444)
PHONE..........................936 262-8000
Linda Pipps, *Sales Staff*
Troy Grice,
Carol Griswold, *Admin Asst*
David Stetson,
Charles Verhelen,
EMP: 50
SQ FT: 50,000
SALES (est): 6.5MM **Privately Held**
WEB: www.batsonlumber.com
SIC: **2411** Timber, cut at logging camp; wood chips, produced in the field

Bay City
Matagorda County

(G-1767)
ALAMO CONCRETE PRODUCTS LTD
Plant 76 End Of Clmbus Rd (77414)
P.O. Box 168 (77404-0168)
PHONE..........................979 245-8365
Armando Garcia, *Manager*
EMP: 19 **Privately Held**
SIC: **3273** Ready-mixed concrete

PA: Alamo Concrete Products, Ltd.
6055 W Green Mountain Rd
Austin TX 78744

(G-1768)
BAY CITY TRIBUNE
Also Called: Daily Tribune
2901 Carey Smith Blvd (77414-3768)
P.O. Box 2450 (77404-2450)
PHONE..................................979 245-2920
Angela Pageo, *President*
Shelley Gormey, *Manager*
EMP: 13 EST: 1958
SALES (est): 830.8K
SALES (corp-wide): 140.3MM **Privately Held**
WEB: www.baycitysentinel.com
SIC: 2711 Commercial printing & newspaper publishing combined; newspapers, publishing & printing
PA: Southern Newspapers, Inc.
5701 Woodway Dr Ste 131
Houston TX 77057
713 266-5481

(G-1769)
BU GROWERS LTD
1800 Avenue E (77414-3950)
P.O. Box 453 (77404-0453)
PHONE..................................979 245-2043
Joe M Crane, *General Ptnr*
Joe Crane, *General Ptnr*
EMP: 25
SALES (est): 6.3MM **Privately Held**
WEB: www.bugrowers.com
SIC: 2044 Rice milling

(G-1770)
CELANESE AMERICAS LLC
2001 Fm 3057 (77414-2968)
P.O. Box 509 (77404-0509)
PHONE..................................979 241-4000
Don Berthelot, *Production*
Nause Reiner, *Branch Mgr*
Rudy Trevino, *Manager*
Marcus Rubio, *Supervisor*
Matt McCall, *Director*
EMP: 36
SALES (corp-wide): 5.6B **Publicly Held**
WEB: www.celanese.com
SIC: 2819 Industrial inorganic chemicals
HQ: Celanese Americas Llc
222 Colinas Blvd W # 900
Irving TX 75039
972 443-4000

(G-1771)
CHEMICALS INCORPORATED
8055 State Highway 60 S (77414-3283)
P.O. Box 8010, Baytown (77522-8010)
PHONE..................................979 244-0100
Ashok Moza, *CEO*
EMP: 50
SALES (corp-wide): 22.8MM **Privately Held**
WEB: www.chemicalsinc.com
SIC: 2869 Industrial organic chemicals
PA: Chemicals Incorporated
12321 Hatcherville Rd
Baytown TX 77521
281 576-5000

(G-1772)
EOG RESOURCES INC
3211 Avenue F (77414-7105)
PHONE..................................979 245-2201
EMP: 37
SALES (corp-wide): 18B **Publicly Held**
SIC: 1311 Crude Petroleum/Natural Gas Production
PA: Eog Resources, Inc.
1111 Bagby St Lbby 2
Houston TX 77002
713 651-7000

(G-1773)
HENDERSON FABRICATION INC
3107 Nichols Ave (77414-7386)
P.O. Box 659 (77404-0659)
PHONE..................................979 245-5350
Lloyd Henderson, *President*
Theresa Henderson, *Admin Sec*
EMP: 30
SQ FT: 22,000

SALES: 10.6MM **Privately Held**
WEB: www.hendersonfabrication.com
SIC: 3441 Building components, structural steel

(G-1774)
LYONDELL CHEMICAL COMPANY
U.S Hwy 60 13 Mi S Of (77414)
P.O. Box 2100 (77404-2100)
PHONE..................................979 245-1225
EMP: 79 **Privately Held**
SIC: 2869 2821 Mfg Industrial Organic Chemicals Mfg Plastic Materials/Resins
HQ: Lyondell Chemical Company
Lyondell Bas Twr Ste 700
Houston TX 77010
713 309-7200

(G-1775)
NEWPARK MATS INTGRTED SVCS LLC
Also Called: Newpark Drilling
Hwy 35 W (77414)
P.O. Box 1192 (77404-1192)
PHONE..................................979 245-3894
Pom Joines, *Manager*
EMP: 55
SALES (corp-wide): 747.7MM **Publicly Held**
WEB: www.newpark.com
SIC: 1389 1382 Oil field services; oil & gas exploration services
HQ: Newpark Mats & Integrated Services Llc
9320 Lkeside Blvd Ste 100
The Woodlands TX 77381
281 362-6800

(G-1776)
OQ CHEMICALS CORPORATION
2001 Fm 3057 (77414-2968)
P.O. Box 1141 (77404-1141)
PHONE..................................972 481-2771
Cristobal Ascencio, *Vice Pres*
Fred Gaytan, *Plant Mgr*
Charles Saverline, *Project Mgr*
Mark Tyler, *Purch Mgr*
Thomas Roye, *Purchasing*
EMP: 112
SALES (corp-wide): 1.3B **Privately Held**
WEB: www.chemicals.oq.com
SIC: 2869 Industrial organic chemicals
HQ: Oq Chemicals Corporation
15375 Memorial Dr
Houston TX 77079

(G-1777)
WILLIAMS FIELD SERVICES CO LLC
2200 Avenue A (77414-4935)
PHONE..................................979 843-7724
Dan Byrne, *Regional Mgr*
EMP: 40
SALES (corp-wide): 8.2B **Publicly Held**
WEB: www.williams.com
SIC: 1311 Crude petroleum & natural gas production
HQ: Williams Field Services Company, Llc
1 Williams Ctr
Tulsa OK 74172

Baytown
Chambers County

(G-1778)
ANT ENTERPRISES INCORPORATED
8602 Tri City Beach Rd (77523-9254)
P.O. Box 24128, Houston (77229-4128)
PHONE..................................281 456-7446
Anthony J Torres, *President*
Susan Arnold, *CFO*
EMP: 55 EST: 1999
SQ FT: 3,500
SALES (est): 5.5MM **Privately Held**
SIC: 3273 Ready-mixed concrete

(G-1779)
ARMOR INDUSTRIAL FABRICATORS
11344 Interstate 10 E (77523-0884)
P.O. Box 1834 (77522-1834)
PHONE..................................281 573-2777
David Snell, *President*
Kevin Parent, *Info Tech Mgr*
EMP: 20 EST: 2011
SALES (est): 1.5MM **Privately Held**
WEB: www.armorfab.com
SIC: 3441 2399 Fabricated structural metal; emblems, badges & insignia

(G-1780)
BORUSAN MANNESMANN PIPE US INC
4949 Borusan Rd (77523-3700)
PHONE..................................832 399-6000
Akin Eren, *QC Mgr*
Buddy Burr, *Branch Mgr*
EMP: 21 **Privately Held**
WEB: www.borusan.com
SIC: 3494 Pipe fittings
HQ: Borusan Mannesmann Pipe U.S., Inc.
363 N Sam H Pkwy E Ste 63
Houston TX 77060
832 399-6000

(G-1781)
CLARK MACHINE INC
6650 W Bay Rd (77523-8622)
PHONE..................................281 303-8698
Leon Clark, *President*
EMP: 14
SQ FT: 8,000
SALES (est): 2.2MM **Privately Held**
WEB: www.clark-machine.com
SIC: 3599 Machine shop, jobbing & repair

(G-1782)
COVESTRO LLC
8500 W Bay Rd (77523-8727)
PHONE..................................281 383-6000
Darlene Beecher, *General Mgr*
Jerry Klink, *Superintendent*
Dave Rzepecki, *Counsel*
Julia Rubino, *Vice Pres*
Herman Campbell, *Opers Mgr*
EMP: 500
SALES (corp-wide): 13.7B **Privately Held**
WEB: www.covestro.us
SIC: 2822 2821 Synthetic rubber; plastics materials & resins
HQ: Covestro Llc
1 Covestro Cir
Pittsburgh PA 15205
866 540-0753

(G-1783)
DIETRICH INDUSTRIES INC
4200 Cedar Blvd (77523-9604)
PHONE..................................281 383-1617
Mark Adams, *Manager*
EMP: 45
SALES (corp-wide): 3B **Publicly Held**
WEB: www.worthingtonindustries.com
SIC: 3441 Fabricated structural metal
HQ: Dietrich Industries, Inc.
200 W Old Wlson Bridge Rd
Worthington OH 43085
800 873-2604

(G-1784)
DOME PETROCHEMICAL LC
6655 W Bay Rd (77523-8615)
PHONE..................................713 540-9075
Rodman A Eggen, *Mng Member*
EMP: 15
SALES (est): 1.5MM **Privately Held**
SIC: 2899 Chemical preparations

(G-1785)
DUNA USA INC (DH)
4210 Fm 1405 Rd (77523-9736)
PHONE..................................281 383-3862
Andrea Benebetti, *CEO*
Andrea Benedetti, *CEO*
Giuliano Caselli, *Division Mgr*
Franco Sala, *Engineer*
Brad Burnett, *Sales Staff*
▲ EMP: 25
SQ FT: 19,000

SALES (est): 14.6MM
SALES (corp-wide): 26.2K **Privately Held**
WEB: www.dunagroup.com
SIC: 5199 3999 Foams & rubber; atomizers, toiletry
HQ: Duna Corradini Spa
Via Modena Carpi 388
Soliera MO 41019
059 565-403

(G-1786)
EL DORADO NITROGEN LP
8490 W Bay Rd (77523)
P.O. Box 2469 (77522-2469)
PHONE..................................281 383-1807
Anne Rendon, *Partner*
▲ EMP: 19 EST: 1996
SALES (est): 13MM
SALES (corp-wide): 365MM **Publicly Held**
SIC: 2873 Nitric acid
PA: Lsb Industries, Inc.
3503 Nw 63rd St Ste 500
Oklahoma City OK 73116
405 235-4546

(G-1787)
FLOMIN INC
Also Called: Snf Flomin
7500 Fm 1405 Rd (77523-8772)
P.O. Box 250, Riceboro GA (31323-0250)
PHONE..................................281 573-6401
EMP: 12 **Privately Held**
SIC: 2899 Mfg Chemical Preparations
HQ: Flomin Inc.
1 Chemical Plant Rd
Riceboro GA 31323

(G-1788)
GREIF INC
233 Delta Pkwy (77523-2002)
PHONE..................................281 573-6380
Siva Sambasivam, *Branch Mgr*
▲ EMP: 10
SALES (corp-wide): 4.5B **Publicly Held**
WEB: www.deltacogroup.com
SIC: 2655 Fiber cans, drums & similar products
PA: Greif, Inc.
425 Winter Rd
Delaware OH 43015
740 549-6000

(G-1789)
GREIF INC
616b Logistics Dr (77523-4530)
PHONE..................................346 263-2639
Peter G Watson, *President*
EMP: 12
SALES (corp-wide): 4.5B **Publicly Held**
WEB: www.deltacogroup.com
SIC: 2671 Packaging paper & plastics film, coated & laminated
PA: Greif, Inc.
425 Winter Rd
Delaware OH 43015
740 549-6000

(G-1790)
HALLIBURTON COMPANY
4000 Cedar Blvd (77523-8616)
PHONE..................................713 455-9547
Danny Fleming, *Manager*
EMP: 20 **Publicly Held**
WEB: www.halliburton.com
SIC: 1389 Oil field services
PA: Halliburton Company
3000 N Sam Houston Pkwy E
Houston TX 77032

(G-1791)
HUNTING ENERGY SERVICES INC
555 Transport Dr (77523-5033)
PHONE..................................832 902-2266
Bradley Matejcek, *Branch Mgr*
EMP: 30
SALES (corp-wide): 960MM **Privately Held**
WEB: www.hunting-intl.com
SIC: 1389 Oil field services
HQ: Hunting Energy Services, Llc
16825 Northchase Dr # 600
Houston TX 77060

G E O G R A P H I C

GEOGRAPHIC

(G-1792)
IGI THE INTL GROUP INC
7106 N Highway 146 (77523-9523)
PHONE....................281 573-9280
Molly Barnes, *Purch Mgr*
Larry Elrod, *Executive*
EMP: 40
SALES (corp-wide): 419.3K **Privately Held**
WEB: www.igiwax.com
SIC: 2821 2891 Polypropylene resins; adhesives & sealants
HQ: Igi The International Group, Inc.
   1007 E Spring St
   Titusville PA 16354
   814 827-3609

(G-1793)
JINDAL SAW USA LLC (HQ)
1411 S Fm 565 Rd (77523-9054)
PHONE....................281 573-3002
Kamal Singh, *General Mgr*
Kamaljit Singh, *General Mgr*
Dhiraj More, *Engineer*
Kamal Jit Singh, *Mng Member*
◆ **EMP:** 22
SQ FT: 5,000
SALES (est): 15.3MM **Privately Held**
WEB: www.jindalsawusa.net
SIC: 3317 Steel pipe & tubes

(G-1794)
JSW STEEL (USA) INC
Also Called: J S W
5200 E Mckinney Rd # 110 (77523-8291)
PHONE....................281 383-2525
Mark Bush, *CEO*
John G Hritz, *President*
Wes Hendricks, *Division Mgr*
Charles Bartholomew, *Vice Pres*
Jason Jamieson, *Vice Pres*
◆ **EMP:** 696
SQ FT: 2,301,362
SALES (est): 293.7MM **Privately Held**
WEB: www.jswsteel.us
SIC: 3317 3312 Steel pipe & tubes; blast furnaces & steel mills; tubes, steel & iron
HQ: Jsw Steel Holding (Usa) Inc.
   5200 E Mckinney Rd
   Baytown TX 77523
   281 383-2525

(G-1795)
LANXESS CORPORATION
8500 W Bay Rd (77523-8727)
PHONE....................281 383-7761
Gerrald John, *Branch Mgr*
Marek Moraczewski, *Technology*
Scott Hebert, *Technician*
EMP: 25
SALES (corp-wide): 7.5B **Privately Held**
WEB: www.lanxess.us
SIC: 2869 2819 Industrial organic chemicals; industrial inorganic chemicals
HQ: Lanxess Corporation
   111 Ridc Park West Dr
   Pittsburgh PA 15275
   412 809-1000

(G-1796)
LS ENERGY FABRICATION LLC (PA)
Also Called: Lonestar Energy Fabrication
2050 Fm 1405 Rd (77523-0992)
PHONE....................281 573-9500
Darryl A Schroeder, *CEO*
Brian Shanklin, *President*
Thomas Desormeaux, *Business Mgr*
Mario Salinas, *Vice Pres*
Patrick McCoy, *Project Mgr*
EMP: 100
SALES (est): 45.2MM **Privately Held**
WEB: www.lsenergyfabrication.com
SIC: 3533 Oil & gas drilling rigs & equipment

(G-1797)
MITCHELL WELL SERVICE INC (PA)
Also Called: Mitchell Industries
15555 Interstate 10 E (77523-9093)
PHONE....................281 576-5007
Mark Mitchell, *President*
Chase Mitchell, *General Mgr*
Naymon Walters, *Opers Mgr*

▲ **EMP:** 24
SQ FT: 1,066
SALES (est): 4.9MM **Privately Held**
WEB: www.mitchellind.com
SIC: 1389 5051 Servicing oil & gas wells; wire screening

(G-1798)
PASADENA TANK CORPORATION
1301 Transport Dr (77523-5903)
PHONE....................281 457-3996
Robert Block Sr, *President*
Bob Easter, *General Mgr*
Yvonne Martinez, *Human Res Mgr*
Kelsey Dedmon, *Manager*
John Mason, *Maintence Staff*
▲ **EMP:** 140 **EST:** 1976
SALES (est): 42.4MM
SALES (corp-wide): 113MM **Privately Held**
WEB: www.ptctanks.com
SIC: 3443 7699 Tanks, standard or custom fabricated: metal plate; vessels, process or storage (from boiler shops): metal plate; tank repair
PA: Hmt Llc
   19241 David Memorial Dr # 150
   Shenandoah TX 77385
   281 681-7000

(G-1799)
PBP INC
Also Called: Plastic Bagging & Packaging
5151 E Grand Pkwy S (77523-5107)
P.O. Box 2583 (77522-2583)
PHONE....................832 902-2231
Hugo L Dell'oglio, *CEO*
Daniela Dell'oglio, *Vice Pres*
Darcy Dell'oglio, *Vice Pres*
Darly Dell'oglio, *Vice Pres*
Claudia C Dell'oglio, *VP Opers*
EMP: 45 **EST:** 2014
SQ FT: 312,000
SALES (est): 12MM **Privately Held**
WEB: www.pbpcorp.com
SIC: 3086 5999 Packaging & shipping materials, foamed plastic; packaging materials: boxes, padding, etc.

(G-1800)
SAMSON CONTROLS INC (HQ)
Also Called: Samson Project Engineering
4111 Cedar Blvd (77523-8588)
PHONE....................281 383-3677
Boguslaw Urbanowicz, *President*
Richard Judd, *Regional Mgr*
David Scott, *Regional Mgr*
Robert Sidler, *Vice Pres*
Joe Ferraro, *Opers Mgr*
▲ **EMP:** 14
SALES (est): 13.8MM
SALES (corp-wide): 735.1MM **Privately Held**
WEB: www.samsoncontrols.com
SIC: 5085 5084 3491 Valves & fittings; industrial machinery & equipment; process control regulator valves
PA: Samson Ag
   Weismullerstr. 3
   Frankfurt Am Main 60314
   694 009-0

(G-1801)
SEAPAC INC
4000 Cedar Blvd (77523-8616)
P.O. Box 1728 (77522-1728)
PHONE....................281 383-2400
Mark Kramer, *Manager*
EMP: 80
SALES (corp-wide): 5.7MM **Privately Held**
WEB: www.seapac-inc.com
SIC: 7389 2899 Packaging & labeling services; chemical preparations
PA: Seapac, Inc.
   502 Bear Creek Rd E Ofc
   Tuscaloosa AL 35405
   205 759-1290

(G-1802)
SONIC SURVEYS LTD
10601 Langston Dr (77523-8991)
P.O. Box 719, Mont Belvieu (77580-0719)
PHONE....................281 385-6500
Ron Hicks, *President*

EMP: 10
SQ FT: 7,200
SALES (est): 2.5MM **Privately Held**
SIC: 3533 1389 Oil field machinery & equipment; well logging

(G-1803)
TAYLOR-WHARTON AMERICA INC
1411 Transport Dr (77523-5905)
PHONE....................281 738-2863
Tim Miller, *President*
Hector Villarreal, *Exec VP*
Chris Catania, *Vice Pres*
EMP: 84
SQ FT: 44,000
SALES (est): 30MM **Privately Held**
WEB: www.twcryo.com
SIC: 3559 Cryogenic machinery, industrial

(G-1804)
UNITED SALT BAYTOWN LLC
7901 Fm 1405 Rd (77523-8632)
PHONE....................281 303-1101
Thomas Ellis, *Technical Mgr*
Karen Berwick, *Office Mgr*
Dennis Bradley, *Manager*
Mike Reed, *Maintence Staff*
EMP: 37
SALES (corp-wide): 247.1MM **Privately Held**
WEB: www.unitedsalt.com
SIC: 1479 Rock salt mining
HQ: United Salt Baytown Llc
   4800 San Felipe St # 100
   Houston TX 77056
   713 877-2600

(G-1805)
WEST TEXAS DRUM COMPANY LTD II
8950 Fm 1405 Rd (77523-8665)
PHONE....................281 383-1901
Charles R Ridge, *President*
EMP: 41
SALES (est): 14MM **Privately Held**
WEB: www.westtexasdrum.net
SIC: 5085 3089 Commercial containers; plastic containers, except foam

Baytown
Harris County

(G-1806)
A & M MACHINE & WLDG WORKS INC
7108 East Fwy (77521-9503)
P.O. Box 1243 (77522-1243)
PHONE....................281 421-1281
Carl E Morris Jr, *President*
Raymond Quinones, *Owner*
Clarice Morris, *Treasurer*
EMP: 9 **EST:** 1959
SQ FT: 8,400
SALES (est): 1.4MM **Privately Held**
WEB: www.aandmmachineweld.com
SIC: 3599 7692 Machine shop, jobbing & repair; welding repair

(G-1807)
ALL AMERICAN FILTERS INC
5334 East Rd (77521-9004)
P.O. Box 1367 (77522-1367)
PHONE....................281 421-1909
Jim Reynolds, *President*
Ramoni Reynolds, *Vice Pres*
EMP: 10
SALES (est): 1.3MM **Privately Held**
SIC: 3569 Filters, general line: industrial

(G-1808)
BBB TANK SERVICES LLC
162 Independence Pkwy N (77520-1033)
PHONE....................832 695-2132
Robert E Swain, *President*
Dewayne Benavides, *Superintendent*
Mike Files, *Area Mgr*
Roy Dennis, *Vice Pres*
John Wells, *Opers Staff*
EMP: 108
SQ FT: 6,000

SALES (est): 33.2MM **Privately Held**
WEB: www.bbbtankservices.com
SIC: 1389 Lease tanks, oil field: erecting, cleaning & repairing

(G-1809)
BEMIS SHEET METAL INC
1207 S Airhart Dr (77520-4103)
PHONE....................281 427-1538
Ralph Ugalde, *President*
David Salinas, *Vice Pres*
Robert Salinas, *CFO*
EMP: 9
SQ FT: 11,000
SALES (est): 1.4MM **Privately Held**
WEB: www.bemissheetmetal.com
SIC: 3444 Sheet metalwork

(G-1810)
CAMPBELL CONCRETE & MTLS LP
4704 W Cedar Bayou Lynchb (77521)
PHONE....................281 424-5650
Robert Wiggims, *Manager*
EMP: 18
SALES (corp-wide): 20.8B **Privately Held**
WEB: www.michaeljames.com
SIC: 3273 Ready-mixed concrete
HQ: Campbell Concrete & Materials, L.P.
   16155 Park Row Ste 120
   Houston TX 77084
   281 592-5201

(G-1811)
CENTURY ASPHALT LTD
4008 N Highway 146 (77520)
PHONE....................281 421-2621
Philip King, *Manager*
EMP: 15 **Privately Held**
WEB: www.centuryasphalt.com
SIC: 2951 Asphalt paving mixtures & blocks
PA: Century Asphalt, Ltd.
   5303 Navigation Blvd
   Houston TX 77011

(G-1812)
CERTIFIED PIPE SVC HOUSTON INC
Also Called: CPS Houston
6225 Fm 1942 Rd (77521-9471)
PHONE....................281 457-2454
Travis Badeaux, *Branch Mgr*
Ragena Graham, *Manager*
EMP: 25
SALES (corp-wide): 21.9MM **Privately Held**
WEB: www.cpshouston.net
SIC: 3441 4225 Fabricated structural metal; general warehousing & storage
PA: Certified Pipe Service Houston, Inc.
   301 Sheldon Rd
   Channelview TX 77530
   281 457-2454

(G-1813)
CHEMICALS INCORPORATED (PA)
12321 Hatcherville Rd (77521-7700)
PHONE....................281 576-5000
Ashok Moza, *President*
Tina Goetschius, *Senior VP*
Stephen Rohde, *Vice Pres*
Indra Bhopale, *Mfg Staff*
Robin McIntosh, *Office Mgr*
▼ **EMP:** 75
SQ FT: 25,000
SALES (est): 22.8MM **Privately Held**
WEB: www.chemicalsinc.com
SIC: 2834 2869 2899 Pharmaceutical preparations; industrial organic chemicals; industrial inorganic chemicals; chemical preparations; flavoring extracts & syrups

(G-1814)
CHEVRON PHILLIPS CHEM CO LP
Chemical-Olefins
9500 I 10 East Exit 796 (77521)
PHONE....................281 421-6500
Thomas Fisseler, *Superintendent*
Jeffrey Gates, *Superintendent*
Van Long, *Plant Mgr*
Chris Oehler, *Project Mgr*

▲ = Import ▼=Export
◆ =Import/Export

Janie Nguyen, *Opers Staff*
EMP: 600
SALES (corp-wide): 3.5B **Privately Held**
WEB: www.cpchem.com
SIC: 2821 2899 Polyethylene resins;
chemical preparations
HQ: Chevron Phillips Chemical Company
Lp
10001 Six Pines Dr
The Woodlands TX 77380
832 813-4100

(G-1815)
DEER PARK CNSTR ASSOC INC
5300 Barkaloo Rd (77521-9253)
P.O. Box 128, Deer Park (77536-0128)
PHONE................................281 839-0020
Joe L Koch Jr, *President*
Chris Gentry, *Vice Pres*
Pete Taylor, *Manager*
Joe Koch III, *Executive*
EMP: 35
SQ FT: 4,000
SALES (est): 6MM **Privately Held**
WEB: www.dpcindustrial.com
SIC: 1541 1389 Prefabricated building
erection, industrial; construction, repair &
dismantling services

(G-1816)
**ELECTROMAGNETIC
INDUSTRIES LLC**
1507 Beaumont Rd (77520-3103)
P.O. Box 1066 (77522-1066)
PHONE................................281 422-5225
Christopher J Lahowetz, *President*
Mark Jennings, *Manager*
Ann Lahowetz, *Manager*
Jacqulyn Champlin, *Assistant*
▲ **EMP:** 26
SQ FT: 15,000
SALES (est): 3.8MM **Privately Held**
WEB: www.electromagnetic.biz
SIC: 3612 Instrument transformers (except
portable)

(G-1817)
**EXXONMOBIL CHEMICAL
COMPANY**
Also Called: Baytown Tech & Engg Complex
5200 Bayway Dr (77520-2100)
P.O. Box 5200 (77522-5200)
PHONE................................281 834-5200
Jeffrey Brinen, *Research*
LI Ding, *Research*
Jose Vargas, *Research*
G Bindi, *Manager*
Larry Hjelle, *Research Analys*
EMP: 680
SALES (corp-wide): 264.9B **Publicly
Held**
WEB: www.exxonmobilchemical.com
SIC: 2821 Plastics materials & resins
HQ: Exxonmobil Chemical Company
22777 Sprngwoods Vlg Pkwy
Spring TX 77389
800 243-9966

(G-1818)
**GENERAL POLYMER SERVICES
LLC (PA)**
4724 Decker Dr (77520-1416)
PHONE................................281 424-4673
Davide Danese, *Branch Mgr*
Reynaldo Barrera, *Administration*
Russell Foreman,
EMP: 30 **EST:** 2012
SQ FT: 20,000
SALES (est): 4MM **Privately Held**
WEB: www.polymerservices.com
SIC: 2822 Ethylene-propylene rubbers,
EPDM polymers

(G-1819)
**GENERAL POLYMER SERVICES
LLC**
5110 Decker Dr (77520-1440)
PHONE................................281 424-4673
David Danefe, *Branch Mgr*
EMP: 60
SALES (corp-wide): 4MM **Privately Held**
WEB: www.polymerservices.com
SIC: 2822 Ethylene-propylene rubbers,
EPDM polymers

PA: General Polymer Services, Llc
4724 Decker Dr
Baytown TX 77520
281 424-4673

(G-1820)
GORDON MARTIN INC
Also Called: Industrial Instrument Co
5810 Wade Rd (77521-9743)
P.O. Box 2190 (77522-2190)
PHONE................................281 424-1301
Gordon Martin, *President*
Ricky Martin, *Vice Pres*
Jo Ann Martin, *Admin Sec*
EMP: 15
SQ FT: 12,000
SALES (est): 2.9MM **Privately Held**
WEB:
www.industrialinstrumentcompany.com
SIC: 3491 Process control regulator
valves; valves, automatic control

(G-1821)
H & S METALS INC
820 Sharon Ln (77520-9663)
P.O. Box 89 (77522-0089)
PHONE................................281 421-9488
Wille R Harvey, *President*
Willie R Harvey, *President*
Rick Sheldon, *Vice Pres*
EMP: 18
SALES (est): 2.3MM **Privately Held**
WEB: www.hns-metals.com
SIC: 3444 3441 Sheet metal specialties,
not stamped; fabricated structural metal

(G-1822)
IPSCO KOPPEL TUBULARS LLC
Also Called: Koppel Steel Corp Baytown
2600 East Fwy 99 (77521-1312)
PHONE................................281 383-2603
Joshua Gee, *Buyer*
Charlie Canatella, *Manager*
EMP: 125
SALES (corp-wide): 183.7K **Privately
Held**
WEB: www.tmk-group.com
SIC: 3312 Bar, rod & wire products; pipes
& tubes
HQ: Ipsco Koppel Tubulars, L.L.C.
6403 6th Ave
Koppel PA 16136

(G-1823)
JACK SAUNDERS
Also Called: Bay Pro Computers
4506 Adobe Ln (77521-2503)
PHONE................................713 806-7997
Jack Sauders, *Owner*
EMP: 12
SQ FT: 640
SALES (est): 1.6MM **Privately Held**
SIC: 3571 7378 Personal computers (mi-
crocomputers); computer maintenance &
repair

(G-1824)
KIRBY STONE COMPANY LLC
1300 Rollingbrook Dr # 500 (77521-3863)
P.O. Box 819, Deer Park (77536-0819)
PHONE................................281 427-7990
Doug Cox, *VP Opers*
James E Cox, *Mng Member*
EMP: 45
SALES (est): 8.2MM **Privately Held**
WEB: www.kirbystone.com
SIC: 1422 Cement rock, crushed & broken-
quarrying

(G-1825)
**KNIGHT INDUSTRIAL SERVICES
INC**
6802 East Fwy (77521-8172)
P.O. Box 1650, Mont Belvieu (77580-1650)
PHONE................................281 421-5049
Marc Knight, *President*
EMP: 250
SQ FT: 17,000
SALES (est): 17.5MM **Privately Held**
WEB: www.knightis.com
SIC: 3471 Sand blasting of metal parts

(G-1826)
LCY ELASTOMERS LP
4803 Decker Dr (77520-1447)
PHONE................................281 424-6100

Cliferd Menezes, *General Mgr*
Nolan Smith, *General Mgr*
Bowei Lee, *General Ptnr*
Garry Osan, *Plant Mgr*
Nyla Franklin, *Warehouse Mgr*
◆ **EMP:** 84
SQ FT: 1,902,210
SALES (est): 71.9MM **Publicly Held**
SIC: 2822 Styrene-butadiene rubbers,
(over 50% butadiene), SBR, GRS
HQ: Lcy Chemical Corp. (Lee Chang Yung
Chemical Industry Corporation)
3f, 4f, 5f, 85, Bade Rd., Sec. 4,
Taipei City TAP 10561

(G-1827)
LYNCHBURG SHIPYARD INC
Also Called: Channel Shipyard
999 McCollum Pkwy N (77520-1040)
P.O. Box 926, Highlands (77562-0926)
PHONE................................281 426-2474
H Dennis Steger, *President*
Floyd Anderson, *Vice Pres*
EMP: 50
SQ FT: 1,600
SALES (est): 12.9MM **Privately Held**
WEB: www.channelshipyard.net
SIC: 3731 7699 Shipbuilding & repairing;
ship boiler & tank cleaning & repair, con-
tractors

(G-1828)
MARKING SERVICES INC
5518 Decker Dr (77520-1400)
PHONE................................281 424-6710
Jeff Gault, *Vice Pres*
Cody Landon, *Sales Mgr*
EMP: 10
SALES (corp-wide): 23MM **Privately
Held**
WEB: www.markserv.com
SIC: 2679 Labels, paper: made from pur-
chased material
PA: Marking Services, Inc.
8265 N Faulkner Rd
Milwaukee WI 53224
414 973-1331

(G-1829)
MESSER LLC
Also Called: Boc Gases
100 S Airhart Dr (77520-2244)
PHONE................................281 837-0184
Charlie Crutcher, *Manager*
EMP: 25
SQ FT: 18,245
SALES (corp-wide): 1.2B **Privately Held**
WEB: www.praxair.com
SIC: 5169 2813 Industrial gases; industrial
gases
HQ: Messer Llc
200 Somerset Corp Blvd # 7000
Bridgewater NJ 08807
908 464-8100

(G-1830)
OSR SERVICES LP (PA)
2315 W Main St (77520-6216)
PHONE................................281 422-7206
Richea Powell, *Partner*
Joe Powell, *Partner*
Karen Powell, *Partner*
EMP: 30
SQ FT: 10,000
SALES (est): 5.4MM **Privately Held**
WEB: www.ossrs.com
SIC: 3398 3567 Metal heat treating; indus-
trial furnaces & ovens

(G-1831)
PAUL SMOKE
Also Called: Design Ventures
6730 Independence Blvd # 300
(77521-0204)
PHONE................................281 422-4228
Paul Smoke, *Owner*
EMP: 12
SALES (est): 332.7K **Privately Held**
SIC: 3993 2672 Signs, not made in cus-
tom sign painting shops; coated & lami-
nated paper; labels (unprinted), gummed:
made from purchased materials

(G-1832)
RANGER LIFT TRUCKS LLC (PA)
Also Called: Ranger Opco
2100 I 10 E (77521)
PHONE................................281 424-2111
Todd Ford, *President*
Omar Muhammad, *Controller*
Chris Herrera, *Sales Staff*
Galen Gardner,
▼ **EMP:** 15
SALES (est): 3MM **Privately Held**
WEB: www.rangerlifttrucks.com
SIC: 3537 5084 5511 7699 Forklift
trucks; trucks, industrial; trucks, tractors &
trailers: new & used; industrial truck repair

(G-1833)
RAVEN BUTENE-1 LLC
9520 East Fwy (77521-8155)
PHONE................................251 414-6955
Stephanie Bryers,
EMP: 50
SALES (est): 1.8MM **Privately Held**
SIC: 2911 Liquefied petroleum gases, LPG

(G-1834)
SNOW FLAKE BAKERY
Also Called: Snow Flake & Co
1906 N Alexander Dr (77520-3405)
PHONE................................281 427-4423
Ed K Cammack, *Owner*
EMP: 22
SQ FT: 12,000
SALES (est): 1.2MM **Privately Held**
SIC: 5461 2041 6794 Bakeries; flour
mixes; franchises, selling or licensing

(G-1835)
SOUTHERN NEWSPAPERS INC
Also Called: Baytown Sun, The
1301 Memorial Dr (77520-2401)
P.O. Box 90 (77522-0090)
PHONE................................281 422-8302
Carol Skewes, *Publisher*
Michael Pineda, *Editor*
Misty Warner, *Business Mgr*
Cathy Loftin, *Accounts Exec*
Dean West, *Adv Mgr*
EMP: 22
SALES (corp-wide): 140.3MM **Privately
Held**
WEB: www.sninews.com
SIC: 2711 Newspapers, publishing & print-
ing
PA: Southern Newspapers, Inc.
5701 Woodway Dr Ste 131
Houston TX 77057
713 266-5481

(G-1836)
**SPECIALTY LOCOMOTIVE
SERVICES**
Also Called: Speciluty Locomotive Service
115 N Main St (77520-4063)
P.O. Box 58291, Houston (77258-8291)
PHONE................................281 425-9850
Fred Hawley, *President*
Vince Augustine, *Vice Pres*
EMP: 12
SQ FT: 16,000
SALES (est): 833.8K **Privately Held**
SIC: 3743 4789 4741 Railroad equip-
ment; railroad car repair; rental of railroad
cars

(G-1837)
STRIKE LLC
10919 I 10 E (77520)
PHONE................................888 353-1444
James Harrison, *Superintendent*
Neri Perez, *Superintendent*
Juan Sanchez, *Superintendent*
Otis Sparkman, *Superintendent*
Terry Watkins, *Superintendent*
EMP: 275
SALES (corp-wide): 1.4B **Privately Held**
WEB: www.strikeusa.com
SIC: 1389 Servicing oil & gas wells
PA: Strike, Llc
1800 Hughes Landing Blvd # 500
The Woodlands TX 77380
713 389-2400

G
E
O
G
R
A
P
H
I
C

(G-1838)
UNITED ENERGY GROUP LLC
8010 Needlepoint Rd (77521-9585)
PHONE..............................281 839-0080
Richard Looney, *President*
Daniel Mullins, *Project Mgr*
EMP: 99
SALES (est): 12.1MM **Privately Held**
WEB: www.unitedenergygroupllc.com
SIC: 2911 Petroleum refining

(G-1839)
WORLD WIDE FILTRATION INC
5340 East Rd (77521-9004)
P.O. Box 1186 (77522-1186)
PHONE..............................281 421-7676
Ralph Oler, *President*
Mike Guthrie, *Treasurer*
EMP: 15
SALES (est): 3.3MM **Privately Held**
WEB: www.worldwidefiltration.com
SIC: 3569 Filters, general line: industrial

Beasley
Fort Bend County

(G-1840)
FINORIC LLC
8115 Loop 540 (77417-9485)
PHONE..............................855 346-6742
Ambrish Kamdar, *President*
◆ EMP: 80
SALES (est): 881.4K **Privately Held**
WEB: www.finoric.com
SIC: 2819 Industrial inorganic chemicals

(G-1841)
HUDSON PRODUCTS CORPORATION (HQ)
9660 Grunwald Rd (77417-8600)
P.O. Box 20029, Sugar Land (77496-0029)
PHONE..............................281 396-8195
Grady Walker, *President*
Hector Perez, *General Mgr*
Rachel East, *Superintendent*
Salem Abouabsi, *Project Mgr*
Jim Goldsmith, *Project Mgr*
◆ EMP: 25
SQ FT: 26,000
SALES (est): 150.4MM **Publicly Held**
WEB: www.chartindustries.com
SIC: 3443 Heat exchangers, condensers & components

(G-1842)
HUDSON PRODUCTS HOLDINGS INC (HQ)
9660 Grunwald Rd (77417-8600)
PHONE..............................281 396-8100
Grady Walker, *CEO*
Sam Chapple, *President*
Bob Giammaruti, *Vice Pres*
Steve Boes, *Director*
◆ EMP: 50
SALES (est): 138.2MM **Publicly Held**
WEB: www.chartindustries.com
SIC: 3443 Air coolers, metal plate

(G-1843)
PIPE COATINGS INTL LLC
Also Called: PCI
9028 Vincik Ehlert Rd (77417)
PHONE..............................979 387-3150
Steve Broussard, *General Mgr*
Sealy Morris,
EMP: 35
SQ FT: 50,000
SALES (est): 5.4MM
SALES (corp-wide): 29.6MM **Privately Held**
SIC: 2295 Sealing or insulating tape for pipe: coated fiberglass
HQ: Rotary Drilling Tools Usa Llc
1201 Louisiana St Fl 28
Houston TX 77002

(G-1844)
POWDER COATERS OF TEXAS INC
8723 Loop 540 (77417-9505)
PHONE..............................979 387-2049
Eric Talley, *President*
EMP: 10

SALES (est): 571K **Privately Held**
WEB: www.powdercoatersoftexas.com
SIC: 3399 2851 Powder, metal; paints & paint additives

(G-1845)
RDT INC
9022 Vincik Ehlert (77417)
PHONE..............................979 387-3223
Carlos Lopez, *Ch of Bd*
Francesc Ribas, *Vice Pres*
EMP: 99
SALES (est): 1.2MM **Privately Held**
WEB: www.rdt-usa.com
SIC: 1389 Pipe testing, oil field service

Beaumont
Jefferson County

(G-1846)
A-1 SHEET METAL AND AC INC
2935 Milam St (77701-4816)
PHONE..............................409 833-4715
David Gallier, *President*
Jeremy Kotlarz, *President*
Debbie Foreman, *Opers Staff*
Linda Gallier, *Treasurer*
EMP: 28
SQ FT: 43,500
SALES (est): 5.8MM **Privately Held**
WEB: www.a-1sheetmetal.com
SIC: 3444 1711 Sheet metal specialties, not stamped; ducts, sheet metal; plumbing, heating, air-conditioning contractors

(G-1847)
AA FLOOD MASTERS LLC
10655 Fm 365 Rd (77705-9479)
PHONE..............................409 796-2620
Michael Wright, *Pastor*
Randy Clark, *Bishop*
Henry Labrie, *Mng Member*
Henry A Labrie, *Mng Member*
EMP: 45
SALES (est): 7.8MM **Privately Held**
WEB: www.aaafloodmasters.com
SIC: 3823 7641 8999 Water quality monitoring & control systems; antique furniture repair & restoration; actuarial consultant

(G-1848)
AKCORP INC (PA)
Also Called: Premier Corporate Housing
1280 S 11th St (77701-4721)
PHONE..............................409 833-8002
EMP: 18
SQ FT: 27,000
SALES: 11MM **Privately Held**
WEB: www.boomtownfurniture.com
SIC: 2519 7359 5712 Furniture, household: glass, fiberglass & plastic; furniture rental; furniture stores

(G-1849)
ALLEGIANT INDUSTRIAL LLC
850 Pine St (77701-1851)
P.O. Box 4259 (77704-4259)
PHONE..............................409 782-7963
Robert Thayer, *CEO*
Ronald Yawn, *President*
EMP: 25 EST: 2017
SALES (est): 2.1MM **Privately Held**
WEB: www.allegiantindustrial.com
SIC: 1623 2655 7389 Oil & gas pipeline construction; fiber spools, tubes & cones; safety inspection service

(G-1850)
ALTUS HEALTH SYSTEM
390 N 11th St (77702-1802)
PHONE..............................409 554-0131
Taseer A Badar, *Branch Mgr*
EMP: 17
SALES (corp-wide): 4.4MM **Privately Held**
WEB: www.ztcorporate.com
SIC: 3826 Magnetic resonance imaging apparatus
PA: Altus Health System
1626 W Baker Rd
Baytown TX 77521
281 837-7600

(G-1851)
AMERICAN BOTTLING COMPANY
Also Called: 7 Up Bottling of Beaumont
7410 Frint Dr (77705-7332)
PHONE..............................409 842-6061
Ricky Mout, *Manager*
EMP: 35 **Publicly Held**
WEB: www.keurigdrpepper.com
SIC: 2086 Soft drinks: packaged in cans, bottles, etc.
HQ: The American Bottling Company
5301 Legacy Dr
Plano TX 75024

(G-1852)
AMERICAN VALVE HYDRANT MFG CO (HQ)
Also Called: American Darling Valve
3525 Hollywood St (77701-3832)
PHONE..............................409 832-7721
Van Richey, *Ch of Bd*
Tim Sudela, *President*
Ken R La Fleur, *Vice Pres*
John Cook, *Treasurer*
J M O Brien, *Admin Sec*
▲ EMP: 16
SQ FT: 18,638
SALES (est): 29MM
SALES (corp-wide): 1.3B **Privately Held**
WEB: www.avhmc.com
SIC: 3491 Water works valves; fire hydrant valves
PA: American Cast Iron Pipe Company
1500 32nd Ave N
Birmingham AL 35207
205 325-7701

(G-1853)
AMERICAN VALVE HYDRANT MFG CO
3350 Hollywood St (77701-3820)
PHONE..............................409 832-7721
Tim Sudela, *President*
EMP: 157
SALES (corp-wide): 1.3B **Privately Held**
WEB: www.avhmc.com
SIC: 3491 5085 Water works valves; valves & fittings
HQ: American Valve & Hydrant Manufacturing Company
3525 Hollywood St
Beaumont TX 77701
409 832-7721

(G-1854)
ARKEMA INC
Also Called: Beaumont Plant
2810 Gulf States Rd (77701)
P.O. Box 1427 (77704-1427)
PHONE..............................409 838-3981
EMP: 85
SALES (corp-wide): 120.6MM **Privately Held**
WEB: www.arkema-americas.com
SIC: 2819 2899 2869 Industrial inorganic chemicals; chemical preparations; industrial organic chemicals
HQ: Arkema Inc.
900 First Ave
King Of Prussia PA 19406
610 205-7000

(G-1855)
AUSTIN COCA-COLA BOTTLING CO
11450 Eastex Fwy (77708-0900)
PHONE..............................409 899-5080
Brutch Taylor, *Manager*
EMP: 85
SQ FT: 163,746
SALES (corp-wide): 309.5MM **Privately Held**
SIC: 2086 Bottled & canned soft drinks
PA: Austin Coca-Cola Bottling Company
1 Coca Cola Pl
San Antonio TX 78219
210 225-2601

(G-1856)
AZZ INC
5885 Industrial Rd (77705-6960)
PHONE..............................409 842-0216
Henry Netherland, *Principal*
EMP: 37

SALES (corp-wide): 1B **Publicly Held**
WEB: www.azz.com
SIC: 3699 Electrical equipment & supplies
PA: Azz Inc.
3100 W 7th St Ste 500
Fort Worth TX 76107
817 810-0095

(G-1857)
BABIN MACHINE WORKS INC
2510 N 9th St (77703-4740)
P.O. Box 2007 (77704-2007)
PHONE..............................409 892-1231
Joya Cruthirds, *Vice Pres*
Rod Cistrunk, *Admin Sec*
EMP: 10 EST: 1938
SQ FT: 3,000
SALES (est): 637K **Privately Held**
WEB: www.babinmachine.com
SIC: 3599 3541 Machine shop, jobbing & repair; drilling machine tools (metal cutting)

(G-1858)
BASF CORPORATION
14385 W Port Arthur Rd (77705-9290)
PHONE..............................409 981-5000
John Smoter, *Branch Mgr*
Truyen Nguyen, *Planning*
Terrence Young, *Planning*
Laura Austin, *Representative*
Madonna Johnson, *Associate*
EMP: 95
SALES (corp-wide): 65.6B **Privately Held**
WEB: www.basf.com
SIC: 2869 2879 Industrial organic chemicals; agricultural chemicals
HQ: Basf Corporation
100 Park Ave
Florham Park NJ 07932
973 245-6000

(G-1859)
BEAUMONT BOLT & GASKET INC (DH)
1060 Fannin St (77701-2792)
PHONE..............................409 838-6304
Michael Vaughn, *Vice Pres*
▲ EMP: 25 EST: 1970
SQ FT: 50,000
SALES (est): 4.4MM
SALES (corp-wide): 182.5MM **Privately Held**
WEB: www.lamons.com
SIC: 5085 3452 3053 Fasteners, industrial: nuts, bolts, screws, etc.; bolts, nuts, rivets & washers; gaskets, packing & sealing devices
HQ: Lamons Gasket Company
7300 Airport Blvd
Houston TX 77061
713 222-0284

(G-1860)
BEAUMONT COCA-COLA BOTTLING CO
11450 Eastex Fwy (77708-0900)
PHONE..............................409 899-5080
Crawford Rainwater, *Ch of Bd*
William A Morrison Jr, *President*
Patrick J Pate Jr, *Vice Pres*
EMP: 150 EST: 1912
SQ FT: 16,000
SALES (est): 11.4MM **Privately Held**
SIC: 2086 5149 Soft drinks: packaged in cans, bottles, etc.; soft drinks

(G-1861)
BEAUMONT METAL INDUSTRIES INC
3115 Milam St (77701-4830)
PHONE..............................409 833-1777
Mike Jenkins, *President*
Rodney Jenkins, *Vice Pres*
Jean Campbell, *Admin Sec*
EMP: 20
SQ FT: 5,000
SALES (est): 2.4MM **Privately Held**
SIC: 3444 Sheet metal specialties, not stamped

(G-1862)
BEAUMONT RICE MILLS INC
1800 Pecos St (77701-2500)
P.O. Box 3111 (77704-3111)
PHONE......................409 832-2521
Louis M Broussard Jr, *President*
Fred C Adams Jr, *Corp Secy*
Ben E Broussard, *Vice Pres*
Brenda D Cook, *Treasurer*
Rhonda Rubel, *Practice Mgr*
EMP: 40 **EST:** 1892
SQ FT: 29,230
SALES (est): 11.5MM **Privately Held**
WEB: www.bmtricemills.com
SIC: 5153 2044 Rice, unpolished; rice milling

(G-1863)
BERRY GLOBAL INC
10463 Highway 124 (77705-0631)
P.O. Box 20483 (77720-0483)
PHONE......................409 794-1011
Burnice Wilson, *Branch Mgr*
EMP: 127 **Publicly Held**
WEB: www.berryplastics.com
SIC: 3089 Bottle caps, molded plastic
HQ: Berry Global, Inc.
101 Oakley St
Evansville IN 47710

(G-1864)
BERTRAND ENTERPRISES INC
2400 Gulf St (77703-5206)
PHONE......................409 833-0922
Robert Bertrand, *President*
Cheryl Bertrand, *Vice Pres*
EMP: 16
SQ FT: 20,000 **Privately Held**
WEB: www.hotcurrenttees.com
SIC: 2395 2396 2759 Embroidery & art needlework; screen printing on fabric articles; screen printing

(G-1865)
BGI ENTERPRISE INC (PA)
1325 Spindletop Rd (77705-6611)
P.O. Box 22077 (77720-2077)
PHONE......................409 833-0303
A B Bernard Jr, *President*
Randy Donin, *Vice Pres*
Lorenza Fitch, *Manager*
EMP: 50
SQ FT: 30,000
SALES (est): 15.6MM **Privately Held**
WEB: www.bgitexas.us
SIC: 1629 8711 3731 1541 Industrial plant construction; engineering services; shipbuilding & repairing; industrial buildings & warehouses; concrete work; non-residential construction

(G-1866)
BLP SETTLEMENT COMPANY
4175 W Cardinal Dr (77705-4408)
PHONE......................713 674-2266
Dan Rose, *Train & Dev Mgr*
Jimmy Mowlam, *Manager*
EMP: 15
SALES (corp-wide): 3.1B **Privately Held**
WEB: www.lifting.com
SIC: 3496 Miscellaneous fabricated wire products
HQ: Blp Settlement Company
125 Mccarty St
Houston TX 77029
713 674-2266

(G-1867)
CB&I LLC
Also Called: CB&i Beaumont
Edison Plaza 350 Pine St (77701)
PHONE......................409 980-5500
EMP: 216
SALES (corp-wide): 8.4B **Privately Held**
WEB: www.cbi.com
SIC: 1791 3443 3312 Structural steel erection; fabricated plate work (boiler shop); blast furnaces & steel mills
HQ: Cb&l Llc
915 N Eldridge Pkwy # 10
Houston TX 77079
281 870-5000

(G-1868)
CHEMAX CORPORATION
12175 Highway 90 (77713-3505)
P.O. Box 7453 (77726-7453)
PHONE......................409 866-4232
Polly Lyons, *Ch of Bd*
Rebecca Hinshaw, *President*
Jason Greene, *Sales Mgr*
Brandi Griffin, *Sales Staff*
Krista Hernandez, *Office Mgr*
EMP: 23 **EST:** 1977
SQ FT: 10,000
SALES (est): 5.9MM **Privately Held**
WEB: www.chemax.com
SIC: 5169 2842 2992 2899 Industrial chemicals; cleaning or polishing preparations; lubricating oils & greases; chemical preparations

(G-1869)
CHEMTRADE REFINERY SVCS INC
1400 Olin Rd (77705-5754)
P.O. Box 30 (77704-0030)
PHONE......................409 835-6641
Kevin Goes, *Plant Mgr*
Michael Shepherd, *Plant Mgr*
Dwayne Taveney, *Project Mgr*
Patricia Munoz, *Purchasing*
Lane Benford, *Engineer*
EMP: 45
SALES (corp-wide): 1.1B **Privately Held**
WEB: www.chemtradelogistics.com
SIC: 2819 Sulfuric acid, oleum
HQ: Chemtrade Refinery Services Inc.
440 N 9th St
Lawrence KS 66044
785 843-2290

(G-1870)
CLARK PILLOW COMPANY
6281 Industrial Rd (77705-6964)
PHONE......................409 842-5767
Deborah Fertitta, *CEO*
Tony Fertitta, *CEO*
Jan Wallace, *Corp Secy*
Candyce Edwards, *Vice Pres*
▲ **EMP:** 20
SQ FT: 30,000
SALES (est): 2.2MM **Privately Held**
WEB: www.clarkpillow.com
SIC: 2392 Pillows, bed: made from purchased materials; cushions & pillows; slip covers & pads

(G-1871)
CO CO MO JOES
Also Called: Cocomo Joe's
2024 Calder St (77701-1519)
PHONE......................409 212-9892
Joe Ramey, *Owner*
EMP: 15
SQ FT: 10,474
SALES (est): 106K **Privately Held**
WEB: www.cocomojoes.net
SIC: 2395 2759 Emblems, embroidered; embroidery & art needlework; screen printing

(G-1872)
COASTAL CAVERNS INC
6045 Highland Ave (77705-6517)
P.O. Box 22779 (77720-2779)
PHONE......................409 833-5504
Caliche Coastal LLC,
EMP: 9
SALES (est): 1.1MM
SALES (corp-wide): 7.4MM **Privately Held**
SIC: 2911 Liquefied petroleum gases, LPG
HQ: Vitol Services Limited
160 Victoria Street
London SW1E
207 973-4200

(G-1873)
COLGAN-WILSON METALS LLC
Also Called: Triangle Bolt
3165 Milam St (77701-4831)
PHONE......................409 882-9296
John Colgan, *CEO*
Eddie Hebert, *Sales Staff*
EMP: 10 **EST:** 1981
SQ FT: 10,000

SALES (est): 3.2MM **Privately Held**
WEB: www.stsindustrial.com
SIC: 5085 3452 Fasteners, industrial: nuts, bolts, screws, etc.; bolts, metal

(G-1874)
COLT SERVICES LP
6029 Industrial Rd (77705-6962)
PHONE......................409 842-6929
David Davis, *Branch Mgr*
EMP: 10
SALES (corp-wide): 11.5MM **Privately Held**
WEB: www.coltonline.com
SIC: 1389 7699 Construction, repair & dismantling services; boiler & heating repair services
PA: Colt Services, L.P.
626 N 16th St
La Porte TX 77571
281 471-9099

(G-1875)
COMMERCIAL METALS COMPANY
Also Called: CMC Recycling
5250 College St (77707-3712)
P.O. Box 20317 (77720-0317)
PHONE......................409 842-3316
Carlos Breeden, *Branch Mgr*
EMP: 55
SALES (corp-wide): 5.4B **Publicly Held**
WEB: www.cmc.com
SIC: 5093 4953 3312 Ferrous metal scrap & waste; nonferrous metals scrap; recycling, waste materials; blast furnaces & steel mills
PA: Commercial Metals Company
6565 N Macarthur Blvd # 800
Irving TX 75039
214 689-4300

(G-1876)
CONSOLIDATED CONTAINMENT LLC
5450 Avenue A (77705-6402)
P.O. Box 23165 (77720-3165)
PHONE......................409 781-4254
William J Petree,
Michael G Shrum,
Richard Wilkes,
EMP: 25
SALES (est): 5.1MM **Privately Held**
WEB: www.consolidatedcontainment.com
SIC: 3089 Plastic containers, except foam

(G-1877)
CRABTREE BARRICADE SYSTEMS INC
Also Called: C-Stripe
7375 Frint Dr (77705-7305)
P.O. Box 20195 (77720-0195)
PHONE......................409 842-2073
Marjorie Crabtree, *President*
Guy E Crabtree, *Vice Pres*
EMP: 34
SQ FT: 9,000
SALES (est): 3.8MM **Privately Held**
WEB: www.c-stripe.com
SIC: 1721 7521 3993 1799 Pavement marking contractor; parking lots; signs & advertising specialties; parking lot maintenance

(G-1878)
CRH AMERICAS MATERIALS INC
Also Called: APAC
12907 Highway 90 (77713-4114)
P.O. Box 20779 (77720-0779)
PHONE......................409 866-1444
Scott Blanchard, *General Mgr*
Eddie McCoy, *Purch Mgr*
Angela Kvarme, *Controller*
Kal Kinciad, *Systems Staff*
EMP: 162
SALES (corp-wide): 30.6B **Privately Held**
WEB: www.crhamericasmaterials.com
SIC: 1611 3273 2951 General contractor, highway & street construction; highway & street paving contractor; ready-mixed concrete; asphalt paving mixtures & blocks

HQ: Crh Americas Materials, Inc.
900 Ashwood Pkwy Ste 700
Atlanta GA 30338

(G-1879)
CULLIGAN SOUTHEAST TEXAS WATER
850 Mcfaddin St (77701-1865)
PHONE......................409 838-6261
Henry Strait, *Owner*
EMP: 25 **EST:** 2002
SQ FT: 14,700
SALES (est): 1.2MM **Privately Held**
WEB: www.southeasttexaswater.com
SIC: 5999 2086 5963 5074 Water purification equipment; pasteurized & mineral waters, bottled & canned; bottled water delivery; water softeners

(G-1880)
DBT INC (PA)
Also Called: Fastsigns
4108 Dowlen Rd (77706-6851)
PHONE......................409 892-2300
Russell Fontana, *President*
Don Pippin, *COO*
EMP: 13
SQ FT: 1,250
SALES (est): 2.2MM **Privately Held**
WEB: www.fastsigns.com
SIC: 3993 5999 Signs & advertising specialties; banners, flags, decals & posters

(G-1881)
DEBES ICE COMPANY
3750 Milam St (77701-4734)
PHONE......................409 835-4431
Wallace Debes Sr, *Owner*
Wallace Debes Jr, *Owner*
Sam Debes, *Co-Owner*
EMP: 10
SQ FT: 8,800
SALES (est): 707K **Privately Held**
SIC: 2097 5999 Manufactured ice; ice

(G-1882)
DEEPWELL ENERGY SERVICES LLC
1245 W Cardinal Dr (77705-6410)
PHONE......................337 780-8297
EMP: 21
SALES (corp-wide): 254.8MM **Privately Held**
WEB: www.dwservices.com
SIC: 1381 Drilling oil & gas wells
PA: Deepwell Energy Services, Llc
4025 Highway 35 N
Columbia MS 39429
800 477-2855

(G-1883)
DOGUETS RICE MILLING COMPANY
795 S Major Dr (77707-1532)
PHONE......................409 866-2297
Debbie Robbins, *President*
Greg Devillier, *Vice Pres*
Kyle Kurth, *QC Mgr*
Kaitlin Lowery, *Sales Staff*
EMP: 25
SQ FT: 21,200
SALES (est): 7.4MM **Privately Held**
WEB: www.doguets.com
SIC: 0723 2044 Rice drying services; rice milling

(G-1884)
DOW CHEMICAL COMPANY
Hwy 347 (77705)
P.O. Box 3269 (77704-3269)
PHONE......................409 722-3451
Verlon Bradley, *Branch Mgr*
EMP: 60
SALES (corp-wide): 38.5B **Publicly Held**
WEB: www.dow.com
SIC: 2822 2899 2819 2869 Synthetic rubber; chemical preparations; industrial inorganic chemicals; industrial organic chemicals
HQ: The Dow Chemical Company
2211 H H Dow Way
Midland MI 48642
989 636-1000

(G-1885)
DRAGON ESP LTD (PA)
1655 Louisiana St (77701-1120)
PHONE..................................409 833-2665
Randy Prater, *Principal*
EMP: 17
SALES (est): 5.7MM **Privately Held**
WEB: www.dragonproductsltd.com
SIC: 3533 Oil field machinery & equipment

(G-1886)
DRAGON PRODUCTS LLC (DH)
1655 Louisiana St (77701-1120)
P.O. Box 790 (77704-0790)
PHONE..................................409 833-2665
Will Crenshaw, *CEO*
Chuck Childress, *Vice Pres*
John Crenshaw, *Vice Pres*
Steve Stump, *Vice Pres*
Alyssa Ortega, *Accountant*
▼ **EMP:** 200 **EST:** 1998
SALES (est): 20MM **Privately Held**
WEB: www.dragonproductsltd.com
SIC: 3443 Fuel tanks (oil, gas, etc.): metal
plate
HQ: Modern Ag Products, Llc
1655 Louisiana St
Beaumont TX 77701
409 833-2665

(G-1887)
ENGINERED PACKAGED SYSTEMS INC
Also Called: Eps
6280 Westwood Blvd (77707-3412)
P.O. Box 3644 (77704-3644)
PHONE..................................409 866-5213
Marvin Spears, *President*
Casey Spears, *Vice Pres*
Lisa Spears, *Controller*
Whitney Wilson, *Sales Staff*
Jacqueline Suire, *Admin Sec*
EMP: 21
SQ FT: 35,625
SALES: 5.2MM **Privately Held**
WEB: www.engpkgsys.com
SIC: 3585 3433 Refrigeration equipment,
complete; heating equipment, except
electric

(G-1888)
ENGLOBAL CORPORATION
3105 Executive Blvd (77705-1044)
PHONE..................................409 840-2100
Wiliam A Coskey, *President*
EMP: 250
SALES (corp-wide): 56.4MM **Publicly
Held**
WEB: www.englobal.com
SIC: 3575 Computer terminals, monitors &
components
PA: Englobal Corporation
654 N Sam Houston Pkwy E # 400
Houston TX 77060
281 878-1000

(G-1889)
EXAMINER CORPORATION
Also Called: Examiner Newspaper, The
795 Willow St (77701-1829)
PHONE..................................409 833-1755
Don Dodd, *President*
Taryn Sykes, *General Mgr*
Dana Moore, *Sales Mgr*
Kristi Dodd, *Director*
Aaron Alverson, *Executive*
EMP: 32
SQ FT: 1,900
SALES (est): 2.2MM **Privately Held**
WEB: www.theexaminer.com
SIC: 2711 Newspapers, publishing & print-
ing

(G-1890)
EXCEL MEDIA LLC
Also Called: Excel Media Kxxf Radio
80 Interstate 10 N # 209 (77702-2128)
PHONE..................................409 832-5770
John Walton, *Mng Member*
Karen Ollier,
EMP: 10
SALES (est): 148K **Privately Held**
WEB: www.freefm.net
SIC: 4832 7372 Radio broadcasting sta-
tions; application computer software

(G-1891)
EXXONMOBIL CHEMICAL COMPANY
Also Called: Beaumont Polyethylene Plant
11440 Highway 90 (77713-3486)
P.O. Box 2295 (77704-2295)
PHONE..................................409 860-1300
Ricky Wood, *Production*
Chris Graham, *Engineer*
J R Townsend, *Branch Mgr*
EMP: 370
SALES (corp-wide): 264.9B **Publicly
Held**
WEB: www.exxonmobilchemical.com
SIC: 2821 Polyethylene resins
HQ: Exxonmobil Chemical Company
22777 Sprngwoods Vlg Pkwy
Spring TX 77389
800 243-9966

(G-1892)
FEDEX OFFICE & PRINT SVCS INC
5775 Eastex Fwy (77706-6922)
PHONE..................................409 895-4000
Lori Harrison, *Accounts Exec*
EMP: 12
SALES (corp-wide): 69.2B **Publicly Held**
WEB: www.fedex.com
SIC: 7334 2759 2752 Photocopying & du-
plicating services; commercial printing;
commercial printing, lithographic
HQ: Fedex Office And Print Services, Inc.
7900 Legacy Dr
Plano TX 75024
800 463-3339

(G-1893)
FESCO LTD
2205 W Florida St (77705-6352)
PHONE..................................409 842-3000
James Jordan, *Manager*
EMP: 25
SQ FT: 28,050
SALES (corp-wide): 201MM **Privately
Held**
WEB: www.fescoinc.com
SIC: 8711 1389 Petroleum engineering; oil
field services
PA: Fesco, Ltd.
1000 Fesco Dr
Alice TX 78332
361 664-3479

(G-1894)
FLOWBACK GREEN SERVICES LLC
3005 Silver St (77703-4017)
PHONE..................................409 217-1482
Keith A Viator,
EMP: 25
SALES (est): 448.8K **Privately Held**
SIC: 1389 Oil & gas field services

(G-1895)
FLOWSERVE CORPORATION
2920 W Cardinal Dr (77705-4536)
PHONE..................................409 842-5594
Benny Elisar, *General Mgr*
Jeremy Brottem, *Engineer*
David Lowe, *Sales Staff*
EMP: 10
SALES (corp-wide): 3.9B **Publicly Held**
WEB: www.flowserve.com
SIC: 3561 Industrial pumps & parts
PA: Flowserve Corporation
5215 N Ocnnor Blvd Ste 23 Connor
Irving TX 75039
972 443-6500

(G-1896)
FOR HEAVENS SAKE
4190 Calder Ave (77706-4926)
PHONE..................................409 898-3340
Gina Crenshaw, *Principal*
EMP: 14
SALES (est): 777.3K **Privately Held**
WEB:
www.forheavenssake.bridgecatalog.com
SIC: 2759 Commercial printing

(G-1897)
FRED CLARK FELT CO BEAUMONT (PA)
6305 Industrial Rd (77705-6966)
PHONE..................................409 842-5080
Deborah Clark Fertitta, *President*
Candyce M Edwards, *Vice Pres*
Janyce Wallace, *Admin Sec*
◆ **EMP:** 20 **EST:** 1974
SQ FT: 27,000
SALES: 2.7MM **Privately Held**
SIC: 2299 Felts & felt products

(G-1898)
GHX INDUSTRIAL LLC
Also Called: Bayou Gasket & Hose Co
3155 W Cardinal Dr (77705-4418)
P.O. Box 3303 (77704-3303)
PHONE..................................409 832-3461
Gary Schnur, *Manager*
EMP: 31
SALES (corp-wide): 366.9MM **Privately
Held**
WEB: www.ghxinc.com
SIC: 3053 5085 5199 3599 Gaskets, all
materials; packing materials; packing,
metallic; packing, rubber; rubber goods,
mechanical; hose, belting & packing;
leather belting, packing; packaging mate-
rials; flexible metal hose, tubing & bellows; hose & tube fittings & assemblies,
hydraulic/pneumatic
HQ: Ghx Industrial, Llc
13311 Lockwood Rd
Houston TX 77044
713 341-3407

(G-1899)
GONZALES ELEC SYSTEMS LLC
4950 Washington Blvd (77707-4312)
PHONE..................................409 860-3802
Don Gonzales Jr, *Mng Member*
EMP: 40
SQ FT: 8,000
SALES (est): 3MM **Privately Held**
WEB: www.gonzaleselectric.com
SIC: 5063 3613 Electrical apparatus &
equipment; distribution boards, electric

(G-1900)
GULF COAST FABRICATORS INC
9695 Walden Rd (77707-5232)
PHONE..................................409 866-6721
Louis Falgout, *Vice Pres*
Annette Schwartzenburg, *Office Mgr*
EMP: 40 **Privately Held**
WEB: www.gulfcoastsheetmetal.com
SIC: 3498 3441 Pipe fittings, fabricated
from purchased pipe; fabricated structural
metal
PA: Gulf Coast Fabricators, Inc.
6711 N Twin City Hwy
Port Arthur TX 77642

(G-1901)
HELENA LABORATORIES CORP (PA)
1530 Lindbergh Dr (77707-4131)
P.O. Box 752 (77704-0752)
PHONE..................................409 842-3714
Tipton L Golias, *CEO*
Britt Curtice, *President*
Joe Golias, *President*
Noel Bartlett, *Vice Pres*
David Mayes, *Vice Pres*
▲ **EMP:** 500
SQ FT: 200,000
SALES (est): 221.1MM **Privately Held**
WEB: www.helena.com
SIC: 3841 3826 Medical instruments &
equipment, blood & bone work; elec-
trophoresis equipment

(G-1902)
HELENA LABORATORIES CORP
Also Called: Electronics Division
3795 Washington Blvd (77705-1137)
P.O. Box 752 (77704-0752)
PHONE..................................409 842-3714
James Simmons, *Program Mgr*
David Mayes, *Manager*
EMP: 400

SALES (corp-wide): 221.1MM **Privately
Held**
WEB: www.helena.com
SIC: 3827 3841 3826 3821 Optical instruments & apparatus; surgical & medical instruments; analytical instruments;
laboratory apparatus & furniture; in vitro &
in vivo diagnostic substances
PA: Helena Laboratories Corporation
1530 Lindbergh Dr
Beaumont TX 77707
409 842-3714

(G-1903)
HERCULES LLC
10658 Highway 90 (77713-3472)
PHONE..................................409 866-4778
Hern Lorraine, *Branch Mgr*
EMP: 54
SALES (corp-wide): 2.3B **Publicly Held**
WEB: www.hercules.com
SIC: 2899 Water treating compounds
HQ: Hercules Llc
500 Hercules Rd
Wilmington DE 19808
302 594-5000

(G-1904)
HONEYWELL INTERNATIONAL INC
350 Pine St Ste 250 (77701-2431)
PHONE..................................409 833-4601
Frank Whitsura, *Branch Mgr*
EMP: 20
SALES (corp-wide): 36.7B **Publicly Held**
WEB: www.honeywell.com
SIC: 3724 Aircraft engines & engine parts
PA: Honeywell International Inc.
300 S Tryon St
Charlotte NC 28202
704 627-6200

(G-1905)
I CORP INC
4933 Fannett Rd (77705-4305)
PHONE..................................409 981-9090
Charles E Randolph, *Branch Mgr*
EMP: 11 **Privately Held**
WEB: www.icorptx.com
SIC: 3599 Machine shop, jobbing & repair
PA: I Corp, Inc.
4935 Fannett Rd
Beaumont TX 77705
409 842-9765

(G-1906)
INDUSTRIAL ALLOY FBRCATION INC
3780 Milam St (77701-4734)
PHONE..................................409 600-8222
Ron Hillenburg, *President*
Mike Heinen, *Manager*
Tracy Huey, *Manager*
John Stewart, *Executive*
EMP: 15
SQ FT: 14,000
SALES (est): 1.9MM **Privately Held**
WEB: www.iaftx.com
SIC: 3443 Industrial vessels, tanks & con-
tainers

(G-1907)
INFRARED CAMERAS INC
Also Called: Infrared Training Institute
2105 W Cardinal Dr (77705-6336)
PHONE..................................409 861-0788
Gary E Strahan, *CEO*
EMP: 15
SQ FT: 1,500
SALES (est): 2.6MM **Privately Held**
WEB: www.infraredcameras.com
SIC: 3861 Cameras & related equipment

(G-1908)
INSTRUMENT & VALVE SERVICES CO
Also Called: Emerson
4870 Romeda Rd (77705-1129)
PHONE..................................409 840-8400
Jeremiah Hazi, *Branch Mgr*
EMP: 14
SALES (corp-wide): 16.7B **Publicly Held**
WEB: www.scalloncontrols.com
SIC: 3823 Industrial instrmnts msrmnt dis-
play/control process variable

▲ = Import ▼=Export
◆ =Import/Export

HQ: Instrument & Valve Services Company
205 S Center St
Marshalltown IA 50158

(G-1909)
INTEGRATED POWER SERVICES LLC
1320 Jim Gilligan Way (77705-6234)
PHONE...................................409 833-9477
Karl Huch, *General Mgr*
Jean Stedman, *Principal*
Nancy Choate, *Accounts Mgr*
EMP: 42
SALES (corp-wide): 843.2MM **Privately Held**
WEB: www.ips.us
SIC: 7694 Electric motor repair
HQ: Integrated Power Services Llc
250 Executive Center Dr # 100
Greenville SC 29615

(G-1910)
INTERNTNAL GLVNZERS PARTNR LTD
Also Called: Azz Galvanizing-Beaumont
5885 Industrial Rd (77705-6960)
PHONE...................................409 842-0216
Bobby McKinney, *Sales Staff*
Bobby Mc Kinney, *Branch Mgr*
EMP: 35
SALES (corp-wide): 1B **Publicly Held**
WEB: www.azz.com
SIC: 3479 Galvanizing of iron, steel or end-formed products
HQ: International Galvanizers Partnership, Ltd.
3100 W 7th St Ste 500
Fort Worth TX 76107

(G-1911)
J & E WELDING INC
10930 E Clubb Rd (77705-7154)
P.O. Box 22123 (77720-2123)
PHONE...................................409 794-2311
Carl Freeman, *President*
Sheri Freeman, *Vice Pres*
EMP: 11
SQ FT: 16,000
SALES (est): 2.2MM **Privately Held**
WEB: www.jewelding.com
SIC: 7692 Welding repair

(G-1912)
J & J MANUFACTURING COMPANY
5455 Ohio St (77705-6211)
P.O. Box 1119, Vidor (77670-1119)
PHONE...................................409 835-1330
EMP: 60 EST: 1960
SQ FT: 60,000
SALES: 2.8MM **Privately Held**
SIC: 3565 3535 3823 3547 Mfg Packaging Machinery Mfg Conveyors/Equipment Mfg Process Cntrl Instr Mfg Rolling Mill Mach

(G-1913)
JONES ALUMINUM
9805 Mallot Rd (77713-3119)
PHONE...................................409 866-5585
Raymond Keith Jones, *Owner*
EMP: 10
SALES (est): 1.3MM **Privately Held**
WEB: www.jonesalum.com
SIC: 1761 5999 5211 2394 Siding contractor; awnings; screens, door & window; canvas awnings & canopies; patio & deck construction & repair

(G-1914)
KIESCHNICK INDUSTRIES INC
3050 W Cedar St (77702-2528)
PHONE...................................409 833-5611
Todd Kieschnick, *President*
Stuart Kieschnick, *Vice Pres*
Thad Kieschnick, *Vice Pres*
Wade Kieschnick, *Vice Pres*
EMP: 27 EST: 2001
SQ FT: 20,000
SALES: 4.1MM **Privately Held**
WEB: www.kieschnickind.com
SIC: 3444 Sheet metal specialties, not stamped

(G-1915)
KNIFE RIVER CORPORATION
4825 Romeda Rd (77705-1198)
P.O. Box 20257 (77720-0257)
PHONE...................................409 842-2100
Mark Baker, *Branch Mgr*
EMP: 75
SALES (corp-wide): 5.3B **Publicly Held**
WEB: www.kniferiver.com
SIC: 3273 5032 Ready-mixed concrete; aggregate
HQ: Knife River Corporation
1150 W Century Ave
Bismarck ND 58503
701 530-1400

(G-1916)
LABELLECO FAB LLC
Also Called: Labelleco Fabrication
7335 Frint Dr (77705-7305)
P.O. Box 20516 (77720-0516)
PHONE...................................409 225-5499
Ryan Merendino, *CEO*
Chris Waldrup, *Project Mgr*
John Moore, *Prdtn Mgr*
Johnnie Erickson, *Manager*
Mike Simon, *Officer*
EMP: 60
SQ FT: 7,500
SALES (est): 4MM **Privately Held**
WEB: www.labellecofab.com
SIC: 3441 Building components, structural steel

(G-1917)
LETOURNEAU LFLIKE ORTHTICS PRS (PA)
2452 Calder St (77702-1920)
P.O. Box 21698 (77720-1698)
PHONE...................................409 832-5005
Tom Letourneau, *President*
Sandra Letourneau, *CFO*
EMP: 15
SQ FT: 3,852
SALES (est): 1.3MM **Privately Held**
WEB: www.llop.com
SIC: 3842 Orthopedic appliances; prosthetic appliances

(G-1918)
LIMA REFINING COMPANY
Also Called: Premcor Refining
9405 W Port Arthur Rd (77705-9294)
PHONE...................................409 839-3500
Gary Projcak, *Manager*
EMP: 16
SALES (corp-wide): 1.6B **Privately Held**
WEB: www.huskyenergy.com
SIC: 2911 Petroleum refining
HQ: Lima Refining Company
1150 S Metcalf St
Lima OH 45804
419 226-2300

(G-1919)
LINDE INC
Also Called: Praxair
3077 Calder St (77702-1408)
PHONE...................................409 835-3939
Larry Darst, *Exec VP*
Daniel Peoples, *Exec VP*
Mark Choate, *Vice Pres*
Eugene Humphrey, *Vice Pres*
EMP: 20 **Privately Held**
WEB: www.praxair.com
SIC: 2813 Industrial gases
HQ: Linde Inc.
10 Riverview Dr
Danbury CT 06810
203 837-2000

(G-1920)
LONE STAR RIGGING LP
4175 W Cardinal Dr (77705-4408)
PHONE...................................409 842-2263
Annie James, *Sales Mgr*
Chris Richardson, *Manager*
Chris L Richardson, *Manager*
Andrew Wilson, *Manager*
EMP: 13
SQ FT: 10,000
SALES (est): 4.2MM **Privately Held**
WEB: www.lonestarrigging.com
SIC: 3496 Slings, lifting: made from purchased wire

(G-1921)
M & T PALLET COMPANY INC
11397 Highway 90 (77713-3485)
P.O. Box 27, China (77613-0027)
PHONE...................................409 866-8136
Michael G Hamons, *President*
Trisha Hamons, *Vice Pres*
EMP: 20
SQ FT: 1,200
SALES (est): 2.7MM **Privately Held**
SIC: 2448 Pallets, wood

(G-1922)
M&I ELECTRIC LLC
4775 S Mlk Jr Pkwy (77705-5651)
PHONE...................................409 838-0441
Diana Grootonk, *CEO*
Leslie Chow, *Controller*
EMP: 210
SALES (est): 45MM
SALES (corp-wide): 120.8MM **Privately Held**
WEB: www.mielectric.com
SIC: 3448 3613 3629 Prefabricated metal buildings; control panels, electric; switchgear & switchgear accessories; power conversion units, a.c. to d.c.: static-electric
PA: Myers Power Products, Inc.
2950 E Philadelphia St
Ontario CA 91761
909 923-1800

(G-1923)
MAIL & PARCELS PLUS INC
Also Called: Kirkseys Sprint Prtg & Signs
3865 W Lucas Dr (77706-7110)
PHONE...................................409 899-1771
Doug Mullins, *President*
Charlene Mullins, *Admin Sec*
EMP: 10
SQ FT: 5,800
SALES (est): 1.5MM **Privately Held**
WEB: www.kirkseys.com
SIC: 2752 3953 7389 5943 Commercial printing, offset; embossing seals & hand stamps; mailbox rental & related service; office forms & supplies

(G-1924)
MAIN GATE
1225 Main St (77701-3648)
PHONE...................................409 832-1546
David C Fisher, *Exec Dir*
▼ EMP: 39
SALES (est): 2.4MM **Privately Held**
SIC: 2441 Shipping cases, wood: nailed or lock corner

(G-1925)
MANUFACTURING SOLUTIONS INC
Also Called: MSI
9485 College St (77707-2705)
PHONE...................................409 842-4404
Wayne Moncla, *President*
Stephen Parker, *Sales Staff*
EMP: 10
SQ FT: 7,200
SALES (est): 1.5MM **Privately Held**
WEB: www.msi-tx.com
SIC: 3599 Machine shop, jobbing & repair

(G-1926)
MARTIN MARIETTA MATERIALS INC
5675 Fannett Rd (77705-6833)
PHONE...................................409 835-4933
Brian Abney, *Office Mgr*
EMP: 21 **Publicly Held**
WEB: www.martinmarietta.com
SIC: 3273 Ready-mixed concrete
PA: Martin Marietta Materials Inc
2710 Wycliff Rd
Raleigh NC 27607

(G-1927)
MCLEOD MACHINE WORKS INC
5455 Ohio St (77705-6211)
PHONE...................................409 835-3429
Cal Smith, *President*
James A Smith, *Vice Pres*
Debra Hanks, *Purchasing*
Anita Smith, *Admin Sec*
EMP: 16 EST: 1948

SALES (est): 2.9MM **Privately Held**
WEB: www.mcleodmachine.com
SIC: 3599 Custom machinery; machine shop, jobbing & repair

(G-1928)
METALFORMS LTD
7218 Garth St (77705-6884)
P.O. Box 20118 (77720-0118)
PHONE...................................409 842-1626
David Hearn, *Principal*
Joe Phillips, *Buyer*
Gowri Jayamani, *Engineer*
Robert Long, *CFO*
Daniel Hearn, *Marketing Staff*
EMP: 59
SALES (est): 25MM **Privately Held**
WEB: www.metalformsltd.com
SIC: 3443 Fabricated plate work (boiler shop)

(G-1929)
MODERN CONCRETE & MTLS LLC
2090 W Cardinal Dr (77705-4741)
PHONE...................................409 840-2080
Trent Almond, *Mng Member*
EMP: 16
SALES (est): 116.8K **Privately Held**
WEB: www.modernconcretetx.com
SIC: 1771 3273 Concrete work; ready-mixed concrete

(G-1930)
MODERN GROUP LTD (PA)
1655 Louisiana St (77701-1120)
P.O. Box 790 (77704-0790)
PHONE...................................800 231-8198
Will Crenshaw, *CEO*
Casey Crenshaw, *President*
Adam Baylor, *Plant Mgr*
Paula Allen, *Purchasing*
Melissa Staggs, *Accountant*
▲ EMP: 53
SQ FT: 25,000
SALES (est): 294.9MM **Privately Held**
WEB: www.modernusa.com
SIC: 7359 3441 Equipment rental & leasing; fabricated structural metal

(G-1931)
MOMETRIX MEDIA LLC (PA)
Also Called: Mometrix Test Preparation
3827 Phelan Blvd Ste 179 (77707-2243)
PHONE...................................888 248-1219
Ryan Bowling, *CEO*
Eric Manthei, *Vice Pres*
Peter Rench, *Vice Pres*
Jake Glenn, *Facilities Mgr*
Ben Maas, *Accountant*
EMP: 38
SQ FT: 10,000
SALES (est): 12MM **Privately Held**
WEB: www.mometrix.com
SIC: 2731 2741 Book publishing; miscellaneous publishing; guides: publishing & printing

(G-1932)
NANCE INTERNATIONAL INC
Also Called: Nance Marine & Industrial AC
2915 Milam St (77701-4816)
PHONE...................................409 838-6127
R D Nance, *President*
Tara Holland, *Corp Secy*
Craig Miller, *Vice Pres*
John Trescott, *Vice Pres*
Jacob Johnson, *Opers Staff*
▲ EMP: 55
SQ FT: 40,000
SALES (est): 23.6MM **Privately Held**
WEB: www.nanceinternational.com
SIC: 3585 Refrigeration & heating equipment

(G-1933)
NATIONAL OILWELL VARCO INC
5780 Hagner Rd (77705-6430)
PHONE...................................409 842-2114
Toby Richard, *Mfg Staff*
Gary Hightower, *QC Mgr*
Scott Ray, *Engineer*
Robert Shiflet, *Engineer*
Crystal Curl, *Controller*
EMP: 100

SQ FT: 8,888
SALES (corp-wide): 8.4B **Publicly Held**
WEB: www.nov.com
SIC: 3541 8711 1389 Pipe cutting &
threading machines; engineering serv-
ices; oil field services
PA: National Oilwell Varco, Inc.
7909 Parkwood Circle Dr
Houston TX 77036
713 346-7500

(G-1934)
NEWPARK MATS INTGRTED
SVCS LLC
Also Called: Soloco-Mallard
16341 Highway 90 (77713-3697)
PHONE............................409 752-5800
Jamie Dishman, *Manager*
Shane Forse, *Manager*
EMP: 50
SALES (corp-wide): 747.7MM **Publicly**
Held
WEB: www.newpark.com
SIC: 1389 5082 1382 Construction, repair
& dismantling services; oil field equip-
ment; oil & gas exploration services
HQ: Newpark Mats & Integrated Services
Llc
9320 Lkeside Blvd Ste 100
The Woodlands TX 77381
281 362-6800

(G-1935)
OHMSTEDE LTD (HQ)
895 N Main St (77701-1813)
PHONE............................409 833-6375
William Reid, *CEO*
Glenda Barnwell, *Partner*
Douglas Harrington, *Partner*
John Marcotte, *Partner*
Bill Harkins, *District Mgr*
◆ **EMP:** 500
SQ FT: 112,000
SALES (est): 323.2MM
SALES (corp-wide): 9.1B **Publicly Held**
WEB: www.ohmstede.com
SIC: 5075 3443 Heat exchangers; heat
exchangers: coolers (after, inter), con-
densers, etc.
PA: Emcor Group, Inc.
301 Merritt 7 Fl 6
Norwalk CT 06851
203 849-7800

(G-1936)
OSBORNE CABINETS &
MILLWORK (PA)
Also Called: Osborne Cabinet & Millworks
8080 Eastex Fwy (77708-2403)
PHONE............................409 899-1191
Doyle Osborne, *President*
Angela Osborne, *Vice Pres*
EMP: 25
SQ FT: 18,156
SALES (est): 2.2MM **Privately Held**
WEB: www.osbornecabinets.com
SIC: 2434 Wood kitchen cabinets

(G-1937)
OVERTIME LLC
801 Laurel St (77701-2228)
PHONE............................409 833-3300
Glen W Morgan, *Owner*
EMP: 30
SALES (est): 190.2K **Privately Held**
WEB: www.drinkovertime.com
SIC: 3421 Table & food cutlery, including
butchers'

(G-1938)
PARKER BUSINESS FORMS INC
30 Interstate 10 N (77702-2110)
PHONE............................409 842-5251
Sheryl Parker, *Owner*
James Parker, *Vice Pres*
Heather Camp, *Sales Staff*
Clint Mathis, *Manager*
Becki Moore, *Manager*
EMP: 20
SALES (est): 2.7MM **Privately Held**
WEB: www.parkerbf.com
SIC: 2759 5943 Business forms: printing;
office forms & supplies

(G-1939)
PEPSI-COLA METRO BTLG CO
INC
2750 W Cardinal Dr (77705-4538)
PHONE............................409 842-2111
Joel Abbo, *Vice Pres*
Ward Lowe, *Site Mgr*
Dale Christian, *Sales Dir*
EMP: 45
SQ FT: 19,773
SALES (corp-wide): 67.1B **Publicly Held**
WEB: www.pepsico.com
SIC: 2086 Carbonated soft drinks, bottled
& canned
HQ: Pepsi-Cola Metropolitan Bottling Com-
pany, Inc.
1111 Westchester Ave
White Plains NY 10604
914 767-6000

(G-1940)
PERFORMANCE PRESSURE
PUMPING
5320 Gorman Rd (77705-6417)
PHONE............................409 980-8188
William J Rigby, *Vice Pres*
Antoine Broussard Jr,
EMP: 18 **EST:** 2011
SQ FT: 6,000
SALES (est): 4.3MM **Privately Held**
SIC: 1389 Oil field services

(G-1941)
PINCHBACK INDUSTRIAL INC
Also Called: Industrial Metal Co
695 Pinchback Rd (77707-3158)
P.O. Box 20316 (77720-0316)
PHONE............................409 860-1964
Carl E Skiles, *President*
Carl Higginbotham, *Superintendent*
Thomas Spear, *Opers Mgr*
EMP: 25
SQ FT: 24,000
SALES (est): 6MM **Privately Held**
SIC: 3441 Building components, structural
steel

(G-1942)
PIPING ACCESSORIES INC
7322 Garth St (77705-6886)
PHONE............................409 842-5000
Kenneth Clemmer, *President*
Lavell Harris, *Principal*
Chase Ellis, *Vice Pres*
Cody Murphy, *Sales Staff*
Joe Lavelle, *Technical Staff*
EMP: 25
SQ FT: 22,000
SALES (est): 5.3MM **Privately Held**
WEB: www.pipingaccessories.com
SIC: 3441 3498 3494 3429 Fabricated
structural metal; fabricated pipe & fittings;
valves & pipe fittings; manufactured hard-
ware (general)

(G-1943)
QUALITY CASE & FIXTURE INC
2070 Gulf St (77703-5202)
PHONE............................409 832-3200
Scott Jennings, *President*
John Bartlett, *Vice Pres*
EMP: 25
SQ FT: 63,500
SALES (est): 1.6MM **Privately Held**
SIC: 2541 Cabinets, except refrigerated:
show, display, etc.: wood

(G-1944)
QUALITY MAT COMPANY (PA)
6550 Tram Rd (77713-8703)
PHONE............................409 898-1170
Joe E Penland Sr, *CEO*
Joe Penland Jr, *President*
Joe Ehrhart, *General Mgr*
Scott Nance, *General Mgr*
Tina Ledoux, *Human Res Mgr*
◆ **EMP:** 105 **EST:** 1973
SQ FT: 480,000
SALES (est): 49.3MM **Privately Held**
WEB: www.qmat.com
SIC: 1389 3496 Oil field services; mats &
matting

(G-1945)
QUALITY MILL OF TEXAS LLC
550 Tram Rd (77713)
PHONE............................409 722-4594
Joe Penland, *Vice Pres*
EMP: 12
SALES (est): 594.7K **Privately Held**
SIC: 2421 Sawmills & planing mills, gen-
eral

(G-1946)
REAGENT CHEMICAL & RES INC
210 Office Park Dr (77707-2238)
PHONE............................409 899-3400
Jerry Smith, *QC Mgr*
Clara Whatley, *Branch Mgr*
Allen Baumgarte, *Director*
EMP: 12
SQ FT: 3,658
SALES (corp-wide): 376.8MM **Privately**
Held
WEB: www.prosysfill.com
SIC: 2819 Industrial inorganic chemicals
PA: Reagent Chemical & Research, Inc.
115 Rte 202
Ringoes NJ 08551
908 284-2800

(G-1947)
REE HOLDING INC
Also Called: Tool Tech
5420 Gorman Rd (77705-6419)
PHONE............................409 840-5650
Emmit Morales, *President*
Emmit Morales, *President*
Earl Williams, *Vice Pres*
Cara Derouen, *Manager*
EMP: 38
SQ FT: 26,000
SALES (est): 5.8MM **Privately Held**
WEB: www.tooltechmachining.com
SIC: 3599 3444 3441 7389 Custom ma-
chinery; sheet metalwork; fabricated
structural metal; grinding, precision: com-
mercial or industrial

(G-1948)
SENTRY SUPPLY INC
Also Called: Superior Supply & Steel
4855 Fannett Rd (77705-4303)
PHONE............................409 840-4800
J R Hardin, *Manager*
EMP: 15
SALES (corp-wide): 160.3MM **Privately**
Held
WEB: www.supstl.com
SIC: 5085 5051 3498 Industrial supplies;
steel; pipe fittings, fabricated from pur-
chased pipe
PA: Sentry Supply, Inc.
318 S Cities Service Hwy
Sulphur LA 70663
337 625-2300

(G-1949)
SIGN INTERNATIONAL INC
Also Called: Sign International Express
7398 College St (77707-3116)
P.O. Box 20054 (77720-0054)
PHONE............................409 832-0117
David Meriwether, *President*
Alan Meriwether, *Principal*
Michael Meriwether, *Vice Pres*
EMP: 14
SQ FT: 6,500
SALES (est): 2.2MM **Privately Held**
WEB: www.signinternational.com
SIC: 3993 Signs, not made in custom sign
painting shops

(G-1950)
SMITH INTERNATIONAL INC
6405 Highway 347 (77705-7631)
PHONE............................409 724-2471
Johnnie Willis, *Manager*
EMP: 40 **Publicly Held**
WEB: www.smithcodevelopment.com
SIC: 1389 Oil field services
HQ: Smith International, Inc.
1310 Rankin Rd
Houston TX 77073
281 443-3370

(G-1951)
SOUTHEAST TEXAS
INDUSTRIES INC
9561 Viterbo Rd (77705-0347)
PHONE............................409 722-7351
Jerrold Gill, *Manager*
EMP: 50 **Privately Held**
WEB: www.setxind.com
SIC: 3441 Fabricated structural metal
PA: Southeast Texas Industries, Inc.
35911 Us Highway 96 S
Buna TX 77612

(G-1952)
SOUTHERN AVIONICS CO
5055 Belmont St (77707-3701)
P.O. Box 5345 (77726-5345)
PHONE............................409 842-1717
John B Goodhue II, *President*
Brooks Goodhue, *President*
Jill Broussard, *Purch Mgr*
Amy Carre, *Purch Mgr*
Barney Ellis, *Technical Mgr*
EMP: 40
SQ FT: 30,000
SALES (est): 7.3MM **Privately Held**
WEB: www.southernavionics.com
SIC: 3812 8731 3663 Search & naviga-
tion equipment; commercial physical re-
search; radio & TV communications
equipment

(G-1953)
SOUTHERN STATE STEEL CO
9675 Walden Rd (77707-5232)
P.O. Box 3195, Austin (78764-3195)
PHONE............................409 866-1409
Fax: 409 866-6926
EMP: 40
SQ FT: 49,969
SALES (est): 4.5MM **Privately Held**
SIC: 3449 Mfg Misc Structural Metalwork

(G-1954)
STEEL INSULATOR GROUP LLC
7870 College St (77707-3142)
PHONE............................409 284-4407
Judd P Adams,
EMP: 15
SALES (est): 292.9K **Privately Held**
SIC: 1389 Construction, repair & disman-
tling services

(G-1955)
SUEZ WTS USA INC
W Hwy 90 (77713)
PHONE............................409 866-4756
Hern Lorraine, *Manager*
EMP: 50
SALES (corp-wide): 100.8MM **Privately**
Held
WEB: www.gewater.com
SIC: 2899 Water treating compounds
HQ: Suez Wts Usa, Inc.
4636 Somerton Rd
Trevose PA 19053
215 355-3300

(G-1956)
TCW INVESTMENTS INC
Also Called: Tri-City Investments
8505 Hwy 365 (77705)
P.O. Box 1352, Nederland (77627-1352)
PHONE............................409 796-1883
Larry Merendino, *President*
Daniel Fultz, *General Mgr*
EMP: 15
SQ FT: 4,000
SALES (est): 1.9MM **Privately Held**
WEB: www.tricitywelding.com
SIC: 3441 7692 3625 Fabricated struc-
tural metal; welding repair; electric con-
trols & control accessories, industrial

(G-1957)
TEAM INC
Also Called: Team Industrial Services
3875 W Cardinal Dr (77705-4411)
PHONE............................409 840-9955
Sarah Garza, *Office Mgr*
Brandon Brooks, *Manager*
EMP: 30

SALES (corp-wide): 1.1B **Publicly Held**
WEB: www.teaminc.com
SIC: 1389 8734 Oil & gas wells: building, repairing & dismantling; X-ray inspection service, industrial
PA: Team, Inc.
13131 Dar Ashford Ste 600
Sugar Land TX 77478
281 331-6154

(G-1958)
TEXAS COFFEE COMPANY
3297 S M L King Jr Pkwy (77705-2513)
P.O. Box 31 (77704-0031)
PHONE....................409 835-3434
Carlo Busceme III, *President*
Donald P Fertitta, *Vice Pres*
Joseph Fertitta Jr, *Vice Pres*
EMP: 40
SQ FT: 44,000
SALES (est): 5.1MM **Privately Held**
WEB: www.texjoy.com
SIC: 5499 5149 2099 2095 Coffee; coffee, green or roasted; food preparations; roasted coffee

(G-1959)
TIGER OFFSHORE RENTALS LLC (PA)
1655 Louisiana St (77701-1120)
PHONE....................409 951-4048
Will Crenshaw II, *CEO*
Colby Crenshaw, *President*
William Drost, *General Mgr*
Enyer Mata, *Engineer*
Brian Bomer, *CFO*
◆ **EMP:** 51 EST: 1998
SQ FT: 10,946
SALES (est): 206.5MM **Privately Held**
WEB: www.tigeroffshorerentals.com
SIC: 2911 8322 Oils, fuel; disaster service; emergency shelters

(G-1960)
TMS INTERNATIONAL LLC
100 Old Hwy 90 (77707)
P.O. Box 2749 (77704-2749)
PHONE....................409 768-1241
EMP: 17
SALES (corp-wide): 216.9MM **Privately Held**
SIC: 3295 Mfg Minerals-Ground/Treated
HQ: Tms International Group Llc
12 Monongahela Ave
Glassport PA 15203
412 678-6141

(G-1961)
TOTAL PTRCHEMICALS REF USA INC
11455 Ih 10 (77705-7043)
PHONE....................409 291-7296
Tom Voltz, *Mfg Dir*
Carrie Cunningham, *Branch Mgr*
EMP: 30
SALES (corp-wide): 7B **Publicly Held**
WEB: www.totalpetrochemicalsrefiningusa.com
SIC: 2821 Plastics materials & resins
HQ: Total Petrochemicals & Refining Usa, Inc.
1201 La St Ste 1800
Houston TX 77002
713 483-5000

(G-1962)
TRIANGLE BLUE PRINT COMPANY
1123 Calder St (77701-1798)
PHONE....................409 835-6810
Jaylynn Lavergne, *President*
Marinell Dominick, *Corp Secy*
George Lavergne, *Vice Pres*
Jay Lavergne, *Manager*
Randall Lavergne, *Technology*
EMP: 10
SQ FT: 12,000
SALES (est): 1.7MM **Privately Held**
WEB: www.triangleblueprint.com
SIC: 7334 2752 Blueprinting service; commercial printing, lithographic

(G-1963)
TRIANGLE RESOURCES INC
9869 Highway 90 (77713-3461)
P.O. Box 12364 (77726-2364)
PHONE....................409 861-2267
Margie Linder, *President*
Ronnie Linder, *Vice Pres*
EMP: 50
SALES (est): 9.7MM **Privately Held**
SIC: 3523 Soil sampling machines

(G-1964)
TRINITY INDUSTRIAL SVCS LLC (PA)
13071 W Port Arthur Rd (77705-0213)
PHONE....................409 722-6700
Bart E Umphrey, *President*
Mohamed Alli, *CFO*
Mohammed Alli, *CFO*
Anthony Tacker, *Director*
Bart Umphrey,
EMP: 450
SALES (est): 52.8MM **Privately Held**
WEB: www.trinityindustrialsvc.com
SIC: 8748 8742 3441 Industrial development planning; industrial & labor consulting services; fabricated structural metal

(G-1965)
UNITED MARINE ENTERPRISE INC
Also Called: United Marine Shipyard
1440 Spindletop Rd (77705-6613)
P.O. Box 22077 (77720-2077)
PHONE....................409 833-0303
A B Bernard Jr, *President*
EMP: 75
SQ FT: 30,000
SALES (est): 9.6MM **Privately Held**
WEB: www.umtexas.us
SIC: 3731 4499 1541 8711 Shipbuilding & repairing; marine salvaging & surveying services; industrial buildings & warehouses; engineering services; fabricated structural metal; fabricated plate work (boiler shop)
PA: Bgi Enterprise, Inc.
1325 Spindletop Rd
Beaumont TX 77705

(G-1966)
USA MILLENNIUM LP
2710 S 11th St (77701-7601)
PHONE....................409 840-6801
▲ **EMP:** 10
SALES (est): 980K **Privately Held**
SIC: 2834 Mfg Pharmaceutical Preparations

(G-1967)
VULCAN MATERIALS COMPANY
1399 Carroll St (77701-5806)
PHONE....................409 833-4177
EMP: 14 **Publicly Held**
WEB: www.vulcanmaterials.com
SIC: 3273 Ready-mixed concrete
PA: Vulcan Materials Company
1200 Urban Center Dr
Vestavia AL 35242

(G-1968)
WALSTON VENTURES LLC
Also Called: Tri-City Welding & Fabrication
8505 Fm 365 Rd (77705-9371)
PHONE....................409 796-1883
EMP: 15 EST: 2014
SQ FT: 2,800
SALES (est): 3MM **Privately Held**
WEB: www.tricitywelding.com
SIC: 3441 Fabricated structural metal

(G-1969)
WEST LTD
11025 Highway 124 (77705-6985)
P.O. Box 2298 (77704-2298)
PHONE....................409 794-9090
Clint West,
Clay West,
EMP: 10
SALES (est): 3MM **Privately Held**
WEB: www.apacheip.com
SIC: 3471 Sand blasting of metal parts

(G-1970)
WORLDWIDE SORBENT PRODUCTS INC
6600 Tram Rd Ste 2 (77713-8818)
PHONE....................409 983-7800
Chad Clay, *CEO*
William George, *President*
John Cooper, *Plant Mgr*
Andrea Tongue, *Purch Agent*
EMP: 45
SALES (est): 11.1MM **Privately Held**
WEB: www.wspsorbents.com
SIC: 2821 Polypropylene resins

Beckville
Panola County

(G-1971)
LACY OPERATIONS LTD
657 Fm 2792 (75631-8587)
PHONE....................903 693-3501
Rickey Simmons, *Manager*
EMP: 20
SALES (corp-wide): 6.3MM **Privately Held**
WEB: www.rlacy.com
SIC: 2911 1321 Gases & liquefied petroleum gases; natural gas liquids
PA: Lacy Operations Ltd
222 E Tyler St
Longview TX 75601
903 758-8276

(G-1972)
PIERCE CONSTRUCTION INC (PA)
4324 State Hwy 149 (75631)
PHONE....................903 678-3748
Kenneth Pierce, *President*
Justin Pierce, *Vice Pres*
Brenda Pierce, *Treasurer*
EMP: 57
SQ FT: 4,000
SALES (est): 34.9MM **Privately Held**
SIC: 1389 Oil & gas wells: building, repairing & dismantling

Bedford
Tarrant County

(G-1973)
AMERICAN POLYMERS CORP
2100 Reliance Pkwy (76021-6102)
PHONE....................817 684-7335
Vivek Varshney, *President*
Laxmi C Gupta, *Branch Mgr*
EMP: 11
SALES (corp-wide): 98.2MM **Privately Held**
WEB: www.polycoatusa.com
SIC: 2899 Waterproofing compounds
PA: American Polymers Corp.
14722 Spring Ave
Santa Fe Springs CA 90670
562 802-8834

(G-1974)
IMMEDIATEK INC
3301 Airport Fwy Ste 200 (76021-6034)
PHONE....................888 661-6565
Robert Hart, *Ch of Bd*
Timothy M Rice, *President*
Chetan Jaitly, *Vice Pres*
Timothy McCrory, *CFO*
Martin Woodall, *Director*
EMP: 20
SQ FT: 9,900
SALES: 3.2MM **Publicly Held**
WEB: www.immediatek.com
SIC: 7372 Application computer software; business oriented computer software
PA: Radical Holdings Lp
5424 Deloache Ave
Dallas TX 75220

(G-1975)
IMMUNOTEK BIO CENTERS LLC
1401 Brown Trl (76022-6491)
PHONE....................404 345-3570
Jerome Parnell III, *Branch Mgr*
EMP: 15

SALES (corp-wide): 27MM **Privately Held**
WEB: www.immunotek.com
SIC: 2836 Blood derivatives
PA: Immunotek Bio Centers, L.L.C.
3900 N Causeway Blvd # 1200
Metairie LA 70002
337 500-1175

(G-1976)
LEGACY HOUSING CORPORATION (PA)
1600 Airport Fwy Ste 100 (76022-6881)
PHONE....................817 799-4900
Curtis D Hodgson, *Ch of Bd*
Kenneth E Shipley, *President*
Jeff Burt, *CFO*
Thomas Kerkaert, *CFO*
Joey Powell, *Director*
▲ **EMP:** 181
SQ FT: 5,398
SALES: 168.9MM **Publicly Held**
WEB: www.legacyhousingcorp.com
SIC: 2541 Wood partitions & fixtures

(G-1977)
PLAYNET INC
1901 Central Dr Ste 600 (76021-5826)
P.O. Box 210218 (76095-7218)
PHONE....................817 358-7580
Jim Mesteller, *President*
Mike Carter, *Administration*
EMP: 50
SALES (est): 4MM **Privately Held**
WEB: www.wiionline.com
SIC: 4813 7372 ; prepackaged software

(G-1978)
REB TECHNOLOGIES INC
Also Called: Rebtech
1500 Brown Trl Ste 100 (76022-6418)
PHONE....................817 285-7740
Richard Borkowski, *President*
Jeff Stubbs, *Senior VP*
Lynne Borkowski, *Vice Pres*
Jim Garrett, *VP Prdtn*
EMP: 20
SQ FT: 2,000
SALES (est): 3.5MM **Privately Held**
WEB: www.rebtechnvg.com
SIC: 3728 Aircraft parts & equipment

(G-1979)
SHIELD BEARER INC (PA)
1316 Shirley Way (76022-6734)
PHONE....................817 868-1400
John Brookshire, *President*
June Brookshire, *Vice Pres*
EMP: 9
SALES (est): 871.9K **Privately Held**
SIC: 2834 Pharmaceutical preparations

(G-1980)
TRU-FORM OPTICS INC (PA)
400 Harwood Rd (76021-4150)
PHONE....................817 267-9261
Jan Svochak II, *President*
Jo Svochak, *President*
Frank Svochak II, *Treasurer*
Barbara Svockak, *Marketing Staff*
Truitt Hoover, *Consultant*
EMP: 20 EST: 1975
SQ FT: 5,300
SALES (est): 2.7MM **Privately Held**
WEB: www.tfoptics.com
SIC: 3851 Contact lenses

Bedias
Grimes County

(G-1981)
DURAMAST INDUSTRIES INC
9756 Fm 1696 Rd (77831-9496)
P.O. Box 158 (77831-0158)
PHONE....................936 395-0334
Karl E Johnson, *Exec Dir*
EMP: 25 EST: 2010
SALES (est): 4.4MM **Privately Held**
WEB: www.duramast.com
SIC: 3599 Machine shop, jobbing & repair

Beeville
Bee County

(G-1982)
BASIC ENERGY SERVICES LP
4638 Fish Ln (78102-8479)
P.O. Box 1419 (78104-1419)
PHONE..................................361 358-2505
Robert Fish, *President*
Richard Wegner, *Vice Pres*
EMP: 45
SALES (corp-wide): 567.2MM **Publicly Held**
WEB: www.basices.com
SIC: 1389 Oil field services
HQ: Basic Energy Services, L.P.
　　801 Cherry St Unit 2
　　Fort Worth TX 76102

(G-1983)
BECK BROS INC
2171 Ellis Rd (78102-8903)
PHONE..................................361 289-6082
Roland H Beck Jr, *President*
EMP: 85
SALES (est): 14MM **Privately Held**
WEB: www.beckbrosinc.com
SIC: 1389 Oil field services

(G-1984)
BEEVILLE PUBLISHING COMPANY (PA)
Also Called: Beeville Bee-Picayune
111 N Washington St (78102-4508)
P.O. Box 10 (78104-0010)
PHONE..................................361 358-2550
Fred C Latcham Jr, *President*
George Geoffrey Latcham, *General Mgr*
Fred C Latcham III, *Vice Pres*
EMP: 23 **EST:** 1886
SQ FT: 6,750
SALES (est): 3.1MM **Privately Held**
WEB: www.mysoutex.com
SIC: 2711 2791 2789 2759 Job printing & newspaper publishing combined; typesetting; bookbinding & related work; commercial printing; commercial printing, lithographic; automotive & apparel trimmings

(G-1985)
HUGHES DAN A COMPANY LP (PA)
Also Called: Dan A. Hughes Company
208 E Houston St (78102-4820)
P.O. Box 669 (78104-0669)
PHONE..................................361 358-3752
Dan A Hughes Sr, *Partner*
Dan A Hughes Jr, *Partner*
EMP: 27
SQ FT: 40,000
SALES (est): 9.5MM **Privately Held**
WEB: www.danahughescompany.bzzp.net
SIC: 1311 Crude petroleum production; natural gas production

(G-1986)
INTERNATIONAL WELL TESTERS
3720 Highway 59 W (78102-8795)
PHONE..................................361 358-1990
Jude Duffer, *Office Mgr*
Joann Cormier, *Office Mgr*
EMP: 14
SALES (corp-wide): 1.5MM **Privately Held**
SIC: 1389 Testing, measuring, surveying & analysis services
PA: International Well Testers Inc
　　803-E Mills Hwy
　　Breaux Bridge LA 70517
　　337 237-3000

(G-1987)
POLARIS EXPLORATION CORP
2863 Central Ln (78102-4706)
P.O. Box 60015, Corpus Christi (78466-0015)
PHONE..................................361 857-7176
William Carl, *President*
Savage Ken, *Exec VP*
Sandra Carl, *Treasurer*
EMP: 10

SALES (est): 674.7K **Privately Held**
SIC: 1382 Oil & gas exploration services

(G-1988)
STREAM-FLO USA LLC
3102 Highway 59 E (78102-8586)
PHONE..................................361 362-2600
Cody Cole, *Branch Mgr*
EMP: 35
SALES (corp-wide): 38.3MM **Privately Held**
WEB: www.streamflo.com
SIC: 3533 Oil field machinery & equipment
HQ: Stream-Flo Usa Llc
　　8726 Fallbrook Dr
　　Houston TX 77064
　　903 912-1022

(G-1989)
TW TANKS AND CONSTRUCTION CO
Also Called: Todd Weldings
671 W Fm 351 (78102-8348)
P.O. Box 4219 (78104-4219)
PHONE..................................361 358-8869
David Todd, *President*
Mike Todd, *Vice Pres*
Darlene Todd, *Admin Sec*
▲ **EMP:** 15
SQ FT: 3,300
SALES (est): 3.3MM **Privately Held**
SIC: 3533 7692 1799 3599 Oil & gas field machinery; welding repair; welding on site; machine shop, jobbing & repair; plastics plumbing fixtures

Bellaire
Harris County

(G-1990)
BIO-PATH HOLDINGS INC
4710 Bellaire Blvd # 210 (77401-4526)
PHONE..................................832 742-1357
Peter H Nielsen, *Ch of Bd*
Ulrich W Mueller, *COO*
Michael Roberts, *Mfg Staff*
Ana Tari, *Research*
Tara Sadeghi, *Director*
EMP: 11
SQ FT: 3,002
SALES (est): 44.7K **Privately Held**
WEB: www.biopathholdings.com
SIC: 2834 Pharmaceutical preparations

(G-1991)
BRIDGELINE HOLDINGS LP (DH)
4800 Fournace Pl (77401-2324)
PHONE..................................713 432-6000
Randal Curry, *President*
Randal L Curry, *President*
Hugh H Connett, *Vice Pres*
Robert Morgan, *Vice Pres*
Trevor Mihalik, *CFO*
EMP: 11
SQ FT: 5,000
SALES (est): 3.5MM
SALES (corp-wide): 6B **Publicly Held**
WEB: www.bridgeline.enlink.com
SIC: 1321 Natural gas liquids
HQ: Enlink Midstream Operating, Lp
　　1722 Routh St Ste 1300
　　Dallas TX 75201
　　214 953-9500

(G-1992)
C K HIGGS
Also Called: Galt Wine Cellars
5007 Elm St (77401-2811)
P.O. Box 25046, Houston (77265-5046)
PHONE..................................713 666-5739
Mike Stanton, *Owner*
C K Higgs, *Owner*
EMP: 40
SALES (est): 2.8MM **Privately Held**
WEB: www.galtwine.com
SIC: 2084 5182 3585 2434 Wine cellars, bonded: engaged in blending wines; wine; refrigeration & heating equipment; wood kitchen cabinets

(G-1993)
DELTA PAPER STOCK CORP
4814 Linden St (77401-4433)
PHONE..................................713 666-1440
Richard M Schultz, *President*
Michael Schultz, *Vice Pres*
EMP: 22
SQ FT: 30,000
SALES (est): 2.4MM **Privately Held**
SIC: 5093 4953 2611 Waste paper; refuse systems; pulp mills

(G-1994)
DOW CHEMICAL COMPANY
4709 Laurel St (77401-4408)
PHONE..................................713 667-5133
Oliver Holden, *Principal*
Kristin Page, *Technical Staff*
Anntwanette Chase, *Technician*
EMP: 68
SALES (corp-wide): 38.5B **Publicly Held**
WEB: www.dow.com
SIC: 2821 Thermoplastic materials
HQ: The Dow Chemical Company
　　2211 H H Dow Way
　　Midland MI 48642
　　989 636-1000

(G-1995)
EASTHAM DRILLING INC
Also Called: Big E Drilling Co.
4710 Bellaire Blvd # 350 (77401-4531)
PHONE..................................713 661-6890
Lyle Eastham, *CEO*
Becky Veronie, *Accountant*
EMP: 120
SALES (est): 9.5MM
SALES (corp-wide): 66.4MM **Privately Held**
WEB: www.bigedrilling.com
SIC: 1389 Oil field services
PA: Eastham Enterprises, Inc.
　　4710 Bellaire Blvd # 350
　　Bellaire TX 77401
　　713 661-6890

(G-1996)
GEOPHYSICAL TECHNOLOGY INC
800 Mulberry Ln (77401-3808)
PHONE..................................281 222-3078
Richard Degner, *President*
Heidi Brown, *Vice Pres*
Brown Heidi, *Vice Pres*
Ryan Khan, *Electrical Engi*
Mike Strain, *CFO*
EMP: 14
SALES (est): 1.7MM **Privately Held**
WEB: www.geophysicaltechnology.com
SIC: 3829 Geophysical or meteorological electronic equipment

(G-1997)
H J GRUY AND ASSOCIATES INC (PA)
6575 West Loop S Ste 550 (77401-3506)
PHONE..................................713 739-1000
Marilyn Wilson, *President*
Robert Rasor, *Exec VP*
Donaldson G E, *Vice Pres*
EMP: 13
SQ FT: 9,000
SALES (est): 2.5MM **Privately Held**
WEB: www.hjgruy.com
SIC: 8711 1382 7389 Consulting engineer; petroleum engineering; geological exploration, oil & gas field; geophysical exploration, oil & gas field; photogrammatic mapping

(G-1998)
MEDICAL UNIFORM MFG INC
Also Called: Syntheticomp
4951 Terminal St Ste G (77401-6009)
PHONE..................................713 838-2233
Mustafa Ebrahim, *President*
▲ **EMP:** 9
SQ FT: 8,000
SALES (est): 2.6MM **Privately Held**
WEB: www.med-uniform.com
SIC: 5137 5136 2326 Uniforms, women's & children's; uniforms, men's & boys'; medical & hospital uniforms, men's

(G-1999)
NEWS PUBLICATIONS INC
Also Called: Village News
5160 Spruce St (77401-3309)
PHONE..................................713 668-9293
Kathleen Ballanfant, *President*
EMP: 15
SQ FT: 3,807
SALES (est): 924.9K **Privately Held**
WEB: www.village-southwest-news.com
SIC: 2711 Newspapers: publishing only, not printed on site

(G-2000)
OFT ENTERPRISES INC (PA)
4950 Terminal St (77401-6013)
PHONE..................................713 787-5373
Omar Tuna, *President*
Atilla Tuna, *Vice Pres*
EMP: 30 **EST:** 1999
SQ FT: 5,000
SALES (est): 10.8MM **Privately Held**
WEB: www.oftent.com
SIC: 3531 5047 5072 5084 Construction machinery; medical equipment & supplies; hardware; industrial machinery & equipment; industrial trucks & tractors

(G-2001)
PERFOMIX LLC
1 Greenway Plz Ste 930 (77401)
PHONE..................................713 893-8310
EMP: 70
SALES (est): 2.6MM
SALES (corp-wide): 122B **Publicly Held**
SIC: 7372 Prepackaged Software Services
HQ: Baker Hughes, A Ge Company, Llc
　　17021 Aldine Westfield Rd
　　Houston TX 77073
　　713 439-8600

(G-2002)
SCHMIDT MANUFACTURING INC
6330 West Loop S Ste 900 (77401-2928)
PHONE..................................281 431-0581
Matt Sharpe, *Principal*
EMP: 11
SQ FT: 35,000
SALES (est): 8.1MM **Privately Held**
SIC: 3629 3625 3443 3412 Blasting machines, electrical; relays & industrial controls; fabricated plate work (boiler shop); metal barrels, drums & pails
HQ: Wheelabrator Group, Inc.
　　1606 Executive Dr
　　Lagrange GA 30240

(G-2003)
TEXAS AUTOMATIC FOODS INC
Also Called: T A F
1331 N 1st St (77401-6001)
PHONE..................................713 432-1331
Don L Berger, *President*
Donald M Berger, *Principal*
Lillian Berger, *Vice Pres*
Gregory J Berger, *Treasurer*
EMP: 31
SQ FT: 20,000
SALES (est): 3MM **Privately Held**
SIC: 2099 5962 Sandwiches, assembled & packaged: for wholesale market; salads, fresh or refrigerated; food vending machines

(G-2004)
VOSS CATERING INC
5422 Bellaire Blvd (77401-3906)
P.O. Box 2122 (77402-2122)
PHONE..................................713 257-9898
Shaun Leva, *President*
EMP: 55 **EST:** 2013
SALES (est): 73.8K **Privately Held**
WEB: www.houstoncatering.com
SIC: 5812 2051 Caterers

Bells
Grayson County

(G-2005)
C&C WELDING
302 Sunshine Trl (75414-3418)
PHONE..................................903 436-9150
Caleb Powers, *Principal*
EMP: 9

▲ = Import ▼ =Export
◆ =Import/Export

SALES (est): 94.9K **Privately Held**
SIC: 7692 Welding repair

(G-2006)
FOUR-STAR FABRICATORS & SVC CO
1140 N Pecan St (75414-2774)
P.O. Box 6 (75414-0006)
PHONE.........................903 965-4309
Christopher Slaughter, *President*
EMP: 32
SQ FT: 4,000
SALES (est): 5.6MM **Privately Held**
WEB: www.4starfab.com
SIC: 1711 3599 Mechanical contractor; machine & other job shop work

---

Bellville
Austin County

(G-2007)
AMERITRAIL INC (PA)
1005 S Front St (77418-2973)
P.O. Box 1118 (77418-1118)
PHONE.........................281 375-5458
Bernard Vlahakis, *President*
EMP: 42
SQ FT: 47,000
SALES (est): 9.5MM **Privately Held**
WEB: www.ranchkingtexas.com
SIC: 3713 Truck bodies & parts

(G-2008)
BELLVILLE TUBE COMPANY
141 Miller Rd E (77418-7096)
PHONE.........................281 467-7177
Joseph Lahey, *CEO*
Brendan Lahey, *CFO*
EMP: 50
SALES (est): 2MM **Privately Held**
SIC: 3533 Oil field machinery & equipment

(G-2009)
G E HUEBNER CONCRETE INC
217 S Mathews St (77418-2247)
P.O. Box 636 (77418-0636)
PHONE.........................979 865-2274
Glen Huebner, *President*
Donna Huebner, *Principal*
EMP: 10 EST: 1945
SQ FT: 1,000
SALES (est): 900K **Privately Held**
WEB: www.bellville.com
SIC: 3273 Ready-mixed concrete

(G-2010)
LONESTAR PRESTRESS MFG INC
Also Called: Lpmi
8892 Highway 159 E (77418-5888)
P.O. Box 400 (77418-0400)
PHONE.........................713 896-0994
Mark L Boyer, *CEO*
Brad B Boyer, *President*
Lyda Boyer, *Vice Pres*
Deborah Boyer, *Treasurer*
EMP: 48
SALES (est): 7.6MM **Privately Held**
WEB: www.lonestarprestress.com
SIC: 3272 Prestressed concrete products

(G-2011)
NELSON FACILITIES INC
12355 Highway 36 (77418-7047)
P.O. Box 638 (77418-0638)
PHONE.........................979 865-8596
James Dean-Nelson, *President*
James Dean Nelson, *President*
Julie K Nelson, *Corp Secy*
EMP: 15
SQ FT: 4,000
SALES (est): 2.2MM **Privately Held**
WEB: www.nelsonplantfood.com
SIC: 2875 Fertilizers, mixing only

(G-2012)
TESCO INDUSTRIES LP
1035 E Hacienda St (77418-2827)
PHONE.........................979 865-2163
Norman Kiecke, *General Ptnr*
Dennise Rother, *General Ptnr*
Larry W Rother, *General Ptnr*
▲ EMP: 85

SQ FT: 150,000
SALES (est): 12.7MM **Privately Held**
WEB: www.tesco-ind.com
SIC: 2531 2522 School furniture; office furniture, except wood

(G-2013)
VALMONT INDUSTRIES INC
11308 Highway 36 (77418-7056)
P.O. Box 640 (77418-0640)
PHONE.........................979 865-9137
Lenoal Hartwick, *Branch Mgr*
EMP: 76
SALES (corp-wide): 2.7B **Publicly Held**
WEB: www.valmont.com
SIC: 3441 Fabricated structural metal
PA: Valmont Industries, Inc.
1 Valmont Plz Ste 500
Omaha NE 68154
402 963-1000

(G-2014)
VALMONT NEWMARK INC
Also Called: Newmark International 14
11308 Highway 36 (77418-7056)
P.O. Box 640 (77418-0640)
PHONE.........................979 865-9137
Gerald Carter, *Finance Mgr*
Barbara Gremmel, *Executive*
EMP: 45
SALES (corp-wide): 2.7B **Publicly Held**
WEB: www.valmont.com
SIC: 3441 Fabricated structural metal
HQ: Valmont Newmark, Inc.
2 Perimeter Park S 475w
Birmingham AL 35243
205 968-7200

(G-2015)
WESTERN INTL GAS CYLINDERS INC (DH)
7173 Highway 159 E (77418-5309)
P.O. Box 668 (77418-0668)
PHONE.........................979 865-5991
Thomas S Kallman, *Ch of Bd*
Corey Birdwell, *Purch Agent*
Kenneth Kaase, *Engineer*
Jason Bombard, *Project Engr*
Chris Kramr, *Project Engr*
▲ EMP: 104
SQ FT: 15,000
SALES (est): 89.1MM **Privately Held**
WEB: www.westernintl.com
SIC: 5169 2813 Industrial gases; acetylene
HQ: Matheson Tri-Gas, Inc.
3 Mountainview Rd Ste 3 # 3
Warren NJ 07059
908 991-9200

Belton
Bell County

(G-2016)
AG-MEIER INDUSTRIES LLC
920 E 6th Ave (76513-2712)
PHONE.........................254 939-3731
Lyle Meier,
▲ EMP: 40
SALES (est): 3.2MM **Privately Held**
WEB: www.ag-meier.net
SIC: 0711 3569 Soil chemical treatment services; firefighting apparatus & related equipment

(G-2017)
AGE INDUSTRIES LTD
801 Industrial Park Rd (76513-1923)
PHONE.........................254 939-5828
Misty Coe, *Opers Mgr*
Gerry Lundy, *CFO*
Jim Linton, *Sales Staff*
Michael Coe, *Branch Mgr*
Mike Coe, *Manager*
EMP: 25
SQ FT: 15,000
SALES (corp-wide): 140.8MM **Privately Held**
WEB: www.ageindustries.com
SIC: 2653 Boxes, corrugated: made from purchased materials

PA: Age Industries, Ltd.
3601 County Road 316c
Cleburne TX 76031
817 477-5266

(G-2018)
AMERICAN SPINCAST INC
Also Called: Amstock Supply
2505 Taylors Valley Rd (76513-9622)
P.O. Box 769 (76513-0769)
PHONE.........................254 939-0292
Ivy J Breaux, *President*
Ellen Morris, *Vice Pres*
Robert Bell, *Purch Agent*
Mary Otoole, *Human Res Mgr*
Jason Jones, *Technical Staff*
▲ EMP: 70
SQ FT: 50,000
SALES (est): 15MM **Privately Held**
WEB: www.americanspincast.us
SIC: 3325 Alloy steel castings, except investment

(G-2019)
BELCO MANUFACTURING CO INC
2303 Taylors Valley Rd (76513-9606)
P.O. Box 210 (76513-0210)
PHONE.........................254 933-9000
Steve Macy, *President*
Robert B Bennett, *Vice Pres*
Victor Felix, *Plant Mgr*
Mark Guenat, *QC Mgr*
Denise Severson, *QC Mgr*
EMP: 160 EST: 1980
SQ FT: 75,000
SALES (est): 43.5MM
SALES (corp-wide): 8.4B **Publicly Held**
WEB: www.belco-mfg.com
SIC: 3089 Plastic & fiberglass tanks
HQ: Denali Incorporated
9910 E 56th St N
Tulsa OK 74117

(G-2020)
BELLTEC INDUSTRIES INC
2057 Commerce St (76513-1968)
P.O. Box 270 (76513-0270)
PHONE.........................254 939-9404
Clyde Jones, *President*
Donny Jones, *Vice Pres*
Tamara Brown, *Purch Agent*
Cory Wheeler, *Sales Staff*
Alan Jones, *Marketing Staff*
▲ EMP: 18
SQ FT: 35,000
SALES (est): 3.8MM **Privately Held**
WEB: www.belltec.net
SIC: 3531 3523 Construction machinery; farm machinery & equipment

(G-2021)
BELTON NEWSPAPER INC
Also Called: Belton Journal
210 N Penelope St (76513-3159)
P.O. Box 180 (76513-0180)
PHONE.........................254 939-5754
David Tuma, *President*
Anna Tuma, *Vice Pres*
Darci Miller, *Sales Staff*
EMP: 12
SALES (est): 721.3K **Privately Held**
WEB: www.beltonjournal.com
SIC: 2711 Newspapers, publishing & printing

(G-2022)
CAPITOL SEATING COMPANY
Also Called: USA Capitol
209 E Grove Rd (76513-9425)
PHONE.........................254 939-1853
Terry Mantz, *President*
Todd Mantz, *Vice Pres*
EMP: 50
SQ FT: 150,000
SALES (est): 7.7MM **Privately Held**
WEB: www.usacapitol.com
SIC: 2531 5712 School furniture; chairs, table & arm; furniture stores

(G-2023)
H & H T-SHIRT PRINTING INC
5696 Fm 439 (76513-4736)
PHONE.........................254 628-1453
Bill Hale, *President*
Laurie Hale, *Manager*

EMP: 9
SQ FT: 4,200
SALES (est): 1.2MM **Privately Held**
WEB: www.hhtexas.com
SIC: 5699 2329 5136 T-shirts, custom printed; lumber jackets: men's, youths' & boys'; shirts, men's & boys'

(G-2024)
HARVEST INCORPORATED (DH)
Also Called: Stratasys Direct Manufacturing
815 Kirkley Blvd (76513-4158)
PHONE.........................254 933-1000
David K Leigh, *President*
David E Leigh, *President*
Dorothy Musacchio, *Project Mgr*
Carlos Berumen, *Production*
Jeromy Knapp, *Engineer*
▲ EMP: 24
SQ FT: 40,000
SALES (est): 5.4MM
SALES (corp-wide): 620.5MM **Privately Held**
WEB: www.stratasysdirect.com
SIC: 2821 Plastics materials & resins

(G-2025)
INDECO SALES INC (PA)
805 E 4th Ave (76513-2769)
PHONE.........................254 939-5742
Byron L Mays, *President*
Mike Anderson, *Vice Pres*
Patrick Lynn Mays, *Vice Pres*
Carlton Beck, *Project Mgr*
Doris Mays, *Treasurer*
▲ EMP: 25 EST: 1971
SQ FT: 285,000
SALES (est): 35.5MM **Privately Held**
WEB: www.indecosales.com
SIC: 5021 2531 2521 School desks; public building & related furniture; wood office furniture

(G-2026)
JONES-BELL LLC
Also Called: Engineer Composite System
2201 Taylors Valley Rd (76513-9600)
P.O. Box 127 (76513-0127)
PHONE.........................254 933-2270
Jeffrey Jones, *President*
Alisa J Leinart, *Corp Secy*
Michael G Jones, *Vice Pres*
Lina Nemeth, *Assistant*
EMP: 50
SALES (est): 14MM **Privately Held**
WEB: www.ecs-env.com
SIC: 2221 Fiberglass fabrics

(G-2027)
MACO MANUFACTURING INC
805 E 4th Ave (76513-2769)
P.O. Box 208 (76513-0208)
PHONE.........................254 939-5742
Byron Lee Mays, *President*
Doris Mays, *Corp Secy*
Lynn Mays, *Vice Pres*
▲ EMP: 25 EST: 1974
SALES (est): 3.4MM **Privately Held**
SIC: 2531 2541 School furniture; wood partitions & fixtures

(G-2028)
SOUTHWESTERN FOAM TECH INC
1106 Industrial Park Rd (76513-1926)
P.O. Box 240 (76513-0240)
PHONE.........................254 939-6379
Carl Thies, *Branch Mgr*
EMP: 15
SALES (corp-wide): 183.7MM **Privately Held**
WEB: www.grft.com
SIC: 3086 Plastics foam products
HQ: Southwestern Foam Technologies, Inc.
1700 Alpine Ave Nw
Grand Rapids MI 49504

(G-2029)
TRU
520 Sparta Rd (76513-1400)
PHONE.........................254 831-6002
EMP: 50
SALES (est): 1.5MM **Privately Held**
WEB: www.beltonedc.org
SIC: 3724 Aircraft engines & engine parts

Ben Wheeler
Van Zandt County

(G-2030)
ACE AUTOMATICS INC
7439 Fm 314 (75754-5043)
P.O. Box 1270, Van (75790-1270)
PHONE.................................903 852-3004
James Gilchrist, *President*
Carla Shackelford, *Manager*
EMP: 12
SALES (est): 1.7MM Privately Held
SIC: 2541 3442 Store fronts, prefabricated: wood; store fronts, prefabricated, metal

(G-2031)
AMERI SOURCE MANUFACTURING INC
Also Called: Crick Tool
17785 Fm 773 (75754-6025)
P.O. Box 1656, Athens (75751-1656)
PHONE.................................903 677-7734
Sam Alford, *President*
Charlotte Alford, *Corp Secy*
Lonnie Hodges, *Plant Mgr*
Scott Brown, *Sales Executive*
EMP: 11
SQ FT: 16,000
SALES (est): 2.2MM Privately Held
WEB: www.cricktool.com
SIC: 3823 3829 Level & bulk measuring instruments, industrial process; measuring & controlling devices

(G-2032)
DOOR CONTROL SERVICES
Also Called: A 1 Automatic Door Systems
321 Vz County Road 4500 (75754-3184)
PHONE.................................210 732-1214
Fax: 210 735-8621
EMP: 16
SQ FT: 5,000
SALES (est): 1.1MM Privately Held
SIC: 1751 7699 3699 Carpentry Contractor Repair Services Mfg Electrical Equipment/Supplies

(G-2033)
DOOR CONTROLS USA INC
321 Vz County Road 4500 (75754-3184)
PHONE.................................903 833-5815
Jimmy D Gilchrist, *CEO*
Kristine Shores, *CFO*
Matt Lucas, *Manager*
Greg Bishop, *Administration*
EMP: 185
SALES (est): 32MM Privately Held
WEB: www.doorcontrolsusa.com
SIC: 3429 Door locks, bolts & checks

(G-2034)
RAL & ASSOCIATES INC
14750 State Highway 64 (75754-2118)
P.O. Box 442 (75754-0442)
PHONE.................................903 833-5191
Rita Lyness, *President*
Patrick Lyness, *Director*
EMP: 23 Privately Held
SIC: 2591 5719 Window blinds; venetian blinds; vertical blinds

Benavides
Duval County

(G-2035)
PRICE DRILLING COMPANY INC
Hwy 359 E (78341)
P.O. Box 470 (78341-0470)
PHONE.................................361 256-3363
Richard B Shaw, *President*
Robert W Cadwell, *Vice Pres*
Robert Cadwell, *Vice Pres*
Shad C Shaw, *CFO*
EMP: 100
SQ FT: 1,400
SALES (est): 6.4MM Privately Held
WEB: www.pricedrilling.com
SIC: 1381 Drilling oil & gas wells

Benbrook
Tarrant County

(G-2036)
ADVANCED DIVERSIFIED SVCS INC
Also Called: A D S Steel Services
7461 W Vickery Blvd (76116-9253)
PHONE.................................817 377-2718
Frank Keith Shaw, *President*
Stuart Shaw, *Vice Pres*
Lee Gilbert, *Purch Agent*
EMP: 40
SQ FT: 25,000
SALES (est): 12.5MM Privately Held
SIC: 3441 1791 Fabricated structural metal; structural steel erection

(G-2037)
APPLIED SYSTEMS ENGRG INC
Also Called: A S E
7510 Benbrook Pkwy (76126-2112)
PHONE.................................817 249-4180
Kenneth Reed, *President*
Michael Reed, *VP Opers*
Laneva Kidd, *Manager*
Gil Valdez, *Technology*
B V Jostrand, *Director*
EMP: 55
SQ FT: 20,000
SALES (est): 25.2MM Privately Held
WEB: www.applsys.com
SIC: 3663 Radio & TV communications equipment

(G-2038)
AVX AIRCRAFT COMPANY
6310 Southwest Blvd # 106 (76109-3998)
PHONE.................................817 731-8003
David E Brody, *CEO*
Don Taylor, *Ch of Bd*
Kendall Goodman, *President*
Frank King, *Senior VP*
Keith Stevenson, *Engineer*
EMP: 35
SALES (est): 1.9MM Privately Held
WEB: www.avxaircraft.com
SIC: 3721 Helicopters

(G-2039)
FRIEDSON HILL INC
Also Called: Line-X of West Ft Worth
8155 Camp Bowie West Blvd A (76116-6314)
PHONE.................................817 244-6500
David Friedson, *President*
EMP: 10
SALES (corp-wide): 1.3MM Privately Held
WEB: www.linexfortworthtexas.com
SIC: 5531 2821 Truck equipment & parts; plastics materials & resins
PA: Friedson Hill Inc
6804 Trinity Landing Dr N
Fort Worth TX 76132
817 294-3309

(G-2040)
GARDNER DENVER INC
441 Winscott Rd (76126-2115)
PHONE.................................817 248-4500
Michael Mace, *Production*
Vanessa Sanabria, *Engineer*
Roy Childs, *Sales Mgr*
Russel Stewart, *Manager*
EMP: 24
SALES (corp-wide): 2.4B Publicly Held
WEB: www.gardnerdenver.com
SIC: 3533 3561 Oil field machinery & equipment; pumps & pumping equipment
HQ: Gardner Denver, Inc.
800 Beaty St
Davidson NC 28036

(G-2041)
HERRING TANK COMPANY INC (PA)
7201 W Vickery Blvd (76116-9038)
PHONE.................................817 377-1851
Ricky Don Herring, *President*
Charles T Roper Jr, *Corp Secy*
Rick Herring, *CFO*
Dale Herring, *Treasurer*

Roper Charile, *Manager*
▼ EMP: 25
SQ FT: 100,000
SALES (est): 7.6MM Privately Held
WEB: www.herringtank.com
SIC: 1791 3443 Storage tanks, metal: erection; fabricated plate work (boiler shop)

(G-2042)
LOCKHEED MARTIN CORPORATION
6116 Southwest Blvd (76109-3986)
P.O. Box 748, Fort Worth (76101-7450)
PHONE.................................817 777-2000
Mark Caesar, *Senior Engr*
Rick Couck, *Manager*
Randy Cochran, *Executive*
Kevin Isley, *Analyst*
EMP: 100 Publicly Held
WEB: www.lockheedmartin.com
SIC: 3761 3663 3764 3812 Space vehicles, complete; guided missiles, complete; ballistic missiles, complete; guided missiles & space vehicles, research & development; satellites, communications; propulsion units for guided missiles & space vehicles; guided missile & space vehicle engines, research & devel.; warfare counter-measure equipment; missile guidance systems & equipment; sonar systems & equipment; radar systems & equipment; aircraft parts & equipment; research & dev by manuf., aircraft parts & auxiliary equip; research & development on aircraft by the manufacturer
PA: Lockheed Martin Corporation
6801 Rockledge Dr
Bethesda MD 20817

(G-2043)
MAVERICK POLES & STRUCTURE LLC
3559 Williams Rd Ste 106 (76116-7041)
PHONE.................................817 441-9688
Courtney Wooten, *Accounts Mgr*
Pamela A Wooten, *Mng Member*
▼ EMP: 9
SQ FT: 2,000
SALES (est): 1MM Privately Held
WEB: www.maverickpoles.com
SIC: 3648 Lighting equipment

(G-2044)
PALADIN SIGNS AND GRAPHICS INC
324 Rhineland Rd (76126-3113)
PHONE.................................817 744-7361
Jaysen Lamb, *President*
EMP: 18 EST: 2012
SALES (est): 800K Privately Held
WEB: www.paladinsigns.com
SIC: 3993 1742 Signs & advertising specialties; solar reflecting insulation film

(G-2045)
PULIDO ASSOCIATES INC
Also Called: Pulido Tortilla Factory
7601 Benbrook Pkwy (76126-2102)
PHONE.................................817 249-6728
Robert Pulido, *President*
John Rodriguez, *Vice Pres*
EMP: 20
SQ FT: 14,800
SALES (corp-wide): 11.4MM Privately Held
WEB: www.pulidonassociates.com
SIC: 5141 2099 Groceries, general line; tortillas, fresh or refrigerated
PA: Pulido Associates, Inc.
4924 Old Benbrook Rd
Fort Worth TX 76116
817 731-4241

(G-2046)
TRIDENT WATER SERVICES LLC
325 Trinidad Ct (76126-3148)
PHONE.................................817 889-4334
Jud Sustala, *CEO*
Cody Lode, *President*
Monte Lode, *COO*
EMP: 30 EST: 2008

SALES (est): 2.6MM Privately Held
WEB: www.tridentwater.com
SIC: 1389 Gas field services

(G-2047)
U S WEATHERFORD L P
500 Winscott Rd (76126-2116)
PHONE.................................817 249-7200
Randy Cassady, *Vice Pres*
Hamid Nayyeri, *Sales Mgr*
EMP: 26 Privately Held
WEB: www.weatherford.com
SIC: 3498 3533 Fabricated pipe & fittings; oil & gas field machinery; oil field machinery & equipment
HQ: U S Weatherford L P
179 Weatherford Dr
Schriever LA 70395
985 493-6100

(G-2048)
WEATHERFORD INTERNATIONAL LLC
7500 Benbrook Pkwy (76126-2112)
PHONE.................................817 443-3000
EMP: 9 Privately Held
WEB: www.weatherford.com
SIC: 1389 1382 Oil field services; oil & gas exploration services
HQ: Weatherford International, Llc
2000 Saint James Pl
Houston TX 77056
713 693-4000

Bergheim
Kendall County

(G-2049)
MMMIX LTD
Also Called: Margarita Man
33 Fm 3351 N (78004-1905)
PHONE.................................830 336-4252
EMP: 20
SQ FT: 1,620
SALES (est): 3.2MM Privately Held
WEB: www.margaritaman.com
SIC: 2087 Cocktail mixes, nonalcoholic

Bertram
Burnet County

(G-2050)
ALKUSARI TEXAS LIMESTONE CORP
4121 E State Highway 29 (78605-4271)
PHONE.................................512 339-2299
Tom Alkusari, *President*
EMP: 10
SQ FT: 60,000
SALES (est): 595.8K Privately Held
WEB: www.alkusaristone.com
SIC: 1411 Limestone & marble dimension stone

(G-2051)
ANTIQUESTONE INC
Also Called: Stone Art
330 N Lampasas St (78605-4329)
P.O. Box 434 (78605-0434)
PHONE.................................512 355-2722
Jim Dyke, *President*
James Dyke Jr, *Corp Secy*
EMP: 12
SQ FT: 20,000
SALES (est): 790K Privately Held
WEB: www.uscustomtile.com
SIC: 3272 Floor slabs & tiles, precast concrete

(G-2052)
DIVERSIFIED MACHINING INC
3703 E State Highway 29 (78605-4572)
P.O. Box 1716 (78605-1716)
PHONE.................................512 355-3270
A Charles, *President*
Charles A Null, *President*
Denise Null, *CFO*
EMP: 15
SQ FT: 15,000

SALES (est): 2.1MM **Privately Held**
WEB: www.diversifiedmachining.net
SIC: 3599 7692 Machine shop, jobbing &
repair; welding repair

(G-2053)
RIVER CITY MANUFACTURING INC
1255 E State Highway 29 (78605-4332)
PHONE..................................512 335-5194
Gene Kilmer, *President*
▼ EMP: 15
SALES (est): 2.8MM **Privately Held**
WEB: www.hydrawheel.com
SIC: 3541 5085 3531 Machine tools,
metal cutting type; industrial supplies;
construction machinery

Big Lake
Reagan County

(G-2054)
BASIC ENERGY SERVICES INC
101 N Mississippi Ave (76932-5111)
PHONE..................................325 884-5901
Arturo Ramirez, *Manager*
EMP: 70
SALES (corp-wide): 567.2MM **Publicly Held**
WEB: www.basices.com
SIC: 1389 Oil field services
PA: Basic Energy Services, Inc.
801 Cherry St Unit 2
Fort Worth TX 76102
817 334-4100

(G-2055)
CHRISTEROS SERVICES LLC
108 N Ohio Ave (76932-5427)
PHONE..................................325 884-1100
Mario De Julios, *Owner*
EMP: 30
SALES (est): 983.5K **Privately Held**
SIC: 1382 Oil & gas exploration services

(G-2056)
FISHER LEASE SERVICE INC (PA)
Also Called: F & W Disposal
303 N State Highway 137 (76932-3005)
P.O. Box 926 (76932-0926)
PHONE..................................325 884-2701
Cecil Dale Fisher, *President*
EMP: 45
SALES (est): 4.3MM **Privately Held**
SIC: 1389 7363 Oil field services; help
supply services

(G-2057)
GLOBE WELL SERVICE INC
Also Called: Big Lake Fluid Services
159 Santa Rita Rd (76932)
PHONE..................................325 884-3091
Troy Botts Jr, *President*
Troy Burton, *Senior VP*
Philip Wright, *CFO*
EMP: 70 EST: 1963
SQ FT: 6,000
SALES (est): 211.7K
SALES (corp-wide): 567.2MM **Publicly Held**
WEB: www.phoenixoilfieldservices.com
SIC: 1389 Oil field services
HQ: Basic Energy Services, L.P.
801 Cherry St Unit 2
Fort Worth TX 76102

(G-2058)
KODIAK PRODUCTION LTD
303 N State Highway 137 (76932-3005)
P.O. Box 926 (76932-0926)
PHONE..................................325 884-2040
Cecil Dale Fisher, *Principal*
John Ashby,
EMP: 40
SALES (est): 1.4MM **Privately Held**
SIC: 1381 Drilling oil & gas wells

(G-2059)
NABORS WELL SERVICES CO
Also Called: CNJ
100 W Highway 67 (76932-3024)
PHONE..................................325 884-2536

Ray Wootall, *President*
Ray Woodall, *Branch Mgr*
Juan Rivera, *Manager*
EMP: 55 EST: 2013
SALES (est): 1.4MM **Privately Held**
SIC: 1389 Oil field services

(G-2060)
NATIONAL OILWELL VARCO INC
506 W Us Highway 67 (76932-1802)
PHONE..................................325 884-2556
John Hodge, *Branch Mgr*
EMP: 13
SALES (corp-wide): 8.4B **Publicly Held**
WEB: www.nov.com
SIC: 5084 5082 1389 Industrial machin-
ery & equipment; oil field equipment; oil
field services
PA: National Oilwell Varco, Inc.
7909 Parkwood Circle Dr
Houston TX 77036
713 346-7500

(G-2061)
RAMCO ROUSTABOUT INC
1401 E 3rd St (76932)
P.O. Box 280 (76932-0280)
PHONE..................................325 884-5734
Pedro Ramirez, *President*
Jorge Ramirez, *Corp Secy*
Humberto Ramirez, *Vice Pres*
EMP: 25
SALES (est): 3.3MM **Privately Held**
WEB: www.eugeneiv.com
SIC: 1389 Roustabout service

(G-2062)
T HILL PRODUCTION SVCS INC
1700 N State Highway 137 (76932-1903)
P.O. Box 424 (76932-0424)
PHONE..................................325 884-2670
Tommy L Hill Jr, *President*
Deborah L Hill, *Treasurer*
EMP: 19
SALES (est): 2.6MM **Privately Held**
WEB: www.thillpro.com
SIC: 1389 Oil field services

(G-2063)
WEST TEXAS ANCHOR INC
103 S Utah Ave (76932-6214)
P.O. Box 548 (76932-0548)
PHONE..................................325 884-3402
Jokellie Kuykendall, *Director*
EMP: 20
SALES (est): 3.8MM **Privately Held**
SIC: 1389 Oil field services

Big Sandy
Upshur County

(G-2064)
AGPRO SYSTEMS INC (PA)
242 Private Road 3341 (75755-4658)
PHONE..................................903 636-5545
Donald Mischnick, *President*
▲ EMP: 10
SALES (est): 1.6MM **Privately Held**
WEB: www.agprosystems.com
SIC: 2879 Agricultural chemicals

(G-2065)
KENNETH M BURGIN
Also Called: K & D Woodwork
381 Pine Rd (75755-5580)
PHONE..................................903 636-4086
Kenneth M Burgin, *Owner*
EMP: 12
SALES (est): 957.8K **Privately Held**
WEB: www.kdwoodwork.com
SIC: 2434 Wood kitchen cabinets

(G-2066)
PAVEMENT TOOL MFG INC
6339 Scrub Pine Rd (75755-5177)
P.O. Box 1048, Gladewater (75647-1048)
PHONE..................................903 734-7531
Patty Smith, *President*
Jack A Smith, *Shareholder*
EMP: 12
SQ FT: 6,000 **Privately Held**
WEB: www.pavementtool.com

SIC: 3953 2951 5032 Stencils, painting &
marking; asphalt paving mixtures &
blocks; paving materials

Big Spring
Howard County

(G-2067)
A & B GLASS LLC
1811 S Gregg St (79720-5433)
PHONE..................................432 517-4565
Kenneth Rowell, *Principal*
Don Avent, *Mng Member*
EMP: 10
SALES (est): 411.4K **Privately Held**
WEB: www.abglassmirrorcompany.com
SIC: 1793 3211 3231 5039 Glass & glaz-
ing work; construction glass; building
glass, flat; ornamental glass; cut, en-
graved or otherwise decorated; exterior
flat glass: plate or window

(G-2068)
A & M COMPOSITES CORPORATION
1409 E Highway 350 (79720-0477)
PHONE..................................432 267-6525
Michael R Niklasch, *President*
Jeannie K Niklasch, *Vice Pres*
EMP: 40
SQ FT: 52,000
SALES (est): 8.8MM **Privately Held**
SIC: 3089 2221 Plastic processing; fiber-
glass fabrics

(G-2069)
ALON USA LP
200 Refinery Rd (79720-2173)
P.O. Box 1311 (79721-1311)
PHONE..................................432 263-7661
Deann Cannon, *Buyer*
Dave Foster, *Branch Mgr*
Joebrice Wright, *Supervisor*
Darren Byrd, *Technology*
Gary Barnard, *Maintence Staff*
EMP: 280
SALES (corp-wide): 9.3B **Publicly Held**
WEB: www.alonusa.com
SIC: 2911 Oils, fuel
HQ: Alon Usa, Lp
7102 Commerce Way
Brentwood TN 37027

(G-2070)
B & E ROUSTABOUT INC
103 Aztec St (79720-2159)
P.O. Box 3582 (79721-3582)
PHONE..................................432 393-5672
Barry McBee, *President*
Barry Mc Bee, *President*
EMP: 22
SALES (est): 2.7MM **Privately Held**
WEB: www.hostprodirect.com
SIC: 1389 1382 Servicing oil & gas wells;
oil & gas exploration services

(G-2071)
BAKER HUGHES INCORPORATED
3609 E Interstate 20 (79720-3545)
PHONE..................................432 264-9007
EMP: 85
SALES (corp-wide): 24.5B **Publicly Held**
SIC: 3533 Mfg Oil/Gas Field Machinery
PA: Baker Hughes Incorporated
2929 Allen Pkwy Ste 2100
Houston TX 77073
713 439-8600

(G-2072)
BASIC ENERGY SERVICES INC
1203 Highway 176 (79720-0390)
PHONE..................................432 267-8885
Roger Sparks, *Manager*
EMP: 40
SALES (corp-wide): 567.2MM **Publicly Held**
WEB: www.basices.com
SIC: 1389 Oil field services
PA: Basic Energy Services, Inc.
801 Cherry St Unit 2
Fort Worth TX 76102
817 334-4100

(G-2073)
BASIC ENERGY SERVICES LP
2206 N Hwy 87 (79720)
P.O. Box 2887 (79721-2887)
PHONE..................................432 264-1212
Lynn Wigington, *Manager*
EMP: 80
SALES (corp-wide): 567.2MM **Publicly Held**
WEB: www.basices.com
SIC: 1389 Running, cutting & pulling cas-
ings, tubes & rods; oil field services
HQ: Basic Energy Services, L.P.
801 Cherry St Unit 2
Fort Worth TX 76102

(G-2074)
CERAM-KOTE COATINGS INC
Also Called: Freecom
1800 Industrial Park (79720-7894)
P.O. Box 2119 (79721-2119)
PHONE..................................432 263-8497
John E Freeman, *CEO*
Kevin Freeman, *President*
Chad Freeman, *Vice Pres*
Jack Richardson, *Vice Pres*
Zac Terry, *Plant Mgr*
▼ EMP: 35
SQ FT: 40,000
SALES (est): 5.1MM **Privately Held**
WEB: www.ceram-kote.com
SIC: 3479 2851 Coating, rust preventive;
paints & allied products

(G-2075)
CLINE CONSTRUCTION INC
Also Called: Cline Construction and Paving
1807 N Fm 700 (79720-0323)
P.O. Box 832 (79721-0832)
PHONE..................................432 267-6006
Greg Cline, *President*
EMP: 25
SQ FT: 2,000
SALES (est): 3.4MM **Privately Held**
SIC: 1623 1611 1389 Telephone & com-
munication line construction; highway &
street paving contractor; construction, re-
pair & dismantling services

(G-2076)
CNHI LLC
Also Called: Big Spring Herald
710 Scurry St (79720-2723)
P.O. Box 1431 (79721-1431)
PHONE..................................432 263-7331
Susanne Reed, *Sales/Mktg Mgr*
EMP: 30
SALES (corp-wide): 23.7B **Privately Held**
WEB: www.cnhi.com
SIC: 2711 Newspapers, publishing & print-
ing
HQ: Cnhi, Llc
445 Dexter Ave Ste 7000
Montgomery AL 36104

(G-2077)
CO-EX PIPE CO
714 Anna St (79720-1800)
P.O. Box 3507 (79721-3507)
PHONE..................................432 263-0206
Dale Waldron, *President*
Dennis Bolin, *Vice Pres*
Carol S Waldron, *Vice Pres*
EMP: 20
SALES (est): 9.4MM **Privately Held**
WEB: www.coexpipe.com
SIC: 3084 Plastics pipe

(G-2078)
D & R CASING SERVICES INC
1317 E 11th Pl (79720-4803)
P.O. Box 3421 (79721-3421)
PHONE..................................432 263-8900
Betty Pearson, *President*
Ava Blair, *Corp Secy*
Tyson Blair, *Admin Sec*
EMP: 15
SALES (est): 1.4MM **Privately Held**
SIC: 1389 Oil field services

(G-2079)
DAVES TUBING TESTING &HOT OIL
5901 N Service Rd (79720-0603)
P.O. Box 3129 (79721-3129)
PHONE..................................432 263-1747

G
E
O
G
R
A
P
H
I
C

Jimmy Hector, *President*
Sandra Hector, *Corp Secy*
Gwyn Sparks, *Manager*
EMP: 22
SALES (est): 4.3MM **Privately Held**
WEB: www.summit.com
SIC: 1389 Oil field services

(G-2080)
DRACO TECHNOLOGIES LLC
711 Colgate Ave (79720-3443)
P.O. Box 65 (79721-0065)
PHONE............................432 213-5626
EMP: 10 **EST:** 2015
SALES (est): 1MM **Privately Held**
WEB: www.draco.tech
SIC: 1382 Oil & gas exploration services

(G-2081)
DUNCAN DRILLING COMPANY
402 E Fm 700 Rd 700th (79720)
P.O. Box 109 (79721-0109)
PHONE............................432 263-7721
EMP: 9
SQ FT: 4,000
SALES (est): 921.2K **Privately Held**
SIC: 1311 Crude petroleum production

(G-2082)
FEDERAL PRISON INDUSTRIES
Also Called: Unicor
1900 Simler Ave (79720-7789)
PHONE............................432 466-2300
Wayne Huffman, *Superintendent*
EMP: 250 **Publicly Held**
WEB: www.bop.gov
SIC: 2298 9223 Cable, fiber; correctional institutions;
HQ: Federal Prison Industries, Inc
　　320 1st St Nw
　　Washington DC 20534

(G-2083)
IC-I REMEDIATE LLC
7600 Brandon Rd (79720-7088)
PHONE............................432 213-7813
Mike Tredaway,
Sherida Tredaway,
EMP: 11
SQ FT: 900
SALES (est): 568.8K **Privately Held**
WEB: www.iciremediate.com
SIC: 1389 Servicing oil & gas wells

(G-2084)
JOHNSON TOOL COMPANY INC
Also Called: Southwest Tool Co
901 E 2nd St (79720-3201)
P.O. Box 1007 (79721-1007)
PHONE............................432 267-7612
Emma Jean Johnson, *President*
James L Johnson III, *Treasurer*
EMP: 20 **EST:** 1924
SQ FT: 12,800
SALES (est): 15.2MM **Privately Held**
SIC: 5051 7692 5085 3599 Steel; welding repair; valves & fittings; machine shop, jobbing & repair; industrial machinery & equipment

(G-2085)
JSPAZ GUARDIAN ENERGY SVCS LLC
1009 W 5th St (79720-2144)
P.O. Box 2338 (79721-2338)
PHONE............................432 606-5003
Steve A Claus, *Treasurer*
Jackson Thompson, *Mng Member*
EMP: 25
SALES (est): 6MM **Privately Held**
WEB: www.guardianenergy.us
SIC: 1389 Oil field services

(G-2086)
KEY ENERGY SERVICES INC
3404 E F M 700 (79720)
P.O. Box 584, Forsan (79733-0584)
PHONE............................432 267-5291
Fax: 432 267-1805
EMP: 40
SALES (corp-wide): 436.1MM **Publicly Held**
SIC: 1389 1381 Oil/Gas Field Services Oil/Gas Well Drilling

PA: Key Energy Services, Inc.
　　1301 Mckinney St Ste 1800
　　Houston TX 77010
　　713 651-4300

(G-2087)
MB ROBINSON INC
607 Main St (79720)
P.O. Box 311 (79721-0311)
PHONE............................432 267-5277
Mike Robinson, *President*
Ray B Alexander, *Vice Pres*
EMP: 35
SQ FT: 4,100
SALES (est): 2.1MM **Privately Held**
SIC: 1381 1311 Drilling oil & gas wells; crude petroleum & natural gas

(G-2088)
MOVENTAS GEARS INC
604 Owens St (79720-3112)
PHONE............................432 517-4518
Jessica Moreno, *Branch Mgr*
EMP: 11
SALES (corp-wide): 970.5K **Privately Held**
WEB: www.moventas.com
SIC: 3599 Machine shop, jobbing & repair
HQ: Moventas Gears Inc.
　　2002 Timberloch Pl # 200
　　Spring TX 77380
　　503 247-6107

(G-2089)
NOLTEX TRUSS BIG SPRING INC
1700 Rickabaugh Dr (79720)
PHONE............................432 267-4700
EMP: 13
SALES (est): 1.5MM **Privately Held**
SIC: 2439 Mfg Structural Wood Members

(G-2090)
OLD DT HOLDINGS
2515 Apron Dr (79720-7812)
P.O. Box 351 (79721-0351)
PHONE............................432 267-7141
Randy Phillips, *Principal*
Arturo Del Valle,
EMP: 200
SALES (est): 26.2MM **Privately Held**
SIC: 3443 Tanks, standard or custom fabricated: metal plate

(G-2091)
OXY USA INC
4518 S Us Highway 87 (79720-7974)
PHONE............................432 634-2247
Gary O Lee Jr, *Branch Mgr*
EMP: 15
SALES (corp-wide): 21.2B **Publicly Held**
SIC: 1311 Crude petroleum production
HQ: Oxy Usa Inc.
　　1001 S County Rd W
　　Odessa TX 79763
　　432 335-0995

(G-2092)
PARTEE ENTERPRISES
110 W 22nd St Ste A (79720-5522)
PHONE............................432 263-0632
Stanley E Partee, *Owner*
EMP: 17 **EST:** 1979
SQ FT: 8,000
SALES (est): 1MM **Privately Held**
SIC: 1311 Crude petroleum production

(G-2093)
PHILLIPS FABRICATION INC
1305 E Airpark Dr (79720-3850)
P.O. Box 791 (79721-0791)
PHONE............................432 264-6600
Randy Phillips, *President*
Cecilia Phillips, *Vice Pres*
EMP: 44
SQ FT: 11,000
SALES (est): 8.5MM **Privately Held**
WEB: www.philfab.com
SIC: 3444 7692 Sheet metalwork; welding repair

(G-2094)
R2R AND D LLC
Also Called: Finalrod
610 S Main St (79720-2731)
PHONE............................432 264-7500

EMP: 70 **EST:** 2011
SQ FT: 101,000
SALES (est): 25MM **Privately Held**
WEB: www.superod.com
SIC: 3312 Bar, rod & wire products

(G-2095)
RH WELL SERVICE
7608 S Service Rd I20 (79720-0586)
P.O. Box 551 (79721-0551)
PHONE............................432 393-5305
Gene Hector, *Principal*
EMP: 19
SALES (est): 3MM **Privately Held**
SIC: 1389 Oil field services

(G-2096)
ROBINSON DRILLING TEXAS LTD
1200 N Fm 700 (79720-0321)
P.O. Box 311 (79721-0311)
PHONE............................432 267-5277
Steve Suarez, *Vice Pres*
Randall Hanson, *Opers Mgr*
Geneva Legg, *Controller*
Rodene Bomir, *Mng Member*
Richard Tapio, *Director*
EMP: 29
SALES (est): 7.7MM **Privately Held**
WEB: www.robinsondrlg.com
SIC: 1381 3533 Directional drilling oil & gas wells; oil & gas drilling rigs & equipment

(G-2097)
S C S TECHNOLOGIES LLC
Also Called: S & S Technologies
3423 Ih 20 E (79720-3545)
P.O. Box 807 (79721-0807)
PHONE............................432 264-6500
Jess Slaughter, *Project Mgr*
Damon Lehning, *CFO*
Daniel Jones, *Sales Staff*
Clifford Castilaw, *Mng Member*
Cliff Castilaw, *Manager*
EMP: 50
SALES (est): 20.2MM **Privately Held**
WEB: www.scstechnologiesllc.com
SIC: 3441 Fabricated structural metal

(G-2098)
SHERIDAN PRODUCTION CO LLC
400 Ranch Road 33 (79720-7808)
PHONE............................432 263-4301
Bruce Thompson, *Branch Mgr*
EMP: 83 **Privately Held**
WEB: www.sheridanproduction.com
SIC: 1382 Oil & gas exploration services
PA: Sheridan Production Company Llc
　　1360 Post Oak Blvd # 2500
　　Houston TX 77056

(G-2099)
STELLAR AUTOMATION INC
711 E 3rd St (79720-3009)
P.O. Box 910 (79721-0910)
PHONE............................432 517-4502
EMP: 14
SALES (est): 7.9MM **Privately Held**
WEB: www.stellarautomationinc.com
SIC: 1389 Gas field services

(G-2100)
TOKAI CARBON CB LTD
Also Called: Sid Richardson Carbn Enrgy Co
1211 N Midway Rd (79720-0819)
PHONE............................432 263-7389
Eric Dand, *Plant Mgr*
EMP: 87 **Privately Held**
WEB: www.sidrichardson.org
SIC: 2895 2899 Carbon black; chemical preparations
HQ: Tokai Carbon Cb Ltd.
　　301 Commerce St Ste 500
　　Fort Worth TX 76102
　　817 390-8600

(G-2101)
TRONOX INCORPORATED
Hc 63 (79720)
PHONE............................432 263-4301
Philip Endris, *Manager*
EMP: 17

SALES (corp-wide): 2.6B **Privately Held**
WEB: www.tronox.com
SIC: 1311 Crude petroleum production
HQ: Tronox Incorporated
　　1 Stamford Plz
　　Stamford CT 06901
　　203 705-3800

(G-2102)
WEST TEXAS ENERGY SEVICES LLC
3215 S Us Highway 87 (79720-7137)
P.O. Box 1888 (79721-1888)
PHONE............................432 267-3126
Mike Evans, *CEO*
Vincent Hatfield,
EMP: 12
SALES (est): 2.1MM **Privately Held**
SIC: 1381 Drilling oil & gas wells
PA: Sharp Image Energy, Inc.
　　505 N Big Spring St Ste 2
　　Midland TX 79701

(G-2103)
WESTERN CONTAINER CORPORATION
1600 W 1st St (79720-1734)
PHONE............................432 263-8361
Chad Chesworth, *Manager*
EMP: 105
SALES (corp-wide): 37.2B **Publicly Held**
WEB: www.westerncontainercoke.com
SIC: 3085 Plastics bottles
HQ: Western Container Corporation
　　2277 Plaza Dr Ste 270
　　Sugar Land TX 77479
　　346 309-3238

Big Wells
Dimmit County

(G-2104)
SELECT ENERGY SERVICES LLC
Also Called: Select Oilfield Construction
15386 Hwy 85 W (78830)
PHONE............................830 457-2215
Kyle Wanjura, *Office Mgr*
EMP: 130
SALES (corp-wide): 1.2B **Publicly Held**
WEB: www.selectenergyservices.com
SIC: 1389 7353 Oil field services; oil field equipment, rental or leasing
HQ: Select Energy Services, Llc
　　1820 N I 35
　　Gainesville TX 76240
　　940 668-1818

Bishop
Nueces County

(G-2105)
CELANESE AMERICAS LLC
Us Hwy 77 (78343)
P.O. Box 428 (78343-0428)
PHONE............................361 584-6000
Brian Connley, *Plant Mgr*
Veronica Olsson, *Purch Mgr*
Samyak Patel, *Engineer*
James Price, *Controller*
Michael Deering, *Manager*
EMP: 90
SALES (corp-wide): 5.6B **Publicly Held**
WEB: www.celanese.com
SIC: 2819 Industrial inorganic chemicals
HQ: Celanese Americas Llc
　　222 Colinas Blvd W # 900
　　Irving TX 75039
　　972 443-4000

(G-2106)
DCP MIDSTREAM LLC
Also Called: Gulf Plains Plant
7202 County Road 16 (78343-3230)
PHONE............................361 584-8500
Rob King, *Manager*
EMP: 25
SALES (corp-wide): 1.9B **Privately Held**
WEB: www.dcpmidstream.com
SIC: 1321 1311 Natural gas liquids; natural gas production

PA: Dcp Midstream, Llc
370 17th St Ste 2500
Denver CO 80202
303 633-2900

(G-2107)

DCP OPERATING COMPANY LP
7202 County Road 16 (78343-3230)
P.O. Box 982265, El Paso (79998-2265)
PHONE..............................361 584-8509
Rhonda Rosa, *Administration*
EMP: 188 Publicly Held
WEB: www.dcpmidstream.com
SIC: 1311 5172 3999 Crude petroleum
production; petroleum products; atomiz-
ers, toiletry
HQ: Dcp Operating Company, Lp
370 17th St Ste 2500
Denver CO 80202
303 595-3331

(G-2108)

OQ CHEMICALS BISHOP LLC
Also Called: Oxea Bishop, LLC
U.S Highway 77 Business (78343)
P.O. Box 9 (78343-0009)
PHONE..............................361 584-6920
Wolfgang Hackenberg, *Mng Member*
Joey Giomcaspero,
EMP: 27
SALES (est): 7MM
SALES (corp-wide): 1.3B Privately Held
WEB: www.chemicals.oq.com
SIC: 2899 Chemical preparations
HQ: Oq Chemicals Corporation
15375 Memorial Dr
Houston TX 77079

(G-2109)

SOLUTION INTEGRATED CHEM LLC (PA)
5398 County Road 4 (78343-3309)
PHONE..............................361 584-5000
Bren Bull, *CEO*
Bren Calhoun Bull, *Mng Member*
EMP: 18
SQ FT: 2,000
SALES (est): 2.5MM Privately Held
WEB: www.tomball-homesforsale.com
SIC: 2899 Chemical preparations

Blanco
Blanco County

(G-2110)

D AND H EQUIPMENT LTD
1564 S Loop 163 (78606)
P.O. Box 1660 (78606-1660)
PHONE..............................830 833-5366
Andy Cox, *Partner*
Jason Cox, *Marketing Staff*
Marykay Massey, *Office Mgr*
Randy Watt, *Manager*
◆ **EMP:** 25
SALES (est): 4.9MM Privately Held
WEB: www.dhequip.com
SIC: 3531 Asphalt plant, including gravel-
mix type

Bloomington
Victoria County

(G-2111)

CDW CONSULTANT GROUP LLC
Also Called: Cdw Consulting
624 Traylor Rd (77951)
PHONE..............................361 237-9339
Charles Donovan White, *President*
EMP: 29 EST: 2012
SQ FT: 5,000
SALES (est): 1.3MM Privately Held
WEB: www.cdwconsultant.com
SIC: 8711 2411 1382 5989 Building con-
struction consultant; energy conservation
engineering; fuel wood harvesting; wood
chips, produced in the field; oil & gas ex-
ploration services; wood (fuel)

Blossom
Lamar County

(G-2112)

BLOSSOM MACHINE & MFG INC
121 E Front St (75416-2501)
P.O. Box 615 (75416-0615)
PHONE..............................903 982-5500
EMP: 43
SQ FT: 15,000
SALES (est): 4.6MM Privately Held
WEB: www.blossommachine.com
SIC: 3599 3089 Machine shop, jobbing &
repair

Boerne
Kendall County

(G-2113)

ALBANY ENGNERED COMPOSITES INC
Also Called: AEC Boerne
1281 N Main St (78006-3014)
PHONE..............................830 249-4400
Randal Carlson, *Senior Buyer*
Carol Ford, *Buyer*
Steve Barrett, *Engineer*
Clayton Black, *Engineer*
Stephen Lavrack, *Finance*
EMP: 100
SALES (corp-wide): 1B Publicly Held
WEB: www.albint.com
SIC: 3728 3769 3714 Aircraft assemblies,
subassemblies & parts; guided missile &
space vehicle parts & auxiliary equip-
ment; motor vehicle parts & accessories
HQ: Albany Engineered Composites, Inc.
216 Airport Dr
Rochester NH 03867
603 330-5800

(G-2114)

BEE JAY MOLDING INC (PA)
39500 Interstate 10 W (78006-8845)
PHONE..............................830 249-2425
EMP: 19
SALES (est): 3.1MM Privately Held
WEB: www.beejaymolding.com
SIC: 3089 Injection molding of plastics

(G-2115)

BERNIE STAR NEWSPAPER
941 N School St (78006-5922)
P.O. Box 820 (78006-0820)
PHONE..............................830 249-2441
Brian Cartwright, *Publisher*
Keith Domke, *Manager*
EMP: 15 EST: 1906
SALES (est): 538K Privately Held
WEB: www.boernestar.com
SIC: 2711 Newspapers, publishing & print-
ing

(G-2116)

CELLTEKS INC
Also Called: Concept Cellular International
113 Parkway (78006-9224)
PHONE..............................830 249-8999
Brent Holmes, *President*
Hershel Craig, *VP Bus Dvlpt*
▲ **EMP:** 10
SQ FT: 5,600
SALES (est): 2.3MM Privately Held
WEB: www.cellteks.com
SIC: 5065 5999 1731 7629 Mobile tele-
phone equipment; mobile telephones &
equipment; telephone & telephone equip-
ment installation; telephone set repair;
telegraph or telephone carrier & repeater
equipment

(G-2117)

CREATIVE INDUSTRIES LLC
140 Old San Antonio Rd (78006-3413)
P.O. Box 2332 (78006-6332)
PHONE..............................830 249-1200
Maggie Bennette, *President*
Richard Bennette, *Vice Pres*
▲ **EMP:** 12

SALES (est): 1.3MM Privately Held
WEB: www.creative-prc.us
SIC: 3645 Garden, patio, walkway & yard
lighting fixtures: electric

(G-2118)

ELECTROLAB INC
Also Called: E9 Treatments
159 Enterprise Pkwy (78006-8634)
PHONE..............................210 824-5364
Robert W Drees, *President*
Jim Schulte, *President*
Karl Senghaas, *President*
Sean Drees, *Vice Pres*
Michelle Hernandez, *Purch Mgr*
EMP: 30
SQ FT: 8,400
SALES (est): 6MM Privately Held
WEB: www.electrolabcontrols.com
SIC: 3625 3823 Control circuit devices,
magnet & solid state; industrial instrmnts
msrmnt display/control process variable

(G-2119)

ENVIRONMENTAL FUEL SYSTEMS
213 Commerce Ave (78006-3010)
P.O. Box 1305 (78006-1305)
PHONE..............................800 375-7747
EMP: 10
SALES (est): 1.2MM Privately Held
SIC: 3822 Mfg Environmental Controls

(G-2120)

FINLEY CO
306 Wollschlaeger Dr (78006-5930)
PHONE..............................830 816-2107
EMP: 26
SALES (est): 1.1MM Privately Held
SIC: 1382 Oil & gas exploration services

(G-2121)

FLYING CIRCLE BAG CO
Also Called: Flying Circle Bags
10045 Johns Rd (78006-8814)
P.O. Box 1857 (78006-6857)
PHONE..............................830 249-2480
Joy Chittim, *President*
Alma Kuttner, *General Mgr*
Christine Chittim, *Exec VP*
Jim H Chittim, *Vice Pres*
Margo Freedman, *Manager*
◆ **EMP: 24 EST:** 1975
SQ FT: 160,000
SALES: 5MM Privately Held
WEB: www.flyingcirclegear.com
SIC: 2393 Textile bags

(G-2122)

INGRAM READYMIX INC
37345 Interstate 10 W (78006-8906)
PHONE..............................830 249-3506
Brandon Crowder, *Manager*
EMP: 17
SQ FT: 5,449
SALES (corp-wide): 125.6MM Privately Held
WEB: www.ingramreadymixinc.com
SIC: 3273 Ready-mixed concrete
PA: Ingram Readymix, Inc.
3580 Farm Market 482
New Braunfels TX 78132
830 625-9156

(G-2123)

INSTRUMENT SPECIALISTS INC
32390 Interstate 10 W (78006-9214)
PHONE..............................830 249-9535
Sandra S Kabanek, *President*
Lori Brown, *Vice Pres*
Lisa L Hernandez, *Vice Pres*
James Kabanek, *Vice Pres*
Casey Shephard, *Vice Pres*
EMP: 14 EST: 1979
SQ FT: 5,700
SALES (est): 2.6MM Privately Held
WEB: www.isisurgery.com
SIC: 5047 3841 7699 Instruments, surgi-
cal & medical; surgical & medical instru-
ments; surgical instrument repair

(G-2124)

JCJH LLC
Also Called: J Groomed
1685 River Rd Ste 200 (78006-2469)
PHONE..............................830 331-2240

Janet Hoffheins, *Mng Member*
Julie Whaley,
EMP: 12 EST: 2016
SALES (est): 49.2K Privately Held
WEB: www.jgroomed.com
SIC: 7241 7372 Barber shops; application
computer software

(G-2125)

JOY PIPE USA LP (PA)
39850 Interstate 10 W (78006-8805)
P.O. Box 1619 (78006-6619)
PHONE..............................830 249-7400
Tom Bibb, *Partner*
William Thomas, *Partner*
Bibb Thomas, *Vice Pres*
Luella Dufner, *Accountant*
Colin Bibb, *Sales Staff*
◆ **EMP:** 12
SQ FT: 3,000
SALES (est): 10.6MM Privately Held
WEB: www.joypipe.com
SIC: 3494 Pipe fittings

(G-2126)

LEBCO GRAPHICS INC
31400 Interstate 10 W (78006-9239)
PHONE..............................830 755-8226
Lanne E Brehmer, *President*
Delores Ragsdale, *Corp Secy*
Darren Brehmer, *Vice Pres*
EMP: 28
SQ FT: 20,000
SALES (est): 3MM Privately Held
WEB: www.lebcographics.com
SIC: 2752 2791 2789 2759 Commercial
printing, offset; typesetting; bookbinding &
related work; commercial printing

(G-2127)

LOSOYA INDUSTRIES LLC
205 Rosebud St (78006-2145)
PHONE..............................210 559-6066
Paige Losoya, *Managing Prtnr*
Rubin Losoya,
EMP: 15
SALES (est): 1MM Privately Held
SIC: 3999 Manufacturing industries

(G-2128)

MAGIC IN SKY LLC
26926 Hardy Run (78015-6581)
PHONE..............................210 267-5371
Jacob Dell, *CEO*
Steven Parra, *Project Mgr*
Rachel E Dell, *Admin Sec*
▲ **EMP: 10 EST:** 2007
SALES (est): 1.3MM Privately Held
WEB: www.magicinthesky.com
SIC: 2899 Fireworks

(G-2129)

MISSION PHARMACAL COMPANY
38505 Interstate 10 W (78006-9005)
PHONE..............................210 696-8400
Chris Huggins, *Vice Pres*
Stuart Schoenherr, *Research*
Jay Avers, *Accountant*
Justin Tran, *Accountant*
Anthony Nwajei, *Sales Staff*
EMP: 225
SALES (corp-wide): 180.5MM Privately Held
WEB: www.missionpharmacal.com
SIC: 2834 Pharmaceutical preparations
PA: Mission Pharmacal Company
10999 W Interstate 10
San Antonio TX 78230
210 696-8400

(G-2130)

NEOM LLC
27711 Woodway Bnd (78006-6552)
PHONE..............................210 372-3475
Nancy Ortiz,
Robert Saunders,
EMP: 12 EST: 2011
SALES (est): 1.4MM Privately Held
WEB: www.neomllc.com
SIC: 8741 5172 5983 1542 Construction
management; petroleum products; fuel oil
dealers; commercial & office building,
new construction; fuels

(G-2131)
PARKING SENSE USA INC
37535 Interstate 10 W # 2 (78006-8903)
PHONE..................................830 428-0299
Jake Bezzant, *CEO*
Jimmy Dumont, *President*
EMP: 15
SQ FT: 7,500
SALES (est): 811.1K **Privately Held**
WEB: www.parkhelp.com
SIC: 1799 3559 Parking facility equipment
& maintenance; parking facility equipment
& supplies
PA: Parkhelp Technologies Limited
22 Northpoint Street
Porirua

(G-2132)
**PRYTIME MEDICAL DEVICES
INC (PA)**
229 N Main St (78006-2035)
PHONE..................................210 340-0116
David Spencer, *CEO*
Brian Ferrari, *Vice Pres*
Nelson Whistance, *Vice Pres*
Eric Pointer, *Engineer*
Brian Gorman, *Sales Staff*
EMP: 19
SQ FT: 5,000
SALES (est): 6MM **Privately Held**
WEB: www.prytimemedical.com
SIC: 3841 Inhalation therapy equipment

(G-2133)
**QUALITY ACCESS CONTROL
SYSTEMS**
28993 Interstate 10 W (78006-9119)
P.O. Box 691928, San Antonio (78269-
1928)
PHONE..................................830 981-5400
Todd Chakales, *President*
EMP: 16
SQ FT: 6,500
SALES (est): 2.4MM **Privately Held**
WEB:
www.qualityaccesscontrolsystems.com
SIC: 1731 1799 3446 Access control sys-
tems specialization; fence construction;
gates, ornamental metal

(G-2134)
ROBERT U NEESE
Also Called: Gravity Services Group
307 Wollschlaeger Dr (78006-5933)
PHONE..................................281 342-2884
Robert U Neese, *Owner*
EMP: 15
SQ FT: 2,250
SALES (est): 1MM **Privately Held**
WEB: www.gravityservices.com
SIC: 3829 7629 Measuring & controlling
devices; electronic equipment repair

(G-2135)
**SAND CREEK TIMBER FRAMES
LLC**
613 State Highway 46 E (78006-5978)
PHONE..................................210 698-6156
Alex Arizpe, *Branch Mgr*
EMP: 50
SALES (corp-wide): 13.9MM **Privately
Held**
SIC: 2439 Timbers, structural: laminated
lumber
HQ: Sand Creek Timber Frames, L.L.C.
116 W 1st St
Wayne NE 68787
402 833-5600

(G-2136)
**SEPARATION TECHNOLOGY
INC**
Also Called: S T I
1261 N Main St (78006-3014)
PHONE..................................830 249-0772
Lisa Fox, *CEO*
Jami Meeks, *President*
Ed Hitchler, *General Mgr*
EMP: 15
SQ FT: 6,000

SALES (est): 2.7MM
SALES (corp-wide): 58MM **Privately
Held**
WEB: www.ekfusa.com
SIC: 2835 3821 In vitro & in vivo diagnos-
tic substances; laboratory measuring ap-
paratus
PA: Ekf Diagnostics Holdings Plc
Avon House, 19 Stanwell Road
Penarth S GLAM CF64
292 071-0570

(G-2137)
**STANBIO LABORATORY LP
(HQ)**
Also Called: Ekf Life Sciences
1261 N Main St (78006-3014)
PHONE..................................830 824-0772
Ed Hitchler, *General Mgr*
Ben Denlinger, *General Mgr*
Kathryn Marnell, *Export Mgr*
June Wieringa, *Human Res Mgr*
Edward Balmelli, *Sales Staff*
◆ **EMP:** 85
SQ FT: 19,990
SALES (est): 40MM
SALES (corp-wide): 58MM **Privately
Held**
WEB: www.ekfusa.com
SIC: 2835 8071 In vitro & in vivo diagnos-
tic substances; testing laboratories
PA: Ekf Diagnostics Holdings Plc
Avon House, 19 Stanwell Road
Penarth S GLAM CF64
292 071-0570

(G-2138)
SWEENEY ENTERPRISES INC
321 Waring Welfare Rd (78006-7927)
PHONE..................................830 537-4631
Zachary S Sweeney, *President*
Kim Sweeney, *Manager*
◆ **EMP:** 9
SQ FT: 16,000
SALES (est): 1.8MM **Privately Held**
WEB: www.sweeneyfeeders.com
SIC: 3523 Farm machinery & equipment

(G-2139)
**TAYLORMADE PLLETS
LGISTICS LLC**
Also Called: P R S Pallet Repair Services
30023 Fairway Vista Dr (78015-4952)
PHONE..................................210 566-3833
Jenny Gill, *CEO*
Jeff Gill, *President*
Veronica Gill, *Admin Asst*
EMP: 23
SALES (est): 4.6MM **Privately Held**
WEB: www.taylormadepallets.com
SIC: 2653 7699 Pallets, corrugated: made
from purchased materials; tool repair
services

(G-2140)
**TEXAS STAR NUT AND FOOD
CO INC**
Also Called: Natures Eat
206 Market Ave (78006-3003)
P.O. Box 2353 (78006-6353)
PHONE..................................830 249-8300
John C Taylor Jr, *President*
Ray Goodman, *Plant Mgr*
Kelly Carver, *QC Mgr*
Robert Henarie, *VP Sales*
Anne Bearden, *Sales Staff*
▲ **EMP:** 70
SQ FT: 45,000
SALES (est): 85.1MM **Privately Held**
WEB: www.texasnut.com
SIC: 5145 2068 Nuts, salted or roasted;
nuts: dried, dehydrated, salted or roasted

(G-2141)
**THOMAS INSTRUMENT
INCORPORATED**
110 Commerce Ave (78006-3060)
PHONE..................................830 331-1325
Randy Coggins, *Vice Pres*
Kristin Jay, *Vice Pres*
Ben Holmes, *Branch Mgr*
Nathan Massey, *Manager*
EMP: 20

SALES (corp-wide): 25MM **Privately
Held**
WEB: www.thomasinstrument.com
SIC: 3812 Acceleration indicators & sys-
tems components, aerospace
PA: Thomas Instrument, Incorporated
3440 1st St
Brookshire TX 77423
281 375-6300

(G-2142)
TIMEKEEPERS INC
Also Called: Timekeepers Security
115 Bess St (78006-2806)
PHONE..................................830 331-1224
Shawn Fluitt, *President*
EMP: 90
SALES (est): 2.9MM **Privately Held**
SIC: 7382 7381 1382 4922 Burglar alarm
maintenance & monitoring; security guard
service; oil & gas exploration services;
pipelines, natural gas

(G-2143)
TOOTIE PIE COMPANY INC (PA)
Also Called: Tootie Pie Gourmet Cafe
129 Industrial Dr (78006-3307)
PHONE..................................210 737-6600
Leslie D Int, *CEO*
Leslie E Doss, *CEO*
Brandi Stewart, *Sales Staff*
Brian Gile, *Officer*
Bobbie Keese, *Executive*
EMP: 56
SQ FT: 5,000
SALES: 2.7MM **Privately Held**
WEB: www.tootiepieco.com
SIC: 2053 2051 Pies, bakery: frozen; bak-
ery: wholesale or wholesale/retail com-
bined

(G-2144)
TRC CONSULTANTS LC (PA)
120 Dietert Ave Ste 100 (78006-2406)
PHONE..................................830 249-9968
Gary Gonzenbach, *President*
EMP: 11
SQ FT: 4,000
SALES (est): 2.1MM **Privately Held**
WEB: www.phdwin.com
SIC: 1389 Gas field services

Bogata
Red River County

(G-2145)
**CHIP MCCORMICK CUSTOM
LLC**
Also Called: CMC Products
150 County Road 4603 (75417-7167)
PHONE..................................830 798-2863
Brandon Robert, *General Mgr*
Joyce Wilson, *Accountant*
Kim McCormick, *Mng Member*
EMP: 20
SALES (est): 1MM **Privately Held**
WEB: www.cmcproducts.com
SIC: 2721 3484 5099 5941 Magazines:
publishing & printing; guns (firearms) or
gun parts, 30 mm. & below; firearms &
ammunition, except sporting; firearms

Boling
Wharton County

(G-2146)
B & S SERVICES INC
11928 Fm 1301 Rd (77420-9354)
P.O. Box 6 (77420-0006)
PHONE..................................281 342-1052
Leon Bannert, *President*
Kevin Bannert, *Vice Pres*
EMP: 17 **EST:** 1981
SALES (est): 2.3MM **Privately Held**
SIC: 1389 Cementing oil & gas well cas-
ings; acidizing wells; pumping of oil & gas
wells

(G-2147)
DRAWWORKS LP
Also Called: McCoy
10555 Fm 1301 Rd (77420-9660)
P.O. Box 280 (77420-0280)
PHONE..................................512 610-5200
Gus Mullins, *Managing Prtnr*
John Lara, *Technician*
▼ **EMP:** 10
SQ FT: 2,700
SALES (est): 1.6MM
SALES (corp-wide): 40.1MM **Privately
Held**
WEB: www.drawworkslp.com
SIC: 3599 Machine shop, jobbing & repair
PA: Mccoy Global Inc
9910 39th Ave Nw Suite 201
Edmonton AB T6B 3
780 453-8451

(G-2148)
STERLINGS VACUUM SERVICE
11708 Fm 1301 Rd (77420-9379)
P.O. Box 188 (77420-0188)
PHONE..................................979 657-4633
Leslie Lopez, *Office Mgr*
Roger Pahmiyer, *Mng Member*
Ross Sterling,
EMP: 15
SQ FT: 1,500
SALES (est): 2MM **Privately Held**
SIC: 1389 Gas field services; oil field serv-
ices

Bon Wier
Newton County

(G-2149)
MS LOGGING INC
1 Newton County Rd (75928)
PHONE..................................409 382-2424
Michael Stivender, *President*
EMP: 13 **EST:** 2000
SALES (est): 1.6MM **Privately Held**
SIC: 2411 Logging camps & contractors

(G-2150)
**SOUTHERN FOREST PRODUCTS
LLC**
Fm 2626 N St (75928)
P.O. Box 207 (75928-0207)
PHONE..................................409 634-3365
John Langford, *President*
Harold Estes, *General Mgr*
Josh Lowe, *General Mgr*
Jim Ulmer, *Info Tech Dir*
EMP: 80 **EST:** 1998
SALES (est): 9.4MM
SALES (corp-wide): 47.7MM **Privately
Held**
SIC: 2421 2431 2426 Sawmills & planing
mills, general; millwork; hardwood dimen-
sion & flooring mills
HQ: Texas Timberjack, Inc.
6004 S First St
Lufkin TX 75901
936 634-3365

(G-2151)
TEXAS TIMBERJACK INC
Also Called: Southern Forest Products
Fm 2626 (75928)
P.O. Box 207 (75928-0207)
PHONE..................................409 397-4221
Tony Damron, *President*
EMP: 60
SALES (corp-wide): 47.7MM **Privately
Held**
WEB: www.texastimberjack.com
SIC: 2411 2421 2431 Logging; sawmills &
planing mills, general; millwork
HQ: Texas Timberjack, Inc.
6004 S First St
Lufkin TX 75901
936 634-3365

Bonham
Fannin County

(G-2152)
CMH MANUFACTURING INC
333 Austin Dr (75418-4558)
PHONE.................................800 445-3516
Francis Moran, *Plant Mgr*
EMP: 200
SALES (corp-wide): 254.6B **Publicly Held**
WEB: www.claytonhomes.com
SIC: 2451 Mobile homes
HQ: Cmh Manufacturing, Inc.
5000 Clayton Rd
Maryville TN 37804
865 380-3000

(G-2153)
FANNIN COUNTY LEADER LLC
224 N Main Bonham (75418)
P.O. Box 296 (75418-0296)
PHONE.................................903 583-3280
Thomas H Turner, *President*
John W Burnett, *Admin Sec*
EMP: 10
SALES (est): 765K **Privately Held**
WEB: www.fannincountytexas.com
SIC: 2711 Commercial printing & newspaper publishing combined

(G-2154)
RENLITA DOORS NORTH AMER LLC
2430 Albert Broadfoot St (75418-2020)
P.O. Box B (75418-0179)
PHONE.................................903 583-7500
Byron Royse, *President*
Jason Royse, *Vice Pres*
Barbara Reeves, *Marketing Staff*
Beverly Royse, *Mng Member*
▲ EMP: 22
SQ FT: 45,000
SALES (est): 5.1MM **Privately Held**
WEB: www.renlitausa.com
SIC: 2431 Doors, wood

(G-2155)
TEAM MANUFACTURING INC
1438 N State Highway 78 (75418-5532)
P.O. Box 400 (75418-0400)
PHONE.................................903 583-7722
Gerald Sladd, *President*
Gerald Sledd, *President*
Euvonna Sledd, *Vice Pres*
EMP: 14
SALES (est): 2MM **Privately Held**
WEB: www.ewmfg.com
SIC: 3544 Industrial molds

(G-2156)
TRANS CABLE INTERNATIONAL INC
800 E 2nd St (75418-4301)
PHONE.................................903 449-4622
Carlos Medina, *CEO*
Sam Jazayri, *President*
EMP: 30
SQ FT: 40,000
SALES (est): 8.1MM **Privately Held**
WEB: www.transcableusa.com
SIC: 3357 5131 Coaxial cable, nonferrous; textiles, woven

Booker
Lipscomb County

(G-2157)
OVERFLOW ENERGY LLC
723 W Industrial Rd (79005-1100)
P.O. Box 354 (79005-0354)
PHONE.................................806 658-7832
Duwane Skipper, *Mng Member*
EMP: 50 EST: 2007
SALES (est): 25MM **Privately Held**
WEB: www.overflowenergy.com
SIC: 1382 Oil & gas exploration services

(G-2158)
PREFERRED BEEF GROUP LP
Also Called: Texas Protein
910 E Industrial Rd (79005-6035)
P.O. Box 290 (79005-0290)
PHONE.................................806 658-4561
Roy Goldsmith, *General Mgr*
Stephen N Holmes, *COO*
Jim Gardner, *Safety Mgr*
John Orel, *Purch Mgr*
Wrex Phipps, *Buyer*
EMP: 210
SALES (est): 35.9MM **Privately Held**
WEB: www.preferredbeef.com
SIC: 2011 Meat packing plants

(G-2159)
TOM MCGEE CORP
319 W Industrial Rd (79005-1209)
P.O. Box 276 (79005-0276)
PHONE.................................806 658-4591
Tam McGee, *President*
Becky McGee, *Admin Sec*
EMP: 9
SQ FT: 1,000
SALES (est): 887.4K **Privately Held**
SIC: 1311 Crude petroleum production; natural gas production

(G-2160)
UNIT CORPORATION
Also Called: Unit Petroleum
112 S Main St (79005-6028)
P.O. Box 489, Shattuck OK (73858-0489)
PHONE.................................806 658-2262
Kent Simms, *Branch Mgr*
EMP: 9
SALES (corp-wide): 674.6MM **Privately Held**
WEB: www.unitcorp.com
SIC: 1311 Crude petroleum production
PA: Unit Corporation
8200 S Unit Dr
Tulsa OK 74132
918 493-7700

Borger
Hutchinson County

(G-2161)
AGRIUM US INC
9201 Fm 1551 (79007-6722)
P.O. Box 5067 (79008-5067)
PHONE.................................806 274-5204
Michael J Frank, *Exec VP*
Susan Jones, *Exec VP*
Michael Webb, *Exec VP*
Richard Downey, *Vice Pres*
Rod Oglesby, *Enginr/R&D Mgr*
EMP: 60
SALES (corp-wide): 20B **Privately Held**
WEB: www.nutrien.com
SIC: 2873 5261 2875 Anhydrous ammonia; fertilizer; fertilizers, mixing only
HQ: Agrium U.S. Inc.
5296 Harvest Lake Dr
Loveland CO 80538

(G-2162)
BAKER HUGHES
Also Called: Unichem
Magic Plains Indus Park (79007)
P.O. Box 572 (79008-0572)
PHONE.................................806 273-6531
Gary Roberts, *Branch Mgr*
EMP: 16
SALES (corp-wide): 23.8B **Publicly Held**
WEB: www.bakerhughes.com
SIC: 1389 Cementing oil & gas well casings; oil field services
HQ: Baker Hughes Holdings Llc
17021 Aldine Westfield Rd
Houston TX 77073
713 439-8600

(G-2163)
BEAGLE STEAM SERVICE INC
400 Dallas St (79007-6418)
P.O. Box 3416 (79008-3416)
PHONE.................................806 274-6892
Arnold Beagle, *President*
Arden Beagle, *Vice Pres*
Leslie Beagle, *Admin Sec*
EMP: 9

SALES (est): 1.4MM **Privately Held**
SIC: 1389 Oil field services

(G-2164)
BIG CREEK SAND AND GRAVEL INC
3300 S Cedar (79007)
P.O. Box 3190 (79008-3190)
PHONE.................................806 273-7501
Dwight Rice, *President*
Mike Williams, *Opers Staff*
Heidi Prock, *Bookkeeper*
EMP: 25
SQ FT: 4,000
SALES (est): 4.1MM **Privately Held**
WEB: www.bigcreeksg.com
SIC: 2951 Asphalt paving mixtures & blocks

(G-2165)
BORGER OIL CHEMICAL INDUS PLAS
Also Called: Oil Chem Industrial Plastics
Airport Rd (79007)
P.O. Box 948 (79008-0948)
PHONE.................................806 273-9518
Bill Owen, *President*
Wanda Purvis, *Corp Secy*
Purvis McNeal, *Vice Pres*
Gerald Purvis, *Vice Pres*
Mc Neal Purvis, *Vice Pres*
EMP: 12 EST: 1981
SQ FT: 20,100
SALES (est): 2.1MM **Privately Held**
WEB: www.borgeredc.com
SIC: 5084 3592 3082 Compressors, except air conditioning; pistons & piston rings; rods, unsupported plastic; tubes, unsupported plastic

(G-2166)
BORGER REDI-MIX CON CO INC
529 N Florida St (79007-4333)
PHONE.................................806 273-2874
Bill J Williamson, *President*
EMP: 35 EST: 1962
SQ FT: 5,000
SALES (est): 4.2MM **Privately Held**
SIC: 3273 5032 Ready-mixed concrete; concrete & cinder block; cement; masons' materials

(G-2167)
CHESAPEAKE OPERATING LLC
303 Industrial Blvd (79007)
PHONE.................................806 273-5820
Dustin Dunlap, *Superintendent*
Justin Langford, *Consultant*
EMP: 26 **Publicly Held**
WEB: www.chk.com
SIC: 1311 Crude petroleum production
HQ: Chesapeake Operating, L.L.C.
6100 N Western Ave
Oklahoma City OK 73118

(G-2168)
CHEVRON PHILLIPS CHEM CO LP
Spur 119 N (79007)
P.O. Box 968 (79008-0968)
PHONE.................................806 275-5500
Joe Kerr, *Project Mgr*
James Stark, *Project Mgr*
EMP: 230
SALES (corp-wide): 3.5B **Privately Held**
WEB: www.cpchem.com
SIC: 2821 Plastics materials & resins
HQ: Chevron Phillips Chemical Company Lp
10001 Six Pines Dr
The Woodlands TX 77380
832 813-4100

(G-2169)
CNHI LLC
Also Called: Borger News Herald
207 S Main St (79007-4715)
P.O. Box 5130 (79008-5130)
PHONE.................................806 273-5611
Tom Hinde, *Branch Mgr*
Tara Hopkins, *Executive*
EMP: 20
SQ FT: 4,000

SALES (corp-wide): 23.7B **Privately Held**
WEB: www.cnhi.com
SIC: 2711 7313 2752 Newspapers: publishing only, not printed on site; newspaper advertising representative; commercial printing, lithographic
HQ: Cnhi, Llc
445 Dexter Ave Ste 7000
Montgomery AL 36104

(G-2170)
COMAC WELL SERVICE INC
1100 Industrial Blvd (79007)
P.O. Box 5141 (79008-5141)
PHONE.................................806 274-2259
Chester Mc Kee, *President*
Mary E Mc Kee, *President*
Janet Hazlett, *Corp Secy*
EMP: 35
SQ FT: 3,000
SALES (est): 3.8MM **Privately Held**
SIC: 1389 Roustabout service; running, cutting & pulling casings, tubes & rods; servicing oil & gas wells

(G-2171)
CONNER MACHINE AND WELDING INC
Also Called: Conner Industries
118 Bunton St (79007-2058)
P.O. Box 905 (79008-0905)
PHONE.................................806 274-2281
Ben Conner, *President*
Elizabeth A Conner, *Vice Pres*
James Morton, *Opers Staff*
Perry Rowell, *Opers Staff*
EMP: 125
SQ FT: 22,000
SALES: 12.7MM **Privately Held**
WEB: www.connerindustriestx.com
SIC: 1629 1389 3531 Industrial plant construction; cementing oil & gas well casings; construction machinery

(G-2172)
D-JS WELL SVC ROUSTABOUT INC
Also Called: D-J's Well Svc Roustabout Off
1621 N Main St (79007-2042)
P.O. Box 1160 (79008-1160)
PHONE.................................806 273-2667
Jamie Perkins, *President*
Vicki Ramsay, *Corp Secy*
EMP: 40 EST: 1980
SALES (est): 3.2MM **Privately Held**
SIC: 1389 Oil field services

(G-2173)
DISCO MACHINE LIBERAL COMPANY (PA)
103 Texas St (79007-2119)
P.O. Box 5030 (79008-5030)
PHONE.................................806 274-2214
Michael James Haning, *President*
Andrew Green, *Corp Secy*
EMP: 24
SQ FT: 25,000
SALES (est): 10MM **Privately Held**
WEB: www.disco-inc.com
SIC: 3599 Machine shop, jobbing & repair

(G-2174)
DIVERSIFIED INDUSTRIAL SVC CO (PA)
Also Called: Disco Compressor
1400 N Main St (79007-2010)
P.O. Box 5030 (79008-5030)
PHONE.................................806 274-2214
James Haning, *President*
James Hannings, *President*
Andrew E Green, *Vice Pres*
John Garren, *Sales Dir*
Kent Junell, *Sales Staff*
EMP: 20
SQ FT: 22,500
SALES (est): 13MM **Privately Held**
WEB: www.disco-inc.com
SIC: 3563 3533 3561 3599 Air & gas compressors; gas field machinery & equipment; pumps & pumping equipment; machine & other job shop work

GEOGRAPHIC

(G-2175)
DIVERSIFIED INDUSTRIAL SVC CO
Also Called: Disco
1400 N Main St (79007-2010)
P.O. Box 5030 (79008-5030)
PHONE.....................................806 274-2214
Michael Haning, *President*
EMP: 22
SALES (corp-wide): 13MM **Privately Held**
WEB: www.disco-inc.com
SIC: 3599 Machine shop, jobbing & repair
PA: Diversified Industrial Service Company
1400 N Main St
Borger TX 79007
806 274-2214

(G-2176)
DYNE OIL & GAS INC
116 W 7th St (79007-3502)
PHONE.....................................806 274-2952
Billy M Gillman, *Ch of Bd*
Greg Hill, *President*
Robert H Windle, *Treasurer*
EMP: 14
SQ FT: 3,100
SALES (est): 850K **Privately Held**
SIC: 1311 Crude petroleum production; natural gas production

(G-2177)
ED PRINCE ENTERPRISES INC
Also Called: Crown Supply
515 E 10th St (79007-3701)
P.O. Box 5198 (79008-5198)
PHONE.....................................806 274-7178
Edward E Prince, *President*
Nedra Prince, *Corp Secy*
Jason McCown, *Sales Staff*
EMP: 14
SQ FT: 10,000
SALES (est): 9.8MM **Privately Held**
WEB: www.crownsupplyind.com
SIC: 5251 5099 5085 5082 Tools; safety equipment & supplies; industrial supplies; oil field equipment; flexible metal hose, tubing & bellows; oil well machinery, equipment & supplies

(G-2178)
ENGINEERED CARBONS INC
Fm 1559 (79007)
P.O. Box 7777 (79008-7777)
PHONE.....................................806 274-6347
Jack Klem, *President*
EMP: 84
SALES (est): 10.6MM **Privately Held**
WEB: www.orioncarbons.com
SIC: 2895 Carbon black

(G-2179)
FUZZYS INDUS MINT MNFACTURE LP (PA)
Also Called: Fuzzy's Radiator
204 W 1st St (79007-4720)
P.O. Box 467 (79008-0467)
PHONE.....................................806 273-2818
Richard A Jones, *Partner*
Kenneth Jones, *Partner*
Alan Jones, *General Ptnr*
Chris Martinez, *Project Engr*
EMP: 95
SQ FT: 10,000
SALES (est): 21.5MM **Privately Held**
WEB: www.fuzzysradiator.com
SIC: 3433 7699 Heating equipment, except electric; industrial machinery & equipment repair; agricultural equipment repair services

(G-2180)
NATIONAL OILWELL VARCO LP
Also Called: Nov Completion Prod Solutions
301 Premier Rd (79007-7713)
PHONE.....................................806 274-5293
Tim Clifton, *Branch Mgr*
EMP: 60
SALES (corp-wide): 8.4B **Publicly Held**
WEB: www.nov.com
SIC: 3491 3533 Industrial valves; oil & gas field machinery

HQ: National Oilwell Varco, L.P.
7909 Parkwood Circle Dr
Houston TX 77036
713 375-3700

(G-2181)
ORION ENGINEERED CARBONS LLC
Also Called: Advanced Fillers & Pigments
9440 Fm Hwy 1559 W Of Cy (79007)
P.O. Box 7777 (79008-7777)
PHONE.....................................806 274-6347
Ryan Birge, *Branch Mgr*
Jaronne King, *Manager*
EMP: 76
SALES (corp-wide): 889.5K **Privately Held**
WEB: www.orioncarbons.com
SIC: 2895 Carbon black
HQ: Orion Engineered Carbons Llc
4501 Magnolia Cove Dr
Kingwood TX 77345
832 445-3300

(G-2182)
PAYTON MACHINE & SUPPLY INC
3100 S Cedar (79007)
P.O. Box 387 (79008-0387)
PHONE.....................................806 274-5221
Gerald Payton, *President*
George W Payton Jr, *President*
Gerald L Payton, *Corp Secy*
Lois Payton, *Controller*
Stephanie Payton, *Admin Sec*
EMP: 22
SQ FT: 19,600
SALES (est): 4.9MM **Privately Held**
WEB: www.paytonmachine.com
SIC: 3599 7699 Machine shop, jobbing & repair; aircraft & heavy equipment repair services

(G-2183)
R & R SHEET METAL AND MCH SP
110 E Grand St (79007-5430)
PHONE.....................................806 274-2361
Robert E Haynes Jr, *President*
Eric Shopsteese, *Vice Pres*
Danny Haynes, *Treasurer*
EMP: 15 **EST:** 1944
SQ FT: 25,000
SALES (est): 2MM **Privately Held**
SIC: 7692 3599 Welding repair; custom machinery; machine shop, jobbing & repair

(G-2184)
RAY MAC ENERGY
Also Called: O H M Orperating
1601 Fairlanes Blvd (79007-6701)
P.O. Box 1475 (79008-1475)
PHONE.....................................806 274-5881
EMP: 13
SALES (est): 1.8MM **Privately Held**
SIC: 1311 6512 Oil And Gas Production Operators Of Commercial Real Estate

(G-2185)
SNW OPERATING COMPANY INC
1621 N Main St (79007-2042)
P.O. Box 1130 (79008-1130)
PHONE.....................................806 273-2667
Jerry Nolen, *President*
Vickie Ramsey, *Corp Secy*
EMP: 12
SQ FT: 1,600
SALES (est): 1.1MM **Privately Held**
SIC: 1311 Crude petroleum production

(G-2186)
SOLVAY SPCLTY POLYMERS USA LLC
600 Spur 119 N (79007)
P.O. Box 27328, Houston (77227-7328)
PHONE.....................................770 772-8200
EMP: 21
SALES (corp-wide): 13.8MM **Privately Held**
WEB: www.solvay.com
SIC: 2819 Industrial inorganic chemicals

HQ: Solvay Specialty Polymers Usa, L.L.C.
4500 Mcginnis Ferry Rd
Alpharetta GA 30005
770 772-8200

(G-2187)
SPECIALTY COMPRSR & ENG CO INC (PA)
2 Industrial Blvd (79007)
P.O. Box 783 (79008-0783)
PHONE.....................................806 274-7135
Toll Free:...........................888 -
Roland S Ledford, *Chairman*
Sarah Ledford, *Corp Secy*
Ronnie Ledford, *Vice Pres*
Silver Welch, *Manager*
EMP: 25
SQ FT: 38,000
SALES (est): 8.2MM **Privately Held**
WEB: www.specialtycompressor.com
SIC: 5084 3599 3592 Compressors, except air conditioning; engines & transportation equipment; machine shop, jobbing & repair; pistons & piston rings

(G-2188)
TOKAI CARBON CB LTD
9455 Fm 1559 Rd 1559th (79007)
P.O. Box 3118 (79008-3118)
PHONE.....................................806 274-7213
Terry Bevins, *Principal*
EMP: 125 **Privately Held**
WEB: www.sidrichardson.org
SIC: 2895 Carbon black
HQ: Tokai Carbon Cb Ltd.
301 Commerce St Ste 500
Fort Worth TX 76102
817 390-8600

Bowie
Montague County

(G-2189)
ABSHIER ENERGY LLC
301 Elvis Rd (76230-8456)
P.O. Box 14737, Odessa (79768-4737)
PHONE.....................................432 352-4338
Susan Abshier, *Sales Staff*
Susan Snyder-Abshier,
EMP: 9
SALES (est): 377.1K **Privately Held**
WEB: www.abshierenergy.com
SIC: 4911 1389 1731 Electric services; construction, repair & dismantling services; building oil & gas well foundations on site; oil field services; roustabout service; standby or emergency power specialization

(G-2190)
AHC WESTERN HATTERS LTD LBLTY
Also Called: American Hat Company
3091 Highway 81 N (76230-6348)
P.O. Box 1288 (76230-1288)
PHONE.....................................940 872-2404
Sherry Huff, *CFO*
Stan Redding, *Natl Sales Mgr*
Keith Maddox, *Mng Member*
Susan Maddox,
▲ **EMP:** 25
SQ FT: 35,000
SALES (est): 2.5MM **Privately Held**
WEB: www.americanhat.net
SIC: 2353 Harvest hats, straw

(G-2191)
BENNETT PRODUCTION CORP
815 Highway 59 N (76230-3634)
P.O. Box 391 (76230-0391)
PHONE.....................................940 872-1183
Tod R Dearman, *President*
Ronnie Bell, *Corp Secy*
John Bennett, *Vice Pres*
Charles E Suhr, *Vice Pres*
EMP: 10 **EST:** 1967
SQ FT: 3,200
SALES (est): 950K **Privately Held**
SIC: 1311 Crude petroleum production

(G-2192)
BOWIE INDUSTRIES INCORPORATED
Also Called: Hydro-Mulcher
1004 E Wise St (76230-5233)
P.O. Box 931 (76230-0931)
PHONE.....................................940 872-1106
Bob Jones, *Corp Secy*
Dean Myers, *Vice Pres*
Gary Meyer, *Vice Pres*
Carrie Davis, *Sales Executive*
EMP: 47
SQ FT: 65,000
SALES (est): 13.3MM **Privately Held**
WEB: www.bowieindustries.com
SIC: 3561 3523 5085 Pumps, oil well & field; fertilizing machinery, farm; industrial supplies

(G-2193)
BOWIE NEWS INC
301 Sanders St (76230-4821)
P.O. Box 831 (76230-0831)
PHONE.....................................940 872-2247
Michael Winter, *President*
Barbara Green, *General Mgr*
Winter Mike, *Vice Pres*
EMP: 12 **EST:** 1930
SALES (est): 720.3K **Privately Held**
WEB: www.bowienewsonline.com
SIC: 2711 Newspapers, publishing & printing

(G-2194)
EOG RESOURCES INC
2100 Briar Creek Rd (76230-7725)
P.O. Box B (76230)
PHONE.....................................940 696-6000
Randy Lewellen, *Office Mgr*
EMP: 30
SALES (corp-wide): 17.3B **Publicly Held**
WEB: www.eogresources.com
SIC: 1382 1311 Oil & gas exploration services; crude petroleum production
PA: Eog Resources, Inc.
1111 Bagby Sky Lbby 2
Houston TX 77002
713 651-7000

(G-2195)
GAS ACQUISITION & SUPPLY INC
815 Highway 59 N (76230-3634)
P.O. Box 391 (76230-0391)
PHONE.....................................940 872-1183
Todd Dearman, *President*
EMP: 15
SALES (est): 412.3K **Privately Held**
SIC: 1311 Crude petroleum production

(G-2196)
GIBBONS INC
1007 E Wise St (76230-5232)
P.O. Box 632 (76230-0632)
PHONE.....................................940 872-2452
M L Sanders, *President*
Connie Patterson, *Admin Sec*
▲ **EMP:** 15 **EST:** 1964
SQ FT: 6,000
SALES (est): 880K **Privately Held**
WEB: www.gibbonsinc.com
SIC: 1389 7692 3599 Oil & gas wells: building, repairing & dismantling; welding repair; machine shop, jobbing & repair

(G-2197)
M C(RED)GIBBINS INC
1007 E Wise St (76230-5232)
P.O. Box 632 (76230-0632)
PHONE.....................................940 872-1681
Buster Sanders, *President*
EMP: 20
SALES (est): 1.7MM **Privately Held**
SIC: 3599 Machine shop, jobbing & repair

(G-2198)
NEW VENTURES LEASING LLC
820 State Highway 101 (76230-1949)
P.O. Box 278, Sunset (76270-0278)
PHONE.....................................940 577-7789
Mike Richey,
EMP: 10

SALES (est): 201.3K **Privately Held**
WEB: www.newventuresleasingllc.com
SIC: 7359 1382 Equipment rental & leasing; oil & gas exploration services

(G-2199)
NORTH TEXAS FARM & RANCH
200 Walnut St (76230-4841)
PHONE...................................940 872-5922
Brenda Bingham, *Principal*
Jessica Bartel, *Editor*
EMP: 17
SALES (est): 958.3K **Privately Held**
WEB: www.ntfronline.com
SIC: 2721 Periodicals

(G-2200)
S & V WELL SERVICE INC
1500 Nugent St (76230-2702)
P.O. Box 550 (76230-0550)
PHONE...................................940 872-3535
David Wise, *President*
Vicki Wise, *Corp Secy*
EMP: 10
SQ FT: 4,800
SALES (est): 1.1MM **Privately Held**
SIC: 1389 Servicing oil & gas wells; oil field services

(G-2201)
SHOPPER
Also Called: Montague County Shopper
30 Lyndsey St (76230)
PHONE...................................940 872-6186
Carol Johnson, *President*
EMP: 9 EST: 1980
SQ FT: 25,000
SALES (est): 801.2K **Privately Held**
WEB: www.theshopperonline.biz
SIC: 2741 7375 2721 Shopping news: publishing & printing; information retrieval services; periodicals

(G-2202)
WL PLASTICS CORPORATION
1110 Old Wise Rd (76230-4753)
PHONE...................................940 872-8300
Larry Marcella, *Plant Mgr*
Holly Thompson, *Accountant*
Jerry Rogers, *Branch Mgr*
EMP: 53 **Privately Held**
WEB: www.wlplastics.com
SIC: 3084 Plastics pipe
PA: W.L. Plastics Corporation
3575 Lone Star Cir Ste 30
Fort Worth TX 76177

Boyd
Wise County

(G-2203)
BOYD INDUSTRIES INC
Also Called: Boyd Built Buildings
200 E Lawrence (76023)
P.O. Box 315 (76023-0315)
PHONE...................................940 433-2315
Deborah Maatsch, *President*
Jason Maatsch, *Treasurer*
Gordon Maatsch, *Asst Sec*
EMP: 35 EST: 1961
SQ FT: 60,000
SALES (est): 3MM **Privately Held**
WEB: www.boydbuilt.com
SIC: 3523 1542 Cattle feeding, handling & watering equipment; commercial & office building, new construction
PA: D G J D, Inc.
490 Redhill Rd
Fairplay CO 80440

(G-2204)
CONCORD MECHANICAL INC
1715 County Road 4757 (76023-5006)
P.O. Box 2045 (76023-2045)
PHONE...................................817 319-5575
Cavin Clamon, *President*
Chad Lytle, *Vice Pres*
EMP: 14
SQ FT: 3,200
SALES (est): 2.5MM **Privately Held**
WEB: www.concordmechanicalinc.com
SIC: 1711 3822 Heating & air conditioning contractors; air flow controllers; air conditioning & refrigeration

(G-2205)
KINGS TRUCK BEDS INC
1667 E Highway 114 (76023-6013)
P.O. Box 125 (76023-0125)
PHONE...................................940 433-2360
Bob King, *President*
EMP: 15
SQ FT: 20,000
SALES (est): 1MM **Privately Held**
WEB: www.bobkingstruckbeds.com
SIC: 3713 Truck beds

(G-2206)
LUTTRELL WELDING SERVICES
2840 E Highway 114 (76023-6036)
P.O. Box 1123 (76023-1123)
PHONE...................................940 433-3131
Henry E Luttrell III, *Principal*
Wendy Luttrell, *Principal*
EMP: 21
SALES (est): 2MM **Privately Held**
WEB: www.luttrellweldingservices.com
SIC: 7692 Welding repair

(G-2207)
TEXAS AEROPLASTICS
1803 E Highway 114 (76023-6057)
PHONE...................................817 430-3651
Scott Evans, *General Mgr*
Cristal Broussard, *Manager*
EMP: 10
SALES (est): 1MM **Privately Held**
WEB: www.buyplaneparts.com
SIC: 3728 Aircraft parts & equipment

(G-2208)
TIPPEN STEEL SERVICES INC
100 E Lawrence Ave (76023-3034)
PHONE...................................940 433-3132
Lee Jack Tippen, *President*
Brady Tippen, *Director*
EMP: 35
SQ FT: 25,000
SALES (est): 10.3MM **Privately Held**
WEB: www.tippensteel.com
SIC: 3441 1791 Fabricated structural metal; structural steel erection

(G-2209)
TRI STAR METALS INC
Also Called: Direct Animal Products
554 S Allen St (76023-3340)
P.O. Box 928 (76023-0928)
PHONE...................................940 433-2173
Lupe Batterton, *CEO*
Richard Batterton Jr, *President*
Cindy Powers, *Treasurer*
EMP: 20
SQ FT: 12,000
SALES (est): 5.7MM **Privately Held**
WEB: www.directanimal.com
SIC: 3589 3841 Commercial cooking & foodwarming equipment; veterinarians' instruments & apparatus

(G-2210)
YOUNGS TANK INCORPORATED
3500 E Hwy 114 (76023)
P.O. Box 491 (76023-0491)
PHONE...................................800 345-7952
Roy Young, *President*
Michael C Young, *Corp Secy*
EMP: 26
SQ FT: 21,000
SALES (est): 5.5MM **Privately Held**
WEB: www.youngstank.com
SIC: 3443 3714 Tanks for tank trucks, metal plate; motor vehicle parts & accessories

Brady
Mcculloch County

(G-2211)
BRADY STANDARD HERALD INC
201 S Bridge St (76825-4917)
P.O. Box 1151 (76825-1151)
PHONE...................................325 597-2959
Larry B Smith, *President*
Holly Stewart, *Editor*
Mary Ann Smith, *Treasurer*
James Stewart, *Advt Staff*
James Holloway, *Manager*
EMP: 10 EST: 1942

SQ FT: 4,750
SALES (est): 842.5K **Privately Held**
WEB: www.bradystandard.com
SIC: 2711 5948 5947 Newspapers, publishing & printing; luggage, except footlockers & trunks; souvenirs

(G-2212)
CLEAR DIAMOND INC
807 San Angelo Hwy (76825-3836)
PHONE...................................325 597-9240
Daniel McBride, *President*
EMP: 12
SQ FT: 3,000
SALES (est): 5MM **Privately Held**
WEB: www.mkgas.com
SIC: 2869 Fuels

(G-2213)
DAMUTH TAXIDERMY INC
2300 S Bridge St (76825-7444)
PHONE...................................325 597-0001
Gary Damuth, *President*
EMP: 10
SALES (est): 945.7K **Privately Held**
WEB: www.damuthtaxidermy.com
SIC: 7699 3111 Taxidermists; leather tanning & finishing

(G-2214)
LOADCRAFT INDUSTRIES LTD (PA)
3811 N Bridge St (76825)
PHONE...................................325 597-2911
Terry McIver, *Managing Prtnr*
Donald Barley, *Partner*
Cary Brown, *Partner*
Dale Brown, *Partner*
Ray Jones, *Partner*
▼ EMP: 117
SALES (est): 67.5MM **Privately Held**
WEB: www.loadcraft.com
SIC: 3533 Oil field machinery & equipment

(G-2215)
LOADCRAFT INDUSTRIES LTD
3811 N Brg (76825)
PHONE...................................325 597-1930
Terry McIver, *President*
Reece McIver, *COO*
Gary Weatherman, *Exec VP*
Grady McIver, *Vice Pres*
Luis Collazo, *CFO*
▼ EMP: 12
SALES (est): 1.3MM **Privately Held**
WEB: www.loadcraft.com
SIC: 3999 Barber & beauty shop equipment

(G-2216)
PIONEER SANDS LLC
1000 Oglebay Norton Dr (76825)
PHONE...................................325 597-0721
Ron Jordon, *Opers-Prdtn-Mfg*
Joe Tinebra, *Sales Mgr*
EMP: 9
SALES (corp-wide): 9.3B **Publicly Held**
WEB: www.pwgillibrand.com
SIC: 1446 Silica sand mining
HQ: Pioneer Sands Llc
777 Hidden Rdg
Irving TX 75038
972 444-9001

(G-2217)
RODDIE WOOL SCOURING INC
601 Grand Ave (76825-6531)
P.O. Box 452 (76825-0452)
PHONE...................................325 597-2138
Kurt Roddie, *President*
Rodney Behrenf, *Vice Pres*
Roddie Kirk, *Director*
EMP: 17 EST: 1955
SQ FT: 130,000
SALES (est): 1MM **Privately Held**
SIC: 2299 2231 Scouring: wool, mohair & similar fibers; broadwoven fabric mills, wool

Brazoria
Brazoria County

(G-2218)
CHEVRON PHILLIPS CHEM CO LP
2611 County Road 314 (77422-6365)
PHONE...................................979 798-3950
Jim Gailagly, *Manager*
EMP: 39
SQ FT: 43,560
SALES (corp-wide): 3.5B **Privately Held**
WEB: www.cpchem.com
SIC: 2821 Plastics materials & resins
HQ: Chevron Phillips Chemical Company Lp
10001 Six Pines Dr
The Woodlands TX 77380
832 813-4100

Breckenridge
Stephens County

(G-2219)
ABC PRINTING SERVICE
Also Called: ABC Printing and Office Sups
139 E Walker St (76424-3624)
P.O. Box 930 (76424-0930)
PHONE...................................254 559-3561
Jon Jackson, *Owner*
EMP: 11 EST: 1953
SQ FT: 2,000
SALES (est): 500K **Privately Held**
WEB: www.abcprintingandofficesupply.com
SIC: 2752 2759 Commercial printing, offset; letterpress printing

(G-2220)
B B L LTD
Also Called: Petco
300 N Breckenridge Ave (76424-3506)
P.O. Box 911 (76424-0911)
PHONE...................................254 559-3355
John Connlee, *President*
Umesh Zende, *General Mgr*
Fred Dueser, *Principal*
Ajay Parashar, *Sales Staff*
Jai Sharma, *Sales Staff*
EMP: 40
SALES (est): 2.5MM **Privately Held**
WEB: www.bharatbijlee.com
SIC: 1311 Crude petroleum production

(G-2221)
BASA RESOURCES INC
566 Fm 2231e (76424)
P.O. Box 1778 (76424-1778)
PHONE...................................254 559-3366
Gary Phillips, *Manager*
EMP: 15 **Privately Held**
WEB: www.basaresources.com
SIC: 1311 Crude petroleum production; natural gas production
PA: Basa Resources, Inc.
14875 Landmark Blvd # 400
Dallas TX 75254

(G-2222)
BORETS US INC
1586 Us Highway 180 E (76424-4893)
PHONE...................................254 559-5502
Lev Stulberg, *Branch Mgr*
EMP: 15 **Privately Held**
WEB: www.borets.com
SIC: 5084 1382 Pumps & pumping equipment; oil & gas exploration services
HQ: Borets U.S., Inc.
1600 N Garnett Rd
Tulsa OK 74116

(G-2223)
BRECK OPERATING CORP (HQ)
300 N Breckenridge Ave (76424-3506)
P.O. Box 911 (76424-0911)
PHONE...................................254 559-3355
Fred F Dueser, *CEO*
John Connally, *President*
O H Reaugh, *Senior VP*
Daniel Wilson, *Vice Pres*
Steve Deavzy, *Treasurer*
EMP: 27

G E O G R A P H I C

SQ FT: 25,000
SALES (est): 3.6MM **Privately Held**
WEB: www.breckop.com
SIC: 1311 Crude petroleum production;
natural gas production

(G-2224)
BRECKENRIDGE AUTO & ENGINE SUP (PA)
Also Called: Leonard's Service Center
1811 W Walker St (76424-3233)
P.O. Box 1575 (76424-1575)
PHONE..................................254 559-8241
EMP: 11
SQ FT: 11,800
SALES (est): 2.4MM **Privately Held**
WEB: www.breckenridgeairshow.com
SIC: 5013 5084 3599 Automotive sup-
plies & parts; engines & parts, air-cooled;
machine shop, jobbing & repair

(G-2225)
BRECKENRIDGE EXPLORATION CO
2301 E Us Highway 180 (76424-4982)
P.O. Box 1032, Cisco (76437-1032)
PHONE..................................254 559-7566
Johnny Rowe, President
James T Clay Jr, Vice Pres
EMP: 20
SQ FT: 7,500
SALES (est): 1.9MM **Privately Held**
WEB: www.breckex.com
SIC: 1382 1389 Geophysical exploration,
oil & gas field; gas compressing (natural
gas) at the fields

(G-2226)
BRECKENRIDGE READY MIX INC
Also Called: Tri Cities Ready Mix Div
508 E Lindsey St (76424)
PHONE..................................254 559-3775
William J Sandbrook, President
EMP: 15 **EST:** 1961
SQ FT: 1,000
SALES (est): 926.4K
SALES (corp-wide): 1.4B **Publicly Held**
SIC: 3273 Ready-mixed concrete
PA: U.S. Concrete, Inc.
331 N Main St
Euless TX 76039
817 835-4105

(G-2227)
BRIDGEPORT TRUCK MFG INC
Also Called: Bridgeport Refuse Trucks
1000 Industrial Pkwy (76424-2367)
P.O. Box 1212 (76424-1212)
PHONE..................................254 559-2533
Anthony Kouri, President
Paul Butcher, Regl Sales Mgr
▲ **EMP:** 70
SALES (est): 20MM **Privately Held**
WEB: www.bridgeportmfg.com
SIC: 3713 Garbage, refuse truck bodies

(G-2228)
DELTA OIL & GAS LTD (PA)
1851 E Us Highway 180 # 1 (76424-4971)
P.O. Box 387 (76424-0387)
PHONE..................................254 559-9841
Greg Thomas, President
Kidd Lee, Vice Pres
EMP: 23
SQ FT: 1,200
SALES (est): 4.2MM **Privately Held**
WEB: www.deltaoandg.com
SIC: 1311 Crude petroleum production;
natural gas production

(G-2229)
IBEX INC
300 N Breckenridge Ave (76424-3506)
P.O. Box 911 (76424-0911)
PHONE..................................254 559-3355
John Connally, President
EMP: 50
SALES (est): 2.3MM **Privately Held**
WEB: www.chambermaster.com
SIC: 1311 Crude petroleum production;
natural gas production

(G-2230)
JONELL FILTRATION PRODUCTS INC
900 Industrial Pkwy (76424-2369)
P.O. Box 1092 (76424-1092)
PHONE..................................254 559-7591
Alan Clarke, President
George Clarke, Exec VP
Hebron Burkhall, Vice Pres
John W Clarke Jr, Vice Pres
Joseph Ciminella, Regl Sales Mgr
▼ **EMP:** 85
SQ FT: 84,000
SALES (est): 22.4MM **Privately Held**
WEB: www.processtechnologies.filtra-
tiongroup.com
SIC: 3677 Filtration devices, electronic

(G-2231)
LAKE COUNTY NEWSPAPER
Also Called: Breckenridge American
114 E Elm St (76424-3613)
P.O. Box 871 (76424-0871)
PHONE..................................254 559-5412
Rick Tidrow, General Mgr
Roy Robinson, Principal
Moore Virgil E Jr, Director
EMP: 10 **EST:** 1960
SALES (est): 525K
SALES (corp-wide): 3.4B **Privately Held**
WEB: www.breckenridgeamerican.com
SIC: 2711 Commercial printing & newspa-
per publishing combined; newspapers:
publishing only, not printed on site
HQ: Medianews Group, Inc.
101 W Colfax Ave Ste 1100
Denver CO 80202

(G-2232)
PAT GARCIA
6512 Us Highway 180 W (76424-7717)
PHONE..................................254 559-2815
EMP: 19
SALES (est): 999.5K **Privately Held**
SIC: 3089 Mfg Plastic Products

(G-2233)
PETROLEUM EXPLORATION CO LTD
Also Called: Petex
220 W Elm St (76424-3532)
PHONE..................................254 559-5453
Curtiss McClymond, President
EMP: 35
SALES (est): 4.6MM **Privately Held**
WEB: www.petexltd.com
SIC: 1382 Oil & gas exploration services

(G-2234)
PRODUCTION METER & TESTING
506 E Walker St (76424-3643)
P.O. Box 1724 (76424-1724)
PHONE..................................254 559-7271
Michael Tennison, President
Bob Griffin, Corp Secy
Wayne Vinson, Vice Pres
EMP: 10
SQ FT: 1,500
SALES (est): 511.1K **Privately Held**
WEB: www.pmttexas.com
SIC: 1389 Pipe testing, oil field service

(G-2235)
RAYDON INC (PA)
Also Called: Raydon Construction
300 Fm 3099 N (76424)
PHONE..................................254 559-5012
Darrell E Shortes, President
EMP: 42
SQ FT: 7,200
SALES (est): 29.5MM **Privately Held**
WEB: www.raydon-inc.com
SIC: 1389 1623 1794 1611 Roustabout
service; sewer line construction; excava-
tion work; highway & street construction

(G-2236)
RIDGE OIL COMPANY INC
6628 Us Highway 180 E (76424-8109)
P.O. Box 232 (76424-0232)
PHONE..................................254 559-2297
EMP: 10 **EST:** 1973
SQ FT: 7,500

SALES (est): 1.4MM **Privately Held**
SIC: 1311 Crude petroleum production;
natural gas production

(G-2237)
SINGLETON MOULDINGS INC
1895 E Us Highway 180 (76424-4954)
PHONE..................................254 559-7541
Vance Singleton, President
Trish Singleton, Corp Secy
EMP: 14
SQ FT: 40,000 **Privately Held**
WEB: www.singletonmouldings.com
SIC: 2431 5031 Moldings, wood: unfin-
ished & prefinished; molding, all materials

(G-2238)
SOUTHWEST OILFIELD PDTS INC
1000 Industrial Pkwy (76424-2367)
PHONE..................................254 559-8667
Terry Brumfield, Opers-Prdtn-Mfg
EMP: 9
SALES (corp-wide): 152.8MM **Privately
Held**
WEB: www.swoil.com
SIC: 3599 Machine shop, jobbing & repair
HQ: Southwest Oilfield Products, Inc.
10340 Wallisville Rd
Houston TX 77013
713 675-7541

(G-2239)
STATES INC (PA)
300 N Breckenridge Ave (76424-3506)
PHONE..................................254 559-3355
John Connally, President
Fred F Dueser, Co-COB
O H Reaugh, Co-COB
E Bruce Street, Director
Eileen Speer, Executive
EMP: 40
SQ FT: 25,000
SALES (est): 11.5MM **Privately Held**
SIC: 1311 Crude petroleum production;
natural gas production

(G-2240)
TRI RESOURCES INC
Also Called: Dynegy
2209 Us Highway 180 E (76424-4974)
P.O. Box 991 (76424-0991)
PHONE..................................940 549-8340
David Ishmael, Opers-Prdtn-Mfg
EMP: 21 **Publicly Held**
WEB: www.triresources.com
SIC: 1321 Natural gas liquids
HQ: Tri Resources Inc.
811 Louisiana St Ste 2100
Houston TX 77002
713 584-1000

(G-2241)
TRI RESOURCES INC
Also Called: Dynegy
4 Market Rd 2231 (76424)
PHONE..................................254 559-7533
David Ishmore, Area Mgr
David Ishmael, Opers Mgr
Debra Clark, Administration
EMP: 14 **Publicly Held**
WEB: www.triresources.com
SIC: 1321 Fractionating natural gas liquids
HQ: Tri Resources Inc.
811 Louisiana St Ste 2100
Houston TX 77002
713 584-1000

Brenham
Washington County

(G-2242)
6-K INC
Also Called: Triple C Sheetmetal
1802 Buchannan St (77833-4447)
PHONE..................................979 830-0251
Robert Kitzman, President
EMP: 10
SALES (est): 1.1MM **Privately Held**
WEB: www.schubertsheetmetal.com
SIC: 1711 3444 Ventilation & duct work
contractor; ducts, sheet metal

(G-2243)
BENCOR LLC
4629 Highway 290 W (77833-2090)
P.O. Box 521 (77834-0521)
PHONE..................................979 830-5252
Christine Giese, President
Cynthia Martinez, Vice Pres
Dalton Schulze, Purch Agent
Valarie Cienega, Purchasing
Sonya Schulze, Sales Staff
◆ **EMP:** 20
SALES (est): 2.3MM **Privately Held**
WEB: www.bencor-llc.com
SIC: 3672 Printed circuit boards

(G-2244)
BRAZOS VALLEY BREWING CO LLC
206 S Jackson St (77833-3502)
PHONE..................................979 353-5361
Joshua Bass, Mng Member
EMP: 10
SALES (est): 60.7K **Privately Held**
SIC: 5813 2082 Bar (drinking places);
beer (alcoholic beverage)

(G-2245)
BRENHAM AUTO LTD
Also Called: Fleetfilter
1102 S Austin St (77833-4514)
P.O. Box 589 (77834-0589)
PHONE..................................979 836-4524
EMP: 12
SALES (est): 620K **Privately Held**
SIC: 3714 Mfg Motor Vehicle Parts/Acces-
sories

(G-2246)
BRENHAM READY MIX INC
2200 Highway 290 E (77833-7137)
P.O. Box 827 (77834-0827)
PHONE..................................979 830-1989
Felix Meyer, President
Rayburn Klussmann, Vice Pres
EMP: 15
SQ FT: 800
SALES (est): 3.7MM **Privately Held**
WEB: www.laurenconcrete.com
SIC: 3273 Ready-mixed concrete

(G-2247)
BRENHAM REPAIR CENTER LLC
1404 W Main St (77833-3412)
PHONE..................................979 277-9071
Gregory Peck,
Allan Stelter,
EMP: 10
SQ FT: 6,000
SALES (est): 1.1MM **Privately Held**
WEB: www.brenhamrepair.com
SIC: 7694 7999 Motor repair services; tour
& guide services

(G-2248)
BULLGANG TOOLS LLC
2450 Highway 290 E (77833-7087)
PHONE..................................979 203-9009
EMP: 9 **EST:** 2015
SALES (est): 500K **Privately Held**
WEB: www.bullgangtools.com
SIC: 3441 3315 5947 Fabricated struc-
tural metal; fence gates posts & fittings:
steel; gift shop

(G-2249)
C & P PLASTICS INC
8005 Highway 36 N (77833-8098)
P.O. Box 917 (77834-0917)
PHONE..................................979 251-7991
Carmen Gore, CEO
Cameron Gore, Vice Pres
Rodney Price, Vice Pres
EMP: 22
SQ FT: 9,000
SALES (est): 2MM **Privately Held**
WEB: www.candpplasticsinc.com
SIC: 2821 Plastics materials & resins

(G-2250)
CATO CONSTRUCTION COMPANY
1906 Longwood Dr (77833-5230)
PHONE..................................979 830-1398
James N Cato, President
Rosie Cato, Vice Pres

James Cato, *Info Tech Mgr*
Rosie A Cato, *Admin Sec*
EMP: 20
SQ FT: 66,000
SALES (est): 6MM **Privately Held**
WEB: www.catoconstruction.com
SIC: 1542 3448 Commercial & office building, new construction; agricultural building contractors; prefabricated metal buildings

(G-2251)
DEL SOL FOOD COMPANY INC
Also Called: Briannas Salad Dressings
3015 S Blue Bell Rd (77833-5169)
P.O. Box 2243 (77834-2243)
PHONE................................979 836-5978
Jerry G Brown, *President*
Scott Eckert, *President*
Kathryn Brown, *Vice Pres*
Sherald Bell, *Plant Mgr*
Barbara Dozier, *Production*
▼ **EMP:** 50
SQ FT: 42,000
SALES (est): 7.2MM **Privately Held**
WEB: www.briannas.com
SIC: 2035 Dressings, salad: raw & cooked (except dry mixes)

(G-2252)
DOUBLE R BRAND MFG LLC
11700 Highway 290 W (77833-1647)
P.O. Box 118, Burton (77835-0118)
PHONE................................979 289-3421
Paul Spack, *Controller*
Rodney Roth, *Mng Member*
EMP: 80
SALES (est): 9.5MM
SALES (corp-wide): 13.2MM **Privately Held**
SIC: 2011 Bacon, slab & sliced from meat slaughtered on site
PA: Double R Brand Foods, Llc
6633 Portwest Dr Ste 110
Houston TX 77024
713 868-0030

(G-2253)
EVANS CABINET AND DOOR LTD (PA)
308 W First St (77833-3606)
PHONE................................979 836-6934
James A Evans, *Managing Prtnr*
Bill Christian, *Partner*
Eddie Rogers, *Partner*
Brent McCord, *Vice Pres*
EMP: 38
SQ FT: 40,000
SALES (est): 6.3MM **Privately Held**
WEB: www.evanscabinetanddoor.com
SIC: 2434 2431 Wood kitchen cabinets; doors, wood

(G-2254)
FLAGSHIP TRANSPORT LP
Also Called: Flagship Carrier.
6500 Earlywine Rd (77833-7249)
PHONE................................713 253-7785
CK Moye, *Managing Prtnr*
EMP: 9
SALES (est): 2MM **Privately Held**
SIC: 3537 Trucks: freight, baggage, etc.: industrial, except mining

(G-2255)
GEOSOUTHERN ENERGY CORPORATION
5416 Highway 290 W (77833-8506)
P.O. Box 1329 (77834-1329)
PHONE................................979 836-5203
Richard Borstmayer, *General Mgr*
Greg Colburn, *Production*
Josh Greenleaf, *Engineer*
Herb Rohloff, *Engineer*
Wesley Hicks, *Accountant*
EMP: 15
SALES (corp-wide): 47.7MM **Privately Held**
SIC: 1382 Oil & gas exploration services
PA: Geosouthern Energy Corporation
1425 Lake Front Cir # 200
The Woodlands TX 77380
281 363-9161

(G-2256)
H & H MACHINE SERVICE LLC
1503 Industrial Blvd (77833-5233)
P.O. Box 162 (77834-0162)
PHONE................................979 836-2599
Tommy Ladewig, *Mng Member*
Frank Thomas, *Manager*
EMP: 18
SQ FT: 23,360
SALES (est): 2.4MM **Privately Held**
WEB: www.hh-machine.com
SIC: 3599 1711 1799 7699 Machine shop, jobbing & repair; mechanical contractor; welding on site; aircraft & heavy equipment repair services

(G-2257)
HL INDUSTRIES INC
Also Called: Hi-Line Industries
1208 Industrial Blvd (77833-1776)
P.O. Box 673 (77834-0673)
PHONE................................979 836-2661
Dennis J Kocian, *President*
Ben Heramis, *Engineer*
Marie Rosenhoover, *Treasurer*
Phil Keil, *Sales Staff*
Thomas Bedrich, *Prgrmr*
EMP: 65 **EST:** 1976
SQ FT: 90,000
SALES (est): 11.3MM **Privately Held**
WEB: www.hi-lineindustries.com
SIC: 3535 Conveyors & conveying equipment

(G-2258)
INNOCOR FORM TECH BRENHAM LLC
1200 Rink St (77833-2354)
P.O. Box 643 (77834-0643)
PHONE................................732 945-6222
Carol S Eicher,
▲ **EMP:** 18
SALES (est): 2.3MM **Privately Held**
WEB: www.brenhambanner.com
SIC: 3086 Plastics foam products
HQ: Innocor Foam Technologies, Llc
200 Schulz Dr Ste 2
Red Bank NJ 07701

(G-2259)
JIMMIE HAHN PARTNERSHIP LTD (PA)
1503 N Park St (77833-2335)
PHONE................................979 836-3664
Jimmie Hahn Jr, *President*
Charles Ray Hahn, *Vice Pres*
Charles Schulte, *Vice Pres*
EMP: 40 **EST:** 1935
SQ FT: 1,000
SALES (est): 7.6MM **Privately Held**
WEB: www.laurenconcrete.com
SIC: 3273 4212 Ready-mixed concrete; local trucking, without storage

(G-2260)
LA GRANGE CON & AGGREGATES (PA)
1503 N Park St (77833-2335)
PHONE................................979 836-3664
Jimmie Hahn Jr, *President*
Alma Hahn, *Principal*
Mary Ann Schulte, *Corp Secy*
Charles Ray Hahn, *Vice Pres*
Charles Schulte, *Vice Pres*
EMP: 19
SQ FT: 600
SALES (est): 2.6MM **Privately Held**
WEB: www.laurenconcrete.com
SIC: 3273 4212 Ready-mixed concrete; local trucking, without storage

(G-2261)
LONGWOOD ELASTOMERS INC
Also Called: Gates Molder Products Company
1901 Longwood Dr (77833-5238)
PHONE................................979 830-1111
Michael Groves, *Manager*
EMP: 130 **Publicly Held**
WEB: www.longwoodindustries.com
SIC: 3053 3561 2822 3533 Gaskets, all materials; pumps & pumping equipment; synthetic rubber; oil & gas field machinery; mining machinery

HQ: Longwood Elastomers, Inc.
655 Fairview Rd
Wytheville VA 24382

(G-2262)
MAGNETIC INSTRUMENTS CORP (HQ)
Also Called: M I C Group
3140 S Blue Bell Rd (77833-5153)
PHONE................................800 836-6696
John B Poindexter, *Ch of Bd*
Nelson Byman, *President*
Stan Stafford, *President*
Jeff McKnight, *General Mgr*
Stephen Magee, *Corp Secy*
EMP: 207 **EST:** 1963
SQ FT: 115,000
SALES (est): 69.3MM
SALES (corp-wide): 1.2B **Privately Held**
WEB: www.micgrp.com
SIC: 3599 Machine shop, jobbing & repair
PA: J. B. Poindexter & Co., Inc
600 Travis St Ste 200
Houston TX 77002
713 655-9800

(G-2263)
MIC GROUP LLC
3140 S Blue Bell Rd (77833-5153)
PHONE................................979 277-7806
James C Taylor, *President*
Brad Leuschner, *CFO*
▲ **EMP:** 18
SALES (est): 1.5MM **Privately Held**
WEB: www.micgrp.com
SIC: 3542 Mechanical (pneumatic or hydraulic) metal forming machines

(G-2264)
MIC GROUP LLC (PA)
3140 S Blue Bell Rd (77833-5153)
PHONE................................979 277-7800
Tom Hoyer, *President*
Rick Welch, *Vice Pres*
Trenton Carroll, *Engineer*
Bradley Leuschner, *CFO*
Shelby Smith, *Sales Mgr*
EMP: 59 **Privately Held**
WEB: www.micgrp.com
SIC: 3599 7539 Machine shop, jobbing & repair; machine shop, automotive

(G-2265)
MOUNT VERNON MILLS INC
Also Called: Brentex Division
1100 Highway 290 W (77833-5423)
P.O. Box 625 (77834-0625)
PHONE................................979 836-5255
James Bowden, *Marketing Staff*
David Nagy, *Manager*
EMP: 300 **Privately Held**
WEB: www.mvmills.com
SIC: 2221 2211 Polyester broadwoven fabrics; broadwoven fabric mills, cotton
HQ: Mount Vernon Mills, Inc.
503 S Main St
Mauldin SC 29662
864 688-7100

(G-2266)
NUECES CANYON COMPANIES
Also Called: Nueces Canyon Cattle Company
9501 Highway 290 W (77833-9138)
PHONE................................979 289-5600
Beverly Caloudas, *Owner*
EMP: 15
SALES (est): 390K **Privately Held**
WEB: www.nuecescanyon.com
SIC: 0752 7999 0212 7011 Boarding services, horses: racing & non-racing; baseball batting cage; beef cattle except feedlots; bed & breakfast inn; seasonings, meat sauces (except tomato & dry); frozen meats from purchased meat

(G-2267)
P I COMPONENTS CORP
Also Called: Pic Texas
1951 Highway 290 W (77833-5219)
PHONE................................979 830-5400
Mark S Schumacher, *President*
Eric Claggett, *Vice Pres*
Bruce Muske, *Technical Staff*
Steven A Chelesnik, *Admin Sec*
Marcus Weidemann, *Maintence Staff*
EMP: 95

SQ FT: 70,000
SALES (est): 25.4MM
SALES (corp-wide): 16.7B **Publicly Held**
SIC: 3061 3053 3999 Oil & gas field machinery rubber goods (mechanical); gaskets, packing & sealing devices; atomizers, toiletry
HQ: Rosemount Inc.
8200 Market Blvd
Chanhassen MN 55317
952 906-8888

(G-2268)
PEPSI-COLA METRO BTLG CO INC
Also Called: Pepsico
Geers Rd (77833)
P.O. Box 660 (77834-0660)
PHONE................................979 836-3755
Niel Campbell, *Manager*
EMP: 20
SALES (corp-wide): 67.1B **Publicly Held**
WEB: www.pepsico.com
SIC: 2086 Soft drinks: packaged in cans, bottles, etc.
HQ: Pepsi-Cola Metropolitan Bottling Company, Inc.
1111 Westchester Ave
White Plains NY 10604
914 767-6000

(G-2269)
POLAR ICE INC
2106 Longwood Dr (77833-5247)
P.O. Box 2312 (77834-2312)
PHONE................................979 830-1954
Roy Horton, *President*
Patti Horton, *Director*
EMP: 10
SALES (est): 387.7K **Privately Held**
WEB: www.polaricetexas.com
SIC: 2097 Manufactured ice

(G-2270)
PPE LLC
3201 S Blue Bell Rd (77833-5183)
PHONE................................979 353-7300
Paul Gillyon, *President*
Mark Gorman, *Chairman*
Paolo Benedetto, *Treasurer*
EMP: 16 **EST:** 2013
SALES (est): 370.9K
SALES (corp-wide): 2.4B **Publicly Held**
WEB: www.prepol.com
SIC: 2821 Polymethyl methacrylate resins (plexiglass)
PA: Idex Corporation
3100 Sanders Rd Ste 301
Northbrook IL 60062
847 498-7070

(G-2271)
QUESTSPECIALTY CORPORATION (PA)
2001 E Tom Green St (77833-5126)
P.O. Box 624 (77834-0624)
PHONE................................713 896-8188
Carl Hubble, *President*
Beverley Hubble, *Corp Secy*
Scott Garner, *Vice Pres*
Mitch Whitney, *Vice Pres*
Shay Morrow, *Human Resources*
EMP: 100
SQ FT: 158,000
SALES (est): 50MM **Privately Held**
WEB: www.questspecialty.com
SIC: 2842 2819 Specialty cleaning, polishes & sanitation goods; nonmetallic compounds

(G-2272)
R R DONNELLEY & SONS COMPANY
Continental Ribbon & Carbn Div
1903 Fm 389 (77833-5206)
PHONE................................979 836-4451
EMP: 100
SALES (corp-wide): 6.2B **Publicly Held**
WEB: www.rrd.com
SIC: 2759 Screen printing
PA: R. R. Donnelley & Sons Company
35 W Wacker Dr
Chicago IL 60601
312 326-8000

(G-2273)
SOUTHWEST RESOURCES
205 N Market St Ste 207 (77833-3216)
P.O. Box 1805 (77834-1805)
PHONE...............................979 836-5500
Keith Sanders, *President*
EMP: 10 **Privately Held**
SIC: **1311** Crude petroleum production

(G-2274)
T F E COMPANY INC
1311 Highway 290 W (77833-5203)
P.O. Box 661 (77834-0661)
PHONE...............................979 836-6111
C H Harvey, *President*
Ryan Beaudet, *Vice Pres*
Jason Draehn, *Prdtn Mgr*
Carrie Baker, *Accounting Mgr*
Heather Kirby, *Sales Mgr*
EMP: 27 **EST: 1963**
SQ FT: 38,000
SALES (est): 5.4MM **Privately Held**
WEB: www.tfecompany.com
SIC: **3053** Gaskets, all materials

(G-2275)
TAYLOR COMMUNICATIONS INC
1609 S Blue Bell Rd (77833-5103)
PHONE...............................800 755-6405
J W Burchfield, *Branch Mgr*
EMP: 53
SALES (corp-wide): 2.5B **Privately Held**
WEB: www.taylorcorp.com
SIC: **2754** Commercial printing, gravure
HQ: Taylor Communications, Inc.
    1725 Roe Crest Dr
    North Mankato MN 56003
    866 541-0937

(G-2276)
TRU-VISION PLASTICS INC
401 W Blue Bell Rd (77833-2347)
P.O. Box 653 (77834-0653)
PHONE...............................979 836-1091
Ted Dean, *President*
Wanda Olsen, *Vice Pres*
Jose Rios, *Production*
EMP: 12
SQ FT: 82,000
SALES (est): 2.1MM **Privately Held**
WEB: www.tru-vision.com
SIC: **3081** 2671 Plastic film & sheet; plastic film, coated or laminated for packaging

(G-2277)
VALMONT INDUSTRIES INC
2551 Valmont Dr (77833-5418)
PHONE...............................979 836-9395
Roger Cardwell, *Branch Mgr*
EMP: 230
SALES (corp-wide): 2.7B **Publicly Held**
WEB: www.valmont.com
SIC: **3441** Tower sections, radio & television transmission
PA: Valmont Industries, Inc.
    1 Valmont Plz Ste 500
    Omaha NE 68154
    402 963-1000

(G-2278)
VALMONT INDUSTRIES INC
Also Called: Texas Galvanizing
2569 Valmont Dr (77833-5418)
PHONE...............................979 277-3359
Michael Riley, *Branch Mgr*
EMP: 75
SALES (corp-wide): 2.7B **Publicly Held**
WEB: www.valmont.com
SIC: **3441** Fabricated structural metal
PA: Valmont Industries, Inc.
    1 Valmont Plz Ste 500
    Omaha NE 68154
    402 963-1000

(G-2279)
WHITE WING INSPECTION INC
12505 New Wehdem Rd (77833-9179)
PHONE...............................979 421-8255
David Booth, *President*
EMP: 45
SALES (est): 500K **Privately Held**
WEB: www.whitewinginspection.com
SIC: **1389** Pipe testing, oil field service; oil field services

---

Bridge City
Orange County

(G-2280)
BJHR INC
Also Called: Penny Record
333 W Round Bunch Rd (77611-2445)
P.O. Box 1008 (77611-1008)
PHONE...............................409 735-5305
Roy Dunn, *President*
John Dubose, *Treasurer*
EMP: 40
SALES (est): 1.2MM **Privately Held**
WEB: www.therecordlive.com
SIC: **2711** 5735 Newspapers: publishing only, not printed on site; records

(G-2281)
BURTON SHIPYARD INC
E Roundbunch Rd (77611)
P.O. Box 278 (77611-0278)
PHONE...............................409 735-2491
Len Hartman, *President*
Rachel Wheeler, *Vice Pres*
EMP: 50
SQ FT: 5,000
SALES (est): 7.7MM **Privately Held**
WEB: www.inlandboats.com
SIC: **3731** 3732 Shipbuilding & repairing; boat building & repairing

(G-2282)
CRUMPLERS MCH & WLDG SVC INC
335 Bland Dr (77611-3705)
P.O. Box 848 (77611-0848)
PHONE...............................409 886-7934
Stephen Crumpler, *President*
Steve Crumpler, *Principal*
James Michael Crumpler, *Vice Pres*
Ava Crumpler, *Treasurer*
Jana Fifete, *Treasurer*
EMP: 26 **EST: 1957**
SQ FT: 30,000
SALES (est): 4.3MM **Privately Held**
WEB: www.crumplermachine.com
SIC: **3599** 7692 Machine shop, jobbing & repair; welding repair

(G-2283)
FABRICATING SOLUTIONS
745 Jones St (77611-3909)
P.O. Box 608 (77611-0608)
PHONE...............................409 735-7141
Matthew Wright, *Vice Pres*
Bonnie Wright, *Office Mgr*
Matthew D Wright, *Mng Member*
Bonnie L Wright,
EMP: 18
SQ FT: 9,000
SALES (est): 4.7MM **Privately Held**
WEB: www.fabsollc.com
SIC: **3443** 7692 Fabricated plate work (boiler shop); welding repair

(G-2284)
HBREAUX COMPANIES INC
Also Called: Eye On Security Systems
3165 Texas Ave (77611-4919)
P.O. Box 595 (77611-0595)
PHONE...............................409 792-9212
Henry R Breaux Jr, *President*
EMP: 10 **EST: 1999**
SALES (est): 723.5K **Privately Held**
WEB: www.pinpointsecurity.us
SIC: **2041** Pizza dough, prepared

(G-2285)
HYETT MFG & INSTR CO INC
Also Called: Hyett Instrument Company
130 Granger Dr (77611-2813)
P.O. Box 1640 (77611-1640)
PHONE...............................409 735-5383
Nick Scallon, *Ch of Bd*
Rusty Adkins, *President*
Murray Anderson, *Vice Pres*
EMP: 10 **EST: 1966**
SQ FT: 6,600 **Privately Held**
WEB: www.hyettinstrument.com
SIC: **2819** Industrial inorganic chemicals

(G-2286)
SOUTHEAST TEXAS INDUSTRIES INC
325 Nevils St (77611-3825)
P.O. Box 1449, Buna (77612-1449)
PHONE...............................409 792-0084
Gene Purkey, *Manager*
Jimmie Clark, *Admin Asst*
EMP: 120 **Privately Held**
WEB: www.setxind.com
SIC: **3312** 3498 3444 3441 Blast furnaces & steel mills; fabricated pipe & fittings; sheet metalwork; fabricated structural metal
PA: Southeast Texas Industries, Inc.
    35911 Us Highway 96 S
    Buna TX 77612

(G-2287)
STIS INC
Also Called: Southeast Texas Indus Svcs
3127 Texas Ave (77611-4919)
P.O. Box 1284 (77611-1284)
PHONE...............................409 697-3350
Paul Spence, *President*
Richard Purkey, *Vice Pres*
Robin McGlothlin, *Project Mgr*
Janet Telles, *Purch Agent*
Dale Montgomery, *Project Engr*
EMP: 400
SQ FT: 30,000
SALES (est): 82.6MM **Privately Held**
WEB: www.setxind.com
SIC: **3441** Fabricated structural metal

Bridgeport
Wise County

(G-2288)
BASIC ENERGY SERVICES INC
G & L Tool
2103 Hwy 114 (76426)
P.O. Box R, Aspermont (79502-0916)
PHONE...............................940 683-5484
Doug Wilkinson, *Branch Mgr*
EMP: 10
SALES (corp-wide): 567.2MM **Publicly Held**
WEB: www.basices.com
SIC: **1389** Oil field services
PA: Basic Energy Services, Inc.
    801 Cherry St Unit 2
    Fort Worth TX 76102
    817 334-4100

(G-2289)
BRANDT A VARCO COMPANY
5764 Us Highway 380 (76426-6421)
PHONE...............................940 683-6286
EMP: 45
SALES (est): 1MM **Privately Held**
SIC: **1389** Oil/Gas Field Services

(G-2290)
BRIDGEPORT TANK TRUCKS LLC (HQ)
Also Called: Btt
601 Us Highway 380 (76426-2235)
P.O. Box 6 (76426-0006)
PHONE...............................940 683-9440
Ronald Holley, *CEO*
Gene Melton, *COO*
Bob Earley, *CFO*
EMP: 60
SQ FT: 23,000
SALES (est): 69.4MM
SALES (corp-wide): 1.5B **Privately Held**
WEB: www.bridgeporttanktrucks.com
SIC: **1389** Oil field services
PA: Audax Group Limited Partnership
    101 Huntington Ave # 2450
    Boston MA 02199
    617 859-1500

(G-2291)
BRIDWELL PUBLISHING COMPANY
Also Called: Bridgeport Index
916 Halsell St (76426-3028)
P.O. Box 1150 (76426-1150)
PHONE...............................940 683-4021
Keith Bridwell, *President*
Jo Gilbreath, *Editor*

Francine West, *Prdtn Dir*
Whitney Bridwell, *Manager*
EMP: 12 **EST: 1957**
SQ FT: 1,500
SALES (est): 803.9K **Privately Held**
WEB: www.bridgeportindex.com
SIC: **2711** 2759 Newspapers: publishing only, not printed on site; commercial printing

(G-2292)
ELITE WELLSITE SERVICES LLC
1804 Overland Dr (76426-2632)
P.O. Box 1600 (76426-1600)
PHONE...............................940 393-2116
Jerrod S Mowery,
EMP: 10
SALES (est): 584.3K
SALES (corp-wide): 1.2B **Publicly Held**
SIC: **1382** Geophysical exploration, oil & gas field
HQ: Select Energy Services, Llc
    1820 N I 35
    Gainesville TX 76240
    940 668-1818

(G-2293)
ENERVEST OPERATING LLC
306 Us Highway 380 (76426-2243)
P.O. Box 1280 (76426-1280)
PHONE...............................940 683-1966
Sam Bluewinters, *Manager*
EMP: 40 **Privately Held**
WEB: www.enervest.net
SIC: **1382** Oil & gas exploration services
HQ: Enervest Operating, L.L.C.
    1001 Fannin St Ste 800
    Houston TX 77002

(G-2294)
HAMMER CONSTRUCTION INC
3232 S Hwy 101 (76426)
P.O. Box 600 (76426-0600)
PHONE...............................940 683-3131
Javier Luna, *Branch Mgr*
EMP: 70 **Privately Held**
WEB: www.hammerok.com
SIC: **1389** 1794 Oil field services; excavation & grading, building construction
PA: Hammer Construction, Inc.
    4320 Adams Rd
    Norman OK 73069

(G-2295)
HANSON AGGREGATES LLC
Chico Hwy 101 (76426)
P.O. Box 6, Chico (76431-0006)
PHONE...............................940 683-4294
David Carlton, *Manager*
EMP: 86
SALES (corp-wide): 20.8B **Privately Held**
WEB: www.heidelbergcement.com
SIC: **1442** Common sand mining; construction sand mining
HQ: Hanson Aggregates Llc
    8505 Freport Pkwy Ste 500
    Irving TX 75063
    469 417-1200

(G-2296)
KOKOMO ENERGY INC
101 Turkey Creek Trl (76426-2242)
P.O. Box 1200 (76426-1200)
PHONE...............................940 683-1102
Cecil L Everton, *President*
Lelland Everton, *Corp Secy*
Birdsong Thomas H III, *Director*
EMP: 13
SQ FT: 2,000
SALES (est): 1.8MM **Privately Held**
SIC: **1382** Oil & gas exploration services

(G-2297)
NORTH TEXAS COMPRESSION
101 Turkey Creek Trl (76426-2242)
P.O. Box 1105 (76426-1105)
PHONE...............................940 683-5025
Dwanye Garrett, *Owner*
EMP: 10
SQ FT: 7,500
SALES (est): 1.9MM **Privately Held**
WEB: www.flatrockcompression.com
SIC: **1389** Oil field services

(G-2298)
PEAK OILFIELD SERVICES LLC (HQ)
1502 10th St (76426-2339)
P.O. Box 548 (76426-0548)
PHONE.................................940 683-1627
John Schmitz, *CEO*
Pat Anderle, *President*
Matt Brennan, *Area Mgr*
Cody Ortowski, *COO*
James Perkins, *Opers Mgr*
EMP: 31
SQ FT: 4,258
SALES (est): 75.4MM
SALES (corp-wide): 1.2B **Publicly Held**
WEB: www.peakoilservices.com
SIC: 1389 Oil field services
PA: Select Energy Services, Inc.
1233 West Loop S Ste 1400
Houston TX 77027
713 235-9500

(G-2299)
PROTOCOL TECHNOLOGIES INC
Also Called: Protocol Feeds
210 Lake Rd (76426-2226)
PHONE.................................940 683-8123
Dr Jimmy Horner, *President*
Cindy Poore, *Corp Secy*
Randy Harms, *Vice Pres*
Abby Broussard, *Mktg Dir*
Chad Horner, *Manager*
EMP: 15
SALES (est): 2.4MM **Privately Held**
WEB: www.protocolnaturals.net
SIC: 2048 Feed supplements

(G-2300)
ROC SERVICE COMPANY LLC (DH)
191 Energy Way (76426-6122)
P.O. Box 1337 (76426-1337)
PHONE.................................940 683-0159
Brandon Johnson, *President*
Lacee King, *Business Mgr*
Billy Greenwood, *COO*
Robert Johnson, *Vice Pres*
Paul Coscia, *CFO*
EMP: 122
SALES (est): 72.6MM
SALES (corp-wide): 93.7MM **Privately Held**
WEB: www.rocserviceco.com
SIC: 1794 1731 1389 Excavation & grading, building construction; energy management controls; building oil & gas well foundations on site; roustabout service; servicing oil & gas wells
HQ: Roc Holdings, Llc
191 Energy Way
Bridgeport TX 76426
940 683-0159

(G-2301)
SMITH OILFIELD SERVICES INC
172 County Road 3503 (76426-4620)
P.O. Box 562 (76426-0562)
PHONE.................................940 683-5722
Rick Smith, *President*
Landon Smith, *Vice Pres*
Mark Norwood, *Director*
EMP: 50
SQ FT: 4,800
SALES (est): 9.4MM **Privately Held**
WEB: www.smithoilfieldservices.com
SIC: 4959 1389 Oil spill cleanup; environmental cleanup services; oil field services

(G-2302)
T & W TIRE LLC
1908 Chico Hwy (76426-2222)
PHONE.................................940 683-3558
Charlie Wilson, *Branch Mgr*
Billy Hutchison, *Manager*
Leslie Hutchison, *Asst Mgr*
EMP: 9
SALES (corp-wide): 185.1MM **Privately Held**
WEB: www.tandwtire.com
SIC: 3011 7534 Truck or bus tires, pneumatic; tire repair shop

PA: T & W Tire, L.L.C.
25 N Council Rd
Oklahoma City OK 73127
405 787-6711

(G-2303)
TEXAS INDUSTRIES INC
Also Called: Txi
1795 S Hwy 101 (76426)
P.O. Box 487 (76426-0487)
PHONE.................................940 683-4277
Todd Lacy, *General Mgr*
EMP: 102 **Publicly Held**
WEB: www.martinmarietta.com
SIC: 3273 Ready-mixed concrete
HQ: Texas Industries, Inc.
1503 Lyndon B Johnson Fwy
Dallas TX 75234
972 647-6700

(G-2304)
VULCAN MATERIALS COMPANY
Also Called: Chico
2560 S State Highway 101 (76426-6116)
PHONE.................................940 683-4996
J Thomas Hill, *Ch of Bd*
EMP: 25 **Publicly Held**
WEB: www.vulcanmaterials.com
SIC: 1422 Crushed & broken limestone
PA: Vulcan Materials Company
1200 Urban Center Dr
Vestavia AL 35242

(G-2305)
WISE READY MIX CONCRETE (PA)
2005 16th St (76426-2107)
P.O. Box 488 (76426-0488)
PHONE.................................940 683-5260
Alton J Baker, *President*
Linda K Baker, *Vice Pres*
Alan Baker, *Admin Sec*
EMP: 30
SQ FT: 1,000
SALES (est): 9.4MM **Privately Held**
WEB: www.wisereadymix.com
SIC: 3273 Ready-mixed concrete

Bronte
Coke County

(G-2306)
SAGO ENERGY LLC
209 Ne Railraod St (76933)
PHONE.................................325 473-5161
Bob Boyd, *Manager*
EMP: 55
SALES (corp-wide): 3.9MM **Privately Held**
WEB: www.westtexasgas.com
SIC: 1311 4924 Natural gas production; natural gas distribution
PA: Sago Energy Llc
211 N Colorado St
Midland TX 79701
432 682-6311

(G-2307)
WTG GAS PROCESSING LP
209 Ne Railroad St (76933)
P.O. Box D (76933-0380)
PHONE.................................325 473-5161
Jeff Shepard, *Manager*
EMP: 20
SALES (corp-wide): 30.2MM **Privately Held**
WEB: www.wtggasprocessing.com
SIC: 1321 1311 Natural gasoline production; crude petroleum & natural gas production
PA: Wtg Gas Processing, L.P.
211 N Colorado St
Midland TX 79701
432 682-4349

Brookeland
Jasper County

(G-2308)
RAYBAR SERVICES LLC
105 Don Woods Dr (75931-3844)
P.O. Box 530 (75931-0530)
PHONE.................................409 698-2548
Donald Wood Jr, *President*
Charles Beckett, *Principal*
EMP: 15
SQ FT: 12,000
SALES (est): 2MM **Privately Held**
SIC: 1623 8744 3531 Oil & gas pipeline construction; ; rakes, land clearing: mechanical

Brookshire
Waller County

(G-2309)
ACCURATE INC
37233 Fm 529 Rd (77423-9493)
PHONE.................................979 921-7777
Henry Hutcherson, *CEO*
EMP: 137 **Privately Held**
WEB: www.accuratecoatings.com
SIC: 3479 Painting, coating & hot dipping
PA: Accurate, Inc.
207 Allison
Taylor TX 76574

(G-2310)
B & H BAG COMPANY
35220 Cooper Rd (77423-9847)
PHONE.................................713 641-0921
Tom Robson, *President*
EMP: 30
SALES (est): 3.8MM **Privately Held**
WEB: www.bhbag.com
SIC: 2674 Paper bags: made from purchased materials

(G-2311)
BROOKSHIRE CHEMICAL SVCS LLC
30653 Fm 529 Rd (77423-9131)
PHONE.................................281 371-2600
Pascal Estienne,
Gerald Eaton,
Allen Ebert,
◆ **EMP:** 20
SQ FT: 125,000
SALES (est): 4.1MM **Privately Held**
SIC: 2819 Catalysts, chemical

(G-2312)
CARDET WHOLESALE INC
Also Called: Goya Foods of Texas
30602 Goya Rd (77423-9604)
PHONE.................................713 266-9834
Evelio Fernandez, *President*
Carlos Ortiz, *President*
Miguel Lugo, *Principal*
Peter Unanue, *Principal*
Robert Unanue, *Principal*
◆ **EMP:** 100
SALES (est): 64.1MM
SALES (corp-wide): 1.5B **Privately Held**
WEB: www.goya.com
SIC: 5141 5499 2673 Groceries, general line; beverage stores; food storage & frozen food bags, plastic
PA: Goya Foods, Inc.
350 County Rd
Jersey City NJ 07307
201 348-4900

(G-2313)
CERDA-FIED SPECIALISTS INC
707 Bains St (77423-4313)
PHONE.................................281 392-8063
Charlie Cerda, *President*
Lianna Cerda, *Assistant*
EMP: 16

SALES (est): 2.4MM **Privately Held**
WEB: www.cerdafied.com
SIC: 1761 3442 3446 3462 Skylight installation; window & door frames; stairs, staircases, stair treads: prefabricated metal; fences or posts, ornamental iron or steel; ornamental metal forgings, ferrous; doors, safe & vault: metal

(G-2314)
CUSTOM HELIARC INC
34430 Sunset Ln (77423-8524)
PHONE.................................281 375-2075
Matt Stewart, *President*
Charles R Sledge, *President*
▲ **EMP:** 11
SQ FT: 16,400
SALES (est): 1.5MM **Privately Held**
WEB: www.customheliarcinc.com
SIC: 7692 Welding repair

(G-2315)
D&R PIPE FAB PLUS INC
520 Purdy St (77423-9456)
P.O. Box 159 (77423-0159)
PHONE.................................281 375-2401
Dewayne Lanier, *President*
EMP: 10
SQ FT: 6,400
SALES (est): 1.9MM **Privately Held**
WEB: www.drpipefabplus.com
SIC: 3498 Fabricated pipe & fittings

(G-2316)
GRUNDFOS CBS INC (DH)
Also Called: Paco Pumps By Grundfos
902 Koomey Rd (77423-8216)
PHONE.................................281 994-2700
Gregers Johansen, *President*
Stephanie Welda, *Business Mgr*
Luna WEI, *Controller*
Chau Nguyen, *Human Resources*
Trevor Lain, *Manager*
◆ **EMP:** 225
SALES (est): 64.5MM
SALES (corp-wide): 4B **Privately Held**
WEB: www.pacopumps.com
SIC: 3561 Pumps & pumping equipment
HQ: Grundfos Holding Ag
C/O Bratschi Ag, Zweigniederlassung Zug
Zug ZG 6300
417 692-222

(G-2317)
GULF STATES TUBE LLC
34066 Sunset Ln (77423-8518)
PHONE.................................281 375-5113
Henry Pavlick, *Branch Mgr*
EMP: 30 **Privately Held**
SIC: 3317 Steel pipe & tubes
PA: Gulf States Tube, Llc
9401 Telge Rd
Houston TX

(G-2318)
LEADING TESTING LABS LLC (PA)
Also Called: Ltl Group
839 Fm 1489 Rd (77423-8804)
PHONE.................................281 600-8227
Grace Liu, *Opers Staff*
Yang Wang, *Technical Staff*
Peng Xiang Nie,
EMP: 45
SQ FT: 50,000
SALES (est): 30.8MM **Privately Held**
WEB: www.ltlg.us
SIC: 5047 3559 Diagnostic equipment, medical; electronic component making machinery

(G-2319)
MAN ENERGY SOLUTIONS USA INC (DH)
1758 Twinwood Pkwy (77423-4700)
PHONE.................................713 780-4200
Yvonne Benkert, *President*
David Finn, *General Mgr*
William Anthony Ruegger, *Managing Dir*
Gary Benard, *Vice Pres*
Sven Feyer, *CFO*
◆ **EMP:** 15

SALES (est): 40.5MM
SALES (corp-wide): 279.5B **Privately Held**
WEB: www.usa.man-es.com
SIC: 7538 5999 7539 3621 Engine repair; engines & parts, air-cooled; automotive turbocharger & blower repair; rotor retainers or housings
HQ: Man Energy Solutions Se
Stadtbachstr. 1
Augsburg 86153
821 322-0

(G-2320)
MAN ENERGY SOLUTIONS USA INC
Man Diesel Turbo
1758 Twinwood Pkwy (77423-4700)
PHONE....................................713 780-4200
Jim Otto, *General Mgr*
Steve Taylor, *Plant Mgr*
Chris Gray, *Sales Staff*
Diorgenes Borges, *Manager*
EMP: 15
SALES (corp-wide): 279.5B **Privately Held**
WEB: www.usa.man-es.com
SIC: 3519 Diesel, semi-diesel or duel-fuel engines, including marine
HQ: Man Energy Solutions Usa Inc
1758 Twinwood Pkwy
Brookshire TX 77423
713 780-4200

(G-2321)
OLDCASTLE INFRASTRUCTURE INC
2120 Fm 359 Rd S (77423-9023)
PHONE....................................713 991-2400
Asher Kazman, *Branch Mgr*
Fabian Dehoyos, *Manager*
Jason Frost, *Manager*
EMP: 50
SALES (corp-wide): 30.6B **Privately Held**
WEB: www.oldcastleinfrastructure.com
SIC: 3272 Concrete products, precast
HQ: Oldcastle Infrastructure, Inc.
7000 Central Pkwy Ste 800
Atlanta GA 30328
470 602-2000

(G-2322)
ORIZON INDUSTRIES INC
7007 Fm 362 Rd (77423-9418)
PHONE....................................281 375-7700
Curtis F Jones, *President*
Cullen R Spitzer, *Chairman*
Ted Johnson, *Corp Secy*
Charles O'Hara, *Vice Pres*
Will Essner, *VP Opers*
EMP: 250
SQ FT: 252,669
SALES (est): 106.8MM
SALES (corp-wide): 185MM **Privately Held**
WEB: www.orizonindustries.com
SIC: 3441 Building components, structural steel
PA: Spitzer Industries, Inc.
12141 Wickc Ln Ste 750
Houston TX 77079
832 783-7000

(G-2323)
PROCON CONSTRUCTION CO INC
2875 Woods Rd (77423-9047)
PHONE....................................281 375-6829
Royce Reid, *President*
Lawrence Reid, *Treasurer*
EMP: 10
SQ FT: 5,000
SALES (est): 1.4MM **Privately Held**
WEB: www.procon.com.au
SIC: 3312 Structural shapes & pilings, steel; pipes, iron & steel

(G-2324)
SATURN MACHINE INC
4815 Front St (77423-9409)
P.O. Box 1276 (77423-1276)
PHONE....................................281 391-7800
Salvador Soliz, *President*
Bill Richards, *Vice Pres*
William F Richards, *Vice Pres*
Melinda Johnson, *Accountant*

Shaun Lawler, *Info Tech Dir*
▲ **EMP:** 65
SQ FT: 14,700
SALES (est): 21.3MM **Privately Held**
WEB: www.saturnmachine.com
SIC: 3599 Machine shop, jobbing & repair

(G-2325)
SULZER PUMPS HOUSTON INC
800 Koomey Rd (77423-8202)
PHONE....................................281 934-6014
URS Rathgeb, *President*
Jack O Connor, *Vice Pres*
Gene Krupala, *Purch Agent*
Paul Patterson, *Sales Staff*
Julie Likewise, *Marketing Staff*
◆ **EMP:** 104
SQ FT: 230,000
SALES (est): 49.6MM
SALES (corp-wide): 3.7B **Privately Held**
SIC: 3561 Pumps, oil well & field
HQ: Sulzer Us Holding Inc.
1255 Enclave Pkwy Ste 300
Houston TX 77077
346 207-9660

(G-2326)
SUPERIOR ENERGY SERVICES LLC
Also Called: Superior Pressure Pumping Svcs
3943 Fm 362 Rd (77423-2525)
PHONE....................................281 934-2181
EMP: 23 **Publicly Held**
SIC: 1389 7353 Oil/Gas Field Services Heavy Construction Equip Rental
HQ: Superior Energy Services, L.L.C.
5801 Highway 90 E
Broussard LA 70508
337 714-4545

(G-2327)
TEXAS FIRST INDUS CORP INC
32473 Morton Rd (77423-8010)
PHONE....................................281 934-1190
Bin Hao, *President*
Vera Zhang, *Accountant*
Zhang Lishu, *Sales Mgr*
Yu Zhang, *Director*
Guangxia Qiu, *Admin Secy*
◆ **EMP:** 20
SALES (est): 9.1MM **Privately Held**
WEB: www.tfi-corp.com
SIC: 3533 Drilling tools for gas, oil or water wells

Brookston
Lamar County

(G-2328)
NORSTAR INDUSTRIES LLC
5500 Farm Road 38 N (75421-2519)
PHONE....................................903 784-8900
John Harms, *Manager*
David Harms,
Abraham Harms,
Johan Harms,
▲ **EMP:** 47
SQ FT: 56,000
SALES (est): 2.4MM **Privately Held**
WEB: www.norstarcompany.com
SIC: 3713 3799 Truck beds; trailers & trailer equipment

Brownfield
Terry County

(G-2329)
BAKER HUGHES HOLDINGS LLC
702 S 14th St (79316-5021)
PHONE....................................806 637-4745
Paul Mason, *Branch Mgr*
EMP: 15
SALES (corp-wide): 23.8B **Publicly Held**
WEB: www.bakerhughes.com
SIC: 1389 Oil field services
HQ: Baker Hughes Holdings Llc
17021 Aldine Westfield Rd
Houston TX 77073
713 439-8600

(G-2330)
BIRDSONG CORPORATION
Birdsong Peanut Company
1564 C R 474 (79316)
P.O. Box 1375 (79316-1375)
PHONE....................................806 637-7200
EMP: 10
SALES (corp-wide): 46.7MM **Privately Held**
SIC: 5159 5441 2099 2068 Whol Farm Prdt Raw Mtrls Ret Candy/Confectionery Mfg Food Preparations Mfg Roasted Nuts/Seeds
PA: Birdsong Corporation
612 Madison Ave
Suffolk VA 23434
757 539-3456

(G-2331)
GUAR RESOURCES LLC
807 N 5th St (79316-2443)
P.O. Box 528 (79316-0528)
PHONE....................................806 637-4662
Arie Genger, *Ch of Bd*
Jessica Garcia, *Controller*
Ashley Watkins, *Controller*
EMP: 50
SQ FT: 40,000
SALES (est): 9MM **Privately Held**
WEB: www.guarresources.com
SIC: 2032 Bean sprouts: packaged in cans, jars, etc.

(G-2332)
W & R INDUSTRIAL SERVICES INC
720 W Broadway St (79316-4214)
P.O. Box 1321 (79316-1321)
PHONE....................................806 637-8204
Ross Ward, *President*
Kelley Ward, *Admin Sec*
EMP: 25 **EST:** 1978
SQ FT: 60,000
SALES (est): 2.5MM **Privately Held**
WEB: www.wrindustrialservices.com
SIC: 3523 Planting machines, agricultural

Brownsboro
Henderson County

(G-2333)
WILSON STEEL SERVICES LLC
13501 County Road 3300 (75756-3523)
PHONE....................................903 275-2995
P Kristine Wilson, *Mng Member*
Phyllis Kristine Wilson, *Mng Member*
EMP: 10
SALES (est): 300K **Privately Held**
WEB: www.wilsonsteelservices.com
SIC: 3441 3211 3449 Fabricated structural metal; structural glass; miscellaneous metalwork

---

Brownsville
Cameron County

(G-2334)
ADIENT CLANTON INC
4694 Coffeeport Rd (78521)
PHONE....................................956 525-4515
EMP: 251 **Privately Held**
WEB: www.clantonadvertiser.com
SIC: 2531 Vehicle furniture
HQ: Adient Clanton Inc.
2541 7th St S
Clanton AL 35046
205 755-9994

(G-2335)
ADVANCE FIBERGLASS LLC
Also Called: Fib-R-Dor Division
5224 Ruben Torres Sr Blvd (78526-5217)
PHONE....................................956 544-1000
Jason Dileo,
▲ **EMP:** 18
SQ FT: 12,500
SALES (est): 1.7MM **Privately Held**
WEB: www.chem-pruf.com
SIC: 3089 Fiberglass doors

(G-2336)
ALLIED MINERAL PRODUCTS INC
3025 Mineral Loop (78521-1042)
PHONE....................................956 831-2022
Mario Gonzales, *Manager*
EMP: 9
SALES (corp-wide): 119.8MM **Privately Held**
WEB: www.alliedmineral.com
SIC: 3297 3255 Nonclay refractories; clay refractories
PA: Allied Mineral Products, Llc
2700 Scioto Pkwy
Columbus OH 43221
614 876-0244

(G-2337)
AUSTIN STAR DETONATOR COMPANY
901 Cantu Rd (78521-9200)
PHONE....................................956 831-7751
Sam Hatley, *President*
Ignacio Reyes, *Manager*
▲ **EMP:** 27
SQ FT: 16,000
SALES (est): 9.2MM
SALES (corp-wide): 509.6MM **Privately Held**
SIC: 2892 Detonators, high explosives
HQ: Austin Powder Company
25800 Science Park Dr # 300
Cleveland OH 44122
216 464-2400

(G-2338)
BORDER MANUFACTURER CONTRS LLC
3320 E 14th St (78521-3232)
PHONE....................................956 982-0910
Luis Ramirez, *Controller*
Rolando A Gonzalez, *Mng Member*
EMP: 25
SALES (est): 6.5MM **Privately Held**
SIC: 2899 Fire extinguisher charges

(G-2339)
BORDER STATES INDUSTRIES INC
Bush Sup A Div Border States
2781 Robindale Rd (78526-2507)
PHONE....................................956 831-3441
Allan Jensen, *Branch Mgr*
EMP: 21
SALES (corp-wide): 2.4B **Privately Held**
WEB: www.borderstates.com
SIC: 5063 5065 5074 1711 Electrical supplies; electronic parts & equipment; plumbing & hydronic heating supplies; plumbing, heating, air-conditioning contractors; plastics plumbing fixtures; vitreous plumbing fixtures
PA: Border States Industries, Inc.
2400 38th St S
Fargo ND 58104
701 293-5834

(G-2340)
BROWNSVILLE SHEET METAL WORKS
1954 S Price Rd (78521-2496)
PHONE....................................956 546-4517
Harry Lee Richardson, *President*
Ivianne Merril, *Vice Pres*
EMP: 26
SQ FT: 11,000
SALES (est): 3.5MM **Privately Held**
WEB:
www.brownsvillesheetmetalworks.com
SIC: 1711 3499 Ventilation & duct work contractor; metal household articles

(G-2341)
BROWNSVLLE ARCHITECTURAL MLLWK
Also Called: Brownsville Millwork
4764 Martinal Rd (78526-9626)
PHONE....................................956 592-5423
Darrell Spieckermann, *President*
Minnie Spieckermann, *Vice Pres*
EMP: 35
SQ FT: 5,000

SALES (est): 4.3MM **Privately Held**
SIC: 2431 5211 1751 Millwork; millwork & lumber; cabinet & finish carpentry

(G-2342)
BUENA VISTA BURIAL PARK INC
5 Mcdavitt Blvd (78521-2122)
PHONE...........................956 542-5271
Juan Garcia, *General Mgr*
Vicky Trevino, *Manager*
EMP: 15
SALES (est): 639.3K **Privately Held**
WEB: www.buenavistaburialpark.com
SIC: 6553 3272 5999 Cemeteries, real estate operation; burial vaults, concrete or precast terrazzo; monuments & tombstones

(G-2343)
CAPISTRAN TORTILLA FACTORY
Also Called: Capistran Tortillas Bar-B-Que
1305 Lincoln St (78521-2058)
PHONE...........................956 541-3053
Ramon Capistran, *Owner*
Mike Capistran, *Owner*
EMP: 35
SALES (est): 2.1MM **Privately Held**
SIC: 2099 5411 5812 Tortillas, fresh or refrigerated; grocery stores, independent; eating places

(G-2344)
CARLING TECHNOLOGIES INC
3734 International Blvd (78521-3230)
PHONE...........................956 546-5564
Ryan Roth, *Vice Pres*
Rogelio Guerra, *Maint Spvr*
Esteban Saucedo, *Buyer*
Martin Pizana, *Engineer*
Francisco Miranda, *Human Resources*
EMP: 50
SALES (corp-wide): 1.5MM **Privately Held**
WEB: www.carlingtech.com
SIC: 3625 Switches, electric power
PA: Carling Technologies, Inc.
60 Johnson Ave
Plainville CT 06062
860 793-9281

(G-2345)
CELEBRITY GROUP MAGAZINE
2353 Old Port Isabel Rd (78521-7416)
PHONE...........................956 579-2020
Marco Romero, *CEO*
EMP: 23
SQ FT: 800
SALES (est): 1.4MM **Privately Held**
SIC: 2721 Magazines: publishing & printing

(G-2346)
CHEM-PRUF DOOR CO LTD
5224 Ruben Torres Sr Blvd (78526-5217)
P.O. Box 4560 (78523-4560)
PHONE...........................956 544-1000
Tony McDermid, *Principal*
EMP: 75
SALES (est): 14MM **Privately Held**
WEB: www.chem-pruf.com
SIC: 3089 3442 Fiberglass doors; metal doors, sash & trim

(G-2347)
CONSULTINGPOINT INC
301 Mexico Blvd Ste 700 (78520-4021)
PHONE...........................956 986-2727
Joel Gonzalez, *President*
Rosa Gonzalez, *Vice Pres*
Rosie Gonzalez, *Vice Pres*
Jose Rocha, *Mfg Staff*
Oscar Flores, *Controller*
EMP: 46
SALES (est): 2.4MM **Privately Held**
WEB: www.cpi-manufacturing.com
SIC: 3621 Motors & generators

(G-2348)
DELCAS INDUSTRIES LLC
4630 Mar St (78521-5252)
PHONE...........................956 831-3311
Fernando Del, *Director*
Fernando Del Castillo,
EMP: 9
SQ FT: 8,000

SALES (est): 997.8K **Privately Held**
SIC: 3544 Special dies & tools

(G-2349)
DELTATECH CONTROLS INC
594 S Vermillion Ave (78521-6881)
PHONE...........................956 755-9634
Enrique Lopez, *Manager*
▲ EMP: 18
SALES (est): 4.8MM **Privately Held**
SIC: 3559 Cement making machinery

(G-2350)
DLHBOWLES INC
3301 Nafta Pkwy Ste A (78526-9733)
PHONE...........................956 986-6000
Dennis Robish, *CFO*
EMP: 57
SALES (corp-wide): 252.6MM **Privately Held**
WEB: www.dlhbowles.com
SIC: 3089 3082 Injection molding of plastics; tubes, unsupported plastic
PA: Dlhbowles, Inc.
2422 Leo Ave Sw
Canton OH 44706
330 478-2503

(G-2351)
DUS OPERATING INC
Also Called: Dura
3201 Nafta Pkwy (78526-9764)
PHONE...........................956 371-3057
Rafael Crocker, *Branch Mgr*
EMP: 378
SALES (corp-wide): 152.7MM **Privately Held**
WEB: www.duraauto.com
SIC: 3714 Motor vehicle parts & accessories
PA: Dus Operating Inc.
1780 Pond Run
Auburn Hills MI 48326
248 299-7500

(G-2352)
EASY WAY LEISURE CORPORATION
2705 Quality Ln Ste B (78526-5107)
PHONE...........................956 831-6442
Glen Napolitano, *CFO*
EMP: 250
SALES (corp-wide): 45MM **Privately Held**
WEB: www.easywayproducts.com
SIC: 2392 Cushions & pillows
PA: Easy Way Leisure Corporation
8950 Rossash Rd
Cincinnati OH 45236
513 731-5640

(G-2353)
ELIZONDO ENTERPRISES INC
Also Called: Elizondo Crane Service
4699 Ruben Torres Sr Blvd (78526-7401)
P.O. Box 5748 (78523-5748)
PHONE...........................956 831-7174
Ethelvina Elizondo, *President*
Jorge A Elizondo, *Vice Pres*
EMP: 9
SQ FT: 5,000
SALES (est): 1.6MM **Privately Held**
WEB: www.elizondocrane.com
SIC: 5084 7353 3531 Cranes, industrial; cranes & aerial lift equipment, rental or leasing; backhoes, tractors, cranes, plows & similar equipment

(G-2354)
ENTAIL ENGINE LLC
1445 E Madison St Ste 177 (78520-5759)
PHONE...........................956 467-5198
Orlando Urzua,
EMP: 9 EST: 2009
SALES (est): 1.1MM **Privately Held**
WEB: www.entailengine.com
SIC: 2851 Paints & allied products

(G-2355)
EXEL BOBBINS & PLAS COMPONENTS
3301 Nafta Pkwy Ste C (78526-9733)
PHONE...........................956 832-0807
Steve Becker, *President*
▲ EMP: 25
SQ FT: 40,000

SALES (est): 5.3MM **Privately Held**
WEB: www.exelbpc.com
SIC: 3089 Injection molding of plastics

(G-2356)
FIESTA GRAPHICS
Also Called: Ernie's Fiesta Graphics
205 Paredes Line Rd (78521-2247)
PHONE...........................956 546-1722
Ernie Hernandez, *Owner*
Nena Ramirez, *Manager*
EMP: 12
SQ FT: 3,500
SALES (est): 585K **Privately Held**
WEB: www.embroiderycontracts.com
SIC: 2397 5111 Schiffli machine embroideries; printing & writing paper

(G-2357)
FISHER & COMPANY INCORPORATED
Also Called: Fisher Dynamics
2045 Les Mauldin Rd 3f (78521-6471)
PHONE...........................586 746-1961
Robert Kupras, *Branch Mgr*
EMP: 40
SALES (corp-wide): 477.8MM **Privately Held**
WEB: www.fisherco.com
SIC: 3714 Motor vehicle parts & accessories
PA: Fisher & Company, Incorporated
33300 Fisher Dr
Saint Clair Shores MI 48082
586 746-2000

(G-2358)
GATEHOUSE MEDIA LLC
Also Called: Valley Bargain Book
2494 Central Blvd Ste A (78520-8458)
PHONE...........................956 546-5113
Yvonne Gomez, *Branch Mgr*
EMP: 13
SALES (corp-wide): 1.8B **Publicly Held**
WEB: www.gannett.com
SIC: 2711 7311 2759 Newspapers, publishing & printing; advertising agencies; commercial printing
HQ: Gatehouse Media, Llc
175 Sullys Trl Fl 3
Pittsford NY 14534
585 598-0030

(G-2359)
GATEWAY PRINTING & OFF SUP INC
Also Called: Jones & Cook Stationers
1460 N Expressway 77 (78521-1457)
PHONE...........................956 546-0632
Tony Cantu, *Branch Mgr*
Rudy Castilleja, *Manager*
EMP: 9
SALES (corp-wide): 25.9MM **Privately Held**
WEB: www.gatewayp.com
SIC: 2752 Commercial printing, offset
PA: Gateway Printing & Office Supply, Inc.
14803 Bulverde Rd
San Antonio TX 78247
210 650-3995

(G-2360)
GOBAR SYSTEMS INC
3320 E 14th St (78521-3232)
PHONE...........................956 377-4836
Rolando A Gonzalez, *President*
Luis Ramirez, *General Mgr*
Raul Gonzalez, *Corp Secy*
Humberto Hernandez, *Engineer*
Victor Rivero, *Engineer*
▲ EMP: 12
SQ FT: 20,000
SALES (est): 4.6MM **Privately Held**
WEB: www.gobarsystems.com
SIC: 3469 Stamping metal for the trade

(G-2361)
GULF SPECIAL SERVICES INC
7770 Padre Island Hwy (78521-3456)
PHONE...........................956 541-1445
Reynaldo Santos Jr, *Manager*
EMP: 20
SQ FT: 12,133 **Privately Held**
SIC: 3536 Cranes, industrial plant

HQ: Gulf Special Services, Inc.
7455 Cullen Blvd
Houston TX 77051
713 733-4341

(G-2362)
INTERNATIONAL ASSEMBLY INC
Also Called: Iai
4402 Austin Rd Ste B (78521-4273)
PHONE...........................956 525-4533
Robert Katusak, *President*
EMP: 10 EST: 1992
SALES (est): 985.3K **Privately Held**
SIC: 3465 7532 5015 Moldings or trim, automobile: stamped metal; paint shop, automotive; automotive accessories, used

(G-2363)
INTERNATIONAL MACHINE SHOP
Also Called: Feldlo
2250 Anglers Place Rd (78521-9250)
PHONE...........................956 838-1234
Felipe Mendez, *President*
EMP: 9 EST: 1995
SQ FT: 5,900
SALES (est): 372.4K **Privately Held**
SIC: 3599 Machine shop, jobbing & repair

(G-2364)
INTERNTNAL SHPBREAKING LTD LLC
18501 Rl Ostos Rd (78521-1038)
P.O. Box 6048 (78523-6048)
PHONE...........................956 831-4112
Joel Dupre, *CEO*
David Farnsworth, *CFO*
Kevin McCabe, *Mng Member*
Robert Berry,
Michael Donovan,
EMP: 120
SALES (est): 13.2MM
SALES (corp-wide): 3.5B **Privately Held**
WEB: www.shiprecycling.com
SIC: 4499 3341 Ship dismantling; marine dismantling & scrapping services; marine wrecking ships for scrap; recovery & refining of nonferrous metals
HQ: European Metal Recycling Limited
Sirius House
Warrington

(G-2365)
INTEVA PRODUCTS LLC
3501 Nafta Pkwy Ste C (78526-8413)
PHONE...........................248 655-8777
Robert Baker, *Branch Mgr*
EMP: 300
SALES (corp-wide): 4.4B **Privately Held**
WEB: www.intevaproducts.com
SIC: 3714 Motor vehicle parts & accessories
HQ: Inteva Products, Llc
1401 Crooks Rd
Troy MI 48084

(G-2366)
IRENT
3460 Southmost Rd (78521-4856)
PHONE...........................956 592-4061
Sergio A Lezama, *Owner*
EMP: 15 EST: 2017
SALES (est): 1.1MM **Privately Held**
WEB: www.brownsvilleherald.com
SIC: 2711 Newspapers, publishing & printing

(G-2367)
JAMES AVERY CRAFTSMAN INC
2355 N Xpwy Ste 1 (78520)
PHONE...........................956 509-2912
Gabriel Hernandez, *Manager*
EMP: 16
SALES (corp-wide): 180.9MM **Privately Held**
WEB: www.jamesavery.com
SIC: 5944 7631 3911 Jewelry, precious stones & precious metals; jewelry repair services; jewelry mountings & trimmings
PA: James Avery Craftsman, Inc.
145 Avery Rd
Kerrville TX 78028
830 353-4001

(G-2368)
JAMESTOWN PLASTICS INC
3200 Fm 511 (78526-9730)
PHONE..................................956 831-8800
Jeff Baker, *Manager*
Fernando Baca, *Manager*
EMP: 20
SQ FT: 28,480
SALES (corp-wide): 10.3MM **Privately Held**
WEB: www.jamestownplastics.com
SIC: 3089 Injection molding of plastics
PA: Jamestown Plastics, Inc.
8806 Highland Ave
Brocton NY 14716
716 792-4144

(G-2369)
JEFFERSON ELECTRIC INC
Also Called: Real Products
3330 E 14th St (78521-3232)
PHONE..................................956 542-5491
EMP: 18
SALES (corp-wide): 92.1MM **Publicly Held**
SIC: 3612 Mfg Transformers
HQ: Jefferson Electric, Inc.
9650 S Franklin Dr
Franklin WI 30607

(G-2370)
JM CONSTRUCTION
6304 Sioux Fls (78521-6509)
PHONE..................................956 518-2113
Juan Esquivel, *CEO*
EMP: 25
SALES (est): 1.2MM **Privately Held**
WEB: www.jmconstructiontexas.com
SIC: 1522 1721 1742 1771 Remodeling,
multi-family dwellings; painting & paper
hanging; stucco work, interior; stucco, gu-
nite & grouting contractors; construction,
repair & dismantling services; custom
builders, non-residential

(G-2371)
JOBRAN UNLIMITED LLC
Also Called: Berry Pool
3009 J C S Industrial Dr (78526-5140)
PHONE..................................956 541-1309
Michael Diaz,
Anita Diaz,
EMP: 27
SQ FT: 4,000
SALES (est): 3.4MM **Privately Held**
WEB: www.berrypool.com
SIC: 5091 3949 5999 Swimming pools,
equipment & supplies; swimming pools,
except plastic; swimming pool chemicals,
equipment & supplies; swimming pools,
above ground

(G-2372)
JUICEUS LLC
3090 Pablo Kisel Blvd A (78526-4443)
PHONE..................................956 667-0153
Ernesto Anzaldua, *Mng Member*
Alexandra Anzaldua, *Administration*
EMP: 28 EST: 2017
SALES (est): 76.1K **Privately Held**
SIC: 5499 5812 2033 Juices, fruit or veg-
etable; health food restaurant; fruit juices:
fresh; vegetable juices: fresh

(G-2373)
KEMET ELECTRONICS CORPORATION
1705 Billy Mitchell Blvd (78521-5000)
P.O. Box 3126 (78523-3126)
PHONE..................................956 548-7200
Luis La Garza, *Mfg Staff*
Emilio Garza, *Branch Mgr*
Jose Rodriguez, *Manager*
EMP: 16 **Privately Held**
WEB: www.kemet.com
SIC: 3675 Electronic capacitors
HQ: Kemet Electronics Corporation
1 E Broward Blvd Ste 200
Fort Lauderdale FL 33301
864 963-6700

(G-2374)
KEPPEL AMFELS INC (DH)
20000 State Highway 48 (78521-8910)
PHONE..................................956 838-3110
Mohamed Sahlan Bin Salleh, *President*

Caroline Chang, *General Mgr*
Tay Chew, *General Mgr*
Lynn Koh, *General Mgr*
Sepalika Kulasekera, *General Mgr*
▲ EMP: 1528
SQ FT: 332,000
SALES: 235MM **Privately Held**
WEB: www.keppelom.com
SIC: 1629 3731 1389 3449 Oil refinery
construction; shipbuilding & repairing; oil
& gas wells: building, repairing & disman-
tling; miscellaneous metalwork; power-dri-
ven handtools; fabricated plate work
(boiler shop)

(G-2375)
LASH MFG & DEV GROUP LLC
2005 Matehuala Ct (78526-1740)
PHONE..................................956 465-0330
Guillermo Lash,
▲ EMP: 15
SALES (est): 1MM **Privately Held**
WEB: www.glmanufacturas.com
SIC: 3999 Manufacturing industries

(G-2376)
LEGACY VULCAN LLC
Also Called: Brownsville Yard
10905 Rl Ostos Rd (78521-1027)
PHONE..................................956 831-8888
Jesus Narro, *Branch Mgr*
Sonya Lopez, *Manager*
EMP: 22 **Publicly Held**
WEB: www.vulcanmaterials.com
SIC: 3273 Ready-mixed concrete
HQ: Legacy Vulcan, Llc
1200 Urban Center Dr
Vestavia AL 35242
205 298-3000

(G-2377)
LEONARD ELC PDTS CO TEXAS INC
Also Called: Lepco
2600 Old Alice Rd Ste E (78521-1456)
PHONE..................................956 350-5650
Robert Blatnik, *President*
Claude Harrari, *Vice Pres*
Tom Sartychoff, *Treasurer*
EMP: 16
SQ FT: 20,000
SALES (est): 1.4MM **Privately Held**
SIC: 3679 Electronic circuits

(G-2378)
LUGRA INC
Also Called: Specialty Advertisers
3664 Commerce Dr (78521-3249)
PHONE..................................956 986-0958
Lucila Richa, *President*
Carlos E Richa, *Treasurer*
EMP: 12
SQ FT: 5,000
SALES (est): 1.6MM **Privately Held**
WEB: www.specialtyadvertisers.com
SIC: 8743 7311 2395 Sales promotion;
advertising consultant; embroidery prod-
ucts, except schiffli machine

(G-2379)
M SOSA WHITE CHEESE LA PINTITA
5294 Southmost Rd (78521-8072)
PHONE..................................956 546-7078
Gerardo Sosa, *Owner*
EMP: 9
SQ FT: 2,400
SALES (est): 2MM **Privately Held**
SIC: 2022 Processed cheese

(G-2380)
MAQUILAPLEX LLC
2500 Courage Blvd (78521-6447)
PHONE..................................956 542-4138
▲ EMP: 19
SQ FT: 35,000
SALES (est): 550K **Privately Held**
WEB: www.maquilaplex.com
SIC: 2326 Work apparel, except uniforms

(G-2381)
MARTEX FIBER SOUTHERN CORP
4656 Towerwood Dr (78521-6433)
PHONE..................................956 831-7707

James F Jarrett, *President*
EMP: 35
SALES (corp-wide): 94.5MM **Privately Held**
WEB: www.martexfiber.com
SIC: 3552 Fiber & yarn preparation ma-
chinery & equipment
PA: Martex Fiber Southern Corp.
3200b Southport Rd
Spartanburg SC 29302
864 583-6412

(G-2382)
MAVERICK TRMNALS THREE RVERS L
14301 Rl Ostos Rd (78521-1029)
PHONE..................................956 371-6530
David Villareal, *Branch Mgr*
EMP: 17
SALES (corp-wide): 6.2MM **Privately Held**
WEB: www.howardenergypartners.com
SIC: 1382 Oil & gas exploration services
PA: Maverick Terminals Three Rivers, Llc
17806 W Interstate 10
San Antonio TX 78257
361 792-3028

(G-2383)
MILWHITE INC (PA)
5487 Padre Island Hwy (78521-8300)
PHONE..................................956 547-1970
Armando Leon C, *Ch of Bd*
Michael P Hughes, *President*
Hector Guerrero, *Finance Mgr*
Isabel D De La Garza, *Office Admin*
Alberto De Leon, *Director*
▼ EMP: 20 EST: 1931
SQ FT: 37,308
SALES (est): 15.6MM **Privately Held**
WEB: www.milwhite.com
SIC: 1459 Fuller's earth mining; clays
(common) quarrying

(G-2384)
MUELLER CO LLC
3351 Ruben Torres Sr Blvd (78526-2834)
PHONE..................................956 621-3086
Kimberly Nash, *Manager*
EMP: 107
SALES (corp-wide): 964.1MM **Publicly Held**
WEB: www.muellercompany.com
SIC: 3823 3494 Flow instruments, indus-
trial process type; valves & pipe fittings
HQ: Mueller Co. Llc
633 Chestnut St Ste 1200
Chattanooga TN 37450
423 209-4800

(G-2385)
NATIONAL ELECTRIC COIL CO LP
3330 E 14th St (78521-3232)
P.O. Box 370, Columbus OH (43216-0370)
PHONE..................................956 541-1759
Fred Dawson, *Partner*
Armando Arista, *Plant Mgr*
Edvardo Ramon, *Engineer*
Jorge Zamarripa, *Supervisor*
◆ EMP: 50
SALES (est): 16.7MM **Privately Held**
WEB: www.national-electric-coil.com
SIC: 3621 Coils, for electric motors or gen-
erators
PA: National Electric Coil, Inc.
800 King Ave
Columbus OH 43212

(G-2386)
NAVCO OILFIELD SERVICES LLC (PA)
2500 Courage Blvd (78521-6447)
PHONE..................................956 542-4426
James Griffin Jr, *Vice Pres*
James T Griffin, *Mng Member*
Dail Obryant,
EMP: 9
SQ FT: 3,000
SALES (est): 10.8MM **Privately Held**
SIC: 1382 Oil & gas exploration services

(G-2387)
NEXNOL LLC
5250 Coffee Port Rd (78521-5361)
PHONE..................................833 463-9665
Jaki Owen,
EMP: 10
SALES (est): 409.5K **Privately Held**
SIC: 2842 Sanitation preparations, disin-
fectants & deodorants

(G-2388)
OHMITE HOLDING LLC
Also Called: Ohmite Manufacturing
2400 Courage Blvd # 1110 (78521-5160)
PHONE..................................956 542-0276
Gary Innocenti, *General Mgr*
Sean Pyritz, *General Mgr*
Terri Tracz-King, *General Mgr*
Gustavo Jimenez, *Engineer*
Amado Rivas, *Branch Mgr*
EMP: 12 **Privately Held**
WEB: www.ohmite.com
SIC: 3625 3612 Industrial electrical relays
& switches; power & distribution trans-
formers
HQ: Ohmite Holding, L.L.C.
27501 Bella Vista Pkwy
Warrenville IL 60555
847 258-0300

(G-2389)
ORC INDUSTRIES INC
2807 N Central Ave (78526-5105)
PHONE..................................956 831-0618
Amado Espinosa, *Manager*
Wally Avelar, *Info Tech Mgr*
Adele Gasparro, *Executive*
EMP: 100
SALES (corp-wide): 12.9MM **Privately Held**
WEB: www.orcind.com
SIC: 8331 2385 2394 Sheltered work-
shop; waterproof outerwear; raincoats,
except vulcanized rubber: purchased ma-
terials; tents: made from purchased mate-
rials
PA: Orc Industries, Inc.
2700 Commerce St
La Crosse WI 54603
608 781-7727

(G-2390)
PALLETS911 LLC
602 S Indiana Ave (78521-7301)
PHONE..................................956 203-2671
Jorge L Sandoval, *Mng Member*
Daniel S Sandoval,
EMP: 18
SALES (est): 1.9MM **Privately Held**
WEB: www.pallet911.net
SIC: 2448 Pallets, wood
PA: Vlm Embalajes, S. De R.L. M.I.
Carretera Victoria Km. 10
Matamoros TAMPS.

(G-2391)
PARAGON RIO GRANDE LLC
Also Called: Rio Grande Tool Co
5295 Commercial Dr (78521-5286)
P.O. Box 4320 (78523-4320)
PHONE..................................956 831-8249
Dave Muir, *CEO*
EMP: 16 EST: 1986
SQ FT: 21,432
SALES (est): 3.1MM
SALES (corp-wide): 35.8MM **Privately Held**
WEB: www.riograndeapc.com
SIC: 3544 3089 Dies, plastics forming; in-
jection molding of plastics
PA: Paragon Die & Engineering Company
5225 33rd St Se
Grand Rapids MI 49512
616 949-2220

(G-2392)
PESA LABELING SYSTEMS INC
4401 Paredes Line Rd (78526-1117)
PHONE..................................956 544-3323
Mary Alice Scott, *President*
Damian Galvan, *Vice Pres*
Anna Maria Villarrea, *Vice Pres*
▲ EMP: 25
SQ FT: 12,000

SALES (est): 8.3MM **Privately Held**
WEB: www.pesalabeling.com
SIC: 2759 Flexographic printing; labels &
seals: printing

(G-2393)
PHILIPS NORTH AMERICA LLC
Also Called: Airpax
1000 Billy Mitchell Blvd (78521-5182)
PHONE..................................956 541-1224
David Lopez, *General Mgr*
EMP: 15
SALES (corp-wide): 21.5B **Privately Held**
WEB: www.usa.philips.com
SIC: 3613 Switchgear & switchboard appa-
ratus
HQ: Philips North America Llc
   222 Jacobs St Fl 3
   Cambridge MA 02141
   978 659-3000

(G-2394)
POLIBRID COATINGS INC
Also Called: Polobrid Coating
6700 Ruben Torres Sr Blvd (78526-6914)
PHONE..................................956 831-7818
Jorge M Ramirez, *President*
Enrique Perez, *Treasurer*
◆ EMP: 12
SQ FT: 7,000
SALES (est): 2MM **Privately Held**
WEB: www.polibrid.com
SIC: 3479 Coating of metals & formed
products

(G-2395)
PORTAGE PLASTICS CORPORATION
1900 Billy Mitchell Blvd (78521-5612)
PHONE..................................956 504-6102
Tony Cappella, *Branch Mgr*
EMP: 10 **Privately Held**
WEB: www.portageplastics.com
SIC: 3089 Injection molding of plastics
PA: Portage Plastics Corporation
   3000 Boeck Rd
   Portage WI 53901

(G-2396)
R & I ENTERPRISES INC
Also Called: Compulogic Design Co
233 Paredes Line Rd (78521-2247)
PHONE..................................956 544-7948
Rene Regalado, *President*
Mirna Vasquez, *Principal*
EMP: 12
SQ FT: 1,500
SALES (est): 1.1MM **Privately Held**
WEB: www.compulogicdesign.com
SIC: 3545 3569 Machine tool accessories;
assembly machines, non-metalworking

(G-2397)
RAIL PRODUCTS INTL INC
3600 E 14th St (78521-3238)
PHONE..................................956 541-1759
Brian Barton, *Principal*
EMP: 92
SALES (est): 3.2MM **Privately Held**
WEB: www.railproductsinternational.com
SIC: 7694 3613 Electric motor repair;
switchgear & switchboard apparatus
PA: National Electric Coil, Inc.
   800 King Ave
   Columbus OH 43212

(G-2398)
REINFRO LLC
3320 E 14th St (78521-3232)
PHONE..................................956 838-9814
Abelardo Gonzalez, *President*
Raul Gonzalez, *Vice Pres*
Faustino Villalon, *Engineer*
Eloy Conde, *Controller*
▲ EMP: 100
SALES (est): 9.5MM **Privately Held**
WEB: www.reinfro.com
SIC: 3471 Plating of metals or formed
products

(G-2399)
RICH PRODUCTS CORPORATION
Also Called: Sea Pak Shrimp Company
3555 E 14th St (78521-3235)
PHONE..................................956 542-0001

Eddie Velarosa, *Plant Mgr*
Mike Heggie, *Plant Mgr*
Eddie De La Rosa, *Plant Mgr*
Bea Quintanilla, *Warehouse Mgr*
Kevin Parker, *Production*
EMP: 269
SALES (corp-wide): 6.7B **Privately Held**
WEB: www.richs.com
SIC: 2092 Fresh or frozen packaged fish
PA: Rich Products Corporation
   1 Robert Rich Way
   Buffalo NY 14213
   716 878-8000

(G-2400)
RIO GRANDE VALLEY BUSINESS
1300 Wildrose Ln (78520-8600)
P.O. Box 4195 (78523-4195)
PHONE..................................956 546-5113
F Mike McKinney, *Owner*
EMP: 35
SALES (est): 556.2K **Privately Held**
SIC: 2711 Newspapers, publishing & print-
ing

(G-2401)
RIO PLASTICS INC
Also Called: Aqua Swim Spas
2700 Rl Ostos Rd (78521-1055)
P.O. Box 3707 (78523-3707)
PHONE..................................956 831-2715
▼ EMP: 25
SQ FT: 1,800
SALES (est): 2.7MM **Privately Held**
SIC: 3949 3089 Mfg Sporting/Athletic
Goods Mfg Plastic Products

(G-2402)
ROBERTSHAW CONTROLS COMPANY
Also Called: Invensys Controls
5845 Padre Island Hwy (78521-4463)
PHONE..................................956 831-9000
EMP: 108 **Privately Held**
WEB: www.robertshaw.com
SIC: 3822 3823 Auto controls regulating
residntl & coml environmt & applncs; in-
dustrial instrmnts msrmnt display/control
process variable
HQ: Robertshaw Controls Company
   1222 Hamilton Pkwy
   Itasca IL 60143

(G-2403)
S A FABTECMEX C V
Also Called: Collado-Ryerson
4200 Las Palmas Cir # 327 (78521-2791)
PHONE..................................956 504-0707
Lee Husinger, *Branch Mgr*
EMP: 300 **Privately Held**
SIC: 3443 Perforating on heavy metal
PA: Fabtecmex, S.A. De C.V.
   Av. Prolg. Av. Uniones S/N
   H. Matamoros TAMPS.

(G-2404)
SAINT-GOBAIN ABRASIVES INC
Also Called: Bonded Abrasives
1505 Morningside Rd (78521-7630)
PHONE..................................956 541-5285
Frederick Timm, *Sales/Mktg Mgr*
EMP: 110
SALES (corp-wide): 328.4MM **Privately Held**
WEB: www.saint-gobain.com
SIC: 3291 Abrasive products
HQ: Saint-Gobain Abrasives, Inc.
   1 New Bond St
   Worcester MA 01606
   508 795-5000

(G-2405)
SERAFY LABORATORIES LTD
Also Called: Proficiency Testing
205 W Levee St (78520-5558)
PHONE..................................956 546-5313
Nicholas Serafy Jr, *Partner*
Nicholas Serafy Sr, *Ltd Ptnr*
EMP: 20
SQ FT: 10,000
SALES (est): 2.7MM **Privately Held**
WEB: www.serafy.com
SIC: 2869 8071 Industrial organic chemi-
cals; medical laboratories

(G-2406)
SOUTH TEXAS MOULDING INC
Also Called: South Texas Moulding & Ply-
wood
4668 Ruben Torres Sr Blvd (78526-7400)
PHONE..................................956 831-0340
Tom Gomez, *General Mgr*
Eddie Cantu, *Manager*
EMP: 10
SALES (corp-wide): 11.1MM **Privately Held**
WEB: www.texaswoodsupply.com
SIC: 5039 5211 3446 Metal buildings;
lumber products; stairs, staircases, stair
treads: prefabricated metal
PA: South Texas Moulding, Inc.
   940 W Expressway 83
   Donna TX 78537
   956 464-0560

(G-2407)
STANDARD TEXTILE CO INC
3300 Nafta Pkwy Ste C (78526-9735)
PHONE..................................956 831-9040
Al George, *President*
EMP: 76
SALES (corp-wide): 639.8MM **Privately Held**
WEB: www.standardtextile.com
SIC: 2231 7389 Bleaching, dying & spe-
cialty treating: wool, mohair, etc.; textile &
apparel services
PA: Standard Textile Co., Inc.
   1 Knollcrest Dr
   Cincinnati OH 45237
   513 761-9255

(G-2408)
STARKEY LABORATORIES INC
Also Called: Distribution Center
615 Elca Ln Ste A (78521-5700)
PHONE..................................956 541-1917
Dora Ayala, *Manager*
Viraj Menon, *Manager*
EMP: 417
SALES (corp-wide): 495.7MM **Privately Held**
WEB: www.starkey.com
SIC: 3842 Hearing aids
PA: Starkey Laboratories, Inc.
   6700 Washington Ave S
   Eden Prairie MN 55344
   952 941-6401

(G-2409)
TEX-MEX COLD STORAGE INC (PA)
21 Poinsettia Pl (78520-8032)
PHONE..................................956 831-4531
Emilio A Sanchez, *President*
Norma Sanchez, *Vice Pres*
EMP: 160
SQ FT: 160,000
SALES (est): 16MM **Privately Held**
SIC: 4222 2092 Warehousing, cold stor-
age or refrigerated; fresh or frozen pack-
aged fish

(G-2410)
TEXAS HOME & PROJECTS LLC
2685 N Coria St Rear (78520-8821)
PHONE..................................956 546-8400
Rogelio Magana, *Vice Pres*
Raul Caballero,
EMP: 9
SQ FT: 10,000
SALES (est): 431K **Privately Held**
SIC: 2431 2434 2517 3281 Jalousies,
glass, wood frame; wood kitchen cabi-
nets; home entertainment unit cabinets,
wood; table tops, marble; kitchen cabinets

(G-2411)
TEXAS WIPERS & RAGS LLC
739 Mcnair Family Dr (78520-5246)
PHONE..................................956 554-7500
Enrique Melguizo, *Owner*
Enrique A Melguizo,
EMP: 9
SALES (est): 330K **Privately Held**
WEB: www.valleywipers.com
SIC: 5136 5137 2211 Men's & boys' cloth-
ing; women's & children's clothing; tow-
els, dishcloths & washcloths: cotton

(G-2412)
THUR-CO INC
Also Called: Thirlwall Sheet Metal Co
225 Industrial Dr (78521-3246)
PHONE..................................956 982-4424
Chuck Thirlwall, *President*
Thomas Thirlwall, *Vice Pres*
Tanya Thirlwall, *Director*
EMP: 15
SQ FT: 21,000
SALES (est): 2MM **Privately Held**
SIC: 1761 3444 Architectural sheet metal
work; sheet metalwork; ducts, sheet metal

(G-2413)
TITAN INTERNATIONAL INC
Also Called: Titan Tire Corp of Texas
6700 Paredes Line Rd (78526-3539)
PHONE..................................956 541-7500
Dave Fines, *Manager*
EMP: 230
SALES (corp-wide): 1.4B **Publicly Held**
WEB: www.titan-intl.com
SIC: 3011 Pneumatic tires, all types
PA: Titan International, Inc.
   2701 Spruce St
   Quincy IL 62301
   217 228-6011

(G-2414)
TORQON INC (PA)
Also Called: Tek Turbine
253 W Elizabeth St (78520-5548)
PHONE..................................956 546-3239
Alfred J Ottolino, *President*
Cassady Angela, *Vice Pres*
EMP: 10
SQ FT: 6,000
SALES (est): 1MM **Privately Held**
SIC: 5013 3714 Motor vehicle supplies &
new parts; transmissions, motor vehicle

(G-2415)
TORTILLRIA MONTERREY GROCERIES
364 Us Highway 281 (78520-4403)
PHONE..................................956 544-7222
Javiar Vivero, *Owner*
EMP: 10
SALES (est): 651K **Privately Held**
WEB: www.monterreytortilleria.com
SIC: 2099 Tortillas, fresh or refrigerated

(G-2416)
TRICO TECHNOLOGIES CORPORATION (DH)
1995 Billy Mitchell Blvd (78521-5697)
PHONE..................................956 544-2722
Greg Flake, *President*
David Cummings, *President*
Alma Martinez, *Purchasing*
◆ EMP: 150
SQ FT: 350,000
SALES (est): 243MM
SALES (corp-wide): 332.6MM **Privately Held**
SIC: 3714 Windshield wiper systems,
motor vehicle
HQ: Trico Holding Corporation
   50 Thielman Dr
   Buffalo NY 14206
   716 852-5700

(G-2417)
ULTIMATE TRINING MUNITIONS INC
1555 N Central Ave Ste A (78521-7565)
PHONE..................................908 392-5390
Maxine Nordmeyer, *President*
Pete Minoui, *Sales Staff*
EMP: 10 **Privately Held**
WEB: www.utmworldwide.com
SIC: 5941 3949 Ammunition; shooting
equipment & supplies, general
PA: Ultimate Training Munitions Inc.
   55 Readington Rd
   Branchburg NJ 08876

(G-2418)
UNITED COMMODITIES LLC
44 Fireside Dr (78521-1645)
PHONE..................................956 621-1798
Luis Muzquiz,
EMP: 11

SALES (est): 1.4MM **Privately Held**
SIC: 6221 3089 Commodity contracts brokers, dealers; molding primary plastic

(G-2419)
VALLEY MEDIA INC (PA)
Also Called: Bargain Book
2494 Central Blvd Ste A (78520-8458)
PHONE....................................956 546-5113
Frank M Mc Kinney Jr, *President*
Jack L Wilson, *Vice Pres*
Roger McKnight, *Manager*
Dixie Garza, *Consultant*
Alex Tavares, *Administration*
EMP: 20
SALES (est): 1.7MM **Privately Held**
WEB: www.valleybargainbook.com
SIC: 2741 2711 Shopping news: publishing & printing; newspapers

(G-2420)
VAUGHAN INVESTMENTS INC
Also Called: Burton Co
3800 International Blvd (78521-3254)
PHONE....................................956 546-5175
Joe Touchet, *Sales Staff*
Scott Vaughan, *Manager*
Carlos Rivas, *Manager*
EMP: 25
SQ FT: 26,600
SALES (corp-wide): 34MM **Privately Held**
WEB: www.burtoncompanies.com
SIC: 5013 7539 3599 Automotive supplies & parts; machine shop, automotive; machine shop, jobbing & repair
PA: Vaughan Investments, Inc.
529 E Hwy 83
Weslaco TX 78596
956 968-3121

(G-2421)
WELDING WORKS INTL INC
7620 Victoria Ct Ste 4 (78521-6937)
P.O. Box 3561 (78523-3561)
PHONE....................................956 838-5636
Alfredo De La Fuente, *President*
Paulina Garcia, *Accountant*
EMP: 38 **EST:** 2003
SALES (est): 2.6MM **Privately Held**
WEB: www.weldingworks.us
SIC: 7692 Welding repair

(G-2422)
ZIMCO MARINE LLC
1170 Bayou Ct (78521-9235)
PHONE....................................956 831-7828
Cecil Moses, *Manager*
EMP: 14
SALES (corp-wide): 8.8MM **Privately Held**
WEB: www.texasgoldshrimp.com
SIC: 5551 7699 5088 3429 Marine supplies; boat repair; marine crafts & supplies; manufactured hardware (general)
PA: Zimco Marine, L.L.C.
1430 Everglades Rd
Brownsville TX 78521
956 831-7828

Brownwood
Brown County

(G-2423)
3M COMPANY
4501 Highway 377 S (76801-5907)
P.O. Box 1669 (76804-1669)
PHONE....................................325 643-9798
Mike Benson, *Superintendent*
Hak Shin, *Exec VP*
Richard Ziegler, *Vice Pres*
Rick Kleypas, *Engineer*
Travis Leigh, *Engineer*
EMP: 750
SALES (corp-wide): 32.1B **Publicly Held**
WEB: www.3m.com
SIC: 3081 3669 Unsupported plastics film & sheet; traffic signals, electric
PA: 3m Company
3m Center
Saint Paul MN 55144
651 733-1110

(G-2424)
AIRMARK INDUSTRIES INC
5701 Highway 377 S (76801)
P.O. Box 3370 (76803-3370)
PHONE....................................325 641-1999
Charlotte Dendy, *President*
Ray Dendy, *Corp Secy*
Doug Dendy, *Vice Pres*
Greg Dendy, *Vice Pres*
EMP: 23
SQ FT: 12,000
SALES (est): 1.8MM **Privately Held**
WEB: www.airmarkusa.com
SIC: 3993 2395 Advertising novelties; embroidery products, except schiffli machine

(G-2425)
BARR FABRICATION LLC
4501 Danhil Dr (76801-8519)
P.O. Box 2217 (76804-2217)
PHONE....................................325 643-2277
Sandra Barr, *President*
Bo Barr, *Vice Pres*
Rebecca Wiles, *Opers Staff*
Brett Froh, *CFO*
Henry Skaggs, *Manager*
EMP: 50
SALES (est): 6.4MM **Privately Held**
WEB: www.barrfab.com
SIC: 3441 Fabricated structural metal

(G-2426)
BOBS FUELS INC
Also Called: Seawalt Butane
1107 W Commerce St (76801-2010)
PHONE....................................325 646-7571
John B Gordon II, *President*
Vannessa R Stewart, *Corp Secy*
EMP: 9
SALES (est): 1.4MM **Privately Held**
WEB: www.bobsfuelsinc.com
SIC: 2869 Fuels

(G-2427)
CHEVRON PHILLIPS CHEM CO LP
Also Called: Performance Pipe
1400 Drisco Dr (76801-6439)
P.O. Box 1060 (76804-1060)
PHONE....................................325 646-6561
Leo Karnes, *Manager*
Barrett Jesseph, *Technical Staff*
EMP: 60
SALES (corp-wide): 3.5B **Privately Held**
WEB: www.cpchem.com
SIC: 2821 Plastics materials & resins
HQ: Chevron Phillips Chemical Company Lp
10001 Six Pines Dr
The Woodlands TX 77380
832 813-4100

(G-2428)
FENTON ENVIRONMENTAL TECH INC
4306 Highway 377 S (76801-5921)
P.O. Box 1916 (76804-1916)
PHONE....................................800 521-1708
Dan Bolton, *Branch Mgr*
EMP: 35
SALES (corp-wide): 10.8MM **Privately Held**
SIC: 3531 Construction machinery
HQ: Fenton Environmental Technologies, Inc.
228 Charles Ave Ste 1323
New Orleans LA 70130
504 581-2355

(G-2429)
GATOR PUMP INC
302 Corrigan Ave (76801-5001)
P.O. Box 57 (76804-0057)
PHONE....................................325 643-3502
Carol Lemmons, *President*
Robert Dale Lemmons, *Vice Pres*
▼ **EMP:** 9
SQ FT: 12,000
SALES (est): 1.9MM **Privately Held**
WEB: www.gatorpump.com
SIC: 3561 5084 Industrial pumps & parts; industrial machinery & equipment

(G-2430)
GREENHAW CABINETS INC
2815 Stephen F Austin Dr (76801-6454)
PHONE....................................325 646-8319
Charles Greenhaw, *President*
Paul W Greenhaw Jr, *Treasurer*
EMP: 12
SQ FT: 6,000
SALES (est): 1.2MM **Privately Held**
SIC: 5712 2434 2541 Cabinet work, custom; wood kitchen cabinets; wood partitions & fixtures

(G-2431)
KJD ENTERPRISES
Also Called: Day Ranch & Cattle
2700 Virgil Gray Dr (76801-8515)
P.O. Box 726 (76804-0726)
PHONE....................................325 641-0420
Kenneth Day, *Owner*
▲ **EMP:** 16 **EST:** 1955
SQ FT: 10,000
SALES (est): 4.8MM **Privately Held**
WEB: www.kdloaders.com
SIC: 5083 3537 Farm implements; industrial trucks & tractors

(G-2432)
KOHLER CO
Also Called: Kohler Company Plumbing
4601 Highway 377 S (76801-5901)
PHONE....................................325 643-2661
EMP: 280
SALES (corp-wide): 9B **Privately Held**
WEB: www.us.kohler.com
SIC: 3432 Plumbing fixture fittings & trim
PA: Kohler Co.
444 Highland Dr
Kohler WI 53044
920 457-4441

(G-2433)
KOHLER CO
Highway 37 (76801)
PHONE....................................325 643-2661
Buddy Hollt, *Plant Mgr*
EMP: 900
SALES (corp-wide): 9B **Privately Held**
WEB: www.us.kohler.com
SIC: 3431 Metal sanitary ware
PA: Kohler Co.
444 Highland Dr
Kohler WI 53044
920 457-4441

(G-2434)
LEDSOME MACHINE & WELDING CO
2508 Stephen F Austin Dr (76801-6414)
P.O. Box 1168 (76804-1168)
PHONE....................................325 646-4691
Gerard Ledsome, *President*
EMP: 14
SQ FT: 10,000
SALES (est): 1.5MM **Privately Held**
WEB: www.ledsome.com
SIC: 3599 1796 7692 3444 Machine shop, jobbing & repair; installing building equipment; welding repair; sheet metalwork

(G-2435)
LEGACY VULCAN LLC
Southwest Division
377 S Brady Hwy (76801)
P.O. Box 518 (76804-0518)
PHONE....................................325 646-8526
Mike Harris, *Manager*
Mike Harrington, *Executive*
EMP: 40 **Publicly Held**
WEB: www.vulcanmaterials.com
SIC: 1442 2951 1422 Construction sand & gravel; asphalt paving mixtures & blocks; crushed & broken limestone
HQ: Legacy Vulcan, Llc
1200 Urban Center Dr
Vestavia AL 35242
205 298-3000

(G-2436)
LIDDELL INDUSTRIES INC
4306 Highway 377 S (76801-5921)
PHONE....................................325 646-7581
Alejandro Gil, *CEO*
Jesus S Gil, *Co-Owner*
Salvador Gil, *Co-Owner*

Ray Jones, *COO*
Lonnie McDonald, *Purchasing*
EMP: 13
SALES (est): 10MM **Privately Held**
WEB: www.liddellindustriesinc.com
SIC: 3713 Truck bodies & parts

(G-2437)
LINDE INC
Also Called: Praxair
813 Early Blvd (76802-2130)
PHONE....................................325 643-5813
Larry Dempsey, *Principal*
EMP: 20 **Privately Held**
WEB: www.praxair.com
SIC: 2813 Industrial gases
HQ: Linde Inc.
10 Riverview Dr
Danbury CT 06810
203 837-2000

(G-2438)
LOADCRAFT INDUSTRIES LTD
4306 Highway 377 S (76801-5921)
PHONE....................................325 646-7581
Terry McIver, *Branch Mgr*
EMP: 213
SALES (corp-wide): 67.5MM **Privately Held**
WEB: www.loadcraft.com
SIC: 3533 Oil & gas field machinery
PA: Loadcraft Industries, Ltd.
3811 N Bridge St
Brady TX 76825
325 597-2911

(G-2439)
M & F GAUGE & SPECIALTY CO INC
Also Called: Mf Guage
3104 Morris Sheppard Dr (76801-6461)
P.O. Box 693 (76804-0693)
PHONE....................................325 643-2655
Jack Matthaei, *CEO*
Monelle Manley, *President*
David Huggins, *Manager*
Roger Matthews, *Director*
▼ **EMP:** 40
SQ FT: 33,000
SALES (est): 7MM **Privately Held**
WEB: www.realtuffbaler.com
SIC: 3599 3545 Machine shop, jobbing & repair; gauges (machine tool accessories)

(G-2440)
MCBERMETT MILNER LLC
4501 Danhil Dr (76801-8519)
PHONE....................................325 643-2277
Sandra Barr,
EMP: 50
SALES (est): 3.8MM **Privately Held**
SIC: 3441 Fabricated structural metal

(G-2441)
P DIAMOND ENTERPRISES INC (PA)
3300 Milam Dr (76801-6948)
P.O. Box 483 (76804-0483)
PHONE....................................325 643-5629
Domingo Perez, *President*
▲ **EMP:** 10
SALES (est): 21.6MM **Privately Held**
WEB: www.diamondpenterprises.com
SIC: 2499 3086 Reels, plywood; packaging & shipping materials, foamed plastic

(G-2442)
POTTERS INDUSTRIES LLC
Potter Industries
5650 Highway 279 (76801-8864)
PHONE....................................325 752-6711
Gary Whyte, *General Mgr*
Ken Loewrigkeit, *Plant Mgr*
Deb Day, *Manager*
EMP: 30
SALES (corp-wide): 167.9MM **Privately Held**
WEB: www.pqcorp.com
SIC: 3231 3229 Reflector glass beads, for highway signs or reflectors; pressed & blown glass
PA: Potters Industries, Llc
300 Lindenwood Dr
Malvern PA 19355
610 651-4700

(G-2443)
SAWYER OILFIELD PRODUCTS LLC
Also Called: Sawyer Industries
2700 Virgil Gray Dr (76801-8515)
PHONE....................................254 644-7261
Jamey Finstad,
Willard Hammonds II,
EMP: 30
SALES (est): 1MM Privately Held
WEB: www.sawyerindustries.com
SIC: 3229 Yarn, fiberglass

(G-2444)
SIGN SHOP
4300 Fm 3021 (76801-0807)
PHONE....................................325 641-2424
Gary Mass, Owner
Trey Akin, Owner
EMP: 9
SALES (est): 516.1K Privately Held
WEB: www.signshopmarket.com
SIC: 3993 Signs & advertising specialties

(G-2445)
SIVALLS INC
2300 Dickman Dr (76801-6930)
P.O. Box 1326 (76804-1326)
PHONE....................................325 643-3621
Clayton Kuykendall, Plant Mgr
Clay Kirkindal, Manager
EMP: 26
SALES (corp-wide): 90MM Privately Held
WEB: www.sivalls.com
SIC: 3533 3443 Oil field machinery & equipment; fabricated plate work (boiler shop)
PA: Sivalls, Inc.
2200 E 2nd St
Odessa TX 79761
432 337-3571

(G-2446)
SUPERIOR ESSEX INTL LP
Also Called: Superior Essex Communications
2900 Morris Sheppard Dr (76801-6457)
PHONE....................................325 646-8591
Rhonda Buchanan, Accounting Mgr
Bob Stearns, Branch Mgr
EMP: 20
SQ FT: 191,000 Privately Held
WEB: www.superioressex.com
SIC: 3357 3661 3315 Communication wire; telephone & telegraph apparatus; wire & fabricated wire products
HQ: Superior Essex International Lp
5770 Powers Ferry Rd # 300
Atlanta GA 30327
770 657-6000

(G-2447)
VRC TECHNOLOGIES INC (PA)
1412 Custer Rd (76801-6433)
PHONE....................................325 643-8038
Martin Beirne III, CEO
Robert Green, Vice Pres
Kayla Haddix, Director
▲ EMP: 15
SALES (est): 2.4MM Privately Held
WEB: www.vrctexas.com
SIC: 2869 Industrial organic chemicals

(G-2448)
W T HARRIS COMPANY INC
Also Called: W.T. Harris Company
2908 Stephen F Austin Dr (76801-6474)
PHONE....................................325 646-7521
William Barton Harris, President
Ann Harris, Vice Pres
▲ EMP: 30 EST: 1978
SQ FT: 160,000
SALES (est): 3MM Privately Held
WEB: www.wtharriscompany.com
SIC: 2449 Wood containers

(G-2449)
WEST TEXAS PRINTING COMPANY
2909 Stephen F Austin Dr (76801-6475)
P.O. Box 1509 (76804-1509)
PHONE....................................325 646-3598
James Blake, President
Juliet Lemond, Sales Staff
Sarah Blake, Info Tech Dir

Richard Bleth, Info Tech Mgr
EMP: 60 EST: 1948
SQ FT: 55,500
SALES (est): 4.9MM Privately Held
WEB: www.wes-tex.com
SIC: 2752 2791 Commercial printing, off-set; typesetting

Bruni
Webb County

(G-2450)
ROBERT MARSHALL CNSTR INC
980 Rr 8054c (78344)
P.O. Box 205 (78344-0205)
PHONE....................................361 747-5253
Robert Marshall, President
EMP: 10
SALES (corp-wide): 3.4MM Privately Held
SIC: 1629 1389 Land clearing contractor; construction, repair & dismantling services
PA: Robert Marshall Construction, Inc.
19274 Road 17
Madera CA 93637
559 673-8781

Bryan
Brazos County

(G-2451)
ADVANCE HYDROCARBON CORP
1559 Crosswind Dr (77808-9696)
PHONE....................................979 778-8100
EMP: 10
SALES (corp-wide): 7.4MM Privately Held
WEB: www.ahcus.com
SIC: 1389 Saltwater Disposal Wells
HQ: Advance Hydrocarbon Corporation
10343 Sam Houston Park Dr # 325
Houston TX 77064

(G-2452)
AIRFOIL IMPELLERS CORPORATION
2010 Fountain Ave (77801-1117)
P.O. Box 9966, College Station (77842-7966)
PHONE....................................979 822-6418
Dennis K Anderholm, President
EMP: 25
SQ FT: 109,000
SALES (est): 6.9MM Privately Held
WEB: www.airfoil.com
SIC: 3365 3564 3469 Machinery castings, aluminum; blowers & fans; metal stampings

(G-2453)
ALENCO HOLDING CORPORATION (DH)
Also Called: All Seasons
615 W Carson St (77801-1199)
PHONE....................................979 779-1051
Bryan Redpath, President
Chuck Gessler, CFO
EMP: 450
SQ FT: 250,000
SALES (est): 110.1MM
SALES (corp-wide): 4.8B Publicly Held
SIC: 3442 Window & door frames
HQ: Ply Gem Industries, Inc.
5020 Weston Pkwy Ste 400
Cary NC 27513
919 677-3900

(G-2454)
ALL SEASONS COMMERCIAL DIV INC
1293 N Hrvey Mtchll Pkwy (77803-2062)
PHONE....................................979 823-6557
William K Akins, President
▲ EMP: 35
SALES (est): 5.1MM Privately Held
WEB: www.aswcommercial.com
SIC: 3442 Sash, door or window: metal

(G-2455)
AXIS PIPE AND TUBE INC
1451 Louis Mikulin Rd (77807)
P.O. Box 6780 (77805-6780)
PHONE....................................979 703-6847
Lou Sanders, Business Mgr
Nick Johnson, Purch Mgr
Connor Thompson, Sales Staff
EMP: 23
SALES (corp-wide): 38.3MM Privately Held
WEB: www.axispipeandtube.com
SIC: 3312 Blast furnaces & steel mills
PA: Axis Pipe And Tube Llc
770 S Post Oak Ln Ste 200
Houston TX 77056
281 494-0900

(G-2456)
BCS EAGLE
Also Called: Bryan College Station Eagle
1729 Briarcrest Dr (77802-2712)
P.O. Box 3000 (77805-3000)
PHONE....................................979 776-4444
Crystal Dupre, Publisher
Jesse Wright, General Mgr
James Wilson, Principal
Rob Clark, Editor
Melissa Sullivan, Editor
EMP: 16
SALES (est): 946K Privately Held
WEB: www.theeagle.com
SIC: 2711 Commercial printing & newspaper publishing combined

(G-2457)
BELO CORP
1729 Briarcrest Dr (77802-2712)
P.O. Box 3000 (77805-3000)
PHONE....................................979 776-4444
Donnis Baggett, Manager
EMP: 150
SQ FT: 40,000
SALES (corp-wide): 2.3B Publicly Held
WEB: www.13newsnow.com
SIC: 2711 Newspapers, publishing & printing
HQ: Belo Corp.
7950 Jones Branch Dr
Mc Lean VA 22102
703 854-6000

(G-2458)
BOYD READY MIX INC
2853 N Hrvey Mtchll Pkwy (77807-1008)
P.O. Box 4787 (77805-4787)
PHONE....................................979 778-5199
Greg Boyd, President
EMP: 25
SALES (est): 4.7MM Privately Held
WEB: www.boydreadymix.com
SIC: 3273 Ready-mixed concrete

(G-2459)
BRAZOS VALLEY DRIVELINES INC
840 N Hrvey Mitchell Pkwy (77807-1015)
PHONE....................................979 775-3535
Robert Averyt, President
EMP: 10
SQ FT: 13,000
SALES (est): 1.4MM Privately Held
WEB: www.bvd.cc
SIC: 3599 7539 Machine shop, jobbing & repair; powertrain components repair services

(G-2460)
BREC INC
Also Called: Bryan Research Equipment Co.
400 Stone City Dr (77803-2019)
P.O. Box 4232 (77805-4232)
PHONE....................................979 823-4466
Vincent A Neal, President
EMP: 15
SALES (est): 1.1MM Privately Held
WEB: www.brecinc.com
SIC: 5999 3523 3496 Pet supplies; farm machinery & equipment; miscellaneous fabricated wire products

(G-2461)
BRYAN BAKING INC (HQ)
Also Called: Mid South Baking Company
600 Phil Gramm Blvd (77807-9101)
PHONE....................................979 778-6600

Steve Warden, President
Lee Boyer, Prdtn Mgr
Mark Eldridge, Safety Mgr
Craig Shaefer, CFO
Fred Bowers, Manager
EMP: 200
SQ FT: 300,000
SALES (est): 42.9MM
SALES (corp-wide): 758.5MM Privately Held
WEB: www.midsouthbakingllc.com
SIC: 2051 5149 Buns, bread type: fresh or frozen; groceries & related products
PA: C.H. Guenther & Son Llc
2201 Broadway St
San Antonio TX 78215
210 227-1401

(G-2462)
BRYAN BAKING COMPANY LLC
Also Called: New Southwest Baking Co
600 Phil Gramm Blvd (77807-9101)
PHONE....................................979 778-6600
Leonardo Garcia, QC Mgr
Don Dickens, Plant Engr
Craig Shaefer, CFO
Pamela Bond, Persnl Mgr
Fred Bauer,
EMP: 258
SQ FT: 300,000
SALES (est): 23.1MM Privately Held
WEB: www.midsouthbakingllc.com
SIC: 2051 Buns, bread type: fresh or frozen

(G-2463)
BRYAN CONTAINER COMPANY INC
Also Called: Technology Plastics
1121 Turkey Creek Rd (77801-1522)
P.O. Box 32 (77806-0032)
PHONE....................................979 822-7998
Charles Cobos, President
Jane Cobos, Treasurer
Brent Murray, VP Sales
Donald A Ball, Director
EMP: 9
SQ FT: 20,000
SALES (est): 1.4MM Privately Held
WEB: www.bryancontainers.com
SIC: 3443 3082 Industrial vessels, tanks & containers; unsupported plastics profile shapes

(G-2464)
BWAY
1591 N Hrvey Mtchll Pkwy (77803-2068)
PHONE....................................979 779-5900
Stephan Dechert, Principal
Fabian Sanchez, Supervisor
EMP: 15
SALES (est): 4.2MM Privately Held
WEB: www.mauserpackaging.com
SIC: 3411 Metal cans

(G-2465)
CALIBER BIOTHERAPEUTICS LLC
8800 Hlth Scence Ctr Pkwy (77807)
P.O. Box 15922, College Station (77841-5123)
PHONE....................................979 314-7740
Barry Holtz, President
EMP: 24
SALES (est): 5.2MM Privately Held
WEB: www.fullspectrum.com
SIC: 2836 Vaccines

(G-2466)
COPY STOP PRINT AND POSTAL
2290 Boonville Rd Ste 800 (77808-2271)
PHONE....................................979 774-4111
Jeff Plotts, General Mgr
Gene Smith, Principal
Carole Williams, Store Mgr
EMP: 10 EST: 2009
SALES (est): 1.2MM Privately Held
WEB: www.copystopprint.com
SIC: 2752 Commercial printing, offset

(G-2467)
CRAB VENTURES LLC
Also Called: Batten Flow Testing
6328 Fm 1179 (77808-7273)
PHONE....................................979 571-0258
Doug Batten, CEO

GEOGRAPHIC

Ross Batten,
Hank Robertson,
EMP: 20
SQ FT: 2,000
SALES (est): 1.3MM **Privately Held**
WEB: www.battenflowtesting.com
SIC: 1389 Construction, repair & dismantling services

(G-2468)
CUSTOM FABRICATORS & RPS INC
1379 N Hrvey Mtchell Pkwy (77803-2064)
PHONE...................................979 775-4297
Paul R Hundl, *President*
EMP: 15
SQ FT: 4,000
SALES (est): 4.1MM **Privately Held**
WEB: www.bcscustomfab.com
SIC: 3441 Fabricated structural metal

(G-2469)
DARLING INGREDIENTS INC
601 Liberty Dr (77807-3901)
PHONE...................................979 778-0298
Irene Vasquez, *Office Mgr*
Rick Speak, *Manager*
EMP: 15
SALES (corp-wide): 3.3B **Publicly Held**
WEB: www.darlingii.com
SIC: 2077 Animal & marine fats & oils
PA: Darling Ingredients Inc.
　　5601 N Macarthur Blvd
　　Irving TX 75038
　　972 717-0300

(G-2470)
DYNACON INC
831 Industrial Blvd (77803-2097)
PHONE...................................979 823-2690
Dennis Brunson, *COO*
Dennis P Brunson, *COO*
Joe R Janac, *Exec VP*
Wesley Keppers, *Vice Pres*
David Janac, *VP Prdtn*
◆ **EMP:** 74
SQ FT: 75,000
SALES (est): 21.9MM **Publicly Held**
WEB: www.f-e-t.com
SIC: 3531 Marine related equipment
HQ: Forum Us, Inc.
　　10344 Sam Houston Park Dr # 300
　　Houston TX 77064
　　713 351-7900

(G-2471)
EAGLE PRINTING COMPANY
1729 Briarcrest Dr (77802-2712)
P.O. Box 3000 (77805-3000)
PHONE...................................979 776-4444
Gerald Garcia, *President*
Ben Tedrick, *President*
EMP: 140
SALES (est): 4.6MM
SALES (corp-wide): 217.5MM **Privately Held**
WEB: www.theeagle.com
SIC: 2711 Newspapers, publishing & printing
PA: Harte Hanks, Inc.
　　2800 Wells Branch Pkwy
　　Austin TX 78728
　　512 343-1100

(G-2472)
EXPRESS ENERGY SVCS OPER LP
9637 E State Highway 21 (77808-9470)
PHONE...................................979 589-2255
Justin Irwin, *General Mgr*
EMP: 25
SALES (corp-wide): 770.4MM **Privately Held**
WEB: www.eeslp.com
SIC: 1389 Oil field services
PA: Express Energy Services Operating, Lp
　　9800 Richmond Ave Ste 500
　　Houston TX 77042
　　713 625-7400

(G-2473)
FESCO LTD
450 Stone City Dr (77803-2019)
PHONE...................................979 775-1825
Jay Langdon, *Manager*
EMP: 17

SALES (corp-wide): 201MM **Privately Held**
WEB: www.fescoinc.com
SIC: 1389 Oil field services
PA: Fesco, Ltd.
　　1000 Fesco Dr
　　Alice TX 78332
　　361 664-3479

(G-2474)
FRANKS INTERNATIONAL LLC
4100 Carrabba Rd (77808-9044)
P.O. Box 2757 (77805-2757)
PHONE...................................979 778-8700
Justin Conrad, *Branch Mgr*
EMP: 65
SQ FT: 6,000
SALES (corp-wide): 581MM **Privately Held**
SIC: 1389 7353 Oil field services; oil field equipment, rental or leasing
HQ: Frank's International, Llc
　　10260 Westheimer Rd
　　Houston TX 77042
　　281 966-7300

(G-2475)
GAZOO INC
120 N Main St (77803-3234)
PHONE...................................979 220-7753
Chris McDonald, *Business Mgr*
EMP: 10
SALES (est): 870.7K **Privately Held**
WEB: www.gazoohpc.com
SIC: 3571 Electronic computers

(G-2476)
HEATH INC
Also Called: Flying Penguin Ice
422 Dellwood St (77801-2523)
PHONE...................................979 822-6924
Robert P Heath Jr, *President*
Dorothy Carmichael, *Vice Pres*
EMP: 20
SQ FT: 5,000
SALES (est): 375K **Privately Held**
WEB: www.flyingpenguinice.com
SIC: 2097 Block ice; ice cubes

(G-2477)
HOLICKS MANUFACTURING CO LLC
4315 Wellborn Rd (77801-4665)
P.O. Box 264, College Station (77841-0264)
PHONE...................................979 846-6721
Leo Belbostey,
EMP: 10
SQ FT: 3,750
SALES (est): 500K **Privately Held**
WEB: www.holicks.com
SIC: 3999 3143 5661 Barber & beauty shop equipment; boots, dress or casual: men's; shoe stores

(G-2478)
HONEYWELL INTERNATIONAL INC
6200 Mumford Rd (77807-7712)
PHONE...................................979 778-4477
Rodney Mayerhoff, *Opers Staff*
Ralph Day, *Manager*
EMP: 17
SALES (corp-wide): 36.7B **Publicly Held**
WEB: www.honeywell.com
SIC: 8999 2899 Chemical consultant; chemical preparations
PA: Honeywell International Inc.
　　300 S Tryon St
　　Charlotte NC 28202
　　704 627-6200

(G-2479)
IBIO INC (PA)
8800 Hsc Pkwy (77807-1107)
PHONE...................................979 446-0027
Thomas F Isett, *Ch of Bd*
Randy J Maddux, *COO*
John Delta, *CFO*
Robert B Kay, *Treasurer*
EMP: 15 **EST:** 2008
SALES: 1.6MM **Publicly Held**
WEB: www.ibioinc.com
SIC: 2834 Pharmaceutical preparations

(G-2480)
JAGUAR ENERGY SERVICES LLC
1850 Roughneck Dr (77808-8487)
PHONE...................................337 250-4030
Jason Monk, *Branch Mgr*
EMP: 23
SALES (corp-wide): 61.2MM **Privately Held**
WEB: www.jaguar-energy.com
SIC: 1389 Oil field services
PA: Jaguar Energy Services, Llc
　　301 N Parkerson Ave
　　Crowley LA 70526
　　800 734-5803

(G-2481)
JAMES D ATKINS
Also Called: Turbo Tech Engineering
3100 Leonard Rd (77803-4313)
PHONE...................................979 209-2121
EMP: 10
SALES (est): 490K **Privately Held**
SIC: 3599 Machine Shop Jobbing And Repair Mfg

(G-2482)
KENT MOORE CABINETS INC (PA)
1460 Fountain Ave (77801-1129)
PHONE...................................979 775-2906
R Kent Moore, *President*
Anna Adler, *Regional Mgr*
Jesse Sherlock, *Business Mgr*
Jack Marino, *Vice Pres*
Giacomo Marino, *VP Opers*
EMP: 35
SQ FT: 136,000
SALES (est): 81.4MM **Privately Held**
WEB: www.kmc.net
SIC: 2434 Vanities, bathroom: wood

(G-2483)
KEY ENERGY SERVICES INC
4585 Andert Rd (77808-9409)
P.O. Box 4748 (77805-4748)
PHONE...................................979 589-2594
EMP: 50
SALES (corp-wide): 1.4B **Publicly Held**
SIC: 1389 Oil & Gas Field Service
PA: Key Energy Services, Inc.
　　1301 Mckinney St Ste 1800
　　Houston TX 77010
　　713 651-4300

(G-2484)
KEY ENERGY SERVICES INC
6115 E State Highway 21 (77808-8643)
P.O. Box 29, Giddings (78942-0029)
PHONE...................................979 778-1800
Chad Ussery, *District Mgr*
Lynn Stroud, *Manager*
EMP: 100
SALES (corp-wide): 413.8MM **Publicly Held**
WEB: www.keyenergy.com
SIC: 1389 7353 Oil field services; oil equipment rental services
PA: Key Energy Services, Inc.
　　1301 Mckinney St Ste 1800
　　Houston TX 77010
　　713 651-4300

(G-2485)
KEYSTONE MILLWORK INC
1740 Shiloh Ave (77803-2026)
PHONE...................................979 823-4846
Robert Kraus, *President*
Mary Kraus, *Vice Pres*
Jessie Ayers, *Plant Mgr*
Jim Reda, *Project Mgr*
Aaron Barnes, *Engineer*
EMP: 40
SQ FT: 3,500
SALES (est): 6MM **Privately Held**
WEB: www.keystone-millwork.com
SIC: 2521 5031 5712 2541 Cabinets, office: wood; lumber, plywood & millwork; cabinet work, custom; counter & sink tops

(G-2486)
KJ RUSTIC DESIGNS LLC
6458 Dick Elliott Rd (77808-7720)
PHONE...................................832 477-6545
EMP: 100 **EST:** 2015

SALES (est): 5MM **Privately Held**
SIC: 1389 Construction, repair & dismantling services

(G-2487)
KNIFE RIVER CORPORATION
9867 Fm 1227 (77806)
P.O. Box 674 (77806-0674)
PHONE...................................979 779-1112
Tracy Radtke, *Human Res Mgr*
Ben Carlson, *Branch Mgr*
EMP: 69
SALES (corp-wide): 5.3B **Publicly Held**
WEB: www.kniferiver.com
SIC: 3273 Ready-mixed concrete
HQ: Knife River Corporation
　　1150 W Century Ave
　　Bismarck ND 58503
　　701 530-1400

(G-2488)
KNIFE RIVER CORPORATION
6310 W State Highway 21 (77807-4921)
P.O. Box 674 (77806-0674)
PHONE...................................979 361-2900
Carol Vann Stone, *Principal*
EMP: 69
SALES (corp-wide): 5.3B **Publicly Held**
WEB: www.kniferiver.com
SIC: 1442 3273 3241 1221 Construction sand & gravel; ready-mixed concrete; cement, hydraulic; bituminous coal & lignite-surface mining
HQ: Knife River Corporation
　　1150 W Century Ave
　　Bismarck ND 58503
　　701 530-1400

(G-2489)
KRISTEN DISTRIBUTING CO (PA)
8301 N State Highway 6 (77807-7431)
PHONE...................................979 775-6322
▲ **EMP:** 20
SQ FT: 44,800
SALES (est): 40.7MM **Privately Held**
WEB: www.kristendistributing.com
SIC: 5181 5149 2086 Beer & other fermented malt liquors; soft drinks; water, pasteurized: packaged in cans, bottles, etc.

(G-2490)
LINDE INC
Also Called: Praxair
3030 E 29th St Ste 112 (77802-2740)
PHONE...................................979 774-0638
Wayne Jeske, *Branch Mgr*
EMP: 20 **Privately Held**
WEB: www.praxair.com
SIC: 2813 Industrial gases
HQ: Linde Inc.
　　10 Riverview Dr
　　Danbury CT 06810
　　203 837-2000

(G-2491)
LISAM AMERICA INC
3091 University Dr E # 430 (77802-3494)
PHONE...................................979 307-7384
Andrew Nelson, *CEO*
Brett Brewer, *Sales Executive*
EMP: 20
SALES (est): 286.5K
SALES (corp-wide): 1.6MM **Privately Held**
WEB: www.lisam.com
SIC: 7371 7372 7373 Computer software development; application computer software; systems software development services
HQ: Lisam Systems
　　Boulevard De La Sennette 42a
　　Ecaussinnes 7190
　　674 900-03

(G-2492)
MACK LARRY
Also Called: Mack Bolt & Steel
5875 E State Highway 21 (77808-8637)
PHONE...................................979 778-8088
Larry Mack, *Owner*
Deon Thurmon, *General Mgr*
Janet Mack, *Co-Owner*
EMP: 12
SQ FT: 9,000

▲ = Import ▼=Export
◆ =Import/Export

SALES (est): 1.5MM **Privately Held**
WEB: www.mackbolt.com
SIC: 3452 3599 Bolts, nuts, rivets & washers; machine shop, jobbing & repair

(G-2493)
MESSINA HOF WINE CELLARS INC (PA)
Also Called: Villa At Messina Hof
4545 Old Reliance Rd (77808-8995)
PHONE.................................979 778-9463
Paul V Bonarrigo, *President*
Joseph Behrens, *Opers Mgr*
Robin Allen, *Sales Staff*
Merrill Bonarrigo, *Admin Sec*
▲ EMP: 49
SQ FT: 25,000
SALES (est): 5.6MM **Privately Held**
WEB: www.messinahof.com
SIC: 2084 Wines

(G-2494)
NEUTRAL POSTURE INC
3904 N Texas Ave (77803-0555)
PHONE.................................979 778-0502
Rebecca E Boenigk, *Ch of Bd*
Brian Rutherford, *President*
Paula Overall, *General Mgr*
Christine Wuensche, *General Mgr*
Jaye E Congleton, *Exec VP*
▲ EMP: 85
SQ FT: 66,000
SALES (est): 19.3MM **Privately Held**
WEB: www.neutralposture.com
SIC: 2522 Chairs, office: padded or plain, except wood

(G-2495)
NEWMAN PRINTING COMPANY INC (PA)
1300 E 29th St (77802-1203)
PHONE.................................979 779-7700
Louis Newman III, *Ch of Bd*
Mike Newman, *Vice Pres*
John Viens, *Purchasing*
Donna Muegge, *Sales Staff*
Matthew Garrett, *Marketing Staff*
EMP: 37 EST: 1950
SQ FT: 23,000
SALES (est): 4.4MM **Privately Held**
WEB: www.newmanprint.com
SIC: 2752 Commercial printing, offset

(G-2496)
NORTH AMERICA PACKAGING CORP
Also Called: Rheem Container
1591 N Hrvey Mtchell Pkwy (77803-2068)
PHONE.................................979 779-5900
Stepher Dechart, *Branch Mgr*
EMP: 150
SQ FT: 79,164
SALES (corp-wide): 1.1B **Privately Held**
WEB: www.mauserpackaging.com
SIC: 3089 Pallets, plastic
HQ: North America Packaging Corp
1515 W 22nd St Ste 550
Oak Brook IL 60523
630 203-4100

(G-2497)
PEPSI-COLA METRO BTLG CO INC
1801 Shiloh Ave (77803-2018)
PHONE.................................979 779-6324
Colby Muth, *Safety Mgr*
James Bryant, *Sales & Mktg St*
EMP: 40
SQ FT: 17,900
SALES (corp-wide): 67.1B **Publicly Held**
WEB: www.pepsico.com
SIC: 2086 5149 Carbonated soft drinks, bottled & canned; soft drinks
HQ: Pepsi-Cola Metropolitan Bottling Company, Inc.
1111 Westchester Ave
White Plains NY 10604
914 767-6000

(G-2498)
PLY GEM INDUSTRIES INC
615 W Carson St (77801-1102)
PHONE.................................979 361-3514
Ellie Hunt, *Purchasing*
David Webb, *Sales Staff*

James Dean, *Manager*
EMP: 250
SALES (corp-wide): 4.8B **Publicly Held**
WEB: www.plygem.com
SIC: 2431 Windows, wood; doors, wood
HQ: Ply Gem Industries, Inc.
5020 Weston Pkwy Ste 400
Cary NC 27513
919 677-3900

(G-2499)
PRO STAR INDUSTRIES INC (HQ)
1590a N Harvey Mitchell (77803-2067)
PHONE.................................979 779-9399
Doryaneh Howell, *President*
Randy Niblett, *Vice Pres*
Dan Quinn, *Vice Pres*
O J Howell, *VP Sales*
Orlen Howell, *Sales Staff*
EMP: 20 EST: 1997
SQ FT: 17,850
SALES (est): 7.3MM **Privately Held**
WEB: www.prostarindustries.com
SIC: 2842 2841 5087 Cleaning or polishing preparations; soap & other detergents; janitors' supplies

(G-2500)
REFRIGRTION VSSELS SYSTEMS COR
Also Called: Refrigrtion Vlves Systems Corp
1520 Crosswind Dr (77808-9600)
P.O. Box 1300, Westminster MD (21158-5300)
PHONE.................................979 778-0095
EMP: 70
SQ FT: 50,000
SALES (est): 21.9MM
SALES (corp-wide): 447.5MM **Privately Held**
WEB: www.rvscorp.com
SIC: 3585 3443 Refrigeration equipment, complete; fabricated plate work (boiler shop)
PA: Evapco, Inc.
5151 Allendale Ln
Taneytown MD 21787
410 756-2600

(G-2501)
RIK-MAR FABRICATORS INC
400 Stone City Dr (77803-2019)
P.O. Box 4232 (77805-4232)
PHONE.................................979 779-1616
Richard Neal, *President*
Vince Neal, *Vice Pres*
EMP: 12
SQ FT: 30,000
SALES (est): 1.8MM **Privately Held**
WEB: www.rik-mar.com
SIC: 3449 3567 Bars, concrete reinforcing: fabricated steel; fuel-fired furnaces & ovens

(G-2502)
RODS SERVICE LLC
7932 W State Highway 21 (77807-4953)
PHONE.................................979 775-5000
Tony Zaragoza, *Plant Mgr*
Jerry Allen,
EMP: 28
SALES (est): 1.6MM **Privately Held**
WEB: www.rtsinspection.com
SIC: 1389 Oil field services

(G-2503)
RUSTEX INC
1776 Frieda Ln (77808-7285)
PHONE.................................979 778-7551
John H Williams Jr, *President*
Wendy Williams, *Vice Pres*
EMP: 25
SQ FT: 200
SALES (est): 3MM **Privately Held**
WEB: www.rustexinc.net
SIC: 1389 Oil & gas wells: building, repairing & dismantling

(G-2504)
SANDERSON FARMS INC PROC DIV
2000 Shiloh Ave (77803-2044)
PHONE.................................979 361-3410
Paul Smith, *Division Mgr*

Bennie King, *Purchasing*
Yefenia Saldana, *Chief Acct*
David Reynolds, *Auditor*
Denise Cabrera, *Human Res Mgr*
EMP: 1600
SALES (corp-wide): 3.5B **Publicly Held**
WEB: www.sandersonfarms.com
SIC: 0251 2015 Broiling chickens, raising of; poultry slaughtering & processing
HQ: Sanderson Farms, Inc. (Processing Division)
127 Flynt Rd
Laurel MS 39443
601 649-4030

(G-2505)
SANDERSON FARMS INC PROD DIV
701 Capitol Pkwy (77807-9102)
PHONE.................................979 778-5730
Karl King, *Manager*
Jed Haby, *Manager*
EMP: 1000
SQ FT: 64,095
SALES (corp-wide): 3.5B **Publicly Held**
WEB: www.sandersonfarms.com
SIC: 2015 Poultry slaughtering & processing
HQ: Sanderson Farms, Inc. (Production Division)
127 Flynt Rd
Laurel MS 39443
601 425-2552

(G-2506)
SCREENED IMAGES INC
725 E Vlla Mria Rd Ste 23 (77801)
PHONE.................................979 260-9891
Robert L Luckie, *President*
Debra Luckie, *Admin Sec*
EMP: 15
SQ FT: 2,200
SALES (est): 1.5MM **Privately Held**
WEB: www.screenedimagesonline.com
SIC: 2395 2396 Embroidery products, except schiffli machine; screen printing on fabric articles

(G-2507)
SECOND GNRATION ARC SPARK WLDG
7502 E State Highway 21 (77808-8658)
PHONE.................................979 778-1999
EMP: 40
SALES (est): 80.2K **Privately Held**
WEB: www.2genarcnspark.com
SIC: 7692 Welding repair

(G-2508)
SELECT ENERGY SERVICES LLC
Also Called: Alice Southern Equipment
7740 E State Highway 21 (77808-8662)
PHONE.................................361 701-8465
Jason Dugan, *Branch Mgr*
EMP: 50
SALES (corp-wide): 1.2B **Publicly Held**
WEB: www.selectenergyservices.com
SIC: 1389 Oil field services
HQ: Select Energy Services, Llc
1820 N I 35
Gainesville TX 76240
940 668-1818

(G-2509)
T G & P INC
Also Called: Texas Gate and Panel
2600 Fm 2223 (77808-6070)
PHONE.................................979 778-8255
Pat Fisher, *President*
Alex Estrella, *Vice Pres*
EMP: 10
SQ FT: 2,400
SALES (est): 1.6MM **Privately Held**
SIC: 3446 Fences, gates, posts & flagpoles

(G-2510)
TEMPLE BOTTLING COMPANY LTD
1820 Roughneck Dr (77808-8487)
PHONE.................................979 778-1203
EMP: 9

SALES (corp-wide): 26.6MM **Privately Held**
SIC: 2086 Mfg Bottled/Canned Soft Drinks
PA: Temple Bottling Company, Ltd.
3510 Parkway Dr
Temple TX 76504
254 773-3376

(G-2511)
TEXAS HIGH ROLLER INC
13810 S State Highway 6 (77807-4161)
PHONE.................................979 778-7460
John R Riley, *President*
Elizabeth Riley, *Vice Pres*
Weldon R Lloyd Jr, *Treasurer*
EMP: 20
SQ FT: 3,000
SALES (est): 1.8MM **Privately Held**
SIC: 3523 3541 3531 Fertilizing machinery, farm; machine tools, metal cutting type; construction machinery

(G-2512)
TOPS PRINTING INC
Also Called: Alphagrphics Bryan/College Stn
2023 S Texas Ave (77802-1834)
PHONE.................................979 779-1234
Steve Britton, *President*
EMP: 27
SQ FT: 3,500
SALES (est): 4.8MM **Privately Held**
WEB: www.topsprinting.com
SIC: 2752 2732 Commercial printing, lithographic; book printing

(G-2513)
TOYO INK AMERICA LLC
2400 N Hrvey Mtchell Pkwy (77807-1202)
PHONE.................................979 778-1538
Johnna Hanly, *Site Mgr*
Jeff Altmeyer, *Purch Agent*
Dominick Martinez, *Accounts Mgr*
EMP: 50 **Privately Held**
WEB: www.toyoink.com
SIC: 2893 Printing ink
HQ: Toyo Ink America, Llc
1225 N Michael Dr
Wood Dale IL 60191
630 930-5100

(G-2514)
TRISEUM LLC
1733 Briarcrest Dr # 213 (77802-2755)
PHONE.................................979 773-8909
Ben House, *Technical Staff*
Andre Thomas,
EMP: 15
SALES (est): 540.7K **Privately Held**
WEB: www.triseum.com
SIC: 7372 Educational computer software

(G-2515)
V T I OF TEXAS INC
6201 Mumford Rd (77807-9786)
PHONE.................................979 778-2804
Greg Petter, *General Mgr*
John Muller, *Manager*
Larry Adams, *Maintence Staff*
EMP: 35
SALES (corp-wide): 276.6MM **Privately Held**
WEB: www.vtindustries.com
SIC: 2542 2541 Counters or counter display cases: except wood; wood partitions & fixtures
HQ: V T I Of Texas, Inc.
1000 Industrial Park
Holstein IA 51025
712 368-4381

(G-2516)
XTO ENERGY INC
14596 Hilltop Ln (77803)
PHONE.................................979 828-1963
Noel Evans, *Branch Mgr*
EMP: 44
SALES (corp-wide): 264.9B **Publicly Held**
WEB: www.xtoenergy.com
SIC: 1311 Crude petroleum production
HQ: Xto Energy Inc.
22777 Sprngwoods Vlg Pkwy
Spring TX 77389

Buchanan Dam
Llano County

(G-2517)
BUCHANAN SEPTIC TANKS INC
15648 E State Highway 29 (78609-4418)
P.O. Box 297 (78609-0297)
PHONE..................................512 793-3100
David Parker, *President*
Beth Parker, *Admin Sec*
EMP: 14
SQ FT: 4,000
SALES (est): 2.2MM **Privately Held**
WEB: www.buchananseptictanks.com
SIC: 3272 Septic tanks, concrete

(G-2518)
LOWER COLORADO RIVER AUTHORITY
815 Buchanan Plant Rd (78609-2629)
P.O. Box 8 (78609-0008)
PHONE..................................512 473-3270
Ryan Rowney, *Manager*
EMP: 16
SALES (corp-wide): 1.3B **Privately Held**
WEB: www.lcra.org
SIC: 3822 Damper operators: pneumatic,
thermostatic, electric
PA: Lower Colorado River Authority
3700 Lake Austin Blvd
Austin TX 78703
512 473-3200

Buda
Hays County

(G-2519)
AMPERSAND ART SUPPLY INC
1235 S Loop 4 Ste 400 (78610-5838)
P.O. Box 1440 (78610-1440)
PHONE..................................512 322-0278
Elaine Salazar, *CEO*
▲ **EMP:** 26
SQ FT: 12,000
SALES (est): 5.4MM **Privately Held**
WEB: www.ampersandart.com
SIC: 2621 Art paper

(G-2520)
AUSTIN ARMATURE WORKS LP
496 Commercial Dr (78610-3536)
PHONE..................................512 312-0088
J F Kramer III, *Partner*
Jay Kramer, *Partner*
J F Kramer Jr, *General Ptnr*
Brian Kruse, *Sales Staff*
Chuck Moore, *Sales Staff*
EMP: 35
SQ FT: 10,500
SALES (est): 9.7MM **Privately Held**
WEB: www.aawems.com
SIC: 7694 6512 5063 Rebuilding motors,
except automotive; shopping center, prop-
erty operation only; motors, electric

(G-2521)
BUDA WOODWORKS LLC
2041 Fm 2001 (78610-3849)
P.O. Box 1067 (78610-1067)
PHONE..................................512 312-0550
Brandon Dykes, *Project Mgr*
Richie Gonzalez, *Project Mgr*
Jason Hair, *Engineer*
Alyson Jackson, *Accounts Mgr*
Chris Cloran,
EMP: 51
SQ FT: 55,000
SALES (est): 7.8MM **Privately Held**
WEB: www.budawoodworks.com
SIC: 2431 Woodwork, interior & ornamen-
tal

(G-2522)
C M C STEEL FABRICATORS INC
Exit 221 At I 35 N (78610)
P.O. Box 3195, Austin (78764-3195)
PHONE..................................512 282-8820
Rick Jenkins, *Branch Mgr*
EMP: 73

SALES (corp-wide): 5.4B **Publicly Held**
WEB: www.cmc.com
SIC: 3441 3496 Fabricated structural
metal; miscellaneous fabricated wire
products
HQ: C M C Steel Fabricators, Inc.
1 Steel Mill Dr
Seguin TX 78155
830 372-8200

(G-2523)
CAPITAL CITY CONTAINER CORP
150 Precision (78610-6002)
P.O. Box 870 (78610-0870)
PHONE..................................512 312-1222
John McLeod, *President*
David M Patten, *Treasurer*
Jerry C Hardison, *Admin Sec*
▲ **EMP:** 15
SQ FT: 196,000
SALES (est): 2.7MM **Privately Held**
SIC: 2653 Boxes, corrugated: made from
purchased materials

(G-2524)
CAPITAL SPECTRUM INC
Also Called: Communication Specialists
502 S Loop 4 (78610-9388)
P.O. Box 17936, Austin (78760-7936)
PHONE..................................512 478-3448
Charles T Sack, *President*
Vance Sack, *Vice Pres*
Pat Whalen, *Sales Staff*
Paul Barnes, *Manager*
Billy Donley, *Manager*
EMP: 150
SQ FT: 100,000
SALES (est): 33.1MM **Privately Held**
WEB: www.capspec.com
SIC: 2752 7331 Color lithography; mailing
service

(G-2525)
CENTEX MATERIALS LLC
1100 Hwy 2770 (78610)
P.O. Box 928 (78610-0928)
PHONE..................................512 295-4801
Mike Meyer, *Manager*
EMP: 20
SALES (corp-wide): 1.4B **Publicly Held**
WEB: www.centexmaterials.com
SIC: 3273 Ready-mixed concrete
HQ: Centex Materials Llc
3019 Alvin Devane Blvd # 100
Austin TX 78741
512 460-3003

(G-2526)
COMMERCIAL METALS COMPANY
14501 S Ih 35 (78610-9701)
PHONE..................................512 282-8820
Barney Cruz, *Branch Mgr*
EMP: 10
SALES (corp-wide): 5.4B **Publicly Held**
WEB: www.cmc.com
SIC: 3312 Blast furnaces & steel mills
PA: Commercial Metals Company
6565 N Macarthur Blvd # 800
Irving TX 75039
214 689-4300

(G-2527)
DEALERS TRUCK EQUIPMENT CO INC
16201 S Ih 35 (78610-9799)
PHONE..................................512 312-2100
Austin Sweeper, *Manager*
EMP: 16
SALES (corp-wide): 25.5MM **Privately Held**
WEB: www.dealerstruck.com
SIC: 5531 5084 5014 3531 Truck equip-
ment & parts; winches; truck tires &
tubes; backhoes, tractors, cranes, plows
& similar equipment
PA: Dealers Truck Equipment Company,
Inc.
2460 Midway St
Shreveport LA 71108
318 635-7567

(G-2528)
DUDLEY J PERIO INC
Also Called: Hydraulic Power Technology
18109 Foust Dr (78610-9711)
PHONE..................................512 295-4234
Dudley J Perio, *President*
Davie Benner, *Engineer*
Ron Blower, *Finance Mgr*
Auday Saffar, *Admin Sec*
EMP: 50
SALES (est): 10.2MM **Privately Held**
WEB: www.hpt-texas.com
SIC: 3533 Oil field machinery & equipment

(G-2529)
HENDERSON CONTROLS INC
900 W Goforth Rd (78610-3509)
P.O. Box 60, Lockhart (78644-0060)
PHONE..................................512 398-5700
Randall R Henderson, *President*
Cecilia Henderson, *Officer*
EMP: 35
SALES (est): 6.2MM **Privately Held**
SIC: 3585 Refrigeration & heating equip-
ment

(G-2530)
HYDRAULIC PWR TECHNOLOGY-TEXAS
18109 Foust Dr (78610-9711)
PHONE..................................512 295-4234
Ramadan Ismail, *President*
Auday Al Saffar, *General Mgr*
◆ **EMP:** 21
SQ FT: 25,000
SALES (est): 5.9MM **Privately Held**
WEB: www.hpt-texas.com
SIC: 3533 Oil field machinery & equipment

(G-2531)
JARDINE FOODS INC
Also Called: Jardine's Texas Foods
1 Chisholm Trl (78610-3350)
P.O. Box 1530 (78610-1530)
PHONE..................................512 295-4600
Robert McGee, *CEO*
Tom Keim, *President*
Richard Garland, *CFO*
▲ **EMP:** 40 **EST:** 1979
SQ FT: 26,000
SALES (est): 12.9MM
SALES (corp-wide): 380.6MM **Privately Held**
WEB: www.jardinefoods.com
SIC: 2033 2099 2035 Jellies, edible, in-
cluding imitation: in cans, jars, etc.; bar-
becue sauce: packaged in cans, jars, etc.;
food preparations; relishes, fruit & veg-
etable; seasonings, vegetable sauces
(except tomato & dry)
PA: Teasdale Foods, Inc.
3041 Churchill Dr Ste 100
Flower Mound TX 75022
209 358-5616

(G-2532)
LEWIS SIGN BUILDERS INC
16910 Interstate 35 (78610-3518)
P.O. Box 1665 (78610-1665)
PHONE..................................512 312-4555
John Lewis, *President*
Ann Lewis, *Corp Secy*
Leon Apostolo, *Sales Mgr*
Taelor Harris, *Office Admin*
EMP: 39
SQ FT: 7,500
SALES (est): 7.5MM **Privately Held**
WEB: www.lewissign.com
SIC: 3993 Electric signs; neon signs

(G-2533)
NIGHT HAWK FROZEN FOODS INC
100 Nighthawk Cir (78610-9100)
P.O. Box 867 (78610-0867)
PHONE..................................800 580-4166
Leanne H Logan, *Ch of Bd*
Charles V Hill, *President*
Michelle Anselment, *COO*
Scott L Logan, *COO*
John E Hyde, *Vice Pres*
EMP: 64
SQ FT: 30,000

SALES (est): 14.5MM **Privately Held**
WEB: www.nighthawkfoods.com
SIC: 2038 Dinners, frozen & packaged

(G-2534)
PWF ENTERPRISES
Also Called: Plastic Welding & Fabrication
2457 S Loop 4 Ste 3b (78610-9359)
PHONE..................................512 295-6412
Shaun Shoemake, *Partner*
Julie Hicsman, *Partner*
Fred L Shoemake, *Partner*
Ona K Shoemake, *Partner*
Mari Shoemake, *Office Mgr*
EMP: 14
SQ FT: 6,000
SALES (est): 1.2MM **Privately Held**
WEB:
www.plasticweldingandfabrication.com
SIC: 7692 Welding repair

(G-2535)
ROYAL BATHS MFG CO LTD
Also Called: Royal Bath Mfg
199 Park 35 Cv N (78610-3521)
PHONE..................................512 707-0094
Anne Cano, *Manager*
EMP: 30
SALES (corp-wide): 170.5MM **Privately Held**
WEB: www.royal-mfg.com
SIC: 5719 3281 Bath accessories; marble,
building: cut & shaped
PA: Royal Baths Manufacturing Company
14635 Chrisman Rd
Houston TX 77039
281 442-3400

(G-2536)
SAND SOCKS
5381 Industrial Way Dr (78610-5750)
PHONE..................................512 284-7706
Mike Sickmiller, *Principal*
EMP: 13 **EST:** 2010
SALES (est): 1.3MM **Privately Held**
WEB: www.sandsocks.net
SIC: 2252 Socks

(G-2537)
SCHNEIDER ELECTRIC USA INC
576 Commercial Dr (78610-3553)
PHONE..................................512 295-8060
Dean Conley, *Branch Mgr*
EMP: 143
SALES (corp-wide): 177.9K **Privately Held**
WEB: www.ccagp.com
SIC: 3699 1731 Electrical equipment &
supplies; electrical work
HQ: Schneider Electric Usa, Inc.
1 Boston Pl Ste 2700
Boston MA 02108
978 975-9600

(G-2538)
SPARTAN REINFORCING LLC
1955 Fm 2001 Ste 320 (78610-2043)
PHONE..................................915 269-5222
Alejandro Mitchell, *Branch Mgr*
EMP: 20
SALES (corp-wide): 15MM **Privately Held**
WEB: www.spartanreinforcing.com
SIC: 3449 5051 Miscellaneous metalwork;
metals service centers & offices
PA: Spartan Reinforcing, Llc
15840 Fm 529 Rd Ste 303
Houston TX 77095
832 271-1721

(G-2539)
SPEEDTECH LIGHTS INC
2809 Business Park Dr (78610-9413)
PHONE..................................800 757-2581
Ahmed Deyaf, *President*
Mostafa Abdallah, *Sales Mgr*
Mohamed Deyaf, *Sales Staff*
Andrew Knoy, *Mktg Coord*
Ferdous Deyaf, *Manager*
▲ **EMP:** 20
SALES (est): 3.8MM **Privately Held**
WEB: www.speedtechlights.com
SIC: 3648 5063 5719 Lighting equipment;
light bulbs & related supplies; lighting,
lamps & accessories

(G-2540)
TEXAS LEHIGH CEMENT COMPANY LP
701 Cement Plant Rd (78610)
P.O. Box 610 (78610-0610)
PHONE.....................512 295-6111
John Jenkins, *Traffic Mgr*
Alfred Carrillo, *Terminal Mgr*
Marvin Bragewitz, *Sales Mgr*
Stuart Tomlinson, *Manager*
Victor Gonzalez, *Manager*
EMP: 120
SALES (corp-wide): 1.4B **Publicly Held**
WEB: www.texaslehigh.com
SIC: 3241 Portland cement
HQ: Texas Lehigh Cement Company Lp
1000 Jack C Hays Trl
Buda TX 78610
512 295-6111

(G-2541)
TEXAS LEHIGH CEMENT COMPANY LP (HQ)
1000 Jack C Hays Trl (78610-3335)
P.O. Box 610 (78610-0610)
PHONE.....................512 295-6111
Robert Kidnew, *President*
Bob Kidnew, *Partner*
Steve Adkins, *Safety Dir*
Larry Covert, *Plant Mgr*
Jeff Main, *Sales Staff*
▲ EMP: 155 EST: 1976
SQ FT: 500,000
SALES (est): 68MM
SALES (corp-wide): 1.4B **Publicly Held**
WEB: www.texaslehigh.com
SIC: 3241 Portland cement
PA: Eagle Materials Inc.
5960 Berkshire Ln Ste 900
Dallas TX 75225
214 432-2000

Buffalo
Leon County

(G-2542)
ANADARKO PETROLEUM CORPORATION
921 S Hgwy 75 (75831)
PHONE.....................903 389-3814
Kendall Madden, *Supervisor*
EMP: 50
SALES (corp-wide): 21.2B **Publicly Held**
WEB: www.oxy.com
SIC: 1382 Oil & gas exploration services
HQ: Anadarko Petroleum Corporation
1201 Lake Robbins Dr
The Woodlands TX 77380
832 636-1000

(G-2543)
BUFFALO TANK COMPANY INC
219 Donie Rd (75831-7634)
P.O. Box 506 (75831-0506)
PHONE.....................903 322-4153
Joe Cheek, *President*
Margaret Cheek, *Corp Secy*
EMP: 9
SQ FT: 5,000
SALES (est): 1.2MM **Privately Held**
WEB: www.buffalotank.com
SIC: 3443 Tanks, standard or custom fabricated: metal plate

(G-2544)
J & S CONSTRUCTION LLC
10823 Hwy 75 S (75831-8327)
P.O. Box 400 (75831-0400)
PHONE.....................903 322-4942
Jeff Rodell, *Mng Member*
Susan Rodell,
EMP: 50
SALES (est): 10.9MM **Privately Held**
SIC: 1381 Service well drilling

(G-2545)
KC FIELD SERVICES INC
13498 N Us Highway 75 (75831-8211)
PHONE.....................903 322-9353
John Carmeans, *President*
Markay Carmeans, *Treasurer*
EMP: 15

SALES (est): 900K **Privately Held**
SIC: 1389 Servicing oil & gas wells

(G-2546)
LS ROPE LLC
Also Called: Lone Star Rope
213 Lanely Rd (75831-6297)
PHONE.....................903 322-6580
Guy Alford, *Mng Member*
Kevin Pate, *Shareholder*
Richie Pate, *Shareholder*
▲ EMP: 21
SALES (est): 2.8MM **Privately Held**
SIC: 2298 Rope, except asbestos & wire

(G-2547)
R CONSTRUCTION COMPANY (PA)
1313 W Us Highway 79 (75831-3521)
P.O. Box 189 (75831-0189)
PHONE.....................903 322-4639
Brody Maedgen, *President*
Matt Buchanan, *VP Business*
A David Williams, *CFO*
David Williams, *CFO*
Kevin Purington, *Director*
EMP: 137
SQ FT: 8,000
SALES (est): 58.1MM **Privately Held**
WEB: www.rconstructionco.com
SIC: 1389 1794 Oil field services; excavation & grading, building construction

(G-2548)
RIDLEY USA INC
Also Called: Ridley Block Operations
125 Industrial Blvd (75831)
P.O. Box 1130 (75831-1130)
PHONE.....................903 322-4228
Sandy Lumley, *Branch Mgr*
EMP: 10
SALES (corp-wide): 1.7B **Privately Held**
WEB: www.hubbardfeeds.com
SIC: 2048 5191 Livestock feeds; animal feeds
HQ: Ridley Usa Inc.
111 W Cherry St Ste 500
Mankato MN 56001
507 388-9400

(G-2549)
WIL CALL SERVICES LTD
12762 Fm 2539 (75831-8164)
P.O. Box 473 (75831-0473)
PHONE.....................903 322-2911
Jon Wilson, *Partner*
Connie Wilson, *Partner*
David Harcrow, *Vice Pres*
Charlotte Cooper, *Office Mgr*
EMP: 67
SALES (est): 43.7MM **Privately Held**
WEB: www.wilcall.com
SIC: 1381 Directional drilling oil & gas wells

Buffalo Gap
Taylor County

(G-2550)
COMANCHE MOON PUBLISHING LLC
3002 Fm 89 (79508-2202)
P.O. Box 728 (79508-0728)
PHONE.....................325 572-3339
Tom Perini,
EMP: 20
SALES (est): 1.3MM **Privately Held**
SIC: 2741 Miscellaneous publishing

Bullard
Smith County

(G-2551)
CONSOLIDATED WOOD PRODUCTS INC
Also Called: Consolidated Crate
1940 County Road 3703 (75757-7834)
P.O. Box 457 (75757-0457)
PHONE.....................903 894-7745
Cindy Tarrant, *President*
Jim Tarrant, *Corp Secy*

Ed Bernd, *Director*
◆ EMP: 30
SQ FT: 20,000
SALES (est): 5MM **Privately Held**
WEB: www.consolidatedwoodproducts.com
SIC: 2448 Pallets, wood

(G-2552)
TRIPLE S ONSHORE OPRATIONS LLC
117 Pecan Valley Dr (75757-5478)
PHONE.....................903 658-0489
Derek St Amant, *Mng Member*
Jon St Amant,
Katherine St Amant,
EMP: 20
SQ FT: 1,000
SALES (est): 4MM **Privately Held**
SIC: 1389 Construction, repair & dismantling services

Bulverde
Comal County

(G-2553)
ALLY WHOLESALE SIGNS LLC
20540 Hwy 45 E Ste 115 St (78163)
PHONE.....................830 438-2500
Michele Bowman, *Sales Staff*
EMP: 21 **Privately Held**
WEB: www.allysigns.com
SIC: 3993 Signs & advertising specialties
PA: Ally Wholesale Signs Llc
300 Broyles Ln
Bulverde TX 78163

(G-2554)
ALLY WHOLESALE SIGNS LLC (PA)
300 Broyles Ln (78163-3207)
PHONE.....................830 438-2500
Jeffrey Barton,
Travis Popp,
EMP: 15
SALES (est): 4MM **Privately Held**
WEB: www.allysigns.com
SIC: 3993 Signs & advertising specialties

(G-2555)
KELLOGG COMPANY
5357 Honeysuckle Br (78163-2277)
PHONE.....................830 438-2254
EMP: 699
SALES (corp-wide): 13.5B **Publicly Held**
WEB: www.kelloggcompany.com
SIC: 2043 Cereal breakfast foods
PA: Kellogg Company
1 Kellogg Sq
Battle Creek MI 49017
269 961-2000

(G-2556)
MEDTRONIC MINIMED INC
2880 John Charles Rd (78163-1847)
PHONE.....................830 438-0383
EMP: 603 **Privately Held**
WEB: www.medtronicdiabetes.com
SIC: 3841 Surgical & medical instruments
HQ: Medtronic Minimed, Inc.
18000 Devonshire St
Northridge CA 91325

(G-2557)
NYTEX AUTOMATIC PRODUCTS INC
535 E Ammann Rd (78163-2009)
P.O. Box 12356, San Antonio (78212-0356)
PHONE.....................830 997-8986
EMP: 21
SQ FT: 12,800
SALES (est): 4.2MM **Privately Held**
SIC: 3451 Mfg Screw Machine Products

(G-2558)
RANGER COML CON CONTRS LLC
771 Brand Rd Rc (78163-3410)
P.O. Box 937, Spring Branch (78070-0937)
PHONE.....................210 831-7052
Monica Salinas, *President*
EMP: 15 EST: 2015
SALES (est): 1.6MM **Privately Held**
SIC: 3272 Slabs, crossing: concrete

Buna
Jasper County

(G-2559)
APPLIED MAINTENANCE SPC INC
Also Called: Metal Ink Wear Technologies
34369 Us Highway 96 S (77612-5919)
P.O. Box 209 (77612-0209)
PHONE.....................409 994-5849
Rodney Robison, *President*
Debra Robison, *Corp Secy*
Gary Vanpelt, *Sales Staff*
◆ EMP: 15
SQ FT: 12,500
SALES (est): 2MM **Privately Held**
WEB: www.appliedmaintenance.com
SIC: 3541 Machine tools, metal cutting type

(G-2560)
BAILEY & HARLEY SERVICES LLC
Also Called: Merit Oil Field Services
227 Business Hwy 96 S (77612)
PHONE.....................409 994-5857
Jeremy Baily,
Scott Harley,
EMP: 45
SQ FT: 1,000
SALES (est): 10.5MM **Privately Held**
SIC: 1382 1389 Oil & gas exploration services; construction, repair & dismantling services

(G-2561)
C&F FABRICATION INDUS SVCS LLC
537 County Road 737 (77612-2649)
PHONE.....................409 994-2135
EMP: 20
SALES (est): 3.9MM **Privately Held**
SIC: 3441 3479 1795 Structural Metal Fabrication Coating/Engraving Service Wrecking/Demolition Contractor

(G-2562)
SOUTHEAST TEXAS INDUSTRIES INC (PA)
Also Called: STI Group
35911 Us Highway 96 S (77612-4031)
P.O. Box 1449 (77612-1449)
PHONE.....................409 994-3570
Paul T Spence, *President*
Jimmy Willson, *Division Mgr*
Richard Broussard, *General Mgr*
Earnest Moore, *Superintendent*
Pat Pairsh, *Business Mgr*
▲ EMP: 350
SQ FT: 10,000
SALES (est): 194.4MM **Privately Held**
WEB: www.setxind.com
SIC: 3312 3443 Structural shapes & pilings, steel; hot-rolled iron & steel products; fabricated plate work (boiler shop)

Burkburnett
Wichita County

(G-2563)
AMERON INTERNATIONAL CORP
Ameron Fiberglass & Pipe
1004 Ameron Rd (76354-2912)
P.O. Box 878 (76354-0878)
PHONE.....................940 569-1471
Mark Nowak, *Principal*
EMP: 165
SALES (corp-wide): 8.4B **Publicly Held**
WEB: www.nov.com
SIC: 3498 2821 Fabricated pipe & fittings; plastics materials & resins
HQ: Ameron International Corporation
7909 Parkwood Circle Dr
Houston TX 77036
713 375-3700

GEOGRAPHIC

(G-2564)
SUPERIOR PLLET WICHITA FLS LTD (PA)
160 Gresham Rd (76354-1822)
P.O. Box 965 (76354-0965)
PHONE....................................940 569-5244
Sam S Lobaugh Jr, *President*
Sam S Lobaugh Sr, *President*
Dwayne Lobaugh, *Vice Pres*
EMP: 18
SQ FT: 45,000
SALES (est): 2.5MM **Privately Held**
SIC: 2448 2449 2441 Cargo containers, wood; rectangular boxes & crates, wood; nailed wood boxes & shook

Burleson
Johnson County

(G-2565)
AERO CNC INC
960 S Burleson Blvd (76097-5506)
P.O. Box 35 (76097-0035)
PHONE....................................817 295-0184
Mary Layne, *President*
Chris Layne, *General Mgr*
Richard Layne, *Vice Pres*
Michael Kline, *Prgrmr*
Fred Rogers, *Director*
EMP: 32
SQ FT: 19,200
SALES: 6.7MM **Privately Held**
WEB: www.aerocnc.com
SIC: 3599 Machine shop, jobbing & repair

(G-2566)
ALL STAR CORRUGATED
208 Hiddenglen St (76028-2220)
PHONE....................................817 454-8640
Kimberly Stephens, *Branch Mgr*
EMP: 60
SALES (corp-wide): 12.6MM **Privately Held**
WEB: www.allstarbox.com
SIC: 2653 Boxes, corrugated: made from purchased materials
PA: All Star Corrugated
1425 Forum Way S
Fort Worth TX 76140
817 551-5580

(G-2567)
AMERICAN COMPLETION TOOLS INC (HQ)
3084 S Burleson Blvd (76028-1879)
PHONE....................................817 790-6608
Prabhat Kumar, *President*
Neel Grag, *CFO*
Ahmad Said, *Sales Staff*
Kumar Prakash, *Director*
◆ EMP: 25
SQ FT: 30,000
SALES (est): 4.7MM **Privately Held**
WEB: www.americancompletiontools.com
SIC: 3599 Oil & gas field machinery

(G-2568)
BAKER HUGHES HOLDINGS LLC
Also Called: Baker Hughes Oilfld Operations
1980 Sw Wilshire Blvd (76028-6322)
PHONE....................................817 426-7080
Justin Adams, *District Mgr*
EMP: 86
SALES (corp-wide): 23.8B **Publicly Held**
WEB: www.bakerhughes.com
SIC: 1389 Oil field services
HQ: Baker Hughes Holdings Llc
17021 Aldine Westfield Rd
Houston TX 77073
713 439-8600

(G-2569)
BASDEN STEEL AND ERECTION INC (HQ)
645 E Renfro St Ste C (76028-4992)
P.O. Box 1061 (76097-1061)
PHONE....................................817 295-6100
Bruce Basden, *President*
Donnie Doan, *Department Mgr*
Linda Webb, *Admin Sec*
EMP: 30
SQ FT: 80,000

SALES (est): 32.3MM **Privately Held**
WEB: www.basdensteel.com
SIC: 3312 7353 7389 5082 Structural shapes & pilings, steel; cranes & aerial lift equipment, rental or leasing; crane & aerial lift service; cranes, construction; fabricated structural metal; structural steel erection

(G-2570)
BASDEN STEEL CORPORATION
645 E Renfro St Ste C (76028-4992)
P.O. Box 1061 (76097-1061)
PHONE....................................817 295-6100
Bruce Basden, *President*
EMP: 70
SALES (est): 5.9MM **Privately Held**
WEB: www.basdensteel.com
SIC: 3441 Fabricated structural metal
PA: Renfro Street Holdings, Ltd.
645 E Renfro St
Burleson TX 76028

(G-2571)
BERRY MACHINE SHOP
7782 Berry Rd (76028-2821)
P.O. Box 171 (76097-0171)
PHONE....................................817 572-0948
Clyde T Berry, *Owner*
EMP: 31
SQ FT: 14,000
SALES (est): 3.6MM **Privately Held**
SIC: 3599 7692 3728 3555 Machine shop, jobbing & repair; welding repair; aircraft parts & equipment; printing trades machinery; metals service centers & offices

(G-2572)
BIRDWELL CLEANING PRODUCTS INC
1075 Nw John Jones Dr (76028-5153)
P.O. Box 1388 (76097-1388)
PHONE....................................800 722-8006
David Birdwell, *President*
Greg Birdwell, *VP Opers*
◆ EMP: 52 EST: 1982
SQ FT: 50,000
SALES (est): 8.9MM **Privately Held**
WEB: www.birdwellcleaning.com
SIC: 3991 Brooms & brushes

(G-2573)
BURLY CORP (PA)
754 N Burleson Blvd (76028-2902)
PHONE....................................817 295-1128
David B Davenport, *President*
Brett Davenport, *Exec VP*
Bryan Davenport, *Exec VP*
Morris B Davenport, *Vice Pres*
James Matthews, *Legal Staff*
◆ EMP: 25
SALES (est): 40.4MM **Privately Held**
WEB: www.burlycorp.com
SIC: 3496 3822 Fencing, made from purchased wire; hardware for environmental regulators

(G-2574)
CLASSIC FOODS LP
3165 S Burleson Blvd (76028-1882)
P.O. Box 549, Temple (76503-0549)
PHONE....................................817 332-1071
Drayton McLane III, *Partner*
Bret Gailey, *Partner*
Carl Worthington, *Partner*
Joel Nearing, *Research*
Jim Plummer, *Sales Staff*
▲ EMP: 16
SQ FT: 22,700
SALES (est): 4.1MM **Privately Held**
WEB: www.mclaneclassicfoods.com
SIC: 2099 Sauces: gravy, dressing & dip mixes
PA: Mclane Group, L.P.
4001 Central Pointe Pkwy
Temple TX 76504

(G-2575)
CNC FABRICATION AND MAINT
2171 E Renfro St (76028-2217)
PHONE....................................817 295-9055
Charles N Choate, *President*
Charles Choate, *Director*
EMP: 11
SQ FT: 2,500

SALES (est): 3.2MM **Privately Held**
WEB: www.cncfabinc.com
SIC: 1542 3535 3556 4222 Commercial & office building, new construction; belt conveyor systems, general industrial use; meat, poultry & seafood processing machinery; warehousing, cold storage or refrigerated; food products manufacturing or packing plant construction; grain elevator construction

(G-2576)
CONFAB OILFIELD CONTRACTORS
4014 Windmill Rd (76097)
PHONE....................................817 992-6563
Mark Shipman, *Owner*
EMP: 15
SALES (est): 882.3K **Privately Held**
SIC: 1382 Oil & gas exploration services

(G-2577)
CORDOVA CORPORATION
Also Called: Pmr Global Aerospace
4290 E Fm 1187 (76028-7912)
PHONE....................................817 484-1100
John Rymell, *President*
Steve Michell, *Vice Pres*
Chad Parsons, *Vice Pres*
EMP: 27
SQ FT: 12,500
SALES (est): 205K
SALES (corp-wide): 5.4MM **Privately Held**
SIC: 5088 8742 3599 Helicopter parts; management consulting services; machine & other job shop work
PA: Pmr Global, Inc.
4290 E Fm 1187
Burleson TX 76028
817 484-1100

(G-2578)
ERWIN CONTAINERS INC
535 Memorial Plz (76028-4917)
P.O. Box 51 (76097-0051)
PHONE....................................817 295-5256
Mike Erwin, *President*
EMP: 24
SQ FT: 51,000
SALES (est): 2.2MM **Privately Held**
WEB: www.erwincontainers.com
SIC: 2441 Packing cases, wood: nailed or lock corner

(G-2579)
FWAVE LLC
921 S Burleson Blvd (76028-4906)
PHONE....................................817 754-9021
Scott McDonald, *President*
James Sauter, *Vice Pres*
Daniel Dejarnette, *VP Opers*
▼ EMP: 10
SQ FT: 37,000
SALES (est): 523.9K
SALES (corp-wide): 828K **Privately Held**
WEB: www.f-wave.com
SIC: 3089 Plastic hardware & building products
PA: Zinniatek, Inc.
19 Elmer St
Cambridge MA 02138
617 714-4847

(G-2580)
HALF PRICE BKS REC MGZINES INC
12616 South Fwy Ste 134 (76028-8441)
PHONE....................................817 295-8560
Aaron Williamson, *Manager*
EMP: 16
SALES (corp-wide): 211.7MM **Privately Held**
WEB: www.becomegreen.info
SIC: 5932 2721 Rare books; magazines: publishing & printing
PA: Half Price Books, Records, Magazines, Incorporated
5803 E Northwest Hwy
Dallas TX 75231
214 360-0833

(G-2581)
HAYES & STOLZ INDUS MFG CO LLC
6500 Cirrus Dr (76028-1576)
PHONE....................................817 926-3391
B J Masters, *President*
Kathy Byford, *Human Res Mgr*
Jerry Ferguson, *Manager*
Jim Nickels, *Manager*
Gary Schilling, *Manager*
EMP: 50 EST: 1945
SQ FT: 7,000
SALES (est): 18.3MM **Privately Held**
WEB: www.hayes-stolz.com
SIC: 3523 3559 Feed grinders, crushers & mixers; plastics working machinery

(G-2582)
INDICOM BUILDINGS INC
721 N Burleson Blvd (76028-2912)
P.O. Box 1567 (76097-1567)
PHONE....................................817 447-1213
Ron Procunier, *CEO*
Devin Duvak, *General Mgr*
Nety Duenas, *Accounting Mgr*
Ron Livingston, *Sales Staff*
Rusty Pearse, *Sales Executive*
EMP: 90
SQ FT: 50,000
SALES (est): 24.7MM **Privately Held**
WEB: www.indicombuildings.com
SIC: 2452 3448 Prefabricated buildings, wood; buildings, portable: prefabricated metal

(G-2583)
ISC MANUFACTURING LLC
Also Called: ISC Industrial Manufacturing
4133 Conveyor Dr (76028-1819)
PHONE....................................817 641-0691
Bill Hartley,
EMP: 40
SALES (est): 2.6MM **Privately Held**
WEB: www.iscmfg.com
SIC: 3535 Bulk handling conveyor systems

(G-2584)
KERR COLLECTION
1100 E Rendon Crowley Rd (76028-7529)
PHONE....................................817 572-4663
Shawn Kerr, *Manager*
EMP: 14 **Privately Held**
WEB: www.kerrcollection.com
SIC: 2519 5712 2521 2511 Household furniture, except wood or metal: upholstered; furniture stores; wood office furniture; wood household furniture
PA: Kerr Collection
8024 Rose Creek Ct
Burleson TX 76028

(G-2585)
KMP GRAPHICS INC
105 Black Jack Ln (76028-1406)
PHONE....................................817 295-5350
Keith Kelly, *President*
Bradley Doughty, *Art Dir*
EMP: 9
SALES (est): 887.1K **Privately Held**
WEB: www.kmpgraphics.com
SIC: 3993 Signs & advertising specialties

(G-2586)
KWS MANUFACTURING COMPANY LTD
3041 Conveyor Dr (76028-1857)
PHONE....................................817 295-2247
William C Mecke, *Partner*
Jim Collins, *Vice Pres*
Maurice McAdory, *Project Mgr*
Kent Thomas, *Regl Sales Mgr*
John Ringgold, *Sales Staff*
▼ EMP: 135
SQ FT: 128,000
SALES (est): 56.1MM **Privately Held**
WEB: www.kwsmfg.com
SIC: 3535 5084 Belt conveyor systems, general industrial use; industrial machinery & equipment

(G-2587)
LIQUID-STONE CONCRETE
221 Centre Dr (76028-4315)
PHONE....................................817 295-5151
Paul Karmy, *Partner*

David Karmy, *Partner*
John Carter, *Sales Associate*
EMP: 22
SQ FT: 10,000
SALES (est): 4MM **Privately Held**
WEB: www.lsctx.com
SIC: 3273 Ready-mixed concrete

(G-2588)
LSRI LLC
Also Called: Lone Star Rebar Installers
417 N Rudd St (76028-3922)
PHONE.....................817 770-0937
EMP: 60
SALES (est): 719.8K **Privately Held**
SIC: 1389 Oil/Gas Field Services

(G-2589)
M W BUTLER COMPANY
12390 Rendon Rd (76028-3012)
PHONE.....................817 572-3306
Mitchel Butler, *Owner*
Nopi Butler, *Owner*
EMP: 10
SQ FT: 7,500
SALES (est): 850K **Privately Held**
SIC: 3724 Aircraft engines & engine parts

(G-2590)
MDU CNSTRUCTION SVCS GROUP INC
5701 Highpoint Pkwy (76028-1582)
PHONE.....................817 447-8085
James Pace, *Branch Mgr*
▲ **EMP:** 41
SALES (corp-wide): 5.3B **Publicly Held**
WEB: www.mducsg.com
SIC: 3531 Construction machinery
HQ: Mdu Construction Services Group, Inc.
1150 W Century Ave
Bismarck ND 58503
701 530-1000

(G-2591)
MIDWAY MACHINE & WLDG SP INC
121 Industrial Park Blvd (76028-2905)
PHONE.....................817 447-0985
William Lewis, *President*
Bud Lewis, *President*
Sharon Lewis, *Corp Secy*
EMP: 10
SQ FT: 10,000
SALES (est): 1.5MM **Privately Held**
SIC: 3599 Machine shop, jobbing & repair

(G-2592)
OLAERIS INC
717 Creekview Dr (76028-4447)
PHONE.....................877 750-5500
Edward Lindsley, *CEO*
Dr Paul Pounds, *Vice Pres*
EMP: 11
SALES (est): 950K **Privately Held**
WEB: www.olaeris.com
SIC: 3721 Aircraft

(G-2593)
PMR GLOBAL INC (PA)
4290 E Fm 1187 (76028-7912)
PHONE.....................817 484-1100
John Rymell, *President*
Steve Michell, *Vice Pres*
Chad Parsons, *Vice Pres*
Lisa Sciuto, *Vice Pres*
Chad Morgan, *Mfg Mgr*
▲ **EMP:** 23
SQ FT: 12,500
SALES (est): 5.4MM **Privately Held**
WEB: www.pmrglobal.com
SIC: 3469 Machine parts, stamped or pressed metal

(G-2594)
PROVENCE HARDWARE CORPORATION
Also Called: Shawn Austin Furnishings
1112 E Rendon Crowley Rd (76028-7529)
PHONE.....................817 572-4663
Shawn Kerr, *President*
EMP: 13
SQ FT: 3,000
SALES (est): 1.7MM **Privately Held**
WEB: www.shawnaustinfurnishings.com
SIC: 2599 Factory furniture & fixtures

(G-2595)
R J SMELLEY COMPANY INC
Also Called: Burleson Feed Mill
123 N Commerce St (76028-4250)
PHONE.....................817 295-4241
Greg Graham, *Branch Mgr*
EMP: 10
SQ FT: 1,140
SALES (corp-wide): 1.1MM **Privately Held**
WEB: www.supergrassdirt.com
SIC: 2048 5191 Livestock feeds; animal feeds
PA: R. J. Smelley Company, Inc.
4750 Cattlebaron Dr
Fort Worth TX
817 448-8520

(G-2596)
RENFRO STREET HOLDINGS LTD (PA)
645 E Renfro St (76028-4932)
P.O. Box 1061 (76097-1061)
PHONE.....................817 295-6100
Bruce Basden, *CEO*
Linda Webb, *Admin Sec*
EMP: 24
SQ FT: 60,000
SALES (est): 63.8MM **Privately Held**
SIC: 3312 6719 Blast furnaces & steel mills; investment holding companies, except banks

(G-2597)
SYNERGY INDUSTRIES LP
12963 Oak Grove Rd S (76028-6669)
PHONE.....................817 295-1161
Paul Morrison, *President*
Steve Randell, *Vice Pres*
Bart Adams, *Manager*
Bacilio Orosco, *Manager*
EMP: 65
SQ FT: 12,000
SALES (est): 18.4MM
SALES (corp-wide): 20.3MM **Privately Held**
WEB: www.synergywirelineequipment.com
SIC: 3533 5082 3713 Oil field machinery & equipment; oil field equipment; truck & bus bodies
PA: Synergy Holdings Management, Ltd.
13504 Almeda School Rd
Houston TX 77047
713 433-3756

(G-2598)
TEX TECH ENVIRONMENTAL INC
1125 S Burleson Blvd (76028-4900)
P.O. Box 2047 (76097-2047)
PHONE.....................817 295-3701
Cleve Weyenberg Jr, *President*
EMP: 9
SQ FT: 5,000
SALES (est): 1.2MM **Privately Held**
WEB: www.textechenvironmental.com
SIC: 3589 Sewage treatment equipment

(G-2599)
TRUE GRIT TRANSPORTATION INC
2724 E Renfro St (76028-1204)
P.O. Box 68 (76097-0068)
PHONE.....................682 708-5847
Joshua Christian, *President*
Paula Heaslet, *Vice Pres*
EMP: 20
SALES (est): 582.9K **Privately Held**
WEB: www.truegrittransportation.com
SIC: 4789 1389 Cargo loading & unloading services; oil field services

(G-2600)
UNITED AVIATION ACC INC
Also Called: Miller Company
2075 S Burleson Blvd (76028-6138)
PHONE.....................817 447-8000
Rick A Miller, *President*
Virgel Miller, *Vice Pres*
Denise Russ, *Prdtn Mgr*
Debra Jann, *Buyer*
Lori Evans, *Purchasing*
EMP: 48
SQ FT: 50,000

SALES (est): 9MM **Privately Held**
SIC: 2531 2273 2221 Seats, aircraft; aircraft floor coverings, except rubber or plastic; wall covering fabrics, manmade fiber & silk

(G-2601)
WAHOO INC
Also Called: Printing Plus
149 Loy St (76028-4908)
PHONE.....................817 332-2310
Sue Johnson, *President*
Johnson Robert, *Vice Pres*
EMP: 9
SALES (est): 1.2MM **Privately Held**
WEB: www.printingplustexas.com
SIC: 2759 7336 Screen printing; graphic arts & related design

Burnet
Burnet County

(G-2602)
ATMI MATERIALS LTD (DH)
706 Houston Clinton Dr (78611-4533)
PHONE.....................512 715-5343
Doug Neugold, *President*
Tim Carlson, *Exec VP*
Tod Higinbotham, *Exec VP*
Dan Sharkey, *Exec VP*
Mario Philips, *Senior VP*
◆ **EMP:** 115
SQ FT: 75,000
SALES (est): 69.3MM
SALES (corp-wide): 1.8B **Publicly Held**
WEB: www.atmi.com
SIC: 3674 Semiconductors & related devices
HQ: Entegris Professional Solutions, Inc.
7 Commerce Dr
Danbury CT 06810
203 794-1100

(G-2603)
AUSTIN AMERICAN TECH CORP
Also Called: A A T
401 Industrial Blvd (78611-4541)
P.O. Box 1489 (78611-7489)
PHONE.....................512 756-4150
Steve Stach, *Ch of Bd*
Wayne Kruemcke, *Opers Mgr*
Jack Harris, *Sales Mgr*
Phillip Mandel, *Accounts Exec*
Sheryl Cota, *Sales Staff*
▲ **EMP:** 12
SQ FT: 12,500
SALES (est): 2.7MM **Privately Held**
WEB: www.aat-corp.com
SIC: 3679 Electronic circuits

(G-2604)
CHEMICAL LIME-SOUTHWEST LLC
Also Called: Marble Falls Plant Us61
7829 S Us Highway 281 (78611-4571)
P.O. Box 927, Marble Falls (78654-0927)
PHONE.....................512 756-8668
Rick Hohman, *Plant Mgr*
EMP: 17
SALES (corp-wide): 2.6MM **Privately Held**
WEB: www.lhoist.com
SIC: 3274 Quicklime
HQ: Chemical Lime-Southwest, Llc
3700 Hulen St
Fort Worth TX 76107
817 732-8164

(G-2605)
CPI PRODUCTS LLC
Also Called: Freeman Ep
307 Industrial Blvd (78611-4526)
PHONE.....................877 756-2388
Michael Parette, *Finance*
Daniel Clarke, *Mng Member*
Terry Nielsen,
EMP: 45
SALES (est): 5.5MM **Privately Held**
WEB: www.cpiproducts.com
SIC: 3089 Injection molding of plastics

(G-2606)
EAST LAKE BUCAHANAN
101 County Road 128 (78611-3087)
PHONE.....................512 756-4566
James Tilley, *Chief*
EMP: 12
SALES (est): 1.3MM **Privately Held**
WEB: www.eastlakefellowshipchurch.com
SIC: 3711 Fire department vehicles (motor vehicles), assembly of

(G-2607)
ENTEGRIS INC
706 Houston Clinton Dr (78611-4533)
PHONE.....................512 715-5344
Bertrand Loy, *CEO*
Kenneth Metting, *Production*
Joel Robison, *Production*
Melissa Herrera, *Purch Agent*
David Davila, *Buyer*
EMP: 13
SALES (corp-wide): 1.8B **Publicly Held**
WEB: www.entegris.com
SIC: 3674 Semiconductors & related devices
PA: Entegris, Inc.
129 Concord Rd
Billerica MA 01821
978 436-6500

(G-2608)
FREEMAN DAVID PRODUCTS INC
3303 Ranch Rd 620 N (78611)
P.O. Box 887 (78611-0887)
PHONE.....................866 310-2556
David Freeman, *President*
Zach McKeown, *Vice Pres*
▼ **EMP:** 46
SALES (est): 12.3MM **Privately Held** –
SIC: 3089 5084 5088 Plastic & fiberglass tanks; septic tanks, plastic; tanks, storage; tanks & tank components

(G-2609)
HANSON AGGREGATES LLC
4901 S Us Highway 281 (78611-4542)
PHONE.....................512 756-8255
Leslie Hassell, *Manager*
EMP: 30
SALES (corp-wide): 20.8B **Privately Held**
WEB: www.heidelbergcement.com
SIC: 1422 Crushed & broken limestone
HQ: Hanson Aggregates Llc
8505 Freport Pkwy Ste 500
Irving TX 75063
469 417-1200

(G-2610)
HCR ELECTRONICS INC
2708 S Water St (78611-4507)
P.O. Box 868 (78611-0868)
PHONE.....................512 756-8164
Glen E Morris, *President*
▲ **EMP:** 20
SQ FT: 3,000
SALES (est): 3.2MM **Privately Held**
WEB: www.hcrelectronics.com
SIC: 3523 Barn, silo, poultry, dairy & livestock machinery

(G-2611)
LHOIST NORTH AMERICA TEXAS LTD
Also Called: Marble Falls Plant Us61
7829 S Us Highway 281 (78611-4571)
PHONE.....................512 756-8668
Rick Hohman, *Plant Mgr*
EMP: 23
SALES (corp-wide): 2.6MM **Privately Held**
WEB: www.lhoist.com
SIC: 3274 Quicklime
HQ: Lhoist North America Of Texas, Ltd.
5600 Clearfork Main St
Fort Worth TX 76109
817 732-8164

(G-2612)
METICULOUS MACHINING INC
102 John Kelly St (78611-4513)
P.O. Box 458 (78611-0458)
PHONE.....................512 756-7471
Lorenzo Romero, *President*
Elizabeth Romero, *Treasurer*

EMP: 40
SQ FT: 11,000
SALES (est): 1MM **Privately Held**
WEB: www.stealthproducts.com
SIC: **3599** Machine shop, jobbing & repair

(G-2613)
NAILHEAD SPUR COMPANY INC
Polk St 1840 E Hwy 29 (78611)
PHONE......................................512 588-6112
Richard V Wendt, *President*
Valerie Wendt, *Vice Pres*
EMP: 14
SQ FT: 9,000
SALES (est): 1MM **Privately Held**
WEB: www.nailheadspur.com
SIC: **3499** Aerosol valves, metal

(G-2614)
STEALTH PRODUCTS LLC
104 John Kelly St (78611-4569)
PHONE......................................512 715-9995
Lorenzo Romero, *CEO*
Marietta Williams, *Accounting Mgr*
Rafael Vila, *Software Dev*
▲ EMP: 99
SALES (est): 5MM **Privately Held**
WEB: www.stealthproducts.com
SIC: **3841** Surgical & medical instruments

(G-2615)
SURE CAST INC
200 Sure Cast (78611-4540)
P.O. Box 930 (78611-0930)
PHONE......................................512 756-6500
William Wurster, *CEO*
Dale Wurster, *President*
Chris Parr, *Purch Agent*
Terry Sterling, *Purchasing*
Walter Tubocick, *Treasurer*
EMP: 100
SQ FT: 3,200
SALES (est): 26.2MM **Privately Held**
WEB: www.surecast.com
SIC: **3324** Commercial investment castings, ferrous

(G-2616)
TEXAS SPA COVERS INC
Also Called: Absolute Spa Cover and More
1801 S Water St (78611-4505)
PHONE......................................512 756-2043
Ned Little, *President*
Kyla Bible, *Mfg Staff*
EMP: 9
SQ FT: 6,000
SALES (est): 1.4MM **Privately Held**
WEB: www.texasspacovers.com
SIC: **3714** 5013 Motor vehicle parts & accessories; automotive supplies & parts

(G-2617)
TORR NA LOCHS LLC
Also Called: Torr NA Lochs Vinyrd & Winery
7055 W State Highway 29 (78611-4100)
PHONE......................................832 606-7575
Karen Deberry, *Principal*
EMP: 12
SALES (est): 147K **Privately Held**
SIC: **2084** 5182 5921 Wines; wine; wine

(G-2618)
VALOR PLASTICS LLC
307 Industrial Blvd (78611-4526)
PHONE......................................512 663-2489
David Freeman,
EMP: 45
SALES (est): 1.4MM **Privately Held**
WEB: www.valorplastics.com
SIC: **2821** Plastics materials & resins

Burton
Washington County

(G-2619)
MIC-ALL MACHINING INC
4254 E Fm 389 Rd (77835-7090)
PHONE......................................979 830-8558
Leslie Little, *CEO*
Annette Little, *Principal*
EMP: 10

SALES (est): 750K **Privately Held**
WEB: www.micallmachining.com
SIC: **3599** Machine shop, jobbing & repair

(G-2620)
ROCK CRUSHERS INC
7000 Fm 390 Rd W (77835-5416)
PHONE......................................979 289-3768
Samuel J Wostal, *President*
June Wostal, *Corp Secy*
EMP: 10
SALES (est): 892K **Privately Held**
SIC: **1422** Crushed & broken limestone

Bushland
Potter County

(G-2621)
CUDA EXPRESS II INC
5255 Adkisson Rd (79012)
P.O. Box 189 (79012-0189)
PHONE......................................806 433-1896
Apryl Albracht, *President*
EMP: 20
SALES (est): 750K **Privately Held**
SIC: **3661** 7389 Carrier equipment, telephone or telegraph;

Cactus
Moore County

(G-2622)
JBS USA FOOD COMPANY
Also Called: Swift Beef Plant
5950 Trails End Rd (79013)
P.O. Box 524, Dumas (79029-0524)
PHONE......................................806 966-5103
Risius Todd, *Opers Mgr*
Edith Leyva, *Safety Mgr*
Hernandez Salvador, *Sales Staff*
Scot Brinkley, *Branch Mgr*
Drew Brown, *Manager*
EMP: 100 **Publicly Held**
WEB: www.jbssa.com
SIC: **2011** Meat packing plants
HQ: Jbs Usa Food Company
1770 Promontory Cir
Greeley CO 80634
970 506-8000

Caddo Mills
Hunt County

(G-2623)
EAST CREEK CORPORATION
Also Called: Stainless Drains Com
4894 Interstate 30 W (75135-7410)
P.O. Box 1278, Greenville (75403-1278)
PHONE......................................903 527-5190
Darla G Henry, *President*
Sheila A Heller, *Vice Pres*
Shelby Farmer, *Sales Staff*
Shannon Mes, *Marketing Staff*
Graham Henry, *CTO*
EMP: 25
SALES (est): 5.6MM **Privately Held**
WEB: www.stainlessdrains.com
SIC: **3499** Metal household articles

(G-2624)
HIXSON LUMBER SALES INC
1 Brewton Industrial Dr (75135)
P.O. Box 997 (75135-0997)
PHONE......................................903 527-4010
Lue Peacock, *Manager*
Susie Donny Broughton, *Systems Staff*
EMP: 35 **Privately Held**
WEB: www.hixsonlumbersales.com
SIC: **5211** 2491 Planing mill products & lumber; wood preserving
PA: Hixson Lumber Sales, Inc.
310 S Tennessee St
Pine Bluff AR 71601
870 535-1436

Caldwell
Burleson County

(G-2625)
ALLIED PRECISION FABG INC
1105 Foundation Dr (77836-1165)
PHONE......................................713 757-9810
Marcy Norman, *CEO*
Rance Norman, *President*
Kim Streams, *Marketing Mgr*
Kenneth Moore, *Admin Mgr*
Roy Norman, *Executive*
EMP: 25 EST: 1977
SQ FT: 33,000
SALES (est): 7.2MM **Privately Held**
WEB: www.apf-inc.com
SIC: **3441** 3444 Fabricated structural metal; metal housings, enclosures, casings & other containers; sheet metal specialties, not stamped

(G-2626)
ANADARKO PETROLEUM CORPORATION
206 S Wright St (77836-1845)
PHONE......................................979 567-7013
EMP: 18
SALES (corp-wide): 7.8B **Publicly Held**
SIC: **1311** Crude Petroleum/Natural Gas Production
PA: Anadarko Petroleum Corporation
1201 Lake Robbins Dr
The Woodlands TX 77380
832 636-1000

(G-2627)
BAKER PETROLITE LLC
Cty Rd 108 Hwy 21 W (77836)
PHONE......................................979 567-9859
James Loftan, *Manager*
EMP: 11 **Privately Held**
WEB:
www.bakerhughesdirect.lookchem.com
SIC: **1389** Oil & gas wells: building, repairing & dismantling
HQ: Baker Petrolite Llc
12645 W Airport Blvd
Sugar Land TX 77478
281 276-5400

(G-2628)
BASSLER ENERGY SERVICES INC (PA)
8050 State Highway 21 E (77836-6559)
P.O. Box 33, Deanville (77852-0033)
PHONE......................................979 535-4593
L Miller Bassler, *President*
Blade Bassler, *COO*
Kathie Bassler, *Vice Pres*
Mickey Hunt, *Opers Staff*
Jason Seale, *Opers Staff*
EMP: 43
SQ FT: 1,000
SALES (est): 24.5MM **Privately Held**
WEB: www.basslerenergyservices.com
SIC: **1389** Roustabout service; pumping of oil & gas wells

(G-2629)
BWM SERVICES LP
4007 State Highway 21 E (77836-5135)
P.O. Box 176 (77836-0176)
PHONE......................................979 272-7708
Pete Bednar, *Partner*
EMP: 25
SALES (est): 3.1MM **Privately Held**
WEB: www.bwmservices.cc
SIC: **7692** Welding repair

(G-2630)
CHISHOLM TRAIL OILFIELD SVC
545 State Highway 36 S (77836-7566)
P.O. Box 671 (77836-0671)
PHONE......................................979 567-4943
Terry L Garrett, *President*
EMP: 10
SALES (est): 842.5K **Privately Held**
SIC: **1389** Oil field services; impounding & storing salt water, oil & gas field

(G-2631)
DIAMOND P LEASE & WELL SVC INC
400 S Banks St (77836-1628)
PHONE......................................979 567-1919
Pete Vega, *President*
EMP: 25
SALES (corp-wide): 11.8MM **Privately Held**
SIC: **1389** Oil field services
PA: Diamond P. Lease & Well Service, Inc.
7981 Fm 141
Dime Box TX 77853
979 884-6111

(G-2632)
EVERS AND SONS INC
12905 State Highway 36 S (77836-6543)
P.O. Box 385, Somerville (77879-0385)
PHONE......................................979 596-2139
Teressa J Evers, *President*
Richard Breland, *Vice Pres*
Christopher Evers, *Vice Pres*
Casey Best, *Director*
Julie Strickland, *Admin Sec*
EMP: 100
SQ FT: 1,416
SALES (est): 50.9MM **Privately Held**
WEB: www.eversandsons.com
SIC: **1389** Construction, repair & dismantling services

(G-2633)
NOVOSAD ENTERPRISES INC
Also Called: Hot Point Energy
2080 State Highway 21 W (77836-5201)
PHONE......................................979 272-9203
Pat Novosad, *President*
Thomas Novosad II, *President*
Karen Taylor, *Principal*
Tommy Novosad Jr, *Vice Pres*
EMP: 17
SALES (est): 4MM **Privately Held**
WEB: www.neiconstruction.com
SIC: **1389** Oil field services

(G-2634)
SAGE ENERGY COMPANY
1516 Fm 166 (77836)
PHONE......................................979 567-7629
Glen McDaniel, *Manager*
EMP: 16
SALES (corp-wide): 6.7MM **Privately Held**
WEB: www.sage-energy.com
SIC: **1311** 1381 Crude petroleum production; drilling oil & gas wells
PA: Sage Energy Company
100 Ne Loop 410 Ste 1300
San Antonio TX 78216
210 404-2828

(G-2635)
SHERIDAN PRODUCTION CO LLC
1516 Fm 166 (77836-4616)
PHONE......................................979 567-7629
Mike Dorcy, *Branch Mgr*
EMP: 12 **Privately Held**
WEB: www.sheridanproduction.com
SIC: **1382** Oil & gas exploration services
PA: Sheridan Production Company Llc
1360 Post Oak Blvd # 2500
Houston TX 77056

(G-2636)
SNOE INC MACHINING & WELDING
215 County Road 300 (77836)
PHONE......................................979 567-0808
Gary Snoe, *CEO*
Karen Adams, *Human Resources*
EMP: 48
SALES: 7.8MM **Privately Held**
WEB: www.snoeinc.com
SIC: **3599** 7692 Machine shop, jobbing & repair; welding repair

(G-2637)
SUMMIT PUMP & SAFETY INC
1203 Commerce St (77836-1076)
PHONE......................................979 567-7867
Bo Zboril, *Sales Mgr*
Dana K Spacek, *Director*
EMP: 20 EST: 2010

SALES (est): 3.2MM **Privately Held**
WEB: www.summitpump.net
SIC: **1389** Oil field services

Camden
Polk County

(G-2638)
GEORGIA-PACIFIC WD PDTS S LLC
Also Called: Georgia Pacific
20000125 E Fm 942 Sm 62 (75934)
PHONE..............................936 398-2511
Robert Jewell, *Manager*
EMP: 700
SALES (corp-wide): 36.8B **Privately Held**
WEB: www.buildgp.com
SIC: **2656** 2436 2421 2435 Paper cups, plates, dishes & utensils; panels, softwood plywood; sawmills & planing mills, general; panels, hardwood plywood
HQ: Georgia-Pacific Wood Products South Llc
    133 Peachtree St Ne
    Atlanta GA 30303

Cameron
Milam County

(G-2639)
BROWN PRECISION INC
1484 County Road 241a (76520-1035)
PHONE..............................530 384-2506
EMP: 9 **EST:** 1968
SALES (est): 750K **Privately Held**
WEB: www.brownprecision.com
SIC: **3089** 3484 Stock shapes, plastic; rifles or rifle parts, 30 mm. & below

(G-2640)
BUTLER WELDMENTS CORPORATION
Also Called: B W
1200 Industrial Blvd (76520-1178)
P.O. Box 1000 (76520-0300)
PHONE..............................254 697-6416
Bryan Harris, *Project Mgr*
Dominic Riola, *Facilities Mgr*
Cody Allison, *Production*
John Kropp, *Engineer*
James Armstrong, *Director*
EMP: 54 **EST:** 1977
SQ FT: 55,000
SALES (est): 17.5MM **Privately Held**
WEB: www.butler-weldments.com
SIC: **3441** 3599 3444 3443 Fabricated structural metal; machine shop, jobbing & repair; sheet metalwork; metal parts

(G-2641)
CHARLOTTE PIPE AND FOUNDRY CO
Also Called: Charlotte Plastic S/W
2700 N Blake Ave (76520-1145)
P.O. Box 671 (76520-0671)
PHONE..............................254 697-6556
Jerald Brunson, *Manager*
EMP: 44
SALES (corp-wide): 510.5MM **Privately Held**
WEB: www.charlottepipe.com
SIC: **3089** 3084 Molding primary plastic; plastics pipe
PA: Charlotte Pipe And Foundry Company
    2109 Randolph Rd
    Charlotte NC 28207
    704 372-5030

(G-2642)
IDEAL PLTY BREEDING FARMS INC
215 W Main St (76520-3941)
P.O. Box 591 (76520-0591)
PHONE..............................254 697-6677
EMP: 35
SQ FT: 12,000
SALES (est): 6.2MM **Privately Held**
WEB: www.idealpoultry.com
SIC: **2015** Poultry slaughtering & processing

(G-2643)
MILAM BROADCASTING CO INC
Also Called: K M I L
901 E 1st St (76520-3404)
P.O. Box 832 (76520-0832)
PHONE..............................254 697-6633
Joe Smitherman, *President*
EMP: 10 **EST:** 1955
SQ FT: 2,500
SALES (est): 553.9K **Privately Held**
WEB: www.kmil.com
SIC: **4832** 2711 Radio broadcasting stations, music format; newspapers

(G-2644)
TEXWOOD LTD
Also Called: School Specialty
1110 Industrial Blvd (76520-1177)
PHONE..............................888 388-3224
Jeff Whittle, *General Ptnr*
Patrick Fisk, *Sales Staff*
Christopher Corder, *Manager*
Reeder Dossett, *Director*
▲ **EMP:** 65
SQ FT: 30,000
SALES (est): 5MM **Privately Held**
WEB: www.schoolspecialty.com
SIC: **2531** Library furniture

Campbell
Hunt County

(G-2645)
D F W ELITE NEWS
5258 County Road 3110 (75422-3266)
PHONE..............................214 372-6500
Darryl Blair, *President*
Deborah Blair-Abron, *Publisher*
BJ Fullylove, *Director*
EMP: 9
SQ FT: 1,800
SALES (est): 659.3K **Privately Held**
SIC: **2711** Newspapers, publishing & printing

(G-2646)
QMF STEEL INC
Also Called: QMF Supply Fab Manufacturing
3846 E Interstate 30 (75422-1393)
P.O. Box 460 (75422-0460)
PHONE..............................903 455-3618
Sherrill Lester, *President*
Steve Lester, *Treasurer*
Ronald S Lester, *Admin Sec*
EMP: 20
SQ FT: 37,500
SALES (est): 5.5MM **Privately Held**
WEB: www.qmfsteel.com
SIC: **3599** 3443 3353 3317 Machine & other job shop work; fabricated plate work (boiler shop); aluminum sheet, plate & foil; steel pipe & tubes; steel wire & related products

Canadian
Hemphill County

(G-2647)
CANADIAN REDI-MIX INC
11130 Us Highway 60 (79014-5110)
P.O. Box 157 (79014-0157)
PHONE..............................806 323-5379
Jerry Smith, *President*
EMP: 17
SALES (est): 2.4MM **Privately Held**
WEB: www.canadiantxredimix.com
SIC: **3273** Ready-mixed concrete

(G-2648)
EAGLE ROCK FIELD SERVICES LP
Also Called: Eagle Rock Energy
9898 County Rd 3 (79014)
PHONE..............................806 323-5381
Chad Knips, *Branch Mgr*
EMP: 11
SALES (corp-wide): 460.2MM **Publicly Held**
SIC: **1311** Crude petroleum & natural gas

HQ: Eagle Rock Field Services, L.P.
    1415 La St Ste 2700
    Houston TX 77002

(G-2649)
FESCO LTD
10919 Us Highway 60 (79014-5009)
PHONE..............................361 661-7000
EMP: 17
SALES (corp-wide): 201MM **Privately Held**
WEB: www.fescoinc.com
SIC: **1389** Oil field services
PA: Fesco, Ltd.
    1000 Fesco Dr
    Alice TX 78332
    361 664-3479

(G-2650)
FOUR K SERVICES INC
1821 Willard St (79014-3602)
PHONE..............................806 323-8560
Wallace Hill, *President*
Rhcalen Hill, *Corp Secy*
EMP: 15
SALES (est): 820K **Privately Held**
SIC: **1389** Oil field services

(G-2651)
GRANITE OPERATING COMPANY
8450 E Crescent Pkwy St (79014)
PHONE..............................806 323-9118
George Sullage, *President*
Bailey Peyton, *Principal*
Tad Herz, *CFO*
EMP: 30
SQ FT: 3,000
SALES (est): 1.7MM
SALES (corp-wide): 6.4B **Publicly Held**
SIC: **1311** Crude petroleum production; natural gas production
HQ: Cordillera Energy Partners Iii, Llc
    8450 E Crescent Pkwy # 400
    Greenwood Village CO 80111

(G-2652)
KING WELL SERVICE INC
10925 Us Highway 60 (79014-5009)
PHONE..............................806 323-6664
Willard L King, *CEO*
Terrel Hardin, *President*
Kenneth King, *Treasurer*
Ada Rex, *Office Mgr*
EMP: 57
SQ FT: 2,500
SALES (est): 8MM **Privately Held**
WEB: www.kingwell.com
SIC: **1389** Servicing oil & gas wells; oil field services

(G-2653)
PCS OILFIELD SERVICES LLC
10918 Shanna St (79014-5731)
P.O. Box 1300 (79014-1300)
PHONE..............................806 323-8007
Shad Fowler, *Manager*
Bill Purcell, *Info Tech Dir*
William M Purcell,
Derek S Cooper,
Edward E Purell,
EMP: 42
SALES (est): 7.3MM **Privately Held**
SIC: **1389** Oil field services

(G-2654)
SUPERIOR PIPELINE COMPANY
15041 Fm 3044 (79014-5601)
PHONE..............................806 323-8145
Patty Tyler, *Administration*
EMP: 68
SALES (est): 3.1MM **Privately Held**
WEB: www.superiorpipeline.com
SIC: **1382** Energy conservation consultant

(G-2655)
TRI RESOURCES INC
Also Called: Dynegy
3 Mi S On Hwy 60 (79014)
P.O. Box 278 (79014-0278)
PHONE..............................806 323-9125
Rodney Krogh, *Principal*
EMP: 9 **Publicly Held**
WEB: www.triresources.com
SIC: **1321** Natural gas liquids

HQ: Tri Resources Inc.
    811 Louisiana St Ste 2100
    Houston TX 77002
    713 584-1000

(G-2656)
TURNER ENERGY SERVICES LLC
111 Airport Rd (79014-5030)
PHONE..............................806 323-8844
John Turner, *Branch Mgr*
EMP: 11 **Publicly Held**
WEB: www.turnertransportation.com
SIC: **1389** Haulage, oil field
HQ: Turner Energy Services Llc

    Enid OK 73702
    806 323-8844

Canton
Van Zandt County

(G-2657)
INGRAM INDUSTRIES INC
Also Called: Coloc Manufacturing
465 Vz County Road 2516 (75103-3893)
P.O. Box 249 (75103-0249)
PHONE..............................903 848-8411
Richard S Ingram, *President*
Sherie Woods, *Vice Pres*
EMP: 20
SQ FT: 15,000
SALES (est): 4.1MM **Privately Held**
WEB: www.colocmfg.com
SIC: **3452** Nuts, metal

(G-2658)
MILLWOOD CABINETS LLP
1200 1st Monday Ln (75103-1058)
PHONE..............................903 567-3333
Jearl Cunningham, *Partner*
EMP: 20
SALES (est): 1.6MM **Privately Held**
WEB: www.millwoodcabinets.com
SIC: **1751** 2434 Cabinet building & installation; wood kitchen cabinets

(G-2659)
RISING S COMPANY LLC
17729 Interstate 20 (75103-3585)
PHONE..............................903 469-4452
Gary Lynch, *Branch Mgr*
EMP: 10
SALES (corp-wide): 4MM **Privately Held**
WEB: www.risingsbunkers.com
SIC: **3441** Fabricated structural metal
PA: Rising S Company Llc
    9350 State Highway 31 E
    Murchison TX 75778
    214 455-0560

(G-2660)
SBI INDUSTRIAL LLC
21739 State Highway 64 (75103-6146)
PHONE..............................972 284-1250
John Krawietz, *Vice Pres*
Michael D Cope, *Mng Member*
Rex Ramsey,
▲ **EMP:** 32
SQ FT: 52,000
SALES (est): 12MM **Privately Held**
WEB: www.sbiindustrial.com
SIC: **3441** Floor posts, adjustable: metal

(G-2661)
VALERO ENERGY CORPORATION
Also Called: Lloyd's
310 E Hwy 243 (75103)
PHONE..............................903 567-6001
Barbie Kuykandall, *Manager*
EMP: 25
SALES (corp-wide): 108.3B **Publicly Held**
WEB: www.valero.com
SIC: **2911** Petroleum refining
PA: Valero Energy Corporation
    1 Valero Way
    San Antonio TX 78249
    210 345-2000

Canutillo
El Paso County

(G-2662)
AL KNOCH INTERIORS INC
9010 N Desert Blvd (79835-8511)
P.O. Box 484 (79835-0484)
PHONE...................915 886-5800
Al Knoch, *President*
▲ EMP: 62
SQ FT: 30,000
SALES (est): 8.5MM **Privately Held**
WEB: www.alknochinteriors.com
SIC: 2273 3714 3544 Floor coverings;
    textile fiber; motor vehicle parts & acces-
    sories; special dies, tools, jigs & fixtures

(G-2663)
**CUSTOM CRATES & PALLETS
LTD**
1501 Westway Blvd (79835-8910)
P.O. Box 1038 (79835-1038)
PHONE...................915 886-4985
Adolfo Torres, *Partner*
Misael Garcia, *Partner*
Oscar Garcia, *Partner*
EMP: 53
SALES (est): 9.4MM **Privately Held**
WEB: www.ccptx.com
SIC: 2448 Pallets, wood; pallets, wood &
    wood with metal

(G-2664)
GUESS INC
Also Called: Guess Factory
7051 S Desert Blvd A177 (79835-8560)
PHONE...................915 877-1948
Christi Martinez, *Branch Mgr*
EMP: 25
SALES (corp-wide): 2.6B **Publicly Held**
WEB: www.guess.com
SIC: 2325 2389 Men's & boys' jeans &
    dungarees; men's miscellaneous acces-
    sories
PA: Guess , Inc.
    1444 S Alameda St
    Los Angeles CA 90021
    213 765-3100

(G-2665)
TEXAS BARRICADE SERVICE
6621 Doniphan Dr (79835-5002)
PHONE...................915 355-6653
Angelita Enriquez, *President*
EMP: 12
SALES (est): 667.9K **Privately Held**
WEB: www.tbarricade.com
SIC: 3669 Communications equipment

(G-2666)
TORTILLERIA CUAUHTEMOC
809 Westway Blvd (79835-8504)
PHONE...................915 886-4480
Geronimo Hernandez, *Principal*
EMP: 14
SALES (est): 1.9MM **Privately Held**
WEB: www.tortilleriacu.com
SIC: 2099 Tortillas, fresh or refrigerated

(G-2667)
VALLEY BY PRODUCTS INC
7740 Kiely Rd (79835)
P.O. Box 628 (79835-0628)
PHONE...................915 877-3131
Natalie Jerome, *President*
Virgie Jerome, *Vice Pres*
EMP: 28 EST: 1995
SALES (est): 4.6MM **Privately Held**
SIC: 2077 Grease rendering, inedible

(G-2668)
WESTSIDE WELDING INC
141 El Chanate Dr (79835-6034)
PHONE...................915 877-5345
Teresita Arzate, *President*
Miguel Arzate, *Vice Pres*
EMP: 20
SALES (est): 3MM **Privately Held**
WEB: www.westsidewelding.net
SIC: 1791 3444 Structural steel erection;
    siding, sheet metal

Canyon
Randall County

(G-2669)
BIOCOPE INC
23711 Hix Dr (79015-4938)
PHONE...................806 655-2933
Pat McDaniel, *President*
Gary McDaniel, *Vice Pres*
EMP: 10
SALES (est): 1.5MM **Privately Held**
WEB: www.biocope.com
SIC: 5169 3589 Chemicals & allied prod-
    ucts; sewage treatment equipment

(G-2670)
DOBBS CORPORATION
100 Highway 60 (79015-1918)
P.O. Box 928 (79015-0928)
PHONE...................806 655-7791
Debbie Green, *President*
Tiffany Green, *Sales Staff*
EMP: 9
SQ FT: 20,647
SALES (est): 2MM **Privately Held**
WEB: www.dobbspumps.com
SIC: 3561 5084 Pumps, domestic: water
    or sump; pumps & pumping equipment

(G-2671)
KEELING HOMES INC
Also Called: Cabinet Shoppe, The
3101 N I 27 (79015)
P.O. Box 487 (79015-0487)
PHONE...................806 655-2071
Keith Keeling, *President*
Jan Keeling, *Admin Sec*
EMP: 15
SALES (est): 1MM **Privately Held**
WEB: www.cabinet-shoppe.com
SIC: 2434 Wood kitchen cabinets

(G-2672)
**KEITH WEIGHING SYSTEMS
LLC**
Also Called: Express Scale Svc
10511 W Us Highway 60 (79015-5712)
P.O. Box 748 (79015-0748)
PHONE...................806 655-3033
Steven A Keith, *Principal*
EMP: 15
SALES (est): 2.3MM **Privately Held**
WEB: www.expressscale.com
SIC: 3596 Scales & balances, except labo-
    ratory; industrial scales; weighing ma-
    chines & apparatus

(G-2673)
**LONE STAR DAIRY PRODUCTS
LLC**
401 Highway 60 (79015-1927)
P.O. Box 1676 (79015-1676)
PHONE...................806 567-5623
Cody Gruwell, *Principal*
Travis Bland, *Controller*
EMP: 60
SALES (est): 100MM **Privately Held**
WEB: www.canyonnews.com
SIC: 2023 Baby formulas; cream substi-
    tutes; condensed milk; powdered cream

(G-2674)
MORGAN TRIM INC
18700 S Us Highway 87 (79015-5923)
PHONE...................806 655-9777
Kerry S Morgan, *President*
Patricia Morgan, *Treasurer*
EMP: 12
SQ FT: 6,000
SALES (est): 1.3MM **Privately Held**
SIC: 1751 2431 5211 Finish & trim car-
    pentry; millwork; millwork & lumber

(G-2675)
NUTRITION PLUS LLP
2308 10th Ave (79015-5200)
P.O. Box 29 (79015-0029)
PHONE...................806 655-0505
Paul Williams, *Partner*
Albert Bailey, *Partner*
Steve Carlisle, *Partner*
Stephanie Rodriguez, *Partner*
Preston Tuckett, *Partner*

EMP: 9
SALES (est): 2.5MM **Privately Held**
WEB: www.nutritionplus.biz
SIC: 2048 Feed supplements

(G-2676)
VANZANDT CONTROLS (DH)
700 Highway 60 (79015-2201)
P.O. Box 1056 (79015-1056)
PHONE...................806 655-9367
David A Criswell, *President*
Alexia Criswell, *Vice Pres*
Jennifer Nix, *Controller*
EMP: 9
SQ FT: 3,000
SALES (est): 3.7MM
SALES (corp-wide): 9.7MM **Privately
Held**
WEB: www.vanzandtcontrols.com
SIC: 5085 5084 3625 Valves & fittings;
    controlling instruments & accessories; ac-
    tuators, industrial
HQ: Vanzandt Controls, Llc
    13409 W County Road 132
    Odessa TX 79765
    432 242-8000

Canyon Lake
Comal County

(G-2677)
**AL TEX CONCRETE PRODUCTS
INC**
1398 Fm 2673 Ste B (78133-4591)
PHONE...................830 964-5150
Walker Chapman, *President*
EMP: 10
SALES (est): 1MM **Privately Held**
WEB: www.yellowstonechurch.org
SIC: 3272 Concrete products

(G-2678)
**CERTIFIED TECHNICAL
PROFESSION**
14613 Fm 306 (78133-4164)
PHONE...................757 831-9235
Robert Schultz, *President*
EMP: 9
SALES (est): 323.8K **Privately Held**
SIC: 3843 Dental equipment & supplies

(G-2679)
EBLING WELDING LLC
621 Ridgehaven St (78133-6247)
PHONE...................830 905-7235
Richard Ebling, *Principal*
EMP: 9 EST: 2018
SALES (est): 112.3K **Privately Held**
SIC: 7692 Welding repair

(G-2680)
T L W ARCHERY INC
Also Called: Viking Archery
41000 Fm 3159 (78133-5082)
PHONE...................830 227-5171
Tim Whiteford, *President*
Lannie Whiteford, *Corp Secy*
EMP: 9
SQ FT: 14,000
SALES (est): 761.8K **Privately Held**
SIC: 5941 3949 7999 Archery supplies;
    archery equipment, general; archery
    lanes

(G-2681)
**TARGET WELL SERVICES INC
(PA)**
212 Flat Crk (78133-4982)
PHONE...................361 883-8100
Mance Richardson, *President*
Rose Richardson, *Corp Secy*
Heather Thomas, *Vice Pres*
EMP: 14
SALES (est): 1.9MM **Privately Held**
WEB: www.targetwell.com
SIC: 1389 Oil field services

Carbon
Eastland County

(G-2682)
CHUTEHELP INC
500 S Main St (76435-3206)
PHONE...................855 248-8343
Tom Gipson, *President*
Austin Laramore, *Principal*
EMP: 11
SALES (est): 1.2MM **Privately Held**
WEB: www.chutehelp.com
SIC: 3443 Fabricated plate work (boiler
    shop)

Carrizo Springs
Dimmit County

(G-2683)
686 INC
Also Called: Hamilton Ranch
1908 N 1st St (78834-2026)
P.O. Box 516 (78834-6516)
PHONE...................830 876-5541
James R Hamilton, *President*
EMP: 15
SALES (est): 1.5MM **Privately Held**
SIC: 1382 0212 Oil & gas exploration
    services; beef cattle except feedlots

(G-2684)
**ANADARKO PETROLEUM
CORPORATION**
4674 Us Hwy 277 N Gate (78834)
P.O. Box 4995, Spring (77387-4995)
PHONE...................830 491-3300
Benjamin M Fink, *Exec VP*
EMP: 20
SALES (corp-wide): 21.2B **Publicly Held**
WEB: www.oxy.com
SIC: 1382 Oil & gas exploration services
HQ: Anadarko Petroleum Corporation
    1201 Lake Robbins Dr
    The Woodlands TX 77380
    832 636-1000

(G-2685)
DHW WELL SERVICE INC (PA)
255 Loop 517 (78834)
PHONE...................830 876-9615
Don H Wilson, *President*
Martin Keith, *COO*
Keith Martin, *COO*
Herminio Aguirre, *Vice Pres*
Suzanne Brown, *Admin Sec*
EMP: 250
SALES (est): 40MM **Privately Held**
WEB: www.dhwtx.com
SIC: 1381 Reworking oil & gas wells

(G-2686)
MID-COUNTY READY MIX
Also Called: Ubalde Concrete
5940 N Us Hwy 83 (78834)
PHONE...................830 876-3800
Nicolas Ayala, *Owner*
EMP: 25
SALES (est): 1.5MM **Privately Held**
SIC: 3273 Ready-mixed concrete

(G-2687)
PRIME OPERATING COMPANY
Also Called: Eastern Oil Well Service
1595 Hwy 83 S (78834)
P.O. Box 797, Stamford CT (06904-0797)
PHONE...................830 876-2441
Beverly Cummings, *Vice Pres*
Ricardo Rodriguez, *Plant Mgr*
Mark Gonzales, *Safety Mgr*
EMP: 50
SALES (corp-wide): 104.8MM **Publicly
Held**
SIC: 1382 Oil & gas exploration services
HQ: Prime Operating Company
    9821 Katy Fwy Ste 1050
    Houston TX 77024

(G-2688)
PRIMEENERGY CORPORATION
1684 S Us Highway 83 (78834-4897)
PHONE...................830 876-2441

Gerardo Nanding, *Branch Mgr*
EMP: 11
SALES (corp-wide): 104.8MM **Publicly Held**
WEB: www.primeenergy.com
SIC: 1389 Construction, repair & dismantling services
PA: Primeenergy Corporation
9821 Katy Fwy Ste 1050
Houston TX 77024
713 735-0000

(G-2689)
ZEDI US INC
Also Called: Southern Flow
3415 N Hwy 277 (78834-5045)
PHONE..........................830 876-2777
Scott Schap, *Branch Mgr*
EMP: 15
SALES (corp-wide): 16.7B **Publicly Held**
WEB: www.zedisolutions.com
SIC: 1389 Oil field services
HQ: Zedi Us Inc.
101 Ibex Ln
Broussard LA 70518
337 233-2066

Carrollton
Dallas County

(G-2690)
4FRONT ENGNEERED SOLUTIONS INC (DH)
1612 Hutton Dr Ste 140 (75006-6642)
PHONE..........................972 466-0707
Keith F Moore, *President*
Al Thomson, *Vice Pres*
Kendall Norby, *Prdtn Mgr*
Michael Hughes, *Materials Mgr*
Mike Phipps, *Purch Agent*
◆ **EMP:** 120
SQ FT: 189,000
SALES (est): 151.4MM
SALES (corp-wide): 9.7B **Privately Held**
WEB: www.entrematic.com
SIC: 3537 Loading docks: portable, adjustable & hydraulic
HQ: Assa Abloy Entrance Systems Us Inc.
1900 Airport Rd
Monroe NC 28110
704 290-5520

(G-2691)
ADVERTISERS DYNMC SVCS CO INC
Also Called: C & L Printing
1100 Valwood Pkwy Ste 118 (75006-8388)
PHONE..........................972 392-9722
Kenneth Gerew, *President*
Mary Cobb Conley, *Director*
EMP: 13
SALES (est): 1.9MM **Privately Held**
WEB: www.lawpublications.net
SIC: 2721 Magazines: publishing & printing

(G-2692)
AEGLE NUTRITION LLC
Also Called: FSI Nutritional Products
1300 Hutton Dr Ste 110 (75006-6659)
PHONE..........................972 446-9600
John Ramsey, *Mng Member*
Parrish Whitaker, *Mng Member*
EMP: 26
SQ FT: 40,000
SALES (est): 7.3MM **Privately Held**
WEB: www.aeglenutrition.com
SIC: 2834 5122 Vitamin, nutrient & hematinic preparations for human use; vitamins & minerals

(G-2693)
AEI COMMUNICATIONS CORP
3310 Keller Springs Rd # 160 (75006-5057)
PHONE..........................650 552-9416
Mario Jauryegui, *CEO*
Peter Chen, *Engineer*
Abel Soria, *Manager*
Mario Jauregui, *CTO*
▲ **EMP:** 20
SALES (est): 2.3MM **Privately Held**
WEB: www.aeicommunications.com
SIC: 3661 Telephones & telephone apparatus

(G-2694)
AER MANUFACTURING INC
3420 Wiley Post Rd (75006-5132)
PHONE..........................972 418-6499
Bob McGraw, *VP Opers*
Fred Barajas, *Purchasing*
Clint Buchanan, *Supervisor*
Lupe Martinez, *Supervisor*
EMP: 296
SALES (corp-wide): 139MM **Privately Held**
WEB: www.aermanufacturing.com
SIC: 3714 Motor vehicle parts & accessories
PA: Aer Manufacturing, Inc.
1605 Surveyor Blvd
Carrollton TX 75006
972 418-6499

(G-2695)
AERO COMPOSITES STRUCTURES INC
1533 Crescent Dr Ste 102 (75006-3642)
PHONE..........................972 694-5330
Glen Daugherty, *President*
Russell Oonk, *Vice Pres*
Ed Schauer, *Admin Sec*
EMP: 14
SALES (est): 2.6MM **Privately Held**
WEB: www.acs-repair.com
SIC: 3728 Aircraft parts & equipment

(G-2696)
AMERICA ILSIN TECH LLC
Also Called: Swift
3330 Earhart Dr Ste 208 (75006-4919)
PHONE..........................972 556-0916
Chan Seol Park, *President*
Brad Everette, *Principal*
You Daniel, *COO*
Richard Case, *Engineer*
Scott Brown, *Sales Staff*
▲ **EMP:** 18
SQ FT: 1,000
SALES (est): 346.1K **Privately Held**
WEB: www.americailsintech.com
SIC: 3827 5084 Optical instruments & lenses; industrial machinery & equipment

(G-2697)
AMERICA PLASTICS LLC
Texas Division
1420 Vinylex Dr (75006-3872)
PHONE..........................972 245-4525
Robert Pena, *Opers Mgr*
Thomas Edgman, *Branch Mgr*
EMP: 163
SQ FT: 76,707
SALES (corp-wide): 59.9MM **Privately Held**
WEB: www.omegaplastics.com
SIC: 2824 3089 Polyvinylidene chloride fibers; extruded finished plastic products
PA: America Plastics, Llc
2636 Byington Solway Rd
Knoxville TN 37931
865 690-2211

(G-2698)
AMI INVESTMENTS LLC
Also Called: Nighthawk
2304 Tarpley Rd Ste 110 (75006-2469)
PHONE..........................972 717-5555
Charles Kitowski, *CEO*
Key Foster, *Senior VP*
G Ruffner Page, *Senior VP*
Glenda D Burson, *Vice Pres*
Charles E Nowlin, *Vice Pres*
EMP: 20 **EST:** 2010
SALES (est): 1MM
SALES (corp-wide): 970.3MM **Privately Held**
WEB: www.nighthawkcontrol.com
SIC: 3829 Measuring & controlling devices
HQ: Mcwane Technology, Llc
2900 Highway 280 S # 300
Birmingham AL 35223
205 414-3100

(G-2699)
AVERY DENNISON CORPORATION
2025 Mckenzie Dr Ste 100 (75006-6860)
PHONE..........................972 919-6900
Mike Bukowski, *Accountant*

Jose Campos, *Branch Mgr*
EMP: 30
SALES (corp-wide): 7B **Publicly Held**
WEB: www.averydennison.com
SIC: 2672 Coated paper, except photographic, carbon or abrasive
PA: Avery Dennison Corporation
207 N Goode Ave
Glendale CA 91203
626 304-2000

(G-2700)
B BRAUN MEDICAL INC
1601 Wallace Dr Ste 150 (75006-6690)
PHONE..........................972 245-2243
Gale White, *Principal*
Alyssa Taylor, *Purchasing*
Kitti Hughes, *Credit Staff*
Joern Lubadel, *Sales Staff*
Bruce Nunn, *Manager*
EMP: 1300
SALES (corp-wide): 2.6MM **Privately Held**
WEB: www.bbraunusa.com
SIC: 3841 Catheters
HQ: B. Braun Medical Inc.
824 12th Ave
Bethlehem PA 18018
610 691-5400

(G-2701)
BAKER HGHES OLFLD OPRTIONS LLC
Also Called: Baker Atlas
1875 Monetary Ln (75006-7012)
PHONE..........................972 466-2673
EMP: 95
SALES (corp-wide): 22.8B **Publicly Held**
SIC: 1389 1382 Oil/Gas Field Services Oil/Gas Exploration Services
HQ: Baker Hughes Oilfield Operations Llc
17021 Aldine Westfield Rd
Houston TX 77073
713 879-1000

(G-2702)
BASF CORPORATION
1216 Trend Dr (75006-5408)
PHONE..........................973 245-6000
Steven A Zoeller, *Principal*
James Woodruff, *Sales Staff*
EMP: 11
SQ FT: 20,000
SALES (corp-wide): 65.6B **Privately Held**
WEB: www.basf.com
SIC: 2869 Industrial organic chemicals
HQ: Basf Corporation
100 Park Ave
Florham Park NJ 07932
973 245-6000

(G-2703)
BC CONNECT LLC
2340 E Trinity Mills Rd # 300 (75006-1942)
PHONE..........................800 347-0855
Michele Burke, *President*
EMP: 110
SALES (est): 5.8MM **Privately Held**
SIC: 7372 Operating systems computer software

(G-2704)
BE-TECHNOLOGIES LTD
1540 Selene Dr Ste 100 (75006-6490)
PHONE..........................972 242-1853
Jeffery Henderson, *General Mgr*
Michael Berdan,
EMP: 15
SQ FT: 36,000
SALES (est): 2.9MM **Privately Held**
WEB: www.be-technologies.org
SIC: 3365 7299 3728 3721 Aerospace castings, aluminum; consumer purchasing services; aircraft parts & equipment; aircraft; composite board products, woodboard; assembly machines, including robotic

(G-2705)
BLACK & DECKER CORPORATION
1300 N Interstate 35 # 112 (75006-3800)
PHONE..........................972 446-2996
Kenny Kimbrell, *QC Mgr*
Matt Willard, *Manager*
EMP: 11

SALES (corp-wide): 14.4B **Publicly Held**
WEB: www.blackanddecker.com
SIC: 3546 Power-driven handtools
HQ: The Black & Decker Corporation
701 E Joppa Rd
Towson MD 21286
410 716-3900

(G-2706)
BUSINESS PRINTING INC (PA)
Also Called: Business Printing Service
3209 Commander Dr (75006-2506)
P.O. Box 113236 (75011-3236)
PHONE..........................214 445-5000
EMP: 16
SALES (est): 2.3MM **Privately Held**
WEB: www.businessprinting.com
SIC: 2759 2796 2791 2789 Commercial printing; platemaking services; typesetting; bookbinding & related work; commercial printing, lithographic

(G-2707)
BUZZBALLZ LLC
Also Called: Southern Champion
2114 Mcdaniel Dr (75006-6839)
PHONE..........................972 242-3777
Merrilee A Kick, *President*
Tracy Frisbie, *Vice Pres*
Alex Kick, *Vice Pres*
Alexander C Kick, *Vice Pres*
Andrew Kick, *Vice Pres*
▲ **EMP:** 65 **EST:** 2009
SALES (est): 22.8MM **Privately Held**
WEB: www.buzzballz.com
SIC: 2085 Vodka (alcoholic beverage)

(G-2708)
BWI COMPANIES INC
Also Called: Bwi of Dallas/Fort Worth
1418 Upfield Dr (75006-6915)
PHONE..........................972 242-4755
Patrick Wilder, *Advt Staff*
Joel Green, *Manager*
EMP: 60
SQ FT: 83,010
SALES (corp-wide): 270.1MM **Privately Held**
WEB: www.bwicompanies.com
SIC: 5191 5083 3423 Insecticides; garden supplies; seeds & bulbs; landscaping equipment; hand & edge tools
PA: Bwi Companies, Inc.
1355 N Kings Hwy
Nash TX 75569
903 838-8561

(G-2709)
C H INDUSTRIES INC (HQ)
1700 Columbian Club Dr (75006-5517)
PHONE..........................972 416-1304
Charles E Hasty, *President*
John A Carbona, *Senior VP*
Laurie Hasty, *Vice Pres*
▲ **EMP:** 75 **EST:** 1958
SQ FT: 52,000
SALES (est): 79.9MM
SALES (corp-wide): 71.6MM **Privately Held**
WEB: www.delawaredynamicsmi.com
SIC: 2599 3444 3469 Hospital beds; sheet metalwork; metal stampings
PA: Ii Millennium Holdings Co.
1700 Columbian Club Dr
Carrollton TX 75006
972 343-7000

(G-2710)
C H INDUSTRIES INC
Also Called: Humanetics Ii
1700 Columbian Club Dr (75006-5517)
PHONE..........................972 416-1304
Ed Charba Jr, *Manager*
EMP: 260
SALES (corp-wide): 71.6MM **Privately Held**
WEB: www.delawaredynamicsmi.com
SIC: 3444 5047 Sheet metalwork; hospital equipment & furniture
HQ: C H Industries, Inc
1700 Columbian Club Dr
Carrollton TX 75006
972 416-1304

(G-2711)
CEDAR SUPPLY INC (PA)
1200 Denton Dr (75006-3823)
P.O. Box 110229 (75011-0229)
PHONE..........................972 242-6561
C Mayo Carrington Jr, *President*
Lance M Carrington, *Vice Pres*
Amy Carrington, *Treasurer*
EMP: 20
SQ FT: 8,000
SALES (est): 13MM **Privately Held**
WEB: www.cedarsupply.net
SIC: 5031 2421 Lumber: rough, dressed &
finished; sawmills & planing mills, general

(G-2712)
CENTERPOINT PRODUCTIONS INC
1232 Crowley Dr (75006-1373)
PHONE..........................214 905-0000
David Horowitz, *President*
Julie Horowitz, *Admin Sec*
EMP: 50 **EST:** 1996
SQ FT: 26,500
SALES (est): 8.7MM **Privately Held**
SIC: 2431 Moldings, wood: unfinished &
prefinished

(G-2713)
CENTRAL ADMXTURE PHRM SVCS INC
Also Called: C A P S
1601 Wallace Dr Ste 130 (75006-6652)
PHONE..........................972 242-2788
Anita Punch, *Branch Mgr*
EMP: 18
SALES (corp-wide): 2.6MM **Privately Held**
WEB: www.capspharmacy.com
SIC: 2834 5122 Pharmaceutical preparations; pharmaceuticals
HQ: Central Admixture Pharmacy Services,
Inc.
2525 Mcgaw Ave
Irvine CA 92614

(G-2714)
CHAPAL/ZENRAY INC (PA)
Also Called: Chana Enterprises
2452 Lacy Ln Ste 116 (75006-6570)
P.O. Box 111622 (75011-1622)
PHONE..........................214 638-0402
Vivit Lervisit, *CEO*
Gray Stacy, *President*
Mike McWilliams, *COO*
Sumritti Lervisit, *Vice Pres*
▲ **EMP:** 78
SQ FT: 25,000
SALES (est): 18.4MM **Privately Held**
WEB: www.chapal.com
SIC: 3911 5094 Jewelry, precious metal;
jewelry; precious metals

(G-2715)
CI SYSTEMS INC
1500 N Interstate 35 # 116 (75006-3871)
PHONE..........................805 520-2233
Robert Buckwald, *President*
Dario Cabib, *Vice Pres*
Yael Baharav, *Engineer*
David Daunt, *Senior Engr*
Tracy Little, *Accounts Mgr*
◆ **EMP:** 10
SQ FT: 3,500
SALES (est): 2.1MM
SALES (corp-wide): 4.3MM **Privately Held**
WEB: www.ci-systems.com
SIC: 3827 Optical test & inspection equipment
HQ: C I Systems (Israel) Ltd.
Ramat Gavriel Ind. Zone
Migdal Haemek

(G-2716)
COLORADO STONE PDTS TEXAS INC
2025 Country Club Dr (75006-5702)
P.O. Box 430, Lewisville (75067-0430)
PHONE..........................972 434-2515
Melton Bacon, *President*
▼ **EMP:** 100
SQ FT: 45,000

SALES (est): 19.7MM
SALES (corp-wide): 65.2MM **Privately Held**
WEB: www.coronado.com
SIC: 3281 5032 Cut stone & stone products; stucco
PA: Creative Stone Mfg., Inc.
11191 Calabash Ave
Fontana CA 92337
909 357-8295

(G-2717)
COMMSCOPE TECHNOLOGIES LLC
2430 Lacy Ln (75006-6534)
PHONE..........................972 243-0965
Paul Stewart, *Branch Mgr*
EMP: 15 **Publicly Held**
SIC: 3663 Radio & TV communications
equipment
HQ: Commscope Technologies Llc
4 Westbrook Corporate Ctr
Westchester IL 60154
708 236-6600

(G-2718)
COMPLETE TCHNCAL RPRSNTTION IN
Also Called: C T R
1705 John Connally Dr (75006-5418)
PHONE..........................972 621-1111
H N Symonds, *CEO*
Stace Symonds, *President*
EMP: 48 **EST:** 1965
SQ FT: 38,000
SALES (est): 11.3MM **Privately Held**
WEB: www.ctraero.com
SIC: 3499 5085 5088 Automobile seat
frames, metal; machine bases, metal; filters, industrial; aircraft equipment & supplies

(G-2719)
CPM ACQUISITION CORP
Also Called: TSA Griddle System
2009 Mckenzie Dr Ste 116 (75006-8366)
PHONE..........................972 243-8070
Ted Waitman, *President*
EMP: 10
SALES (corp-wide): 215MM **Privately Held**
WEB: www.cpmroskamp.com
SIC: 3634 Griddles or grills, electric:
household
HQ: Cpm Acquisition Corp.
2975 Airline Cir
Waterloo IA 50703
319 232-8444

(G-2720)
CREE VISUAL MARKETING COMPANY
Also Called: Southwest Displays and Events
1200 Crowley Dr (75006-1315)
PHONE..........................214 905-8485
Brian Cree, *CEO*
Richard Slack, *President*
EMP: 45
SQ FT: 43,000
SALES (est): 4.4MM **Privately Held**
WEB: www.southwestdisplays.com
SIC: 7389 3999 7319 Advertising, promotional & trade show services; advertising
display products; display advertising service

(G-2721)
DAS BROT INC
Also Called: Texas Crumb and Food Products
2441 Midway Rd (75006-2503)
PHONE..........................972 243-8443
Steven L Holtsclaw, *President*
EMP: 20
SQ FT: 7,150
SALES (est): 3.5MM **Privately Held**
WEB: www.dasbrot.com
SIC: 2099 2045 Bread crumbs, not made
in bakeries; doughs & batters: from purchased flour

(G-2722)
DDSEP LLC
Also Called: Digital
3305 Wiley Post Rd (75006-5113)
PHONE..........................972 931-8000

Greg Brown, *Project Mgr*
Cynthia Wise, *Project Mgr*
Mason Sanders, *CFO*
Sharon Spataro, *Sales Staff*
Gary Mix, *Sales Executive*
EMP: 60
SQ FT: 40,000
SALES (est): 9.9MM **Privately Held**
WEB: www.digitalimps.com
SIC: 2721 2759 Periodicals; commercial
printing

(G-2723)
DIEM DIGITAL INTERIORS LLC
Also Called: Bora Gear
2420 Tarpley Rd Ste 210 (75006-2401)
PHONE..........................972 899-1189
Megan Tubbs, *Vice Pres*
John Dorsey, *Mng Member*
EMP: 17
SQ FT: 3,000
SALES (est): 4.6MM **Privately Held**
WEB: www.diemdigital.com
SIC: 3651 Home entertainment equipment,
electronic

(G-2724)
DIMACO LTD
1100 Valwood Pkwy Ste 104 (75006-8388)
PHONE..........................972 242-2427
Mark Risley, *Partner*
EMP: 18
SALES (est): 3.8MM **Privately Held**
WEB: www.directmailcompany.com
SIC: 2752 Commercial printing, offset

(G-2725)
DIVERSCO INC
Also Called: Custom Label Converter
1100 Venture Ct Ste 100 (75006-5459)
P.O. Box 551089, Dallas (75355-1089)
PHONE..........................972 478-6400
Craig Burton, *President*
Greg Hamilton, *Corp Secy*
Joseph S Haas, *Vice Pres*
James Struhar, *CFO*
▲ **EMP:** 55
SQ FT: 51,000
SALES (est): 11.7MM
SALES (corp-wide): 305.3MM **Privately Held**
WEB: www.nosco.com
SIC: 2759 Laser printing
HQ: Nosco, Inc
2199 N Delany Rd
Gurnee IL 60031
847 336-4200

(G-2726)
DOOSAN HF CONTROLS CORPORATION
1624 W Crosby Rd Ste 124 (75006-6601)
PHONE..........................469 568-6500
Jong Min Kim, *CEO*
Timothy McCreary, *President*
Steve Yang, *Senior VP*
Rob Waletzko, *Engineer*
Ciaran McConville, *Treasurer*
EMP: 40
SQ FT: 25,000
SALES (est): 8.6MM **Privately Held**
WEB: www.hfcontrols.com
SIC: 3491 Automatic regulating & control
valves
PA: Doosan Heavy Industries & Construction Co., Ltd.
22 Doosanvolvo-Ro, Seongsan-Gu
Changwon 51711

(G-2727)
EAGLE EYE SIGNS LP
13375 N Stmmons Fwy Ste 4 (75006)
PHONE..........................972 466-2100
Craig Davidson, *General Ptnr*
EMP: 12
SQ FT: 1,800
SALES (est): 965.1K **Privately Held**
WEB: www.eagleeyesigns.net
SIC: 3993 Signs & advertising specialties

(G-2728)
EGH PRINTING LLC
Also Called: Sir Speedy 4043
2001 Midway Rd Ste 128 (75006-4916)
PHONE..........................972 788-4266
Phillip Crum, *Marketing Mgr*

EMP: 14
SALES (corp-wide): 1.7MM **Privately Held**
WEB: www.sirspeedy.com
SIC: 2752 Commercial printing, lithographic
PA: Egh Printing, Llc
8837 Golden Sunset Trl
Fort Worth TX 76244
682 225-4872

(G-2729)
EINSTEINS INC
1800 Surveyor Blvd (75006-5108)
PHONE..........................972 387-8485
James Keith Einstein, *President*
Judith Kaplan Einstein, *Admin Sec*
EMP: 10
SQ FT: 5,600
SALES (est): 1.7MM **Privately Held**
WEB: www.einsteinprinting.com
SIC: 2752 7334 2791 Commercial printing, offset; photocopying & duplicating
services; typesetting, computer controlled

(G-2730)
ELECTRO PLATE CIRCUITRY INC (PA)
1430 Century Dr (75006-3697)
PHONE..........................972 466-0818
James McNeal, *Vice Pres*
Sharon Kirkland, *QC Mgr*
Gloria Garcia, *Sales Mgr*
Amarnath Nuggehalli, *Director*
EMP: 70
SQ FT: 10,000
SALES (est): 11.4MM **Privately Held**
WEB: www.eplate.com
SIC: 3672 Printed circuit boards

(G-2731)
ENERSYS
1600 Wallace Dr Ste 120 (75006-8009)
PHONE..........................972 245-6601
Dawn Shadwick, *Regional Mgr*
Mike Rogers, *Manager*
Ryan Shadwick, *Manager*
Aaron Felt, *Supervisor*
EMP: 15
SALES (corp-wide): 3B **Publicly Held**
WEB: www.enersys.com
SIC: 3691 Storage batteries
PA: Enersys
2366 Bernville Rd
Reading PA 19605
610 208-1991

(G-2732)
ENTREMATIC LOADING DOCK PDTS
1612 Hutton Dr Ste 140 (75006-6642)
PHONE..........................972 466-0707
Brian Boleyn, *General Mgr*
Ryan Geltmeier, *General Mgr*
Bob Hawk, *General Mgr*
Carl Nethercutt, *General Mgr*
Steve Sprunger, *Vice Pres*
EMP: 27
SALES (est): 5.1MM **Privately Held**
WEB: www.entrematic.com
SIC: 3634 Ceiling fans

(G-2733)
EXACTA PACKAGING DESIGNS INC
1223 Crowley Dr (75006-1314)
PHONE..........................972 323-1063
William Seanor, *President*
Tom Spitz, *Managing Dir*
Elizabeth Spitz, *Admin Sec*
▲ **EMP:** 65
SQ FT: 60,000
SALES (est): 3.1MM **Privately Held**
WEB: www.exactapak.com
SIC: 3253 3544 Mosaic tile, glazed &
unglazed: ceramic; dies, steel rule

(G-2734)
EXALT PRINTING SOLUTIONS LLC
1628 W Crosby Rd Ste 104 (75006-8004)
PHONE..........................972 245-3858
Cari Self, *Accounts Mgr*
Lisa Marta, *Mng Member*
Dominic Cinquepalmi, *Executive*

▲ = Import ▼=Export
◆ =Import/Export

EMP: 30
SALES (est): 9MM **Privately Held**
WEB: www.exaltprinting.com
SIC: 2752 Commercial printing, offset

(G-2735)
EXPANSION INDUSTRIES LLC
Also Called: Expansion Arms and Ammunition
2410 Luna Rd Ste 130 (75006-6536)
PHONE..................................888 707-9343
Richie Smissen, *CEO*
Lucas Smissen, *Owner*
EMP: 20
SALES (est): 500K **Privately Held**
WEB: www.expansion-ammunition.com
SIC: 3482 5099 Cartridge cases for ammunition, 30 mm. & below; firearms & ammunition, except sporting

(G-2736)
FASTSIGNS INTERNATIONAL INC (PA)
Also Called: American Fastsigns
2542 Highlander Way (75006-3312)
PHONE..................................888 285-5935
Catherine Monson, *CEO*
Chris Nosil, *Owner*
Jeff Collier, *Partner*
Danell McGinley, *Partner*
Valerie Jackson, *Publisher*
EMP: 88
SQ FT: 37,000
SALES (est): 23.9MM **Privately Held**
WEB: www.fastsigns.com
SIC: 3993 Signs & advertising specialties

(G-2737)
FASTSIGNS NAT ADVG COUNCIL INC
2542 Highlander Way (75006-3312)
PHONE..................................214 346-5600
Catherine Monson, *Ch of Bd*
Oren Newton, *General Mgr*
Drue Townsend, *Vice Pres*
Brandon Basara, *Opers Staff*
Garth Allison, *Director*
EMP: 30
SALES (est): 3.1MM **Privately Held**
WEB: www.fastsigns.com
SIC: 3993 Signs & advertising specialties

(G-2738)
FISHER SELECT PRODUCTS INC
3201 Skylane Dr Ste 110 (75006-2527)
PHONE..................................972 484-1188
Carl Fisher, *President*
Carl M Fisher III, *Vice Pres*
Patrick T Fisher, *Vice Pres*
Carl Fisher, *Treasurer*
EMP: 25
SALES (est): 1.6MM **Privately Held**
WEB: www.skylightheatblocker.com
SIC: 7389 3444 Design services; skylights, sheet metal

(G-2739)
FLECO INDUSTRIES LLC (HQ)
Also Called: Lights Fantastic
2055 Luna Rd Ste 142 (75006-6436)
PHONE..................................972 247-3171
Jon Sayah, *CEO*
Larry Sayah, *Manager*
▲ EMP: 190
SQ FT: 120,000
SALES (est): 77.5MM **Privately Held**
WEB: www.texasfluorescents.com
SIC: 5063 3674 3646 3645 Lighting fixtures; light emitting diodes; commercial indusl & institutional electric lighting fixtures; residential lighting fixtures; tubes, electric light
PA: Saylite Holdings Llc
2055 Luna Rd Ste 142
Carrollton TX 75006
972 247-3171

(G-2740)
FONG KAI USA INC (HQ)
Also Called: Fki USA
2525 Carter Dr (75006-1310)
PHONE..................................972 644-1584
Derek Dooley, *President*
Fred Yang, *Opers Staff*
Robin Dooley, *Human Res Mgr*

Ken Sikora, *Sales Mgr*
Charles Overman, *Sales Engr*
▲ EMP: 34
SQ FT: 12,000
SALES (est): 6.7MM **Privately Held**
WEB: www.fkiusa.net
SIC: 3444 Sheet metalwork

(G-2741)
FUJIFILM NORTH AMERICA CORP
Also Called: Fuji Photo U S A
1628 W Crosby Rd Ste 100 (75006-6632)
PHONE..................................972 242-0662
EMP: 100
SALES (corp-wide): 22.8B **Privately Held**
SIC: 7384 3861 5043 Photofinishing Laboratory Mfg Photographic Equipment/Supplies Whol Photo Equipment/Supplies
HQ: Fujifilm North America Corporation
200 Summit Lake Dr Fl 2
Valhalla NY 10595
914 789-8100

(G-2742)
FUJIFILM ULTRA PURE SLTONS INC
1200 W Jackson Rd (75006-1317)
PHONE..................................972 245-3797
Bill Robb, *Branch Mgr*
EMP: 20
SQ FT: 25,934 **Privately Held**
WEB: www.fujifilm.com
SIC: 2819 Alkali metals: lithium, cesium, francium, rubidium
HQ: Fujifilm Ultra Pure Solutions, Inc.
11225 Commercial Pkwy
Castroville CA 95012
831 632-2120

(G-2743)
FUTUREMEDIA GROUP INC
2120 Hutton Dr Ste 800 (75006-8391)
PHONE..................................972 770-0000
Joseph Wilson, *President*
EMP: 40
SQ FT: 22,000
SALES (est): 634.8K **Privately Held**
SIC: 3571 Electronic computers

(G-2744)
GANART TECHNOLOGIES INC
1700 Columbian Club Dr (75006-5517)
PHONE..................................972 512-6933
Art Holbrook, *President*
Wayne McHugh, *Managing Dir*
Purnendu Mishra, *Finance*
Janie White, *Admin Sec*
EMP: 20
SQ FT: 10,000
SALES (est): 10MM **Privately Held**
WEB: www.ganart.com
SIC: 3578 Automatic teller machines (ATM)

(G-2745)
GLOBAL INDUSTRIES INC
2025 W Belt Line Rd # 100 (75006-6447)
PHONE..................................972 236-1366
Larry Gantt, *Manager*
Ron Gilmore, *Manager*
EMP: 9
SALES (corp-wide): 109.9MM **Privately Held**
WEB: www.evolvefurnituregroup.com
SIC: 1389 Construction, repair & dismantling services
PA: Global Industries, Inc.
17 W Stow Rd
Marlton NJ 08053
856 596-3390

(G-2746)
GOLF TIME LLC
Also Called: Team Golf
2221 Luna Rd (75006-6505)
PHONE..................................214 366-1595
Emily Russell, *Opers Mgr*
Brad Wallin, *Sales Staff*
David McDevitt, *Mng Member*
◆ EMP: 20
SQ FT: 102,000
SALES (est): 9.3MM **Privately Held**
WEB: www.teamgolfusa.com
SIC: 5091 3949 Golf & skiing equipment & supplies; golf equipment

(G-2747)
GRAPHIC CONVERTING LTD
1210 Champion Cir Ste 100 (75006-8331)
PHONE..................................972 554-8000
EMP: 43 EST: 1998
SQ FT: 35,000
SALES (est): 10.8MM **Privately Held**
SIC: 2679 Building, insulating & packaging paperboard

(G-2748)
GREENSMITHS INC
1419 Upfield Dr (75006-6921)
PHONE..................................972 242-5310
James Montgomery, *President*
Gary Mayberry, *Exec VP*
TI Morgan, *Vice Pres*
Lee Langley, *Sales Staff*
▼ EMP: 9
SQ FT: 100,000
SALES (est): 1.5MM **Privately Held**
WEB: www.greensmiths.com
SIC: 5261 2875 5191 Fertilizer; fertilizers, mixing only; fertilizer & fertilizer materials

(G-2749)
GTCR GOLDER RAUNER LLC
Also Called: Honeywell Security Monitoring
3414 Midcourt Rd Ste 100 (75006-5913)
PHONE..................................972 670-7975
Tom Phelan, *Branch Mgr*
EMP: 15
SALES (corp-wide): 303.3MM **Privately Held**
WEB: www.gtcr.com
SIC: 2834 Pharmaceutical preparations
PA: Gtcr Golder Rauner, L.L.C.
300 N La Salle Dr # 5600
Chicago IL 60654
312 329-0225

(G-2750)
HAGER CONTAINERS L P
Also Called: Dzignpak
1015 Hayden Dr (75006-5741)
PHONE..................................972 417-7660
Carl Renner, *Partner*
Steve Hager, *Partner*
Doug Zadow, *Partner*
EMP: 71
SQ FT: 125,000
SALES (est): 14.5MM **Privately Held**
WEB: www.englanderdzp.com
SIC: 2653 Boxes, corrugated: made from purchased materials; boxes, solid fiber: made from purchased materials

(G-2751)
HALLIBURTON COMPANY
3220 Keller Springs Rd # 128 (75006-5049)
PHONE..................................972 418-3221
EMP: 40 **Publicly Held**
WEB: www.halliburton.com
SIC: 1389 Oil field services
PA: Halliburton Company
3000 N Sam Houston Pkwy E
Houston TX 77032

(G-2752)
HALLIBURTON COMPANY
2601 E Belt Line Rd (75006-5401)
PHONE..................................972 418-3000
William Wood, *Production*
Don Perkins, *Technical Mgr*
Lisa Cox, *Research*
Tyson Eiman, *Engineer*
Ken Schwendemann, *Engineer*
EMP: 24 **Publicly Held**
WEB: www.halliburton.com
SIC: 1389 Oil field services; cementing oil & gas well casings; well logging; perforating well casings
PA: Halliburton Company
3000 N Sam Houston Pkwy E
Houston TX 77032

(G-2753)
HANITATEK LLC
Also Called: Hanita Tek Window Films
2025 Mckenzie Dr Ste 100 (75006-6860)
PHONE..................................214 351-5818
Jim Brown, *CEO*
Kevin Menig, *Sales Mgr*
Randall Garcia, *Sales Staff*
▲ EMP: 9

SALES (est): 964.9K **Privately Held**
SIC: 1799 2295 Coating, caulking & weather, water & fireproofing; coated fabrics, not rubberized

(G-2754)
HC INTERIORS INC
1000 W Crosby Rd Ste 100 (75006-6982)
PHONE..................................214 350-0468
Christine Reilly, *CEO*
Doug Michel, *President*
Michael Oriely, *Principal*
Ryan Reed, *Sales Dir*
Mike Reilly, *Sales Executive*
EMP: 40
SALES (est): 4.7MM **Privately Held**
WEB: www.hcinteriors.com
SIC: 2391 2591 2221 Curtains & draperies; shade, curtain & drapery hardware; bedspreads, silk & manmade fiber

(G-2755)
HEADS UP TECHNOLOGIES INC
2033 Chenault Dr Ste 100 (75006-5119)
PHONE..................................972 980-4890
Robert Harshaw, *CEO*
Keith Dennis, *Vice Pres*
Jim Found, *Vice Pres*
David Gross, *Vice Pres*
John Header, *Engineer*
EMP: 50
SQ FT: 15,000
SALES (est): 11.8MM **Privately Held**
WEB: www.heads-up.com
SIC: 3769 Guided missile & space vehicle parts & auxiliary equipment

(G-2756)
HIGH VOLTAGE POWER SYSTEMS INC
Also Called: Fuji Semiconductor
2532 Highlander Way (75006-2323)
PHONE..................................972 733-1700
Joseph Jan Collmer, *President*
James L Mathis, *Exec VP*
Reggie Scheu, *Vice Pres*
Bonnie Keating, *Engineer*
Lynn Roszel, *Engineer*
EMP: 110 EST: 1979
SQ FT: 47,000
SALES (est): 14.2MM **Privately Held**
WEB: www.deantechnology.com
SIC: 5065 3612 Electronic parts; transistors; diodes; voltage regulating transformers, electric power
PA: Fuji Electric Co., Ltd.
1-11-2, Osaki
Shinagawa-Ku TKY 141-0

(G-2757)
HILITE INDUSTRIES AUTO LP
1671 S Broadway St (75006-7496)
PHONE..................................972 242-2116
Karl Hammer, *CEO*
Andreas Aumueller, *CFO*
EMP: 99
SALES (est): 12.7MM **Privately Held**
SIC: 3714 Motor vehicle parts & accessories
HQ: Hilite International, Inc.
1671 S Broadway St
Carrollton TX 75006
972 242-2116

(G-2758)
HILITE INTERNATIONAL INC
Hilite Intl Dallas Div
1671 S Broadway St (75006-7496)
PHONE..................................972 242-2116
Steve Nance, *Engineer*
Mike Bush, *Manager*
EMP: 320 **Privately Held**
WEB: www.hilite.com
SIC: 3714 Motor vehicle parts & accessories
HQ: Hilite International, Inc.
1671 S Broadway St
Carrollton TX 75006
972 242-2116

(G-2759)
HILITE INTERNATIONAL INC (DH)
1671 S Broadway St (75006-7496)
PHONE..................................972 242-2116
Karl Hammer, *President*

GEOGRAPHIC

Joerge Feuring, *COO*
Marco Hernandez, *Plant Mgr*
Bill Green, *Production*
Quang Tran, *Production*
▲ **EMP:** 12
SALES (est): 198.8MM **Privately Held**
WEB: www.hilite.com
SIC: 3714 Motor vehicle parts & accessories
HQ: Hilite Germany Gmbh
Am Schlossfeld 5
Marktheidenfeld 97828
939 191-10

(G-2760)
HILLSHIRE BRANDS COMPANY
1820 N Josey Ln (75006-6047)
PHONE.................................972 416-4395
Justin Vannoy, *Branch Mgr*
EMP: 400
SALES (corp-wide): 43.1B **Publicly Held**
WEB: www.sterlingbay.com
SIC: 2013 Sausages & other prepared meats
HQ: The Hillshire Brands Company
400 S Jefferson St Ste 1n
Chicago IL 60607
312 614-6000

(G-2761)
HITACHI AMERICA LTD
2315 Luna Rd (75006-6524)
PHONE.................................972 488-3824
Creg Gerkove, *Branch Mgr*
EMP: 80 **Privately Held**
WEB: www.hitachi.us
SIC: 3823 5065 Thermal conductivity instruments, industrial process type; semiconductor devices
HQ: Hitachi America Ltd
50 Prospect Ave
Tarrytown NY 10591
914 332-5800

(G-2762)
HOWMET AEROSPACE INC
2625 E Belt Line Rd (75006-5435)
PHONE.................................972 416-6500
EMP: 135
SALES (corp-wide): 14.1B **Publicly Held**
WEB: www.howmet.com
SIC: 3353 Aluminum sheet & strip
PA: Howmet Aerospace Inc.
201 Isabella St Ste 200
Pittsburgh PA 15212
412 553-1940

(G-2763)
HUMANETICS II LTD (DH)
1700 Columbian Club Dr (75006-5534)
PHONE.................................972 416-1304
▲ **EMP:** 115
SALES (est): 77.5MM
SALES (corp-wide): 71.6MM **Privately Held**
WEB: www.humanetics.com
SIC: 3444 3599 Sheet metalwork; custom machinery
HQ: C H Industries, Inc
1700 Columbian Club Dr
Carrollton TX 75006
972 416-1304

(G-2764)
ILLES FOOD INGREDIENTS LTD (PA)
Also Called: Illes Seasonings & Flavors
2200 Luna Rd Ste 120 (75006-6559)
PHONE.................................800 683-4553
George M Illes Jr, *Ch of Bd*
Marc Aymond, *Vice Pres*
Tom Bailey, *Vice Pres*
Cristin Kahale, *Vice Pres*
Linda Mullin, *Vice Pres*
▼ **EMP:** 75
SQ FT: 22,500
SALES (est): 28.6MM **Privately Held**
WEB: www.illesfoods.com
SIC: 2087 2099 Flavoring extracts & syrups; powders, drink; pastes, flavoring; concentrates, drink; food preparations

(G-2765)
INSTRUMENT TECH CORP
3333 Earhart Dr Ste 230 (75006-5127)
PHONE.................................972 458-8785

Billy L Prewitt Jr, *President*
Lori Prewitt, *Vice Pres*
Jesse Villegas, *Opers Mgr*
◆ **EMP:** 18
SALES (est): 2.8MM **Privately Held**
WEB: www.shopinstrumenttech.com
SIC: 3812 5088 Aircraft flight instruments; aircraft equipment & supplies

(G-2766)
INTERNATIONAL PAPER COMPANY
2605 E Belt Line Rd (75006-5444)
PHONE.................................972 417-1350
Russell Gipson, *Branch Mgr*
Daryl Mason, *Info Tech Mgr*
EMP: 135
SALES (corp-wide): 22.3B **Publicly Held**
WEB: www.internationalpaper.com
SIC: 2653 Boxes, corrugated: made from purchased materials
PA: International Paper Company
6400 Poplar Ave
Memphis TN 38197
901 419-9000

(G-2767)
INTERNATIONAL PAPER COMPANY
1655 S I 35 (75006-7415)
PHONE.................................972 512-0400
Scott Jeffrey, *Manager*
Steve Hall, *Maintence Staff*
EMP: 125
SQ FT: 157,854
SALES (corp-wide): 22.3B **Publicly Held**
WEB: www.internationalpaper.com
SIC: 2621 Paper mills
PA: International Paper Company
6400 Poplar Ave
Memphis TN 38197
901 419-9000

(G-2768)
INTERNATIONAL PAPER COMPANY
2015 Country Club Dr (75006-5702)
PHONE.................................972 416-8680
John McCage, *Plant Supt*
Reed Tibbets, *Manager*
EMP: 35
SQ FT: 34,175
SALES (corp-wide): 22.3B **Publicly Held**
WEB: www.internationalpaper.com
SIC: 2621 Paper mills
PA: International Paper Company
6400 Poplar Ave
Memphis TN 38197
901 419-9000

(G-2769)
INTERNATIONAL TOOL & MFG CO
3218 Skylane Dr Ste 102 (75006-2587)
PHONE.................................800 753-1004
Joseph J Koncewicz, *President*
Michael Koncewicz, *Vice Pres*
EMP: 10
SQ FT: 31,476
SALES (est): 3.1MM **Privately Held**
SIC: 3843 Dental equipment & supplies

(G-2770)
INTERNTNAL FLVORS FRGRNCES INC
Iff International Flavors
1620 W Crosby Rd Ste 102 (75006-6656)
PHONE.................................496 557-7001
Lance Laplante, *QC Mgr*
Melanie Fischer, *Engineer*
Kathi Johnson, *Marketing Staff*
John Heffernan, *Manager*
Michael Hughes, *Supervisor*
EMP: 100
SALES (corp-wide): 5.1B **Publicly Held**
WEB: www.iff.com
SIC: 2869 Flavors or flavoring materials, synthetic; perfume materials, synthetic
PA: International Flavors & Fragrances Inc.
521 W 57th St
New York NY 10019
212 765-5500

(G-2771)
JAYNA INC
2555 Tarpley Rd (75006-2329)
PHONE.................................972 417-8922
Damaroo Shah, *Branch Mgr*
EMP: 31
SALES (corp-wide): 9.3MM **Privately Held**
WEB: www.jaynainc.com
SIC: 3599 Machine shop, jobbing & repair
PA: Jayna, Inc.
15 Marybill Dr S
Troy OH 45373
937 335-8922

(G-2772)
K & S PRODUCTS INC
Also Called: Legacy Blind Mfg
1000 Crowley Dr (75006-1329)
PHONE.................................972 820-0007
Yun Hui Park, *Principal*
EMP: 12
SALES (est): 932.6K **Privately Held**
WEB: www.legacyblindsmfg.com
SIC: 2591 Window blinds

(G-2773)
L C COLORMARK
Also Called: Colormark Printing
1840 Hutton Dr Ste 208 (75006-6660)
PHONE.................................972 243-1919
David R Hudson, *President*
David Hudson, *Partner*
Hudson Andy, *Vice Pres*
Carlyn Scott, *Production*
Jerry Landry, *Purchasing*
EMP: 95
SALES (est): 22.5MM **Privately Held**
WEB: www.colormark-lc.com
SIC: 2752 7336 2791 2789 Commercial printing, offset; commercial art & graphic design; typesetting; bookbinding & related work

(G-2774)
LAW PUBLICATIONS INC
1100 Valwood Pkwy Ste 118 (75006-8388)
PHONE.................................800 527-0156
EMP: 14 **EST:** 1974
SALES (est): 1.9MM **Privately Held**
WEB: www.lawpublications.net
SIC: 2752 7371 Commercial printing, lithographic; computer software development & applications

(G-2775)
LEGACY AERONAUTICS INC
2145 Chenault Dr Ste 110 (75006-5056)
PHONE.................................855 622-8600
EMP: 30
SALES (est): 1.1MM **Privately Held**
SIC: 3728 Mfg Aircraft Parts/Equipment

(G-2776)
LESCO DISTRIBUTING INC
Also Called: L E S Distribrs
1628 W Crosby Rd Ste 115 (75006-6679)
PHONE.................................972 446-1605
Steve Elmore, *Manager*
EMP: 13 **Privately Held**
WEB: www.lescodistributing.com
SIC: 3651 5064 Audio electronic systems; radios
PA: Iesco Distributing, Inc.
1203 E Industrial Dr
Orange City FL 32763

(G-2777)
MANS DISTRIBUTORS INC
Also Called: Mans Distributors
3120 Kellway Dr Ste 108 (75006-3311)
PHONE.................................972 930-0330
Purnima Kara, *CEO*
Suresh Kara, *President*
Arvin Kara, *General Mgr*
Sadhna Patel, *General Mgr*
Akhil Kara, *Vice Pres*
EMP: 10
SALES (est): 3.9MM **Privately Held**
WEB: www.mans.us
SIC: 5087 2656 5046 Janitors' supplies; cleaning & maintenance equipment & supplies; sanitary food containers; restaurant equipment & supplies

(G-2778)
MARFIELD INC
Also Called: Marfield Corporate Stationary
1225 E Crosby Rd Ste B1 (75006-8522)
P.O. Box 814210, Dallas (75381-4210)
PHONE.................................972 245-9122
Lee Ann Packard, *President*
Joe Packard, *Vice Pres*
Andrea Rowe, *Vice Pres*
Joseph Packard, *CFO*
Kathryn Crawford, *Treasurer*
EMP: 20 **EST:** 1971
SQ FT: 17,100
SALES (est): 3.4MM **Privately Held**
WEB: www.marfieldprinting.com
SIC: 2752 7389 Commercial printing, offset; engraving service

(G-2779)
MERIDIAN BRICK LLC
Also Called: Boral Building Products
1400 N Broadway St (75006-3817)
PHONE.................................972 245-1542
Jim Wise, *Vice Pres*
Bill Hughes, *Manager*
Jason Collins, *Manager*
EMP: 18
SALES (corp-wide): 441MM **Privately Held**
WEB: www.meridianbrick.com
SIC: 5085 3251 Refractory material; brick & structural clay tile
PA: Meridian Brick Llc
6455 Shiloh Rd D
Alpharetta GA 30005
770 645-4500

(G-2780)
MID-WEST HOSE & SPECIALTY
1132 Valwood Pkwy Ste 100 (75006-8311)
PHONE.................................214 638-3210
James Hatley, *Manager*
EMP: 11
SALES (corp-wide): 223.9MM **Privately Held**
WEB: www.midwesthose.com
SIC: 5085 3492 Hose, belting & packing; rubber goods, mechanical; hose & tube fittings & assemblies, hydraulic/pneumatic
PA: Mid-West Hose & Specialty, Inc.
3312 S I 35 Service Rd
Oklahoma City OK 73129
405 670-6718

(G-2781)
MIX PRINTING COMPANY INC
2441 Midway Rd (75006-2503)
P.O. Box 112460 (75011-2460)
PHONE.................................972 248-9000
Joanne Mix, *President*
Gary A Mix, *Corp Secy*
Darryl Mix, *Vice Pres*
John C Mix, *Vice Pres*
Tom Switser, *Vice Pres*
EMP: 23 **EST:** 1966
SQ FT: 33,800
SALES (est): 2.7MM **Privately Held**
WEB: www.mixprinting.com
SIC: 2752 Commercial printing, offset

(G-2782)
MTC MARKETING INC (PA)
Also Called: RR Design
1415 Hutton Dr (75006-6613)
PHONE.................................972 488-0577
Sandeep Malik, *President*
▲ **EMP:** 25
SQ FT: 28,000
SALES (est): 2.7MM **Privately Held**
WEB: www.mtcmarketinginc.com
SIC: 2389 5136 Men's miscellaneous accessories; work clothing, men's & boys'

(G-2783)
MTC PRINTING INC (PA)
Also Called: Thompson's Quick Print
1840 Hutton Dr Ste 200 (75006-6685)
PHONE.................................972 620-3212
Dave Hudson, *President*
EMP: 9
SQ FT: 3,500
SALES (est): 1.1MM **Privately Held**
WEB: www.thompsonsprinting.net
SIC: 2752 Commercial printing, offset

▲ = Import ▼=Export
◆ =Import/Export

(G-2784)
NATURELAB CORP
1606 Vantage Dr (75006-5613)
PHONE.....................972 417-3000
Charles Shea, *President*
EMP: 9 EST: 2016
SQ FT: 20,000
SALES (est): 1MM **Privately Held**
WEB: www.naturelabusa.com
SIC: 2023 Dietary supplements, dairy &
non-dairy based

(G-2785)
NOVA CONSTRUCTION CO INC
1713 E Crosby Rd (75006-7348)
PHONE.....................972 869-3041
Donald Pevehouse, *President*
Novice Northington, *Vice Pres*
Raymond Pinero, *Vice Pres*
Carla Woody, *Vice Pres*
EMP: 22
SQ FT: 6,746
SALES (est): 1.5MM **Privately Held**
SIC: 1794 1771 3444 1611 Excavation
work; parking lot construction; blacktop
(asphalt) work; culverts, sheet metal; sur-
facing & paving

(G-2786)
OPTEK TECHNOLOGY INC (HQ)
1645 Wallace Dr (75006-6696)
PHONE.....................972 323-2200
Billal Hammoud, *President*
Robert Taber, *President*
Geraint Anderson, *Chairman*
Tom Sward, *Vice Pres*
Walter Brooks, *Engineer*
◆ EMP: 100
SQ FT: 40,000
SALES (est): 90.2MM
SALES (corp-wide): 617.6MM **Publicly
Held**
WEB: www.optekinc.com
SIC: 3825 3812 3661 3643 Instruments
to measure electricity; search & naviga-
tion equipment; telephone & telegraph ap-
paratus; current-carrying wiring devices;
light sensitive devices
PA: Tt Electronics Plc
St. Andrews House
Woking GU21
193 282-5300

(G-2787)
**ORBIS INTERNATIONAL TECH
INC**
2081 Hutton Dr Ste 201 (75006-6873)
PHONE.....................972 929-5705
Mark Linnaro, *President*
Jane Livingston, *Vice Pres*
EMP: 20
SQ FT: 5,867
SALES (corp-wide): 23MM **Privately
Held**
WEB: www.orbissystems.eu
SIC: 3663 3679 Mobile communication
equipment; electronic circuits
PA: Orbis Systems Oy
Ayritie 8d
Vantaa 01510
290 040-800

(G-2788)
PACIFIC SENSOR LLC
2501 Mayes Rd Ste 100 (75006-1378)
PHONE.....................972 242-5750
Paul Fletcher, *Vice Pres*
William Ritter, *Opers Mgr*
EMP: 12
SALES (est): 2MM **Privately Held**
WEB: www.pacificsensor.com
SIC: 1389 2899 Cementing oil & gas well
casings; corrosion preventive lubricant

(G-2789)
**PACKAGING CORPORATION
AMERICA**
Also Called: Englander-Sonntag
1015 Hayden Dr (75006-5741)
PHONE.....................469 568-7000
Gary Springer, *General Mgr*
EMP: 70

SALES (corp-wide): 6.9B **Publicly Held**
WEB: www.englanderdzp.com
SIC: 2631 2653 Container board; container, packaging & boxboard; corrugated
& solid fiber boxes
PA: Packaging Corporation Of America
1 N Field Ct
Lake Forest IL 60045
847 482-3000

(G-2790)
PARTNERS CONVERTING INC
1800 Kelly Blvd (75006-5529)
PHONE.....................469 568-5000
Gale Woelffer, *President*
EMP: 14
SQ FT: 55,000
SALES (est): 1.9MM **Privately Held**
SIC: 2679 Paper products, converted

(G-2791)
PHOENIX MOBILE AIR INC
2320 Apollo Cir (75006-5516)
PHONE.....................972 418-6444
Scott Carter, *CEO*
Ray Rutledge, *Sales Staff*
Sara Perez, *Office Mgr*
Carter Scott, *Manager*
▲ EMP: 16
SALES (est): 3MM **Privately Held**
WEB: www.phoenixmobileair.com
SIC: 3585 Air conditioning equipment,
complete; air conditioning, motor vehicle

(G-2792)
**PRECISION DCMENT
SOLUTIONS INC (PA)**
2452 Lacy Ln Ste 100 (75006-6569)
P.O. Box 814850, Dallas (75381-4850)
PHONE.....................866 916-1177
David A Smith, *President*
Steve Jenkins, *President*
Mark Carver, *Regional Mgr*
Mark Turner, *COO*
Jerry Dixon, *Exec VP*
EMP: 40
SQ FT: 11,000
SALES (est): 35.2MM **Privately Held**
WEB: www.pdsnow.com
SIC: 3861 5044 7629 Reproduction ma-
chines & equipment; toners, prepared
photographic (not made in chemical
plants); office equipment; copying equip-
ment; business machine repair, electric

(G-2793)
PRECISION WATER TECH INC
1225 Capital Dr Ste 180 (75006-3503)
PHONE.....................972 488-6755
Charles Heineman, *President*
John Loiseau, *Vice Pres*
EMP: 12
SALES (est): 1.1MM **Privately Held**
WEB: www.precisionwater.net
SIC: 3589 Water treatment equipment, in-
dustrial

(G-2794)
PREMIER LIGHTING ENTPS LLC
Also Called: Premier Christmas
1300 Hutton Dr Ste 104 (75006-6634)
PHONE.....................855 426-4544
Justin Lubbers, *Vice Pres*
EMP: 15
SALES (est): 2MM **Privately Held**
WEB: www.premier-christmas.com
SIC: 3648 Decorative area lighting fixtures

(G-2795)
PRETZELS INC
Also Called: Texas Twist
2305 E Belt Line Rd # 210 (75006-5463)
PHONE.....................972 416-3660
Gary Powell, *President*
Dennis Moore, *Vice Pres*
Gerald Shreiber, *Director*
Allison Snyder, *Admin Sec*
EMP: 45
SQ FT: 3,200
SALES (est): 9.5MM
SALES (corp-wide): 1B **Publicly Held**
SIC: 2052 2099 2096 2053 Pretzels;
food preparations; potato chips & similar
snacks; frozen bakery products, except
bread; frozen specialties

PA: J & J Snack Foods Corp.
6000 Central Hwy
Pennsauken NJ 08109
856 665-9533

(G-2796)
PRICEVISION INC
1505 Wallace Dr Ste 140 (75006-6639)
PHONE.....................972 770-0000
Joseph Wilson, *President*
Arnon Wilson, *President*
EMP: 35
SALES (est): 8MM **Privately Held**
WEB: www.pricevision.com
SIC: 3674 Semiconductors & related de-
vices

(G-2797)
PRIME TURBINES LLC (DH)
1615 Diplomat Dr Ste 120 (75006-8392)
PHONE.....................972 406-2100
Russell Starr, *President*
Criss Berry, *General Mgr*
Bruce Weaver, *Corp Secy*
Mike Murtha, *Purch Mgr*
Nicole Covington, *Accountant*
EMP: 34
SALES (est): 8.8MM **Privately Held**
WEB: www.primeturbines.com
SIC: 3724 Aircraft engines & engine parts
HQ: Ptb Holdings Usa, Llc
1615 Diplomat Dr Ste 120
Carrollton TX 75006
972 406-2100

(G-2798)
**PROACTIVE TECHNOLOGIES
INC**
2833 Trinty Sq Dr Ste 105 (75006-2384)
PHONE.....................972 416-6298
Kenny Kremm, *President*
Archie Martin, *Sales Staff*
EMP: 10
SQ FT: 13,500
SALES (est): 2.8MM **Privately Held**
WEB: www.proactivetechnologies.com
SIC: 7373 3572 Systems integration serv-
ices; computer storage devices

(G-2799)
PROMOS DISTRIBUTORS INC
2520 Tarpley Rd Ste 500 (75006-2284)
PHONE.....................972 478-7298
EMP: 52 EST: 1999
SQ FT: 3,000
SALES (est): 386.5K **Privately Held**
WEB: www.promosdistributors.com
SIC: 2262 5947 Screen printing: man-
made fiber & silk broadwoven fabrics; gift,
novelty & souvenir shop

(G-2800)
**PROTECTIVE PACKAGING
CORP INC**
1746 W Crosby Rd Ste 108 (75006-6498)
PHONE.....................972 446-2247
Steve Hanna, *President*
Matthew Hanna, *Principal*
Lucas Hanna, *Business Mgr*
Debra Hernandez, *Controller*
Angela Yantes, *Manager*
EMP: 36
SQ FT: 15,000
SALES (est): 11MM **Privately Held**
WEB: www.protectivepackaging.net
SIC: 2674 5199 Bags: uncoated paper &
multiwall; packaging materials

(G-2801)
**QUALITY POWDER COATING
INC (PA)**
Also Called: Pro Coat
1838 Forms Dr (75006-3743)
PHONE.....................972 466-0655
Roland P Schurrer, *President*
Taylor Arnold, *Sales Staff*
Jim Hester, *Manager*
▲ EMP: 9
SALES (est): 1.7MM **Privately Held**
WEB: www.specifyqpc.com
SIC: 3479 Coating of metals & formed
products

(G-2802)
QUINN PRINTING CO INC
Also Called: Sir Speedy
2001 Midway Rd Ste 128 (75006-4916)
PHONE.....................972 788-4266
James Quinn, *President*
EMP: 16
SQ FT: 7,500
SALES: 2.7MM **Privately Held**
WEB: www.sirspeedy.com
SIC: 2752 Commercial printing, litho-
graphic

(G-2803)
REBEL ATHLETIC INC
2554 Tarpley Rd Ste 114 (75006-2385)
PHONE.....................972 418-0827
▲ EMP: 10 EST: 2012
SALES (est): 931.4K **Privately Held**
WEB: www.rebelathletic.com
SIC: 2389 Band uniforms

(G-2804)
REGAL HARDWOODS INC (PA)
1540 Selene Dr Ste 110 (75006-6484)
PHONE.....................972 620-8833
Patrick Luke, *President*
Gui X Xu, *Vice Pres*
John Stage, *Manager*
Gene Fan, *Admin Sec*
▲ EMP: 12
SQ FT: 66,000
SALES (est): 1.7MM **Privately Held**
WEB: www.regalhardwoods.com
SIC: 2426 5023 5211 Flooring, hardwood;
wood flooring; flooring, wood

(G-2805)
REICHERT CORPORATION
1625 Crescent Cir Ste 210 (75006-3653)
PHONE.....................972 267-1300
Joe Reichert, *President*
EMP: 10
SQ FT: 5,000
SALES (est): 1.2MM **Privately Held**
WEB: www.padprintingdfw.com
SIC: 2754 Commercial printing, gravure

(G-2806)
**REVOLUTION RETAIL SYSTEMS
LLC**
1400 Valwood Pkwy Ste 100 (75006-8336)
PHONE.....................469 317-2910
Mark K Levenick, *Ch of Bd*
Tony Walker, *Exec VP*
Sandra Hayes, *VP Opers*
Brad Britton, *Project Mgr*
Andrew Rodo, *Project Mgr*
▲ EMP: 9
SALES (est): 7MM **Privately Held**
WEB: www.revolutionretailsystems.com
SIC: 3578 Accounting machines & cash
registers

(G-2807)
**REYNOLDS PRESTO PRODUCTS
INC**
Also Called: Presto Products Company
2625 E Belt Line Rd (75006-5435)
P.O. Box 815849, Dallas (75381-5849)
PHONE.....................972 416-6500
Glenn Thaxton, *Vice Pres*
Paul Johnson, *Branch Mgr*
EMP: 320 **Privately Held**
WEB: www.prestoproducts.com
SIC: 2671 2673 Plastic film, coated or
laminated for packaging; bags: plastic,
laminated & coated
HQ: Reynolds Presto Products Inc.
670 N Perkins St
Appleton WI 54914
800 558-3525

(G-2808)
RISO INC
2081 Hutton Dr Ste 208 (75006-6873)
PHONE.....................800 942-7476
Gary Plannerio, *Manager*
Richard Stavis, *Manager*
EMP: 12 **Privately Held**
WEB: www.us.riso.com
SIC: 3663 5084 Digital encoders; printing
trades machinery, equipment & supplies

HQ: Riso, Inc.
10 State St Ste 201
Woburn MA 01801
978 777-7377

(G-2809)
ROOFTOP SYSTEMS INC
Also Called: Rrs
1625 Diplomat Dr (75006-6848)
PHONE...............................972 247-7447
Thomas Robert Edwards, *President*
Phil Rutledge, *President*
Tony Moffett, *Exec VP*
John Pinkston, *Engineer*
David Wise, *Engineer*
EMP: 80
SALES (est): 22.1MM **Privately Held**
WEB: www.ruskinrooftopsystems.com
SIC: 3444 Sheet metalwork

(G-2810)
RPMTRONICS INCORPORATED
Also Called: Rpm-Tronics
2201 Midway Rd Ste 108s (75006-5242)
PHONE...............................972 865-1330
Roger Melo, *President*
Carl Cook, *Sales Staff*
Richard Haug, *Product Mgr*
EMP: 600
SALES (est): 38.6MM **Privately Held**
WEB: www.rpm-tronics.com
SIC: 3679 Liquid crystal displays (LCD)

(G-2811)
RUSKIN COMPANY
2405 Mciver Ln (75006-6512)
PHONE...............................972 247-7448
EMP: 16 **Privately Held**
WEB: www.ruskin.com
SIC: 3822 Auto controls regulating residntl
& coml environmt & applncs
HQ: Ruskin Company
3900 Doctor Greaves Rd
Grandview MO 64030
816 761-7476

(G-2812)
SANMINA CORPORATION
1201 W Crosby Rd (75006-6905)
PHONE...............................972 512-3333
Mary Littlefield, *Purch Mgr*
Linda Long, *Buyer*
Sally Meyers, *Buyer*
Mike Baker, *Engineer*
Randy Thomas, *VP Bus Dvlpt*
EMP: 400 **Publicly Held**
WEB: www.sanmina.com
SIC: 3672 Printed circuit boards
PA: Sanmina Corporation
2700 N 1st St
San Jose CA 95134

(G-2813)
SCHNEDER ELC BLDNGS AMRCAS INC (DH)
1650 W Crosby Rd (75006-6628)
P.O. Box 841868, Dallas (75284-1868)
PHONE...............................972 323-1111
James Sandlan, *President*
Travis Schneweis, *Partner*
Kirrilly Cooper, *Business Mgr*
Eric Cassagne, *Vice Pres*
Johnathan Donovan, *Vice Pres*
▼ EMP: 400
SQ FT: 85,000
SALES (est): 519MM
SALES (corp-wide): 177.9K **Privately Held**
WEB: www.se.com
SIC: 1731 3822 Electronic controls instal-
lation; air conditioning & refrigeration con-
trols

(G-2814)
SCHNEIDER ELECTRIC USA INC
1650 W Crosby Rd (75006-6628)
PHONE...............................972 323-1111
Bob Klein, *Partner*
Donald Lemenager, *Partner*
Ken Broach, *Area Mgr*
Kevin Self, *Senior VP*
Vinay Moorthy, *Vice Pres*
EMP: 140

SALES (corp-wide): 177.9K **Privately Held**
WEB: www.ccagp.com
SIC: 3613 Switchgear & switchboard appa-
ratus
HQ: Schneider Electric Usa, Inc.
1 Boston Pl Ste 2700
Boston MA 02108
978 975-9600

(G-2815)
SCIENCE APPLICATIONS INTL CORP
2440 Marsh Ln (75006-2216)
PHONE...............................469 557-8249
EMP: 17
SALES (corp-wide): 6.3B **Publicly Held**
WEB: www.saic.com
SIC: 8731 7371 7373 8742 Commercial
physical research; energy research; environmental research; medical research,
commercial; computer software development; systems engineering, computer related; training & development consultant;
integrated circuits, semiconductor networks, etc.
PA: Science Applications International Corporation
12010 Sunset Hills Rd # 5
Reston VA 20190
703 676-4300

(G-2816)
SMITH SYSTEM MANUFACTURING CO
1150 Luna Rd (75006-6630)
P.O. Box 860415, Plano (75086-0415)
PHONE...............................800 328-1061
Charles Risdall, *CEO*
Jim Austin, *President*
Jim Stelter, *President*
Andrea Nodorft, *Business Mgr*
Michelle Shade, *Purchasing*
▲ EMP: 172 EST: 1982
SQ FT: 160,000
SALES (est): 44.1MM
SALES (corp-wide): 3.7B **Publicly Held**
WEB: www.smithsystem.com
SIC: 2531 2522 2521 5021 School furni-
ture; office furniture, except wood; wood
office furniture; furniture
PA: Steelcase Inc.
901 44th St Se
Grand Rapids MI 49508
616 247-2710

(G-2817)
SONOCO PRODUCTS COMPANY
1925 Country Club Dr (75006-5851)
PHONE...............................972 416-2595
Mario Hernandez, *Manager*
Timothy Sperry, *Manager*
EMP: 55
SALES (corp-wide): 5.3B **Publicly Held**
WEB: www.sonoco.com
SIC: 2655 Fiber cans, drums & similar
products
PA: Sonoco Products Company
1 N 2nd St
Hartsville SC 29550
843 383-7000

(G-2818)
SPINNER PRINTING CO (PA)
Also Called: Spinner The Printer
3335 Keller Springs Rd # 1 (75006-5098)
PHONE...............................972 380-0789
Teri Cragle, *CEO*
Mike Richards, *President*
Sherri Urias, *President*
Debbie Morales, *Vice Pres*
Dennis Rose, *Prdtn Mgr*
EMP: 30
SQ FT: 9,200
SALES (est): 2.3MM **Privately Held**
WEB: www.spinnerprinting.com
SIC: 2752 Commercial printing, offset

(G-2819)
SPX DOCK PRODUCTS INC
1612 Hutton Dr Ste 140 (75006-6642)
PHONE...............................972 466-0707
Amy Skoug, *Principal*
EMP: 9

SALES (est): 1.3MM **Privately Held**
WEB: www.sercoentrematic.com
SIC: 3537 Loading docks: portable, ad-
justable & hydraulic

(G-2820)
STMICRLCTRNICS N AMER HLDG INC
1310 Electronics Dr (75006-7005)
PHONE...............................972 466-6000
Alfred Eiblmayr, *President*
Antonio Giuffrida, *Partner*
Mark Crum, *General Mgr*
Neil Frost, *Chief*
Giancarla Zucchetti, *Area Mgr*
EMP: 22
SALES (est): 244.4MM
SALES (corp-wide): 9.5B **Privately Held**
WEB: www.st.com
SIC: 3674 Memories, solid state
PA: Stmicroelectronics N.V.
Schiphol Boulevard 265
Luchthaven Schiphol
206 543-210

(G-2821)
STYLEACCESS LLC
Also Called: Northstar Ceramic Trading
1613 Hutton Dr Ste 110 (75006-6841)
PHONE...............................972 392-3800
Marc Powell, *Mng Member*
Patrick Bonlan,
David Farrage Jr,
Norman Tracy,
◆ EMP: 70
SALES (est): 13.1MM **Privately Held**
SIC: 3253 5032 Floor tile, ceramic; tile &
clay products; tile, clay or other ceramic,
excluding refractory

(G-2822)
SWISS-AMERICAN CDMO LLC
2055 Luna Rd Ste 126 (75006-6623)
PHONE...............................214 239-2280
Phil Oneill, *President*
Ede Payne, *COO*
Cory Johnson, *CFO*
EMP: 160
SQ FT: 134,000
SALES (est): 41.2MM
SALES (corp-wide): 27.9MM **Privately Held**
WEB: www.swissamericancdmo.com
SIC: 2834 2844 Ointments; face creams
or lotions
PA: Swiss American Llc
2055 Luna Rd Ste 126
Carrollton TX 75006
214 239-2280

(G-2823)
TACONIC INDUSTRIES CORPORATION
Also Called: Image Industries
2151 Hutton Dr (75006-6808)
PHONE...............................972 241-5200
U K Gupta, *President*
Sharda Gupta, *Project Mgr*
Amy Yoon, *Controller*
EMP: 32
SQ FT: 108,000
SALES (est): 3.3MM **Privately Held**
WEB: www.image-industries.com
SIC: 3479 2759 Painting of metal prod-
ucts; coating of metals & formed prod-
ucts; screen printing

(G-2824)
TAOTAO USA INC (PA)
2201 Luna Rd (75006-6505)
PHONE...............................214 635-3980
Tarry Matao Cao, *President*
◆ EMP: 10
SALES (est): 2.9MM **Privately Held**
WEB: www.taotao.us
SIC: 3711 Motor vehicles & car bodies

(G-2825)
TAYLOR DESIGN GROUP INC
Also Called: Incratools
1605 Crescent Cir Ste 400 (75006-3502)
P.O. Box 810262, Dallas (75381-0262)
PHONE...............................972 243-7943
Christopher Taylor, *President*
Alice Taylor, *Vice Pres*
Cindy Liang, *Art Dir*

EMP: 17
SQ FT: 8,600
SALES (est): 3.1MM **Privately Held**
WEB: www.incra.com
SIC: 3423 5084 Carpenters' hand tools,
except saws: levels, chisels, etc.; wood-
working machinery

(G-2826)
TE CONNECTIVITY CORPORATION
1628 W Crosby Rd Ste 100 (75006-6632)
PHONE...............................469 568-0657
EMP: 20
SALES (corp-wide): 13.3B **Privately Held**
WEB: www.tycoelectronics.com
SIC: 3089 Thermoformed finished plastic
products
HQ: Te Connectivity Corporation
1050 Westlakes Dr
Berwyn PA 19312
610 893-9800

(G-2827)
TEMPERATSURE LLC
1520 Luna Rd Ste 126 (75006-3446)
PHONE...............................502 715-2819
Eric Loisranoi, *Branch Mgr*
EMP: 20
SALES (corp-wide): 47MM **Privately Held**
WEB: www.nordiccoldchain.com
SIC: 3053 Packing materials
PA: Temperatsure, Llc
2705 Clemens Rd Ste 103
Hatfield PA 19440
866 427-1919

(G-2828)
TESTAMERICA AIR EMISSION CORP (DH)
Also Called: Metco Environmental
3226 Commander Dr (75006-2507)
PHONE...............................800 394-1194
Heather Villemaire, *CFO*
Jenny Stewart, *Admin Sec*
EMP: 15 EST: 2002
SALES (est): 1.8MM
SALES (corp-wide): 2.7B **Privately Held**
WEB: www.metcoenv.com
SIC: 3826 Analytical instruments
HQ: Testamerica Environmental Services,
Llc
4101 Shuffel St Nw
North Canton OH 44720
330 497-9396

(G-2829)
TESTEQUITY LLC
Also Called: Ewd Solutions
2434 Mciver Ln (75006-6511)
PHONE...............................972 247-2470
Scott Maclin, *Partner*
Christine Kubisak-Scales, *Accounts Mgr*
John Bates, *Sales Staff*
David Cornett, *Sales Staff*
Monique Phillips, *Sales Staff*
EMP: 60 **Privately Held**
WEB: www.jensentools.com
SIC: 3825 Instruments to measure electric-
ity
PA: Testequity Llc
6100 Condor Dr
Moorpark CA 93021

(G-2830)
TEXAS FINISHING COMPANY
1801 Surveyor Blvd (75006-5124)
P.O. Box 59445, Dallas (75229-1445)
PHONE...............................972 416-2961
Carolyn B Beard, *President*
Toni Thomas, *Sales Executive*
EMP: 50
SQ FT: 30,000
SALES (est): 8.8MM **Privately Held**
WEB: www.texasfinishing.com
SIC: 3479 2851 Coating of metals &
formed products; paints & allied products

(G-2831)
TEXAS PROFAB CORPORATION
2151 Hutton Dr (75006-6808)
PHONE...............................972 241-5050
Uttar K Gupta, *President*
Vivek Kumar Gupta, *Managing Dir*
EMP: 32

▲ = Import ▼=Export
◆ =Import/Export

SQ FT: 108,000
SALES (est): 5MM **Privately Held**
WEB: www.texasprofab.com
SIC: 3444 Sheet metalwork

(G-2832)
THOMSON REUTERS CORPORATION
2395 Midway Rd (75006-2521)
PHONE...................................972 250-7000
Carl Tobiasen, *General Mgr*
Andrew Scherf, *Editor*
Warren Schaefer, *Counsel*
Tina Arend, *Vice Pres*
Maria Diaz, *Vice Pres*
EMP: 89
SALES (corp-wide): 10.6B **Publicly Held**
WEB: www.thomsonreuters.com
SIC: 2731 8111 7372 Books: publishing only; legal services; prepackaged software
HQ: Thomson Reuters Corporation
333 Bay St
Toronto ON M5H 2
416 687-7500

(G-2833)
THOMSON RTERS TAX ACCNTING INC (DH)
2395 Midway Rd (75006-2521)
PHONE...................................800 431-9025
Brian Pecarrelli, *President*
Roy Martin, *President*
Lori Sheehy, *Principal*
Sari Dwek, *Vice Pres*
Dalton Conley, *Engineer*
EMP: 400
SQ FT: 400,000
SALES (est): 424.8MM
SALES (corp-wide): 10.6B **Publicly Held**
WEB: www.thomsonreuters.com
SIC: 2721 7371 Periodicals: publishing only; computer software development

(G-2834)
TIDEL ENGINEERING LP
2025 W Belt Line Rd # 114 (75006-6453)
PHONE...................................972 484-3358
Gary Landry, *President*
Flynt Moreland, *Exec VP*
Troy Richard, *Exec VP*
Darren Taylor, *Exec VP*
Glenn Mason, *Vice Pres*
▲ EMP: 134
SQ FT: 50,000
SALES (est): 28.6MM **Privately Held**
WEB: www.tidel.com
SIC: 3499 Money chests, steel; safes & vaults, metal

(G-2835)
TITAN CHAIR LLC (PA)
Also Called: Titanchair.com
1001 W Crosby Rd (75006-6901)
PHONE...................................888 848-2630
Michael Cha, *President*
Steven Cha,
▲ EMP: 25
SALES (est): 30MM **Privately Held**
WEB: www.titanchair.com
SIC: 3634 Massage machines, electric, except for beauty/barber shops

(G-2836)
TRANE US INC
1617 Hutton Dr (75006-6610)
PHONE...................................239 277-7400
EMP: 10 **Privately Held**
SIC: 3585 Mfg Refrigeration/Heating Equipment
HQ: Trane U.S. Inc.
3600 Pammel Creek Rd
La Crosse WI 54601
608 787-2000

(G-2837)
TRANE US INC
1617 Hutton Dr (75006-6610)
PHONE...................................469 758-3128
Tim Engebretsen, *Accounts Mgr*
Felix Wilson, *Branch Mgr*
Kim Gates, *Manager*
Micah Lightfoot, *Manager*
EMP: 300 **Privately Held**
WEB: www.trane.com

SIC: 3585 Refrigeration & heating equipment
HQ: Trane U.S. Inc.
3600 Pammel Creek Rd
La Crosse WI 54601
608 787-2000

(G-2838)
TRANSCENDIA INC
Also Called: Transilwrap Texas
2001 Westgate Dr Ste 100 (75006-6477)
PHONE...................................800 659-4254
Adam Shea, *Plant Mgr*
Rose Olsen, *Sales Mgr*
John G Sakelaris, *Branch Mgr*
Cody Waits, *Analyst*
Glen Skajewski, *Representative*
EMP: 20
SALES (corp-wide): 314.1MM **Privately Held**
WEB: www.transcendia.com
SIC: 2869 3081 2671 Industrial organic chemicals; unsupported plastics film & sheet; packaging paper & plastics film, coated & laminated
PA: Transcendia, Inc.
9201 Belmont Ave Ste 100a
Franklin Park IL 60131
847 678-1800

(G-2839)
TRANSDATA INC
2560 Tarpley Rd (75006-2328)
PHONE...................................972 418-7717
Edward J Gleibs III, *President*
Larry Porter, *President*
Edward J Gleibs Jr, *Chairman*
Stephen R Clegg, *Exec VP*
Rebecca A Foster, *Vice Pres*
EMP: 35
SQ FT: 26,000
SALES (est): 7MM **Privately Held**
WEB: www.transdatainc.com
SIC: 3825 Transducers for volts, amperes, watts, vars, frequency, etc.

(G-2840)
TREND OFFSET PRINTING SVCS INC
Also Called: TREND OFFSET PRINTING SERVICES INCORPORATED
2323 Mcdaniel Dr Ste 100 (75006-8355)
PHONE...................................972 243-3556
David Wickstrom, *President*
Tom Vargas, *Production*
Steve Priester, *Purchasing*
Tim Brown, *Cust Mgr*
Jeff O' Brien, *Manager*
EMP: 200
SALES (corp-wide): 422.2MM **Privately Held**
WEB: www.trendoffset.com
SIC: 2752 Commercial printing, offset
PA: Trend Offset Printing Services, Inc.
3701 Catalina St
Los Alamitos CA 90720
562 598-2446

(G-2841)
TSA GRIDDLE SYSTEMS INC
2009 Mckenzie Dr Ste 116 (75006-8366)
PHONE...................................972 243-8070
EMP: 10
SALES: 3.9MM **Privately Held**
SIC: 3634 Electric Housewares And Fans

(G-2842)
UNIFRAX I LLC
2340 E Trinty Mls Rd # 300 (75006-1942)
PHONE...................................281 251-5595
EMP: 44
SALES (corp-wide): 176.8MM **Privately Held**
SIC: 3299 Mfg Nonmetallic Mineral Products
HQ: Unifrax I Llc
600 Rverwalk Pkwy Ste 120
Tonawanda NY 14150
716 768-6400

(G-2843)
UNITED LABORATORIES MFG LLC (DH)
Also Called: United 1 International Labs
1541 Champion Dr (75006-6814)
PHONE...................................972 490-3300

George Mitchell, *President*
Matt Donnell, *COO*
James Mitchell, *Exec VP*
Joe Cooper, *Vice Pres*
Lorena Macias, *Vice Pres*
▲ EMP: 150
SALES (est): 75MM
SALES (corp-wide): 90.9MM **Privately Held**
WEB: www.inw-group.com
SIC: 2834 2844 Vitamin, nutrient & hematinic preparations for human use; cosmetic preparations
HQ: Inw Manufacturing, Llc
2101 Cedar Springs Rd # 16
Dallas TX 75201
972 490-3300

(G-2844)
VAREL MINING AND INDUS LLC (DH)
1625 W Crosby Rd Ste 124 (75006-6694)
P.O. Box 111397 (75011-1397)
PHONE...................................469 476-4870
David Harrington, *CEO*
EMP: 11
SALES (est): 23.4MM
SALES (corp-wide): 10.7B **Privately Held**
WEB: www.varelmining.com
SIC: 3545 Drill bits, metalworking
HQ: Sandvik, Inc.
17-02 Nevins Rd
Fair Lawn NJ 07410
201 794-5000

(G-2845)
WARFIELD ELECTRIC TEXAS INC
Also Called: Jim Warfield Electric
1221 Champion Cir Ste 105 (75006-8389)
PHONE...................................214 637-1200
Barbara Warfield, *President*
▲ EMP: 12
SQ FT: 26,000
SALES (est): 2.1MM **Privately Held**
WEB: www.butbid.com
SIC: 7694 Rebuilding motors, except automotive; electric motor repair

(G-2846)
WATER EVENT GULF COAST LLC
2109 Luna Rd Ste 100 (75006-6437)
PHONE...................................713 937-8630
Brian Rose, *Mng Member*
Chivone Thompson, *Manager*
EMP: 30
SQ FT: 10,000
SALES (est): 1.2MM **Privately Held**
WEB: www.waterevent.com
SIC: 2086 Mineral water, carbonated: packaged in cans, bottles, etc.

(G-2847)
WATKINS ORNAMENTAL IRON INC
3219 Commander Dr Ste 120 (75006-2537)
PHONE...................................972 931-5350
▲ EMP: 16
SQ FT: 12,000
SALES (est): 2.9MM **Privately Held**
SIC: 3446 Architectural metalwork

(G-2848)
WESTERN INDUSTRIES CORPORATION
Also Called: Wic
2161 Hutton Dr Ste 116 (75006-6895)
PHONE...................................214 503-8322
Louis Morelli, *Branch Mgr*
EMP: 65
SALES (corp-wide): 27.5MM **Privately Held**
WEB: www.wicpack.com
SIC: 3086 2449 Packaging & shipping materials, foamed plastic; wood containers
PA: Western Industries Corporation
5500 S Hattie Ave
Oklahoma City OK 73129
405 419-3100

(G-2849)
WHRZT INC
2418 Marsh Ln Ste 106 (75006-3338)
PHONE...................................888 507-9985
Jim Nalley, *CEO*
Gary Menees, *COO*
Chris Buehler, *CTO*
EMP: 10 EST: 2015
SQ FT: 2,500
SALES (est): 327.2K **Privately Held**
WEB: www.whrzt.com
SIC: 3812 Search & navigation equipment

(G-2850)
WOODHAUS INC
1207 Tappan Cir Ste 104 (75006-6943)
PHONE...................................972 245-8117
Jeff Dale, *President*
Robbie Hesselbacher, *Vice Pres*
EMP: 100
SALES (est): 17.1MM **Privately Held**
WEB: www.woodhausinc.com
SIC: 2431 Millwork

(G-2851)
YELLOW FOLDER LLC
1617 W Crosby Rd Ste 100 (75006-6486)
PHONE...................................214 431-3600
Kelby Hagar, *Principal*
Chris Dyess, *Exec VP*
Jason Addams, *Engineer*
Claudia Mullins, *Engineer*
Jhenelle Smith, *Accounting Mgr*
EMP: 33 EST: 2013
SALES (est): 5.1MM **Privately Held**
WEB: www.yellowfolder.com
SIC: 7372 8231 Educational computer software; documentation center

(G-2852)
ZURN INDUSTRIES LLC
2055 Luna Rd Ste 182 (75006-6466)
PHONE...................................972 277-0900
Jim Sauter, *Branch Mgr*
Sharon Fisher, *Supervisor*
Christina Smoke, *Supervisor*
EMP: 20 **Publicly Held**
WEB: www.zurn.com
SIC: 3431 5074 Bathroom fixtures, including sinks; plumbing fittings & supplies
HQ: Zurn Industries, Llc
1801 Pittsburgh Ave
Erie PA 16502
814 455-0921

Carrollton
Denton County

(G-2853)
ADDVANTAGE TECH GROUP INC (PA)
1430 Bradley Ln Ste 196 (75007-4952)
PHONE...................................918 251-9121
James C McGill, *Ch of Bd*
Joseph E Hart, *President*
Reginald Jaramillo, *President*
Donald E Kinison, *President*
Jimmy Taylor, *President*
EMP: 21
SALES: 50.1MM **Publicly Held**
WEB: www.addvantagetech.com
SIC: 5051 4841 3663 Cable, wire; cable & other pay television services; cable television equipment

(G-2854)
ADVANTAGE SUPPLIES INC
4257 Marsh Ridge Rd (75010-4456)
PHONE...................................972 250-1339
Lisa Thompson, *President*
Michael Thompson, *Vice Pres*
▲ EMP: 18
SQ FT: 4,800
SALES (est): 2.3MM **Privately Held**
WEB: www.advantagesupplies.com
SIC: 2311 2329 3999 Military uniforms, men's & youths': purchased materials; field jackets, military; military insignia

(G-2855)
ALLMETAL INC
Also Called: All Metal
1413 Bradley Ln (75007-4897)
PHONE..................................972 245-9264
Kevin Dugan, *General Mgr*
Kelvin Dugan, *Plant Mgr*
Cathy Richards, *Sales Staff*
Kathy Richards, *Sales Staff*
EMP: 35
SALES (corp-wide): 70.6MM **Privately Held**
WEB: www.allmetalinc.de
SIC: 3442 3446 3444 Window & door frames; architectural metalwork; sheet metalwork
PA: Allmetal, Inc.
1 Pierce Pl Ste 295w
Itasca IL 60143
630 250-8090

(G-2856)
AMERISOURCE COMPANIES LP
2828 Trade Ctr Ste 110 (75007-4654)
P.O. Box 2088, Addison (75001-2088)
PHONE..................................972 380-2000
▲ EMP: 40 EST: 1995
SALES (est): 12.2MM **Privately Held**
WEB: www.myamerisource.com
SIC: 2653 Corrugated & solid fiber boxes

(G-2857)
ARCANUM CORP
Also Called: Arcanum Consulting
2918 Panorama Dr (75007-4302)
PHONE..................................214 507-3433
EMP: 16
SQ FT: 1,500
SALES (est): 970K **Privately Held**
SIC: 7379 8748 2396 It Consulting Business Consulting & Apparel Print Svcs

(G-2858)
ASSURANCE SYSTEMS INC
Also Called: Accuauto
1415 Halsey Way Ste 314 (75007-4455)
PHONE..................................770 242-6832
William R Capps, *CEO*
Kurt Hedberg, *Business Mgr*
Katherine Capps, *CFO*
EMP: 15
SALES (est): 1.7MM
SALES (corp-wide): 41.4MM **Privately Held**
WEB: www.accuauto.net
SIC: 7372 Operating systems computer software
HQ: Insurance Technologies Corp
1415 Halsey Way Ste 314
Carrollton TX 75007
972 245-3660

(G-2859)
CHATEAU NOBLESSE INC
Also Called: Latin Orchid
4228 N Josey Ln 112 (75010-4600)
PHONE..................................972 365-7017
EMP: 64
SQ FT: 500
SALES (est): 5MM **Privately Held**
SIC: 2844 5087 7231 Manufactures Cosmetic Products

(G-2860)
CORRADI USA INC
1433 W Frankford Rd # 100 (75007-4959)
PHONE..................................972 466-0721
Alberto Tanzi, *President*
Beatrice Arouati, *Corp Secy*
Christopher Taylor, *Natl Sales Mgr*
Erin Collis, *Marketing Mgr*
Francesco Tanzi, *Manager*
◆ EMP: 50
SQ FT: 67,000
SALES (est): 17MM
SALES (corp-wide): 3.7MM **Privately Held**
WEB: www.corradiusa.com
SIC: 5023 2431 2394 Window furnishings; moldings, wood: unfinished & prefinished; canvas awnings & canopies
PA: Corradi Spa
Via Marosticana 25
Maser TV
042 392-3083

(G-2861)
CROWN EXPLORATION LTD
4024 Nazarene Dr Ste A (75010-6425)
PHONE..................................972 395-1133
Shawn M Grisham, *President*
Jennifer Carlton, *Human Res Mgr*
Danice Grisham, *Admin Sec*
EMP: 14
SQ FT: 3,000
SALES (est): 1.4MM **Privately Held**
WEB: www.crownexploration.com
SIC: 1382 Oil & gas exploration services

(G-2862)
CT-TECHNOLOGY INC (PA)
1448 Halsey Way Ste 112 (75007-4441)
PHONE..................................469 531-9472
Le Tran, *President*
Lynn Cao, *Vice Pres*
EMP: 9
SQ FT: 1,100
SALES (est): 1.2MM **Privately Held**
WEB: www.ct-technology.net
SIC: 3679 Harness assemblies for electronic use: wire or cable

(G-2863)
DACOS BOWLING INTERNATIONAL (PA)
3618 Canyon Oaks Dr (75007-2779)
PHONE..................................972 394-6507
Richard Donahue, *President*
EMP: 25
SALES (est): 1.5MM **Privately Held**
SIC: 3949 Bowling equipment & supplies

(G-2864)
DALLAS FABRICATION INC
1520 Halsey Way (75007-4438)
P.O. Box 59474, Dallas (75229-1474)
PHONE..................................972 245-8771
William Mosher, *CEO*
Bill Mosher, *Research*
EMP: 20
SQ FT: 18,000
SALES (est): 7.5MM **Privately Held**
SIC: 3441 Fabricated structural metal

(G-2865)
DIESEL DISPLAYS & INTERIOR LLC
2941 Commodore Dr (75007-4615)
PHONE..................................800 747-4417
Brian Karr,
EMP: 72
SALES (est): 2.4MM **Privately Held**
SIC: 2541 Store & office display cases & fixtures

(G-2866)
DM HOME ENTERTAINMENT LLC
4300 Marsh Ridge Rd # 112 (75010-4450)
PHONE..................................972 992-3155
EMP: 9
SQ FT: 3,500
SALES (est): 1.4MM **Privately Held**
SIC: 3651 Mfg Home Audio/Video Equipment

(G-2867)
GVI SECURITY SOLUTIONS INC
2801 Trade Ctr Ste 120 (75007-4637)
PHONE..................................972 236-6235
Steven E Walin, *Ch of Bd*
Joseph Restivo, *COO*
EMP: 53
SQ FT: 58,850
SALES (est): 6.4MM **Privately Held**
WEB: www.myvideobell.com
SIC: 3812 Detection apparatus: electronic/magnetic field, light/heat

(G-2868)
HESEYEON LLC
1001 E Hbron Pkwy Ste 114 (75010)
PHONE..................................214 483-3800
Young M Kwon, *Principal*
EMP: 9
SALES (est): 1MM **Privately Held**
SIC: 2869 Laboratory chemicals, organic

(G-2869)
HEWELL ENTERPRISES INC
Also Called: AlphaGraphics
2722 N Josey Ln Ste 100 (75007-5433)
PHONE..................................972 466-2442
Martie Cowan, *President*
Jim Hewell, *CFO*
Dennis McCabe, *Manager*
EMP: 39
SQ FT: 10,000
SALES (est): 5.8MM **Privately Held**
WEB: www.agnortheast.com
SIC: 2752 2759 2791 Commercial printing, lithographic; photocopying & duplicating services; commercial art & graphic design; typesetting; bookbinding & related work; commercial printing

(G-2870)
IB SUPPLY LLC (PA)
Also Called: International Builders Supply
2933 Eisenhower St # 110 (75007-4981)
PHONE..................................469 709-9650
Andrew Sanders, *Opers Mgr*
Robyn Zumwalt, *VP Sales*
John Shofner, *Mng Member*
Tyler Laughlin, *Graphic Designe*
David Clift,
EMP: 16
SQ FT: 2,500
SALES (est): 12MM **Privately Held**
WEB: www.ib-supply.com
SIC: 5032 3253 5211 5713 Tile, clay or other ceramic, excluding refractory; ceramic wall & floor tile; tile, ceramic; floor tile

(G-2871)
INTERCERAMIC INC (HQ)
Also Called: Intercramic Tile Stone Gallery
1950 Parker Rd (75010-4735)
PHONE..................................214 503-5501
Victor Almeida, *President*
Edmeerto Maese, *Senior VP*
Humberto Maese, *Senior VP*
Tom Smolarek, *Opers Mgr*
Kevin Thompson, *Opers Mgr*
◆ EMP: 400
SQ FT: 250,000
SALES (est): 188.6MM **Privately Held**
WEB: www.interceramicusa.com
SIC: 3253 5032 Ceramic wall & floor tile; tile, structural clay

(G-2872)
INTERPHASE CORPORATION (PA)
4240 Intl Pkwy Ste 105 (75007)
PHONE..................................214 654-5000
Gregory B Kalush, *Ch of Bd*
Randall E McComas, *Vice Pres*
Yoram Solomon, *Vice Pres*
Thomas N Tipton Jr, *CFO*
Ed Von Adelung, *Sr Project Mgr*
▲ EMP: 67
SQ FT: 43,000
SALES: 13.7MM **Privately Held**
WEB: www.interphase.com
SIC: 3577 Input/output equipment, computer

(G-2873)
J & J NAMEPLATE AND LABEL LLC
Also Called: Texas Label and Tag
2425 Parker Rd Bldg 6 (75010-4742)
PHONE..................................972 939-1157
Fernando Dacosta,
Robin Dacosta,
EMP: 9
SQ FT: 22,000
SALES (est): 1.2MM **Privately Held**
WEB: www.jjnameplate.com
SIC: 2759 2796 Screen printing; platemaking services

(G-2874)
JOHN W GASPARINI INC
Also Called: Mark's Plumbing Parts
2720 Commodore Dr Ste 130 (75007-6479)
PHONE..................................972 466-4104
Randy Acker, *Sales Mgr*
Rene Garcia, *Sales Staff*
Joe Lewis, *Manager*
EMP: 55
SALES (corp-wide): 44.4MM **Privately Held**
WEB: www.marksmro.com
SIC: 3432 Plumbing fixture fittings & trim
PA: John W Gasparini, Inc.
3312 Ramona Dr
Fort Worth TX 76116
817 731-6211

(G-2875)
JOHN WILEY & SONS INC
1649 W Frankford Rd (75007-4605)
PHONE..................................972 245-0480
EMP: 63
SALES (corp-wide): 1.8B **Publicly Held**
WEB: www.wiley.com
SIC: 2731 Books: publishing only
PA: John Wiley & Sons, Inc.
111 River St Ste 2000
Hoboken NJ 07030
201 748-6000

(G-2876)
LA BLANC BOB
4309 Fairway Dr (75010-3233)
PHONE..................................972 492-1898
Bob Leblanc, *President*
EMP: 23
SALES (est): 2MM **Privately Held**
SIC: 2892 Explosives

(G-2877)
LADY HLTH FTNESS-ROCKWALL INC (PA)
Also Called: Results Fitness For Women
4009 Old Denton Rd # 114 (75007-1000)
PHONE..................................972 906-0400
John Gauthier, *Principal*
EMP: 10
SALES (est): 1.3MM **Privately Held**
WEB: www.treehealthlady.com
SIC: 7991 3634 Physical fitness clubs with training equipment; sauna heaters, electric

(G-2878)
LOGICAL CONTROL SERVICES LLP
Also Called: Lcs
1421 Lemay Dr (75007-4930)
PHONE..................................972 820-0100
Ron Pogue, *Partner*
James Murphy, *Partner*
Glenda Howerton, *Controller*
Deanna King, *Controller*
Josh Bump, *Supervisor*
EMP: 42
SQ FT: 13,000
SALES (est): 8.2MM **Privately Held**
WEB: www.lcstexas.com
SIC: 1711 3822 1731 Warm air heating & air conditioning contractor; building services monitoring controls, automatic; fire detection & burglar alarm systems specialization

(G-2879)
LYONDELL CHEMICAL COMPANY
4025 Midway Rd (75007-1904)
PHONE..................................972 512-3171
EMP: 79
SALES (corp-wide): 32.8B **Privately Held**
SIC: 2869 Mfg Industrial Organic Chemicals
HQ: Lyondell Chemical Company
1221 Mckinney St Ste 300
Houston TX 77010
713 309-7200

(G-2880)
NAPCO BAG & FILM GP LLC (PA)
1435 Bradley Ln Ste 130 (75007-4956)
PHONE..................................972 245-8190
Steve Rife, *Exec VP*
Mike Milton, *VP Sales*
David Monroe, *Regl Sales Mgr*
Nolan Sittig, *Manager*
Todd Garrett,
▲ EMP: 45
SALES (est): 14.3MM **Privately Held**
WEB: www.napcobag.com
SIC: 2821 Plastics materials & resins

(G-2881)
PHILIPS NORTH AMERICA LLC
Also Called: Entertainment Technology
2828 Trade Ctr Ste 130 (75007-4636)
PHONE..................................800 526-2731
EMP: 126
SALES (corp-wide): 20.1B Privately Held
SIC: 3646 Mfg Commercial Lighting Fixtures
HQ: Philips North America Llc
222 Jacobs St Fl 3
Cambridge MA 02141
978 659-3000

(G-2882)
PRECISE FOOD INGREDIENTS INC
1432 Wainwright Way # 150 (75007-4948)
PHONE..................................972 323-4951
Scott Miller, President
Morris Mahaley, Vice Pres
Morris Mahalley, Vice Pres
Danny Orr, Prdtn Mgr
Chinda Sivannarath, Production
EMP: 41
SQ FT: 98,000
SALES (est): 16.8MM Privately Held
WEB: www.precisefood.com
SIC: 2099 Seasonings & spices

(G-2883)
R & R CUSTOM CABINETS INC
1213 Wiltshire Dr (75007-4810)
PHONE..................................972 247-4697
Russell Shaffer, President
Rick Mc Cance, Vice Pres
Marsha Mc Cance, Treasurer
Linda Shaffer, Admin Sec
EMP: 15
SQ FT: 18,500
SALES (est): 1.3MM Privately Held
SIC: 2434 2541 2542 Wood kitchen cabinets; store & office display cases & fixtures; cabinets, except refrigerated: show, display, etc.: wood; counters or counter display cases: except wood; fixtures, store: except wood; cabinets: show, display or storage: except wood

(G-2884)
RAYTHEON COMPANY
2816 Commodore Dr (75007-4612)
PHONE..................................972 952-4195
Gordon Prendergast, Info Tech Dir
EMP: 22 EST: 1922
SALES (est): 9.5MM Privately Held
WEB: www.rtx.com
SIC: 3812 Search & navigation equipment

(G-2885)
REDI-MIX LP (DH)
1445 Mac Arthur Dr # 136 (75007-4461)
PHONE..................................972 242-4550
Bill Mabry, Partner
John C Miller, Partner
Chuck Powell, Partner
EMP: 20 EST: 1979
SQ FT: 6,500
SALES (est): 102.8MM
SALES (corp-wide): 1.4B Publicly Held
SIC: 3273 Ready-mixed concrete
HQ: Alberta Investments Inc
1445 Mac Arthur Dr Ste 13
Carrollton TX 75007
972 242-4550

(G-2886)
RF MONOLITHICS INC (DH)
Also Called: Rfm
4100 Midway Rd Ste 2050 (75007-1976)
PHONE..................................972 233-2903
Farlin A Halsey, President
James P Farley, Vice Pres
Jon S Prokop, Vice Pres
David B Crawford, VP Sls/Mktg
Harley E Barnes III, CFO
▲ EMP: 39 EST: 1979
SQ FT: 31,000
SALES (est): 7.2MM Privately Held
WEB: www.wireless.murata.com
SIC: 3663 Carrier equipment, radio communications
HQ: Murata Electronics North America, Inc.
2200 Lake Park Dr Se
Smyrna GA 30080
770 436-1300

(G-2887)
SIGNS UNIVERSE
3733 N Josey Ln Ste 105 (75007-2475)
PHONE..................................972 880-2884
Wajahap Siddiqui, Owner
EMP: 9
SALES (est): 947.3K Privately Held
WEB: www.signsuniverse.com
SIC: 3993 Signs, not made in custom sign painting shops

(G-2888)
SKW ALLIANCE MED LLC
2256 Longwood Dr (75010-4912)
PHONE..................................972 358-5171
EMP: 9
SALES (est): 150K Privately Held
SIC: 2836 Mfg Biological Products

(G-2889)
SOLA PROSTHETICS INC
4541 N Josey Ln Ste 240 (75010-4781)
P.O. Box 1565, Little Elm (75068-1565)
PHONE..................................972 492-7652
EMP: 10
SALES (est): 1.2MM Privately Held
SIC: 3842 Mfg Surgical Appliances/Supplies

(G-2890)
TELLABS INC (HQ)
4240 Intl Pkwy Ste 105 (75007)
PHONE............/.....................800 690-2324
▲ EMP: 20
SALES (est): 350.1MM Privately Held
WEB: www.tellabs.com
SIC: 3661 1731 Telephones & telephone apparatus; multiplex equipment, telephone & telegraph; communications specialization

(G-2891)
TELLABS ENTERPRISE INC
4240 Intl Pkwy Ste 105 (75007)
PHONE..................................972 588-7951
James D Norrod, President
Richard Cuthill, Vice Pres
Thomas Ruvarac, Vice Pres
David Brown, CFO
Alan Malone, Technology
▲ EMP: 51
SALES (est): 6.5MM Privately Held
WEB: www.tellabs.com
SIC: 3669 Intercommunication systems, electric
HQ: Tellabs Access Llc
338 Pier Ave
Hermosa Beach CA 90254
630 798-8671

(G-2892)
TURBOCHEF TECHNOLOGIES INC
4240 Intl Pkwy Ste 105 (75007)
PHONE..................................214 379-6000
April J McLain, President
EMP: 26
SALES (corp-wide): 2.7B Publicly Held
WEB: www.turbochef.com
SIC: 3631 3589 Household cooking equipment; cooking equipment, commercial
HQ: Turbochef Technologies Inc.
2801 Trade Ctr
Carrollton TX 75007

(G-2893)
TURBOCHEF TECHNOLOGIES INC (HQ)
2801 Trade Ctr (75007-4630)
PHONE..................................214 379-6000
Timothy J Fitzgerald, Vice Pres
Martin M Lindsay, Treasurer
◆ EMP: 28
SQ FT: 7,000
SALES (est): 51.6MM
SALES (corp-wide): 2.7B Publicly Held
WEB: www.turbochef.com
SIC: 3631 3589 Convection ovens, including portable: household; microwave ovens (cooking equipment), commercial
PA: The Middleby Corporation
1400 Toastmaster Dr
Elgin IL 60120
847 741-3300

(G-2894)
VASTAV INC
Also Called: AlphaGraphics
2722 N Josey Ln Ste 100 (75007-5433)
PHONE..................................972 466-2442
Pratul Kumar, President
EMP: 33
SALES (est): 4.8MM Privately Held
WEB: www.agnortheast.com
SIC: 2752 Commercial printing, lithographic

(G-2895)
VEDERO SOFTWARE INC
4100 Midway Rd Ste 2050 (75007-1976)
PHONE..................................972 309-9870
Joe Pollard, CEO
David Booty, COO
Michael Green, CFO
Tobe Thompson, CTO
EMP: 9
SALES (est): 1.1MM Privately Held
WEB: www.murata.com
SIC: 7372 7371 Prepackaged software; computer software development

(G-2896)
VERITY INSTRUMENTS INC
2901 Eisenhower St (75007-4887)
PHONE..................................972 446-9990
Mike Whelan, President
Paul Whelan, Vice Pres
Dianne Treneman, Senior Buyer
Dianne Zacha, Senior Buyer
Dean Wellman, Purchasing
▲ EMP: 60 EST: 1965
SQ FT: 40,000
SALES (est): 13MM Privately Held
WEB: www.verityinst.com
SIC: 3825 3575 Instruments to measure electricity; computer terminals

(G-2897)
WHITE WING WEAPONRY LLC
1629 W Hebron Pkwy (75010-6334)
PHONE..................................940 382-0830
Jeremy Hubnik, Owner
Brenna Albright,
EMP: 10
SALES (est): 908.2K Privately Held
WEB: www.whitewingweaponry.net
SIC: 3484 5941 Guns (firearms) or gun parts, 30 mm. & below; firearms

Carthage
Panola County

(G-2898)
ANDERSON MUD LOGGING SERVICE
1401 Hills Lake Rd (75633-3168)
P.O. Box 726 (75633-0726)
PHONE..................................903 693-5817
Royce Anderson, Owner
Scott Anderson, Principal
EMP: 11
SALES (est): 604.7K Privately Held
SIC: 1389 Mud service, oil field drilling

(G-2899)
BAKER HUGHES A GE COMPANY LLC
3115 Sw Loop (75633)
PHONE..................................903 690-0026
Bob Hughes, Branch Mgr
Shannon Weatherford, Manager
EMP: 41
SALES (corp-wide): 23.8B Publicly Held
WEB: www.bakerhughes.com
SIC: 1389 Oil field services
HQ: Baker Hughes Holdings Llc
17021 Aldine Westfield Rd
Houston TX 77073
713 439-8600

(G-2900)
CAPPS CONSTRUCTION AND GAS CO
Also Called: Capps Construction Co
1108 N Saint Mary St (75633-1122)
PHONE..................................903 693-2580
Mike Capps, President
R N Capps, President

Phyllis Capps, Vice Pres
EMP: 10
SQ FT: 300
SALES (est): 1.2MM Privately Held
SIC: 1389 Building oil & gas well foundations on site

(G-2901)
CAR-TEX TRANSPORT & VACUUM SVC
County Rd 301 (75633)
P.O. Box 647 (75633-0647)
PHONE..................................903 693-6271
Henry L Howard, President
Robert Howard, Vice Pres
Deborah Patrick, Treasurer
EMP: 78
SQ FT: 1,500
SALES (est): 5.7MM Privately Held
SIC: 1389 Gas field services

(G-2902)
CARTHAGE CUP CO
505 E Cotton St (75633-2753)
P.O. Box 668 (75633-0668)
PHONE..................................903 693-7151
John Bates, Principal
EMP: 9
SALES (est): 1.1MM
SALES (corp-wide): 3.7B Privately Held
WEB: www.carthageisd.org
SIC: 3089 Plastics products
PA: Cascades Inc
404 Boul Marie-Victorin
Kingsey Falls QC J0A 1
819 363-5100

(G-2903)
CARTHAGE HARDWOODS LLC
1314 Hills Lake Rd (75633-3169)
P.O. Box 1317 (75633-7317)
PHONE..................................903 693-9300
Michael Anthony, Principal
EMP: 11
SALES (est): 1.8MM Privately Held
SIC: 2421 Sawmills & planing mills, general

(G-2904)
COMMIATOS MCH & REPR SVC INC
1141 Ne Loop (75633-1245)
PHONE..................................903 694-9378
Rebecia Commiato, President
Pete Commiato, Vice Pres
Pete Commiatos, Vice Pres
EMP: 9
SALES (est): 1.5MM Privately Held
WEB: www.commiatosmachine.com
SIC: 3599 Machine shop, jobbing & repair

(G-2905)
D COURTNEY CONSTRUCTION INC
1300 Ne Loop Carthage (75633)
P.O. Box 549 (75633-0549)
PHONE..................................903 694-2911
Daphne Courtney, President
K Shane Courtney, Vice Pres
Donna Courtney, Treasurer
Karlos Courtney, Treasurer
David Holcomb, Sr Project Mgr
EMP: 265
SQ FT: 6,000
SALES (est): 55.4MM Privately Held
WEB: www.courtneyconstruction.com
SIC: 1389 Oil field services

(G-2906)
DEVON ENERGY CORPORATION
611 S Shelby St (75633-3025)
P.O. Box 270 (75633-0270)
PHONE..................................903 693-7196
Harold Hawkin, Manager
EMP: 15
SALES (corp-wide): 6.2B Publicly Held
WEB: www.devonenergy.com
SIC: 1311 1381 1382 Crude petroleum production; drilling oil & gas wells; oil & gas exploration services
PA: Devon Energy Corporation
333 W Sheridan Ave
Oklahoma City OK 73102
405 235-3611

GEOGRAPHIC

(G-2907)
FIELDCO ENERGY SERVICES INC
Also Called: Wellpath Solutions
101 Timberlane Dr (75633-2228)
P.O. Box 518 (75633-0580)
PHONE...............................903 693-5900
Larry W Fields, President
EMP: 11
SALES (est): 1MM Privately Held
WEB: www.fieldcoenergy.com
SIC: 1389 Oil field services

(G-2908)
GENPAK LLC
505 E Cotton St (75633-2753)
PHONE...............................903 693-7151
Paul Haviland, Transportation
Dennis Patterson, Production
Matthew Altimari, Controller
Kristine Arthurs, Controller
William Oconnell, VP Finance
EMP: 117 Privately Held
WEB: www.genpak.com
SIC: 3089 Plastic containers, except foam
HQ: Genpak Llc
    10601 Westlake Dr
    Charlotte NC 28273
    800 626-6695

(G-2909)
GENPAK SOUTHWEST LP
505 E Cotton St (75633-2753)
PHONE...............................903 693-7151
Edward P Fitts, Partner
Lois A Meeth, Partner
Susan Scadden, Partner
Richard J Scanlan, Partner
EMP: 180 EST: 1960
SQ FT: 4,200
SALES (est): 16.7MM Privately Held
SIC: 3089 Kitchenware, plastic; cups, plastic, except foam; plates, plastic; plastic containers, except foam
HQ: Genpak Llc
    10601 Westlake Dr
    Charlotte NC 28273
    800 626-6695

(G-2910)
KEY ENERGY DRILLING INC
1771 Ne Loop (75633-1966)
PHONE...............................903 693-2622
Ishmael Wynn, Branch Mgr
EMP: 25
SALES (corp-wide): 413.8MM Publicly Held
WEB: www.keyenergy.com
SIC: 1389 Oil field services
HQ: Key Energy Drilling, Inc.
    1301 Mckinney St Ste 1800
    Houston TX 77010

(G-2911)
KOCH INDUSTRIES INC
606 S Shelby St (75633-3026)
PHONE...............................903 693-5172
Ed McMullen, Manager
EMP: 35
SALES (corp-wide): 36.8B Privately Held
WEB: www.kochindusinc.com
SIC: 1389 4613 4612 Gas compressing (natural gas) at the fields; refined petroleum pipelines; crude petroleum pipelines
PA: Koch Industries, Inc.
    4111 E 37th St N
    Wichita KS 67220
    316 828-5500

(G-2912)
LEGACY FIELD SERVICES LLC
457 W Panola St (75633-2536)
P.O. Box 1539 (75633-7539)
PHONE...............................903 694-9445
Shirlene Daniel, CFO
Jennifer Leggett, Mng Member
Sam Pullig, Mng Member
Kathryn B Leggett,
Shannon Mayfield,
EMP: 63
SQ FT: 2,000
SALES (est): 9.9MM Privately Held
WEB: www.legacyfieldservices.com
SIC: 1389 Oil field services

(G-2913)
LINDSAY FOREST PRODUCTS INC
2113 Se Loop (75633-3159)
P.O. Box 289 (75633-0289)
PHONE...............................903 693-7526
Brad Eberenz, Opers-Prdtn-Mfg
Joy Meaux, Admin Mgr
EMP: 11
SALES (corp-wide): 2.8MM Privately Held
WEB: www.lindsayforestproducts.com
SIC: 3553 3599 2411 Woodworking machinery; machine shop, jobbing & repair; logging
PA: Forest Lindsay Products Inc
    2711 Ne Columbia Blvd
    Portland OR
    503 331-0783

(G-2914)
MARKWEST ENRGY E TEXAS GAS LP
3239 Sw Loop (75633-4973)
P.O. Box 310 (75633-0310)
PHONE...............................903 694-2225
Elizabeth Greenup, Branch Mgr
EMP: 37
SALES (corp-wide): 9B Publicly Held
SIC: 1321 4922 1389 Fractionating natural gas liquids; pipelines, natural gas; storage, natural gas; gas compressing (natural gas) at the fields
HQ: Markwest Energy East Texas Gas Company L.P.
    2448 E 81st St Ste 5400
    Tulsa OK 74137

(G-2915)
PANOLA WIRE LINE SERVICES INC
Hwy 79 (75633)
P.O. Box 672 (75633-0672)
PHONE...............................903 693-3966
Sam W Strong, President
Rick Conway, Admin Sec
EMP: 19
SQ FT: 2,000
SALES (est): 1.2MM Privately Held
SIC: 1389 Oil field services

(G-2916)
PINNERGY LTD
1156 Hills Lake Rd (75633-2084)
P.O. Box 202 (75633-0202)
PHONE...............................903 693-6300
Kinny Weeks, Branch Mgr
Toni Hamm, Manager
EMP: 97 Privately Held
WEB: www.pinnergy.com
SIC: 1389 Oil field services
PA: Pinnergy, Ltd.
    111 Congress Ave Ste 2020
    Austin TX 78701

(G-2917)
PINNERGY LTD
325 W Sabine St Ste G (75633-2549)
P.O. Box B (75633-0160)
PHONE...............................903 693-8400
John Randall Taylor, Branch Mgr
EMP: 83 Privately Held
WEB: www.pinnergy.com
SIC: 1389 Oil field services
PA: Pinnergy, Ltd.
    111 Congress Ave Ste 2020
    Austin TX 78701

(G-2918)
SABINE MUD LOGGING INC
1018 University Cir (75633-1328)
P.O. Box 269 (75633-0269)
PHONE...............................903 693-2912
Frank P Willis III, President
Lela Collins, Office Mgr
EMP: 15
SALES (est): 1.9MM Privately Held
SIC: 1389 Mud service, oil field drilling

(G-2919)
SMITH ENERGY SERVICES INC (PA)
Also Called: Smith Equipment Rental & Svcs
932 S Shelby St (75633-3032)
PHONE...............................903 693-8872

Michael Smith, President
Judy Smith, Exec VP
EMP: 233
SQ FT: 9,600
SALES (est): 25.2MM Privately Held
WEB: www.smithenergyservices.com
SIC: 7353 1389 Oil field equipment, rental or leasing; oil field services

(G-2920)
SMITH INTERNATIONAL INC
114 Wilson St (75633-3193)
PHONE...............................903 693-2596
Mark Shoffner, Branch Mgr
EMP: 12 Publicly Held
WEB: www.smithcodevelopment.com
SIC: 1389 Oil field services
HQ: Smith International, Inc.
    1310 Rankin Rd
    Houston TX 77073
    281 443-3370

(G-2921)
SOUTHERN PETROLEUM LABS INC
Also Called: Spl
1595 S Us Highway 79 (75633-6163)
PHONE...............................903 693-6242
Dan Parker, Manager
EMP: 50
SALES (corp-wide): 157.5MM Privately Held
WEB: www.spl-inc.com
SIC: 1389 Oil sampling service for oil companies
PA: Southern Petroleum Laboratories, Inc.
    8850 Interchange Dr
    Houston TX 77054
    713 660-0901

(G-2922)
STRONG SERVICES LP (PA)
3784 S Us Highway 79 (75633-6572)
P.O. Box 672 (75633-0672)
PHONE...............................903 693-3966
Sam Strong, Partner
EMP: 95
SALES (est): 68MM Privately Held
WEB: www.strongservicelp.com
SIC: 1382 Oil & gas exploration services

(G-2923)
TETRA TECHNOLOGIES INC
1743 Ne Loop (75633-1966)
PHONE...............................903 693-9500
Todd Worthan, Manager
Robert Ortigo, Supervisor
EMP: 25
SALES (corp-wide): 1B Publicly Held
WEB: www.tetratec.com
SIC: 1389 1382 Oil field services; oil & gas exploration services
PA: Tetra Technologies, Inc.
    24955 Interstate 45
    The Woodlands TX 77380
    281 367-1983

(G-2924)
TIMCO SERVICES INC
850 S Shelby St (75633-3030)
PHONE...............................903 693-9400
Hector Plata, Branch Mgr
EMP: 39
SALES (corp-wide): 91.6MM Privately Held
SIC: 1389 Running, cutting & pulling casings, tubes & rods
PA: Timco Services, Inc.
    1724 E Milton Ave
    Lafayette LA 70508
    337 233-5185

(G-2925)
TYSON FOODS INC
1484 Ne Loop (75633-1250)
PHONE...............................903 297-4200
Jack Hammond, Safety Mgr
Mike Steele, Controller
Mark Haecker, Branch Mgr
Gerald Broussard, Manager
Jeffrey Davidson, Director
EMP: 730
SALES (corp-wide): 43.1B Publicly Held
WEB: www.tysonfoods.com
SIC: 2015 Poultry slaughtering & processing

PA: Tyson Foods, Inc.
    2200 W Don Tyson Pkwy
    Springdale AR 72762
    479 290-4000

Castroville
Medina County

(G-2926)
CEMEX MATERIALS LLC
Also Called: Rinker Materials
6145 Mechler Ln N (78009-9583)
P.O. Box 27256, San Antonio (78227-0256)
PHONE...............................210 677-8191
EMP: 25
SQ FT: 33,642 Privately Held
WEB: www.cemexusa.com
SIC: 3273 Ready-mixed concrete
HQ: Cemex Materials Llc
    1501 Belvedere Rd
    West Palm Beach FL 33406
    561 833-5555

(G-2927)
D&R STEEL WORKS INC
252 County Road 485 (78009-5824)
PHONE...............................210 639-8314
Duane Zurovec, Principal
EMP: 12
SALES (est): 1.2MM Privately Held
WEB: www.dnrsteelworks.com
SIC: 7692 Welding repair

(G-2928)
DZIUK MEAT MARKET INC
608 Us Highway 90 W (78009-4546)
PHONE...............................830 538-3082
Marvin Dziuk, President
EMP: 14
SQ FT: 5,000
SALES (est): 1MM Privately Held
WEB: www.dziuks.com
SIC: 5421 2011 5147 2013 Meat markets, including freezer provisioners; meat packing plants; meats & meat products; sausages & other prepared meats

(G-2929)
ZINSMEYER MECH & WLDG LTD
2891 Us Highway 90 E (78009-5408)
PHONE...............................830 985-3498
Leroy Zinsmeyer, President
Kevin Zinsmeyer, Partner
Troy Zinsmeyer, Partner
EMP: 40
SQ FT: 5,000
SALES (est): 6.6MM Privately Held
WEB: www.zinsmeyerach.com
SIC: 1711 3441 1791 Warm air heating & air conditioning contractor; fabricated structural metal; structural steel erection

Cat Spring
Austin County

(G-2930)
HOLLY YAUPON TEA LLC
Also Called: Catspring Yaupon
202 N Front St (78933-5234)
P.O. Box 43 (78933-0043)
PHONE...............................512 677-4907
Abianne Falla,
Jennadee Detro,
EMP: 9
SALES (est): 385.8K Privately Held
WEB: www.catspringtea.com
SIC: 5149 2043 Coffee & tea; coffee substitutes, made from grain

(G-2931)
NEVINS LLC
14006 Newberg Rd (78933-5111)
P.O. Box 108 (78933-0108)
PHONE...............................713 230-2100
Melanie Miller, Engineer
Catherine Grell, Marketing Mgr
Marsha Tipp, Manager
Brian Nevins,
Karen Nevins,
EMP: 21
SQ FT: 10,000

SALES (est): 4.1MM **Privately Held**
WEB: www.nevins.co
SIC: 2521 2522 Wood office furniture; office furniture, except wood

(G-2932)
PHOENIX METALWORKS LP
1135 Dunlavy Rd (78933-5316)
PHONE.................................979 992-3909
John W B Huckaby, *Partner*
Diana Huckaby, *Partner*
EMP: 12
SALES (est): 2.1MM **Privately Held**
SIC: 3441 Fabricated structural metal

Catarina
Dimmit County

(G-2933)
SANCHEZ OIL & GAS CORPORATION
30888 S Us Hwy 83 (78836)
PHONE.................................210 208-1300
Antonio R Sanchez III, *President*
EMP: 51
SALES (corp-wide): 396.4MM **Privately Held**
WEB: www.sanchezog.com
SIC: 1311 Natural gas production
PA: Sanchez Oil & Gas Corporation
1360 Post Oak Blvd # 2400
Houston TX 77056
713 783-8000

Cedar Creek
Bastrop County

(G-2934)
CND SIGNS LLC
5213 Tucker Hill Ln (78612-4185)
PHONE.................................512 394-5421
EMP: 25 EST: 2013
SALES (est): 423K **Privately Held**
WEB: www.cndsigns.com
SIC: 3993 Electric signs

(G-2935)
DUKE FORMS & PRINTING
Also Called: Page Design
417 Colorado Dr (78612-3556)
PHONE.................................512 985-6587
Susan O'Neal, *Owner*
EMP: 18
SALES (est): 799.2K **Privately Held**
SIC: 7389 2752 Printing broker; commercial printing, lithographic

Cedar Hill
Dallas County

(G-2936)
ARGOS USA LLC
Also Called: Gifford-Hill Concrete Products
2138 S Highway 67 (75104-3605)
P.O. Box 847 (75106-0847)
PHONE.................................972 299-5274
Grage Minteer, *General Mgr*
EMP: 60
SQ FT: 16,000 **Privately Held**
WEB: www.argos-us.com
SIC: 3272 5032 Concrete products; sewer pipe, clay
HQ: Argos Usa Llc
3015 Windward Plz Ste 300
Alpharetta GA 30005
678 368-4300

(G-2937)
CENTER-LINE CURTAINS INC
1213 S Cedar Hill Rd (75104-8103)
PHONE.................................972 299-5902
Richard B Benton, *President*
Susan N Benton, *Vice Pres*
▲ EMP: 15
SQ FT: 20,000
SALES (est): 2.8MM **Privately Held**
WEB: www.center-linecurtains.com
SIC: 2259 Curtains, knit

(G-2938)
CENTRAL STATES MFG INC
660 Grigsby Way (75104-2538)
P.O. Box 4087 (75106-4087)
PHONE.................................469 272-0041
Randy Lutz, *Branch Mgr*
EMP: 45
SALES (corp-wide): 219.5MM **Privately Held**
WEB: www.centralstatesmfg.com
SIC: 3448 Panels for prefabricated metal buildings
PA: Central States Manufacturing, Inc.
302 Jane Pl
Lowell AR 72745
800 356-2733

(G-2939)
DIAMOND MANUFACTURING COMPANY
Also Called: Diamond Mfg Co Southwest
1548 Edgefield Way (75104-8400)
PHONE.................................972 291-8800
Billy Lewis, *General Mgr*
EMP: 63
SALES (corp-wide): 10.9B **Publicly Held**
WEB: www.diamondman.com
SIC: 3469 Perforated metal, stamped
HQ: Diamond Manufacturing Company
243 W Eigth St
Wyoming PA 18644
570 693-0300

(G-2940)
EPIC PRODUCTS INTL CORP
902 Kck Way (75104-8000)
PHONE.................................817 640-3037
Max Dahlgren, *CEO*
Harvey Dahlgren, *Ch of Bd*
Mary Barnes, *President*
Jennifer Lark, *President*
Michael Barisonek, *Vice Pres*
▲ EMP: 60
SALES (est): 11MM **Privately Held**
WEB: www.epicproducts.com
SIC: 3555 Printing trades machinery

(G-2941)
FORTERRA PIPE & PRECAST LLC
2138 S Highway 67 (75104-3605)
PHONE.................................972 262-3600
Todd Arnolds, *Branch Mgr*
Pati Page, *Clerk*
EMP: 33
SALES (corp-wide): 1.5B **Publicly Held**
WEB: www.forterrabp.com
SIC: 3272 Precast terrazo or concrete products
HQ: Forterra Pipe & Precast, Llc
511 E John Carpenter Fwy
Irving TX 75062
469 458-7973

(G-2942)
GEL INVESTMENTS
2135 Becky Ln (75104-1004)
PHONE.................................214 699-6996
Gregory Preston, *Partner*
EMP: 15
SALES (est): 528.8K **Privately Held**
SIC: 3843 Investment material, dental

(G-2943)
IDX CORPORATION
621 Hall St (75104-2536)
PHONE.................................314 739-4120
Lin Courtois, *Vice Pres*
EMP: 122
SALES (corp-wide): 4.4B **Publicly Held**
WEB: www.idxcorporation.com
SIC: 2542 Office & store showcases & display fixtures
HQ: Idx Corporation
13213 Corporate Exch Dr
Bridgeton MO 63044
314 739-4120

(G-2944)
IDX DALLAS LLC
Also Called: Universal Forest Products
621 Hall St (75104-2536)
PHONE.................................972 637-1525
Scott Carpenter, *General Mgr*
EMP: 71

SALES (est): 8.3MM
SALES (corp-wide): 4.4B **Publicly Held**
WEB: www.idxcorporation.com
SIC: 2542 2541 Partitions & fixtures, except wood; wood partitions & fixtures; display fixtures, wood; store & office display cases & fixtures
PA: Ufp Industries, Inc.
2801 E Beltline Ave Ne
Grand Rapids MI 49525
616 364-6161

(G-2945)
INDUSTRIAL THERMOFORM INC
Also Called: ITI
1211 Industrial Way (75104-8027)
P.O. Box 802 (75106-0802)
PHONE.................................972 299-5391
Keith A Martinez, *President*
EMP: 27
SQ FT: 30,000
SALES (est): 4.1MM **Privately Held**
WEB: www.industrialthermoform.com
SIC: 3089 Injection molding of plastics

(G-2946)
JOHNSTON PRODUCTS DALLAS INC
604 Jealouse Way (75104-2548)
PHONE.................................469 272-7212
Gene A Johnston, *President*
Lori Chung, *Mktg Coord*
Leslie Johnston, *Admin Sec*
EMP: 38
SQ FT: 23,000
SALES: 9.3MM **Privately Held**
WEB: www.johnstonproducts.com
SIC: 7692 1799 3444 3441 Welding repair; ornamental metal work; sheet metalwork; fabricated structural metal

(G-2947)
JW INDUSTRIES LTD (PA)
1001 Mount Lebanon Rd (75104-8003)
PHONE.................................972 291-7474
A B Jones Jr, *General Ptnr*
Mark Winkelman, *Ltd Ptnr*
Jon Winkelman, *Director*
▲ EMP: 18
SALES (est): 2.1MM **Privately Held**
SIC: 2952 Coating compounds, tar

(G-2948)
MG DOORS & MORE LLC
902 Kck Way (75104-8000)
P.O. Box 851, Waxahachie (75168-0851)
PHONE.................................972 291-4389
Michael Mahlstedt, *CFO*
Gavin Cantu,
EMP: 10 EST: 2010
SQ FT: 11,000
SALES: 3.2MM **Privately Held**
WEB: www.mgdoors.net
SIC: 5031 2431 Doors; doors, wood

(G-2949)
P & W QUALITY MACHINES INC (PA)
707 S Highway 67 (75104-6619)
PHONE.................................972 299-0500
Mike Parnell, *Owner*
Charlie Jones, *Sales Mgr*
Devin Glasscock, *Sales Staff*
Ryan Parnell, *Sales Staff*
Jason Sims, *Manager*
EMP: 46
SQ FT: 16,000
SALES (est): 26.4MM **Privately Held**
WEB: www.pwmachine.com
SIC: 3599 3444 7699 Machine shop, jobbing & repair; culverts, flumes & pipes; professional instrument repair services

(G-2950)
PHASE ELECTRIC MOTORS INC
1105 S Cedar Hill Rd (75104-3108)
PHONE.................................972 291-9221
Gene Hickson, *President*
Kent Burks,
EMP: 14
SQ FT: 7,500
SALES (est): 3.1MM **Privately Held**
WEB: www.phaseelectric.com
SIC: 7694 5999 Electric motor repair; motors, electric

(G-2951)
PRECISION WOOD PRODUCTS INC
Also Called: MJB Supply
1585 High Meadows Way (75104-8413)
PHONE.................................972 293-2252
Alan Bennett, *Ch of Bd*
Joe Aulds, *President*
Joe Caldwell, *Vice Pres*
Christine Compton, *Office Mgr*
EMP: 75
SQ FT: 600,000
SALES (est): 14MM
SALES (corp-wide): 236.2MM **Privately Held**
SIC: 2511 Wood household furniture
PA: Mjb Wood Group, Llc
3100 Olympus Blvd Ste 480
Coppell TX 75019
972 401-0005

(G-2952)
PROFESSIONAL COATING TECH INC
Also Called: Fastphalt
1001 Mount Lebanon Rd (75104-8003)
PHONE.................................972 291-7474
Mark Winkleman, *President*
Steve Mayberry, *CFO*
Joyce Maberry, *Accounting Mgr*
Steve Maberry, *IT/INT Sup*
EMP: 18
SQ FT: 22,000
SALES (est): 5.2MM
SALES (corp-wide): 2.1MM **Privately Held**
WEB: www.procoat.tech
SIC: 2952 Coating compounds, tar
PA: Jw Industries, Ltd.
1001 Mount Lebanon Rd
Cedar Hill TX 75104
972 291-7474

(G-2953)
TEXAS CABINET INC
Also Called: Texas Cabinet Doors
1001 Cedarview Dr (75104-2518)
PHONE.................................972 293-2450
Stan Tidwell, *President*
Jeff Elseman, *Corp Secy*
Tom Waid, *Marketing Mgr*
EMP: 40
SQ FT: 15,000 **Privately Held**
SIC: 2431 Doors, wood

(G-2954)
VACUUMPODSCOM INC
135 Hunter Dr (75104-5103)
PHONE.................................972 986-8876
Laura D Moore, *President*
EMP: 10
SALES (est): 1.5MM **Privately Held**
WEB: www.vacuumpods.com
SIC: 3553 Woodworking machinery

(G-2955)
WESTERN CABINETS INC
1001 Cedarview Dr (75104-2518)
PHONE.................................972 293-2450
George Bellomusto, *Vice Pres*
Shelley Pitts, *Cust Mgr*
Scott Gullett, *Branch Mgr*
EMP: 50
SALES (corp-wide): 34MM **Privately Held**
WEB: www.woodmontcabinetry.com
SIC: 2434 Wood kitchen cabinets
PA: Western Cabinets, Inc.
3444 Morse Dr
Dallas TX 75236
469 916-5350

(G-2956)
WILBERT FUNERAL SERVICES INC
Also Called: Si Funeral Svcs & Con Precast
611 Jealouse Way (75104-2547)
PHONE.................................972 291-7854
Robert McCool, *Branch Mgr*
EMP: 12
SQ FT: 20,140
SALES (corp-wide): 9B **Publicly Held**
WEB: www.greensborowilbert.com
SIC: 3272 Burial vaults, concrete or precast terrazzo

HQ: Wilbert Funeral Services, Inc.
10965 Granada Ln Ste 300
Overland Park KS 66211
913 345-2120

Cedar Park
Williamson County

(G-2957)
360 PRESS SOLUTIONS LLC
2009 Windy Ter (78613-3507)
PHONE.................................512 381-2360
Mitchell Gray, *Accounts Exec*
Cindy Salome, *Accounts Exec*
Teri Diaz, *Sales Staff*
Sean Lane, *Sales Staff*
James Anderson, *Mng Member*
EMP: 30
SALES (est): 4.4MM **Privately Held**
WEB: www.360presssolutions.com
SIC: 2741 Miscellaneous publishing

(G-2958)
3PS INC
Also Called: 3 Point Solutions
1300 Arrow Point Dr (78613-7594)
PHONE.................................512 610-5200
EMP: 60 **EST:** 1999
SQ FT: 30,000
SALES (est): 15.1MM
SALES (corp-wide): 222MM **Privately Held**
WEB: www.mccoyglobal.com
SIC: 3531 Cranes; crane carriers
PA: Pason Systems Inc
6130 3 St Se
Calgary AB T2H 1
403 301-3400

(G-2959)
ADVANCED METAL FUSION INC
3507 Valley Pike Rd (78613-5207)
PHONE.................................512 422-0888
Ronald M April, *President*
Marie R Hamm, *Vice Pres*
EMP: 10
SALES (est): 748K **Privately Held**
WEB: www.advancedmetalfusion.com
SIC: 1799 7692 Welding on site; welding repair

(G-2960)
ANTX INC
3005 Glacier Pass (78613-7628)
PHONE.................................512 255-2800
Stephen Allen, *President*
Jon Catanzarita, *Business Mgr*
Alan Thomas, *Senior Engr*
Rhonda Stubblefield, *Accounts Exec*
EMP: 11
SALES (est): 1.9MM **Privately Held**
WEB: www.antx.com
SIC: 3429 3625 Manufactured hardware (general); relays & industrial controls

(G-2961)
AUSTIN DYNAMICS INC
3200 W Whitestone Blvd D (78613-1906)
P.O. Box 80094, Austin (78708-0094)
PHONE.................................512 267-3117
Craig Hobdy, *President*
Tony Gonzalez, *Manager*
EMP: 30
SQ FT: 8,000
SALES (est): 6.7MM **Privately Held**
WEB: www.austindynamics.com
SIC: 3599 Machine shop, jobbing & repair

(G-2962)
BMC MILLWORK
1920 E Whitestone Blvd (78613-7371)
PHONE.................................512 456-2000
Doug Davidson, *Principal*
EMP: 10
SALES (est): 1.2MM **Privately Held**
SIC: 2431 Millwork

(G-2963)
CHRISTOPHER RAD NADER
Also Called: Austin Duraclean
1511 Dandridge Dr (78613-5458)
PHONE.................................512 442-5326
Christopher N RAD, *Owner*
EMP: 10

SALES (est): 250K **Privately Held**
SIC: 7217 7349 3564 1799 Carpet & upholstery cleaning; air duct cleaning; filters, air: furnaces, air conditioning equipment, etc.; post-disaster renovations; heating & air conditioning contractors

(G-2964)
CORESLAB STRUCTURES TEXAS INC (DH)
15916 Anderson Mill Rd (78613-7470)
P.O. Box 1868 (78630-1868)
PHONE.................................512 250-0755
Mario Franciosa, *CEO*
Sidney Spiegel, *Corp Secy*
Wilbur Whitcher, *Exec VP*
Bob McGee, *Vice Pres*
Robert McGee, *Vice Pres*
EMP: 135
SQ FT: 31,784
SALES (est): 35.8MM
SALES (corp-wide): 27.3MM **Privately Held**
WEB: www.coreslab.com
SIC: 3272 Concrete products, precast
HQ: Coreslab Structures (Ont) Inc
205 Coreslab Dr
Dundas ON L9H 0
905 689-3993

(G-2965)
CORVALENT CORPORATION
1101 Arrwpint Dr Bldg 501 (78613)
PHONE.................................512 456-2400
Ed Trevis, *President*
Denise Manchester, *Vice Pres*
Mark Bartholomew, *Engineer*
Steve Hall, *Accounts Mgr*
Andrew Mrozewski, *Sales Staff*
▲ **EMP:** 42
SQ FT: 24,500
SALES (est): 10.1MM **Privately Held**
WEB: www.corvalent.com
SIC: 3672 3577 3571 Printed circuit boards; computer peripheral equipment; electronic computers

(G-2966)
DRW HOLDINGS
Also Called: Visual Lighting Technologies
1809 Hur Industrial Blvd (78613-7252)
PHONE.................................949 581-9398
Daniel K Haydt, *President*
Monica Haydt, *Admin Sec*
▲ **EMP:** 45
SQ FT: 22,000
SALES (est): 7.8MM **Privately Held**
WEB: www.vltcorp.com
SIC: 3648 Lighting equipment

(G-2967)
EESTOR INC
715 Discovery Blvd # 107 (78613-2294)
PHONE.................................512 259-7601
Richard D Weir, *President*
Thomas Weir, *Vice Pres*
Betty Weir, *Purch Mgr*
▲ **EMP:** 9
SQ FT: 7,500
SALES (est): 1.6MM
SALES (corp-wide): 1.7MM **Privately Held**
WEB: www.zenncars.com
SIC: 3691 Storage batteries
PA: Eestor Corporation
82 Richmond St E
Toronto ON M5C 1
416 535-8395

(G-2968)
ETS-LINDGREN INC (HQ)
Also Called: Ets Lindgren
1301 Arrow Point Dr (78613-6936)
PHONE.................................512 531-6400
B E Butler, *President*
Dou Qinchuan, *Managing Dir*
Bill Giacone, *Vice Pres*
Mark Mawdsley, *Vice Pres*
Tom Woods, *Vice Pres*
◆ **EMP:** 150
SQ FT: 80,000

SALES (est): 45.8MM **Publicly Held**
WEB: www.ets-lindgren.com
SIC: 3569 3677 3469 3444 Testing chambers for altitude, temperature, ordnance, power; electronic coils, transformers & other inductors; metal stampings; sheet metalwork; partitions & fixtures, except wood; laboratory measuring apparatus

(G-2969)
FEDEX OFFICE & PRINT SVCS INC
1335 E Whitestone Blvd # 300 (78613-7598)
PHONE.................................512 528-9690
Christopher Young, *Director*
EMP: 11
SALES (corp-wide): 69.2B **Publicly Held**
WEB: www.fedex.com
SIC: 7389 7334 4215 2759 Packaging & labeling services; photocopying & duplicating services; courier services, except by air; commercial printing
HQ: Fedex Office And Print Services, Inc.
7900 Legacy Dr
Plano TX 75024
800 463-3339

(G-2970)
FIREFLY AEROSPACE INC (HQ)
1320 Arrow Point Dr # 109 (78613-2167)
PHONE.................................512 277-6959
Thomas Markusic, *President*
Shea Ferring, *Vice Pres*
Leslie Kovacs, *Vice Pres*
Adam Oakes, *Production*
Terry Boardman, *Chief Engr*
EMP: 126
SQ FT: 20,000
SALES (est): 4.1MM
SALES (corp-wide): 34.4MM **Privately Held**
WEB: www.firefly.com
SIC: 3761 Rockets, space & military, complete
PA: Noosphere Venture Partners Lp
1906 El Camino Real
Menlo Park CA 94027
650 646-2700

(G-2971)
FREEDOM POWER SYSTEMS INC
1620 La Jaita Dr Ste 100 (78613-6942)
PHONE.................................512 259-0941
James B Russell, *President*
Mark Cihlar, *QC Mgr*
Daryl Cabrera, *Engineer*
Jim Mann, *Engineer*
Brandi Green, *Accountant*
EMP: 19
SQ FT: 7,500
SALES (est): 3.9MM
SALES (corp-wide): 262.9MM **Publicly Held**
WEB: www.freedompower.biz
SIC: 3629 Electronic generation equipment
PA: Vicor Corporation
25 Frontage Rd
Andover MA 01810
978 470-2900

(G-2972)
GRENIER SERVICE COMPANY LLC
1408 N Bell Blvd (78613-7080)
PHONE.................................512 335-7441
Donald Grenier, *President*
EMP: 50
SALES (est): 671.4K **Privately Held**
SIC: 2431 3442 Garage doors, overhead: wood; fire doors, metal; garage doors, overhead: metal

(G-2973)
HILL COUNTRY NEWS
715 Discovery Blvd # 304 (78613-2289)
P.O. Box 1777 (78630-1777)
PHONE.................................512 259-4449
Don Moore, *President*
Jim Grimes, *Vice Pres*
EMP: 13
SQ FT: 2,888

SALES (est): 730.3K **Privately Held**
WEB: www.hillcountry-sc.com
SIC: 2711 Newspapers, publishing & printing

(G-2974)
HODYON LP (HQ)
Also Called: Hancock Industries
2620 Brushy Creek Loop (78613-3196)
PHONE.................................512 225-0165
David Hancock, *Exec VP*
Sharon Oleary, *CFO*
Jim Thompson, *Info Tech Dir*
Todd A Self,
▲ **EMP:** 16
SQ FT: 90,000
SALES (est): 6.7MM
SALES (corp-wide): 17.3MM **Privately Held**
WEB: www.fallbrooktech.com
SIC: 3585 7699 Compressors for refrigeration & air conditioning equipment; compressor repair
PA: Fallbrook Technologies Inc.
1501 Leander Dr
Leander TX 78641
512 714-1964

(G-2975)
JUSTIN INDUSTRIES INC
Also Called: Texas Quarries
1800 W Whitestone Blvd (78613-7199)
P.O. Box 179, Liberty Hill (78642-0179)
PHONE.................................512 258-1474
Robert Copeland, *Prdtn Mgr*
Clint Jones, *Maintence Staff*
EMP: 84
SALES (corp-wide): 254.6B **Publicly Held**
WEB: www.brick.com
SIC: 5211 3281 Brick; cut stone & stone products
HQ: Justin Industries, Inc.
3024 Acme Brick Plz
Fort Worth TX 76109
817 332-4101

(G-2976)
KEY OVATION LLC
Also Called: Goldtouch
1320 Arrow Point Dr # 101 (78613-2167)
PHONE.................................512 259-5688
Mark Norwalk, *CEO*
Christopher Linegar, *Chairman*
Mary McElveen, *Accounting Mgr*
Tesha Norwalk, *Mktg Coord*
▲ **EMP:** 10
SQ FT: 10,000
SALES (est): 2.3MM **Privately Held**
WEB: www.goldtouch.com
SIC: 3575 Keyboards, computer, office machine

(G-2977)
M E RUBY JR INC
15700 Anderson Mill Rd (78613-7469)
PHONE.................................512 258-1601
Mark McKinsey, *President*
EMP: 200
SQ FT: 1,200
SALES (est): 6.5MM **Privately Held**
SIC: 1422 Crushed & broken limestone

(G-2978)
MARTIN-DECKER TOTCO INC (HQ)
Also Called: MD Totco
1200 Cypress Creek Rd (78613-3614)
P.O. Box 808, Houston (77001-0808)
PHONE.................................512 340-5000
Clay Willams, *President*
◆ **EMP:** 400
SQ FT: 203,400
SALES (est): 85.9MM
SALES (corp-wide): 8.4B **Publicly Held**
SIC: 7353 3533 5082 3823 Oil field equipment, rental or leasing; oil & gas field machinery; oil field equipment; industrial instrmnts msrmnt display/control process variable; electronic coils, transformers & other inductors; scales & balances, except laboratory
PA: National Oilwell Varco, Inc.
7909 Parkwood Circle Dr
Houston TX 77036
713 346-7500

(G-2979)
MYSTIC PHARMACEUTICALS INC
2006 Windy Ter Ste A (78613-4294)
P.O. Box 342216, Austin (78734-0037)
PHONE...............................512 918-2900
Doug Topkis, *Ch of Bd*
Timothy Sullivan, *President*
EMP: 24
SQ FT: 11,000
SALES (est): 531.4K **Privately Held**
WEB: www.mysticpharmaceuticals.com
SIC: 2834 Pharmaceutical preparations

(G-2980)
NATIONAL OILWELL VARCO INC
Also Called: MD Totco
1200 Cypress Creek Rd (78613-3614)
PHONE...............................512 340-5000
Gregg Elling, *Engineer*
Dave Murray, *Engineer*
Graciela Tyson, *Accountant*
Rebecca Dodd, *Manager*
David Shaver, *Software Engr*
EMP: 72
SALES (corp-wide): 8.4B **Publicly Held**
WEB: www.nov.com
SIC: 3533 Oil & gas field machinery
PA: National Oilwell Varco, Inc.
7909 Parkwood Circle Dr
Houston TX 77036
713 346-7500

(G-2981)
PAINTED ROCK LLC (PA)
Also Called: Swagelok Austin
1017 Innovation Way (78613-2459)
PHONE...............................512 832-5057
Frederich C Kaimer,
EMP: 25
SALES (est): 3.8MM **Privately Held**
WEB: www.austin.swagelok.com
SIC: 3674 Wafers (semiconductor devices)

(G-2982)
PAPA BEARS PIZZA
1420 Colorado Bend Dr (78613-6981)
P.O. Box 1026, Leander (78646-1026)
PHONE...............................512 351-5421
EMP: 30
SALES (est): 1.8MM **Privately Held**
SIC: 2099 Mfg Food Preparations

(G-2983)
PRESCRPTION DSPENSING LABS INC
101 Commercial Pkwy (78613-2913)
PHONE...............................512 219-0724
Dan Volney, *President*
Patricia Lundblade, *Manager*
EMP: 12 **EST:** 1998
SQ FT: 4,000
SALES (est): 2.3MM **Privately Held**
WEB: www.pdlabs.net
SIC: 2834 Pharmaceutical preparations

(G-2984)
RF IDENTITY LLC
413 Ridgetop Bnd (78613-7479)
PHONE...............................512 689-1586
Jeff Kimmel, *Officer*
EMP: 14
SALES (est): 1.9MM **Privately Held**
WEB: www.rfidentity.com
SIC: 3699 Security devices

(G-2985)
SHERMCO INDUSTRIES INC
1705 Hur Industrial Blvd (78613-7229)
PHONE...............................512 267-2324
Kevin Ewing, *Principal*
Chad Bruck, *Accounts Mgr*
Paul Jackson, *Accounts Mgr*
Danny Granillo, *Manager*
Brian Hasley, *Manager*
EMP: 9 **Privately Held**
WEB: www.shermco.com
SIC: 3999 Barber & beauty shop equipment
HQ: Shermco Industries, Inc.
2425 E Pioneer Dr
Irving TX 75061
972 793-5523

(G-2986)
TAILWIND BUSINESS VENTURES LLC
11901 W Parmer Ln Ste 220 (78613-7653)
PHONE...............................210 268-2717
Paulo Vieira, *Principal*
James Bindseil, *Principal*
EMP: 205 **EST:** 2016
SALES (est): 8MM **Privately Held**
WEB: www.tailwindsw.com
SIC: 3652 7372 Pre-recorded records & tapes; custom computer programming services

(G-2987)
TDK RF SOLUTIONS INC
1101 Cypress Creek Rd (78613-3615)
PHONE...............................512 258-9478
Robert Sutton, *President*
Bleicher Pete, *Engineer*
James McLean, *Design Engr*
Tom Kossmann, *Treasurer*
Jim Ott, *Sales Mgr*
▲ **EMP:** 35
SALES (est): 8.5MM **Privately Held**
WEB: www.tdkrfsolutions.com
SIC: 7373 3829 3825 Computer systems analysis & design; measuring & controlling devices; instruments to measure electricity
PA: Tdk Corporation
2-5-1, Nihombashi
Chuo-Ku TKY 103-0

(G-2988)
TOLTEQ GROUP LLC
1200 Cypress Creek Rd (78613-3614)
P.O. Box 4207 (78630-4207)
PHONE...............................512 331-4241
Paul Deere, *President*
EMP: 100
SQ FT: 19,000
SALES (est): 19MM
SALES (corp-wide): 8.4B **Publicly Held**
WEB: www.nov.com
SIC: 3823 Industrial process measurement equipment
PA: National Oilwell Varco, Inc.
7909 Parkwood Circle Dr
Houston TX 77036
713 346-7500

(G-2989)
TRIPLE D SERVICES LLC
Also Called: Philco Tubing Testers
2930 Grand Oaks Loop # 2002 (78613-4363)
PHONE...............................512 750-6052
Donald Davis, *Mng Member*
EMP: 14
SALES (est): 1.1MM **Privately Held**
SIC: 1389 Testing, measuring, surveying & analysis services

(G-2990)
WHITE CLOUD SECURITY INC
1464 E Whitestone Blvd (78613-9058)
P.O. Box 170422, Austin (78717-0027)
PHONE...............................512 887-8783
Steven Shanklin, *Partner*
James McLendon, *COO*
David Grajek, *CFO*
Jess Elshere, *Sales Mgr*
Robert Ott, *Consultant*
EMP: 10
SALES (est): 171.5K **Privately Held**
WEB: www.whitecloudsecurity.com
SIC: 7372 7389 Operating systems computer software;

Celina
Collin County

(G-2991)
CHEMTRADE SULFATE CHEM INC (DH)
Also Called: Fini Enterprises, Inc.
Business Hwy 289 N (75009)
P.O. Box 808 (75009-0808)
PHONE...............................416 496-4176
Mark Davis, *President*
EMP: 32
SQ FT: 30,800

SALES (est): 7.5MM
SALES (corp-wide): 1.1B **Privately Held**
WEB: www.ceofiniole.com
SIC: 2899 Water treating compounds

(G-2992)
MARTINEK GRAIN & BINS INC
104 W Ash St (75009)
P.O. Box 430, Gunter (75058-0430)
PHONE...............................972 382-8500
Donnie Martinek, *President*
EMP: 12
SALES (est): 1.3MM **Privately Held**
WEB: www.whitewrightfeed.com
SIC: 5261 2819 Fertilizer; industrial inorganic chemicals

(G-2993)
RDA CORPORATION
Also Called: PSI Automation
4295 County Road 86 # 180 (75009-4749)
PHONE...............................281 474-2881
Robert D Arnett Jr, *CEO*
Robert D Arnett III, *President*
Miriam H Arnett, *Admin Sec*
◆ **EMP:** 20
SALES (est): 3.1MM **Privately Held**
WEB: www.psiautomation.com
SIC: 3594 Motors: hydraulic, fluid power or air

(G-2994)
S AND S PALLETS
11189 County Road 95 (75009-3729)
PHONE...............................972 382-8142
EMP: 10
SALES (est): 724.7K **Privately Held**
WEB: www.sandspallets.com
SIC: 2448 Pallets, wood

Center
Shelby County

(G-2995)
CEN-TEX TANKS LLC
946 Loop 500 (75935-7510)
PHONE...............................936 590-4441
EMP: 100 **EST:** 2011
SALES (est): 15.9MM **Privately Held**
WEB: www.dragonproductsltd.com
SIC: 3443 Fuel tanks (oil, gas, etc.): metal plate

(G-2996)
CENTER FIXTURES
1010 Logansport St (75935-3216)
P.O. Box 1775 (75935-1775)
PHONE...............................936 598-2247
Paul Weise, *President*
EMP: 91
SALES (est): 8.1MM **Privately Held**
SIC: 2541 2542 Store & office display cases & fixtures; partitions & fixtures, except wood

(G-2997)
DMI INTERNATIONAL INC
2055 Loop 500 E (75935-9069)
PHONE...............................936 591-8006
Terry Tubb, *Owner*
EMP: 10 **Privately Held**
WEB: www.dmiinternational.com
SIC: 3999 Barber & beauty shop equipment
PA: Dmi International, Inc.
15615 E Pine St
Tulsa OK 74116

(G-2998)
GENERAL SHLTERS OF BVLLE TEXAS
1639 State Highway 87 N (75935-5657)
P.O. Box 2108 (75935-2108)
PHONE...............................936 598-3389
EMP: 32
SALES: 3.3MM **Privately Held**
SIC: 2452 3448 Mfg Prefabricated Wood Buildings Mfg Prefabricated Metal Buildings

(G-2999)
HIGH ROLLER WELLS LLC
1008 Southview Cir (75935-4537)
PHONE...............................936 598-5577
Terry Bailey, *Principal*
EMP: 20
SALES (est): 9.5MM **Privately Held**
WEB: www.highrollersand.com
SIC: 1389 Oil & gas wells: building, repairing & dismantling

(G-3000)
JML MANAGEMENT INC
748 State Highway 7 W (75935-5818)
PHONE...............................936 591-9782
Mike Lout, *President*
Patricia Lout, *Vice Pres*
Rebecca Parfait, *Office Mgr*
EMP: 15
SALES (est): 1.9MM **Privately Held**
WEB: www.jmlmanagementinc.com
SIC: 2411 Logging

(G-3001)
K&L CONTRACTORS INC
748 State Highway 7 W (75935-5818)
P.O. Box 2107 (75935-2107)
PHONE...............................936 591-8333
John Michael Lout, *President*
Roy D Klein, *Exec VP*
Natalia Klein, *Treasurer*
Patricia Lout, *Treasurer*
Becky Parfait, *Manager*
EMP: 35
SALES (est): 12.2MM **Privately Held**
WEB: www.klcontractorsinc.com
SIC: 1382 Oil & gas exploration services

(G-3002)
LIGHT & CHAMPION PUBLISHING (PA)
137 San Augustine St (75935-3951)
P.O. Box 1989 (75935-1989)
PHONE...............................936 598-3377
Phillip Smith, *President*
EMP: 25
SQ FT: 7,500
SALES (est): 1.6MM **Privately Held**
WEB: www.lightandchampion.com
SIC: 2711 Newspapers: publishing only, not printed on site

(G-3003)
OMNI ENERGY SERVICES CORP
1524 Shelbyville St (75935-4606)
PHONE...............................936 591-8598
Raif Tawakal, *Branch Mgr*
EMP: 25
SALES (corp-wide): 773.9MM **Privately Held**
WEB:
www.omnienvironmentalsolutions.com
SIC: 1389 Energy management controls
PA: Omni Energy Services Corp.
4500 Ne Evangeline Trwy
Carencro LA 70520
337 896-6664

(G-3004)
PILGRIMS PRIDE CORPORATION
Also Called: Pilgrim's Pride Chicken Operat
1102 Logansport St (75935-3218)
PHONE...............................936 598-3356
Scott Magee, *Manager*
EMP: 80 **Publicly Held**
WEB: www.pilgrims.com
SIC: 2015 Chicken, slaughtered & dressed
HQ: Pilgrim's Pride Corporation
1770 Promontory Cir
Greeley CO 80634
970 506-8000

(G-3005)
PORTACOOL LLC (DH)
711 Fm 2468 (75935-7234)
P.O. Box 2167 (75935-2167)
PHONE...............................936 598-5651
Ben Wulf, *President*
Todd Waldhauser, *Division Mgr*
Stacey Mikesh, *Principal*
Robert Mangiaforte, *Vice Pres*
Michael O'Brien, *Vice Pres*
◆ **EMP:** 285
SQ FT: 450,000

SALES (est): 80MM
SALES (corp-wide): 500.3K **Privately Held**
WEB: www.portacool.com
SIC: 3585 Parts for heating, cooling & refrigerating equipment
HQ: Portacool Group Corp.
711 Fm 2468
Center TX 75935
936 598-5651

(G-3006)
PORTACOOL LLC
721 Fm 2468 (75935-7234)
P.O. Box 2167 (75935-2167)
PHONE..............................936 598-6353
Rodney Roderick, *General Mgr*
Ben Wulf, *General Mgr*
Jason Locke, *Branch Mgr*
Stacey Mikesh, *Director*
EMP: 17
SALES (corp-wide): 500.3K **Privately Held**
WEB: www.portacool.com
SIC: 3585 Parts for heating, cooling & refrigerating equipment
HQ: Portacool, Llc
711 Fm 2468
Center TX 75935

(G-3007)
PORTERFIELD TIMBER HARVESTING
349 County Road 1005 (75935-5906)
P.O. Box 942 (75935-0942)
PHONE..............................936 598-4203
Danny Porterfield, *President*
Gina Porterfield, *Treasurer*
EMP: 9
SQ FT: 4,400
SALES (est): 500K **Privately Held**
WEB: www.porterfield-timber-harvesting.hub.biz
SIC: 2411 Logging camps & contractors

(G-3008)
SPARTAN STRUCTURES LLC (PA)
1084 State Highway 7 E (75935-7417)
PHONE..............................936 591-9280
Brett Scarber, *Vice Pres*
Matthew Bowman Little,
Brett Delane Scarber,
Michael Brady Scarber,
EMP: 29 **EST:** 2013
SALES (est): 10.1MM **Privately Held**
WEB: www.spartan-llc.com
SIC: 3531 Bituminous, cement & concrete related products & equipment

(G-3009)
STEEL BUILDING SUPPLY INC
1154 State Highway 7 E (75935-5310)
PHONE..............................936 598-6373
Toll Free:..............................888 -
James R Teske, *CEO*
Tommy Huff, *Vice Pres*
Blake Phillips, *Sales Staff*
Bruce Samford, *Sales Staff*
Matt Strong, *Manager*
EMP: 25
SQ FT: 59,330
SALES (est): 6.4MM **Privately Held**
WEB: www.steelbuildingsupply.com
SIC: 3448 3441 2439 Prefabricated metal buildings; fabricated structural metal; structural wood members

(G-3010)
TYSON FARMS OF TEXAS INC
1019 Shelbyville St (75935-3741)
P.O. Box 1960 (75935-1960)
PHONE..............................936 598-2474
John H Tyson, *President*
Leland E Tollett, *President*
Gerald Johnston, *Exec VP*
Barbara Tyson, *Vice Pres*
Amber Dodd, *Personnel*
EMP: 1100
SALES (est): 142.3MM
SALES (corp-wide): 43.1B **Publicly Held**
WEB: www.tyson.com
SIC: 2015 Chicken, processed: fresh; poultry, slaughtered & dressed

PA: Tyson Foods, Inc.
2200 W Don Tyson Pkwy
Springdale AR 72762
479 290-4000

Centerville
Leon County

(G-3011)
BEAR PAW CUSTOM EMBROIDERY LLC
3678 S County Road 481 (75833-1914)
PHONE..............................903 394-0722
EMP: 9
SALES (corp-wide): 997.9K **Privately Held**
SIC: 2395 Embroidery products, except schiffli machine
PA: Bear Paw Custom Embroidery, Llc
213 S Canyon St
Carlsbad NM 88220
575 234-2614

Channelview
Harris County

(G-3012)
ASSOCIATED CANVAS PDTS I LTD
16917 Market St (77530-3837)
PHONE..............................281 457-1480
Bebe Brasher, *Partner*
Clifton Brasher, *Partner*
James Brasher, *General Ptnr*
EMP: 19
SQ FT: 12,000
SALES (est): 2.1MM **Privately Held**
WEB: www.acpgloballogistics.com
SIC: 2394 5999 5091 Tarpaulins, fabric: made from purchased materials; awnings, fabric: made from purchased materials; awnings; boat accessories & parts

(G-3013)
BESTWAY OILFIELD INC (PA)
16030 Market St (77530-4512)
PHONE..............................281 452-2525
Ronny Dwairy, *CEO*
Mark Albert, *President*
Gus Dwairy, *President*
Ray Morgan, *District Mgr*
Derek Broussard, *Vice Pres*
▲ **EMP:** 50
SALES (est): 45.2MM **Privately Held**
WEB: www.bestwayoilfield.com
SIC: 5084 3533 Oil well machinery, equipment & supplies; oil field machinery & equipment

(G-3014)
BUDGET READY MIX
14915 Market St (77530-4229)
PHONE..............................281 452-5233
Pete Sanchez, *Owner*
EMP: 11
SALES (est): 943.7K **Privately Held**
WEB: www.budgetreadymix.com
SIC: 3273 Ready-mixed concrete

(G-3015)
CEMEX CONSTRUCTION MTLS S LLC
Also Called: Cem - De Zavala Terminal
16530 De Zavalla Rd (77530-4616)
PHONE..............................281 457-0031
Raymond Foreman, *Manager*
EMP: 12 **Privately Held**
WEB: www.cemexusa.com
SIC: 3273 5211 Ready-mixed concrete; cement
HQ: Cemex Construction Materials South, Llc
2088 E 20th St
Yuma AZ 85365
928 343-4100

(G-3016)
COCA-COLA REFRESHMENTS USA INC
15221 Market St (77530-4232)
PHONE..............................281 452-7635

EMP: 68
SQ FT: 55,450
SALES (corp-wide): 35.4B **Publicly Held**
SIC: 2086 Carb Sft Drnkbtlcn
HQ: Coca-Cola Refreshments Usa, Inc.
2500 Windy Ridge Pkwy Se
Atlanta GA 30339
770 989-3000

(G-3017)
DOWNSTREAM AGGREGATOR LLC (HQ)
16315 Market St (77530-4427)
PHONE..............................281 247-8118
Ruben Lah, *President*
John Furka, *CFO*
EMP: 10 **EST:** 2015
SALES (est): 47.9MM
SALES (corp-wide): 1.1B **Publicly Held**
SIC: 3491 6719 8711 Industrial valves; personal holding companies, except banks; engineering services
PA: Circor International, Inc.
30 Corporate Dr Ste 200
Burlington MA 01803
781 270-1200

(G-3018)
ENERGY SERVICES GROUP AMER INC
15019 N Brentwood St (77530-3901)
P.O. Box 96229, Houston (77213-6229)
PHONE..............................281 452-5335
Eric Olafson, *President*
Silivia Olafson, *Vice Pres*
Dan Reed, *Manager*
EMP: 15
SQ FT: 10,000
SALES (est): 3.7MM **Privately Held**
WEB: www.energy-service.biz
SIC: 3567 Industrial furnaces & ovens

(G-3019)
ENVIRO-TECH SPECIALTIES INC
121 Dell Dale St (77530-4225)
P.O. Box 1609 (77530-1609)
PHONE..............................281 476-9803
Mary Ann Fox, *President*
◆ **EMP:** 10
SQ FT: 9,000
SALES (est): 2.2MM **Privately Held**
WEB: www.enviro-techspecialties.com
SIC: 2819 Industrial inorganic chemicals

(G-3020)
EQUISTAR CHEMICALS LP
Also Called: A Lyondell Chemical Company
2502 Sheldon Rd (77530-2681)
P.O. Box 30 (77530-0030)
PHONE..............................281 862-4000
Lonnie Lindsey, *General Mgr*
Randolph Smith, *Engineer*
Charles Etter, *Manager*
Becky Keasler, *Manager*
EMP: 44
SALES (corp-wide): 34.9B **Privately Held**
WEB: www.lyondellbasell.com
SIC: 2869 2899 2821 Olefins; chemical preparations; plastics materials & resins
HQ: Equistar Chemicals, Lp
1221 Mckinney St Ste 300
Houston TX 77010

(G-3021)
EXCALIBAR MINERALS LLC
2400 Appelt (77530)
PHONE..............................281 864-9550
David Henrick, *Branch Mgr*
EMP: 22
SALES (corp-wide): 747.7MM **Publicly Held**
WEB: www.newpark.com
SIC: 3295 Minerals, ground or treated
HQ: Excalibar Minerals Llc
21920 Merchants Way
Katy TX 77449

(G-3022)
FLEX TANK SYSTEMS LLC
16514 De Zavalla Rd (77530-4690)
PHONE..............................281 862-2900
Hank Thomas,
Rex P Bryan,
Richard Riassetto,

EMP: 20
SQ FT: 2,500
SALES (est): 1.9MM **Privately Held**
WEB: www.flexoilservices.com
SIC: 4953 2992 Hazardous waste collection & disposal; lubricating oils & greases

(G-3023)
GLENDALE BOAT WORKS INC
18300 Market St (77530-3856)
PHONE..............................281 452-7146
Richard A Batson, *President*
Sue Barrentine, *Office Mgr*
EMP: 15 **EST:** 1963
SQ FT: 600
SALES (est): 2.5MM **Privately Held**
WEB: www.glendaleboatworks.com
SIC: 3731 Towboats, building & repairing; barges, building & repairing

(G-3024)
HARSCO CORPORATION
Also Called: Harsco Ikg Industries
1514 Sheldon Rd (77530-2622)
PHONE..............................713 378-3944
Roger Buffkin, *Site Mgr*
Groves Brian, *Design Engr*
Martin Ng, *Technology*
Gregory Moller, *Director*
Brandi Rice, *Representative*
EMP: 60
SALES (corp-wide): 1.5B **Publicly Held**
WEB: www.harsco.com
SIC: 3446 Architectural metalwork
PA: Harsco Corporation
350 Poplar Church Rd
Camp Hill PA 17011
717 763-7064

(G-3025)
HASCO MARINE
Also Called: Saoza's Market
906 Elsbeth St (77530-4624)
PHONE..............................281 452-5017
Hugo A Salazar, *Owner*
EMP: 11
SALES (est): 400K **Privately Held**
SIC: 3731 Shipbuilding & repairing

(G-3026)
HOUSTON PRODUCTS PROC INC (PA)
Also Called: Hpp Recycle
15201 East Fwy Ste 100 (77530-4137)
PHONE..............................281 487-0766
Wayne W Webber, *President*
Charles A Burnett, *Vice Pres*
Melinda Haschke, *Personnel*
Laura Short, *Mktg Dir*
Mark Briggs, *Marketing Staff*
EMP: 9
SALES (est): 1.4MM **Privately Held**
WEB: www.hpprecycles.com
SIC: 3271 Concrete block & brick

(G-3027)
JAS MARKETING INC
1328 Sheldon Rd (77530-2602)
PHONE..............................281 879-1844
Vas P Kenyen, *President*
Beth Kenyen, *Vice Pres*
Amie Kenyen, *Shareholder*
EMP: 14
SALES (est): 3MM **Privately Held**
WEB: www.jasmarketing.com
SIC: 8741 3559 8711 Construction management; chemical machinery & equipment; engineering services

(G-3028)
LABARGE COATING LLC
711 Shields St (77530-3032)
P.O. Box 2005 (77530-8005)
PHONE..............................713 378-7225
Mark Yager, *Principal*
Melanie Holt, *HR Admin*
Donna Puleo, *Office Mgr*
EMP: 100 **Privately Held**
WEB: www.labargecoating.com
SIC: 3479 3498 5051 3317 Coating of metals & formed products; tube fabricating (contract bending & shaping); structural shapes, iron or steel; steel pipe & tubes

136   2021 Harris Texas
Manufacturers Directory   ▲ = Import ▼=Export
◆ =Import/Export

PA: Labarge Coating, Llc
211 N Broadway Ste 3050
Saint Louis MO 63102

(G-3029)
LABARGE COATING LLC
400 S Sheldon Rd (77530-1409)
PHONE...................................281 457-0200
Labarge Coating, *VP Opers*
Mark Yager, *Branch Mgr*
Lori Iberg, *Executive Asst*
Scott Kincaid,
EMP: 40 **Privately Held**
WEB: www.labargecoating.com
SIC: 3479 Coating of metals & formed
products
PA: Labarge Coating, Llc
211 N Broadway Ste 3050
Saint Louis MO 63102

(G-3030)
LYONDELL CHEMICAL
COMPANY
8280 Sheldon Rd (77530-2693)
PHONE...................................281 862-4000
Morris Gelb, *President*
Tony Schmanske, *Engineer*
Catherine Gunton, *Manager*
Nancy Mc Conville, *Manager*
Amy Ng, *Manager*
EMP: 16
SALES (corp-wide): 34.9B **Privately Held**
WEB: www.lyondellbasell.com
SIC: 2869 Industrial organic chemicals
HQ: Lyondell Chemical Company
1221 Mckinney St Ste 300
Houston TX 77010
713 309-7200

(G-3031)
PARAMOUNT PETROLEUM
CORP
704 Sheldon Rd Ste B (77530-3569)
PHONE...................................800 882-6541
Doug Goodson, *General Mgr*
EMP: 34
SALES (corp-wide): 9.3B **Publicly Held**
WEB: www.ppcla.com
SIC: 2911 Fractionation products of crude
petroleum, hydrocarbons
HQ: Paramount Petroleum Corporation
14700 Downey Ave
Paramount CA 90723
562 531-2060

(G-3032)
PATTERSON TUBULAR
SERVICES INC (HQ)
539 S Sheldon Rd (77530-1400)
PHONE...................................281 452-5443
Charles Coleman, *President*
David Vela, *Opers Mgr*
Brandon Baker, *Opers Staff*
Anibal Cruz, *Supervisor*
Cynthia Alvarez, *Clerk*
EMP: 42 **EST:** 1994
SALES (est): 41.9MM
SALES (corp-wide): 1.7B **Publicly Held**
WEB: www.pattersontubular.com
SIC: 1389 Oil field services
PA: Rpc, Inc.
2801 Buford Hwy Ne # 300
Brookhaven GA 30329
404 321-2140

(G-3033)
RUS INDUSTRIAL LLC
Also Called: Cornerstone Infield Services
16030 Bear Bayou Dr (77530-2821)
P.O. Box 1479 (77530-1479)
PHONE...................................281 864-9070
Kevin P Laird, *CEO*
Roy L Johnson, *President*
Roy Johnson, *COO*
Kevin Laird, *Exec VP*
Pete Thurman, *Prdtn Mgr*
EMP: 242
SQ FT: 72,000
SALES: 24.5MM **Privately Held**
WEB: www.rusindustrial.com
SIC: 1731 3823 3441 Electrical work; in-
dustrial instrmnts msrmnt display/control
process variable; fabricated structural
metal

(G-3034)
RUSSELL MARINE LLC
16828 Market St (77530-3836)
PHONE...................................281 860-0011
Chris Milligan, *Superintendent*
Bob Andrews, *Vice Pres*
Tim Linden, *Vice Pres*
Frank Thielen, *Vice Pres*
Aaron Vasquez, *Project Mgr*
EMP: 170 **EST:** 2010
SQ FT: 3,000
SALES: 89.9MM **Privately Held**
WEB: www.russellmarinellc.com
SIC: 1629 2491 Marine construction; rail-
road cross bridges & switch ties, treated
wood

(G-3035)
SAN JAC MARINE LLC
17112 Market St (77530-3842)
PHONE...................................281 862-9764
Christian O'Niel, *Mng Member*
EMP: 120
SALES (est): 12MM
SALES (corp-wide): 2.8B **Publicly Held**
WEB: www.sanjacmarine.com
SIC: 3731 Barges, building & repairing
PA: Kirby Corporation
55 Waugh Dr Ste 1000
Houston TX 77007
713 435-1000

(G-3036)
SHAWCOR PIPE PROTECTION
LLC
711 Shields St (77530-3032)
PHONE...................................713 378-7200
Miguel Mendez, *Branch Mgr*
EMP: 15
SALES (corp-wide): 1.1B **Privately Held**
WEB: www.shawcor.com
SIC: 3479 Coating or wrapping steel pipe
HQ: Shawcor Pipe Protection Llc
5875 N Sam Houston Pkwy W # 200
Houston TX 77086

(G-3037)
SNEED SHIPBUILDING INC (PA)
17112 Market St (77530-3842)
PHONE...................................281 862-2266
Clyde E Sneed, *President*
Mitchell S Jones, *Vice Pres*
▼ **EMP:** 25
SQ FT: 3,000
SALES (est): 40.8MM **Privately Held**
WEB: www.sneedshipbuilding.com
SIC: 3731 Shipbuilding & repairing

(G-3038)
SOLAR TURBINES
INCORPORATED
16504 De Zavalla Rd (77530-4616)
PHONE...................................281 860-6703
Bill Hanna, *General Mgr*
John Schulze, *Safety Mgr*
Eddie Shaw, *Engineer*
Rigoberto Valencia, *Engineer*
Marissa Munoz, *Human Res Mgr*
EMP: 200
SALES (corp-wide): 53.8B **Publicly Held**
WEB: www.solarturbines.com
SIC: 3511 Gas turbine generator set units,
complete
HQ: Solar Turbines Incorporated
2200 Pacific Hwy
San Diego CA 92101
619 544-5000

(G-3039)
TAG WATERBLOCK LLC
16023 East Fwy Ste 7 (77530-4358)
P.O. Box 1398, Pasadena (77501-1398)
PHONE...................................281 862-0300
Robert Lockhart,
▲ **EMP:** 22
SALES (est): 850K **Privately Held**
SIC: 3999 Barber & beauty shop equip-
ment

(G-3040)
TAPCOENPRO LLC (DH)
16315 Market St (77530-4427)
PHONE...................................281 247-8100
Ruben Lah, *President*
John Furka, *CFO*

◆ **EMP:** 100
SQ FT: 35,000
SALES (est): 47.6MM
SALES (corp-wide): 1.1B **Publicly Held**
WEB: www.tapcoenpro.com
SIC: 3491 Industrial valves
HQ: Downstream Aggregator, Llc
16315 Market St
Channelview TX 77530
281 247-8118

(G-3041)
TAPCOENPRO INTERNATIONAL
INC
16315 Market St (77530-4427)
PHONE...................................281 247-8100
David J Linton, *President*
Joe Ditolla, *General Mgr*
Ron Napper, *Mfg Mgr*
Jeremy Meadows, *Opers Staff*
Bob Stoddard, *Engineer*
EMP: 200
SQ FT: 65,000
SALES (est): 23.9MM **Privately Held**
WEB: www.tapcoenpro.com
SIC: 3599 3494 3491 3443 Machine
shop, jobbing & repair; valves & pipe fit-
tings; industrial valves; fabricated plate
work (boiler shop)

(G-3042)
TARGA RESOURCES CORP
Also Called: Targa Term Channelview
16514 De Zavalla Rd Ste B (77530-4691)
PHONE...................................713 584-1053
Phil Applegate, *Branch Mgr*
Jerry Parrish, *Manager*
Michael Grace, *Supervisor*
EMP: 20 **Publicly Held**
WEB: www.targaresources.com
SIC: 1382 Oil & gas exploration services
PA: Targa Resources Corp.
811 Louisiana St Ste 2100
Houston TX 77002

(G-3043)
TOTAL PTRCHEMICALS REF
USA INC
8280 Sheldon Rd (77530-2693)
PHONE...................................281 452-8577
Ken Sweeney, *Manager*
EMP: 9
SALES (corp-wide): 7B **Publicly Held**
WEB: www.totalpetrochemicalsre-
finingusa.com
SIC: 2821 2869 2819 Plastics materials &
resins; industrial organic chemicals; in-
dustrial inorganic chemicals
HQ: Total Petrochemicals & Refining Usa,
Inc.
1201 La St Ste 1800
Houston TX 77002
713 483-5000

(G-3044)
WESTERN TOWING COMPANY
18350 Market St (77530-3865)
PHONE...................................713 435-1800
Joseph H Pyne, *CEO*
Steve Valerius, *President*
Robert Goolsby, *Vice Pres*
EMP: 35
SQ FT: 6,520
SALES (est): 2.4MM
SALES (corp-wide): 2.8B **Publicly Held**
SIC: 4492 3731 4499 Marine towing serv-
ices; barges, building & repairing; water
transportation cleaning services
HQ: Kirby Inland Marine, Lp
55 Waugh Dr Ste 1000
Houston TX 77007
713 435-1000

Channing
Hartley County

(G-3045)
SOONER TRADING INC
Hwy 385 N (79018)
P.O. Box 27 (79018-0027)
PHONE...................................806 235-3904
Jeff Earles, *President*
EMP: 12

SALES (corp-wide): 6.3MM **Privately**
Held
SIC: 2048 4231 Livestock feeds; trucking
terminal facilities
PA: Sooner Trading, Inc.
108 N Easton
Ravia OK 73455
580 371-9413

Chappell Hill
Washington County

(G-3046)
HOUSTON UNLIMITED METAL
PROC
9400 Highway 290 E (77426-6278)
P.O. Box 143 (77426-0143)
PHONE...................................979 836-7568
Joe Kuciemba, *President*
EMP: 25
SQ FT: 6,000
SALES (est): 998.2K **Privately Held**
WEB: www.houstonunlimitedinc.com
SIC: 3479 Coating of metals & formed
products

Charlotte
Atascosa County

(G-3047)
FLA SAFETY & PROD SVCS INC
Also Called: Pneumatech Safety Systems
11404 W Fm 140 (78011-3578)
PHONE...................................830 570-7286
William C Fehr Jr, *President*
Richard P Allen, *Vice Pres*
James K Lambeth, *Treasurer*
EMP: 35
SALES (est): 2.4MM **Privately Held**
SIC: 1389 Oil field services

(G-3048)
NEXTIER CMPLTION
SOLUTIONS INC
303 E Hindes (78011-3525)
PHONE...................................830 277-1200
Nick Jenkins, *Branch Mgr*
EMP: 13
SALES (corp-wide): 1.8B **Publicly Held**
WEB: www.cjenergy.com
SIC: 1389 Oil field services
HQ: Nextier Completion Solutions Inc.
3990 Rogerdale Rd
Houston TX 77042
713 325-6000

(G-3049)
VENADO OIL & GAS LLC
490 E Hindes Ave (78011)
PHONE...................................512 518-2900
EMP: 10
SALES (corp-wide): 15.6MM **Privately**
Held
WEB: www.vogllc.com
SIC: 1382 Oil & gas exploration services
PA: Venado Oil & Gas, Llc
13301 Galleria Cir # 300
Austin TX 78738
512 518-2900

Chico
Wise County

(G-3050)
AUSTIN POWDER COMPANY
306 County Road 1347 (76431-2633)
PHONE...................................940 644-5771
David Glesen, *President*
Hunter Hughes, *General Mgr*
Brian Foerster, *Manager*
EMP: 21
SALES (corp-wide): 509.6MM **Privately**
Held
WEB: www.austinpowder.com
SIC: 2892 5169 Explosives; explosives
HQ: Austin Powder Company
25800 Science Park Dr # 300
Cleveland OH 44122
216 464-2400

(G-3051)
BLACK SHEEP OILFIELD SVCS LLC
691 N Davis St (76431-2829)
P.O. Box 129 (76431-0129)
PHONE..................................940 644-1720
Neil W Richey, *President*
Morris L Busby, *Vice Pres*
Lloyd Chisum, *Admin Sec*
EMP: 19 **EST:** 2011
SALES (est): 5.9MM **Privately Held**
SIC: 1389 Oil field services

(G-3052)
CATALYST PARTNERS INC
Also Called: Catalyst Partners Oil Field
146 Prvate Rd 1738 Unit 2 (76431)
PHONE..................................940 644-5625
Landy Moran, *President*
Bill Fiero, *Principal*
Amelia Cox, *Marketing Staff*
Ladona Paul, *Manager*
EMP: 9
SQ FT: 2,000
SALES (est): 2.7MM **Privately Held**
WEB: www.catalyst.partners
SIC: 5169 2911 Chemicals & allied products; petroleum refining

(G-3053)
MARTIN MRTTA MTLS SUTHWEST LLC
856 Fm 2952 (76431-2241)
PHONE..................................940 644-5084
Richard Perkins, *Branch Mgr*
EMP: 62 **Publicly Held**
WEB: www.chenega.com
SIC: 1422 Crushed & broken limestone
HQ: Martin Marietta Materials Southwest, Llc
　5710 W Hausman Rd Ste 121
　San Antonio TX 78249
　210 208-4400

(G-3054)
TRI RESOURCES INC
Also Called: Dynegy
383 County Road 1745 (76431-2121)
PHONE..................................940 644-2233
Joe Clark, *Manager*
Shane Tribe, *Manager*
EMP: 23 **Publicly Held**
WEB: www.triresources.com
SIC: 4922 1321 2911 Natural gas transmission; natural gas liquids; petroleum refining
HQ: Tri Resources Inc.
　811 Louisiana St Ste 2100
　Houston TX 77002
　713 584-1000

Childress
Childress County

(G-3055)
JUSTIN BRANDS INC
700 Avenue F Nw (79201-3514)
PHONE..................................940 226-1706
Ann Statham, *Branch Mgr*
EMP: 315
SALES (corp-wide): 254.6B **Publicly Held**
WEB: www.justinbrands.com
SIC: 3143 Men's footwear, except athletic
HQ: Justin Brands, Inc.
　610 W Daggett Ave
　Fort Worth TX 76104

(G-3056)
TRANSPORTATION TEXAS DEPT
Also Called: Driver License Office
1700 Avenue F Nw (79201-3321)
PHONE..................................940 937-2571
David Casteel, *Director*
EMP: 14
SALES (corp-wide): 128.4B **Privately Held**
WEB: www.txdot.gov
SIC: 3469 9621 Automobile license tags, stamped metal;
HQ: Texas Department Of Transportation
　150 E Riverside Dr
　Austin TX 78704

China Grove
Bexar County

(G-3057)
LONE STAR BAKERY INC (PA)
6905 Us Highway 87 E (78263-6029)
PHONE..................................210 648-6400
Mac S Morris Jr, *President*
Tracy Fletcher, *Partner*
Don McComas, *Vice Pres*
Deborah Morris, *Vice Pres*
Jim Herzfeld, *Maint Spvr*
▲ **EMP:** 400 **EST:** 1800
SQ FT: 140,000
SALES (est): 135.3MM **Privately Held**
WEB: www.lonestarbakery.com
SIC: 2053 2051 Frozen bakery products, except bread; bread, cake & related products

(G-3058)
LONE STAR BAKERY INC
8100 Us Highway 87 E (78263-2225)
PHONE..................................210 648-6400
Tomas Pacheco, *Principal*
Mike Brehm, *Chief Engr*
John Sant, *Engineer*
Chris Donlon, *Maintence Staff*
EMP: 200
SALES (corp-wide): 135.3MM **Privately Held**
WEB: www.lonestarbakery.com
SIC: 2053 Frozen bakery products, except bread
PA: Lone Star Bakery, Inc.
　6905 Us Highway 87 E
　China Grove TX 78263
　210 648-6400

Christine
Atascosa County

(G-3059)
NORTH AMERICAN COAL CORP
Also Called: San Miguel Lignite Mine
9200 Peeler Ln (78012-2017)
P.O. Box 399, Jourdanton (78026-0399)
PHONE..................................830 784-3545
Stephen Mullaney, *Manager*
Christopher Friez, *Manager*
Shawn Woods, *Technology*
EMP: 240
SALES (corp-wide): 140.9MM **Publicly Held**
WEB: www.nacoal.com
SIC: 1221 Bituminous coal & lignite-surface mining
HQ: The North American Coal Corporation
　5340 Legacy Dr Ste 300
　Plano TX 75024
　972 448-5400

Cibolo
Guadalupe County

(G-3060)
AGE INDUSTRIES LTD
1204 Schneider (78108-3221)
PHONE..................................210 659-1301
Chris Hughes, *General Mgr*
Christopher Hughes, *Vice Pres*
Troy Redmon, *Plant Mgr*
Leny Andal, *Office Mgr*
Missy Garcia, *Executive*
EMP: 75
SQ FT: 624
SALES (corp-wide): 140.8MM **Privately Held**
WEB: www.ageindustries.com
SIC: 2653 2449 2448 Boxes, corrugated: made from purchased materials; containers, plywood & veneer wood; wood pallets & skids
PA: Age Industries, Ltd.
　3601 County Road 316c
　Cleburne TX 76031
　817 477-5266

(G-3061)
AMBASSADOR FACILITY SVCS LLC
220 Country Vale (78108-3472)
P.O. Box 477 (78108-0477)
PHONE..................................210 849-7677
Daniel Jones, *Principal*
EMP: 20
SALES (est): 593.3K **Privately Held**
SIC: 2842 7217 7389 7349 Window cleaning preparations; carpet & upholstery cleaning plants; ; janitorial service, contract basis

(G-3062)
B&B WORLDWIDE TECHNOLOGY
Also Called: B & B Technology
608 Hinge Fls (78108-3350)
PHONE..................................713 471-2387
Kevin Brink, *Partner*
Davin Broussard, *Partner*
D Broussard, *Associate*
EMP: 10
SALES (est): 264.7K **Privately Held**
SIC: 7379 7372 7373 ; application computer software; systems engineering, computer related

(G-3063)
INDEPNDENT RUGH TRRAIN CTR LLC
103 Guadalupe Dr (78108-3144)
P.O. Box 1028 (78108-1028)
PHONE..................................210 599-6541
Steven Speakes, *President*
◆ **EMP:** 160
SQ FT: 31,000
SALES (est): 25MM **Privately Held**
WEB: www.irtc-tx.com
SIC: 3537 6399 5531 Forklift trucks; warranty insurance, automobile; truck equipment & parts

(G-3064)
ROY C GARRETT INC
411 Fm 1103 (78108-3573)
P.O. Box 569 (78108-0569)
PHONE..................................210 659-6701
B Tom Dreher, *President*
Dan Hale, *General Mgr*
Chris Benson, *Vice Pres*
Jennifer Benson, *Admin Sec*
EMP: 10
SQ FT: 5,000
SALES (est): 1.6MM **Privately Held**
WEB: www.roycgarrett.com
SIC: 1711 2499 Mechanical contractor; cooling towers, wood or wood & sheet metal combination

(G-3065)
SIGNATURE PLATING LTD
1135 Guadalupe Dr (78108-3232)
PHONE..................................210 380-0020
Lawrence Donoho, *President*
Matthew McKnight, *QA Dir*
Zane Leake, *VP Sales*
EMP: 22
SALES (est): 3.7MM **Privately Held**
WEB: www.signatureplating.com
SIC: 3471 Plating of metals or formed products

Cisco
Eastland County

(G-3066)
EASTLAND COUNTY NEWSPAPER INC
Also Called: Cisco Press
700 Conrad Hilton Blvd (76437-3140)
P.O. Box 29 (76437-0029)
PHONE..................................254 442-2000
Hv O'Brien, *Manager*
EMP: 12
SALES (corp-wide): 1.5MM **Privately Held**
WEB: www.eastlandcountytoday.com
SIC: 2711 Newspapers: publishing only, not printed on site

PA: Eastland County Newspaper Inc
　215 S Seaman St
　Eastland TX 76448
　254 629-1707

(G-3067)
INTERSTATE EXPLORATIONS LLC
17010 Interstate 20 (76437-6471)
P.O. Box 984 (76437-0984)
PHONE..................................254 442-1057
JC Williams, *Superintendent*
Dan H Wilks, *Manager*
Robert B Early,
Farris C Wilks,
EMP: 10 **EST:** 1998
SQ FT: 800
SALES (est): 4MM **Privately Held**
WEB: www.interstateexplorations.com
SIC: 1389 Oil field services

(G-3068)
RESEARCH ADVANCED METHODS INDS
Also Called: R A M
808 E 6th St (76437-2114)
P.O. Box 47 (76437-0047)
PHONE..................................254 442-1008
Richard Williams, *CEO*
Diann Morris, *President*
Daniel Bray, *QC Mgr*
Jeb Hudson, *Engineer*
Dustin Williams, *Engineer*
▼ **EMP:** 44
SQ FT: 37,900
SALES (est): 4MM **Privately Held**
WEB: www.raminc-cisco.com
SIC: 3089 3544 3083 Injection molding of plastics; special dies, tools, jigs & fixtures; laminated plastics plate & sheet

(G-3069)
UNITED ENERGEX INC
517 Spur 490 (76437-6530)
PHONE..................................254 629-8560
Irvin Robinson, *District Mgr*
EMP: 25
SALES (corp-wide): 12.8MM **Privately Held**
SIC: 1389 Servicing oil & gas wells
HQ: United Energex, Inc.
　7709 Broadway St Apt 106
　San Antonio TX 78209
　210 826-0681

Clarendon
Donley County

(G-3070)
CLARENDON MFG & DISTRG CO INC
Also Called: Cmd
200 W 1st St (79226)
P.O. Box 948 (79226-0948)
PHONE..................................806 874-3584
Darrell Leffew, *President*
Wilma K Leffew, *Admin Sec*
EMP: 10 **EST:** 1971
SQ FT: 13,280
SALES (est): 775K **Privately Held**
SIC: 3531 5083 Scrapers (construction machinery); farm equipment parts & supplies

(G-3071)
WALLACE MONUMENT COMPANY (PA)
213 E 2nd St (79226)
PHONE..................................806 874-2442
Mark White, *President*
Kim Fowler, *Vice Pres*
EMP: 11 **EST:** 1930
SQ FT: 3,000
SALES (est): 1.3MM **Privately Held**
WEB: www.wallacemonumentco.net
SIC: 5999 3281 3272 Monuments, finished to custom order; tombstones; curbing, granite or stone; burial vaults, concrete or precast terrazzo

Clarksville
Red River County

(G-3072)
COMPLIANT POWER SYSTEMS LLC
1801 Industrial Way (75426-2564)
PHONE..................................903 427-0071
Doyle Hess,
Chris A Hess,
Frank J Hess,
Laverna M Nasche,
EMP: 12 EST: 2012
SALES (est): 2.2MM Privately Held
WEB: www.compliantpowersystems.com
SIC: 3523 3694 3621 5083 Fertilizing, spraying, dusting & irrigation machinery; engine electrical equipment; power generators; irrigation equipment; electrical apparatus & equipment; generators; electrical repair shops

(G-3073)
HUHTAMAKI INC
500 Industrial Blvd (75426-2493)
PHONE..................................903 427-5711
EMP: 300
SALES (corp-wide): 3.7B Privately Held
WEB: www.huhtamaki.com
SIC: 3565 2656 Labeling machines, industrial; ice cream containers: made from purchased material
HQ: Huhtamaki, Inc.
9201 Packaging Dr
De Soto KS 66018
913 583-3025

(G-3074)
MAGNOLIA BRUSH MFRS INC
1001 N Cedar St (75426-2700)
P.O. Box 932 (75426-0932)
PHONE..................................903 427-2261
Kenneth Backus, President
▲ EMP: 95 EST: 1907
SQ FT: 87,500
SALES (est): 17.2MM Privately Held
WEB: www.magnoliabrush.com
SIC: 3991 2499 Brushes, household or industrial; handles, wood

(G-3075)
MARTIN SPROCKET & GEAR INC
300 Industrial Blvd (75426-2489)
PHONE..................................903 427-2217
Shawn Beck, Branch Mgr
EMP: 60
SALES (corp-wide): 539MM Privately Held
WEB: www.martinsprocket.com
SIC: 3566 3568 Gears, power transmission, except automotive; power transmission equipment
PA: Martin Sprocket & Gear, Inc.
3100 Sprocket Dr
Arlington TX 76015
817 258-3000

(G-3076)
NORTHAST TXAS MCHNING WLDG HRD
121 North St (75426-2343)
PHONE..................................903 427-2277
Rachel Ward Atnip, President
Zach Ward, General Mgr
Zachary Scott Ward, Treasurer
EMP: 15
SQ FT: 60,000
SALES (est): 300K Privately Held
WEB: www.nethardfacing.com
SIC: 7692 3599 3448 3443 Welding repair; machine shop, jobbing & repair; prefabricated metal buildings; fabricated plate work (boiler shop); sheet metalwork

(G-3077)
PALLETONE INC
670 Us Highway 82 E (75426-8147)
PHONE..................................903 427-3030
Howe Q Wallace, CEO
EMP: 65

SALES (corp-wide): 476.2MM Privately Held
WEB: www.palletone.com
SIC: 2448 Pallets, wood
PA: Palletone, Inc
6001 Foxtrot Ave
Bartow FL 33830
800 771-1147

(G-3078)
WABB INDUSTRIES INC
Also Called: K & B Steel
525 Industrial Blvd (75426-2494)
PHONE..................................903 427-3980
Richard Cobb, President
EMP: 25
SQ FT: 40,000
SALES (est): 4.7MM Privately Held
WEB: www.kandbsteel.com
SIC: 3441 Fabricated structural metal

Cleburne
Johnson County

(G-3079)
AGE INDUSTRIES LTD (PA)
3601 County Road 316c (76031-9098)
P.O. Box 539 (76033-0539)
PHONE..................................817 477-5266
EMP: 75
SQ FT: 56,832
SALES (est): 140.8MM Privately Held
WEB: www.ageindustries.com
SIC: 2653 2655 2671 Boxes, corrugated: made from purchased materials; fiber cans, drums & similar products; packaging paper & plastics film, coated & laminated

(G-3080)
B & H ENTERPRISES
803 Rose Ave (76033-7442)
P.O. Box 676 (76033-0676)
PHONE..................................817 558-2667
EMP: 20
SALES (est): 1.3MM Privately Held
SIC: 3547 Mfg Rolling Mill Machinery

(G-3081)
BEACON ENERGY (TEXAS) CORP
3102 Windmill Rd (76033-7734)
PHONE..................................817 558-9255
Bylan Renlay, President
EMP: 15
SQ FT: 14,000
SALES (est): 3.9MM Publicly Held
WEB: www.bestbiofuels.com
SIC: 2869 Industrial organic chemicals
PA: Eqm Technologies & Energy Inc.
1800 Carillion Blvd
Cincinnati OH 45240

(G-3082)
C & S TRUCKING
5154 N Fm 199 (76033-9427)
PHONE..................................817 517-9172
Casey W Seidl, Owner
EMP: 10
SALES (est): 642.2K Privately Held
SIC: 3715 Truck trailers

(G-3083)
CHILDS READY-MIX CONCRETE CO
4989 N Fm 199 (76033-9433)
PHONE..................................817 477-5151
Roy Wesson, Manager
EMP: 22
SALES (corp-wide): 1.4B Publicly Held
WEB: www.ingramconcrete.com
SIC: 5032 1442 Brick, stone & related material; construction sand & gravel
HQ: Childs Ready-Mix Concrete Company
4301 Danhil Dr
Brownwood TX 76801
325 646-6518

(G-3084)
COVIA HOLDINGS CORPORATION
1788 County Road 308 (76033-9409)
PHONE..................................254 897-4408

Christopher Sluder, Safety Dir
Adam Eatheron, Plant Mgr
EMP: 50
SALES (corp-wide): 125.5MM Privately Held
WEB: www.coviacorp.com
SIC: 1446 Industrial sand
HQ: Covia Holdings Corporation
3 Summit Park Dr Ste 700
Independence OH 44131
440 214-3284

(G-3085)
COWAN COSTUMES INC
108 S Caddo St (76031-5503)
PHONE..................................817 641-3126
Karen Cowan, President
Penny Bell, Production
Bradley Cowan, Treasurer
EMP: 13
SQ FT: 8,000
SALES (est): 1.4MM Privately Held
WEB: www.cowancostumes.com
SIC: 2389 7299 Costumes; costume rental

(G-3086)
DA SCHOGGIN INC
Also Called: Tech Lite Mfg
1701 Hal Ave (76031-7617)
PHONE..................................817 641-6800
Jerry Riley, Manager
Adam Toro, Supervisor
EMP: 50
SALES (corp-wide): 17.3MM Privately Held
WEB: www.techlightusa.com
SIC: 3648 3645 3646 Decorative area lighting fixtures; garden, patio, walkway & yard lighting fixtures: electric; commercial indusl & institutional electric lighting fixtures
PA: D.A. Schoggin, Inc.
2707 Satsuma Dr
Dallas TX 75229
214 350-0591

(G-3087)
DEFENSE SOLUTIONS GROUP INC
Also Called: Dsgi
6100 Conveyor Dr (76031-0988)
PHONE..................................800 382-7571
Russell G Hague, President
Zack Jones, Vice Pres
Dorothy Hague, Admin Sec
▲ EMP: 10 EST: 1995
SALES (est): 1.6MM Privately Held
WEB: www.dsgarms.com
SIC: 7374 7375 2741 7699 Data processing & preparation; information retrieval services; miscellaneous publishing; gunsmith shop

(G-3088)
DELEK RENEWABLES LLC
3102 Windmill Rd (76033-7734)
PHONE..................................817 558-9255
Frank Roy, Branch Mgr
EMP: 22
SALES (corp-wide): 9.3B Publicly Held
SIC: 2911 Petroleum refining
HQ: Delek Renewables, Llc
7102 Commerce Way
Brentwood TN 37027
615 771-6701

(G-3089)
FRED BENNETT PRINTING COMPANY (PA)
Also Called: Bennetts Printing & Office Sup
300 E Chambers St (76031-5613)
P.O. Box 729 (76033-0729)
PHONE..................................817 641-9861
Gary Bennett, President
Dave Lester, Sales Mgr
Norma Canon, Info Tech Dir
EMP: 35
SQ FT: 15,000
SALES (est): 6.5MM Privately Held
WEB: www.bennettsprinting.com
SIC: 5943 2752 Office forms & supplies; commercial printing, offset

(G-3090)
FUQUA ENTERPRISES INC
205 E Vaughn Rd (76031)
PHONE..................................817 641-1074
John Fuqua, Manager
EMP: 9
SALES (corp-wide): 852.2K Privately Held
WEB: www.fuqua3.com
SIC: 3444 Sheet metalwork
PA: Fuqua Enterprises, Inc.
418 W Vaughn Rd
Cleburne TX 76033
817 641-1074

(G-3091)
GENES PAUL ENTERPRISES INC
Also Called: Gene's Paul MBL Wshsand Blast
301 N Pendell Ave (76033-8729)
PHONE..................................817 558-7868
Paul Warrick, President
EMP: 25
SALES (est): 860.9K Privately Held
WEB: www.paulgenesenterprises.com
SIC: 7542 3471 1721 Carwashes; sand blasting of metal parts; painting & paper hanging

(G-3092)
GRAVITY OILFIELD SERVICES LLC
1717 Hal Ave (76031-7617)
PHONE..................................817 558-9194
Ted Hogan, Owner
EMP: 59
SQ FT: 340
SALES (corp-wide): 422.8MM Privately Held
WEB: www.gravityoilfieldservices.com
SIC: 1389 Oil field services
HQ: Gravity Oilfield Services Llc
3300 N A St Bldg 4-100
Midland TX 79705

(G-3093)
GS LIQUID TECHNOLOGIES LLC
601 W Industrial Blvd A (76033-7880)
P.O. Box 3185 (76033-3185)
PHONE..................................817 556-6262
Eric Rodela, General Mgr
Scott Elgin, Principal
Gino Inman,
EMP: 10
SQ FT: 40,000
SALES (est): 1.8MM Privately Held
WEB: www.gsliquid.com
SIC: 3053 3565 7389 3677 Packing materials; labeling machines, industrial; packaging & labeling services; filtration devices, electronic; quality assurance consultant; blow molded finished plastic products

(G-3094)
GUNDERSON RAIL SERVICES LLC
101 Park St (76031-4038)
PHONE..................................817 556-9191
Tim Stucky, President
Jason Green, QC Mgr
EMP: 275
SALES (corp-wide): 2.7B Publicly Held
WEB: www.gbrx.com
SIC: 3743 Railroad car repair
HQ: Gunderson Rail Services Llc
1 Centerpointe Dr Ste 200
Lake Oswego OR 97035
503 684-7000

(G-3095)
HLI RESOURCES LLC
Also Called: Hli Energy Services
3600 W Highway 67 (76033-8523)
PHONE..................................817 240-4361
Ross Gatlin, CEO
John R Hardee, President
Trevor Cohen, Senior VP
Don Heierman, CFO
EMP: 250
SQ FT: 40,000
SALES (est): 36MM Privately Held
WEB: www.hlienergy.com
SIC: 1389 Oil field services

(G-3096)
INTERNATIONAL INGREDIENT CORP
2701 Pipeline Rd (76033-7789)
PHONE......................817 645-1328
Steve Moore, *Branch Mgr*
EMP: 15
SALES (corp-wide): 26.3MM **Privately Held**
WEB: www.iicag.com
SIC: 2048 Prepared feeds
PA: International Ingredient Corporation
150 Lrkin Williams Ind Ct
Fenton MO 63026
636 343-4111

(G-3097)
JAMES HARDIE BUILDING PDTS INC
820 Sparks Dr (76033-7700)
PHONE......................817 556-7000
Jamie Korcenowski, *Principal*
Clara Childress, *Business Mgr*
Mark Moore, *Business Mgr*
Rob Gilfert, *Opers Staff*
William Munch, *Engineer*
EMP: 200 **Privately Held**
WEB: www.jameshardie.com
SIC: 3272 2823 Dry mixture concrete; cellulosic manmade fibers
HQ: James Hardie Building Products Inc.
231 S La Salle St # 2000
Chicago IL 60604
312 291-5072

(G-3098)
JOHNS MANVILLE CORPORATION
200 W Industrial Blvd (76033-5062)
PHONE......................817 645-9101
Paula Wakeland, *Business Mgr*
Todd Neighbor, *Branch Mgr*
Ed Hughes, *Manager*
Tom Sampson, *Executive*
Harold Brookshire, *Admin Sec*
EMP: 360
SALES (corp-wide): 254.6B **Publicly Held**
WEB: www.jm.com
SIC: 3296 Fiberglass insulation
HQ: Johns Manville Corporation
717 17th St Ste 800
Denver CO 80202
303 978-2000

(G-3099)
JOHNSON COUNTY REDI-MIX LTD
1905 N Main St (76033-5021)
P.O. Box 597 (76033-0597)
PHONE......................817 556-9214
Ricky Allen, *President*
Don Brown, *Vice Pres*
Curtis Rives, *Vice Pres*
EMP: 11
SALES (est): 2.8MM **Privately Held**
WEB: www.johnsoncountyredi-mix.com
SIC: 3273 Ready-mixed concrete

(G-3100)
LEE PRODUCTS INC
Also Called: Bill's Welding Service
4308 E Highway 67 (76031-9111)
PHONE......................817 641-9893
Raymond Lee, *President*
Bill Lee, *Vice Pres*
Juanita Lee, *Vice Pres*
Kay Harwell, *Treasurer*
Randy Branham, *VP Mktg*
EMP: 15
SQ FT: 12,000
SALES (est): 3.5MM **Privately Held**
WEB: www.metalranch.com
SIC: 3523 3429 5013 Farm machinery & equipment; fireplace equipment, hardware: andirons, grates, screens; trailer parts & accessories

(G-3101)
MCBROOM INDUSTRIES
4385 S Highway 174 (76033-8606)
P.O. Box 271 (76033-0271)
PHONE......................817 645-2248
Ronald R McBroom, *Owner*
EMP: 11

SQ FT: 960
SALES (est): 1MM **Privately Held**
SIC: 3229 Glass fiber products

(G-3102)
NEWSPAPER HOLDING INC
Also Called: Cleburne Times Review
108 S Anglin St (76031-5602)
P.O. Box 1569 (76031-1569)
PHONE......................817 645-2441
Renae Alexander, *Accounts Exec*
Kay Helms, *Branch Mgr*
EMP: 35
SQ FT: 9,936
SALES (corp-wide): 23.7B **Privately Held**
WEB: www.oskaloosa.com
SIC: 2711 2752 Newspapers: publishing only, not printed on site; commercial printing, lithographic
HQ: Newspaper Holding, Inc.
425 Locust St
Johnstown PA 15901
814 532-5102

(G-3103)
NEWTON CONVEYORS INC
1204 County Road 1123 (76033-8090)
P.O. Box 816 (76033-0816)
PHONE......................817 558-1722
Bob Newton, *President*
David Newton, *Vice Pres*
Carolyn Newton, *Admin Sec*
EMP: 15
SQ FT: 5,000
SALES (est): 1.6MM **Privately Held**
WEB: www.newtonconveyors.com
SIC: 3535 Conveyors & conveying equipment

(G-3104)
NG OPERATIONS LLC
Also Called: National Gypsum Company
811 Sparks Dr (76033-7700)
P.O. Box 1688 (76033-1688)
PHONE......................817 645-3435
Dana Pearson, *Principal*
EMP: 99
SALES (corp-wide): 478MM **Privately Held**
WEB: www.nationalgypsum.com
SIC: 3275 Gypsum products
HQ: Proform Finishing Products, Llc
2001 Rexford Rd
Charlotte NC 28211

(G-3105)
PATTERSON-UTI ENERGY INC
3205 Windmill Rd (76033-7743)
PHONE......................817 556-5300
Tony Waltrep, *Branch Mgr.*
Jay Bowen, *Director*
EMP: 35
SALES (corp-wide): 1.1B **Publicly Held**
WEB: www.patenergy.com
SIC: 1389 Oil field services
PA: Patterson-Uti Energy, Inc.
10713 W Sam Houston Pkwy
Houston TX 77064
281 765-7100

(G-3106)
PYTHON PRESSURE PUMPING LLC
111 Hyde Park Blvd # 500 (76033-4583)
PHONE......................940 549-6900
Terry Glover, *President*
Clay Wells, *Sales Mgr*
Anthony Briseno, *Manager*
Michael Winder, *Maintence Staff*
EMP: 40
SQ FT: 1,000
SALES (est): 3.3MM **Privately Held**
WEB: www.pythonpressurepumping.com
SIC: 1382 Oil & gas exploration services

(G-3107)
RANGAIRE MANUFACTURING CO LP
Also Called: Jensen
501 S Wilhite St (76031-6399)
PHONE......................817 556-6500
Alan M Crawford, *Mng Member*
Stephen Fitchett,
◆ EMP: 80
SQ FT: 210,000

SALES (est): 11MM **Privately Held**
WEB: www.rangairemfg.com
SIC: 2514 Medicine cabinets & vanities: metal

(G-3108)
SACHEM INC
2311 Pipeline Rd (76033-7747)
PHONE......................817 202-3200
Eric Riden, *Vice Pres*
Jeff Pakeltis, *Plant Mgr*
Andy Kenny, *Opers Staff*
Tyler Bullard, *Production*
John Hattenbach, *Buyer*
EMP: 60
SALES (corp-wide): 91.2MM **Privately Held**
WEB: www.sacheminc.com
SIC: 2869 2899 Industrial organic chemicals; chemical preparations
PA: Sachem, Inc.
821 Woodward St
Austin TX 78704
512 421-4900

(G-3109)
SMITHFIELD BIOENERGY LLC (DH)
3102 Windmill Rd (76033-7734)
PHONE......................817 558-9255
Robert W Manly, *President*
Mark Farrer, *General Mgr*
Michael B Cole, *Principal*
James Boushka, *Vice Pres*
EMP: 32
SQ FT: 15,000
SALES (est): 2.7MM **Privately Held**
SIC: 2869 Industrial organic chemicals
HQ: Smithfield Foods, Inc.
200 Commerce St
Smithfield VA 23430
757 365-3000

(G-3110)
SUPERIOR CON FENCE TEXAS INC
2020 S Highway 171 (76031-7629)
PHONE......................817 558-6658
Raul Rodriguez, *Manager*
EMP: 40 **Privately Held**
WEB: www.concretefence.com
SIC: 3272 Concrete products
PA: Superior Concrete Fence Of Texas, Inc.
1203 Raider Dr
Euless TX 76040

(G-3111)
SUPREME CORPORATION OF TEXAS (DH)
500 Commerce Blvd (76033-5026)
P.O. Box 2828 (76033-2828)
PHONE......................817 641-6282
Herbert Gardner, *Chairman*
William Barrett, *Vice Pres*
Matthew Long, *CFO*
Lynn Stevens, *Human Res Mgr*
▲ EMP: 175 EST: 1978
SQ FT: 94,000
SALES (est): 27.8MM
SALES (corp-wide): 2.2B **Publicly Held**
WEB: www.supremecorp.com
SIC: 3713 Truck bodies (motor vehicles)
HQ: Supreme Industries, Inc.
2581 Kercher Rd
Goshen IN 46528
574 642-3070

(G-3112)
SUPREME CORPORATION OF TEXAS
Also Called: Supreme Armored
3001 N Main St (76033-5001)
PHONE......................817 641-8002
EMP: 120
SALES (corp-wide): 2.2B **Publicly Held**
WEB: www.supremecorp.com
SIC: 3537 3799 3713 Industrial trucks & tractors; trailers & trailer equipment; stake, platform truck bodies
HQ: Supreme Corporation Of Texas
500 Commerce Blvd
Cleburne TX 76033
817 641-6282

(G-3113)
TEXAS INGREDIENT CORPORATION
Also Called: Texas Ingredients
2701 Pipeline Rd (76033-7789)
PHONE......................817 645-1328
Fred Brown, *President*
James Sullivan, *Vice Pres*
▲ EMP: 70
SQ FT: 20,000 **Privately Held**
SIC: 2082 2869 Brewers' grain; ethyl alcohol, ethanol

(G-3114)
TEXAS LIME COMPANY
Also Called: United States Lime & Minerals
15865 Farm Road 1434 (76033)
P.O. Box 851 (76033-0851)
PHONE......................817 641-4433
Julius Harris, *Branch Mgr*
EMP: 100
SALES (corp-wide): 4.1MM **Publicly Held**
WEB: www.uslm.com
SIC: 3274 1422 Lime; crushed & broken limestone
HQ: Texas Lime Company
5429 Lyndon B Johnson Fwy # 230
Dallas TX 75240
972 385-1335

(G-3115)
TRIANGLE PUMP COMPONENTS INC (PA)
3644 W Highway 67 (76033-8523)
PHONE......................817 202-8530
David Moser, *President*
Sam Kelton, *Vice Pres*
Mark Otwell, *Opers Staff*
Patti Humphrey, *Accounting Mgr*
Dana Miller, *Sales Mgr*
▲ EMP: 12
SQ FT: 14,000
SALES (est): 3.6MM **Privately Held**
WEB: www.triangle-pump.com
SIC: 3533 3561 Oil & gas field machinery; pumps & pumping equipment

(G-3116)
UNIFIX INC
811 Sparks Dr (76033-7700)
PHONE......................817 645-3435
Tom Nelson, *Branch Mgr*
EMP: 30
SQ FT: 50,058
SALES (corp-wide): 478MM **Privately Held**
WEB: www.unifixinc.com
SIC: 2439 3275 Timbers, structural: laminated lumber; gypsum products
HQ: Unifix Inc
35 Rue Unifix
Bromont QC J2L 1
450 534-0955

(G-3117)
URBANOVSKY ADVANCED CNSTR LLC
4301 County Road 312b (76031-8938)
PHONE......................817 556-3288
Patricia Chapman, *Principal*
Caleb Rohm, *Principal*
John Palomares, *Manager*
Ricky W Urbanovsky,
EMP: 55
SALES (est): 4.3MM **Privately Held**
WEB: www.myadvancedconstruction.com
SIC: 3441 Fabricated structural metal

Cleveland
Liberty County

(G-3118)
ACE INDUSTRIES INC
Also Called: Gaffey Crane Div
1436 N Duck Creek Rd (77328-5815)
PHONE......................281 443-6690
Gary Wallace, *Principal*
EMP: 54
SQ FT: 1,488
SALES (corp-wide): 111.2MM **Privately Held**
WEB: www.aceindustries.com
SIC: 3536 Hoists, cranes & monorails

PA: Ace Industries, Inc.
6295 Mcdonough Dr
Norcross GA 30093
770 441-0898

(G-3119)
B E R PRECISION INC
Also Called: Ber Precission
1100 N Washington Ave (77327-3733)
PHONE..................................281 659-0100
Thomas E Berry, *President*
Todd Berry, *Vice Pres*
EMP: 10 **EST:** 1986
SQ FT: 8,000
SALES (est): 1.8MM **Privately Held**
WEB: www.berprecision.com
SIC: 3599 Machine shop, jobbing & repair

(G-3120)
B&B AGGREGATES INC
3469 Fm 1010 Rd (77327-8790)
PHONE..................................281 659-9004
Paul Brockner, *President*
Jan Brockner, *Treasurer*
EMP: 10
SALES (est): 662.3K **Privately Held**
SIC: 1442 Gravel & pebble mining

(G-3121)
BROCKS LOGGING INC
3469 Fm 1010 Rd (77327-8790)
PHONE..................................281 593-1531
Paul Brockner, *President*
Jan Brockner, *Admin Sec*
EMP: 20 **EST:** 1984
SQ FT: 576
SALES (est): 3.2MM **Privately Held**
SIC: 2411 Logging camps & contractors

(G-3122)
CHEESEMAKERS INC
2266 S Walker Rd (77328-6336)
PHONE..................................281 593-1319
James C Keliehor, *President*
Mark Tesch, *General Mgr*
Amy Keliehor, *Vice Pres*
Tim Carpenter, *Plant Mgr*
Kathleen Cawthon, *Marketing Staff*
EMP: 20
SQ FT: 8,200
SALES (est): 4.5MM **Privately Held**
WEB: www.cheesemakers.com
SIC: 2022 5143 Cheese, natural & processed; cheese

(G-3123)
CLW INC (PA)
10001 Fm 2025 Rd (77328-8334)
P.O. Box 1677 (77328-1677)
PHONE..................................281 592-4691
Brian Weinheimer, *President*
H P Coleman, *Chairman*
Hugh Lowe, *Vice Pres*
Claudette Coleman Lowe, *Treasurer*
Rosemary Coleman Weinheimer, *Treasurer*
EMP: 65
SALES (est): 29.8MM **Privately Held**
SIC: 2421 Lumber: rough, sawed or planed

(G-3124)
COLUMBUS MCKINNON CORPORATION
Gaffey
1436 N Duck Creek Rd (77328-5815)
PHONE..................................281 443-6690
Richard O'Toole, *Manager*
EMP: 30
SALES (corp-wide): 809.1MM **Publicly Held**
WEB: www.columbusmckinnon.com
SIC: 3536 Hoists, cranes & monorails
PA: Columbus Mckinnon Corporation
205 Crosspoint Pkwy
Getzville NY 14068
716 689-5400

(G-3125)
FREEDOM ARCHITECTURAL MILLWORK
12380 Fm 1725 Rd (77328-5416)
PHONE..................................281 592-5377
David Smith, *Owner*
Janice Smith, *Co-Owner*
EMP: 10 **Privately Held**
WEB: www.freedommillwork.com
SIC: 2431 Millwork

(G-3126)
FWM TUBULAR & EQUIPMENT CORP
10111 Fostoria Rd (77328-6923)
PHONE..................................281 806-7918
William Huebel, *President*
Ray Routhier, *Vice Pres*
Amy Wilms, *CFO*
Neva Huebel, *Director*
◆ **EMP:** 25
SQ FT: 3,000
SALES (est): 5.4MM **Privately Held**
WEB: www.fwmtubular.com
SIC: 3533 Oil & gas field machinery

(G-3127)
GILL METALLURGICAL INC
691 County Road 2201 (77327-2867)
PHONE..................................281 593-0807
Parwinder Gill, *Principal*
EMP: 10
SALES (est): 1.3MM **Privately Held**
WEB: www.gillmet.com
SIC: 3398 Metal heat treating

(G-3128)
HERB HILLTOP FARM & RESTAURANT
235 Chain O Lakes Resort (77327-8698)
PHONE..................................832 397-4020
James Smith, *Partner*
Steve Ough, *Partner*
Helena Smith, *Partner*
EMP: 55
SALES (est): 4MM **Privately Held**
WEB: www.artesianlakes.com
SIC: 2033 Canned fruits & specialties

(G-3129)
J-W OPERATING COMPANY
4748 Us Highway 59 S (77327-6035)
PHONE..................................281 592-2351
Mike Douthwaite, *Owner*
EMP: 54 **Privately Held**
WEB: www.jwpower.net
SIC: 1389 Oil field services
HQ: J-W Operating Company
15505 Wright Brothers Dr
Addison TX 75001
972 233-8191

(G-3130)
JAMES BARKER III
Also Called: Precise Industrial Maintenance
3301 Highway 105 (77327-8061)
PHONE..................................936 298-2851
James Barker III, *Owner*
▲ **EMP:** 10 **EST:** 1998
SALES (est): 244K **Privately Held**
WEB: www.precisemachinefab.com
SIC: 3441 Fabricated structural metal

(G-3131)
KATS GLASS LLC
Also Called: City Glass
901 E Houston St Ste A (77327-4602)
PHONE..................................281 592-5211
David Bates,
Wayne Nelson,
EMP: 40
SALES (est): 5.7MM **Privately Held**
WEB: www.cityglassoftexas.com
SIC: 3211 Flat glass
PA: Dp Organization, Inc.
901 E Houston St Ste A
Cleveland TX 77327
281 592-5211

(G-3132)
NON-TYPICAL PIPELINE LLC
Also Called: Non Typical Pipeline
418 Fm 2025 Rd (77328-8617)
P.O. Box 1849 (77328-1849)
PHONE..................................281 622-5002
Marshall Kirst, *Business Mgr*
Jaqueline Crawford, *Mng Member*
EMP: 43
SQ FT: 3,000
SALES (est): 4.6MM **Privately Held**
WEB: www.ntpipeline.com
SIC: 1389 Construction, repair & dismantling services; building oil & gas well foundations on site; derrick building, repairing & dismantling

(G-3133)
PRECISE MACHINE & FABRICATIONS
3301 Highway 105 (77327-8061)
PHONE..................................936 298-2851
Janes R Barker III, *CEO*
EMP: 10
SALES (est): 1.1MM **Privately Held**
WEB: www.precisemachinefab.com
SIC: 3599 Machine shop, jobbing & repair

(G-3134)
ROUNHOUSE CORPORATION
18488 Highway 105 (77328-2404)
P.O. Box 1744 (77328-1744)
PHONE..................................281 593-1118
EMP: 12 **EST:** 1976
SQ FT: 2,072
SALES (est): 2.2MM **Privately Held**
WEB: www.rounhouse.com
SIC: 3448 Greenhouses: prefabricated metal

(G-3135)
SCP INTERNATIONAL INC
1447 Fm 1010 Rd (77327-9311)
PHONE..................................817 326-0257
Stephen C Pahls, *President*
Alan Burns, *COO*
Marcy Pound, *CFO*
▼ **EMP:** 10
SQ FT: 12,500
SALES (est): 925.4K **Privately Held**
WEB:
www.marcyssurplusandequipment.com
SIC: 2834 Vitamin preparations

(G-3136)
SPLENDORA PIPE SERVICES LLC
26670 Midline Rd (77328-7390)
PHONE..................................281 432-1400
Federico Garcia, *Mng Member*
Ronald E Bell,
EMP: 100
SALES (est): 15MM **Privately Held**
WEB: www.splendorapipeservices.com
SIC: 3317 1791 3444 Steel pipe & tubes; structural steel erection; sheet metalwork

(G-3137)
STETSON INTERNATIONAL LP
21189 Highway 321 (77327-1693)
P.O. Box 1645 (77328-1645)
PHONE..................................281 592-4788
Dorinda Stetson, *Partner*
David Stetson, *General Ptnr*
EMP: 9 **EST:** 1985
SQ FT: 1,600
SALES (est): 990K **Privately Held**
SIC: 2411 Wooden logs

(G-3138)
SUPERIOR SHOT PEENING INC
2350 Security Forest Dr (77328-7257)
PHONE..................................281 432-0900
Dan Spinner, *Manager*
EMP: 41 **Privately Held**
WEB: www.superiorshotpeening.com
SIC: 3398 3479 Metal heat treating; painting, coating & hot dipping; coating of metals & formed products
PA: Superior Shot Peening, Inc.
13930 Luthe Rd
Houston TX 77039

(G-3139)
THICK N THIN LUMBER CO INC
8591 Fm 787 Rd W (77327-9768)
P.O. Box 42 (77328-0042)
PHONE..................................281 592-0437
Mark Jones, *President*
Teresa Jones, *Office Mgr*
EMP: 14
SQ FT: 2,800
SALES (est): 2.5MM **Privately Held**
SIC: 2421 Sawmills & planing mills, general

(G-3140)
UNION TANK CAR COMPANY
604 County Road 2205 (77327-2754)
PHONE..................................281 592-6424
Douglas Trollope, *Branch Mgr*
EMP: 150

SALES (corp-wide): 254.6B **Publicly Held**
WEB: www.utlx.com
SIC: 3743 Railway motor cars
HQ: Union Tank Car Company
175 W Jackson Blvd # 2100
Chicago IL 60604
312 431-3111

(G-3141)
WESTERN FORGE & FLANGE CO INC (HQ)
687 County Road 2201 (77327-2867)
P.O. Box 1788 (77328-1788)
PHONE..................................800 352-6433
Walter R Pierce, *President*
James Smith, *Vice Pres*
▲ **EMP:** 45 **EST:** 1944
SQ FT: 40,000
SALES (est): 7.7MM
SALES (corp-wide): 42.7MM **Privately Held**
WEB: www.western-forge.com
SIC: 3462 Flange, valve & pipe fitting forgings, ferrous
PA: Pennsylvania Machine Works, Llc
201 Bethel Ave
Upper Chichester PA 19014
610 497-3300

Clifton
Bosque County

(G-3142)
CHEMICAL LIME-SOUTHWEST LLC
Clifton Plant Us60
2861 Fm 2602 (76634)
P.O. Box 473 (76634-0473)
PHONE..................................254 675-8668
Sam Wells, *Plant Mgr*
EMP: 130
SALES (corp-wide): 2.6MM **Privately Held**
WEB: www.lhoist.com
SIC: 1411 3274 1422 Limestone, dimension-quarrying; lime; crushed & broken limestone
HQ: Chemical Lime-Southwest, Llc
3700 Hulen St
Fort Worth TX 76107
817 732-8164

(G-3143)
CLIFTON MOULDING CORP
100 S Avenue B (76634-1729)
P.O. Box 77 (76634-0077)
PHONE..................................877 882-1803
Charles L Burton, *Principal*
Robbie Allen, *Plant Mgr*
Paige Sibila, *Purch Mgr*
Alice Brewer, *Treasurer*
Alicia Brewer, *Treasurer*
▼ **EMP:** 100
SQ FT: 100,000
SALES (est): 15.2MM **Privately Held**
WEB: www.cliftonmoulding.com
SIC: 2431 Moldings, wood: unfinished & prefinished

(G-3144)
HANSON AGGREGATES LLC
856 Sm 2114 (76634)
PHONE..................................254 622-3239
Bill Tufts, *Branch Mgr*
EMP: 16
SALES (corp-wide): 20.8B **Privately Held**
WEB: www.heidelbergcement.com
SIC: 3273 Ready-mixed concrete
HQ: Hanson Aggregates Llc
8505 Freeport Pkwy Ste 500
Irving TX 75063
469 417-1200

(G-3145)
ORBIX CORPORATION
Also Called: Gearench
4450 S Hwy 6 (76634)
P.O. Box 192 (76634-0192)
PHONE..................................254 675-8651
Debra Embry, *Opers Dir*
Keith Hollingsworth, *Materials Mgr*
Brent Grelle, *QC Mgr*
Ben Stenmark, *Engineer*

Krist Hall, *Human Res Dir*
EMP: 50
SALES (corp-wide): 15.7MM **Privately Held**
WEB: www.petol.com
SIC: 3533 5082 3462 Oil field machinery & equipment; oil field equipment; iron & steel forgings
PA: Orbix Corporation
　　4450 S Highway 6
　　Clifton TX 76634
　　254 675-8371

(G-3146)
PROGRSSIVE MDIA COMMUNICATIONS
Also Called: Clifton Record
310 W 5th St (76634-1611)
P.O. Box 343, Meridian (76665-0343)
PHONE..................254 675-3336
Jim Masseur, *President*
W Leon Smith, *President*
James W Smith, *Admin Sec*
EMP: 18
SALES (est): 450K **Privately Held**
WEB: www.cliftonrecord.com
SIC: 2711 Commercial printing & newspaper publishing combined

Clint
El Paso County

(G-3147)
RAMIREZ PECAN FARM LLC
Also Called: Hajost Pecan Farm
13709 N Loop Dr (79836-5102)
PHONE..................915 851-2003
Guadalupe Ramirez Jr,
Norma Ramirez,
EMP: 15
SQ FT: 2,000
SALES (est): 450K **Privately Held**
WEB: www.ramirezpecanfarm.com
SIC: 2068 5441 0173 Nuts: dried, dehydrated, salted or roasted; nuts; tree nuts

(G-3148)
T & R CHEMICALS INC
700 Celum Rd (79836-4906)
P.O. Box 330 (79836-0330)
PHONE..................915 851-2761
Fredo Arias, *President*
Lilly Chairez, *Treasurer*
Martin Lopez, *Sales Mgr*
Vasilios Fotopoulos, *Sales Staff*
◆ **EMP:** 20 **EST:** 1952
SQ FT: 40,000
SALES (est): 5.2MM **Privately Held**
WEB: www.trchemicals.com
SIC: 2869 Industrial organic chemicals

Clute
Brazoria County

(G-3149)
CHEM FABRICATION LLC
911 Highway 288 S B (77531-5724)
PHONE..................979 265-6600
Norman Schaaf, *President*
Keith Oliver, *General Mgr*
Perry Jinkins, *Vice Pres*
Skip Jones, *Purch Mgr*
David Jones, *Purch Agent*
EMP: 52
SQ FT: 40,000
SALES (est): 10MM **Privately Held**
WEB: www.chemfab.net
SIC: 3443 3498 5075 5085 Heat exchangers, condensers & components; process vessels, industrial: metal plate; manifolds, pipe: fabricated from purchased pipe; heat exchangers; tanks, pressurized; flange, valve or pipe fitting forgings, nonferrous; flange, valve & pipe fitting forgings, ferrous

(G-3150)
COMMERCIAL METALS COMPANY
Also Called: CMC Recycling
215 Mockingbird Ln (77531-4953)
P.O. Box 458 (77531-0458)
PHONE..................979 265-4642
Bill Welch, *Branch Mgr*
EMP: 20
SALES (corp-wide): 5.4B **Publicly Held**
WEB: www.cmc.com
SIC: 5093 3341 Ferrous metal scrap & waste; nonferrous metals scrap; secondary nonferrous metals
PA: Commercial Metals Company
　　6565 N Macarthur Blvd # 800
　　Irving TX 75039
　　214 689-4300

(G-3151)
CURTIS TECHNICAL SERVICE INC
Also Called: CTS
920 S Shanks St (77531-5629)
P.O. Box 517 (77531-0517)
PHONE..................979 388-0007
Curtis A Wells, *President*
Cindy Wells, *Manager*
EMP: 19 **EST:** 2000
SQ FT: 12,000 **Privately Held**
WEB: www.curtistechnicalservice.com
SIC: 3089 Injection molding of plastics

(G-3152)
DETAIL PRODUCTS INC
1604 Old Angleton Rd (77531-3512)
PHONE..................713 722-7789
Joseph C Allen, *President*
EMP: 11
SALES (est): 1.7MM **Privately Held**
WEB: www.detail-products.com
SIC: 2752 Commercial printing, offset

(G-3153)
EAGLEBURGMANN INDUSTRIES LP
Also Called: Eagle Burgmann Industries
228 W Plantation Dr (77531-5406)
PHONE..................979 265-2320
Kimberly Longoria, *Manager*
EMP: 25
SALES (corp-wide): 10.5B **Privately Held**
WEB: www.eaglburgmann.us
SIC: 3053 5085 Gaskets, packing & sealing devices; seals, industrial
HQ: Eagleburgmann Industries Lp
　　10035 Brookriver Dr
　　Houston TX 77040
　　713 939-9515

(G-3154)
FACTS
720 S Main St (77531-5411)
P.O. Box 549 (77531-0549)
PHONE..................979 237-0100
Judy Strons, *Owner*
Joel Luna, *Editor*
Lynn Webb, *Sales Staff*
Cindy Cornette, *Adv Dir*
Yvonne Mintz, *Manager*
EMP: 11
SQ FT: 66,696
SALES (est): 460.9K **Privately Held**
WEB: www.thefacts.com
SIC: 2711 Newspapers: publishing only, not printed on site

(G-3155)
GULF COAST CABINET DOORS LLC
220 Highway 332 (77531-5613)
PHONE..................979 265-1519
Ross Watkins,
EMP: 12
SQ FT: 6,500
SALES (est): 1MM **Privately Held**
WEB: www.gulfcoastcabinetdoors.net
SIC: 2434 Wood kitchen cabinets

(G-3156)
MAC FABRICATORS
617 Mockingbird Ln (77531-4945)
PHONE..................979 265-0235
Mike Ahearen, *Owner*
EMP: 9

SQ FT: 30,000
SALES (est): 1.2MM **Privately Held**
SIC: 3441 3444 3331 3312 Fabricated structural metal; sheet metalwork; primary copper; blast furnaces & steel mills

(G-3157)
OFFSHORE OIL SERVICES INC
Also Called: Muchowich Offshore Oil Service
1608 Old Angleton Rd (77531-3512)
PHONE..................979 265-3300
Stacy Stanley, *President*
Michael Gay, *Exec VP*
Dermot Saltibus, *Human Resources*
EMP: 45
SQ FT: 3,500
SALES (est): 6.1MM **Privately Held**
WEB: www.offshoreoil.com
SIC: 3731 Offshore supply boats, building & repairing; crew boats, building & repairing

(G-3158)
RPS COMPOSITES ALABAMA INC (PA)
1402 County Road 434 (77531-5016)
PHONE..................979 265-4262
Ven Cote, *CEO*
Rick Crawford, *Vice Pres*
EMP: 14
SQ FT: 10,000
SALES (est): 2.1MM **Privately Held**
WEB: www.rpscomposites.com
SIC: 2221 Fiberglass fabrics

(G-3159)
SOUTHERN GULF SOLUTIONS LLC
1227 Highway 332 Ste 8 (77531-5236)
P.O. Box 3096, Lake Jackson (77566-3096)
PHONE..................979 299-8808
EMP: 10
SALES (est): 4.3MM **Privately Held**
WEB: www.sogulf.com
SIC: 3731 Offshore supply boats, building & repairing

(G-3160)
SOUTHERN NEWSPAPERS INC
Also Called: Brazosport Facts
720 S Main St (77531-5411)
P.O. Box 549 (77531-0549)
PHONE..................979 237-0100
Neice Bell, *Publisher*
Bill Cornwell, *Principal*
Mikala Compton, *Editor*
Ian Goodrum, *Editor*
Tucker Stephenson, *Editor*
EMP: 100
SALES (corp-wide): 140.3MM **Privately Held**
WEB: www.sninews.com
SIC: 2711 Newspapers, publishing & printing
PA: Southern Newspapers, Inc.
　　5701 Woodway Dr Ste 131
　　Houston TX 77057
　　713 266-5481

(G-3161)
UNITED ELEC INSTRMENTATION LTD (DH)
622 Commerce St (77531-5612)
P.O. Box 448 (77531-0448)
PHONE..................979 265-1256
Tammi Blevins, *Partner*
Brad McIntyre, *Partner*
Mark Monical, *Partner*
Harold E Monical, *General Ptnr*
EMP: 70
SQ FT: 30,000
SALES: 42.1MM
SALES (corp-wide): 12.7B **Privately Held**
WEB: www.ueiltd.com
SIC: 1731 1761 1711 3829 General electrical contractor; sheet metalwork; refrigeration contractor; instrumentation for reactor controls, auxiliary
HQ: Wood Group Psn, Inc.
　　17325 Park Row
　　Houston TX 77084
　　281 647-1041

Clyde
Callahan County

(G-3162)
BULLDOG STEEL PRODUCTS INC (PA)
1217 S Access Rd (79510-3860)
P.O. Box 569 (79510-0569)
PHONE..................325 893-5806
Nathan M Tinkle, *President*
Scott Campbell, *General Mgr*
Nathan Tinkle, *Vice Pres*
Raymond Ward, *Vice Pres*
Scott S Campbell, *Opers Mgr*
EMP: 28
SQ FT: 42,000
SALES (est): 4.9MM **Privately Held**
WEB: www.bulldogsteel.com
SIC: 3441 3443 Fabricated structural metal; tanks, lined: metal plate

(G-3163)
HAWK PORTABLE BUILDINGS INC (PA)
1825 S Access Rd (79510-3814)
PHONE..................325 893-5120
John Hawk III, *President*
Endgate Hawk, *President*
Kathy Hawk, *Vice Pres*
Race Schlemeyer, *Sales Mgr*
Chad Robinson, *Sales Staff*
EMP: 35
SQ FT: 15,000
SALES (est): 7.5MM **Privately Held**
WEB: www.hawkbuildings.com
SIC: 3448 2452 Buildings, portable: prefabricated metal; prefabricated buildings, wood

Coahoma
Howard County

(G-3164)
BIG SPRING CAT CNSTR INC
600 Se Broadway (79511)
P.O. Box 3672
PHONE..................432 394-4161
Michael Blissard, *President*
Amanda Blissard, *Admin Sec*
EMP: 14
SALES (est): 3.1MM **Privately Held**
SIC: 1389 1521 Oil field services; new construction, single-family houses

(G-3165)
J L DAVIS COMPANY
Also Called: East Fieldmore Gas Plant
11703 Fm 846 (79511-2321)
PHONE..................432 399-4575
Allan Worthington, *Branch Mgr*
EMP: 22
SALES (corp-wide): 350MM **Privately Held**
WEB: www.westtexasgas.com
SIC: 1321 2911 Natural gas liquids; petroleum refining
PA: James Lee Davis
　　211 N Colorado St
　　Midland TX 79701
　　432 682-6311

Coldspring
San Jacinto County

(G-3166)
JET OIL PRODUCERS INC
Hwy 150 (77331)
P.O. Box 930 (77331-0930)
PHONE..................936 653-3379
Phillip Stalder, *President*
Ted R Stalder, *Vice Pres*
Chris Stalder, *Vice Pres*
EMP: 10
SALES (est): 940.5K **Privately Held**
WEB: www.jetoilproducers.com
SIC: 1311 Crude petroleum production

▲ = Import ▼=Export
◆ =Import/Export

(G-3167)
SIGNATURE ENVELOPE COMPANY INC
13180 State Highway 150 W (77331-9365)
P.O. Box 1550 (77331-1550)
PHONE..................713 538-1177
Dennis Ready, *President*
EMP: 10
SQ FT: 10,000
SALES (est): 3.8MM **Privately Held**
SIC: 2677 Envelopes

(G-3168)
YOKOGAWA CORPORATION AMERICA
35 Petroleum Rd (77331-7904)
PHONE..................936 653-2120
John Williams, *Manager*
Terri Macintyre, *Admin Asst*
EMP: 30 **Privately Held**
WEB: www.yokogawa.com
SIC: 3823 Analyzers, industrial process type
HQ: Yokogawa Corporation Of America
12530 W Airport Blvd
Sugar Land TX 77478
281 340-3800

Coleman
Coleman County

(G-3169)
COLEMAN MACHINE & WELDING SVC
800 W 24th St (76834-7520)
P.O. Box 878 (76834-0878)
PHONE..................325 625-5186
Garry Cox, *Owner*
EMP: 10
SQ FT: 3,000
SALES (est): 867.6K **Privately Held**
WEB: www.colemantexas.org
SIC: 3599 7692 3441 Machine shop, jobbing & repair; welding repair; fabricated structural metal

(G-3170)
KENTEX FABRICATIONS
220 Santa Anna Ave (76834-7412)
PHONE..................325 214-0025
Ken Miller, *Owner*
EMP: 10
SQ FT: 2,500
SALES (est): 70K **Privately Held**
SIC: 3446 Architectural metalwork

College Station
Brazos County

(G-3171)
AA SCIENTIFIC INC
2151 Harvey Mitchell Pkwy (77840-5281)
PHONE..................979 696-8080
D Ravichandran, *President*
Duraiswamy Ravichandran, *President*
EMP: 10
SALES (est): 585.7K **Privately Held**
WEB: www.aascientific.com
SIC: 2869 Industrial organic chemicals

(G-3172)
ACCMACH INC
Also Called: Accurate Machine Works
4400 Pate Rd (77845-7873)
PHONE..................979 774-0062
EMP: 25 **EST:** 1995
SQ FT: 24,000
SALES (est): 6.9MM **Privately Held**
WEB: www.accmachtech.com
SIC: 3599 Machine shop, jobbing & repair

(G-3173)
AKHU THERAPEUTICS INC
2713 Horse Haven Ln (77845-6044)
PHONE..................979 820-2740
Caurnel Morgan, *CEO*
EMP: 9

SALES (est): 375K **Privately Held**
WEB: www.akhutherapeutics.com
SIC: 2834 7389 Drugs acting on the central nervous system & sense organs;

(G-3174)
ARBIN CORPORATION
Also Called: Arbin Instruments
762 Peach Creek Cut Off (77845-8704)
PHONE..................979 690-2751
Chaojiong Zang, *President*
Kevin Duff, *General Mgr*
Ping Jiang, *Vice Pres*
Andrew Kuvlesky, *Opers Mgr*
MEI Liu, *Production*
▲ **EMP:** 40
SQ FT: 60,000
SALES (est): 9.9MM **Privately Held**
WEB: www.arbin.com
SIC: 3825 3829 3699 Battery testers, electrical; measuring & controlling devices; electrical equipment & supplies

(G-3175)
ARBIN INSTRUMENTS INC
762 Peach Creek Cut Off (77845-8704)
PHONE..................979 690-2751
EMP: 20
SALES (est): 1.2MM **Privately Held**
WEB: www.arbin.com
SIC: 3829 Mfg Measuring/Controlling Devices

(G-3176)
ARBIN INSTRUMENTS LLC
762 Peach Creek Cut Off (77845-8704)
PHONE..................979 690-2751
John Zhang, *Plant Mgr*
Andrew Kuvlesky, *Opers Mgr*
Salah Zayouna, *Research*
Xiaomei Zhang, *Engineer*
Grace Santana, *Controller*
◆ **EMP:** 40
SALES (est): 10MM **Privately Held**
WEB: www.arbin.com
SIC: 3825 Instruments to measure electricity

(G-3177)
BECKMAN COULTER INC
Also Called: AP Fullerton
1450 Texas Ave S (77840-2435)
PHONE..................714 961-6558
Earl Beckman, *Branch Mgr*
EMP: 82
SALES (corp-wide): 17.9B **Publicly Held**
WEB: www.beckmancoulter.com
SIC: 3826 Analytical instruments
HQ: Beckman Coulter, Inc.
250 S Kraemer Blvd
Brea CA 92821
714 993-5321

(G-3178)
BRAZOS RUNNING COMPANY LLC
1667 Texas Ave S (77840-3326)
PHONE..................979 485-9830
Dara T Nugent, *Mng Member*
EMP: 9
SALES (est): 1.1MM **Privately Held**
WEB: www.brazosrunning.com
SIC: 2253 Jogging & warm-up suits, knit

(G-3179)
BULLDOG WIRELINE INC (PA)
13757 S Dowling Rd (77845-3338)
PHONE..................979 260-9034
Adolphus Y Jennings, *President*
Sara Adams Jennings, *Vice Pres*
EMP: 11
SQ FT: 5,000
SALES (est): 1.8MM **Privately Held**
WEB: www.bulldogwireline.com
SIC: 1389 Oil field services

(G-3180)
CARDIOQUIP LLC
8422 Calibration Ct (77845-5328)
PHONE..................979 691-0202
Allen Pate, *Partner*
Robin Pate, *General Mgr*
Douglas Platt, *Engineer*
Will Otto, *Mktg Dir*
EMP: 37

SALES (est): 1.6MM **Privately Held**
WEB: www.cardioquip.com
SIC: 3841 Surgical instruments & apparatus

(G-3181)
CC CREATIONS LTD (PA)
Also Called: Custom Imprint Wearables
114 Holleman Dr (77840-4235)
PHONE..................979 693-9664
Ken Lawson, *General Ptnr*
Kristen Atkinson, *Sales Staff*
▲ **EMP:** 107 **EST:** 1990
SQ FT: 1,500
SALES (est): 23.4MM **Privately Held**
WEB: www.cccreationsusa.com
SIC: 2759 2395 Screen printing; embroidery products, except schiffli machine

(G-3182)
FENNER & ASSOCIATES INC
Also Called: Otto H Fenner & Associates
5257 Vintage Oaks Dr (77845-6182)
PHONE..................281 970-9977
Richard Fenner, *President*
Kaylon Fenner, *Corp Secy*
EMP: 14
SALES (est): 1.7MM **Privately Held**
WEB: www.alloyidkit.com
SIC: 3829 Testing equipment: abrasion, shearing strength, etc.

(G-3183)
FUJIFILM DIOSYNTH BIOTECHNOLOG
3939 Biomedical Way (77845-2037)
PHONE..................979 431-3500
EMP: 16 **Privately Held**
WEB: www.fujifilmdiosynth.com
SIC: 2836 Biological products, except diagnostic
HQ: Fujifilm Diosynth Biotechnologies Texas, Llc
100 Discovery Dr Ste 200
College Station TX 77845
979 431-3500

(G-3184)
G-CON LLC
6161 Imperial Loop (77845-5766)
P.O. Box 15922 (77841-5123)
PHONE..................214 220-4303
Robert P Landin, *Vice Pres*
David M Shanahan,
David M Haselwood,
EMP: 13
SALES (est): 2.5MM **Privately Held**
WEB: www.gconbio.com
SIC: 2451 Mobile buildings: for commercial use

(G-3185)
H & B COPIES INC
Also Called: Copy Corner
2307 Texas Ave S Ste B (77840-4737)
PHONE..................979 694-2679
Lawrence B Hodges Jr, *President*
Nick Bregenzer, *Vice Pres*
Jill Becka, *Sales Staff*
Rick Archibeque, *Manager*
EMP: 50
SQ FT: 9,800
SALES (est): 6.8MM **Privately Held**
WEB: www.copycorner.com
SIC: 7334 2759 Blueprinting service; publication printing

(G-3186)
HEWLETT-PACKARD COMPANY
Also Called: HP
1700 Res Pkwy Ste 200 (77845)
PHONE..................979 691-4540
EMP: 60
SALES (corp-wide): 120.3B **Publicly Held**
SIC: 3571 8748 Commercial Nonphysical Research Business Consulting Services
PA: Hewlett-Packard Company
3000 Hanover St
Palo Alto CA 94304
650 857-1501

(G-3187)
ISP SUPPLIES LLC
10770 State Highway 30 # 20 (77845-7939)
PHONE..................855 947-7776
Logan Helms, *Opers Mgr*
Jonathan Nicholson, *Sales Staff*
Richard Frey, *Network Enginr*
Brad Smith, *Director*
Steve Discher,
EMP: 23
SALES (est): 4.7MM **Privately Held**
WEB: www.ispsupplies.com
SIC: 3663 Television antennas (transmitting) & ground equipment

(G-3188)
J M SADDLER INC (PA)
9107 Riverstone Ct (77845-9365)
PHONE..................979 693-5114
Janet Sauber, *President*
Jerome Sauber, *Corp Secy*
Margret Hannes, *Vice Pres*
▼ **EMP:** 9
SQ FT: 20,000
SALES (est): 1MM **Privately Held**
WEB: www.jmsaddler.com
SIC: 2048 Prepared feeds

(G-3189)
KB & KB ENTERPRISES INC
Also Called: Fastsigns
404 University Dr E Ste C (77840-1743)
PHONE..................979 764-7446
Kevin Brightwell, *President*
EMP: 10
SALES (est): 1MM **Privately Held**
WEB: www.fastsigns.com
SIC: 3993 Signs & advertising specialties

(G-3190)
KEYTRAK INC
200 Quality Cir (77845-4468)
PHONE..................979 595-2600
Carl Hanly, *Regional Mgr*
Carlan Cooper, *Vice Pres*
CB Huchingson, *Vice Pres*
Todd Emerson, *Opers Staff*
Steve Robinson, *Opers Staff*
EMP: 70
SQ FT: 60,000
SALES (est): 5.3MM **Privately Held**
WEB: www.keytrak.com
SIC: 7299 7372 Personal financial services; prepackaged software

(G-3191)
KNIFE RIVER CORP - SOUTH (HQ)
1553 Greens Prairie Rd W (77845-8417)
PHONE..................979 361-2900
Robert Kover, *President*
Ben Carlson, *President*
James Snyder, *Vice Pres*
EMP: 18
SALES (est): 245.7MM
SALES (corp-wide): 5.3B **Publicly Held**
WEB: www.kniferiver.com
SIC: 1442 3273 1521 Construction sand & gravel; ready-mixed concrete; single-family housing construction
PA: Mdu Resources Group, Inc.
1200 W Century Ave
Bismarck ND 58503
701 530-1000

(G-3192)
MATICA BIOTECHNOLOGY INC
1645 Grens Prrie Rd W Ste (77845)
PHONE..................979 321-7500
EMP: 12
SALES (est): 553.1K **Privately Held**
SIC: 2836 Mfg Biological Products

(G-3193)
MOBILE TOYS INC
909 University Dr E Ste B (77840-2359)
PHONE..................979 268-6066
Brandon Goodlett, *Principal*
EMP: 10
SALES (est): 1.4MM **Privately Held**
WEB: www.mobiletoysinc.com
SIC: 3944 2451 Electronic games & toys; mobile homes

(G-3194)
MONOGRAMS & MORE
1806 Welsh Ave Ste G (77840-6807)
PHONE...................................979 693-7773
Robert Harp, *Partner*
Brian Pendergraff, *Partner*
Todd Weingand, *Partner*
EMP: 14
SQ FT: 2,750
SALES (est): 1MM **Privately Held**
WEB: www.m-mapparel.com
SIC: 7299 2395 2396 Stitching, custom;
embroidery & art needlework; screen
printing on fabric articles

(G-3195)
NBL PERMIAN LLC
707 Texas Ave S Ste 109a (77840-1900)
PHONE...................................979 764-4030
EMP: 16
SALES (corp-wide): 3.4B **Publicly Held**
SIC: 1311 1382 5171 Crude
Petroleum/Natural Gas Production
Oil/Gas Exploration Services Petroleum
Bulk Station
HQ: Nbl Permian Llc
1001 Noble Energy Way
Houston TX 77070
281 872-3100

(G-3196)
OI CORPORATION (HQ)
Also Called: O I Analytical
151 Graham Rd (77845-9654)
P.O. Box 9010 (77842-9010)
PHONE...................................979 690-1711
J Bruce Lancaster, *CEO*
Donald P Segers, *President*
Laura Cummings, *General Mgr*
Guillermo Jimenez, *Vice Pres*
Lisa Yeagin, *Buyer*
EMP: 173 EST: 1963
SQ FT: 68,650
SALES (est): 161.5MM **Publicly Held**
WEB: www.oico.com
SIC: 3826 Gas chromatographic instru-
ments

(G-3197)
PPG INDUSTRIES INC
Also Called: PPG 8327
3800 State Highway 6 S # 200
(77845-5840)
PHONE...................................979 693-7097
Will Mc Clure, *Branch Mgr*
EMP: 24
SALES (corp-wide): 15.3B **Publicly Held**
WEB: www.ppg.com
SIC: 2851 Paints & allied products
PA: Ppg Industries, Inc.
1 Ppg Pl
Pittsburgh PA 15272
412 434-3131

(G-3198)
**QUICK INTRNET SFTWR
SLTONS INC**
3206 Earl Rudder Fwy S (77845-6457)
PHONE...................................979 846-3008
David Quick, *President*
Art Barry, *Supervisor*
Kathryn Adams, *Prgrmr*
Philip Van Ruitenbeek, *Software Dev*
Terrell Wright, *Software Dev*
EMP: 15
SALES: 1.7MM **Privately Held**
WEB: www.eqiss.com
SIC: 5045 7372 Computer software;
prepackaged software

(G-3199)
REDLINE INSTRUMENTS INC
10350 State Highway 30 (77845-7888)
PHONE...................................979 776-7200
Gary Keating, *Vice Pres*
EMP: 11 **Privately Held**
WEB: www.rlii.net
SIC: 3829 Gas detectors
PA: Redline Instruments, Inc.
1091 Fletcher Rd
Sulphur OK 73086

(G-3200)
RV STATION LTD (PA)
4520 State Highway 6 S (77845-8968)
PHONE...................................979 778-8000

Chris Falcone, *Partner*
Kirk Falcone, *Partner*
Mark Homeyer, *Partner*
EMP: 20
SQ FT: 5,000
SALES (est): 4.8MM **Privately Held**
WEB: www.rvstationbryan.com
SIC: 3799 5511 Recreational vehicles; au-
tomobiles, new & used

(G-3201)
SANOFI-AVENTIS US LLC
211 Quality Cir (77845-4470)
P.O. Box 696410, San Antonio (78269-
6410)
PHONE...................................800 981-2491
Tom Deaver, *Director*
EMP: 224 **Privately Held**
WEB: www.sanofi.us
SIC: 2834 Pharmaceutical preparations
HQ: Sanofi-Aventis U.S. Llc
55 Corporate Dr
Bridgewater NJ 08807

(G-3202)
STATACORP LLC
4905 Lakeway Dr (77845-4512)
PHONE...................................979 696-4600
Finis Welch, *Ch of Bd*
William Gould, *President*
Alan Riley, *COO*
Monica Sheppard, *Vice Pres*
Vince Wiggins, *Vice Pres*
▼ EMP: 120
SQ FT: 39,000
SALES (est): 13.5MM **Privately Held**
WEB: www.stata.com
SIC: 7371 7372 Computer software devel-
opment; prepackaged software

(G-3203)
**TENNECO AUTOMOTIVE OPER
CO INC**
211 Quality Cir (77845-4470)
PHONE...................................979 691-7732
Andrew Baker, *Branch Mgr*
EMP: 204
SALES (corp-wide): 17.4B **Publicly Held**
SIC: 3714 Motor vehicle parts & acces-
sories
HQ: Tenneco Automotive Operating Com-
pany, Inc.
500 N Field Dr
Lake Forest IL 60045
847 482-5000

(G-3204)
TEXAS DIGITAL SYSTEMS INC
400 Technology Pkwy (77845-5826)
PHONE...................................979 693-0933
Robert Bower Jr PHD, *Ch of Bd*
Dennis Davidson, *President*
Brian Gray, *Exec VP*
Linda Fitzpatrick, *Vice Pres*
Russ Manning, *Vice Pres*
▲ EMP: 90
SQ FT: 31,000
SALES (est): 31.7MM
SALES (corp-wide): 6.9B **Publicly Held**
WEB: www.ncr.com
SIC: 3577 Graphic displays, except
graphic terminals
PA: Ncr Corporation
864 Spring St Nw
Atlanta GA 30308
937 445-1936

(G-3205)
**THE TEXAS A&M UNIVERSITY
SYS**
Also Called: Veternary Diagnostic Lab
1 Sippel Rd (77843-0001)
P.O. Box 3040 (77841-3040)
PHONE...................................979 845-3414
Lelve Gayle, *Manager*
Robert K Phillips, *Supervisor*
Ernesto Ramos, *Technician*
Jennifer Wollock, *Professor*
EMP: 108
SALES (corp-wide): 167.1MM **Privately
Held**
WEB: www.tamus.edu
SIC: 2221 Broadwoven fabric mills, man-
made

PA: The Texas A&M University System
301 Tarrow St Fl 3
College Station TX 77840
979 458-6100

(G-3206)
**THE TEXAS A&M UNIVERSITY
SYS**
Also Called: University Press
4354 Tamu (77843-0001)
PHONE...................................979 845-1436
Mary Jacob, *Manager*
Charles Backus, *Director*
EMP: 25
SQ FT: 5,000
SALES (corp-wide): 167.1MM **Privately
Held**
WEB: www.tamus.edu
SIC: 2731 8221 Textbooks: publishing
only, not printed on site; university
PA: The Texas A&M University System
301 Tarrow St Fl 3
College Station TX 77840
979 458-6100

(G-3207)
**THE TEXAS A&M UNIVERSITY
SYS**
Also Called: Instructional Materials Svc
2588 Tamus (77843-0001)
PHONE...................................979 845-6601
John Dillingham, *Director*
EMP: 17
SALES (corp-wide): 167.1MM **Privately
Held**
WEB: www.tamus.edu
SIC: 2732 2741 2731 Books: printing
only; miscellaneous publishing; book pub-
lishing
PA: The Texas A&M University System
301 Tarrow St Fl 3
College Station TX 77840
979 458-6100

(G-3208)
UNIFIRST CORPORATION
12700 Highway 30 Bldg 100 (77845-7756)
PHONE...................................979 774-0577
Jason McFarland, *Branch Mgr*
EMP: 20
SALES (corp-wide): 1.8B **Publicly Held**
WEB: www.unifirst.com
SIC: 7218 2841 Industrial uniform supply;
soap & other detergents
PA: Unifirst Corporation
68 Jonspin Rd
Wilmington MA 01887
978 658-8888

(G-3209)
VICEROY PETROLEUM LP
4359 Roans Chapel Rd (77845-4096)
PHONE...................................832 783-5790
Matt Ferguson, *President*
EMP: 34 EST: 2006
SALES (est): 9MM **Privately Held**
WEB: www.viceroypetroleum.com
SIC: 1382 Oil & gas exploration services

Colleyville
Tarrant County

(G-3210)
**ALLSTAR DOOR &
MAINTENANCE LP**
4205 Colleyville Blvd (76034-3726)
P.O. Box 92565, Southlake (76092-0565)
PHONE...................................817 748-0667
Michelle Jones, *Partner*
Steven Jones, *Partner*
EMP: 10
SQ FT: 2,000
SALES (est): 500K **Privately Held**
WEB: www.allstardoor.com
SIC: 7349 1751 2431 Window cleaning;
window & door installation & erection;
window & door (prefabricated) installation;
doors & door parts & trim, wood; door
frames, wood; doors, wood

(G-3211)
**CHRISTNES CON SWING
SALING LLC**
2916 Meadowview Dr (76034-4755)
PHONE...................................214 212-4808
Christine Diamond-Bond, *CEO*
EMP: 10
SALES (est): 980K **Privately Held**
SIC: 3559 Special industry machinery

(G-3212)
CLARKE PRODUCTS INC
820 Central Dr (76034-3071)
PHONE...................................972 660-1992
Donald H Clarke, *President*
Colleen E Clarke, *Vice Pres*
◆ EMP: 110
SQ FT: 96,000
SALES (est): 34.7MM **Privately Held**
WEB: www.clarkeproducts.com
SIC: 3088 3949 Plastics plumbing fixtures;
sporting & athletic goods

(G-3213)
**EDMONDS PUBG & MEDIA
GROUP LLC**
3101 Woodland Heights Cir (76034-4679)
P.O. Box 92940, Southlake (76092-0940)
PHONE...................................214 460-7560
Robert Lee Edmonds, *CEO*
Linda Edmonds,
EMP: 11
SALES (est): 753.9K **Privately Held**
SIC: 2731 7389 Books: publishing only;

(G-3214)
ITEXASPOLITICS LLC
Also Called: Texan News The
5212 Elm St (76034-3257)
PHONE...................................512 200-4035
Konni Lyn Burton, *Principal*
EMP: 9
SALES (est): 75K **Privately Held**
SIC: 2711 Newspapers

(G-3215)
KATHY & JANES CO
5615 Colleyville Blvd # 340 (76034-6083)
PHONE...................................817 605-9335
EMP: 9 EST: 2010
SALES (est): 360K **Privately Held**
SIC: 2024 Mfg Ice Cream/Frozen Desert

(G-3216)
KFL PROMOTIONS LLC
4703 Mill Creek Dr (76034-3646)
PHONE...................................817 822-9116
Karen Lucchesi, *CEO*
EMP: 38
SALES (est): 1.3MM **Privately Held**
SIC: 2097 8742 Manufactured ice; manu-
facturing management consultant

(G-3217)
KNOWLES PUBLISHING INC
4708 Shadycreek Ln (76034-4734)
P.O. Box 911004, Fort Worth (76111-9104)
PHONE...................................817 838-0202
EMP: 66 EST: 1983
SALES (est): 5.4MM **Privately Held**
WEB: www.knowlespublishing.com
SIC: 2731 Books: publishing only

(G-3218)
KTECH PRODUCTS LLC
5114 Heritage Oaks Dr (76034-5975)
PHONE...................................972 333-7092
Jaideep Chitkara, *Mng Member*
EMP: 25
SALES (est): 3MM **Privately Held**
WEB: www.ktechproducts.com
SIC: 3575 Computer terminals, monitors &
components

(G-3219)
**LOCKHEED MARTIN
CORPORATION**
4707 Mill Crossing W (76034-3682)
PHONE...................................817 763-2663
Randy Hooper, *Manager*
EMP: 473 **Publicly Held**
WEB: www.lockheedmartin.com
SIC: 3812 Search & navigation equipment

▲ = Import ▼=Export
◆ =Import/Export

PA: Lockheed Martin Corporation
6801 Rockledge Dr
Bethesda MD 20817

(G-3220)
MEASUREMENT TECHNOLOGIES LTD
Also Called: Mtech
4843 Colleyville Blvd (76034-3923)
P.O. Box 668 (76034-0668)
PHONE..................................817 571-9981
Don Hudson, *Partner*
Hudson Holdings, *General Ptnr*
EMP: 9
SQ FT: 2,500
SALES (est): 750.2K **Privately Held**
WEB: www.mtech.biz
SIC: 3829 Measuring & controlling devices

(G-3221)
MEDIFACTS INC
1105 S Airport Cir Ste B (76034)
P.O. Box 1258 (76034-1258)
PHONE..................................817 571-8181
Mark E Self, *President*
Diana Self, *Vice Pres*
Stanley Cohen, *Treasurer*
David Bennett, *Info Tech Dir*
Diane Self, *Admin Sec*
EMP: 50
SALES (est): 3MM **Privately Held**
WEB: www.medifacts.net
SIC: 7372 Application computer software

Colmesneil
Tyler County

(G-3222)
RANDY L GARDNER INC
301 S Wheeler (75938-3259)
PHONE..................................409 837-5111
EMP: 13
SALES (est): 1MM **Privately Held**
SIC: 2411 Logging

Colorado City
Mitchell County

(G-3223)
CONCRETE MOBILITY LLC
373 Concrete Mobility Way (79512-2657)
PHONE..................................325 728-5858
Brenda Flood, *Owner*
EMP: 14 **Privately Held**
WEB: www.concretemobility.com
SIC: 3273 Ready-mixed concrete
PA: Concrete Mobility, Llc
1207 Cardinal Ave N
Glencoe MN 55336

(G-3224)
CS WELL SERVICE LLC
2313 N State Highway 208 (79512-2637)
PHONE..................................325 242-2438
Bryne Joe Stone,
Robert Boyd Cox,
EMP: 12
SALES (est): 1.5MM **Privately Held**
SIC: 1389 Oil & gas wells: building, repairing & dismantling

(G-3225)
OILTEK SYSTEMS LLC
278 W 2nd St (79512-6002)
PHONE..................................325 200-0423
David Allen,
EMP: 20
SALES (est): 329.3K **Privately Held**
SIC: 8748 7379 2869 0781 Environmental consultant; computer related maintenance services; industrial organic chemicals; horticultural counseling services

(G-3226)
RED ROCK OILFIELD SERVICE LLC
199 S Fm 1229 (79512-7533)
P.O. Box 1003 (79512-1003)
PHONE..................................325 933-0224
George Guerra, *Opers Mgr*

Beki Denison, *Office Mgr*
Blaine Dudley Lemons, *Mng Member*
James Corey Beavers,
Kyle D Lemons,
EMP: 15
SALES (est): 1.6MM **Privately Held**
WEB: www.redrockofs.com
SIC: 1382 1389 3533 Oil & gas exploration services; testing, measuring, surveying & analysis services; pipe testing, oil field service; servicing oil & gas wells; fishing for tools, oil & gas field; oil & gas field machinery

(G-3227)
T & T TRANSPORTS INC
2308 N State Highway 208 (79512-2636)
P.O. Box 872 (79512-0872)
PHONE..................................325 728-2669
Donny Lindsey, *President*
Tom Mann, *Training Spec*
EMP: 50
SQ FT: 2,000
SALES (est): 8.7MM **Privately Held**
WEB: www.tttransports.com
SIC: 8299 1389 Truck driving training; oil field services

Columbus
Colorado County

(G-3228)
ALLEYTON RESOURCE COMPANY LLC (DH)
Also Called: Alcomat
755 Fm 762 (78934)
P.O. Box 80, Thompsons (77481-0080)
PHONE..................................281 238-1010
Bryan Kalbfleisch, *President*
EMP: 24
SALES (est): 58.3MM
SALES (corp-wide): 2.2B **Publicly Held**
WEB: www.alleytonresource.net
SIC: 3273 Ready-mixed concrete
HQ: Summit Materials, Llc
1550 Wynkoop St Ste 300
Denver CO 80202
303 893-0012

(G-3229)
BARCO INDUSTRIES
Also Called: Barton and Company
3554 Fm 109 (78934-5106)
PHONE..................................979 732-2086
Mark Barton, *President*
Dolores Toenitzsch, *Admin Sec*
EMP: 11
SALES (est): 2.4MM **Privately Held**
WEB: www.barcoind.com
SIC: 1442 Gravel mining

(G-3230)
BARTEN INDUSTRIAL COATINGS LLC
4176 Highway 71 (78934-4902)
P.O. Box 687 (78934-0687)
PHONE..................................979 732-8441
John Barten, *President*
EMP: 14 EST: 2004
SALES (est): 4.5MM **Privately Held**
SIC: 2851 Paints & allied products

(G-3231)
DIVERSITECH CORPORATION
Fm 949 At Interstate 10 (78934)
P.O. Box 357 (78934-0357)
PHONE..................................678 542-3600
Paula Frnka, *Manager*
EMP: 90
SALES (corp-wide): 96.3MM **Privately Held**
WEB: www.diversitech.com
SIC: 3272 Concrete products
HQ: Diversitech Corporation
3039 Premiere Pkwy # 600
Duluth GA 30097
678 542-3600

(G-3232)
QUIKRETE COMPANIES LLC
Also Called: Sand Express
1083 Kleimann (78934-5267)
PHONE..................................979 732-8210

John Lentz, *Partner*
EMP: 45 **Privately Held**
WEB: www.quikrete.com
SIC: 3272 3255 3251 3241 Dry mixture concrete; clay refractories; brick & structural clay tile; cement, hydraulic
HQ: The Quikrete Companies Llc
5 Concourse Pkwy Ste 1900
Atlanta GA 30328
404 634-9100

(G-3233)
SOUTHWEST CONCRETE PRODUCTS CO
Also Called: Headwaters Construction Mtls
Ih 10 E (78934)
PHONE..................................888 464-9341
Bob Whisnant, *President*
Jim Pouns, *CFO*
EMP: 210
SALES (est): 32.4MM **Privately Held**
SIC: 3271 Concrete block & brick
HQ: Headwaters Incorporated
10701 S River Front Pkwy # 300
South Jordan UT 84095

(G-3234)
TEXAS LUMBER CONSTRUCTION
939 Fannin St (78934-2234)
P.O. Box 203 (78934-0203)
PHONE..................................979 732-2063
Dorris Dvorak, *Owner*
EMP: 13
SALES (est): 596.2K **Privately Held**
SIC: 1389 1442 Construction, repair & dismantling services; gravel mining

Comanche
Comanche County

(G-3235)
ARCHER-DANIELS-MIDLAND COMPANY
Also Called: ADM
508 Moorman Rd (76442-2175)
P.O. Box 950 (76442-0948)
PHONE..................................325 356-2511
Gale Lahr, *Plant Mgr*
Richard Steele, *Plant Mgr*
Beon Miles, *Branch Mgr*
Jale Lahr, *Branch Mgr*
Eddie McGettes, *Maintence Staff*
EMP: 27
SALES (corp-wide): 64.6B **Publicly Held**
WEB: www.adm.com
SIC: 2041 Flour & other grain mill products
PA: Archer-Daniels-Midland Company
77 W Wacker Dr Ste 4600
Chicago IL 60601
312 634-8100

(G-3236)
TEXAS SODIUM BENTONITE INC
18301 Highway 16 (76442-7132)
PHONE..................................325 885-2339
George Burton, *President*
Jeannie Burton, *Vice Pres*
EMP: 9 EST: 1987
SQ FT: 2,500
SALES (est): 1.5MM **Privately Held**
WEB: www.texassodiumbentonite.com
SIC: 2819 Sodium compounds or salts, inorg., ex. refined sod. chloride

(G-3237)
YOUGHALL ENTERPRISES INC
Also Called: Professional Ambulance Sls Svc
309 Highway 3381 (76442-2047)
PHONE..................................325 356-2233
Kem Bales, *Accounts Mgr*
James McGregor, *Branch Mgr*
Troy Miceli, *Mng Member*
Tanner Jacob, *Manager*
George Vickery, *Manager*
EMP: 32
SALES (est): 5.9MM **Privately Held**
WEB: www.proambulance.net
SIC: 3713 Ambulance bodies

Comfort
Kendall County

(G-3238)
CONNEXA ENERGY LLC
147 Us Highway 87 (78013-3703)
P.O. Box 219 (78013-0219)
PHONE..................................830 995-3600
Michael W Postel Jr, *President*
Coleman Rogers, *Sales Staff*
Deborah Mey, *Marketing Staff*
EMP: 29
SQ FT: 35,000
SALES (est): 6.6MM **Privately Held**
WEB: www.connexa.com
SIC: 3699 3674 Electrical equipment & supplies; photovoltaic devices, solid state

(G-3239)
LLT INC
120 Hermann Sons Rd (78013)
P.O. Box 658 (78013-0658)
PHONE..................................830 995-3465
Clinton Wood, *President*
▼ **EMP:** 10 EST: 2013
SALES (est): 1.4MM **Privately Held**
WEB: www.largelifttruck.com
SIC: 3537 Forklift trucks

(G-3240)
PSD3 ENTERPRISES LLC
Also Called: Apache Rifleworks
50502 Ih 10 W (78013-3447)
PHONE..................................830 995-3894
Paul Duran III, *President*
EMP: 10
SALES (est): 292.3K **Privately Held**
WEB: www.apacherifleworks.com
SIC: 7699 5941 3484 Gun services; firearms; rifles or rifle parts, 30 mm. & below

Commerce
Hunt County

(G-3241)
ALLIANCE CARPET CUSHION CO
3100 Industrial Dr (75428)
PHONE..................................903 886-4153
Joe Fetuccia, *Manager*
EMP: 62 **Publicly Held**
SIC: 2282 Carpet yarn: twisting, winding or spooling
HQ: Alliance Carpet Cushion Co
180 Church St
Torrington CT 06790
860 489-4273

(G-3242)
COVIDIEN LP
Also Called: Medical Supplies
400 Maple St (75428-3604)
P.O. Box 1140 (75429-1140)
PHONE..................................903 886-3153
EMP: 400
SQ FT: 125,000 **Privately Held**
WEB: www.nellcor.com
SIC: 3841 Surgical & medical instruments
HQ: Covidien Lp
15 Hampshire St
Mansfield MA 02048
763 514-4000

(G-3243)
ESQUIRE TOOLING & MFG INC
111 State Highway 224 (75428-2170)
P.O. Box 43 (75429-0043)
PHONE..................................903 886-4779
Nelson Chapman, *President*
Linda Chapman, *Admin Sec*
EMP: 20
SALES (est): 465.8K **Privately Held**
WEB: www.esquiretooling.com
SIC: 3444 Sheet metalwork

(G-3244)
NEWSPAPER HOLDING INC
Also Called: Commerce Journal
1219 Washington St (75428-2613)
PHONE..................................903 886-3196

EMP: 38 Privately Held
SIC: 2711 Newspapers-Publishing/Printing
HQ: Newspaper Holding, Inc.
425 Locust St
Johnstown PA 15901
814 532-5102

(G-3245)
PERSONALIZED PRINTING INC
1300 Bonham St (75428-2530)
PHONE.................................903 886-7173
Floyd Black, *President*
James R Atchley, *Vice Pres*
Randy Atchley, *Vice Pres*
Chris Black, *Treasurer*
Christopher A Black, *Admin Sec*
EMP: 10
SQ FT: 17,000
SALES (est): 1.7MM Privately Held
WEB: www.personalizedprinting.com
SIC: 2752 Commercial printing, offset

(G-3246)
RANDOLPH D & L COMPANY LLC
Also Called: Quality Concrete Products
915 Bois D Arc St (75428-2165)
PHONE.................................903 886-3055
Lori Gordon,
David Gordon,
EMP: 13
SALES (est): 2.2MM Privately Held
WEB: www.qualityconcreteproducts.com
SIC: 3272 Septic tanks, concrete

Como
Hopkins County

(G-3247)
CRYSTAL FEED MILLS INC
700 W Main St (75431-2819)
P.O. Box 19 (75431-0019)
PHONE.................................903 488-3261
Allan Spencer, *President*
EMP: 20
SQ FT: 100,000
SALES (est): 4.8MM Privately Held
SIC: 2048 Prepared feeds

(G-3248)
CUSTOM SHUTTERS INC
811 W Main St (75431-2805)
P.O. Box 17 (75431-0017)
PHONE.................................903 488-3224
Carey Gibson, *President*
Sara Gibson, *Treasurer*
Felecia Smith, *Office Mgr*
Jo Watts, *Shareholder*
EMP: 25
SQ FT: 100,000
SALES (est): 4.2MM Privately Held
WEB: www.customshutters.com
SIC: 2431 Blinds (shutters), wood

(G-3249)
PETRO-HUNT LLC
6524 Fm 69 (75431-2310)
PHONE.................................903 629-3205
EMP: 41
SALES (corp-wide): 4.1B Privately Held
WEB: www.petrohunt.com
SIC: 1311 Crude petroleum production
HQ: Petro-Hunt, L.L.C.
2101 Cedar Springs Rd # 60
Dallas TX 75201
214 880-8400

(G-3250)
STEEL METAL DAIRY INC
Also Called: Steel Metal Daddy
3362 County Road 2346 (75431-3431)
PHONE.................................903 866-2536
Jack H Kempenaar, *President*
Sakje Kempenaar, *Vice Pres*
EMP: 32 **EST:** 1986
SALES (est): 4MM Privately Held
SIC: 3523 Dairy equipment (farm)

Conroe
Montgomery County

(G-3251)
5L ENERGY SERVICES LLC
5750 W Davis St (77304-4862)
P.O. Box 247 (77305-0247)
PHONE.................................936 539-1232
John Kevin Libhart, *Principal*
EMP: 14 **EST:** 2012
SALES (est): 2.5MM Privately Held
SIC: 1389 Oil field services

(G-3252)
ADCORP SIGN SYSTEMS LLC
10965 Highway 242 (77385-4347)
P.O. Box 2423 (77305-2423)
PHONE.................................936 321-4888
Larry Slade, *Sales Staff*
Darrell Tinsley, *Mng Member*
EMP: 12
SALES (est): 1.3MM Privately Held
WEB: www.darrellsign.com
SIC: 7319 3993 Display advertising service; signs & advertising specialties

(G-3253)
ADOBE FAB CONSULTANTS INC
7187 Old Highway 105 W (77304-4545)
P.O. Box 1244, Montgomery (77356-1244)
PHONE.................................936 447-6400
Mario Ramos, *Principal*
EMP: 20
SALES (est): 2.7MM Privately Held
WEB: www.adobefab.com
SIC: 3449 Bars, concrete reinforcing: fabricated steel

(G-3254)
AIRBRUSH IMAGES INC
Also Called: ABI Digital Solutions
851 N Fm 3083 Rd E (77303-1858)
PHONE.................................936 523-1000
Daniel E Henrichs, *President*
Tobe Basher, *General Mgr*
Tobe Bashor, *General Mgr*
Heidi Henrichs, *CFO*
Nancy Dennis, *Accounts Mgr*
▲ **EMP:** 25
SQ FT: 40,000
SALES (est): 3.2MM Privately Held
WEB: www.abidigitalsolutions.com
SIC: 3993 Signs & advertising specialties

(G-3255)
AMERA-SEIKI CORPORATION
4213 N Frazier St Ste B1 (77303-1678)
PHONE.................................832 234-5960
Richard Welsh, *President*
Scott Murray, *Partner*
◆ **EMP:** 15
SALES (est): 3MM Privately Held
WEB: www.ameraseikicnc.com
SIC: 3545 Cutting tools for machine tools

(G-3256)
ANALYTICAL INSTRUMENTS CORP
Also Called: Aic
12621 Highway 105 W # 205 (77304-1612)
PHONE.................................713 460-5757
EMP: 13
SQ FT: 7,000
SALES (est): 2.4MM Privately Held
WEB: www.aicgc.net
SIC: 3823 Chromatographs, industrial process type

(G-3257)
APPLIED RUBBER TECHNOLOGY INC
116a Industrial Ct (77301-4029)
P.O. Box 779 (77305-0779)
PHONE.................................936 760-4100
Ray Snow, *CEO*
▲ **EMP:** 68
SQ FT: 35,000
SALES (est): 8.5MM
SALES (corp-wide): 164.4MM Privately Held
WEB: www.utexind.com
SIC: 3053 Gaskets, packing & sealing devices

HQ: Utex Industries, Inc.
10810 Katy Fwy Ste 100
Houston TX 77043
713 467-1000

(G-3258)
ATLANTIS LABORATORIES INC
1601 Airport Rd (77301-3125)
PHONE.................................936 760-1255
Mark Potter, *President*
▲ **EMP:** 10
SQ FT: 4,000
SALES (est): 2.1MM Privately Held
SIC: 2844 Cosmetic preparations; hair preparations, including shampoos

(G-3259)
AUSTRAL INTEGRATED SERVICES
8601 Fawn Trl Bldg 3 (77385-3307)
PHONE.................................936 266-0945
Ewert Munoz, *Director*
EMP: 10
SALES (est): 615.9K Privately Held
WEB: www.austral.ca
SIC: 1381 Directional drilling oil & gas wells

(G-3260)
AUTO FIRE AND SAFETY CONS
7398 Teaswood Dr (77304-5400)
PHONE.................................832 585-0423
CAM Cope, *Owner*
Danielle Cope, *Corp Secy*
Sherri Cope, *Vice Pres*
EMP: 9
SALES (est): 815K Privately Held
WEB: www.firesafetyconsultant.com
SIC: 7389 1389 Safety inspection service; construction, repair & dismantling services

(G-3261)
BALL METAL BEVERAGE CONT CORP
Metal Beverage Packaging Div
1001 N Fm 3083 Rd E (77303-1862)
PHONE.................................936 760-2255
Ellis Freeman, *Opers Mgr*
Charles Nollkamper, *Production*
Bob Martin, *Branch Mgr*
Devin Ranson, *Supervisor*
Scott Lowrey, *Admin Mgr*
EMP: 115
SALES (corp-wide): 11.4B Publicly Held
WEB: www.ball.com
SIC: 3411 Metal cans
HQ: Ball Metal Beverage Container Corp.
9300 W 108th Cir
Westminster CO 80021

(G-3262)
BAUER MANUFACTURING LLC
100 N Fm 3083 Rd E (77303-1866)
PHONE.................................936 539-5030
Wolfgang Puennel, *CEO*
Sebastian Bauer, *Vice Pres*
Gerald Huber, *Opers Dir*
◆ **EMP:** 74
SALES (est): 23.2MM
SALES (corp-wide): 1.6B Privately Held
WEB: www.bauer-conroe.com
SIC: 3541 Drilling & boring machines
HQ: Bauer Maschinen Gmbh
Bauer-Str. 1
Schrobenhausen 86529
825 297-0

(G-3263)
BOEING COMPANY
4724 S Parkway St (77303-4355)
PHONE.................................936 756-0505
Michael Trapp, *Principal*
EMP: 996
SALES (corp-wide): 58.1B Publicly Held
WEB: www.boeing.com
SIC: 3721 Airplanes, fixed or rotary wing
PA: The Boeing Company
100 N Riverside Plz
Chicago IL 60606
312 544-2000

(G-3264)
BRITE LITE SIGN SERVICE INC
2603 Sand Shore Dr (77304-4331)
PHONE.................................713 849-5545

EMP: 35
SQ FT: 250,000
SALES (est): 5.8MM Privately Held
SIC: 3993 Signs, not made in custom sign painting shops

(G-3265)
BROEN INC
27657 Commerce Oaks Dr (77385-4405)
PHONE.................................713 300-0480
Ben Marchisio, *President*
EMP: 25
SALES (est): 4.2MM Privately Held
WEB: www.broen.us
SIC: 3491 3592 Industrial valves; valves

(G-3266)
BRUKER OPTICS INC
3750 Fm 1488 Rd Ste 104 (77384-3902)
PHONE.................................978 439-9899
Jack Robbins, *Branch Mgr*
EMP: 14
SQ FT: 13,277
SALES (corp-wide): 2B Publicly Held
WEB: www.bruker.com
SIC: 3826 Analytical instruments
HQ: Bruker Optics Inc.
40 Manning Rd
Billerica MA 01821

(G-3267)
BULLET CONCRETE MATERIALS INC
9393 Broadway Ave (77385-5505)
PHONE.................................281 367-9747
Harold Denton Jr, *President*
Calvin Denton, *Vice Pres*
EMP: 10 **EST:** 1969
SQ FT: 10,000
SALES (est): 1.3MM Privately Held
SIC: 3273 Ready-mixed concrete
PA: Root Co
9393 Broadway Ave
Conroe TX
936 756-1906

(G-3268)
BUZZARD INDUSTRIES INC
12826 Highway 105 E (77306-5310)
P.O. Box 132378, The Woodlands (77393-2378)
PHONE.................................936 264-1010
M Sims S Sr, *President*
Lisa Sims, *Corp Secy*
M Sims Jr, *Vice Pres*
EMP: 15
SALES (est): 272.9K Privately Held
WEB: www.buzzardind.com
SIC: 3441 Building components, structural steel

(G-3269)
BYRNE MEDICAL INC
3150 Pollok Dr (77303-2104)
P.O. Box 958 (77305-0958)
PHONE.................................936 539-0391
Donny M Byrne, *President*
Travis Bendele, *Design Engr*
Chris Hartwig, *Design Engr*
Carlotta Lansford, *CFO*
Vanessa Miller, *Manager*
EMP: 210
SQ FT: 60,000 **Privately Held**
WEB: www.medivators.com
SIC: 3841 Surgical & medical instruments

(G-3270)
C & C METALS INC
1402 E Davis St (77301-3110)
PHONE.................................936 760-5640
EMP: 42 **EST:** 2011
SALES (est): 2.7MM Privately Held
WEB: www.candcmetals.com
SIC: 3441 Fabricated structural metal

(G-3271)
C2 PIPELINE SERVICES LLC
16525 Old Houston Rd (77302-6963)
PHONE.................................713 253-6980
Kevin Burnette, *Manager*
EMP: 20
SALES (corp-wide): 10MM Privately Held
WEB: www.c2pipeline.com
SIC: 1389 Oil field services

▲ = Import ▼=Export
◆ =Import/Export

PA: C2 Pipeline Services, Llc
16 Cascade Caverns Rd
Boerne TX 78015
830 651-3089

(G-3272)
CALVARY STEEL MFG LLC
2418 N Frazier St Ste 108 (77303-1899)
P.O. Box 720 (77305-0720)
PHONE................................936 494-5775
Gary Buckaloo, *Mng Member*
Richard Christoffersen, *Director*
Lisa Buckaloo, *Admin Sec*
EMP: 18
SALES (est): 3.5MM **Privately Held**
WEB: www.cs-ministriestx.org
SIC: 3533 Oil field machinery & equipment

(G-3273)
CAMPBELL-RANDALL MACHINERY CO
405 Fm 3083 Rd (77301-6431)
P.O. Box 2468 (77305-2468)
PHONE................................936 539-1400
EMP: 12
SALES (est): 2.2MM **Privately Held**
WEB: www.campbell-randall.com
SIC: 3559 Special industry machinery

(G-3274)
CAROLS LIGHTING AND FAN SP INC
Also Called: Lighting One
27132 Interstate 45 N (77385-8714)
PHONE................................281 292-1661
Nina McClendon, *Manager*
EMP: 16
SALES (corp-wide): 15.7MM **Privately Held**
WEB: www.carolslighting.com
SIC: 5719 3564 Lighting fixtures; blowers
& fans
PA: Carol's Lighting And Fan Shop, Inc.
1710 Humble Place Dr
Humble TX 77338
281 446-7613

(G-3275)
CHEVRON PHILLIPS CHEM CO LP
Also Called: Drilling Spc Animal Plants
5450 Jefferson Chem Rd (77301-6836)
P.O. Box 2567 (77305-2567)
PHONE................................936 539-3154
Sherry Ramthal, *Plant Mgr*
EMP: 34
SQ FT: 30,000
SALES (corp-wide): 3.5B **Privately Held**
WEB: www.cpchem.com
SIC: 2821 Plastics materials & resins
HQ: Chevron Phillips Chemical Company
Lp
10001 Six Pines Dr
The Woodlands TX 77380
832 813-4100

(G-3276)
CHROMATIC INDUSTRIES INC
15b S Trade Center Pkwy (77385-8214)
PHONE................................936 539-5770
▲ EMP: 31
SALES (est): 7MM **Privately Held**
WEB: www.chromaticindustries.com
SIC: 3491 Industrial valves

(G-3277)
CHROMATIC INDUSTRIES LLC (DH)
15b S Trade Center Pkwy (77385-8214)
PHONE................................936 539-5770
Mark Gamber, *CEO*
Bill Losa, *Exec VP*
Brett Wesley, *Exec VP*
EMP: 19 EST: 2016
SALES (est): 10.4MM
SALES (corp-wide): 80.7MM **Privately Held**
WEB: www.chromaticindustries.com
SIC: 3592 Valves
HQ: Sequitur Energy Resources, Llc
2050 W Sam Houston Pkwy S # 1850
Houston TX 77042
713 395-3000

(G-3278)
COAST PRECAST LLC
11261 Meador Rd (77303-2351)
PHONE................................936 890-5500
Boardman L Munson,
EMP: 10 EST: 1976
SQ FT: 22,000
SALES (est): 1.3MM **Privately Held**
WEB: www.coastprecast.com
SIC: 3272 Concrete products, precast

(G-3279)
COMPLETION TECHNOLOGIES INC
1925 Longmire Rd Ste 2 (77304-4892)
PHONE................................936 760-2734
EMP: 10 EST: 2010
SALES (est): 420K **Privately Held**
SIC: 1389 Oil/Gas Field Services

(G-3280)
COMPONENT MANUFACTURING CORP
3565 S Loop 336 E (77301-6850)
PHONE................................800 275-3011
Ty M Tipton, *CEO*
Rose Renteria, *Corp Secy*
▲ EMP: 20
SQ FT: 20,500
SALES (est): 20MM **Privately Held**
WEB: www.componentmfg.com
SIC: 3432 3423 3069 Plumbing fixture fit-
tings & trim; plumbers' hand tools;
plumbers' rubber goods

(G-3281)
CONROE CONCRETE LTD
Also Called: Yancey Ready-Mix
1701 Royal College Hl Rd (77304-2564)
P.O. Box 3159 (77305-3159)
PHONE................................936 539-1761
Bobby Yancey, *President*
Jo Ann Yancey, *Vice Pres*
▲ EMP: 65
SQ FT: 1,500
SALES (est): 14.5MM **Privately Held**
WEB: www.concretecontractorssupply.com
SIC: 3273 Ready-mixed concrete

(G-3282)
CONROE MACHINE LLC
701 Conroe Park North Dr (77303-2257)
P.O. Box 689, Broussard LA (70518-0689)
PHONE................................936 494-2566
Murray Touchette, *President*
Kevin McBride, *Vice Pres*
Nora Tucker, *Vice Pres*
James Wardell, *Prgrmr*
Ronald E Brumley,
EMP: 100
SALES (est): 14.9MM **Privately Held**
WEB: www.conroemachine.com
SIC: 3599 Machine shop, jobbing & repair

(G-3283)
CONROE PLASTICS MOLDING INC
1700 Orval Rd (77301-4834)
PHONE................................936 539-2005
Randy Clark, *Manager*
▲ EMP: 70
SQ FT: 18,000
SALES (est): 10.4MM
SALES (corp-wide): 2.4B **Publicly Held**
WEB: www.phoenixplastics.com
SIC: 3053 Gaskets, all materials; oil seals,
rubber
HQ: Gardner Denver, Inc.
800 Beaty St
Davidson NC 28036

(G-3284)
CONSERVATEK INDUSTRIES INC
Also Called: CST Covers
498 N Loop 336 E (77301-1433)
PHONE................................713 290-9944
Dave Abbott, *Ch of Bd*
Donald R Brown, *President*
Chris Bridgnell, *Corp Secy*
John Delaney, *Senior VP*
Steven Ducotey, *Vice Pres*
▼ EMP: 100
SQ FT: 65,000

SALES (est): 32MM **Privately Held**
WEB: www.cstindustries.com
SIC: 3441 Fabricated structural metal
PA: Tank Wind-Down Corp.
903 E 104th St Ste 900
Kansas City MO 64131

(G-3285)
CONSOLIDATED PRESSURE CTRL LLC
27264 Oakridge Park Dr (77385-2770)
PHONE................................281 893-5900
Otto Windholz Jr, *President*
Vk Dhawan, *Chairman*
Fenil Mistry, *Purch Agent*
Hitendra Kale, *CFO*
EMP: 84
SQ FT: 37,000
SALES (est): 21MM
SALES (corp-wide): 5MM **Privately Held**
WEB: www.cpcmfg.com
SIC: 3533 1799 Oil & gas field machinery;
service station equipment installation,
maintenance & repair
PA: Sts Products Inc.
27264 Okrdge Pk Dr Bldg 2
Conroe TX 77385
832 375-1444

(G-3286)
CONTAINMENT SOLUTIONS INC (DH)
Also Called: Fluid Containment Acquisition
500 Conroe Park West Dr (77303-1931)
PHONE................................936 756-7731
Robert Clay Findley, *President*
Todd Bogenrief, *Area Mgr*
Demetrio Salazar, *Engineer*
Bob Tirocchi, *CFO*
Jeff Shaffer, *Human Res Mgr*
◆ EMP: 50
SALES (est): 56.9MM
SALES (corp-wide): 8.4B **Publicly Held**
WEB: www.containmentsolutions.com
SIC: 3443 Tanks, lined: metal plate

(G-3287)
CROWN CORK & SEAL USA INC
Also Called: Crown Beverage Packaging
2501 N Frazier St (77303-1586)
P.O. Box 2628 (77305-2628)
PHONE................................936 539-5401
Holly Pozadzides, *Human Resources*
George Rice, *Manager*
Daniel Abramowicz, *CTO*
EMP: 153
SQ FT: 375,000
SALES (corp-wide): 11.6B **Publicly Held**
WEB: www.crowncork.com
SIC: 3411 3545 3354 Metal cans; cams
(machine tool accessories); aluminum ex-
truded products
HQ: Crown Cork & Seal Usa, Inc.
770 Township Line Rd # 100
Yardley PA 19067
215 698-5100

(G-3288)
CUDE OILFIELD CONTRACTORS INC
Also Called: Cude Energy Services
100 Interstate 45 N # 400 (77301-2701)
P.O. Box 131441, The Woodlands (77393-
1441)
PHONE................................281 298-0600
Lea Ann Peterson, *President*
Marlon McAdams, *Vice Pres*
EMP: 10
SQ FT: 1,000
SALES (est): 3MM **Privately Held**
WEB: www.totalenergyservices.us
SIC: 1381 Drilling oil & gas wells

(G-3289)
DB BITS LLC
12072 Fm 3083 Rd (77301-6104)
P.O. Box 1698, Fredericksburg (78624-
1901)
PHONE................................936 539-4948
Brian Ballard, *Mfg Mgr*
Zachary Sample, *Production*
Ed Martin, *Engineer*
Kody Bodine, *Sales Staff*
Chris Box, *Manager*
EMP: 9

SALES (est): 1.3MM **Privately Held**
WEB: www.dbbits.com
SIC: 3532 Drills, bits & similar equipment

(G-3290)
DCL AMERICA INC
27603 Commerce Oaks Dr (77385-4405)
P.O. Box 560, Houston (77001-0560)
PHONE................................281 651-5900
Brendan Filby, *Principal*
Inderpreet Sran, *Engineer*
Jonathan U Abaee, *Regl Sales Mgr*
Brent Anderson, *Regl Sales Mgr*
Lisa Barber, *Regl Sales Mgr*
EMP: 14
SQ FT: 25,000
SALES (est): 30MM
SALES (corp-wide): 15.6MM **Privately Held**
WEB: www.dcl-inc.com
SIC: 2396 3823 Automotive & apparel
trimmings; combustion control instru-
ments
PA: Dcl International Inc
140 Cidermill Ave
Concord ON L4K 4
905 660-6450

(G-3291)
DFI PILING INC
Also Called: D F I
610 Aurora Business Pk Dr (77301-4768)
PHONE................................877 334-7453
David A Freeland, *President*
Jane Freeland, *Corp Secy*
Sean Freeland, *Vice Pres*
Barry Strauss, *CFO*
EMP: 10
SALES (est): 322.8K
SALES (corp-wide): 11.6MM **Privately Held**
WEB: www.dfipiling.com
SIC: 1389 1629 4213 Building oil & gas
well foundations on site; oil & gas wells:
building, repairing & dismantling; pile driv-
ing contractor; trucking, except local
PA: Freeland Holdings Inc
3403 74 Ave Nw
Edmonton AB T6B 3
780 466-5237

(G-3292)
DIALOG WIRELINE SERVICES L L C
13040 Highway 105 E (77306-5312)
PHONE................................936 264-3847
Chris Chitwood, *Branch Mgr*
EMP: 19
SALES (corp-wide): 20.4MM **Privately Held**
WEB: www.dialogwireline.com
SIC: 1389 Oil field services
PA: Dialog Wireline Services L L C
3100 Maverick Dr
Kilgore TX 75662
903 988-2311

(G-3293)
DIAMOND FAB
1150 Beach Airport Rd (77301-7168)
PHONE................................936 441-9353
Ricky Mizell, *Owner*
Karen Mizell, *Partner*
James Diamond, *Partner*
EMP: 15
SQ FT: 10,000
SALES (est): 4MM **Privately Held**
WEB: www.diamondfab.com
SIC: 3498 1799 Fabricated pipe & fittings;
welding on site

(G-3294)
DIVINE LTG & FABRICATION LLC
Also Called: Divine Lighting and Mfg
3704 Hilltop Dr Ste 200 (77303-1640)
PHONE................................936 494-3900
Robin Donahou, *Prdtn Mgr*
Sallie Campbell, *Opers Staff*
Bob Meador, *Purchasing*
Rory Watkins, *Sales Mgr*
Micheal A Krest, *Mng Member*
▲ EMP: 28
SALES (est): 6MM **Privately Held**
WEB: www.divinelighting.net
SIC: 3646 Commercial indusl & institu-
tional electric lighting fixtures

(G-3295)
DMG EQUIPMENT COMPANY LLC (PA)
Also Called: Smith & Company
1575 Fm 1485 Rd (77301-6839)
P.O. Box 691 (77305-0691)
PHONE................................936 756-6960
Dave Smith, *Partner*
Gene Smith, *Partner*
Mike C Smith, *General Ptnr*
▲ **EMP:** 200 **EST:** 1946
SQ FT: 90,000
SALES: 85.4MM **Privately Held**
WEB: www.smithandcompany.net
SIC: 1611 2951 Highway & street paving
contractor; asphalt & asphaltic paving
mixtures (not from refineries)

(G-3296)
FARRZ INC
Also Called: Fastsigns Conroe
206h S Loop 336 W (77304-3300)
PHONE................................936 539-3278
Chris Farr, *President*
Lisa Farr, *Vice Pres*
EMP: 10
SALES (est): 1.4MM **Privately Held**
WEB: www.fastsigns.com
SIC: 3993 Signs & advertising specialties

(G-3297)
FLARES & STACKS INC
12697 Johnson Rd (77302-3935)
PHONE................................281 356-1408
EMP: 12 **EST:** 1998
SALES (est): 3.7MM **Privately Held**
WEB: www.flares-stacks.com
SIC: 2899 3433 Flares; heating equip-
ment, except electric

(G-3298)
FRAZIER & SON LP
101 Longview St (77301-4075)
P.O. Box 2847 (77305-2847)
PHONE................................936 494-4040
Mark Frazier, *Partner*
Gregory Frazier, *Partner*
Kyle Frazier, *Vice Pres*
Greg Frazier, *VP Opers*
Robert Gennario, *VP Opers*
EMP: 15 **EST:** 1928
SQ FT: 53,000
SALES (est): 5.5MM **Privately Held**
WEB: www.frazierandson.com
SIC: 3535 Bucket type conveyor systems;
bulk handling conveyor systems; over-
head conveyor systems

(G-3299)
GULF COAST ENVMTL SYSTEMS LLC
Also Called: Gces
1689 Hawthorne Dr (77301-3284)
PHONE................................832 476-9024
Ken Rogers, *President*
Jay Swoboda, *Vice Pres*
Charles H Clark IV, *CFO*
▲ **EMP:** 30
SALES (est): 18.7MM **Privately Held**
WEB: www.gcesystems.com
SIC: 5075 8711 3826 Air pollution control
equipment & supplies; pollution control
engineering; environmental testing equip-
ment

(G-3300)
HALLIBURTON COMPANY
Also Called: Halliburton Energy Services
16548 Donwick Dr (77385-3506)
PHONE................................936 442-4700
Tom M Hann, *Mktg Dir*
Joyce Winn, *Branch Mgr*
EMP: 24 **Publicly Held**
WEB: www.halliburton.com
SIC: 1389 Oil field services
PA: Halliburton Company
3000 N Sam Houston Pkwy E
Houston TX 77032

(G-3301)
HANSON AGGREGATES LLC
12541 Sleepy Hollow Rd (77385-5103)
PHONE................................281 367-4557
Michael Hunt, *Manager*
EMP: 10

SALES (corp-wide): 20.8B **Privately Held**
WEB: www.heidelbergcement.com
SIC: 3273 Ready-mixed concrete
HQ: Hanson Aggregates Llc
8505 Freport Pkwy Ste 500
Irving TX 75063
469 417-1200

(G-3302)
HEMPEL (USA) INC (DH)
Also Called: Neogard
600 Conroe Park North Dr (77303-2207)
PHONE................................936 523-6000
Greg Bengtson, *President*
Ken Mackey, *Area Mgr*
Lars J Dollerup, *Exec VP*
Michael Hansen, *Exec VP*
Peter Kirkegaard, *Exec VP*
◆ **EMP:** 90 **EST:** 1951
SQ FT: 12,000
SALES (est): 155.4MM
SALES (corp-wide): 1.8MM **Privately Held**
WEB: www.north-america.hempel.com
SIC: 2851 Marine paints; paints & paint ad-
ditives; lacquers, varnishes, enamels &
other coatings
HQ: Hempel A/S
Lundtoftegardsvej 91
Kongens Lyngby 2800
459 338-00

(G-3303)
HESHKA OIL LLC
2929 E Davis St (77301-7216)
PHONE................................936 760-3453
Michael Perschke, *President*
Michael T Perschke, *Mng Member*
▲ **EMP:** 9
SQ FT: 9,980
SALES (est): 2.1MM **Privately Held**
WEB: www.heshkaoil.com
SIC: 3533 Oil field machinery & equipment

(G-3304)
HIGHER PLANES INC
513 Bryant Rd (77303-1763)
PHONE................................936 494-1717
Barry Cain, *President*
Carol Cain, *CFO*
Elizabeth Caruthers, *Admin Sec*
EMP: 9
SALES (est): 1.2MM **Privately Held**
WEB: www.higherplanes.com
SIC: 3728 Aircraft parts & equipment

(G-3305)
HILFLO LLC
Also Called: Engenuity
12076 Fm 3083 Rd (77301-6104)
P.O. Box 2351 (77305-2351)
PHONE................................936 756-2020
Jeff Hilpert, *President*
Lee Hilpert, *COO*
Melissa Atchley, *VP Sales*
EMP: 10
SALES (est): 1.1MM **Privately Held**
WEB: www.engenuityinc.com
SIC: 3829 Measuring & controlling devices

(G-3306)
HOFFLAND ENVIRONMENTAL INC
10391 Silver Springs Rd (77303-2373)
PHONE................................936 856-4515
Robert O Hoffland, *President*
Ryan Hoffland, *Chairman*
Carol Hoffland, *Corp Secy*
John Hoffland, *Vice Pres*
◆ **EMP:** 27
SQ FT: 36,000
SALES (est): 6.4MM **Privately Held**
WEB: www.heienv.com
SIC: 3823 Water quality monitoring & con-
trol systems

(G-3307)
HOOKS INDUSTEIAL SERVICE CTR
101 Industrial Ct (77301-6203)
PHONE................................361 299-6112
John Valentine, *President*
EMP: 12 **EST:** 2010

SALES (est): 808K **Privately Held**
WEB: www.hooksindustrial.com
SIC: 3999 Dock equipment & supplies, in-
dustrial

(G-3308)
HUNTSMAN CHEMICAL
5451 Jefferson Chem Rd (77301-6837)
PHONE................................936 539-1961
Joe Castagna, *Owner*
EMP: 9
SALES (est): 1.1MM **Privately Held**
WEB: www.huntsman.com
SIC: 2821 Plastics materials & resins

(G-3309)
HUNTSMAN PETROCHEMICAL LLC
5451 Jefferson Chem Rd (77301-6837)
PHONE................................936 756-3381
Victor Mena, *Purchasing*
Bill Ray, *Engineer*
Frederick Timothy, *Engineer*
Randi Weber, *Engineer*
Walter L Greer, *Human Res Mgr*
EMP: 175
SQ FT: 960
SALES (corp-wide): 6.8B **Publicly Held**
SIC: 2821 Plastics materials & resins
HQ: Huntsman Petrochemical Llc
500 S Huntsman Way
Salt Lake City UT 84108
801 584-5700

(G-3310)
IMMI TURBINES INC
1410 S Frazier St (77301-4416)
PHONE................................936 788-2229
Lance R Shearer, *President*
Chrystal A Shearer, *Vice Pres*
EMP: 15 **EST:** 1999
SQ FT: 3,000
SALES (est): 2.9MM **Privately Held**
WEB: www.immiturbines.com
SIC: 7389 3511 8742 Purchasing service;
gas turbines, mechanical drive; mainte-
nance management consultant

(G-3311)
IPS INTERNATIONAL LLC
2615 Industrial Ln (77301-4033)
PHONE................................936 521-1981
Austreberto F Cobos Rojas, *Principal*
EMP: 12
SALES (est): 1.6MM **Privately Held**
SIC: 1382 Oil & gas exploration services

(G-3312)
J B EDWARDS COMPANY
18960 Moorhead Rd (77302-6630)
PHONE................................281 429-7143
Jack Edwards, *Owner*
EMP: 9
SALES (est): 732.8K **Privately Held**
SIC: 3444 Booths, spray: prefabricated
sheet metal

(G-3313)
JAMES WALKER OIL & GAS CO
26797 Hanna Rd Ste D7 (77385-6630)
P.O. Box 467, Glenwood IL (60425-0467)
PHONE................................281 875-0002
Nigel Page, *Vice Pres*
Lena Pickett, *Finance*
EMP: 18
SALES (est): 2.8MM **Privately Held**
WEB: www.jameswalker.biz
SIC: 2992 Lubricating oils & greases

(G-3314)
JD PRO-SERVICE LLC (PA)
17220 Highway 105 E (77306-5902)
P.O. Box 2426 (77305-2426)
PHONE................................936 264-4003
Agustin Diaz, *President*
EMP: 15
SALES (est): 1.3MM **Privately Held**
WEB: www.jdproservices.net
SIC: 1799 3441 7389 Welding on site;
fabricated structural metal;

(G-3315)
JOHN BEAN TECHNOLOGIES CORP
Also Called: Jbt Aerotech Services
100 Interstate 45 N 152a (77301-2890)
PHONE................................936 441-2077
John Eifler, *Office Mgr*
EMP: 9 **Publicly Held**
WEB: www.jbtc.com
SIC: 3556 Food products machinery
PA: John Bean Technologies Corporation
70 W Madison St Ste 4400
Chicago IL 60602

(G-3316)
JYOTI INTERNATIONAL INC
Also Called: Jyoti Americas
3575 Pollok Dr (77303-5706)
PHONE................................936 523-4700
Prakash Thakur, *President*
EMP: 157
SQ FT: 2,000
SALES (est): 15.6MM **Privately Held**
WEB: www.jyotiamericas.com
SIC: 3568 Power transmission equipment
PA: Jyoti Structures Limited
6th Floor, Valecha Chambers, New
Link Road,
Mumbai MH 40005

(G-3317)
KIMRAY INC
Also Called: Kimray Sales & Service
11133 I 45 S Ste A (77302)
PHONE................................936 441-2468
Larry Johnson, *Manager*
Shelvin Voudrie, *Manager*
Hugh Sauer, *Maintence Staff*
EMP: 10
SALES (corp-wide): 113.4MM **Privately Held**
WEB: www.kimray.com
SIC: 3829 Measuring & controlling devices
PA: Kimray, Inc.
52 Nw 42nd St
Oklahoma City OK 73118
405 525-6601

(G-3318)
LEAM DRILLING SYSTEMS LLC
2027a Airport Rd (77301-3250)
PHONE................................936 539-1351
Matt Colerick, *COO*
Mark Arnspiger, *Engineer*
Travis Schwope, *Manager*
Stephen Senn, *Manager*
Shawn Pellerin, *Executive*
EMP: 20
SALES (corp-wide): 13.2MM **Privately Held**
WEB: www.leam.net
SIC: 1389 Oil field services
PA: Leam Drilling Systems Llc
3114 W Old Spanish Trl
New Iberia LA 70560
337 367-3552

(G-3319)
LEWIS-QUINN CNSTR SVCS INC (PA)
11355 Highway 242 (77385-4354)
PHONE................................936 321-8111
Ted Lewis, *President*
Jimmy Quinn, *Vice Pres*
EMP: 20
SQ FT: 1,400 **Privately Held**
SIC: 3531 Chippers: brush, limb & log

(G-3320)
LIBERTY MATERIALS INC (PA)
18214 E River Rd (77302-5754)
P.O. Box 1172, Liberty (77575-1172)
PHONE................................281 572-4003
James E Welch, *President*
Billy Hoppes, *General Mgr*
Joe Hitzfeld, *Business Mgr*
Paul Welch, *Vice Pres*
Evelyn Welch, *Treasurer*
EMP: 23 **EST:** 1989
SQ FT: 1,500
SALES (est): 16.3MM **Privately Held**
WEB: www.libertymaterials.com
SIC: 3273 Ready-mixed concrete

(G-3321)
LINCOLN LUMBER LLC (PA)
1390 Fm 1314 (77301)
P.O. Box 778 (77305-0778)
PHONE.................................936 539-4421
Edwin M Blazek, *Mng Member*
Jim Kelly,
EMP: 80
SQ FT: 1,000
SALES (est): 48.6MM **Privately Held**
WEB: www.lincolnusa.com
SIC: 2421 5031 Building & structural materials, wood; lumber: rough, dressed & finished

(G-3322)
LITTLEFIELD BROTHERS CON CNSTR
Also Called: Littlefield Brothers Mini Stor
15285 Fm 1485 Rd (77306-8915)
PHONE.................................281 399-1488
Tim Littlefield, *Vice Pres*
Glenda Littlefield, *Manager*
EMP: 30
SQ FT: 5,000
SALES (est): 3.2MM **Privately Held**
WEB: www.littlefieldbrothers.com
SIC: 1771 3272 1611 Foundation & footing contractor; slabs, crossing: concrete; highway & street paving contractor

(G-3323)
LOGIC CONTROL LLC
Also Called: Electrical Automation Controls
27331 Robinson Rd (77385-8931)
PHONE.................................281 362-9600
Karen Pinckard, *Office Mgr*
Mike Weathers, *Mng Member*
Jack Cates,
Storm Ruffin,
Jerry Smith,
EMP: 10
SALES (est): 4MM **Privately Held**
SIC: 3613 Control panels, electric

(G-3324)
LONE STAR MOLDING INC
12686 Fm 1314 Rd (77302-3443)
PHONE.................................936 539-0008
Terry Dillard, *President*
EMP: 40
SALES (est): 3MM **Privately Held**
WEB: www.lonestarmolding.com
SIC: 3089 2296 Molding primary plastic; fabric for reinforcing rubber tires

(G-3325)
LONG BEACH SHAVINGS CO INC (PA)
Also Called: Texpak
14369 Fm 1314 Rd (77302-3421)
PHONE.................................936 231-4400
Jack Price, *President*
Russell Wayne Price, *Treasurer*
Matt Niccum, *Manager*
EMP: 13
SQ FT: 12,000
SALES (est): 2.4MM **Privately Held**
WEB: www.lbsc.com
SIC: 2421 Sawdust & shavings

(G-3326)
LUC URETHANES INC
3411 Pollok Dr (77303-5343)
PHONE.................................936 539-2170
Dean Enterline, *Production*
Ryan Martin, *Technical Staff*
Charles Krutzen, *Director*
Suzanne Krutzen-Winkens, *Director*
EMP: 11
SALES (est): 2.2MM
SALES (corp-wide): 484.2K **Privately Held**
WEB: www.lucgroup.com
SIC: 2821 Thermosetting materials
HQ: Limburgse Urethaan Chemie B.V.
Boschstraat 31
Brunssum 6442
455 270-300

(G-3327)
M FAB & MACHINE
17781 Highway 105 E (77306-5913)
PHONE.................................936 264-2388
Robert Masterson, *Owner*

EMP: 10
SQ FT: 20,500
SALES (est): 600K **Privately Held**
WEB: www.amstechnologygroup.com
SIC: 3599 1799 3494 Machine shop, jobbing & repair; welding on site; valves & pipe fittings

(G-3328)
MAUSER USA LLC
410 S Trade Center Pkwy B13
(77385-8246)
PHONE.................................936 273-1279
Ron Lesniak, *Plant Mgr*
Jerry Dunlevy, *Warehouse Mgr*
Dennis Platek, *Controller*
William Cave, *Regl Sales Mgr*
Kurt Gary, *Manager*
EMP: 60
SALES (corp-wide): 1.1B **Privately Held**
WEB: www.mauserpackaging.com
SIC: 3089 5085 Pallets, plastic; commercial containers
HQ: Mauser Usa, Llc
35 Cotters Ln Ste C
East Brunswick NJ 08816

(G-3329)
MAVERICK TUBE CORPORATION
Also Called: Tenaris
699 Fm 3083 Rd (77301-6435)
PHONE.................................936 539-2136
Matthew Machacek, *Research*
Linda Flory, *Personnel Exec*
Joel Smith, *Human Resources*
Alejandro Altamirano, *Branch Mgr*
Facundo Gomila, *Info Tech Mgr*
EMP: 400
SALES (corp-wide): 183.7K **Privately Held**
WEB: www.tenaris.com
SIC: 3317 Steel pipe & tubes; pipes, seamless steel
HQ: Maverick Tube Corporation
2200 West Loop S Ste 800
Houston TX 77027
713 767-4400

(G-3330)
MEDIVATORS INC
Also Called: Byrne Medical
3150 Pollok Dr (77303-2104)
PHONE.................................936 539-0391
Norberto Castillo, *Mfg Mgr*
Richard Jackson, *Mfg Staff*
Brittney Mastrian, *Production*
Holli Gilbert, *Buyer*
Jeremy Kehn, *Engineer*
EMP: 210
SALES (corp-wide): 1B **Publicly Held**
WEB: www.minntech.com
SIC: 3841 Surgical & medical instruments
HQ: Medivators Inc.
14585 Northdale Blvd
Rogers MN 55374
763 553-3300

(G-3331)
MODCO INDUSTRIES INC
10650 Fm 1484 Rd (77303-4324)
P.O. Box 657 (77305-0657)
PHONE.................................936 539-9222
Joe Bartlett, *President*
EMP: 25
SALES (est): 6.1MM **Privately Held**
WEB: www.modcoind.com
SIC: 3494 Valves & pipe fittings; crowns & closures

(G-3332)
MS DIRECTIONAL LLC (HQ)
Also Called: Ms Energy Services
3335 Pollok Dr (77303-5702)
P.O. Box 3047 (77305-3047)
PHONE.................................936 442-2500
Allen Neel, *CEO*
Paul Culbreth, *President*
Bart Lantis, *District Mgr*
Tim Johnson, *Buyer*
Bob Graham, *Engineer*
EMP: 96
SQ FT: 2,400

SALES (est): 143.2MM
SALES (corp-wide): 1.1B **Publicly Held**
WEB: www.msenergyservices.com
SIC: 1389 1381 Servicing oil & gas wells; drilling oil & gas wells
PA: Patterson-Uti Energy, Inc.
10713 W Sam Houston Pkwy
Houston TX 77064
281 765-7100

(G-3333)
NATIONAL ELECTRONIC DEVICES
15 S Trade Center Pkwy (77385-8214)
PHONE.................................936 273-4111
Prabhakara Reddy, *President*
Kantha Reddy, *Treasurer*
▲ **EMP:** 10 **EST:** 1979
SQ FT: 28,500
SALES (est): 1.9MM **Privately Held**
WEB: www.national-electronic-devices-ltd.com
SIC: 3663 Cable television equipment

(G-3334)
NATIONAL OILWELL VARCO INC
Also Called: Nov Wellbore Technologies
500 Conroe Park West Dr (77303-1931)
PHONE.................................936 856-9180
Bill McMahon, *Manager*
EMP: 24
SALES (corp-wide): 8.4B **Publicly Held**
WEB: www.nov.com
SIC: 3533 Oil & gas field machinery
PA: National Oilwell Varco, Inc.
7909 Parkwood Circle Dr
Houston TX 77036
713 346-7500

(G-3335)
NATIONAL OILWELL VARCO INC
National Oilwell Varco DH
500 Conroe Park West Dr (77303-1931)
PHONE.................................936 444-4000
Fred Hampton, *Vice Pres*
Parul Dhall, *QC Mgr*
Daniel Debrosse, *Engineer*
Ahmed Gaffar, *Engineer*
Michael Garner, *Engineer*
EMP: 150
SALES (corp-wide): 8.4B **Publicly Held**
WEB: www.nov.com
SIC: 3825 3545 3546 Instruments to measure electricity; machine tool accessories; power-driven handtools
PA: National Oilwell Varco, Inc.
7909 Parkwood Circle Dr
Houston TX 77036
713 346-7500

(G-3336)
NATIONAL OILWELL VARCO INC
Texas Oil Tool
3770 Pollok Dr (77303-5703)
P.O. Box 2488 (77305-2488)
PHONE.................................936 777-6100
Bryant Cardwell, *General Mgr*
Ken Barnes, *Engineer*
Daniel Piperato, *Supervisor*
EMP: 150
SALES (corp-wide): 8.4B **Publicly Held**
WEB: www.nov.com
SIC: 3533 Oil & gas field machinery
PA: National Oilwell Varco, Inc.
7909 Parkwood Circle Dr
Houston TX 77036
713 346-7500

(G-3337)
NATIONAL OILWELL VARCO INC
500 Conroe Park West Dr (77303-1931)
PHONE.................................832 575-2000
EMP: 24
SALES (corp-wide): 8.4B **Publicly Held**
WEB: www.nov.com
SIC: 3533 Oil & gas field machinery
PA: National Oilwell Varco, Inc.
7909 Parkwood Circle Dr
Houston TX 77036
713 346-7500

(G-3338)
NATIONAL OILWELL VARCO INC
Also Called: Advanced Wire Cloth
2800 N Frazier St (77303-1528)
PHONE.................................936 441-0006
Jeff Walker, *Regional Mgr*
Kim Gale, *Prdtn Mgr*
Jackie Clark, *Export Mgr*
Rebekah Warzon, *Buyer*
Eric Scott, *VP Engrg*
EMP: 27
SALES (corp-wide): 8.4B **Publicly Held**
WEB: www.nov.com
SIC: 3496 Fourdrinier wire cloth
PA: National Oilwell Varco, Inc.
7909 Parkwood Circle Dr
Houston TX 77036
713 346-7500

(G-3339)
NATIONAL OILWELL VARCO LP
Also Called: Nov Ctes
3770 Pollock Dr (77303)
PHONE.................................936 777-6200
Edward Smalley, *General Mgr*
EMP: 32
SALES (est): 192.3K **Privately Held**
WEB: www.nov.com
SIC: 1389 Oil field services

(G-3340)
NATIONAL OILWELL VARCO LP
Also Called: Brandt N O V
2800 N Frazier St (77303-1528)
PHONE.................................936 756-4800
Linda Furlan, *Manager*
EMP: 365
SALES (corp-wide): 8.4B **Publicly Held**
WEB: www.nov.com
SIC: 3533 Oil field machinery & equipment
HQ: National Oilwell Varco, L.P.
7909 Parkwood Circle Dr
Houston TX 77036
713 375-3700

(G-3341)
NATURES WAY RESOURCES INC
101 Sherbrook Cir (77385-7750)
PHONE.................................936 273-1200
John C Ferguson, *President*
EMP: 10
SALES (est): 1.5MM **Privately Held**
WEB: www.natureswayresources.com
SIC: 2499 2875 5261 Mulch, wood & bark; compost; top soil

(G-3342)
NICKENS BROTHERS RACING ENGS
200 Beach Airport Rd (77301-7108)
PHONE.................................936 441-1131
Robert Nickens, *President*
David Nickens, *Vice Pres*
EMP: 12
SQ FT: 4,000
SALES (est): 1.8MM **Privately Held**
WEB: www.nickensracing.com
SIC: 3519 Internal combustion engines

(G-3343)
NORTHSIDE CULTURED MARBLE INC
19627 Fm 1314 Rd 1314th (77302)
PHONE.................................281 429-5288
Andres Ugalde, *President*
EMP: 9
SALES (est): 591.8K **Privately Held**
SIC: 1743 3281 Marble installation, interior; marble, building: cut & shaped

(G-3344)
NOVOSCI CORP
2021 Airport Rd (77301-3250)
PHONE.................................281 363-4949
Michael J Sorna, *President*
Chris Bares, *Vice Pres*
Steve Ford, *VP Opers*
Nicole Cavazos, *Opers Mgr*
Daniel Ovalle, *Prdtn Mgr*
▲ **EMP:** 26
SALES (est): 4.1MM **Privately Held**
WEB: www.novosci.us
SIC: 3841 Surgical & medical instruments

GEOGRAPHIC

(G-3345)
ODOM TRAILER MFG CO INC
213 Porter Rd (77301-4098)
PHONE..............................936 756-3910
Rocky Cates, *Manager*
EMP: 13
SALES (corp-wide): 1.2MM **Privately Held**
WEB: www.odomtrailer.com
SIC: 3715 Trailer bodies
PA: Odom Trailer Mfg. Co., Inc.
　213 Porter Rd Ste 1314
　Conroe TX
　936 539-3324

(G-3346)
PACKARD INTERNATIONAL INC
22397 White Oak Dr (77306-8859)
PHONE..............................281 399-8771
Antoine Deeb, *President*
James Oliver Henry Jr, *Chief Engr*
Joseph Halabi, *Design Engr*
Nadia Deeb-Newton, *Sales Mgr*
Tina Bark, *Office Mgr*
▲ EMP: 19
SQ FT: 12,500
SALES (est): 15.4MM **Privately Held**
WEB: www.packardusa.com
SIC: 1389 Oil field services

(G-3347)
PENTAIR RSDNTIAL FLTRATION LLC
Also Called: Pentair Filtration Solutions
4301 W Davis St (77304-4285)
PHONE..............................936 525-2310
Marcus Reeves, *Technical Staff*
EMP: 18
SALES (corp-wide): 7.8MM **Privately Held**
WEB: www.pentair.com
SIC: 3589 Water purification equipment, household type
PA: Pentair Residential Filtration, Llc
　5500 Wayzata Blvd Ste 600
　Minneapolis MN 55416
　763 656-5258

(G-3348)
PEPSI-COLA METRO BTLG CO INC
222 N Loop 336 E (77301-1429)
PHONE..............................936 522-4400
Ricky Lyles, *Warehouse Mgr*
Terry Woods, *Manager*
EMP: 100
SQ FT: 142,789
SALES (corp-wide): 67.1B **Publicly Held**
WEB: www.pepsico.com
SIC: 2086 Carbonated soft drinks, bottled & canned
HQ: Pepsi-Cola Metropolitan Bottling Company, Inc.
　1111 Westchester Ave
　White Plains NY 10604
　914 767-6000

(G-3349)
PHOENIX PLASTICS LP
5400 Jefferson Chem Rd (77301-6836)
PHONE..............................936 760-2311
Rod A Garcia, *President*
Ricardo Olmos, *Production*
Amy Gula, *Human Resources*
Maria Garcia, *Manager*
Abel Garcia, *Administration*
◆ EMP: 13
SALES (est): 3.3MM **Privately Held**
WEB: www.phoenixplastics.com
SIC: 2821 Plastics materials & resins

(G-3350)
PLANEVIEW-WMI LLC
Also Called: Wesso Metals
13639 Poplar Cir Ste 101 (77304-2223)
PHONE..............................936 588-8988
Ida Tanaka, *Office Mgr*
Ross A Bernstein,
▲ EMP: 15 EST: 2013
SALES (est): 1.9MM **Privately Held**
SIC: 3569 5072 Centrifuges, industrial; nozzles

(G-3351)
POOL CUSTOM IRON WORKS INC
923 S 1st St (77301-4386)
P.O. Box 2746 (77305-2746)
PHONE..............................936 756-4292
Frank D Adams, *Principal*
Dusty Adams, *Manager*
EMP: 15
SQ FT: 7,000
SALES (est): 3.6MM **Privately Held**
WEB: www.pooliron.com
SIC: 3446 Fences or posts, ornamental iron or steel

(G-3352)
PORTELE PRINTING COMPANY INC
Also Called: Precision Printing
3606 N Frazier St (77301-1431)
P.O. Box 3656 (77305-3656)
PHONE..............................936 441-3738
George A Portele, *President*
EMP: 15
SQ FT: 10,000
SALES (est): 2.9MM **Privately Held**
WEB: www.precisionprinting.org
SIC: 2752 Commercial printing, offset

(G-3353)
PPG INDUSTRIES INC
Also Called: PPG 8339
910 W Dallas St (77301-2234)
PHONE..............................936 441-1533
Bill McConnell, *Branch Mgr*
EMP: 24
SALES (corp-wide): 15.3B **Publicly Held**
WEB: www.ppg.com
SIC: 2851 Paints & allied products
PA: Ppg Industries, Inc.
　1 Ppg Pl
　Pittsburgh PA 15272
　412 434-3131

(G-3354)
PROFESSNAL DRCTIONAL ENTPS INC (PA)
Also Called: Pro Directional
850 Conroe Park West Dr (77303-1966)
P.O. Box 750 (77305-0750)
PHONE..............................936 441-7266
Karen O'Neil, *President*
Lee Wright, *President*
Wayne Mills, *VP Opers*
Steven Brewer, *CFO*
Vince Ekleberry, *CFO*
EMP: 115
SQ FT: 50,000
SALES (est): 289.6MM **Privately Held**
WEB: www.prodirectional.com
SIC: 1389 1381 Oil field services; drilling oil & gas wells

(G-3355)
PROTECT CONTROLS INC
3212 Old Highway 105 E (77301-6458)
PHONE..............................713 691-5183
▲ EMP: 215 EST: 1973
SQ FT: 182,000
SALES (est): 29.5MM **Privately Held**
WEB: www.protectcontrols.com
SIC: 3448 Buildings, portable: prefabricated metal

(G-3356)
RAMROD ENTERPRISES LLC
Also Called: Texans Agri Products
12286 Highway 105 E (77306-5304)
PHONE..............................936 756-4846
William B Mitchell, *President*
Stephen D Smith, *Treasurer*
EMP: 50 EST: 2000
SALES (est): 4.4MM **Privately Held**
SIC: 2499 2875 5191 5199 Mulch, wood & bark; potting soil, mixed; phosphate rock, ground; baling of wood shavings for mulch

(G-3357)
RHR ACQUISITION CO LLC
Also Called: SEI Heat Treat
4400 N Frazier St (77303-1441)
PHONE..............................936 856-6607
Richard Rau, *Branch Mgr*
EMP: 11

SALES (corp-wide): 2.3MM **Privately Held**
WEB: www.seiheat.com
SIC: 3398 Metal heat treating
PA: Rhr Acquisition Co., Llc
　6910 Fulton St
　Houston TX 77022
　713 699-3892

(G-3358)
RIVER AGGREGATES LLC
13070 Sh 242 (77302)
P.O. Box 8609, The Woodlands (77387-8609)
PHONE..............................936 446-2000
Rob Van Til,
Carl Davis,
EMP: 20
SALES (est): 4.6MM
SALES (corp-wide): 7.9MM **Privately Held**
WEB: www.riveraggregates.com
SIC: 1442 Construction sand & gravel
PA: Stonepoint Materials Llc
　30 S 17th St Ste 840
　Philadelphia PA 19103
　215 874-0609

(G-3359)
ROBOTIC WELDING SOLUTIONS LLC
1525 Airport Rd (77301-3123)
PHONE..............................281 706-5967
April Ann Bergquist-Nobs,
EMP: 9
SALES (est): 104.4K **Privately Held**
WEB: www.roboticweldingsolutions.com
SIC: 7692 Welding repair

(G-3360)
RWS CABINETS LLC
5797 Rolling Hills Rd (77303-4686)
PHONE..............................936 760-2407
Lucas R Shipley, *Mng Member*
EMP: 11 EST: 2011
SALES (est): 1.1MM **Privately Held**
WEB: www.rwscabinets.com
SIC: 2434 Wood kitchen cabinets

(G-3361)
SAWYER TECHNICAL MATERIALS LLC
Also Called: Sawyer Crystal
1601 Airport Rd (77301-3125)
P.O. Box 2707 (77305-2707)
PHONE..............................936 756-8886
EMP: 70 **Privately Held**
SIC: 3281 Mfg Cut Stone/Products
HQ: Sawyer Technical Materials Llc
　35400 Lakeland Blvd
　Willoughby OH 44095
　440 951-8770

(G-3362)
SCOUT DOWNHOLE INC
1125 Beach Airport Rd (77301-7169)
PHONE..............................936 756-3255
Scout Downhole, *President*
Sheldon Ritchie, *Vice Pres*
Juan Castro, *Manager*
Bryan Woloshyn, *Director*
Chris Tragesser, *Administration*
▲ EMP: 11 EST: 2009
SALES (est): 901.6K **Privately Held**
WEB: www.scoutdownhole.com
SIC: 1389 Construction, repair & dismantling services

(G-3363)
SHAKUN SOLUTIONS LLC
Also Called: AlphaGraphics
3606 N Frazier St (77303-1431)
PHONE..............................936 756-3738
Girish Sethi,
EMP: 10
SQ FT: 9,500
SALES (est): 809.9K **Privately Held**
WEB: www.precisionprinting.org
SIC: 2752 Commercial printing, lithographic

(G-3364)
SHUMATE ENERGY TECH LLC
12060 Fm 3083 Rd (77301-6104)
PHONE..............................936 539-9533
Johnny Primacio, *CEO*

Ben Rogers, *CFO*
EMP: 34
SQ FT: 30,000
SALES (est): 7.1MM **Privately Held**
SIC: 3325 Alloy steel castings, except investment

(G-3365)
SPARKLER GROUP INC (PA)
101 N Loop 336 E (77301-1446)
P.O. Box 19 (77305-0019)
PHONE..............................936 756-4471
James T Reneau Jr, *President*
A F Kracklauer, *Vice Pres*
K B Kracklauer, *Treasurer*
Mary Rose Kracklauer, *Controller*
EMP: 38
SQ FT: 8,400
SALES (est): 7.4MM **Privately Held**
WEB: www.sparklerfilters.org
SIC: 3569 5084 5085 Filters, general line: industrial; industrial machinery & equipment; filters, industrial

(G-3366)
SPEED PRINTING CONROE INC (PA)
Also Called: Speed Printing & Office Supply
1105 W Dallas St (77301-2295)
PHONE..............................936 441-2248
Van Gillen Jr, *President*
Betty S Gillen, *Vice Pres*
Brad Hayes, *Sales Mgr*
Adam Gillen, *Sales Staff*
EMP: 12 EST: 1979
SQ FT: 6,000
SALES (est): 2.3MM **Privately Held**
WEB: www.speedprinting.net
SIC: 5943 5712 5044 2752 Office forms & supplies; office furniture; office equipment; commercial printing, offset

(G-3367)
STITT SPARK PLUG COMPANY INC
204 N Loop 336 E (77301-1429)
P.O. Box 327 (77305-0327)
PHONE..............................936 441-7796
Alfred R Brenholts Jr, *President*
Greg Slaughter, *Prdtn Mgr*
EMP: 40 EST: 1918
SQ FT: 14,000
SALES (est): 7.5MM **Privately Held**
WEB: www.stitt-sparkplug.com
SIC: 3694 Spark plugs for internal combustion engines

(G-3368)
STONE MACHINERY MOVERS INC
13905 Henry Harris Rd (77306-6719)
PHONE..............................936 446-2805
Steven D Stone, *President*
EMP: 24
SALES (est): 4.5MM **Privately Held**
WEB: www.stonemachinerymovers.net
SIC: 3599 Machine shop, jobbing & repair

(G-3369)
TANK WIND-DOWN CORP
Also Called: CST Covers
498 N Loop 336 E (77301-1433)
PHONE..............................936 539-1747
Martha Bryan, *Manager*
EMP: 14 **Privately Held**
WEB: www.cstindustries.com
SIC: 3443 Tanks, standard or custom fabricated: metal plate
PA: Tank Wind-Down Corp.
　903 E 104th St Ste 900
　Kansas City MO 64131

(G-3370)
TEXAS FIRECRCKRS FSTPTCH SOFTB
11093 Darby Loop (77385-7413)
PHONE..............................713 818-4661
Joel Bartsch, *Director*
Connie May, *Director*
EMP: 12
SALES (est): 768.2K **Privately Held**
SIC: 3949 Softball equipment & supplies

(G-3371)
TEXAS PRECISION POLYMERS INC
13843 Highway 105 W # 423 (77304-5705)
PHONE...........................936 588-4333
Alex Rivera, *President*
Theresa Brown, *Principal*
EMP: 9
SALES (est): 1MM **Privately Held**
WEB: www.texpoly.com
SIC: 3053 5085 Gaskets, packing & sealing devices; gaskets & seals; seals, industrial

(G-3372)
TISDALE AC & HTG CO
Also Called: Tisdale Company
5111 N Frazier St (77303-6403)
P.O. Box 2728 (77305-2728)
PHONE...........................936 856-1500
Brenda Tisdale, *President*
Paul Tisdale, *Vice Pres*
Hamid Mekioui, *Project Mgr*
Lisa Fuller, *Treasurer*
Rusty O'Dell, *Agent*
▲ EMP: 15 EST: 1967
SQ FT: 40,000
SALES (est): 4MM **Privately Held**
WEB: www.tisdalecompany.com
SIC: 3585 1711 3433 Refrigeration & heating equipment; plumbing, heating, air-conditioning contractors; heating equipment, except electric

(G-3373)
TRICOR INDUSTRIAL INC
3517 N Loop 336 W (77304-3623)
PHONE...........................936 273-2661
Bill Austin, *Branch Mgr*
EMP: 20
SALES (corp-wide): 60.5MM **Privately Held**
WEB: www.tricormetals.com
SIC: 5051 5169 3444 5085 Metals service centers & offices; chemicals & allied products; sheet metalwork; fasteners, industrial: nuts, bolts, screws, etc.
PA: Tricor Industrial, Inc.
3225 W Old Lincoln Way
Wooster OH 44691
330 264-3299

(G-3374)
TUBULAR PRFRTING MFR OF CONROE
Also Called: Tpm
2611 Industrial Ln (77301-4033)
P.O. Box 2039 (77305-2039)
PHONE...........................936 441-8660
Ed Blackburne Jr, *Partner*
Janet Blackburn, *Corp Secy*
Janette Blackburne, *Treasurer*
Sara Holloway, *Office Mgr*
▼ EMP: 30
SQ FT: 12,500
SALES (est): 7.9MM **Privately Held**
WEB: www.tpmltd.com
SIC: 3498 Tube fabricating (contract bending & shaping)

(G-3375)
TURBO DRILL INDUSTRIES INC (PA)
Also Called: Scout Downhole
1125 Beach Airport Rd (77301-7169)
PHONE...........................936 756-3210
Myles G Woloshyn, *President*
John Schwalm, *Engineer*
Amado Azua, *Human Res Dir*
Linda Owens, *Human Resources*
Jake Blacklaws, *Sales Staff*
▼ EMP: 60
SQ FT: 20,000
SALES (est): 22.2MM **Privately Held**
WEB: www.turbodrillind.com
SIC: 3533 Oil field machinery & equipment

(G-3376)
ULTIMATE DECALS INC
Also Called: Ultimate Banners
808 W Dallas St Ste B (77301-2259)
PHONE...........................936 539-5719
Greg Bloh, *President*
Randy Sebesta, *Manager*
David Bloh, *Admin Sec*

EMP: 11
SALES (est): 752.7K **Privately Held**
WEB: www.ultimatebanner.com
SIC: 3993 Signs & advertising specialties

(G-3377)
ULTRA FINE SILICA LP
2251 N Loop 336 W Ste B (77304-3585)
PHONE...........................936 444-7338
Lance Hammond, *Partner*
Isaac Franke, *Partner*
Levi Love, *Partner*
David Stevens, *Partner*
EMP: 10
SALES (est): 293.1K **Privately Held**
WEB: www.ultrafinesilica.com
SIC: 1429 Grits mining (crushed stone)

(G-3378)
UNISERT MULTI WALL SYSTEMS INC
13295 Rocky Rd (77306-7133)
PHONE...........................936 441-7722
Kenneth Tierling, *President*
Jeanie Tierling, *Vice Pres*
▲ EMP: 20
SQ FT: 4,000
SALES (est): 1.8MM **Privately Held**
WEB: www.unisert.com
SIC: 3498 Piping systems for pulp paper & chemical industries

(G-3379)
UNITED MACHINING SERVICES INC
1009 Ivey St (77301-4369)
PHONE...........................936 760-1153
Joe Waddle Jr, *President*
Ronald Michael, *Opers Mgr*
Teresa Linney, *Office Mgr*
EMP: 10
SALES (est): 1.8MM **Privately Held**
WEB: www.unitedmachiningservices.com
SIC: 3599 Machine shop, jobbing & repair

(G-3380)
US RUBBER CORPORATION
211 N Loop 336 E (77301-1428)
P.O. Box 520 (77305-0520)
PHONE...........................936 756-1977
Gregory Torre, *Engineer*
Gail Warner, *Human Res Mgr*
Kevin Durbin, *Regl Sales Mgr*
Michelle Grantom, *Marketing Staff*
Sherrie Chen, *Office Mgr*
◆ EMP: 40
SQ FT: 125,000
SALES (est): 10MM **Privately Held**
WEB: www.usrubbercorp.com
SIC: 3559 3496 Rubber working machinery, including tires; conveyor belts

(G-3381)
UTEX INDUSTRIES INC
116a Industrial Ct (77301-4029)
P.O. Box 779 (77305-0779)
PHONE...........................936 760-4100
Joe Hermis, *Engineer*
Michael Balas, *Branch Mgr*
EMP: 68
SALES (corp-wide): 164.4MM **Privately Held**
WEB: www.utexind.com
SIC: 3053 3061 Packing, rubber; oil & gas field machinery rubber goods (mechanical)
HQ: Utex Industries, Inc.
10810 Katy Fwy Ste 100
Houston TX 77043
713 467-1000

(G-3382)
VAUGHN ENERGY SERVICES
500 N Loop 336 E Ste 100 (77301-1435)
PHONE...........................936 539-9096
Randy Holcomb, *Office Mgr*
EMP: 14
SALES (est): 708.1K **Privately Held**
SIC: 1382 Geological exploration, oil & gas field

(G-3383)
VERDIA INC
11133 Interstate 45 S (77302-5833)
PHONE...........................713 999-5090
Anthony Crowell, *Director*

EMP: 13
SQ FT: 15,000
SALES (est): 6.1MM **Privately Held**
WEB: www.verdia.com
SIC: 2851 5198 Paints & allied products; paints

(G-3384)
WAPCO INC (PA)
Also Called: NAPA Auto Parts
201 S Frazier St (77301-3511)
PHONE...........................936 539-6272
Craig Whitehead, *President*
Kimberly Whitehead, *Admin Sec*
EMP: 16
SQ FT: 14,600
SALES (est): 2.4MM **Privately Held**
SIC: 5531 3599 5013 7539 Automotive parts; machine shop, jobbing & repair; automotive supplies & parts; machine shop, automotive

(G-3385)
WESTERN RUBBER AND MFG CO
7015 Old Highway 105 W (77304-4468)
PHONE...........................936 588-3033
Paul Eberhardt, *President*
John Stroh, *Vice Pres*
▼ EMP: 35 EST: 1977
SQ FT: 24,000
SALES (est): 7.2MM **Privately Held**
WEB: www.westernrm.com
SIC: 3053 3061 Oil seals, rubber; oil & gas field machinery rubber goods (mechanical)

(G-3386)
WMC STEEL LLC
18490 Old Harvey Rd (77385)
PHONE...........................706 922-5179
Jordi Barrenechea, *Director*
EMP: 20
SALES (corp-wide): 2.1MM **Privately Held**
WEB: www.wmc-us.com
SIC: 3496 Miscellaneous fabricated wire products
PA: Wmc Steel, Llc
25219 Kuykendahl Rd # 290
The Woodlands TX 77375
706 922-5179

Converse
Bexar County

(G-3387)
ALAMO PLATING INC
9230 Converse Business Ln (78109-2011)
PHONE...........................210 658-4024
Ralph Arnold, *President*
EMP: 10
SQ FT: 8,000
SALES (est): 1.1MM **Privately Held**
WEB: www.alamoplating.com
SIC: 3471 Chromium plating of metals or formed products; gold plating

(G-3388)
ALAMO PLATING & MET FINSHG LTD
9230 Converse Ln (78109)
PHONE...........................210 658-4024
Jana Wallace, *Partner*
Tymonee Arnold-Piel, *CFO*
Tyson S Stephens, *Manager*
EMP: 24
SALES (est): 2.2MM **Privately Held**
WEB: www.alamoplating.com
SIC: 3471 Plating of metals or formed products

(G-3389)
BECK MANUFACTURING INTL INC
Also Called: Beck Industrial
2510 Fm 1516 N (78109-3533)
PHONE...........................210 246-7510
James F Beck, *President*
J Frank Beck III, *Vice Pres*
Thomas Beck, *Vice Pres*
Amy Frias, *Purch Agent*
Jared Downs, *Senior Engr*

◆ EMP: 57
SALES (est): 25.8MM **Privately Held**
WEB: www.beckindustrial.com
SIC: 3711 Truck & tractor truck assembly

(G-3390)
BUSINESS PRINT CENTER INC
10313 Vigilante Trl (78109-1701)
PHONE...........................505 864-3553
Bruce Flemming, *President*
Sherie Flemming, *Vice Pres*
EMP: 22
SALES (est): 180K **Privately Held**
WEB: www.businessprintcenter.com
SIC: 2321 Sport shirts, men's & boys': from purchased materials

(G-3391)
CALFRAC WELL SERVICES CORP
11226 Interstate 10 E (78109-9797)
PHONE...........................210 268-0800
Thomas Migchelbrink, *Accounts Mgr*
Rod Humphrey, *Branch Mgr*
EMP: 234
SALES (corp-wide): 11.2MM **Privately Held**
WEB: www.calfrac.com
SIC: 1389 Hydraulic fracturing wells
HQ: Calfrac Well Services Corp.
717 17th St Ste 1445
Denver CO 80202

(G-3392)
EPICA APPLIED TECHNOLOGIES LLC
Also Called: Tetra Technologies
2290 Fm 1516 N Unit 1 (78109-3284)
PHONE...........................281 367-1983
Martin Aguirre, *Manager*
EMP: 45
SALES (corp-wide): 1B **Publicly Held**
WEB: www.tetratec.com
SIC: 1389 Well plugging & abandoning, oil & gas
HQ: Epica Applied Technologies Llc
1080 Eldridge Pkwy # 130
Houston TX 77077

(G-3393)
EPICA APPLIED TECHNOLOGIES LLC
Also Called: Tetra Services
2290 Fm 1516 N Unit 1 (78109-3284)
PHONE...........................210 310-7710
Roger Villarreal, *Manager*
EMP: 42
SALES (corp-wide): 1B **Publicly Held**
WEB: www.tetratec.com
SIC: 1389 8734 Oil field services; testing laboratories
HQ: Epica Applied Technologies Llc
1080 Eldridge Pkwy # 130
Houston TX 77077

(G-3394)
HALFEN USA INC (DH)
402 Gibbs Sprawl Rd (78109-1546)
P.O. Box 18687, San Antonio (78218-0687)
PHONE...........................210 945-1399
Oliver Holleber, *CEO*
Brenda Fuentes, *Production*
John Shedleski, *Sales Staff*
▲ EMP: 35
SALES (est): 12.4MM
SALES (corp-wide): 30.6B **Privately Held**
WEB: www.helifix.com
SIC: 3531 Construction machinery
HQ: Crh Americas, Inc.
900 Ashwood Pkwy Ste 600
Atlanta GA 30338
770 804-3363

(G-3395)
HANDCRAFTED METAL INC
310 Avenue E St (78109-1417)
PHONE...........................512 386-5433
William Bentz, *President*
Pamela Bentz, *Corp Secy*
Erik Bentz, *Vice Pres*
Suzanne Osborne, *Accountant*
▲ EMP: 19

SALES (est): 3.2MM **Privately Held**
WEB: www.handcraftedmetal.com
SIC: 3639 Major kitchen appliances, except refrigerators & stoves

(G-3396)
HILL COUNTRY STEEL LP
13638 E Ih 10 Unit 2 (78109-3134)
PHONE...................................210 667-9737
Todd Whittaker, *General Ptnr*
EMP: 48
SALES (est): 20.4MM **Privately Held**
WEB: www.hillcountrysteel.com
SIC: 3441 Fabricated structural metal

(G-3397)
INGRAM READYMIX INC
9450 Fm 78 (78109-2902)
PHONE...................................210 659-4468
Bruce Ingram Jr, *Manager*
EMP: 31
SQ FT: 8,100
SALES (corp-wide): 125.6MM **Privately Held**
WEB: www.ingramreadymixinc.com
SIC: 3273 Ready-mixed concrete
PA: Ingram Readymix, Inc.
　　3580 Farm Market 482
　　New Braunfels TX 78132
　　830 625-9156

(G-3398)
MISSION WRECKER SERVICE S A
4535 Fm 1516 N (78109-3484)
PHONE...................................210 341-0333
Muhammad Choudary, *President*
Johnny Reicherzer, *Sales Staff*
EMP: 40
SALES (est): 6.1MM **Privately Held**
WEB: www.missionwrecker.com
SIC: 3711 1795 Wreckers (tow truck), assembly of; wrecking & demolition work

(G-3399)
NAT G CNG SOLUTIONS LLC
9402 Converse Business Ln (78109-2042)
PHONE...................................512 998-9316
Balu Balagopal, *Branch Mgr*
EMP: 15
SALES (corp-wide): 6MM **Privately Held**
WEB: www.nat-g.com
SIC: 7549 3714 Fuel system conversion, automotive; motor vehicle parts & accessories
PA: Nat G Cng Solutions, Llc
　　16504 Aldine Westfield Rd A1
　　Houston TX 77032
　　281 954-4600

(G-3400)
PRONTO PUBLISHINGS & PRTG CO
304 Crown Ct (78109-1828)
PHONE...................................210 658-6857
Evelyn A Niland, *President*
Christy Niland, *Vice Pres*
EMP: 10
SALES (est): 660K **Privately Held**
SIC: 2741 2752 Miscellaneous publishing; commercial printing, offset

(G-3401)
RCSS
Also Called: Redondo Manufacturing
2919 Fm 1516 N (78109-3345)
PHONE...................................210 661-8474
Charles Schoenfeld, *President*
Christian Slayer, *Facilities Mgr*
Miguel Flores, *Engineer*
Janet Frelich, *Controller*
Chuck Schoenfeld, *VP Sales*
EMP: 65
SQ FT: 75,000
SALES (est): 12.6MM **Privately Held**
WEB: www.precastbollards.com
SIC: 3272 Cast stone, concrete

(G-3402)
RODRILL INC
Also Called: Rodrill Manufacturing
11670 Interstate 10 E (78109-3032)
P.O. Box 489 (78109-0489)
PHONE...................................210 667-2130
Francisco Rodriguez, *President*
◆ **EMP:** 20

SQ FT: 5,000
SALES (est): 5.9MM **Privately Held**
WEB: www.rodrill.com
SIC: 3449 Miscellaneous metalwork

(G-3403)
SPECIALIZED CNSTR SVCS LLC
8715 Business Cir Ste 1 (78109-2092)
PHONE...................................210 262-7263
Clayton Huebner, *President*
Keith Parma,
EMP: 20
SALES (est): 810K **Privately Held**
SIC: 1389 Construction, repair & dismantling services

Cookville
Titus County

(G-3404)
HORSE CREEK MFG & FABRICATION
405 County Road 3095 (75558-4057)
P.O. Box 158 (75558-0158)
PHONE...................................903 572-4211
John Stevens, *President*
Harold Jackson Smith III, *Vice Pres*
Riki Nicole Perez, *Treasurer*
EMP: 20
SALES (est): 2.4MM **Privately Held**
SIC: 3799 Trailers & trailer equipment

(G-3405)
LEONARD RAY VAUGHT
Also Called: Pleasant Pallet
1182 County Road 3425 (75558-2083)
P.O. Box 248 (75558-0248)
PHONE...................................903 572-0352
Leonard Ray Vaught, *Vice Pres*
EMP: 30
SQ FT: 10,000
SALES (est): 2.5MM **Privately Held**
WEB: www.pleasantpallet.com
SIC: 2448 2449 Pallets, wood; wood containers

(G-3406)
PLEASANT FENCING & CNSTR
1182 County Road 3425 (75558-2083)
P.O. Box 248 (75558-0248)
PHONE...................................903 572-0352
Jerrod Vaught, *President*
Leonard Ray Vaught, *Vice Pres*
Brandi Denson, *Treasurer*
Freddy Vaught, *Admin Sec*
EMP: 41
SQ FT: 10,000
SALES (est): 4.7MM **Privately Held**
WEB: www.pleasantpallet.com
SIC: 2448 Pallets, wood

Coolidge
Limestone County

(G-3407)
FRAZIER & FRAZIER INDS INC
817 S 1st St (76635-3041)
P.O. Box 279 (76635-0279)
PHONE...................................254 786-2293
Charles W Frazier, *President*
Bob Pranger, *General Mgr*
Kim Bailey, *Principal*
Lee Ann Ewing, *Corp Secy*
Harlon Easton, *Vice Pres*
EMP: 280
SQ FT: 43,000
SALES (est): 53.2MM **Privately Held**
WEB: www.ffcastings.com
SIC: 3321 Gray iron castings

Coppell
Dallas County

(G-3408)
AMERICAN BUILDING SUPPLY INC
350 Northpoint Dr (75019-3931)
PHONE...................................469 322-8100
EMP: 73 **Publicly Held**

WEB: www.abs-abs.com
SIC: 5031 3231 Doors; door frames, all materials; doors, glass; made from purchased glass
HQ: American Building Supply, Inc.
　　8360 Elder Creek Rd
　　Sacramento CA 95828
　　916 503-4100

(G-3409)
AMERICAN WOODMARK CORPORATION
Timberlake Cabinet Company
1350 Lakeshore Dr Ste 160 (75019-5167)
PHONE...................................469 635-1960
S Cary Dunston, *President*
Paul Fairless, *Opers Mgr*
Stephen Lang, *Opers Mgr*
Ron Jolly, *Prdtn Mgr*
Ethan Roebuck, *Human Res Mgr*
EMP: 228
SALES (corp-wide): 1.6B **Publicly Held**
WEB: www.americanwoodmark.com
SIC: 2434 Wood kitchen cabinets
PA: American Woodmark Corporation
　　561 Shady Elm Rd
　　Winchester VA 22602
　　540 665-9100

(G-3410)
BEAUTY MFG SOLUTIONS CORP
Also Called: Bmsc
1250 Freeport Pkwy (75019-4410)
PHONE...................................972 241-9665
Peter Song, *CEO*
Maurice McAllister, *Opers Mgr*
Diane Lewis, *QC Mgr*
Oscar Garcia, *Controller*
Ben Lorimer, *Sales Mgr*
▲ **EMP:** 150
SQ FT: 300,000
SALES (est): 70.2MM **Privately Held**
WEB: www.beautymanufacture.com
SIC: 2844 Cosmetic preparations

(G-3411)
CLASSIC AUTO AIR MFG LP
910 Freeport Pkwy Ste 100 (75019-4793)
PHONE...................................817 442-4822
Mike Oliveras, *Purchasing*
Dwight Dow, *Sales Staff*
Gary Wayman, *Sales Associate*
Dan Acosta, *Marketing Staff*
Pat Morris, *Branch Mgr*
EMP: 12 **Privately Held**
WEB: www.classicautoair.com
SIC: 3559 Automotive related machinery
PA: Classic Auto Air Manufacturing Lp
　　100 Park Pl
　　Chagrin Falls OH

(G-3412)
CONCOTE CORPORATION (PA)
Also Called: Insul-Fab
600 Freeport Pkwy Ste 150 (75019-3871)
PHONE...................................214 956-0077
Shelby Ricketts, *CEO*
Robert Hanton, *Ch of Bd*
Andy Webb, *President*
John Frederiksen, *Exec VP*
Ron Sinclair, *Research*
◆ **EMP:** 110
SQ FT: 250,000
SALES (est): 29.4MM **Privately Held**
WEB: www.concote.com
SIC: 3086 5085 2675 3471 Plastics foam products; adhesives, tape & plasters; packing, industrial; die-cut paper & board; electroplating of metals or formed products

(G-3413)
CONTRINEX INC
480 Wrangler Dr Ste 100 (75019-4691)
PHONE...................................574 340-7089
Adrian Johnson, *President*
Temba Henry, *Principal*
EMP: 11 **EST:** 1998

SALES (est): 2.1MM
SALES (corp-wide): 24MM **Privately Held**
WEB: www.contrinex.com
SIC: 3674 3823 3625 Photoelectric cells, solid state (electronic eye); industrial process control instruments; positioning controls, electric
PA: Contrinex S.A.
　　Route Du Paqui 5
　　Corminboeuf FR 1720
　　264 604-646

(G-3414)
DERSE INC
586 S Royal Ln (75019-3806)
PHONE...................................972 393-9046
Eric Lewis, *General Mgr*
Frank Occhiogrosso, *Vice Pres*
Kenney Rheinfeldt, *Production*
Justin Laney, *Purchasing*
Mark McLain, *VP Bus Dvlpt*
EMP: 80
SALES (corp-wide): 98.7MM **Privately Held**
WEB: www.derse.com
SIC: 3993 Signs & advertising specialties
PA: Derse, Inc.
　　3800 W Canal St
　　Milwaukee WI 53208
　　414 257-2000

(G-3415)
DEXAS INTERNATIONAL LTD
585 S Royal Ln Ste 200 (75019-3838)
PHONE...................................469 635-8100
Ellis Shamoon, *President*
Gabe Sandoval, *Safety Mgr*
Fernando Chu, *Purch Mgr*
Sapna Patel, *Design Engr*
John W Dagg, *CFO*
◆ **EMP:** 100
SQ FT: 200,000
SALES (est): 23.5MM **Privately Held**
WEB: www.dexas.com
SIC: 3089 3421 Injection molded finished plastic products; cutlery

(G-3416)
EPIC BOTTLING LLC
204 Airline Dr Ste 700 (75019-4681)
PHONE...................................512 947-8608
Deepak Bajaj,
EMP: 20
SALES (est): 671.8K **Privately Held**
SIC: 2087 Beverage bases

(G-3417)
GEMMY INDUSTRIES CORPORATION (PA)
Also Called: Varidesk
117 Wrangler Dr Ste 100 (75019-4711)
PHONE...................................972 538-4200
Jason McCann, *President*
Daniel G Flaherty, *Chairman*
Morgan Broom, *Business Mgr*
Matt Little, *Business Mgr*
Jeff Lamb, *COO*
◆ **EMP:** 105 **EST:** 1984
SQ FT: 80,000
SALES (est): 23.9MM **Privately Held**
WEB: www.gemmy.com
SIC: 3999 5045 Boutiquing: decorating gift items with sequins, fruit, etc.; computer peripheral equipment

(G-3418)
GULFSTREAM AEROSPACE CORP
812 Kilbridge Ln (75019-2070)
PHONE...................................972 899-1625
George Xia, *Principal*
EMP: 1303
SALES (corp-wide): 37.9B **Publicly Held**
WEB: www.gulfstream.com
SIC: 3721 Aircraft
HQ: Gulfstream Aerospace Corporation
　　500 Gulfstream Rd
　　Savannah GA 31408

(G-3419)
HUSSMANN CORPORATION
925 Freeport Pkwy Ste 200 (75019-4492)
P.O. Box 612667, Dallas (75261-2667)
PHONE...................................972 956-9045
David Denney, *Project Mgr*

Aaron Harrington, *Sales Staff*
Dave Smith, *Manager*
EMP: 60 **Privately Held**
WEB: www.hussmann.com
SIC: 3585 Refrigeration & heating equipment
HQ: Hussmann Corporation
12999 St Charles Rock Rd
Bridgeton MO 63044
314 291-2000

(G-3420)
IDIS AMERICA CO LTD
801 Hammond St Ste 200 (75019-4471)
PHONE.................................866 986-1312
EMP: 18
SALES (est): 3.9MM **Privately Held**
WEB: www.idisglobal.com
SIC: 3569 Surveillance ovens for aging & testing powder
PA: Idis Co.,Ltd.
Rm 1430
Goyang-Si

(G-3421)
IMPRESO INC (PA)
Also Called: Tstimpreso
652 Southwestern Blvd (75019-4419)
P.O. Box 506 (75019-0506)
PHONE.................................972 462-0100
Marshall D Sorokwasz, *Ch of Bd*
Susan M Atkins, *Vice Pres*
Jeff Boren, *Vice Pres*
John L Graves, *Vice Pres*
Don Cozzi, *Purch Agent*
◆ **EMP:** 75
SQ FT: 75,000
SALES: 115.2MM **Publicly Held**
WEB: www.tstimpreso.com
SIC: 2761 2679 2086 Manifold business forms; telegraph, teletype & adding machine paper; paper products, converted; water, pasteurized: packaged in cans, bottles, etc.

(G-3422)
INTELLIGRATED SYSTEMS INC
701 Canyon Dr Ste 110 (75019-3843)
PHONE.................................972 899-9636
Martin Augustyn, *Manager*
EMP: 264
SALES (corp-wide): 36.7B **Publicly Held**
WEB: www.intelligrated.com
SIC: 3535 5084 Conveyors & conveying equipment; industrial machinery & equipment
HQ: Intelligrated Systems, Inc.
7901 Innovation Way
Mason OH 45040
866 936-7300

(G-3423)
JACK BLACK LLC
551 Sthwstern Blvd Ste 10 (75019)
PHONE.................................469 341-2700
Becky Kilgore, *Vice Pres*
Sue Goble, *Opers Staff*
Lorraine McClellan, *Sales Staff*
Gabrielle Douthitt, *Mktg Dir*
Brandace Chatman, *Marketing Staff*
▲ **EMP:** 60
SALES (est): 20.1MM
SALES (corp-wide): 1.9B **Publicly Held**
WEB: www.getjackblack.com
SIC: 2844 Cosmetic preparations
PA: Edgewell Personal Care Company
6 Research Dr Ste 400
Shelton CT 06484
203 944-5500

(G-3424)
JORMAC AEROSPACE INC
820 W Sandy Lake Rd # 400 (75019-4111)
PHONE.................................972 436-7069
Steve Jourdenais, *President*
EMP: 48 **EST:** 2008
SALES (est): 6.5MM **Privately Held**
WEB: www.jormac.com
SIC: 2514 2434 Kitchen cabinets: metal; wood kitchen cabinets

(G-3425)
KAWNEER COMPANY INC
Also Called: Kawneer North TX
710 Gateway Blvd Unit 140 (75019-4791)
PHONE.................................972 829-7160

EMP: 47
SALES (corp-wide): 7.2B **Publicly Held**
WEB: www.alcoa.com
SIC: 3442 Metal doors
HQ: Kawneer Company, Inc.
555 Guthridge Ct
Norcross GA 30092
770 449-5555

(G-3426)
KERR CORPORATION
800 W Sandy Lake Rd # 100 (75019-3802)
PHONE.................................800 355-5063
Tom Kempers, *Opers Staff*
Callie Hartman, *Branch Mgr*
Lisa Islas, *Executive Asst*
EMP: 167
SALES (corp-wide): 17.9B **Publicly Held**
WEB: www.kerrdental.com
SIC: 3843 Dental hand instruments
HQ: Kerr Corporation
1717 W Collins Ave
Orange CA 92867
714 516-7400

(G-3427)
KPT INC
700 Freeport Pkwy Ste 100 (75019-4465)
PHONE.................................214 620-9700
Kurt J Pyka, *Ch of Bd*
John Cox, *Senior VP*
Nancy Creamer Pyka, *Chm Emeritus*
EMP: 65
SQ FT: 47,000
SALES (est): 3.2MM **Privately Held**
SIC: 8721 2759 Billing & bookkeeping service; commercial printing

(G-3428)
MJB WOOD GROUP LLC (PA)
Also Called: MJB Precision Wood Group
3100 Olympus Blvd Ste 480 (75019-5473)
PHONE.................................972 401-0005
Joe A Caldwell, *CEO*
Scott Griggs, *President*
Cliff Caudill, *Division Mgr*
Darrell Land, *Division Mgr*
Ward Harris, *Business Mgr*
◆ **EMP:** 50
SALES (est): 236.2MM **Privately Held**
WEB: www.mjbwood.com
SIC: 2426 2434 Furniture dimension stock, hardwood; wood kitchen cabinets

(G-3429)
NATERRA INTERNATIONAL INC
1250 Freeport Pkwy (75019-4410)
PHONE.................................972 616-6100
Jin K Song, *President*
John Ku, *Business Mgr*
Peter Song, *Exec VP*
Mark Pence, *Sales Staff*
Jilliann Gonzalez, *Manager*
▼ **EMP:** 60
SQ FT: 65,000
SALES (est): 23.2MM **Privately Held**
WEB: www.naterra.us
SIC: 2844 Toilet preparations

(G-3430)
NEFAB COMPANIES INC (DH)
204 Airline Dr Ste 100 (75019-4602)
PHONE.................................866 332-4425
Wade Mullis, *President*
Brian Bulatao, *President*
Kenneth Wilson, *President*
Jeb Baum, *General Mgr*
Paul Frisch, *General Mgr*
▲ **EMP:** 50 **EST:** 1870
SQ FT: 60,000
SALES (est): 186.1MM
SALES (corp-wide): 503.9MM **Privately Held**
WEB: www.nefab.com
SIC: 2448 2449 2441 Pallets, wood & wood with metal; skids, wood & wood with metal; rectangular boxes & crates, wood; nailed wood boxes & shook
HQ: Nefab Ab
Lantmatargrand 5
Jonkoping 553 2
771 590-000

(G-3431)
NEFAB PACKAGING INC (DH)
Also Called: Nefab Companies
204 Airline Dr Ste 100 (75019-4602)
PHONE.................................469 444-5264
Rodney W Mullus, *President*
Rodney W Mullis, *President*
Mike Murphy, *General Mgr*
Gary Chisholm, *Managing Dir*
Koen Adams, *Vice Pres*
◆ **EMP:** 50
SQ FT: 25,000
SALES (est): 169.1MM
SALES (corp-wide): 503.9MM **Privately Held**
WEB: www.nefab.com
SIC: 2448 2449 2441 Pallets, wood & wood with metal; skids, wood & wood with metal; rectangular boxes & crates, wood; nailed wood boxes & shook
HQ: Nefab Companies, Inc.
204 Airline Dr Ste 100
Coppell TX 75019
866 332-4425

(G-3432)
NOKIA SLUTIONS NETWORKS US LLC (DH)
3201 Olympus Blvd (75019-4520)
PHONE.................................972 374-3000
Stephen Trowbridge, *Vice Chairman*
Frank Shelton, *Business Mgr*
Jim Weiss, *Business Mgr*
Stephen Wyse, *Counsel*
Tammy Couture, *Vice Pres*
▲ **EMP:** 300
SALES (est): 815.4MM
SALES (corp-wide): 25.8B **Privately Held**
WEB: www.nokia.com
SIC: 3663 5999 4813 Radio broadcasting & communications equipment; telephone & communication equipment; telephone communication, except radio
HQ: Nokia Solutions And Networks Branch Operations Oy
Karakaari 7
Espoo 02610
104 488-000

(G-3433)
NORWEX USA INC
800 W Bethel Rd Ste 100 (75019-4422)
PHONE.................................214 614-6707
Kristi Hubbard, *CEO*
Dixie Martin, *CEO*
Phillip Yarbrough, *Vice Pres*
Brandye Horn, *Opers Staff*
Justin Moen, *Engineer*
▲ **EMP:** 200
SALES (est): 13.7MM
SALES (corp-wide): 16.1MM **Privately Held**
WEB: www.norwex.biz
SIC: 2842 Cleaning or polishing preparations
PA: Norwex Canada Inc
871 Whitmore Ave E
Dauphin MB R7N 3
204 622-3600

(G-3434)
PEAK NANOSYSTEMS LLC (PA)
8951 Cypress Waters Blvd (75019-4661)
PHONE.................................469 464-4504
Wendy Hoenig, *Senior VP*
Chad Lewis,
Elisa Garza,
James Welsh,
EMP: 30
SQ FT: 2,000
SALES (est): 5.9MM **Privately Held**
WEB: www.peaknano.com
SIC: 3827 3089 2819 Gun sights, optical; lenses, except optical: plastic; alkali metals: lithium, cesium, francium, rubidium

(G-3435)
PRISM MICROWAVE INC
440 Wrangler Dr Ste 500 (75019-7606)
PHONE.................................972 745-7222
Juha Mort, *President*
Rodney Roderick, *Controller*
EMP: 60
SQ FT: 5,500

SALES (est): 30MM **Privately Held**
SIC: 3663 Microwave communication equipment

(G-3436)
QUALITY FABRICATION DESIGN LP
955 Freeport Pkwy Ste 400 (75019-4455)
PHONE.................................972 304-3266
Alexander P Pier, *President*
Brian Stowell, *General Mgr*
Vondel Kremeier, *Vice Pres*
Harvey Norman, *Sales Staff*
Martha Pier, *Admin Sec*
▼ **EMP:** 60
SQ FT: 89,000
SALES (est): 12.1MM **Privately Held**
WEB: www.quality-fabrication.com
SIC: 3444 8711 5084 3556 Sheet metalwork; mechanical engineering; food product manufacturing machinery; food products machinery

(G-3437)
RAPID REPROGRAPHICS LP
156 Kingston Cir (75019-6254)
PHONE.................................214 357-5444
Stuart Marlow, *President*
Katie Marlow, *Vice Pres*
Kari Daelke, *Manager*
EMP: 19 **EST:** 1981
SALES (est): 2.5MM **Privately Held**
SIC: 2752 2791 2789 Commercial printing, offset; typesetting; bookbinding & related work

(G-3438)
REDIFORM INC
555 Airline Dr (75019-4697)
PHONE.................................972 393-8080
Harolde Savoy, *President*
◆ **EMP:** 36
SQ FT: 140,800
SALES (est): 51.5MM
SALES (corp-wide): 8.5MM **Privately Held**
WEB: www.rediform.com
SIC: 5112 2752 2761 2759 Business forms; business forms, lithographed; manifold business forms; commercial printing
PA: Dominion Blue Line Inc
1027 Northern Prospect Cres
Newmarket ON L3X 1
416 409-0583

(G-3439)
RIGHT PATHWAYS LLC
106 N Denton Tap Rd (75019-2138)
PHONE.................................817 522-3600
Kevin L Seay, *CEO*
Allison Seay, *Vice Pres*
EMP: 75
SQ FT: 1,500
SALES (est): 2.5MM **Privately Held**
WEB: www.rightpathways.com
SIC: 8071 3845 Medical laboratories; electromedical equipment

(G-3440)
RK GLOBAL INC
726 Cheshire Dr (75019-5453)
PHONE.................................972 339-8016
Rakesh Kanjani, *Principal*
EMP: 13
SALES (est): 956K **Privately Held**
SIC: 3949 Playground equipment

(G-3441)
ROHDE & SCHWARZ USA INC
410 Freeport Pkwy (75019-3854)
PHONE.................................469 713-5300
Hans-Guenter Titze, *Branch Mgr*
Kimberly Frank, *Program Mgr*
EMP: 30
SALES (corp-wide): 2.3B **Privately Held**
WEB: www.rohde-schwarz.com
SIC: 3825 Instruments to measure electricity
HQ: Rohde & Schwarz Usa, Inc.
6821 Benjamin Franklin Dr
Columbia MD 21046
410 910-7800

(G-3442)
RSI VISUAL SYSTEMS INC
Also Called: RSI Visuals
615 Freeport Pkwy (75019-3866)
PHONE.................................817 510-0350
Edgar Phillips, *Ch of Bd*
Jeff Everett, *President*
Robert Bordovsky, *Vice Pres*
Robert Rossow, *Vice Pres*
Neil Wheatley, *Vice Pres*
▼ EMP: 65
SALES (est): 12.7MM **Privately Held**
WEB: www.rsi-visuals.com
SIC: 3728 Aircraft parts & equipment

(G-3443)
SAFERTEK SOFTWARE LLC
153 E State Highway 121 # 100
(75019-7908)
PHONE.................................972 331-2984
Maruti Tangirala, *President*
EMP: 20
SALES (est): 1.2MM **Privately Held**
WEB: www.safertek.com
SIC: 7372 Business oriented computer
  software

(G-3444)
SCHNEIDER ELECTRIC USA INC
204 Airline Dr Ste 300 (75019-4663)
PHONE.................................972 236-0300
Art Rosales, *Principal*
EMP: 225
SALES (corp-wide): 177.9K **Privately
Held**
WEB: www.ccagp.com
SIC: 3643 3612 3823 3625 Bus bars
  (electrical conductors); power transform-
  ers, electric; controllers for process vari-
  ables, all types; relays & industrial
  controls; electrical apparatus & equip-
  ment; power circuit breakers
HQ: Schneider Electric Usa, Inc.
  1 Boston Pl Ste 2700
  Boston MA 02108
  978 975-9600

(G-3445)
SCOTT STUDIOS CORPORATION
Also Called: Computer Concepts P
701 Canyon Dr Ste 120 (75019-3899)
PHONE.................................972 620-2211
Dave Scott Blyth, *CEO*
David Blyth, *President*
Karen Blyth, *Exec VP*
EMP: 50
SQ FT: 25,000 **Privately Held**
SIC: 3663 Radio & TV communications
  equipment

(G-3446)
SOLOPROTECT US LLC
701 Canyon Dr Ste 100 (75019-3873)
PHONE.................................866 632-6577
Kevin Rippentrop, *Partner*
Daniel Hendrickson, *Business Mgr*
Dee Rasmussen, *Opers Staff*
Felicia Eninas, *Sales Staff*
Dee Rassmussen, *Manager*
EMP: 85 EST: 2017
SALES (est): 3MM **Privately Held**
WEB: www.kingsiii.com
SIC: 3661 3663 7389 7382 Telephone &
  telegraph apparatus; radio & TV commu-
  nications equipment; telemarketing serv-
  ices; security systems services

(G-3447)
SUPERIOR AIR PARTS INC
621 S Royal Ln Ste 100 (75019-3877)
PHONE.................................800 420-4727
Keith Chatten, *CEO*
Timothy T Archer, *President*
Scott Hayes, *Vice Pres*
Bill Ross, *Vice Pres*
Wes Rayon, *Production*
▲ EMP: 42
SQ FT: 40,000
SALES (est): 11.3MM
SALES (corp-wide): 76.7MM **Privately
Held**
WEB: www.superiorairparts.com
SIC: 3724 Aircraft engines & engine parts

PA: Thielert Ag
  Albert-Einstein-Ring 11
  Hamburg 22761
  406 969-500

(G-3448)
SYBRON DENTAL SPECIALTIES INC
Axis Sybronendo
800 W Sandy Lake Rd # 100 (75019-3802)
PHONE.................................469 635-6100
Perry Lowe, *President*
Doug Baker, *Office Mgr*
EMP: 550
SALES (corp-wide): 17.9B **Publicly Held**
WEB: www.kavokerr.com
SIC: 3843 Burs, dental
HQ: Sybron Dental Specialties, Inc.
  1717 W Collins Ave
  Orange CA 92867

(G-3449)
SYNERGY CATALYST LLC
1122 W Bethel Rd Ste 400 (75019-4425)
PHONE.................................248 786-7145
Michael Van Fatten, *Mng Member*
▲ EMP: 11
SALES (est): 2.7MM **Privately Held**
WEB: www.synergycatalyst.com
SIC: 3699 Heat emission operating appa-
  ratus

(G-3450)
TRADE SOURCE INTERNATIONAL (DH)
Also Called: Tsi Prime
650 S Royal Ln Ste 200 (75019-3837)
P.O. Box 1037 (75019-1037)
PHONE.................................972 393-3800
John Deblois, *Treasurer*
◆ EMP: 30
SQ FT: 25,000
SALES (est): 13.6MM
SALES (corp-wide): 106.3MM **Privately
Held**
SIC: 5063 3645 Lighting fixtures, residen-
  tial; residential lighting fixtures
HQ: Craftmade International, Inc.
  650 S Royal Ln Ste 100
  Coppell TX 75019
  972 393-3800

(G-3451)
TST/IMPRESO INC (HQ)
652 Southwestern Blvd (75019-4419)
P.O. Box 506 (75019-0506)
PHONE.................................972 462-0100
Marshall D Sorokwasz, *CEO*
Jeff Boren, *President*
John Graves, *VP Mfg*
Damon Murphy, *Purch Mgr*
Ashley Delamotte, *Sales Staff*
◆ EMP: 75 EST: 1976
SQ FT: 75,000
SALES (est): 83.3MM
SALES (corp-wide): 115.2MM **Publicly
Held**
WEB: www.tstimpreso.com
SIC: 2679 2761 2086 Adding machine
  rolls, paper: made from purchased mate-
  rial; computer forms, manifold or continu-
  ous; continuous forms, office & business;
  water, pasteurized: packaged in cans,
  bottles, etc.
PA: Impreso, Inc.
  652 Southwestern Blvd
  Coppell TX 75019
  972 462-0100

(G-3452)
UNIVERSAL DISPLAY & FIXS CO
200 Northpoint Dr Ste 100 (75019-7412)
PHONE.................................972 829-2366
EMP: 250
SALES (corp-wide): 110.7MM **Privately
Held**
WEB: www.udfc.com
SIC: 2542 Partitions & fixtures, except
  wood
PA: Universal Display And Fixture Com-
  pany
  726 E Hwy 121
  Lewisville TX 75057
  972 434-8067

(G-3453)
WOODARD—CM LLC (DH)
Also Called: Woodard Furniture
650 S Royal Ln Ste 100 (75019-3836)
P.O. Box 1037 (75019-1037)
PHONE.................................972 393-3800
Jean C Liu, *CEO*
John Mares, *President*
Brad D Heimann, *Principal*
Clifford Crimmings, *Vice Pres*
James Goff, *Vice Pres*
▲ EMP: 41 EST: 2007
SALES (est): 29.7MM
SALES (corp-wide): 106.3MM **Privately
Held**
WEB: www.woodard-furniture.com
SIC: 2511 Wood household furniture
HQ: Craftmade International, Inc.
  650 S Royal Ln Ste 100
  Coppell TX 75019
  972 393-3800

(G-3454)
YKK AP AMERICA INC
346 E Belt Line Rd # 600 (75019-4721)
PHONE.................................972 245-9551
Yoshi Yamamoto, *President*
EMP: 30 **Privately Held**
WEB: www.ykkap.com
SIC: 3365 Aluminum foundries
HQ: Ykk Ap America Inc.
  270 Riverside Pkwy Sw # 100
  Austell GA 30168

Copperas Cove
Coryell County

(G-3455)
MAKS FAMILY FUN & EVENTS LLC
14859 E Business 190 (76522-6357)
P.O. Box 129, Kempner (76539-0129)
PHONE.................................254 518-0005
Makayla Barbee, *Owner*
Alyssa McDowel, *General Mgr*
EMP: 20
SALES (est): 1.7MM **Privately Held**
WEB: www.maksfamilyfun.com
SIC: 3944 7993 Go-carts, children's;
  amusement arcade

(G-3456)
TACH SERVICES INC
Also Called: TAC Services
103 Wolf Rd (76522-1939)
PHONE.................................254 547-7121
Teri Bates, *President*
EMP: 20
SALES (est): 1.3MM **Privately Held**
WEB: www.tacservicesoftexas.com
SIC: 1611 5211 3315 2499 General con-
  tractor, highway & street construction;
  fencing; chain link fencing; fencing, wood

Corinth
Denton County

(G-3457)
METROPLEX CABINETS INC
3100 Walton Dr (76208-5420)
P.O. Box 1200, Lake Dallas (75065-1200)
PHONE.................................940 321-5151
Butch Honse, *President*
Brian Elliott, *Managing Prtnr*
Justin Houser, *Prdtn Mgr*
▲ EMP: 60
SQ FT: 70,000
SALES (est): 9.6MM **Privately Held**
WEB: www.metroplexcabinets.com
SIC: 2434 Wood kitchen cabinets

(G-3458)
METROPLEX ROOF AND FENCE INC (PA)
6801 S Interstate 35 E (76210-2406)
PHONE.................................469 417-8003
Charles Fairchild, *President*
Chris Kephart, *Principal*
EMP: 15
SQ FT: 5,000

SALES (est): 4.2MM **Privately Held**
WEB: www.metroplexroof.com
SIC: 1761 1799 1521 2851 Roofing contractor; fence construction; patio & deck
  construction & repair; polyurethane coatings; general contractor, highway & street
  construction; exterior concrete stucco
  contractor

(G-3459)
PACCAR INC
2111 Redrock Dr (76210-1934)
PHONE.................................940 566-7329
EMP: 200
SALES (corp-wide): 24.1B **Publicly Held**
WEB: www.paccar.com
SIC: 3537 Industrial trucks & tractors
PA: Paccar Inc
  777 106th Ave Ne
  Bellevue WA 98004
  425 468-7400

(G-3460)
PACCAR INC
2501 Mountainview Dr (76210-2666)
PHONE.................................940 566-7752
Lee Yarbrough, *Sales Staff*
EMP: 319
SALES (corp-wide): 24.1B **Publicly Held**
WEB: www.paccar.com
SIC: 3711 Motor vehicles & car bodies
PA: Paccar Inc
  777 106th Ave Ne
  Bellevue WA 98004
  425 468-7400

(G-3461)
PATTTY BRINLEE
Also Called: Pattycakes Sweetreats
1715 Vintage Dr (76210-3073)
PHONE.................................940 600-0878
Pattty Brinlee, *Owner*
EMP: 10
SALES (est): 283.4K **Privately Held**
SIC: 2051 Bakery: wholesale or whole-
  sale/retail combined

Corpus Christi
Nueces County

(G-3462)
3-C VALVE & EQUIPMENT LP (PA)
1825 N Lexington Blvd (78409-1325)
P.O. Box 4883 (78469-4883)
PHONE.................................281 361-3283
Layne Smith, *President*
Will Beauchamp, *Sales Staff*
Mark Lafleur, *Sales Staff*
Colton Smith, *Sales Staff*
Chase Steward, *Sales Staff*
EMP: 16
SALES (est): 3.4MM **Privately Held**
WEB: www.3cve.com
SIC: 3592 Valves

(G-3463)
AB INTERCONNECT INC
4222 S Staples St (78411-2702)
PHONE.................................919 934-5181
Robert A Fletcher, *President*
Barry Rolison, *Vice Pres*
Barbara Bannister, *Director*
Gary Dickson, *Admin Sec*
▲ EMP: 110 EST: 1996
SQ FT: 52,000
SALES (est): 11.9MM
SALES (corp-wide): 617.6MM **Publicly
Held**
WEB: www.ttelectronics.com
SIC: 3676 3679 Electronic resistors; har-
  ness assemblies for electronic use: wire
  or cable
HQ: International Resistive Company, Inc.
  4222 S Staples St
  Corpus Christi TX 78411
  361 992-7900

(G-3464)
ABSOLUTE CMMNCTONS NTWRK SLTON (PA)
Also Called: Discount Telephone
2333 Pollex Ave (78415-9721)
P.O. Box 271563 (78427-1563)
PHONE.....................361 888-6776
Robert Dener, *President*
Bobbie Smith, *Chairman*
Gary Smith, *Corp Secy*
Kevin Hostins, *Vice Pres*
EMP: 24
SQ FT: 4,500
SALES (est): 4MM **Privately Held**
WEB: www.callabsolute.com
SIC: 3699 6211 7373 4813 Security control equipment & systems; dealers, security; local area network (LAN) systems integrator; data telephone communications; voice telephone communications; information services, consumer

(G-3465)
ACADEMY VENETIAN BLINDS CO INC
4303 S Padre Island Dr (78411-4407)
PHONE.....................361 852-6088
Richard R Valadez, *President*
Roy Valadez, *Vice Pres*
Ernestine Valadez, *Treasurer*
EMP: 10 EST: 1946
SQ FT: 4,500
SALES (est): 1.3MM **Privately Held**
WEB: www.academywindowcoverings.com
SIC: 2591 5719 Venetian blinds; venetian blinds

(G-3466)
AD SACK INC
Also Called: Ad Sack Area Weekly Shopper
2660 S Padre Island Dr (78415-1806)
P.O. Box 60069 (78466-0069)
PHONE.....................361 854-0137
Elda Ortiz, *President*
EMP: 20
SQ FT: 1,200
SALES (est): 1MM **Privately Held**
WEB: www.adsack.com
SIC: 2711 Newspapers: publishing only, not printed on site

(G-3467)
AIM DIRECTIONAL SERVICES LLC (PA)
500 N Water St Ste 400 (78401-0214)
P.O. Box 181015 (78480-1015)
PHONE.....................361 653-6500
Thomas Rinald, *President*
Alan Foust, *District Mgr*
Allison Reinert, *VP Engrg*
Kristina Gonzales, *Bookkeeper*
Trinidad Pena, *VP Sales*
EMP: 53
SQ FT: 4,000
SALES (est): 24.5MM **Privately Held**
WEB: www.aimdir.com
SIC: 1381 Directional drilling oil & gas wells

(G-3468)
AIR LIQUIDE AMERICA LP
5880 Up River Rd (78407-1129)
PHONE.....................361 299-2999
John Mitchell, *Branch Mgr*
EMP: 10
SALES (corp-wide): 129.8MM **Privately Held**
WEB: www.industry.airliquide.us
SIC: 2813 Industrial gases
HQ: Air Liquide America L.P.
9811 Katy Fwy Ste 100
Houston TX 77024
713 624-8000

(G-3469)
AIRGAS USA LLC
301 Hereford Rd (78408-2307)
PHONE.....................361 533-0758
Jim Wilson, *Branch Mgr*
EMP: 14
SQ FT: 35,000

SALES (corp-wide): 129.8MM **Privately Held**
WEB: www.airgas.com
SIC: 2813 5172 5085 Industrial gases; petroleum products; welding supplies
HQ: Airgas Usa, Llc
259 N Radnor Chester Rd
Radnor PA 19087
216 642-6600

(G-3470)
AJ COMMERCIAL SERVICES INC
Also Called: ASC Paving
6429 Crosstown Expy Ste D (78417-3418)
PHONE.....................361 336-2113
Rafalita Avalos, *President*
EMP: 9
SALES (est): 442.6K **Privately Held**
WEB: www.ajcommserv.com
SIC: 1611 3272 1791 1542 Highway & street paving contractor; slabs, crossing: concrete; structural steel erection; institutional building construction

(G-3471)
ALAMO CONCRETE PRODUCTS LTD
6129 Agnes St (78406-1907)
PHONE.....................361 289-9200
Romero Rodriguez, *Branch Mgr*
EMP: 45 **Privately Held**
SIC: 5082 5032 3273 1442 Masonry equipment & supplies; brick, stone & related material; ready-mixed concrete; construction sand & gravel
PA: Alamo Concrete Products, Ltd.
6055 W Green Mountain Rd
Austin TX 78744

(G-3472)
AMERICAN BOTTLING COMPANY
Also Called: Seven Up Bottling Company
3127 Cabaniss Rd (78415-5907)
PHONE.....................361 851-9977
Larry Quintanilla, *Manager*
EMP: 82 **Publicly Held**
WEB: www.keurigdrpepper.com
SIC: 2086 Soft drinks: packaged in cans, bottles, etc.
HQ: The American Bottling Company
5301 Legacy Dr
Plano TX 75024

(G-3473)
ANALYTIC STRESS RELIEVING INC
1302 Cathead Rd (78409-1901)
PHONE.....................361 883-0315
Scott Libia, *Manager*
EMP: 36
SALES (corp-wide): 224.8MM **Privately Held**
WEB: www.analyticstress.com
SIC: 3398 Metal heat treating
PA: Analytic Stress Relieving, Inc.
3118 W Pinhook Rd Ste 202
Lafayette LA 70508
337 237-8790

(G-3474)
ARANSAS FUEL LLC
Also Called: Lac Fleet
5858 S Padre Island Dr (78412-3932)
P.O. Box 60267 (78466-0267)
PHONE.....................361 992-5223
EMP: 25
SALES (est): 1.2MM **Privately Held**
WEB: www.aransasfuel.com
SIC: 1389 Haulage, oil field

(G-3475)
ARIS DESIGNS INC
4451 Baldwin Blvd (78408-2707)
PHONE.....................361 881-8131
Gary Males, *President*
Teresa Ward, *Office Mgr*
EMP: 10 EST: 1982
SQ FT: 18,000
SALES (est): 1.4MM **Privately Held**
SIC: 2521 Cabinets, office: wood

(G-3476)
ASIEL ENTERPRISES INC
Also Called: Adaptor Content
8306 Serenity Ct (78414-6458)
PHONE.....................361 765-6670
Gloria D Perez, *President*
EMP: 71
SALES (est): 270K **Privately Held**
WEB: www.asielenterprises.com
SIC: 2099 7349 Food preparations; janitorial service, contract basis

(G-3477)
ATLAS RADIATOR INC
824 N Chaparral St (78401-2027)
P.O. Box 331214 (78463-1214)
PHONE.....................361 882-5661
Larry H Frederick, *President*
Donna Frederick, *Corp Secy*
Bobbie Jo Blocker, *Systems Mgr*
EMP: 38
SQ FT: 20,000
SALES (est): 7.5MM **Privately Held**
WEB: www.atlasradiator.cc
SIC: 3519 Radiators, stationary engine

(G-3478)
B D PRODUCTION CO INC
615 N Upr Brdway St # 1900 (78401-0776)
PHONE.....................361 888-4741
L A Durst Jr, *President*
EMP: 54
SALES (est): 4MM **Privately Held**
SIC: 1311 Oil shale mining; natural gas production

(G-3479)
BAKER HGHES OLFLD OPRTIONS LLC
Also Called: Baker Hughs Inteq
322 Manning Rd (78409-3401)
PHONE.....................361 289-0373
Lee Enderle, *Manager*
Joe Garcia, *Administration*
EMP: 17 **Privately Held**
WEB: www.bakerhughes.com
SIC: 1389 Oil field services
PA: Baker Hughes Oilfield Operations Llc
2001 Rankin Rd
Houston TX 77073

(G-3480)
BAKER HUGHES A GE COMPANY LLC
Also Called: Hughes Christensen
430 Navigation Blvd (78408-2748)
P.O. Box 9546 (78469-9546)
PHONE.....................361 883-1591
Wayne Hall, *Branch Mgr*
EMP: 9
SALES (corp-wide): 23.8B **Publicly Held**
WEB: www.bakerhughes.com
SIC: 1389 Oil field services
HQ: Baker Hughes Holdings Llc
17021 Aldine Westfield Rd
Houston TX 77073
713 439-8600

(G-3481)
BALLEW CASTING REPAIR INC
673 Omaha Dr (78408-2952)
P.O. Box 9052 (78469-9052)
PHONE.....................361 882-9901
Tommy Ballew, *President*
Wanda Ballew, *Corp Secy*
Dewayne Ballew, *Vice Pres*
EMP: 10
SALES (est): 586.1K **Privately Held**
SIC: 7692 Welding repair

(G-3482)
BAY AREA ANESTHESIA ASSOCIATES
4444 Corona Dr Ste 232 (78411-4323)
PHONE.....................361 857-8588
Libardo Taboada, *President*
Ben A Meisenheimer, *Med Doctor*
EMP: 17 EST: 1999
SALES (est): 1.3MM **Privately Held**
SIC: 8011 3841 General & family practice, physician/surgeon; anesthesia apparatus

(G-3483)
BAYTEK INTERNATIONAL INC
401 N Shoreline Blvd (78401-2527)
PHONE.....................361 887-8988
Dan Richter, *CEO*
Sarah Jasso, *Accounting Mgr*
Joe McGough, *Sales Mgr*
Charles T White, *Info Tech Mgr*
EMP: 17
SQ FT: 9,750
SALES (est): 2.1MM **Privately Held**
WEB: www.baytekinternational.com
SIC: 7372 Prepackaged software

(G-3484)
BERRY GP INC (PA)
1414 Corn Product Rd (78409-3020)
P.O. Box 9908 (78469-9908)
PHONE.....................361 693-2100
Edward A Martin, *President*
Ken Luhan, *President*
Bill Parker, *President*
Dj Smith, *Senior VP*
Jim Bliss, *Vice Pres*
EMP: 3000 EST: 1952
SQ FT: 40,000
SALES (est): 151.7MM **Privately Held**
WEB: www.bayltd.com
SIC: 1541 1611 3498 Industrial buildings, new construction; highway & street construction; highway & street paving contractor; general contractor, highway & street construction; fabricated pipe & fittings

(G-3485)
BERRY HOLDINGS LP (PA)
Also Called: Bay Limited
1414 Corn Product Rd (78409-3020)
P.O. Box 9908 (78469-9908)
PHONE.....................361 693-2100
Edward Martin, *CEO*
Ken Luhan, *President*
Robert Blair, *Vice Pres*
Walter Brothers, *Vice Pres*
David Carlin, *Vice Pres*
◆ EMP: 850
SQ FT: 280,000
SALES: 432.6MM **Privately Held**
WEB: www.bayltd.com
SIC: 1541 1611 3498 Industrial buildings, new construction; highway & street paving contractor; fabricated pipe & fittings

(G-3486)
BEST STRL FABRICATORS INC
8631 Old Brownsville Rd (78415-6937)
P.O. Box 270323 (78427-0323)
PHONE.....................361 265-0550
Brad Larza, *President*
EMP: 10
SQ FT: 10,000
SALES (est): 3MM **Privately Held**
SIC: 3441 Fabricated structural metal

(G-3487)
BIGTRAK TECHNOLOGIES LLC
5262 S Staples St Ste 300 (78411-4137)
PHONE.....................361 944-3982
Randy Vondrasek, *Mng Member*
EMP: 9
SALES (est): 409.5K **Privately Held**
WEB: www.bigtraktech.com
SIC: 3944 Electronic games & toys

(G-3488)
BRANDON WLDG & FABRICATION INC
9002 Leopard St (78409-2501)
P.O. Box 260247 (78426-0247)
PHONE.....................361 242-3344
Stewart Brandon, *President*
Lyn-Dee Brandon, *Vice Pres*
Carlos Martinez, *Vice Pres*
Divina H Hernandez, *Purch Mgr*
Santos Garza, *VP Mktg*
EMP: 28
SQ FT: 21,000
SALES (est): 5.9MM **Privately Held**
WEB: www.brandonwelding.com
SIC: 3443 1799 Tanks, standard or custom fabricated: metal plate; welding on site

(G-3489)
BRAYTON OPERATING CORP
606 N Carancahua St # 615 (78401-0699)
PHONE................................361 884-8741
EMP: 15
SALES (est): 1.5MM **Privately Held**
SIC: 1382 1311 Oil/Gas Exploration Services Crude Petroleum/Natural Gas Production

(G-3490)
BTB REFINING LLC (PA)
6600 Up River Rd (78409-3034)
P.O. Box 9606 (78469-9606)
PHONE................................561 347-5500
Kevin G Kirkeide,
EMP: 11
SALES (est): 3.1MM **Privately Held**
SIC: 2951 Asphalt paving mixtures & blocks

(G-3491)
BULLET PRODUCTION SERVICES LLC
4250 Ih 69 Access Rd (78410)
P.O. Box 260838 (78426-0838)
PHONE................................361 504-4200
Roger Floyd, *Mng Member*
Terrence Gordon Allen,
EMP: 20 EST: 2015
SQ FT: 1,800
SALES (est): 1.6MM **Privately Held**
SIC: 1389 Oil field services

(G-3492)
C C BATTERY COMPANY INC
3513 Agnes St (78405-2706)
P.O. Box 2823 (78403-2823)
PHONE................................361 882-5561
Kenneth G Turner, *President*
Kenneth G Turner Jr, *Vice Pres*
Ted Turner, *Vice Pres*
▲ EMP: 30 EST: 1923
SQ FT: 30,000
SALES (est): 5.8MM **Privately Held**
WEB: www.ccbattery.com
SIC: 3694 5531 3714 Ignition apparatus, internal combustion engines; automotive parts; motor vehicle parts & accessories

(G-3493)
CALLER-TIMES PUBLISHING CO
Also Called: Corpus Christi Caller Times
820 N Lower Broadway St (78401-2025)
P.O. Box 9136 (78469-9136)
PHONE................................361 883-1111
Patrick Birmingham, *President*
Mary Ann Beckett, *Opers Staff*
Michelle Coosmer, *CFO*
Diana Hinojosa, *Sales Staff*
Jeff De Loach, *Sales Executive*
EMP: 350 EST: 1877
SQ FT: 30,000
SALES (est): 10.6MM **Privately Held**
WEB: www.cctexas.com
SIC: 2711 Newspapers, publishing & printing

(G-3494)
CAMERON INTERNATIONAL CORP
6441 Interstate 37 (78409-2717)
PHONE................................361 289-1455
EMP: 40 **Publicly Held**
WEB: www.products.slb.com
SIC: 1389 Oil field services
HQ: Cameron International Corporation
    4646 W Sam Houston Pkwy N
    Houston TX 77041

(G-3495)
CAMIN CARGO CONTROL INC
218 Centaurus St (78405-3622)
PHONE................................361 884-3922
Mark Rodriguez, *COO*
Kim Holloway, *Branch Mgr*
Michael Villarreal, *Manager*
Ariel Klein, *Supervisor*
Justin Gutierrez, *Technician*
EMP: 19
SALES (corp-wide): 67.5MM **Privately Held**
WEB: www.camincargo.com
SIC: 1389 Oil field services

PA: Camin Cargo Control, Inc.
    230 Marion Ave
    Linden NJ 07036
    908 523-0616

(G-3496)
CANTWELL MATTRESS COMPANY (PA)
Also Called: Cantwell Sleep Stores
4634 Baldwin Blvd (78408-2712)
P.O. Box 4067 (78469-4067)
PHONE................................361 883-8525
Curtis B Cantwell Jr, *President*
EMP: 14 EST: 1920
SQ FT: 50,000
SALES (est): 4MM **Privately Held**
WEB: www.cantwellmattress.com
SIC: 2515 5712 Mattresses & foundations; box springs, assembled; beds & accessories; bedding & bedsprings; mattresses

(G-3497)
CC COATING & MACHINE INC
658 Omaha Dr (78408-2953)
P.O. Box 4244 (78469-4244)
PHONE................................361 884-9753
EMP: 21
SALES (est): 3MM **Privately Held**
WEB: www.cccoating.com
SIC: 3469 3312 7692 2851 Machine parts, stamped or pressed metal; plate, sheet & strip, except coated products; welding repair; paints & allied products

(G-3498)
CEC CORROSION SERVICES LLC
3388 County Rd 48 (78403)
P.O. Box D, Sinton (78387-0169)
PHONE................................361 883-6930
Daniel R Cook, *Mng Member*
EMP: 15 EST: 2014
SQ FT: 2,000
SALES (est): 1MM **Privately Held**
WEB: www.ceccorrosionservices.com
SIC: 1389 Testing, measuring, surveying & analysis services; pipe testing, oil field service; hot shot service; servicing oil & gas wells

(G-3499)
CITY OF CORPUS CHRISTI
Also Called: Ccisd Print Shop
801 Leopard St (78401-2421)
P.O. Box 110 (78403-0110)
PHONE................................361 695-7350
Jesus Chavez, *Superintendent*
Jose Hernandez, *Opers Staff*
EMP: 225
SALES (corp-wide): 372.8MM **Privately Held**
WEB: www.cctexas.com
SIC: 2752 Commercial printing, lithographic
PA: City Of Corpus Christi
    1201 Leopard St
    Corpus Christi TX 78401
    361 880-3000

(G-3500)
CLARIOS
Also Called: Johnson Controls
2209 N Padre Island Dr (78408-2432)
PHONE................................361 289-9675
Brant Pate, *Sales Executive*
Jackson Teddlie, *Manager*
Cynthia Canales, *Info Tech Mgr*
EMP: 15 **Privately Held**
WEB: www.johnsoncontrols.com
SIC: 3822 Building services monitoring controls, automatic
HQ: Johnson Controls, Inc.
    5757 N Green Bay Ave
    Glendale WI 53209
    800 382-2804

(G-3501)
CLASSIC PRINTING
4639 Corona Dr Ste 101 (78411-5402)
PHONE................................361 852-7261
Rick Cervantes, *President*
Ron Cervantes, *Treasurer*
Louis Cervantes Sr, *Admin Sec*
EMP: 10
SALES (est): 1.1MM **Privately Held**
SIC: 2752 Commercial printing, offset

(G-3502)
COASTAL BEND TOOLING & AUTOMTN
510 S Staples St (78401-3333)
PHONE................................361 883-0376
Richard Reinhart, *President*
Steven Reinhart, *Vice Pres*
EMP: 10
SQ FT: 10,000
SALES (est): 800K **Privately Held**
WEB: www.coastalbendtooling.com
SIC: 3599 Machine shop, jobbing & repair

(G-3503)
COASTAL DRILLING COMPANY L L C
Also Called: Cdc
311 Saratoga Blvd (78417-3506)
PHONE................................361 852-6195
J C McClanahan,
▲ EMP: 180
SALES (est): 53.5MM **Privately Held**
WEB: www.coastaldrilling.com
SIC: 1381 Directional drilling oil & gas wells

(G-3504)
COLT SERVICES LP
Also Called: Hcf Group
4822 Leopard St (78408-2622)
P.O. Box 9194 (78469-9194)
PHONE................................361 299-2284
Matt Rohmfeld, *Manager*
EMP: 12
SALES (corp-wide): 11.5MM **Privately Held**
WEB: www.coltonline.com
SIC: 3559 Refinery, chemical processing & similar machinery
PA: Colt Services, L.P.
    626 N 16th St
    La Porte TX 77571
    281 471-9099

(G-3505)
COMMERCIAL METALS COMPANY
Also Called: CMC Recycling
4614 Agnes St (78405-3617)
P.O. Box 9067 (78469-9067)
PHONE................................361 884-4071
EMP: 68
SALES (corp-wide): 5.4B **Publicly Held**
WEB: www.cmc.com
SIC: 5093 3341 Ferrous metal scrap & waste; nonferrous metals scrap; secondary nonferrous metals
PA: Commercial Metals Company
    6565 N Macarthur Blvd # 800
    Irving TX 75039
    214 689-4300

(G-3506)
CONRECO INC
414 Saratoga Blvd (78417-3507)
PHONE................................361 851-0352
William Sanderson, *President*
Tonia Simpson, *Consultant*
EMP: 9 EST: 1962
SQ FT: 12,500
SALES (est): 1.6MM **Privately Held**
SIC: 3441 Fabricated structural metal

(G-3507)
CORD KEEPER LLC
5801 S Staples St Ste D (78413-3783)
PHONE................................361 992-1122
Will K Deaton, *CEO*
EMP: 15
SQ FT: 6,000
SALES (est): 1.1MM **Privately Held**
SIC: 3429 Manufactured hardware (general)

(G-3508)
CORPUS CHRISTI CD ELECTRIC LP (PA)
Also Called: C-D Electric Motor Sales & Svc
617 High Starr Dr (78408-2512)
PHONE................................361 888-4133
Mary Pittaway, *Partner*
William J Pittaway, *General Ptnr*
Eddie Salinas, *Cust Mgr*
Gilbert Perez, *Manager*
EMP: 17

SQ FT: 13,400
SALES (est): 2.5MM **Privately Held**
WEB: www.c-delectric.com
SIC: 7694 5063 Electric motor repair; motors, electric

(G-3509)
CORPUS CHRISTI STAMP WORKS INC
Also Called: National Signage Affiliates
502 S Staples St (78401-3333)
P.O. Box 2189 (78403-2189)
PHONE................................361 884-4801
Harry Lee Chester, *President*
Georganne Gasaway, *Vice Pres*
EMP: 20 EST: 1949
SQ FT: 28,000
SALES (est): 3.1MM **Privately Held**
WEB: www.nationalsignageaffiliates.com
SIC: 2796 3953 Platemaking services; marking devices

(G-3510)
CORPUS CHRSTI GSKET FSTNER INC
341 Westchester Dr (78408-2936)
P.O. Box 4074 (78469-4074)
PHONE................................361 884-6366
David E Massie, *President*
Ian Massie, *Vice Pres*
Melaine Massie, *Vice Pres*
Sean Massie, *Vice Pres*
Brad Tindall, *Vice Pres*
◆ EMP: 135 EST: 1967
SQ FT: 40,000
SALES (est): 30MM **Privately Held**
WEB: www.ccgasket.com
SIC: 3053 3452 3965 5085 Gasket materials; gaskets, all materials; bolts, metal; fasteners; packing, industrial

(G-3511)
DAVENPORT ELECTRIC MOTORS LLC
421 Junior Beck Dr Ste B (78405-4411)
PHONE................................361 299-6440
Jimmy Enriquez, *CEO*
Donna Keith, *Manager*
EMP: 13
SALES (est): 376K **Privately Held**
WEB: www.davenportelectricmotors.com
SIC: 7694 Electric motor repair

(G-3512)
DEWBRE PETROLEUM CORPORATION
802 N Carancahua St # 1800 (78401-0098)
PHONE................................361 888-7978
Jerry C Dewbre, *Ch of Bd*
Lina Hall, *Business Mgr*
Rusty Douglas, *Project Mgr*
Jane Russell, *Treasurer*
Nita Russell, *Treasurer*
EMP: 17
SQ FT: 5,000
SALES (est): 2.9MM **Privately Held**
WEB: www.dewbre.com
SIC: 1381 8711 Drilling oil & gas wells; petroleum engineering

(G-3513)
DFA DAIRY BRANDS FLUID LLC
Also Called: Hygeia Dairy
5330 Ayers St (78415-2104)
PHONE................................361 854-4561
Gene Bentley, *Vice Pres*
Doug Purl, *Vice Pres*
Donald R Shelton, *Vice Pres*
Scott McClaren, *Sales & Mktg St*
Carol E Law, *Treasurer*
EMP: 14
SALES (corp-wide): 15.8B **Privately Held**
SIC: 2026 5143 Milk processing (pasteurizing, homogenizing, bottling); dairy products, except dried or canned
HQ: Dfa Dairy Brands Fluid, Llc
    1405 N 98th St
    Kansas City KS 66111
    816 801-6455

(G-3514)
DIVERSIFIED MATERIALS INC
857 Cantwell Ln (78408-2605)
PHONE................................361 993-4600

Steven A Cox, *President*
EMP: 31
SQ FT: 12,000
SALES (est): 8.8MM **Privately Held**
SIC: 3569 Filters

(G-3515)
DOGGETT HEAVY MCHY SVCS LLC
Also Called: John Deere Authorized Dealer
134 N Padre Island Dr (78406-2001)
P.O. Box 4918 (78469-4918)
PHONE..................................361 289-0727
Brian Paulmyer, *Principal*
EMP: 15
SALES (corp-wide): 29.5MM **Privately Held**
WEB: www.doggett.com
SIC: 5084 3545 Industrial machine parts; machine tool attachments & accessories
PA: Doggett Heavy Machinery Services, Llc
901 E Interstate 2
San Juan TX 78589
956 787-0001

(G-3516)
DORADO OIL COMPANY (PA)
9101 Up River Rd (78409-3213)
P.O. Box 578 (78403-0578)
PHONE..................................361 241-3200
Jim C Schuchardt, *President*
Frances Schuchardt, *Corp Secy*
EMP: 25
SQ FT: 3,000
SALES (est): 8MM **Privately Held**
WEB: www.doradooil.com
SIC: 1311 Crude petroleum production

(G-3517)
DRESSER LLC
Also Called: Dresser Flow Control
1257 Southern Minerals Rd (78409-1819)
PHONE..................................361 881-8182
John Thornberry, *Manager*
EMP: 32
SALES (corp-wide): 95.2B **Publicly Held**
WEB: www.dresserngs.com
SIC: 3491 3825 Industrial valves; instruments to measure electricity
HQ: Dresser, Llc
4425 Westway Park Blvd
Houston TX 77041
262 549-2626

(G-3518)
EL TEJANO HISPANIC COMMUNITY
2505 Sarita St (78405-1943)
PHONE..................................361 884-2238
Mersedes Sanchez, *Partner*
Angel Dela Paz, *Partner*
EMP: 14
SALES (est): 617K **Privately Held**
WEB: www.eltejanomagazine.com
SIC: 2711 7389 Newspapers, publishing & printing;

(G-3519)
EOG RESOURCES INC
539 N Carancahua St # 900 (78401-0999)
PHONE..................................361 866-4300
Mel Ryan, *Superintendent*
Jeremy Coleman, *Engineer*
Robert K Garrison, *Manager*
EMP: 80
SQ FT: 1,000
SALES (corp-wide): 17.3B **Publicly Held**
WEB: www.eogresources.com
SIC: 1382 1311 Oil & gas exploration services; crude petroleum production; natural gas production
PA: Eog Resources, Inc.
1111 Bagby Sky Lbby 2
Houston TX 77002
713 651-7000

(G-3520)
ESENJAY EXPLORATION INC (PA)
500 N Water St Ste 1100 (78401-0236)
PHONE..................................361 883-7464
David W Berry, *Ch of Bd*
Alex M Cranberg, *Vice Ch Bd*
Michael Johnson, *President*
David Christofferson, *Senior VP*

EMP: 25
SALES (est): 5.3MM **Privately Held**
WEB: www.tripointehomes.com
SIC: 1382 Oil & gas exploration services

(G-3521)
ESENJAY PETROLEUM CORPORATION
500 N Water St Ste 1100 (78401-0236)
PHONE..................................361 883-7464
Charles J Smith, *Ch of Bd*
Dale Alexander, *COO*
Howard Williams, *Vice Pres*
Samuel Cortez, *Opers Mgr*
Rolf Woods, *Exploration*
EMP: 17
SALES (est): 1.4MM **Privately Held**
SIC: 1311 Crude petroleum production; natural gas production

(G-3522)
EW SCRIPPS COMPANY
Also Called: Corpus Christi Caller Times
820 N Lower Broadway St (78401-2025)
P.O. Box 9136 (78469-9136)
PHONE..................................361 886-3652
EMP: 200
SALES (corp-wide): 715.6MM **Publicly Held**
SIC: 2711 Newspapers
PA: The E W Scripps Company
312 Walnut St Ste 2800
Cincinnati OH 45202
513 977-3000

(G-3523)
EXCALIBAR MINERALS LLC
4138 Joe Fulton Intl Tc (78402-1926)
PHONE..................................361 883-5227
Rodney Baxter, *Plant Supt*
Scott Richard, *Manager*
EMP: 15
SALES (corp-wide): 747.7MM **Publicly Held**
WEB: www.newpark.com
SIC: 1389 Oil field services
HQ: Excalibar Minerals Llc
21920 Merchants Way
Katy TX 77449

(G-3524)
EXPRESS DRILLING FLUIDS LLC
5412 Leopard St (78408-2509)
PHONE..................................361 289-1631
Ronnie King, *Principal*
Ronnie D King, *Principal*
EMP: 30
SALES (est): 585.7K **Privately Held**
SIC: 3546 Drills & drilling tools

(G-3525)
EXXENE CORPORATION
5939 Holly Rd (78412-4554)
P.O. Box 81203 (78468-1203)
PHONE..................................361 991-8391
Lili Karsh, *CEO*
Edward A Bernheim, *President*
Bea Olivarez, *Personnel*
EMP: 50
SQ FT: 55,000
SALES (est): 7.9MM **Privately Held**
WEB: www.exxene.com
SIC: 3544 Special dies & tools

(G-3526)
FEDEX OFFICE & PRINT SVCS INC
3850 S Padre Island Dr (78415-2921)
PHONE..................................361 806-2220
EMP: 25
SALES (corp-wide): 69.2B **Publicly Held**
WEB: www.fedex.com
SIC: 7334 2759 Photocopying & duplicating services; commercial printing
HQ: Fedex Office And Print Services, Inc.
7900 Legacy Dr
Plano TX 75024
800 463-3339

(G-3527)
FESCO LTD
627 Omaha Dr (78408-2952)
PHONE..................................361 882-4124
Randy Winters, *Manager*

EMP: 30
SALES (corp-wide): 201MM **Privately Held**
WEB: www.fescoinc.com
SIC: 1389 Oil field services
PA: Fesco, Ltd.
1000 Fesco Dr
Alice TX 78332
361 664-3479

(G-3528)
FLEETPRIDE INC
Fleetpride/Fleetcare
424 S Port Ave (78405-2238)
P.O. Box 9156 (78469-9156)
PHONE..................................361 883-4358
Lee Stockseth, *Vice Pres*
EMP: 15 **Privately Held**
WEB: www.fleetpride.com
SIC: 5013 3537 Truck parts & accessories; forklift trucks
HQ: Fleetpride, Inc.
600 Las Colinas Blvd E # 400
Irving TX 75039
469 249-7500

(G-3529)
FLINT HILLS RESOURCES LP
1700 Nueces Bay Blvd (78407-2540)
P.O. Box 2608 (78403-2608)
PHONE..................................361 889-7282
Spencer Beard, *Project Mgr*
Renee Gardner, *Project Mgr*
Larry Webb, *Safety Mgr*
Charles Walker, *Engineer*
Janie Garcia, *Electrical Engi*
EMP: 250
SALES (corp-wide): 36.8B **Privately Held**
WEB: www.fhr.com
SIC: 2911 Oils, fuel
HQ: Flint Hills Resources, Lp
4111 E 37th St N
Wichita KS 67220
800 292-3133

(G-3530)
FLINT HILLS RESOURCES LP
2825 Suntide Rd (78409-2100)
PHONE..................................361 241-4811
Rick Crossland, *COO*
Rick Rod, *Project Mgr*
Bob Shenkle, *Opers Mgr*
Oswaldo Medellin, *Engineer*
Chris Saldana, *Project Engr*
EMP: 26
SALES (corp-wide): 36.8B **Privately Held**
WEB: www.fhr.com
SIC: 2911 Petroleum refining
HQ: Flint Hills Resources, Lp
4111 E 37th St N
Wichita KS 67220
800 292-3133

(G-3531)
FLINT HILLS RESOURCES LP
8606 Ih 37 (78409-3114)
P.O. Box 2625 (78403-2625)
PHONE..................................361 241-4811
Jim Simmons, *General Mgr*
EMP: 120
SALES (corp-wide): 36.8B **Privately Held**
WEB: www.fhr.com
SIC: 5172 4612 1382 2911 Gases, liquefied petroleum (propane); crude petroleum pipelines; oil & gas exploration services; petroleum refining
HQ: Flint Hills Resources, Lp
4111 E 37th St N
Wichita KS 67220
800 292-3133

(G-3532)
FLOWERS BAKERIES LLC
3717 Saratoga Blvd (78415-5812)
PHONE..................................361 814-0558
Maria Montez, *Manager*
EMP: 47
SALES (corp-wide): 4.1B **Publicly Held**
WEB: www.flowersfoods.com
SIC: 2051 Bakery: wholesale or wholesale/retail combined
HQ: Flowers Bakeries, Llc
1919 Flowers Cir
Thomasville GA 31757

(G-3533)
GATES E&S NORTH AMERICA INC (DH)
134 44th St Bldg 7 (78405-3302)
PHONE..................................361 887-9807
EMP: 56
SQ FT: 60,000
SALES (est): 10.5MM
SALES (corp-wide): 2.7B **Publicly Held**
SIC: 3052 Rubber hose
HQ: The Gates Corporation
1144 15th St Ste 1400
Denver CO 80202
303 744-1911

(G-3534)
GE OIL & GAS LOGGING SVCS INC
4910 Leopard St Ste 400 (78408-2640)
PHONE..................................361 299-9457
David Brinkman, *Manager*
EMP: 27
SALES (corp-wide): 95.2B **Publicly Held**
WEB: www.bhge.com
SIC: 1389 Oil field services
HQ: Ge Oil & Gas Logging Services, Inc.
13000 Executive Dr
Sugar Land TX 77478

(G-3535)
GJR MEYER SERVICE INC
Also Called: Meyer Service Company
6733 Leopard St (78409-1701)
PHONE..................................361 289-2130
Greg Meyer, *President*
Jeff Meyer, *Corp Secy*
Randy Meyer, *Vice Pres*
Allison Meyer, *Purch Mgr*
Noel McKim, *Engineer*
EMP: 20
SALES (est): 5.8MM **Privately Held**
WEB: www.meyernow.com
SIC: 3533 Oil & gas field machinery

(G-3536)
GK TECHSTAR LLC
5541 Bear Ln (78405-4129)
PHONE..................................361 289-6825
Jon Fotorny, *Branch Mgr*
EMP: 29
SALES (corp-wide): 29.8MM **Privately Held**
WEB: www.techstar.com
SIC: 3823 Water quality monitoring & control systems
PA: Gk Techstar, Llc
802 W 13th St
Deer Park TX 77536
281 884-8257

(G-3537)
GOODYEAR TIRE & RUBBER COMPANY
1134 S Navigation Blvd (78405-3804)
PHONE..................................361 289-8251
Ronnie Villarreal, *Branch Mgr*
EMP: 2018
SALES (corp-wide): 12.3B **Publicly Held**
WEB: www.goodyear.com
SIC: 5531 7534 7538 7539 Automotive tires; tire retreading & repair shops; rebuilding & retreading tires; general automotive repair shops; truck engine repair, except industrial; automotive repair shops; brake services; shock absorber replacement; tune-up service, automotive; motor vehicle supplies & new parts; automotive servicing equipment; automotive supplies & parts; inner tubes, all types
PA: The Goodyear Tire & Rubber Company
200 E Innovation Way
Akron OH 44316
330 796-2121

(G-3538)
GRUNWALD PRINTING COMPANY
1418 Morgan Ave (78404-3350)
P.O. Box 3219 (78463-3219)
PHONE..................................361 882-5654
John E Grunwald, *President*
Jennifer Alfano, *Comptroller*
Nora Tristan, *Sales Associate*
Gabriel Gonzalez, *Manager*
Sandra Simmons, *Manager*

GEOGRAPHIC

EMP: 300 **EST:** 1946
SQ FT: 42,000
SALES (est): 8.1MM **Privately Held**
WEB: www.gpprint.com
SIC: 2752 Commercial printing, offset

(G-3539)
GULF COAST REPAIR & MCH SP INC
Also Called: Gulf Coast Machine Shop
6802 Leopard St (78409-1704)
P.O. Box 260591 (78426-0591)
PHONE................................361 289-1273
Weldon Riebschleager, *President*
Bullet Riebschleager, *General Mgr*
Jorge Tovar, *General Mgr*
Justin Lamb, *Sales Executive*
Bobby Taylor, *Manager*
EMP: 22
SQ FT: 10,000
SALES (est): 4.5MM **Privately Held**
WEB: www.gulfcoastrepair.com
SIC: 3599 Machine shop, jobbing & repair

(G-3540)
GULF COPPER SHIP REPAIR INC
4385 Joe Fulton Intl Tc (78402-1928)
P.O. Box 23043 (78403-3043)
PHONE................................361 883-1040
Steven Hale, *President*
Steven Dockler, *General Mgr*
Carl Trent, *General Mgr*
Harold Austell, *Project Mgr*
Pat S Guillory, *CFO*
◆ **EMP:** 80
SQ FT: 10,500
SALES (est): 17.1MM
SALES (corp-wide): 65.3MM **Privately Held**
WEB: www.gulfcopper.com
SIC: 3444 3731 Sheet metalwork; dredges, building & repairing
PA: Gulf Copper & Manufacturing Corporation
5700 Procter Ext
Port Arthur TX 77642
409 989-0300

(G-3541)
GYRODATA INCORPORATED
1805 N Lexington Blvd (78409-1325)
PHONE................................361 289-1031
Rony Mayrang, *District Mgr*
EMP: 57
SALES (corp-wide): 394.1MM **Privately Held**
WEB: www.gyrodata.com
SIC: 1389 7353 Testing, measuring, surveying & analysis services; heavy construction equipment rental
PA: Gyrodata Incorporated
23000 Nw Lake Dr
Houston TX 77095
713 461-3146

(G-3542)
H & S FABRICATORS INC
1133 E Port Ave (78401-1047)
P.O. Box 9014 (78469-9014)
PHONE................................361 884-1212
Patrick Horn, *President*
EMP: 22
SALES (est): 3.6MM **Privately Held**
SIC: 3731 Shipbuilding & repairing

(G-3543)
HACIENDA REC RECORDING STUDIO
1236 S Staples St (78404-3241)
P.O. Box 331298 (78463-1298)
PHONE................................361 882-7066
Roland Garcia, *CEO*
Gilbert Garcia, *President*
Annie Garcia, *Corp Secy*
Rick Garcia, *Exec VP*
EMP: 10
SQ FT: 24,500
SALES (est): 798.5K **Privately Held**
WEB: www.hacienda-records.myshopify.com
SIC: 7389 3652 Recording studio, non-commercial records; phonograph record blanks

(G-3544)
HALLIBURTON COMPANY
Also Called: Halliburton Energy Services
555 N Carancahua St # 775 (78401-0899)
PHONE................................281 575-5000
Ed Peacock, *Manager*
Hailey Guillemette, *Technical Staff*
EMP: 26 **Publicly Held**
WEB: www.halliburton.com
SIC: 1389 1382 Well logging; oil & gas exploration services
PA: Halliburton Company
3000 N Sam Houston Pkwy E
Houston TX 77032

(G-3545)
HARBOR ENGINE & GRINDING INC
2845 Agnes St (78405-2296)
PHONE................................361 882-1571
W R Laurel Sr, *President*
Tiffany Peterson, *Office Mgr*
Laurel J G, *Director*
EMP: 10 **EST:** 1962
SQ FT: 6,700
SALES (est): 700K **Privately Held**
SIC: 3519 Internal combustion engines

(G-3546)
HEADINGTON OIL LIMITED 1993 LP
Also Called: Headington Energy Partners
500 N Shoreline Blvd # 902 (78401-0399)
PHONE................................361 885-0110
William Johnston, *Manager*
Bill Johnston, *Manager*
EMP: 14
SALES (corp-wide): 35.3MM **Privately Held**
WEB: www.headingtonenergy.com
SIC: 1382 Oil & gas exploration services
PA: Headington Oil Limited 1993, L.P.
2711 N Haskell Ave # 2800
Dallas TX 75204
214 696-0606

(G-3547)
HESCO GATHERING COMPANY L L C
500 N Shoreline Blvd (78401-0399)
PHONE................................361 883-8398
Gary Hollowell,
Steve Loy,
Steve Mauch,
Dustin Roach,
EMP: 18
SQ FT: 3,000
SALES (est): 1.4MM **Privately Held**
WEB: www.gulfcoastgasgathering.com
SIC: 1311 Natural gas production

(G-3548)
HIGHWAY BARRICADES & SVCS LLC (PA)
Also Called: Corpus Christi Readymix
7775 Leopard St (78409-2020)
P.O. Box 9104 (78469-9104)
PHONE................................361 883-6300
Mitra M Khan, *President*
Mark Penuelaz, *Purchasing*
EMP: 85 **EST:** 2007
SQ FT: 5,902
SALES (est): 14.4MM **Privately Held**
WEB: www.hbstexas.com
SIC: 1611 3499 Highway & street paving contractor; barricades, metal

(G-3549)
HOFFMAN COMPANY
1306 Laredo St (78401-3249)
P.O. Box 893 (78403-0893)
PHONE................................361 882-9281
Bryan Hoffman, *President*
J Bryan Hoffman, *President*
A S Hoffman, *Corp Secy*
Ed Ybanez, *Vice Pres*
Michael Maitland, *Client Mgr*
EMP: 38 **EST:** 1950
SQ FT: 21,000
SALES (est): 7.2MM **Privately Held**
WEB: www.thehoffmancompany.com
SIC: 3089 Plastic processing

(G-3550)
HOLLON SAFE COMPANY LLC
227 44th St (78405-3303)
PHONE................................888 455-2337
Zack Gilmore, *President*
Margo Jones, *General Mgr*
Danny Burns, *Natl Sales Mgr*
Daniel Coleman, *Sales Staff*
▲ **EMP:** 10
SALES (est): 1.6MM **Privately Held**
WEB: www.hollonsafe.com
SIC: 3499 5044 Safe deposit boxes or chests, metal; safes & vaults, metal; vaults & safes

(G-3551)
HONEYWELL INTERNATIONAL INC
308 Crecy St (78419-5211)
PHONE................................361 937-1082
EMP: 679
SALES (corp-wide): 36.7B **Publicly Held**
WEB: www.honeywell.com
SIC: 3724 Aircraft engines & engine parts
PA: Honeywell International Inc.
300 S Tryon St
Charlotte NC 28202
704 627-6200

(G-3552)
ICONIC SIGN GROUP LLC
5819 Leopard St (78408-2326)
P.O. Box 271483 (78427-1483)
PHONE................................361 883-7446
Ray Hernandez, *VP Business*
David De La Fuente, *Mng Member*
EMP: 19
SALES (est): 1.4MM **Privately Held**
WEB: www.iconicsg.com
SIC: 3993 1799 Signs & advertising specialties; sign installation & maintenance

(G-3553)
INGRAM READYMIX INC
5635 Holly Rd (78412-4550)
PHONE................................361 533-2225
Bruce Ingram, *President*
EMP: 20
SALES (corp-wide): 125.6MM **Privately Held**
WEB: www.ingramreadymixinc.com
SIC: 3273 Ready-mixed concrete
PA: Ingram Readymix, Inc.
3580 Farm Market 482
New Braunfels TX 78132
830 625-9156

(G-3554)
INGRAM READYMIX INC
101 Omaha Dr (78408-2736)
P.O. Box 81383 (78468-1383)
PHONE................................361 888-9281
Fax: 361 888-9283
EMP: 55
SALES (corp-wide): 87MM **Privately Held**
SIC: 3273 Mfg Ready-Mixed Concrete
PA: Ingram Readymix, Inc.
3580 Farm Market 482
New Braunfels TX 78132
830 625-9156

(G-3555)
INTERNTONAL RESISTIVE TEXAS LP
Also Called: Advanced Film Division
4222 S Staples St (78411-2702)
PHONE................................361 992-7900
Christine Amaro, *Executive*
▼ **EMP:** 244
SQ FT: 100,000
SALES (est): 29.5MM
SALES (corp-wide): 617.6MM **Publicly Held**
WEB: www.ttelectronics.com
SIC: 3676 3674 5065 Electronic resistors; semiconductors & related devices; electronic parts & equipment
HQ: International Resistive Company, Inc.
4222 S Staples St
Corpus Christi TX 78411
361 992-7900

(G-3556)
INTERTEK USA INC
Also Called: Intertek Caleb Brett
4702 Westway Dr (78408-2726)
P.O. Box 4685 (78469-4685)
PHONE................................361 289-7474
Brad Hicks, *Branch Mgr*
EMP: 25
SALES (corp-wide): 3.8B **Privately Held**
WEB: www.intertek.com
SIC: 2911 Liquefied petroleum gases, LPG
HQ: Intertek Usa Inc.
200 Westlake Park Blvd # 400
Houston TX 77079
713 543-3600

(G-3557)
IRON RAM SERVICES LLC
8263 Leopard St (78409-2232)
PHONE................................361 241-2346
Ramiro Rodriguez, *Mng Member*
EMP: 13
SALES (est): 2.3MM **Privately Held**
WEB: www.ironramservices.com
SIC: 3715 3443 Truck trailers; industrial vessels, tanks & containers

(G-3558)
JOHN BLUDWORTH SHIPYARD LLC
3909 Joe Fulton Intl Tc (78402-1924)
P.O. Box 2441 (78403-2441)
PHONE................................361 887-7981
Gasper D'Anna, *President*
Matthew Kearns, *Vice Pres*
Ronald L Janota, *Executive*
John L Bludworth III,
▲ **EMP:** 65 **EST:** 1980
SQ FT: 10,000
SALES (est): 15MM **Privately Held**
WEB: www.jbludshipyard.com
SIC: 3731 Tugboats, building & repairing; barges, building & repairing; cargo vessels, building & repairing

(G-3559)
JV INDUSTRIAL COMPANIES LTD
1920 N Port Ave (78401-1204)
PHONE................................361 884-4022
John Durham, *CEO*
Pete Latka, *Supervisor*
EMP: 60 **Privately Held**
WEB: www.jvic.com
SIC: 3599 Machine shop, jobbing & repair
HQ: J.V. Industrial Companies, Ltd.
527 Logwood Ave
San Antonio TX 78221
713 568-2600

(G-3560)
KENNEDY WIRE ROPE & SLING CO (PA)
302 Flato Rd (78405-4205)
P.O. Box 4016 (78469-4016)
PHONE................................361 289-1444
Jacqueline Kennedy, *CEO*
Garland M Kennedy Jr, *President*
Aaron Bohnert, *COO*
Garland Kennedy, *Vice Pres*
Jonathan Cloutet, *Treasurer*
▲ **EMP:** 90
SQ FT: 90,000
SALES (est): 48MM **Privately Held**
WEB: www.kwrs.com
SIC: 3496 Miscellaneous fabricated wire products

(G-3561)
KONECRANES INC
1959 Saratoga Blvd Bldg 5 (78417-3417)
PHONE................................361 289-9400
Holly Emery, *Manager*
EMP: 9
SALES (corp-wide): 3.6B **Privately Held**
WEB: www.konecranes.com
SIC: 3536 Industrial machinery & equipment repair
HQ: Konecranes, Inc.
4401 Gateway Blvd
Springfield OH 45502

(G-3562)
LAREDO COCA-COLA BOTTLING CO
5126 Greenwood Dr (78417-2011)
PHONE.............................361 693-4200
Robert Wardlay, *Manager*
Lorenzo Cardona, *Manager*
Bernard P Cantu, *Supervisor*
EMP: 17
SALES (corp-wide): 309.5MM **Privately Held**
WEB: www.coca-colacompany.com
SIC: 2086 Bottled & canned soft drinks
HQ: The Laredo Coca-Cola Bottling Company
    1402 Industrial Blvd
    Laredo TX 78041
    956 726-2671

(G-3563)
LEADER GASKET TECHNOLOGIES INC
International Gasket and Sup
5819 Leopard St (78408-2326)
PHONE.............................361 289-1614
Hector Sanchez, *Manager*
Bastiaan Calis, *Director*
EMP: 12 **Privately Held**
WEB: www.leadergt.com
SIC: 3053 Gaskets, packing & sealing devices
HQ: Leader Gasket Technologies, Inc.
    850 Sens Rd
    La Porte TX 77571
    281 542-0600

(G-3564)
LORELEI BREWING COMPANY LLC
520 Nas Dr (78418-3254)
PHONE.............................361 445-1084
Varian Criser, *Mng Member*
Laura Criser,
EMP: 9 EST: 2015
SALES (est): 650K **Privately Held**
WEB: www.lazybeachbrewing.com
SIC: 2082 Malt beverages

(G-3565)
LYONDELL CHEMICAL COMPANY
1501 Mckinzie Rd (78410-9706)
P.O. Box 10940 (78460-0940)
PHONE.............................361 242-8000
Curtis Strezinek, *Purchasing*
Bryan Barrington, *Engineer*
Randy Tatum, *Manager*
EMP: 79
SALES (corp-wide): 34.9B **Privately Held**
WEB: www.lyondellbasell.com
SIC: 2869 2822 Olefins; ethylene; polyethylene, chlorosulfonated (hypalon)
HQ: Lyondell Chemical Company
    1221 Mckinney St Ste 300
    Houston TX 77010
    713 309-7200

(G-3566)
M & G RESINS USA LLC
Also Called: M&G Chemicals
7001 Joe Fulton (78402-1902)
PHONE.............................304 576-2041
EMP: 13
SALES (corp-wide): 22.5MM **Privately Held**
WEB: www.mgcorpuschristi.com
SIC: 3089 Air mattresses, plastic
HQ: M & G Resins Usa, Llc
    450 Gears Rd Ste 240
    Houston TX 77067
    281 873-5780

(G-3567)
M-I LLC
Also Called: Swaco
1102 Heinsohn Rd (78406-1904)
PHONE.............................361 886-3400
Jamie Huval, *Branch Mgr*
EMP: 31 **Publicly Held**
WEB: www.products.slb.com
SIC: 1389 Oil field services
HQ: M-I L.L.C.
    5950 N Course Dr
    Houston TX 77072
    281 561-1300

(G-3568)
MAGNUM ENGINEERING COMPANY
Also Called: Magnum Producing & Operating
500 N Shoreline Blvd # 32 (78401-0399)
PHONE.............................361 882-3858
Avinash C Ahuja, *President*
P L Ahuja, *Vice Pres*
Ahuja Peggy B, *Vice Pres*
EMP: 9
SQ FT: 2,100
SALES (est): 1.3MM **Privately Held**
WEB: www.magnumproducing.com
SIC: 1311 Crude petroleum production; natural gas production

(G-3569)
MAGNUM PRODUCING LP (PA)
500 N Shoreline Blvd # 322 (78401-0399)
PHONE.............................361 882-3858
Avinash C Ahuja, *Partner*
Peggy B Ahuja, *Partner*
EMP: 11
SQ FT: 2,750
SALES (est): 5.7MM **Privately Held**
WEB: www.magnumproducing.com
SIC: 1311 1389 Crude petroleum production; servicing oil & gas wells

(G-3570)
MAINTECH INTERNATIONAL LLC
299 Gilliam St (78409-3301)
PHONE.............................361 265-9901
Robert M Gough, *President*
Richard Lane, *Vice Pres*
◆ EMP: 40 EST: 1981
SQ FT: 50,000
SALES (est): 6.6MM **Privately Held**
SIC: 3599 Machine shop, jobbing & repair

(G-3571)
MAINTENANCE TOOL & SUPPLY CO (PA)
Also Called: MTS Threaded Products Company
1902 Mestina St (78408-3944)
P.O. Box 4748 (78469-4748)
PHONE.............................361 888-8801
Mack Rodriguez, *President*
Tony Rodriguez, *Vice Pres*
Rudy Perez, *Sales Mgr*
EMP: 15
SALES (est): 3.2MM **Privately Held**
WEB: www.mtsthreadedproducts.com
SIC: 3452 3545 Nuts, metal; bolts, metal; machine tool accessories

(G-3572)
MANTI OPERATING COMPANY
800 N Shoreline Blvd 900s (78401-3700)
P.O. Box 2907 (78403-2907)
PHONE.............................361 888-7708
Lee D Barberito, *President*
Rober Hill, *CFO*
EMP: 28
SALES (est): 4MM **Privately Held**
WEB: www.sabaloenergy.com
SIC: 1382 Oil & gas exploration services

(G-3573)
MARKWEST JAVELINA COMPANY LLC
5438 Union St (78407-1410)
PHONE.............................361 289-4900
Frank M Semple, *CEO*
EMP: 54
SALES (corp-wide): 9B **Publicly Held**
WEB: www.markwest.com
SIC: 1389 Processing service, gas
HQ: Markwest Javelina Company, L.L.C.
    1515 Arapahoe St 1
    Denver CO 80202
    303 925-9200

(G-3574)
MARROQUIN TORTILLA FACTORY
Also Called: Marroquin's Tortilla Factory
2737 Greenwood Dr (78405-2465)
PHONE.............................361 883-7051
Martha Marriqin, *Owner*
EMP: 13

SALES (est): 367.8K **Privately Held**
SIC: 5812 2099 Eating places; tortillas, fresh or refrigerated

(G-3575)
MATHESON TRI-GAS INC
4863 Baldwin Blvd (78408-2715)
PHONE.............................361 887-0011
Mike Power, *Sales Staff*
Jeff Bergman, *Branch Mgr*
EMP: 9 **Privately Held**
WEB: www.mathesongas.com
SIC: 2813 5084 Industrial gases; welding machinery & equipment
HQ: Matheson Tri-Gas, Inc.
    3 Mountainview Rd Ste 3 # 3
    Warren NJ 07059
    908 991-9200

(G-3576)
MC WELDING & FABRICATION INC
8337 Up River Rd Ste A (78409-3109)
PHONE.............................361 289-9605
Albert Carrales, *President*
Keith McLendon, *Vice Pres*
EMP: 14
SQ FT: 5,000
SALES (est): 2.2MM **Privately Held**
WEB: www.mcweldfab.com
SIC: 1799 3441 Welding on site; fabricated structural metal

(G-3577)
MESTENA URANIUM LLC
500 N Shoreline Blvd (78401-0399)
PHONE.............................361 884-2191
Benjamin Eshleman III,
EMP: 9
SALES (est): 641.9K **Privately Held**
WEB: www.uraniumenergy.com
SIC: 1094 Uranium ore mining
PA: Energy Fuels Inc.
    82 Richmond St E Suite 308
    Toronto ON M5C 1
    416 214-2810

(G-3578)
MOFFITT & ASSOC INC
615 Leopard St Ste 707 (78401-7801)
P.O. Box 2786 (78403-2786)
PHONE.............................361 884-9273
William Moffitt, *President*
Megan Welch, *Manager*
EMP: 25 EST: 1990
SALES (est): 1.9MM **Privately Held**
WEB: www.moffittandassociates.com
SIC: 1389 Oil & gas wells: building, repairing & dismantling

(G-3579)
MORENOS AUTO GLASS INC
Also Called: MO Glass
2617 Holly Rd (78415-4111)
P.O. Box 7632 (78467-7632)
PHONE.............................361 855-1471
Charles Patrick, *President*
EMP: 16 EST: 1977
SALES (est): 2.6MM **Privately Held**
SIC: 5231 7536 1793 1542 Glass; automotive glass replacement shops; glass & glazing work; store front construction; mirrored glass

(G-3580)
MTLV PROPERTIES LLC
15338 Dasmarinas Dr (78418-6314)
P.O. Box 273, Tilden (78072-0273)
PHONE.............................361 946-6145
Mark Ramert, *President*
Johnny Oneal, *Vice Pres*
Thomas Criser, *CFO*
EMP: 22 EST: 2012
SQ FT: 1,200
SALES (est): 846.2K **Privately Held**
SIC: 1389 Oil field services

(G-3581)
NUECES VALVE SOLUTIONS LLC
730 Diamond Cut Dr Ste A (78409-1619)
P.O. Box 4893 (78469-4893)
PHONE.............................361 248-1700
Derek Bingham, *Manager*
EMP: 10

SALES (est): 460K **Privately Held**
SIC: 3592 Valves

(G-3582)
OCCIDENTAL CHEMICAL CORP
1501 Mckinzie Rd (78410-9706)
P.O. Box 10940 (78460-0940)
PHONE.............................361 242-8000
James R Gibson, *Plant Mgr*
EMP: 18
SALES (corp-wide): 21.2B **Publicly Held**
WEB: www.oxy.com
SIC: 2874 Phosphatic fertilizers
HQ: Occidental Chemical Corporation
    14555 Dallas Pkwy Ste 400
    Dallas TX 75254
    972 404-3800

(G-3583)
OGINFOCOM LLC
3802 Saturn Rd (78413-1917)
P.O. Box 271120 (78427-1120)
PHONE.............................361 904-0071
James H Davis, *General Mgr*
Shawn Rancatore, *Vice Pres*
Nicole Trevino, *Webmaster*
Amruta Karnik, *Software Dev*
Sonia Rodriguez, *Officer*
EMP: 20
SQ FT: 5,500
SALES (est): 2.2MM **Privately Held**
WEB: www.oginfo.com
SIC: 1382 Geological exploration, oil & gas field

(G-3584)
OHMSTEDE LTD
410 Flato Rd (78405-4301)
P.O. Box 5607 (78465-5607)
PHONE.............................361 289-1701
Will Ohmstede, *General Mgr*
Charles Varney, *QC Mgr*
Gene Haisler, *Engineer*
Kevin Dielman, *Design Engr*
John Odle, *Manager*
EMP: 80
SALES (corp-wide): 9.1B **Publicly Held**
WEB: www.ohmstede.com
SIC: 3443 7699 Heat exchangers, plate type; heat exchangers: coolers (after, inter), condensers, etc.; industrial equipment services
HQ: Ohmstede Ltd.
    895 N Main St
    Beaumont TX 77701
    409 833-6375

(G-3585)
ONETA COMPANY (PA)
Also Called: Pepsi-Cola
1401 S Padre Island Dr (78416-1322)
PHONE.............................361 853-0123
Julia Kriegel, *CEO*
Karl Koch, *CEO*
Kimberly Koch, *President*
Stephanie Koch, *Vice Pres*
Ana Duda, *Sales Executive*
EMP: 160 EST: 1977
SQ FT: 90,000
SALES (est): 68.7MM **Privately Held**
WEB: www.onetacc.com
SIC: 2086 Carbonated soft drinks, bottled & canned

(G-3586)
OVERHEAD DOOR CORPORATION
Also Called: Horton Automatics
4242 Baldwin Blvd (78405-3325)
PHONE.............................361 884-6640
Peter Finnegan, *General Mgr*
Dave Tanger, *Vice Pres*
Tim Cassidy, *Project Mgr*
Zac Parker, *Project Mgr*
Lynnet Ritter, *Buyer*
EMP: 275
SQ FT: 15,149 **Privately Held**
WEB: www.overheaddoor.com
SIC: 3442 2431 3699 3625 Garage doors, overhead: metal; doors, wood; electrical equipment & supplies; relays & industrial controls; valves & pipe fittings; products of purchased glass

HQ: Overhead Door Corporation
2501 S State Hwy 121 Ste
Lewisville TX 75067
469 549-7100

(G-3587)
P & K SERVICES LLC
5741 Leopard St Ste A (78408-2367)
PHONE..................................361 299-1800
Kenneth W Yarbrough Jr,
Paul Galvan,
EMP: 40
SALES (est): 8.9MM Privately Held
WEB: www.pnkservices.com
SIC: 3441 Fabricated structural metal

(G-3588)
P-AMERICAS LLC
Also Called: Pepsico
1401 S Padre Island Dr (78416-1322)
PHONE..................................361 853-0123
Terry Brandon, Manager
EMP: 38
SALES (corp-wide): 67.1B Publicly Held
SIC: 2086 Carbonated soft drinks, bottled
& canned
HQ: P-Americas Llc
1 Pepsi Way
Somers NY 10589
336 896-5740

(G-3589)
PAUL KRIVOY
Also Called: Precision Parts Center
2106 Cord 20b (78415)
PHONE..................................361 854-7911
Gary White, Branch Mgr
EMP: 21
SALES (corp-wide): 2.8MM Privately
Held
SIC: 3479 Coating of metals & formed
products
PA: Paul Krivoy
2106 County Road 20b
Corpus Christi TX 78415
361 854-7911

(G-3590)
**PEPSI-COLA BTLG CRPUS
CHRSTI V**
1401 S Padre Island Dr (78416-1397)
PHONE..................................361 853-0123
Kim Koch, President
Terry Brandon, Vice Pres
Julia Koch, Treasurer
Julia Kriegel, Treasurer
EMP: 40
SQ FT: 5,000
SALES (est): 1.4MM Privately Held
WEB: www.pepsicolacorpuschristi.com
SIC: 5962 2086 Cold drinks vending ma-
chines; water, pasteurized: packaged in
cans, bottles, etc.

(G-3591)
**PIONEER DRILLING SERVICES
LTD**
334 Flato Rd (78405-4205)
P.O. Box 2963 (78403-2963)
PHONE..................................361 289-9241
Buddy Shamblin, Branch Mgr
EMP: 210
SALES (corp-wide): 575.7MM Privately
Held
WEB: www.pioneeres.com
SIC: 1311 1381 Crude petroleum produc-
tion; drilling oil & gas wells
HQ: Pioneer Drilling Services, Ltd.
1250 Ne Loop 410 Ste 1000
San Antonio TX 78209
210 828-7689

(G-3592)
PIPE PROS LLC (PA)
1729 N Clarkwood Rd # 10 (78409-2411)
PHONE..................................361 289-9090
Gary Edwards, President
Mando Valdez, Vice Pres
EMP: 41
SQ FT: 9,000
SALES (est): 100.6MM Privately Held
WEB: www.pipe-pros.com
SIC: 1389 Oil & gas wells: building, repair-
ing & dismantling

(G-3593)
POLK PRODUCTION TECH INC
Also Called: Phoenix Production Tech
4910 Leopard St Ste 500 (78408-2658)
P.O. Box 260778 (78426-0778)
PHONE..................................361 815-1245
Kenneth Polk, President
EMP: 10 EST: 2011
SALES (est): 2MM Privately Held
SIC: 1382 Oil & gas exploration services

(G-3594)
POWER REPAIR SERVICE INC
314 Mcbride Ln (78408-2340)
PHONE..................................361 289-1471
James W Power II, President
Herbert O Power, Treasurer
Nicholas Power, Manager
Denise Williams, Executive
Dudley C Power, Admin Sec
EMP: 78
SQ FT: 25,200
SALES (est): 14.4MM Privately Held
WEB: www.powerrepair.net
SIC: 3599 4226 Machine shop, jobbing &
repair; special warehousing & storage

(G-3595)
PPG INDUSTRIES INC
Also Called: PPG 8334
6764 Weber Rd (78413-2047)
PHONE..................................361 225-2250
Randy Kyle, Branch Mgr
EMP: 24
SALES (corp-wide): 15.3B Publicly Held
WEB: www.ppg.com
SIC: 2851 Paints & allied products
PA: Ppg Industries, Inc.
1 Ppg Pl
Pittsburgh PA 15272
412 434-3131

(G-3596)
PREMIER BOARD INC
138 45th St (78405)
P.O. Box 9697 (78469-9697)
PHONE..................................361 883-6553
Regis Barber, Principal
Barbara Price, Vice Pres
Joseph Cortez, Admin Sec
EMP: 10
SALES: 14.9K
SALES (corp-wide): 50.8MM Privately
Held
SIC: 2381 Fabric dress & work gloves
PA: South Texas Lighthouse For The Blind
4421 Agnes St
Corpus Christi TX 78405
361 883-6553

(G-3597)
**PROCESS ENGINEERED EQP
CO**
Also Called: Peeco
438 Mcbride Ln (78408-2342)
P.O. Box 9549 (78469-9549)
PHONE..................................361 289-8891
Larry B Green, President
Mark Snyder, Vice Pres
Kelli Koehl, Office Mgr
Sue Green, Admin Sec
Kelli L Koehl, Admin Sec
EMP: 15
SQ FT: 5,000
SALES (est): 2.6MM Privately Held
WEB: www.peeco.com
SIC: 3589 5084 Water treatment equip-
ment, industrial; pumps & pumping equip-
ment

(G-3598)
**PROTECTIVE POWDER
COATINGS LLC**
502 Mccampbell Rd (78408-2410)
PHONE..................................361 854-7911
EMP: 12
SALES (est): 1.4MM Privately Held
WEB: www.protectivepowder.com
SIC: 3479 Coating of metals & formed
products

(G-3599)
**PUFFER-SWEIVEN HOLDINGS
INC**
621 Navigation Blvd (78408-2699)
PHONE..................................361 883-6215
Lynda Almendarez, Hum Res Coord
Ryan Baker, Accounts Mgr
Douglas Brubaker, Accounts Mgr
Ben Burnett, Accounts Mgr
Robert Haertig, Accounts Mgr
EMP: 16
SALES (corp-wide): 300.7MM Privately
Held
WEB: www.puffer.com
SIC: 1389 Oil field services
PA: Puffer-Sweiven Holdings, Inc.
4230 Greenbriar Dr
Stafford TX 77477
281 240-2000

(G-3600)
PUGH ACQUISITION COMPANY
Also Called: Billy Pugh Company
5878 Agnes St (78406-1938)
P.O. Box 802 (78403-0802)
PHONE..................................361 884-9351
Paul Liberato, President
Kipling Layton, Corp Secy
Frank Liberato, Vice Pres
EMP: 37 EST: 1950
SQ FT: 19,000
SALES (est): 6MM Privately Held
WEB: www.billypugh.com
SIC: 3069 Life rafts, rubber; baby pacifiers,
rubber

(G-3601)
PUT-IN-CUPS LLC
14510 Whitman Pond (78418-6292)
P.O. Box 181148 (78480-1148)
PHONE..................................800 506-7891
Randall Hunt, Mng Member
EMP: 13
SALES (est): 2.1MM Privately Held
WEB: www.putincups.com
SIC: 3089 Fences, gates & accessories:
plastic

(G-3602)
PWC INDUSTRIES INC
6650 Leopard St (78409-1611)
PHONE..................................361 289-0557
Tim Bowen, CEO
Robin Bowen, President
Cheryl Darden, Vice Pres
Gary Wells, Sales Mgr
EMP: 35 EST: 1980
SQ FT: 38,000
SALES (est): 8.2MM Privately Held
WEB: www.pwcindustries.com
SIC: 3441 Fabricated structural metal

(G-3603)
QUALITY READYMIX LTD LLP
333 Mcbride Ln (78408-2339)
PHONE..................................361 289-2515
Donnie Ham, Partner
Arturo Cuellar, Partner
Henry Lozano III, Partner
EMP: 17
SALES (est): 3.8MM Privately Held
WEB: www.qualityreadymixtx.com
SIC: 3273 Ready-mixed concrete

(G-3604)
R & R OILFIELD SERVICES INC
Also Called: R & R Contractors
7619 Up River Rd (78409-2809)
P.O. Box 10286 (78460-0286)
PHONE..................................361 289-5892
Richard C Custer Jr, President
Lonnie Finkhaus, Division Mgr
Don C Chapman, Vice Pres
Donald Murphey, Opers Mgr
Brenda Jurach, Office Mgr
EMP: 100
SQ FT: 5,000
SALES (est): 18.1MM Privately Held
WEB: www.pickettsystems.com
SIC: 3443 1389 3824 3823 Fabricated
plate work (boiler shop); oil field services;
fluid meters & counting devices; industrial
instrmnts msrmnt display/control process
variable; electrical equipment & supplies;
fabricated pipe & fittings

(G-3605)
RAM INTERNATIONAL INC
1848 Suntide Rd (78409-2108)
P.O. Box 4802 (78469-4802)
PHONE..................................361 688-1966
▲ EMP: 12 EST: 2007
SALES (est): 4.5MM Privately Held
WEB: www.ramoiltools.com
SIC: 3533 5082 Oil & gas field machinery;
oil field equipment

(G-3606)
RDHS INC
Also Called: Randolph Door & Hearth Shoppe
6767 Weber Rd (78413-2048)
P.O. Box 270635 (78427-0635)
PHONE..................................361 852-4094
Jack Randolph, President
EMP: 14
SQ FT: 21,000
SALES (est): 3.5MM Privately Held
SIC: 5211 2431 1799 5063 Garage
doors, sale & installation; doors & door
parts & trim, wood; prefabricated fireplace
installation; lighting fixtures, residential

(G-3607)
REDDY ICE CORPORATION
Also Called: Packaged Ice
5874 State Highway 44 Byp (78406-1908)
PHONE..................................361 289-0276
James Cox, Manager
EMP: 25 Privately Held
WEB: www.reddyice.com
SIC: 2097 Manufactured ice
HQ: Reddy Ice Corporation
5710 Lbj Fwy Ste 300
Dallas TX 75240
214 526-6740

(G-3608)
RENFROW & CO INC
1123 Agnes St (78401-3303)
P.O. Box 3519 (78463-3519)
PHONE..................................361 884-5541
William B Renfrow, President
Gladys Kieschnik, Vice Pres
Rustin Myers, Sales Staff
Lonnie Garcia, Technology
Cindy Jimenez, Representative
EMP: 30 EST: 1931
SQ FT: 12,000
SALES (est): 4.2MM Privately Held
WEB: www.renfrowprint.com
SIC: 2761 2759 Continuous forms, office
& business; letterpress printing

(G-3609)
REPCON INC (HQ)
7501 Up River Rd (78409-2807)
P.O. Box 9316 (78469-9316)
PHONE..................................361 289-6342
Robert E Parker, President
Brad Myers, Superintendent
James Yanik, Superintendent
Josh Causey, Vice Pres
Shane Green, Project Mgr
▲ EMP: 500
SQ FT: 10,000
SALES (est): 202.2MM
SALES (corp-wide): 9.1B Publicly Held
WEB: www.repcon.com
SIC: 1629 1389 Chemical plant & refinery
construction; oil field services
PA: Emcor Group, Inc.
301 Merritt 7 Fl 6
Norwalk CT 06851
203 849-7800

(G-3610)
**RISTER CRNKSHAFT SPCIALIST
LTD**
Also Called: Coastal Plating Company
5317 Leopard St (78408-2506)
PHONE..................................361 289-0588
Roy C Rister, President
Hattaway Frances, Vice Pres
Wright N Patricia, Admin Sec
▲ EMP: 32
SQ FT: 30,000
SALES (est): 7.1MM Privately Held
WEB: www.coastalplatinginc.com
SIC: 3471 Chromium plating of metals or
formed products

(G-3611)
ROYAL PRODUCTION COMPANY INC (HQ)
500 N Shoreline Blvd # 807 (78401-0399)
PHONE....................................361 888-4792
J Scott Smith, *President*
Bill Gregorcyk, *President*
Donald S Kersting, *Vice Pres*
Scott Smith, *Vice Pres*
Paul F Brown Jr, *Treasurer*
EMP: 15
SALES (est): 10.6MM
SALES (corp-wide): 13.7MM **Privately Held**
SIC: 1311 Crude petroleum production; natural gas production
PA: Royal Oil & Gas Corporation
1 Indian Springs Rd
Indiana PA 15701
724 463-0246

(G-3612)
RPC INC
820 Mcbride Ln (78408-2242)
PHONE....................................361 289-7088
Gabriel Rodriguez, *Manager*
EMP: 20
SALES (corp-wide): 1.7B **Publicly Held**
WEB: www.rpc.net
SIC: 7353 7699 5082 1389 Oil field equipment, rental or leasing; industrial equipment services; oil field equipment; oil field services
PA: Rpc, Inc.
2801 Buford Hwy Ne # 300
Brookhaven GA 30329
404 321-2140

(G-3613)
S Y G CORPORATION
105 Villa Dr (78408-2758)
P.O. Box 9275 (78469-9275)
PHONE....................................361 884-4927
Mike Yankee, *President*
EMP: 65
SALES (est): 4.3MM **Privately Held**
SIC: 3315 Steel wire & related products

(G-3614)
SABALO EXPLRTION OPERATING LLC (PA)
800 N Shoreline Blvd (78401-3700)
PHONE....................................361 888-7708
Barry Clark, *President*
Philip Bell, *Vice Pres*
Mike Dignam, *Vice Pres*
Tom Medary, *Vice Pres*
Wayne Psencik, *Vice Pres*
EMP: 23
SALES (est): 23.8MM **Privately Held**
WEB: www.sabaloenergy.com
SIC: 1382 Oil & gas exploration services

(G-3615)
SAT RADIO COMMUNICATIONS LTD
Also Called: Industrial Communications
730 Diamond Cut Dr Ste F (78409-1619)
PHONE....................................361 853-9943
Donna Graham, *Office Mgr*
Dottie King, *Manager*
Kevin Lopez, *Manager*
Jeff Poole, *Technology*
EMP: 12
SALES (corp-wide): 6.9MM **Privately Held**
WEB: www.indcom.net
SIC: 5731 7622 3663 Radios, two-way, citizens' band, weather, short-wave, etc.; radio repair & installation; radio broadcasting & communications equipment
PA: Sat Radio Communications, Ltd.
1019 E Euclid Ave
San Antonio TX 78212
210 226-3682

(G-3616)
SATCO SOUTH 1 LLC
Ste Tc 12b Bldg 1824 (78419)
PHONE....................................361 961-1181
Patrick Blackman, *Manager*
EMP: 13
SALES (est): 1,000K **Privately Held**
SIC: 3699 Flight simulators (training aids), electronic

(G-3617)
SCHNEIDER ELECTRIC USA INC
555 N Carancahua St # 230 (78401-0899)
PHONE....................................361 887-5055
Ron Pool, *Branch Mgr*
EMP: 136
SALES (corp-wide): 177.9K **Privately Held**
WEB: www.ccagp.com
SIC: 3613 Switchgear & switchboard apparatus
HQ: Schneider Electric Usa, Inc.
1 Boston Pl Ste 2700
Boston MA 02108
978 975-9600

(G-3618)
SEAPORT STEEL FAB INC
333 45th St (78405-3313)
PHONE....................................361 884-1670
Patricia Rikke, *President*
Al Rikke Sr, *Vice Pres*
Jason Rikke, *Admin Sec*
EMP: 12
SQ FT: 80,000
SALES (est): 1MM **Privately Held**
SIC: 3629 Condensers, fixed or variable

(G-3619)
SECCO INC
1411 Corn Pdts Rd Rear (78409)
P.O. Box 67 (78403-0067)
PHONE....................................361 289-1722
Jim West, *President*
Greg West, *Vice Pres*
Marvin West, *Treasurer*
Wanda J West, *Admin Sec*
EMP: 9
SQ FT: 8,000
SALES (est): 1.8MM **Privately Held**
SIC: 5169 1389 5084 Chemicals & allied products; oil field services; cleaning equipment, high pressure, sand or steam

(G-3620)
SECHRIST-HALL COMPANY (PA)
102 Omaha Dr (78408-2737)
P.O. Box 2347, Harlingen (78551-2347)
PHONE....................................361 884-5264
William McBride Jr, *President*
Henry M Sapp, *President*
Peggy Thomas, *COO*
Dudley Bluhm Sr, *Senior VP*
Carlos Coronado, *Senior VP*
EMP: 45 **EST:** 1959
SQ FT: 20,000
SALES (est): 9.3MM **Privately Held**
SIC: 1761 3444 Roofing contractor; sheet metalwork; sheet metalwork

(G-3621)
SERPA FABRICATION INC
1302 Mary St (78401-3257)
PHONE....................................361 883-2266
Rodney Serpa, *President*
Manuel Arispe, *Vice Pres*
EMP: 18
SQ FT: 20,000
SALES (est): 3.8MM **Privately Held**
WEB: www.serpafab.com
SIC: 3441 Fabricated structural metal

(G-3622)
SHELL MACHINE WORKS INC
5317 Agnes St (78405-3709)
P.O. Box 4788 (78469-4788)
PHONE....................................361 883-7073
David Shell, *President*
Robert Knippa, *General Mgr*
Neil Mathews, *General Mgr*
Justin Thomas, *Engineer*
Lonnie Shell, *Finance Mgr*
EMP: 23 **EST:** 1958
SQ FT: 7,750
SALES (est): 6.6MM **Privately Held**
WEB: www.shellmachineworks.com
SIC: 3533 3599 Oil field machinery & equipment; machine shop, jobbing & repair

(G-3623)
SOUTH TEXAS EYE CONS PLLC (PA)
Also Called: Eyecare Optical
5402 S Staples St Ste 100 (78411-4656)
PHONE....................................361 992-9400
John B Sohocki II, *Partner*
Dr Thomas R Dietze, *Partner*
Dr Angel Saenz, *Partner*
EMP: 21
SQ FT: 3,200
SALES (est): 3MM **Privately Held**
WEB: www.southtexaseye.com
SIC: 8011 8042 3851 Ophthalmologist; physicians' office, including specialists; offices & clinics of optometrists; ophthalmic goods

(G-3624)
SOUTH TEXAS MINING VENTURE LLP
500 N Shoreline Blvd # 800 (78401-0333)
PHONE....................................361 888-8235
Larry McGonagle, *Partner*
EMP: 20
SALES (est): 1.5MM **Publicly Held**
WEB: www.uraniumenergy.com
SIC: 1094 Uranium-radium-vanadium ores
PA: Uranium Energy Corp.
500 N Shoreline Blvd # 800
Corpus Christi TX 78401

(G-3625)
SOUTH TEXAS MOULDING INC
6525 Ayers St (78415-5720)
P.O. Box 271123 (78427-1123)
PHONE....................................361 857-7770
Albert Lichtenberger, *Principal*
EMP: 15
SALES (corp-wide): 11.1MM **Privately Held**
WEB: www.texaswoodsupply.com
SIC: 2431 5031 Moldings, wood: unfinished & prefinished; window frames, all materials
PA: South Texas Moulding, Inc.
940 W Expressway 83
Donna TX 78537
956 464-0560

(G-3626)
SOUTH TEXAS SPORTS ACADEMY
525 Belleview Dr (78412-3125)
PHONE....................................361 992-3364
John Hays, *Owner*
EMP: 13
SALES (est): 724K **Privately Held**
SIC: 3949 Sporting & athletic goods

(G-3627)
SOUTH TXAS LGHTHOUSE FOR BLIND (PA)
4421 Agnes St (78405-3321)
P.O. Box 9697 (78469-9697)
PHONE....................................361 883-6553
Nicky Ooi, *President*
Denise Perez, *Vice Pres*
David Wells, *Vice Pres*
Len Sralla, *CFO*
John Morgan, *Accounts Mgr*
▲ **EMP:** 125
SQ FT: 76,000
SALES: 50.8MM **Privately Held**
WEB: www.stlb.net
SIC: 8331 3999 2782 2542 Skill training center; candles; looseleaf binders & devices; mail racks & lock boxes, postal service: except wood; computer peripheral equipment

(G-3628)
STAINLESS STEEL PRODUCTS INC
502 Westchester Dr (78408-2928)
P.O. Box 4050 (78469-4050)
PHONE....................................361 884-1281
Jorge Alegria, *President*
Diana Alegria, *Vice Pres*
Daniel Alegria, *Treasurer*
Danny Alegria, *Supervisor*
Ricardo Alegria, *Admin Sec*
EMP: 9 **EST:** 1960
SQ FT: 9,000
SALES (est): 630K **Privately Held**
WEB: www.sspmetalworks.com
SIC: 3441 Fabricated structural metal

(G-3629)
STEWART STEVENSON PWR PDTS LLC
6530 Agnes St (78406-1900)
P.O. Box 4975 (78469-4975)
PHONE....................................361 299-6839
Darrell Wheeler,
EMP: 30
SALES (corp-wide): 2.8B **Publicly Held**
WEB: www.stewartandstevenson.com
SIC: 5084 3531 Engines & parts, diesel; road construction & maintenance machinery
HQ: Stewart & Stevenson Power Products, Llc
55 Waugh Dr Ste 800
Houston TX 77007

(G-3630)
STREAMLINE ENERGY SERVICES LLC
2610 Holly Rd (78415-4110)
PHONE....................................361 852-0907
John K Smith, *President*
Darrell Eaker, *Accounts Mgr*
EMP: 15
SALES (corp-wide): 1.9MM **Privately Held**
WEB: www.slenergyservices.com
SIC: 1794 1389 1611 Excavation & grading, building construction; oil & gas wells: building, repairing & dismantling; gravel or dirt road construction
PA: Streamline Energy Services, Llc
1220 Valley Rd Ste 25
Valley Forge PA 19482
610 415-1220

(G-3631)
STRIKE LLC
7619 Up River Rd (78409-2809)
PHONE....................................361 939-0800
Jerry Jentry, *Foreman/Supr*
Marcos Vargas, *Foreman/Supr*
Shannon Sorrells, *Sr Project Mgr*
Richard Custer, *Manager*
Kent Stpe, *Director*
EMP: 2060
SALES (corp-wide): 1.4B **Privately Held**
WEB: www.strikeusa.com
SIC: 3443 Fabricated plate work (boiler shop)
PA: Strike, Llc
1800 Hughes Landing Blvd # 500
The Woodlands TX 77380
713 389-2400

(G-3632)
STX BEEF COMPANY LLC
9001 Leopard St (78409-2502)
P.O. Box 9254 (78469-9254)
PHONE....................................361 241-5000
Terry Maul, *CEO*
Ryan Connelly, *Mng Member*
▼ **EMP:** 700
SQ FT: 175,000
SALES (est): 14.3MM
SALES (corp-wide): 36.3MM **Privately Held**
WEB: www.stxbeef.com
SIC: 2011 Meat packing plants
PA: Jdh Capital, Llc
3735 Beam Rd Unit B
Charlotte NC 28217
704 357-1220

(G-3633)
SUPERIOR WEIGHTING PDTS LLC
4030 Rincon Rd (78402-1801)
PHONE....................................361 880-7160
Tom Eisenman, *General Mgr*
EMP: 10
SALES (corp-wide): 959.2MM **Privately Held**
WEB: www.swproducts.com
SIC: 3541 Grinding, polishing, buffing, lapping & honing machines
HQ: Superior Weighting Products, Llc
11767 Katy Fwy Ste 230
Houston TX 77079
888 556-4533

(G-3634)
T L R GROUP (PA)
Also Called: Sun Splash
3149 Crestwater Dr (78415-2441)
PHONE..........................361 500-4136
Tim Ryan, *President*
Lynn Ryan, *Vice Pres*
EMP: 20
SQ FT: 2,500
SALES (est): 1.3MM **Privately Held**
SIC: 2844 Suntan lotions & oils

(G-3635)
TANDEM MARKETING SERVICES INC (PA)
Also Called: Pier 99
2822 N Shoreline Blvd (78402-1006)
PHONE..........................361 949-7703
John M Astin, *President*
EMP: 70
SALES (est): 1.9MM **Privately Held**
WEB: www.tandemmarketinggroup.com
SIC: 5812 2741 Eating places; miscellaneous publishing

(G-3636)
TEXAS AIR & WATER LLC
Also Called: Rainsoft Corpus Christi
3818 Wow Rd (78413-1952)
PHONE..........................361 814-3131
Joel Sanuelson, *President*
Melissa Garcia Sanuelson, *Principal*
EMP: 11
SALES (est): 2MM **Privately Held**
WEB: www.rainsoftofcorpuschristi.com
SIC: 3589 7371 Water treatment equipment, industrial; computer software development & applications

(G-3637)
TEXAS PIPE FABRICATORS INC
709 High Starr Dr (78408-2512)
P.O. Box 9162 (78469-9162)
PHONE..........................361 882-5541
Joe Fleck, *President*
Linda Fleck, *Treasurer*
EMP: 50
SQ FT: 15,000
SALES (est): 3MM **Privately Held**
WEB: www.txpipefab.com
SIC: 3443 1761 Pipe, standpipe & culverts; process vessels, industrial: metal plate; sheet metalwork

(G-3638)
TEXAS PUBLISHING CO
Also Called: Grader Corpus Christi Tele
4455 S Padre Island Dr. 21-O (78411-5151)
PHONE..........................361 991-1306
Dan Albey, *CEO*
Bob Jones, *Principal*
EMP: 20
SALES (est): 1MM **Privately Held**
WEB: www.101corpuschristi.com
SIC: 2741 Telephone & other directory publishing

(G-3639)
THIRD COAST RX INC
Also Called: Carter's Pharmacy
3845 S Padre Island Dr (78415-2919)
PHONE..........................361 749-6337
EMP: 10
SALES (est): 1.8MM **Privately Held**
SIC: 2834 Mfg Pharmaceutical Preparations

(G-3640)
THRIFTY NCKEL WANT ADS CRPUS C
1308 Airline Rd (78412-3910)
PHONE..........................361 980-0008
Galen Niles, *President*
Judy Carson, *Vice Pres*
EMP: 19 EST: 1996
SALES (est): 250.8K **Privately Held**
WEB: www.tylerthriftynickel.com
SIC: 2711 Newspapers: publishing only, not printed on site

(G-3641)
THRU TUBING SOLUTIONS INC
6769 Ih 37 Access Rd (78409)
PHONE..........................361 883-4600
Cody Trebing, *Regl Sales Mgr*

James McCornick, *Branch Mgr*
EMP: 11
SALES (corp-wide): 1.7B **Publicly Held**
WEB: www.thrutubing.com
SIC: 1389 Oil field services
HQ: Thru Tubing Solutions, Inc.
11515 S Portland Ave
Oklahoma City OK 73170
405 692-1900

(G-3642)
TOR MINERALS INTERNATIONAL INC (PA)
722 Burleson St (78402-1344)
PHONE..........................361 883-5591
Douglas M Hartman, *Ch of Bd*
Olaf Karasch, *President*
Mark J Schomp, *Exec VP*
Mark Schomp, *Exec VP*
Ted Gonzalez, *Maint Spvr*
▲ EMP: 82
SALES: 38.9MM **Publicly Held**
WEB: www.torminerals.com
SIC: 2816 2819 Titanium dioxide, anatase or rutile (pigments); industrial inorganic chemicals; barium compounds

(G-3643)
TRIUMPH INC
445 44th St (78405-3307)
PHONE..........................361 946-4658
Paul Sale, *President*
EMP: 10
SALES (est): 516.5K **Privately Held**
WEB: www.triumphdownhole.com
SIC: 1389 Gas field services

(G-3644)
TSGC INC
Also Called: Industrial Fbrctors Crpus Chrs
300 Mcbride Ln (78408-2339)
P.O. Box 5446 (78465-5446)
PHONE..........................361 289-0901
Gus Cargile III, *President*
Tom Painschab, *Superintendent*
Cody Cargile, *Vice Pres*
Eddie Mireles, *Purchasing*
Wayne Melton, *Sales Staff*
▲ EMP: 116
SQ FT: 185,000
SALES (est): 31.5MM **Privately Held**
WEB: www.indfabcc.com
SIC: 3441 3499 Fabricated structural metal; metal ladders

(G-3645)
U S WEATHERFORD L P
Also Called: Weatherford Enterra
6002 Hopkins Rd (78409-1200)
P.O. Box 9607 (78469-9607)
PHONE..........................361 289-1551
William Keenan, *Manager*
EMP: 21 **Privately Held**
WEB: www.weatherford.com
SIC: 1389 Oil field services
HQ: U S Weatherford L P
179 Weatherford Dr
Schriever LA 70395
985 493-6100

(G-3646)
U S WEATHERFORD L P
5821 Agnes St (78406-1922)
P.O. Box 9756 (78469-9756)
PHONE..........................361 289-5111
Bob Chederquist, *Opers Staff*
Rene Fernandez, *Opers Staff*
Lupe Iglesias, *Branch Mgr*
EMP: 100 **Privately Held**
WEB: www.weatherford.com
SIC: 1389 Oil field services
HQ: U S Weatherford L P
179 Weatherford Dr
Schriever LA 70395
985 493-6100

(G-3647)
UNIVERSAL WLLHEAD SVCS HLDNGS
5729 Leopard St Bldg 9 (78408-2363)
PHONE..........................361 299-1100
Neil Havard, *District Mgr*
Michael Mino, *CFO*
John Madeiro, *Sales Staff*
Alvin H Dueitt, *Mng Member*
J Richard Espinosa,

EMP: 18
SALES (est): 2.4MM **Privately Held**
WEB: www.universalwellhead.com
SIC: 1389 Oil field services

(G-3648)
URANIUM ENERGY CORP (PA)
500 N Shoreline Blvd # 800 (78401-0333)
PHONE..........................361 888-8235
Spencer Abraham, *Ch of Bd*
Amir Adnani, *President*
Scott Melbye, *Exec VP*
Pat Obara, *CFO*
EMP: 33
SALES (est): 2MM **Publicly Held**
WEB: www.uraniumenergy.com
SIC: 1094 Uranium-radium-vanadium ores

(G-3649)
VAL AND VAL INC
5815a A Weber Rd (78413)
PHONE..........................361 852-8992
Andrea Marie Valenti, *Director*
Andrea Valenti, *Director*
EMP: 30
SALES (est): 4.4MM **Privately Held**
WEB: www.tshirtgalleryandsports.com
SIC: 2759 Screen printing

(G-3650)
VARCO LP
Also Called: Tubscope Nov
401 Saratoga Blvd (78417-3508)
PHONE..........................361 854-1167
Joe Koenig, *Marketing Staff*
Rex Childers, *Manager*
EMP: 30
SALES (corp-wide): 8.4B **Publicly Held**
WEB: www.nov.com
SIC: 1389 Oil field services
HQ: Varco, L.P.
2835 Holmes Rd
Houston TX 77051
713 799-5272

(G-3651)
VAREL INTERNATIONAL IND LLC
4531 Ayers St (78415-1419)
PHONE..........................713 304-5813
EMP: 14
SALES (corp-wide): 10.7B **Privately Held**
WEB: www.varelintl.com
SIC: 3545 Drill bits, metalworking
HQ: Varel International Ind., Llc
4730 Consulate Plaza Dr # 190
Houston TX 77032
281 272-6000

(G-3652)
VIRTEX HOLDINGS LLP
Also Called: Operating Company
615 N Upper Broadway St # 525 (78401-0712)
PHONE..........................361 882-3046
Dale Phipps, *Managing Prtnr*
Matt Conrad, *Vice Pres*
Basil Phipps, *Vice Pres*
Leo Verrett, *Vice Pres*
Stephen Broll, *Engineer*
EMP: 49
SALES (est): 14MM **Privately Held**
WEB: www.virtexoperating.com
SIC: 1311 Crude petroleum production

(G-3653)
WEATHERFORD INTERNATIONAL INC
210 S Carancahua St (78401-3044)
PHONE..........................361 693-6800
EMP: 23
SALES (corp-wide): 194.6B **Publicly Held**
SIC: 3533 Mfg Oil/Gas Field Machinery
HQ: Weatherford International, Llc
2000 Saint James Pl
Houston TX 77056
713 693-4000

(G-3654)
WESTERN CHEMICAL TRADING LLC
14493 S Padre Island Dr A (78418-5931)
PHONE..........................405 923-4211
Kris Rittenberry, *Vice Pres*

EMP: 15
SALES (est): 552.9K **Privately Held**
WEB: www.westernchemicaltrading.com
SIC: 1389 Oil field services

(G-3655)
WHIPPED UP INC
4101 Intrstate Hwy 69 Acc (78410)
P.O. Box 260417 (78426-0417)
PHONE..........................361 248-4639
Monica Case, *Owner*
EMP: 9
SALES (est): 813K **Privately Held**
SIC: 2053 5143 Cakes, bakery: frozen; yogurt

(G-3656)
WHITECAP WASTEWATER TREATMENT
13409 Whitecap Blvd (78418-7008)
PHONE..........................361 826-4142
Larry Gonzales, *President*
EMP: 15
SALES (est): 1MM **Privately Held**
SIC: 2899 Water treating compounds

(G-3657)
WINN EXPLORATION CO INC
800 N Shoreline Blvd 1900n (78401-3754)
PHONE..........................361 844-6900
C C Winn, *President*
M W Calley, *Vice Pres*
Michael Calley, *Vice Pres*
EMP: 16 EST: 1951
SQ FT: 2,500
SALES (est): 4.7MM **Privately Held**
WEB: www.xerox.com
SIC: 1311 1382 Crude petroleum production; natural gas production; oil & gas exploration services

(G-3658)
ZARSKY LUMBER COMPANY INC
Also Called: Zarsky Oil Field
510 N Port Ave (78408-3946)
P.O. Box 4205 (78469-4205)
PHONE..........................361 882-2575
Martin Magallan, *Store Mgr*
Christopher Soliz, *Store Mgr*
Steve Weaver, *Manager*
Denise Robinson, *Manager*
EMP: 40
SQ FT: 18,000
SALES (corp-wide): 137.6MM **Privately Held**
WEB: www.zarsky.com
SIC: 5211 1389 1381 Lumber products; construction, repair & dismantling services; drilling oil & gas wells
HQ: Zarsky Lumber Company, Inc.
604 E Rio Grande St
Victoria TX 77901
361 573-2479

Corrigan
Polk County

(G-3659)
CORRIGAN OSB LLC (DH)
Also Called: Royomartin
1923 Us Highway 287 W (75939-6221)
P.O. Box 1110, Alexandria LA (71309-1110)
PHONE..........................318 448-0405
Terry Secrest, *Vice Pres*
Raymond A Peters,
E Scott Poole,
Terry W Secrest Jr,
EMP: 26
SALES (est): 7.2MM
SALES (corp-wide): 300.1MM **Privately Held**
WEB: www.royomartin.com
SIC: 2493 Reconstituted wood products
HQ: Martco L.L.C.
2189 Memorial Dr
Alexandria LA 71301
318 448-0405

Corsicana
Navarro County

(G-3660)
AMERICAN BOTTLING COMPANY
Also Called: Corsicana Dr Pepper Btlg Co
2401 S Business 45 (75110-9116)
P.O. Box 801 (75151-0801)
PHONE...............................903 874-5666
Michael Haferkamp, *Manager*
EMP: 40 **Publicly Held**
WEB: www.keurigdrpepper.com
SIC: 2086 Soft drinks: packaged in cans, bottles, etc.
HQ: The American Bottling Company
5301 Legacy Dr
Plano TX 75024

(G-3661)
AQUA TRANSFER & ENRGY SVCS LLC
309 N Beaton St (75110-4623)
P.O. Box 959 (75151-0959)
PHONE...............................903 874-4946
Chadwick Kindle, *President*
EMP: 45
SALES (est): 6.5MM **Privately Held**
WEB: www.aquaoilfieldservices.com
SIC: 1382 Oil & gas exploration services

(G-3662)
COR-TEX STEEL
Also Called: Jennifer Harper
3701 S Business 45 (75109-9162)
PHONE...............................903 872-3991
Jennifer Harper, *Owner*
EMP: 12
SALES (est): 2.6MM **Privately Held**
SIC: 5051 3441 Steel; fabricated structural metal

(G-3663)
CORSICANA BEDDING LLC
2700 E Hwy 31 (75109-8905)
P.O. Box 1050 (75151-1050)
PHONE...............................903 872-2591
EMP: 67
SALES (corp-wide): 414.9MM **Privately Held**
WEB: www.corsicanamattress.com
SIC: 2515 Mattresses, innerspring or box spring; box springs, assembled
PA: Corsicana Bedding, Llc
1420 W Mockingbird Ln
Dallas TX 75247
800 323-4349

(G-3664)
CORSICANA BEDDING LLC
Also Called: Corsicana Mattress Company
2700 E State Highway 31 (75109-8905)
PHONE...............................903 257-3360
Ashley Welch, *Project Mgr*
Lara Pattison, *Manager*
Jennifer Richards, *Administration*
Becky Smith, *Clerk*
EMP: 105
SALES (corp-wide): 414.9MM **Privately Held**
WEB: www.corsicanamattress.com
SIC: 2515 Mattresses & bedsprings
PA: Corsicana Bedding, Llc
1420 W Mockingbird Ln
Dallas TX 75247
800 323-4349

(G-3665)
CORSICANA BOX COMPANY INC
1000 Ferguson St (75110)
P.O. Box 675 (75151-0675)
PHONE...............................903 874-5615
Robert Deleon, *General Mgr*
EMP: 10
SQ FT: 16,000
SALES (corp-wide): 2.3MM **Privately Held**
WEB: www.aetnaglass.com
SIC: 2441 Shipping cases, wood: nailed or lock corner

HQ: Corsicana Box Company, Inc.
1000 Ferguson Dr
Corsicana TX 75110
903 874-5615

(G-3666)
CORSICANA SHEET METAL CO INC
Also Called: Corsicana Air Conditioning
625 W 2nd Ave (75110-2943)
PHONE...............................903 872-8434
Ray Cobb, *President*
Marvie James, *Corp Secy*
Billy Ray Cobb Jr, *Vice Pres*
EMP: 14
SQ FT: 3,360
SALES (est): 2.1MM **Privately Held**
WEB: www.watkinselectric.com
SIC: 1711 7623 1761 0212 Warm air heating & air conditioning contractor; air conditioning repair; sheet metalwork; beef cattle except feedlots; sheet metalwork

(G-3667)
CRESLINE PLASTIC PIPE CO INC
3801 E State Highway 31 (75109-9691)
PHONE...............................903 872-7418
Billy Owen, *Purchasing*
John Heard, *Sales Staff*
EMP: 50
SALES (corp-wide): 146.9MM **Privately Held**
WEB: www.cresline.com
SIC: 3084 Plastics pipe
PA: Cresline Plastic Pipe Co Inc
600 N Cross Pointe Blvd
Evansville IN 47715
812 428-9300

(G-3668)
CUSTOM TS
1712 W 2nd Ave (75110-4110)
PHONE...............................903 874-7626
Tyson Chandler, *President*
EMP: 11
SQ FT: 6,000
SALES (est): 900.6K **Privately Held**
WEB: www.customt-s.com
SIC: 2759 Screen printing

(G-3669)
DALCO ATHLETIC LETTERING INC
2030 Haggar St (75110-9613)
P.O. Box 2299 (75151-2299)
PHONE...............................903 201-6244
Gene F Feil, *President*
Linda Feil, *Corp Secy*
▲ **EMP:** 52
SQ FT: 34,000
SALES (est): 5.1MM **Privately Held**
WEB: www.dalcoathletics.com
SIC: 2399 Emblems, badges & insignia

(G-3670)
ELECTRICO INC
2500 S Business 45 (75110-9117)
P.O. Box 3097 (75151-3097)
PHONE...............................903 872-6567
Janet Noblett, *President*
Harmon Noblett, *Chairman*
Mark A Noblett, *Vice Pres*
Mark Noblett, *Vice Pres*
EMP: 15
SQ FT: 16,000
SALES (est): 5.4MM **Privately Held**
WEB: www.electricoinc.com
SIC: 5063 7694 Motors, electric; motor repair services

(G-3671)
ENTERPRISE PRCAST CON TXAS LLC
800 N Interstate 45 (75110)
PHONE...............................903 875-1077
Thomas L Egan, *President*
John Arehart, *Vice Pres*
Sam Kakish, *Vice Pres*
EMP: 50
SQ FT: 27,800
SALES (est): 10MM **Privately Held**
WEB: www.enterpriseprecast.com
SIC: 3272 Concrete products, precast

(G-3672)
GRANDOR CORPORATION (PA)
Also Called: Oil City Iron Works
814 S Main St (75110-7231)
P.O. Box 1560 (75151-1560)
PHONE...............................903 872-6571
EMP: 156 **EST:** 1965
SQ FT: 250,000
SALES (est): 33.2MM **Privately Held**
WEB: www.ociw.com
SIC: 3321 Gray & ductile iron foundries

(G-3673)
GUARDIAN INDUSTRIES LLC
3801 S Hwy 287 (75109-9373)
PHONE...............................903 872-4871
Jesse Meason, *Engineer*
Chuck Warrington, *Engineer*
Dan Zalace, *Engineer*
Eric Drain, *Plant Engr*
Walter Palma, *Manager*
EMP: 400
SALES (corp-wide): 36.8B **Privately Held**
WEB: www.guardian.com
SIC: 3211 5039 3231 Float glass; glass construction materials; products of purchased glass
HQ: Guardian Industries, Llc
2300 Harmon Rd
Auburn Hills MI 48326
248 340-1800

(G-3674)
INDUSTRIAL PIPE FITTINGS LLC
305 N 7th St (75110-4642)
PHONE...............................903 872-7890
Les Phillips, *Principal*
EMP: 40 **Privately Held**
WEB: www.plassonusa.com
SIC: 2679 Pipes & fittings, fiber: made from purchased material
PA: Industrial Pipe Fittings, L.L.C.
10707 Corp Dr Ste 220
Stafford TX 77477

(G-3675)
JAMES MANUFACTURING INC
550 Hardy Ave (75110-1904)
P.O. Box 125 (75151-0125)
PHONE...............................903 872-2346
James Shanahan, *President*
EMP: 25
SQ FT: 32,000
SALES (est): 4.3MM **Privately Held**
WEB: www.jamesmanufacturingservices.com
SIC: 7699 3531 3549 3537 Aircraft & heavy equipment repair services; construction machinery; metalworking machinery; industrial trucks & tractors

(G-3676)
LONE STAR WHEEL COMPONENTS
3129 E Hwy 31 (75110)
P.O. Box 531 (75151-0531)
PHONE...............................903 654-1132
Larry L Coffey, *President*
Jerry Coffey, *Vice Pres*
▲ **EMP:** 52
SALES (est): 9.9MM **Privately Held**
WEB: www.lswctx.com
SIC: 3011 Tires & inner tubes

(G-3677)
MCKEE TRUE VALUE HDWR & LBR
104 N 7th St (75110-5318)
PHONE...............................903 874-6581
Larry Morrison, *Owner*
EMP: 20 **EST:** 2001
SALES (est): 852.3K **Privately Held**
SIC: 5251 3999 5231 5211 Hardware; manufacturing industries; paint; lumber products

(G-3678)
MIDWEST ENERGY EMISSIONS CORP (PA)
1810 Jester Dr (75109-9593)
P.O. Box 1277 (75151-1277)
PHONE...............................614 505-6115
Christopher Greenberg, *Ch of Bd*
Richard Macpherson, *President*
John Pavlish, *Senior VP*

James Trettel, *Vice Pres*
EMP: 13
SALES: 11.4MM **Publicly Held**
WEB: www.midwestemissions.com
SIC: 3822 Auto controls regulating residntl & coml environmt & applncs

(G-3679)
MORGAN TRUCK BODY LLC
8051 Morgan Cir (75109-9063)
P.O. Box 1318 (75151-1318)
PHONE...............................903 872-7445
Erick Bugg, *Opers-Prdtn-Mfg*
Guivini Nava, *Buyer*
Brant Hickman, *Regl Sales Mgr*
EMP: 100
SALES (corp-wide): 1.2B **Privately Held**
WEB: www.morgancorp.com
SIC: 3713 3537 2657 Truck bodies (motor vehicles); industrial trucks & tractors; folding paperboard boxes
HQ: Morgan Truck Body, Llc
111 Morgan Way
Morgantown PA 19543
610 286-5025

(G-3680)
NOW MAGAZINES LLC
413 W Main St (75151)
PHONE...............................972 937-8447
Sandra Strong, *Editor*
Dustin Dauenhauer, *Accounts Exec*
Linda Dean, *Accounts Exec*
Joyce Sebesta, *Accounts Exec*
Angela Mixon, *Manager*
EMP: 20
SALES (est): 810K **Privately Held**
WEB: www.nowmagazines.com
SIC: 2721 Magazines: publishing only, not printed on site

(G-3681)
OIL CITY IRON WORKS INC
814 S Main St (75110-7231)
PHONE...............................903 872-6571
Eric Meyers, *CEO*
Eric R Meyers, *President*
Harry Phillips, *Exec VP*
EMP: 220
SQ FT: 250,000
SALES (est): 32.7MM
SALES (corp-wide): 33.2MM **Privately Held**
WEB: www.ociw.com
SIC: 3321 Gray & ductile iron foundries
PA: The Grandor Corporation
814 S Main St
Corsicana TX 75110
903 872-6571

(G-3682)
OMP SPECIALTIES INC
2201 S Business 45 (75110-9112)
P.O. Box 1479 (75151-1479)
PHONE...............................903 874-0045
Olimpia De Marchena, *President*
EMP: 25
SALES (est): 5.8MM **Privately Held**
WEB: www.ompspecialties.com
SIC: 3449 Bars, concrete reinforcing: fabricated steel

(G-3683)
PACTIV LLC
4501 E Hwy 31 (75109-9762)
PHONE...............................903 654-4745
Todd Missbach, *Branch Mgr*
EMP: 30 **Publicly Held**
WEB: www.pactiv.com
SIC: 3086 2821 Packaging & shipping materials, foamed plastic; plastics materials & resins
HQ: Pactiv Llc
1900 W Field Ct
Lake Forest IL 60045
847 482-2000

(G-3684)
SMBG CORSICANA LLC
3501 Crscana Crssngs Blvd (75109-9304)
PHONE...............................254 262-4400
Mark Schulman,
EMP: 10
SALES (est): 85.9K **Privately Held**
SIC: 3651 Home entertainment equipment, electronic

G E O G R A P H I C

(G-3685)
TEXAS MPP LP (PA)
Also Called: Mpp Group of Companies
2900 E State Highway 31 (75109-9482)
PHONE......................................903 874-5781
Edgar F Bozarth, *Chairman*
Jo Ann Cleveland, *Credit Mgr*
EMP: 25
SQ FT: 65,000
SALES (est): 5.2MM **Privately Held**
WEB: www.mppgroup.com
SIC: 3471 Electroplating of metals or
　formed products

(G-3686)
TOMCAT DRILLING LLC
716 Grandview Dr (75109-0542)
PHONE......................................316 262-8554
Timothy Sanders, *Partner*
Spence Hummel, *Partner*
EMP: 90
SALES (est): 14.4MM **Privately Held**
SIC: 1381 Redrilling oil & gas wells

(G-3687)
TRIMMINGS INC
2030 Haggar St (75110-9613)
P.O. Box 118 (75151-0118)
PHONE......................................903 872-1556
Robert Wright, *President*
Jacque Wright, *Vice Pres*
▲ EMP: 106
SQ FT: 80,000
SALES (est): 7.7MM **Privately Held**
WEB: www.trimmingsinc.com
SIC: 3999 5947 Potpourri; gift, novelty &
　souvenir shop

(G-3688)
TRUE VALUE COMPANY LLC
2601 E Highway 31 (75109-8988)
PHONE......................................903 872-8365
Dan Wilkie, *Manager*
Marjorie Braddick, *Consultant*
EMP: 156 **Privately Held**
WEB: www.truevaluecompany.com
SIC: 5251 2851 3991 4225 Hardware;
　paints & paint additives; paint & varnish
　brushes; general warehousing & storage
HQ: True Value Company, L.L.C.
　8600 W Bryn Mawr Ave 100s
　Chicago IL 60631
　773 695-5000

Cotulla
La Salle County

(G-3689)
4L OILFIELD SERVICES LLC
902 S Main St (78014-2415)
PHONE......................................830 879-5300
EMP: 27
SALES (corp-wide): 11MM **Privately Held**
WEB: www.4loilfield.com
SIC: 1389 Oil field services
PA: 4l Oilfield Services, Llc
　81 Us Highway 380
　Bridgeport TX 76426
　940 626-8100

(G-3690)
EOG RESOURCES INC
402 N Main St (78014-2155)
PHONE......................................830 879-4614
EMP: 42
SALES (corp-wide): 18B **Publicly Held**
SIC: 1382 1311 Oil/Gas Exploration Serv-
　ices Crude Petroleum/Natural Gas Pro-
　duction
PA: Eog Resources, Inc.
　1111 Bagby St Lbby 2
　Houston TX 77002
　713 651-7000

(G-3691)
**SS EQUIPMENT SERVICES II
LLC**
1162 Fm 3408 (78014-2792)
P.O. Box 493 (78014-0493)
PHONE......................................830 483-0187
Alejandro Narvaiv, *General Mgr*
EMP: 50
SQ FT: 217,800

SALES (est): 800K **Privately Held**
SIC: 1389 Construction, repair & disman-
　tling services

(G-3692)
WILDCAT WIRELINE
6159 N Interstate 35 (78014-5010)
PHONE......................................830 879-5100
EMP: 57
SALES (est): 389.6K
SALES (corp-wide): 56.5B **Publicly Held**
SIC: 1389 Removal of condensate gaso-
　line from field (gathering) lines
HQ: La-Tex Pump And Transportation, L.P.
　3040 Post Oak Blvd 15thf
　Houston TX 77056
　832 844-1015

Coupland
Williamson County

(G-3693)
TYPE EXCELLENCE INC
20406 Wilson Rd (78615-4840)
PHONE......................................830 833-9005
Rose Peterson, *President*
EMP: 10
SALES (est): 496.6K **Privately Held**
SIC: 2791 Typesetting

Covington
Hill County

(G-3694)
AUSTIN POWDER COMPANY
2793 Fm 67 (76636-4629)
PHONE......................................817 371-6147
EMP: 26
SALES (corp-wide): 509.6MM **Privately
Held**
WEB: www.austinpowder.com
SIC: 2892 Explosives
HQ: Austin Powder Company
　25800 Science Park Dr # 300
　Cleveland OH 44122
　216 464-2400

Coyanosa
Pecos County

(G-3695)
DCP MIDSTREAM LLC
2821 Waha Rd (79730)
P.O. Box 38 (79730-0038)
PHONE......................................432 343-7112
Jaime Gonazalez, *Manager*
EMP: 47
SALES (corp-wide): 1.9B **Privately Held**
WEB: www.dcpmidstream.com
SIC: 1389 Servicing oil & gas wells
PA: Dcp Midstream, Llc
　370 17th St Ste 2500
　Denver CO 80202
　303 633-2900

Crandall
Kaufman County

(G-3696)
INK IT PRINTING
402 E Trunk St Ste C (75114-2555)
PHONE......................................972 428-9623
Beth Maroney, *Principal*
EMP: 10
SALES (est): 1.2MM **Privately Held**
WEB: www.inkitprint.com
SIC: 2752 Commercial printing, offset

Crane
Crane County

(G-3697)
APACHE CORPORATION
1 Mile N Of Crane Hwy 385 (79731)
PHONE......................................432 558-2065

Danny Galvan, *Manager*
EMP: 20
SALES (corp-wide): 6.4B **Publicly Held**
WEB: www.apachecorp.com
SIC: 1311 Crude petroleum production
PA: Apache Corporation
　2000 Post Oak Blvd Ste 10
　Houston TX 77056
　713 296-6000

(G-3698)
APACHE CORPORATION
8602 Exxon Loop (79731-6507)
PHONE......................................432 558-2572
Harry Gryder, *Manager*
EMP: 15
SALES (corp-wide): 6.4B **Publicly Held**
WEB: www.apachecorp.com
SIC: 1311 Crude petroleum production
PA: Apache Corporation
　2000 Post Oak Blvd Ste 10
　Houston TX 77056
　713 296-6000

(G-3699)
KEY ENERGY SERVICES INC
111th North Gaston St (79731)
P.O. Box 1086 (79731-1086)
PHONE......................................432 558-3574
Alfonso Baron, *Branch Mgr*
Daniel Nuno, *Supervisor*
EMP: 120
SALES (corp-wide): 413.8MM **Publicly
Held**
WEB: www.keyenergy.com
SIC: 1389 Servicing oil & gas wells; oil field
　services
PA: Key Energy Services, Inc.
　1301 Mckinney St Ste 1800
　Houston TX 77010
　713 651-4300

(G-3700)
NATIONAL FOUNDRY & MFG CO
299 Foundry Rd (79731)
P.O. Box 1146 (79731-1146)
PHONE......................................432 558-3444
Gayla Tibbitts, *President*
Donnie Tibbitts, *Sales Staff*
EMP: 26
SALES (est): 5.7MM **Privately Held**
WEB: www.nationalfoundry.com
SIC: 3462 Anchors, forged

(G-3701)
T-P RENTALS LLC
1204 Se County Rd (79731-2209)
P.O. Box 964 (79731-0964)
PHONE......................................432 558-7218
Ronna M Aguilar, *Vice Pres*
Doak Painter, *CFO*
EMP: 29 EST: 2009
SALES (est): 5MM **Privately Held**
SIC: 7353 1389 Oil field equipment, rental
　or leasing; pipe testing, oil field service

(G-3702)
TREY TRUCKS LTD
1160 Sw 6th St (79731-6500)
P.O. Box 366 (79731-0366)
PHONE......................................432 558-7966
Ridgely Holifield, *Partner*
Steve Holifield Jr, *Partner*
Dwayne Tarpley, *Manager*
EMP: 84 EST: 1990
SALES (est): 9.9MM **Privately Held**
SIC: 1389 Haulage, oil field

(G-3703)
TRI RESOURCES INC
Also Called: Targa Resources
5880 Fm 1233 (79731-6514)
PHONE......................................432 558-3996
Randy Compton, *Safety Mgr*
Jeremy Tiller, *Opers Staff*
Debbie Gerndt, *Sales Staff*
Paul Ivey, *Manager*
Anthony Wheat, *Manager*
EMP: 35 **Publicly Held**
WEB: www.triresources.com
SIC: 1321 1311 Natural gas liquids; crude
　petroleum & natural gas
HQ: Tri Resources Inc.
　811 Louisiana St Ste 2100
　Houston TX 77002
　713 584-1000

Crawford
Mclennan County

(G-3704)
**LHOIST NORTH AMERICA TENN
INC**
Also Called: Franklin Industrial Minerals
8759 5th St (76638-3030)
P.O. Box 59 (76638-0059)
PHONE......................................254 486-2105
Richard Dunbar, *Branch Mgr*
Jeff Bullard, *Maintence Staff*
EMP: 40
SALES (corp-wide): 2.6MM **Privately
Held**
SIC: 1422 Crushed & broken limestone
HQ: Lhoist North America Of Tennessee,
　Inc.
　750 Old Hickry Blvd 200-2
　Brentwood TN 37027
　615 259-4222

Creedmoor
Hays County

(G-3705)
**AUSTIN ARCHTCTRAL
GRAPHICS INC**
11400 Old Lockhart Hwy (78610-2073)
PHONE......................................512 473-2075
Thomas B Dunn, *President*
Beverly S Dunn, *Vice Pres*
Eric Maag, *Sales Staff*
Kathy Hemphill, *Admin Sec*
EMP: 30
SALES (est): 4.4MM **Privately Held**
WEB: www.aagsigns.com
SIC: 3993 Signs, not made in custom sign
　painting shops

Cresson
Hood County

(G-3706)
BRIDGES HOLDINGS INC
Also Called: Bridges Equipment
14400 Cleburne Hwy (76035)
PHONE......................................817 396-4340
Tom Simmons, *Branch Mgr*
EMP: 40
SALES (corp-wide): 19.7MM **Privately
Held**
WEB: www.bridgesequipment.com
SIC: 1389 Oil field services
PA: Bridges Holdings, Inc.
　2122 Maurice Rd
　Odessa TX 79763
　432 333-9741

(G-3707)
DEVON ENERGY CORPORATION
9500 Glasscock Dr (76035-4103)
PHONE......................................817 396-4000
Dickie Smith, *Branch Mgr*
EMP: 50
SALES (corp-wide): 6.2B **Publicly Held**
WEB: www.devonenergy.com
SIC: 1382 Oil & gas exploration services
PA: Devon Energy Corporation
　333 W Sheridan Ave
　Oklahoma City OK 73102
　405 235-3611

(G-3708)
DIGITAL PRINT INC
217 Performance Ln # 102 (76035-4365)
P.O. Box 679 (76035-0679)
PHONE......................................817 512-3153
Jack Farr, *President*
Bob Whitman, *Purch Mgr*
▼ EMP: 10
SQ FT: 6,000
SALES (est): 2.9MM **Privately Held**
WEB: www.digitalprint.com
SIC: 2752 Commercial printing, offset

▲ = Import ▼ =Export
◆ =Import/Export

(G-3709)
INTEGRITY BIO-CHEMICALS LLC
1100 N Cresson Hwy (76035-4121)
PHONE..................408 396-7797
James Jett, *Mng Member*
Jake Galm, *Manager*
Max Duncan,
Steve Erikson,
Scott Schroeder,
EMP: 35
SQ FT: 30,000
SALES (est): 49MM **Privately Held**
WEB: www.integritybiochem.com
SIC: 2869 Laboratory chemicals, organic

(G-3710)
NABORS WELL SERVICES CO
Also Called: Nabors Wells Service
12890 Cleburne Hwy (76035-3128)
PHONE..................817 396-4310
Jay Jones, *Manager*
EMP: 76 **Privately Held**
WEB: www.nabors.com
SIC: 1389 Oil field services
HQ: Nabors Well Services Co.
515 W Greens Rd Ste 1000
Houston TX 77067
281 874-0035

(G-3711)
PRECISION DRILLING COMPANY LP
1415 Hughie Long Rd (76035-4183)
PHONE..................817 396-4714
Forrest Conley, *Vice Pres*
Forrest M Conley Jr, *Vice Pres*
Mike Skuce, *Engineer*
EMP: 30
SALES (corp-wide): 1.1B **Privately Held**
WEB: www.precisiondrilling.com
SIC: 1381 Drilling oil & gas wells
HQ: Precision Drilling Company, Lp
10350 Richmond Ave # 700
Houston TX 77042

(G-3712)
QES WIRELINE LLC
Also Called: Granberry Gray Wireline
12052 Cleburne Hwy (76035-3115)
PHONE..................432 813-6088
EMP: 18
SALES (corp-wide): 1B **Privately Held**
WEB: www.quintanaenergyservices.com
SIC: 1389 Well logging
HQ: Qes Wireline Llc
801 Cherry St Ste 800
Fort Worth TX 76102
817 546-4970

(G-3713)
SPUR INDUSTRIAL LLC
Also Called: Spur Environmental Services
1420 Hughie Long Rd (76035-4182)
PHONE..................817 293-1515
John Wesley Sheffielr, *Principal*
EMP: 27
SALES (est): 13.5MM **Privately Held**
WEB: www.spurindustrial.com
SIC: 1542 1629 1791 3312 Commercial & office building, new construction

(G-3714)
STANDARD INDUS MFG PRTNERS LLC
8500 Silver Spur Ct (76035-4387)
PHONE..................682 500-1718
EMP: 19
SALES (corp-wide): 27.2MM **Privately Held**
WEB: www.standardpumpparts.com
SIC: 3561 Industrial pumps & parts
PA: Standard Industrial
901 W 3rd St
Odessa TX 79763
432 332-5955

(G-3715)
TRINKOTE INDUS FINISHES INC
800 Hughie Long Rd (76035-4170)
P.O. Box 310 (76035-0310)
PHONE..................817 396-4747
James Gardner, *President*
David Phillips, *Opers Staff*
Gary Hillis, *Purch Mgr*

Michael Reichling, *Controller*
Glenn Wilson, *Manager*
▲ **EMP:** 30
SQ FT: 44,000
SALES (est): 6.6MM **Privately Held**
WEB: www.trinkote.com
SIC: 2851 Paints & allied products

Crockett
Houston County

(G-3716)
CROCKETT SAND AND GRAVEL INC
9812 State Highway 7 W (75835-7559)
P.O. Box 389 (75835-0389)
PHONE..................936 545-1021
Lee Holsey, *President*
EMP: 44
SQ FT: 960
SALES (est): 8.4MM **Privately Held**
WEB: www.crockettsandandgravel.com
SIC: 1442 Gravel mining

(G-3717)
EARLS APPAREL INC
908 S 4th St (75835-3202)
P.O. Box 939 (75835-0939)
PHONE..................936 544-5521
Earl M Beard, *President*
Larry Beard, *Principal*
Billy Jean Beard, *Vice Pres*
EMP: 100 **EST:** 1975
SQ FT: 16,000
SALES (est): 8.8MM **Privately Held**
WEB: www.earlsapparel.com
SIC: 2321 2325 2326 Men's & boys' furnishings; men's & boys' trousers & slacks; overalls & coveralls

(G-3718)
ELASTOTECH SOUTHWEST INC
1700 Sw Loop 304 (75835-3510)
PHONE..................936 545-8550
Bob Lewallen, *President*
John Bobbitt, *Vice Pres*
Wesley Brown, *Sales Staff*
Connie Larue, *Office Mgr*
▲ **EMP:** 28
SQ FT: 21,000
SALES (est): 4.8MM **Privately Held**
WEB: www.elastotechsouthwest.com
SIC: 3061 Mechanical rubber goods

(G-3719)
HOLSEY MINING INC
9812 State Highway 7 W (75835-7559)
P.O. Box 389 (75835-0389)
PHONE..................936 545-1021
Lee Holsey, *President*
EMP: 15
SALES (est): 50.1K **Privately Held**
SIC: 1081 Metal mining services

(G-3720)
HOUSTON CNTY READY-MIX CON CO
Hwy 19 S (75835)
P.O. Box 389 (75835-0389)
PHONE..................936 544-7200
Barrington J Hosley, *President*
Lee Hosley, *Vice Pres*
EMP: 15
SQ FT: 400 **Privately Held**
WEB: www.houstoncountyreadymix.com
SIC: 3273 Ready-mixed concrete

(G-3721)
PARTEN OPERATING INC
19354 State Highway 21 W (75835-9013)
PHONE..................936 624-3100
Donald Adams, *Manager*
EMP: 20 **Privately Held**
SIC: 1382 Oil & gas exploration services
PA: Parten Operating Inc.
211 Hghland Crotx Dr Ste
Houston TX 77073

(G-3722)
POLK COUNTY PUBLISHING CO
Also Called: Houston County Courier
102 S 7th St (75835-2146)
P.O. Box 551 (75835-0551)
PHONE..................936 544-0540
Jeannine Rhone, *Branch Mgr*
EMP: 15
SQ FT: 6,000
SALES (corp-wide): 6MM **Privately Held**
WEB: www.easttexasnews.com
SIC: 2711 Newspapers: publishing only, not printed on site
PA: Polk County Publishing Co.
100 E Calhoun St
Livingston TX 77351
936 327-4357

(G-3723)
QUANTEX INSTRUMENT COMPANY
1503 E Loop 304 (75835-3401)
P.O. Box 520 (75835-0520)
PHONE..................936 544-5732
▲ **EMP:** 20 **EST:** 1971
SQ FT: 15,500
SALES (est): 4MM **Privately Held**
WEB: www.quantexinstruments.com
SIC: 3599 3544 3469 3451 Machine shop, jobbing & repair; special dies, tools, jigs & fixtures; metal stampings; screw machine products

(G-3724)
STANLEY JEANS CORP (PA)
908 S 4th St (75835-3202)
P.O. Box 939 (75835-0939)
PHONE..................936 544-5521
Larry Beard, *President*
Stanley Beard, *Director*
EMP: 70
SQ FT: 30,000
SALES (est): 3.9MM **Privately Held**
WEB: www.stanley-jeans.com
SIC: 2325 2326 Men's & boys' jeans & dungarees; men's & boys' work clothing

Crosby
Harris County

(G-3725)
ARKEMA INC
Crosby Plant
18000 Crosby Eastgate Rd (77532-3924)
PHONE..................281 328-3561
Randy Nycz, *Plant Mgr*
Paul Shelton, *Manager*
Michael Washington, *Manager*
EMP: 100
SALES (corp-wide): 120.6MM **Privately Held**
WEB: www.arkema-americas.com
SIC: 5169 2819 Organic chemicals, synthetic; industrial inorganic chemicals
HQ: Arkema Inc.
900 First Ave
King Of Prussia PA 19406
610 205-7000

(G-3726)
B H M PIPE & SUPPLY INC
11615 F M Road 2100 (77532)
P.O. Box 928 (77532-0928)
PHONE..................281 328-5552
Billy Miller, *President*
▲ **EMP:** 25
SQ FT: 11,508
SALES (est): 3.7MM **Privately Held**
WEB: www.bhmpipesupply.com
SIC: 3541 5051 Pipe cutting & threading machines; pipe & tubing, steel

(G-3727)
BO-GE ASSEMBLY INC
1123 Church St (77532-8704)
P.O. Box 1567 (77532-1567)
PHONE..................281 462-0073
Maureen Bohne, *President*
Alan Stephenson, *General Mgr*
Donald H Bohne, *Corp Secy*
Gronstedt Rande, *Sales Mgr*
Rande Gronstedt, *Sales Staff*
EMP: 25

SQ FT: 26,234
SALES (est): 4.8MM **Privately Held**
WEB: www.bo-ge.com
SIC: 7699 2891 Precision instrument repair; sealants

(G-3728)
CERTI-FAB INDUSTRIES INC
Also Called: Certi-Fab Steel Fabricators
25150 Crosby Fwy (77532-2756)
P.O. Box 1627 (77532-1627)
PHONE..................281 328-7244
James M Lewis, *President*
Jason M Lewis, *Vice Pres*
Jeana M McCall, *Vice Pres*
Jennifer M Eidson, *Treasurer*
Julie K Lewis, *Admin Sec*
EMP: 19
SQ FT: 20,000
SALES (est): 3.8MM **Privately Held**
SIC: 3441 Fabricated structural metal

(G-3729)
DOCRESOURCES LLC
5010 Fm 2100 Rd Ste 107 (77532)
P.O. Box 315 (77532-0315)
PHONE..................832 802-6008
Eric Jennings,
EMP: 12
SALES (est): 1.8MM **Privately Held**
WEB: www.docresources.com
SIC: 7379 3861 3555 ; photocopy machines; printing trades machinery

(G-3730)
DOWNHOLE THREADING SVCS INC
2935 Highway 90 (77532-6604)
PHONE..................281 462-9800
Eric Couch, *President*
Kim Alexander, *Production*
Sammy Schubert, *Sales Staff*
Ramiro Monsivais, *Admin Sec*
EMP: 28
SALES (est): 6.7MM **Privately Held**
WEB: www.downholethreading.com
SIC: 3541 5051 Pipe cutting & threading machines; metals service centers & offices

(G-3731)
G FABRICATING LLC
4101 Barbers Hill Rd (77532-7781)
PHONE..................281 421-3100
Randall Garcia, *Mng Member*
EMP: 22
SQ FT: 20,000
SALES (est): 1.2MM **Privately Held**
SIC: 3441 3443 3444 3449 Fabricated structural metal; chutes & troughs; sheet metalwork; miscellaneous metalwork; fabricated pipe & fittings

(G-3732)
GROTHE INDUSTRIAL COATING LLC
20115 Fm 2100 Rd (77532-3716)
PHONE..................281 354-1574
Melvin Wayne Grothe,
EMP: 10 **EST:** 2008
SALES (est): 1MM **Privately Held**
WEB: www.grotheindustrialcoating.info
SIC: 3479 Coating of metals & formed products

(G-3733)
HOU FAB & MAINTENANCE INC
716 Sundown Meadows St (77532-7542)
PHONE..................713 672-1993
Eddie Glass, *President*
Wayne Glass, *Shareholder*
Harrison Heirs, *Shareholder*
Diana Orelana, *Admin Sec*
EMP: 9
SALES (est): 893.1K **Privately Held**
WEB: www.hou-fab.com
SIC: 3443 3567 7699 3535 Tanks, lined: metal plate; tanks, standard or custom fabricated: metal plate; industrial furnaces & ovens; tank repair; boiler & heating repair services; industrial equipment services; pneumatic tube conveyor systems

(G-3734)
HUNTING ENERGY SERVICES INC
16818 Ramsey Rd (77532-7490)
PHONE........................281 328-1400
Chet Fielden, *Vice Pres*
John Acosta, *Opers Mgr*
Andy Galloway, *Purchasing*
David Bowar, *Senior Engr*
Brad Jeter, *Sales Staff*
EMP: 18
SALES (corp-wide): 960MM **Privately Held**
WEB: www.hunting-intl.com
SIC: 1389 8741 Oil field services; management services
HQ: Hunting Energy Services, Llc
   16825 Northchase Dr # 600
   Houston TX 77060

(G-3735)
JMJ ORGANICS LTD (PA)
Also Called: Warren's Southern Gardens
1006 Spanish Cove Dr (77532-3017)
P.O. Box 927, Huffman (77336-0927)
PHONE........................281 798-3056
Carey Dean Warren, *Partner*
Bernice Warren, *Partner*
EMP: 15
SALES (est): 1.2MM **Privately Held**
SIC: 5261 1741 2875 7389 Nurseries & garden centers; masonry & other stonework; fertilizers, mixing only;

(G-3736)
JML SERVICES INC
Also Called: Loftin Mechanical Services
2902 Skimmer Way (77532-7273)
P.O. Box 2165 (77532-8165)
PHONE........................713 582-9500
Jennifer Loftin, *President*
John Loftin, *Vice Pres*
EMP: 16
SALES (est): 1.8MM **Privately Held**
WEB: www.loftinmechanicalservices.com
SIC: 1711 2499 Mechanical contractor; cooling towers, wood or wood & sheet metal combination

(G-3737)
JP TUBULAR SERVICES INC
11621 Fm 2100 (77532)
P.O. Box 1486 (77532-1486)
PHONE........................281 426-8596
Scott Stiles, *President*
Scott Fleming, *Vice Pres*
Maria Salinas, *Purch Agent*
EMP: 22
SQ FT: 100,000
SALES (est): 1.6MM **Privately Held**
WEB: www.jptubular.com
SIC: 1389 Oil field services

(G-3738)
NABORS DRILLING TECH USA INC
2100 Crosby Dayton Rd (77532-4714)
PHONE........................281 462-1730
Billy Rogers, *Manager*
Cory Lucas, *Technology*
EMP: 20 **Privately Held**
WEB: www.nabors.com
SIC: 1381 1389 Drilling oil & gas wells; oil field services
HQ: Nabors Drilling Technologies Usa, Inc.
   515 W Greens Rd Ste 1200
   Houston TX 77067
   281 874-0035

(G-3739)
NUMERICAL PRECISION INC (PA)
1630 E Stroker Rd (77532-4310)
P.O. Box 1228 (77532-1228)
PHONE........................281 328-7343
Randy Bentley, *President*
Shane Bentley, *Vice Pres*
Brett Thomas, *Mfg Mgr*
Terry Fruge, *Sales Mgr*
Kenneth N Bentley, *Shareholder*
◆ EMP: 89
SQ FT: 30,000
SALES (est): 26.2MM **Privately Held**
WEB: www.numerical.net
SIC: 3599 Machine shop, jobbing & repair

(G-3740)
OILWELL TUBULAR CONSULTANTS
14630 Bohemian Hall Rd (77532-6034)
P.O. Box 1267 (77532-1267)
PHONE........................281 328-6220
Wilton Schexnayder, *President*
EMP: 21
SQ FT: 2,000
SALES (est): 1.4MM **Privately Held**
WEB: www.oilwelltubular.com
SIC: 1389 Oil field services

(G-3741)
RAMSEY PROPERTIES LP (PA)
Also Called: Kmtex
16503 Ramsey Rd (77532-5916)
PHONE........................281 328-3501
◆ EMP: 110
SQ FT: 20,000
SALES (est): 34.7MM **Privately Held**
WEB: www.kmcoinc.com
SIC: 2899 2992 Chemical preparations; antifreeze compounds; brake fluid (hydraulic): made from purchased materials

(G-3742)
SEABOARD CONTROLS LLC
4807 Highway 90 (77532-5964)
P.O. Box 1869 (77532-1869)
PHONE........................281 328-8620
Philip G Muro, *CEO*
Jack Harvey, *Vice Pres*
Anthony Muro, *Controller*
▲ EMP: 25
SQ FT: 18,000
SALES (est): 5.9MM **Privately Held**
WEB: www.seaboardcontrols.com
SIC: 3699 Electrical equipment & supplies

(G-3743)
SOONER PIPE LLC
Also Called: AZ Terminal
1919 Highway 90 (77532-7832)
P.O. Box 250 (77532-0250)
PHONE........................281 328-4877
Joe Ottaviani, *Vice Pres*
Terra Calloway, *Sales Staff*
Randy REA, *Director*
EMP: 36 **Privately Held**
WEB: www.soonerpipe.com
SIC: 1389 3491 Oil field services; industrial valves
HQ: Sooner Pipe, L.L.C.
   909 Fannin St Ste 3100
   Houston TX 77010
   713 759-1200

(G-3744)
T O F ENTERPRISES INC
1609 Kennings Rd (77532-5113)
P.O. Box 806 (77532-0806)
PHONE........................281 328-2553
Linda Hays, *President*
Jim Hays, *Vice Pres*
EMP: 10
SQ FT: 4,000
SALES (est): 500K **Privately Held**
SIC: 3441 7692 Fabricated structural metal; welding repair

(G-3745)
TOP THREADING SERVICES INC
11613 Fm 2100 (77532)
P.O. Box 1572 (77532-1572)
PHONE........................281 426-8461
Charles M Hall, *President*
EMP: 40 EST: 2005
SALES (est): 6.8MM **Privately Held**
WEB: www.topthreadingservices.com
SIC: 3547 5051 Pipe & tube mills; pipe & tubing, steel

Cross Plains
Callahan County

(G-3746)
ALEXANDER MANUFACTURING CO
Also Called: Metro Tool & Manufacturing
11573 County Road 436 (76443-6729)
PHONE........................972 641-7355
Dennis Heffernan, *President*

Dana Yanez, *Human Res Mgr*
EMP: 12
SQ FT: 10,000
SALES (est): 800K **Privately Held**
WEB: www.alexandermfg.com
SIC: 3599 Machine shop, jobbing & repair

Crossroads
Denton County

(G-3747)
CARTER GLASSBLOWING INC
5751 Fm 424 (76227-7299)
P.O. Box 489, Santo (76472-0489)
PHONE........................940 440-3090
Royce E Carter, *President*
Laura Petty, *Office Mgr*
▲ EMP: 12
SQ FT: 9,000
SALES (est): 2MM **Privately Held**
WEB: www.cgquartz.com
SIC: 3679 Quartz crystals, for electronic application

(G-3748)
HAYES BUILDING SERVICE INC
1011 E Oak Shores Dr (76227-2410)
PHONE........................940 484-7775
Greg Hayes, *President*
EMP: 12
SQ FT: 20,000
SALES (est): 2.1MM **Privately Held**
WEB: www.hayesbuildingservices.com
SIC: 2521 Wood office filing cabinets & bookcases

(G-3749)
RP WELDING INC
9000 King Ranch Dr (76227-8294)
PHONE........................940 315-1024
Pedro Ramirez, *Branch Mgr*
EMP: 13 **Privately Held**
SIC: 7692 Welding repair
PA: Rp Welding Inc
   2412 Old North Rd Ste 101
   Denton TX 76209

(G-3750)
SORENSEN INDUSTRIES INC
Also Called: Titan Fence & Supply
301 S Highway 377 (76227-2511)
PHONE........................940 365-9999
Jeffrey P Sorensen, *President*
Andrew Craft, *CFO*
Roger Dowell, *Sales Staff*
Cindy Osborne, *Manager*
EMP: 45
SQ FT: 5,000
SALES: 7.1MM **Privately Held**
WEB: www.titanfence.com
SIC: 1799 2499 3446 3496 Fence construction; fencing, wood; fences or posts, ornamental iron or steel; fencing, made from purchased wire; wire fence, gates & accessories

Crowley
Tarrant County

(G-3751)
AZZ INC
Also Called: Aztec Galvanizing Services
200 N Beverly St (76036-2506)
P.O. Box 647 (76036-0647)
PHONE........................817 297-4361
Jim Duggan, *Sales Staff*
Rick Wood, *Manager*
EMP: 33
SALES (corp-wide): 1B **Publicly Held**
WEB: www.azz.com
SIC: 3699 3547 3312 Electrical equipment & supplies; galvanizing lines (rolling mill equipment); iron & steel: galvanized, pipes, plates, sheets, etc.
PA: Azz Inc.
   3100 W 7th St Ste 500
   Fort Worth TX 76107
   817 810-0095

(G-3752)
AZZ INC
Aztec Manufacturing Co
400 N Tarrant St (76036-2527)
PHONE........................713 225-9340
Rupam Saikia, *Business Mgr*
Marla Waldoch, *Project Mgr*
Michael Knopp, *Project Engr*
Robert Sloan, *Project Engr*
Michael Carroll, *Controller*
EMP: 33
SALES (corp-wide): 1B **Publicly Held**
WEB: www.azz.com
SIC: 3699 3498 Electrical equipment & supplies; pipe sections fabricated from purchased pipe
PA: Azz Inc.
   3100 W 7th St Ste 500
   Fort Worth TX 76107
   817 810-0095

(G-3753)
CHARLEYS CONCRETE CO LTD
10016 E Crowley Rd (76036)
P.O. Box 1106, Keller (76244-1106)
PHONE........................817 568-2400
Danny Flowers, *Manager*
EMP: 28
SALES (corp-wide): 39MM **Privately Held**
WEB: www.charleysconcrete.com
SIC: 3273 Ready-mixed concrete
PA: Charley's Concrete Co., Ltd.
   11801 Katy Rd
   Fort Worth TX 76244
   817 431-3515

(G-3754)
DALWORTH TECHNOLOGIES INC
Also Called: Dalworth Molds & Tools
1065 Floyd Hampton Rd (76036-4657)
PHONE........................817 297-7976
Ferdinand A Olinger, *President*
James F Olinger, *Vice Pres*
Ted Jagen, *Plant Mgr*
EMP: 9
SQ FT: 2,500
SALES (est): 1.8MM **Privately Held**
WEB: www.dalworthtools-molding.com
SIC: 3089 Injection molding of plastics

(G-3755)
HARBISON-FISCHER INC (DH)
Also Called: Harbison-Fischer Manufacturing
901 N Crowley Rd (76036-3798)
PHONE........................817 297-2211
David Martin, *President*
Darryl Polasek, *Vice Pres*
Bitz Sandra, *Vice Pres*
Jason Thompson, *Vice Pres*
Jason Taylor, *CFO*
▲ EMP: 280 EST: 1933
SQ FT: 335,000
SALES (est): 181.1MM
SALES (corp-wide): 1.1B **Publicly Held**
WEB: www.apergyals.com
SIC: 3533 3443 Oil field machinery & equipment; tanks, lined: metal plate
HQ: Apergy Artificial Lift International, Llc
   2445 Tech Frest Blvd Ste
   Spring TX 77381
   281 403-5742

Crystal City
Zavala County

(G-3756)
DEL MONTE FOODS INC
2205 Old Uvalde Hwy (78839-1532)
PHONE........................830 374-3451
James Johnson, *Business Mgr*
Alejandra Ramirez, *Controller*
David Archer, *Branch Mgr*
Rene Terrazas, *Manager*
David Vogl, *Technical Staff*
EMP: 500 **Privately Held**
WEB: www.delmonte.com
SIC: 2033 2035 Canned fruits & specialties; pickles, sauces & salad dressings
HQ: Del Monte Foods, Inc.
   205 N Wiget Ln
   Walnut Creek CA 94598
   925 949-2772

▲ = Import ▼=Export
◆ =Import/Export

(G-3757)
SOLANSKY WELDING AND PUMP INC
501 W Zavala St (78839-2828)
PHONE..........................830 374-3318
Freddie Solansky, *President*
Frank Solansky, *Corp Secy*
EMP: 25
SALES (est): 8.4MM **Privately Held**
WEB: www.solanskyhardwarerental-sandgifts.com
SIC: 5191 7699 7692 Greenhouse equipment & supplies; harness equipment; saddlery; beekeeping supplies (non-durable); pumps & pumping equipment repair; automotive welding; brazing; cracked casting repair

Cuero
Dewitt County

(G-3758)
ALAMO LUMBER COMPANY
Also Called: Alamo 25
704 N Esplanade St (77954-3502)
PHONE..........................361 275-2321
David Wisherd, *Branch Mgr*
EMP: 10
SALES (corp-wide): 52.9MM **Privately Held**
WEB: www.alamo.doitbest.com
SIC: 5251 3273 Hardware; ready-mixed concrete
HQ: Alamo Lumber Company
10800 Sentinel St
San Antonio TX 78217
210 590-9300

(G-3759)
DLUGOSCH III LLC
101 W Heaton St (77954-3941)
P.O. Box 338, Yorktown (78164-0338)
PHONE..........................361 275-9282
EMP: 16
SALES (corp-wide): 18.4MM **Privately Held**
SIC: 3494 Valves & pipe fittings
PA: Dlugosch Iii, Llc
507 E Main St
Yorktown TX 78164
361 564-9504

(G-3760)
DUNN SERVICES INC
9827 Us Highway 183 S (77954-6555)
PHONE..........................361 275-3952
Blake Dunn, *President*
Kathy Dunn, *Admin Sec*
EMP: 20
SALES (est): 2.8MM **Privately Held**
WEB: www.dunnservices.net
SIC: 1799 1611 1389 Welding on site; highway & street construction; oil field services

(G-3761)
HOOKEN R LLC
186 Smith Ranch Rd (77954-6132)
PHONE..........................817 304-7645
Russell E Harrod,
EMP: 80
SQ FT: 2,000
SALES (est): 3.4MM **Privately Held**
SIC: 1389 Construction, repair & dismantling services

(G-3762)
LARRY MCHORSE SERVICES LLC
Also Called: Bluhms
401 2nd St (77954-2543)
PHONE..........................361 275-4978
Shannon McHorse, *President*
Larry McHorse, *Vice Pres*
EMP: 10
SALES: 950.2K **Privately Held**
WEB: www.larrymchorseservices.com
SIC: 1389 1623 1794 Oil field services; pipeline wrapping; pipe laying construction; excavation work; excavation & grading, building construction

(G-3763)
MCMAHAN WELDING SERVICE LTD
Also Called: McMahan Trailer Sales
269 Us Highway 183 S (77954-6504)
PHONE..........................361 275-0111
Jeff McMahan, *Partner*
Denise McMahan, *Partner*
EMP: 11
SQ FT: 5,000
SALES (est): 2.8MM **Privately Held**
WEB: www.mcmahanwelding.com
SIC: 7692 7539 5084 1799 Welding repair; trailer repair; welding machinery & equipment; welding on site

(G-3764)
MOUNT VERNON MILLS INC
Brentex Division
202 N Gazzie St (77954-3730)
P.O. Box 100, Mauldin SC (29662-0100)
PHONE..........................361 275-2393
Craven Will, *Controller*
Ray Orosco, *Sales Staff*
Ray Rorsco, *Branch Mgr*
EMP: 250 **Privately Held**
WEB: www.mvmills.com
SIC: 2211 2221 Cotton broad woven goods; polyester broadwoven fabrics
HQ: Mount Vernon Mills, Inc.
503 S Main St
Mauldin SC 29662
864 688-7100

(G-3765)
PAISANO SERVICE & SUPPLY INC
751 Us Highway 183 S (77954-6544)
P.O. Box 112 (77954-0112)
PHONE..........................361 572-0322
Ed Harvey, *CEO*
Peggy Tomlinson, *President*
Brad Tomlinson, *Vice Pres*
Tom Tomlinson, *Vice Pres*
Michael Holt, *CFO*
EMP: 24
SALES (est): 5.7MM **Privately Held**
WEB: www.paisanoservice.com
SIC: 1389 Haulage, oil field

(G-3766)
SURFACE BURIAL VAULT MONUMENT
Also Called: Surface Burial Vaults Monu Co
1319 E Broadway St (77954-2139)
P.O. Box 288 (77954-0288)
PHONE..........................361 275-3213
Justin Cooper, *President*
Darrel Foster, *Manager*
Elaine Foster, *Manager*
EMP: 14 EST: 1938
SALES (est): 2.8MM **Privately Held**
WEB: www.surfaceburialvault.com
SIC: 5099 3272 Monuments & grave markers; burial vaults, concrete or precast terrazzo

Cushing
Nacogdoches County

(G-3767)
BALLQUBE LC
12146 County Road 4233 W (75760-6232)
PHONE..........................903 863-5572
Suzanne Pham, *President*
Sally L Rogers, *President*
Kenneth D Rogers, *Corp Secy*
Brendan Rogers, *Treasurer*
Kathryn Kendall, *Sales Staff*
▲ EMP: 20
SQ FT: 20,000
SALES (est): 3.7MM **Privately Held**
WEB: www.ballqube.com
SIC: 3089 Injection molded finished plastic products; extruded finished plastic products

Cut and Shoot
Montgomery County

(G-3768)
T AND S MACHINE COMPANY
19160 Fm 1484 Rd 105 (77303-4744)
P.O. Box 7188, Conroe (77306-0188)
PHONE..........................936 264-1030
Sandra Welch, *President*
Deidra Welch, *General Mgr*
Travis Welch, *Vice Pres*
Debbie Welch, *Sales Staff*
Wayne Welch, *Marketing Mgr*
EMP: 35
SQ FT: 1,216
SALES (est): 5.2MM **Privately Held**
WEB: www.tnsmachine.com
SIC: 3599 Machine shop, jobbing & repair

Cypress
Harris County

(G-3769)
5 FAB ENERGY INC
16703 Steinhagen Rd (77429-7152)
PHONE..........................832 596-7140
Magdaleno Bonilla, *President*
EMP: 9
SALES (est): 1.6MM **Privately Held**
WEB: www.5fabenergy.com
SIC: 3441 Fabricated structural metal

(G-3770)
A E MACHINE WORKS INC
14602 Cypress N Huston Rd (77429-3316)
P.O. Box 40305, Houston (77240-0305)
PHONE..........................281 970-2020
Wesley Mills, *President*
Michael Sicola, *Corp Secy*
Edwin Konvicka, *Vice Pres*
Brandon Kocher, *Sales Mgr*
EMP: 25 EST: 1966
SQ FT: 25,000
SALES (est): 4.8MM **Privately Held**
WEB: www.aemachine.com
SIC: 3599 Machine shop, jobbing & repair

(G-3771)
AMERICAN MAINTENANCE SUPS LLC
15922 Cyprs N Hstn Rd (77429-2193)
PHONE..........................281 304-8369
Brian Simmons, *Mng Member*
Jackie Simmons,
EMP: 15
SALES (est): 2.7MM **Privately Held**
WEB: www.americanmaintenancesupplies.com
SIC: 3524 Lawn & garden equipment

(G-3772)
AMERICAN WHL THERMOGRAPHERS (HQ)
Also Called: Kwik Kopy Printing
12715 Telge Rd (77429-2289)
PHONE..........................281 256-4100
Steve Hammerstein, *President*
EMP: 120
SQ FT: 31,000
SALES (est): 5.6MM **Privately Held**
WEB: www.awt.com
SIC: 2759 2752 Thermography; commercial printing, lithographic

(G-3773)
AMERICAN WHL THERMOGRAPHERS
Also Called: Awt
12715 Telge Rd (77429-2289)
PHONE..........................713 896-9008
Brian Gay, *President*
EMP: 10 **Privately Held**
WEB: www.awt.com
SIC: 2752 Commercial printing, lithographic
HQ: American Wholesale Thermographers, Inc
12715 Telge Rd
Cypress TX 77429
281 256-4100

(G-3774)
AMKIN TECHNOLOGIES LLC
12320 Barker Cypress Rd (77429-8325)
PHONE..........................281 755-2046
Gary Stratulate, *CEO*
Jeff Merecka, *CFO*
EMP: 15
SALES (est): 2.3MM **Privately Held**
WEB: www.aggregatetechnologies.com
SIC: 3677 Electronic coils, transformers & other inductors

(G-3775)
AQUAJET MANUFACTURING
18635 Telge Rd (77429-1781)
PHONE..........................832 484-9244
James Trew, *Owner*
EMP: 20
SALES (est): 1.9MM **Privately Held**
WEB: www.aquajetmfg.com
SIC: 3999 Manufacturing industries

(G-3776)
ARTISTIC IRON & FORGE
11834 Dula Ln (77429-5842)
PHONE..........................281 807-3440
David Cruey, *Owner*
Jeremiah Cruey, *Owner*
EMP: 12
SALES (est): 1MM **Privately Held**
WEB: www.artisticironandforge.com
SIC: 3446 Architectural metalwork

(G-3777)
AUTOMATION TECHNOLOGY INC (PA)
Also Called: ATI Actuators
21225 Fm 529 Rd (77433-5139)
PHONE..........................713 934-0171
Cooper Etheridge, *President*
Todd Howard, *Vice Pres*
Reagie Ebner, *Production*
Paul Martinez, *Production*
Jackie Brandes, *Buyer*
EMP: 25
SALES (est): 13.2MM **Privately Held**
WEB: www.atiactuators.com
SIC: 3593 Fluid power cylinders & actuators

(G-3778)
BEXXT INC
21233 Fm 529 Rd (77433-5139)
PHONE..........................832 209-7970
Robert Bird, *Principal*
Ken Breaux, *Principal*
Nick Fontenot, *Controller*
EMP: 13 EST: 2009
SALES (est): 2.5MM **Privately Held**
WEB: www.bexxt.com
SIC: 3599 3491 Machine shop, jobbing & repair; industrial valves

(G-3779)
BLESS-SCENT CANDLE COMPANY LLC
8803 Clemens Dr (77433-3673)
PHONE..........................832 431-9923
Tascha Stith, *Mng Member*
Tascha L Stith,
EMP: 18
SALES (est): 508.4K **Privately Held**
SIC: 3999 5199 5999 7389 Candles; candles; candle shops;

(G-3780)
BLUE HORSE EXPRESS LLC
15214 Flintridge Lake Ln (77429-7352)
PHONE..........................832 966-1053
Victor Sandhu, *Mng Member*
EMP: 12
SALES (est): 900.1K **Privately Held**
SIC: 3715 Truck trailers

(G-3781)
BLUE MEDICAL SERVICES INC
Also Called: Medical Practice Management
7522 Alpine Park Ln (77433-1534)
PHONE..........................954 417-5442
Joseph Barthol, *CEO*
EMP: 24

SALES (est): 1MM Privately Held
SIC: 3841 8099 3061 2326 Surgical & medical instruments; medical services organization; medical & surgical rubber tubing (extruded & lathe-cut); medical & hospital uniforms, men's

(G-3782)
BOLFING BROTHERS MARBLE INC
18407 Telge Rd (77429-7027)
PHONE..................................281 351-7195
Phil Bolfing, *President*
Rose Anne Bolfing, *Vice Pres*
Chris Felix, *Plant Mgr*
EMP: 50
SQ FT: 20,000
SALES (est): 5.9MM Privately Held
WEB: www.bolfingbrothers.com
SIC: 3281 Marble, building: cut & shaped

(G-3783)
CS&P TECHNOLOGIES LP (PA)
Also Called: C S & P Cryogenics
18119 Telge Rd (77429-1301)
P.O. Box 130 (77410-0130)
PHONE..................................713 467-0869
◆ **EMP: 99**
SQ FT: 15,000
SALES (est): 84.9MM Privately Held
WEB: www.csphouston.com
SIC: 3561 Pumps & pumping equipment

(G-3784)
CY-FAIR COATINGS INC
18115 Telge Rd 1 (77429-1301)
P.O. Box 1440, Tomball (77377-1440)
PHONE..................................281 351-7427
Cheryl Shuck, *President*
EMP: 12
SQ FT: 154,000
SALES (est): 1.5MM Privately Held
WEB: www.cy-faircoatings.com
SIC: 1799 3479 3471 1721 Exterior cleaning, including sandblasting; sandblasting of building exteriors; painting, coating & hot dipping; coating, rust preventive; painting of metal products; plating & polishing; industrial painting

(G-3785)
DELTA CONTROLS COMPANY INC
18410 E Paloma Dr (77433-5904)
PHONE..................................281 469-4891
EMP: 11
SQ FT: 4,000
SALES (est): 1.6MM Privately Held
SIC: 3823 Mfg Control Panels

(G-3786)
DIVERSIFIED STEEL
15922 Stenbury Ct (77429-6971)
PHONE..................................281 213-3340
Michael Wayne Owens, *Owner*
EMP: 50
SALES (est): 4.5MM Privately Held
WEB: www.diversifiedsteelfab.com
SIC: 3441 Fabricated structural metal

(G-3787)
ENERFLEX ENERGY SYSTEMS INC
12015 Barker Cypress Rd (77433-1804)
PHONE..................................281 758-4900
EMP: 88
SALES (corp-wide): 1.5B Privately Held
SIC: 3585 7623 7699 3563 Mfg Refrig/Heat Equip Refrigeration Svc/Repair Repair Services Mfg Air/Gas Compressors
HQ: Enerflex Energy Systems Inc.
10815 Telge Rd
Houston TX 77095
281 345-9300

(G-3788)
ENVIRO-SAN CORPORATION
16522 Cypress Rosehill Rd (77429-1426)
P.O. Box 655 (77410-0655)
PHONE..................................281 373-4200
Gordon Clunn, *Vice Pres*
Sandra Clunn, *Vice Pres*
EMP: 12

SALES (est): 1MM Privately Held
WEB: www.envirosan.com
SIC: 3275 Acoustical plaster, gypsum

(G-3789)
EXCEL STAMPING & MFG INC
20101 Schiel Rd (77433-4234)
PHONE..................................281 304-0771
Fred Yaggi Jr, *President*
Charlotte Schoedinger, *Corp Secy*
Lee Kinney, *Safety Mgr*
EMP: 20
SQ FT: 15,000
SALES (est): 5.2MM Privately Held
WEB: www.excelstamping-mfg.com
SIC: 3441 3469 Fabricated structural metal; stamping metal for the trade

(G-3790)
FLOW PROCESS TECHNOLOGIES INC
17818 Grant Rd (77429-7116)
PHONE..................................281 351-9427
Allyn B Conwell, *President*
Olga Conwell, *Treasurer*
▲ **EMP: 14**
SQ FT: 20,000
SALES (est): 2.8MM Privately Held
WEB: www.flowprocess.com
SIC: 3533 Oil & gas field machinery

(G-3791)
FOTOWN PRODUCTIONS
Also Called: Fotown Diaster Solutions
19034 Greenview Glen Dr (77433-0051)
PHONE..................................225 773-1894
Adam Nelson, *Partner*
EMP: 10
SALES (est): 126.1K Privately Held
SIC: 7291 8322 3577 Tax return preparation services; disaster service; data conversion equipment, media-to-media: computer

(G-3792)
FRAC FUEL SOLUTIONS LLC
17811 Fairhaven Sunset Ct (77433-6169)
PHONE..................................713 907-4371
Roy Moffitt Jr, *Mng Member*
EMP: 21
SALES (est): 500K Privately Held
WEB: www.fracfuelsolutions.com
SIC: 1389 Oil field services

(G-3793)
FYCO TOOL & DIE INC
20101 Schiel Rd (77433-4234)
PHONE..................................281 304-4480
Charlotte Schoedinger, *Principal*
Matt Yaggi, *Vice Pres*
James Lundgren, *Sales Staff*
Fred C Yaggi Jr, *Director*
Freddie Yaggi, *Executive*
EMP: 17
SALES (est): 2.5MM Privately Held
WEB: www.fycotool-die.com
SIC: 3544 Special dies & tools

(G-3794)
G-III APPAREL GROUP LTD
29300 Highway 290 Ste 946 (77433-3808)
PHONE..................................281 256-3661
Karl Zummallen, *Branch Mgr*
EMP: 14 Publicly Held
WEB: www.giii.com
SIC: 2335 5621 Women's, juniors' & misses' dresses; women's specialty clothing stores
PA: G-Iii Apparel Group, Ltd.
512 7th Ave Fl 35
New York NY 10018

(G-3795)
GEOMETRICA INC (PA)
12300 Dundee Ct Ste 200 (77429-8363)
PHONE..................................832 220-1200
Francisco Castano, *President*
▲ **EMP: 18**
SQ FT: 1,984
SALES (est): 12.5MM Privately Held
WEB: www.geometrica.com
SIC: 3448 Prefabricated metal buildings

(G-3796)
GEOTHERM USA LLC
21239 Fm 529 Rd Ste F (77433-8061)
PHONE..................................281 985-9344
Deepak Parma, *Mng Member*
Geeta Parmar, *Mng Member*
Meera Patel, *Mng Member*
Nimesh Patel, *Manager*
EMP: 11
SQ FT: 10,000
SALES (est): 576.5K Privately Held
WEB: www.geothermusa.com
SIC: 8734 3826 Soil analysis; thermal analysis instruments, laboratory type

(G-3797)
GNC CABLE TECHNOLOGIES INC
Also Called: B J'S Custom Cables
18222 Alemarble Oak St (77429-1414)
PHONE..................................832 876-1780
Betty Burgess, *President*
EMP: 10
SALES (est): 1.3MM Privately Held
WEB: www.gnc.com
SIC: 3679 Harness assemblies for electronic use: wire or cable

(G-3798)
GOOEYS
15407 Hickory Dale St (77429-4991)
PHONE..................................832 788-9644
Ginger Jones,
EMP: 10 EST: 2018
SALES (est): 325K Privately Held
WEB:
www.gooeysicecreamsandwiches.com
SIC: 2024 Ice cream & frozen desserts

(G-3799)
HMC INSTRMENTATION CONTRLS LLC
16940 Grant Rd (77429-7357)
PHONE..................................832 252-9280
Jason McDaniel, *Vice Pres*
Jay Rodriguez, *Project Mgr*
Ryan Scott, *Purchasing*
Sam Gosdin, *Manager*
Bryan Harris, *Manager*
EMP: 203
SQ FT: 1,500
SALES (est): 16.8MM Privately Held
WEB: www.hmcic.com
SIC: 3533 7699 Oil & gas field machinery; machinery cleaning

(G-3800)
HOLD PHONE LLC
12320 Barker Cypress Rd (77429-8325)
PHONE..................................281 304-4777
Marc Langland,
EMP: 13
SALES (est): 1.5MM Privately Held
SIC: 3661 Telephone answering machines

(G-3801)
HONEYWELL INTERNATIONAL INC
21300 Northwest Fwy (77429-4551)
PHONE..................................281 890-0088
Billy Abshire, *Branch Mgr*
EMP: 657
SALES (corp-wide): 36.7B Publicly Held
WEB: www.honeywell.com
SIC: 3724 3812 3728 2824 Aircraft engines & engine parts; aircraft control systems, electronic; brakes, aircraft; nylon fibers; polyethylene resins; motor vehicle parts & accessories
PA: Honeywell International Inc.
300 S Tryon St
Charlotte NC 28202
704 627-6200

(G-3802)
HUNTING SPECIALTY SUPPLY LP
13730 Cypress N Huston Rd (77429-3237)
PHONE..................................281 970-8444
Gerald Byrd, *Partner*
Gerald R Byrd, *Partner*
James Chambers, *General Ptnr*
Raul Luna, *Foreman/Supr*
EMP: 50
SQ FT: 9,500

SALES (est): 14.5MM
SALES (corp-wide): 960MM Privately Held
SIC: 3533 Oil & gas drilling rigs & equipment
HQ: Hunting Energy Services, Llc
16825 Northchase Dr # 600
Houston TX 77060

(G-3803)
J K WELDING SERVICE LLC
18433 Fm 529 Rd (77433-1163)
PHONE..................................281 550-1008
John J King,
EMP: 25
SALES (est): 5.9MM Privately Held
WEB: www.jkwelding.net
SIC: 1761 1799 3444 Roofing contractor; welding on site; sheet metal specialties, not stamped

(G-3804)
JAMES D VOSSLER
14022 Sunrise Arbor Ln (77429-7721)
PHONE..................................281 376-6420
James D Vossler, *Owner*
EMP: 10
SALES (est): 694.7K Privately Held
SIC: 2621 Printing paper

(G-3805)
JONES TAPE DUPLICATING INC
17408 Bobcat Trl (77429-1200)
PHONE..................................281 351-8109
Doyle E Jones, *President*
Jones Bruce, *Vice Pres*
David Bruce Jones, *Vice Pres*
Mary Jones, *Treasurer*
EMP: 9 EST: 1971
SQ FT: 10,000
SALES (est): 835.7K Privately Held
SIC: 3652 Master records or tapes, preparation of

(G-3806)
K&P OILFIELD SOLUTIONS
15207 Waverly Canyon Ct (77429-4421)
PHONE..................................254 290-4862
Jeffrey Krueger, *Owner*
EMP: 9
SALES (est): 200.6K Privately Held
SIC: 1389 Oil field services

(G-3807)
KK MEIER CO LLC
Also Called: Bohama
14030 Telge Rd Ste J (77429-6201)
PHONE..................................281 256-7366
Kevin Meier,
EMP: 18
SALES (est): 425K Privately Held
SIC: 2024 Ice cream & frozen desserts

(G-3808)
KWIK-KOPY CORPORATION
Also Called: Kwik Kopy Printing
1 Kwik Kopy Ln (77429-5785)
PHONE..................................281 256-4100
Frederick Hadfield, *Ch of Bd*
Steven Hammerstien, *President*
Brian Gay, *Vice Pres*
Scott Krueger, *CFO*
Deborah Clifford, *Admin Sec*
EMP: 140 EST: 1967
SQ FT: 31,000
SALES (est): 12MM Privately Held
WEB: www.kwikkopy.com
SIC: 2752 6794 5084 6153 Commercial printing, offset; franchises, selling or licensing; printing trades machinery, equipment & supplies; working capital financing; business training services
PA: International Center For Entrepreneurial Development Inc
12715 Telge Rd
Cypress TX 77429

(G-3809)
MCGUFFY ENERGY SERVICES LP
18635 Telge Rd (77429-1781)
P.O. Box 697, Tomball (77377-0697)
PHONE..................................281 255-6955
Steven Wormald, *Managing Prtnr*
▼ **EMP: 85**
SQ FT: 28,000

SALES (est): 23.5MM **Privately Held**
WEB: www.mcguffy.com
SIC: **2813** Industrial gases

(G-3810)
PARIS CONSTRUCTION LLC
16518 House Hahl Rd (77433-1901)
PHONE..................................832 752-5271
Tony Paris, *CEO*
EMP: 10
SALES (est): 64.1K **Privately Held**
SIC: **1389** 1799 Construction, repair & dismantling services; welding on site

(G-3811)
PERFORMANCE GEAR HDQTR LLC
Also Called: Rtic Custom Shop
17689 Telge Rd (77477-7080)
PHONE..................................281 402-6816
Jacob Thomas Daniels, *Mng Member*
EMP: 21
SQ FT: 15,000
SALES (est): 203.8K **Privately Held**
WEB: www.rticcustomshop.com
SIC: **3089** Tumblers, plastic

(G-3812)
PETRA OIL COMPANY INC
11085 Regency Green Dr (77429-4756)
PHONE..................................888 738-7261
Arnold Gacita, *President*
Steven Burns, *Vice Pres*
Keith Orr, *Director*
EMP: 15 EST: 2010
SALES (est): 2.9MM **Privately Held**
WEB: www.petraoilco.com
SIC: **2911** Oils, fuel

(G-3813)
PRESTIGE CUSTOM CABINETRY
18902 Fm 529 Rd Ste D (77433-3396)
PHONE..................................832 674-8074
EMP: 9 EST: 2014
SALES (est): 643.4K **Privately Held**
WEB: www.prestigecabinetdoors.net
SIC: **2434** Wood kitchen cabinets

(G-3814)
PROFESSIONAL PROJECTS INC
Also Called: P P I
18115 Telge Rd (77429)
PHONE..................................281 351-6315
Meredith Gibbs, *President*
EMP: 60 EST: 1979
SQ FT: 8,000
SALES (est): 7.3MM **Privately Held**
WEB: www.professionalprojectsinc.com
SIC: **1389** 3441 3443 Gas field services; fabricated structural metal; vessels, process or storage (from boiler shops); metal plate

(G-3815)
PROPTESTER INCORPORATED (PA)
17222 Huffmeister Rd B (77429-1643)
PHONE..................................281 256-8880
Don Anaschutz, *CEO*
Jason J Renkes, *Chairman*
Earl Freeman, *Exec VP*
Ian Renkes, *Opers Staff*
Ashley Rich, *Manager*
▲ EMP: 13
SALES (est): 4.1MM **Privately Held**
WEB: www.proptester.com
SIC: **1389** Oil consultants

(G-3816)
PROTECTIVE CONCEPTS INC
17803 Grant Rd (77429-7124)
PHONE..................................832 843-7619
Adam Ester, *President*
Natalie Ester, *Sales Staff*
EMP: 15
SQ FT: 8,000
SALES (est): 935K **Privately Held**
WEB: www.pci-worldwide.com
SIC: **5033** 2261 2262 1799 Insulation, thermal; fire resistance finishing of cotton broadwoven fabrics; fire resistance finishing: manmade & silk broadwoven; insulation of pipes & boilers; mineral wool insulation products; acoustical & insulation work

(G-3817)
R & N MANUFACTURING LTD
21235 Fm 529 Rd (77433-5139)
PHONE..................................713 466-6252
Richard Noppe, *President*
Sherry Noppe, *Exec VP*
Jessica Noppe, *Engineer*
Justin James, *Manager*
EMP: 60
SQ FT: 17,500
SALES (est): 16.4MM **Privately Held**
WEB: www.rnmanufacturing.com
SIC: **3443** 7692 3441 Bins, prefabricated metal plate; welding repair; fabricated structural metal

(G-3818)
S + S INSTRUMENTS INC
19001 Fm 529 Rd (77433-2284)
P.O. Box 957 (77410-0957)
PHONE..................................281 463-1600
Herman Schuller, *President*
Louis Sellers, *Vice Pres*
EMP: 13
SQ FT: 25,000
SALES (est): 2.5MM **Privately Held**
WEB: www.ssinstruments.com
SIC: **3599** Machine shop, jobbing & repair

(G-3819)
SBI PRECISION COMPONENTS LLC
17643 Telge Rd (77429-7080)
PHONE..................................713 715-6111
Kenneth Scott Ward, *Mng Member*
John Stephen Baker,
Ty Lee Larsen,
EMP: 9
SQ FT: 7,500
SALES (est): 500K **Privately Held**
WEB: www.sbiprecision.com
SIC: **3599** Machine shop, jobbing & repair

(G-3820)
SLZ REBAR LLC
7719 Serene Wood Ln (77433-6563)
PHONE..................................832 427-5860
Jorge Salazar, *Mng Member*
Marcial Salazar,
EMP: 13
SALES (est): 420.9K **Privately Held**
SIC: **1791** 3449 7389 Structural steel erection; bars, concrete reinforcing: fabricated steel;

(G-3821)
SOFTECH CONTROLS INC
15710 Cascading Brook Way (77433-5557)
PHONE..................................713 553-0365
Ronnie K Robinson, *CEO*
C M Witherspon, *President*
EMP: 10
SALES (est): 1.2MM **Privately Held**
SIC: **3823** Industrial instrmnts msrmnt display/control process variable

(G-3822)
SS MACHINE LP
Also Called: Specialty Supply
13730 Cypress N Huston Rd (77429-3237)
PHONE..................................281 970-8444
James Chambers, *General Ptnr*
EMP: 40
SALES (est): 4.7MM **Privately Held**
SIC: **3545** Machine tool accessories

(G-3823)
TRAW MACHINE WORKS LLC
18635 Telge Rd (77429-1781)
PHONE..................................281 893-1710
Brian K Traw, *President*
Linda Traw, *Owner*
EMP: 39
SQ FT: 12,500
SALES (est): 8.5MM **Privately Held**
WEB: www.trawmachine.com
SIC: **3599** Machine shop, jobbing & repair

(G-3824)
TYSON GLOBL TRNSPT & CNSTR LLC
15507 Stallion Point Cir (77429-7095)
PHONE..................................470 481-6161
Toni Scott, *Principal*
Ronald Hampton, *Principal*

EMP: 27
SALES (est): 1.7MM **Privately Held**
SIC: **3731** Transport vessels, troop: building & repairing

(G-3825)
VITRUVIAN EXPLORATION II LLC (PA)
13814 Riverton Manor Ct (77429-8164)
PHONE..................................832 458-3100
John D Thaeler, *President*
Richard Lane, *Chairman*
Mark Blumenshine, *Senior VP*
Karl Knudson, *Senior VP*
John Davies, *Vice Pres*
EMP: 17
SALES (est): 13.8MM **Privately Held**
WEB: www.vexpl.com
SIC: **1382** Oil & gas exploration services

(G-3826)
VITRUVIAN EXPLORATION IV LLC
13814 Riverton Manor Ct (77429-8164)
PHONE..................................832 458-3100
Brian L Rickmers, *President*
Rhuben Coffey, *Vice Pres*
Cindy Giacona, *Treasurer*
Jasen Bradley, *Manager*
Trey Hebert, *Info Tech Mgr*
EMP: 41
SALES (est): 119.9K **Privately Held**
SIC: **1382** Geological exploration, oil & gas field

(G-3827)
WILLIAMS MACHINE INC
19738 Ashley Terrace Ln (77433-2522)
P.O. Box 924088, Houston (77292-4088)
PHONE..................................713 462-2229
Sarah Hopkins, *President*
Vicky Lyman, *Admin Sec*
EMP: 17
SQ FT: 14,400
SALES (est): 1.4MM **Privately Held**
SIC: **3625** Actuators, industrial

D Hanis
Medina County

(G-3828)
CLAY DHANIS PRODUCTS INC
Also Called: D'Hanis Brick & Tile Co
Old Eagle Pass Rd (78850)
P.O. Box 308 (78850-0308)
PHONE..................................830 363-7636
Mark Garrison, *Manager*
EMP: 28 **Privately Held**
WEB: www.dhanisbricktile.com
SIC: **3251** Brick & structural clay tile
PA: Clay D'hanis Products Inc
   311 E Nakoma St
   San Antonio TX 78216

(G-3829)
H6 AIRCRAFT LLC
Also Called: Hangar 6
732 County Road 312 (78850-6819)
PHONE..................................830 741-3836
Russell Lindeman, *President*
Anthony Tice, *Vice Pres*
Geoffrey Hall, *CFO*
EMP: 12
SQ FT: 45,000
SALES (est): 752.1K **Privately Held**
SIC: **3721** Aircraft

Daingerfield
Morris County

(G-3830)
ATLAS ROOFING CORPORATION
Gypsum and Roofing Division
1100 E Georgia Pacific Dr (75638-1161)
P.O. Box 700 (75638-0700)
PHONE..................................903 645-3988
Russ Addison, *Production*
Wade Kerley, *Purch Mgr*
Marla Bullard, *Human Res Mgr*
Greg Frost,

Tommy Fisher, *Administration*
EMP: 150 **Privately Held**
WEB: www.atlasroofing.com
SIC: **3086** Insulation or cushioning material, foamed plastic
HQ: Atlas Roofing Corporation
   802 Highway 19 N Ste 190
   Meridian MS 39307
   601 484-8900

(G-3831)
DELTA FABRICATION AND MCH INC (PA)
1379 County Road 2110 (75638-4421)
P.O. Box 980 (75638-0980)
PHONE..................................903 645-3994
Gerald W Williams, *President*
Paula Williams, *Corp Secy*
Joshua Williams, *Vice Pres*
Dwayne Staples, *Mfg Staff*
Randy Wright, *Human Resources*
▲ EMP: 95
SQ FT: 22,000
SALES (est): 64.8MM **Privately Held**
WEB: www.deltafab.net
SIC: **1541** 3599 3441 Industrial buildings, new construction; paper/pulp mill construction; machine shop, jobbing & repair; fabricated structural metal

Daisetta
Liberty County

(G-3832)
B & J VACUUM TANK SERVICE INC
Hwy 770 1 Mile S (77533)
P.O. Box 400 (77533-0400)
PHONE..................................936 536-6148
Jeff Green, *President*
EMP: 9 EST: 1964
SQ FT: 3,000
SALES (est): 1.8MM **Privately Held**
SIC: **1389** Oil field services

Dalhart
Dallam County

(G-3833)
DALHART PUBLISHING CO
Also Called: Dalhart Daily Texan
410 Denrock Ave (79022-2628)
PHONE..................................806 244-4511
Robert S Clay, *President*
EMP: 10
SQ FT: 3,500
SALES (est): 505K **Privately Held**
WEB: www.thedalharttexan.com
SIC: **2711** Newspapers: publishing only, not printed on site

(G-3834)
DALHART R & R MCH WORKS INC
Also Called: R&R Machine
1006 Liberal St (79022-2916)
P.O. Box 1330 (79022-1330)
PHONE..................................806 244-5686
Warren Cornelius, *President*
▼ EMP: 40 EST: 1976
SQ FT: 33,400
SALES (est): 8.1MM **Privately Held**
WEB: www.randrmachineworks.com
SIC: **3523** 3569 Farm machinery & equipment; filters

(G-3835)
HUNTER CONSTRUCTION INC
Also Called: Transmix Redi Mix
Highway 54 W (79022)
P.O. Box 564 (79022-0564)
PHONE..................................806 244-5331
Jerry Hunter, *President*
EMP: 55
SALES (est): 5.1MM **Privately Held**
SIC: **3273** 1542 Ready-mixed concrete; nonresidential construction

(G-3836)
XIT SAND AND GRAVEL LLC
3212 Us Highway 54 (79022-8001)
PHONE.....................................806 249-8743
Wally N Johnson,
EMP: 9
SALES (est): 3.2MM
SALES (corp-wide): 2.2B **Publicly Held**
WEB: www.xit.net
SIC: 3531 Batching plants, for aggregate concrete & bulk cement
PA: Summit Materials, Inc.
   1550 Wynkoop St Ste 300
   Denver CO 80202
   303 893-0012

Dallas
Collin County

(G-3837)
ALLIED WEAR SYSTEMS LLC
Also Called: Allied Welding Systems
17810 Davenport Rd # 109 (75252-5889)
P.O. Box 795459 (75379-5459)
PHONE.....................................972 248-8838
Douglas Hamblin,
▲ **EMP:** 18
SQ FT: 3,200
SALES (est): 2.4MM **Privately Held**
WEB: www.alliedweldingsystems.com
SIC: 3548 3599 Welding apparatus; machine shop, jobbing & repair

(G-3838)
BAE SYSTEMS INFO & ELEC SYS
17111 Waterview Pkwy (75252-8002)
PHONE.....................................972 994-4176
Kara Quarles, *Human Resources*
John Brickman, *Director*
EMP: 84
SALES (corp-wide): 23.6B **Privately Held**
WEB: www.baesystems.com
SIC: 3812 Aircraft/aerospace flight instruments & guidance systems
HQ: Bae Systems Information And Electronic Systems Integration Inc.
   65 Spit Brook Rd
   Nashua NH 03060
   603 885-4321

(G-3839)
CAMBIUM LEARNING GROUP INC (HQ)
17855 Dallas Pkwy Ste 400 (75287-6857)
PHONE.....................................214 932-9500
John Campbell, *CEO*
Jeffrey A Elliott, *President*
Bob Holl, *President*
Aaron Ingold, *President*
Lisa Omasta, *President*
EMP: 62
SALES: 158.1MM
SALES (corp-wide): 39.2MM **Privately Held**
WEB: www.cambiumlearning.com
SIC: 8299 8211 7372 Educational services; specialty education; educational computer software
PA: Cambium Holding Corp.
   17855 Dallas Pkwy Ste 400
   Dallas TX 75287
   214 932-9500

(G-3840)
CAMBIUM LEARNING INC (DH)
Also Called: Voyager
17855 Dallas Pkwy Ste 400 (75287-6857)
PHONE.....................................214 932-9500
John Campbelle, *CEO*
Carolynn Archer, *Business Mgr*
Barbara Benson, *CFO*
Brian Peters, *Human Res Dir*
Silas Schulze, *Info Tech Mgr*
EMP: 10
SQ FT: 10,000
SALES (est): 108.1MM
SALES (corp-wide): 39.2MM **Privately Held**
WEB: www.cambiumlearning.com
SIC: 2731 Book publishing

(G-3841)
ERIC INDUSTRIES INC
5934 Tree Shadow Trl (75252-5104)
PHONE.....................................972 248-8009
Robert Quat, *President*
Kathryn Ricard, *Vice Pres*
Thomas Crotzer, *Manager*
EMP: 29
SQ FT: 19,000
SALES (est): 5.1MM **Privately Held**
WEB: www.plasticenvelopes.com
SIC: 2677 Envelopes

(G-3842)
ESHIP GLOBAL INC
18111 Preston Rd Ste 650 (75252-6606)
PHONE.....................................972 518-1775
Srini Vasan, *President*
Lawrence Howorth, *COO*
Tomika Hicks, *Manager*
Akash Vasan, *Manager*
Karthik Nathan, *Prgrmr*
EMP: 10
SQ FT: 1,551
SALES (est): 2.2MM **Privately Held**
WEB: www.eshipglobal.com
SIC: 7331 4731 7372 8742 Mailing service; freight transportation arrangement; prepackaged software; management consulting services

(G-3843)
GLOBAL BUSINESS & COMMERCE INC
18208 Preston Rd (75252-6007)
PHONE.....................................214 449-0566
Pj Putnam, *COO*
▲ **EMP:** 10
SQ FT: 7,500
SALES (est): 495.5K **Privately Held**
SIC: 2899 Oils & essential oils

(G-3844)
IDEA PLANET LP (PA)
Also Called: Idea Planet Collectibles
18170 Hillcrest Rd (75252-2742)
PHONE.....................................972 380-9867
Kimberly Flecker, *CEO*
Michael Ableman, *Partner*
Michael Flecker, *Partner*
Michael Selz, *Partner*
Kim Taylor-Flecker, *Partner*
▲ **EMP:** 22
SQ FT: 8,000
SALES (est): 4.3MM **Privately Held**
WEB: www.ideaplanetlp.com
SIC: 8742 2671 2821 3942 Marketing consulting services; paper coated or laminated for packaging; plastics materials & resins; dolls & stuffed toys; art goods; aerial advertising services

(G-3845)
INTERVOICE LLC
17787 Waterview Pkwy (75252-8027)
PHONE.....................................972 454-8000
Fax: 972 454-8707
EMP: 34
SALES (est): 9.8MM **Privately Held**
SIC: 3661 Telephone And Telegraph Apparatus

(G-3846)
INTERVOICE LLC (DH)
17787 Waterview Pkwy (75252-8027)
PHONE.....................................972 454-8000
Jeffrey Daly, *President*
Marc Gardner, *VP Engrg*
John Harrison, *Engineer*
H Don Brown, *VP Human Res*
Kenneth Goldberg, *Marketing Staff*
EMP: 51
SQ FT: 225,000
SALES (est): 88.9MM
SALES (corp-wide): 24.6B **Publicly Held**
WEB: www.intervoice.com
SIC: 3661 PBX equipment, manual or automatic
HQ: Concentrix Cvg Corporation
   201 E 4th St
   Cincinnati OH 45202
   800 747-0583

(G-3847)
LAZEL INC (DH)
Also Called: Voyager
17855 Dallas Pkwy Ste 400 (75287-6857)
PHONE.....................................214 932-9500
Ronald Klausner, *CEO*
Dr Vernon Johnson, *President*
Eric Frenchak, *Regional Mgr*
Scott McWhorter, *Counsel*
Todd Buchardt, *Vice Pres*
EMP: 16
SALES (est): 4.8MM
SALES (corp-wide): 39.2MM **Privately Held**
WEB: www.explorelearning.com
SIC: 3999 Education aids, devices & supplies
HQ: Cambium Learning, Inc.
   17855 Dallas Pkwy Ste 400
   Dallas TX 75287
   214 932-9500

(G-3848)
LETOILE APPAREL INC
Also Called: L'Etoile Children's Apparel
7503 Maribeth Dr (75252-6819)
P.O. Box 797563 (75379-7563)
PHONE.....................................972 701-8916
▲ **EMP:** 25 EST: 1997
SALES (est): 1.8MM **Privately Held**
SIC: 2369 2339 2337 Mfg Girl/Youth Outerwear Mfg Women's/Misses' Outerwear Mfg Women's/Misses' Suits/Coats

(G-3849)
MOBILE SURGICAL TECH INC
17817 Davenport Rd # 315 (75252-5871)
PHONE.....................................972 735-8003
Glenn Yeik, *President*
Kate Rohsner, *Sales Staff*
EMP: 11
SALES (est): 1.4MM
SALES (corp-wide): 4.7MM **Publicly Held**
WEB: www.mstlaser.com
SIC: 3841 Surgical & medical instruments
PA: Trimedyne, Inc.
   519 N Smith Ave Ste 105
   Corona CA 92878
   949 951-3800

(G-3850)
PEAG LLC (PA)
Also Called: Jlab Audio
17950 Preston Rd Ste 360 (75252-4611)
PHONE.....................................858 683-3634
Winthrop Cramer, *CEO*
Gary Wilks, *CFO*
Scott Fesler,
Robert A Smith,
Matt Sotelo,
▲ **EMP:** 22 EST: 2015
SQ FT: 5,000
SALES (est): 4.2MM **Privately Held**
WEB: www.jlabaudio.com
SIC: 3651 Household audio & video equipment

(G-3851)
RER APPAREL INC (PA)
7527 Bromwich Ct (75252-6451)
PHONE.....................................417 673-5786
Richard Rosenbaum, *President*
Eleanor Rosenbaum, *Vice Pres*
EMP: 25
SALES (est): 2.7MM **Privately Held**
SIC: 2326 2339 Work pants; women's & misses' outerwear

(G-3852)
SYNDIANT INC (PA)
18325 Waterview Pkwy A101 (75252-8013)
PHONE.....................................972 248-3331
Daniel Wong, *CEO*
Timothy Rost, *General Mgr*
Amanda Darr, *Sales Staff*
Pete Petropoulos, *Manager*
Steven Chan, *Director*
EMP: 26
SALES (est): 3MM **Privately Held**
WEB: www.syndiant.com
SIC: 3674 Semiconductors & related devices

(G-3853)
TRIPLE DIAMOND ENERGY OPER LLC
17855 Dallas Pkwy Ste 140 (75287-6857)
PHONE.....................................972 267-8600
EMP: 10 EST: 2008
SQ FT: 2,800
SALES (est): 720K **Privately Held**
SIC: 1382 Oil/Gas Exploration Services

(G-3854)
U S COMPANIES INC (PA)
17210 Campbell Rd Ste 100 (75252-4203)
P.O. Box 794608 (75379-4608)
PHONE.....................................214 891-3300
Max Williams, *Ch of Bd*
George Burns, *President*
David R Latchford, *President*
Steve Whitehead, *Treasurer*
Nancy Gee, *Admin Sec*
EMP: 16
SALES (est): 3MM **Privately Held**
WEB: www.uscompanies.com
SIC: 1311 Crude petroleum production

(G-3855)
US AMERICAN RESOURCES INC
3839 Briargrove Ln # 6305 (75287-6360)
PHONE.....................................972 662-9070
John Owen, *President*
Robert Palmer, *Vice Pres*
EMP: 26
SALES (est): 6MM **Privately Held**
WEB: www.usarinc.com
SIC: 1481 Nonmetallic mineral services

(G-3856)
US OPERATING INC (HQ)
17210 Campbell Rd Ste 100 (75252-4203)
P.O. Box 794608 (75379-4608)
PHONE.....................................214 393-3992
Max Williams, *Ch of Bd*
David R Latchford, *President*
Steve Whitehead, *Vice Pres*
Nancy Gee, *Admin Sec*
EMP: 14
SQ FT: 10,000
SALES (est): 1.9MM
SALES (corp-wide): 3MM **Privately Held**
SIC: 1382 Oil & gas exploration services
PA: U S Companies, Inc
   17210 Campbell Rd Ste 100
   Dallas TX 75252
   214 891-3300

(G-3857)
VALKYRIE SYSTEMS AEROSPACE INC
17440 Dallas Pkwy Ste 230 (75287-7397)
PHONE.....................................888 426-2113
Glenn Dawson, *CEO*
EMP: 17
SQ FT: 28,000
SALES (est): 1.5MM **Privately Held**
WEB: www.valkyrieuav.com
SIC: 3812 3721 Aircraft/aerospace flight instruments & guidance systems; aircraft; research & development on aircraft by the manufacturer; airplanes, fixed or rotary wing

(G-3858)
VOYAGER LEARNING COMPANY (DH)
17855 Dallas Pkwy Ste 400 (75287-6857)
PHONE.....................................214 932-9500
David Cappellucci, *President*
Vince Starner, *President*
Scott McWhorter, *Principal*
Todd W Buchardt, *Senior VP*
Bradley C Almond, *CFO*
EMP: 40 EST: 1907
SQ FT: 164,131
SALES (est): 107.8MM
SALES (corp-wide): 39.2MM **Privately Held**
WEB: www.voyagersopris.com
SIC: 2741 2759 Miscellaneous publishing; commercial printing

▲ = Import ▼=Export
◆ =Import/Export

(G-3859)
WARRIOR ENERGY SERVICES CORP
4242 N Capistrano Dr # 17 (75287-4033)
PHONE.....................504 220-8080
EMP: 15 **Publicly Held**
WEB: www.superiorenergy.com
SIC: 1389 Oil field services
HQ: Warrior Energy Services Corporation
5801 Highway 90 E
Broussard LA 70518
337 714-2400

(G-3860)
WILLBNKS FNCL CNSLTING GROUP L
Also Called: Cornerstone Commercial Svcs
3635 Eden Dr (75287-6262)
P.O. Box 703568 (75370-3568)
PHONE.....................469 444-0170
Russell Willbanks, CEO
EMP: 15
SALES (est): 3MM **Privately Held**
WEB: www.cornerstonecommercial.us
SIC: 1542 1389 1522 1531 Restaurant construction; construction, repair & dismantling services; multi-family dwellings, new construction; condominium developers

(G-3861)
XTENTI LLC
17304 Preston Rd Ste 800 (75252-5645)
PHONE.....................818 434-5239
Daniel Lim, President
Robert Murrill, Exec VP
EMP: 9 EST: 2016
SALES (est): 167.7K **Privately Held**
WEB: www.xtenti.com
SIC: 3769 Guided missile & space vehicle parts & aux eqpt, rsch & dev

Dallas
Dallas County

(G-3862)
123PRINT INC
12750 Merit Dr Ste 900 (75251-1237)
PHONE.....................800 877-5147
Mark Latouceur, President
Richard Nelson, VP Mktg
EMP: 150
SALES (est): 8.7MM
SALES (corp-wide): 2.5B **Privately Held**
WEB: www.123print.com
SIC: 2752 Commercial printing, offset
HQ: Navitor, Inc.
1625 Roe Crest Dr
North Mankato MN 56003

(G-3863)
20 SPC INC
14901 Quorum Dr Ste 425 (75254-6907)
PHONE.....................972 687-6700
Craig S Stevens, CEO
EMP: 62
SQ FT: 17,169
SALES (est): 3.2MM **Privately Held**
SIC: 2721 Magazines: publishing only, not printed on site; trade journals: publishing only, not printed on site
PA: 1105 Media, Inc.
6300 Canoga Ave Ste 1150
Woodland Hills CA 91367

(G-3864)
2018 KIDWELL LLC
6324 Prospect Ave (75214-3936)
PHONE.....................214 824-9463
Robert Wilson,
EMP: 20
SALES (est): 847.9K **Privately Held**
SIC: 2084 Wines

(G-3865)
21ST CENTURY FOX AMERICA INC
2626 Howell St Ste 960 (75204-0906)
PHONE.....................214 981-0800
Darin Lee, Manager
EMP: 15
SALES (corp-wide): 65.3B **Publicly Held**
WEB: www.thewaltdisneycompany.com
SIC: 2711 Newspapers: publishing only, not printed on site
HQ: 21st Century Fox America, Inc.
1211 Ave Of The Americas
New York NY 10036
212 852-7000

(G-3866)
2LOGO INC
10859 Shady Trl Ste 102 (75220-1323)
P.O. Box 59685 (75229-1685)
PHONE.....................214 350-2505
Dipam Patel, President
EMP: 12
SQ FT: 4,000
SALES (est): 1.1MM **Privately Held**
WEB: www.2logo.com
SIC: 7389 2395 Embroidering of advertising on shirts, etc.; embroidery products, except schiffli machine

(G-3867)
3 L DESIGNS INC
8821 Directors Row (75247-5507)
PHONE.....................214 920-9223
Lindsey Littrell, President
Denise Littrell, Vice Pres
Mike Jackson, Manager
EMP: 31
SALES (est): 1.6MM **Privately Held**
SIC: 2434 2511 Wood kitchen cabinets; wood household furniture

(G-3868)
34 OAKS FINE CABINETRY LLC
2605 Rodney Ln (75229-3426)
P.O. Box 29324 (75229-0324)
PHONE.....................469 533-0730
Arturo Valdez, Mng Member
Luis Alcala,
Thomas Sukach,
EMP: 70
SQ FT: 2,000
SALES (est): 3MM **Privately Held**
WEB: www.34oaks.com
SIC: 2434 Wood kitchen cabinets

(G-3869)
3DGENCE AMERICA INC
1841 E Levee St (75207-6803)
PHONE.....................469 466-2950
Ron Faruqui, CEO
Kristin Booth, Principal
EMP: 12 EST: 2018
SALES (est): 263.9K **Privately Held**
SIC: 2759 Screen printing

(G-3870)
A G VAN & TRUCK EQP INC
2323 N Support Rd (75261)
PHONE.....................214 638-8805
Harley J Westfall, President
Dorian Page, Sales Staff
Joseph E Emens, Asst Sec
EMP: 31
SQ FT: 22,000
SALES (est): 7.7MM
SALES (corp-wide): 128.9MM **Privately Held**
WEB: www.agvan.com
SIC: 5013 5531 5014 3713 Automotive supplies & parts; automobile & truck equipment & parts; truck tires & tubes; truck bodies & parts
PA: Adrian Steel Company
906 James St
Adrian MI 49221
517 265-6194

(G-3871)
A H BELO CORPORATION (PA)
1954 Commerce St (75201-5205)
P.O. Box 224866 (75222-4866)
PHONE.....................214 977-8222
Robert W Decherd, Ch of Bd
Christine E Larkin, Senior VP
Teri Andrews, Vice Pres
Mitchell Belitz, Vice Pres
Christine Larkin, Vice Pres
EMP: 61

SALES (corp-wide): 183.5MM **Publicly Held**
WEB: www.ahbelo.com
SIC: 2711 7313 Newspapers, publishing & printing; electronic media advertising representatives

(G-3872)
A&B FOUNDRY LLC
11165 Denton Dr (75229-4707)
PHONE.....................972 247-3579
Trisha Cubit, CEO
Ernest Cubit,
EMP: 10 EST: 1965
SQ FT: 5,240
SALES (est): 2MM **Privately Held**
WEB: www.abfoundryllc.com
SIC: 3365 3366 3993 5091 Aluminum & aluminum-based alloy castings; brass foundry; castings (except die): brass; signs & advertising specialties; swimming pools, equipment & supplies

(G-3873)
AAA PRODUCTS INTERNATIONAL INC
7114 Harry Hines Blvd (75235-4010)
PHONE.....................214 357-3851
Harry Womack, President
Kent Wiaite, Vice Pres
Kent Waite, VP Mfg
▲ EMP: 17 EST: 1960
SQ FT: 6,000
SALES (est): 3.1MM **Privately Held**
WEB: www.aaaproducts.com
SIC: 3533 3491 3494 3492 Drilling tools for gas, oil or water wells; industrial valves; valves & pipe fittings; fluid power valves & hose fittings

(G-3874)
AALFS MANUFACTURING INC
Also Called: W J Denims
5440 Harvest Hill Rd # 182 (75230-1605)
PHONE.....................972 991-3945
Brad Fritts, Vice Pres
EMP: 400
SALES (corp-wide): 28.7MM **Privately Held**
WEB: www.aalfs.com
SIC: 2325 Jeans: men's, youths' & boys'
PA: Aalfs Manufacturing, Inc.
1005 4th St
Sioux City IA 51101
712 252-1877

(G-3875)
AAP METALS LLC
Also Called: Arbor Metals
811 Regal Row (75247-4406)
PHONE.....................214 357-6161
Jack Matheson,
Shelly Bledsoe,
Bill Sultzbaugh,
Robert Vannoord,
◆ EMP: 45
SQ FT: 90,000
SALES (est): 21.4MM
SALES (corp-wide): 640.1MM **Privately Held**
WEB: www.arbormetals.com
SIC: 3469 5051 Stamping metal for the trade; metals service centers & offices
PA: Triple-S Steel Holdings, Inc.
6000 Jensen Dr
Houston TX 77026
713 697-7105

(G-3876)
ABBCO DISPLAY COMPANY
13910 Distribution Way B (75234-3469)
PHONE.....................214 319-8148
Leon Schroeder, Partner
C P Owens, Partner
EMP: 9
SQ FT: 7,500
SALES (est): 1.3MM **Privately Held**
SIC: 3312 5046 Bar, rod & wire products; store fixtures & display equipment

(G-3877)
ABBOTT LABEL INC (PA)
11440 Hillguard Rd (75243-5502)
P.O. Box 551627 (75355-1627)
PHONE.....................866 228-0100
John L Abbott, President
Steve Puschmann, General Mgr
Joe Hood, Vice Pres
Paul Garcia, Assoc VP
Ken Young, Opers Staff
EMP: 60 EST: 2000
SQ FT: 11,000
SALES (est): 20.4MM **Privately Held**
WEB: www.abbottlabel.com
SIC: 2759 Labels & seals: printing

(G-3878)
ABCO INC
1621 Wall St (75215-1864)
PHONE.....................214 428-8996
Leon J Kaplan, President
Scott Jeffrey, CFO
EMP: 75
SQ FT: 66,000
SALES (est): 13.5MM **Privately Held**
WEB: www.abcodigital.com
SIC: 7334 2782 2752 2675 Photocopying & duplicating services; looseleaf binders & devices; commercial printing, offset; cards, folders & mats: die-cut
PA: American Graphics Press Inc
1621 Wall St
Dallas TX

(G-3879)
ABEONA THERAPEUTICS INC
3333 Lee Pkwy Ste 600 (75219-5117)
PHONE.....................214 784-7177
Phil Maples, Vice Pres
Ron Fleming, Director
Magdalena Tyrpien, Director
Todd Wider, Bd of Directors
EMP: 17
SALES (est): 2.2MM **Privately Held**
WEB: www.abeonatherapeutics.com
SIC: 2834 Pharmaceutical preparations

(G-3880)
AC METALS LLC
256 Regal Row (75247-5202)
PHONE.....................214 630-5554
Brad Lockett, Vice Pres
Raleigh Davis, Mng Member
▲ EMP: 21 EST: 1960
SQ FT: 13,800
SALES (est): 7.9MM **Privately Held**
WEB: www.wootenmetal.com
SIC: 3444 Sheet metal specialties, not stamped

(G-3881)
ACCELERATE RESOURCES OPER LLC
5949 Sherry Ln Ste 1060 (75225-8112)
PHONE.....................214 292-8960
Michael Reel, Mng Member
EMP: 20
SALES (est): 1.1MM **Privately Held**
WEB: www.accelerate-resources.com
SIC: 1382 Oil & gas exploration services

(G-3882)
ACE HANGER STRAP INC
334 Rock Island St (75207-7407)
PHONE.....................214 742-8585
Truman Kerbo, CEO
Jack Pruitt, President
EMP: 10
SQ FT: 25,000
SALES (est): 649.5K **Privately Held**
SIC: 2295 Sealing or insulating tape for pipe: coated fiberglass

(G-3883)
ACME BRICK COMPANY
3815 Singleton Blvd (75212-3502)
P.O. Box 560725 (75356-0725)
PHONE.....................214 637-2720
Rebeca Whatley, Credit Staff
Peet Walker, Manager
Lori Everage, Analyst
Erik Golan, Analyst
EMP: 45
SALES (corp-wide): 254.6B **Publicly Held**
WEB: www.brick.com
SIC: 3271 Blocks, concrete or cinder: standard
HQ: Acme Brick Company
3024 Acme Brick Plz
Fort Worth TX 76109

(G-3884)
ACTIVE NETWORK LLC (HQ)
717 N Harwood St Ste 2500 (75201-6527)
PHONE..................................888 543-7223
Dana Jones, *CEO*
Scott Brown, *Editor*
Pam Bailey, *Business Mgr*
Kyla Oropeza, *Business Mgr*
Jeff McWilliams, *Vice Pres*
▲ **EMP:** 600
SALES (est): 217.5MM
SALES (corp-wide): 4.9B **Publicly Held**
WEB: www.activenetwork.com
SIC: 7372 Prepackaged software
PA: Global Payments Inc.
3550 Lenox Rd Ne Ste 3000
Atlanta GA 30326
770 829-8000

(G-3885)
ACUITY BRANDS LIGHTING INC
2700 Easter Ave Ste 100 (75216-3244)
P.O. Box 612388, Dfw Airport (75261-2388)
PHONE..................................972 456-1451
EMP: 113
SALES (corp-wide): 3.3B **Publicly Held**
WEB: www.lithonia.acuitybrands.com
SIC: 3646 Commercial indusl & institu-
tional electric lighting fixtures
HQ: Acuity Brands Lighting, Inc.
1 Acuity Way
Conyers GA 30012

(G-3886)
ACUITY SURGICAL DEVICES LLC
14215 Proton Rd (75244-3606)
PHONE..................................214 862-5017
Bryan Cowan, *President*
Shawn Thomas, *Vice Pres*
Tony Carlone, *VP Bus Dvlpt*
EMP: 11
SQ FT: 2,500
SALES (est): 1.5MM **Privately Held**
WEB: www.acuitysurgical.com
SIC: 3842 Implants, surgical

(G-3887)
ADCO INC
13911 Distribution Way (75234-3436)
P.O. Box 815382 (75381-5382)
PHONE..................................972 484-6177
John Helms, *Vice Pres*
Greg Reinhardt, *Natl Sales Mgr*
Brenda Jo Anderson, *Office Mgr*
▲ **EMP:** 35
SQ FT: 110,000
SALES (est): 2.7MM **Privately Held**
WEB: www.gluesticksdirect.com
SIC: 2891 Glue

(G-3888)
ADDAX MINERALS LLC
5950 Berkshire Ln # 1250 (75225-5846)
PHONE..................................214 445-6000
Ryan Watts, *Principal*
Liz Young, *Vice Pres*
Brett Braun, *Asst Controller*
EMP: 19
SALES (est): 2.8MM **Privately Held**
WEB: www.springbokenergy.com
SIC: 3299 Nonmetallic mineral products

(G-3889)
ADI ELECTRONICS INC
3920 Bryan St Frnt Frnt (75204-6528)
PHONE..................................214 818-4720
Raman Kalidas, *President*
Harish Kalidas, *Vice Pres*
Steve Youkers, *Opers Mgr*
Y Banach, *Safety Mgr*
Johnny Mullis, *Engineer*
EMP: 19
SQ FT: 15,000
SALES (est): 3MM **Privately Held**
WEB: www.adielectronics.com
SIC: 3678 Electronic connectors

(G-3890)
ADOBE INC
15950 Dallas Pkwy Ste 400 (75248-6628)
PHONE..................................469 955-9500
Michael O'Neill, *Marketing Staff*
Aaron Cockrill, *Consultant*
EMP: 32

SALES (corp-wide): 12.8B **Publicly Held**
WEB: www.adobe.com
SIC: 7372 Prepackaged software
PA: Adobe Inc.
345 Park Ave
San Jose CA 95110
408 536-6000

(G-3891)
ADVANCED WATERJET CUTTING INC
2825 Reward Ln (75220-1507)
PHONE..................................214 358-2194
Larry Elison, *President*
Clif Gibson, *President*
Kirk Dudley, *General Mgr*
Larry Ellison, *Vice Pres*
Sal Copado, *Sales Executive*
EMP: 55
SQ FT: 50,000
SALES (est): 9MM **Privately Held**
WEB: www.awcwaterjet.com
SIC: 3449 Miscellaneous metalwork

(G-3892)
ADVANTAGE AVIATION TECH
201 Regal Row (75247-5201)
P.O. Box 560088 (75356-0088)
PHONE..................................972 647-7300
Debbie Macdonald, *President*
Steve Dewasme, *Manager*
EMP: 23 **EST:** 2013
SALES (est): 6.2MM **Privately Held**
WEB: www.aatinc.net
SIC: 3728 Aircraft parts & equipment

(G-3893)
ADVANTAGE AVIATION TECH II LLC
201 Regal Row (75247-5201)
P.O. Box 560088 (75356-0088)
PHONE..................................972 647-7300
Glenn Mayberry, *General Mgr*
Stacy Cors, *Purchasing*
Randy McCollough, *QC Mgr*
Joe Simpson, *Regl Sales Mgr*
Mari Olvera, *Cust Mgr*
EMP: 48
SQ FT: 50,000
SALES (est): 7MM **Privately Held**
WEB: www.aatinc.net
SIC: 3728 Aircraft parts & equipment

(G-3894)
ADVANTAGE MARKING & LABELING
Also Called: Advantage Label Company
8727 Empress Row (75247-3901)
P.O. Box 560006 (75356-0006)
PHONE..................................214 638-5225
Kyle Phillips, *CEO*
John Fields, *President*
Curtis Pennington, *President*
Eddie Fields, *Sales Staff*
Royce Smith, *Sales Staff*
EMP: 30
SQ FT: 30,000
SALES (est): 8MM **Privately Held**
WEB: www.adlabel.com
SIC: 2672 2679 Adhesive papers, labels
or tapes: from purchased material; tags &
labels, paper

(G-3895)
AEGIS OIL LIMITED VENTURES LLC (PA)
Also Called: Aegis Ventures
100 Crescent Ct Ste 700 (75201-2112)
PHONE..................................214 431-5201
James R Freiman, *CEO*
Andrew Cabot, *President*
Wiiliam Perkins,
EMP: 15
SALES (est): 955.3K **Privately Held**
SIC: 1382 Oil & gas exploration services

(G-3896)
AERUS HOLDINGS LLC (PA)
14841 Dallas Pkwy Ste 500 (75254-7689)
PHONE..................................214 378-4000
Joseph Urso, *Ch of Bd*
Carl Christoff, *President*
Kevin Hickey, *COO*
Bret Holland, *Vice Pres*
Leda Simer, *Comms Mgr*

EMP: 11
SALES (est): 62.9MM **Privately Held**
WEB: www.beyondbyaerus.com
SIC: 5722 3634 Vacuum cleaners; electric
housewares & fans

(G-3897)
AERUS LLC (HQ)
14841 Dallas Pkwy Ste 500 (75254-7689)
PHONE..................................214 378-4000
Joseph Urso, *CEO*
Kevin Hickey, *President*
James McCain, *COO*
Cortney Carroll, *Vice Pres*
Mike Wilkin, *Vice Pres*
◆ **EMP:** 40
SQ FT: 18,000
SALES (est): 49.6MM **Privately Held**
WEB: www.beyondbyaerus.com
SIC: 3635 3564 Household vacuum clean-
ers; blowers & fans

(G-3898)
AETHON ENERGY MANAGEMENT LLC
12377 Merit Dr Ste 1200 (75251-2248)
PHONE..................................214 750-3820
EMP: 42 **EST:** 2014
SALES (est): 3.8MM **Privately Held**
WEB: www.aethonenergy.com
SIC: 6799 1382 Investors; oil & gas explo-
ration services; geophysical exploration,
oil & gas field

(G-3899)
AETHON ENERGY OPERATING LLC
12377 Merit Dr Ste 1200 (75251-2248)
PHONE..................................214 750-3833
Ben Barr, *Treasurer*
Don McClur, *Mng Member*
Preston Phillips,
EMP: 240
SALES (est): 1.3MM
SALES (corp-wide): 50MM **Privately Held**
WEB: www.aethonenergy.com
SIC: 1382 Oil & gas exploration services
PA: Aethon United Br Lp
12377 Merit Dr Ste 1200
Dallas TX 75251
214 750-3829

(G-3900)
AETHON I LP
5910 N Central Expy (75206-5125)
PHONE..................................214 750-1522
Robert Bruce Thompson, *Partner*
Helios A LLC, *General Ptnr*
EMP: 60
SALES (est): 14.1MM **Privately Held**
WEB: www.edens.com
SIC: 3731 Drilling & production platforms,
floating (oil & gas)

(G-3901)
AFFINITY CHEMICAL LLC (PA)
3016 Southwestern Blvd (75225-7840)
PHONE..................................214 696-1037
EMP: 18
SALES (est): 11.4MM **Privately Held**
WEB: www.affinitychemical.com
SIC: 3354 Aluminum extruded products

(G-3902)
AGENT SYSTEMS INC
13375 N Stemmons Fwy # 300
(75234-5744)
PHONE..................................972 774-0400
Brian G Waters, *President*
Carol Waters, *Corp Secy*
Waters Douglas, *Vice Pres*
EMP: 9
SQ FT: 14,000
SALES (est): 830K **Privately Held**
SIC: 3577 Computer peripheral equipment

(G-3903)
AIBUY INC
13455 Noel Rd (75240-6620)
PHONE..................................972 616-6400
Jim Roundtree, *CEO*
Eugene Terekhov, *COO*
Serge Kononov, *QC Mgr*
Rob Smith, *Manager*
EMP: 33

SALES (est): 822.1K **Privately Held**
WEB: www.aibuy.io
SIC: 7372 Business oriented computer
software

(G-3904)
AIM SOLUTIONS INC
10440 N Cntl Expy Ste 240 (75231)
PHONE..................................214 373-6084
Ava Idom, *President*
Patrick Idom, *Consultant*
Terry Sample, *Sr Software Eng*
EMP: 16
SALES (est): 1.7MM **Privately Held**
WEB: www.aimsolutionsinc.com
SIC: 7372 7371 Prepackaged software;
computer software systems analysis &
design, custom

(G-3905)
AIR LIQUIDE ELECTRONICS US LP (DH)
9101 Lyndon B Johnson Fwy # 800
(75243-1920)
P.O. Box 301046 (75303-1046)
PHONE..................................972 301-5200
Benot Potier, *CEO*
Deborah Hutchinson, *General Mgr*
David Lockhart, *General Mgr*
Jorge Lopez, *General Mgr*
Netta Washington, *General Mgr*
▲ **EMP:** 3000
SQ FT: 10,000
SALES (est): 3B
SALES (corp-wide): 129.8MM **Privately
Held**
WEB: www.airliquide.com
SIC: 2813 3564 8631 2819 Industrial
gases; dust or fume collecting equipment,
industrial; labor unions & similar labor or-
ganizations; industrial inorganic chemi-
cals
HQ: American Air Liquide Holdings, Inc.
2700 Post Oak Blvd
Houston TX 77056
713 624-8000

(G-3906)
AIR LIQUIDE ELECTRONICS US LP
13140 T I Blvd (75243-1508)
PHONE..................................972 994-2403
Dale McQuiston, *Branch Mgr*
EMP: 151
SALES (corp-wide): 129.8MM **Privately
Held**
WEB: www.airliquide.com
SIC: 2813 Industrial gases
HQ: Air Liquide Electronics U.S. Lp
9101 Lyndon B Johnson Fwy # 800
Dallas TX 75243
972 301-5200

(G-3907)
AIR PERFORMANCE SERVICE INC (PA)
Also Called: Honeywell Authorized Dealer
10510 Markison Rd (75238-1652)
PHONE..................................972 387-3334
EMP: 40
SQ FT: 4,800
SALES (est): 12.6MM **Privately Held**
WEB: www.airperformance.com
SIC: 1711 7623 3567 Warm air heating &
air conditioning contractor; air condition-
ing repair; industrial furnaces & ovens

(G-3908)
AIR-SERV GROUP LLC (DH)
3201 W Royal Ln Ste 100 (75229)
PHONE..................................651 454-0465
Thomas J Bauer, *General Mgr*
Greg Muldoon, *Mng Member*
EMP: 39
SQ FT: 20,000
SALES (est): 32MM
SALES (corp-wide): 330.2MM **Privately
Held**
WEB: www.air-serv.com
SIC: 3563 Tire inflators, hand or compres-
sor operated; vacuum (air extraction) sys-
tems, industrial
HQ: Csc Sw Holdco, Inc.
303 Sunnyside Blvd # 70
Plainview NY 11803
516 349-8555

▲ = Import ▼=Export
◆ =Import/Export

(G-3909)
AIRCRAFT COMPOSITE INC
2777 Irving Blvd Ste 112 (75207-2309)
PHONE..................................214 638-0138
Domingo Martinez, *President*
Clara Mejias, *Purch Mgr*
EMP: 10
SQ FT: 2,500
SALES (est): 2MM **Privately Held**
SIC: 2541 Cabinets, except refrigerated:
show, display, etc.: wood

(G-3910)
AIRCRAFT ENGINE & ACCESSORY CO
2275 Crown Rd (75229-2099)
PHONE..................................972 243-7404
Paul Skelton, *Principal*
Paul E Skelton, *Vice Pres*
Greg Berg, *Plant Mgr*
Bob Wilkinson, *Executive*
▲ EMP: 14
SQ FT: 8,000
SALES (est): 1.9MM **Privately Held**
WEB: www.aea-precision.com
SIC: 3728 4581 3724 Aircraft parts &
equipment; airports, flying fields & serv-
ices; aircraft engines & engine parts

(G-3911)
AIRFLOW SYSTEMS INC
11221 Pagemill Rd (75243-8314)
PHONE..................................800 818-6185
Michael A Bodmer, *President*
Jerry Browning, *Vice Pres*
EMP: 65
SQ FT: 80,000
SALES (est): 29.2MM **Privately Held**
WEB: www.airflowsystems.com
SIC: 5084 3564 Pollution control equip-
ment, air (environmental); air cleaning
systems; dust or fume collecting equip-
ment, industrial

(G-3912)
AIRGAS USA LLC
13140 T I Blvd (75243-1508)
PHONE..................................972 994-2400
Dale McQuiston, *Manager*
Kent Harer, *Manager*
EMP: 60
SQ FT: 4,960
SALES (corp-wide): 129.8MM **Privately Held**
WEB: www.airgas.com
SIC: 2813 5084 Industrial gases; welding
machinery & equipment
HQ: Airgas Usa, Llc
259 N Radnor Chester Rd
Radnor PA 19087
216 642-6600

(G-3913)
AIX ENERGY INC
8401 N Central Expy # 840 (75225-4403)
PHONE..................................214 292-3482
Robert A Imil, *CEO*
Robert A Imel, *President*
EMP: 15
SALES (est): 5.3MM **Privately Held**
WEB: www.aixenergy.com
SIC: 1311 Crude petroleum production

(G-3914)
AJOOO INC
13526 Vargon St (75243-1440)
PHONE..................................469 494-7317
Jesurobo Agbonkonkon, *President*
EMP: 10
SALES (est): 305.8K **Privately Held**
SIC: 2023 Baby formulas

(G-3915)
AKIDCO INC
Also Called: Rainbow Building Systems
3420 Singleton Blvd (75212-3641)
PHONE..................................214 905-6064
Nathan King, *President*
Jane King, *Corp Secy*
EMP: 16
SQ FT: 52,000
SALES (est): 4MM **Privately Held**
WEB: www.rainbowbuildings.com
SIC: 3441 Fabricated structural metal

(G-3916)
AL LEGACY PARTNERS INC
Also Called: John Charles Designs
4501 Mountain Creek Pkwy (75236-4600)
PHONE..................................972 296-9599
Robert Duncan, *CEO*
Sanjay Chandra, *Vice Chairman*
Cary Benson, *Vice Pres*
James Barrow, *Purchasing*
Cesar Valenzuela, *Manager*
◆ EMP: 373
SQ FT: 250,000
SALES (est): 70.4MM **Privately Held**
WEB: www.americanleather.com
SIC: 2512 5712 Upholstered household
furniture; furniture stores

(G-3917)
ALAMO PALLET RECYCLERS INC
Also Called: First Choice Pallets
5623 W Ledbetter Dr (75236-1305)
PHONE..................................972 296-2090
Philip Shoffner, *Principal*
EMP: 17 EST: 1994
SALES (est): 2.4MM **Privately Held**
WEB: www.fcpallet.com
SIC: 2448 Pallets, wood; pallets, wood &
wood with metal

(G-3918)
ALECOM METAL WORKS INC
2803 Chalk Hill Rd (75212-4511)
PHONE..................................972 438-1032
Jeffery Cates, *President*
Allen Cates, *Vice Pres*
Wes Kriska Jr, *Vice Pres*
EMP: 21
SQ FT: 12,000
SALES (est): 6.7MM **Privately Held**
WEB: www.alecommw.com
SIC: 3441 Fabricated structural metal

(G-3919)
ALL AMERICAN AWNINGS INC
Also Called: Clanton's Quality Awning
4612 S Buckner Blvd (75227-4208)
PHONE..................................214 388-5444
P Curt Richmond, *President*
EMP: 20
SQ FT: 9,600 **Privately Held**
WEB: www.clantonsqualityawnings.com
SIC: 2394 Canvas & related products;
awnings, fabric: made from purchased
materials; liners & covers, fabric: made
from purchased materials

(G-3920)
ALL COLOR PRESS TEXAS INC
4818 Woodall St (75247-6709)
PHONE..................................214 744-2258
Abdul Khemani, *President*
Ray Khemani, *President*
EMP: 12
SQ FT: 6,250
SALES (est): 1.7MM **Privately Held**
SIC: 5199 2752 Badges; commercial print-
ing, offset

(G-3921)
ALL FORKLIFTSCOM INC
1616 Tantor Rd (75229-3136)
PHONE..................................972 506-9108
EMP: 10 EST: 2014
SALES (est): 561.5K **Privately Held**
WEB: www.pro-liftequipment.com
SIC: 3537 Lift trucks, industrial: fork, plat-
form, straddle, etc.

(G-3922)
ALL TRUSS BUILDING SYSTEMS INC
5930 Royal Ln Ste E (75230-3896)
PHONE..................................817 247-7671
James N Cooper, *Branch Mgr*
EMP: 14 **Privately Held**
SIC: 2439 Trusses, wooden roof
PA: All Truss Building Systems, Inc.
167 Sentry Dr
Mansfield TX 76063

(G-3923)
ALLAN KNIGHT & ASSOCIATES INC
150 Turtle Creek Blvd # 101 (75207-6809)
PHONE..................................214 741-2227
Allan Knight, *President*
Tom Briscoe, *General Mgr*
Arnoldo Carmona, *Warehouse Mgr*
Christopher Poller, *Production*
Darrell Turner, *Purchasing*
▲ EMP: 15
SALES (est): 3.5MM **Privately Held**
WEB: www.allan-knight.com
SIC: 2519 Household furniture, except
wood or metal: upholstered

(G-3924)
ALLFLEX USA INC (HQ)
2805 E 14th St (75261)
P.O. Box 612266 (75261-2266)
PHONE..................................972 456-3686
Brian W Bolton, *President*
C Dickinson Hill, *Corp Secy*
Glenn Fischer, *Vice Pres*
Kip Kernodle, *Vice Pres*
▲ EMP: 68
SQ FT: 60,000
SALES (est): 16MM **Privately Held**
WEB: www.allflexusa.com
SIC: 3089 5199 Molding primary plastic;
pet supplies

(G-3925)
ALLIANCE PETROLEUM INTERESTS
17311 Dallas Pkwy Ste 200 (75248-1150)
PHONE..................................469 249-8985
Taylor Stilovich, *President*
EMP: 10
SALES (est): 380.3K **Privately Held**
WEB: www.alliancepetro.com
SIC: 1382 Oil & gas exploration services

(G-3926)
ALLIED FENCE CO OF DALLAS (PA)
Also Called: Allied Gate Company
266 W Commerce St (75208-1992)
PHONE..................................903 892-9640
Dewayne Cooper, *President*
Sean Cooper, *Corp Secy*
Tom Roth, *Exec VP*
Margie Cooper, *Vice Pres*
John Roth, *Sales Staff*
EMP: 18
SQ FT: 2,000
SALES (est): 1.9MM **Privately Held**
WEB: www.alliedfencedallas.com
SIC: 3446 5031 5211 Fences, gates,
posts & flagpoles; fencing, wood; fencing

(G-3927)
ALLIED STONE INC (HQ)
2405 Crown Rd (75229-2103)
P.O. Box 559, Durant OK (74740-0559)
PHONE..................................214 838-2225
Jerry Lim, *President*
Allan Foo, *General Mgr*
Katie Fleischer, *Project Mgr*
Chris Roberts, *Production*
James Rivera, *Human Resources*
◆ EMP: 100
SQ FT: 66,000
SALES (est): 49.7MM **Privately Held**
WEB: www.alliedstoneinc.com
SIC: 3281 Marble, building: cut & shaped;
granite, cut & shaped

(G-3928)
ALM MEDIA LLC
Also Called: Texas Lawyer
1999 Bryan St (75201-3136)
PHONE..................................214 744-9300
Colleen NC Gushin, *Manager*
EMP: 45
SALES (corp-wide): 200MM **Privately Held**
WEB: www.alm.com
SIC: 2711 Newspapers
HQ: Alm Media, Llc
150 E 42nd St
New York NY 10017
212 457-9400

(G-3929)
ALOE VERA OF AMERICA INC (PA)
Also Called: Forever Aloe Plantations
13745 Jupiter Rd (75238-2418)
PHONE..................................214 355-5400
Gregg Maughan, *President*
Rex Maughan, *Chairman*
Garin Breinholt, *Exec VP*
Navaz Ghaswala, *Exec VP*
Rjay Lloyd, *Exec VP*
◆ EMP: 80
SQ FT: 275,000
SALES (est): 76.3MM **Privately Held**
SIC: 2844 Toilet preparations

(G-3930)
ALON USA PARTNERS LP
12700 Park Central Dr # 1600
(75251-1500)
PHONE..................................972 367-3600
Alan Moret, *CEO*
Shai Even, *President*
Jeff Morris, *Vice Chairman*
Alon U GP, *General Ptnr*
Alan P Moret, *Vice Pres*
EMP: 2830 EST: 2012
SALES: 1.8B
SALES (corp-wide): 9.3B **Publicly Held**
WEB: www.alonpartners.com
SIC: 2911 Gasoline
HQ: Alon Usa Energy, Inc.
7102 Commerce Way
Brentwood TN 37027

(G-3931)
ALPHATRUST CORPORATION
8226 Douglas Ave Ste 625 (75225-5968)
PHONE..................................214 234-9200
Jody Bennett, *Vice Pres*
▼ EMP: 9
SQ FT: 1,279
SALES (est): 1.5MM **Privately Held**
WEB: www.alphatrust.com
SIC: 7372 Business oriented computer
software
PA: Internet Pipeline, Inc.
222 Valley Creek Blvd # 300
Exton PA 19341

(G-3932)
ALTA MESA RESOURCES INC (PA)
2101 Cedar Springs Rd # 1100
(75201-2158)
PHONE..................................214 647-7630
Mark P Castiglione, *CEO*
James T Hackett, *Ch of Bd*
John H Campbell Jr, *President*
Randy L Limbacher, *Exec VP*
Kevin J Bourque, *Vice Pres*
EMP: 11
SALES: 489.8MM **Publicly Held**
WEB: www.altamesa.net
SIC: 1382 Oil & gas exploration services

(G-3933)
ALTERSTART SYSTEMS INC
4919 W Davis St (75211-1217)
PHONE..................................214 330-2277
Patrick Nolan, *President*
Rosie Nolan, *Admin Sec*
EMP: 9
SQ FT: 6,000
SALES (est): 1.2MM **Privately Held**
WEB: www.alterstart.biz
SIC: 3694 Alternators, automotive

(G-3934)
ALTIUM PACKAGING
4525 Joseph Hardin Dr # 101
(75236-1915)
PHONE..................................214 333-4179
Chris Stables, *President*
EMP: 9
SALES (corp-wide): 12.5B **Publicly Held**
WEB: www.altiumpkg.com
SIC: 3089 Plastic containers, except foam
HQ: Altium Packaging Llc
2500 Windy Ridge Pkwy Se # 1400
Atlanta GA 30339
678 742-4600

(G-3935)
ALTLITE LLC
11520 N Cntl Expy Ste 154 (75243)
PHONE...................................469 767-1959
Michael Sedat, *Manager*
EMP: 15
SALES (est): 2.7MM **Privately Held**
SIC: 2679 2752 Tags & labels, paper; filter
paper: made from purchased material;
photo-offset printing

(G-3936)
AMBERNET TECHNOLOGIES INC
3010 Lbj Fwy Fl 1200 (75234-2710)
PHONE...................................972 707-4000
EMP: 15 EST: 2006
SALES (est): 1.3MM **Privately Held**
SIC: 8742 7371 7372 Management Con-
sulting Services Custom Computer Pro-
graming Prepackaged Software Services

(G-3937)
AMERICAN ACHIEVEMENT CORP (DH)
Also Called: AAC
1550 W Mockingbird Ln (75235-5007)
PHONE...................................512 444-0571
Steven Parr, *CEO*
Jerry Ellis, *President*
Benjamin Norwick, *Partner*
Donald J Percenti, *Chairman*
Sherice P Bench, *Exec VP*
▲ EMP: 32
SQ FT: 23,000
SALES (est): 607.6MM **Privately Held**
WEB: www.balfour.com
SIC: 3911 2741 Mfg Precious Metal Jew-
elry Misc Publishing

(G-3938)
AMERICAN BOTTLING COMPANY
4350 Mint Way (75237-1610)
PHONE...................................214 330-0491
Byron Rodenburg, *Manager*
EMP: 50
SQ FT: 36,530 **Publicly Held**
WEB: www.keurigdrpepper.com
SIC: 2086 Soft drinks: packaged in cans,
bottles, etc.
HQ: The American Bottling Company
5301 Legacy Dr
Plano TX 75024

(G-3939)
AMERICAN EGLE MAILBOX MFR CORP
2618 Manana Dr (75220-1302)
P.O. Box 29287 (75229-0287)
PHONE...................................214 358-2873
Able Lozano, *President*
EMP: 12
SQ FT: 4,000
SALES (est): 1.7MM **Privately Held**
WEB: www.americaneaglemailbox.com
SIC: 2542 Locker boxes, postal service:
except wood

(G-3940)
AMERICAN ENVIRCON INC (PA)
8305 Sovereign Row (75247-4715)
P.O. Box 560744 (75356-0744)
PHONE...................................214 634-1744
Robert F Powell, *President*
Thomas W Dillard, *Vice Pres*
EMP: 9
SALES (est): 1.7MM **Privately Held**
SIC: 3585 Compressors for refrigeration &
air conditioning equipment

(G-3941)
AMERICAN GASKET MFG CO INC
3828 Samuell Blvd (75228-6718)
P.O. Box 271044 (75227-1044)
PHONE...................................214 388-0603
O Lewis Mc Pherson, *President*
O Lewis Mc Pherson Jr, *Vice Pres*
Eric Mc Pherson, *Treasurer*
Eric McPherson, *Manager*
Johnny Johnson, *Admin Sec*
▲ EMP: 20
SQ FT: 25,000

SALES (est): 2.7MM **Privately Held**
WEB: www.americangasket.biz
SIC: 3053 Gaskets, all materials

(G-3942)
AMERICAN GRAND STAND INC
Also Called: American Grandstands
8604 Chancellor Row (75247-5522)
P.O. Box 560623 (75356-0623)
PHONE...................................214 638-7007
Paul Byars, *President*
Eldon Hampton, *Partner*
William Glassner, *Shareholder*
George Lucas, *Shareholder*
EMP: 16
SQ FT: 16,000
SALES (est): 2.2MM **Privately Held**
WEB: www.americangrandstands.com
SIC: 7359 2531 Equipment rental & leas-
ing; stadium furniture

(G-3943)
AMERICAN GYPSUM COMPANY (HQ)
5960 Berkshire Ln Ste 800 (75225-6068)
PHONE...................................214 530-5500
Craig Kesler, *President*
Gary King, *Superintendent*
Dave Powers, *Chairman*
David Drews, *Purch Mgr*
Chip Steedly, *Engineer*
▲ EMP: 245
SALES (est): 95MM
SALES (corp-wide): 1.4B **Publicly Held**
WEB: www.americangypsum.com
SIC: 3275 5031 Wallboard, gypsum; wall-
board
PA: Eagle Materials Inc.
5960 Berkshire Ln Ste 900
Dallas TX 75225
214 432-2000

(G-3944)
AMERICAN LEA OPERATIONS LLC
4501 Mountain Creek Pkwy (75236-4600)
PHONE...................................972 296-8016
Bruce Birnbach, *President*
Veronica Schnitzius, *COO*
Rico Berrios, *Vice Pres*
Veronica Londono, *VP Opers*
Willie Palomo, *Safety Mgr*
EMP: 400
SALES (est): 63.3MM **Privately Held**
WEB: www.americanleather.com
SIC: 2512 Upholstered household furniture

(G-3945)
AMERICAN QUARTZ LLC
11129 Zodiac Ln Ste 300 (75229-4872)
PHONE...................................214 243-6676
EMP: 100
SALES (est): 1.3MM **Privately Held**
SIC: 1499 Quartz crystal (pure) mining

(G-3946)
AMERITEX PETROLEUM LLC
13140 Coit Rd Ste 510 (75240-5751)
PHONE...................................972 528-6644
Reese Bostick, *Exec VP*
Judith Jurica, *Manager*
Christian E Wise, *
EMP: 12 EST: 2007
SALES (est): 1.2MM **Privately Held**
WEB: www.ameritexpetro.com
SIC: 1382 Oil & gas exploration services

(G-3947)
AMFAN CORPORATION
Also Called: R & D Machine Shop
3443 Morse Dr (75236-1119)
PHONE...................................214 638-2451
David K Williams, *President*
Dennis Williams, *Vice Pres*
Chris Ganzer, *Design Engr*
Mike Hortman, *Design Engr*
Irene F Williams, *Treasurer*
▲ EMP: 50
SQ FT: 132,000
SALES (est): 12.4MM **Privately Held**
WEB: www.amfan.com
SIC: 3599 Machine shop, jobbing & repair

(G-3948)
AMWELD INTERNATIONAL LLC
13901 Midway Rd (75244-4359)
PHONE...................................888 775-2397
Scott Willson, *
EMP: 65
SALES (est): 6.8MM **Privately Held**
WEB: www.amweld.com
SIC: 2514 5072 Metal household furniture;
hardware

(G-3949)
ANSUNG-USA LLC
5200 E Grand Ave Ste 505 (75223-2230)
PHONE...................................469 877-5242
Sung Doo Kim, *Mng Member*
Steve Kam, *
▲ EMP: 20
SALES (est): 1.1MM **Privately Held**
WEB: www.ansungusa.com
SIC: 3537 Industrial trucks & tractors

(G-3950)
APHTHORIA SOLUTIONS INC
9125 Viscount Row (75247-5413)
PHONE...................................214 821-8607
Jon C Loshinsky, *President*
EMP: 55
SQ FT: 53,000
SALES (est): 13.5MM **Privately Held**
WEB: www.standardcontrols.com
SIC: 3613 3625 Control panels, electric;
control equipment, electric

(G-3951)
API PRECISION MACHINING INC
617 W Commerce St (75208-1821)
PHONE...................................214 748-4994
Karen Lynch, *President*
James Rogers, *Sales Mgr*
EMP: 15
SQ FT: 13,000
SALES (est): 2.5MM **Privately Held**
WEB: www.apipm.com
SIC: 3599 Machine shop, jobbing & repair

(G-3952)
APOLLO RESOURCES INTL INC
3001 Knox St Ste 403 (75205-5584)
PHONE...................................214 389-9800
EMP: 41
SQ FT: 2,500
SALES (est): 3.7MM **Privately Held**
SIC: 1311 Crude Petroleum/Natural Gas
Production

(G-3953)
APPLETON GRP LLC
11404 Pagemill Rd (75243)
P.O. Box 740155 (75374-0155)
PHONE...................................214 349-2310
EMP: 13
SALES (corp-wide): 16.7B **Publicly Held**
WEB: www.emerson.com
SIC: 3823 Industrial instrmnts msrmnt dis-
play/cntrol process variable
HQ: Appleton Grp Llc
9377 W Higgins Rd
Rosemont IL 60018
847 268-6000

(G-3954)
APPLIED SERVICES CORPORATION
Also Called: Applied Magnets
7523 Midbury Dr (75230-3207)
PHONE...................................972 432-6509
Allen Wang, *President*
Jon Pierracos, *Sales Dir*
▲ EMP: 11
SQ FT: 2,000
SALES (est): 890K **Privately Held**
SIC: 3499 Magnets, permanent: metallic

(G-3955)
APPY HEALTH INC
8204 Elmbrook Dr Ste 228 (75247-4060)
PHONE...................................844 764-2779
William Grimes, *President*
EMP: 12 EST: 2018
SALES (est): 256K **Privately Held**
SIC: 7372 Application computer software

(G-3956)
AQUA ELECTRIC INC
Also Called: Aqua-Tech Electric
11252 Goodnight Ln # 900 (75229-4424)
PHONE...................................972 243-2162
Larry Klutter, *CFO*
EMP: 12
SQ FT: 2,000
SALES (est): 1.8MM **Privately Held**
WEB: www.aquatechelectric.com
SIC: 3822 3625 Thermostats, except built-
in; timing devices, electronic

(G-3957)
ARCHER-DANIELS-MIDLAND COMPANY
Also Called: ADM
9965 Monroe Dr (75220-1401)
PHONE...................................214 357-3331
Dennis Hennigar, *Manager*
EMP: 16
SALES (corp-wide): 64.6B **Publicly Held**
WEB: www.adm.com
SIC: 2041 Flour & other grain mill products
PA: Archer-Daniels-Midland Company
77 W Wacker Dr Ste 4600
Chicago IL 60601
312 634-8100

(G-3958)
ARCOSA INC (PA)
500 N Akard St Ste 400 (75201-3332)
PHONE...................................972 942-6500
Rhys J Best, *Ch of Bd*
Antonio Carrillo, *President*
Kerry S Cole, *President*
Jesse E Collins Jr, *President*
Reid S Essl, *President*
EMP: 103
SALES: 1.7B **Publicly Held**
WEB: www.arcosa.com
SIC: 3568 3612 3731 3271 Power trans-
mission equipment; transformers, except
electric; barges, building & repairing; con-
crete block & brick

(G-3959)
ARCOSA LW HPB LLC (HQ)
Also Called: Arcosa Lightweight
500 N Akard St (75201-3302)
PHONE...................................214 631-4420
Antonio Carrillo, *Mng Member*
EMP: 23
SALES (est): 580.8K
SALES (corp-wide): 1.7B **Publicly Held**
SIC: 3295 3532 Minerals, ground or
treated; mining machinery
PA: Arcosa, Inc.
500 N Akard St Ste 400
Dallas TX 75201
972 942-6500

(G-3960)
ARCOSA LW KY LLC
500 N Akard St (75201-3302)
PHONE...................................214 631-4420
Antonio Carrillo, *Mng Member*
EMP: 24
SALES (est): 1.1MM
SALES (corp-wide): 1.7B **Publicly Held**
SIC: 3273 Ready-mixed concrete
PA: Arcosa, Inc.
500 N Akard St Ste 400
Dallas TX 75201
972 942-6500

(G-3961)
ARCOSA MARINE PRODUCTS INC (HQ)
500 N Akard St (75201-3302)
P.O. Box 35721 (75235-0721)
PHONE...................................214 631-4420
Thomas Faherty, *President*
Stephen Sheridan, *Exec VP*
Theis Rice, *Vice Pres*
Tommy Marciniak, *Marketing Mgr*
Bryan Stevenson, *Admin Sec*
▲ EMP: 118
SALES: 78.4MM
SALES (corp-wide): 1.7B **Publicly Held**
WEB: www.nabrico-marine.com
SIC: 3731 Barges, building & repairing

▲ = Import ▼=Export
◆ =Import/Export

PA: Arcosa, Inc.
500 N Akard St Ste 400
Dallas TX 75201
972 942-6500

(G-3962)
ARCOSA TANK LLC
500 N Akard St (75201-3302)
PHONE.....................214 631-4420
Kerry Cole, *President*
Jared Wallace, *Vice Pres*
Gail M Peck, *Treasurer*
▼ **EMP:** 40
SALES (est): 19.4MM
SALES (corp-wide): 1.7B **Publicly Held**
WEB: www.arcosatank.com
SIC: 3443 Tanks, lined: metal plate
PA: Arcosa, Inc.
500 N Akard St Ste 400
Dallas TX 75201
972 942-6500

(G-3963)
ARCTURUS CORPORATION
2828 N Harwood St # 2000 (75201-2124)
PHONE.....................214 720-0075
Ali Parvizian, *President*
Marc Weinberg, *Managing Prtnr*
John Hanley, *CFO*
EMP: 18
SQ FT: 8,500
SALES (est): 1.8MM **Privately Held**
WEB: www.arcturusgrp.com
SIC: 1382 8999 Oil & gas exploration
services; information bureau

(G-3964)
ARGENBRGHT NAT SHTMTL
WRKS INC
9121 King Arthur Dr (75247-3607)
P.O. Box 540845 (75354-0845)
PHONE.....................214 357-9161
Don A Argenbright, *President*
Gail Argenbright, *Vice Pres*
EMP: 35
SQ FT: 25,000
SALES (est): 2MM **Privately Held**
SIC: 3444 Sheet metalwork

(G-3965)
ARGOS USA LLC
1946 California Xing (75220-7006)
P.O. Box 140998, Irving (75014-0998)
PHONE.....................972 556-0735
Tim Morison, *General Mgr*
EMP: 30 **Privately Held**
WEB: www.argos-us.com
SIC: 3273 Ready-mixed concrete
HQ: Argos Usa Llc
3015 Windward Plz Ste 300
Alpharetta GA 30005
678 368-4300

(G-3966)
ARNIM TOOL INC
2204 Joe Field Rd (75229-3325)
PHONE.....................972 247-0802
Kingston Arnim, *President*
EMP: 15
SQ FT: 4,160
SALES (est): 2.2MM **Privately Held**
WEB: www.arnimtoolinc.com
SIC: 3544 Special dies & tools

(G-3967)
ARROW-MAGNOLIA INTL INC
2646 Rodney Ln (75229-3425)
P.O. Box 59089 (75229-1089)
PHONE.....................972 247-7111
David Tippeconnic, *CEO*
Tanya Shaw, *Chairman*
Brad Arnold, *Regional Mgr*
Cliff Trammell, *Business Mgr*
John Niland, *Vice Pres*
EMP: 46
SQ FT: 70,000
SALES (est): 16.6MM **Privately Held**
WEB: www.arrowmagnolia.com
SIC: 2819 Industrial inorganic chemicals

(G-3968)
ARTLUX INC (PA)
Also Called: Toff
10925 Alder Cir (75238-1354)
PHONE.....................214 716-1990
Oscar Martinez, *President*

Shane Dierking, *Vice Pres*
Jacinto Ramos, *Accountant*
Gerald R Macias, *Sales Staff*
Bobby Bailey, *Manager*
◆ **EMP:** 12
SALES (est): 1.2MM **Privately Held**
WEB: www.toffliners.com
SIC: 2819 5169 Industrial inorganic chem-
icals; industrial chemicals

(G-3969)
ARTOGRAFX INC
2611 Andjon Dr (75220-1309)
PHONE.....................214 349-1075
Richard M Santoyo, *President*
Sean Thorp, *Prdtn Mgr*
Steve Benson, *Sales Mgr*
Mindi McMorris, *Office Mgr*
EMP: 34
SQ FT: 20,000
SALES: 5.5MM **Privately Held**
WEB: www.artografx.com
SIC: 3993 Neon signs; signs, not made in
custom sign painting shops

(G-3970)
ASHMORE & ASHMORE
PROPERTIES
6865 Westlake Ave (75214-3446)
PHONE.....................214 327-9228
Frank Ashmore, *President*
EMP: 70 **EST:** 1941
SALES (est): 5.5MM **Privately Held**
SIC: 2842 Drycleaning preparations

(G-3971)
ASMAR CUSTOM CABINETS INC
Also Called: Asmar Custom Furn & Cabinets
2643 Brenner Dr (75220-1319)
PHONE.....................972 241-7676
Allen Asad Asmar, *President*
▲ **EMP:** 10
SQ FT: 5,500
SALES (est): 1.3MM **Privately Held**
WEB: www.asmarcabinets.com
SIC: 2514 2521 1751 Kitchen cabinets:
metal; wood office furniture; cabinet & fin-
ish carpentry

(G-3972)
ASSOCIATED LABEL & TAPE CO
2009 Farrington St (75207-6607)
P.O. Box 568343 (75356-8343)
PHONE.....................214 744-1662
Donald R Florez Sr, *President*
Pamela K Florez, *Treasurer*
Kirk Florez, *Software Dev*
EMP: 22
SQ FT: 13,500
SALES (est): 1.1MM **Privately Held**
WEB: www.associatedlabel.com
SIC: 2759 2672 Labels & seals: printing;
coated & laminated paper

(G-3973)
ASSOCIATED LOCKSMITHS
AMER INC
1408 N Riverfront Blvd # 30 (75207-3912)
PHONE.....................214 819-9733
EMP: 17
SALES (est): 2.4MM **Privately Held**
WEB: www.aloa.org
SIC: 2721 8611 Magazines: publishing
only, not printed on site; trade associa-
tions

(G-3974)
ASSOCIATED PRO INC
3620 Pallos Verdas Dr (75229-2625)
P.O. Box 59864 (75229-1864)
PHONE.....................214 902-8211
James Weis, *CEO*
EMP: 810
SALES (est): 26.4MM **Privately Held**
SIC: 3861 Motion picture film

(G-3975)
ASSOCIATED TIME INSTRS CO
INC (PA)
Also Called: Associated Time & Prkg Contrls
9104 Diplomacy Row (75247-5306)
PHONE.....................214 637-2763
Christopher Archer, *President*
Stacey Archer, *Vice Pres*
Greg Brewer, *Vice Pres*

Robert Collier, *Vice Pres*
Edward Lammer, *Vice Pres*
EMP: 20
SQ FT: 8,500
SALES: 19MM **Privately Held**
WEB: www.associatedtime.com
SIC: 5072 5046 3579 Computers,
peripherals & software; security devices,
locks; parking meters; time clocks & time
recording devices; parking facility equip-
ment & supplies; access control systems
specialization

(G-3976)
ASTANZA HOLDINGS LLC
Also Called: Astanza Laser
1810 S Akard St Ste 500 (75215-1943)
PHONE.....................800 364-9010
Justin Arnosky, *Vice Pres*
Brian Hasenbauer, *Vice Pres*
Holly Lambert, *Vice Pres*
Opal Taskila, *Vice Pres*
Brent Nixon, *VP Sales*
EMP: 12
SALES (est): 1.3MM **Privately Held**
WEB: www.astanzalaser.com
SIC: 3845 Laser systems & equipment,
medical

(G-3977)
ASTRO FOODS INTERNATIONAL
CORP
10720 Miller Rd Ste 300 (75238-5336)
PHONE.....................214 349-7840
John Jauregui, *President*
EMP: 15 **EST:** 1981
SQ FT: 1,500
SALES (est): 5.2MM **Privately Held**
WEB: www.astrofoodsinternational.com
SIC: 3556 5149 Dehydrating equipment,
food processing; specialty food items

(G-3978)
AT&T INC (PA)
208 S Akard St (75202-4295)
PHONE.....................210 821-4105
Randall L Stephenson, *Ch of Bd*
John T Stankey, *President*
John J Stephens, *CFO*
David S Huntley, *Ch Credit Ofcr*
David R McAtee II, *Executive*
EMP: 590
SALES (est): 181.1B **Publicly Held**
WEB: www.att.com
SIC: 4812 3663 3661 2741 Cellular tele-
phone services; cellular radio telephone;
pagers (one-way); telephone & telegraph
apparatus; telephones & telephone appa-
ratus; directories, telephone: publishing &
printing; local & long distance telephone
communications

(G-3979)
ATLANTIC BLOWERS LLC
Also Called: Canada Blower
1134 Longpoint Ave (75247-6810)
PHONE.....................214 233-0280
Gary Miledi,
Cynthia Villalobos,
▲ **EMP:** 11
SALES (est): 12MM **Privately Held**
WEB: www.atlanticblowers.com
SIC: 5084 8711 3564 Industrial machinery
& equipment; engineering services; air-
curtains (blower)

(G-3980)
ATLANTIC DWNTWN DLLAS
VNTR LLC
Also Called: Element Dallas Downtown East
4005 Gaston Ave (75246-1514)
PHONE.....................469 399-1049
Perwez Molubhoy,
Salim Molubhoy,
EMP: 40
SALES (est): 2.4MM **Privately Held**
SIC: 2819 Elements

(G-3981)
ATLAS IRON & SCRAP METAL
CO
Also Called: Atlas Scrap Management
9506 S Central Expy (75241-7302)
PHONE.....................972 225-4221
Alan Eisenberg, *President*

Jay Eisenberg, *Treasurer*
EMP: 48
SQ FT: 15,000
SALES (est): 5.5MM **Privately Held**
WEB: www.gachman.com
SIC: 3341 3312 4953 Recovery & refining
of nonferrous metals; blast furnaces &
steel mills; refuse systems

(G-3982)
ATLAS METAL WORKS INC
818 Singleton Blvd (75212-4013)
P.O. Box 225208 (75222-5208)
PHONE.....................214 741-4788
James Storey, *President*
Boude E Storey II, *Director*
EMP: 18
SQ FT: 60,000
SALES (est): 4.4MM **Privately Held**
WEB: www.atlasmetalworks.com
SIC: 3523 3444 3312 Farm machinery &
equipment; sheet metalwork; primary fin-
ished or semifinished shapes

(G-3983)
ATRIUM WINDOWS AND DOORS
INC (DH)
9001 Ambassador Row (75247-4509)
PHONE.....................214 583-1840
Robert Kirby, *CEO*
Scott St Clair, *President*
Robert E Burns, *COO*
Brian Slobodow, *COO*
Nancy Litzler, *Senior VP*
▲ **EMP:** 100 **EST:** 1953
SALES (est): 913.9MM
SALES (corp-wide): 4.8B **Publicly Held**
WEB: www.atrium.com
SIC: 2431 3089 3354 7629 Doors & door
parts & trim, wood; windows & window
parts & trim, wood; windows, plastic; win-
dow frames & sash, plastic; doors, fold-
ing: plastic or plastic coated fabric;
extruded finished plastic products; alu-
minum extruded products; tool repair,
electric; window & door frames
HQ: Ply Gem Holdings, Inc.
5020 Weston Pkwy Ste 400
Cary NC 27513
919 677-3900

(G-3984)
ATRON GROUP LLC
Also Called: Atron Cs
9125 Viscount Row (75247-5413)
PHONE.....................214 292-9840
▲ **EMP:** 65 **EST:** 2011
SQ FT: 18,000
SALES (est): 25.5MM **Privately Held**
WEB: www.atrongroup.com
SIC: 3563 3679 3089 7699 Air & gas
compressors; air & gas compressors in-
cluding vacuum pumps; electronic cir-
cuits; injection molding of plastics;
compressor repair; sheet metalwork;
switchgear & switchboard apparatus; con-
trol panels, electric

(G-3985)
ATROPOS EXPLORATION
COMPANY (PA)
8117 Preston Rd Ste 600 (75225-6326)
PHONE.....................214 691-2377
Todd M Hunt, *President*
Clay M Hunt, *Vice Pres*
Clay Hunt, *Vice Pres*
Paul Lee, *CFO*
Savannah McClure, *Analyst*
EMP: 10
SALES (est): 2.9MM **Privately Held**
SIC: 1382 1311 Oil & gas exploration serv-
ices; crude petroleum production; natural
gas production

(G-3986)
AUTHENTIC GELATO LLC (HQ)
Also Called: Paciugo Italian Gelato
1215 Viceroy Dr (75247-3908)
PHONE.....................214 654-9501
Ugo Ginatta,
Cristiana Acerbi Ginatta,
Vincent J Ginatta,
▲ **EMP:** 14 **EST:** 2000
SQ FT: 17,000

GEOGRAPHIC

SALES (est): 2.1MM
SALES (corp-wide): 14.8MM **Privately Held**
WEB: www.paciugo.com
SIC: 2024 Ice cream & frozen desserts
PA: Paciugo Holdings, Llc
1215 Viceroy Dr
Dallas TX 75247
214 654-9501

(G-3987)
AUTISTIC TREATMENT CTR
Also Called: Authesism Treatment Center
10503 Metric Dr (75243-5514)
PHONE...................................972 644-2076
Carolyn Garner, *Director*
EMP: 35 **EST:** 1992
SALES (est): 2MM **Privately Held**
SIC: 3999 8331 Barber & beauty shop equipment; job training & vocational rehabilitation services

(G-3988)
AUTO WAX COMPANY INC
Also Called: Clay Magic
1275 Round Table Dr (75247-3503)
PHONE...................................214 631-4000
Wray Rives, *General Mgr*
Bill Andrichik, *Vice Pres*
◆ **EMP:** 45 **EST:** 1960
SQ FT: 12,000
SALES (est): 8.9MM **Privately Held**
WEB: www.automagic.com
SIC: 2842 7532 Polishing preparations & related products; specialty cleaning preparations; top & body repair & paint shops

(G-3989)
AUTOSEIS INC
17103 Preston Rd Ste 200 (75248-1332)
PHONE...................................972 332-3388
Sean M Gore, *CEO*
Ralph Muse, *President*
Caroline Branch, *Vice Pres*
Robert Moss, *Manager*
Richard C White, *Director*
EMP: 10 **EST:** 2007
SALES (est): 776.8K **Privately Held**
SIC: 1382 Oil & gas exploration services

(G-3990)
AVAZZIA INC
13140 Coit Rd Ste 515 (75240-5751)
PHONE...................................214 575-2820
Tim Smith, *CEO*
Tom Lahutsky, *President*
EMP: 15
SALES (est): 2.8MM **Privately Held**
WEB: www.avazzia.com
SIC: 3845 Electromedical equipment

(G-3991)
AVO MULTI-AMP CORPORATION (DH)
Also Called: Megger
4545 W Davis St (75211-3422)
PHONE...................................214 330-3201
Alan Hardie, *CEO*
Richard Brown, *President*
Chris Burns, *General Mgr*
Ted Kim, *Regional Mgr*
Bruce Buxkemper, *Vice Pres*
▼ **EMP:** 110
SALES (est): 42.4MM **Privately Held**
WEB: www.megger.com
SIC: 3825 Test equipment for electronic & electric measurement

(G-3992)
AVO MULTI-AMP CORPORATION
States Trml Blcks Test Swtches
4545 W Davis St (75211-3422)
PHONE...................................800 325-4574
Rick Beaver, *Branch Mgr*
EMP: 15 **Privately Held**
WEB:
SIC: 3625 Switches, electric power
HQ: Avo Multi-Amp Corporation
4545 W Davis St
Dallas TX 75211
214 330-3201

(G-3993)
AVO USA INC
4271 Bronze Way (75237-1019)
PHONE...................................214 333-3201
Peter Frank, *President*
Michael Foster, *Sales Mgr*
Yovanda Bennett, *Accounts Exec*
West B Linvel, *Accounts Exec*
Bernadette Pitts, *Accounts Exec*
EMP: 225
SQ FT: 60,000
SALES (est): 17.2MM
SALES (corp-wide): 500.3K **Privately Held**
WEB: www.avotraining.com
SIC: 3825 Instruments to measure electricity
HQ: Tbg Europe N.V.
J.J. Viottastraat 43
Amsterdam 1071
205 474-800

(G-3994)
AVTEQ INC
9003 Governors Row (75247-3709)
P.O. Box 560607 (75356-0607)
PHONE...................................214 905-9001
◆ **EMP:** 9 **EST:** 1999
SQ FT: 32,000
SALES (est): 4MM **Privately Held**
WEB: www.avteq.net
SIC: 2599 Factory furniture & fixtures

(G-3995)
B & S PREMIUM SHEET METAL INC
Also Called: Miller Sheet Metal Mfg
7877 Carr St (75227-4020)
P.O. Box 1924, Rockwall (75087-2024)
PHONE...................................214 388-4724
Bryan Miller, *President*
Stephanie Miller, *Treasurer*
Veronica Vega, *Admin Sec*
EMP: 30
SQ FT: 1,000
SALES (est): 529.3K **Privately Held**
SIC: 3444 Forming machine work, sheet metal

(G-3996)
B C WILLIAMS INDUSTRIES INC
6000 Denton Dr (75235-6626)
P.O. Box 35947 (75235-0947)
PHONE...................................214 352-4255
Dudley Taylor, *President*
Steve Bolton, *Vice Pres*
Candy Krywalski, *Purch Agent*
L L Brown, *Shareholder*
James B Williams, *Shareholder*
▲ **EMP:** 14
SALES (est): 3.5MM **Privately Held**
WEB: www.bcwilliams.com
SIC: 2842 7349 Specialty cleaning preparations; disinfectants, household or industrial plant; deodorants, nonpersonal; chemical cleaning services

(G-3997)
B&B ORNAMENTAL IRON COMPANY
Also Called: Excel Steel
1760 W Northwest Hwy (75220-7016)
P.O. Box 541381 (75354-1381)
PHONE...................................214 350-0639
Steve Boone, *President*
Walt Atchley, *Controller*
EMP: 50
SQ FT: 28,000
SALES (est): 6.5MM **Privately Held**
WEB: www.excelsteelcorp.biz
SIC: 3446 Stairs, staircases, stair treads: prefabricated metal

(G-3998)
BAINBRIDGE UINTA LLC
8150 N Central Expy # 650 (75206-1809)
PHONE...................................214 580-2059
Steve Moore, *CFO*
Paul Ching,
Brian Ching,
EMP: 19
SALES (est): 602.6K **Privately Held**
SIC: 1311 Crude petroleum & natural gas

PA: Bainbridge Uinta Holdings, Llc
8150 N Central Expy # 650
Dallas TX

(G-3999)
BAKER METAL PRODUCTS INC (PA)
11140 Zodiac Ln (75229-4721)
P.O. Box 59445 (75229-1445)
PHONE...................................972 241-3553
Robert F Baker, *President*
Peggy B Baker, *Corp Secy*
Carolyn B Beard, *Vice Pres*
Dave Wortman, *Vice Pres*
David E Wortman, *Vice Pres*
▲ **EMP:** 135
SQ FT: 70,000
SALES (est): 39.2MM **Privately Held**
WEB: www.bakermetal.com
SIC: 3449 3353 Curtain walls for buildings, steel; aluminum sheet, plate & foil

(G-4000)
BALDWIN METALS COMPANY INC
Also Called: Stricklin Company
1901 W Commerce St (75208-8196)
PHONE...................................214 637-1030
Tom Johnson, *President*
Quinn Johnson, *Technology*
Dianne Johnson, *Admin Sec*
EMP: 35 **EST:** 1961
SQ FT: 30,500
SALES (est): 8.6MM **Privately Held**
WEB: www.baldwinmetals.com
SIC: 3443 3444 3441 3541 Fabricated plate work (boiler shop); sheet metalwork; fabricated structural metal; grinding machines, metalworking; crushers, grinders & similar equipment

(G-4001)
BALLQUBE INC
3317 Stanford Ave (75225-7617)
PHONE...................................800 543-1470
Susan Pham, *Principal*
Brandon Rogers, *Vice Pres*
Kenneth D Rogers, *Treasurer*
EMP: 15
SALES (est): 656.8K **Privately Held**
WEB: www.ballqube.com
SIC: 3949 Sporting & athletic goods

(G-4002)
BAM DENTON MGT VENTURES LLC
Also Called: Business Air Management
7515 Lemmon Ave (75209-3017)
PHONE...................................940 898-1200
Patrick Hall, *Vice Pres*
Richard D Ward, *Mng Member*
Peterson Ginger, *Director*
J Philip Jordan,
EMP: 30
SQ FT: 1,500
SALES (est): 8MM **Privately Held**
WEB: www.business-air.com
SIC: 4522 8741 2869 Flying charter service; management services; fuels

(G-4003)
BAND MANS CO SOUTHWEST INC (PA)
Also Called: Bates Embroidery & Digitizing
2845 Ladybird Ln (75220-1413)
PHONE...................................214 350-0631
Edward J Bates, *President*
Nicole Bates, *Corp Secy*
Paul Phillips, *Vice Pres*
▲ **EMP:** 15
SQ FT: 8,900
SALES (est): 4.5MM **Privately Held**
WEB: www.dallas-embroidery.com
SIC: 2389 Band uniforms

(G-4004)
BANK OF NEW YORK MELLON CORP
Also Called: Bank of NY M Trust Co N A
2001 Bryan St Fl 11 (75201-3020)
PHONE...................................214 239-6420
B Mellon, *Principal*
David Ramsey, *Vice Pres*
Jason Stephens, *Vice Pres*
Darren Brown, *Administration*

EMP: 16
SALES (corp-wide): 16.4B **Publicly Held**
WEB: www.bnymellon.com
SIC: 3944 Banks, toy
PA: The Bank Of New York Mellon Corporation
240 E Greenwich St
New York NY 10007
212 495-1784

(G-4005)
BARKER & BRATTON STEEL INC
10733 Newkirk St (75220-2305)
P.O. Box 541716 (75354-1716)
PHONE...................................972 556-1951
J W Bratton, *Exec VP*
EMP: 25 **EST:** 1961
SQ FT: 110,300
SALES (est): 3.8MM **Privately Held**
SIC: 3441 Fabricated structural metal

(G-4006)
BARRINGTON GROUP LTD INC
2300 N Haskell Ave (75204-3703)
P.O. Box 192099 (75219-8512)
PHONE...................................214 528-6990
Gil Sheehan, *President*
David Gowdey, *Vice Pres*
Pete Wilhelm, *Vice Pres*
▲ **EMP:** 15
SALES (est): 2.4MM **Privately Held**
WEB: www.barringtongifts.com
SIC: 3951 3172 5112 5099 Pens & mechanical pencils; personal leather goods; writing instruments & supplies; luggage

(G-4007)
BARRON MANUFACTURING INC
Also Called: Performance Specialty Service
1195 Empire Central Dr (75247-4301)
PHONE...................................214 747-2544
Mark Barron, *President*
Roxann B Barron, *Director*
EMP: 15
SALES (est): 656.2K **Privately Held**
SIC: 7389 2759 Printers' services: folding, collating; embossing on paper

(G-4008)
BASA RESOURCES INC (PA)
14875 Landmark Blvd # 400 (75254-1489)
PHONE...................................214 580-5203
Michael N Foster Jr, *CEO*
Frances Whittington, *COO*
Lary D Knowlton, *Exec VP*
Nicholas C Duane, *Vice Pres*
Steve Limke, *Vice Pres*
▲ **EMP:** 20
SQ FT: 11,000
SALES (est): 60.4MM **Privately Held**
WEB: www.basaresources.com
SIC: 1382 Oil & gas exploration services

(G-4009)
BCT INTERNATIONAL INC
10580 Newkirk St Ste 110 (75220-2329)
PHONE...................................972 401-9171
Brian Henderson, *Manager*
EMP: 30
SALES (corp-wide): 4.2MM **Privately Held**
WEB: www.bct-net.com
SIC: 2752 Commercial printing, lithographic
HQ: Bct International, Inc.
2810 E Oklnd Prk Blvd # 308
Fort Lauderdale FL 33306
305 563-1224

(G-4010)
BCW FOOD PRODUCTS INC
6000 Denton Dr (75235-6626)
P.O. Box 35947 (75235-0947)
PHONE...................................214 350-3320
J Bowman Williams, *Principal*
Oscar Garcia, *Plant Mgr*
Mary R Williams, *Admin Sec*
EMP: 22
SQ FT: 8,000
SALES (est): 8.9MM **Privately Held**
WEB: www.bcwilliams.com
SIC: 2045 2087 2041 Prepared flour mixes & doughs; flavoring extracts & syrups; flour & other grain mill products

(G-4011)
BECKETT COLLECTIBLES INC
Also Called: Beckett Media
4635 Mcewen Rd (75244-5308)
PHONE................................855 777-2325
Sandeep Dua, *President*
Gaurav Sharma, *Manager*
EMP: 57
SQ FT: 32,000
SALES (est): 10MM **Privately Held**
WEB: www.beckett.com
SIC: 2721 5947 Magazines: publishing &
printing; trading cards: baseball or other
sports, entertainment, etc.

(G-4012)
BECKETT MEDIA LLC
4635 Mcewen Rd (75244-5308)
P.O. Box 975384 (75397-5384)
PHONE................................972 991-6657
Greg E Lindberg, *Owner*
Alex Soriano, *Accounts Exec*
Casey Clifford, *Advt Staff*
▲ EMP: 135
SQ FT: 75,000
SALES (est): 41.6MM **Privately Held**
WEB: www.beckett.com
SIC: 2721 Magazines: publishing only, not
printed on site

(G-4013)
BEDROCK MANUFACTURING CO LP (PA)
301 N Crowdus St Ste 200 (75226-1419)
PHONE................................214 247-2453
Steve Obrien, *Managing Prtnr*
Lynda Zimmerman, *Counsel*
EMP: 101
SALES (est): 18.3MM **Privately Held**
WEB: www.bedrockmanufacturing.com
SIC: 3281 Granite, cut & shaped

(G-4014)
BEECON LEARNING LLC
2012 Farrington St (75207-6608)
PHONE................................877 923-3266
Jeffrey C Brooks, *CEO*
Michelle Roberts, *Mng Member*
EMP: 10
SALES (est): 1.5MM **Privately Held**
WEB: www.beeconlearning.com
SIC: 3942 3944 5942 Stuffed toys, includ-
ing animals; games, toys & children's ve-
hicles; children's books

(G-4015)
BEHAVIORAL SCIENCE RES PRESS
12803 Demetra Dr Ste 100 (75234-6185)
PHONE................................972 243-8543
Shannon Goodson, *President*
George Dudley, *Chairman*
Trelitha R Bryant, *Vice Pres*
Jacqueline Calder, *Sales Staff*
Jeanne Ketchersid, *Manager*
EMP: 11
SQ FT: 4,000
SALES (est): 1MM **Privately Held**
WEB: www.salescallreluctance.com
SIC: 8742 2731 Personnel management
consultant; books: publishing only

(G-4016)
BELL WOODEN PRODUCTS INC
4341 Cedar Lake Dr (75227-4029)
PHONE................................214 388-5421
John Andrew Shoemaker, *President*
EMP: 35 EST: 1939
SQ FT: 10,000
SALES (est): 5.7MM **Privately Held**
SIC: 2448 2449 2441 Pallets, wood;
wood containers; boxes, wood: wire-
bound; nailed wood boxes & shook

(G-4017)
BENBELLA BOOKS INC
10440 N Cntl Expy Ste 800 (75231)
PHONE................................214 750-3600
Glenn Yeffeth, *President*
Claire Schulz, *Editor*
Vy Tran, *Editor*
Monica Lowry, *Prdtn Mgr*
Jessika Rieck, *Production*
▲ EMP: 19

SALES (est): 1.2MM **Privately Held**
WEB: www.benbellabooks.com
SIC: 2731 Books: publishing only

(G-4018)
BENTINTOSHAPE LLC
10590 King William Dr (75220-2411)
PHONE................................214 228-2985
Roland Curt,
EMP: 10 EST: 2010
SQ FT: 2,000
SALES (est): 1.2MM **Privately Held**
WEB: www.bentintoshape.net
SIC: 3441 Fabricated structural metal

(G-4019)
BERLIN PACKAGING LLC
3737 Rock Quarry Rd # 100 (75211-1827)
PHONE................................214 339-0054
David Glazier, *Warehouse Mgr*
Nydia Jenks, *QC Mgr*
Mark Gray, *Manager*
EMP: 18
SALES (corp-wide): 621.4MM **Privately Held**
WEB: www.berlinpackaging.com
SIC: 5085 3545 Packing, industrial; cams
(machine tool accessories)
PA: Berlin Packaging L.L.C.
525 W Monroe St Ste 1400
Chicago IL 60661
312 876-9292

(G-4020)
BERRIDGE MANUFACTURING COMPANY
2015 Cal Crossing Rd (75220-2309)
PHONE................................972 506-8496
EMP: 70
SALES (corp-wide): 59.5MM **Privately Held**
WEB: www.berridge.com
SIC: 3444 Sheet metalwork
PA: Berridge Manufacturing Company, Inc
6515 Fratt Rd
San Antonio TX 78218
210 650-7056

(G-4021)
BERRY CORPORATION (BRY) (PA)
16000 Dallas Pkwy Ste 500 (75248-6619)
PHONE................................661 616-3900
A T Smith, *Ch of Bd*
Arthur T Smith, *Ch of Bd*
Fernando Araujo, *COO*
Danielle Hunter, *Exec VP*
Kurt Neher, *Exec VP*
EMP: 26
SALES: 559.4MM **Publicly Held**
WEB: www.bry.com
SIC: 1311 Crude petroleum production

(G-4022)
BETA ARKANSAS LLC
Also Called: R.G. Morgan & Son Central Ark
14185 Dallas Pkwy # 1020 (75254-1319)
PHONE................................972 490-2340
Nathan Collins,
EMP: 15
SQ FT: 1,300
SALES (est): 1.1MM **Privately Held**
WEB: www.billybobharris.com
SIC: 3462 3533 7699 Construction or
mining equipment forgings, ferrous; oil
field machinery & equipment; construction
equipment repair

(G-4023)
BIG D CONCRETE INC
Also Called: Big D Ready Mix
10361 Bickham Rd (75220-4205)
PHONE................................972 737-7976
Muamar Anani, *President*
Hanadi Anani, *President*
Masoud Khayyat, *Vice Pres*
EMP: 22
SQ FT: 7,000
SALES (est): 6.4MM **Privately Held**
WEB: www.bigdreadymix.com
SIC: 3271 5032 Concrete block & brick;
concrete & cinder building products

(G-4024)
BILINGUAL YELLOW PAGES
4310 N Central Expy (75206-6536)
PHONE................................214 823-4384
Michael A Gonzalez, *Owner*
EMP: 9
SALES (est): 509.4K **Privately Held**
WEB: www.byptexas.com
SIC: 2741 Telephone & other directory
publishing

(G-4025)
BIO TRUST NUTRITION LLC (PA)
Also Called: Biotrust Nutrition
4100 Spring Valley Rd # 32 (75244-3629)
PHONE................................800 766-5086
Kim Eschner, *Partner*
Cristina Powell, *Consultant*
Karen Boatwright, *Supervisor*
Justine Schuler, *Software Engr*
Jordan Hyde, *Director*
EMP: 20
SALES (est): 19.7MM **Privately Held**
WEB: www.biotrust.com
SIC: 2023 8049 Dietary supplements,
dairy & non-dairy based; nutrition special-
ist

(G-4026)
BIOMED LABORATORIES LLC
8181 Eastpoint Dr Ste 500 (75227-2071)
PHONE................................972 707-1210
Roger Liebelt, *CEO*
EMP: 48
SQ FT: 54,000
SALES (est): 10.2MM
SALES (corp-wide): 414.3MM **Privately Held**
WEB: www.biomedlabs.com
SIC: 2834 Pharmaceutical preparations
HQ: Scapa North America Inc
111 Great Pond Dr
Windsor CT 06095
860 688-8000

(G-4027)
BLACK EAGLE INC
100 Crescent Ct Ste 1600 (75201-6915)
PHONE................................214 871-3555
Matthew Clifton, *President*
Kenneth Polsinelli, *Director*
EMP: 50
SQ FT: 10,000
SALES (est): 4.9MM
SALES (corp-wide): 17.4B **Publicly Held**
WEB: www.blackeagleconsulting.com
SIC: 2911 Petroleum refining
PA: Hollyfrontier Corporation
2828 N Harwood St # 1300
Dallas TX 75201
214 871-3555

(G-4028)
BLACKLAND AEROSPACE LP
13355 Noel Rd Ste 1805 (75240-6813)
PHONE................................972 980-5970
EMP: 136
SALES (corp-wide): 3.1MM **Privately Held**
WEB: www.blacklandgroup.com
SIC: 3728 Blades, aircraft propeller: metal
or wood
PA: Blackland Aerospace, Lp
222 Las Colinas Blvd W 1650e
Irving TX 75039
972 980-5970

(G-4029)
BLAINES MOTOR SUPPLY INC
4700 Scyene Rd (75210-2220)
PHONE................................214 426-4400
Bertha L Taylor, *President*
Timothy B Taylor, *Vice Pres*
Judith Taylor, *Treasurer*
EMP: 60
SQ FT: 250,000
SALES (est): 8.8MM **Privately Held**
WEB: www.blainesmotorsupply.com
SIC: 5013 3599 Automotive supplies &
parts; machine shop, jobbing & repair

(G-4030)
BLANKS PRINTING & IMAGING INC
2343 N Beckley Ave (75208-2116)
PHONE................................214 741-3905
Leron Blanks, *President*
Mark Connor, *Vice Pres*
Doug Heyerdahl, *CFO*
Thomas Leron Blanks, *Treasurer*
Mike Plouff, *Accounts Exec*
EMP: 90
SQ FT: 88,000
SALES (est): 22.4MM **Privately Held**
WEB: www.blanks.com
SIC: 2752 2759 2796 2791 Commercial
printing, offset; catalogs, lithographed;
promotional printing, lithographic; bag,
wrapper & seal printing & engraving;
platemaking services; typesetting

(G-4031)
BLUE BOX AIR LLC
Also Called: Blue Box Filtration
3927 Main St Ste 130 (75226-1229)
PHONE................................424 241-3060
Maria Leftakis, *Accounts Mgr*
James Metropoulos, *Mng Member*
EMP: 80
SALES (est): 10.4MM **Privately Held**
WEB: www.blueboxair.com
SIC: 3677 7349 Filtration devices, elec-
tronic; cleaning service, industrial or com-
mercial

(G-4032)
BLUE RACER FINANCE CORP
5949 Sherry Ln Ste 1300 (75225-8036)
PHONE................................214 580-3700
Rick Moncrief, *President*
EMP: 26
SALES (est): 1.7MM
SALES (corp-wide): 47.7MM **Privately Held**
WEB: www.blueracermidstream.com
SIC: 1382 Oil & gas exploration services
PA: Blue Racer Midstream, Llc
5949 Sherry Ln Ste 1300
Dallas TX 75225
214 580-3700

(G-4033)
BLUESCAPE RESOURCES CO LLC
200 Crescent Ct Ste 1900 (75201-7843)
PHONE................................469 398-2202
C John Wilder, *Ch of Bd*
David Campbell, *President*
Doug Strebel, *President*
Philip Roach, *General Mgr*
Nathan Langston, *Vice Pres*
EMP: 19
SQ FT: 11,000
SALES (est): 5.9MM **Privately Held**
WEB: www.bluescaperesources.com
SIC: 1311 Natural gas production

(G-4034)
BMC SOFTWARE INC
1501 Lbj Fwy Ste 450 (75234-6076)
PHONE................................972 484-1200
Michael Pero, *Sales Staff*
James Treviling, *Branch Mgr*
EMP: 36
SALES (corp-wide): 1.4B **Privately Held**
WEB: www.bmc.com
SIC: 7372 Prepackaged software
PA: Bmc Software, Inc.
2103 Citywest Blvd # 2100
Houston TX 77042
713 918-8800

(G-4035)
BOBBY PINS LLC
2828 Hood St Apt 1408 (75219-7811)
PHONE................................920 267-6388
Charles Schwab Jr, *President*
EMP: 19 EST: 2014
SALES (est): 3MM **Privately Held**
SIC: 3999 7231 3965 Hair & hair-based
products; hairdressers; hairpins, except
rubber

(G-4036)
BOCK TECHNOLOGIES INC
11496 Luna Rd Ste 1200 (75234-9440)
PHONE..................................972 869-2625
Daniel Bock, *President*
Brittany Bock, *CFO*
Sara Johns, *Office Mgr*
EMP: 20
SALES (est): 2.5MM **Privately Held**
WEB: www.bocktech.com
SIC: 3663 Radio broadcasting & communications equipment

(G-4037)
BODYCOTE K-TECH INC (DH)
12750 Merit Dr Ste 1400 (75251-1248)
PHONE..................................214 904-2420
Tracey Glende, *President*
David Hair, *President*
Jeff Carr, *Vice Pres*
David Landless, *Vice Pres*
David Starkie, *CFO*
EMP: 12
SQ FT: 13,000
SALES (est): 1.7MM
SALES (corp-wide): 929.6MM **Privately Held**
SIC: 3398 Metal heat treating
HQ: Bodycote Usa, Inc.
    12750 Merit Dr Ste 1400
    Dallas TX 75251
    214 904-2420

(G-4038)
BODYCOTE THERMAL PROC INC (DH)
Also Called: Bird Electron Beam
12750 Merit Dr Ste 1400 (75251-1248)
PHONE..................................214 904-2420
Steven A Harris, *CEO*
Ron Perkins, *General Mgr*
Albert Sarabia, *General Mgr*
Anthony Schaut, *General Mgr*
Thomas J Gibbons, *Division Pres*
EMP: 35
SQ FT: 10,000
SALES (est): 338.8MM
SALES (corp-wide): 929.6MM **Privately Held**
WEB: www.bodycote.com
SIC: 3398 Brazing (hardening) of metal
HQ: Bodycote Usa, Inc.
    12750 Merit Dr Ste 1400
    Dallas TX 75251
    214 904-2420

(G-4039)
BODYCOTE USA INC (HQ)
12750 Merit Dr Ste 1400 (75251-1248)
PHONE..................................214 904-2420
Dan McCurdy, *President*
Jake Byrne, *General Mgr*
David Chirichello, *General Mgr*
Joe Dyer, *General Mgr*
Paul Dymond, *General Mgr*
◆ EMP: 100
SALES (est): 982.1MM
SALES (corp-wide): 929.6MM **Privately Held**
WEB: www.bodycote.com
SIC: 3398 Brazing (hardening) of metal
PA: Bodycote Plc
    Springwood Court
    Macclesfield SK10
    162 550-5300

(G-4040)
BOMBARDIER AEROSPACE CORP (HQ)
7336 Aviation Pl (75235-2802)
PHONE..................................972 960-3810
Francois Ouellette, *President*
Gaetano Pengue, *Project Mgr*
Denise Petrone, *Opers Staff*
Scott Nelson, *Controller*
Michael Anckner, *Sales Dir*
◆ EMP: 10
SQ FT: 50,000
SALES (est): 317.9MM
SALES (corp-wide): 15.7B **Privately Held**
WEB: www.aero.bombardier.com
SIC: 5088 3721 Aircraft & parts; aircraft
PA: Bombardier Inc
    800 Boul Rene-Levesque O 29e etage
    Montreal QC H3B 1
    514 861-9481

(G-4041)
BOMBARDIER SERVICES CORP
Also Called: Bombardier Arospc - Dallas Mro
4039 Rock Quarry Rd # 600 (75211-1585)
PHONE..................................214 331-9400
Michael Nadolski, *President*
Nicky McKay, *Manager*
Anna Cristofaro, *Manager*
Mark Masluch, *Director*
Nathalie Scott, *Relations*
EMP: 100
SALES (corp-wide): 15.7B **Privately Held**
WEB: www.bombardier.com
SIC: 3721 Aircraft
HQ: Bombardier Services Corp
    2400 Aviation Way
    Bridgeport WV 26330

(G-4042)
BORDEN DAIRY COMPANY (HQ)
8750 N Central Expy # 400 (75231-6417)
PHONE..................................855 311-1583
Stephen Gorman, *CEO*
Richard Thomas, *President*
Ed Medors, *General Mgr*
Kevin Gallagher, *Vice Pres*
Dennis Hills, *Plant Mgr*
EMP: 20
SALES (est): 1.8B
SALES (corp-wide): 2.2MM **Privately Held**
WEB: www.bordendairy.com
SIC: 2026 2033 Milk processing (pasteurizing, homogenizing, bottling); fruit juices: packaged in cans, jars, etc.
PA: Borden Dairy Holdings, Llc
    8750 N Central Expy # 400
    Dallas TX 75231
    855 311-1583

(G-4043)
BORDEN TRANSPORT CO OHIO LLC
8750 N Central Expy # 400 (75231-6436)
PHONE..................................214 459-1100
Frederick J Fowler, *President*
EMP: 92
SALES (est): 2.4MM
SALES (corp-wide): 2.2MM **Privately Held**
SIC: 2026 Milk processing (pasteurizing, homogenizing, bottling)
HQ: Borden Dairy Company Of Ohio, Llc
    3068 W 106th St
    Cleveland OH 44111
    216 671-2300

(G-4044)
BORIACK INTERIORS INC
1230 E Ledbetter Dr (75216-6988)
PHONE..................................214 376-1814
Dorothy Boriack, *President*
Ann Bush, *Corp Secy*
Phillip Boriack, *Senior VP*
EMP: 20
SQ FT: 15,000
SALES (est): 4.8MM **Privately Held**
WEB: www.quiltcraft.com
SIC: 5023 5131 5714 7217 Window furnishings; upholstery fabrics, woven; drapery & upholstery stores; carpet & upholstery cleaning; drapery hardware & blinds & shades; curtains & draperies

(G-4045)
BOWENS REED AND CALLOWAY INC
4315 S Lancaster Rd (75216-7105)
P.O. Box 398646 (75339-8646)
PHONE..................................214 389-0002
Tracie Reed, *CEO*
Alan Reed, *Vice Pres*
Miles Calloway, *Admin Sec*
EMP: 10
SALES: 3.5MM **Privately Held**
SIC: 3577 Input/output equipment, computer

(G-4046)
BRATTON INTERIM INC (PA)
10733 Newkirk St (75220-2305)
P.O. Box 541716 (75354-1716)
PHONE..................................972 556-1951
Jerry Bratton, *President*
David Bratton, *Vice Pres*

Linda Dodson, *Manager*
EMP: 55
SQ FT: 65,000
SALES (est): 10.7MM **Privately Held**
WEB: www.bratsteel.com
SIC: 3441 Fabricated structural metal

(G-4047)
BRATTON STEEL LP
10733 Newkirk St (75220-2305)
P.O. Box 541716 (75354-1716)
PHONE..................................972 556-1951
Jerry Bratton, *President*
David Bratton, *Vice Pres*
EMP: 50
SALES (est): 13.8MM **Privately Held**
WEB: www.brattonsteel.net
SIC: 3441 Fabricated structural metal
PA: Bratton Interim, Inc.
    10733 Newkirk St
    Dallas TX 75220

(G-4048)
BRC OPERATING COMPANY LLC
Also Called: Bluescape Resources Company
200 Crescent Ct Ste 1900 (75201-7843)
PHONE..................................214 855-2260
Jonathan Siegler,
EMP: 20
SALES (est): 1MM **Privately Held**
WEB: www.bluescapepartners.com
SIC: 1382 Oil & gas exploration services

(G-4049)
BRICK STONE GRAPHICS BY GARTEX
10310 Plano Rd Ste B (75238-1700)
PHONE..................................214 343-0573
Freddie McNeel, *President*
EMP: 10
SALES (est): 934.4K **Privately Held**
WEB: www.brickstonegraphics.com
SIC: 3993 7336 Signs & advertising specialties; commercial art & graphic design

(G-4050)
BRIDGFORD FOOD PROC TEXAS LP
1601 S Good Latimer (75226)
PHONE..................................214 428-1535
Ray Lancy, *Vice Pres*
EMP: 99
SALES (est): 6.3MM
SALES (corp-wide): 188.7MM **Publicly Held**
WEB: www.bridgford.com
SIC: 2099 Food preparations
HQ: Bridgford Foods Corporation
    1308 N Patt St
    Anaheim CA 92801
    714 526-5533

(G-4051)
BRIDGFORD FOODS CORPORATION
Also Called: Bridgford Frozen Rite Foods
1707 S Good Latimer Expy (75226-2257)
PHONE..................................214 428-1535
Marina Reeves, *Plant Mgr*
Linda Tuttel, *Cust Svc Dir*
Alvin Blackmon, *Manager*
Joe Dealcuaz, *Director*
EMP: 90
SQ FT: 3,200
SALES (corp-wide): 188.7MM **Publicly Held**
WEB: www.bridgford.com
SIC: 2041 2099 2051 2038 Doughs, frozen or refrigerated; food preparations; bread, cake & related products; frozen specialties
HQ: Bridgford Foods Corporation
    1308 N Patt St
    Anaheim CA 92801
    714 526-5533

(G-4052)
BRIDGFORD FOODS CORPORATION
Superior Division
9001 Chancellor Row (75247-5313)
PHONE..................................214 631-7970
Blaine Bridgford, *Vice Pres*
EMP: 40
SQ FT: 26,000

SALES (corp-wide): 188.7MM **Publicly Held**
WEB: www.bridgford.com
SIC: 2099 Food preparations
HQ: Bridgford Foods Corporation
    1308 N Patt St
    Anaheim CA 92801
    714 526-5533

(G-4053)
BRIDGFORD INDUSTRIES INC (PA)
Also Called: Bridgford Foods
1601 S Good Latimer Expy (75226)
PHONE..................................214 428-1535
John Simmons, *President*
William L Bridgford, *Chairman*
Daniel R Yost, *Senior VP*
Allan Bridgford, *Vice Pres*
Dan Yost, *Vice Pres*
EMP: 32
SALES (est): 188.7MM **Publicly Held**
WEB: www.bridgford.com
SIC: 2045 2099 2015 2013 Biscuit dough, prepared: from purchased flour; doughs, frozen or refrigerated: from purchased flour; sandwiches, assembled & packaged: for wholesale market; salads, fresh or refrigerated; poultry sausage, luncheon meats & other poultry products; snack sticks, including jerky: from purchased meat; cheese, natural & processed; dips, cheese-based; frozen specialties

(G-4054)
BRIDGFORD MARKETING COMPANY
Also Called: Bridgford Foods
1707 S Good Latimer Expy (75226-2211)
PHONE..................................214 428-1535
Joe Dealcuaz, *Manager*
EMP: 90
SALES (corp-wide): 188.7MM **Publicly Held**
WEB: www.bridgford.com
SIC: 5141 2099 Groceries, general line; sandwiches, assembled & packaged: for wholesale market
HQ: Bridgford Marketing Company
    1308 N Patt St
    Anaheim CA 92801
    714 526-5533

(G-4055)
BRILL INC
10741 Miller Rd (75238-1303)
PHONE..................................214 343-4816
Martha Arguello, *Production*
Tucker Lisa, *Sales Staff*
Mike Haden, *Branch Mgr*
Travis Raine, *Manager*
EMP: 137
SALES (corp-wide): 177.9K **Privately Held**
WEB: www.csmbakerysolutions.com
SIC: 2051 Bread, cake & related products
HQ: Brill, Inc.
    1912 Montreal Rd
    Tucker GA 30084
    770 724-8214

(G-4056)
BRISTOL-MYERS SQUIBB COMPANY
8901 Forney Rd (75227-4506)
P.O. Box 271128 (75227-1128)
PHONE..................................214 381-5050
Patricia Pope, *Oncology*
EMP: 20
SALES (corp-wide): 42.5B **Publicly Held**
WEB: www.bms.com
SIC: 2834 Pharmaceutical preparations
PA: Bristol-Myers Squibb Company
    430 E 29th St Fl 14
    New York NY 10016
    212 546-4000

(G-4057)
BRIT SYSTEMS LLC
13737 Noel Rd Ste 100 (75240-2017)
PHONE..................................214 630-0636
Mirza Baige, *CEO*
Michelle Fisher, *President*
Kim Herman, *General Mgr*
Thomas Dapice, *COO*

Dr Robert Murray, *Vice Pres*
EMP: 10
SQ FT: 11,000
SALES (est): 24MM **Privately Held**
WEB: www.brit.com
SIC: 5047 7372 Hospital equipment & furniture; prepackaged software

(G-4058)
BRODNAX PRINTING COMPANY I LLC
737 Regal Row (75247-5211)
PHONE..................................214 528-2622
Robert W Singer, *President*
Michael N Campbell, *Chairman*
Jim Singer, *Vice Pres*
Meg Paxton, *Sales Staff*
Robert Spalding, *Manager*
EMP: 33
SQ FT: 10,000
SALES (est): 10.7MM **Privately Held**
WEB: www.brodnax21c.com
SIC: 2752 Commercial printing, offset

(G-4059)
BROOKHOLLOW RENTAL CO INC (PA)
Also Called: Brookhollow Concrete
8200 Harry Hines Blvd (75235-3396)
P.O. Box 571230 (75357-1230)
PHONE..................................214 631-6883
James Wilson, *President*
Skip Wilson, *President*
Julie Wilson, *Corp Secy*
EMP: 10 EST: 1956
SQ FT: 2,000
SALES (est): 1.5MM **Privately Held**
WEB: www.brookhollowrental.com
SIC: 7359 3273 Party supplies rental services; ready-mixed concrete

(G-4060)
BROWN FNDTION REPR IN CNSLTING
Also Called: Brown Fndation Repr Consulting
1619 Bluebank Rd (75229-3103)
PHONE..................................972 271-2621
Robert L Brown, *President*
EMP: 24 EST: 1971
SQ FT: 3,000
SALES (est): 981.4K **Privately Held**
WEB: www.brownfoundationrepair.com
SIC: 6512 1311 Commercial & industrial building operation; crude petroleum production

(G-4061)
BROWNING OFFSHORE INC
12377 Merit Dr Ste 450 (75251-2343)
PHONE..................................214 739-3481
Michael R McWilliams, *President*
Jane Browning, *Owner*
Bill Patterson, *Treasurer*
EMP: 15
SALES (est): 759K **Privately Held**
WEB: www.browningoil.com
SIC: 1382 1311 Oil & gas exploration services; crude petroleum & natural gas production

(G-4062)
BROWNING OIL COMPANY INC (PA)
12377 Merit Dr Ste 450 (75251-2343)
PHONE..................................214 739-3481
Michael McWilliams, *President*
Michael R McWilliams, *President*
Jane H Browning, *Vice Pres*
James L Buron, *Vice Pres*
Bill Patterson, *Vice Pres*
EMP: 19
SQ FT: 14,411
SALES (est): 22.4MM **Privately Held**
WEB: www.browningoil.com
SIC: 1311 1382 Crude petroleum production; oil & gas exploration services

(G-4063)
BRUNTON INTERNATIONAL INC
3310 Quebec St (75247-6608)
PHONE..................................214 638-4600
Roy Brunton, *President*
Brad Bowers,
EMP: 22
SQ FT: 60,000

SALES (est): 5MM **Privately Held**
WEB: www.bii-usa.com
SIC: 2392 5131 Cushions & pillows; textiles, woven

(G-4064)
BTP MANUFACTURING INC
5535 Red Bird Center Dr (75237-1921)
PHONE..................................214 467-0094
Walter Johnson Sr, *President*
Jasper Daniels, *Vice Pres*
Asberry Hodge, *Vice Pres*
Walter Johnson Jr, *Vice Pres*
EMP: 25
SQ FT: 6,000
SALES (est): 1.6MM **Privately Held**
WEB: www.btpmfginc.com
SIC: 3357 3672 Aircraft wire & cable, nonferrous; printed circuit boards

(G-4065)
BUILDERS FIRSTSOURCE - SE GRP (HQ)
2001 Bryan St Ste 1600 (75201-3017)
PHONE..................................214 880-3500
Jim Read, *Purch Mgr*
Amy Turner, *Buyer*
Jeanie Kyker, *Credit Mgr*
Russ Buice, *Sales Staff*
Korey Roach, *Sales Staff*
◆ **EMP:** 80
SALES (est): 432.2MM
SALES (corp-wide): 7.2B **Publicly Held**
WEB: www.bldr.com
SIC: 2431 5211 Doors, wood; millwork & lumber
PA: Builders Firstsource, Inc.
2001 Bryan St Ste 1600
Dallas TX 75201
214 880-3500

(G-4066)
BUILDERS FIRSTSOURCE INC (PA)
2001 Bryan St Ste 1600 (75201-3017)
PHONE..................................214 880-3500
Paul S Levy, *Ch of Bd*
M Chad Crow, *President*
Chad Arnold, *General Mgr*
Jonathan Hale, *General Mgr*
Kelly Manuel, *General Mgr*
EMP: 40
SALES: 7.2B **Publicly Held**
WEB: www.bldr.com
SIC: 2421 5211 2431 Building & structural materials, wood; lumber & other building materials; doors & door parts & trim, wood

(G-4067)
BUILDERS FIRSTSOURCE-OHIO VALL (HQ)
2001 Bryan St Ste 1600 (75201-3017)
PHONE..................................214 880-3500
Bruce Allen, *General Mgr*
Don Baxter, *General Mgr*
Matthew Epler, *General Mgr*
Randy Fleischman, *General Mgr*
Derrick Geiger, *General Mgr*
EMP: 150 EST: 1937
SQ FT: 120,000
SALES (est): 119.9MM
SALES (corp-wide): 7.2B **Publicly Held**
WEB: www.bldr.com
SIC: 5031 2439 5211 2434 Lumber: rough, dressed & finished; millwork; trusses, wooden roof; millwork & lumber; wood kitchen cabinets; millwork; staircases & stairs, wood; doors, wood; sawmills & planing mills, general
PA: Builders Firstsource, Inc.
2001 Bryan St Ste 1600
Dallas TX 75201
214 880-3500

(G-4068)
BUTLER & LAND INC (PA)
10823 Sanden Dr (75238-1338)
P.O. Box 550399 (75355-0399)
PHONE..................................214 343-8800
Mike Woods, *President*
John Cook, *Vice Pres*
Robert Krause, *Vice Pres*
Phillip Amburn, *Engineer*
Lynell Huffmaster, *Treasurer*
EMP: 22

SQ FT: 18,000
SALES (est): 5.1MM **Privately Held**
WEB: www.butlerandland.com
SIC: 3825 Test equipment for electronic & electrical circuits

(G-4069)
BUZZI UNICEM USA INC
1801 Lone Star Dr (75212-5046)
PHONE..................................214 638-8391
Carroll Mulanax, *Principal*
EMP: 23
SALES (corp-wide): 395.5MM **Privately Held**
WEB: www.buzziunicemusa.com
SIC: 3241 Portland cement
HQ: Buzzi Unicem Usa Inc
100 Brodhead Rd Ste 230
Bethlehem PA 18017
610 882-5000

(G-4070)
BYNARI INC
2639 Electronic Ln # 110 (75220-1225)
PHONE..................................214 350-5772
EMP: 17
SQ FT: 10,000
SALES (est): 1.4MM **Privately Held**
SIC: 7372 Prepackaged Software Services

(G-4071)
C & H LABEL CO INC
6928 S R L Thornton Fwy (75232-3666)
PHONE..................................214 371-2355
Lisa M Lynn, *President*
Larry Lynn, *Vice Pres*
EMP: 10 EST: 1966
SQ FT: 7,000
SALES (est): 900K **Privately Held**
WEB: www.chlabel.net
SIC: 2752 Commercial printing, lithographic

(G-4072)
C & R BINDERY INC
2935 Irving Blvd Ste 201 (75247-6236)
PHONE..................................214 688-5258
Hung Kuo Chan, *President*
Anthony L Romaniello, *Vice Pres*
EMP: 14
SALES (est): 1.9MM **Privately Held**
SIC: 2732 Books: printing & binding

(G-4073)
C M C STEEL FABRICATORS INC
Also Called: CMC Construction Services
2323 Irving Blvd (75207-6001)
PHONE..................................214 631-6699
Calvin Oglee, *Manager*
EMP: 56
SALES (corp-wide): 5.4B **Publicly Held**
WEB: www.cmc.com
SIC: 5051 3441 3316 Concrete reinforcing bars; reinforcement mesh, wire; fabricated structural metal; cold finishing of steel shapes
HQ: C M C Steel Fabricators, Inc.
1 Steel Mill Dr
Seguin TX 78155
830 372-8200

(G-4074)
C R D N N DALLAS RESTORATION
4830 Lakawana St (75247-6712)
PHONE..................................214 698-0059
Shane Cook, *President*
EMP: 45
SALES (est): 3.8MM **Privately Held**
WEB: www.crdn.com
SIC: 3582 Drycleaning equipment & machinery, commercial

(G-4075)
CABFIXCO INC
Also Called: Metro Store Fixtures
10350 Brockwood Rd (75238-1611)
PHONE..................................214 389-1520
David Andrews, *President*
Audrey Andrews, *CFO*
EMP: 23
SQ FT: 30,000
SALES (est): 2.3MM **Privately Held**
SIC: 2541 2542 Store fixtures, wood; fixtures, store: except wood

(G-4076)
CADDY PRINTING & GRAPHICS
Also Called: Caddy Quick Print
13701 Neutron Rd (75244-4413)
PHONE..................................972 991-1770
Maddy Kapoor, *President*
Subash Kapoor, *Exec VP*
Amit Kapoor, *Vice Pres*
EMP: 18
SQ FT: 14,500
SALES (est): 2.8MM **Privately Held**
WEB: www.caddyprinting.com
SIC: 2752 Commercial printing, offset

(G-4077)
CAELUS ENERGY ALASKA LLC (PA)
8401 N Central Expy # 400 (75225-4046)
PHONE..................................214 368-6050
Barbara Pearl, *Engineer*
James Musselman,
EMP: 23
SALES (est): 79.9MM **Privately Held**
WEB: www.caelusenergy.com
SIC: 1311 Crude petroleum & natural gas production

(G-4078)
CAIMAN ENERGY LLC (PA)
5949 Sherry Ln Ste 1300 (75225-8036)
PHONE..................................214 580-3700
Jack M Lafield, *President*
Brent Breon, *President*
Richard D Moncrief, *President*
Daniel Wentworth, *COO*
Stephen L Arata, *Exec VP*
EMP: 22
SALES (est): 4.8MM **Privately Held**
WEB: www.caimanenergy.com
SIC: 1382 Oil & gas exploration services

(G-4079)
CAIN FOOD INDUSTRIES INC
8401 Sovereign Row (75247-4683)
P.O. Box 35066 (75235-0066)
PHONE..................................214 630-4511
Gary L Cain, *President*
Kent Burris, *Regional Mgr*
Bradley Cain, *Vice Pres*
Matt Feder, *Vice Pres*
▲ **EMP:** 26
SQ FT: 29,100
SALES (est): 7.6MM **Privately Held**
WEB: www.cainfood.com
SIC: 2099 Emulsifiers, food; yeast

(G-4080)
CAPITAL CITY PROCESSORS LLC
2621 State St (75204-2602)
PHONE..................................405 232-5511
Randy Mc Kiddie, *Manager*
EMP: 25
SALES (est): 3.9MM **Privately Held**
SIC: 2299 Textile mill waste & remnant processing
PA: Pascal Enterprises, Inc.
2621 State St
Dallas TX 75204

(G-4081)
CAPITAL DALLAS ELC MTR SVC
Also Called: Capital Mechanical
9109 Sovereign Row (75247-4515)
PHONE..................................214 630-8487
Mark Manning, *Partner*
Myles Manning, *General Mgr*
Stephen Manning, *General Ptnr*
Francisco Sifuentes, *Foreman/Supr*
Tammy Ormand, *CFO*
EMP: 17
SQ FT: 6,000
SALES (est): 4.4MM **Privately Held**
WEB: www.capitalelectricmotor.com
SIC: 7694 Electric motor repair

(G-4082)
CARBOLINE COMPANY
8888 Governors Row (75247-3916)
PHONE..................................800 848-4645
EMP: 20
SALES (corp-wide): 5.5B **Publicly Held**
WEB: www.carboline.com
SIC: 2851 Lacquers, varnishes, enamels & other coatings

HQ: Carboline Company
2150 Schuetz Rd Fl 1
Saint Louis MO 63146
314 644-1000

(G-4083)
CARDINAL AUTOMATION INC
Also Called: Atlaswerks
11036 Aladdin Dr (75229-4005)
P.O. Box 670421 (75367-0421)
PHONE..............................214 233-3773
John Kasik, *President*
Patrick Kiggins, *Exec VP*
Harry Cummins III, *CFO*
Khaled Hassan, *CTO*
EMP: 15
SQ FT: 1,439
SALES (est): 614K **Privately Held**
WEB: www.cardinalautomation.com
SIC: 7372 Business oriented computer
software; application computer software

(G-4084)
CARDINAL MIDSTREAM II LLC
8150 N Cntrl Expy # 1725 (75206-0504)
PHONE..............................214 468-0700
Mark Ward, *Vice Pres*
Douglas E Dormer Jr,
EMP: 20 EST: 2013
SALES (est): 4.2MM **Privately Held**
WEB: www.cardinalmidstream.com
SIC: 1382 Oil & gas exploration services

(G-4085)
CARPENTER CO
Also Called: Er Carpenter
4443 Bronze Way (75236-2099)
P.O. Box 1007, Temple (76503-1007)
PHONE..............................214 330-0373
Mike Mc Henrick, *General Mgr*
EMP: 50
SALES (corp-wide): 1.8B **Privately Held**
WEB: www.carpenterftp.com
SIC: 3086 2821 Insulation or cushioning
material, foamed plastic; plastics materi-
als & resins
PA: Carpenter Co.
5016 Monument Ave
Richmond VA 23230
804 359-0800

(G-4086)
CARREKER CORPORATION (DH)
Also Called: Genisys Group
4055 Valley View Ln # 800 (75244-5070)
PHONE..............................800 486-1981
John D Carreker Jr, *President*
John D Carreker III, *President*
Michael Glover, *President*
Suzette Massie, *President*
Blake A Williams, *President*
EMP: 170
SQ FT: 72,433
SALES (est): 25.4MM
SALES (corp-wide): 10.1B **Publicly Held**
WEB: www.gens1.com
SIC: 7372 7379 Prepackaged software;
computer related consulting services
HQ: Checkfree Corporation
2900 Westside Pkwy
Alpharetta GA 30004
678 375-3000

(G-4087)
CARTA MUNDI INC (HQ)
5101 Highland Place Dr (75236-1449)
P.O. Box 211099 (75211-4301)
PHONE..............................214 330-7761
Steve Young, *CEO*
Stephen Venable, *Exec VP*
Keith Chandler, *Vice Pres*
Bob Nickel, *Vice Pres*
Greg Hughes, *Purch Mgr*
▲ EMP: 75
SALES (est): 137MM
SALES (corp-wide): 177.9K **Privately
Held**
WEB: www.cartamundi.com
SIC: 7999 2752 Card & game services;
playing cards, lithographed
PA: Cartamundi
Visbeekstraat 22
Turnhout
144 202-01

(G-4088)
CASCI ORNAMENTAL PLASTER INC
2615 S Good Latimer Expy (75215-2208)
PHONE..............................214 421-3390
Royce L Renfro, *President*
Jan Renfro, *Vice Pres*
EMP: 10
SQ FT: 37,000
SALES (est): 1.2MM **Privately Held**
WEB: www.casciplaster.com
SIC: 3299 Ornamental & architectural plas-
ter work

(G-4089)
CASEROS IMPORTS INC
Also Called: Casero's and Associates
4343 Sigma Rd Ste 300 (75244-4450)
PHONE..............................972 247-1991
Maria Casero, *President*
Francisco Casero Jr, *Vice Pres*
Philippe Lacorne, *Treasurer*
▲ EMP: 10
SQ FT: 4,000
SALES (est): 1.2MM **Privately Held**
WEB: www.luliandme.com
SIC: 2361 Dresses: girls', children's & in-
fants'

(G-4090)
CASINO SUPPLY COMPANY
Also Called: A Touch of Vegas
2416 Walnut Ridge St (75229-4528)
PHONE..............................972 241-4833
Jay Simon, *Owner*
Jeff Simon, *General Mgr*
▲ EMP: 10
SQ FT: 35,000
SALES (est): 2.2MM **Privately Held**
WEB: www.casinosupply.com
SIC: 3944 5092 Bingo boards (games);
poker chips; playing cards

(G-4091)
CASTEEL & ASSOCIATES INC
Also Called: Casteel Sign
11106 Morrison Ln (75229-5607)
PHONE..............................214 352-7446
Warren Casteel, *President*
Audre Casteel, *President*
EMP: 13
SQ FT: 11,000
SALES (est): 1.8MM **Privately Held**
WEB: www.casteelsign.com
SIC: 3993 8742 Signs & advertising spe-
cialties; management consulting services

(G-4092)
CECO ENVIRONMENTAL CORP (PA)
14651 Dallas Pkwy Ste 50 (75254-7476)
PHONE..............................214 357-6181
Todd Gleason, *CEO*
Jason Dezwirek, *Ch of Bd*
Tim Shippy, *Vice Pres*
Pamela Turay, *Vice Pres*
John Allison, *Opers Staff*
EMP: 107
SQ FT: 18,267
SALES (est): 341.8MM **Publicly Held**
WEB: www.cecoenviro.com
SIC: 3564 Purification & dust collection
equipment

(G-4093)
CELANESE ACETATE LLC
1601 Lyndon B Johnson Fwy (75234-6512)
PHONE..............................972 443-4000
Lou Purvis, *President*
Dan Gill, *Business Mgr*
Belinda Hyde, *Vice Pres*
Beverly Sharpe, *Vice Pres*
Rudy Velez, *Purch Mgr*
▼ EMP: 800
SALES (est): 110.7MM
SALES (corp-wide): 5.6B **Publicly Held**
WEB: www.celanese.com
SIC: 2281 Manmade & synthetic fiber
yarns, spun; acetate yarn, spun: made
from purchased staple
HQ: Cna Holdings Llc
222 Las Colinas Blvd W
Irving TX 75039
972 443-4000

(G-4094)
CELANESE US HOLDINGS LLC
1601 Lyndon B Johnson Fwy (75234-6034)
PHONE..............................972 443-4000
▼ EMP: 880
SALES (est): 863.3MM
SALES (corp-wide): 5.6B **Publicly Held**
WEB: www.celanese.com
SIC: 2821 2879 2819 Plastics materials &
resins; agricultural chemicals; industrial
inorganic chemicals
PA: Celanese Corporation
222 Las Colinas Blvd W
Irving TX 75039
972 443-4000

(G-4095)
CEMS ACQUIRE CO LLC
811 N Bishop Ave Apt 2 (75208-4254)
PHONE..............................817 308-0165
Robert Ryan,
EMP: 25
SQ FT: 20,000
SALES (est): 211.7K **Privately Held**
SIC: 7694 Motor repair services

(G-4096)
CENTENNIAL RADIATOR INC (PA)
Also Called: Centennial Radiator Service
447 W Mockingbird Ln (75247-6687)
PHONE..............................214 634-8262
Kenneth W Wood, *President*
Dina Wood, *Principal*
Vivian Wood, *Corp Secy*
Don Kimberlin, *Vice Pres*
Wood Vivian, *Director*
EMP: 25
SQ FT: 4,000
SALES (est): 5.4MM **Privately Held**
WEB: www.centennialradiator.com
SIC: 5013 7539 3675 Radiators; radiator
repair shop, automotive; condensers,
electronic

(G-4097)
CENTEX CORPORATION (HQ)
2728 N Harwood St (75201-1516)
PHONE..............................214 981-5000
Timothy R Eller, *President*
Richard Dugas Jr, *President*
James Ellinghausen, *Exec VP*
Joseph A Bosch, *Senior VP*
Mark D Kemp, *Senior VP*
▲ EMP: 155
SQ FT: 100,000
SALES (est): 439.3MM
SALES (corp-wide): 11B **Publicly Held**
WEB: www.centex.com
SIC: 1531 2451 6162 1542 Speculative
builder, single-family houses; mobile
homes; mortgage bankers; nonresidential
construction; commercial & office build-
ing, new construction; hospital construc-
tion; school building construction;
industrial buildings & warehouses; industrial buildings, new construction; residential construction; hotel/motel, new
construction; condominium construction
PA: Pultegroup, Inc.
3350 Peachtree Rd Ne # 15
Atlanta GA 30326
404 978-6400

(G-4098)
CENTRAL HARDWOODS INC (PA)
1959 W Northwest Hwy (75220-2313)
PHONE..............................972 241-3571
Joseph P Wilbert Jr, *President*
Jerry Kerr, *Controller*
Jay Fisher, *Sales Staff*
Dean Webb, *Sales Staff*
Marie Erickson, *Manager*
EMP: 42 EST: 1946
SQ FT: 100,000
SALES (est): 20.3MM **Privately Held**
WEB: www.centralhardwoods.com
SIC: 5031 2431 Lumber: rough, dressed &
finished; millwork

(G-4099)
CENTRAL JEWELRY & REFINING (PA)
2650 Andjon Dr (75220-1310)
PHONE..............................214 350-4653
EMP: 13 EST: 2011
SALES (est): 2.2MM **Privately Held**
WEB: www.centraljewelryrefining.com
SIC: 3339 Gold refining (primary)

(G-4100)
CENTRAL MILLWORK LLC
Blystone Ln (75220)
PHONE..............................925 963-5448
Eric Thornton,
EMP: 25
SQ FT: 48,000
SALES (est): 3.4MM **Privately Held**
WEB: www.centralmillwork.com
SIC: 2431 Millwork

(G-4101)
CENTRIC PIPE LLC
14850 Montfort Dr Ste 100 (75254-6756)
PHONE..............................214 526-4423
Mike Knafelc, *President*
EMP: 22
SALES (est): 6.7MM **Privately Held**
WEB: www.centricpipe.com
SIC: 3317 Steel pipe & tubes

(G-4102)
CENVEO WORLDWIDE LIMITED
14001 Inwood Rd (75244-4602)
PHONE..............................972 729-5700
Donald Stark, *Project Mgr*
Charlie Detruit, *Production*
Audrey Noll, *Purch Agent*
Kelli Parmer, *Accounts Mgr*
Dan Kreber, *Cust Mgr*
EMP: 150
SQ FT: 150,000
SALES (corp-wide): 1B **Privately Held**
WEB: www.cenveo.com
SIC: 2677 5112 Envelopes; envelopes
HQ: Cenveo Worldwide Limited
200 First Stamford Pl # 2
Stamford CT 06902
203 595-3000

(G-4103)
CERTAINTEED LLC
3000 W Commerce St (75212-4841)
PHONE..............................214 630-7377
Sam Ansley, *Division Pres*
Jeff Hansen, *Vice Pres*
Jeff Hausen, *Vice Pres*
Rudy Schneider, *Purch Mgr*
John Smrcina, *CFO*
EMP: 100
SALES (corp-wide): 328.4MM **Privately
Held**
WEB: www.certainteed.com
SIC: 3292 Roofing, asbestos felt roll
HQ: Certainteed Llc
20 Moores Rd
Malvern PA 19355
610 893-5000

(G-4104)
CHAPARRAL WLDG FABRICATION INC
2453 Merrell Rd (75229-4516)
PHONE..............................972 243-7747
Charles Pittman, *President*
Amanda Rogers, *Safety Mgr*
Linda Pittman, *Treasurer*
EMP: 25
SQ FT: 14,000
SALES (est): 4.2MM **Privately Held**
WEB: www.chaparralwelding.com
SIC: 1761 7692 3441 Architectural sheet
metal work; welding repair; fabricated
structural metal

(G-4105)
CHAPMAN ELECTRIC COMPANY
3131 S Haskell Ave (75223-3120)
PHONE..............................214 824-8095
James Chapman, *President*
Chris Chapman, *Vice Pres*
EMP: 14
SQ FT: 8,500

SALES (est): 1.3MM **Privately Held**
WEB: www.forkliftmotors.com
SIC: 7694 Rebuilding motors, except auto-
motive; electric motor repair

(G-4106)
CHEERLEADING COMPANY INC
11350 Hillguard Rd (75243-8311)
PHONE................................800 411-4105
James G Hazlewood, *President*
Angelica Alcala, *Production*
Quortni Hunt, *Production*
Amanda Marsh, *Production*
Edward Knuth, *Finance*
▲ EMP: 45
SQ FT: 62,000
SALES (est): 7.8MM **Privately Held**
WEB: www.cheerleading.com
SIC: 2389 5632 2339 5139 Band uni-
forms; women's dancewear, hosiery & lin-
gerie; apparel accessories; women's &
misses' athletic clothing & sportswear;
uniforms, athletic: women's, misses' &
juniors'; footwear, athletic

(G-4107)
CHEESECAKE ROYALE INC (PA)
Also Called: Cheesecake Royale Bakery
9016 Garland Rd (75218-3919)
PHONE................................214 328-9102
Dino Roidopoulous, *President*
Gina Roidopoulos, *Vice Pres*
Jessica Gump, *Manager*
▲ EMP: 25
SQ FT: 2,200
SALES (est): 3.8MM **Privately Held**
WEB: www.cheesecakeroyale.com
SIC: 2051 Cakes, bakery: except frozen

(G-4108)
CHEM-COAT INDUSTRIES INC
729 3rd Ave (75226-2017)
PHONE................................972 485-8648
David Tatom, *President*
Marie Kaufman, *Office Mgr*
EMP: 10
SALES (est): 2.6MM **Privately Held**
WEB: www.chem-coat.com
SIC: 2851 Paints & allied products

(G-4109)
CHEP (USA) INC
Also Called: National Pallet Company
2805 Mican Dr (75212-4602)
P.O. Box 560041 (75356-0041)
PHONE................................214 688-4108
Bobby Hall, *Branch Mgr*
EMP: 75 **Privately Held**
WEB: www.chep.com
SIC: 2448 Pallets, wood; skids, wood
HQ: Chep (U.S.A.) Inc.
5897 Windward Pkwy
Alpharetta GA 30005
770 668-8100

(G-4110)
CHEQUEDCOM INC
13355 Noel Rd Ste 1500 (75240-6894)
PHONE................................888 412-0699
Greg Moran, *CEO*
John Tobison, *COO*
Gary Ito, *CFO*
Kevin Williams, *Security Dir*
EMP: 30 EST: 2012
SALES (est): 2.5MM
SALES (corp-wide): 12.9MM **Privately
Held**
SIC: 7372 8742 Business oriented com-
puter software; human resource consult-
ing services
PA: Chequed Holdings, Llc
513 Broadway Ste 1
Saratoga Springs NY 12866
888 412-0699

(G-4111)
**CHEROKEE HORN
PRODUCTION LP**
5950 Berkshire Ln # 1250 (75225-5846)
PHONE................................619 435-8950
Carl G McCaslin Jr, *Principal*
EMP: 15
SALES (est): 1.8MM **Privately Held**
WEB: www.springbokenergy.com
SIC: 1382 Oil & gas exploration services

(G-4112)
CHIEF OIL & GAS LLC (PA)
Also Called: Chief Operating
8111 Westchester Dr # 600 (75225-6140)
PHONE................................214 265-9590
Trevor D Rees-Jones, *CEO*
Russell Parker, *President*
Steven Haworth, *Vice Pres*
John E Hinton, *Vice Pres*
David Hundley, *Vice Pres*
EMP: 12
SQ FT: 4,500
SALES (est): 22.6MM **Privately Held**
WEB: www.chiefog.com
SIC: 1311 Crude petroleum production;
natural gas production

(G-4113)
CHOLLA PETROLEUM INC (HQ)
6688 N Central Expy # 1610 (75206-3951)
P.O. Box 12208 (75225-0208)
PHONE................................214 692-7052
Loyd W Powell Jr, *President*
Loyd Powell Jr, *Managing Prtnr*
Terry Cahill, *CFO*
Chris Cahill, *Manager*
Gideon Powell, *Director*
EMP: 37
SQ FT: 4,300
SALES (est): 10.2MM
SALES (corp-wide): 3.7MM **Privately
Held**
WEB: www.chollapetro.com
SIC: 1311 Crude petroleum production;
natural gas production
PA: Palo Verde Oil Company
5949 Sherry Ln Ste 850
Dallas TX 75225
214 692-7052

(G-4114)
**CHROMALLOY GAS TURBINE
LLC**
14042 Distribution Way (75234-3439)
PHONE................................972 241-2501
Sam Malone, *Director*
EMP: 12
SALES (corp-wide): 3.3B **Publicly Held**
WEB: www.chromalloy.com
SIC: 3812 5088 7699 3724 Search &
navigation equipment; aircraft engines &
engine parts; fountain repair; aircraft en-
gines & engine parts; brazing (hardening)
of metal
HQ: Chromalloy Gas Turbine Llc
3999 Rca Blvd
Palm Beach Gardens FL 33410
561 935-3571

(G-4115)
CHROMIUM CORPORATION (DH)
14911 Quorum Dr Ste 600 (75254-1491)
PHONE................................972 851-0500
Frank Jalili, *Exec VP*
Joseph Gary, *Vice Pres*
▲ EMP: 12
SALES (est): 5.9MM
SALES (corp-wide): 2.5B **Privately Held**
SIC: 3443 Liners, industrial: metal plate
HQ: Elkcorp
14911 Quorum Dr Ste 600
Dallas TX 75254
972 851-0500

(G-4116)
CHURRO FACTORY LLC
2156 W Northwest Hwy # 302
(75220-4221)
PHONE................................214 566-5894
Edgar Meza, *Principal*
Edgar N Meza,
EMP: 9
SALES (est): 618.4K **Privately Held**
WEB: www.thechurrofactory.com
SIC: 2051 Bread, cake & related products

(G-4117)
**CINCO NATURAL RESOURCES
CORP**
Also Called: Cinco Resources
2626 Howell St Ste 800 (75204-0831)
PHONE................................214 520-7727
Jon Glass, *President*
Jon L Glass, *President*
Chris Kidd, *Vice Pres*

Chris M Kidd, *Vice Pres*
Leigh T Prieto, *Vice Pres*
EMP: 49
SALES (est): 7.6MM
SALES (corp-wide): 70.6MM **Privately
Held**
WEB: www.cincoog.com
SIC: 1382 Oil & gas exploration services
HQ: Cinco Resources, Inc.
2626 Howell St Ste 800
Dallas TX 75204

(G-4118)
CINCO OIL & GAS LLC
2626 Howell St Ste 800 (75204-0831)
PHONE................................214 520-7727
Edward Travis, *COO*
Sharon Featherstone, *Human Res Mgr*
Craig Pollard, *Executive*
Wayne Stoltenberg,
EMP: 25
SALES (est): 1.3MM **Privately Held**
WEB: www.cincoog.com
SIC: 1382 Geological exploration, oil & gas
field

(G-4119)
CINCO RESOURCES INC (HQ)
2626 Howell St Ste 800 (75204-0831)
PHONE................................214 520-7727
Jon Glass, *President*
Ed Travis, *COO*
Leigh Prieto, *Vice Pres*
Wayne B Stoltenberg, *CFO*
EMP: 9
SALES (est): 7.6MM
SALES (corp-wide): 70.6MM **Privately
Held**
WEB: www.cincoog.com
SIC: 1382 Oil & gas exploration services
PA: Riley Exploration Group, Llc
29 E Reno Ave Ste 5
Oklahoma City OK 73104
405 485-8200

(G-4120)
CIRCLE R EMBROIDERY CO INC
Also Called: Classic Caps & Embroidery
4901 Woodall St (75247-6710)
PHONE................................214 741-1555
Frank Rosenbloom, *President*
Rosalie Rosenbloom, *Vice Pres*
▲ EMP: 40
SQ FT: 42,000
SALES (est): 4.5MM **Privately Held**
WEB: www.classicce.com
SIC: 2395 2353 Emblems, embroidered;
hats, caps & millinery

(G-4121)
**CIRCLE T WESTERN WEAR LTD
(PA)**
Also Called: Roughrider
5349 Drane Dr (75209-5501)
PHONE................................214 808-1100
William W Lenox, *President*
Marilyn Lenox, *Vice Pres*
EMP: 13
SQ FT: 18,000
SALES (est): 1MM **Privately Held**
SIC: 2337 2331 Skirts, separate:
women's, misses' & juniors'; shirts,
women's & juniors': made from purchased
materials

(G-4122)
CITY HATZ/CITY FLAGZ
6708 Sweet Sue Ln (75241-3745)
PHONE................................214 376-2589
Johnathan R Willis, *Principal*
EMP: 54
SALES (est): 950K **Privately Held**
SIC: 2353 Hats, caps & millinery

(G-4123)
**CITY NEWSPAPERS
MANAGEMENT LLC**
Also Called: People News Papers
750 N Saint Paul St # 2100 (75201-3236)
PHONE................................214 739-2244
Kate Martin, *Executive*
Wick Allison,
EMP: 130
SQ FT: 5,500

SALES (est): 7.7MM **Privately Held**
WEB: www.peoplenewspapers.com
SIC: 2711 Newspapers: publishing only,
not printed on site; newspapers, publishing & printing

(G-4124)
CITY SIGN SERVICES INC
3914 Elm St (75226-1218)
PHONE................................214 826-4475
Patsy Waits, *President*
Shellie Peters, *Corp Secy*
Kenneth Waits, *Vice Pres*
Wayne Waits, *Vice Pres*
EMP: 26 EST: 1956
SQ FT: 20,000
SALES (est): 4.7MM **Privately Held**
WEB: www.citysignservices.com
SIC: 4212 7699 3993 Truck rental with
drivers; miscellaneous building item repair
services; electric signs

(G-4125)
CKS PACKAGING INC
Also Called: C K S Regal Plastics
2818 Merrell Rd (75229-4701)
P.O. Box 29306 (75229-0306)
PHONE................................214 358-2441
John Beasley, *Plant Mgr*
Tracy Escobar, *Branch Mgr*
EMP: 50
SALES (corp-wide): 439.3MM **Privately
Held**
WEB: www.ckspackaging.com
SIC: 3089 5085 3085 Plastic containers,
except foam; bottler supplies; plastics bot-
tles
PA: C.K.S. Packaging, Inc.
350 Great Sw Pkwy
Atlanta GA 30336
404 691-8900

(G-4126)
CLARKE HARLAND CORP
10575 Vista Park Rd (75238-1647)
PHONE................................210 694-1492
Richard Martin, *Manager*
EMP: 100 **Publicly Held**
WEB: www.harlandclarke.com
SIC: 2752 2782 2759 Business form &
card printing, lithographic; checkbooks;
commercial printing
HQ: Harland Clarke Corp.
15955 La Cantera Pkwy
San Antonio TX 78256
830 609-5500

(G-4127)
**CLASSIC BALLOON
CORPORATION**
Also Called: Fineline Packaging
2200 Ross Ave Ste 3300 (75201-7965)
PHONE................................972 242-2711
Leslie W Barton, *President*
Les Barton, *President*
Marci Barton, *Admin Sec*
▲ EMP: 120
SQ FT: 56,000
SALES (est): 16.2MM **Privately Held**
WEB: www.trammellcrow.com
SIC: 3069 Balloons, metal foil laminated
with rubber

(G-4128)
CLASSIC DOORS SYSTEMS CO
151 Regal Row Ste 220 (75247-5609)
P.O. Box 591759, San Antonio (78259-
0137)
PHONE................................214 678-9555
EMP: 14
SQ FT: 20,000
SALES: 1.6MM **Privately Held**
SIC: 2431 Mfg Millwork

(G-4129)
CLASSIC STAINLESS INC
4031 Bronze Way (75237-1028)
PHONE................................214 467-8700
Son Tran, *President*
William E Newton, *Vice Pres*
Gustavo Macias, *Treasurer*
Belen Macias, *Office Mgr*
EMP: 20
SALES (est): 3.8MM **Privately Held**
WEB: www.classicstainless.net
SIC: 3444 Sheet metalwork

(G-4130)
CLIMAX INVESTORS LLC
7272 Marvin D Love Fwy # 518
(75237-3173)
P.O. Box 442012, Houston (77244-2012)
PHONE..................................832 582-9622
Layton Williams, *Partner*
EMP: 22
SALES (est): 976.7K **Privately Held**
SIC: 1541 1542 1522 0781 Industrial
buildings & warehouses; nonresidential
construction; residential construction;
landscape counseling & planning; sports
apparel; customized clothing & apparel;
apparel & outerwear fabrics, cotton

(G-4131)
**CNC PRECISION
MANUFACTURING**
14850 Venture Dr (75234-2426)
P.O. Box 815668 (75381-5668)
PHONE..................................972 241-4226
Gary Embrey, *Partner*
Emy Embrey, *Partner*
Kiah Buchner, *Manager*
EMP: 40
SQ FT: 4,000
SALES (est): 6.4MM **Privately Held**
SIC: 3699 Electrical equipment & supplies

(G-4132)
**CNOOC PETROLEUM OFFSHR
USA INC**
Also Called: Nexen Petroleum Offshr USA Inc
12790 Merit Dr Ste 800 (75251-1217)
PHONE..................................972 450-4600
Douglas Otten, *President*
Grant W Dreger, *Vice Pres*
Ian W Macleod, *Vice Pres*
Ronald E Manz, *Vice Pres*
R M Nall, *Vice Pres*
EMP: 130
SALES (est): 5.1MM **Privately Held**
SIC: 1382 Oil & gas exploration services
HQ: Nexen Petroleum U.S.A. Inc.
945 Bunker Hill Rd # 1400
Houston TX 77024
972 450-4600

(G-4133)
COBB CARPET SUPPLY CO (PA)
Also Called: Dyna-Chem
1314 Viceroy Dr (75247-3911)
PHONE..................................214 634-2622
Randall R Cobb, *President*
Lawrence J Cobb, *Vice Pres*
Mats Berg, *Purchasing*
▼ **EMP:** 15 **EST:** 1975
SQ FT: 40,000
SALES (est): 8.7MM **Privately Held**
WEB: www.cobbcarpet.com
SIC: 5084 2842 Industrial machinery &
equipment; cleaning or polishing prepara-
tions

(G-4134)
**COCA COLA BTLG OF
SHREVEPORT (DH)**
Also Called: Coca-Cola
14185 Dallas Pkwy # 1400 (75254-1319)
PHONE..................................214 902-2600
Henry A Schimberg, *President*
Susan Gambardella, *Executive Asst*
▲ **EMP:** 120 **EST:** 1902
SALES (est): 49.4MM
SALES (corp-wide): 37.2B **Publicly Held**
WEB: www.na.ko.com
SIC: 2086 5046 5962 Bottled & canned
soft drinks; vending machines, coin-oper-
ated; cold drinks vending machines
HQ: Coca-Cola Refreshments Usa, Inc.
2500 Windy Ridge Pkwy Se
Atlanta GA 30339
770 989-3000

(G-4135)
COCA-COLA COMPANY
6445 Lemmon Ave (75209-5794)
P.O. Box 7186 (75209)
PHONE..................................214 351-4797
Trenton Busby, *Sales Mgr*
Rachel Chahal, *Marketing Staff*
J T Cantrell, *Branch Mgr*
Frank Comito, *Manager*
Susan Stading, *Director*

EMP: 130
SALES (corp-wide): 37.2B **Publicly Held**
WEB: www.coca-colacompany.com
SIC: 2086 2087 Bottled & canned soft
drinks; flavoring extracts & syrups
PA: The Coca-Cola Company
1 Coca Cola Plz Nw
Atlanta GA 30313
404 676-2121

(G-4136)
**COCA-COLA ENTERPRISES
BOTTLING**
14185 Dallas Pkwy # 1400 (75254-1319)
P.O. Box 132008 (75313-2008)
PHONE..................................214 253-5747
Danny Holstead, *Principal*
EMP: 200
SALES (est): 25.1MM
SALES (corp-wide): 37.2B **Publicly Held**
WEB: www.cokecce.com
SIC: 2086 Bottled & canned soft drinks
HQ: Coca-Cola Refreshments Usa, Inc.
2500 Windy Ridge Pkwy Se
Atlanta GA 30339
770 989-3000

(G-4137)
**COCA-COLA REFRESHMENTS
USA INC**
13727 Noel Rd Ste 900 (75240-1355)
PHONE..................................214 253-5600
Dave Van Houten, *Principal*
EMP: 65
SALES (corp-wide): 37.2B **Publicly Held**
WEB: www.coca-colacompany.com
SIC: 2086 Bottled & canned soft drinks
HQ: Coca-Cola Refreshments Usa, Inc.
2500 Windy Ridge Pkwy Se
Atlanta GA 30339
770 989-3000

(G-4138)
**COCA-COLA SOUTHWEST BEVS
LLC (DH)**
Also Called: Ccswb
14185 Dallas Pkwy # 1300 (75254-1319)
PHONE..................................214 902-2600
Mark Schortman, *President*
EMP: 110
SALES (est): 2.4B **Privately Held**
SIC: 2086 2087 Bottled & canned soft
drinks; soft drinks: packaged in cans, bot-
tles, etc.; fruit drinks (less than 100%
juice): packaged in cans, etc.; syrups,
drink; concentrates, drink

(G-4139)
**COCA-COLA SOUTHWEST BEVS
LLC**
8161 Moberly Ln (75227-2322)
PHONE..................................214 388-6000
Billy Walker, *Branch Mgr*
Luis Acosta, *Manager*
Cardell Armstrong, *Manager*
Marilee O Horn, *Manager*
John Santiago, *Manager*
EMP: 400 **Privately Held**
WEB: www.coca-cola.com
SIC: 2086 5149 Bottled & canned soft
drinks; groceries & related products
HQ: Coca-Cola Southwest Beverages Llc
14185 Dallas Pkwy # 1300
Dallas TX 75254
214 902-2600

(G-4140)
**COGENT MIDSTREAM WESTEX
LLC**
2305 Cedar Springs Rd # 100
(75201-1854)
PHONE..................................469 290-4100
Dennis McCanless, *CEO*
Stan Golemon, *COO*
Scott Brown, *Senior VP*
Rodney Madden, *Senior VP*
Bradley K Alford, *CFO*
EMP: 37
SALES (est): 11.5MM **Privately Held**
WEB: www.lucid-energy.com
SIC: 1382 Oil & gas exploration services

(G-4141)
COLO4 LLC
3004 Irving Blvd (75247-6213)
PHONE..................................214 630-3100
Pat Thompson, *Owner*
EMP: 16
SALES (est): 3.7MM **Privately Held**
WEB: www.colo4.com
SIC: 3661 Telegraph or telephone carrier &
repeater equipment

(G-4142)
COLONIAL TRUSS CO LLC
2825 Storey Ln (75220-4513)
PHONE..................................469 320-1000
EMP: 28
SALES (corp-wide): 2.6MM **Privately
Held**
WEB: www.colonialtruss.com
SIC: 2439 Trusses, wooden roof
PA: Colonial Truss Co., Llc
7557 Rambler Rd Ste 1020
Dallas TX 75231
469 364-3134

(G-4143)
COLOR CONTORL NETWORK
1908 Royal Ln (75229-3128)
PHONE..................................972 754-1912
Henry Martinez, *CEO*
David Culotta, *VP Finance*
EMP: 9
SALES (est): 859.2K **Privately Held**
WEB: www.colorcontrolnetwork.com
SIC: 2752 Color lithography

(G-4144)
**COLUMBIA PACKING CO INC
(PA)**
2807 E 11th St (75203-2010)
P.O. Box 151336 (75315-1336)
PHONE..................................214 946-8171
Joseph C Ondrusek, *President*
Amber Ferry, *Vice Pres*
Jim Liska, *Controller*
EMP: 35 **EST:** 1913
SQ FT: 75,000
SALES (est): 40MM **Privately Held**
WEB: www.columbiapacking.com
SIC: 5147 2011 2013 5143 Lard; canned
meats (except baby food), meat slaugh-
tered on site; boneless meat, from pur-
chased meat; cheese

(G-4145)
**COMMEMORATIVE BRANDS
INC**
Balfour Sports
1550 W Mockingbird Ln (75235-5007)
PHONE..................................800 225-3687
Michael Foltz, *Regional Mgr*
Curt Langford, *Vice Pres*
Larry Pennington, *Facilities Mgr*
Steven Bauer, *Train & Dev Mgr*
Ann Harris, *Accounts Exec*
EMP: 22 **Privately Held**
WEB: www.balfour.com
SIC: 3911 Jewelry, precious metal
HQ: Commemorative Brands, Inc.
1550 W Mockingbird Ln
Dallas TX 75235

(G-4146)
**COMMERCIAL METALS
COMPANY**
CMC Recycling American
2215 S Good Latimer Expy (75226-2221)
PHONE..................................214 565-0668
Joe Blair, *Branch Mgr*
EMP: 101
SALES (corp-wide): 5.4B **Publicly Held**
WEB: www.cmc.com
SIC: 5093 4953 3341 Ferrous metal
scrap & waste; nonferrous metals scrap;
refuse systems; secondary nonferrous
metals
PA: Commercial Metals Company
6565 N Macarthur Blvd # 800
Irving TX 75039
214 689-4300

(G-4147)
**COMMERCIAL METALS
COMPANY**
Also Called: CMC Recycling
1839 W Commerce St (75208-8102)
PHONE..................................469 729-0180
Allan White, *Branch Mgr*
EMP: 40
SALES (corp-wide): 5.4B **Publicly Held**
WEB: www.cmc.com
SIC: 5093 3341 Ferrous metal scrap &
waste; secondary nonferrous metals
PA: Commercial Metals Company
6565 N Macarthur Blvd # 800
Irving TX 75039
214 689-4300

(G-4148)
**COMMSCOPE INC NORTH
CAROLINA**
8635 N Stemmons Fwy (75247)
PHONE..................................214 583-6750
Michael Abela, *Principal*
Philip Sorrells, *Vice Pres*
Amit Kaistha, *Engineer*
Jim Noel, *Manager*
Kevin Volkert, *Director*
EMP: 246 **Publicly Held**
WEB: www.commscope.com
SIC: 3663 Radio & TV communications
equipment
HQ: Commscope, Inc. Of North Carolina
1100 Commscope Pl Se
Hickory NC 28602
866 277-2410

(G-4149)
**COMMSCOPE TECHNOLOGIES
LLC**
Decibel Products
8635 N Stemmons Fwy (75247)
PHONE..................................214 634-8502
Peter Mailandt, *President*
EMP: 600 **Publicly Held**
SIC: 3663 1799 3661 3651 Radio & TV
communications equipment; antenna in-
stallation; telephone & telegraph appara-
tus; household audio & video equipment;
blowers & fans; porcelain electrical sup-
plies
HQ: Commscope Technologies Llc
4 Westbrook Corporate Ctr
Westchester IL 60154
708 236-6600

(G-4150)
**COMPLETE RESTAURANT SVCS
INC**
2668 Myrtle Springs Ave (75220-2537)
PHONE..................................214 350-1110
David Tunnell, *President*
Michael J Bell, *Vice Pres*
John R Welborn, *Vice Pres*
Crue Welborn, *Technical Staff*
EMP: 39
SALES (est): 8.6MM **Privately Held**
WEB: www.completerestaurantservices.net
SIC: 2599 Carts, restaurant equipment;
food wagons, restaurant; restaurant furni-
ture, wood or metal

(G-4151)
**COMPOSITE TECHNOLOGY INC
(DH)**
Also Called: C T I
1727 S Main St (75261-4602)
P.O. Box 610407 (75261-0407)
PHONE..................................972 456-6900
Timothy Adanti, *General Mgr*
John Hay, *Chief Engr*
▲ **EMP:** 48
SQ FT: 60,000
SALES (est): 17.3MM **Publicly Held**
WEB: www.rotorblades.com
SIC: 4581 3728 Aircraft servicing & repair-
ing; aircraft parts & equipment

(G-4152)
**COMPRESSORS UNLIMITED
INTL LLC**
2531 S Belt Line Rd (75253-4602)
P.O. Box 361027 (75336-1027)
PHONE..................................972 286-2264
Brian Robertson, *Opers Staff*

▲ = Import ▼=Export
◆ =Import/Export

Gwen McCollum, *Mng Member*
James McCollum,
David Wilcox,
EMP: 19
SQ FT: 60,000
SALES (est): 4.5MM **Privately Held**
WEB: www.compressorsunlimited.com
SIC: 5075 3585 Air conditioning & ventilation equipment & supplies; air conditioning units, complete: domestic or industrial

(G-4153)
COMPUTER SERVICE TECHNOLOGY
2336 Lufield Dr (75229-2022)
PHONE..............................972 241-2662
Cecil Ho, *President*
Joseph Goh, *Vice Pres*
Kitty Seto, *Purch Mgr*
Patty Ho, *Admin Sec*
▲ **EMP:** 20
SQ FT: 4,000
SALES (est): 4.5MM **Privately Held**
WEB: www.simmtester.com
SIC: 3825 Test equipment for electronic & electric measurement

(G-4154)
COMPX INTERNATIONAL INC (DH)
Also Called: NL INDUSTRIES
5430 Lyndon B Johnson Fwy (75240-2601)
PHONE..............................972 448-1400
Loretta J Feehan, *Ch of Bd*
Robert D Graham, *Vice Ch Bd*
Scott C James, *President*
Andrew B Nace, *Exec VP*
Steven S Eaton, *Vice Pres*
▲ **EMP:** 55
SALES: 124.2MM
SALES (corp-wide): 2B **Publicly Held**
WEB: www.compx.com
SIC: 3699 3714 Security devices; mufflers (exhaust), motor vehicle
HQ: N L Industries, Inc.
5430 Lbj Fwy Ste 1700
Dallas TX 75240
972 233-1700

(G-4155)
COMSOVEREIGN HOLDING CORP (PA)
5000 Quorum Dr Ste 400 (75254-7114)
PHONE..............................469 930-2661
Daniel L Hodges, *Ch of Bd*
John E Howell, *President*
Mohan Tammisetti, *Senior VP*
Brian T Mihelich, *CFO*
Dustin McIntire, *CTO*
EMP: 21
SQ FT: 15,289
SALES (est): 4.7MM **Publicly Held**
WEB: www.droneaviationcorp.com
SIC: 4812 3728 7382 Radio telephone communication; target drones; confinement surveillance systems maintenance & monitoring

(G-4156)
CONSOLIDATED FABRICATORS INC
5480 La Sierra Dr (75231-4108)
PHONE..............................214 376-4389
Norm Osstad, *President*
EMP: 9
SQ FT: 8,800 **Privately Held**
WEB: www.cfidallas.com
SIC: 3443 Fabricated plate work (boiler shop)

(G-4157)
CONTINENTAL AMERICAN CORP
Also Called: Pioneer Balloon Co
4025 Singleton Blvd (75212-3506)
PHONE..............................214 630-3121
Fred Karr, *General Mgr*
Nolan Collins, *Controller*
Carl Hartschuh, *Planning Mgr*
EMP: 120
SALES (corp-wide): 228.7MM **Privately Held**
WEB: www.us.qualatex.com
SIC: 3069 Balloons, advertising & toy: rubber

PA: Continental American Corporation
5000 E 29th St N
Wichita KS 67220
316 685-2266

(G-4158)
CONTINENTAL BATTERY COMPANY (PA)
4919 Woodall St (75247-6710)
PHONE..............................214 631-5701
James McCann, *President*
William McCann, *Vice Pres*
David G Nelson, *Treasurer*
Danny Coffman, *Sales Staff*
Rex Gibson, *Marketing Mgr*
▲ **EMP:** 60
SQ FT: 10,000
SALES (est): 79MM **Privately Held**
WEB: www.continentalbattery.com
SIC: 3691 Storage batteries

(G-4159)
CONTINENTAL ELECTRONICS CORP (HQ)
Also Called: C E C
4212 S Buckner Blvd (75227-4201)
PHONE..............................214 381-7161
Daniel Dickey, *CEO*
Daniel L Dickey, *CEO*
Mike Rosso, *Vice Pres*
Karen Stephens, *Vice Pres*
Richard Key, *Mfg Dir*
▲ **EMP:** 75
SQ FT: 148,000
SALES (est): 15.5MM **Privately Held**
WEB: www.contelec.com
SIC: 3663 Radio broadcasting & communications equipment

(G-4160)
CONTINENTAL NH3 PDTS CO INC
Also Called: Continental Manufacturing
130 Yorktown St (75208-2136)
P.O. Box 225323 (75222-5323)
PHONE..............................214 741-6083
Joyce Ward, *Chairman*
Judd Stretcher, *Vice Pres*
Claudia Ferguson, *Exec Sec*
▲ **EMP:** 60
SQ FT: 28,600
SALES (est): 56.2MM **Privately Held**
WEB: www.continental-manufacturing.com
SIC: 5085 3599 Valves & fittings; custom machinery

(G-4161)
CONTRAN CORPORATION (PA)
5430 Lyndon B Johnson Fwy (75240-2601)
PHONE..............................972 233-1700
Harold C Simmons, *CEO*
Glenn R Simmons, *Vice Ch Bd*
Steve Watson, *President*
Tim Hafer, *Principal*
David Carlson, *COO*
EMP: 20
SQ FT: 4,000
SALES (est): 2B **Publicly Held**
WEB: www.valhi.net
SIC: 2816 Titanium dioxide, anatase or rutile (pigments)

(G-4162)
CONTROLR SOFTWARE INC
3309 Elm St Ste 3w1 (75226-1637)
PHONE..............................214 909-8676
EMP: 10
SALES (est): 197.9K **Privately Held**
SIC: 7372 Prepackaged software

(G-4163)
CONVEY COMPUTER CORPORATION
5542 Merrimac Ave (75206-5832)
PHONE..............................214 576-9630
Bruce Poal, *President*
Kent Coker, *Vice Pres*
Scott Tracey, *Vice Pres*
▲ **EMP:** 31
SQ FT: 20,000
SALES (est): 8.3MM **Privately Held**
WEB: www.micron.com
SIC: 3571 Electronic computers

(G-4164)
CONVEYOR AGGREGATE PDTS CORP (HQ)
10500 N Stemmons Fwy (75220-2425)
PHONE..............................214 358-5588
Robert W Purvis, *President*
Gail Purvis, *Corp Secy*
Robert Moran, *CFO*
EMP: 23
SALES (est): 28.2MM
SALES (corp-wide): 270.9MM **Privately Held**
SIC: 3496 Conveyor belts
PA: Purvis Industries, Llc
10500 N Stemmons Fwy
Dallas TX 75220
214 358-5500

(G-4165)
COOK & BOARDMAN GROUP LLC
Also Called: Rdl Supply
11240 Gemini Ln (75229-4710)
PHONE..............................214 630-3965
Ed Lawrence, *Manager*
Mark Sanford, *Executive*
EMP: 50
SALES (corp-wide): 36.5MM **Privately Held**
WEB: www.cookandboardman.com
SIC: 3442 2431 Metal doors; millwork
HQ: The Cook & Boardman Group Llc
3916 Westpoint Blvd
Winston Salem NC 27103
336 768-8872

(G-4166)
COPPERBECK ENERGY PARTNERS LLC (PA)
750 N Saint Paul St # 1320 (75201-3239)
PHONE..............................214 238-4881
Wes Martin, *CEO*
John Suchand, *Vice Pres*
Matt Vermillion, *Vice Pres*
EMP: 33
SQ FT: 4,312
SALES (est): 30.9MM **Privately Held**
WEB: www.copperbeck.com
SIC: 1389 Gas field services

(G-4167)
CORELITE INC
5101 Norwood Rd (75247-5828)
PHONE..............................214 905-4359
Giancarlo D Cioppo, *Treasurer*
EMP: 15
SALES (corp-wide): 9MM **Privately Held**
WEB: www.corelitecomposites.com
SIC: 2436 Softwood veneer & plywood
PA: Corelite, Inc
1060 E 30th St
Hialeah FL 33013
305 921-4292

(G-4168)
CORETECH INDUSTRIES LLC
8300 S Central Expy (75241-7815)
PHONE..............................440 949-9592
Robert Foster, *Manager*
Richard Arn,
EMP: 10
SQ FT: 16,000
SALES (est): 300K **Privately Held**
WEB: www.coretechprecision.com
SIC: 3353 Tubes, welded, aluminum

(G-4169)
CORONADO RESOURCES GP LLC
3811 Trtl Crk Blvd (75219-4693)
PHONE..............................214 651-6245
Campbell Lewis, *Principal*
Hayley Rife, *Controller*
EMP: 11
SALES (est): 1.5MM **Privately Held**
WEB: www.coronado-resources.com
SIC: 1382 Oil & gas exploration services

(G-4170)
CORONET ENTERPRISES INC
Also Called: Suntec Industries
3220 Quebec St (75247-6606)
PHONE..............................214 630-1116
Robert Baron, *President*
David Tabayes, *Vice Pres*

David Tobias, *Vice Pres*
Tom Gibson, *Accounts Exec*
Jim Clark, *VP Mktg*
▲ **EMP:** 25
SQ FT: 25,000
SALES (est): 3.6MM **Privately Held**
WEB: www.suntecindustries.com
SIC: 2394 Awnings, fabric: made from purchased materials

(G-4171)
CORPORATE RECORDS MANAGEMENT
Also Called: Maxxsafe Company
3141 Hansboro Ave (75233-1415)
PHONE..............................214 333-3453
Denise Chadima, *President*
Martin Devitt, *Manager*
EMP: 9
SALES (est): 1.4MM **Privately Held**
WEB: www.crmfiles.com
SIC: 4226 7389 3589 Document & office records storage; document & office record destruction; shredders, industrial & commercial

(G-4172)
CORPORATE VSUAL CMMNCTIONS
9011 John W Carpenter Fwy (75247-4525)
P.O. Box 560804 (75356-0804)
PHONE..............................214 206-3763
Jaime Herrera, *President*
Pam Herrera, *Vice Pres*
EMP: 20
SQ FT: 18,000
SALES (est): 3.8MM **Privately Held**
WEB: www.corporatevisual.net
SIC: 2752 Commercial printing, offset

(G-4173)
CORSICANA BEDDING LLC (PA)
Also Called: Corsicana Mattress Company
1420 W Mockingbird Ln (75247-4931)
P.O. Box 1050, Corsicana (75151-1050)
PHONE..............................800 323-4349
Michael Thompson, *CEO*
James Booth, *COO*
Stuart Fallen, *Vice Pres*
Chad Reinsel, *Opers Mgr*
Luis Cervantes, *Prdtn Mgr*
◆ **EMP:** 30
SQ FT: 106,000
SALES (est): 414.9MM **Privately Held**
WEB: www.corsicanamattress.com
SIC: 2515 Mattresses, innerspring or box spring; box springs, assembled

(G-4174)
CORTEZ RESOURCES LLC
3131 Mckinney Ave Ste 430 (75204-8529)
PHONE..............................214 628-9155
J Patrick Collins, *President*
Michael Catrino, *COO*
Peggy Lloyd, *Vice Pres*
Ryan Allen, *CFO*
EMP: 9
SALES (est): 240.8K **Privately Held**
WEB: www.cortezoil.com
SIC: 1382 Oil & gas exploration services

(G-4175)
COUNTRY FRESH LLC (DH)
Also Called: Country Fresh Wesley
2711 N Haskell Ave # 3400 (75204-2911)
PHONE..............................616 243-0173
Kevin Begin, *General Mgr*
Rob Hollandsworth, *Vice Pres*
Larry Hughes, *Plant Mgr*
Denise Glowacki, *Purch Agent*
Craig Macmillan, *Sales Mgr*
EMP: 347 **EST:** 1946
SALES (est): 136.7MM **Publicly Held**
WEB: www.deanfoods.com
SIC: 2097 2024 2026 Manufactured ice; ice cream & frozen desserts; milk processing (pasteurizing, homogenizing, bottling)
HQ: Dean East, Llc
2900 Bristol Hwy
Johnson City TN 37601
423 283-5700

GEOGRAPHIC

(G-4176)
COVEY PARK ENERGY HOLDINGS LLC
8401 N Central Expy # 700 (75225-4405)
PHONE..................................214 548-6000
Delwin Johnson, *Superintendent*
Omar Ghneim, *Vice Pres*
Frank Hernandez, *Vice Pres*
Sherry Hodges, *Vice Pres*
Whitney Ward, *Marketing Mgr*
EMP: 9
SALES (est): 788.9K **Privately Held**
SIC: 1382 Oil & gas exploration services

(G-4177)
COX OIL LLC (PA)
4514 Cole Ave Ste 1175 (75205-4183)
PHONE..................................214 420-7710
Jeffery Wallace, *Purch Dir*
Brad E Cox, *Mng Member*
EMP: 15
SALES (est): 66.8MM **Privately Held**
WEB: www.coxoperating.com
SIC: 1382 Oil & gas exploration services

(G-4178)
COX OPERATING LLC (HQ)
4514 Cole Ave Ste 1175 (75205-4183)
PHONE..................................504 267-9138
Craig Sanders, *CEO*
Brad E Cox, *President*
Rodney Dykes, *President*
William L Graham, *Director*
EMP: 15
SALES (est): 66.8MM **Privately Held**
WEB: www.coxoperating.com
SIC: 1382 Oil & gas exploration services

(G-4179)
CPI IMPORTERS INC
Also Called: Globex America
2324 Shorecrest Dr (75235-1804)
PHONE..................................214 353-0328
Bonnie Itzig, *President*
Jerry Itzig, *Vice Pres*
▲ EMP: 10
SQ FT: 10,000
SALES (est): 1.1MM **Privately Held**
WEB: www.cavallinicoffee.com
SIC: 2095 7389 5078 5046 Coffee roasting (except by wholesale grocers); coffee service; ice cream cabinets; coffee brewing equipment & supplies

(G-4180)
CRAIN CHEMICAL COMPANY INC
2624 Andjon Dr (75220-1310)
P.O. Box 540995 (75354-0995)
PHONE..................................214 358-3301
Lacy E Crain, *Ch of Bd*
Bob Queen, *President*
Aaron Jones, *Exec VP*
Patsy Lee Queen, *Vice Pres*
EMP: 42
SQ FT: 87,000
SALES (est): 5.9MM **Privately Held**
SIC: 2842 5169 Waxes for wood, leather & other materials; furniture polish or wax; specialty cleaning preparations; chemicals & allied products; detergents & soaps, except specialty cleaning

(G-4181)
CRAYON SOFTWARE EXPERTS LLC (DH)
12221 Merit Dr Ste 800 (75251-3105)
PHONE..................................469 329-0290
Glenn Orcutt, *General Mgr*
Regina Manfredi, *Vice Pres*
Ken Pharr, *Vice Pres*
Jon B Syvertsen, *CFO*
Thomas Stave, *Sales Dir*
EMP: 24 EST: 2014
SQ FT: 4,000
SALES (est): 6.6MM **Privately Held**
WEB: www.crayon.com
SIC: 7372 8243 7373 Business oriented computer software; software training, computer; systems software development services
HQ: Crayon Group As
Sandakerveien 114a
Oslo 0484
230 067-00

(G-4182)
CREATIVE TILE INC (PA)
Also Called: Artisan Collection
2906 N Fitzhugh Ave (75204-3161)
PHONE..................................214 827-0552
Bobby Gene Moore, *President*
EMP: 9
SQ FT: 2,000
SALES (est): 984.8K **Privately Held**
WEB: www.creativetile-inc.com
SIC: 3253 5211 5032 1799 Ceramic wall & floor tile; tile, ceramic; ceramic wall & floor tile; counter top installation; tile installation, ceramic

(G-4183)
CREATIVE TYPE
1350 Mnscture Ring Ste 11 (75207)
PHONE..................................214 420-1980
Mindi Rosenquist, *CEO*
David Rosenquist, *President*
EMP: 23
SQ FT: 40,000
SALES (est): 2.2MM **Privately Held**
SIC: 3577 Printers, computer

(G-4184)
CREATIVE WOOD CONCEPTS INC
Also Called: Lewis Manufacturing Co
1959 W Northwest Hwy (75220-2313)
PHONE..................................972 539-2555
Tracy Edgemon, *President*
Karan Edgemon, *Vice Pres*
EMP: 12
SQ FT: 30,000
SALES (est): 970K **Privately Held**
SIC: 2431 2434 Woodwork, interior & ornamental; wood kitchen cabinets

(G-4185)
CROSSVALE INC (PA)
4201 Spring Valley Rd # 306 (75244-3808)
PHONE..................................972 714-4782
Jason Sharp, *President*
Conor Brankin, *Managing Prtnr*
Leon McKenzie, *Vice Pres*
Rocio Molina, *Human Res Mgr*
Akshith Arremreddy, *Consultant*
EMP: 26
SQ FT: 12,000
SALES (est): 2.4MM **Privately Held**
WEB: www.crossvale.com
SIC: 7372 Educational computer software

(G-4186)
CROW CHANDELIERS INC
Also Called: Crow Chandelier Service
1333 Slocum St (75207-3801)
PHONE..................................214 744-5488
Bob Crow, *President*
EMP: 12
SALES (est): 1.2MM **Privately Held**
WEB: www.crowchandeliers.com
SIC: 3645 Chandeliers, residential

(G-4187)
CRYO ZONE LLC
3326 Courtyard Pl (75234-3758)
PHONE..................................972 523-6060
Dale Montross, *Mng Member*
EMP: 15
SALES (est): 750K **Privately Held**
SIC: 3842 Hydrotherapy equipment

(G-4188)
CSL PLASMA INC
10121 Lake June Rd 503 (75217-3002)
PHONE..................................972 329-0186
Brenda Greenfield, *Manager*
EMP: 20 **Privately Held**
WEB: www.cslplasma.com
SIC: 8099 2836 Plasmapherous center; blood derivatives
HQ: Csl Plasma Inc.
900 Broken Sound Pkwy Nw # 400
Boca Raton FL 33487
561 981-3700

(G-4189)
CSW INDUSTRIALS INC (PA)
5420 Lyndon B Johnson Fwy (75240-6222)
PHONE..................................214 884-3777
Joseph B Armes, *Ch of Bd*
Greggory Branning, *Exec VP*

Don Sullivan, *Exec VP*
Luke E Alverson, *Senior VP*
Craig J Foster, *Senior VP*
EMP: 35
SALES: 385.8MM **Publicly Held**
WEB: www.cswindustrials.com
SIC: 3569 Assembly machines, non-metal-working

(G-4190)
CSW INDUSTRIALS HOLDINGS INC
5420 Lyndon B Johnson Fwy (75240-6222)
PHONE..................................214 884-3777
Joseph B Armes, *CEO*
EMP: 14
SALES (est): 225.1K
SALES (corp-wide): 385.8MM **Publicly Held**
WEB: www.cswindustrials.com
SIC: 3569 Assembly machines, non-metal-working
PA: Csw Industrials, Inc.
5420 Lyndon B Johnson Fwy
Dallas TX 75240
214 884-3777

(G-4191)
CUBE SOLUTIONS LLC (PA)
7331 Maplecrest Dr (75254-2728)
PHONE..................................972 783-4880
Chris Mathers, *Partner*
Phil Plasko, *Vice Pres*
Pam Strong, *Accounts Mgr*
Mark Rainbolt, *Marketing Staff*
Michael Warren, *Office Mgr*
▲ EMP: 12
SALES (est): 4.1MM **Privately Held**
WEB: www.cubesolutions.com
SIC: 5712 2521 Office furniture; wood office furniture

(G-4192)
CUMMINS - ALLISON CORP
Also Called: Cummins-Allison
13721 Gamma Rd (75244-4409)
PHONE..................................972 661-5390
David Allen, *Manager*
EMP: 12
SQ FT: 1,000
SALES (corp-wide): 3.2B **Publicly Held**
WEB: www.cumminsallison.com
SIC: 5044 5087 3579 3578 Office equipment; shredders, industrial & commercial; perforators (office machines); change making machines; internal combustion engines
HQ: Cummins-Allison Corp.
852 Feehanville Dr
Mount Prospect IL 60056
800 786-5528

(G-4193)
CUMMINS SOUTHERN PLAINS LLC
4895 Mountain Creek Pkwy (75236-4603)
PHONE..................................800 286-6467
Dana Crockett, *Project Mgr*
EMP: 25
SALES (corp-wide): 19.8B **Publicly Held**
WEB: www.cummins.com
SIC: 3714 Engines & parts, diesel
HQ: Cummins Southern Plains Llc
600 N Watson Rd
Arlington TX 76011
817 640-6801

(G-4194)
CUSTOM CHENILLE EMBROIDERY INC
11330 Hillguard Rd (75243-8311)
PHONE..................................214 343-0888
R L Gilmer, *President*
Christine Gilmer, *Corp Secy*
Marla Platt, *Accounting Mgr*
EMP: 40
SQ FT: 18,000
SALES (est): 3.9MM **Privately Held**
WEB: www.chenille.com
SIC: 2395 Embroidery products, except schiffli machine

(G-4195)
CUSTOM CRETE INC (HQ)
Also Called: Custom Stone Supply
2624 Joe Field Rd (75229-4601)
PHONE..................................972 243-4466
Steve Bond, *President*
Cullen Davies, *Sales Staff*
Dee Stephens, *Sales Staff*
◆ EMP: 200 EST: 1969
SQ FT: 10,000
SALES (est): 142.5MM
SALES (corp-wide): 1.4B **Publicly Held**
WEB: www.custom-crete.com
SIC: 5032 3273 Building stone; ready-mixed concrete
PA: U.S. Concrete, Inc.
331 N Main St
Euless TX 76039
817 835-4105

(G-4196)
CUSTOM MANUFACTURING COMPANY
5501 S Lamar St (75215-5199)
PHONE..................................214 428-5173
Bruce Frazer, *President*
Misses Frazer, *Vice Pres*
Edgar Frazer, *Treasurer*
Travis Frazer, *Technician*
EMP: 25
SQ FT: 35,000
SALES (est): 6MM **Privately Held**
WEB: www.custommfgco.com
SIC: 3442 3443 3446 Garage doors, overhead; metal; metal parts; channels, furring

(G-4197)
CUSTOM WORK ROOM SERVICES
1307 Medical District Dr (75207-2305)
PHONE..................................214 631-2795
Danny Senter, *President*
Sara Senter, *Vice Pres*
EMP: 12
SQ FT: 6,000
SALES (est): 750K **Privately Held**
SIC: 2391 5023 Curtains & draperies; draperies

(G-4198)
CUTTING SOLUTIONS INC
Also Called: Gladu Southwest
4647 Leston St Ste 603 (75247-5726)
PHONE..................................214 637-4849
Jean Jr Gladu, *President*
EMP: 35
SALES (est): 4.5MM **Privately Held**
SIC: 3545 3425 Bits for use on lathes, planers, shapers, etc.; saw blades & handsaws

(G-4199)
D & S CONTAINER INC
Also Called: Budget Box Company
3304 Halifax St (75247-5902)
P.O. Box 560086 (75356-0086)
PHONE..................................214 637-7957
David Sutton, *President*
Scott Minter, *General Mgr*
David Wiens, *General Mgr*
Kathy Clement, *COO*
Darrel Williams, *Prdtn Mgr*
EMP: 90
SQ FT: 85,000
SALES (est): 37.2MM **Privately Held**
WEB: www.budgetboxco.com
SIC: 2653 5113 Boxes, corrugated: made from purchased materials; boxes, paperboard & disposable plastic

(G-4200)
D C LITES INC
10740 Goodnight Ln (75220-2497)
PHONE..................................972 556-0260
Jack P Jeter, *President*
Cora Jeter, *Vice Pres*
EMP: 16
SQ FT: 8,100
SALES (est): 2.1MM **Privately Held**
WEB: www.dclites.net
SIC: 3545 Scales, measuring (machinists' precision tools)

(G-4201)
D C LITES COMPANY
10740 Goodnight Ln (75220-2497)
PHONE..................................972 556-0260
Jack P Jeter, *President*
Rich Castellano, *QC Mgr*
Cora Jeter, *Treasurer*
Gary Flanagan, *Manager*
EMP: 18
SQ FT: 8,100
SALES (est): 2.3MM **Privately Held**
WEB: www.dclites.net
SIC: 3545 Machine tool accessories

(G-4202)
D CUSTOM
750 N Saint Paul St # 2100 (75201-3236)
PHONE..................................214 523-0300
Wick Alison, *Partner*
Gordon Laoke, *Partner*
JAS Robertson, *General Mgr*
Kirsten Faulder, *Editor*
Pedro Armstrong, *Production*
EMP: 15
SALES (est): 1.1MM **Privately Held**
WEB: www.dcustom.com
SIC: 7313 2759 Printed media advertising
representatives; commercial printing

(G-4203)
D MAGAZINE PARTNERS LP
750 N Saint Paul St # 2100 (75201-3214)
PHONE..................................214 939-3636
Christine Allison, *CEO*
Gillea Allison, *President*
Wick Allison, *Partner*
Phyllis McKnight, *Publisher*
Caitlin Clark, *Editor*
EMP: 30
SQ FT: 9,436
SALES (est): 5.4MM **Privately Held**
WEB: www.dmagazine.com
SIC: 2721 Magazines: publishing only, not
printed on site

(G-4204)
DA SCHOGGIN INC (PA)
Also Called: Techlight
2707 Satsuma Dr (75229-3521)
PHONE..................................214 350-0591
Jackie Schoggin, *President*
Doug Schoggin, *Corp Secy*
John Bohannon, *CFO*
Ellen Lollnan, *CFO*
Ed Oswald, *Regl Sales Mgr*
◆ EMP: 75
SQ FT: 26,500
SALES (est): 17.3MM **Privately Held**
WEB: www.wqsu.com
SIC: 3648 3645 3646 5063 Decorative
area lighting fixtures; garden, patio, walk-
way & yard lighting fixtures: electric; com-
mercial indusl & institutional electric
lighting fixtures; lighting fixtures, commer-
cial & industrial; lighting fixtures, residen-
tial; light bulbs & related supplies

(G-4205)
DAC LABELS & GRAPHIC SPC
10491 Brockwood Rd (75238-1641)
PHONE..................................214 340-2055
Harlan Leeds, *President*
Judy Weghorst Vinson, *Vice Pres*
EMP: 14
SQ FT: 9,000
SALES (est): 1.3MM **Privately Held**
WEB: www.daclabels.com
SIC: 2754 2759 5999 2679 Labels:
gravure printing; poster & decal printing &
engraving; decals; labels, paper: made
from purchased material; packaging
paper & plastics film, coated & laminated

(G-4206)
DAILY COMMERCIAL RECORD INC
Also Called: Collin County Coml Record
706 Main St Bsmt (75202-3620)
PHONE..................................214 741-6366
E Nuel Cates Jr, *President*
Nuel Cates, *Publisher*
Emily Cates, *Editor*
Chasity Johnson, *Prdtn Mgr*
EMP: 10
SQ FT: 2,500
SALES (est): 900.5K **Privately Held**
WEB: www.dailycommercialrecord.com
SIC: 2711 Newspapers, publishing & print-
ing

(G-4207)
DAISY BRAND LLC (PA)
12750 Merit Dr Ste 600 (75251-1261)
PHONE..................................972 726-0800
David M Sokolsky, *CEO*
Vince Taylor, *President*
Rick Fagan, *General Mgr*
Derek Garwood, *General Mgr*
Eric Lafleur, *General Mgr*
▲ EMP: 104
SQ FT: 12,000
SALES (est): 211MM **Privately Held**
WEB: www.daisybrand.com
SIC: 2026 Milk processing (pasteurizing,
homogenizing, bottling)

(G-4208)
DALE OPERATING COMPANY
2100 Ross Ave Ste 1870 (75201-6773)
PHONE..................................214 979-9010
Lawrence B Dale, *President*
Michael Taliaferro, *Exec VP*
Brandon W Buford, *CFO*
Paul Harlan, *Manager*
Pete Dale, *General Counsel*
EMP: 28
SQ FT: 9,000
SALES (est): 5.4MM **Privately Held**
WEB: www.daleoperating.com
SIC: 1311 1382 Crude petroleum produc-
tion; oil & gas exploration services

(G-4209)
DALLA COMPRESS ENER SOLUTIO LL
Also Called: Wesco
8150 N Central Expy (75206-1815)
PHONE..................................214 265-0400
Niel Rootare, *VP Business*
Steve Weyel, *Mng Member*
Robert Stiles, *Mng Member*
EMP: 35
SALES (est): 3.5MM
SALES (corp-wide): 5MM **Privately Held**
WEB: www.e2energyservices.com
SIC: 1382 Oil & gas exploration services
PA: Enerven, Llc
8150 N Central Expy
Dallas TX 75206
214 265-0400

(G-4210)
DALLAS A C HORN & COMPANY INC
Also Called: Cantrell International Div
1269 Majesty Dr (75247-3917)
P.O. Box 560687 (75356-0687)
PHONE..................................214 630-3311
Michael Horn, *President*
Paul Lima, *Opers Mgr*
Jesse Melton, *Safety Mgr*
Autry Green, *Traffic Mgr*
Elizabeth Durban, *Buyer*
◆ EMP: 85
SQ FT: 65,000
SALES (est): 23.3MM **Privately Held**
WEB: www.achornmfg.com
SIC: 3535 5084 3556 3589 Conveyors &
conveying equipment; processing & pack-
aging equipment; mills, food; smoking or
roasting machinery, including ovens; pop-
corn machines, commercial

(G-4211)
DALLAS AIRMOTIVE INC
6114 Forest Park Rd (75235-6410)
PHONE..................................214 956-2505
Jim Dunlan, *President*
Brian Gilbert, *Opers Mgr*
John Hocking, *Controller*
David Daniel, *Human Res Dir*
Angela McDade, *Publications*
EMP: 435
SALES (corp-wide): 2.2B **Privately Held**
WEB: www.dallasairmotive.com
SIC: 7699 3724 Aircraft & heavy equip-
ment repair services; aircraft engines &
engine parts

HQ: Dallas Airmotive, Inc.
2988 W Walnut Hill Ln
Dfw Airport TX 75261
214 956-3001

(G-4212)
DALLAS BIAS FABRICS INC (PA)
1401 N Carroll Ave (75204-5012)
P.O. Box 638, Forney (75126-0638)
PHONE..................................214 824-2036
Stewart Kipness, *President*
Jack Kipness, *Vice Pres*
James Kipness, *Vice Pres*
Jim Kipness, *Vice Pres*
EMP: 30 EST: 1948
SQ FT: 55,000
SALES (est): 7MM **Privately Held**
WEB: www.dallasbias.com
SIC: 2396 2369 Waistbands, trouser; bind-
ings, bias: made from purchased materi-
als; trimming, fabric; girls' & children's
outerwear

(G-4213)
DALLAS CAST STONE II CORP
4107 Hancock St (75210-2942)
PHONE..................................940 382-6922
Mark S Ragsdale, *CEO*
Kirk Ragsdale, *CEO*
Luke Ragsdale, *Manager*
EMP: 20 EST: 1922
SQ FT: 1,500
SALES (est): 3.1MM **Privately Held**
WEB: www.dallasstone.com
SIC: 3272 3281 Cast stone, concrete; cut
stone & stone products

(G-4214)
DALLAS CHRISTIE LITES INC
12121 N Stemmons Fwy # 100
(75234-5805)
PHONE..................................214 637-3535
Huntley Christie, *President*
Shane Gillespie, *Vice Pres*
▲ EMP: 15 EST: 2002
SALES (est): 2.8MM
SALES (corp-wide): 20.2MM **Privately Held**
WEB: www.christielites.com
SIC: 3648 Lighting equipment
HQ: Christie Lites Orlando, Llc
2479 Eunice Ave
Orlando FL 32808
206 223-7200

(G-4215)
DALLAS DIRECTIONAL DRLG INC
6212 Lovett Ave (75227-3522)
PHONE..................................214 254-6985
Vanessa C Aleman-Padilla, *President*
EMP: 10
SALES (est): 669K **Privately Held**
WEB: www.dallasdirectionalboring.com
SIC: 1381 4813 Directional drilling oil &
gas wells; telephone communication, ex-
cept radio

(G-4216)
DALLAS FLAG & FLAGPOLE CO LC (PA)
Also Called: Flag Systems
2300 Valley View Ln # 109 (75234-5753)
PHONE..................................972 607-0958
Shawna Williams,
EMP: 15 EST: 2015
SQ FT: 4,500
SALES (est): 1.5MM **Privately Held**
WEB: www.flagsystems.org
SIC: 7389 5999 2399 5131 Personal
service agents, brokers & bureaus; ban-
ners, flags, decals & posters; flags; ban-
ners, pennants & flags; flags, fabric; flags
& banners

(G-4217)
DALLAS LGHTHOUSE FOR BLIND INC
Also Called: Envision Dallas
4306 Capitol Ave (75204-8817)
PHONE..................................214 821-2375
Michael J Monteferrante, *President*
Nikki Freeman, *Vice Pres*
Sandra Rice, *Purchasing*

Mark D Eaton, *CFO*
Mark Eaton, *CFO*
▲ EMP: 220 EST: 1931
SQ FT: 180,000
SALES: 4MM
SALES (corp-wide): 207.5MM **Privately Held**
WEB: www.envisionus.com
SIC: 8322 3951 2782 Association for the
handicapped; pens & mechanical pencils;
looseleaf binders & devices
PA: Envision, Inc.
610 N Main St Ste 400
Wichita KS 67203
316 440-1500

(G-4218)
DALLAS LITE AND BARRICADE INC (PA)
Also Called: Ft Worth Lite & Barricade
1607 Fort Worth Ave (75208-1508)
P.O. Box 223786 (75222-3786)
PHONE..................................214 748-5791
B D Howell, *CEO*
Shane D Howell, *President*
Sheryl S Howell, *Corp Secy*
Jay Galler, *Vice Pres*
Gary K Howell, *Vice Pres*
▲ EMP: 45
SQ FT: 5,000
SALES (est): 18.5MM **Privately Held**
WEB: www.dlbinc.net
SIC: 3531 7359 3499 1799 Construction
machinery; work zone traffic equipment
(flags, cones, barrels, etc.); barricades,
metal; sign installation & maintenance;
traffic signals, electric; highway & street
sign installation

(G-4219)
DALLAS MARKET CENTER CO LTD (PA)
Also Called: Trade Mart
2100 N Stemmons Fwy # 1000
(75207-3009)
PHONE..................................214 655-6100
Bill Winsor, *Partner*
Laura Dumas, *Partner*
Penni Barton, *Exec VP*
Mitzi Tally, *Exec VP*
Eva Walsh, *Exec VP*
▲ EMP: 177
SALES (est): 85.2MM **Privately Held**
WEB: www.dallasmarketcenter.com
SIC: 3999 7999 Preparation of slides &
exhibits; exhibition operation

(G-4220)
DALLAS METAL FABRICATORS INC
2817 Logan St (75215-1465)
PHONE..................................214 421-7417
William Ross Sr, *President*
EMP: 11
SALES (est): 2.4MM **Privately Held**
WEB: www.dallasmetalfab.com
SIC: 3441 5051 Fabricated structural
metal; metals service centers & offices

(G-4221)
DALLAS METAL SERVICE
Also Called: Dallas Metal Services
13346 Bee St Ste 102 (75234-6101)
PHONE..................................972 481-1700
Gary Miller, *Owner*
Raylene Gleghorn, *Director*
EMP: 10
SQ FT: 2,000
SALES (est): 860K **Privately Held**
WEB: www.dallasmetalservice.com
SIC: 3559 Metal finishing equipment for
plating, etc.

(G-4222)
DALLAS OBSERVER LP
Also Called: Voice Media Group
2030 Main St Ste 410 (75201-4446)
P.O. Box 190289 (75219-0289)
PHONE..................................214 757-9000
Stewart Folb, *Partner*
Gregg Diamond, *Editor*
Beth Rankin, *Editor*
Kelly Foster, *Business Mgr*
Patrick Williams, *Opers Staff*
EMP: 20

SALES (est): 1.9MM
SALES (corp-wide): 241.4MM **Privately Held**
WEB: www.dallasobserver.com
SIC: 2711 Newspapers, publishing & printing
PA: Voice Media Group, Inc.
969 N Broadway
Denver CO 80203
303 296-7744

(G-4223)
DALLAS OIL
Also Called: Dallas Oil Service
3018 Ruder St (75212-3006)
PHONE..........................214 638-9055
Ernie Slaughter, *Owner*
Vonna Boyer, *Vice Pres*
EMP: 30
SALES (est): 2.3MM **Privately Held**
SIC: 1381 Drilling oil & gas wells

(G-4224)
DALLAS PRODUCTION INC (PA)
Also Called: Pitts Energy Group
4600 Greenville Ave # 300 (75206-5038)
PHONE..........................214 369-9266
William A Custard, *President*
Douglas Sheetz, *Vice Pres*
Marla Custard, *Engineer*
Ron D Johnson, *CFO*
Ronald Johnson, *Treasurer*
EMP: 30
SQ FT: 26,000
SALES (est): 48MM **Privately Held**
SIC: 1311 Crude petroleum production;
natural gas production

(G-4225)
DALLAS SIGHT AND SOUND INC
14354 Proton Rd (75244-3511)
PHONE..........................972 392-3202
David Rogers, *CEO*
Tim Graham, *President*
Eva Walsh, *President*
Dee Jones, *Vice Pres*
Jim Lugannani, *Vice Pres*
EMP: 21
SQ FT: 12,000
SALES (est): 3.4MM **Privately Held**
WEB: www.dallassightandsound.com
SIC: 5731 1731 5072 3699 High fidelity
stereo equipment; sound equipment spe-
cialization; security devices, locks; secu-
rity devices; security control equipment &
systems

(G-4226)
DALLAS STEEL DRUMS INC
2214 Singleton Blvd (75212-3732)
PHONE..........................214 638-7027
Stanley C Thomas, *President*
Aline Callaway, *Corp Secy*
Phillip A Thomas, *Vice Pres*
Dana Moore, *Instructor*
EMP: 26 **EST:** 1936
SQ FT: 500
SALES (est): 184.7K
SALES (corp-wide): 5.2MM **Privately Held**
WEB: www.dallassteeldrums.com
SIC: 3412 Drums, shipping: metal; barrels,
shipping: metal
PA: Curtis Thomas Investments Inc
2517 Ne 35th St
Fort Worth TX 76111
817 336-5569

(G-4227)
DALLAS TEXAS TOOL AND DIE INC
Also Called: Texas Tool & Die
2925 Mican Dr (75212-4604)
PHONE..........................214 634-7175
Darrell Bravenec, *President*
Raven League, *Manager*
EMP: 17
SQ FT: 10,000
SALES (est): 1.7MM **Privately Held**
WEB: www.txtooldie.com
SIC: 3444 3599 Sheet metalwork; ma-
chine shop, jobbing & repair

(G-4228)
DALLAS TORTILLAS INC (PA)
Also Called: Dallas Tortilla & Tamale Fctry
309 N Marsalis Ave (75203-1713)
PHONE..........................214 943-7681
Ruben L Leal Sr, *President*
Edward Leal, *Vice Pres*
Matias Leal, *Vice Pres*
Roland Leal, *Vice Pres*
Ruben Leal, *Manager*
EMP: 17 **EST:** 1952
SQ FT: 6,000
SALES (est): 2.4MM **Privately Held**
WEB: www.dallastortilla.com
SIC: 2099 2032 2096 Tortillas, fresh or re-
frigerated; tamales: packaged in cans,
jars, etc.; tortilla chips

(G-4229)
DALLAS USA FOODS INC
1880 Lone Star Dr (75212-5045)
PHONE..........................214 905-1511
Ellen Lan Guan, *President*
EMP: 84
SQ FT: 22,000
SALES (est): 30MM **Privately Held**
WEB: www.dallasusafoods.com
SIC: 2015 Chicken, processed: fresh

(G-4230)
DALLAS WESTPORT INC
2180 French Settlement Rd (75212-6001)
P.O. Box 224685 (75222-4685)
PHONE..........................214 231-1450
John R Bacon, *President*
Bobby Bridges, *Superintendent*
William J Calvert, *Vice Pres*
Leslie Boyd, *Human Res Mgr*
Leslie Boyd-Stigler, *Human Res Mgr*
▲ **EMP:** 130
SALES (est): 24.7MM
SALES (corp-wide): 305.3MM **Privately Held**
WEB: www.wingpowersystem.service.west-
port.com
SIC: 3714 Fuel systems & parts, motor ve-
hicle
HQ: Westport Innovations (U.S.) Holdings
Inc.
2180 French Settlement Rd
Dallas TX 75212
214 231-1450

(G-4231)
DALLCO MARKETING INC
Also Called: American Distributing
11333 Pagemill Rd (75243-8305)
PHONE..........................214 217-7800
Ray Davis, *President*
Ann Davis, *Vice Pres*
Kevin Silvey, *Administration*
▲ **EMP:** 40
SQ FT: 44,000
SALES (est): 10.2MM **Privately Held**
WEB: www.adcoindustries.com
SIC: 2679 Tags, paper (unprinted): made
from purchased paper; labels, paper:
made from purchased material

(G-4232)
DANCAR INVESTMENT GROUP INC
Also Called: Dancar Printing Group
10551 Miller Rd Ste 100 (75238-1226)
PHONE..........................972 633-1200
Daniel Wells, *President*
Chris Hall, *Partner*
Michael Dawson, *Vice Pres*
Pam Cordell, *Accounting Mgr*
Thomas Montgomery, *Manager*
EMP: 10
SALES (est): 539.3K **Privately Held**
WEB: www.dancargroup.com
SIC: 2759 Commercial printing

(G-4233)
DANHARD INC (PA)
3839 Dilido Rd (75228-5595)
PHONE..........................214 328-8541
Sherry Jackson, *CEO*
Gerhard Dankowski, *Ch of Bd*
Detlef Dankowski, *Vice Pres*
EMP: 15 **EST:** 1963
SQ FT: 39,000

SALES (est): 2.8MM **Privately Held**
WEB: www.danhard.com
SIC: 3585 3443 Air conditioning units,
complete: domestic or industrial; heat exchangers, plate type

(G-4234)
DANICK RESOURCES
5005 Lyndon B Johnson Fwy # 1250
(75244-6105)
PHONE..........................214 827-2222
Otto Harrison, *Chairman*
EMP: 25
SALES (est): 1.1MM **Privately Held**
WEB: www.danickresources.com
SIC: 1382 Oil & gas exploration services

(G-4235)
DANIEL AYALA
Also Called: Eda Label Products
8414 Endicott Ln (75227-2309)
PHONE..........................469 245-3181
Daniel Ayala, *Owner*
EMP: 10
SALES (est): 334.8K **Privately Held**
SIC: 2759 Labels & seals: printing

(G-4236)
DANIELLE HOWARD
Also Called: Fabuluex
5210 Bexar St Apt 204 (75215-4930)
PHONE..........................469 554-6772
Danielle Howard, *Owner*
EMP: 10
SALES (est): 283.1K **Privately Held**
SIC: 3999 Hair & hair-based products

(G-4237)
DAP PRODUCTS INC
13555 Jupiter Rd (75238-2405)
PHONE..........................214 349-9951
Tony Nguyen, *Plant Engr Mgr*
Patrick Devlin, *Plant Engr*
Craig Zentz, *Controller*
Jason Holt, *Human Res Mgr*
Bill Marsheck, *Sales Mgr*
EMP: 80
SQ FT: 30,000
SALES (corp-wide): 5.5B **Publicly Held**
WEB: www.dap.com
SIC: 2851 2891 Putty; caulking com-
pounds
HQ: Dap Products Inc.
2400 Boston St Ste 200
Baltimore MD 21224
800 543-3840

(G-4238)
DARLING INGREDIENTS INC
1240 Sargent Rd (75203-4607)
PHONE..........................214 948-7501
Tyler McGann, *Plant Mgr*
Mitchell McGee, *Export Mgr*
Martijn Van Steenpaal, *Treasurer*
Brian Smith, *Sales Staff*
Mike Molini, *Manager*
EMP: 50
SALES (corp-wide): 3.3B **Publicly Held**
WEB: www.darlingii.com
SIC: 2077 5172 2048 Grease rendering,
inedible; tallow rendering, inedible; bone
meal, except as animal feed; meat meal &
tankage, except as animal feed; lubricat-
ing oils & greases; prepared feeds
PA: Darling Ingredients Inc.
5601 N Macarthur Blvd
Irving TX 75038
972 717-0300

(G-4239)
DARYAN DESIGN INC
Also Called: Daryan Displays
3145 Halifax St (75247-6013)
PHONE..........................214 905-6022
Robert Brody, *President*
Gary Cathey, *General Mgr*
Mark Doby, *Graphic Designe*
EMP: 12
SQ FT: 25,000
SALES (est): 1.5MM **Privately Held**
WEB: www.daryandisplay.com
SIC: 7389 2541 7319 5999 Advertising,
promotional & trade show services; dis-
play fixtures, wood; display advertising
service; Christmas lights & decorations;
Christmas trees, including artificial

(G-4240)
DATA CONNECTION INC
Also Called: Green It Connection
11420 Chairman Dr (75243-8502)
P.O. Box 830878, Richardson (75083-
0878)
PHONE..........................972 231-2185
Wayne Bowles, *President*
John Frizzell, *General Mgr*
Jo Bowles, *Treasurer*
Wayne D Bowles, *Info Tech Dir*
David Bowles, *Admin Sec*
EMP: 12
SQ FT: 3,250
SALES (est): 2.2MM **Privately Held**
WEB: www.dci123.com
SIC: 1731 3577 3357 Computer installa-
tion; computer peripheral equipment; non-
ferrous wiredrawing & insulating

(G-4241)
DATA DALLAS CORPORATION
1111 W Mockingbird Ln # 300
(75247-5017)
PHONE..........................214 662-5165
Gerald Garcia, *President*
Ron Rocek, *Marketing Staff*
EMP: 20
SQ FT: 17,287
SALES (est): 1.8MM **Privately Held**
WEB: www.datadallas.com
SIC: 7374 2759 7373 Data processing
service; laser printing; systems integration
services

(G-4242)
DEAN FOODS COMPANY (PA)
2711 N Haskell Ave # 340 (75204-2911)
PHONE..........................214 303-3400
Jim L Turner, *Ch of Bd*
Eric Beringause, *President*
Terence Roche, *Dean*
Brad Cashaw, *Exec VP*
Russell F Coleman, *Exec VP*
EMP: 432
SALES: 7.3B **Publicly Held**
WEB: www.deanfoods.com
SIC: 2023 2026 Dry, condensed, evapo-
rated dairy products; milk processing
(pasteurizing, homogenizing, bottling)

(G-4243)
DEAN HOLDING COMPANY (HQ)
2711 N Haskell Ave # 340 (75204-2911)
PHONE..........................214 303-3400
Gregg L Engles, *CEO*
Barry A Fromberg, *CFO*
V J Hill, *Director*
Ronald L McCrummen, *Director*
▲ **EMP:** 47 **EST:** 1921
SALES (est): 1.7B **Publicly Held**
WEB: www.deanfoods.com
SIC: 2023 5143 5451 Dry, condensed,
evaporated dairy products; dairy prod-
ucts, except dried or canned; dairy prod-
ucts stores

(G-4244)
DEAN INTLLCTUAL PRPRTY SVCS II
2515 Mckinney Ave (75201-1908)
PHONE..........................214 303-3400
Gary Rahlfs, *Senior VP*
EMP: 5000
SALES (est): 131.2K **Publicly Held**
SIC: 2026 Fluid milk
HQ: Dips Limited Partner Ii
2515 Mckinney Ave # 1200
Dallas TX 75201
214 303-3400

(G-4245)
DEEP ELLUM BREWING COMPANY LLC
2823 Saint Louis St (75226-1904)
PHONE..........................214 888-3322
Shareese Harrell, *Office Mgr*
John C Reardon, *Mng Member*
Scott Frieling, *Mng Member*
James D Piel, *Mng Member*
▲ **EMP:** 35
SQ FT: 16,000
SALES (est): 1.9MM **Privately Held**
WEB: www.deepellumbrewing.com
SIC: 2082 Beer (alcoholic beverage)

(G-4246)
DEEP VELLUM PUBLISHING INC
3000 Commerce St (75226-1626)
PHONE...................................972 638-7741
William Evans, *Principal*
EMP: 11
SALES (est): 170.4K **Privately Held**
WEB: www.deepvellum.org
SIC: 2741 Miscellaneous publishing

(G-4247)
DEFENSE LOGISTICS AGENCY
Also Called: Defense Contracting
600 N Pearl St (75201-2822)
PHONE...................................214 670-9259
Paul McQueen, *Principal*
EMP: 360 **Publicly Held**
WEB: www.dla.mil
SIC: 3812 Defense systems & equipment
HQ: Defense Logistics Agency
8725 John J Kingman Rd # 2533
Fort Belvoir VA 22060

(G-4248)
DEFIANT SAFE CO INC
3140 Towerwood Dr (75234-2313)
PHONE...................................972 243-3711
Richard Rolland, *President*
Walter Adler, *Corp Secy*
▲ **EMP:** 25
SQ FT: 6,500
SALES (est): 3.1MM **Privately Held**
WEB: www.rollandsolutions.com
SIC: 5999 5044 3499 7699 Vaults &
safes; vaults & safes; safes & vaults,
metal; lock & key services

(G-4249)
DESOTO ENVIRONMENTAL MGT
5430 Lyndon B Johnson Fwy # 800
(75240-2601)
PHONE...................................972 458-0028
Troy Taylor, *Principal*
EMP: 208
SALES (est): 8.5MM
SALES (corp-wide): 928.5K **Privately Held**
WEB: www.kci-corp.com
SIC: 3312 Bar, rod & wire products
HQ: Keystone Consolidated Industries, Inc.
5430 Lyndon B Johnson Fwy
Dallas TX 75240
800 441-0308

(G-4250)
DFA DAIRY BRANDS DISTRG N LLC
2711 N Haskell Ave # 340 (75204-2911)
PHONE...................................214 303-3400
Alan Bernon, *President*
Kevin Strathman, *CFO*
Danelle Bender, *Treasurer*
Alex Bachelor, *Admin Sec*
EMP: 34
SALES (est): 862.8K
SALES (corp-wide): 15.8B **Privately Held**
SIC: 2023 2026 Dry, condensed, evapo-
rated dairy products; milk processing
(pasteurizing, homogenizing, bottling)
HQ: Dfa Dairy Brands Transportation, Llc
2711 N Haskell Ave # 340
Dallas TX 75204
214 303-3400

(G-4251)
DFA DAIRY BRANDS DISTRG S LLC
2711 N Haskell Ave # 340 (75204-2911)
PHONE...................................214 303-3400
Alan Bernon, *President*
Kevin Strathman, *CFO*
Danelle Bender, *Treasurer*
Alex Bachelor, *Admin Sec*
EMP: 34
SALES (est): 862.8K
SALES (corp-wide): 15.8B **Privately Held**
SIC: 2023 2026 Dry, condensed, evapo-
rated dairy products; milk processing
(pasteurizing, homogenizing, bottling)
HQ: Dfa Dairy Brands Transportation, Llc
2711 N Haskell Ave # 340
Dallas TX 75204
214 303-3400

(G-4252)
DFA DAIRY BRANDS DISTRG W LLC
2711 N Haskell Ave # 340 (75204-2911)
PHONE...................................214 303-3400
Alan Bernon, *President*
Kevin Strathman, *CFO*
Danelle Bender, *Treasurer*
Alex Bachelor, *Admin Sec*
EMP: 34
SALES (est): 862.8K
SALES (corp-wide): 15.8B **Privately Held**
SIC: 2023 2026 Dry, condensed, evapo-
rated dairy products; milk processing
(pasteurizing, homogenizing, bottling)
HQ: Dfa Dairy Brands Transportation, Llc
2711 N Haskell Ave # 340
Dallas TX 75204
214 303-3400

(G-4253)
DFA DAIRY BRANDS IP LLC
2711 N Haskell Ave # 340 (75204-2911)
PHONE...................................214 303-3400
Alan Bernon, *President*
Kevin Strathman, *CFO*
Danelle Bender, *Treasurer*
Alex Bachelor, *Admin Sec*
EMP: 158
SALES (est): 3.5MM
SALES (corp-wide): 15.8B **Privately Held**
SIC: 2023 2026 Dry, condensed, evapo-
rated dairy products; milk processing
(pasteurizing, homogenizing, bottling)
HQ: Dfa Dairy Brands, Llc
1405 N 98th St
Kansas City KS 66111
816 801-6455

(G-4254)
DFA DAIRY BRANDS TRNSP LLC (DH)
2711 N Haskell Ave # 340 (75204-2911)
PHONE...................................214 303-3400
Alan Bernon, *President*
Kevin Strathman, *CFO*
Danelle Bender, *Treasurer*
Alex Bachelor, *Admin Sec*
EMP: 105
SALES (est): 3.8MM
SALES (corp-wide): 15.8B **Privately Held**
SIC: 2023 2026 Dry, condensed, evapo-
rated dairy products; milk processing
(pasteurizing, homogenizing, bottling)
HQ: Dfa Dairy Brands, Llc
1405 N 98th St
Kansas City KS 66111
816 801-6455

(G-4255)
DFW CAMPER CORRAL INC
Also Called: Truck Accessory Store
11600 N Stemmons Fwy (75229-2125)
PHONE...................................972 241-6443
Robert Abbott, *Vice Pres*
Bruce Hunter, *Branch Mgr*
John Strong, *Manager*
EMP: 10
SALES (corp-wide): 12.6MM **Privately Held**
WEB: www.dfwcamper.com
SIC: 3714 5561 5531 5014 Motor vehicle
parts & accessories; recreational vehicle
parts & accessories; trailer hitches, auto-
motive; truck tires & tubes
PA: Dfw Camper Corral, Inc.
1450 E Interstate 20
Arlington TX 76018
817 461-8663

(G-4256)
DHALIWAL LABORATORIES LLC (PA)
Also Called: Dhaliwal Labs
11910 Shiloh Rd Ste 130 (75228-1590)
PHONE...................................214 446-5862
Mina D O'Hearn, *Managing Prtnr*
Tammy Stuckey, *General Mgr*
Sammy Afifi, *Vice Pres*
Natalie Dill, *Vice Pres*
Varsha Nainani, *Vice Pres*
▲ **EMP:** 150 **EST:** 2008
SQ FT: 65,000
SALES (est): 75.1MM **Privately Held**
WEB: www.dhaliwal-labs.com
SIC: 2844 Cosmetic preparations

(G-4257)
DIAPER SPORTS GROUP LLC
6565 Hillcrest Ave # 100 (75205-1840)
PHONE...................................214 871-5131
Alan Dorbitz, *COO*
Gerald J Ford,
EMP: 10
SALES (est): 422.8K **Privately Held**
SIC: 2211 5137 Diaper fabrics; diapers

(G-4258)
DIGITAL COPY LLC
500 N Akard St Ste 250 (75201-6668)
PHONE...................................214 740-2480
Thanh Nguyen,
EMP: 25
SALES (est): 1.1MM **Privately Held**
SIC: 3993 7389 Signs & advertising spe-
cialties; printing broker

(G-4259)
DILLON GAGE REFINING INC
11231 Gemini Ln (75229-4711)
PHONE...................................972 484-3377
John Christianson, *President*
Kristen Compton, *Executive Asst*
EMP: 34
SALES (est): 4.7MM **Privately Held**
WEB: www.dillongage.com
SIC: 3339 Precious metals

(G-4260)
DIME EMB LLC (PA)
Also Called: Designs In Machine Embroidery
10495 Olympic Dr Ste 100 (75220-4418)
PHONE...................................888 739-0555
Samuel Solomon, *Sales Executive*
Denise Holguin, *Manager*
William Fenimore III,
Eileen Roche,
▲ **EMP:** 30
SALES (est): 5.5MM **Privately Held**
WEB: www.dzgns.com
SIC: 2759 Magazines: printing

(G-4261)
DIRECTORS ASSISTANT LLC
2115 Irving Blvd (75207-6503)
PHONE...................................972 816-5553
Chris Walls,
▲ **EMP:** 10 **EST:** 2012
SQ FT: 250
SALES (est): 1MM **Privately Held**
SIC: 2339 5621 5699 2389 Service ap-
parel, washable: women's; ready-to-wear
apparel, women's; customized clothing &
apparel; band uniforms; tailored suits &
formal jackets

(G-4262)
DISPLAY PRODUCTS INC
Also Called: Radius Display Products
800 Fabric Xpress Way (75234-7260)
PHONE...................................972 406-1221
Tim Lightfoot, *President*
Sherry Hanes, *Vice Pres*
Ross Trayler, *Vice Pres*
Sharon Parker, *Prdtn Mgr*
Geoffrey Duncan, *Sales Staff*
▲ **EMP:** 52
SQ FT: 40,000
SALES (est): 7.1MM **Privately Held**
WEB: www.radiusdp.com
SIC: 2391 2392 3993 Draperies, plastic &
textile: from purchased materials; table-
cloths & table settings; signs & advertis-
ing specialties

(G-4263)
DISTRIBUTION INTERNATIONAL INC
2322 French Settlement Rd # 300
(75212-6034)
PHONE...................................214 637-0151
David Dzina, *General Mgr*
Randy Smith, *Regional Mgr*
EMP: 30
SALES (corp-wide): 421MM **Privately Held**
WEB: www.distributioninternational.com
SIC: 5033 3296 Insulation, thermal; min-
eral wool
PA: Distribution International, Inc.
601 Jefferson St Ste 600
Houston TX 77002
713 428-3740

(G-4264)
DIYATECH CORP
Also Called: Alachisoft
12005 Ford Rd Ste 520 (75234-7284)
PHONE...................................214 769-6933
Iqbal Khan, *President*
Josh Hamid, *Mktg Dir*
Sam Awan, *Marketing Staff*
EMP: 35
SQ FT: 1,600
SALES (est): 303K **Privately Held**
WEB: www.alachisoft.com
SIC: 7371 7372 Computer software devel-
opment; prepackaged software

(G-4265)
DLK MEDICAL TECHNOLOGIES INC
5440 Red Bird Center Dr (75237-1937)
PHONE...................................214 613-5682
Darren Henderson, *CEO*
EMP: 21 **EST:** 2017
SALES (est): 1.8MM **Privately Held**
WEB: www.dlkmedicaltechnologies.com
SIC: 3841 Surgical & medical instruments

(G-4266)
DLT MANUFACTURING INC
4081 Shilling Way (75237-1009)
PHONE...................................214 330-8334
Guadalupe Calderon, *President*
Hector Calderon, *Opers Mgr*
Robert La Torre, *Purchasing*
Jamee Calderon, *IT/INT Sup*
Henry Garcia, *Prgrmr*
EMP: 67 **EST:** 1977
SQ FT: 20,000
SALES (est): 14.8MM **Privately Held**
WEB: www.dltmanufacturing.com
SIC: 3444 Sheet metalwork

(G-4267)
DMN INC (HQ)
Also Called: Dallas Morning News
1954 Commerce St (75201-5205)
P.O. Box 655237 (75265-5237)
PHONE...................................214 977-8222
James M Moroney III, *CEO*
Grant Moise, *President*
Robert W Mong Jr, *President*
Priscilla Presley, *Partner*
Jason Taylor, *Partner*
▲ **EMP:** 1000
SALES (est): 214.9MM **Publicly Held**
WEB: www.dallasnews.com
SIC: 2711 Newspapers, publishing & print-
ing

(G-4268)
DNS TOOL CUTTER GRINDING LLC
Also Called: D & S Tool
12029 Denton Dr (75234-7211)
PHONE...................................972 484-7491
Charles Gilbert, *Mng Member*
EMP: 13
SQ FT: 6,000
SALES (est): 2.3MM **Privately Held**
WEB: www.dnstool.us
SIC: 3599 Machine shop, jobbing & repair

(G-4269)
DOBBS-STANFORD CORPORATION
Also Called: Infomotion
2715 Electronic Ln (75220-1217)
PHONE...................................214 350-4222
▲ **EMP:** 43 **EST:** 1970
SQ FT: 35,000
SALES (est): 13MM **Privately Held**
WEB: www.dobbsstanford.com
SIC: 3695 5045 5065 Magnetic tape;
computers, peripherals & software; video
equipment, electronic

(G-4270)
DOIY LLC
325 N Saint Paul St # 3100 (75201-3801)
PHONE...................................469 513-4159
Elodie Joelle Deviras, *Manager*

Jaime Monfort Arroyo, *Manager*
Leila Etemadi,
EMP: 14
SALES (est): 500K
SALES (corp-wide): 5.6MM **Privately Held**
SIC: 2599 3111 3269 3499 Factory furniture & fixtures; accessory products, leather; stationery articles, pottery; novelties & giftware, including trophies; furniture; stationery & office supplies
PA: Doiycustom Sl
Calle Avila, 24 - S 2
Barcelona 08005
931 275-030

(G-4271)
DOLCO PACKAGING CORP
4700 S Westmoreland Rd (75237-1698)
PHONE..................................214 337-4711
Patrick F Smith, *CEO*
EMP: 200
SALES (est): 32.1MM **Privately Held**
SIC: 3086 Packaging & shipping materials, foamed plastic

(G-4272)
DON YOUNG COMPANY INCORPORATED (PA)
8181 Ambassador Row (75247-4703)
P.O. Box 560608 (75356-0608)
PHONE..................................214 630-0934
Don Young, *President*
Sue Young, *Corp Secy*
Scott Young, *Vice Pres*
Renee Schere, *Credit Mgr*
Mary Slaughter, *Human Res Mgr*
EMP: 70
SQ FT: 65,000
SALES (est): 21.7MM **Privately Held**
WEB: www.dycwindows.com
SIC: 3442 Storm doors or windows, metal; screen doors, metal

(G-4273)
DORCHESTER MINERALS LP (PA)
3838 Oak Lawn Ave Ste 300 (75219-4541)
PHONE..................................214 559-0300
William Casey McManemin, *CEO*
Dorchester M LP, *General Ptnr*
Brad Ehrman, *COO*
Bradley J Ehrman, *COO*
C W Russell, *Manager*
EMP: 24
SQ FT: 11,847
SALES: 78.8MM **Publicly Held**
WEB: www.dmlp.net
SIC: 1311 Crude petroleum production; natural gas production

(G-4274)
DOUBLE JJ CORPORATION (PA)
2604 Freewood Dr (75220-2511)
PHONE..................................214 353-0230
John Stickle, *President*
James Stickle, *Vice Pres*
EMP: 35
SQ FT: 23,250
SALES (est): 5.4MM **Privately Held**
SIC: 3556 2096 Food products machinery; corn chips & other corn-based snacks

(G-4275)
DOW JONES & COMPANY INC
3333 Lee Pkwy Ste 600 (75219-5117)
PHONE..................................214 951-7251
William Geiler, *Senior VP*
Don Young, *Mktg Dir*
Bob Broussard, *Manager*
Tim Goldsberry, *Manager*
Andrew Johnson, *Exec Dir*
EMP: 50
SALES (corp-wide): 9B **Publicly Held**
WEB: www.dowjones.com
SIC: 2711 Newspapers, publishing & printing
HQ: Dow Jones & Company, Inc.
1211 Avenue Of The Americ
New York NY 10036
609 627-2999

(G-4276)
DOWNTOWN COLOR EXPRESS INC
2707 N Stemmons Fwy (75207-2289)
P.O. Box 270022, Flower Mound ۷(75027-0022)
PHONE..................................214 630-5533
EMP: 10
SALES (corp-wide): 1.9MM **Privately Held**
SIC: 2752 Commercial Offset Printing Service
PA: Downtown Color Express, Inc.
520 W Elm St
Lake City MN 55041
651 994-4653

(G-4277)
DPS TECK LLC
11937 Denton Dr Ste 102 (75234-7785)
PHONE..................................972 241-0339
James F Carroll, *CEO*
Darrell Starnes, *President*
Frank J Carroll, *Officer*
EMP: 20
SALES (est): 1.8MM **Privately Held**
WEB: www.dpsteck.com
SIC: 2759 Commercial printing

(G-4278)
DRAFFT ROOT BEER INC
Also Called: Metro Sweet Products
3138 Quebec St Ste 106 (75247-6722)
PHONE..................................214 638-8442
Theodore Clay Long, *President*
Carolyn Jaquess, *Corp Secy*
Carolyn J Long, *Director*
EMP: 14
SQ FT: 34,000
SALES (est): 4.1MM **Privately Held**
WEB: www.drafft.com
SIC: 5149 2087 Sugar, honey, molasses & syrups; concentrates, drink

(G-4279)
DRS NTWORK IMAGING SYSTEMS LLC
Infrared Technologies Division
13544 N Central Expy (75243-1108)
PHONE..................................214 996-2837
Stephanie Moore, *Manager*
Chad Ottosen, *Technology*
Scott Winburn, *Director*
EMP: 122
SALES (corp-wide): 9.9B **Privately Held**
WEB: www.leonardodrs.com
SIC: 3674 Infrared sensors, solid state
HQ: Drs Network & Imaging Systems, Llc
100 N Babcock St
Melbourne FL 32935

(G-4280)
DRS NTWORK IMAGING SYSTEMS LLC
Also Called: Drs Infrared Technology
13532 N Central Expy (75243-1108)
PHONE..................................877 377-4783
Terry Murphy, *COO*
Jim Robinson, *VP Engrg*
Patty Benken, *Engineer*
Tim Haese, *Engineer*
Shawn Tobin, *Engineer*
EMP: 122
SALES (corp-wide): 9.9B **Privately Held**
WEB: www.leonardodrs.com
SIC: 3812 Search & navigation equipment
HQ: Drs Network & Imaging Systems, Llc
100 N Babcock St
Melbourne FL 32935

(G-4281)
DRS TRAINING CTRL SYSTEMS LLC
4212 S Buckner Blvd (75227-4201)
PHONE..................................214 381-7161
John Uvodich, *President*
EMP: 150
SQ FT: 242,000
SALES (corp-wide): 9.9B **Privately Held**
WEB: www.leonardodrs.com
SIC: 3812 Radar systems & equipment
HQ: Drs Training & Control Systems, Llc
645 Anchors St Nw
Fort Walton Beach FL 32548
850 302-3000

(G-4282)
DSX ACCESS SYSTEMS INC
10731 Rockwall Rd (75238-1219)
P.O. Box 550909 (75355-0909)
PHONE..................................214 553-6140
Albert Havrilla, *President*
Bart Holzer, *Vice Pres*
A Meadows, *Vice Pres*
William Monroe, *Vice Pres*
Marty Monroe, *Production*
▲ **EMP:** 25
SQ FT: 15,000
SALES (est): 4.6MM **Privately Held**
WEB: www.dsxinc.com
SIC: 1731 3829 Access control systems specialization; measuring & controlling devices

(G-4283)
E & T PLASTIC MFG CO INC
1174 Security Dr (75247-6812)
PHONE..................................214 622-6263
Greg Gillen, *Vice Pres*
Stephen Ward, *Credit Mgr*
Erik Carlson, *Manager*
EMP: 10
SALES (corp-wide): 75MM **Privately Held**
WEB: www.e-tplastics.com
SIC: 3089 Injection molding of plastics
PA: E & T Plastic Manufacturing Co., Inc.
4545 37th St
Long Island City NY 11101
718 729-6226

(G-4284)
E R CARPENTER LP
4443 Bronze Way (75236-2005)
P.O. Box 1007, Temple (76503-1007)
PHONE..................................804 359-0800
Mike McKendrick, *Branch Mgr*
EMP: 30
SALES (corp-wide): 54.6MM **Privately Held**
WEB: www.carpenter.com
SIC: 3086 Insulation or cushioning material, foamed plastic
PA: E. R. Carpenter, L.P.
2611 N General Bruce Dr
Temple TX 76501
804 359-0800

(G-4285)
E T C COMPANY
8111 Westchester Dr # 600 (75225-6140)
PHONE..................................210 403-6402
Kelcy Warren, *Partner*
Ray Davis, *Partner*
EMP: 30
SALES (est): 1MM **Privately Held**
WEB: www.energytransfer.com
SIC: 1389 1382 Gas compressing (natural gas) at the fields; oil & gas exploration services

(G-4286)
E Z CLEANING SOLUTIONS
2603 N Carroll Ave (75204-3000)
P.O. Box 600481 (75360-0481)
PHONE..................................214 841-9626
Todd Welch, *Owner*
EMP: 10
SALES (est): 578.1K **Privately Held**
SIC: 7217 2899 Carpet & upholstery cleaning; rifle bore cleaning compounds

(G-4287)
E-M DESIGN TIME INC
3915 Fairlakes Dr (75228-1437)
PHONE..................................972 279-4720
Benny D Hopper, *President*
Mary E Hopper, *Treasurer*
EMP: 18
SALES (est): 1.1MM **Privately Held**
SIC: 8748 3679 Business consulting; electronic circuits

(G-4288)
E2 ENERGY SERVICES LLC
8150 N Central Expy (75206-1815)
PHONE..................................214 365-3200
Tom Little, *President*
Earl Ashley, *VP Opers*
Mack Mays, *Opers Mgr*
Ahlaam Varachia, *Human Resources*
Rod Brumlow, *Director*

EMP: 24 **EST:** 2014
SALES (est): 5.3MM **Privately Held**
WEB: www.e2energyservices.com
SIC: 1382 Oil & gas exploration services

(G-4289)
EAGLE BRUSH & CHEMICAL INC
Also Called: Eagle Specialty Brush
11242 Indian Trl (75229-3518)
P.O. Box 59068 (75229-1068)
PHONE..................................972 484-0391
Ben Carriker, *President*
EMP: 12
SQ FT: 21,000
SALES (est): 3.4MM **Privately Held**
WEB: www.eagle-hawk.com
SIC: 5087 3991 Janitors' supplies; brooms & brushes

(G-4290)
EAGLE CIRCUITS INC
10820 Sanden Dr (75238-5325)
PHONE..................................214 349-0288
H R Savalia, *President*
Nilesh Naik, *Vice Pres*
Patel Rasikial A, *Director*
J D Cajera, *Director*
D D Ramolia, *Director*
▲ **EMP:** 40
SQ FT: 18,500
SALES (est): 6.9MM **Privately Held**
WEB: www.eaglecircuits.com
SIC: 3672 Circuit boards, television & radio printed

(G-4291)
EAGLE GAS & OIL CO INC
5950 Berkshire Ln # 1100 (75225-5846)
PHONE..................................214 369-1545
Pat S Bolin, *CEO*
Darrell S Lohoefer, *President*
Scott Wright, *Engineer*
Bradley W Ayres, *Info Tech Mgr*
Mary Bayne Lambert, *Admin Asst*
EMP: 13
SALES (est): 4MM **Privately Held**
WEB: www.eagleog.com
SIC: 1382 Oil & gas exploration services

(G-4292)
EAGLE MATERIALS INC (PA)
5960 Berkshire Ln Ste 900 (75225-6068)
PHONE..................................214 432-2000
Michael R Nicolais, *Ch of Bd*
Michael R Haack, *President*
Keith W Metcalf, *President*
Gerald J Essl, *Exec VP*
James H Graass, *Exec VP*
EMP: 143
SALES: 1.4B **Publicly Held**
WEB: www.eaglematerials.com
SIC: 3241 3275 3273 Cement, hydraulic; wallboard, gypsum; cement, keene's; plaster & plasterboard, gypsum; ready-mixed concrete

(G-4293)
EAGLERIDGE ENERGY LLC
Also Called: Eagleridge Operating
3300 Oak Lawn Ave Ste 500 (75219-6430)
P.O. Box 191447 (75219-8447)
PHONE..................................214 295-6704
Michael V Ronca, *CEO*
Mark L Grawe, *COO*
Jessica Savell, *Accountant*
Andrea Molinar, *Analyst*
Sam Showman, *Analyst*
EMP: 10 **EST:** 2009
SQ FT: 3,000
SALES (est): 4.7MM **Privately Held**
WEB: www.eagleridgeenergy.com
SIC: 1382 Oil & gas exploration services

(G-4294)
EAST DLLAS-LAKEWOOD PEOPLE INC
Also Called: Advocate Publishing
6301 Gaston Ave Ste 820 (75214-6291)
PHONE..................................214 823-5885
Rick Wamre, *President*
Elissa Chudwin, *Editor*
Lisa Kresl, *Editor*
Keri Mitchell, *Editor*
Rachel Stone, *Editor*
EMP: 23

SQ FT: 4,500
SALES (est): 3.2MM **Privately Held**
WEB: www.advocatemag.com
SIC: 2721 2711 2741 Magazines: publishing only, not printed on site; newspapers: publishing only, not printed on site; guides: publishing only, not printed on site; shopping news: publishing & printing

(G-4295)
EASTMAN KODAK COMPANY
3400 Carlisle St (75204-1285)
PHONE...................................972 241-1611
Robert Corder, *Branch Mgr*
EMP: 78
SALES (corp-wide): 1.2B **Publicly Held**
WEB: www.kodak.com
SIC: 3861 Film, sensitized motion picture, X-ray, still camera, etc.
PA: Eastman Kodak Company
343 State St
Rochester NY 14650
585 724-4000

(G-4296)
EASTMAN PARK MICROGRAPHICS INC (PA)
Also Called: E P M
6300 Cedar Springs Rd (75235-5809)
P.O. Box 541028 (75354-1028)
PHONE...................................214 580-8390
William D Oates, *President*
Kevin Harvell, *COO*
Tim Mortenson, *Vice Pres*
Timothy Mortenson, *Vice Pres*
Pamela A Schneider, *Vice Pres*
◆ EMP: 25
SQ FT: 52,000
SALES (est): 18.4MM **Privately Held**
WEB: www.epminc.com
SIC: 5044 3861 Microfilm equipment; microfilm equipment: cameras, projectors, readers, etc.

(G-4297)
EASY PROTECT INC
2035 Royal Ln Ste 290 (75229-3266)
PHONE...................................469 916-1099
Young Yi, *President*
▲ EMP: 24
SQ FT: 5,000
SALES (est): 2.7MM **Privately Held**
SIC: 3699 5065 Security control equipment & systems; security control equipment & systems

(G-4298)
EBT NEWCO LLC
2777 N Stemmons Fwy # 18 (75207-2277)
PHONE...................................972 996-0458
Marcus Randolph,
EMP: 13
SALES (est): 556.8K **Privately Held**
SIC: 3341 Lead smelting & refining (secondary)

(G-4299)
ECO-BAT AMERICA LLC (DH)
2777 N Stemmons Fwy # 185 (75207-2277)
PHONE...................................214 631-6070
George Cummins, *Mng Member*
Peter King,
EMP: 214
SALES (est): 87.7MM
SALES (corp-wide): 6.3MM **Privately Held**
WEB: www.ecobat.com
SIC: 3339 Primary nonferrous metals

(G-4300)
EDWARDS PRINTING SERVICE INC
13643 Beta Rd (75244-4511)
PHONE...................................972 387-3575
Richard Larry Edwards, *President*
Kimberly M Puckett, *Admin Sec*
EMP: 12
SALES (est): 2.3MM **Privately Held**
WEB: www.edwardsprintingservice.com
SIC: 2752 Commercial printing, offset

(G-4301)
EDWIN JONES COMPANY INC (PA)
Also Called: Entertainment Networks
6445 Prestonshire Ln (75225-2310)
PHONE...................................214 361-4000
Edwin G Jones, *President*
Brenda Merritt, *CFO*
Cheryl Brauner,
Paul Kavanagh, *Advisor*
Lynn Zukley, *Representative*
EMP: 9
SQ FT: 2,200
SALES (est): 3.2MM **Privately Held**
WEB: www.edwinjones.com
SIC: 5063 3625 Electrical supplies; electric controls & control accessories, industrial

(G-4302)
EFFICIENT-TEC INTL LLC
9659 Wendell Rd (75243-5510)
PHONE...................................214 221-9405
Molly Wilson, *Prdtn Mgr*
Jerry Nickell,
◆ EMP: 25
SQ FT: 18,000
SALES (est): 6.3MM **Privately Held**
WEB: www.solavantilighting.com
SIC: 5065 3441 Electronic parts; building components, structural steel

(G-4303)
EGMA LLC
11234 Goodnight Ln (75229-7807)
PHONE...................................972 488-3462
Alan Yuster, *Senior VP*
Allan Yustr, *Vice Pres*
Ricky Lee, *Mfg Staff*
Poya Eghterafi, *Exec Dir*
EMP: 18
SALES (est): 1.6MM **Privately Held**
WEB: www.egmallc.com
SIC: 3827 Optical instruments & lenses

(G-4304)
EL DORADO LOGISTICS LLC
2828 N Harwood St (75201-1518)
PHONE...................................214 871-3555
Leslie Simmons, *Principal*
EMP: 16
SALES (est): 298.3K
SALES (corp-wide): 17.4B **Publicly Held**
SIC: 2752 Schedules, transportation: lithographed
HQ: Holly Energy Partners, L.P.
2828 N Harwood St # 1300
Dallas TX 75201
214 871-3555

(G-4305)
EL EXTRA SPNISH LNGAGE NEWSPPR
Also Called: El Extra Newspaper
1214 Gardenview Dr (75217-4311)
P.O. Box 270432 (75227-0432)
PHONE...................................214 309-0990
Emmy Silva, *Owner*
EMP: 18
SALES (est): 1.2MM **Privately Held**
WEB: www.elextranewspaper.com
SIC: 2721 2711 Periodicals; newspapers

(G-4306)
EL HERALDO NEWS INCORPORATED
4532 Columbia Ave (75226-1016)
P.O. Box 141354 (75214-1354)
PHONE...................................214 827-9700
Francisco Rayo, *President*
Jim L Byrd, *CFO*
Ellie Byrd, *Exec Dir*
EMP: 32
SQ FT: 4,000
SALES (est): 1.7MM **Privately Held**
WEB: www.elheraldonews.com
SIC: 2711 Newspapers: publishing only, not printed on site

(G-4307)
ELAH HOLDINGS INC (PA)
Also Called: Real Industry
8214 Westchester Dr # 950 (75225-6100)
PHONE...................................805 435-1255
C Clark Webb, *Ch of Bd*

Michael J Hobey, *President*
Terrance Hogan, *President*
Kelly G Howard, *Exec VP*
Kyle Ross, *Exec VP*
EMP: 12
SQ FT: 20,000
SALES (est): 981.5MM **Publicly Held**
WEB: www.elahholdings.com
SIC: 3341 3313 3613 Secondary nonferrous metals; alloys, additive, except copper: not made in blast furnaces; ferromanganese, not made in blast furnaces; power circuit breakers; circuit breakers, air

(G-4308)
ELAND ENERGY INC (PA)
16400 Dallas Pkwy Ste 100 (75248-2640)
PHONE...................................214 368-6100
Tim Allen, *President*
Gregg Allen, *Vice Pres*
Ralph Butler, *Opers Staff*
Ross Pearson, *QC Mgr*
Steve Flynn, *Engineer*
EMP: 20
SQ FT: 20,000
SALES (est): 17.2MM **Privately Held**
WEB: www.elandenergy.com
SIC: 1382 Oil & gas exploration services

(G-4309)
ELEMETAL LLC (PA)
15850 Dallas Pkwy (75248-3308)
PHONE...................................214 956-7600
Brittany Kernodle, *Opers Staff*
Alan Buehler, *CFO*
Matthew Eden, *CFO*
Tobias Bernal, *Human Res Mgr*
Alan Stockmeister, *Mng Member*
EMP: 9 EST: 2008
SQ FT: 80,000
SALES (est): 96.3MM **Privately Held**
WEB: www.elemetal.com
SIC: 3341 3356 3339 Secondary precious metals; nonferrous rolling & drawing; primary nonferrous metals

(G-4310)
ELGIE COMPANY INC
4600 Greenville Ave # 200 (75206-5037)
PHONE...................................214 691-6216
Stephanie Shelby, *President*
Arlene Shriver, *Corp Secy*
Ron Johnson, *Vice Pres*
EMP: 12
SQ FT: 1,200
SALES (est): 1.4MM **Privately Held**
SIC: 1311 Crude petroleum production; natural gas production

(G-4311)
ELJER INDUSTRIES INC (DH)
Also Called: Eljer Plumbing Ware
14801 Quorum Dr Fl 3 (75254-7589)
PHONE...................................972 560-2000
James A Harris, *President*
Patty Puttnicki, *Exec VP*
Steven M Rodman, *Vice Pres*
Rich Rosselet, *Vice Pres*
◆ EMP: 23
SQ FT: 212,300
SALES (est): 3.1MM **Publicly Held**
SIC: 3432 3431 3088 3261 Plumbing fixture fittings & trim; metal sanitary ware; plastics plumbing fixtures; vitreous plumbing fixtures; registers (air), metal; grilles & grillework, woven wire
HQ: Zurn Industries, Llc
1801 Pittsburgh Ave
Erie PA 16502
814 455-0921

(G-4312)
ELK CORPORATION OF TEXAS (DH)
14911 Quorum Dr Ste 600 (75254-1491)
PHONE...................................972 851-0500
Richard Nowak, *President*
Gregory J Fisher, *CFO*
Steve Peterson, *Controller*
▼ EMP: 100
SALES (est): 40.2MM
SALES (corp-wide): 2.5B **Privately Held**
WEB: www.elkcorp.com
SIC: 2952 2273 Roofing materials; carpets & rugs

(G-4313)
ELKCORP (DH)
Also Called: GAF Materials
14911 Quorum Dr Ste 600 (75254-1491)
PHONE...................................972 851-0500
Thomas D Karol, *Ch of Bd*
Richard A Nowak, *President*
David Tuttle, *General Mgr*
Matti Kiik, *Senior VP*
Andrew Vetter, *Transportation*
◆ EMP: 35 EST: 1956
SQ FT: 1,958
SALES (est): 699.8MM
SALES (corp-wide): 2.5B **Privately Held**
WEB: www.gaf.com
SIC: 2952 5033 2426 2431 Roofing materials; roofing, asphalt & sheet metal; flooring, hardwood; stair railings, wood; plating & polishing

(G-4314)
ELLARD JOHN
Also Called: Manda Machine Co
2683 Myrtle Springs Ave (75220-2514)
P.O. Box 541236 (75354-1236)
PHONE...................................214 352-5946
EMP: 15
SALES (est): 826K **Privately Held**
SIC: 2052 Management Consulting Services

(G-4315)
ELM RIDGE EXPLORATION CO LLC
12225 Grnvlle Ave Ste 950 (75243)
PHONE...................................972 889-2100
James M Clark Jr,
EMP: 40
SALES (est): 8.2MM **Privately Held**
SIC: 1382 Oil & gas exploration services

(G-4316)
ELM RIDGE RESOURCES INC (PA)
12225 Grnvlle Ave Ste 950 (75243)
PHONE...................................972 889-2100
James M Clark Jr, *President*
James M Clark Sr, *Vice Pres*
EMP: 18
SALES (est): 8.3MM **Privately Held**
SIC: 1382 1311 Oil & gas exploration services; crude petroleum production

(G-4317)
EMC CORPORATION
14755 Preston Rd Ste 200 (75254-9200)
PHONE...................................972 892-7700
Lillian Andree, *Partner*
Austin Bell, *Engineer*
Eric Merriweather, *Senior Engr*
Dan Lumbra, *Accountant*
Krisha Osteen, *Branch Mgr*
EMP: 135 **Publicly Held**
WEB: www.emc.com
SIC: 3572 7372 7374 5045 Computer storage devices; prepackaged software; data processing service; computers, peripherals & software
HQ: Emc Corporation
176 South St
Hopkinton MA 01748
508 435-1000

(G-4318)
EMERGENCY ICE INC (PA)
8700 Diplomacy Row (75247-5402)
PHONE...................................972 988-0577
Earl Toler, *President*
Paul Toler, *Senior VP*
Donnel Toler, *Vice Pres*
Mary Killion, *Accountant*
EMP: 10
SQ FT: 6,000
SALES (est): 2.4MM **Privately Held**
WEB: www.emergencyice.com
SIC: 2097 Manufactured ice

(G-4319)
EMF COMPANY INC
106 Regal Row (75247-5606)
P.O. Box 560345 (75356-0345)
PHONE...................................214 350-6848
Mike Tignor, *President*
Dolores Tignor, *Corp Secy*
Kurt Tignor, *Vice Pres*

Tim Winker, *Purch Mgr*
Cheryl Winker, *Controller*
EMP: 61
SQ FT: 65,000
SALES (est): 13.1MM **Privately Held**
WEB: www.emfcompany.com
SIC: 3469 3699 Electronic enclosures, stamped or pressed metal; electrical equipment & supplies

(G-4320)
EMPIRE BAKING COMPANY L P (PA)
6440 N Central Expy # 508 (75206-4133)
PHONE.................................972 851-5677
Robert Ozarow, *Partner*
EMP: 38
SQ FT: 9,000
SALES (est): 5MM **Privately Held**
WEB: www.empirebaking.com
SIC: 5461 2051 Cookies; bread, cake & related products

(G-4321)
EMSOLUTIONS LLC
10810 Alder Cir (75238-1347)
PHONE.................................214 575-5327
Barry Hurley, *Sales Executive*
Nilesh Naik,
Shirish D Patel,
Hasmukhlal Savalia,
EMP: 50
SQ FT: 20,000
SALES (est): 7.1MM **Privately Held**
SIC: 3672 Printed circuit boards

(G-4322)
ENERCON STEAM SOLUTIONS LLC
8401 N Central Expy # 840 (75225-4402)
P.O. Box 600788 (75360-0788)
PHONE.................................214 292-3485
Barry Hayes, *Mng Member*
Carey Nash,
EMP: 10
SALES (est): 754.6K **Privately Held**
WEB: www.enerconsteam.com
SIC: 3494 Plumbing & heating valves

(G-4323)
ENERGY MANAGEMENT COMPANY (PA)
Also Called: Energy Management Co Texas
5910 N Central Expy # 1300 (75206-5126)
PHONE.................................972 885-6799
Joe Vaughan, *CEO*
David Vaughan, *President*
EMP: 10
SQ FT: 10,000
SALES (est): 23MM **Privately Held**
WEB: www.emcotexas.com
SIC: 1382 Oil & gas exploration services

(G-4324)
ENLINK MIDSTREAM INC (HQ)
2501 Cedar Springs Rd # 600 (75201-7614)
PHONE.................................214 953-9500
Barry E Davis, *Ch of Bd*
William W Davis, *COO*
William Davis, *COO*
A Chris Aulds, *Exec VP*
Joe A Davis, *Exec VP*
EMP: 46
SQ FT: 108,500
SALES (est): 19MM
SALES (corp-wide): 6B **Publicly Held**
WEB: www.enlink.com
SIC: 1311 5712 Natural gas production; mattresses
PA: Enlink Midstream, Llc
     1722 Routh St Ste 1300
     Dallas TX 75201
     214 953-9500

(G-4325)
ENTECH TECHNOLOGY INC
16326 Sunset Valley Dr (75248-2834)
P.O. Box 797887 (75379-7887)
PHONE.................................972 542-0210
Loyde N De Berry, *President*
Sharon D De Berry, *Treasurer*
Loyde De Berry, *Manager*
EMP: 50 **EST:** 1979
SQ FT: 40,000

SALES (est): 4.5MM **Privately Held**
SIC: 1541 3441 2448 Industrial buildings, new construction; renovation, remodeling & repairs: industrial buildings; fabricated structural metal; wood pallets & skids

(G-4326)
ENTERPRISE CONCRETE PDTS LLC
Also Called: American Concrete Products
4040 Singleton Blvd (75212-3505)
PHONE.................................214 631-7006
Thomas L Egan Jr,
Kimberly H Egan,
▲ **EMP:** 100
SQ FT: 40,000
SALES (est): 23.3MM
SALES (corp-wide): 56.8MM **Privately Held**
SIC: 3272 Concrete products, precast
PA: Enterprise Properties, Inc.
     10220 F St
     Omaha NE 68127
     402 339-3670

(G-4327)
ENVIROMENTAL INDUSTRIES LP
8801 Governors Row (75247-3915)
PHONE.................................972 390-9899
Chris Cowman, *Principal*
EMP: 16
SALES (est): 2MM **Privately Held**
SIC: 3999 Manufacturing industries

(G-4328)
EOA HOLDING CO INC
Also Called: Essilor Labs of America
13555 N Stemmons Fwy (75234-5765)
PHONE.................................214 496-4000
Laurent Vacherot, *President*
Eric Leonard, *Exec VP*
Kevin Rupp, *Senior VP*
Ray Schroeder, *Treasurer*
Morey Thompson, *Finance*
EMP: 13
SALES (est): 432.7K
SALES (corp-wide): 1.7MM **Privately Held**
WEB: www.essilorusa.com
SIC: 3851 Ophthalmic goods
PA: Essilorluxottica
     147 Rue De Paris
     Charenton Le Pont 94220
     149 774-224

(G-4329)
EQUIPMENT STORAGE SERVICE INC (HQ)
3839 E Overton Rd (75216-2802)
P.O. Box 397525 (75339-7525)
PHONE.................................214 374-3995
Edwin S Bell, *President*
Pepper Kuykendall, *Vice Pres*
Gus Brair, *Treasurer*
EMP: 12
SQ FT: 2,400
SALES (est): 3.4MM
SALES (corp-wide): 87.9MM **Privately Held**
WEB: www.equipmentstorageservice.business.site
SIC: 2655 4731 Containers, liquid tight fiber: from purchased material; freight forwarding
PA: Ed Bell Investments, Inc.
     10605 Harry Hines Blvd
     Dallas TX 75220
     214 358-3414

(G-4330)
ERECT-A-LINE INC
3912 W Illinois Ave (75211-8451)
P.O. Box 541087 (75354-1087)
PHONE.................................214 630-1154
Jeff Barnes, *President*
Ray Harper, *General Mgr*
Gary Barnes, *Vice Pres*
▲ **EMP:** 15
SQ FT: 36,242
SALES (est): 4.7MM
SALES (corp-wide): 108.2MM **Privately Held**
WEB: www.ealmfg.com
SIC: 3272 5032 Concrete products, precast; concrete building products

PA: Georgeco, Inc.
     2609 Willowbrook Rd
     Dallas TX 75220
     214 352-9091

(G-4331)
ERGOTECT CORPORATION
Also Called: Ergomart
5200 E Grand Ave Ste 500 (75223-2228)
P.O. Box 710130 (75371-0130)
PHONE.................................214 747-3746
Michael J Sears, *President*
Dianna Diaz, *Plant Mgr*
Nick Johnson, *Project Engr*
Stephanie Herrington, *Sales Staff*
James Pace, *Business Anlyst*
▲ **EMP:** 22
SALES (est): 4.1MM **Privately Held**
WEB: www.ergomart.com
SIC: 2522 5712 5021 Office furniture, except wood; office furniture; office & public building furniture

(G-4332)
ESSILOR LABORATORIES AMER INC (DH)
Also Called: Distrilens
13515 N Stemmons Fwy (75234-5765)
PHONE.................................972 241-4141
Hubert Sagnires, *CEO*
Weldon Lucas, *President*
Carl Bracy, *VP Sales*
Wilston Nkangoh, *Technology*
Gary Duffens, *Software Engr*
◆ **EMP:** 252
SQ FT: 126,176
SALES (est): 918.4MM
SALES (corp-wide): 1.7MM **Privately Held**
WEB: www.essilorrichrewards.com
SIC: 3851 Eyeglasses, lenses & frames; contact lenses; ophthalmic goods; frames, ophthalmic; lenses, ophthalmic
HQ: Essilor Laboratories Of America Holding Co., Inc.
     13555 N Stemmons Fwy
     Dallas TX 75234
     214 496-4141

(G-4333)
ESSILOR OF AMERICA INC
13515 N Stemmons Fwy (75234-5765)
PHONE.................................214 496-4000
Bruno Barajuan, *General Mgr*
Dan Limbert, *District Mgr*
Susan Kim, *Counsel*
Jeremy Benson, *Vice Pres*
Rick Piper, *Vice Pres*
EMP: 367
SALES (corp-wide): 1.7MM **Privately Held**
WEB: www.essilorusa.com
SIC: 3851 Ophthalmic goods
HQ: Essilor Of America, Inc.
     13555 N Stemmons Fwy
     Dallas TX 75234

(G-4334)
ESSILOR OF AMERICA INC (DH)
Also Called: Omega Dallas
13555 N Stemmons Fwy (75234-5765)
P.O. Box 961268, El Paso (79996-1268)
PHONE.................................214 496-4000
John Carrier, *President*
Cindy Bunn, *General Mgr*
Inta Larson, *General Mgr*
Carl Bracy, *Exec VP*
David Milan, *Senior VP*
▲ **EMP:** 348
SQ FT: 274,000
SALES (est): 1.8B
SALES (corp-wide): 1.7MM **Privately Held**
WEB: www.essilorusa.com
SIC: 3851 5048 Ophthalmic goods; ophthalmic goods
HQ: Essilor Of America Holding Company, Inc.
     1209 N Orange St
     Wilmington DE 19801
     214 496-4000

(G-4335)
ESSILOR OF AMERICA INC
13455 Branch View Ln (75234-5703)
PHONE.................................214 496-4235
Joey Lowery, *Branch Mgr*
Jacob Gray, *Manager*
Jessica Jacobs, *Manager*
EMP: 367
SALES (corp-wide): 1.7MM **Privately Held**
WEB: www.essilorusa.com
SIC: 3851 Ophthalmic goods
HQ: Essilor Of America, Inc.
     13555 N Stemmons Fwy
     Dallas TX 75234

(G-4336)
EUROPA DESIGNS
Also Called: Kelli Kouri Leather
13720 Neutron Rd (75244-4412)
PHONE.................................972 792-0997
Kelli Neagle, *Owner*
EMP: 16
SALES (est): 1MM **Privately Held**
SIC: 3199 2371 Leather garments; apparel, fur

(G-4337)
EVEREST GLOBAL INC
13455 Noel Rd Ste 2100 (75240-6615)
PHONE.................................972 980-0013
Peter Bendor-Samuel, *CEO*
Ronak Doshi, *Vice Pres*
Anurag Srivastava, *Vice Pres*
Bill Berry, *CFO*
Bandreena Kharumnuid, *Sales Staff*
EMP: 16 **Privately Held**
WEB: www.everestgrp.com
SIC: 7372 Prepackaged software
PA: Everest Global, Inc.
     12770 Merit Dr Ste 800
     Dallas TX 75251

(G-4338)
EVOLUTION FUELS INC
3001 Knox St Ste 403 (75205-5584)
PHONE.................................214 389-9800
EMP: 39
SALES (est): 184.5K **Privately Held**
SIC: 2869 Mfg Industrial Organic Chemicals

(G-4339)
EVOLUTION SPINE LLC
4225 Office Pkwy (75204-3628)
PHONE.................................214 228-6252
Munear Ashton Kouzbari, *President*
EMP: 13
SQ FT: 2,500
SALES (corp-wide): 11MM **Privately Held**
SIC: 3841 Surgical & medical instruments
PA: Evolution Spine Llc
     2300 N Haskell Ave
     Dallas TX 75204
     214 228-6252

(G-4340)
EXCELERGY CORP
3102 Maple Ave Ste 450 (75201-1261)
PHONE.................................214 953-9373
Kevin Swenke, *Manager*
EMP: 10
SALES (corp-wide): 5.6MM **Privately Held**
WEB: www.excelergy.com
SIC: 7372 8731 Prepackaged software; energy research
PA: Excelergy Corp
     10 Maguire Rd Ste 111
     Lexington MA

(G-4341)
EXCELERON SOFTWARE LLC
8144 Walnut Hill Ln # 905 (75231-4388)
PHONE.................................972 852-2700
Dave Griffee, *Regl Sales Mgr*
Ravi Raju, *Chief Mktg Ofcr*
Bob Crenshaw, *Manager*
EMP: 12
SQ FT: 1,498
SALES (est): 798.5K **Privately Held**
WEB: www.exceleron.com
SIC: 7372 Business oriented computer software

▲ = Import ▼=Export
◆ =Import/Export

(G-4342)
EXCLUSIVE ORIENTAL RUGS INC
2050 N Stemmons Fwy # 111
(75207-3206)
P.O. Box 421293 (75342-1293)
PHONE................................214 747-5557
Abde Esmaili, *President*
EMP: 10
SQ FT: 7,000
SALES (est): 2.1MM **Privately Held**
WEB: www.exclusiveorientalrugs.com
SIC: 5023 2273 7217 Carpets; rugs; rugs, braided & hooked; carpet & rug cleaning & repairing plant

(G-4343)
EXCO HOLDINGS INC
12377 Merit Dr Ste 1700 (75251-2256)
PHONE................................214 368-2084
Stephaen F Smith, *President*
EMP: 471
SQ FT: 13,400
SALES (est): 22.2MM
SALES (corp-wide): 24.3B **Privately Held**
WEB: www.excoresources.com
SIC: 1311 Crude petroleum production
HQ: Cerberus Partners, L.P.
450 Park Ave Fl 28
New York NY 10022

(G-4344)
EXCO OPERATING COMPANY LP (DH)
12377 Merit Dr Ste 1700 (75251-2256)
PHONE................................214 368-2084
Harold L Hickey, *Partner*
William L Boeing, *Vice Pres*
Michael R Chambers, *Vice Pres*
Ronald G Edelen, *Vice Pres*
Stephen F Smith,
EMP: 32
SALES (est): 191.7MM
SALES (corp-wide): 394MM **Privately Held**
WEB: www.excoresources.com
SIC: 1382 Oil & gas exploration services

(G-4345)
EXCO RESOURCES INC (PA)
12377 Merit Dr Ste 1700 (75251-2256)
PHONE................................214 368-2084
Harold L Hickey, *President*
David Rivet, *Superintendent*
Keith Pitts, *Vice Chairman*
Harold H Jameson, *COO*
Heather Lamparter, *Counsel*
▲ **EMP:** 114
SQ FT: 155,000
SALES: 394MM **Privately Held**
WEB: www.excoresources.com
SIC: 1382 Oil & gas exploration services

(G-4346)
EXECUTIVE ENTERPRISES LLC (PA)
Also Called: Woodlands Apothecary
8360 Lbj Fwy Ste 215 (75243-1222)
PHONE................................346 224-2125
Michael Burch, *Mng Member*
Linh Nguyen,
EMP: 11
SQ FT: 2,500
SALES (est): 4.8MM **Privately Held**
SIC: 2834 5122 Digitalis pharmaceutical preparations; pharmaceuticals

(G-4347)
EXIGO OFFICE INC (PA)
1600 Viceroy Dr Ste 125 (75235-2313)
PHONE................................214 367-9999
David Thompson, *President*
Sam Harrower, *Accounts Exec*
Matt Eastman, *Director*
Sarah Dittrich, *Tech Recruiter*
EMP: 12
SALES (est): 1.5MM **Privately Held**
WEB: www.exigo.com
SIC: 7371 5045 7372 Computer software development; computer software; application computer software

(G-4348)
EXPERT TOOL & MACHINE INC
2433 Arbuckle Ct (75229-4506)
PHONE................................972 241-5353
Rudy Kobus, *President*
Anthony Dilday, *Project Mgr*
Gwen Sparkman, *Office Mgr*
EMP: 11
SQ FT: 8,000
SALES (est): 2.1MM **Privately Held**
WEB: www.etmusa.com
SIC: 3599 Machine shop, jobbing & repair

(G-4349)
EXPRESS INC
13350 Dallas Pkwy # 2300 (75240-1548)
PHONE................................972 233-2986
Katherine Dickerson, *Principal*
Jatin Rana, *Software Dev*
EMP: 2113 **Publicly Held**
WEB: www.express.com
SIC: 2741 Miscellaneous publishing
PA: Express, Inc.
1 Express Dr
Columbus OH 43230

(G-4350)
F & R MACHINE SERVICES INC
7217 Harry Hines Blvd (75235-4011)
P.O. Box 36307 (75235-1307)
PHONE................................214 631-4946
Frank Rosner, *President*
Goldie Rosner, *Vice Pres*
Daniel Titus, *Foreman/Supr*
EMP: 12 **EST:** 1978
SQ FT: 7,200
SALES (est): 1.3MM **Privately Held**
WEB: www.fandrmachine.com
SIC: 7692 3441 3599 7699 Welding repair; fabricated structural metal; machine shop, jobbing & repair; industrial machinery & equipment repair

(G-4351)
FANLIGHT CORPORATION INC
11011 Regency Crest Dr # 800
(75238-1718)
PHONE................................909 930-6868
Cecilia Liem, *Principal*
EMP: 13
SALES (corp-wide): 11.9MM **Privately Held**
WEB: www.fanlightinc.com
SIC: 3641 Electric lamps
PA: Fanlight Corporation, Inc.
2000 S Grove Ave Bldg B
Ontario CA 91761
909 930-6868

(G-4352)
FARO SERVICES INC
3701 La Reunion Pkwy (75212-6106)
PHONE................................214 631-1888
Charlene Vartlett, *Manager*
Charlene N Vartlett, *Manager*
EMP: 10 **Privately Held**
WEB: www.farousa.com
SIC: 3565 4225 Packaging machinery; general warehousing
PA: Faro Services, Inc.
7070 Pontius Rd
Groveport OH 43125

(G-4353)
FAS HOLDINGS GROUP LLC
10480 Markison Rd (75238-1650)
P.O. Box 550128 (75355-0128)
PHONE................................214 343-5300
Stephen Newman, *President*
Miguel Friedrich, *Vice Pres*
EMP: 25
SALES (est): 10.2MM **Privately Held**
WEB: www.ntact.com
SIC: 3559 5084 Semiconductor manufacturing machinery; industrial machinery & equipment

(G-4354)
FAS TECHNOLOGIES LLC
10480 Markison Rd (75238-1650)
P.O. Box 550128 (75355-0128)
PHONE................................214 343-5300
Leah Delong, *Office Mgr*
Hugo Abarca Ntact, *Manager*
Ted Snodgrss,
EMP: 20

SALES (est): 3.4MM **Privately Held**
SIC: 3674 Computer logic modules

(G-4355)
FAUBION ASSOCIATES INC
1000 Forest Ave (75215-3126)
P.O. Box 150159 (75315-0159)
PHONE................................214 565-1000
Leo Faubion, *President*
Tom Prebensen, *Vice Pres*
James Gallagher, *Project Mgr*
Wayne Austin, *CFO*
◆ **EMP:** 250
SQ FT: 300,000
SALES (est): 29.7MM **Privately Held**
WEB: www.faubionassoc.com
SIC: 2431 2542 2541 Millwork; doors & door parts & trim, wood; partitions & fixtures, except wood; store & office display cases & fixtures

(G-4356)
FCI ENVIRONMENTAL INC
13111 N Cntl Expy Ste 440 (75243)
PHONE................................702 262-3953
Jeffrey Hewitt, *Ch of Bd*
Ken Culver, *CFO*
EMP: 30
SQ FT: 15,000
SALES (est): 4.4MM **Privately Held**
SIC: 3823 3829 3826 3812 Industrial instrmnts msrmnt display/control process variable; measuring & controlling devices; analytical instruments; search & navigation equipment

(G-4357)
FCX PERFORMANCE INC
Also Called: Pierce Pump Company
9010 John W Carpenter Fwy (75247-4520)
PHONE................................214 320-3604
Don Reece, *Branch Mgr*
EMP: 30
SALES (corp-wide): 3.2B **Publicly Held**
WEB: www.fcxperformance.com
SIC: 5084 3563 Pumps & pumping equipment; air & gas compressors including vacuum pumps
HQ: Fcx Performance, Inc
3000 E 14th Ave
Columbus OH 43219
614 324-6050

(G-4358)
FEDERAL RESERVE BANK DALLAS (HQ)
Also Called: Board of Gvrnors of Fdral Rsrv
2200 N Pearl St (75201-2272)
P.O. Box 655906 (75265-5906)
PHONE................................214 922-6000
▲ **EMP:** 946 **EST:** 1913
SQ FT: 388,956
SALES (est): 191.3MM **Privately Held**
WEB: www.dallasfed.org
SIC: 2895 Carbon black
PA: Board Of Governors Of The Federal Reserve System
20th St Cnsttution Ave Nw
Washington DC 20551
202 452-3000

(G-4359)
FERREIRA HOLDING GROUP LLC
Also Called: Tender Mercies
9319 L B Jhnson Ste 208-A Johnson (75243)
PHONE................................214 293-9233
Bertha Ferreira,
EMP: 48
SQ FT: 800
SALES (est): 213K **Privately Held**
WEB: www.fhg-cjallc.com
SIC: 3423 1542 1721 Carpenters' hand tools, except saws: levels, chisels, etc.; commercial & office building contractors; interior residential painting contractor

(G-4360)
FIBERGRATE COMPOSITE (HQ)
5151 Belt Line Rd Ste 700 (75254-7028)
P.O. Box 208, Stephenville (76401-0003)
PHONE................................972 250-1633
Eric Breiner, *President*
Wendell Hollingsworth, *Vice Pres*
Sean Lovison, *CFO*

Amy Sayasan, *Accountant*
Carlos Angulo, *Sales Mgr*
◆ **EMP:** 20
SALES (est): 55.9MM
SALES (corp-wide): 5.5B **Publicly Held**
WEB: www.fibergrate.com
SIC: 3089 Synthetic resin finished products
PA: Rpm International Inc.
2628 Pearl Rd
Medina OH 44256
330 273-5090

(G-4361)
FILTRATION GROUP LLC
11500 Hillguard Rd (75243-5504)
PHONE................................815 726-4600
Chris Koeppen, *Vice Pres*
John Sheehan, *Branch Mgr*
EMP: 45
SALES (corp-wide): 16MM **Privately Held**
WEB: www.filtrationgroup.com
SIC: 3569 Filters
HQ: Filtration Group Llc
912 E Washington St Ste 1
Joliet IL 60433
803 628-2410

(G-4362)
FINISHING & MAILING CENTER LLC
2151 W Commerce St (75212-5015)
PHONE................................214 747-6244
Mike Showen, *Production*
Elena Squiric, *Accounts Exec*
Rance Peevy, *Sales Staff*
William Squiric, *Mng Member*
Silvia Vacio, *Manager*
EMP: 45
SQ FT: 40,000
SALES (est): 6MM **Privately Held**
WEB: www.mailingcenter.net
SIC: 7331 2789 2732 Mailing service; bookbinding & related work; book printing

(G-4363)
FIRST QUALITY FABRICATING INC
1529 N Edgefield Ave (75208-2950)
P.O. Box 4910 (75208-0910)
PHONE................................214 748-0071
Richard Thrailkill, *President*
Rick Thrailkill, *Vice Pres*
EMP: 16
SQ FT: 15,000
SALES (est): 3.8MM **Privately Held**
WEB: www.firstqualityfabricating.com
SIC: 3444 Sheet metal specialties, not stamped

(G-4364)
FIRST TEXAS PRECAST INC
Also Called: First Texas Concrete Repair
6839 Harry Hines Blvd (75235-4210)
PHONE................................214 350-5612
Michael E Roberts, *President*
EMP: 35
SQ FT: 20,000
SALES (est): 5.9MM **Privately Held**
WEB: www.firsttexasprecast.com
SIC: 3272 3446 Concrete products, precast; architectural metalwork

(G-4365)
FISCHBACH TEXAS LP
1901 Hutton Ct Ste 100 (75234-9033)
PHONE................................469 533-5500
Fabio Scagliarini, *Principal*
Heidi Grube, *COO*
David Fisher, *Executive*
Dena Richmond,
Rolf-Udo Schneider,
▲ **EMP:** 12
SALES (est): 2MM **Privately Held**
WEB: www.fischbach-fi.com
SIC: 3089 Injection molding of plastics

(G-4366)
FISHBOWL GAMES LLC
2707 N Fitzhugh Ave # 1122 (75204-3247)
PHONE................................469 449-3275
Maxime Preaux,
EMP: 14
SALES (est): 840K **Privately Held**
SIC: 7372 7389 Home entertainment computer software;

(G-4367)
FIVE POINTS HOLDINGS LLC
1919 Mckinney Ave Ste 100 (75201-2496)
PHONE..............................214 525-6700
Mark Hulme, *Ch Credit Ofcr*
Jake Davis, *Manager*
David Wharton, *Manager*
Jason Stone, *Technology*
Amy Kauffman, *Exec Dir*
EMP: 50
SALES (est): 1.5MM **Privately Held**
WEB: www.dsnews.com
SIC: 2741 Miscellaneous publishing

(G-4368)
FLECO INDUSTRIES LLC
Also Called: Texas Fluorescents
4637 Greenville Ave (75206-5009)
PHONE..............................214 369-1101
Tom Hack, *Opers Staff*
EMP: 80
SALES (corp-wide): 77.5MM **Privately Held**
WEB: www.lighting-one.com
SIC: 3645 5063 3646 Garden, patio, walkway & yard lighting fixtures: electric; lighting fixtures; commercial indusl & institutional electric lighting fixtures
HQ: Fleco Industries, Llc
2055 Luna Rd Ste 142
Carrollton TX 75006
972 247-3171

(G-4369)
FLEURON ENTERPRISES INC
Also Called: Finial Company, The
4030 La Reunion Pkwy # 10 (75212-6023)
PHONE..............................214 678-0805
Martha Beck, *President*
Tiffany Bui, *Engineer*
Kelly Crabtree, *Director*
◆ **EMP:** 75 **EST:** 2005
SQ FT: 28,000
SALES (est): 11.5MM
SALES (corp-wide): 48MM **Privately Held**
WEB: www.thefinialcompany.com
SIC: 2591 Drapery hardware & blinds & shades
PA: Rowley Company, Llc
230 Meek Rd
Gastonia NC 28056
704 866-0650

(G-4370)
FLINT GROUP US LLC
Also Called: Flint Group Print Media N Amer
11625 Columbia Center Dr # 300 (75229-7302)
PHONE..............................214 638-6700
Clayton Shores, *Manager*
Eric Gibbs, *Manager*
Mike Green, *Technician*
EMP: 30
SALES (corp-wide): 53.9B **Publicly Held**
WEB: www.flintgrp.com
SIC: 2893 Printing ink
HQ: Flint Group Us Llc
17177 N Laurel Park Dr # 300
Livonia MI 48152
734 781-4600

(G-4371)
FLOWERS BAKING CO DENTON LLC
10879 Bekay St (75238-1313)
PHONE..............................214 343-6796
Dennis Lewis, *Sales Executive*
Garrett Felts, *Manager*
Denis Lewis, *Director*
EMP: 15
SQ FT: 11,375
SALES (corp-wide): 4.1B **Publicly Held**
WEB: www.flowersfoods.com
SIC: 2051 Bread, cake & related products
HQ: Flowers Baking Co. Of Denton, Llc
4210 Edwards Rd
Denton TX 76208
940 383-5280

(G-4372)
FLOWTRONEX PSI LLC (HQ)
10661 Newkirk St (75220-2303)
PHONE..............................469 221-1200
◆ **EMP:** 220
SQ FT: 48,600

SALES (est): 71.9MM **Publicly Held**
SIC: 3561 3949 3523 3432 Pumps, domestic: water or sump; sporting & athletic goods; farm machinery & equipment; plumbing fixture fittings & trim

(G-4373)
FOUR-STAR FABRICATION INC
2041 W Commerce St (75208-8026)
PHONE..............................214 748-3494
Doug McWilliams, *President*
Kevin Kiesling, *Vice Pres*
Debora McWilliams, *Admin Sec*
EMP: 9
SQ FT: 13,000
SALES (est): 2.1MM **Privately Held**
WEB: www.fourstarfabinc.com
SIC: 3441 Building components, structural steel

(G-4374)
FOURCE COMMUNICATIONS LIMITED
1351 Regal Row (75247-3615)
PHONE..............................214 630-2125
Murphy Webster III, *Partner*
Marcia Webster, *Manager*
Jon Hendrickson, *Director*
Tiffany Homan, *Graphic Designe*
EMP: 16
SQ FT: 30,253
SALES (est): 4.1MM **Privately Held**
WEB: www.fource.net
SIC: 7311 8742 3993 Advertising agencies; marketing consulting services; signs & advertising specialties

(G-4375)
FOXTRONICS INC
3448 W Mockingbird Ln (75235-5941)
P.O. Box 706, Haslet (76052-0706)
PHONE..............................214 358-4425
Wayne Ostrander, *CEO*
Janeet Hill, *President*
Robert Underwood, *Admin Sec*
▼ **EMP:** 10
SQ FT: 14,630
SALES (est): 2.8MM **Privately Held**
WEB: www.foxtronics.com
SIC: 3812 Airspeed instrumentation (aeronautical instruments)

(G-4376)
FR GLOBAL TRADING CO INC
11311 Harry Hines Blvd (75229-3451)
PHONE..............................214 281-8668
◆ **EMP:** 25
SQ FT: 2,500
SALES: 1.5MM **Privately Held**
SIC: 8099 3443 Health Srvcs & Mfg Fabricated Plate Work

(G-4377)
FRANKIE VS KITCHEN LLC
2101 Cedar Springs Rd # 1220 (75201-2164)
PHONE..............................214 303-9910
EMP: 60 **EST:** 2012
SALES (est): 26.1MM **Privately Held**
WEB: www.frankievskitchen.com
SIC: 2035 Seasonings & sauces, except tomato & dry; dressings, salad: raw & cooked (except dry mixes)

(G-4378)
FREEMAN EXPOSITIONS LLC
3801 Adler Dr Ste 150 (75211-1420)
PHONE..............................214 623-1300
Barbara Leschak, *Info Tech Mgr*
Hope Hennessey, *Director*
Jessie Robinson, *Executive*
EMP: 12
SALES (corp-wide): 1.5B **Privately Held**
WEB: www.freeman.com
SIC: 3651 Electronic kits for home assembly: radio, TV, phonograph
HQ: Freeman Expositions, Llc
1600 Viceroy Dr Ste 100
Dallas TX 75235
214 445-1000

(G-4379)
FRITO-LAY NORTH AMERICA INC
1141 Regal Row (75247-3646)
PHONE..............................214 631-8485

Bill Howard, *Department Mgr*
Bob George, *Manager*
Tonya James, *Admin Asst*
Debbie Johnson, *Legal Staff*
EMP: 30
SQ FT: 58,784
SALES (corp-wide): 67.1B **Publicly Held**
WEB: www.fritolay.com
SIC: 2096 2099 Potato chips & similar snacks; food preparations
HQ: Frito-Lay North America, Inc.
7701 Legacy Dr,
Plano TX 75024

(G-4380)
FRITO-LAY NORTH AMERICA INC
3420 Duncanville Rd (75236-1010)
PHONE..............................214 944-5238
Mike Kavavi, *Manager*
EMP: 60
SQ FT: 61,051
SALES (corp-wide): 67.1B **Publicly Held**
WEB: www.fritolay.com
SIC: 2096 8731 2099 Potato chips & other potato-based snacks; commercial physical research; food preparations
HQ: Frito-Lay North America, Inc.
7701 Legacy Dr
Plano TX 75024

(G-4381)
FRITO-LAY NORTH AMERICA INC
Also Called: Dallas Baked Snacks
3548 Duncanville Rd (75236-1012)
PHONE..............................214 331-7000
Jim Smith, *Opers Mgr*
Ned Searles, *Branch Mgr*
EMP: 360
SALES (corp-wide): 67.1B **Publicly Held**
WEB: www.fritolay.com
SIC: 2051 2099 2096 Biscuits, baked: baking powder & raised; food preparations; potato chips & similar snacks
HQ: Frito-Lay North America, Inc.
7701 Legacy Dr
Plano TX 75024

(G-4382)
FRONTIER FIRE SYSTEMS INC
9671 Wendell Rd (75243-5510)
P.O. Box 550365 (75355-0365)
PHONE..............................214 343-9500
EMP: 20 **EST:** 1999
SQ FT: 5,300
SALES (est): 2.7MM **Privately Held**
SIC: 1711 3569 Contractor - Fire Sprinkler Systems Installation Mfg Automatic Fire Sprinkler Systems

(G-4383)
FRONTIER OIL CORPORATION (HQ)
2828 N Harwood St # 1300 (75201-2174)
PHONE..............................214 871-3555
Michael C Jennings, *President*
J Currie Bechtol, *Vice Pres*
Jon D Galvin, *Vice Pres*
Nancy J Zupan, *Vice Pres*
Douglas S Aron, *CFO*
▲ **EMP:** 10
SQ FT: 6,500
SALES (est): 114.4MM
SALES (corp-wide): 17.4B **Publicly Held**
WEB: www.hollyfrontier.com
SIC: 5172 2911 Petroleum products; gasoline
PA: Hollyfrontier Corporation
2828 N Harwood St # 1300
Dallas TX 75201
214 871-3555

(G-4384)
FUJIKOKI AMERICA INC (HQ)
4040 Bronze Way (75237-1081)
PHONE..............................214 333-4266
Takayoshi Yokoyama, *President*
Osamu Inoue, *General Mgr*
Donnie Anderson, *Vice Pres*
Don Glover, *Facilities Mgr*
David Clemons, *Mfg Spvr*
◆ **EMP:** 121
SQ FT: 80,000

SALES (est): 60MM **Privately Held**
WEB: www.fujikoki.us
SIC: 3585 5063 3494 Refrigeration & heating equipment; switches, except electronic; expansion joints pipe

(G-4385)
FUNGOMAN LLC
10840 Switzer Ave Ste 102 (75238-1361)
P.O. Box 29336, Shreveport LA (71149-9336)
PHONE..............................318 775-0000
Romy Cucjen, *President*
Christine Cucjen, *Mktg Dir*
EMP: 17
SALES (est): 2.9MM **Privately Held**
WEB: www.fungoman.com
SIC: 3949 Sporting & athletic goods

(G-4386)
FUTURE FOAM INC
10726 Doric St (75220-2627)
PHONE..............................214 350-6611
Kia Tabibian, *Plant Mgr*
George La Garza, *Mfg Staff*
George Delagarza, *Branch Mgr*
Minh Tran, *Director*
EMP: 51
SALES (corp-wide): 383.5MM **Privately Held**
WEB: www.futurefoam.com
SIC: 3086 Plastics foam products
PA: Future Foam, Inc.
1610 Avenue N
Council Bluffs IA 51501
712 323-9122

(G-4387)
FUTURE FOAM INC
8611 Ambassador Row (75247-4605)
PHONE..............................214 905-6043
Randy Reynolds, *General Mgr*
EMP: 40
SALES (corp-wide): 383.5MM **Privately Held**
WEB: www.futurefoam.com
SIC: 3086 Insulation or cushioning material, foamed plastic
PA: Future Foam, Inc.
1610 Avenue N
Council Bluffs IA 51501
712 323-9122

(G-4388)
G T SOUTHWEST HOSE INC
644 W Mockingbird Ln (75247-6026)
P.O. Box 560545 (75356-0545)
PHONE..............................214 689-4673
Gordon Pendergraft, *President*
Michael Carothers, *General Mgr*
Lee McCullough, *Prdtn Mgr*
Nancy White, *Info Tech Mgr*
EMP: 12
SQ FT: 12,000
SALES (est): 5MM **Privately Held**
WEB: www.gtsouthwest.com
SIC: 4731 3052 Freight forwarding; rubber & plastics hose & beltings

(G-4389)
G W VINES COMPANY INC
3839 Singleton Blvd (75212-3502)
P.O. Box 227416 (75222-7416)
PHONE..............................214 742-8371
Russell Thompson, *President*
William D Thompson, *Vice Pres*
Tish Thompson, *Treasurer*
Joan Tanner, *Admin Sec*
EMP: 40
SALES (est): 3.7MM **Privately Held**
WEB: www.gwvines.com
SIC: 3444 7692 1711 Sheet metal specialties, not stamped; welding repair; mechanical contractor

(G-4390)
G2 AUTOMATED TECHNOLOGIES LLC
10500 Metric Dr Ste 122 (75243-5524)
PHONE..............................972 479-0699
Leigh Griffis, *CEO*
Simon Fang, *President*
Dave Rediger, *General Mgr*
David Rediger, *General Mgr*
Jonathan Lamb, *Accounts Mgr*
◆ **EMP:** 31

SQ FT: 20,000
SALES (est): 7.4MM **Privately Held**
WEB: www.g2automatedtechnologies.com
SIC: **3312** 3499 2542 2599 Stainless
  steel; chair frames, metal; furniture parts,
  metal; partitions & fixtures, except wood;
  cabinets, factory; stools, factory

(G-4391)
**GARRATT-CALLAHAN
COMPANY**
13721 Welch Rd (75244-4521)
PHONE..................................972 661-5006
Cordellia Gard, *Manager*
EMP: 9
SQ FT: 26,153
SALES (corp-wide): 67.3MM **Privately
Held**
WEB: www.g-c.com
SIC: **2899** Water treating compounds
PA: Garratt-Callahan Company
  50 Ingold Rd
  Burlingame CA 94010
  650 697-5811

(G-4392)
GARVON INC (HQ)
Also Called: Caribbean Marine
12015 Shiloh Rd Ste 120 (75228-1551)
PHONE..................................214 691-0711
Patrick Sullivan, *President*
Vergie Berry, *Vice Pres*
EMP: 14
SQ FT: 1,600
SALES (est): 2.5MM
SALES (corp-wide): 2.4MM **Privately
Held**
SIC: **0212** 6531 1311 Beef cattle except
  feedlots; real estate agent, commercial;
  crude petroleum production; natural gas
  production
PA: Caribbean Marine, Inc

  Christiansted VI
  340 773-0289

(G-4393)
**GAS EQUIPMENT COMPANY
INC (HQ)**
11616 Harry Hines Blvd (75229-2203)
P.O. Box 29242 (75229-0242)
PHONE..................................972 241-2333
Milton Ladue III, *President*
M J La Due III, *President*
C K La Due, *Vice Pres*
Brett Roberts, *Opers Mgr*
Debbie Cannon, *Sales Staff*
◆ EMP: 120 EST: 1937
SQ FT: 200,000
SALES (est): 121.4MM
SALES (corp-wide): 130.5MM **Privately
Held**
WEB: www.gasequipment.com
SIC: **5084** 5085 3321 Instruments & con-
  trol equipment; pumps & pumping equip-
  ment; hose, belting & packing; valves &
  fittings; ductile iron castings

(G-4394)
GAVSON INC
Also Called: Gavson Salon Classics
9880 Chartwell Dr (75243-8304)
P.O. Box 551030 (75355-1030)
PHONE..................................214 341-0440
Kevin Gavson, *President*
Marian Shaffer Gavson, *Vice Pres*
Marian Gavson, *Vice Pres*
Dawn Shirley, *Sales Staff*
▲ EMP: 21
SQ FT: 13,000
SALES (est): 2.4MM **Privately Held**
WEB: www.gavsonsalon.com
SIC: **2389** Uniforms & vestments

(G-4395)
GCA PRODUCTS INC
10671 N Stemmons Fwy (75220-2428)
PHONE..................................972 506-3196
Gary Carter, *President*
Hunter Dunlap, *VP Opers*
▲ EMP: 9
SALES (est): 4.5MM **Privately Held**
WEB: www.gcaproducts.com
SIC: **2656** Straws, drinking: made from
  purchased material

(G-4396)
GEM ASSET ACQUISITION LLC
Also Called: Gemseal Pvements Pdts - Dallas
3111 W Saner Ave (75233-1425)
PHONE..................................214 333-4343
EMP: 23
SALES (corp-wide): 127.6MM **Privately
Held**
WEB: www.gemsealproducts.com
SIC: **2951** Asphalt paving mixtures &
  blocks
PA: Gem Asset Acquisition Llc
  3700 Arco Corprt Dr # 425
  Charlotte NC 28273
  704 225-3321

(G-4397)
GEMINI COATINGS INC
7230 C F Hawn Fwy (75217)
PHONE..................................405 262-5710
Scott Rott, *Plant Mgr*
Larry Hunt, *Manager*
Brent Cooksey, *Technical Staff*
EMP: 11
SQ FT: 4,000
SALES (corp-wide): 1.6MM **Privately
Held**
WEB: www.gemini-coatings.com
SIC: **2851** Lacquer: bases, dopes, thinner
HQ: Gemini Coatings, Inc.
  421 Se 27th St
  El Reno OK 73036
  405 262-5710

(G-4398)
GENERAL DATATECH LP
Gdt Manufacturing
1212 Medical District Dr (75207-2302)
PHONE..................................214 857-6194
Tom Garrow, *Branch Mgr*
EMP: 35
SALES (corp-wide): 369.6MM **Privately
Held**
WEB: www.gdt.com
SIC: **3679** Harness assemblies for elec-
  tronic use: wire or cable
PA: General Datatech, L.P.
  999 Metro Media Pl
  Dallas TX 75247
  214 631-5600

(G-4399)
GENERAL ELECTRIC COMPANY
3202 Manor Way (75235-5999)
PHONE..................................214 902-6600
Melissa McPherson, *Human Res Mgr*
Adam McAnally, *Mng Member*
Alicia Scott, *Manager*
Leonard Duncan, *Maintence Staff*
EMP: 90
SALES (corp-wide): 95.2B **Publicly Held**
WEB: www.ge.com
SIC: **3511** Turbines & turbine generator
  sets
PA: General Electric Company
  5 Necco St
  Boston MA 02210
  617 443-3000

(G-4400)
GENERAL ELECTRIC COMPANY
3020 Manor (75235)
PHONE..................................214 902-6600
Adam McAnally, *Manager*
EMP: 80
SALES (corp-wide): 95.2B **Publicly Held**
WEB: www.ge.com
SIC: **7694** 4911 Electric motor repair; elec-
  tric services
PA: General Electric Company
  5 Necco St
  Boston MA 02210
  617 443-3000

(G-4401)
GENMZ LP
2101 Cedar Springs Rd # 1875
(75201-2152)
PHONE..................................214 683-6635
EMP: 10
SALES (est): 201.1K **Privately Held**
SIC: **8732** 7372 Business research serv-
  ice; application computer software

(G-4402)
GENTI STUDIOS INC (PA)
Also Called: City Colour
1825 W Mockingbird Ln (75235-5012)
PHONE..................................214 951-9696
Kiran Genti, *President*
Lorenzo Magdaleno, *VP Opers*
EMP: 41 EST: 1983
SQ FT: 56,000
SALES (est): 8.6MM **Privately Held**
SIC: **7389** 7336 2754 Design services;
  commercial art & graphic design; graphic
  arts & related design; commercial print-
  ing, gravure

(G-4403)
**GEORG FISCHER CENTRAL
PLAS LLC**
4949 Joseph Hardin Dr (75236-1904)
PHONE..................................972 641-2080
Rocky Wade, *Managing Dir*
Elizabeth Latham, *Human Resources*
EMP: 110
SALES (corp-wide): 3.7B **Privately Held**
WEB: www.centralplastics.com
SIC: **3089** Fittings for pipe, plastic
HQ: Georg Fischer Central Plastics Llc
  39605 Independence St
  Shawnee OK 74804
  405 273-6302

(G-4404)
GEORGEJEAN INC
Also Called: Gaby's Shoppe
1311 Dragon St (75207-4007)
PHONE..................................214 748-6644
Jean Astie, *President*
George Asti, *Treasurer*
▲ EMP: 9
SQ FT: 13,500
SALES (est): 1.2MM **Privately Held**
WEB: www.gabys.com
SIC: **3446** Architectural metalwork

(G-4405)
GERBER TECHNOLOGY INC
12225 Grnvlle Ave Ste 900 (75243)
PHONE..................................972 238-7211
EMP: 150
SALES (corp-wide): 277.1MM **Privately
Held**
SIC: **7622** 3552 3541 Radio/Television
  Repair Mfg Textile Machinery Mfg Ma-
  chine Tools-Cutting
HQ: Gerber Technology Llc
  24 Industrial Park Rd W
  Tolland CT 06084
  860 871-8082

(G-4406)
GHM CORP (PA)
12700 Hillcrest Rd Ste C (75230-2161)
P.O. Box 660280 (75266-0280)
PHONE..................................972 840-1200
Guy H Morgan, *President*
Hicks B Morgan, *Corp Secy*
Jeff Glajch, *CFO*
Peter Lewis, *CTO*
Patrick Miller, *Info Tech Mgr*
EMP: 125
SQ FT: 32,000
SALES (est): 147.4MM **Privately Held**
WEB: www.morganusa.com
SIC: **3448** 1799 5999 5561 Buildings,
  portable: prefabricated metal; spa or hot
  tub installation or construction; swimming
  pools, above ground; recreational vehicle
  dealers

(G-4407)
GL AUTOMATION INC
Also Called: G L A
10710 Sandhill Rd (75238-1216)
PHONE..................................214 503-9888
Galle Lin, *President*
Ondat Truong, *General Mgr*
Gonzalo Amador, *Engineer*
Rick McDonald, *Engineer*
Irene Lin, *Bookkeeper*
EMP: 18
SQ FT: 8,000
SALES (est): 3.6MM **Privately Held**
WEB: www.glautomation.com
SIC: **3559** 8742 Semiconductor manufac-
  turing machinery; industry specialist con-
  sultants

(G-4408)
**GLASS MOUNTAIN PIPELINE
LLC**
Also Called: GM Pipeline
2626 Cole Ave Ste 900 (75204-1078)
PHONE..................................214 880-6000
Matthew Vining,
EMP: 30
SALES (est): 745.9K **Privately Held**
SIC: **1382** Oil & gas exploration services

(G-4409)
**GLEN OAKS INDUSTRIES INC
(PA)**
Also Called: Rendevous
1201 Elm St Ste 2500 (75270-2169)
PHONE..................................214 631-1340
Fax: 214 688-0354
▼ EMP: 13 EST: 1928
SQ FT: 100,000
SALES (est): 10.5MM **Privately Held**
SIC: **2325** 5136 Mfg Men's/Boy's Trousers
  Whol Men's/Boy's Clothing

(G-4410)
GLOBAL WATER GROUP INC
Also Called: Global Water Home Systems
8601 Sovereign Row (75247-4613)
PHONE..................................214 678-9866
Alan M Weiss, *President*
Volker Hohmann, *Vice Pres*
EMP: 20
SQ FT: 12,000
SALES (est): 3MM **Privately Held**
WEB: www.globalwater.com
SIC: **4952** 4941 3589 Sewerage systems;
  water supply; water treatment equipment,
  industrial
PA: Eastern Water Resources Develop-
  ment And Management Public Com-
  pany Limited
  1 Soi Vipavadeerangsit 5,
  Vipavadeerangsit Road
  Chatuchak 10900

(G-4411)
GMI STONE LLC
Also Called: Kiva Stone
10574 King William Dr (75220-2411)
PHONE..................................469 360-8847
Sanjay Singh, *CEO*
EMP: 10
SALES (est): 103.6K **Privately Held**
WEB: www.kivastone.com
SIC: **3281** Cut stone & stone products

(G-4412)
GOLDEN PEDIC INC
Also Called: Golden Mattress Co
1240 Titan Dr (75247-3712)
PHONE..................................214 630-5588
Tang Tran, *President*
◆ EMP: 37
SQ FT: 25,000
SALES (est): 6.6MM **Privately Held**
WEB: www.goldenmattressdallas.com
SIC: **2515** Mattresses, innerspring or box
  spring; mattresses & foundations

(G-4413)
GOODRICH CORPORATION
Also Called: Goodrich Wheel and Brake Svcs
9151 King Arthur Dr (75247-3607)
PHONE..................................214 689-9588
Jim Caudill, *Manager*
EMP: 19
SALES (corp-wide): 56.5B **Publicly Held**
WEB: www.collinsaerospace.com
SIC: **3728** Aircraft parts & equipment
HQ: Goodrich Corporation
  2730 W Tyvola Rd
  Charlotte NC 28217
  704 423-7000

(G-4414)
GREAT DANE LLC
Also Called: Great Dane Trailers
4115 Port Blvd (75241-7635)
PHONE..................................214 637-2425
Eddy Sarten, *General Mgr*
EMP: 16
SALES (corp-wide): 811.6MM **Privately
Held**
WEB: www.greatdane.com
SIC: **3715** Truck trailers

HQ: Great Dane Llc
222 N Lasalle St Ste 920
Chicago IL 60601

(G-4415)
GREENPACKS USA
3331 Towerwood Dr Ste 304 (75234-2328)
PHONE..............................888 498-7774
Kunitake Kobayashi, *President*
EMP: 12
SALES (est): 1.9MM **Privately Held**
WEB: www.greenpacksusa.com
SIC: 3053 Packing materials

(G-4416)
GREYHELLER LLC
Also Called: Appsian
8111 Lyndon B Johnson Fwy (75251-1313)
PHONE..............................925 415-5050
Shelley Nelson, *Vice Pres*
Keith Waggoner, *Engineer*
Jim Henderson, *Sales Dir*
Piyush Pandey, *Mng Member*
Mark Martin, *Manager*
EMP: 90
SQ FT: 1,500
SALES (est): 12MM **Privately Held**
WEB: www.appsian.com
SIC: 7372 Prepackaged software

(G-4417)
GROCO PAINT MFG CO INC
10818 C F Hawn Fwy (75217-8057)
P.O. Box 170790 (75217-0790)
PHONE..............................972 286-7890
George W Grogan, *President*
Jimmie Jo Grogan, *Vice Pres*
EMP: 22
SQ FT: 29,000
SALES (est): 4.1MM **Privately Held**
WEB: www.grocosc.com
SIC: 2851 Paints & paint additives

(G-4418)
GROWTH HOLDINGS LLC
Also Called: Signature Millwork
2861 Merrell Rd (75229-4702)
PHONE..............................972 241-9535
Jeff Makohon, *President*
Jeff Maohon, *Mng Member*
EMP: 40
SQ FT: 13,000
SALES (est): 3MM **Privately Held**
WEB: www.signaturemillwork.com
SIC: 2431 2434 2542 5211 Millwork;
wood kitchen cabinets; partitions & fix-
tures, except wood; millwork & lumber;
wood office furniture

(G-4419)
GRUMA CORPORATION
Also Called: Mission Foods
4000 Dan Morton Dr # 100 (75236-1300)
PHONE..............................972 709-1217
German Chavez, *General Mgr*
Jay Desai, *Opers Staff*
Beverly Everett, *Benefits Mgr*
Rosemary Anaya, *Manager*
Horacio Garza, *Manager*
EMP: 500 **Privately Held**
WEB: www.missionfoods.com
SIC: 2096 0723 2099 Tortilla chips; flour
milling custom services; food preparations
HQ: Gruma Corporation
5601 Executive Dr Ste 800
Irving TX 75038
972 232-5000

(G-4420)
**GUARD-ALL BLDG SLTIONS
MFG LLC**
1011 Regal Row (75247-4404)
PHONE..............................877 397-1594
DOT Haymann, *Chairman*
Basil A Haymann, *Senior VP*
Alfredo Davila, *Mfg Staff*
Cori Ponsford, *Purchasing*
Ryan Widger, *Engineer*
EMP: 48
SQ FT: 127,000
SALES (est): 8.6MM **Privately Held**
WEB: www.guard-all.com
SIC: 3448 5039 Prefabricated metal build-
ings; prefabricated buildings

(G-4421)
**GULF COAST WESTERN LLC
(PA)**
14160 Dallas Pkwy (75254-4319)
PHONE..............................972 284-0600
Matthew H Fleeger, *CEO*
John Engel, *Vice Pres*
Beverly Fleeger, *Vice Pres*
Aaron Hoffee, *Vice Pres*
Mark Orbach, *Vice Pres*
EMP: 30 EST: 1970
SQ FT: 12,000
SALES (est): 29.4MM **Privately Held**
WEB: www.gulfcoastwestern.com
SIC: 1382 Oil & gas exploration services

(G-4422)
**GULFSTREAM AEROSPACE
CORP**
8555 Lemmon Ave (75209-2647)
PHONE..............................912 965-3000
Roy Grumman, *Engineer*
Eric Hanson, *Sales Dir*
Grady Ebensberger, *Manager*
John Longbotham, *Manager*
Leanne McIntosh, *Manager*
EMP: 1303
SALES (corp-wide): 37.9B **Publicly Held**
WEB: www.gulfstream.com
SIC: 3721 Aircraft
HQ: Gulfstream Aerospace Corporation
500 Gulfstream Rd
Savannah GA 31408

(G-4423)
**GULFSTREAM AEROSPACE
CORP**
7350 Cedar Springs Rd (75235-2812)
P.O. Box 7145 (75209-0145)
PHONE..............................214 902-7520
Charles Celli, *Manager*
EMP: 1000
SALES (corp-wide): 37.9B **Publicly Held**
WEB: www.gulfstream.com
SIC: 3721 3728 3296 2851 Aircraft; air-
craft parts & equipment; mineral wool;
paints & allied products
HQ: Gulfstream Aerospace Corporation
500 Gulfstream Rd
Savannah GA 31408

(G-4424)
**GULFSTREAM AEROSPACE
CORP GA**
7440 Aviation Pl (75235-2804)
PHONE..............................214 350-4177
EMP: 750
SALES (corp-wide): 37.9B **Publicly Held**
WEB: www.gulfstream.com
SIC: 3721 8711 1721 Airplanes, fixed or
rotary wing; aviation &/or aeronautical en-
gineering; painting & paper hanging
HQ: Gulfstream Aerospace Corporation
(Georgia)
500 Gulfstream Rd
Savannah GA 31408
912 965-3000

(G-4425)
H POWER I LLC
1900 N Akard St (75201-2300)
PHONE..............................214 978-8943
Hunter L Hunt, *Mng Member*
W Kirk Baker, *Manager*
◆ EMP: 90
SALES (est): 3.5MM **Privately Held**
WEB: www.huntoil.com
SIC: 1382 Oil & gas exploration services

(G-4426)
HAASTECH INC
Also Called: Advanced Starter Service
2711 Irving Blvd (75207-2307)
PHONE..............................214 688-0280
Richard William Haas, *President*
EMP: 16 EST: 2017
SALES (est): 1.4MM **Privately Held**
WEB: www.advancedstarter.com
SIC: 3621 5511 Electric motor & generator
parts; new & used car dealers

(G-4427)
HAGGAR WOMENS WEAR LTD
Also Called: Haggar Clothing Co
1507 Lyndon B Johnson Fwy (75234-6088)
PHONE..............................214 637-5300
Edward M Jones III, *President*
Ana Ortega, *Marketing Staff*
▲ EMP: 200 EST: 1964
SALES (est): 9.5MM **Privately Held**
WEB: www.haggar.com
SIC: 2253 Pants, slacks or trousers, knit;
T-shirts & tops, knit
HQ: Haggar Corp.
1507 Lyndon B Johnson Fwy # 100
Farmers Branch TX 75234
214 352-8481

(G-4428)
HALEAUX INC
Also Called: Ingalls Custom Lamps
2025 Irving Blvd Ste 108 (75207-6617)
PHONE..............................214 742-2795
Emanuel Leon, *President*
Owen Greg, *Vice Pres*
Robert Greg Owen, *Vice Pres*
EMP: 16
SQ FT: 7,500
SALES (est): 1.1MM **Privately Held**
SIC: 3229 3645 3999 Lamp parts &
shades, glass; lamp shades, metal; lamp
shade frames

(G-4429)
**HALLIBURTON INTERNATIONAL
INC**
500 N Akard St Ste 3600 (75201-3328)
PHONE..............................214 759-2600
David J Lesar, *CEO*
Gayle Moritz, *Manager*
EMP: 5004
SALES (est): 114K **Publicly Held**
SIC: 1389 1381 Construction, repair & dis-
mantling services; drilling oil & gas wells
HQ: Halliburton Delaware, Inc.
3000 Houston Ave
Houston TX 77009

(G-4430)
**HALLWOOD GROUP
INCORPORATED (HQ)**
10440 N Cntl Expy Ste 240 (75231)
PHONE..............................214 528-5588
▲ EMP: 28 EST: 1981
SALES (est): 408.1MM **Privately Held**
WEB: www.hallwood.com
SIC: 2221 7389 Broadwoven fabric mills,
manmade; textile & apparel services

(G-4431)
HALLWOOD PETROLEUM LLC
Also Called: Hallwood Energy
10440 N Cntl Expy Ste 240 (75231)
PHONE..............................214 528-5588
Anthony J Gumbiner, *CEO*
William L Guzzetti, *President*
Richard Kelley, *Vice Pres*
Tony L Strehlow, *CFO*
Joseph T Koenig, *Treasurer*
EMP: 20
SALES (est): 2MM **Privately Held**
WEB: www.hallwood.com
SIC: 1311 Crude petroleum & natural gas
production

(G-4432)
**HALO BRANDED SOLUTIONS
INC**
Also Called: Harvey Dayco
12801 N Stemmons Fwy # 8 (75234-5835)
PHONE..............................972 536-4069
Ruth Warrick, *Manager*
EMP: 25
SALES (corp-wide): 160MM **Privately
Held**
WEB: www.halo.com
SIC: 3993 8743 Signs & advertising spe-
cialties; sales promotion
PA: Halo Branded Solutions, Inc.
1500 Halo Way
Sterling IL 61081
815 625-0980

(G-4433)
HANSON AGGREGATES LLC
Also Called: Hanson Concrete Truck Maint
1946 California Xing (75220-7006)
PHONE..............................972 556-0735
Tim Morrison, *Branch Mgr*
EMP: 15
SALES (corp-wide): 20.8B **Privately Held**
WEB: www.heidelbergcement.com
SIC: 3272 3273 Concrete products; ready-
mixed concrete
HQ: Hanson Aggregates Llc
8505 Freport Pkwy Ste 500
Irving TX 75063
469 417-1200

(G-4434)
HANSON LEHIGH INC
Also Called: Accounts Payable Department
10620 Coldine Rd (75265)
PHONE..............................281 491-7376
Dana Osburn, *Office Mgr*
Deanna Morrison, *Manager*
Leslie Russell, *Administration*
Raman Vinocha, *Analyst*
EMP: 9
SALES (corp-wide): 20.8B **Privately Held**
WEB: www.lehighhanson.com
SIC: 3273 Ready-mixed concrete
HQ: Hanson Lehigh Inc
300 E John Carpenter Fwy
Irving TX 75062

(G-4435)
**HARDING ENERGY PARTNERS
LLC**
13465 Midway Rd Ste 400 (75244-5106)
PHONE..............................214 723-5112
Steve Carter,
Mike Burnaman,
Rick Harding,
EMP: 15
SALES (est): 1.2MM **Privately Held**
SIC: 1382 Oil & gas exploration services

(G-4436)
**HARMAN PROPERTY SERVICES
LLC**
Also Called: Express Commercial Services
9538 Mossridge Cir (75238-5000)
PHONE..............................469 446-2909
Jim Harman, *President*
EMP: 15
SQ FT: 2,000
SALES (est): 1.9MM **Privately Held**
WEB: www.expresscommercial.com
SIC: 3991 1799 Street sweeping brooms,
hand or machine; cleaning building exteri-
ors

(G-4437)
**HARRIS INDUSTRIES
INCORPORATED**
13355 Noel Rd (75240-6602)
P.O. Box 33477, Kansas City MO (64120-
3477)
PHONE..............................903 759-4485
Mark Casey, *President*
Jill Pratt, *Vice Pres*
EMP: 70
SALES (est): 15.3MM **Privately Held**
WEB: www.harrisindustries.com
SIC: 3321 3599 Gray iron castings; ductile
iron castings; machine shop, jobbing & re-
pair

(G-4438)
HARRISON FABRICATORS INC
3402 E Illinois Ave (75216-3958)
P.O. Box 1412, Hutchins (75141-1412)
PHONE..............................214 374-1684
Marshall Harrison, *President*
Michael Harrison, *Vice Pres*
EMP: 10
SQ FT: 4,200
SALES (est): 225K **Privately Held**
SIC: 1799 7692 3443 Welding on site;
welding repair; boiler shop products: boil-
ers, smokestacks, steel tanks

(G-4439)
**HARVEST NATURAL
RESOURCES INC**
8117 Preston Rd Ste 300 (75225-6347)
PHONE..............................281 899-5700

Stephen D Chesebro, *Ch of Bd*
James A Edmiston, *President*
Robert Speirs, *Senior VP*
Keith L Head, *Vice Pres*
Karl L Nesselrode, *VP Engrg*
▼ **EMP:** 27
SALES (est): 4.8MM **Privately Held**
WEB: www.harvestnr.com
SIC: 1382 Oil & gas exploration services

(G-4440)
HARVEY DUPRIEST & SONS INC
633 Sunnyside Ave (75211-4660)
PHONE.....................214 337-4731
Harvey R Du Priest Jr, *President*
Benny J Du Priest, *Vice Pres*
EMP: 60 **EST:** 2001
SQ FT: 89,000
SALES (est): 8.2MM **Privately Held**
WEB: www.thedupriest.com
SIC: 2759 3993 2396 Screen printing; signs & advertising specialties; automotive & apparel trimmings

(G-4441)
HAWKWOOD ENERGY EAST TEXAS LLC
1999 Bryan St Ste 900 (75201-3140)
PHONE.....................303 823-4175
Patrick R Oenbring, *CEO*
Leonard Gurule, *President*
Matthew O'Neill, *CFO*
EMP: 6993
SALES (est): 357K
SALES (corp-wide): 35MM **Privately Held**
WEB: www.hawkwoodenergy.com
SIC: 1382 Oil & gas exploration services
PA: Hawkwood Energy, Llc
4582 S Ulster St Ste 500
Denver CO 80237
303 823-4175

(G-4442)
HEADINGTON OIL COMPANY
2711 N Haskell Ave # 2800 (75204-2940)
PHONE.....................214 696-0606
Pat L Smith, *Principal*
Julie Ciesielski, *COO*
Jeny Bania, *Vice Pres*
Nick Galen, *Vice Pres*
Nick Seaman, *Vice Pres*
EMP: 20
SALES (est): 1.9MM **Privately Held**
SIC: 1311 Investors

(G-4443)
HEADINGTON OIL LIMITED 1993 LP (PA)
Also Called: Headington Companies
2711 N Haskell Ave # 2800 (75204-2940)
PHONE.....................214 696-0606
Brooks Purnell, *Partner*
Pat Smith, *Partner*
Tim Headington, *General Ptnr*
Michael E Tregoning, *CFO*
R Keith Bunch, *Treasurer*
EMP: 53
SQ FT: 15,000
SALES (est): 35.3MM **Privately Held**
WEB: www.headingtoncompanies.com
SIC: 1311 Crude petroleum production; natural gas production

(G-4444)
HEADINGTRON OIL LP
Also Called: Headington Oil
2711 N Haskell Ave # 2800 (75204-2911)
PHONE.....................214 696-0606
Timothy Headington, *Partner*
Brooks Prennel, *Partner*
Pat Smith, *Partner*
Michael Tregoning, *Partner*
John Ambler, *Vice Pres*
EMP: 60
SQ FT: 22,000
SALES (est): 14.3MM **Privately Held**
SIC: 1311 Crude petroleum production; natural gas production

(G-4445)
HEALTHMARK MEDICAL GROUP LLC
Also Called: Healthmark Group
325 N Saint Paul St # 1650 (75201-3812)
PHONE.....................800 659-4035
Scott Bagley, *Principal*
Chance Turner, *Director*
EMP: 16
SALES (est): 2.5MM **Privately Held**
WEB: www.healthmark-group.com
SIC: 7372 Prepackaged software

(G-4446)
HELEN GORDON INTERESTS LTD
Also Called: The Dallas Greensheet
7929 Brookriver Dr # 350 (75247-4900)
PHONE.....................214 853-6088
Clint Finch, *Sales/Mktg Mgr*
EMP: 100
SALES (corp-wide): 62.3MM **Privately Held**
WEB: www.thegreensheet.com
SIC: 2711 Newspapers: publishing only, not printed on site
PA: Helen Gordon Interests, Ltd.
2020 North Loop W Ste 220
Houston TX 77018
713 371-3500

(G-4447)
HELENS HEART LLC
Also Called: Helen's Heart and Vienna Prom
13628 Beta Rd Ste A (75244-4531)
PHONE.....................972 247-1414
Terry Jeffreys, *Mng Member*
Jimme Huang,
Helen Zheng,
▲ **EMP:** 12 **EST:** 2005
SQ FT: 10,000
SALES (est): 4.2MM **Privately Held**
WEB: www.helensheart.com
SIC: 2339 Women's & misses' accessories

(G-4448)
HEMPEL (USA) INC
2728 Empire Central (75235-4409)
PHONE.....................214 353-1600
Jeffrey Powell, *Exec VP*
Ronaldo Nicolas, *Manager*
EMP: 160
SQ FT: 5,000
SALES (corp-wide): 1.8MM **Privately Held**
WEB: www.north-america.hempel.com
SIC: 2851 Paints & paint additives; marine paints; lacquers, varnishes, enamels & other coatings
HQ: Hempel (Usa), Inc.
600 Conroe Park North Dr
Conroe TX 77303
936 523-6000

(G-4449)
HENRY OIL LC
Also Called: John Henry Petroleum
8117 Preston Rd Ste 300 (75225-6347)
PHONE.....................214 696-5150
Donald John Henry, *President*
EMP: 12
SQ FT: 5,000
SALES (est): 1.9MM **Privately Held**
WEB: www.jhpenergy.com
SIC: 1382 Oil & gas exploration services

(G-4450)
HENSLEY INDUSTRIES INC (DH)
Also Called: Hensley Attachments
2108 Joe Field Rd (75229-3255)
P.O. Box 29779 (75229-0779)
PHONE.....................972 241-2321
Hidekichi Kuribayashi, *President*
Albert Vega, *General Mgr*
H Shinozuka, *Chairman*
Ralph Huebner, *Exec VP*
K Tatsumikawa, *Vice Pres*
◆ **EMP:** 425
SALES (est): 135.4MM **Privately Held**
WEB: www.hensleyind.com
SIC: 3531 Construction machinery

(G-4451)
HEP EL DORADO LLC
2828 N Harwood St # 1300 (75201-1518)
PHONE.....................214 871-3555
EMP: 13
SALES (est): 1.1MM
SALES (corp-wide): 17.4B **Publicly Held**
WEB: www.hollyenergy.com
SIC: 1311 Crude petroleum & natural gas
HQ: Holly Energy Partners, L.P.
2828 N Harwood St # 1300
Dallas TX 75201
214 871-3555

(G-4452)
HEREFORD BIOFUELS LP
4100 Spring Valley Rd (75244-3629)
PHONE.....................972 980-7159
Robert W Carter,
Natasha Ray,
EMP: 60
SALES (est): 3.3MM **Privately Held**
SIC: 2869 8731 Ethyl alcohol, ethanol; energy research

(G-4453)
HERMAN MILLER INC
2811 Mckinney Ave Ste 20 (75204-8563)
PHONE.....................214 855-0200
Jesse Garcia, *Branch Mgr*
EMP: 10
SALES (corp-wide): 2.4B **Publicly Held**
WEB: www.hermanmiller.com
SIC: 2521 2522 2541 2542 Wood office furniture; office furniture, except wood; wood partitions & fixtures; partitions & fixtures, except wood; public building & related furniture
PA: Herman Miller, Inc.
855 E Main Ave
Zeeland MI 49464
616 654-3000

(G-4454)
HFS HOLDING CORPORATION (PA)
Also Called: Hospital Forms & Systems
8900 Ambassador Row (75247-4510)
PHONE.....................214 634-8600
Peter A Pyhrr, *President*
Kim Orlando, *Accountant*
Tom Helenbrook, *Manager*
Michael Martin, *Director*
EMP: 14
SQ FT: 25,000
SALES (est): 114.9MM **Privately Held**
WEB: www.hforms.com
SIC: 2679 5112 2675 Labels, paper: made from purchased material; business forms; die-cut paper & board

(G-4455)
HI-CRUSH PERMIAN SAND LLC
1999 Bryan St Ste 900 (75201-3140)
PHONE.....................713 960-4777
J Philip McCormick Jr,
EMP: 33
SALES (est): 342.5K **Privately Held**
SIC: 1442 Sand mining
PA: Hi-Crush Inc.
1330 Post Oak Blvd # 600
Houston TX 77056

(G-4456)
HI-TECH PRCOUS MTLS RFNERY LLC (PA)
13620 Gamma Rd (75244-4406)
PHONE.....................972 239-0597
Mike Charori, *Opers Mgr*
Abe Hamideh, *Opers Staff*
Nadim Shabout, *Engineer*
Shelby Laney, *Cust Mgr*
Ashley Quariab,
▲ **EMP:** 21 **EST:** 2007
SALES (est): 2.7MM **Privately Held**
WEB: www.hitechpmr.com
SIC: 3339 Precious metals

(G-4457)
HILITE INDUSTRIES INC
990 S Saint Paul St (75120-6120)
P.O. Box 814649 (75381-4649)
PHONE.....................972 242-2116
Art D Johnson, *Principal*
Lakreece Allen, *Manager*

Bryan Holman, *Info Tech Mgr*
EMP: 20 **Privately Held**
WEB: www.pittsindustries.com
SIC: 3714 Motor vehicle parts & accessories
HQ: Hilite Industries Inc
1671 S Broadway St
Carrollton TX 75006
972 242-2116

(G-4458)
HILL PRINT SOLUTIONS LTD
915 S Peak St (75223-2849)
PHONE.....................214 826-0092
Jolene Hill, *President*
John Whisnant, *President*
Michael Hill, *Manager*
Gregg Hill, *Admin Sec*
EMP: 10 **EST:** 1925
SQ FT: 30,000
SALES (est): 1.8MM **Privately Held**
WEB: www.hillprintsolutions.com
SIC: 2752 2732 2754 Commercial printing, offset; book printing; commercial printing, gravure

(G-4459)
HILLTOP ENERGY LLC (PA)
4925 Grnvlle Ave Ste 1200 (75206)
PHONE.....................972 686-0369
EMP: 10 **EST:** 1978
SALES (est): 15.8MM **Privately Held**
WEB: www.smarterenergy360.com
SIC: 1382 Oil & gas exploration services

(G-4460)
HISPANIC FMLY CHRSTN NTWRK INC
Also Called: La Nueva 106.5 FM
8330 Lyndon B Johnson Fwy (75243-1166)
PHONE.....................214 331-2800
Maria C Guel, *President*
EMP: 10
SALES (est): 419K **Privately Held**
SIC: 3663 Radio broadcasting & communications equipment

(G-4461)
HOFFMAN CONTROLS CORP
2463 Merrell Rd (75229-4543)
PHONE.....................972 243-7425
EMP: 31
SQ FT: 8,300
SALES (est): 4.8MM **Privately Held**
WEB: www.hoffmancontrols.com
SIC: 3823 Industrial instrmnts msrmnt display/control process variable; on-stream gas/liquid analysis instruments, industrial

(G-4462)
HOLLYFRONTIER CORPORATION (PA)
2828 N Harwood St # 1300 (75201-1518)
PHONE.....................214 871-3555
Franklin Myers, *Ch of Bd*
Michael C Jennings, *President*
Thomas G Creery, *Senior VP*
James M Stump, *Senior VP*
Tom Creery, *Vice Pres*
EMP: 380
SQ FT: 60,000
SALES (est): 17.4B **Publicly Held**
WEB: www.hollyfrontier.com
SIC: 2911 4613 Petroleum refining; gasoline; jet fuels; diesel fuels; refined petroleum pipelines

(G-4463)
HOLLYFRONTIER REF & MKTG LLC (HQ)
2828 N Harwood St # 1300 (75201-1518)
PHONE.....................214 871-3555
Michael C Jennings, *Ch of Bd*
George J Damiris, *Senior VP*
Denise S McWatters, *Senior VP*
James M Stump, *Senior VP*
Marie Perry, *Vice Pres*
▼ **EMP:** 114
SALES (est): 200.1MM
SALES (corp-wide): 17.4B **Publicly Held**
WEB: www.hollyfrontier.com
SIC: 4612 2911 Crude petroleum pipelines; gasoline

PA: Hollyfrontier Corporation
2828 N Harwood St # 1300
Dallas TX 75201
214 871-3555

(G-4464)
HOLLYWOOD OVRHD DOOR OF DALLAS (PA)
Also Called: South Wstn Stl Rolling Door Co
9525 White Rock Trl (75238-2556)
PHONE..................................214 348-7240
Jack Pierce, *Exec VP*
Larry Freed, *CIO*
Pierce Pat, *Director*
▲ EMP: 37
SQ FT: 40,000
SALES (est): 6.4MM **Privately Held**
WEB: www.hollywoodohd.com
SIC: 5211 5031 3442 3429 Garage doors, sale & installation; doors, garage; metal doors, sash & trim; manufactured hardware (general)

(G-4465)
HONEYWELL INTERNATIONAL INC
10318 Markison Rd (75238-1648)
PHONE..................................972 896-0004
Scot Skinner, *Branch Mgr*
EMP: 84
SALES (corp-wide): 36.7B **Publicly Held**
WEB: www.honeywell.com
SIC: 3724 Aircraft engines & engine parts
PA: Honeywell International Inc.
300 S Tryon St
Charlotte NC 28202
704 627-6200

(G-4466)
HOPE AGRI PRODUCTS INC
Also Called: Hope Agri Products of Texas
4930 River Oaks Rd (75241-7704)
PHONE..................................214 371-7120
Tom Duncan, *Manager*
EMP: 12
SQ FT: 6,450
SALES (corp-wide): 4.9MM **Privately Held**
WEB: www.oldcastlelogistics.com
SIC: 2875 5083 Potting soil, mixed; landscaping equipment
PA: Hope Agri Products, Inc.
2400 S Main St
Hope AR 71801
870 777-2200

(G-4467)
HOPEWELL OPERATING INC (PA)
4600 Greenville Ave # 200 (75206-5037)
PHONE..................................214 691-6216
Michael Shelby, *President*
EMP: 12
SALES (est): 2.4MM **Privately Held**
SIC: 1311 Crude petroleum production

(G-4468)
HOUSTON BUSINESS JOURNALS INC
Dallas Business Journal
2515 Mckinney Ave (75201-1908)
PHONE..................................214 696-5959
Susan Parker, *Business Mgr*
Rachel McCarty, *Advt Staff*
EMP: 50
SALES (corp-wide): 5B **Privately Held**
WEB: www.discountednewspapers.com
SIC: 2711 Newspapers, publishing & printing; newspapers: publishing only, not printed on site
HQ: Houston Business Journals Inc
5444 Westheimr Rd # 1000
Houston TX 77056
713 688-8811

(G-4469)
HOWMET AEROSPACE INC
8740 John Carpenter Fwy (75247-4626)
PHONE..................................214 631-0200
Mike Phillips, *Branch Mgr*
EMP: 135
SALES (corp-wide): 14.1B **Publicly Held**
WEB: www.howmet.com
SIC: 3353 Aluminum sheet & strip

PA: Howmet Aerospace Inc.
201 Isabella St Ste 200
Pittsburgh PA 15212
412 553-1940

(G-4470)
HUFCOR INC
454 W Mockingbird Ln (75247-6614)
PHONE..................................972 850-2200
Lorrie Shelton, *Office Mgr*
Jason Edmonson, *Branch Mgr*
Randy Wheeler, *Manager*
EMP: 15
SALES (corp-wide): 233.7MM **Privately Held**
WEB: www.hufcor.com
SIC: 2542 3442 Partitions for floor attachment, prefabricated: except wood; metal doors, sash & trim
PA: Hufcor, Inc.
2101 Kennedy Rd
Janesville WI 53545
608 756-1241

(G-4471)
HUNT NLSON BNKER TRUST ESTT-T (PA)
3811 Trtl Crk Blvd (75219-4693)
PHONE..................................214 979-9072
Carroll Huntress, *Trustee*
EMP: 15 EST: 1935
SALES (est): 1MM **Privately Held**
SIC: 1382 1311 Oil & gas exploration services; crude petroleum production

(G-4472)
HUNT DOMINION CORPORATION (PA)
1601 Elm St Ste 3900 (75201-4708)
PHONE..................................214 880-8400
Bruce Hunt, *President*
Alan Bain, *Vice Pres*
Tom Nelson, *Vice Pres*
Steve Chisler, *Opers Mgr*
Justin Shepherd, *Engineer*
EMP: 120
SQ FT: 15,000
SALES (est): 192.9MM **Privately Held**
WEB: www.petrohunt.com
SIC: 1311 1382 1241 Crude petroleum production; natural gas production; oil & gas exploration services; coal mining services

(G-4473)
HUNT EXPLORATION MINING CO
Also Called: Hemco
1601 Elm St Ste 3650 (75201-7275)
PHONE..................................214 979-9072
Chuck Middlekauf, *President*
▲ EMP: 14
SALES (est): 2.1MM **Privately Held**
WEB: www.huntoil.com
SIC: 1382 Oil & gas exploration services

(G-4474)
HUNT MARCELLUS LLC
1900 N Akard St (75201-2300)
PHONE..................................214 978-8000
Paul Habenicht, *President*
Diane Prier, *General Mgr*
Dennis Grindinger, *Senior VP*
Travis Armayor, *Vice Pres*
Bruce Cope, *Vice Pres*
EMP: 20
SALES (est): 861.2K **Privately Held**
WEB: www.huntoil.com
SIC: 1382 Oil & gas exploration services

(G-4475)
HUNT OIL COMPANY
Also Called: Lamar Ranch
1900 N Akard St (75201-2300)
PHONE..................................214 978-8000
Mark Gunnin, *President*
Mike N Bierman, *Managing Dir*
Mark Wagley, *Superintendent*
Hunter L Hunt, *Chairman*
Steve Suellentrop, *Chairman*
EMP: 28
SALES (est): 20.4MM
SALES (corp-wide): 5.3B **Privately Held**
WEB: www.huntoil.com
SIC: 1382 Oil & gas exploration services

HQ: Hunt Oil Usa, Inc.
1900 N Akard St
Dallas TX 75201
214 978-8000

(G-4476)
HVAC CORROSION TECH LLC
Also Called: Corrotec
12160 Abrams Rd Ste 610 (75243-4533)
PHONE..................................214 790-9609
Ronn Croston, *President*
Wouter Scheffer, *COO*
Virginia Sue Smith, *CFO*
EMP: 10
SQ FT: 10,000
SALES (est): 465.8K **Privately Held**
SIC: 2851 Coating, air curing

(G-4477)
HYDROTEX HOLDINGS INC
12920 Senlac Dr Ste 190 (75234-9237)
PHONE..................................972 389-8500
John Beasley, *President*
Phil Kramer, *President*
Chuck Bailey, *Partner*
John Cummins, *Vice Pres*
Bill Dewberry, *Vice Pres*
EMP: 65
SQ FT: 20,000
SALES (est): 13.9MM **Privately Held**
WEB: www.hydrotexlube.com
SIC: 2992 Oils & greases, blending & compounding; lubricating oils

(G-4478)
HYPERION ENERGY LP (PA)
12377 Merit Dr Ste 1200 (75251-2248)
PHONE..................................214 750-3820
Bruce Thompson, *President*
Legacy Resources LP, *Partner*
Miro Vranac, *CFO*
EMP: 12
SQ FT: 12,000
SALES (est): 12.8MM **Privately Held**
WEB: www.hyperionoil.com
SIC: 1311 6726 6531 Crude petroleum production; natural gas production; investment offices; real estate agents & managers

(G-4479)
HYPERION RESOURCES INC
5910 N Central Expy # 1520 (75206-5125)
PHONE..................................214 750-1522
Robert Bruce Thompson, *President*
Bob Ankerd, *Vice Pres*
Miro Vranac, *CFO*
EMP: 12
SQ FT: 7,500
SALES (est): 1MM **Privately Held**
WEB: www.hyperionoil.com
SIC: 1311 6531 6722 Crude petroleum production; real estate agents & managers; management investment, openend
PA: Legacy Investments, Inc.
12377 Merit Dr Ste 1200
Dallas TX 75251

(G-4480)
HYPHEN SOLUTIONS LLC (PA)
Also Called: Michaelholigan.com
1507 Lyndon B Johnson Fwy (75234-6088)
PHONE..................................972 728-8100
John Ballard, *President*
Clay K Deniger, *Partner*
Michael Holigan, *Partner*
Felix Vasquez, *Partner*
David B Deniger, *General Ptnr*
EMP: 53
SALES (est): 12.1MM **Privately Held**
WEB: www.hyphensolutions.com
SIC: 7372 Application computer software

(G-4481)
I&G DESIGNS AND LOGISTICS LLC
Also Called: Fashionit
14114 Dallas Pkwy Ste 420 (75254-1303)
P.O. Box 260111, Plano (75026-0111)
PHONE..................................214 543-4461
Annabel Inbal Wolman, *Owner*
Lawrence Hirson,
▲ EMP: 10 EST: 2010
SQ FT: 2,000

SALES (est): 3.2MM **Privately Held**
WEB: www.justfashionit.com
SIC: 2339 Women's & misses' accessories

(G-4482)
I2 TECHNOLOGIES INC (DH)
11701 Luna Rd (75234-6072)
PHONE..................................469 357-1000
Jackson L Wilson Jr, *CEO*
Raymond B Greer, *President*
Hiten D Varia, *Exec VP*
John Harvey, *Senior VP*
Nancy J Litzler, *Senior VP*
EMP: 42
SALES (est): 62MM
SALES (corp-wide): 305.8MM **Privately Held**
SIC: 7372 Business oriented computer software

(G-4483)
IACX ENERGY LLC (PA)
5001 Lyndon B Johnson Fwy (75244-6120)
PHONE..................................972 960-3210
Jeff Lee, *Vice Pres*
Loran Zimmerman, *Vice Pres*
Russell Gibbs, *Opers Staff*
Michael Sutton, *Engineer*
Cody Compton, *CFO*
EMP: 11
SALES (est): 250MM **Privately Held**
WEB: www.iacx.com
SIC: 1311 1541 Natural gas production; factory construction

(G-4484)
ICON OILFIELD SERVICES LLC (PA)
5950 Berkshire Ln # 1401 (75225-5857)
PHONE..................................214 758-0315
EMP: 13
SALES (est): 6MM **Privately Held**
SIC: 1389 Oil/Gas Field Services

(G-4485)
IFCO SYSTEMS NORTH AMERICA INC
Also Called: Palex
6909 Harry Hines Blvd (75235-4212)
PHONE..................................214 637-4840
EMP: 60 **Privately Held**
SIC: 2448 Mfg Wood Pallets/Skids

(G-4486)
IMAGE CONCRETE INC
2030 Walnut Hill Ln (75229-3154)
P.O. Box 1693, Roanoke (76262-1693)
PHONE..................................817 430-0339
Vaughn Proffitt, *President*
Annette Proffitt, *Vice Pres*
EMP: 30
SQ FT: 1,500
SALES (est): 4.5MM **Privately Held**
SIC: 3273 Ready-mixed concrete

(G-4487)
IMAGE IMPRINTING INC
2675 Freewood Dr (75220-2510)
PHONE..................................972 243-8125
John Barr, *President*
EMP: 37
SALES (est): 1.6MM **Privately Held**
WEB: www.imageofdallas.com
SIC: 2759 Screen printing

(G-4488)
IMAGE TYPE CORPORATION
1601 Prudential Dr (75235-4214)
PHONE..................................214 956-9050
Phil Winstead, *President*
Luis Gonzalez, *Project Mgr*
Ariel Seitz, *Sales Staff*
Dan Glenn, *Info Tech Dir*
▲ EMP: 12
SQ FT: 4,000
SALES (est): 1.8MM **Privately Held**
WEB: www.itc-cuttingedge.com
SIC: 2791 Typesetting

(G-4489)
IMAGERY MARKETING DESIGN INC
Also Called: AlphaGraphics
2372 Irving Blvd (75207-6002)
PHONE..................................817 576-3735

Barbara Adams, *President*
Ken Adams, *Vice Pres*
EMP: 10
SQ FT: 6,700
SALES (est): 2.5MM **Privately Held**
WEB: www.agnortheast.com
SIC: 2752 Commercial printing, litho-
graphic

(G-4490)
IMAGINATION STATION INC
Also Called: Istation
8150 N Cntrl Expy # 2000 (75206-1815)
PHONE....................214 237-9300
EMP: 12 **EST:** 2011
SALES (est): 930K **Privately Held**
SIC: 7372 Prepackaged Software Services

(G-4491)
IMAGING PRODUCTS CORP
Also Called: Buzz Print
1850 Empire Central (75235-4202)
PHONE....................214 631-8899
Robin Burns, *President*
Amy Berry, *Vice Pres*
Paul Foley, *Vice Pres*
Robert C Foley, *CFO*
Irene Foley, *Admin Sec*
EMP: 10
SQ FT: 15,000
SALES (est): 3MM **Privately Held**
WEB: www.buzprint.com
SIC: 2752 7334 Commercial printing, off-
set; photocopying & duplicating services

(G-4492)
IMMUNOTEK BIO CENTERS LLC
8989 Forest Ln Ste 100 (75243-4159)
PHONE....................214 453-2748
Maritza Belin, *Manager*
EMP: 21
SALES (corp-wide): 27MM **Privately
Held**
WEB: www.immunotek.com
SIC: 2836 Blood derivatives
PA: Immunotek Bio Centers, L.L.C.
3900 N Causeway Blvd # 1200
Metairie LA 70002
337 500-1175

(G-4493)
IMMUNOTEK BIO CENTERS LLC
1080 N Westmoreland Rd (75211-2444)
PHONE....................404 345-3570
Jerome Parnell III, *Branch Mgr*
EMP: 15
SALES (corp-wide): 27MM **Privately
Held**
WEB: www.immunotek.com
SIC: 2836 Blood derivatives
PA: Immunotek Bio Centers, L.L.C.
3900 N Causeway Blvd # 1200
Metairie LA 70002
337 500-1175

(G-4494)
IMPACT PRINTING & GRAPHICS
2618 Perth St (75220-1318)
PHONE....................214 904-0808
Marc P Freedman, *Partner*
Lacie Rowan, *Assistant*
▲ **EMP:** 13
SQ FT: 17,600
SALES (est): 2.3MM **Privately Held**
WEB: www.impactprinting.biz
SIC: 2752 Commercial printing, offset

(G-4495)
INCONGRUITY LLC
539 W Commerce St (75208-1953)
PHONE....................954 889-6854
Mike Boudet, *President*
EMP: 10
SALES (est): 441.8K **Privately Held**
SIC: 2741

(G-4496)
INFOR (US) LLC
Also Called: Peopleanswers
14185 Dallas Pkwy Ste 550 (75254-4332)
PHONE....................800 915-3243
Charles Cagle, *Vice Pres*
Larry Wright, *Engineer*
Kelley Taylor, *Marketing Mgr*
Holly Williams, *Sr Project Mgr*
Alyson Schneller, *Program Mgr*

EMP: 188
SALES (corp-wide): 36.8B **Privately Held**
WEB: www.infor.com
SIC: 7372 Application computer software
HQ: Infor (Us), Llc
641 Ave Of The Americas
New York NY 10011
866 244-5479

(G-4497)
INFRATECH INC
10440 Miller Rd (75238-1210)
PHONE....................214 503-1087
Chao T Tang, *President*
MEI H Lee, *Corp Secy*
Y Lee, *Vice Pres*
EMP: 12
SQ FT: 6,300
SALES (est): 1.8MM **Privately Held**
SIC: 3679 Electronic circuits

(G-4498)
**INFUSED MEDICAL
TECHNOLOGY INC**
4559 S Westmoreland Rd (75237-1015)
PHONE....................214 330-4000
Patricia Henderson, *CEO*
Darren Henderson, *President*
Franklin Hunter, *CFO*
EMP: 12
SQ FT: 4,500 **Privately Held**
WEB: www.infusedmedical.com
SIC: 3841 Surgical & medical instruments

(G-4499)
INGAMIA INC
Also Called: Helena & Harry The IV
4949 Beeman Ave (75223-3012)
PHONE....................214 828-1660
Susan Ingram, *President*
EMP: 13
SQ FT: 11,000
SALES (est): 1.4MM **Privately Held**
SIC: 2311 2361 5137 2369 Men's &
boys' suits & coats; coats, tailored, men's
& boys': from purchased materials; girls'
& children's dresses, blouses & shirts;
dresses: girls', children's & infants'; chil-
dren's goods; coats: girls', children's & in-
fants'

(G-4500)
INKJET PARTNERS INC
Also Called: Inkjet International
4443 Simonton Rd (75244-5214)
PHONE....................972 991-4577
Jittu Sarna, *President*
Alok Sarna, *Exec VP*
Shirley Sarna, *Exec VP*
▲ **EMP:** 27
SQ FT: 48,500
SALES (est): 5MM **Privately Held**
WEB: www.inkjetintl.com
SIC: 2759 3993 Commercial printing;
signs & advertising specialties

(G-4501)
INNOSYNC INC
13111 N Central Expy (75243-1138)
P.O. Box 833639, Richardson (75083-
3639)
PHONE....................972 644-7962
Eric Sczepanik, *President*
Larry Johnson, *VP Opers*
EMP: 27
SQ FT: 14,000
SALES (est): 2MM **Privately Held**
SIC: 3674 7373 1731 Semiconductors &
related devices; systems software devel-
opment services; electrical work

(G-4502)
**INNOVATIVE MACHINE & LASER
LLC**
3131 Winnequah St (75212-3031)
PHONE....................214 330-1141
Chris Williams, *Managing Prtnr*
Chris Lewis, *Project Mgr*
Kevin G Moore, *Mng Member*
Kim H Smith,
EMP: 32
SALES (est): 6.8MM **Privately Held**
WEB: www.iml-mfg.com
SIC: 3499 Fire- or burglary-resistive prod-
ucts

(G-4503)
**INNOVATIVE MILLWORK
SYSTEMS**
11319 Tantor Rd A (75229-3143)
PHONE....................972 869-9892
Deborah Sutton, *President*
Mark Sutton, *Vice Pres*
Lloyd Hagler, *Project Mgr*
EMP: 40
SQ FT: 10,000
SALES (est): 6MM **Privately Held**
WEB: www.innovativemillworksystems.com
SIC: 1751 2431 Cabinet & finish carpen-
try; millwork

(G-4504)
**INOVAR PACKAGING GROUP
LLC (HQ)**
Also Called: DOT-It Restaurant Fulfillment
10470 Miller Rd (75238-1210)
PHONE....................817 277-6666
John Attayek, *CEO*
Robin Hamilton, *Vice Pres*
Brent Steineman, *Vice Pres*
Megan Rosenow, *Opers Staff*
Ross Owen, *Buyer*
◆ **EMP:** 12
SQ FT: 42,000
SALES (est): 16.4MM
SALES (corp-wide): 3.1B **Privately Held**
WEB: www.inovarpackaging.com
SIC: 2759 3086 5963 Labels & seals:
printing; packaging & shipping materials,
foamed plastic; home related products, di-
rect sales
PA: Aea Investors Lp
666 5th Ave Fl 36
New York NY 10103
212 644-5900

(G-4505)
**INTEGRATED ROADWAY SVCS
INC**
11300 Kline Dr (75229-3108)
P.O. Box 540128 (75354-0128)
PHONE....................214 352-1937
Seyed M Mirtaheri, *President*
David Mirtaheri, *President*
Smith Andy, *Opers Mgr*
Conrad Alagaban, *Controller*
Christian Lemus, *Manager*
EMP: 25
SQ FT: 1,620
SALES (est): 5.4MM **Privately Held**
WEB: www.integratedroadway.com
SIC: 3669 Traffic signals, electric

(G-4506)
INTERLAKE MECALUX INC
12301 N Stemmons Fwy # 110
(75234-5825)
PHONE....................972 245-3910
Nancy Peterson, *Accounts Exec*
Miguel Lopez, *Manager*
Miquel Lopez, *Manager*
Amy Martinez,
EMP: 30
SALES (corp-wide): 9.9MM **Privately
Held**
WEB: www.interlakemecalux.com
SIC: 5084 2542 Materials handling ma-
chinery; partitions & fixtures, except wood
HQ: Interlake Mecalux, Inc.
1600 N 25th Ave
Melrose Park IL 60160

(G-4507)
**INTERSTATE BATTERIES INC
(HQ)**
12770 Merit Dr Ste 300 (75251-1402)
PHONE....................972 991-1444
Scott Miller, *President*
Bobby McClain, *Principal*
Brandon Spencer, *Business Mgr*
Dale Herold, *Vice Pres*
Walt Holmes, *Vice Pres*
◆ **EMP:** 120 **EST:** 2013
SALES (est): 268.2MM **Privately Held**
WEB: www.interstatebatteries.com
SIC: 5531 3694 Batteries, automotive &
truck; battery charging alternators & gen-
erators

(G-4508)
INTERSTATE FITTINGS INC (PA)
2200 Singleton Blvd (75212-3732)
P.O. Box 224429 (75222-4429)
PHONE....................214 637-6720
EMP: 78 **EST:** 1973
SQ FT: 20,000
SALES (est): 12.9MM **Privately Held**
WEB: www.interstatethreadedproducts.com
SIC: 3312 3356 Bars & bar shapes, steel,
cold-finished: own hot-rolled; bars & bar
shapes, steel, hot-rolled; bars, iron: made
in steel mills; nonferrous rolling & drawing

(G-4509)
INTRAPACK CORPORATION
10650 Markison Rd (75238-1654)
PHONE....................214 348-7105
Tracy L Zaffino, *President*
Leslie Rettig, *Buyer*
Ryan Peck, *Engineer*
Tina M Harrison, *Controller*
Rochelle Jones, *Controller*
▲ **EMP:** 50
SQ FT: 34,362
SALES (est): 11MM **Privately Held**
WEB: www.intrapack.com
SIC: 3679 1731 2542 Power supplies, all
types: static; computer installation; parti-
tions & fixtures, except wood

(G-4510)
INTRAPACK INDUSTRIES INC
10650 Markison Rd (75238-1654)
PHONE....................214 348-7105
▲ **EMP:** 20 **EST:** 1986
SQ FT: 20,000
SALES (est): 6.3MM **Privately Held**
WEB: www.intrapack.com
SIC: 3444 Sheet metalwork

(G-4511)
INVOLTA LLC
15770 Dallas Pkwy # 1100 (75248-3329)
PHONE....................817 937-8943
David Kramer, *Manager*
EMP: 15
SALES (corp-wide): 39.1MM **Privately
Held**
WEB: www.medcoiowa.org
SIC: 7379 7371 7372 ; computer soft-
ware development & applications; busi-
ness oriented computer software
PA: Involta, Llc
460 12th Ave Se Ste 100
Cedar Rapids IA 52401
319 261-3000

(G-4512)
IREO REPRODUCTIONS LLC
Also Called: Dupriest Company The
633 Sunnyside Ave (75211-4660)
PHONE....................214 337-4731
EMP: 20 **EST:** 2011
SALES (est): 468.1K **Privately Held**
WEB: www.thedupriest.com
SIC: 7822 2759 Motion picture & tape dis-
tribution; commercial printing

(G-4513)
**ISENBERG BATH
CORPORATION**
11927 Mustang Rd Ste 100 (75234)
P.O. Box 630283, Irving (75063-0116)
PHONE....................888 342-2284
Prakhar Jain, *Engineer*
Abbas Poonawala, *Manager*
Leslie Garza, *Associate*
▲ **EMP:** 17
SALES (est): 674.7K **Privately Held**
WEB: www.isenbergfaucets.com
SIC: 3432 Plumbing fixture fittings & trim

(G-4514)
**ISTICK CAPITAL MANAGEMENT
LLC**
600 N Pearl St Ste S226 (75201-2822)
P.O. Box 191289 (75219-8289)
PHONE....................214 231-4000
Chad Willis, *CEO*
Brandi Van Loon, *Opers Staff*
Chris Athens, *Finance*
EMP: 20

SALES (est): 1.8MM **Privately Held**
WEB: www.istickcapital.com
SIC: 3533 Oil & gas drilling rigs & equip-

(G-4515)
ITT LLC
10661 Newkirk St (75220-2303)
PHONE..................................469 221-1200
Laura Kindred, *Branch Mgr*
John Swanson, *Director*
EMP: 58
SALES (corp-wide): 2.8B **Publicly Held**
WEB: www.itt.com
SIC: 3561 Pumps & pumping equipment
HQ: Itt Llc
    1133 Westchester Ave N-100
    White Plains NY 10604
    914 641-2000

(G-4516)
J & L PARTNERS
Also Called: Rite Weld Supply
4246 Woodfin Dr (75220-6416)
P.O. Box 700397 (75370-0397)
PHONE..................................972 417-3977
Carolyn Huckabee, *President*
EMP: 49 EST: 1944
SQ FT: 4,000
SALES (est): 2.3MM **Privately Held**
WEB: www.jlbpartners.com
SIC: 1311 5084 Crude petroleum & natu-
ral gas production; welding machinery &
equipment

(G-4517)
**J CLEO THMPSON JMES CLEO
THMP**
325 N Saint Paul St # 4300 (75201-3801)
PHONE..................................432 550-8887
James C Thompson, *Principal*
Linda Gordon, *Vice Pres*
EMP: 11
SALES (est): 389.9K **Privately Held**
WEB: www.lynnllp.com
SIC: 1311 Natural gas production

(G-4518)
J D DOCUMENTS INC
17130 Dallas Pkwy Ste 115 (75248-1175)
PHONE..................................972 733-1080
Don Ledbetter, *President*
EMP: 12
SALES (est): 504.4K **Privately Held**
SIC: 2759 Business forms: printing

(G-4519)
J LEWIS PARTNERS LP
Also Called: Lewis Company
13355 Noel Rd Ste 1750 (75240-6821)
PHONE..................................972 702-7390
John P Lewis, *Managing Prtnr*
EMP: 556
SQ FT: 4,000
SALES (est): 28.7MM **Privately Held**
WEB: www.johnson-photo.com
SIC: 6799 2211 2221 5131 Venture capi-
tal companies; apparel & outerwear fab-
rics, cotton; manmade & synthetic
broadwoven fabrics; synthetic fabrics;
trucking, except local; grain elevators

(G-4520)
JACK PHIPPS
Also Called: J & J Fabricators
11545 Pagemill Rd Ste 100 (75243-5508)
PHONE..................................972 278-3186
Fax: 214 221-2998
EMP: 13
SQ FT: 11,600
SALES (est): 751.2K **Privately Held**
SIC: 3599 7692 6411 Mfg Industrial Ma-
chinery Welding Repair Insurance
Agent/Broker

(G-4521)
**JACKSON DEERFIELD MFG
CORP**
14330 Midway Rd Ste 119 (75244-3513)
P.O. Box 801329 (75380-1329)
PHONE..................................972 233-7513
Daniel Rego, *President*
◆ EMP: 50
SALES (est): 7MM **Privately Held**
WEB: www.amertac.com
SIC: 2431 Millwork

(G-4522)
JAGUAR DESIGNS INC
9034 Diplomacy Row (75247-5304)
P.O. Box 560192 (75356-0192)
PHONE..................................214 634-7733
Harold Bridges, *CEO*
Darren Bridges, *President*
Judy Bridges, *Vice Pres*
Bridges Darrin, *Info Tech Dir*
EMP: 20
SQ FT: 12,500
SALES (est): 2MM **Privately Held**
WEB: www.jaguarltg.com
SIC: 3648 5063 3646 3645 Lighting
equipment; lighting fixtures; commercial
indusl & institutional electric lighting fix-
tures; residential lighting fixtures

(G-4523)
JAMCO SERVICES LLC
Also Called: Jam Construction
8080 Park Ln Ste 700 (75231-5920)
PHONE..................................432 242-6051
Roman Gilmer, *Manager*
Javier Almodova,
EMP: 60
SALES: 33.2MM **Privately Held**
WEB: www.jamcoservices.com
SIC: 1389 1629 Building oil & gas well
foundations on site; earthmoving contrac-
tor

(G-4524)
**JAMIESON MANUFACTURING
CO (DH)**
Also Called: Jamieson Fence Supply
3010 Lyndon B Johnson Fwy # 800
(75234-2776)
PHONE..................................214 339-8384
Jeffrey Wallace, *CEO*
Richard Calhoun, *President*
David Milton, *President*
Chad Kearney, *Regional Mgr*
Justin McMichael, *Regional Mgr*
▲ EMP: 35 EST: 1961
SALES (est): 85.1MM **Privately Held**
WEB: www.jamiesonfence.com
SIC: 5039 2499 Wire fence, gates & ac-
cessories; fencing, docks & other outdoor
wood structural products
HQ: Master-Halco, Inc.
    3010 Lbj Fwy Ste 800
    Dallas TX 75234
    972 714-7300

(G-4525)
JANUS SIGNS INC (PA)
Also Called: Fastsigns
9742 Skillman St (75243-5150)
PHONE..................................214 503-1333
Sarosh Nayar, *President*
Bridgit Rivas, *Executive*
EMP: 10
SQ FT: 3,600
SALES (est): 1.2MM **Privately Held**
WEB: www.fastsigns.com
SIC: 3993 Signs & advertising specialties

(G-4526)
JARVIS PRESS INC
9112 Viscount Row (75247-5497)
PHONE..................................214 637-2340
Steve Zisler, *President*
Linda Post, *Principal*
Chris Brady, *Production*
Jennifer B Hampton, *Controller*
Scott Wolf, *Accounts Mgr*
EMP: 90
SQ FT: 25,050
SALES (est): 28.5MM
SALES (corp-wide): 6.2B **Publicly Held**
WEB: www.jarvispress.com
SIC: 2752 Commercial printing, offset
HQ: Consolidated Graphics, Inc.
    5858 Westheimer Rd # 200
    Houston TX 77057
    713 787-0977

(G-4527)
JAYDEN INC
2632 Freewood Dr (75220-2511)
PHONE..................................214 389-7300
James T Furrate, *President*
EMP: 25
SQ FT: 12,000

SALES (est): 1.2MM **Privately Held**
WEB: www.jadenfabrics.com
SIC: 3999 Potpourri

(G-4528)
JAYROE LITHO INC
Also Called: Jayroe Printing
13240 Valley Branch Ln (75234-5748)
PHONE..................................972 243-3835
John Jayroe, *President*
Florine Jayroe, *Corp Secy*
Robert Jayroe, *Vice Pres*
Vicky Sangster, *Vice Pres*
Kris Jayroe, *Prdtn Mgr*
EMP: 14
SQ FT: 8,000
SALES (est): 1.6MM **Privately Held**
WEB: www.jayroeprinting.com
SIC: 2752 Commercial printing, offset

(G-4529)
JBC STEEL PRODUCTS LLC
10904 Sanden Dr Ste 102 (75238-5396)
PHONE..................................214 340-1510
Jack Pratley, *President*
Chris G Redmond, *Vice Pres*
EMP: 40
SQ FT: 40,000
SALES (est): 11.5MM **Privately Held**
WEB: www.jbcsteel.com
SIC: 3441 Fabricated structural metal

(G-4530)
**JEFFERSON AT MONTFORT
LIMITED**
14332 Montfort Dr (75254-8486)
PHONE..................................972 789-3600
Henry Miller, *President*
EMP: 20
SALES (est): 1.8MM **Privately Held**
WEB: www.hydeparkmontfort.com
SIC: 2791 2759 Typesetting; commercial
printing

(G-4531)
**JENTEK WATER TREATMENT
INC**
11524 Pagemill Rd (75243-5507)
PHONE..................................214 349-7111
Mark Jenkins, *President*
Doug Minnick, *Project Mgr*
Sherre Bishop, *Office Mgr*
John Todd, *Director*
EMP: 11
SALES (est): 1.3MM **Privately Held**
WEB: www.jentekwater.com
SIC: 5074 2899 8744 Water purification
equipment; chemical preparations; facili-
ties support services

(G-4532)
**JERELL CLOTHING COMPANY
LLC**
Also Called: Jerell Clothing Multiples
10367 Brockwood Rd (75238-1656)
PHONE..................................214 349-1891
Sharon A Young, *Mng Member*
John Bourgeois,
Sam Kapholz,
Leroy Spencer,
Edward D Vierling,
▲ EMP: 19
SQ FT: 27,000
SALES (est): 1.8MM
SALES (corp-wide): 9MM **Privately Held**
WEB: www.slimsation.com
SIC: 2339 Women's & misses' accessories
PA: Sharon Young, Inc.
    10367 Brockwood Rd
    Dallas TX 75238
    214 349-1891

(G-4533)
**JERICHO SYSTEMS
CORPORATION**
25 Highland Park Vlg (75205-2789)
PHONE..................................972 231-2000
Brynn Mow, *CEO*
EMP: 23
SQ FT: 8,269

SALES (est): 1MM **Privately Held**
WEB: www.jerichosystems.com
SIC: 7372 5045 Application computer software; business oriented computer software; utility computer software; computer
software

(G-4534)
JF FILTRATION INC (PA)
Also Called: Joe W. Fly Co.
4820 Memphis St (75207-5210)
PHONE..................................214 634-2200
Joe W Fly III, *President*
Hunt Foster, *Vice Pres*
Joe Fly Jr, *Treasurer*
Mary Fly, *Admin Sec*
EMP: 14
SQ FT: 10,000
SALES (est): 14MM **Privately Held**
WEB: www.joeflyco.com
SIC: 3564 5075 Filters, air: furnaces, air
conditioning equipment, etc.; air filters

(G-4535)
JOHN D BLANKENSHIP
Also Called: Custom Wood Workers
1715 E Levee St (75207-6801)
PHONE..................................214 752-9191
John D Blankenship, *Owner*
EMP: 20
SQ FT: 10,000
SALES (est): 3MM **Privately Held**
SIC: 1751 2499 Cabinet building & instal-
lation; decorative wood & woodwork

(G-4536)
**JOHN GALT DEVELOPMENT
INC (PA)**
1919 Mckinney Ave (75201-2495)
PHONE..................................312 701-9026
Anne Omord, *President*
Brandon Anton, *Consultant*
EMP: 10
SQ FT: 2,000
SALES (est): 8MM **Privately Held**
WEB: www.johngalt.com
SIC: 7372 Publishers' computer software

(G-4537)
JOHN HOGAN INTERESTS INC
Also Called: First Food Company
4561 Leston St (75247-5709)
P.O. Box 560029 (75356-0029)
PHONE..................................214 637-0214
Bradford Brooke Hogan, *President*
Dial Anderson, *Vice Pres*
Jon Colt, *Regl Sales Mgr*
Jerry Brewer, *Admin Sec*
EMP: 50
SQ FT: 45,000
SALES (est): 14.3MM **Privately Held**
WEB: www.firstfoodco.com
SIC: 2087 2099 Powders, drink; gelatin
dessert preparations

(G-4538)
**JONES LANG LASALLE IP INC
(HQ)**
Also Called: B R G
10440 N Central Expy # 1150
(75231-2221)
PHONE..................................214 777-5100
Traci Doane, *President*
Stephan Cloitre, *Exec VP*
Reeves Davis, *Exec VP*
Michael Levine, *Exec VP*
Allan Neill, *Exec VP*
EMP: 20
SALES (est): 7.3MM
SALES (corp-wide): 17.9B **Publicly Held**
WEB: www.brg.com
SIC: 7371 7372 7379 Computer software
development & applications; application
computer software; computer related con-
sulting services
PA: Jones Lang Lasalle Incorporated
    200 E Randolph St # 4300
    Chicago IL 60601
    312 782-5800

(G-4539)
**JOSHUAS RESPIRATORY CARE
INC**
11880 Shiloh Rd (75228-1501)
PHONE..................................469 916-9354

▲ = Import ▼=Export
◆ =Import/Export

Donald A Boswell, *President*
EMP: 14
SALES (est): 2.7MM **Privately Held**
WEB: www.joshuasrci.com
SIC: 3842 Respirators

(G-4540)
JOURNAL AIR LAW COMMERCE
3315 Daniel Ave (75205-1439)
PHONE..............................214 768-2570
Amanda Peters, *President*
EMP: 35
SALES (est): 1.5MM **Privately Held**
SIC: 2721 Magazines: publishing only, not printed on site

(G-4541)
K & R SCREEN GRAPHICS
3915 Main St (75226-1229)
PHONE..............................214 821-9562
Kruse Rojas Sr, *Owner*
EMP: 9
SQ FT: 14,000
SALES (est): 700K **Privately Held**
WEB: www.krscreen.com
SIC: 2759 Screen printing

(G-4542)
K S W CORP
Also Called: Ksw
2970 Blystone Ln Ste 101 (75220-1515)
PHONE..............................214 350-1943
Larry Cox, *Manager*
EMP: 11
SQ FT: 5,000
SALES (corp-wide): 2.4MM **Privately Held**
WEB: www.kswcorporation.com
SIC: 3599 Machine shop, jobbing & repair
PA: K. S. W., Corp.
1731 Guthrie Ave
Des Moines IA 50316
515 265-5269

(G-4543)
KALE NATURALS LLC
3309 Villanova St (75225-4842)
PHONE..............................214 402-6040
Dana Kale, *Mng Member*
Tia Pettijohn, *Mng Member*
EMP: 10 **EST:** 2008
SALES (est): 500K **Privately Held**
WEB: www.kalenaturals.com
SIC: 5122 2844 Cosmetics; toilet preparations

(G-4544)
KASTON FIXS & DESIGN GROUP LLC
8610 Directors Row (75247-5504)
PHONE..............................972 243-5334
John Steger,
◆ **EMP:** 21
SQ FT: 20,000
SALES (est): 4.1MM **Privately Held**
WEB: www.kastongroup.com
SIC: 3089 5072 Boxes, plastic; hardware

(G-4545)
KAURINAS LLC
4434 Mcewen Rd (75244-5205)
PHONE..............................972 888-9990
Hari P Singh, *Mng Member*
Aman Singh,
EMP: 18 **EST:** 1997
SALES (est): 2.5MM **Privately Held**
WEB: www.kaurinas.com
SIC: 2024 Ice cream & frozen desserts

(G-4546)
KBS RESEARCH LLC
15770 Dallas Pkwy Ste 500 (75248-3387)
PHONE..............................214 984-3724
Charles Scott, *CEO*
Mike Logsdon, *Managing Dir*
EMP: 20
SALES (est): 500K **Privately Held**
WEB: www.atrantil.com
SIC: 2833 Medicinals & botanicals

(G-4547)
KEDDIE ENTERPRISES INC
4304 Shilling Way (75237-1021)
PHONE..............................214 337-5387
Kevin Ferrell, *President*
Mace Turner, *Vice Pres*

EMP: 9
SQ FT: 8,000
SALES (est): 1.2MM **Privately Held**
WEB: www.keddieco.com
SIC: 3599 Machine shop, jobbing & repair

(G-4548)
KELLY ASSOCIATES
4165 Meadowdale Ln (75229-5318)
PHONE..............................214 357-8752
Donovan M Kelly, *Owner*
EMP: 10
SALES (est): 368.9K **Privately Held**
WEB: www.bradkellyassociates.com
SIC: 2752 2796 5064 2759 Lithographing on metal; engraving on copper, steel, wood or rubber: printing plates; plates & cylinders for rotogravure printing; answering machines, telephone; commercial printing

(G-4549)
KEN JORDAN SHUTTERS INC
Also Called: Ken Jordan Custom Shutters
10306 Hedgeway Dr (75229-6122)
PHONE..............................972 241-7776
Johnny Jordan, *President*
Jordan Oren K, *Director*
EMP: 15
SALES (est): 1.8MM **Privately Held**
WEB: www.kenjordanshutters.com
SIC: 2431 Blinds (shutters), wood; window shutters, wood; window trim, wood

(G-4550)
KENMARK ARCHITECTURAL PDTS INC (PA)
9865 Chartwell Dr (75243-8303)
PHONE..............................800 788-8263
Franklin Kisberg, *CEO*
Lamana J Tramonte, *President*
Suzanne Brooks, *Vice Pres*
Adrian Calixte, *Project Mgr*
Jim Schnefke, *Business Dir*
EMP: 10
SQ FT: 10,000
SALES: 3MM **Privately Held**
WEB: www.gokenmark.com
SIC: 8712 3259 1742 5211 Architectural services; architectural clay products; acoustical & insulation work; wallboard (composition) & paneling; interior decorating

(G-4551)
KENNEY INDUSTRIES INC
Also Called: Commercial Machining
2110 Panoramic Cir (75212-6305)
PHONE..............................214 421-4175
Michael Kenney, *President*
EMP: 65
SQ FT: 15,000
SALES (est): 20.5MM **Privately Held**
WEB: www.kenneyind.com
SIC: 3599 Machine shop, jobbing & repair

(G-4552)
KERICK INDUSTRIES
815 Wood River Rd (75232-2049)
PHONE..............................214 432-2446
Joannia Johnson, *Owner*
EMP: 12
SQ FT: 6,000 **Privately Held**
SIC: 3089 2393 2221 Plastic processing; canvas bags; broadwoven fabric mills, manmade

(G-4553)
KEVIN M EHRINGER ENTPS INC
Also Called: Data Center Systems
1881 Valley View Ln # 100 (75234-8939)
PHONE..............................972 620-4997
Kevin M Ehringer, *President*
Jerod Green, *Business Mgr*
Steven Gutman, *Business Mgr*
Michael Cox, *COO*
John Amato, *Vice Pres*
EMP: 66
SQ FT: 30,000
SALES (est): 16.6MM **Privately Held**
WEB: www.datacentersys.com
SIC: 2298 1731 Cable, fiber; fiber optic cable installation

(G-4554)
KI MEMORIES INC
4343 Sigma Rd (75244-4402)
PHONE..............................972 333-3015
Ira L Sabel, *President*
Kimberly Sabel, *Vice Pres*
▲ **EMP:** 40
SQ FT: 38,000 **Privately Held**
SIC: 2679 Gift wrap & novelties, paper

(G-4555)
KIBO SOFTWARE INC (PA)
717 N Harwood St Ste 1800 (75201-6552)
PHONE..............................707 780-1600
David Post, *CEO*
Jennifer Sherman, *Senior VP*
Euwart Anderson, *Vice Pres*
Keith Blankenship, *Vice Pres*
Eric Buhrfeind, *Vice Pres*
EMP: 71 **EST:** 2015
SALES (est): 57.2MM **Privately Held**
WEB: www.kibocommerce.com
SIC: 7372 Prepackaged software

(G-4556)
KING OPERATING CORPORATION
6142 Campbell Rd (75248-1370)
PHONE..............................214 420-3000
James R Young, *President*
Tom Gray, *President*
Todd Garner, *COO*
Ronnie Franz, *Vice Pres*
Ray Kong, *Vice Pres*
EMP: 10
SQ FT: 1,416
SALES (est): 4.5MM **Privately Held**
WEB: www.kingoperating.com
SIC: 1382 Oil & gas exploration services

(G-4557)
KINGFISHER MIDSTREAM LLC (HQ)
2101 Cedar Springs Rd # 1100 (75201-2158)
PHONE..............................281 655-3200
John Regan, *Mng Member*
Zachary Lee,
EMP: 11
SALES (est): 7.5MM
SALES (corp-wide): 100MM **Privately Held**
WEB: www.armenergy.com
SIC: 1389 Processing service, gas
PA: Bce - Mach Iii Llc
14201 Wireless Way # 300
Oklahoma City OK 73134
405 252-8100

(G-4558)
KIRBY MIDCO INC (PA)
Also Called: Midco Demolition Tool Co
9101 John W Carpenter Fwy (75247-4532)
PHONE..............................214 688-0444
Douglas F Dry, *President*
Robert T Dry, *Vice Pres*
Robby Read, *Sales Staff*
▲ **EMP:** 19
SQ FT: 80,000
SALES (est): 11MM **Privately Held**
WEB: www.midcosling.com
SIC: 5051 3496 Rope, wire (not insulated); slings, lifting: made from purchased wire

(G-4559)
KJ ENERGY LLC
8150 N Central Expy # 900 (75206-1815)
PHONE..............................214 297-5013
Jon Grottis, *Principal*
EMP: 10
SALES (corp-wide): 1.8MM **Privately Held**
WEB: www.kjenergy.com
SIC: 1389 Oil field services
PA: Kj Energy, Llc
5106 Knickerbocker Rd
San Angelo TX 76904
325 942-8792

(G-4560)
KLN MANUFACTURING LLC
1151 Empire Central Dr (75247-4301)
P.O. Box 565821 (75356-5821)
PHONE..............................210 227-4747

Kelly O Donnell, *Mng Member*
John O Donnell,
◆ **EMP:** 130
SQ FT: 100,000
SALES (est): 25MM **Privately Held**
WEB: www.kerrylogistics.com
SIC: 2514 5021 Metal household furniture; furniture

(G-4561)
KLN STEEL PRODUCTS COMPANY LLC (PA)
1161 Empire Central Dr (75247-4301)
P.O. Box 565821 (75356-5821)
PHONE..............................210 227-4747
Kris Benson, *Vice Pres*
Tabitha Martinez, *Production*
Kelly Flynn, *Purch Mgr*
Stephanie Diaz, *Accountant*
Gilbert Benavides, *Prgrmr*
▲ **EMP:** 154 **EST:** 2006
SQ FT: 500,000
SALES (est): 17.1MM **Privately Held**
WEB: www.kerrylogistics.com
SIC: 2514 Metal household furniture

(G-4562)
KNOLL INC
1722 Routh St Ste 112 (75201-2536)
PHONE..............................214 741-5819
Gracie Bolner, *Sales Staff*
Jan Flatt, *Sales Staff*
Andrea Pickens, *Sales Staff*
Susan Sallock, *Manager*
Diana Lachica, *Manager*
EMP: 18 **Publicly Held**
WEB: www.knoll.com
SIC: 2521 Wood office furniture
PA: Knoll, Inc.
1235 Water St
East Greenville PA 18041

(G-4563)
KNOTTSMITH CONSTRUCTION CO INC
Also Called: Ksc
2620 Willowbrook Rd (75220-4423)
PHONE..............................214 499-5667
Brennan M Knott, *President*
Benjamin R Smith, *Vice Pres*
EMP: 50
SQ FT: 10,000
SALES (est): 3.6MM **Privately Held**
WEB: www.knottsmith.com
SIC: 1542 3444 Commercial & office building, new construction; metal roofing & roof drainage equipment

(G-4564)
KOCH-GLITSCH LP
4900 Singleton Blvd (75212-3300)
P.O. Box 660053 (75266-0053)
PHONE..............................214 583-3000
Alessandro Auttura, *Principal*
Fred Cash, *Sales Staff*
Ronny Bakkum, *Officer*
EMP: 70
SALES (corp-wide): 36.8B **Privately Held**
WEB: www.koch-glitsch.com
SIC: 3443 Metal parts
HQ: Koch-Glitsch, Lp
4111 E 37th St N
Wichita KS 67220
316 828-5000

(G-4565)
KOSMOS ENERGY LLC (PA)
Also Called: Kosmos Energy Holdings
8176 Park Ln Ste 500 (75231-5988)
PHONE..............................214 445-9600
Brian F Maxted, *President*
Phillip Feiner, *Counsel*
Kenny Goh, *Senior VP*
Eric J Haas, *Senior VP*
William S Hayes, *Senior VP*
▲ **EMP:** 14
SQ FT: 50,000
SALES (est): 38.9MM **Privately Held**
WEB: www.kosmosenergy.com
SIC: 1382 Oil & gas exploration services

(G-4566)
KOSMOS ENERGY LTD (PA)
8176 Park Ln Ste 500 (75231-5988)
PHONE..............................214 445-9600
Brian F Maxted, *CEO*

Kelly Hoffmann, *Principal*
Darrell L McKenna, *COO*
Paul Dailly, *Senior VP*
Kevin Bourgeois, *Vice Pres*
EMP: 9
SALES (est) 55.1MM **Privately Held**
WEB: www.kosmosenergy.com
SIC: 1382 Oil & gas exploration services

(G-4567)
KPW ENTERPRISES INC
Also Called: Walls Printing Company
9171 King Arthur Dr (75247-3607)
PHONE.................................214 630-8088
Kevin P Walls, *President*
Royce Gregory, *Vice Pres*
Dolores Whittenburg, *Admin Asst*
EMP: 9
SQ FT: 13,400
SALES (est): 1.9MM **Privately Held**
WEB: www.wallsprinting.com
SIC: 2752 Commercial printing, offset

(G-4568)
KRONOS INTERNATIONAL INC (DH)
5430 Lyndon B Johnson Fwy (75240-2601)
PHONE.........................972 233-1700
Steven L Watson, *President*
EMP: 13
SALES (est): 289.8MM
SALES (corp-wide): 2B **Publicly Held**
WEB: www.kronostio2.com
SIC: 2816 Inorganic pigments

(G-4569)
KRONOS WORLDWIDE INC (DH)
5430 Lbj Fwy Ste 1700 (75240-2620)
PHONE.........................972 233-1700
Loretta J Feehan, *Ch of Bd*
Robert D Graham, *President*
Benjamin R Corona, *President*
James Buch, *COO*
Brian W Christian, *Exec VP*
EMP: 95
SALES: 1.7B
SALES (corp-wide): 2B **Publicly Held**
WEB: www.kronostio2.com
SIC: 2816 Titanium dioxide, anatase or rutile (pigments)
HQ: Valhi, Inc.
    5430 Lbj Fwy Ste 1700
    Dallas TX 75240
    972 233-1700

(G-4570)
KRONOS WORLDWIDE INC
5430 Lyndon B Johnson Fwy (75240-2601)
PHONE.........................609 860-6200
Dr Larry Wigdor, *CEO*
Ronny Duquet, *Technology*
Paulraj Selvanayagam, *Prgrmr*
EMP: 35
SALES (corp-wide): 2B **Publicly Held**
WEB: www.kronostio2.com
SIC: 2816 2899 Titanium dioxide, anatase or rutile (pigments); chemical preparations
HQ: Kronos Worldwide, Inc.
    5430 Lbj Fwy Ste 1700
    Dallas TX 75240

(G-4571)
KS LITTLE SHOP
5825 Spring Glen Dr (75232-2435)
PHONE.........................214 371-4113
Kattie B Richie, *Owner*
EMP: 13
SALES (est): 585.1K **Privately Held**
SIC: 7389 5714 5719 2392 Interior designer; draperies; bedding (sheets, blankets, spreads & pillows); household furnishings

(G-4572)
KUBYS SAUSAGE HOUSE INC (PA)
6601 Snider Plz (75205-1351)
PHONE.........................214 363-2231
Karl F Kuby, *President*
Dieter Probson, *General Mgr*
Terri Ghent, *Controller*
EMP: 12 **EST:** 1961
SQ FT: 12,000

SALES (est): 1.2MM **Privately Held**
WEB: www.kubys.com
SIC: 5812 2013 5411 Caterers; German restaurant; sausages from purchased meat; delicatessens

(G-4573)
L L PALLETS
4060 Duncanville Rd (75236-1406)
PHONE.........................469 916-7552
Steve Fowler, *Owner*
EMP: 15
SALES (est): 1.3MM **Privately Held**
SIC: 2448 Pallets, wood

(G-4574)
L3 TECHNOLOGIES INC
Also Called: Warrior Systems Division
9827 Chartwell Dr (75243-8303)
P.O. Box 910099 (75391-0099)
PHONE.........................972 840-5600
Gregg Bell, *President*
EMP: 301
SALES (corp-wide): 11.3B **Publicly Held**
WEB: www.l3t.com
SIC: 3679 Attenuators
HQ: L3 Technologies, Inc.
    600 3rd Ave Fl 34
    New York NY 10016
    212 805-5234

(G-4575)
LA HACENDA MEXICAN FD PDTS INC
2604 Freewood Dr (75220-2511)
PHONE.........................214 353-0230
John Stickle, *President*
Tom McIntyre, *Vice Pres*
Martha Salazar, *Human Res Mgr*
EMP: 35
SQ FT: 26,000
SALES (est): 4.7MM
SALES (corp-wide): 5.4MM **Privately Held**
SIC: 2099 Food preparations
PA: Double Jj Corporation
    2604 Freewood Dr
    Dallas TX 75220
    214 353-0230

(G-4576)
LA PALETERIA
4225 Ross Ave (75204-5126)
PHONE.........................214 887-8278
Havier Tenoco, *Manager*
EMP: 75
SALES (est): 4.3MM **Privately Held**
SIC: 2599 Food wagons, restaurant

(G-4577)
LA SUBASTA INCORPORATED
502 N Haskell Ave (75246-1419)
PHONE.........................214 951-9500
Oscar Salinas, *Sales Mgr*
Dalena Salinas, *Accounts Mgr*
Sergio Budini, *Chief Mktg Ofcr*
Oscar Salina, *Manager*
Angel Flores, *IT Executive*
EMP: 16
SALES (corp-wide): 2.3MM **Privately Held**
WEB: www.lasubasta.com
SIC: 2711 7313 Newspapers, publishing & printing; newspaper advertising representative
PA: La Subasta Incorporated
    6120 Tarnef Dr Ste 100
    Houston TX 77074
    713 777-1010

(G-4578)
LALA US INC
5301 Alpha Rd Ste 80-300 (75240-4355)
PHONE.........................469 804-3850
Jorge Ramos, *CEO*
Aaron Armas, *VP Human Res*
Kevin Herbert, *VP Sales*
Daniel Espinosa, *IT/INT Sup*
Armando Banda, *Director*
EMP: 289
SALES (est): 100.4K **Privately Held**
WEB: www.lala-us.com
SIC: 2026 2023 Fluid milk; dry, condensed, evaporated dairy products

PA: Grupo Lala, S.A.B. De C.V.
    Calzada Carlos Herrera Araluce No. 185
    Gomez Palacio DGO. 35079

(G-4579)
LAMAR HUNT TRUST ESTATE INC
1601 Elm St Ste 4000 (75201-7202)
PHONE.........................214 720-1600
J R Holland, *President*
Linda Williams, *Vice Pres*
Alan Tompkins, *General Counsel*
EMP: 55 **EST:** 1935
SQ FT: 2,000
SALES (est): 4.6MM **Privately Held**
SIC: 1311 1382 Crude petroleum production; oil & gas exploration services

(G-4580)
LAMINATE WORKS INC
4051 La Reunion Pkwy # 170 (75212-6031)
PHONE.........................913 281-7474
Ben Young, *Plant Mgr*
Tom Riley, *Mfg Staff*
Mike Keller, *Branch Mgr*
EMP: 50
SALES (corp-wide): 22MM **Privately Held**
WEB: www.laminateworks.com
SIC: 2493 Particleboard, plastic laminated
PA: Laminate Works, Inc.
    15900 College Blvd # 200
    Lenexa KS 66219
    913 800-8263

(G-4581)
LANGLEY ENERGY
10405 E Northwest Hwy # 304 (75238-4619)
PHONE.........................214 221-2669
Mike Langley, *Principal*
EMP: 10
SALES (est): 971.3K **Privately Held**
WEB: www.langleyenergy.com
SIC: 1311 Crude petroleum production

(G-4582)
LASER IMAGE INC
2451 N Stemmons Fwy (75207-2601)
PHONE.........................214 267-1313
Barbara Morris, *President*
Chele Butler, *Vice Pres*
Olga Escobedo, *Vice Pres*
Sharon Chapman, *Accounting Mgr*
Curtis Smith, *Accounting Mgr*
EMP: 40
SQ FT: 42,000
SALES (est): 6.2MM **Privately Held**
WEB: www.fusemind.com
SIC: 2759 7331 7374 2752 Laser printing; direct mail advertising services; data processing service; commercial printing, lithographic

(G-4583)
LASSO TECHNOLOGIES LLC
8750 N Central Expy # 300 (75231-6464)
PHONE.........................866 392-0923
Peter McCormick, *President*
Patti Flowers, *Admin Asst*
Richard S Kumpf,
EMP: 17 **EST:** 2008
SALES (est): 2.9MM **Privately Held**
WEB: www.lasso.com
SIC: 3663

(G-4584)
LATINA STYLE INC
Also Called: Latina Style Magazine
2102 Empire Central (75235-4302)
PHONE.........................214 357-2186
Robert Bard, *CEO*
EMP: 20 **EST:** 2011
SALES (est): 2.8MM **Privately Held**
WEB: www.latinastyle.com
SIC: 2721 Magazines: publishing & printing

(G-4585)
LAVENDER ENTERPRISES INC
Also Called: Stone Images
4939 Cash Rd (75247-6307)
P.O. Box 560686 (75356-0686)
PHONE.........................214 631-8080
Jim Lavender, *President*

Cece Verges, *Sales Staff*
EMP: 44
SALES (est): 3.9MM **Privately Held**
SIC: 3272 3281 Stone, cast concrete; cut stone & stone products

(G-4586)
LE STITCH N DESIGNS INC
12215 Forestgate Dr # 101 (75243-5495)
PHONE.........................214 340-1592
Hong Lee, *Owner*
▲ **EMP:** 50
SALES (est): 2.5MM **Privately Held**
SIC: 2326 Men's & boys' work clothing

(G-4587)
LEGACY INVESTMENTS INC (PA)
12377 Merit Dr Ste 1200 (75251-2248)
PHONE.........................214 750-1522
Bruce Thompson, *President*
Mike Caruthers, *VP Finance*
Stoney Heflin, *IT/INT Sup*
EMP: 39
SQ FT: 17,000
SALES (est): 14.1MM **Privately Held**
WEB: www.hyperionoil.com
SIC: 1311 6531 Crude petroleum production; natural gas production; real estate agents & managers

(G-4588)
LEGACY LOCKERS LLC
4433 Bronze Way (75236-2005)
PHONE.........................972 937-1088
Jeffrey Reedy, *Vice Pres*
Scott Henson, *Warehouse Mgr*
Jeff Reedy, *Sales Mgr*
James Esely, *Sales Staff*
Will Rudolph, *Sales Staff*
▲ **EMP:** 20
SALES (est): 3.4MM **Privately Held**
WEB: www.legacylockers.com
SIC: 2541 Lockers, except refrigerated: wood

(G-4589)
LEGACY NATIONAL SIGNS
11330 Luna Rd (75229-3114)
PHONE.........................972 790-8900
Nathan Lohri, *General Mgr*
Jonathan Lohri, *Principal*
Brian Lohri, *Master*
EMP: 24
SALES (est): 3.1MM **Privately Held**
WEB: www.lnssigns.com
SIC: 3993 Electric signs

(G-4590)
LEGGETT & PLATT INCORPORATED
Also Called: Duro Metals
440 Hillburn Dr (75217-6552)
PHONE.........................214 391-3181
EMP: 99
SQ FT: 3,600
SALES (corp-wide): 3.7B **Publicly Held**
SIC: 2515 Mfg Mattresses/Bedsprings
PA: Leggett & Platt, Incorporated
    1 Leggett Rd
    Carthage MO 64836
    417 358-8131

(G-4591)
LEONARD SLOAN & ASSOCIATES INC
2720 Manor Way (75235-5616)
PHONE.........................214 350-2440
Leonard R Sloan, *CEO*
Jane Sloan, *General Mgr*
Marsha J Sloan, *CFO*
EMP: 16 **EST:** 1976
SQ FT: 7,200
SALES (est): 1.7MM **Privately Held**
WEB: www.wholesalecontractscreenprinting.com
SIC: 2337 2395 Uniforms, except athletic: women's, misses' & juniors'; art goods for embroidering, stamped: purchased materials

(G-4592)
LETCO GROUP LLC (PA)
Also Called: Living Earth
1901 Cal Crossing Rd (75220-7005)
PHONE....................................972 506-8575
Mark Rose, *President*
Scott Donahue, *CFO*
Wes Ringgenberg, *Credit Mgr*
Paul Tomaso, *Branch Mgr*
Mike Conroy, *Manager*
▲ EMP: 70
SQ FT: 10,000
SALES (est): 78.3MM **Privately Held**
WEB: www.livingearth.net
SIC: 2875 Compost; potting soil, mixed

(G-4593)
LETCO GROUP LLC
1901 California Xing (75220-7005)
PHONE....................................972 869-4332
Paul Tomaso, *Branch Mgr*
EMP: 50
SALES (corp-wide): 78.3MM **Privately Held**
WEB: www.livingearth.net
SIC: 2875 Compost
PA: The Letco Group Llc
1901 Cal Crossing Rd
Dallas TX 75220
972 506-8575

(G-4594)
LIBERTY CARDS LP
2020 Singleton Blvd (75212-3829)
PHONE....................................214 646-9923
Mohammad Kamal, *Partner*
EMP: 15
SQ FT: 476,000
SALES (est): 147.1K **Privately Held**
SIC: 2759 Commercial printing

(G-4595)
LIGHTHOUSE DISTRIBUTION INC
Also Called: Lighthouse Converting
2176 French Settlement Rd (75212-6001)
PHONE....................................214 630-1630
David R Olson, *President*
John J Hennessey, *Vice Pres*
Sheri J Olson, *Director*
EMP: 14 EST: 1998
SALES (est): 3.6MM **Privately Held**
WEB: www.lighthousepaperconverting.com
SIC: 2679 5111 Pressed fiber & molded pulp products except food products; printing & writing paper

(G-4596)
LINUX TECH INC
Also Called: SW Technology
5050 Quorum Dr 700-360 (75254-7564)
P.O. Box 250185, Plano (75025-0185)
PHONE....................................972 907-0871
Marvin Wu, *President*
Stephen LI, *Vice Pres*
Allison Wu, *Legal Staff*
EMP: 10
SQ FT: 3,000
SALES (est): 2.5MM **Privately Held**
WEB: www.swt.com
SIC: 7379 7373 3571 Computer related consulting services; systems integration services; electronic computers

(G-4597)
LISTO INC
1025 W Commerce St (75208-1704)
PHONE....................................469 544-4555
Walter Huerta, *CEO*
Augusto Huerta, *Treasurer*
EMP: 40
SQ FT: 2,500
SALES (est): 5.9MM **Privately Held**
SIC: 3559 Concrete products machinery

(G-4598)
LLANO OPERATING CORPORATION
Also Called: North Texas Llano Operating
5944 Luther Ln Ste 1003 (75225-5922)
PHONE....................................972 677-7690
Steve Looper, *President*
EMP: 10
SALES (est): 565.5K **Privately Held**
SIC: 1382 Oil & gas exploration services

(G-4599)
LOBO TORTILLA FACTORY INC
7777 Hines Pl (75235-3312)
PHONE....................................972 388-8000
Tom Rowell, *CFO*
Brett Landes, *Director*
Nickie Landes, *Director*
▲ EMP: 160
SALES (est): 23.4MM **Privately Held**
WEB: www.landesfoods.com
SIC: 2099 Tortillas, fresh or refrigerated

(G-4600)
LODOR ENTERPRISES INC
Also Called: Commerce Grinding Co.
635 Fort Worth Ave (75208-1801)
PHONE....................................214 651-1977
Joe Lodor, *President*
Mike Johnson, *Exec VP*
Tim Johnson, *Exec VP*
Don Henexson, *Treasurer*
James Clark, *Manager*
EMP: 70 EST: 1976
SQ FT: 8,500
SALES (est): 9.8MM **Privately Held**
WEB: www.commercegrinding.com
SIC: 3599 Machine shop, jobbing & repair

(G-4601)
LOFTUS & WOOSLEY INC
Also Called: Premier Printing
8607 Ambtxdor Row Ste 190 (75247)
PHONE....................................214 631-1975
Clarence Woosley, *President*
Robert Loftus, *Vice Pres*
EMP: 18
SQ FT: 11,000
SALES (est): 2.7MM **Privately Held**
WEB: www.premierdallas.com
SIC: 2752 Commercial printing, offset

(G-4602)
LOLOI INC (PA)
Also Called: Loloi Rugs
4501 Spring Valley Rd (75244-3706)
PHONE....................................972 503-5656
Amir Loloi, *President*
Steve McKee, *General Mgr*
Sussan Loloi, *Vice Pres*
Heather Garcia, *Project Mgr*
Joanna Vargas, *Production*
◆ EMP: 179
SQ FT: 8,000
SALES (est): 68.1MM **Privately Held**
WEB: www.loloirugs.com
SIC: 2273 2392 Carpets & rugs; cushions & pillows

(G-4603)
LONE STAR CERAMICS COMPANY
2408 Fruitland Ave (75234-4720)
PHONE....................................972 247-3111
Fax: 972 247-3113
EMP: 35
SQ FT: 31,000
SALES (est): 1.4MM **Privately Held**
SIC: 3253 Mfg Ceramic Wall/Floor Tile

(G-4604)
LONE STAR TECHNOLOGIES INC (HQ)
15660 Dallas Pkwy Ste 500 (75248-3354)
PHONE....................................972 770-6401
Rhys J Best, *CEO*
Joseph Alvarado, *President*
Robert F Spears, *Vice Pres*
Charles J Keszler, *CFO*
◆ EMP: 70
SQ FT: 25,000
SALES (est): 145.6MM
SALES (corp-wide): 12.9B **Publicly Held**
WEB: www.lonestartech.com
SIC: 3312 3317 Sheet or strip, steel, hot-rolled; welded pipe & tubes
PA: United States Steel Corp
600 Grant St
Pittsburgh PA 15219
412 433-1121

(G-4605)
LONGHORN TUBE LP
1891 Ryan Rd (75220-7019)
PHONE....................................972 556-0234
Jim Hutchins, *President*

Phillip Groves, *Partner*
Danni Norris, *Sales Staff*
EMP: 15
SALES (est): 3.3MM **Privately Held**
WEB: www.longhorntube.com
SIC: 3317 Steel pipe & tubes

(G-4606)
LOPEZ TORTILLA FOODS INC
9727 Brockbank Dr (75220-2926)
PHONE....................................214 353-9538
Armando Lopez, *President*
EMP: 25
SQ FT: 60,000
SALES (est): 11.1MM **Privately Held**
WEB: www.lopezfoodstortillasdallas.com
SIC: 2096 Tortilla chips

(G-4607)
LP & M GROUP INC
Also Called: Leather Leather
13465 Inwood Rd Apt 1312 (75244-5323)
PHONE....................................972 458-9393
Leonard Feiner, *President*
Creighton Kent, *Controller*
Jane Nelson, *Office Mgr*
EMP: 45
SQ FT: 40,000
SALES (est): 20.6K **Privately Held**
SIC: 2519 5712 Household furniture, except wood or metal: upholstered; furniture stores

(G-4608)
LR ENERGY INC (PA)
8150 N Central Expy (75206-1815)
PHONE....................................214 691-5800
John Burke, *COO*
Paul J Coughlin III, *Exec Dir*
▲ EMP: 50 EST: 2010
SALES (est): 3.4MM **Privately Held**
WEB: www.lrenergyinc.com
SIC: 1382 Oil & gas exploration services

(G-4609)
LSF8 GYPSUM HOLDINGS LP
2711 N Haskell Ave (75204-2911)
PHONE....................................703 480-3800
Isaac Preston, *Principal*
EMP: 504
SALES (est): 22.1MM **Privately Held**
WEB: www.zix.com
SIC: 3275 Gypsum board

(G-4610)
LUCID ENERGY GROUP LLC
Also Called: Agave Midstream Company
3100 Mckinnon St Ste 800 (75201-7014)
PHONE....................................575 810-6025
Michael Latchem, *CEO*
EMP: 50
SALES (est): 5.9MM
SALES (corp-wide): 8.4MM **Privately Held**
WEB: www.lucid-energy.com
SIC: 1382 Oil & gas exploration services
PA: Lucid Energy Group Ii, Llc
3100 Mckinnon St Ste 800
Dallas TX 75201
214 420-4950

(G-4611)
LUCID ENERGY GROUP II LLC (PA)
3100 Mckinnon St Ste 800 (75201-7014)
PHONE....................................214 420-4950
Michael J Latchem, *President*
EMP: 13 EST: 2015
SALES (est): 8.4MM **Privately Held**
WEB: www.lucid-energy.com
SIC: 1382 Oil & gas exploration services

(G-4612)
LUNAS TORTILLAS FACTORY
Also Called: Luna's Tortillas Y Hacienda
2225 Connector Dr (75220-4318)
PHONE....................................214 747-2661
Fernando Luna, *Owner*
Francisco X Luna Sr, *Director*
EMP: 16
SQ FT: 10,000
SALES (est): 1.2MM **Privately Held**
WEB: www.lunastortillas.com
SIC: 2099 2096 Tortillas, fresh or refrigerated; tortilla chips

(G-4613)
LWC BRANDS INC
Also Called: Lady Walton's Cookies
151 Regal Row Ste 118 (75247-5609)
P.O. Box 560762 (75356-0762)
PHONE....................................214 630-9101
Mary Alizon-Walton, *President*
Susan Walton, *Chairman*
Scott Royal, *Sales Staff*
▲ EMP: 20
SQ FT: 13,000
SALES (est): 4.5MM **Privately Held**
WEB: www.ladywaltons.com
SIC: 2052 Cookies

(G-4614)
LYNX ENERGY COMPANY INC
2100 Ross Ave Ste 860 (75201-7941)
PHONE....................................214 969-5555
Robert S Craine, *President*
Karen Murphy, *Admin Sec*
EMP: 17
SALES (est): 2.1MM **Privately Held**
SIC: 1311 Crude petroleum production; natural gas production

(G-4615)
LYONS MANUFACTURING INC
8900 Forney Rd (75227-4505)
PHONE....................................214 381-8100
Rhonald D Morris, *President*
Robert J Morris, *Vice Pres*
EMP: 20
SQ FT: 20,000
SALES (est): 5MM **Privately Held**
WEB: www.lyonsmanufacturing.com
SIC: 3272 Building materials, except block or brick: concrete

(G-4616)
M & H METAL SPECIALITIES INC
5711 W Ledbetter Dr (75236-1307)
P.O. Box 210092 (75211-0092)
PHONE....................................972 296-9057
Clifford B Sauer, *President*
EMP: 14 EST: 1975
SQ FT: 14,000
SALES (est): 3MM **Privately Held**
WEB: www.mandhmetal.com
SIC: 3441 Fabricated structural metal

(G-4617)
M & L ROSE ENTERPRISES INC (PA)
Also Called: Rose Tree Linen
4639 N Lindhurst Ave (75229-6517)
PHONE....................................214 637-8000
Lydia Rose, *President*
Maurice Rose, *Corp Secy*
Mark Rose, *Vice Pres*
▲ EMP: 17
SALES (est): 15MM **Privately Held**
SIC: 2299 Linen fabrics

(G-4618)
M & M UPHOLSTERY INC
8337 Lake June Rd Ste B (75217-2169)
PHONE....................................214 391-2666
Marlin Ray Martin Jr, *President*
EMP: 20 EST: 1957
SQ FT: 7,500
SALES (est): 1.4MM **Privately Held**
WEB: www.mandmupholstery.com
SIC: 2512 Upholstered household furniture

(G-4619)
M BROWN BOOKS PUBG GROUP INC
16250 Knoll Trail Dr (75248-2874)
PHONE....................................972 381-0009
Milli Brown, *CEO*
Sherry Levine, *Publisher*
▲ EMP: 10
SALES (est): 956.6K **Privately Held**
WEB: www.brownbooks.com
SIC: 2731 8999 Books: publishing only; commercial & literary writings

(G-4620)
M C SYSTEMS INC
2412 Richland Ave Ste 101 (75234-5307)
PHONE....................................972 247-6785
Fax: 972 247-6709
EMP: 15
SQ FT: 12,000

SALES (est): 1.6MM **Privately Held**
SIC: 3674 Mfg Semiconductor Circuit Networks

(G-4621)
M N GUMBERT CORPORATION
Also Called: Sandpaper of Texas
10750 Metric Dr (75243-8504)
PHONE..........................214 340-8383
Michael N Gumbert, *President*
Rick Henkhaus, *General Mgr*
Steve Gumbert, *Vice Pres*
EMP: 35
SQ FT: 4,000
SALES (est): 6.8MM **Privately Held**
WEB: www.sotabrasives.com
SIC: 5085 5084 5169 2819 Abrasives;
metal polishes; industrial machinery &
equipment; metalworking machinery; industrial inorganic chemicals

(G-4622)
M W PERISCOPE INC
2025 Royal Ln Ste 310 (75229-3229)
P.O. Box 29005 (75229-0005)
PHONE..........................972 247-4202
Mary M Wood, *President*
Susan Anderson, *Corp Secy*
▲ **EMP:** 47
SQ FT: 36,000
SALES (est): 5.7MM **Privately Held**
SIC: 2759 2396 Screen printing; automotive & apparel trimmings

(G-4623)
M4 PRODUCTS LLC
Also Called: M4 Performance Exhaust
2227 Joe Field Rd (75229-3326)
PHONE..........................972 481-9300
Richard Martin, *Mng Member*
Kyle Martin,
EMP: 10
SQ FT: 16,000
SALES (est): 1.5MM **Privately Held**
WEB: www.m4exhaust.com
SIC: 3498 Fabricated pipe & fittings

(G-4624)
MACE SECURITY INTL INC
Also Called: Industrial Vision Source
13710 Hutton Dr (75234-9005)
PHONE..........................800 627-6734
EMP: 35
SALES (corp-wide): 28.8MM **Publicly Held**
WEB: www.mace.com
SIC: 3663 5043 Television closed circuit
equipment; photographic equipment &
supplies
PA: Mace Security International, Inc.
4400 Carnegie Ave
Cleveland OH 44103
440 424-5325

(G-4625)
MADDOX METAL WORKS INC (PA)
Also Called: Maddox Adams International
4116 Bronze Way (75237-1002)
PHONE..........................214 333-2311
Samuel Louis Maddox, *President*
James Carlin, *Corp Secy*
Phil Moss, *Plant Mgr*
Steve McAfee, *Purch Agent*
Ann Elles, *Buyer*
◆ **EMP:** 65 **EST:** 1952
SQ FT: 60,000
SALES (est): 14.4MM **Privately Held**
WEB: www.maddoxmetalworks.com
SIC: 3556 3728 3462 Food products machinery; aircraft parts & equipment; iron &
steel forgings

(G-4626)
MAGNETIC TICKET & LABEL CORP (HQ)
Also Called: MT&I Card Products
8719 Diplomacy Row (75247-5401)
PHONE..........................214 634-8600
Peter Pyhrr, *President*
Stan Welker, *Senior VP*
Barbara Fulenwiter, *Vice Pres*
Michael Hale, *Vice Pres*
Yahya Kashani, *Vice Pres*
EMP: 123
SQ FT: 28,000

SALES (est): 99.3MM
SALES (corp-wide): 114.9MM **Privately Held**
SIC: 2759 Commercial printing; labels &
seals; printing
PA: Hfs Holding Corporation
8900 Ambassador Row
Dallas TX 75247
214 634-8600

(G-4627)
MAGNUS MOBILITY SYSTEMS INC
2605 Joe Field Rd (75229-4602)
PHONE..........................800 527-5142
Andrew Madrid, *Opers Mgr*
Wally Barrera, *Sales Staff*
EMP: 10
SALES (corp-wide): 12.1MM **Privately Held**
WEB: www.magnusinc.com
SIC: 5072 3562 Casters & glides; casters
PA: Monroe Magnus Llc
2805 Barranca Pkwy
Irvine CA 92606
714 771-2630

(G-4628)
MAIL CONTRACTORS AMERICA INC
Also Called: Hartco
1936 W Commerce St (75208-8127)
PHONE..........................214 742-6103
Kelly Ross, *Manager*
EMP: 25
SQ FT: 700
SALES (corp-wide): 352.2MM **Privately Held**
WEB: www.mailcontractors.com
SIC: 3579 Mailing, letter handling & addressing machines
HQ: Mail Contractors Of America, Inc.
3809 Roundtop Dr
North Little Rock AR 72117
501 280-0500

(G-4629)
MAIL MART INC
4812 Top Line Dr (75247-6315)
P.O. Box 224849 (75222-4849)
PHONE..........................214 630-9643
Jamie Huffaker, *President*
Roy Bullion, *CFO*
Ray Suppe, *Marketing Staff*
Carol Beseda, *Admin Sec*
EMP: 65
SQ FT: 50,000
SALES (est): 9.1MM **Privately Held**
WEB: www.themailmart.com
SIC: 7331 7374 2752 Mailing service;
data processing service; commercial
printing, lithographic

(G-4630)
MANDA MACHINE COMPANY
2683 Myrtle Springs Ave (75220-2514)
P.O. Box 541236 (75354-1236)
PHONE..........................214 352-5946
Richard Ellard, *President*
Christopher Ellard, *Vice Pres*
John Ellard, *Vice Pres*
EMP: 27
SQ FT: 8,000
SALES (est): 5.6MM **Privately Held**
WEB: www.mandamachine.com
SIC: 3599 Machine shop, jobbing & repair

(G-4631)
MANHATTAN PROJECT LLC
Also Called: Manhattan Project Beer Company
2215 Sulphur St (75208-2033)
PHONE..........................469 678-8870
Karl Sanford, *Mng Member*
EMP: 29 **EST:** 2016
SALES (est): 1.7MM **Privately Held**
WEB: www.manhattanproject.beer
SIC: 2082 Beer (alcoholic beverage)

(G-4632)
MANHEIM COMPANIES INC
Also Called: Manheim Ruseau
13736 Beta Rd (75244-4512)
PHONE..........................972 387-4578
James Brown, *Chairman*

James D Pratt, *Chairman*
Glaucia Mosher, *Production*
EMP: 23
SQ FT: 30,000
SALES (est): 2.7MM **Privately Held**
WEB: www.hhruseau.com
SIC: 2511 Wood household furniture

(G-4633)
MANUFACTURING GROUP AMER INC
2841 Pierce St (75233-1535)
P.O. Box 210247 (75211-0247)
PHONE..........................214 467-4444
James Bradley West, *CEO*
Mike Ferguson, *Senior VP*
Paul Zipp, *Admin Sec*
EMP: 700
SQ FT: 10,000
SALES (est): 43.9MM **Privately Held**
SIC: 5031 2434 Structural assemblies,
prefabricated: wood; vanities, bathroom:
wood

(G-4634)
MARCOS N SUAREZ
Also Called: El Hispano Newspaper
2102 Empire Central (75235-4302)
PHONE..........................214 357-2186
Marcos Nelson Suarez, *Owner*
EMP: 12
SQ FT: 26,000
SALES (est): 500K **Privately Held**
WEB: www.elhispanonews.com
SIC: 2711 7313 Newspapers: publishing
only, not printed on site; newspaper advertising representative

(G-4635)
MARLIN CONTROLS INC (PA)
11011 Regency Crest Dr # 200
(75238-1719)
P.O. Box 550457 (75355-0457)
PHONE..........................214 553-5700
Moe Chigani, *President*
Ken Chigani, *Project Mgr*
Robert Cardinali, *Natl Sales Mgr*
Nava Pradappet, *Graphic Designe*
▲ **EMP:** 10
SQ FT: 5,950
SALES (est): 1.9MM **Privately Held**
WEB: www.marlincontrols.com
SIC: 3829 Instrumentation for reactor controls, auxiliary; hydrometers, except industrial process type

(G-4636)
MARMON HIGHWAY TECH LLC
3030 Irving Blvd (75247-6213)
P.O. Box 560094 (75356-0094)
PHONE..........................214 631-8810
Earl Tucker, *Sales/Mktg Mgr*
EMP: 20
SALES (corp-wide): 254.6B **Publicly Held**
WEB: www.marmonhitech.com
SIC: 7389 3714 5084 5082 Crane & aerial lift service; motor vehicle parts & accessories; winches; cranes, construction;
truck bodies & parts
HQ: Marmon Highway Technologies Llc
5915 Chalkville Rd 300
Birmingham AL 35235
205 508-2000

(G-4637)
MARROQUIN CUSTOM UPHOLSTERY
Also Called: Marroquin and Associates
4835 Reading St (75247-6716)
PHONE..........................214 905-0461
Jesus Marroquin, *President*
Elsa Maroquin, *Vice Pres*
EMP: 25
SQ FT: 35,000
SALES (est): 3.2MM **Privately Held**
WEB: www.marroquincustomuph.com
SIC: 2512 7641 Upholstered household
furniture; upholstery work

(G-4638)
MARSMITH ENTERPRISES INC
Also Called: Advanced Beverages
2403 Walnut Ridge St (75229-4529)
PHONE..........................972 488-9339
Mark Smith, *President*

Marke Smith, *Engineer*
EMP: 15
SALES (est): 3.2MM **Privately Held**
WEB: www.advancedbeverages.com
SIC: 2086 5078 5149 Bottled & canned
soft drinks; refrigerated beverage dispensers; beverages, except coffee & tea

(G-4639)
MARTIN INC
Also Called: Morrison Architectural Sign
3108 Garden Brook Dr (75234-2307)
PHONE..........................972 247-7160
Buddy Kanizar, *President*
Michelle Smiley, *Project Mgr*
Jessica Ferguson, *Graphic Designe*
EMP: 33
SQ FT: 11,900
SALES (est): 318.1K **Privately Held**
WEB: www.morrisonsign.com
SIC: 3993 Signs, not made in custom sign
painting shops

(G-4640)
MARTIN MARIETTA MATERIALS INC
Also Called: Alamo North Texas RR
1503 Lyndon B Johnson Fwy # 400
(75234-6059)
PHONE..........................972 350-8200
David Mitteis, *General Mgr*
Jason Stilwell, *Sales Staff*
Ron Kopplin, *Manager*
Stefanie Gaines, *Manager*
Michael Taylor, *Manager*
EMP: 25 **Publicly Held**
WEB: www.martinmarietta.com
SIC: 1422 Crushed & broken limestone
PA: Martin Marietta Materials Inc
2710 Wycliff Rd
Raleigh NC 27607

(G-4641)
MARTIN SPROCKET & GEAR INC
Martin Foundry
2944 Oak Ln (75215-1559)
PHONE..........................214 428-2191
Noel Bell, *Vice Pres*
Johnny Hill, *Prdtn Mgr*
Brenda Juarez, *Business Anlyst*
Rogers Ozment, *Branch Mgr*
EMP: 60
SALES (corp-wide): 539MM **Privately Held**
WEB: www.martinsprocket.com
SIC: 3566 5085 3462 3568 Gears, power
transmission, except automotive; sprockets; iron & steel forgings; power transmission equipment
PA: Martin Sprocket & Gear, Inc.
3100 Sprocket Dr
Arlington TX 76015
817 258-3000

(G-4642)
MARY AND MEGAN FOOD CO LLC (PA)
314 N Bishop Ave (75208-4655)
PHONE..........................972 921-9618
Megan Wilkes,
Mary Sparks,
EMP: 25 **EST:** 2012
SALES (est): 7.4MM **Privately Held**
SIC: 2051 Bakery: wholesale or wholesale/retail combined

(G-4643)
MASONITE INTERNATIONAL CORP
11990 Shiloh Rd (75228-1503)
PHONE..........................972 686-5500
Christopher Beth, *Branch Mgr*
Mary Murante, *Director*
EMP: 55
SALES (corp-wide): 2.1B **Publicly Held**
WEB: www.masonite.com
SIC: 5031 3442 2431 Doors & windows;
metal doors; doors, wood
PA: Masonite International Corporation
1242 E 5th Ave
Tampa FL 33605
800 895-2723

(G-4644)
MASSOUD FURNITURE MFG CO
8351 Moberly Ln (75227-2316)
PHONE..................................214 388-8655
Charles E Massoud Sr, *President*
Charles E Massoud Jr, *Vice Pres*
Adam Messick, *Supervisor*
Gilann Garcia,
Taryn Payne,
EMP: 60
SQ FT: 40,000
SALES (est): 12.5MM Privately Held
WEB: www.massoudfurniture.com
SIC: 2512 Living room furniture: upholstered on wood frames; couches, sofas & davenports: upholstered on wood frames; chairs: upholstered on wood frames

(G-4645)
MASTER-HALCO INC (DH)
Also Called: Master Halco
3010 Lbj Fwy Ste 800 (75234-2776)
PHONE..................................972 714-7300
Ken Fishbein, *CEO*
Randy Ryker, *Plant Mgr*
Danielle Frazier, *Buyer*
Ariel Sutton, *Purchasing*
Scott Suh, *CFO*
▲ EMP: 60
SQ FT: 20,000
SALES (est): 508.2MM Privately Held
WEB: www.masterhalco.com
SIC: 3315 5039 3496 3446 Chain link fencing; wire fence, gates & accessories; miscellaneous fabricated wire products; architectural metalwork; lumber, plywood & millwork; fence construction
HQ: Itochu International Inc.
1251 Ave Of The Amrcas 51
New York NY 10020
212 818-8000

(G-4646)
MASTER-HALCO INC
8330 Lovett Ave (75227-4232)
PHONE..................................214 275-3100
Seth Peirce, *Branch Mgr*
EMP: 11 Privately Held
WEB: www.masterhalco.com
SIC: 3315 5039 Chain link fencing; wire fence, gates & accessories
HQ: Master-Halco, Inc.
3010 Lbj Fwy Ste 800
Dallas TX 75234
972 714-7300

(G-4647)
MASTER-HALCO INC
8250 Lovett Ave (75227-4230)
PHONE..................................214 391-3190
Juan Garibay, *Superintendent*
Ryan Gelhausen, *Superintendent*
Tony Hernandez, *Superintendent*
Tom Coopman, *Business Mgr*
Jerry Hart, *Branch Mgr*
EMP: 70 Privately Held
WEB: www.masterhalco.com
SIC: 3315 Chain link fencing
HQ: Master-Halco, Inc.
3010 Lbj Fwy Ste 800
Dallas TX 75234
972 714-7300

(G-4648)
MASTERCO INC
Also Called: Signmaster Wholesale Sign Co
3925 Cresthill Rd (75227-3210)
PHONE..................................214 381-5690
Bob Green, *President*
EMP: 9
SALES (corp-wide): 1.7MM Privately Held
SIC: 3993 Neon signs
PA: Masterco, Inc.
5545 Parkdale Dr
Dallas TX
214 388-4727

(G-4649)
MATADOR PRODUCTION COMPANY
5400 Lbj Fwy Ste 1500l (75240-1000)
P.O. Box 164336, Fort Worth (76161-4336)
PHONE..................................972 371-5200
Joseph W Foran, *CEO*
Craig N Adams, *Exec VP*

David E Lancaster, *Exec VP*
Matthew V Hairford, *Vice Pres*
Kathy Wayne, *Treasurer*
EMP: 20
SALES (est): 9.1MM
SALES (corp-wide): 983.6MM Publicly Held
WEB: www.matadorresources.com
SIC: 1382 Oil & gas exploration services
PA: Matador Resources Company
5400 Lbj Fwy Ste 1500
Dallas TX 75240
972 371-5200

(G-4650)
MATADOR RESOURCES COMPANY (PA)
5400 Lbj Fwy Ste 1500 (75240-1017)
PHONE..................................972 371-5200
Joseph Wm Foran, *Ch of Bd*
Matthew V Hairford, *President*
Dee Smith, *Superintendent*
Craig N Adams, *COO*
Billy E Goodwin, *COO*
EMP: 23
SALES: 983.6MM Publicly Held
WEB: www.matadorresources.com
SIC: 1311 Crude petroleum & natural gas; natural gas production; oil shale mining

(G-4651)
MATHESON TRI-GAS INC
2040 California Xing (75220-2310)
PHONE..................................972 432-8800
EMP: 20 Privately Held
WEB: www.mathesongas.com
SIC: 2813 5084 Industrial gases; welding machinery & equipment
HQ: Matheson Tri-Gas, Inc.
3 Mountainview Rd Ste 3 # 3
Warren NJ 07059
908 991-9200

(G-4652)
MATHESON TRI-GAS INC
2040 Cal Crossing Rd (75220-2310)
PHONE..................................817 354-9536
Fax: 817 354-9547
EMP: 15
SALES (corp-wide): 4.7B Privately Held
SIC: 2813 5084 Mfg Industrial Gases Whol Industrial Equipment
HQ: Matheson Tri-Gas, Inc.
150 Allen Rd Ste 302
Basking Ridge NJ 07059
908 991-9200

(G-4653)
MAVERICK STAINLESS LLC
4525 Production Dr (75235-8024)
PHONE..................................214 884-2700
Ray Broussard, *President*
Marty Palazeti, *Vice Pres*
Bruce Lisbin,
EMP: 25 EST: 2008
SALES (est): 7.7MM Privately Held
WEB: www.maverickstainless.com
SIC: 3312 Hot-rolled iron & steel products

(G-4654)
MAXIM INTEGRATED PRODUCTS INC
4345 Innovation Dr (75244)
P.O. Box 801549 (75380-1549)
PHONE..................................972 371-4000
Lin Zhu, *Technology*
EMP: 528
SALES (corp-wide): 2.1B Publicly Held
WEB: www.maximintegrated.com
SIC: 3674 Microcircuits, integrated (semiconductor)
PA: Maxim Integrated Products, Inc.
160 Rio Robles
San Jose CA 95134
408 601-1000

(G-4655)
MAXWELL PAPERS LP
Also Called: Maxwell Paper Products
615 Regal Row (75247-5209)
PHONE..................................214 631-5550
Rod Smith, *CEO*
▲ EMP: 68
SQ FT: 50,000

SALES (est): 20.1MM Privately Held
WEB: www.maxwellpaper.com
SIC: 2679 Adding machine rolls, paper: made from purchased material; teletypewriter paper, rolls with carbon; paper products, converted
PA: Maxwell Papers Holdings, Llp
615 Regal Row
Dallas TX 75247
214 631-5550

(G-4656)
MAXWELL PAPERS HOLDINGS LLP (PA)
615 Regal Row (75247-5209)
PHONE..................................214 631-5550
◆ EMP: 10 EST: 1974
SQ FT: 50,000
SALES (est): 20.1MM Privately Held
WEB: www.maxwellpaper.com
SIC: 2679 Adding machine rolls, paper: made from purchased material

(G-4657)
MAYCO INC
2811 Mican Dr (75212-4602)
P.O. Box 560543 (75356-0543)
PHONE..................................214 638-4848
David Gwinn, *President*
Melba Gwinn, *Vice Pres*
Kyle Thomason, *Plant Mgr*
Ricky Thomason, *Accountant*
EMP: 12 EST: 1976
SQ FT: 60,000
SALES (est): 2MM Privately Held
WEB: www.maycopallet.com
SIC: 2448 Pallets, wood

(G-4658)
MCBEE OPERATING COMPANY LLC (PA)
4301 Westside Dr Ste 200 (75209-6571)
PHONE..................................214 526-1500
EMP: 11
SQ FT: 3,600
SALES (est): 2.2MM Privately Held
SIC: 1311 Crude petroleum production; natural gas production

(G-4659)
MCCARTNEY INVESTMENT CORP
Also Called: McCartney's University Spirit
6407 Hillcrest Ave (75205-1852)
PHONE..................................214 521-8410
Carolyn Culbert, *President*
Blake McCartney, *President*
EMP: 10
SALES (est): 651K Privately Held
WEB: www.blakejonesdesigns.com
SIC: 5947 5944 2389 Gift shop; jewelry stores; regalia

(G-4660)
MCCORD PRINTING INC
1111 Regal Row (75247-3611)
PHONE..................................214 631-1809
EMP: 22
SALES (est): 1.4MM Privately Held
SIC: 2752 Lithographic Commercial Printing

(G-4661)
MCGREW ENERGY CORPORATION
4849 Grnvlle Ave Ste 1310 (75206)
PHONE..................................214 265-1135
Richard M McGrew, *President*
John A Stewart, *Vice Pres*
EMP: 9
SQ FT: 2,000
SALES (est): 2.5MM Privately Held
SIC: 1311 Crude petroleum production

(G-4662)
MEDICAL TEXTILES INC
107 Pittsburg St (75207-7207)
PHONE..................................214 744-1246
Anthony Borino Jr, *President*
Richard Gamble, *Vice Pres*
EMP: 30
SQ FT: 3,000
SALES (est): 1.9MM Privately Held
SIC: 2211 Draperies & drapery fabrics, cotton

(G-4663)
MEDICAL WEB EXPERTS LLC
5950 Sherry Ln Ste 405 (75225-6538)
PHONE..................................619 819-8610
Yanina Libenson, *President*
John Deutsch, *Chairman*
Kortney Orueta, *CFO*
EMP: 30
SALES (est): 700.9K Privately Held
WEB: www.medicalwebexperts.com
SIC: 7372 Prepackaged software

(G-4664)
MEDITRRNEAN SPCIALTY FOODS LLC
Also Called: Tykhe Foods
6433 Norway Rd (75230-5146)
PHONE..................................214 680-8820
Sam Paulos, *Partner*
David James Nayfa, *Mng Member*
EMP: 100
SQ FT: 8,000
SALES (est): 3MM Privately Held
SIC: 2099 5143 Desserts, ready-to-mix; frozen dairy desserts

(G-4665)
MELISSA LIGHTING INC
4859 Olson Dr (75227-2100)
PHONE..................................214 388-7487
Peter Macaluso, *President*
▲ EMP: 47
SQ FT: 17,000
SALES (est): 7.3MM Privately Held
WEB: www.melissalighting.com
SIC: 3645 3646 Residential lighting fixtures; commercial indusl & institutional electric lighting fixtures

(G-4666)
MERIT ENERGY COMPANY LLC (PA)
13737 Noel Rd Ste 1200 (75240-1335)
PHONE..................................972 701-8377
Robert R Matejek, *President*
Debbie Remphrey, *Chairman*
Kathryn Lyles, *Counsel*
Ben Moffett, *Counsel*
Thomas Porter Trimble, *Exec VP*
▲ EMP: 200
SQ FT: 60,000
SALES (est): 3.9B Privately Held
WEB: www.meritenergy.com
SIC: 1311 Crude petroleum production; natural gas production

(G-4667)
MERIT ENERGY PARTNERS F-I LP
132727 Noel Rd Ste 500 (75240)
PHONE..................................972 701-8377
Megan Cuddihy, *Managing Prtnr*
EMP: 10
SALES (est): 550K Privately Held
WEB: www.meritenergy.com
SIC: 1389 Oil & gas field services

(G-4668)
MESTEX LTD
4830 Transport Dr (75247-6310)
PHONE..................................214 638-6010
Tommy Nsuk, *Engineer*
Linzi Hernandez, *Sales Staff*
Dale Bennett, *Mng Member*
▲ EMP: 240
SALES (est): 68.6MM
SALES (corp-wide): 642MM Privately Held
WEB: www.mestex.com
SIC: 3585 1711 Heating & air conditioning combination units; plumbing, heating, air-conditioning contractors
PA: Mestek, Inc.
260 N Elm St
Westfield MA 01085
470 898-4533

(G-4669)
METAL DETAIL INC
4120 Shilling Way (75237-1025)
PHONE..................................214 330-7757
Woodrow W Thompson II, *President*
Judy Thompson, *Corp Secy*
EMP: 16 EST: 1958
SQ FT: 15,000

SALES (est): 2.4MM **Privately Held**
WEB: www.metaldetail.com
SIC: **3599** Machine shop, jobbing & repair

(G-4670)
METRO MINI COURSES INC
Also Called: Metropolitian Newsletter
6400 Maple Ave Ste 850 (75235-5521)
PHONE..........................214 826-2300
Chris Kerrigan, *President*
Stephen Mandala, *Vice Pres*
EMP: 15
SQ FT: 4,000
SALES (est): 1.4MM **Privately Held**
SIC: **2759** Publication printing

(G-4671)
METRO-GRAPHICS INC
1311 Regal Row (75247-3615)
P.O. Box 36046 (75235-1046)
PHONE..........................214 638-6780
Raymond Mosman, *President*
Dolores J Mosman, *Corp Secy*
Randy Mosman, *Vice Pres*
Dolores Mosman, *Admin Sec*
EMP: 10
SALES (est): 1.8MM **Privately Held**
WEB: www.metrodallas.com
SIC: **2752** Commercial printing, offset

(G-4672)
METROPLEX MILLWORKS INC
2665 Perth St (75220-1317)
P.O. Box 542677 (75354-2677)
PHONE..........................214 358-1770
Charles Hargrave, *President*
Debra Hargrave, *Corp Secy*
EMP: 18
SQ FT: 14,000
SALES (est): 2.6MM **Privately Held**
SIC: **2599 2434 5211** Cabinets, factory; wood kitchen cabinets; millwork & lumber

(G-4673)
METROPOLEX WOOD SPECIALTY
1357 N Walton Walker Blvd (75211-1042)
PHONE..........................214 339-5115
Russell Heydenreich, *Partner*
Marley Heydenreich, *Partner*
EMP: 24
SALES (est): 2.9MM **Privately Held**
SIC: **2499** Applicators, wood

(G-4674)
MICK & DAVID ENTERPRISES INC
Also Called: Pro Panels
9017 Diplomacy Row (75247-5303)
PHONE..........................214 350-5765
David Curry, *President*
Mark Burris, *General Mgr*
Michael M Dixon, *Vice Pres*
EMP: 10
SQ FT: 12,000
SALES (est): 2MM **Privately Held**
WEB: www.propanels.com
SIC: **2653 5199 7319** Display items, corrugated: made from purchased materials; canvas products; display advertising service

(G-4675)
MICRO-DESIGN INC
Also Called: M D I
1805 Royal Ln Ste 111 (75229-7520)
P.O. Box 59449 (75229-1449)
PHONE..........................972 488-8725
EMP: 9
SALES (est): 1.9MM **Privately Held**
WEB: www.micro-design.com
SIC: **3823** Liquid level instruments, industrial process type

(G-4676)
MICROSPACE INSTRUMENTS INC
4751 Wilburton Dr (75227-2318)
P.O. Box 270982 (75227-0982)
PHONE..........................214 388-0461
Stanley A Bennett Sr, *President*
Stanley A Bennett Jr, *Corp Secy*
Kyle T Bennett, *Vice Pres*
Kyle Bennett, *Vice Pres*
Malcom White, *Vice Pres*

EMP: 16
SQ FT: 7,000
SALES (est): 1.2MM **Privately Held**
WEB: www.mspace.com
SIC: **3599** Machine shop, jobbing & repair

(G-4677)
MIKE SANDONE PRODUCTIONS INC
403 S Haskell Ave (75226-1116)
P.O. Box 150365 (75315-0365)
PHONE..........................800 652-5635
Mike Sandone, *President*
Marc Brizendine, *QC Mgr*
Sara Okey, *Office Mgr*
Frank Villarreal, *Manager*
Bill Glassner, *Executive*
EMP: 32
SQ FT: 15,000
SALES (est): 2.4MM **Privately Held**
WEB: www.sandoneproductions.com
SIC: **2394 7359 5999 5947** Canvas awnings & canopies; tents: made from purchased materials; tent & tarpaulin rental; awnings; tents; gifts & novelties

(G-4678)
MINEARC SYSTEMS AMERICA LLC
4850 W Ledbetter Dr (75236-1514)
PHONE..........................214 337-5100
Heath Ramirez, *Design Engr*
James Rau, *Mng Member*
Jameas A Rau, *Director*
Gerald Ness,
Paul Ness,
▲ EMP: 15
SQ FT: 10,000
SALES (est): 4.8MM **Privately Held**
WEB: www.minearc.com
SIC: **3448** Buildings, portable: prefabricated metal

(G-4679)
MIZKAN AMERICA INC
4515 Bronze Way (75236-2007)
PHONE..........................214 339-5551
Koichi Yuki, *CEO*
EMP: 99 **Privately Held**
WEB: www.mizkan.com
SIC: **2099** Food preparations
HQ: Mizkan America, Inc.
1661 Feehanville Dr 100a
Mount Prospect IL 60056
847 590-0059

(G-4680)
MIZKAN AMERICAS INC
4647 Bronze Way (75236-2009)
PHONE..........................214 339-5551
Timothy Hakimi, *Plant Mgr*
Darren James, *Plant Mgr*
Paul Mamola, *Manager*
EMP: 22
SQ FT: 21,282 **Privately Held**
WEB: www.mizkan.com
SIC: **2099** Vinegar
HQ: Mizkan America, Inc.
1661 Feehanville Dr 100a
Mount Prospect IL 60056
847 590-0059

(G-4681)
MJM SOURCING LLC
1050 Metro Media Pl (75247-4717)
PHONE..........................214 769-7881
Mary Bang, *Mng Member*
▲ EMP: 10 EST: 2011
SQ FT: 25,000
SALES (est): 10MM **Privately Held**
WEB: www.mybiomiracle.com
SIC: **2389** Men's miscellaneous accessories

(G-4682)
MO2 INC (PA)
13111 N Cntl Expy Ste 440 (75243)
PHONE..........................214 575-7600
Peter A Gerard, *President*
Ken Culver, *CFO*
Robert Culver, *CFO*
EMP: 10
SQ FT: 3,000

SALES (est): 783.8K **Privately Held**
SIC: **3823 4841 3812 3826** Absorption analyzers: infrared, X-ray, etc.: industrial; satellite master antenna systems services (SMATV); search & navigation equipment; analytical instruments; measuring & controlling devices; personal holding companies, except banks

(G-4683)
MOHAWK INDUSTRIES INC
7834 C F Hawn Fwy (75217-6529)
P.O. Box 170130 (75217-9131)
PHONE..........................214 309-4848
Guy Hargrove, *Division Mgr*
Claudio Caselli, *Vice Pres*
John Cousins, *Vice Pres*
Jon Shedlosky, *Vice Pres*
Tom Kennedy, *Materials Dir*
EMP: 24 **Publicly Held**
WEB: www.mohawkind.com
SIC: **2273** Finishers of tufted carpets & rugs
PA: Mohawk Industries, Inc.
160 S Industrial Blvd
Calhoun GA 30701

(G-4684)
MOLL MCNEILL INC
Also Called: Finley
3901 Main St (75226-1229)
PHONE..........................214 748-7272
Heather McNeill, *President*
Susan Finley Moll, *Vice Pres*
Moll Susan Finley, *Director*
EMP: 9
SQ FT: 3,000
SALES (est): 946K **Privately Held**
WEB: www.thefinleyshirt.com
SIC: **2331 2339 2337 2335** Shirts, women's & juniors': made from purchased materials; slacks: women's, misses' & juniors'; jackets & vests, except fur & leather: women's; women's, juniors' & misses' dresses

(G-4685)
MONEYONMOBILE INC
500 N Akard St Ste 2850 (75201-6620)
PHONE..........................214 758-8600
Harold H Montgomery, *Ch of Bd*
Will Dawson, *COO*
Scott S Arey, *CFO*
Wendy Pritchett, *Human Res Mgr*
EMP: 308
SALES (est): 15.9MM **Privately Held**
WEB: www.calpian.com
SIC: **7372 7389 6099** Prepackaged software; process serving service; electronic funds transfer network, including switching

(G-4686)
MONTANA WEST USA
2606 Brenner Dr (75220-1320)
PHONE..........................972 241-9998
▲ EMP: 17
SALES (est): 1.8MM **Privately Held**
WEB: www.montanawestusa.com
SIC: **2389** Men's miscellaneous accessories

(G-4687)
MOOALA BRANDS LLC
2633 Mckinney Ave Ste 130 (75204-8630)
PHONE..........................214 206-1902
Jeffrey Richards, *President*
EMP: 10
SALES (est): 1MM **Privately Held**
WEB: www.mooala.com
SIC: **2087 7389** Beverage bases;

(G-4688)
MORGAN BUILDING TRANSPORT
Also Called: Morgan Buildings & Spas
12700 Hillcrest Rd Ste C (75230-2161)
P.O. Box 660280 (75266-0280)
PHONE..........................972 864-7300
Guy Morgan, *Manager*
EMP: 20 **Privately Held**
WEB: www.morganusa.com
SIC: **5999 2452** Swimming pools, hot tubs & sauna equipment & supplies; prefabricated buildings; prefabricated wood buildings

HQ: Morgan Building Transport Corp
12700 Hillcrest Rd Ste C
Dallas TX 75230
972 864-7300

(G-4689)
MORRELL PLATING CO INC
2712 Anson Rd (75235-3762)
PHONE..........................214 357-9850
James Morrell Jr, *President*
Bill Morrell, *Vice Pres*
EMP: 10
SQ FT: 9,000
SALES (est): 1.2MM **Privately Held**
WEB: www.morrellplating.com
SIC: **3471** Electroplating of metals or formed products

(G-4690)
MOTION ENVELOPE INC
Also Called: I3 Plastic Cards
1628 Terre Colony Ct (75212-6221)
PHONE..........................214 634-2131
John Searfoss, *President*
Frank Artinger, *Exec VP*
Ralph P Searfoss, *Vice Pres*
Michael Foley, *Opers Mgr*
EMP: 40
SQ FT: 25,000
SALES (est): 14.3MM **Privately Held**
WEB: www.i3plasticcards.com
SIC: **2677** Envelopes

(G-4691)
MOTOR CONTROLS INC
Also Called: MCI Flowtronex
10661 Newkirk St (75220-2303)
P.O. Box 59986 (75229-1986)
PHONE..........................972 247-4440
James Carter, *CEO*
Craig Carter, *President*
Jeff Haines, *Vice Pres*
John Murtaugh, *Vice Pres*
Roger Vowell, *Vice Pres*
EMP: 275
SQ FT: 138,775
SALES (est): 76.6MM **Privately Held**
WEB: www.motorcontrols.com
SIC: **3444 3561 3625 3565** Metal housings, enclosures, casings & other containers; pumps & pumping equipment; industrial controls: push button, selector switches, pilot; packaging machinery

(G-4692)
MOTOROLA SOLUTIONS INC
1507 L B Johnson Fwy # 700 (75234-6174)
PHONE..........................972 277-4600
Patrick Philp, *Branch Mgr*
EMP: 55
SALES (corp-wide): 7.8B **Publicly Held**
WEB: www.motorolasolutions.com
SIC: **3663** Radio & TV communications equipment
PA: Motorola Solutions, Inc.
500 W Monroe St Ste 4400
Chicago IL 60661
847 576-5000

(G-4693)
MOTOROLA SOLUTIONS INC
1701 Valley View Ln (75234-9027)
PHONE..........................972 587-5360
Wesley D Thrash, *Branch Mgr*
Timothy Erichson, *Senior Mgr*
EMP: 36
SALES (corp-wide): 7.8B **Publicly Held**
WEB: www.motorolasolutions.com
SIC: **3663** Radio & TV communications equipment
PA: Motorola Solutions, Inc.
500 W Monroe St Ste 4400
Chicago IL 60661
847 576-5000

(G-4694)
MOYES & CO INC
8235 Douglas Ave Ste 1221 (75225-6012)
PHONE..........................214 623-6700
Christopher P Moyes, *President*
Christopher R Moore, *Managing Dir*
EMP: 21
SQ FT: 3,000
SALES (est): 3.3MM **Privately Held**
WEB: www.moyesco.com
SIC: **1382** Oil & gas exploration services

(G-4695)
MOZZARELLA COMPANY
2944 Elm St (75226-1509)
PHONE..................214 741-4072
Paula S Lambert, *President*
Suzanne S Bartolucci, *Vice Pres*
Mauricio Travesi, *Plant Mgr*
Ross Adami, *Project Mgr*
Carole B Jordan, *Admin Sec*
EMP: 20
SQ FT: 4,500
SALES: 1.7MM **Privately Held**
WEB: www.mozzco.com
SIC: 2022 5451 Natural cheese; cheese

(G-4696)
MPL INDUSTRIES INC (PA)
Also Called: SOUTHERN METALS COMPANY
10877 Rockwall Rd (75238-1213)
P.O. Box 551354 (75355-1354)
PHONE..................214 253-2332
Michael P Long, *President*
Michael Knize, *COO*
Melissa Mitchell, *COO*
EMP: 13
SQ FT: 2,200
SALES (est): 6.7MM **Privately Held**
WEB: www.metaltechcompany.com
SIC: 5051 3469 Tubing, metal; stamping metal for the trade

(G-4697)
MPL INDUSTRIES INC
Southern Metals Company
10877 Rockwall Rd (75238-1213)
PHONE..................972 233-0757
John Karo, *Enginr/R&D Mgr*
EMP: 9
SQ FT: 8,000
SALES (corp-wide): 6.7MM **Privately Held**
WEB: www.metaltechcompany.com
SIC: 3599 Machine shop, jobbing & repair
PA: Mpl Industries, Inc
10877 Rockwall Rd
Dallas TX 75238
214 253-2332

(G-4698)
MR NAMS FOODS INCORPORATED
3435 Jane Ln (75247-6528)
PHONE..................214 689-4688
EMP: 10
SQ FT: 5,656
SALES (est): 1MM **Privately Held**
SIC: 2032 Mfg Canned Specialties

(G-4699)
MR SIGN INC (PA)
Also Called: Fast Signs Oaklawn
2629 Oak Lawn Ave (75219-4021)
PHONE..................214 526-7446
Bill Becker, *President*
Adrian Becker, *Vice Pres*
Rita Becker, *Treasurer*
EMP: 9
SQ FT: 18,000
SALES (est): 1.8MM **Privately Held**
WEB: www.fastsigns.com
SIC: 3993 7334 5999 Signs & advertising specialties; photocopying & duplicating services; banners

(G-4700)
MRC ENERGY COMPANY
Also Called: Matador Resources Company
5400 Lyndon B Johnson Fwy (75240-1000)
PHONE..................972 371-5200
Joseph Wm Foran, *Ch of Bd*
Craig Adams, *Vice Pres*
Matthew Hairford, *Vice Pres*
Scott King, *Vice Pres*
David E Lancaster, *Vice Pres*
EMP: 40
SQ FT: 21,000
SALES (corp-wide): 983.6MM **Publicly Held**
WEB: www.matadorresources.com
SIC: 1382 Oil & gas exploration services
PA: Matador Resources Company
5400 Lbj Fwy Ste 1500
Dallas TX 75240
972 371-5200

(G-4701)
MS DALLAS REPROGRAPHICS INC
1130 Dragon St Ste 110 (75207-4233)
PHONE..................214 521-7000
Daphne Best, *President*
EMP: 20
SQ FT: 17,000
SALES (est): 2.7MM **Privately Held**
WEB: www.msdallas.com
SIC: 7334 2752 Blueprinting service; commercial printing, lithographic

(G-4702)
MSF ELECTRIC INC
9622 Chartwell Dr (75243-8302)
PHONE..................214 377-8710
EMP: 36 **Privately Held**
WEB: www.msfelectric.com
SIC: 3699 1731 Electrical equipment & supplies; electrical work
PA: Msf Electric, Inc.
10455 Fountaingate Dr
Stafford TX 77477

(G-4703)
MUDSMITH
2114 Greenville Ave (75206-7126)
PHONE..................214 370-9535
EMP: 13 **EST:** 2013
SALES (est): 787.6K **Privately Held**
WEB: www.mudsmithcoffee.com
SIC: 1389 Oil & gas field services

(G-4704)
MULTI PACKAGING SOLUTIONS INC
Also Called: MPS Dallas
13465 Jupiter Rd (75238-2434)
PHONE..................214 343-7600
Sherry Benavidez, *Production*
Reno Lawrence, *Production*
Bob Carlson, *Research*
Sara Carmichael, *Accounts Exec*
Travis McDonough, *Branch Mgr*
EMP: 150
SALES (corp-wide): 17.5B **Publicly Held**
WEB: www.westrock.com
SIC: 2759 Commercial printing
HQ: Multi Packaging Solutions, Inc.
885 3rd Ave Fl 28
New York NY 10022

(G-4705)
MULTI PACKG SOLUTIONS INTL LTD
1455 Terre Colony Ct (75212-6220)
PHONE..................214 634-2131
EMP: 35
SALES (corp-wide): 17.5B **Publicly Held**
WEB: www.westrock.com
SIC: 3089 Identification cards, plastic
HQ: Multi Packaging Solutions International Limited
885 3rd Ave Fl 28
New York NY 10022
646 885-0005

(G-4706)
MULTI PLASTICS
10554 King William Dr (75220-2411)
PHONE..................972 402-9100
John Parsio, *Owner*
Matt Farris, *Manager*
Anthony A Dziurawiec, *Executive*
EMP: 10
SALES (est): 952.9K **Privately Held**
WEB: www.multi-plastics.com
SIC: 2821 Plastics materials & resins

(G-4707)
MULTICAM INC (HQ)
1025 Royal Ln (75261-4527)
P.O. Box 612048 (75261-2048)
PHONE..................972 929-4070
David Morse, *CEO*
David Scheffrahn, *Vice Pres*
Jeff Dirickson, *Engineer*
Douglas Trinh, *CFO*
Corie Clifton, *Human Res Mgr*
◆ **EMP:** 135
SQ FT: 100,000

SALES (est): 32.3MM **Privately Held**
WEB: www.multicam.com
SIC: 3545 Machine tool attachments & accessories

(G-4708)
MUROC SYSTEMS INC
Also Called: Teamsupport.com
100 Highland Park Vlg (75205-2722)
PHONE..................214 295-9442
Robert C Johnson, *President*
Tamiko Fletcher, *VP Sales*
Leon Choi, *Accounts Exec*
Kevin Jones, *CTO*
Eric Harrington, *Officer*
EMP: 15
SALES (est): 1.8MM **Privately Held**
WEB: www.teamsupport.com
SIC: 7372 Business oriented computer software

(G-4709)
MURRAY LABEL & PRINTING LTD
10470 Miller Rd (75238-1210)
PHONE..................972 234-2220
Jeff Murray, *Partner*
James Murray, *Principal*
▼ **EMP:** 16
SQ FT: 10,000
SALES (est): 2.1MM **Privately Held**
WEB: www.inovarpackaging.com
SIC: 2759 Commercial printing, lithographic

(G-4710)
MY SONS LAUNDRY LLC
Also Called: Texas Coin and Commercial Ldry
8700 Chancellor Row (75247-5524)
PHONE..................214 634-2080
Kellie Blumberg, *President*
Mike Blumberg, *Vice Pres*
EMP: 12
SALES (est): 2.5MM
SALES (corp-wide): 22.3MM **Privately Held**
WEB: www.txcoinlaundry.com
SIC: 5087 3582 5999 Laundry equipment & supplies; commercial laundry equipment; cleaning equipment & supplies
PA: Bermil Industries Corporation
461 Doughty Blvd
Inwood NY 11096
516 371-4400

(G-4711)
N L INDUSTRIES INC (DH)
Also Called: Nl Industries
5430 Lbj Fwy Ste 1700 (75240-2620)
PHONE..................972 233-1700
Loretta J Feehan, *Ch of Bd*
Courtney J Riley, *President*
Robert D Graham, *Vice Chairman*
Kelly D Luttmer, *Exec VP*
Kelly Luttmer, *Exec VP*
EMP: 29 **EST:** 1891
SALES: 124.2MM
SALES (corp-wide): 2B **Publicly Held**
WEB: www.nl-ind.com
SIC: 2819 3572 3699 Industrial inorganic chemicals; computer storage devices; security devices
HQ: Valhi, Inc.
5430 Lbj Fwy Ste 1700
Dallas TX 75240
972 233-1700

(G-4712)
NATIONAL BANNER COMPANY INC (PA)
Also Called: World Division USA
11938 Harry Hines Blvd (75234-5999)
P.O. Box 842372 (75284-2372)
PHONE..................972 241-2131
Abraham Goldfarb, *Ch of Bd*
Marc Goldfarb, *President*
Don Girard, *Treasurer*
Brandon Westmoreland, *Sales Staff*
◆ **EMP:** 120 **EST:** 1952
SQ FT: 131,500
SALES (est): 24.7MM **Privately Held**
WEB: www.nationalbanner.com
SIC: 3993 Signs & advertising specialties

(G-4713)
NATIONAL BANNER COMPANY INC
Also Called: World Division USA
12023 Denton Dr (75234-7211)
PHONE..................972 241-2131
Melissa McLaughlin, *VP Admin*
David Fry, *Manager*
EMP: 70
SALES (corp-wide): 24.7MM **Privately Held**
WEB: www.nationalbanner.com
SIC: 3993 Signs & advertising specialties
PA: National Banner Company, Inc.
11938 Harry Hines Blvd
Dallas TX 75234
972 241-2131

(G-4714)
NATIONAL DIAMOND LAB TEXAS INC
1435 Round Table Dr (75247-3507)
PHONE..................214 638-1435
Jody Nichols, *CEO*
Richard Burrola, *President*
EMP: 13
SQ FT: 10,000
SALES (est): 1.1MM **Privately Held**
WEB: www.ndlab.com
SIC: 3545 Diamond cutting tools for turning, boring, burnishing, etc.; diamond dressing & wheel crushing attachments

(G-4715)
NATIONAL FOOD AND BEVERAGE INC
9030 Premier Row (75247-5406)
PHONE..................214 905-9700
Johnny Lee Stanley, *President*
Shawn Cantrell, *Vice Pres*
Katie Lee, *Vice Pres*
Todd Thomasson, *Production*
Carissa Kennedy, *Human Res Mgr*
EMP: 80
SQ FT: 30,000
SALES (est): 6.2MM **Privately Held**
WEB: www.national-foods.com
SIC: 2099 2033 2035 Sauces: gravy, dressing & dip mixes; dips, except cheese & sour cream based; barbecue sauce: packaged in cans, jars, etc.; jams, including imitation: packaged in cans, jars, etc.; jellies, edible, including imitation: in cans, jars, etc.; pickles, sauces & salad dressings

(G-4716)
NATIONAL WHOLESALE SUPPLY INC (PA)
Also Called: National Hot Water
1972 Cal Crossing Rd (75220-7006)
PHONE..................972 331-7770
Charles Reynolds, *President*
Kathy Shaw, *Sales Staff*
Patricia Vessels, *Info Tech Dir*
Dario Meucci, *Technology*
EMP: 21
SQ FT: 18,000
SALES (est): 91.2MM **Privately Held**
WEB: www.nationalwholesalesupply.com
SIC: 5074 3589 3491 3585 Plumbing fittings & supplies; water purification equipment, household type; water works valves; air conditioning equipment, complete

(G-4717)
NATURAL GAS VEHICLES TEXAS INC
Also Called: Ngv Texas
10733 Spangler Rd (75220-7101)
PHONE..................214 630-1000
Fury Zaidi, *President*
Marci Malinder, *Vice Pres*
Marci Millender, *Opers Staff*
◆ **EMP:** 15 **EST:** 2008
SALES: 4.2MM **Privately Held**
WEB: www.ngvtexas.com
SIC: 3519 1321 Gasoline engines; natural gas liquids

(G-4718)
NEARBURG PRODUCING COMPANY (PA)
5447 Glen Lakes Dr (75231-4307)
P.O. Box 823085 (75382-3085)
PHONE......................................214 739-1778
Charles E Nearburg, *President*
Frederick E White, *COO*
Bill Fairhurst, *Vice Pres*
Duane Davis, *Director*
EMP: 15
SQ FT: 6,540
SALES (est): 19.9MM **Privately Held**
SIC: 1311 Crude petroleum production

(G-4719)
NEC CORPORATION OF AMERICA
Also Called: N E C America Radio Division
1213 N 28th Ave (75261-5003)
P.O. Box 730037 (75373-0037)
PHONE......................................214 262-2387
EMP: 45 **Privately Held**
WEB: www.necam.com
SIC: 3663 5999 5065 Microwave communication equipment; telephone equipment & systems; telephone equipment
HQ: Nec Corporation Of America
    3929 W John Carpenter Fwy
    Irving TX 75063
    214 262-6000

(G-4720)
NELSON HUNT BUNKER
Also Called: Hunt Mining & Exploration
3811 Trtl Crk Blvd # 1825 (75219-4444)
PHONE......................................214 979-9072
Nelson Bunker Hunt, *Owner*
EMP: 15
SALES (est): 706.5K **Privately Held**
SIC: 1382 Oil & gas exploration services

(G-4721)
NEORA LLC (HQ)
Also Called: Nerium International
4201 Spring Valley Rd (75244-3631)
PHONE......................................855 463-7486
Jeff Olson, *CEO*
Jeffrey Dahl, *CEO*
Bo Short, *President*
Roy Truett, *President*
Deborah K Heisz, *Co-CEO*
EMP: 10 EST: 2011
SALES (est): 2.4MM **Privately Held**
WEB: www.neora.com
SIC: 5122 8731 2834 2844 Cosmetics; commercial physical research; pharmaceutical preparations; toilet preparations

(G-4722)
NEW CROSSLINK LP
11122 Morrison Ln (75229-5607)
PHONE......................................972 484-3322
Patrick Flynn, *Partner*
EMP: 11
SQ FT: 11,000
SALES (est): 1.1MM **Privately Held**
SIC: 3399 Metal powders, pastes & flakes

(G-4723)
NEW DAIRY MADISONVILLE LLC
8750 N Central Expy # 400 (75231-6436)
PHONE......................................863 297-7342
Gregg Engles, *CEO*
EMP: 15
SALES (est): 49.9K
SALES (corp-wide): 56MM **Privately Held**
SIC: 2023 Condensed, concentrated & evaporated milk products
PA: New Dairy Opco, Llc
    8750 N Central Expy # 400
    Dallas TX 75231
    972 619-1535

(G-4724)
NEW DAIRY NDH TRANSPORT LLC
8750 N Central Expy # 400 (75231-6436)
PHONE......................................214 459-1100
Gregg Engles, *CEO*
EMP: 15

SALES (est): 68.6K
SALES (corp-wide): 56MM **Privately Held**
SIC: 2023 Condensed, concentrated & evaporated milk products
PA: New Dairy Opco, Llc
    8750 N Central Expy # 400
    Dallas TX 75231
    972 619-1535

(G-4725)
NEW DAIRY OPCO LLC (PA)
Also Called: Borden Dairy
8750 N Central Expy # 400 (75231-6417)
PHONE......................................972 619-1535
Pat Boyle, *President*
Stephen Harper, *CFO*
Pat Ford, *Finance*
EMP: 80
SALES (est): 56MM **Privately Held**
SIC: 2023 Dry, condensed, evaporated dairy products

(G-4726)
NEW DAIRY TEXAS LLC
8750 N Central Expy # 400 (75231-6436)
PHONE......................................214 459-1100
Gregg Engles, *CEO*
EMP: 15
SALES (est): 59.8K
SALES (corp-wide): 56MM **Privately Held**
SIC: 2023 Condensed, concentrated & evaporated milk products
PA: New Dairy Opco, Llc
    8750 N Central Expy # 400
    Dallas TX 75231
    972 619-1535

(G-4727)
NEW DAIRY TRADEMARK HOLDG LLC
8750 N Central Expy (75231-6436)
PHONE......................................803 297-7342
Gregg Engles, *CEO*
EMP: 15
SALES (est): 54.1K
SALES (corp-wide): 56MM **Privately Held**
SIC: 2021 Creamery butter
PA: New Dairy Opco, Llc
    8750 N Central Expy # 400
    Dallas TX 75231
    972 619-1535

(G-4728)
NEW DIRY CLIMS ADJSTING SVCS L
8750 N Central Expy # 400 (75231-6436)
PHONE......................................863 297-7342
Gregg Engles,
EMP: 10
SALES (est): 283.4K
SALES (corp-wide): 56MM **Privately Held**
SIC: 2023 Dry, condensed, evaporated dairy products
PA: New Dairy Opco, Llc
    8750 N Central Expy # 400
    Dallas TX 75231
    972 619-1535

(G-4729)
NEW LIFESTYLES INC
4144 N Cntl Expy Ste 1000 (75204)
PHONE......................................214 824-0022
Doug Fusella, *President*
Pamela Fusella, *Corp Secy*
Pam Fusella, *CFO*
Megan Blaser, *Accounts Exec*
Stacee Howse, *Director*
EMP: 30
SQ FT: 10,249
SALES (est): 3.8MM **Privately Held**
WEB: www.newlifestyles.com
SIC: 2741 Directories: publishing only, not printed on site

(G-4730)
NEW NATIONAL DAIRY LLC
8750 N Cntl Ex Way Ste 40 (75231)
PHONE......................................863 297-7342
Gregg Engles, *CEO*
EMP: 10

SALES (est): 43.5K
SALES (corp-wide): 56MM **Privately Held**
SIC: 2023 Dry, condensed, evaporated dairy products
PA: New Dairy Opco, Llc
    8750 N Central Expy # 400
    Dallas TX 75231
    972 619-1535

(G-4731)
NEW WORLD JEWELRY INC
Also Called: World Jewelry Associates
10830 Grissom Ln Ste 100 (75229-3501)
PHONE......................................972 243-2931
Steve Sohn, *President*
EMP: 13
SQ FT: 5,000
SALES (est): 3.1MM **Privately Held**
SIC: 5094 3911 Jewelry; jewelry, precious metal

(G-4732)
NEWCOMB SPRING CORP
Also Called: Newcomb Spring of Texas
2831 Satsuma Dr (75229-3524)
PHONE......................................972 241-6781
Ron Hubbard, *General Mgr*
Tim Coker, *Manager*
EMP: 35
SQ FT: 25,000
SALES (corp-wide): 60.1MM **Privately Held**
WEB: www.newcombspring.com
SIC: 3495 5085 3496 3493 Mechanical springs, precision; springs; miscellaneous fabricated wire products; steel springs, except wire; metal stampings
PA: Spring Newcomb Corp
    3155 North Point Pkwy G220
    Alpharetta GA 30005
    770 981-2803

(G-4733)
NEWS KOREA TEXAS INC
2000 Royal Ln Ste 200 (75229-3882)
PHONE......................................972 247-9111
Timothy Choe, *Principal*
Ji Mok, *CFO*
▲ EMP: 20
SALES (est): 902.1K **Privately Held**
WEB: www.newskorea.com
SIC: 2711 Newspapers, publishing & printing

(G-4734)
NEWSLETTER COMPANY
Also Called: Newletter Company, The
4901 Cole Ave (75205-3401)
PHONE......................................214 871-7997
Sherry McKinley, *President*
Mary Ann McKinley, *Vice Pres*
EMP: 10
SQ FT: 9,000
SALES (est): 975.1K **Privately Held**
WEB: www.thenewslettercompany.com
SIC: 2741 Newsletter publishing

(G-4735)
NEXEON MEDSYSTEMS INC
1910 Pcf Ave Ste 20000 (75201)
PHONE......................................844 919-9990
William Rosellini, *Ch of Bd*
Christopher R Miller, *CFO*
EMP: 55 EST: 2015
SQ FT: 800
SALES: 3.3MM **Privately Held**
WEB: www.nexeonmedsystems.com
SIC: 3821 Clinical laboratory instruments, except medical & dental

(G-4736)
NEXTECH SOLUTIONS INC
10480 Markison Rd (75238-1650)
PHONE......................................214 343-5300
Antonio Di Napoli, *CEO*
David A Torres, *Vice Pres*
Gerald M Bowers, *CTO*
Darrell McCauley, *Director*
EMP: 20
SQ FT: 9,800
SALES (est): 2.2MM **Privately Held**
SIC: 3674 Semiconductors & related devices

(G-4737)
NEXUS ALARM & SUPPRESSION INC
10575 Vista Park Rd (75238-1647)
PHONE......................................877 828-1200
Roddy Bieber, *General Mgr*
EMP: 50 **Privately Held**
WEB: www.afpgusa.com
SIC: 1731 1711 3569 Fire detection & burglar alarm systems specialization; fire sprinkler system installation; firefighting apparatus & related equipment
HQ: Nexus Alarm And Suppression, Inc.
    10575 Vista Park Rd
    Dallas TX 75238
    214 341-1200

(G-4738)
NICHOLSON METAL FABRICATORS
5127 Mercantile Row (75247-5927)
PHONE......................................214 920-3654
Victor Nicholson, *President*
Sandra Nicholson, *Admin Sec*
▲ EMP: 28
SALES (est): 3MM **Privately Held**
SIC: 3444 Sheet metalwork

(G-4739)
NIEMAN PRINTING INC (PA)
10615 Newkirk St Ste 100 (75220-2333)
PHONE......................................972 506-7400
Garrett Graves, *President*
EMP: 185 EST: 1979
SQ FT: 137,000
SALES (est): 62.7MM **Privately Held**
WEB: www.niemanprinting.com
SIC: 2752 2791 2796 Commercial printing, offset; typesetting; platemaking services

(G-4740)
NIKE INC
14241 Dallas Pkwy Ste 100 (75254-2937)
PHONE......................................972 980-1946
EMP: 50
SALES (corp-wide): 32.3B **Publicly Held**
SIC: 3021 Mfg Rubber/Plastic Footwear
PA: Nike, Inc.
    1 Sw Bowerman Dr
    Beaverton OR 97005
    503 671-6453

(G-4741)
NOLES DAVIS PLATING CO
Also Called: Noles Plating Co
2711 Manor Way (75235-5615)
PHONE......................................214 358-1731
Robert L Davis, *Owner*
EMP: 9
SQ FT: 1,800
SALES (est): 350K **Privately Held**
WEB: www.noles-davis.com
SIC: 3471 Gold plating

(G-4742)
NORAL HOLDING COMPANY
5495 Belt Line Rd (75254-7683)
P.O. Box 541743 (75354-1743)
PHONE......................................972 392-7780
J Glynn Gross, *President*
Jeff Cannon, *CFO*
EMP: 41
SALES (est): 275.2K **Privately Held**
SIC: 3669 1389 Intercommunication systems, electric; oil field services

(G-4743)
NORTHROP GRUMMAN SYSTEMS CORP
Also Called: Northrop Grmman Coml Arcft Div
9314 W Jefferson Blvd (75211-9301)
P.O. Box 655907 (75265-5907)
PHONE......................................972 946-9000
Ralph Crosby, *President*
Lynn Patterson, *Technology*
Barbara Caplan, *Software Dev*
David Tanner, *Software Dev*
Glenn McCoy, *Administration*
EMP: 2000 **Publicly Held**
WEB: www.northropgrumman.com
SIC: 3423 5599 Soldering tools; aircraft, self-propelled

▲ = Import ▼=Export
◆ =Import/Export

HQ: Northrop Grumman Systems Corporation
2980 Fairview Park Dr
Falls Church VA 22042
703 280-2900

(G-4744)
NOVOLEX INC
12118 Corporate Dr (75228-8111)
PHONE..................................972 686-5090
Mike Graubard, *Engineer*
Butch Fant, *Branch Mgr*
EMP: 129
SALES (corp-wide): 3.3B **Publicly Held**
WEB: www.novolex.com
SIC: 2673 5162 Plastic bags: made from purchased materials; plastics sheets & rods
HQ: Hilex Poly Co. Llc
101 E Carolina Ave
Hartsville SC 29550
843 857-4800

(G-4745)
NRPC OPERATING LLC
4925 Greenville Ave # 550 (75206-4026)
PHONE..................................512 428-4753
Kelly W Hoffman, *Mng Member*
EMP: 9
SALES (est): 475.1K **Privately Held**
SIC: 1382 Oil & gas exploration services

(G-4746)
NTL-BRANDS LTD (PA)
Also Called: Thermoserv
3901 Pipestone Rd (75212-6017)
PHONE..................................214 631-0307
Tom Neth, *CEO*
Dwayne Warren, *CFO*
Darryl Gaines, *Marketing Staff*
Mike Meyers, *Supervisor*
Kim Platt, *Info Tech Dir*
▲ **EMP:** 100
SQ FT: 185,000
SALES (est): 40.6MM **Privately Held**
WEB: www.thermoserv.com
SIC: 3089 Cups, plastic, except foam

(G-4747)
NUCOR CORPORATION
Vulcraft Division
7616 Lyndon B Johnson Fwy (75251-1100)
PHONE..................................214 340-1883
Driscoll Otto, *Sales/Mktg Mgr*
EMP: 13
SALES (corp-wide): 22.5B **Publicly Held**
WEB: www.nucor.com
SIC: 3312 Blast furnaces & steel mills
PA: Nucor Corporation
1915 Rexford Rd Ste 400
Charlotte NC 28211
704 366-7000

(G-4748)
O E M INDUSTRIES INC
1015 N Justin Ave (75211-1139)
P.O. Box 210427 (75211-0427)
PHONE..................................214 330-7271
Edward C Steiner Jr, *President*
EMP: 10
SQ FT: 4,200
SALES (est): 1MM **Privately Held**
WEB: www.oemindustries.com
SIC: 3462 Gear & chain forgings

(G-4749)
O9 SOLUTIONS INC (PA)
1501 Lyndon B Johnson Fwy # 140 (75234-6399)
P.O. Box 670634 (75367-0634)
PHONE..................................214 838-3125
Chakri Gottemukkala, *President*
Sanjiv Sidhu, *Chairman*
Igor Rikalo, *COO*
Umesh Arasu, *Vice Pres*
Koustuv Chatterjee, *Vice Pres*
EMP: 30
SALES (est): 7.2MM **Privately Held**
WEB: www.o9solutions.com
SIC: 7372 Prepackaged software

(G-4750)
OAK CLIFF OFFICE SUP PRTG INC
1876 Lone Star Dr (75212-5045)
PHONE..................................214 943-7421

Kenneth A Caldwell, *President*
Judi G Caldwell, *Corp Secy*
Rick Ivey, *Accounts Exec*
Toni Wyatt, *Sales Staff*
EMP: 22
SQ FT: 10,000
SALES (est): 1.9MM **Privately Held**
WEB: www.ocopexpress.com
SIC: 5943 2752 5712 Office forms & supplies; commercial printing, offset; office furniture

(G-4751)
OCCIDENTAL CHEMICAL CORP (HQ)
Also Called: O X Y
14555 Dallas Pkwy Ste 400 (75254-4362)
PHONE..................................972 404-3800
◆ **EMP:** 350
SQ FT: 133,000
SALES (est): 341.9MM
SALES (corp-wide): 21.2B **Publicly Held**
WEB: www.oxy.com
SIC: 2812 Chlorine, compressed or liquefied
PA: Occidental Petroleum Corporation
5 Greenway Plz Ste 110
Houston TX 77046
713 215-7000

(G-4752)
OCCIDENTAL CHEMICAL CORP
1100 Lenway St (75215-3364)
PHONE..................................214 421-7607
Patricia Ledbetter, *Purch Mgr*
Gary Ernst, *Branch Mgr*
EMP: 48
SQ FT: 69,046
SALES (corp-wide): 21.2B **Publicly Held**
WEB: www.oxy.com
SIC: 2874 Phosphatic fertilizers
HQ: Occidental Chemical Corporation
14555 Dallas Pkwy Ste 400
Dallas TX 75254
972 404-3800

(G-4753)
OCCIDENTAL CHEMICAL HOLDG CORP
5005 Lb Johnson Fwy Fl 22 Flr 22 (75244)
PHONE..................................972 404-3800
Raghaven Rajaji, *President*
Michael J Rudick, *Vice Pres*
Nigel Hopkinson, *VP Opers*
EMP: 50
SQ FT: 255,000
SALES (est): 68.8MM
SALES (corp-wide): 21.2B **Publicly Held**
WEB: www.oxy.com
SIC: 2869 3089 2873 2874 Industrial organic chemicals; plastic processing; nitrogenous fertilizers; phosphatic fertilizers; agricultural chemicals
PA: Occidental Petroleum Corporation
5 Greenway Plz Ste 110
Houston TX 77046
713 215-7000

(G-4754)
ODEE COMPANY
10630 Control Pl (75238-5323)
P.O. Box 550488 (75355-0488)
PHONE..................................214 340-0415
James Tatom Jr, *President*
Travis Baggett, *President*
Lucy Tatom, *Corp Secy*
James R Tatom Sr, *Vice Pres*
Travis Stein, *Manager*
EMP: 48 **EST:** 1923
SQ FT: 22,000
SALES (est): 11.8MM **Privately Held**
WEB: www.odeecompany.com
SIC: 5112 2759 2752 3993 Stationery & office supplies; thermography; commercial printing, offset; signs & advertising specialties; bookbinding & related work

(G-4755)
OGP OPERATING INC
8140 Walnut Hill Ln # 610 (75231-4350)
PHONE..................................214 696-2393
C Mitchell Johnston, *President*
Mary Arnold, *Corp Secy*
David Burns, *Vice Pres*
EMP: 9
SQ FT: 4,200

SALES (est): 949.1K **Privately Held**
WEB: www.ogpenergy.com
SIC: 1382 Oil & gas exploration services

(G-4756)
OIL & GAS PRODUCERS INC
8140 Walnut Hill Ln # 610 (75231-4350)
PHONE..................................214 696-2393
S Brooks Gremmels, *CEO*
EMP: 11
SQ FT: 4,200
SALES (est): 844.4K **Privately Held**
SIC: 1311 Crude petroleum & natural gas

(G-4757)
OILFIELD WATER LOGISTICS LLC
Also Called: Owl Swd Operating
8201 Preston Rd Ste 520 (75225-6210)
PHONE..................................214 292-2011
Christopher Cooper, *CEO*
Nevin Bannister, *COO*
Nick Hines, *Exec VP*
Roger Johnson, *Exec VP*
Matthew Thiel, *Exec VP*
EMP: 80 **EST:** 2014
SALES (est): 13MM
SALES (corp-wide): 3.3MM **Privately Held**
WEB: www.oilfieldwaterlogistics.com
SIC: 1389 Impounding & storing salt water, oil & gas field; oil field services
PA: Instaragf Asset Management Inc
66 Wellington St W Fl 31
Toronto ON M5K 1
416 815-6224

(G-4758)
OLD WORLD DESIGN LLC
134 Riveredge Dr (75207-6806)
PHONE..................................214 741-6858
Lynn Hamilton, *Marketing Staff*
Melisa Groth,
Jim Groth,
▲ **EMP:** 19
SQ FT: 20,000
SALES (est): 4.6MM **Privately Held**
WEB: www.owddallas.com
SIC: 5023 3641 Lamps: floor, boudoir, desk; lamps, incandescent filament, electric

(G-4759)
OLDCASTLE BUILDINGENVELOPE INC (DH)
5005 Lyndon B Johnson Fwy # 1050 (75244-6116)
PHONE..................................214 273-3400
Edwin B Hathaway, *CEO*
Liam O'Nahony, *Ch of Bd*
Doug Black, *President*
Kraig Garmaker, *General Mgr*
Rick Peters, *General Mgr*
◆ **EMP:** 13
SALES (est): 1B
SALES (corp-wide): 30.6B **Privately Held**
WEB: www.obe.com
SIC: 3231 5231 Tempered glass: made from purchased glass; insulating glass: made from purchased glass; glass
HQ: Crh Americas, Inc.
900 Ashwood Pkwy Ste 600
Atlanta GA 30338
770 804-3363

(G-4760)
OMEGA OPTICAL CO LP (PA)
13515 N Stemmons Fwy (75234-5765)
PHONE..................................972 241-4141
Hubert Sagnieres, *Principal*
EMP: 12
SALES (est): 6.7MM **Privately Held**
SIC: 3851 5048 5049 Eyeglasses, lenses & frames; contact lenses; ophthalmic goods; frames, ophthalmic; lenses, ophthalmic; optical goods

(G-4761)
OMRON MANAGEMENT CTR AMER INC
2801 W Rchlle Rd Bldg 100 (75261)
PHONE..................................489 724-2899
EMP: 20 **Privately Held**
SIC: 3829 Measuring And Controlling Devices, Nec

HQ: Omron Management Center Of America, Inc.
2895 Grnspint Pkwy Ste 10
Hoffman Estates IL 60169

(G-4762)
ON-BOARD COMMUNICATIONS INC
12850 Spurling Dr. Ste 280 (75230-1267)
PHONE..................................214 346-0300
Donald M Kennedy, *President*
William C Kennedy Jr, *Chairman*
Susie Marshall, *Corp Secy*
Wm C Kennedy III, *Vice Pres*
Larry Simmons, *Vice Pres*
EMP: 21
SQ FT: 5,600
SALES (est): 4MM **Privately Held**
WEB: www.onboardcommunications.com
SIC: 3663

(G-4763)
OPENCONNECT SYSTEMS INC
2711 Lbj Fwy Ste 700 (75234-7323)
PHONE..................................972 484-5200
John D Ferguson, *Vice Pres*
EMP: 28
SALES (corp-wide): 15.3MM **Privately Held**
WEB: www.activeops.com
SIC: 7372 Prepackaged software
PA: Openconnect Systems Incorporated
2711 Lyndon B Johnson Fwy
Dallas TX 75234
972 484-5200

(G-4764)
OPTEX SYSTEMS INC
Also Called: Applied Optics Center
9827 Chartwell Dr (75243-8303)
PHONE..................................972 629-1701
Bill Bates, *General Mgr*
EMP: 31
SALES (corp-wide): 25.8MM **Publicly Held**
WEB: www.optexsys.com
SIC: 3827 Lens coating equipment
HQ: Optex Systems, Inc.
1420 Presidential Dr
Richardson TX 75081
972 764-5700

(G-4765)
OQ CHEMICALS HOLDING CORP (DH)
Also Called: Oxea Holding Corp
1505 Lyndon B Johnson Fwy (75234-6069)
PHONE..................................972 481-2700
Wolfgang Hackenberc, *President*
Robert Gengelbach, *Principal*
Oliver Borgmeier, *COO*
Jan Hille, *Exec VP*
Markus Hoschke, *Exec VP*
EMP: 9
SALES (est): 94.4MM
SALES (corp-wide): 1.3B **Privately Held**
WEB: www.chemicals.oq.com
SIC: 2899 Chemical preparations
HQ: Oq Chemicals Gmbh
Rheinpromenade 4a
Monheim Am Rhein 40789
217 399-930

(G-4766)
ORACLE AMERICA INC
Also Called: Storagetek
12750 Merit Dr Ste 800 (75251-1251)
PHONE..................................972 980-7799
Tom Smits, *Branch Mgr*
EMP: 120
SALES (corp-wide): 39B **Publicly Held**
WEB: www.ea.com
SIC: 7372 Prepackaged software
HQ: Oracle America, Inc.
500 Oracle Pkwy
Redwood City CA 94065
650 506-7000

(G-4767)
ORDERMYGEAR LLC
2211 Commerce St Ste 300 (75201-4307)
PHONE..................................214 945-4000
Dave Dutch, *CEO*
Meredith Chapman, *Accounts Mgr*
Brett Messerall, *Accounts Mgr*
Bryan Sander, *Accounts Mgr*

Ben Truehart, *Security Dir*
EMP: 15
SALES (est): 1.6MM **Privately Held**
WEB: www.ordermygear.com
SIC: 7372 Prepackaged software

(G-4768)
ORION COMMUNICATIONS INC
8350 N Central Expy # 700 (75206-1600)
PHONE..................214 361-1203
EMP: 20 EST: 1998
SQ FT: 2,500
SALES (est): 3.1MM **Privately Held**
WEB: www.orioncom.com
SIC: 7372 Application computer software

(G-4769)
ORTEGAS CUSTOM INTERIORS INC
10885 Alder Cir Ste A (75238-1348)
PHONE..................214 341-4003
Delores Ortega, *President*
EMP: 16
SQ FT: 9,400
SALES (est): 1.5MM **Privately Held**
WEB: www.ocidesigns.com
SIC: 2221 Apparel & outerwear fabric,
manmade fiber or silk; draperies & drapery fabrics, manmade fiber & silk

(G-4770)
OSSEUS FUSION SYSTEMS LLC
1931 Greenville Ave (75206-7438)
PHONE..................888 330-5960
Robert Pace, *CEO*
Eric Hansen, *CEO*
Chase Tipping, *Engineer*
Robert D Pace, *CFO*
EMP: 12
SQ FT: 4,100
SALES (est): 871.8K **Privately Held**
WEB: www.osseus.com
SIC: 3841 Surgical & medical instruments

(G-4771)
OSV INVESTMENT LLC
Also Called: Onsiteview.com
3333 Lee Pkwy Ste 600 (75219-5117)
P.O. Box 190139 (75219-0139)
PHONE..................512 301-2848
Jeff Tomlins, *Mng Member*
EMP: 20
SALES (est): 2.1MM **Privately Held**
WEB: www.onsiteview.com
SIC: 3861 Cameras & related equipment

(G-4772)
OTIS ELEVATOR COMPANY
1444 N Cockrell Hill Rd # 102
(75211-1381)
PHONE..................214 741-6207
Sharon O'Quinn, *Principal*
EMP: 16
SALES (corp-wide): 12.7B **Publicly Held**
WEB: www.otis.com
SIC: 3534 1796 7699 Elevators & equipment; escalators, passenger & freight;
walkways, moving; installing building equipment; elevator installation & conversion; miscellaneous building item repair services; elevators: inspection, service & repair
HQ: Otis Elevator Company
11760 Us Highway 1 W600
Palm Beach Gardens FL 33408
860 674-3000

(G-4773)
OVERHEAD DOOR CORPORATION
2170 French Settlement Rd (75212-6001)
PHONE..................214 630-4669
Mark Dewolfe, *General Mgr*
Melanie Thompson, *Credit Mgr*
Angela Burgess, *Sr Project Mgr*
Mark De Wolfe, *Manager*
EMP: 70 **Privately Held**
WEB: www.overheaddoor.com
SIC: 3442 2431 Garage doors, overhead:
metal; doors, wood
HQ: Overhead Door Corporation
2501 S State Hwy 121 Ste
Lewisville TX 75067
469 549-7100

(G-4774)
OVERWRAPS PACKAGING INC
3950 La Reunion Pkwy (75212-6011)
PHONE..................214 634-0427
William C Seanor, *CEO*
Lanny Howell, *President*
Chris Donnelly, *Vice Pres*
Carlton Ferguson, *Vice Pres*
Nicole Seanor, *Vice Pres*
▲ EMP: 70
SQ FT: 120,000
SALES (est): 30MM **Privately Held**
WEB: www.overwraps.com
SIC: 2759 Flexographic printing

(G-4775)
OXY VINYLS LP (HQ)
14555 Dallas Pkwy Ste 400 (75254-4362)
P.O. Box 809050 (75380-9050)
PHONE..................877 699-8465
Ray R Irani, *Chairman*
◆ EMP: 12 EST: 1999
SALES (est): 1B
SALES (corp-wide): 21.2B **Publicly Held**
WEB: www.oxy.com
SIC: 2821 2899 2819 1382 Vinyl resins;
chemical preparations; industrial inorganic chemicals; oil & gas exploration services
PA: Occidental Petroleum Corporation
5 Greenway Plz Ste 110
Houston TX 77046
713 215-7000

(G-4776)
P-R-O MANAGEMENT INC
13601 Preston Rd Ste 309e (75240-4933)
PHONE..................972 720-1475
EMP: 34 EST: 1972
SALES (est): 1.9MM **Privately Held**
SIC: 1311 8742 Crude petroleum production; general management consultant

(G-4777)
PALACIO IVIS
Also Called: E & I Contractors
811 Pleasant Hills Dr (75217-3634)
PHONE..................214 402-6856
Ivis Palacio, *Owner*
EMP: 10
SALES (est): 569.7K **Privately Held**
SIC: 2952 Mastic roofing composition

(G-4778)
PALLADIUM EXCHANGE LLC
1208 S Riverfront Blvd (75207-4703)
PHONE..................214 421-8600
Preston Dargan,
EMP: 13
SQ FT: 1,500
SALES (est): 1.4MM **Privately Held**
SIC: 3411 Aluminum cans

(G-4779)
PALLAS ARCHTCTRAL WODWORKS LLC
9008 Chancellor Row (75247-5314)
PHONE..................214 741-1125
Lynn Parkerson, *Bookkeeper*
James Schragin, *Office Mgr*
Gregor Schragin,
EMP: 16
SALES (est): 1.6MM **Privately Held**
WEB: www.pallaswoodworks.com
SIC: 2511 Wood household furniture

(G-4780)
PALLET ADVISOR LLC
Also Called: All Star Pallet
8770 S Central Expy (75241-7502)
PHONE..................817 271-4840
Lawrence Snyder, *Mng Member*
Lawrence C Snyder Jr,
EMP: 40
SALES (est): 1.6MM **Privately Held**
SIC: 2448 Pallets, wood

(G-4781)
PALO PETROLEUM INC (PA)
5944 Luther Ln Ste 900 (75225-5921)
P.O. Box 601544 (75360-1544)
PHONE..................214 691-3676
James Graham, *President*
James P Graham, *President*
Patricia A Snyder, *Vice Pres*

Debbie Holt, *Manager*
Pamela Graham, *Director*
EMP: 12
SQ FT: 4,500
SALES (est): 2.9MM **Privately Held**
WEB: www.palopetro.com
SIC: 1311 1382 Crude petroleum production; oil & gas exploration services

(G-4782)
PALO VERDE OIL COMPANY (PA)
5949 Sherry Ln Ste 850 (75225-8060)
PHONE..................214 692-7052
Loyd W Powell Jr, *President*
Terry Cahill, *Vice Pres*
Laverne Parker, *Vice Pres*
EMP: 51
SQ FT: 4,300
SALES (est): 3.7MM **Privately Held**
SIC: 1311 Crude petroleum production;
natural gas production

(G-4783)
PANDA ETHANOL INC (PA)
Also Called: (A DEVELOPMENT STAGE COMPANY)
4100 Spring Valley Rd # 675 (75244-3603)
PHONE..................972 361-1200
Janice Carter, *CEO*
Robert W Carter, *Ch of Bd*
Darol Lindloff, *President*
Don Thorpe, *Vice Pres*
Creede Williams, *Vice Pres*
EMP: 10
SALES (est): 3MM **Privately Held**
WEB: www.pandaethanol.com
SIC: 2869 Ethyl alcohol, ethanol

(G-4784)
PANDA PWR GNRTION INFRSTRCTURE
Also Called: Panda Power Fund
5001 Spring Valley Rd 1150w
(75244-3946)
PHONE..................972 361-2000
R W Carter, *Partner*
Robert W Carter, *Partner*
Sean Hausman, *General Mgr*
Paula Robinson, *Chairman*
Richard Evans, *Vice Pres*
EMP: 35
SALES (est): 11.2MM **Privately Held**
SIC: 1382 Oil & gas exploration services

(G-4785)
PANDA-BRANDYWINE L P
4100 Spring Valley Rd (75244-3629)
PHONE..................972 980-7159
Robert W Carter, *Managing Prtnr*
EMP: 29
SALES (est): 3.1MM **Privately Held**
SIC: 3612 2899 Autotransformers, electric (power transformers); distilled water

(G-4786)
PAPER NETWORK INC (PA)
4652 Nall Rd (75244-4617)
PHONE..................972 239-6567
John G Schmerien, *President*
EMP: 41
SALES (est): 11.9MM **Privately Held**
SIC: 2789 4226 7377 Paper cutting; special warehousing & storage; computer hardware rental or leasing, except finance leasing

(G-4787)
PAPER TUBES & SALES CO
Also Called: A-1 Paper Tubes & Sales
Hinton St (75235)
PHONE..................214 631-0973
Scott Stewart, *President*
Laura Elkenan, *Safety Mgr*
Bob Womack, *Sales Staff*
▲ EMP: 49 EST: 1968
SQ FT: 122,000
SALES (est): 12.8MM **Privately Held**
WEB: www.pts-mfg.com
SIC: 2655 Cans, fiber: made from purchased material; cores, fiber: made from purchased material

(G-4788)
PARCO DOUBLE-E LLC
Also Called: Double-E, Inc.
1261 Profit Dr (75247-3919)
PHONE..................214 631-2290
James A Wilson, *Ch of Bd*
Joe Fiore, *President*
Eric Cassidy, *Vice Pres*
Mark Rose, *QC Mgr*
J M Allen, *Admin Sec*
EMP: 52 EST: 1923
SQ FT: 20,800
SALES (est): 12MM
SALES (corp-wide): 1.3B **Privately Held**
WEB: www.doubleeinc.com
SIC: 3533 3069 Oil field machinery & equipment; molded rubber products
HQ: Parco, Llc
1801 S Archibald Ave
Ontario CA 91761
909 947-2200

(G-4789)
PARTS KRAFTERS CO (PA)
13130 Glenside Dr (75234-5004)
P.O. Box 233, Haslet (76052-0233)
PHONE..................515 981-4749
Don Kanz, *President*
Lois Mace, *Corp Secy*
▲ EMP: 16
SALES (est): 2.5MM **Privately Held**
WEB: www.reliabilityprovin.com
SIC: 3579 5084 Stapling machines (hand or power); industrial machinery & equipment

(G-4790)
PATARA OIL & GAS LLC
333 Clay St Ste 3960 (75219)
P.O. Box 199113 (75219-9113)
PHONE..................214 295-6704
Bill A Berilgen, *CEO*
Curtis Carver,
George R Hutchinson,
Edward Seeman,
EMP: 69
SQ FT: 7,300
SALES (est): 13.2MM **Privately Held**
WEB: www.pataraog.com
SIC: 1382 Oil & gas exploration services

(G-4791)
PC CALENDAR 2010 LLC (PA)
2501 N Harwood St # 2600 (75201-1607)
PHONE..................214 491-5103
Robert J Schlegel, *CEO*
Bobby L Staten, *President*
Kerry Dowling, *General Mgr*
Scott Hughes, *General Mgr*
Tim Berns, *Vice Pres*
▲ EMP: 40
SQ FT: 6,000
SALES (est): 7.4MM **Privately Held**
WEB: www.pavestone.com
SIC: 3271 Blocks, concrete: drystack interlocking; blocks, concrete: landscape or retaining wall

(G-4792)
PCORE EXPLORATION PROD II LLC
2200 Ross Ave Ste 4900e (75201-7907)
PHONE..................469 802-1400
Colin O'Farrell, *Exec VP*
Billy Hannes, *General Counsel*
Mike Hiduke,
EMP: 11 EST: 2016
SALES (est): 278.1K **Privately Held**
WEB: www.pcoreep.com
SIC: 1382 Oil & gas exploration services

(G-4793)
PEACOCK ALLEY INC (PA)
Also Called: Peacock Alley Dsign Stdio Atln
2050 Postal Way (75212-6318)
PHONE..................214 744-0399
Jason L Needleman, *CEO*
Mary Ella Gabler, *Chairman*
Paul Hamilton, *Vice Pres*
Josh Needleman, *Vice Pres*
▲ EMP: 70
SQ FT: 84,000

SALES (est): 14.5MM Privately Held
WEB: www.peacockalley.com
SIC: 2392 5023 5719 Blankets, comforters & beddings; pillowcases; bedspreads; sheets, textile; towels; beddings & linens

(G-4794)
PEERLESS MFG CO (HQ)
14651 Dallas Pkwy Ste 50 (75254-7476)
PHONE.................................214 357-6181
Kevin King, *Business Mgr*
Ed Prajzner, *Vice Pres*
Tim Shippy, *Vice Pres*
Pedro Hernandez, *Project Mgr*
Amit Shah, *Purch Agent*
◆ EMP: 100
SQ FT: 26,886
SALES (est): 66.1MM Publicly Held
WEB: www.cecoenviro.com
SIC: 3569 3823 3822 Separators for steam, gas, vapor or air (machinery); industrial instrmnts msrmnt display/control process variable; damper operators: pneumatic, thermostatic, electric

(G-4795)
PELOTON THERAPEUTICS INC
2330 Inwood Rd Ste 226 (75235-7323)
PHONE.................................972 629-4100
David V Goeddel, *Ch of Bd*
John A Josey, *President*
Alan A Musso, *CFO*
Mohammad Hirmand, *Chief Mktg Ofcr*
Eli M Wallace, *Security Dir*
EMP: 64 EST: 2010
SQ FT: 26,474
SALES (est): 17.3MM
SALES (corp-wide): 46.8B Publicly Held
WEB: www.pelotontherapeutics.com
SIC: 2836 Biological products, except diagnostic
PA: Merck & Co., Inc.
    2000 Galloping Hill Rd
    Kenilworth NJ 07033
    908 740-4000

(G-4796)
PEREGRINE PETROLEUM LLC (PA)
2101 Cedar Springs Rd (75201-2104)
PHONE.................................214 231-6800
Michael B Wisenbaker, *President*
Jeremy T Greene, *Senior VP*
Tamara L Gannon, *Vice Pres*
Deborah Kitchens, *CFO*
Mike White, *Controller*
EMP: 30
SALES (est): 34.9MM Privately Held
WEB:
SIC: 1382 Oil & gas exploration services

(G-4797)
PERFORMANCE COMPANIES LP
Also Called: Performance Pop
2929 N Stemmons Fwy (75247-6102)
P.O. Box 436, Argyle (76226-0436)
PHONE.................................214 665-1000
John T White, *Partner*
Kelley Ball, *COO*
Maria Serratore-Gunter, *CFO*
Jeff Mathis, *Natl Sales Mgr*
Greg White, *VP Sales*
EMP: 185
SALES (est): 59.4MM Privately Held
WEB: www.performancepop.com
SIC: 2752 2759 2542 Commercial printing, lithographic; commercial printing; partitions & fixtures, except wood

(G-4798)
PETRO HARVESTER OPER CO LLC (HQ)
5005 Lyndon B Johnson Fwy # 700 (75244-6145)
PHONE.................................214 618-7600
Lewis Gillies, *President*
Joe Schimelpfening, *COO*
Joe Townsend, *CFO*
Steve Margerum, *Controller*
EMP: 54
SQ FT: 17,268
SALES (est): 91MM Privately Held
SIC: 1311 Crude petroleum production

PA: Rockall Energy, Llc
    5005 Lyndon B Johnson Fwy # 700
    Dallas TX 75244
    214 618-7600

(G-4799)
PETRO-HUNT LLC (HQ)
2101 Cedar Springs Rd # 60 (75201-2104)
PHONE.................................214 880-8400
EMP: 100 EST: 1998
SQ FT: 60,000
SALES (est): 4.1B Privately Held
WEB: www.petrohunt.com
SIC: 1311 Crude petroleum production; natural gas production
PA: The William Herbert Hunt Trust Estate
    1601 Elm St Ste 3900
    Dallas TX 75201
    214 880-8400

(G-4800)
PETTIGREWS CUSTOM IRON & MTLS
7301 Hines Pl (75235-4017)
PHONE.................................214 637-1494
Lee Pettigrew, *President*
Billy Pettigrew, *Vice Pres*
Betty Pettigrew, *Treasurer*
EMP: 10
SQ FT: 12,070
SALES (est): 1.5MM Privately Held
WEB: www.pettigrewscustomiron.com
SIC: 3446 Architectural metalwork

(G-4801)
PHASE 1 PROTOTYPES LLC
10580 Newkirk St Ste 301 (75220-2329)
P.O. Box 140698, Irving (75014-0698)
PHONE.................................972 406-9988
Kristin Lanoue, *Mng Member*
William Ramirez,
EMP: 15
SQ FT: 6,000
SALES (est): 2.6MM Privately Held
WEB: www.phase1prototypes.com
SIC: 2752 Commercial printing, offset

(G-4802)
PHILBO ENTERPRISES INC
1201 S Ervay St (75215-1124)
PHONE.................................214 747-7018
Gus W Kamis, *President*
Sara Kamis, *Corp Secy*
Andrew Atkinson, *Vice Pres*
Bruce Kamis, *Vice Pres*
EMP: 32 EST: 1973
SQ FT: 40,000
SALES (est): 3.2MM Privately Held
SIC: 5021 2759 5112 Office furniture; commercial printing; computer & photocopying supplies

(G-4803)
PICKENS COMPANY INC
8111 Preston Rd Ste 800 (75225-6378)
PHONE.................................214 369-7471
Robert H Pickens, *President*
Rick Clark, *Sheriff*
William C Pickens Sr, *Vice Pres*
William C Pickens Jr, *Vice Pres*
EMP: 10 EST: 1930
SQ FT: 4,000
SALES (est): 1.3MM Privately Held
SIC: 1311 Crude petroleum production; natural gas production

(G-4804)
PICKENS ENERGY CORPORATION
10100 N Cntl Expy Ste 200 (75231)
PHONE.................................214 503-1271
John T Pickens, *President*
V Robert Milner, *Corp Secy*
EMP: 10
SALES (est): 1.1MM Privately Held
SIC: 1311 Crude petroleum production

(G-4805)
PILGRIMS PRIDE CORPORATION
1900 S Central Expy (75215-1301)
P.O. Box 150129 (75315-0129)
PHONE.................................214 565-8600
David Vanhoose, *CEO*
EMP: 2000

SQ FT: 32,184 Publicly Held
WEB: www.pilgrims.com
SIC: 2015 Turkey, processed: fresh
HQ: Pilgrim's Pride Corporation
    1770 Promontory Cir
    Greeley CO 80634
    970 506-8000

(G-4806)
PITTS OIL COMPANY LLC
4600 Greenville Ave # 300 (75206-5085)
PHONE.................................214 369-9266
Barbara Chapman, *Info Tech Mgr*
L Frank Pitts,
EMP: 10
SQ FT: 15,000
SALES (est): 770.9K Privately Held
WEB: www.pittsoil.com
SIC: 1382 1311 Oil & gas exploration services; crude petroleum production

(G-4807)
PITZER FAMILY LTD PARTNERSHIP
8388 C F Hawn Fwy (75217-7009)
PHONE.................................214 398-1491
Starr L Pitzer, *General Ptnr*
EMP: 30 EST: 1998
SQ FT: 16,300
SALES (est): 5.1MM Privately Held
SIC: 2851 Lead-in-oil paints

(G-4808)
PIXEL AND TEXEL LLC
Also Called: Computer Software
2933 Commerce St (75226-1610)
PHONE.................................214 240-0013
Andrew Strickland, *CEO*
EMP: 12
SALES (est): 881K Privately Held
WEB: www.pixelandtexel.com
SIC: 7371 7372 Computer software development & applications; computer software development; business oriented computer software

(G-4809)
PLANTATION SHUTTER
11649 Chairman Dr Ste 1 (75243-5222)
PHONE.................................214 341-3677
Dora Sewell, *President*
Doug Sewell, *Vice Pres*
EMP: 19
SALES (est): 2.7MM Privately Held
WEB: www.theplantationshutter.com
SIC: 3442 5719 2591 Shutters, door or window: metal; vertical blinds; blinds vertical

(G-4810)
PLAYERS MEDIA GROUP INC
5960 Berkshire Ln (75225-6066)
PHONE.................................509 254-4949
Collin Castellaw, *Partner*
EMP: 15
SALES (est): 491.1K Privately Held
SIC: 2836 Culture media

(G-4811)
POLYSPEDE ELECTRONICS CORP
6770 Twin Hills Ave (75231-6510)
P.O. Box 822720 (75382-2720)
PHONE.................................214 363-7245
Babu G'Vam, *CEO*
Michael J Looney, *President*
Babu G Sivam, *COO*
Thila G'Vam, *Manager*
▲ EMP: 10 EST: 1959
SQ FT: 13,000
SALES (est): 2.6MM Privately Held
WEB: www.polyspede.com
SIC: 3566 Speed changers, drives & gears

(G-4812)
POP STAR LLC
1350 Manufacturing St # 212 (75207-6500)
PHONE.................................214 244-2502
John Doumas,
EMP: 10 EST: 2012
SQ FT: 2,250
SALES (est): 401.6K Privately Held
WEB: www.popstardallas.com
SIC: 2024 Ice cream & frozen desserts

(G-4813)
POSITIVE MARKETING (USA) INC
11277 N Stemmons Fwy (75229-4547)
PHONE.................................877 284-4488
Hagop Dekirmenjian, *Director*
EMP: 11 EST: 2015
SALES (est): 204.8K Privately Held
WEB: www.positivemarketingusa.com
SIC: 2396 2752 Fabric printing & stamping; commercial printing, lithographic

(G-4814)
POST UP TOWN INC
3000 Mckinney Ave (75204-2433)
PHONE.................................214 965-6565
Orlala Iceenberger, *Manager*
EMP: 9
SALES (est): 517.3K Privately Held
SIC: 7359 2711 Equipment rental & leasing; newspapers

(G-4815)
PPG INDUSTRIES INC
Also Called: PPG 8344
2515 Willowbrook Rd # 109 (75220-4435)
PHONE.................................214 902-8922
Raymond Robinett, *Branch Mgr*
EMP: 24
SALES (corp-wide): 15.3B Publicly Held
WEB: www.ppg.com
SIC: 2851 Paints & allied products
PA: Ppg Industries, Inc.
    1 Ppg Pl
    Pittsburgh PA 15272
    412 434-3131

(G-4816)
PRATT INDUSTRIES INC
Also Called: Converting Division
3700 Eagle Place Dr # 800 (75236-1450)
PHONE.................................972 296-2900
Mike Tansey, *General Mgr*
Richard Reyes, *Plant Mgr*
Russell Gipson, *Opers Mgr*
James Kemp, *Maint Spvr*
Angela Roundtree, *Purchasing*
EMP: 25 Privately Held
WEB: www.prattindustries.com
SIC: 2653 Boxes, corrugated: made from purchased materials
PA: Pratt Industries, Inc.
    1800 Sarasot Bus Pkwy Ne S
    Conyers GA 30013

(G-4817)
PRATT WHTNEY LINE MINT SVCS IN
Also Called: Pratt & Whitney Dallas Dist
2701 Regent Blvd Ste 300 (75261)
P.O. Box 3107, Coppell (75019-7001)
PHONE.................................972 894-0139
Richard Brant, *President*
EMP: 9 EST: 2007
SQ FT: 25,000
SALES (est): 2.4MM
SALES (corp-wide): 56.5B Publicly Held
WEB: www.prattwhitney.com
SIC: 3519 Jet propulsion engines
HQ: Pratt & Whitney Engine Services, Inc.
    1525 Midway Park Rd
    Bridgeport WV 26330
    304 842-5421

(G-4818)
PRECISION ALLOYS CORPORATION
811 Regal Row (75247-4406)
PHONE.................................800 321-0759
Bill Sultzbaugh, *Principal*
EMP: 45
SALES (est): 5.4MM Privately Held
WEB: www.palcoweldingsupply.com
SIC: 3469 5051 Stamping metal for the trade; metals service centers & offices

(G-4819)
PRECISION FORMULATIONS LLC
9660 Dilworth Rd (75243-8315)
PHONE.................................972 393-7170
Cheryl Cahill, *President*
Monty Lloyd, *Corp Secy*
▲ EMP: 68
SQ FT: 52,000

SALES (est): 13.8MM **Privately Held**
WEB: www.precisionformulations.com
SIC: 2037 Fruit juices

(G-4820)
PRECISION PACK
10725 Sandhill Rd Ste 102 (75238-1227)
PHONE..........................214 553-8044
Keith Burns, *CEO*
Don Shotland, *Vice Pres*
EMP: 11
SALES (est): 1.4MM **Privately Held**
SIC: 2899 Foam charge mixtures

(G-4821)
PRECISION SET INCORPORATED
13711 Omega Rd (75244-4517)
P.O. Box 819049 (75381-9049)
PHONE..........................972 385-6732
Don Jopling, *President*
James Jordan, *Vice Pres*
Lisa Calhoun, *Office Mgr*
EMP: 35
SQ FT: 7,000
SALES (est): 5.2MM **Privately Held**
WEB: www.precisionset.com
SIC: 3911 Jewelry, precious metal

(G-4822)
PRENTEX ALLOY FABRICATORS INC
3108 Sylvan Ave (75212-4096)
PHONE..........................214 748-7837
Carolyn Wester, *CEO*
David Wester, *President*
Tink Durbin, *Engineer*
Chris Wester, *CFO*
EMP: 24
SQ FT: 800
SALES (est): 3MM **Privately Held**
WEB: www.prentex.com
SIC: 3443 Fabricated plate work (boiler shop)

(G-4823)
PRIMARY COLOR LLC
9239 Premier Row (75247-5409)
PHONE..........................214 630-8800
Mark Truan, *President*
▲ EMP: 50
SALES (est): 2.7MM **Privately Held**
WEB: www.primarycolorinc.com
SIC: 2752 Commercial printing, offset

(G-4824)
PRIMEXX OPERATING CORPORATION (PA)
4849 Grnvlle Ave Ste 1600 (75206)
PHONE..........................214 369-5909
Thomas H Fagadau, *President*
Sanford P Fagadau, *President*
Sam Blatt, *Vice Pres*
Anthony Walker, *Vice Pres*
Chase White, *Vice Pres*
EMP: 14 EST: 1960
SQ FT: 6,500
SALES (est): 24.2MM **Privately Held**
WEB: www.primexx.com
SIC: 1311 Crude petroleum production; natural gas production

(G-4825)
PRINTCITYCOM
9020 Directors Row (75247-5321)
PHONE..........................214 728-1230
EMP: 10
SALES (est): 610K **Privately Held**
SIC: 2752 Commercial Printing, Lithographic

(G-4826)
PRINTDALLAS INC
Also Called: AlphaGraphics
3001 Knox St Ste 102 (75205-5552)
PHONE..........................214 363-1101
Sherry Perry, *President*
EMP: 11
SQ FT: 3,700
SALES (est): 2.6MM **Privately Held**
WEB: www.alphagraphics.com
SIC: 2752 2759 3993 Commercial printing, lithographic; commercial printing; signs & advertising specialties

(G-4827)
PRINTING RESEARCH CORPORATION
Also Called: Superblue.net
10760 Shady Trl Ste 300 (75220-1329)
PHONE..........................214 353-9000
Howard De Moore, *Ch of Bd*
Dave Douglas, *Vice Pres*
David D Douglas, *Vice Pres*
Debbie Deller, *CFO*
Ofelia Diaz, *Accounts Mgr*
▲ EMP: 75
SQ FT: 50,000
SALES (est): 18MM **Privately Held**
WEB: www.superblue.net
SIC: 3555 Printing trades machinery

(G-4828)
PRITCHETT LP
Also Called: Rummler-Brache Group
8150 N Central Expy (75206-1815)
PHONE..........................214 239-9600
Joe Aberger, *Partner*
Price Prichett, *Partner*
Kim Webster, *Exec VP*
Bradford Chuck, *Vice Pres*
Dee Overley, *Finance Mgr*
EMP: 25
SQ FT: 11,000
SALES (est): 2.6MM **Privately Held**
WEB: www.pritchettnet.com
SIC: 2731 8742 Books: publishing only; management consulting services

(G-4829)
PRIVACY INC
12720 Hillcrest Rd # 720 (75230-2035)
PHONE..........................214 760-8700
Kenneth M Good, *Ch of Bd*
Steven Romeo, *Exec VP*
Tom Allen, *Vice Pres*
Phyllis Kramer, *Vice Pres*
EMP: 25
SQ FT: 5,300
SALES (est): 2.1MM **Privately Held**
SIC: 7372 Prepackaged software

(G-4830)
PRO LINE PRODUCTS INC
Also Called: Proline Hs
11625 Columbia Center Dr # 1 (75229-2075)
PHONE..........................972 488-4200
Luke Thorburn, *Vice Pres*
Kris McConniel, *Manager*
EMP: 19 EST: 2005
SALES (est): 4.6MM **Privately Held**
WEB: www.prolineproductsinc.com
SIC: 2891 Sealants

(G-4831)
PROCRAFT CABINETRY DALLAS LLC
2330 Alberta Dr 100 (75229-2063)
PHONE..........................469 607-2588
Sophia Chen, *Info Tech Dir*
Gary Bynum, *Director*
Tao Zheng,
EMP: 10
SALES (est): 629.6K **Privately Held**
WEB: www.procraftcabinetry.com
SIC: 2434 Wood kitchen cabinets

(G-4832)
PRODUCERS MIDSTREAM LP
2311 Cedar Springs Rd # 100 (75201-7816)
PHONE..........................214 238-5740
James Bryant, *CEO*
James W Hagger, *COO*
Joseph Styer, *Opers Staff*
Hudson White, *CFO*
Will McCraney, *Manager*
EMP: 15 EST: 2016
SALES: 56.1K **Privately Held**
WEB: www.producersmidstream.com
SIC: 4922 1389 4612 Pipelines, natural gas; processing service, gas; crude petroleum pipelines

(G-4833)
PROVIDENCE ENERGY CORPORATION
14860 Montfort Dr Ste 115 (75254-6873)
PHONE..........................214 522-9131

Mike Allen, *President*
EMP: 30
SQ FT: 900
SALES (est): 1.2MM **Privately Held**
WEB: www.providence-energy.com
SIC: 1382 Oil & gas exploration services

(G-4834)
PT HARDWARE INC
Also Called: Paris Texas Hardware
4030 La Reunion Pkwy (75212-6023)
PHONE..........................214 744-4491
Kerri Green, *President*
Matthew Gabay, *CFO*
▲ EMP: 75
SQ FT: 55,000
SALES (est): 11MM **Privately Held**
WEB: www.paristexashardware.com
SIC: 3429 5023 Manufactured hardware (general); window furnishings
HQ: Hunter Douglas N.V.
Piekstraat 2
Rotterdam 3071
104 869-911

(G-4835)
PUBLISHING CONCEPTS LP
4835 Lbj Fwy Ste 1100 (75244-6057)
PHONE..........................214 530-0335
Andrew Clancy, *President*
Deborah Dale, *Vice Pres*
Alex Morin, *Accounts Exec*
Daniel Nash, *Accounts Exec*
Colin Stewart, *Accounts Exec*
EMP: 325
SQ FT: 170,100
SALES (est): 16.8MM **Privately Held**
WEB: www.publishingconcepts.com
SIC: 2741 Directories: publishing only, not printed on site

(G-4836)
PURITY OILFIELD SERVICES LLC (DH)
2101 Cedar Springs Rd # 650 (75201-2333)
PHONE..........................214 880-8400
Marshall T Hunt, *President*
Ed Oconnor, *Opers Staff*
Max Goodroe, *Pub Rel Staff*
Ralph Jannise, *Manager*
Melanie Kiker, *Manager*
EMP: 44
SALES (est): 120.7MM
SALES (corp-wide): 4.1B **Privately Held**
WEB: www.purityoilfieldservices.com
SIC: 1389 Oil field services
HQ: Petro-Hunt, L.L.C.
2101 Cedar Springs Rd # 60
Dallas TX 75201
214 880-8400

(G-4837)
PURVIS INDUSTRIES LLC (PA)
10500 N Stemmons Fwy (75220-2425)
P.O. Box 540757 (75354-0757)
PHONE..........................214 358-5500
Robert W Purvis, *President*
Vern Eldred, *Regional Mgr*
Gail Purvis, *Corp Secy*
Cameron Barker, *Vice Pres*
Jay Gilbert, *Vice Pres*
▲ EMP: 65
SQ FT: 45,000
SALES (est): 270.9MM **Privately Held**
WEB: www.purvisindustries.com
SIC: 5085 8711 3441 5084 Bearings; engineering services; fabricated structural metal; materials handling machinery; rubber & plastics hose & beltings; power transmission equipment

(G-4838)
QNET INC
Also Called: Qnet Information Services
12021 Plano Rd Ste 150 (75243-5427)
P.O. Box 550744 (75355-0744)
PHONE..........................214 341-7638
Larry Hall, *President*
Sam Pierre Auguste, *Vice Pres*
Bob Snodgrass, *Engineer*
EMP: 55
SQ FT: 3,000

SALES (est): 8.8MM **Privately Held**
WEB: www.qnetms.com
SIC: 7373 7371 7372 7374 Systems integration services; custom computer programming services; prepackaged software; data processing & preparation; computer related maintenance services

(G-4839)
QT DOG LLC
4419 Mint Way (75236-2011)
PHONE..........................214 333-4477
Michael Thomas, *Mng Member*
Yami Harper,
▲ EMP: 12
SALES (est): 1.5MM **Privately Held**
WEB: www.qtdog.com
SIC: 5199 3999 Pet supplies; pet supplies

(G-4840)
QT INDUSTRIES LLC
Also Called: Quality Tool
7410 Ambassador Row (75247-4804)
PHONE..........................972 221-0537
Anand Patel, *General Mgr*
Bill Gilliand,
EMP: 17
SQ FT: 11,000
SALES (est): 3.8MM **Privately Held**
WEB: www.qtmfg.com
SIC: 3089 Injection molding of plastics

(G-4841)
QUAD/GRAPHICS INC
6700 Denton Dr (75235-4433)
PHONE..........................972 892-3803
Amy Ziemer, *Accounts Exec*
Raimol John, *Analyst*
EMP: 200
SALES (corp-wide): 3.9B **Publicly Held**
WEB: www.quad.com
SIC: 2752 2771 2759 2796 Commercial printing, offset; greeting cards; catalogs: printing; color separations for printing; photocopying & duplicating services
PA: Quad/Graphics Inc.
N61w23044 Harrys Way
Sussex WI 53089
414 566-6000

(G-4842)
QUAKER OATS COMPANY
2822 Glenfield Ave (75233-1497)
PHONE..........................214 333-1200
Sally Zelinsky, *Production*
Tom Dixon, *Manager*
EMP: 200
SALES (corp-wide): 67.1B **Publicly Held**
WEB: www.quakeroats.com
SIC: 4225 2086 General warehousing & storage; bottled & canned soft drinks
HQ: The Quaker Oats Company
555 W Monroe St Fl 1
Chicago IL 60661
312 821-1000

(G-4843)
QUALITY BUMPER SERVICE DALLAS
1155 S Haskell Ave (75223-2999)
PHONE..........................214 824-7300
Joe Landtroop, *President*
Daniel C Castloo, *Treasurer*
EMP: 24
SQ FT: 12,000
SALES (est): 3.1MM **Privately Held**
WEB: www.qualitybumperservice.com
SIC: 5013 5531 3471 Bumpers; truck equipment & parts; plating of metals or formed products

(G-4844)
QUALITY IRONWORKS INC
1607 W Commerce St (75208-1408)
PHONE..........................214 688-0180
Guy Ringer, *President*
Jim Branham, *Vice Pres*
Jeff Seeley, *CFO*
EMP: 55
SQ FT: 128,000
SALES (est): 19.8MM **Privately Held**
WEB: www.qiworks.com
SIC: 1799 3446 Ornamental metal work; fences, gates, posts & flagpoles

(G-4845)

QUALITY SAUSAGE COMPANY INC (PA)

1925 Lone Star Dr (75212-6300)
PHONE...................................214 634-3400
Gene Eisen, *President*
Tim Burns, *Vice Pres*
Fred Koelewyn, *Vice Pres*
Joe Cruz, *Plant Mgr*
Skipper Adams, *Safety Mgr*
▲ EMP: 133
SQ FT: 100,000
SALES (est): 73MM **Privately Held**
WEB: www.qualitysausage.com
SIC: 2013 Sausages from purchased
  meat; sausages & related products, from
  purchased meat; bacon, side & sliced:
  from purchased meat; prepared pork
  products from purchased pork

(G-4846)

QUALITY SAUSAGE COMPANY INC

1919 Lone Star Dr (75212-6302)
PHONE...................................214 634-3400
Joe Cruz, *Manager*
EMP: 200
SQ FT: 60,208
SALES (corp-wide): 73MM **Privately Held**
WEB: www.qualitysausage.com
SIC: 2013 Sausages & other prepared
  meats
PA: Quality Sausage Company, Inc.
  1925 Lone Star Dr
  Dallas TX 75212
  214 634-3400

(G-4847)

QUARRIES DIRECT INTERNATIONAL

2605 Freewood Dr (75220-2510)
PHONE...................................602 269-7900
Michael Demore, *Sales Staff*
Fatih Surmen, *Branch Mgr*
EMP: 22
SALES (corp-wide): 6.9MM **Privately Held**
WEB: www.qdisurfaces.com
SIC: 3281 Cut stone & stone products
PA: Quarries Direct International, Llc
  2633 N 24th Dr
  Phoenix AZ 85009
  602 269-7900

(G-4848)

QUATREFOIL PARTNERS LLC

Also Called: 3 Marthas
5521 Maple Ave (75235-7417)
PHONE...................................214 631-7117
Abigail Davis, *Mng Member*
Julie Dawar,
Rachel Ferguson,
▲ EMP: 16
SQ FT: 8,500
SALES (est): 1.9MM **Privately Held**
WEB: www.3marthas.com
SIC: 2361 2515 2844 Girls' & children's
  dresses, blouses & shirts; mattresses &
  bedsprings; towelettes, premoistened

(G-4849)

QUEMETCO METALS LIMITED INC

2777 N Stemmons Fwy # 1800
(75207-2277)
PHONE...................................214 631-6070
Robert E Finn, *President*
John De Paul, *Exec VP*
Joe Dugger, *Vice Pres*
R David Prengaman, *Director*
▲ EMP: 11
SALES (est): 4.6MM
SALES (corp-wide): 276.4MM **Privately Held**
WEB: www.rsrna.com
SIC: 5051 3341 Anode metal; lead smelting & refining (secondary)
HQ: Rsr Corporation
  2777 N Stemmons Fwy # 2000
  Dallas TX 75207
  214 631-6070

(G-4850)

QUEST SOFTWARE INC

15950 Dallas Pkwy Ste 350 (75248-6602)
PHONE...................................949 754-8000
Joe Kuderer, *Senior Mgr*
EMP: 30
SALES (corp-wide): 1.1B **Privately Held**
WEB: www.quest.com
SIC: 7372 Prepackaged software
HQ: Quest Software, Inc.
  4 Polaris Way
  Aliso Viejo CA 92656
  949 754-8000

(G-4851)

QUEXCO INCORPORATED (PA)

2777 N Stemmons Fwy # 18 (75207-2277)
PHONE...................................214 688-4000
Howard M Meyers, *Ch of Bd*
Cheryl Crim, *Manager*
Albert P Lospinoso, *Director*
◆ EMP: 35
SQ FT: 45,000
SALES (est): 276.4MM **Privately Held**
SIC: 3341 Lead smelting & refining (secondary)

(G-4852)

QUIET LOGISTICS INC

10750 Denton Dr (75220-1516)
PHONE...................................860 841-3892
Derek Morse, *Vice Pres*
Darby French, *CFO*
Paul Difrancesco, *Manager*
Bernard Yelmarie, *Manager*
Mika Puccio, *Personnel Assit*
▲ EMP: 24
SALES (est): 5MM **Privately Held**
WEB: www.quietlogistics.com
SIC: 3549 Assembly machines, including
  robotic

(G-4853)

R C T INC

11527 Hillguard Rd (75243-5503)
P.O. Box 744133 (75374-4133)
PHONE...................................972 231-9698
David Huggins, *President*
EMP: 35
SQ FT: 12,000
SALES (est): 3.8MM **Privately Held**
SIC: 2542 Counters or counter display
  cases: except wood

(G-4854)

R JONES AND ASSOCIATES INC

3054 Irving Blvd (75247-6213)
P.O. Box 560705 (75356-0705)
PHONE...................................214 951-0091
Bryan Campbell, *CEO*
Eric Fidler, *Vice Pres*
Shari Campbell, *Safety Mgr*
Jesse Solano, *Facilities Mgr*
EMP: 40
SQ FT: 34,000
SALES (est): 5.7MM **Privately Held**
WEB: www.rjones.com
SIC: 2511 2512 Wood household furniture;
  upholstered household furniture

(G-4855)

R NEAL JOHN & ASSOCIATES INC

Also Called: NEAL & ASSOCIATES
10610 Boomer Cir (75238-1341)
P.O. Box 550127 (75355-0127)
PHONE...................................214 340-1464
Josh Jones, *President*
John Neal Jr, *Vice Pres*
Jim Tracy, *CFO*
EMP: 31 EST: 1981
SQ FT: 21,000
SALES: 11.6MM **Privately Held**
WEB: www.nealandassociates.com
SIC: 5074 5051 3441 Heating equipment
  (hydronic); steel; fabricated structural
  metal

(G-4856)

R R DONNELLEY & SONS COMPANY

Also Called: Donnelley Financial
3500 Maple Ave Ste 810 (75219-3903)
PHONE...................................214 521-4767
Mike Martin, *Managing Dir*

Mike Williamson, *Branch Mgr*
Carol Bennett, *Analyst*
EMP: 35
SALES (corp-wide): 6.2B **Publicly Held**
WEB: www.rrd.com
SIC: 2759 Commercial printing
PA: R. R. Donnelley & Sons Company
  35 W Wacker Dr
  Chicago IL 60601
  312 326-8000

(G-4857)

R S GLOBAL INC

Also Called: Rsg Southwest
3373 Garden Brook Dr (75234-2310)
PHONE...................................972 406-2930
R Scott Shaw, *President*
Shauna Mitchell, *Business Mgr*
Daniel M Jameson, *Vice Pres*
Daniel Jameson, *Vice Pres*
Thomas Shaw, *Opers Staff*
▲ EMP: 60
SQ FT: 13,000
SALES (est): 19.5MM **Privately Held**
WEB: www.rsglobal.com
SIC: 5023 2273 Floor coverings; carpets &
  rugs

(G-4858)

RADIXON INC

4144 N Central Expy # 600 (75204-3140)
PHONE...................................855 723-4966
Milan Hudecek, *President*
Tariq Hasnie, *Vice Pres*
◆ EMP: 35
SALES (est): 850K **Privately Held**
WEB: www.radixon.com
SIC: 3651 Radio receiving sets
HQ: Radixon Group Pty Ltd
  45-47 Islington St
  Collingwood VIC 3066

(G-4859)

RAYMER ENTERPRISES INC

Also Called: First Place Screen Prtg & Pdts
3355 Garden Brook Dr (75234-2310)
PHONE...................................972 242-8863
Ryan Raymer, *President*
EMP: 12
SQ FT: 26,000
SALES (est): 1.4MM **Privately Held**
SIC: 2759 Screen printing

(G-4860)

RAYTHEON COMPANY

6000 Lemmon Ave (75209-5824)
P.O. Box 660246 (75266-0246)
PHONE...................................972 205-4277
Bruce Blackmon, *Opers Staff*
Randy Dempsey, *Engineer*
Kipp Khamphouy, *Engineer*
David Smith, *Senior Engr*
Alan Hughes, *Financial Analy*
EMP: 600
SALES (corp-wide): 56.5B **Publicly Held**
WEB: www.rtx.com
SIC: 3812 3469 3444 Radar systems &
  equipment; sonar systems & equipment;
  fathometers; warfare counter-measure
  equipment; metal stampings; sheet metal-
  work
HQ: Raytheon Company
  870 Winter St
  Waltham MA 02451
  781 522-3000

(G-4861)

RAYTHEON COMPANY

13588 N Central Expy (75243-1108)
PHONE...................................972 344-3000
David Welp, *Branch Mgr*
EMP: 150
SALES (corp-wide): 56.5B **Publicly Held**
WEB: www.rtx.com
SIC: 3812 Radar systems & equipment;
  sonar systems & equipment; fathometers;
  warfare counter-measure equipment
HQ: Raytheon Company
  870 Winter St
  Waltham MA 02451
  781 522-3000

(G-4862)

RAYTHEON COMPANY

13510 N Central Expy (75243-1108)
P.O. Box 650408 (75265-0408)
PHONE...................................972 344-9133
James Glavin, *Engineer*
Mark Hanna, *Engineer*
Vicky Hsu, *Engineer*
Terry Johnson, *Engineer*
Jana Salles, *Engineer*
EMP: 15
SALES (corp-wide): 56.5B **Publicly Held**
WEB: www.rtx.com
SIC: 3812 Defense systems & equipment
HQ: Raytheon Company
  870 Winter St
  Waltham MA 02451
  781 522-3000

(G-4863)

RB CONVERTING INC (HQ)

Also Called: R B Converting
12855 Valley Branch Ln (75234-5813)
PHONE...................................800 543-7690
Ramzy Bathish, *President*
Scot Decker, *CFO*
Mark Nunn, *Sales Staff*
John G Schmerein, *Admin Sec*
EMP: 32 EST: 1986
SQ FT: 100,000
SALES (est): 11.9MM **Privately Held**
WEB: www.rbconverting.com
SIC: 2679 Paper products, converted

(G-4864)

RCHEMCO INC

Also Called: R Chem Company
2633 Mckinney Ave 130-411 (75204-2581)
PHONE...................................817 791-7304
Richard Rios, *Principal*
EMP: 12
SALES (est): 1.2MM **Privately Held**
WEB: www.rchemco.com
SIC: 2879 Insecticides & pesticides

(G-4865)

RDG REAL ESTATE & CONSTRUCTION

5955 Alpha Rd 1109 (75240-1121)
PHONE...................................469 629-9919
Joseph Lee Rawls, *CEO*
EMP: 10
SALES (est): 185K **Privately Held**
SIC: 1389 Construction, repair & disman-
  tling services

(G-4866)

RDRTEC INCORPORATED

3737 Atwell St Ste 208 (75209-5765)
PHONE...................................214 353-8755
Sidney W Theis, *CEO*
David Hails, *President*
Janice Grote,
EMP: 25
SQ FT: 3,000
SALES (est): 3.3MM **Privately Held**
WEB: www.rdrtec.com
SIC: 8733 3812 Scientific research
  agency; electronic detection systems
  (aeronautical)

(G-4867)

RECLAIMED TEXTILES CO

10777 Shady Trl (75220-1330)
PHONE...................................214 638-7551
Scott Birnbaum, *President*
Mike Courtney, *Vice Pres*
Matt Kersting, *Sales Staff*
▲ EMP: 30
SALES (est): 5.9MM **Privately Held**
WEB: www.reclaimedtextiles.com
SIC: 2299 Recovering textile fibers from
  clippings & rags

(G-4868)

RECONSERVE OF TEXAS INC

Also Called: Recycle To Conserve, Tx, Inc.
3610 Duncanville Rd (75236-1014)
PHONE...................................214 339-4755
Meyer Luskin, *CEO*
Robert McMullen, *President*
Rida Hamed, *Vice Pres*
Jack Starkey, *Vice Pres*
Susan Noland, *Manager*
EMP: 30
SQ FT: 41,044

G E O G R A P H I C

SALES (est): 6.7MM
SALES (corp-wide): 203.7MM **Privately Held**
WEB: www.reconserve.com
SIC: **2048** Pulverized oats, prepared as animal feed
HQ: Reconserve, Inc.
    2811 Wilshire Blvd # 410
    Santa Monica CA 90403
    310 458-1574

(G-4869)
RED MOUNTAIN RESOURCES INC (PA)
6334 Maple Ave Ste 500 (75235-5527)
PHONE....................................214 871-0400
Alan W Barksdale, *President*
Hilda D Kouvelis, *Exec VP*
Jack Bradley, *Vice Pres*
Matthew Jacobs, *Vice Pres*
EMP: 26
SALES: 12.7MM **Publicly Held**
WEB: www.redmountainresources.com
SIC: **1311** Crude petroleum production

(G-4870)
RED RIVER TEA COMPANY
Also Called: Teazzers
13375 Branch View Ln (75234-5701)
PHONE....................................214 956-0373
Jeff Farris, *President*
Craig Dyer, *Vice Pres*
Mike Hamblin, *Vice Pres*
Rick Scheer, *Vice Pres*
Craig Spivey, *Vice Pres*
EMP: 10
SQ FT: 15,000 **Privately Held**
WEB: www.teazzers.com
SIC: **2099** Tea blending

(G-4871)
RED STEEL COMPANY
10566 Spangler Rd (75220-2308)
P.O. Box 541536 (75354-1536)
PHONE....................................972 243-4242
Lee W Owen, *President*
Gerald Gansert, *Vice Pres*
Debbie Owen, *Treasurer*
Jean Harper, *Officer*
EMP: 22
SQ FT: 3,000
SALES (est): 4MM **Privately Held**
SIC: **3441** Fabricated structural metal

(G-4872)
REDDY ICE CORPORATION
4320 Duncanville Rd (75236-1802)
PHONE....................................972 296-4271
Jeff Frey, *Branch Mgr*
Susan Figgins, *Payroll Mgr*
Wallace Nault, *Supervisor*
EMP: 60
SQ FT: 42,305 **Privately Held**
WEB: www.reddyice.com
SIC: **2097** Manufactured ice; ice
HQ: Reddy Ice Corporation
    5710 Lbj Fwy Ste 300
    Dallas TX 75240
    214 526-6740

(G-4873)
REDDY ICE CORPORATION
8750 N Cntl Expy Ste 1800 (75231)
PHONE....................................214 526-6740
Steven Fair, *General Mgr*
Kevin Hansen, *General Mgr*
Doris Bell, *Vice Pres*
Steven Wilson, *Vice Pres*
Yancey Reynolds, *Plant Mgr*
EMP: 17 **Privately Held**
WEB: www.reddyice.com
SIC: **2097** Manufactured ice
HQ: Reddy Ice Corporation
    5710 Lbj Fwy Ste 300
    Dallas TX 75240
    214 526-6740

(G-4874)
REDDY ICE CORPORATION (DH)
5710 Lbj Fwy Ste 300 (75240-6389)
PHONE....................................214 526-6740
Deborah Conklin, *CEO*
Bill Corbin, *Ch of Bd*
Scott McKinnon, *Vice Pres*
Dave Sanborn, *Vice Pres*
Mark A Steffek, *Vice Pres*

EMP: 68
SQ FT: 4,500
SALES (est): 321MM **Privately Held**
WEB: www.reddyice.com
SIC: **2097** Manufactured ice

(G-4875)
REDDY ICE GROUP INC
4320 Duncanville Rd (75236-1802)
PHONE....................................972 263-4359
Steven Janusek, *Branch Mgr*
EMP: 16 **Privately Held**
WEB: www.reddyice.com
SIC: **2097** Manufactured ice
HQ: Reddy Ice Group, Inc.
    5720 Lbj Fwy Ste 200
    Dallas TX 75240

(G-4876)
REDDY ICE GROUP INC (DH)
5720 Lbj Fwy Ste 200 (75240-6396)
PHONE....................................877 295-0024
Steven J Janusek, *Exec VP*
Graham D Davis, *Exec VP*
Mark A Steffek, *Treasurer*
▼ EMP: 50
SQ FT: 16,000
SALES (est): 323.9MM **Privately Held**
WEB: www.reddyice.com
SIC: **5199 2097** Ice, manufactured or natural; manufactured ice
HQ: Reddy Ice Holdings, Inc.
    5720 Lbj Fwy Ste 200
    Dallas TX 75240
    214 526-6740

(G-4877)
REDDY ICE HOLDINGS INC (HQ)
5720 Lbj Fwy Ste 200 (75240-6396)
PHONE....................................214 526-6740
Deborah Conklin, *CEO*
Bill Corbin, *Ch of Bd*
Karen Apperson, *General Mgr*
William A Tolany, *Principal*
William P Brick, *Chairman*
EMP: 45
SQ FT: 32,217
SALES (est): 389.8MM **Privately Held**
WEB: www.reddyice.com
SIC: **2097** Ice cubes

(G-4878)
REDHOUSE VIRTUAL EDUCATION LLC
701 Commerce St (75202-4522)
PHONE....................................210 872-4989
Tony Scallion, *CEO*
Tenequia Smith,
EMP: 10
SALES (est): 300K **Privately Held**
WEB: www.redhouse243.com
SIC: **8299 8243 8211 7372** Educational services; software training, computer; ; educational computer software; computer software development & applications

(G-4879)
REDWINE RESOURCES INC
8214 Westchester Dr # 740 (75225-6199)
PHONE....................................214 691-5800
Gary Redwine, *President*
Shauna Redwine, *Admin Sec*
EMP: 21
SQ FT: 2,500
SALES (est): 3.7MM **Privately Held**
WEB: www.shepherdroyalty.com
SIC: **1382** Oil & gas exploration services

(G-4880)
REFOCUS GROUP INC (PA)
Also Called: Refocus Ocular
10210 N Cntl Expy Ste 400 (75231)
PHONE....................................214 368-0200
Michael Judy, *CEO*
Mark A Cox, *Exec VP*
Selene A Burke, *Vice Pres*
David Ozinga, *Vice Pres*
Zack Thompson, *CFO*
▲ EMP: 16 EST: 2000
SQ FT: 900
SALES (est): 1.8MM **Privately Held**
WEB: www.refocus-group.com
SIC: **3841** Diagnostic apparatus, medical

(G-4881)
REGENCY ENERGY PARTNERS LP (DH)
8111 Westchester Dr # 600 (75225-6142)
PHONE....................................214 750-1771
Michael J Bradley, *President*
Christofer Rozzell, *Exec VP*
Dennie W Dixon, *Senior VP*
Shannon A Ming, *Senior VP*
Thomas E Long, *CFO*
EMP: 74
SALES: 4.9B **Publicly Held**
WEB: www.energytransfer.com
SIC: **1321 4925 5172 4922** Natural gas liquids; liquefied petroleum gas, distribution through mains; gases, liquefied petroleum (propane); natural gas transmission
HQ: Etp Legacy Lp
    8111 Westchester Dr # 600
    Dallas TX 75225
    214 981-0700

(G-4882)
REGENCY PLZ PRTG & OFF SUP INC
Also Called: ASAP
2797 Irving Blvd Ste 118 (75207-2310)
P.O. Box 568629 (75356-8629)
PHONE....................................214 939-3456
Patty Tate, *President*
H M Tate, *Treasurer*
Dallas Owen, *Controller*
Donald Wesolowski, *Manager*
EMP: 14
SQ FT: 6,000
SALES (est): 2.7MM **Privately Held**
WEB: www.regencynow.com
SIC: **5943 2752** Office forms & supplies; commercial printing, offset

(G-4883)
REGENCY WRAPS INC
2731 Satsuma Dr (75229-3521)
PHONE....................................214 357-0099
Doug Cohen, *President*
◆ EMP: 25
SQ FT: 6,500
SALES (est): 4.9MM **Privately Held**
WEB: www.regencywraps.com
SIC: **3589** Cooking equipment, commercial

(G-4884)
REGIS MANUFACTURING COMPANY
1500 Corinth St (75215-5730)
P.O. Box 152900 (75315-2900)
PHONE....................................214 421-5171
Larry Morden, *President*
Frank L Kehr, *President*
Mary Nell Kehr, *Corp Secy*
Patty Wright, *Accountant*
EMP: 10 EST: 1959
SQ FT: 10,000 **Privately Held**
WEB: www.regismanufacturing.com
SIC: **3714** Motor vehicle parts & accessories

(G-4885)
REHRIG PACIFIC COMPANY
625 W Mockingbird Ln (75247-6008)
PHONE....................................214 631-7943
Sheldon Neill, *Safety Dir*
Steve Pappas, *Plant Mgr*
Stephan Papas, *Manager*
EMP: 80 **Privately Held**
WEB: www.rehrigpacific.com
SIC: **3089 5999** Injection molding of plastics; business machines & equipment
HQ: Rehrig Pacific Sales Company
    4010 E 26th St
    Vernon CA 90058
    323 262-5145

(G-4886)
RENAISSANCE PRINTING
1215 Commerce St (75202-4323)
PHONE....................................972 234-0347
Jarrod Danielson, *Owner*
EMP: 20
SALES (est): 2.9MM **Privately Held**
SIC: **2752** Commercial printing, lithographic

(G-4887)
RENEVER INC
Also Called: Old Timber Table Company
908 Dragon St (75207-4204)
PHONE....................................214 761-1882
C H Everett Jr, *President*
EMP: 10
SQ FT: 13,000
SALES (est): 1.1MM **Privately Held**
WEB: www.oldtimbertable.com
SIC: **2511 5712** Wood household furniture; furniture stores

(G-4888)
RENOVATED HOMES INC
Also Called: Act-PSM
4829 Top Line Dr (75247-6316)
PHONE....................................214 678-9114
EMP: 14 EST: 1999
SQ FT: 15,000
SALES (est): 2.1MM **Privately Held**
WEB: www.act-psm.com
SIC: **3444** Sheet metalwork

(G-4889)
REPUBLIC ENERGY INC
Also Called: Warner Group
2621 State St (75204-2602)
PHONE....................................214 369-4800
Jerald T Baldridge, *Ch of Bd*
Frank A King, *President*
Robert Douglas, *COO*
John Swanson, *CFO*
Jolene Brown, *Office Mgr*
EMP: 25
SQ FT: 4,000
SALES (est): 5.1MM **Privately Held**
WEB: www.republicenergy.com
SIC: **1382 1311** Oil & gas exploration services; crude petroleum production; natural gas production

(G-4890)
REPUBLIC SALES & MANUFACTURING
Also Called: Republic Blower Systems
5131 Cash Rd (75247-5805)
PHONE....................................214 631-8070
Zachary Goff, *CEO*
Frank Kiska, *Business Mgr*
Shelley Condon, *Opers Mgr*
Brad Cofer, *Production*
Demi Pratt, *Opers-Prdtn-Mfg*
▲ EMP: 30
SALES (est): 7.1MM **Privately Held**
WEB: www.republic-mfg.com
SIC: **3564** Blowers & fans

(G-4891)
RESOURCE ROYALTY LLC
5949 Sherry Ln Ste 1100 (75225-8007)
PHONE....................................214 691-5234
Gary Redwine, *Mng Member*
Bob Howard,
EMP: 10
SALES (est): 992.1K **Privately Held**
WEB: www.resourceroyaltyllc.com
SIC: **1382** Oil & gas exploration services

(G-4892)
RETCO TOOL COMPANY INC
9030 Viscount Row (75247-5412)
PHONE....................................214 358-5039
John Cade, *President*
Celia Venable, *General Mgr*
Bill Bain, *Vice Pres*
David Martin, *Supervisor*
EMP: 35 EST: 1969
SQ FT: 21,750
SALES (est): 4MM **Privately Held**
WEB: www.retcotool.com
SIC: **3545 5084** Cutting tools for machine tools; machine tools & metalworking machinery

(G-4893)
REVERE SMELTING & REF CORP
2777 N Stemmons Fwy # 1800 (75207-2277)
PHONE....................................214 631-6070
Robert E Finn, *President*
John De Paul, *Vice Pres*
John D Paul, *Vice Pres*
Patrick Moriarty, *Purch Mgr*

▲ = Import ▼ =Export
◆ =Import/Export

Grant Steckler, *Purch Agent*
◆ **EMP:** 189 **EST:** 1970
SQ FT: 45,000
SALES (est): 53.2MM
SALES (corp-wide): 276.4MM **Privately Held**
WEB: www.rsrna.com
SIC: 3341 2899 Lead smelting & refining (secondary); battery acid
HQ: Rsr Corporation
2777 N Stemmons Fwy # 2000
Dallas TX 75207
214 631-6070

(G-4894)
REYNIERS FRENCH BAKERY INC
2156 W Northwest Hwy # 304 (75220-4221)
PHONE..................................972 401-3600
Edwin Mergulhao, *President*
Virginia Mergulhao, *Vice Pres*
Reynier Viviane, *Vice Pres*
EMP: 12 **EST:** 1978
SALES (est): 1.3MM **Privately Held**
WEB: www.windward-realty.com
SIC: 2051 Bread, cake & related products

(G-4895)
RH TAMLYN & SONS LP
10940 Petal St (75238-2423)
PHONE..................................214 348-9676
Betty Hayes, *Controller*
Dana Madden, *Sales Staff*
Lorena Ramirez, *Mktg Coord*
Ron Tamlyn, *Branch Mgr*
Siem Su, *Info Tech Mgr*
EMP: 14
SQ FT: 24,400
SALES (corp-wide): 23.3MM **Privately Held**
WEB: www.tamlyn.com
SIC: 3444 Sheet metalwork
PA: R.H. Tamlyn & Sons
13623 Pike Rd
Stafford TX 77477
281 499-9604

(G-4896)
RICH TRANSPORT LLC
4444 Irving Blvd (75247-5702)
PHONE..................................214 819-3082
Shane Timmons, *Branch Mgr*
EMP: 150
SALES (corp-wide): 1.8B **Publicly Held**
WEB: www.rrts.com
SIC: 3537 4731 Trucks: freight, baggage, etc.: industrial, except mining; freight transportation arrangement
HQ: Rich Transport, Llc
6011 Scott Hamilton Dr
Little Rock AR 72209

(G-4897)
RICHARD E COLGIN I LTD
Also Called: Colgin Companies, The
4111 Mint Way (75237-1605)
PHONE..................................214 951-8687
Elizabeth Gardner, *Managing Prtnr*
Mark Gardner, *Vice Pres*
Elizabeth Gardener, *CFO*
Debora Reed, *Sales Staff*
EMP: 20 **EST:** 1938
SQ FT: 33,600
SALES (est): 4MM **Privately Held**
WEB: www.colgin.com
SIC: 2035 Seasonings & sauces, except tomato & dry

(G-4898)
RICHARD-MARCUS INC
Also Called: Arrowhead Sperior Woodcrafters
13821 Diplomat Dr (75234-8813)
PHONE..................................972 484-0406
Dave Harrison, *CEO*
Kevin Ingram, *General Mgr*
Jason Proctor, *General Mgr*
Bob Doebener, *Purchasing*
Alexis Patman, *Manager*
EMP: 45
SQ FT: 13,000
SALES (est): 15.2MM **Privately Held**
WEB: www.arrowheadstairs.com
SIC: 3446 Stairs, staircases, stair treads: prefabricated metal

(G-4899)
RICK TRIPLETT
Also Called: R Triplett Construction
802 S Haskell Ave (75223-2744)
PHONE..................................214 823-2830
Rick Triplett, *Owner*
EMP: 10
SQ FT: 7,560
SALES (est): 680K **Privately Held**
WEB: www.triplettconstruction.com
SIC: 2434 2521 Wood kitchen cabinets; wood office furniture

(G-4900)
RINGO DRILLING I LP
12900 Preston Rd Ste 730 (75230-1348)
PHONE..................................325 232-5807
Murl Richardson, *Partner*
Danny Covert, *Partner*
Anthony Hutchison, *Principal*
EMP: 230 **EST:** 2005
SALES (est): 13.5MM **Privately Held**
SIC: 1381 Directional drilling oil & gas wells

(G-4901)
RIO STAR FOODS INC
3251 W Commerce St (75212-4837)
P.O. Box 560525 (75356-0525)
PHONE..................................214 630-4455
Samuel N Hazen, *President*
John N Franck II, *Vice Pres*
David G Anderson, *Treasurer*
Dwayne Rohlf, *Sales Dir*
Carlos Vigil, *Manager*
▲ **EMP:** 60
SQ FT: 27,000
SALES (est): 13.1MM **Privately Held**
WEB: www.riostarfoods.com
SIC: 2015 Poultry, processed: fresh

(G-4902)
RIOS PACKAGING CORP
4557 Leston St (75247-5709)
PHONE..................................214 920-9851
Roland Rios, *Owner*
EMP: 14
SQ FT: 42,500
SALES (est): 2MM **Privately Held**
WEB: www.riospackagingcorp.com
SIC: 2679 Paper products, converted

(G-4903)
RJ & RC ASSOCIATES LLC
4103 Crossing Ln (75220-5035)
PHONE..................................214 352-4690
Robert J Schuetz, *Mng Member*
Richard Clay Young, *Director*
EMP: 10
SALES (est): 792K **Privately Held**
SIC: 2542 Racks, merchandise display or storage: except wood

(G-4904)
RMG ENTERPRISE SOLUTIONS INC (DH)
Also Called: Rmg Networks
15770 Dallas Pkwy # 1100 (75248-3387)
PHONE..................................877 796-6634
Robert Michelson, *CEO*
Jana Bell, *CFO*
Garrett McCloud, *Manager*
Melissa Flores, *Executive Asst*
EMP: 50 **EST:** 1980
SALES: 42.5MM
SALES (corp-wide): 9.8MM **Privately Held**
WEB: www.rmgnetworks.com
SIC: 7371 7372 Computer software development; prepackaged software

(G-4905)
ROBERT V JOHNS & ASSOCIATES (PA)
Also Called: Kitchen Source, The
1544 Slocum St (75207-3604)
PHONE..................................214 741-1912
Robert V Johns, *President*
Rachel Schroeder, *Associate*
EMP: 13
SALES (est): 1.4MM **Privately Held**
WEB: www.thekitchensource.net
SIC: 2434 Wood kitchen cabinets

(G-4906)
ROBINSON AEROSPACE INC
539 W Commerce St (75208-1953)
PHONE..................................817 253-0639
Jeff Robinson, *President*
Ronnie Hudson, *General Mgr*
Joe Robinson, *Vice Pres*
Mark Robinson, *Vice Pres*
Scott Rendleman, *Controller*
EMP: 50
SALES (est): 2MM **Privately Held**
WEB: www.robinsonaero.com
SIC: 2599 3444 Cabinets, factory; sheet metalwork

(G-4907)
ROCHESTER GAUGES LLC (DH)
11616 Harry Hines Blvd (75229-2203)
P.O. Box 29242 (75229-0242)
PHONE..................................972 280-8478
Jack W La Due, *Ch of Bd*
Benjamin Lease, *President*
Herbert Ross, *Exec VP*
C K La Due, *Vice Pres*
H G Ross, *Vice Pres*
▲ **EMP:** 250
SQ FT: 110,000
SALES (est): 61MM
SALES (corp-wide): 130.5MM **Privately Held**
WEB: www.rochestergauges.com
SIC: 3823 Industrial instrmnts msrmnt display/control process variable; liquid level instruments, industrial process type; pressure gauges, dial & digital; temperature instruments: industrial process type
HQ: Gas Equipment Company, Inc.
11616 Harry Hines Blvd
Dallas TX 75229
972 241-2333

(G-4908)
ROCKALL ENERGY LLC (PA)
5005 Lyndon B Johnson Fwy # 700 (75244-6145)
PHONE..................................214 618-7600
Lewis Gillies, *President*
Joe Schimepfening, *COO*
K Bradleigh Leblanc, *Senior VP*
Graeme Miller, *Senior VP*
Dennis Justus, *CFO*
EMP: 75
SALES (est): 91MM **Privately Held**
WEB: www.rockallenergy.com
SIC: 1382 Oil & gas exploration services

(G-4909)
ROLLAND SAFE & LOCK CO LLC (PA)
Also Called: Rolland Centuries of Security
3140 Towerwood Dr (75234-2313)
PHONE..................................972 243-3711
Rick Rolland, *CEO*
Vicky C Teherani, *CEO*
Krissy Zimmerman, *General Mgr*
Walter Adler, *Principal*
Frank McCuen, *COO*
◆ **EMP:** 76
SQ FT: 40,000
SALES (est): 28MM **Privately Held**
WEB: www.rollandsolutions.com
SIC: 7699 3429 5251 Locksmith shop; locks or lock sets; door locks & lock sets

(G-4910)
ROSADO WELDING INC
6632 Fireflame Dr (75248-5015)
PHONE..................................469 730-2222
Victor Rosado, *President*
EMP: 12
SALES (est): 62.4K **Privately Held**
WEB: www.rosadowelding.com
SIC: 7692 Welding repair

(G-4911)
ROSEWOOD PRVATE INVSTMENTS INC (PA)
2101 Cedar Springs Rd # 16 (75201-2104)
PHONE..................................214 849-9000
Schuyler Marshall, *Ch of Bd*
Tim Wafford, *COO*
John M Dziminski, *Senior VP*
Loren Greaves, *Senior VP*
C Jedson Nau, *Senior VP*
EMP: 10

SALES (est): 34.7MM **Privately Held**
WEB: www.rosewoodpi.com
SIC: 6799 3423 Investors; cutting dies, except metal cutting

(G-4912)
ROSEWOOD RESOURCES INC (HQ)
2101 Cedar Springs Rd # 1500 (75201-2147)
PHONE..................................214 849-9300
Nathan Mayer, *CEO*
Mark Malinowsky, *President*
Steve Renke, *President*
Angela O'Malley, *VP Admin*
Gary Conrad, *Vice Pres*
▼ **EMP:** 25
SQ FT: 20,134
SALES (est): 12MM
SALES (corp-wide): 91.2MM **Privately Held**
WEB: www.rosewoodresources.com
SIC: 1311 Crude petroleum production; natural gas production
PA: The Rosewood Corporation
2101 Cedar Springs Rd # 1600
Dallas TX 75201
214 849-9000

(G-4913)
ROYAL CHEMICAL COMPANY LTD
2851 Reward Ln (75220-1507)
PHONE..................................214 358-1861
Dan Zelman, *Branch Mgr*
EMP: 15
SALES (corp-wide): 10.8MM **Privately Held**
WEB: www.royalchemical.com
SIC: 2841 2869 2819 Soap: granulated, liquid, cake, flaked or chip; industrial organic chemicals; industrial inorganic chemicals
HQ: Royal Chemical Company, Ltd.
8679 Freeway Dr
Macedonia OH 44056
330 467-1300

(G-4914)
ROYAL PRINTING GROUP INC
2035 Royal Ln Ste 250 (75229-7203)
PHONE..................................972 241-5686
Winston Manning, *President*
EMP: 14
SQ FT: 9,500
SALES (est): 1.9MM **Privately Held**
SIC: 2752 Commercial printing, offset

(G-4915)
RPS ENVIRONMENTAL SOLUTIONS LP
12200 N Stemmons Fwy (75234-5888)
PHONE..................................972 247-1556
Robert Hill, *President*
Scott Olson, *Principal*
Grant Gifford, *Vice Pres*
Paul Waggoner, *CFO*
John Ross, *Technology*
EMP: 20
SQ FT: 2,500
SALES (est): 318.2K **Privately Held**
WEB: www.rpsenvironmental.com
SIC: 2899 Vegetable oils, vulcanized or sulfurized

(G-4916)
RSP PERMIAN LLC (DH)
3141 Hood St Ste 700 (75219-5022)
PHONE..................................214 252-2700
Erik B Daugbjerg, *Exec VP*
Mark Ellis, *Engineer*
Steven Smith, *Accounting Mgr*
Steven Loh, *Finance*
Sam August, *Human Resources*
EMP: 40
SALES (est): 83MM **Privately Held**
WEB: www.rsppermian.com
SIC: 1382 Oil & gas exploration services
HQ: Rsp Permian, Inc.
600 W Illinois Ave
Midland TX 79701
432 683-7443

(G-4917)
RTS PACKAGING LLC
4105 Bronze Way (75237-1001)
PHONE..........................214 331-6555
Ron Jameson, *General Mgr*
EMP: 64
SQ FT: 59,300
SALES (corp-wide): 17.5B **Publicly Held**
WEB: www.rtspackaging.com
SIC: 2679 2631 Paperboard products,
　converted; paperboard mills
HQ: Rts Packaging, Llc
　504 Thrasher St
　Norcross GA 30071
　800 558-6984

(G-4918)
RUBEN REYES
Also Called: Rare Enterprises
4707 S Cockrell Hill Rd (75236-2020)
PHONE..........................214 331-4307
Ruben Reyes, *Owner*
EMP: 11
SQ FT: 26,000
SALES (est): 1MM **Privately Held**
SIC: 5046 3993 Signs, electrical; signs,
　not made in custom sign painting shops

(G-4919)
RUDOLPH FOODS COMPANY INC
3660 Pipestone Rd (75212-6109)
PHONE..........................214 638-2204
Marc Vondran, *General Mgr*
John Kenning, *VP Sales*
Kathryn Amatrian, *Marketing Staff*
Robert Wallace, *Manager*
Rod Eppley, *Manager*
EMP: 52
SQ FT: 10,223
SALES (corp-wide): 131.1MM **Privately Held**
WEB: www.rudolphfoods.com
SIC: 2096 2099 Potato chips & similar
　snacks; food preparations
PA: Rudolph Foods Company, Inc.
　6575 Bellefontaine Rd
　Lima OH 45804
　909 383-7463

(G-4920)
RUDOLPHS MARKET & SAUSAGE CO
2924 Elm St (75226-1509)
PHONE..........................214 741-1874
Justine M Andreason, *President*
Brandon Andreason, *Vice Pres*
EMP: 15 EST: 1895
SQ FT: 4,750
SALES (est): 1MM **Privately Held**
WEB: www.rudolphsmarket.com
SIC: 5421 5147 2013 Meat markets, in-
　cluding freezer provisioners; meats, fresh;
　sausages & other prepared meats

(G-4921)
RUSSIAN SPIRIT INC
13644 Neutron Rd (75244-4410)
PHONE..........................214 334-3018
Roman Talis, *Principal*
Billy Adcock, *VP Opers*
▲ **EMP:** 11
SALES (est): 1.1MM **Privately Held**
WEB: www.krutovodka.com
SIC: 2085 Distilled & blended liquors

(G-4922)
S C S C INC
Also Called: Cast Stone Commercial Services
301 Pleasant Dr (75217-6512)
P.O. Box 170249 (75217-0249)
PHONE..........................214 398-1199
Richard Carey, *CEO*
Fred Carey, *COO*
▲ **EMP:** 44
SQ FT: 54,000
SALES (est): 20.6MM **Privately Held**
WEB:
www.caststonecommercialservices.com
SIC: 3272 3443 3429 3281 Concrete
　products, precast; fabricated plate work
　(boiler shop); manufactured hardware
　(general); cut stone & stone products

(G-4923)
S N D MANUFACTURING LTD
Also Called: Formals
12215 Forestgate Dr # 101 (75243-5495)
PHONE..........................214 340-1592
Hong Lee, *President*
Victor Vothang, *Vice Pres*
EMP: 85
SALES (est): 2.5MM **Privately Held**
WEB: www.snd-mfg.com
SIC: 2329 2392 3634 Athletic (warmup,
　sweat & jogging) suits: men's & boys';
　cushions & pillows; heating pads, electric

(G-4924)
S W GALLERIES CORP
Also Called: Southwest Gallery
4500 Sigma Rd (75244-4503)
PHONE..........................972 788-2743
Eugene C Carmack, *President*
Bob Malenfant, *Vice Pres*
Michael Downs, *Sales Staff*
EMP: 28
SQ FT: 16,000
SALES (est): 2.1MM **Privately Held**
WEB: www.swgallery.com
SIC: 5999 8412 2499 Art dealers; muse-
　ums & art galleries; picture frame mold-
　ing, finished

(G-4925)
SABLE NATURAL RESOURCES CORP
12222 Merit Dr Ste 1850 (75251-2293)
PHONE..........................972 770-4700
Michael K Galvis, *Ch of Bd*
Cory Hall, *COO*
Mark Randles, *Investment Ofcr*
EMP: 12
SQ FT: 3,700
SALES (est): 1MM **Privately Held**
WEB: www.snrcorp.com
SIC: 1311 Crude petroleum & natural gas

(G-4926)
SAFEGUARD BUSINESS SYSTEMS INC (HQ)
8585 N Stemmons Fwy 600n (75247-3836)
PHONE..........................800 523-2422
John J Sorrenli, *President*
Kipp Kress, *Business Mgr*
Caitlin Martin, *Vice Pres*
Tina Drew, *Project Mgr*
Colyn Locker, *Project Mgr*
◆ **EMP:** 148
SQ FT: 36,300
SALES (est): 125.3MM
SALES (corp-wide): 2B **Publicly Held**
WEB: www.gosafeguard.com
SIC: 7374 2759 5112 5045 Data pro-
　cessing service; commercial printing;
　business forms; computers
PA: Deluxe Corporation
　3680 Victoria St N
　Shoreview MN 55126
　651 483-7111

(G-4927)
SAGEM COMMUNICATIONS USA LLC
14651 Dallas Pkwy Ste 900 (75254-8862)
PHONE..........................972 386-4641
Scott Billings, *CFO*
EMP: 20 **Privately Held**
WEB: www.polarcus.com
SIC: 3661 Modems
HQ: Polarcus Dmcc
　Level 20,Jumeirah Lakes Towers Unit
　No 2001, Plot No Jlt-Ph2-O1a
　Dubai

(G-4928)
SALIENT GLOBAL TECHNOLOGIES
11252 Leo Ln (75229-4726)
PHONE..........................925 526-1234
EMP: 75 EST: 2017
SQ FT: 30,000
SALES (est): 270K **Privately Held**
WEB: www.salientglobaltech.com
SIC: 7373 3571 5045 Systems software
　development services; electronic comput-
　ers; computers, peripherals & software

(G-4929)
SAMPLE HOUSE & RESALE SHOP INC (PA)
Also Called: Sample House & Candle Shop
4722 Bengal St (75235-8008)
PHONE..........................214 688-0751
Foster M Poole, *President*
Mitsui Kimuro, *Vice Pres*
Bradley W Poole, *Vice Pres*
Bradley Poole, *Vice Pres*
Bryan W Poole, *Vice Pres*
EMP: 40 EST: 1958
SQ FT: 35,000
SALES (est): 12.6MM **Privately Held**
WEB: www.samplehouse.com
SIC: 2621 5947 Specialty papers; gift
　shop; novelties

(G-4930)
SAN MATEO MIDSTREAM LLC
5400 Lbj Fwy Ste 1500 (75240-1017)
PHONE..........................972 371-5203
Matthew D Spicer, *Vice Pres*
EMP: 11
SALES (est): 204.6K
SALES (corp-wide): 983.6MM **Publicly Held**
WEB: www.sanmateomidstream.com
SIC: 1311 Natural gas production
PA: Matador Resources Company
　5400 Lbj Fwy Ste 1500
　Dallas TX 75240
　972 371-5200

(G-4931)
SANDENVENDO AMERICA INC (HQ)
10710 Sanden Dr (75238-1335)
PHONE..........................800 344-7216
Frank Kabei, *President*
Kevin Mason, *IT/INT Sup*
◆ **EMP:** 400
SALES (est): 850.1MM **Privately Held**
WEB: www.vendoco.com
SIC: 3581 Automatic vending machines

(G-4932)
SANDFORD PREPRESS SYSTEMS
Also Called: Sanford Howard Litho
4656 Leston St Ste 511 (75247-5725)
PHONE..........................214 808-3070
Howard Sandford, *President*
Sandra Sandford, *Vice Pres*
EMP: 22
SQ FT: 20,000
SALES (est): 1.8MM **Privately Held**
SIC: 2741 2796 2791 Miscellaneous pub-
　lishing; platemaking services; typesetting

(G-4933)
SANTA CRUZ BIOTECHNOLOGY INC (PA)
10410 Finnell St (75220-2443)
PHONE..........................214 902-3900
John R Stephenson, *CEO*
Brenda Stephenson, *Vice Pres*
Jim Hampton, *Finance*
Bonita Keaton, *Manager*
Erik Wild, *Manager*
▲ **EMP:** 115
SQ FT: 18,126
SALES (est): 21.6MM **Privately Held**
WEB: www.scbt.com
SIC: 2836 5122 Biological products, ex-
　cept diagnostic; biologicals & allied prod-
　ucts

(G-4934)
SAPUTO DAIRY FOODS USA LLC (DH)
Also Called: Sulphur Springs Cultured Spc
2711 N Haskell Ave # 370 (75204-2911)
PHONE..........................214 863-2300
Kevin Yost, *President*
Nick Adame, *Vice Pres*
Rachel A Gonzalez, *Vice Pres*
David Rothstein, *Vice Pres*
Mario Skertchly, *Vice Pres*
▲ **EMP:** 250
SALES (est): 5.2B
SALES (corp-wide): 3.7B **Privately Held**
WEB: www.saputo.com
SIC: 2023 2015 2026 Cream substitutes;
　egg substitutes made from eggs; cream,
　sour; milk, reconstituted; whipped top-
　ping, except frozen or dry mix; cottage
　cheese

(G-4935)
SASCH INC
Also Called: Pro Print A Sasch Company
8101a Moberly Ln (75227-2312)
P.O. Box 466, Rowlett (75030-0466)
PHONE..........................214 388-7000
Nancy Cox, *Principal*
EMP: 12
SALES (est): 894.9K **Privately Held**
SIC: 7389 2395 Printing broker; embroi-
　dery & art needlework

(G-4936)
SATCO PRODUCTS INC
2000 Valwood Pkwy (75234-8800)
PHONE..........................972 247-2437
EMP: 228
SALES (corp-wide): 38.9MM **Privately Held**
WEB: www.satco.com
SIC: 3641 3229 Electric light bulbs, com-
　plete; glass lighting equipment parts
PA: Satco Products, Inc.
　110 Heartland Blvd
　Edgewood NY 11717
　631 243-2022

(G-4937)
SATORI HOME LIMITED LLC
13612 Midway Rd Ste 515 (75244-4323)
PHONE..........................855 472-8674
Steve Bonkowski, *CEO*
Ronnie Perlstein, *Exec VP*
EMP: 26
SALES (est): 3MM **Privately Held**
WEB: www.wattceg.com
SIC: 2591 5023 7389 Drapery hardware
　& blinds & shades; home furnishings; in-
　terior decorating

(G-4938)
SAULSBURY INDUSTRIES INC
Also Called: Nuclear Services Division
3010 L B Johnson Fwy # 1100
(75234-7770)
PHONE..........................972 884-6000
Oscar Alvarez, *Superintendent*
Norman Hood, *Principal*
Kim Combs, *Vice Pres*
Jimmy Matthews, *Vice Pres*
Myra Carrasco, *Purchasing*
EMP: 665
SALES (corp-wide): 718.7MM **Privately Held**
WEB: www.saulsbury.com
SIC: 3443 Nuclear reactors, military or in-
　dustrial
PA: Saulsbury Industries, Inc.
　2951 E Interstate 20
　Odessa TX 79766
　432 366-3686

(G-4939)
SAWMILL PARTNERS LLC
Also Called: Richardson Timbers
7557 Rambler Rd Ste 1020 (75231-2385)
PHONE..........................214 358-2314
Lynn Surls, *Mng Member*
EMP: 30
SQ FT: 4,000
SALES (est): 4.1MM **Privately Held**
WEB: www.richardsontimbers.com
SIC: 2421 Sawmills & planing mills, gen-
　eral

(G-4940)
SCHLACHTER OPERATING CORP
Also Called: Schlachter Oil
6211 W Nw Hwy Ste C256 (75225-3477)
PHONE..........................214 692-1567
Mark Schlachter, *President*
EMP: 9 EST: 1999
SALES (est): 1.2MM **Privately Held**
WEB: www.schlachteroil.com
SIC: 1311 Crude petroleum production

(G-4941)
SCHWOB ENERGY SERVICES LLC
2346 Glenda Ln (75229-3317)
PHONE....................................469 917-9023
Andre Rodriguez, *President*
Roman Gonzalez, *COO*
Harlan Smith, *Exec VP*
Paul Lehmann, *CFO*
EMP: 75
SALES: 63.6MM **Privately Held**
WEB: www.schwob.com
SIC: **1389** 1623 Construction, repair & dismantling services; oil & gas line & compressor station construction; oil & gas pipeline construction

(G-4942)
SCLM ENTERPRISES INC
Also Called: Sunbelt Letterpress
11252 Leo Ln (75229-4726)
PHONE....................................972 243-1688
Scott Skinner, *President*
EMP: 20
SALES (est): 2.7MM **Privately Held**
WEB: www.sunbeltletterpress.com
SIC: **2752** 2759 Commercial printing, lithographic; commercial printing

(G-4943)
SCOTCH CORPORATION
1255 Viceroy Dr (75247-3908)
P.O. Box 560126 (75356-0126)
PHONE....................................214 943-4605
Lawrence E Siegel, *President*
Karen Siegel, *Corp Secy*
Zelda Siegel, *Vice Pres*
Charlotte Siegel, *Sales Dir*
◆ EMP: 23
SQ FT: 15,000
SALES (est): 8.5MM **Privately Held**
WEB: www.myinstantpower.com
SIC: **2819** 5169 2899 Industrial inorganic chemicals; chemicals & allied products; chemical preparations

(G-4944)
SCOTT-MERRIMAN INC
Also Called: S/M
2930 Merrell Rd (75229-4904)
PHONE....................................972 484-7113
Melvin A Biggs, *President*
Jeffry Biggs, *President*
Ginni Guimond, *Corp Secy*
EMP: 11
SQ FT: 6,000
SALES (est): 2.1MM **Privately Held**
WEB: www.scott-merriman.com
SIC: **2752** Commercial printing, offset

(G-4945)
SCOUT ENERGY MANAGEMENT LLC (PA)
Also Called: Scout Energy Partners
4901 Lyndon B Johnson Fwy # 300 (75244-6107)
PHONE....................................972 277-1397
Nick Tunnell, *Division Mgr*
John Baschab, *Managing Dir*
Todd Flott, *COO*
Kevin Rathke, *VP Opers*
Mark Caldwell, *Foreman/Supr*
EMP: 19
SQ FT: 6,000
SALES (est): 18.7MM **Privately Held**
WEB: www.scoutep.com
SIC: **1311** Crude petroleum & natural gas production

(G-4946)
SCURRY MIDSTREAM LLC
2311 Cedar Springs Rd # 10 (75201-1856)
PHONE....................................214 238-5740
Matt Flory, *CEO*
EMP: 10
SALES (est): 72K **Privately Held**
SIC: **1389** Processing service, gas

(G-4947)
SEKISUI SPCIALTY CHEM AMER LLC (DH)
1501 Lyndon B Johnson Fwy (75234-6047)
PHONE....................................972 277-2900
Cory Sikora, *CEO*
David Althouse, *Opers Staff*

Phil Sayles, *Opers Staff*
Dustin Peek, *Engineer*
Paul Thompson, *Engineer*
◆ EMP: 50
SALES (est): 95.9MM **Privately Held**
WEB: www.sekisui-sc.com
SIC: **2899** Chemical preparations
HQ: Sekisui America Corporation
    333 Meadowlands Pkwy
    Secaucus NJ 07094
    201 423-7960

(G-4948)
SEL CORPORATE ENTERPRISES INC
Also Called: Dfw Hightech Signs
10660 Plano Rd Ste 118 (75238-1357)
PHONE....................................214 348-8784
Scott Watson, *President*
Aaron Johnson, *Prdtn Mgr*
Marcus Longoria, *Sales Mgr*
Emily Watson, *Admin Sec*
EMP: 9
SQ FT: 5,100
SALES (est): 825K **Privately Held**
WEB: www.dfwvehiclegraphics.com
SIC: **3993** Signs & advertising specialties

(G-4949)
SERVICE ELECTRIC SUPPLY INC
10929 Grissom Ln (75229-3505)
PHONE....................................972 620-2821
J Marcus Young, *President*
Paula K Young, *Vice Pres*
EMP: 10
SQ FT: 25,000
SALES (est): 1.5MM **Privately Held**
WEB: www.seswire.com
SIC: **3714** Automotive wiring harness sets

(G-4950)
SFG MANAGEMENT LTD LBLTY CO
3114 S Haskell Ave (75223-3121)
PHONE....................................214 824-8163
Rick Beaman,
Eddie Tollison,
EMP: 600
SQ FT: 6,026
SALES (est): 138.4MM **Privately Held**
SIC: **2026** Milk processing (pasteurizing, homogenizing, bottling)

(G-4951)
SHADE STRUCTURES INC
Also Called: USA Shade
8319 Chancellor Row (75247-5515)
P.O. Box 3467, Coppell (75019-3406)
PHONE....................................214 905-9500
Melissa Houchins, *COO*
Gary Haymann, *Exec VP*
Deon Kleynhans, *Vice Pres*
Kevin Spence, *Vice Pres*
Matthew Friedman, *Project Mgr*
EMP: 9 **Publicly Held**
WEB: www.usa-shade.com
SIC: **1799** 3444 2394 Welding on site; sheet metalwork; canvas & related products
HQ: Shade Structures, Inc.
    2580 Esters Blvd 100
    Dfw Airport TX 75261
    214 905-9500

(G-4952)
SHAME LINGERIE
8330 Moberly Ln (75227-2315)
PHONE....................................214 823-1454
Kenneth Peters, *Owner*
EMP: 17
SQ FT: 10,000
SALES (est): 1.4MM **Privately Held**
WEB: www.shamecatalog.com
SIC: **2341** 5632 Women's & children's undergarments; lingerie & corsets (underwear)

(G-4953)
SHARON YOUNG INC (PA)
10367 Brockwood Rd (75238-1656)
PHONE....................................214 349-1891
Edward Vierling, *CEO*
Joe Mendenhall, *President*
Sam Klapholz, *Exec VP*

Thomas E Young, *Vice Pres*
Deann Hathaway, *Prdtn Mgr*
▲ EMP: 45
SQ FT: 19,100
SALES (est): 9MM **Privately Held**
WEB: www.sharonyounginc.com
SIC: **2335** Women's, juniors' & misses' dresses

(G-4954)
SHI INTERNATIONAL CORP
13737 Noel Rd Ste 210 (75240-2008)
PHONE....................................732 764-8888
Pat Faram, *Principal*
Eli Buck, *Executive*
EMP: 12 **Privately Held**
WEB: www.shi.com
SIC: **7372** Prepackaged software
PA: Shi International Corp.
    290 Davidson Ave
    Somerset NJ 08873

(G-4955)
SHIFTSMART INC
16000 Dallas Pkwy Ste 550 (75248-6649)
PHONE....................................817 271-3604
Aakash Kumar, *CEO*
EMP: 19
SALES (est): 1.2MM **Privately Held**
WEB: www.shiftsmart.com
SIC: **7372** Prepackaged software

(G-4956)
SHINE LIGHTING GROUP USA INC
1445 Ross Ave Ste 3700 (75202-2755)
PHONE....................................973 865-5893
EMP: 30
SALES (est): 1.3MM
SALES (corp-wide): 651.2K **Privately Held**
SIC: **3646** Ornamental lighting fixtures, commercial
PA: Enchant Christmas Light Maze & Market Ltd
    901 3rd St W Suite 304
    North Vancouver BC V7P 3
    604 220-6332

(G-4957)
SHOCKWATCH INC (DH)
Also Called: Spotsee
5501 Lyndon B Johnson Fwy (75240-6225)
PHONE....................................214 630-9625
Gerry Smith, *CEO*
Monique Allen, *Partner*
Roberto Pinheiro, *General Mgr*
Jeff Kilpatrick, *Senior VP*
Dale Glen, *Vice Pres*
◆ EMP: 44
SQ FT: 48,000
SALES (est): 8.9MM
SALES (corp-wide): 62MM **Publicly Held**
WEB: www.spotsee.io
SIC: **3829** Measuring & controlling devices
HQ: Media Recovery
    5501 Lyndon B Johnson Fwy
    Dallas TX 75240
    800 660-3586

(G-4958)
SIBBITT AND LOTT INC
Also Called: S&L Designs
1813 W Commerce St (75208-8102)
P.O. Box 222325 (75222-2325)
PHONE....................................214 742-6949
Susan Sibbitt Lott, *President*
Brad Lott, *Vice Pres*
Susan Lott, *Office Mgr*
▲ EMP: 9
SQ FT: 10,000
SALES (est): 2MM **Privately Held**
SIC: **2591** 2514 5023 2522 Shade, curtain & drapery hardware; metal household furniture; beds, including folding & cabinet, household: metal; tables, household: metal; window furnishings; office furniture, except wood

(G-4959)
SIEMENS INDUSTRY INC
2700 Esters Blvd Ste 200b (75261-4030)
P.O. Box 61648 (75261)
PHONE....................................972 947-7000
Gert Seidel, *CEO*
Dan Stricklin, *Sales Staff*

EMP: 500
SALES (corp-wide): 67.4B **Privately Held**
WEB: www.new.siemens.com
SIC: **3822** 5063 3669 1731 Air conditioning & refrigeration controls; thermostats & other environmental sensors; electric alarms & signaling equipment; emergency alarms; safety & security specialization; security systems services; relays & industrial controls
HQ: Siemens Industry, Inc.
    1000 Deerfield Pkwy
    Buffalo Grove IL 60089
    847 215-1000

(G-4960)
SIGN WAVE CORPORATION
10225 N Central Expy (75231-3401)
PHONE....................................214 890-4444
Lane Harris, *Ch of Bd*
EMP: 9
SQ FT: 3,600
SALES (est): 1.2MM **Privately Held**
SIC: **3993** Signs, not made in custom sign painting shops; letters for signs, metal

(G-4961)
SIGNIFY NORTH AMERICA CORP
Also Called: Philips Lighting
10911 Petal St (75238-2424)
PHONE....................................214 647-7880
Jeffrey Reese, *Engineer*
Steve Carson, *Manager*
EMP: 150
SALES (corp-wide): 6.9B **Privately Held**
WEB: www.colorkinetics.com
SIC: **3646** Commercial indusl & institutional electric lighting fixtures
HQ: Signify North America Corporation
    200 Franklin Square Dr # 4
    Somerset NJ 08873
    732 563-3000

(G-4962)
SIGNS MANUFACTURING CORP (PA)
4550 Mint Way (75236-2014)
PHONE....................................214 339-2227
Pamela Watson, *President*
James Watson, *Vice Pres*
William K Watson, *Vice Pres*
▲ EMP: 23
SALES (est): 4.4MM **Privately Held**
WEB: www.signsmanufacturing.com
SIC: **3993** Signs & advertising specialties

(G-4963)
SIKA CORPORATION
13524 Welch Rd (75244-5227)
PHONE....................................972 387-4500
EMP: 115
SALES (corp-wide): 8.1B **Privately Held**
WEB: www.usa.sika.com
SIC: **3086** Insulation or cushioning material, foamed plastic
HQ: Sika Corporation
    201 Polito Ave
    Lyndhurst NJ 07071
    201 933-8800

(G-4964)
SILVER HILL ENRGY PARTNERS LLC
5949 Sherry Ln Ste 1550 (75225-8090)
PHONE....................................214 865-6555
Kyle D Miller, *CEO*
Emery M Petrof III, *COO*
Jason A Gordeuk, *Vice Pres*
Matt Huhnke, *Vice Pres*
EMP: 50
SALES (est): 18.6MM **Privately Held**
WEB: www.silverhillenergy.com
SIC: **1382** Oil & gas exploration services
HQ: Rsp Permian, L.L.C.
    3141 Hood St Ste 700
    Dallas TX 75219

(G-4965)
SIX B LABELS CORPORATION
12200 Forestgate Dr (75243-5445)
PHONE....................................214 349-7824
Fariborz Bakhshian, *President*
Babak Bakhshian, *Vice Pres*
Bill Harris, *Sales Associate*
Toni Evans, *Marketing Staff*
Michelle Feldman, *Marketing Staff*

EMP: 45
SQ FT: 33,000
SALES (est): 9MM **Privately Held**
WEB: www.sixb.com
SIC: 2759 Labels & seals: printing

(G-4966)
SKAGEN DESIGNS LTD (DH)
10615 Sanden Dr (75238-1720)
PHONE.................................775 336-5667
Charlotte K Jorst, *President*
Henrick Jorst, *CFO*
Henrik K Jorst, *Treasurer*
Katie Caraway, *Senior Mgr*
Randy S Hyne, *Admin Sec*
◆ **EMP:** 85
SQ FT: 35,000
SALES (est): 16.8MM
SALES (corp-wide): 2.2B **Publicly Held**
WEB: www.skagen.com
SIC: 5094 3873 Watches & parts; watches, clocks, watchcases & parts

(G-4967)
SKIVA TECHNOLOGIES INC
2010 Valley View Ln # 320 (75234-8930)
PHONE.................................214 441-3517
Mandeep Kumar, *President*
▲ **EMP:** 20
SALES (est): 2.8MM **Privately Held**
WEB: www.skivatech.com
SIC: 3571 Electronic computers

(G-4968)
SKUDO USA DISTRIBUTION LLC
11120 Zodiac Ln (75229-4721)
PHONE.................................972 993-0777
Brendon Smith, *President*
EMP: 12 **EST:** 2014
SALES (est): 1.9MM **Privately Held**
WEB: www.skudousa.com
SIC: 2851 Paints & allied products

(G-4969)
SKY GLASS INC (PA)
Also Called: Sky Glass Aluminum
2600 Manana Dr (75220-1302)
PHONE.................................972 807-9616
Hossein Fardi, *CEO*
Darya Fardi, *CFO*
▲ **EMP:** 16
SQ FT: 12,000
SALES (est): 7.5MM **Privately Held**
WEB: www.skyglassaluminum.com
SIC: 3211 3442 Flat glass; metal doors, sash & trim

(G-4970)
SKYLINE CABINETRY INC
2230 Lbj Fwy Ste 400 (75234-7331)
PHONE.................................972 620-8880
Chunbo Zhang, *President*
EMP: 18
SQ FT: 60,000 **Privately Held**
WEB: www.skylinecabinetry.com
SIC: 2434 Wood kitchen cabinets
HQ: Skyline Cabinetry Inc
12301 N Stemmons Fwy # 100
Farmers Branch TX 75234
972 620-8880

(G-4971)
SMART CITY LOCATING INC
1619 N Hall St (75204-5401)
P.O. Box 730381 (75373-0381)
PHONE.................................214 586-0519
Cassandra Brown, *CEO*
Jake Fogel, *Vice Pres*
Mike Seaton, *Office Mgr*
Jordan Bodie, *Agent*
Hilary Faircloth, *Agent*
EMP: 27
SALES (est): 7.7MM **Privately Held**
WEB: www.smartcitylocating.com
SIC: 7299 7372 Apartment locating service; application computer software

(G-4972)
SND OPERATING LLC
13140 Coit Rd Ste 225 (75240-5746)
PHONE.................................214 691-3072
L Ali Sheikh, *Mng Member*
Deborah H Sheikh,
EMP: 30

SALES (est): 7.9MM **Privately Held**
WEB: www.sndenergy.com
SIC: 1382 Oil & gas exploration services

(G-4973)
SNELICK QUALITY TOOL INC
7410 Ambassador Row (75247-4804)
PHONE.................................972 221-0537
Joe Snelick, *President*
EMP: 20
SQ FT: 6,000
SALES (est): 2.3MM **Privately Held**
WEB: www.qtmfg.com
SIC: 3544 Industrial molds

(G-4974)
SNYDERS-LANCE INC
3276 Quebec St (75247-6606)
PHONE.................................214 638-2378
Dean Berwer, *Manager*
EMP: 30
SALES (corp-wide): 8.6B **Publicly Held**
WEB: www.snyderslance.com
SIC: 2064 Candy bars, including chocolate covered bars
HQ: Snyder's-Lance, Inc.
13515 Balntyn Corp Pl
Charlotte NC 28277
704 554-1421

(G-4975)
SOLARA IRONWORKS LLC (PA)
Also Called: Solara Doors
142 Howell St (75207-7104)
PHONE.................................214 744-9900
Malena Gutierrez, *Sales Executive*
Alberto D Perez, *Mng Member*
EMP: 20
SQ FT: 15,000
SALES (est): 4MM **Privately Held**
WEB:
www.solaracustomdoorsandlighting.com
SIC: 3442 3645 3646 Metal doors, sash & trim; residential lighting fixtures; ornamental lighting fixtures, commercial

(G-4976)
SOLAVANTI TRADING LLC
Also Called: Solavanti Lighting
9659 Wendell Rd (75243-5510)
PHONE.................................214 221-9405
Jerry Nickell, *Technical Mgr*
Joerg Zahn,
◆ **EMP:** 24
SALES (est): 4.6MM **Privately Held**
WEB: www.solavantilighting.com
SIC: 3645 Residential lighting fixtures

(G-4977)
SOLO CUP OPERATING CORPORATION
4444 W Ledbetter Dr (75236-1610)
PHONE.................................214 339-3131
Toby Andrews, *QC Mgr*
Sid Smith, *Manager*
EMP: 732
SQ FT: 1,100,000
SALES (corp-wide): 965.8MM **Privately Held**
WEB: www.solocup.com
SIC: 2679 2676 Cups, pressed & molded pulp: made from purchased material; dishes, pressed & molded pulp: from purchased material; plates, pressed & molded pulp: from purchased material; utensils, pressed & molded pulp: from purchased material; sanitary paper products
HQ: Solo Cup Operating Corporation
500 Hogsback Rd
Mason MI 48854
800 248-5960

(G-4978)
SOLUTION TECH HARN GROUP LLC
11601 Plano Rd Ste 107 (75243-5244)
PHONE.................................214 221-0323
Kenneth Leonce,
EMP: 35
SALES (est): 4.1MM **Privately Held**
SIC: 3678 3679 3714 Electronic connectors; harness assemblies for electronic use: wire or cable; automotive wiring harness sets

PA: Technical Manufacturing & Sales, L.L.C.
11601 Plano Rd Ste 107
Dallas TX 75243
214 221-0323

(G-4979)
SOLUTIONS IN SOFTWARE INC
Also Called: Lucid Iq
2201 Main St Ste 1120 (75201-4466)
PHONE.................................214 221-9995
Richard Spies, *President*
Kevin Ames, *Treasurer*
Alex Hancock, *Cust Mgr*
▲ **EMP:** 20
SALES (est): 2.3MM **Privately Held**
WEB: www.lucidiq.com
SIC: 7372 Business oriented computer software

(G-4980)
SOMANI TEXAS INC
Also Called: AlphaGraphics
1505 Federal St Ste 150 (75201-3497)
PHONE.................................214 698-0556
Mehul Patel, *President*
EMP: 10
SALES (est): 1.6MM **Privately Held**
WEB: www.alphagraphics.com
SIC: 2752 Commercial printing, lithographic

(G-4981)
SOUTHCROSS ALA PIPELINE LLC (DH)
1700 Pacific Ave Ste 5200 (75201-4617)
PHONE.................................214 979-3700
John Hamman, *Agent*
Dwight Hill, *Agent*
Michael B Howe,
Michael Hunter,
David Mueller,
EMP: 40
SQ FT: 20,000
SALES (est): 7.9MM
SALES (corp-wide): 618.1MM **Privately Held**
WEB: www.southcrossenergy.com
SIC: 4213 2911 Liquid petroleum transport, non-local; petroleum refining

(G-4982)
SOUTHCROSS CCNG GATHERING LTD
2501 Cedar Springs Rd # 600 (75201-1409)
PHONE.................................214 953-9500
Michael B Howe, *Partner*
EMP: 15
SALES (est): 2.2MM
SALES (corp-wide): 618.1MM **Privately Held**
WEB: www.southcrossenergy.com
SIC: 1321 Natural gas liquids
HQ: Southcross Energy Lp Llc
2103 Citywest Blvd
Houston TX 77042

(G-4983)
SOUTHCROSS GATHERING LTD
1700 Pacific Ave Ste 2900 (75201-4666)
PHONE.................................214 979-3700
Michael B Howe, *Partner*
David Mueller, *Vice Pres*
EMP: 12 **EST:** 2012
SALES (est): 559.7K
SALES (corp-wide): 618.1MM **Privately Held**
WEB: www.southcrossenergy.com
SIC: 1311 Crude petroleum & natural gas
HQ: Southcross Energy Lp Llc
2103 Citywest Blvd
Houston TX 77042

(G-4984)
SOUTHCROSS MARKETING CO LTD
1700 Pacific Ave Ste 2900 (75201-4666)
PHONE.................................214 979-3700
Michael B Howe, *Partner*
EMP: 16

SALES (est): 916.3K
SALES (corp-wide): 618.1MM **Privately Held**
WEB: www.southcrossenergy.com
SIC: 1311 Natural gas production
HQ: Southcross Energy Lp Llc
2103 Citywest Blvd
Houston TX 77042

(G-4985)
SOUTHER EQUIPMENT SALES INC
5409 W Ledbetter Dr (75236-1305)
PHONE.................................972 296-5231
Emory E Souther, *President*
Gene Souther, *President*
Sue Souther, *Vice Pres*
Vanita S Souther, *Vice Pres*
Russell Brewster, *Opers Mgr*
EMP: 10
SQ FT: 2,000
SALES (est): 2MM **Privately Held**
WEB: www.southerequipment.com
SIC: 3531 3535 Concrete plants; unit handling conveying systems

(G-4986)
SOUTHERN FOODS GROUP LLC (DH)
Also Called: Schepps Dairy
3114 S Haskell Ave (75223-3121)
P.O. Box 200300 (75320-0300)
PHONE.................................214 824-8163
Gregg A Tanner, *CEO*
Rachel A Gonzalez, *Vice Pres*
Timothy A Smith, *Vice Pres*
Patrick Ford, *CFO*
Kristy N Waterman, *Admin Sec*
▼ **EMP:** 224
SQ FT: 5,000
SALES (est): 264.8MM **Publicly Held**
WEB: www.deanfoods.com
SIC: 2026 Cream, sour; cottage cheese

(G-4987)
SOUTHERN FOODS GROUP LLC
Morningstar Foods
1114 N Lancaster Ave (75203-1118)
P.O. Box 910067 (75391-0067)
PHONE.................................214 941-0302
Craig Roberts, *Branch Mgr*
EMP: 99 **Publicly Held**
WEB: www.deanfoods.com
SIC: 2026 Fluid milk
HQ: Southern Foods Group, Llc
3114 S Haskell Ave
Dallas TX 75223
214 824-8163

(G-4988)
SOUTHERN METHODIST UNIVERSITY
Also Called: Smu Electron Microprobe Lab
3225 Daniel Ave (75205-1437)
P.O. Box 750395 (75275-0395)
PHONE.................................214 768-2756
Nina Schwartz, *Ch of Bd*
William Detwiler, *Vice Pres*
Steve Snider, *Admin Sec*
EMP: 12
SALES (corp-wide): 652.2MM **Privately Held**
WEB: www.smu.edu
SIC: 3826 Microprobes
PA: Southern Methodist University Inc
6425 Boaz Ln
Dallas TX 75205
214 768-2000

(G-4989)
SOUTHWEST DIAMOND CUTTERS INC
Also Called: LLC
13721 Omega Rd (75244-4517)
PHONE.................................972 387-1078
Ashley Vancreveld, *President*
Barry Adler, *Vice Pres*
Van Creveld, *Vice Pres*
EMP: 9
SALES (est): 1.5MM **Privately Held**
WEB: www.southwestdiamondcutters.com
SIC: 3915 5944 Diamond cutting & polishing; jewelry, precious stones & precious metals

▲ = Import ▼ = Export
◆ = Import/Export

(G-4990)
SOUTHWEST DIST & WINERY LLC
9761 Clifford Dr (75220-5333)
PHONE...................................214 440-4144
Sarvesh Sharma, *CEO*
EMP: 15
SQ FT: 114,000
SALES (est): 1.1MM **Privately Held**
WEB: www.sw-spirits.com
SIC: 2085 Distilled & blended liquors

(G-4991)
SOUTHWEST MANUFACTURING CORP
8720 Empress Row (75247-3902)
PHONE...................................214 638-0323
Humberto Chavez, *President*
Hector Chavez, *Vice Pres*
Pedro Lira, *Vice Pres*
EMP: 9
SQ FT: 8,000
SALES (est): 1.1MM **Privately Held**
WEB: www.gtsouthwest.com
SIC: 3599 Machine shop, jobbing & repair

(G-4992)
SOUTHWEST PROF VEHICLES (PA)
Also Called: Crain M-M Sales
3910 E Overton Rd (75216-2803)
PHONE...................................214 371-3474
Sean Myers, *Owner*
Cheryl Myers, *Vice Pres*
Andrea Dunnahue, *Bookkeeper*
Monty Monzingo, *Sales Staff*
EMP: 11
SQ FT: 20,000
SALES (est): 7.4MM **Privately Held**
WEB: www.limoandhearseforsale.com
SIC: 5012 5511 7515 7542 Automobiles
& other motor vehicles; new & used car
dealers; passenger car leasing; carwash,
self-service; funeral directors' equipment
& supplies; automobile assembly, includ-
ing specialty automobiles

(G-4993)
SOUZA BAKERY
9000 Diplomacy Row (75247-5304)
P.O. Box 560463 (75356-0463)
PHONE...................................214 631-0669
Oscar De Souza, *Owner*
EMP: 15
SQ FT: 28,000
SALES (est): 948.5K **Privately Held**
SIC: 2051 Bakery: wholesale or whole-
sale/retail combined; rolls, bread type:
fresh or frozen

(G-4994)
SOWELL & CO LP
1601 Elm St Ste 3500 (75201-4703)
PHONE...................................214 871-3320
Jim Sowell, *Partner*
Cindy Taylor, *Admin Sec*
EMP: 20
SALES (est): 2MM **Privately Held**
WEB: www.sowellco.com
SIC: 6512 6531 1311 Nonresidential
building operators; real estate agents &
managers; crude petroleum & natural gas

(G-4995)
SPECTRA TEST SOLUTIONS LLC (PA)
Also Called: S T S
10810 Alder Cir (75238-1347)
PHONE...................................214 349-0288
Nilesh Naik, *Manager*
Michael Bennett,
▲ **EMP:** 23
SQ FT: 12,000
SALES (est): 3MM **Privately Held**
SIC: 3825 Test equipment for electronic &
electric measurement

(G-4996)
SPECTRAL MD INC
2515 Mckinney Ave # 1000 (75201-1908)
PHONE...................................972 499-4934
J Michael Dimaio, *CEO*
Wensheng Fan, *Exec VP*
Louis Percoco, *Project Mgr*
Priyanka Das, *Engineer*

Leah Gaither, *Program Mgr*
EMP: 10
SALES (est): 1.8MM **Privately Held**
WEB: www.spectralmd.com
SIC: 3841 Diagnostic apparatus, medical

(G-4997)
SPINDLETOP DRILLING COMPANY
12850 Spurling Dr Ste 200 (75230-1279)
PHONE...................................972 644-2581
Chris G Mazzini, *President*
Tiffany Thornburg, *CFO*
EMP: 21 **EST:** 1975
SALES (est): 1MM
SALES (corp-wide): 5.5MM **Publicly Held**
WEB: www.spindletopdrilling.com
SIC: 1382 Oil & gas exploration services
PA: Spindletop Oil & Gas Co.
12850 Spurling Dr Ste 200
Dallas TX 75230
972 644-2581

(G-4998)
SPINDLETOP OIL & GAS CO (PA)
12850 Spurling Dr Ste 200 (75230-1279)
PHONE...................................972 644-2581
Chris G Mazzini, *Ch of Bd*
David Owen, *Opers Spvr*
Michelle H Mazzini, *Treasurer*
Ted R Munselle, *Director*
Robert Corbin, *Officer*
EMP: 31 **EST:** 1985
SALES: 5.5MM **Publicly Held**
WEB: www.spindletopoil.com
SIC: 1311 1382 7353 6531 Crude petro-
leum & natural gas; natural gas produc-
tion; crude petroleum production; oil &
gas exploration services; oil field equip-
ment, rental or leasing; real estate agent,
commercial

(G-4999)
SPORTS SOLUTIONS INC
Also Called: Guest Solutions
2536 Manana Dr (75220-1206)
PHONE...................................214 351-2834
Laurie Schmidt, *President*
Laurie Agee, *Vice Pres*
EMP: 15
SQ FT: 16,000
SALES (est): 3.1MM **Privately Held**
WEB: www.sportssolutionsinc.com
SIC: 2844 3999 Shampoos, rinses, condi-
tioners: hair; cosmetic preparations; soap
dispensers

(G-5000)
SQUARE CABINETRY LLC
2405 Crown Rd (75229-2103)
PHONE...................................214 838-2225
Jerry Lim,
EMP: 45
SALES (est): 3.2MM **Privately Held**
SIC: 2434 Wood kitchen cabinets
HQ: Allied Stone, Llc
2405 Crown Rd
Dallas TX 75229
214 838-2225

(G-5001)
STAINLESS STEEL CONCEPTS LLC
8908 Sovereign Row (75247-4502)
PHONE...................................214 630-4430
EMP: 18
SQ FT: 20,000
SALES: 1.2MM **Privately Held**
SIC: 3444 Stainless Steel Fabricator

(G-5002)
STAND BY SYSTEMS INC
5956 Sherry Ln Ste 1000 (75225-8021)
PHONE...................................214 346-2980
Kenneth Palmer, *CEO*
Charles Williams, *President*
James Helbig, *Vice Pres*
David Craig, *CFO*
Scott Hatfield, *Accountant*
EMP: 65
SQ FT: 500
SALES (est): 4.8MM **Privately Held**
SIC: 3841 Inhalation therapy equipment

(G-5003)
STANDARD FORGED PRODUCTS LLC (HQ)
Also Called: McKees Rock Forgings Division
500 N Akard St (75201-3302)
P.O. Box 568887 (75356-8887)
PHONE...................................214 631-4420
Timmothy R Wallace, *Mng Member*
James Perry,
◆ **EMP:** 20
SALES (est): 15.3MM
SALES (corp-wide): 1.7B **Publicly Held**
WEB: www.standardforgedproductsinc.com
SIC: 3312 Axles, rolled or forged: made in
steel mills
PA: Arcosa, Inc.
500 N Akard St Ste 400
Dallas TX 75201
972 942-6500

(G-5004)
STANDARD INDUSTRIES INC
Also Called: GAF Materials
14911 Quorum Dr Ste 600 (75254-1491)
P.O. Box 6377, Mobile AL (36660-0377)
PHONE...................................972 851-0460
Ken Walton, *Purch Agent*
Dave Seymour, *Invest Mgr*
EMP: 200
SALES (corp-wide): 2.5B **Privately Held**
WEB: www.gaf.com
SIC: 2493 2952 Insulation & roofing mate-
rial, reconstituted wood; asphalt felts &
coatings
HQ: Standard Industries Inc.
1 Campus Dr
Parsippany NJ 07054

(G-5005)
STANDARD MEAT COMPANY LLC (PA)
5105 Investment Dr (75236-1420)
PHONE...................................214 561-0561
Joe Penshorn, *Partner*
Joseph Penshorn, *Partner*
Billy Rosenthal, *Partner*
William Rosenthal, *Partner*
Garry Custer, *Principal*
▲ **EMP:** 80
SQ FT: 65,304
SALES (est): 17.7MM **Privately Held**
WEB: www.standardmeat.com
SIC: 2013 Sausages & other prepared
meats

(G-5006)
STANLEY BLACK & DECKER INC
12827 Valley Branch Ln (75234-5813)
PHONE...................................972 247-1367
Kevin Lemke, *Opers Staff*
Ron Russell, *Branch Mgr*
EMP: 11
SALES (corp-wide): 14.4B **Publicly Held**
WEB: www.stanleyblackanddecker.com
SIC: 3423 Hand & edge tools
PA: Stanley Black & Decker, Inc.
1000 Stanley Dr
New Britain CT 06053
860 225-5111

(G-5007)
STANLEY INDUSTRIAL & AUTO LLC
Also Called: Proto Industrial Tools
12827 Valley Branch Ln (75234-5813)
PHONE...................................972 247-1367
EMP: 268
SALES (corp-wide): 14.4B **Publicly Held**
WEB: www.mactools.com
SIC: 3423 Hand & edge tools
HQ: Stanley Industrial & Automotive, Llc
505 N Cleveland Ave
Westerville OH 43082
614 755-7000

(G-5008)
STAR GLASS AND METAL SVCS LLC
7601 Churchill Way # 439 (75251-1906)
PHONE...................................770 490-9055
David Harris,
EMP: 15
SALES (est): 1.5MM **Privately Held**
SIC: 3231 Products of purchased glass

(G-5009)
STEELFAST INC (PA)
11281 Leo Ln (75229-4715)
P.O. Box 59401 (75229-1401)
PHONE...................................972 243-5312
John Amis Jr, *President*
John Amis III, *Exec VP*
EMP: 11
SQ FT: 6,000
SALES (est): 100K **Privately Held**
WEB: www.steelfast.com
SIC: 5072 3452 Bolts, nuts & screws;
screws, metal

(G-5010)
STERLING FABRICATION TECH
2707 W Mockingbird Ln (75235-5632)
PHONE...................................713 591-9004
Russel Kehrer, *Principal*
Kevin Bartels, *Regl Sales Mgr*
Jordan Russell, *Sales Staff*
▲ **EMP:** 11
SALES (est): 1.8MM **Privately Held**
WEB: www.sterlingfabtech.com
SIC: 3599 Machine shop, jobbing & repair

(G-5011)
STEWARD PRINTING & ADVG INC
10775 Sanden Dr (75238-1336)
PHONE...................................214 348-1200
Melissa Steward, *President*
Kevin L Steward, *Vice Pres*
Holli Elrod, *Sales Executive*
EMP: 12
SQ FT: 6,500
SALES (est): 3.2MM **Privately Held**
WEB: www.stewardprinting.com
SIC: 2752 Commercial printing, offset

(G-5012)
STONEMODE GRANITE LLC
Also Called: Slab Fabricators
2840 Reward Ln (75220-1508)
PHONE...................................214 484-8820
Edgar Quijada, *Project Mgr*
Jose Quijada,
EMP: 10
SALES (est): 900.3K **Privately Held**
WEB: www.stonemodegranite.com
SIC: 3281 Granite, cut & shaped

(G-5013)
STONEXPRESSIONS LLC
2647 Andjon Dr (75220-1309)
PHONE...................................214 366-2216
Salvador Soriano, *Mng Member*
Tihui Cope, *Manager*
Tihui Soriano, *Manager*
Daniel Soriano, *Consultant*
EMP: 9
SQ FT: 15,000
SALES (est): 959K **Privately Held**
WEB: www.stonexpressionsdfw.com
SIC: 1743 3281 Marble installation, inte-
rior; marble, building: cut & shaped

(G-5014)
STORM VULCAN INC
2225 Burbank St (75235-3124)
PHONE...................................214 637-1430
EMP: 15
SALES (est): 1.2MM **Privately Held**
SIC: 3541 Mfg Automotive Engine Rebuild-
ing Equipment

(G-5015)
STRATAS FOODS LLC
2210 Saint Germain Rd (75212-4811)
PHONE...................................469 341-7055
John Olivingi, *Branch Mgr*
EMP: 10 **Privately Held**
WEB: www.stratasfoods.com
SIC: 2631 Container, packaging &
boxboard
PA: Stratas Foods Llc
7970 Stage Hills Blvd
Bartlett TN 38133

(G-5016)
STREETLOC INC
13101 Preston Rd 110-3 (75240-5237)
PHONE...................................254 274-2500
Grant Jackson, *CEO*
EMP: 15

SALES (est): 366K **Privately Held**
SIC: 2741

(G-5017)
STUART HOSE & PIPE LTD
2621 Irving Blvd (75207-5913)
PHONE......................................214 631-6682
John Boden Miller, *Opers-Prdtn-Mfg*
Kristy Hickman, *Buyer*
Garrett Pinson, *Accounts Mgr*
Cory Cobler, *Director*
EMP: 20
SQ FT: 16,129
SALES (corp-wide): 366.9MM **Privately Held**
WEB: www.stuarthose.com
SIC: 5085 5051 3599 Hose, belting & packing; pipe & tubing, steel; flexible metal hose, tubing & bellows
HQ: Stuart Hose & Pipe Company, Inc.
   701 Riverside Dr
   Fort Worth TX 76111
   817 332-5297

(G-5018)
SUEZ WTS SERVICES USA INC
Also Called: GE Mobile Water
4740 Bronze Way (75236-1902)
PHONE......................................214 339-2135
Joe Berges, *Branch Mgr*
EMP: 10
SQ FT: 11,200
SALES (corp-wide): 100.8MM **Privately Held**
WEB: www.suezwatertechnologies.com
SIC: 3589 Water treatment equipment, industrial
HQ: Suez Wts Services Usa, Inc.
   4545 Patent Rd
   Norfolk VA 23502
   757 855-9000

(G-5019)
SUGAR KRYSTLES LLC
120 Turtle Creek Blvd (75207-6841)
PHONE......................................817 368-6869
Krystle Haynes,
EMP: 10
SALES (est): 296.4K **Privately Held**
SIC: 2051 Cakes, bakery: except frozen

(G-5020)
SUHM SPRING WORKS INC
Also Called: Suhm Spring of Dallas
1601 Terre Colony Ct (75212-6222)
PHONE......................................214 330-9111
Freddie McBride, *Foreman/Supr*
Tim Higginbotham, *Manager*
EMP: 19
SALES (corp-wide): 32.6MM **Privately Held**
WEB: www.suhm.net
SIC: 3493 Coiled flat springs
PA: Spring Suhm Works Inc
   14650 Hathrow Forest Pkwy
   Houston TX 77032
   713 224-9293

(G-5021)
SULPHUR RIVER EXPLORATION INC (PA)
4851 Lyndon B Johnson Fwy # 550 (75244-6046)
PHONE......................................214 373-1091
EMP: 13
SALES (est): 7MM **Privately Held**
SIC: 1311 1389 Crude petroleum production; natural gas production; processing service, gas; gas field services

(G-5022)
SUN CHEMICAL CORPORATION
Also Called: U S Ink Division
12010 Corporate Dr (75228-8102)
PHONE......................................972 270-6735
Hill Stephen, *Plant Mgr*
Steven Bill, *Branch Mgr*
Wade Chuck, *Manager*
EMP: 55 **Privately Held**
WEB: www.sunchemical.com
SIC: 2893 Printing ink
HQ: Sun Chemical Corporation
   35 Waterview Blvd Ste 100
   Parsippany NJ 07054
   973 404-6000

(G-5023)
SUNBELT VACUUM SERVICES INC
2551 S Good Latimer Expy (75215-1435)
P.O. Box 152597 (75315-2597)
PHONE......................................972 449-3830
Dwight Armor, *President*
Judy Armor, *Admin Sec*
EMP: 20
SALES (est): 4.8MM **Privately Held**
WEB: www.sunbeltvacuumservice.com
SIC: 3563 Vacuum (air extraction) systems, industrial

(G-5024)
SUPER SACK BAG INC (PA)
11510 Data Dr (75218-1419)
PHONE......................................214 340-7060
Robert Williamson, *CEO*
Karl Reimers, *President*
Jodi L Simons, *Principal*
Curtis Lindsey, *Treasurer*
Jean P Williamson, *Admin Sec*
◆ **EMP:** 18
SQ FT: 10,000
SALES (est): 148.8MM **Privately Held**
WEB: www.bagcorp.com
SIC: 4953 3556 3081 2673 Recycling, waste materials; packing house machinery; unsupported plastics film & sheet; plastic bags: made from purchased materials

(G-5025)
SUPERIOR COOLING SERVICES INC (PA)
2227 Irving Blvd (75207-6201)
P.O. Box 2368, Red Oak (75154-1576)
PHONE......................................214 637-2162
Mark Spence, *President*
Chad Spence, *Vice Pres*
EMP: 12
SQ FT: 47,000
SALES (est): 2.1MM **Privately Held**
WEB: www.superiorcooling.co
SIC: 3714 Radiators & radiator shells & cores, motor vehicle

(G-5026)
SUPERIOR LABEL SYSTEMS INC
3530 Pipestone Rd (75212-6107)
PHONE......................................214 330-7770
Jack Edwards, *Opers-Prdtn-Mfg*
Carol McWhirter, *Director*
EMP: 14 **Privately Held**
WEB: www.wspackaging.com
SIC: 3565 2679 2759 Labeling machines, industrial; labels, paper: made from purchased material; flexographic printing
HQ: Superior Label Systems Inc
   7500 Industrial Row Dr
   Mason OH 45040
   513 336-0825

(G-5027)
SUPERMEDIA SERVICES INC
Also Called: GTE Directories Distribution
2200 W Airfield Dr (75261-4008)
PHONE......................................972 453-7000
Gary C Hruska, *President*
EMP: 10
SALES (est): 1.9MM
SALES (corp-wide): 1.4B **Publicly Held**
SIC: 2759 Publication printing
HQ: Supermedia Llc
   2200 W Airfield Dr
   Dfw Airport TX 75261
   972 453-7000

(G-5028)
SUPPLYNET INC
1631 Record Crossing Rd (75235-6115)
PHONE......................................484 582-1004
EMP: 35
SALES (corp-wide): 381.2MM **Privately Held**
WEB: www.supplyone.com
SIC: 3081 2673 Polyethylene film; bags: plastic, laminated & coated
HQ: Supplyone, Inc.
   11 Campus Blvd Ste 150
   Newtown Square PA 19073
   800 927-9801

(G-5029)
SUPPLYNET INC
1608 Plantation Rd (75235-5003)
PHONE......................................214 637-0160
Jim Dolehide, *Vice Pres*
Mario Hinojosa, *Plant Mgr*
Michele Kane, *Controller*
James Bowie, *Sales Mgr*
Chris Durden, *Sales Staff*
EMP: 75
SALES (corp-wide): 381.2MM **Privately Held**
WEB: www.supplyone.com
SIC: 3081 2653 2673 Polyethylene film; boxes, corrugated: made from purchased materials; bags: plastic, laminated & coated
HQ: Supplyone, Inc.
   11 Campus Blvd Ste 150
   Newtown Square PA 19073
   800 927-9801

(G-5030)
SUPREME PRINTING COMPANY
148 Pittsburg St (75207-7208)
PHONE......................................214 742-2511
Syed Masoud Azimi, *President*
Keith Goodman, *General Mgr*
Amir Saeed Azimi, *Vice Pres*
Fakhri Najafabadi, *Treasurer*
Frank Monjazeb, *VP Sales*
EMP: 15
SQ FT: 22,000
SALES (est): 1.3MM **Privately Held**
WEB: www.supremeprinting.com
SIC: 2752 Commercial printing, offset

(G-5031)
SURGICAL NOTES INC
3100 Monticello Ave # 450 (75205-3442)
PHONE......................................214 821-3850
Randy Bishop, *CEO*
Courtney Blankinship, *President*
Chuck Meisel, *Vice Pres*
John M Carradine, *CFO*
Paul Ignacio, *Accounts Mgr*
EMP: 41
SALES (est): 5.7MM **Privately Held**
WEB: www.surgicalnotes.com
SIC: 7338 7372 Public stenographers; business oriented computer software

(G-5032)
SYNERGEN HEALTH LLC
3131 Mckinney Ave Ste 602 (75204-7426)
PHONE......................................214 643-6002
▲ **EMP:** 12
SALES (est): 1.4MM **Privately Held**
WEB: www.synergenhealth.com
SIC: 7372 7374 7389 Business oriented computer software; computer processing services; financial services

(G-5033)
T RICH INC
Also Called: Shadow Fax Graphics
4834 Reading St (75247-6705)
PHONE......................................214 748-8700
Tom Manson, *President*
Tom Maunson, *Senior Mgr*
EMP: 9
SALES (est): 1.1MM **Privately Held**
WEB: www.shadowfaxgraphics.com
SIC: 2759 Screen printing

(G-5034)
TALON OIL & GAS LLC
3131 Mckinney Ave Ste 750 (75204-2457)
PHONE......................................214 323-8360
Grant Henderson,
EMP: 11
SALES (est): 47.6MM **Privately Held**
SIC: 1382 Oil & gas exploration services

(G-5035)
TANA EXPLORATION COMPANY LLC
4001 Maple Ave Ste 600 (75219-3241)
PHONE......................................469 276-8262
Kevin D Talley, *President*
Kevin Talley, *President*
Joel Darr, *General Mgr*
Carl E Comstock, *Vice Pres*
Michael J Simon, *Vice Pres*
EMP: 60

SALES (est): 30.8MM **Privately Held**
WEB: www.tanaexp.com
SIC: 1382 Oil & gas exploration services

(G-5036)
TAUREN EXPLORATION INC
9870 Plano Rd (75238-5104)
P.O. Box 551043 (75355-1043)
PHONE......................................972 681-8047
Calvin A Wallen III, *President*
Calvin Wallen III, *President*
EMP: 18
SQ FT: 4,600
SALES (est): 2.8MM **Privately Held**
WEB: www.cretaenergy.com
SIC: 1382 Oil & gas exploration services

(G-5037)
TAXSATION INC
7606 Lairds Ln (75248-2343)
PHONE......................................888 829-1120
Robert Llewellyn, *President*
Stewart Hunt, *Vice Pres*
EMP: 11
SALES (est): 850K **Privately Held**
SIC: 7372 Application computer software

(G-5038)
TAYLOR COMMUNICATIONS INC
8750 Autobahn Dr (75237-3934)
PHONE......................................972 581-7711
Kenny Culbert, *Manager*
Donna Bugher, *Associate*
EMP: 20
SALES (corp-wide): 2.5B **Privately Held**
WEB: www.taylorcorp.com
SIC: 2761 Manifold business forms
HQ: Taylor Communications, Inc.
   1725 Roe Crest Dr
   North Mankato MN 56003
   866 541-0937

(G-5039)
TAYLOR PUBLISHING COMPANY (DH)
1550 W Mockingbird Ln (75235-5007)
PHONE......................................214 637-2800
Donald J Percenti, *President*
Craig Van Pelt, *Sr Corp Ofcr*
Min Chu, *Senior VP*
Kim Hawley, *Vice Pres*
W Gregg Smart, *Vice Pres*
▲ **EMP:** 525
SQ FT: 327,000
SALES (est): 283.2MM **Privately Held**
WEB: www.balfour.com
SIC: 2731 2732 Books-Publishing/Printing Book Printing

(G-5040)
TAYSHA GENE THERAPIES INC
2280 Inwood Rd (75235-7321)
PHONE......................................214 612-0000
Sean P Nolan, *Ch of Bd*
Ra Session II, *President*
Greg Gara, *Senior VP*
Kimberly Lee, *Senior VP*
Kamran Alam, *CFO*
EMP: 10
SALES (est): 824.5K **Privately Held**
WEB: www.tayshagtx.com
SIC: 2834 Pharmaceutical preparations

(G-5041)
TCR BUSINESS SYSTEMS
1801 Royal Ln Ste 600 (75229-3198)
PHONE......................................972 807-8000
Jennifer Trichell, *Owner*
EMP: 11
SALES (est): 1.4MM **Privately Held**
WEB: www.tcr.us
SIC: 2754 Business form & card printing, gravure

(G-5042)
TDINDUSTRIES LTD
13850 Diplomat Dr (75234-8812)
P.O. Box 819060 (75381-9060)
PHONE......................................972 888-9500
Maureen Underwood, *Principal*
EMP: 25
SALES (est): 3.7MM **Privately Held**
WEB: www.tdindustries.com
SIC: 3999 Manufacturing industries

(G-5043)
TEAM GO FIGURE LLP
6140 Goliad Ave (75214-3630)
PHONE..................................972 276-6700
Scott Eskridge, *President*
Sherry Gunter, *Office Mgr*
▲ EMP: 30
SALES (est): 3.4MM **Privately Held**
WEB: www.teamgofigure.com
SIC: 2339 2369 5137 Athletic clothing:
women's, misses' & juniors'; leotards:
women's, misses' & juniors'; jogging &
warmup suits: women's, misses' & jun-
iors'; girls' & children's outerwear; sports-
wear, women's & children's

(G-5044)
TECHNOLOGY MEDIA GROUP INC
1262 Viceroy Dr (75247-3909)
PHONE..................................469 463-7647
Ryon Rhue, *Opers Mgr*
Joseph Varghese, *Info Tech Dir*
Jeanette Vallejo,
EMP: 33
SALES (corp-wide): 13.3MM **Privately Held**
WEB: www.tmgsignworld.com
SIC: 2752 Commercial printing, litho-
graphic
PA: Technology Media Group, Inc.
1208 Viceroy Dr
Dallas TX 75247
800 777-9091

(G-5045)
TECHNOLOGY MEDIA GROUP INC (PA)
Also Called: Technology Printing
1208 Viceroy Dr (75247-3909)
PHONE..................................800 777-9091
Cassandra Byerly, *President*
Patrick Noonan, *Opers Staff*
Bruce Byerly, *Treasurer*
Amanda Rhue, *Marketing Staff*
Diana Shay, *Senior Mgr*
▲ EMP: 52
SQ FT: 50,000
SALES (est): 13.3MM **Privately Held**
WEB: www.tmguniverse.com
SIC: 2752 2759 Commercial printing, litho-
graphic; commercial printing

(G-5046)
TECO METAL PRODUCTS LLC
11477 Pagemill Rd (75243-5505)
PHONE..................................214 221-5020
Terry Roden, *President*
Darlene Roden, *Vice Pres*
EMP: 28
SQ FT: 68,000
SALES (est): 9.4MM **Privately Held**
WEB: www.tecometal.com
SIC: 3441 Fabricated structural metal

(G-5047)
TEJAS VSUAL COMMUNICATIONS INC
Also Called: Lincoln Press
9020 Directors Row (75247-5321)
P.O. Box 561345 (75356-1345)
PHONE..................................972 243-6612
Gerald Wickliffe Jr, *President*
Eric Wickliffe, *Vice Pres*
Randy Cole, *Sales Executive*
Michael Roels, *Manager*
Lori Wickliffe, *Admin Sec*
EMP: 25
SQ FT: 20,000
SALES (est): 7.7MM **Privately Held**
WEB: www.lincolnpress.biz
SIC: 2752 Commercial printing, offset

(G-5048)
TEKNI-PLEX INC
4700 S Westmoreland Rd (75237-1629)
PHONE..................................214 337-4711
Bryant Foster, *Principal*
Marcus Hawn, *Plant Mgr*
Lori Dickirson, *Human Res Mgr*
Jim Davis, *Sales Staff*
Ricky Redmon, *Maintence Staff*
EMP: 140

SALES (corp-wide): 1B **Privately Held**
WEB: www.tekni-plex.com
SIC: 3089 2821 Plastic containers, except
foam; plastics materials & resins
PA: Tekni-Plex, Inc.
460 E Swedesford Rd # 3000
Wayne PA 19087
484 690-1520

(G-5049)
TELECOM SITE SOLUTIONS LLC
7841 Hawn Fwy (75217)
P.O. Box 251171, Plano (75025-1171)
PHONE..................................888 779-9069
Michael Thomas, *Mng Member*
EMP: 18 EST: 2008
SALES (est): 3MM **Privately Held**
WEB: www.telecomsitesolutions.com
SIC: 3661 Telephone & telegraph appara-
tus

(G-5050)
TERRY COSTA INC (PA)
12817 Preston Rd Ste 138 (75230-1261)
PHONE..................................972 385-6100
Terry Costa, *President*
Weathers William, *Vice Pres*
Tina Loyd, *CFO*
Natasha Else, *Director*
EMP: 30
SQ FT: 13,095
SALES: 8.5MM **Privately Held**
WEB: www.terrycosta.com
SIC: 7299 5621 5999 2335 Clothing
rental services; ready-to-wear apparel,
women's; alarm & safety equipment
stores

(G-5051)
TEX CNP/SEAL INC (PA)
8435 Directors Row (75247-5528)
PHONE..................................214 688-7770
Chris Hillen, *President*
Ed Kearney, *General Mgr*
Shelby Frank, *Treasurer*
EMP: 30
SQ FT: 25,000
SALES (est): 4MM **Privately Held**
WEB: www.sealtex.com
SIC: 3585 3441 3053 3444 Parts for
heating, cooling & refrigerating equip-
ment; fabricated structural metal; gaskets
& sealing devices; sheet metalwork

(G-5052)
TEX WEBB LLC
7324 Gaston Ave 124-42 (75214-6126)
PHONE..................................214 770-7073
Joshua K Webb, *Mng Member*
EMP: 12
SALES (est): 35MM **Privately Held**
WEB: www.webbtexllc.com
SIC: 3533 Oil & gas field machinery

(G-5053)
TEX-SUN SHADE SPECIALTIES INC
12150 Shiloh Rd Ste 104 (75228-1595)
PHONE..................................972 279-0132
Cindy Wiethorn, *Vice Pres*
Jodi Wiethorn, *CFO*
Michael K Wiethorn,
EMP: 11
SQ FT: 2,750
SALES (est): 2MM **Privately Held**
WEB: www.tex-sun.com
SIC: 5719 2591 5023 5211 Window fur-
nishings; venetian blinds; window shades;
window blinds; shade pulls, window; win-
dow shades; window furnishings; vene-
tian blinds; window shades; bathroom
fixtures, equipment & supplies; signs, ex-
cept electric; partitions

(G-5054)
TEXAS AND OKLAHOMA ELC SVC LLC
Also Called: Texas Electrical
11233 N Stemmons Fwy (75229-4548)
PHONE..................................972 222-2229
Gary Young, *Mng Member*
EMP: 32

SALES (est): 4MM **Privately Held**
WEB: www.texaselectrical.com
SIC: 1731 3993 General electrical con-
tractor; electric signs

(G-5055)
TEXAS BY-PRODUCTS PARTNERSHIP (PA)
2621 State St (75204-2602)
PHONE..................................214 871-0600
Bill Shirley, *Managing Prtnr*
EMP: 15
SALES (est): 8.9MM **Privately Held**
SIC: 2077 Rendering

(G-5056)
TEXAS CLOTHING HOLDING CORP (PA)
11511 Luna Rd (75234-6449)
PHONE..................................214 956-4494
Nancy Klinkenberg, *Human Res Dir*
Mark Douglas, *Manager*
Randall Pincu, *Technical Staff*
Fang MEI Chen, *Director*
John Glazer, *Director*
EMP: 28
SALES (est): 609.3MM **Privately Held**
WEB: www.haggar.com
SIC: 2311 2321 5611 2325 Tailored suits
& formal jackets; men's & boys' furnish-
ings; men's & boys' clothing stores;
slacks, dress: men's, youths' & boys'

(G-5057)
TEXAS COASTAL ENERGY CO LLC
9330 Lyndon B J Fwy 900 (75243)
PHONE..................................214 429-3700
Jeff Gordon,
EMP: 16
SALES (est): 1.6MM **Privately Held**
SIC: 1382 Oil & gas exploration services

(G-5058)
TEXAS ELECTRONICS INC
4230 Shilling Way (75237-1023)
PHONE..................................214 327-2566
Jason Burson, *CEO*
Carol Westlund, *President*
Jane Tozer-Hansen, *Vice Pres*
Fernando Ayala, *Officer*
Pam Froehner, *Executive*
EMP: 14
SQ FT: 16,000
SALES (est): 3.1MM **Privately Held**
WEB: www.texaselectronics.com
SIC: 3829 Meteorological instruments

(G-5059)
TEXAS ENERGY HOLDINGS INC (PA)
3320 Oak Grove Ave # 100 (75204-2320)
P.O. Box 191289 (75219-8289)
PHONE..................................214 231-4000
Phillip C Willis, *President*
Casey Ladymon, *Senior VP*
Byron Jackson, *Vice Pres*
Michael Garrett, *Treasurer*
Katie Sluder, *Software Dev*
EMP: 45
SQ FT: 7,779
SALES (est): 12.2MM **Privately Held**
WEB: www.istickcapital.com
SIC: 1382 Oil & gas exploration services

(G-5060)
TEXAS ENVELOPE COMPANY
10655 Shady Trl (75220-2506)
PHONE..................................214 358-5661
Ernest M Curtis, *President*
Michael Curtis, *Vice Pres*
Doug Hudgins, *Plant Mgr*
Patricia Pace, *Accountant*
Mike Mouton, *Executive*
▲ EMP: 33
SQ FT: 36,000
SALES (est): 9.7MM **Privately Held**
WEB: www.texenv.com
SIC: 2621 2677 Envelope paper; en-
velopes

(G-5061)
TEXAS FLAMEPROOFING INC
Also Called: Fire Equipment Service Co.
5131 Sharp St (75247-6019)
PHONE..................................214 630-1088
J R Patterson, *President*
EMP: 10
SQ FT: 15,000
SALES (est): 1MM **Privately Held**
WEB: www.texasflame.com
SIC: 2261 7389 5999 5082 Fire resist-
ance finishing of cotton broadwoven fab-
rics; laminating service; fire extinguishers;
contractors' materials

(G-5062)
TEXAS INDUSTRIES INC (HQ)
Also Called: Txi
1503 Lyndon B Johnson Fwy (75234-6059)
PHONE..................................972 647-6700
C Howard Nye, *President*
Edwin J Gerik, *Production*
Lyndon D Zielke, *Purchasing*
George E Eure, *Engineer*
Anne H Lloyd, *CFO*
▲ EMP: 204 EST: 1951
SALES (est): 812.8MM **Publicly Held**
WEB: www.martinmarietta.com
SIC: 3241 3299 3281 3273 Masonry ce-
ment; sand lime products; gravel painting;
limestone, cut & shaped; ready-mixed
concrete

(G-5063)
TEXAS INDUSTRIES INC
Also Called: T X I
10610 Spangler Rd (75220-2317)
PHONE..................................972 556-0751
Pamela Winters, *Manager*
EMP: 75 **Publicly Held**
WEB: www.martinmarietta.com
SIC: 3273 Ready-mixed concrete
HQ: Texas Industries, Inc.
1503 Lyndon B Johnson Fwy
Dallas TX 75234
972 647-6700

(G-5064)
TEXAS INDUSTRIES INC
Also Called: T X I
2202 Chalk Hill Rd (75212-5815)
PHONE..................................972 263-5077
Kevin Grogan, *General Mgr*
EMP: 20
SQ FT: 855 **Publicly Held**
WEB: www.martinmarietta.com
SIC: 3312 Blast furnaces & steel mills
HQ: Texas Industries, Inc.
1503 Lyndon B Johnson Fwy
Dallas TX 75234
972 647-6700

(G-5065)
TEXAS INSTRS PHILIPPINES LLC
12500 T I Blvd (75243-0592)
PHONE..................................972 995-3773
Kun Gchen, *Principal*
David Buechler, *Manager*
Dominic Nguyen, *Manager*
EMP: 11
SALES (est): 1MM
SALES (corp-wide): 14.4B **Publicly Held**
SIC: 3674 Microprocessors
PA: Texas Instruments Incorporated
12500 Ti Blvd
Dallas TX 75243
972 995-3773

(G-5066)
TEXAS INSTRUMENTS INCORPORATED
7800 Banner Dr (75251-1602)
P.O. Box 655012 (75265-5012)
PHONE..................................972 995-2011
Nobuo Suzuki, *COO*
Scott Bryson, *Engineer*
Chin Y Tsai, *Engineer*
Bradley Vance, *Engineer*
Shaoping Tang, *Senior Engr*
EMP: 74
SALES (corp-wide): 14.4B **Publicly Held**
WEB: www.txwx.com
SIC: 3674 Semiconductors & related de-
vices

PA: Texas Instruments Incorporated
12500 Ti Blvd
Dallas TX 75243
972 995-3773

(G-5067)
TEXAS INSTRUMENTS INCORPORATED (PA)
12500 Ti Blvd (75243-0592)
P.O. Box 660199 (75266-0199)
PHONE....................................972 995-3773
Richard K Templeton, *Ch of Bd*
Haviv Ilan, *COO*
Niels Anderskouv, *Senior VP*
Ahmad S Bahai, *Senior VP*
Ellen L Barker, *Senior VP*
▲ EMP: 9800
SALES: 14.4B **Publicly Held**
WEB: www.ti.com
SIC: 3674 3613 3822 3578 Microproces-
sors; microcircuits, integrated (semicon-
ductor); computer logic modules;
memories, solid state; power circuit
breakers; thermostats & other environ-
mental sensors; calculators & adding ma-
chines

(G-5068)
TEXAS INSTRUMENTS INCORPORATED
13020 Ti Blvd (75243)
P.O. Box 655012 (75265-5012)
PHONE....................................214 479-3773
Steve Moore, *Facilities Mgr*
EMP: 52
SALES (corp-wide): 14.4B **Publicly Held**
WEB: www.txwx.com
SIC: 3674 Semiconductors & related de-
vices
PA: Texas Instruments Incorporated
12500 Ti Blvd
Dallas TX 75243
972 995-3773

(G-5069)
TEXAS INSTRUMENTS INCORPORATED
13532 N Central Expy (75243-1108)
P.O. Box 650311 (75265-0311)
PHONE....................................214 567-5185
EMP: 63
SALES (corp-wide): 14.4B **Publicly Held**
WEB: www.txwx.com
SIC: 3674 Semiconductors & related de-
vices
PA: Texas Instruments Incorporated
12500 Ti Blvd
Dallas TX 75243
972 995-3773

(G-5070)
TEXAS INSTRUMENTS INCORPORATED
13570 N Central Expy (75243-1108)
PHONE....................................972 995-2011
Peter McLarty, *Counsel*
Naveen Bhoria, *Design Engr*
Tanmay Neema, *Design Engr*
Kevin P March, *CFO*
David Lara, *Manager*
EMP: 432
SALES (corp-wide): 14.4B **Publicly Held**
WEB: www.txwx.com
SIC: 3674 Microprocessors
PA: Texas Instruments Incorporated
12500 Ti Blvd
Dallas TX 75243
972 995-3773

(G-5071)
TEXAS INSTRUMENTS INCORPORATED
8330 Lbj Fwy Ms3123 (75243-1166)
P.O. Box 660246 (75266-0246)
PHONE....................................972 644-5580
Yuqing Xu, *Business Mgr*
Scott Johannesmeyer, *Design Engr*
Nora Bradfield, *Manager*
Bhaskar Aravind, *Info Tech Mgr*
EMP: 150
SQ FT: 600
SALES (corp-wide): 14.4B **Publicly Held**
WEB: www.txwx.com
SIC: 3674 Semiconductors & related de-
vices

PA: Texas Instruments Incorporated
12500 Ti Blvd
Dallas TX 75243
972 995-3773

(G-5072)
TEXAS INSTRUMENTS INCORPORATED
13536 N Central Expy (75243-1108)
P.O. Box 655012 (75265-5012)
PHONE....................................817 401-5563
Hongwei Liang, *Engineer*
Hulon Pearre, *Engineer*
Julie Blood, *Branch Mgr*
Mary Coles, *Technical Staff*
Diane Vowell, *Maintence Staff*
EMP: 27
SALES (corp-wide): 14.4B **Publicly Held**
WEB: www.txwx.com
SIC: 3674 Semiconductors & related de-
vices
PA: Texas Instruments Incorporated
12500 Ti Blvd
Dallas TX 75243
972 995-3773

(G-5073)
TEXAS INSTRUMENTS INCORPORATED
13588 N Central Expy (75243-1108)
P.O. Box 650311 (75265-0311)
PHONE....................................972 995-2011
William L Eversole, *Vice Pres*
Gene Vallow, *Vice Pres*
Bret Dahl, *Engineer*
Mark Jenson, *Engineer*
David McGaha, *Engineer*
EMP: 350
SALES (corp-wide): 14.4B **Publicly Held**
WEB: www.txwx.com
SIC: 8732 3826 3674 Commercial non-
physical research; infrared analytical in-
struments; semiconductors & related
devices
PA: Texas Instruments Incorporated
12500 Ti Blvd
Dallas TX 75243
972 995-3773

(G-5074)
TEXAS JEWISH POST LTD (PA)
Also Called: Post Printing & Publishing
7920 Belt Line Rd Ste 680 (75254-8150)
PHONE....................................972 458-7283
Sharon Wisch, *President*
Irene Wisch, *President*
Sharon Wisch-Ray, *Minister*
Susan Wisch, *Vice Pres*
Amy Doty, *VP Sales*
EMP: 10 EST: 1945
SQ FT: 4,200
SALES (est): 990.4K **Privately Held**
WEB: www.tjpnews.com
SIC: 2711 Newspapers, publishing & print-
ing

(G-5075)
TEXAS LIME COMPANY (DH)
5429 Lyndon B Johnson Fwy # 230
(75240-2666)
PHONE....................................972 385-1335
Timothy W Byrne, *President*
M Michael Owens, *CFO*
EMP: 24
SQ FT: 2,500
SALES (est): 24.8MM
SALES (corp-wide): 4.1MM **Publicly Held**
WEB: www.uslm.com
SIC: 1422 Crushed & broken limestone
HQ: United States Lime & Minerals, Inc.
5429 Lbj Fwy Ste 230
Dallas TX 75240
972 991-8400

(G-5076)
TEXAS MATERIALS GROUP INC
Also Called: APAC
8201 S Central Expy (75241-7819)
PHONE....................................214 372-7700
Curtis Dove, *Manager*
EMP: 90
SALES (corp-wide): 30.6B **Privately Held**
WEB: www.texasmaterialsgroup.com
SIC: 2819 2821 2899 Industrial inorganic
chemicals; plastics materials & resins;
chemical preparations

HQ: Texas Materials Group, Inc.
1320 Arrow Point Dr # 600
Cedar Park TX 78613
512 861-7100

(G-5077)
TEXAS MRI LP
Also Called: Media Recovery
1111 W Mockingbird Ln # 1050
(75247-5028)
PHONE....................................214 630-9625
Mike Floan, *Exec VP*
Becky Roccaforte, *Marketing Mgr*
Monica Waldorf, *Marketing Mgr*
Steve Bergeon, *Info Tech Mgr*
Kevin Kohlewriter, *Info Tech Mgr*
EMP: 20 **Privately Held**
WEB: www.spotsee.io
SIC: 2759 Commercial printing
PA: Texas Mri, Lp
510 Corporate Dr
Graham TX 76450

(G-5078)
TEXAS OFFSET PRINTING LP (PA)
6730 Oakbrook Blvd (75235-4108)
PHONE....................................214 628-7430
John Barber, *Partner*
Debra Stewart, *Opers Mgr*
EMP: 21
SALES (est): 2.9MM **Privately Held**
WEB: www.txoffset.com
SIC: 2752 Commercial printing, offset

(G-5079)
TEXOD ENERGY LLC
1920 Mckinney Ave Fl 7 (75201-2483)
PHONE....................................214 998-5360
Pablo Trinidad, *Mng Member*
EMP: 10
SALES (est): 52.5K **Privately Held**
WEB: www.texod.com
SIC: 5211 1382 Energy conservation
products; oil & gas exploration services

(G-5080)
TEXOKAN OPERATING INC
5646 Milton St Ste 130 (75206-3929)
PHONE....................................214 484-2322
George C Burrell, *President*
EMP: 11
SALES (est): 1.7MM **Privately Held**
SIC: 3533 1381 Oil field machinery &
equipment; oil & gas drilling rigs & equip-
ment; drilling oil & gas wells

(G-5081)
TFW INDUSTRIAL SUP CNC MCH LLC
1133 S Madison Ave (75208-6726)
P.O. Box 118, Godley (76044-0118)
PHONE....................................817 898-9140
Troy Gilley, *Mng Member*
EMP: 15
SALES (est): 2.5MM **Privately Held**
WEB: www.tfwmachine.com
SIC: 3491 5072 Gas valves & parts, in-
dustrial; bolts, nuts & screws

(G-5082)
THEATRICAL WAREHOUSE INC
Also Called: T W Design & Construction
2808 Mcgowan St (75203-4110)
PHONE....................................214 634-2965
Roger Farkash, *President*
Dorothy Farkash, *CFO*
EMP: 30
SQ FT: 45,000
SALES (est): 3.6MM **Privately Held**
WEB: www.twdesign.com
SIC: 3999 7389 Theatrical scenery; trade
show arrangement

(G-5083)
THERM PROCESSES INC
1609 E 8th St (75203-2522)
P.O. Box 223603 (75222-3603)
PHONE....................................214 942-3131
Steve Coffey, *President*
Cliff Coffey, *Vice Pres*
Clifton Coffey, *Vice Pres*
▲ EMP: 11
SQ FT: 12,000

SALES (est): 2MM **Privately Held**
WEB: www.thermprocesses.com
SIC: 5013 2842 Automotive supplies; specialty cleaning, polishes & sanitation
goods

(G-5084)
THERM-ALL INC
Also Called: Therm All Insulation
4884 Duncanville Rd Ste B (75236-1812)
PHONE....................................214 630-4800
Ben Holmes, *Manager*
EMP: 14
SQ FT: 120,292
SALES (corp-wide): 17.5MM **Privately Held**
WEB: www.therm-all.com
SIC: 3083 5033 Plastic finished products,
laminated; insulation materials
PA: Therm-All, Inc.
31387 Industrial Pkwy
North Olmsted OH 44070
440 779-9494

(G-5085)
THERMO-SERV INC
3901 Pipestone Rd (75212-6017)
PHONE....................................214 631-0307
F Folsom Bell, *President*
Lance Wimmer, *President*
Matthew Huss, *Plant Mgr*
Madny Michael, *Purch Mgr*
Dana Dowdy, *Marketing Mgr*
▲ EMP: 200
SQ FT: 180,000
SALES (est): 31.1MM **Privately Held**
WEB: www.thermoserv.com
SIC: 3089 Cups, plastic, except foam

(G-5086)
THOMPSON & THOMPSON (PA)
Also Called: Double T Ranch
325 N Saint Paul St # 4300 (75201-3806)
PHONE....................................214 953-1177
James Cleo Thompson Jr, *Partner*
Linda Gordon, *Partner*
Christy Thompson, *Partner*
EMP: 23
SQ FT: 11,000
SALES (est): 25.5MM **Privately Held**
SIC: 1311 0212 6211 Crude petroleum
production; beef cattle except feedlots; oil
royalties dealers

(G-5087)
THOMPSON PETROLEUM CORPORATION (PA)
Also Called: Thompson J Cleo
325 N Saint Paul St # 4300 (75201-3801)
PHONE....................................214 953-1177
James Cleo Thompson Jr, *President*
Linda Thompson Gordon, *Vice Pres*
Frank Peterman, *Vice Pres*
Christine Thompson, *Vice Pres*
Dorothy Thompson, *Vice Pres*
EMP: 10 EST: 1978
SQ FT: 12,000
SALES (est): 60.9MM **Privately Held**
SIC: 1311 Crude petroleum production;
natural gas production

(G-5088)
THREE STREAMS ENERGY LLC
3811 Turtle Creek Blvd (75219-4693)
PHONE....................................469 917-1777
Michael Myers,
EMP: 10
SALES (est): 259.7K **Privately Held**
SIC: 1382 Oil & gas exploration services

(G-5089)
THUNDERBIRD FOOD MACHINERY
4602 Brass Way (75236-2004)
PHONE....................................214 331-3000
Charles Lin, *President*
▲ EMP: 25
SQ FT: 17,100
SALES (est): 4.5MM **Privately Held**
WEB: www.thunderbirdfm.com
SIC: 3556 Food products machinery

(G-5090)
THYBAR CORPORATION
Thy Curb Div
13801 Senlac Dr Ste 100 (75234-8835)
PHONE..................972 416-6220
Mike Pease, *Engineer*
Gary Reedy, *Engineer*
Gary Reeby, *Manager*
Steve Ricks, *Manager*
EMP: 35
SALES (corp-wide): 39.3MM **Privately Held**
WEB: www.thybar.com
SIC: 3441 3444 Fabricated structural metal; sheet metalwork
PA: Thybar Corporation
913 S Kay Ave
Addison IL 60101
630 543-5300

(G-5091)
TICONA POLYMERS INC
1601 Lyndon B Johnson Fwy (75234-6512)
PHONE....................972 443-4000
Carolyn Hindley, *Principal*
EMP: 250
SALES (corp-wide): 5.6B **Publicly Held**
WEB: www.celanese.com
SIC: 3087 Custom compound purchased resins
HQ: Ticona Polymers, Inc.
222 Las Colinas Blvd W 900n
Irving TX 75039
859 525-4740

(G-5092)
TIG REAL ESTATE SERVICES INC
2500 Dallas Pkwy Ste 2060 (75254)
PHONE....................972 661-0232
EMP: 20 **Privately Held**
WEB: www.tigusa.com
SIC: 2015 Chicken slaughtering & processing
PA: Tig Real Estate Services, Inc.
4350 Beltway Dr
Addison TX 75001

(G-5093)
TIGERFLOW SYSTEMS LLC (PA)
4034 Mint Way (75237-1604)
PHONE....................214 337-8780
Manny Rodriguez, *President*
Jared Stout, *Prdtn Mgr*
Monroe Guest, *CFO*
Kai Zhang, *Finance*
Nancy Abraham, *Sales Staff*
▲ EMP: 52
SQ FT: 87,600
SALES (est): 16.3MM **Privately Held**
WEB: www.tigerflow.com
SIC: 3585 5084 Parts for heating, cooling & refrigerating equipment; industrial machinery & equipment

(G-5094)
TIME DELAY CORPORATION
Also Called: Mc Quirk, Bob Watchmaker
10440 N Cntl Expy Ste 210 (75231)
PHONE....................214 369-4063
Robert J Mc Quirk, *President*
Gerry Bohmann, *General Mgr*
Gregory Loving, *Controller*
▲ EMP: 25
SQ FT: 4,000
SALES (est): 3.3MM **Privately Held**
WEB: www.timedelay.com
SIC: 3915 3911 Gems, real & imitation: preparation for settings; jewelry, precious metal

(G-5095)
TIMESAVER TEMPLATES INC
5920 Preston Valley Dr (75240-4756)
PHONE....................972 620-2197
Teresa Crouch, *President*
Deborah Hildenbrand, *Vice Pres*
EMP: 10
SQ FT: 11,000
SALES (est): 1.4MM **Privately Held**
SIC: 3083 3953 2796 Laminated plastics plate & sheet; marking devices; platemaking services

(G-5096)
TITAN CUSTOM PRODUCTS INC
2560 W Commerce St (75212-4909)
PHONE....................214 678-9105
Robert Royer, *CEO*
Felix Soliz, *President*
Daniel Merrill, *Vice Pres*
▲ EMP: 15
SQ FT: 8,000
SALES (est): 1.7MM **Privately Held**
WEB: www.titancustom.com
SIC: 2759 Commercial printing

(G-5097)
TITANIUM METALS CORPORATION
Also Called: Valhi Timet
5430 Lyndon B Johnson Fwy # 1700 (75240-2601)
PHONE....................972 233-1700
Gregory Swalwell, *Vice Pres*
Misty Schultz, *Project Mgr*
Chet Sowal, *Project Mgr*
Jennifer Walkowiak, *Export Mgr*
Jason Ulrich, *Foreman/Supr*
EMP: 98
SALES (corp-wide): 254.6B **Publicly Held**
WEB: www.timet.com
SIC: 3356 Titanium; titanium & titanium alloy bars, sheets, strip, etc.
HQ: Titanium Metals Corporation
4832 Richmond Rd Ste 100
Warrensville Heights OH 44128
610 968-1300

(G-5098)
TITUS GROUP INC
Also Called: Titus Industrial
14580 Midway Rd (75244-3109)
PHONE....................469 289-1773
Maxwell Farley, *CEO*
EMP: 22
SALES (est): 1.7MM **Privately Held**
WEB: www.titusindustrial.com
SIC: 3429 Clamps, couplings, nozzles & other metal hose fittings

(G-5099)
TKO TELESYSTEMS LLC
12801 N Stemmons Fwy (75234-5835)
PHONE....................972 484-4900
EMP: 11
SQ FT: 3,500
SALES (est): 600K **Privately Held**
WEB: www.officetelesystems.com
SIC: 3661 Communication headgear, telephone

(G-5100)
TOP CAT READY MIX LLC
2040 Dowdy Ferry Rd (75217-9237)
P.O. Box 308, Scurry (75158-0308)
PHONE....................972 486-3162
John Reeder, *Mng Member*
Rena Huddleston,
Patricia Gibson, *Admin Asst*
EMP: 60
SALES (est): 30MM **Privately Held**
SIC: 3273 Ready-mixed concrete

(G-5101)
TOP LEVEL PRINTING INK INC
1343 Round Table Dr (75247-3505)
PHONE....................214 267-9010
Billy Ragland, *President*
Doug Raley, *Vice Pres*
Tricia Morgan,
▲ EMP: 18
SQ FT: 25,000
SALES (est): 3.7MM **Privately Held**
WEB: www.toplevelink.com
SIC: 2893 Printing ink

(G-5102)
TOTAL METAL PRODUCTS INC
4071 Shilling Way (75237-1009)
PHONE....................214 330-7453
Fred Garcia, *President*
EMP: 66
SQ FT: 17,000
SALES (est): 12.2MM **Privately Held**
SIC: 3444 Sheet metalwork

(G-5103)
TOUTATIS AZTEC SOLUTIONS
Also Called: Aztec Systems
2101 Cedar Springs Rd (75201-2104)
PHONE....................972 484-3060
Andrew Levi, *President*
Vishal Waghmare, *Engineer*
Milind Gawade, *Manager*
Edith Bezuijen, *Agent*
Martin Nordeen, *CTO*
EMP: 53
SQ FT: 13,000
SALES (est): 8.2MM **Privately Held**
WEB: www.aztecsystems.com
SIC: 7372 8742 Prepackaged software; management information systems consultant

(G-5104)
TRANE US INC
Also Called: Trane Supply
11011 Regency Crest Dr (75238-1718)
PHONE....................972 892-3900
Ron Hageman, *Branch Mgr*
EMP: 62 **Privately Held**
WEB: www.trane.com
SIC: 3585 Refrigeration & heating equipment
HQ: Trane U.S. Inc.
3600 Pammel Creek Rd
La Crosse WI 54601
608 787-2000

(G-5105)
TRANS-MATE LLC
5949 Sherry Ln Ste 540 (75225-8096)
PHONE....................800 867-9274
Steven Stockman, *President*
EMP: 20
SALES (est): 6.3MM
SALES (corp-wide): 193.5MM **Privately Held**
WEB: www.trans-mate.com
SIC: 2999 2841 Waxes, petroleum: not produced in petroleum refineries; soap & other detergents
HQ: Niteo Products, Llc
5949 Sherry Ln Ste 540
Dallas TX 75225
214 245-5000

(G-5106)
TREFFINGER INC
Also Called: Collins Concrete
12650 Ravenview Rd (75253-3917)
P.O. Box 360007 (75336-0007)
PHONE....................972 286-8852
Fred Treffinger, *President*
Beverly Treffinger, *Corp Secy*
Kris Barnhill, *Opers Mgr*
Chris Callicutt, *Sales Mgr*
Terance Miller, *Sales Staff*
EMP: 42
SQ FT: 3,000
SALES (est): 16.2MM **Privately Held**
WEB: www.collinsconcrete.com
SIC: 3273 Ready-mixed concrete

(G-5107)
TREK RESOURCES INC
4925 Greenville Ave # 915 (75206-4026)
PHONE....................214 373-0318
Michael E Montgomery, *President*
Kenneth Smith, *Exec VP*
Mary Helen Cole, *Senior VP*
Conrad Mirochna, *Senior VP*
Leslie Wylie, *Senior VP*
EMP: 16
SQ FT: 6,000
SALES (est): 5.7MM **Privately Held**
WEB: www.trekresources.com
SIC: 1382 Oil & gas exploration services

(G-5108)
TRI CAPITAL ENERGY CORPORATION
1 Galleria Tower (75240)
PHONE....................972 996-7486
Gary Allen, *CEO*
EMP: 10
SALES (est): 237.9K **Privately Held**
WEB: www.tricapitalenergy.com
SIC: 1389 Oil & gas field services

(G-5109)
TRI-TEX ENTERPRISES INC (PA)
4909 Lakawana St (75247-6701)
PHONE....................214 744-1246
Anthony V Borino Jr, *President*
Sarah E Borino, *Corp Secy*
Richard Gamble, *Vice Pres*
Gene Davis, *Project Mgr*
Craig Dasse, *Sales Staff*
◆ EMP: 40
SQ FT: 4,000
SALES (est): 28.1MM **Privately Held**
WEB: www.tri-tex.net
SIC: 2391 2392 3842 Draperies, plastic & textile: from purchased materials; bedspreads & bed sets: made from purchased materials; surgical appliances & supplies

(G-5110)
TRI-WIN OUTSOURCING INC
4301 Simonton Rd Ste 100 (75244-5212)
PHONE....................214 826-2244
Scott Stephen Fish, *President*
Robin Fish, *Vice Pres*
Louise Morgan, *CFO*
Daniel Dunsworth, *Sales Mgr*
Brad Salerno, *Accounts Mgr*
EMP: 48
SQ FT: 32,000
SALES (est): 10.5MM **Privately Held**
WEB: www.tri-win.com
SIC: 2759 7331 Commercial printing; mailing service

(G-5111)
TRINITY CASTING SERVICE INC
2127 Cartwright St (75212-5504)
PHONE....................214 631-4248
Terry Huebner, *President*
EMP: 23 EST: 1969
SQ FT: 20,000
SALES (est): 1.9MM **Privately Held**
SIC: 7389 7692 Grinding, precision: commercial or industrial; welding repair

(G-5112)
TRINITY INDUSTRIES INC (PA)
14221 Dallas Pkwy Ste 11 (75254-2942)
PHONE....................214 631-4420
E Jean Savage, *President*
Brian D Madison, *President*
Paul E Mauer, *President*
Timothy R Wallace, *President*
Todd Simmons, *Superintendent*
▼ EMP: 355
SALES (est): 3B **Publicly Held**
WEB: www.trinityindustries.com
SIC: 3743 3731 3531 3444 Freight cars & equipment; tank freight cars & car equipment; barges, building & repairing; offshore supply boats, building & repairing; crew boats, building & repairing; fishing vessels, large: building & repairing; concrete plants; guard rails, highway: sheet metal; fabricated structural metal; building components, structural steel; fabricated structural metal for bridges; industrial vessels, tanks & containers

(G-5113)
TRINITY INDUSTRIES INTL
14221 Dallas Pkwy (75254-2942)
PHONE....................214 589-8967
Timothy R Wallace, *President*
Jeff Ordonez, *Principal*
Michael G Fortado, *Vice Pres*
Jim S Ivy, *Vice Pres*
John M Lee, *Vice Pres*
EMP: 900
SALES (est): 56MM
SALES (corp-wide): 3B **Publicly Held**
WEB: www.trin.net
SIC: 3743 Railway motor cars; sleeping cars, railroad
PA: Trinity Industries, Inc.
14221 Dallas Pkwy Ste 11
Dallas TX 75254
214 631-4420

(G-5114)
TRINITY RAIL GROUP LLC (HQ)
14221 Dallas Pkwy # 1100 (75254-2942)
PHONE....................214 631-4420
Timothy Wallace, *CEO*
Jose Luna, *Superintendent*

GEOGRAPHIC

Clay Howard, *Vice Pres*
Helmut Hvizdalek, *Vice Pres*
Gail Peck, *Vice Pres*
EMP: 10
SQ FT: 107,000
SALES (est): 58.1MM
SALES (corp-wide): 3B **Publicly Held**
WEB: www.trinityrail.com
SIC: 3743 Locomotives & parts; sleeping cars, railroad
PA: Trinity Industries, Inc.
14221 Dallas Pkwy Ste 11
Dallas TX 75254
214 631-4420

(G-5115)
TRIPLE CROWN RESOURCES LLC
1722 Routh St Ste 1750 (75201-2518)
PHONE.............................972 444-8808
Donald Markley, *Vice Pres*
EMP: 13
SALES (corp-wide): 669.9K **Privately Held**
WEB: www.triplecrownresources.com
SIC: 1311 Crude petroleum production
PA: Triple Crown Resources, Llc
1722 Routh St Ste 1750
Dallas TX 75201
214 306-0524

(G-5116)
TRIPLE/S DYNAMICS INC
4215 Gurley St (75223)
P.O. Box 151027 (75315-1027)
PHONE.............................214 828-8600
Marion Cowen, *Branch Mgr*
EMP: 25
SALES (corp-wide): 15.1MM **Privately Held**
WEB: www.sssdynamics.com
SIC: 3599 3589 Custom machinery; shredders, industrial & commercial
PA: Triple/S Dynamics, Inc.
1031 S Haskell Ave
Dallas TX 75223
214 828-8600

(G-5117)
TRIPLE/S DYNAMICS INC (PA)
1031 S Haskell Ave (75223-2925)
P.O. Box 151027 (75315-1027)
PHONE.............................214 828-8600
James F Sullivan Sr, *Ch of Bd*
Kenneth Everill, *President*
James F Sullivan Jr, *Co-President*
Ronnie Mouton, *Plant Mgr*
Jim Cross, *Production*
EMP: 50
SQ FT: 23,000
SALES (est): 15.1MM **Privately Held**
WEB: www.sssdynamics.com
SIC: 3599 3549 3535 Custom machinery; metalworking machinery; conveyors & conveying equipment

(G-5118)
TRISTAR GROUP INC
5220 Spring Valley Rd # 190 (75254-3099)
PHONE.............................972 392-2848
Robert Harrison, *President*
Carl Frenkel, *Vice Pres*
EMP: 35 **EST:** 2001
SALES (est): 3.7MM **Privately Held**
WEB: www.tsgrep.com
SIC: 3559 Semiconductor manufacturing machinery

(G-5119)
TRIUMPH ENERGY PARTNERS LLC
14001 Dallas Pkwy # 1200 (75240-7369)
PHONE.............................918 986-8283
John Kueser, *CEO*
Kerby Hunt, *Vice Pres*
Murray Papke, *Vice Pres*
Kyle Hill, *CFO*
Sheri Addis, *Marketing Staff*
EMP: 9
SALES (est): 617.1K **Privately Held**
WEB: www.triumphep.com
SIC: 1382 Oil & gas exploration services

(G-5120)
TRIUMPH GROUP INC
899 Cassatt Rd Ste 210 (75265)
PHONE.............................610 251-1000
Michael Deshaies, *President*
Rex Johnson, *Branch Mgr*
EMP: 17 **Publicly Held**
WEB: www.triumphgroup.com
SIC: 3728 Aircraft body & wing assemblies & parts
PA: Triumph Group, Inc.
899 Cassatt Rd Ste 210
Berwyn PA 19312

(G-5121)
TRT HOLDINGS INC (PA)
Also Called: Omni Hotels
4001 Maple Ave Ste 600 (75219-3241)
PHONE.............................214 283-8500
Robert B Rowling, *Ch of Bd*
James D Caldwell, *President*
Dave Schnabel, *President*
Joel Darr, *General Mgr*
John Murtha, *General Mgr*
EMP: 30
SALES (est): 1.1B **Privately Held**
WEB: www.trtholdings.com
SIC: 7011 7991 1382 Hotels & motels; physical fitness facilities; physical fitness clubs with training equipment; exercise facilities; aerobic dance & exercise classes; oil & gas exploration services

(G-5122)
TURF TECHNOLOGIES LLC
1525 Hinton St (75235-5101)
PHONE.............................419 422-4356
Alan Richmond,
Jason Craven,
EMP: 50
SALES (est): 4MM **Privately Held**
WEB: www.blackswampcouncil.org
SIC: 2899 Chemical supplies for foundries

(G-5123)
TWBM HOLDING CO INC (PA)
8500 N Stemmons Fwy (75247-3832)
PHONE.............................469 916-9430
T William Mc Intyre, *President*
Donna Alexander, *Vice Pres*
EMP: 10
SALES (est): 1.9MM **Privately Held**
SIC: 1389 Oil field services

(G-5124)
TXCO RESOURCES INC
2001 Ross Ave Ste 400 (75201-2916)
PHONE.............................210 822-8864
James E Sigmon, *Ch of Bd*
James J Bookout, *COO*
Roberto R Thomae, *Vice Pres*
P Mark Stark, *CFO*
Richard A Sartor,
▲ **EMP:** 19
SQ FT: 25,400
SALES (est): 3.7MM **Privately Held**
SIC: 1381 1382 Drilling oil & gas wells; oil & gas exploration services

(G-5125)
TXI OPERATIONS LP (DH)
1341 W Mockingbird Ln 700w (75247-6913)
PHONE.............................972 647-6700
Mel G Brekhus, *CEO*
Robert D Rogers, *President*
Frederick G Anderson, *Vice Pres*
James R Mc Craw, *Vice Pres*
Robert C Moore, *Vice Pres*
▲ **EMP:** 225
SALES (est): 178.2MM **Publicly Held**
WEB: www.martinmarietta.com
SIC: 3273 3271 3272 1442 Ready-mixed concrete; blocks, concrete or cinder; standard; pipe, concrete or lined with concrete; sand mining
HQ: Texas Industries, Inc.
1503 Lyndon B Johnson Fwy
Dallas TX 75234
972 647-6700

(G-5126)
TYSON FOODS INC
4114 Mint Way (75237-1606)
PHONE.............................214 331-1010
David Gladbach, *Principal*

Sara Bratetich, *Manager*
Yasmin Zughni,
EMP: 161
SALES (corp-wide): 43.1B **Publicly Held**
WEB: www.tysonfoods.com
SIC: 2011 Meat packing plants
PA: Tyson Foods, Inc.
2200 W Don Tyson Pkwy
Springdale AR 72762
479 290-4000

(G-5127)
UFP DALLAS LLC (HQ)
Also Called: Bigs Packaging and Lumber
2829 Sea Harbor Rd (75212-4228)
PHONE.............................817 825-6512
Bryan Bigham, *President*
EMP: 30 **EST:** 2014
SALES (est): 22.6MM
SALES (corp-wide): 4.4B **Publicly Held**
WEB: www.bigspackaging.com
SIC: 2449 Wood containers
PA: Ufp Industries, Inc.
2801 E Beltline Ave Ne
Grand Rapids MI 49525
616 364-6161

(G-5128)
UFP DALLAS LLC
Also Called: Universal Forest Products
2829 Sea Harbor Rd (75212-4228)
PHONE.............................972 232-1711
Bryan Bigham, *Branch Mgr*
EMP: 150
SALES (corp-wide): 4.4B **Publicly Held**
WEB: www.bigspackaging.com
SIC: 2493 Reconstituted wood products
HQ: Ufp Dallas, Llc
2829 Sea Harbor Rd
Dallas TX 75212
817 825-6512

(G-5129)
ULTIMATE CONTROL SOLUTIONS INC
13601 Preston Rd Ste 310e (75240-4910)
PHONE.............................972 383-9414
Joe Rumaker, *President*
Patricia Rumaker, *Vice Pres*
Patricia J Rumaker, *Vice Pres*
EMP: 11
SALES (est): 3.7MM **Privately Held**
WEB: www.ultimatecsi.com
SIC: 3822 7389 Temperature controls, automatic;

(G-5130)
ULTRATEST INTERNATIONAL INC
Also Called: Microlabs
7326 Craigshire Ave (75231-4748)
PHONE.............................214 340-5252
EMP: 25
SALES (est): 1.7MM **Privately Held**
SIC: 8734 3825 Testing Laboratory Mfg Electrical Measuring Instruments

(G-5131)
ULTRAVISION INTERNATIONAL
4542 Mcewen Rd (75244-5207)
PHONE.............................214 260-4500
William Hall, *CEO*
Tandy Robinson, *Controller*
Bill Hall, *CTO*
EMP: 32
SALES (est): 7.4MM **Privately Held**
WEB: www.ultravisioninternational.com
SIC: 3646 Fluorescent lighting fixtures, commercial

(G-5132)
UNIFORMS INC
Also Called: Embroidery Graphix
1489 Prudential Dr (75235-4109)
PHONE.............................214 630-0924
Scott Howley, *CEO*
Charles L Howley, *CEO*
Dennis Atkins, *General Mgr*
Nancy Howley, *Vice Pres*
EMP: 18 **EST:** 1978
SQ FT: 9,800

SALES (est): 5.4MM **Privately Held**
WEB: www.embroiderygraphix.com
SIC: 2326 2759 2395 2396 Men's & boys' work clothing; screen printing; emblems, embroidered; embroidery products, except schiffli machine; screen printing on fabric articles; T-shirts, custom printed

(G-5133)
UNILIN NORTH AMERICA LLC (HQ)
7834 C F Hawn Fwy (75217-6529)
PHONE.............................214 398-1411
Frank H Boykin,
Edward R Schleper,
Christoph Schmitz,
▲ **EMP:** 70
SALES (est): 41.2MM **Publicly Held**
SIC: 3996 Hard surface floor coverings

(G-5134)
UNITED GROUP PRINTING
14001 Distribution Way (75234-3438)
PHONE.............................972 428-3000
Jeff Rupley, *Owner*
EMP: 15
SALES (est): 1.9MM **Privately Held**
WEB: www.ugprinting.com
SIC: 2752 Commercial printing, offset

(G-5135)
UNITED LEATHER USA INC
1233 E Levee St (75207-7107)
PHONE.............................214 698-8270
Michael Arredondo, *President*
Juan Leon, *President*
Jose Machado, *President*
Shelly Norman, *Natl Sales Mgr*
Leon Jj, *Info Tech Mgr*
▲ **EMP:** 55
SQ FT: 33,000
SALES (est): 2.3MM **Privately Held**
WEB: www.unitedleatherusa.com
SIC: 2512 Upholstered household furniture

(G-5136)
UNITED OFFICE INTERIORS INC (PA)
Also Called: United Interior Resources
8200 Lovett Ave (75227-4230)
PHONE.............................214 381-0101
Charles Holden, *CEO*
J Tom Holden, *President*
Fabio Jelezoglo, *Superintendent*
Chuck Louden, *Superintendent*
Paul M Holden, *Vice Pres*
EMP: 68
SQ FT: 70,000
SALES (est): 50.7MM **Privately Held**
WEB: www.fcsdallas.com
SIC: 2542 1742 Partitions for floor attachment, prefabricated: except wood; drywall

(G-5137)
UNITED STATES GYPSUM COMPANY
255 Regal Row (75247-5299)
PHONE.............................214 424-2500
Martin Robertson, *Opers Mgr*
Dan Newcomer, *Manager*
EMP: 50
SQ FT: 56,700
SALES (corp-wide): 8.2B **Privately Held**
WEB: www.usg.com
SIC: 5032 3275 Brick, stone & related material; gypsum products
HQ: United States Gypsum Company
550 W Adams St Ste 1300
Chicago IL 60661
312 606-4000

(G-5138)
UNITED STATES LIME & MNRL INC (HQ)
5429 Lbj Fwy Ste 230 (75240-2666)
PHONE.............................972 991-8400
Antoine M Doumet, *Ch of Bd*
Edward A Odishaw, *Vice Ch Bd*
Timothy W Byrne, *President*
Russell W Riggs, *VP Prdtn*
Michael L Wiedemer, *CFO*
EMP: 43

SALES: 158.2MM
SALES (corp-wide): 4.1MM **Publicly Held**
WEB: www.uslm.com
SIC: **1422** 3274 6289 Crushed & broken limestone; quicklime; hydrated lime; royalty owners protective associations
PA: Federal White Cement Ltd
789 Pender St W Suite 1020
Vancouver BC V6C 1
604 683-9641

(G-5139)
UNITRON LP
10925 Miller Rd (75238-1350)
P.O. Box 38902 (75238-0902)
PHONE..................................214 221-9094
Robert King, *Partner*
Raymond L Beutel, *Chairman*
Scott Lefky, *Vice Pres*
Greg Adair, *Materials Mgr*
Larry Denson, *Materials Mgr*
▲ EMP: 70
SQ FT: 40,000
SALES (est): 18.1MM **Privately Held**
WEB: www.unitronlp.com
SIC: **3621** 3613 3679 Motors & generators; switchgear & switchboard apparatus; electronic circuits

(G-5140)
UNITY HUNT INC
5956 Sherry Ln Ste 1500 (75225-8026)
PHONE..................................214 720-1600
Lamar Hunt, *Owner*
Lela Luxen, *Vice Pres*
Suzanne Cornett, *Executive Asst*
EMP: 50 EST: 1937
SQ FT: 1,000
SALES (est): 7.5MM **Privately Held**
WEB: www.trinityhunt.com
SIC: **1311** Crude petroleum production; natural gas production

(G-5141)
UP 1 TRUCKING LLC
11816 Inwood Rd (75244-8011)
PHONE..................................833 398-7825
Sakura Richards, *CEO*
EMP: 10
SALES (est): 302.8K **Privately Held**
SIC: **4213** 3799 5088 Trucking, except local; transportation equipment; transportation equipment & supplies

(G-5142)
UPAY INC (PA)
3010 Lbj Fwy (75234-7770)
PHONE..................................972 888-6052
David Westfere, *President*
EMP: 14
SALES: 1.3MM **Privately Held**
WEB: www.upaytechnology.com
SIC: **7372** Business oriented computer software

(G-5143)
UPELY TRADERS
3811 Turtle Creek Blvd (75219-4693)
PHONE..................................832 998-8432
EMP: 30
SALES (est): 1MM **Privately Held**
WEB: www.upely.com
SIC: **3612** Power & distribution transformers

(G-5144)
UPEX AUTO SUPPLY
3036 Elm St (75226-1511)
P.O. Box 150099 (75315-0099)
PHONE..................................214 741-2400
John Schmitz, *President*
EMP: 13
SQ FT: 12,000
SALES (est): 2.7MM **Privately Held**
WEB: www.upexauto.com
SIC: **5013** 5531 3694 Automotive supplies & parts; automotive parts; automotive electrical equipment

(G-5145)
UPTOWN POPCORN LLC (PA)
10880 Rockwall Rd Ste 200 (75238-1214)
PHONE..................................972 291-4767
Brooks Shankle, *CEO*
Hannah Shankle, *President*
Curtis Foster, *COO*

Brent Shankle, *CFO*
EMP: 15
SQ FT: 600
SALES (est): 1.3MM **Privately Held**
WEB: www.uptownpopcorn.com
SIC: **2064** 5441 Popcorn balls or other treated popcorn products; popcorn, including caramel corn

(G-5146)
URBAN PUBLISHERS INC
Also Called: Paper City Magazine
3303 Lee Pkwy Ste 340 (75219-5116)
PHONE..................................214 521-3439
Maxine Trowbridge, *Chief Engr*
Linda Kenney, *Accounts Exec*
Samantha Olguin, *Sales Staff*
Michelle Giles, *Branch Mgr*
James Work, *Manager*
EMP: 9 **Privately Held**
WEB: www.papercitymag.com
SIC: **2721** Magazines: publishing only, not printed on site
PA: Urban Publishers, Inc.
3411 Richmond Ave Ste 600
Houston TX 77046

(G-5147)
US GALVANIZING LLC
2525 N Stemmons Fwy (75207-2401)
PHONE..................................817 268-6111
EMP: 300
SALES (est): 14.1MM **Privately Held**
SIC: **3479** Coating/Engraving Service

(G-5148)
USPLABS LLC
10761 King William Dr (75220-2445)
P.O. Box 815667 (75381-5667)
PHONE..................................469 484-1927
Jacob E Geissler, *Mng Member*
Brandon Horoho, *Creative Dir*
Adam Schwinghammer, *Officer*
John Doyle,
◆ EMP: 50 EST: 2006
SALES (est): 8.2MM **Privately Held**
WEB: www.usplabsdirect.com
SIC: **2023** Dietary supplements, dairy & non-dairy based

(G-5149)
VAC-U-RAT OILFIELD SVCS LLC
3860 W Northwest Hwy # 325 (75220-5183)
P.O. Box 271, Tilden (78072-0271)
PHONE..................................214 850-1042
Frank McMordie, *President*
Keith Henke, *Vice Pres*
EMP: 12
SALES (est): 947K **Privately Held**
SIC: **1389** Oil field services

(G-5150)
VALEO NORTH AMERICA INC
2520 Esters Blvd Ste 100 (75261)
PHONE..................................972 574-1900
EMP: 37 **Privately Held**
SIC: **3585** Mfg Refrigeration/Heating Equipment
HQ: Valeo North America, Inc.
150 Stephenson Hwy
Troy MI 48083

(G-5151)
VALHI INC (DH)
5430 Lbj Fwy Ste 1700 (75240-2327)
PHONE..................................972 233-1700
Loretta J Feehan, *Ch of Bd*
Robert D Graham, *President*
Diane Adkins, *District Mgr*
Chris Armstrong, *Exec VP*
Andrew B Nace, *Exec VP*
◆ EMP: 40 EST: 1932
SALES: 1.9B
SALES (corp-wide): 2B **Publicly Held**
WEB: www.valhi.net
SIC: **2816** 2899 3429 Titanium dioxide, anatase or rutile (pigments); chemical preparations; keys, locks & related hardware; furniture hardware
HQ: Dixie Rice Agricultural L.L.C.
5430 Lyndon B Johnson Fwy
Dallas TX 75240
972 233-1700

(G-5152)
VALLEY PROTEINS (DE) INC
515 Pontiac Ave (75203-2114)
PHONE..................................469 580-0864
Corey Brazil, *Branch Mgr*
EMP: 53
SALES (corp-wide): 473.5MM **Privately Held**
WEB: www.valleyproteins.com
SIC: **2077** Animal & marine fats & oils
PA: Valley Proteins (De), Inc.
151 Valpro Dr
Winchester VA 22603
540 877-2533

(G-5153)
VAN ORIENTAL FOOD INC
Also Called: Van Foods
4828 Reading St (75247-6705)
PHONE..................................214 630-0333
Theresa Motter, *President*
Cline David, *COO*
Van Nguyen, *Vice Pres*
Brian Krohn, *Prdtn Mgr*
Tim Womack, *Mfg Mgr*
▲ EMP: 77
SQ FT: 56,000
SALES (est): 18MM **Privately Held**
WEB: www.vanskitchen.com
SIC: **2099** 2038 Food preparations; frozen specialties

(G-5154)
VAQUERO MIDSTREAM LLC
2602 Mckinney Ave Ste 400 (75204-2595)
PHONE..................................214 855-5546
EMP: 21
SALES (corp-wide): 15.9MM **Privately Held**
WEB: www.vaqueromidstream.com
SIC: **3569** Gas producers (machinery)
PA: Vaquero Midstream Llc
1790 Hughes Landing Blvd
The Woodlands TX 77380
281 501-5699

(G-5155)
VARI DOC MANAGEMENT GROUP LLC
737 Regal Row (75247-5211)
PHONE..................................214 528-9925
Robert W Singer, *Partner*
Mike Campbell, *Partner*
Brad Bryant, *General Mgr*
Jim Singer, *Sales Executive*
Paul Sherman, *Info Tech Mgr*
EMP: 29
SALES (est): 6.8MM **Privately Held**
WEB: www.brodnax21c.com
SIC: **2752** Commercial printing, offset

(G-5156)
VARI-LITE LLC
10911 Petal St (75238-2424)
PHONE..................................214 647-7880
EMP: 104
SALES: 9.2MM
SALES (corp-wide): 6.9B **Privately Held**
SIC: **3646** Commercial indusl & institutional electric lighting fixtures
HQ: Signify North America Corporation
200 Franklin Square Dr # 4
Somerset NJ 08873
732 563-3000

(G-5157)
VECTORNAV TECHNOLOGIES LLC
10501 Markison Rd (75238-1653)
PHONE..................................512 772-3615
Gerardo Iglesias, *Vice Pres*
Jeff Cheek, *Vice Pres*
Jeremy Davis, *Engineer*
Paul Lucas, *Train & Dev Mgr*
Jakub Maslikowski, *Marketing Staff*
EMP: 13
SALES (est): 3MM **Privately Held**
WEB: www.vectornav.com
SIC: **8711** 3812 Engineering services; navigational systems & instruments

(G-5158)
VERACITY USA INCOPORATED
17000 Preston Rd Ste 260 (75248-1258)
PHONE..................................972 786-6771

Scott Sereboff, *CEO*
Alastair McLeod, *President*
EMP: 11
SALES (est): 2.4MM
SALES (corp-wide): 23.5MM **Privately Held**
WEB: www.veracityglobal.com
SIC: **3699** Security devices
PA: Veracity Uk Limited
4 Dow Road
Prestwick KA9 2
129 226-4967

(G-5159)
VERADO ENERGY INC (PA)
8150 N Central Expy # 850 (75206-1899)
PHONE..................................214 368-5322
Christopher S Graham, *Principal*
John Primdahl, *Asst Controller*
Jamie Markey, *Human Res Mgr*
Brian Furlong, *Officer*
EMP: 12
SQ FT: 3,500
SALES (est): 7.2MM **Privately Held**
WEB: www.veradoenergy.com
SIC: **1311** 1382 Crude petroleum production; natural gas production; oil & gas exploration services

(G-5160)
VERADO OIL AND GAS CORPORATION
8150 N Central Expy # 900 (75206-1913)
PHONE..................................214 368-5322
EMP: 12 EST: 1990
SALES (est): 579.3K **Privately Held**
WEB: www.veradoenergy.com
SIC: **1382** Oil & gas exploration services

(G-5161)
VERCOM SOFTWARE INC
Also Called: Primac Systems
13355 Noel Rd Ste 1100 (75240-6694)
PHONE..................................972 661-9336
Faisal Bhombal, *President*
Muhammad Safder, *President*
Michael Cooke, *COO*
EMP: 20
SQ FT: 9,400
SALES (est): 2MM **Privately Held**
WEB: www.vercom.com
SIC: **7373** 7371 7372 Systems software development services; custom computer programming services; prepackaged software

(G-5162)
VERDAD OIL & GAS CORPORATION (PA)
5950 Sherry Ln Ste 700 (75225-6562)
PHONE..................................214 357-0333
Louis A Beecherl III, *President*
William C Beecherl, *President*
John T Beecherl, *Vice Pres*
Lauren Salazar, *Controller*
Julie Theiss, *Manager*
EMP: 20
SALES (est): 4.9MM **Privately Held**
WEB: www.verdadresources.com
SIC: **1311** Crude petroleum production; natural gas production

(G-5163)
VERSA PRINTING INC
2631 Brenner Dr (75220-1319)
PHONE..................................972 243-5353
Gonzalo Godinez Jr, *President*
Sergio Godinez, *Vice Pres*
Roger Sosa, *Opers Mgr*
Alfredo Aviles, *Treasurer*
EMP: 25
SALES (est): 2MM **Privately Held**
WEB: www.versaprinting.com
SIC: **2752** 2396 2261 2711 Commercial printing, offset; screen printing on fabric articles; screen printing of cotton broadwoven fabrics; newspapers, publishing & printing; book, bond & printing papers; screen printing

(G-5164)
VERTICAL NERVE INC
8350 N Central Expy (75206-1600)
PHONE..................................800 330-9450
Tim Storer, *CEO*
William Stringham, *Principal*

Milan Evans, *CFO*
EMP: 15
SQ FT: 20,000
SALES (est): 2.8MM **Publicly Held**
SIC: 2591 Blinds vertical
PA: A. H. Belo Corporation
1954 Commerce St
Dallas TX 75201

(G-5165)
VIATECH PUBG SOLUTIONS INC (PA)
11935 N Stemmons Fwy # 1 (75234-5834)
PHONE......................214 827-8151
Michael J Bertuch, *Ch of Bd*
Larry Kambas, *Business Mgr*
Ron Simmons, *COO*
Ronald Simmons, *COO*
Moises Gutierrez, *Production*
◆ **EMP:** 95 **EST:** 1961
SQ FT: 50,000
SALES: 55MM **Privately Held**
WEB: www.viatechpub.com
SIC: 2741 Miscellaneous publishing

(G-5166)
VIDEOTEX SYSTEMS INC
10255 Miller Rd (75238-1224)
PHONE......................214 349-6399
Bob Gillman, *President*
Rodney Hood, *Purchasing*
Gene Steiner, *Accounts Exec*
◆ **EMP:** 18
SQ FT: 20,000
SALES (est): 5.8MM **Privately Held**
WEB: www.videotexsystems.com
SIC: 3651 5731 Household audio & video equipment; television sets

(G-5167)
VIKING INTERNATIONAL LIMITED
5910 N Central Expy (75206-5125)
P.O. Box 246, Addison (75001-0246)
PHONE......................214 220-4323
Malone Mitchell, *CEO*
Mike Burnett, *CFO*
EMP: 50
SALES (est): 1.7MM **Privately Held**
WEB: www.viking-intl.com
SIC: 1382 Oil & gas exploration services

(G-5168)
VOICE PUBLISHING CO INC
Also Called: Dallas Voice
1825 Market Center Blvd # 240 (75207-3309)
PHONE......................214 754-8710
Robert Moore, *President*
Leo Cusimano, *Adv Dir*
Chad Mantooth, *Advt Staff*
Kr Murphy, *Art Dir*
EMP: 17
SQ FT: 3,000
SALES (est): 1.2MM **Privately Held**
WEB: www.dallasvoice.com
SIC: 2711 Newspapers, publishing & printing

(G-5169)
VOLLARA LLC (HQ)
4100 Alpha Rd Ste 1100 (75244-4326)
PHONE......................800 989-2299
Joseph Urso, *Principal*
Bill Coyle, *Exec VP*
Troy Sanford, *Vice Pres*
Lynn Nelson, *Buyer*
Bret Holland, *CFO*
▲ **EMP:** 29
SALES (est): 12.2MM **Privately Held**
WEB: www.vollara.com
SIC: 3634 2833 Electric housewares & fans; medicinals & botanicals

(G-5170)
W & S PRECISION FINISHING CO
Also Called: W&S Finishing
4138 Shilling Way (75237-1095)
PHONE......................214 339-7181
David M Stamey, *CEO*
Abbie O Stamey, *Chairman*
Jo Ann Faulkner, *Bookkeeper*
Bud Stamey, *VP Sales*
John B Stamey III, *Director*
EMP: 42
SQ FT: 29,000

SALES (est): 4.1MM **Privately Held**
WEB: www.wsfinishing.com
SIC: 3471 Electroplating of metals or formed products

(G-5171)
W V GRANT INTL MINISTRIES
Also Called: Eagles Nest Cathedral
5600 W Lovers Ln Ste 116 (75209-4360)
PHONE......................214 333-2176
EMP: 14
SQ FT: 90,000
SALES (est): 757.9K **Privately Held**
WEB: www.wvgrant.com
SIC: 8661 2721 4833 4832 Covenant & Evangelical Church; magazines: publishing & printing; television broadcasting stations; radio broadcasting stations

(G-5172)
WARREN RESOURCES INC (PA)
5420 Lbj Fwy Ste 600 (75240-6230)
PHONE......................214 393-9688
James A Watt, *Ch of Bd*
Steve Craig, *Senior VP*
Gregory Fox, *Senior VP*
Zach Waite, *Senior VP*
Greg Fox, *Vice Pres*
EMP: 40
SQ FT: 11,832
SALES (est): 52.1MM **Publicly Held**
WEB: www.warrenresources.com
SIC: 1382 Oil & gas exploration services

(G-5173)
WARRIOR ENERGY SERVICES CORP
5050 Quorum Dr Ste 700 (75254-1410)
PHONE......................972 687-9057
EMP: 15 **Publicly Held**
WEB: www.superiorenergy.com
SIC: 1389 Oil field services
HQ: Warrior Energy Services Corporation
5801 Highway 90 E
Broussard LA 70518
337 714-2400

(G-5174)
WASTEQUIP MANUFACTURING CO LLC
3920 Singleton Blvd (75212-3556)
PHONE......................214 905-9101
Yolanda Saenz, *Production*
Dakota Trammell, *Production*
Veronica White, *Buyer*
Rob Brown, *Branch Mgr*
Jeff Buhring, *Director*
EMP: 17 **Privately Held**
WEB: www.wastequip.com
SIC: 3443 Dumpsters, garbage
HQ: Wastequip Manufacturing Company Llc
6525 Morrison Blvd # 300
Charlotte NC 28211

(G-5175)
WATTSTOCK LLC
4925 Grnvlle Ave Ste 1020 (75206)
PHONE......................713 248-4148
E Patrick Jenevein III,
Jay Manning,
EMP: 10
SQ FT: 2,000
SALES (est): 557.8K **Privately Held**
WEB: www.wattstock.com
SIC: 3612 Electric furnace transformers

(G-5176)
WBC MEDIA LP
8350 N Central Expy (75206-1600)
PHONE......................214 764-2000
James Hines, *Partner*
Ted Case, *Partner*
Bill Dunlap, *Partner*
▲ **EMP:** 10
SALES (est): 1.1MM **Privately Held**
SIC: 2679 Book covers, paper

(G-5177)
WEB TECHNOLOGY INC
11464 Pagemill Rd (75243-5506)
PHONE......................214 343-9238
Keith Williams, *President*
Edward Etess, *Vice Pres*
Jackie Candelier, *Admin Sec*
EMP: 19

SALES (est): 19.8MM **Privately Held**
WEB: www.webtechnology.com
SIC: 3825 Semiconductor test equipment

(G-5178)
WEBB TECHNOLOGY INC
Also Called: Webb Automation
11411 Plano Rd (75243-8512)
PHONE......................214 348-8678
Bart Gilbert, *Partner*
Billy Ingram, *Ltd Ptnr*
Ed Knight, *Ltd Ptnr*
EMP: 12
SQ FT: 2,000
SALES (est): 1.4MM **Privately Held**
WEB: www.webtechnology.com
SIC: 3599 3613 Machine shop, jobbing & repair; switchgear & switchboard apparatus

(G-5179)
WEBB-MASON INC
4131 N Central Expy # 600 (75204-2102)
PHONE......................214 205-1123
Pamela Martin, *Accounts Exec*
Tom Rouse, *Branch Mgr*
Leann Griffin, *Analyst*
EMP: 23 **Privately Held**
WEB: www.webbmason.com
SIC: 2752 Business form & card printing, lithographic
PA: Webb-Mason, Inc.
10830 Gilroy Rd
Hunt Valley MD 21031

(G-5180)
WEST-WARD PHARMACEUTICAL CORP
3030 Lyndon B Johnson Fwy (75234-7781)
PHONE......................800 631-2174
Michael Raya, *CEO*
EMP: 15
SALES (est): 1.7MM **Privately Held**
SIC: 2834 Pharmaceutical preparations

(G-5181)
WESTERN CABINETS INC (PA)
Also Called: Woodmont Cabinetry
3444 Morse Dr (75236-1120)
PHONE......................469 916-5350
Stanley Tidwell, *President*
Joseph Leonard, *COO*
Jeff Elseman, *Opers Mgr*
John Abbott, *Mfg Staff*
Greg Deavers, *Production*
▲ **EMP:** 140
SQ FT: 100,000
SALES (est): 34MM **Privately Held**
WEB: www.woodmontcabinetry.com
SIC: 2434 Wood kitchen cabinets

(G-5182)
WESTERN GRINDING CO INC
9000 S Hampton Rd (75232-6006)
P.O. Box 764739 (75376-4739)
PHONE......................214 631-3090
Johnny Garcia, *President*
EMP: 13
SQ FT: 21,000
SALES (est): 1.7MM **Privately Held**
WEB: www.westerngrindingtx.com
SIC: 3471 3599 7389 Finishing, metals or formed products; grinding castings for the trade; grinding, precision: commercial or industrial

(G-5183)
WESTPORT INNOVATIONS (US) (HQ)
Also Called: Westport Dallas
2180 French Settlement Rd (75212-6001)
P.O. Box 224685 (75222-4685)
PHONE......................214 231-1450
John R Bacon, *Principal*
James Arthurs, *Exec VP*
Michael Snider, *Vice Pres*
Rod Beazley, *Engineer*
David Mumford, *Engineer*
EMP: 12
SALES (est): 24.7MM
SALES (corp-wide): 305.3MM **Privately Held**
WEB: www.westport.com
SIC: 3714 Fuel systems & parts, motor vehicle

PA: Westport Fuel Systems Inc
1750 75th Ave W Suite 101
Vancouver BC
604 718-2000

(G-5184)
WESTROCK RKT LLC
Also Called: Rock-Tenn Paperboard Products
1120 E Clarendon Dr (75203-3135)
P.O. Box 1291 (75221)
PHONE......................214 941-3400
Doug Estridge, *General Mgr*
Everett Jewell, *Manager*
EMP: 120
SALES (corp-wide): 17.5B **Publicly Held**
WEB: www.westrock.com
SIC: 2653 Boxes, corrugated: made from purchased materials
HQ: Westrock Rkt, Llc
1000 Abernathy Rd Ste 125
Atlanta GA 30328
770 448-2193

(G-5185)
WHEELS AMERICA ALLOY WHEEL (PA)
3939 Platinum Way (75237-1611)
PHONE......................214 330-9866
Maggie Hurlburt, *CFO*
David Daliessio, *Manager*
Scott Stretch, *Manager*
Jennifer Delamora, *Admin Mgr*
Robert G Stretch, *Director*
▲ **EMP:** 20
SQ FT: 13,000
SALES (est): 39.5MM **Privately Held**
WEB: www.wheelsamerica.com
SIC: 5531 3312 6794 Automotive tires; wheels; franchises, selling or licensing

(G-5186)
WILDCAT MIDSTREAM OPER LLC
8333 Douglas Ave Ste 400 (75225-5812)
PHONE......................214 310-1213
EMP: 50 **EST:** 2011
SALES (est): 2MM **Privately Held**
SIC: 1382 Oil & gas exploration services

(G-5187)
WILDCAT MINERALS HOLDINGS LLC
2950 N Harwood St # 2200 (75201-1519)
PHONE......................214 706-3553
Drew Armstrong,
EMP: 50 **EST:** 2011
SALES (est): 2MM **Privately Held**
SIC: 1389 Processing service, gas

(G-5188)
WILEY HOLDINGS GROUP INC
Also Called: Wiley Printing
4650 Cole Ave Apt 105 (75205-4085)
PHONE......................214 443-0908
Robert B Wiley, *President*
Billy H Wiley, *Director*
EMP: 11
SALES (est): 1.2MM **Privately Held**
WEB: www.thinkwithink.com
SIC: 2752 Commercial printing, lithographic

(G-5189)
WILLIAM G BURNS
Also Called: Burns Wliam G Mktg Cmmnctions
4601 Langland Rd Ste 106 (75244-3953)
PHONE......................972 233-4700
EMP: 10
SQ FT: 8,200
SALES (est): 1.5MM **Privately Held**
WEB: www.businessexpresspress.com
SIC: 2752 2791 7311 0212 Commercial printing, offset; typesetting; advertising agencies; beef cattle except feedlots

(G-5190)
WILLOW BEND BAKERY INC
6607 Duffield Dr (75248-1452)
PHONE......................214 353-0889
Udomsak Marianukro, *President*
Udomsak Marianukroh, *President*
EMP: 16

SALES (est): 443.8K **Privately Held**
WEB: www.wbbakery.com
SIC: 2051 Bread, cake & related products

(G-5191)
WILSON METAL FABRICATORS INC
1925 N Lncstr Hutchins Rd (75220)
PHONE.................972 227-0200
Darold Wilson, *President*
EMP: 34
SQ FT: 25,000
SALES (est): 4.6MM **Privately Held**
WEB: www.wilsonmetalfab.com
SIC: 3441 Fabricated structural metal

(G-5192)
WILSONART LLC
Also Called: Wilson Art
4051 La Reunion Pkwy # 140
(75212-6031)
PHONE.................214 634-2310
Schuchmann Mark, *Regional Mgr*
Billy Yates, *Regl Sales Mgr*
Kelli Durham, *Sales Staff*
Terry McCormick, *Branch Mgr*
EMP: 17
SALES (corp-wide): 4.9B **Privately Held**
WEB: www.wilsonart.com
SIC: 4225 5162 2891 General warehousing & storage; plastics sheets & rods; adhesives & sealants
HQ: Wilsonart Llc
2501 Wilsonart Dr
Temple TX 76504
254 207-7000

(G-5193)
WINDOW OUTFITTERS LP
Also Called: T W O
10405 Shady Trl Ste 300 (75220-2553)
PHONE.................469 619-0892
Clifford Stanley, *Partner*
Kelly Mitchell, *Partner*
Gary Hudson, *General Mgr*
Amanda Jackson, *Opers Staff*
Dena Dillon, *Marketing Staff*
▲ EMP: 49
SALES (est): 5.4MM **Privately Held**
WEB: www.two-usa.com
SIC: 2431 3442 2591 Window shutters, wood; shutters, door or window: metal; window shades

(G-5194)
WINDSTROM INDUSTRIES & ASSOC
7474 S Lancaster Rd 8a (75241-5733)
PHONE.................214 298-6342
Lawrence H Washington,
Albert Houston,
EMP: 25
SALES (est): 1.6MM **Privately Held**
SIC: 3462 Iron & steel forgings

(G-5195)
WINGATE PARTNERS LP (PA)
750 N Saint Paul St # 1200 (75201-3273)
PHONE.................214 720-1313
Brad Brenneman, *Partner*
Michael B Decker, *Partner*
V Edward Easterling Jr, *Partner*
J I Applebaum, *Partner*
James A Johnson, *Partner*
▲ EMP: 10
SQ FT: 4,000
SALES (est): 486.7MM **Privately Held**
WEB: www.wingatepartners.com
SIC: 2621 2672 3645 2519 Paper mills; coated & laminated paper; floor lamps; wicker furniture: padded or plain; furniture; wood office furniture

(G-5196)
WINGATE PARTNERS V LP (HQ)
750 N Saint Paul St # 1200 (75201-3273)
PHONE.................214 720-1313
Brad Brenneman,
Louise Backa, *Executive Asst*
Michael Decker,
EMP: 10
SALES (est): 486.7MM **Privately Held**
WEB: www.wingatepartners.com
SIC: 6726 3448 Investment offices; prefabricated metal components

(G-5197)
WINIFRED S HAYES INCORPORATED
2711 N Haskell Ave # 145 (75204-2911)
PHONE.................215 855-0615
Trace Devanny, *CEO*
Winifred S Hayes, *President*
Maura Connor, *COO*
Christina G Dietrich, *CFO*
Terri Horn, *Human Res Dir*
EMP: 46
SALES (est): 5.1MM
SALES (corp-wide): 20.3MM **Privately Held**
WEB: www.hayesinc.com
SIC: 8742 2741 Hospital & health services consultant; miscellaneous publishing
PA: Tractmanager, Inc.
1208 King St Ste 405
Chattanooga TN 37403
423 267-9300

(G-5198)
WINZEN FILM INC
11510 Data Dr (75218-1419)
P.O. Box 677, Sulphur Springs (75483-0677)
PHONE.................214 340-7060
Robert Williamson, *CEO*
Karl Reimers, *President*
Jodi L Simons, *President*
Cindy Finley, *Vice Pres*
Ron Futrell, *CFO*
▲ EMP: 20
SQ FT: 77,000
SALES (est): 3.6MM **Privately Held**
SIC: 2673 3081 2221 2282 Plastic bags: made from purchased materials; polyethylene film; polypropylene broadwoven fabrics; polypropylene filament yarn: twisting, winding, etc.
PA: Super Sack Bag Inc
11510 Data Dr
Dallas TX 75218

(G-5199)
WIRELESS MANIAC
11532 Harry Hines Blvd (75229-2212)
PHONE.................817 209-9524
Naomi Edwards, *Manager*
EMP: 25 EST: 2013
SALES (est): 1.3MM **Privately Held**
SIC: 3961 Costume jewelry

(G-5200)
WOOD GALLERY INC
10724 Goodnight Ln (75220-2409)
PHONE.................972 869-9161
▲ EMP: 25
SQ FT: 25,000
SALES (est): 5.1MM **Privately Held**
WEB: www.woodgallery.biz
SIC: 3469 Architectural panels or parts, porcelain enameled

(G-5201)
WOOD PRINTING COMPANY INC
1418 Seegar St (75215-2047)
P.O. Box 152569 (75315-2569)
PHONE.................214 421-7393
Frank Wood, *President*
Martha Crawford, *Corp Secy*
EMP: 13 EST: 1907
SQ FT: 7,500
SALES (est): 1.3MM **Privately Held**
WEB: www.woodprinting.com
SIC: 2759 2752 2761 Letterpress printing; commercial printing, offset; color printing, gravure; manifold business forms

(G-5202)
WOODWRIGHT HARDWOOD FLR CO INC
425 Regal Row (75247-5205)
PHONE.................214 630-8811
Steven C Welch, *President*
Adriene Haynes, *Controller*
Jason Dahl, *Sales Staff*
Daniel Garcia, *Sales Staff*
Jeff Hutchins, *Sales Staff*
▲ EMP: 45

SQ FT: 10,000
SALES (est): 7.6MM **Privately Held**
WEB: www.woodwright.net
SIC: 1752 2426 Wood floor installation & refinishing; flooring, hardwood

(G-5203)
WORLDWIDE WNDOWS TRATMENTS LLC (PA)
4030 La Reunion Pkwy # 100 (75212-6023)
PHONE.................718 893-9370
Richard Holmes,
Jaime Eskobar,
▲ EMP: 26 EST: 1872
SALES (est): 2.7MM **Privately Held**
SIC: 2591 3429 Shade, curtain & drapery hardware; manufactured hardware (general)

(G-5204)
WS GROUP INC (PA)
Also Called: Precision Oxygen & Supply
2829 Fort Worth Ave (75211-2476)
PHONE.................214 337-4761
Mike Wallis, *CEO*
EMP: 9
SQ FT: 3,075
SALES (est): 1.8MM **Privately Held**
WEB: www.veris.com.au
SIC: 2813 Oxygen, compressed or liquefied

(G-5205)
XACT XPRESSIONS INC
13995 Diplomat Dr Ste 200 (75234-8814)
PHONE.................972 242-6332
Shannon Wright, *President*
Andrea Galbraith, *Vice Pres*
Larry Galbraith IV, *Treasurer*
▲ EMP: 22
SALES (est): 1.5MM **Privately Held**
WEB: www.xactx.com
SIC: 7299 3552 5099 Stitching services; silk screens for textile industry; luggage

(G-5206)
XTO ENERGY INC
3250 Love Field Dr (75235-2002)
PHONE.................817 740-0488
Keith Anderson, *Manager*
EMP: 44
SALES (corp-wide): 264.9B **Publicly Held**
WEB: www.xtoenergy.com
SIC: 1311 Crude petroleum production
HQ: Xto Energy Inc.
22777 Sprngwoods Vlg Pkwy
Spring TX 77389

(G-5207)
YES LIGHTING LLC
11220 Grader St Ste 500 (75238-2458)
PHONE.................972 807-9197
Jody Cloud, *Principal*
Gregory L Sweeney, *Manager*
Stephen Arnold, *Manager*
EMP: 9
SALES (est): 250.5K **Privately Held**
SIC: 3648 Lighting equipment

(G-5208)
YOOLOTTO LLC
13760 Noel Rd Ste 855 (75240-1390)
PHONE.................469 383-6488
Eric Yoo, *CEO*
Paul Panza, *Shareholder*
EMP: 29
SQ FT: 2,000
SALES: 5.1MM **Privately Held**
WEB: www.yoolotto.com
SIC: 7372 8742 Application computer software; marketing consulting services

(G-5209)
ZION OIL & GAS INC (PA)
12655 N Cntl Expy Ste 100 (75243)
PHONE.................214 221-4610
John M Brown, *Ch of Bd*
William H Avery, *President*
Robert W A Dunn, *COO*
Michael B Croswell Jr, *CFO*
Martin M Van Brauman, *Treasurer*
EMP: 11

SQ FT: 10,000
SALES (est): 3.9MM **Publicly Held**
WEB: www.zionoil.com
SIC: 1382 1311 Oil & gas exploration services; crude petroleum & natural gas

(G-5210)
ZIX CORPORATION (PA)
2711 N Haskell Ave # 2300 (75204-2960)
PHONE.................214 370-2000
Robert C Hausmann, *Ch of Bd*
David J Wagner, *President*
Justin K Ferguson, *Vice Pres*
Steve Irons, *Vice Pres*
Russell J Morgan, *Vice Pres*
EMP: 85
SALES: 173.4MM **Publicly Held**
WEB: www.zix.com
SIC: 7372 7374 7382 Prepackaged software; data processing & preparation; security systems services

(G-5211)
ZIXCORP SYSTEMS INC (HQ)
2711 N Haskell Ave (75204-2911)
PHONE.................214 370-2000
Richard D Spurr, *CEO*
Ronald A Woessner, *Vice Pres*
Barry W Wilson, *Treasurer*
Darleen Harris, *Asst Sec*
Janice E Rodriguez, *Asst Sec*
EMP: 49
SALES (est): 7.5MM
SALES (corp-wide): 173.4MM **Publicly Held**
WEB: www.zix.com
SIC: 7382 7372 Security systems services; prepackaged software
PA: Zix Corporation
2711 N Haskell Ave # 2300
Dallas TX 75204
214 370-2000

(G-5212)
ZODIAC STONE LLC
11125 Zodiac Ln (75229-4720)
P.O. Box 6050, Monroe LA (71211-6050)
PHONE.................972 243-2112
John Mitchel, *Mng Member*
Joseph H Hakim,
Nouri E Hakim,
Jeff Henner,
EMP: 12
SQ FT: 34,000
SALES (est): 866.2K **Privately Held**
WEB: www.zodiacstonecompany.com
SIC: 3281 Furniture, cut stone

Damon
Brazoria County

(G-5213)
MICHEAL J ARNOLD & CO
3533 County Road 4 (77430-8555)
PHONE.................979 742-3030
Mike Arnold, *CEO*
EMP: 10
SALES (est): 1.1MM **Privately Held**
WEB: www.mjacompany.com
SIC: 3661 5065 Telephones & telephone apparatus; telephone & telegraphic equipment

Darrouzett
Lipscomb County

(G-5214)
O & B TANK CO INC (PA)
511 W Hwy 15 (79024)
P.O. Box 68 (79024-0068)
PHONE.................806 624-3431
Duwane Skipper, *President*
EMP: 91 EST: 1965
SQ FT: 2,500
SALES (est): 7.7MM **Privately Held**
WEB: www.obtank.com
SIC: 1389 Oil field services

(G-5215)
O & B TANK CO INC
Hwy 15 W (79024)
P.O. Box 68 (79024-0068)
PHONE.................806 624-4781

Brent Farney, *Manager*
EMP: 15
SALES (corp-wide): 7.7MM **Privately Held**
WEB: www.obtank.com
SIC: 1389 Haulage, oil field
PA: O & B Tank Co Inc
5511 W Hwy 15
Darrouzett TX 79024
806 624-3431

Dawn
Deaf Smith County

(G-5216)
AZTECA MILLING LP
4819 Fm 809 (79025)
P.O. Box 56 (79025-0056)
PHONE...............................806 258-7704
Oscar Cortazar, *Branch Mgr*
EMP: 111 **Privately Held**
WEB: www.aztecamilling.com
SIC: 2041 Flour & other grain mill products
HQ: Azteca Milling, L.P.
5601 Executive Dr Ste 650
Irving TX 75038
956 383-4911

(G-5217)
PANHANDLE MILLING LLC (PA)
Also Called: Panhandle Milling Co
4805 Fm 809 (79025)
PHONE...............................806 243-4211
Tim Devey, *Marketing Staff*
John Mason, *Mng Member*
Morgan Kesner, *Manager*
EMP: 32 **EST:** 2015
SALES (est): 8MM **Privately Held**
WEB: www.panhandlemilling.com
SIC: 2041 Flour & other grain mill products

(G-5218)
PANHANDLE MILLING LLC
4805 Fm 809 (79025)
PHONE...............................806 258-7253
EMP: 10
SALES (corp-wide): 8MM **Privately Held**
WEB: www.panhandlemilling.com
SIC: 2041 Flour & other grain mill products
PA: Panhandle Milling, Llc
4805 Fm 809
Dawn TX 79025
806 243-4211

(G-5219)
RICHARDSON MILLING INC
Fm 809 At Fm 1062 (79025)
P.O. Box 10 (79025-0010)
PHONE...............................806 258-7227
Lynn Rundle, *Branch Mgr*
EMP: 13
SALES (corp-wide): 2.7B **Privately Held**
WEB: www.richardson.ca
SIC: 2041 Wheat flour
HQ: Richardson Milling, Inc.
1201 Nw Briarcliff Pkwy # 200
Kansas City MO 64116
816 994-7615

Dayton
Liberty County

(G-5220)
AGRIBIOFUELS LLC
138 Seaberg Industrial Rd (77535-6566)
P.O. Box 2612 (77535-0044)
PHONE...............................936 257-0826
Ed Gaiennie, *Mng Member*
EMP: 12
SQ FT: 15,260
SALES (est): 3.2MM **Privately Held**
WEB: www.agribiofuels.com
SIC: 2899 Chemical preparations

(G-5221)
BASIC ENERGY SERVICES LP
1705 Highway 146 (77535-2566)
PHONE...............................409 842-6262
Fax: 409 840-9287
EMP: 45
SALES (est): 3.2MM **Privately Held**
SIC: 1389 Oil/Gas Field Services

(G-5222)
BUDDYS GRASS FARM INC
11574 Fm 686 (77535-4317)
PHONE...............................936 258-7954
Leroy M Janacek Jr, *President*
Barbara Janacek, *Vice Pres*
Brianne Janacek, *Vice Pres*
Emily Janacek, *Vice Pres*
EMP: 10 **Privately Held**
SIC: 3999 Grasses, artificial & preserved

(G-5223)
CLEAN COMBUSTION INC
14210 Highway 146 (77535-1888)
P.O. Box 890, Mont Belvieu (77580-0890)
PHONE...............................832 333-7800
Brian Harless, *Branch Mgr*
EMP: 11
SQ FT: 2,500
SALES (corp-wide): 145.7K **Privately Held**
WEB: www.cleancombustioninc.com
SIC: 1389 Gas field services
PA: Clean Combustion, Inc.
12522 Bunker Cove Dr
Cypress TX 77433
281 746-7558

(G-5224)
COUNTY BARN PRECINCT 4
Also Called: Liberty County Precinct 4
1034 County Road 605 (77535-5014)
P.O. Box 88 (77535-0002)
PHONE...............................936 258-5202
Norman Brown, *Commissioner*
EMP: 19
SALES (est): 3.3MM **Privately Held**
SIC: 3523 Barn cleaners

(G-5225)
CROFT CONSTRUCTION CO INC
4866 Fm 1008 (77535-2789)
P.O. Box 188 (77535-0004)
PHONE...............................936 258-7902
Jane Croft, *President*
Larry Fontenot, *General Mgr*
Sean Leger, *Vice Pres*
Gordan Smith, *Vice Pres*
EMP: 16
SQ FT: 9,339
SALES (est): 3.7MM **Privately Held**
WEB: www.croftconstruction.com
SIC: 3443 3441 Fabricated plate work (boiler shop); fabricated structural metal

(G-5226)
FABRICATION & CNSTR SVCS LP
4665 Fm 1960 (77535-5887)
P.O. Box 788 (77535-0014)
PHONE...............................936 257-0466
Daniel Walsh, *Partner*
Wayne Wood, *Partner*
EMP: 30
SQ FT: 12,500
SALES (est): 7.9MM **Privately Held**
WEB: www.fandcservices.com
SIC: 2911 1799 Petroleum refining; petroleum storage tank installation, underground

(G-5227)
GLOBAL TUBING LLC (HQ)
501 County Road 493 (77535-8149)
P.O. Box 2139 (77535-0036)
PHONE...............................713 265-5000
Ivo Bozukov, *Business Mgr*
Garry McClelland, *Vice Pres*
Ray Rowland, *VP Opers*
Daniel Novak, *Opers Mgr*
Jessica Perez, *Engineer*
◆ **EMP:** 113
SALES (est): 29.6MM **Publicly Held**
WEB: www.global-tubing.com
SIC: 3317 Steel pipe & tubes

(G-5228)
HARRIS REBAR (HQ)
9500 Hwy 90 W At Frost Rd (77535)
P.O. Box 279 (77535-0005)
PHONE...............................936 258-8221
Karl Stumm, *Ch of Bd*
Woflgang Stumm, *President*
Brian Luippold, *Division Mgr*
Lyall Hadden, *General Mgr*
Doug Ewart, *Area Mgr*

◆ **EMP:** 45
SQ FT: 50,000
SALES (est): 9.5MM
SALES (corp-wide): 22.5B **Publicly Held**
WEB: www.harrisrebar.com
SIC: 3312 5051 Bars & bar shapes, steel, cold-finished: own hot-rolled; rods, iron & steel: made in steel mills; steel; bars, metal; rods, wire (not insulated)
PA: Nucor Corporation
1915 Rexford Rd Ste 400
Charlotte NC 28211
704 366-7000

(G-5229)
HOWARD CROFT
201 County Road 2318 (77535-3976)
PHONE...............................936 258-3321
Howard Croft, *Owner*
EMP: 12
SALES (est): 833.5K **Privately Held**
SIC: 2411 Logging camps & contractors

(G-5230)
INSTEEL WIRE PRODUCTS COMPANY
500 Klemp Rd (77535-7288)
P.O. Box 1620 (77535-0027)
PHONE...............................936 258-7625
Rafles Cisneros, *Production*
Bill Davis, *Manager*
Lissa Alexander, *Manager*
EMP: 100
SALES (corp-wide): 472.6MM **Publicly Held**
WEB: www.insteel.com
SIC: 3496 Miscellaneous fabricated wire products
HQ: Insteel Wire Products Company
1373 Boggs Dr
Mount Airy NC 27030
336 719-9000

(G-5231)
J ROLLINS CONSTRUCTION INC
405 W Clayton St (77535-2405)
P.O. Box 2 (77535-0001)
PHONE...............................936 258-3485
Sam Skipper, *CEO*
Loretta Higgins, *CFO*
David Mak, *CFO*
EMP: 78
SALES: 6.4MM **Privately Held**
WEB: www.jrollinsinc.com
SIC: 1623 1389 Oil & gas pipeline construction; pipe testing, oil field service

(G-5232)
JAY MANAGEMENT COMPANY LLC
1252 Fm 1413 (77535-8482)
PHONE...............................936 258-2646
Randy Kalimitchek, *Branch Mgr*
EMP: 9 **Privately Held**
WEB: www.isramcousa.com
SIC: 1382 Aerial geophysical exploration oil & gas
HQ: Jay Management Company, Llc
1001 West Loop S Ste 750
Houston TX 77027
713 621-6785

(G-5233)
LOPEZ TANK LINING LLC
1199 County Road 615 (77535-6537)
P.O. Box 726 (77535-0013)
PHONE...............................936 257-9779
Eleuterio Lopez, *Mng Member*
Francisco Lopez,
EMP: 15
SALES (est): 1.2MM **Privately Held**
WEB: www.lopeztankliningllc.com
SIC: 3443 Tanks, lined: metal plate

(G-5234)
PHOENIX HYDROCARBONS OPERATING
1252 Fm 1413 (77535-8482)
PHONE...............................936 258-2646
Randal Klimitchek, *Manager*
EMP: 12 **Privately Held**
SIC: 1311 Crude petroleum production
PA: Phoenix Hydrocarbons Operating Corp
808 W Wall St
Midland TX 79701

De Berry
Panola County

(G-5235)
SELECT ENERGY SERVICES LLC
Also Called: Impact Energy Services
175 Private Road 7336 (75639-2461)
PHONE...............................318 949-5080
EMP: 59
SALES (corp-wide): 843.8MM **Privately Held**
SIC: 1389 Oil And Gas Field Services
HQ: Select Energy Services, Llc
1820 N Interstate 35
Gainesville TX 76240
940 668-1818

De Kalb
Bowie County

(G-5236)
CECIL PHILLIPS LUMBER MILL
Fm Rd 1326 (75559)
P.O. Box 500 (75559-0500)
PHONE...............................903 684-3516
Chuck Lee Phillips, *President*
EMP: 15
SALES (est): 1.9MM **Privately Held**
WEB: www.phillipsforestproducts.com
SIC: 2421 2426 2411 Lumber: rough, sawed or planed; hardwood dimension & flooring mills; logging

(G-5237)
WCCOG CORP
75 County Road 3303 (75559-4157)
P.O. Box 310 (75559-0310)
PHONE...............................903 667-0264
Tim Blevins, *President*
EMP: 12
SALES (est): 2.5MM **Privately Held**
WEB: www.contractorsoutletgroup.com
SIC: 3792 1542 Trailer coaches, automobile; commercial & office building contractors

De Leon
Comanche County

(G-5238)
GOLDEN PEANUT COMPANY LLC
1401 Highway 1496 (76444-6813)
P.O. Box 226 (76444-0226)
PHONE...............................254 893-2034
Craig Smith, *Manager*
EMP: 60
SALES (corp-wide): 64.6B **Publicly Held**
WEB: www.goldenpeanut.com
SIC: 0723 5159 2068 Peanut shelling; nuts & nut by-products; salted & roasted nuts & seeds
HQ: Golden Peanut Company, Llc
100 N Point Ctr E Ste 400
Alpharetta GA 30022
770 752-8160

De Soto
Dallas County

(G-5239)
JAY H FIXTURES INC
305 N Beckley Rd (75115)
PHONE...............................972 223-2245
EMP: 42 **EST:** 1974
SQ FT: 15,000
SALES (est): 7.2MM **Privately Held**
WEB: www.jayhfixtures.com
SIC: 2541 1751 Store fixtures, wood; store fixture installation

Decatur
Wise County

(G-5240)
AERO BRIGHAM LLC
351 Airport Rd Bldg 500 (76234-3070)
PHONE................................940 626-4849
EMP: 14 EST: 2014
SQ FT: 15,000
SALES: 5.1MM **Privately Held**
WEB: www.aerobrigham.com
SIC: 3721 Aircraft

(G-5241)
ARUBA PETROLEUM INC
15076 Fm 455 (76234-7449)
PHONE................................940 466-9438
John Goforth, *Branch Mgr*
EMP: 16 **Privately Held**
WEB: www.arubapetroleum.com
SIC: 1311 Crude petroleum production
PA: Aruba Petroleum, Inc.
555 Republic Dr Ste 505
Plano TX 75074

(G-5242)
ASSET GUARD PRODUCTS INC
Also Called: Falcon Technologies
2242 E Highway 380 (76234-5538)
P.O. Box 1329 (76234-6144)
PHONE................................940 627-1400
R Ghurston, *General Mgr*
Bishop Bron, *General Mgr*
EMP: 20
SALES (est): 457.1K
SALES (corp-wide): 161.7MM **Privately Held**
SIC: 3291 Abrasive products
PA: Carbo Ceramics Inc.
575 N Dairy Ashford Rd # 300
Houston TX 77079
281 921-6400

(G-5243)
BAKER PETROLITE LLC
Also Called: Baker Hughes
1404 S Fm 51 (76234-2416)
PHONE................................940 626-4436
Carl Walin, *Manager*
EMP: 87 **Privately Held**
WEB:
www.bakerhughesdirect.lookchem.com
SIC: 1389 Oil field services
HQ: Baker Petrolite Llc
12645 W Airport Blvd
Sugar Land TX 77478
281 276-5400

(G-5244)
DECATUR MACHINE SERVICES INC
3720 Us Highway 380 (76234-4701)
PHONE................................940 627-1062
Lisa Bivens, *President*
Miles Bivens, *Vice Pres*
Megan Brawley, *Purchasing*
EMP: 23
SQ FT: 45,000
SALES: 3.5MM **Privately Held**
WEB: www.decaturms.com
SIC: 3544 3728 3599 Jigs & fixtures; aircraft parts & equipment; machine & other job shop work

(G-5245)
E3RIVERS LLC
4163 S Fm 730 (76234-4956)
P.O. Box 1038, Rhome (76078-1038)
PHONE................................817 247-5828
Anthony Woods, *President*
EMP: 35
SALES (est): 8.8MM **Privately Held**
SIC: 3585 5075 Air conditioning, motor vehicle; automotive air conditioners

(G-5246)
ENTEGRIS INC
Also Called: Poco Grathite
300 Old Greenwood Rd (76234-3068)
PHONE................................940 393-4232
Lance Sears, *Buyer*
Linda Rios, *Finance*
EMP: 424

SALES (corp-wide): 1.8B **Publicly Held**
WEB: www.entegris.com
SIC: 3089 Plastic processing
PA: Entegris, Inc.
129 Concord Rd
Billerica MA 01821
978 436-6500

(G-5247)
IMPERIAL GROUP MFG INC
Also Called: Imperial Fabricating Company
2188 E Highway 380 (76234-5541)
P.O. Box 616 (76234-0616)
PHONE................................940 627-1700
Bob Christy, *Manager*
EMP: 230
SALES (corp-wide): 529.1MM **Privately Held**
WEB: www.ironform.com
SIC: 3443 3715 3714 3713 Fabricated plate work (boiler shop); truck trailers; motor vehicle parts & accessories; truck & bus bodies; fabricated structural metal; blast furnaces & steel mills
PA: Imperial Group Manufacturing, Inc.
4545 Airport Rd
Denton TX 76207
940 565-8505

(G-5248)
LANDMARK FABRICATION LP
3496 Gateway Dr (76234-1171)
PHONE................................817 230-8857
Chris Lamon, *Principal*
EMP: 34
SALES (est): 8.8MM **Privately Held**
WEB: www.landmarksteelfabrication.com
SIC: 3441 Fabricated structural metal

(G-5249)
NABORS WELL SERVICES CO
2273 N Highway 287 (76234-6208)
PHONE................................940 626-3735
Nick Petrinio, *President*
EMP: 76 **Privately Held**
WEB: www.nabors.com
SIC: 1389 Haulage, oil field; oil field services
HQ: Nabors Well Services Co.
515 W Greens Rd Ste 1000
Houston TX 77067
281 874-0035

(G-5250)
PLATINUM PRESSURE SERVICES INC (HQ)
2618 S Highway 287 (76234-4301)
P.O. Box 1852 (76234-6152)
PHONE................................866 943-2204
EMP: 50
SALES (est): 15.4MM
SALES (corp-wide): 805.6MM **Publicly Held**
SIC: 1389 Oil/Gas Field Services
PA: Basic Energy Services, Inc.
801 Cherry St Unit 2
Fort Worth TX 76102
817 334-4100

(G-5251)
POCO GRAPHITE HOLDINGS LLC
300 Old Greenwood Rd (76234-3068)
PHONE................................940 627-2121
Corey Rucci,
EMP: 271
SALES (est): 14.8MM
SALES (corp-wide): 1.8B **Publicly Held**
WEB: www.poco.entegris.com
SIC: 3624 Carbon & graphite products
PA: Entegris, Inc.
129 Concord Rd
Billerica MA 01821
978 436-6500

(G-5252)
RENEGADE WELL SERVICES LLC
4348 Us Highway 380 (76234-4705)
P.O. Box 2011 (76234-6155)
PHONE................................940 626-4498
EMP: 27
SALES (corp-wide): 417.2MM **Privately Held**
SIC: 1389 Oil/Gas Field Services

HQ: Renegade Well Services, Llc
3301 E Us Highway 377 # 202
Granbury TX 76049
682 936-4466

(G-5253)
SANDY HILL REDI-MIX CON CO (PA)
3812 S Highway 287 (76234-5003)
PHONE................................940 627-8769
Troy Lutenbaker, *President*
Reba Lutenbaker, *Vice Pres*
EMP: 24
SQ FT: 2,000
SALES (est): 4MM **Privately Held**
SIC: 3273 Ready-mixed concrete

(G-5254)
SELECT ENERGY SERVICES LLC
Also Called: Sweeth2o - Office
1826 E Highway 380 (76234)
PHONE................................940 627-2066
EMP: 59
SALES (corp-wide): 945.3MM **Privately Held**
SIC: 1389 Oil/Gas Field Services
HQ: Select Energy Services, Llc
1820 N Interstate 35
Gainesville TX 76240
940 668-1818

(G-5255)
U S WEATHERFORD L P
Weatherford Fishing Rentl Tls
2045 E Highway 380 # 300 (76234-5558)
PHONE................................940 626-4698
Terry Willis, *Manager*
EMP: 35 **Privately Held**
WEB: www.weatherford.com
SIC: 1389 Oil field services
HQ: U S Weatherford L P
179 Weatherford Dr
Schriever LA 70395
985 493-6100

(G-5256)
UNITED RTORCRAFT SOLUTIONS LLC
1942 N Trinity St (76234-1093)
PHONE................................940 627-0626
David S Brigham, *President*
Beth McCurdy, *Finance Mgr*
Greg Williams, *Manager*
Traci Brigham,
▼ **EMP:** 43
SQ FT: 15,000
SALES (est): 2.3MM
SALES (corp-wide): 1.6B **Privately Held**
WEB: www.unitedrotorcraft.com
SIC: 1799 1721 2273 2531 Renovation of aircraft interiors; aircraft painting; aircraft & automobile floor coverings; seats, aircraft
HQ: Air Methods Corporation
5500 S Quebec St Ste 300
Greenwood Village CO 80111
303 792-7400

(G-5257)
WISE COUNTY MESSENGER INC
Also Called: Messenger Office Supply
115 S Trinity St (76234-1819)
P.O. Box 149 (76234-0149)
PHONE................................940 627-5987
Roy J Eaton, *President*
Jeannine Eaton, *Corp Secy*
Kenneth E Roselle, *Vice Pres*
EMP: 34
SQ FT: 6,000
SALES (est): 2.2MM **Privately Held**
WEB: www.wcmessenger.com
SIC: 2711 5943 5947 Commercial printing & newspaper publishing combined; office forms & supplies; gift, novelty & souvenir shop

Deer Park
Harris County

(G-5258)
A&K INDUSTRIAL REPAIR LLC
1250 Underwood Rd (77536)
PHONE................................281 470-8848
Craig Dodds,
EMP: 20
SALES (est): 3.5MM **Privately Held**
WEB: www.akindustrialrepairllc.com
SIC: 3569 7692 7699 Lubrication equipment, industrial; welding repair; industrial machinery & equipment repair

(G-5259)
ABB ENTERPRISE SOFTWARE INC
Also Called: ABB Turbocharger Co
1109 Howard Dr (77536-2638)
PHONE................................281 930-8383
Michael Kriner, *Manager*
EMP: 11
SALES (corp-wide): 27.9B **Privately Held**
WEB: www.new.abb.com
SIC: 3511 Turbines & turbine generator sets
HQ: Abb Inc.
305 Gregson Dr
Cary NC 27511

(G-5260)
ABLE INDUSTRIAL LLC
1250 Clay Ct Ste 200 (77536-1908)
PHONE................................281 946-2200
Cononver H Able III, *President*
Terence Day, *COO*
Alleman Laurie, *Vice Pres*
Rene Terral, *Vice Pres*
Chris Rairden, *Engrg Dir*
EMP: 85
SALES (est): 24MM **Privately Held**
WEB: www.able-industrial.com
SIC: 3441 Fabricated structural metal

(G-5261)
AQUA SOLUTIONS INC (PA)
6913 Highway 225 (77536-2414)
P.O. Box 70 (77536-0070)
PHONE................................800 256-2586
Thomas C Bedford, *President*
Ashley Billingsley, *Managing Dir*
Chris Bedford, *Vice Pres*
Morgan Lafferty, *Human Res Mgr*
Rick Komm, *Sales Staff*
EMP: 44
SQ FT: 36,500
SALES (est): 7.9MM **Privately Held**
WEB: www.aquasolutions.org
SIC: 2899 Chemical preparations

(G-5262)
ATLAS COPCO RENTAL LLC (DH)
2300 E 13th St (77536-1937)
PHONE................................800 736-8267
Scott Carnell, *President*
Bryan Becknel, *Vice Pres*
Blake Gearhart, *Vice Pres*
Frank McMahon, *Vice Pres*
Hiram Perez, *Vice Pres*
EMP: 31
SALES (est): 35.8MM
SALES (corp-wide): 10.7B **Privately Held**
WEB: www.atlascopcorental.com
SIC: 3563 Air & gas compressors

(G-5263)
CARBER HOLDINGS INC
Also Called: Car-Ber Testing Services
5110 Railroad St (77536-2409)
PHONE................................281 837-8003
Roy Harrold, *Manager*
EMP: 40 **Privately Held**
WEB: www.hydrochempsc.com
SIC: 1389 Testing, measuring, surveying & analysis services; pipe testing, oil field service; surveying wells
PA: Carber Holdings, Inc
12600 N Featherwood Dr # 450
Houston TX 77034

(G-5264)
CLEAN HRBORS EXPLRTION SVCS IN
802 Seaco Ct (77536-3176)
PHONE.................................281 478-2600
Robert Johnston, *President*
Gregory Malerbi, *Treasurer*
Peri Bryan, *Sales Staff*
Mike Terry, *Senior Mgr*
Michael Malm, *Admin Sec*
EMP: 16
SALES (est): 316.9K
SALES (corp-wide): 3.4B **Publicly Held**
WEB: www.cleanharbors.com
SIC: 1799 1389 Boring for building construction; oil field services
HQ: Versant Energy Services, Inc.
   42 Longwater Dr
   Norwell MA 02061
   781 792-5000

(G-5265)
CLIMAX PORTABLE MCH TLS INC
7003 Highway 225 Ste B (77536-2425)
PHONE.................................800 333-8311
Dave Baker, *Branch Mgr*
EMP: 15
SALES (corp-wide): 81.2MM **Privately Held**
WEB: www.climaxportable.com
SIC: 3829 Testing equipment: abrasion, shearing strength, etc.
PA: Climax Portable Machine Tools, Inc.
   2712 E 2nd St
   Newberg OR 97132
   503 538-2185

(G-5266)
CURFLO INC
1113 Howard Dr (77536-2638)
PHONE.................................281 479-5000
Mike Ritchey, *President*
Brad Ritchey, *Vice Pres*
▲ EMP: 10
SALES (est): 1MM **Privately Held**
WEB: www.curflo.com
SIC: 3561 Industrial pumps & parts

(G-5267)
DELTA COMPANIES GROUP
Also Called: Delta Deluxe, L.L.C.
334 Tidal Rd (77536-2405)
PHONE.................................281 479-7288
Kevin Washburn, *Plant Supt*
Andreas Schulz, *Engineer*
Paul B Maxwell, *Mng Member*
William Cope, *Manager*
Kevin Shburn, *Manager*
◆ EMP: 42
SQ FT: 120,000
SALES (est): 12MM
SALES (corp-wide): 4.5B **Publicly Held**
WEB: www.deltacogroup.com
SIC: 2992 Oils & greases, blending & compounding
HQ: Delta Petroleum Company, Inc.
   10352 River Rd
   Saint Rose LA 70087
   740 657-6600

(G-5268)
DOW CHEMICAL COMPANY
4460 Highway 225 (77536-2442)
PHONE.................................281 228-2800
Susan Lee, *Branch Mgr*
EMP: 300
SALES (corp-wide): 38.5B **Publicly Held**
WEB: www.dow.com
SIC: 2819 2821 Industrial inorganic chemicals; plastics materials & resins
HQ: The Dow Chemical Company
   2211 H H Dow Way
   Midland MI 48642
   989 636-1000

(G-5269)
DOW CHEMICAL COMPANY
1800 Tidal Rd (77536-2426)
PHONE.................................713 767-1615
Dean Powers, *Branch Mgr*
EMP: 55

SALES (corp-wide): 38.5B **Publicly Held**
WEB: www.dow.com
SIC: 2819 2821 Industrial inorganic chemicals; plastics materials & resins
HQ: The Dow Chemical Company
   2211 H H Dow Way
   Midland MI 48642
   989 636-1000

(G-5270)
DOW CHEMICAL COMPANY
1900 Tidal Rd (77536-2416)
PHONE.................................281 228-3060
Jeanne Williams, *Accountant*
EMP: 30
SALES (corp-wide): 38.5B **Publicly Held**
WEB: www.dow.com
SIC: 2819 Industrial inorganic chemicals
HQ: The Dow Chemical Company
   2211 H H Dow Way
   Midland MI 48642
   989 636-1000

(G-5271)
DRESSER LLC
Also Called: Dresser-Masoneilan Ctrl Valves
1250 Hall Ct (77536-6557)
PHONE.................................281 884-1000
Jerry Icenhower, *Branch Mgr*
EMP: 80
SALES (corp-wide): 95.2B **Publicly Held**
WEB: www.dressergs.com
SIC: 3491 5085 Industrial valves; valves & fittings
HQ: Dresser, Llc
   4425 Westway Park Blvd
   Houston TX 77041
   262 549-2626

(G-5272)
ENVIROTECH PUMPSYSTEMS INC
920 Seaco Ave (77536-3170)
PHONE.................................832 200-6220
Alex Machenkov, *Manager*
EMP: 9
SALES (corp-wide): 3.4B **Privately Held**
WEB: www.global.weir
SIC: 3541 Machine tool replacement & repair parts, metal cutting types
HQ: Envirotech Pumpsystems, Inc.
   440 W 800 S
   Salt Lake City UT 84101

(G-5273)
FD-THRU POWER SYSTEMS CNNCTORS
Also Called: Pft Systems
212 Deerwood Glen Dr (77536-3269)
PHONE.................................281 476-9100
P Ram Tukkaram, *CEO*
Michael Colescott, *President*
Gene Barnett, *Vice Pres*
Mondher Yassine, *Vice Pres*
Brad Yingst, *Vice Pres*
▼ EMP: 20
SQ FT: 8,200
SALES (est): 4.4MM **Privately Held**
WEB: www.pftsys.com
SIC: 3678 3533 Electronic connectors; oil field machinery & equipment

(G-5274)
FLEXITALLIC GROUP INC
6915 Highway 225 (77536-2414)
PHONE.................................281 604-2400
Gregory English, *Administration*
EMP: 11
SALES (corp-wide): 5.2MM **Privately Held**
WEB: www.flexitallic.com
SIC: 3053 Gasket materials
HQ: The Flexitallic Group Inc
   201 Kngwood Med Dr Ste B2
   Houston TX 77067

(G-5275)
FQE CHEMICALS INC
4820 Railroad St (77536-2412)
PHONE.................................281 476-9249
Karl Gannon, *President*
Jody Black, *General Mgr*
Lisa Choy, *Controller*
EMP: 15

SALES (est): 5MM **Privately Held**
WEB: www.fqechemicals.com
SIC: 2899 Chemical supplies for foundries

(G-5276)
GK TECHSTAR LLC (PA)
802 W 13th St (77536-3166)
PHONE.................................281 884-8257
Kyle Kuhlow, *President*
Dave Bigalke, *Vice Pres*
David Bigalke, *Vice Pres*
Adam Ohayon, *Opers-Prdtn-Mfg*
Jennifer McGinnis, *Accounts Mgr*
EMP: 70
SQ FT: 8,128
SALES (est): 29.8MM **Privately Held**
WEB: www.techstar.com
SIC: 3823 Pressure gauges, dial & digital; industrial flow & liquid measuring instruments; industrial process measurement equipment

(G-5277)
GUARDIAN COMPLIANCE
5110 Railroad St (77536-2409)
PHONE.................................713 641-2020
Steve Saboe, *President*
EMP: 800 EST: 2011
SALES (est): 275K **Privately Held**
WEB: www.hydrochempsc.com
SIC: 3429 5045 Manufactured hardware (general); computer software

(G-5278)
HAMPSHIRE CHEMICAL CORP
739 Battleground Rd (77536)
PHONE.................................281 479-9525
Edward Najjar, *Branch Mgr*
Tina Van Dam, *Admin Sec*
EMP: 100
SALES (corp-wide): 38.5B **Publicly Held**
SIC: 2899 2869 Chemical preparations; industrial organic chemicals
HQ: Hampshire Chemical Corp
   2 E Spit Brook Rd
   Nashua NH 03060

(G-5279)
HEXION INC
5900 Highway 225 (77536-2434)
PHONE.................................281 727-3163
EMP: 52
SALES (corp-wide): 1.5B **Privately Held**
WEB: www.hexion.com
SIC: 2821 Plastics materials & resins
HQ: Hexion Inc.
   180 E Broad St Fl 26
   Columbus OH 43215
   614 225-4000

(G-5280)
INDUSTRIAL SPCLTY SVCS USA LLC
4900 Railroad St (77536-2411)
PHONE.................................713 987-9117
James Craig, *CEO*
Russell Naisbitt, *CFO*
EMP: 13
SALES (est): 1.9MM **Privately Held**
WEB: www.industrialspecialtyservices.com
SIC: 8711 7692 7694 7699 Construction & civil engineering; welding repair; armature rewinding shops; industrial equipment cleaning

(G-5281)
KEITH DARWIN RAINES (PA)
Also Called: Corrosion Products Services
3309 Park Meadows Ave (77536-5239)
PHONE.................................713 477-8534
Darwin Raines, *Owner*
EMP: 16 EST: 2009
SALES (est): 3.2MM **Privately Held**
WEB: www.corrosionproductsservices.com
SIC: 3479 Aluminum coating of metal products

(G-5282)
LINDE INC
Also Called: Praxair
622 Tidal Rd (77536-2441)
P.O. Box 250 (77536-0250)
PHONE.................................281 478-1500
Dustin Davis, *General Mgr*
Pat Penbrook, *Manager*
Ernest Zavala, *Manager*

EMP: 20 **Privately Held**
WEB: www.praxair.com
SIC: 2813 Industrial gases
HQ: Linde Inc.
   10 Riverview Dr
   Danbury CT 06810
   203 837-2000

(G-5283)
MALONE INDUSTRIAL MACHINE LLC
2902 E Pasadena Blvd (77536-5642)
PHONE.................................713 477-7737
Terry Malone, *Mng Member*
Bobby Malone,
EMP: 23
SQ FT: 35,000
SALES (est): 4.2MM **Privately Held**
WEB: www.maloneindustrial.com
SIC: 3599 Machine shop, jobbing & repair

(G-5284)
MASS TRANSFER LIMITED (PA)
5026 Railroad St (77536-2410)
PHONE.................................281 991-8866
Aaron Lund, *President*
John Durham, *General Ptnr*
Sean Richardson, *Regional Mgr*
Mary Osburn, *Controller*
Vince Maniscalco, *Regl Sales Mgr*
▲ EMP: 18
SALES (est): 4.4MM **Privately Held**
WEB: www.mtl-us.com
SIC: 3914 Trays, stainless steel

(G-5285)
MAVIRO INC (DH)
Also Called: Rmis
1102 Howard Dr (77536-2639)
PHONE.................................713 485-5193
Kent Bartley, *President*
Chris Boase, *Senior VP*
Ryan Bogers, *Vice Pres*
Nick Sleming, *Vice Pres*
Michael Tringali, *CFO*
EMP: 80
SALES (est): 50MM
SALES (corp-wide): 651.4MM **Privately Held**
WEB: www.maviro.com
SIC: 3612 Transformers, except electric
HQ: Maviro Holdings Inc.
   350 73rd Ave Ne Ste 1
   Fridley MN 55432
   763 270-0490

(G-5286)
MICOR INC
Also Called: Zach's Spice Company
1001 Georgia Ave (77536-2519)
PHONE.................................281 476-0808
Rick Goolsby, *President*
Vickie Goolsby, *Human Resources*
Vicki Goolsby, *Admin Sec*
EMP: 20
SQ FT: 9,500
SALES (est): 3.3MM **Privately Held**
WEB: www.zachspice.com
SIC: 2099 Spices, including grinding

(G-5287)
NOVVI LLC
2525 Independence Pkwy (77536)
PHONE.................................281 488-0833
Jacob Wilburn, *Plant Mgr*
EMP: 19
SALES (corp-wide): 8.1MM **Privately Held**
WEB: www.novvi.com
SIC: 2911 Oils, lubricating
PA: Novvi Llc
   5885 Hollis St Ste 100
   Emeryville CA 94608
   281 488-0833

(G-5288)
OHMSTEDE LTD
801 Georgia Ave (77536-2515)
PHONE.................................281 867-3260
Mike Lantz, *Safety Mgr*
Norman Thornton, *Branch Mgr*
EMP: 10
SALES (corp-wide): 9.1B **Publicly Held**
WEB: www.ohmstede.com
SIC: 3443 Fabricated plate work (boiler shop)

HQ: Ohmstede Ltd.
895 N Main St
Beaumont TX 77701
409 833-6375

(G-5289)
OXY VINYLS LP
5900 Highway 225 G8a (77536-2434)
P.O. Box 500 (77536-5000)
PHONE......................................281 476-2640
Karenanne Stegmann, *Manager*
EMP: 54
SALES (corp-wide): 21.2B Publicly Held
WEB: www.oxy.com
SIC: 2821 Vinyl resins
HQ: Oxy Vinyls, Lp
14555 Dallas Pkwy Ste 400
Dallas TX 75254
877 699-8465

(G-5290)
RELIANCE INDUSTRIES LLC
Also Called: Reliance Fall Protection
2101 S Battle Ground Rd (77536)
P.O. Box 2046 (77536-2046)
PHONE......................................281 930-8000
Joe Shaw, *President*
Shweta Chaudhari, *Buyer*
Gary Choate, *Sales Executive*
▲ EMP: 45
SQ FT: 12,000
SALES (est): 5MM Privately Held
WEB: www.relsafe.com
SIC: 2399 Belting & belt products; belting,
fabric: made from purchased materials

(G-5291)
**ROHM AND HAAS TEXAS INC
(HQ)**
6600 La Porte Fwy (77536)
PHONE......................................281 476-8304
Rajiv L Gupta, *Ch of Bd*
Robert W Brinly, *President*
Pierre R Brondeau, *President*
Jacques M Croisetiere, *President*
John E Cubertson, *President*
◆ EMP: 115 EST: 1965
SQ FT: 40,000
SALES (est): 185.9MM
SALES (corp-wide): 38.5B Publicly Held
WEB: www.dow.com
SIC: 2869 2899 2819 Industrial organic
chemicals; chemical preparations; indus-
trial inorganic chemicals
PA: Dow Inc.
2211 H H Dow Way
Midland MI 48642
989 636-1000

(G-5292)
ROMCO MANUFACTURING INC
Also Called: Tru Turn
100 W 1st St (77536-2602)
PHONE......................................281 479-9600
EMP: 15 EST: 1975
SQ FT: 4,000
SALES (est): 1MM Privately Held
WEB: www.truturn.com
SIC: 3599 Machine shop, jobbing & repair

(G-5293)
ROMCO MANUFACTURING INC
100 W 1st St (77536-2602)
P.O. Box 1896 (77536-1896)
PHONE......................................281 479-9600
Robert Obenberger, *President*
Amanda H Wright,
EMP: 20
SALES (est): 4MM Privately Held
WEB: www.romco.net
SIC: 3599 Machine shop, jobbing & repair

(G-5294)
SAYBOLT LP
201 Deerwood Glen Dr (77536-3270)
PHONE......................................281 478-1300
Charles Kirkland, *Partner*
EMP: 60
SALES (corp-wide): 668.2MM Privately
Held
WEB: www.corelab.com
SIC: 1389 8734 8731 1382 Testing,
measuring, surveying & analysis services;
testing laboratories; commercial physical
research; oil & gas exploration services

HQ: Saybolt Lp
6316 Windfern Rd
Houston TX 77040
713 328-2673

(G-5295)
**SFC GLOBAL SUPPLY CHAIN
INC**
612 Georgia Ave (77536-2512)
PHONE......................................713 740-7536
EMP: 254 Privately Held
WEB: www.schwanscompany.com
SIC: 2038 Frozen specialties
HQ: Sfc Global Supply Chain, Inc.
115 W College Dr
Marshall MN 56258
507 532-3274

(G-5296)
SHELL OIL COMPANY
5900 Highway 225 (77536-2434)
PHONE......................................713 246-6462
EMP: 100
SALES (corp-wide): 344.8B Privately
Held
WEB: www.shell.com
SIC: 2911 Petroleum refining
HQ: Shell Oil Company
150 N Dairy Ashford Rd A
Houston TX 77079
713 241-6161

(G-5297)
SPM FLOW CONTROL INC
920 Seaco Ave (77536-3170)
PHONE......................................817 246-2461
EMP: 138
SALES (corp-wide): 3.4B Privately Held
WEB: www.global.weir
SIC: 3533 Oil & gas field machinery
HQ: S.P.M. Flow Control, Inc.
7601 Wyatt Dr
Fort Worth TX 76108
817 246-2461

(G-5298)
**SWABY MANUFACTURING
COMPANY**
921 Seaco Ct (77536-3187)
PHONE......................................281 479-7500
MO Khalil, *Branch Mgr*
EMP: 19
SALES (corp-wide): 4.2MM Privately
Held
WEB: www.swabypump.com
SIC: 3561 Pumps, domestic: water or
sump
PA: Swaby Manufacturing Company
5420 W Roosevelt Rd 300b
Chicago IL 60644
773 626-1400

(G-5299)
**TACKABERRY DOOLEY
SYSTEMS (HQ)**
1515 W 13th St (77536-2535)
PHONE......................................281 479-9700
Chris Dooley, *CEO*
Arthur R Dooley Jr, *Ch of Bd*
Glenn Tackaberry, *President*
Robert Reed Tackaberry, *President*
▼ EMP: 145
SQ FT: 13,500
SALES (est): 18.8MM Privately Held
WEB: www.dooleytackaberry.com
SIC: 1731 2899 Fire detection & burglar
alarm systems specialization; anti-glare
material

(G-5300)
**TM CHEMICALS LTD
PARTNERSHIP**
Also Called: Tm Deer Park Services
2525 Independence Pkwy S (77536)
P.O. Box 1914 (77536-1914)
PHONE......................................281 930-2525
Mark Lyons, *Partner*
Casey Borowski, *Partner*
BJ Jungman, *Partner*
Donna Ratliff, *Partner*
Frank Harris, *VP Opers*
▼ EMP: 103

SALES (est): 31.3MM Privately Held
WEB: www.texasmolecular.com
SIC: 4953 2899 Chemical detoxification;
chemical preparations

(G-5301)
**TOTAL PTRCHEMICALS REF
USA INC**
Polypropylene Plant
1818 Battleground Rd (77536)
P.O. Box 888 (77536-0888)
PHONE......................................281 476-3700
Alan Bassinger, *Engineer*
Darrell Bailey, *Branch Mgr*
EMP: 220
SALES (corp-wide): 7B Publicly Held
WEB: www.totalpetrochemicalsre-
finingusa.com
SIC: 2911 5169 Petroleum refining; indus-
trial chemicals
HQ: Total Petrochemicals & Refining Usa,
Inc.
1201 La St Ste 1800
Houston TX 77002
713 483-5000

(G-5302)
WIKA INSTRUMENT LP
Elelctrical Temperature Div
950 Hall Ct (77536-1879)
PHONE......................................713 475-0022
Brian McDowell, *Plant Mgr*
Jon Clifford, *Accounts Mgr*
EMP: 52
SALES (corp-wide): 545.6MM Privately
Held
WEB: www.wika.us
SIC: 3823 Temperature instruments: indus-
trial process type
HQ: Wika Instrument, Lp
1000 Wiegand Blvd
Lawrenceville GA 30043

(G-5303)
**WILLIAMS INDUS SVCS GROUP
INC**
130 W San Augustine St (77536-4024)
PHONE......................................281 884-8364
EMP: 188
SALES (corp-wide): 245.7MM Publicly
Held
WEB: www.globalpower.com
SIC: 3568 Power transmission equipment
PA: Williams Industrial Services Group Inc.
100 Crscent Ctr Pkwy Ste
Tucker GA 30084
770 879-4400

Del Rio
Val Verde County

(G-5304)
AB-TEX BEVERAGE LTD
131 Foster Dr (78840-2662)
PHONE......................................830 775-1543
Ed Sewell, *Branch Mgr*
EMP: 25
SALES (corp-wide): 67.1B Publicly Held
WEB: www.pepsico.com
SIC: 2086 Soft drinks: packaged in cans,
bottles, etc.; water, pasteurized: pack-
aged in cans, bottles, etc.
HQ: Ab-Tex Beverage, Ltd.
650 Colonial Dr
Abilene TX 79603
325 673-7171

(G-5305)
**ARC RITE WELDING &
FABRICATION**
Also Called: Arcrite Welding and Truck Acce
5555 W Us Highway 90 (78840-3377)
PHONE......................................830 774-6058
Clay Taylor, *Owner*
EMP: 16
SQ FT: 10,000
SALES (est): 1.6MM Privately Held
WEB: www.arcrite.com
SIC: 5531 7692 6794 Truck equipment &
parts; welding repair; franchises, selling
or licensing

(G-5306)
AZTEC FR APPAREL INC
2144 Cienegas Rd (78840-7765)
PHONE......................................830 422-1775
Mark Fogle, *CEO*
EMP: 308 EST: 2011
SALES (est): 13MM Privately Held
WEB: www.aztecfrapparel.com
SIC: 2326 Overalls & coveralls

(G-5307)
BACKER MARATHON INC
808 Hackberry Ln (78840-3394)
PHONE......................................830 775-1417
Divian Linares, *Principal*
Joe Gandara, *Safety Mgr*
Wendy Vargas, *Purch Agent*
Dave Finder, *Engineer*
Jose Ocada, *Design Engr*
▲ EMP: 9
SALES (est): 729.5K
SALES (corp-wide): 2.6B Privately Held
WEB: www.backermarathon.com
SIC: 3398 Metal heat treating
HQ: Nibe Ab
Hannabadsvagen 5
Markaryd 285 3
433 730-00

(G-5308)
**BORDER OPPRTNITY SVER
SYSTEMS**
Also Called: B O S S Medical
594 Industrial Blvd (78840-3592)
P.O. Box 1407 (78841-1407)
PHONE......................................830 775-1225
Don P Newton, *President*
Leo Martinez, *President*
Oralia Newton, *Vice Pres*
Bb Moya, *Analyst*
▲ EMP: 25
SQ FT: 40,000
SALES (est): 4.1MM Privately Held
WEB: www.borderopp.com
SIC: 3842 2389 Orthopedic appliances;
cotton, including cotton balls: sterile &
non-sterile; bandages & dressings; band-
ages: plastic, muslin, plaster of paris, etc.;
hospital gowns

(G-5309)
**BRIC MC MANN INDUSTRIES
INC**
505 E 8th St (78840-4019)
PHONE......................................830 775-9153
Eric Hofmann, *President*
Jaime Ramirez, *Vice Pres*
Elwyn C Hofmann, *Treasurer*
Susan Hoffmann, *Admin Sec*
▲ EMP: 10
SALES (est): 2MM Privately Held
WEB: www.bricmcmann.com
SIC: 2389 6531 5812 Uniforms & vest-
ments; real estate agent, commercial;
American restaurant

(G-5310)
**CACTUS WEAPONS SYSTEMS
INC**
109 Pierce St (78840-5503)
PHONE......................................210 858-6703
T Herbert Shriver, *President*
Clay Sinclair, *Vice Pres*
Daniel Chartlend, *Treasurer*
EMP: 10
SALES (est): 700K Privately Held
WEB: www.cactusweapons.com
SIC: 3484 Small arms

(G-5311)
**CATERPLLAR GLOBL MIN
MXICO LLC (DH)**
557 Finegan Rd 10 (78840-8508)
PHONE......................................224 551-4000
Christopher Carl Curfman, *President*
Reene Cvalvetti, *Controller*
Ronald M Defeo,
Eric I Cohen,
Richard Nichols,
▲ EMP: 19
SQ FT: 25,000
SALES (est): 25.6MM
SALES (corp-wide): 53.8B Publicly Held
SIC: 3531 Construction machinery; con-
struction machinery attachments

G
E
O
G
R
A
P
H
I
C

HQ: Caterpillar Global Mining Llc
1118 Rawson Ave
South Milwaukee WI 53172
414 768-4000

(G-5312)
CNI
865 Industrial Blvd (78840-8519)
PHONE..............................830 765-7484
Rosy Barksdale, *Principal*
▲ **EMP:** 14
SALES (est): 2.2MM **Privately Held**
SIC: 3089 Injection molding of plastics

(G-5313)
COCA-COLA BOTTLING CO
1310 E 1st St (78840-4812)
PHONE..............................830 775-8561
Alonzo Barrera, *Principal*
EMP: 9 **EST:** 2012
SALES (est): 1.2MM **Privately Held**
SIC: 2086 Bottled & canned soft drinks

(G-5314)
CONSTRUCTION SPECIALTIES INC
Also Called: Fabricas Elena
107 Industrial Blvd (78840-8502)
PHONE..............................830 774-0151
Nelson Trejo, *Buyer*
Tom Stanley, *Manager*
EMP: 10
SALES (corp-wide): 336.4MM **Privately Held**
WEB: www.c-sgroup.com
SIC: 3446 Architectural metalwork
PA: Construction Specialties Inc.
3 Werner Way Ste 100
Lebanon NJ 08833
908 236-0800

(G-5315)
GENTHERM (TEXAS) INC (HQ)
2121b Frontera Rd (78840-8905)
P.O. Box 1167 (78841-1167)
PHONE..............................830 774-3512
Klaus Wilhelm, *President*
Karla Renovato, *Project Mgr*
Carlos Marin, *Production*
Esmeralda Gaytan, *Purch Agent*
Jorge Pena, *Engineer*
◆ **EMP:** 60 **EST:** 1995
SALES (est): 442.6MM **Publicly Held**
WEB: www.gentherm.com
SIC: 3714 Motor vehicle parts & accessories

(G-5316)
HADLOCK & FOX MFG CO L L C
594 Industrial Blvd (78840-3592)
P.O. Box 1407 (78841-1407)
PHONE..............................830 778-6017
Leo Martinez, *Managing Prtnr*
Patricia Martinez, *Manager*
Patsy Martinez, *Manager*
Don Newton,
EMP: 35 **EST:** 1962
SQ FT: 16,000
SALES (est): 3.5MM **Privately Held**
WEB: www.hadlockfox.com
SIC: 3999 Barber & beauty shop equipment

(G-5317)
HOWMET GLOBL FASTENING SYSTEMS
2162 Cienegas Rd (78840-7765)
PHONE..............................830 774-7156
EMP: 139
SALES (corp-wide): 14.1B **Publicly Held**
WEB: www.arconic.com
SIC: 3353 Aluminum sheet & strip
HQ: Howmet Global Fastening Systems Inc.
3990a Heritage Oak Ct
Simi Valley CA 93063
805 426-2270

(G-5318)
JAROPAMEX
2 A Fawcett Dr (78842)
PHONE..............................830 774-5920
EMP: 15

SALES (est): 6.4MM
SALES (corp-wide): 1.5B **Privately Held**
WEB: www.irvinproducts.com
SIC: 2396 Automotive & apparel trimmings
HQ: Irvin Automotive Products Llc
2600 Centerpoint Pkwy
Pontiac MI 48341
248 451-4100

(G-5319)
JOYSON SAFETY SYSTEMS
Also Called: Jss Airbag
715 Frontera Rd (78840-7520)
P.O. Box 420459 (78842-0459)
PHONE..............................830 703-7191
Juan De Los Santos, *Branch Mgr*
Miguel Del Cascillo, *MIS Mgr*
EMP: 28
SALES (corp-wide): 2.2B **Privately Held**
WEB: www.joysonsafety.com
SIC: 2399 Seat belts, automobile & aircraft
PA: Joyson Safety Systems Acquisition Llc
2500 Innovation Dr
Auburn Hills MI 48326
248 373-8040

(G-5320)
MIDLAND STAMPING AND FABG CORP
S-I Midland Chutes 2150
2022 Cienegas Rd (78840-7862)
PHONE..............................830 422-2052
EMP: 19 **Privately Held**
WEB: www.midlandsf.com
SIC: 3469 Stamping metal for the trade
PA: Midland Stamping And Fabricating Corporation
9521 Ainslie St
Schiller Park IL 60176

(G-5321)
OHARA VALENTE
Also Called: Rivercity Donuts
500 Veterans Blvd (78840-4470)
PHONE..............................830 775-8769
Valente Ohara, *Owner*
Jesus Ohara, *Co-Owner*
EMP: 15
SALES (est): 1.3MM **Privately Held**
SIC: 2051 Doughnuts, except frozen

(G-5322)
REGAL BELOIT CORPORATION
532 Industrial Blvd (78840-8515)
P.O. Box 421087 (78842-1087)
PHONE..............................830 774-2677
Steve Clay, *Branch Mgr*
EMP: 223
SALES (corp-wide): 3.2B **Publicly Held**
WEB: www.regalbeloit.com
SIC: 3621 Motors & generators
PA: Regal Beloit Corporation
200 State St
Beloit WI 53511
608 364-8800

(G-5323)
SAN ANTONIO SHOE INC
Also Called: San Antonio Shoes 121
100 Johnson Blvd (78840)
PHONE..............................830 768-7200
Bill Hammock, *Manager*
EMP: 600
SALES (corp-wide): 272.2MM **Privately Held**
WEB: www.sasshoes.com
SIC: 5661 3144 3131 3172 Shoes, orthopedic; women's footwear, except athletic; footwear cut stock; personal leather goods; men's footwear, except athletic
PA: San Antonio Shoe, Inc.
1717 Sas Dr
San Antonio TX 78224
877 727-7463

(G-5324)
SIGMATRON INTERNATIONAL INC
Nsc Electronics Division
103 Avenue J (78840-4711)
PHONE..............................830 775-5524
Daniel Camp, *Vice Pres*
Dennis McNamara, *Engineer*
Anthony Antista, *Manager*
Sandy Duncan, *Director*
EMP: 11 **Publicly Held**

WEB: www.sigmatronintl.com
SIC: 3672 3663 3354 3577 Printed circuit boards; cable television equipment; coils, rod, extruded, aluminum; data conversion equipment, media-to-media: computer
PA: Sigmatron International, Inc.
2201 Landmeier Rd
Elk Grove Village IL 60007

(G-5325)
SUNBEAM PRODUCTS INC
1653 Frontera Rd Plant126 (78840-9054)
PHONE..............................830 774-4517
Fraz Schlottbohm, *Branch Mgr*
Antonio Rubio, *Manager*
EMP: 15
SALES (corp-wide): 9.7B **Publicly Held**
WEB: www.newellbrands.com
SIC: 3631 Barbecues, grills & braziers (outdoor cooking)
HQ: Sunbeam Products, Inc.
2381 Nw Executive Ctr Dr
Boca Raton FL 33431
561 912-4100

(G-5326)
TOTER LLC
1661 Frontera Rd (78840-9054)
PHONE..............................830 775-3411
Edward Joslyn, *Manager*
EMP: 10 **Privately Held**
WEB: www.toter.com
SIC: 3089 Garbage containers, plastic
HQ: Toter, Llc
841 Meacham Rd
Statesville NC 28677
800 424-0422

(G-5327)
UNION SLAUGHTER HOUSE INC
1000 Plaza Ave (78840-7036)
P.O. Box 1187 (78841-1187)
PHONE..............................830 774-0065
Daryl Hargrove, *President*
EMP: 40
SALES (est): 1.8MM
SALES (corp-wide): 3.2MM **Privately Held**
SIC: 2011 5421 Meat packing plants; meat & fish markets
PA: Southwest Livestock & Trucking Co Inc
1305 E Gibbs St
Del Rio TX 78840
830 775-2471

(G-5328)
VAL VERDE PUBLISHING LLC
Also Called: Del Rio Sun
2116 Veterans Blvd (78840-3178)
PHONE..............................830 774-2198
Robert Garza, *Principal*
EMP: 10
SALES (est): 400.8K **Privately Held**
SIC: 2711 Newspapers: publishing only, not printed on site

Del Valle
Travis County

(G-5329)
CEMEX CONSTRUCTION MTLS S LLC
Also Called: Norwood Quarry
3901 Norwood Ln (78617-3268)
PHONE..............................512 247-3400
Javier Villarreal, *Vice Pres*
James Murphy, *Manager*
EMP: 11 **Privately Held**
WEB: www.cemexusa.com
SIC: 3273 Ready-mixed concrete
HQ: Cemex Construction Materials South, Llc
2088 E 20th St
Yuma AZ 85365
928 343-4100

(G-5330)
DOVETAIL CUSTOM WOODWORKS INC
Also Called: Dovetail Custom Wood & Metal
5235 Hwy 71 E Bldg A (78617-3298)
PHONE..............................512 501-6717
Isaac Alexander, *President*

Jimmy James, *Superintendent*
Cory Choate, *Project Mgr*
Carlos Perez, *Project Mgr*
Marcus Pough, *Project Mgr*
EMP: 49
SQ FT: 25,000
SALES (est): 2.4MM **Privately Held**
WEB: www.dovetailmade.com
SIC: 2431 Millwork

(G-5331)
HOESMAN INDUSTRIES INC
Also Called: Texas Concrete Tank
5264 Highway 71 E (78617-3223)
PHONE..............................512 247-4173
Clark Hoesman, *President*
EMP: 22
SALES (est): 2.3MM **Privately Held**
WEB: www.capitalconcreteproducts.com
SIC: 3272 Septic tanks, concrete

(G-5332)
LIVE OAK BREWING COMPANY LLC
1615 Crozier Ln (78617-2129)
PHONE..............................512 385-2299
Courtland Privat, *Sales Staff*
Hoyt McElroy III, *Mng Member*
Hill Zach, *Manager*
Laura McElroy, *Admin Sec*
Elmer N Baldwin III,
▲ **EMP:** 40
SQ FT: 200
SALES (est): 1.4MM
SALES (corp-wide): 2.4MM **Privately Held**
WEB: www.liveoakbrewing.com
SIC: 5181 2082 5921 Beer & other fermented malt liquors; beer (alcoholic beverage); wine & beer
PA: Zymurgy Holding Company, Lc
1615 Crozier Ln
Del Valle TX 78617
918 251-0490

(G-5333)
TURBINE TOOL CORPORATION
157 Privada Dr (78617-5646)
PHONE..............................512 385-5311
Christian Szakacs, *President*
EMP: 9
SQ FT: 8,000
SALES (est): 1.5MM **Privately Held**
SIC: 3728 Aircraft assemblies, subassemblies & parts

Denison
Grayson County

(G-5334)
ACS MANUFACTURING INC
1601 Commerce Blvd (75020-1905)
PHONE..............................903 462-2001
Dan Knox, *President*
John Puentes, *Vice Pres*
Tony Knox, *Project Mgr*
Brian Munson, *Project Mgr*
Pat Murphree, *Project Mgr*
EMP: 30 **EST:** 1998
SALES (est): 19.2MM **Privately Held**
WEB: www.acsmanufacturing.com
SIC: 3444 3621 Sheet metalwork; motors & generators

(G-5335)
BC WETLANDS LTD
226 Highland Terrace Cir (75020-2678)
PHONE..............................903 718-1530
Kenneth Klug, *General Ptnr*
EMP: 9
SQ FT: 300
SALES: 28.9K **Privately Held**
SIC: 2015 Ducks, slaughtered & dressed

(G-5336)
CATERPILLAR GLOBAL MIN EQP LLC
3501 N Fm Highway 1417 (75020-8904)
PHONE..............................903 786-2981
Timothy Sullivan, *Branch Mgr*
Marty Clemons, *Manager*
EMP: 77

▲ = Import ▼=Export
◆ =Import/Export

SALES (corp-wide): 53.8B **Publicly Held**
WEB: www.caterpillar.com
SIC: 3532 3531 Mining machinery; construction machinery
HQ: Caterpillar Global Mining Equipment Llc
1100 Milwaukee Ave
South Milwaukee WI 53172

(G-5337)
CHAMPION COOLER CORPORATION
Also Called: Champion Steel Processing
2011 Macgregor Dr (75020-1050)
PHONE....................................903 465-3294
Crystal Kingston, *Purch Agent*
Lynn Johnson, *Branch Mgr*
EMP: 111 **Privately Held**
WEB: www.essickair.com
SIC: 3585 5075 Evaporative condensers; heat transfer equipment; air conditioning & ventilation equipment & supplies
HQ: Champion Cooler Corporation
5800 Murray St
Little Rock AR 72209
501 562-1094

(G-5338)
CHAMPION COOLER CORPORATION
3328 Interurban Rd (75021-7834)
PHONE....................................903 463-1408
Jerry Mattox, *Branch Mgr*
EMP: 61 **Privately Held**
WEB: www.essickair.com
SIC: 3585 Coolers, milk & water: electric
HQ: Champion Cooler Corporation
5800 Murray St
Little Rock AR 72209
501 562-1094

(G-5339)
CREATIVE CASTING INC
1827 S Armstrong Ave # 102 (75020-7066)
PHONE....................................903 463-6160
Larry M Mc Gaffey, *President*
Cynthia Mc Gaffer, *Vice Pres*
Mike Skelcher, *Engineer*
EMP: 10
SQ FT: 10,000
SALES (est): 1.2MM **Privately Held**
WEB: www.creativecastinginc.com
SIC: 3965 3446 3961 Buckles & buckle parts; architectural metalwork; rings, finger: gold plated wire

(G-5340)
DENISON INDUSTRIES INC
22 Fielder Dr (75020-8654)
P.O. Box 1459 (75021-1459)
PHONE....................................903 786-4444
Chris Norch, *President*
Thomas J Dagenback, *Vice Pres*
Anthony Ortega, *Opers Mgr*
Steve Ellis, *Facilities Mgr*
John Flood, *Purchasing*
◆ EMP: 170
SQ FT: 218,000
SALES (est): 50.7MM **Privately Held**
WEB: www.denisonindustries.com
SIC: 3365 Aluminum & aluminum-based alloy castings

(G-5341)
KNIVES OF ALASKA INC
3100 Airport Dr (75020-8623)
PHONE....................................903 786-7366
Charles Allen, *President*
Jody M Allen, *Treasurer*
Debbie Carpenter, *Executive*
EMP: 20
SALES (est): 3.1MM **Privately Held**
WEB: www.knivesofalaska.com
SIC: 3421 Knives: butchers', hunting, pocket, etc.

(G-5342)
MOFFITT WEST LLC (HQ)
3100 Juanita Dr (75020-1007)
PHONE....................................903 463-5700
Leanna Chaffin, *Manager*
Tyler Williams, *Manager*
John D Moffitt,
EMP: 12
SQ FT: 20,000

SALES (est): 2.9MM
SALES (corp-wide): 9.1MM **Privately Held**
SIC: 3444 Ventilators, sheet metal
PA: Moffitt Corporation, Inc.
1351 13th Ave S Ste 130
Jacksonville Beach FL 32250
904 241-9944

(G-5343)
NEON SIGNS AND DESIGNS INC
Also Called: Gus Specialty Advertising
103 E Crawford St (75021-4643)
PHONE....................................903 463-7446
Robert Petty, *President*
Jerry Bates, *Vice Pres*
Ricky Bates, *Admin Sec*
EMP: 14
SQ FT: 22,000
SALES (est): 1.6MM **Privately Held**
WEB: www.signmachine.us
SIC: 1799 3993 Sign installation & maintenance; electric signs

(G-5344)
PALLET & CRATING CO INC
Fm 1417 (75021)
P.O. Box 457, Pottsboro (75076-0457)
PHONE....................................903 463-5786
Karen Salyer, *President*
Rick Bechtel, *Manager*
EMP: 45
SALES (est): 4.4MM **Privately Held**
WEB: www.palletandcrating.com
SIC: 2448 2449 2441 Pallets, wood; wood containers; nailed wood boxes & shook

(G-5345)
PLATTS WELDING AND CNSTR LLC
431 E Parnell St (75021-2621)
PHONE....................................972 333-5830
Kimberly Platt, *Mng Member*
EMP: 11
SALES (est): 1.1MM **Privately Held**
WEB: www.plattsweldingandconstruction.com
SIC: 1541 1791 1799 7692 Prefabricated building erection, industrial; structural steel erection; iron work, structural; welding on site; welding repair

(G-5346)
SOUTHERN FOODSERVICE MGT INC
2600 N State Highway 91 (75020-9042)
PHONE....................................903 463-1313
Marty Doyle, *COO*
Paul Woodrick, *Engineer*
Jeff Pearson, *Info Tech Mgr*
Jim Skaggs, *Technical Staff*
EMP: 306
SQ FT: 2,114
SALES (corp-wide): 123.5MM **Privately Held**
WEB: www.southernfoodservice.com
SIC: 3429 Keys, locks & related hardware
PA: Southern Foodservice Management, Inc.
431 Office Park Dr Fl 1
Mountain Brk AL 35223
205 871-8000

(G-5347)
TEREX CORPORATION
Reedrill
3501 N Fm 1417 (75020-8904)
PHONE....................................903 786-2981
Carol Brownlee, *Director*
John Clark, *Director*
EMP: 78
SALES (corp-wide): 4.3B **Publicly Held**
WEB: www.terex.com
SIC: 3531 3532 Construction machinery; mining machinery; drills & drilling equipment, mining (except oil & gas)
PA: Terex Corporation
45 Glover Ave
Norwalk CT 06850
203 222-7170

(G-5348)
TGC INDUSTRIES
3375 Juanita Dr (75020-1009)
PHONE....................................903 464-9908

EMP: 35
SALES (est): 1.2MM **Privately Held**
SIC: 3999 Manufacturing industries

(G-5349)
TWIN DISTRIBUTING INC
2545 E Fm 120 (75021-7043)
P.O. Box 2229 (75021-2229)
PHONE....................................903 463-1194
Bobby West, *President*
Susan M West, *Corp Secy*
Jason Godfredsen, *IT/INT Sup*
EMP: 23
SQ FT: 2,000
SALES (est): 6MM **Privately Held**
WEB: www.twindistributing.com
SIC: 3589 Car washing machinery

Denton
Denton County

(G-5350)
ARYGIN CORPORATION
4101 Mill Run Rd (76208-2229)
PHONE....................................940 597-8275
Ken Mandeville, *CEO*
Giovanni Austin, *President*
Audrey Mackenzie, *Engineer*
Jody Hassemer, *CFO*
Shaya Shivers, *Sales Staff*
EMP: 12 EST: 2018
SALES (est): 832K **Privately Held**
WEB: www.arygin.com
SIC: 3663 7374 7319 Television broadcasting & communications equipment; data processing service; distribution of advertising material or sample services

(G-5351)
ASAP GLASS & DOOR LLC
512 N Locust St (76201-4128)
PHONE....................................214 770-8266
Christina North, *President*
EMP: 12
SALES (est): 496.1K **Privately Held**
SIC: 5231 3429 7699 1793 Glass; door opening & closing devices, except electrical; locksmith shop; glass & glazing work

(G-5352)
AUSTIN POWDER COMPANY
19 Oak Forrest Cir (76210-5549)
PHONE....................................940 382-4111
Sally Hughes, *Manager*
EMP: 10
SALES (corp-wide): 509.6MM **Privately Held**
WEB: www.austinpowder.com
SIC: 2892 Explosives
HQ: Austin Powder Company
25800 Science Park Dr # 300
Cleveland OH 44122
216 464-2400

(G-5353)
BEER DUDES CANNING CO LLC
Also Called: Beer Dudes Mobile Canning
1210 Duncan St Bldg 6 (76205-7318)
PHONE....................................972 342-4819
John Culp, *President*
Douglas Smith, *Director*
EMP: 10
SALES (est): 258.4K **Privately Held**
WEB: www.beerdudescanning.com
SIC: 2086 8742 7389 Carbonated beverages, nonalcoholic: bottled & canned; food & beverage consultant; packaging & labeling services

(G-5354)
CLASSIC CORRUGATED INC
1725 Cooper Creek Rd (76208-1001)
PHONE....................................940 381-0137
Ad Pete Corell, *Ch of Bd*
EMP: 56
SALES (est): 6.7MM
SALES (corp-wide): 36.8B **Privately Held**
SIC: 2679 Corrugated paper: made from purchased material
HQ: Georgia-Pacific Llc
133 Peachtree St Nw
Atlanta GA 30303
404 652-4000

(G-5355)
CODESOURCE LP
4115 Mesa Dr (76207-3436)
PHONE....................................940 891-1281
Phil Anton, *Principal*
Kerry Anton, *Principal*
Bob Hatley, *Opers Staff*
Russell Vanallen, *Opers Staff*
Matthew Reuter, *Sales Staff*
▲ EMP: 10
SQ FT: 5,000
SALES (est): 3MM **Privately Held**
WEB: www.codesource.com
SIC: 3577 Bar code (magnetic ink) printers

(G-5356)
COMPONENT STRUCTURES INC (HQ)
2400 Worthington Dr (76207-3449)
P.O. Box 340, Muenster (76252-0340)
PHONE....................................940 566-1166
EMP: 20
SALES (est): 1.5MM
SALES (corp-wide): 17MM **Privately Held**
SIC: 2439 2452 Mfg Structural Wd Member Mfg Prefabricatd Wd Bldgs
PA: Bowie-Sims-Prange, Inc.
2400 Worthington Dr
Denton TX
940 566-1166

(G-5357)
DELTA INDUSTRIES INC
9129 Perimeter St (76207-5638)
PHONE....................................214 941-3135
Karen B Waggoner, *President*
Jack H Waggoner, *COO*
EMP: 70
SQ FT: 100,000
SALES (est): 8.9MM **Privately Held**
SIC: 3585 Compressors for refrigeration & air conditioning equipment

(G-5358)
DENTON DOOR COMPANY INC
2690 Old Alton Rd (76210-7005)
PHONE....................................940 891-0600
Clas Thelin, *President*
Mark Hallgren, *Corp Secy*
EMP: 16
SALES (est): 3.1MM **Privately Held**
WEB: www.dentondoor.com
SIC: 3089 2431 Doors, folding: plastic or plastic coated fabric; doors & door parts & trim, wood

(G-5359)
DENTON PUBLISHING COMPANY (DH)
Also Called: Denton Record-Chronicle
314 E Hickory St (76201-4281)
P.O. Box 369 (76202-0369)
PHONE....................................940 387-3811
Bill Patterson, *CEO*
Mariel Tam, *Publisher*
Lucinda Breeding, *Editor*
Mark Finley, *Editor*
Kaycee Key, *Editor*
EMP: 115 EST: 1903
SALES (est): 7.8MM
SALES (corp-wide): 2.3B **Publicly Held**
WEB: www.dentonrc.com
SIC: 2711 Newspapers, publishing & printing
HQ: Belo Corp.
7950 Jones Branch Dr
Mc Lean VA 22102
703 854-6000

(G-5360)
DISPLAYS BY MARTIN PAUL INC
9307 Interstate 35 (76207-4924)
P.O. Box 1907 (76202-1907)
PHONE....................................940 458-7976
Paul Belokin, *President*
Martin Belokin, *Vice Pres*
Norman Belokin, *Admin Sec*
◆ EMP: 20
SQ FT: 16,000
SALES (est): 2.9MM **Privately Held**
WEB: www.martinpaul.com
SIC: 2542 Partitions & fixtures, except wood

GEOGRAPHIC

(G-5361)
DOUBLE L LEATHER LLC
2321 N Masch Branch Rd # 329
(76207-3290)
PHONE..................................888 643-5117
Max Gonzalez, *Controller*
Curtis Hannah, *Mng Member*
EMP: 22 **EST:** 2013
SALES (est): 10MM **Privately Held**
WEB: www.doubleleather.com
SIC: 2512 Upholstered household furniture

(G-5362)
EFI INC (PA)
2200 Worthington Dr (76207-3453)
PHONE..................................940 380-8000
Jeff Pieper, *President*
Andrew Gannon, *President*
Kayla Gannon, *Corp Secy*
Don Searcy, *Exec VP*
Mike Sauls, *Sales Staff*
▲ **EMP:** 34
SQ FT: 42,000
SALES (est): 18.2MM **Privately Held**
WEB: www.edsco.com
SIC: 3452 3449 Bolts, metal; miscella-
neous metalwork

(G-5363)
ELIJAH TOOLING INC (PA)
1025 Shady Oaks Dr # 103 (76205-7900)
PHONE..................................940 591-1340
Richard V Miller, *President*
Julie Miller, *Vice Pres*
Kenneth Comeans, *Foreman/Supr*
EMP: 10
SALES (est): 3.1MM **Privately Held**
WEB: www.invert-a-bolt.com
SIC: 5084 3399 Machine tools & acces-
sories; metal fasteners

(G-5364)
EMLS INCORPORATED
Also Called: Elite Manufacturing
3650 Shelby Ln (76207-4713)
PHONE..................................940 566-9500
Gene Schindler, *President*
EMP: 180
SQ FT: 133,000
SALES (est): 15MM **Privately Held**
WEB: www.emls1.com
SIC: 1541 3714 Warehouse construction;
motor vehicle parts & accessories

(G-5365)
ESAB GROUP INC (HQ)
Also Called: ESAB Welding & Cutting Pdts
2800 Airport Rd (76207-2100)
PHONE..................................800 372-2123
Shyam Kambeyanda, *President*
Miguel Maynez, *Controller*
Brandon Boyd, *Accounts Mgr*
◆ **EMP:** 249
SQ FT: 500,000
SALES (est): 209.6MM
SALES (corp-wide): 3.3B **Publicly Held**
WEB: www.esabna.com
SIC: 2899 3548 Fluxes: brazing, solder-
ing, galvanizing & welding; electrodes,
electric welding
PA: Colfax Corporation
420 Natl Bus Pkwy Ste 500
Annapolis Junction MD 20701
301 323-9000

(G-5366)
**FLOWERS BAKING CO DENTON
LLC (HQ)**
4210 Edwards Rd (76208-5964)
PHONE..................................940 383-5280
Bobby Harrison, *President*
Stephen R Avera, *Counsel*
Karyl H Lauder, *Vice Pres*
Karyl Lauder, *Asst Treas*
Robert L Benton, *Officer*
EMP: 177
SALES (est): 44.7MM
SALES (corp-wide): 4.1B **Publicly Held**
WEB: www.flowersfoods.com
SIC: 2051 Bakery: wholesale or whole-
sale/retail combined
PA: Flowers Foods, Inc.
1919 Flowers Cir
Thomasville GA 31757
912 226-9110

(G-5367)
**FULTON SUPPLY AND RECYCL
INC (PA)**
Also Called: Fultons Metal and Hardware
1404 Fort Worth Dr (76205-5842)
P.O. Box 1031 (76202-1031)
PHONE..................................940 382-3611
Suzanne Fulton, *President*
Jane Ann Fulton, *Vice Pres*
EMP: 30 **EST:** 1970
SQ FT: 1,500
SALES (est): 5.4MM **Privately Held**
WEB: www.fultonsupply.net
SIC: 3341 5051 Secondary nonferrous
metals; ferroalloys; nonferrous metal
sheets, bars, rods, etc.

(G-5368)
GEORGIA-PACIFIC LLC
1725 Cooper Creek Rd (76208-1001)
PHONE..................................940 205-9558
Robert M Patrick, *Branch Mgr*
EMP: 60
SALES (corp-wide): 36.8B **Privately Held**
WEB: www.gp.com
SIC: 2431 2421 2621 2631 Millwork;
sawmills & planing mills, general; paper
mills; paperboard mills; printing & writing
paper; stationery & office supplies
HQ: Georgia-Pacific Llc
133 Peachtree St Nw
Atlanta GA 30303
404 652-4000

(G-5369)
**GREENPOINT PRECISION MCH
INC**
Also Called: Odyssey Aerospace Compo-
nents
3561 Shelby Ln (76207-4712)
PHONE..................................940 382-3933
Jon A Buccola, *CEO*
Scott Goodey, *President*
Sloan Benson, *Exec VP*
Terry Guilliams, *Production*
Darin Truby, *Production*
EMP: 30 **EST:** 2011
SALES (est): 6.1MM **Privately Held**
WEB: www.greenpoint.com
SIC: 3728 Aircraft parts & equipment

(G-5370)
**GROGGY DOG SPRTSWEAR
GRPHIC DS (PA)**
4017 Mesa Dr (76207-3435)
PHONE..................................940 891-4022
Christy Cansler, *Human Resources*
Reeve Nettles, *Human Resources*
Wendi Ellis, *Sales Staff*
Alicia Kasper, *Sales Staff*
Stefanie Paterson, *Sales Staff*
EMP: 12
SQ FT: 3,000
SALES (est): 1.3MM **Privately Held**
WEB: www.groggydogonline.com
SIC: 2759 Screen printing

(G-5371)
HALSEY MANUFACTURING
Also Called: Halsey Mfg
209 N Mayhill Rd (76208-4005)
P.O. Box 2833 (76202-2833)
PHONE..................................940 566-3306
Donald J Halsey Jr, *CEO*
Donald James Halsey Sr, *President*
Laurence Halsey, *Director*
EMP: 9
SQ FT: 4,500
SALES (est): 500K **Privately Held**
WEB: www.halseymfg.com
SIC: 3544 3728 Special dies, tools, jigs &
fixtures; aircraft parts & equipment

(G-5372)
**HARPER DIRCTRY DIST GROUP
LLC**
2925 Country Club Rd # 103 (76210-8603)
PHONE..................................940 808-0769
Sean Harper,
Suzanne Harper,
EMP: 10
SALES (est): 159.3K **Privately Held**
WEB: www.harperdistributiongroup.com
SIC: 2741 Directories, telephone: publish-
ing only, not printed on site

(G-5373)
HI-TECH METALS INC
Also Called: Hi-Tech Metal Finishing
3100 Jim Christal Rd (76207-2600)
PHONE..................................940 243-0516
J Spence Nelson, *President*
Mike Nelson, *Vice Pres*
Matt Jesch, *CFO*
EMP: 75 **EST:** 1989
SQ FT: 15,000
SALES (est): 10.1MM **Publicly Held**
WEB: www.hi-techmetalfinishing.com
SIC: 3471 Finishing, metals or formed
products
PA: Esco Technologies Inc.
9900 Clayton Rd Ste A
Saint Louis MO 63124

(G-5374)
HOWMET AEROSPACE INC
4401 N Elm St (76207-7104)
PHONE..................................940 243-4491
Danny Berend, *Plant Mgr*
EMP: 12
SALES (corp-wide): 14.1B **Publicly Held**
WEB: www.howmet.com
SIC: 3353 Aluminum sheet & strip
PA: Howmet Aerospace Inc.
201 Isabella St Ste 200
Pittsburgh PA 15212
412 553-1940

(G-5375)
IG HOLDINGS LP
Also Called: Imperial Fabricating
4545 Airport Rd (76207-3927)
PHONE..................................940 565-8505
Kenny Hartman, *Branch Mgr*
EMP: 10
SALES (corp-wide): 529.1MM **Privately
Held**
SIC: 3443 Fabricated plate work (boiler
shop)
HQ: Ig Holdings, Lp
111 Industrial Dr
Portland TN 37148
615 325-9224

(G-5376)
IMPERIAL GROUP MFG INC (PA)
4545 Airport Rd (76207-3927)
PHONE..................................940 565-8505
Brian Crumbaugh, *President*
John Hatherly, *Vice Pres*
Ian Kirson, *Vice Pres*
EMP: 700
SALES (est): 529.1MM **Privately Held**
WEB: www.ironform.com
SIC: 3715 Trailer bodies

(G-5377)
INDUSTRIAL CHEMICALS CORP
1700 Shady Oaks Dr Ste A (76205-7960)
PHONE..................................940 383-0035
Carl Kelley, *President*
Mike Kelley, *Vice Pres*
EMP: 15
SQ FT: 8,000
SALES (est): 1MM **Privately Held**
SIC: 3479 Painting, coating & hot dipping

(G-5378)
LABINAL SALISBURY LLC
3790 Russell Newman Blvd # 100
(76208-2936)
PHONE..................................410 548-7800
Greg Moffitt, *President*
EMP: 800
SALES (est): 1.1MM
SALES (corp-wide): 799.9MM **Privately
Held**
SIC: 3728 Aircraft parts & equipment
HQ: Safran Usa, Inc.
700 S Washington St # 320
Alexandria VA 22314
703 351-9898

(G-5379)
**M1 SUPPORT SERVICES LP
(PA)**
300 N Elm St Ste 101 (76201-4158)
PHONE..................................940 323-1119
Kathleen S Hildreth, *Managing Prtnr*
William J Shelt, *Partner*
Tom Weeks, *Regional Mgr*
Kevin Denny, *Vice Pres*

Dwaine Esch, *Safety Mgr*
EMP: 68
SQ FT: 5,000
SALES (est): 37.8MM **Privately Held**
WEB: www.m1services.com
SIC: 8742 3728 4581 3721 Maintenance
management consultant; gears, aircraft
power transmission; airports, flying fields
& services; motorized aircraft

(G-5380)
MARTIN PAUL INC
Also Called: Displays By Martin Paul
9307 Interstate 35 (76207-4924)
P.O. Box 1907 (76202-1907)
PHONE..................................940 458-7976
Paul Belokin, *President*
Norman Belokin, *Vice Pres*
Wesley Thompson, *Finance Mgr*
Linden Galyon, *Info Tech Mgr*
EMP: 13
SALES (est): 1.8MM **Privately Held**
WEB: www.martinpaul.com
SIC: 2542 Partitions & fixtures, except
wood

(G-5381)
MAYDAY MANUFACTURING CO
3100 Jim Christal Rd (76207-2600)
PHONE..................................940 898-8301
Tom Shaw, *President*
Matthew Jesch, *Chairman*
James W Brown III, *Vice Pres*
Netzer Maoz, *Vice Pres*
Doug Wulf, *Vice Pres*
▲ **EMP:** 250 **EST:** 1966
SQ FT: 130,000
SALES (est): 40MM **Publicly Held**
WEB: www.maydaymfg.com
SIC: 3728 3769 3568 3452 Aircraft parts
& equipment; guided missile & space ve-
hicle parts & auxiliary equipment; power
transmission equipment; bolts, nuts, rivets
& washers; copper foundries; aluminum
foundries
HQ: Esco Technologies Holding Llc
9900 Clayton Rd Ste A
Saint Louis MO 63124
314 213-7200

(G-5382)
**MORRISON MILLING COMPANY
(HQ)**
319 E Prairie St (76201-6109)
PHONE..................................940 387-6111
Scott Petty Jr, *Ch of Bd*
Dale W Tremblay, *President*
J Steven Stroud, *President*
Thomas A McRae, *Senior VP*
Stephen T Phillips, *Senior VP*
▲ **EMP:** 69 **EST:** 1886
SQ FT: 6,000
SALES (est): 35.5MM
SALES (corp-wide): 758.5MM **Privately
Held**
WEB: www.morrisonmilling.com
SIC: 2041 Wheat flour
PA: C.H. Guenther & Son Llc
2201 Broadway St
San Antonio TX 78215
210 227-1401

(G-5383)
MOTION REPS INC
Also Called: Texon Icx
3801 N Interstate 35 # 110 (76207-2500)
PHONE..................................940 565-9411
Looney Nust, *President*
EMP: 22
SALES (est): 2.5MM **Privately Held**
SIC: 3494 Valves & pipe fittings

(G-5384)
**NUCON STEEL COMMERCIAL
CORP**
3570 Shelby Ln (76207-4711)
PHONE..................................940 891-3050
Richard Biddle, *President*
▼ **EMP:** 10
SQ FT: 34,000
SALES (est): 10MM **Privately Held**
WEB: www.axtellcommercial.com
SIC: 3441 Fabricated structural metal

▲ = Import ▼=Export
◆ =Import/Export

(G-5385)
O D C L INC (PA)
Also Called: Lily of Desert Nutraceuitical
1887 Geesling Rd (76208-1411)
PHONE..................................940 566-9914
E Don Lovelace, *President*
Glen Gillis, *Vice Pres*
Jerry Lovelace, *Vice Pres*
Patty Lovelace, *Vice Pres*
Edgar Valdez, *Vice Pres*
◆ **EMP:** 14
SQ FT: 25,000
SALES (est): 4.6MM **Privately Held**
WEB: www.lilyofthedesert.com
SIC: 2087 2844 Beverage bases, concentrates, syrups, powders & mixes; suntan lotions & oils

(G-5386)
ORBIS RPM LLC
5071 Dakota Ln (76207-4722)
PHONE..................................940 387-6711
Arthur Rodriguez, *Branch Mgr*
Arthur G Rodriguez, *Manager*
EMP: 10
SALES (corp-wide): 1.6B **Privately Held**
WEB: www.corbiplastics.com
SIC: 3081 Unsupported plastics film & sheet
HQ: Orbis Rpm, Llc
1055 Corporate Center Dr
Oconomowoc WI 53066
262 560-5000

(G-5387)
PACCAR INC
3200 Airport Rd (76207-2108)
P.O. Box 550 (76202-0550)
PHONE..................................940 566-7100
Brian Danhof, *Engineer*
David Lindsay, *Engineer*
Larry Skidmore, *Engineer*
Chris Touraine, *Engineer*
Darren White, *Engineer*
EMP: 200
SALES (corp-wide): 24.1B **Publicly Held**
WEB: www.paccar.com
SIC: 3711 Motor vehicles & car bodies
PA: Paccar Inc
777 106th Ave Ne
Bellevue WA 98004
425 468-7400

(G-5388)
PACCAR INC
1700 Woodbrook St (76205-7864)
P.O. Box 90208 (76202-5208)
PHONE..................................940 591-4000
Mike Dozier, *Vice Pres*
Robert Woodall, *Opers Staff*
Jim Aston, *Controller*
Lisa Wiborg, *Human Res Dir*
Dan Sovic, *Manager*
EMP: 200
SALES (corp-wide): 24.1B **Publicly Held**
WEB: www.paccar.com
SIC: 3711 Motor vehicles & car bodies
PA: Paccar Inc
777 106th Ave Ne
Bellevue WA 98004
425 468-7400

(G-5389)
PAN ECTOR INDUSTRIES LLC
1017 Shady Oaks Dr (76205-7981)
PHONE..................................940 566-1414
Michael Little, *Mng Member*
Nick Webber,
EMP: 13 **EST:** 2009
SQ FT: 3,500
SALES (est): 500K **Privately Held**
WEB: www.panector.com
SIC: 7336 2396 2759 7389 Commercial art & graphic design; screen printing on fabric articles; promotional printing; advertising, promotional & trade show services

(G-5390)
PEERLESS MFG CO
1115 Duncan St (76205-7215)
PHONE..................................940 566-9029
Sherrill Stone, *Ch of Bd*
Don Fisher, *IT/INT Sup*
EMP: 28 **Publicly Held**
WEB: www.cecoenviro.com

SIC: 3548 3599 Electric welding equipment; machine shop, jobbing & repair
HQ: Peerless Mfg. Co.
14651 Dallas Pkwy Ste 50
Dallas TX 75254
214 357-6181

(G-5391)
PEERLESS MFG CO INC
5450 Dakota Ln (76207-4730)
PHONE..................................972 559-6380
EMP: 16
SALES (est): 1.8MM **Privately Held**
SIC: 3999 Barber & beauty shop equipment

(G-5392)
PERMIAN BASIN INSTRUMENTS INC
Also Called: Pbi Labs
5014 Oak Bend Cir (76208-3418)
PHONE..................................432 687-4445
EMP: 25
SQ FT: 4,800
SALES (est): 1.7MM **Privately Held**
SIC: 7359 3533 Equipment Rental/Leasing Mfg Oil/Gas Field Machinery

(G-5393)
PRATT INDUSTRIES USA INC
1401 S Mayhill Rd (76208-6211)
PHONE..................................940 387-7291
John Dunlap, *Branch Mgr*
Christina Renfro, *Clerk*
EMP: 40 **Privately Held**
WEB: www.prattindustries.com
SIC: 2611 Pulp manufactured from waste or recycled paper
PA: Pratt Industries, Inc.
1800 Sarasot Bus Pkwy Ne S
Conyers GA 30013

(G-5394)
PROVIDENT RMNFCTURING SVCS INC
2141 Collins Rd Ste 301 (76208-1723)
P.O. Box 270628, Houston (77277-0628)
PHONE..................................940 239-7775
Lyle Delka, *Director*
EMP: 21
SALES (est): 8MM **Privately Held**
SIC: 3537 Industrial trucks & tractors

(G-5395)
QUALITY INDUSTRIES INC
Also Called: QUALITY INDUSTRIES, INCORPORATED
1550 N Wstn Blvd Ste 190 (76207)
PHONE..................................615 708-4980
EMP: 21
SALES (corp-wide): 10.2MM **Privately Held**
WEB: www.qualityindustries.com
SIC: 3444 Sheet metalwork
HQ: Quality Industries, Llc
130 Jones Blvd
La Vergne TN 37086
615 793-3000

(G-5396)
RAGSDALE VISION CTR
Also Called: Ragsdale, Mark S Od
526 N Locust St Ste B (76201-4128)
PHONE..................................940 387-9595
Shane Ragsdale, *Owner*
Jen Ragsdale, *Vice Pres*
Patricia Kelsey, *Manager*
EMP: 12
SALES (est): 1.2MM **Privately Held**
WEB: www.ragsdalevision.com
SIC: 5995 8042 3851 Contact lenses, prescription; offices & clinics of optometrists; eyeglasses, lenses & frames

(G-5397)
REAPER MINIATURES INC
Also Called: Hobby Q
9062 Teasley Ln (76210-4010)
P.O. Box 1985, Lake Dallas (75065-1985)
PHONE..................................940 484-6464
Ed Pugh, *President*
Albert Pare, *Vice Pres*
David Pugh, *Vice Pres*
Ron Hawkins, *Store Mgr*
Bill Yowell, *Manager*
▲ **EMP:** 20

SQ FT: 20,000
SALES (est): 4.9MM **Privately Held**
WEB: www.reapermini.com
SIC: 3331 Blister copper

(G-5398)
SAFRAN ELEC & PWR USA LLC (HQ)
3790 Russell Newman Blvd (76208-2936)
PHONE..................................940 272-5700
Jorge Ortega, *President*
Sander Visan, *General Mgr*
David Vollrath, *General Mgr*
Tom Bauer, *Business Mgr*
Henri Grigure, *Vice Pres*
EMP: 600 **EST:** 1986
SQ FT: 140,000
SALES (est): 312.1MM
SALES (corp-wide): 799.9MM **Privately Held**
WEB: www.safran-electrical-power.com
SIC: 3728 Aircraft parts & equipment
PA: Safran
2 Bd Du General Martial Valin
Paris 75015
140 608-080

(G-5399)
SAN BAY STUDIO INC
1427 Oakland St (76201-3173)
PHONE..................................940 387-4466
Roy Sanchez, *President*
Sanchez Rogelio, *Director*
EMP: 12
SALES (est): 450K **Privately Held**
WEB: www.sanbaystudio.com
SIC: 2759 7213 7218 2395 Screen printing

(G-5400)
SOUTHERN STRTCH FRMING FBRCTIO (PA)
9070 Teasley Ln (76210-4010)
P.O. Box 50047 (76206-0047)
PHONE..................................940 591-0410
David Arthur, *President*
Cherry Stephens, *General Mgr*
Robert Seils, *Natl Sales Mgr*
Micheal Cunningham, *Sales Staff*
EMP: 30
SQ FT: 30,000
SALES (est): 4.3MM **Privately Held**
WEB: www.southernstretch.com
SIC: 3444 Forming machine work, sheet metal; sheet metal specialties, not stamped

(G-5401)
STARLITE SIGN LP
7923 E Mckinney St (76208-2020)
PHONE..................................817 430-8359
Terry L Brockett, *President*
Lynda Brockett, *Partner*
Tessa Miller, *Project Mgr*
Mike Nguyen, *Project Mgr*
Dana Anderson, *Finance*
EMP: 82
SQ FT: 60,000
SALES (est): 13.7MM **Privately Held**
WEB: www.kiefferstarlite.com
SIC: 3993 Electric signs

(G-5402)
SYSTEMS AUTOMATED CONTROLS INC
1512 Interstate 35 W # 108 (76207-2424)
PHONE..................................818 898-1900
Jay Marshall Easley, *CEO*
Janine Easley, *Treasurer*
Kirsten Davidson, *Administration*
EMP: 32
SALES (est): 10.4MM **Privately Held**
WEB: www.systemsautomated.com
SIC: 3535 5084 Conveyors & conveying equipment; conveyor systems; materials handling machinery

(G-5403)
TETRA PAK GLOBAL INFORMATION
3300 Airport Rd Bldg 900b (76207-2199)
PHONE..................................940 565-8800
Mark Meyer, *CEO*
Agripa Munyai, *Manager*
EMP: 9

SALES (est): 1.2MM **Privately Held**
WEB: www.tetrapak.com
SIC: 3556 Food products machinery

(G-5404)
TETRA PAK INC (DH)
Also Called: Tetra Pak CPS
3300 Airport Rd (76207-2199)
PHONE..................................940 565-8800
Michael Zacka, *President*
Keith Krautkramer, *Business Mgr*
Jonas Kristensson, *Business Mgr*
Rod Shreiber, *Business Mgr*
Natalia Vaz, *Business Mgr*
◆ **EMP:** 160
SQ FT: 34,000
SALES (est): 328.5MM
SALES (corp-wide): 355.8K **Privately Held**
WEB: www.tetrapak.com
SIC: 2671 3565 5084 Paper coated or laminated for packaging; packaging machinery; hydraulic systems equipment & supplies

(G-5405)
TETRA PAK MATERIALS LP
3300 Airport Rd (76207-2199)
PHONE..................................940 565-8800
Charles Posey, *Manager*
EMP: 170
SALES (corp-wide): 355.8K **Privately Held**
WEB: www.tetrapak.com
SIC: 2671 2656 Paper coated or laminated for packaging; sanitary food containers
HQ: Tetra Pak Materials Lp
101 Corporate Woods Pkwy
Vernon Hills IL 60061

(G-5406)
TEXAS RIB RANGERS PRODUCT
Also Called: Rib Ranger Products of Texas
2402 Sherwood St (76209-1155)
PHONE..................................940 565-1983
William Milroy, *President*
Barbara Milroy, *Vice Pres*
EMP: 20
SALES (est): 250K **Privately Held**
WEB: www.texasribrangers.com
SIC: 2033 Barbecue sauce: packaged in cans, jars, etc.

(G-5407)
TRANSFER GRAPHICS INC
1024 Dallas Dr (76205-5278)
PHONE..................................940 566-2679
Michael Cooper, *President*
EMP: 12
SQ FT: 8,000
SALES (est): 1.2MM **Privately Held**
SIC: 7334 2752 5999 3993 Photocopying & duplicating services; commercial printing, lithographic; banners; signs & advertising specialties; bookbinding & related work; commercial printing

(G-5408)
UNITED COPPER INDUSTRIES LLC
2727 Geesling Rd (76208-1408)
PHONE..................................940 243-8200
Jeffrey Hykin, *CEO*
Richard Long, *Transportation*
Richard Jones, *Opers Staff*
Wendy Montgomery, *Buyer*
Veronica Powell, *Engineer*
◆ **EMP:** 300
SALES (est): 77.3MM
SALES (corp-wide): 2B **Privately Held**
SIC: 3357 Nonferrous wiredrawing & insulating
PA: Southwire Company, Llc
1 Southwire Dr
Carrollton GA 30119
770 832-4242

(G-5409)
VICTOR EQUIPMENT COMPANY (DH)
Also Called: Victor Technologies
2800 Airport Rd (76207-2100)
PHONE..................................940 566-2000
Paul D Melnuck, *Ch of Bd*
Paul D Melnuk, *Ch of Bd*

Martin Quinn, *President*
Nick Varsam, *Vice Pres*
Patricia Williams, *Vice Pres*
◆ **EMP:** 564 **EST:** 1931
SQ FT: 222,403
SALES (est): 150.9MM
SALES (corp-wide): 3.3B **Publicly Held**
WEB: www.esabna.com
SIC: 3548 3541 5088 Welding & cutting apparatus & accessories; plasma process metal cutting machines; transportation equipment & supplies
HQ: Victor Technologies International, Inc.
2800 Airport Rd
Denton TX 76207
940 381-1353

(G-5410)
VICTOR TECHNOLOGIES GROUP INC
Also Called: Tweco
2800 Airport Rd (76207-2100)
PHONE..................................940 566-2000
Hank Eaws, *President*
EMP: 47
SALES (corp-wide): 3.3B **Publicly Held**
WEB: www.esabna.com
SIC: 3541 3548 Machine tools, metal cutting type; welding apparatus
HQ: Victor Technologies Group, Inc.
16253 Swingley Ridge Rd # 200
Chesterfield MO 63017
636 728-3000

(G-5411)
VICTOR TECHNOLOGIES INTL INC (DH)
Also Called: Tweco-Arcair
2800 Airport Rd (76207-2100)
PHONE..................................940 381-1353
Paul D Melnuk, *Ch of Bd*
Michael Cook, *Business Mgr*
Terry Downes, *COO*
Nick H Varsam, *Vice Pres*
Martin Quinn, *Officer*
▲ **EMP:** 80
SQ FT: 16,109
SALES (est): 150.9MM
SALES (corp-wide): 3.3B **Publicly Held**
SIC: 3541 3548 Plasma process metal cutting machines; welding & cutting apparatus & accessories
HQ: Victor Technologies Group, Inc.
16253 Swingley Ridge Rd # 200
Chesterfield MO 63017
636 728-3000

(G-5412)
WEYERHAEUSER COMPANY
5007 Airport Rd (76207-4505)
PHONE..................................940 230-4670
EMP: 101
SALES (corp-wide): 6.5B **Publicly Held**
WEB: www.weyerhaeuser.com
SIC: 2411 Logging
PA: Weyerhaeuser Company
220 Occidental Ave S
Seattle WA 98104
206 539-3000

(G-5413)
WORLDS OF WOW LLC
Also Called: Wow Funscapes
1800 Shady Oaks Dr (76205-7962)
PHONE..................................817 380-4215
Reagan Hillier, *CEO*
Ashley Altum, *CFO*
▲ **EMP:** 30
SQ FT: 20,000
SALES (est): 5.3MM **Privately Held**
WEB: www.worldsofwow.com
SIC: 1799 3993 Playground construction & equipment installation; float (parade) construction; prop, set or scenery construction, theatrical; signs & advertising specialties; displays, paint process
HQ: Playcore Holdings, Inc.
544 Chestnut St
Chattanooga TN 37402
877 762-7563

Denver City
Yoakum County

(G-5414)
ANDREWS PUMP & SUPPLY INC
1115 W Broadway St (79323-3022)
P.O. Box 1378, Andrews (79714-1378)
PHONE..................................806 592-4567
Bill C Sommers, *Branch Mgr*
EMP: 23
SALES (corp-wide): 8MM **Privately Held**
WEB: www.garnerpump.com
SIC: 3561 5084 Pumps & pumping equipment; pumps & pumping equipment
PA: Andrews Pump & Supply, Inc.
507 Nw Mustang Dr
Andrews TX 79714
432 523-2166

(G-5415)
ATLANTIC RICHFIELD COMPANY
Also Called: A R C O
4 Miles North On Hwy 214 (79323)
P.O. Box 1030 (79323-1030)
PHONE..................................806 592-4900
Mike Brock, *Manager*
EMP: 22
SALES (corp-wide): 278.4B **Privately Held**
WEB: www.arco.com
SIC: 5541 2813 Filling stations, gasoline; industrial gases
HQ: Atlantic Richfield Company Inc
4 Centerpointe Dr
La Palma CA 90623
800 333-3991

(G-5416)
BASIC ENERGY SERVICES LP
2753 Chisholm Trl (79323-5817)
P.O. Box 1576 (79323-1576)
PHONE..................................806 592-4287
Jackie Kleam, *Manager*
EMP: 100
SALES (corp-wide): 567.2MM **Publicly Held**
WEB: www.basices.com
SIC: 1389 Oil & gas wells: building, repairing & dismantling; oil field services
HQ: Basic Energy Services, L.P.
801 Cherry St Unit 2
Fort Worth TX 76102

(G-5417)
CJR CONTRACTORS INC
401 W Broadway St (79323-3016)
P.O. Box 1080 (79323-1080)
PHONE..................................806 592-2232
Rick Cavazos, *President*
Ellen Bovkoon, *Vice Pres*
EMP: 109
SQ FT: 5,000
SALES (est): 14.8MM **Privately Held**
WEB: www.cjrcontractors.com
SIC: 1389 Roustabout service; oil field services

(G-5418)
ESPINOZA SERVICES INC (PA)
2887 Dulin Dr (79323-9553)
P.O. Box 1521 (79323-1521)
PHONE..................................806 592-8463
Gilbert Espinoza, *President*
Richard Espinoza, *Vice Pres*
Ginger Espinoza, *Admin Sec*
EMP: 14
SALES (est): 5.3MM **Privately Held**
WEB: www.espinozaservice.com
SIC: 1389 Oil field services

(G-5419)
FIVE STAR CONSOLIDATED CO LTD (PA)
Plains Hwy (79323)
P.O. Box 1359 (79323-1359)
PHONE..................................806 592-3113
Wayne Harper, *Partner*
EMP: 120
SQ FT: 30,000
SALES (est): 3.5MM **Privately Held**
SIC: 1389 Haulage, oil field

(G-5420)
LUFKIN INDUSTRIES LLC
Also Called: Lufkins Services
2811 State Highway 214 (79323-6079)
P.O. Box 1350 (79323-1350)
PHONE..................................806 592-2586
Frank Ballie, *Manager*
EMP: 45
SALES (corp-wide): 1B **Privately Held**
WEB: www.bhge.com
SIC: 1389 Lease tanks, oil field: erecting, cleaning & repairing
PA: Lufkin Gears Llc
409 Ellis Ave
Lufkin TX 75904
936 634-2211

(G-5421)
NABORS WELL SERVICES LTD
1161 State Hwy 83 (79323-6006)
PHONE..................................806 592-9128
Ali Nejjar, *Manager*
EMP: 27 **Privately Held**
WEB: www.nabors.com
SIC: 1389 Oil field services
HQ: Nabors Well Services Ltd.
515 W Greens Rd Ste 1200
Houston TX 77067
281 874-0035

(G-5422)
OCCIDENTAL PERMIAN LTD
3 Mile N Hwy 214 (79323)
P.O. Box 1650 (79323-1650)
PHONE..................................806 592-3777
Terry Small, *General Mgr*
EMP: 35
SALES (corp-wide): 21.2B **Publicly Held**
WEB: www.oxy.com
SIC: 1311 Crude petroleum production
HQ: Occidental Permian Ltd.
5 Greenway Plz Ste 110
Houston TX 77046

(G-5423)
PRODUCTION DOWNHOLE SVCS INC
1602 State Route 83 (79323)
P.O. Box 780 (79323-0780)
PHONE..................................806 592-0032
Warren Stroud, *Principal*
Zach Stroud, *Technology*
EMP: 15
SALES (est): 3MM **Privately Held**
WEB: www.productiondownhole.com
SIC: 1389 Oil field services

(G-5424)
STATE RBR ENVMTL SOLUTIONS LLC
1390 County Rd 344 (79323)
P.O. Box 732 (79323-0732)
PHONE..................................806 592-3803
Jerry Woosley, *Vice Pres*
Dan Swanson, *Plant Mgr*
Joe Kay, *Mng Member*
EMP: 22
SALES (est): 3.7MM **Privately Held**
SIC: 3069 Rubber floor coverings, mats & wallcoverings; floor coverings, rubber

(G-5425)
U S WEATHERFORD L P
Also Called: Weatherford Enterra
1251 State Hwy 83 (79323-6048)
PHONE..................................806 592-3407
Debbie Dolloff, *District Mgr*
Glen Stroud, *Branch Mgr*
EMP: 20 **Privately Held**
WEB: www.weatherford.com
SIC: 1389 Oil field services
HQ: U S Weatherford L P
179 Weatherford Dr
Schriever LA 70395
985 493-6100

Desoto
Dallas County

(G-5426)
1 PLAY AWAY LLC
504 E Belt Line Rd Unit B (75115-5102)
P.O. Box 894, Cedar Hill (75106-0894)
PHONE..................................972 532-6226
Emily D Sutton, *CEO*
EMP: 34
SQ FT: 1,800
SALES (est): 289K **Privately Held**
SIC: 8742 5651 2329 8748 Marketing consulting services; unisex clothing stores; athletic (warmup, sweat & jogging) suits: men's & boys'; business consulting

(G-5427)
428TRANSPORTERS LLC
205 W Lanett Dr (75115-4925)
PHONE..................................214 212-8648
Devin Moore, *President*
EMP: 14
SALES (est): 795.5K **Privately Held**
SIC: 3537 Trucks: freight, baggage, etc.: industrial, except mining

(G-5428)
AMREP INC
525 E Centre Park Blvd (75115-2485)
PHONE..................................972 227-3304
Randy Heizer, *Opers-Prdtn-Mfg*
EMP: 70
SALES (corp-wide): 978.4MM **Privately Held**
WEB: www.amrepproducts.com
SIC: 2842 5172 Cleaning or polishing preparations; lubricating oils & greases
HQ: Amrep, Inc.
1555 S Cucamonga Ave
Ontario CA 91761
909 923-0430

(G-5429)
DIAB HOLDINGS INC (DH)
315 Seahawk Dr (75115-2419)
PHONE..................................972 228-7600
Steve Jackson, *President*
Martin Heiskell, *President*
Lennart Thalin, *President*
Alvaro Braune, *General Mgr*
Mats Persson, *COO*
◆ **EMP:** 225 **EST:** 1981
SQ FT: 100,000
SALES (est): 68.7MM
SALES (corp-wide): 2.6B **Privately Held**
WEB: www.diabgroup.com
SIC: 3086 Plastics foam products
HQ: Diab International Ab
Norra Sofieroleden 8
Laholm 312 3
430 163-00

(G-5430)
DURA-MAR VENUS INC (PA)
1101 S Hampton Rd (75115-8091)
P.O. Box 565 (75123-0565)
PHONE..................................972 223-8008
Jackie N Dickerson, *President*
Pattie Dickerson, *Treasurer*
EMP: 65
SQ FT: 2,000
SALES (est): 6.3MM **Privately Held**
WEB: www.duramarvenus.com
SIC: 3281 5072 5211 Bathroom fixtures, cut stone; hardware; bathroom fixtures, equipment & supplies

(G-5431)
FOCUS NEWSPAPERS OF DFW INC
Also Called: Best Southwest Focus
1337 Marilyn Ave (75115-6414)
P.O. Box 1714 (75123-1714)
PHONE..................................972 223-9175
Marlon Hanson, *President*
Carmela Hanson, *Vice Pres*
EMP: 20 **EST:** 1987
SQ FT: 4,000
SALES (est): 689.9K **Privately Held**
WEB: www.focusdailynews.com
SIC: 2711 Commercial printing & newspaper publishing combined

(G-5432)
GLASFLOSS INDUSTRIES INC
(PA)
420 E Danieldale Rd (75115-2494)
PHONE..................740 687-1100
Scott Lange, *President*
Cheryl Thompson, *Principal*
Doug Lange, *District Mgr*
Donald Kingston, *Vice Pres*
Cheryl Manrique, *Vice Pres*
▼ EMP: 250
SALES (est): 47MM **Privately Held**
WEB: www.glasfloss.com
SIC: 3564 Filters, air: furnaces, air condi-
tioning equipment, etc.

(G-5433)
IGAHU INC
2607 Prince George Ave # 3601
(75115-2157)
P.O. Box 765335, Dallas (75376-5335)
PHONE..................469 474-9490
Tirfari Smith, *Chairman*
EMP: 10
SALES (est): 359.3K **Privately Held**
SIC: 2741 Miscellaneous publishing

(G-5434)
INTEGHRTY WHLCHAIR VAN
SVC LLC
Also Called: Integhearty Wheelchair Van Svc
1636 N Hampton Rd Ste 227 (75115-8601)
PHONE..................972 224-7017
Vreitta Smith, *Principal*
EMP: 14
SALES (est): 655.6K **Privately Held**
WEB: www.integheartyambser.com
SIC: 3842 Wheelchairs

(G-5435)
J & G TRYBUS CORPORATION
(PA)
320 W Centre Park Blvd (75115-2423)
PHONE..................214 331-5248
Gary Trybus, *President*
Jason Huang, *Vice Pres*
Jack Trybus, *Vice Pres*
▲ EMP: 10
SQ FT: 15,000
SALES (est): 2.1MM **Privately Held**
WEB: www.trybus.com
SIC: 2321 2325 2322 2329 Men's &
boys' furnishings; men's & boys' trousers
& slacks; men's & boys' underwear &
nightwear; men's & boys' sportswear &
athletic clothing

(G-5436)
NATIONAL MRI SHIELDING INC
1604 Kestrel Ave Ste 102 (75115-8808)
PHONE..................855 996-9820
Corey Hess, *General Mgr*
Dustin Hess, *Opers Mgr*
Kristi Hunter, *Office Mgr*
▲ EMP: 12 EST: 2006
SQ FT: 5,000
SALES (est): 2.7MM **Privately Held**
WEB: www.mri-shielding.com
SIC: 3845 Magnetic resonance imaging
device, nuclear

(G-5437)
NOBLE GENT LLC
1801 N Hampton Rd Ste 365 (75115-8308)
PHONE..................214 516-8609
Lynn Miller, *CEO*
EMP: 10
SALES (est): 200K **Privately Held**
SIC: 3999 5813 Chairs, hydraulic, barber
& beauty shop; cocktail lounge

(G-5438)
PALOMAR MODULAR
BUILDINGS LLC
505 N Interstate 35 E (75115-4803)
P.O. Box 909 (75123-0909)
PHONE..................469 727-0727
John Martin, *President*
Dane Clark, *Materials Mgr*
Michael Marlowe, *Purchasing*
Dehn Smith, *CFO*
Frank Laywell, *Manager*
EMP: 130

SALES (est): 52.6MM **Privately Held**
WEB: www.palomarmodular.com
SIC: 1542 2452 3448 Commercial & office building, new construction; prefabricated wood buildings; prefabricated metal
buildings

(G-5439)
PAPER PLATE INCORPORATED
1670 N Hampton Rd Ste 106 (75115-2389)
PHONE..................972 296-7888
Linda Carlisle, *President*
M Garrett Carlisle, *Vice Pres*
Kimberly Carlisle, *Director*
EMP: 60
SALES (est): 16.7MM **Privately Held**
WEB: www.thepaperplate.com
SIC: 2099 Food preparations

(G-5440)
PRECISION BUSINESS MCHS
INC
Also Called: Imagery Graphic Systems
1509 Falcon Dr Ste 106 (75115-8805)
PHONE..................972 224-9119
Renita Massey, *CEO*
Terry F Massey, *President*
Matt Tumelson, *General Mgr*
Shelley Tumelson, *Mktg Dir*
EMP: 10
SQ FT: 7,500
SALES (est): 3MM **Privately Held**
WEB: www.pbminc.com
SIC: 5084 3565 Printing trades machinery,
equipment & supplies; labeling machines,
industrial

(G-5441)
SEW-EURODRIVE INC
202 W Danieldale Rd (75115-2201)
PHONE..................214 330-4824
Debora Frizzell, *Administration*
EMP: 115
SALES (corp-wide): 3.4B **Privately Held**
WEB: www.seweurodrive.com
SIC: 3566 Gears, power transmission, ex-
cept automotive
HQ: Sew-Eurodrive, Inc.
1295 Old Spartanburg Hwy
Lyman SC 29365
864 439-7537

(G-5442)
SOLAR TURBINES
INCORPORATED
215 E Centre Park Blvd (75115-2481)
PHONE..................972 228-5500
Jeremy Downey, *Principal*
Tony Valle, *Project Mgr*
David Simon, *Opers Staff*
Jacob Olson, *Engineer*
Michael Wood, *Engineer*
EMP: 350
SALES (corp-wide): 53.8B **Publicly Held**
WEB: www.solarturbines.com
SIC: 3511 Gas turbine generator set units,
complete
HQ: Solar Turbines Incorporated
2200 Pacific Hwy
San Diego CA 92101
619 544-5000

(G-5443)
SUMITOMO PRECISION USA INC
1639 Falcon Dr (75115-8806)
PHONE..................972 228-9300
Taro Shimizu, *President*
Michael Farnham, *General Mgr*
Darrell Miller, *Vice Pres*
Gary Palla, *Prdtn Mgr*
▲ EMP: 9
SQ FT: 10,000
SALES: 5.2MM **Privately Held**
WEB: www.0370c64.netsolhost.com
SIC: 3728 Aircraft parts & equipment
PA: Sumitomo Precision Products Co., Ltd.
1-10, Fusocho
Amagasaki HYO 660-0

(G-5444)
TECHNOLOGY CONTAINER
CORP
1221 E Cntre Pk Blvd Bldg (75115)
PHONE..................972 228-1617
Frederick J Dowd, *President*

Lil Kurtz, *Vice Pres*
David Ramey, *CFO*
Stephen Westerlind, *CFO*
▼ EMP: 50
SQ FT: 70,000
SALES (est): 15.3MM **Privately Held**
WEB: www.techcontainer.com
SIC: 2653 2679 3083 Boxes, corrugated:
made from purchased materials; paper
products, converted; laminated plastic
sheets

(G-5445)
TODAYS CHILDREN FOOD
PROGRAM
1205 Briarbrook Dr (75115-3006)
PHONE..................214 562-4702
Sheronda Langston, *Director*
EMP: 15 EST: 2010
SALES (est): 1MM **Privately Held**
SIC: 2099 Food preparations

(G-5446)
UNITED LYNN-CON
CORPORATION
1308 S Hampton Rd (75115-8096)
PHONE..................972 223-2540
Bary Saladino, *President*
Edward Watson, *Vice Pres*
Brenda Williams, *Manager*
◆ EMP: 15
SQ FT: 20,000
SALES (est): 7.2MM **Privately Held**
WEB: www.unitedlynncon.com
SIC: 5023 5713 3253 1752 Carpets; re-
silient floor coverings: tile or sheet; car-
pets; floor tile; linoleum; ceramic wall &
floor tile; carpet laying

(G-5447)
VENUS MARBLE CO INC (PA)
1101 S Hampton Rd (75115-8091)
P.O. Box 565 (75123-0565)
PHONE..................972 223-8008
Jackie Dickerson, *President*
Pattie Dickerson, *Admin Sec*
EMP: 60 EST: 1972
SQ FT: 20,000
SALES (est): 3.6MM **Privately Held**
WEB: www.duramarvenus.com
SIC: 3281 1521 2541 Marble, building:
cut & shaped; single-family housing con-
struction; wood partitions & fixtures

Detroit
Red River County

(G-5448)
TEXAS TRIPE INC
110 2nd St Sw (75436-1819)
PHONE..................903 674-8042
Roger Holdeman, *President*
EMP: 11 EST: 2017
SALES (est): 2.2MM **Privately Held**
WEB: www.texastripe.com
SIC: 3556 Meat processing machinery

Devine
Medina County

(G-5449)
DOWNING WELL SERVICE INC
207 State Highway 132 N C (78016-1803)
P.O. Box 654 (78016-0654)
PHONE..................830 665-4923
Mark Downing, *President*
Mary Downing, *President*
EMP: 13
SALES (est): 1.4MM **Privately Held**
SIC: 1389 Well plugging & abandoning, oil
& gas

(G-5450)
J & H MANUFACTURING INC
161 County Road 777 (78016-4519)
PHONE..................830 665-5230
John McNair, *President*
Harrel McNair, *Vice Pres*
Janis McNair, *CFO*
EMP: 15
SQ FT: 36,000

SALES (est): 3.3MM **Privately Held**
WEB: www.jandhmfg.com
SIC: 2542 2541 2431 Fixtures, store: ex-
cept wood; store fixtures, wood; millwork

(G-5451)
WILBUR-ELLIS COMPANY LLC
265 Interstate 35 S (78016)
P.O. Box 450 (78016-0450)
PHONE..................830 663-3644
Larry Stull, *Enginr/R&D Mgr*
EMP: 15
SALES (corp-wide): 3.1B **Privately Held**
WEB: www.wilburellis.com
SIC: 2875 Fertilizers, mixing only
HQ: Wilbur-Ellis Company Llc
345 California St Fl 27
San Francisco CA 94104
415 772-4000

Dfw Airport
Dallas County

(G-5452)
CKI LOCKER LLC
Also Called: Canadian Locker
2701 Regent Blvd Ste 200 (75261)
PHONE..................817 329-1600
Andrew Cashin, *CFO*
Frederick A Cook Jr, *Mng Member*
Efrain Rodriguez, *Manager*
EMP: 12 EST: 2014
SALES (est): 1.2MM **Privately Held**
WEB: www.americanlocker.com
SIC: 3429 3581 Manufactured hardware
(general); locks, coin-operated

(G-5453)
NEC AMERICA INC
1213 N 28th Ave (75261-5003)
PHONE..................214 262-2387
EMP: 45 EST: 2015
SALES (est): 3.9MM **Privately Held**
SIC: 3663 Mfg Radio/Tv Communication
Equipment

(G-5454)
SIEMENS INDUSTRY INC
2700 Esters Blvd Ste 200b (75261-4030)
PHONE..................972 947-7100
EMP: 99
SALES (corp-wide): 67.4B **Privately Held**
WEB: www.new.siemens.com
SIC: 3535 Conveyors & conveying equip-
ment
HQ: Siemens Industry, Inc.
1000 Deerfield Pkwy
Buffalo Grove IL 60089
847 215-1000

(G-5455)
SIEMENS LOGISTICS LLC
2700 Esters Blvd Ste 200b (75261-4030)
P.O. Box 613209 (75261-3209)
PHONE..................972 947-7100
Brian Niccum, *Opers Staff*
Artur Zgoda, *Engineer*
Nicholas Jones, *Client Mgr*
Gert Seidel, *Manager*
Vasu Mahadasu, *Software Dev*
EMP: 600
SQ FT: 300,000
SALES (est): 84.2MM
SALES (corp-wide): 67.4B **Privately Held**
WEB: www.new.siemens.com
SIC: 3535 Belt conveyor systems, general
industrial use
HQ: Siemens Logistics Gmbh
Lilienthalstr. 16/-18
Konstanz 78467
753 186-2500

(G-5456)
SUPERMEDIA LLC (DH)
Also Called: Verizon
2200 W Airfield Dr (75261-4008)
PHONE..................972 453-7000
Gerard Corcoran, *President*
Frank Gatto, *President*
Lester K W Chu, *Vice Pres*
David R Landry, *Vice Pres*
Patrick Marshall, *Vice Pres*
▲ EMP: 48

SALES (est): 235.7MM
SALES (corp-wide): 1.4B **Publicly Held**
WEB: www.thryv.com
SIC: 2741 6719 Directories, telephone: publishing only, not printed on site; investment holding companies, except banks
HQ: Thryv, Inc.
2200 W Airfield Dr
Dfw Airport TX 75261
972 453-7000

(G-5457)
THRYV INC (HQ)
Also Called: Dexyp
2200 W Airfield Dr (75261-4008)
P.O. Box 619810 (75261-9810)
PHONE............................972 453-7000
Alan F Schultz, *Ch of Bd*
Joseph A Walsh, *President*
Suzanne Keen, *President*
Michael Dunn, *Exec VP*
Raymond R Ferrell, *Exec VP*
EMP: 122
SQ FT: 419,000
SALES (est): 781.3MM
SALES (corp-wide): 1.4B **Publicly Held**
WEB: www.thryv.com
SIC: 7311 2741 Advertising agencies; directories: publishing & printing
PA: Thryv Holdings, Inc.
2200 W Airfield Dr
Dfw Airport TX 75261
972 453-7000

(G-5458)
THRYV HOLDINGS INC (PA)
2200 W Airfield Dr (75261-4008)
P.O. Box 619810 (75261-9810)
PHONE............................972 453-7000
Jason Mudrick, *Ch of Bd*
Joseph A Walsh, *President*
Gordon Henry, *Exec VP*
James McCusker, *Exec VP*
John Wholey, *Exec VP*
EMP: 13144
SALES: 1.4B **Publicly Held**
SIC: 7372 7319 Prepackaged software; transit advertising services

Diana
Upshur County

(G-5459)
C WRIGHTS MACHINE TOOL INC
12293 Fm 2879 (75640-4241)
PHONE............................903 777-2344
Carl F Wright, *Vice Pres*
Tiffanie Granbery, *Purch Mgr*
Sharon K Wright, *Treasurer*
EMP: 32
SQ FT: 35,000
SALES (est): 5.9MM **Privately Held**
WEB: www.wrightsmachine.com
SIC: 3599 Machine shop, jobbing & repair

(G-5460)
MAVERICK BUSINESS FORMS INC
10401 Us Hwy 259 (75640)
P.O. Box 6195, Longview (75608-6195)
PHONE............................903 663-7503
James Chitwood, *President*
Sallie McGrede, *General Mgr*
Chris Chitwood, *Vice Pres*
Vickie Holder, *Sales Staff*
EMP: 46
SQ FT: 20,000
SALES (est): 10.1MM **Privately Held**
WEB: www.maverickforms.com
SIC: 2759 Business forms: printing

Diboll
Angelina County

(G-5461)
ATLAS ROOFING CORPORATION
Also Called: Atlas Energy Products Div
101 W Borden St (75941-1222)
PHONE............................936 829-5279

Bobby Lee, *Purch Mgr*
Jerry Handy, *Engineer*
John Gullett, *Branch Mgr*
EMP: 48 **Privately Held**
WEB: www.atlasroofing.com
SIC: 3086 Insulation or cushioning material, foamed plastic
HQ: Atlas Roofing Corporation
802 Highway 19 N Ste 190
Meridian MS 39307
601 484-8900

(G-5462)
DEMCO MANUFACTURING INC
1121 N Temple Dr (75941-1303)
P.O. Box 757 (75941-0757)
PHONE............................936 829-4771
Charles J Schmidt, *President*
Josh Hearne, *Engineer*
Dora Ramirez, *Admin Sec*
Carolyn Schmidt, *Administration*
EMP: 21
SQ FT: 15,000
SALES (est): 318.6K **Privately Held**
WEB: www.demco-mfg.com
SIC: 3499 3366 3446 Giftware, brass goods; giftware, copper goods; copper foundries; architectural metalwork
PA: D Mc Leasing, Inc
722 W Davis St
Dallas TX

(G-5463)
DEMCO MANUFACTURING INC
1121 N Temple Dr (75941-1303)
P.O. Box 757 (75941-0757)
PHONE............................936 829-4771
Fax: 936 829-2861
EMP: 27
SQ FT: 16,865
SALES (est): 4.6MM **Privately Held**
SIC: 3599 Mfg Industrial Machinery

(G-5464)
DENNIS W OATES LOGGING LLC
Also Called: Dwo Enterprises
308 Thompson St (75941-2032)
PHONE............................936 526-2700
Dennis W Oates, *President*
Star Peck, *Opers Mgr*
EMP: 32 EST: 2008
SALES (est): 523.8K **Privately Held**
SIC: 2411 4212 Logging camps & contractors; lumber & timber trucking

(G-5465)
GEORGIA-PACIFIC LLC
303 S Temple Dr (75941-2419)
PHONE............................800 231-6060
M Richard Warner, *Branch Mgr*
EMP: 210
SALES (corp-wide): 36.8B **Privately Held**
WEB: www.gp.com
SIC: 2493 Reconstituted wood products
HQ: Georgia-Pacific Llc
133 Peachtree St Nw
Atlanta GA 30303
404 652-4000

(G-5466)
GEORGIA-PACIFIC LLC
600 A St (75941-1641)
P.O. Box N (75941)
PHONE............................936 829-5511
Jeff Adams, *Branch Mgr*
EMP: 150
SALES (corp-wide): 36.8B **Privately Held**
WEB: www.gp.com
SIC: 2493 3444 3275 Fiberboard, other vegetable pulp; sheet metalwork; gypsum products
HQ: Georgia-Pacific Llc
133 Peachtree St Nw
Atlanta GA 30303
404 652-4000

(G-5467)
HEXION INC
100 W Borden St (75941-1204)
PHONE............................936 829-5566
William Miner, *Branch Mgr*
Bruce Dillion, *Manager*
EMP: 35

SALES (corp-wide): 1.5B **Privately Held**
WEB: www.hexion.com
SIC: 2869 2899 2861 Industrial organic chemicals; chemical preparations; gum & wood chemicals
HQ: Hexion Inc.
180 E Broad St Fl 26
Columbus OH 43215
614 225-4000

Dickinson
Galveston County

(G-5468)
AQUA DRILL INTERNATIONAL LLC (PA)
1300 Fm 646 Rd W (77539-3022)
PHONE............................281 337-0900
Matt Chapmond, *General Mgr*
Jennifer Brennan, *Opers Mgr*
Ivan Hristov, *Project Engr*
Gregory Folks, *Accounts Mgr*
David Jordan, *Manager*
◆ **EMP:** 70
SALES (est): 13.5MM **Privately Held**
WEB: www.aquadrillinternational.com
SIC: 1781 3532 Water well drilling; cleaning machinery, mineral

(G-5469)
ARC MARINE LLC
2921 Windy Hollow Ln (77539-4192)
PHONE............................713 489-7719
Paul Ayala, *Managing Dir*
EMP: 9 EST: 2015
SALES (est): 299.4K **Privately Held**
WEB: www.arc-marine.com
SIC: 1799 3443 Welding on site; fabricated plate work (boiler shop)

(G-5470)
ATLAS AUTOMATICS INC
Also Called: Atlas Automatics Screw Mch Sp
4211 21st St (77539-3802)
P.O. Box 68, League City (77574-0068)
PHONE............................281 337-1128
Chris Patelis, *President*
Karen Blackwell, *Shareholder*
EMP: 9
SQ FT: 10,000
SALES (est): 1MM **Privately Held**
SIC: 3599 Machine shop, jobbing & repair

(G-5471)
CALUMET KARNS CITY REF LLC
4401 Park Ave (77539-6933)
P.O. Box 841311, Dallas (75284-1311)
PHONE............................281 337-1534
Frank Bengtson, *Engineer*
Charles Vogus, *Branch Mgr*
EMP: 54 **Publicly Held**
WEB: www.calumetspecialty.com
SIC: 2911 Petroleum refining
HQ: Calumet Karns City Refining, Llc
2780 Waterfront
Indianapolis IN 46214

(G-5472)
CANOPY SOLUTIONS LLC
2260 Dickinson Ave Ste L (77539-2611)
PHONE............................713 510-3800
EMP: 20
SALES (est): 7MM **Privately Held**
WEB: www.canopy-solutions.com
SIC: 3444 Sheet metalwork

(G-5473)
CLEAN HARBORS SAN LEON INC (PA)
2700 Avenue S (77539-7285)
P.O. Box 58466, Houston (77258-8466)
PHONE............................281 339-1352
Alan McKim, *CEO*
Steve Corbin, *President*
Jack Blonquist, *Vice Pres*
Rob Field, *Vice Pres*
Paul Nowlin, *Vice Pres*
◆ **EMP:** 85
SQ FT: 10,000
SALES (est): 9.3MM **Privately Held**
WEB: www.duratherm-intl.com
SIC: 1389 Gas field services

(G-5474)
HILLMAN SHRIMP & OYSTER CO
10700 Hillman Dr (77539-3058)
PHONE............................281 339-1506
Clifford Hillman, *President*
Stephen Hillman, *Vice Pres*
Darla Hillman, *Treasurer*
EMP: 300
SQ FT: 10,000
SALES (est): 22.1MM **Privately Held**
WEB: www.hillmanoysters.com
SIC: 2092 5146 Shellfish, frozen: prepared; seafoods

(G-5475)
HILLMAN SHRIMP AND OYSTER CO
Also Called: Hillman Oyster Company
10700 Hillman Dr (77539-3058)
PHONE............................281 339-1506
Clifford Hillman, *President*
Darla Hillman, *Corp Secy*
Stephen Hillman, *Vice Pres*
▼ **EMP:** 290
SALES (est): 14.8MM **Privately Held**
WEB: www.hillmanoysters.com
SIC: 2092 5146 Shellfish, frozen: prepared; seafoods

(G-5476)
KARATECH CNC MACHINING LLC
Also Called: Atlas Automatics
4211 21st St (77539-3802)
PHONE............................281 337-1208
Stavros Karamitsos,
EMP: 12
SQ FT: 900
SALES (est): 246.3K **Privately Held**
WEB: www.karatechcnc.com
SIC: 3581 Automatic vending machines

(G-5477)
KARATECH MACHINING LLC
4211 21st St (77539-3802)
PHONE............................281 337-1208
Viset Keo, *Mfg Mgr*
Stavros Karamitsos,
EMP: 15
SALES (est): 3MM **Privately Held**
WEB: www.karatechcnc.com
SIC: 3581 Automatic vending machines

(G-5478)
TEXAS MARINE SHIPYARD LLC
5200 27th St (77539)
P.O. Box 489 (77539-0489)
PHONE............................409 457-6260
Andy Huynh,
Cathy Huynh,
EMP: 15
SALES (est): 1.7MM **Privately Held**
SIC: 3731 Shipbuilding & repairing

(G-5479)
VIRTUAL REALITIES
2706 Wilmington Dr Ste A (77539-4664)
PHONE............................409 599-7863
Armand W Bastien Jr, *President*
EMP: 11
SALES (est): 846.3K **Privately Held**
WEB: www.vrealities.com
SIC: 2253 7389 Hats & headwear, knit;

Dilley
Frio County

(G-5480)
EAGLE OILFIELD WELDING
17544 S Interstate Hwy 35 (78017-4645)
PHONE............................830 965-4255
Carlos Villarreal, *Owner*
EMP: 22
SALES (est): 1.4MM **Privately Held**
SIC: 1381 Drilling oil & gas wells

(G-5481)
HALLIBURTON COMPANY
833 County Road 4614 (78017-4444)
PHONE............................361 527-2780
Corbet Sparks, *Manager*
EMP: 28 **Publicly Held**
WEB: www.halliburton.com

SIC: **1389** Oil field services
PA: Halliburton Company
3000 N Sam Houston Pkwy E
Houston TX 77032

(G-5482)
J B OIL & GAS WELL SERVICE
3387 County Rd 3700 (78017)
P.O. Box 646 (78017-0646)
PHONE............................830 378-5586
Roy Boyd, *President*
EMP: 10
SALES (est): 5MM **Privately Held**
SIC: 1381 Reworking oil & gas wells

(G-5483)
**RENEGADE WELL SERVICES
LLC**
2799 W Fm 117 (78017)
P.O. Box 1897 (78017-1897)
PHONE............................830 378-5977
EMP: 27 **Privately Held**
WEB: www.renegadewellservices.com
SIC: 1389 Servicing oil & gas wells
HQ: Renegade Well Services, Llc
3301 E Us Highway 377 # 202
Granbury TX 76049

Dime Box
Lee County

(G-5484)
**DIAMOND P LEASE & WELL SVC
INC (PA)**
7981 Fm 141 (77853-5045)
P.O. Box 203 (77853-0203)
PHONE............................979 884-6111
Domingo Rodriguez, *President*
Pete Vega, *President*
EMP: 78
SQ FT: 2,000
SALES (est): 11.8MM **Privately Held**
SIC: 1389 7389 Oil field services;

Dimmitt
Castro County

(G-5485)
POOLE CHEMICAL CO INC
Also Called: Dimmitt Sulfur Products
Hwy 194 Se (79027)
P.O. Box 1008 (79027-1008)
PHONE............................806 647-2121
John Furr, *Opers-Prdtn-Mfg*
Bob Moore, *Sales Staff*
EMP: 18
SALES (corp-wide): 35MM **Privately
Held**
WEB: www.poolechemical.com
SIC: 2873 2874 Anhydrous ammonia;
phosphatic fertilizers
PA: Poole Chemical Co., Inc.
111 N 1st St
Texline TX 79087
806 362-4261

Donna
Hidalgo County

(G-5486)
AAA ELECTRICAL SIGNS (PA)
Also Called: Tesoro
2407 E Business Hwy 8 (78537)
P.O. Box 3245, McAllen (78502-3245)
PHONE............................956 464-3221
Paul W Sullivan, *President*
Steve A Smith, *Exec VP*
Martin Vazquez, *Manager*
EMP: 12
SQ FT: 15,000
SALES (est): 2.1MM **Privately Held**
WEB: www.3asigns.com
SIC: 1731 3993 1799 General electrical
contractor; signs & advertising specialties;
sign installation & maintenance

(G-5487)
AVILA STONE LLC
501 South Ave (78537-3162)
PHONE............................956 453-4747
Mike Avila, *Train & Dev Mgr*
Miguel Mike Angel Avila,
Miguel Armando Avila,
Ignacio B Gonzales,
EMP: 30
SALES (est): 500K **Privately Held**
WEB: www.avilastonellc.com
SIC: 1429 0782 Boulder, crushed & bro-
ken-quarrying; riprap quarrying; land-
scape contractors

(G-5488)
DARGEL BOATS INC
4110 N Fm 493 (78537-5088)
PHONE............................956 464-2263
Cleve Ford, *President*
Miriam Ford, *Vice Pres*
EMP: 30 **EST:** 1938
SQ FT: 15,000
SALES (est): 5.8MM **Privately Held**
WEB: www.dargelboats.net
SIC: 3732 5551 7699 Boat kits, not mod-
els; boats, fiberglass: building & repairing;
motor boat dealers; outboard motors;
boat repair

(G-5489)
**PACKAGING CORPORATION
AMERICA**
Also Called: PCA/Donna 319
2111 Hester Ave Ste A (78537-4609)
P.O. Box 968 (78537-0968)
PHONE............................956 464-5664
EMP: 87
SALES (corp-wide): 6.9B **Publicly Held**
WEB: www.packagingcorp.com
SIC: 2653 Boxes, corrugated: made from
purchased materials
PA: Packaging Corporation Of America
1 N Field Ct
Lake Forest IL 60045
847 482-3000

(G-5490)
SAN-CO STEEL LTD
Also Called: Southern Steel Fabricators
9221 N Fm 493 (78537)
P.O. Box 130, La Blanca (78558-0130)
PHONE............................956 464-7766
Ricardo Flores, *President*
Rene Garza, *Vice Pres*
EMP: 130 **EST:** 1999
SQ FT: 15,000
SALES (est): 54.3MM **Privately Held**
WEB: www.southernsteelinc.com
SIC: 3441 3444 Building components,
structural steel; sheet metalwork

(G-5491)
SOUTH TEXAS CONCRETE
E Expy 83 (78537)
PHONE............................956 464-4440
EMP: 10
SALES (corp-wide): 14.1MM **Privately
Held**
SIC: 3273 Mfg Ready-Mixed Concrete
PA: South Texas Concrete
1420 S 28th Ave
Edinburg TX 78542
956 381-9886

(G-5492)
**SOUTH TEXAS MOULDING INC
(PA)**
Also Called: Texas Wood Supply
940 W Expressway 83 (78537-4133)
PHONE............................956 464-0560
Dennis L Seal, *President*
Lock K Seal, *Corp Secy*
Dyver Seal, *Vice Pres*
Lawrence S Seal, *Vice Pres*
Larry L Seal, *Director*
EMP: 20
SQ FT: 60,000
SALES (est): 11.1MM **Privately Held**
WEB: www.texaswoodsupply.com
SIC: 5031 2431 Window frames, all mate-
rials; moldings, wood: unfinished & prefin-
ished

(G-5493)
SUNSHINE PAPER CORP
Also Called: Del Valle Paper Company
90 N Main St (78537-2758)
PHONE............................956 283-9999
Diego Salinas, *Principal*
▲ **EMP:** 16
SALES (est): 3.8MM **Privately Held**
WEB: www.sunshinepapercorp.com
SIC: 2621 Paper mills

(G-5494)
TESORO CORP
Also Called: AAA Custom & Electrical Signs
2407 E Business Hwy 83 (78537-3545)
P.O. Box 2886, McAllen (78502-2886)
PHONE............................956 682-7831
Paul W Sullivan, *President*
Mario Cavazos, *Manager*
Mabel Sullivan, *Admin Sec*
EMP: 50 **EST:** 1970
SQ FT: 11,600
SALES (est): 6.1MM **Privately Held**
WEB: www.3asigns.com
SIC: 3993 Neon signs

(G-5495)
VELAS BUILDERS LLC
Also Called: Star Builders Supply
2617 E Expressway 83 (78537-2976)
PHONE............................956 464-7827
Juan Vela,
EMP: 15
SALES (est): 3.5MM **Privately Held**
SIC: 2821 Molding compounds, plastics

Double Oak
Denton County

(G-5496)
LETCO GROUP LLC
7761 Justin Rd (75077-3039)
PHONE............................817 490-6655
EMP: 11
SALES (corp-wide): 78.3MM **Privately
Held**
WEB: www.livingearth.net
SIC: 2499 Mulch or sawdust products,
wood
PA: The Letco Group Llc
1901 Cal Crossing Rd
Dallas TX 75220
972 506-8575

(G-5497)
**TEXAS INSTRUMENTS
INCORPORATED**
330 Valley View Trl (75077-8433)
PHONE............................214 966-9759
Pat Uszler, *Branch Mgr*
EMP: 418
SALES (corp-wide): 14.4B **Publicly Held**
WEB: www.txwx.com
SIC: 3674 Microprocessors
PA: Texas Instruments Incorporated
12500 Ti Blvd
Dallas TX 75243
972 995-3773

Driftwood
Hays County

(G-5498)
ANGEL SWORD CORP
Also Called: Cavalier Casting
350 Jennifer Ln (78619-9796)
PHONE............................512 847-9679
Daniel Watson, *President*
Barnhart Todd, *Vice Pres*
EMP: 20
SALES (est): 2MM **Privately Held**
WEB: www.angelsword.com
SIC: 5719 3421 Cutlery; cutlery

(G-5499)
CKL DISTILLING LLC
Also Called: Desert Door
211 Darden Hill Rd A200 (78619-2021)
PHONE............................512 963-2373
Brent Looby, *Principal*
EMP: 40

SALES (est): 266.9K **Privately Held**
WEB: www.desertdoor.com
SIC: 2085 Distilled & blended liquors

(G-5500)
**DRIFTWOOD ESTATE WINERY
LLC**
Also Called: Driftwood Vineyard
4001 Elder Hill Rd (78619-4329)
PHONE............................512 692-6229
Laura Rood, *General Mgr*
Gary Elliott,
EMP: 24
SALES (est): 3.4MM **Privately Held**
WEB: www.driftwoodwine.com
SIC: 2084 Wines

Dripping Springs
Hays County

(G-5501)
BARTON SPRINGS MILL INC
16604 Fitzhugh Rd B (78620-2267)
PHONE............................512 554-5981
James Brown, *President*
EMP: 10
SALES (est): 124.7K **Privately Held**
WEB: www.bartonspringsmill.com
SIC: 2044 Rice milling

(G-5502)
CONTAIN WATER SYSTEMS INC
252 Frog Pond Ln Unit C (78620-5534)
PHONE............................512 770-9080
Kelsey Eric Konechny, *President*
Liliya Konechny, *CFO*
Dick Butler, *Sales Mgr*
Larry Konechny, *Sales Staff*
▼ **EMP:** 48
SQ FT: 12,000
SALES (est): 8MM **Privately Held**
WEB: www.containwatersystems.com
SIC: 3443 Water tanks, metal plate

(G-5503)
**CONTROL ALTERNATIVE
SOLUTIONS**
1001 Barton Creek Dr (78620-3716)
PHONE............................512 858-9603
Prakash Jadeja, *Director*
Ruth Jadeja, *Director*
EMP: 10
SALES (est): 853.8K **Privately Held**
WEB: www.casolinc.com
SIC: 3625 Control circuit devices, magnet
& solid state

(G-5504)
**DEVOS CUSTOM
WOODWORKING**
1451 W Highway 290 (78620-3402)
PHONE............................512 894-0464
Daniel J Vos, *Owner*
EMP: 11
SALES (est): 1MM **Privately Held**
WEB: www.devoswoodworking.com
SIC: 2431 Millwork

(G-5505)
**ECLECTIC INNVTIVE SLUTIONS
LLC**
102 Old Fitzhugh Rd Ste 3 (78620-4029)
PHONE............................737 999-1907
Christopher Fletcher, *Owner*
Jeremy Hornback, *Owner*
Art Ardolino, *Vice Pres*
Brian Fletcher, *Mng Member*
EMP: 12 **EST:** 2015
SQ FT: 1,847
SALES (est): 750K **Privately Held**
WEB: www.eis.consulting
SIC: 7379 7389 7371 7372 ; ; computer
software systems analysis & design, cus-
tom; computer software development &
applications; prepackaged software; busi-
ness oriented computer software; local
area network (LAN) systems integrator

(G-5506)
H & L FABRICATION INC
2025 Harmon Hills Rd (78620-3649)
P.O. Box 1365, Cortez CO (81321-1365)
PHONE............................512 894-0918

James M Lindsey, *President*
Al Haffelder, *Admin Sec*
EMP: 10 **EST:** 1997
SQ FT: 1,200
SALES (est): 1MM **Privately Held**
WEB: www.handlfab.com
SIC: 3589 Water treatment equipment, industrial

(G-5507)
HILL CNTRY BB CH DRPPING SPRNG
100 Commons Rd Ste 4 (78620-3966)
PHONE..............................512 843-0035
Jason McNutt, *Pastor*
EMP: 10
SALES: 1.2MM **Privately Held**
WEB: www.hcbcds.com
SIC: 8661 7372 Non-denominational church; application computer software

(G-5508)
LE RAGGE RUGGS INC (PA)
Also Called: Cow Girls & Lace
1111 W Highway 290 (78620-3818)
P.O. Box 896 (78620-0896)
PHONE..............................512 858-4186
Reba Byrd, *President*
EMP: 25
SQ FT: 15,000
SALES (est): 4.9MM **Privately Held**
WEB: www.cowgirlsandlace.com
SIC: 2392 5719 Household furnishings; beddings & linens

(G-5509)
NEW CANAAN FARMS INC
Hwy 290 W (78620)
P.O. Box 386 (78620-0386)
PHONE..............................512 858-7669
Cindy Figer, *President*
Mike Figer, *Treasurer*
Figer Curtis B, *Director*
EMP: 12
SQ FT: 2,500
SALES (est): 1.2MM **Privately Held**
WEB: www.newcanaanfarms.com
SIC: 2033 5149 Jams, including imitation: packaged in cans, jars, etc.; jellies, edible, including imitation: in cans, jars, etc.; groceries & related products

(G-5510)
NICOR INC
100 Commons Rd 7-355 (78620-4400)
PHONE..............................707 484-0835
▲ **EMP:** 12
SALES (est): 2.7MM **Privately Held**
WEB: www.nicorinc.net
SIC: 3643 Connectors & terminals for electrical devices

(G-5511)
PATRIOT ERECTORS LLC
3023 W Highway 290 (78620-5298)
PHONE..............................512 858-9100
Jason Puckett, *Safety Dir*
Evan Webb, *Controller*
Eric Herzog, *Manager*
Rex Webb, *Director*
Parley Dixon,
EMP: 230
SQ FT: 10,000
SALES (est): 95.1MM **Privately Held**
WEB: www.patrioterectors.com
SIC: 1541 3441 1791 Steel building construction; fabricated structural metal; floor jacks, metal; structural steel erection

(G-5512)
PATRIOT PARENT LLC
3023 W Highway 290 (78620-5298)
PHONE..............................512 858-9100
Parley Dixon,
EMP: 330
SALES (est): 80MM **Privately Held**
SIC: 1541 3441 1791 Steel building construction; fabricated structural metal; structural steel erection

(G-5513)
TREATY OAK BREWING DISTLG LLC
Also Called: Treaty Oak Distilling Company
16604 Fitzhugh Rd (78620-2267)
PHONE..............................512 680-1606

Daniel Barnes, *CEO*
David Powell, *Vice Pres*
Nate Powell, *Master*
▲ **EMP:** 38
SQ FT: 6,000
SALES (est): 4.4MM **Privately Held**
WEB: www.treatyoakdistilling.com
SIC: 2082 2085 Beer (alcoholic beverage); distilled & blended liquors

Dublin
Erath County

(G-5514)
ABF PACKING INC
8758 S Us Highway 377 (76446-4375)
PHONE..............................254 968-4919
D L Funderburgh, *President*
Jason Beyer, *Vice Pres*
Gilbert Martinez, *Plant Mgr*
Quioz Jonathan, *Opers Mgr*
Mike Ondrusek, *Sales Mgr*
EMP: 63
SQ FT: 10,000
SALES (est): 8.3MM **Privately Held**
WEB: www.abfpacking.com
SIC: 0751 2011 Slaughtering: custom livestock services; meat packing plants

(G-5515)
DUBLIN BOTTLING WORKS INC
Also Called: Dublin Dr Pepper
221 S Patrick St (76446-2347)
PHONE..............................254 445-3939
William Edward Kloster, *President*
Mark Kloster, *President*
Jeffrey C Kloster, *Treasurer*
James M Mulloy, *Admin Sec*
EMP: 37 **EST:** 1891
SQ FT: 43,000
SALES (est): 6.4MM **Privately Held**
WEB: www.dublinbottlingworks.com
SIC: 2086 5149 Soft drinks: packaged in cans, bottles, etc.; soft drinks

(G-5516)
EL DORADO CHEMICAL COMPANY
300 E Oneil St (76446-2342)
PHONE..............................254 445-2720
Ike Thedford, *Manager*
EMP: 108
SALES (corp-wide): 365MM **Publicly Held**
WEB: www.lsbindustries.com
SIC: 2819 2892 2875 Inorganic acids, except nitric & phosphoric; explosives; fertilizers, mixing only
HQ: El Dorado Chemical Company Inc
3503 Nw 63rd St Ste 500
Oklahoma City OK 73116
405 235-4546

(G-5517)
THOMPSONS CSTM MEATS & PROC LP
Also Called: Thompsons Custom Meats & Proc
111 W Elm St (76446-2209)
P.O. Box 330, Stephenville (76401-0025)
PHONE..............................254 445-4180
Tanner Thompson, *Partner*
EMP: 25
SALES (est): 500K **Privately Held**
SIC: 2011 5421 Meat packing plants; meat markets, including freezer provisioners

(G-5518)
UNIVERSAL BLANCHERS LLC
1033 County Road 343 6w (76446-5633)
P.O. Box 198 (76446-0198)
PHONE..............................254 445-4021
Jackie Mayfield, *Manager*
EMP: 40 **Privately Held**
WEB: www.olamonline.com
SIC: 0723 2099 2068 Field crops, except cash grains; market preparation services; peanut butter; salted & roasted nuts & seeds
HQ: Universal Blanchers, L.L.C.
2077 Convntn Ctr Conc 1
Atlanta GA 30337

Dumas
Moore County

(G-5519)
BP AMERICA PRODUCTION COMPANY
1330 Fm 2203 (79029-7830)
PHONE..............................806 935-8810
Lisa Smith, *Branch Mgr*
EMP: 56
SALES (corp-wide): 278.4B **Privately Held**
WEB: www.bp.com
SIC: 1381 Drilling oil & gas wells
HQ: Bp America Production Company
501 Westlake Park Blvd
Houston TX 77079
281 366-2000

(G-5520)
DUANE OLLINGER (PA)
Also Called: Four Star Construction
1 Mile West On 87 (79029)
P.O. Box 478 (79029-0478)
PHONE..............................806 935-6786
Duane Ollinger, *Owner*
EMP: 20
SQ FT: 30,000
SALES (est): 1.4MM **Privately Held**
SIC: 7692 1794 Welding repair; excavation work

(G-5521)
HIGH PLAINS DRILLING COMPANY
Also Called: Jones, W D Drilling Co
610 N Dumas Ave (79029)
P.O. Box 817 (79029-0817)
PHONE..............................806 935-2132
Jerry E Thompson, *President*
Lola I Thompson, *Corp Secy*
EMP: 12
SQ FT: 9,000
SALES (est): 2.9MM **Privately Held**
SIC: 5083 1781 3599 Irrigation equipment; water well drilling; machine shop, jobbing & repair

(G-5522)
HIGH PLINS CNTRS MGT GROUP INC (PA)
414 S Dumas Ave (79029-3733)
P.O. Box 1444 (79029-1444)
PHONE..............................806 935-5858
Michael J Ramirez, *President*
EMP: 21
SALES (est): 1.9MM **Privately Held**
WEB: www.highplainsmanagement.com
SIC: 1542 8741 7389 3861 Commercial & office building, new construction; construction management; ; aerial cameras; etching & engraving; plumbing, heating, air-conditioning contractors

(G-5523)
J W RESOURCES INC
7 Miles N Of Dumas (79029)
PHONE..............................806 935-0185
EMP: 9 **Privately Held**
SIC: 1381 Oil & Gas Drilling & Operating
PA: J W Resources Inc
3131 Bell St Ste 203
Amarillo TX 79106

(G-5524)
LLANOS ALTOS LLC
Also Called: Pure Element Water
5901 W Road I (79029-7209)
PHONE..............................806 934-4534
Stacey Grall,
Harold Grall,
EMP: 10
SALES (est): 500K **Privately Held**
WEB: www.pureelementwater.com
SIC: 2086 Water, pasteurized: packaged in cans, bottles, etc.

(G-5525)
MONSANTO COMPANY
Hwy 87 W (79029)
P.O. Box 417 (79029-0417)
PHONE..............................806 935-5623
Scott Buchannah, *Manager*

EMP: 30
SALES (corp-wide): 48.1B **Privately Held**
WEB: www.monsanto.com
SIC: 2879 Agricultural chemicals
HQ: Monsanto Company
800 N Lindbergh Blvd
Saint Louis MO 63167
314 694-1000

(G-5526)
MOORE COUNTY NEWS PRESS
Also Called: North Plains Agriculture
702 N Meredith Ave (79029-2558)
P.O. Box 757 (79029-0757)
PHONE..............................806 935-4111
Ineze Lewis, *President*
Charles Lancaster, *Partner*
James Lancaster, *Partner*
Lissa Walls, *Vice Pres*
Garald Hoke, *Treasurer*
EMP: 18
SQ FT: 5,000
SALES (est): 950K
SALES (corp-wide): 140.3MM **Privately Held**
WEB: www.moorenews.com
SIC: 2711 Newspapers: publishing only, not printed on site
PA: Southern Newspapers, Inc.
5701 Woodway Dr Ste 131
Houston TX 77057
713 266-5481

Duncanville
Dallas County

(G-5527)
ALIENTO INC
110 N Main St (75116-3647)
P.O. Box 763849, Dallas (75376-3849)
PHONE..............................214 302-6580
Jose Olide, *CEO*
Marco Barrientos, *Chairman*
EMP: 30
SQ FT: 3,500
SALES (est): 1.2MM **Privately Held**
WEB: www.aliento.org
SIC: 2741 Music book & sheet music publishing

(G-5528)
APPLE CORRUGATED PACKAGING INC
1346 N Main St (75116-2312)
PHONE..............................214 331-9000
Charles Bush, *President*
Marcus Bush, *Vice Pres*
Tommy Hill, *Vice Pres*
EMP: 40
SQ FT: 60,000
SALES (est): 14.8MM **Privately Held**
SIC: 2653 Boxes, corrugated: made from purchased materials

(G-5529)
CH GUENTHER & SON LLC
627 Big Stone Gap Rd (75137-2223)
PHONE..............................972 298-4281
Chuck Hanson, *Branch Mgr*
Susmita Anupoju, *Technology*
EMP: 158
SALES (corp-wide): 758.5MM **Privately Held**
WEB: www.chg.com
SIC: 2041 Wheat flour
PA: C.H. Guenther & Son Llc
2201 Broadway St
San Antonio TX 78215
210 227-1401

(G-5530)
FABRICON INC
1146 Explorer St (75137-3054)
P.O. Box 383059 (75138-3059)
PHONE..............................214 630-5998
Jerry Luce, *President*
Ed Grafe, *Vice Pres*
EMP: 25
SQ FT: 15,500
SALES (est): 5.8MM **Privately Held**
WEB: www.fabriconinc.com
SIC: 3599 Machine shop, jobbing & repair

(G-5531)
GK STEEL FABRICATION LLC
906 Mercury Ave (75137-2232)
PHONE.................................972 291-5514
Mike Owens, *General Mgr*
Sarah Miller, *Project Mgr*
Patricia Wheatley, *Accountant*
Michael Owens, *Mng Member*
Trendon Morton, *Supervisor*
EMP: 12
SALES (est): 3MM **Privately Held**
WEB: www.gksteelfab.com
SIC: 3462 Iron & steel forgings

(G-5532)
LA MEXICANA TORTILLA FCTRY INC
715 Skyline Dr (75116-3923)
PHONE.................................214 943-7770
Ricardo Garza, *President*
Rafael Perez, *General Mgr*
Jose Villarreal, *Opers Mgr*
Becky Garza, *Admin Sec*
EMP: 90
SQ FT: 20,000
SALES (est): 18.8MM **Privately Held**
WEB: www.lamexicanatortillas.com
SIC: 2099 Tortillas, fresh or refrigerated

(G-5533)
MASCO CABINETRY LLC
520 Big Stone Gap Rd (75137-2222)
PHONE.................................972 725-4298
Karen Strauss, *Branch Mgr*
EMP: 115
SALES (corp-wide): 1.7B **Privately Held**
WEB: www.mascocabinetry.com
SIC: 2434 Wood kitchen cabinets
HQ: Cabinetworks Group Michigan, Llc
4600 Arrowhead Dr
Ann Arbor MI 48105
734 205-4600

(G-5534)
MILKE MANUFACTURING JEWELERS
106 S Cedar Ridge Dr (75116-4531)
P.O. Box 380339 (75138-0339)
PHONE.................................972 296-4319
Robert Milke, *President*
Milke Jeanita A, *Vice Pres*
EMP: 9
SQ FT: 2,652
SALES (est): 628.3K **Privately Held**
SIC: 7631 3911 Jewelry repair services; jewelry, precious metal

(G-5535)
MOFFITT WEST LLC
Also Called: Universal Enclosure Systems
1146 S Cedar Ridge Dr (75137-3019)
PHONE.................................972 298-0531
James Wheaton, *Branch Mgr*
EMP: 21
SQ FT: 20,000
SALES (corp-wide): 9.1MM **Privately Held**
WEB: www.moffittcorp.com
SIC: 3469 Electronic enclosures, stamped or pressed metal
HQ: Moffitt West, Llc
3100 Juanita Dr
Denison TX 75020
903 463-5700

(G-5536)
PIONEER FROZEN FOODS INC (HQ)
627 Big Stone Gap Rd (75137-2223)
P.O. Box 118, San Antonio (78291-0118)
PHONE.................................972 298-4281
Dale W Tremblay, *CEO*
Forrest R Word, *Ch of Bd*
J Steven Stroud, *President*
Dennis Daniels, *Vice Pres*
Charles V Hanson, *Vice Pres*
▲ EMP: 750 EST: 1982
SQ FT: 90,000
SALES (est): 124.3MM
SALES (corp-wide): 758.5MM **Privately Held**
WEB: www.chg.com
SIC: 2099 Food preparations

PA: C.H. Guenther & Son Llc
2201 Broadway St
San Antonio TX 78215
210 227-1401

(G-5537)
PRECISE CONNECTIONS INC
1114 Explorer St (75137-3012)
PHONE.................................972 298-1040
Mark Ott, *President*
Joel Krohn, *Purch Agent*
▲ EMP: 25
SQ FT: 12,500
SALES (est): 8.2MM **Privately Held**
WEB: www.preciseconnections.com
SIC: 3672 Printed circuit boards

(G-5538)
PROLIFT EQUIPMENT INC
1314 Heather Glen St (75137-2835)
PHONE.................................214 682-3327
Velma Labastida, *Director*
Edgar Labastida, *Director*
EMP: 15
SALES (est): 2.8MM **Privately Held**
WEB: www.pro-liftequipment.com
SIC: 3537 Forklift trucks

(G-5539)
TRITON CONSOLIDATED INC
815 Mercury Ave (75137-2233)
PHONE.................................972 362-1711
Perry Jasin, *CEO*
Don I Criswell, *President*
EMP: 15
SQ FT: 19,450
SALES (est): 3MM **Privately Held**
SIC: 3728 Elevators, aircraft

Eagle Lake
Colorado County

(G-5540)
COLORADO COUNTY RICE MILL INC
1006 Mccormick Rd (77434-2748)
P.O. Box 367 (77434-0367)
PHONE.................................979 234-5554
Betty G Adams, *Ch of Bd*
Don R Adams Sr, *President*
▼ EMP: 17
SQ FT: 29,000
SALES (est): 6MM **Privately Held**
WEB: www.coloradocountycitizen.com
SIC: 0723 2044 Cash grain crops market preparation services; rice milling

(G-5541)
LONE STAR CRYOGENICS INC
500 Glen Flora Rd (77434-2860)
PHONE.................................979 234-5001
Sarah Wiebold, *Corp Secy*
Bill Weibold, *Director*
EMP: 10
SALES (est): 800K **Privately Held**
WEB: www.lonestarcryo.com
SIC: 3559 Cryogenic machinery, industrial

(G-5542)
MANGUMS OILFIELD SERVICES
4321 Main St (77434)
P.O. Box 786 (77434-0786)
PHONE.................................979 234-7327
Michael R Mangum, *President*
EMP: 40
SALES (est): 2MM **Privately Held**
WEB: www.mangumsoilfield.com
SIC: 1389 Oil field services

(G-5543)
SPECIALTY SAND COMPANY
1096 Parker Rd (77434-7010)
PHONE.................................979 234-7431
Henry Rodriguez, *Manager*
EMP: 9
SALES (corp-wide): 8.2MM **Privately Held**
WEB: www.specialtysand.com
SIC: 1446 Blast sand mining; foundry sand mining
PA: Specialty Sand Company Inc.
16601 Garrett Rd
Houston TX 77044
281 456-9553

(G-5544)
TRAFCO INDUSTRIES INC
413 W Main St (77434-2310)
PHONE.................................979 234-5713
Lesley M Carey, *President*
Lonny Daley, *Vice Pres*
Daley Lonny Earl, *Vice Pres*
EMP: 9
SQ FT: 25,000
SALES (est): 1.7MM **Privately Held**
WEB: www.trafco.net
SIC: 3669 5999 Transportation signaling devices; alarm & safety equipment stores

(G-5545)
TRAFFIC SUPPLY INC
500 Highway 3013 W (77434-9743)
PHONE.................................979 234-5509
Frank Fei, *President*
Janet Yang, *Treasurer*
Debbie Wishert, *Admin Sec*
▲ EMP: 14
SALES (est): 2.2MM **Privately Held**
WEB: www.apexmarker.com
SIC: 3669 Pedestrian traffic control equipment
PA: Apex Universal, Inc.
11033 Forest Pl
Santa Fe Springs CA 90670

(G-5546)
TX QUALITY PRODUCTS LLC
1134 Pioneer Plant Rd (77434-7107)
P.O. Box 625 (77434-0625)
PHONE.................................979 234-7979
Dennis Filson, *Principal*
EMP: 19
SALES (est): 3.1MM **Privately Held**
WEB: www.texasqualityproducts.com
SIC: 2048 Prepared feeds

Eagle Pass
Maverick County

(G-5547)
ALAMO CONCRETE PRODUCTS LTD
Fm 1021 El Indio Hwy (78852)
P.O. Box 2588 (78853-2588)
PHONE.................................830 773-6334
Francisco Billim, *Branch Mgr*
EMP: 16 **Privately Held**
SIC: 3273 Ready-mixed concrete
PA: Alamo Concrete Products, Ltd.
6055 W Green Mountain Rd
Austin TX 78744

(G-5548)
LA HACIENDA TORTILLA FACTORY
2505 El Indio Hwy (78852-5537)
PHONE.................................830 773-9151
Hipolito Gonzales, *Owner*
EMP: 10
SQ FT: 3,600
SALES (est): 400K **Privately Held**
SIC: 2099 5411 5541 Tortillas, fresh or refrigerated; grocery stores, independent; gasoline service stations

(G-5549)
LITTELFUSE INC
1025 Adams Cir (78852-5105)
PHONE.................................830 513-8775
Robert Nostwick, *Branch Mgr*
EMP: 60
SALES (corp-wide): 1.5B **Publicly Held**
WEB: www.littelfuse.com
SIC: 3613 3625 3694 Fuses & fuse equipment; relays, for electronic use; automotive electrical equipment
PA: Littelfuse, Inc.
8755 W Higgins Rd Ste 500
Chicago IL 60631
773 628-1000

(G-5550)
MUSTANG GROUP LTD
4058 Adams Cir (78852-5157)
P.O. Box 4829 (78853-4829)
PHONE.................................830 968-0291
Richard La Cabaoa, *Treasurer*
Mario De La Cabada,
Roberto De Lacabada,
Jorge De La Cabada,
Richard De La Cabaoa,
EMP: 18
SQ FT: 30,000
SALES (est): 1.7MM **Privately Held**
WEB: www.themustanggroup.com
SIC: 3999 5159 Barber & beauty shop equipment; tobacco distributors & products

(G-5551)
NEWS GRAM
2431 Del Rio Blvd (78852-3216)
PHONE.................................830 773-8610
Rueben Carrillo, *Owner*
EMP: 12
SALES (est): 195K **Privately Held**
WEB: www.thenewsgramonline.net
SIC: 2711 Newspapers, publishing & printing

(G-5552)
PARTS SUPPLIERS INC
2913 Diaz St (78852-3643)
P.O. Box 466 (78853-0466)
PHONE.................................830 773-5069
EMP: 14
SALES (est): 1.2MM **Privately Held**
SIC: 3052 Mfg Rubber/Plastic Hose/Belting

(G-5553)
PIEDRAS NEGRAS TORTILLA FCTRY
340 N Pierce St (78852-4628)
PHONE.................................830 773-6706
Jose Moreno, *President*
Moreno Olga Guadalupe, *Vice Pres*
Olga Moreno, *Vice Pres*
EMP: 9
SQ FT: 1,920
SALES (est): 848K **Privately Held**
SIC: 2099 Tortillas, fresh or refrigerated

(G-5554)
REGAL BELOIT AMERICA INC
Also Called: Fasco Eldon Rbc
1305 Industrial Blvd (78852-5293)
P.O. Box 982401, El Paso (79998-2401)
PHONE.................................715 284-9801
Garcia Paul, *Opers Staff*
Oscar Quezada, *Mfg Staff*
Luis Ortiz, *QC Mgr*
EMP: 242
SALES (corp-wide): 3.2B **Publicly Held**
WEB: www.regalbeloit.com
SIC: 3621 Motors & generators
HQ: Regal Beloit America, Inc.
200 State St
Beloit WI 53511
608 364-8800

(G-5555)
REGAL BELOIT AMERICA INC
Also Called: Fasco
11206 Farmer 2182 (78852)
P.O. Box 548, Cassville MO (65625-0548)
PHONE.................................417 847-4775
Mike Atwood, *Branch Mgr*
EMP: 242
SALES (corp-wide): 3.2B **Publicly Held**
WEB: www.regalbeloit.com
SIC: 3564 Blowers & fans
HQ: Regal Beloit America, Inc.
200 State St
Beloit WI 53511
608 364-8800

Early
Brown County

(G-5556)
ALDERSGATE ENRICHMENT CENTER
Also Called: Aldersgate Industries
5001 Highway 84 E (76802-3833)
P.O. Box 1406, Brownwood (76804-1406)
PHONE.................................325 646-2566
Brandy Stanley, *Principal*
Jason Snedegar, *Opers Staff*
Barbara Varner, *Human Res Dir*
Bobbye Gomez, *Supervisor*
Donna Phillips, *Supervisor*

EMP: 65
SQ FT: 900
SALES: 1.6MM **Privately Held**
WEB: www.aldersgatecenter.org
SIC: 8331 2448 7389 2611 Sheltered
workshop; pallets, wood; packaging & la-
beling services; pulp mills

East Bernard
Wharton County

(G-5557)
**EAST BERNARD MILLING CO
LLC**
854 Wallace St (77435-8850)
PHONE..........................979 335-7554
Joe Brady Whitley, *Mng Member*
John Britton Whitley, *Mng Member*
EMP: 9
SQ FT: 12,000
SALES (est): 2.5MM **Privately Held**
WEB: www.simplotgrowersolutions.com
SIC: 2048 Livestock feeds

(G-5558)
GAYLA INDUSTRIES INC
770 Leverage (77435)
P.O. Box 225 (77435-0225)
PHONE..........................979 335-7503
Daniel Pesek, *Manager*
EMP: 30
SALES (corp-wide): 11.1MM **Privately
Held**
WEB: www.gaylainc.com
SIC: 3944 Kites
PA: Gayla Industries, Inc.
6401 Antoine Dr
Houston TX 77091
713 681-2411

(G-5559)
**LEEDO MANUFACTURING CO
LP (PA)**
Also Called: Leedo Cabinetry
16856 Cabinet Rd (77435-5064)
PHONE..........................866 465-3336
H Benjamin Samuels, *Partner*
David Mullis, *Partner*
Larry Pirvul, *Managing Dir*
Randy Bailey, *Exec VP*
Otto Iskandar, *Vice Pres*
▲ **EMP:** 151
SALES (est): 112.1MM **Privately Held**
WEB: www.leedocabinetry.com
SIC: 2434 Vanities, bathroom: wood

(G-5560)
**MANGUMS OILFIELD SERVICES
LTD**
4321 Main St (77435-9004)
P.O. Box 786, Eagle Lake (77434-0786)
PHONE..........................979 234-5203
Michael R Mangum, *President*
EMP: 40
SALES (est): 4.1MM **Privately Held**
WEB: www.mangumsoilfield.com
SIC: 1389 Oil field services

Eastland
Eastland County

(G-5561)
CAM SERVICES INC
Also Called: Bam Operating
Airport Rd (76448)
P.O. Box 688 (76448-0688)
PHONE..........................254 629-8561
EMP: 10
SQ FT: 2,400
SALES (est): 620K **Privately Held**
SIC: 1389 Oil/Gas Field Services

(G-5562)
**CROWDER CONSTRUCTION CO
INC**
318 N Seaman St (76448-1842)
PHONE..........................254 629-1688
Tom Crowder, *President*
EMP: 20

SALES (est): 3.2MM **Privately Held**
WEB: www.crowderconstructioninc.com
SIC: 1389 Construction, repair & disman-
tling services

(G-5563)
**EAGLE RAILCAR SERVICES LP
(PA)**
9701 E I 20 (76448)
PHONE..........................254 631-0168
EMP: 11
SALES (est): 5MM **Privately Held**
WEB: www.eaglerailcar.com
SIC: 3743 Railroad equipment

(G-5564)
**EASTLAND COUNTY
NEWSPAPER INC (PA)**
Also Called: Ranger Times
215 S Seaman St (76448-2745)
P.O. Box 29 (76448-0029)
PHONE..........................254 629-1707
Houston V O'Brien, *President*
Vance O'Brien, *Corp Secy*
Gaynell O'Brien, *Vice Pres*
EMP: 11
SQ FT: 15,000
SALES (est): 1.5MM **Privately Held**
WEB: www.eastlandcountytoday.com
SIC: 2711 2752 5943 Commercial printing
& newspaper publishing combined; com-
mercial printing, offset; office forms &
supplies

(G-5565)
EBAA IRON INC (PA)
County Rd 442 Fm 570 S 1 (76448)
P.O. Box 877 (76448-0877)
PHONE..........................254 629-1737
Earl C Bradley, *President*
Earl Bradley, *Principal*
Billye B Bradley, *Vice Pres*
Earl T Bradley, *Vice Pres*
Billy Moore, *Manager*
▲ **EMP:** 280 **EST:** 1964
SQ FT: 90,000
SALES (est): 91.8MM **Privately Held**
WEB: www.ebaa.com
SIC: 3321 Ductile iron castings

(G-5566)
LEGACY VULCAN LLC
Southwest Division
702 County Road 442 (76448-5738)
P.O. Box 1369 (76448-1369)
PHONE..........................254 629-2850
Ron Hart, *Manager*
EMP: 13 **Publicly Held**
WEB: www.vulcanmaterials.com
SIC: 3273 Ready-mixed concrete
HQ: Legacy Vulcan, Llc
1200 Urban Center Dr
Vestavia AL 35242
205 298-3000

(G-5567)
MIGHTY MOLDING & MFG
Also Called: Mighty Molding & Manufacturing
2016 Old Bankhead Hwy (76448-4001)
P.O. Box 1157 (76448-1157)
PHONE..........................254 629-2525
Stacey Jameson, *Principal*
EMP: 12
SALES (est): 1.6MM **Privately Held**
SIC: 3089 Plastic containers, except foam

(G-5568)
**MORGAN BUILDING & SPA MFG
CORP**
Also Called: Morgan Buildings &AMp Spas
1117 Lower Seman (76448)
PHONE..........................254 629-1599
EMP: 75
SALES (corp-wide): 238.8MM **Privately
Held**
SIC: 2452 3999 Mfg Wood Portable Build-
ings & Hot Tubs
HQ: Morgan Building & Spa Manufacturing
Corporation
12700 Hillcrest Rd # 291
Dallas TX 75230
972 864-7300

(G-5569)
TRI-TEX ENTERPRISES INC
Also Called: Eastlander Designs
202 N College Ave (76448-1606)
PHONE..........................214 744-1246
Tony Borino, *Manager*
EMP: 100
SALES (corp-wide): 28.1MM **Privately
Held**
WEB: www.tri-tex.net
SIC: 2211 2392 2391 Bedspreads, cotton;
draperies & drapery fabrics, cotton;
household furnishings; curtains &
draperies
PA: Tri-Tex Enterprises, Inc.
4909 Lakawana St
Dallas TX 75247
214 744-1246

(G-5570)
**VULCAN CONSTRUCTION MTLS
LLC**
702 County Road 442 (76448-5738)
PHONE..........................254 629-2850
Ron Hart, *Branch Mgr*
EMP: 25 **Publicly Held**
WEB: www.vulcanmaterials.com
SIC: 3273 Ready-mixed concrete
HQ: Vulcan Construction Materials, Llc
1200 Urban Center Dr
Vestavia AL 35242
205 298-3000

Eden
Concho County

(G-5571)
CONCHO SERVICES LLC
814 W Broadway St (76837)
P.O. Box 517 (76837-0517)
PHONE..........................325 869-5242
Ramiro C Ramirez, *Principal*
EMP: 14
SALES (est): 2.3MM **Privately Held**
WEB: www.concho-services-
llc.business.site
SIC: 1389 Servicing oil & gas wells

Edgewood
Van Zandt County

(G-5572)
INFINITY CARPORTS INC
7977 Us Hwy 19 (75117)
PHONE..........................903 765-2057
Eduardo Cardoso, *President*
Alfonso Cardoso, *Vice Pres*
EMP: 18
SALES (est): 1.7MM **Privately Held**
SIC: 3448 Prefabricated metal buildings

Edinburg
Hidalgo County

(G-5573)
**ADVANCED ORTHOTICS
PROSTHETICS**
5428 S Jackson Rd (78539-6672)
PHONE..........................956 971-8200
Anthony Eidman, *Owner*
EMP: 10
SALES (est): 790.1K **Privately Held**
SIC: 3842 5999 Orthopedic appliances;
orthopedic & prosthesis applications

(G-5574)
AMAIDA MACHINE SHOP LLC
919 N 10th Ave Ste C (78541-3105)
PHONE..........................956 287-8824
Norma Tores,
Samuel Tores,
EMP: 9
SALES (est): 600K **Privately Held**
SIC: 3599 Machine shop, jobbing & repair

(G-5575)
ASHLEY WORLDWIDE INC
Also Called: Gerber Manufacturing Company
1500 S 25th Ave (78542-7213)
PHONE..........................956 383-0636
Terry L Gerber, *President*
Deron M Gerber, *VP Mktg*
Maria Patterson, *Manager*
EMP: 50
SALES (corp-wide): 9.5MM **Privately
Held**
WEB: www.gerbertables.com
SIC: 2326 Work uniforms
PA: Ashley Worldwide, Inc.
13388 State Road 23
Granger IN 46530
574 259-2481

(G-5576)
AUTO LICENSE
100 E Cano St Ste 102 (78539-4548)
P.O. Box 178 (78540-0178)
PHONE..........................956 318-2158
Arnold Morin, *Manager*
Armando Berrera Jr, *Exec Dir*
Armando Barrera Jr, *Director*
EMP: 27 **EST:** 1987
SALES (est): 2.5MM **Privately Held**
SIC: 3469 Automobile license tags,
stamped metal

(G-5577)
AZTECA MILLING LP
501 W Chapin St (78541-2412)
PHONE..........................956 383-4911
Hector Segura, *Warehouse Mgr*
Jorge Castro, *Human Res Mgr*
Santoniago Salazar, *Manager*
Isabel Benavides, *MIS Mgr*
Alfredo Perez, *Technical Staff*
EMP: 225
SQ FT: 216 **Privately Held**
WEB: www.aztecamilling.com
SIC: 2041 Flour & other grain mill products
HQ: Azteca Milling, L.P.
5601 Executive Dr Ste 650
Irving TX 75038
956 383-4911

(G-5578)
**BAKER HUGHES A GE
COMPANY LLC**
Fm 1925 E St (78539)
PHONE..........................956 383-0142
Grissey Leary, *Branch Mgr*
EMP: 62
SALES (corp-wide): 23.8B **Publicly Held**
WEB: www.bakerhughes.com
SIC: 1389 Oil field services
HQ: Baker Hughes Holdings Llc
17021 Aldine Westfield Rd
Houston TX 77073
713 439-8600

(G-5579)
BLACK WIDOW ENERGY LLC
4943 S Jackson Rd Ste 105 (78539-7203)
PHONE..........................956 378-5363
Teodulo Cantu,
Orlando Domiguez,
EMP: 18 **EST:** 2014
SQ FT: 144
SALES (est): 771.5K **Privately Held**
SIC: 1389 Roustabout service

(G-5580)
**BUTCHS OILFIELD SERVICES
INC**
12404 Vicksburg Dr (78542-3059)
P.O. Box 1256 (78540-1256)
PHONE..........................956 381-8409
Michael Rogers, *President*
EMP: 40
SALES (est): 4MM **Privately Held**
WEB: www.bosinctx.com
SIC: 1389 Construction, repair & disman-
tling services

(G-5581)
**CEMEX CONSTRUCTION MTLS S
LLC**
Also Called: Edinburg Rm
3710 S Expy 281 (78542-7023)
PHONE..........................956 386-1452
Victor Garza, *Manager*

EMP: 19 **Privately Held**
WEB: www.cemexusa.com
SIC: **3273** Ready-mixed concrete
HQ: Cemex Construction Materials South, Llc
 2088 E 20th St
 Yuma AZ 85365
 928 343-4100

(G-5582)
CHORIZO DE SAN MANUEL GUER
Also Called: Guerra's Grocery & Meat Market
36080 N Hwy 281 (78542-2812)
PHONE....................................956 383-8751
Vicki Flores, *President*
Jaime Flores, *Vice Pres*
Luis Flores III, *Vice Pres*
Jj Flores, *Plant Mgr*
Patricia Los Santos, *Treasurer*
EMP: 25
SQ FT: 20,000
SALES (est): 5.9MM **Privately Held**
WEB: www.chorizodesanmanuel.com
SIC: **2013** 5411 Sausages from purchased meat; grocery stores, independent

(G-5583)
CLAUDIA RODRIGUEZ
Also Called: Cartoon Mascots
1815 Nora Dr (78539-6617)
PHONE....................................956 381-0845
EMP: 15 EST: 1993
SALES: 50K **Privately Held**
SIC: **7929** 2389 Entertainer/Entertainment Group Mfg Apparel/Accessories

(G-5584)
D & R PRECISION MANUFACTURING
1810 S Expressway 281 (78542-7201)
PHONE....................................956 386-0685
Domingo Hinojosa, *President*
Ricardo Hinojosa, *Vice Pres*
EMP: 10
SQ FT: 6,000
SALES (est): 1.3MM **Privately Held**
WEB: www.drprecisionmfg.com
SIC: **3451** Screw machine products

(G-5585)
E&R VACUUM TRUCK SERVICES LLC
8 And A Half Ware Rd (78539)
P.O. Box 1797 (78540-1797)
PHONE....................................956 618-9590
Edward Estrada, *Principal*
EMP: 10
SALES (est): 505.2K **Privately Held**
SIC: **4212** 1389 Local trucking, without storage; haulage, oil field

(G-5586)
EXQUISITA TORTILLAS INC (PA)
700 W Chapin St (78541-2416)
P.O. Box 1078 (78540-1078)
PHONE....................................956 383-6712
J Humberto Rodriguez, *President*
Bill Guerra, *COO*
EMP: 105
SQ FT: 46,000
SALES (est): 31.9MM **Privately Held**
WEB: www.exquisitatortillas.com
SIC: **2099** Tortillas, fresh or refrigerated

(G-5587)
EXQUISITA TORTILLAS INC
320 N 12th Ave (78541-3506)
PHONE....................................956 383-3011
Philip Olvera, *Manager*
EMP: 40
SALES (corp-wide): 31.9MM **Privately Held**
WEB: www.exquisitatortillas.com
SIC: **2099** 2096 2051 Tortillas, fresh or refrigerated; tortilla chips; bread, cake & related products
PA: Exquisita Tortillas, Inc.
 700 W Chapin St
 Edinburg TX 78541
 956 383-6712

(G-5588)
FESCO LTD
4501 W University Dr (78539)
PHONE....................................956 383-8378
James De Vries, *Manager*
EMP: 27
SALES (corp-wide): 201MM **Privately Held**
WEB: www.fescoinc.com
SIC: **1389** Construction, repair & dismantling services
PA: Fesco, Ltd.
 1000 Fesco Dr
 Alice TX 78332
 361 664-3479

(G-5589)
GRUMA CORPORATION
501 W Chapin St (78541-2412)
PHONE....................................956 380-4090
Miguel Arce, *Manager*
EMP: 206 **Privately Held**
WEB: www.missionfoods.com
SIC: **2096** Potato chips & similar snacks
HQ: Gruma Corporation
 5601 Executive Dr Ste 800
 Irving TX 75038
 972 232-5000

(G-5590)
INTERNATIONAL PAPER COMPANY
1501 N Closner Blvd (78541-2595)
PHONE....................................956 383-3811
Kevin Griffin, *General Mgr*
Ofelia Valdez, *Principal*
Lulu Garcia, *Purchasing*
Amelia Leal, *Controller*
Toya Weaver, *Controller*
EMP: 130
SALES (corp-wide): 22.3B **Publicly Held**
WEB: www.internationalpaper.com
SIC: **2621** Paper mills
PA: International Paper Company
 6400 Poplar Ave
 Memphis TN 38197
 901 419-9000

(G-5591)
INTERNATIONAL PAPER COMPANY
1010 E Chapin St (78541-2511)
PHONE....................................956 387-8100
EMP: 133
SALES (corp-wide): 27.8B **Publicly Held**
SIC: **2621** Paper Mill
PA: International Paper Company
 6400 Poplar Ave
 Memphis TN 38197
 901 419-9000

(G-5592)
LA PALOMA TORTILLA FACTORY (PA)
Also Called: La Paloma Tortilla Fctry & Bky
621 E Cano St (78539-4711)
P.O. Box 2139 (78540-2139)
PHONE....................................956 316-1515
Servando Marroquin, *President*
EMP: 17
SALES (est): 719K **Privately Held**
SIC: **5812** 2099 Mexican restaurant; tortillas, fresh or refrigerated

(G-5593)
LONGHORN SERVICES INC
Also Called: Specialty Services
21377 N Moorefield Rd (78541-5386)
PHONE....................................956 655-2360
Monty Awbrey, *President*
EMP: 35
SALES (est): 1.7MM **Privately Held**
WEB: www.longhornstx.com
SIC: **1389** 1611 Pipe testing, oil field service; highway & street construction; highway & street paving contractor

(G-5594)
M J M INTERNATIONAL CORP (PA)
632 S Jackson Rd (78539-2356)
P.O. Box 720054, McAllen (78504-0054)
PHONE....................................956 781-5000
Hector Moroles, *President*
Ben Cantu, *Vice Pres*

Gilbert Moroles, *Vice Pres*
Cristina Ortiz, *Buyer*
Melly Moroles, *CFO*
◆ EMP: 15
SQ FT: 15,000
SALES (est): 5.1MM **Privately Held**
WEB: www.mjminternational.com
SIC: **2522** Office furniture, except wood

(G-5595)
MARTIN MRTTA MTLS SUTHWEST LLC
35700 Fm 3250 (78541-1327)
PHONE....................................956 381-1459
Albert Martinez, *Manager*
EMP: 136 **Publicly Held**
WEB: www.chenega.com
SIC: **1422** Crushed & broken limestone
HQ: Martin Marietta Materials Southwest, Llc
 5710 W Hausman Rd Ste 121
 San Antonio TX 78249
 210 208-4400

(G-5596)
MERIT ENERGY COMPANY LLC
28808 N Fm 681 (78541-6128)
PHONE....................................956 842-3649
EMP: 15 **Privately Held**
WEB: www.meritenergy.com
SIC: **1311** Crude petroleum production
PA: Merit Energy Company, Llc
 13737 Noel Rd Ste 1200
 Dallas TX 75240

(G-5597)
MO-VAC SERVICE COMPANY (PA)
3721 S Mccoll Rd (78539-9618)
P.O. Box 2677, McAllen (78502-2677)
PHONE....................................956 682-6381
Glynn Andrews, *President*
Arnold Perez, *Vice Pres*
Aimee Pimentel, *Accountant*
Junior Contreras, *Manager*
Urbano Garza, *Manager*
EMP: 75 EST: 1960
SQ FT: 15,000
SALES (est): 156.8MM **Privately Held**
WEB: www.mo-vac.com
SIC: **1389** 4959 Mud service, oil field drilling; environmental cleanup services

(G-5598)
PURCHASING DEPT
2802 S Hwy Business 281 (78539)
PHONE....................................956 318-2626
Yolanda Velasquez, *Purch Agent*
Martha L Salazar, *Director*
EMP: 28
SALES (est): 1.7MM **Privately Held**
WEB: www.hidalgocounty.us
SIC: **3087** Custom compound purchased resins

(G-5599)
RLEY ENTERPRISES INC
Also Called: Phoenix EMB & Screen Prtg
1012 E Owassa Rd Ste B (78542-7049)
PHONE....................................956 715-8228
Eric Fernandez, *Principal*
Ruben Castilla,
Lupe Salinas,
EMP: 10
SALES (est): 550.5K **Privately Held**
SIC: **2752** Commercial printing, lithographic

(G-5600)
RO SA VACUUM TRUCKS INC
15751 Wallace Rd (78541-3307)
P.O. Box 419 (78540-0419)
PHONE....................................956 584-8685
EMP: 25
SQ FT: 12,500
SALES (est): 2.4MM **Privately Held**
SIC: **1389** Oil/ As Field Services

(G-5601)
S & S CONTRACT PUMPING SVC INC
1204 S Mccoll Rd (78539-8833)
P.O. Box 3369 (78540-3369)
PHONE....................................956 386-0211
James S Jung, *President*

Susan Jung, *Vice Pres*
EMP: 13
SALES (est): 1.4MM **Privately Held**
WEB:
www.sandscontractpumping.trustab.org
SIC: **1389** Measurement of well flow rates, oil & gas

(G-5602)
SOUTH TEXAS CONCRETE (PA)
Also Called: South-Tex Concrete Ready Mix
1420 S 28th Ave (78542-7299)
P.O. Box 531808, Harlingen (78553-1808)
PHONE....................................956 381-9886
Frederico Palacios Sr, *Partner*
Juan Palacios, *Partner*
Nicolas Palacios, *Partner*
Rene Palacios, *Partner*
EMP: 100 EST: 1979
SQ FT: 10,000
SALES (est): 15.6MM **Privately Held**
WEB: www.j3concrete.com
SIC: **3273** Ready-mixed concrete

(G-5603)
STRIKE LLC
2605 N Closner Blvd (78541-2598)
PHONE....................................888 353-1444
Raul Garza, *Branch Mgr*
EMP: 35
SALES (corp-wide): 1.4B **Privately Held**
WEB: www.strikeusa.com
SIC: **1389** Servicing oil & gas wells
PA: Strike, Llc
 1800 Hughes Landing Blvd # 500
 The Woodlands TX 77380
 713 389-2400

(G-5604)
TREVINOS PAINTING INC
2038 E Richardson Rd (78542-0200)
PHONE....................................956 571-3999
Juan M Trevino, *President*
EMP: 20
SALES (est): 191.5K **Privately Held**
SIC: **1721** 3471 Industrial painting; sand blasting of metal parts

(G-5605)
VALLEY ARMATURE & ELC CO INC
1313 N Expressway 281 (78542-4879)
P.O. Box 3127, McAllen (78502-3127)
PHONE....................................956 393-2233
Kenneth Larry Lewis, *President*
Dominic James, *Purchasing*
Martha Lewis, *Treasurer*
Kasey Lewis, *Office Mgr*
EMP: 19
SQ FT: 20,000
SALES (est): 9.8MM **Privately Held**
WEB: www.valleyarmature.com
SIC: **5063** 7694 Motors, electric; electric motor repair

Edna
Jackson County

(G-5606)
GT OILFIELD REPAIR INC
802 W Main St (77957-2416)
P.O. Box 595 (77957-0595)
PHONE....................................361 782-7300
Gary Thomas, *President*
Marcus Thomas, *Vice Pres*
Debora Thomas, *Treasurer*
Sharon Thomas, *Admin Sec*
EMP: 25
SQ FT: 12,000
SALES (est): 3.1MM **Privately Held**
SIC: **1389** Construction, repair & dismantling services; oil field services

(G-5607)
JACKSON COUNTY HERALD TRIBUNE
Also Called: Edna Harold Publishing
306 N Wells St (77957-2729)
PHONE....................................361 782-2131
Joe Hermes, *President*
Dennis Simons, *Corp Secy*
Harrison Stafford LL, *Vice Pres*
EMP: 16

GEOGRAPHIC

SQ FT: 2,000
SALES (est): 900K **Privately Held**
WEB: www.jacksonconews.com
SIC: 2711 Newspapers, publishing & printing

(G-5608)
KEY ENERGY SERVICES INC
1112 Us Highway 59 S (77957-4662)
PHONE..................................361 578-9975
EMP: 50
SALES (corp-wide): 436.1MM **Publicly Held**
SIC: 1389 Oil/Gas Field Services
PA: Key Energy Services, Inc.
1301 Mckinney St Ste 1800
Houston TX 77010
713 651-4300

(G-5609)
MERCER CONTROLS INC
804 Apollo Dr (77957-3307)
P.O. Box 777 (77957-0777)
PHONE..................................361 782-7168
Sherrel Mercer, *President*
Steve Gabrysch, *Corp Secy*
EMP: 13
SALES (est): 2MM **Privately Held**
WEB: www.mercercontrols.com
SIC: 3823 3699 Programmers, process type; photographic control systems, electronic

El Campo
Wharton County

(G-5610)
APACHE CORPORATION
9625 Pierce Ranch Rd (77437-3567)
PHONE..................................979 543-4391
Tim N Sullivan, *Exec VP*
George Canable, *Manager*
Michael Abrams, *Manager*
EMP: 13
SALES (corp-wide): 6.4B **Publicly Held**
WEB: www.apachecorp.com
SIC: 1311 Crude petroleum production
PA: Apache Corporation
2000 Post Oak Blvd Ste 10
Houston TX 77056
713 296-6000

(G-5611)
AUSTIN COCA-COLA BOTTLING CO
1001 W Jackson St (77437-4030)
PHONE..................................979 543-2522
Ivory Harrison, *Manager*
EMP: 56
SQ FT: 11,502
SALES (corp-wide): 309.5MM **Privately Held**
SIC: 2086 Bottled & canned soft drinks
PA: Austin Coca-Cola Bottling Company
1 Coca Cola Pl
San Antonio TX 78219
210 225-2601

(G-5612)
BASIC ENERGY SERVICES INC
183 Martin St (77437-7801)
PHONE..................................979 733-0488
Monte McCarver, *Manager*
EMP: 35
SALES (corp-wide): 567.2MM **Publicly Held**
WEB: www.basices.com
SIC: 1389 Oil field services
PA: Basic Energy Services, Inc.
801 Cherry St Unit 2
Fort Worth TX 76102
817 334-4100

(G-5613)
BROTHERS WELL SERVICE LTD (PA)
Also Called: Brother's Trucking
County Rd 453 (77437)
P.O. Box 1540 (77437-1540)
PHONE..................................979 543-6851
Donald Nohavitza, *President*
Dorothy Kubala, *Corp Secy*
EMP: 23 **EST:** 1965

SQ FT: 10,000
SALES (est): 3.3MM **Privately Held**
SIC: 1389 5082 7353 1382 Servicing oil & gas wells; haulage, oil field; oil field equipment; oil field equipment, rental or leasing; oil & gas exploration services

(G-5614)
COLORADO CNTY SAND GRAV L L C
Hwy 71 N One Mile (77437)
P.O. Box 1599 (77437-1599)
PHONE..................................979 543-3791
Frank W Marek,
EMP: 33
SALES (est): 11.7MM
SALES (corp-wide): 2.2B **Publicly Held**
SIC: 1442 Sand mining
PA: Summit Materials, Inc.
1550 Wynkoop St Ste 300
Denver CO 80202
303 893-0012

(G-5615)
EL CAMPO MACHINE & REPAIR INC (PA)
Highway 71 (77437)
PHONE..................................979 543-9663
David John Pratka, *President*
EMP: 30
SQ FT: 4,800
SALES (est): 2.8MM **Privately Held**
WEB: www.shopecr.com
SIC: 3599 Machine shop, jobbing & repair

(G-5616)
EL CAMPO NEWSPAPERS INC
Also Called: El Campo Leader News
203 E Jackson St (77437-4413)
P.O. Box 1180 (77437-1180)
PHONE..................................979 543-3363
Fred Barbee Jr, *President*
Christopher F Barbee, *Vice Pres*
EMP: 25
SQ FT: 9,000
SALES (est): 1.4MM **Privately Held**
WEB: www.experienceelcampo.com
SIC: 2711 Newspapers, publishing & printing

(G-5617)
EL CAMPO SHEET METAL LLC
28385 Us 59 Hwy (77437-1901)
P.O. Box 529 (77437-0529)
PHONE..................................979 543-5751
William R Drapela, *Vice Pres*
Gary Mazoch, *Mng Member*
Gary P Mazoch, *Mng Member*
Gary Mozoch, *Mng Member*
Silvan J Dluhos, *Admin Sec*
EMP: 16
SQ FT: 15,200
SALES (est): 3.1MM **Privately Held**
WEB: www.elcamposheetmetal.com
SIC: 3449 3441 Miscellaneous metalwork; fabricated structural metal

(G-5618)
FESCO LTD
310 N Wharton St (77437-4655)
PHONE..................................979 543-9451
Gene Newton, *Division Mgr*
Randy Tarber, *District Mgr*
Chad Bacak, *Project Mgr*
Garron Farrar, *Manager*
EMP: 40
SALES (corp-wide): 201MM **Privately Held**
WEB: www.fescoinc.com
SIC: 1389 Oil field services
PA: Fesco, Ltd.
1000 Fesco Dr
Alice TX 78332
361 664-3479

(G-5619)
KEY ENERGY SERVICES INC
Hwy 59 (77437)
PHONE..................................713 651-4300
Buddy Bornek, *Manager*
EMP: 100
SALES (corp-wide): 413.8MM **Publicly Held**
WEB: www.keyenergy.com
SIC: 1389 Oil field services

PA: Key Energy Services, Inc.
1301 Mckinney St Ste 1800
Houston TX 77010
713 651-4300

(G-5620)
KING WORKOVER SERVICE INC
2882 N Mechanic St (77437-9422)
PHONE..................................979 543-5464
Kevin King, *President*
EMP: 12
SALES (est): 490.4K **Privately Held**
WEB: www.kwsog.com
SIC: 1389 Oil field services

(G-5621)
MARKS MACHINE CO INC
1101 N Blue Creek Rd (77437-9119)
P.O. Box 1596 (77437-1596)
PHONE..................................979 543-9204
Mark C Pratka, *President*
Edgar Garcia, *General Mgr*
Nate Morrow, *General Mgr*
Brent Pratka, *Vice Pres*
Kay Pratka, *Vice Pres*
▲ **EMP:** 70
SQ FT: 27,000
SALES (est): 13.6MM **Privately Held**
WEB: www.marksmachine.com
SIC: 3599 7699 Machine shop, jobbing & repair; valve repair, industrial

(G-5622)
MARTIN ELECTRIC CO INC
1504 W Jackson St (77437-9310)
PHONE..................................979 543-6421
Kenneth Martin, *President*
Evelyn Martin, *Vice Pres*
Pat Martin, *Treasurer*
Lisa Ramczyk, *Office Mgr*
Suzanne Martin, *Admin Sec*
EMP: 30
SQ FT: 10,000
SALES (est): 6.2MM **Privately Held**
WEB: www.martinelectriccompany.com
SIC: 7694 1731 Electric motor repair; general electrical contractor

(G-5623)
NEW ICM LP (HQ)
Also Called: Tom and Jerry
220 Sam Bishkin Rd (77437-4733)
PHONE..................................979 578-0543
Daniel Zalman, *Partner*
Stewart McGowan, *General Mgr*
▲ **EMP:** 32 **EST:** 1999
SQ FT: 60,000
SALES (est): 11.2MM **Privately Held**
WEB: www.newicm.com
SIC: 2341 2322 Women's & children's nightwear; nightwear, men's & boys': from purchased materials
PA: Paty Investments, Inc.
4540 S Pinemont Dr # 110
Houston TX 77041
713 688-7686

(G-5624)
NEW ICM L P
220 Sam Bishkin Rd (77437-4733)
PHONE..................................979 578-0543
Donna Thorton, *Vice Pres*
EMP: 113
SALES (corp-wide): 11.2MM **Privately Held**
WEB: www.newicm.com
SIC: 2341 Women's & children's nightwear
HQ: New Icm, L.P.
220 Sam Bishkin Rd
El Campo TX 77437
979 578-0543

(G-5625)
NICHOLS ENTERPRISES INC
Also Called: Nichols Irrigation
5731 N Sh 71 (77437)
PHONE..................................979 543-4833
Pat Nichols, *President*
EMP: 10 **EST:** 1975
SQ FT: 3,000
SALES (est): 1.4MM **Privately Held**
WEB: www.nicholsirrigation.com
SIC: 1623 3441 Pipe laying construction; fabricated structural metal

(G-5626)
PRASEKS HILLJE SMOKEHOUSE
29714 Us 59 Hwy (77437-4054)
PHONE..................................979 543-8312
Mike Prasek, *President*
Troy Prasek, *President*
Mike Prasek Jr, *Vice Pres*
David Janik, *Production*
David Janiks, *Engineer*
EMP: 95 **EST:** 1950
SQ FT: 22,000
SALES (est): 7.5MM **Privately Held**
WEB: www.praseks.com
SIC: 5461 5411 5421 2013 Bakeries; grocery stores, independent; meat markets, including freezer provisioners; sausages & other prepared meats; gift shop

(G-5627)
QUALITY HOT MIX INC (PA)
1805 N Blue Creek Rd (77437-6482)
P.O. Box 1244 (77437-1244)
PHONE..................................979 543-6464
EMP: 12
SQ FT: 500
SALES: 11.6MM **Privately Held**
SIC: 2951 Asphalt & asphaltic paving mixtures (not from refineries)

(G-5628)
VIPER WELL SERVICES LLC
Also Called: Viper Oil & Gas
402 Dam Rd (77437-2541)
PHONE..................................979 541-5262
David Pratka, *Mng Member*
EMP: 20
SALES (est): 3.5MM **Privately Held**
SIC: 1381 Reworking oil & gas wells

(G-5629)
WILLIAM L BONNELL COMPANY INC
Also Called: Bonnell Campo
902 Gladys St (77437-9220)
PHONE..................................409 543-0600
John Fitzmartin, *Manager*
EMP: 275 **Publicly Held**
WEB: www.bonnellaluminum.com
SIC: 3354 3523 3471 3446 Aluminum extruded products; farm machinery & equipment; plating & polishing; architectural metalwork
HQ: Bonnell Aluminum (Corporate), Inc.
25 Bonnell St
Newnan GA 30263
770 253-2020

El Paso
El Paso County

(G-5630)
21C SIGN COMPANY
6999 Commerce Ave (79915-1101)
PHONE..................................915 775-8514
Kevin Buntyn, *Owner*
EMP: 10
SALES (est): 859K **Privately Held**
WEB: www.centurysignselpaso.com
SIC: 3993 Signs, not made in custom sign painting shops

(G-5631)
77 STONE
337 E Sunset Rd (79922-1021)
PHONE..................................915 590-0770
Edward Dean Lapuma, *Owner*
EMP: 16
SALES (est): 1.5MM **Privately Held**
WEB: www.77stone.net
SIC: 2541 3281 Counter & sink tops; cut stone & stone products

(G-5632)
A & B LABELS AND PRINTING INC
7245 Copperqueen Dr (79915-1228)
PHONE..................................915 774-0007
Juan A Barcena Sr, *President*
Sandra Barcena, *Treasurer*
Daniel Barcena, *Admin Sec*
EMP: 27

SQ FT: 37,000 **Privately Held**
WEB: www.ablabelselpaso.com
SIC: 2759 Labels & seals: printing; calendars: printing; business forms: printing

(G-5633)
A & I INDUSTRIES INC
337 N Zaragoza Rd Ste D (79907-4741)
P.O. Box 71056 (79917-1056)
PHONE..................................915 633-8444
Oscar A Vazquez, *Principal*
EMP: 10 EST: 2010
SQ FT: 2,000
SALES (est): 1MM **Privately Held**
SIC: 3469 Machine parts, stamped or pressed metal

(G-5634)
A O SMITH CORPORATION
1270 Don Haskins Dr Ste A (79936-7805)
P.O. Box 245008, Milwaukee WI (53224-9508)
PHONE..................................915 400-2800
Rene Martinez, *Branch Mgr*
EMP: 40
SALES (corp-wide): 2.9B **Publicly Held**
WEB: www.aosmith.com
SIC: 3639 3433 3621 Hot water heaters, household; boilers, low-pressure heating: steam or hot water; motors, electric
PA: A. O. Smith Corporation
11270 W Park Pl Ste 1200
Milwaukee WI 53224
414 359-4000

(G-5635)
A O SMITH CORPORATION
A.o Smith Warehouse
1265 Peter Cooper Dr (79936-6814)
PHONE..................................915 859-1071
Bob Herlyhy, *Principal*
Bruce Kielgas, *Engineer*
Cesar Valdez, *Info Tech Mgr*
EMP: 122
SALES (corp-wide): 2.9B **Publicly Held**
WEB: www.aosmith.com
SIC: 3621 Motors, electric
PA: A. O. Smith Corporation
11270 W Park Pl Ste 1200
Milwaukee WI 53224
414 359-4000

(G-5636)
ACME BRICK COMPANY
325 N Americas Ave (79907-7006)
PHONE..................................817 332-4101
Vanessa Rocha, *Sales Staff*
Ron Rede, *Manager*
Steve Bush, *Manager*
EMP: 54
SALES (corp-wide): 254.6B **Publicly Held**
WEB: www.brick.com
SIC: 3251 3229 3086 2816 Structural brick & blocks; pressed & blown glass; plastics foam products; inorganic pigments; concrete work; masonry & other stonework
HQ: Acme Brick Company
3024 Acme Brick Plz
Fort Worth TX 76109

(G-5637)
ADEMCO INC
12220 Rojas Dr Ste A (79936-7716)
PHONE..................................915 872-5542
Victor Aguilar, *Branch Mgr*
EMP: 102
SALES (corp-wide): 4.9B **Publicly Held**
SIC: 5063 3669 3822 Electrical apparatus & equipment; emergency alarms; air conditioning & refrigeration controls
HQ: Ademco Inc.
1985 Douglas Dr N
Golden Valley MN 55422
800 468-1502

(G-5638)
ADEMCO INC
Also Called: ADI Global Distribution
3950 Doniphan Dr Ste N&O (79922-1357)
P.O. Box 26549 (79926-6549)
PHONE..................................915 875-0091
Joel Roman, *Branch Mgr*
EMP: 97

SALES (corp-wide): 4.9B **Publicly Held**
SIC: 5063 3669 3822 Electrical apparatus & equipment; emergency alarms; auto controls regulating residntl & coml environmt & applncs
HQ: Ademco Inc.
1985 Douglas Dr N
Golden Valley MN 55422
800 468-1502

(G-5639)
ALAREAL CORPORATION
Also Called: Bin There Dump That
8417 Beverly Pl (79907-3800)
PHONE..................................915 858-4097
Antonio Alarcon, *President*
EMP: 9
SALES (est): 930.3K **Privately Held**
SIC: 3443 5722 Dumpsters, garbage; garbage disposals

(G-5640)
ALCO MACHINE TOOL & STEEL INC
6805 Alameda Ave (79905-4933)
PHONE..................................915 779-7013
Alfredo Borrego, *President*
EMP: 10
SQ FT: 13,000
SALES (est): 715K **Privately Held**
WEB: www.alcoep.net
SIC: 3469 3312 Machine parts, stamped or pressed metal; tool & die steel

(G-5641)
ALIGN TECHNOLOGY INC
10 Leigh Fisher Blvd (79906-5239)
PHONE..................................408 470-1311
Alejandro Erreira, *Branch Mgr*
EMP: 12
SALES (corp-wide): 2.4B **Publicly Held**
WEB: www.aligntech.com
SIC: 3843 Orthodontic appliances
PA: Align Technology, Inc.
2820 Orchard Pkwy
San Jose CA 95134
408 470-1000

(G-5642)
ALPHABET MCD DIVISION
7 Zane Grey St Ste A (79906-5214)
PHONE..................................915 593-2011
Alberto Chretin, *Principal*
▲ EMP: 27 EST: 2010
SALES (est): 9.6MM **Privately Held**
SIC: 3679 Electronic circuits

(G-5643)
AMERI-TECH DIST INC (PA)
Also Called: Inter-Wash-Garment Finishing
5201 El Paso Dr (79905-2820)
PHONE..................................915 772-9090
Alfred Fernandez, *President*
Alfonso Font, *Vice Pres*
Jose Briones, *CFO*
Arthur Fernandez, *Manager*
EMP: 28
SQ FT: 6,000
SALES (est): 9.1MM **Privately Held**
WEB: www.ameritechllc.com
SIC: 2325 Men's & boys' jeans & dungarees

(G-5644)
ANMAR ENTERPRISES INC
Also Called: Airport Printing Service
7 Leigh Fisher Blvd (79906-5210)
P.O. Box 971007 (79997-1007)
PHONE..................................915 772-7488
Anita McCorgary, *President*
Marvin McCorgary, *Vice Pres*
Mike McCorgary, *Vice Pres*
Doug Barton, *Prdtn Mgr*
Ellen Howard, *Cust Svc Dir*
EMP: 27
SQ FT: 21,600
SALES (est): 4.5MM **Privately Held**
WEB: www.airportprinting.com
SIC: 2752 Commercial printing, offset

(G-5645)
APCO BUILDING SPECIALTIES INC
4737 Osborne Dr (79922-1011)
P.O. Box 12807 (79913-0807)
PHONE..................................915 581-6005

Lindsay B Holt, *CEO*
Thomas Buck, *President*
Willie Beltran, *Vice Pres*
Michael Hinojos, *Vice Pres*
Mario Saucedo, *Sales Staff*
EMP: 45 EST: 1955
SALES (est): 11.6MM **Privately Held**
WEB: www.apcobuildingspecialties.com
SIC: 5072 5031 3442 Builders' hardware; security devices, locks; metal doors, sash & trim; metal doors, sash & trim

(G-5646)
APTIV SERVICES US LLC
Also Called: Delphi
48 Walter Jones Blvd (79906-5301)
PHONE..................................915 783-4200
Gary De Arment, *Plant Mgr*
Steven Whitaker, *Engineer*
Jaziel Jimenez, *Design Engr*
Gary Dakolios, *Branch Mgr*
EMP: 26
SALES (corp-wide): 14.4B **Privately Held**
WEB: www.delphi.com
SIC: 3714 Motor vehicle parts & accessories
HQ: Aptiv Services Us, Llc
5725 Innovation Dr
Troy MI 48098

(G-5647)
APTIV SERVICES US LLC
Also Called: Electronics & Safety
48 Walter Jones Blvd (79906-5301)
PHONE..................................915 783-4769
Jeff Owens, *Branch Mgr*
EMP: 157
SALES (corp-wide): 14.4B **Privately Held**
WEB: www.delphi.com
SIC: 3714 Motor vehicle parts & accessories
HQ: Aptiv Services Us, Llc
5725 Innovation Dr
Troy MI 48098

(G-5648)
APTIV SERVICES US LLC
Also Called: Delphi Energy
48 Walter Jones Blvd D (79906-5301)
PHONE..................................915 783-4787
David Panko, *Branch Mgr*
EMP: 14
SALES (corp-wide): 14.4B **Privately Held**
WEB: www.delphi.com
SIC: 3714 Motor vehicle parts & accessories
HQ: Aptiv Services Us, Llc
5725 Innovation Dr
Troy MI 48098

(G-5649)
ARCHITECTURAL PRODUCTS CO INC (PA)
4737 Osborne Dr (79922-1011)
P.O. Box 12807 (79913-0807)
PHONE..................................915 584-9424
Lindsay B Holt, *Chairman*
Harriet Holt, *Vice Pres*
Thomas Buck, *Treasurer*
Denise Sanchez, *Human Res Mgr*
EMP: 46
SQ FT: 12,000
SALES (est): 5.7MM **Privately Held**
WEB: www.apcoinc.net
SIC: 3444 3443 3442 3441 Sheet metalwork; fabricated plate work (boiler shop); metal doors, sash & trim; fabricated structural metal; manufactured hardware (general); builders' hardware

(G-5650)
AREA IRON & STEEL WORKS INC
4605 Osborne Dr (79922-1025)
P.O. Box 13265 (79913-3265)
PHONE..................................915 833-9494
Karen Edmonston, *President*
Frederick Edmonston, *Vice Pres*
EMP: 15
SQ FT: 20,000
SALES (est): 5.1MM **Privately Held**
WEB: www.areaironandsteel.com
SIC: 3441 Fabricated structural metal

(G-5651)
ARIAS LOGISTICS INC (PA)
543 S Americas Ave Ste A1 (79907-5647)
PHONE..................................915 872-0034
Gilberto Arias, *President*
Alex Rivera, *Opers Mgr*
◆ EMP: 34
SQ FT: 48,000
SALES (est): 3.7MM **Privately Held**
WEB: www.ariaslogistics.com
SIC: 3825 Logic circuit testers

(G-5652)
ARMACEUTICA INC
1155 Galloway Dr (79902-2109)
PHONE..................................949 677-6001
Ernest Armstrong, *CEO*
EMP: 14
SALES (est): 629K **Privately Held**
SIC: 2834 Pharmaceutical preparations

(G-5653)
ATOMIC CONTAINER HOMES INC
1575 E San Antonio Ave (79901-1723)
PHONE..................................915 433-4817
Leslie Burk, *President*
Halle Blessings, *COO*
David Torres, *Exec VP*
Ethan Day, *Treasurer*
Diana Burk, *Director*
EMP: 27 EST: 2001
SQ FT: 21,000
SALES (est): 25MM **Privately Held**
WEB: www.containerhome.center
SIC: 2451 1542 1531 1541 Mobile buildings: for commercial use; commercial & office buildings, prefabricated erection; ; steel building construction; buildings, portable: prefabricated metal; agricultural research

(G-5654)
AUTO KABEL NORTH AMERICA INC
1320 Henry Brennan Dr (79936-6803)
PHONE..................................915 217-2253
Jens Schumacher, *Branch Mgr*
EMP: 30
SALES (corp-wide): 391.6MM **Privately Held**
SIC: 3714 Booster (jump-start) cables, automotive
HQ: Auto Kabel Of North America, Inc.
7362 Remcon Cir
El Paso TX 79912
915 217-2253

(G-5655)
AUTO KABEL NORTH AMERICA INC (DH)
7362 Remcon Cir (79912-1623)
PHONE..................................915 217-2253
Jens Schumacher, *CEO*
Dieter F Griesenbach, *President*
Josef Sievering, *CFO*
▲ EMP: 14
SALES (est): 9.9MM
SALES (corp-wide): 391.6MM **Privately Held**
SIC: 3714 Booster (jump-start) cables, automotive
HQ: Auto-Kabel Management Gmbh
Im Grien 1a
Hausen Im Wiesental 79688
762 239-030

(G-5656)
AXXION GROUP CORPORATION
4731 Ripley Dr Ste A (79922-1026)
PHONE..................................915 225-8888
Po-Wen Hu, *President*
Fu Hsiun Lien, *President*
Henry Yoshawirja, *Exec VP*
Carlos Ortega, *Vice Pres*
Kevin Patin, *Engineer*
EMP: 75
SQ FT: 80,000
SALES (est): 24MM **Privately Held**
WEB: www.lfe-ww.com
SIC: 5045 3469 Computer peripheral equipment; metal stampings

GEOGRAPHIC

(G-5657)
AZTEC IMPORTS INC
9701 Pan American Dr # 100 (79927-2141)
PHONE...................................915 858-2287
Esther Armendariz, *CEO*
Mike Balibrera, *President*
Robert Armendariz, *Corp Secy*
Al Balibrera, *Sales Mgr*
▲ EMP: 20
SQ FT: 20,000
SALES (est): 4.1MM **Privately Held**
WEB: www.aztecimports.com
SIC: 2679 5199 Novelties, paper: made
from purchased material; gifts & novelties

(G-5658)
**BALLOFFET DIE CORPORATION
INC**
11450 Rojas Dr Ste D17 (79936-6995)
PHONE...................................915 592-5252
Richard Barthod, *President*
Bill Couse, *Vice Pres*
◆ EMP: 16
SQ FT: 3,300
SALES (est): 2MM **Privately Held**
WEB: www.balloffetdie.com
SIC: 3544 Diamond dies, metalworking

(G-5659)
BASSETT WOODWORKS
Also Called: Basset Wood Work
11905 Golden Gate Rd (79936-5806)
PHONE...................................915 855-2144
Ralph Murillo, *Owner*
EMP: 18
SALES (est): 700K **Privately Held**
WEB: www.bassettwoodworks.com
SIC: 2434 Wood kitchen cabinets

(G-5660)
BECK-DRENNAN INC
Also Called: Printing Corner, The
7741 Lockheed Dr (79925-2403)
P.O. Box 972955 (79997-2955)
PHONE...................................915 772-3800
Vicki Drennan, *President*
Vince Hernandez, *Admin Sec*
EMP: 10
SQ FT: 12,950
SALES (est): 1MM **Privately Held**
SIC: 2752 Commercial printing, offset

(G-5661)
BELTRAN PRECAST INC
860 Kastrin St (79907-2724)
PHONE...................................915 599-8777
Raymundo Beltran, *President*
Juan Beltran, *Admin Sec*
EMP: 10
SQ FT: 2,500
SALES (est): 999.1K **Privately Held**
WEB: www.beltranelp.com
SIC: 3272 Concrete products, precast

(G-5662)
**BIG BEAR OIL COMPANY INC
(HQ)**
Also Called: Ysleta Del Sur Pblo Ltd Prtnr
1025 Wall St (79915-1012)
PHONE...................................915 775-1945
Randolph Maxwell, *CEO*
Carlos Hisa, *President*
EMP: 19
SQ FT: 11,940
SALES (est): 5.2MM **Privately Held**
SIC: 1311 5172 Crude petroleum & natu-
ral gas; petroleum products
PA: Del Ysleta Sur Pueblo
119 S Old Pueblo Dr
Ysleta Sur TX 79907
915 859-7913

(G-5663)
BITECH TOOL & DIE INC
5240 Tetons Dr (79904-2257)
PHONE...................................915 757-8001
David Garcia, *President*
Roberto Garcia, *President*
Jorge Cano, *Vice Pres*
Ruben Garcia, *Vice Pres*
▲ EMP: 25
SALES (est): 4.2MM **Privately Held**
WEB: www.bitech.net
SIC: 3544 Special dies & tools

(G-5664)
BMV MEDIA LLC
6209 Airport Rd (79925-2062)
PHONE...................................915 216-3554
Francisco J Bowler Sr,
Francisco Bowler,
EMP: 20 EST: 2017
SALES (est): 555.1K **Privately Held**
WEB: www.bmvmediasigns.com
SIC: 3999 Manufacturing industries

(G-5665)
BOEING COMPANY
9566 Railroad Dr (79924-6318)
P.O. Box 240002, Huntsville AL (35813-
6402)
PHONE...................................915 834-1000
EMP: 300
SALES (corp-wide): 58.1B **Publicly Held**
WEB: www.boeing.com
SIC: 3721 Aircraft
PA: The Boeing Company
100 N Riverside Plz
Chicago IL 60606
312 544-2000

(G-5666)
**BORDER APPAREL LAUNDRY
LTD**
6969 Industrial Ave (79915-1107)
PHONE...................................915 772-7170
Enrique Cervantes, *Partner*
Jesus Cervantes, *Partner*
Yadira Avalos, *Purchasing*
Saul Cervantes, *Administration*
▲ EMP: 50
SQ FT: 80,000
SALES (est): 176.2MM **Privately Held**
SIC: 2326 7211 Men's & boys' work cloth-
ing; power laundries, family & commercial

(G-5667)
BORDER ASSEMBLY INC
Also Called: Border Delivery
11394 James Watt Dr # 405 (79936-6440)
P.O. Box 447, Gilmer (75644-0447)
PHONE...................................915 592-1172
Brian Busse, *President*
EMP: 20 ◆
SQ FT: 30,000
SALES (est): 2MM **Privately Held**
SIC: 3672 3679 5162 5065 Printed circuit
boards; harness assemblies for electronic
use: wire or cable; plastics basic shapes;
transformers, electronic; insulation, ther-
mal; noise control equipment

(G-5668)
**BORDER INDUSTRIAL MOTORS
INC**
9305 Lait Dr (79925-6638)
PHONE...................................915 542-4266
Juan Saldana Jr, *President*
Soledad C Saldana, *Corp Secy*
Robert King, *Vice Pres*
EMP: 9
SQ FT: 5,600
SALES (est): 1.4MM **Privately Held**
WEB: www.borderstates.com
SIC: 5063 7694 Motors, electric; electric
motor repair

(G-5669)
BORDER PALLETS INC
291 S Darrington Rd (79928-7447)
PHONE...................................915 852-3939
Felipe Truax, *President*
Barbara Truax, *Vice Pres*
EMP: 34
SALES (est): 5.4MM **Privately Held**
WEB: www.borderpallets.com
SIC: 2448 Pallets, wood

(G-5670)
**BORDER STATES INDUSTRIES
INC**
Border States Electric Supply
8101 Lockheed Dr (79925-2501)
PHONE...................................575 434-2022
Dustin Rardin, *Branch Mgr*
EMP: 11

SALES (corp-wide): 2.4B **Privately Held**
WEB: www.borderstates.com
SIC: 5063 5065 5074 1711 Electrical
supplies; electronic parts & equipment;
plumbing & hydronic heating supplies;
plumbing, heating, air-conditioning contractors; plastics plumbing fixtures; vitreous plumbing fixtures
PA: Border States Industries, Inc.
2400 38th St S
Fargo ND 58104
701 293-5834

(G-5671)
BORDER TM INDUSTRIES INC
Also Called: Xceed Resources
201b N Clark Dr (79905-3105)
P.O. Box 9091 (79995-9091)
PHONE...................................915 779-6431
Raul Sifuentes, *General Mgr*
Jesus Sanchez, *Prdtn Mgr*
Juan Gonzalez, *Accounting Mgr*
Graciela Arreola, *Human Resources*
Eddie Sanchez, *Exec Dir*
EMP: 105
SQ FT: 9,000
SALES: 3.5MM **Privately Held**
WEB: www.xceedresources.org
SIC: 0781 8331 3084 Landscape serv-
ices; sheltered workshop; plastics pipe

(G-5672)
**BORGWARNER TRANSM
SYSTEMS LLC**
45 Butterfield Cir Ste D (79906-5222)
PHONE...................................915 217-9268
Cuauhtemoc Eulloqui, *Manager*
EMP: 12
SALES (corp-wide): 10.1B **Publicly Held**
WEB: www.ts.aftermarket.borgwarner.com
SIC: 3714 Motor vehicle parts & acces-
sories
HQ: Borgwarner Transmission Systems Llc
3850 Hamlin Rd
Auburn Hills MI 48326
248 754-9200

(G-5673)
BRK BRANDS INC
1301 Joe Battle Blvd (79936-0903)
PHONE...................................915 860-3500
Olga Garnica, *Manager*
EMP: 10
SALES (corp-wide): 9.7B **Publicly Held**
WEB: www.brkelectronics.com
SIC: 3669 3999 3829 Smoke detectors;
fire extinguishers, portable; gas detectors
HQ: Brk Brands, Inc.
3901 Liberty St
Aurora IL 60504

(G-5674)
BRUCE FOODS CORPORATION
8000 Ashley Rd (79934-2603)
PHONE...................................915 821-2500
Tom Lahut, *COO*
EMP: 10
SALES (corp-wide): 115.8MM **Privately
Held**
WEB: www.brucefoods.com
SIC: 2032 2033 2035 Mexican foods:
packaged in cans, jars, etc.; canned fruits
& specialties; pickles, sauces & salad
dressings
PA: Bruce Foods Corporation
221 Southpark Rd Ste A1
Lafayette LA 70508
337 365-8101

(G-5675)
C N A INC
Also Called: CNA Insurance
2217 E Mills Ave (79901-2000)
PHONE...................................915 533-2425
Sandra Pinard, *President*
EMP: 30
SQ FT: 30,000
SALES (est): 5MM **Privately Held**
WEB: www.cna.com
SIC: 6411 2386 Insurance agents, brokers
& service; leather & sheep-lined clothing

(G-5676)
C R BARD INC
Also Called: C R Bard
6930 Market Ave (79915-1109)
PHONE...................................915 781-2489
Heidi Esquivel, *Engineer*
Brad Smith, *Sales Staff*
EMP: 446
SALES (corp-wide): 17.1B **Publicly Held**
WEB: www.crbard.com
SIC: 3841 Surgical & medical instruments
HQ: C. R. Bard, Inc.
1 Becton Dr
Franklin Lakes NJ 07417
201 847-6800

(G-5677)
CAMBRIAN INDUSTRIES INC
8900 Viscount Blvd (79925-5897)
PHONE...................................915 771-6100
Fernando Cadena, *President*
EMP: 30
SALES (est): 4.9MM **Privately Held**
WEB: www.cambrianind.net
SIC: 3469 Machine parts, stamped or
pressed metal

(G-5678)
CAPABLE CONTROLS INC
3800 Buckner St (79925-1304)
PHONE...................................915 594-7659
EMP: 23 **Privately Held**
WEB: www.capablecontrols.com
SIC: 3625 Electric controls & control ac-
cessories, industrial
PA: Capable Controls, Inc.
1114 Tower Ln
Bensenville IL 60106

(G-5679)
CAPCO PLASTICS INC
Also Called: Capco West
9231 Billy The Kid St (79907-4738)
PHONE...................................915 772-1395
Bob Arno, *Manager*
EMP: 15
SALES (corp-wide): 8.4MM **Privately
Held**
WEB: www.capcoplastics.com
SIC: 3089 Blister or bubble formed pack-
aging, plastic
PA: Capco Plastics, Inc.
297 Dexter St
Providence RI 02907
401 272-3833

(G-5680)
CAPSONIC AUTOMOTIVE INC
7 Zane Grey St Ste B (79906-5214)
PHONE...................................915 872-3585
Edna Camargo, *Buyer*
Fransisco Delgadillo, *Branch Mgr*
EMP: 20 **Privately Held**
WEB: www.capsonic.com
SIC: 3625 Motor controls & accessories;
switches, electric power
PA: Capsonic Automotive, Inc.
460 2nd St
Elgin IL 60123

(G-5681)
CAPSONIC GROUP LLC
7 Zane Grey St (79906-5265)
PHONE...................................915 872-3539
Tom Gillespie, *Branch Mgr*
EMP: 25
SALES (corp-wide): 48.4MM **Privately
Held**
WEB: www.capsonicgroup.com
SIC: 3089 Injection molded finished plastic
products; injection molding of plastics
PA: Capsonic Group Llc
460 2nd St
Elgin IL 60123
847 888-7264

(G-5682)
CARDINAL HEALTH INC
1 Butterfield Trail Blvd (79906-4901)
PHONE...................................915 781-7465
Ignacio Mejolado, *Vice Pres*
EMP: 56
SALES (corp-wide): 152.9B **Publicly
Held**
WEB: www.cardinalhealth.com
SIC: 3842 Surgical appliances & supplies

▲ = Import ▼=Export
◆ =Import/Export

PA: Cardinal Health, Inc.
7000 Cardinal Pl
Dublin OH 43017
614 757-5000

(G-5683)
CAREFUSION 213 LLC
Also Called: Snowden-Pencer
1550 Northwestern Dr (79912-8000)
PHONE................................915 231-5000
Luz Olivas, *Buyer*
Aurelia Rascon, *Research*
Arturo Marquez, *Engineer*
Frank Muro, *Auditor*
Gloria Varela, *Director*
EMP: 500
SALES (corp-wide): 17.1B **Publicly Held**
WEB: www.bd.com
SIC: 2834 3841 Pharmaceutical prepara-
tions; surgical & medical instruments
HQ: Carefusion 213, Llc
3750 Torrey View Ct
San Diego CA 92130

(G-5684)
CARNICRIA Y TORTILLERIA EL
SOL
6215 Upper Valley Rd M (79932-4300)
PHONE................................915 877-5553
Veronica Chavez, *President*
Rene Acosta, *Vice Pres*
EMP: 9
SALES (est): 801.2K **Privately Held**
SIC: 2099 Tortillas, fresh or refrigerated

(G-5685)
CARRIAGE CASTING INC
1206 Mcrae Blvd A (79925-7502)
PHONE................................915 760-6800
Dee Farnum, *President*
Betty Farnum, *Vice Pres*
EMP: 9
SQ FT: 2,500
SALES (est): 997.2K **Privately Held**
SIC: 3915 Jewelers' castings

(G-5686)
CARRION ENTERPRISES INC
Also Called: A & A Custom Engravers
7230 Gateway Blvd E Ste C (79915-1353)
PHONE................................915 593-1338
Andrew Carrion, *President*
EMP: 11 EST: 1972
SALES (est): 350K **Privately Held**
SIC: 2282 7622 5999 7389 Embroidery
yarn: twisting, winding or spooling; radio
repair & installation; trophies & plaques;
engraving service

(G-5687)
CEGA INC
11501 Rojas Dr Ste F (79936-6900)
PHONE................................915 633-1660
Ruben C Mendoza, *President*
Maria E Zubia, *Admin Sec*
EMP: 19
SALES (est): 3.9MM **Privately Held**
SIC: 3599 Machine shop, jobbing & repair

(G-5688)
CEGA INC
1220 Barranca Dr Ste 3 (79935-4606)
PHONE................................915 257-1898
Ruben Cepeda, *President*
EMP: 13
SALES (est): 1.7MM **Privately Held**
SIC: 3599 Machine shop, jobbing & repair

(G-5689)
CEMEX CONSTRUCTION MTLS S
LLC
Also Called: Open-Plant
2050 Cherrington St (79928-5609)
PHONE................................915 855-9658
Rey Loya, *Manager*
EMP: 38 **Privately Held**
WEB: www.cemexusa.com
SIC: 3273 Ready-mixed concrete
HQ: Cemex Construction Materials South,
Llc
2088 E 20th St
Yuma AZ 85365
928 343-4100

(G-5690)
CEMEX CONSTRUCTION MTLS S
LLC
Also Called: El Paso Regional Admin Office
1 Mckelligon Canyon Rd (79930-2634)
PHONE................................915 565-4681
EMP: 36 **Privately Held**
WEB: www.cemexusa.com
SIC: 3273 Ready-mixed concrete
HQ: Cemex Construction Materials South,
Llc
2088 E 20th St
Yuma AZ 85365
928 343-4100

(G-5691)
CEMEX EL PASO INC (DH)
1 Mckelligon Canyon Rd (79930-2634)
PHONE................................915 565-4681
Bill Poole, *President*
Juan Romero, *Exec VP*
EMP: 230
SQ FT: 4,000
SALES (est): 95.8MM **Privately Held**
WEB: www.elpaso.homesandland.com
SIC: 3273 2951 5032 1442 Ready-mixed
concrete; paving blocks; sand, construc-
tion; stone, crushed or broken; construc-
tion sand & gravel
HQ: Rmc Usa, Inc
920 Memorial City Way
Houston TX 77024
713 650-6200

(G-5692)
CEMEX EL PASO INC
6101 Stan Roberts Sr Ave (79934-3306)
PHONE................................915 564-8400
Luis Najera, *General Mgr*
EMP: 200 **Privately Held**
WEB: www.elpaso.homesandland.com
SIC: 1442 Construction sand mining;
gravel mining
HQ: Cemex El Paso, Inc.
1 Mckelligon Canyon Rd
El Paso TX 79930
915 565-4681

(G-5693)
CER TEK INC
5740 Cleveland Ave (79925-3327)
PHONE................................915 772-8290
Joe Bickley, *President*
Ann Louise Floyd, *Vice Pres*
EMP: 10
SQ FT: 5,300
SALES (est): 1.1MM **Privately Held**
SIC: 3549 3674 Metalworking machinery;
semiconductors & related devices

(G-5694)
CESAR-SCOTT INC (PA)
1731 Myrtle Ave (79901-1831)
PHONE................................915 543-3212
Gus Farell, *President*
Gus Farelll, *President*
Paula Farell, *Corp Secy*
Cesar Farell, *Vice Pres*
Fernando Moreno, *Opers Staff*
▲ EMP: 17
SQ FT: 6,000
SALES: 4.5MM **Privately Held**
WEB: www.cesar-scott.com
SIC: 3496 Miscellaneous fabricated wire
products

(G-5695)
CHAMPLAIN CABLE TEXAS
CORP
9560 Plaza Cir (79927-2008)
PHONE................................915 860-0010
Richard Hall, *President*
Timothy Lizotte, *CFO*
Manny Noriega, *Manager*
Manual Noriega, *Technical Staff*
EMP: 10 EST: 2010
SQ FT: 80,000
SALES (est): 1.1MM
SALES (corp-wide): 53MM **Privately**
Held
WEB: www.champcable.com
SIC: 3355 Aluminum wire & cable

PA: Champlain Cable Corporation
175 Hercules Dr
Colchester VT 05446
802 654-4200

(G-5696)
CLASSIC MILLWORK AND
PRODUCTS
275 Rio West Dr (79932-1808)
PHONE................................915 833-9922
Bruce B Spitz, *President*
Bruce Spitz, *CFO*
Cynthia Spitz, *Admin Sec*
EMP: 24
SQ FT: 12,000
SALES (est): 3.1MM **Privately Held**
WEB: www.classicmillworkelpaso.com
SIC: 2542 2521 2434 Cabinets: show,
display or storage: except wood; wood of-
fice furniture; wood kitchen cabinets

(G-5697)
CLAUDES SAUCES INC
935 Loma Verde Dr (79936-7821)
P.O. Box 50157, Albuquerque NM (87181-
0157)
PHONE................................915 858-4299
Glenda J Castaneda, *President*
Stephen L Castaneda, *Vice Pres*
Veronica Castaneda, *Administration*
Christy Cattaneo, *Administration*
EMP: 13
SQ FT: 24,500
SALES (est): 1.5MM **Privately Held**
WEB: www.claudessauces.com
SIC: 2033 5149 Barbecue sauce: pack-
aged in cans, jars, etc.; spices & season-
ings

(G-5698)
CLOVER GROUP INC
2914 Alameda Ave (79905-2208)
PHONE................................915 590-2525
Genoveva T Edmunds, *President*
Maria Casanas, *Export Mgr*
EMP: 30
SQ FT: 15,000
SALES (est): 6.2MM **Privately Held**
SIC: 5085 3425 2273 Industrial tools;
knives, industrial; saw blades & hand-
saws; carpets & rugs

(G-5699)
COLEMAN CABLE LLC
Also Called: South Wire Coleman Cable
7811 Hoover Ave (79912-8801)
PHONE................................915 858-7475
Rick Hernandez, *General Mgr*
EMP: 110
SALES (corp-wide): 2B **Privately Held**
WEB: www.southwire.com
SIC: 3643 Power line cable
HQ: Coleman Cable, Llc
1 Overlook Pt Ste 265
Lincolnshire IL 60069
847 672-2300

(G-5700)
COLUMBUS INDUSTRIES INC
Also Called: Columbus Industry of Texas
32 Spur Dr Ste A (79906-5321)
PHONE................................915 843-2274
Steve Porter, *Vice Pres*
Terry Vourvopoulos, *Vice Pres*
J Dickson, *Warehouse Mgr*
Russell Baldinger, *Engrg Dir*
Jeff Pontius, *Branch Mgr*
EMP: 117
SALES (corp-wide): 184.8MM **Privately**
Held
WEB: www.colind.com
SIC: 3564 Filters, air: furnaces, air condi-
tioning equipment, etc.
PA: Columbus Industries, Inc.
2938 State Route 752
Ashville OH 43103
740 983-2552

(G-5701)
COMPASS ELECTRONICS
GROUP LLC
Also Called: Protech Global
45 Butterfield Cir Ste C (79906-5222)
PHONE................................915 594-0500
John Huhn, *CEO*
EMP: 89

SALES (corp-wide): 10.1MM **Privately**
Held
WEB: www.cgep.com
SIC: 3679 Electronic loads & power sup-
plies
PA: Compass Electronics Group, Llc
7701 Forsyth Blvd Ste 850
Saint Louis MO 63105
314 721-2800

(G-5702)
COMPLETE REPROGRAPHICS
INC
6122 Trowbridge Dr (79905-2199)
PHONE................................915 779-5000
Reagan Williams, *President*
Rhonda Williams, *Vice Pres*
EMP: 14
SQ FT: 12,000
SALES (est): 1.1MM **Privately Held**
WEB: www.completerepro.com
SIC: 7334 5999 2752 2399 Blueprinting
service; architectural supplies; posters,
lithographed; banners, pennants & flags;
commercial art & illustration

(G-5703)
COMPUTER LABS INC
3 Buttrfield Trail Blvd St (79906)
PHONE................................915 775-1839
Rueben Lopez, *President*
EMP: 25
SQ FT: 23,920
SALES (est): 1MM **Privately Held**
WEB: www.4cpubiz.com
SIC: 7372 Prepackaged software

(G-5704)
COWTOWN BOOT COMPANY
(PA)
11401 Gateway Blvd W (79936-6499)
P.O. Box 26428 (79926-6428)
PHONE................................915 593-2929
Paul Calcattera, *President*
Joseph Calcattera Jr, *Vice Pres*
▲ EMP: 75 EST: 1962
SQ FT: 140,000
SALES (est): 9.9MM **Privately Held**
WEB: www.cowtownboots.com
SIC: 5661 3143 5139 3144 Men's boots;
boots, dress or casual: men's; boots;
women's footwear, except athletic

(G-5705)
CREATIVE MOLDED
PACKAGING LLC
Also Called: Market Avenue Packaging
6980 Market Ave (79915-1112)
PHONE................................915 881-8401
Carlos Chavira Rodriguez, *CEO*
EMP: 10
SALES (est): 150.5K **Privately Held**
WEB: www.marketavenuepackaging.com
SIC: 5199 3053 2631 2621 Packaging
materials; packing materials; cardboard;
molded pulp products

(G-5706)
CUMMINS DIESEL FUEL INC
9615 Plaza Cir Ste 100 (79927-2150)
PHONE................................915 858-7310
Rosa Fuentes, *Principal*
EMP: 118
SALES (est): 28.6MM **Privately Held**
SIC: 3519 Internal combustion engines

(G-5707)
CUMMINS INC
14333 Gateway Blvd W (79928-6602)
PHONE................................915 791-6600
Carlos Payan, *Manager*
EMP: 34
SQ FT: 43,600
SALES (corp-wide): 19.8B **Publicly Held**
WEB: www.cummins.com
SIC: 5084 7538 3519 Engines, gasoline;
diesel engine repair: automotive; internal
combustion engines
PA: Cummins Inc.
500 Jackson St
Columbus IN 47201
812 377-5000

G
E
O
G
R
A
P
H
I
C

(G-5708)
CUMMINS INC
9615 Plaza Cir Ste 100 (79927-2150)
PHONE.....................................915 858-7310
David Porter, *Plant Mgr*
Rosa Fuentes, *Supervisor*
EMP: 18
SALES (corp-wide): 19.8B **Publicly Held**
WEB: www.cummins.com
SIC: 3519 Engines, diesel & semi-diesel or dual-fuel
PA: Cummins Inc.
　　500 Jackson St
　　Columbus IN 47201
　　812 377-5000

(G-5709)
CUMMINS JREZ EMISSION SOLUTION
9615 Plaza Cir Ste 100 (79927-2150)
PHONE.....................................844 401-0221
Heriberto Rodriguez, *Manager*
EMP: 56 EST: 2014
SALES (est): 4.7MM **Privately Held**
SIC: 3519 Internal combustion engines

(G-5710)
D & D TOOLING AND MFG INC
1330 Pullman Dr (79936-7780)
PHONE.....................................915 590-2655
Fernando Zeh, *Manager*
EMP: 20
SALES (corp-wide): 23.2MM **Privately Held**
WEB: www.danddmfg.wixsite.com
SIC: 3469 Stamping metal for the trade
PA: D & D Tooling And Manufacturing, Inc.
　　500 Territorial Dr
　　Bolingbrook IL 60440
　　888 300-6869

(G-5711)
D SQUARE INC
1601 Northwestern Dr # 100 (79912-8022)
PHONE.....................................915 834-6400
Angie Biano, *Principal*
EMP: 12 EST: 2010
SALES (est): 2.2MM **Privately Held**
SIC: 3699 Electrical equipment & supplies

(G-5712)
DANA GLOBAL PRODUCTS INC
12150 Rojas Dr Ste A (79936-7710)
PHONE.....................................915 860-7204
EMP: 9 **Publicly Held**
WEB: www.dana.com
SIC: 3714 Motor vehicle parts & accessories
HQ: Dana Global Products, Inc.
　　3939 Technology Dr
　　Maumee OH 43537

(G-5713)
DANRICK INDUSTRIES INC
850 Kastrin St (79907-2724)
PHONE.....................................915 599-2988
Marco A Herrera, *President*
EMP: 18
SQ FT: 8,670
SALES (est): 3.3MM **Privately Held**
WEB: www.danrickindustries.com
SIC: 3544 Special dies & tools

(G-5714)
DARLING QUICK PRINT INC
Also Called: Labels Plus
12130 Freight Ln (79936-6821)
PHONE.....................................915 858-5055
Michael Darling, *President*
Michael J Keller, *Vice Pres*
EMP: 20 EST: 1977
SQ FT: 11,000
SALES (est): 3.2MM **Privately Held**
WEB: www.labelsplus.net
SIC: 2752 2671 Commercial printing, offset; packaging paper & plastics film, coated & laminated

(G-5715)
DAVIDS APPAREL INC
9901 Carnegie Ave (79925-1503)
PHONE.....................................915 590-3744
David Partida, *President*
Refugio Partida, *Corp Secy*
J D Partida, *Vice Pres*
EMP: 25 EST: 1985
SQ FT: 14,400
SALES (est): 2.6MM **Privately Held**
WEB: www.davidsapparel.com
SIC: 2759 2396 2395 Screen printing; automotive & apparel trimmings; pleating & stitching

(G-5716)
DEL NORTE MASONRY PRODUCTS INC
4560 Ripley Dr (79922-1096)
PHONE.....................................915 584-4453
Richard R Backer, *President*
Kay Backer, *Vice Pres*
EMP: 30
SQ FT: 25,000
SALES (est): 5.4MM **Privately Held**
WEB: www.delnortemasonryproducts.com
SIC: 3271 5032 3272 Blocks, concrete or cinder: standard; brick, except refractory; concrete & cinder building products; concrete products

(G-5717)
DELFINGEN US-TEXAS LP (DH)
12270 Rojas Dr Ste 300 (79936-7713)
PHONE.....................................915 858-5577
Gerald Streit, *CEO*
Bernard Streit, *President*
David Streit, *Vice Pres*
Jean Remond, *Plant Mgr*
Albert Bustillos, *Prdtn Mgr*
◆ EMP: 34
SQ FT: 100,000
SALES (est): 19.9MM
SALES (corp-wide): 3.1MM **Privately Held**
WEB: www.delfingen.com
SIC: 3089 3083 Plastic processing; laminated plastics plate & sheet

(G-5718)
DELPHI POWERTRAIN SYSTEMS LLC
48 Walter Jones Blvd (79906-5301)
PHONE.....................................915 783-4733
Juan Ruiz, *Branch Mgr*
EMP: 14
SALES (corp-wide): 1.2MM **Privately Held**
WEB: www.delphi.com
SIC: 3714 Motor vehicle parts & accessories
HQ: Delphi Powertrain Systems, Llc
　　3000 University Dr
　　Auburn Hills MI 48326
　　248 707-5224

(G-5719)
DELPHI POWERTRAIN SYSTEMS LLC
48 Walter Jones Blvd (79906-5301)
PHONE.....................................915 783-4769
David Kronofhek, *Manager*
EMP: 23
SALES (corp-wide): 1.2MM **Privately Held**
WEB: www.delphi.com
SIC: 3714 Motor vehicle parts & accessories
HQ: Delphi Powertrain Systems, Llc
　　3000 University Dr
　　Auburn Hills MI 48326
　　248 707-5224

(G-5720)
DESERT FBRCTION MILLWRIGHT SVC
10342 Grouse Rd (79924-2710)
P.O. Box 640038 (79904-0038)
PHONE.....................................915 821-3172
Neal Kane, *President*
EMP: 9
SQ FT: 7,500
SALES (est): 902.2K **Privately Held**
SIC: 3599 Machine shop, jobbing & repair

(G-5721)
DESERT ROCK CO
8500 Plant Rd (79907-5958)
P.O. Box 17727 (79917-7727)
PHONE.....................................915 859-5969
Gilbert L Sanchez, *President*
Eric Sanchez, *Treasurer*
Cathy Sanchez, *Executive*
Enriquetta Sanchez, *Admin Sec*
EMP: 11
SALES (est): 3.1MM **Privately Held**
WEB: www.desertrockco.com
SIC: 5211 1442 1429 Paving stones; construction sand & gravel; grits mining (crushed stone)

(G-5722)
DLC CONSTRUCTION INC
8411 Lockheed Dr Ste 3 (79925-1259)
PHONE.....................................915 771-7580
Adan Delacueva, *President*
Adan De La Cueva, *President*
EMP: 11
SALES (est): 2.2MM **Privately Held**
SIC: 2951 Paving blocks

(G-5723)
DOOR SA-LUTIONS INC
6840 Industrial Ave (79915-1011)
PHONE.....................................915 781-0664
Jaime Sapien Jr, *President*
Maribel Sapien, *Vice Pres*
EMP: 10
SQ FT: 2,500
SALES (est): 1.7MM **Privately Held**
WEB: www.doorsalutionsinc.com
SIC: 2431 Doors, wood

(G-5724)
DREGON LLC
5108 Bragg Ave (79904-3408)
PHONE.....................................910 670-8211
Raul Pedregon, *CEO*
Thomas Plank, *Principal*
EMP: 15
SALES (est): 586.5K **Privately Held**
SIC: 3484 Small arms

(G-5725)
DURABOX CORRUGATED PDTS INC
9155 Billy The Kid St (79907-4736)
PHONE.....................................915 440-4409
Ricardo Ortega, *President*
EMP: 10
SALES (est): 871.4K **Privately Held**
WEB: www.durabox.com.mx
SIC: 2653 Boxes, corrugated: made from purchased materials

(G-5726)
DYNAMIC TOOL COMPANY INC
1421 Vanderbilt Dr (79935-4893)
PHONE.....................................915 598-2330
Jf Thompson, *President*
Robert Schulz, *Vice Pres*
Robert C Schulz, *Vice Pres*
▲ EMP: 95
SQ FT: 17,250
SALES (est): 19.3MM **Privately Held**
WEB: www.dynamictool.com
SIC: 3599 3544 Machine shop, jobbing & repair; industrial molds; special dies & tools

(G-5727)
DYNATEC SCIENTIFIC LABS
11940 Golden Gate Rd (79936-5805)
PHONE.....................................915 849-1322
Rudolfo Pina, *President*
EMP: 35
SQ FT: 6,000
SALES (est): 3.7MM **Privately Held**
WEB: www.dynatec-labs.com
SIC: 8734 3842 Testing laboratories; surgical appliances & supplies

(G-5728)
E & L GRAPHICS LLC
Also Called: El Paso Mail and Print Service
1144 Vista De Oro Dr A (79935-4904)
P.O. Box 370943 (79937-0943)
PHONE.....................................915 591-8789
Justin Riley, *Accounts Exec*
Lorena Armendariz, *Mng Member*
Edward Armendariz,
EMP: 15
SALES (est): 1.6MM **Privately Held**
WEB: www.epmailprint.com
SIC: 7331 2759 Mailing service; commercial printing

(G-5729)
EAGLE FAMILY FOODS GROUP LLC
255 Montoya Rd (79932-1803)
PHONE.....................................915 584-7189
EMP: 103
SALES (corp-wide): 200MM **Privately Held**
SIC: 2023 Mfg Dry/Evaporated Dairy Products
PA: Eagle Family Foods Group Llc
　　4020 Kinross Lakes Pkwy
　　Richfield OH 44103
　　330 382-3725

(G-5730)
EATON CORPORATION
6 Founders Blvd (79906-9400)
P.O. Box 26129 (79926-6129)
PHONE.....................................915 779-4524
Elisa Ramirez, *Human Res Mgr*
Zeke Barrbra, *Manager*
EMP: 500 **Privately Held**
WEB: www.eatonelectrical.com
SIC: 3625 Relays & industrial controls
HQ: Eaton Corporation
　　1000 Eaton Blvd
　　Cleveland OH 44122
　　440 523-5000

(G-5731)
EATON CORPORATION
7800 Trade Center Ave (79912-8407)
PHONE.....................................262 765-9764
Alexander Cutler, *CEO*
Matthew Nezbeth, *Manager*
EMP: 400 **Privately Held**
WEB: www.eatonelectrical.com
SIC: 3625 Motor controls & accessories
HQ: Eaton Corporation
　　1000 Eaton Blvd
　　Cleveland OH 44122
　　440 523-5000

(G-5732)
EATON CORPORATION
Also Called: Commercial Indus Fcilities Div
60 A Basset Ctr (79925)
PHONE.....................................915 772-6198
Oswaldo Jeffery, *Engineer*
Ruben Rodriguez, *Branch Mgr*
EMP: 19 **Privately Held**
WEB: www.eatonelectrical.com
SIC: 5063 3613 Electrical apparatus & equipment; switchgear & switchboard apparatus
HQ: Eaton Corporation
　　1000 Eaton Blvd
　　Cleveland OH 44122
　　440 523-5000

(G-5733)
EATON CORPORATION
Also Called: Eaton Electrical
45 Butterfield Cir Ste C (79906-5222)
PHONE.....................................915 881-0259
EMP: 217 **Privately Held**
WEB: www.eatonelectrical.com
SIC: 3625 Relays & industrial controls
HQ: Eaton Corporation
　　1000 Eaton Blvd
　　Cleveland OH 44122
　　440 523-5000

(G-5734)
EC WRECKING & SALVAGE CORP
Also Called: Fiesta Auto Salvage
1931 Texas Ave (79901-1916)
PHONE.....................................915 855-7999
▲ EMP: 19 EST: 1996
SQ FT: 35,000
SALES (est): 2.5MM **Privately Held**
SIC: 5093 3341 Automotive wrecking for scrap; secondary nonferrous metals

(G-5735)
EL PASO HEAT TRANSFER INC
5400 Suncrest Dr Ste C6 (79912-5615)
P.O. Box 9902 (79995-2902)
PHONE.....................................915 779-6334
Rodolfo Murra, *President*
Rita De La Fuente, *General Mgr*
Silvia Murra, *Admin Mgr*
EMP: 12

▲ = Import ▼=Export
◆ =Import/Export

SALES (est): 1.8MM **Privately Held**
WEB: www.passotransfer.com
SIC: 2752 3993 Decals, lithographed; advertising novelties

(G-5736)
EL PASO LIGHTHOUSE FOR BLIND
205 Tobin Pl (79905-3826)
PHONE................................915 532-4495
EMP: 45 **EST:** 1934
SQ FT: 25,000
SALES (est): 2.2MM **Privately Held**
WEB: www.lighthouse-elpaso.com
SIC: 2311 Military uniforms, men's & youths': purchased materials

(G-5737)
EL PASO MACHINE & STEEL INC
1600 E 4th Ave (79901-3506)
P.O. Box 175 (79942-0175)
PHONE................................915 533-7483
William Fred Kastrin, *President*
Veronica Callaghan, *Vice Pres*
Deborah C Kastrin, *Admin Sec*
EMP: 30
SQ FT: 5,000
SALES (est): 5.4MM **Privately Held**
WEB: www.kascostructures.com
SIC: 3449 5051 3441 Miscellaneous metalwork; iron & steel (ferrous) products; fabricated structural metal

(G-5738)
EL PASO PROSTHETIC CENTER LLC
1800 N Mesa St Ste 100 (79902-3554)
PHONE................................915 234-2408
Greta Alvarez-Santullano,
EMP: 40
SALES (est): 2.7MM **Privately Held**
WEB: www.elpasoprostheticcenter.com
SIC: 3842 Prosthetic appliances

(G-5739)
EL PASO PWDR CTING HYDRGRPHICS
5559 El Paso Dr (79905-2907)
PHONE................................915 313-9333
Mike Marivani, *CFO*
Aryan Marivani,
EMP: 10
SALES (est): 2.5MM **Privately Held**
WEB: www.eptexcoatings.com
SIC: 3479 Coating of metals & formed products

(G-5740)
EL PASO REPROGRAPHICS LLC
109 Argonaut Dr (79912-6035)
PHONE................................915 532-6255
Eduardo Lujan, *Mng Member*
Guadalupe Madrid,
EMP: 11
SQ FT: 3,000
SALES (est): 900K **Privately Held**
SIC: 7334 5049 5131 7336 Blueprinting service; engineers' equipment & supplies; flags & banners; commercial art & graphic design; letters for signs, metal

(G-5741)
EL PASO SADDLEBLANKET CO LP
6935 Commerce Ave (79915-1101)
PHONE................................915 544-1000
Bonnie Henson, *Partner*
Richard P Henson, *General Ptnr*
◆ **EMP:** 33 **EST:** 1970
SQ FT: 46,000
SALES (est): 4.5MM **Privately Held**
WEB: www.elpasosaddleblanket.com
SIC: 2273 5191 5199 Rugs, machine woven; saddlery; gifts & novelties; curios

(G-5742)
EL PASO STAR READY-MIX
117 S Moon Rd (79927-1842)
PHONE................................915 860-8555
Jose Garcia, *President*
EMP: 20
SALES (est): 2.4MM **Privately Held**
SIC: 3273 Ready-mixed concrete

(G-5743)
EL PASO TIMES CHARITABLE CORP (DH)
500 W Overland Ave # 150 (79901-1108)
PHONE................................915 546-6100
Dionicio Flores, *President*
Cindy L Webber, *CFO*
Malena Field, *Director*
EMP: 420 **EST:** 1977
SQ FT: 80,000
SALES (est): 93.9K
SALES (corp-wide): 1.8B **Publicly Held**
WEB: www.elpasotimes.com
SIC: 2711 Newspapers
HQ: Gannett Media Corp.
7950 Jones Branch Dr
Mc Lean VA 22102
703 854-6000

(G-5744)
EL PASO TOOL & DIE CO INC
10859 Pellicano Dr (79935-4608)
PHONE................................915 591-0346
EMP: 20 **EST:** 1973
SQ FT: 20,000
SALES (est): 3.8MM **Privately Held**
WEB: www.stampcoat.com
SIC: 3469 7692 3479 Stamping metal for the trade; welding repair; coating of metals with plastic or resins

(G-5745)
EL PASO TRUSS INC
9931 Railroad Dr (79924-5006)
PHONE................................915 751-0025
Luis Mendiola, *President*
EMP: 60
SQ FT: 900
SALES (est): 10.2MM **Privately Held**
WEB: www.elpasotruss.com
SIC: 2439 Trusses, except roof: laminated lumber; trusses, wooden roof

(G-5746)
EL PASO WATER INDUS SVCS INC
Also Called: Industrial Water Services
4500 Turf Rd (79938-9731)
PHONE................................915 849-0401
Ruben J Diaz, *President*
Christina Diaz, *Admin Sec*
EMP: 13
SQ FT: 5,000
SALES (est): 3.3MM **Privately Held**
WEB: www.industrialwaterservice.com
SIC: 3589 Water treatment equipment, industrial; water filters & softeners, household type

(G-5747)
EL PASO WOOD PRODUCTS INC
1025 Myrtle Ave (79901-1515)
PHONE................................915 545-2974
Alejandro Fernandez, *Principal*
Margarita Fernandez, *Corp Secy*
EMP: 10
SQ FT: 800
SALES (est): 3.4MM **Privately Held**
WEB: www.portadadoors.com
SIC: 2431 Doors & door parts & trim, wood

(G-5748)
ELAMEX USA CORP
1800 Northwestern Dr (79912-1122)
PHONE................................915 298-3061
Richard Spencer, *President*
Sam L Henry, *CFO*
EMP: 600
SALES (est): 80.2MM **Privately Held**
SIC: 3694 2068 2064 Engine electrical equipment; salted & roasted nuts & seeds; candy & other confectionery products
HQ: Elamex, S.A. De C.V.
Ishikawa No. 9040
Ciudad Juarez CHIH. 32152

(G-5749)
ELCOM INC (DH)
20 Butterfield Trail Blvd (79906-5254)
PHONE................................915 298-2000
Rich Tajer, *President*
Don Winn, *Treasurer*
Dieter Ehrmanntraut, *Director*
Kunio Matsuura, *Director*
Kiyoji Nagai, *Director*
▲ **EMP:** 14
SQ FT: 315,000
SALES (est): 376.6MM **Privately Held**
SIC: 3679 3694 Electronic circuits; engine electrical equipment

(G-5750)
ELECTRICAL COMPONENTS INTL INC
Also Called: E C I
12415 Rojas Dr (79928-5285)
PHONE................................915 217-2700
David J Webster, *CEO*
Rob Sell, *Opers Staff*
Juan Jigashi, *Engineer*
Ruben Perez, *Engineer*
Irisbel Soto, *Supervisor*
EMP: 100
SALES (corp-wide): 24.3B **Privately Held**
WEB: www.ecintl.com
SIC: 3679 Harness assemblies for electronic use: wire or cable
HQ: Electrical Components International, Inc.
1 Cityplace Dr Ste 450
Saint Louis MO 63141

(G-5751)
EMERSON ELECTRIC CO
1281 Joe Battle Blvd B (79936-0987)
PHONE................................314 553-3695
Adela Martinez, *Human Resources*
Monica Moore, *Sales Staff*
Gabriel Lopez, *Branch Mgr*
Victor Herrera, *Clerk*
EMP: 120
SALES (corp-wide): 16.7B **Publicly Held**
WEB: www.emerson.com
SIC: 3823 Industrial instrmnts msrmnt display/control process variable
PA: Emerson Electric Co.
8000 West Florissant Ave
Saint Louis MO 63136
314 553-2000

(G-5752)
EMERSON ELECTRIC CO
Also Called: Emerson Climate Technologies
1281 Joe Battle Blvd B (79936-0987)
PHONE................................915 400-3888
Victor Romero, *Manager*
EMP: 12
SALES (corp-wide): 16.7B **Publicly Held**
WEB: www.emerson.com
SIC: 3823 Industrial instrmnts msrmnt display/control process variable
PA: Emerson Electric Co.
8000 West Florissant Ave
Saint Louis MO 63136
314 553-2000

(G-5753)
EMICON CORPORATION (PA)
12285 Pellicano Dr Ste A5 (79936-6284)
PHONE................................915 857-5128
Timothy Eyerman, *President*
L Schmitz, *Plant Mgr*
EMP: 12
SQ FT: 4,200
SALES (est): 895.2K **Privately Held**
WEB: www.emiconcorp.com
SIC: 3823 Computer interface equipment for industrial process control

(G-5754)
EMICON CORPORATION
1147 Larry Mahan Dr Ste E (79925-6515)
PHONE................................915 593-6422
Lourds Schmitz, *Manager*
EMP: 10
SALES (corp-wide): 895.2K **Privately Held**
WEB: www.emiconcorp.com
SIC: 3823 Computer interface equipment for industrial process control
PA: Emicon Corporation
12285 Pellicano Dr Ste A5
El Paso TX 79936
915 857-5128

(G-5755)
EMPIRE WLDG & FABRICATION LLC
2211 E Missouri Ave # 221 (79903-3836)
PHONE................................915 706-4070
Joshua Velazquez, *President*
Christian Gonzalez, *Vice Pres*
Julian Velazquez, *Vice Pres*
Araceli Velazquez, *Treasurer*
EMP: 13
SALES (est): 98.4K **Privately Held**
WEB: www.empireweldingfabrication.com
SIC: 7692 Welding repair

(G-5756)
EP BIG MEDIA INC
5710 Doniphan Dr (79932-1306)
PHONE................................915 585-0444
Danny Barela, *Partner*
Karen Azpeitia, *Manager*
EMP: 17 **EST:** 2010
SALES (est): 2.2MM **Privately Held**
WEB: www.bigmediaprint.com
SIC: 3993 Signs & advertising specialties

(G-5757)
EPIC TECHNOLOGIES LLC
Also Called: Epic De Juarez SA De RI De Cv
995 Loma Verde Dr (79936-7821)
PHONE................................915 791-5326
Jochen Lipp, *Branch Mgr*
EMP: 200
SALES (corp-wide): 1.1B **Privately Held**
WEB: www.neotech.com
SIC: 3672 Circuit boards, television & radio printed
HQ: Epic Technologies, Llc
9340 Owensmouth Ave
Chatsworth CA 91311
818 495-8617

(G-5758)
EPIC TECHNOLOGIES LLC
Also Called: Neotech
9600 Joe Rodriguez Ste 4 (79927-2139)
PHONE................................915 229-6805
Ceasar Morales, *Branch Mgr*
EMP: 75
SALES (corp-wide): 1.1B **Privately Held**
WEB: www.neotech.com
SIC: 3672 Printed circuit boards
HQ: Epic Technologies, Llc
9340 Owensmouth Ave
Chatsworth CA 91311
818 495-8617

(G-5759)
ESSEX GROUP INC
Also Called: Essex Group Industrial Pdts
24 Spur Dr Ste A (79906-5313)
PHONE................................915 772-6041
Henry Romero, *Manager*
EMP: 15 **Privately Held**
WEB: www.essexgroup.com
SIC: 3357 Nonferrous wiredrawing & insulating
HQ: Essex Furukawa Magnet Wire Usa Llc
1601 Wall St
Fort Wayne IN 46802
260 461-4000

(G-5760)
EXCEL GARMENT MFG LTD
Also Called: Excel Manufacturing
3517 Frutas Ave (79905-1210)
PHONE................................915 544-5006
Blanca Ortega, *President*
Jose Luis Ortega, *Vice Pres*
Garciela Esquivel, *Executive*
▲ **EMP:** 106
SQ FT: 102,000
SALES (est): 18.7MM **Privately Held**
WEB: www.excelmfg.net
SIC: 2325 2369 2339 Jeans: men's, youths' & boys'; men's & boys' jeans & dungarees; jeans: girls', children's & infants'; jeans: women's, misses' & juniors'

(G-5761)
F M EAGLE TOOL CO INC
Also Called: Eagle Tool Company
8810 Yermoland Dr (79907-1804)
PHONE................................915 590-6377
Francisco Melendez, *President*
EMP: 10
SQ FT: 1,500

SALES (est): 1.1MM **Privately Held**
WEB: www.eagletoolco.com
SIC: 3544 Special dies & tools

(G-5762)
FALCONHEAD BOOTS BELTS BUCKLES
Also Called: Tres Outlaws
421 S Cotton St (79901-3113)
PHONE..................................915 544-2727
Jerry Black, *Manager*
EMP: 13
SALES (corp-wide): 799.3K **Privately Held**
WEB: www.falconhead.com
SIC: 3143 Boots, dress or casual: men's
PA: Falconhead Boots, Belts & Buckles, Inc.
11911 San Vicente Blvd
Los Angeles CA 90049
310 471-7075

(G-5763)
FAMCO LOGISTICS INC
11710 Gateway Blvd E (79927-7709)
PHONE..................................915 307-2536
Luis Corral, *President*
Freddy Corral, *Vice Pres*
Vanessa Nila, *Manager*
Maria Corral, *Director*
EMP: 10
SALES (est): 1.7MM **Privately Held**
SIC: 3531 1794 Tractors, construction; excavation & grading, building construction

(G-5764)
FAR EAST PRINTING
3608 Prairie Rose St (79936-1525)
PHONE..................................281 495-6161
Kenny Boung, *President*
Kenny Duong, *Owner*
EMP: 10
SALES (est): 790.5K **Privately Held**
SIC: 2759 Commercial printing

(G-5765)
FASTSIGNS
1355 George Dieter Dr # 103 (79936-7533)
PHONE..................................915 229-8000
Veronica Velasco, *Owner*
EMP: 9 **EST:** 2017
SALES (est): 172.6K **Privately Held**
WEB: www.fastsigns.com
SIC: 3993 5046 5099 Signs & advertising specialties; signs, electrical; signs, except electric

(G-5766)
FEDERAL-MOGUL POWERTRAIN LLC
1273 Joe Battle Blvd A (79936-0966)
PHONE..................................915 860-2300
EMP: 17
SALES (corp-wide): 17.4B **Publicly Held**
WEB: www.federalmogul.com
SIC: 3559 Degreasing machines, automotive & industrial
HQ: Federal-Mogul Powertrain Llc
27300 W 11 Mile Rd # 100
Southfield MI 48034

(G-5767)
FEDERAL-MOGUL POWERTRAIN LLC
1277 Joe Battle Blvd (79936-0966)
PHONE..................................915 860-2300
Julian Arruti, *Manager*
Stuart Cheung, *Manager*
Pierre Darbonnier, *Manager*
EMP: 265
SALES (corp-wide): 17.4B **Publicly Held**
WEB: www.federalmogul.com
SIC: 3083 3053 Laminated plastics plate & sheet; gaskets, packing & sealing devices
HQ: Federal-Mogul Powertrain Llc
27300 W 11 Mile Rd # 100
Southfield MI 48034

(G-5768)
FEDEX OFFICE & PRINT SVCS INC
1410 N Lee Trevino Dr (79936-6426)
PHONE..................................915 592-1190
Fernando Squez, *Opers Mgr*

EMP: 10
SALES (corp-wide): 69.2B **Publicly Held**
WEB: www.fedex.com
SIC: 7334 2759 Photocopying & duplicating services; commercial printing
HQ: Fedex Office And Print Services, Inc.
7900 Legacy Dr
Plano TX 75024
800 463-3339

(G-5769)
FIRST TEXAS PRODUCTS CORP (PA)
1120 Alza Dr (79907-3108)
PHONE..................................915 633-8354
Thomas Walsh, *President*
EMP: 14
SALES (est): 6.4MM **Privately Held**
WEB: www.fisherlab.com
SIC: 3613 Switchboard apparatus, except instruments

(G-5770)
FLEXAUST INC
Also Called: Flexhaust Appliance Div
12134 Esther Lama Dr # 300 (79936-7747)
P.O. Box 4275, Warsaw IN (46581-4275)
PHONE..................................915 872-3100
Morgan Garza, *General Mgr*
Thomas Poore, *Prdtn Mgr*
Mike Stull, *Engineer*
Tom Ryan, *Sales Staff*
Jim Carlisle, *Manager*
EMP: 120
SALES (corp-wide): 223.3MM **Privately Held**
WEB: www.flexaust.com
SIC: 3052 3635 Automobile hose, rubber; automobile hose, plastic; rubber belting; plastic belting; household vacuum cleaners
HQ: Flexaust Inc
1510 Armstrong Rd
Warsaw IN 46580

(G-5771)
FLOWERS BAKERIES LLC
Also Called: Flowers Baking Company El Paso
301 Dallas St (79901-1821)
PHONE..................................915 533-8434
Ruben Arriola, *Engineer*
Mary Vega, *Director*
Eddie Morris,
EMP: 47
SALES (corp-wide): 4.1B **Publicly Held**
WEB: www.flowersfoods.com
SIC: 2051 Bread, cake & related products
HQ: Flowers Bakeries, Llc
1919 Flowers Cir
Thomasville GA 31757

(G-5772)
FLOWERS BAKING CO EL PASO LLC (HQ)
301 Dallas St (79901-1821)
P.O. Box 1768 (79949-1768)
PHONE..................................915 533-8434
Larry Baldwin, *President*
Jesus-Carlos Nunez, *Vice Pres*
David Valles, *Treasurer*
EMP: 12
SQ FT: 36,539
SALES (est): 14.5MM
SALES (corp-wide): 4.1B **Publicly Held**
WEB: www.elpaso.org
SIC: 2051 Bakery: wholesale or wholesale/retail combined
PA: Flowers Foods, Inc.
1919 Flowers Cir
Thomasville GA 31757
912 226-9110

(G-5773)
FOX JOHN
Also Called: American Management
4741 Maxwell Ave Apt 13 (79904-1447)
PHONE..................................915 755-0080
John Fox, *Mng Member*
EMP: 20
SALES (est): 874K **Privately Held**
SIC: 2431 Windows & window parts & trim, wood

(G-5774)
FREEPORT MINERALS CORPORATION
897 Hawkins Blvd (79915-1217)
P.O. Box 2001 (79950-2001)
PHONE..................................915 778-9881
John Holzenthaler, *Manager*
EMP: 250
SALES (corp-wide): 14.4B **Publicly Held**
WEB: www.fcx.com
SIC: 1021 3331 2819 Copper ore mining & preparation; primary copper; industrial inorganic chemicals
HQ: Freeport Minerals Corporation
333 N Central Ave
Phoenix AZ 85004
602 366-8100

(G-5775)
FRL INC
Also Called: Fisher Research Laboratory
1120 Alza Dr (79907-3108)
PHONE..................................915 633-8354
Thomas Walsh, *President*
Charles Schwan, *CFO*
▲ **EMP:** 800 **EST:** 1931
SQ FT: 23,000
SALES (est): 87.8MM
SALES (corp-wide): 102.8MM **Privately Held**
WEB: www.fisherlab.com
SIC: 3699 Electrical equipment & supplies
HQ: First Texas Products, Llc
1120 Alza Dr
El Paso TX 79907
915 633-8354

(G-5776)
FUTABA CORPORATION OF AMERICA
26 Walter Jones Blvd B (79906-5305)
PHONE..................................915 771-7858
Abel Cisneros, *Branch Mgr*
EMP: 10 **Privately Held**
WEB: www.futaba.com
SIC: 3679 Electronic crystals
HQ: Futaba Corporation Of America
711 E State Pkwy
Schaumburg IL 60173
847 884-1444

(G-5777)
G & A LABEL INC
1601 Wyoming Ave (79902-5625)
P.O. Box 3505 (79923-3505)
PHONE..................................915 544-1766
Amelia Saldana, *President*
Alice Higgins, *Corp Secy*
Frank Ramirez, *Vice Pres*
George Myers, *CFO*
EMP: 35
SQ FT: 15,900
SALES (est): 8.4MM **Privately Held**
WEB: www.gna30.com
SIC: 5131 2269 2759 5085 Labels; labels, cotton: printed; labels & seals: printing; ink, printers'

(G-5778)
G & C MOLD COMPANY
11430 Cedar Oak Dr (79936-6000)
PHONE..................................915 590-6670
Carlos Martinez, *Owner*
EMP: 14
SQ FT: 6,000
SALES (est): 2.2MM **Privately Held**
WEB: www.gncmold.com
SIC: 3599 Machine shop, jobbing & repair

(G-5779)
GCC RIO GRANDE INC
Also Called: Rio Grande Portland Cement
2825 W Paisano Dr (79922-1632)
PHONE..................................915 544-1750
Enrique Escanlante, *President*
Jaime Ramirez, *General Mgr*
Jonathan Dennis, *Manager*
EMP: 15 **Privately Held**
WEB: www.gccusa.com
SIC: 3273 Ready-mixed concrete
HQ: Gcc Rio Grande, Inc.
11783 Hwy 337
Tijeras NM 87059
505 281-3311

(G-5780)
GENERAL ASSEMBLY CORPORATION (HQ)
7101 N Mesa St Ste 544 (79912-3613)
PHONE..................................915 701-0605
Roman Brenner, *President*
Cesar Aguilera Saucedo, *General Mgr*
Chris Karanicolas, *Corp Secy*
George McPherson, *Treasurer*
Josef Bornbaum, *Admin Sec*
▲ **EMP:** 10
SALES (est): 81.4MM
SALES (corp-wide): 8.6B **Publicly Held**
SIC: 3679 Harness assemblies for electronic use: wire or cable
PA: Amphenol Corporation
358 Hall Ave
Wallingford CT 06492
203 265-8900

(G-5781)
GENERAL LABELS & PRINTING LLC
2000 E Mills Ave (79901-1931)
PHONE..................................915 532-7131
Jose Gerardo,
Marissa Gerardo,
EMP: 37
SQ FT: 7,000
SALES (est): 7.6MM **Privately Held**
WEB: www.glabels.com
SIC: 2752 5199 Commercial printing, offset; packaging materials

(G-5782)
GENESIS TOOL INC
111 S Concepcion St (79905-3908)
PHONE..................................915 781-1000
George Cantore, *President*
Deborah Cantore, *President*
▲ **EMP:** 10 **EST:** 1994
SQ FT: 2,500
SALES (est): 1MM **Privately Held**
WEB: www.genesistoolinc.com
SIC: 3544 Industrial molds

(G-5783)
GEORGIA-PACIFIC LLC
Plant 1610 (79998)
P.O. Box 981957 (79998-1957)
PHONE..................................434 283-6202
EMP: 9
SALES (corp-wide): 36.8B **Privately Held**
WEB: www.gp.com
SIC: 2676 Sanitary paper products
HQ: Georgia-Pacific Llc
133 Peachtree St Nw
Atlanta GA 30303
404 652-4000

(G-5784)
GEORGIA-PACIFIC LLC
6 Founders Blvd (79906-9400)
PHONE..................................866 924-1397
EMP: 330
SALES (corp-wide): 36.8B **Privately Held**
WEB: www.gp.com
SIC: 2435 2821 3275 Hardwood veneer & plywood; plastics materials & resins; gypsum products
HQ: Georgia-Pacific Llc
133 Peachtree St Nw
Atlanta GA 30303
404 652-4000

(G-5785)
GH DAIRY
Also Called: Gh Dairy El Paso
9747 Pan American Dr (79927-2122)
PHONE..................................915 790-2609
Patrick Byrne, *Branch Mgr*
EMP: 145 **Privately Held**
WEB: www.sarahfarmsep.com
SIC: 2026 Milk processing (pasteurizing, homogenizing, bottling)
PA: Gh Dairy
14651 Grove Ave
Ontario CA 91762

(G-5786)
GIANT INDUSTRIES INC
6500 Trowbridge Dr (79905-3402)
PHONE..................................915 775-3300
Anthony Bernitsky, *Director*
EMP: 2809

▲ = Import ▼ =Export
◆ =Import/Export

SALES (est): 2.8B **Publicly Held**
WEB: www.giant.com
SIC: **2911** Petroleum refining
HQ: Northern Tier Energy Lp
1250 W Washington St # 101
Tempe AZ 85281
602 302-5450

(G-5787)
GLOBAL ALTERNATIVE FUELS LLC
Also Called: Vital Fuels
3500 Doniphan Dr (79922-1408)
PHONE..................................915 791-8720
Heidi Avedician, *Purch Mgr*
Ignacio Meza, *Info Tech Mgr*
Mesilla Valley Biofuels,
Rio Grande,
Carlos Guzman,
EMP: 20
SQ FT: 80,000
SALES (est): 9.4MM
SALES (corp-wide): 166.4MM **Privately Held**
WEB: www.riovalleybiofuels.com
SIC: **2911** Oils, fuel
PA: Mvt Services, Llc
3590 W Picacho Ave
Las Cruces NM 88007
575 524-2835

(G-5788)
GONZALEZ MECHANICAL CONTR LLC (PA)
7201 Stiles Dr (79915-2409)
PHONE..................................915 345-1282
Miguel Gonzalez, *Owner*
EMP: 9
SALES (est): 85.7K **Privately Held**
WEB: www.gonzalezair.com
SIC: **1711 3441** Mechanical contractor;
fabricated structural metal

(G-5789)
GREAT SOUTHWEST TOOL CO
1220 Barranca Dr Ste 1c (79935-4606)
PHONE..................................915 594-7804
Andres Gutierrez, *President*
Ramon Bobadilla, *Vice Pres*
EMP: 20
SQ FT: 5,000
SALES (est): 1.8MM **Privately Held**
SIC: **3544 3599** Special dies & tools; ma-
chine shop, jobbing & repair

(G-5790)
GREATER SOUTHWEST ART CENTER
3101 E Yandell Dr (79903-4114)
PHONE..................................915 566-2410
Daniel Hamicha, *President*
Henry Rothchild, *President*
Susan Rothchild, *Treasurer*
EMP: 9
SQ FT: 5,000
SALES (est): 949.4K **Privately Held**
WEB: www.artcenterelpaso.com
SIC: **7336 5999 5199 2499** Graphic arts
& related design; artists' supplies & mate-
rials; artists' materials; picture & mirror
frames, wood; picture framing, custom

(G-5791)
GREEN BAY PACKAGING INC
10515 Railroad Dr (79924-1670)
PHONE..................................915 822-9700
Bill Sharrett, *Manager*
EMP: 50
SALES (corp-wide): 1.7B **Privately Held**
WEB: www.gbpcoated.com
SIC: **2631 2672 2653 2491** Paperboard
mills; coated & laminated paper; corru-
gated & solid fiber boxes; wood preserv-
ing
PA: Green Bay Packaging Inc.
1700 N Webster Ave
Green Bay WI 54302
920 433-5111

(G-5792)
H & H DINERO TREE INC
Also Called: H & H Mailing Services
9431 Carnegie Ave (79925-1421)
P.O. Box 971116 (79997-1116)
PHONE..................................915 591-6245

Ronald J Harris, *President*
EMP: 12 EST: 1980
SQ FT: 8,600
SALES (est): 500K **Privately Held**
WEB: www.hnhmailmarketing.com
SIC: **7331 2759** Mailing service; commer-
cial printing

(G-5793)
HAN-D-PAC PRODUCTS INC
9420 Carnegie Ave (79925-1422)
P.O. Box 971456 (79997-1456)
PHONE..................................915 595-2212
Raul Ramos, *President*
Rosalie Ramos, *Corp Secy*
Rosalie Venecia, *Corp Secy*
Romelia Juarez, *Vice Pres*
Romelia Ramos, *Vice Pres*
EMP: 45 EST: 1967
SQ FT: 28,000
SALES (est): 9.5MM **Privately Held**
WEB: www.han-d-pac.com
SIC: **5141 2099** Groceries, general line;
food preparations

(G-5794)
HANDGARDS LLC (HQ)
901 Hawkins Blvd (79915-1202)
PHONE..................................915 779-6606
Joe Kubicek, *CEO*
John Carpenter, *District Mgr*
Tony Williams, *Business Mgr*
John Lewchenko, *Exec VP*
Brian Bain, *Vice Pres*
◆ EMP: 154
SQ FT: 380,000
SALES (est): 59.2MM
SALES (corp-wide): 988.6MM **Privately Held**
WEB: www.handgards.com
SIC: **3089 2673 3021 2385** Work gloves,
plastic; plastic containers, except foam;
plastic bags: made from purchased mate-
rials; boots, plastic; aprons, waterproof:
made from purchased materials; bibs, wa-
terproof: made from purchased materials;
unsupported plastics film & sheet; men's
& boys' work clothing
PA: Wind Point Partners, L.P.
676 N Michigan Ave # 3700
Chicago IL 60611
312 255-4800

(G-5795)
HANGAR WELDING & FABRICATION
15501 Peggy Hopkins (79938-8377)
PHONE..................................915 857-2899
Jay Jones, *Owner*
EMP: 10
SALES (est): 737.2K **Privately Held**
SIC: **3548** Welding & cutting apparatus &
accessories

(G-5796)
HONCHO BOOTS LLC
3505 Lee Blvd Ste E (79936-1497)
PHONE..................................915 855-9300
Sidney Meyers,
Bob Davidson,
EMP: 18
SQ FT: 12,500
SALES (est): 1.7MM **Privately Held**
WEB: www.honchoboots.com
SIC: **3131 3143** Footwear cut stock; men's
footwear, except athletic

(G-5797)
HONEYWELL INTERNATIONAL INC
3509 Durazno Ave (79905-1206)
P.O. Box 981162 (79998-1162)
PHONE..................................480 353-4053
Adolfo Carmona, *Manager*
EMP: 86
SALES (corp-wide): 36.7B **Publicly Held**
WEB: www.honeywell.com
SIC: **3724** Aircraft engines & engine parts
PA: Honeywell International Inc.
300 S Tryon St
Charlotte NC 28202
704 627-6200

(G-5798)
HONEYWELL INTERNATIONAL INC
3518 Durazno Ave (79905-1207)
PHONE..................................480 592-2047
Ken Swanson, *Manager*
EMP: 214
SALES (corp-wide): 36.7B **Publicly Held**
WEB: www.honeywell.com
SIC: **3724** Aircraft engines & engine parts
PA: Honeywell International Inc.
300 S Tryon St
Charlotte NC 28202
704 627-6200

(G-5799)
HONEYWELL INTERNATIONAL INC
10 Leigh Fisher Blvd 9h (79906-5239)
P.O. Box 981230 (79998-1230)
PHONE..................................915 778-7401
EMP: 33
SALES (corp-wide): 36.7B **Publicly Held**
WEB: www.honeywell.com
SIC: **3724** Aircraft engines & engine parts
PA: Honeywell International Inc.
300 S Tryon St
Charlotte NC 28202
704 627-6200

(G-5800)
HONEYWELL INTERNATIONAL INC
3509 Durazno Ave (79905-1206)
PHONE..................................915 544-6634
Ken Swanson, *Branch Mgr*
EMP: 35
SALES (corp-wide): 36.7B **Publicly Held**
WEB: www.honeywell.com
SIC: **3724** Aircraft engines & engine parts
PA: Honeywell International Inc.
300 S Tryon St
Charlotte NC 28202
704 627-6200

(G-5801)
HONEYWELL INTERNATIONAL INC
8260 S Hrdy Dr Golden Dv (79901)
PHONE..................................480 592-2052
Julie Carlson, *Principal*
EMP: 14
SALES (corp-wide): 36.7B **Publicly Held**
WEB: www.honeywell.com
SIC: **3724** Aircraft engines & engine parts
PA: Honeywell International Inc.
300 S Tryon St
Charlotte NC 28202
704 627-6200

(G-5802)
HONEYWELL INTERNATIONAL INC
3509 Durazno Ave (79905-1206)
P.O. Box 981163 (79998-1163)
PHONE..................................480 592-7380
EMP: 41
SALES (corp-wide): 36.7B **Publicly Held**
WEB: www.honeywell.com
SIC: **3724** Aircraft engines & engine parts
PA: Honeywell International Inc.
300 S Tryon St
Charlotte NC 28202
704 627-6200

(G-5803)
HONEYWELL INTERNATIONAL INC
3509 Durazno Ave (79905-1206)
P.O. Box 981771 (79998-1771)
PHONE..................................717 771-8100
EMP: 657
SALES (corp-wide): 36.7B **Publicly Held**
WEB: www.honeywell.com
SIC: **3724** Aircraft engines & engine parts
PA: Honeywell International Inc.
300 S Tryon St
Charlotte NC 28202
704 627-6200

(G-5804)
HORIZON GLOBAL AMERICAS INC
8460 Grand Vis (79907)
PHONE..................................915 545-2720
Norman Candellaria, *Opers-Prdtn-Mfg*
EMP: 12
SALES (corp-wide): 690.4MM **Publicly Held**
WEB: www.horizonglobal.com
SIC: **3799 3714** Automobile trailer chassis;
axles, motor vehicle
HQ: Horizon Global Americas Inc.
47912 Halyard Dr Ste 100
Plymouth MI 48170

(G-5805)
HRH DOOR CORP
Also Called: Wayne - Dalton of El Paso
1477 Lomaland Dr Ste B10 (79935-4704)
PHONE..................................915 590-8997
Danny Alvarez, *Branch Mgr*
EMP: 13
SALES (corp-wide): 634.1MM **Privately Held**
WEB: www.wayne-dalton.com
SIC: **3699 5211** Door opening & closing
devices, electrical; door & window prod-
ucts
PA: Hrh Door Corp.
1 Door Dr
Mount Hope OH 44660
850 208-3400

(G-5806)
HUECO QUARRY INC
Also Called: MTI Materials
15583 Faith Rd (79938-9586)
PHONE..................................915 859-5767
Anthony Mullen, *President*
EMP: 10
SQ FT: 5,000
SALES (est): 2.5MM **Privately Held**
WEB: www.mtireadymix.com
SIC: **3273** Ready-mixed concrete

(G-5807)
ICS ENTERPRISES LTD
Also Called: Box Company The
9560 Joe Rodriguez (79927-2146)
P.O. Box 220332 (79913-2332)
PHONE..................................915 539-5415
Albert Lanza, *President*
EMP: 35
SQ FT: 22,900
SALES (est): 4.7MM **Privately Held**
SIC: **2657 5199** Folding paperboard
boxes; packaging materials

(G-5808)
ICS ENTERPRISES LLP
Also Called: Ics Vmi Group
12273 Gateway Blvd W (79936-7809)
P.O. Box 220488 (79913-2488)
PHONE..................................915 239-9256
Albert Lanza, *Partner*
EMP: 300
SALES (est): 30.2MM **Privately Held**
SIC: **2653 2449 4225** Corrugated boxes,
partitions, display items, sheets & pad;
rectangular boxes & crates, wood; gen-
eral warehousing

(G-5809)
IDEA CORPORATION
Also Called: T 2 C 3 Group
1013 Ada Ln (79932-2801)
PHONE..................................915 845-6606
Stephen C Harvey, *President*
Stephen Harvey, *Engineer*
Theresa V Harvey, *Marketing Staff*
EMP: 10 EST: 1992
SQ FT: 9,000
SALES (est): 1.6MM **Privately Held**
WEB: www.espwebsite.com
SIC: **3575** Computer terminals

(G-5810)
IMPRESA LABEL INC (PA)
Also Called: Iq Graphics
1410 Gail Borden Pl B1 (79935-4814)
PHONE..................................915 592-4500
Doug Young, *President*
Bruce Young, *Vice Pres*
James Milligan III, *Treasurer*
▲ EMP: 26

SQ FT: 22,000
SALES (est): 2.4MM **Privately Held**
WEB: www.impresalabel.com
SIC: 2759 Labels & seals: printing

(G-5811)
IMUNIZE EL PASO
1580 Grge Dter Dr Ste 102 (79936)
PHONE.................................915 857-2474
Diana Garcia, *Branch Mgr*
EMP: 15
SALES (est): 1.2MM **Privately Held**
WEB: www.immunizeelpaso.org
SIC: 2836 Vaccines & other immunizing products

(G-5812)
INTERCARNES TEXAS CORPORATION
12160 Rojas Dr Ste H (79936-7705)
PHONE.................................281 360-3825
Eugenio Baeza, *CEO*
Walter Burr, *President*
Guillermo Baeza, *Admin Sec*
EMP: 60
SALES (est): 7.4MM **Privately Held**
SIC: 2013 Head cheese from purchased meat products

(G-5813)
INTERMATIC INCORPORATED
12429 Rojas Dr Ste B (79928-5243)
PHONE.................................915 858-9204
Martin Martinez, *Branch Mgr*
Luis Brun, *Manager*
Zofriah Summer, *Manager*
EMP: 16
SALES (corp-wide): 124.7MM **Privately Held**
WEB: www.shop.intermatic.com
SIC: 3612 3645 Line voltage regulators; residential lighting fixtures
PA: Intermatic Incorporated
　　7777 Winn Rd
　　Spring Grove IL 60081
　　815 675-7000

(G-5814)
INTERNATIONAL FLATBED SVCS INC (PA)
11425 Stockyard Dr (79927-4800)
PHONE.................................915 858-1200
Mariano Hidalgo, *President*
EMP: 18
SQ FT: 2,000
SALES (est): 3.7MM **Privately Held**
SIC: 3715 Bus trailers, tractor type

(G-5815)
INTERNATIONAL PAPER COMPANY
9301 Billy The Kid St (79907-4880)
PHONE.................................915 858-8877
Alfonso Duran, *Safety Mgr*
Luis Fernandez, *Buyer*
Ricaro Trutva, *Manager*
Korina Candia, *Personnel Assit*
EMP: 125
SALES (corp-wide): 22.3B **Publicly Held**
WEB: www.internationalpaper.com
SIC: 2621 Paper mills
PA: International Paper Company
　　6400 Poplar Ave
　　Memphis TN 38197
　　901 419-9000

(G-5816)
INTERNATIONAL WIRE GROUP INC
1700 Commerce Park Dr (79912-8400)
PHONE.................................915 877-5500
Bruce Plumley, *Manager*
EMP: 53
SALES (corp-wide): 3B **Publicly Held**
WEB: www.internationalwiregroup.com
SIC: 3351 Wire, copper & copper alloy
HQ: International Wire Group, Inc.
　　12 Masonic Ave
　　Camden NY 13316

(G-5817)
INVESTOR PUBLICATIONS INC (PA)
Also Called: El Paso
208 N Octavia St (79901-1533)
PHONE.................................915 534-4422
Thomas Fenton, *President*
Secret Wherrett, *Publisher*
Debra Fraire, *Principal*
Ellie D Fenton, *Treasurer*
▲ **EMP:** 26
SALES (est): 2.3MM **Privately Held**
WEB: www.elpasoinc.com
SIC: 2711 Newspapers, publishing & printing

(G-5818)
ISABELLA FOODS INC (PA)
1133 Barranca Dr (79935-5001)
PHONE.................................915 590-1899
Nelson Guerra, *President*
Diego Guerra, *General Mgr*
Veronica Guerra, *Vice Pres*
Veronica Gerra, *Controller*
▲ **EMP:** 55
SQ FT: 42,000
SALES (est): 9MM **Privately Held**
WEB: www.isabellafoods.com
SIC: 2038 2096 2099 Frozen specialties; tortilla chips; tortillas, fresh or refrigerated

(G-5819)
ISOMEDIX OPERATIONS INC
1435 Isomedix Pl (79936-6810)
PHONE.................................915 855-2001
Emmanuel Mendoza, *Prdtn Mgr*
Molina Ana, *Purch Mgr*
EMP: 40 **Privately Held**
WEB: www.steris.com
SIC: 3842 Surgical appliances & supplies
HQ: Isomedix Operations Inc.
　　5960 Heisley Rd
　　Mentor OH 44060

(G-5820)
JC VIRAMONTES INC
Also Called: Interntonal Garment Processors
12651 Montana Ave (79938-9695)
P.O. Box 9777 (79995-2777)
PHONE.................................915 857-4545
Julio C Viramontes, *CEO*
Heidi Viramontes, *President*
Charlie Heredia, *CFO*
Wendy Viramontes, *Admin Sec*
▲ **EMP:** 46 **EST:** 1973
SQ FT: 100,000
SALES (est): 6.3MM **Privately Held**
SIC: 2261 Bleaching cotton broadwoven fabrics

(G-5821)
JOBE MATERIALS LP (PA)
1150 Southview Dr Ste A (79928-5240)
PHONE.................................915 298-9900
Irene Eperson, *Partner*
Stanley Jobe, *General Ptnr*
Irene Epperson, *Exec VP*
Ralph Richards, *Vice Pres*
Hector Paquian, *Safety Dir*
EMP: 430
SQ FT: 13,000
SALES (est): 92.9MM **Privately Held**
WEB: www.jobematerials.com
SIC: 3273 Ready-mixed concrete

(G-5822)
JOHN BEAN TECHNOLOGIES CORP
Also Called: Jbt Aero Tech
6930 Market Ave Ste C (79915-1100)
PHONE.................................915 859-3776
Arturo Adame, *Executive*
EMP: 13
SALES (est): 3.1MM **Publicly Held**
WEB: www.jbtc.com
SIC: 3556 Food products machinery
PA: John Bean Technologies Corporation
　　70 W Madison St Ste 4400
　　Chicago IL 60602

(G-5823)
JONSIL MANUFACTURING CORP
11812 Pete Rose Dr (79936-7014)
PHONE.................................915 544-4244

Gabriel Sparagana, *President*
David Cervantes, *General Mgr*
Shirley Sparagana, *Vice Pres*
EMP: 17 **EST:** 1971
SALES: 387.5K
SALES (corp-wide): 2.9MM **Privately Held**
WEB: www.propsmagtv.com
SIC: 3911 Jewelry apparel; rings, finger: precious metal
PA: Shaudra Company, Inc.
　　1801 Whitehead Rd
　　Baltimore MD 21207
　　410 265-5200

(G-5824)
JUSTIN BRANDS INC
Tony Lama
1137 Tony Lama St (79915-1307)
PHONE.................................915 778-8311
John Justin, *Branch Mgr*
EMP: 916
SALES (corp-wide): 254.6B **Publicly Held**
WEB: www.justinbrands.com
SIC: 3172 3111 3143 3144 Personal leather goods; shoe leather; sole leather; boots, dress or casual: men's; women's footwear, except athletic
HQ: Justin Brands, Inc.
　　610 W Daggett Ave
　　Fort Worth TX 76104

(G-5825)
KALIL BOTTLING CO
Also Called: Kalil Bottling Co of El Paso
7328 Boeing Dr (79925-1116)
PHONE.................................915 778-4413
Steve Yankovich, *General Mgr*
Paul Neeley, *Opers Staff*
Eddie Gonzalez, *Manager*
Michele Holloman, *Supervisor*
EMP: 40
SQ FT: 19,834
SALES (corp-wide): 225.2MM **Privately Held**
WEB: www.kalilbottling.com
SIC: 2086 Soft drinks: packaged in cans, bottles, etc.
PA: Kalil Bottling Co
　　931 S Highland Ave
　　Tucson AZ 85719
　　520 624-1788

(G-5826)
KASTROS WOOD PALLETS INC
13781 Davidson Blvd (79938-8054)
PHONE.................................915 855-8011
Juan Jesus Castro Jr, *President*
Maria C Castro, *Treasurer*
EMP: 15
SQ FT: 1,000
SALES (est): 1.9MM **Privately Held**
SIC: 2448 Pallets, wood

(G-5827)
KEATS SOUTHWEST INC
11425 Rojas Dr (79936-6424)
PHONE.................................915 599-2950
Wade Keats, *CEO*
John Matthew Eggameyer, *President*
Ron McConvile, *CFO*
Brad Keats, *Accounts Exec*
Mario Ramirez, *Sales Staff*
▲ **EMP:** 50
SQ FT: 25,000
SALES (est): 12.6MM
SALES (corp-wide): 19.4MM **Privately Held**
WEB: www.keatsmfg.com
SIC: 3496 Cylinder wire cloth; clips & fasteners, made from purchased wire
PA: Keats Manufacturing Co.
　　350 Holbrook Dr
　　Wheeling IL 60090
　　847 520-1133

(G-5828)
KESSLER INDUSTRIES INC
Also Called: Kessler Enterprises
8600 Gateway Blvd E Ste B (79907-1714)
P.O. Box 17549 (79917-7549)
PHONE.................................915 591-8161
Calvin K Kessler Sr, *President*
Kalvin K Kessler, *Plant Mgr*
Geraldine Kessler, *Treasurer*

◆ **EMP:** 50 **EST:** 1958
SQ FT: 350,000 **Privately Held**
WEB: www.kesslerind.com
SIC: 3365 2514 Aluminum foundries; novelty furniture, household: metal

(G-5829)
KESSLER PACKAGING INC
8600 Gateway Blvd E (79907-1704)
PHONE.................................915 591-8161
Calvin K Kessler, *President*
Geraldine Kessler, *Admin Sec*
EMP: 32
SALES (est): 3.5MM **Privately Held**
WEB: www.kesslerind.com
SIC: 2653 Boxes, corrugated: made from purchased materials

(G-5830)
KITCHEN BATH CBINETS DOORS INC
13682 Nayarit Dr (79928-5645)
PHONE.................................915 852-0499
Martin Ramirez, *President*
EMP: 29
SALES (est): 2.9MM **Privately Held**
WEB: www.kbcelp.com
SIC: 2499 5712 2431 Kitchen, bathroom & household ware: wood; cabinet work, custom; millwork

(G-5831)
KOHLHAAS CORPORATION
6831 El Paso Dr (79905-3306)
PHONE.................................915 778-5357
Charles Kohlhaas, *President*
Mike Alexis, *Sales Staff*
EMP: 22
SQ FT: 10,000
SALES (est): 4.9MM **Privately Held**
WEB: www.kohlhaastanks.com
SIC: 5032 3443 Asphalt mixture; bins, prefabricated metal plate

(G-5832)
KOMAX CORPORATION
9641 Plaza Cir (79927-2151)
PHONE.................................915 591-4551
Remi Bochsler, *Purch Agent*
Maurice Grenier, *Controller*
Enrique Romero, *Regl Sales Mgr*
Martha Porres, *Manager*
Erich Bachmann, *Manager*
EMP: 10
SALES (corp-wide): 421MM **Privately Held**
WEB: www.komaxgroup.com
SIC: 3549 Wiredrawing & fabricating machinery & equipment, ex. die
HQ: Komax Corporation
　　1100 E Corp Grove Dr
　　Buffalo Grove IL 60089
　　888 465-6629

(G-5833)
KUZZY INDUSTRIAL SUPPLIER
2909 Alameda Ave (79905-2207)
PHONE.................................915 881-4105
Elia Hernandez, *Owner*
Hugo Valverde, *Manager*
EMP: 10
SALES (est): 118.7K **Privately Held**
SIC: 3566 Gears, power transmission, except automotive

(G-5834)
LA ROTATIVA TORTILLA INC
Also Called: La Rotativa Tortilla Factory
2010 Montana Ave (79903-3414)
PHONE.................................915 533-2317
Tomas Carrera, *President*
Efran Carrera, *Vice Pres*
Elma R Carrera, *Admin Sec*
EMP: 9
SQ FT: 3,350
SALES (est): 540K **Privately Held**
SIC: 2099 Tortillas, fresh or refrigerated

(G-5835)
LA TAPATIA INC
8941 Old County Dr (79907-6325)
PHONE.................................915 859-9616
Esther Rosencrans, *President*
Alicia Chacon, *President*
Ester Rosencrans, *President*
Joseph Chacon, *Vice Pres*

EMP: 20 EST: 1969
SQ FT: 5,869
SALES (est): 2.2MM Privately Held
SIC: 2099 5812 Tortillas, fresh or refrigerated; Mexican restaurant

(G-5836)
LACHMANN VLLNEVA HLDNGS GP LLC
Also Called: Protech Globl Solutions GP LLC
45 Buttrfeld Trail Blvd S (79906)
PHONE....................915 594-0500
Jose L Villanueva,
Leonard P Lachmann,
Leonard Lachmann,
Leonard P Lachmann,
▲ EMP: 17
SQ FT: 23,000
SALES (est): 5.1MM
SALES (corp-wide): 131.4MM Privately Held
WEB: www.compasses.net
SIC: 3679 Electronic circuits
PA: Logic Pd, Inc.
     6201 Bury Dr
     Eden Prairie MN 55346
     952 646-1191

(G-5837)
LAGARTO INC
Also Called: Black Jack Boots
10787 Gateway Blvd W (79935-4906)
PHONE....................915 598-2668
Dane Ledet, President
Gerardo Guerra, Vice Pres
EMP: 29
SALES (est): 364.6K Privately Held
WEB: www.blackjackboots.net
SIC: 3143 2387 Boots, dress or casual: men's; apparel belts

(G-5838)
LAKE REGION MEDICAL INC
31 Butterfield Trail Blvd C (79906-5263)
PHONE....................978 570-6900
EMP: 187
SALES (corp-wide): 1.4B Publicly Held
SIC: 3841 Mfg Surgical/Medical Instruments
HQ: Lake Region Medical, Inc.
     100 Fordham Rd Ste 3
     Wilmington MA 01887

(G-5839)
LARK INDUSTRIAL LLC
7198 Merch Ave Ste C2 (79915)
PHONE....................915 500-4347
Jesse Ornelas, Managing Prtnr
Sinai Rivas, Partner
Jorge Romero, Partner
EMP: 15
SALES (est): 2.5MM Privately Held
WEB: www.larkindustries.com
SIC: 3544 Special dies & tools

(G-5840)
LARSEN MANUFACTURING LLC
12150 Rojas Dr Ste E (79936-7710)
PHONE....................915 790-0762
Denis Larson, Manager
Jeff Lorenz, Manager
EMP: 80
SALES (corp-wide): 43MM Privately Held
WEB: www.larsenmfg.com
SIC: 3469 Stamping metal for the trade
PA: Larsen Manufacturing, L.L.C.
     1201 Allanson Rd
     Mundelein IL 60060
     847 970-9600

(G-5841)
LEAR CORPORATION
11970 Pellicano Dr (79936-7289)
PHONE....................915 791-5400
Dave M Kee, Manager
Juan Perez, Manager
Scott Oliver, Supervisor
EMP: 300
SALES (corp-wide): 17B Publicly Held
WEB: www.lear.com
SIC: 3714 Motor vehicle parts & accessories

PA: Lear Corporation
     21557 Telegraph Rd
     Southfield MI 48033
     724 248-1500

(G-5842)
LEAR CORPORATION
Also Called: Lear Electrical Systems Group
950 Loma Verde Dr (79936-7899)
PHONE....................915 307-9237
David Rico, Research
Scott Oliver, Engineer
Tim Wagoner, Technology
Jerry Pizzo, Director
Marco Escarcega, Director
EMP: 328
SALES (corp-wide): 17B Publicly Held
WEB: www.lear.com
SIC: 3714 Motor vehicle parts & accessories
PA: Lear Corporation
     21557 Telegraph Rd
     Southfield MI 48033
     724 248-1500

(G-5843)
LEAR CORPORATION
Plant 195
950 Loma Verde Dr (79936-7899)
PHONE....................915 787-5012
Robert Taylor, Manager
EMP: 300
SALES (corp-wide): 17B Publicly Held
WEB: www.lear.com
SIC: 3714 Motor vehicle parts & accessories
PA: Lear Corporation
     21557 Telegraph Rd
     Southfield MI 48033
     724 248-1500

(G-5844)
LEAR TRIM LP
1440 Don Haskins Dr (79936-6830)
PHONE....................915 849-5660
EMP: 31 Privately Held
WEB: www.lear.com
SIC: 3714 Motor vehicle parts & accessories
PA: Lear Trim L.P.
     21557 Telegraph Rd
     Southfield MI 48033

(G-5845)
LOCKHEED MARTIN CORPORATION
1 Ltv Dr (79928-7700)
PHONE....................915 852-1100
Lew Deen, Manager
EMP: 50 Publicly Held
WEB: www.lockheedmartin.com
SIC: 3761 3728 3711 3721 Guided missiles & space vehicles; aircraft parts & equipment; motor vehicles & car bodies; aircraft; search & navigation equipment
PA: Lockheed Martin Corporation
     6801 Rockledge Dr
     Bethesda MD 20817

(G-5846)
LONE STAR INDUS CORP TEXAS
6985 Industrial Ave (79915-1107)
P.O. Box 26911 (79926-6911)
PHONE....................915 779-7255
Ralph Navar, President
Carolyn Navar, Corp Secy
Alex Estrada, Site Mgr
Mark Atchley, CFO
EMP: 25
SQ FT: 12,000
SALES (est): 2.4MM Privately Held
WEB: www.lonestarindustrial.com
SIC: 3495 3643 Precision springs; current-carrying wiring devices

(G-5847)
LOPEZ SCRAP METAL INC (PA)
Also Called: Lopez Houston Metals
351 N Nevarez Rd (79927-4120)
PHONE....................915 859-0770
◆ EMP: 52
SQ FT: 30,000

SALES: 103.3MM Privately Held
WEB: www.lopezscrapmetal.com
SIC: 5093 3341 Ferrous metal scrap & waste; nonferrous metals scrap; secondary nonferrous metals

(G-5848)
LOWN BROTHERS INC
Also Called: Apparel Art
11601 Pellicano Dr A15 (79936-6279)
PHONE....................915 594-4499
Valerie Steinbergh, President
James Lown, Treasurer
▲ EMP: 20
SQ FT: 10,000
SALES (est): 1.9MM Privately Held
WEB: www.apparelart.com
SIC: 3993 7389 2759 Signs & advertising specialties; embroidering of advertising on shirts, etc.; screen printing

(G-5849)
LUCCHESE INC
40 Walter Jones Blvd (79906-5301)
PHONE....................915 778-8585
Dough Kindy, Branch Mgr
EMP: 360 Privately Held
WEB: www.lucchese.com
SIC: 3143 3144 Boots, dress or casual: men's; boots, canvas or leather: women's
HQ: Lucchese, Inc.
     40 Walter Jones Blvd
     El Paso TX 79906
     915 778-8585

(G-5850)
LUCCHESE INC (DH)
Also Called: Lucchese Boot Co
40 Walter Jones Blvd (79906-5301)
PHONE....................915 778-8585
Doug Kindy, President
Carlos Armendariz, Store Mgr
Ricardo Barcenas, QC Mgr
Ty Harris, Sales Staff
Jennifer Huggins, Marketing Staff
▲ EMP: 390
SQ FT: 100,000
SALES (est): 106.8MM Privately Held
WEB: www.lucchese.com
SIC: 3143 3144 Boots, dress or casual: men's; boots, canvas or leather: women's
HQ: Arena Brands, Inc.
     601 Marion Dr
     Garland TX 75042
     972 494-7133

(G-5851)
M & F WHOLESALE FLORAL SUPS (PA)
212 S Oregon St Ste 212 # 212 (79901-2322)
PHONE....................915 542-1238
Frank Perez, President
Margarito De Los Santos, Vice Pres
EMP: 11
SQ FT: 10,000
SALES (est): 1.2MM Privately Held
SIC: 3999 Artificial flower arrangements; barber & beauty shop equipment

(G-5852)
M AND N PLASTICS INC
7750 Trade Center Ave (79912-8404)
PHONE....................915 877-1900
Tommy Jenkins, Plant Mgr
Alvaro Mancilla, Engineer
Marty Nagle, Engineer
Tom Jenkins, Manager
Mary Sloat, Director
EMP: 14
SALES (corp-wide): 21.1MM Privately Held
WEB: www.mandn.com
SIC: 3089 Blow molded finished plastic products; injection molding of plastics
PA: M And N Plastics, Inc.
     6450 Dobry Dr
     Sterling Heights MI 48314
     586 726-8850

(G-5853)
M G PRODUCTS COMPANY (PA)
6825 Cielo Vista Dr 25 (79925-2205)
PHONE....................915 541-8950
Roberto Moya, President
Sergio Molinar, Vice Pres

EMP: 20
SQ FT: 40,000
SALES (est): 12.6MM Privately Held
WEB: www.mgproducts-pemjusa.com
SIC: 3365 3366 Aluminum foundries; copper foundries

(G-5854)
M J CELCO INC
Also Called: Celco Industries
1455 Vanderbilt Dr (79935-4808)
PHONE....................915 594-1777
Thomas Sikorski, General Mgr
EMP: 55
SALES (corp-wide): 50MM Privately Held
WEB: www.mjcelco.com
SIC: 3469 Stamping metal for the trade
PA: M J Celco, Inc.
     3900 Wesley Ter
     Schiller Park IL 60176
     847 671-1900

(G-5855)
M-MASTER LLC
221 N Kansas St Ste 700 (79901-1443)
PHONE....................915 242-2315
Anaid R Alvarez,
EMP: 10 EST: 2015
SALES (est): 1.3MM Privately Held
WEB: www.m-masterllc.com
SIC: 2821 5999 Polyvinyl chloride resins (PVC); safety supplies & equipment

(G-5856)
M3 IMAGE LLC
4709 Ripley Dr (79922-1028)
PHONE....................915 845-7676
James Stewart, Mng Member
EMP: 12
SQ FT: 10,000
SALES (est): 1.2MM Privately Held
WEB: www.m3image.com
SIC: 3993 Signs & advertising specialties

(G-5857)
MAGGIE CHACON
Also Called: Structural Steel Services
13351 Montana Ave (79938-9640)
PHONE....................915 857-3100
Roy Chacon, General Mgr
Maggie Chacon, Principal
EMP: 23
SQ FT: 6,000
SALES (est): 6.9MM Privately Held
WEB: www.structuralsteelservices.com
SIC: 3441 Fabricated structural metal

(G-5858)
MAGNA LEATHER CORP
6841 Commerce Ave (79915-1024)
PHONE....................915 772-0004
Natalio Churba, President
▲ EMP: 15
SQ FT: 9,522
SALES (est): 2.3MM Privately Held
WEB: www.alligatorbeltsbymagna.com
SIC: 3111 Leather tanning & finishing

(G-5859)
MAGNOLIA COCA-COLA BOTTLING CO (PA)
11001 Gateway Blvd W (79935-5003)
PHONE....................915 593-2653
J W Wolslager Sr, Ch of Bd
J W Wolslager Jr, President
Paula L Wolslager, Treasurer
EMP: 44
SQ FT: 156,000
SALES: 2.5MM Privately Held
SIC: 2086 Bottled & canned soft drinks

(G-5860)
MAHLE BEHR MFG MGT INC
41 Butterfield Cir (79906-5202)
PHONE....................915 783-4213
Bruce Moorehouse, Vice Pres
Dennis Kimsey, Manager
EMP: 10
SALES (est): 663.8K Privately Held
SIC: 3714 Air conditioner parts, motor vehicle

(G-5861)
MAHLE BEHR MFG MGT INC
48 Walter Jones Blvd (79906-5301)
PHONE..........................248 735-3623
EMP: 10
SALES (est): 374.7K **Privately Held**
SIC: 3714 Mfg Motor Vehicle Parts/Accessories

(G-5862)
MALLINCKRODT LLC
9560 Joe Rodriguez (79927-2146)
PHONE..........................915 298-6010
Brett Gideon, *Sales Staff*
Paul Sullivan, *Branch Mgr*
EMP: 39 **Privately Held**
WEB: www.mallinckrodt.com
SIC: 2834 Pharmaceutical preparations
HQ: Mallinckrodt Llc
675 Jmes S Mcdonnell Blvd
Hazelwood MO 63042
314 654-2000

(G-5863)
MAQUILA MAGAZINE INC
114 S Oregon St (79901-2320)
PHONE..........................915 544-5845
Randy Lore, *President*
EMP: 22
SALES (est): 988.8K **Privately Held**
WEB: www.maquila.com
SIC: 2721 Magazines: publishing only, not printed on site

(G-5864)
MARELLI AUTOMOTIVE LTG USA LLC
12112 Rojas Dr Ste B (79936-7733)
P.O. Box 972270 (79997-2270)
PHONE..........................915 872-1104
Ernesto Corral, *Engineer*
Antonio Pelizza, *Branch Mgr*
EMP: 15
SALES (corp-wide): 959.6MM **Privately Held**
WEB: www.al-lighting.com
SIC: 8711 3647 Engineering services; headlights (fixtures), vehicular
HQ: Marelli Automotive Lighting Usa Llc
3900 Automation Ave
Auburn Hills MI 48326
248 418-3000

(G-5865)
MARIAN GRAPHICS INC
11401 Pellicano Dr (79936-5906)
PHONE..........................915 542-0033
Werner H Widmar, *President*
Armando Valadez, *Sales Mgr*
Andrea Herrera, *Administration*
EMP: 30
SQ FT: 8,000
SALES (est): 3MM **Privately Held**
WEB: www.marianinc.com
SIC: 2759 Screen printing

(G-5866)
MARIAN MEXICO INC
11401 Pellicano Dr (79936-5906)
PHONE..........................915 591-8558
David Connelly, *President*
Neal Rebuck, *Sales Executive*
Cynthia Romero, *Manager*
▲ **EMP:** 35 **EST:** 1998
SQ FT: 50,000
SALES (est): 7.3MM
SALES (corp-wide): 181.3MM **Privately Held**
WEB: www.marianinc.com
SIC: 3089 Injection molding of plastics
HQ: Marian, Inc.
1011 E Saint Clair St
Indianapolis IN 46202
317 638-6525

(G-5867)
MARICK FOODS INC
Also Called: Sandy's Baking Company
1013 Cedar St (79903-2404)
P.O. Box 221257 (79913-4257)
PHONE..........................915 593-2271
Richard Chatterton, *President*
Mary Chatterton, *Vice Pres*
EMP: 55 **EST:** 1980
SQ FT: 50,000
SALES (est): 2MM **Privately Held**
SIC: 2051 5149 Bread, all types (white, wheat, rye, etc): fresh or frozen; pastries, e.g. danish: except frozen; groceries & related products

(G-5868)
MASTER FIBERS INC (HQ)
1710 E Paisano Dr (79901-3157)
PHONE..........................915 544-2299
Alonso Gonzalez, *President*
Ricardo Ordaz, *President*
Sandra Bravo, *Manager*
Juventino Villareal, *Admin Sec*
EMP: 54
SALES (est): 26.2MM **Privately Held**
WEB: www.masterfibers.com
SIC: 5093 5113 4953 2611 Waste paper; cardboard & products; refuse systems; pulp mills

(G-5869)
MASTER PRECISION MACHINING LLC
4683 Pistolero Ln B (79912-6050)
PHONE..........................915 877-0776
Jose Ramos, *Mng Member*
EMP: 11
SALES (est): 450.1K **Privately Held**
SIC: 3545 Precision tools, machinists'

(G-5870)
MAXIMS IMPORTS INC
1001 E Missouri Ave (79902-5408)
PHONE..........................915 577-9228
Ricardo Gutierrez, *President*
Ricardo Guiterrez, *President*
EMP: 13
SQ FT: 4,235
SALES (est): 1.1MM **Privately Held**
WEB: www.maximsimports.com
SIC: 2387 Apparel belts

(G-5871)
MBS MEDICAL TECHNOLOGIES INC
6750 N Desert Blvd (79912)
PHONE..........................888 482-4201
Randy Roth, *CEO*
Matt Lowe, *President*
Diana Vizcarra, *Ch Credit Ofcr*
EMP: 25
SALES (est): 2.1MM **Privately Held**
SIC: 2842 Sanitation preparations, disinfectants & deodorants

(G-5872)
MEDICAL CONCEPTS DEV INC
1 Butterfield Trail Blvd (79906-4901)
PHONE..........................651 735-0498
Lee Annett, *CEO*
David Padget, *COO*
De Ann Salley, *Accountant*
◆ **EMP:** 100
SQ FT: 40,000
SALES (est): 11.4MM **Privately Held**
WEB: www.medconceptsdev.com
SIC: 3842 Surgical appliances & supplies

(G-5873)
METAL TRANSFORMATION & DESIGN
5959 Gateway Blvd W # 315 (79925-3331)
PHONE..........................915 235-4645
Hugo Romo, *CEO*
Sergio Trujillo, *Principal*
EMP: 13
SALES (est): 1.5MM **Privately Held**
SIC: 3441 Fabricated structural metal

(G-5874)
MEXI-SNAX CORPORATION
Also Called: Las Cruces Brand Products
6860 El Paso Dr (79905-3399)
PHONE..........................915 779-5709
EMP: 30 **EST:** 1961
SQ FT: 6,000
SALES (est): 2.9MM **Privately Held**
SIC: 2099 2096 2035 Mfg Food Preparations Mfg Potato Chips/Snacks Mfg Pickles/Sauces/Dressing

(G-5875)
MEXICAN TECHNOLOGIES CO INC
Also Called: M T C
8650 Yermoland Dr (79907-1718)
PHONE..........................915 595-2285
Michael Johnson, *President*
Sergio Cordova, *Vice Pres*
▲ **EMP:** 10
SQ FT: 50,064
SALES (est): 1.2MM **Privately Held**
SIC: 3544 Special dies & tools

(G-5876)
MFI INTERNATIONAL MFG LLC (PA)
Also Called: M F I International
9570 Pan American Dr (79927-2001)
PHONE..........................915 858-0971
Lawrence Wollschlager, *CEO*
Cecilia Levine, *President*
Jabibb Flores, *Purchasing*
Victor Salas, *Engineer*
Paola Ramos, *Mktg Dir*
▲ **EMP:** 515
SQ FT: 62,000
SALES (est): 47.8MM **Privately Held**
WEB: www.mfiintl.com
SIC: 2399 5719 5047 2511 Seat covers, automobile; bedding (sheets, blankets, spreads & pillows); medical & hospital equipment; bed frames, except water bed frames: wood

(G-5877)
MICHELIN NORTH AMERICA INC
1301 Horizon Blvd (79928-4835)
PHONE..........................864 458-5000
EMP: 447
SALES (corp-wide): 1.1B **Privately Held**
WEB: www.michelinman.com
SIC: 3011 Automobile tires, pneumatic; truck or bus tires, pneumatic
HQ: Michelin North America, Inc.
1 Parkway S
Greenville SC 29615
864 458-5000

(G-5878)
MILLENNIUM PLASTICS TECH LLC (PA)
1305 Henry Brennan Dr (79936-6804)
PHONE..........................915 834-2700
George Jordan, *Manager*
Mike Seipel, *Executive*
Tom Talboys,
Kris Lovell,
EMP: 45
SQ FT: 96,000
SALES (est): 3.3MM **Privately Held**
WEB: www.integrated-internet.com
SIC: 7539 3083 Automotive repair shops; laminated plastics plate & sheet

(G-5879)
MILVIAN SOLUTIONS LLC
2407 E Yandell Dr Ste A (79903-3625)
PHONE..........................915 219-5260
Richard Lewis, *Vice Pres*
Rick Lewis, *Vice Pres*
Miguel Vergara III,
EMP: 17
SALES (est): 1.8MM **Privately Held**
WEB: www.milviansolutions.com
SIC: 3812 Defense systems & equipment

(G-5880)
MINICONCRETE MATERIALS INC
15001 Horizon Blvd (79928-8567)
PHONE..........................915 852-4468
Jose B Soto, *President*
EMP: 15
SALES (est): 3.2MM **Privately Held**
WEB: www.miniconcrete.com
SIC: 3273 Ready-mixed concrete

(G-5881)
MODERN IRON WORKS INC
2101 E Mills Ave (79901-2025)
P.O. Box 10035 (79995-0035)
PHONE..........................915 778-6469
Kenneth Schillinger, *President*
Lucy Atilano, *Corp Secy*
EMP: 20

SALES (est): 4.5MM **Privately Held**
WEB: www.miwelpaso.com
SIC: 3446 Stairs, fire escapes, balconies, railings & ladders

(G-5882)
MOLEX LLC
Also Called: Woodhead
11501 James Watt Dr (79936-6902)
PHONE..........................915 591-5600
EMP: 65
SQ FT: 54,000
SALES (corp-wide): 36.8B **Privately Held**
WEB: www.molex.com
SIC: 3613 3643 Power connectors, electric; current-carrying wiring devices
HQ: Molex, Llc
2222 Wellington Ct
Lisle IL 60532
630 969-4550

(G-5883)
MONDELEZ GLOBAL LLC
11210 Armour Dr Ste 3 (79935-4815)
P.O. Box 982140 (79998-2140)
PHONE..........................847 943-4000
EMP: 132 **Publicly Held**
WEB: www.mondelezinternational.com
SIC: 2022 Processed cheese
HQ: Mondelez Global Llc
905 W Fulton Market
Chicago IL 60607
847 943-4000

(G-5884)
MOTOROLA SOLUTIONS INC
1220 Don Haskins Dr Ste A (79936-7815)
PHONE..........................915 872-1229
Fax: 915 872-8290
EMP: 20
SALES (corp-wide): 6B **Publicly Held**
SIC: 3577 Mfg Bar Code Optical Scanning Devices
PA: Motorola Solutions, Inc.
500 W Monroe St Ste 4400
Chicago IL 60661
847 576-5000

(G-5885)
MOUNT FRANKLIN FOODS LLC
9820 Railroad Dr (79924-5029)
PHONE..........................800 351-8178
EMP: 369
SALES (corp-wide): 724.8MM **Privately Held**
WEB: www.azarnutco.com
SIC: 2064 Candy & other confectionery products
PA: Mount Franklin Foods, Llc
1800 Northwestern Dr
El Paso TX 79912
915 877-4079

(G-5886)
MP PRECISION SERVICES INC
11501 Rojas Dr Ste O (79936-6900)
PHONE..........................915 599-9188
Miguel Angel Picos Jr, *President*
EMP: 16
SALES (est): 1.6MM **Privately Held**
WEB: www.mpps-us.com
SIC: 3542 5084 7692 Bending machines; tool & die makers' equipment; brazing

(G-5887)
MPA INTERNATIONAL LP (PA)
7453 Le Conte Dr (79912-7150)
P.O. Box 13286 (79913-3286)
PHONE..........................915 474-7832
Jose Luis Mena, *Partner*
Jose Mena, *General Ptnr*
EMP: 160
SALES (est): 5MM **Privately Held**
SIC: 3469 3089 3829 Metal stampings; injection molding of plastics; thermometers, including digital: clinical

(G-5888)
MR MAIZ-ITO-INC
1901 E Yandell Dr Ste B (79903-3416)
PHONE..........................915 873-9270
Cesar Sifuentes, *President*
EMP: 12
SALES (est): 950K **Privately Held**
SIC: 3999 Manufacturing industries

▲ = Import ▼=Export
◆ =Import/Export

(G-5889)
MSDP GROUP LLC (HQ)
Also Called: Msd Performance
1350 Pullman Dr 14 (79936-7737)
PHONE....................................915 857-5200
Rick Ruebusch, *CEO*
Arnulfo Lara, *Mfg Mgr*
Frankie Hernandez, *Engineer*
Agustin Franco, *Manager*
Carlos Porras, *Supervisor*
EMP: 12
SALES (est): 34.8MM
SALES (corp-wide): 159.3MM **Privately Held**
WEB: www.holley.com
SIC: 3694 Ignition systems, high frequency
PA: Holley Performance Products Inc.
1801 Russellville Rd
Bowling Green KY 42101
270 782-2900

(G-5890)
MSSL WIRING SYSTEM INC
7 Zane Grey St Ste A (79906-5214)
PHONE....................................830 776-9221
Ismael Chavira, *Manager*
EMP: 41 **Privately Held**
SIC: 3679 Harness assemblies for electronic use: wire or cable
HQ: Mssl Wiring System Inc.
700 Intdl Dr
Portland IN 47371
330 856-3366

(G-5891)
MULLEN-TELLES INC
Also Called: MTI Ready Mix
905 Loma Verde Dr (79936-7897)
PHONE....................................915 859-5767
Anthony Mullen, *President*
John Clark, *Manager*
Gary Anderson, *Info Tech Mgr*
Julie Levine Mullen, *Admin Sec*
EMP: 80
SQ FT: 4,000
SALES (est): 16.2MM **Privately Held**
WEB: www.mtireadymix.com
SIC: 3273 Ready-mixed concrete

(G-5892)
MUSSHORN ENTERPRISES INC
Also Called: B & M Machinery Company
7170 Copperqueen Dr (79915-1225)
PHONE....................................915 772-9007
Elmer Musshorn, *President*
Rodolpho Morales, *Vice Pres*
Gary Sales, *Vice Pres*
Thomas Valdez, *Vice Pres*
Tony Cruz, *Buyer*
▲ **EMP:** 102
SQ FT: 36,400
SALES (est): 14.2MM **Privately Held**
WEB: www.coiltec.com
SIC: 7694 7629 1731 3621 Electric motor repair; generator repair; general electrical contractor; coils, for electric motors or generators; motors, electric; generators; machine shop, jobbing & repair

(G-5893)
NATIONAL AERONAUTICS
Also Called: NASA
8101 Boeing Dr (79925-1139)
PHONE....................................915 782-5250
Michael Sierchio, *Division Mgr*
Julie C Kliesing, *Business Mgr*
Teresa Gilchrist, *Buyer*
Ilse Alcantara, *Engineer*
Charles Moss, *Engineer*
EMP: 23 **Publicly Held**
WEB: www.nasa.gov
SIC: 3761 9611 Rockets, space & military, complete; consumer protection office, government; economic development agency, government;
HQ: National Aeronautics And Space Administration
300 E St Sw Ste 5r30
Washington DC 20546
202 358-0000

(G-5894)
NEW MLLENNIUM BLDG SYSTEMS LLC
6248 Edgemere Blvd (79925-3414)
PHONE....................................915 298-5050
Francisco Sanchez, *General Mgr*
Angelo Nieves, *Engineer*
EMP: 101 **Publicly Held**
WEB: www.newmill.com
SIC: 3441 Joists, open web steel: longspan series
HQ: New Millennium Building Systems Llc
7575 W Jefferson Blvd
Fort Wayne IN 46804
260 969-3500

(G-5895)
NFS INC
Also Called: Adams Moulding and Lumber Co
6002 Doniphan Dr (79932-1202)
PHONE....................................915 584-1440
Thomas R Swahlen, *President*
Bridget Swahlen, *Vice Pres*
EMP: 10 **EST:** 1962
SQ FT: 20,000
SALES (est): 1.5MM **Privately Held**
WEB: www.adamsmoulding.com
SIC: 2431 Moldings, wood: unfinished & prefinished

(G-5896)
NICHIRIN-FLEX USA INC
Also Called: Nichirin Coupler
9600 Plaza Cir (79927-2105)
PHONE....................................915 859-1199
Yoshiaki Takashima, *President*
Shinya Imai, *Admin Sec*
▲ **EMP:** 350
SQ FT: 35,030
SALES (est): 56.3MM **Privately Held**
SIC: 3498 3714 3585 Fabricated pipe & fittings; motor vehicle parts & accessories; refrigeration & heating equipment
PA: Nichirin Co., Ltd.
1118, Sazuchi, Besshocho
Himeji HYO 671-0

(G-5897)
NIVISYS LLC
1120 Alza Dr (79907-3108)
PHONE....................................915 633-8354
Joe T Walsh,
EMP: 9
SALES (est): 1.2MM **Privately Held**
WEB: www.nivisys.com
SIC: 3827 Optical instruments & lenses

(G-5898)
NOORMAC LLC
12309 Rojas Dr Unit B4b3 (79928-5249)
PHONE....................................303 261-2818
Raul Saenz, *President*
EMP: 15
SALES (est): 62.5K **Privately Held**
WEB: www.noormac.com
SIC: 3599 Machine shop, jobbing & repair

(G-5899)
NORLUS GROUP INC
Also Called: Professional Machines Co
1217 Barranca Dr Ste A (79935-4601)
PHONE....................................915 590-2041
EMP: 10
SQ FT: 12,000
SALES (est): 970K **Privately Held**
SIC: 3544 Mfg Dies/Tools/Jigs/Fixtures

(G-5900)
OK-GO PACKAGING INC
201 Inglwood Ave Bldg 1-A (79927)
P.O. Box 292348 (79929-2348)
PHONE....................................915 440-2500
Bryan Eichler, *President*
Jorge Calderon, *Plant Mgr*
Emery Eichler, *Sales Associate*
Jaime Eichler, *Director*
EMP: 30
SQ FT: 25,000
SALES (est): 10.5MM **Privately Held**
WEB: www.okgopackaging.com
SIC: 2653 Boxes, corrugated: made from purchased materials

(G-5901)
OMEGA PAVING CONTRACTOR INC
428 Frederick Rd (79905-1809)
PHONE....................................915 595-1280
Jorge Valenzuela, *President*
◆ **EMP:** 14
SQ FT: 6,000

SALES (est): 8MM **Privately Held**
WEB: www.omegapaving.com
SIC: 2951 Asphalt & asphaltic paving mixtures (not from refineries)

(G-5902)
ONEOK INC
4600 Pollard St (79930-6836)
PHONE....................................915 680-7200
Cory Mikles, *CTO*
EMP: 47
SALES (corp-wide): 10.1B **Publicly Held**
WEB: www.oneok.com
SIC: 1321 Natural gas liquids
PA: Oneok, Inc.
100 W 5th St Ste Ll
Tulsa OK 74103
918 588-7000

(G-5903)
PACKAGING CORPORATION AMERICA
Also Called: PCA/El Paso 327
21 Leigh Fisher Blvd (79906-5241)
PHONE....................................915 779-1291
Kathy Cartwright, *General Mgr*
Kathy Partwright, *Branch Mgr*
EMP: 50
SALES (corp-wide): 6.9B **Publicly Held**
WEB: www.packagingcorp.com
SIC: 2653 Boxes, corrugated: made from purchased materials
PA: Packaging Corporation Of America
1 N Field Ct
Lake Forest IL 60045
847 482-3000

(G-5904)
PASO DEL NORTE HARDWARE LLC
Also Called: Ace Hardware
2200 N Yarbrough Dr E43 (79925-6337)
PHONE....................................915 591-6200
Rick Elliott, *Mng Member*
EMP: 13 **EST:** 2015
SALES (est): 587.8K **Privately Held**
WEB: www.healthypasodelnorte.org
SIC: 5251 3089 Hardware; window screening, plastic

(G-5905)
PASO DEL NORTE PUBLISHING INC
Also Called: El Diario De Elpaso
1801 Texas Ave (79901-1811)
PHONE....................................915 838-1601
Adrian Rodriguez, *President*
Armando Velez, *Chief*
Osvaldo Rodriguez, *Vice Pres*
EMP: 82
SQ FT: 29,000
SALES (est): 6.5MM **Privately Held**
WEB: www.pdnp.com
SIC: 2711 Commercial printing & newspaper publishing combined

(G-5906)
PDN SSL LLC
Also Called: Superior Sign & Lighting
11445 Cedar Oak Dr (79936-6009)
P.O. Box 371173 (79937-1173)
PHONE....................................915 629-9100
Rebeca Quintana, *General Mgr*
Alex Del Moral, *Vice Pres*
Fred Reynosa, *Foreman/Supr*
Gilberto Quezada, *Mng Member*
EMP: 33
SQ FT: 15,000
SALES (est): 3.3MM **Privately Held**
WEB: www.superiorsignandlighting.com
SIC: 1799 3993 Sign installation & maintenance; electric signs

(G-5907)
PENCIL CUP OFFICE PRODUCTS INC
1220 Texas Ave (79901-1638)
PHONE....................................915 838-0026
Teresa Gandara, *CEO*
Carlos Gandara, *Vice Pres*
Christina Gandara, *Vice Pres*
EMP: 13
SQ FT: 10,841

SALES (est): 1.5MM **Privately Held**
WEB: www.pencil-cup.com
SIC: 5112 2521 Office supplies; wood office furniture

(G-5908)
PEPSI-COLA METRO BTLG CO INC
10841 Pellicano Dr (79935-4612)
PHONE....................................915 590-6965
Randy Majors, *Manager*
Bonnie Aranda, *Administration*
EMP: 75
SQ FT: 34,480
SALES (corp-wide): 67.1B **Publicly Held**
WEB: www.pepsico.com
SIC: 2086 Carbonated soft drinks, bottled & canned
HQ: Pepsi-Cola Metropolitan Bottling Company, Inc.
1111 Westchester Ave
White Plains NY 10604
914 767-6000

(G-5909)
PHILIPS CONSUMER ELECTRONIC CO
Also Called: Phillips Consumer Electronics
12430 Mercantile Ave (79928-5235)
PHONE....................................915 298-4111
Roger De Moor, *CEO*
Philips Juarez, *Principal*
▲ **EMP:** 1000
SALES (est): 87.5MM **Privately Held**
SIC: 3663 Cameras, television

(G-5910)
PHILIPS NORTH AMERICA LLC
Also Called: Philips Lighting
12430 Mercantile Ave (79928-5235)
PHONE....................................915 298-4111
Rene Zeschitz, *Branch Mgr*
EMP: 25
SQ FT: 20,000
SALES (corp-wide): 21.5B **Privately Held**
WEB: www.usa.philips.com
SIC: 3612 5063 4225 Ballasts for lighting fixtures; electrical apparatus & equipment; miniwarehouse, warehousing
HQ: Philips North America Llc
222 Jacobs St Fl 3
Cambridge MA 02141
978 659-3000

(G-5911)
PLASTIC MOLDING TECHNOLOGY INC
Also Called: P M T
12280 Rojas Dr Ste A (79936-7749)
PHONE....................................915 593-6922
Charles A Sholtis, *CEO*
Jim Vanolli, *General Mgr*
Steve Thompson, *Plant Mgr*
Sam Alvarado, *Prdtn Mgr*
Henry Ramos, *Buyer*
▼ **EMP:** 110
SQ FT: 60,000
SALES (est): 21MM **Privately Held**
WEB: www.pmtinc.com
SIC: 3089 Thermoformed finished plastic products; injection molding of plastics

(G-5912)
PLAYGROUND CONSTRUCTORS INC
205 Teramar Way (79922-1029)
P.O. Box 12531 (79913-0531)
PHONE....................................915 585-6336
Robert Millard, *President*
EMP: 12
SALES (est): 886.9K **Privately Held**
SIC: 3949 5039 Playground equipment; air ducts, sheet metal

(G-5913)
PMC ACQUISITION COMPANY INC
Also Called: Nn Inc V-S Products Division
11355 Rojas Dr Ste 13-14 (79936-6465)
P.O. Box 9856 (79995-2856)
PHONE....................................915 225-8758
James H Dorton, *President*
EMP: 250 **EST:** 2014
SQ FT: 1,000

SALES (est): 6.7MM
SALES (corp-wide): 847.4MM **Publicly Held**
SIC: 3315 Steel wire & related products
PA: Nn, Inc.
  6210 Ardrey Kell Rd # 600
  Charlotte NC 28277
  980 264-4300

(G-5914)
POLLOK INC
Also Called: Pollok Electronics
21 Butterfield Trail Blvd (79906-5268)
PHONE............................915 592-5700
David M Draime, *Ch of Bd*
Cloyd J Abruzzo, *President*
Victor Pineda, *Engineer*
Kevin Bagby, *CFO*
Avery S Cohen, *Admin Sec*
▲ **EMP:** 600
SALES (est): 90MM **Publicly Held**
SIC: 5065 3823 3714 3545 Electronic
  parts & equipment; industrial instrmnts
  msrmnt display/control process variable;
  motor vehicle parts & accessories; ma-
  chine tool accessories
PA: Stoneridge, Inc.
  39675 Mackenzie Dr # 400
  Novi MI 48377

(G-5915)
POLYMERICA LTD
Also Called: Global Enterprises
6055 Luckett Ct (79932-1806)
PHONE............................915 845-6288
Frank Kladzyk, *Branch Mgr*
EMP: 125
SALES (corp-wide): 86MM **Privately Held**
WEB: www.globalent.org
SIC: 3089 Extruded finished plastic prod-
  ucts
PA: Polymerica Limited Company
  26909 Woodward Ave
  Huntington Woods MI 48070
  248 542-2000

(G-5916)
PORFIRIO DIAZ EXIT LP
Also Called: Pdx Printing
208 N Octavia St (79901-1533)
PHONE............................915 544-6688
Tom Fenton, *Partner*
Ellie D Fenton, *Partner*
John Bauer, *General Mgr*
Erin Pfirman, *Sales Staff*
Jesse Galvan, *Graphic Designe*
EMP: 11
SALES (est): 1.7MM **Privately Held**
WEB: www.pdxprinting.com
SIC: 2752 Commercial printing, offset

(G-5917)
**PRECISION PROSTHETIC INC
(PA)**
1501 E Missouri Ave (79902-5615)
PHONE............................915 544-2961
Katherine Lee, *President*
John Lee, *Admin Sec*
EMP: 10
SQ FT: 3,400
SALES (est): 1.2MM **Privately Held**
WEB: www.precision-prosthetics.com
SIC: 3842 Limbs, artificial

(G-5918)
**PRINCE MANUFACTURING
CORP**
6248 Edgemere Blvd (79925-3414)
PHONE............................915 217-2664
EMP: 105
SALES (corp-wide): 150.3MM **Privately Held**
WEB: www.princemanufacturing.com
SIC: 2759 3479 Commercial printing;
  coating of metals & formed products
HQ: Prince Manufacturing Corporation
  203 W Main St Ste A3
  Lexington SC 29072
  803 708-4789

(G-5919)
**PRODUCTION MANUFACTURING
INC**
1515 Goodyear Dr (79936-6039)
PHONE............................915 629-9668
Greg Harper, *President*
Joe Mergili, *Vice Pres*
EMP: 22
SQ FT: 7,500
SALES (est): 1.6MM **Privately Held**
WEB: www.productionmanufacturing.net
SIC: 3599 Machine shop, jobbing & repair

(G-5920)
**PRODUCTION WAREHOUSING
INC**
320 N Clark Dr (79905-3134)
PHONE............................915 779-1405
Thomas M Niland, *President*
EMP: 55
SALES (est): 3.9MM **Privately Held**
SIC: 3648 Street lighting fixtures

(G-5921)
**PROGRESSIVE RESOURCES
INC (PA)**
Also Called: Asmar Truck Equipment
7713 Alameda Ave (79915-3920)
PHONE............................915 778-9548
Juan Sandoval, *President*
Carlos Sandoval, *Vice Pres*
Raul Sandoval, *Treasurer*
G Edward Sandoval, *Admin Sec*
EMP: 9 **EST:** 1978
SQ FT: 9,000
SALES (est): 1MM **Privately Held**
SIC: 3713 Truck bodies (motor vehicles)

(G-5922)
**QUALITY GRAPHICS & FORMS
INC**
1410 Gail Borden Pl B1 (79935-4814)
PHONE............................915 592-4500
Doug Young, *President*
EMP: 15
SQ FT: 21,000
SALES (est): 2MM **Privately Held**
WEB: www.impresalabel.com
SIC: 2752 2761 Commercial printing, off-
  set; manifold business forms
PA: Impresa Label Inc
  1410 Gail Borden Pl B1
  El Paso TX 79935

(G-5923)
**QUICKIE MANUFACTURING
CORP**
12058 Rojas Dr Ste A (79936-7736)
PHONE............................915 859-2522
Craig Learn, *Manager*
EMP: 55
SALES (corp-wide): 9.7B **Publicly Held**
WEB: www.quickie.com
SIC: 3991 2392 Brooms; mops, floor &
  dust
HQ: Quickie Manufacturing Corp
  3124 Valley Ave
  Winchester VA 22601
  856 829-7900

(G-5924)
R E M INDUSTRIES INC
Also Called: El Paso Saddlery
2025 E Yandell Dr (79903-3513)
P.O. Box 27194 (79926-7194)
PHONE............................915 544-2233
Ryan McNellis, *President*
Robert E Mc Nellis, *President*
Don Long, *Finance Mgr*
EMP: 15
SQ FT: 6,200
SALES (est): 2MM **Privately Held**
WEB: www.epsaddlery.com
SIC: 3199 3172 5948 Holsters, leather;
  personal leather goods; luggage & leather
  goods stores

(G-5925)
R-J TYPESETTERS INC
Also Called: Fast Printing
2717 E Missouri Ave (79903-3998)
PHONE............................915 562-4461
Joseph Olivas, *President*
Maggie Olivas, *Vice Pres*

EMP: 9
SQ FT: 3,000
SALES (est): 350K **Privately Held**
WEB: www.rjrubberstampco.com
SIC: 3953 Marking devices

(G-5926)
RAMIREZ EVERARDO
Also Called: Pro Print & Label Group
8701 Castner Dr (79907-1858)
P.O. Box 17739 (79917-7739)
PHONE............................915 593-5349
Everardo Ramirez, *Owner*
Rose Heredia, *Principal*
EMP: 47
SQ FT: 18,000
SALES (est): 5.5MM **Privately Held**
WEB: www.proprintandlabel.com
SIC: 2752 7389 Commercial printing, off-
  set; packaging & labeling services

(G-5927)
**RANGER SECURITY
DETECTORS INC**
11900 Montana Ave (79936-1503)
PHONE............................915 590-4441
John E Turner, *CEO*
Roger Turner, *President*
Estele Turner, *Vice Pres*
▲ **EMP:** 49
SQ FT: 12,000
SALES (est): 10MM **Privately Held**
WEB: www.rangersecurity.com
SIC: 3812 Navigational systems & instru-
  ments

(G-5928)
RAYTHEON COMPANY
7201 Montana Ave (79925)
PHONE............................915 779-7666
Rosalinda Rubio, *Engineer*
Rick Reynolds, *Manager*
Rosendo Dominguez, *Representative*
EMP: 284
SQ FT: 48,182
SALES (corp-wide): 56.5B **Publicly Held**
WEB: www.rtx.com
SIC: 3812 Search & navigation equipment
HQ: Raytheon Company
  870 Winter St
  Waltham MA 02451
  781 522-3000

(G-5929)
RCT GLOBAL INC
1520 Goodyear Dr Ste S (79936-6020)
PHONE............................915 595-8750
Roberto Holguin III, *President*
EMP: 15
SALES (est): 1.3MM **Privately Held**
WEB: www.rctprecision.com
SIC: 7373 3544 Computer-aided manufac-
  turing (CAM) systems service; special
  dies & tools

(G-5930)
**RD FOOD MANUFACTURING
INC**
Also Called: Productos Real
1100 Pendale Rd (79907-1711)
PHONE............................915 594-4488
Ramon Dominguez, *President*
Argelia Dominguez, *Office Mgr*
EMP: 25
SALES (est): 4MM **Privately Held**
WEB: www.productosreal.com
SIC: 2032 Spanish foods: packaged in
  cans, jars, etc.

(G-5931)
READYONE INDUSTRIES INC
1414 Ability Dr (79936-6415)
PHONE............................915 858-7277
Luis Alvarez, *President*
Daniel Nunez, *General Mgr*
Cynthia Deharo, *Vice Pres*
Asaf Picciotto, *Vice Pres*
Cody Bachmeier, *Project Mgr*
◆ **EMP:** 1000
SQ FT: 350,000
SALES: 120.6MM **Privately Held**
WEB: www.readyone.org
SIC: 2331 2311 Women's & misses'
  blouses & shirts; military uniforms, men's
  & youths': purchased materials

(G-5932)
**REBUILDING TGETHER EL PASO
INC**
6400 Airport Rd Ste G (79925-1049)
PHONE............................915 342-3882
Anna Gill, *President*
EMP: 16
SALES: 234.7K **Privately Held**
WEB: www.rebuildingtogetherelpaso.org
SIC: 1389 Oil & gas field services

(G-5933)
REDDY ICE CORPORATION
1621 Texas Ave (79901-1749)
PHONE............................915 532-2495
David Tankersley, *Manager*
EMP: 50
SQ FT: 32,742 **Privately Held**
WEB: www.reddyice.com
SIC: 5999 2097 Ice; awnings; manufac-
  tured ice
HQ: Reddy Ice Corporation
  5710 Lbj Fwy Ste 300
  Dallas TX 75240
  214 526-6740

(G-5934)
REGAL BELOIT CORPORATION
1265 Peter Cooper Dr (79936-6814)
PHONE............................412 968-0100
Rafael Elias, *Buyer*
Ricardo Alcala, *Engineer*
Jesus De Lira, *Engineer*
John Boyne, *Sales Staff*
Oscar Lugo, *Sr Project Mgr*
EMP: 35
SALES (corp-wide): 3.2B **Publicly Held**
WEB: www.regalbeloit.com
SIC: 3621 Motors & generators
PA: Regal Beloit Corporation
  200 State St
  Beloit WI 53511
  608 364-8800

(G-5935)
**REGENCY PLASTICS - UBLY
INC**
Also Called: Sierra Plastics
1101 Burgundy Dr (79907-3461)
PHONE............................915 860-1997
Rosa Fuentes, *Prdtn Mgr*
Julie Kennedy, *Marketing Staff*
Danny Provencio, *Branch Mgr*
EMP: 100 **Privately Held**
WEB: www.geminigroup.net
SIC: 3089 Injection molding of plastics
HQ: Regency Plastics - Ubly, Inc.
  4147 N Ubly Rd
  Ubly MI 48475

(G-5936)
**RELIANT LABELS AND PRTG
INC**
11400 Rojas Dr Ste B (79936-6423)
PHONE............................915 595-2999
Richard Aguilera, *President*
Wanda Medina, *Vice Pres*
Armando Valadez, *Sales Staff*
Stephen Griffin, *Graphic Designe*
Sujeil Terrazas,
EMP: 20
SQ FT: 9,000
SALES (est): 3.5MM **Privately Held**
WEB: www.reliantlabels.com
SIC: 2759 Letterpress printing; labels &
  seals: printing

(G-5937)
REMSA USA INC
14500 Sam Hawken Rd (79938-9717)
PHONE............................915 855-8621
Luis A Ramirez, *President*
Jorge Ramirez, *Vice Pres*
Abdiel Ramirez, *Sales Mgr*
▲ **EMP:** 10
SQ FT: 43,000
SALES (est): 3MM **Privately Held**
WEB: www.remsausainc.com
SIC: 7694 7699 Electric motor repair;
  pumps & pumping equipment repair

(G-5938)
REXCEL COATINGS CORPORATION (PA)
4600 Ripley Dr (79922-1016)
P.O. Box 12310 (79913-0310)
PHONE................................915 581-2797
Rex B Smith, *Ch of Bd*
Geoffrey L Smith, *President*
Kristen B Smith, *Corp Secy*
Dennis Lukehart, *Vice Pres*
Clayton H Smith, *Vice Pres*
EMP: 18
SQ FT: 19,034
SALES (est): 7.8MM **Privately Held**
WEB: www.rexcelcoatings.com
SIC: 5084 2851 Paint spray equipment, industrial; coating, air curing; epoxy coatings

(G-5939)
RIGBA INTERNATIONAL INC (PA)
820 Hawkins Blvd Ste G (79915-1229)
PHONE................................915 239-1070
Nestor Riggs, *President*
▲ **EMP:** 12
SALES (est): 1.4MM **Privately Held**
WEB: www.rigbainternational.com
SIC: 2752 Promotional printing, lithographic

(G-5940)
RIO VALLEY BIOFUEL TRANSPORT
3500 Doniphan Dr (79922-1408)
P.O. Box 1300, Anthony NM (88021-1300)
PHONE................................915 791-8720
Donna Belcher, *Exec Dir*
EMP: 30
SALES (est): 1.4MM **Privately Held**
WEB: www.riovalleybiofuels.com
SIC: 2869 Fuels

(G-5941)
RIO VALLEY BIOFUELS LLC
3500 Doniphan Dr (79922-1408)
P.O. Box 1300, Anthony NM (88021-1300)
PHONE................................915 791-8720
Noah Smith, *COO*
Dean Belcher, *Plant Mgr*
Seth Jenkins, *Manager*
Elle Mitchell, *Manager*
EMP: 70
SQ FT: 17,566
SALES (est): 1.8MM **Privately Held**
WEB: www.riovalleybiofuels.com
SIC: 2911 Diesel fuels

(G-5942)
ROBERT F HERNDON CORPORATION
Also Called: Herndon's Rod Iron Furniture
7360 Stiles Dr (79915-2518)
PHONE................................915 779-7905
Robert F Herndon, *President*
EMP: 10
SQ FT: 57,213
SALES (est): 1.2MM **Privately Held**
SIC: 5099 2514 Brass goods; novelty furniture, household: metal

(G-5943)
ROCKA SOLUTIONS INC
14005 Sandy Point Ln (79938-5002)
PHONE................................514 602-9449
Rodrigo Cacho, *President*
EMP: 18
SALES (est): 775.6K **Privately Held**
SIC: 2891 Adhesives

(G-5944)
ROICOM USA LLC
1414 Ability Dr (79936-6415)
PHONE................................915 471-3071
Mercedes Gil, *Credit Mgr*
Tony Martinez,
EMP: 50
SALES (est): 3.2MM **Privately Held**
WEB: www.roicomusa.com
SIC: 2311 Men's & boys' uniforms

(G-5945)
ROM INDUSTRIAL INC
2120 E Paisano Dr Ste D (79905-4076)
PHONE................................915 875-1186

Roman Bojorquez, *President*
EMP: 12
SQ FT: 250
SALES (est): 2.5MM **Privately Held**
WEB: www.rom-industrial.com
SIC: 5085 3599 Industrial supplies; air intake filters, internal combustion engine, except auto

(G-5946)
ROSS OPTICAL INDUSTRIES INC
1410 Gail Borden Pl A3 (79935-4814)
PHONE................................915 595-5417
Ed Ross, *CEO*
Divaker Mangadu, *President*
Erika Salayandia, *QC Mgr*
Jing Zheng, *Engineer*
Steele Jones, *Treasurer*
EMP: 13
SQ FT: 9,500
SALES (est): 3MM
SALES (corp-wide): 9.9MM **Publicly Held**
WEB: www.rossoptical.com
SIC: 3827 Optical instruments & lenses
PA: Precision Optics Corporation, Inc.
22 E Broadway
Gardner MA 01440
978 630-1800

(G-5947)
RSD SECURITY SCANNERS LLC
11900 Montana Ave (79936-1503)
PHONE................................915 590-4441
Alfonso Bernal, *Engineer*
John Turner, *Sales Mgr*
Isac Salido, *Mng Member*
Yancy Gonzalez, *Admin Dir*
EMP: 25
SQ FT: 5,000
SALES (est): 3MM **Privately Held**
WEB: www.rsdsecurityscanners.com
SIC: 3829 Measuring & controlling devices

(G-5948)
RUBENS ELECTROPLATING INC
Also Called: Electroplating of El Paso
1040 Hawkins Blvd (79915-1213)
PHONE................................915 779-3796
Ruben Nares Jr, *President*
Ruben Nares Sr, *Vice Pres*
EMP: 14
SQ FT: 6,000
SALES (est): 1.3MM **Privately Held**
WEB: www.electroplatingelpaso.com
SIC: 3471 Electroplating of metals or formed products

(G-5949)
RUDDOCK MANUFACTURING CO INC
Also Called: Ruddock Brothers
1801 Magoffin Ave (79901-1825)
P.O. Box 10205 (79995-0205)
PHONE................................915 544-3530
Leon L Ruddock, *President*
John Ruddock, *Vice Pres*
Jeff Ruddock, *Sales Staff*
▲ **EMP:** 110 **EST:** 1955
SQ FT: 60,000
SALES (est): 9.3MM **Privately Held**
WEB: www.ruddock-shirts.com
SIC: 2321 2339 2326 Men's & boys' furnishings; women's & misses' outerwear; men's & boys' work clothing

(G-5950)
RUDDOCK MANUFACTURING CO INC
1825 Magoffin Ave (79901-1882)
P.O. Box 10205 (79995-0205)
PHONE................................915 544-3530
John Ruddock, *President*
Leon Ruddock, *Manager*
EMP: 120
SQ FT: 50,000
SALES (est): 7.2MM **Privately Held**
WEB: www.ruddock-shirts.com
SIC: 2321 Men's & boys' dress shirts

(G-5951)
S & M AIRE LLC
Also Called: Perfect Weather Htg & Coolg
13340 Ayla Rd (79938-8979)
PHONE................................915 921-9677

Sergio Macedo, *Mng Member*
Dane Felix,
EMP: 12
SALES (est): 2.2MM **Privately Held**
WEB: www.elpasoperfectweather.com
SIC: 3585 Refrigeration & heating equipment

(G-5952)
SASA MOLDING INC
Also Called: Rogupe Sasa Molding
32 Via Placita (79927-5050)
PHONE................................915 726-9290
Humberto Salas Jr, *President*
Rosaura Salas, *Vice Pres*
Mireya Salas, *Treasurer*
Marilu Salas, *Admin Sec*
EMP: 40
SQ FT: 150,000
SALES (est): 6.7MM **Privately Held**
SIC: 2431 Trim, wood

(G-5953)
SCHNEIDER ELECTRIC
1601 Northwestern Dr (79912-8024)
PHONE................................915 834-6451
Ceci Leon, *Manager*
EMP: 13
SALES (est): 4MM **Privately Held**
SIC: 3699 Electrical equipment & supplies

(G-5954)
SEISA MEDICAL INC (PA)
9005 Montana Ave (79925-1313)
P.O. Box 221616 (79913-4616)
PHONE................................915 774-4321
Julio Chiu, *CEO*
Aaron Chiu, *COO*
Isaac Chiu, *Vice Pres*
Jocobo Chiu, *Vice Pres*
▲ **EMP:** 44
SALES (est): 360.6MM **Privately Held**
WEB: www.seisa.com
SIC: 3841 Surgical & medical instruments

(G-5955)
SELTEK INTERNATIONAL INC
2301 Wyoming Ave (79903-3818)
PHONE................................915 772-8444
Manuel Vargas, *President*
MA Elena Vargas, *Admin Sec*
▲ **EMP:** 27
SQ FT: 4,500
SALES (est): 6.5MM **Privately Held**
WEB: www.seltek.net
SIC: 3569 Heaters, swimming pool: electric

(G-5956)
SEVENDIPITY JEWELRY MFG LLC
1528 Sioux Dr Ste A (79925-2158)
PHONE................................915 594-8500
Jesus O Gonzalez,
EMP: 9 **EST:** 2007
SALES (est): 831.3K **Privately Held**
SIC: 3911 Jewelry, precious metal

(G-5957)
SHAUDRA COMPANY INC
Also Called: Jonsil Manufacturing Co
11812 Pete Rose Dr (79936-7014)
PHONE................................915 544-4244
David Cervantez, *Branch Mgr*
EMP: 20
SALES (corp-wide): 2.9MM **Privately Held**
WEB: www.jjenkinssonscoinc.com
SIC: 3914 3911 Trophies; jewelry apparel
PA: Shaudra Company, Inc.
1801 Whitehead Rd
Baltimore MD 21207
410 265-5200

(G-5958)
SHEET METAL AIR PLUS CO LLC
4016 Johnson Ave (79930-6856)
PHONE................................915 566-8131
Alberto Ortiz,
EMP: 10
SALES (est): 880.7K **Privately Held**
SIC: 3444 Sheet metalwork

(G-5959)
SHURE ELECTRONICS
Also Called: Shure Brothers
12425 Rojas Dr 1 (79928-5201)
PHONE................................915 782-2800
Fax: 915 782-2730
▲ **EMP:** 23 **EST:** 1997
SALES (est): 3.9MM **Privately Held**
SIC: 3651 Mfg Microphones

(G-5960)
SIEMENS INDUSTRY INC
9494 Escobar Dr Ste A (79907-3106)
PHONE................................915 790-0219
Ruby Ciciretti, *Manager*
Rebecca Boetto, *Consultant*
EMP: 150
SALES (corp-wide): 67.4B **Privately Held**
WEB: www.new.siemens.com
SIC: 3621 3613 Motors & generators; switchgear & switchboard apparatus
HQ: Siemens Industry, Inc.
1000 Deerfield Pkwy
Buffalo Grove IL 60089
847 215-1000

(G-5961)
SIGNS & GRAPHICS PLUS LLC
Also Called: Sgp
1302 Gail Borden Pl Ste B (79935-5309)
PHONE................................915 590-7446
Maria Kondow, *President*
EMP: 10
SQ FT: 1,400
SALES (est): 625.5K **Privately Held**
WEB: www.signsgp.com
SIC: 3993 7389 7336 Electric signs; neon signs; letters for signs, metal; lettering & sign painting services; graphic arts & related design

(G-5962)
SINGER DATA PRODUCTS INC
3800 Buckner St (79925-1304)
PHONE................................915 594-7650
Toni Ceniceros, *Manager*
EMP: 24
SALES (corp-wide): 4.1MM **Privately Held**
SIC: 3575 3577 3625 Computer terminals; computer peripheral equipment; relays & industrial controls
PA: Singer Data Products Inc
790 Maple Ln
Bensenville IL 60106
630 860-6500

(G-5963)
SLE ELECTRONICS-USA INC
9641 Plaza Cir Ste A (79927-2152)
PHONE................................915 594-4998
Jesus Duarte, *President*
Joseph Liebl, *Principal*
EMP: 40
SQ FT: 3,000
SALES (est): 6.6MM
SALES (corp-wide): 421MM **Privately Held**
WEB: www.sle-usa.com
SIC: 3429 Harness hardware
HQ: Komax Sle Gmbh & Co. Kg
Technopark 4
Grafenau 94481
855 272-3000

(G-5964)
SNAPP TOOL & DIE INC
10885 Dyer St Ste A (79934-2941)
P.O. Box 4487 (79914-4487)
PHONE................................915 821-2046
Gregory Snapp, *President*
Kay Snapp, *Corp Secy*
Bob Baker, *Exec VP*
Todd Snapp, *Vice Pres*
EMP: 30
SALES (est): 4.9MM **Privately Held**
WEB: www.snapptool.com
SIC: 3544 3444 Special dies & tools; sheet metalwork

(G-5965)
SNOWBALL LIGHTING INC
1555 Goodyear Dr Ste A (79936-6047)
PHONE................................915 227-7210
EMP: 11

SALES (est): 1.6MM **Privately Held**
WEB: www.snowball-inc.com
SIC: 3646 Commercial indusl & institutional electric lighting fixtures

(G-5966)
SOLERA CO
500 W Overland Ave # 250 (79901-1085)
PHONE.....................915 637-6471
Hugo Pardo, *President*
EMP: 16
SALES (est): 736.5K **Privately Held**
SIC: 3999 Manufacturing industries

(G-5967)
SOLID DISTRIBUTION LLC
8900 Viscount Blvd # 722 (79925-5897)
PHONE.....................915 235-4357
Lidia Ruiz, *Mng Member*
EMP: 9
SALES (est): 450K **Privately Held**
WEB: www.solidistribution.com
SIC: 3089 Injection molding of plastics

(G-5968)
SOLID INTEGRATIONS LLC
7101 N Mesa St (79912-3613)
PHONE.....................915 235-4357
Arturo Chavez, *Mng Member*
Rodolfo De La Ree, *Mng Member*
EMP: 30
SALES (est): 1.5MM **Privately Held**
WEB: www.solidintegrations.net
SIC: 7372 7389 Prepackaged software; design, commercial & industrial

(G-5969)
SOLRAC CORPORATION
Also Called: Block Component Div
19 Leigh Fisher Blvd B (79906-5218)
PHONE.....................915 772-3073
Carlos Rodriguez, *President*
Oscar Rodriguez, *Corp Secy*
Mauricio Rodriguez, *CFO*
Irene Morales, *Human Res Mgr*
EMP: 300
SQ FT: 55,000
SALES (est): 29.3MM **Privately Held**
WEB: www.solraccorp.com
SIC: 3694 3714 Harness wiring sets, internal combustion engines; motor vehicle parts & accessories

(G-5970)
SOUTHANCHOR MANUFACTURING LLC
Also Called: Sam
525 Canal Rd Ste C (79901-2200)
P.O. Box 3613 (79923-3613)
PHONE.....................915 590-6718
Elizabeth S Rome,
EMP: 20
SALES (est): 3.7MM **Privately Held**
WEB: www.api-ep.com
SIC: 3083 3423 3554 Laminated plastics plate & sheet; cutting dies, except metal cutting; coating & finishing machinery, paper

(G-5971)
SOUTHWEST CUTTERS LLC
1430 Gail Borden Pl 1c (79935-4810)
PHONE.....................915 858-2200
Shane Martinez, *Mng Member*
Donald Martinez, *Manager*
▲ **EMP:** 85
SQ FT: 60,000
SALES (est): 15.6MM **Privately Held**
WEB: www.swcutters.com
SIC: 2211 3639 3999 Glove fabrics, cotton; sewing equipment; pet supplies

(G-5972)
SOUTHWEST TACTICAL LLC
11201 Armour Dr Ste D (79935-4817)
PHONE.....................915 726-0634
John M Himes, *Principal*
EMP: 195
SALES (est): 13.8MM **Privately Held**
SIC: 2394 Canvas & related products

(G-5973)
SS ELECTRIC INC
Also Called: Electric Supply Source
3650 Buckner St (79925-1321)
P.O. Box 962047 (79996-2047)
PHONE.....................915 217-2200
Sandra Sanchez, *President*
Alex Sanchez, *Project Mgr*
EMP: 15
SQ FT: 4,000
SALES (est): 2.8MM **Privately Held**
WEB: www.electricsupplysource.com
SIC: 8742 3625 3613 7373 Automation & robotics consultant; electric controls & control accessories, industrial; control panels, electric; office computer automation systems integration; electrical work

(G-5974)
STALLION BOOT CO INC
100 N Cotton St (79901-1792)
PHONE.....................915 532-6268
Pedro Munoz, *President*
Norma Loera, *Office Mgr*
EMP: 30 **EST:** 1981
SQ FT: 5,000
SALES (est): 3.8MM **Privately Held**
WEB: www.stallionboots.com
SIC: 3143 3144 5661 3172 Boots, dress or casual: men's; boots, canvas or leather: women's; men's boots; women's boots; personal leather goods; apparel belts

(G-5975)
STAMPCOAT INC
10863 Pellicano Dr (79935-4608)
PHONE.....................915 591-0346
Sal Robles, *President*
EMP: 20
SALES (est): 3.7MM **Privately Held**
WEB: www.stampcoat.com
SIC: 3479 Painting, coating & hot dipping

(G-5976)
STEEL SPECIALTIES INC
750 Pendale Rd (79907-2722)
PHONE.....................915 590-2337
Juan Gonzalez, *President*
Javier Espinoza, *Manager*
EMP: 29
SQ FT: 800
SALES (est): 9.4MM **Privately Held**
WEB: www.steelspecialtiesinc.net
SIC: 3446 Stairs, staircases, stair treads: prefabricated metal; railings, prefabricated metal; open flooring & grating for construction

(G-5977)
STELLA HASEGAWA
Also Called: Accents and Accessories
9801 Montwood Dr (79925-6001)
P.O. Box 371075 (79937-1075)
PHONE.....................915 594-7633
Stella Hasegawa, *Owner*
EMP: 10
SQ FT: 2,000
SALES (est): 1.1MM **Privately Held**
WEB: www.aaaaccents.com
SIC: 1542 1721 5023 2521 Commercial & office buildings, renovation & repair; commercial painting; carpets; wood office furniture; window treatment installation

(G-5978)
STEWART EFI LLC
27 Leigh Fisher Blvd (79906-5241)
PHONE.....................915 775-2558
Daniel Stokes,
EMP: 50
SALES (corp-wide): 47.4MM **Privately Held**
WEB: www.stewartefi.com
SIC: 3469 Stamping metal for the trade
PA: Stewart Efi, Llc
　　45 Old Waterbury Rd
　　Thomaston CT 06787
　　860 283-8213

(G-5979)
STEWART EFI FINISHING LLC
44 Butterfield Cir (79906-5200)
PHONE.....................915 775-2558
Bernie Rosselli, *President*
Cruz Smith, *Purch Mgr*

▲ **EMP:** 10
SALES (est): 1.7MM
SALES (corp-wide): 47.4MM **Privately Held**
WEB: www.stewartefi.com
SIC: 3469 Stamping metal for the trade
PA: Stewart Efi, Llc
　　45 Old Waterbury Rd
　　Thomaston CT 06787
　　860 283-8213

(G-5980)
STEWART STEVENSON PWR PDTS LLC
11100 Gateway Blvd E (79927-8701)
PHONE.....................915 790-1848
Pablo Sierros, *General Mgr*
EMP: 14
SALES (corp-wide): 2.8B **Publicly Held**
WEB: www.stewartandstevenson.com
SIC: 5084 3531 7538 Engines & parts, diesel; road construction & maintenance machinery; general automotive repair shops
HQ: Stewart & Stevenson Power Products, Llc
　　55 Waugh Dr Ste 800
　　Houston TX 77007

(G-5981)
STITCHES INC
360 Ridgemont Dr (79912-5331)
PHONE.....................915 591-9260
Raymond W Klein, *Ch of Bd*
Rachael I Klein, *Vice Pres*
EMP: 40
SQ FT: 40,000
SALES (est): 1.8MM **Privately Held**
SIC: 2325 2339 2389 2326 Jeans: men's, youths' & boys'; slacks, dress: men's, youths' & boys'; jeans: women's, misses' & juniors'; slacks: women's, misses' & juniors'; hospital gowns; men's & boys' work clothing

(G-5982)
STONE MASTERS
1201 Berryville St (79928-5659)
PHONE.....................915 216-1702
Roberto Peru, *Owner*
Mario Vera, *Co-Owner*
EMP: 10.
SALES (est): 466.8K **Privately Held**
SIC: 3281 Cut stone & stone products

(G-5983)
STONERIDGE INC
Warehouse Division
21 Butterfield Trail Blvd A (79906-5269)
PHONE.....................915 778-1331
John C Corey, *President*
EMP: 319 **Publicly Held**
WEB: www.stoneridge.com
SIC: 3714 3679 3625 Motor vehicle electrical equipment; instrument board assemblies, motor vehicle; harness assemblies for electronic use: wire or cable; electronic switches; actuators, industrial
PA: Stoneridge, Inc.
　　39675 Mackenzie Dr # 400
　　Novi MI 48377

(G-5984)
STONERIDGE ELECTRONICS INC
Also Called: Stoneridge Electronics NA
21 Buttrfield Trail Blvd 1 # 100 (79906)
PHONE.....................915 621-6111
John C Corey, *President*
Thomas A Beaver, *Vice Pres*
Kevin B Kramer, *Vice Pres*
Michael D Sloan, *Vice Pres*
George E Strickler, *Vice Pres*
▲ **EMP:** 1000
SALES (est): 228.8MM **Publicly Held**
WEB: www.srisupplier.com
SIC: 3679 3714 Electronic circuits; motor vehicle electrical equipment
PA: Stoneridge, Inc.
　　39675 Mackenzie Dr # 400
　　Novi MI 48377

(G-5985)
STRATTEC SECURITY CORPORATION
Also Called: F/K/A Nextlock
12170 Rojas Dr Ste E (79936-7723)
PHONE.....................915 790-5400
Victor Valero, *Branch Mgr*
Patrick Hansen, *Officer*
EMP: 22 **Publicly Held**
WEB: www.strattec.com
SIC: 3699 Security devices
PA: Strattec Security Corporation
　　3333 W Good Hope Rd
　　Milwaukee WI 53209

(G-5986)
SUMITOMO ELC WIRG SYSTEMS INC
6500 N Desert Blvd (79912-8401)
PHONE.....................915 845-7700
Yoshiro Yamane, *Principal*
Rosa Simental, *Buyer*
Robert Ornelas, *Manager*
EMP: 128 **Privately Held**
WEB: www.sewus.com
SIC: 3315 Wire & fabricated wire products
HQ: Sumitomo Electric Wiring Systems, Inc.
　　1018 Ashley St
　　Bowling Green KY 42103
　　270 782-7397

(G-5987)
SUMITOMO ELC WIRG SYSTEMS INC
12110 Esther Lama Dr # 100 (79936-7741)
PHONE.....................915 859-0555
Don Walsh, *Branch Mgr*
EMP: 10 **Privately Held**
WEB: www.sewus.com
SIC: 3714 Motor vehicle parts & accessories
HQ: Sumitomo Electric Wiring Systems, Inc.
　　1018 Ashley St
　　Bowling Green KY 42103
　　270 782-7397

(G-5988)
SUPPLYONE TUCSON INC
Also Called: Supplyone El Paso
12135 Esther Lama Dr (79936-7762)
PHONE.....................915 860-9911
William T Leith, *Branch Mgr*
EMP: 9
SALES (corp-wide): 381.2MM **Privately Held**
WEB: www.supplyone.com
SIC: 2821 5113 Thermoplastic materials; corrugated & solid fiber boxes
HQ: Supplyone Tucson, Inc.
　　6874 S Palo Verde Rd # 100
　　Tucson AZ 85756
　　520 573-7080

(G-5989)
SW FOAM LLC
9900 Railroad Dr (79924-5000)
PHONE.....................915 751-1000
Robert Bislorek, *Mng Member*
Charles Daly,
Charles Little,
Masashi Ozekl,
Daryl Schuett,
EMP: 34
SALES (est): 6.9MM **Privately Held**
WEB: www.woodbridgegroup.com
SIC: 3069 Medical & laboratory rubber sundries & related products

(G-5990)
SYSTEM SENSOR
1101b Burgundy Dr (79907-3461)
PHONE.....................915 778-1301
EMP: 9
SALES (est): 41.1K **Privately Held**
WEB: www.systemsensor.com
SIC: 3669 Smoke detectors

(G-5991)
T S K INNOVATIONS COMPANY
1057 Doniphan Park Cir B (79922-1347)
PHONE.....................915 581-9718
Tim Macalpine, *President*
Maurice Grenier, *Controller*

▲ = Import ▼=Export
◆ =Import/Export

Lee Humphreys, *Manager*
▲ **EMP:** 42 **EST:** 1994
SQ FT: 6,000
SALES (est): 5.9MM
SALES (corp-wide): 421MM **Privately Held**
SIC: 3699 Electrical equipment & supplies
HQ: Komax Corporation
1100 E Corp Grove Dr
Buffalo Grove IL 60089
888 465-6629

(G-5992)
T S K INNOVATIONS COMPANY
9641 Plaza Cir Ste B (79927-2152)
PHONE..............................915 581-9718
Tim Macalpine, *President*
EMP: 19 **EST:** 2015
SALES (est): 2.9MM **Privately Held**
SIC: 3699 Electrical equipment & supplies

(G-5993)
TE CONNECTIVITY CORPORATION
Also Called: El Paso Distribution Center
1321 Joe Battle Blvd (79936-0903)
PHONE..............................610 893-9800
Manuel Alvarado, *Manager*
EMP: 100
SALES (corp-wide): 13.3B **Privately Held**
WEB: www.te.com
SIC: 3678 Electronic connectors
HQ: Te Connectivity Corporation
1050 Westlakes Dr
Berwyn PA 19312
610 893-9800

(G-5994)
TEASDALE FOODS INC
Also Called: Ashley S Division
8000 Ashley Rd (79934-2603)
PHONE..............................915 821-2500
Pat Rocha, *Manager*
EMP: 120
SALES (corp-wide): 380.6MM **Privately Held**
WEB: www.teasdalelatinfoods.com
SIC: 2033 2099 Canned fruits & specialties; food preparations
PA: Teasdale Foods, Inc.
3041 Churchill Dr Ste 100
Flower Mound TX 75022
209 358-5616

(G-5995)
TECAL MANUFACTURING LLC
9100 Mayflower Ave Ste E (79925-1306)
PHONE..............................915 593-1413
Eddy Ozomaro, *Partner*
EMP: 15 **EST:** 1981
SQ FT: 4,500
SALES (est): 500K **Privately Held**
WEB: www.tecal-mfg.com
SIC: 3677 Electronic coils, transformers & other inductors

(G-5996)
TECHNICOLOR USA INC
12430 Mercantile Ave (79928-5235)
PHONE..............................915 872-8001
EMP: 157
SALES (corp-wide): 59.7MM **Privately Held**
SIC: 3651 Household audio & video equipment
HQ: Technicolor Usa, Inc.
6040 W Sunset Blvd
Hollywood CA 90028
317 587-4287

(G-5997)
TENNECO INC
7801 Trade Center Ave A (79912-8495)
P.O. Box 221410 (79913-4410)
PHONE..............................915 832-4661
Leonardo Scuderi, *Branch Mgr*
EMP: 800
SALES (corp-wide): 17.4B **Publicly Held**
WEB: www.tenneco-automotive.com
SIC: 3647 3714 3053 3592 Automotive lighting fixtures; motor vehicle parts & accessories; gaskets & sealing devices; pistons & piston rings

PA: Tenneco Inc.
500 N Field Dr
Lake Forest IL 60045
847 482-5000

(G-5998)
TEXAS EAGLE STAR MGT INC
10747 Ululani Dr (79927-3860)
PHONE..............................915 858-3144
Enrique Felix, *General Mgr*
Margarita Felix, *Exec Dir*
EMP: 14
SALES (est): 522.1K **Privately Held**
SIC: 2231 Skirtings: wool, mohair or similar fibers

(G-5999)
TEXAS INTL GAS & OIL CO
124 W Castellano Dr # 211 (79912-6139)
PHONE..............................915 860-8803
Eduardo Fuentes, *President*
J Magness, *Exec VP*
Cary K Silahian, *Vice Pres*
EMP: 10
SQ FT: 2,500
SALES (est): 3.7MM **Privately Held**
WEB: www.texasinternationalgas.com
SIC: 1382 Oil & gas exploration services

(G-6000)
THERM-O-DISC INCORPORATED
Also Called: Thermo Disc
12425 Rojas Dr (79928-5201)
PHONE..............................915 860-9167
Don Williams, *Branch Mgr*
EMP: 451
SALES (corp-wide): 16.7B **Publicly Held**
WEB: www.climate.emerson.com
SIC: 3823 Built-in thermostats, filled system & bimetal types
HQ: Therm-O-Disc, Incorporated
1320 S Main St
Mansfield OH 44907
419 525-8500

(G-6001)
THERM-O-LINK INC
Also Called: Thermolink
1295 Henry Brennan Dr (79936-6811)
PHONE..............................915 860-9933
Guillermo Villasenor, *Manager*
Rodolfo Rodriguez, *Supervisor*
EMP: 88
SALES (corp-wide): 45.3MM **Privately Held**
WEB: www.tolwire.com
SIC: 3357 3315 Nonferrous wiredrawing & insulating; steel wire & related products
PA: Therm-O-Link, Inc.
10513 Freedom St
Garrettsville OH 44231
330 527-2124

(G-6002)
THOMAS M NILAND COMPANY
320 N Clark Dr (79905-3134)
PHONE..............................915 779-1405
Thomas M Niland, *President*
Jack W Niland, *Vice Pres*
▲ **EMP:** 42
SQ FT: 87,000
SALES (est): 9.2MM **Privately Held**
WEB: www.nilandco.com
SIC: 3089 3648 Blow molded finished plastic products; street lighting fixtures

(G-6003)
THRIFTY NICKEL WANT ADS INC
Also Called: Thriftynickel.com
10921 Pellicano Dr # 100 (79935-4603)
PHONE..............................915 751-3494
Grady Lee, *President*
EMP: 15
SALES (est): 720.8K **Privately Held**
SIC: 2711 Newspapers: publishing only, not printed on site

(G-6004)
TIANHAI ELECTRIC N AMER INC
19 Leigh Fisher Blvd (79906-5216)
PHONE..............................915 881-9740
Timothy Howick, *Branch Mgr*
EMP: 24

SALES (corp-wide): 1.3MM **Privately Held**
WEB: www.te-na.com
SIC: 3714 Motor vehicle parts & accessories
HQ: Tianhai Electric North America, Inc.
70 E Silverdome Indus Par
Pontiac MI 48342
248 987-2100

(G-6005)
TIGER CONSTRUCTION
688 Bluff Canyon Cir (79912-5174)
PHONE..............................915 999-1260
Jesus Martinez, *Owner*
EMP: 15
SALES (est): 808.3K **Privately Held**
SIC: 2045 Prepared flour mixes & doughs

(G-6006)
TIGUA ENTERPRISES INC (HQ)
12 Leigh Fisher Blvd (79906-5239)
PHONE..............................915 298-0700
John Baily, *President*
William Kilmer, *General Mgr*
Joshua Allen, *Opers Mgr*
EMP: 21
SALES: 5.2MM **Privately Held**
WEB: www.tiguainc.us
SIC: 8744 7349 2522 Facilities support services; janitorial service, contract basis; office furniture, except wood

(G-6007)
TONY LAMA COMPANY INC
1137 Tony Lama St (79915-1307)
PHONE..............................915 778-8311
John Justin Jr, *Ch of Bd*
Frank Scivetti, *President*
▲ **EMP:** 1534 **EST:** 1911
SQ FT: 147,600
SALES (est): 65MM
SALES (corp-wide): 254.6B **Publicly Held**
WEB: www.sheplers.com
SIC: 3143 3172 3111 3144 Boots, dress or casual: men's; personal leather goods; shoe leather; sole leather; women's footwear, except athletic
HQ: Justin Industries, Inc.
3024 Acme Brick Plz
Fort Worth TX 76109
817 332-4101

(G-6008)
TORO COMPANY
9455 Railroad Dr (79924-6330)
P.O. Box 4289 (79914-4289)
PHONE..............................915 231-7200
Gabriel Portillo, *Plant Mgr*
Martha Matsushita, *Buyer*
Aubrey Jarrett, *Finance Mgr*
Dennis Campbell, *Manager*
Richard Nunez, *Manager*
EMP: 215
SQ FT: 55,000
SALES (corp-wide): 3.3B **Publicly Held**
WEB: www.thetorocompany.com
SIC: 3523 3564 3469 Irrigation equipment, self-propelled; blowers & fans; metal stampings
PA: The Toro Company
8111 Lyndale Ave S
Bloomington MN 55420
952 888-8801

(G-6009)
TOTAL ORTHTIC PRSTHTIC SLTIONS (PA)
900 E Yandell Dr (79902-5428)
PHONE..............................915 541-8677
Miguel Guerra, *President*
Susan Guerra, *CFO*
EMP: 9
SQ FT: 6,500
SALES (est): 1.3MM **Privately Held**
WEB: www.totalorthoticandprostheticsolutions.com
SIC: 3842 Orthopedic appliances; prosthetic appliances

(G-6010)
TOVAR PRINTING INC
1230 Texas Ave (79901-1638)
PHONE..............................915 584-5900
David Tovar, *President*

Noemi Tovar, *Vice Pres*
EMP: 15 **EST:** 2007
SQ FT: 2,500
SALES (est): 3MM **Privately Held**
WEB: www.tovarprinting.com
SIC: 2752 Commercial printing, offset

(G-6011)
TPI MEXICO LLC (HQ)
700 N Zaragoza Rd Ste N (79907-9997)
P.O. Box 310 (79943-0310)
PHONE..............................915 881-5808
Steve C Lockard,
Wayne G Monie,
▲ **EMP:** 24
SQ FT: 18,000
SALES (est): 12.3MM
SALES (corp-wide): 1.4B **Publicly Held**
SIC: 2752 Schedules, transportation: lithographed
PA: Tpi Composites, Inc.
8501 N Scottsdale Rd # 280
Scottsdale AZ 85253
480 305-8910

(G-6012)
TRANE COMPANY
Also Called: Trane Global Parts
1405 Vanderbilt Dr (79935-4808)
PHONE..............................915 593-3484
Warren Michelson, *General Mgr*
Martin Monedero, *Manager*
Katie Stone, *Manager*
EMP: 39 **Privately Held**
WEB: www.trane.com
SIC: 3585 Refrigeration & heating equipment
HQ: The Trane Company
3600 Pammel Creek Rd
La Crosse WI 54601
608 787-2000

(G-6013)
TRANE US INC
Also Called: Trane Company, The
1405 Vanderbilt Dr (79935-4808)
P.O. Box 981394 (79998-1394)
PHONE..............................915 593-3484
Warren Michelson, *General Mgr*
EMP: 33 **Privately Held**
WEB: www.trane.com
SIC: 3585 Refrigeration & heating equipment
HQ: Trane U.S. Inc.
3600 Pammel Creek Rd
La Crosse WI 54601
608 787-2000

(G-6014)
TRE STARS INCORPORATED
Also Called: Smartz Printing Services
6800 Gateway Blvd E (79915-1040)
P.O. Box 971727 (79997-1727)
PHONE..............................915 351-1433
Robt Martz, *President*
EMP: 10
SQ FT: 4,000
SALES (est): 1.4MM **Privately Held**
SIC: 2759 Screen printing

(G-6015)
TREY INDUSTRY SW
1221 Barranca Dr (79935-4601)
PHONE..............................915 591-5100
Tomas Rey, *President*
EMP: 46
SALES (est): 1.6MM **Privately Held**
SIC: 3714 Motor vehicle parts & accessories

(G-6016)
TRIMCO MASTER MILLWORK INC
3500 Lee Blvd (79936-1413)
PHONE..............................915 855-8501
Christopher Elguea, *President*
Sergio Elguea, *Admin Sec*
EMP: 45
SQ FT: 16,000
SALES (est): 9.3MM **Privately Held**
SIC: 2431 Doors, wood; door trim, wood

(G-6017)
TROY HELEN TEXAS CORPORATION (DH)
1 Helen Of Troy Plz (79912-1148)
PHONE....................................915 225-8000
Julien Mininberg, *CEO*
William Levy, *President*
Shannon Rhoads, *Counsel*
Arthur August, *Exec VP*
Michael Cafaro, *Exec VP*
◆ **EMP:** 91
SQ FT: 240,000
SALES (est): 388.2MM **Privately Held**
WEB: www.bedheadstyling.com
SIC: 3999 Hair driers, designed for beauty parlors

(G-6018)
UFP TECHNOLOGIES INC
Also Called: Pacific Foam Technologies Div
1400 Henry Brennan Dr (79936-6805)
PHONE....................................915 598-7377
EMP: 100
SALES (corp-wide): 198.3MM **Publicly Held**
WEB: www.ufpt.com
SIC: 3086 Packaging & shipping materials, foamed plastic
PA: Ufp Technologies, Inc.
100 Hale St
Newburyport MA 01950
978 352-2200

(G-6019)
UNIQUE PRODUCTS MFG LLC
8650 Yermoland Dr (79907-1718)
PHONE....................................915 590-2444
Michael Johnson,
Lorena Bolanos,
Michael J Johnson,
Anna Loya,
▼ **EMP:** 30
SALES (est): 9.8MM **Privately Held**
WEB: www.boydcorp.com
SIC: 3554 Die cutting & stamping machinery, paper converting

(G-6020)
UNIVERSAL GRAPHICS INC
1217 Barranca Dr Ste B (79935-4601)
PHONE....................................915 591-8943
Gilberto Lespron, *President*
Lidia Lespron, *Corp Secy*
EMP: 10
SQ FT: 6,000
SALES (est): 1.3MM **Privately Held**
WEB: www.ug-inc.com
SIC: 2752 Commercial printing, offset

(G-6021)
UTAX SOFTWARE LLC (PA)
11985 Pellicano Dr G123 (79936-6289)
PHONE....................................844 440-8829
Paul Slagle, *Opers Staff*
James Marks, *Engineer*
John Colver, *Sales Staff*
Loretta Amezquita, *Manager*
Daniel Montoya, *Executive*
EMP: 9
SALES (est): 1.7MM **Privately Held**
WEB: www.utaxsoftware.com
SIC: 7372 Prepackaged software

(G-6022)
V-S PRECISION USA LLC
2150 Trawood Dr (79935-3322)
P.O. Box 9856 (79995-2856)
PHONE....................................915 590-2707
Carlos Castillo, *President*
Jack Schwieteit, *Vice Pres*
EMP: 325
SQ FT: 50,000
SALES (est): 42.2MM **Privately Held**
WEB: www.v-sp.com
SIC: 3369 3443 Castings, except die-castings, precision; metal parts

(G-6023)
VALEO NORTH AMERICA INC
Also Called: Valeo Wiper Systems
5 Zane Grey St (79906-5223)
P.O. Box 10075 (79995-0075)
PHONE....................................915 774-9340
Flabio Lujan, *Manager*
Mauro Alvarado, *Info Tech Mgr*
EMP: 700

SALES (corp-wide): 177.9K **Privately Held**
SIC: 3621 Motors & generators
HQ: Valeo North America, Inc.
150 Stephenson Hwy
Troy MI 48083

(G-6024)
VALEO NORTH AMERICA INC
Also Called: Valeo Wipers Systems
5a Zane Grey St (79906-5223)
PHONE....................................915 779-1625
Felipe Martinesec, *Principal*
EMP: 700
SALES (corp-wide): 177.9K **Privately Held**
SIC: 3621 Motors & generators
HQ: Valeo North America, Inc.
150 Stephenson Hwy
Troy MI 48083

(G-6025)
VALTREK GROUP LLC
3523 Confederate Rd (79936-1402)
PHONE....................................915 201-7559
Jose Rosario Valdez, *President*
EMP: 13
SALES (est): 3MM **Privately Held**
WEB: www.valtrek.com
SIC: 3569 Liquid automation machinery & equipment

(G-6026)
VEOLIA NORTH AMERICA REG SERV
6501 Trowbridge Dr (79905-3401)
PHONE....................................915 782-5550
Timothy Palculict, *Manager*
EMP: 37
SALES (corp-wide): 559.3MM **Privately Held**
WEB: www.veolianorthamerica.com
SIC: 2819 Sulfuric acid, oleum
HQ: Veolia North America Regeneration Services, Llc
4760 World Houston Pkwy
Houston TX 77032
832 300-5708

(G-6027)
W SILVER RECYCLING INC (PA)
Also Called: W Silver Recycling
1720 Magoffin Ave (79901-1824)
P.O. Box 307 (79943-0307)
PHONE....................................915 532-5643
Lane B Gaddy, *President*
Bernard Fenbneock, *Chairman*
Chimene Mark, *Business Mgr*
Jeanette Fenenbock, *Corp Secy*
John Korey, *Vice Pres*
◆ **EMP:** 53
SQ FT: 5,000
SALES (est): 52.4MM **Privately Held**
WEB: www.wsilverrecycling.com
SIC: 5093 3341 Nonferrous metals scrap; secondary nonferrous metals

(G-6028)
WCSC LLC
150 E Sunset Rd (79922-1018)
PHONE....................................915 774-0348
Daniel Heredia,
EMP: 11
SALES (est): 700K **Privately Held**
SIC: 3599 Water leak detectors

(G-6029)
WESMAR CORPORATION
4720 Osborne Dr Ste 300 (79922-1023)
PHONE....................................915 599-1572
Kim Gerhart, *CFO*
Thomas W Gerhart, *Director*
▲ **EMP:** 30
SQ FT: 9,000
SALES (est): 4.7MM **Privately Held**
WEB: www.wesmarcompany.com
SIC: 3069 3089 Heels, boot or shoe: rubber, composition or fiber; heels, boot or shoe: plastic

(G-6030)
WEST TEXAS CHAPTR OF ARCHTCTRL
275 Rio West Dr (79932-1808)
PHONE....................................915 833-9922
Bruce Spitz, *President*

EMP: 25
SALES (est): 127K **Privately Held**
SIC: 2431 Millwork

(G-6031)
WEST TEXAS CONTAINER CORP
12345 Rojas Dr (79928-5260)
PHONE....................................915 859-6712
John Widera, *President*
Jose Rangel, *Sales Executive*
▲ **EMP:** 31
SQ FT: 83,000
SALES (est): 5.4MM **Privately Held**
WEB: www.westtexascontainer.com
SIC: 2653 Boxes, corrugated: made from purchased materials

(G-6032)
WESTERN PRECAST CONCRETE INC
9101 Roseway Dr (79907-5536)
P.O. Box 17961 (79917-7961)
PHONE....................................915 859-9362
Leo Feuerstein, *CEO*
John E Kramer, *President*
David Feuerstein, *Vice Pres*
Alex Leyva, *Project Mgr*
Richard Alvarado, *QC Mgr*
EMP: 53
SQ FT: 5,000
SALES (est): 10.6MM **Privately Held**
WEB: www.westernprecast.com
SIC: 3272 Concrete products, precast

(G-6033)
WESTERN REFINING INC (DH)
Also Called: Andeavor
212 N Clark Dr (79905-3106)
PHONE....................................915 775-3300
Jeff A Stevens, *CEO*
David L Lamp, *President*
Gary Rees, *General Mgr*
Cynthia Warner, *Exec VP*
Lowry Barfield, *Senior VP*
EMP: 277
SALES: 7.7B **Publicly Held**
WEB: www.wnr.com
SIC: 2911 5983 Petroleum refining; fuel oil dealers
HQ: Andeavor Llc
19100 Ridgewood Pkwy
San Antonio TX 78259
210 626-6000

(G-6034)
WESTERN REFINING COMPANY LP
6550 Gateway Blvd E (79905-2017)
PHONE....................................915 775-3246
Servando Rojas, *Technical Mgr*
Scott Steven, *Branch Mgr*
Leonard Bloom, *Director*
EMP: 19 **Publicly Held**
WEB: www.westernrefining.com
SIC: 2911 3531 Petroleum refining; asphalt plant, including gravel-mix type
HQ: Western Refining Company, L.P.
212 N Clark Dr
El Paso TX 79905

(G-6035)
WESTERN REFINING COMPANY LP (DH)
Also Called: Andeavor
212 N Clark Dr (79905-3106)
PHONE....................................915 534-1400
Gary Dalke, *Partner*
Jeff A Stevens, *Partner*
Greg Tauscher, *Controller*
Dane Neumann, *Financial Analy*
Tessa Aguirre, *Human Res Mgr*
EMP: 10
SQ FT: 13,000
SALES (est): 163.7MM **Publicly Held**
WEB: www.westernrefining.com
SIC: 2911 Petroleum refining

(G-6036)
WESTERN STUCCO PRODUCT
Also Called: Rio Grande Stucco Product
9151 Roseway Dr (79907-5536)
PHONE....................................915 858-3494
Louis Winchell, *President*
Winchell B G, *Vice Pres*
EMP: 11

SALES (est): 948K **Privately Held**
WEB: www.westernblended.com
SIC: 3299 Stucco

(G-6037)
WESTROCK CP LLC
7350 Stiles Dr (79915-2518)
PHONE....................................915 778-7350
Don Tinkoff, *Branch Mgr*
EMP: 500
SALES (corp-wide): 17.5B **Publicly Held**
WEB: www.westrock.com
SIC: 2653 Boxes, corrugated: made from purchased materials
HQ: Westrock Cp, Llc
1000 Abernathy Rd Ste 125
Atlanta GA 30328

(G-6038)
WESTROCK CP LLC
7350 Stiles Dr (79915-2518)
PHONE....................................915 778-7350
Don Tinkoff, *Manager*
EMP: 101
SALES (corp-wide): 17.5B **Publicly Held**
WEB: www.westrock.com
SIC: 2653 Boxes, corrugated: made from purchased materials
HQ: Westrock Cp, Llc
1000 Abernathy Rd Ste 125
Atlanta GA 30328

(G-6039)
WILMOT PRINTING COMPANY INC
10618 Montwood Dr (79935-2704)
PHONE....................................915 843-6424
Richard S Wilmot Sr, *President*
Julia Wilmot, *Vice Pres*
EMP: 20
SQ FT: 10,000
SALES (est): 1.2MM **Privately Held**
SIC: 2759 Commercial printing

(G-6040)
WOODBRIDGE SALES & ENGRG INC
Also Called: Woodbridge Group, The
9900 Railroad Dr (79924-5000)
PHONE....................................915 751-1000
Isabel Thurman, *Human Resources*
Bob Magee, *Branch Mgr*
Isabel Lloyd, *Program Mgr*
Carlos Vazquez, *Senior Mgr*
EMP: 103
SALES (corp-wide): 157.8MM **Privately Held**
WEB: www.woodbridgegroup.com
SIC: 3069 2821 Foam rubber; plastics materials & resins
HQ: Woodbridge Sales & Engineering, Inc.
1515 Equity Dr
Troy MI 48084
248 288-0100

(G-6041)
YAZAKI NORTH AMERICA INC
12435 Rojas Dr (79928-5201)
PHONE....................................618 512-8723
Wade Jenks, *Branch Mgr*
EMP: 18 **Privately Held**
WEB: www.yazaki-na.com
SIC: 5013 3679 3694 Automotive supplies & parts; electronic circuits; engine electrical equipment
HQ: Yazaki North America, Inc.
6801 N Haggerty Rd
Canton MI 48187
734 983-1000

(G-6042)
ZF ELEC SYS PLSNT PRAIRE LLC
Also Called: Cherry De Mexico
12420 Mercantile Ave (79928-5228)
PHONE....................................915 790-5000
Felipe Sanchez, *Engineer*
Craig Esparca, *Branch Mgr*
EMP: 12
SALES (corp-wide): 216.2K **Privately Held**
WEB: www.cherryamericas.com
SIC: 3714 Motor vehicle parts & accessories

HQ: Zf Electronic Systems Pleasant Prairie, Llc
11200 88th Ave
Pleasant Prairie WI 53158
262 942-6500

(G-6043)
ZF PASSIVE SAFETY US INC
9780 Plaza Cir Ste A (79927-2109)
PHONE................................734 582-1139
Rocio Cordero, *Controller*
EMP: 500
SALES (corp-wide): 216.2K **Privately Held**
SIC: 3714 2399 Motor vehicle parts & accessories; seat belts, automobile & aircraft
HQ: Zf Passive Safety Us Inc.
12001 Tech Center Dr
Livonia MI 48150
734 855-2600

Eldorado
Schleicher County

(G-6044)
BAKER HUGHES HOLDINGS LLC
Hwy 277 (76936)
PHONE................................325 853-2553
EMP: 55
SALES (corp-wide): 23.8B **Publicly Held**
WEB: www.bakerhughes.com
SIC: 1389 Oil field services
HQ: Baker Hughes Holdings Llc
17021 Aldine Westfield Rd
Houston TX 77073
713 439-8600

(G-6045)
CROWDER SERVICES INC
306 S Us Highway 277 (76936-4011)
P.O. Box 1056 (76936-1056)
PHONE................................325 853-2852
Danny Crowder, *President*
Denise Capps, *Manager*
EMP: 34
SQ FT: 800
SALES (est): 3MM **Privately Held**
SIC: 1389 Oil field services

(G-6046)
HM ROUSTABOUT SERVICE INC
8 W Louise Ave (76936)
P.O. Box 502, Brackettville (78832-0502)
PHONE................................830 563-5449
EMP: 12
SQ FT: 8,200
SALES (est): 510K **Privately Held**
SIC: 1389 Oil/Gas Field Services

(G-6047)
NIBLETTS OILFIELD SERVICES INC
Hwy 277 S (76936)
P.O. Box 910 (76936-0910)
PHONE................................325 853-2521
Charles A Niblett, *President*
Cherie E Niblett, *Corp Secy*
EMP: 41
SQ FT: 3,600
SALES (est): 3.3MM **Privately Held**
SIC: 1389 4213 4212 Oil field services; haulage, oil field; trucking, except local; local trucking, without storage

Electra
Wichita County

(G-6048)
NASON SERVICES LLC
102 Hwy 287 E (76360)
P.O. Box 127 (76360-0127)
PHONE................................940 495-2558
Sam Nason,
EMP: 11
SALES (est): 512.4K **Privately Held**
SIC: 1389 Oil field services

(G-6049)
O S & S OPERATING INC
1305 S Bailey St (76360-3223)
P.O. Box 311 (76360-0311)
PHONE................................940 495-3645
Scott Strange, *Principal*
Leola Kent, *Manager*
EMP: 9
SALES (est): 913.3K **Privately Held**
WEB: www.ossopr.com
SIC: 1389 Oil field services

(G-6050)
U S MACHINE SHOP INC
501 E Cleveland Ave (76360-3025)
P.O. Box 871 (76360-0871)
PHONE................................940 495-3964
Benny Dorland, *President*
EMP: 10
SQ FT: 9,200
SALES (est): 890K **Privately Held**
SIC: 3599 2899 Machine shop, jobbing & repair; oil absorption equipment

Elgin
Bastrop County

(G-6051)
ACME BRICK COMPANY
Also Called: Featherlite Building Products
1776 Old Mcdade Rd (78621-3136)
PHONE................................512 255-2573
Don Nowak, *Safety Mgr*
Ron Benningfield, *Branch Mgr*
Rodney Ebeling, *Manager*
EMP: 30
SALES (corp-wide): 254.6B **Publicly Held**
WEB: www.brick.com
SIC: 3272 3271 Concrete products, pre-cast; concrete block & brick
HQ: Acme Brick Company
3024 Acme Brick Plz
Fort Worth TX 76109

(G-6052)
ACME BRICK COMPANY
Also Called: Acme Building Brands
1776 Old Mcdade Rd (78621-3136)
PHONE................................512 281-5744
Leon Prince, *Planning Mgr*
EMP: 100
SALES (corp-wide): 254.6B **Publicly Held**
WEB: www.brick.com
SIC: 3251 5211 3271 Brick & structural clay tile; brick; concrete block & brick
HQ: Acme Brick Company
3024 Acme Brick Plz
Fort Worth TX 76109

(G-6053)
CENTURY ASPHALT LTD
1858 Old Mcdade Rd (78621-3167)
PHONE................................512 285-4499
EMP: 14 **Privately Held**
WEB: www.centuryasphalt.com
SIC: 2951 Asphalt paving mixtures & blocks
PA: Century Asphalt, Ltd.
5303 Navigation Blvd
Houston TX 77011

(G-6054)
EMPLOYEE OWNED NURSERY ENTPS
Also Called: Organics By Gosh
2040 Fm 969 (78621-6102)
PHONE................................512 276-1211
Phillip Gosh, *Partner*
Donna J Shaver Gosh, *CFO*
Donnaj Shaver Gosh, *CFO*
Noelle Bugaj, *Accountant*
John Garza, *Accountant*
EMP: 11
SALES (est): 1.8MM
SALES (corp-wide): 10.3MM **Privately Held**
WEB: www.organicsbygosh.com
SIC: 7389 2875 Packaging & labeling services; compost

PA: Earth Property Holdings Llc
420 Royal Palm Way # 100
Palm Beach FL 33480
561 693-1423

(G-6055)
I & R MACHINING INC
401 Hwy 290 E (78621-3209)
P.O. Box 181 (78621-0181)
PHONE................................512 281-2251
Geno Chavarria, *President*
Robert Chavarria, *Vice Pres*
EMP: 15
SQ FT: 8,000
SALES (est): 1.8MM **Privately Held**
SIC: 3599 Machine shop, jobbing & repair

(G-6056)
ONEPOINTE SOLUTIONS LLC
Also Called: Chemtops
1112 Swenson Blvd (78621-3259)
PHONE................................866 222-7494
Aaron Boto, *CEO*
Don Carlson, *Vice Pres*
Thomas Costello, *Vice Pres*
Roy Richards, *Vice Pres*
Ashley Wright, *Opers Mgr*
▼ **EMP:** 56
SQ FT: 45,000
SALES (est): 14.2MM **Privately Held**
WEB: www.onepointesolutions.com
SIC: 3821 2599 Laboratory furniture; worktables, laboratory; work benches, factory

(G-6057)
YERICO MANUFACTURING INC (PA)
619 Mogonye Ln (78621-1018)
PHONE................................512 285-3444
Ihn Hong Min, *President*
Gabriel Sidatt, *Sales Mgr*
EMP: 44
SQ FT: 40,000
SALES: 12.9MM **Privately Held**
WEB: www.yericomfg.com
SIC: 3674 Semiconductors & related devices

Elkhart
Anderson County

(G-6058)
BANDANA INSTALLATION LP
215 N Us Highway 287 (75839-7328)
P.O. Box 975 (75839-0975)
PHONE................................903 764-2933
James W Davenport, *Partner*
Sharon Davenport, *Partner*
Jan Collins, *Finance Dir*
EMP: 35
SQ FT: 3,600
SALES (est): 4.7MM **Privately Held**
WEB: www.bandanainstallation.com
SIC: 1796 3446 Installing building equipment; architectural metalwork

(G-6059)
DON H WILSON INC
3499 Fm 2022 (75839-4487)
PHONE................................903 478-3860
Don H Wilson, *President*
Loretta A Wilson, *Vice Pres*
EMP: 16
SALES (est): 1.5MM **Privately Held**
SIC: 1381 Drilling oil & gas wells

(G-6060)
LA MACHINE & ENGINEERING INC
3202 An County Road 179 (75839-5844)
P.O. Box 248 (75839-0248)
PHONE................................903 764-5634
Walter Chaffin, *President*
EMP: 15 **EST:** 1975
SQ FT: 10,000
SALES (est): 1.1MM **Privately Held**
SIC: 3599 Machine shop, jobbing & repair

(G-6061)
WILSON CULVERTS INC
699 Fm 1817 (75839-4508)
P.O. Box 940 (75839-0940)
PHONE................................903 764-5605
H C Wilson, *President*
Terry Huffines, *Vice Pres*
Betty Wilson, *Vice Pres*
Jamesjame Ballard, *Sales Staff*
EMP: 20 **EST:** 1978
SQ FT: 2,500
SALES (est): 6.3MM **Privately Held**
WEB: www.wilsonculverts.com
SIC: 3444 Culverts, sheet metal

Ellinger
Fayette County

(G-6062)
FR HRUSKA STORE
109 W State Highway 71 (78938-5126)
PHONE................................979 378-2333
Teresa James, *Owner*
EMP: 24
SALES (est): 2.3MM **Privately Held**
WEB: www.hruskas-bakery.com
SIC: 2051 Bakery: wholesale or wholesale/retail combined

Elm Mott
Mclennan County

(G-6063)
DUNLAPS CUSTOM CABINETS INC
6448 Old Dallas Rd (76640-3699)
PHONE................................254 829-2279
Steve Dunlap, *President*
Larry Dunlap, *Vice Pres*
Joyce Dunlap, *Treasurer*
EMP: 11
SALES (est): 1.2MM **Privately Held**
SIC: 2434 Vanities, bathroom: wood

(G-6064)
ELM MOTT MARBLE CO
1064 N Mclennan Dr # 104 (76640-3946)
P.O. Box 837 (76640-0837)
PHONE................................254 829-1552
Fidel Lopez, *Owner*
EMP: 10
SALES (est): 823.5K **Privately Held**
SIC: 3281 Marble, building: cut & shaped

(G-6065)
TEXAS CONCRETE PARTNERS LP (PA)
1690 Mesquite Tree Rd (76640)
P.O. Box 338 (76640-0338)
PHONE................................254 822-1351
R D Carr Jr, *President*
Paul M Guthrie, *Vice Pres*
Ralph Castillo, *Purchasing*
EMP: 95
SQ FT: 5,000
SALES (est): 61.1MM **Privately Held**
WEB: www.texasconcrete.com
SIC: 3272 Prestressed concrete products

Elmendorf
Bexar County

(G-6066)
AMCO STEEL FABRICATION LLC
8051 S Loop 1604 E (78112-5001)
PHONE................................210 488-9023
Alberto Macias, *Mng Member*
EMP: 15
SQ FT: 10,000
SALES (est): 5.1MM **Privately Held**
WEB: www.amco-llc.com
SIC: 3441 1791 Fabricated structural metal; structural steel erection

(G-6067)
BURKE & COMPANY INC
13105 Donop Rd (78112-9720)
PHONE......................................210 271-0008
Michael J Burke, *CEO*
Mike Burke, *Partner*
Jim Pruski, *Vice Pres*
EMP: 13
SALES (est): 2.4MM **Privately Held**
WEB: www.burkeandco.com
SIC: 3444 Sheet metalwork

(G-6068)
EL PASO FIELD SERVICES LP
20733 Lamm Rd (78112)
PHONE......................................210 621-2031
Maurice Tchirhart, *Manager*
EMP: 10
SQ FT: 2,000 **Publicly Held**
WEB: www.kindermorgan.com
SIC: 1321 4923 Natural gas liquids; gas
transmission & distribution
HQ: El Paso Field Services, L.P.
1001 Louisiana St
Houston TX 77002

(G-6069)
**HIGUCHI INTERNATIONAL CORP
(HQ)**
14901 Southton Rd (78112-9699)
P.O. Box 166 (78112-0166)
PHONE......................................210 633-2877
Nariie Higuchi, *President*
▲ **EMP:** 32 **EST:** 2006
SALES (est): 30.1MM **Privately Held**
SIC: 3829 Automatic turnstiles & related
apparatus

(G-6070)
HOWMET AEROSPACE INC
14555 Old Crpus Chrsti Rd (78112-9607)
PHONE......................................775 343-4010
Neil Vernon, *Manager*
EMP: 28
SALES (corp-wide): 14.1B **Publicly Held**
WEB: www.howmet.com
SIC: 3443 Fabricated plate work (boiler
shop)
PA: Howmet Aerospace Inc.
201 Isabella St Ste 200
Pittsburgh PA 15212
412 553-1940

(G-6071)
PRO LINE NEWWATER INC
Also Called: Newwater Boatworks
13406 Donop Rd (78112-5628)
PHONE......................................210 648-2206
Tim Clancey, *President*
Leslie Clancey, *Manager*
EMP: 15
SQ FT: 10,000
SALES (est): 1MM **Privately Held**
WEB: www.newwaterboatworks.com
SIC: 3732 Fishing boats: lobster, crab, oys-
ter, etc.: small

(G-6072)
**TRANS-TEX FABRICATING CO
INC**
Also Called: Jackson Steel Company
13165 Donop Rd (78112-9720)
PHONE......................................210 633-0100
Adrian Augustine, *Branch Mgr*
EMP: 34 **Privately Held**
WEB: www.bexar.org
SIC: 3441 Fabricated structural metal
PA: Trans-Tex Fabricating Co., Inc.
549 Heimer Rd Ste 100
San Antonio TX 78232

(G-6073)
U S WEATHERFORD L P
Also Called: Weatherford CPS
19685 Interstate 37 S (78112-9623)
PHONE......................................361 668-8362
EMP: 23 **Privately Held**
SIC: 3533 Mfg Drill Pipe And Oil Field
Equipment
HQ: U S Weatherford L P
2000 Saint James Pl
Houston TX 70395
713 693-4000

(G-6074)
**WEATHERFORD
INTERNATIONAL LLC**
19685 Interstate 37 S (78112-9623)
PHONE......................................210 306-3431
James Harper, *Opers Staff*
Johnnie Howard, *Branch Mgr*
Gary Dellinger, *Manager*
Joseph Hernandez, *Supervisor*
EMP: 23 **Privately Held**
WEB: www.weatherford.com
SIC: 1389 Oil field services
HQ: Weatherford International, Llc
2000 Saint James Pl
Houston TX 77056
713 693-4000

(G-6075)
**WEATHERFORD
INTERNATIONAL LLC**
Also Called: Weathford Engneered Chem-
istry
4420 S Flores Rd (78112-9712)
PHONE......................................210 621-2156
Jamie Rawlyck, *Sales Staff*
Scott Lisko, *Branch Mgr*
EMP: 40 **Privately Held**
WEB: www.weatherford.com
SIC: 3498 3533 Fabricated pipe & fittings;
oil field machinery & equipment
HQ: Weatherford International, Llc
2000 Saint James Pl
Houston TX 77056
713 693-4000

(G-6076)
**WEATHERFORD
INTERNATIONAL LTD**
4426 S Flores Rd (78112-9712)
PHONE......................................210 626-0831
Gil Rodriguez, *Principal*
Jimmy Cooper, *Opers Spvr*
EMP: 9 **EST:** 2012
SALES (est): 717.1K **Privately Held**
WEB: www.weatherford.com
SIC: 1389 Oil field services

(G-6077)
WEATHERFORD US LP
19685 Ih 37 S (78112-9623)
PHONE......................................210 306-3400
Robert Soliz, *Branch Mgr*
EMP: 24 **Privately Held**
WEB: www.weatherford.com
SIC: 1389 Oil field services
HQ: U S Weatherford L P
179 Weatherford Dr
Schriever LA 70395
985 493-6100

(G-6078)
**WHOLEARTH ORGANIC
COMPOSTING**
20805 Lamm Rd (78112)
PHONE......................................210 621-2411
Jim Allred, *Partner*
EMP: 16
SALES (est): 1.6MM **Privately Held**
SIC: 2875 Compost

Elsa
Hidalgo County

(G-6079)
FRONTERA MATERIALS INC
22630 N Fm 88 (78543)
P.O. Box 1449 (78543-1449)
PHONE......................................956 316-8952
Edwin E Forshage III, *President*
Joseph Forshage, *Corp Secy*
EMP: 63
SALES (est): 13.4MM **Privately Held**
WEB: www.fmitex.com
SIC: 2951 Asphalt paving mixtures &
blocks

(G-6080)
RAUL GONZALEZ
Also Called: RG Builders
300 E 5th St (78543)
P.O. Box 1396 (78543-1396)
PHONE......................................956 793-5359

Raul Gonzalez, *Owner*
EMP: 15
SQ FT: 16,000
SALES (est): 928.9K **Privately Held**
WEB: www.rggroup.in
SIC: 2452 Prefabricated wood buildings

Emory
Rains County

(G-6081)
AASTEK ELECTRONICS CORP
212 Enterprise Rd (75440-5261)
PHONE......................................903 953-0888
EMP: 12 **EST:** 1998
SALES (est): 1.8MM **Privately Held**
WEB: www.aastekmfg.com
SIC: 3334 Primary aluminum

(G-6082)
CAROLINA CARPORTS INC
3740 Fm 2324 (75440-7169)
P.O. Box 838 (75440-0838)
PHONE......................................800 670-4262
Javier Herera, *Manager*
EMP: 27
SALES (corp-wide): 24.8MM **Privately
Held**
WEB: www.carolinacarportsinc.com
SIC: 3448 Prefabricated metal buildings
PA: Carolina Carports, Inc.
187 Cardinal Ridge Ln
Dobson NC 27017
336 367-6400

(G-6083)
J C MANUFACTURING INC
201 Prosperity (75440-5250)
P.O. Box 940 (75440-0940)
PHONE......................................903 473-3770
Daryl Meeks, *President*
Joyce Watkins, *Office Mgr*
Tom Hale, *Manager*
Mike Horn, *Manager*
EMP: 10 **EST:** 1977
SQ FT: 2,000
SALES (est): 1.3MM **Privately Held**
WEB: www.jcmfgcorp.com
SIC: 2521 Cabinets, office: wood

(G-6084)
JENNINGS TRAILERS INC
421 Rs County Road 1301 (75440-5925)
P.O. Box 911 (75440-0911)
PHONE......................................903 473-4562
Timothy Jennings, *President*
EMP: 20
SALES (est): 3.7MM **Privately Held**
WEB: www.surepull.net
SIC: 3799 Trailers & trailer equipment

(G-6085)
RAINS COUNTY LEADER
239 N Texas St (75440-2405)
P.O. Box 127 (75440-0127)
PHONE......................................903 473-2653
Earl C Hill Jr, *Owner*
Nancy Fenter, *Office Mgr*
EMP: 9
SALES (est): 407.6K **Privately Held**
WEB: www.rainscountyleader.com
SIC: 2711 Newspapers, publishing & print-
ing

Encinal
La Salle County

(G-6086)
LEWIS ENERGY GROUP LP
3 4 Mi W Hwy 44 (78019)
PHONE......................................956 728-6000
EMP: 1000 **Privately Held**
WEB: www.lewisenergy.com
SIC: 1382 Oil & gas exploration services
PA: Lewis Energy Group, L.P.
10101 Reunion Pl Ste 1000
San Antonio TX 78216

Ennis
Ellis County

(G-6087)
**ADVANCED DRAINAGE
SYSTEMS INC**
210 Metro Park Blvd (75119-7031)
PHONE......................................972 878-9600
Danny Due, *Manager*
Linda Williams, *Executive*
EMP: 75
SALES (corp-wide): 1.6B **Publicly Held**
WEB: www.ads-pipe.com
SIC: 3084 3083 Plastics pipe; laminated
plastics plate & sheet
PA: Advanced Drainage Systems, Inc.
4640 Trueman Blvd
Hilliard OH 43026
800 821-6710

(G-6088)
**AMERICASE FBRICATION
CNSTR LLC**
Also Called: Americase Ennis
1001 S Kaufman St (75119-6606)
P.O. Box 854, Waxahachie (75168-0854)
PHONE......................................972 910-2296
Cole Morgan,
Robby Kinsala,
EMP: 15
SQ FT: 35,000
SALES (est): 100K
SALES (corp-wide): 8.5MM **Privately
Held**
WEB: www.afc-llc.com
SIC: 3441 Fabricated structural metal
PA: Americase, Llc
6200 N Interstate 35 E
Waxahachie TX 75165
972 937-3629

(G-6089)
BWF ENTERPRISES INC (PA)
Also Called: Barbeque Wood Flavors
141 Lyons Rd (75119-0767)
PHONE......................................972 875-8391
George C Wartsbaugh, *President*
▲ **EMP:** 98
SQ FT: 12,500
SALES (est): 16.4MM **Privately Held**
WEB: www.bbqwf.com
SIC: 2421 Wood chips, produced at mill

(G-6090)
CERTAINTEED LLC
2901 N Kaufman St (75119-2815)
P.O. Box 518 (75120-0518)
PHONE......................................972 875-9661
Jerome Williams, *Manager*
EMP: 75
SALES (corp-wide): 328.4MM **Privately
Held**
WEB: www.certainteed.com
SIC: 2952 Roofing felts, cements or coat-
ings
HQ: Certainteed Llc
20 Moores Rd
Malvern PA 19355
610 893-5000

(G-6091)
CODY COMPANY LLC (HQ)
4200 N Interstate Hwy 45 (75119-0985)
P.O. Box 1320 (75120-1320)
PHONE......................................972 875-5884
Suzi Agar, *Purch Mgr*
Jackie Martinez, *Officer*
BJ Hancock,
▲ **EMP:** 100
SQ FT: 200,000
SALES (est): 18.1MM
SALES (corp-wide): 795.7MM **Privately
Held**
WEB: www.codycompany.com
SIC: 3444 Ducts, sheet metal
PA: Locke Supply Co.
1300 Se 82nd St
Oklahoma City OK 73149
405 631-9701

▲ = Import ▼=Export
◆ =Import/Export

(G-6092)
DENOVUS LLC
4101 S Hwy 45 (75119)
P.O. Box 280, Moberly MO (65270-0280)
PHONE.................................214 789-5725
EMP: 35
SALES (est): 2.6MM **Privately Held**
SIC: 2891 Mfg Adhesives/Sealants

(G-6093)
DISINGERM INC
1200 Nesuda Rd Ste B (75119-0993)
PHONE.................................214 482-9135
Brittany Spaniel, CEO
Thomas Stokes, Vice Pres
EMP: 10
SALES (est): 316.3K **Privately Held**
WEB: www.disingerm.com
SIC: 7342 2842 2879 Disinfecting services; disinfecting & deodorizing; disinfectants, household or industrial plant; agricultural disinfectants

(G-6094)
EDDIE RICHARDSON
751 Cody Rd (75119-8831)
PHONE.................................972 878-6181
Eddie Richardson, Owner
EMP: 12
SQ FT: 3,464
SALES (est): 481.1K **Privately Held**
SIC: 3441 Fabricated structural metal

(G-6095)
ELK CORPORATION OF TEXAS
202 Cedar Rd (75119-8449)
P.O. Box 500 (75120-0500)
PHONE.................................972 875-9611
CJ Searcy, Project Engr
Larry Reed, Manager
EMP: 200
SQ FT: 228,000
SALES (corp-wide): 2.5B **Privately Held**
WEB: www.elkcorp.com
SIC: 2952 2273 Roofing materials; carpets & rugs
HQ: Elk Corporation Of Texas
14911 Quorum Dr Ste 600
Dallas TX 75254

(G-6096)
ELLIS CO NEWSPAPERS
Also Called: Ennis Daily News
213 N Dallas St (75119-4011)
P.O. Box 100 (75120-0100)
PHONE.................................972 875-3801
Marc Richard, President
Boward Ratliff, Corp Secy
Deb Thompson, Manager
Keenan Gingles, Exec Dir
EMP: 30
SQ FT: 4,800
SALES (est): 1.8MM **Privately Held**
WEB: www.ennisdailynews.com
SIC: 2711 2752 Newspapers, publishing & printing; commercial printing, offset

(G-6097)
ELLIS COUNTY NEWSPAPERS INC
Also Called: Ennis Daily News, The
213 N Dallas St (75119-4011)
P.O. Box 100 (75120-0100)
PHONE.................................972 872-9113
Mark Richard, President
EMP: 20
SQ FT: 4,340
SALES (est): 927K **Privately Held**
WEB: www.ennisdailynews.com
SIC: 2711 Newspapers, publishing & printing

(G-6098)
ENNIS INC
Also Called: Star Award Ribbon Company
114 Ne Main St (75119-4045)
P.O. Box 488 (75120-0488)
PHONE.................................972 875-5873
Joe Boulin, Vice Pres
EMP: 20
SALES (corp-wide): 438.4MM **Publicly Held**
WEB: www.ennis.com
SIC: 2752 Commercial printing, lithographic

PA: Ennis, Inc.
2441 Presidential Pkwy
Midlothian TX 76065
972 775-9801

(G-6099)
ENNIS-FLINT INC
2802 Spur 469 (75119)
PHONE.................................817 706-3777
EMP: 10
SALES (corp-wide): 15.3B **Publicly Held**
WEB: www.ennisflintamericas.com
SIC: 2851 Paints & allied products
HQ: Ennis-Flint, Inc.
4161 Piedmont Pkwy # 370
Greensboro NC 27410
800 331-8118

(G-6100)
ERGON INC
203 Cedar Rd (75119-8450)
P.O. Box 489 (75120-0489)
PHONE.................................972 875-1122
Tony Doblado, Manager
EMP: 11
SALES (corp-wide): 891MM **Privately Held**
WEB: www.ergon.com
SIC: 2911 Gases & liquefied petroleum gases
PA: Ergon, Inc.
2829 Lakeland Dr Ste 2000
Flowood MS 39232
601 933-3000

(G-6101)
EXTRUDED ENNIS PRODUCTS
4200 Knighthurst St (75119-9050)
PHONE.................................972 875-1770
Roger Stevens, Principal
▲ EMP: 13
SALES (est): 2.5MM **Privately Held**
SIC: 2952 Siding materials

(G-6102)
FINE LINE RIBBON INC
Also Called: Fine Line Ribbon Company
2405 N Preston St (75119-7719)
P.O. Box 697 (75120-0697)
PHONE.................................972 875-8681
Theresa Strunc, President
EMP: 20
SQ FT: 15,000
SALES (est): 2.1MM **Privately Held**
WEB: www.finelineribbon.com
SIC: 3955 Ribbons, inked: typewriter, adding machine, register, etc.

(G-6103)
GARDNER-GIBSON MFG INC
2801 N Old Hwy 75 (75119)
P.O. Box 777 (75120-0777)
PHONE.................................972 878-1602
James White, Manager
EMP: 13
SALES (corp-wide): 424.6MM **Privately Held**
WEB: www.gardner-gibson.com
SIC: 2952 2891 Roofing felts, cements or coatings; caulking compounds
HQ: Gardner-Gibson Manufacturing, Inc.
4161 E 7th Ave
Tampa FL 33605
813 248-2101

(G-6104)
GENESIS CSTM CHEM BLENDING LLC
2708 Ne Main St (75119-8426)
P.O. Box 1299 (75120-1299)
PHONE.................................469 309-2790
Donnie Lourd, President
EMP: 10
SALES (est): 1.4MM
SALES (corp-wide): 68.8MM **Privately Held**
WEB: www.genesisccb.com
SIC: 2899 Chemical preparations
PA: Smart Chemical Services, Lp
905 S Polk St
Amarillo TX 79101
806 367-8031

(G-6105)
GLOBE PRODUCTS COMPANY INC
1490 Jack Mckay Blvd (75119-6502)
PHONE.................................972 875-1660
Jess Haupt, President
Jesse Haupt, Principal
Brenda Haupt, Vice Pres
Tony Rodriquez, Plant Mgr
Herb Williams, Natl Sales Mgr
EMP: 60
SQ FT: 15,000
SALES (est): 21.8MM **Privately Held**
WEB: www.globeproducts.com
SIC: 3492 3965 Fluid power valves & hose fittings; eyelets, metal: clothing, fabrics, boots or shoes

(G-6106)
GUARDIAR USA LLC (DH)
3309 Sw Interstate 45 (75119)
PHONE.................................972 878-7000
Paul Skertchly, President
Sharon Christopher, Sales Staff
Jean Slease, Sales Staff
Tony Thompson, Marketing Staff
Roosevelt Dorval, Manager
▲ EMP: 92
SALES (est): 16.6MM
SALES (corp-wide): 3MM **Privately Held**
WEB: www.betafenceusa.com
SIC: 3441 Building components, structural steel
HQ: Guardiar Europe
Blokkestraat 34b
Zwevegem 8550
567 079-27

(G-6107)
HANSON AGGREGATES LLC
Also Called: Hanson Aggregates Bristol
7000 E Highway 34 (75119-1581)
PHONE.................................972 875-9590
Allen Lathem, Branch Mgr
EMP: 16
SALES (corp-wide): 20.8B **Privately Held**
WEB: www.heidelbergcement.com
SIC: 3273 Ready-mixed concrete
HQ: Hanson Aggregates Llc
8505 Freport Pkwy Ste 500
Irving TX 75063
469 417-1200

(G-6108)
J WATERS INC
100 Arnold St (75119-8052)
P.O. Box 1056 (75119-1056)
PHONE.................................502 896-0850
John Waters, President
Linda Waters, Vice Pres
EMP: 13
SQ FT: 10,000
SALES (est): 1.1MM **Privately Held**
WEB: www.jwaters.com
SIC: 2431 Doors, wood

(G-6109)
LEGGETT & PLATT INCORPORATED
Leggett & Platt 0003
4100 S Interstate 45 (75119-0884)
PHONE.................................972 875-8401
Rhonda Lawson, Human Res Mgr
Joan Norch, Office Mgr
Kevin Fincher, Manager
Michelele Slovak, Info Tech Mgr
EMP: 310
SALES (corp-wide): 4.7B **Publicly Held**
WEB: www.leggett.com
SIC: 2515 3495 Bedsprings, assembled; wire springs
PA: Leggett & Platt, Incorporated
1 Leggett Rd
Carthage MO 64836
417 358-8131

(G-6110)
MITEK CORPORATION
Also Called: Atlas Soundolier
1601 Jack Mckay Blvd (75119-6507)
PHONE.................................972 875-8413
David Moriarty, Regional Mgr
Steve Brooks, Vice Pres
Zaid Ahmed, Engineer
Tim Byrnes, Engineer

Steve Clay, Engineer
EMP: 100
SALES (corp-wide): 77MM **Privately Held**
WEB: www.mitekusa.com
SIC: 3651 Sound reproducing equipment
PA: Mitek Corporation
4545 E Baseline Rd
Phoenix AZ 85042
602 438-4545

(G-6111)
MUNCASTER CAPITAL TEXAS INC (PA)
Also Called: Polyguard Products
4101 S Interstate Hwy 45 (75119-0882)
P.O. Box 755 (75120-0755)
PHONE.................................214 515-5000
John W Muncaster, CEO
Shawn Eastham, President
Paul Doud, Regional Mgr
Robert Nee, Vice Pres
Carlos Montoya, VP Opers
▲ EMP: 35
SQ FT: 44,000
SALES (est): 14.2MM **Privately Held**
WEB: www.polyguardproducts.com
SIC: 2295 Tape, varnished: plastic & other coated (except magnetic)

(G-6112)
NATIONAL CNVERTING FULFILLMENT
2708 Ne Main St (75119-8426)
PHONE.................................972 875-5096
Melvin Riecke, President
Kathy Riecke, Corp Secy
▲ EMP: 26
SQ FT: 144,000
SALES (est): 6.7MM **Privately Held**
SIC: 2653 7389 Corrugated boxes, partitions, display items, sheets & pad; packaging & labeling services

(G-6113)
NIGHTNGALE ARCHTCTRAL DORS INC
100 Arnold St (75119)
P.O. Box 1056 (75120-1056)
PHONE.................................972 875-1134
Roger Nightingale, Principal
EMP: 9
SALES (est): 1.6MM **Privately Held**
WEB: www.nightingaledoors.com
SIC: 2431 Millwork

(G-6114)
POLYGUARD PRODUCTS INC (HQ)
3801 S Interstate Hwy 45 (75119-0804)
P.O. Box 755 (75120-0755)
PHONE.................................972 875-8421
John W Muncaster, Ch of Bd
Shawn Eastham, President
Bryan Coulter, Vice Pres
Patrick Dunn, Vice Pres
Chic Hughes, Vice Pres
▲ EMP: 41
SQ FT: 44,000
SALES (est): 14.2MM **Privately Held**
WEB: www.polyguardproducts.com
SIC: 2295 Tape, varnished: plastic & other coated (except magnetic)
PA: Muncaster Capital Of Texas, Inc.
4101 S Interstate Hwy 45
Ennis TX 75119
214 515-5000

(G-6115)
POLYNT COMPOSITES USA INC
201 Cedar Rd (75119-8450)
PHONE.................................972 875-8634
Dolores Scott, Purch Mgr
Dianne Shrum, Purch Mgr
Matthew Hayden, Train & Dev Mgr
Jon Cremers, Branch Mgr
Jim Lensmire, Info Tech Mgr
EMP: 60
SALES (corp-wide): 2.2B **Privately Held**
WEB: www.polynt.com
SIC: 2821 Polyethylene resins
HQ: Polynt Composites Usa Inc.
99 E Cottage Ave
Carpentersville IL 60110

(G-6116)
RC CHRISTOPHER INDUSTRIES INC
1504 S Kaufman St (75119-7037)
P.O. Box 1270 (75120-1270)
PHONE....................................972 875-6555
Robert Christopher, *President*
Patrick C Henry, *Vice Pres*
F M Koppersmith III, *CFO*
EMP: 37
SQ FT: 77,000
SALES: 3.2MM **Privately Held**
SIC: 3088 Shower stalls, fiberglass & plastic

(G-6117)
SCHIRM USA INC
Also Called: AG Warehouse
4101 Knighthurst St (75119-6655)
P.O. Box 237 (75120-0237)
PHONE....................................972 878-4400
Colten Watson, *Plant Engr*
Dob Bryant, *Manager*
EMP: 40 **Privately Held**
WEB: www.imperial-international.com
SIC: 2879 Pesticides, agricultural or household
HQ: Schirm U.S.A., Inc.
2801 S Oak Grove Rd
Ennis TX 75119

(G-6118)
SOUTHWEST SPRAY INC
1702 Jack Mckay Blvd (75119-6508)
PHONE....................................972 875-5665
Jim Rainey, *President*
EMP: 30
SQ FT: 25,000
SALES (est): 2.8MM **Privately Held**
WEB: www.headpaint.com
SIC: 3479 Coating of metals & formed products

(G-6119)
THREET PALLET LLC
801 Lakeway Dr (75119-8010)
PHONE....................................972 489-6887
Scott Threet,
EMP: 30
SALES (est): 4.4MM **Privately Held**
SIC: 2448 7389 Pallets, wood;

(G-6120)
TOTAL STEEL FABRICATION LLC
2705 Brombeck (75119-7933)
PHONE....................................972 846-4703
Valerie Scoggin, *Controller*
Robert Emerick,
Sharon Emerick,
James Bradley Wilson,
EMP: 23
SALES (est): 5MM **Privately Held**
WEB: www.totalstlfab.com
SIC: 3441 Fabricated structural metal

(G-6121)
TROPAR MANUFACTURING CO INC
2313 N Preston St (75119-7717)
PHONE....................................972 875-5831
Charles Yowell, *Plant Mgr*
Buckingham Gina, *Engineer*
EMP: 15 **Privately Held**
WEB: www.airflyte.com
SIC: 3499 5999 Trophies, metal, except silver; trophies & plaques
PA: Tropar Manufacturing Co Inc
5 Vreeland Rd
Florham Park NJ 07932

(G-6122)
US POLYCO INC
3901 S Interstate Hwy 45 (75119-0803)
PHONE....................................972 875-9300
Thomas Nichols, *Principal*
Dave Harlan, *Plant Mgr*
Gabrell Gray, *Opers Staff*
Hans Vrij, *Manager*
EMP: 19
SALES (corp-wide): 7.5MM **Privately Held**
WEB: www.uspolyco.com
SIC: 2951 Asphalt paving mixtures & blocks

PA: U.S. Polyco, Inc.
9110 Double Dmnd Pkwy B
Reno NV 89521
775 626-8818

(G-6123)
WILBERT FUNERAL SERVICES INC
Also Called: Si Precast Concrete
5203 N Interstate Hwy 45 (75119-0937)
PHONE....................................972 875-9605
Joe Wright, *Manager*
EMP: 28
SQ FT: 27,250
SALES (corp-wide): 9B **Publicly Held**
WEB: www.greensborowilbert.com
SIC: 3272 5085 0782 1711 Burial vaults, concrete or precast terrazzo; concrete products, precast; industrial supplies; cemetery upkeep services; septic system construction
HQ: Wilbert Funeral Services, Inc.
10965 Granada Ln Ste 300
Overland Park KS 66211
913 345-2120

Eola
Concho County

(G-6124)
JENSCO TRANSPORT SERVICES LLC
13880 Whitfield Rd (76937-9755)
P.O. Box 340, Wall (76957-0340)
PHONE....................................325 234-1412
Carlton Michael Jenschke, *President*
David Adam Jenschke, *Vice Pres*
Carl Jenschke, *Director*
EMP: 18 **EST:** 2012
SQ FT: 3,600
SALES (est): 130K **Privately Held**
SIC: 1389 Oil field services

Euless
Tarrant County

(G-6125)
AC PRINTING LLC
3400 Raider Dr Ste 1 (76040-6651)
PHONE....................................817 267-8990
Shiraz Kanji, *President*
Les Ewell, *Purchasing*
Tyler McLain, *Accounts Mgr*
McCarthy Teresa, *Accounts Mgr*
John Portwood, *Sales Staff*
▲ **EMP:** 25
SQ FT: 27,000
SALES (est): 6.2MM **Privately Held**
WEB: www.acprinting.com
SIC: 2752 Commercial printing, offset

(G-6126)
AEREOS INC (PA)
Also Called: Euless Aero Components
1100 S Pipeline Rd W (76040-6913)
P.O. Box 519 (76039-0519)
PHONE....................................817 267-1371
Ben Hinterlong, *Ch of Bd*
William Montgomery, *President*
David Baker, *Exec VP*
David Tarrant, *Vice Pres*
Sarah Ryan, *Purchasing*
EMP: 55
SQ FT: 28,600
SALES (est): 15.5MM **Privately Held**
WEB: www.aereos.com
SIC: 3728 Aircraft parts & equipment

(G-6127)
AERO DYNAMIX INC
3227 W Euless Blvd (76040-6254)
PHONE....................................817 571-0729
Daniel Hewitt, *President*
Tonka Hufford, *COO*
Laura Hewitt, *Vice Pres*
David Lam, *Production*
Paul Carter, *QC Mgr*
EMP: 77
SQ FT: 23,000

SALES (est): 8.6MM **Privately Held**
WEB: www.aerodynamix.com
SIC: 3728 Aircraft parts & equipment

(G-6128)
AEROTECH ENGINEERING INC
1100 S Pipeline Rd W (76040-6913)
P.O. Box 519 (76039-0519)
PHONE....................................817 267-1371
William Montgomery, *President*
David Tarrant, *COO*
Sarah Ryan, *Sales Mgr*
EMP: 40
SALES (est): 5.5MM **Privately Held**
SIC: 3728 Aircraft parts & equipment

(G-6129)
AGH INDUSTRIES INC
1103 Stanley Dr (76040-6817)
PHONE....................................817 284-1742
Kenneth H Wanamaker, *CEO*
Jeremy S Wanamaker, *President*
Jeremy Wanamaker, *President*
Kyle Blake, *Vice Pres*
Debra S Chambers, *Vice Pres*
EMP: 20 **EST:** 1971
SQ FT: 21,000
SALES (est): 4.8MM **Privately Held**
WEB: www.aghindustries.com
SIC: 3728 3462 3463 Aircraft parts & equipment; missile & ordnance forgings; missile & ordnance forgings

(G-6130)
AMERICAN MICRO SYSTEMS LTD
Also Called: American Microsystems
2190 Regal Pkwy (76040-6732)
PHONE....................................817 571-9015
Rusty Herod, *Partner*
Buddy Herod, *Partner*
R K Herod, *Partner*
Mike Kearby, *Partner*
Mitch Martin, *Partner*
▲ **EMP:** 26
SQ FT: 10,000
SALES (est): 8.7MM **Privately Held**
WEB: www.amltd.com
SIC: 3577 7372 5044 7389 Magnetic ink & optical scanning devices; bar code (magnetic ink) printers; decoders, computer peripheral equipment; application computer software; office equipment; packaging & labeling services

(G-6131)
ATLAS MATCH LLC (PA)
1301 Texas Star Pkwy (76040-6862)
P.O. Box 348, Jaffrey NH (03452-0348)
PHONE....................................817 267-1500
Mitch Gorstein, *VP Sales*
David Bradley,
Regina Clark, *Administration*
Hal Carew, *Maintence Staff*
Doug Lamb,
◆ **EMP:** 43
SQ FT: 65,000
SALES (est): 14.3MM **Privately Held**
WEB: www.atlasmatch.com
SIC: 3999 Matches & match books

(G-6132)
AWNTECH CORPORATION
10950 S Pipeline Rd (76040-6658)
PHONE....................................817 354-9600
Sean Konda, *CEO*
Katherine Konda, *President*
Coe Steal, *Facilities Mgr*
Shawn Konda, *CFO*
Lilly Konda, *Marketing Mgr*
◆ **EMP:** 49
SQ FT: 250,000
SALES (est): 7MM **Privately Held**
WEB: www.awntech.com
SIC: 5999 3444 2431 2591 Awnings; awnings & canopies; awnings, blinds & shutters, wood; drapery hardware & blinds & shades; canvas awnings & canopies; fiberglass building materials

(G-6133)
BLAKEMAN INDUSTRIES INC
Also Called: Southwest Air Products
13108 Euless St (76040-7266)
P.O. Box 1155 (76039-1155)
PHONE....................................817 267-4444

Alan Blakeman, *President*
◆ **EMP:** 40
SQ FT: 68,000
SALES (est): 7.9MM **Privately Held**
WEB: www.swairproducts.com
SIC: 3086 Packaging & shipping materials, foamed plastic

(G-6134)
CAMTECH PRECISION MFG INC
1400 Westpark Way (76040-6734)
PHONE....................................404 444-9646
Wayne Reid, *CEO*
EMP: 30 **Privately Held**
SIC: 3469 Machine parts, stamped or pressed metal

(G-6135)
CHARLEYS CONCRETE CO LTD
Fm 1171 & I 35w (76039)
P.O. Box 1106, Keller (76244-1106)
PHONE....................................817 431-2016
Charley Pennington, *President*
EMP: 31
SALES (corp-wide): 39MM **Privately Held**
WEB: www.charleysconcrete.com
SIC: 3273 Ready-mixed concrete
PA: Charley's Concrete Co., Ltd.
11801 Katy Rd
Fort Worth TX 76244
817 431-3515

(G-6136)
CHASSIS LINER
11500 S Pipeline Rd (76040-6712)
PHONE....................................817 284-2545
▲ **EMP:** 13
SALES (est): 1.5MM **Privately Held**
WEB: www.chassisliner.com
SIC: 3999 5099 Manufacturing industries; durable goods

(G-6137)
COBRA MANUFACTURING CO INC
1001 Pamela Dr (76040-6809)
PHONE....................................918 366-7622
Tom McClendon, *CEO*
Russ Freeman, *President*
▲ **EMP:** 50
SQ FT: 30,000
SALES (est): 5.3MM **Privately Held**
SIC: 3949 Archery equipment, general

(G-6138)
COMMSCOPE TECHNOLOGIES LLC
Also Called: St Andrew
11312 S Pipeline Rd (76040-6629)
PHONE....................................817 864-4100
Kevin Paswalk, *Branch Mgr*
EMP: 50 **Publicly Held**
WEB: www.commscope.com
SIC: 3663 Radio & TV communications equipment
HQ: Commscope Technologies Llc
4 Westbrook Corporate Ctr
Westchester IL 60154
708 236-6600

(G-6139)
CURRY PRINTING LTD
1109 Pamela Dr (76040-6811)
PHONE....................................817 540-5252
Cody Curry, *President*
Linda Curry, *Vice Pres*
Laquinta Garcia, *Graphic Designe*
EMP: 25
SQ FT: 15,000
SALES (est): 4MM **Privately Held**
WEB: www.curryprintinginc.com
SIC: 2752 2789 2759 Commercial printing, offset; bookbinding & related work; commercial printing

(G-6140)
DAVIS MACHINE & MFG CO
Also Called: R W McNamara
1503 Royal Pkwy (76040-6727)
PHONE....................................817 684-8703
Robert McNamara, *Owner*
Judy McNamara, *Vice Pres*
EMP: 20 **EST:** 1952
SQ FT: 27,000

▲ = Import ▼ =Export
◆ =Import/Export

SALES (est): 3.6MM **Privately Held**
WEB: www.davismachine.com
SIC: 3599 Machine shop, jobbing & repair

(G-6141)
EARTH HAULERS INC
11500 Mosier Valley Rd (76040-2104)
PHONE...................................817 540-2777
Allen M Tucker, *President*
Benny Tucker, *Vice Pres*
Danielle Tucker, *Office Mgr*
EMP: 10 EST: 1977
SQ FT: 4,000
SALES (est): 2.2MM **Privately Held**
WEB: www.earthhaulers.com
SIC: 1442 4959 1794 4212 Construction
sand & gravel; environmental cleanup
services; excavation work; dump truck
haulage; heavy hauling

(G-6142)
**EASTMAN PERFORMANCE
FILMS LLC**
1385 Westpark Way (76040-6731)
PHONE...................................817 445-1102
David Mussett, *Branch Mgr*
EMP: 32 **Publicly Held**
SIC: 2821 Plastics materials & resins
HQ: Eastman Performance Films, Llc
4210 The Great Rd
Fieldale VA 24089
276 627-3000

(G-6143)
**EULESS AERO COMPONENTS
LLC**
1100 S Pipeline Rd W (76040-6913)
P.O. Box 519 (76039-0519)
PHONE...................................817 267-1371
William Montgomery, *President*
Chris Baumann, *COO*
Tammy Smith, *Controller*
EMP: 55
SALES (est): 1.7MM
SALES (corp-wide): 15.5MM **Privately
Held**
WEB: www.aereos.com
SIC: 3728 Aircraft parts & equipment
PA: Aereos, Inc.
1100 S Pipeline Rd W
Euless TX 76040
817 267-1371

(G-6144)
**EVANS SONS PRTBLE ROCK
CRSHING**
2100 Heritage Ave # 5202 (76039-5429)
PHONE...................................830 214-3629
EMP: 10 EST: 2015
SALES (est): 417.4K **Privately Held**
WEB: www.evansandsonscrushing.com
SIC: 3462 1499 Railroad, construction &
mining forgings; asphalt mining & bitumi-
nous stone quarrying

(G-6145)
F & H RIBBON COMPANY INC
3010 S Pipeline Rd (76040-6637)
P.O. Box 1338, Hurst (76053-1338)
PHONE...................................817 283-5891
Rhea Ann Pope, *CEO*
Rene Brown, *Vice Pres*
▲ EMP: 70
SQ FT: 40,000
SALES (est): 7.3MM **Privately Held**
WEB: www.fhribbon.com
SIC: 2399 2396 Banners, pennants &
flags; automotive & apparel trimmings

(G-6146)
**FEDERAL HEATH SIGN
COMPANY LLC (HQ)**
2300 St Hwy 121 (76040-4061)
PHONE...................................817 685-9075
Stew Edinger, *Vice Pres*
Tammy Baker, *Project Mgr*
Toni Miller, *Project Mgr*
John Love, *Opers Mgr*
Terry Smith, *Foreman/Supr*
◆ EMP: 83
SQ FT: 50,000
SALES (est): 135.6MM
SALES (corp-wide): 3.2B **Privately Held**
WEB: www.federalheath.com
SIC: 3993 Neon signs

PA: Diane M Hendricks Enterprises Inc.
1 Abc Pkwy
Beloit WI 53511
608 362-7777

(G-6147)
GUND COMPANY INC
3010 S Pipeline Rd (76040-6637)
PHONE...................................972 389-0615
Jordan Adams, *Branch Mgr*
EMP: 25
SALES (corp-wide): 77MM **Privately
Held**
WEB: www.thegundcompany.com
SIC: 3644 3053 Insulators & insulation
materials, electrical; gaskets, packing &
sealing devices; gasket materials
PA: The Gund Company Inc
9333 Dielman Indus Dr
Saint Louis MO 63132
314 423-5200

(G-6148)
**KEIZER TECHNOLOGIES
AMERICAS**
10908 S Pipeline Rd (76040-6650)
PHONE...................................817 685-7090
Rudy Trevino, *President*
Judd Adcock, *Vice Pres*
EMP: 10
SQ FT: 8,000
SALES (est): 3.5MM **Privately Held**
WEB: www.torbousa.com
SIC: 3589 Commercial cleaning equipment

(G-6149)
MICA STEELWORKS INC
3501 House Anderson Rd (76040-2005)
PHONE...................................817 267-9699
Gene Swofford, *Branch Mgr*
EMP: 31
SALES (corp-wide): 93.4MM **Privately
Held**
WEB: www.micacorporation.com
SIC: 3312 Blast furnaces & steel mills
PA: Mica Steelworks, Inc.
5750 N Riverside Dr
Fort Worth TX 76137
817 529-5000

(G-6150)
**MODERN TEKTRONIX
ASSEMBLY**
Also Called: M T A
1107 Pamela Dr (76040-6811)
PHONE...................................817 868-7173
Paul H Trang, *President*
▲ EMP: 30
SQ FT: 10,000
SALES (est): 5MM **Privately Held**
WEB: www.mtai.com
SIC: 3679 Electronic circuits

(G-6151)
OP2 LABS LLC (PA)
601 Bridgewater St Euless (76039)
PHONE...................................888 448-8468
Alexander Kunz, *CEO*
Jeff Byers, *COO*
Eric Pollard, *Senior VP*
Mike Janke,
EMP: 10
SQ FT: 12,000
SALES (est): 2.6MM **Privately Held**
WEB: www.frogfuel.com
SIC: 2023 2834 Dietary supplements,
dairy & non-dairy based; solutions, phar-
maceutical

(G-6152)
**PARKERLANE DIRECTIONAL
DRLG LP**
2504 Kodiak Cir (76039-6080)
P.O. Box 609 (76039-0609)
PHONE...................................817 235-4050
Steve Parker, *Partner*
Brent Lyane, *Partner*
EMP: 20
SALES (est): 1.3MM **Privately Held**
WEB: www.parkerlane.com
SIC: 1381 Directional drilling oil & gas
wells

(G-6153)
REDI-MIX LLC (HQ)
Also Called: Redi-Mix Concrete
331 N Main St (76039-3636)
PHONE...................................817 835-4105
William J Sandbrook, *CEO*
Wallace H Johnson, *Vice Pres*
Paul M Jolas, *Vice Pres*
Mark B Peabody, *Vice Pres*
William M Brown, *CFO*
EMP: 86
SALES (est): 58.2MM
SALES (corp-wide): 1.4B **Publicly Held**
WEB: www.us-concrete.com
SIC: 3273 Ready-mixed concrete
PA: U.S. Concrete, Inc.
331 N Main St
Euless TX 76039
817 835-4105

(G-6154)
REDI-MIX LP
Also Called: Redi-Mix Concrete
1100 Westpark Way Ste 100 (76040-6350)
PHONE...................................817 485-4850
Will Glusac, *Manager*
EMP: 20
SALES (corp-wide): 1.4B **Publicly Held**
SIC: 3273 Ready-mixed concrete
HQ: Redi-Mix Lp
1445 Mac Arthur Dr # 136
Carrollton TX 75007
972 242-4550

(G-6155)
RICHARD H SMITH LLC
Also Called: Fineline Production
2221 Regal Pkwy (76040-6710)
PHONE...................................817 267-6750
Gerard Smith, *President*
Alex J Ferguson, *COO*
Richard Smith, *Vice Pres*
Penny Gamblin, *Senior Buyer*
Daphine Peters,
EMP: 30
SALES (est): 6.2MM **Privately Held**
WEB: www.finelineproduction.com
SIC: 3599 3469 3465 Machine shop, job-
bing & repair; metal stampings; automo-
tive stampings

(G-6156)
ROMIX CHEMICALS INC
Also Called: Romix Chemical & Brush
3608 Liston Ln (76040-6606)
P.O. Box 1110, Colleyville (76034-1110)
PHONE...................................817 685-0006
Roger Anderson, *President*
Pam Anderson, *Corp Secy*
Cliff L Anderson, *Vice Pres*
Cliff Anderson, *Vice Pres*
Craig W Anderson, *Vice Pres*
▼ EMP: 30
SQ FT: 22,200
SALES (est): 6.7MM **Privately Held**
WEB: www.romixchem.com
SIC: 2842 5169 Cleaning or polishing
preparations; chemicals & allied products

(G-6157)
SCOTT MC GAHA
Also Called: Precision Orthodonics
700 S Main St (76040-5317)
PHONE...................................817 540-2309
Scott McGaha, *President*
Scott Mc Gaha, *Owner*
EMP: 10
SQ FT: 392
SALES (est): 911K **Privately Held**
WEB: www.precisionortho.biz
SIC: 3843 Orthodontic appliances

(G-6158)
SIGN ERECTION LTD
Also Called: Sign Company
11128 S Pipeline Rd (76040-6639)
P.O. Box 9 (76039-0009)
PHONE...................................817 267-1554
EMP: 20 EST: 1976
SQ FT: 14,000
SALES (est): 4MM **Privately Held**
SIC: 3993 Electric signs

(G-6159)
SIMTEK INC
1505 Royal Pkwy (76040-6727)
PHONE...................................817 283-1801
Chad Cowley, *President*
Tad Buck, *Vice Pres*
Steve Smith, *Vice Pres*
David Towns, *Vice Pres*
Brandon Kuecker, *Opers Dir*
EMP: 86 EST: 1978
SQ FT: 29,000
SALES: 8.8MM **Privately Held**
WEB: www.simtekinc.com
SIC: 3699 3812 Flight simulators (training
aids), electronic; search & navigation
equipment

(G-6160)
**SUPERIOR CON FENCE TEXAS
INC (PA)**
Also Called: Superior Concrete Products
1203 Raider Dr (76040-6238)
PHONE...................................817 277-9255
Todd Sternfeld, *CEO*
Calvin Clarke, *President*
Mike Taylor, *Vice Pres*
Kyle Wilson, *Vice Pres*
Lex Kruit, *Project Mgr*
EMP: 15
SQ FT: 4,000
SALES (est): 10.4MM **Privately Held**
WEB: www.concretefence.com
SIC: 1771 3272 Concrete work; concrete
products, precast

(G-6161)
TA FABRICATION LLC
2307 Harrington Ct (76039-4241)
PHONE...................................330 301-6800
Thomas Andres, *CEO*
EMP: 10
SALES (est): 367.3K **Privately Held**
SIC: 3549 Metalworking machinery

(G-6162)
TEXAS POLY INC
1375 Westpark Way (76040-6798)
PHONE...................................817 540-2351
Justin Earl, *President*
▲ EMP: 20
SQ FT: 15,000
SALES (est): 4MM **Privately Held**
WEB: www.texaspoly.com
SIC: 2673 Plastic bags: made from pur-
chased materials

(G-6163)
TURBINE RESOURCES INC
1005 Stanley Dr (76040-6815)
P.O. Box 428, Colleyville (76034-0428)
PHONE...................................817 540-0249
William J McCall, *President*
Carolyn McCall, *Vice Pres*
Mark Suneson, *Project Engr*
Aaron Kramer, *Manager*
▲ EMP: 25
SQ FT: 16,000
SALES (est): 5.6MM **Privately Held**
WEB: www.turbineresourcesinc.com
SIC: 3511 7699 Gas turbines, mechanical
drive; steam turbines; industrial machin-
ery & equipment repair

(G-6164)
UALLY LLC
718 Bordeaux Dr (76039-4018)
PHONE...................................936 252-7476
Yanbo Zhang,
EMP: 30
SALES (est): 946.4K **Privately Held**
SIC: 2426 Furniture stock & parts, hard-
wood

(G-6165)
**UNITED PETRO TRANSPORTS
INC**
3520 S Main St (76040-7114)
PHONE...................................817 540-6178
Gregory Price, *Owner*
Keith Mears, *Manager*
Shari Ardies, *Executive Asst*
EMP: 30

GEOGRAPHIC

SALES (corp-wide): 71.6MM **Privately
Held**
WEB: www.drive4upt.com
SIC: 4212 1389 4213 Petroleum haulage,
local; haulage, oil field; trucking, except
local
HQ: United Petroleum Transports, Inc.
4312 S Georgia Pl
Oklahoma City OK 73129
316 263-6868

(G-6166)
US CONCRETE INC (PA)
331 N Main St (76039-3636)
PHONE.....................817 835-4105
William J Sandbrook, *Ch of Bd*
Ronnie Pruitt, *President*
Chris Kissick, *General Mgr*
Niel L Poulsen, *Exec VP*
Paul M Jolas, *Senior VP*
▼ **EMP:** 23
SALES: 1.4B **Publicly Held**
WEB: www.us-concrete.com
SIC: 3273 3272 Ready-mixed concrete;
concrete products

Evadale
Jasper County

(G-6167)
WESTROCK MWV LLC
Also Called: Evadale Paperboard Mill
1913 Hwy 105 S (77615)
PHONE.....................409 276-3243
Rod Strong, *Manager*
EMP: 250
SALES (corp-wide): 17.5B **Publicly Held**
WEB: www.westrock.com
SIC: 2653 Boxes, corrugated: made from
purchased materials
HQ: Westrock Mwv, Llc
501 S 5th St
Richmond VA 23219
804 444-1000

Fairfield
Freestone County

(G-6168)
ARCHROCK INC
105 Bailiff Dr (75840-2453)
PHONE.....................903 389-5666
Don Vance, *Branch Mgr*
Darriel Hopson, *Manager*
EMP: 11 **Publicly Held**
WEB: www.archrock.com
SIC: 1389 5084 Gas compressing (natural
gas) at the fields; compressors, except air
conditioning
PA: Archrock, Inc.
9807 Katy Fwy Ste 100
Houston TX 77024

(G-6169)
BAKER PETROLITE
Also Called: Baker Hughes
111 Bailiff Dr (75840-2453)
P.O. Box B (75840)
PHONE.....................903 389-2903
Bill Turner, *Manager*
EMP: 30
SALES (corp-wide): 23.8B **Publicly Held**
WEB: www.bakerhughes.com
SIC: 2865 3533 Cyclic organic crudes;
cyclic organic intermediates; bits, oil &
gas field tools: rock
HQ: Baker Petrolite
2121 W Mary St
Garden City KS 67846

(G-6170)
**CHRIS CHRISTENSEN SYSTEMS
INC**
325 Industrial Park Dr (75840)
P.O. Box 961 (75840-0018)
PHONE.....................903 389-7949
Adrian J Christensen, *President*
Lisa L Christensen, *Vice Pres*
▲ **EMP:** 28
SQ FT: 10,000

SALES (est): 4.1MM **Privately Held**
WEB: www.chrissystems.com
SIC: 3999 Pet supplies

(G-6171)
**CLEAN ENERGY TECH ASSN
INC**
123 E Commerce St (75840-1507)
PHONE.....................903 389-4136
Roy W Hill, *President*
Michelle Moore, *Exec VP*
Rebecca Dodge, *Vice Pres*
Scooter Long, *Vice Pres*
Brandi Rhodes, *Vice Pres*
EMP: 32
SALES (est): 5.9MM **Privately Held**
WEB: www.cetaenergy.com
SIC: 8731 3533 3567 Energy research;
gas field machinery & equipment; oil field
machinery & equipment; distillation
ovens, charcoal & coke

(G-6172)
**DANIEL MIKE CONSTRUCTION
INC**
Also Called: Indy Construction
366 West St 27 (75840-3044)
P.O. Box 787 (75840-0015)
PHONE.....................903 389-2595
Mike Daniel, *President*
EMP: 50
SALES (est): 7MM **Privately Held**
WEB: www.mikedanielconstruction.com
SIC: 1389 Oil & gas wells: building, repair-
ing & dismantling

(G-6173)
FE HILL CO LLP
300 S Keechi St (75840-1524)
P.O. Box 226 (75840-0004)
PHONE.....................903 389-3616
F R Hill Jr, *Partner*
Marilyn S Toomey, *Partner*
Rich Hill, *General Ptnr*
EMP: 15
SQ FT: 30,000
SALES (est): 1MM **Privately Held**
WEB: www.huntfehillranch.com
SIC: 0212 1382 6512 Beef cattle except
feedlots; oil & gas exploration services;
commercial & industrial building operation

(G-6174)
FLINT ENERGY SERVICES INC
341 Hwy 45 (75840)
PHONE.....................903 389-8716
Tab Allenman, *Manager*
EMP: 100
SALES (corp-wide): 13.2B **Publicly Held**
WEB: www.aecom.com
SIC: 7699 5084 1389 Industrial machin-
ery & equipment repair; oil well machin-
ery, equipment & supplies; oil field
services
HQ: Flint Energy Services Inc.
6200 S Quebec St Ste 1
Greenwood Village CO 80111
918 294-3030

(G-6175)
**GREEN ENERGY OILFIELD
SVCS LLC**
335 Industrial Dr (75840-2415)
PHONE.....................210 904-3400
Roger Nevill, *President*
Joe Monroe, *Principal*
Marla Aaron Collins, *Vice Pres*
J R Nevill, *Vice Pres*
John Renger, *Vice Pres*
EMP: 170 **EST:** 2011
SALES (est): 48.7MM **Privately Held**
WEB:
www.greenenergyoilfieldservices.com
SIC: 1389 Oil field services

(G-6176)
HALLIBURTON COMPANY
Also Called: Mokey Chem
114 W Us Highway 84 (75840-4900)
PHONE.....................903 389-9275
Dane Yowell, *Branch Mgr*
EMP: 12 **Publicly Held**
WEB: www.halliburton.com
SIC: 1389 Oil field services

PA: Halliburton Company
3000 N Sam Houston Pkwy E
Houston TX 77032

(G-6177)
JEFES WELDING COMPANY
234 County Road 1171 (75840-5129)
PHONE.....................903 389-4036
Jesus Francisco Espinoza, *Principal*
EMP: 10
SALES (est): 185.2K **Privately Held**
WEB: www.jefeswelding.com
SIC: 7692 Welding repair

(G-6178)
MD CONSTRUCTION INC
Also Called: Mike Daniel Construction
366 West St 27 (75840-3044)
P.O. Box 787 (75840-0015)
PHONE.....................903 389-2595
Mike Daniel, *President*
EMP: 115
SALES (est): 5MM **Privately Held**
SIC: 1389 Construction, repair & disman-
tling services

(G-6179)
**MUSTANG OILFIELD SERVICES
LLC**
117 County Road 946 (75840-5124)
P.O. Box 107 (75840-0002)
PHONE.....................903 389-4200
Al Gibson,
Kyle Glicksman,
EMP: 41
SALES (est): 6.1MM **Privately Held**
WEB: www.mos-tx.com
SIC: 1389 Oil field services

(G-6180)
TXU ENERGY SERVICES CO LLC
488 Fm 2570 (75840-5444)
P.O. Box 948 (75840-0018)
PHONE.....................903 389-6074
EMP: 150
SALES (corp-wide): 9.1B **Publicly Held**
SIC: 3621 4911 Mfg Motors/Generators
HQ: Txu Energy Services Company Llc
1601 Bryan St
Dallas TX 75201
214 812-4600

Falfurrias
Brooks County

(G-6181)
ALS INC
Also Called: Als Welding
3660 E Highway 285 (78355-5903)
PHONE.....................361 325-2154
Alonzo Barrera, *President*
Albino Barrera, *Principal*
EMP: 10
SALES (est): 590K **Privately Held**
SIC: 7692 Welding repair

Falls City
Karnes County

(G-6182)
B & M OILFIELD SERVICES LLC
Also Called: Jose Lucio Sandblasting & Pntg
11174 Us Highway 181 S (78113-3087)
PHONE.....................979 241-2051
Berry Monteau, *Mng Member*
EMP: 10 **EST:** 2009
SALES (est): 673.3K **Privately Held**
SIC: 3589 Sandblasting equipment

(G-6183)
MESQUITE CONCRETE INC
7566 Fm 541 E (78113-2447)
PHONE.....................830 216-1530
Kevin Janek, *President*
Bryan Camber, *Vice Pres*
Kathy Janek, *Treasurer*
EMP: 10
SQ FT: 3,535
SALES (est): 1.5MM **Privately Held**
WEB: www.mesquiteconcrete.com
SIC: 3273 Ready-mixed concrete

Farmers Branch
Dallas County

(G-6184)
ADEMCO INC
Also Called: ADI Global Distribution
12880 Valley Branch Ln (75234-5848)
PHONE.....................972 402-8612
Steven Motz, *Business Mgr*
Dean Cobourn, *Branch Mgr*
Steve Beshear, *Manager*
EMP: 21
SALES (corp-wide): 4.9B **Publicly Held**
WEB: www.adi-dist.com
SIC: 5063 3669 3822 Electrical apparatus
& equipment; emergency alarms; air con-
ditioning & refrigeration controls
HQ: Ademco Inc.
1985 Douglas Dr N
Golden Valley MN 55422
800 468-1502

(G-6185)
AEROXCHANGE LTD
1503 Lbj Fwy Ste 275 (75234-6450)
PHONE.....................972 556-8500
Albert Koszarek, *CEO*
Jon Andre, *Vice Pres*
Mike Folsom, *Vice Pres*
Mike Mills, *Project Mgr*
Wendy Ll, *CFO*
EMP: 37 **EST:** 2000
SQ FT: 30,000
SALES (est): 10.7MM **Privately Held**
WEB: www.aeroxchange.com
SIC: 3728 7699 Aircraft parts & equip-
ment; aircraft & heavy equipment repair
services

(G-6186)
ANKEM OF TEXAS INC
Also Called: Ankem Chemicals
3500 Garden Brook Dr (75234-2443)
PHONE.....................903 802-7133
Ronnie E Anderson Jr, *President*
Catherine Anderson, *Vice Pres*
▼ **EMP:** 35
SQ FT: 10,000
SALES (est): 397.2K **Privately Held**
WEB: www.ankem.com
SIC: 5169 2842 2841 Specialty cleaning
& sanitation preparations; specialty clean-
ing, polishes & sanitation goods; soap &
other detergents

(G-6187)
APPLEGATE EDM INC
2405 Squire Pl (75234-4707)
PHONE.....................972 488-8997
Wayne Applegate, *President*
EMP: 28
SQ FT: 28,000
SALES (est): 5.6MM **Privately Held**
WEB: www.applegateedm.com
SIC: 3599 Machine shop, jobbing & repair

(G-6188)
ARROWHEAD STAIRS AND TRIM
2115 Valley View Ln # 100 (75234-8934)
PHONE.....................972 484-0406
EMP: 16 **EST:** 2013
SALES (est): 3.6MM **Privately Held**
SIC: 3446 Mfg Architectural Metalwork

(G-6189)
**ASTI MANUFACTURING CORP
INC**
Also Called: Maevn Uniforms
13950 Senlac Dr Ste 300 (75234-8828)
PHONE.....................972 241-3055
Thomas Lee, *President*
Mathew Ninan, *Opers Mgr*
Mathew-US Ninan, *Opers Mgr*
▲ **EMP:** 20
SALES (est): 1.1MM **Privately Held**
WEB: www.maevn.com
SIC: 5136 2326 Uniforms, men's & boys';
medical & hospital uniforms, men's

(G-6190)
BAKERYWORKS LLC
Also Called: Local Oven
4436 Mcewen Rd (75244-5205)
PHONE.....................972 250-1818

▲ = Import ▼=Export
◆ =Import/Export

Linda Fitzerman, *Owner*
EMP: 50
SQ FT: 8,000
SALES (est): 1.2MM **Privately Held**
WEB: www.localoven.com
SIC: 2051 Biscuits, baked: baking powder
& raised

(G-6191)
CBD FARMHOUSE
4360 Spring Valley Rd (75244-3701)
PHONE.....................214 971-6688
EMP: 10
SALES (est): 601.2K **Privately Held**
WEB: www.cbdfarmhouse.com
SIC: 3999 5159 5993 ; ;

(G-6192)
DALLAS LABEL AND
PACKAGING INC
Also Called: Prime Lables
14832 Venture Dr (75234-2426)
P.O. Box 119017, Carrollton (75011-9017)
PHONE.....................972 487-6064
Howard Horton, *President*
EMP: 13
SQ FT: 11,200
SALES (est): 3.4MM **Privately Held**
WEB: www.dallaslabel.com
SIC: 2679 Labels, paper: made from pur-
chased material

(G-6193)
DIVCON EMS AUSTIN LLC
Also Called: Divcon Controls
1801 Royal Ln Ste 100 (75229-3192)
PHONE.....................214 821-6958
Sandy Forbes, *Controller*
Todd Dempsey, *Sales Mgr*
Ben Crowell,
Hilary Edwards, *Administration*
John Palacios,
EMP: 30 EST: 2009
SQ FT: 6,000
SALES (est): 6.1MM **Privately Held**
WEB: www.divconcontrols.com
SIC: 3822 Building services monitoring
controls, automatic

(G-6194)
E MAJOR TECH LLC
13620 Omega Rd (75244-4514)
PHONE.....................972 385-6466
K Chen, *President*
Lily Lin, *Opers Staff*
▲ **EMP:** 16
SQ FT: 6,000
SALES (est): 800K **Privately Held**
WEB: www.emajortech.com
SIC: 3577 Computer peripheral equipment

(G-6195)
ELEGANTE IRON INC
13619 Inwood Rd Ste 360 (75244-4649)
P.O. Box 821973, Dallas (75382-1973)
PHONE.....................214 342-8987
Jenny Sandlin, *President*
Don Sandlin, *Vice Pres*
EMP: 10
SALES (est): 1.4MM **Privately Held**
WEB: www.eleganteiron.com
SIC: 3446 Architectural metalwork

(G-6196)
EPIMED INTERNATIONAL INC
(PA)
13958 Diplomat Dr (75234-8805)
PHONE.....................972 373-9090
Gabor Jerome Racz, *President*
Sandor Racz, *Exec VP*
Nicholas Sandor Racz, *Vice Pres*
Bruce Whitcavitch, *Vice Pres*
Frank Williams, *Sales Staff*
▲ **EMP:** 43
SQ FT: 27,000
SALES (est): 8.7MM **Privately Held**
WEB: www.epimed.com
SIC: 3841 Surgical & medical instruments

(G-6197)
GMYP MANUFACTURING LLC
4260 Spring Valley Rd (75244-3616)
PHONE.....................682 313-3023
Calvin Young, *Mng Member*
EMP: 10 EST: 2017

SALES (est): 365K **Privately Held**
WEB: www.gmypmanufacturing.com
SIC: 2329 2339 Men's & boys' sportswear
& athletic clothing; athletic clothing:
women's, misses' & juniors'

(G-6198)
GT SILICONES INC
13700 Diplomat Dr (75234-8916)
PHONE.....................610 252-5800
Kevin Hickey, *Principal*
EMP: 20
SALES (est): 504.6K **Privately Held**
SIC: 3999 Manufacturing industries

(G-6199)
HAGGAR CLOTHING CO (DH)
1507 Lyndon B Johnson Fwy # 100
(75234-6058)
PHONE.....................214 352-8481
Michael B Stitt, *President*
David Yarbrough, *President*
Tad Parnell, *Senior VP*
Jeanne Bonaguro, *Project Mgr*
Lauren Bradley, *Production*
◆ **EMP:** 500 EST: 1926
SALES (est): 599.6MM **Privately Held**
WEB: www.haggar.com
SIC: 2311 2321 5611 5651 Tailored suits
& formal jackets; suits, men's & boys':
made from purchased materials; tailored
dress & sport coats: men's & boys'; men's
& boys' furnishings; men's & boys' dress
shirts: sport shirts, men's & boys': from
purchased materials; flannel shirts, except work: men's, youths' & boys'; men's
& boys' clothing stores; family clothing
stores; men's & boys' jeans & dungarees
HQ: Haggar Corp.
1507 Lyndon B Johnson Fwy # 100
Farmers Branch TX 75234
214 352-8481

(G-6200)
HAGGAR CORP (HQ)
Also Called: Haggar Clothing Company
1507 Lyndon B Johnson Fwy # 100
(75234-6058)
PHONE.....................214 352-8481
Michael B Stitt, *CEO*
David Heine, *Area Mgr*
Steve Barr, *Vice Pres*
Don Schneider, *Vice Pres*
Pradeep Sethi, *Vice Pres*
◆ **EMP:** 1000
SQ FT: 443,000
SALES (est): 609.2MM **Privately Held**
WEB: www.haggar.com
SIC: 2311 2321 5611 6794 Tailored suits
& formal jackets; suits, men's & boys':
made from purchased materials; tailored
dress & sport coats: men's & boys'; men's
& boys' furnishings; men's & boys' dress
shirts; sport shirts, men's & boys': from
purchased materials; flannel shirts, except work: men's, youths' & boys'; men's
& boys' clothing stores; copyright buying
& licensing; slacks, dress: men's, youths'
& boys'

(G-6201)
HARTUNG GLASS INDUSTRIES
INC
Also Called: Agalite - Dallas
12900 Nicholson Rd (75234-9215)
PHONE.....................972 629-6890
EMP: 9
SALES (corp-wide): 109.3MM **Privately
Held**
WEB: www.hartung-glass.com
SIC: 3211 5039 Flat glass; exterior flat
glass: plate or window
PA: Hartung Glass Industries, Inc.
17830 W Valley Hwy
Tukwila WA 98188
425 656-2626

(G-6202)
HINES CHAUNTE
Also Called: Exceptional Signs
2691 Hearthstone Dr (75234-4757)
PHONE.....................469 583-0985
Chaunte Hines, *Owner*
EMP: 10
SALES (est): 50K **Privately Held**
SIC: 3993 Signs & advertising specialties

(G-6203)
HYDROTEX PARTNERS (PA)
12920 Senlac Dr Ste 190 (75234-9237)
PHONE.....................972 389-8500
John Beasley, *CEO*
Lee Doren, *President*
John Cummins, *Partner*
Bill Dewberry, *Partner*
Dwight Gleades, *Partner*
EMP: 20 EST: 1936
SQ FT: 20,000
SALES (est): 16.7MM **Privately Held**
WEB: www.hydrotexlube.com
SIC: 2992 Oils & greases, blending & com-
pounding; lubricating oils

(G-6204)
JADTIS INDUSTRIES LP
13365 Branch View Ln (75234-5701)
PHONE.....................214 905-9566
Bill Sultzbaugh, *President*
David Haas, *Partner*
▲ **EMP:** 61
SQ FT: 85,000
SALES (est): 2.1MM **Privately Held**
WEB: www.jadtis.com
SIC: 2296 Steel tire cords & tire cord fab-
rics

(G-6205)
KOVACH ENCLOSURE
SYSTEMS LLC
13649 Beta Rd (75244-4511)
PHONE.....................480 926-9292
EMP: 70
SALES (est): 1.6MM
SALES (corp-wide): 66.4MM **Privately
Held**
SIC: 1761 1793 3211 Roofing, siding &
sheet metal work; glass & glazing work;
flat glass
PA: Kovach Enclosure Systems, Llc
3195 W Armstrong Pl
Chandler AZ 85286
480 926-9292

(G-6206)
LORENTE INTERNATIONAL LLC
Also Called: World Class Awards
4435 Simonton Rd (75244-5214)
PHONE.....................877 281-6469
Susan Daproza, *Vice Pres*
Cindy Roberson, *Natl Sales Mgr*
Kevin Caffey, *Office Mgr*
Alfredo Lorente,
Angela Lorente,
◆ **EMP:** 35
SQ FT: 28,000
SALES (est): 4.3MM **Privately Held**
WEB: www.lorente.us
SIC: 3993 2396 Advertising novelties; au-
tomotive & apparel trimmings

(G-6207)
MED COUTURE INC
Also Called: Peaches
1901 Hutton Ct Ste 200 (75234-9032)
PHONE.....................214 231-2500
Barry Rothschild, *President*
Mark Wilcoxson, *Vice Pres*
Justin Lee, *Prdtn Dir*
Alayna Gallant, *Accounts Mgr*
Michael Clements, *Cust Mgr*
◆ **EMP:** 87
SQ FT: 60,000
SALES (est): 22.5MM **Privately Held**
WEB: www.medcouture.com
SIC: 2326 Work uniforms

(G-6208)
NEW OPTIONS INC
Also Called: New Options Sports
1850 Diplomat Dr 100 (75234-9013)
PHONE.....................214 638-6422
John Scott, *President*
Barry Bledsoe, *Vice Pres*
Dan Gibson, *Vice Pres*
Shawn King, *Director*
Rosie Gallegos,
◆ **EMP:** 61
SQ FT: 10,000
SALES (est): 10MM **Privately Held**
WEB: www.newoptionssports.com
SIC: 3842 5999 Orthopedic appliances;
orthopedic & prosthesis applications

(G-6209)
NEWGEN BIOTECH USA INC
12901 Nicholson Rd # 100 (75234-9229)
PHONE.....................972 241-1438
Jim Titus, *President*
EMP: 10
SALES (est): 1.5MM **Privately Held**
WEB: www.newgenbiotech.com
SIC: 2834 Pharmaceutical preparations

(G-6210)
NORTEX REDIMIX LLC (PA)
2010 Valley View Ln (75234-7821)
P.O. Box 542404, Dallas (75354-2404)
PHONE.....................214 681-5200
Zachary Weir, *Mng Member*
EMP: 10
SALES (est): 10.2MM **Privately Held**
SIC: 3273 Ready-mixed concrete

(G-6211)
QORVO INC
Also Called: Qorvo Logistics
4345 Innovation Dr Bldg D (75234)
PHONE.....................336 678-5099
Ralph Knupp, *Vice Pres*
Hans Schwarz, *Vice Pres*
Mark Murphy, *CFO*
Robert Bruggeworth, *Branch Mgr*
Jk Givens, *General Counsel*
EMP: 1000
SALES (corp-wide): 3.2B **Publicly Held**
WEB: www.qorvo.com
SIC: 3674 Semiconductors & related de-
vices
PA: Qorvo, Inc.
7628 Thorndike Rd
Greensboro NC 27409
336 664-1233

(G-6212)
RAZBERI TECHNOLOGIES INC
13755 Hutton Dr Ste 500 (75234-9037)
PHONE.....................469 828-3380
Doug Dickerson, *CEO*
Mig Paredes, *Principal*
David Watts, *Vice Pres*
Kevin Chester, *Opers Mgr*
Joe Mahfouz, *Opers Mgr*
▲ **EMP:** 35
SALES (est): 10.2MM **Privately Held**
WEB: www.razberi.net
SIC: 3699 5065 Security devices; security
control equipment & systems

(G-6213)
SHAMROCK PRECISION USA
LLC
14850 Venture Dr (75234-2426)
PHONE.....................972 241-4226
EMP: 49 EST: 2008
SQ FT: 8,000
SALES (est): 8MM **Privately Held**
WEB: www.shamrockprecision.com
SIC: 3452 Bolts, nuts, rivets & washers

(G-6214)
SKYLINE CABINETRY INC (HQ)
Also Called: Skyline Cabinets
12301 N Stemmons Fwy # 100
(75234-5847)
PHONE.....................972 620-8880
Chunbo Zhang, *President*
EMP: 17
SQ FT: 70,000
SALES (est): 50K **Privately Held**
WEB: www.skylinecabinetry.com
SIC: 2434 Wood kitchen cabinets

(G-6215)
SOUTHERN GLAZERS WINE
AND SP (HQ)
Also Called: Glazers Wholesale Distributors
2001 Diplomat Dr (75234-8919)
P.O. Box 809013, Dallas (75380-9013)
PHONE.....................972 277-2000
Bennett Glazer, *President*
Kyle Miller, *Division Mgr*
Robert M Swartz, *COO*
Alan Greenspan, *Exec VP*
James Campbell, *Vice Pres*
◆ **EMP:** 200 EST: 1909
SQ FT: 12,000

SALES (est): 1.7B
SALES (corp-wide): 12.5B **Privately Held**
WEB: www.southernglazers.com
SIC: 2082 5182 5199 Beer (alcoholic beverage); ale (alcoholic beverage); wine & distilled beverages; general merchandise, non-durable; art goods & supplies
PA: Southern Glazer's Wine And Spirits Of Nebraska, Llc
1600 Nw 163rd St
Miami FL 33169
305 625-4171

(G-6216)
SPECTRA METAL SALES INC
11425 Mathis Ave Ste 406 (75234-9413)
PHONE......................972 556-2564
Steven Moore, *Branch Mgr*
EMP: 94
SALES (corp-wide): 271.2MM **Privately Held**
WEB: www.spectrametals.com
SIC: 3444 Sheet metalwork
PA: Spectra Metal Sales, Inc.
6104 Boat Rock Blvd Sw
Atlanta GA 30336
404 344-4305

(G-6217)
SUPER COLOR DIGITAL LLC
2010 Valley View Ln # 230 (75234-8900)
PHONE......................702 242-6335
EMP: 10
SALES (corp-wide): 32MM **Privately Held**
SIC: 2759 Commercial Printing
PA: Super Color Digital, Llc
16761 Hale Ave
Irvine CA 92606
949 622-0010

(G-6218)
VICKY CAKES PANCAKE MIX LLC
4601 Langland Rd Ste 103 (75244-3953)
PHONE......................469 573-2773
Christian Westbrook,
EMP: 9
SALES (est): 362K **Privately Held**
WEB: www.vickycakesonline.com
SIC: 2045 Pancake mixes, prepared: from purchased flour

(G-6219)
WOMACK MACHINE SUPPLY CO (HQ)
13835 Senlac Dr (75234-8822)
PHONE......................800 569-9800
Mike J Rowlett, *Ch of Bd*
Kevin Kampe, *President*
Robert E Savage, *Corp Secy*
Irby Bennett, *Vice Pres*
Sam Durard, *Vice Pres*
▲ **EMP:** 97 **EST:** 1942
SQ FT: 125,000
SALES (est): 95.1MM **Privately Held**
WEB: www.womackmachine.com
SIC: 3491 3532 5084 3594 Industrial valves; mining machinery; industrial machinery & equipment; fluid power pumps & motors

Farmersville
Collin County

(G-6220)
ADVANCED FIXTURES INC
Also Called: A F I
2655 E Audie Murphy Pkwy (75442-2538)
PHONE......................972 784-8800
Tony Ewing, *President*
Stephanie Hurst, *Vice Pres*
Kelly Delancey, *Project Mgr*
Eva Conley, *Opers Mgr*
Tim Cloud, *Safety Mgr*
▲ **EMP:** 125
SQ FT: 140,000
SALES (est): 25.7MM **Privately Held**
WEB: www.advancedfixtures.com
SIC: 2541 5078 5046 Display fixtures, wood; store fixtures, wood; commercial refrigeration equipment; store fixtures

(G-6221)
AMERICAN ACRYLIC INJECTION INC
419 Welch Dr (75442-3415)
PHONE......................972 784-7759
Kevin Wallace, *President*
Dolly Wallace, *Corp Secy*
Stacy Price, *Natl Sales Mgr*
Alexa Price, *Manager*
▲ **EMP:** 42
SQ FT: 77,000
SALES (est): 6.9MM **Privately Held**
WEB: www.bathtubs.com
SIC: 3088 3544 3561 3594 Tubs (bath, shower & laundry), plastic; industrial molds; pumps & pumping equipment; fluid power motors; plumbing fixtures: enameled iron cast iron or pressed metal; sporting & athletic goods

(G-6222)
EXPRESS FABRICATORS LLC
708 State Highway 78 S (75442-3410)
PHONE......................972 734-3855
Ronnie Welborn, *Owner*
Andrea Rater,
EMP: 10
SALES (est): 1.1MM **Privately Held**
WEB: www.expfab.com
SIC: 3312 3441 Plate, steel; structural shapes & pilings, steel; tubes, steel & iron; building components, structural steel

(G-6223)
GERDAU AMERISTEEL US INC
2411 E Audie Murphy Pkwy (75442-2533)
PHONE......................972 782-7902
EMP: 9 **Privately Held**
WEB: www.gerdau.com
SIC: 3325 Steel foundries
HQ: Gerdau Ameristeel Us Inc.
4221 W Boy Scout Blvd # 600
Tampa FL 33607
813 286-8383

(G-6224)
J & S PLATING AND REPAIR INC
1318 County Road 655 (75442-6006)
P.O. Box 54877, Hurst (76054-4877)
PHONE......................972 784-8718
James Schulte, *President*
Justice Gary, *Vice Pres*
Gary Juastice, *Vice Pres*
EMP: 19
SQ FT: 2,500
SALES (est): 213.1K **Privately Held**
SIC: 3471 Electroplating of metals or formed products

(G-6225)
PM ASSEMBLY LLC
17141 County Road 566 (75442-6799)
PHONE......................972 814-3727
Patrick McGarity, *General Mgr*
Wynda McGarity, *Info Tech Mgr*
Wanda McGarity,
EMP: 10
SALES (est): 750K **Privately Held**
WEB: www.pmassembly.com
SIC: 3672 Printed circuit boards

(G-6226)
UNIVERSAL TRANSFORMER COMPANY
411 Welch Dr (75442-3415)
P.O. Box 472 (75442-0472)
PHONE......................972 784-7700
Mark E Cooper, *President*
Jan Morgan, *Corp Secy*
Christian Cooper, *Vice Pres*
Mark Cooper, *Sales Staff*
EMP: 19
SQ FT: 15,000
SALES (est): 3.3MM **Privately Held**
WEB: www.universal-transformer-co.farmersville.tx.amfibi.company
SIC: 3677 Electronic transformers

Farnsworth
Ochiltree County

(G-6227)
FOSTER TESTING CO INC (PA)
376 S 2 Fm (79033)
P.O. Box 1940, Weatherford OK (73096-1940)
PHONE......................806 435-6876
Roger D Wright, *President*
Eleanor Wright, *Principal*
Whittenberg Verl, *Vice Pres*
Craig Wright, *Vice Pres*
EMP: 15
SQ FT: 3,500
SALES (est): 4.5MM **Privately Held**
SIC: 1389 5169 Chemically treating wells; chemicals, industrial & heavy

Fate
Rockwall County

(G-6228)
OMI CRANE SYSTEMS INC (PA)
1515 E Interstate 30 (75189-8513)
P.O. Box 1719, Rockwall (75087-1719)
PHONE......................972 636-8000
Mike Bunnel, *President*
Eugene E Oard, *President*
James O'Shea, *General Mgr*
Kimberly L Bunnel, *Corp Secy*
Thomas G Codiana, *Vice Pres*
◆ **EMP:** 50
SQ FT: 70,000
SALES (est): 36.8MM **Privately Held**
WEB: www.omicranes.com
SIC: 5084 3565 Cranes, industrial; packaging machinery

Ferris
Ellis County

(G-6229)
ARCOSA AGGREGATES INC (HQ)
401 N Interstate Hwy 45 (75125-1800)
P.O. Box 373 (75125-0373)
PHONE......................972 544-5900
Carl Campbell, *President*
Bret Johnston, *CFO*
Gail M Peck, *Treasurer*
Jared S Richardson, *Admin Sec*
EMP: 50 **EST:** 1998
SQ FT: 4,000
SALES (est): 156.5MM
SALES (corp-wide): 1.7B **Publicly Held**
WEB: www.trinitymaterialsinc.com
SIC: 1442 Construction sand & gravel
PA: Arcosa, Inc.
500 N Akard St Ste 400
Dallas TX 75201
972 942-6500

(G-6230)
ATCO PRODUCTS INC
601 S Interstate Hwy 45 (75125-5101)
P.O. Box 430 (75125-0430)
PHONE......................972 842-8178
Alan Gatlin, *President*
Mike Ferguson, *Vice Pres*
Gilberto Garcia, *Plant Mgr*
Reza Habibi, *QC Mgr*
Andy Gasser, *CFO*
◆ **EMP:** 203
SALES (est): 39.9MM **Privately Held**
WEB: www.atcomail.com
SIC: 3714 Air conditioner parts, motor vehicle
HQ: Transtar Industries Llc
7350 Young Dr
Cleveland OH 44146
440 232-5100

(G-6231)
CAJUN ELECTRIC MOTORS INC
205 N Main St (75125-2009)
P.O. Box 2459, Red Oak (75154-1577)
PHONE......................972 227-9000
Jude Comeaux, *President*

EMP: 10
SALES (est): 1.6MM **Privately Held**
WEB: www.cajunelectricmotors.com
SIC: 7694 Electric motor repair

(G-6232)
SUNRISE WOODS DESIGNS (PA)
410 N Interstate Hwy 45 (75125-1821)
P.O. Box 384 (75125-0384)
PHONE......................972 842-3579
Ed Gatlin, *President*
EMP: 82
SQ FT: 47,000
SALES (est): 26.9MM **Privately Held**
SIC: 2541 Cabinets, except refrigerated: show, display, etc.: wood

Flatonia
Fayette County

(G-6233)
MID TEX MINERALS INC
Barrium Ln (78941)
P.O. Box 389 (78941-0389)
PHONE......................361 865-3530
Frank Shemanski, *President*
EMP: 10
SQ FT: 126,900
SALES (est): 987.5K **Privately Held**
WEB: www.midtexmineralsinc.com
SIC: 1459 Clays, except kaolin & ball; bentonite mining

(G-6234)
SELLERS LEASE SERVICE INC
Also Called: Sellers' Pump & Supply
2033 Fm 609 (78941-5193)
P.O. Box 369 (78941-0369)
PHONE......................361 865-2142
EMP: 15 **EST:** 1968
SALES (est): 1.7MM **Privately Held**
SIC: 1311 7353 1389 Crude petroleum production; oil field equipment, rental or leasing; servicing oil & gas wells

(G-6235)
V & V PRODUCTS INC
Also Called: V & V Sausage
12705 N Hwy 5 (78941)
P.O. Box 238, Smithville (78957-0238)
PHONE......................361 865-3841
Robert Vinklarek, *President*
Donald Vinklarek, *Vice Pres*
EMP: 15
SQ FT: 3,200
SALES (est): 500K **Privately Held**
WEB: www.vandvsausage.com
SIC: 2013 Sausages from purchased meat; smoked meats from purchased meat

Flint
Smith County

(G-6236)
CONINE MANUFACTURING COMPANY
10891 Fm 346 W (75762-8711)
P.O. Box 2188 (75762-2188)
PHONE......................903 894-6150
Greg Conine, *President*
Valli Conine, *Corp Secy*
▼ **EMP:** 9
SQ FT: 10,000
SALES (est): 2.5MM **Privately Held**
WEB: www.castironsovent.com
SIC: 3321 Cast iron pipe & fittings

(G-6237)
FTS INTERNATIONAL INC
19081 State Highway 155 S (75762-4625)
PHONE......................903 590-2440
Elizabeth Kirven, *Branch Mgr*
EMP: 431 **Publicly Held**
WEB: www.ftsi.com
SIC: 1389 Removal of condensate gasoline from field (gathering) lines
PA: Fts International, Inc.
777 Main St Ste 2900
Fort Worth TX 76102

Florence
Williamson County

(G-6238)
CONTINENTAL CUT STONE INC
460 County Road 219 (76527-4302)
P.O. Box 37 (76527-0037)
PHONE....................................254 793-2329
Robert Teel, *President*
Corey Ford, *Vice Pres*
EMP: 42
SQ FT: 10,000
SALES (est): 5.9MM **Privately Held**
WEB: www.continentalcutstone.com
SIC: 3281 Cut stone & stone products

(G-6239)
DIONYSUS GROUP LLLP
Also Called: Vineyard At Florence, The
8711 W Fm 487 (76527)
PHONE....................................512 572-7000
Kambrah Garland, *President*
◆ **EMP:** 15
SALES (est): 2.1MM **Privately Held**
WEB: www.thevineyardatflorence.com
SIC: 2084 6552 Wines; land subdividers & developers, residential

(G-6240)
LITHIC INDUSTRIES INC (PA)
Also Called: Quality Stone Co
3450 Fm 2843 (76527-3922)
P.O. Box 1 (76527-0001)
PHONE....................................254 793-3791
Toll Free:............................888 -
Kirk Coyne,
EMP: 19
SQ FT: 12,000
SALES (est): 3.8MM **Privately Held**
WEB: www.qualitystone.com
SIC: 3281 1411 Stone, quarrying & processing of own stone products; dimension stone

(G-6241)
LUEDERS LIMESTONE LP
Also Called: Lueders Limestone Quarry
3500 Fm 2843 (76527-3952)
PHONE....................................325 228-4370
Dale Higginbotham, *Partner*
Doreta Higginbotham, *Partner*
EMP: 52
SALES (est): 4.9MM **Privately Held**
WEB: www.saladousa.com
SIC: 1411 Limestone, dimension-quarrying

(G-6242)
RLF SALADO QUARRIES LLC
Also Called: Salado Quarry
3500 Fm 2843 (76527-3952)
P.O. Box 1006 (76527-1006)
PHONE....................................254 793-3355
Tom Wood,
Tommy Edwards,
Resource Land Fund II,
Rlf Salado Properies LL,
Shawn Webb,
EMP: 50
SQ FT: 1,200
SALES (est): 9.1MM
SALES (corp-wide): 9.2MM **Privately Held**
WEB: www.saladousa.com
SIC: 1499 Asphalt mining & bituminous stone quarrying
PA: Resource Land Holdings, L.L.C.
619 N Cascade Ave Ste 201
Colorado Springs CO 80903
719 633-1505

(G-6243)
SALADO OPERATIONS LLC
3500 Fm 2843 (76527-3952)
P.O. Box 1006 (76527-1006)
PHONE....................................254 793-3355
Cori White Eagle, *CEO*
Michelle Acosta, *Accountant*
Byron Davis, *Marketing Staff*
EMP: 130
SALES (est): 2MM **Privately Held**
SIC: 1411 Limestone, dimension-quarrying

(G-6244)
TEBO CONCRE FENCE LLC
Also Called: Concretex
11800 N Highway 183 (76527-4456)
PHONE....................................512 219-1018
Jim Bohard,
Len Tesoro,
EMP: 14 **EST:** 2017
SALES (est): 593.6K **Privately Held**
WEB: www.concretex.com
SIC: 3446 Fences, gates, posts & flagpoles

(G-6245)
TEXAS CARVED STONE LP
6621 Hwy 195 (76527-4532)
PHONE....................................254 793-2384
Mary Condon, *Partner*
EMP: 10
SQ FT: 5,625
SALES (est): 1MM **Privately Held**
WEB: www.texascarvedstone.com
SIC: 5039 7336 3272 Construction materials; commercial art & graphic design; stone, cast concrete

Floresville
Wilson County

(G-6246)
CAMINO AGAVE INC (PA)
Also Called: Z S L
314 Us Highway 181 N (78114-3137)
P.O. Box 129 (78114-0129)
PHONE....................................830 393-1051
Darren Kolbe, *President*
Fernando Soto, *Treasurer*
EMP: 250
SQ FT: 10,000
SALES (est): 55MM **Privately Held**
WEB: www.caminoagave.com
SIC: 1389 Lease tanks, oil field: erecting, cleaning & repairing; oil field services

(G-6247)
FAIFER ARLIN D WOODMILL CO
6850 Us Highway 181 N (78114-6253)
PHONE....................................830 216-4189
Arlin D Faifer, *Co-Owner*
Carla Faifer, *Co-Owner*
EMP: 10
SALES (est): 680K **Privately Held**
WEB: www.mesquitefloors.com
SIC: 2431 Millwork

(G-6248)
MISSION CLAY PRODUCTS LLC
8854 County Road 128 (78114-6622)
PHONE....................................830 393-2568
Lewis Bertalotto, *Manager*
EMP: 12
SALES (corp-wide): 158.7MM **Privately Held**
WEB: www.missionclay.com
SIC: 3259 3251 Sewer pipe or fittings, clay; brick & structural clay tile
HQ: Mission Clay Products Llc
23835 Temescal Canyon Rd
Corona CA 92883

(G-6249)
PLANT FABRICATORS INC
6893 Us Highway 181 N (78114-6277)
PHONE....................................830 393-3064
N A Fitzsimon, *President*
Carleen Fitzsimon, *Corp Secy*
Byron Hensch, *Vice Pres*
John Ploch, *Project Mgr*
Patti Foster, *Purchasing*
EMP: 25 **EST:** 1979
SQ FT: 5,000
SALES (est): 7.3MM **Privately Held**
WEB: www.plantfab.com
SIC: 3441 3535 3443 Fabricated structural metal; conveyors & conveying equipment; fabricated plate work (boiler shop)

(G-6250)
SWAT INC
9835 State Highway 97 W (78114-4166)
PHONE....................................409 296-4976
Wayben R Touchet Jr, *CEO*
Reed Touchet, *President*
Damon Touchet, *Vice Pres*
Kristine Touchet, *Admin Sec*
EMP: 30
SQ FT: 4,200
SALES (est): 10.6MM **Privately Held**
WEB: www.swatconstructioninc.com
SIC: 1389 Oil field services

(G-6251)
TEX SUN MANUFACTURING CO
1912 Virginia Ln (78114-6711)
PHONE....................................830 393-5186
EMP: 32 **EST:** 1946
SQ FT: 15,500
SALES (est): 3.2MM **Privately Held**
SIC: 2591 Mfg Drapery Hardware/Blinds

(G-6252)
TEXALOY FOUNDRY COMPANY
710 4th St (78114-1606)
P.O. Box 37 (78114-0037)
PHONE....................................830 393-6679
Jack Rice, *President*
Gary Banse, *Vice Pres*
Matt Stetler, *Purchasing*
Jane Rice Coy, *Treasurer*
Robert Hons, *Manager*
EMP: 37 **EST:** 1929
SQ FT: 9,500
SALES (est): 7.8MM **Privately Held**
WEB: www.texaloy.com
SIC: 3321 Gray iron castings

(G-6253)
TEXANA FEEDERS LTD
3493 Fm 539 (78114-3542)
PHONE....................................830 947-3396
Jason Peeler, *Owner*
Alonzo M Peeler Jr, *General Ptnr*
EMP: 20
SALES (est): 3.6MM **Privately Held**
SIC: 2011 Beef products from beef slaughtered on site

(G-6254)
TRIFECTA OILFIELD SERVICES LLC
Also Called: Trifecta Environmental Svcs
2840 Bus Loop 181 N Ste 1 (78114)
PHONE....................................930 730-4800
James Parham, *Mng Member*
Melba Locke,
EMP: 186
SQ FT: 800
SALES: 20.5MM **Privately Held**
SIC: 1389 Gas field services

(G-6255)
UDELHOVEN INC
1210 Fm 537 (78114-3663)
PHONE....................................210 635-8833
EMP: 75 **EST:** 1997
SALES (est): 252.1K
SALES (corp-wide): 106.8MM **Privately Held**
SIC: 1731 1389 Electrical work; building oil & gas well foundations on site
PA: Harding Holdings Inc
184 E 53rd Ave
Anchorage AK 99518
907 344-1577

(G-6256)
UNIVERSAL TECH
200 County Road 120 (78114-0045)
PHONE....................................832 584-9460
EMP: 14 **EST:** 2018
SALES (est): 2.6MM **Privately Held**
SIC: 3699 Security devices

(G-6257)
WATCO TANKS INC
5877 Fm 539 (78114-3520)
PHONE....................................830 947-0101
James W Watson, *President*
Sandra Watson, *Human Res Mgr*
Jason Holland, *Sales Mgr*
EMP: 35 **EST:** 1966
SALES (est): 9.5MM **Privately Held**
WEB: www.watcotanksinc.com
SIC: 3443 Tanks, lined: metal plate; tanks, standard or custom fabricated: metal plate

(G-6258)
WCN INC
Also Called: Wilson County News
1012 C St (78114-2224)
PHONE....................................830 216-4519
Elaine Kolodziej, *President*
Kristen Weaver, *Vice Pres*
EMP: 25
SQ FT: 2,000
SALES (est): 1MM **Privately Held**
WEB: www.wilsoncountynews.com
SIC: 2711 2752 Commercial printing & newspaper publishing combined; commercial printing, lithographic

Flower Mound
Denton County

(G-6259)
ALECOM TECHNOLOGIES GROUP INC
Also Called: Conti Systems
1001 Spinks Rd Ste 230 (75028-4216)
PHONE....................................972 870-9400
Louis Conti, *President*
Angel Lara, *Warehouse Mgr*
Thomas Eppes, *Opers Staff*
Elissa Conti, *CFO*
Sam Parrish, *Cust Mgr*
EMP: 9
SQ FT: 2,500
SALES (est): 4.4MM **Privately Held**
WEB: www.contisystems.com
SIC: 5045 5131 2759 2679 Computers; labels; labels & seals: printing; tags & labels, paper; labels, cotton: printed; printers, computer

(G-6260)
BERCHTOLD CORPORATION
571 Silveron (75028-4095)
PHONE....................................843 569-6100
Matthew W Weismiller, *President*
Sid Stark, *Vice Pres*
Samuel Gilner, *CFO*
◆ **EMP:** 180 **EST:** 1982
SQ FT: 50,000
SALES (est): 41.9MM
SALES (corp-wide): 14.3B **Publicly Held**
WEB: www.stryker.com
SIC: 3841 Surgical instruments & apparatus
PA: Stryker Corporation
2825 Airview Blvd
Portage MI 49002
269 385-2600

(G-6261)
BOUND TREE MEDICAL LLC
1420 Lkeside Pkwy Ste 105 (75028)
PHONE....................................469 771-4010
Damon Knopps, *Branch Mgr*
EMP: 20
SALES (corp-wide): 5.4B **Privately Held**
WEB: www.boundtree.com
SIC: 3842 First aid, snake bite & burn kits
HQ: Bound Tree Medical, Llc
5000 Tuttle Crossing Blvd
Dublin OH 43016
614 760-5000

(G-6262)
CFS BRANDS LLC (PA)
Also Called: Snap Drape Brands
3304 Druid Way (75028-2926)
PHONE....................................972 466-1030
▼ **EMP:** 50
SALES (est): 8.1MM **Privately Held**
WEB: www.snapdrape.com
SIC: 2392 2391 Tablecloths: made from purchased materials; draperies, plastic & textile: from purchased materials

(G-6263)
CHARLES W WEAVER MFG CO INC
3101 Justin Rd (75028-2430)
PHONE....................................972 539-1537
Timothy A Horner, *CEO*
Rod Person, *President*
Guillermo Taleno, *Vice Pres*
Raul Castro, *Cust Mgr*
Mark Thomas, *Business Dir*

▲ EMP: 300 EST: 1962
SQ FT: 100,000
SALES (est): 37.1MM **Privately Held**
WEB: www.weavermanufacturing.com
SIC: 3499 3443 Novelties & giftware, in-
cluding trophies; fabricated plate work
(boiler shop)

(G-6264)
CT GREGGS AND SONS LLC
(PA)
Also Called: Hightower Company
1400 Harvest Glen Dr (75028-3898)
PHONE..............................972 333-1960
Cory Greggs, *Principal*
EMP: 12 EST: 2010
SALES (est): 1.6MM **Privately Held**
WEB: www.hightowercompany.com
SIC: 3089 Windows, plastic

(G-6265)
ENDIPREV USA INC
1045 Cross Timbers Rd (75028-1371)
PHONE..............................214 897-5740
Andre Pereira, *President*
Vince Botto, *General Mgr*
Rod Elrifay, *Vice Pres*
EMP: 17
SQ FT: 450
SALES (est): 1.2MM
SALES (corp-wide): 39.8K **Privately Held**
WEB: www.endiprev.com
SIC: 3511 Turbines & turbine generator set
units, complete
HQ: Endiprev, S.A.
Rua AntOnio Nicolau D'almeida, 45
4.10
Porto 4100-
231 927-035

(G-6266)
GENERAL ALUMINUM CO
TEXAS LP (HQ)
1900 Lakeside Pkwy (75028-4078)
P.O. Box 819022, Dallas (75381-9022)
PHONE..............................972 242-5271
Dean P Guerin, *Ch of Bd*
Chris Rix, *President*
John Russell, *COO*
Mark Swoverland, *CFO*
EMP: 200
SQ FT: 233,000
SALES (est): 72MM
SALES (corp-wide): 765.7MM **Privately
Held**
SIC: 3442 5031 Window & door frames;
casements, aluminum; metal doors, sash
& trim
PA: Mi Windows And Doors, Llc
650 W Market St
Gratz PA 17030
717 365-3300

(G-6267)
GRAPHIC IMAGE INC
601 Silveron Ste 200 (75028-4030)
P.O. Box 271067 (75027-1067)
PHONE..............................563 285-5214
Warren Ivie, *President*
Sharon Kay Ivie, *Corp Secy*
Gary Long, *CFO*
◆ EMP: 25
SALES: 5.7MM
SALES (corp-wide): 3.9B **Publicly Held**
SIC: 2731 2791 2789 2752 Book publish-
ing; typesetting; bookbinding & related
work; commercial printing, lithographic
PA: Quad/Graphics Inc.
N61w23044 Harrys Way
Sussex WI 53089
414 566-6000

(G-6268)
INTELLICENTRICS INC (PA)
Also Called: Reptrax
1420 Lakeside Pkwy # 110 (75028-4035)
PHONE..............................214 222-7484
Michael Sheehan, *President*
Eli Spirer, *Exec VP*
Jason McGee, *Production*
Charles Christopherson, *CFO*
Peggy Cowart, *Cust Mgr*
EMP: 43
SALES (est): 6.8MM **Privately Held**
WEB: www.intellicentrics.com
SIC: 7372 Prepackaged software

(G-6269)
JC MILLWORK INC
501 Lakeside Pkwy Ste 150 (75028-4073)
PHONE..............................469 702-2570
Jim Copp, *President*
Billy Palmertree, *Vice Pres*
Bobby Palmertree, *Production*
Beth Lopez, *Purch Mgr*
EMP: 125
SQ FT: 20,000
SALES: 14.2MM **Privately Held**
WEB: www.jcmillwork.com
SIC: 2431 Millwork

(G-6270)
MANNATECH INCORPORATED
(PA)
1410 Lkeside Pkwy Ste 200 (75028)
PHONE..............................972 471-7400
J Stanley Fredrick, *Ch of Bd*
Robert A Toth, *Vice Ch Bd*
Alfredo Bala, *President*
Christopher J Simons, *President*
Curt Craig, *Vice Pres*
EMP: 154
SQ FT: 52,992
SALES: 157.7MM **Publicly Held**
WEB: www.mannatechscience.org
SIC: 2833 Medicinals & botanicals

(G-6271)
MAPSCO INC
2521 Lakeshore Dr (75028-7549)
PHONE..............................214 476-5480
Paul E Babb, *Principal*
EMP: 53
SALES (est): 1.9MM
SALES (corp-wide): 148.2MM **Privately
Held**
SIC: 2741 Maps: publishing & printing
HQ: Kappa Map Group, Llc
6198 Butler Pike
Blue Bell PA 19422

(G-6272)
MOHAWK INDUSTRIES INC
100 Enterprise Dr Ste 200 (75028-4069)
P.O. Box 12069, Calhoun GA (30703-7002)
PHONE..............................972 874-5820
EMP: 15 **Publicly Held**
WEB: www.mohawkind.com
SIC: 2273 Finishers of tufted carpets &
rugs
PA: Mohawk Industries, Inc.
160 S Industrial Blvd
Calhoun GA 30701

(G-6273)
NATIONAL ELEVATOR
COMPANY INC
6000 Pine Valley Dr (75022-6510)
PHONE..............................925 484-5050
EMP: 26 EST: 1968
SQ FT: 15,000
SALES (est): 3.7MM **Privately Held**
SIC: 3534 7699 Elevators & equipment;
elevators: inspection, service & repair

(G-6274)
NATUS MEDICAL
INCORPORATED
Also Called: Natus Peloton
2670 Firewheel Dr Ste B (75028-7596)
PHONE..............................650 802-0400
James Hawkins, *Branch Mgr*
EMP: 20
SALES (corp-wide): 495.1MM **Publicly
Held**
WEB: www.natus.com
SIC: 3845 Electromedical equipment
PA: Natus Medical Incorporated
6701 Koll Center Pkwy # 12
Pleasanton CA 94566
925 223-6700

(G-6275)
NIAGARA CONSERVATION
CORP (PA)
1200 Lkeside Pkwy Ste 450 (75028)
PHONE..............................817 391-0800
William Cutler, *President*
Carl Wehmeyer, *Exec VP*
Kyle Cutler, *Vice Pres*
Kevin Wilham, *Vice Pres*
Julian Noriega, *Warehouse Mgr*

▲ EMP: 40
SALES (est): 13.4MM **Privately Held**
WEB: www.niagaraconservation.com
SIC: 3088 Toilet fixtures, plastic

(G-6276)
PREMIER MANUFACTURING LP
3151 Justin Rd (75028-2430)
PHONE..............................972 355-3285
Timothy A Horner, *General Ptnr*
Philip Bell, *Purchasing*
Karen Oaks, *Manager*
▲ EMP: 20
SQ FT: 65,580
SALES (est): 4.2MM **Privately Held**
WEB: www.premfg.com
SIC: 3961 3911 Costume jewelry; jewelry,
precious metal

(G-6277)
PROTOM INTERNATIONAL INC
(PA)
610 Parker Sq (75028-7427)
PHONE..............................972 410-3551
Stephen L Spotts, *CEO*
Thomas Carman, *Senior VP*
Nancy E Corbett, *Senior VP*
Nancy Corbett, *Senior VP*
Michael A Williams, *Senior VP*
EMP: 65
SALES (est): 10.7MM **Privately Held**
WEB: www.protominternational.com
SIC: 3844 Beta-ray irradiation equipment

(G-6278)
REEF PROCESS SYSTEMS LLC
(PA)
2604 Long Prairie Rd # 300 (75022-4839)
PHONE..............................972 874-9300
Danny Griffin,
Andrew Avila Jr,
EMP: 16 EST: 2013
SALES (est): 2.5MM **Privately Held**
WEB: www.quadcomply.com
SIC: 3599 Gasoline filters, internal com-
bustion engine, except auto

(G-6279)
RUBY RED PAINT INC
Also Called: Lk252
5312 Meadow Chase Ln (75028-1968)
PHONE..............................972 221-8665
▲ EMP: 12 EST: 1996
SALES (est): 2MM **Privately Held**
WEB: www.rubyredpaint.com
SIC: 3944 Paint sets, children's

(G-6280)
SEALANT SOLUTION INC
4809 Neptune Ct (75022-5473)
PHONE..............................214 886-6688
Richard Alan Davis, *President*
Dominic Adams, *Project Mgr*
EMP: 13
SALES (est): 2.6MM **Privately Held**
WEB: www.sealantsolution.com
SIC: 2891 Sealants

(G-6281)
SIGNATURE SYSTEMS GROUP
LLC (HQ)
Also Called: American Turf & Carpet
1201 Lkeside Pkwy Ste 150 (75028)
PHONE..............................972 684-5736
Pradeep Saha, *CEO*
Jason Frew, *Vice Pres*
Jeff Condino, *VP Opers*
David Egbert, *CFO*
Marnie Knauer, *Accounting Mgr*
◆ EMP: 30
SQ FT: 32,000
SALES (est): 48.4MM
SALES (corp-wide): 71.2MM **Privately
Held**
WEB: www.signaturecorp.com
SIC: 3996 1752 Hard surface floor cover-
ings; floor laying & floor work
PA: Center Rock Capital Partners, Lp
8725 W Higgins Rd
Chicago IL 60631
312 635-8075

(G-6282)
SPEARS MANUFACTURING CO
1000 Lakeside Pkwy (75028-4047)
PHONE..............................469 528-3000
Wayne Spears, *President*
Dennis Littleford, *Controller*
EMP: 30
SALES (corp-wide): 1.3B **Privately Held**
WEB: www.spearsmfg.com
SIC: 3089 Plastic containers, except foam
PA: Spears Manufacturing Co.
15853 Olden St
Sylmar CA 91342
818 364-1611

(G-6283)
STRYKER COMMUNICATIONS
INC (HQ)
571 Silveron (75028-4095)
PHONE..............................972 410-7000
William Enquist, *President*
Wanda Diaz, *Project Mgr*
Orlando Vega, *Buyer*
Nathan Croutch, *Purchasing*
Glorianne Gonzalez, *Research*
▲ EMP: 148
SALES (est): 26.5MM
SALES (corp-wide): 14.3B **Publicly Held**
WEB: www.stryker.com
SIC: 3841 Surgical & medical instruments
PA: Stryker Corporation
2825 Airview Blvd
Portage MI 49002
269 385-2600

(G-6284)
STURROCK & ROBSON USA
SVCS INC
Also Called: Sturrock and Robson Mfg
1420 Lkeside Pkwy Ste 109 (75028)
PHONE..............................281 907-8928
Jeff Shorter, *CEO*
Leon Wetherford, *President*
Bryan Kenski, *CFO*
EMP: 10 EST: 2015
SQ FT: 3,000
SALES (est): 1.4MM
SALES (corp-wide): 177.9K **Privately
Held**
WEB: www.sturrockandrobson.com
SIC: 3491 Industrial valves
HQ: Sturrock And Robson (Uk) Limited
4 Fitzhardinge Street
London W1H 6
207 034-4070

(G-6285)
SUSTAIN ABILITY SOLUTIONS
INC
1200 Lkeside Pkwy Ste 425 (75028)
PHONE..............................888 657-7582
EMP: 11
SALES (est): 1.1MM **Privately Held**
WEB: www.sasconserve.com
SIC: 3088 Plastics plumbing fixtures

(G-6286)
TDI LLC
4816 Pack Saddle Way (75028-3125)
PHONE..............................972 877-5780
Tony Dean, *Executive*
EMP: 35
SALES (est): 4.8MM **Privately Held**
WEB: www.tdismarttechnologies.com
SIC: 3089 Cases, plastic

(G-6287)
TEASDALE FOODS INC (PA)
Also Called: Teasdale Latin Foods
3041 Churchill Dr Ste 100 (75022-2733)
P.O. Box 814, Atwater CA (95301-0814)
PHONE..............................209 358-5616
Chris Kiser, *CEO*
Jerry Cook, *Exec VP*
Marco Casillas, *Vice Pres*
Hoerning Corey, *Vice Pres*
Mike Knuth, *Vice Pres*
▼ EMP: 246
SQ FT: 250,000

SALES (est): 380.6MM **Privately Held**
WEB: www.teasdalelatinfoods.com
SIC: 2032 2034 Beans, baked without meat: packaged in cans, jars, etc.; chili with or without meat: packaged in cans, jars, etc.; Mexican foods: packaged in cans, jars, etc.; dehydrated fruits, vegetables, soups

(G-6288)
TEASDALE FOODS INC
Also Called: Hoopeston Foods
3041 Churchill Dr Ste 100 (75022-2733)
PHONE..................................952 854-0903
Corey Hoerning, *Vice Pres*
EMP: 120
SALES (corp-wide): 380.6MM **Privately Held**
WEB: www.teasdalelatinfoods.com
SIC: 2099 Food preparations
PA: Teasdale Foods, Inc.
3041 Churchill Dr Ste 100
Flower Mound TX 75022
209 358-5616

(G-6289)
TITAN CORRUGATED INC
801 Lakeside Pkwy (75028-4043)
PHONE..................................214 513-2691
Jon Reneau, *President*
Taylor Leggett, *President*
Jenny Reneau, *Vice Pres*
Bonnie Randall, *CFO*
EMP: 22
SQ FT: 64,000
SALES (est): 9.7MM **Privately Held**
WEB: www.titancorrugated.com
SIC: 2653 Boxes, corrugated: made from purchased materials

(G-6290)
TRAX HOLDINGS INC
Also Called: Fleet Trax
3051 Churchill Dr Ste 116 (75022-5900)
P.O. Box 270186 (75027-0186)
PHONE..................................855 999-7828
Scott A McCurdy, *President*
EMP: 15
SALES (est): 2MM
SALES (corp-wide): 10.8MM **Privately Held**
WEB: www.fleettrax.net
SIC: 7372 Prepackaged software
PA: Gpstrackit Holdings, Llc
1080 Holcomb Bridge Rd # 350
Roswell GA 30076
951 296-1316

(G-6291)
UNIVERSAL DISPLAY AND FIX CO
1650 Lakeside Pkwy # 200 (75028-4093)
PHONE..................................972 221-5157
Fransico D De Jesus, *CEO*
EMP: 250
SALES (corp-wide): 110.7MM **Privately Held**
WEB: www.udfc.com
SIC: 2542 3993 3496 Partitions & fixtures, except wood; signs & advertising specialties; miscellaneous fabricated wire products
PA: Universal Display And Fixture Company
726 E Hwy 121
Lewisville TX 75057
972 434-8067

Floydada
Floyd County

(G-6292)
DON HARDY RACE CARS INC
Also Called: Hardy Don Fuel Effcent Eng Svc
202 W Missouri St (79235-2713)
PHONE..................................806 983-3774
Donald D Hardy, *President*
▲ EMP: 10
SQ FT: 6,000
SALES (est): 2MM **Privately Held**
WEB: www.donhardyracecars.com
SIC: 3714 Motor vehicle parts & accessories

(G-6293)
FLOYD COUNTY HESPERIAN-BEACON
Also Called: Lockney Beacon
201 W California St Ste A (79235-2700)
PHONE..................................888 400-1083
Roland K Towery, *President*
Chris Blackburn, *President*
EMP: 11 EST: 1962
SALES (est): 406K **Privately Held**
WEB: www.hesperianbecononline.com
SIC: 2711 5994 Newspapers: publishing only, not printed on site; news dealers & newsstands

Forest Hill
Tarrant County

(G-6294)
3024 EAST SEMINARY GROUP LLC
Also Called: Chief Adhesive
3024 E Seminary Dr (76119-5646)
PHONE..................................817 534-6755
Leonard Goode, *Mng Member*
EMP: 12
SQ FT: 36,653
SALES (est): 2.4MM **Privately Held**
WEB: www.reynoldsglue.com
SIC: 3821 Melting point apparatus, laboratory

(G-6295)
CLS METAL FABRICATION LLC
2915 Horton Rd (76119-5635)
P.O. Box 10745, Fort Worth (76114-0745)
PHONE..................................817 994-0891
Shane Wheat,
Shirley Wheat,
EMP: 15
SQ FT: 1,000
SALES (est): 1.6MM **Privately Held**
SIC: 3441 Fabricated structural metal

(G-6296)
GLOBAL SIGNS INC
5105 E California Pkwy (76119-7606)
PHONE..................................817 834-1123
Rick Robertson, *President*
EMP: 16
SALES (est): 2.8MM **Privately Held**
WEB: www.globalsignsinc.com
SIC: 3993 Electric signs

(G-6297)
INPRO FABRICATION LTD
Also Called: Buck's Awning
5111 E California Pkwy (76119-7606)
P.O. Box 11878, Fort Worth (76110-0878)
PHONE..................................817 926-5050
David Meyer, *Partner*
EMP: 26
SALES (est): 4.5MM **Privately Held**
WEB: www.inproltd.com
SIC: 2394 Canvas awnings & canopies

(G-6298)
LONESTAR LANDSCAPE DFW LLC
6807 Anglin Dr (76140-1511)
PHONE..................................817 863-5609
Kevin Marshall, *Mng Member*
EMP: 12
SQ FT: 7,500
SALES (est): 857.4K **Privately Held**
WEB: www.lonestarlandscape.com
SIC: 0782 3271 0181 Landscape contractors; blocks, concrete: landscape or retaining wall; mats, preseeded: soil erosion, growing of

Forestburg
Montague County

(G-6299)
ADVANCED INDUSTRIAL METAL FABR
1541 Merritt Rd (76239-3378)
PHONE..................................940 964-2691
Jill A Roark, *Principal*

Ronnie Roark, *Vice Pres*
EMP: 11
SALES (est): 1.9MM **Privately Held**
SIC: 3499 Fabricated metal products

(G-6300)
RIFE ENERGY OPERATING INC
167 County Road 345 (76239-2143)
PHONE..................................940 964-2822
Trey Rife, *Branch Mgr*
EMP: 9
SALES (corp-wide): 781.5K **Privately Held**
WEB: www.rifeenergyoperating.com
SIC: 1382 Oil & gas exploration services
PA: Rife Energy Operating Incorporated
4775 North Fwy 200
Fort Worth TX 76106
817 732-8739

Forney
Kaufman County

(G-6301)
ABOX PAPERBOARD COMPANY (PA)
Also Called: Abox Packaging
12950 Fm 1641 (75126-7606)
P.O. Box 2639 (75126-2639)
PHONE..................................972 932-9800
H Keith Thompson, *President*
John Kirkpatrick, *General Mgr*
Sara Sommer, *Exec VP*
Jeffrey Byers, *Human Resources*
Barbara Norman, *Human Resources*
EMP: 76 EST: 1976
SQ FT: 110,000
SALES (est): 16.5MM **Privately Held**
WEB: www.aboxpackaging.com
SIC: 2652 2657 Setup paperboard boxes; folding paperboard boxes

(G-6302)
ALL STAR WHEEL REPAIR LLC
220 Industrial Dr (75126-8508)
P.O. Box 3114 (75126-3114)
PHONE..................................972 564-1610
Travis Rile,
EMP: 18
SALES (est): 3MM **Privately Held**
SIC: 3714 Wheels, motor vehicle

(G-6303)
CANDEO INTERACTIVE LLC
Also Called: 12 Adaptive Marketing
408 S Center St (75126-9309)
PHONE..................................214 394-8499
Robert Portillo,
EMP: 15
SALES (est): 500K **Privately Held**
WEB: www.12amagency.com
SIC: 7371 8742 7372 8732 Computer software development & applications; software programming applications; computer software writing services; marketing consulting services; application computer software; market analysis or research

(G-6304)
CARDINAL TOOL CO
2 Mustang Cir (75126-9135)
PHONE..................................972 564-2314
Charles D Weber, *President*
EMP: 15 EST: 1965
SQ FT: 22,000
SALES (est): 3.1MM **Privately Held**
WEB: www.cardinaltoolco.com
SIC: 3444 Sheet metalwork

(G-6305)
CLASSIC INDUSTRIES LP
13020 Fm 1641 (75126-7607)
P.O. Box 1917 (75126-1917)
PHONE..................................972 564-2192
Sandra Wilson, *Partner*
Rick Wilson, *General Ptnr*
John Clement, *Vice Pres*
Philip Wilson, *Project Mgr*
◆ EMP: 50
SQ FT: 200,000

SALES (est): 9.1MM **Privately Held**
WEB: www.classicusa.com
SIC: 1542 8712 3442 Commercial & office building, new construction; commercial & office buildings, renovation & repair; architectural services; moldings & trim, except automobile: metal

(G-6306)
CROWNED PLUS ENTERPRISES LLC
1812 Chadwick Ln (75126-2399)
PHONE..................................469 585-9658
Shanikka Caraway,
EMP: 11
SALES (est): 306.5K **Privately Held**
SIC: 3999 Hair & hair-based products

(G-6307)
DDR MANUFACTURING INC
12034 S Profit Row (75126-7036)
PHONE..................................469 728-7242
Darrel Ralph, *President*
Sharon Ralph, *Vice Pres*
▼ EMP: 9
SQ FT: 2,000
SALES (est): 1MM **Privately Held**
WEB: www.darrelralph.com
SIC: 3421 3484 Knife blades & blanks; guns (firearms) or gun parts, 30 mm. & below

(G-6308)
G N P INC SHEET METAL
Also Called: G N P Inc Sheet Metal
202 Fm 1641 (75126-4015)
PHONE..................................972 564-0450
Charles Partney, *President*
EMP: 25
SQ FT: 4,000
SALES (est): 3MM **Privately Held**
WEB: www.gnpsheetmetal.com
SIC: 1761 3446 3444 Sheet metalwork; architectural metalwork; sheet metalwork

(G-6309)
INFRAMARK LLC
9550 Helms Trl Ste 800 (75126-7735)
PHONE..................................281 579-4500
EMP: 16
SALES (corp-wide): 73.2MM **Privately Held**
WEB: www.inframark.com
SIC: 8748 3589 Environmental consultant; water treatment equipment, industrial
PA: Inframark, Llc
220 Gibraltar Rd Ste 200
Horsham PA 19044
215 646-9201

(G-6310)
INTELLIGENT SURVEILLANCE CORP
122 Industrial Dr (75126-8571)
P.O. Box 12168, College Station (77842-2168)
PHONE..................................979 323-6900
Galen Green, *Treasurer*
EMP: 27
SALES (est): 6MM **Privately Held**
WEB: www.intelligentsurveillancecorp.com
SIC: 3699 Security devices

(G-6311)
INWOOD FURNITURE MANUFACTURING
11821 N Profit Row (75126-7061)
P.O. Box 639 (75126-0639)
PHONE..................................972 564-4444
Ramin Gilani, *President*
Valerie Gilani, *Vice Pres*
EMP: 100
SQ FT: 70,000
SALES (est): 9.6MM **Privately Held**
WEB: www.inwoodfurniture.net
SIC: 2511 5021 Wood household furniture; furniture

(G-6312)
LINDEN STEEL LP
12418 Fm 1641 (75126-7602)
PHONE..................................972 285-0200
Brian Anderson, *President*
Bonnie Anderson, *Vice Pres*
EMP: 60

SALES (est): 4MM **Privately Held**
WEB: www.lindensteellp.com
SIC: 3315 Steel wire & related products

(G-6313)
MAR-TEK INDUSTRIES INC
301 Industrial Dr (75126-8500)
P.O. Box 29555, Dallas (75229-0555)
PHONE.....................214 350-9401
Takeitha Thorn, *President*
Thomas Lundberg, *Vice Pres*
Kiki Thorn, *Vice Pres*
Josh Thorn, *Marketing Staff*
▲ **EMP:** 9
SALES (est): 1.3MM **Privately Held**
WEB: www.mar-tekindustries.com
SIC: 2891 Adhesives

(G-6314)
SMURFIT KAPPA NORTH AMER LLC
Also Called: Smurfit Kappa Forney
855 E Us Highway 80 (75126-8614)
P.O. Box 847 (75126-0847)
PHONE.....................214 515-6400
Dave Nelson, *Vice Pres*
Bryan Norwood, *Branch Mgr*
EMP: 300 **Privately Held**
WEB: www.smurfitkappa.com
SIC: 2653 2671 2657 Boxes, corrugated: made from purchased materials; packaging paper & plastics film, coated & laminated; folding paperboard boxes
HQ: Smurfit Kappa North America Llc
125 E John Carpenter Fwy # 925
Irving TX 75062
800 306-8326

(G-6315)
TEXAS LAMP MANUFACTURERS INC
Also Called: Gallery Designs
505 E Us Highway 80 (75126-8671)
PHONE.....................972 564-5267
F J Pinnell, *Ch of Bd*
Julie Pinnell, *Vice Pres*
Tom Pinnell, *Vice Pres*
Jerry V Pinnell, *Treasurer*
▲ **EMP:** 40
SQ FT: 47,000
SALES (est): 5MM **Privately Held**
WEB: www.txlampparts.net
SIC: 3999 3231 3641 Shades, lamp or candle; decorated glassware: chipped, engraved, etched, etc.; electric lamps

(G-6316)
VRT INVESTMENTS INC
Also Called: Sunnyvale Fence
10600 W Us Highway 80 (75126-7046)
PHONE.....................972 226-1981
Terry Shupp, *President*
Betty Shupp, *Admin Sec*
EMP: 25 **EST:** 1990
SQ FT: 2,200
SALES (est): 3.4MM **Privately Held**
WEB: www.sunnyvalefence.com
SIC: 2499 3315 Fencing, wood; chain link fencing

Fort Bliss
El Paso County

(G-6317)
LOCKHEED MARTIN CORPORATION
Abernathy Rd Bldg 5808 (79916)
P.O. Box 3504, Sunnyvale CA (94088-3504)
PHONE.....................915 568-6264
Ivan Hall, *Engineer*
Kunisch Jack, *Engineer*
Dave Hulett, *Manager*
Terri Hinderman, *Executive Asst*
EMP: 15 **Publicly Held**
WEB: www.lockheedmartin.com
SIC: 3812 Search & navigation equipment
PA: Lockheed Martin Corporation
6801 Rockledge Dr
Bethesda MD 20817

Fort Davis
Jeff Davis County

(G-6318)
ARCHITECTURAL STAINED GLASS
506 Limpia Canyon Trl (79734-5016)
P.O. Box 1126 (79734-1126)
PHONE.....................432 426-3311
Jeff G Smith, *President*
Pam S Edwards, *Treasurer*
EMP: 10
SQ FT: 1,500
SALES (est): 250K **Privately Held**
WEB: www.archstglassinc.com
SIC: 3231 Products of purchased glass

(G-6319)
SOLAMOTOR OF TEXAS
Hc 74 Box 117 (79734-5003)
PHONE.....................432 426-3246
Jeffrey W Fisher, *Partner*
Charles W McAnally, *Partner*
EMP: 10
SALES (est): 1.1MM **Privately Held**
WEB: www.solamotor.com
SIC: 3561 Pumps, domestic: water or sump

(G-6320)
VILLAGE FARMS LP
Also Called: Ft. Davis Division
State Highway 17 S (79734)
P.O. Box 1309 (79734-1309)
PHONE.....................432 426-2301
Carlos Flores, *Purch Mgr*
Jan Korteland, *Branch Mgr*
Jose Cruz, *Manager*
EMP: 200
SALES (corp-wide): 144.5MM **Privately Held**
WEB: www.villagefarms.com
SIC: 0181 2879 Flowers: grown under cover (e.g. greenhouse production); pesticides, agricultural or household
HQ: Village Farms, L.P.
90 Colonial Center Pkwy # 100
Lake Mary FL 32746

Fort Hancock
Hudspeth County

(G-6321)
GSC CHIPOTLE TEXAS LTD
101 Port Of Entry Rd (79839)
P.O. Box 250 (79839-0250)
PHONE.....................915 769-0097
Gale Carr, *Partner*
Kenneth Carr, *Partner*
EMP: 20
SQ FT: 46,000
SALES (est): 2.2MM **Privately Held**
WEB: www.chipotletexas.com
SIC: 2099 Chili pepper or powder

Fort Hood
Bell County

(G-6322)
FORT HOOD SPORTSMENS CENTER
Bldg 1937 (76544)
PHONE.....................254 532-4552
Judy Johnson, *Manager*
EMP: 13
SALES (est): 524K **Privately Held**
SIC: 3949 Hunting equipment

(G-6323)
GENERAL DYNAMICS MISSION
Terminal Ave Bldg 3820 (76544)
PHONE.....................254 532-2927
Bobby Dunn, *Manager*
Don Bechtel, *Technician*
EMP: 42
SALES (corp-wide): 37.9B **Publicly Held**
WEB: www.gdmissionsystems.com
SIC: 3663 Radio & TV communications equipment

HQ: General Dynamics Mission Systems, Inc.
12450 Fair Lakes Cir
Fairfax VA 22033
877 449-0600

(G-6324)
GENERAL DYNMICS LAND SYSTEMS I
Also Called: Customer Service & Support Co
Logistics Ln Bldg 88037 (76544)
PHONE.....................586 825-7242
Bob Rathbun, *Supervisor*
EMP: 23
SALES (corp-wide): 37.9B **Publicly Held**
WEB: www.gdls.com
SIC: 3795 Tanks & tank components
HQ: General Dynamics Land Systems Inc.
38500 Mound Rd
Sterling Heights MI 48310
586 825-4000

(G-6325)
LOCKHEED MARTIN CORPORATION
62nd Nrth Ave Bldg 26011 (76544)
PHONE.....................254 285-5503
Rosario Martinez, *Manager*
Vassar Holamon, *Technician*
EMP: 20 **Publicly Held**
WEB: www.lockheedmartin.com
SIC: 3812 Search & navigation equipment
PA: Lockheed Martin Corporation
6801 Rockledge Dr
Bethesda MD 20817

Fort Stockton
Pecos County

(G-6326)
ACE SAND AND GRAVEL
8818 N 1053 (79735)
P.O. Box 1146 (79735-1146)
PHONE.....................432 290-1205
Yvonne Aterrera, *Partner*
EMP: 10
SALES (est): 360.4K **Privately Held**
SIC: 1442 Construction sand & gravel

(G-6327)
APACHE INSTRUMENTATIONS & GAS (PA)
Also Called: Apache Instrmntation Gen Cnstr
4501 N State Highway 18 (79735-9493)
P.O. Box 355 (79735-0355)
PHONE.....................432 336-7755
Ramondo P Franco, *Owner*
R P Franco, *Owner*
EMP: 27
SQ FT: 5,000
SALES (est): 7.8MM **Privately Held**
SIC: 1382 5082 7692 Oil & gas exploration services; oil field equipment; welding repair

(G-6328)
ARCHROCK INC
3105 W 9th St (79735-4510)
PHONE.....................432 336-8632
Randy Archer, *Manager*
EMP: 16 **Publicly Held**
WEB: www.archrock.com
SIC: 1389 4225 Gas compressing (natural gas) at the fields; general warehousing
PA: Archrock, Inc.
9807 Katy Fwy Ste 100
Houston TX 77024

(G-6329)
D & L WELL SERVICE INC
4451 N State Highway 18 (79735-9463)
P.O. Box 254 (79735-0254)
PHONE.....................432 336-8101
Gene A Dunn, *President*
Jamie Dunn, *Corp Secy*
EMP: 15 **EST:** 1980
SQ FT: 1,524
SALES (est): 1.4MM **Privately Held**
SIC: 1389 1382 Cleaning wells; lease tanks, oil field: erecting, cleaning & repairing; servicing oil & gas wells; oil & gas exploration services

(G-6330)
TRIPLE R WELDING LLC
2215 W 9th St (79735-4763)
PHONE.....................432 336-5289
Andy Rivera, *Mng Member*
Belinda Rivera, *Mng Member*
Michael Rivera,
EMP: 50
SQ FT: 2,000
SALES (est): 8.6MM **Privately Held**
WEB: www.triplerweldingllc.com
SIC: 7353 1389 Heavy construction equipment rental; oil field services

(G-6331)
WESTERN GAS RESOURCES INC
S On Fm 2023 (79735)
P.O. Box 1566 (79735-1566)
PHONE.....................432 395-2448
James Gonzales, *Manager*
EMP: 25
SALES (corp-wide): 21.2B **Publicly Held**
WEB: www.oxy.com
SIC: 4923 2911 1321 Gas transmission & distribution; petroleum refining; natural gas liquids
HQ: Western Gas Resources, Inc.
1099 18th St
Denver CO 80202

(G-6332)
WESTERN GAS RESOURCES INC
Also Called: Gomez Plant
3368310 Gomez Rd (79735)
P.O. Box 1566 (79735-1566)
PHONE.....................432 395-2973
Rick Young, *Manager*
EMP: 15
SALES (corp-wide): 21.2B **Publicly Held**
WEB: www.oxy.com
SIC: 1382 Oil & gas exploration services
HQ: Western Gas Resources, Inc.
1099 18th St
Denver CO 80202

Fort Worth
Tarrant County

(G-6333)
1ST ORIGINAL TEXAS CHILI INC
3313 N Jones St (76164-4339)
P.O. Box 4281 (76164-0281)
PHONE.....................817 626-0983
Danny Owens, *President*
Deborah Owens, *Corp Secy*
Garret Flynt, *Vice Pres*
EMP: 9 **EST:** 1952
SQ FT: 7,000
SALES (est): 1.3MM **Privately Held**
WEB: www.texaschili.com
SIC: 2038 Ethnic foods, frozen

(G-6334)
A & C CABINET CO
5681 Kelly Rd (76126-5500)
P.O. Box 26766 (76126-0766)
PHONE.....................817 244-4303
Brent Hickey, *President*
Glen McKittrick, *Principal*
Bill Hickey, *Vice Pres*
Brett Neill, *Vice Pres*
EMP: 25
SQ FT: 5,000
SALES (est): 2.9MM **Privately Held**
SIC: 2434 Wood kitchen cabinets

(G-6335)
A & S FABRICATION INC
1701 Brennan Ave (76106-8315)
PHONE.....................817 626-7720
Stephen Alexander, *President*
EMP: 19 **EST:** 2000
SQ FT: 12,000
SALES (est): 3.3MM **Privately Held**
WEB: www.asfabrication.com
SIC: 3441 Fabricated structural metal

(G-6336)
A B C FLAG ACQUISITION CORP
Also Called: A B C Flag Manufacturing
212 S Main St (76104-1223)
PHONE..........................817 335-2548
EMP: 20 EST: 1960
SQ FT: 15,000
SALES (est): 2.2MM **Privately Held**
WEB: www.lonestarbannersandflags.com
SIC: 2399 5131 5999 Flags, fabric; pennants; banners, made from fabric; flags & banners; flags; banners

(G-6337)
A M FABRICATION INC
Also Called: Ctj Energy Solutions
8932 South Fwy (76140-4943)
PHONE..........................817 345-7600
Micah D Martin, President
Anna V Martin, Admin Sec
EMP: 25 EST: 2011
SALES (est): 8.7MM **Privately Held**
WEB: www.amfabtx.com
SIC: 3446 3443 Stairs, fire escapes, balconies, railings & ladders; tanks, standard or custom fabricated: metal plate

(G-6338)
A&W ENERGY INC
1301 Forum Way S (76140-5013)
PHONE..........................817 704-7346
Benjamin M Allen, Director
Charles M Allen, Director
Samuel M Allen, Director
Michie White, Director
EMP: 12
SALES (est): 2.6MM **Privately Held**
WEB: www.aw.energy
SIC: 3533 Oil & gas field machinery

(G-6339)
AARON ARCHITECTURAL IRON LLC
Also Called: Aaron Iron Parts
107 W Barron Ave (76140-3801)
PHONE..........................817 731-9281
Belinda Hackleman,
Todd Brock,
EMP: 43 EST: 2005
SQ FT: 5,000
SALES (est): 6.7MM **Privately Held**
WEB: www.aaronornamental.com
SIC: 3446 Architectural metalwork

(G-6340)
ABBYS THRES NO PL LIKE HM FUR
Also Called: Abbys Thres No Pl Like HM Furn
855 Foch St (76107-2916)
PHONE..........................817 244-3371
Valerie Abby Slayton, President
EMP: 10
SQ FT: 5,800
SALES (est): 2.4MM **Privately Held**
WEB: www.furnishfw.com
SIC: 5712 5021 3645 Mattresses; furniture; residential lighting fixtures

(G-6341)
ACE ENGINEERING LTD
10200 Jacksboro Hwy (76135-4706)
PHONE..........................817 237-7700
Ace Ghanemi, CEO
John Watson, President
Jon Standley, General Mgr
Rick Reeves, Exec VP
EMP: 140
SQ FT: 70,000
SALES (est): 25.6MM **Privately Held**
SIC: 3536 Hoists

(G-6342)
ACE TRUCKS LTD
10200 Jacksboro Hwy (76135-4706)
PHONE..........................817 237-7700
Rick Reeves, Partner
Ace World Companies, Partner
Ace Ghanemi, Partner
Mike Harris, Partner
Camron Ghanemi, Vice Pres
▲ EMP: 88
SQ FT: 55,000
SALES (est): 11.3MM **Privately Held**
WEB: www.aceworldcompanies.com
SIC: 3536 Hoists, cranes & monorails

(G-6343)
ACME BRICK COMPANY (HQ)
3024 Acme Brick Plz (76109-4104)
P.O. Box 425 (76101-0425)
PHONE..........................817 332-4101
Dennis D Knautz, President
Craig Dudley, General Mgr
Bill Smith, General Mgr
Ray Ribble, Superintendent
Sean Austin, Counsel
▲ EMP: 164
SQ FT: 36,000
SALES (est): 646.7MM
SALES (corp-wide): 254.6B **Publicly Held**
WEB: www.brick.com
SIC: 3251 5032 5211 Structural brick & blocks; brick, except refractory; building blocks; brick
PA: Berkshire Hathaway Inc.
3555 Farnam St Ste 1140
Omaha NE 68131
402 346-1400

(G-6344)
ADDISON COLLECTION LP
2901 W Bolt St (76110-5808)
PHONE..........................817 921-4450
Dan Addison,
EMP: 9
SQ FT: 22,000
SALES (est): 851.8K **Privately Held**
SIC: 2299 Textile mill waste & remnant processing

(G-6345)
ADEXCO OPERATING COMPANY
309 W 7th St Ste 400 (76102-6902)
PHONE..........................817 332-3891
Glenn A Adams, President
EMP: 9
SQ FT: 5,000
SALES (est): 1.1MM **Privately Held**
SIC: 1311 Crude petroleum production

(G-6346)
ADVANCE TOOL & DIE INC
3428 S Jones St (76110-4313)
PHONE..........................817 923-8787
William Schmidt, President
Joe Jarrett, Vice Pres
EMP: 22
SQ FT: 8,000
SALES (est): 2.6MM **Privately Held**
WEB: www.advancemachineandtool.com
SIC: 3599 Machine shop, jobbing & repair

(G-6347)
ADVANCED CAST STONE INC
Also Called: Advanced Architectural Stone
115 Lee St (76140-3029)
PHONE..........................817 572-0018
Eddie Lesok, CEO
Pete Boogren, President
Tim Michaels, Vice Pres
Jacob Pendley, Purchasing
EMP: 128
SQ FT: 75,000
SALES (est): 10MM **Privately Held**
WEB:
www.advancedarchitecturalstone.com
SIC: 3272 Stone, cast concrete

(G-6348)
ADVANCED MBL FLTRTION SVCS LLC
6300 Ridglea Plste 1011 (76116)
PHONE..........................800 484-4590
Mike Atkinson, CEO
Tim Smith, President
Gerard Simon, COO
EMP: 12
SALES (est): 510.6K **Privately Held**
WEB: www.amfsfiltration.com
SIC: 3589 Commercial cleaning equipment

(G-6349)
ADVANTAGE STEEL SERVICE INC
3700 Flory St (76180-8834)
P.O. Box 820040 (76182-0040)
PHONE..........................817 589-0088
Tom Church, President
Claude Cain, Sales Associate
Thomas Church, Technology
EMP: 45
SQ FT: 100,000
SALES (est): 12.4MM **Privately Held**
WEB: www.advantagesteelservice.com
SIC: 3441 Fabricated structural metal
PA: Walker Building Corporation
3733 Flory St
Fort Worth TX

(G-6350)
ADVISORY CONS STL ERECTION MFG
Also Called: Acsem
3113 Saint Louis Ave (76110-4132)
PHONE..........................817 924-1991
Donald Corlett, President
EMP: 50
SQ FT: 10,000
SALES (est): 6.2MM **Privately Held**
WEB: www.jimcosales.com
SIC: 3444 Sheet metalwork

(G-6351)
AERO COMPONENTS LLC
5124 Kaltenbrun Rd (76119-6400)
PHONE..........................817 834-6251
Jon Williams Sr, President
Jon Williams Jr, Vice Pres
Clark Fraser, Purchasing
Vicki Blake, Treasurer
Vecki Blake, Sales Staff
EMP: 65
SALES (est): 12.4MM **Privately Held**
WEB: www.foreaero.com
SIC: 3728 Aircraft parts & equipment

(G-6352)
AEROMAX INDUSTRIES INC
1310 Ranchers Legacy Trl (76126-1750)
PHONE..........................818 701-9500
Thomas Brizes, CEO
Thelma Martinez, Principal
Micki Brizes, Controller
Jessica Lopez, Sales Staff
Aimee Donadio, Manager
EMP: 10
SQ FT: 7,000
SALES: 6.4MM **Privately Held**
WEB: www.aeromax.com
SIC: 3724 5088 Aircraft engines & engine parts; aircraft & space vehicle supplies & parts

(G-6353)
AEROSPACE & COML TECH INC
Also Called: A C T
970 Fm 2871 (76126-9410)
PHONE..........................817 560-6600
David Smith, President
John R Demlow, Vice Pres
Hal Smith, Vice Pres
Ross Smith, Vice Pres
Jerry Bayless, Opers Mgr
◆ EMP: 13
SQ FT: 26,000
SALES (est): 3.9MM **Publicly Held**
WEB: www.aero-com-tech.com
SIC: 3728 Aircraft parts & equipment
PA: Heico Corporation
3000 Taft St
Hollywood FL 33021

(G-6354)
AFFIRM OILFIELD SERVICES LLC
3575 Lone Star Cir Ste 41 (76177-8904)
PHONE..........................817 644-3360
John Schmitz, CEO
Cody Ortowski, COO
Sam Gandy, Controller
Ismael Cabrales, Manager
Regina Davis, Manager
EMP: 672 EST: 2014
SALES (est): 11.5MM
SALES (corp-wide): 1.2B **Publicly Held**
WEB: www.4xindustrial.com
SIC: 1389 Oil field services
HQ: Select Energy Services, Llc
1820 N I 35
Gainesville TX 76240
940 668-1818

(G-6355)
AGRANA FRUIT US INC
2400 Northeast Pkwy (76106-1815)
PHONE..........................817 625-9053
Tim Petty, Engineer
Brianne Pressler, Human Resources
Mark Porter, Manager
Jesus Rivas, Technician
Burt Pardue, Regional
EMP: 57
SALES (corp-wide): 51.7MM **Privately Held**
WEB: www.us.agrana.com
SIC: 2033 2087 Fruits: packaged in cans, jars, etc.; flavoring extracts & syrups
HQ: Agrana Fruit Us, Inc.
6850 Southpointe Pkwy
Brecksville OH 44141
440 546-1199

(G-6356)
AGS TECHNOLOGY INC
Also Called: Advanced Corrosion Technology
4800 Alliance Gateway Fwy # 130 (76177-3709)
PHONE..........................817 490-0086
EMP: 50
SALES (est): 4.6MM **Privately Held**
SIC: 3663 Cellphone Manufacturing

(G-6357)
AIR RELIEF TECHNOLOGIES INC (PA)
Also Called: Tex Air Filters
5757 E Rosedale St (76112-7732)
PHONE..........................817 261-3791
Jim Rosenthal, CEO
Stevan Brown, President
EMP: 45
SQ FT: 20,000
SALES (est): 14MM **Privately Held**
WEB: www.texairfilters.com
SIC: 3564 Filters, air: furnaces, air conditioning equipment, etc.

(G-6358)
AIRCO INDUSTRIES, INC.
Also Called: Photo Etch
5600 Blue Mound Rd (76131-1410)
PHONE..........................817 332-3806
EMP: 57
SALES (corp-wide): 167.7B **Privately Held**
SIC: 3728 Aircraft parts & equipment
HQ: Abelconn Llc
9210 Science Center Dr
Minneapolis MN 55428
763 533-3533

(G-6359)
AKZO NOBEL COATINGS INC
Also Called: Akzo Coatings
3201 Ne Loop 820 Ste 200 (76137-2434)
PHONE..........................817 232-9745
Greg Barber, Accounts Mgr
Jack Edgin, Manager
EMP: 15
SALES (corp-wide): 10.2B **Privately Held**
WEB: www.akzonobel.com
SIC: 2851 Paints: oil or alkyd vehicle or water thinned
HQ: Akzo Nobel Coatings Inc.
8220 Mohawk Dr
Strongsville OH 44136
440 297-5100

(G-6360)
AKZO NOBEL INC
611 E Northside Dr (76164-9243)
PHONE..........................817 625-1500
Henry Snow, Opers-Prdtn-Mfg
John Piercy, Maintence Staff
EMP: 50
SALES (corp-wide): 10.2B **Privately Held**
WEB: www.akzonobel.com
SIC: 2841 2879 2842 Detergents, synthetic organic or inorganic alkaline; agricultural chemicals; specialty cleaning, polishes & sanitation goods
HQ: Akzo Nobel Inc.
535 Marriott Dr Ste 500
Nashville TN 37214

(G-6361)
AL/TEX HOMES INC
Also Called: Southern Energy Homes of Texas
8701 Harmon Rd (76177-7501)
PHONE..........................817 847-1355
Keith Holbrook, President

Johnny Long, *Vice Pres*
EMP: 160
SQ FT: 100,000
SALES (est): 36.3MM
SALES (corp-wide): 254.6B **Publicly Held**
WEB: www.sehomestexas.com
SIC: 2451 Mobile homes
HQ: Southern Energy Homes, Inc.
144 Corporate Way
Addison AL 35540
256 747-8589

(G-6362)
ALAN CHARLES INCORPORATED
3446 May St (76110-4127)
PHONE...................................817 922-9834
Margaret Sevadjian, *President*
Cissy Wells, *Project Mgr*
▲ **EMP:** 23
SQ FT: 40,000
SALES (est): 2.9MM **Privately Held**
WEB: www.charlesalaninc.com
SIC: 2511 2512 2531 Wood household furniture; upholstered household furniture; public building & related furniture

(G-6363)
ALCON LABORATORIES INC (DH)
6201 South Fwy (76134-2001)
PHONE...................................817 293-0450
David Endicott, *CEO*
Kevin Stiner, *Division Mgr*
Jeanne Lim, *General Mgr*
Michael Ball, *Chairman*
Laurent Attias, *Senior VP*
▲ **EMP:** 2400 **EST:** 1957
SALES (est): 1.2B
SALES (corp-wide): 7.5B **Privately Held**
SIC: 3841 2834 Ophthalmic instruments & apparatus; solutions, pharmaceutical
HQ: Alcon, Inc.
1132 Ferris Rd
Amelia OH 45102
513 722-1037

(G-6364)
ALCON LABORATORIES INC
Also Called: Alcon Surgical
6201 South Fwy (76134-2001)
PHONE...................................817 293-7276
EMP: 170
SALES (corp-wide): 49.4B **Privately Held**
SIC: 3845 Mfg And Sales Of Medical Laser Systems
HQ: Alcon Laboratories, Inc.
6201 South Fwy
Fort Worth TX 76134
817 293-0450

(G-6365)
ALCON LABORATORIES HOLDG CORP (DH)
6201 South Fwy (76134-2001)
P.O. Box 6600 (76115-0600)
PHONE...................................817 293-0450
Robert K Warner, *President*
Todd Deneault, *Division Mgr*
Chuck Kerzner, *Division Mgr*
Bettina Maunz, *Vice Pres*
Michael Pfleger, *Vice Pres*
▲ **EMP:** 2500
SQ FT: 1,667,000
SALES (est): 2.7B
SALES (corp-wide): 7.5B **Privately Held**
WEB: www.alcon.com
SIC: 2834 3841 Solutions, pharmaceutical; ophthalmic instruments & apparatus
HQ: Alcon Management Sa
Chemin De Blandonnet 8
Vernier GE
589 112-000

(G-6366)
ALCON RESEARCH LLC (PA)
6201 South Fwy (76134-2001)
PHONE...................................817 551-4555
David Endicott, *CEO*
Teresa Moore, *Buyer*
Bill Shwaiko, *Project Engr*
Tom Callaghan, *Manager*
Danney Stanley, *Manager*
EMP: 148 **EST:** 1945

SALES (est): 180.4MM **Privately Held**
WEB: www.alcon.com
SIC: 8733 3841 2834 Research institute; surgical & medical instruments; pharmaceutical preparations

(G-6367)
ALCON SURGICAL INC
6201 South Fwy (76134-2001)
P.O. Box 6600 (76115-0600)
PHONE...................................817 293-0450
David Bass, *CEO*
Gary Rayman, *President*
Heather Attra, *Senior VP*
Rajkumar Narayanan, *Senior VP*
Dale Schaper, *Engineer*
EMP: 3000
SALES (est): 156.8MM **Privately Held**
WEB: www.alcon.com
SIC: 3841 Ophthalmic instruments & apparatus

(G-6368)
ALCON VISION LLC (HQ)
6201 South Fwy (76134-2001)
PHONE...................................817 293-0450
Jim Murphy, *Vice Pres*
George Yao, *Vice Pres*
Christine Mathew, *Purch Agent*
Susan Millard, *Human Resources*
Bill Kucera, *Sales Staff*
EMP: 57
SALES (est): 1.7B
SALES (corp-wide): 7.5B **Privately Held**
WEB: www.alcon.com
SIC: 3841 3851 Ophthalmic instruments & apparatus; contact lenses
PA: Alcon Ag
0
Freiburg FR 1701
417 637-711

(G-6369)
ALEXANDERS MCH MAINT SVC INC
Also Called: Alexander Machine & Maint Svc
3700 N Commerce St (76106-2710)
PHONE...................................817 625-4175
EMP: 38 **EST:** 1970
SQ FT: 4,700
SALES (est): 9.2MM **Privately Held**
WEB: www.alexandersmachine.com
SIC: 3599 7692 Machine shop, jobbing & repair; welding repair

(G-6370)
ALL MARK IMPRESSIONS LTD
823 N Riverside Dr (76111-4249)
P.O. Box 7575 (76111-0575)
PHONE...................................817 834-0080
Richard Spraberry, *President*
Harold Sample, *Treasurer*
Nancy Menchaza, *Admin Sec*
▲ **EMP:** 10
SQ FT: 2,500
SALES (est): 1.4MM **Privately Held**
WEB: www.allmarkimpressions.com
SIC: 3069 Medical & laboratory rubber sundries & related products
PA: Fort Worth Rubber Stamp Co, . Inc.
823 N Riverside Dr
Fort Worth TX

(G-6371)
ALL STAR CORRUGATED (PA)
1425 Forum Way S (76140-5086)
PHONE...................................817 551-5580
Ronnie Branch, *Partner*
George V Baker, *Partner*
R W Leeth, *Partner*
Russell McCasland, *Purch Dir*
Ladonna Anthony, *Sales Staff*
EMP: 50
SQ FT: 69,000
SALES (est): 12.6MM **Privately Held**
WEB: www.allstarbox.com
SIC: 2653 Boxes, corrugated: made from purchased materials

(G-6372)
ALLIANCE COATINGS LLC
1001 N Blue Mound Rd (76131-4809)
PHONE...................................817 834-8817
Brendon Graft, *Vice Pres*
John D Willbanks III, *Director*
Fred Redd III,

Fred Eric Redd,
EMP: 20
SQ FT: 8,050
SALES (est): 2.9MM **Privately Held**
SIC: 3479 Coating of metals with plastic or resins

(G-6373)
ALS ASSOCIATES
2829 Bryan Ave (76104-6712)
PHONE...................................817 921-2679
James Johnson, *President*
Tommy Johnson, *Vice Pres*
EMP: 20
SQ FT: 2,500
SALES (est): 1.8MM **Privately Held**
SIC: 3471 Plating of metals or formed products; electroplating of metals or formed products

(G-6374)
ALTERNATIVE CUTTING METHODS
120 E Felix St Ste 310 (76115-3557)
PHONE...................................817 927-3332
James M Clark, *President*
Tony Dawson, *Foreman/Supr*
EMP: 12
SALES (est): 1.7MM **Privately Held**
WEB: www.alternativecuttingmethods.com
SIC: 3599 Machine shop, jobbing & repair

(G-6375)
ALTIUM PACKAGING
Also Called: Fort Worth Plastics
5651 Alliance Gateway Fwy # 1 (76177-3737)
PHONE...................................817 491-9229
Monty Dirickson, *Manager*
EMP: 26
SALES (corp-wide): 12.5B **Publicly Held**
WEB: www.altiumpkg.com
SIC: 3089 Plastic containers, except foam
HQ: Altium Packaging Llc
2500 Windy Ridge Pkwy Se # 1400
Atlanta GA 30339
678 742-4600

(G-6376)
ALUMINUM TANK & TANK ACC INC
2702 N Nichols St Ste B (76106-7235)
PHONE...................................817 378-8455
Brad C Hackett, *President*
Jeanette Weber, *General Mgr*
Nicholas Humphrey, *Plant Mgr*
Jeanette Weber, *Credit Mgr*
EMP: 10 **EST:** 2010
SALES (est): 1.2MM **Privately Held**
WEB: www.attatank.com
SIC: 3353 Aluminum sheet, plate & foil

(G-6377)
AMCOR RIGID PACKAGING USA LLC
4324 Fleetwood Rd (76155-2720)
PHONE...................................817 267-5917
James Brooks, *Buyer*
Jose Celio, *Branch Mgr*
Charles Bullock, *Manager*
EMP: 100
SALES (corp-wide): 12.4B **Privately Held**
WEB: www.amcor.com
SIC: 3089 Plastic containers, except foam
HQ: Amcor Rigid Packaging Usa, Llc
40600 Ann Arbor Rd E
Plymouth MI 48170

(G-6378)
AMERICAN CANVAS PRODUCTS INC (PA)
1319 N Main St (76164-9118)
P.O. Box 4585 (76164-0585)
PHONE...................................817 429-3108
James Fred Cordell II, *President*
Kimla Cordell, *Corp Secy*
Carl Ryan Cordell, *Vice Pres*
EMP: 10
SQ FT: 4,000

SALES (est): 1.3MM **Privately Held**
WEB: www.amcanvas.com
SIC: 2394 Awnings, fabric: made from purchased materials; canopies, fabric: made from purchased materials; liners & covers, fabric: made from purchased materials

(G-6379)
AMERICAN COMMODITIES INC (PA)
3701 N Grove St (76106-3733)
P.O. Box 161729 (76161-1729)
PHONE...................................817 740-8326
Krista M Blanton, *President*
Krista Blanton, *President*
Greg Gardner, *Vice Pres*
Irene Sullivent, *Controller*
Jerrod Burton, *Director*
EMP: 20
SQ FT: 1,000
SALES (est): 4.2MM **Privately Held**
WEB: www.acitexas.net
SIC: 2079 2077 Cooking oils, except corn: vegetable refined; grease rendering, inedible

(G-6380)
AMERICAN ELECTRO OPTICS LLC
210 Shelby Rd (76140-5604)
P.O. Box 15007 (76119-0007)
PHONE...................................817 546-0993
Morris Rodgers, *VP Opers*
Dana Prather,
▲ **EMP:** 15
SQ FT: 30,000
SALES (est): 6MM **Privately Held**
WEB: www.aeoptics.com
SIC: 3827 Optical instruments & lenses

(G-6381)
AMERICAN MARAZZI TILE INC
6313 Airport Fwy Ste A (76117-5380)
PHONE...................................972 232-3800
Justina Ash, *Manager*
EMP: 9
SQ FT: 20,000 **Publicly Held**
WEB: www.marazziusa.com
SIC: 3253 5211 5032 Floor tile, ceramic; tile, ceramic; ceramic wall & floor tile
HQ: American Marazzi Tile, Inc.
7834 C F Hawn Fwy
Dallas TX 75217
972 232-3801

(G-6382)
AMERICAN PAINT HORSE ASSN
Also Called: Apha
122 E Exchange Ave (76164-8210)
P.O. Box 961023 (76161-0023)
PHONE...................................817 834-2742
▲ **EMP:** 140 **EST:** 1962
SALES (est): 9.9MM **Privately Held**
WEB: www.apha.com
SIC: 8699 2721 Personal interest organization; periodicals: publishing & printing

(G-6383)
AMERICAN PLANT FOOD CORP
3800 Deen Rd (76106-4109)
P.O. Box 161697 (76161-1697)
PHONE...................................817 624-7132
EMP: 12
SQ FT: 86,570
SALES (corp-wide): 194.6MM **Privately Held**
WEB: www.apfcorp.net
SIC: 2879 2875 Agricultural chemicals; fertilizers, mixing only
PA: American Plant Food Corporation
903 Mayo Shell Rd
Galena Park TX 77547
713 675-2231

(G-6384)
AMERICAN POWDER COATING CORP
5950 Tension Dr (76112-6936)
PHONE...................................817 446-9400
EMP: 12
SALES (est): 1.6MM **Privately Held**
WEB: www.dfwpowdercoating.com
SIC: 3479 Coating of metals & formed products

(G-6385)
AMERICAN SHREDDER ENTPS LLC
3800 N Commerce St (76106-2712)
PHONE..................................817 378-8511
Ronnie Smith, *Mng Member*
August Stanislawaki III,
EMP: 17
SALES (est): 2.2MM **Privately Held**
SIC: 3442 7389 Rolling doors for industrial buildings or warehouses, metal; metal cutting services

(G-6386)
AMTECH MANUFACTURING INC
5129 Vesta Farley Rd (76119-6413)
P.O. Box 172765, Arlington (76003-2765)
PHONE..................................817 563-1251
Amir Morshed, *President*
Denise Tolman, *Purchasing*
Haleh Morshed, *Admin Sec*
EMP: 28 EST: 2000
SQ FT: 27,732
SALES (est): 5.5MM **Privately Held**
WEB: www.amtech-eng.com
SIC: 1761 3679 Sheet metalwork; electronic switches

(G-6387)
AN AUTHORIZED AFFILIATE OF PRI
Also Called: PCI
1712 Lacy Dr (76177-6501)
PHONE..................................817 430-6202
Michael Walker, *President*
EMP: 9
SALES (est): 652.8K **Privately Held**
WEB: www.pciprinters.com
SIC: 2752 5045 Commercial printing, lithographic; printers, computer

(G-6388)
ANADARKO PETROLEUM CORPORATION
4200 N Main St Bldg 27n (76106-2756)
PHONE..................................817 877-7449
John White, *Branch Mgr*
EMP: 10
SALES (corp-wide): 21.2B **Publicly Held**
WEB: www.oxy.com
SIC: 1382 Oil & gas exploration services
HQ: Anadarko Petroleum Corporation
1201 Lake Robbins Dr
The Woodlands TX 77380
832 636-1000

(G-6389)
ANODICS INC
4105 Murray Ave (76117-1779)
PHONE..................................817 281-2743
Stephen Sones, *President*
EMP: 14 EST: 1965
SQ FT: 9,700
SALES (est): 2MM **Privately Held**
WEB: www.anodics.com
SIC: 3471 Electroplating of metals or formed products

(G-6390)
APARTMENT FURNISHINGS CO INC
1200 W Risinger Rd (76134-5670)
PHONE..................................817 568-2002
Daniel Stage, *CEO*
Gary O Street, *President*
Joy Street, *Corp Secy*
Dan Stage, *Vice Pres*
Gary Street, *Vice Pres*
EMP: 45 EST: 1968
SQ FT: 80,000
SALES (est): 13MM **Privately Held**
WEB: www.apartmentfurnishingsco.com
SIC: 5021 7359 2515 Household furniture; furniture rental; sofa beds (convertible sofas)

(G-6391)
APCI INC
Also Called: Arrow Plating Co
3129 May St (76110-4122)
P.O. Box 11451 (76110-0451)
PHONE..................................817 927-5362
James L Shafer, *President*
Simon Serrano, *General Mgr*
Richard Barnett, *Plant Mgr*

Tommy Hencke, *Manager*
EMP: 21 EST: 1953
SQ FT: 31,000
SALES (est): 2.6MM **Privately Held**
WEB: www.arrowplating.com
SIC: 3471 Electroplating of metals or formed products

(G-6392)
APPLIED AVIONICS INC (PA)
Also Called: Aerospace Optics
3201 Sandy Ln (76112-7203)
P.O. Box 732575, Dallas (75373-2575)
PHONE..................................817 451-1141
Loren K Jensen, *Ch of Bd*
Craig Morgan, *Vice Pres*
Mike Perry, *Vice Pres*
Matt Hawkins, *CFO*
Kay Roberson, *Asst Controller*
EMP: 75
SQ FT: 34,000
SALES (est): 10.8MM **Privately Held**
WEB: www.appliedavionics.com
SIC: 3728 Aircraft parts & equipment

(G-6393)
APPROACH MDSTREAM HOLDINGS LLC
1 Ridgmar Ctr 6500 W Fwy (76116)
PHONE..................................817 989-9000
Theodore Oldham, *Opers Staff*
Sergei Krylov,
EMP: 13 EST: 2014
SALES (est): 385K
SALES (corp-wide): 114MM **Privately Held**
WEB: www.approachresources.com
SIC: 1382 Oil & gas exploration services
PA: Approach Resources Inc.
6500 West Fwy Ste 900
Fort Worth TX 76116
817 989-9000

(G-6394)
APPROACH RESOURCES I LP
6500 West Fwy Ste 900 (76116-2177)
PHONE..................................817 989-9000
Steven P Smart, *CFO*
EMP: 13
SALES (est): 300.5K
SALES (corp-wide): 114MM **Privately Held**
WEB: www.approachresources.com
SIC: 1382 Oil & gas exploration services
PA: Approach Resources Inc.
6500 West Fwy Ste 900
Fort Worth TX 76116
817 989-9000

(G-6395)
APPROACH RESOURCES INC (PA)
6500 West Fwy Ste 900 (76116-2177)
PHONE..................................817 989-9000
Sergei Krylov, *President*
James C Crain, *Chairman*
Qingming Yang, *COO*
Joshua Dazey, *Exec VP*
Josh Dazey, *Vice Pres*
EMP: 41 EST: 2002
SALES: 114MM **Privately Held**
WEB: www.approachresources.com
SIC: 1311 1382 Crude petroleum & natural gas; oil & gas exploration services

(G-6396)
APPROACH SERVICES LLC
6500 West Fwy Ste 800 (76116-2178)
PHONE..................................817 989-9000
Suzanne Ogle,
EMP: 17
SALES (est): 226.1K
SALES (corp-wide): 114MM **Privately Held**
WEB: www.approachresources.com
SIC: 1382 Oil & gas exploration services
PA: Approach Resources Inc.
6500 West Fwy Ste 900
Fort Worth TX 76116
817 989-9000

(G-6397)
AQUILA ENVIRONMENTAL LLC
509 Pecan St Ste 200 (76102-4070)
PHONE..................................817 953-3171
John Sledge, *CEO*

EMP: 9 EST: 2015
SALES (est): 402.2K **Privately Held**
WEB: www.aquilaenv.com
SIC: 8748 7359 3646 Environmental consultant; equipment rental & leasing; commercial indusl & institutional electric lighting fixtures

(G-6398)
ARCOSA WIND TOWERS INC
Also Called: Tsti
1000 Ne 28th St R (76106-7221)
PHONE..................................817 378-3700
Gary Schmidt, *Manager*
David Peraza, *Director*
EMP: 9
SQ FT: 108,951
SALES (corp-wide): 1.7B **Publicly Held**
SIC: 3441 3621 Fabricated structural metal; windmills, electric generating
HQ: Arcosa Wind Towers, Inc.
500 N Akard St
Dallas TX 75201
972 942-6500

(G-6399)
ARCTIC COOLER-FREEZER REPR INC
Also Called: Arctic Warehouse Facility Repr
7331 John T White Rd (76120-3307)
P.O. Box 2102, Hurst (76053-2102)
PHONE..................................817 492-0200
Johnny Hyatt, *President*
Mary Hyatt, *Vice Pres*
EMP: 12
SQ FT: 5,000
SALES (est): 2.5MM **Privately Held**
WEB: www.arcticrepair.com
SIC: 3632 Household refrigerators & freezers

(G-6400)
ARGOS USA LLC
6100 Old Hemphill Rd (76134-1408)
PHONE..................................817 551-0931
Lee Farris, *Branch Mgr*
EMP: 70 **Privately Held**
WEB: www.argos-us.com
SIC: 3273 Ready-mixed concrete
HQ: Argos Usa Llc
3015 Windward Plz Ste 300
Alpharetta GA 30005
678 368-4300

(G-6401)
ARISMENDY JOSIAS
Also Called: Beyond Ordinary Services
340 Bellvue Ct (76134-3944)
PHONE..................................817 353-1244
Josias Arismendy, *Owner*
EMP: 25
SALES (est): 780.4K **Privately Held**
WEB: www.beyondordinaryservices.com
SIC: 1611 1752 2541 1741 Highway & street maintenance; wood floor installation & refinishing; table or counter tops, plastic laminated; masonry & other stonework; foundation & retaining wall construction;

(G-6402)
ARROW CRUSHED STONE INC
4641 Ivanhoe Dr (76132-2030)
PHONE..................................817 423-1337
Suzanne Arnold, *President*
John Whitehorn, *Vice Pres*
EMP: 11
SQ FT: 1,300
SALES (est): 607.3K **Privately Held**
SIC: 1422 1411 Crushed & broken limestone; limestone & marble dimension stone

(G-6403)
ASK INDUSTRIES INC
Also Called: AK
301 Commerce St Ste 1810 (76102-4163)
PHONE..................................432 686-2520
Scott Wilson, *President*
▲ EMP: 18
SALES (est): 5.9MM **Privately Held**
WEB: www.askindustries.com
SIC: 2899 Chemical preparations

(G-6404)
ASPEN MARBLE INC
5399 Oak St (76140-7909)
P.O. Box 641, Crowley (76036-0641)
PHONE..................................817 478-5140
Don Frieze, *President*
EMP: 13
SQ FT: 4,200
SALES (est): 1.2MM **Privately Held**
WEB: www.aspenmarble.com
SIC: 1743 3281 Marble installation, interior; marble, building: cut & shaped

(G-6405)
ASPEN OPERATING COMPANY LLC
6777 Camp Bowie Blvd # 600 (76116-7195)
PHONE..................................817 882-9063
Garry Sargent, *Managing Prtnr*
Steven E Baker, *Mng Member*
EMP: 28
SQ FT: 9,000
SALES (est): 4.1MM **Privately Held**
SIC: 1382 Oil & gas exploration services

(G-6406)
ATCO RUBBER PRODUCTS INC (HQ)
7101 Atco Dr (76118-7098)
PHONE..................................817 595-2894
Ramesh Bhatia, *President*
Bill McReynolds, *Engineer*
Randall Calaway, *CFO*
Julie Decker, *Natl Sales Mgr*
Nancy Harris, *Cust Mgr*
◆ EMP: 600
SQ FT: 260,000
SALES (est): 166MM **Publicly Held**
WEB: www.atcoflex.com
SIC: 3443 3084 3585 3444 Ducting, metal plate; plastics pipe; refrigeration & heating equipment; sheet metalwork; laminated plastics plate & sheet

(G-6407)
ATHLON ENERGY INC
420 Throckmorton St # 1200 (76102-3700)
PHONE..................................817 984-8200
Robert C Reeves, *President*
Nelson K Treadway, *Senior VP*
John C Souders, *Vice Pres*
Bud W Holmes, *VP Engrg*
William B D Butler, *CFO*
EMP: 40
SALES (est): 93.9MM
SALES (corp-wide): 9.3MM **Publicly Held**
WEB: www.athlonenergy.com
SIC: 1311 Crude petroleum & natural gas
HQ: Alenco, Inc.
16201 W 110th St
Lenexa KS 66219

(G-6408)
ATLAS ENERGY GROUP LLC (PA)
425 Houston St Ste 300 (76102-7433)
PHONE..................................412 489-0006
Jonathan Z Cohen, *Ch of Bd*
Edward E Cohen, *President*
Daniel C Herz, *President*
Jeffrey M Slotterback, *CFO*
Walter Jones, *Director*
EMP: 13
SALES: 9MM **Publicly Held**
WEB: www.atlasenergy.com
SIC: 1311 4922 Crude petroleum & natural gas; natural gas transmission

(G-6409)
ATLAS GROWTH PARTNERS GP LLC
425 Houston St Ste 300 (76102-7433)
PHONE..................................412 489-0006
Edward E Cohen, *Ch of Bd*
John P Hanna, *President*
Jeffrey M Slotterback, *CFO*
EMP: 35
SALES: 512.9K
SALES (corp-wide): 9MM **Publicly Held**
SIC: 1311 4922 Crude petroleum & natural gas; natural gas transmission

G E O G R A P H I C

PA: Atlas Energy Group, Llc
425 Houston St Ste 300
Fort Worth TX 76102
412 489-0006

(G-6410)
AUSTIN COCA-COLA BOTTLING CO
3400 Fossil Creek Blvd (76137-2402)
PHONE.....................817 232-8600
Sol Eaton, *Manager*
EMP: 800
SALES (corp-wide): 309.5MM **Privately Held**
SIC: 2086 Bottled & canned soft drinks
PA: Austin Coca-Cola Bottling Company
1 Coca Cola Pl
San Antonio TX 78219
210 225-2601

(G-6411)
AUTOMOTIVE RENTALS INC
Also Called: Fleet Body Equipment
711 Airway Dr (76106-1902)
PHONE.....................817 624-3650
Mark Marutani, *General Mgr*
Henry Jones, *Manager*
David Geisler, *Technician*
EMP: 25
SQ FT: 43,200
SALES (corp-wide): 1.2B **Privately Held**
WEB: www.arifleet.com
SIC: 7513 7515 3713 3743 Truck rental & leasing, no drivers; passenger car leasing; truck bodies & parts; railroad equipment; blast furnaces & steel mills
HQ: Automotive Rentals, Inc.
4001 Leadenhall Rd
Mount Laurel NJ 08054
856 778-1500

(G-6412)
AVIATION DVCS ELCTRNIC CMPNNTS
Also Called: Avdec
3215 W Loop 820 S (76116-5941)
PHONE.....................817 738-9161
Kelly Templin, *Project Mgr*
Kent Boomer, *Engineer*
Miguel Garcia, *Sales Staff*
Becky Kern, *Sales Staff*
Leonel Rodriguez, *Sales Staff*
EMP: 32 **EST:** 1997
SALES (est): 7.9MM **Privately Held**
WEB: www.avdec.com
SIC: 3728 3669 Aircraft parts & equipment; transportation signaling devices

(G-6413)
AVIATION PRODUCTS INC
Also Called: Talco Industries
5621 E Rosedale St Ste A (76112-6948)
P.O. Box 918, Rhome (76078-0918)
PHONE.....................817 457-2040
Charles Sean Talley, *President*
EMP: 10
SQ FT: 7,500
SALES (est): 2MM **Privately Held**
WEB: www.aviationproducts.com
SIC: 2891 3724 Adhesives; aircraft engines & engine parts

(G-6414)
AZZ INC (PA)
3100 W 7th St Ste 500 (76107-8701)
PHONE.....................817 810-0095
Kevern R Joyce, *Ch of Bd*
Thomas E Ferguson, *President*
Gary Hill, *COO*
Bryan Stovall, *COO*
David Nark, *Senior VP*
◆ **EMP:** 75 **EST:** 1956
SALES: 1B **Publicly Held**
WEB: www.azz.com
SIC: 3699 3613 3494 3312 Electrical equipment & supplies; switchgear & switchboard apparatus; valves & pipe fittings; blast furnaces & steel mills; coated or plated products

(G-6415)
AZZ INC
7410 Pebble Dr (76118-6961)
PHONE.....................817 284-0119
Edward Taylor, *Sales Staff*
Matt Sweeney, *Branch Mgr*

Keith Reeser, *Executive*
EMP: 37
SALES (corp-wide): 1B **Publicly Held**
WEB: www.azz.com
SIC: 3699 Electrical equipment & supplies
PA: Azz Inc.
3100 W 7th St Ste 500
Fort Worth TX 76107
817 810-0095

(G-6416)
AZZ INCORPORATED
3100 W 7th St Ste 500 (76107-8701)
PHONE.....................817 810-0095
EMP: 37
SALES (corp-wide): 1B **Publicly Held**
WEB: www.azz.com
SIC: 3699 Electrical equipment & supplies
PA: Azz Inc.
3100 W 7th St Ste 500
Fort Worth TX 76107
817 810-0095

(G-6417)
B & B WINDOWS INC
7714 Camp Bowie West Blvd (76116-6416)
PHONE.....................817 237-2212
Kenneth Black Jr, *President*
EMP: 10 **EST:** 1978
SQ FT: 12,000 **Privately Held**
SIC: 5031 3442 Windows; storm doors or windows, metal

(G-6418)
BA-KER TANK HEAD COMPANY INC
10405 North Fwy (76177-7127)
P.O. Box 77021 (76177-0021)
PHONE.....................817 232-8030
Austin Baker, *President*
Cody Caldwell, *General Mgr*
Randy Button, *Maint Spvr*
Wes Perdew, *Purch Agent*
Robert Paine, *Purchasing*
▼ **EMP:** 42
SQ FT: 46,000
SALES (est): 21.2MM **Privately Held**
WEB: www.bakertankhead.com
SIC: 3795 3443 Tanks & tank components; tanks, standard or custom fabricated: metal plate

(G-6419)
BAILEYS PREMIER SERVICES LLC
4200 S Hulen St (76109-4914)
P.O. Box 16454 (76162-0454)
PHONE.....................817 292-2423
Tamiko W Bailey, *President*
EMP: 200
SALES (est): 371.3K **Privately Held**
WEB: www.baileyspremierservices.com
SIC: 4581 3089 Aircraft maintenance & repair services

(G-6420)
BAKER MACY EDWARD
Also Called: Baker Sign
5213 Sun Valley Dr (76119-6440)
PHONE.....................817 572-7346
Macy Edward Baker, *Owner*
Sherilyn Baker, *Bookkeeper*
EMP: 12
SQ FT: 8,500
SALES (est): 1MM **Privately Held**
SIC: 1799 3993 Sign installation & maintenance; electric signs

(G-6421)
BAKER HGHES OLFLD OPRTIONS LLC
Also Called: BJ Services 7833
309 W 7th St Ste 1520 (76102-5113)
PHONE.....................817 806-3200
Jeff Jordan, *Branch Mgr*
EMP: 42 **Privately Held**
WEB: www.bakerhughes.com
SIC: 1389 Oil field services
PA: Baker Hughes Oilfield Operations Llc
2001 Rankin Rd
Houston TX 77073

(G-6422)
BAKER HUGHES INCORPORATED
2426 Ne 35th St (76111-1903)
PHONE.....................817 838-0583
EMP: 87
SALES (corp-wide): 24.5B **Publicly Held**
SIC: 3533 Mfg Equip & Provides Services For Oil And Gas Field
PA: Baker Hughes Incorporated
2929 Allen Pkwy Ste 2100
Houston TX 77073
713 439-8600

(G-6423)
BAKER O & P ENTERPRISES INC (HQ)
Also Called: Baker Orthotics & Prosthetics
810 Lipscomb St Ste A (76104-3116)
PHONE.....................817 332-7313
Gordon Steven, *President*
Mattie Stevens, *Treasurer*
EMP: 15 **EST:** 1946
SQ FT: 5,000
SALES (est): 2.5MM
SALES (corp-wide): 27.3MM **Privately Held**
WEB: www.baker-oandp.com
SIC: 3842 Braces, orthopedic; abdominal supporters, braces & trusses; foot appliances, orthopedic
PA: Bulow Holdings, Llc
102 Woodmont Blvd Ste 120
Nashville TN 37205
615 550-8774

(G-6424)
BALL CORPORATION
6600 Will Rogers Blvd (76140-6006)
PHONE.....................817 551-3100
Glenn Jost, *Plant Mgr*
Bob Monaco, *Prdtn Mgr*
Ronny Newton, *Production*
Ron Wheeler, *Purch Agent*
Quang Chau, *Engineer*
EMP: 151
SALES (corp-wide): 11.4B **Publicly Held**
WEB: www.ball.com
SIC: 3411 Food & beverage containers
PA: Ball Corporation
10 Longs Peak Dr
Broomfield CO 80021
303 469-3131

(G-6425)
BALL METAL BEVERAGE CONT CORP
Ball Metal Beverage Cont Div
6600 Will Rogers Blvd (76140-6006)
PHONE.....................817 551-3100
Glenn Jost, *Manager*
Merle Ridlen, *CTO*
EMP: 250
SALES (corp-wide): 11.4B **Publicly Held**
WEB: www.ball.com
SIC: 3411 Metal cans
HQ: Ball Metal Beverage Container Corp.
9300 W 108th Cir
Westminster CO 80021

(G-6426)
BANYAN INDUSTRIES INC
2701 Ludelle St Ste A (76105-1212)
P.O. Box 838, Cleburne (76033-0838)
PHONE.....................817 413-7945
Mary Bender, *President*
EMP: 22
SQ FT: 20,000
SALES (est): 1.8MM **Privately Held**
SIC: 2392 5021 4225 Cushions & pillows; furniture; general warehousing & storage

(G-6427)
BARNETT GATHERING LLC (DH)
810 Houston St (76102-6203)
PHONE.....................817 870-2800
Frank G McDonald, *Partner*
EMP: 11
SALES (est): 2.6MM
SALES (corp-wide): 264.9B **Publicly Held**
WEB: www.xtoenergy.com
SIC: 1389 Oil consultants

(G-6428)
BASELINE ENERGY SERVICES LP (PA)
201 N Foch St (76107-1321)
P.O. Box 470929 (76147-0929)
PHONE.....................817 889-0056
Graham Radler, *Partner*
Dave Whisenhunt, *Business Mgr*
Kaes Dejong, *Vice Pres*
Jeffry Mills, *Opers Staff*
John Gil, *Accountant*
EMP: 32
SQ FT: 6,000
SALES (est): 10.1MM **Privately Held**
WEB: www.baseline-enserv.com
SIC: 3621 Power generators

(G-6429)
BASIC ENERGY SERVICES INC (PA)
801 Cherry St Unit 2 (76102-6886)
PHONE.....................817 334-4100
Timothy H Day, *Ch of Bd*
Thomas Monroe Patterson, *President*
Arturo Ramirez, *General Mgr*
Jason Deleon, *Superintendent*
Jay Fryar, *Superintendent*
EMP: 60 **EST:** 1992
SALES: 567.2MM **Publicly Held**
WEB: www.basices.com
SIC: 1389 Servicing oil & gas wells; swabbing wells

(G-6430)
BASIC ENERGY SERVICES INC
801 Cherry St Unit 21 (76102-6884)
PHONE.....................817 645-0853
EMP: 35
SALES (corp-wide): 567.2MM **Publicly Held**
WEB: www.basices.com
SIC: 1389 Oil field services
PA: Basic Energy Services, Inc.
801 Cherry St Unit 2
Fort Worth TX 76102
817 334-4100

(G-6431)
BASIC ENERGY SERVICES INC
801 Cherry St Unit 21 (76102-6884)
PHONE.....................918 225-1111
Steve Dilley, *Manager*
Kurt Onstott, *Manager*
EMP: 35
SALES (corp-wide): 567.2MM **Publicly Held**
WEB: www.basices.com
SIC: 1389 Oil field services
PA: Basic Energy Services, Inc.
801 Cherry St Unit 2
Fort Worth TX 76102
817 334-4100

(G-6432)
BASIC ENERGY SERVICES INC
801 Cherry St Unit 21 (76102-6884)
PHONE.....................254 442-2200
Tim Dame, *Vice Pres*
Bradlee Rains, *Facilities Mgr*
Jackie Hart, *Opers Staff*
Tim Rains, *Engineer*
Kelly Swift, *Human Res Mgr*
EMP: 75
SALES (corp-wide): 567.2MM **Publicly Held**
WEB: www.basices.com
SIC: 1389 Oil field services
PA: Basic Energy Services, Inc.
801 Cherry St Unit 2
Fort Worth TX 76102
817 334-4100

(G-6433)
BASIC ENERGY SERVICES LP (DH)
Also Called: Basic Oil & Gas Well Services
801 Cherry St Unit 2 (76102-6886)
P.O. Box 53710, Midland (79710-3710)
PHONE.....................817 334-4100
T M Roe Patterson, *CEO*
Steven A Webster, *Partner*
James J Carter, *Partner*
Dub Harrison, *Partner*
Ken V Huseman, *Partner*
EMP: 25

▲ = Import ▼ = Export
◆ = Import/Export

SQ FT: 20,000
SALES (est): 1.2B
SALES (corp-wide): 567.2MM **Publicly Held**
WEB: www.basices.com
SIC: 1389 Oil & gas wells: building, repairing & dismantling; oil field services
HQ: Basic Energy Services Lp, Llc
801 Cherry St Unit 2
Fort Worth TX 76102
817 334-4100

(G-6434)
BASIC ENERGY SERVICES LP
801 Cherry St Unit 21 (76102-6884)
PHONE..............................903 643-1140
Marvin Hall, *Manager*
EMP: 30
SALES (corp-wide): 567.2MM **Publicly Held**
WEB: www.basices.com
SIC: 7359 1389 Tool rental; oil field services
HQ: Basic Energy Services, L.P.
801 Cherry St Unit 2
Fort Worth TX 76102

(G-6435)
BASIC MARINE SERVICES INC
801 Cherry St Unit 2 (76102-6886)
P.O. Box 10460, Midland (79702-7460)
PHONE..............................817 334-4100
Kenneth V Huseman, *President*
Alan Krenek, *Senior VP*
Dub Harrison, *Vice Pres*
Mark D Rankin, *Vice Pres*
James E Tyner, *Vice Pres*
EMP: 225
SALES (est): 5.6MM
SALES (corp-wide): 567.2MM **Publicly Held**
SIC: 1389 Oil field services
HQ: Basic Energy Services, L.P.
801 Cherry St Unit 2
Fort Worth TX 76102

(G-6436)
BASIN OIL & GAS LLC
1320 S University Dr (76107-5764)
PHONE..............................817 820-8910
Carl T Ratner, *Mng Member*
EMP: 12 **EST:** 1998
SALES (est): 597.4K **Privately Held**
WEB: www.basinoilandgas.com
SIC: 1382 Oil & gas exploration services

(G-6437)
BASIN PIPELINE LLC
7950 John T White Rd (76120-3608)
PHONE..............................817 460-7777
Naresh K Vashisht, *Principal*
EMP: 25
SALES (est): 592.6K
SALES (corp-wide): 38.2MM **Privately Held**
SIC: 1389 Oil & gas field services
HQ: Omimex Energy, Inc.
7950 John T White Rd
Fort Worth TX 76120

(G-6438)
BASS ENTERPRISES PRODUCTION CO (PA)
Also Called: Bass Bros Enterprises
201 Main St Ste 2700 (76102-3195)
PHONE..............................817 698-0200
Perry R Bass, *Ch of Bd*
Sid R Bass, *President*
Robert Cottham, *Vice Pres*
W H Medary, *Vice Pres*
John Smitherman, *VP Opers*
◆ **EMP:** 250
SQ FT: 120,000
SALES (est): 255.7MM **Privately Held**
WEB: www.texaco.com
SIC: 5541 1382 Filling stations, gasoline; oil & gas exploration services

(G-6439)
BASS PRINTING INC
4620 S Edgewood Ter (76119-8204)
P.O. Box 820822, North Richland Hills (76182-0822)
PHONE..............................817 293-4913
Mark Pafford, *President*
Rosemary Gillespie, *Vice Pres*

EMP: 11
SQ FT: 5,000
SALES (est): 1.4MM **Privately Held**
WEB: www.bassprinting.com
SIC: 2752 Commercial printing, offset

(G-6440)
BAUMANN SPRINGS USA INC
14813 Trinity Blvd (76155-2609)
P.O. Box 536089, Grand Prairie (75053-6089)
PHONE..............................972 641-7272
Hans R Ruegg, *CEO*
EMP: 10
SALES (corp-wide): 187.1MM **Privately Held**
WEB: www.baumann-springs.com
SIC: 3469 Metal stampings
HQ: Baumann Springs Usa, Inc.
3075 N Great Sw Pkwy
Grand Prairie TX 75050
972 641-7272

(G-6441)
BEAN IN MOTION LOGISTICS LLC
8200 Willow Glen Ct (76134-4810)
PHONE..............................682 465-9083
EMP: 10
SALES (est): 300K **Privately Held**
SIC: 3537 Mfg Industrial Trucks/Tractors

(G-6442)
BEHR SERVICE AMERICA
5020 Augusta Dr (76106-1891)
PHONE..............................817 624-7273
Harrel Alcorn, *Principal*
▲ **EMP:** 18
SALES (est): 3.4MM **Privately Held**
SIC: 3714 Motor vehicle parts & accessories

(G-6443)
BELL TEXTRON INC
Also Called: Shared Svcs Accounts Payable
3255 Bell Flight Blvd (76118)
P.O. Box 77007 (76177-0007)
PHONE..............................817 837-4700
Stanley Young, *Engineer*
Joseph Ginty, *Commissioner*
Joel Best, *Director*
Aldo Olivas, *Instructor*
EMP: 36
SALES (corp-wide): 13.6B **Publicly Held**
WEB: www.bellflight.com
SIC: 3728 Aircraft parts & equipment
HQ: Bell Textron Inc.
3255 Bell Flight Blvd
Fort Worth TX 76118
817 280-2011

(G-6444)
BELL TEXTRON INC (HQ)
3255 Bell Flight Blvd (76118)
P.O. Box 482 (76101-0482)
PHONE..............................817 280-2011
Mitchell L Snyder, *President*
Natalie Taylor, *Business Mgr*
Jessica Kulkarni, *Counsel*
Felipe Gumucio, *Exec VP*
Gunnar Kleveland, *Exec VP*
◆ **EMP:** 2500
SQ FT: 230,000
SALES (est): 3.3B
SALES (corp-wide): 13.6B **Publicly Held**
WEB: www.bellflight.com
SIC: 3728 5088 3721 Aircraft parts & equipment; transportation equipment & supplies; helicopters; motorized aircraft
PA: Textron Inc.
40 Westminster St
Providence RI 02903
401 421-2800

(G-6445)
BELL TEXTRON INC
Also Called: Bell Helicptr Training Academy
13901 Aviator Way (76177-4308)
P.O. Box 482 (76101-0482)
PHONE..............................817 280-2011
Ray Lamas, *General Mgr*
David Archer, *Engineer*
Carey Cross, *Engineer*
Jeffery Krause, *Engineer*
Alana Keeton, *Branch Mgr*
EMP: 131

SALES (corp-wide): 13.6B **Publicly Held**
WEB: www.bellflight.com
SIC: 3721 Helicopters; motorized aircraft
HQ: Bell Textron Inc.
3255 Bell Flight Blvd
Fort Worth TX 76118
817 280-2011

(G-6446)
BELL TEXTRON SERVICES INC (DH)
Also Called: Bell Helicopter Services Inc.
3255 Bell Flight Blvd (76118)
PHONE..............................817 280-2011
Jessica Kulkarni, *Counsel*
David Shurtleff, *Vice Pres*
Lauris Higgins, *Project Mgr*
Dustin Larkin, *Production*
Rachel Barnette, *Purchasing*
EMP: 15
SALES (est): 8.4MM
SALES (corp-wide): 13.6B **Publicly Held**
WEB: www.bellflight.com
SIC: 3728 5088 3721 Aircraft parts & equipment; transportation equipment & supplies; helicopters; motorized aircraft
HQ: Bell Textron Inc.
3255 Bell Flight Blvd
Fort Worth TX 76118
817 280-2011

(G-6447)
BENZ COMPANIES LTD
Also Called: Benz Airborne Systems
2400 Handley Ederville Rd (76118-6946)
PHONE..............................817 280-0000
Roy H Coleman Jr, *Partner*
Charles Sanzone, *Engineer*
EMP: 10 **EST:** 1964
SALES (est): 1.8MM **Privately Held**
WEB: www.benzairborne.com
SIC: 3728 Aircraft parts & equipment

(G-6448)
BEST PUMP AND FLOW LP
Also Called: Best Machining Services
1329 Markum Gate Way (76126-1517)
PHONE..............................713 690-4511
Gail Garner, *Partner*
Marty Blacklock, *Partner*
Evelyn Martinez, *Purch Agent*
Curtis Thierry, *Engineer*
Melissa Martindale, *Manager*
▲ **EMP:** 40
SALES (est): 16.3MM **Privately Held**
WEB: www.bestflowline.com
SIC: 3494 3568 Valves & pipe fittings; power transmission equipment

(G-6449)
BIANCO BROTHERS
Also Called: Bianco Brothers Mfg Co
3008 Stuart Dr (76104-6767)
PHONE..............................817 922-0885
Don Bianco, *Owner*
EMP: 17 **EST:** 1952
SQ FT: 20,000
SALES (est): 1.7MM **Privately Held**
WEB: www.biancobros.com
SIC: 2599 Restaurant furniture, wood or metal

(G-6450)
BIG RED ENGINEERING LLC (PA)
6070 Copperfield Dr # 614 (76132-2613)
PHONE..............................817 539-9560
Labib Arafat, *Vice Pres*
Nadal Diya, *Mng Member*
EMP: 15 **EST:** 2014
SALES (est): 20MM **Privately Held**
WEB: www.bigredeng.com
SIC: 3533 1381 Oil field machinery & equipment; service well drilling

(G-6451)
BILLMARK COMPANY
2232 Solona St (76117-5314)
P.O. Box 14471 (76117-0471)
PHONE..............................817 834-2481
Charles M Shafer, *President*
Brenda Shafer, *Vice Pres*
EMP: 12
SQ FT: 27,500

SALES (corp-wide): 13.6B **Publicly Held**
WEB: www.billmarkplating.com
SIC: 3471 Electroplating of metals or formed products

(G-6452)
BIONICHE ANIMAL HEALTH USA INC (DH)
4250 N Sylvania Ave (76137-5014)
PHONE..............................706 549-4503
Andrew Grant, *CEO*
EMP: 14
SALES (est): 1.8MM
SALES (corp-wide): 3.6MM **Privately Held**
SIC: 2834 8731 3841 Veterinary pharmaceutical preparations; commercial physical research; surgical & medical instruments

(G-6453)
BIRDVIEW SKYLIGHTS
201 Longhorn Rd (76179-2403)
PHONE..............................817 439-9266
Guy Bird, *President*
Tim Reich, *General Mgr*
Debbie Bird, *Vice Pres*
Max Legett, *Sales Staff*
EMP: 15
SQ FT: 30,000
SALES (est): 3.2MM **Privately Held**
WEB: www.birdviewskylights.com
SIC: 3444 1761 Skylights, sheet metal; skylight installation

(G-6454)
BLACK MOUNTAIN SAND LLC (PA)
420 Commerce St Ste 500 (76102-4066)
PHONE..............................817 698-9901
Rhett Bennett, *CEO*
Jacob Smith,
EMP: 15
SALES (est): 33.4MM **Privately Held**
WEB: www.blackmountainsand.com
SIC: 1382 Oil & gas exploration services

(G-6455)
BLACK MTN ROYALTY I 2009 LP
500 Main St (76102-3937)
PHONE..............................888 698-9901
Rhett Bennett, *Principal*
EMP: 11
SALES (est): 2.9MM **Privately Held**
WEB: www.blackmtn.com
SIC: 1382 Oil & gas exploration services

(G-6456)
BLAYLOCK INDUSTRIES INC
5600 Midway Rd (76117-4632)
PHONE..............................817 831-0170
Ralph D Larovere, *CEO*
Rory Connor, *CEO*
Colinda Storms, *Executive*
EMP: 25
SALES (est): 7.1MM
SALES (corp-wide): 3.3MM **Privately Held**
WEB: www.blaylockind.com
SIC: 3365 Aluminum & aluminum-based alloy castings
PA: Winkleman & Winkleman Partners, Llc
5600 Midway Rd
Fort Worth TX 76117
817 831-0170

(G-6457)
BLAZING NEEDLES LP
Also Called: Golden Needle
401 N Beach St (76111-7011)
PHONE..............................817 831-2668
H A Shaban, *Partner*
▲ **EMP:** 30
SALES (est): 3.7MM **Privately Held**
WEB: www.eblazingneedles.com
SIC: 2392 Cushions & pillows

(G-6458)
BLUEBONNET BAKERY INC
Also Called: Harper's Bluebonnet Bakery
4705 Camp Bowie Blvd (76107-4154)
PHONE..............................817 731-4233
Margie Hart, *President*
EMP: 15 **EST:** 1950
SQ FT: 2,275

SALES (est): 797.8K **Privately Held**
WEB: www.bluebonnetbakery.com
SIC: 5461 5812 2052 2051 Cakes; caterers; cookies & crackers; bread, cake & related products

(G-6459)
BLUECREST ENERGY INC (PA)
1320 S University Dr # 825 (76107-5764)
PHONE..................................817 731-0066
J Benjamin Johnson, *CEO*
Robert Israel, *Ch of Bd*
John Martineck, *COO*
Jack Eells, *Vice Pres*
John Eells, *Vice Pres*
EMP: 25
SQ FT: 5,000
SALES (est): 19.9MM **Privately Held**
WEB: www.bluecrestenergy.com
SIC: 1382 Oil & gas exploration services

(G-6460)
BLUFF HOLDINGS INC
Also Called: Bluff Manufacturing
1400 Everman Pkwy Ste 156 (76140-5034)
PHONE..................................817 293-3018
Andrea Curreri, *President*
Tom Hobbs, *VP Opers*
Bruce Parker, *CFO*
Clark Smith, *Exec Dir*
◆ **EMP:** 75
SALES (est): 31.4K
SALES (corp-wide): 62.8K **Privately Held**
WEB: www.bluffmanufacturing.com
SIC: 3448 Docks: prefabricated metal
PA: Hadley Capital Fund Ii Lp
    1200 Central Ave Ste 300
    Wilmette IL 60091
    847 906-5300

(G-6461)
BLUFF MANUFACTURING INC (HQ)
1400 Everman Pkwy Ste 130 (76140-5031)
PHONE..................................817 293-3018
Clay Brock, *Ch of Bd*
Andrea Curreri, *President*
Paul Rusk, *Senior VP*
Scott Witt, *Vice Pres*
Jae Bills, *Purch Agent*
▲ **EMP:** 52
SALES (est): 33.2MM
SALES (corp-wide): 13.5MM **Privately Held**
WEB: www.bluffmanufacturing.com
SIC: 3448 Prefabricated metal buildings
PA: Wincove Private Holdings, L.P.
    75 Arlington St Ste 500
    Boston MA 02116
    617 848-4504

(G-6462)
BOSQUE DISPOSAL SYSTEMS LLC
420 Throckmorton St # 640 (76102-3723)
P.O. Box 614, Meridian (76665-0614)
PHONE..................................254 435-2260
Clane Lacrosse, *President*
Phillip Boren, *Vice Pres*
Ryan McAlister, *Vice Pres*
Robert Mitchell, *Vice Pres*
Peter Pappas, *Vice Pres*
EMP: 93
SALES (est): 31.3MM **Privately Held**
WEB: www.bosquesystems.com
SIC: 3589 Water treatment equipment, industrial

(G-6463)
BOSQUE SYSTEMS LLC
420 Throckmorton St # 640 (76102-3700)
PHONE..................................817 289-9900
EMP: 75
SALES (est): 23.2MM **Privately Held**
WEB: www.bosquesystems.com
SIC: 3589 Water treatment equipment, industrial

(G-6464)
BOXX MODULAR INC (HQ)
3475 High River Rd (76155-1900)
PHONE..................................972 492-4040
Trevor Haynes, *President*
Harry Klukas, *Exec VP*
Chris Rowe, *Vice Pres*
Neil Runion, *Vice Pres*

Gregory Roy, *Opers Staff*
EMP: 19
SQ FT: 2,000
SALES (est): 13.9MM
SALES (corp-wide): 139.6MM **Privately Held**
WEB: www.blackdiamondgroup.com
SIC: 7359 2452 Equipment rental & leasing; panels & sections, prefabricated, wood
PA: Black Diamond Group Limited
    440 2 Ave Sw Suite 1000
    Calgary AB T2P 5
    403 206-4747

(G-6465)
BRACKET SYSTEMS INC
Also Called: BSI
8781 Harmon Rd (76177-7501)
PHONE..................................817 232-8199
William E Hughes, *President*
Ed Ondrej, *Maint Spvr*
Daniel Nellessen, *Mfg Staff*
Shane Patrick, *Engineer*
Linda L Hughes, *Director*
▲ **EMP:** 40
SQ FT: 10,000
SALES (est): 10.8MM **Privately Held**
WEB: www.bracketrysystems.com
SIC: 3714 Air conditioner parts, motor vehicle

(G-6466)
BRADEN EXPLORATION LLC
307 W 7th St Ste 1300 (76102-5122)
P.O. Box 1270, Aledo (76008-1270)
PHONE..................................817 717-7020
Bruce F Braden, *Mng Member*
EMP: 15
SQ FT: 3,906
SALES (est): 1.4MM **Privately Held**
SIC: 1382 Oil & gas exploration services

(G-6467)
BRADEN EXPLORATION II LLC
307 W 7th St Ste 1300 (76102-5122)
P.O. Box 1270, Aledo (76008-1270)
PHONE..................................817 717-7020
Jennifer Braden,
EMP: 15 EST: 2012
SALES (est): 1.1MM **Privately Held**
WEB: www.bradenexpl.com
SIC: 1382 Oil & gas exploration services

(G-6468)
BRANDFX LLC (PA)
Also Called: Brand Fx Body Co
2800 Golden Triangle Blvd (76177-7016)
P.O. Box 77027 (76177-0027)
PHONE..................................817 431-1131
Lee Finley, *Ch of Bd*
Gary Heisterkamp, *President*
Perry Shatley, *Manager*
EMP: 48
SALES (est): 19.3MM **Privately Held**
WEB: www.brandfxbody.com
SIC: 3711 Trucks, pickup, assembly of

(G-6469)
BRANDON & CLARK INC
Also Called: Fort Worth Division
2475 E Long Ave (76106-6564)
PHONE..................................817 838-5593
Noah Hudgeons, *General Mgr*
Jody Lawrence, *Sales Staff*
Russ Burran, *Branch Mgr*
Scott Steggs, *Supervisor*
EMP: 36
SALES (corp-wide): 49.3MM **Privately Held**
WEB: www.brandonclark.com
SIC: 7694 5063 Electric motor repair; power transmission equipment, electric
PA: Brandon & Clark, Inc.
    3623 Interstate 27
    Lubbock TX 79404
    806 771-5600

(G-6470)
BRAZOS DELAWARE GAS LLC
Also Called: Brazos Midstream
3017 W 7th St Ste 300 (76107-2223)
PHONE..................................817 332-6800
Brad Iles, *CEO*
Ryan Jaggi, *COO*
Geoff Cole, *Vice Pres*

William Butler, *CFO*
EMP: 13
SALES (est): 2.3MM **Privately Held**
WEB: www.brazosmidstream.com
SIC: 1382 Oil & gas exploration services

(G-6471)
BRAZOS MDSTREAM HLDINGS II LLC
777 Main St Ste 3700 (76102-5376)
PHONE..................................817 332-6800
Brad Iles, *CEO*
Ryan Jaggi, *COO*
Bernadette Escamilla, *Opers Staff*
William Butler, *CFO*
Stephen Luskey, *Ch Credit Ofcr*
EMP: 34
SALES (est): 99.1K **Privately Held**
WEB: www.brazosmidstream.com
SIC: 1382 Oil & gas exploration services

(G-6472)
BROADWING AVIATION LLC
5300 W Vickery Blvd (76107-7520)
PHONE..................................817 332-0011
Mark Anderson, *Partner*
Michael Mills, *General Ptnr*
Domonic Eleby, *Opers Mgr*
Mark Pierce, *Opers Staff*
Tabor Chambers, *Buyer*
EMP: 30
SQ FT: 14,500
SALES (est): 9.7MM **Privately Held**
WEB: www.broadwingaviation.com
SIC: 3724 3728 5088 3721 Aircraft engines & engine parts; aircraft parts & equipment; aircraft & parts; aircraft

(G-6473)
BROWNLOW PUBLISHING COMPANY
Also Called: Brownlow Gifts
6309 Airport Fwy (76117-5393)
PHONE..................................817 831-3831
Paul C Brownlow, *President*
Fentress Sheppard, *General Mgr*
Andrew Brownlow, *Vice Pres*
John Paul Brownlow, *Vice Pres*
Lesha Henderson, *Prdtn Mgr*
◆ **EMP:** 41
SQ FT: 24,500
SALES (est): 6.1MM **Privately Held**
WEB: www.brownlowgift.com
SIC: 2731 Books: publishing & printing

(G-6474)
BRUMLEY PRINTING INC
820 N Main St (76164-9419)
PHONE..................................817 336-5551
EMP: 17
SQ FT: 20,000
SALES (est): 2.2MM **Privately Held**
WEB: www.brumleyprinting.com
SIC: 2752 Commercial printing, offset

(G-6475)
BSCO INC
2934 Se Loop 820 (76140-1020)
PHONE..................................817 568-0390
William Shelton, *President*
William H Shelton, *President*
EMP: 11
SQ FT: 10,000
SALES (est): 150K **Privately Held**
WEB: www.bsco-inc.com
SIC: 3699 5084 Electrical welding equipment; welding machinery & equipment

(G-6476)
BUILDERS FIRSTSOURCE INC
500 Terminal Rd (76106-1923)
PHONE..................................817 625-1200
Chris Reynolds, *General Mgr*
Bart Hall, *Sales Staff*
Chris Renalds, *Branch Mgr*
EMP: 30
SALES (corp-wide): 7.2B **Publicly Held**
WEB: www.bldr.com
SIC: 5031 2439 Lumber, plywood & millwork; structural wood members
PA: Builders Firstsource, Inc.
    2001 Bryan St Ste 1600
    Dallas TX 75201
    214 880-3500

(G-6477)
BUMPER MANUFACTURING CO INC
2500 Minnis Dr (76117-4858)
P.O. Box 7537 (76111-0537)
PHONE..................................817 831-4401
James J Ford, *President*
Marlene K Ford, *Corp Secy*
EMP: 20
SQ FT: 50,000
SALES (est): 3.9MM **Privately Held**
SIC: 5013 3714 Truck parts & accessories; motor vehicle parts & accessories

(G-6478)
BUNGE OILS INC
6700 Snowden Rd (76140-6030)
PHONE..................................817 568-4900
Mile Skein, *Branch Mgr*
EMP: 72 **Privately Held**
WEB: www.bungenorthamerica.com
SIC: 2076 Vegetable oil mills
HQ: Bunge Oils, Inc.
    1391 Tmbarlake Manor Pkwy
    Chesterfield MO 63017
    314 292-2000

(G-6479)
BURNETT OIL CO INC (PA)
801 Cherry St Unit 9 (76102-6881)
PHONE..................................817 332-5108
William Pollard, *President*
Bobby Claborn, *Principal*
Jack McCaslin, *Corp Secy*
Elizabeth Babb, *Counsel*
Neils Agather, *Vice Pres*
EMP: 26
SQ FT: 12,000
SALES (est): 44.6MM **Privately Held**
WEB: www.burnettoil.com
SIC: 1382 1311 Oil & gas exploration services; crude petroleum production; natural gas production

(G-6480)
BUZZ SERVICES LLC (PA)
Also Called: Buzz Custom Fence
5104 W Vickery Blvd (76107-7518)
P.O. Box 101442 (76185-1442)
PHONE..................................817 263-9788
Denise Bristow, *Production*
Sean Gremmer, *Sales Mgr*
Nicolena Matranga, *Sales Staff*
Denise Schrader,
Eric Schrader,
EMP: 20 EST: 1998
SQ FT: 11,000
SALES (est): 3.5MM **Privately Held**
WEB: www.buzzfence.com
SIC: 1799 3496 3315 Fence construction; miscellaneous fabricated wire products; steel wire & related products

(G-6481)
C & G PRINTING COMPANY INC
Also Called: Graphic Technologies
6237 Genoa Rd (76116-2025)
PHONE..................................817 738-8350
EMP: 30 EST: 1977
SQ FT: 17,000
SALES (est): 2.4MM **Privately Held**
SIC: 2752 2789 7336 Lithographic Commercial Printing Bookbinding/Related Work Commercial Art/Graphic Design

(G-6482)
C & H HARDWOODS INC
320 Thomas Pl (76140-4610)
P.O. Box 40885 (76140-0885)
PHONE..................................817 561-7711
Clifford Famers, *President*
Clifford Farmer, *President*
EMP: 17 EST: 1997
SQ FT: 15,000
SALES (est): 1.8MM **Privately Held**
SIC: 2435 Hardwood veneer & plywood

(G-6483)
C & L ALUMINUM FOUNDRY INC
3024 S Main St (76110-4283)
PHONE..................................817 923-0533
Nicholas Ferguson, *President*
Bryan Ferguson, *Vice Pres*
Ann Haugt, *Treasurer*
EMP: 16 EST: 1956
SQ FT: 10,000

▲ = Import ▼=Export
◆ =Import/Export

SALES (est): 3.2MM **Privately Held**
WEB: www.claluminum.com
SIC: 3366 Copper foundries

(G-6484)
C M C STEEL FABRICATORS INC
Also Called: CMC Construction Services
2400 Ne 36th St (76111-1905)
PHONE...................................817 838-6811
Mike McCoy, *Branch Mgr*
Scott Brown, *Manager*
Erik Vadte, *Manager*
EMP: 50
SALES (corp-wide): 5.4B **Publicly Held**
WEB: www.cmc.com
SIC: 5051 3449 3441 Steel; miscellaneous metalwork; fabricated structural metal
HQ: C M C Steel Fabricators, Inc.
1 Steel Mill Dr
Seguin TX 78155
830 372-8200

(G-6485)
CABINETS BY MICHAEL INC
Also Called: Vitality Construction
4301 Murray Ave (76117-1822)
PHONE...................................817 485-1962
Michael Wells, *President*
Forrest Ewing, *Manager*
EMP: 14
SQ FT: 10,000
SALES (est): 1.3MM **Privately Held**
WEB: www.cabinetsbymichael.com
SIC: 2521 1521 Cabinets, office: wood; new construction, single-family houses

(G-6486)
CALCOMP INC
1001 Le Loop 820 Ste 425 (76131)
PHONE...................................817 862-9311
Fred Donnelly, *President*
EMP: 45
SQ FT: 25,000
SALES (est): 2.8MM **Privately Held**
WEB: www.calcompinc.net
SIC: 3728 Aircraft parts & equipment

(G-6487)
CALIFORNIA EXPANDED MET PDTS
Also Called: California Expanded Metals Co
8600 Will Rogers Blvd (76140-6216)
PHONE...................................817 568-1525
Chad Rodgers, *Branch Mgr*
EMP: 83
SALES (corp-wide): 69.4MM **Privately Held**
WEB: www.cemcosteel.com
SIC: 3446 Lintels light gauge steel
PA: California Expanded Metal Products Company
13191 Crssrads Pkwy N Ste
City Of Industry CA 91746
626 369-3564

(G-6488)
CALIFORNIA EXPANDED MET PDTS
8600 Ill Rogers (76140)
PHONE...................................817 568-1525
EMP: 13
SALES (corp-wide): 76.3MM **Privately Held**
SIC: 3444 Mfg Sheet Metalwork
PA: California Expanded Metal Products Company
263 N Covina Ln
City Of Industry CA 91746
626 369-3564

(G-6489)
CALLAWAY GOLF BALL OPRTONS INC
Ben Hogan Div
9200 Oak Grove Rd (76140-5138)
PHONE...................................844 534-6426
Steve Dreyer, *Branch Mgr*
EMP: 100
SALES (corp-wide): 1.7B **Publicly Held**
SIC: 3949 5091 Golf equipment; golf equipment

HQ: Callaway Golf Ball Operations, Inc.
425 Meadow St
Chicopee MA 01013
413 536-1200

(G-6490)
CAMDEN MACHINE & TOOL INC
4900 Northeast Pkwy (76106-1817)
PHONE...................................817 838-6731
Ty Jones, *President*
David Durham, *Vice Pres*
EMP: 28 EST: 2014
SALES (est): 353.8K **Privately Held**
SIC: 3599 Machine & other job shop work

(G-6491)
CANTEX INC (DH)
301 Commerce St Ste 2700 (76102-4127)
PHONE...................................817 215-7000
Hisayoshi Uno, *CEO*
Don Wirtanon, *President*
Don Wirtanen, *President*
Mark Bauer, *General Mgr*
Claudio Najum, *Principal*
◆ EMP: 60
SALES (est): 187.8MM **Privately Held**
WEB: www.cantexinc.com
SIC: 3084 3089 Plastics pipe; fittings for pipe, plastic
HQ: Mitsubishi International Corporation
655 3rd Ave Fl 5
New York NY 10017
212 605-2000

(G-6492)
CAPELLON PHRMCTCALS LTD PARTNR
7509 Flagstone St (76118-6953)
PHONE...................................817 595-5820
David Brown, *Partner*
Ralph Brown, *General Ptnr*
Amy Brown, *Sales Associate*
Kris Torres, *Info Tech Dir*
Mike Fitz, *Info Tech Mgr*
EMP: 35
SALES (est): 7.7MM **Privately Held**
WEB: www.capellon.com
SIC: 5122 2834 Pharmaceuticals; pharmaceutical preparations

(G-6493)
CAPITAL RETURNS INC
4332 Empire Rd (76155-2716)
PHONE...................................414 466-2418
Lawrence G Hruska, *President*
Claude Dance, *Vice Pres*
EMP: 80
SALES (est): 7.3MM
SALES (corp-wide): 69.2B **Publicly Held**
SIC: 7389 2834 4953 Salvaging of damaged merchandise, service only; pharmaceutical preparations; refuse systems
HQ: Fedex Supply Chain Distribution System, Inc.
700 Cranberry Woods Dr
Cranberry Township PA 16066

(G-6494)
CASCADE ENGINEERING INC
5400 Alliance Gateway Fwy (76177-3732)
PHONE...................................817 490-6300
Fred Keller, *Branch Mgr*
EMP: 460
SALES (corp-wide): 667.4MM **Privately Held**
WEB: www.cascadecartsolutions.com
SIC: 3089 Injection molding of plastics
PA: Cascade Engineering, Inc.
3400 Innovation Ct Se
Grand Rapids MI 49512
616 975-4800

(G-6495)
CASH ENGRAVING CO
Also Called: Label Graphics
1403 Oak Knoll Dr (76117-5599)
PHONE...................................817 831-8585
David Harris, *Owner*
EMP: 15 EST: 1986
SQ FT: 6,700

SALES (est): 1MM **Privately Held**
SIC: 2796 2752 2672 2761 Photoengraving plates, linecuts or halftones; commercial printing, offset; labels (unprinted), gummed; made from purchased materials; manifold business forms; therapy equipment

(G-6496)
CASTING DESIGNS INC
Also Called: CDI
9320 Crowley Rd (76134-5903)
PHONE...................................817 551-7373
Jerry Bransom, *President*
Jeannie Bransom, *Vice Pres*
Casey Glendenning, *Design Engr*
Terri Vaughn, *Sales Executive*
Troy Russom, *MIS Mgr*
EMP: 125
SQ FT: 70,000
SALES (est): 18.2MM **Privately Held**
WEB: www.castingdesignsinc.com
SIC: 3275 2221 3271 Gypsum products; glass & fiberglass broadwoven fabrics; architectural concrete: block, split, fluted, screen, etc.

(G-6497)
CBI LABORATORIES INC
Also Called: Voyant Beauty
4201 Diplomacy Rd (76155-2633)
PHONE...................................972 241-7546
David Pair, *COO*
Bill Basinski, *Vice Pres*
Vicky Marin, *Production*
Vicky Rodriguez, *Research*
Michael Seay, *CFO*
▲ EMP: 75
SQ FT: 110,000
SALES (est): 20MM **Privately Held**
WEB: www.cbiskincare.com
SIC: 3841 Cystoscopes; bone drills
PA: Suntx Capital Partners Ii Gp, L.P.
5420 Lyndon B Johnson Fwy # 1000
Dallas TX 75240

(G-6498)
CC3
Also Called: Business
5600 Stratum Dr (76137-2710)
PHONE...................................817 230-2700
Scott Turner, *Vice Pres*
EMP: 50
SALES (est): 3.4MM **Privately Held**
SIC: 2759 Commercial printing

(G-6499)
CCS CUPCAKE HEAVEN
1420 Heidi Ct (76108-3569)
PHONE...................................817 732-2993
Michelle McCrccken, *Owner*
EMP: 11 EST: 2013
SALES (est): 821.8K **Privately Held**
WEB: www.cupcakesfortworth.com
SIC: 2051 Bakery: wholesale or wholesale/retail combined

(G-6500)
CDK PERFORATING
8101 Boat Club Rd Ste 330 (76179-3633)
PHONE...................................817 945-1051
EMP: 20 EST: 2012
SALES (est): 870K **Privately Held**
SIC: 1389 Oil/Gas Field Services

(G-6501)
CDK PERFORATING LLC (HQ)
Also Called: Nine Energy Service
6500 West Fwy Ste 600 (76116-2118)
PHONE...................................817 945-1051
Christopher A Payson,
Kenneth Preston,
Arezeki Seheb,
Karen Walton,
EMP: 110
SALES (est): 139.7MM
SALES (corp-wide): 832.9MM **Publicly Held**
WEB: www.nineenergyservice.com
SIC: 1389 Oil field services
PA: Nine Energy Service, Inc.
2001 Kirby Dr Ste 200
Houston TX 77019
281 730-5100

(G-6502)
CDK PERFORATING HOLDINGS INC
6500 West Fwy Ste 600 (76116-2118)
PHONE...................................817 945-1051
Ann Fox, *CFO*
Andrew Waite, *Director*
Christopher Payson, *Director*
EMP: 180
SALES (est): 8.1MM **Privately Held**
WEB: www.nineenergyservice.com
SIC: 1389 Oil field services

(G-6503)
CELERO ENERGY (PA)
301 Commerce St Ste 2001 (76102-4129)
PHONE...................................817 708-3800
Scott Lakey, *Owner*
John Lodge, *Vice Pres*
Michelle Gutierrez, *Manager*
EMP: 9
SQ FT: 14,000
SALES (est): 2.3MM **Privately Held**
WEB: www.celeroenergy.com
SIC: 1382 Oil & gas exploration services

(G-6504)
CELERO ENERGY II LP
301 Commerce St Ste 2001 (76102-4129)
PHONE...................................817 708-3800
Lakey Scott, *Branch Mgr*
EMP: 25
SALES (est): 1.8MM **Privately Held**
SIC: 1382 Oil & gas exploration services

(G-6505)
CENTURY COMPONENTS CORPORATION
5524 Midway Rd Ste 1 (76117-4641)
P.O. Box 399, Santo (76472-0399)
PHONE...................................817 831-8301
Annie Laurie Hyde, *President*
Lori Cook, *Vice Pres*
▲ EMP: 10 EST: 1998
SQ FT: 3,600
SALES (est): 1.2MM **Privately Held**
WEB: www.centurycomponents.com
SIC: 3728 Aircraft parts & equipment

(G-6506)
CFJ MANUFACTURING LP (PA)
Also Called: Collections Fine Jewelry
701 Eight Twenty Blvd # 145 (76106-2002)
PHONE...................................817 625-9559
Sharon Evans, *CEO*
Kim Sissen, *President*
Javier Johnston, *Opers Dir*
Seni Efunshile, *Controller*
Chanda Campbell, *Accountant*
◆ EMP: 85
SALES (est): 18.2MM **Privately Held**
WEB: www.cfjmanufacturinglp.com
SIC: 3911 3993 5094 5199 Jewelry, precious metal; signs & advertising specialties; jewelry; advertising specialties; jewelry, precious stones & precious metals

(G-6507)
CHAMPION CUSTOM CABINETS INC
875 Haltom Rd (76117-6422)
PHONE...................................817 834-8552
Keith Ivy, *President*
Hoffman Evelyn, *Vice Pres*
EMP: 18 EST: 1980
SQ FT: 6,000
SALES (est): 1.5MM **Privately Held**
SIC: 2434 5712 Wood kitchen cabinets; cabinets, except custom made: kitchen

(G-6508)
CHANDLER SIGNS LLC
14201 Sovereign Rd 101 (76155-2644)
PHONE...................................760 734-1708
Chuck Riffe, *Vice Pres*
Brenda Jimenez, *Project Mgr*
Erin Myers, *Project Mgr*
Therese Pennington, *Project Mgr*
Samantha Rodd, *Project Mgr*
EMP: 100
SALES (corp-wide): 74MM **Privately Held**
WEB: www.chandlersigns.com
SIC: 3993 Electric signs

GEOGRAPHIC

PA: Chandler Signs, Llc
14201 Sovereign Rd 101
Fort Worth TX 76155
214 902-2000

(G-6509)
CHANDLER SIGNS LLC (PA)
14201 Sovereign Rd 101 (76155-2644)
PHONE..................................214 902-2000
Rockford Gray, *Ch of Bd*
Chuck Riffe, *President*
Gary Stevens, *President*
Bill Macrum, *Vice Pres*
Mark J Vergenz, *Vice Pres*
EMP: 250
SQ FT: 80,000
SALES (est): 74MM **Privately Held**
WEB: www.chandlersigns.com
SIC: 3993 Signs & advertising specialties;
electric signs; neon signs

(G-6510)
CHARLEYS CONCRETE CO LTD
(PA)
11801 Katy Rd (76244-8824)
P.O. Box 1106, Keller (76244-1106)
PHONE..................................817 431-3515
Brent Pennington, *CEO*
Patsy Pennington, *Partner*
Tanya Shaw, *Credit Mgr*
Julie Zuefeldt, *Accountant*
Liz Starkey, *Human Res Mgr*
EMP: 40
SQ FT: 2,400
SALES (est): 39MM **Privately Held**
WEB: www.charleysconcrete.com
SIC: 3273 Ready-mixed concrete

(G-6511)
CHASE PECAN LP
201 Main St Ste 1801 (76102-3121)
PHONE..................................706 556-6216
Nancy Chavis, *Manager*
EMP: 75
SALES (corp-wide): 11.8MM **Privately Held**
WEB: www.oliverpecan.com
SIC: 2068 Nuts: dried, dehydrated, salted
or roasted
PA: Chase Pecan Lp
2803 W Wallace St
San Saba TX 76877
325 372-5727

(G-6512)
CHESAPEAKE ENERGY
CORPORATION
100 Energy Way (76102-2661)
PHONE..................................817 502-5000
EMP: 50
SALES (corp-wide): 12.7B **Publicly Held**
SIC: 1311 Oil & Gas Exploration Produc-
tion And Marketing
PA: Chesapeake Energy Corporation
6100 N Western Ave
Oklahoma City OK 73118
405 848-8000

(G-6513)
CHICAGO FLAMEPROOF WD
SPC CORP
Also Called: North Texas Flameproof & Wood
4215 Chickasaw Ave (76119-4023)
PHONE..................................817 534-9800
Jason Nichols, *Branch Mgr*
EMP: 12 **Privately Held**
WEB: www.flameproof.com
SIC: 5031 2491 Building materials, exte-
rior; building materials, interior; wood pre-
serving
PA: Chicago Flameproof And Wood Spe-
cialties Corp.
1200 S Lake St
Montgomery IL 60538

(G-6514)
CHISHOLM ENERGY
OPERATING LLC
801 Cherry St Ste 1200 (76102-6825)
PHONE..................................817 953-6063
Aaron Gaydosik, *CFO*
EMP: 17
SQ FT: 23,000

SALES (est): 40MM
SALES (corp-wide): 2.7MM **Privately
Held**
WEB: www.chisholmenergy.com
SIC: 1382 Oil & gas exploration services
PA: Chisholm Energy Holdings, Llc
801 Cherry St Ste 1200
Fort Worth TX 76102
817 953-6063

(G-6515)
CHOICE FABRICATED STONE
LLC
6308 Eden Dr (76117-6129)
PHONE..................................817 222-2201
Wes Cooper, *Mng Member*
Chris Campbell, *Supervisor*
EMP: 22
SALES (est): 4.4MM **Privately Held**
WEB: www.choicestone.net
SIC: 5032 3281 Granite building stone;
building stone products; curbing, granite
or stone

(G-6516)
CHUCK ATKINSON INC
Also Called: Cap Software
7250 W Vickery Blvd (76116-9071)
PHONE..................................817 560-8139
Chuck Atkinson, *CEO*
William Atkinson, *President*
Charles A Atkinson Jr, *Chairman*
Derrick Atkinson, *Vice Pres*
Jan Atkinson, *Vice Pres*
EMP: 10
SQ FT: 3,300
SALES (est): 1.6MM **Privately Held**
WEB: www.capretail.com
SIC: 7372 Prepackaged software

(G-6517)
CIBA VISION CORPORATION
Also Called: Alcon
6201 South Fwy (76134-2001)
PHONE..................................817 551-6881
Seba Leoni, *President*
Tom Steiner, *Principal*
Trang Nguyen, *Project Mgr*
Jean Wagner, *VP Human Res*
David Nixon, *Sales Staff*
▲ **EMP:** 869 **EST:** 2011
SALES (est): 228.8MM **Privately Held**
WEB: www.alcon.com
SIC: 3851 Contact lenses

(G-6518)
CIBA VISION INC
6201 South Fwy (76134-2001)
PHONE..................................847 294-3000
Bernie Bartlette, *General Mgr*
EMP: 2820
SQ FT: 340,000
SALES (est): 203.9MM **Privately Held**
WEB: www.alcon.com
SIC: 3851 Contact lenses

(G-6519)
CIRCLE J FABRICATION INC
8020 White Settlement Rd (76108-1725)
PHONE..................................817 367-3877
Joseph Jones, *President*
Justin Jones, *Associate*
EMP: 20
SALES (est): 3.5MM **Privately Held**
WEB: www.circlejfirepits.com
SIC: 3631 Barbecues, grills & braziers
(outdoor cooking)

(G-6520)
CIRCLE U FOODS INC
751 Eight Twenty Blvd # 101 (76106-1972)
PHONE..................................817 626-6918
Lynn Ulmer, *President*
Debbie Ulmer, *Corp Secy*
EMP: 16
SQ FT: 32,000
SALES (est): 7.1MM **Privately Held**
WEB: www.circleufoods.com
SIC: 2099 5141 Spices, including grinding;
food brokers

(G-6521)
CKS PACKAGING INC
109 E Felix St S (76115-3533)
PHONE..................................817 924-2205
David Shafer, *Branch Mgr*

EMP: 125
SALES (corp-wide): 439.3MM **Privately
Held**
WEB: www.ckspackaging.com
SIC: 3089 3085 Plastic containers, except
foam; plastics bottles
PA: C.K.S. Packaging, Inc.
350 Great Sw Pkwy
Atlanta GA 30336
404 691-8900

(G-6522)
CLARIOS
Also Called: Johnson Controls
2500 Lou Menk Dr (76131-2828)
PHONE..................................817 733-4326
EMP: 88 **Privately Held**
WEB: www.johnsoncontrols.com
SIC: 2531 Seats, automobile
HQ: Johnson Controls, Inc.
5757 N Green Bay Ave
Glendale WI 53209
800 382-2804

(G-6523)
CLEBURNE METAL WORKS LLC
Also Called: Cleburne Sheet Metal
6432 Nine Mile Bridge Rd (76135-9260)
P.O. Box 137088 (76136-1088)
PHONE..................................817 237-5060
Brandon Caster, *General Mgr*
Bruce Huff, *Sales Executive*
Fred Couch, *Mng Member*
Nathan Avanzini, *Prgrmr*
EMP: 40
SQ FT: 21,000
SALES (est): 11.3MM **Privately Held**
WEB: www.cleburnesheetmetal.com
SIC: 3444 Sheet metalwork

(G-6524)
CMC MATERIALS INC (HQ)
Also Called: Kmg Chemicals
300 Throckmorton St (76102-2921)
PHONE..................................817 761-6100
Christopher T Fraser, *President*
Jeffrey S Handelman, *Senior VP*
Chris Gonser, *Vice Pres*
Tim Hagensen, *Vice Pres*
Jennifer Pomales, *Manager*
◆ **EMP:** 64 **EST:** 1985
SQ FT: 27,778
SALES: 465.5MM
SALES (corp-wide): 1.1B **Publicly Held**
WEB: www.kmgchemicals.com
SIC: 2899 Chemical preparations
PA: Cmc Materials, Inc.
870 N Commons Dr
Aurora IL 60504
630 375-6631

(G-6525)
CO-OPERATIVE INDS DEF LLC
Also Called: Co-Operative Inds Arospc & Def
1401 S Cherry Ln (76108-3622)
PHONE..................................817 740-4700
Oanh Vo, *Mfg Spvr*
Sam Symonds, *Mng Member*
Martin Angella, *Manager*
Scott Moore, *Manager*
Jim W Green,
EMP: 95
SQ FT: 122,000
SALES (est): 3.3MM **Privately Held**
WEB: www.coopind.com
SIC: 3679 Harness assemblies for elec-
tronic use: wire or cable
PA: Ksaria Corporation
300 Griffin Brook Dr
Methuen MA 01844

(G-6526)
COCA-COLA COMPANY
3400 Fossil Creek Blvd (76137-2402)
PHONE..................................817 847-3000
Derek McCoy, *Branch Mgr*
EMP: 500
SALES (corp-wide): 37.2B **Publicly Held**
WEB: www.coca-colacompany.com
SIC: 2086 Bottled & canned soft drinks
PA: The Coca-Cola Company
1 Coca Cola Plz Nw
Atlanta GA 30313
404 676-2121

(G-6527)
COCA-COLA ENTERPRISES
3400 Fossil Creek Blvd (76137-2402)
PHONE..................................817 232-8600
EMP: 23
SALES (est): 3.8MM **Privately Held**
SIC: 2086 Bottled & canned soft drinks

(G-6528)
COCKRELL PRINTING CO (PA)
Also Called: Cockrell Enovation
218 W Broadway Ave (76104-1206)
P.O. Box 1568 (76101-1568)
PHONE..................................817 336-0571
John Cockrell, *President*
Lynn Cockrell, *Corp Secy*
Mary E Cockrell, *Admin Sec*
EMP: 85
SQ FT: 65,000
SALES (est): 21.8MM **Privately Held**
WEB: www.cockrellprinting.com
SIC: 2752 2791 2789 Commercial print-
ing, offset; typesetting; bookbinding & re-
lated work

(G-6529)
COHN & GREGORY SUPPLY LLC
2710 N Nichols St (76106-7225)
PHONE..................................817 624-1141
EMP: 19
SALES (corp-wide): 35MM **Privately
Held**
WEB: www.cgsupply.com
SIC: 3443 Tanks, standard or custom fabri-
cated: metal plate
PA: Cohn & Gregory Supply Llc
5450 Midway Rd
Haltom City TX 76117
817 831-9998

(G-6530)
COLD AIR PRODUCTS INC
1201 Forum Way S (76140-5011)
P.O. Box 40386 (76140-0386)
PHONE..................................817 531-2665
Darrow Cowart, *President*
Scott Hutto, *Vice Pres*
Dalynn Ybarra, *Office Mgr*
▲ **EMP:** 28
SQ FT: 5,000
SALES (est): 5.8MM **Privately Held**
WEB: www.oldairproducts.com
SIC: 3585 Air conditioning, motor vehicle

(G-6531)
COMMERCIAL METALS
COMPANY
Also Called: CMC Recycling & Express Retail
4500 Old Decatur Rd (76106-2405)
P.O. Box 4405 (76164-0405)
PHONE..................................817 429-4005
Daniel Leal, *Sales Mgr*
Tabatha Day, *Marketing Staff*
John Sims, *Marketing Staff*
Mitch Alverson, *Branch Mgr*
EMP: 39
SALES (corp-wide): 5.4B **Publicly Held**
WEB: www.cmc.com
SIC: 5093 3341 Ferrous metal scrap &
waste; nonferrous metals scrap; second-
ary nonferrous metals
PA: Commercial Metals Company
6565 N Macarthur Blvd # 800
Irving TX 75039
214 689-4300

(G-6532)
COMPASS WELL SERVICES
LLC (PA)
Also Called: Compass Cementing Services
4100 Intl Plz Ste 500 (76109)
PHONE..................................817 244-2555
Colin F Raymond, *Chairman*
Buddy Petersen, *Vice Pres*
Edgar Gonzalez, *Foreman/Supr*
Johnathon Siegenthaler, *Opers Staff*
Dick Mocksfield, *Engineer*
EMP: 83
SQ FT: 7,059
SALES (est): 80MM **Privately Held**
WEB: www.compasswellservices.com
SIC: 1389 1382 Cementing oil & gas well
casings; oil & gas exploration services

(G-6533)
COMPLETE SOLIDS CONTROL LLC
944 Hemlock Trl (76131-3550)
PHONE..............................817 372-2702
Rachel Nicodemus, *Manager*
EMP: 10
SALES (est): 557.9K Privately Held
WEB: www.completesolidscontrol.com
SIC: 1389 Building oil & gas well foundations on site

(G-6534)
COMPONENT PARTS MACHINE CO INC (PA)
3100 Chesser Boyer Rd (76111-3005)
P.O. Box 7514 (76111-0514)
PHONE..............................817 834-4771
Don Sanders, *President*
EMP: 25
SQ FT: 14,000
SALES (est): 2MM Privately Held
SIC: 3599 3714 3585 Machine shop, jobbing & repair; motor vehicle parts & accessories; refrigeration & heating equipment

(G-6535)
COMPONENT PARTS MACHINE CO INC
Fabrication Division
4100 Hahn Blvd (76117-1709)
P.O. Box 7514 (76111-0514)
PHONE..............................817 834-4771
John Rueles, *General Mgr*
EMP: 10
SQ FT: 7,500
SALES (corp-wide): 2MM Privately Held
SIC: 7539 3599 Machine shop, automotive; machine shop, jobbing & repair
PA: Component Parts Machine Co., Inc.
3100 Chesser Boyer Rd
Fort Worth TX 76111
817 834-4771

(G-6536)
COMPOSITE COOLING SOLUTIONS LP
Also Called: Ccsolutions
4150 Intl Plz Ste 500 (76109)
PHONE..............................817 246-8700
William Rector, *CEO*
Charles Bardo, *Partner*
Jamie Bland, *Partner*
Jess Seawell, *Partner*
Shane Weyant, *Partner*
◆ EMP: 57
SQ FT: 10,000
SALES (est): 59.8MM Privately Held
WEB: www.compositecooling.com
SIC: 3444 Cooling towers, sheet metal

(G-6537)
COMPOSITES ONE LLC
905 Railhead Dr (76177-3904)
PHONE..............................817 595-4991
Dionicio Sifuentez, *Warehouse Mgr*
Stephen Smith, *Manager*
EMP: 25
SALES (corp-wide): 355.3MM Privately Held
WEB: www.compositesone.com
SIC: 2821 Plastics materials & resins
HQ: Composites One Llc
85 W Algonquin Rd Ste 600
Arlington Heights IL 60005
847 437-0200

(G-6538)
COMPROBE INC
9632 Crowley Rd (76134-5999)
PHONE..............................817 293-7333
Mike Hawkins, *President*
Eric Nellis, *Principal*
Ken Fowler, *Vice Pres*
EMP: 15
SQ FT: 15,000
SALES (est): 2.2MM Privately Held
WEB: www.comprobeinc.com
SIC: 3812 3713 Search & detection systems & instruments; truck & bus bodies

(G-6539)
CONAGRA BRANDS INC
4701 Gold Spike Dr (76106-1988)
PHONE..............................817 210-1600
Christopher Brantley, *Branch Mgr*
EMP: 54
SALES (corp-wide): 11B Publicly Held
WEB: www.conagrabrands.com
SIC: 2099 Food preparations
PA: Conagra Brands, Inc.
222 Mdse Mart Plz Ste 1
Chicago IL 60654
312 549-5000

(G-6540)
CONECRAFT INCORPORATED
3209 S Grove St (76110-4304)
PHONE..............................817 922-9200
James A Austin, *President*
Anthony C Cox, *Vice Pres*
Tony Cox, *Vice Pres*
Sarah J Schultz, *Vice Pres*
Jonathan Dow, *Design Engr*
EMP: 83
SQ FT: 40,000
SALES (est): 16.6MM Privately Held
WEB: www.conecraft.com
SIC: 3559 Pharmaceutical machinery

(G-6541)
CONNER INDUSTRIES INC
1951 Keller Hicks Rd (76177-6907)
PHONE..............................817 439-3555
Floyd Farquhar, *Branch Mgr*
EMP: 20
SALES (corp-wide): 171.2MM Privately Held
WEB: www.connerindustries.com
SIC: 5031 2421 2493 2449 Lumber: rough, dressed & finished; cut stock, softwood; reconstituted wood products; wood containers
PA: Conner Industries, Inc.
3800 Sandshell Dr Ste 235
Fort Worth TX 76137
800 413-8006

(G-6542)
CONNOR MEDIA GROUP LLC
Also Called: Texas Community Newspapers
101 Summit Ave Ste 803 (76102-2622)
PHONE..............................817 336-8300
Richard Conner, *President*
EMP: 20
SALES (est): 1.3MM Privately Held
SIC: 2711 Newspapers, publishing & printing

(G-6543)
CONSLIDATED RIGWORKS LP
6000 E Berry St (76119-1807)
PHONE..............................817 446-5272
Kenneth Butler, *President*
EMP: 45
SQ FT: 57,000
SALES (est): 4.3MM Privately Held
WEB: www.crwlp.com
SIC: 3711 3533 5013 1799 Wreckers (tow truck), assembly of; oil field machinery & equipment; automotive servicing equipment; welding on site

(G-6544)
CONSOLIDATED RIG WORKS LP
6000 E Berry St (76119-1807)
PHONE..............................817 446-5272
Rick Coon, *CEO*
Kenneth Butler, *Partner*
Caleb Fulks, *Vice Pres*
Billy Wood, *CFO*
EMP: 50
SALES (est): 14MM Privately Held
WEB: www.crwlp.com
SIC: 3533 Oil & gas drilling rigs & equipment

(G-6545)
COOKSEY LUTHER PRINTING CO
1920 Wenneca Ave (76102-4321)
PHONE..............................817 332-2842
James Dugger, *President*
Dwayne Dugger, *Vice Pres*
EMP: 10 EST: 1950

SQ FT: 5,000
SALES (est): 1.3MM Privately Held
SIC: 2752 2796 Lithographing on metal; letterpress plates, preparation of

(G-6546)
COOPER OIL COMPANY INC
Also Called: Cooper Operating
777 Main St Ste 800 (76102-5350)
PHONE..............................817 332-7755
Jimmy Cooper, *President*
EMP: 12
SALES (est): 2.9MM Privately Held
SIC: 1389 5171 Oil field services; petroleum bulk stations & terminals

(G-6547)
COOPER SHEET METAL INC
10056 Hicks Field Rd (76179-5240)
P.O. Box 79730 (76179-0730)
PHONE..............................817 232-4250
Chris Cooper, *President*
Donna Cooper, *Corp Secy*
EMP: 45
SQ FT: 15,000
SALES (est): 7.3MM Privately Held
SIC: 3444 Ducts, sheet metal

(G-6548)
COOPER SUPPLY INC
2524 Minnis Dr (76117-4858)
PHONE..............................817 222-9055
Stephanie Paul, *General Mgr*
Christi Minnis, *Opers Dir*
Greg Corbelli, *Sales Staff*
Raymond Escoto, *Sales Staff*
Damon Walters, *Manager*
EMP: 21
SALES (corp-wide): 8.4MM Privately Held
WEB: www.coopersupply.com
SIC: 5074 3081 Plumbing & hydronic heating supplies; polyethylene film
PA: Cooper Supply, Inc.
216 Santa Anna Ave
Coleman TX 76834
325 625-3543

(G-6549)
COPPER CRAFT INC
300 Railhead Rd (76106-1974)
PHONE..............................817 490-9622
Bob West, *President*
▼ EMP: 35
SQ FT: 20,000
SALES (est): 8.2MM Privately Held
WEB: www.coppercraft.com
SIC: 3351 1761 3463 3444 Extruded shapes, copper & copper alloy; roofing, siding & sheet metal work; nonferrous forgings; sheet metalwork

(G-6550)
CORNING OPTICAL COMMUNICATIONS
5940 Optical Way (76244-2009)
PHONE..............................817 431-7120
▲ EMP: 20 EST: 2015
SALES (est): 4.3MM
SALES (corp-wide): 11.5B Publicly Held
SIC: 3229 Fiber optics strands
PA: Corning Incorporated
1 Riverfront Plz
Corning NY 14831
607 974-9000

(G-6551)
COWBOY PUBLISHING GROUP
2112 Montgomery St (76107-4517)
PHONE..............................817 737-6397
Patty Tiberg, *Sales Staff*
Carl Mullins, *Sales Staff*
EMP: 50
SALES (est): 2.7MM Privately Held
WEB: www.barrelhorsenews.com
SIC: 2721 Magazines: publishing only, not printed on site
HQ: Morris Communications Company Llc
725 Broad St
Augusta GA 30901
706 724-0851

(G-6552)
COWTOWN REDI MIX INC
3401 Bethlehem St (76111-1923)
P.O. Box 162327 (76161-2327)
PHONE..............................817 759-1919
Mariam El Hourani, *President*
Sam Shamisani, *Corp Secy*
EMP: 10
SQ FT: 1,200
SALES (est): 80MM Privately Held
WEB: www.cowtownredimix.com
SIC: 3273 Ready-mixed concrete

(G-6553)
COWTOWN TRAFFIC CONTROL INC (PA)
112 W Jessamine St (76110-2757)
PHONE..............................817 924-4524
Roosevelt Burrell Jr, *President*
Ronita B Moore, *Manager*
EMP: 9
SQ FT: 24,000
SALES (est): 882.9K Privately Held
WEB: www.cowtowntrafficcontrolinc.wordpress.com
SIC: 3499 Barricades, metal

(G-6554)
COWTOWN WESTERN BELT INC
Also Called: Bryan Enterprise
5608 Scoggins St (76114-1136)
PHONE..............................817 625-4411
Arturo Alcocer, *President*
EMP: 30 EST: 1979
SALES (est): 1.9MM Privately Held
SIC: 2387 Apparel belts

(G-6555)
COZART MTAL BLDNGS SYSTEMS INC
6428 Nine Mile Bridge Rd (76135-9260)
P.O. Box 1195, Azle (76098-1195)
PHONE..............................817 237-2282
James Cozart, *President*
Jeremy Cozart, *Vice Pres*
Pam Cozart, *Admin Sec*
Pamela Cozart, *Admin Sec*
EMP: 9
SALES (est): 950K Privately Held
WEB: www.cozartmbs.com
SIC: 3448 Prefabricated metal buildings

(G-6556)
CRAFTMARK PRODUCTS INC
Also Called: Craftmark Idntfication Systems
3212 S Cravens Rd (76119-1862)
P.O. Box 50668 (76105-0668)
PHONE..............................817 457-8753
Brabham Vernon Jr, *CEO*
Glen Christianson, *President*
Kelly Priest, *Executive*
▲ EMP: 45
SQ FT: 30,000
SALES (est): 5.6MM Privately Held
WEB: www.craftmarkid.com
SIC: 3993 Signs & advertising specialties

(G-6557)
CRANE EQUIPMENT & SERVICE INC
Also Called: Gaffey Cranes & Hoists
2426 Gravel Dr (76118-6938)
PHONE..............................817 740-7911
Jim Kritzmire, *Manager*
EMP: 25
SALES (corp-wide): 809.1MM Publicly Held
SIC: 5084 3536 Hoists; hoists, cranes & monorails
HQ: Crane Equipment & Service, Inc.
140 John Jmes Adubon Pkwy
Amherst NY 14228
716 689-5400

(G-6558)
CREATIVE NIGHTSCAPES
5755 Carlisle Ct Ste 300 (76180-6038)
PHONE..............................817 581-6936
David Rosenbame, *Principal*
Frances Martinez, *Office Mgr*
EMP: 10
SALES (est): 650K Privately Held
WEB: www.creativenightscapes.com
SIC: 3645 Garden, patio, walkway & yard lighting fixtures: electric

---

(G-6559)
CREATIVE STITCHES INC
578 N Beach St (76111-5940)
PHONE................................817 284-0061
Darrell Norrid, *President*
Jon Hawkins, *Regional Mgr*
Ken Hubbard, *Regl Sales Mgr*
EMP: 23
SQ FT: 18,000 **Privately Held**
WEB: www.creativestitchesinc.com
SIC: 2395 Embroidery products, except
schiffli machine

(G-6560)
CREST PUMPING
TECHNOLOGIES LLC (HQ)
6500 West Fwy Ste 601 (76116-2181)
PHONE................................817 484-5100
David Crombie, *President*
Bryan Besselaar, *Opers Mgr*
Kevin Palma, *CFO*
Jeff Gleason, *Director*
EMP: 80
SALES (est): 194MM
SALES (corp-wide): 832.9MM **Publicly**
Held
WEB: www.nineenergyservice.com
SIC: 1389 Oil field services
PA: Nine Energy Service, Inc.
2001 Kirby Dr Ste 200
Houston TX 77019
281 730-5100

(G-6561)
CRIST INDUSTRIES INC
9965 Saginaw Blvd (76179-5206)
P.O. Box 79320 (76179-0320)
PHONE................................817 847-8500
Celia Crist, *President*
Steve Murphy, *President*
Larry Crist, *Vice Chairman*
EMP: 75
SQ FT: 40,000
SALES (est): 15.1MM **Privately Held**
WEB: www.ennissteel.com
SIC: 3441 Fabricated structural metal

(G-6562)
CROW PRECISION
COMPONENTS LLC
Also Called: W. Pat Crow Forgings
200 Luxton St (76104-1719)
P.O. Box 1720 (76101-1720)
PHONE.......:........................817 536-2861
Al Altieri, *CEO*
Khalid Rokhami, *General Mgr*
EMP: 100 **EST:** 2014
SALES (est): 13.8MM
SALES (corp-wide): 20.4MM **Privately**
Held
WEB: www.wpatcrow.com
SIC: 3462 Iron & steel forgings
PA: Whi Global, Llc
90 New Dutch Ln
Fairfield NJ 07004
855 944-4562

(G-6563)
CSG SYSTEMS INC
5600 Stratum Dr (76137-2710)
PHONE................................817 230-2700
EMP: 123 **Publicly Held**
WEB: www.csgi.com
SIC: 2752 Commercial printing, litho-
graphic
HQ: Csg Systems, Inc.
18020 Burt St
Elkhorn NE 68022

(G-6564)
CTC INC
9601 Camp Bowie West Blvd (76116-5939)
PHONE................................817 886-8210
Rick Campbell, *President*
Mike Cunningham, *COO*
Kurt Anderson, *Vice Pres*
Janie Hollingsworth, *Vice Pres*
John Sharkey, *Vice Pres*
EMP: 45
SQ FT: 10,366
SALES (est): 11.4MM **Privately Held**
WEB: www.riotechnology.com
SIC: 3743 1629 8711 Railroad equipment;
railroad & subway construction; construc-
tion & civil engineering

PA: Rio Grande Pacific Corporation
6100 Southwest Blvd # 320
Benbrook TX 76109

(G-6565)
CUGAR MACHINE INC
3579 Mccart Ave (76110-4694)
PHONE................................817 927-0411
Gary Greene, *President*
EMP: 10
SQ FT: 7,000
SALES (est): 1MM **Privately Held**
SIC: 3535 3556 Belt conveyor systems,
general industrial use; food products ma-
chinery

(G-6566)
CUMMINS SOUTHERN PLAINS
LLC
3250 North Fwy (76111-1812)
PHONE................................817 624-2107
Leo Mendez, *Branch Mgr*
EMP: 40
SQ FT: 28,080
SALES (corp-wide): 19.8B **Publicly Held**
WEB: www.cummins.com
SIC: 7538 3519 Diesel engine repair: au-
tomotive; internal combustion engines
HQ: Cummins Southern Plains Llc
600 N Watson Rd
Arlington TX 76011
817 640-6801

(G-6567)
CUSTOM DELIS EQUIPMENT CO
INC
153 N Riverside Dr (76111-3911)
PHONE................................817 831-7080
Ken Severe, *CEO*
Leo Garcia, *President*
Yolanda Garcia, *Corp Secy*
EMP: 25
SQ FT: 36,000
SALES (est): 6.9MM **Privately Held**
WEB: www.customdelisinc.com
SIC: 3556 5084 3444 2542 Food prod-
ucts machinery; food industry machinery;
sheet metalwork; partitions & fixtures, ex-
cept wood

(G-6568)
D & D FABRICATION &
ERECTION
4200 White St (76135-2208)
P.O. Box 136577 (76136-0577)
PHONE................................817 237-3306
Ronnie Polston, *Ch of Bd*
Connie Ellis, *Vice Pres*
Don Strickland, *Vice Pres*
EMP: 25 **EST:** 1963
SQ FT: 4,000
SALES (est): 4MM **Privately Held**
SIC: 1791 3441 Structural steel erection;
fabricated structural metal

(G-6569)
D & D PERFORMANCE
ENTERPRISES
Also Called: B&R Leasing
2923 Edith Ln (76117-4322)
PHONE................................817 834-8961
David Rash, *President*
Susan Rash, *Vice Pres*
▼ **EMP:** 35
SQ FT: 12,000
SALES (est): 7.3MM **Privately Held**
WEB: www.danddexhaust.com
SIC: 3714 Exhaust systems & parts, motor
vehicle

(G-6570)
D & J TECHNOLOGIES INC
2010 Mrtin Lther King Fwy (76104-6303)
PHONE................................817 536-0718
David Pastusek, *President*
Joanne Hedrick, *Vice Pres*
Tiffany Strebeck, *Controller*
Trisha Fewell, *Receptionist*
◆ **EMP:** 30
SQ FT: 64,000
SALES (est): 12MM **Privately Held**
WEB: www.dnjtech.com
SIC: 3599 Machine shop, jobbing & repair

(G-6571)
D&D PALLETS INC
3251 Weber St (76106)
P.O. Box 667 (76101-0667)
PHONE................................817 625-7966
Dan Davis, *President*
EMP: 30
SALES (est): 2.7MM **Privately Held**
SIC: 2448 Pallets, wood

(G-6572)
DAGGETT STREET PROPERTIES
Also Called: Armoloy Co
204 E Daggett Ave (76104-1312)
PHONE................................817 332-5604
David Richards, *President*
EMP: 18
SALES (est): 720K **Privately Held**
WEB: www.armoloyfw.com
SIC: 3479 3471 Coating of metals &
formed products; chromium plating of
metals or formed products

(G-6573)
DALLAS FORT WRTH
FYRESTONE LLC
5955 Eden Dr (76117-6122)
PHONE................................817 429-0999
Gene Binnion, *General Mgr*
Jim Fanning,
EMP: 35
SALES (est): 3.3MM **Privately Held**
WEB: www.fyre-stone.com
SIC: 2431 5023 Moldings & baseboards,
ornamental & trim; mantels, wood; fire-
place equipment & accessories

(G-6574)
DALTONS BEST MAID
PRODUCTS INC
Also Called: Del-Dixi
1401 S Riverside Dr (76104-5841)
P.O. Box 1809 (76101-1809)
PHONE................................800 447-3581
Gary Dalton, *CEO*
Brian Dalton, *President*
Robert McCready, *Plant Mgr*
Lance Heinen, *Production*
Mike Wuller, *Engineer*
▲ **EMP:** 250 **EST:** 1926
SQ FT: 200,000
SALES (est): 55.1MM **Privately Held**
WEB: www.bestmaidproducts.com
SIC: 2035 Pickles, vinegar; dressings,
salad: raw & cooked (except dry mixes);
mayonnaise

(G-6575)
DANIELS TERRY CSTM TRIM
MLLWK
2026 Haltom Rd (76117-5003)
PHONE................................817 295-6750
EMP: 10
SALES (est): 654.4K **Privately Held**
SIC: 2431 Mfg Millwork

(G-6576)
DANONE US LLC
1313 Samuels Ave (76102-1130)
PHONE................................817 336-2320
Bruce Horkley, *Branch Mgr*
EMP: 225
SALES (corp-wide): 656MM **Privately**
Held
WEB: www.danonenorthamerica.com
SIC: 2026 Yogurt
HQ: Danone Us, Llc
1 Maple Ave
White Plains NY 10605
914 872-8400

(G-6577)
DANONE US LLC
Also Called: Dannon Yogurt
1300 W Peter Smith St (76104-2116)
PHONE................................817 332-1264
Dwane Tincher, *Manager*
Jory Bailey, *Manager*
Steve Hoggard, *Director*
Steve Barney, *Technician*
Alberto Arana, *Analyst*
EMP: 250

SALES (corp-wide): 656MM **Privately**
Held
WEB: www.danonenorthamerica.com
SIC: 2026 Yogurt
HQ: Danone Us, Llc
1 Maple Ave
White Plains NY 10605
914 872-8400

(G-6578)
DAVOIL INC (PA)
6300 Ridglea Pl Ste 1208 (76116-5738)
P.O. Box 122269 (76121-2269)
PHONE................................817 737-6678
William S Davis Sr, *Ch of Bd*
William S Davis Jr, *Vice Pres*
Bill Roach, *CFO*
Darrell Brown, *Treasurer*
Richard Fleck, *Treasurer*
◆ **EMP:** 12 **EST:** 1976
SQ FT: 6,000
SALES (est): 122.1MM **Privately Held**
WEB: www.quoruminternational.com
SIC: 1382 Oil & gas exploration services

(G-6579)
DDB CANDLES INC (PA)
Also Called: Deejay's Candles By Diane
2612 W Waggoman St (76110-4629)
PHONE................................817 927-3377
Debbie Allen, *Vice Pres*
EMP: 15
SQ FT: 3,400
SALES (est): 1.4MM **Privately Held**
SIC: 3999 5199 Candles; candles

(G-6580)
DEAN FOODS COMPANY
1114 N Lancaster (76102)
P.O. Box 955265 (76155-9265)
PHONE................................214 944-4960
Harlen Jenkins, *Branch Mgr*
EMP: 200 **Publicly Held**
WEB: www.deanfoods.com
SIC: 2026 Fluid milk
PA: Dean Foods Company
2711 N Haskell Ave # 340
Dallas TX 75204

(G-6581)
DEAN FOODS COMPANY
14760 Trinity Blvd (76155-2642)
PHONE................................817 684-3600
Cameron Harris, *Human Resources*
Lori Mack, *Manager*
Patricia Smith, *Supervisor*
Lisa Garcia, *Analyst*
EMP: 300 **Publicly Held**
WEB: www.deanfoods.com
SIC: 2033 2097 5143 5149 Fruit juices:
packaged in cans, jars, etc.; manufac-
tured ice; ice cubes; ice cream & ices;
coffee, green or roasted; milk processing
(pasteurizing, homogenizing, bottling)
PA: Dean Foods Company
2711 N Haskell Ave # 340
Dallas TX 75204

(G-6582)
DEEN WHOLESALE MEAT CO
Also Called: Deen Meats and Cooked Foods
813 E Northside Dr (76102-1017)
P.O. Box 4155 (76164-0155)
PHONE................................817 335-2257
Nancy Deen, *CEO*
Danny Deen, *President*
Pat Harrington, *Partner*
Matthew Deen, *Vice Pres*
Mike Pritchard, *Vice Pres*
EMP: 50
SQ FT: 24,000
SALES (est): 13MM **Privately Held**
WEB: www.deenmeat.com
SIC: 2011 Meat packing plants

(G-6583)
DELTA STEEL INC
9217 South Fwy (76140-4999)
PHONE................................918 437-7501
Randy Berkovsky, *General Mgr*
Brad Blankenship, *Opers Mgr*
Bob Demarco, *Branch Mgr*
Yesenia Gonzalez, *Manager*
EMP: 20

▲ = Import ▼=Export
◆ =Import/Export

SALES (corp-wide): 10.9B **Publicly Held**
WEB: www.deltasteel.com
SIC: **5051** 3312 Iron or steel semifinished products; blast furnaces & steel mills
HQ: Delta Steel, Inc.
7355 Roundhouse Ln
Houston TX 77078
713 635-1200

(G-6584)
DFB PHARMACEUTICALS LLC (PA)
3909 Hulen St (76107-7253)
PHONE................................817 900-4050
H Paul Dorman, *CEO*
Michael E Steadman, *President*
Harald Heckenm Ller, *General Mgr*
Maxwell Lea, *Vice Pres*
Maxwell A Lea, *Vice Pres*
EMP: 30
SQ FT: 35,000
SALES (est): 58.2MM **Privately Held**
WEB: www.dfb.com
SIC: **2834** Pharmaceutical preparations

(G-6585)
DFR ACQUISITION CORPORATION
Also Called: Dragonfire Racing
4900 Alliance Gateway Fwy (76177-3722)
PHONE................................480 834-4392
Andrew Graves, *CEO*
Brian Etter, *CEO*
Michael Moore, *President*
Arnold W Ackerman, *Chairman*
Scott Christman, *Corp Secy*
◆ EMP: 30
SALES (est): 4MM
SALES (corp-wide): 251.1MM **Privately Held**
WEB: www.dragonfireracing.com
SIC: **3799** All terrain vehicles (ATV)
PA: Motorsport Aftermarket Group, Inc.
13861 Rosecrans Ave
Santa Fe Springs CA 90670
917 838-4002

(G-6586)
DIGITAL COMMUNICATION SVCS INC
Also Called: Digitcom
1021 S Handley Dr (76112-7014)
P.O. Box 120308, Arlington (76012-0308)
PHONE................................682 478-2134
James Labenz, *President*
Jeff Reis, *Vice Pres*
Nancy Tomerlin, *Office Mgr*
EMP: 17
SQ FT: 10,000 **Privately Held**
WEB: www.digitcominc.com
SIC: **2493** Insulation board, cellular fiber

(G-6587)
DIRECT INTERNATIONAL
2309 E Loop 820 N (76118-7103)
P.O. Box 11184 (76110-0184)
PHONE................................817 284-7722
EE S Song, *Owner*
EMP: 9
SQ FT: 50,000
SALES (est): 580K **Privately Held**
SIC: **3728** 5088 Aircraft parts & equipment; helicopter parts

(G-6588)
DIVERSE EDUCATN RESOURCES LLC
2951 Northern Cross Blvd (76137-3630)
P.O. Box 161082 (76161-1082)
PHONE................................817 769-8968
Phillip Deats, *CEO*
Phil Deats, *President*
EMP: 20 EST: 2016
SALES (est): 163.5K **Privately Held**
SIC: **2759** Commercial printing

(G-6589)
DOLLAMUR LP (PA)
Also Called: Dollamur Sport Surfaces
1734 E El Paso St Ste 110 (76102-6771)
PHONE................................817 534-3344
Don Ochsenreiter, *Principal*
Mike Peller, *Vice Pres*
Dave Rossi, *Vice Pres*
Chuck Thompson, *Vice Pres*

Brad Boultinghouse, *Purchasing*
◆ EMP: 92
SQ FT: 50,000
SALES (est): 25MM **Privately Held**
WEB: www.dollamur.com
SIC: **3949** Gymnasium equipment

(G-6590)
DOUBLE EAGLE ENERGY OPER LLC
3724 Hulen St (76107-6816)
PHONE................................817 928-3260
Cody Campbell, *Principal*
John Sellers, *Principal*
EMP: 30
SALES (est): 3.5MM **Privately Held**
WEB: www.doubleeagledevelopment.com
SIC: **1382** Oil & gas exploration services

(G-6591)
DOUBLE EAGLE LONE STAR LLC
3724 Hulen St (76107-6816)
PHONE................................817 928-3260
Cody Campbell, *CEO*
John A Sellers, *President*
Blake A Carpenter, *COO*
Joshua A Gregg, *CFO*
EMP: 14
SALES (est): 2.8MM
SALES (corp-wide): 9.3B **Publicly Held**
WEB: www.doubleeagledevelopment.com
SIC: **1311** Crude petroleum & natural gas
HQ: Parsley Energy, Inc.
303 Colorado St Ste 3000
Austin TX 78701
737 704-2300

(G-6592)
DOYLE & HAMILTON INC
Also Called: Red Dog Studios
2927 Morton St (76107-2925)
PHONE................................817 882-8080
Roger H Smith, *President*
Melissa Smith, *Vice Pres*
Jerry Mitchell, *Sales Mgr*
EMP: 16
SQ FT: 5,200
SALES (est): 1.9MM **Privately Held**
SIC: **2395** 7389 5199 Embroidery products, except schiffli machine; advertising, promotional & trade show services; embroidering of advertising on shirts, etc.; advertising specialties

(G-6593)
DRAKEN INTERNATIONAL LLC (PA)
9800 Hillwood Pkwy # 100 (76177-1527)
PHONE................................863 289-0849
Jared Isaacman, *CEO*
John Baun, *Vice Pres*
Sean Gustafson, *Vice Pres*
Jerry Kerby, *Vice Pres*
Gordon Kevin, *Opers Mgr*
▲ EMP: 47
SQ FT: 11,000
SALES (est): 46.5MM **Privately Held**
WEB: www.drakenintl.com
SIC: **3721** Aircraft

(G-6594)
DRC MEDIA LLC
Also Called: Fort Worth Business Press
101 Summit Ave Ste 803 (76102-2622)
P.O. Box 65 (76101-0065)
PHONE................................817 336-8300
Richard Connor,
Deborah Connor,
EMP: 18 EST: 2010
SALES (est): 1MM **Privately Held**
WEB: www.fortworthbusiness.com
SIC: **2711** Newspapers, publishing & printing

(G-6595)
DTE GAS RESOURCES LLC
301 Commerce St Ste 1800 (76102-4109)
PHONE................................817 302-4600
Steven Prelipp,
Lance Sheehy,
EMP: 34
SALES (est): 1.4MM **Publicly Held**
SIC: **1382** Oil & gas exploration services

PA: Dte Energy Company
1 Energy Plz
Detroit MI 48226

(G-6596)
DUMPZIT LLC
10021 Jacksboro Hwy (76135-4701)
PHONE................................817 238-6563
Chandra Ambrose, *Office Mgr*
Terry Autrey,
Bob Autrey,
Mark Knutp,
Lynn Pervis,
EMP: 11
SALES (est): 750K **Privately Held**
SIC: **3272** Concrete products

(G-6597)
DYNAMIC INC (PA)
2801 Glenda St (76117-4326)
PHONE................................817 838-1800
John H Harvison, *President*
Donna Cottongame, *Treasurer*
Gerald Graham, *Administration*
EMP: 20
SQ FT: 20,000
SALES (est): 10.5MM **Privately Held**
WEB: www.dynamicproduction.net
SIC: **6512** 1311 1382 Commercial & industrial building operation; crude petroleum production; oil & gas exploration services

(G-6598)
DYNAMIC PRODUCTION (HQ)
5070 Mark Iv Pkwy (76106-2219)
PHONE................................817 838-1800
John H Harvison, *Ch of Bd*
John D Harvison, *President*
Gerald H Graham, *Vice Pres*
Jonathon G Weiss, *Vice Pres*
J Mark Bronson, *CFO*
EMP: 20
SQ FT: 20,000
SALES (est): 10.5MM **Privately Held**
WEB: www.dynamicproduction.net
SIC: **1311** Crude petroleum production
PA: Dynamic Inc
2801 Glenda St
Fort Worth TX 76117
817 838-1800

(G-6599)
DYNASTY CONSOLIDATED INDS INC
Also Called: Posture Beauty Sleep Products
4250 Cambridge Rd (76155-2626)
PHONE................................214 630-3132
Amirali G Sunderji, *CEO*
Rizwan Sunderji, *President*
Jim Bailey, *Division Mgr*
Alim A G Sunderji, *COO*
Jameel Sunderji, *Vice Pres*
▲ EMP: 97
SQ FT: 208,000
SALES (est): 17.6MM **Privately Held**
WEB: www.sleeptronic.com
SIC: **2515** 5021 Mattresses & foundations; mattresses

(G-6600)
DYNOCOM INDUSTRIES INC
2447 Riverbend West Dr (76118-7024)
PHONE................................817 284-8844
Bill Pitts, *President*
Allison Blackstein, *Sales Mgr*
Steve Wallace, *Manager*
▲ EMP: 25
SQ FT: 50,000
SALES (est): 5.6MM **Privately Held**
WEB: www.dynocom.net
SIC: **3559** Automotive maintenance equipment

(G-6601)
E-MIST INNOVATIONS INC
Also Called: Electrostatic Misting
3013 Joyce Dr (76116-4013)
P.O. Box 122717 (76121-2717)
PHONE................................844 563-6478
George Robertson, *President*
EMP: 10 EST: 2010
SALES (est): 2.5MM **Privately Held**
WEB: www.emist.com
SIC: **2842** Sanitation preparations, disinfectants & deodorants

(G-6602)
ECI SOFTWARE SOLUTIONS INC (HQ)
Also Called: Eci2
4400 Alliance Gateway Fwy # 154 (76177-3706)
PHONE................................703 737-6620
Ron Books, *CEO*
Trevor Gruenewald, *President*
Jeff Ralyea, *President*
Gary Peterson, *Partner*
Lipetz David, *Vice Pres*
EMP: 120
SQ FT: 35,000
SALES (est): 164MM **Privately Held**
WEB: www.ecisolutions.com
SIC: **7372** Prepackaged software

(G-6603)
ECKELS - BILT INC
Also Called: Eckels-Bilt
7700 Harwell St (76108-1806)
PHONE................................817 246-4555
John Mickunas, *President*
Tracye Mickunas, *Vice Pres*
Sheryl Aldridge, *Accountant*
Tony Keeton, *Sales Mgr*
Nikki Sanborn, *Office Mgr*
EMP: 12
SQ FT: 7,000
SALES (est): 3.4MM **Privately Held**
WEB: www.eckelsbilt.com
SIC: **3535** Conveyors & conveying equipment

(G-6604)
EDGE ADHESIVES INC (PA)
5117 Northeast Pkwy (76106-1822)
PHONE................................817 232-2026
Jim Turner, *President*
Freddie Cole, *General Mgr*
Darren Ourth, *Vice Pres*
Todd Strange, *Production*
Christy Liles, *Office Mgr*
▲ EMP: 75
SALES (est): 21.6MM **Privately Held**
WEB: www.edgeadhesives.com
SIC: **2891** Adhesives

(G-6605)
EDGE INTEGRITY SERVICES LLC
5225 El Campo Ave (76107-4841)
PHONE................................817 585-1007
Jack Martin King III,
Scott Thornton,
EMP: 9
SQ FT: 2,600
SALES (est): 2.4MM **Privately Held**
WEB: www.edgeintegrity.com
SIC: **1389** 8713 Oil consultants; surveying services

(G-6606)
EFW INC (DH)
4700 Marine Creek Pkwy (76179-3598)
P.O. Box 136969 (76136-0969)
PHONE................................817 916-1359
Raanan Horowitz, *CEO*
Randy R Burns, *Project Dir*
Efi Marco, *Opers Staff*
Julie Filips, *Engineer*
Steve Marsh, *Engineer*
◆ EMP: 800
SQ FT: 156,000
SALES (est): 263.7MM
SALES (corp-wide): 1.3B **Privately Held**
WEB: www.elbitsystems-us.com
SIC: **3812** Search & navigation equipment

(G-6607)
EICA INDUSTRIES INC
Also Called: Eica Tankheads
1700 E Hicks Field Rd (76179-5250)
P.O. Box 79144, Saginaw (76179-0144)
PHONE................................817 847-0917
Nelson De Abrea, *President*
EMP: 9
SALES (est): 3MM **Privately Held**
WEB: www.eicatankheads.com
SIC: **3443** Tanks, standard or custom fabricated; metal plate

(G-6608)
EL HABR CORPORATION
Also Called: Michel's Tiffany
4115 W Vickery Blvd (76107-6422)
PHONE..................................817 731-4660
Michelle Elhabr, *Manager*
EMP: 17
SALES (corp-wide): 1.2MM Privately Held
SIC: 3231 Stained glass: made from purchased glass
PA: El Habr Corporation
   3030 W Pafford St
   Fort Worth TX 76110
   817 737-9391

(G-6609)
ELBIT SYSTEMS OF AMERICA LLC (HQ)
4700 Marine Creek Pkwy (76179-3505)
PHONE..................................817 234-6600
Raanan Horowitz, *President*
Toby Corey, *Business Mgr*
Elad Aharonson, *Exec VP*
Gideon Sheffer, *Exec VP*
Bob Edmonds, *Vice Pres*
▲ EMP: 20
SALES (est): 739.9MM
SALES (corp-wide): 1.3B Privately Held
WEB: www.elbitsystems-us.com
SIC: 3827 Optical instruments & apparatus
PA: Elbit Systems Ltd
   Advanced Technology Center
   Haifa
   772 946-341

(G-6610)
EMERGE ENERGY SERVICES LP (PA)
6500 West Fwy Ste 800 (76116-2178)
PHONE..................................817 618-4020
Rick Shearer, *Partner*
Emerge Energy Services GP LLC, *General Ptnr*
Deborah Deibert, *CFO*
Christopher Welch, *CFO*
Kara Dahm, *Human Resources*
EMP: 42
SALES: 313.5MM Privately Held
WEB: www.emergelp.com
SIC: 1311 1389 4613 Oil sand mining; sand & shale oil mining; oil field services; processing service, gas; refined petroleum pipelines

(G-6611)
ENDURANCE LIFT SOLUTIONS LLC
420 Throckmorton St # 740 (76102-3700)
PHONE..................................903 595-8600
Dan Newman, *CEO*
EMP: 200
SALES (corp-wide): 343.1MM Privately Held
WEB: www.endurancelift.com
SIC: 3533 3561 5084 Gas field machinery & equipment; pumps & pumping equipment; industrial machinery & equipment
PA: Endurance Lift Solutions, Llc
   114 E Foreline St
   Gainesville TX 76240
   281 269-6880

(G-6612)
ENDURO RESOURCE PARTNERS LLC (HQ)
777 Main St Ste 800 (76102-5350)
PHONE..................................817 744-8200
David Bruce, *Opers Staff*
Trey Courtney, *Senior Engr*
Leonard Kariuki, *Accountant*
John W Arms, *Mng Member*
I Jon Brumley, *Mng Member*
EMP: 20
SALES (est): 8.8MM
SALES (corp-wide): 1.9MM Privately Held
WEB: www.washplc.com
SIC: 1382 Oil & gas exploration services

(G-6613)
ENERGY EXPLRATION PARTNERS INC
420 Throckmorton St # 120 (76102-3700)
PHONE..................................817 789-6712

Hunt Pettit, *CEO*
Brian H Pettit, *President*
Chad Galloway, *COO*
Robert Karpman, *Exec VP*
Tom McNutt, *Exec VP*
EMP: 25 EST: 2012
SALES (est): 2.8MM Privately Held
WEB: www.pardusog.com
SIC: 1382 Oil & gas exploration services

(G-6614)
ENERGY RETROFITTERS INC
4090 H C Meacham Blvd (76135-9572)
PHONE..................................817 319-2796
Steven S Norris, *President*
EMP: 10
SALES (est): 1.2MM Privately Held
WEB: www.texas-generator.com
SIC: 3646 1731 7699 5063 Commercial indusl & institutional electric lighting fixtures; general electrical contractor; industrial equipment services; light bulbs & related supplies

(G-6615)
ENGRAVING AND PRINTING BUREAU
Also Called: Fort Worth Facility
9000 Blue Mound Rd (76131-3304)
PHONE..................................817 847-3800
Tom Harris, *Branch Mgr*
EMP: 29 Publicly Held
WEB: www.moneyfactory.gov
SIC: 2796 2754 9311 Platemaking services; commercial printing, gravure; finance, taxation & monetary policy;
HQ: Bureau Of Engraving And Printing
   14th And C St Sw
   Washington DC 20228
   202 874-2361

(G-6616)
EOG RESOURCES INC
421 W 3rd St Ste 300 (76102-3827)
PHONE..................................817 339-9380
Jared Gabro, *Opers Mgr*
Robert Richardson, *Safety Mgr*
Bradley Lindsey, *Foreman/Supr*
Rick Burton, *Opers Staff*
Keith Elliott, *Opers Staff*
EMP: 110
SALES (corp-wide): 17.3B Publicly Held
WEB: www.eogresources.com
SIC: 1382 Oil & gas exploration services
PA: Eog Resources, Inc.
   1111 Bagby Sky Lbby 2
   Houston TX 77002
   713 651-7000

(G-6617)
EOSERA INC
5000 South Fwy (76115-3902)
PHONE..................................844 732-7929
Elyse Dickerson, *CEO*
Joseph Griffin, *Admin Sec*
EMP: 10
SALES (est): 471.5K Privately Held
WEB: www.eosera.com
SIC: 2834 Pharmaceutical preparations

(G-6618)
ESSNER MANUFACTURING LP
6651 Will Rogers Blvd B (76140-6055)
PHONE..................................817 551-5511
Dale R Westerfeld, *President*
Jon Alt, *President*
Brian Edmiston, *General Mgr*
Nelly Barefoot, *Purch Mgr*
Chase Bagley, *Engineer*
EMP: 65 EST: 1939
SQ FT: 73,800
SALES (est): 16.3MM Privately Held
WEB: www.essner.com
SIC: 3469 3441 3444 Stamping metal for the trade; fabricated structural metal; sheet metalwork

(G-6619)
ESSNER PRECISION MFG LLC
Also Called: Precision Mfg Co Fort Worth
6651 Will Rogers Blvd B (76140-6055)
PHONE..................................817 529-2580
Rhonda Van Kirk, *Purchasing*
Dale Westerfeld,
Jonathan Alt,
Andrew Bushell,

EMP: 50
SQ FT: 41,028
SALES (est): 950K Privately Held
WEB: www.essner.com
SIC: 3728 Aircraft parts & equipment

(G-6620)
EXACT DIAGNOSTICS LLC
3400 Camp Bowie Blvd (76107-2729)
PHONE..................................817 989-9262
Winnie Boonyaratanakor, *General Mgr*
Tara Cisneros, *Sales Staff*
Richard Petronis,
Jerry Boonyaratanakornkit,
EMP: 25
SALES (est): 414.5K Privately Held
WEB: www.exactdiagnostics.com
SIC: 2835 In vitro diagnostics

(G-6621)
EZ FLEX LLC
Also Called: EZ Flex Sport Mats
1701 Pharr St (76102-1717)
PHONE..................................817 632-4800
Liz Anderson, *CEO*
Jeff Anderson, *Accounts Mgr*
Kevin Coons, *Accounts Mgr*
Jeremy Rockwell, *Accounts Mgr*
Blake Wientge, *Accounts Mgr*
▲ EMP: 40
SALES (est): 8.3MM Privately Held
WEB: www.ezflexmats.com
SIC: 3069 Rubber floor coverings, mats & wallcoverings

(G-6622)
F & F COMPOSITE GROUP INC
5800 Egg Farm Rd Ste 260 (76244-8899)
P.O. Box 247, Keller (76244-0247)
PHONE..................................817 379-4411
John Fakhari, *President*
Suzanne Seely, *Admin Sec*
▲ EMP: 48
SALES (est): 4.7MM Privately Held
WEB: www.fandfcompositegroup.com
SIC: 1799 5162 2221 3089 Fiberglass work; resins; glass & fiberglass broadwoven fabrics; fiberglass fabrics; fences, gates & accessories: plastic; fiberglass materials, except insulation

(G-6623)
FALCON PHARMACEUTICALS LTD
6201 South Fwy (76134-2001)
PHONE..................................800 343-2133
Cary Rayment, *President*
Shelley Delgado, *Exec VP*
Gerald Cagle PHD, *Senior VP*
Kevin Buehler, *Vice Pres*
Andre Bens PHD, *Vice Pres*
EMP: 3000
SALES (est): 228.8MM Privately Held
WEB: www.alcon.com
SIC: 2834 3841 Solutions, pharmaceutical; ophthalmic instruments & apparatus

(G-6624)
FBC ENTERPRISES INC
Also Called: CUSTOM GRAPHIC SERVICES
5110 Rondo Dr (76106-1827)
PHONE..................................817 740-1951
Fax: 817 740-1785
EMP: 50
SQ FT: 45,000
SALES: 4MM Privately Held
SIC: 2752 Lithographic Commercial Printing

(G-6625)
FEATHERLITE CORPORATION (DH)
3024 Acme Brick Plz (76109-4104)
P.O. Box 425 (76101-0425)
PHONE..................................817 332-4101
Dennis Kanell, *President*
EMP: 131
SALES (est): 57.2MM
SALES (corp-wide): 254.6B Publicly Held
WEB: www.featherlitetexas.com
SIC: 3272 Concrete products, precast
HQ: Justin Industries, Inc.
   3024 Acme Brick Plz
   Fort Worth TX 76109
   817 332-4101

(G-6626)
FEDEX SUP CHAIN LGSTICS ELEC I
Also Called: Genco Atc
13500 Independence Pkwy (76177-4010)
P.O. Box 1940, Roanoke (76262-1940)
PHONE..................................817 491-7700
Todd R Peters, *CEO*
Anthony Francis, *President*
Dan Gardner, *Vice Pres*
Marc Sherman, *Vice Pres*
Randy Engel, *VP Opers*
▲ EMP: 2400
SALES (est): 91.1MM
SALES (corp-wide): 69.2B Publicly Held
SIC: 4225 3714 3694 General warehousing & storage; rebuilding engines & transmissions, factory basis; motor vehicle transmissions, drive assemblies & parts; engine electrical equipment
HQ: Atc Technology Corporation
   700 Cranberry Woods Dr
   Cranberry Township PA 16066

(G-6627)
FELLFAB CORPORATION
2680 Gravel Dr Bldg 5 (76118-6976)
PHONE..................................817 595-7408
Don Fell, *CEO*
Sophia Alexander, *QC Mgr*
Charlie Picou, *Accounts Exec*
Pablo Alcantar, *Manager*
EMP: 30
SALES (corp-wide): 34.4MM Privately Held
WEB: www.fellfab.com
SIC: 2531 4581 Public building & related furniture; aircraft maintenance & repair services
HQ: Fellfab Corporation
   200 Tradeport Dr Ste 100
   Atlanta GA 30354
   404 363-8905

(G-6628)
FIBERCO INC (PA)
1300 Eden Dr (76117-6115)
P.O. Box 14728 (76117-0728)
PHONE..................................682 647-1332
Charles I Kaplan, *President*
Gary Varner, *Vice Pres*
Teresa Bryden, *Admin Sec*
EMP: 15 EST: 1965
SQ FT: 35,000
SALES (est): 10.4MM Privately Held
WEB: www.fiberco.com
SIC: 2297 2395 2211 Nonwoven fabrics; quilting, for the trade; broadwoven fabric mills, cotton

(G-6629)
FIELDTECH AVIONICS INSTRS INC (PA)
4151 N Main St (76106-2704)
P.O. Box 4455 (76164-0455)
PHONE..................................817 740-7110
Kevin Nelms, *President*
Bryan Pichler, *Business Mgr*
David Mills, *Vice Pres*
Laura Chavez, *Purch Mgr*
Ashley Althoff, *Purchasing*
▲ EMP: 49 EST: 1979
SQ FT: 11,000
SALES (est): 7.3MM Privately Held
WEB: www.ftav.com
SIC: 3812 7622 Aircraft/aerospace flight instruments & guidance systems; radar systems & equipment; aircraft radio equipment repair

(G-6630)
FIFO TECHNOLOGIES INC
8949 First Hills Dr (76101)
PHONE..................................817 991-1388
Charles Ice, *CEO*
EMP: 10
SALES (est): 888.9K Privately Held
SIC: 3533 Oil field machinery & equipment

(G-6631)
FINLEY RESOURCES INC
Also Called: Finley Production Company
1308 Lake St Ste 200 (76102-4505)
P.O. Box 2200 (76113-2200)
PHONE..................................817 336-1924

2021 Harris Texas
Manufacturers Directory

▲ = Import ▼ =Export
◆ =Import/Export

Jim Finley, *CEO*
Brent Talbot, *President*
Clinton Koerth, *Vice Pres*
Stephen M Clark, *CFO*
EMP: 95
SALES (est): 46.7MM **Privately Held**
WEB: www.finleyresources.com
SIC: 1382 1381 1321 Oil & gas exploration services; drilling oil & gas wells; natural gas liquids

(G-6632)
FIRESTONE ROBERTSON DISTLG LLC
2601 Whiskey Ranch Rd (76119-1610)
PHONE.............................817 840-9140
Drew S Calvert, *Principal*
Ken Graham, *Opers Staff*
Frank Meyer, *Controller*
Kathleen Dooley, *Manager*
Megan Affrica, *Director*
▲ **EMP:** 27
SALES (est): 2.2MM
SALES (corp-wide): 224.6MM **Privately Held**
WEB: www.frdistilling.com
SIC: 2085 2084 Distilled & blended liquors; wines, brandy & brandy spirits
HQ: Pernod Ricard Usa, Llc
250 Park Ave Ste 17a
New York NY 10177
212 372-5400

(G-6633)
FIRST ENERGY SERVICES COMPANY
801 Cherry St Unit 2 (76102-6886)
PHONE.............................817 334-4100
David C Johnston, *Risk Mgmt Dir*
EMP: 304
SALES (est): 3.4MM
SALES (corp-wide): 567.2MM **Publicly Held**
SIC: 1389 Servicing oil & gas wells
HQ: Basic Energy Services, L.P.
801 Cherry St Unit 2
Fort Worth TX 76102

(G-6634)
FITTINGS INC
3300 Fisher Ave (76111-4506)
PHONE.............................817 332-3300
Lewis Graves, *President*
Margie Graves, *Corp Secy*
Mark K Gannon, *Vice Pres*
Ladonna Davis, *Buyer*
◆ **EMP:** 55
SQ FT: 38,000
SALES (est): 10.7MM **Privately Held**
WEB: www.fitandcp.com
SIC: 3089 3586 3492 Fittings for pipe, plastic; measuring & dispensing pumps; fluid power valves & hose fittings

(G-6635)
FIVE STAR CUSTOM FOODS LTD (DH)
3709 E 1st St (76111-5804)
PHONE.............................682 647-2700
Jess Bledsoe, *Partner*
Jeffrey Bledsoe, *Partner*
Steven Phillips, *Partner*
Arthur Wolf, *Partner*
▲ **EMP:** 25
SALES (est): 28.8MM
SALES (corp-wide): 113.4B **Privately Held**
WEB: www.fivestarcustomfoods.com
SIC: 5141 2099 Food brokers; food preparations
HQ: Cargill Meat Solutions Corp
151 N Main St Ste 900
Wichita KS 67202
316 291-2500

(G-6636)
FLAMESTOP INC
924 S Blue Mound Rd (76131-1402)
PHONE.............................817 306-1222
James Bower, *President*
Chris Obal, *Sales Associate*
EMP: 25
SALES (est): 3.9MM **Privately Held**
WEB: www.flamestop.com
SIC: 2899 Fire retardant chemicals

(G-6637)
FLAT CREEK RESOURCES LLC
777 Main St Ste 3600 (76102-5341)
PHONE.............................817 310-8570
Chandler Quisenberry, *CFO*
Michael McCracken, *Mng Member*
William Flanagan, *Technology*
EMP: 11
SALES (est): 429.3K **Privately Held**
WEB: www.flatcreekresources.com
SIC: 1389 Oil & gas wells: building, repairing & dismantling

(G-6638)
FLIGHTSAFETY INTERNATIONAL INC
4660 Diplomacy Rd (76155-2650)
PHONE.............................817 571-5925
Amy Jenny, *Partner*
Jamie Buckley, *Engineer*
Andrew Morris, *Engineer*
Irina Davidoff, *Accountant*
Maureen Maloney, *Sales Staff*
EMP: 200
SQ FT: 34,965
SALES (corp-wide): 254.6B **Publicly Held**
WEB: www.flightsafety.com
SIC: 6331 2731 3635 5441 Property damage insurance: fire, marine & casualty insurance: stock; books: publishing only; textbooks: publishing only, not printed on site; pamphlets: publishing only, not printed on site; household vacuum cleaners; candy; confectionery produced for direct sale on the premises; newspapers: publishing only, not printed on site; carpets
HQ: Flightsafety International Inc.
290 Brdhllow Rd Ste 402e
Melville NY 11747
718 565-4100

(G-6639)
FMC TECHNOLOGIES INC
777 Main St Ste 600 (76102-5368)
PHONE.............................817 887-8063
EMP: 24
SALES (corp-wide): 13.4B **Privately Held**
WEB: www.technipfmc.com
SIC: 3533 Oil & gas field machinery
HQ: Fmc Technologies, Inc.
11740 Katy Fwy Enrgy Twr
Houston TX 77079
281 591-4000

(G-6640)
FORBES RBUILT AUTOMITIVE PARTS
2712 White Settlement Rd (76107-1332)
PHONE.............................817 332-7643
David Forbes, *President*
Debbie Forbes, *Vice Pres*
Mona Forbes, *Treasurer*
Walton Forbes, *Admin Sec*
EMP: 12 EST: 1964
SQ FT: 30,000
SALES (est): 700K **Privately Held**
WEB: www.forbesrebuiltautoparts.com
SIC: 6512 3714 Commercial & industrial building operation; rebuilding engines & transmissions, factory basis

(G-6641)
FORT DEARBORN COMPANY
4601 Pylon St (76106-1918)
PHONE.............................817 625-1116
Lane Jett, *Manager*
EMP: 170
SALES (corp-wide): 7.9B **Privately Held**
WEB: www.fortdearborn.com
SIC: 2752 2759 Tickets, lithographed; commercial printing
HQ: Fort Dearborn Company
1530 Morse Ave
Elk Grove Village IL 60007
847 357-9500

(G-6642)
FORT WORTH F AND D HEAD CO
Also Called: Fort Worth F&D Head Company
3040 Peden Rd (76179-5523)
P.O. Box 79700, Saginaw (76179-0700)
PHONE.............................817 236-8773

Q D Gilliland, *President*
John Taylor, *Principal*
Dorothy Frizzell, *Corp Secy*
Wilma Jo Gilliland, *Corp Secy*
Walter Frizzell, *Vice Pres*
▲ **EMP:** 70 EST: 1967
SQ FT: 16,000
SALES (est): 33.9MM **Privately Held**
WEB: www.fwfdhead.com
SIC: 3443 Tanks, standard or custom fabricated: metal plate

(G-6643)
FORT WORTH FABRICATION INC
5316 Blue Mound Rd (76106-1940)
PHONE.............................817 625-2321
Tracy Montgomery, *President*
Robert Montgomery, *Vice Pres*
Donna Montgomery, *Treasurer*
EMP: 10
SQ FT: 20,000
SALES (est): 1.4MM **Privately Held**
WEB: www.fortworthfab.com
SIC: 3715 Truck trailers

(G-6644)
FORT WORTH FORGING DIE LP
Also Called: Tooling Manufacturing
2579 Berner St (76111-1828)
PHONE.............................817 529-9990
Al Turner, *President*
Gary Shumate, *General Mgr*
Pat Potts, *Vice Pres*
EMP: 19 EST: 1955
SQ FT: 13,000
SALES (est): 2.7MM **Privately Held**
WEB: www.fwforgedie.com
SIC: 3544 Special dies & tools

(G-6645)
FORTSON OIL COMPANY
306 W 7th St Ste 901 (76102-4929)
PHONE.............................817 335-5641
Ben J Fortson Jr, *CEO*
Dinah Dupuy, *Vice Pres*
Jeff Stanton, *Production*
David Frazier, *CFO*
David Frasier, *Finance Mgr*
EMP: 20
SALES (est): 6.9MM **Privately Held**
WEB: www.fortsonoil.com
SIC: 1311 Crude petroleum production; natural gas production

(G-6646)
FOUR CORNERSTONE SOLUTIONS LLC
316 Bailey Ave (76107-1828)
PHONE.............................817 377-1144
Hunter Herren, *President*
EMP: 40
SQ FT: 12,000
SALES (est): 2.9MM **Privately Held**
WEB: www.fourcornerstone.com
SIC: 7371 7372 8711 8748 Computer software development & applications; prepackaged software; consulting engineer; systems analysis & engineering consulting services; computer related consulting services

(G-6647)
FOUR SEVENS OPERATING CO LTD
Also Called: Bsg Pipeline
306 W 7th St Ste 1045 (76102-4909)
PHONE.............................817 870-9088
Dick Lowe, *Partner*
Hunter Ennis, *Partner*
EMP: 12
SALES (est): 917.2K **Privately Held**
WEB: www.foursevensoperating.com
SIC: 1311 Crude petroleum & natural gas

(G-6648)
FRANKLIN-LEDDY CORPORATION (PA)
Also Called: M. L. Leddy's
2455 N Main St (76164-8522)
PHONE.............................817 624-3149
Wilson D Franklin, *President*
Martha Franklin, *Vice Pres*
Michael Morrison, *Treasurer*
EMP: 52 EST: 1922

SQ FT: 20,000
SALES (est): 9.7MM **Privately Held**
WEB: www.leddys.com
SIC: 3143 5699 3199 Boots, dress or casual: men's; western apparel; saddles or parts

(G-6649)
FRIEDSON HILL INC (PA)
6804 Trinity Landing Dr N (76132-3742)
PHONE.............................817 294-3309
David Friedson, *Principal*
EMP: 13
SALES (est): 1.3MM **Privately Held**
SIC: 2821 Plastics materials & resins

(G-6650)
FTG AEROSPACE INC
4084 Sandshell Dr (76137-2422)
PHONE.............................817 332-3806
Michael Labrador, *President*
EMP: 57
SALES (corp-wide): 84.2MM **Privately Held**
WEB: www.ftgcorp.com
SIC: 3559 8711 Electronic component making machinery; engineering services
HQ: Ftg Aerospace Inc.
20740 Marilla St
Chatsworth CA 91311

(G-6651)
FTG AEROSPACE INC
4084 Sandshell Dr (76137-2422)
PHONE.............................818 577-6126
Michael Labrador, *President*
John Zachmeyer, *Software Engr*
EMP: 51
SALES (corp-wide): 84.2MM **Privately Held**
WEB: www.ftgcorp.com
SIC: 3728 Aircraft parts & equipment
HQ: Ftg Aerospace Inc.
20740 Marilla St
Chatsworth CA 91311

(G-6652)
FTS INTERNATIONAL INC (PA)
777 Main St Ste 2900 (76102-5318)
PHONE.............................817 862-2000
Michael J Doss, *CEO*
Buddy Petersen, *COO*
Juston Parker, *Parts Mgr*
Ronald Powell, *Research*
Lance Turner, *CFO*
EMP: 47
SQ FT: 89,522
SALES (est): 776.6MM **Publicly Held**
WEB: www.ftsi.com
SIC: 1389 Hydraulic fracturing wells; oil field services

(G-6653)
FTS INTERNATIONAL MFG LLC
4700 S Edgewood Ter (76119-8201)
PHONE.............................682 647-3300
Dan Wilks, *Branch Mgr*
EMP: 9 **Publicly Held**
WEB: www.ftsi.com
SIC: 3561 Pumps & pumping equipment
HQ: Fts International Manufacturing, Llc
777 Main St Ste 2900
Fort Worth TX 76102

(G-6654)
FTS INTERNATIONAL SERVICES LLC
777 Main St Ste 1600 (76102-5364)
PHONE.............................817 334-0002
EMP: 11 **Publicly Held**
WEB: www.ftsi.com
SIC: 3561 8711 7353 4225 Pumps & pumping equipment; chemical engineering; oil field equipment, rental or leasing; general warehousing
HQ: Fts International Services, Llc
777 Main St Ste 2900
Fort Worth TX 76102
817 862-2000

(G-6655)
FTS INTERNATIONAL SERVICES LLC (HQ)
777 Main St Ste 2900 (76102-5318)
PHONE.............................817 862-2000
Larry Carroll, *District Mgr*

Sean Parker, *Opers Staff*
Bill Ables, *Engineer*
Dean Hartman, *Controller*
Lance Turner, *Mng Member*
◆ **EMP:** 146
SALES (est): 142.8MM **Publicly Held**
WEB: www.ftsi.com
SIC: 3561 8711 7353 4225 Pumps &
pumping equipment; chemical engineer-
ing; oil field equipment, rental or leasing;
general warehousing

(G-6656)
FTS INTERNATIONAL SERVICES
LLC
777 Main St Ste 3000 (76102-5365)
PHONE................................817 862-2000
Drew Witter, *Opers Staff*
Garrett Damich, *Engineer*
Kathy Kluge, *Branch Mgr*
Carlos Griffith, *Supervisor*
Andre Malone, *Supervisor*
EMP: 50 **Publicly Held**
WEB: www.ftsi.com
SIC: 1382 Oil & gas exploration services
HQ: Fts International Services, Llc
777 Main St Ste 2900
Fort Worth TX 76102
817 862-2000

(G-6657)
FWT LLC (DH)
5750 E Interstate 20 (76119-7034)
PHONE................................817 255-2965
Fred Moore, *CEO*
Bill Sales, *Exec VP*
Lee Mitchell, *Sales Staff*
Jared Orzolek, *Sales Staff*
Jeremy Moore, *Marketing Staff*
▲ **EMP:** 101 **EST:** 1957
SQ FT: 160,000
SALES (est): 64.6MM
SALES (corp-wide): 5.6B **Privately Held**
WEB: www.fwtllc.com
SIC: 3441 Tower sections, radio & televi-
sion transmission
HQ: Sabre Industries, Inc.
8653 E Highway 67
Alvarado TX 76009
817 852-1700

(G-6658)
G KUSTOMS AUTO
CUSTOMIZING LLC
1929 Golden Heights Rd (76177-7098)
PHONE................................682 703-1583
Glen Nichols, *President*
EMP: 10
SALES (est): 250K **Privately Held**
SIC: 3089 7532 Automotive parts, plastic;
body shop, automotive

(G-6659)
GALDERMA LABORATORIES LP
Also Called: Galderma USA
2929 Texas Longhorn Way (76177-3303)
PHONE................................817 961-5000
Nancy Boyd, *Sales Staff*
Patrick Rumble, *Sales Staff*
Robert Justman, *Manager*
EMP: 150
SALES (corp-wide): 500.3K **Privately**
Held
WEB: www.galderma.com
SIC: 4225 2834 General warehousing &
storage; dermatologicals
HQ: Galderma Laboratories, L.P.
14501 North Fwy
Fort Worth TX 76177
817 961-5000

(G-6660)
GALDERMA LABORATORIES LP
(DH)
14501 North Fwy (76177-3304)
PHONE................................817 961-5000
Todd Zavodnick, *President*
Fournier Francois, *Principal*
Shannon Gohler, *Business Mgr*
Jessica Mikus, *Counsel*
Phil Brown, *Senior VP*
◆ **EMP:** 250
SQ FT: 120,000

SALES (est): 197.5MM
SALES (corp-wide): 500.3K **Privately**
Held
WEB: www.galderma.com
SIC: 2834 Dermatologicals
HQ: Galderma Pharma S.A.
Rue D'entre-Deux-Villes 10
La Tour-De-Peilz VD 1814
216 427-800

(G-6661)
GALDERMA RESEARCH & DEV
INC
14501 North Fwy (76177-3304)
PHONE................................817 961-5000
Todd Zavodnick, *President*
Quintin Cassady, *Vice Pres*
EMP: 75
SQ FT: 50,000
SALES (est): 11.3MM
SALES (corp-wide): 500.3K **Privately**
Held
WEB: www.galderma.com
SIC: 2834 Dermatologicals
HQ: Galderma Pharma S.A.
Rue D'entre-Deux-Villes 10
La Tour-De-Peilz VD 1814
216 427-800

(G-6662)
GARDNER DENVER INC
2600 Sylvania Cross Dr (76137-5023)
PHONE................................817 248-4510
Roger Hanson, *Engineer*
EMP: 9
SALES (est): 1.2MM **Privately Held**
WEB: www.gardnerdenver.com
SIC: 2911 1382 Gases & liquefied petro-
leum gases; oil & gas exploration services

(G-6663)
GDC TECHNICS LLC (PA)
Also Called: Gore Completions
2060 Eagle Pkwy (76177-2300)
PHONE................................210 496-5614
Roland C Mowermail, *CEO*
Orlando Lopez, *General Mgr*
Rick Crider A A E, *Exec VP*
Dan Ferris CPA, *Exec VP*
Adrienne Cox, *Vice Pres*
▲ **EMP:** 100
SQ FT: 120,000
SALES (est): 30.9MM **Privately Held**
WEB: www.gdctechnics.com
SIC: 3728 Aircraft parts & equipment

(G-6664)
GENERAL WRELESS
OPERATIONS INC (HQ)
Also Called: Radioshack
801 Ne 38th St (76106-3732)
PHONE................................800 843-7422
Steve Moroneso, *CEO*
Jeff Liu, *President*
Nick Cannon, *Ch Credit Ofcr*
Donna Bottoms, *Accountant*
Windy Wynne, *Cust Mgr*
▲ **EMP:** 153
SALES (est): 1.5B **Privately Held**
WEB: www.radioshack.com
SIC: 5065 3651 5731 Telephone equip-
ment; electronic kits for home assembly:
radio, TV, phonograph; radio, television &
electronic stores

(G-6665)
GEORGIA-PACIFIC LLC
4747 Mark Iv Pkwy (76106-2215)
PHONE................................817 625-9091
EMP: 104
SALES (corp-wide): 36.8B **Privately Held**
WEB: www.gp.com
SIC: 2421 Sawmills & planing mills, gen-
eral
HQ: Georgia-Pacific Llc
133 Peachtree St Nw
Atlanta GA 30303
404 652-4000

(G-6666)
GEOTEX INC
6700 Davis Blvd Ste A (76182-4016)
PHONE................................817 656-9797
Marcus Blagg, *President*
John Ladkins, *Production*
Gary McKelvey, *Shareholder*

EMP: 21
SQ FT: 20,000
SALES (est): 4.1MM **Privately Held**
WEB: www.geotex.com
SIC: 3089 3423 Thermoformed finished
plastic products; hand & edge tools

(G-6667)
GGM EXPLORATION INC (PA)
420 Throckmorton St # 200 (76102-3700)
PHONE................................817 338-1137
George Young, *President*
EMP: 48
SQ FT: 1,000
SALES (est): 15MM **Privately Held**
SIC: 1382 Geophysical exploration, oil &
gas field

(G-6668)
GI LEGACY LLC
Also Called: Greer Industries, LLC
2521 E Loop 820 N (76118-6919)
PHONE................................817 222-1414
Mitch Rosenbleeth, *President*
Kim Cravens, *Principal*
Glenn Cato, *Treasurer*
EMP: 12
SQ FT: 8,000
SALES (est): 3.1MM **Privately Held**
WEB: www.greerfasteners.com
SIC: 3728 Aircraft parts & equipment
PA: Peloton Aerospace, Llc
3843 Meadowdale Ln
Dallas TX 75229
214 632-2653

(G-6669)
GIB LEWIS PROPERTIES INC
2300 Race St (76111-1225)
PHONE................................817 834-7334
Gibson D Lewis, *CEO*
EMP: 45
SQ FT: 36,310
SALES (est): 6.5MM **Privately Held**
WEB: www.lewislabel.com
SIC: 2759 Labels & seals: printing

(G-6670)
GL BRANDS INC (PA)
Also Called: Freedom Leaf
3101 W 6th St (76147-1501)
P.O. Box 470458 (76147-0458)
PHONE................................888 811-4367
Carlos Frias, *CEO*
David Goldburg, *Ch of Bd*
Brian Moon, *CFO*
Alex Frias, *VP Finance*
Daniel Nguyen, *Security Dir*
EMP: 14
SALES: 2.3MM **Publicly Held**
WEB: www.freedomleaf.com
SIC: 2833 2621 Medicinals & botanicals;
catalog, magazine & newsprint papers

(G-6671)
GLASSVIEW LLC (PA)
813 May St Ste 3 (76104-3218)
PHONE................................646 844-4922
Alyssa Rodia, *Business Mgr*
Patrick Kirby, *Vice Pres*
James Brooks, *Mng Member*
Mike Parent, *Exec Dir*
Michael Goefron, *Security Dir*
EMP: 40
SALES (est): 51MM **Privately Held**
WEB: www.glassview.com
SIC: 2741 Miscellaneous publishing

(G-6672)
GLENN METALCRAFT TEXAS
LLC
2101 Franklin Dr (76106-2206)
PHONE................................817 838-9000
Joseph Glenn, *President*
EMP: 10 **EST:** 2011
SALES (est): 2MM **Privately Held**
WEB: www.glennmetalcraft.com
SIC: 3469 Stamping metal for the trade

(G-6673)
GLOBAL CO PAK LLC
2600 Ne Loop 820 130 (76106-1839)
PHONE................................817 449-3115
Clayton Musselman, *Mng Member*
EMP: 22

SALES (est): 546.4K **Privately Held**
SIC: 3999 Manufacturing industries

(G-6674)
GREAT SOUTHWEST VENTURES
LLC
Also Called: Alpha Graphics 544
4296 Western Center Blvd (76137-2042)
PHONE................................817 306-9204
Barrie Keiser, *Mng Member*
Jim Lombardo,
EMP: 13
SQ FT: 5,000
SALES (est): 1.6MM **Privately Held**
WEB:
www.fortworth544.alphagraphics.com
SIC: 2752 Commercial printing, litho-
graphic

(G-6675)
GREEN BAY PACKAGING INC
Fort Worth Division
7901 South Fwy (76134-5102)
P.O. Box 303 (76101-0303)
PHONE................................817 551-1934
EMP: 150
SALES (corp-wide): 1.7B **Privately Held**
WEB: www.gbpcoated.com
SIC: 2653 5199 Boxes, corrugated: made
from purchased materials; packaging ma-
terials
PA: Green Bay Packaging Inc.
1700 N Webster Ave
Green Bay WI 54302
920 433-5111

(G-6676)
GREEN EQUIPMENT CO INC
2563 Gravel Dr (76118-6944)
PHONE................................817 589-2704
Ed Green, *President*
Zane Smith, *Vice Pres*
Derek Dickens, *Regl Sales Mgr*
Brandon Baker, *Sales Staff*
Jason Crowe, *Sales Staff*
EMP: 10
SQ FT: 2,800
SALES (est): 13MM **Privately Held**
WEB: www.greenequipco.com
SIC: 3533 Oil field machinery & equipment

(G-6677)
GREENS SPECIALTY SERVICES
Also Called: Green Specialty
301 W Morningside Dr (76110-2712)
PHONE................................817 924-4323
Richard Green, *President*
Robin Green Willis, *Corp Secy*
Patty Sisson, *COO*
Janet Green, *Vice Pres*
Patricia L Sisson, *Technology*
EMP: 13
SQ FT: 11,000
SALES (est): 2.4MM **Privately Held**
WEB: www.greenspecialty.com
SIC: 3599 Machine shop, jobbing & repair

(G-6678)
GREENSLADE & COMPANY INC
2234 Wenneca Ave (76102-4325)
PHONE................................817 870-8888
Larry Borowski, *President*
Joe E Greenslade, *President*
EMP: 14 **EST:** 1978
SQ FT: 3,000
SALES (est): 3.7MM **Privately Held**
WEB: www.greensladeandcompany.com
SIC: 5084 3823 Measuring & testing
equipment, electrical; industrial instrmnts
msrmnt display/control process variable

(G-6679)
GREG-CO PISTON RINGS INC
4407 Ne 28th St (76117-4306)
PHONE................................817 831-0253
Kerri Hill, *President*
Dean Hill, *Vice Pres*
Gregory Yvonne, *Vice Pres*
EMP: 25
SQ FT: 8,700
SALES (est): 4.7MM **Privately Held**
SIC: 3592 Pistons & piston rings

▲ = Import ▼=Export
◆ =Import/Export

(G-6680)
GREINER AEROSPACE INC
7621 Pebble Dr (76118-6918)
PHONE..............................817 686-3100
Jon Frazier, *President*
Victor Pena, *Prdtn Mgr*
Fanar Berger, *Purch Mgr*
Christoph Mittendorfer, *VP Engrg*
Joanna Faulkner, *Project Engr*
▲ EMP: 60
SQ FT: 40,000
SALES (est): 12MM
SALES (corp-wide): 1.6B **Privately Held**
WEB: www.greiner-aerospace.com
SIC: 3728 Aircraft parts & equipment
HQ: Greiner Purtec Gmbh
Erwin GreinerstraBe 5
Schwanenstadt 4690
505 412-2255

(G-6681)
GRISSOMS FINE JEWELRY
Also Called: Grissom & Friends
9524 Camp Bowie West Blvd B
(76116-5988)
PHONE..............................817 244-9754
Shirley Grissom, *Partner*
Patrick Grissom, *Partner*
EMP: 9 EST: 1968
SQ FT: 1,000
SALES (est): 1.9MM **Privately Held**
WEB: www.grissoms.com
SIC: 3911 5944 Jewelry, precious metal;
jewelry, precious stones & precious metals

(G-6682)
GUNOOK PRODUCTS INC
2401 Ludelle St (76105-1018)
PHONE..............................817 536-0136
Ed Tastusek, *President*
John Tastusek, *Vice Pres*
EMP: 40
SALES (est): 3.3MM **Privately Held**
WEB: www.gunookproducts.com
SIC: 3545 Tool holders

(G-6683)
H J G TRUCKING INC (PA)
701 Denair St (76111-4497)
PHONE..............................817 834-7181
Sharon Fentress, *President*
Cheryl Albrecht, *Corp Secy*
EMP: 12 EST: 1960
SQ FT: 1,500
SALES (est): 1.4MM **Privately Held**
WEB: www.hjgtrucking.com
SIC: 4212 1442 Local trucking, without
storage; gravel mining

(G-6684)
HALO COATINGS
5221 Pyramid Blvd (76126-8383)
P.O. Box 1174, Granbury (76048-8174)
PHONE..............................817 443-3710
Jo Beth Southard, *Exec Dir*
EMP: 9
SALES (est): 1.3MM **Privately Held**
WEB: www.halocoatings.com
SIC: 3399 Powder, metal

(G-6685)
HAMAR INDUSTRIES INC
5216 David Strickland Rd (76119-5306)
PHONE..............................817 756-8990
Blake Hamar, *President*
Matthew Sanregret, *CFO*
EMP: 38 EST: 2013
SALES (est): 5.4MM **Privately Held**
WEB: www.caliraisedled.com
SIC: 3441 3824 3647 Fabricated structural metal; vehicle instruments; vehicular
lighting equipment

(G-6686)
HAN-BOONE INTERNATIONAL INC
Also Called: Fort Worth Gasket & Supply
2200 Gravel Dr (76118-7123)
PHONE..............................817 838-5196
CHI-Yeh H Boone, *President*
Derek Boone, *Vice Pres*
Anthony Kallas, *Engineer*
Duy Nguyen, *Controller*
Stephen Scales, *Government*
▲ EMP: 10
SQ FT: 13,000
SALES (est): 7MM **Privately Held**
WEB: www.fortworthgasket.com
SIC: 5085 3053 Fasteners, industrial:
nuts, bolts, screws, etc.; gaskets & seals;
gasket materials; cup packing, leather

(G-6687)
HANGER INC
1401 W Magnolia Ave (76104-4250)
PHONE..............................817 923-2101
Brenda North, *General Mgr*
Mark Ashford, *Manager*
Patsy Debaca, *CTO*
EMP: 22
SALES (corp-wide): 1.1B **Publicly Held**
WEB: www.hangerclinic.com
SIC: 5999 3842 Artificial limbs; limbs, artificial
PA: Hanger, Inc.
10910 Domain Dr Ste 300
Austin TX 78758
512 777-3800

(G-6688)
HANGER PROSTHETICS & ORTHOTICS
1401 W Magnolia Ave (76104-4250)
PHONE..............................817 923-2101
Van Sable, *President*
EMP: 24
SQ FT: 5,500
SALES (est): 2.7MM **Privately Held**
SIC: 3842 Prosthetic appliances

(G-6689)
HAR-CONN CHROME COMPANY
Also Called: Har-Conn Chrome Co of Texas
5000 Augusta Dr (76106-1803)
PHONE..............................817 626-5437
Daniel Backus, *Vice Pres*
John Adamowicz, *Engineer*
Jon Kautz, *Branch Mgr*
EMP: 40
SALES (corp-wide): 11.2MM **Privately
Held**
WEB: www.har-conn.com
SIC: 3471 Electroplating of metals or
formed products
PA: The Har-Conn Chrome Company
603 New Park Ave
West Hartford CT 06110
860 236-6801

(G-6690)
HARRIS CABINET & WDWKG INC
Also Called: Taramar Products
5090 Dick Price Rd (76140-7720)
PHONE..............................817 561-2959
Tommy R Harris, *President*
EMP: 9
SQ FT: 5,564
SALES (est): 1.3MM **Privately Held**
SIC: 2499 3993 Decorative wood & woodwork; displays & cutouts, window & lobby

(G-6691)
HEALTHCARE PYMNT SPCALISTS LLC
100 Lexington St Ste 300 (76102-2753)
PHONE..............................800 784-2175
Todd Doze, *President*
Adam Seymour, *COO*
Carol Stuckley, *CFO*
Mary Sackleh, *Asst Controller*
John Atkinson, *Manager*
EMP: 45
SQ FT: 10,000
SALES (est): 10.4MM
SALES (corp-wide): 2.6B **Publicly Held**
WEB: www.transunion.com
SIC: 7372 Business oriented computer
software
PA: Transunion
555 W Adams St Fl 1
Chicago IL 60661
312 985-2000

(G-6692)
HEALTHPOINT LTD
Also Called: Coria Pharmaceuticals
5600 Clearfork Main St (76109-3571)
PHONE..............................817 900-4000
Travis E Baugh, *President*

Michael E Steadman, *President*
Chad Miller, *District Mgr*
Paul H Duesterhoft, *Vice Pres*
F B Fitzgerald, *Vice Pres*
EMP: 220
SALES (est): 34.3MM **Privately Held**
WEB: www.smith-nephew.com
SIC: 3841 Surgical & medical instruments

(G-6693)
HEARING LAB TECHNOLOGY LLC (PA)
Also Called: GSM - Walker Products
14301 F A A Blvd (76155)
PHONE..............................469 586-0448
Timothy D Schnell, *CEO*
Christina Tul, *President*
David Beattie, *District Mgr*
Jennifer Brown, *District Mgr*
Abbie Gold, *District Mgr*
◆ EMP: 84
SQ FT: 70,000
SALES (est): 126.3MM **Privately Held**
WEB: www.lucidhearing.com
SIC: 3842 Hearing aids

(G-6694)
HEAT AIR PRODUCTS COMPANY
Also Called: Hapco
3024 N Sylvania Ave (76111-3012)
P.O. Box 14866, Haltom City (76117-0866)
PHONE..............................817 222-9567
Ann Van Schuyver, *President*
EMP: 23
SQ FT: 25,000
SALES (est): 3MM **Privately Held**
WEB: www.hapcometal.com
SIC: 3585 5075 3444 Parts for heating,
cooling & refrigerating equipment; warm
air heating & air conditioning; sheet metalwork

(G-6695)
HICKORY SPRINGS MFG CO
3629 E 1st St (76111-5802)
PHONE..............................817 831-1785
Frank Grosskreuz, *Branch Mgr*
EMP: 15
SALES (corp-wide): 783.9MM **Privately
Held**
WEB: www.hsmsolutions.com
SIC: 3069 3495 2514 2821 Foam rubber;
furniture springs, unassembled; frames
for box springs or bedsprings; metal; plastics materials & resins
PA: Hickory Springs Manufacturing Company
235 2nd Ave Nw
Hickory NC 28601
828 328-2201

(G-6696)
HIGHPEAK ENERGY PARTNERS LP
421 W 3rd St Ste 1000 (76102-3826)
PHONE..............................817 850-9200
Jack Hightower, *President*
Connie Forbes, *Engineer*
EMP: 25
SQ FT: 18,000
SALES (est): 2MM **Privately Held**
WEB: www.highpeakenergy.com
SIC: 1382 Oil & gas exploration services

(G-6697)
HIGHRISE SYSTEMS INC (PA)
3313 May St (76110-4126)
P.O. Box 12436 (76110-8436)
PHONE..............................817 927-8711
David B Jaffe, *President*
Milton Torrecillas, *General Mgr*
EMP: 25
SQ FT: 70,000
SALES (est): 1.6MM **Privately Held**
WEB: www.highrise-systems.com
SIC: 3699 8711 Cleaning equipment, ultrasonic, except medical & dental; consulting
engineer

(G-6698)
HIGHT MARINE PRODUCTS INC
Also Called: Edd's & Towing
708 Katy Rd Unit B (76244-7821)
PHONE..............................817 431-4569
Rhonda Hight, *President*
Nate Hight, *Principal*

EMP: 9
SQ FT: 36,000
SALES (est): 1MM **Privately Held**
WEB: www.eddstowing.com
SIC: 7549 3536 Towing service, automotive; boat lifts

(G-6699)
HIGHTECH GRAFIX INC
7660 Pebble Dr (76118-6959)
PHONE..............................817 616-3204
Bryan Nichols, *President*
Robert Ray, *Vice Pres*
Paulina Province, *Sales Staff*
Monica Draper, *Manager*
Bryce Nichols, *Web Dvlpr*
◆ EMP: 9
SQ FT: 3,000
SALES (est): 1.7MM **Privately Held**
WEB: www.hightechgrafix.com
SIC: 3993 8742 Signs & advertising specialties; marketing consulting services

(G-6700)
HILLSHIRE BRANDS COMPANY
3900 Meacham Blvd (76117-1603)
PHONE..............................817 427-7700
Bob Taggart, *General Mgr*
EMP: 14
SALES (corp-wide): 43.1B **Publicly Held**
WEB: www.sterlingbay.com
SIC: 2013 Sausages & other prepared
meats
HQ: The Hillshire Brands Company
400 S Jefferson St Ste 1n
Chicago IL 60607
312 614-6000

(G-6701)
HOHMANN & BARNARD INC
2415 Cold Springs Rd (76106-8404)
PHONE..............................817 625-9781
Robert Hohmann, *Branch Mgr*
EMP: 20
SQ FT: 38,496
SALES (corp-wide): 254.6B **Publicly
Held**
WEB: www.h-b.com
SIC: 3496 Miscellaneous fabricated wire
products
HQ: Hohmann & Barnard, Inc.
30 Rasons Ct
Hauppauge NY 11788
631 234-0600

(G-6702)
HOLDTITE USA INC
1051 Fm 1187 S (76036)
P.O. Box 126260 (76126-0260)
PHONE..............................817 441-1723
H T Priddy, *President*
EMP: 12
SALES (est): 300K **Privately Held**
WEB: www.global.dopa.com
SIC: 2891 Adhesives

(G-6703)
HORIZON TECH INDUSTRIES INC
2401 Ludelle St (76105-1018)
PHONE..............................817 536-2263
John Pastusek, *President*
Ed Pastusek, *President*
Mary C Pastusek, *Principal*
EMP: 26
SQ FT: 7,200
SALES (est): 5.4MM **Privately Held**
WEB: www.hti-fw.com
SIC: 3599 Machine shop, jobbing & repair

(G-6704)
HOSHIZAKI AMERICA INC
Also Called: Hoshizaki Dallas DC
15121 Frye Rd (76155-2704)
PHONE..............................817 540-4665
Greg Cavender, *Branch Mgr*
EMP: 20
SQ FT: 25,080 **Privately Held**
WEB: www.hoshizakiamerica.com
SIC: 3585 Refrigeration & heating equipment
HQ: Hoshizaki America, Inc.
618 Highway 74 S
Peachtree City GA 30269
770 487-2331

GEOGRAPHIC

(G-6705)
HOUGHTON MIFFLIN HARCOURT PUBG
301 Commerce St Ste 3700 (76102-4137)
P.O. Box 966 (76101-0966)
PHONE..................................817 302-0006
Ted Bucholz, *President*
EMP: 220
SQ FT: 70,000
SALES (corp-wide): 1.3B **Publicly Held**
WEB: www.hmhco.com
SIC: 2731 Books: publishing only
HQ: Houghton Mifflin Harcourt Publishing
Company
125 High St Ste 900
Boston MA 02110
617 351-5000

(G-6706)
HRK ENTERPRISES INC
5019 Mrtin Lther King Fwy (76119-4139)
PHONE..................................817 654-2008
Helen Killingsworth, *CEO*
Rickey Kuhn, *Vice Pres*
Ross Bigbie, *Manager*
EMP: 12
SQ FT: 10,000
SALES (est): 2.3MM **Privately Held**
WEB: www.hrke.com
SIC: 3441 Fabricated structural metal

(G-6707)
HUCKABY ENTERPRISES INC
Also Called: Bob Davis Fences & Gates
3805 W Vickery Blvd (76107-5623)
PHONE..................................817 732-5541
Stan Huckaby, *President*
EMP: 10 EST: 1946
SQ FT: 8,000
SALES (est): 1.4MM **Privately Held**
WEB: www.bobdavisfences.com
SIC: 1799 3496 Fence construction; miscellaneous fabricated wire products

(G-6708)
HULL HISTORICAL INC
201 Lipscomb St (76104-1138)
PHONE..................................817 332-1495
Brent Hull, *President*
EMP: 25
SQ FT: 8,000
SALES (est): 5MM **Privately Held**
WEB: www.hullhistorical.com
SIC: 2431 Millwork

(G-6709)
HUNNICUTT DIGITAL ELECTRONICS
Also Called: Hde
4300 South Dr (76109-5338)
PHONE..................................817 336-5449
Jack Hunnicutt, *President*
Val Hunnicutt, *Vice Pres*
Hunnicutt Valerie T, *Vice Pres*
EMP: 17
SQ FT: 12,000
SALES (est): 1.7MM **Privately Held**
WEB: www.hdemfg.com
SIC: 3699 3825 Electrical equipment & supplies; instruments to measure electricity

(G-6710)
HUNT PETROLEUM CORPORATION (DH)
110 W 7th St (76102-7018)
PHONE..................................214 880-8400
Keith A Hutton, *Exec VP*
David Levy, *Vice Pres*
Randy J Cleveland, *Vice Pres*
J A Podraza, *Vice Pres*
Robert N Schleckser, *Vice Pres*
EMP: 120 EST: 1983
SQ FT: 50,000
SALES: 72.8MM
SALES (corp-wide): 264.9B **Publicly Held**
WEB: www.petrohunt.com
SIC: 1382 1311 2911 Oil & gas exploration services; crude petroleum production; natural gas production; petroleum refining

(G-6711)
HYDRAULICS INC
3000 Saint Louis Ave (76110-4105)
PHONE..................................817 923-1965
Frank Howeth, *Principal*
Beverly Sharp,
EMP: 12
SALES (corp-wide): 10.3MM **Privately Held**
WEB: www.hydraulicsinc.com
SIC: 3492 Fluid power valves & hose fittings
PA: Hydraulics, Inc.
2935 Saint Louis Ave
Fort Worth TX 76110
817 923-1965

(G-6712)
I DO IT WITH INK
2433 Gelbray Pl (76131-2412)
PHONE..................................817 715-0681
Tyan Austin, *Owner*
EMP: 9
SALES (est): 586.1K **Privately Held**
SIC: 2731 Books: publishing only

(G-6713)
ID TECHNOLOGY LLC (DH)
5051 N Sylvania Ave # 405 (76137-4037)
PHONE..................................817 626-7779
Bob Barnard, *General Mgr*
Mark W Anderson, *Vice Pres*
Robert Zuilhof, *Vice Pres*
Mark Snedecor, *Opers Staff*
Paul B Shiller, *Mfg Staff*
◆ EMP: 70
SQ FT: 35,000
SALES (est): 88.7MM **Privately Held**
WEB: www.idtechnology.com
SIC: 5084 3565 3953 2759 Printing trades machinery, equipment & supplies; labeling machines, industrial; marking devices; commercial printing
HQ: Pro Mach, Inc.
50 E Rvrcnter Blvd Ste 18
Covington KY 41011
513 831-8778

(G-6714)
IDAHO TIMBER OF TEXAS LLC
900 W Risinger Rd (76140-5335)
PHONE..................................817 293-1001
Ted Ellis,
Scott Beechie,
Jill Fisher,
EMP: 82
SQ FT: 4,000
SALES (est): 14.1MM
SALES (corp-wide): 6B **Publicly Held**
SIC: 5031 2421 Lumber: rough, dressed & finished; lumber: rough, sawed or planed
PA: Jefferies Financial Group Inc.
520 Madison Ave
New York NY 10022
212 460-1900

(G-6715)
IGLO LLC
Also Called: Iglo Led
4924 Cambridge Rd (76155-2248)
PHONE..................................214 893-8703
Sonny Menon, *CEO*
Ritu Kher, *Director*
Michael Bowen,
Ramzanali M Karimi,
Aziz Muscatwalla,
▲ EMP: 10
SALES (est): 1.3MM **Privately Held**
WEB: www.igloled.net
SIC: 3641 3645 3646 Electric light bulbs, complete; residential lighting fixtures; commercial indusl & institutional electric lighting fixtures

(G-6716)
ILLINOIS TOOL WORKS INC
Also Called: Kairak
4401 Blue Mound Rd (76106-1928)
PHONE..................................714 870-8661
Baldo Torres, *Branch Mgr*
EMP: 19
SALES (corp-wide): 14.1B **Publicly Held**
WEB: www.itw.com
SIC: 3089 Injection molded finished plastic products

PA: Illinois Tool Works Inc.
155 Harlem Ave
Glenview IL 60025
847 724-7500

(G-6717)
IMPRESSION INKS LTD
7333 Jack Newell Blvd N # 200 (76118-7151)
PHONE..................................817 590-9711
Jesse Samaniego, *President*
▼ EMP: 37
SQ FT: 27,000
SALES (est): 18.3MM **Privately Held**
WEB: www.impressioninks.com
SIC: 2893 Printing ink

(G-6718)
INDUSTRIAL CNVYOR FBRCTION LTD
646 Aviator Dr (76179-5442)
PHONE..................................817 439-0735
Toni Pearson, *Partner*
Calvin Pearson, *General Ptnr*
EMP: 11
SQ FT: 8,000
SALES (est): 2MM **Privately Held**
WEB: www.industrialconveyorandfab.com
SIC: 3535 5084 Conveyors & conveying equipment; conveyor systems

(G-6719)
INDUSTROTECH INC
1009 Wickwood Ct (76131-3803)
PHONE..................................817 847-1358
Peggy Antilley Morris, *CEO*
Gary Wayne Morris, *President*
EMP: 10
SALES (est): 1.8MM **Privately Held**
WEB: www.industrotech.com
SIC: 3537 8711 Skids, metal; building construction consultant

(G-6720)
INK SPOT
576 N Beach St (76111-5940)
PHONE..................................817 831-4438
Karen Dixson, *President*
Renee Romines, *Graphic Designe*
EMP: 10
SALES (est): 1.1MM **Privately Held**
WEB: www.gmdirectinc.com
SIC: 2752 Commercial printing, offset

(G-6721)
INNOVATIVE IMPRESSIONS INC
2333 Minnis Dr Ste D (76117-5364)
PHONE..................................817 838-6466
Robert Breese, *President*
Fred Breese, *President*
Pat Ray, *Vice Pres*
EMP: 40
SQ FT: 7,500
SALES (est): 2.8MM **Privately Held**
SIC: 2395 Embroidery products, except schiffli machine

(G-6722)
INNOVATIVE SAND SOLUTIONS LLC
201 Main St Ste 801 (76102-3121)
PHONE..................................817 421-7428
Dale Behan, *President*
EMP: 10 EST: 2015
SQ FT: 600
SALES (est): 290.8K **Privately Held**
SIC: 1446 Filtration sand mining

(G-6723)
INTERCONNECT WIRING LLP
5024 W Vickery Blvd (76107-7517)
PHONE..................................817 377-9473
John B Ashour, *President*
Clare Martin, *COO*
Clare E McGarrey, *Vice Pres*
Clare McGarry, *Vice Pres*
Marc Piloian, *Vice Pres*
EMP: 150
SQ FT: 35,000

SALES: 15.5MM **Privately Held**
WEB: www.interconnect-wiring.com
SIC: 3694 3613 5063 3699 Harness wiring sets, internal combustion engines; panel & distribution boards & other related apparatus; wire & cable; flight simulators (training aids); electronic; aircraft maintenance & repair services

(G-6724)
INTERNATIONAL PAINT LLC
Also Called: Akzo Nobel
2951 Nthrn Cross Blvd Bld (76137)
PHONE..................................817 834-0141
Richard Farrell, *Sales Staff*
Joshua Koonz, *Branch Mgr*
EMP: 10
SALES (corp-wide): 10.2B **Privately Held**
WEB: www.akzonobel.com
SIC: 2851 Paint
HQ: International Paint Llc
6001 Antoine Dr
Houston TX 77091
713 682-1711

(G-6725)
INTERNATIONAL PAPER COMPANY
2400 Shamrock Ave (76107-1429)
PHONE..................................817 338-4000
Val Miranda, *Prdtn Mgr*
Chris Harding, *Manager*
EMP: 102
SALES (corp-wide): 22.3B **Publicly Held**
WEB: www.internationalpaper.com
SIC: 2621 Paper mills
PA: International Paper Company
6400 Poplar Ave
Memphis TN 38197
901 419-9000

(G-6726)
INTERNTNAL GLVNZERS PARTNR LTD (HQ)
Also Called: Azz Galvanizing
3100 W 7th St Ste 500 (76107-8701)
PHONE..................................817 810-0095
Kent Furche, *Principal*
John Lincoln, *Vice Pres*
Ross Bamburg, *Plant Mgr*
Duane Bickers, *Plant Mgr*
Anthony Dipaolo, *Plant Mgr*
EMP: 50
SALES (est): 10.1MM
SALES (corp-wide): 1B **Publicly Held**
WEB: www.azz.com
SIC: 3479 Galvanizing of iron, steel or end-formed products
PA: Azz Inc.
3100 W 7th St Ste 500
Fort Worth TX 76107
817 810-0095

(G-6727)
INWESCO INCORPORATED
2824 N Sylvania Ave (76111-2932)
PHONE..................................817 538-0387
Bob Delagarza, *Manager*
EMP: 10
SALES (corp-wide): 25MM **Privately Held**
WEB: www.inwesco.com
SIC: 3441 Fabricated structural metal
PA: Inwesco Incorporated
746 N Coney Ave
Azusa CA 91702
626 334-7115

(G-6728)
IQ ENTERPRISES INC
2521 5th Ave (76110-2509)
PHONE..................................866 789-0508
◆ EMP: 40 EST: 1998
SQ FT: 3,800
SALES (est): 3.5MM **Privately Held**
WEB: www.iqagroup.com
SIC: 7374 7336 2752 Computer graphics service; commercial art & graphic design; offset & photolithographic printing

(G-6729)
J BRANDT RECOGNITION LTD
2816 W Lancaster Ave (76107-3007)
PHONE..................................817 877-0513
Jerry Brandt, *President*
Melissa Brandt, *Treasurer*

EMP: 10
SQ FT: 3,500
SALES (est): 1.7MM **Privately Held**
WEB: www.jbrandt.com
SIC: 3911 Rings, finger: precious metal; pins (jewelry), precious metal; collar/cuff buttons, precious/semiprecious metal or stone

(G-6730)
J L ROBERTS INDUSTRIES INC
2501 Ne 36th St (76111-1907)
PHONE....................817 831-0676
Larry Roberts, *President*
Stephen W Roberts, *Vice Pres*
Deborah L Roberts, *Admin Sec*
Deborah Roberts, *Admin Sec*
◆ EMP: 18 EST: 1975
SQ FT: 40,000
SALES (est): 2.7MM **Privately Held**
SIC: 3713 Truck & bus bodies

(G-6731)
J&D INTERIORS INC (PA)
2015 N Main St (76164-8510)
PHONE....................817 626-2365
Juan A Castro Jr, *President*
Jane Cevancez, *Sales Executive*
EMP: 18 EST: 1979
SQ FT: 35,000
SALES (est): 1.5MM **Privately Held**
WEB: www.ilovejd.com
SIC: 2512 5712 5949 Upholstered household furniture; furniture stores; fabric, remnants

(G-6732)
J-MAC TOOL INC
8701 Eagle Mountain Cir (76135-9497)
PHONE....................817 237-6309
Jack Coleman, *President*
Janet Coleman, *Director*
▲ EMP: 50
SQ FT: 16,500
SALES (est): 21MM **Publicly Held**
WEB: www.f-e-t.com
SIC: 3549 Metalworking machinery
PA: Forum Energy Technologies, Inc.
10344 Sam Houston Park Dr # 300
Houston TX 77064

(G-6733)
J-PEAM LLC
Also Called: John Sons Press
3300 South Fwy (76110-4316)
PHONE....................817 927-1819
John J Hernandez, *President*
J Phillip Hernandez, *Vice Pres*
Dolores Roberts, *Bookkeeper*
Marc Hernandez, *VP Sales*
Wendy Talkington, *Accounts Mgr*
EMP: 26
SQ FT: 28,000
SALES (est): 5.2MM **Privately Held**
WEB: www.johnsonspress.com
SIC: 2752 Commercial printing, offset

(G-6734)
JAGEE PETRO INC
2918 Wingate St (76107-1948)
P.O. Box 9600 (76147-2600)
PHONE....................817 335-5881
Richard F Garvey, *President*
Shirley Garvey, *Admin Sec*
EMP: 10
SQ FT: 15,000
SALES (est): 532.4K
SALES (corp-wide): 13.7MM **Privately Held**
WEB: www.jagee.com
SIC: 1311 Crude petroleum production
PA: Jagee Holdings, Llp
2918 Wingate St
Fort Worth TX 76107
817 335-5881

(G-6735)
JAR-TEX INDUSTRIES INC
Also Called: Armoloy Company of Fort Worth
204 E Daggett Ave (76104-1312)
PHONE....................817 332-9922
Joan M Austin, *President*
David Richards, *Vice Pres*
Tony De Paul, *Plant Mgr*
Todd Holloway, *Manager*
EMP: 27 EST: 1970

SQ FT: 20,000
SALES (est): 1.8MM **Privately Held**
WEB: www.jartex.com
SIC: 3479 Coating of metals & formed products

(G-6736)
JBS USA FOOD COMPANY
Also Called: Swift Sales Office
3906 Sandshell Dr (76137-2403)
PHONE....................817 306-9900
Pete Hicks, *Manager*
EMP: 272 **Publicly Held**
WEB: www.jbssa.com
SIC: 2011 Meat packing plants
HQ: Jbs Usa Food Company
1770 Promontory Cir
Greeley CO 80634
970 506-8000

(G-6737)
JDP MANUFACTURING INC
2016 Mrtin Lther King Fwy (76104-6303)
PHONE....................817 529-4009
John W Pastusek, *President*
Anna L Pastusek, *Vice Pres*
David Pastusek, *Vice Pres*
EMP: 22
SQ FT: 20,000
SALES (est): 4.9MM **Privately Held**
WEB: www.jdpmfg.com
SIC: 3089 Injection molding of plastics

(G-6738)
JENSAR CORPORATION (PA)
Also Called: Edible Arrngements - Grapevine
2014 5th Ave (76110-1901)
P.O. Box 2652, Keller (76244-2652)
PHONE....................817 542-4327
Jennifer Brown, *President*
EMP: 9
SALES (est): 2MM **Privately Held**
SIC: 2033 Jellies, edible, including imitation: in cans, jars, etc.

(G-6739)
JETTA OPERATING COMPANY INC (PA)
640 Taylor St Ste 2400 (76102-4846)
PHONE....................817 335-1179
Gregory A Bird, *President*
Mike Richardson, *Exec VP*
Jeanette Clark, *Vice Pres*
Richard Cornelius, *Vice Pres*
Mike McKee, *Vice Pres*
EMP: 68
SALES (est): 47.7MM **Privately Held**
WEB: www.jettaoperating.com
SIC: 1311 Crude petroleum production

(G-6740)
JETTA PRODUCTION COMPANY INC (PA)
777 Taylor St Ph P1d (76102-4919)
PHONE....................817 335-1179
Gregory A Bird, *President*
Michael G Radler, *Exec VP*
EMP: 27
SQ FT: 4,500
SALES (est): 10.2MM **Privately Held**
WEB: www.jettaoperating.com
SIC: 1311 Crude petroleum production

(G-6741)
JGR ENTERPRISES LLC
Also Called: O. B. Macaroni Company
108 South Fwy I35w (76104-1341)
P.O. Box 53 (76101-0053)
PHONE....................817 335-4629
Gene Ratliff, *Managing Prtnr*
Jennifer S Ratliff, *Mng Member*
Jody Strader, *Manager*
EMP: 23
SQ FT: 35,000
SALES (est): 5.7MM **Privately Held**
WEB: www.obmacaroni.com
SIC: 2099 Food preparations

(G-6742)
JIMCO SALES & MFG INC
3113 Saint Louis Ave (76110-4132)
PHONE....................817 924-6173
James P Hendricks, *President*
Chad Volner, *Opers Staff*
Patricia Dimick, *Purchasing*
Ann Salazar, *Personnel*

Daryl Bates, *Sales Staff*
EMP: 40
SQ FT: 20,000
SALES (est): 12.2MM **Privately Held**
WEB: www.jimcosales.com
SIC: 3444 Fabricated structural metal

(G-6743)
JMN ENERGY EXPERTS
6229 Brentwood Dr (76112-3101)
PHONE....................817 703-9539
Talanna Reyes, *President*
EMP: 40
SALES (est): 3MM **Privately Held**
SIC: 3585 Air conditioning units, complete: domestic or industrial

(G-6744)
JOE WHITE TANK COMPANY INC
2710 N Nichols St (76106-7289)
P.O. Box 4146 (76164-0146)
PHONE....................817 624-1141
Scott Mahaffey, *CEO*
EMP: 19 EST: 1963
SQ FT: 44,000
SALES (est): 7MM **Privately Held**
WEB: www.jwtank.net
SIC: 3443 Tanks, standard or custom fabricated: metal plate

(G-6745)
JORDANS MANUFACTURING COMPANY
4205 Garland Dr (76117-1708)
P.O. Box 14829, Haltom City (76117-0829)
PHONE....................817 656-1033
Wendell Jordan III, *President*
EMP: 13
SQ FT: 8,000
SALES (est): 2.8MM **Privately Held**
SIC: 3441 Fabricated structural metal

(G-6746)
JPS ALLIANCE INC
Also Called: Alliance Loose Leaf
4625 Martin St (76119-4081)
P.O. Box 68, Lillian (76061-0068)
PHONE....................817 534-0044
Jerry Stults, *President*
Patricia Stults, *Corp Secy*
EMP: 30
SQ FT: 20,000
SALES (est): 6.4MM **Privately Held**
WEB: www.jpshealthnet.org
SIC: 2675 2782 Folders, filing, die-cut: made from purchased materials; blankbooks & looseleaf binders

(G-6747)
JUNCTION INDUSTRIES LLC (PA)
Also Called: Anchor Industrial
3348 Peden Rd Ste 500 .(76179-5558)
PHONE....................817 607-8873
Matthew Wiatrek, *Vice Pres*
Ryan McElvain, *Engineer*
Clay Trantham,
EMP: 42
SALES (est): 22.5MM **Privately Held**
WEB: www.trident-structures.com
SIC: 8741 3441 7699 Construction management; fabricated structural metal; industrial machinery & equipment repair

(G-6748)
JUSTIN BRANDS INC (HQ)
Also Called: Justin Original Work Boot
610 W Daggett Ave (76104-1103)
P.O. Box 548 (76101-0548)
PHONE....................817 332-4385
Greg Crouchley, *President*
Donna Lasater, *Human Res Dir*
◆ EMP: 200
SQ FT: 26,000
SALES (est): 99.8MM
SALES (corp-wide): 254.6B **Publicly Held**
WEB: www.justinbrands.com
SIC: 3144 3143 3149 Boots, canvas or leather: women's; boots, dress or casual: men's; children's footwear, except athletic

PA: Berkshire Hathaway Inc.
3555 Farnam St Ste 1140
Omaha NE 68131
402 346-1400

(G-6749)
JUSTIN INDUSTRIES INC
Chippewa Footwear
610 W Daggett Ave (76104-1103)
P.O. Box 548 (76101-0548)
PHONE....................817 332-4385
Chuck Caverly, *Branch Mgr*
Steve White, *Telecom Exec*
EMP: 500
SALES (corp-wide): 254.6B **Publicly Held**
WEB: www.brick.com
SIC: 3143 Boots, dress or casual: men's
HQ: Justin Industries, Inc.
3024 Acme Brick Plz
Fort Worth TX 76109
817 332-4101

(G-6750)
JUSTIN INDUSTRIES INC (HQ)
3024 Acme Brick Plz (76109-4104)
P.O. Box 425 (76101-0425)
PHONE....................817 332-4101
Warren Buffett, *CEO*
Dennis D Knautz, *President*
Judy B Hunter, *Corp Secy*
Edward L Stout Jr, *Vice Pres*
J Randy Watson, *Vice Pres*
▲ EMP: 100 EST: 1891
SQ FT: 43,800
SALES (est): 651.9MM
SALES (corp-wide): 254.6B **Publicly Held**
WEB: www.brick.com
SIC: 3251 3271 5211 5032 Brick clay: common face, glazed, vitrified or hollow; concrete block & brick; brick; brick, except refractory
PA: Berkshire Hathaway Inc.
3555 Farnam St Ste 1140
Omaha NE 68131
402 346-1400

(G-6751)
KAIRAK INC
Also Called: Kairak Innovations
4401 Blue Mound Rd (76106-1928)
PHONE....................800 825-8220
Craig S Kushen, *CEO*
EMP: 150
SALES (est): 18.1MM **Privately Held**
WEB: www.kairak.com
SIC: 3585 5078 5064 Refrigeration equipment, complete; refrigeration equipment & supplies; refrigerators & freezers

(G-6752)
KDM HOLDING INC (DH)
3700 Hulen St (76107-6816)
PHONE....................817 732-8164
Ludwig De Mot, *CEO*
▲ EMP: 100 EST: 1997
SALES: 603.2MM
SALES (corp-wide): 2.6MM **Privately Held**
WEB: www.lhoist.com
SIC: 3274 Quicklime
HQ: Lhoist
Rue Charles Dubois 28
Ottignies-Louvain-La-Neuve 1342
102 307-11

(G-6753)
KEEBLER COMPANY
4300 Diplomacy Rd Ste 200 (76155-2669)
PHONE....................817 868-2800
EMP: 20
SQ FT: 1,776
SALES (corp-wide): 12.9B **Publicly Held**
SIC: 2052 Mfg Cookies/Crackers
HQ: Keebler Company
1 Kellogg Sq
Battle Creek MI 49017
269 961-2000

(G-6754)
KELFORD ENERGY LLC
8553 N Beach St 167 (76244-4919)
PHONE....................817 615-0263
EMP: 16

GEOGRAPHIC

SALES (est): 1.5MM **Privately Held**
SIC: 7353 1381 Heavy Construction
Equipment Rental Oil/Gas Well Drilling

(G-6755)
KELLER NORTH AMERICA INC
15850 Highway 377 S (76126-5526)
P.O. Box 5000, Little Elm (75068-9000)
PHONE..............................817 443-1465
Marshall Frye, *Manager*
Duane Frye, *Manager*
EMP: 22
SALES (corp-wide): 2.9B **Privately Held**
WEB: www.keller-na.com
SIC: 1741 1771 1081 Foundation build-
ing; concrete work; metal mining services
HQ: Keller North America, Inc.
7550 Teague Rd Ste 300
Hanover MD 21076
410 551-8200

(G-6756)
KEV GROUP INC
3000 S Hulen St Ste 124 (76109-1934)
PHONE..............................866 891-9138
Bram Belzberg, *CEO*
Evelyn Eagle, *President*
Joshua Shuval, *Sales Dir*
Jennifer Rivera, *Manager*
Josh Shuval, *Director*
EMP: 26
SALES (est): 1.2MM **Privately Held**
WEB: www.kevgroup.com
SIC: 7372 Prepackaged software

(G-6757)
KEY 3 CASTING LLC (HQ)
301 Commerce St Ste 3200 (76102-4150)
PHONE..............................817 332-9500
Tanya McClanahan, *Corp Secy*
Robert Tamburrino,
◆ **EMP:** 60
SALES (est): 43.1MM
SALES (corp-wide): 261.8MM **Privately
Held**
SIC: 3365 3321 Aluminum & aluminum-
based alloy castings; gray iron castings
PA: Metal Technologies Of Indiana Llc
1401 S Grandstaff Dr
Auburn IN 46706
260 925-4717

(G-6758)
KEYSTONE EXPLORATION LTD
777 Main St Ste 3100 (76102-5325)
P.O. Box 4247 (76164-0247)
PHONE..............................817 820-7029
Thomas B Blanton, *President*
Paula Davis, *Office Mgr*
EMP: 10
SALES (est): 1.6MM **Privately Held**
SIC: 1382 Oil & gas exploration services

(G-6759)
KGP GROUP INC
Speqtrum Aerospace
1401 Everman Pkwy Ste 130 (76140-5005)
PHONE..............................817 349-3135
Gregory D Burger, *CEO*
Brian Whalen, *Manager*
EMP: 12
SALES (corp-wide): 20.2MM **Privately
Held**
WEB: www.speqtrum-pps.net
SIC: 3369 Aerospace castings, nonferrous:
except aluminum
PA: Kgp Group, Inc.
1000 Pennsylvania Ave
Fort Worth TX 76104
817 354-0766

(G-6760)
KGP GROUP INC (PA)
Also Called: Speqtrum
1000 Pennsylvania Ave (76104-2227)
PHONE..............................817 354-0766
Gregory D Burger, *CEO*
Kelly G Vaughn, *President*
Steven R Purvis, *Chairman*
Garrison Gillespie, *Buyer*
Sal Perez, *Accounts Mgr*
▲ **EMP:** 50

SALES (est): 20.2MM **Privately Held**
WEB: www.speqtrum-pps.net
SIC: 3423 3555 3069 Cutting dies, except
metal cutting; printing plates; sponge rubber & sponge rubber products

(G-6761)
**KIMBERLY-CLARK
CORPORATION**
8715 Harmon Rd (76177-7501)
PHONE..............................817 847-0211
EMP: 11
SALES (corp-wide): 18.2B **Publicly Held**
SIC: 2621 2676 Paper Mill Mfg Sanitary
Paper Products
PA: Kimberly-Clark Corporation
351 Phelps Dr
Irving TX 75038
972 281-1200

(G-6762)
KING PIPELINE SERVICES LLC
3805 Summercrest Dr (76109-3418)
PHONE..............................903 530-8667
Tripp King,
EMP: 22
SALES (est): 1.1MM **Privately Held**
SIC: 1389 4212 6541 8713 Testing,
measuring, surveying & analysis services;
petroleum haulage, local; title abstract of-
fices; surveying services; oil & gas explo-
ration services

(G-6763)
KIRBY - SMITH MACHINERY INC
1450 Ne Loop 820 (76106-1728)
PHONE..............................817 378-0600
Mike Wenske, *Manager*
EMP: 15
SQ FT: 11,428
SALES (corp-wide): 575.9MM **Privately
Held**
WEB: www.kirby-smith.com
SIC: 3569 5082 7389 Assembly ma-
chines, non-metalworking; cranes, con-
struction; crane & aerial lift service
PA: Kirby - Smith Machinery, Inc.
6715 W Reno Ave
Oklahoma City OK 73127
888 861-0219

(G-6764)
KITES DRAPERIES INC
Also Called: Kite's Interiors
2711 White Settlement Rd (76107-1331)
PHONE..............................817 336-1027
Samuel E Kite, *President*
Fran Pixler, *Corp Secy*
Wanda A Kite, *Vice Pres*
EMP: 25 **EST:** 1962
SQ FT: 20,000
SALES (est): 3.1MM **Privately Held**
WEB: www.kitesinteriors.com
SIC: 2391 5714 2591 Curtains &
draperies; draperies; drapery hardware &
blinds & shades

(G-6765)
KLABZUBA OIL & GAS INC (PA)
Also Called: Klabzuba, Robert
100 Lexington St Ste 50 (76102-2795)
PHONE..............................817 336-5757
EMP: 15 **EST:** 1967
SQ FT: 20,000
SALES (est): 3.3MM **Privately Held**
WEB: www.klabzuba.com
SIC: 1311 Crude petroleum production;
natural gas production

(G-6766)
**KMG ELECTRONIC CHEMICALS
INC (DH)**
300 Throckmorton St # 1800 (76102-2933)
PHONE..............................817 761-6100
Christopher T Fraser, *CEO*
Tim Hagensen, *Vice Pres*
Jeff Handelman, *Vice Pres*
Ernest C Kremling II, *Vice Pres*
Mark Panger, *Engineer*
◆ **EMP:** 20
SQ FT: 17,527
SALES (est): 107.4MM
SALES (corp-wide): 1.1B **Publicly Held**
WEB: www.kmgchemicals.com
SIC: 2899 Chemical preparations

HQ: Cmc Materials, Inc.
300 Throckmorton St
Fort Worth TX 76102
817 761-6100

(G-6767)
KMG-BERNUTH INC (DH)
300 Throckmorton St (76102-2921)
PHONE..............................817 761-6100
David L Hatcher, *Ch of Bd*
Neal Butler, *President*
Michael A Hoffman, *Vice Pres*
Roger Jackson, *Vice Pres*
Ernest C Kremling III, *Vice Pres*
◆ **EMP:** 19
SQ FT: 8,000
SALES (est): 43.9MM
SALES (corp-wide): 1.1B **Publicly Held**
WEB: www.kmgchemicals.com
SIC: 5169 2869 Chemicals, industrial &
heavy; industrial organic chemicals
HQ: Cmc Materials, Inc.
300 Throckmorton St
Fort Worth TX 76102
817 761-6100

(G-6768)
KOBI ELECTRIC LLC
301 E Risinger Rd Ste 109 (76140-5348)
PHONE..............................817 297-3200
Frank Saade, *CEO*
Nicholas Peragine, *President*
Michael Sawilowsky, *CFO*
▲ **EMP:** 15 **EST:** 2011
SALES (est): 25.5MM **Privately Held**
WEB: www.yujiatech.com
SIC: 3674 Light emitting diodes

(G-6769)
KOLD PACK INCORPORATED
5609 Azle Ave (76114-1119)
PHONE..............................800 824-2661
Glen Stuard, *President*
Abbie Stuard, *Vice Pres*
Michelle Stohler, *Treasurer*
EMP: 16 **EST:** 1971
SQ FT: 8,000
SALES (est): 2.1MM **Privately Held**
WEB: www.koldpack.com
SIC: 3585 Refrigeration equipment, com-
plete

(G-6770)
KPS GLOBAL LLC (PA)
4201 N Beach St (76137-3212)
PHONE..............................817 281-5121
Mike Eakins, *CEO*
Eojin Lee, *Vice Pres*
Dan Zeddy, *CFO*
EMP: 220
SALES (est): 276.7MM **Privately Held**
WEB: www.kpsglobal.com
SIC: 3089 3585 Panels, building: plastic;
refrigeration & heating equipment

(G-6771)
KPS GLOBAL LLC
505 Pecan St Ste 200 (76102-4061)
PHONE..............................817 339-2100
EMP: 44
SALES (corp-wide): 99.6MM **Privately
Held**
SIC: 3585 Manufacturing
Refrigeration/Heating Equipment
PA: Kps Global Llc
4201 N Beach St
Fort Worth TX 76137
817 281-5121

(G-6772)
KRAFT HEINZ FOODS COMPANY
1005 Railhead Dr (76177-3901)
PHONE..............................817 837-4100
EMP: 324
SALES (corp-wide): 24.9B **Publicly Held**
WEB: www.kraftheinzcompany.com
SIC: 2033 Canned fruits & specialties
HQ: Kraft Heinz Foods Company
1 Ppg Pl Ste 3400
Pittsburgh PA 15222
412 456-5700

(G-6773)
KROGER CO
Also Called: Vandervoort Dairy
900 S Main St (76104-3407)
P.O. Box 1525, Cincinnati OH (45201-
1525)
PHONE..............................817 698-4357
Joe Lastingy, *Branch Mgr*
EMP: 225
SALES (corp-wide): 122.2B **Publicly
Held**
WEB: www.thekrogerco.com
SIC: 2026 Milk processing (pasteurizing,
homogenizing, bottling); cream, sour; yo-
gurt
PA: The Kroger Co
1014 Vine St Ste 1000
Cincinnati OH 45202
513 762-4000

(G-6774)
KROWN MANUFACTURING INC
3408 Indale Rd (76116-7348)
PHONE..............................817 738-2485
Barbara Ander, *President*
Barabra Anders, *President*
Sidney Anders, *Vice Pres*
Billy Geeslin, *Production*
▲ **EMP:** 15
SQ FT: 15,000
SALES (est): 2.7MM **Privately Held**
WEB: www.krownmfg.com
SIC: 3661 5999 5065 Telephone & tele-
graph apparatus; telephone & communi-
cation equipment; telephone &
telegraphic equipment

(G-6775)
KUBA-TECH INDUSTRIES LLC
801 Ozona Ave (76108-1224)
PHONE..............................817 924-5520
Raykel Rodriguez, *Mng Member*
EMP: 15
SALES (est): 2.4MM **Privately Held**
WEB: www.kticabinets.com
SIC: 2521 2599 Cabinets, office: wood;
cabinets, factory

(G-6776)
**KUROSKY & CO PNTG CONTRS
INC**
6220 Anderson Rd (76117-6100)
P.O. Box 14468 (76117-0468)
PHONE..............................817 834-7179
Gary Kurosky, *President*
Cliff Kurosky, *Vice Pres*
EMP: 50
SQ FT: 6,000
SALES (est): 3.7MM **Privately Held**
WEB: www.kurosky.com
SIC: 1721 1799 3443 Commercial paint-
ing; industrial painting; sandblasting of
building exteriors; liners/lining

(G-6777)
LA NUEVA RIOGRANDESE INC
4241 Mccart Ave (76115-1020)
PHONE..............................817 921-0440
Arcenio V Munoz, *Branch Mgr*
EMP: 28
SALES (corp-wide): 490.4K **Privately
Held**
SIC: 2099 Tortillas, fresh or refrigerated
PA: La Nueva Riograndese Inc
831 N Sylvania Ave
Fort Worth TX 76111
817 222-0090

(G-6778)
LA SUPERIOR FOODS INC
Also Called: La Superior Tortillas Y Mas
500 E Central Ave (76164-9218)
PHONE..............................682 703-1165
EMP: 11
SALES (corp-wide): 1MM **Privately Held**
WEB: www.superiortortillas.com
SIC: 2099 Tortillas, fresh or refrigerated
PA: La Superior Foods, Inc.
1128 E Seminary Dr
Fort Worth TX
817 927-7688

(G-6779)
LANDERS MACHINE CO
Also Called: Manufacturing Plant
3601 N Sylvania Ave (76111-3196)
PHONE.................................817 834-6383
Tony Barnett, *Branch Mgr*
EMP: 25
SQ FT: 60,000
SALES (corp-wide): 8.5MM **Privately Held**
SIC: 3556 3541 Mills, food; machine tools, metal cutting type
PA: Landers Machine Co.
3601 N Sylvania Ave
Fort Worth TX 76111
817 834-6383

(G-6780)
LASKO PRODUCTS LLC
1700 Meacham Blvd (76106-2199)
PHONE.................................817 625-6381
Mark Khashram, *Vice Pres*
Eddie Yarbrough, *Opers-Prdtn-Mfg*
Ron Lamberg, *Natl Sales Mgr*
Jack Arwood, *Manager*
EMP: 400 **Privately Held**
WEB: www.lasko.com
SIC: 3634 3564 Electric housewares & fans; blowers & fans
HQ: Lasko Products, Llc
820 Lincoln Ave
West Chester PA 19380
610 692-7400

(G-6781)
LATHAM STAIRS & MILLWORKS INC
1212 Ruby Lea Ln (76179-9173)
P.O. Box 669, Sanger (76266-0669)
PHONE.................................940 458-3075
Toll Free:.................................866 -
David Todd Greenwood, *President*
Denise Greenwood, *Vice Pres*
EMP: 40
SQ FT: 48,000
SALES (est): 7.2MM **Privately Held**
WEB: www.lathamstairsandcabinets.com
SIC: 2431 Staircases, stairs & railings

(G-6782)
LEGGETT & PLATT INCORPORATED
2107 Franklin Dr (76106-2206)
PHONE.................................817 378-0108
Stephanie Westbrook, *Manager*
EMP: 35
SALES (corp-wide): 4.7B **Publicly Held**
WEB: www.leggett.com
SIC: 2515 Mattresses & bedsprings
PA: Leggett & Platt, Incorporated
1 Leggett Rd
Carthage MO 64836
417 358-8131

(G-6783)
LEGGETT & PLATT INCORPORATED
Leggett & Platt 1701
307 W 7th St Ste 1800 (76102-5118)
PHONE.................................817 626-6690
Larry Heppe, *President*
Brian Jennings, *Manager*
EMP: 38
SALES (corp-wide): 4.7B **Publicly Held**
WEB: www.leggett.com
SIC: 2515 Mattresses & bedsprings
PA: Leggett & Platt, Incorporated
1 Leggett Rd
Carthage MO 64836
417 358-8131

(G-6784)
LEGGETT & PLATT INCORPORATED
Also Called: Leggett & Platt 0117
5000 South Fwy (76115-3902)
PHONE.................................817 922-5000
Fax: 817 921-1624
EMP: 200
SALES (corp-wide): 3.7B **Publicly Held**
SIC: 2541 Mfg Store And Office Display Cases And Fixtures

PA: Leggett & Platt, Incorporated
1 Leggett Rd
Carthage MO 64836
417 358-8131

(G-6785)
LHOIST NORTH AMERICA ALA LLC (DH)
5600 Clearfork Main St # 300 (76109-3572)
P.O. Box 985004 (76185-5004)
PHONE.................................817 732-8164
Ron Thompson, *CEO*
Kyle Colde, *CFO*
Bob Nordin, *Treasurer*
Tollie Smith, *Sales Staff*
▲ EMP: 80
SALES (est): 52.3MM
SALES (corp-wide): 2.6MM **Privately Held**
SIC: 3274 1422 Lime; crushed & broken limestone
HQ: Lhoist North America, Inc.
5600 Clearfork Main St # 300
Fort Worth TX 76109
817 732-8164

(G-6786)
LHOIST NORTH AMERICA MO INC (DH)
Also Called: Headquarters
5600 Clearfork Main St # 300 (76109-3572)
P.O. Box 985004 (76185-5004)
PHONE.................................817 732-8164
Ludwig De Mot, *CEO*
David Reilly, *President*
Tom Reeder, *Plant Mgr*
Randy Thomas, *Mfg Staff*
Steve Darnish, *CFO*
EMP: 56
SALES (est): 10.5MM
SALES (corp-wide): 2.6MM **Privately Held**
WEB: www.lhoist.com
SIC: 3274 Quicklime
HQ: Lhoist North America, Inc.
5600 Clearfork Main St # 300
Fort Worth TX 76109
817 732-8164

(G-6787)
LHOIST NORTH AMERICA TENN INC
5600 Clearfrk Main St 3 # 300 (76109)
P.O. Box 985004 (76185-5004)
PHONE.................................817 732-8164
Carolyn Hussey, *Credit Mgr*
EMP: 41
SALES (corp-wide): 2.6MM **Privately Held**
SIC: 1422 Crushed & broken limestone
HQ: Lhoist North America Of Tennessee, Inc.
750 Old Hickry Blvd 200-2
Brentwood TN 37027
615 259-4222

(G-6788)
LIBERTY COMPANY
Lauritzen & Makin
101 W Felix (76115)
P.O. Box 6214 (76115-0214)
PHONE.................................817 921-0218
EMP: 20
SALES (corp-wide): 2.1MM **Privately Held**
SIC: 2541 5211 2542 2499 Mfg Wood Partitions/Fixt Nonwd Partition/Fixt Ret Lumber/Building Mtrl Carpentry Contractor
PA: The Liberty Company
101 W Felix St
Fort Worth TX
817 921-0218

(G-6789)
LILIS ENERGY INC (PA)
201 Main St Ste 700 (76102-3134)
PHONE.................................817 585-9001
Joseph C Daches, *CEO*
Joseph Daches, *CEO*
James W Denny III, *Exec VP*
Austin Brooks, *Vice Pres*
Geok Lim, *Vice Pres*
EMP: 17

SALES: 66MM **Privately Held**
WEB: www.lilisenergy.com
SIC: 1382 Oil & gas exploration services

(G-6790)
LIME HOLDING INC (DH)
3700 Hulen St (76107-6816)
PHONE.................................817 732-8164
Ludwig De Mot, *CEO*
▲ EMP: 183
SQ FT: 45,000
SALES (est): 574.9MM
SALES (corp-wide): 2.6MM **Privately Held**
SIC: 3274 Quicklime
HQ: Kdm Holding Inc.
3700 Hulen St
Fort Worth TX 76107
817 732-8164

(G-6791)
LLEBROC INDUSTRIES INC
3601 Conway St (76111-4615)
PHONE.................................817 831-3158
Wayne Corbell, *President*
Bonnie Corbell, *Corp Secy*
Nicholas Covey, *Controller*
Sharon Smith, *Human Res Dir*
Kitsi Eakins, *Accounts Mgr*
▲ EMP: 29
SQ FT: 80,000
SALES (est): 5.4MM **Privately Held**
WEB: www.llebroc.com
SIC: 2531 Seats, automobile

(G-6792)
LOCKHEED MARTIN CORPORATION
1029 Lindstrom Dr (76131-5312)
P.O. Box 748 (76101-7450)
PHONE.................................817 763-3035
Jim Burke, *Engineer*
Von Clement, *Engineer*
Thomas Ek, *Engineer*
Joan Koebert, *Engineer*
Gary Downs, *Manager*
EMP: 55 **Publicly Held**
WEB: www.lockheedmartin.com
SIC: 3812 Search & navigation equipment
PA: Lockheed Martin Corporation
6801 Rockledge Dr
Bethesda MD 20817

(G-6793)
LOCKHEED MARTIN CORPORATION
6937 Aspen Wood Trl (76132-3511)
P.O. Box 748 (76101-7450)
PHONE.................................817 935-1363
David Babb, *Engineer*
Dain Hancock, *Manager*
Jovante Ham, *Software Engr*
EMP: 1265 **Publicly Held**
WEB: www.lockheedmartin.com
SIC: 3812 Search & navigation equipment
PA: Lockheed Martin Corporation
6801 Rockledge Dr
Bethesda MD 20817

(G-6794)
LOCKHEED MARTIN CORPORATION
7000 Calmont Ave (76116-4183)
PHONE.................................817 495-0200
Anna Wideska, *Engineer*
Kevin E Organ, *Manager*
Tony Barrett, *Administration*
EMP: 458 **Publicly Held**
WEB: www.lockheedmartin.com
SIC: 3812 Search & navigation equipment
PA: Lockheed Martin Corporation
6801 Rockledge Dr
Bethesda MD 20817

(G-6795)
LOCKHEED MARTIN CORPORATION
Also Called: Lockheed Mrtin Crprtn-Rnautics
1 Lockheed Blvd Bldg 10 (76108-3619)
PHONE.................................817 777-2000
J Smith, *Principal*
EMP: 50 **Publicly Held**
WEB: www.lockheedmartin.com
SIC: 3812 Search & navigation equipment

PA: Lockheed Martin Corporation
6801 Rockledge Dr
Bethesda MD 20817

(G-6796)
LOCKHEED MARTIN CORPORATION
Wilcox Plz 7000 Clmt Ave Wilcox Plaza (76116)
PHONE.................................817 777-2000
Kevin Organ, *Contract Mgr*
EMP: 500 **Publicly Held**
WEB: www.lockheedmartin.com
SIC: 3812 Search & navigation equipment
PA: Lockheed Martin Corporation
6801 Rockledge Dr
Bethesda MD 20817

(G-6797)
LOCKHEED MARTIN CORPORATION
Also Called: Aero - Ft Worth
7501 Calmont Ave (76116-4047)
PHONE.................................817 777-0786
Bryan Henderson, *Engineer*
Juan Moya, *Engineer*
Fred Samudio, *Manager*
EMP: 15 **Publicly Held**
WEB: www.lockheedmartin.com
SIC: 3812 Search & navigation equipment
PA: Lockheed Martin Corporation
6801 Rockledge Dr
Bethesda MD 20817

(G-6798)
LOCKHEED MARTIN CORPORATION
6100 Western Pl Ste 700 (76107-4678)
PHONE.................................817 777-2000
Jack P Guthrie, *Principal*
Quinn Kelly, *Engineer*
Natasha Buck, *Manager*
David Wade, *Manager*
Charles Felts, *IT/INT Sup*
EMP: 435 **Publicly Held**
WEB: www.lockheedmartin.com
SIC: 3761 3663 3764 3812 Space vehicles, complete; guided missiles, complete; ballistic missiles, complete; guided missiles & space vehicles, research & development; satellites, communications; propulsion units for guided missiles & space vehicles; guided missile & space vehicle engines, research & devel.; warfare counter-measure equipment; missile guidance systems & equipment; sonar systems & equipment; radar systems & equipment; aircraft parts & equipment; research & dev by manuf., aircraft parts & auxiliary equip; research & development on aircraft by the manufacturer
PA: Lockheed Martin Corporation
6801 Rockledge Dr
Bethesda MD 20817

(G-6799)
LONESTAR PROSPECTS LTD (DH)
Also Called: Vista Sand
4413 Carey St (76119-4219)
PHONE.................................817 279-1660
Roger Sikes, *Partner*
Justin Thomas, *General Mgr*
Patrick Washington, *Vice Pres*
Felipe Lembcke, *Production*
Kristin Smith, *CFO*
EMP: 42
SALES (est): 172.8MM
SALES (corp-wide): 254.2MM **Privately Held**
WEB: www.vistasand.com
SIC: 1446 Silica sand mining

(G-6800)
LONESTAR RESOURCES US INC (PA)
111 Boland St Ste 301 (76107-1265)
PHONE.................................817 921-1889
Frank D Bracken III, *CEO*
John H Pinkerton, *Ch of Bd*
Barry D Schneider, *COO*
Barry Schneider, *COO*
Thomas H Olle, *Vice Pres*
EMP: 21

SALES: 195.1MM **Privately Held**
WEB: www.lonestarresources.com
SIC: 1311 Crude petroleum & natural gas

(G-6801)
LOUIS BARRIGA
Also Called: Precision Mold Builders
3244 Stuart Dr (76110-4320)
PHONE............................817 923-7370
Louis Barriga, *Owner*
EMP: 22 **EST:** 1967
SQ FT: 5,500
SALES (est): 594.8K **Privately Held**
WEB: www.fiestafortworth.net
SIC: 5812 3089 Mexican restaurant; caterers; injection molding of plastics

(G-6802)
M & K PLATING INC
2621 Finley St (76111-1031)
P.O. Box 7302 (76111-0302)
PHONE............................817 332-6021
James G Curry, *President*
J V Curry, *Vice Pres*
Charles Mc Crory, *Vice Pres*
EMP: 20 **EST:** 1975
SQ FT: 6,000
SALES (est): 2.2MM **Privately Held**
WEB: www.mandkplating.com
SIC: 3471 Chromium plating of metals or formed products; electroplating of metals or formed products

(G-6803)
M L HOLDINGS INC
Also Called: AlphaGraphics
5836 Camp Bowie Blvd (76107-5008)
PHONE............................817 732-1708
Suzanne Cowan, *President*
EMP: 12
SQ FT: 6,500
SALES (est): 2.7MM **Privately Held**
WEB: www.alphagraphics.com
SIC: 2752 7334 Commercial printing, lithographic; photocopying & duplicating services

(G-6804)
M&M MANUFACTURING INC (DH)
Also Called: M&M Manufacturing Company
4001 Mark Iv Pkwy (76106-4129)
P.O. Box 163409 (76161-3409)
PHONE............................817 336-2311
Rob Felton, *President*
Melvin Nobles, *Vice Pres*
Steve Priester, *Vice Pres*
Michael D Stepp, *Vice Pres*
Jim Strong, *Vice Pres*
◆ **EMP:** 200 **EST:** 1958
SQ FT: 95,000
SALES (est): 143.5MM
SALES (corp-wide): 254.6B **Publicly Held**
WEB: www.mmmfg.com
SIC: 3444 Ducts, sheet metal
HQ: Mitek Industries, Inc.
16023 Swinly Rdg
Chesterfield MO 63017
314 434-1200

(G-6805)
M&M MANUFACTURING INC
200 Adolph St (76107-1497)
PHONE............................817 334-0034
Terry Clements, *Manager*
EMP: 50
SALES (corp-wide): 254.6B **Publicly Held**
WEB: www.mmmfg.com
SIC: 3444 Ducts, sheet metal
HQ: M&M Manufacturing, Inc.
4001 Mark Iv Pkwy
Fort Worth TX 76106
817 336-2311

(G-6806)
MAHLE BEHR SERVICE AMERICA LLC (DH)
5020 Augusta Dr (76106-1803)
PHONE............................817 624-7273
Torsten Waldhelm, *Managing Dir*
▲ **EMP:** 30 **EST:** 2004

SALES (est): 9.3MM
SALES (corp-wide): 504.6K **Privately Held**
SIC: 5531 3714 Automobile air conditioning equipment, sale, installation; radiators & radiator shells & cores, motor vehicle

(G-6807)
MAKERS COMPANY INC
2723 Weaver St (76117-4867)
P.O. Box 14537 (76117-0537)
PHONE............................817 834-5538
Charles C Haskin, *Ch of Bd*
Greg Haskin, *President*
Terry Smith, *General Mgr*
Laura Haskin, *Corp Secy*
B J Haskin, *Vice Pres*
EMP: 30
SQ FT: 1,000
SALES (est): 7MM **Privately Held**
WEB: www.makerssales.com
SIC: 3441 Fabricated structural metal

(G-6808)
MALOR MANUFACTURING INC
3245 Saint Louis Ave (76110-4181)
PHONE............................817 926-0278
J Don Willis Sr, *President*
Mary Willis, *Corp Secy*
Mindy Hanzik, *Vice Pres*
EMP: 25 **EST:** 1957
SQ FT: 25,000
SALES (est): 3.5MM **Privately Held**
WEB: www.malormfg.com
SIC: 3599 Machine shop, jobbing & repair

(G-6809)
MARCO DISPLAY SPECIALISTS LP
3209 Marquita Dr (76116-5120)
P.O. Box 123439 (76121-3439)
PHONE............................817 244-8300
Darrell L Cooper, *Principal*
◆ **EMP:** 500
SQ FT: 80,000
SALES (est): 54.6MM
SALES (corp-wide): 147.3MM **Privately Held**
WEB: www.marcocompany.com
SIC: 2541 3993 Store & office display cases & fixtures; signs & advertising specialties
PA: Marco Display Specialists Gp, Lc
3209 Marquita Dr
Fort Worth TX 76116
817 244-8300

(G-6810)
MARCO DSPLAY SPECIALISTS GP LC (PA)
Also Called: Marco Company, The
3209 Marquita Dr (76116-5120)
P.O. Box 123439 (76121-3439)
PHONE............................817 244-8300
Jon W Stewart, *CFO*
Darrell L Cooper,
Dan Cooper,
Craig Nickell,
Douglas E Pentecost,
◆ **EMP:** 200
SQ FT: 225,000
SALES (est): 147.3MM **Privately Held**
WEB: www.marcocompany.com
SIC: 2521 2541 3993 3089 Tables, office: wood; store & office display cases & fixtures; signs & advertising specialties; washers, plastic; unsupported plastics film & sheet

(G-6811)
MARIAN FORT WORTH INC
1501 Northpark Dr (76102-1007)
PHONE............................817 332-6151
Andrew J Lirette, *President*
Brenda James, *Production*
Oscar Cruz, *Controller*
Sue Batdorf, *Accountant*
Lee Vansyckle, *Human Res Mgr*
EMP: 30
SALES (est): 9.5MM
SALES (corp-wide): 181.3MM **Privately Held**
WEB: www.marianinc.com
SIC: 3069 3081 Hard rubber & molded rubber products; unsupported plastics film & sheet

HQ: Marian, Inc.
1011 E Saint Clair St
Indianapolis IN 46202
317 638-6525

(G-6812)
MARSHALL R YOUNG OIL CO (PA)
200 Bailey Ave Ste 102 (76107-1219)
PHONE............................817 335-1216
George M Young, *Ch of Bd*
Shannon Ray, *President*
J Greg Wilson, *Vice Pres*
Marshall R Young, *Vice Pres*
Sherman S Young, *Admin Sec*
EMP: 11
SQ FT: 8,000
SALES (est): 2.6MM **Privately Held**
WEB: www.wilsonroyalty.com
SIC: 1311 Crude petroleum production; natural gas production

(G-6813)
MARTIN SPROCKET & GEAR INC
Martin Tool & Forge
3600 Mccart Ave (76110-4692)
PHONE............................817 258-3000
Jim Johnson, *President*
Robert Robbins, *General Mgr*
Manny Vasquez, *Mfg Staff*
Melissa Moses, *Production*
Pamela Bush, *Purchasing*
EMP: 190
SALES (corp-wide): 539MM **Privately Held**
WEB: www.martinsprocket.com
SIC: 3566 3535 Gears, power transmission, except automotive; conveyors & conveying equipment
PA: Martin Sprocket & Gear, Inc.
3100 Sprocket Dr
Arlington TX 76015
817 258-3000

(G-6814)
MARVEL COMMUNICATIONS COMPANY
Also Called: Everhardt Antennas
6000 Old Hemphill Rd D (76134-1407)
PHONE............................817 568-0177
Sheila Simmons, *President*
Jack Wadsworth, *VP Admin*
Mike Simmons, *Vice Pres*
▲ **EMP:** 47
SQ FT: 20,000
SALES (est): 8.1MM **Privately Held**
WEB: www.marvelcommunicationstx.com
SIC: 3663 Antennas, transmitting & communications

(G-6815)
MASTER-HALCO INC
500 South Fwy (76104-3504)
PHONE............................817 378-8086
Mike Reitz, *Manager*
EMP: 27 **Privately Held**
WEB: www.masterhalco.com
SIC: 3315 Chain link fencing; fence gates posts & fittings: steel
HQ: Master-Halco, Inc.
3010 Lbj Fwy Ste 800
Dallas TX 75234
972 714-7300

(G-6816)
MATEK PERFORMANCE INC
Also Called: A G R
4920 Rondo Dr (76106-1823)
PHONE............................817 626-9006
Matt Burkett, *President*
Lary Szuhy, *Vice Pres*
EMP: 20
SQ FT: 10,000
SALES (est): 2.5MM **Privately Held**
WEB: www.agrperformance.com
SIC: 3714 5531 3462 Power steering equipment, motor vehicle; automotive parts; iron & steel forgings

(G-6817)
MATHESON TRI-GAS INC
Also Called: Matheson Tri-Gas 506
5932 South Fwy (76134-1402)
PHONE............................817 551-0550

Trey Leftwich, *Sales Staff*
Chad Dowdy, *Manager*
EMP: 10 **Privately Held**
WEB: www.mathesongas.com
SIC: 2813 5084 5169 Industrial gases; welding machinery & equipment; industrial gases
HQ: Matheson Tri-Gas, Inc.
3 Mountainview Rd Ste 3 # 3
Warren NJ 07059
908 991-9200

(G-6818)
MATSON INC
Also Called: A C F Tarp & Awning
5960 E Loop 820 S (76119-7028)
PHONE............................817 478-1800
Mark Matson, *President*
Nan Matson, *Vice Pres*
EMP: 20 **EST:** 1980
SQ FT: 17,000
SALES (est): 2.6MM **Privately Held**
WEB: www.acfdfw.com
SIC: 2394 Awnings, fabric: made from purchased materials

(G-6819)
MATTEL INC
501 Meacham Blvd (76106-1969)
PHONE............................817 302-3300
Teresa Taylor, *Branch Mgr*
Stuart Strauch, *Manager*
Mary Serrato, *Supervisor*
Nicole Habeck, *Technician*
EMP: 9
SALES (corp-wide): 4.5B **Publicly Held**
WEB: www.mattel.com
SIC: 3944 Games, toys & children's vehicles
PA: Mattel, Inc.
333 Continental Blvd
El Segundo CA 90245
310 252-2000

(G-6820)
MAVERICK COMPANIES LLC
801 Cherry St Unit 2 (76102-6886)
PHONE............................817 334-4100
Krisian E Grimland, *General Mgr*
Robert Bruce, *Treasurer*
EMP: 150
SALES (est): 305.5K
SALES (corp-wide): 567.2MM **Publicly Held**
SIC: 1389 Oil field services
HQ: Basic Energy Services, L.P.
801 Cherry St Unit 2
Fort Worth TX 76102

(G-6821)
MAVERICK SOLUTIONS LLC
801 Cherry St Unit 2 (76102-6886)
PHONE............................817 334-4100
David C Johnston,
EMP: 228
SALES (est): 3.2MM
SALES (corp-wide): 567.2MM **Publicly Held**
SIC: 1389 Servicing oil & gas wells
HQ: Basic Energy Services, L.P.
801 Cherry St Unit 2
Fort Worth TX 76102

(G-6822)
MCKINLEY IRON WORKS INC
4720 Esco Dr (76140-2208)
P.O. Box 790 (76101-0790)
PHONE............................817 335-1268
Judith Mc Kinley-Crowder, *President*
Deann McKinley, *Admin Sec*
EMP: 50 **EST:** 1906
SQ FT: 58,011
SALES (est): 9.8MM **Privately Held**
WEB: www.mckinleyironworks.com
SIC: 3321 Gray iron castings

(G-6823)
MCQUEARY INDUSTRIES INC
3120 E 4th St (76111-3805)
P.O. Box 145 (76101-0145)
PHONE............................817 335-1988
Michael McQueary, *President*
EMP: 11
SQ FT: 8,200

SALES (est): 1.6MM **Privately Held**
WEB: www.mcquearyindustries.com
SIC: 3599 7699 Machine shop, jobbing & repair; industrial machinery & equipment repair

(G-6824)
MD3 INDUSTRIES LTD
Also Called: Empire Precision Machining
4901 Keller Haslet Rd (76244-8106)
PHONE..............................682 831-1414
Michael Strader, *Partner*
Jared McCreight, *Plant Mgr*
EMP: 12 EST: 1980
SQ FT: 30,000
SALES (est): 1MM **Privately Held**
WEB: www.empirepremac.com
SIC: 3599 Machine shop, jobbing & repair

(G-6825)
MECO CONSTRUCTION COMPANY LLC
7113 Frenton Ter (76131-3012)
PHONE..............................817 975-4599
Glenn D Martin,
EMP: 20
SQ FT: 600
SALES (est): 1MM **Privately Held**
SIC: 1389 Construction, repair & dismantling services

(G-6826)
MERCH LEGACY
3054 Se Loop 820 (76140-1014)
PHONE..............................817 682-6855
Matthew Davis, *Owner*
EMP: 10
SALES (est): 456.8K **Privately Held**
WEB: www.legacymerch.com
SIC: 2759 Screen printing

(G-6827)
MERCHANTS METALS INC
Meadow Burke Products
7000 Will Rogers Blvd (76140-6010)
PHONE..............................817 293-9641
Ron Potter, *Manager*
EMP: 25
SALES (corp-wide): 3B **Publicly Held**
WEB: www.merchantsmetals.com
SIC: 3496 Fencing, made from purchased wire; mesh, made from purchased wire; concrete reinforcing mesh & wire
HQ: Merchants Metals Llc
211 Perimeter Center Pkwy
Atlanta GA 30346
770 741-0306

(G-6828)
MERCK & CO INC
1414 W Bowie St (76110-3437)
PHONE..............................908 740-4000
Brian Schroeder, *Plant Mgr*
Misti Halastaras, *Sales Staff*
Jonathan Maziarz, *Technology*
Afshan Irani, *Associate*
EMP: 48
SALES (corp-wide): 46.8B **Publicly Held**
WEB: www.merck.com
SIC: 2834 Pharmaceutical preparations
PA: Merck & Co., Inc.
2000 Galloping Hill Rd
Kenilworth NJ 07033
908 740-4000

(G-6829)
MESA PROCESSING INC
3701 N Grove St Ste G (76106-3733)
P.O. Box 4247 (76164-0247)
PHONE..............................817 626-0319
Krista Blanton, *President*
Thomas B Blanton, *President*
Lois Blanton, *Principal*
Greg Gardner, *Vice Pres*
Irene Sullivant, *Treasurer*
EMP: 10
SQ FT: 1,000
SALES (est): 100K **Privately Held**
SIC: 2899 Chemical preparations

(G-6830)
METCON INC
8800 Kirk Ln (76182-7502)
PHONE..............................817 281-1620
R Figueroa, *Principal*
EMP: 9

SALES (est): 1.4MM **Privately Held**
WEB: www.metconmetal.com
SIC: 3441 Fabricated structural metal

(G-6831)
METRO MFG SUPPORT SVCS INC
8949 Forest Hill Dr (76140-9701)
PHONE..............................817 330-3430
William B Jenkins, *President*
Donna Jenkins, *Manager*
Stacey Smith, *Admin Asst*
EMP: 30
SQ FT: 16,725
SALES (est): 1.9MM **Privately Held**
WEB: www.msi-services.org
SIC: 3545 Cutting tools for machine tools

(G-6832)
METROPLEX PRODUCTS INC
2901 Saint Louis Ave (76110-4104)
P.O. Box 6517 (76115-0517)
PHONE..............................817 923-8241
EMP: 12
SALES (est): 1.9MM **Privately Held**
SIC: 3564 Air cleaning systems

(G-6833)
METROPLEX SAND & GRAVEL LTD (PA)
2620 Trinity Trail Way (76118-2025)
P.O. Box 185219 (76181-0219)
PHONE..............................817 589-9001
Kenneth B Newell, *Partner*
EMP: 55
SALES (est): 11.1MM **Privately Held**
WEB: www.metroplexsand.com
SIC: 1442 5032 Common sand mining; gravel mining; stone, crushed or broken

(G-6834)
METROPLEX WOOD PRODUCTS LTD
Also Called: Mwp
2201 W Risinger Rd (76134-5922)
P.O. Box 240, Crowley (76036-0240)
PHONE..............................817 538-0375
Pamela Anderson, *General Ptnr*
EMP: 20
SQ FT: 9,000
SALES (est): 3.9MM **Privately Held**
WEB: www.metroplexpallet.com
SIC: 2448 4953 Pallets, wood; recycling, waste materials

(G-6835)
MIBO FRESH FOODS LLC
715 E 9th St (76102-5512)
PHONE..............................817 882-9600
Uzor Nwoko, *President*
Paul Janiak,
EMP: 81
SALES (est): 14.1MM **Privately Held**
WEB: www.mibofreshfoods.com
SIC: 2037 Frozen fruits & vegetables

(G-6836)
MICA STEELWORKS INC (PA)
5750 N Riverside Dr (76137-2430)
PHONE..............................817 529-5000
L C Tubb Jr, *President*
EMP: 40
SALES (est): 93.4MM **Privately Held**
WEB: www.micacorporation.com
SIC: 3312 Tubes, steel & iron

(G-6837)
MICRO MOLD PLASTICS INC
2314 Ludelle St (76105-1014)
PHONE..............................817 536-0930
Fax: 817 536-2868
EMP: 38
SQ FT: 12,000
SALES (est): 2MM **Privately Held**
SIC: 3089 Mfg Plastic Products

(G-6838)
MICRO MOLD PLASTICS USA INC
2314 Ludelle St (76105-1014)
PHONE..............................817 536-0930
Lisa K Allison, *President*
Lori L Walterscheid, *Vice Pres*
Brent Hamilton, *Opers Mgr*
Steven R Allison, *Treasurer*

Douglas M Walterscheid, *Admin Sec*
EMP: 31
SALES (est): 3MM **Privately Held**
WEB: www.micromoldplasticsusa.com
SIC: 3089 Injection molding of plastics

(G-6839)
MID-SOUTH METALS LLC
3201 N Sylvania Ave (76111-3117)
PHONE..............................817 838-8000
Dwayne Defatta, *Branch Mgr*
EMP: 25 **Privately Held**
WEB: www.midsouthmetals.com
SIC: 3322 Malleable iron foundries
PA: Mid-South Metals, Llc
3849 Southern Ave
Shreveport LA 71106

(G-6840)
MILLENNIUM RECYCLING LLP
3717 N Commerce St (76106-2711)
PHONE..............................817 624-4307
Skipp Ryder,
EMP: 9
SALES (est): 1.8MM **Privately Held**
SIC: 3559 Recycling machinery

(G-6841)
MILLER BREWING
Also Called: Miller Coors
7001 South Fwy (76134-4001)
PHONE..............................817 551-3300
Tom Bober, *Vice Pres*
▲ EMP: 27
SALES (est): 5.2MM **Privately Held**
SIC: 2082 Beer (alcoholic beverage)

(G-6842)
MILLER WASTE MILLS INC
Also Called: R T P Company
1301 Joel East Rd (76140-6037)
PHONE..............................817 293-6163
Dan Doerr, *General Mgr*
Russell Williams, *Prdtn Mgr*
Tim Fitzgerald, *Production*
Ray Munn, *Engineer*
Curt Goretcki, *Sales Engr*
EMP: 55
SQ FT: 120,000
SALES (corp-wide): 331MM **Privately Held**
WEB: www.millerwastemills.com
SIC: 3087 2448 Custom compound purchased resins; wood pallets & skids
PA: Miller Waste Mills, Incorporated
580 E Front St
Winona MN 55987
507 454-6906

(G-6843)
MINUTEMAN PRESS
2567 Gravel Dr (76118-6906)
PHONE..............................817 864-3000
William Lynch, *Mng Member*
EMP: 11
SQ FT: 3,000
SALES (est): 1MM **Privately Held**
WEB: www.minutemanpress.com
SIC: 2752 Commercial printing, lithographic

(G-6844)
MODERN LANTERN
2212 Lipscomb St (76110-2049)
PHONE..............................214 507-8608
EMP: 12
SALES (est): 1.8MM **Privately Held**
WEB: www.modernlantern.com
SIC: 3648 Lighting equipment

(G-6845)
MODULAR CONCEPTS INC
6602 Plaza Pkwy (76116-2400)
PHONE..............................817 945-1667
Francisco N Saenz, *CEO*
John Bennett, *COO*
Wayne Mitchell, *CFO*
Franc Saenz, *Director*
EMP: 11
SALES: 26.2MM **Privately Held**
WEB: www.modularci.com
SIC: 7389 1541 3448 Design services; prefabricated building erection, industrial; buildings, portable: prefabricated metal

(G-6846)
MOLDING ACQUISITION CORP (HQ)
Also Called: Rotoplas
685 John B Sias Mem Pkwy (76134-1302)
PHONE..............................209 723-5000
Magda Hudson, *Human Resources*
Gerber Martinez, *Consultant*
EMP: 20
SQ FT: 60,000
SALES (est): 8.4MM **Privately Held**
WEB: www.rotoplas.com
SIC: 2822 Polyethylene, chlorosulfonated (hypalon)

(G-6847)
MOLSON COORS BEV CO USA LLC
7001 South Fwy (76134-4001)
PHONE..............................817 551-3300
Craig Ringer, *Plant Engr*
James Jackson, *Manager*
Mark Hubartt, *Manager*
Rebecca Jones, *Manager*
Patricia Fannin, *Information Mgr*
EMP: 80
SALES (corp-wide): 9.6B **Publicly Held**
WEB: www.molsoncoors.com
SIC: 2082 Beer (alcoholic beverage)
HQ: Molson Coors Beverage Company Usa Llc
250 S Wacker Dr Ste 800
Chicago IL 60606
312 496-2700

(G-6848)
MONCRIEF OIL INTERNATIONAL INC
Also Called: Moil
950 Commerce St (76102-5418)
PHONE..............................817 348-8454
Richard W Moncrief, *Ch of Bd*
Susan Donald, *Admin Sec*
EMP: 15
SQ FT: 2,000
SALES (est): 2.3MM **Privately Held**
WEB: www.moncriefoil.com
SIC: 1382 Oil & gas exploration services

(G-6849)
MONCRIEF PARTNERS LP (PA)
Also Called: Moncrief Oil
950 Commerce St (76102-5418)
PHONE..............................817 336-7232
William A Moncrieff Jr, *Partner*
Charlie Moncrief, *Partner*
Gary Allen, *CFO*
Annawaynette Kennard, *Accountant*
EMP: 30
SQ FT: 3,000
SALES (est): 5.2MM **Privately Held**
WEB: www.moncriefoil.com
SIC: 1311 Crude petroleum production

(G-6850)
MONCRIES FAXEL OIL INTERESTS
777 Taylor St Ste 1030 (76102-4915)
PHONE..............................817 335-5656
Moncries Faxel, *Owner*
Linda Black, *Exec Dir*
EMP: 10
SQ FT: 600
SALES (est): 620.9K **Privately Held**
WEB: www.moncriefoil.com
SIC: 1311 Crude petroleum production

(G-6851)
MONTEX DRILLING COMPANY (PA)
950 Commerce St (76102-5418)
PHONE..............................817 336-7232
W A Moncrief Jr, *President*
Ted Harter, *General Mgr*
Gary Allen, *CFO*
Tom Moncrief, *Admin Sec*
Moncrief Oil, *Legal Staff*
EMP: 30
SQ FT: 3,000
SALES (est): 10.7MM **Privately Held**
WEB: www.moncriefoil.com
SIC: 1311 0111 0212 Crude petroleum production; natural gas production; wheat; beef cattle except feedlots

(G-6852)
MORNINGSTAR PARTNERS LP (PA)
400 W 7th St (76102-4701)
PHONE............................817 334-7800
Timothy L petrus, *Exec VP*
Bill Frey, *Opers Staff*
Brent Clum, *CFO*
Scott Agosta, *Controller*
Sara Bond, *Accountant*
EMP: 31
SALES (est): 52.8MM **Privately Held**
WEB: www.mspartners.com
SIC: 1381 Drilling oil & gas wells

(G-6853)
MORTEX PRODUCTS INC
Also Called: Summit
501 Terminal Rd (76106-1954)
P.O. Box 471456 (76147-1456)
PHONE............................817 624-0820
▲ **EMP:** 300 EST: 1957
SQ FT: 300,000
SALES (est): 119.9MM **Privately Held**
WEB: www. mortx.com
SIC: 3585 3433 1711 3999 Parts for heating, cooling & refrigerating equipment; heating equipment, except electric; heating & air conditioning contractors; atomizers, toiletry

(G-6854)
MOSITES RUBBER COMPANY INC
2720 Tillar St (76107-1382)
P.O. Box 2115 (76113-2115)
PHONE............................817 335-3451
Billie B Mosites, *Ch of Bd*
Raymond D Garvey, *President*
Rick Heady, *General Mgr*
Kyle Hearne, *General Mgr*
Amber Franz, *Purch Agent*
▲ **EMP:** 45 EST: 1946
SQ FT: 20,000
SALES (est): 9.7MM **Privately Held**
WEB: www.mositesrubber.com
SIC: 3069 2674 Molded rubber products; vacuum cleaner bags: made from purchased materials

(G-6855)
MOTHER PARKERS TEA COF USA LTD (HQ)
Also Called: Mother Parker's Tea and Coffee
7800 Will Rogers Blvd (76140-6026)
PHONE............................817 551-5500
Paul Higgins, *Managing Prtnr*
Van Johnson, *Managing Prtnr*
Michael Higgins, *Partner*
Cindy Malhotra, *General Mgr*
Jonathan Holt, *Opers Mgr*
▲ **EMP:** 155
SQ FT: 100,000
SALES (est): 58.1MM
SALES (corp-wide): 207.1MM **Privately Held**
WEB: www.mother-parkers.com
SIC: 5149 2095 2099 Tea; roasted coffee; food preparations
PA: Mother Parker's Tea & Coffee Inc
2531 Stanfield Rd
Mississauga ON L4Y 1
905 279-9100

(G-6856)
MOTOROLA SOLUTIONS INC
2101 Eagle Pkwy (76177-2720)
PHONE............................817 245-6000
Ralph Kamin, *Principal*
John Landry, *Manager*
EMP: 141
SALES (corp-wide): 7.8B **Publicly Held**
WEB: www.motorolasolutions.com
SIC: 3663 Radio broadcasting & communications equipment
PA: Motorola Solutions, Inc.
500 W Monroe St Ste 4400
Chicago IL 60661
847 576-5000

(G-6857)
MRS BAIRDS BAKERIES BUS TR (DH)
14401 Statler Blvd (76155-2861)
P.O. Box 937 (76101-0937)
PHONE............................800 355-1260
Reynaldo Reyna, *President*
Jim Brennan, *Senior VP*
Joe Dangelmaier, *Senior VP*
Andy Lang, *Senior VP*
H Darrell Miller, *Vice Pres*
▲ **EMP:** 300 EST: 1997
SALES (est): 216.9MM **Privately Held**
WEB: www.mrsbairds.com
SIC: 2051 Bread, cake & related products
HQ: Bimbo Bakeries Usa, Inc.
255 Business Center Dr # 200
Horsham PA 19044
215 347-5500

(G-6858)
MUSTANG EXTREME ENVMTL SVCS LL (PA)
5049 Edwards Ranch Rd # 2 (76109-4133)
P.O. Box 430, Floresville (78114-0430)
PHONE............................830 393-1034
Jay Minmier, *CEO*
Tabor Smith, *VP Opers*
Scott Jones, *CFO*
Whitney Creel, *Admin Sec*
EMP: 19
SALES (est): 14.2MM **Privately Held**
WEB: www.mustangextreme.com
SIC: 1382 Oil & gas exploration services

(G-6859)
NA ACQUISITION COMPANY
3400 Northern Cross Blvd (76137-3600)
PHONE............................817 231-1300
Kevin W Kile, *President*
Ismael Gonzalez, *Manager*
EMP: 130
SALES (est): 11.5MM **Privately Held**
WEB: www.stericaresolutions.com
SIC: 3841 5047 Surgical & medical instruments; medical & hospital equipment

(G-6860)
NASH MANUFACTURING INC (HQ)
6363 Lansdale Rd (76116-1621)
P.O. Box 11526 (76110-0526)
PHONE............................817 926-5223
Keith D Parten, *President*
Bart Napier, *Vice Pres*
Wes Thomas, *Vice Pres*
◆ **EMP:** 80 EST: 1955
SALES (est): 12.5MM **Privately Held**
WEB: www.nashmfg.com
SIC: 3949 Lures, fishing: artificial; water skis; skateboards; playground equipment

(G-6861)
NATIONAL OILWELL VARCO INC
Also Called: Hydra-Rig
1020 Emerman Pkwy (76140)
P.O. Box 15951 (76119-0951)
PHONE............................817 985-5000
F A Waters, *General Mgr*
Curtis Fowler, *Chief*
Albert Gonzales, *Chief*
Chris Hunt, *Chief*
Albert Santo, *Mfg Spvr*
EMP: 16
SALES (corp-wide): 8.4B **Publicly Held**
WEB: www.nov.com
SIC: 3533 5082 3594 3443 Oil field machinery & equipment; oil field equipment; fluid power pumps & motors; fabricated plate work (boiler shop)
PA: National Oilwell Varco, Inc.
7909 Parkwood Circle Dr
Houston TX 77036
713 346-7500

(G-6862)
NATIONAL PRESORT LP (PA)
14901 Trinity Blvd (76155-2611)
PHONE............................214 634-2288
Henry Daboub, *Partner*
Catherine Daboub, *Partner*
Marcel De, *Project Mgr*
Mike Iserman, *Opers Mgr*
David Harvey, *Purch Mgr*
▲ **EMP:** 100
SQ FT: 85,000
SALES (est): 29.8MM **Privately Held**
WEB: www.npisorters.com
SIC: 3579 7629 Mailing, letter handling & addressing machines; business machine repair, electric

(G-6863)
NATIVE AMERICAN INDUSTRIES INC
3470 River Bend Blvd # 404 (76116-0934)
PHONE............................817 731-6786
Purdy Sheila, *President*
Sheila M Purdy, *President*
EMP: 10
SQ FT: 4,300
SALES (est): 1.8MM **Privately Held**
SIC: 3444 3469 Sheet metalwork; machine parts, stamped or pressed metal

(G-6864)
NESTLE USA INC
1313 Samuels Ave (76102-1130)
PHONE............................817 420-9971
EMP: 133
SALES (corp-wide): 93.5B **Privately Held**
WEB: www.nestleusa.com
SIC: 2023 Evaporated milk
HQ: Nestle Usa, Inc.
1812 N Moore St Ste 118
Rosslyn VA 22209
440 264-7249

(G-6865)
NESTLE USA INC
Also Called: Nestle Distribution Center
13600 Independence Pkwy (76177-4000)
PHONE............................817 491-5500
Dave Baker, *Principal*
EMP: 139
SALES (corp-wide): 93.5B **Privately Held**
WEB: www.nestleusa.com
SIC: 2023 Evaporated milk
HQ: Nestle Usa, Inc.
1812 N Moore St Ste 118
Rosslyn VA 22209
440 264-7249

(G-6866)
NORTH AMERICAN STEEL CORP
Also Called: Nasco Steel
1909 Northpark Dr (76102-1095)
PHONE............................817 332-7069
EMP: 21 EST: 1975
SQ FT: 20,000
SALES (est): 6.3MM **Privately Held**
WEB: www.nascosteel.com
SIC: 3441 Fabricated structural metal

(G-6867)
NORTH AMRCN GLVNZING CTNGS INC
Also Called: Azz Galvanizing Services
3100 W 7th St Ste 500 (76107-8701)
PHONE............................817 810-0095
Tom Ferguson, *CEO*
Deanna Perry, *Vice Pres*
Maurice Giasson, *Plant Mgr*
Sam Hartley, *Plant Mgr*
Eddie Sloan, *Plant Mgr*
EMP: 1156 EST: 1955
SQ FT: 4,600
SALES (est): 567.2K
SALES (corp-wide): 1B **Publicly Held**
WEB: www.azz.com
SIC: 7539 3312 Electrical services; iron & steel: galvanized, pipes, plates, sheets, etc.
PA: Azz Inc.
3100 W 7th St Ste 500
Fort Worth TX 76107
817 810-0095

(G-6868)
NORTH AMRCN SLING SLUTIONS LLC
4116 Cockrell Ave (76133-1110)
PHONE............................817 984-8000
Thomas Oswald, *Principal*
Michael Henderson, *Opers Mgr*
EMP: 14

SALES (est): 2.9MM **Privately Held**
WEB: www.northamericansealingsolutions.com
SIC: 3452 Washers, metal

(G-6869)
NORTHWEST INDEPENDENT SCHL DST
1350 Eagle Dr (76111-4924)
PHONE............................817 698-7300
Carri Eddy, *Branch Mgr*
Deyon Moore, *Assistant*
EMP: 230
SALES (corp-wide): 335.7MM **Privately Held**
WEB: www.nisdtx.org
SIC: 3625 Motor controls & accessories
PA: Northwest Independent School District
2001 Texan Dr
Justin TX 76247
817 215-0000

(G-6870)
NOVARIA GROUP LLC (PA)
6300 Ridglea Pl Ste 800 (76116-5708)
PHONE............................817 381-3810
Bryan D Perkins, *CEO*
Matthew McMahan, *President*
Monty W Gillespie, *Exec VP*
Mike Wagner, *Exec VP*
Robert J Batton, *Vice Pres*
EMP: 25 EST: 2011
SALES (est): 166.5MM **Privately Held**
WEB: www.novariagroup.com
SIC: 3542 3728 3812 3452 Machine tools, metal forming type; aircraft parts & equipment; search & navigation equipment; bolts, nuts, rivets & washers

(G-6871)
NOVARTIS PHARMACEUTICALS CORP
6201 South Fwy (76134-2001)
PHONE............................817 293-0450
Shaileen Shah, *Research*
Brian Huss, *Marketing Staff*
Ali Berens, *Manager*
Rosemary Besrutschko, *Manager*
Alan Ochoa, *Manager*
EMP: 16
SALES (corp-wide): 47.5B **Privately Held**
WEB: www.novartis.com
SIC: 2834 Pharmaceutical preparations
HQ: Novartis Pharmaceuticals Corporation
1 Health Plz
East Hanover NJ 07936
862 778-8300

(G-6872)
NOVARTIS SERVICES INC
6201 South Fwy (76134-2001)
PHONE............................817 293-0450
Stephen Wilson, *Vice Pres*
John Sarmento, *Project Mgr*
Michelle Prosperi, *Opers Staff*
Antony Springfield, *Research*
Robert Dee, *Engineer*
EMP: 24
SALES (corp-wide): 47.5B **Privately Held**
WEB: www.novartis.com
SIC: 2834 Pharmaceutical preparations
HQ: Novartis Services, Inc.
1 S Ridgedale Ave
East Hanover NJ 07936
862 778-2100

(G-6873)
NSH SERVICES INC
14501 North Fwy (76177-3304)
PHONE............................817 961-5045
EMP: 11 EST: 1980
SALES (est): 1.2MM
SALES (corp-wide): 93.5B **Privately Held**
SIC: 2043 Cereal breakfast foods
PA: Nestle S.A.
Avenue Nestle 55
Vevey VD 1800
219 242-111

(G-6874)
NTX GATES & FENCES INC
Also Called: Swinger Gate Company
632 S Cherry Ln (76108-2524)
P.O. Box 4051 (76164-0051)
PHONE............................817 740-9449
Shawn Morrow, *President*

EMP: 25 EST: 2013
SQ FT: 11,000
SALES (est): 3MM Privately Held
WEB: www.swingergatecompany.com
SIC: 1799 3317 3315 3446 Fence construction; tubes, wrought: welded or lock joint; pipes, wrought: welded, lock joint or heavy riveted; fence gates posts & fittings: steel; fences or posts, ornamental iron or steel

(G-6875)
ODES INDUSTRIES LLC
2423 E Loop 820 N (76118-6933)
PHONE..................................866 572-8420
Jessica Taylor, Vice Pres
Michael Smith, Mng Member
Michael G Smith,
▲ EMP: 35 EST: 2011
SALES (est): 10.6MM Privately Held
WEB: www.odesindustries.com
SIC: 3799 5012 All terrain vehicles (ATV); recreation vehicles, all-terrain

(G-6876)
OGF LLC
3333 E Loop 820 S (76119-1816)
PHONE..................................817 484-4004
Jigarkumar Barot, Mng Member
EMP: 10
SALES (est): 885.6K Privately Held
SIC: 3728 Aircraft body assemblies & parts

(G-6877)
OMIMEX CANADA LTD
7950 John T White Rd (76120-3608)
PHONE..................................817 460-7777
Naresh Vashisht, President
EMP: 25
SQ FT: 25,000
SALES (est): 1.2MM
SALES (corp-wide): 38.2MM Privately Held
WEB: www.omimex.com
SIC: 1311 Crude petroleum production
PA: Omimex Resources, Inc.
7950 John T White Rd
Fort Worth TX 76120
817 460-7777

(G-6878)
OMIMEX ENERGY INC (HQ)
7950 John T White Rd (76120-3608)
PHONE..................................817 460-7777
Naresh K Vashisht, President
Clark P Storms, Vice Pres
Arnold Campos, Controller
EMP: 10
SQ FT: 5,000
SALES: 14.1MM
SALES (corp-wide): 38.2MM Privately Held
WEB: www.omimex.com
SIC: 1311 1382 Crude petroleum production; natural gas production; oil & gas exploration services
PA: Omimex Resources, Inc.
7950 John T White Rd
Fort Worth TX 76120
817 460-7777

(G-6879)
OMIMEX PETROLEUM INC
7950 John T White Rd (76120-3608)
PHONE..................................817 460-7777
Naresh K Vashisht, President
Rajeev Lal, Production
Niti Vashisht Ross, Admin Sec
EMP: 15
SQ FT: 25,000
SALES (est): 1.3MM
SALES (corp-wide): 38.2MM Privately Held
WEB: www.omimex.com
SIC: 1389 Processing service, gas
PA: Omimex Resources, Inc.
7950 John T White Rd
Fort Worth TX 76120
817 460-7777

(G-6880)
OMIMEX RESOURCES INC (PA)
7950 John T White Rd (76120-3608)
P.O. Box 369, Cut Bank MT (59427-0369)
PHONE..................................817 460-7777
Naresh Vashisht, President

Clark Storms, Vice Pres
Arnold Campos, Treasurer
Tiffany Diggins, Analyst
EMP: 10
SQ FT: 25,000
SALES (est): 38.2MM Privately Held
WEB: www.omimex.com
SIC: 1382 1311 Oil & gas exploration services; crude petroleum production

(G-6881)
OMNIMAX HOLDINGS INC
Also Called: Amerimax Building Products
300 Railhead Rd (76106-1974)
PHONE..................................469 366-3208
Dave Oatman, Manager
EMP: 32
SALES (corp-wide): 542MM Privately Held
WEB: www.omnimax.com
SIC: 3444 Sheet metalwork
PA: Omnimax Holdings, Inc.
303 Research Dr Ste 400
Norcross GA 30092
770 449-7066

(G-6882)
OMNIMAX INTERNATIONAL INC
Vicwest
300 Railhead Rd (76106-1974)
PHONE..................................817 481-3521
Mitchell B Lewis, CEO
EMP: 50 Privately Held
WEB: www.omnimax.com
SIC: 3312 3448 3441 3444 Blast furnaces & steel mills; prefabricated metal buildings; fabricated structural metal; roof deck, sheet metal
HQ: Omnimax International, Inc.
30 Technology Pkwy S # 400
Peachtree Corners GA 30092

(G-6883)
OMNIMAX INTERNATIONAL INC
Amerimax Building Products
300 Railhead Rd (76106-1974)
PHONE..................................469 366-3200
Mitchell B Lewis, CEO
Diana Depedro, Clerk
EMP: 600 Privately Held
WEB: www.omnimax.com
SIC: 3444 Sheet metalwork
HQ: Omnimax International, Inc.
30 Technology Pkwy S # 400
Peachtree Corners GA 30092

(G-6884)
OMNIMAX INTERNATIONAL INC
Fabral
300 Railhead Rd (76106-1974)
PHONE..................................817 481-3521
Mitchell B Lewis, CEO
EMP: 30 Privately Held
WEB: www.omnimax.com
SIC: 3444 Sheet metalwork
HQ: Omnimax International, Inc.
30 Technology Pkwy S # 400
Peachtree Corners GA 30092

(G-6885)
ONE STOP PRINTING INC
Also Called: Plaque World
2904 Cullen St (76107-1307)
PHONE..................................817 338-1962
Virigina Bronner, President
Wayne Bronner, Vice Pres
EMP: 13
SQ FT: 2,000
SALES (est): 1MM Privately Held
WEB: www.onestopprinting.com
SIC: 2796 Engraving platemaking services; steel line engraving for the printing trade; etching on copper, steel, wood or rubber: printing plates; embossing plates for printing

(G-6886)
OPERATING TECHNICAL ELEC
Also Called: Ote
1289 Hemphill St Ste 231 (76104-4651)
PHONE..................................817 288-2600
James Dernehl, CEO
Gina Chiu, President
Ivy Chen, Project Mgr
▲ EMP: 22
SQ FT: 30,000

SALES (est): 5.8MM Privately Held
WEB: www.operatingtech.com
SIC: 3612 Specialty transformers

(G-6887)
P & W SALES INCORPORATED
6676 Corp Pkwy Ste 100 (76126)
PHONE..................................817 244-6565
Waymand McMillan, Owner
Melisa Tennison, Office Mgr
EMP: 9
SALES (corp-wide): 12.3MM Privately Held
WEB: www.p-wsales.com
SIC: 1389 Oil field services
PA: P & W Sales Incorporated
405 N Hwy 135
Kilgore TX 75662
903 984-2102

(G-6888)
P-MCOM INCORPORATED
Also Called: Plastic-Mart.com
685 John B Sias Mem Pkwy (76134-1302)
PHONE..................................866 310-2556
Tony Roucloux, President
Joseph Distefano, Treasurer
Mohammad Waseem, Accounting Mgr
Travis Calvert, Natl Sales Mgr
Kyle Gaines, Sales Mgr
EMP: 20
SALES (est): 2.1MM
SALES (corp-wide): 39.9MM Privately Held
WEB: www.plastic-mart.com
SIC: 3089 Plastic containers, except foam
PA: County Plastics Corp
361 Neptune Ave
West Babylon NY 11704
631 422-8300

(G-6889)
PACKAGE CONVEYER CO INC
123 S Main St (76104-1222)
PHONE..................................817 332-7195
Jack W Powers, President
Linda L Powers, Corp Secy
Donna Sue Powers, Vice Pres
Doyle R Powers, Vice Pres
EMP: 15
SQ FT: 98,000
SALES (est): 3.5MM Privately Held
WEB: www.packageconvey.com
SIC: 3535 Conveyors & conveying equipment

(G-6890)
PAGE CHESTER LTD
Also Called: Cooperative Industries
1401 S Cherry Ln (76108-3622)
PHONE..................................817 624-4001
Sam Symonds, CEO
Paul Diviano, Vice Pres
Jimmy W Green, Vice Pres
David S Symonds Jr, Vice Pres
Benjamin Symonds, Opers Staff
EMP: 126
SQ FT: 122,000
SALES (est): 22.8MM Privately Held
WEB: www.coopind.com
SIC: 3724 Aircraft engines & engine parts

(G-6891)
PAN AMERICAN WIRE INC
2301 Hemphill St (76110-2601)
P.O. Box 1808 (76101-1808)
PHONE..................................817 332-6486
Robert F Dunlap, President
Jennifer Dunlap, Corp Secy
▲ EMP: 16
SQ FT: 5,000
SALES (est): 5.2MM Privately Held
WEB: www.panamericanwire.com
SIC: 3496 5051 0723 Miscellaneous fabricated wire products; wire; hay baling services

(G-6892)
PANYANOUVONG JOSE & LE MALYSA
Also Called: Panya Fabricate Welding & Mch
2804 N Nichols St (76106-7227)
PHONE..................................310 279-7065
Jose Panyanouvong, Co-Owner
Malysa Le, Co-Owner
EMP: 12

SALES (est): 600K Privately Held
SIC: 3599 7692 Machine shop, jobbing & repair; welding repair

(G-6893)
PAPER PLANET
6515 E Lancaster Ave (76112-7006)
PHONE..................................817 451-8898
Juliana Marie West, President
Jonathan Burns, Accounts Mgr
EMP: 10
SALES (est): 1.1MM Privately Held
WEB: www.paperplanetdesign.com
SIC: 2759 Invitations: printing

(G-6894)
PARAMOUNT MILLWORK CORPORATION
3220 May St (76110-4123)
PHONE..................................817 429-1145
Samuel D Weir, President
EMP: 22
SQ FT: 40,000
SALES (est): 3.3MM Privately Held
SIC: 2431 5211 Millwork; millwork & lumber

(G-6895)
PARKER-HANNIFIN CORPORATION
Parflex Division
4700 Lone Star Blvd (76106-2105)
PHONE..................................817 625-5081
Carrie Gentry, Business Mgr
John Fox, Branch Mgr
Matthew Conner, Products
Jessica Downey,
EMP: 100
SQ FT: 54,340
SALES (corp-wide): 13.7B Publicly Held
WEB: www.phtruck.com
SIC: 3594 Fluid power pumps & motors
PA: Parker-Hannifin Corporation
6035 Parkland Blvd
Cleveland OH 44124
216 896-3000

(G-6896)
PASTUSEK INDUSTRIES INC
2008 Mrtin Lther King Fwy (76104-6303)
PHONE..................................972 291-0511
Mike J Pastusek, President
Fran Findley, Treasurer
EMP: 38
SQ FT: 50,000
SALES (est): 6.8MM Privately Held
SIC: 3599 Machine shop, jobbing & repair

(G-6897)
PATTONAIR USA INC
Also Called: Uniseal Division
1900 Robotics Pl (76118-7128)
PHONE..................................817 284-4449
Chris Hoffman, Controller
Igor Fox, Branch Mgr
Maria Voutsina, Manager
David Weddle, Technician
EMP: 20
SALES (corp-wide): 1.7B Privately Held
SIC: 5072 3429 3452 3399 Screws; metal fasteners; screws, metal; metal fasteners
HQ: Pattonair Usa, Inc.
1900 Robotics Pl Kitting
Fort Worth TX 76118
817 284-4449

(G-6898)
PCI INDUSTRIES INC (PA)
Also Called: Pottorff
5101 Blue Mound Rd (76106-1937)
PHONE..................................817 509-2300
Patrick A Cockrum, President
Judith E Scilley, Corp Secy
Ali Nikzad, COO
Brad Bauer, Vice Pres
Marty Mellin, Vice Pres
▲ EMP: 120 EST: 1928
SQ FT: 18,000
SALES (est): 51.2MM Privately Held
WEB: www.pottorff.com
SIC: 3444 5075 Metal ventilating equipment; air conditioning equipment, except room units

(G-6899)
PEAK COMPLETION TECH INC
309 W 7th St Ste 720 (76102-6902)
PHONE................................817 529-2030
EMP: 27
SALES (corp-wide): 104.3MM **Privately Held**
WEB: www.peakcompletions.com
SIC: 1389 Oil field services
PA: Peak Completion Technologies, Inc.
7710 W Highway 80
Midland TX 79706
432 617-0178

(G-6900)
PENNTEX INDUSTRIES INC
7620 Flagstone St (76118-6900)
PHONE................................817 589-7501
Roy Hamlin, Director
EMP: 23 **Privately Held**
WEB: www.penntexusa.com
SIC: 3694 5013 Alternators, automotive;
automotive electrical equipment; automotive supplies & parts
PA: Penntex Industries, Inc.
202 Plaza Dr
Manchester PA 17345

(G-6901)
PEPSI-COLA METRO BTLG CO INC
Also Called: Pepsico
5201 Blue Mound Rd (76106-1939)
PHONE................................817 625-4101
Tony Barton, Sales & Mktg St
Shanda Edwards, Manager
Brian Gilley, Manager
Dilip Rane, Exec Dir
Byron Johnson, Director
EMP: 160
SQ FT: 38,574
SALES (corp-wide): 67.1B **Publicly Held**
WEB: www.pepsico.com
SIC: 2086 Carbonated soft drinks, bottled & canned
HQ: Pepsi-Cola Metropolitan Bottling Company, Inc.
1111 Westchester Ave
White Plains NY 10604
914 767-6000

(G-6902)
PERFECT PERFORMANCE PDTS LLC
Also Called: Painless Performance
2501 Ludelle St (76105-1036)
PHONE................................817 244-6898
Adrian Murray, President
Bart Banks, Safety Mgr
Nick Weinert, Safety Mgr
Krista Benefield, CFO
Derek Love, Natl Sales Mgr
EMP: 50
SQ FT: 43,000
SALES (est): 19MM **Privately Held**
WEB: www.painlessperformance.com
SIC: 3694 Automotive electrical equipment

(G-6903)
PERFORMANCE ELASTOMERS INC
1300 Forum Way S Ste G (76140-5014)
PHONE................................817 293-7503
Rod Stokes, President
Gerald Hansen, Vice Pres
Tim Johns, Vice Pres
Steve Kyker, Vice Pres
EMP: 9
SQ FT: 2,500
SALES (est): 1.1MM **Privately Held**
WEB: www.pei-texas.us
SIC: 3069 Foam rubber

(G-6904)
PETROLEUM FINANCIAL INC
100 Throckmorton St # 400 (76102-2800)
PHONE................................817 339-1075
Thomas M Ray III, President
Tripp Ray, President
EMP: 30
SQ FT: 11,000
SALES (est): 3.8MM **Privately Held**
SIC: 6282 6141 1389 Investment advice;
financing: automobiles, furniture, etc., not
a deposit bank; oil consultants

HQ: P2es Holdings, Llc
1670 Broadway Ste 2800
Denver CO 80202
303 292-0990

(G-6905)
PFIZER INC
6601 Will Rogers Blvd A (76140-6053)
PHONE................................817 293-8887
Jim Mobley, Manager
Rick Francis, Manager
Ajinkya Karve, Planning
Treci Watkin, Representative
EMP: 9
SALES (corp-wide): 51.7B **Publicly Held**
WEB: www.pfizer.com
SIC: 2834 Pharmaceutical preparations
PA: Pfizer Inc.
235 E 42nd St Rm 107
New York NY 10017
212 733-2323

(G-6906)
PHYTON BIOTECH LLC
3909 Hulen St (76107-7253)
PHONE................................817 900-4050
Mark Mitchell, Exec Dir
Marc Iacobucci, Exec Dir
Maxwell Lea, Exec Dir
EMP: 50
SQ FT: 20,000
SALES (est): 12MM **Privately Held**
SIC: 2819 Industrial inorganic chemicals
PA: Dfb Pharmaceuticals, Llc
3909 Hulen St
Fort Worth TX 76107

(G-6907)
PILOT PLASTICS LLC
Also Called: Triton Barn Systems
4360 Western Center Blvd (76137-2043)
PHONE................................800 918-6765
Curtis Gardner,
◆ EMP: 9
SQ FT: 1,100
SALES (est): 4MM **Privately Held**
WEB: www.tritonbarns.com
SIC: 3523 5999 2452 5083 Farm machinery & equipment; farm equipment &
supplies; panels & sections, prefabricated, wood; farm equipment parts & supplies

(G-6908)
PILOT THOMAS LOGISTICS LLC (DH)
Also Called: Pilot Logistic Services
201 N Rupert St Ste 101 (76107-1460)
PHONE................................817 877-8300
Dennis Cassidy, CEO
Chris Anderson, Terminal Mgr
Kenneth Toudouze, Opers Staff
Janis Kline, CFO
Mary Perri, Credit Staff
EMP: 141 EST: 2002
SQ FT: 7,000
SALES (est): 277.9MM
SALES (corp-wide): 5B **Privately Held**
WEB: www.pilotthomas.com
SIC: 5172 2899 Petroleum products; fuel
treating compounds
HQ: Pilot Travel Centers Llc
5508 Lonas Dr
Knoxville TN 37909
877 866-7378

(G-6909)
PLATINUM PRESS INC
4251 Empire Rd (76155-2713)
PHONE................................469 733-1506
Tom Miller, President
Mike Miller, Exec VP
Chris Hicks, Vice Pres
Andrew Vale, Vice Pres
Jack Edwards, Plant Mgr
EMP: 75
SQ FT: 200,000
SALES (est): 21.3MM **Privately Held**
WEB: www.platinumpress.com
SIC: 2741 Miscellaneous publishing

(G-6910)
POINTWISE INC
213 S Jennings Ave (76104-1107)
PHONE................................817 377-2807
John Chawner, President

John Steinbrenner, COO
Richard J Matus, Vice Pres
John P Steinbrenner, Vice Pres
Carolyn Dear, Engineer
EMP: 15
SQ FT: 5,500
SALES (est): 2MM **Privately Held**
WEB: www.pointwise.com
SIC: 7372 7373 Prepackaged software;
computer integrated systems design

(G-6911)
PORT PLASTICS INC
6312 Airport Fwy Ste C (76117-5377)
PHONE................................817 834-7678
Jason Askew, COO
Todd Kriechbaum, Sales Staff
Wade Wells, Sales Staff
Tony Adams, Manager
EMP: 10 **Privately Held**
WEB: www.calsakplastics.com
SIC: 5162 3089 Plastics products; molding
primary plastic
HQ: Port Plastics, Inc.
5800 Campus Circle Dr E 150a
Irving TX 75063
469 299-7000

(G-6912)
PREFERRED PUMP & EQUIPMENT LP (HQ)
2201 Scott Ave Ste 100 (76103-2238)
PHONE................................817 536-9800
▲ EMP: 30 EST: 1982
SQ FT: 8,000
SALES (est): 268.1MM **Privately Held**
WEB: www.preferredpump.com
SIC: 5084 5083 5074 3533 Water pumps
(industrial); irrigation equipment; plumbing
& hydronic heating supplies; drilling tools
for gas, oil or water wells; construction &
mining machinery
PA: Ppe Genpar, Inc.
2201 Scott Ave Ste 100
Fort Worth TX 76103
817 413-2617

(G-6913)
PREMIER ENTRY SYSTEMS LLC
5001 Mosson Rd (76119-6474)
PHONE................................817 422-5908
Matthew K Houchin,
EMP: 16 EST: 2010
SALES (est): 1.7MM **Privately Held**
WEB: www.premierentrysystems.com
SIC: 5211 3446 Garage doors, sale & installation; fences, gates, posts & flagpoles

(G-6914)
PRESIDIO PETROLEUM LLC
500 W 7th St (76102-4700)
PHONE................................814 589-3550
Christopher J Hammack, Co-CEO
William A Ulrich, Co-CEO
EMP: 9
SALES (est): 109K
SALES (corp-wide): 503.8K **Privately Held**
WEB: www.presidiopetroleum.com
SIC: 1382 Oil & gas exploration services
PA: Presidio Investment Holdings Llc
500 W 7th St
Fort Worth TX 76102
800 674-9573

(G-6915)
PRESSURE PRODUCTS INC
15920 Highway 377 S A (76126-5703)
P.O. Box 126080 (76126-0080)
PHONE................................817 249-1338
Bernice Morris, President
Jack Morris, Treasurer
Jack E Morris III, Treasurer
Bo Morris, Sales Mgr
EMP: 11
SQ FT: 12,000
SALES (est): 3.1MM **Privately Held**
WEB: www.ppitx.com
SIC: 3443 Industrial vessels, tanks & containers

(G-6916)
PRINT GROUP
Also Called: Printing Edge The
4296 Western Center Blvd (76137-2042)
PHONE................................817 847-7860

Mike Marsh, Owner
Angela Marsh, Info Tech Dir
EMP: 10
SQ FT: 12,000
SALES (est): 1MM **Privately Held**
SIC: 2752 Offset & photolithographic printing

(G-6917)
PRINT WORLD INC
6025 E Lancaster Ave (76112-6534)
PHONE................................817 446-9555
Shawn Petrie, President
Neil Garry, Vice Pres
EMP: 12
SQ FT: 6,000
SALES (est): 2.3MM **Privately Held**
WEB: www.printworldtx.com
SIC: 2752 Commercial printing, offset

(G-6918)
PRO TECH MWD SERVICES INC
9729 South Fwy (76140-5309)
PHONE................................817 568-1038
Roy A Noble, President
Karl R Spring, Vice Pres
EMP: 10
SALES (est): 670K **Privately Held**
SIC: 1389 Testing, measuring, surveying &
analysis services

(G-6919)
PRO-STEEL INC
5121 Kaltenbrun Rd (76119-6401)
PHONE................................817 572-4959
John Pereda, President
Ray Pereda, Treasurer
Charles Wells, Treasurer
Raymond Pereda, Director
EMP: 38
SQ FT: 9,000
SALES (est): 9.8MM **Privately Held**
WEB: www.pro-steel.com
SIC: 3429 5083 3524 3423 Manufactured hardware (general); landscaping
equipment; lawn & garden equipment;
hand & edge tools

(G-6920)
PROBE TECHNOLOGY SERVICES INC (PA)
1132 Everman Pkwy Ste 100 (76140-4940)
PHONE................................817 568-8528
David Coppe, President
Federico Casavantes, Vice Pres
Thomas P Dunn, CFO
Alan Williamson, Manager
Marcella Pate, Admin Sec
▲ EMP: 25
SQ FT: 26,000
SALES (est): 4.7MM **Privately Held**
WEB: www.probe1.com
SIC: 3533 Water well drilling equipment

(G-6921)
PROGRESS RAIL SERVICES CORP
13601 North Fwy Ste 100 (76177-3009)
PHONE................................817 693-2550
Tom Schlueter, Engineer
Orville Jennings, Branch Mgr
EMP: 9
SALES (corp-wide): 53.8B **Publicly Held**
WEB: www.progressrail.com
SIC: 3743 Railroad equipment
HQ: Progress Rail Services Corporation
1600 Progress Dr
Albertville AL 35950
256 505-6421

(G-6922)
PURINA ANIMAL NUTRITION LLC
5500 South Fwy Ste 180 (76115-3906)
PHONE................................817 492-9159
Jerry Vooren,
EMP: 35
SALES (corp-wide): 6.1B **Privately Held**
WEB: www.purinamills.com
SIC: 2048 Prepared feeds
HQ: Purina Animal Nutrition Llc
100 Danforth Dr
Gray Summit MO 63039

▲ = Import ▼=Export
◆ =Import/Export

(G-6923)
PURINA ANIMAL NUTRITION LLC
1501 E 4th St (76102-4235)
PHONE....................817 878-0280
Peter Markovich, *Manager*
EMP: 80
SALES (corp-wide): 6.1B **Privately Held**
WEB: www.purinamills.com
SIC: 2048 Prepared feeds
HQ: Purina Animal Nutrition Llc
100 Danforth Dr
Gray Summit MO 63039

(G-6924)
PYLE MACHINE COMPANY INC
4201 Clay Ave (76117-1704)
PHONE....................817 485-6011
Mark Winstead, *President*
Tammy Radford, *Corp Secy*
EMP: 30
SQ FT: 9,000
SALES (est): 8MM **Privately Held**
WEB: www.pylemachine.com
SIC: 3599 3451 Machine shop, jobbing &
repair; screw machine products

(G-6925)
QES WIRELINE LLC (HQ)
801 Cherry St Ste 800 (76102-6813)
P.O. Box 829, Cresson (76035-0829)
PHONE....................817 546-4970
John Castetter, *President*
David Chapple, *Vice Pres*
Neil Mills, *Vice Pres*
Richard Mathews, *Controller*
Max Bouthillette, *General Counsel*
EMP: 16
SQ FT: 5,000
SALES (est): 297.2MM
SALES (corp-wide): 1B **Privately Held**
WEB: www.quintanaenergyservices.com
SIC: 1389 Well logging
PA: Quintana Energy Services Lp
1415 La St Ste 2900
Houston TX 77002
832 518-4094

(G-6926)
QTRAN CORP
1334 E 4th St (76102-4230)
P.O. Box 161938 (76161-1938)
PHONE....................817 870-1855
Louis Coomer, *President*
Lea Hobbs, *Corp Secy*
EMP: 12
SQ FT: 10,000
SALES (est): 2MM **Privately Held**
SIC: 1711 3433 Heating systems repair &
maintenance; burners, furnaces, boilers &
stokers

(G-6927)
QUALITY CAST METALS INC
3000 S Jones St (76104-6747)
P.O. Box 6494 (76115-0494)
PHONE....................817 921-3595
EMP: 24
SQ FT: 22,000
SALES (est): 5.4MM **Privately Held**
SIC: 3363 3364 3355 3354 Aluminum
die-castings; magnesium & magnesium-
base alloy die-castings; aluminum rolling
& drawing; aluminum extruded products;
primary aluminum

(G-6928)
**QUICKSILVER RESOURCES INC
(PA)**
801 Cherry St Unit 19 (76102-6883)
P.O. Box 1564, West Chester OH (45071-
1564)
PHONE....................817 665-5000
W Yandell Rogers III, *Ch of Bd*
Glenn Darden, *President*
Romy Massey, *Vice Pres*
Vanessa Gomez Lagatta, *CFO*
Anne Darden Self, *VP Human Res*
EMP: 90 EST: 1997
SALES: 569.4MM **Publicly Held**
WEB: www.qrinc.com
SIC: 1321 1311 Natural gas liquids; crude
petroleum & natural gas production

(G-6929)
QUIKTRIP CORPORATION
2501 Ne 28th St (76106-7508)
PHONE....................817 378-8410
Ryan Jeziorak, *Branch Mgr*
EMP: 25
SALES (corp-wide): 864.1MM **Privately
Held**
WEB: www.quiktrip.com
SIC: 5541 2099 Filling stations, gasoline;
ready-to-eat meals, salads & sandwiches
PA: Quiktrip Corporation
4705 S 129th East Ave
Tulsa OK 74134
918 615-7700

(G-6930)
**R & E TOOLING & PLASTICS
INC**
3939 Broadway Ave (76117-3544)
P.O. Box 14156 (76117-0156)
PHONE....................817 834-2858
Ryan C Dickey, *President*
Roger Dickey, *President*
Ryan Dickey, *President*
Pat Dickey, *Admin Sec*
EMP: 13
SQ FT: 17,090
SALES: 1.9MM **Privately Held**
WEB: www.randetooling.com
SIC: 3089 3544 Injection molding of plas-
tics; special dies & tools

(G-6931)
R IBARRAS INC
Also Called: Ibarra's Tortilleria
5410 Basswood Blvd 21 (76137-4400)
P.O. Box 163646 (76161-3646)
PHONE....................817 625-8962
Hilda Ibarra, *President*
Cynthia Ibarra, *Vice Pres*
EMP: 60
SQ FT: 40,000
SALES (est): 6.3MM **Privately Held**
WEB: www.ibarrastortilleria.com
SIC: 2041 2099 Flour & other grain mill
products; food preparations

(G-6932)
R S GRAPHIC SERVICES INC
Also Called: Redstone Visual Impressions
3300 S Jones St (76110-4311)
PHONE....................817 921-6266
Sharon Grant, *President*
Linda Kriz, *Treasurer*
Steven Schmidt, *Admin Sec*
EMP: 45
SQ FT: 50,000
SALES (est): 6.3MM **Privately Held**
WEB: www.redstonevisual.com
SIC: 2796 7336 2791 2752 Color separa-
tions for printing; commercial art &
graphic design; typesetting; commercial
printing, lithographic

(G-6933)
R-D SHEET METAL INC
200 N Foch St (76107-1339)
P.O. Box 471393 (76147-1393)
PHONE....................817 332-2177
Ronald Dale Witt, *President*
Peggy Hamilton, *Treasurer*
EMP: 15
SQ FT: 14,000
SALES (est): 2.7MM **Privately Held**
SIC: 3444 Sheet metalwork

(G-6934)
R-O MFG CO
7701 Will Rogers Blvd (76140-6025)
PHONE....................817 293-6150
J D Russell, *President*
EMP: 18
SALES (est): 4MM **Privately Held**
WEB: www.romfg.com
SIC: 3444 Sheet metal specialties, not
stamped

(G-6935)
R2 FABRICATION INC
804 S Blue Mound Rd (76131-1023)
PHONE....................817 230-2015
Kevin Rasburry, *President*
Glen Belota, *Vice Pres*
Ty Lamb, *Vice Pres*
Matt Rasburry, *Vice Pres*

Kenny Rasbury, *Project Mgr*
EMP: 24
SQ FT: 30,000
SALES (est): 4.6MM **Privately Held**
WEB: www.r2fab.com
SIC: 1711 3441 Heating & air conditioning
contractors; fabricated structural metal

(G-6936)
**RADFORD MANUFACTURING
INC**
1800 Duval St (76104-5996)
PHONE....................817 536-7706
Troy R Radford, *President*
Patrick Bobbitt, *QC Mgr*
Elva Fuentes, *Treasurer*
Rick Radford, *Director*
EMP: 12
SQ FT: 12,000
SALES (est): 2.9MM **Privately Held**
WEB: www.radfordmfg.com
SIC: 3599 Machine shop, jobbing & repair

(G-6937)
**RADIOLOGY ASSOCIATES N
TEXAS (PA)**
816 W Cannon St (76104-3194)
P.O. Box 1723, Indianapolis IN (46206-
1723)
PHONE....................817 321-0300
Corbin Wilson, *CEO*
Richard Granaghan, *President*
David Phelps, *President*
John Queralt, *President*
Craig Carter, *COO*
EMP: 43
SQ FT: 7,800
SALES (est): 21.8MM **Privately Held**
WEB: www.radntx.com
SIC: 8011 8071 3845 Radiologist; X-ray
laboratory, including dental; magnetic res-
onance imaging device, nuclear

(G-6938)
**RAMANN ENTERPRISES INC
(PA)**
Also Called: Mesa Distributors
3134 Marquita Dr (76116-5119)
PHONE....................817 560-4222
James Buck, *President*
Terry Davis, *General Mgr*
Ada Rodroguez, *General Mgr*
Paula Buck, *Vice Pres*
Stacy Shanto, *Info Tech Mgr*
▲ EMP: 30
SQ FT: 20,000
SALES (est): 17.6MM **Privately Held**
WEB: www.mesadist.com
SIC: 5084 3552 Textile & leather machin-
ery; embroidery machines

(G-6939)
**RANGE PRODUCTION PARENT
CO (HQ)**
Also Called: Range Resources
100 Throckmorton St # 120 (76102-2870)
PHONE....................817 870-2601
Jeffrey L Ventura, *CEO*
John H Pinkerton, *Chairman*
Ray N Walker Jr, *COO*
Alan W Farquharson, *Senior VP*
David P Poole, *Senior VP*
EMP: 28
SALES (est): 24.2MM
SALES (corp-wide): 2.8B **Publicly Held**
WEB: www.rangeresources.com
SIC: 1311 Crude petroleum production;
natural gas production
PA: Range Resources Corporation
100 Throckmorton St # 1200
Fort Worth TX 76102
817 870-2601

(G-6940)
**RANGE RESOURCES - LA INC
(HQ)**
100 Throckmorton St # 1200 (76102-2842)
PHONE....................713 588-8300
Jeffrey L Ventura, *President*
Morgan Aaron, *Superintendent*
Rick Armstrong, *Superintendent*
Ray N Walker Jr, *COO*
Alan Engberg, *Vice Pres*
EMP: 46 EST: 2014

SALES: 732.1MM
SALES (corp-wide): 2.8B **Publicly Held**
WEB: www.rangeresources.com
SIC: 1382 Oil & gas exploration services
PA: Range Resources Corporation
100 Throckmorton St # 1200
Fort Worth TX 76102
817 870-2601

(G-6941)
**RANGE RESOURCES
CORPORATION (PA)**
100 Throckmorton St # 1200 (76102-2842)
PHONE....................817 870-2601
Jeffrey L Ventura, *Ch of Bd*
Dennis Degner, *COO*
Dori A Ginn, *Senior VP*
David P Poole, *Senior VP*
David Goldberg, *VP Legal*
EMP: 85
SALES (est): 2.8B **Publicly Held**
WEB: www.rangeresources.com
SIC: 1382 Oil & gas exploration services

(G-6942)
**RANGE RESOURCES
CORPORATION**
100 Throckmorton St # 1200 (76102-2842)
PHONE....................817 870-2601
Steve Grose, *Manager*
EMP: 115
SALES (corp-wide): 2.8B **Publicly Held**
WEB: www.rangeresources.com
SIC: 1382 Oil & gas exploration services
PA: Range Resources Corporation
100 Throckmorton St # 1200
Fort Worth TX 76102
817 870-2601

(G-6943)
**RAYS CHMPN SPRING & MTR
SVC**
Also Called: Precision Motor Rebuilder
3336 South Fwy (76110-4316)
PHONE....................817 921-3600
Maxin Hawkins, *President*
Maxine Hawkins, *President*
Robert Hawkins, *Corp Secy*
Larry Hawkins, *Vice Pres*
Michael Hawkins, *Vice Pres*
EMP: 25
SQ FT: 48,000
SALES (est): 1.1MM **Privately Held**
WEB: www.rayschampionspring.com
SIC: 7537 7538 7539 3493 Automotive
transmission repair shops; general auto-
motive repair shops; automotive repair
shops; steel springs, except wire

(G-6944)
RAYTHEON COMPANY
6500 West Fwy Ste 400 (76116-2118)
PHONE....................817 735-1251
William McFarlande, *Manager*
Alan Brackett, *Manager*
EMP: 131
SALES (corp-wide): 56.5B **Publicly Held**
WEB: www.rtx.com
SIC: 3812 Defense systems & equipment
HQ: Raytheon Company
870 Winter St
Waltham MA 02451
781 522-3000

(G-6945)
RDS PRODUCTS INC
4301 Clay Ave (76117-1808)
PHONE....................817 656-8277
Curtis Pixler, *President*
EMP: 15
SQ FT: 10,000
SALES (est): 2.4MM **Privately Held**
WEB: www.rdsproductsinc.com
SIC: 3451 Screw machine products

(G-6946)
**RECARO ARCFT STING
AMRICAS LLC (DH)**
2275 Eagle Pkwy (76177-2312)
PHONE....................817 490-9160
Thomas Keller, *General Mgr*
Jean Pierre Foulon, *Vice Pres*
Joachim Ley, *Vice Pres*
Yvonne McConachie, *Vice Pres*
Bernhardt Seiter, *Vice Pres*

▲ **EMP:** 135
SQ FT: 103,000
SALES (est): 71MM
SALES (corp-wide): 806.9MM **Privately Held**
WEB: www.recaro-as.com
SIC: 3728 Aircraft parts & equipment
HQ: Recaro Aircraft Seating Gmbh & Co. Kg
　　Daimlerstr. 21
　　Schwabisch Hall 74523
　　791 503-7000

(G-6947)
RECORDER PUBLISHING CO INC
Also Called: Fort Worth Commercial Recorder
3032 S Jones St (76104-6747)
P.O. Box 11038 (76110-0038)
PHONE....................................817 926-5351
Genevieve Ratcliff, *President*
Richard Ratcliff, *Vice Pres*
EMP: 10 **EST:** 1903
SQ FT: 4,000
SALES (est): 674.7K **Privately Held**
WEB: www.commercialrecorder.com
SIC: 2711 Newspapers: publishing only, not printed on site

(G-6948)
REDDY ICE CORPORATION
601 N Sylvania Ave (76111-2421)
PHONE....................................817 654-9020
Stephen Waters, *Manager*
EMP: 15 **Privately Held**
WEB: www.reddyice.com
SIC: 2097 Manufactured ice
HQ: Reddy Ice Corporation
　　5710 Lbj Fwy Ste 300
　　Dallas TX 75240
　　214 526-6740

(G-6949)
REDMAN PIPE ORGANS LLC (PA)
816 E Vickery Blvd (76104-1444)
PHONE....................................817 332-2953
Roy A Redman,
EMP: 9
SQ FT: 15,000
SALES (est): 829K **Privately Held**
WEB: www.redmanpipeorgans.com
SIC: 3931 Organs, all types: pipe, reed, hand, electronic, etc.

(G-6950)
REDSTONE IMPRESSIONS INC
3300 S Jones St (76110-4311)
PHONE....................................817 921-6266
Robert Morris, *President*
EMP: 30 **EST:** 2018
SALES (est): 6MM **Privately Held**
WEB: www.redstonevisual.com
SIC: 2759 Commercial printing

(G-6951)
REFRESCO BEVERAGES US INC
15200 Trinity Blvd (76155-2707)
PHONE....................................817 359-4500
EMP: 80
SALES (corp-wide): 1.3B **Privately Held**
WEB: www.primowatercorp.com
SIC: 2082 Malt beverages
HQ: Refresco Beverages Us Inc.
　　8112 Woodland Center Blvd
　　Tampa FL 33614

(G-6952)
REGAL WARE INC
Also Called: Kitchen Fare
4300 Amon Carter Blvd # 100 (76155-2670)
PHONE....................................817 652-8151
Gary Stephen, *Branch Mgr*
EMP: 25
SALES (corp-wide): 89.4MM **Privately Held**
WEB: www.regalware.com
SIC: 3634 Electric housewares & fans
PA: Regal Ware, Inc.
　　1675 Reigle Dr
　　Kewaskum WI 53040
　　262 626-2121

(G-6953)
REGENCY CONVERSIONS INC
Also Called: Regency Rv
4709 Lone Star Blvd (76106-2106)
PHONE....................................800 839-7551
Ron Wiseman, *Sales Staff*
Gordon W Davis, *Exec Dir*
EMP: 55
SALES (est): 7.3MM **Privately Held**
WEB: www.regencyrv.com
SIC: 3799 Recreational vehicles

(G-6954)
REMINGTON HEALTH PRODUCTS LLC
808 S Blue Mound Rd (76131-1023)
PHONE....................................817 847-0606
Sue Ooten, *Controller*
William E Steele III,
George Steele,
Leslie Steele,
William E Steele IV,
▲ **EMP:** 10
SALES (est): 2MM **Privately Held**
WEB: www.drinkables.com
SIC: 2834 Vitamin preparations

(G-6955)
RENFRO FOODS INC
815 Stella St (76104-1495)
P.O. Box 321 (76101-0321)
PHONE....................................817 336-3849
Bill Renfro, *CEO*
John Renfro, *CEO*
Doug Renfro, *President*
Becky Borbolla, *Vice Pres*
Becky Renfro, *Vice Pres*
EMP: 40 **EST:** 1940
SQ FT: 50,000
SALES (est): 9.1MM **Privately Held**
WEB: www.renfrofoods.com
SIC: 2035 2032 Relishes, fruit & vegetable; Mexican foods: packaged in cans, jars, etc.

(G-6956)
REPCO REPLACEMENT PARTS INC
Also Called: Repcoreplacement
1021 W Enon Ave (76140-3624)
PHONE....................................817 293-3639
Carla Chandler, *CEO*
Ronald J Chandler, *President*
Rosa Hernandez, *Director*
EMP: 22 **EST:** 1962
SQ FT: 15,000
SALES (est): 3.9MM **Privately Held**
WEB: www.erepco.com
SIC: 3822 Auto controls regulating residntl & coml environmt & applncs

(G-6957)
REQUIRED TEAM GEAR LLC
2600 Cherry Ln (76116-3958)
P.O. Box 100952 (76185-0952)
PHONE....................................817 922-8448
Jonathan Castano, *Sales Staff*
Frank Kratch, *Software Engr*
Patrick Kratch,
John Whitten, *Graphic Designe*
EMP: 39
SALES (est): 5.1MM **Privately Held**
WEB: www.requiredteamgear.com
SIC: 2329 Athletic (warmup, sweat & jogging) suits: men's & boys'

(G-6958)
RIDLEY USA INC
Also Called: Ridley Block Operations
5100 Blue Mound Rd (76106-1936)
PHONE....................................817 625-6680
Daniel Rexroat, *Manager*
EMP: 16
SQ FT: 73,842
SALES (corp-wide): 1.7B **Privately Held**
WEB: www.hubbardfeeds.com
SIC: 2048 Prepared feeds
HQ: Ridley Usa Inc.
　　111 W Cherry St Ste 500
　　Mankato MN 56001
　　507 388-9400

(G-6959)
RIMROCK ENERGY LLC
5128 Apache Plume Rd # 300 (76109-1506)
PHONE....................................303 308-1300
Sandy McCormack, *Chairman*
Wallace Wilson, *CFO*
Terrell Dobkins, *Mng Member*
EMP: 30
SALES (est): 50MM **Privately Held**
WEB: www.rimrockenergy.com
SIC: 1382 Oil & gas exploration services

(G-6960)
RINGWOOD CONTAINERS LP
841 Railhead Rd (76106-1996)
PHONE....................................817 625-7214
Chris Gebhart, *Project Engr*
Chuck Cieble, *Manager*
EMP: 35 **Privately Held**
WEB: www.ringcompanies.com
SIC: 3085 5085 Plastics bottles; bottler supplies
PA: Ringwood Containers, L.P.
　　1 Industrial Park
　　Oakland TN 38060

(G-6961)
RM MANIFOLD GROUP INC
120 S Sylvania Ave Ste A (76111-2275)
PHONE....................................817 897-5330
Timothy E McNulty, *Principal*
EMP: 10
SALES (est): 1.1MM **Privately Held**
WEB: www.rmmanifold.com
SIC: 3433 Heating equipment, except electric

(G-6962)
ROBERT SHAW MFG CO INC
2820 Bryan Ave (76104-6711)
PHONE....................................817 927-2557
Robert H Shaw, *President*
Elaine Shaw, *Vice Pres*
Julie L Shaw, *Vice Pres*
William W Shaw, *Treasurer*
William Shaw, *Treasurer*
EMP: 30 **EST:** 1947
SQ FT: 90,000
SALES (est): 5.2MM **Privately Held**
WEB: www.robertshawmfg.com
SIC: 2541 2521 2431 Office fixtures, wood; showcases, except refrigerated: wood; cabinets, except refrigerated: show, display, etc.: wood; wood office furniture; millwork

(G-6963)
RODGERS ORNAMENTAL IRON INC
2248 E Lancaster Ave (76103-2221)
PHONE....................................817 535-2127
Louise Rodgers, *President*
Bernie Rodgers, *Vice Pres*
EMP: 12 **EST:** 1966
SQ FT: 5,000
SALES (est): 700K **Privately Held**
WEB: www.rodgersiron.com
SIC: 3446 Architectural metalwork

(G-6964)
RODRIGUEZ FOODS LTD
2901 Decatur Ave (76106-7232)
PHONE....................................817 626-3961
Charles Rodriquez, *Partner*
EMP: 30
SQ FT: 17,985
SALES (est): 5MM **Privately Held**
WEB: www.rodriguezfoods.net
SIC: 2032 Mexican foods: packaged in cans, jars, etc.

(G-6965)
ROLL MASTER CORP
7432 Ranger Way (76133-8931)
PHONE....................................817 292-4319
EMP: 54
SALES: 3.3MM **Privately Held**
SIC: 3562 Mfg Ball/Roller Bearings

(G-6966)
ROMEO ENGINEERING INCORPORATED
4217 Hahn Blvd (76117-1712)
PHONE....................................817 656-0048

Frank Romeo, *President*
Florence Romeo, *Corp Secy*
EMP: 28
SQ FT: 17,000
SALES (est): 8.1MM **Privately Held**
WEB: www.romeoeng.com
SIC: 3569 8711 8742 Robots, assembly line: industrial & commercial; liquid automation machinery & equipment; engineering services; automation & robotics consultant

(G-6967)
ROYAL SLEEP PRODUCTS LTD (PA)
Also Called: City Mattress Co
900 Haltom Rd (76117-6423)
PHONE....................................817 834-7522
Mark Gerrick, *President*
Katarina Kolkmeier, *Accounting Mgr*
◆ **EMP:** 63
SQ FT: 200,000
SALES (est): 11MM **Privately Held**
WEB: www.royalsleepproducts.com
SIC: 2515 Mattresses & bedsprings

(G-6968)
RPC INC
Also Called: RPC Logistics Express
1616 Grantland Cir (76112-3122)
P.O. Box 6, Keller (76244-0006)
PHONE....................................817 689-7660
EMP: 39
SALES (corp-wide): 1.7B **Publicly Held**
WEB: www.rpc.net
SIC: 1389 Oil field services
PA: Rpc, Inc.
　　2801 Buford Hwy Ne # 300
　　Brookhaven GA 30329
　　404 321-2140

(G-6969)
RSG AERODESIGN LLC
Also Called: Ranger Aerodesign
3901 N Main St Hngr 2s (76106-2723)
PHONE....................................817 625-9000
Brian Nerney, *CEO*
Daniel Dross, *Director*
Clint Georg, *Director*
EMP: 76
SQ FT: 10,000
SALES (est): 5.2MM **Privately Held**
WEB: www.rotorcraftservices.com
SIC: 3728 Aircraft assemblies, subassemblies & parts

(G-6970)
S & B TECHNICAL PRODUCTS INC
Also Called: Maloney Technical Products
1300 E Berry St (76119-3003)
PHONE....................................800 432-8213
Bradford Corbett Sr, *Ch of Bd*
Bradford Corbett Jr, *President*
Pamela Murrin, *Exec VP*
Tonya Bartlett, *Vice Pres*
Oscar Navarro, *Purch Mgr*
◆ **EMP:** 100
SQ FT: 360,000
SALES (est): 26.3MM **Privately Held**
WEB: www.sbtechprod.com
SIC: 3069 Molded rubber products

(G-6971)
SADDLE CREEK CORP
5000 Low Iron Crossing Dr (76131-2720)
P.O. Box 161126 (76161-1126)
PHONE....................................817 306-2000
Rick Willis, *Principal*
EMP: 18
SALES (est): 2.7MM **Privately Held**
WEB: www.sclogistics.com
SIC: 7372 Prepackaged software

(G-6972)
SAMSILL CORPORATION (PA)
5740 Hartman Rd (76119-6234)
P.O. Box 15066 (76119-0066)
PHONE....................................817 536-1906
James R Bankes, *President*
Mark Samsil, *Chairman*
Bob Shulz, *Exec VP*
Tom Dexter, *VP Opers*
Robert Lane, *Facilities Mgr*
◆ **EMP:** 140 **EST:** 1953
SQ FT: 250,000

▲ = Import ▼=Export
◆ =Import/Export

SALES (est): 24.5MM **Privately Held**
WEB: www.samsill.com
SIC: 2782 3081 3172 3577 Blankbooks & looseleaf binders; plastic film & sheet; leather cases; computer peripheral equipment

(G-6973)
SANARA MEDTECH INC (PA)
1200 Summit Ave Ste 414 (76102-4407)
PHONE.....................................817 529-2300
Ronald T Nixon, *Ch of Bd*
J Michael Carmena, *Vice Ch Bd*
Shawn M Bowman, *President*
Zachary B Fleming, *President*
Michael D McNeil, *CFO*
EMP: 11
SALES: 11.7MM **Publicly Held**
WEB: www.sanaramedtech.com
SIC: 2834 8731 Pharmaceutical preparations; commercial physical research; biotechnical research, commercial

(G-6974)
SANOTECH 360 LLC
Also Called: E-Mist
1000 Frest Pk Blvd Ste 40 (76110)
PHONE.....................................817 697-7116
George R Robertson, *CEO*
Joshua T Robertson, *President*
Hernan Rizo, *CFO*
EMP: 10
SALES (est): 159.9K **Privately Held**
WEB: www.sanotech360.com
SIC: 2842 3563 Specialty cleaning, polishes & sanitation goods; spraying & dusting equipment

(G-6975)
SCADA PRODUCTS LLC
Also Called: Eagle Automation
800 S Blue Mound Rd (76131-1023)
PHONE.....................................888 649-4283
Russell Abendroth, *Branch Mgr*
EMP: 32 **Privately Held**
WEB: www.eagleautomation.com
SIC: 3823 5085 5084 3492 Industrial instrmnts msrmnt display/control process variable; valves & fittings; instruments & control equipment; control valves, fluid power: hydraulic & pneumatic
PA: Scada Products, Llc
1600 Stout St Ste 450
Denver CO 80202

(G-6976)
SCHAEFER MOLD INC
2358 Blue Smoke Ct N (76105-1007)
PHONE.....................................817 534-7461
EMP: 16 EST: 1977
SQ FT: 20,000
SALES (est): 3.3MM **Privately Held**
WEB: www.schaefermold.com
SIC: 3544 Dies, plastics forming; industrial molds; forms (molds), for foundry & plastics working machinery

(G-6977)
SCHAEFER VENTURES LLC
Also Called: Schaefer Outfitters
6715 Cpration Pkwy Ste A (76126)
PHONE.....................................800 426-2074
Richard Grant, *President*
Lynn Grant, *Vice Pres*
EMP: 9
SQ FT: 13,000
SALES (est): 4MM **Privately Held**
WEB: www.schaeferoutfitter.com
SIC: 2326 Work apparel, except uniforms

(G-6978)
SCHLUMBERGER TECHNOLOGY CORP
100 Throckmorton St # 150 (76102-2870)
PHONE.....................................817 870-9040
Jeff Gorski, *Manager*
EMP: 14 **Publicly Held**
SIC: 1389 Construction, repair & dismantling services
HQ: Schlumberger Technology Corp
300 Schlumberger Dr
Sugar Land TX 77478
281 285-8500

(G-6979)
SCHRADER ELECTRONICS LIMITED
13601 Independence Pkwy (76177-4001)
PHONE.....................................817 608-2289
Martha Sullivan, *CEO*
EMP: 300
SALES (corp-wide): 3.4B **Privately Held**
WEB: www.schradertpms.com
SIC: 3714 Motor vehicle parts & accessories
HQ: Schrader Electronics Limited
11 Technology Park Belfast Road
Antrim BT41
289 446-1300

(G-6980)
SCHWEIZER RSG LLC
3901 N Main St 2s (76106-2723)
PHONE.....................................817 405-2100
Brian Nerney, *CEO*
David Horton, *President*
Rachel Laplante, *Treasurer*
EMP: 10
SQ FT: 18,000
SALES (est): 436.1K **Privately Held**
WEB: www.schweizerrsg.com
SIC: 3721 Helicopters

(G-6981)
SCOTT PUBLISHING LLC
Also Called: 360 West Magazine
1612 Summit Ave Ste 150 (76102-5955)
PHONE.....................................817 632-8100
Robert Granfeldt, *General Mgr*
Babs Rodriguez, *Editor*
Toni Stevens, *Sales Executive*
Jerry Scott, *Mng Member*
Sherry Miles, *Executive*
EMP: 12 EST: 2009
SALES (est): 2.5MM **Privately Held**
WEB: www.360westmagazine.com
SIC: 2741 Miscellaneous publishing

(G-6982)
SELECT PLASTICS LLC (HQ)
8800 South Fwy (76140-4910)
PHONE.....................................817 595-3804
Greg Nagel, *President*
EMP: 30
SQ FT: 30,000
SALES (est): 9.6MM
SALES (corp-wide): 147.3MM **Privately Held**
WEB: www.selectplastics.net
SIC: 3089 3081 Washers, plastic; unsupported plastics film & sheet
PA: Marco Display Specialists Gp, Lc
3209 Marquita Dr
Fort Worth TX 76116
817 244-8300

(G-6983)
SENSATA TECHNOLOGIES INC
Also Called: Borderfree
13601 Indpdnc Pkwy 400 (76177-4001)
PHONE.....................................817 608-2289
Michael Brown, *Manager*
EMP: 17
SALES (corp-wide): 3.4B **Privately Held**
WEB: www.sensata.com
SIC: 3676 Thermistors, except temperature sensors
HQ: Sensata Technologies, Inc.
529 Pleasant St
Attleboro MA 02703

(G-6984)
SHAMROCK INDUSTRIES LTD
400 E Vickery Blvd Ste A (76104-1300)
P.O. Box 105 (76101-0105)
PHONE.....................................817 336-1413
Manis Mullarkey, *Partner*
Vic Graffigna, *Partner*
Victor Graffigna, *Partner*
EMP: 26
SQ FT: 40,000
SALES (est): 3MM **Privately Held**
WEB: www.shamrockdiecast.com
SIC: 3363 Aluminum die-castings

(G-6985)
SHEEPSKIN RANCH INC
3408 Indale Rd (76116-7348)
PHONE.....................................817 738-2485
Barbara Ander, *President*

Paulette Shepard, *General Mgr*
Sidney Ander, *Vice Pres*
EMP: 10
SALES (est): 951.6K **Privately Held**
WEB: www.sheepskinranch.com
SIC: 3842 5047 Orthopedic appliances; medical equipment & supplies

(G-6986)
SIGMAPRO ENGINEERING & MFG LLC
13241 Harmon Rd (76177-6533)
PHONE.....................................682 888-1234
David T Underwood, *President*
Susan Olson, *Mng Member*
Christine L Underwood,
▲ EMP: 12
SALES (est): 4.2MM **Privately Held**
WEB: www.sigmaproeng.com
SIC: 3089 Injection molding of plastics

(G-6987)
SIGN & AWNING SERVICES INC
Also Called: Architectural Fabrication
2100 E Richmond Ave (76104-6304)
PHONE.....................................817 926-7270
Sudie Graham, *CEO*
Thomas Graham, *President*
Jeffrey Cash, *Vice Pres*
Ben Davis, *Vice Pres*
Jeff Kenny, *Vice Pres*
EMP: 25
SQ FT: 18,000
SALES (est): 7.9MM **Privately Held**
WEB: www.arch-fab.com
SIC: 2394 3444 Awnings, fabric: made from purchased materials; awnings, sheet metal

(G-6988)
SIKORSKY AIRCRAFT CORPORATION
Also Called: System & Tech Integration Ctr
7000 Calmont Ave 300 (76116-4183)
PHONE.....................................817 377-7500
Jeffrey Pino, *Branch Mgr*
EMP: 138 **Publicly Held**
WEB: www.lockheedmartin.com
SIC: 3812 Search & navigation equipment
HQ: Sikorsky Aircraft Corporation
6900 Main St
Stratford CT 06614

(G-6989)
SILVER CREEK MATERIALS INC (PA)
2251 Silver Creek Rd (76108-9710)
P.O. Box 150665 (76108-0665)
PHONE.....................................817 246-2426
Robert Dow, *President*
Colby Karr, *Principal*
Bart McKay, *Vice Pres*
Joel Simpson, *Vice Pres*
Ted Ruesewald, *Opers Staff*
EMP: 50
SQ FT: 800
SALES (est): 27.1MM **Privately Held**
WEB: www.silvercreekmaterials.com
SIC: 1442 1446 Gravel mining; silica sand mining

(G-6990)
SIR HC20 INC
3201 Wstn Ctr Blvd Ste 10 (76137)
PHONE.....................................817 228-9449
Chris White, *Branch Mgr*
EMP: 14
SALES (corp-wide): 3.1MM **Privately Held**
SIC: 3421 Table & food cutlery, including butchers'
PA: Sir Hc20, Inc.
6305 Diamond Loch N
North Richland Hills TX 76180
817 847-5454

(G-6991)
SITTON ENTERPRISES LLC (PA)
Also Called: SEI Oilfields
4055 International Plz # 410 (76109-4878)
PHONE.....................................817 737-8500
Lynn Grayburn, *Opers Mgr*
Jeffrey Sitton,
EMP: 15
SQ FT: 1,700

SALES (est): 33MM **Privately Held**
WEB: www.seioilfield.com
SIC: 1389 Oil field services

(G-6992)
SKYCAM LLC
Also Called: Cablecam Systems
2751 Northern Cross Blvd # 333 (76137-3651)
PHONE.....................................817 984-6840
Marci Champagne, *Prdtn Mgr*
Denny Graham, *Engineer*
Santosh Junnala, *Engineer*
Endre Buxton, *Mng Member*
Joe Ward, *Director*
EMP: 12
SALES (est): 2.4MM **Privately Held**
WEB: www.skycam.tv
SIC: 3861 Aerial cameras

(G-6993)
SMARTTRUCK UNDERTRAY SYSTEMS
Also Called: Smarttruck Systems
201 Main St Ste 2600 (76102-3134)
PHONE.....................................864 990-0781
Stephen S Ingham Jr, *CEO*
Steven Wulff, *COO*
Charles G Nichols, *CFO*
Charles Nichols, *CFO*
John Manchulenko, *Sales Staff*
EMP: 13
SALES (est): 1.3MM **Privately Held**
WEB: www.transtex-llc.com
SIC: 3537 Trucks: freight, baggage, etc.: industrial, except mining

(G-6994)
SMITH & NEPHEW INC
Also Called: Smith & Nephew Biotherapeutics
5600 Clearfork Main St (76109-3571)
PHONE.....................................817 900-4000
Gail Detoro, *General Mgr*
Price Pritchard, *Opers Staff*
Amy Rawls, *Engineer*
Julius Rotich, *Engineer*
Monica Arkfeld, *Human Res Dir*
EMP: 409
SALES (corp-wide): 5.1B **Privately Held**
WEB: www.smith-nephew.com
SIC: 7352 3842 Medical equipment rental; bandages & dressings
HQ: Smith & Nephew, Inc.
7135 Goodlett Farms Pkwy
Cordova TN 38016
901 396-2121

(G-6995)
SMITH & NEPHEW WOUND MGT
4900 W Vickery Blvd (76107-7290)
PHONE.....................................800 876-1261
Roy Trayhern, *President*
Jennifer Crittenden, *Vice Pres*
Rob Sorensen, *Vice Pres*
Amanda Giddings, *Opers Staff*
Rachael Norton, *Finance*
EMP: 116
SALES (est): 1.6MM
SALES (corp-wide): 5.1B **Privately Held**
WEB: www.smith-nephew.com
SIC: 3841 Surgical & medical instruments
HQ: Smith & Nephew, Inc.
7135 Goodlett Farms Pkwy
Cordova TN 38016
901 396-2121

(G-6996)
SMITH PUMP COMPANY INC
4624 Martin St 100 (76119-4080)
PHONE.....................................817 589-2060
Toll Free:.....................................888 -
James Schumacher, *Manager*
EMP: 9
SALES (corp-wide): 52.1MM **Privately Held**
WEB: www.smithpump.com
SIC: 5084 7699 7694 5999 Water pumps (industrial); pumps & pumping equipment repair; electric motor repair; engine & motor equipment & supplies
PA: Smith Pump Company, Inc.
301 M&B Industrial
Waco TX 76712
254 776-0377

(G-6997)
SMITH WOOD PRODUCTS INC
4220 Clay Ave (76117-1703)
P.O. Box 161459 (76161-1459)
PHONE..............................817 581-5200
Larry C Smith, *President*
Alan McGowan, *Vice Pres*
Lorin Laroux, *Warehouse Mgr*
Smith Kenneth E, *Director*
▲ EMP: 39
SQ FT: 10,000
SALES (est): 4.5MM **Privately Held**
WEB: www.smithwood.com
SIC: 5031 2499 Millwork; carved & turned wood

(G-6998)
SNELSON OILFIELD LTG CO INC (PA)
3619 Alice St (76110-5398)
PHONE..............................817 926-0571
Sharon Drury, *Ch of Bd*
Wes Mohr, *President*
Derrex Drury, *Vice Pres*
Reyna Ed, *Manager*
EMP: 20 EST: 1957
SQ FT: 20,000
SALES (est): 3.2MM **Privately Held**
WEB: www.snelsonlights.com
SIC: 3533 3646 Oil field machinery & equipment; commercial indusl & institutional electric lighting fixtures

(G-6999)
SNF INC (PA)
Also Called: Bfx Fire Apparatus
2800 Golden Triangle Blvd (76177-7016)
P.O. Box 77027 (76177-0027)
PHONE..............................817 402-8040
Susie Finley, *President*
Alfred L Finley, *Vice Pres*
Sara Preston, *Buyer*
Jim Sanborn, *Manager*
▼ EMP: 55
SQ FT: 450,000
SALES (est): 52.7MM **Privately Held**
WEB: www.bfxfire.com
SIC: 3713 Truck bodies (motor vehicles)

(G-7000)
SOLIDIFORM INC
3928 Lawnwood St (76111-6539)
P.O. Box 7656 (76111-0656)
PHONE..............................817 831-2626
Claudia Andre, *President*
Larry Andre, *Vice Pres*
Simon Rico, *Plant Mgr*
Jeff Engelke, *IT/INT Sup*
▲ EMP: 42 EST: 1981
SQ FT: 21,000
SALES (est): 12MM **Privately Held**
WEB: www.solidiform.com
SIC: 3366 Copper foundries

(G-7001)
SOUTHWEST DATA SYSTEMS INC
2501 Parkview Dr Ste 317 (76102-5842)
P.O. Box 136787 (76136-0787)
PHONE..............................817 370-9966
Jack Lambeth, *General Mgr*
Michael Winters, *Principal*
Sue McCauley, *Office Mgr*
EMP: 14
SALES (est): 1.7MM **Privately Held**
WEB: www.swdatasystems.com
SIC: 7372 Prepackaged software

(G-7002)
SOUTHWEST INDUSTRIAL SVCS INC
2413 Whitmore St (76107-1443)
PHONE..............................817 332-6481
Michael D Goold, *President*
Ruby Goold, *Chairman*
Laraine Goold, *Corp Secy*
Chuck Schabow, *Mktg Dir*
Lari Goold, *Office Mgr*
EMP: 35 EST: 1956
SQ FT: 24,000
SALES (est): 6.6MM **Privately Held**
WEB: www.aaaswis.com
SIC: 3599 Machine shop, jobbing & repair

(G-7003)
SOUTHWEST METAL TREATING CORP
9516 Lynwood St (76134-5900)
P.O. Box 6270 (76115-0270)
PHONE..............................817 551-1004
Ryan Fussell, *President*
James Arnold, *Plant Mgr*
Sherry Raushuber, *Controller*
Garrett Bodkin, *Sales Mgr*
EMP: 33
SQ FT: 50,000
SALES (est): 8.6MM **Privately Held**
WEB: www.southwestmetaltreating.com
SIC: 3398 Metal heat treating

(G-7004)
SOUTHWEST METRICS INC (PA)
Also Called: Amco Enterprises
4209 Hahn Blvd (76117-1712)
PHONE..............................817 281-7697
Rick Neil, *CEO*
Richard Neil, *President*
David Manning, *Vice Pres*
Lori Bowden, *Director*
Karen Stephens, *Executive*
◆ EMP: 12 EST: 1970
SQ FT: 45,000
SALES (est): 7MM **Privately Held**
WEB: www.amcoenterprises.com
SIC: 3599 5085 4783 Machine shop, jobbing & repair; fasteners, industrial: nuts, bolts, screws, etc.; packing goods for shipping

(G-7005)
SOUTHWEST METRICS INC
Also Called: Arrowhead Manufacturing
4212 Murray Ave (76117-1715)
PHONE..............................817 581-4474
Jim Hunter, *Manager*
EMP: 20
SALES (corp-wide): 7MM **Privately Held**
WEB: www.amcoenterprises.com
SIC: 3599 3541 Machine shop, jobbing & repair; machine tools, metal cutting type
PA: Southwest Metrics, Inc.
4209 Hahn Blvd
Fort Worth TX 76117
817 281-7697

(G-7006)
SOUTHWESTERN PETROLEUM CORP (PA)
Also Called: Swepco
534 N Main St (76164-9507)
PHONE..............................817 348-7233
Arthur J Dickerson, *Ch of Bd*
Robert C Dickerson, *President*
Phillip Frazier, *Senior VP*
Walker L Thomas, *Senior VP*
Ron Spratlen, *Mfg Spvr*
◆ EMP: 46 EST: 1933
SQ FT: 50,000
SALES (est): 14.5MM **Privately Held**
WEB: www.swepcousa.com
SIC: 2992 2851 Oils & greases, blending & compounding; paints & allied products

(G-7007)
SOVEREIGN PHARMACEUTICALS LLC
7590 Sand St (76118-6977)
PHONE..............................817 284-0429
Miles Davis, *President*
Suresh Dixit, *President*
Paul D Hafey, *Vice Pres*
Johanna Hunter, *Vice Pres*
Kenneth Miles, *Vice Pres*
EMP: 150
SALES (est): 52MM **Privately Held**
WEB: www.sovpharm.com
SIC: 2834 Pharmaceutical preparations

(G-7008)
SPEARS MANUFACTURING CO
3132 Wichita Ct K (76140-1754)
PHONE..............................817 293-0292
Chris Henning, *Manager*
EMP: 18
SALES (corp-wide): 1.3B **Privately Held**
WEB: www.spearsmfg.com
SIC: 3089 Fittings for pipe, plastic

PA: Spears Manufacturing Co.
15853 Olden St
Sylmar CA 91342
818 364-1611

(G-7009)
SPECIALTY ELECTRICAL LLC
14900 Grand River Rd # 124 (76155-2749)
PHONE..............................817 355-5315
Tim Cummings, *President*
EMP: 15
SALES (est): 1.2MM **Privately Held**
SIC: 1731 3699 General electrical contractor; electrical equipment & supplies

(G-7010)
SPECIALTY PACKAGING INC
3250 W Seminary Dr (76133-1145)
PHONE..............................817 922-9727
Hank Dorris, *President*
Bobby Reynolds, *Corp Secy*
Dave Morris, *Senior VP*
Robert Reynolds, *Vice Pres*
Victor Arevalo, *Production*
▲ EMP: 103
SQ FT: 85,000
SALES (est): 32MM **Privately Held**
WEB: www.specialtypackaginginc.com
SIC: 2621 Wrapping paper; asbestos filled paper

(G-7011)
SPECTRUM TECHNOLOGIES USA INC
3934 Sandshell Dr (76137-2403)
PHONE..............................817 232-2373
Peter Dickinson, *President*
Elane Hardy, *Principal*
Jeff Pelsang, *Manager*
Eloy Salinas, *Manager*
EMP: 10
SQ FT: 4,500
SALES (est): 1.9MM
SALES (corp-wide): 9.7MM **Privately Held**
WEB: www.spectrumtech.com
SIC: 3699 7629 Laser systems & equipment; electrical repair shops
PA: Spectrum Technologies Limited
Western Avenue
Bridgend M GLAM CF31
165 665-5437

(G-7012)
SPIRAL DINERS
1314 W Magnolia Ave (76104-4340)
PHONE..............................817 332-8834
Amy McNutt, *Principal*
EMP: 15
SALES (est): 401.1K **Privately Held**
WEB: www.spiraldiner.com
SIC: 5812 2051 Diner; bakery, for home service delivery

(G-7013)
SPM FLOW CONTROL INC (HQ)
Also Called: Weir Oil & Gas
7601 Wyatt Dr (76108-2530)
PHONE..............................817 246-2461
Paul M Coppinger, *President*
Mary A Gilcrease, *Managing Dir*
Muhammad Samir, *Business Mgr*
Keith Peach, *Exec VP*
Ronnie Phelps, *Vice Pres*
◆ EMP: 250 EST: 1958
SALES (est): 500.5MM
SALES (corp-wide): 3.4B **Privately Held**
WEB: www.weir.co.uk
SIC: 3533 3599 Oil & gas field machinery; machine shop, jobbing & repair
PA: Weir Group Plc(The)
1 West Regent Street
Glasgow G2 1R
141 637-7111

(G-7014)
SPORTS WEAR GRAPHICS INC
Also Called: Sportswear Graphics
110 Saint Louis Ave (76104-1228)
PHONE..............................817 870-9900
Ted Settle, *President*
John Hart, *Corp Secy*
Bill Davis, *Vice Pres*
Jamie Settle,
EMP: 9
SQ FT: 5,000

SALES (est): 600K **Privately Held**
WEB: www.sportsweargraphics.com
SIC: 2262 7336 Screen printing: manmade fiber & silk broadwoven fabrics; commercial art & graphic design

(G-7015)
STAR-TELEGRAM OPERATING LTD
685 John B Sias Mem Pkwy (76134-1302)
PHONE..............................817 215-2100
Gerald Zenick, *Vice Pres*
EMP: 400
SALES (corp-wide): 709.5MM **Privately Held**
WEB: www.fwsistercities.org
SIC: 2711 Newspapers, publishing & printing
HQ: Star-Telegram Operating, Ltd.
808 Throckmorton St
Fort Worth TX 76102
817 390-7400

(G-7016)
STAR-TELEGRAM OPERATING LTD (DH)
Also Called: Fort Worth Star Telegram
808 Throckmorton St (76102-6315)
P.O. Box 1870 (76101-1870)
PHONE..............................817 390-7400
Gary Wortel, *President*
Marhta Wilson, *President*
Ryan Mote, *Publisher*
Amy McDaniel, *Editor*
Ryan Rusak, *Editor*
EMP: 700
SQ FT: 25,000
SALES (est): 951.9K
SALES (corp-wide): 709.5MM **Privately Held**
WEB: www.star-telegram.com
SIC: 2711 Newspapers, publishing & printing

(G-7017)
STARKE MACHINE CO
2109 Brennan Ave (76106-8318)
PHONE..............................817 625-6821
Dennis Starke, *President*
Judy Starke, *Vice Pres*
Rhonda Hamilton, *Treasurer*
David Yarbrough, *Human Resources*
Kathy Frazier, *Info Tech Mgr*
EMP: 65 EST: 1980
SQ FT: 20,000
SALES (est): 12MM **Privately Held**
WEB: www.starkemachine.com
SIC: 3599 Machine shop, jobbing & repair

(G-7018)
STERIGENICS US LLC
3125 Wichita Ct (76140-1755)
PHONE..............................817 293-0999
Chris Bonilla, *General Mgr*
Kyle Mead, *Opers Mgr*
Dean Read, *Production*
Adam Russell, *QC Mgr*
Sarah Peterson, *Sales Staff*
EMP: 30
SQ FT: 20,950
SALES (corp-wide): 413.4MM **Privately Held**
WEB: www.sterigenics.com
SIC: 7389 3821 Product sterilization service; sterilizers
HQ: Sterigenics U.S., Llc
2015 Spring Rd Ste 650
Oak Brook IL 60523
630 928-1700

(G-7019)
STEVENS TECHNOLOGY LLC (PA)
4205 Stadium Dr Ste 300 (76133-1000)
P.O. Box 100953 (76185-0953)
PHONE..............................817 831-3500
Mary Wheeler, *Vice Pres*
Steve Parker, *Business Dir*
Paul Stevens,
▲ EMP: 10
SQ FT: 65,080
SALES (est): 2.1MM **Privately Held**
WEB: www.stevenstechnology.com
SIC: 3555 Printing trades machinery

▲ = Import ▼=Export
◆ =Import/Export

(G-7020)
STRIKE LLC
1525 Gilman Rd (76140-1633)
PHONE.....................................888 353-1444
EMP: 75
SALES (corp-wide): 1.4B Privately Held
WEB: www.strikeusa.com
SIC: 1389 Servicing oil & gas wells
PA: Strike, Llc
1800 Hughes Landing Blvd # 500
The Woodlands TX 77380
713 389-2400

(G-7021)
STRUCTURAL & STL PDTS MFG LTD
3001 W Pafford St (76110-5833)
PHONE.....................................817 869-2301
Dan Banks, President
Harold V Price Jr, Partner
EMP: 100
SQ FT: 180,000
SALES (est): 35.1MM
SALES (corp-wide): 311.3MM Privately Held
WEB: www.s-steel.com
SIC: 3312 Structural shapes & pilings, steel
HQ: Structural And Steel Products, Inc.
1320 S University Dr # 701
Fort Worth TX 76107
817 332-7417

(G-7022)
SUMMIT CASING SERVICES LLC (PA)
Also Called: Summit Casing Equipment
6575 Corporation Pkwy (76126-1735)
P.O. Box 34210 (76162-4210)
PHONE.....................................877 860-0969
Andy Eldridge, President
Matt Einck, Principal
Mitchel Hansen, COO
Mark R Lamar, Prdtn Mgr
Matt Larsen, Controller
◆ EMP: 10
SALES (est): 4.4MM Privately Held
WEB: www.summitcasing.com
SIC: 3533 Oil & gas field machinery

(G-7023)
SUNSHINE CUSTOM CABINETS INC
5212 Saunders Rd Ste C (76119-6472)
PHONE.....................................817 572-5201
Danny L Moore, President
Palomares Trini, Vice Pres
Rodney Erwin, Admin Sec
EMP: 17
SQ FT: 10,000
SALES (est): 2MM Privately Held
WEB: www.sunshinecustomcabinets.com
SIC: 2434 2431 Wood kitchen cabinets; vanities, bathroom: wood; door frames, wood

(G-7024)
SUPERIOR OPTIMIZATION LTD
2100 N Main St Ste 212 (76164-8575)
PHONE.....................................817 244-4900
Kirk Mehaffey, COO
Renee Lopez, Sales Staff
Marivel Ortiz, Manager
EMP: 10
SALES (est): 2.1MM Privately Held
WEB: www.superioroptimization.com
SIC: 1389 Oil field services

(G-7025)
SWISS PASTRY SHOP
3936 W Vickery Blvd (76107-5626)
PHONE.....................................817 732-5661
Hans Muller, Owner
EMP: 13
SQ FT: 2,000
SALES (est): 655K Privately Held
WEB: www.swisspastryonline.com
SIC: 5461 5812 2051 Bread; eating places; bread, cake & related products

(G-7026)
SYMONDS FLAGS & POLES INC
7503 Flagstone St Bldg 30 (76118-6953)
PHONE.....................................214 596-1900
Stephen M Symonds, President

Bo Green, Vice Pres
Aimee Chesnut, Office Mgr
Aimee Chesnut, Manager
Erin Symonds, Representative
EMP: 30
SALES (est): 5.7MM Privately Held
WEB: www.symondsflags.com
SIC: 3446 2399 5999 Flagpoles, metal; banners, pennants & flags; banners, flags, decals & posters

(G-7027)
SYNERGY SIGNS & SERVICES LLC
2815 Prestige Rd (76244-9536)
PHONE.....................................817 745-2330
Lisa Tumlinson,
Mike Lewis,
EMP: 21 EST: 2010
SALES (est): 3.2MM Privately Held
WEB: www.synergysigns.com
SIC: 3993 Signs & advertising specialties

(G-7028)
T W HAVENS METALS INC
Also Called: Fabrications
6360 Airport Fwy Ste 100 (76117-5375)
PHONE.....................................817 834-2621
Terry W Havens, President
C C Havens, Treasurer
Clifford Havens, Admin Sec
EMP: 12
SQ FT: 21,260
SALES (est): 1.5MM Privately Held
SIC: 3599 3444 Machine shop, jobbing & repair; sheet metalwork

(G-7029)
T-B & S MFG CO
4901 Blue Mound Rd (76106-1914)
P.O. Box 14608, Haltom City (76117-0608)
PHONE.....................................817 281-9315
Joyce Barrett, President
Tony Berkner, General Mgr
EMP: 14
SQ FT: 6,000
SALES (est): 3.6MM Privately Held
WEB: www.tbandsmfg.com
SIC: 3728 Aircraft parts & equipment

(G-7030)
TACONY CORPORATION
Powr-Flite
3101 Wichita Ct (76140-1755)
PHONE.....................................817 551-0700
Sandie Santos, Human Res Mgr
Michelle Kerr, Sales Staff
Steve Savage, Branch Mgr
Steve Day, Branch Mgr
EMP: 70
SQ FT: 63,530
SALES (corp-wide): 206.2MM Privately Held
WEB: www.tacony.com
SIC: 4225 3589 5064 General warehousing & storage; floor washing & polishing machines, commercial; vacuum cleaners
PA: Tacony Corporation
1760 Gilsinn Ln
Fenton MO 63026
636 349-3000

(G-7031)
TALLA-COM TLLHSSEE CMMNCTONS I (DH)
Also Called: Talla-Com Industries
4700 Marine Creek Pkwy (76179-3505)
P.O. Box 136969 (76136-0969)
PHONE.....................................817 234-6726
Raanan Horowitz, CEO
Cletus Glasener, Principal
Yossi Bechor, Director
EMP: 15
SQ FT: 76,800
SALES (est): 35.1MM
SALES (corp-wide): 1.3B Privately Held
WEB: www.elbitsystems-us.com
SIC: 3669 3672 Intercommunication systems, electric; printed circuit boards

(G-7032)
TALLAHASSEE TECHNOLOGIES INC (DH)
Also Called: Elbit Systems
4700 Marine Creek Pkwy (76179-3505)
P.O. Box 136969 (76136-0969)
PHONE.....................................817 234-6726
Raanan Horowitz, CEO
Uri Vered, Exec VP
Thomas Carter, Vice Pres
Mark Cleveland, Vice Pres
Scott Evers, Vice Pres
EMP: 99
SQ FT: 37,000
SALES (est): 35MM
SALES (corp-wide): 1.3B Privately Held
WEB: www.elbitsystems-us.com
SIC: 3669 Intercommunication systems, electric

(G-7033)
TANGLEWOOD MOMS LLC
3200 Sweetbriar Ln (76109-2059)
PHONE.....................................817 247-1474
EMP: 10
SALES (est): 323.4K Privately Held
WEB: www.tanglewoodmoms.com
SIC: 2721 Periodicals

(G-7034)
TAPE INNOVATIONS LLC (PA)
201 E Risinger Rd Ste 101 (76140-5346)
PHONE.....................................817 568-1212
John Cockerham, President
EMP: 48
SQ FT: 20,000
SALES (est): 13.5MM Privately Held
WEB: www.tapeinnovations.com
SIC: 2675 3699 2672 3053 Die-cut paper & board; laser welding, drilling & cutting equipment; adhesive backed films, foams & foils; gaskets & sealing devices

(G-7035)
TARRANT CONCRETE CO INC (DH)
5400 Thelin St (76115-4426)
P.O. Box 6194 (76115-0194)
PHONE.....................................817 926-6660
James E Rainbolt, President
Bill W Gandy, Admin Sec
EMP: 60
SQ FT: 2,400
SALES (est): 17.4MM
SALES (corp-wide): 1.7B Privately Held
WEB: www.tarrantconcrete.com
SIC: 3273 Ready-mixed concrete
HQ: Lattimore Materials Corp.
15900 Dooley Rd
Addison TX 75001
972 221-4646

(G-7036)
TAYLOR CMMNCTONS SCURE CSTMER
4401 Cambridge Rd (76155-2629)
PHONE.....................................817 283-9500
Jonathan Craig, Accounts Mgr
Deadra Harden, Accounts Mgr
Sharon Brock, Branch Mgr
Alicia Dilley, Manager
Jacob Gonzalez, Manager
EMP: 200
SALES (corp-wide): 2.5B Privately Held
WEB: www.venturesolutions.com
SIC: 2759 Business forms: printing
HQ: Venture Solutions, Inc
1170 Grey Fox Rd
Arden Hills MN 55112
651 494-1740

(G-7037)
TAYLOR DISTRIBUTING CO INC
Also Called: Jesse C Taylor Oil Company
3701 N Sylvania Ave (76137-5006)
PHONE.....................................817 831-0601
James C Taylor, President
Jerry Taylor, Admin Sec
EMP: 24 EST: 1948
SQ FT: 12,000
SALES (est): 14.9MM Privately Held
WEB: www.taylordistributing.com
SIC: 5013 5172 1321 Filters, air & oil; fuel oil; lubricating oils & greases; natural gas liquids

(G-7038)
TAYLOR INDUSTRIES LLC (DH)
801 Cherry St Unit 2 (76102-6886)
PHONE.....................................918 266-7301
Brett Taylor, Mng Member
David C Johnston,
Kenneth V Huseman,
Alan Krenek,
Stephen J McCoy,
EMP: 63
SALES (est): 27.3MM
SALES (corp-wide): 567.2MM Publicly Held
WEB: www.taylorindustries.net
SIC: 1389 Oil field services

(G-7039)
TEAM PROMARK LLC
5001 North Fwy Ste C (76106-1835)
PHONE.....................................303 926-1328
Bill Skinner, President
Brian Moon, CFO
Ray Benz, Sales Staff
Jamie Lockwood, Director
▲ EMP: 20 EST: 1999
SALES (est): 10MM Privately Held
WEB: www.fanmats.com
SIC: 5531 2821 3089 Automotive accessories; casein plastics; cases, plastic

(G-7040)
TECH TOOL PLASTICS INC
7800 Skyline Park Dr (76108-2589)
PHONE.....................................817 246-4694
John E Wilson, President
Gala Dubois, Vice Pres
Grady Aldarondo, Sales Executive
EMP: 25 EST: 1965
SQ FT: 22,000
SALES (est): 4.6MM Privately Held
WEB: www.tech-tool.com
SIC: 3089 Injection molding of plastics

(G-7041)
TECHNOGRAPHIX LLC
Also Called: May Group International
1200 Forum Way S (76140-5012)
PHONE.....................................817 336-5671
Allan Meyer, CEO
Pat Meredith, President
Pete Campbell, Plant Mgr
Bobby Rees, Maint Spvr
David Garcia, Purch Mgr
▲ EMP: 120
SQ FT: 138,000
SALES (est): 20MM Privately Held
WEB: www.shopmaygroup.com
SIC: 7359 3993 Sign rental; electric signs

(G-7042)
TENSION ENVELOPE CORPORATION
5900 Tension Dr (76112-6997)
PHONE.....................................817 451-5811
Deidre Bockelman, Plant Mgr
Tim Tlunk, Branch Mgr
EMP: 86
SQ FT: 64,175
SALES (corp-wide): 234MM Privately Held
WEB: www.tensionenvelope.com
SIC: 2759 Commercial printing
PA: Tension Envelope Corporation
819 E 19th St
Kansas City MO 64108
816 471-3800

(G-7043)
TEP BARNETT USA LLC
301 Commerce St Ste 3700 (76102-4137)
P.O. Box 17209 (76102-0209)
PHONE.....................................817 720-1130
Dave Leopold, President
EMP: 190 EST: 2016
SALES (est): 17.4MM
SALES (corp-wide): 7B Publicly Held
WEB: www.tepbarnett.com
SIC: 1311 Crude petroleum & natural gas
PA: Total Se
La Defense 6
Courbevoie 92400

(G-7044)
TERRACE ENERGY LLC
301 Commerce St Ste 3635 (76102-4143)
PHONE.....................................817 546-7490

Casey Patterson, *President*
Randy Hulme, *Vice Pres*
Keith Godwin, *CFO*
Sarah Topham, *Controller*
Smith A Brownlie III, *Mng Member*
EMP: 11 **EST:** 2010
SALES (est): 1.4MM **Privately Held**
WEB: www.terrace-energy.com
SIC: 1382 Oil & gas exploration services

(G-7045)
TEXAS ALUMINUM FOUNDRY INC
204 Penland St (76111-4623)
P.O. Box 150749 (76108-0749)
PHONE.............................817 834-5568
Stephen Meador, *President*
Paul Meador, *Vice Pres*
EMP: 25 **EST:** 1945
SQ FT: 18,000
SALES (est): 5.7MM **Privately Held**
WEB: www.texasaluminumfoundry.com
SIC: 3365 Aluminum & aluminum-based alloy castings

(G-7046)
TEXAS CORRUGATED BOX PACKG LLC
1624 Intermodal Pkwy (76177)
P.O. Box 77250 (76177-0250)
PHONE.............................817 454-2037
Don Hepburn, *Sales Staff*
Donald Hepburn,
Ray G Clark,
Timothy G Clark,
EMP: 20
SALES (est): 20MM **Privately Held**
SIC: 2653 7389 Boxes, corrugated: made from purchased materials; packaging & labeling services

(G-7047)
TEXAS ENVIRONMENTAL TECH LLC
3453 E Vickery Blvd (76105-1622)
PHONE.............................817 534-4275
William F Rucker, *Principal*
EMP: 9 **EST:** 1997
SQ FT: 5,000
SALES (est): 460.6K **Privately Held**
SIC: 8734 3519 Testing laboratories; parts & accessories, internal combustion engines

(G-7048)
TEXAS INDUSTRIES INC
Also Called: T X I
3601 Lawnwood St (76111-5820)
PHONE.............................817 838-4212
Rick Benson, *Manager*
EMP: 60
SQ FT: 4,980 **Publicly Held**
WEB: www.martinmarietta.com
SIC: 3241 3273 3271 5082 Cement, hydraulic; ready-mixed concrete; blocks, concrete or cinder: standard; concrete processing equipment; bars & bar shapes, steel, hot-rolled
HQ: Texas Industries, Inc.
1503 Lyndon B Johnson Fwy
Dallas TX 75234
972 647-6700

(G-7049)
TEXAS LEATHER TRIM INC
Also Called: Tlt Leather
2422 Blue Smoke Ct S (76105-1009)
P.O. Box 50008 (76105-0008)
PHONE.............................817 535-5883
Gregory S Cooper, *President*
Jim Guckert, *Plant Mgr*
Carol White, *CFO*
Hilda Cooper, *Treasurer*
John C Cooper, *Treasurer*
▲ **EMP:** 39
SQ FT: 32,000
SALES (est): 5.4MM **Privately Held**
WEB: www.tltleather.com
SIC: 2258 3131 Lace & warp knit fabric mills; boot & shoe accessories

(G-7050)
TEXAS MARINE HOLDINGS LTD (PA)
2177 E Loop 820 N (76118-7158)
PHONE.............................817 589-7547
Jimmy Harvell, *Partner*
EMP: 25 **EST:** 2001
SQ FT: 5,000
SALES (est): 9.6MM **Privately Held**
WEB: www.texasmastercraft.com
SIC: 5551 3732 Motor boat dealers; boat building & repairing

(G-7051)
TEXAS WIRELINE MFG LLC
8821 Forum Way Ste 101 (76140-5030)
PHONE.............................817 546-0772
Mark A Petty, *President*
Dawn M Petty, *Corp Secy*
Elise Conley, *Office Mgr*
▼ **EMP:** 17
SALES (est): 2.7MM **Privately Held**
WEB: www.texaswireline.com
SIC: 1389 Oil field services

(G-7052)
TEXPAC HIDE & SKIN LTD (PA)
Also Called: Tex-Pac Hide & Skin
601 Ne 29th St (76106-5915)
PHONE.............................817 626-6586
James Zitnik, *President*
Daniel W Dondero, *Corp Secy*
James Fata, *Vice Pres*
Gary W King, *Vice Pres*
◆ **EMP:** 75
SQ FT: 40,000
SALES (est): 18.8MM **Privately Held**
SIC: 3111 3199 Hides: tanning, currying & finishing; leather belting & strapping

(G-7053)
THE CUMMING COMPANY INC
Also Called: C C I
6300 Ridglea Pl Ste 800 (76116-5708)
PHONE.............................817 737-2393
Dwight Cumming, *President*
Linda Johnson, *Exec VP*
EMP: 13
SQ FT: 3,400
SALES (est): 2.9MM **Privately Held**
WEB: www.thecummingcompany.com
SIC: 1382 Oil & gas exploration services

(G-7054)
THERMACOR PROCESS INC (PA)
1670 E Hicks Field Rd (76179-5248)
P.O. Box 79670 (76179-0670)
PHONE.............................817 847-7300
Caroline Kerzman, *President*
Richard B Bender II, *Partner*
Joe Keyes, *Partner*
Rick Bender, *Senior VP*
Clint Riggin, *Vice Pres*
◆ **EMP:** 100
SQ FT: 95,000
SALES (est): 25.7MM **Privately Held**
WEB: www.thermacor.com
SIC: 3498 3317 Piping systems for pulp paper & chemical industries; steel pipe & tubes

(G-7055)
THERMAL SPECIALTIES TEXAS LLC
212 Page Ave (76110-2737)
PHONE.............................918 836-4800
Mitch Myers, *Mng Member*
Darren Dietrich, *Manager*
EMP: 9
SALES (est): 1.2MM
SALES (corp-wide): 24.8MM **Privately Held**
WEB: www.thermalspecialties.com
SIC: 1741 2895 7389 Refractory or acid brick masonry; furnace black; finishing services
PA: Thermal Specialties, Llc
6314 E 15th St
Tulsa OK 74112
918 836-4800

(G-7056)
THERMO PLASTICS CORPORATION
4101 Hahn Blvd (76117-1782)
P.O. Box 14275 (76117-0275)
PHONE.............................817 281-9010
John C Boyer, *President*
Imogene Boyer, *Vice Pres*
Tammy Ramirez, *Office Mgr*
Pat Neal, *Asst Sec*
EMP: 25 **EST:** 1958
SQ FT: 27,000
SALES (est): 5.2MM **Privately Held**
WEB: www.thermoplasticscorp.com
SIC: 3089 3356 Extruded finished plastic products; nonferrous rolling & drawing

(G-7057)
THOMAS PLASTICS INC
4121 Stadium Dr (76133-1031)
PHONE.............................817 654-3238
Roy Thomas, *President*
Luda Thomas, *Corp Secy*
Mack Thomas, *Vice Pres*
EMP: 53
SQ FT: 69,336
SALES (est): 10.1MM **Privately Held**
WEB: www.thomasplasticsinc.com
SIC: 3085 Plastics bottles

(G-7058)
THOMAS STEEL DRUMS INC
2517 Ne 35th St (76111-1911)
P.O. Box 7122 (76111-0122)
PHONE.............................817 838-6891
Aline Callaway, *Corp Secy*
Stan Thomas, *Exec VP*
Phillip A Thomas, *Vice Pres*
Rosalia Kirby, *Admin Sec*
EMP: 24
SQ FT: 500
SALES (est): 3.6MM
SALES (corp-wide): 5.2MM **Privately Held**
WEB: www.lincnetwork.com
SIC: 3412 Drums, shipping: metal; barrels, shipping: metal
PA: Curtis Thomas Investments Inc
2517 Ne 35th St
Fort Worth TX 76111
817 336-5569

(G-7059)
THORNTON STEEL HOLDINGS INC
2700 W Pafford St (76110-5893)
PHONE.............................817 926-3324
Donny R Lassetter, *President*
Randall Vanzandt, *Project Mgr*
Kerry R Lee, *CFO*
Kerry Lee, *CFO*
Gary Alsup, *Manager*
EMP: 80
SQ FT: 80,000
SALES (est): 45.8MM **Privately Held**
WEB: www.thorntonsteel.com
SIC: 3441 Fabricated structural metal

(G-7060)
THRESHOLD DEVELOPMENT COMPANY
777 Taylor St (76102-4919)
PHONE.............................817 870-1483
Bud Vinson, *President*
Jerry Ross, *CFO*
EMP: 12
SQ FT: 10,000
SALES (est): 2.7MM **Privately Held**
WEB: www.777oil.com
SIC: 1311 Crude petroleum production; natural gas production

(G-7061)
THYSSENKRUPP ARPRT SYSTEMS INC
Also Called: T & T Airport Services
3201 N Sylvania Ave # 117 (76111-3124)
PHONE.............................817 834-6984
Mark Jones, *Principal*
Enver Sarliar, *Vice Pres*
Laura Suarez, *CFO*
Mark Rose, *Information Mgr*
Enver Sarilar, *Director*
◆ **EMP:** 150

SALES (est): 61.2MM
SALES (corp-wide): 34B **Privately Held**
WEB: www.thyssenkrupp-elevator.com
SIC: 3569 3441 Bridge or gate machinery, hydraulic; fabricated structural metal
HQ: Thyssenkrupp North America, Llc
111 W Jackson Blvd # 2400
Chicago IL 60604
312 525-2800

(G-7062)
THYSSENKRUPP ELEVATOR CORP
7425 Pebble Dr (76118-6945)
PHONE.............................817 922-9590
Robert Lusk, *Manager*
EMP: 22
SALES (corp-wide): 918MM **Privately Held**
WEB: www.thyssenkruppelevator.com
SIC: 3999 5084 1796 Wheelchair lifts; elevators; elevator installation & conversion
HQ: Thyssenkrupp Elevator Corporation
11605 Haynes Bridge Rd
Alpharetta GA 30009
678 319-3240

(G-7063)
TIDAL LOGISTICS INC
12319 Us 287 Bus (76179)
PHONE.............................940 668-1818
Joey Fanguy, *President*
Debbie Burgess, *Manager*
EMP: 150
SALES (est): 1.5MM
SALES (corp-wide): 1.2B **Publicly Held**
WEB: www.tidallogistics.com
SIC: 1389 Oil field services
PA: Select Energy Services, Inc.
1233 West Loop S Ste 1400
Houston TX 77027
713 235-9500

(G-7064)
TJP ENTERPRISES LLC
Also Called: All American Tire Recyclers
5225 Teague Rd (76140-8119)
PHONE.............................817 779-4360
Tom Parker, *CEO*
Jodi Parker, *COO*
EMP: 30
SALES (est): 1.7MM **Privately Held**
WEB: www.aatr.biz
SIC: 3011 Tires & inner tubes

(G-7065)
TOKAI CARBON CB LTD (HQ)
301 Commerce St Ste 500 (76102-4178)
PHONE.............................817 390-8600
William Jones, *President*
Ryan Kettle, *Vice Pres*
Wesley A Wampler, *Vice Pres*
Ravi Singh, *Engineer*
Lydia Granado, *Credit Staff*
◆ **EMP:** 33 **EST:** 1993
SQ FT: 20,000
SALES (est): 142.1MM **Privately Held**
WEB: www.sidrichardson.org
SIC: 2895 Carbon black

(G-7066)
TOON LLC
2312 Monarch Dr Apt 616 (76119-5822)
PHONE.............................817 609-0672
Mohamud Abdi, *Mng Member*
EMP: 10
SALES (est): 419K **Privately Held**
SIC: 3669 Transportation signaling devices

(G-7067)
TOTAL SAND SERVICES LLC
Also Called: Tssands
300 Throckmorton St # 300 (76102-2921)
PHONE.............................817 420-7474
Stuart Weinman, *CEO*
Jamie Peace, *President*
Lynn Thompson, *CFO*
EMP: 9
SALES (est): 104.9K **Privately Held**
WEB: www.tssands.com
SIC: 1389 Servicing oil & gas wells

(G-7068)
TOTE SYSTEMS INTERNATIONAL LP
8821 Forum Way Ste 113 (76140-5030)
PHONE..................................817 447-9110
Rick Humke, *Partner*
Mike Ames, *Partner*
Rayce D Gibson, *Production*
Branden Neal, *Engineer*
Rayce Gibson, *Sales Mgr*
▲ EMP: 38
SQ FT: 25,000
SALES (est): 11.6MM **Privately Held**
WEB: www.totesystems.com
SIC: 3559 Pharmaceutical machinery

(G-7069)
TPG CAPITAL MANAGEMENT LP (PA)
Also Called: Texas Pacific Group
301 Commerce St Ste 3300 (76102-4133)
PHONE..................................817 871-4000
Jack Weingart, *Managing Prtnr*
David Bonderman, *Partner*
James G Coulter, *Partner*
Joshua Easterly, *Partner*
Vivek Paul, *Partner*
◆ EMP: 500
SALES (est): 2.3B **Privately Held**
WEB: www.tpg.com
SIC: 6726 3674 6799 3993 Investment offices; silicon wafers, chemically doped; venture capital companies; signs & advertising specialties; investment holding companies, except banks

(G-7070)
TRACE METAL INDUSTRIES INC
2944 S Main St (76110-4225)
PHONE..................................817 921-6251
Andrew Schoening, *President*
EMP: 24 EST: 1979
SQ FT: 15,000
SALES (est): 9MM **Privately Held**
WEB: www.tracemetalindustries.com
SIC: 3441 Fabricated structural metal

(G-7071)
TRANE US INC
4200 N Sylvania Ave (76137-5014)
PHONE..................................817 838-1310
Nanette Hunter, *CFO*
Austin Faeth, *Accounts Mgr*
EMP: 46 **Privately Held**
WEB: www.fortworth-air.com
SIC: 3585 Refrigeration & heating equipment
HQ: Trane U.S. Inc.
    3600 Pammel Creek Rd
    La Crosse WI 54601
    608 787-2000

(G-7072)
TRAULSEN & CO INC
Also Called: Traulsen Companies
4401 Blue Mound Rd (76106-1928)
PHONE..................................817 625-9671
Stewart Hudnut, *President*
Betty Edwards, *Opers Mgr*
Andres Bolivar, *Safety Mgr*
Joe Harris, *Production*
George Maxwell, *Purchasing*
▲ EMP: 300 EST: 1939
SQ FT: 300,000
SALES (est): 103MM
SALES (corp-wide): 14.1B **Publicly Held**
WEB: www.traulsen.com
SIC: 3585 Refrigeration & heating equipment
HQ: Itw Food Equipment Group Llc
    701 S Ridge Ave
    Troy OH 45374

(G-7073)
TREND GATHERING & TREATING LP (DH)
810 Houston St Ste 2000 (76102-6223)
PHONE..................................817 885-2524
Rose Steve, *Principal*
EMP: 14
SALES (est): 7.3MM
SALES (corp-wide): 264.9B **Publicly Held**
SIC: 1311 Crude petroleum production; natural gas production

(G-7074)
TRESKA INC (PA)
3801 Austin Ln (76111-6513)
PHONE..................................682 647-0352
Gary Fields, *CEO*
Larry Thornton, *Vice Pres*
◆ EMP: 26
SQ FT: 18,000
SALES (est): 4MM **Privately Held**
WEB: www.treska.com
SIC: 3961 5023 5632 2331 Costume jewelry, ex. precious metal & semi-precious stones; home furnishings; apparel accessories; women's & misses' blouses & shirts

(G-7075)
TRINITY INDUSTRIES INC
Also Called: Trinity Parts & Components
2548 Ne 28th St (76111-1701)
PHONE..................................817 665-1499
Gary Blevins, *Manager*
Juan Rodriguez, *Supervisor*
EMP: 100
SALES (corp-wide): 3B **Publicly Held**
WEB: www.trin.net
SIC: 3443 3743 Tanks, standard or custom fabricated: metal plate; railroad equipment
PA: Trinity Industries, Inc.
    14221 Dallas Pkwy Ste 11
    Dallas TX 75254
    214 631-4420

(G-7076)
TRINITY PARTS & COMPONENTS LLC (DH)
2548 Ne 28th St (76111-1701)
PHONE..................................817 378-2003
Paul Brown,
Neal Langdon,
EMP: 10
SALES (est): 16.1MM
SALES (corp-wide): 3B **Publicly Held**
WEB: www.trinityrail.com
SIC: 3743 Freight cars & equipment
HQ: Trinity Rail Group, Llc
    14221 Dallas Pkwy # 1100
    Dallas TX 75254
    214 631-4420

(G-7077)
TRINITY RIVER DISTILLERY LLC
1734 E El Paso St Ste 130 (76102-6771)
PHONE..................................214 293-6011
Benjamin Justus Alexander,
Donald Frederick Alexander,
Bruce 'N Conti,
Mark S Lusignan,
EMP: 15
SQ FT: 50,000
SALES (est): 2MM **Privately Held**
WEB: www.silverstarspirits.com
SIC: 2085 Distilled & blended liquors

(G-7078)
TRIPAC INTERNATIONAL INC
9000 Forum Way (76140-5019)
PHONE..................................817 534-9278
Stephen Obrien, *Ch of Bd*
Michael Todd Timmons, *President*
Todd Timmons, *Principal*
Cheree Eller, *Vice Pres*
Bill Kolhagen, *Production*
▲ EMP: 40
SQ FT: 67,000
SALES (est): 15MM **Privately Held**
WEB: www.tripacfans.com
SIC: 3585 5013 Air conditioning, motor vehicle; automotive supplies & parts

(G-7079)
TRIPLE S MANUFACTURING COMPANY
4208 Murray Ave (76117-1715)
P.O. Box 14083 (76117-0083)
PHONE..................................817 281-0602
▼ EMP: 11 EST: 1975
SQ FT: 40,000
SALES (est): 1.9MM **Privately Held**
WEB: www.tsmboilers.com
SIC: 1711 3443 5074 Boiler maintenance contractor; heat exchangers, condensers & components; boilers, hot water heating

(G-7080)
TROTHYHIDE LLC (PA)
Also Called: Smokehouse Salt Company
5371 Rendon Rd (76140-9675)
PHONE..................................817 455-1118
Lowell Stynisky, *President*
Brent Edwards, *Mng Member*
EMP: 10 EST: 2010
SQ FT: 19,000
SALES (est): 1.1MM **Privately Held**
SIC: 2899 Salt

(G-7081)
TRUE GRIT REDI MIX LTD
12150 N Saginaw Blvd (76179)
PHONE..................................817 439-5914
Barbara Warner, *President*
EMP: 21
SALES (est): 6.2MM **Privately Held**
WEB: www.truegritconcrete.com
SIC: 3273 Ready-mixed concrete

(G-7082)
TRUST PRINTSHOP INC
2506 Tillar St (76107-8404)
PHONE..................................817 453-3121
Matthew Lucas, *President*
Janell Johnson, *Manager*
Ryan Johnson, *Manager*
Travis Bryant, *Representative*
Justin White, *Associate*
◆ EMP: 16
SALES (est): 1.9MM **Privately Held**
WEB: www.trustprintshop.com
SIC: 2759 Screen printing

(G-7083)
TRWA INC (PA)
Also Called: American Right Way Associates
925 N University Dr (76114-2336)
P.O. Box 167 (76101-0167)
PHONE..................................817 361-8839
Don Valden, *CEO*
Tedd Valdez, *President*
Anna Marie Valden, *Treasurer*
Anya Valdez, *Admin Sec*
EMP: 55
SALES (est): 6.6MM **Privately Held**
WEB: www.americanrightofwayacquisitions.com
SIC: 1382 Oil & gas exploration services

(G-7084)
TRWA INC
Also Called: Texas Right of Way Association
6502 Sabrosa Ct E (76133-5244)
PHONE..................................817 361-8839
Don Valden, *Exec Dir*
EMP: 30 **Privately Held**
WEB: www.americanrightofwayacquisitions.com
SIC: 1382 Oil & gas exploration services
PA: Trwa, Inc.
    925 N University Dr
    Fort Worth TX 76114

(G-7085)
TSAR OPERATING COMPANY
6500 West Fwy Ste 222 (76116-2116)
PHONE..................................817 731-9595
Duer Wagner, *President*
Dean Cochran, *Vice Pres*
Brenda Smart, *CFO*
EMP: 12
SQ FT: 5,000
SALES (est): 750K **Privately Held**
SIC: 1381 Drilling oil & gas wells

(G-7086)
TWO TALENTS IMAGE PLUS PRTG
12001 Katy Rd (76244-8881)
P.O. Box 8, Keller (76244-0008)
PHONE..................................817 379-5926
Kirk Nance, *President*
Jim Sturgis, *Vice Pres*
EMP: 20
SQ FT: 10,000
SALES (est): 3.6MM **Privately Held**
WEB: www.imageplusprinting.net
SIC: 2752 Commercial printing, offset

(G-7087)
TX TINMAN ENTERPRISES LLC
6731 Bridge St Ste 64 (76112-0817)
PHONE..................................817 288-6116
Tracy L Green, *President*
Timothy E Delce, *Vice Pres*
EMP: 10
SQ FT: 5,500
SALES (est): 2.4MM **Privately Held**
WEB: www.tin-man.net
SIC: 3441 7692 3462 Fabricated structural metal; welding repair; iron & steel forgings

(G-7088)
TYSON FOODS INC
7401 Will Rogers Blvd (76140-6019)
PHONE..................................817 568-9000
Estella Garza, *Personnel*
Greg Irby, *Manager*
Suzanne Osborn, *Director*
EMP: 200
SQ FT: 173,107
SALES (corp-wide): 43.1B **Publicly Held**
WEB: www.tysonfoods.com
SIC: 2015 Chicken, processed: canned
PA: Tyson Foods, Inc.
    2200 W Don Tyson Pkwy
    Springdale AR 72762
    479 290-4000

(G-7089)
TYSON FOODS INC
6350 Browning Ct (76180-6013)
PHONE..................................817 656-5507
Luge Rainbolt, *Branch Mgr*
EMP: 375
SALES (corp-wide): 43.1B **Publicly Held**
WEB: www.tysonfoods.com
SIC: 2013 2099 Sausages & other prepared meats; food preparations
PA: Tyson Foods, Inc.
    2200 W Don Tyson Pkwy
    Springdale AR 72762
    479 290-4000

(G-7090)
U S WEATHERFORD L P
Also Called: Weatherford International
751 Eight Twenty Blvd # 103 (76106-1972)
PHONE..................................817 293-5192
EMP: 18 **Privately Held**
WEB: www.weatherford.com
SIC: 1389 Oil field services
HQ: U S Weatherford L P
    179 Weatherford Dr
    Schriever LA 70395
    985 493-6100

(G-7091)
U S WEATHERFORD L P
3044 Wichita Ct (76140-1710)
PHONE..................................817 293-5192
EMP: 13 **Privately Held**
WEB: www.weatherford.com
SIC: 3533 Oil & gas field machinery
HQ: U S Weatherford L P
    179 Weatherford Dr
    Schriever LA 70395
    985 493-6100

(G-7092)
ULTERRA DRILLING TECH LP (HQ)
201 Main St Ste 1660 (76102-3120)
PHONE..................................817 293-7555
John Clunan, *President*
Danny Delmas, *District Mgr*
Matt H Hardin, *District Mgr*
Danny Jordan, *District Mgr*
David Stark, *District Mgr*
▲ EMP: 25
SALES (est): 140MM **Privately Held**
WEB: www.ulterra.com
SIC: 5084 3533 Drilling equipment, excluding bits; bits, oil & gas field tools: rock

(G-7093)
UNITED PARCEL SERVICE INC
Also Called: UPS
13700 Independence Pkwy (76177-4002)
PHONE..................................817 490-7300
EMP: 14

SALES (corp-wide): 74B **Publicly Held**
WEB: www.ups.com
SIC: 3444 Mail (post office) collection or storage boxes, sheet metal
HQ: United Parcel Service, Inc.
　　55 Glenlake Pkwy
　　Atlanta GA 30328
　　404 828-6000

(G-7094)
UNIWELL LABORATORIES LLC
Also Called: Uniwell Labs
14801 Sovereign Rd (76155-2645)
PHONE.................................817 510-1850
Eduardo Soto,
EMP: 50
SQ FT: 130,000
SALES (est): 1.4MM **Privately Held**
WEB: www.uniwelllabs.com
SIC: 2834 Adrenal pharmaceutical preparations

(G-7095)
UST-MAMIYA INC
14950 Faa Blvd Ste 200 (76155-2235)
PHONE.................................817 267-2219
Suzuki Satoru, *CEO*
Robert Drury, *COO*
Robert Niebeling, *Vice Pres*
Don Rahrig, *Vice Pres*
Darren Young, *Purch Agent*
◆ **EMP:** 35
SQ FT: 57,000
SALES (est): 5.7MM **Privately Held**
WEB: www.ustmamiya.com
SIC: 3949 5091 Shafts, golf club; golf equipment
PA: Mamiya-Op Co.,Ltd.
　　6-18-1, Nishishinjuku
　　Shinjuku-Ku TKY 160-0

(G-7096)
V I J CORPORATION
Also Called: Nuco
1700 Hickory Dr (76117-6011)
P.O. Box 14639 (76117-0639)
PHONE.................................817 838-2020
Jennifer Greer-Cozens, *President*
Alex Cozens, *President*
John Hoyer, *Finance Dir*
Jane Greer, *Admin Sec*
EMP: 49 **EST:** 1950
SQ FT: 35,000
SALES (est): 12MM **Privately Held**
WEB: www.nationalutilities.com
SIC: 3728 3494 Aircraft assemblies, sub-assemblies & parts; valves & pipe fittings

(G-7097)
VENTURA FOODS LLC
3201 Ne Loop 820 Ste 150 (76137-2447)
PHONE.................................817 232-6800
Sara Schiflett, *Manager*
Rachel Pharris, *Admin Asst*
EMP: 15 **Privately Held**
WEB: www.venturafoods.com
SIC: 5411 5141 2099 Grocery stores; groceries, general line; food preparations
PA: Ventura Foods, Llc
　　40 Pointe Dr
　　Brea CA 92821

(G-7098)
VETOQUINOL USA INC (DH)
4250 N Sylvania Ave (76137-5014)
PHONE.................................817 529-7500
Eric Alsup, *President*
Amy Davis, *Sales Staff*
Tabitha Cromer, *Marketing Staff*
Tammy Driscoll, *Manager*
Marty Gick, *Manager*
◆ **EMP:** 37
SQ FT: 25,000
SALES (est): 20.5MM
SALES (corp-wide): 166.7K **Privately Held**
WEB: www.vetoquinolusa.com
SIC: 2834 2836 Pharmaceutical preparations; veterinary biological products
HQ: Vetoquinol N.-A. Inc
　　2000 Ch Georges
　　Lavaltrie QC J5T 3
　　450 586-2252

(G-7099)
VF OUTDOOR LLC
Also Called: Dickies
125 S Jennings Ave (76104-1105)
PHONE.................................817 348-0567
Philip Williamson, *Ch of Bd*
EMP: 500
SALES (corp-wide): 10.4B **Publicly Held**
WEB: www.dickies.com
SIC: 2339 2326 Women's & misses' outerwear; industrial garments, men's & boys'
HQ: Vf Outdoor, Llc
　　2701 Harbor Bay Pkwy
　　Alameda CA 94502
　　855 500-8639

(G-7100)
VF OUTDOOR LLC
Also Called: Dickies
509 W Vickery Blvd (76104-1110)
PHONE.................................817 336-7201
Scott Baxter, *President*
Marie Johnson Moore, *General Mgr*
Cindy Almond, *Marketing Staff*
Juan Olvera, *Technology*
Donnie Richard, *Director*
EMP: 5300
SALES (corp-wide): 10.4B **Publicly Held**
WEB: www.thenorthface.com
SIC: 2326 2339 Men's & boys' work clothing; industrial garments, men's & boys'; women's & misses' outerwear
HQ: Vf Outdoor, Llc
　　2701 Harbor Bay Pkwy
　　Alameda CA 94502
　　855 500-8639

(G-7101)
VF OUTDOOR LLC
Also Called: Dickies
9400 Blue Mound Rd (76131-3308)
PHONE.................................817 810-4401
Scott Stroh, *Superintendent*
Peggy Bickel, *Production*
Larry McKinney, *Manager*
Shannon Thacker, *Manager*
Tammy Atchley, *Admin Asst*
EMP: 150
SALES (corp-wide): 10.4B **Publicly Held**
WEB: www.dickies.com
SIC: 2326 Men's & boys' work clothing
HQ: Vf Outdoor, Llc
　　2701 Harbor Bay Pkwy
　　Alameda CA 94502
　　855 500-8639

(G-7102)
VF OUTDOOR LLC
Also Called: Fort Worth II Distribution Ctr
201 Intermodal Pkwy (76177-3908)
PHONE.................................817 491-4949
John Milhone, *Branch Mgr*
EMP: 25
SALES (corp-wide): 10.4B **Publicly Held**
WEB: www.dickies.com
SIC: 2326 2671 2339 Men's & boys' work clothing; packaging paper & plastics film, coated & laminated; women's & misses' outerwear
HQ: Vf Outdoor, Llc
　　2701 Harbor Bay Pkwy
　　Alameda CA 94502
　　855 500-8639

(G-7103)
VF SAGEBRUSH ENTERPRISES LLC (HQ)
319 Lipscomb St (76104-1140)
P.O. Box 1779 (76101-1779)
PHONE.................................817 336-7201
Steve Rendle, *CEO*
Ray Maddox, *Senior Buyer*
Scott A Roe, *CFO*
Stacy Glaspie, *Admin Asst*
◆ **EMP:** 29

SALES (est): 710.7MM
SALES (corp-wide): 10.4B **Publicly Held**
WEB: www.dickies.com
SIC: 2325 2321 2329 2339 Jeans: men's, youths' & boys'; slacks, dress: men's, youths' & boys'; trousers, dress (separate): men's, youths' & boys'; men's & boys' dress shirts; jackets (suede, leatherette, etc.), men's & boys'; sweaters & sweater jackets: men's & boys'; jeans: women's, misses' & juniors'; slacks: women's, misses' & juniors'; women's & misses' blouses & shirts; jeans: girls', children's & infants'; slacks: girls' & children's; warm-up, jogging & sweat suits: girls' & children's; bathing suits & swimwear: girls', children's & infants'
PA: V.F. Corporation
　　1551 Wewatta St
　　Greenwood Village CO 80110
　　720 778-4000

(G-7104)
VICTORY AWNING INC
6801 Old Randol Mill Rd (76120-1209)
PHONE.................................817 759-1600
Larry Buck, *President*
Earl Gauntt, *Vice Pres*
Scott Luttrell, *Sales Staff*
Susan Buck, *Executive*
Bayardo Bonilla, *Administration*
EMP: 45
SQ FT: 18,000
SALES (est): 5.5MM **Privately Held**
WEB: www.victoryawning.net
SIC: 2394 Awnings, fabric: made from purchased materials

(G-7105)
VICTORY CLIMATE SYSTEMS LLC
8912 South Fwy Ste C (76140-4937)
P.O. Box 40917 (76140-0917)
PHONE.................................817 293-3331
Robert Tigner, *President*
Mike Stutzman, *Mfg Staff*
Don Coggins, *Purch Mgr*
Deanna Williams, *Buyer*
Alex Coronel, *QC Mgr*
▲ **EMP:** 126
SALES (est): 12.1MM **Privately Held**
WEB: www.vcsemail.com
SIC: 3714 Motor vehicle parts & accessories

(G-7106)
VIRUS LIGHT RX LLC
Also Called: Virus Armor
4924 Cambridge Rd (76155-2248)
PHONE.................................817 917-2800
Shari Menon, *Mng Member*
EMP: 10
SALES (est): 600K **Privately Held**
SIC: 2842 Sanitation preparations, disinfectants & deodorants

(G-7107)
VISION SYSTEMS INTL LLC
Also Called: V S I
4700 Marine Creek Pkwy (76179-3505)
P.O. Box 136969 (76136-0969)
PHONE.................................817 234-6600
Philip King, *President*
Scott Evers, *President*
Brian Linden, *Treasurer*
David Mc Dearmid, *Manager*
Darron Blakely, *Admin Sec*
EMP: 10
SQ FT: 227,000
SALES (est): 128.9K **Privately Held**
WEB: www.elbitsystems-us.com
SIC: 8711 3429 Engineering services; manufactured hardware (general)

(G-7108)
VISTA MACHINING COMPANY LLC
3559 Williams Rd Ste 101 (76116-7041)
PHONE.................................817 710-2987
Richard R Hyde, *President*
EMP: 15
SALES (est): 3.2MM **Privately Held**
SIC: 3444 Sheet metalwork

(G-7109)
VISTA PROPPANTS LOGISTICS LLC (HQ)
4413 Carey St (76119-4219)
PHONE.................................817 563-3500
Gary B Humphreys,
EMP: 568
SALES (est): 254.2MM **Privately Held**
WEB: www.vprop.com
SIC: 1442 Sand mining
PA: Vista Proppants And Logistics Inc.
　　4413 Carey St
　　Fort Worth TX 76119
　　817 563-3500

(G-7110)
VLGC LLC
Also Called: Woven Remembrance
6811 Corporation Pkwy (76126-1748)
PHONE.................................817 926-5209
Kathy Cole, *Office Mgr*
Jennifer Branton,
Sharon Johnson, *Administration*
Randy Pack,
EMP: 20
SALES (est): 2MM **Privately Held**
WEB: www.veralee.com
SIC: 2389 Burial garments; disposable garments & accessories

(G-7111)
VOIDFORM PRODUCTS INC
6151 Cowley Rd (76119-1882)
PHONE.................................817 429-0888
Mike Turner, *Manager*
Linda Sanchez, *Admin Asst*
EMP: 45
SQ FT: 40,070
SALES (corp-wide): 15MM **Privately Held**
WEB: www.voidform.com
SIC: 2679 5082 Corrugated paper: made from purchased material; contractors' materials
PA: Voidform Products, Inc.
　　1895 W Dartmouth Ave
　　Englewood CO 80110
　　303 762-0324

(G-7112)
W & W SILKSCREENING INC
2451 Riverbend West Dr (76118-7024)
P.O. Box 185099 (76181-0099)
PHONE.................................817 590-4479
Michelle Wells, *CEO*
Richard Wells, *President*
Barry D Wells, *Vice Pres*
EMP: 20
SQ FT: 30,000
SALES (est): 3.4MM **Privately Held**
WEB: www.w4graphics.com
SIC: 2759 2396 3479 Screen printing; automotive & apparel trimmings; painting of metal products

(G-7113)
W R MEADOWS INC
Also Called: Wr Meadows of Texas
2555 Ne 33rd St (76111-1902)
P.O. Box 7752 (76111-0752)
PHONE.................................817 834-1969
Andrew W Tam, *Opers-Prdtn-Mfg*
Britt Weber, *Finance Mgr*
Delia Kehr, *Administration*
EMP: 35
SQ FT: 67,268
SALES (corp-wide): 110.9MM **Privately Held**
WEB: www.wrmeadows.com
SIC: 5085 3272 Industrial supplies; concrete products
PA: W. R. Meadows, Inc.
　　300 Industrial Dr
　　Hampshire IL 60140
　　847 214-2100

(G-7114)
WABTEC MFG SOLUTIONS LLC
16201 Three Wide Dr (76177-2161)
PHONE.................................814 449-9619
Michael Patton, *President*
Kyra Yates, *Treasurer*
Laura Woolford, *Admin Sec*
EMP: 13

SALES (est): 3.4MM **Publicly Held**
WEB: www.wabtec.com
SIC: **3825** Internal combustion engine analyzers, to test electronics
PA: Westinghouse Air Brake Technologies Corporation
30 Isabella St
Pittsburgh PA 15212

(G-7115)
WAGGONER LAND SERVICES
316 Bailey Ave Ste 100 (76107-1866)
PHONE................817 763-8112
John Osborne, *Owner*
EMP: 30
SALES (est): 2.2MM **Privately Held**
SIC: **1389** Oil & gas field services

(G-7116)
WAGNER OIL COMPANY (PA)
500 Commerce St Ste 600 (76102-5477)
PHONE................817 335-2222
Bryan Wagner, *President*
William Waggoner, *Principal*
Joshua Nevin, *COO*
Mark Belcher, *Vice Pres*
He Patterson, *Vice Pres*
EMP: 40 EST: 1955
SQ FT: 19,000
SALES (est): 22MM **Privately Held**
WEB: www.wagneroil.com
SIC: **1311** Crude petroleum production; natural gas production

(G-7117)
WALLS & FORMS INC
Also Called: Display and Exibit Store, The
15000 Grand River Rd (76155-2737)
P.O. Box 741112, Dallas (75374-1112)
PHONE................972 745-0800
Dan L South, *President*
Flavian Ban, *Purchasing*
Cheryl Cox, *Purchasing*
Jason Hernandez, *Design Engr Mgr*
Santiago Vallejo, *Engineer*
▲ EMP: 62
SQ FT: 147,000
SALES: 9.5MM **Privately Held**
WEB: www.wallsforms.com
SIC: **2541 2426** Store & office display cases & fixtures; store fixtures, wood; frames for upholstered furniture, wood

(G-7118)
WALLS INDUSTRIES LLC (DH)
125 S Jennings Ave (76104-1105)
P.O. Box 1779 (76101-1779)
PHONE................844 259-2557
Jerry Meyer, *Chairman*
Jeffrey Cordes, *COO*
Jeff Fronterhouse, *Vice Pres*
Patrick McGee, *Vice Pres*
William Aisenberg, *CFO*
◆ EMP: 70
SQ FT: 450,000
SALES (est): 17.5MM
SALES (corp-wide): 10.4B **Publicly Held**
WEB: www.walls.com
SIC: **2326 2369 2385 2311** Men's & boys' work clothing; girls' & children's outerwear; waterproof outerwear; men's & boys' suits & coats
HQ: Vf Outdoor, Llc
2701 Harbor Bay Pkwy
Alameda CA 94502
855 500-8639

(G-7119)
WALLS INDUSTRIES LLC
301 E Risinger Rd (76140-5347)
PHONE................817 357-8040
Craig Ferdic, *Branch Mgr*
EMP: 30
SALES (corp-wide): 10.4B **Publicly Held**
WEB: www.walls.com
SIC: **2326** Men's & boys' work clothing
HQ: Walls Industries Llc
125 S Jennings Ave
Fort Worth TX 76104
844 259-2557

(G-7120)
WALSH AND WATTS INC (PA)
500 W 7th St Ste 1007 (76102-4769)
PHONE................817 335-5417
Howard Walsh Jr, *President*

Gary Goble, *Corp Secy*
Alfred B Guinn, *Vice Pres*
G M Louden, *Vice Pres*
EMP: 85
SQ FT: 10,000
SALES (est): 63.2MM **Privately Held**
SIC: **1311** Crude petroleum production

(G-7121)
WALSH COMPANY
500 W 7th St Unit 27 (76102-4773)
PHONE................817 335-3741
Gary Gople, *CEO*
F Howard Walsh Jr, *Partner*
George Malcom Louden, *Partner*
EMP: 40
SQ FT: 2,500
SALES: 510.6K **Privately Held**
WEB: www.walshtx.com
SIC: **1311** Crude petroleum production

(G-7122)
WALSH F HOWARD JR OPER CO INC
500 W 7th St Ste 1007 (76102-4732)
PHONE................817 336-2062
F Howard Walsh Jr, *President*
G Malcolm Louden, *Exec VP*
EMP: 60
SQ FT: 22,500
SALES (est): 4.8MM **Privately Held**
SIC: **1311** Crude petroleum production

(G-7123)
WALSH OIL CO
Also Called: Walsh & Watts
500 W 7th St Ste 1007 (76102-4732)
PHONE................817 336-2062
F Howard Walsh Jr, *Owner*
Denice Elliott-Heim, *Manager*
Alicia Miller, *Manager*
EMP: 25
SALES (est): 1MM **Privately Held**
SIC: **1311** Crude petroleum production; natural gas production

(G-7124)
WANT ADS OF FORT WORTH INC (PA)
Also Called: Thrifty Nickel
2800 W Lancaster Ave (76107-3007)
PHONE................817 870-0055
Victor A Verstraeta Jr, *President*
EMP: 15
SQ FT: 4,500
SALES (est): 1.7MM **Privately Held**
WEB: www.wacoamericanclassifieds.com
SIC: **2711** Newspapers: publishing only, not printed on site

(G-7125)
WAPLES HOLDINGS INC
Also Called: Waples Manufacturing
8900 Forum Way (76140-5017)
PHONE................817 568-1600
EMP: 38 EST: 1964
SQ FT: 10,700
SALES (est): 11.5MM **Privately Held**
WEB: www.waples.com
SIC: **3599** Machine shop, jobbing & repair

(G-7126)
WARD PACKAGING OF FORT WORTH
2848 Cullen St (76107-1306)
PHONE................817 334-0484
J Tim Ward, *President*
Zelime Amen Ward, *Corp Secy*
EMP: 50
SQ FT: 50,000
SALES (est): 9.4MM **Privately Held**
WEB: www.fortworthtexas.gov
SIC: **2653** Boxes, corrugated: made from purchased materials

(G-7127)
WARREN WATTS TECHNOLOGY LLC
Also Called: Auto-Out
1911 Windsor Pl (76110-1845)
PHONE................817 924-1370
Brent Williams, *President*
Robin Williams, *Vice Pres*
Kelli Esposito, *Marketing Staff*
Elvin Caraway,

Bob Freeman,
EMP: 13
SQ FT: 8,000
SALES (est): 1MM **Privately Held**
WEB: www.auto-out.com
SIC: **3669 4813 3577** Fire alarm apparatus, electric; ; computer peripheral equipment

(G-7128)
WEATHERFORD ARTIFICIA
800 Railhead Rd Ste 328 (76106-1981)
PHONE................817 624-7810
EMP: 12 **Privately Held**
SIC: **3561** Mfg Pumps/Pumping Equipment
HQ: Weatherford Artificial Lift Systems, Llc
2000 Saint James Pl
Houston TX 77056
713 836-4000

(G-7129)
WEATHERFORD ARTIFICIA
300 Burnett St Ste 350 (76102-2736)
PHONE................817 882-9955
Diana Little, *Technical Staff*
Caleb Mooneyham, *Technical Staff*
EMP: 32 **Privately Held**
WEB: www.weatherford.com
SIC: **1389** Oil field services
HQ: Weatherford Artificial Lift Systems, Llc
2000 Saint James Pl
Houston TX 77056
713 836-4000

(G-7130)
WEATHERFORD FRACTURING TECH
300 Burnett St Ste 350 (76102-2736)
PHONE................817 882-9955
Barry Estrand, *President*
EMP: 18
SALES (est): 401.5K **Privately Held**
WEB: www.weatherford.com
SIC: **8731 1382** Commercial physical research; oil & gas exploration services

(G-7131)
WEATHERFORD INTERNATIONAL LLC
3044 Wichita Ct (76140-1710)
PHONE................817 568-0282
EMP: 21 **Privately Held**
WEB: www.weatherford.com
SIC: **1389** Oil field services
HQ: Weatherford International, Llc
2000 Saint James Pl
Houston TX 77056
713 693-4000

(G-7132)
WEBB-MASON INC
3125 W Bolt St (76110-5813)
PHONE................800 992-2665
Frank Poeschel, *Vice Pres*
EMP: 23 **Privately Held**
WEB: www.webbmason.com
SIC: **2752** Business form & card printing, lithographic
PA: Webb-Mason, Inc.
10830 Gilroy Rd
Hunt Valley MD 21031

(G-7133)
WEBBMASON
3125 W Bolt St (76110-5813)
PHONE................682 432-0548
EMP: 14
SALES (est): 1.6MM **Privately Held**
SIC: **2752** Lithographic Commercial Printing

(G-7134)
WELBILT WALK-INS LP (HQ)
Also Called: Kysor Panel Systems
4201 N Beach St (76137-3212)
P.O. Box 14248 (76117-0248)
PHONE................817 281-5121
◆ EMP: 176 EST: 1996
SALES (est): 111.2MM
SALES (corp-wide): 276.7MM **Privately Held**
WEB: www.kpsglobal.com
SIC: **3089 3585** Panels, building: plastic; refrigeration & heating equipment

PA: Kps Global Llc
4201 N Beach St
Fort Worth TX 76137
817 281-5121

(G-7135)
WELDON MANUFACTURING INC
Also Called: Weldon Quality Truck Sleepers
3488 Bethlehem St (76111-1924)
P.O. Box 161206 (76161-1206)
PHONE................817 834-2229
Craig Fredrick, *President*
Lesa Turnbo, *Purchasing*
EMP: 17
SQ FT: 20,000
SALES (est): 3.4MM **Privately Held**
WEB: www.weldonusa.com
SIC: **3713 7532** Truck beds; truck painting & lettering

(G-7136)
WESCO AIRCRAFT HARDWARE CORP (DH)
Also Called: Incora
2601 Meacham Blvd Ste 400 (76137-4204)
PHONE................661 775-7200
Todd Snyder, *General Mgr*
Paul Woodard, *General Mgr*
Alex Murray, *COO*
Bertrand Pan, *Counsel*
Alexis McClure, *Site Mgr*
▲ EMP: 370 EST: 1953
SALES (est): 635.7MM
SALES (corp-wide): 1.7B **Privately Held**
WEB: www.wescoair.com
SIC: **5088 3728** Aircraft & parts; research & dev by manuf., aircraft parts & auxiliary equip

(G-7137)
WESCO INDUSTRIES INC
8717 Forum Way Ste 101 (76140-5029)
PHONE................817 551-7063
Mary Riley, *President*
Steven Riley, *Vice Pres*
Wes Riley, *Vice Pres*
EMP: 24
SQ FT: 20,000
SALES (est): 2.8MM **Privately Held**
WEB: www.wescoinc.com
SIC: **3599 2299 7389 5088** Machine shop, jobbing & repair; fabrics: linen, jute, hemp, ramie; sewing contractor; helicopter parts

(G-7138)
WESTERLY EXPLORATION INC
6640 Camp Bowie Blvd (76116-4230)
PHONE................817 738-1917
Kane C Weiner, *Principal*
EMP: 10
SALES (corp-wide): 11MM **Privately Held**
SIC: **1311** Crude petroleum production
PA: Westerly Exploration, Inc.
3701 Kirby Dr Ste 514
Houston TX 77098
713 524-7755

(G-7139)
WESTERN HAULER ENTERPRISES
Also Called: J T W Motor Co
2420 White Settlement Rd (76107-1466)
PHONE................817 332-1121
Larry Roberts, *President*
Jan Bell, *President*
EMP: 15
SQ FT: 57,000
SALES (est): 3.8MM **Privately Held**
SIC: **3537 7538** Industrial trucks & tractors; general automotive repair shops

(G-7140)
WESTERN HORSEMAN MAGAZINE
2112 Montgomery St (76107-4517)
PHONE................817 737-6397
Ernie King, *General Mgr*
Christine Hamilton, *Editor*
Penny Gibson, *Finance Dir*
Rayanne Engel-Currin, *Manager*
Teri Lee, *Manager*
EMP: 28
SQ FT: 10,600

SALES (est): 3.2MM **Privately Held**
WEB: www.westernhorseman.com
SIC: 2721 5961 Magazines: publishing only, not printed on site; books, mail order (except book clubs)
HQ: Morris Communications Company Llc
725 Broad St
Augusta GA 30901
706 724-0851

(G-7141)
WESTERN WIRE WORKS INC
Also Called: Western Group, The
4921 Rondo Dr (76106-1824)
PHONE.................................817 654-3373
Frank Mathews, *Branch Mgr*
EMP: 16
SQ FT: 3,000
SALES (corp-wide): 33.6MM **Privately Held**
WEB: www.thewesterngroup.com
SIC: 3496 2821 Miscellaneous fabricated wire products; polyurethane resins
PA: Western Wire Works, Inc.
3950 Nw Saint Helens Rd
Portland OR 97210
503 222-1644

(G-7142)
WESTMOOR CORP (PA)
4901 North Fwy (76106-1810)
P.O. Box 162749 (76161-2749)
PHONE.................................817 625-2841
Ernest Hochster, *Ch of Bd*
Jeffrey Hochster, *General Mgr*
Leonard F Hochster, *General Mgr*
McCullough C Thomas, *Vice Pres*
Tom McCullough, *CFO*
▲ **EMP:** 40
SQ FT: 65,000
SALES (est): 13.2MM **Privately Held**
WEB: www.panhandleww.com
SIC: 2321 3143 2331 2339 Men's & boys' furnishings; boots, dress or casual: men's; blouses, women's & juniors': made from purchased material; shirts, women's & juniors': made from purchased materials; jeans: women's, misses' & juniors'; girls' & children's outerwear

(G-7143)
WESTMOOR MFG CO
Also Called: Panhandle Slim
4901 North Fwy (76106-1810)
P.O. Box 162749 (76161-2749)
PHONE.................................817 625-2841
Jeffrey Hochster, *President*
Leonard S Hochster, *Exec VP*
C Thomas McCullough, *CFO*
Herb Bogart, *Manager*
▲ **EMP:** 50 **EST:** 1946
SQ FT: 65,000
SALES (est): 8.5MM
SALES (corp-wide): 13.2MM **Privately Held**
WEB: www.westmoormfg.com
SIC: 2321 2331 2339 2369 Men's & boys' dress shirts; blouses, women's & juniors': made from purchased material; shirts, women's & juniors': made from purchased materials; jeans: women's, misses' & juniors'; children's culottes & shorts
PA: Westmoor Corp.
4901 North Fwy
Fort Worth TX 76106
817 625-2841

(G-7144)
WESTROCK CP LLC
Also Called: Corrugated Container Div
6701 South Fwy (76134-3001)
PHONE.................................817 568-0918
John Klevorn, *Manager*
EMP: 150
SALES (corp-wide): 17.5B **Publicly Held**
WEB: www.westrock.com
SIC: 2653 Boxes, corrugated: made from purchased materials
HQ: Westrock Cp, Llc
1000 Abernathy Rd Ste 125
Atlanta GA 30328

(G-7145)
WHIP INDUSTRIES INC (PA)
3010 S Main St (76110-4284)
PHONE.................................817 289-1404
Gary McGee, *President*
Munoz Emily, *Mfg Staff*
◆ **EMP:** 99
SQ FT: 26,000
SALES (est): 25.9MM **Privately Held**
WEB: www.whipindustries.com
SIC: 3599 Machine shop, jobbing & repair

(G-7146)
WILLBANKS METALS INC
2400 Ne 36th St (76111-1905)
PHONE.................................817 625-6161
Carlos Feliciano, *Branch Mgr*
EMP: 15 **Privately Held**
WEB: www.willbanksmetals.com
SIC: 5051 3449 Steel; miscellaneous metalwork
PA: Willbanks Metals, Inc.
1155 Ne 28th St
Fort Worth TX 76106

(G-7147)
WILLBANKS METALS INC (PA)
1155 Ne 28th St (76106-7241)
PHONE.................................817 625-6161
Ryan Letz, *CEO*
Eric Letz, *Ch of Bd*
Scott Begin, *President*
Joe Culpepper, *Vice Pres*
Jim Ely, *Vice Pres*
◆ **EMP:** 135
SQ FT: 5,000
SALES (est): 100MM **Privately Held**
WEB: www.willbanksmetals.com
SIC: 5051 3449 Steel; miscellaneous metalwork

(G-7148)
WILLIAMSRDM INC
200 Greenleaf St (76107-1471)
PHONE.................................817 872-1500
Della H Williams, *President*
Melissa Hoskins, *Principal*
John Williams, *Principal*
James Walters, *Vice Pres*
Kisoo Jung, *Engineer*
▲ **EMP:** 88 **EST:** 1963
SQ FT: 80,000
SALES (est): 28.3MM **Privately Held**
WEB: www.williamsrdm.com
SIC: 3812 3679 3829 3613 Aircraft/aerospace flight instruments & guidance systems; harness assemblies for electronic use: wire or cable; measuring & controlling devices; panel & distribution boards & other related apparatus; engineering services; aircraft parts & equipment

(G-7149)
WILLS PRO CUSTOM MFG INC
4920 Northeast Pkwy (76106-1817)
P.O. Box 163918 (76161-3918)
PHONE.................................817 534-6009
William A Pels, *President*
Kyle Pels, *Vice Pres*
Teresa G Pels, *Vice Pres*
William Pels, *Sales Executive*
EMP: 11
SQ FT: 1,750
SALES (est): 2.1MM **Privately Held**
WEB: www.wpcmfg.com
SIC: 3441 Fabricated structural metal

(G-7150)
WINKLMAN WNKLEMAN PARTNERS LLC (PA)
5600 Midway Rd (76117-4632)
PHONE.................................817 831-0170
Rory Connor, *Mng Member*
Ralph D Larovere,
EMP: 25
SALES (est): 3.3MM **Privately Held**
SIC: 3365 Aluminum & aluminum-based alloy castings

(G-7151)
WORTH TRAILER PARTS INC
4312 E Loop 820 S (76119-4448)
PHONE.................................817 496-7841
Wes Dorrum, *Principal*
EMP: 24 **EST:** 2010

SALES (est): 4.4MM **Privately Held**
WEB: www.worthtrailer.com
SIC: 5599 5013 3799 5084 Utility trailers; trailer parts & accessories; trailers & trailer equipment; trailers, industrial; trailer maintenance; trailer repair

(G-7152)
WRKCO INC
4675 Railhead Rd (76106-0900)
PHONE.................................817 624-8000
JD Mercer, *Branch Mgr*
EMP: 15
SALES (corp-wide): 17.5B **Publicly Held**
WEB: www.westrock.com
SIC: 2653 Boxes, corrugated: made from purchased materials
HQ: Wrkco Inc.
1000 Abernathy Rd Ste 12
Atlanta GA 30328
770 448-2193

(G-7153)
XTERRA FISHING & RENTAL TLS CO
801 Cherry St Unit 2 (76102-6886)
PHONE.................................817 334-4100
Larry Rankin, *President*
EMP: 40
SQ FT: 8,000
SALES (est): 2.2MM
SALES (corp-wide): 567.2MM **Publicly Held**
SIC: 1389 Oil field services
HQ: Basic Energy Services, L.P.
801 Cherry St Unit 2
Fort Worth TX 76102

(G-7154)
XTO ENERGY INC
210 W 6th St (76102-4803)
PHONE.................................817 885-2195
Vickie Augustus, *Opers Staff*
Dacia Montoya, *Manager*
Bobby Stark, *Manager*
Joni Vanmeter, *Manager*
Cameron Webster, *Manager*
EMP: 44
SALES (corp-wide): 264.9B **Publicly Held**
WEB: www.xtoenergy.com
SIC: 1311 Crude petroleum production
HQ: Xto Energy Inc.
22777 Sprngwoods Vlg Pkwy
Spring TX 77389

(G-7155)
XTO ENERGY INC
600 E Exchange Ave (76164-8246)
PHONE.................................505 333-3100
EMP: 14
SALES (corp-wide): 244.3B **Publicly Held**
SIC: 1382 Oil/Gas Exploration Services
HQ: Xto Energy Inc.
810 Houston St Ste 2000
Fort Worth TX 77389

(G-7156)
XTO ENERGY INC
600 E Exchange Ave (76164-8246)
P.O. Box 131931, Dallas (75313-1931)
PHONE.................................713 871-3453
EMP: 44
SALES (corp-wide): 268.8B **Publicly Held**
SIC: 1311 Crude Petroleum And Natural Gas, Nsk
HQ: Xto Energy Inc.
810 Houston St Ste 2000
Fort Worth TX 77389
817 870-2800

(G-7157)
YOHAWK ENERGY LLC
6209 Sandra Dr (76133-4315)
PHONE.................................817 484-9642
JB Yowell, *President*
Chuck Hawkins, *Vice Pres*
EMP: 9
SALES (est): 788.1K **Privately Held**
SIC: 1381 Drilling oil & gas wells

(G-7158)
YOUNGER COLORPRESS INC
4050 Hildring Dr W (76109-4720)
PHONE.................................817 923-1331
M W Younger, *President*
Alice Younger, *Vice Pres*
Thomas Younger, *Vice Pres*
EMP: 12
SQ FT: 18,000
SALES (est): 1.1MM **Privately Held**
SIC: 2752 Commercial printing, offset

(G-7159)
Z FAB USA INC
5929 S Hampshire Blvd (76112-6902)
PHONE.................................817 380-1156
Ursula Zubizarreta, *President*
Emilio Zubizarreta, *Vice Pres*
EMP: 15 **EST:** 2013
SALES (est): 1.9MM **Privately Held**
WEB: www.zfabusa.com
SIC: 3086 Plastics foam products

(G-7160)
ZIMAIR LP
Also Called: Zimair Dsplay Systems Florplan
2024 Belle Ave (76164-7616)
PHONE.................................817 624-7245
Richard Davidovich, *CEO*
Randy Rutledge, *President*
Kw Capital Southwest, *Partner*
▲ **EMP:** 56 **EST:** 1945
SQ FT: 60,000
SALES (est): 10.2MM **Privately Held**
WEB: www.zimair.com
SIC: 3496 6512 1721 Shelving, made from purchased wire; commercial & industrial building operation; painting & paper hanging

---

Fowlerton
La Salle County

(G-7161)
FOWLERTON ENERGY SERVICES LLC
Sherman Ave 110 (78021)
P.O. Box 417 (78021-0417)
PHONE.................................830 570-4507
John Barnes,
EMP: 9
SALES (est): 438.2K **Privately Held**
SIC: 1389 Gas field services; oil field services

(G-7162)
RWC MATERIAL LLC
2514 Irvin Rd (78021)
P.O. Box 366, Cotulla (78014-0366)
PHONE.................................210 219-2987
Russell Crisp, *President*
Kristy Lewis, *Admin Sec*
EMP: 10
SALES (est): 5MM **Privately Held**
SIC: 5032 3446 Gravel; open flooring & grating for construction

---

Franklin
Robertson County

(G-7163)
ANADARKO PETROLEUM CORPORATION
3436 Fm 2096 (77856-5254)
PHONE.................................979 828-1668
EMP: 24
SALES (corp-wide): 21.2B **Publicly Held**
WEB: www.oxy.com
SIC: 1311 Crude petroleum production
HQ: Anadarko Petroleum Corporation
1201 Lake Robbins Dr
The Woodlands TX 77380
832 636-1000

(G-7164)
CESSAC WELDING SERVICE INC (PA)
Also Called: Cws
13345 E Us Highway 79 (77856-4122)
P.O. Box 389 (77856-0389)
PHONE.................................979 828-9067
Alan Cessac, *President*
Sandra Cessac, *Vice Pres*
Andy Kutz, *Supervisor*
Juan Ordonez, *Supervisor*
EMP: 18
SQ FT: 1,500
SALES (est): 3.5MM **Privately Held**
WEB: www.cwsquality.com
SIC: 7692 3441 Welding repair; fabricated structural metal

Frankston

Anderson County

(G-7165)
EMERGENT MACHINE SVCS LTD CO
23628 County Road 4117 (75763-5164)
P.O. Box 1210 (75763-1210)
PHONE.................................903 876-3679
Shelly Thomas, *Principal*
Billy Wedin, *Supervisor*
EMP: 16
SALES (est): 951.3K **Privately Held**
WEB: www.emergentmfg.com
SIC: 3494 Valves & pipe fittings

(G-7166)
EMERGENT MANUFACTURING SYSTEMS
23628 County Road 4117 (75763-5164)
P.O. Box 1210 (75763-1210)
PHONE.................................903 876-3679
Ronald Thomas, *Owner*
Sagliy Thomas, *Co-Owner*
Phil Gill, *QC Mgr*
Miller Jenkins, *Prgrmr*
Aron Green,
EMP: 11
SALES (est): 1MM **Privately Held**
WEB: www.emergentmfg.com
SIC: 3949 Bows, archery

(G-7167)
LANG & MITCHELL CONTRS INC
1499 Us Highway 175 (75763-5559)
P.O. Box 42 (75763-0042)
PHONE.................................903 876-2882
EMP: 12 EST: 1972
SQ FT: 2,000
SALES (est): 2.3MM **Privately Held**
SIC: 1629 1389 Earthmoving contractor; oil field services

Fredericksburg

Gillespie County

(G-7168)
1851 VINEYARDS LLC
Also Called: Slate Mill Wine Collective
4222 S State Highway 16 (78624-9445)
PHONE.................................830 391-8510
Tim Drake,
EMP: 20
SALES (est): 671.8K **Privately Held**
WEB: www.slatemillwinecollective.com
SIC: 2084 Wine cellars, bonded: engaged in blending wines

(G-7169)
ALFRED KAGER
Also Called: Kager Industries
3168 N State Highway 16 (78624-5803)
PHONE.................................830 997-9391
Alfred Kager, *Partner*
Robert Kager, *Partner*
Brooke K Kager, *COO*
EMP: 20
SQ FT: 10,000
SALES (est): 2.6MM **Privately Held**
WEB: www.kagerind.com
SIC: 3469 Machine parts, stamped or pressed metal

(G-7170)
AUGUSTA VIN LLC
140 Augusta Vin Ln (78624-2474)
P.O. Box 3409 (78624-1934)
PHONE.................................830 307-1007
Scott Felder,
EMP: 12
SALES (est): 1.5MM **Privately Held**
WEB: www.augustavin.com
SIC: 2084 Wines

(G-7171)
BARONS CREEK VINEYARDS LLC
5963 E Us Highway 290 (78624-5787)
PHONE.................................830 304-3000
Marta Chase, *General Mgr*
Anthony Makoujy, *General Mgr*
Mark Collins, *Principal*
EMP: 10 EST: 2014
SALES (est): 842.2K **Privately Held**
WEB: www.baronscreekvineyards.com
SIC: 2084 Wines

(G-7172)
BEHRENDS FEED & FERTILIZER LLC
3599 Ranch Road 1376 (78624-4934)
PHONE.................................830 997-3410
Monroe Behrends, *Partner*
Clark Behrends, *Partner*
Scott Behrends, *Partner*
EMP: 25
SQ FT: 29,000
SALES (est): 4MM **Privately Held**
WEB: www.behrendsfeed.net
SIC: 2048 Poultry feeds; livestock feeds; feed premixes

(G-7173)
CIRCLE E CANDLES INC
4181 E Us Highway 290 (78624-5403)
PHONE.................................830 990-4478
D K Enloe, *CEO*
Thomas Enloe, *President*
Rob Davidson, *General Mgr*
Kimber Wunderlich, *Manager*
Dena Kay Enloe, *Admin Sec*
▲ EMP: 15
SQ FT: 18,000
SALES (est): 2.7MM **Privately Held**
WEB: www.circleecandles.com
SIC: 3999 Candles; potpourri

(G-7174)
COMPLETE WOODWORKS INC
895 Teague Ln (78624-6563)
P.O. Box 2387 (78624-1921)
PHONE.................................830 992-3163
Ward Johnson, *President*
EMP: 9
SQ FT: 6,000
SALES (est): 1MM **Privately Held**
SIC: 2431 Millwork

(G-7175)
D & R CUSTOM WLDG & CNSTR INC
Also Called: Dr Welding & Construction
3494 Ranch Road 1631 (78624-6052)
PHONE.................................830 997-1058
Donald Reeh, *President*
Wade Reeh, *Treasurer*
Wendy Reeh, *Admin Sec*
EMP: 26
SALES (est): 4MM **Privately Held**
WEB: www.drweldinginc.com
SIC: 3448 Farm & utility buildings; silos, metal

(G-7176)
DUNN AUTOMOTIVE SYSTEMS LLC
165 S Oak Trl (78624-5857)
PHONE.................................956 283-5544
Teresa Ground Dunn, *CEO*
EMP: 600
SALES (est): 13.4MM **Privately Held**
SIC: 3711 Automobile assembly, including specialty automobiles

(G-7177)
DUTCHMANS MARKET INC
1609 E Main St (78624-5405)
PHONE.................................830 997-5693

Barry Beyer, *President*
EMP: 14
SQ FT: 4,700
SALES (est): 1.4MM **Privately Held**
WEB: www.dutchmansmarket.com
SIC: 2013 5421 2011 Sausages & other prepared meats; meat markets, including freezer provisioners; meat packing plants

(G-7178)
FREDERICKSBURG BREWING COMPANY
245 E Main St (78624-4114)
PHONE.................................830 997-1646
Richard Estenson, *President*
EMP: 70
SQ FT: 16,000
SALES (est): 7.8MM **Privately Held**
WEB: www.yourbrewery.com
SIC: 5921 2082 7011 5812 Wine & beer; beer (alcoholic beverage); bed & breakfast inn; restaurant, family: independent

(G-7179)
FREDERICKSBURG PUBLISHING CO
Also Called: Frederckburg Stndrd-Rdio Post
712 W Main St (78624-3134)
P.O. Box 1639 (78624-1900)
PHONE.................................830 997-2155
Ken Cook, *Principal*
Alicia Trinkle, *Adv Mgr*
Beth Tucker, *Advt Staff*
Christine Granados, *Manager*
Marc Land, *Graphic Designe*
EMP: 30 EST: 1915
SQ FT: 15,000
SALES (est): 1.9MM **Privately Held**
WEB: www.fredericksburgstandard.com
SIC: 2711 Commercial printing & newspaper publishing combined; newspapers: publishing only, not printed on site

(G-7180)
GCV ENTERPRISE LLC
Also Called: Grape Creek Vineyard
10587 E Us Highway 290 (78624-7587)
P.O. Box 1068 (78624-1068)
PHONE.................................830 644-2710
E L Simes MD, *President*
Philip Hawkins, *Project Mgr*
Doug Kitchens, *Opers Staff*
Maureen Ohara, *Mktg Coord*
Patrick Goodman, *Manager*
EMP: 10
SALES (est): 377K **Privately Held**
WEB: www.grapecreek.com
SIC: 2084 7011 Wines; hotels & motels

(G-7181)
GEORGIA-PACIFIC BLDG PDTS LLC
1650 Gypsum Mine Rd (78624-6238)
PHONE.................................830 997-4341
Joe Crawford,
EMP: 12
SALES (corp-wide): 36.8B **Privately Held**
WEB: www.buildgp.com
SIC: 1499 3275 Gypsum mining; wallboard, gypsum
HQ: Georgia-Pacific Building Products Llc
133 Peachtree St Ne
Atlanta GA 30303

(G-7182)
HEARTLAND ENTERPRISES LTD
1039 Kerr Rd (78624-3042)
PHONE.................................830 997-9434
Dave Campbell, *Partner*
Jay Mallinckrodt, *Vice Pres*
Chris Magee, *Engineer*
Barbara Feller, *Office Mgr*
Clif Burch, *Executive*
EMP: 31
SQ FT: 28,000
SALES (est): 7.2MM **Privately Held**
WEB: www.heartlandmachining.com
SIC: 3563 3533 3769 3728 Air & gas compressors; oil & gas drilling rigs & equipment; guided missile & space vehicle parts & auxiliary equipment; aircraft parts & equipment

(G-7183)
INGRAM READYMIX INC
490 Fm 2093 (78624-7151)
PHONE.................................830 997-6506
Jym Chenault, *Manager*
EMP: 12
SALES (corp-wide): 125.6MM **Privately Held**
WEB: www.ingramreadymixinc.com
SIC: 3273 Ready-mixed concrete
PA: Ingram Readymix, Inc.
3580 Farm Market 482
New Braunfels TX 78132
830 625-9156

(G-7184)
JEEP COLLINS JEWELRY MAKER
2089 N Llano St (78624-2959)
PHONE.................................830 997-3135
George P Collins, *President*
Christian Collins, *Corp Secy*
Dana Collins, *Vice Pres*
Lara Collins, *Bd of Directors*
EMP: 61
SQ FT: 6,175
SALES (est): 5.1MM **Privately Held**
WEB: www.jeepcollins.com
SIC: 3911 5944 Jewelry apparel; jewelry stores

(G-7185)
KINGS LTD
Also Called: K-I Cabinets
401 S Lincoln St (78624-4502)
PHONE.................................830 990-0565
Gregory King, *Managing Prtnr*
EMP: 38
SQ FT: 10,000
SALES (est): 6MM **Privately Held**
WEB: www.kingwoodcabinets.com
SIC: 2431 Millwork

(G-7186)
ML INDUSTRIES INC (PA)
165 S Oak Trl (78624-5857)
PHONE.................................956 279-8678
Mickey T Dunn, *CEO*
Gary Dunham, *CFO*
EMP: 9
SALES (est): 723.4MM **Privately Held**
WEB: www.mlindustries.org
SIC: 2396 7389 Automotive & apparel trimmings; automotive trimmings, fabric; furniture trimmings, fabric; apparel designers, commercial

(G-7187)
QUINTESSENTIAL CHOCOLATES INC
251 W Main St (78624-3709)
P.O. Box 687 (78624-0687)
PHONE.................................830 990-9382
Lecia C Duke, *President*
EMP: 10
SALES (est): 300K **Privately Held**
WEB: www.liquidchocolates.com
SIC: 5441 2064 5149 Candy; candy & other confectionery products; chocolate

(G-7188)
RF SAW INC
1725 Old Mason Rd (78624-2346)
P.O. Box 1874 (78624-1902)
PHONE.................................469 227-0322
Clinton Hartmann, *President*
Paul Hartmann, *President*
EMP: 10
SQ FT: 12,000
SALES (est): 250K **Privately Held**
WEB: www.rfsaw.com
SIC: 3825 Radio frequency measuring equipment

(G-7189)
TELEDYNE REAL TIME SYSTEMS INC
103 Industrial Loop # 1100 (78624-5462)
PHONE.................................830 990-2340
EMP: 20
SQ FT: 7,000
SALES: 3.8MM
SALES (corp-wide): 2.3B **Publicly Held**
SIC: 3829 Measuring And Controlling Devices, Nec, N

HQ: Teledyne Bolt, Inc.
4 Duke Pl
Norwalk CT 06854
203 853-0700

Freeport
Brazoria County

(G-7190)
AIR LIQUIDE AMERICA LP
1811 Fm 523 Rd (77541-8661)
P.O. Box 2487 (77542-2487)
PHONE................................979 239-5250
Justin Bednarz, *Branch Mgr*
Bobby Hornback, *Maintence Staff*
EMP: 12
SALES (corp-wide): 129.8MM **Privately Held**
WEB: www.industry.airliquide.us
SIC: 2813 Industrial gases
HQ: Air Liquide America L.P.
9811 Katy Fwy Ste 100
Houston TX 77024
713 624-8000

(G-7191)
AMERICAN RICE INC
505 Port Rd (77541)
PHONE................................979 233-8248
Dick Schneider, *Opers-Prdtn-Mfg*
EMP: 120 **Privately Held**
SIC: 2044 Rice milling
HQ: American Rice Inc.
10700 North Fwy Ste 800
Houston TX 77037
281 272-8800

(G-7192)
BLUE CUBE OPERATIONS LLC
2301 N Brazosport Blvd (77541-3203)
PHONE................................979 238-2011
John E Fischer, *President*
Jim Varilek, *Exec VP*
Pat Dawson, *Vice Pres*
Clive Grannum, *Vice Pres*
John L McIntosh, *Vice Pres*
◆ **EMP:** 11
SALES (est): 5.2MM
SALES (corp-wide): 6.1B **Publicly Held**
SIC: 2611 Pulp mills, chemical & semi-chemical processing
PA: Olin Corporation
190 Carondelet Plz # 1530
Saint Louis MO 63105
314 480-1400

(G-7193)
BRASKEM AMERICA INC
2301 N Brazosport Blvd (77541-3203)
PHONE................................979 705-2532
EMP: 12 **Privately Held**
WEB: www.braskem.com
SIC: 2821 2865 2869 Polypropylene resins; cyclic crudes & intermediates; acetone, synthetic
HQ: Braskem America, Inc.
1735 Market St Fl 28
Philadelphia PA 19103
215 841-3100

(G-7194)
BRAZOS PIPE STL FBRICATORS INC
3135 E Highway 332 (77541-6636)
PHONE................................979 233-7895
Luca Albelice, *President*
Marla Noia, *Corp Secy*
Robby Kiefer, *Vice Pres*
Robert Kiefer III, *Vice Pres*
Leroy Kutac, *Vice Pres*
▲ **EMP:** 25
SQ FT: 2,800
SALES (est): 10MM **Privately Held**
WEB: www.brazospipe.com
SIC: 3443 3441 3312 3317 Vessels, process or storage (from boiler shops): metal plate; fabricated structural metal; blast furnaces & steel mills; steel pipe & tubes

(G-7195)
CABINETS DELUXE BY DALE INC (PA)
Also Called: Euro Tex
3232 Brazos River Rd (77541-8230)
PHONE................................512 259-2531
Robert Baxter, *President*
David Dallmeyer, *Engineer*
Linda Baxter, *Treasurer*
EMP: 55
SQ FT: 65,000
SALES (est): 5.2MM **Privately Held**
WEB: www.cabinetsdeluxe.com
SIC: 2511 2521 2517 Kitchen & dining room furniture; cabinets, office: wood; home entertainment unit cabinets, wood

(G-7196)
DOW CHEMICAL COMPANY
2301 N Brazosport Blvd (77541-3257)
PHONE................................979 238-2011
Alan Chaput, *General Mgr*
Lindsay Sosinski, *General Mgr*
Ty Berilgen, *Business Mgr*
Shian Sweeton, *Exec Officer*
Darryl Frickey, *Counsel*
EMP: 38
SALES (corp-wide): 38.5B **Publicly Held**
WEB: www.dow.com
SIC: 2819 2899 2851 2821 Industrial inorganic chemicals; chemical preparations; paints & allied products; plastics materials & resins; industrial gases; alkalies & chlorine
HQ: The Dow Chemical Company
2211 H H Dow Way
Midland MI 48642
989 636-1000

(G-7197)
DSM NUTRITIONAL PRODUCTS LLC
1000 County Road 227 A (77541-3027)
PHONE................................979 373-5010
Suzette Peel, *Purchasing*
Mark Michna, *Engineer*
Floris Fooij, *Manager*
Ashley Saenz, *Technician*
EMP: 10
SALES (corp-wide): 9.9B **Privately Held**
WEB: www.dsm.com
SIC: 2834 2836 Vitamin, nutrient & hematinic preparations for human use; veterinary biological products
HQ: Dsm Nutritional Products, Llc
45 Waterview Blvd
Parsippany NJ 07054
800 526-0189

(G-7198)
FREEPORT WELDING AND FABG INC (PA)
200 Navigation Blvd (77541-5874)
P.O. Box 2076 (77542-2076)
PHONE................................979 233-0121
Roy E Yates, *President*
Daniel L Yates, *Vice Pres*
Mike Moss, *CFO*
◆ **EMP:** 103
SQ FT: 110,000
SALES (est): 34.2MM **Privately Held**
WEB: www.freeweld.com
SIC: 3443 3441 Industrial vessels, tanks & containers; fabricated structural metal

(G-7199)
INEOS
2305 N Brazosport Blvd (77541-3203)
PHONE................................979 415-8500
Tom Crotty, *CEO*
Jim Ratcliffe, *Ch of Bd*
Todd Peltier, *Opers Staff*
Joe Montemayor, *Manager*
Luke Bryant, *Technician*
EMP: 13
SALES (est): 3.1MM **Privately Held**
WEB: www.ineos.com
SIC: 2821 Plastics materials & resins

(G-7200)
JOHN CRANE INC
115 Linda Ln (77541-7687)
PHONE................................979 239-1201
Sam Elledge, *Manager*
EMP: 11

SQ FT: 10,000
SALES (corp-wide): 3.1B **Privately Held**
WEB: www.johncrane.com
SIC: 3295 Minerals, ground or treated; lapping machines
HQ: John Crane Inc.
227 W Monroe St Ste 1800
Chicago IL 60606
312 605-7800

(G-7201)
JV INDUSTRIAL COMPANIES LTD
217 Commerce St (77541-3109)
PHONE................................979 373-0376
Scott John, *Project Mgr*
James Reynolds, *Manager*
Martha Vargas, *Consultant*
Kameron Holder, *Supervisor*
EMP: 20
SQ FT: 108,944 **Privately Held**
WEB: www.jvic.com
SIC: 3599 Machine shop, jobbing & repair
HQ: J.V. Industrial Companies, Ltd.
527 Logwood Ave
San Antonio TX 78221
713 568-2600

(G-7202)
K-BIN INC
5616 E Highway 332 (77541-3113)
PHONE................................979 233-6610
Ervin Schroeder, *President*
H Kitamura, *Vice Pres*
Yoshiko Saitoh, *Admin Sec*
◆ **EMP:** 30
SQ FT: 7,000
SALES (est): 12.9MM **Privately Held**
SIC: 2821 Plastics materials & resins
HQ: Shintech Incorporated
3 Greenway Plz Ste 1150
Houston TX 77046
713 965-0713

(G-7203)
MCGILL MAINTENANCE PARTNR LTD (PA)
Also Called: McGill Maint & Fabrication
6402 E Highway 332 (77541-3011)
P.O. Box 2521 (77542-2521)
PHONE................................979 233-5438
John K McGill, *President*
Steve Schroeter, *General Mgr*
Clifford L Guidry, *Corp Secy*
John W Woods, *Vice Pres*
Jaci Reese, *Accountant*
EMP: 130 **EST:** 1962
SQ FT: 44,160
SALES (est): 27.1MM **Privately Held**
WEB: www.mcgillmaintenance.com
SIC: 3599 1799 3443 7699 Machine shop, jobbing & repair; welding on site; fabricated plate work (boiler shop); industrial equipment services; pumps & pumping equipment repair; compressor repair

(G-7204)
MEASUREMENTATION
1744 W 4th St Ste 208 (77541-5050)
PHONE................................979 373-9991
Bill White, *Manager*
EMP: 20
SALES (est): 1.9MM **Privately Held**
SIC: 3823 Analyzers, industrial process type

(G-7205)
MIKES MACHINE WORKS INC
403 S Avenue A (77541-4709)
P.O. Box 3010 (77542-1210)
PHONE................................979 233-1257
EMP: 9
SQ FT: 2,000
SALES (est): 850K **Privately Held**
SIC: 3599 Machine shop, jobbing & repair

(G-7206)
OLIN BLUE CUBELLC
2301 N Brazosport Blvd (77541-3203)
PHONE................................979 201-1789
EMP: 10
SALES (est): 1.5MM **Privately Held**
SIC: 2869 Industrial organic chemicals

(G-7207)
PRAXAIR INC FREEPORT PSA
5619 E Highway 332 (77541-3112)
PHONE................................281 203-3682
Daniel Davison, *Plant Mgr*
EMP: 9
SALES (est): 412.5K **Privately Held**
SIC: 2813 Hydrogen

(G-7208)
S F SULPHUR COMPANY
Also Called: Stauffer/Freeport
608 E 2nd St (77541-5959)
P.O. Box 2009 (77542-2009)
PHONE................................979 233-3555
K M Watson, *Manager*
EMP: 12
SQ FT: 130,680
SALES (corp-wide): 18.7MM **Privately Held**
WEB: www.georgiagulfsulfur.com
SIC: 2819 Industrial inorganic chemicals
HQ: S F Sulphur Company
1729 Dow St
Valdosta GA 31601

(G-7209)
S G & P INCORPORATED
Also Called: Scientific Glass & Plastic
1022 N Avenue G (77541-3474)
P.O. Box 2518 (77542-2518)
PHONE................................979 233-7491
Joseph R Epps II, *President*
Christopher M Epps, *Vice Pres*
Jody Epps, *Vice Pres*
Cecile Johnson, *Manager*
▲ **EMP:** 10 **EST:** 1968
SQ FT: 12,500
SALES (est): 1.5MM **Privately Held**
WEB: www.sg-p.com
SIC: 3083 3231 Thermoplastic laminates: rods, tubes, plates & sheet; medical & laboratory glassware: made from purchased glass

(G-7210)
SHINTECH INCORPORATED
5618 E Highway 332 (77541-3198)
PHONE................................979 233-7861
Ervin E Schroeder, *Director*
EMP: 115
SQ FT: 25,000 **Privately Held**
WEB: www.shintech.com
SIC: 2821 5169 Polyvinylidene chloride resins; synthetic resins, rubber & plastic materials
HQ: Shintech Incorporated
3 Greenway Plz Ste 1150
Houston TX 77046
713 965-0713

(G-7211)
SI GROUP INC
702 Fm 523 Rd (77541-8615)
PHONE................................979 238-8000
EMP: 126
SQ FT: 87,120
SALES (corp-wide): 1.1B **Privately Held**
SIC: 2865 2869 Mfg Cyclic Crudes/Intermediates/Dyes Mfg Industrial Organic Chemicals
PA: Si Group, Inc.
2750 Balltown Rd
Schenectady NY 12309
518 347-4200

(G-7212)
SIMMONS CUSTOM BOATS LLC
800 Peach Pt (77541-9342)
PHONE................................832 864-2331
EMP: 15
SALES (est): 1.9MM **Privately Held**
WEB: www.scbboats.com
SIC: 3732 Boat building & repairing

(G-7213)
SORRELL CNSTR EQP & MTLS LLC
2101 Oyster Creek Bnd (77541-7983)
P.O. Box 2049 (77542-2049)
PHONE................................979 233-6655
Lori Sorrell, *President*
Mike Sorrell, *Vice Pres*
Don Barrett, *Project Mgr*
Eric Winstanley, *Safety Mgr*
Sunny Sorrell, *Manager*

EMP: 80
SALES (est): 11.5MM **Privately Held**
WEB: www.sorrelltx.com
SIC: 4212 1442 1795 5032 Local trucking, without storage; construction sand & gravel; demolition, buildings & other structures; stone, crushed or broken

(G-7214)
STANCO MARINE INC
1201 E Brazos St (77541-5956)
P.O. Box 3184 (77542-1384)
PHONE..................................979 233-1614
Jeff Stanley, *President*
Marc Jordan, *Vice Pres*
John Hoss, *Sales Executive*
EMP: 12
SALES (est): 617.2K **Privately Held**
SIC: 1389 Oil field services

(G-7215)
THERIOT INC
315 E Park St (77541-5935)
PHONE..................................979 233-6391
Ronald Theriot Jr, *President*
Ronald Theriot Sr, *Vice Pres*
Julie Theriot, *Treasurer*
EMP: 21
SQ FT: 5,000
SALES (est): 2.1MM **Privately Held**
WEB: www.theriotinc.com
SIC: 3499 3444 Metal household articles; ducts, sheet metal

(G-7216)
TOP COAT INC
9720 Hwy 36 (77541)
P.O. Box 3305 (77542-1505)
PHONE..................................979 233-9558
Kenneth Hayes, *President*
Jason Hayes, *General Mgr*
Donna Hayes, *Vice Pres*
Jeff Smirch, *Manager*
EMP: 30
SQ FT: 60,000
SALES: 8.7MM **Privately Held**
WEB: www.topcoatfab.com
SIC: 1382 1721 Oil & gas exploration services; industrial painting

(G-7217)
TRI-CONSTRUCTION CO INC
5550 E Highway 332 (77541-3111)
P.O. Box 3100 (77542-1300)
PHONE..................................979 233-7211
Kyle Nairn, *Facilities Mgr*
Lisa Bundick Cobler, *CFO*
Barbara Bundick, *Director*
Carol Bundick, *Director*
Darren Bundick, *Director*
EMP: 130 EST: 1971
SQ FT: 27,450
SALES (est): 19.9MM **Privately Held**
WEB: www.abctxgulfcoast.org
SIC: 1629 7692 3444 3441 Industrial plant construction; welding repair; sheet metalwork; fabricated structural metal; general contractor, highway & street construction; concrete work

(G-7218)
VENATOR CHEMICALS LLC
Mineral Research & Development
302 Midway Rd (77541)
PHONE..................................979 233-8183
EMP: 18
SALES (corp-wide): 6.8B **Publicly Held**
WEB: www.mrdc.com
SIC: 2819 Industrial inorganic chemicals
HQ: Venator Chemicals Llc
5910 Pharr Mill Rd
Harrisburg NC 28075
704 455-4135

(G-7219)
VENCOREX US INC (DH)
Also Called: Vencorex Holding France
6213 E Highway 332 (77541-3006)
PHONE..................................979 233-7871
Shane E Steelman, *President*
David Wolf, *President*
Shaw Norma, *Purch Mgr*
Patrick Miller, *Engineer*
Faul Skierski, *Treasurer*
▲ EMP: 50

SALES (est): 16.9MM
SALES (corp-wide): 436.8MM **Privately Held**
WEB: www.vencorex.com
SIC: 2869 Industrial organic chemicals
HQ: Vencorex Holding
196 Allee Alexandre Borodine
St Priest 69800
426 223-805

(G-7220)
VENCOREX US INC
Perstorp Coatings
6213 E Highway 332 (77541-3006)
PHONE..................................979 233-7871
Tomas Hagstrom, *Principal*
EMP: 42
SALES (corp-wide): 436.8MM **Privately Held**
WEB: www.vencorex.com
SIC: 2869 Industrial organic chemicals
HQ: Vencorex Us, Inc.
6213 E Highway 332
Freeport TX 77541

(G-7221)
VERNOR MATERIAL & EQP CO INC
Also Called: VME
545 County Road 227a (77541-3039)
P.O. Box 967, Clute (77531-0967)
PHONE..................................409 233-3366
Kenny Vernor, *President*
Wayne Pavlu, *Superintendent*
Jeremy Vernor, *Corp Secy*
Randall Vernor, *Vice Pres*
George Rodriguez, *Opers Mgr*
EMP: 85
SQ FT: 6,000
SALES (est): 33.2MM **Privately Held**
WEB: www.vernor.com
SIC: 1611 1795 0782 7353 Highway & street construction; wrecking & demolition work; mowing services, lawn; heavy construction equipment rental; local trucking, without storage; sand mining

Freer
Duval County

(G-7222)
BAKER PETROLITE LLC
Hwy 59 N (78357)
PHONE..................................361 394-7544
Mark Fisher, *Manager*
EMP: 17 **Privately Held**
WEB: www.bakerhughesdirect.lookchem.com
SIC: 1389 Oil field services
HQ: Baker Petrolite Llc
12645 W Airport Blvd
Sugar Land TX 77478
281 276-5400

(G-7223)
DUVAL WELL SERVICE INC
Us Hwy 59 Ne (78357)
P.O. Box 360 (78357-0360)
PHONE..................................361 394-7079
EMP: 35 EST: 2000
SALES (est): 5.1MM **Privately Held**
SIC: 1389 Oil/Gas Field Services

(G-7224)
FINO OILFIELD SERVICES CORP
5109 Highway 44 (78357-1270)
P.O. Box 1806 (78357-1806)
PHONE..................................361 394-7700
Cesar Rivera, *President*
Alfredo Cantu, *President*
EMP: 50
SALES (est): 4.2MM **Privately Held**
SIC: 2819 Chemicals, high purity: refined from technical grade

(G-7225)
FREER IRON WORKS INC
202 N Norton St (78357-1983)
P.O. Box 330, Kenedy (78119-0330)
PHONE..................................361 394-7273
Jesus Rudy Casas, *President*
Ann Casas, *Vice Pres*
EMP: 22 EST: 1931
SQ FT: 3,500

SALES (est): 458K **Privately Held**
SIC: 7692 3599 7629 3533 Welding repair; machine shop, jobbing & repair; electrical repair shops; oil & gas field machinery; installing building equipment

(G-7226)
H & K WELL SERVICE LLC
2762 Cr 409 (78357)
P.O. Box 1778 (78357-1778)
PHONE..................................361 394-7165
Jamie Whitley,
Kenneth Whitley,
EMP: 13
SALES (est): 1MM **Privately Held**
SIC: 1381 Service well drilling

(G-7227)
HERNANDEZ SANDBLASTING
4957 County Road 403 (78357-1670)
P.O. Box 1534 (78357-1534)
PHONE..................................361 701-2522
Tiberio Hernandez, *Owner*
EMP: 12
SALES (est): 241K **Privately Held**
SIC: 1389 Oil field services

(G-7228)
HIGH TIDE OILFIELD SVCS LLC
5109 Highway 44 E (78357-1947)
P.O. Box 1657 (78357-1657)
PHONE..................................361 394-1731
EMP: 9
SALES (est): 864.4K **Privately Held**
SIC: 1389 Oil field services

(G-7229)
KILLAM OIL CO LTD
3 Miles W Of Hwy 59 (78357)
P.O. Box 1760 (78357-1760)
PHONE..................................361 394-7680
Ron Richardson, *General Mgr*
EMP: 28
SALES (corp-wide): 41.7K **Privately Held**
WEB: www.killamoil.com
SIC: 1382 Oil & gas exploration services
PA: Killam Oil Co., Ltd.
4320 University Blvd
Laredo TX 78041
956 724-7141

(G-7230)
L T D EXPLORATIONS INC
690 N Highway 16 (78357-1240)
P.O. Box 4199, Alice (78333-4199)
PHONE..................................361 664-9108
Larry T Donaho, *President*
Debbie Donaho, *Admin Sec*
EMP: 9
SALES (est): 600K **Privately Held**
SIC: 1311 Crude petroleum & natural gas

(G-7231)
NEWMAN OPERATING CO
5002 Highway 44 E (78357-0788)
P.O. Box 448 (78357-0448)
PHONE..................................361 394-5516
Robert L Newman, *President*
Norman Newman, *Vice Pres*
EMP: 75
SALES (est): 17.1MM **Privately Held**
WEB: www.newmanoperating.com
SIC: 1311 Crude petroleum production

(G-7232)
SOUTH TEXAS OILFIELD SVCS LLC
5115 Hwy 59 (78357)
P.O. Box 353 (78357-0353)
PHONE..................................361 701-7064
Kathy Soto, *Mng Member*
EMP: 74
SALES (est): 1.2MM **Privately Held**
SIC: 1389 Oil field services

(G-7233)
STRAIGHT LINE CONSTRUCTION INC (PA)
5115 N Hwy 59 (78357)
PHONE..................................361 394-7656
Joe P Garza, *President*
Annie Perez, *Executive*
Rox-Anne Guajardo, *Teacher*
Analisa Garcia, *Education*
Mary Alice Cantu, *Nurse*

EMP: 47
SQ FT: 1,800
SALES (est): 79.7MM **Privately Held**
WEB: www.straightlineconst.org
SIC: 1389 1611 Oil field services; general contractor, highway & street construction

(G-7234)
SUPER-TECH HVAC LLC
Also Called: S & S Hvac
611 Huisache St (78357-1740)
PHONE..................................361 394-5549
Jorge Salinas, *Mng Member*
EMP: 11
SALES (est): 1.9MM **Privately Held**
SIC: 3822 Air conditioning & refrigeration controls

(G-7235)
XYTEX INC
690 N Highway 16 (78357-1240)
P.O. Box 536 (78357-0536)
PHONE..................................361 394-5524
Larry Donaho, *President*
EMP: 10
SALES (est): 480K **Privately Held**
WEB: www.xytex.com
SIC: 1389 Oil field services

Fresno
Fort Bend County

(G-7236)
51 HOME TECHNOLOGIES LLC
2531 Harpers Creek Ct (77545-6075)
P.O. Box 1875 (77545-1626)
PHONE..................................713 589-5747
Ronnie Bullock,
EMP: 11
SQ FT: 2,671
SALES (est): 1.1MM **Privately Held**
SIC: 3651 Household audio & video equipment

(G-7237)
FRESNO MANFACTURING LLC
810 Fm 521 Rd (77545-8213)
P.O. Box 99 (77545-0099)
PHONE..................................281 437-6000
Robert Wehman, *President*
▲ EMP: 75
SALES (est): 32.6K **Publicly Held**
SIC: 3086 Insulation or cushioning material, foamed plastic
HQ: Pittsburgh Corning, Llc
1 Owens Corning Pkwy
Toledo OH 43659
724 327-6100

(G-7238)
HEFCO ENTERPRISES INC
3523 Fm 521 Rd (77545-7925)
P.O. Box 330 (77545-0330)
PHONE..................................281 431-1571
Jim Dudley Sr, *President*
Forest R Dudley, *Vice Pres*
Ray Dudley Jr, *Vice Pres*
Adam Jones, *Manager*
Robert Wharton, *Shareholder*
EMP: 50
SALES (est): 7.9MM **Privately Held**
WEB: www.hefco.com
SIC: 7692 3441 Welding repair; building components, structural steel

(G-7239)
HERBAL ESSENTIALS LLC
3435 Dartmouth Field Ln (77545-7004)
PHONE..................................832 439-3114
John Vasquez, *Manager*
EMP: 10
SALES (est): 409.5K **Privately Held**
WEB: www.herbal-essentials.com
SIC: 2899 Essential oils

(G-7240)
PITTSBURGH CORNING LLC
Also Called: Fresno Manufacturing
810 Fm 521 Rd (77545-8213)
PHONE..................................281 437-6000
Robert Wehman, *Branch Mgr*
EMP: 18 **Publicly Held**
WEB: www.foamglas.com
SIC: 3296 Mineral wool

HQ: Pittsburgh Corning, Llc
1 Owens Corning Pkwy
Toledo OH 43659
724 327-6100

Friendswood
Galveston County

(G-7241)
AAA BLAST-COTE INC
14302 Beamer Rd (77546-2204)
PHONE.....................281 482-1236
Kenneth E Crockett, *President*
Gary Gaston, *Vice Pres*
Monica Lopez, *Office Mgr*
Joe Landa, *Manager*
EMP: 20
SQ FT: 65,000
SALES (est): 2.7MM **Privately Held**
WEB: www.aaablastcote.com
SIC: 3479 3471 Coating of metals & formed products; plating & polishing

(G-7242)
CASTLE BIOSCIENCES INC
820 S Friendswood Dr # 20 (77546-4591)
PHONE.....................866 788-9007
Daniel M Bradbury, *Ch of Bd*
Derek J Maetzold, *President*
Bernhard E Spiess, *COO*
Kristen Oelschlager, *Senior VP*
Robert W Cook, *Vice Pres*
EMP: 96
SQ FT: 4,195
SALES (est): 51.8MM **Privately Held**
WEB: www.castlebiosciences.com
SIC: 2835 8071 In vitro & in vivo diagnostic substances; medical laboratories

(G-7243)
CHESTER R WRIGHT III
Also Called: Commercial Eqp Specialist
3104 Tyler Ct (77546-5675)
PHONE.....................832 693-8038
Chester R Wright III, *Owner*
Leanne Wright, *Co-Owner*
EMP: 11
SQ FT: 1,400
SALES (est): 251.5K **Privately Held**
SIC: 7694 7629 Motor repair services; vacuum cleaner repair

(G-7244)
CUSTOM SAFETY PRODUCTS INC
1030 County Rd 129 (77546)
P.O. Box 833 (77549-0833)
PHONE.....................281 482-8668
Kendall Kichen, *President*
Alyssah Jillett, *Vice Pres*
Kinchen Kendall, *Vice Pres*
Dan Gloger, *Opers Mgr*
Andy Kimball, *Opers Mgr*
EMP: 10
SQ FT: 3,500
SALES (est): 1.7MM **Privately Held**
WEB: www.customsafetyproducts.com
SIC: 3496 Mats & matting

(G-7245)
CYPRESS INDUSTRIES OILFIELD SE
1302 Buttonwood Dr (77546-5269)
P.O. Box 880 (77549-0880)
PHONE.....................281 482-3464
Edward Chamrad, *President*
EMP: 10
SALES (est): 101K **Privately Held**
WEB: www.cypressoilfield.com
SIC: 3999 Manufacturing industries

(G-7246)
ISO-TEX DIAGNOSTICS INC
1511 County Rd 129 (77546)
PHONE.....................281 482-1231
Thomas J Maloney, *President*
EMP: 10
SQ FT: 29,800
SALES (est): 1.8MM **Privately Held**
WEB: www.isotexdiagnostics.com
SIC: 2834 Pharmaceutical preparations

(G-7247)
JT OILFILED MANUFACTURING CO (PA)
1882 Flat Rock St (77546-5476)
P.O. Box 750459, Houston (77275-0459)
PHONE.....................713 947-7006
Tom Mooney, *President*
Leona Mooney, *Vice Pres*
EMP: 24
SALES (est): 3.9MM **Privately Held**
WEB: www.jtoilfield.com
SIC: 3533 Oil field machinery & equipment

(G-7248)
LOCKHEED MARTIN CORPORATION
4943 Mountain Timber Dr (77546-7910)
PHONE.....................281 335-2318
EMP: 473 **Publicly Held**
WEB: www.lockheedmartin.com
SIC: 3812 Search & navigation equipment
PA: Lockheed Martin Corporation
6801 Rockledge Dr
Bethesda MD 20817

(G-7249)
LONE STAR COMPRESSOR CORP
316 Old Course Dr (77546-5637)
PHONE.....................713 947-9975
Fax: 713 947-9978
EMP: 20 EST: 1978
SQ FT: 6,000
SALES (est): 4.9MM **Privately Held**
SIC: 3563 Mfg Air/Gas Compressors

(G-7250)
TEX ISO INC
Also Called: ISO Tex Diagnostics
1511 County Rd 129 (77546)
P.O. Box 909 (77549-0909)
PHONE.....................281 482-1231
EMP: 15 EST: 1974
SQ FT: 29,500
SALES (est): 3.2MM **Privately Held**
WEB: www.isotexdiagnostics.com
SIC: 2834 Solutions, pharmaceutical

Friona
Parmer County

(G-7251)
CAMPBELL TRAILERS & LEASING
Also Called: American Canvas
1106 W 11th St (79035-1650)
PHONE.....................806 250-3611
Randy Campbell, *President*
Debra Campbell, *Vice Pres*
EMP: 10
SQ FT: 12,000
SALES (est): 904.7K **Privately Held**
SIC: 2394 7539 4213 Tarpaulins, fabric: made from purchased materials; trailer repair; heavy hauling

(G-7252)
CARGILL MEAT SOLUTIONS CORP
Also Called: Friona Division Beef Plant
4 Miles W Hgwy60 Ste 60 (79035)
P.O. Box 579 (79035-0579)
PHONE.....................806 295-8393
Jamina Hipps, *Branch Mgr*
EMP: 20
SALES (corp-wide): 113.4B **Privately Held**
WEB: www.cargill.com
SIC: 2011 Meat packing plants
HQ: Cargill Meat Solutions Corp
151 N Main St Ste 900
Wichita KS 67202
316 291-2500

(G-7253)
CARGILL MEAT SOLUTIONS CORP
1530 W Us Highway 60 (79035-1658)
PHONE.....................806 295-8243
Jarrod Gillig, *Branch Mgr*
EMP: 15

SALES (corp-wide): 113.4B **Privately Held**
WEB: www.cargill.com
SIC: 5147 2011 Meats & meat products; beef products from beef slaughtered on site
HQ: Cargill Meat Solutions Corp
151 N Main St Ste 900
Wichita KS 67202
316 291-2500

(G-7254)
TREVINOS WELDING
701 W 11th St (79035-1747)
PHONE.....................806 250-3669
Johnny Trevino, *Owner*
EMP: 12
SALES (est): 405K **Privately Held**
WEB: www.twm-friona.com
SIC: 7692 Welding repair

Frisco
Collin County

(G-7255)
4693057371
9300 John Hickman Pkwy (75035-5711)
PHONE.....................469 305-7371
Aucencio Rodriguez, *CEO*
EMP: 15
SALES (est): 538.1K **Privately Held**
SIC: 3272 Floor slabs & tiles, precast concrete

(G-7256)
BBA&J&V INC
11625 Custer Rd 110-20 (75035-8783)
PHONE.....................469 998-0660
Bogdan Alexe, *CEO*
EMP: 10
SALES (est): 240K **Privately Held**
SIC: 2599 Food wagons, restaurant

(G-7257)
DOLAN NORTHWEST LLC
Also Called: Meletio Lighting and Elec Sup
4855 Ohio Dr (75035-7381)
PHONE.....................972 559-6900
David Meletio, *Principal*
EMP: 41
SQ FT: 4,500 **Privately Held**
WEB: www.globelighting.com
SIC: 3645 3699 5063 5719 Residential lighting fixtures; electrical equipment & supplies; electrical apparatus & equipment; lighting, lamps & accessories
PA: Dolan Northwest Llc
1919 Nw 19th Ave
Portland OR 97209

(G-7258)
EGANA OF SWITZERLAND (AMERICA)
Also Called: Eganagoldpfeil USA
10810 Spring Lake Rd (75035-8475)
PHONE.....................972 839-2808
Daniel Blunschi, *President*
▲ EMP: 12
SQ FT: 5,000
SALES (est): 7MM **Privately Held**
SIC: 5094 3873 Clocks, watches & parts; watches, clocks, watchcases & parts
PA: Eganagoldpfeil (Holdings) Ltd
C/O: The Harbour Trust Co. Ltd
George Town GR CAYMAN

(G-7259)
GREENBASKET INC
Also Called: Omnisling
14679 Maroon Bells Ln (75035-0262)
PHONE.....................212 203-3302
Venugopal Reddy, *President*
Gururaj Kulkarni, *Bd of Directors*
EMP: 20
SALES (est): 896.6K **Privately Held**
WEB: www.gogreenbasket.com
SIC: 7372 7389 Prepackaged software;

(G-7260)
LUMA VUE INC
11625 Custer Rd Ste 150 (75035-8795)
PHONE.....................214 842-8347
EMP: 33

SALES (corp-wide): 4.4MM **Privately Held**
SIC: 3993 Mfg Signs/Advertising Specialties
PA: Luma Vue, Inc.
1724 Se Moberly Ln
Bentonville AR 72712
479 271-7550

(G-7261)
MOTHERS JOURNEY INC
15922 Eldorado Pkwy # 50 (75035-5836)
PHONE.....................877 279-7975
Carlton Ellis, *CEO*
Jennifer Gore, *Opers Staff*
Kandace Ellis, *CFO*
Wilton Gore, *Director*
Rebertha Pope-Matthews, *Director*
EMP: 10
SALES (est): 488.8K **Privately Held**
SIC: 2833 5499 Drugs & herbs: grading, grinding & milling; spices & herbs

(G-7262)
NEW ERA SOLUTIONS INTL LLC
Also Called: Nes International
6686 Simon Ave (75035-4411)
PHONE.....................972 360-6112
EMP: 20
SALES (est): 3.1MM **Privately Held**
SIC: 3577 5065 3572 Mfg Computer Storage Dvc Mfg Computer Peripherals Whol Electronic Parts

(G-7263)
REDI-MIX LP
14800 State Highway 121 (75035-4603)
PHONE.....................972 335-2060
Tim Vaughn, *Vice Pres*
Pete Hebert, *Sales Mgr*
Steve Barton, *Branch Mgr*
EMP: 30
SALES (corp-wide): 1.4B **Publicly Held**
SIC: 3273 Ready-mixed concrete
HQ: Redi-Mix Lp
1445 Mac Arthur Dr # 136
Carrollton TX 75007
972 242-4550

(G-7264)
SPOTTED DOG PRINTING INC
14648 Snowshill Dr (75035-7232)
PHONE.....................972 234-4391
Toni Wilson, *Branch Mgr*
EMP: 20
SALES (corp-wide): 2.1MM **Privately Held**
WEB: www.alphagraphics.com
SIC: 2752 Commercial printing, lithographic
PA: Spotted Dog Printing, Inc.
1750 Alma Rd Ste 118
Richardson TX 75081
972 234-3033

Frisco
Denton County

(G-7265)
ACESCHEM INC
5454 Surrey Path Ste 205 (75034-9582)
PHONE.....................817 863-6948
Yuebiao Jing, *CEO*
EMP: 10
SALES (est): 409.5K **Privately Held**
SIC: 2819 Chemicals, reagent grade: refined from technical grade

(G-7266)
ARGON MEDICAL DEVICES INC (HQ)
2600 Dallas Pkwy Ste 440 (75034-8128)
PHONE.....................903 675-9321
Mike Hudson, *President*
Belynda Daniel, *General Mgr*
Tommy Sawyer, *Principal*
Kurt Baltutat, *Vice Pres*
Christian Chilcott, *Vice Pres*
◆ EMP: 277
SQ FT: 145,000

▲ = Import ▼=Export
◆ =Import/Export

SALES (est): 83.7MM
SALES (corp-wide): 240.9MM **Privately Held**
WEB: www.argonmedical.com
SIC: 3845 3842 3841 Electromedical equipment; surgical appliances & supplies; surgical & medical instruments
PA: Roundtable Healthcare Partners, Lp
272 E Deerpath Ste 350
Lake Forest IL 60045
847 739-3200

(G-7267)
AVATAR SYSTEMS INC (PA)
2801 Network Blvd Ste 210 (75034-1940)
PHONE..................................972 720-1800
Robert Charles Shreve, *Ch of Bd*
Jo A Loftin, *Opers Staff*
Eric Wood, *Opers Staff*
Scott White, *Sales Staff*
Kellie Williams, *Sales Staff*
EMP: 29
SQ FT: 6,192
SALES (est): 4.3MM **Privately Held**
WEB: www.avatarsystems.net
SIC: 7372 Prepackaged software

(G-7268)
AVATAR SYSTEMS INC
2801 Network Blvd Ste 210 (75034-1940)
PHONE..................................972 334-0162
EMP: 15
SALES (est): 504.3K **Privately Held**
SIC: 7372 Prepackaged Software Services

(G-7269)
B & J ACCESSORIES INC
Also Called: Isabel/B & J
5068 Lakehill Blvd (75034-6640)
PHONE..................................972 494-6939
Isabel Sky, *President*
Yefim Sky, *Vice Pres*
◆ **EMP:** 25
SALES (est): 2.4MM **Privately Held**
SIC: 2339 Sportswear, women's

(G-7270)
BKBL HOLDINGS LTD (PA)
Also Called: Quest Drape
2591 Dallas Pkwy Ste 201 (75034-8543)
PHONE..................................214 436-4161
Lee Dunlap, *CEO*
Bobby Lutz, *Partner*
Joshua Hall, *General Mgr*
Patrick Loia, *General Mgr*
Justin Murray, *General Mgr*
▲ **EMP:** 15
SALES (est): 19.8MM **Privately Held**
WEB: www.questevents.com
SIC: 2391 Curtains & draperies

(G-7271)
BLADE ENERGY PARTNERS LTD (PA)
2600 Network Blvd Ste 550 (75034-6036)
PHONE..................................972 712-8407
Sriram Vasantharajan, *President*
Charlie Leslie, *Partner*
Thiago Dasilva, *Technology*
Ravi Krishnamurthy, *Director*
EMP: 43
SALES (est): 15.7MM **Privately Held**
WEB: www.blade-energy.com
SIC: 1382 Oil & gas exploration services

(G-7272)
CDM SOFTWARE SOLUTIONS INC
2591 Dallas Pkwy Ste 300 (75034-8563)
PHONE..................................972 469-3082
Darrell Ortiz, *CEO*
EMP: 47
SALES (est): 7.6MM **Privately Held**
WEB: www.cdmsoft.com
SIC: 7371 7372 7373 Computer software development; application computer software; systems software development services; systems engineering, computer related

(G-7273)
COMSTOCK OIL & GAS LLC (HQ)
Also Called: Comstock Oil & Gas, LP
5300 Twn Cntry Blvd (75034-6894)
PHONE..................................972 668-8800
M Jay Allison, *Partner*
Roland O Burns, *Partner*
Gary Guyton, *Planning*
Tami Ross, *Analyst*
EMP: 45
SQ FT: 6,000
SALES (est): 43.5MM
SALES (corp-wide): 768.6MM **Publicly Held**
WEB: www.comstockresources.com
SIC: 1311 Crude petroleum production; natural gas production
PA: Comstock Resources, Inc.
5300 Twn Cntry Blvd # 500
Frisco TX 75034
972 668-8800

(G-7274)
COMSTOCK RESOURCES INC (PA)
5300 Twn Cntry Blvd # 500 (75034-6892)
PHONE..................................972 668-8800
M Jay Allison, *CEO*
Roland O Burns, *President*
Dale Gillette, *Vice Pres*
Dan Harrison, *Vice Pres*
Daniel Harrison, *Vice Pres*
EMP: 74 **EST:** 1919
SQ FT: 66,382
SALES (est): 768.6MM **Publicly Held**
WEB: www.crkfrisco.com
SIC: 1311 Crude petroleum production; natural gas production

(G-7275)
CORNERSTONE ATOMTN SYSTEMS LLC
Also Called: Casi
10601 Clarence Dr Ste 100 (75033-3866)
PHONE..................................972 346-2242
Thomas Karol, *CEO*
Matt Ramon, *Vice Pres*
Jackie Bonakadar, *Mfg Staff*
Kevin Beattie, *CFO*
Jackie Taylor, *Human Resources*
EMP: 75
SALES (est): 16MM **Privately Held**
WEB: www.casiusa.com
SIC: 8742 7372 Automation & robotics consultant; utility computer software

(G-7276)
COVEY PARK II LLC (PA)
5300 Twn Cntry Blvd # 500 (75034-6892)
PHONE..................................214 548-6000
Katy McLeod, *Finance Dir*
Pricilla Benitez, *Accounts Mgr*
Craig Smith, *Technology*
Kelsi Sorelle, *Information Mgr*
EMP: 64
SALES (est): 200MM **Privately Held**
SIC: 1311 Natural gas production

(G-7277)
CURTIS MATHES INC (PA)
Also Called: Curtis Mathes International
6201 Tech Dr Ste 106 (75033)
PHONE..................................888 725-0309
Erik Hill, *CEO*
Michael Chester, *President*
Mike Piazza, *COO*
Paul Williams, *CFO*
Edwin Pang, *CTO*
◆ **EMP:** 12 **EST:** 2013
SQ FT: 4,000
SALES (est): 4.5MM **Privately Held**
WEB: www.curtismathesstore.com
SIC: 3674 3663 Light emitting diodes; radio & TV communications equipment

(G-7278)
DAIRY LLC (HQ)
Also Called: Dairy.com
3801 Parkwood Blvd # 300 (75034-8649)
PHONE..................................214 442-5928
Scott Sexton, *CEO*
Jon Cunningham, *COO*
Eric Dennis, *Vice Pres*
Jim Boykin, *Sales Staff*

Matthew Denecke, *Manager*
EMP: 25 **EST:** 2000
SQ FT: 11,500
SALES (est): 4.8MM
SALES (corp-wide): 5.4MM **Privately Held**
SIC: 7372 7374 7371 Application computer software; data processing & preparation; custom computer programming services
PA: Momentx Corporation
3801 Parkwood Blvd # 300
Frisco TX 75034
214 360-0061

(G-7279)
DALLAS GOURMET BAKERY INC (PA)
Also Called: Dallas Bakery
3766 Summit Ct (75034-6306)
PHONE..................................972 247-9835
Mark Molter, *President*
EMP: 10
SALES (est): 1.5MM **Privately Held**
WEB: www.netgear.com
SIC: 2051 Breads, rolls & buns

(G-7280)
DEKA TEXAS INC
8000 Dallas Pkwy (75034-4057)
PHONE..................................214 618-1176
Ken Alvarez, *President*
EMP: 20
SALES (est): 2.2MM **Privately Held**
WEB: www.dekatexas.com
SIC: 3544 3565 Forms (molds), for foundry & plastics working machinery; packaging machinery

(G-7281)
ECONOMIC TRNSFRMTION TECH CORP
Also Called: Ett
1 Cowboys Way Ste 575 (75034-2025)
PHONE..................................253 332-7362
Greg Carson, *Principal*
Brittany Burtz, *Principal*
EMP: 12
SALES (est): 68.4K **Privately Held**
WEB: www.skylab.world
SIC: 7372 Application computer software

(G-7282)
ENERGY EXCHANGE 3 LP
Also Called: Emk3
1415 Legacy Dr Ste 220 (75034-6025)
PHONE..................................972 668-6601
Gary Wittsche, *President*
Terry Coulter, *Vice Pres*
William Wittsche, *CTO*
EMP: 12
SALES (est): 151.2K **Privately Held**
SIC: 7372 Prepackaged software

(G-7283)
EPIC SOURCE FOOD COMPANY LLC
Also Called: Bonsavor Foods
7158 Main St (75033-4225)
P.O. Box 2244 (75034-0041)
PHONE..................................214 407-7154
Fernando Gomez, *CEO*
Fernando Jimenez Gomez, *Ch of Bd*
Kari Thibeault, *Controller*
Gayle Franks, *Marketing Staff*
EMP: 13
SALES (est): 2.9MM **Privately Held**
WEB: www.epicsourcefoods.com
SIC: 2051 2024 Bakery products, partially cooked (except frozen); ice cream & frozen desserts

(G-7284)
EXIDE TECHNOLOGIES
7471 5th St (75034-5047)
P.O. Box 250 (75034-0005)
PHONE..................................972 335-2121
EMP: 130
SALES (corp-wide): 2.8B **Publicly Held**
SIC: 3341 Secondary Nonferrous Metal Producer

PA: Exide Technologies
13000 Deerfield Pkwy # 200
Milton GA 30004
678 566-9000

(G-7285)
FALCHION PUBLICATIONS LLC
3635 Navarro Way (75034-8444)
PHONE..................................214 244-9645
Bradley Glenn Reynolds,
EMP: 12
SALES (est): 100K **Privately Held**
SIC: 2721 Magazines: publishing only, not printed on site

(G-7286)
FORTIS FOODS INTERNATIONAL LP
2591 Dallas Pkwy Ste 103 (75034-8543)
PHONE..................................214 472-6400
Rhod Williams, *Managing Prtnr*
Steve Winkler, *Managing Prtnr*
Katty Santana, *Purchasing*
◆ **EMP:** 40
SQ FT: 5,000
SALES (est): 11.5MM **Privately Held**
WEB: www.fortisfoods.com
SIC: 2013 Cooked meats from purchased meat

(G-7287)
GEARBOX PUBLISHING LLC
5757 Main St Ste 500 (75034-3262)
PHONE..................................972 312-8202
Randall S Pitchford II,
Stephen Bahl,
Steve Gibson, *Publishing*
EMP: 75
SALES (est): 1.1MM **Privately Held**
WEB: www.gearboxpublishing.com
SIC: 7372 Operating systems computer software

(G-7288)
GENUINE LETTERPRESS INC
40 Clear Pond Dr (75034-8581)
PHONE..................................214 748-8215
Scott Beavan, *President*
EMP: 50
SQ FT: 30,750
SALES (est): 5.2MM **Privately Held**
SIC: 2759 Letterpress printing

(G-7289)
GRACO FISHING & RENTAL TLS INC (PA)
Also Called: Graco Oilfield Services
5300 Town And Cntry Blvd (75034-6894)
PHONE..................................214 618-3930
Dan Rambo, *CEO*
Jonathan E Rambo, *President*
Mark Mixon, *COO*
Mark Eason, *Vice Pres*
Jason Rambo, *Vice Pres*
EMP: 19
SALES (est): 25.6MM **Privately Held**
WEB: www.gracooilfieldservices.com
SIC: 1389 Oil field services

(G-7290)
HOBBY LOBBY STORES INC
5550 Preston Rd (75034-7418)
PHONE..................................214 872-3184
EMP: 18
SALES (corp-wide): 2.3B **Privately Held**
WEB: www.hobbylobby.com
SIC: 2392 Household furnishings
PA: Hobby Lobby Stores, Inc.
7707 Sw 44th St
Oklahoma City OK 73179
405 745-1100

(G-7291)
HOLDINGCROSS
Also Called: Holdingcross.com
3245 Main St Ste 235 (75034-4412)
PHONE..................................214 705-6502
Jack Scott, *Owner*
EMP: 15
SALES (est): 1MM **Privately Held**
WEB: www.holdingcross.com
SIC: 2861 Wood distillation products

(G-7292)
IMAGINE COMMUNICATIONS CORP (HQ)
3001 Dallas Pkwy Ste 300 (75034-8639)
PHONE..............................469 803-4900
Tom Cotney, *CEO*
Jack Brickey, *President*
Steve Foreman, *President*
Pablo Gargiulo, *President*
Hal York, *Business Mgr*
EMP: 70 **EST:** 1995
SALES (est): 462.2MM
SALES (corp-wide): 2.7B **Privately Held**
WEB: www.imaginecommunications.com
SIC: 4899 3663 Data communication services; radio broadcasting & communications equipment; television broadcasting & communications equipment
PA: The Gores Group Llc
9800 Wilshire Blvd
Beverly Hills CA 90212
310 209-3010

(G-7293)
JF CONSTRUCTION INC
1801 Mccord Way Apt 715 (75033-1143)
P.O. Box 800847, Balch Springs (75180-0847)
PHONE..............................214 272-1902
Jimmy Flores, *President*
EMP: 33 **EST:** 1985
SQ FT: 3,200
SALES (est): 8.9MM **Privately Held**
SIC: 1381 1623 Directional drilling oil & gas wells; oil & gas pipeline construction

(G-7294)
KABA ILCO CORP
5750 Genesis Ct Ste 150 (75034-4167)
PHONE..............................972 668-7996
George K Broady, *Chairman*
EMP: 400
SALES (corp-wide): 2.7B **Privately Held**
WEB: www.ilco.us
SIC: 3429 Keys, locks & related hardware
HQ: Kaba Ilco Corp.
400 Jeffreys Rd
Rocky Mount NC 27804
252 446-3321

(G-7295)
KATHREIN BROADCAST USA INC
5 Cowboys Way Ste 300 (75034-2074)
PHONE..............................541 879-2300
Marc Dunham, *CEO*
EMP: 25
SALES (est): 3.2MM
SALES (corp-wide): 418.9K **Privately Held**
WEB: www.kathreinusa.com
SIC: 3663 Radio & TV communications equipment
HQ: Kathrein Broadcast Gmbh
Ing.-Anton-Kathrein-Str. 1-7
Rohrdorf 83101
803 161-9310

(G-7296)
KLOUDNATION LLC
2611 Internet Blvd # 109 (75034-9085)
PHONE..............................214 682-8692
Bryan Merckling, *CEO*
Reagan V Jobe, *Vice Pres*
Sean Rucker, *Director*
EMP: 24
SQ FT: 2,500
SALES (est): 1MM **Privately Held**
WEB: www.kloudnation.com
SIC: 7372 Application computer software

(G-7297)
MASH GROUP HOLDINGS LLC
5329 Spanish Oaks (75034-4895)
PHONE..............................314 638-4200
EMP: 20
SQ FT: 100,000
SALES (est): 4MM **Privately Held**
SIC: 3999 Mfg Miscellaneous Products Mfg Signs & Advertising Specialties

(G-7298)
MK SYSTEMS USA INC (PA)
Also Called: Mediakind
3001 Dallas Pkwy Ste 300 (75034-8639)
PHONE..............................469 626-9523
Cary Daniel, *Counsel*
Mario Asiain-Diaz, *Vice Pres*
Ravi Chilamkurti, *Opers Staff*
Ann Lim, *Opers Staff*
JB Monson, *Controller*
EMP: 29
SALES (est): 30.8MM **Privately Held**
SIC: 3663 Television broadcasting & communications equipment

(G-7299)
MONOLITH TECH HOLDINGS LLC (PA)
Also Called: Federos
7164 Tech Dr Ste 100 (75033)
P.O. Box 385, Wasco IL (60183-0385)
PHONE..............................972 532-7387
David Knight, *CEO*
Susan Williamson, *Partner*
Jason Kojro-Badziak, *Engineer*
William J Fitton, *CFO*
Neil Dowie, *Sales Dir*
EMP: 20
SALES (est): 4.9MM **Privately Held**
WEB: www.federos.com
SIC: 7372 Prepackaged software

(G-7300)
MTWD HOLDINGS INC
10601 Clarence Dr Ste 100 (75033-3866)
P.O. Box 729, Prosper (75078-0729)
PHONE..............................972 346-2242
Michael Cannonie, *President*
Michael Doke, *Vice Pres*
Richard Steele, *VP Engrg*
Mike Ocando, *Engineer*
Tuan Luong, *Software Engr*
EMP: 45
SQ FT: 36,000
SALES (est): 8.1MM **Privately Held**
WEB: www.casiusa.com
SIC: 7372 3577 Business oriented computer software; computer peripheral equipment

(G-7301)
NEV HOLDINGS LLC
3211 Internet Blvd # 200 (75034-1948)
PHONE..............................972 731-1100
Shelby Marlowe, *CFO*
Valerie Skrivanek, *Credit Mgr*
Rowena Pura, *Director*
EMP: 3401
SQ FT: 16,534
SALES (est): 194.8MM **Privately Held**
SIC: 2677 Envelopes

(G-7302)
OLDCASTLE APG TEXAS INC
Also Called: Custom Stone Supply
9850 John W Elliott Dr (75033-2046)
PHONE..............................972 335-4122
Steve Bond, *President*
EMP: 12
SQ FT: 3,795
SALES (corp-wide): 30.6B **Privately Held**
WEB: www.jewellcp.com
SIC: 3291 Stones, abrasive
HQ: Oldcastle Apg Texas, Inc.
2561 Sw Grapevine Pkwy # 200
Grapevine TX 76051

(G-7303)
ORACLE AMERICA INC
7460 Warren Pkwy Ste 300 (75034-4832)
PHONE..............................214 494-4527
Chris Zink, *Sales Staff*
Michael Cullen, *Branch Mgr*
EMP: 95
SALES (corp-wide): 39B **Publicly Held**
WEB: www.ea.com
SIC: 7372 Business oriented computer software
HQ: Oracle America, Inc.
500 Oracle Pkwy
Redwood City CA 94065
650 506-7000

(G-7304)
ORACLE CORPORATION
7460 Warren Pkwy Ste 300 (75034-4832)
PHONE..............................972 652-8000
Curt Richardson, *Principal*
Damon Arnett, *Engineer*
Scott Schnitzius, *Sales Staff*
Danielle Oakley, *Marketing Staff*
Hari Menon, *Manager*
EMP: 302
SALES (corp-wide): 39B **Publicly Held**
WEB: www.oracle.com
SIC: 7372 Business oriented computer software
PA: Oracle Corporation
2300 Oracle Way
Austin TX 78741
737 867-1000

(G-7305)
PANASONIC CORP NORTH AMERICA
Also Called: Panasonic Indus Dvcs Sls Amer
2600 Network Blvd Ste 600 (75034-6015)
PHONE..............................956 984-3700
Jiro Takeda, *President*
Chris Antonellis, *Executive*
EMP: 80 **Privately Held**
WEB: www.na.panasonic.com
SIC: 3691 5999 3692 Storage batteries; batteries, non-automotive; dry cell batteries, single or multiple cell
HQ: Panasonic Corporation Of North America
2 Riverfront Plz Ste 200
Newark NJ 07102
201 348-7000

(G-7306)
POWERSECURE INC
Also Called: Powersecure Lighting
8655 Corporate Dr (75033-3910)
PHONE..............................203 683-6222
Singing Cheng, *Superintendent*
Chris Hartswick, *Vice Pres*
EMP: 20
SALES (corp-wide): 21.4B **Publicly Held**
WEB: www.powersecure.com
SIC: 4931 3629 ; electronic generation equipment
HQ: Powersecure, Inc.
1609 Heritage Commerce Ct
Wake Forest NC 27587
919 556-3056

(G-7307)
PRECISION WIRE PRODUCTS LLC (PA)
108 Muntain View Indus Ln (75034)
PHONE..............................214 436-4923
Glenn Earley,
Bart Wallace,
EMP: 15
SQ FT: 10,000
SALES (est): 2.1MM **Privately Held**
SIC: 3531 5082 Crane carriers; general construction machinery & equipment

(G-7308)
PROSUPPS USA LLC (HQ)
Also Called: Professional Supplements
5757 Main St Ste 205 (75034-3256)
PHONE..............................214 310-1188
Thomas B Humphreys, *CEO*
David Sandler, *COO*
Blake Roberts, *Prdtn Mgr*
Lyne Donovan, *CFO*
David Hayes, *Sales Staff*
◆ **EMP:** 54
SALES (est): 36.4MM
SALES (corp-wide): 3.7MM **Privately Held**
WEB: www.prosupps.com
SIC: 2833 Vitamins, natural or synthetic: bulk, uncompounded
PA: Prosupps Holdings, Llc
7460 Warren Pkwy Ste 150
Frisco TX 75034
214 310-1188

(G-7309)
ROCKSOLID LLC
1 Cowboys Way Ste 190 (75034-2001)
PHONE..............................855 282-8880
Joey Larocque, *CEO*

Caleb Hanie, *COO*
Izzy Murdy, *CFO*
EMP: 19
SQ FT: 5,000
SALES (est): 2.2MM **Privately Held**
WEB: www.liverocksolid.com
SIC: 3949 Football equipment & supplies, general

(G-7310)
SCHLUMBERGER TECHNOLOGY CORP
Also Called: Schlumberger CMF
3011 Internet Blvd # 200 (75034-1873)
PHONE..............................940 442-6566
William Coates, *President*
EMP: 148 **Publicly Held**
SIC: 1389 Oil field services
HQ: Schlumberger Technology Corp
300 Schlumberger Dr
Sugar Land TX 77478
281 285-8500

(G-7311)
SCHNEIDER OPTICAL MACHINES INC
6644 All Stars Ave Ste 10 (75033-2202)
PHONE..............................972 247-4000
Kurt Atchison, *CEO*
Trey Hoegenauer, *Opers Staff*
Kelly Hodge, *Engineer*
Bill Yee, *Engineer*
Josh Chandonnet, *Manager*
▲ **EMP:** 19
SQ FT: 1,900
SALES (est): 7.4MM **Privately Held**
WEB: www.schneider-om.com
SIC: 3827 Optical instruments & lenses

(G-7312)
SIX & MANGO EQUIPMENT LLP (PA)
Also Called: Kubota Authorized Dealer
8741 Main St (75034-3080)
P.O. Box 1269 (75034-0022)
PHONE..............................972 335-2731
David Six, *Partner*
James Mango, *Partner*
Asa Durocher, *Credit Staff*
Brent Yates, *Sales Staff*
EMP: 30
SQ FT: 10,000
SALES (est): 16.3MM **Privately Held**
WEB: www.sixandmango.com
SIC: 7359 3524 5083 Equipment rental & leasing; lawn & garden tractors & equipment; loaders (garden tractor equipment); farm & garden machinery

(G-7313)
SOLAIS LIGHTING LLC
Also Called: Solais Lighting Group
8655 Corporate Dr Ste 100 (75033-3911)
PHONE..............................469 294-1516
Samuel Newberry, *CEO*
EMP: 38
SALES (est): 758.2K **Privately Held**
WEB: www.solais.com
SIC: 3648 Lighting equipment

(G-7314)
STEWARD ENERGY II LLC
2600 Dallas Pkwy Ste 400 (75034-8128)
PHONE..............................214 297-0500
Cletis Smith, *Superintendent*
Dusty Buck, *Vice Pres*
Shane Seals, *Vice Pres*
Mark Warren, *Vice Pres*
Christina Savage, *Asst Controller*
EMP: 12
SQ FT: 10,000
SALES (est): 1.5MM **Privately Held**
WEB: www.stewardenergy.net
SIC: 1381 Drilling oil & gas wells

(G-7315)
STYLE PUBLISHING GROUP LLC
Also Called: Frisco Style Magazine
8020 Main St Frisco (75033)
P.O. Box 1676 (75034-0028)
PHONE..............................972 335-1181
George Rodriguez, *Sales Staff*
Leah Ratliff, *Art Dir*
C Chris Johnson,

▲ = Import ▼=Export
◆ =Import/Export

EMP: 10
SQ FT: 3,000
SALES (est): 1.2MM **Privately Held**
WEB: www.friscostyle.com
SIC: 2721 Magazines: publishing only, not printed on site

(G-7316)
SUNBELT PLASTICS INCORPORATED
8940 Alpha Ave (75034-5679)
P.O. Box 370 (75034-0007)
PHONE.................................972 335-4100
John R Anselmi, *President*
Maureen Anselmi, *Vice Pres*
Celeste Bernard, *Human Res Mgr*
EMP: 40
SQ FT: 10,000
SALES (est): 5.6MM **Privately Held**
WEB: www.sunbeltplasticsmolding.com
SIC: 3089 Injection molding of plastics

(G-7317)
SWYE360 LEARNING INC
6782 Irongate Pl (75036-4372)
PHONE.................................214 263-2932
Jacob Makuvire, *CEO*
EMP: 13
SALES (est): 378.5K **Privately Held**
SIC: 7372 Educational computer software

(G-7318)
TANGO NETWORKS INC (PA)
2801 Network Blvd Ste 200 (75034-1880)
PHONE.................................469 920-2100
Douglas Bartek, *CEO*
Adam Boone, *Vice Pres*
Jim O'Brey, *Vice Pres*
Nigel Smith, *Vice Pres*
Pamela Strong, *Vice Pres*
EMP: 24
SQ FT: 10,000
SALES (est): 3.6MM **Privately Held**
WEB: www.tango-networks.com
SIC: 3669 Intercommunication systems, electric

(G-7319)
THINKGEO LLC (PA)
2770 Main St Ste 185 (75033-4407)
PHONE.................................785 727-4133
Clint Batman, *President*
David Rehagen, *Exec Officer*
Kyle Day, *Prgrmr*
Val Guillou,
Felix Llueberes,
EMP: 13
SALES (est): 2.1MM **Privately Held**
WEB: www.thinkgeo.com
SIC: 7372 7371 Publishers' computer software; computer software development

(G-7320)
TRINITY STAIRS INC (PA)
12750 Preston Rd Ste 1100 (75033-6448)
PHONE.................................972 335-0700
Richard Bush, *President*
Tracy Bush, *Corp Secy*
EMP: 24
SQ FT: 20,000
SALES (est): 2.9MM **Privately Held**
WEB: www.trinitystairs.com
SIC: 2431 3446 3272 Staircases & stairs, wood; architectural metalwork; concrete products

(G-7321)
US BIOSERVICES
3101 Gaylord Pkwy (75034-8655)
PHONE.................................214 572-8300
Bill Chauvin, *General Mgr*
Michelle Fazio, *General Mgr*
Alex Maverick, *Vice Pres*
Randall Maloziec, *VP Bus Dvlpt*
Susan Heslin, *Accounting Mgr*
EMP: 200 **Privately Held**
WEB: www.usbioservices.com
SIC: 2851 Paints & allied products
PA: Us Bioservices
5100 E Hunter Ave
Anaheim CA 92807

(G-7322)
VELOCITY AEROSPACE GROUP INC (PA)
7460 Warren Pkwy Ste 180 (75034-4170)
PHONE.................................214 988-9898
Dale Gable, *CEO*
Edan Kurzweil, *General Mgr*
Jeff Black, *Vice Pres*
Enrique Mendoza, *Vice Pres*
David Jackson, *QA Dir*
EMP: 55 **EST:** 2013
SALES (est): 32.8MM **Privately Held**
WEB: www.velocityaerospace.com
SIC: 7699 3721 Aircraft & heavy equipment repair services; aircraft

(G-7323)
VIRGIN FIELDS LLC
7236 Yellowstone Dr (75033-3170)
PHONE.................................972 322-7902
Francis Dogvey, *CEO*
EMP: 21
SALES (est): 180K **Privately Held**
SIC: 2911 7379 Diesel fuels;

(G-7324)
VOLKS RESOURCES LLC
7460 Warren Pkwy Ste 100 (75034-4170)
PHONE.................................972 636-1880
Daniel Livelli, *Vice Pres*
Daniel Patricio Livelli, *Manager*
EMP: 12 **EST:** 2014
SQ FT: 45,000
SALES (est): 1.1MM **Privately Held**
WEB: www.volksresources.com
SIC: 1389 7361 8748 8742 Oil consultants; labor contractors (employment agency); telecommunications consultant; business planning & organizing services

(G-7325)
VULCAN MATERIALS COMPANY
6601 Eubanks St (75034-5062)
PHONE.................................972 335-0008
EMP: 16 **Publicly Held**
WEB: www.vulcanmaterials.com
SIC: 3273 Ready-mixed concrete
PA: Vulcan Materials Company
1200 Urban Center Dr
Vestavia AL 35242

(G-7326)
WHITE ENERGY HOLDING CO LLC (PA)
2595 Dallas Pkwy Ste 310 (75034-8530)
PHONE.................................972 715-6490
Brian Steenhard, *CEO*
Zack Deaton, *Controller*
EMP: 12
SALES (est): 17.1MM **Privately Held**
WEB: www.white-energy.com
SIC: 2869 Fuels

Fulshear
Fort Bend County

(G-7327)
ASH AUTOMATED CTRL SYSTEMS LLC
32810 Rogers Rd (77441-6325)
P.O. Box 1113 (77441-2013)
PHONE.................................281 346-1400
Todd Toole, *Engineer*
Randall B Ash,
EMP: 11 **EST:** 2009
SALES (est): 2.3MM **Privately Held**
WEB: www.ash-acs.com
SIC: 3822 7389 Auto controls regulating resid.ntl & coml environmt & applncs;

(G-7328)
CAREY CRUTCHER INC
7330 Fm 359 Rd S (77441)
P.O. Box 965, Katy (77492-0965)
PHONE.................................281 346-0045
Carey Crutcher III, *President*
William Crutcher, *President*
Clay A Crutcher, *Vice Pres*
Sandra Gillum, *Admin Sec*
EMP: 20
SQ FT: 5,000

SALES (est): 3.1MM **Privately Held**
WEB: www.careycrutcherinc.com
SIC: 3531 Construction machinery

(G-7329)
PEREGRINE STIMULATION SVCS LLC
30510 Cedar Woods St (77441-3720)
PHONE.................................713 201-6787
John Piehl II, *Mng Member*
EMP: 9
SALES (est): 801.2K **Privately Held**
SIC: 1389 Servicing oil & gas wells

(G-7330)
SOMERSET HOUSE PUBLISHING INC
Also Called: Somerset Fine Art
29370 Mckinnon Rd (77406-9743)
P.O. Box 869 (77441-0869)
PHONE.................................281 346-8900
Larry Smith, *President*
Allison Sutton, *Cust Mgr*
Patrick Thomas, *Sales Staff*
Norma Hicks, *Manager*
Samantha Demello, *Executive*
▲ **EMP:** 15
SALES (est): 1.6MM **Privately Held**
WEB: www.somersetfineart.com
SIC: 2741 5719 Art copy: publishing only, not printed on site; pictures, wall

(G-7331)
SPECTRUM BATTERIES INC
6910 Sprigg St (77441-6300)
PHONE.................................281 533-9735
Linda Dutchak, *President*
EMP: 45
SQ FT: 4,648
SALES (est): 9MM **Privately Held**
WEB: www.spectrumbatteries.com
SIC: 3533 3692 Oil & gas field machinery; primary batteries, dry & wet

(G-7332)
WYATT RESOURCES INC
5623 Fm Rd 359 (77441)
P.O. Box 744 (77441-0744)
PHONE.................................281 346-6100
Deborah G Beatty, *President*
Everett W Beatty Jr, *Vice Pres*
Jerry Miller, *Vice Pres*
Debby Beatty Holmes, *CFO*
Phyllis Greene, *Accounting Mgr*
EMP: 75
SQ FT: 50,000
SALES (est): 21.9MM **Privately Held**
WEB: www.wyattresources.com
SIC: 3441 Fabricated structural metal for bridges

Gainesville
Cooke County

(G-7333)
ADVANCED PEDESTALS LTD
Also Called: API
2227 Foundry Rd (76240)
P.O. Box 1037 (76241-1037)
PHONE.................................940 668-7283
Jim C Allen, *Partner*
Pete Shauf, *Partner*
Mitchell E Shauf, *General Ptnr*
Gina Craigie, *CFO*
EMP: 75
SQ FT: 28,000
SALES (est): 4.2MM **Privately Held**
WEB: www.petroflexna.com
SIC: 3089 Injection molding of plastics

(G-7334)
B-29 INVESTMENTS LP
201 W California St (76240-3904)
P.O. Box 170 (76241-0170)
PHONE.................................940 665-4373
John D Schmitz, *President*
Steve M Schmitz, *Partner*
Kevin M Palma, *CFO*
EMP: 100
SALES (est): 10.4MM **Privately Held**
WEB: www.b29investments.com
SIC: 1382 6798 Oil & gas exploration services; real estate investment trusts

PA: Schmitz & Schmitz Properties Incorporated
211 W California St
Gainesville TX 76240

(G-7335)
BRAMMER PETROLEUM INC
Also Called: Brammer Pipe and Steel
6178 E Us Highway 82 (76240-7167)
P.O. Box 243 (76241-0243)
PHONE.................................940 665-4807
Gary H Brammer, *President*
Billy C Brammer, *Corp Secy*
Larry R Brammer, *Vice Pres*
EMP: 12 **EST:** 1974
SQ FT: 35,000
SALES (est): 1.2MM **Privately Held**
WEB: www.brammerpipe.net
SIC: 1389 Oil field services

(G-7336)
BRAMMER PIPE AND STEEL INC (PA)
Also Called: Brammer Pipe & Steel
6178 E Us Highway 82 (76240-7167)
P.O. Box 243 (76241-0243)
PHONE.................................940 665-4807
Larry Brammer, *President*
Billie Brammer, *Corp Secy*
▲ **EMP:** 10
SQ FT: 4,000
SALES (est): 1.3MM **Privately Held**
WEB: www.brammerpipe.net
SIC: 1389 Oil field services

(G-7337)
CEMEX MATERIALS LLC
1310 N Clements St (76240-2806)
PHONE.................................940 665-8355
EMP: 28 **Privately Held**
SIC: 3273 Ready-mixed concrete
HQ: Cemex Materials Llc
1501 Belvedere Rd
West Palm Beach FL 33406
561 833-5555

(G-7338)
CIRCUIT BREAKER SALES LLC (HQ)
Also Called: Circuit Breaker Sales Co Inc
1315 Columbine Dr (76240-2010)
P.O. Box 1098 (76241-1098)
PHONE.................................940 665-4444
Finley Ledbetter, *CEO*
Bill Schofield, *President*
William A Schofield, *President*
Bill Stephens, *Vice Pres*
Mike Briley, *Safety Mgr*
◆ **EMP:** 159
SQ FT: 300,000
SALES (est): 11.9MM **Privately Held**
WEB: www.circuitbreaker.com
SIC: 3613 5063 3353 3612 Power circuit breakers; switchgear & switchgear accessories; circuit breakers; aluminum sheet, plate & foil; transformers, except electric; painting & paper hanging

(G-7339)
CNHI LLC
Also Called: Gainesville Daily Register
306 E California St (76240-4006)
P.O. Box 309 (76241-0309)
PHONE.................................940 665-5511
David Scott, *CEO*
David Mann, *Advt Staff*
Jerry Prickett, *Cashier*
EMP: 36
SALES (corp-wide): 23.7B **Privately Held**
WEB: www.cnhi.com
SIC: 2711 7313 2759 Newspapers: publishing only, not printed on site; newspaper advertising representative; commercial printing
HQ: Cnhi, Llc
445 Dexter Ave Ste 7000
Montgomery AL 36104

(G-7340)
COMPLETE ENERGY SERVICES INC
Spindletop Production Tools
3333 Ih 35 N Bldg F (76240)
PHONE.................................940 668-5186
EMP: 22 **Publicly Held**

WEB: www.superiorenergy.com
SIC: **1389** Oil field services
HQ: Complete Energy Services, Inc.
　　220 N Sara Rd
　　Yukon OK 73099

(G-7341)
COMPLETE ENERGY SERVICES INC
201 W California St (76240-3904)
PHONE......................940 665-4373
Shauna Clark, *Personnel Exec*
John Schmidt, *Branch Mgr*
EMP: 725 Publicly Held
WEB: www.superiorenergy.com
SIC: 1389 Butane (natural) production
HQ: Complete Energy Services, Inc.
　　220 N Sara Rd
　　Yukon OK 73099

(G-7342)
DOLLAR B R SR ET AL A TX PTNR
Also Called: Dollar Enterprise
1908 N Weaver St (76240-2230)
P.O. Box 410 (76241-0410)
PHONE......................940 665-6262
EMP: 60 EST: 1983
SQ FT: 42,300
SALES (est): 5MM **Privately Held**
SIC: 2759 7359 Commercial printing; equipment rental & leasing

(G-7343)
ENDURANCE LIFT SOLUTIONS LLC (PA)
114 E Foreline St (76240-3320)
PHONE......................281 269-6880
EMP: 68 EST: 2016
SALES (est): 343.1MM **Privately Held**
WEB: www.endurancelift.com
SIC: 1389 Oil field services

(G-7344)
GAINESVILLE PRINTING CO INC
200 Denison St (76240-4141)
P.O. Box 1011 (76241-1011)
PHONE......................940 665-5517
Roger R Fleitman, *President*
Carol Turner, *Vice Pres*
Roger Fleitman, *Sales Staff*
Janet D Moss, *Graphic Designe*
EMP: 32
SQ FT: 20,800
SALES (est): 4.5MM **Privately Held**
WEB: www.gpctx.com
SIC: 2752 2791 2789 2759 Commercial printing, offset; typesetting; bookbinding & related work; commercial printing

(G-7345)
IFS COATINGS INC (HQ)
3601 N Interstate 35 (76240-1939)
PHONE......................940 668-1062
Glynn Mason, *President*
Patrick H Donahue, *Vice Pres*
Patrick Donahue, *Vice Pres*
Tommy Reno, *VP Opers*
Debra Kohut, *Controller*
▲ **EMP:** 50
SALES (est): 61.7MM
SALES (corp-wide): 76.7MM **Privately Held**
WEB: www.ifscoatings.com
SIC: 2899 2851 2821 Chemical preparations; epoxy coatings; polyesters

(G-7346)
INDUSTRIAL MODELS INC
1711 Westaire Dr (76240-1770)
P.O. Box 1018 (76241-1018)
PHONE......................940 665-7841
Albert Sanches, *CEO*
Lynn Sanches, *President*
Albert Sanches Jr, *Vice Pres*
EMP: 125
SQ FT: 75,000
SALES (est): 2.3MM **Privately Held**
SIC: 3713 3089 Truck & bus bodies; molding primary plastic

(G-7347)
MERIT ENERGY COMPANY LLC
9600 Fm 371 (76240-1124)
PHONE......................940 683-4059

EMP: 25 Privately Held
WEB: www.meritenergy.com
SIC: 1311 Crude petroleum production; natural gas production
PA: Merit Energy Company, Llc
　　13737 Noel Rd Ste 1200
　　Dallas TX 75240

(G-7348)
MIDWEST ASPHALT CORPORATION
Also Called: Midwest Asphalt Company
3609 E Highway 82 (76240-7062)
PHONE......................940 668-1480
Fax: 940 668-6200
EMP: 15
SALES (corp-wide): 34.9MM **Privately Held**
SIC: 2951 Mfg Asphalt Mixtures/Blocks
HQ: Midwest Asphalt Corporation
　　6340 Industrial Dr # 200
　　Eden Prairie MN 55422
　　952 937-8033

(G-7349)
MOLDED FIBER GLASS COMPANIES
3333 N I 35 Bldg 5 (76240-1909)
P.O. Box 1459 (76241-1459)
PHONE......................940 668-0302
Rich Lafountain, *Mfg Spvr*
Wes Shamp, *Branch Mgr*
Wesley Shamp, *Manager*
EMP: 100
SALES (corp-wide): 626.3MM **Privately Held**
WEB: www.moldedfiberglass.com
SIC: 3089 5999 Gutters (glass fiber reinforced), fiberglass or plastic; fiberglass materials, except insulation
PA: Molded Fiber Glass Companies
　　2925 Mfg Pl
　　Ashtabula OH 44004
　　440 997-5851

(G-7350)
N A PETROFLEX LTD
1920 N Weaver St (76240-2230)
PHONE......................800 433-5711
Mitchell Shauf, *General Ptnr*
EMP: 32 Privately Held
WEB: www.petroflexna.com
SIC: 3084 Plastics pipe
PA: N A Petroflex Ltd
　　1305 N Interstate 35
　　Gainesville TX 76240

(G-7351)
N A PETROFLEX LTD (PA)
Also Called: P N A
1305 N Interstate 35 (76240-4673)
P.O. Box 1356 (76241-1356)
PHONE......................940 668-7283
Pete Shauf, *CEO*
Marcie Croft, *Sales Staff*
Patti Hunnicutt, *Admin Asst*
EMP: 86
SQ FT: 70,000
SALES (est): 14.2MM **Privately Held**
WEB: www.petroflexna.com
SIC: 3089 Injection molding of plastics

(G-7352)
NAP INDUSTRIES LLC
202 S Dixon St Ste 201 (76240-4764)
PHONE......................940 668-8111
EMP: 12
SALES (est): 1.8MM **Privately Held**
WEB: www.napindustries.com
SIC: 3589 Water treatment equipment, industrial

(G-7353)
NIBLETT ENTERPRISES INC
Also Called: United Cast Stone Company
4400 W Highway 82 (76240-1767)
P.O. Box 1239, Decatur (76234-6142)
PHONE......................940 383-2887
Gene Niblett, *President*
Don McCarter, *Treasurer*
EMP: 55
SALES (est): 7.3MM **Privately Held**
SIC: 3272 Siding, precast stone

(G-7354)
NORMANS WELL SERVICE INC
3728 E Highway 82 (76240-7056)
P.O. Box 875 (76241-0875)
PHONE......................940 668-8201
Wayne Harper, *President*
EMP: 14
SQ FT: 10,000
SALES (est): 931.7K **Privately Held**
WEB: www.normanswellservice.com
SIC: 1389 Servicing oil & gas wells; oil field services

(G-7355)
NORTH TEXAS CRUSHED STONE
14 County Road 460 (76240)
P.O. Box 1477 (76241-1477)
PHONE......................940 665-9100
Donald Denton, *President*
Cheryl Denton, *Vice Pres*
EMP: 10
SQ FT: 650
SALES (est): 220.2K **Privately Held**
SIC: 1422 Crushed & broken limestone

(G-7356)
ORTEQ ENERGY TECHNOLOGIES LLC
3401 W Highway 82 (76240-2001)
P.O. Box 2060 (76241-2060)
PHONE......................940 665-2316
Rick Dixon, *Engineer*
Cody Ortowski,
Cole Ortowski,
▲ **EMP:** 35
SALES (est): 25MM **Privately Held**
WEB: www.orteqmfg.com
SIC: 5082 1389 Oil field equipment; oil field services

(G-7357)
POND KING INC
5924 W Us Highway 82 (76240-1790)
PHONE......................940 668-2573
Brad Metzler, *President*
EMP: 12
SALES (est): 1.7MM **Privately Held**
WEB: www.pondking.com
SIC: 8741 3732 Management services; boat building & repairing

(G-7358)
PPG INDUSTRIES INC
3333 N Interstate 35 C (76240-1909)
PHONE......................940 665-9590
Robert Schmuck, *Branch Mgr*
EMP: 23
SALES (corp-wide): 15.3B **Publicly Held**
WEB: www.corporate.ppg.com
SIC: 2851 Paints & paint additives
PA: Ppg Industries, Inc.
　　1 Ppg Pl
　　Pittsburgh PA 15272
　　412 434-3131

(G-7359)
QUASAR ENERGY SERVICES INC
3288 Fm 51 (76240-0208)
PHONE......................940 612-3336
Tim Sicking, *President*
EMP: 15
SALES (est): 5.1MM **Privately Held**
WEB: www.quasarenergyservices.com
SIC: 1389 Oil field services

(G-7360)
RECOVERED WATER INDUSTRIES LLC
Also Called: Rwi
202 Suth Dixon St Ste 203 (76240)
PHONE......................940 668-8200
Patrick Shane Lee, *President*
Jeff Isbell, *Vice Pres*
Stormy Lee, *Treasurer*
Cory Enderby, *Admin Sec*
EMP: 35
SQ FT: 1,000
SALES (est): 10MM **Privately Held**
WEB: www.sitesafeteam.com
SIC: 1389 Servicing oil & gas wells

(G-7361)
RELIANT WORLDWIDE PLASTICS LLC
4430 W Highway 82 (76240-1767)
PHONE......................214 382-9672
Craig Clark, *CEO*
Kyle Crawford, *COO*
William Maslakow, *Vice Pres*
Chris Hughes, *CFO*
Randi Reed, *Accountant*
▲ **EMP:** 201
SALES (est): 51.8MM **Privately Held**
WEB: www.reliantplastics.com
SIC: 3089 Injection molding of plastics

(G-7362)
SAFRAN SEATS USA LLC (DH)
2000 Weber Dr (76240-9699)
PHONE......................940 668-4825
Jeff Barger, *President*
Scott Devine, *Vice Pres*
Jeremy Green, *Vice Pres*
Keith Jennette, *Vice Pres*
Dee Robinson, *Vice Pres*
◆ **EMP:** 1800
SQ FT: 500,000
SALES (est): 650MM
SALES (corp-wide): 799.9MM **Privately Held**
WEB: www.myzsus.com
SIC: 3728 5088 Aircraft parts & equipment; transportation equipment & supplies
HQ: Zodiac Us Corporation
　　1747 State Route 34
　　Wall Township NJ 07727
　　732 681-3527

(G-7363)
SELECT ENERGY SERVICES INC
1820 N Interstate 35 (76240-2179)
PHONE......................903 766-2600
EMP: 1376
SALES (corp-wide): 1.2B **Publicly Held**
WEB: www.selectenergyservices.com
SIC: 1389 Oil field services
PA: Select Energy Services, Inc.
　　1233 West Loop S Ste 1400
　　Houston TX 77027
　　713 235-9500

(G-7364)
SELECT ENERGY SERVICES LLC (DH)
1820 N I 35 (76240-2179)
P.O. Box 1715 (76241-1715)
PHONE......................940 668-1818
Cody Ortowski, *Exec VP*
Michael Skarke, *Exec VP*
J Brady Crouch, *Vice Pres*
Danny Grant, *Vice Pres*
Glenn Guthmann, *Vice Pres*
EMP: 100
SALES (est): 1.8B
SALES (corp-wide): 1.2B **Publicly Held**
WEB: www.selectenergyservices.com
SIC: 1389 Oil field services
HQ: Ses Holdings, Llc
　　1820 N Interstate 35
　　Gainesville TX 76240
　　940 668-1818

(G-7365)
SELECT ENERGY SERVICES LLC
Also Called: Tejas Oilfield Service
4337 E Us Highway 82 (76240-1629)
PHONE......................940 665-8223
Fax: 940 665-7218
EMP: 50
SALES (corp-wide): 843.8MM **Privately Held**
SIC: 1389 Oil And Gas Field Services, Nec, Nsk
HQ: Select Energy Services, Llc
　　1820 N Interstate 35
　　Gainesville TX 76240
　　940 668-1818

(G-7366)
SELECT ENERGY SERVICES LLC
Also Called: Impact Energy Services
4506 S Interstate 35 (76240-8236)
P.O. Box 1715 (76241-1715)
PHONE...................................940 665-1767
John Schmitz, *Branch Mgr*
Travis Middlebrooks, *Director*
Joshua Seydler, *Analyst*
EMP: 59
SALES (corp-wide): 1.2B **Publicly Held**
WEB: www.selectenergyservices.com
SIC: 1389 Oil field services
HQ: Select Energy Services, Llc
  1820 N I 35
  Gainesville TX 76240
  940 668-1818

(G-7367)
SHARP OILFIELD SERVICES LLC
212 W Main St (76240-4739)
P.O. Box 680 (76241-0680)
PHONE...................................877 742-7784
Bradley Cox, *Opers Staff*
Micah Davenport,
Joseph B Beck,
EMP: 53
SALES (est): 20MM **Privately Held**
WEB: www.sharpoilfieldservices.com
SIC: 1389 Oil field services

(G-7368)
SITE SAFE SOLUTIONS LTD (PA)
Also Called: Recovered Water Industries
202 S Dixon St Ste 214 (76240-4764)
PHONE...................................940 612-2286
Patrick Shane Lee, *President*
Stormy Lee, *Vice Pres*
Roy Quinby, *Vice Pres*
Charlie Carnevale, *Opers Staff*
Toby Reynolds, *Sales Staff*
▲ EMP: 54 EST: 2010
SALES (est): 24.7MM **Privately Held**
WEB: www.sitesafecontainment.com
SIC: 1382 Oil & gas exploration services

(G-7369)
STANDARD INDUS MFG PRTNERS LLC
1804 Independence Ave (76240-2484)
PHONE...................................940 580-3512
Shelton Medlock, *Manager*
EMP: 19
SALES (corp-wide): 27.2MM **Privately Held**
WEB: www.standardpumpparts.com
SIC: 7699 3561 Pumps & pumping equipment repair; pumps & pumping equipment
PA: Standard Industrial
  901 W 3rd St
  Odessa TX 79763
  432 332-5955

(G-7370)
SUPERIOR ENERGY SERVICES INC
Also Called: Complete Enrgy Svcs Well Svcs
3333 N I 35 Bldg F (76240-1910)
PHONE...................................940 668-5100
Canaan Factor, *CEO*
EMP: 11 **Publicly Held**
WEB: www.superiorenergy.com
SIC: 1389 Oil field services
PA: Superior Energy Services, Inc.
  1001 La St Ste 2900
  Houston TX 77002

(G-7371)
T & S MACHINES AND TOOLS INC
12 Whitleys Ridge Ln (76240-1510)
PHONE...................................940 668-1002
Tim Whitley, *President*
Shanna Whitley, *Vice Pres*
Chris Carter, *Prgrmr*
▲ EMP: 10
SQ FT: 3,500

SALES (est): 1.2MM **Privately Held**
WEB: www.tnsmachines.com
SIC: 3559 3545 Automotive related machinery; machine tool attachments & accessories

(G-7372)
THOMPSON JR INC
3500 N Grand Ave (76240-2369)
PHONE...................................940 665-2533
Johnny R Thompson, *President*
EMP: 25
SQ FT: 1,000
SALES (est): 3.7MM **Privately Held**
SIC: 1422 3531 1442 2951 Crushed & broken limestone; asphalt plant, including gravel-mix type; sand mining; asphalt paving mixtures & blocks

(G-7373)
TRIDENT PROCESS SYSTEMS LLC
2300 N I 35 (76240-2161)
PHONE...................................940 372-1535
Cory Enderby, *Corp Secy*
Kari Hutcherson, *Vice Pres*
Stormy Lee, *Vice Pres*
Phil Neelley, *Vice Pres*
Philip Neelley, *Vice Pres*
EMP: 15
SALES (est): 551.6K **Privately Held**
WEB: www.tridentprosystems.com
SIC: 3548 Welding apparatus

(G-7374)
UNITED COMMERCIAL CAST STONE
4400 W Highway 82 (76240-1767)
P.O. Box 1239, Decatur (76234-6142)
PHONE...................................940 668-8133
Gene Niblett, *President*
EMP: 11
SALES (est): 1.6MM **Privately Held**
WEB:
www.unitedcommercialcaststone.business.site
SIC: 3272 Concrete products

(G-7375)
ZODIAC SEATS CALIFORNIA LLC
8595 Milliken Ave Ste 101 (76240)
PHONE...................................909 652-9700
Mike Rozenblatt, *Mng Member*
▲ EMP: 240
SALES (est): 44.1MM
SALES (corp-wide): 799.9MM **Privately Held**
WEB: www.zodiacaerospace.com
SIC: 3728 Aircraft parts & equipment
HQ: Safran Seats Usa Llc
  2000 Weber Dr
  Gainesville TX 76240
  940 668-4825

Galena Park
Harris County

(G-7376)
AMERICAN PLANT FOOD CORP (PA)
Also Called: A P F
903 Mayo Shell Rd (77547-3291)
P.O. Box 584 (77547-0584)
PHONE...................................713 675-2231
Jerry L Newcomb, *President*
Donald R Ford, *President*
Phillip Kramer, *Vice Pres*
Josh Long, *Vice Pres*
Mark Murphy, *Safety Dir*
▼ EMP: 56 EST: 1964
SQ FT: 150,000
SALES: 194.6MM **Privately Held**
WEB: www.apfcorp.net
SIC: 2873 Fertilizer & fertilizer materials

(G-7377)
ARDENT MILLS LLC
1100 S Main St (77547-3500)
PHONE...................................512 789-5165
Scott Dillingham, *General Mgr*
Bill Stoufer, *COO*
Kellen Lyons, *Plant Mgr*

Jesse McLaren, *Plant Mgr*
Jim Pulverenti, *Plant Mgr*
EMP: 23
SALES (corp-wide): 634.7MM **Privately Held**
WEB: www.ardentmills.com
SIC: 2041 Flour & other grain mill products
PA: Ardent Mills, Llc
  1875 Lawrence St Ste 1400
  Denver CO 80202
  800 851-9618

(G-7378)
CHEMICAL EXCHANGE INDS INC (PA)
Also Called: C X I
900 Clinton Dr (77547-3461)
P.O. Box 67 (77547-0067)
PHONE...................................713 455-1206
David M Smith, *Ch of Bd*
Richard Wall, *President*
Charis W Smith, *Vice Pres*
Debra Greife, *Admin Sec*
EMP: 22 EST: 1961
SQ FT: 2,000
SALES (est): 26.3MM **Privately Held**
WEB: www.texmark.com
SIC: 2819 Industrial inorganic chemicals

(G-7379)
CONGLOBAL INDUSTRIES LLC
Also Called: Con Global
500 Mayo Shell Rd (77547)
P.O. Box 72 (77547-0072)
PHONE...................................713 675-7587
David Eiehl, *Manager*
EMP: 30
SALES (corp-wide): 163.2MM **Privately Held**
WEB: www.cgicontainersales.com
SIC: 3731 7539 4212 Shipbuilding & repairing; frame repair shops, automotive; trailer repair; local trucking, without storage
HQ: Conglobal Industries, Llc
  8200 185th St Ste A
  Tinley Park IL 60487

(G-7380)
GP TERMINALS LLC
1606 Clinton Dr (77547-3274)
PHONE...................................713 209-7780
David Groves, *Director*
▲ EMP: 15
SALES (est): 3.7MM **Privately Held**
SIC: 3537 Containers (metal), air cargo

(G-7381)
PICK INSTRUMENT PRODUCTS CO
102 Eastway St (77547-2857)
P.O. Box 66 (77547-0066)
PHONE...................................713 672-1686
Hershel A Pickens Jr, *President*
Frank Pickens, *Vice Pres*
EMP: 20 EST: 1955
SQ FT: 60,000
SALES (est): 1.7MM **Privately Held**
WEB: www.pickinstrument.com
SIC: 3599 7692 3444 Machine shop, jobbing & repair; welding repair; sheet metalwork

(G-7382)
SOUTH COAST MANUFACTURING LLC
Also Called: SCM
502 S Main St (77547-3530)
PHONE...................................713 670-0900
Joe Ditta, *Managing Prtnr*
Joseph Ditta, *Mng Member*
EMP: 30
SQ FT: 25,000
SALES (est): 2.8MM **Privately Held**
WEB: www.southcoastmfg.com
SIC: 3549 Wiredrawing & fabricating machinery & equipment, ex. die

(G-7383)
TEXMARK CHEMICALS INC
900 Clinton Dr (77547-3461)
P.O. Box 67 (77547-0067)
PHONE...................................713 455-1206
Douglas H Smith, *President*
Sarah S Ragsdale, *Vice Pres*

Rory Moran, *CFO*
Eric Spore, *VP Sales*
George Sladecek, *Manager*
◆ EMP: 43
SQ FT: 4,000
SALES (est): 26.1MM
SALES (corp-wide): 26.3MM **Privately Held**
WEB: www.texmark.com
SIC: 2819 Industrial inorganic chemicals
PA: Chemical Exchange Industries, Inc.
  900 Clinton Dr
  Galena Park TX 77547
  713 455-1206

(G-7384)
UNION TANK CAR COMPANY
2011 Clinton Dr (77547-2836)
PHONE...................................713 926-6980
Denver Christian, *Area Mgr*
EMP: 29
SALES (corp-wide): 254.6B **Publicly Held**
WEB: www.utlx.com
SIC: 3743 Railroad equipment
HQ: Union Tank Car Company
  175 W Jackson Blvd # 2100
  Chicago IL 60604
  312 431-3111

(G-7385)
UNITED STATES GYPSUM COMPANY
1201 Mayo Shell Rd (77547)
P.O. Box 525 (77547-0525)
PHONE...................................713 308-5400
Dale Creed, *Maint Spvr*
George Mitchell, *Systems Staff*
EMP: 175
SALES (corp-wide): 8.2B **Privately Held**
WEB: www.usg.com
SIC: 3275 Wallboard, gypsum
HQ: United States Gypsum Company
  550 W Adams St Ste 1300
  Chicago IL 60661
  312 606-4000

(G-7386)
WESCO ACQUISITION PARTNERS INC
Also Called: Wesco Equipment
2333 Clinton Dr (77547-2623)
P.O. Box 924068, Houston (77292-4068)
PHONE...................................713 688-5551
Ronnie Davis, *President*
Sam Browne, *Senior VP*
▼ EMP: 36
SQ FT: 28,000
SALES (est): 5.6MM **Publicly Held**
SIC: 3625 5084 3823 3643 Actuators, industrial; industrial machinery & equipment; industrial instrmnts msrmnt display/control process variable; current-carrying wiring devices
HQ: Mrc Global (Us) Inc.
  1301 Mckinney St Ste 2300
  Houston TX 77010
  877 294-7574

Galveston
Galveston County

(G-7387)
ARAMCO HOME IMPROVEMENT LLC
208 Coconut St (77554-6130)
PHONE...................................409 762-9652
James Milan, *President*
Ronald Low, *Vice Pres*
EMP: 20 EST: 1938
SQ FT: 23,000
SALES (est): 3.2MM **Privately Held**
SIC: 2591 3442 Window blinds; shutters, door or window: metal

(G-7388)
BAYPORT MACHINE INC
314 Barracuda Ave (77550-3225)
P.O. Box 567, La Porte (77572-0567)
PHONE...................................281 471-6223
Mary Jo Naschke, *President*
Leroy J Naschke Jr, *Treasurer*
EMP: 10

G E O G R A P H I C

SALES (est): 1MM **Privately Held**
WEB: www.bayportmachine.com
SIC: 3599 Machine shop, jobbing & repair

(G-7389)
BLUDWORTH MARINE LLC
Also Called: Bludwrth Mar Galveston Shipyrd
6200 Harborside Dr (77554-2841)
PHONE..................................713 644-1595
Larry Burrows, *Purch Agent*
EMP: 9
SALES (corp-wide): 25.6MM **Privately Held**
WEB: www.vesselrepair.com
SIC: 3731 Shipbuilding & repairing
PA: Bludworth Marine, L.L.C.
320 77th St
Galveston TX 77554
713 644-1595

(G-7390)
BROOME WELDING CO
Also Called: Broome Welding & Machine Co.
7909 Bayside Ave (77554-7189)
PHONE..................................409 744-0407
Herbert C Broome, *President*
Chris Rupert, *Vice Pres*
Rogers Ruiz, *Foreman/Supr*
Dennis Sievers, *Supervisor*
EMP: 35
SQ FT: 15,000
SALES (est): 4.8MM **Privately Held**
WEB: www.broomewelding.com
SIC: 3446 3441 3599 Ornamental metal-work; fabricated structural metal; machine shop, jobbing & repair

(G-7391)
CANDY KINGS INC
Also Called: La King's Confectionery
2323 Strand St (77550-1517)
PHONE..................................409 762-6100
Jack King, *President*
EMP: 12 **EST:** 1997
SQ FT: 15,000
SALES (est): 835.4K **Privately Held**
WEB: www.lakingsconfectionery.com
SIC: 5441 2095 2066 2064 Candy; roasted coffee; chocolate & cocoa products; candy & other confectionery products; ice cream & frozen desserts

(G-7392)
CELESTE STEIN DESIGNS INC
7801 Bayside Ave (77554-7142)
PHONE..................................409 763-1009
Celeste Stein, *CEO*
Dori Golan, *President*
Kim Stein, *COO*
Ben Jay Stein, *Vice Pres*
▲ **EMP:** 15
SQ FT: 15,000
SALES (est): 2MM **Privately Held**
WEB: www.celestestein.com
SIC: 2252 Socks

(G-7393)
CNM HORIZON INVESTMENTS LLC
Also Called: Horizon Trailers
8126 Broadway St (77554-9167)
PHONE..................................713 333-3400
Charles E Pattillo, *Mng Member*
Darryl Swaby,
EMP: 22
SQ FT: 5,000
SALES (est): 1.8MM **Privately Held**
WEB: www.horizontrailers.com
SIC: 3799 Boat trailers

(G-7394)
CONVERSATION PIECES INC
Also Called: Old Strand Emporium
1428 Ball St (77550-4854)
PHONE..................................409 762-2799
Kyle Albright, *President*
Kathleen Albright, *Vice Pres*
EMP: 9
SQ FT: 5,700
SALES (est): 680.3K **Privately Held**
WEB: www.galveston.com
SIC: 5621 2339 5632 Ready-to-wear apparel, women's; women's & misses' outerwear; apparel accessories

(G-7395)
CROCODILE DIGITAL CORPORATION
305 21st St Ste 243 (77550-1678)
PHONE..................................713 382-1891
Stephen Fulcher, *CEO*
EMP: 15
SALES (est): 305.2K **Privately Held**
WEB: www.crocodiledigital.net
SIC: 7372 Application computer software

(G-7396)
FJCJ LLC
Also Called: Fairmont Minerals
5712 Harborside Dr (77554-2821)
PHONE..................................409 740-3355
Mark A Wnsio, *President*
Arturo Estrada, *Branch Mgr*
EMP: 10
SALES (corp-wide): 7.5MM **Privately Held**
WEB: www.us-minerals.com
SIC: 3295 Blast furnace slag
PA: Fjcj, Llc
2105 Northwinds Dr
Dyer IN

(G-7397)
FOUR BROTHERS BOAT WORKS INC
7500 Harborside Dr (77554-2876)
PHONE..................................409 229-4302
Richard R Ryan Sr, *President*
Jannette E Ryan, *Vice Pres*
Richard R Ryan Jr, *Vice Pres*
Tammy L Seiler, *Admin Sec*
EMP: 18 **EST:** 1952
SQ FT: 1,200
SALES (est): 3MM **Privately Held**
SIC: 3732 Boat building & repairing
PA: Columbia Star, Inc.
7500 Harborside Dr
Galveston TX 77554

(G-7398)
GALVESTON NEWSPAPERS INC (HQ)
Also Called: Galveston County Daily News
8522 Teichman Rd (77554-9119)
P.O. Box 628 (77553-0628)
PHONE..................................409 683-5200
Martha Walls, *President*
Dolph Pillotson, *President*
Amy Hollis, *Editor*
James Lacombe, *Editor*
Dlorah Collier, *Business Mgr*
EMP: 98 **EST:** 1842
SQ FT: 25,000
SALES (est): 69.8MM
SALES (corp-wide): 140.3MM **Privately Held**
WEB: www.galvnews.com
SIC: 2711 Commercial printing & newspaper publishing combined; newspapers, publishing & printing
PA: Southern Newspapers, Inc.
5701 Woodway Dr Ste 131
Houston TX 77057
713 266-5481

(G-7399)
GULF COPPER & MFG CORP
Also Called: Gulf Copper Drydock & Rig Repr
2920 Todd Rd (77554-2806)
PHONE..................................409 941-6200
Craig Marston, *General Mgr*
Lenar Hill, *Vice Pres*
Jonathan Hale, *Vice Pres*
Leonard Hale, *Vice Pres*
EMP: 9
SALES (corp-wide): 65.3MM **Privately Held**
WEB: www.gulfcopper.com
SIC: 3999 Barber & beauty shop equipment
PA: Gulf Copper & Manufacturing Corporation
5700 Procter Ext
Port Arthur TX 77642
409 989-0300

(G-7400)
HEMPSTEAD HALIDE INC
305 21st St Ste 228 (77550-1695)
P.O. Box 2630 (77553-2630)
PHONE..................................409 572-2505
Thomas E Hays, *President*
EMP: 12
SALES (est): 717.6K **Privately Held**
WEB: www.hempsteadhalide.com
SIC: 3826 7389 Analytical instruments;

(G-7401)
ISLAND CARRIAGES
2528 Post Office St (77550-1708)
PHONE..................................409 765-6951
Deborah L Steffens, *Owner*
EMP: 10
SALES (est): 578.1K **Privately Held**
SIC: 3799 Carriages, horse drawn

(G-7402)
JOSEPHINE TUG INC
Also Called: T & T Marine
9723 Teichman Rd (77554-9141)
PHONE..................................409 744-1222
EMP: 44
SQ FT: 10,000
SALES (est): 3MM **Privately Held**
WEB: www.teichmangroup.com
SIC: 4492 3732 7359 Tugboat service; boat building & repairing; equipment rental & leasing

(G-7403)
M-I LLC
Also Called: M-I Drilling Fluids
4814 Port Industrial Blvd (77554-2934)
P.O. Box 2117 (77553-2117)
PHONE..................................409 763-2249
Terry Barker, *Branch Mgr*
EMP: 20 **Publicly Held**
WEB: www.products.slb.com
SIC: 1389 3295 Oil field services; minerals, ground or treated
HQ: M-I L.L.C.
5950 N Course Dr
Houston TX 77072
281 561-1300

(G-7404)
MORGAN ROOFING
1311 42nd St (77550-3936)
P.O. Box 381, La Marque (77568-0381)
PHONE..................................409 762-8068
David Morgan, *Owner*
Linda Smith,
EMP: 34
SQ FT: 16,000
SALES (est): 2.7MM **Privately Held**
WEB: www.morganroofingtexas.com
SIC: 3444 1761 Sheet metalwork; roofing contractor

(G-7405)
PIER 19 MARINE FIELD
Also Called: Pier 19 Marine Fuel
19 Pier (77550-1787)
PHONE..................................409 763-5423
Edward Schroeder, *President*
Acosta C L Sr, *Vice Pres*
EMP: 30
SQ FT: 1,500
SALES (est): 3.3MM **Privately Held**
WEB: www.pier19marinefuels.com
SIC: 2869 5172 Fuels; fuel oil

(G-7406)
PRECISION MACHINE
6815 Stewart Rd (77551-1841)
P.O. Box 608, Athens (75751-0608)
PHONE..................................903 675-2300
EMP: 10
SALES (est): 1.1MM **Privately Held**
SIC: 3599 Mfg Industrial Machinery

(G-7407)
REAMA INC (PA)
Also Called: G & M Welding
5320 Sealy St (77551-4154)
P.O. Box 3629 (77552-0629)
PHONE..................................409 744-9222
George Sims, *President*
EMP: 12
SQ FT: 18,400

SALES (est): 1.4MM **Privately Held**
SIC: 7692 3441 3444 3089 Welding repair; fabricated structural metal; sheet metalwork; extruded finished plastic products; machine shop, jobbing & repair

(G-7408)
SMITH-HAMM INC
320 77th St (77554-9038)
PHONE..................................409 740-3314
Tad Humphreys, *President*
George H Lorton, *Director*
EMP: 85
SQ FT: 32,000
SALES (est): 41.9K **Privately Held**
WEB: www.malinshiprepair.com
SIC: 3731 Landing ships, building & repairing

(G-7409)
STEVEN-SHARON CORPORATION
Also Called: Industrial Material
7701 Harborside Dr (77554-2865)
PHONE..................................409 744-4538
Jayson Levy, *President*
Dave Hutchens, *Vice Pres*
David Hutchens, *Vice Pres*
Roger Pritchett, *Vice Pres*
Shawn Nelson, *Warehouse Mgr*
EMP: 66
SQ FT: 22,500
SALES (est): 13.2MM **Privately Held**
WEB: www.industrialmaterial.com
SIC: 3441 5051 5085 Fabricated structural metal; iron & steel (ferrous) products; steel; industrial supplies

(G-7410)
T & T MARINE SALVAGE INC
Also Called: T & T Offshore
2915 Todd Rd (77554-2807)
PHONE..................................409 621-4500
Phil Leasure, *Manager*
EMP: 16
SALES (corp-wide): 6MM **Privately Held**
WEB: www.teichmangroup.com
SIC: 1389 Oil field services
PA: T & T Marine Salvage, Inc.
9723 Teichman Rd
Galveston TX 77554
281 488-5757

(G-7411)
UNIVERSITY OF TX MED BRNCH GAL
Also Called: U T M B Biocommunication
1902 Harborside Dr # 2104 (77550-1692)
PHONE..................................409 772-5900
Vel Watkins, *Branch Mgr*
EMP: 71
SALES (corp-wide): 16.3B **Privately Held**
WEB: www.utmb.edu
SIC: 8221 2741 7374 University; business service newsletters: publishing & printing; computer graphics service
HQ: University Of Texas Medical Branch At Galveston
301 University Blvd
Galveston TX 77555

(G-7412)
US MINERALS INC
5712 Harborside Dr (77554-2821)
PHONE..................................409 740-3355
Glenn Hyzak, *Plant Mgr*
EMP: 15
SALES (corp-wide): 35.5MM **Privately Held**
WEB: www.us-minerals.com
SIC: 3291 Abrasive products
PA: U.S. Minerals, Inc.
18635 West Creek Dr Ste 1
Tinley Park IL 60477
708 623-1935

(G-7413)
WEST GULF MARINE LTD
6000 Harborside Dr (77554)
PHONE..................................409 744-0492
Brian Fiegel, *President*
Lloyd Dawson, *Vice Pres*
Keith Fiegel, *Vice Pres*
Bill Wood, *Vice Pres*
Anna Lander, *Payroll Mgr*
EMP: 70 **EST:** 1998

SALES (est): 24.1MM **Privately Held**
WEB: www.wgma.org
SIC: 3731 Barges, building & repairing

(G-7414)
YOGURT TECHNOLOGIES LLC
Also Called: Ytec
1202 Post Office St (77550-5041)
PHONE....................409 621-2060
Ralph McMorris, *CEO*
Clifton Morris, *COO*
Vivian Ho, *Sales Staff*
Lyndall McMorris, *Admin Sec*
◆ **EMP:** 18
SQ FT: 11,000
SALES (est): 3MM **Privately Held**
WEB: www.ltblender.com
SIC: 2023 Yogurt mix

Ganado
Jackson County

(G-7415)
JANSSEN LEASE SERVICE INC
204 York St (77962)
P.O. Box 375 (77962-0375)
PHONE....................361 771-3556
Bill F Janssen, *President*
Raunda Janssen, *Admin Sec*
EMP: 25
SQ FT: 600
SALES (est): 873K **Privately Held**
SIC: 1389 Oil field services

(G-7416)
W E HAYDEN LEASE SERVICE INC
281 Hwy 172 S (77962)
P.O. Box 290 (77962-0290)
PHONE....................361 771-3684
William Craig Hayden, *President*
Ed Prove, *Corp Secy*
Edward Prove, *Admin Sec*
EMP: 45 **EST:** 1960
SQ FT: 1,500
SALES (est): 3.8MM **Privately Held**
SIC: 1389 Oil field services

Garden City
Glasscock County

(G-7417)
TEXASTONE QUARRIES LLC
1400 Sherrod Rd (79739)
P.O. Box 38 (79739-0038)
PHONE....................432 354-2569
Wilson C Edwards, *Principal*
Brenda Edwards,
▲ **EMP:** 31
SQ FT: 54,000
SALES (est): 3.9MM **Privately Held**
WEB: www.texastone.com
SIC: 1411 1422 Limestone, dimension-quarrying; crushed & broken limestone

Garden Ridge
Comal County

(G-7418)
ARTISTIC COUNTERS INC
18630 Goll St (78266-2807)
PHONE....................210 651-3281
Scott Tonick, *President*
Susan Tonick, *Vice Pres*
Larry Tonick, *Treasurer*
EMP: 120
SQ FT: 26,000
SALES (est): 10.4MM
SALES (corp-wide): 19.4MM **Privately Held**
WEB: www.artisticcounters.com
SIC: 3281 1799 Granite, cut & shaped; counter top installation
PA: Empire Countertops, Llc
1137 Enterprise Dr
Pilot Point TX 76258
940 686-0000

(G-7419)
REDI-MIX LLC
Also Called: Custom-Crete
7998 Jethro Ln (78266-2157)
PHONE....................210 651-4141
John Scofield, *Managing Prtnr*
EMP: 20
SALES (corp-wide): 1.4B **Publicly Held**
WEB: www.us-concrete.com
SIC: 3273 Ready-mixed concrete
HQ: Redi-Mix, Llc
331 N Main St
Euless TX 76039
817 835-4105

Gardendale
Ector County

(G-7420)
CATALYST OILFLD SVCS 2016 LLC (HQ)
11999 E Us Highway 158 (79758-4341)
P.O. Box 8485, Midland (79708-8485)
PHONE....................432 563-0727
Justin Disney, *Engineer*
Wacey Moore, *Accounts Mgr*
Joseph Warner, *Accounts Mgr*
Crystal Castillo, *Technical Staff*
Dallas Disney, *Technical Staff*
EMP: 56
SALES (est): 157.7MM
SALES (corp-wide): 959.2MM **Privately Held**
WEB: www.catalystoilfield.com
SIC: 1389 Oil field services
PA: Ces Energy Solutions Corp
332 6 Ave Sw Suite 1400
Calgary AB T2P 0
403 269-2800

(G-7421)
PERMIAN POWER TONG INC
4512 E Us Highway 158 (79758-4331)
P.O. Box 625 (79758-0625)
PHONE....................432 550-7386
Curtis S Lemons, *President*
Liz Lemons, *Corp Secy*
Elizabeth Lemons, *Treasurer*
EMP: 50
SQ FT: 2,500
SALES (est): 4.4MM **Privately Held**
WEB: www.permianpowertong.com
SIC: 1389 Running, cutting & pulling casings, tubes & rods; oil field services

Garland
Dallas County

(G-7422)
3JG PRINTING LLC
614 N 1st St (75040-5704)
PHONE....................214 553-8664
Joshua Hewitt, *CEO*
Gary Hewitt, *Vice Pres*
Julie Hewitt, *Vice Pres*
Scott Hayes, *Production*
Joanna Hewitt, *CFO*
EMP: 17
SQ FT: 15,000
SALES (est): 3MM **Privately Held**
WEB: www.3jgprinting.com
SIC: 2752 Commercial printing, offset

(G-7423)
A&C GREEN ENERGY INC
1839 Wall St (75041-4052)
P.O. Box 251694, Plano (75025-1516)
PHONE....................972 516-0692
Jeff Lee, *President*
EMP: 9
SALES (est): 886.6K **Privately Held**
WEB: www.acgreenenergy.com
SIC: 3511 Turbines & turbine generator sets

(G-7424)
A-1 POWDER COAT PAINT INC
1410 N 1st St (75040-5108)
PHONE....................972 494-6861
O E Collier, *President*
EMP: 18

SALES (est): 2.4MM **Privately Held**
WEB: www.a1powdercoat.com
SIC: 3479 Coating of metals & formed products

(G-7425)
ABC EXCLUSIVE INC
430 Forest Gate Dr (75042-6513)
PHONE....................972 485-8182
Nicholas Burgstein, *President*
▲ **EMP:** 60
SQ FT: 10,000
SALES (est): 2MM **Privately Held**
WEB: www.abcexclusive.com
SIC: 3465 5531 3711 3429 Body parts, automobile: stamped metal; automotive & home supply stores; motor vehicles & car bodies; manufactured hardware (general)

(G-7426)
ABRASIVE BLAST SYSTEMS LLC
Also Called: ABS Blast
250 S Shiloh Rd (75042-6633)
PHONE....................972 205-9309
Eric G Thomas, *President*
Cassie Carlisle, *General Mgr*
Lance E Gayle, *Vice Pres*
Johan Van Zyl, *Engineer*
Lance Gayle, *VP Sales*
EMP: 20
SALES (est): 5.6MM **Privately Held**
WEB: www.absblast.com
SIC: 3312 Blast furnaces & steel mills

(G-7427)
ACTION SPORTSWEAR INC
Also Called: Action Signs & Banner
1101 Main St (75040-6130)
PHONE....................972 487-6960
Norman Martin, *President*
Sally Barber Martin, *Vice Pres*
EMP: 20
SQ FT: 20,000
SALES (est): 1.9MM **Privately Held**
WEB: www.actionshirts.com
SIC: 2759 3993 Screen printing; signs & advertising specialties

(G-7428)
ADVANCED MATERIALS GROUP INC
2364 Merritt Dr Ste A (75041-6174)
PHONE....................469 246-4100
Timothy R Busch, *Ch of Bd*
Marty Lehman, *Interim Pres*
EMP: 66 **Privately Held**
SIC: 3069 3955 Medical & laboratory rubber sundries & related products; carbon paper & inked ribbons

(G-7429)
AFB MANUFACTURING LLC
Also Called: Atlantic Food Bars
2450 Merritt Dr (75041-6145)
PHONE....................410 581-0300
Carl Feldman, *President*
EMP: 100
SALES (est): 20MM **Privately Held**
WEB: www.atlanticfoodbars.com
SIC: 3585 Refrigeration & heating equipment

(G-7430)
AFFECTS SAT CORPORATION
7109 Christina Ln (75043-6620)
PHONE....................713 897-9935
Ray Ashton, *Chairman*
EMP: 55
SALES (est): 1.8MM **Privately Held**
SIC: 3812 Search & navigation equipment

(G-7431)
AKFIX USA INC
238 Lavon Dr (75040-6522)
PHONE....................972 276-9600
Yasser Alhamzawi, *Vice Pres*
▲ **EMP:** 86
SALES (est): 5.5MM **Privately Held**
SIC: 2891 Adhesives & sealants

(G-7432)
ALLTEK CIRCUITS INCORPORATED
3524 Dividend Dr (75042-7606)
PHONE....................949 250-4499
Aneel Romolia, *President*
EMP: 9
SQ FT: 4,800
SALES (est): 800K **Privately Held**
WEB: www.alltekcircuit.com
SIC: 3672 Printed circuit boards

(G-7433)
AMERICAN DUCT SYSTEMS INC
601 E Walnut Cir (75040-6540)
PHONE....................972 494-7300
Cary Hearn, *CEO*
EMP: 9
SALES (est): 1.4MM **Privately Held**
WEB: www.americanduct.net
SIC: 3444 Sheet metalwork

(G-7434)
AMERICAN EAGLE ENTENPRISE
Also Called: Shutters Manufacturers
3114 Benton St (75042-7410)
PHONE....................972 494-3357
Mark Nguyen, *Owner*
EMP: 10
SALES (est): 739.2K **Privately Held**
WEB: www.aeshutters.com
SIC: 2431 Blinds (shutters), wood

(G-7435)
AMERICAN SIGNAL CORPORATION
3524 Dividend Dr (75042-7606)
PHONE....................414 358-8000
Sheetal Ghelani, *President*
Jaysharee Vekaria, *Principal*
Dougalsa Holub, *Vice Pres*
Alckal Thomas, *Vice Pres*
John Beimborn, *Purch Mgr*
EMP: 20
SQ FT: 18,000
SALES (est): 2MM **Privately Held**
WEB: www.americansignal.com
SIC: 3669 Traffic signals, electric

(G-7436)
AMORPHOUS MATERIALS INC
3130 Benton St (75042-7410)
PHONE....................972 494-5624
Albert Ray Hilton II, *Ch of Bd*
Albert Ray Hilton III, *President*
Greg Whaley, *President*
Madora Hilton, *Vice Pres*
EMP: 9
SQ FT: 7,000
SALES (est): 1.5MM **Privately Held**
WEB: www.amorphousmaterials.com
SIC: 3339 3827 Silicon, pure; optical elements & assemblies, except ophthalmic

(G-7437)
AMTEX CORP (HQ)
Also Called: Sunbelt Modular
832 E Walnut St (75040-6698)
PHONE....................972 276-7626
Ronald Procunier, *President*
Joe Reid, *General Mgr*
William Richardson, *Purch Mgr*
Tim Haviland, *Engineer*
Dean Kennedy, *CFO*
EMP: 100
SALES (est): 12.4MM
SALES (corp-wide): 87.7MM **Privately Held**
WEB: www.amtexcorp.com
SIC: 2452 Modular homes, prefabricated, wood
PA: Sunbelt Modular, Inc.
832 E Walnut St
Garland TX 75040
972 276-7626

(G-7438)
APEX PLASTICS & TOOLING INC
3625 Miller Park Dr Ste A (75042-7536)
PHONE....................972 205-9000
Brian Anderson, *CEO*
Thomas O'Connor, *President*
Ed Dobrzenski, *Purchasing*
Howard Cohen, *Sales Mgr*

Bryan Hagan, *Sales Mgr*
▲ **EMP:** 27
SQ FT: 44,000
SALES (est): 6.1MM **Privately Held**
WEB: www.prototypesfdm.com
SIC: 3089 3544 Injection molding of plastics; special dies & tools

(G-7439)
APPLIANCE CONTROLS TEXAS CORP
2734 W Kingsley Rd Ste J2 (75041-2434)
P.O. Box 1068, Rowlett (75030-1068)
PHONE..............................214 501-3880
Edward Gray, *President*
Doretha Gray, *Corp Secy*
Brad Gray, *Vice Pres*
Dennis Gray, *Vice Pres*
▲ **EMP:** 45 **EST:** 1981
SQ FT: 8,000
SALES (est): 7.6MM **Privately Held**
WEB: www.actexas.com
SIC: 3625 3566 Motor controls, electric; speed changers, drives & gears

(G-7440)
ARA AUTOMOTIVE SYSTEMS INC
3405 Express Dr (75041-6128)
P.O. Box 602, Frisco (75034-0011)
PHONE..............................214 537-1659
Robert M Foley, *President*
William Gonzales, *Vice Pres*
Allen R Smith, *Admin Sec*
▲ **EMP:** 25
SQ FT: 12,000
SALES (est): 3.2MM **Privately Held**
SIC: 3714 5075 Air conditioner parts, motor vehicle; automotive air conditioners

(G-7441)
ARENA BRANDS INC (HQ)
601 Marion Dr (75042-7930)
PHONE..............................972 494-7133
John R Muse, *Ch of Bd*
Paul E Lavoie, *President*
Thomas A Hough, *CFO*
Patrick J Corbett, *Controller*
Jane Buchanan, *Executive Asst*
▲ **EMP:** 11
SQ FT: 285,000
SALES (est): 155.7MM **Privately Held**
SIC: 2353 Caps: cloth, straw & felt; hats: cloth, straw & felt; uniform hats & caps

(G-7442)
ARROW FABRICATED TUBING LTD (PA)
1010 E Walnut St (75040-6614)
PHONE..............................972 276-3010
Arlene Navias, *Partner*
Louis K Navias, *General Ptnr*
Ken Lamb, *Vice Pres*
Gary Scarbro, *Plant Mgr*
Ken Harmon, *Materials Mgr*
▼ **EMP:** 200
SQ FT: 200,000
SALES (est): 46.6MM **Privately Held**
WEB: www.arrowtube.com
SIC: 3444 Sheet metalwork

(G-7443)
ATLANTIC FOOD BARS INC
2450 Merritt Dr (75041-6145)
PHONE..............................888 632-5765
Carl Feldman, *President*
Michael Granados, *Purch Mgr*
Aron Thiehoff, *Engineer*
Jeannine Clack, *Manager*
Julia Truitt, *Assistant*
EMP: 100
SALES (est): 17MM **Privately Held**
WEB: www.atlanticfoodbars.com
SIC: 3585 Refrigeration & heating equipment

(G-7444)
AUTOMATIC PRODUCTS CORP
2735 Forest Ln (75042-6510)
PHONE..............................972 272-6422
Chris Tedford, *President*
Jim Boyd, *Principal*
Gary Tedford, *Chairman*
Tom Jamnongjit, *Engineer*
▲ **EMP:** 125

SQ FT: 155,000
SALES: 8.5MM **Privately Held**
WEB: www.ap-corp.com
SIC: 3599 3829 3451 Machine shop, jobbing & repair; measuring & controlling devices; screw machine products

(G-7445)
AYC GROUP LLC
1036 S Jupiter Rd Ste 200 (75042-7779)
PHONE..............................214 838-2630
EC Chen, *President*
Philip Chen, *General Mgr*
Linda Chen, *Admin Sec*
▲ **EMP:** 12
SQ FT: 6,000
SALES (est): 1.7MM **Privately Held**
WEB: www.aycllc.com
SIC: 3999 Massage machines, electric: barber & beauty shops

(G-7446)
AZZ INC
Also Called: Azz Pwder Coating Pltg Garland
2314 Executive Dr (75041-6121)
PHONE..............................972 840-0934
Thomas Ferguson, *President*
EMP: 40
SALES (corp-wide): 1B **Publicly Held**
WEB: www.azz.com
SIC: 3443 3471 Fabricated plate work (boiler shop); plating & polishing
PA: Azz Inc.
  3100 W 7th St Ste 500
  Fort Worth TX 76107
  817 810-0095

(G-7447)
BALLY UNITED PRODUCE LTD
429 Forest Gate Dr (75042-6514)
PHONE..............................972 487-7788
Sergio Wong, *CEO*
EMP: 40
SQ FT: 42,000
SALES (est): 5MM **Privately Held**
SIC: 2015 Chicken, processed: fresh

(G-7448)
BANDY INCORPORATED
201 S International Rd (75042-6535)
PHONE..............................972 276-6516
Dow P Young, *President*
Aaron Young, *Marketing Staff*
Young Dow, *Technology*
Daisy Young, *Training Spec*
▲ **EMP:** 15
SQ FT: 45,000
SALES (est): 2.6MM **Privately Held**
WEB: www.bandyco.com
SIC: 3499 2522 Chair frames, metal; office furniture, except wood

(G-7449)
BOB LILLYS PROF MKTG GROUP INC
Also Called: Bob Lilly Prof Promotions
4002 W Miller Rd Ste 140 (75041-6160)
PHONE..............................214 231-2082
Bob Lilly, *President*
Andrea Weston, *Opers Staff*
Julie Lilly, *CFO*
Courtney Langley, *Accounts Mgr*
Thom Roberts, *Accounts Exec*
▲ **EMP:** 20
SQ FT: 6,500
SALES (est): 6MM **Privately Held**
WEB: www.boblillypromo.com
SIC: 5199 7336 2732 8743 Advertising specialties; commercial art & graphic design; commercial art & illustration; pamphlets: printing only, not published on site; sales promotion

(G-7450)
BRACE STEEL COMPONENTS LLC
Also Called: Brace Manufacturing Company
540 Easy St (75042-6809)
PHONE..............................972 272-2016
Matthew Brace, *CEO*
Nichole Brace, *President*
EMP: 10
SALES (est): 440.4K **Privately Held**
WEB: www.bracesteel.com
SIC: 3484 Guns (firearms) or gun parts, 30 mm. & below

(G-7451)
BUFERD COMPANY INC
Also Called: Unity Manufacturing
210 E Buckingham Rd (75040-4710)
P.O. Box 462321 (75046-2321)
PHONE..............................972 272-9502
Richard M Buferd II, *President*
Cullen York, *COO*
Moises Solano, *Vice Pres*
Bernice Buferd, *Admin Sec*
Sandra Bailey, *Assistant*
EMP: 95 **EST:** 1958
SQ FT: 122,000
SALES (est): 29.9MM **Privately Held**
WEB: www.unitymfg.com
SIC: 3469 3444 Electronic enclosures, stamped or pressed metal; sheet metalwork

(G-7452)
CAKE CRAFT FACTORY LLC
2001 Platinum St (75042-6662)
PHONE..............................469 782-2500
William Naim, *CEO*
Harry Steck, *CFO*
EMP: 35
SQ FT: 42,000
SALES (est): 5.9MM **Privately Held**
WEB: www.cakecraftusa.com
SIC: 2051 Bread, cake & related products

(G-7453)
CAREER CONCEPTS INC
Also Called: Reflections of Dallas
210 Bronze St (75042-6650)
PHONE..............................972 276-9332
Barbara Lambert, *President*
▲ **EMP:** 22
SALES (est): 2.1MM **Privately Held**
WEB: www.reflectionsofdallas.com
SIC: 2337 Uniforms, except athletic: women's, misses' & juniors'

(G-7454)
CDR MACHINE & FABRICATING INC
209 S Kirby St Ste 312 (75042-7423)
PHONE..............................972 272-9145
Charles Robinson, *President*
Gary Madole, *Director*
EMP: 14
SQ FT: 10,000
SALES (est): 2.4MM **Privately Held**
WEB: www.cdrmachine.com
SIC: 3599 Machine shop, jobbing & repair

(G-7455)
CE LABS LLC
3209 Wood Dr (75041-6142)
PHONE..............................469 429-9200
John Swanson, *CEO*
Jeff Thorne, *Engineer*
Sealtiel Avalos, *Design Engr*
Bob Paton, *CFO*
Blaine Semple, *Marketing Staff*
EMP: 40
SALES (est): 1.4MM **Privately Held**
WEB: www.proav.celabs.net
SIC: 3651 Household audio & video equipment

(G-7456)
CHICO STONE INC
4217 N Garland Ave (75040-8512)
P.O. Box 461012 (75046-1012)
PHONE..............................972 276-2284
Thomas E Chambers, *Ch of Bd*
Eugene A Chambers, *President*
Alice Nicholson, *Admin Sec*
EMP: 30
SALES (est): 1.6MM **Privately Held**
SIC: 1422 Crushed & broken limestone

(G-7457)
CLARION TECH LONESTAR INC
2405 S Shiloh Rd (75041-1344)
PHONE..............................972 278-9700
John Brownlow, *President*
Patrick Kinstle, *CFO*
EMP: 100
SQ FT: 64,000
SALES (est): 2.8MM **Privately Held**
SIC: 3089 Plastic containers, except foam

(G-7458)
CLEAN AIR CONSULTANTS INC
Also Called: Filter 1 Clean Air Consultants
2525 National Dr (75041-2351)
PHONE..............................972 278-2664
Frank Watson, *President*
Clifford Watson, *Owner*
EMP: 80
SQ FT: 20,000
SALES (est): 6.5MM **Privately Held**
WEB: www.filter-1.com
SIC: 5075 3564 8748 7389 Air pollution control equipment & supplies; ventilating equipment & supplies; dust collecting equipment; air cleaning systems; ventilating fans: industrial or commercial; dust or fume collecting equipment, industrial; environmental consultant; air pollution measuring service

(G-7459)
COL-MET GP LLC
3333 Miller Park S (75042-7772)
PHONE..............................972 494-3900
Jim Collier, *President*
Diane Collier, *Admin Sec*
EMP: 45
SALES (est): 10.8MM **Privately Held**
WEB: www.colmet.com
SIC: 3444 Forming machine work, sheet metal

(G-7460)
COLE INDUSTRIES INC
2644 National Pl (75041-2343)
PHONE..............................972 271-0280
Lawrence L Cole, *President*
Chris Reviel, *Sales Engr*
Angela Cisneros, *Admin Asst*
▼ **EMP:** 13 **EST:** 1974
SQ FT: 20,000
SALES (est): 3MM **Privately Held**
WEB: www.coleindustries.com
SIC: 3365 Aluminum & aluminum-based alloy castings

(G-7461)
COLLIER METAL SPECIALTIES LTD
Also Called: Col-Met
3333 Miller Park S (75042-7772)
PHONE..............................972 494-3900
James C Collier Jr, *Principal*
Isaac Simmons, *Opers Staff*
EMP: 11
SALES (est): 578.1K **Privately Held**
WEB: www.colmet.com
SIC: 3444 Sheet metalwork

(G-7462)
CONTRACT POWDER COATING INC
Also Called: Southwest Industrial Eqp Svc
549 N 5th St (75040-5005)
P.O. Box 180175, Dallas (75218-0175)
PHONE..............................972 494-4444
Tom Grunheid, *President*
EMP: 15
SQ FT: 20,000
SALES (est): 1.7MM **Privately Held**
WEB: www.contractpowder.com
SIC: 3479 Coating of metals & formed products; painting, coating & hot dipping

(G-7463)
COOPER CONCRETE CO
1100 N 5th St (75040-5036)
P.O. Box 461118 (75046-1118)
PHONE..............................972 276-1167
Thomas Cooper, *President*
Deborah Ross, *Vice Pres*
John Cooper, *Treasurer*
EMP: 22
SQ FT: 4,000
SALES (est): 7.3MM **Privately Held**
WEB: www.cooperconcrete.com
SIC: 3273 Ready-mixed concrete

(G-7464)
CORONA DESIGNS INC
828 E Walnut St (75040-6610)
P.O. Box 774, Rowlett (75030-0774)
PHONE..............................972 272-0471
EMP: 25 **EST:** 1974
SQ FT: 15,000

▲ = Import ▼ =Export
◆ =Import/Export

SALES (est): 326.7K **Privately Held**
SIC: 3559 Mfg Misc Industry Machinery

(G-7465)
CORRUGATED SERVICES GARLAND
726 E Walnut St (75040-6608)
PHONE..................................972 494-4059
Forest Felvey, *Principal*
EMP: 9
SALES (est): 1.2MM **Privately Held**
WEB: www.garlandisd.net
SIC: 2653 Corrugated & solid fiber boxes

(G-7466)
COSMAX NBT USA INC
3350 Marquis Dr (75042-7743)
PHONE..................................469 661-9700
EMP: 200
SALES (est): 7.5MM **Privately Held**
SIC: 2023 Mfg Dry/Evaporated Dairy Products

(G-7467)
COSMAX NBT USA INC
3366 Miller Park S (75042-7771)
PHONE..................................469 298-2222
Kwon Jin Hyuk, *CEO*
Byung Joo Lee, *President*
James Lee, *Accounts Mgr*
▲ EMP: 100
SALES: 9.7MM **Privately Held**
WEB: www.nutribiotechusa.com
SIC: 2023 Dietary supplements, dairy & non-dairy based

(G-7468)
COURTER-HALL COMPANY
1910 N 1st St (75040-4799)
PHONE..................................972 276-8531
Corky Hall, *President*
Martha Dean, *Vice Pres*
EMP: 16
SQ FT: 8,000
SALES (est): 876.9K **Privately Held**
WEB: www.courterhall.com
SIC: 3471 Electroplating of metals or formed products

(G-7469)
COUTURE AMERICAN LIFESTYLE
3620 Marquis Dr (75042-7513)
PHONE..................................972 487-1641
Nan Martin, *President*
EMP: 30
SALES (est): 550K **Privately Held**
SIC: 2339 Women's & misses' athletic clothing & sportswear

(G-7470)
CPM INC
Also Called: Custom Photo Manufacturing
2447 Merritt Dr (75041-6146)
P.O. Box 550367, Dallas (75355-0367)
PHONE..................................214 349-6886
Stephen Crane, *President*
▲ EMP: 10
SQ FT: 20,300
SALES (est): 1.7MM **Privately Held**
WEB: www.cpmdelta1.com
SIC: 3861 3648 Motion picture film; lighting equipment

(G-7471)
CROWN TEXAS INC
2350 Crist Rd Ste 1300 (75040-3716)
PHONE..................................972 905-4680
EMP: 80
SALES (est): 11.3MM **Privately Held**
SIC: 3613 Control panels, electric
PA: Crown Technical Systems
13470 Philadelphia Ave
Fontana CA 92337

(G-7472)
D C A E INC (PA)
Also Called: Delta Communications & Elec
2162 S Jupiter Rd (75041-6004)
PHONE..................................972 278-0202
Wayne E Lott, *President*
EMP: 24
SQ FT: 6,000

SALES (est): 3MM **Privately Held**
WEB: www.delta2000.com
SIC: 5065 5999 5731 3663 Communication equipment; communication equipment; radios, two-way, citizens' band, weather, short-wave, etc.; radio broadcasting & communications equipment

(G-7473)
D-SIGNS INC
2602 National Pl (75041-2343)
PHONE..................................214 327-2373
Jason Horton, *President*
Eric Horton, *Treasurer*
EMP: 50
SQ FT: 5,000
SALES (est): 5MM **Privately Held**
SIC: 3993 7312 Signs & advertising specialties; outdoor advertising services

(G-7474)
DAC VISION INCORPORATED (DH)
3630 W Miller Rd Ste 350 (75041-6050)
PHONE..................................972 677-2700
Richard Bullwinkle, *CEO*
Jean Michel Balmelle, *President*
David Meisekheimer, *President*
Denny Hall, *Area Mgr*
Cdric Pannetier, *Area Mgr*
◆ EMP: 51
SQ FT: 47,000
SALES (est): 42.1MM
SALES (corp-wide): 1.7MM **Privately Held**
WEB: www.dactechnologies.com
SIC: 5049 3851 5048 3827 Optical goods; ophthalmic goods; ophthalmic goods; optical instruments & lenses
HQ: Dac Vision
Zone Industrielle
Perigny 17180
546 272-724

(G-7475)
DAISY BRAND LLC
3636 Leon Rd (75041-4037)
PHONE..................................972 271-7314
Kevin Longville, *Buyer*
Ashraf Hassan, *Research*
Jordan Bryan, *Engineer*
Ted Rodgers, *Human Res Mgr*
Charlie Bucheit, *Sales Mgr*
EMP: 70
SALES (corp-wide): 211MM **Privately Held**
WEB: www.daisybrand.com
SIC: 2026 Milk processing (pasteurizing, homogenizing, bottling); cream, sour
PA: Daisy Brand, Llc
12750 Merit Dr Ste 600
Dallas TX 75251
972 726-0800

(G-7476)
DATA MATIQUE PROPERTIES LP
2110 Sherwin St (75041-1217)
PHONE..................................972 272-3446
C A Theis, *General Mgr*
Allen R Werner, *General Ptnr*
Terry Edney, *Purchasing*
Scott Young, *Info Tech Mgr*
▲ EMP: 104 EST: 2004
SQ FT: 80,000
SALES (est): 13MM **Privately Held**
WEB: www.data-matique.com
SIC: 3444 7692 3541 Housings for business machines, sheet metal; welding repair; machine tools, metal cutting type

(G-7477)
DAWN FOOD PRODUCTS INC
3353 Miller Park S # 100 (75042-7798)
PHONE..................................972 485-8004
Becky Dost, *General Mgr*
Kevin Tarpley, *General Mgr*
Jeff Robertson, *Warehouse Mgr*
Matt Weber, *Sales Mgr*
Wendy Westmoreland, *Marketing Staff*
EMP: 30

SALES (corp-wide): 1.7B **Privately Held**
WEB: www.dawnfoods.com
SIC: 2045 5084 5046 Doughnut mixes, prepared: from purchased flour; food industry machinery; bakery equipment & supplies
HQ: Dawn Food Products, Inc.
3333 Sargent Rd
Jackson MI 49201

(G-7478)
DENSONONE LLC
Also Called: Garland Service Company
714 Shepherd Dr (75042-6833)
PHONE..................................972 494-1911
Eric Nelson, *COO*
Todd Crawford, *Supervisor*
Britt Smith,
EMP: 27
SQ FT: 17,100
SALES (est): 4.4MM **Privately Held**
WEB: www.gscusa.net
SIC: 3544 Special dies, tools, jigs & fixtures

(G-7479)
DISPLAY SOURCE ALLIANCE LLC (HQ)
4010 Dist Dr Ste 200 (75041)
PHONE..................................972 288-7471
Henry Leaverton, *CEO*
Tom Norman, *Vice Pres*
Martin Harper, *CFO*
▲ EMP: 130
SALES (est): 30.2MM
SALES (corp-wide): 39.2MM **Privately Held**
WEB: www.dsadisplay.com
SIC: 3496 Miscellaneous fabricated wire products
PA: Display Source Design & Factory, Ltd.
1371 S Town East Blvd
Mesquite TX 75149
972 288-7471

(G-7480)
DMN INC
613 W State St (75040-6328)
PHONE..................................214 745-8383
Ray Leszcynski, *Manager*
EMP: 30 **Publicly Held**
WEB: www.dallasnews.com
SIC: 2711 7313 Newspapers, publishing & printing; newspaper advertising representative
HQ: Dmn, Inc.
1954 Commerce St
Dallas TX 75201

(G-7481)
DOWNHOLE ENERGY LLC
310 E Interstate 30 (75043-8000)
PHONE..................................469 250-7179
EMP: 9 EST: 2014
SALES (est): 395.8K **Privately Held**
SIC: 1381 Drilling oil & gas wells

(G-7482)
E Z FILTER BASE MANUFACTURING
406 S Barnes Dr (75042-7325)
PHONE..................................972 272-5800
Terry Youngblood, *President*
Gail Jackson, *Vice Pres*
Jeff Jackson, *VP Sales*
EMP: 15
SQ FT: 20,000
SALES (est): 2.1MM **Privately Held**
WEB: www.ezfilterbase.com
SIC: 3624 Carbon & graphite products

(G-7483)
ECOLAB INC
2305 Sherwin St (75041-1222)
PHONE..................................972 840-3994
Kevin Smith, *Prdtn Mgr*
Roger Billmer, *Branch Mgr*
Ignacio Martinez, *Manager*
EMP: 75
SQ FT: 186,340
SALES (corp-wide): 14.9B **Publicly Held**
WEB: www.ecolab.com
SIC: 2841 2842 Detergents, synthetic organic or inorganic alkaline; specialty cleaning, polishes & sanitation goods

PA: Ecolab Inc.
1 Ecolab Pl
Saint Paul MN 55102
800 232-6522

(G-7484)
EGRET MEDICAL PRODUCTS INC
2713 Industrial Ln (75041-2304)
PHONE..................................214 291-0238
August Eltz, *President*
Richard Cdowdy, *Vice Pres*
EMP: 10
SALES (est): 891.4K **Privately Held**
WEB: www.egretmedical.com
SIC: 3841 Medical instruments & equipment, blood & bone work

(G-7485)
EISENBECK CORPORATION
Also Called: Eisenbeck Corp SEC Fire Div
3814 Marquis Dr Ste 103 (75042-7510)
PHONE..................................972 526-5235
Robert K Eisenbeck II, *President*
EMP: 10
SQ FT: 4,000
SALES (est): 898.5K **Privately Held**
WEB: www.eisenbeck.com
SIC: 1731 3699 5063 Fire detection & burglar alarm systems specialization; photographic control systems, electronic; fire alarm systems

(G-7486)
EPIROC DRILLING SOLUTIONS LLC (HQ)
2100 N 1st St (75040-4102)
P.O. Box 462288 (75046-2288)
PHONE..................................972 496-7400
Jose Manuel Sanchez, *President*
Jerry Enyeart, *District Mgr*
Tom Schwind, *Vice Pres*
Timothy Storm, *Vice Pres*
◆ EMP: 800
SALES (est): 647.2MM
SALES (corp-wide): 4.2B **Privately Held**
WEB: www.us.atlascopco.com
SIC: 3541 Drilling & boring machines
PA: Epiroc Ab
Sickla Industrivag 19
Nacka 131 5
107 550-000

(G-7487)
EPIROC NORTH AMERICA CORP
2100 N 1st St (75040-4102)
PHONE..................................972 496-7353
Roger Goransson, *Vice Pres*
Billye Kudrna, *Purchasing*
Sherry Dealmas, *Auditor*
Tanya Tyler, *Human Resources*
Gregory Gawlik, *Manager*
EMP: 2696
SALES (corp-wide): 184.5MM **Privately Held**
SIC: 3532 Mining machinery
PA: Epiroc North America Corp.
3700 E 68th Ave
Commerce City CO 80022
303 287-8822

(G-7488)
EPSILON INDUSTRIES INC
3538 Dividend Dr (75042-7606)
PHONE..................................469 573-9566
Daniel Naramor, *President*
Trey Austin, *Director*
EMP: 10
SALES (est): 1.4MM **Privately Held**
WEB: www.epsilonindustries.com
SIC: 3089 Injection molding of plastics

(G-7489)
FGL GROUP LLC
Also Called: Montgomery Manufacturing
2900 W Kingsley Rd (75042-2311)
PHONE..................................817 478-3221
Peter G Zehr, *Principal*
EMP: 50
SALES (est): 9.1MM **Privately Held**
WEB: www.fglgroup.com
SIC: 3086 Business consulting

(G-7490)
FIRST PLACE FOODS LLC
515 Mills Rd (75040-6833)
PHONE..................................972 272-1111
Pat Hunn, *President*
Collin Hunn, *Vice Pres*
John Wilson, *Vice Pres*
Tyler Hansen, *Supervisor*
EMP: 30
SQ FT: 20,800
SALES (est): 7.2MM **Privately Held**
WEB: www.firstplacefoods.com
SIC: 2035 Pickled fruits & vegetables; pickles, vinegar; relishes, fruit & vegetable

(G-7491)
FORTRESS IRON LP
Also Called: Fortress Company, The
1720 N 1st St (75040-4702)
PHONE..................................972 231-4001
Matt Sherstad, *Managing Prtnr*
Floyd A Young, *Accounting Mgr*
Floyd Young, *Accounting Mgr*
Pat Bailey, *Sales Staff*
Paul Francis, *Sales Staff*
▲ **EMP:** 93
SQ FT: 50,000
SALES (est): 13.5MM **Privately Held**
WEB: www.fortressbp.com
SIC: 3446 Fences or posts, ornamental iron or steel

(G-7492)
GALT MEDICAL CORP (DH)
2220 Merritt Dr (75041-6137)
PHONE..................................972 271-5177
M Christine Jacobs, *President*
James R Eddings, *President*
Donald Fuhrmann, *Prdtn Mgr*
Emmett Harrison, *Materials Mgr*
Bruce Nedd, *Engineer*
EMP: 36
SQ FT: 14,000
SALES (est): 13.5MM
SALES (corp-wide): 88.1MM **Privately Held**
WEB: www.galtmedical.com
SIC: 3841 Surgical & medical instruments
HQ: Theragenics Corporation
    5203 Bristol Indus Way
    Buford GA 30518
    770 373-7099

(G-7493)
GARLAND DRAPERY INC
1918 Copper St (75042-6677)
PHONE..................................972 276-5297
Sarah Butler, *President*
Bobby Butler, *Vice Pres*
EMP: 10
SQ FT: 4,000
SALES (est): 1MM **Privately Held**
SIC: 5714 2391 Draperies; curtains & draperies

(G-7494)
GARLAND INDEPENDENT SCHOOL DST
Also Called: Print Shop
414 Stadium Dr (75040-4698)
PHONE..................................972 494-8580
Alan Smith, *Branch Mgr*
Tom Vaughan, *Asst Director*
Mary Garcia, *Admin Sec*
EMP: 75
SALES (corp-wide): 669.7MM **Privately Held**
WEB: www.garlandisd.net
SIC: 8211 2621 Public elementary & secondary schools; printing paper
PA: Garland Independent School District
    501 S Jupiter Rd
    Garland TX 75042
    972 494-8201

(G-7495)
GARLAND STEEL INC (PA)
312 S International Rd (75042-6536)
P.O. Box 460730 (75046-0730)
PHONE..................................972 494-6000
David Becker, *President*
William R Becker, *Vice Pres*
Marc I Becker, *Vice Pres*
▲ **EMP:** 25
SQ FT: 200,000
SALES (est): 12.2MM **Privately Held**
WEB: www.garlandsteel.com
SIC: 5051 3341 Steel; secondary nonferrous metals

(G-7496)
GARLAND VENTURES LTD
Also Called: Bally Plus
115 S Intl Rd Ste A (75042)
PHONE..................................972 485-8878
Leon Hsu, *President*
Laurence Hsu, *Plant Mgr*
Lin Chao, *QC Mgr*
▲ **EMP:** 40
SQ FT: 32,000
SALES (est): 8.5MM **Privately Held**
WEB: www.ballyplus.com
SIC: 2038 Dinners, frozen & packaged

(G-7497)
GARRETT ELECTRONICS INC
Also Called: Garrett Metal Detectors
1881 W State St (75042-6797)
PHONE..................................972 494-6151
Charles L Garrett, *President*
Eleanor Garrett, *Vice Pres*
Perry Bohling, *Director*
◆ **EMP:** 180 **EST:** 1965
SQ FT: 75,000
SALES (est): 69.9MM **Privately Held**
WEB: www.garrett.com
SIC: 3812 Search & navigation equipment

(G-7498)
GDMI INC
Also Called: Greater Dallas Mfg Intl
2763 Marquis Dr (75042-7833)
PHONE..................................972 494-7477
Gina Ferrall, *President*
Myron L Ferrall, *President*
Terry Meacham, *Vice Pres*
Carole Ferrall, *Director*
EMP: 85 **EST:** 1982
SQ FT: 63,000
SALES (est): 19.3MM **Privately Held**
WEB: www.gdmiinc.com
SIC: 2844 Cosmetic preparations

(G-7499)
GENERAL DYNAMICS ORDNANCE
General Dynamics Ots Garland
1200 N Glenbrook Dr (75040-5029)
PHONE..................................972 276-5131
Marlin West, *Marketing Staff*
Dan Paul, *Manager*
Bill Grewe, *Supervisor*
John Starks, *Master*
EMP: 450
SALES (corp-wide): 37.9B **Publicly Held**
WEB: www.gd-ots.com
SIC: 3769 3463 Guided missile & space vehicle parts & aux eqpt, rsch & dev; aluminum forgings
HQ: General Dynamics Ordnance And Tactical Systems, Inc.
    11399 16th Ct N Ste 200
    Saint Petersburg FL 33716
    727 578-8100

(G-7500)
GENERAL DYNAMICS ORDNANCE
1201 N 5th St (75040-5039)
PHONE..................................972 276-5131
▲ **EMP:** 15
SALES (corp-wide): 37.9B **Publicly Held**
WEB: www.gd-ots.com
SIC: 3312 Blast furnaces & steel mills
HQ: General Dynamics Ordnance And Tactical Systems, Inc.
    11399 16th Ct N Ste 200
    Saint Petersburg FL 33716
    727 578-8100

(G-7501)
GENESIS MILLWORK LLC (PA)
920 Profit Dr (75040-5731)
P.O. Box 462187 (75046-2187)
PHONE..................................469 402-3940
EMP: 30
SALES (est): 6.1MM **Privately Held**
WEB: www.genesis-millwork.com
SIC: 2431 Millwork

(G-7502)
GEORGIA TRE MAGAZINE LLC (PA)
Also Called: Tre Printing
3202 N Shiloh Rd (75044-8016)
PHONE..................................770 755-5420
Tan Nguyen,
EMP: 22 **EST:** 2007
SQ FT: 2,000
SALES (est): 900K **Privately Held**
WEB: www.baotreonline.com
SIC: 2721 Magazines: publishing only, not printed on site

(G-7503)
GFRC 360 LLC
Also Called: Gfrc Cladding
118 N Shiloh Rd (75042-6639)
PHONE..................................972 494-9000
John Foy, *Sales Staff*
Melvin Bryant, *Mng Member*
EMP: 40 **EST:** 2015
SQ FT: 180,000
SALES (est): 9MM **Privately Held**
WEB: www.gfrccladding.com
SIC: 1771 3272 2452 Concrete work; concrete products; prefabricated wood buildings

(G-7504)
GIFFORD SPRING CO INC
219 Gold St (75042-6642)
PHONE..................................972 272-5645
Melany Gifford, *President*
Blake Gifford, *QC Mgr*
Ralph Gifford, *Treasurer*
EMP: 16
SQ FT: 16,000
SALES (est): 2.7MM **Privately Held**
WEB: www.giffordspring.com
SIC: 3495 Wire springs

(G-7505)
GIL-MAR & ASSOCIATES INC
Also Called: Tajas Machine
2418 Executive Dr (75041-6123)
PHONE..................................972 926-9100
Gilbert Santana, *President*
Margaret Santana, *Vice Pres*
Diane Barrientes, *Purchasing*
EMP: 30
SQ FT: 16,000
SALES (est): 2.5MM **Privately Held**
WEB: www.gil-mar.net
SIC: 3599 Machine shop, jobbing & repair

(G-7506)
GOZA PRODUCTS INC
405 S Kirby St (75042-7418)
PHONE..................................972 494-5956
Roy Wayne Goza, *President*
EMP: 32
SQ FT: 16,800
SALES (est): 3MM **Privately Held**
SIC: 3599 Machine shop, jobbing & repair

(G-7507)
GUARDIAN PACKAGING INDS LP
3615 Security St (75042-7629)
PHONE..................................214 349-1500
Kheng Oeur, *General Mgr*
Norman Stuart, *General Ptnr*
Norm Stuart, *Sales Mgr*
Grace Butterfield, *Sales Staff*
Steve Carlton, *Manager*
EMP: 40
SQ FT: 65,000
SALES (est): 13.2MM **Privately Held**
WEB: www.guardianpackaging.com
SIC: 5113 3086 Corrugated & solid fiber boxes; packaging & shipping materials, foamed plastic

(G-7508)
HCO HOLDING I CORPORATION
Also Called: Office
3810 Miller Park Dr (75042-7525)
PHONE..................................214 764-3021
Andy Hastings, *Vice Pres*
EMP: 10

SALES (corp-wide): 254.1MM **Privately Held**
WEB: www.henry.com
SIC: 2952 Roof cement: asphalt, fibrous or plastic
HQ: Hco Holding I Corporation
    999 N Pacific Coast Hwy
    El Segundo CA 90245

(G-7509)
HEADWAY RESEARCH INC
3637 Marquis Dr Ste 102 (75042-6998)
PHONE..................................972 272-5431
Vern D Shipman, *President*
Diana L Brake, *Director*
Joseph P Brake, *Director*
EMP: 14 **EST:** 1964
SQ FT: 18,000
SALES (est): 2.3MM **Privately Held**
WEB: www.headwayresearch.com
SIC: 3674 Semiconductors & related devices

(G-7510)
HENRY COMPANY
3802 Miller Park Dr (75042-7525)
PHONE..................................972 272-5488
Andy Hastings, *Vice Pres*
Zachary Tresatti, *Technical Staff*
EMP: 30
SALES (corp-wide): 254.1MM **Privately Held**
WEB: www.henry.com
SIC: 2952 2951 2851 Asphalt felts & coatings; asphalt paving mixtures & blocks; paints & allied products
HQ: Hco Holding I Corporation
    999 N Pacific Coast Hwy
    El Segundo CA 90245

(G-7511)
HEUBACH CORPORATION
2713 Industrial Ln (75041-2304)
PHONE..................................214 291-0238
August Eltz III, *CEO*
Matt Eltz, *President*
Tricia Whitley, *Vice Pres*
Lori Eltz, *Info Tech Mgr*
◆ **EMP:** 35
SQ FT: 60,000
SALES (est): 7.7MM **Privately Held**
WEB: www.heubachcorp.com
SIC: 3086 3842 Plastics foam products; surgical appliances & supplies

(G-7512)
HG SOLUTIONS INC
2020 Copper St (75042-6656)
PHONE..................................972 205-0888
EMP: 10
SALES (est): 1.4MM **Privately Held**
SIC: 3674 Mfg Semiconductors/Related Devices

(G-7513)
HILL & SMITH INC
Also Called: Work Area Protection
2205 Hightower Dr (75041-6100)
PHONE..................................972 278-0553
EMP: 23
SALES (corp-wide): 819.3MM **Privately Held**
WEB: www.hillandsmith.com
SIC: 3648 Lighting equipment
HQ: Hill & Smith Inc.
    987 Buckeye Park Rd
    Columbus OH 43207

(G-7514)
HILLARYS SWEET TEMPTATIONS INC
2677 Forest Ln (75042-6546)
PHONE..................................972 485-1005
Dean D'Ambrosia, *President*
Aphrodite Divine, *Dean*
EMP: 16
SQ FT: 10,000
SALES (est): 4.5MM **Privately Held**
WEB: www.aphroditedesserts.com
SIC: 2051 2052 Bakery: wholesale or wholesale/retail combined; cookies & crackers; cookies

(G-7515)

IDENTITY SOLUTIONS INC

Also Called: Prosigns
3200 Broadway Blvd # 450 (75043-1573)
PHONE..........................972 926-0929
Kerry B Foster, *President*
EMP: 25
SALES (est): 1.6MM **Privately Held**
SIC: 3993 1799 Electric signs; sign installation & maintenance

(G-7516)

IDQ ACQUISITION CORP

2447 Merritt Dr 200 (75041-6146)
PHONE..........................214 778-4600
Michael Klein, *CEO*
EMP: 41
SALES (est): 149.1K
SALES (corp-wide): 3.9B **Publicly Held**
WEB: www.shortener.secureserver.net
SIC: 3585 Air conditioning equipment, complete
HQ: Armored Autogroup Parent Inc.
44 Old Ridgebury Rd # 300
Danbury CT 06810
203 205-2900

(G-7517)

IFS INDUSTRIES INC

2222 Lonnecker Dr (75041-1203)
PHONE..........................972 864-2202
Lee Strande, *Branch Mgr*
EMP: 20
SALES (corp-wide): 141.7MM **Privately Held**
WEB: www.ifscos.com
SIC: 3255 Plastic refractories
PA: Ifs Industries, Inc.
400 Orton Ave
Reading PA 19603
610 378-1381

(G-7518)

INDEPENDENT DOOR CO INC

525 N 5th St (75040-5005)
P.O. Box 461383 (75046-1383)
PHONE..........................972 487-0511
James W Franklin, *President*
James M Franklin, *Vice Pres*
EMP: 10
SQ FT: 20,000
SALES (est): 1.7MM **Privately Held**
WEB: www.independentdoortx.com
SIC: 2431 5211 Doors, wood; lumber & other building materials; lumber products

(G-7519)

INTERCO PRODUCTS

624 San Carlos Dr (75043-5134)
PHONE..........................972 613-6749
Dennis Tsai, *President*
EMP: 11
SQ FT: 600
SALES (est): 1MM **Privately Held**
SIC: 3663 Satellites, communications

(G-7520)

INTERPRESS TECHNOLOGIES INC

3302 W Miller Rd Ste 100 (75041-6173)
PHONE..........................972 926-6768
Jessie Goodspeed, *Manager*
EMP: 13
SALES (corp-wide): 30MM **Privately Held**
WEB: www.interpresstechnologies.com
SIC: 2759 Commercial printing
HQ: Interpress Technologies, Inc.
1120 Del Paso Rd
Sacramento CA 95834
916 929-9771

(G-7521)

IRVING TOOL & MFG CO INC

2249 Wall St (75041-4033)
P.O. Box 461586 (75046-1586)
PHONE..........................972 926-4000
Linda C Stringer, *CEO*
Harold E Stringer, *President*
Ellen Cain, *Vice Pres*
Cheryl Pierce, *Treasurer*
EMP: 100
SQ FT: 60,000
SALES (est): 20.2MM **Privately Held**
WEB: www.irvingtool.com
SIC: 3444 3599 Sheet metal specialties, not stamped; machine shop, jobbing & repair

(G-7522)

J & A MANUFACTURING INC

2805 E Centerville Rd (75040-6818)
P.O. Box 472309 (75047-2309)
PHONE..........................972 494-5552
David J Johnson, *Officer*
Tambi Johnson, *Officer*
Aranda Johnson, *Shareholder*
EMP: 52
SQ FT: 32,000
SALES (est): 9.1MM **Privately Held**
WEB: www.jamfg.com
SIC: 3599 3444 Machine shop, jobbing & repair; sheet metalwork

(G-7523)

J S TECHNOLOGY INC

3000 W Kingsley Rd (75041-2313)
PHONE..........................469 326-5900
Atul Patel, *President*
EMP: 60
SQ FT: 43,000
SALES (est): 7.5MM **Privately Held**
SIC: 3423 Hand & edge tools

(G-7524)

J&J WELDING & AWNING

2605 National Cir (75041-2316)
PHONE..........................214 227-5606
John E Long, *Owner*
EMP: 10
SALES (est): 640.7K **Privately Held**
SIC: 7692 Welding repair

(G-7525)

JACQUELINE CONSTRUCTION INC

2302 Jacqueline Dr (75042-3912)
PHONE..........................469 258-4402
Mohammad Jangda, *President*
EMP: 16 EST: 2016
SALES (est): 861.2K **Privately Held**
SIC: 3357 Fiber optic cable (insulated)

(G-7526)

JELD-WEN INC

Also Called: Jeld-Wen Doors
4409 Action St (75042-6808)
PHONE..........................972 272-3667
Brent Dewey, *General Mgr*
EMP: 100 **Publicly Held**
WEB: www.jeld-wen.com
SIC: 5211 2431 Door & window products; millwork
HQ: Jeld-Wen, Inc.
2645 Silver Crescent Dr
Charlotte NC 28273
800 535-3936

(G-7527)

JOE TIPTON INC

2202 Executive Dr (75041-6119)
PHONE..........................972 271-6666
Mike Tipton, *President*
EMP: 18
SQ FT: 15,000
SALES (est): 1.8MM **Privately Held**
WEB: www.filterclone.com
SIC: 3564 Dust or fume collecting equipment, industrial

(G-7528)

JPON GLASS COMPANY INC

1825 S Jupiter Rd (75042-7720)
PHONE..........................214 349-1400
Melinda O'Neal, *President*
Pat O'Neal, *Vice Pres*
Oneal John P, *Vice Pres*
Scott McCombs, *Project Mgr*
Sharon Ledbetter, *Sales Staff*
EMP: 20
SQ FT: 9,000
SALES (est): 3.9MM **Privately Held**
WEB: www.jponglass.com
SIC: 1793 5719 3211 Glass & glazing work; mirrors; building glass, flat

(G-7529)

KAISER FOODLINE LLC

Also Called: Colonel Kababz
1801 Reserve St Ste A (75042-7644)
PHONE..........................972 705-9595
Kass Kaiser, *Opers Mgr*
Mansur Kaiser, *Mng Member*
EMP: 30
SQ FT: 43,000
SALES (est): 3MM **Privately Held**
WEB: www.kaisergourmet.com
SIC: 2038 Ethnic foods, frozen

(G-7530)

KARLEE INTEGRATION FACILITY

2905 Miller Park N (75042-7756)
PHONE..........................972 543-3175
Goenne Brumit, *CEO*
Lee Brumit, *President*
EMP: 50
SALES (est): 4.4MM **Privately Held**
WEB: www.karlee.com
SIC: 3499 Boxes for packing & shipping, metal

(G-7531)

KIRCHHOFF AUTO DALLAS INC (DH)

3901 W Miller Rd Ste 500 (75041-6051)
PHONE..........................214 553-0208
Stefan Leitzgen, *COO*
Stephen Cotter, *Info Tech Dir*
EMP: 200
SQ FT: 4,500
SALES (est): 41.3MM
SALES (corp-wide): 1.7B **Privately Held**
SIC: 3465 Body parts, automobile: stamped metal
HQ: Kirchhoff Automotive Canada Inc
200 Vandorf Sideroad
Aurora ON L4G 0
905 727-8585

(G-7532)

KIRCHHOFF AUTO DALLAS INC

Also Called: Van Rob Dallas
3901 W Miller Rd Ste 200 (75041-6051)
PHONE..........................214 553-0208
Marco Graza, *Branch Mgr*
EMP: 200
SALES (corp-wide): 1.7B **Privately Held**
SIC: 3465 Body parts, automobile: stamped metal
HQ: Kirchhoff Automotive Dallas Inc.
3901 W Miller Rd Ste 500
Garland TX 75041
214 553-0208

(G-7533)

KIRKLAND SALES INC

Also Called: Ksi
2210 Sherwin St (75041-1219)
PHONE..........................972 864-1424
David Kirkland, *President*
Paul Kirkland, *General Mgr*
Aaron Yoquelet, *Pastor*
Claude McClure, *Engineer*
Janet Harrington, *Treasurer*
EMP: 20
SQ FT: 40,000
SALES (est): 4.7MM **Privately Held**
WEB: www.kirklandsales.com
SIC: 3069 5999 Foam rubber; foam & foam products

(G-7534)

KRAFT HEINZ COMPANY

Also Called: Kraft Foods
2340 Forest Ln (75042-7924)
PHONE..........................972 272-7511
Chris Doherty, *Vice Pres*
Michael Pagano, *QC Mgr*
Bart Huchel, *Engineer*
Alex Jaurrieta, *Engineer*
Claire Walters, *Marketing Staff*
EMP: 500
SALES (corp-wide): 24.9B **Publicly Held**
WEB: www.kraftheinzcompany.com
SIC: 2033 2035 2064 4225 Jams, including imitation: packaged in cans, jars, etc.; dressings, salad: raw & cooked (except dry mixes); candy & other confectionery products; general warehousing
PA: The Kraft Heinz Company
1 Ppg Pl Ste 3400
Pittsburgh PA 15222
412 456-5700

(G-7535)

L3 TECHNOLOGIES INC

Also Called: Insight Technology Division
3414 Herrmann Dr (75041-6134)
PHONE..........................972 840-5600
Gregg Bell, *President*
Todd Stirtzinger, *President*
EMP: 301
SALES (corp-wide): 11.3B **Publicly Held**
WEB: www.l3t.com
SIC: 3679 Attenuators
HQ: L3 Technologies, Inc.
600 3rd Ave Fl 34
New York NY 10016
212 805-5234

(G-7536)

LASER PRINTING INC

3002 W Campbell Rd (75044-8100)
PHONE..........................972 235-2488
Stanton M Laser, *President*
Robin Laser, *Manager*
EMP: 9
SQ FT: 3,200
SALES (est): 1.1MM **Privately Held**
WEB: www.laserprintinginc.com
SIC: 2752 2731 Commercial printing, offset; book publishing

(G-7537)

LINDE INC

Praxair
2225 Lonnecker Dr (75041-1204)
PHONE..........................972 271-1531
Carl Brooks, *Manager*
EMP: 32 **Privately Held**
WEB: www.praxair.com
SIC: 2813 Industrial gases
HQ: Linde Inc.
10 Riverview Dr
Danbury CT 06810
203 837-2000

(G-7538)

LIVING COMPANY HOLDINGS LLC

2149 S Jupiter Rd (75041-6003)
PHONE..........................469 687-8991
Parker Pieri, *COO*
Paul Dougan,
James Garner,
EMP: 38 EST: 2017
SALES (est): 2MM **Privately Held**
WEB: www.livingcompany.com
SIC: 2514 Household furniture: upholstered on metal frames

(G-7539)

LUNDY SERVICES LLC

221 Garvon St (75040-6515)
PHONE..........................972 494-2554
James Lundy, *President*
EMP: 40
SALES (corp-wide): 36.7MM **Privately Held**
WEB: www.lundy-services.com
SIC: 1799 2521 2434 2431 Home/office interiors finishing, furnishing & remodeling; wood office furniture; wood kitchen cabinets; millwork; carpentry work
PA: Lundy Services, L.L.C.
13525 Denton Dr
Dallas TX 75234
214 951-8181

(G-7540)

M&M MANUFACTURING INC

360 S Shiloh Rd (75042-6616)
PHONE..........................972 485-1504
Jim Strong, *Manager*
EMP: 110
SALES (corp-wide): 254.6B **Publicly Held**
WEB: www.mmmfg.com
SIC: 3444 Sheet metalwork
HQ: M&M Manufacturing, Inc.
4001 Mark Iv Pkwy
Fort Worth TX 76106
817 336-2311

(G-7541)
MAG FLUX CORPORATION (PA)
Also Called: Magflux
1101 E Walnut St (75040-6615)
PHONE...............................972 272-8576
Matt Davis, *President*
C Glynn Davis, *President*
J Clay Hogan, *Vice Pres*
EMP: 50
SQ FT: 27,900
SALES (est): 3.9MM **Privately Held**
SIC: 3677 3612 Electronic transformers;
transformers, except electric

(G-7542)
MAPEI CORPORATION
1501 Wall St (75041-4046)
PHONE...............................972 271-9500
Carlo Naggi, *Project Mgr*
Fir Yahya, *Manager*
Roger Alvarez, *Manager*
Jose Navarra, *Manager*
EMP: 80 **Privately Held**
WEB: www.mapei.com
SIC: 2891 Adhesives
HQ: Mapei Corporation
1144 E Newport Center Dr
Deerfield Beach FL 33442
954 246-8888

(G-7543)
MARKING SYSTEMS INC
Also Called: MSI
2601 Market St (75041-2423)
PHONE...............................972 475-0770
Mathew Van Beber, *President*
Greg V Beber, *Vice Pres*
Greg Van Beber, *Vice Pres*
Tim Vandeventer, *Production*
Ashton Beber, *Sales Staff*
EMP: 74 EST: 1971
SQ FT: 40,000
SALES (est): 29.9MM **Privately Held**
WEB: www.markingsystems.com
SIC: 2679 3479 Labels, paper: made from
purchased material; name plates: en-
graved, etched, etc.

(G-7544)
MASTER HATTERS OF TEXAS INC
Also Called: Wrangler Hats
2945 Market St (75041-2429)
PHONE...............................972 864-5523
▲ EMP: 18
SQ FT: 65,000
SALES (est): 2MM **Privately Held**
WEB: www.masterhatters.com
SIC: 2353 Hats: cloth, straw & felt

(G-7545)
MASTERWERKES
100 N Shiloh Rd Ste 120 (75042-6697)
PHONE...............................214 315-6479
William Phillip Pittman, *Owner*
EMP: 15 EST: 1996
SQ FT: 3,600
SALES (est): 1.5MM **Privately Held**
WEB: www.masterwerkes.com
SIC: 2499 Decorative wood & woodwork

(G-7546)
MAVERICK CONCEPTS LLC
3402 W Miller Rd (75041-6114)
PHONE...............................972 418-7189
Lucas D Meldrum, *Mng Member*
Lisa Howard, *Manager*
Phil Macnamara,
EMP: 30
SQ FT: 20,000
SALES (est): 4.5MM **Privately Held**
WEB: www.mavconcepts.com
SIC: 2741 Posters: publishing & printing

(G-7547)
MCELROY METAL MILL INC
3014 Lincoln Ct (75041-2210)
PHONE...............................214 703-3113
Jack McElroy, *Branch Mgr*
EMP: 280
SALES (corp-wide): 362MM **Privately Held**
WEB: www.mcelroymetal.com
SIC: 3448 Prefabricated metal buildings

PA: Mcelroy Metal Mill, Inc.
1500 Hamilton Rd
Bossier City LA 71111
318 747-8000

(G-7548)
MCNICHOLS COMPANY
3540 W Miller Rd Ste 240 (75041-6014)
PHONE...............................877 884-4653
Kevin Pressler, *General Mgr*
Dan Taylor, *General Mgr*
Brenda Huttash, *Sales Staff*
Bill Ulmer, *Sales Staff*
Jeremy Mishork, *Marketing Staff*
EMP: 40
SQ FT: 15,000
SALES (corp-wide): 191.3MM **Privately Held**
WEB: www.mcnichols.com
SIC: 5051 3496 3446 Steel; wire screen-
ing; bars, metal; wire cloth & woven wire
products; open flooring & grating for con-
struction
PA: Mcnichols Company
2502 N Rocky Point Dr # 750
Tampa FL 33607
877 884-4653

(G-7549)
METRO LABEL CORPORATION (DH)
3366 Miller Park S (75042-7771)
P.O. Box 3245, Edgartown MA (02539-3245)
PHONE...............................214 369-9377
Scott Metko, *President*
Leonard J Suazo, *CFO*
Stacey Ehle, *Human Res Dir*
EMP: 62 EST: 1977
SQ FT: 73,000
SALES: 5.3MM
SALES (corp-wide): 45.1MM **Privately Held**
SIC: 2759 Labels & seals: printing
HQ: Ingenious Packaging Group
580 Gateway Dr
Napa CA 94558
707 252-8300

(G-7550)
METROPLEX SHEET METAL INC
3701 Marquis Dr Ste 139 (75042-7596)
PHONE...............................972 276-6736
Robert J Sable, *President*
EMP: 33
SQ FT: 30,000
SALES (est): 2.2MM **Privately Held**
WEB: www.metroplexsheetmetal.com
SIC: 3444 Metal ventilating equipment

(G-7551)
MICROPAC INDUSTRIES INC (PA)
905 E Walnut St (75040-6696)
PHONE...............................972 272-3571
Mark King, *Ch of Bd*
Patrick S Cefalu, *CFO*
Richard K Hoesterey, *Admin Sec*
EMP: 82 EST: 1963
SQ FT: 37,000
SALES: 22.2MM **Publicly Held**
WEB: www.micropac.com
SIC: 3612 3663 3674 3823 Voltage regu-
lating transformers, electric power; ampli-
fiers, RF power & IF; light emitting diodes;
microcircuits, integrated (semiconductor);
digital displays of process variables; in-
strument relays, all types

(G-7552)
MICROPAC INDUSTRIES INC
Also Called: Opto Electronics Group
912 E Walnut St (75040-6612)
PHONE...............................972 272-3571
Connie Wood, *President*
Barbara Hall, *Personnel Exec*
EMP: 65
SALES (corp-wide): 22.2MM **Publicly Held**
WEB: www.micropac.com
SIC: 3674 Semiconductors & related de-
vices
PA: Micropac Industries, Inc.
905 E Walnut St
Garland TX 75040
972 272-3571

(G-7553)
MILLER EQUIPMENT CO (PA)
1000 N 1st St (75040-5712)
PHONE...............................469 366-4227
Foster K Miller, *Principal*
Cayedee Rhoades, *Office Mgr*
EMP: 12
SALES (est): 7.9MM **Privately Held**
WEB: www.millerequipco.com
SIC: 5046 5084 Commercial equip-
ment; forklift trucks; materials handling
machinery

(G-7554)
MILLTECH MANUFACTURING COMPANY
537 Easy St (75042-6810)
PHONE...............................972 276-1786
Robert Black, *President*
Dan Ash, *Vice Pres*
Bobbi Meads, *Buyer*
Chris Bee, *Sales Staff*
EMP: 60
SQ FT: 32,000
SALES (est): 8.3MM **Privately Held**
WEB: www.milltechmfg.com
SIC: 3599 3545 3444 Machine shop, job-
bing & repair; machine tool accessories;
sheet metalwork

(G-7555)
MORGAN CABINETRY INC
2775 W Kingsley Rd (75041-2406)
PHONE...............................972 278-8836
EMP: 10
SQ FT: 24,000
SALES (est): 900K **Privately Held**
SIC: 2541 2491 Mfg Cabinets & Millwork

(G-7556)
MTC AMERICA ENTERPRISES INC
3302 W Miller Rd Ste 300 (75041-6173)
PHONE...............................972 926-0600
Yechiel Cohen, *President*
David Attar, *Engineer*
EMP: 11
SALES (est): 2.3MM **Privately Held**
WEB: www.mtcamerica.com
SIC: 3625 3795 3812 3621 Solenoid
switches (industrial controls); tanks & tank
components; aircraft/aerospace flight in-
struments & guidance systems; sliprings,
for motors or generators

(G-7557)
NATIONAL CIRCUIT ASSEMBLY INC (PA)
Also Called: N C A
2908 National Dr Ste 100 (75041-2337)
PHONE...............................972 278-2009
Michael Tan Tieu, *CEO*
Tan Tieu, *President*
Cruz Alvarado, *Vice Pres*
Raul Cantero, *Vice Pres*
Eric Nguyen, *VP Mfg*
EMP: 75
SQ FT: 40,000
SALES (est): 20.4MM **Privately Held**
WEB: www.ncatx.com
SIC: 3672 1731 3669 7622 Printed circuit
boards; electrical work; emergency
alarms; radio & television repair; commu-
nication equipment repair

(G-7558)
NATIONAL INSTRUMENTS CORP
505 Fairway Meadows Dr (75044-5069)
PHONE...............................214 227-4788
EMP: 338
SALES (corp-wide): 1.3B **Publicly Held**
WEB: www.ni.com
SIC: 7372 Application computer software
PA: National Instruments Corporation
11500 N Mopac Expy
Austin TX 78759
512 683-0100

(G-7559)
NATURICH COSMETIQUE LABS INC
Also Called: Naturich Labs
2505 Merritt Dr (75041-6158)
PHONE...............................972 926-9200
Prakash Purohit, *President*

Richa Purohit, *Vice Pres*
Karyne Law, *Project Mgr*
Christine Valdez, *Project Mgr*
Cindy Nuss, *Purch Mgr*
▲ EMP: 35
SQ FT: 60,000
SALES (est): 6MM **Privately Held**
WEB: www.naturich.com
SIC: 2844 2834 Cosmetic preparations;
dermatologicals

(G-7560)
NAVISTAR INTERNATIONAL CORP
801 Easy St (75042-6816)
PHONE...............................972 487-6509
Luis Gonzalez, *Engineer*
Eugenio Torres, *Engineer*
John McPherson, *Branch Mgr*
Jorge Gonzalez, *Manager*
Jeff Polich, *Consultant*
EMP: 80
SALES (corp-wide): 7.5B **Publicly Held**
WEB: www.navistar.com
SIC: 3711 Motor vehicles & car bodies
PA: Navistar International Corporation
2701 Navistar Dr
Lisle IL 60532
331 332-5000

(G-7561)
NEMESIS UVC LLC
3301 Wood Dr Ste 100 (75041-6154)
PHONE...............................972 423-0075
Eric Wade, *Mng Member*
EMP: 22
SALES (est): 5MM **Privately Held**
WEB: www.nemesisuvc.com
SIC: 3648 Ultraviolet lamp fixtures

(G-7562)
NEW CENTURY ENTERPRISES INC
Also Called: Greater Dallas Press
601 Shepherd Dr (75042-6832)
PHONE...............................972 926-6062
Frank Vu, *President*
Jim Jarvis, *Vice Pres*
EMP: 35
SALES (est): 5.4MM **Privately Held**
WEB: www.greaterdallaspress.com
SIC: 2759 2711 Catalogs: printing;
coupons: printing; commercial printing &
newspaper publishing combined

(G-7563)
NEXT CENTURY SCREENS INC
575 S Intl Rd Ste 200 (75042)
PHONE...............................972 496-4981
Peter Fay, *President*
Kelly Fay, *Vice Pres*
EMP: 13
SQ FT: 5,000
SALES (est): 2.3MM **Privately Held**
WEB: www.nextcenturyscreens.com
SIC: 5211 3442 Screens, door & window;
screen doors, metal

(G-7564)
NOVA MAGNETICS INC (PA)
1101 E Walnut St (75040-6697)
PHONE...............................972 272-8287
C Glynn Davis, *President*
Clay Hogan, *Vice Pres*
Jason King, *Mfg Spvr*
Mitch Minter, *Buyer*
Don McDade, *Engineer*
EMP: 80 EST: 1981
SQ FT: 26,478
SALES (est): 18.7MM **Privately Held**
WEB: www.novamagnetics.net
SIC: 3677 3612 Electronic transformers;
transformers, except electric

(G-7565)
PACKAGING CORPORATION AMERICA
Also Called: Pca/Garland 322
2510 W Miller Rd (75041-1311)
PHONE...............................214 227-5124
Donna Rommer, *Controller*
EMP: 110
SQ FT: 5,491

SALES (corp-wide): 6.9B **Publicly Held**
WEB: www.packagingcorp.com
SIC: 2653 Boxes, corrugated: made from purchased materials
PA: Packaging Corporation Of America
    1 N Field Ct
    Lake Forest IL 60045
    847 482-3000

(G-7566)
PEACOCK PRESS LLC
538 Shepherd Dr (75042-6829)
PHONE................................972 272-7764
Jyotshma Patel,
Pravin Patel,
EMP: 15
SQ FT: 7,000
SALES (est): 2.8MM **Privately Held**
WEB: www.peacockpress.net
SIC: 2752 Commercial printing, offset

(G-7567)
PINNER WIRE & CABLE INC
932 N Shiloh Rd (75042-5718)
PHONE................................972 494-3333
Dick Pinner, *President*
Ken Fox, *Vice Pres*
Ty Tompkins, *Purch Agent*
Lisa Pinner, *Manager*
EMP: 67
SQ FT: 42,000
SALES (est): 5.5MM **Privately Held**
WEB: www.pinnerwire.com
SIC: 3679 Harness assemblies for electronic use: wire or cable

(G-7568)
PLASTIPAK PACKAGING INC
3201 Miller Park N (75042-7762)
PHONE................................972 276-8660
David Leclair, *Plant Engr*
Byron Williams, *Project Engr*
Chad Powell, *Controller*
Cheryl Shepard, *Branch Mgr*
Alan Hamill, *Manager*
EMP: 150
SALES (corp-wide): 2.3B **Privately Held**
WEB: www.plastipak.com
SIC: 3085 7389 Plastics bottles; packaging & labeling services
HQ: Plastipak Packaging, Inc.
    41605 Ann Arbor Rd E
    Plymouth MI 48170
    734 455-3600

(G-7569)
POHAKU CLASSIC - OKLAHOMA LLC
2914 National Ct (75041-2327)
PHONE................................972 840-8660
Jason Engel,
EMP: 25
SALES (est): 947.1K **Privately Held**
SIC: 3711 Automobile assembly, including specialty automobiles

(G-7570)
PONY XPRESS PRINTING LLC
2485 Merritt Dr (75041-6146)
PHONE................................214 221-7669
John Alexander, *Vice Pres*
Lisa Keith, *Accountant*
Jerry Baxter, *Accounts Exec*
Cece Renner, *Sales Executive*
Diane Atkinson, *Director*
▲ EMP: 46
SALES (est): 6.5MM **Privately Held**
WEB: www.pxpsolutions.com
SIC: 2759 Screen printing

(G-7571)
POWELL MANUFACTURING COMPANY
2720 Industrial Ln (75041-2303)
PHONE................................972 278-9507
Richard Powell, *President*
Debbie Duncan, *Office Mgr*
EMP: 21
SQ FT: 24,000
SALES (est): 5.2MM **Privately Held**
WEB: www.powellmfgco.com
SIC: 3533 Bits, oil & gas field tools: rock

(G-7572)
PREMEX DOOR SUPPLY INC
Also Called: Southwest Door & Window
3630 W Miller Rd Ste 320 (75041-6050)
PHONE................................214 341-2212
Brandon Devore, *President*
▲ EMP: 13
SALES (est): 1.1MM **Privately Held**
WEB: www.southwestdw.com
SIC: 1751 3442 5023 Window & door (prefabricated) installation; window & door frames; window furnishings

(G-7573)
PUROCOL LLC
2001 Platinum St (75042-6662)
PHONE................................310 926-9007
Nader Naim, *Mng Member*
EMP: 10
SALES (est): 409.5K **Privately Held**
SIC: 2842 Sanitation preparations

(G-7574)
QUALITY STAR PRODUCTS LTD
3930 Miller Park Dr (75042-7614)
PHONE................................214 680-7448
Tony Loung, *CEO*
Kenneth Chu, *General Mgr*
James Jiang, *Principal*
Kit Kwok, *COO*
▲ EMP: 54
SALES (est): 12.6MM **Privately Held**
WEB: www.globalgourmetfs.com
SIC: 2038 Frozen specialties

(G-7575)
QUESTECH SERVICES CORPORATION
2201 Executive Dr (75041-6120)
PHONE................................972 278-8006
Robert W Chapman, *President*
Ronald W Bazanele, *Vice Pres*
Gaither C Laser, *Technician*
EMP: 31
SQ FT: 10,000
SALES: 4.5MM **Privately Held**
WEB: www.questlaser.com
SIC: 3599 3676 Machine shop, jobbing & repair; electronic resistors

(G-7576)
RAYTHEON COMPANY
1110 Sunset Dr (75040-4873)
PHONE................................972 494-2073
King Burgess, *Branch Mgr*
EMP: 170
SALES (corp-wide): 56.5B **Publicly Held**
WEB: www.rtx.com
SIC: 3812 Defense systems & equipment
HQ: Raytheon Company
    870 Winter St
    Waltham MA 02451
    781 522-3000

(G-7577)
RELIANCE STEEL & ALUMINUM CO
Also Called: Bralco Metals
410 Mars Dr (75040-6622)
PHONE................................972 276-2676
Tim Williamson, *Division Mgr*
David Appleby, *Division Mgr*
Shaun Thomas, *General Mgr*
Shaun Wells, *Export Mgr*
Ben Terry, *Opers Staff*
EMP: 21
SALES (corp-wide): 10.9B **Publicly Held**
WEB: www.rsac.com
SIC: 3444 5051 Sheet metalwork; structural shapes, iron or steel
PA: Reliance Steel & Aluminum Co.
    350 S Grand Ave Ste 5100
    Los Angeles CA 90071
    213 687-7700

(G-7578)
RHE HATCO INC (PA)
Also Called: Stetson Hats
601 Marion Dr (75042-7930)
PHONE................................972 494-0511
Stan Redding, *President*
John Rosenthal, *Plant Mgr*
Dan Brown, *Cust Mgr*
Kaci Riggs, *Director*
▲ EMP: 380

SQ FT: 200,000
SALES (est): 96MM **Privately Held**
WEB: www.hat-co.com
SIC: 2353 Hats: cloth, straw & felt

(G-7579)
RHE HATCO INC
Also Called: Resistol Hats
601 Marion Dr (75042-7930)
PHONE................................972 494-0511
John Tillitson, *Manager*
EMP: 350
SALES (corp-wide): 96MM **Privately Held**
WEB: www.resistol.com
SIC: 2353 Hats & caps
PA: Rhe Hatco, Inc.
    601 Marion Dr
    Garland TX 75042
    972 494-0511

(G-7580)
ROBINSON ENGINEERING CO INC
Also Called: Job Boss
1914 Silver St (75042-6645)
PHONE................................972 272-2001
Brad Robinson, *President*
Flavy Correa, *Purch Mgr*
Jason Lechner, *Sales Mgr*
Flavy Ann Correa, *Manager*
▲ EMP: 25
SQ FT: 6,900
SALES (est): 5.2MM **Privately Held**
WEB: www.craneboss.com
SIC: 3625 3822 Crane & hoist controls, including metal mill; auto controls regulating residntl & coml environmt & applncs

(G-7581)
SATELLINK INC
3525 Miller Park Dr (75042-7520)
P.O. Box 472967 (75047-2967)
PHONE................................972 487-1434
Robert P Goodrich, *President*
Lorie Goodrich, *Engineer*
Debbie Morgan, *Engineer*
Ed Williams, *Sales Mgr*
Carroll Bunch, *Manager*
EMP: 45
SQ FT: 15,000
SALES (est): 8.5MM **Privately Held**
WEB: www.satellink.com
SIC: 3663 5065 3651 Amplifiers, RF power & IF; electronic parts & equipment; household audio & video equipment

(G-7582)
SATPRO NETWORK INC
7406 Spicewood Dr (75044-2574)
PHONE................................972 675-8475
Paul Colombo, *CEO*
Paul V Colombo, *CEO*
Diane Rose, *President*
EMP: 25
SQ FT: 4,390
SALES (est): 2.2MM **Privately Held**
WEB: www.satpro.net
SIC: 3679 5731 4841 Antennas, satellite: household use; radio, television & electronic stores; satellite master antenna systems services (SMATV)

(G-7583)
SC AUTOSPORTS LLC
Also Called: Kandi America
3101 W Miller Rd (75041-6107)
PHONE................................972 271-0888
EMP: 18
SALES (est): 18.1MM **Privately Held**
WEB: www.scautosports.com
SIC: 3711 Motor vehicles & car bodies
PA: Kandi Technologies Group, Inc.
    3101 W Miller Rd
    Garland TX 75041
    972 271-0888

(G-7584)
SC INDUSTRIAL RESOURCE GROUP
Also Called: Industrial Woodworking Mch
601 Shepherd Dr (75042-6832)
P.O. Box 473066 (75047-3066)
PHONE................................972 272-4521
David Spencer, *CEO*
EMP: 30

SQ FT: 67,000
SALES (est): 4.7MM **Privately Held**
WEB: www.scindustrial.com
SIC: 5084 3553 Industrial machinery & equipment; woodworking machinery

(G-7585)
SCENT SHOP INC
2614 National Pl (75041-2343)
PHONE................................972 271-4661
John H Stuart, *President*
Mark Stuart, *Vice Pres*
Sylvia Samaieco, *Credit Mgr*
Jacci Tipton, *Office Mgr*
EMP: 30
SQ FT: 50,000
SALES (est): 5.1MM **Privately Held**
WEB: www.scentshop.com
SIC: 2844 Toilet preparations

(G-7586)
SEMICON PHTMTRLOGY SLTIONS LLC
413 Trails Ct (75043-5635)
P.O. Box 831731, Richardson (75083-1731)
PHONE................................214 957-0295
Patrick Gagnon,
George Elliott,
EMP: 13
SALES (est): 20K **Privately Held**
WEB: www.semiphotomet.com
SIC: 3823 Industrial instrmnts msrmnt display/control process variable

(G-7587)
SENTINEL PLATING INC
610 N 1st St (75040-5704)
P.O. Box 460336 (75046-0336)
PHONE................................972 276-2780
Philip E Teeling Jr, *President*
Gloria Teeling, *Vice Pres*
EMP: 10 EST: 1963
SQ FT: 11,000
SALES (est): 800K **Privately Held**
SIC: 3471 Electroplating of metals or formed products

(G-7588)
SHAPE CORP
3901 W Miller Rd (75041-6051)
PHONE................................616 846-8700
Andrew Tallman, *Branch Mgr*
EMP: 95
SALES (corp-wide): 705MM **Privately Held**
WEB: www.shapecorp.com
SIC: 3449 Miscellaneous metalwork
PA: Shape Corp.
    1900 Hayes St
    Grand Haven MI 49417
    616 846-8700

(G-7589)
SPECTRUM BRANDS INC
Also Called: Spectrum Brand Global Autocare
2447 Merritt Dr 200 (75041-6146)
PHONE................................214 778-4600
Michael Klein, *CEO*
Michael Tennant, *Associate*
EMP: 100
SALES (corp-wide): 3.9B **Publicly Held**
WEB: www.rayovac.com
SIC: 3691 Storage batteries
HQ: Spectrum Brands, Inc.
    3001 Deming Way
    Middleton WI 53562
    608 275-3340

(G-7590)
SPIRAL X LLC
3532 Miller Park Dr (75042-7519)
P.O. Box 539, Fate (75132-0539)
PHONE................................855 346-8823
Brian Holland, *Mng Member*
EMP: 15 EST: 2009
SALES (est): 2.8MM **Privately Held**
WEB: www.spiralxllc.com
SIC: 3699 Heat emission operating apparatus

(G-7591)
SST TRUCK COMPANY LLC
4030 Forest Ln (75042-6933)
PHONE................................972 487-2900
Craig N Holmes, *President*

GEOGRAPHIC

James M Moran, *Vice Pres*
Richard Tarapchak, *Vice Pres*
▲ **EMP:** 450
SQ FT: 500,000
SALES (est): 54.2MM
SALES (corp-wide): 7.5B **Publicly Held**
SIC: 3711 3713 Truck & tractor truck assembly; truck & bus bodies
HQ: Navistar, Inc.
2701 Navistar Dr
Lisle IL 60532
331 332-5000

(G-7592)
STILLERS PRCISION FIREARMS LLC
Also Called: Spf
543 N 5th St (75040-5005)
PHONE................................972 429-5000
Jerry Stiller,
EMP: 10 **EST:** 1998
SALES (est): 1.3MM **Privately Held**
WEB: www.stilleractions.com
SIC: 3484 Guns (firearms) or gun parts, 30 mm. & below

(G-7593)
SUB ASSEMBLY GROUP
1035 Nicholson Rd (75042-7858)
PHONE................................214 420-8367
David Bristol, *CEO*
Collin Carpenter, *Warehouse Mgr*
EMP: 12 **EST:** 2010
SALES (est): 2MM **Privately Held**
WEB: www.sagtx.com
SIC: 3711 Motor trucks, except off-highway, assembly of

(G-7594)
SWIFT SCREEN PRINTING INC
Also Called: Xtreme Powder Coating
3848 Marquis Dr (75042-7517)
PHONE................................972 494-1144
Michael Bowen, *President*
Nicole R Bowen, *Vice Pres*
EMP: 15
SQ FT: 2,000
SALES (est): 220K **Privately Held**
WEB: www.swiftscreenprintinginc.com
SIC: 2759 Screen printing

(G-7595)
T SHIRTS N TRENDS
Also Called: Wolford, Carroll L.
2050 Forest Ln Ste 320 (75042-7901)
PHONE................................972 272-2581
Carroll L Wolford, *Owner*
▲ **EMP:** 10
SQ FT: 7,000
SALES (est): 843.1K **Privately Held**
WEB: www.tshirtsandtrends.com
SIC: 2759 Screen printing

(G-7596)
TECPLATE LP
3609 Marquis Dr (75042-7514)
PHONE................................972 487-0636
Richard Stertz, *Managing Prtnr*
EMP: 10
SALES (est): 635.2K **Privately Held**
SIC: 3471 Finishing, metals or formed products

(G-7597)
TELSCO INDUSTRIES INC (PA)
Also Called: Weather-Matic
3301 W Kingsley Rd (75041-2299)
P.O. Box 472545 (75047-2545)
PHONE................................972 278-6131
Malcolm S Morris, *Ch of Bd*
L O Snoddy, *Ch of Bd*
Michael Mason, *President*
Darryl Halbert, *COO*
Brodie Bruner, *Vice Pres*
◆ **EMP:** 9 **EST:** 1945
SQ FT: 72,000
SALES (est): 25MM **Privately Held**
WEB: www.weathermatic.com
SIC: 3523 Irrigation equipment, self-propelled

(G-7598)
TEXAS CIRCUITRY INC
2960 Market St (75041-2428)
P.O. Box 181258, Arlington (76096-1258)
PHONE................................972 278-3838

Chatur K Patel, *President*
Rajan Patel, *Engineer*
Arvind Patel, *Treasurer*
Cindy Klein, *Sales Mgr*
EMP: 50
SQ FT: 31,000
SALES (est): 3.4MM **Privately Held**
WEB: www.txcircuitry.com
SIC: 3672 Circuit boards, television & radio printed

(G-7599)
TEXAS PRECISION PLATING INC
3002 Benton St (75042-7497)
PHONE................................972 494-1547
Steve Gordon, *President*
Doug Gordon, *Vice Pres*
Donna Simmons, *Office Mgr*
EMP: 40
SQ FT: 35,000
SALES (est): 5MM **Privately Held**
WEB: www.texasprecision.net
SIC: 3471 3443 Plating of metals or formed products; fabricated plate work (boiler shop)

(G-7600)
TEXTON INC
114 S Kirby St (75042-7490)
PHONE................................972 494-5941
William E Williams Jr, *Principal*
Doug Tischler, *Purch Mgr*
Pam Rogers, *CFO*
Joshua Emard, *Manager*
EMP: 53 **EST:** 1970
SQ FT: 40,000
SALES (est): 5.7MM **Privately Held**
WEB: www.texton.com
SIC: 2591 5023 Blinds vertical; window covering parts & accessories

(G-7601)
THERMO SENSORS CORPORATION (PA)
405 Gautney St (75040-6538)
P.O. Box 461947 (75046-1947)
PHONE................................972 494-1566
Mark M Medcalf, *President*
Mark Medcalf, *President*
Andy Blakely, *Sales Staff*
Dwayne Blue, *Manager*
EMP: 16
SQ FT: 12,000
SALES (est): 2.4MM **Privately Held**
WEB: www.thermosensors.com
SIC: 3829 Temperature sensors, except industrial process & aircraft

(G-7602)
TNT DIRECTIONAL DRILLING INC
5435 N Garland Ave 140-205 (75040-2785)
PHONE................................972 333-3410
Kenny Vancil, *President*
EMP: 15
SALES (est): 1.1MM **Privately Held**
SIC: 1381 Directional drilling oil & gas wells

(G-7603)
TOLBERT ELECTRIC MOTOR COMPANY
3822 Dividend Dr (75042-7612)
PHONE................................972 272-6541
Laymon Tolbert, *President*
EMP: 13 **EST:** 1975
SQ FT: 10,300
SALES (est): 3.7MM **Privately Held**
WEB: www.tgrayelectric.com
SIC: 5063 7694 5084 Motors, electric; electric motor repair; industrial machinery & equipment

(G-7604)
TPI
Also Called: Telecom Products
1136 N 1st St (75040-5102)
PHONE................................972 276-2901
Barbara Silber, *President*
Bob Silber, *Treasurer*
Tim Thurston, *Sales Mgr*
EMP: 30

SALES (est): 7.3MM **Privately Held**
WEB: www.tpitexas.com
SIC: 3661 3334 3443 3354 Telephone station equipment & parts, wire; primary aluminum; fabricated plate work (boiler shop); aluminum extruded products

(G-7605)
TRINITY POWDER COATING
2850 Industrial Ln (75041-2305)
PHONE................................214 703-3609
Leroy Alaniz Sr, *Owner*
EMP: 13
SALES (est): 2.8MM **Privately Held**
WEB: www.trinitypowdercoatings.com
SIC: 5084 3471 Paint spray equipment, industrial; sand blasting of metal parts

(G-7606)
TRUE VELOCITY AMMUNITION LLC
Also Called: TV Ammo
2735 Forest Ln (75042-6510)
PHONE................................972 487-6500
Kevin Boscamp, *CEO*
Christopher Tedford, *President*
EMP: 72
SALES (est): 113.4K **Privately Held**
WEB: www.tvammo.com
SIC: 5941 3482 Ammunition; small arms ammunition

(G-7607)
VARO LLC
2800 W Kingsley Rd (75041-2400)
PHONE................................972 840-5506
Jacob Armon, *Ch of Bd*
Harry Armon, *President*
Alan J Weiss, *Exec VP*
EMP: 412 **EST:** 1946
SQ FT: 120,000
SALES (est): 37.6MM
SALES (corp-wide): 44.1MM **Privately Held**
SIC: 3629 3823 3812 Power conversion units, a.c. to d.c.: static-electric; industrial instrmnts msrmnt display/control process variable; search & navigation equipment
PA: Imrex, Llc
55 Sandy Hill Rd
Oyster Bay NY 11771
516 479-3675

(G-7608)
VENUS BEAUTY INC
1041 S Jupiter Rd (75042-7708)
PHONE................................301 503-4052
Vu Tran, *President*
EMP: 12
SALES (est): 329.6K **Privately Held**
WEB: www.vbstrading.com
SIC: 3999 Manufacturing industries

(G-7609)
WAVEWARE TECHNOLOGIES INC
2630 National Dr (75041-2331)
PHONE................................972 479-1702
Janet Rock, *President*
Jamie Davis, *Business Mgr*
A C Hickman, *Business Mgr*
Curtis Rock, *Exec VP*
EMP: 10
SQ FT: 5,000
SALES (est): 2MM **Privately Held**
WEB: www.wirelessmessaging.com
SIC: 3663 5065 Pagers (one-way); paging & signaling equipment

(G-7610)
WOLTERS HOLDINGS INC
Also Called: Nor Tex Metal Finishing
1917 Silver St (75042-6671)
PHONE................................972 272-4600
Shelby L Wolters, *CEO*
EMP: 9
SALES (est): 500K **Privately Held**
SIC: 3559 Metal finishing equipment for plating, etc.

(G-7611)
K L BARTON & SONS TIE CO
703 S Us Highway 59 (75946)
P.O. Box 540 (75946-0540)
PHONE................................936 347-2744
Bob J Barton, *President*
K Lane Barton, *Corp Secy*
Mike Barton, *Vice Pres*
EMP: 17 **EST:** 1957
SQ FT: 2,000
SALES (est): 2.4MM **Privately Held**
WEB: www.klbartontie.com
SIC: 2421 2448 2426 Railroad ties, sawed; pallets, wood; hardwood dimension & flooring mills

(G-7612)
LLC HUBER LAND
703 N Us Highway 59 (75946)
PHONE................................936 347-2744
Bob J Barton, *Principal*
EMP: 11
SALES (est): 501.2K **Privately Held**
SIC: 2491 Railroad cross-ties, treated wood

(G-7613)
M & D COMPANIES INC (PA)
156 E Main St (75946-6576)
P.O. Box 2 (75946-0002)
PHONE................................936 347-2138
Marty Reneau, *President*
Richard Arvello, *Manager*
Susan Berry, *Admin Sec*
Dianna Reneau, *Admin Sec*
EMP: 25
SALES (est): 4.9MM **Privately Held**
WEB: www.mdsupply.net
SIC: 1389 Oil field services

(G-7614)
HANSON AGGREGATES LLC
County Road 111 (77442)
P.O. Box 339, Altair (77412-0339)
PHONE................................979 758-3662
Jimmy Smith, *Manager*
EMP: 50
SALES (corp-wide): 20.8B **Privately Held**
WEB: www.heidelbergcement.com
SIC: 3531 1442 Batching plants, for aggregate concrete & bulk cement; construction sand & gravel
HQ: Hanson Aggregates Llc
8505 Freeport Pkwy Ste 500
Irving TX 75063
469 417-1200

(G-7615)
MARIETTA MARTIN MATERIALS INC
Also Called: Garwood Sand & Gravel
6747 Highway 71 (77442-4175)
PHONE................................979 758-3960
David Cook, *Branch Mgr*
EMP: 17 **Publicly Held**
WEB: www.martinmarietta.com
SIC: 1422 Crushed & broken limestone
PA: Martin Marietta Materials Inc
2710 Wycliff Rd
Raleigh NC 27607

(G-7616)
S&M ENERGY SERVICES LLC
153 Private Road 8202 (75643-4398)
PHONE................................318 210-5166
Richard Mayfield, *Mng Member*
EMP: 11
SALES (est): 213.2K **Privately Held**
WEB: www.sm-energy.com
SIC: 1389 Oil & gas field services

Gatesville
Coryell County

(G-7617)
ATTIC BREEZE LLC
1370 Fm 116 (76528-3785)
P.O. Box 1318 (76528-6318)
PHONE..................................254 865-9999
Travis Hipp, *President*
Jim Hudson, *Business Mgr*
Jeff Van Wagner, *Sales Staff*
Brandi Hipp, *Marketing Staff*
▲ EMP: 42
SQ FT: 2,000
SALES (est): 6MM **Privately Held**
WEB: www.atticbreeze.net
SIC: 3564 Blowers & fans

(G-7618)
HEIL TRAILER INTERNATIONAL LLC
Also Called: Kalyn Siebert
1505 W Main St (76528-1024)
PHONE..................................254 865-7235
Ryan Rockafellow, *VP Sales*
William Harris, *Branch Mgr*
Bill Nehrkorn, *Director*
EMP: 125 **Privately Held**
WEB: www.heiltrailer.com
SIC: 7538 3715 3537 General automotive repair shops; truck trailers; industrial trucks & tractors
HQ: Heil Trailer International, Llc
1125 Congress Pkwy N
Athens TN 37303

(G-7619)
MEDICAL PLASTICS LABORATORY
226 Fm 116 (76528-1061)
PHONE..................................254 865-7221
David Broussard, *President*
EMP: 310
SQ FT: 90,000
SALES (est): 22.9MM
SALES (corp-wide): 120.3MM **Privately Held**
SIC: 3083 5046 Laminated plastics plate & sheet; mannequins
PA: Laerdal Medical Corporation
167 Myers Corners Rd
Wappingers Falls NY 12590
845 297-7770

(G-7620)
MESSENGER PUBLISHING CO INC
Also Called: Gatesville Messenger, The
116 S 6th St (76528-2052)
P.O. Box 799 (76528-0799)
PHONE..................................254 865-5212
Marshall Day, *President*
Tidwell Jerry, *Vice Pres*
Roy McQueen, *Admin Sec*
EMP: 10
SQ FT: 4,000
SALES (est): 500K **Privately Held**
WEB: www.gatesvillemessenger.com
SIC: 2711 5943 Newspapers: publishing only, not printed on site; office forms & supplies

(G-7621)
NOLTEX TRUSS BIG SPRING INC
1705 E Main St (76528-2516)
P.O. Box 1060, Grandview (76050-1060)
PHONE..................................254 216-0904
Jeff Browning, *General Mgr*
Joseph Nolte, *Principal*
Amos Davila, *Manager*
Joann Esquibel, *Manager*
EMP: 11 EST: 2009
SALES (est): 1.6MM **Privately Held**
WEB: www.noltextruss.com
SIC: 2439 Trusses, wooden roof

(G-7622)
PADGETT MACHINE TOOLS CO INC
4212 E Us Highway 84 (76528-4094)
P.O. Box 33 (76528-0033)
PHONE..................................254 865-9771
Morris Padgett, *President*
Paige Hargrove, *Vice Pres*
EMP: 28
SQ FT: 8,000
SALES (est): 4.5MM Privately Held
WEB: www.padgettmachinetool.com
SIC: 3599 Machine shop, jobbing & repair

George West
Live Oak County

(G-7623)
CHOCTAW LEASE SERVICE LLC
2272 Hwy 59 (78022-3970)
P.O. Box 171 (78022-0171)
PHONE..................................361 449-3506
Sheila Schroeder, *Partner*
James Schroeder,
EMP: 12
SALES (est): 1.7MM **Privately Held**
SIC: 1389 Oil field services

(G-7624)
FLINT ENERGY SERVICES INC
3425 Highway 281 (78022-3645)
PHONE..................................361 449-2405
Joseph Oddonetto, *Manager*
EMP: 136
SALES (corp-wide): 13.2B **Publicly Held**
WEB: www.aecom.com
SIC: 1389 3594 1623 Servicing oil & gas wells; fluid power pumps; oil & gas pipeline construction
HQ: Flint Energy Services Inc.
6200 S Quebec St Ste 1
Greenwood Village CO 80111
918 294-3030

(G-7625)
JAG ENERGY USA INC
1869 N Ih 37 Access Rd (78022-4083)
PHONE..................................361 449-1400
Danny Foley, *Branch Mgr*
EMP: 27
SALES (corp-wide): 15.7MM **Privately Held**
WEB: www.jagenergy.com
SIC: 1389 Measurement of well flow rates, oil & gas
PA: Jag Energy Usa, Inc.
16300 Katy Fwy Ste 225
Houston TX 77094
281 579-0888

(G-7626)
JOE GARCIA
Also Called: Broken Duckfeet Cafe
100 S Nueces St (78022)
P.O. Box 1124, Three Rivers (78071-1124)
PHONE..................................361 436-2130
Joe Garcia, *Owner*
EMP: 10 EST: 2016
SQ FT: 4,000
SALES (est): 50K **Privately Held**
SIC: 2599 Bar, restaurant & cafeteria furniture

(G-7627)
ONLINE CONSTRUCTION LP
411 Catholic Cemetery Rd (78022-3610)
P.O. Box 1630 (78022-1630)
PHONE..................................361 445-6161
James Williams, *Partner*
EMP: 10 EST: 2011
SALES (est): 791.8K **Privately Held**
SIC: 1389 7353 Oil field services; oil equipment rental services

(G-7628)
PALOMA LEASE SERVICE INC
3466 Highway 281 (78022-3644)
P.O. Box 1116 (78022-1116)
PHONE..................................361 449-2815
Lucio Morin, *President*
Monroe Schroeder, *Corp Secy*
EMP: 32
SQ FT: 5,000
SALES (est): 2.2MM **Privately Held**
SIC: 1389 Oil field services

(G-7629)
SOUTHERN LEASE SERVICE LTD
100 County Rd 121 (78022)
P.O. Box 868 (78022-0868)
PHONE..................................361 449-3048
Larry Holm, *Partner*
John Lyne, *Partner*
Lavanche Lyne, *Partner*
EMP: 15
SALES (est): 1MM **Privately Held**
SIC: 1389 Servicing oil & gas wells

(G-7630)
TOWNSEND OILFIELD SERVICES LP
3122 Highway 281 (78022-3828)
PHONE..................................361 449-1444
Shain Townsend, *Owner*
David Townsend, *Owner*
EMP: 13
SALES (est): 1.5MM **Privately Held**
WEB: www.tosmachineshop.com
SIC: 3999 Atomizers, toiletry

Georgetown
Williamson County

(G-7631)
ADAO GLOBAL LLC
308 Goodnight Dr (78628-6929)
P.O. Box 2241, Cedar Park (78630-2241)
PHONE..................................512 431-7743
Josh Arnold, *Sales Staff*
David Arnold,
▲ EMP: 15
SQ FT: 600
SALES (est): 5.7MM **Privately Held**
WEB: www.soleusrunning.com
SIC: 3873 Watches, clocks, watchcases & parts

(G-7632)
AGUADO STONE INCORPORATED
3601 County Road 239 (78633-4418)
PHONE..................................512 746-5094
Martin Aguado, *President*
▲ EMP: 65
SQ FT: 2,200
SALES (est): 17.7MM **Privately Held**
WEB: www.aguadostone.com
SIC: 5032 3281 Clay construction materials, except refractory; flagstones

(G-7633)
AIRBORN INTERCONNECT INC
Also Called: Airborn Georgetown
3500 Airborn Cir (78626-8215)
PHONE..................................512 863-5585
Cindy Lewis, *Branch Mgr*
EMP: 300
SQ FT: 56,000
SALES (corp-wide): 221.1MM **Privately Held**
WEB: www.airborn.com
SIC: 3678 3679 8711 7373 Electronic connectors; harness assemblies for electronic use: wire or cable; engineering services; computer integrated systems design
PA: Airborn Interconnect, Inc.
3500 Airborn Cir
Georgetown TX 78626
512 863-5585

(G-7634)
AMERICAN FENCE AND SUP CO INC
3501 N Interstate 35 (78628-0904)
PHONE..................................512 930-4000
Milos Miladan, *Manager*
EMP: 12
SALES (corp-wide): 10MM **Privately Held**
WEB: www.afence.com
SIC: 5211 5039 5031 5083 Fencing; wire fence, gates & accessories; fencing, wood; livestock equipment; culverts, sheet metal; welding on site

PA: American Fence And Supply Company, Inc.
2215 Gulf Fwy S
League City TX 77573
281 332-0511

(G-7635)
ARTECH MANUFACTURING INC
1840 County Road 120 (78626-2285)
PHONE..................................512 863-9050
Albert Rychlik, *President*
EMP: 12
SQ FT: 4,500
SALES (est): 1.6MM **Privately Held**
WEB: www.artechmfg.com
SIC: 3599 Machine shop, jobbing & repair

(G-7636)
ARTISANS CABINETRY & WOODWORK
2200 S Church St Ste 103 (78626-8093)
PHONE..................................512 626-7311
Chris Wallace, *CEO*
EMP: 61
SALES (est): 6MM **Privately Held**
SIC: 2431 1751 Millwork; cabinet building & installation

(G-7637)
AT-INTEGRATION INC
204 S Interstate 35 # 105 (78628-4126)
PHONE..................................512 819-4629
Lynn Nations, *President*
EMP: 9
SALES (est): 883.1K **Privately Held**
WEB: www.atintegration.com
SIC: 3695 5734 Computer software tape & disks: blank, rigid & floppy; computer & software stores

(G-7638)
AUSTIN POWDER COMPANY
8850 W Hwy 29 (78626)
P.O. Box 879 (78627-0879)
PHONE..................................512 863-3676
Matt Parker, *General Mgr*
EMP: 9
SALES (corp-wide): 509.6MM **Privately Held**
WEB: www.austinpowder.com
SIC: 2892 5169 Explosives; explosives
HQ: Austin Powder Company
25800 Science Park Dr # 300
Cleveland OH 44122
216 464-2400

(G-7639)
BALCONES TECHNOLOGIES LLC
104 Alabaster Caverns Dr (78628-7228)
PHONE..................................512 699-5828
Michael Lewis, *Vice Pres*
Scott Pish, *Vice Pres*
Angelo Gattozzi, *Research*
Shannon Strank, *Asst Director*
Joseph H Beno Jr,
EMP: 10
SALES (est): 490.2K **Privately Held**
WEB: www.balconestech.com
SIC: 3568 Power transmission equipment

(G-7640)
BENCH TREE GROUP LLC (PA)
4681 County Road 110 (78626-7402)
PHONE..................................512 869-6900
Aubrey L Holt Jr, *President*
Billy Wolf, *Engineer*
Dan Flores, *Director*
Jane Carolyn Holt, *Admin Sec*
▲ EMP: 27
SQ FT: 9,100
SALES (est): 5.8MM **Privately Held**
WEB: www.benchtree.com
SIC: 3679 Electronic circuits

(G-7641)
BEST QUALITY MACHINING INC
3205 Vortac Ln (78628-1842)
PHONE..................................512 864-1667
Lynn G Schneider, *President*
Thomas Stephens, *Director*
Jerome McCain, *Admin Sec*
EMP: 10 EST: 1991
SQ FT: 2,000
SALES (est): 1.1MM **Privately Held**
SIC: 3599 Machine shop, jobbing & repair

(G-7642)
BOYD AG LLC
3208 Sierra Dr (78628-1829)
PHONE......................512 863-2589
Ron Boyd, *President*
EMP: 10
SQ FT: 10,000
SALES (est): 6.6MM **Privately Held**
WEB: www.boydag.com
SIC: 5083 3523 Farm implements;
spreaders, fertilizer

(G-7643)
CFT DISPENSERS INC
Also Called: Clean Fueling Technologies
116 Halmar Cv (78628-2331)
PHONE......................512 942-8300
Curtis Donaldson, *Director*
EMP: 9
SQ FT: 5,200
SALES (est): 220.8K **Privately Held**
WEB: www.cftdispensers.com
SIC: 3586 Gasoline pumps, measuring or
dispensing

(G-7644)
CHATSWORTH PRODUCTS INC
Also Called: CPI
3004 S Austin Ave (78626-7544)
PHONE......................512 863-7800
Henry Erazo, *Engineer*
Daniel Perkins, *Engineer*
Mike Tanner, *Regl Sales Mgr*
Wesley Gass, *Branch Mgr*
Dean Peters, *Program Mgr*
EMP: 125
SQ FT: 51,440 **Privately Held**
WEB: www.chatsworth.com
SIC: 3498 3444 Fabricated pipe & fittings;
sheet metalwork
PA: Chatsworth Products, Inc.
29899 Agoura Rd Ste 120
Agoura Hills CA 91301

(G-7645)
**CREST ORTHOPEDIC IMPLANTS
LLC**
7200 N Intrstate 35 Bldg (78626)
PHONE......................254 931-6996
David Freehill,
EMP: 10
SALES (est): 707K **Privately Held**
WEB: www.crestoi.com
SIC: 3841 Medical instruments & equip-
ment, blood & bone work

(G-7646)
D & L PRINTING INC
552 Stadium Dr (78626-4794)
P.O. Box 210 (78627-0210)
PHONE......................512 863-8145
John Lee Gregory, *President*
Janice Clark, *Manager*
EMP: 10
SQ FT: 2,500
SALES (est): 1.6MM **Privately Held**
WEB: www.dlprint.com
SIC: 2752 Commercial printing, offset

(G-7647)
DETAIL MOLD & MFG LLC
14773 Ranch Road 2338 (78633-6644)
PHONE......................512 255-0525
Dan Berg, *General Mgr*
Mariah Joseph, *Accountant*
Todd Tatro, *Mng Member*
Ray Lensing, *Manager*
EMP: 18
SALES (est): 2.5MM **Privately Held**
WEB: www.detailmold.com
SIC: 3544 Special dies & tools

(G-7648)
DISPLAYS & OPTICAL TECH
110 Market St (78626-3698)
PHONE......................512 246-6400
Monty MA Gill, *President*
Michael Itz, *Vice Pres*
Tyler Hehn, *Engineer*
EMP: 22
SQ FT: 17,000
SALES (est): 2.8MM **Privately Held**
WEB: www.doti-optics.com
SIC: 3229 3827 Pressed & blown glass;
lenses, optical: all types except oph-
thalmic; reflectors, optical

(G-7649)
EMINENT SPINE LLC
7200 N Interstate 35 # 1 (78626-1862)
PHONE......................512 868-5980
Matt Winkler, *Engineer*
George Singeltary, *Business Anlyst*
Kimberly Williams, *Manager*
Aaron Williams, *General Counsel*
Stephen P Courtney,
EMP: 14
SQ FT: 16,000
SALES (est): 2.4MM **Privately Held**
WEB: www.eminentspine.com
SIC: 3841 Surgical & medical instruments

(G-7650)
ENFLITE LLC
105 W Cooperative Way (78626-8200)
PHONE......................512 868-3399
Dana Fiatarone, *President*
Kevin Kieper, *COO*
Corliss Montesi, *Vice Pres*
Ken Ward, *Engineer*
EMP: 58
SQ FT: 20,000
SALES (est): 12.2MM **Privately Held**
WEB: www.lifeport.com
SIC: 3728 Aircraft parts & equipment
PA: Lifeport , Llc
1610 Heritage St
Woodland WA 98674

(G-7651)
ENVIRONMENTAL FLOORS INC
505 Martin Creek Ln (78633-2087)
PHONE......................713 956-5526
EMP: 10
SALES (est): 595.9K **Privately Held**
SIC: 1389 Ceramic Tile & Grout Restora-
tion

(G-7652)
**GEORGETOWN WINERY LLC
(PA)**
715 S Main St (78626-5700)
P.O. Box 2389 (78627-2389)
PHONE......................512 869-8600
Daniel R Marek, *Principal*
EMP: 9 EST: 2010
SALES (est): 1.7MM **Privately Held**
WEB: www.georgetownwinery.com
SIC: 2084 Wines

(G-7653)
**GEORGETOWN WOODWORKS
LLC**
500 Wildflower Ln (78626-1958)
PHONE......................512 868-9048
Stephen Baldwin, *Division Mgr*
Rusty Bowman, *Controller*
Tricia Morrison, *Mng Member*
Collins Morrison, *Mng Member*
EMP: 21
SQ FT: 4,500
SALES (est): 3.5MM **Privately Held**
WEB: www.georgetownwoodworks.com
SIC: 2431 Millwork

(G-7654)
GIPSON GROUP LLC
Also Called: Minuteman Press
1904 S Austin Ave (78626-7808)
PHONE......................512 931-2211
Ty Gipson,
Crystal Gipson,
EMP: 9
SQ FT: 1,300
SALES (est): 1.7MM **Privately Held**
WEB: www.mmptx.com
SIC: 2752 2621 2732 2741 Commercial
printing, lithographic; book, bond & print-
ing papers; books: printing & binding;
posters: publishing & printing

(G-7655)
GRESHARE ENTERPRISES INC
Also Called: Affordable Signs
4185 E University Ave A (78626-3868)
PHONE......................512 869-7446
Sharen K Kohutek, *President*
Dana Noworyta, *Graphic Designe*
EMP: 10
SQ FT: 3,500

SALES (est): 500K **Privately Held**
WEB: www.affsigns.com
SIC: 3993 Signs, not made in custom sign
painting shops

(G-7656)
**HILL COUNTRY DIRECTORIES
LTD**
508 Cedar Dr (78628-4103)
PHONE......................512 864-2973
Bill McEntire, *Partner*
Earline Gibson, *Partner*
EMP: 18
SALES (est): 1.4MM **Privately Held**
WEB: www.hcdyp.com
SIC: 2741 Telephone & other directory
publishing

(G-7657)
IDEAL SIGNS
79 Eastview Dr Ste 101 (78626-3862)
PHONE......................512 930-7446
EMP: 17 EST: 2011
SALES (est): 2.3MM **Privately Held**
WEB: www.ideal-signs.com
SIC: 3993 Signs, not made in custom sign
painting shops

(G-7658)
INSERVIO3 LLC (PA)
624 S Austin Ave Ste 230 (78626-5758)
PHONE......................213 439-9656
David Vandygriff, *CEO*
James Dedakis, *Vice Pres*
Felix Nolasco, *Opers Staff*
John Vandygriff, *CFO*
Ryan Haas, *Accounts Exec*
EMP: 9 EST: 2017
SALES (est): 4.9MM **Privately Held**
WEB: www.inservio3.com
SIC: 7374 7334 2621 7375 Optical scan-
ning data service; photocopying & dupli-
cating services; blueprinting service;
book, bond & printing papers; on-line data
base information retrieval

(G-7659)
**KTEC CLEANROOM SYSTEMS
INC**
5040 E State Highway 29 (78626-3802)
PHONE......................512 388-2396
Randall Jackson, *President*
Sandra Cramer, *General Mgr*
Mark Wells, *Vice Pres*
Patricia C Jackson, *Admin Sec*
EMP: 12
SALES (est): 2.3MM **Privately Held**
WEB: www.kteccleanrooms.com
SIC: 3448 Panels for prefabricated metal
buildings

(G-7660)
LOMONT MOLDING LLC
107 Park Central Blvd (78626-7548)
PHONE......................512 763-3600
Gregory Brown, *Principal*
EMP: 102
SALES (corp-wide): 26.5MM **Privately
Held**
WEB: www.lomont.com
SIC: 3089 Blow molded finished plastic
products
PA: Lomont Molding Llc
1516 E Mapleleaf Dr
Mount Pleasant IA 52641
319 385-1528

(G-7661)
M&H MACHINING INC
102 Meadow Dr (78633-9556)
PHONE......................512 930-9059
Hudson Ingram, *President*
Diane Ingram, *Vice Pres*
Mark Wangler, *Vice Pres*
Brandon Ingram,
EMP: 15 EST: 1973
SQ FT: 5,000
SALES (est): 1.2MM **Privately Held**
WEB: www.mhmachining.com
SIC: 3599 Machine shop, jobbing & repair

(G-7662)
MANITEX INC (HQ)
3000 S Austin Ave (78626-7544)
PHONE......................512 942-3000
David J Langevin, *CEO*

Bob Latchab, *President*
Bob Litchev, *COO*
Sam Hawkins, *Plant Mgr*
James Corey, *Mfg Mgr*
◆ EMP: 140
SQ FT: 2,000
SALES (est): 37.9MM **Publicly Held**
WEB: www.manitex.com
SIC: 3536 3537 Hoists, cranes & mono-
rails; cranes, industrial truck

(G-7663)
MEDIMOBILE
1918 Leander Rd (78628-8835)
PHONE......................512 686-0817
James Enis, *President*
Emil Indradjaja, *Engineer*
Tammy Knight, *Comptroller*
Samantha Huizar, *Marketing Mgr*
Will Enis, *Manager*
EMP: 12
SALES (est): 1.4MM **Privately Held**
WEB: www.medimobile.com
SIC: 7372 Business oriented computer
software

(G-7664)
MERIT SALES INC
Also Called: Merit Industries
119 Serenada Dr (78628-1364)
P.O. Box 878 (78627-0878)
PHONE......................512 863-8541
Herbert Piller, *President*
Lisa Piller, *Vice Pres*
EMP: 55
SQ FT: 50,000
SALES (est): 5.6MM **Privately Held**
WEB: www.meritind.com
SIC: 5199 3999 Advertising specialties;
novelties, bric-a-brac & hobby kits

(G-7665)
**MOONEY SAENGER
ENTERPRISES**
Also Called: Georgetown Shirt Co
40204 Industrial Park Cir (78626-4712)
PHONE......................512 869-0979
Sandy Mooney, *President*
Craig Mooney, *President*
Jay Saenger, *Admin Sec*
EMP: 10
SQ FT: 15,500
SALES (est): 1.4MM **Privately Held**
WEB: www.georgetownshirtcompany.com
SIC: 2759 2395 Screen printing; embroi-
dery & art needlework

(G-7666)
NEXT TECHNOLOGIES INC (PA)
Also Called: Nextdesk
2530 Shell Rd (78628-9235)
PHONE......................512 212-7758
▲ EMP: 14
SALES (est): 6.7MM **Privately Held**
WEB: www.xdesk.com
SIC: 2521 2522 Wood office desks & ta-
bles; desks, office: except wood

(G-7667)
NEXTUS INC
101 Halmar Cv (78628-2331)
PHONE......................512 288-9080
Klaus Bollmann, *CEO*
Susan Vaughan, *COO*
Hannelore Bollmann, *CFO*
Steve Daniel, *VP Mktg*
EMP: 25
SQ FT: 13,500
SALES (est): 5.5MM **Privately Held**
WEB: www.nextus.com
SIC: 3679 3577 Hermetic seals for elec-
tronic equipment; computer peripheral
equipment
PA: Network Technology Limited
26 Victoria Way
Burgess Hill W SUSSEX RH15

(G-7668)
**NOVAK COMMERCIAL CNSTR
LLC**
1500 Rivery Blvd Ste 2200 (78628-3065)
PHONE......................512 688-5644
Morgan McLaughlin, *President*
EMP: 15 EST: 2017

SALES (est): 110.1K **Privately Held**
WEB: www.novakbros.com
SIC: 1531 1389 ; construction, repair & dismantling services

(G-7669)
OLD CASTLE APG TEXAS INC
15811 Hwy 195 (78626)
PHONE..................................512 864-9601
EMP: 30
SALES (corp-wide): 24.2B **Privately Held**
SIC: 3273 5032 Mfg Ready-Mixed Concrete Whol Brick/Stone Material
HQ: Oldcastle Apg Texas, Inc.
2624 Joe Field Rd
Dallas TX 75229
972 488-8131

(G-7670)
PLATINUM UNDERGROUND LLC
3200 Vortac Ln (78628-1845)
PHONE..................................512 770-9410
Teresa Lemons, *CFO*
Paul Lemons, *Mng Member*
EMP: 42
SALES (est): 5.1MM **Privately Held**
SIC: 1442 Construction sand & gravel

(G-7671)
R D MCMILLAN COMPANY INC
Also Called: Mc Millan Company
7075 Ranch Road 2338 (78633-4314)
P.O. Box 1340 (78627-1340)
PHONE..................................512 863-0231
R D Mc Millan, *CEO*
Bob M McMillan, *President*
Phillip S McMillan, *Vice Pres*
EMP: 23
SQ FT: 15,000
SALES (est): 4.8MM **Privately Held**
WEB: www.mcmflow.com
SIC: 3823 Industrial instrmnts msrmnt display/control process variable

(G-7672)
RANGER READY MIX LLC (PA)
40206 Industrial Park Cir (78626-4761)
PHONE..................................512 363-7630
Dan McBride, *Mng Member*
EMP: 27
SALES (est): 6.4MM **Privately Held**
SIC: 3272 Concrete products

(G-7673)
REALITY PUBLISHING CO
1322 Eagle Point Dr (78628-0203)
PHONE..................................281 493-4105
Michael Miller, *President*
EMP: 15
SALES (est): 1.4MM **Privately Held**
WEB: www.realityratings.com
SIC: 2741 Miscellaneous publishing

(G-7674)
REEDHOLM INSTRUMENTS CO
4 Sierra Way St (78626-7574)
PHONE..................................512 869-1935
Joseph P Reedholm Sr, *President*
Frank Siskovic, *Vice Pres*
Karolyn Reedholm, *Treasurer*
EMP: 30
SQ FT: 8,000
SALES (est): 4.4MM **Privately Held**
WEB: www.reedholmsystems.com
SIC: 3679 3829 3825 3674 Parametric amplifiers; measuring & controlling devices; instruments to measure electricity; semiconductors & related devices

(G-7675)
RINGDALE INC (HQ)
101 Halmar Cv (78628-2331)
PHONE..................................512 288-9080
EMP: 15 EST: 1985
SALES (est): 1MM **Privately Held**
WEB: www.ringdale.com
SIC: 4899 3625 3577 Communication signal enhancement network system; relays & industrial controls; computer peripheral equipment

(G-7676)
SCHUNK XYCARB TECHNOLOGY INC
Also Called: Schunk Semiconductor
101 Se Inner Loop (78626-7597)
P.O. Box 1699 (78627-1699)
PHONE..................................512 863-0033
Win Van Velzen, *CEO*
Ramon Martinez, *Maint Spvr*
John Martino, *Regl Sales Mgr*
Paul Arguelles, *Manager*
Michael Thompson, *Manager*
▲ EMP: 35
SQ FT: 12,000
SALES (est): 6.7MM
SALES (corp-wide): 1.2B **Privately Held**
WEB: www.schunk-xycarbtechnology.com
SIC: 3674 Semiconductors & related devices
HQ: Schunk Of North America, Inc
W146n9300 Held Dr
Menomonee Falls WI 53051
262 253-8720

(G-7677)
SOLOMON TRANSFORMERS LLC
100 W Cooperative Way (78626-8200)
PHONE..................................512 763-3306
Clinton Gehrmann, *Principal*
EMP: 60
SALES (corp-wide): 131.1MM **Privately Held**
WEB: www.solomoncorp.com
SIC: 3612 Voltage regulating transformers, electric power
PA: Solomon Transformers, Llc
103 W Main St
Solomon KS 67480
785 655-2191

(G-7678)
SOUTHWEST QUARTZ LTD CO
6024 Williams Dr Ste 110 (78633-4327)
P.O. Box 715, Liberty Hill (78642-0715)
PHONE..................................512 863-8415
Rick Coone, *President*
Pam Coone, *Office Mgr*
EMP: 12
SQ FT: 5,400
SALES (est): 2MM **Privately Held**
SIC: 3679 Quartz crystals, for electronic application

(G-7679)
SPM TECHNOLOGY INC
Also Called: S P M
300 Park Central Blvd (78626-7502)
PHONE..................................512 931-0201
Alvin W Sather, *President*
Geraldene Sather, *Vice Pres*
▲ EMP: 30
SQ FT: 40,000
SALES (est): 6.1MM **Privately Held**
WEB: www.spmtechnology.com
SIC: 3599 Machine shop, jobbing & repair

(G-7680)
STACCATO 2011 LLC (PA)
Also Called: STI International
114 Halmar Cv (78628-2331)
PHONE..................................512 819-0656
Gregory Mooney, *CEO*
Josh Dow, *Prdtn Mgr*
James Rosales, *Prdtn Mgr*
Robert Parker, *Safety Mgr*
Mike Willis, *QC Mgr*
EMP: 59
SQ FT: 9,700
SALES (est): 20MM **Privately Held**
WEB: www.staccato2011.com
SIC: 3484 Guns (firearms) or gun parts, 30 mm. & below

(G-7681)
STARKS WELDING & MFG SVCS INC
Also Called: Motor Pwr Prtction Systems Div
1255 Old 1460 Trl (78626-3903)
P.O. Box 966 (78627-0966)
PHONE..................................512 863-2424
Donald W Starks, *Principal*
Belinda Braddock, *Manager*
EMP: 40

SALES (est): 4.6MM **Privately Held**
SIC: 3441 7692 Building components, structural steel; welding repair; automotive welding

(G-7682)
TASUS CORPORATION
211 Tasus Way (78626-7750)
P.O. Box 1310 (78627-1310)
PHONE..................................512 869-7766
Robbie Grace, *Materials Mgr*
Susan Deckard, *Production*
Shane Green, *Senior Buyer*
Patti Ramien, *QC Mgr*
Cody Coburn, *Engineer*
EMP: 75 **Privately Held**
WEB: www.tasus.com
SIC: 3089 Injection molding of plastics
HQ: Tasus Corporation
1151 W 2nd St
Bloomington IN 47403
812 333-6500

(G-7683)
TASUS TEXAS CORPORATION
211 Tasus Way (78626-7750)
PHONE..................................512 869-7766
Melanie Walker, *President*
Craig Slater, *Corp Secy*
Mark Coburn, *Manager*
◆ EMP: 140
SALES: 25.3MM **Privately Held**
WEB: www.tasus.com
SIC: 3086 3089 Plastics foam products; injection molding of plastics
HQ: Tasus Corporation
1151 W 2nd St
Bloomington IN 47403
812 333-6500

(G-7684)
TEXAS CRUSHED STONE COMPANY (PA)
5300 S Interstate 35 (78626-7764)
P.O. Box 1000 (78627-1000)
PHONE..................................512 255-4405
W B Snead, *President*
▲ EMP: 135 EST: 1947
SALES (est): 82.5MM **Privately Held**
WEB: www.texascrushedstoneco.com
SIC: 1422 2951 1442 Crushed & broken limestone; asphalt paving mixtures & blocks; construction sand & gravel

(G-7685)
TEXAS ELECTRIC COOPS INC
Also Called: TEC Utility Supply & Services
100 W Cooperative Way (78626-8200)
PHONE..................................512 868-8610
EMP: 53
SQ FT: 147,726
SALES (corp-wide): 200MM **Privately Held**
WEB: www.texas-ec.org
SIC: 2491 5063 3677 Poles & pole crossarms, treated wood; electrical apparatus & equipment; transformers power supply, electronic type
PA: Texas Electric Cooperatives, Inc.
1122 Colorado St Ste 2400
Austin TX 78701
512 454-0311

(G-7686)
TIPS INCORPORATED
2402 Williams Dr (78628-3248)
PHONE..................................512 863-3653
Robert Weibel, *President*
Ted Stoltenberg, *CFO*
Lisa Jones, *Sales Staff*
Kelsey Wright, *Mktg Coord*
Bob Weibel, *Software Dev*
EMP: 15
SQ FT: 2,928
SALES (est): 1.9MM **Privately Held**
WEB: www.tipsweb.com
SIC: 7372 Prepackaged software

(G-7687)
TRIFECTIX INC
Also Called: Orcaconfig
20126 West Lake Pkwy (78628-9512)
PHONE..................................512 580-2809
Timothy E Wall, *President*
Shannon Heidemann, *Sales Executive*
EMP: 20

SALES (est): 168.6K **Privately Held**
WEB: www.orcaconfig.com
SIC: 7372 Application computer software

(G-7688)
WESTERN GLASS LLC
3871 E University Ave # 185 (78626-2632)
PHONE..................................512 820-2475
Kyle Winston, *President*
EMP: 12
SALES (est): 1MM **Privately Held**
SIC: 3231 Products of purchased glass

(G-7689)
WILLIAMSON COUNTY SUN INC
Also Called: Sun System
707 S Main St (78626-5700)
P.O. Box 39 (78627-0039)
PHONE..................................512 930-3072
Linda Scarbrough, *President*
Clark Thurmond, *Corp Secy*
Olga Solis, *Manager*
EMP: 34 EST: 1875
SALES (est): 2.9MM **Privately Held**
WEB: www.wilcosun.com
SIC: 2711 Newspapers, publishing & printing

Giddings
Lee County

(G-7690)
ADVANCE HYDROCARBON CORP
1003 County Road 237 (78942-9418)
P.O. Box 908 (78942-0908)
PHONE..................................979 542-1520
EMP: 10
SALES (corp-wide): 7.4MM **Privately Held**
WEB: www.ahcus.com
SIC: 1389 Impounding & storing salt water, oil & gas field
HQ: Advance Hydrocarbon Corporation
10343 Sam Houston Park Dr # 325
Houston TX 77064

(G-7691)
AMERICAN INDUSTRIAL POLYMERS
1233 N Orange St (78942-1449)
P.O. Box 209 (78942-0209)
PHONE..................................979 542-3654
Leonard F Mitschke, *President*
Creek Allen, *Vice Pres*
Alan Creek, *Treasurer*
Calvin V Mitschke, *Shareholder*
EMP: 35
SQ FT: 3,200
SALES (est): 5.3MM **Privately Held**
WEB: www.aiptfe.com
SIC: 2821 3053 Polytetrafluoroethylene resins (teflon); gaskets, packing & sealing devices

(G-7692)
BEG LIQUID MUD SERVICES CORP
2502 E Austin St (78942-3651)
P.O. Box 540 (78942-0540)
PHONE..................................979 542-7000
Brian J Recatto, *CEO*
Gregory Milton, *Vice Pres*
Dan Keen, *Director*
EMP: 15
SALES (est): 1.3MM
SALES (corp-wide): 5.5B **Privately Held**
SIC: 1389 Mud service, oil field drilling; oil field services
PA: Gibson Energy Inc
440 2 Ave Sw Suite 1700
Calgary AB T2P 5
403 206-4000

(G-7693)
CNC PLASTICS
4031 County Road 117 B (78942-5088)
PHONE..................................979 884-0608
Allen Taylor Creek, *Owner*
▲ EMP: 14 EST: 2004
SALES (est): 1MM **Privately Held**
WEB: www.cncplastics.net
SIC: 3086 Plastics foam products

(G-7694)
ENERVEST OPERATING LLC
1055 County Road 237 (78942-9418)
PHONE.................................979 542-2054
John B Walker, *President*
Mark A Houser, *COO*
James M Vanderhider, *CFO*
EMP: 23 **EST:** 1996
SALES (est): 2MM **Privately Held**
SIC: 1382 Oil & gas exploration services

(G-7695)
GIDDINGS VOLUNTEER FIRE DEPT
151 W Independence St (78942-1913)
P.O. Box 1450 (78942-2350)
PHONE.................................979 492-1156
Torri Stadge, *Administration*
Paula Schatte, *Administration*
EMP: 22
SALES: 66.2K **Privately Held**
WEB: www.giddingstx.com
SIC: 0851 1389 8322 Fire fighting services, forest; fire prevention services, forest; fire fighting, oil & gas field; first aid service

(G-7696)
HUGHES MANUFACTURING INC
2301 W Highway 290 (78942-5735)
PHONE.................................979 542-0333
Renata Hughes, *President*
Linda Hughes-Ehlers, *Vice Pres*
EMP: 18
SALES (est): 1.3MM **Privately Held**
WEB: www.hughesmanufacturing.com
SIC: 3993 Signs, not made in custom sign painting shops

(G-7697)
J & P SERVICES INC
1103 Private Road 7703 (78942-6027)
P.O. Box 207 (78942-0207)
PHONE.................................979 542-0500
Jon Olsen, *President*
Pam Olsen, *Corp Secy*
Amanda O Parks, *Vice Pres*
EMP: 15
SQ FT: 5,000
SALES (est): 4.6MM **Privately Held**
WEB: www.pumpingunit.net
SIC: 1389 Construction, repair & dismantling services

(G-7698)
KEY ENERGY SERVICES INC
2144 Fm 448 (78942)
P.O. Box 29 (78942-0029)
PHONE.................................979 542-3344
Danny Kovar, *General Mgr*
Brandy Smith, *Opers Staff*
EMP: 100
SALES (corp-wide): 413.8MM **Publicly Held**
WEB: www.keyenergy.com
SIC: 1389 1382 Servicing oil & gas wells; oil & gas exploration services
PA: Key Energy Services, Inc.
　1301 Mckinney St Ste 1800
　Houston TX 77010
　713 651-4300

(G-7699)
L F MANUFACTURING INC (PA)
5528 E Highway 290 (78942-2972)
P.O. Box 578 (78942-0578)
PHONE.................................979 542-8027
Dan Edling, *President*
Jack Murray, *General Mgr*
Bernard J Ofczarzak, *District Mgr*
David Johnston, *VP Opers*
Roger Anderson, *Project Mgr*
▲ **EMP:** 90
SQ FT: 81,000
SALES (est): 36MM **Privately Held**
WEB: www.lfm-frp.com
SIC: 3089 1629 3088 Plastic & fiberglass tanks; waste water & sewage treatment plant construction; plastics plumbing fixtures

(G-7700)
PUMPCO INC
1209 S Main St (78942-4922)
P.O. Box 742 (78942-0742)
PHONE.................................979 542-9054
Alan Roberts, *President*
Robyn Roberts, *Corp Secy*
EMP: 175
SQ FT: 1,800
SALES (est): 117.1MM
SALES (corp-wide): 7.1B **Publicly Held**
WEB: www.pumpco.cc
SIC: 1623 1389 Pipeline construction; oil field services
HQ: Mastec North America, Inc.
　800 S Douglas Rd Ste 1200
　Coral Gables FL 33134
　305 599-1800

(G-7701)
RHOS INC
Also Called: Richard's Hot Oil Service
716 E Austin St (78942-3404)
P.O. Box 816 (78942-0816)
PHONE.................................979 542-5420
Richard Holt, *President*
EMP: 15
SQ FT: 5,000
SALES (est): 1.5MM **Privately Held**
SIC: 1389 Servicing oil & gas wells

(G-7702)
TEXAS GEOLOGIC SERVICES LLC
2946 E Austin St (78942-9744)
PHONE.................................979 542-3893
Jeff Armstrong,
Scott Rohloff,
EMP: 20
SQ FT: 1,200
SALES (est): 1.5MM **Privately Held**
WEB: www.texasgeologic.com
SIC: 1382 Geological exploration, oil & gas field

(G-7703)
TEXAS HOT OILERS INC
Hwy 77 (78942)
P.O. Box 1007 (78942-1007)
PHONE.................................979 542-9341
Fax: 979 542-1736
EMP: 15
SQ FT: 5,000
SALES (est): 1.5MM **Privately Held**
SIC: 1389 Oil Field Services

(G-7704)
WCS OIL & GAS CORPORATION
451 Cactus St (78942-1456)
P.O. Box 1109 (78942-1509)
PHONE.................................979 542-0021
William C Shuford, *Manager*
EMP: 12
SALES (corp-wide): 2.3MM **Privately Held**
SIC: 1311 Crude petroleum production; natural gas production
PA: Wcs Oil & Gas Corporation
　4807 W Lovers Ln
　Dallas TX 75209
　214 357-9116

Gilmer
Upshur County

(G-7705)
APEX COIL LLC
204 Dean St (75644-7913)
PHONE.................................903 843-4534
Sandra Howard,
Jack Howard,
EMP: 21
SQ FT: 30,000
SALES (est): 2MM **Privately Held**
SIC: 3585 3498 Refrigeration & heating equipment; fabricated pipe & fittings

(G-7706)
DUOLINE TECHNOLOGIES LLC (HQ)
250 W Bluebird Rd (75645-7234)
PHONE.................................903 734-1371
David A Marshall, *President*
Peter Mc Ilroy II, *Partner*
Mike Posson, *Partner*
Michael T Deane, *Vice Pres*
Eric Nichols, *Opers Mgr*
◆ **EMP:** 25

SQ FT: 18,000
SALES (est): 22.7MM
SALES (corp-wide): 70.2MM **Privately Held**
WEB: www.duoline.com
SIC: 3533 1389 Oil field machinery & equipment; servicing oil & gas wells
PA: Robroy Industries, Inc.
　10 River Rd
　Verona PA 15147
　412 828-2100

(G-7707)
GREENEWAY ENTERPRISES INC
Also Called: Gilmer Mirror, The
214 E Marshall St (75644-2228)
P.O. Box 250 (75644-0250)
PHONE.................................903 843-2503
Sarah L Greene, *President*
William Greene, *Admin Sec*
EMP: 12
SQ FT: 4,000
SALES (est): 668.2K **Privately Held**
WEB: www.uber.matchbin.com
SIC: 2711 2752 Newspapers: publishing only, not printed on site; commercial printing, lithographic

(G-7708)
LABELING EQUIPMENT SPECIALISTS
3115 Locust Rd (75645-2774)
PHONE.................................903 734-5873
Everett Bickford, *President*
Jeremy Gaines, *General Mgr*
Jodi Still, *General Mgr*
Mary Bickford, *Treasurer*
Jennifer Gunn, *Sales Staff*
EMP: 10
SALES (est): 500K **Privately Held**
WEB: www.lesincorporated.com
SIC: 3556 Food products machinery

(G-7709)
MAYHAN FABRICATORS INC
7525 Us Highway 271 S (75645-7795)
PHONE.................................903 734-4198
Stanley Shane Mayhan, *President*
Teresia Mayhan, *Corp Secy*
Ross Mayhan, *Vice Pres*
Shane Mayhan, *Manager*
EMP: 35 **EST:** 1981
SQ FT: 14,000
SALES (est): 7.9MM **Privately Held**
WEB: www.mayhan.us
SIC: 3567 3554 3441 3316 Industrial furnaces & ovens; paper industries machinery; fabricated structural metal; cold finishing of steel shapes; blast furnaces & steel mills

(G-7710)
PARLAND INC
Also Called: Total Quality Machining
1205 Industrial Blvd (75644)
PHONE.................................903 843-3467
Mike Newland, *President*
Darel Parsons, *Treasurer*
EMP: 10
SQ FT: 6,900
SALES (est): 1.3MM **Privately Held**
WEB: www.totalqualitymachining.net
SIC: 3599 Machine shop, jobbing & repair

(G-7711)
REDCO ENDEAVORS INC
4200 State Highway 155 S (75645-8076)
P.O. Box 1509 (75644-1509)
PHONE.................................832 421-8549
Justin Donaho, *CEO*
Robbie Tompkins, *Business Mgr*
Quyen Tong, *CFO*
EMP: 15
SALES (est): 570.6K **Privately Held**
WEB: www.redcoendeavors.com
SIC: 1442 1799 1771 1794 Construction sand & gravel; construction site cleanup; fence construction; curb construction; excavation & grading, building construction

(G-7712)
ROBROY INDUSTRIES INC
Also Called: Electrical Productions Div
1100 Us Highway 271 S (75644-7702)
PHONE.................................412 828-2100
Steve Voelzke, *General Mgr*

Craig Mitchell, *Vice Pres*
Brenda Eidd, *Accountant*
Jon Wagner, *VP Sales*
David Marshall, *Branch Mgr*
EMP: 110
SALES (corp-wide): 70.2MM **Privately Held**
WEB: www.robroy.com
SIC: 3644 2851 Electric conduits & fittings; paints & allied products
PA: Robroy Industries, Inc.
　10 River Rd
　Verona PA 15147
　412 828-2100

(G-7713)
ROBROY INDUSTRIES-TEXAS LLC
Also Called: Robroy Industries - Texas LP
1100 Us Highway 271 S (75644-7702)
PHONE.................................903 843-5591
Robert McIlroy II, *CEO*
Steven Voelzke, *President*
Vijay Kumar, *CFO*
Kristen Edge, *Controller*
Stephanie Sipes, *Executive Asst*
EMP: 100
SQ FT: 18,000
SALES (est): 20.3MM
SALES (corp-wide): 70.2MM **Privately Held**
WEB: www.robroy.com
SIC: 3444 Elbows, for air ducts, stovepipes, etc.: sheet metal
PA: Robroy Industries, Inc.
　10 River Rd
　Verona PA 15147
　412 828-2100

(G-7714)
SULPHUR RIVER EXPLORATION INC
Caddo Resources
2186 State Highway 300 (75645-4037)
P.O. Box 948 (75644-0948)
PHONE.................................903 734-7248
Danny Davis, *Branch Mgr*
EMP: 16
SALES (corp-wide): 7MM **Privately Held**
SIC: 1311 1389 Crude petroleum production; natural gas production; processing service, gas; gas field services
PA: Sulphur River Exploration, Inc.
　4851 Lyndon B Johnson Fwy # 550
　Dallas TX 75244
　214 373-1091

(G-7715)
TEXAS INDUSTRIES INC
320 Walnut St (75644-1661)
PHONE.................................903 843-2327
EMP: 24 **Publicly Held**
WEB: www.martinmarietta.com
SIC: 3241 Cement, hydraulic
HQ: Texas Industries, Inc.
　1503 Lyndon B Johnson Fwy
　Dallas TX 75234
　972 647-6700

Gladewater
Gregg County

(G-7716)
3D PLASTICS LLC
1095 E Commerce Ave (75647-3012)
P.O. Box 6797, Longview (75608-6797)
PHONE.................................903 844-9333
David Frye, *President*
Dena Woods, *Vice Pres*
▲ **EMP:** 65
SQ FT: 10,500
SALES (est): 13.6MM
SALES (corp-wide): 122.4MM **Privately Held**
WEB: www.quantumplastics.com
SIC: 3089 Injection molded finished plastic products
PA: Qp Holdings, Llc
　3730 Wheeler Ave
　Fort Smith AR 72901
　479 646-3473

▲ = Import ▼=Export
◆ =Import/Export

(G-7717)
ARK-LA-TEX CUSTOM COATINGS
100 N Lee Dr (75647-2509)
PHONE..................................903 845-6436
Tracey Charlson, *President*
Betty Charlson, *Vice Pres*
EMP: 15
SQ FT: 22,000
SALES (est): 2.6MM **Privately Held**
SIC: 2951 2952 Asphalt paving mixtures & blocks; coating compounds, tar

(G-7718)
ASP WESTWARD LP
Also Called: Gladewater Mirror
211 N Main St (75647-2335)
P.O. Box 1549 (75647-1549)
PHONE..................................903 845-2235
Jim Barwell, *Principal*
EMP: 20
SQ FT: 10,017
SALES (corp-wide): 91.3MM **Privately Held**
WEB: www.chron.com
SIC: 2711 Newspapers, publishing & printing
PA: Asp Westward, L.P.
523 N Sam Houston Pkwy E
Houston TX 77060
713 256-0953

(G-7719)
BLASTROOM EQP & CNSTR INC
Also Called: Breco
605 E Pacific Ave (75647-2426)
P.O. Box 1109, White Oak (75693-6109)
PHONE..................................903 845-2083
Lewis Wright, *President*
Toni Wright, *Treasurer*
Zac Wright, *Manager*
EMP: 20
SQ FT: 10,000
SALES (est): 1MM **Privately Held**
WEB: www.brecoinc.com
SIC: 3441 Fabricated structural metal

(G-7720)
DELZOTTO PRODUCTS MINN INC
5701 Highway 135 (75647-6511)
PHONE..................................903 981-0400
Eric Childress, *Opers Mgr*
EMP: 27
SQ FT: 1,000
SALES (corp-wide): 2.5MM **Privately Held**
WEB: www.delzottoprecastforms.com
SIC: 3449 3272 3443 Miscellaneous metalwork; concrete products; fabricated plate work (boiler shop)
PA: Delzotto Products Of Minnesota, Inc.
1900 County Road 1
Wrenshall MN 55797
218 384-3066

(G-7721)
DELZOTTO PRODUCTS TEXAS INC
5701 State Highway 135 (75647-6511)
PHONE..................................903 981-0400
William M Del Zotto, *President*
Duane Johnson, *Vice Pres*
EMP: 38
SALES (est): 12.2MM **Privately Held**
WEB: www.delzottoprecastforms.com
SIC: 3449 3272 Bars, concrete reinforcing: fabricated steel; sewer pipe, concrete

(G-7722)
HEAT SHIELD INC
Also Called: American Canopies
1710 N Main St (75647-5406)
PHONE..................................903 845-4066
Carol Muckleroy, *President*
Lisa Malone, *Corp Secy*
Jimmie Muckleroy, *Vice Pres*
EMP: 18
SQ FT: 5,500
SALES (est): 3MM **Privately Held**
SIC: 3444 5999 Canopies, sheet metal; siding, sheet metal; awnings

(G-7723)
JDW SERVICES INC (PA)
405 Riverside Dr (75647-5501)
P.O. Box 1523 (75647-1523)
PHONE..................................903 845-5586
EMP: 36 EST: 1972
SQ FT: 3,000
SALES (est): 11.2MM **Privately Held**
SIC: 1389 Oil field services

(G-7724)
JOHN LINDER OPERATING CO LLC
200 Griffin St (75647-9508)
P.O. Box 97 (75647-0097)
PHONE..................................903 845-4240
John G Linder,
EMP: 20
SALES (est): 1.5MM **Privately Held**
SIC: 1389 Gas field services; oil field services

(G-7725)
LBS ENTERPRISES LLC
Also Called: Allstates Coatings Company
100 N Lee Dr (75647-2509)
PHONE..................................903 845-6436
Tracey Charlson, *President*
Luke Charlson, *Vice Pres*
Jon Cook, *Purch Mgr*
EMP: 15 EST: 1996
SALES (est): 4.9MM **Privately Held**
WEB: www.washingtonmover.com
SIC: 2851 Paints & allied products

(G-7726)
MAVERICK TECHNICAL SYSTEMS INC
315 E Us Highway 80 (75647-3978)
P.O. Box 1588 (75647-1588)
PHONE..................................903 845-5574
D Mark Friend, *President*
Sheila M Friend, *Admin Sec*
EMP: 9 EST: 1981
SQ FT: 16,000
SALES (est): 1.6MM **Privately Held**
WEB: www.mavmetal.com
SIC: 3613 3625 Switchgear & switchgear accessories; control panels, electric; control equipment, electric

(G-7727)
TEXAS DIE CASTING LLC
600 S Loop 485 (75647-3316)
P.O. Box 1617 (75647-1617)
PHONE..................................903 845-2224
John Oxton, *Vice Pres*
David Pack, *QC Mgr*
Billy Diviney, *Engineer*
Kevin Patterson, *Engineer*
Ray Voisin, *Sales Mgr*
EMP: 120
SALES (est): 17MM **Privately Held**
WEB: www.texasdiecasting.com
SIC: 3363 Aluminum die-castings

(G-7728)
TRENDSETTER CONSTRUCTION INC (PA)
Also Called: Trendsetter Recycling Services
2173 Turkey Rd (75647-7896)
P.O. Box 246, White Oak (75693-0246)
PHONE..................................903 759-4955
Joel Campbell, *President*
Steven Harris, *Assistant VP*
Robby Campbell, *Vice Pres*
Robert Campbell, *Vice Pres*
Roger Davidson, *Foreman/Supr*
EMP: 110
SQ FT: 4,500
SALES (est): 29.9MM **Privately Held**
WEB: www.trendsetterconstruction.com
SIC: 1629 1795 1799 1389 Land clearing contractor; wrecking & demolition work; athletic & recreation facilities construction; diamond drilling & sawing; roustabout service; mud service, oil field drilling; servicing oil & gas wells; concrete construction: roads, highways, sidewalks, etc.; excavation & grading, building construction

(G-7729)
TRI RESOURCES INC
Also Called: Dynegy
3018 Barrow Ln (75647)
PHONE..................................903 845-2617
Bobby Larence, *Manager*
EMP: 15 **Publicly Held**
WEB: www.triresources.com
SIC: 1389 Servicing oil & gas wells
HQ: Tri Resources Inc.
811 Louisiana St Ste 2100
Houston TX 77002
713 584-1000

(G-7730)
WINCO MACHINE & REPAIR INC
1011 E Commerce Ave (75647-3012)
PHONE..................................903 844-2200
Winn King, *President*
EMP: 17
SQ FT: 16,000
SALES (est): 2.3MM **Privately Held**
SIC: 3599 Machine shop, jobbing & repair

Glen Rose
Somervell County

(G-7731)
BANC PROFESSIONAL SERVICES
100 Progress St (76043-4312)
PHONE..................................972 734-1200
Robert Garner Jr, *Ch of Bd*
Renee Garner, *President*
EMP: 15
SQ FT: 6,000
SALES (est): 2.3MM **Privately Held**
SIC: 2752 2759 5943 Commercial printing, offset; letterpress printing; office forms & supplies

(G-7732)
MW SUPPLY INC
Also Called: Bustin Industrial Products
100 Progress St (76043-4312)
PHONE..................................254 897-4590
Michael B Williams, *President*
Tad Timmons, *Vice Pres*
Brian Blair, *Purch Mgr*
Clint Nickell, *CFO*
Ryan Breton, *Marketing Staff*
▲ **EMP:** 97
SQ FT: 20,000
SALES (est): 17.2MM **Privately Held**
WEB: www.mwsupply.com
SIC: 3714 Sanders, motor vehicle safety

(G-7733)
SKIPPER INDUSTRIES INC
650 Bo Gibbs Blvd (76043)
P.O. Box 71, Iredell (76649-0071)
PHONE..................................254 897-1292
Tony Skipper, *President*
EMP: 21
SALES (est): 2.8MM **Privately Held**
WEB: www.skipperindustriesinc.com
SIC: 3462 Construction or mining equipment forgings, ferrous

Godley
Johnson County

(G-7734)
DAIRYMANS CHOICE ORGANICS INC
Also Called: D C Organics
3101 Fm 2331 (76044-4412)
PHONE..................................817 641-2015
Ronnie West, *President*
Bob Lang, *Vice Pres*
Raylene West, *Treasurer*
Michael Lang, *Admin Sec*
EMP: 11
SQ FT: 4,800
SALES (est): 500K **Privately Held**
SIC: 2875 Compost

(G-7735)
DON SPENCER CO
12656 Fm 2331 (76044-3329)
PHONE..................................817 389-4413

EMP: 200
SALES (est): 4.2MM **Privately Held**
SIC: 1389 Builds Nursing Homes

(G-7736)
MIDWAY OILFIELD CONSTRS INC
Also Called: Midway Energy
11400 Fm 2331 (76044-3526)
PHONE..................................817 389-2525
Landon Martin, *General Mgr*
Jake Cain, *Vice Pres*
EMP: 250
SALES (corp-wide): 385.5MM **Privately Held**
WEB: www.midwayoilfield.com
SIC: 1389 Oil field services
PA: Midway Oilfield Constructors, Inc.
12627 State Highway 21 E
Midway TX 75852
936 348-3721

(G-7737)
NATIONAL OILWELL VARCO INC
Tuboscope Nov
8000 County Road 1001 (76044-5201)
PHONE..................................817 389-2444
Cody Alexander, *Branch Mgr*
EMP: 10
SALES (corp-wide): 8.4B **Publicly Held**
WEB: www.nov.com
SIC: 1389 Oil field services
PA: National Oilwell Varco, Inc.
7909 Parkwood Circle Dr
Houston TX 77036
713 346-7500

(G-7738)
OWEN OIL TOOLS LP (DH)
12001 County Road 1000 (76044-3141)
P.O. Box 568 (76044-0568)
PHONE..................................817 551-0540
Jeff West, *Partner*
Dan W Pratt, *Partner*
Les Weisner, *Partner*
Dan Pratt, *Vice Pres*
Cory Day, *Opers Staff*
◆ **EMP:** 245
SQ FT: 20,000
SALES (est): 183.9MM
SALES (corp-wide): 668.2MM **Privately Held**
WEB: www.ocsresponds.com
SIC: 3533 2892 Drilling tools for gas, oil or water wells; well shooting torpedoes (explosive)

(G-7739)
PINNERGY LTD
9913 N Highway 171 (76044-3435)
PHONE..................................817 389-2105
Joy Mike, *Manager*
Erik Smith, *Manager*
EMP: 111 **Privately Held**
WEB: www.pinnergy.com
SIC: 1389 Oil field services
PA: Pinnergy, Ltd.
111 Congress Ave Ste 2020
Austin TX 78701

(G-7740)
RENEGADE WELL SERVICES LLC
7501 County Road 1128 (76044-3419)
PHONE..................................817 389-2496
EMP: 27 **Privately Held**
WEB: www.renegadewellservices.com
SIC: 1389 Servicing oil & gas wells
HQ: Renegade Well Services, Llc
3301 E Us Highway 377 # 202
Granbury TX 76049

Goldsmith
Ector County

(G-7741)
DCP MIDSTREAM LLC
Highway 158 (79741)
P.O. Box 738 (79741-0738)
PHONE..................................432 827-1945
Bart Collins, *Manager*
Gary Amburgey, *Supervisor*

EMP: 80
SALES (corp-wide): 1.9B **Privately Held**
WEB: www.dcpmidstream.com
SIC: 2911 5191 5172 Gasoline blending plants; fertilizers & agricultural chemicals; petroleum products
PA: Dcp Midstream, Llc
370 17th St Ste 2500
Denver CO 80202
303 633-2900

(G-7742)
FIFE SERVICES INC
Also Called: Fife, J M Welding
616 Odessa St (79741)
P.O. Box 174 (79741-0174)
PHONE.................................432 827-3601
Daniel Fife, *President*
EMP: 44
SQ FT: 3,000
SALES (est): 7MM **Privately Held**
WEB: www.fifeservices.com
SIC: 7629 7692 7641 1629 Electrical repair shops; welding repair; office furniture repair & maintenance; oil refinery construction

(G-7743)
WATERS & WATERS SERVICES INC (PA)
Also Called: Shores Lift Solutions
616 N Odessa St (79741)
PHONE.................................432 827-3354
Ron Waters, *President*
Jamie Waters, *Corp Secy*
Raul Garza, *Vice Pres*
Gerald Waters, *Vice Pres*
Jesse Waters, *Vice Pres*
EMP: 70
SQ FT: 3,000
SALES (est): 10.1MM **Privately Held**
SIC: 4212 1389 Petroleum haulage, local; oil field services

Goldthwaite
Mills County

(G-7744)
SCHUSTERS OF TEXAS INC
2109 Priddy Rd (76844-2035)
P.O. Box 97 (76844-0097)
PHONE.................................325 648-2267
Ronald Schuster, *Vice Pres*
Dale Schuster, *Treasurer*
Tammie Cloud, *Office Mgr*
Vance Schuster, *Admin Sec*
◆ **EMP:** 14 EST: 1950
SQ FT: 75,000
SALES (est): 1.4MM **Privately Held**
WEB: www.schustersoftexas.com
SIC: 3999 5193 5999 Flowers, artificial & preserved; artificial flowers; artificial flowers

(G-7745)
SOUTHERN NUT N TREE EQUIPMENT
324 State Highway 16 S (76844-3404)
PHONE.................................325 938-5460
Dewayne McCasland, *President*
Patty McCasland, *Principal*
Brooke Seely, *Principal*
Brent McCasland, *Vice Pres*
EMP: 50
SALES (est): 1.9MM **Privately Held**
WEB: www.sntequipment.com
SIC: 5083 3523 5999 Harvesting machinery & equipment; planting, haying, harvesting & processing machinery; farm machinery

Goliad
Goliad County

(G-7746)
2W SERVICES LLC
145 N Jefferson St (77963-4007)
P.O. Box 1028 (77963-1028)
PHONE.................................361 645-1010
Dustin E Wright, *Principal*
EMP: 10

SALES (est): 3.4MM **Privately Held**
SIC: 1389 Oil & gas field services

(G-7747)
GOLIAD BREWING COMPANY INC
252 Metting Rd (77963-3966)
PHONE.................................936 441-6100
Jimmy M Rogers, *President*
John Wilkerson, *Vice Pres*
EMP: 12 EST: 2013
SALES (est): 1.6MM **Privately Held**
WEB: www.goliadcc.org
SIC: 2082 Beer (alcoholic beverage)

Gonzales
Gonzales County

(G-7748)
ADAMS FLVORS FODS INGRDNTS LLC
Also Called: Adam's Extract & Spice
3217 Johnson Rd (78629-8008)
P.O. Box 1726 (78629-1226)
PHONE.................................830 672-1850
Brian Rainosek, *VP Opers*
Laura Soto, *Purchasing*
Donald Brown, *CFO*
Zulema Gonzales, *Controller*
Ryan Heger, *Sales Staff*
▲ **EMP:** 163
SQ FT: 36,000
SALES (est): 23.3MM **Privately Held**
WEB: www.adamsextract.com
SIC: 5149 2087 2099 Spices & seasonings; flavoring extracts & syrups; food preparations; seasonings & spices; spices, including grinding

(G-7749)
BUDDYS NATURAL CHICKENS INC
2430 Church St (78629)
PHONE.................................830 672-6262
David Lindeman, *President*
Ruby Lindeman, *Treasurer*
EMP: 76
SALES (est): 8.1MM **Privately Held**
SIC: 2015 Poultry slaughtering & processing

(G-7750)
BUDDYS NATURAL CHICKENS INC
2548 Church St (78629-2100)
P.O. Box 1657 (78629-1157)
PHONE.................................830 305-0553
Fax: 830 672-2968
EMP: 75
SALES (corp-wide): 6.8MM **Privately Held**
SIC: 2015 Poultry Processing
PA: Buddy's Natural Chickens, Inc.
2430 Church St
Gonzales TX 78629
830 672-6262

(G-7751)
DAVIS APPLICATORS LLC
18 Park Place Dr (78629-2705)
PHONE.................................830 857-3222
Taylor Davis, *Principal*
EMP: 9 EST: 2015
SALES (est): 1MM **Privately Held**
WEB: www.davisapplicators.com
SIC: 2015 Poultry slaughtering & processing

(G-7752)
E BARR FEEDS INC
212 Saint Louis St (78629-3954)
PHONE.................................830 672-6515
Steve Ehrig, *President*
Larry Ehrig, *Principal*
Bert Ehrig, *Vice Pres*
EMP: 10
SQ FT: 4,500

SALES (est): 1.4MM **Privately Held**
WEB: www.ebarrfeeds.com
SIC: 2048 5261 5999 5083 Livestock feeds; lawn & garden supplies; fertilizer; insecticides; lawn & garden machinery & equipment; farm supplies; insecticides; fertilizer & fertilizer materials

(G-7753)
GRAVITY OILFIELD SERVICES LLC
1915 E Sarah Dewitt Dr (78629-3812)
PHONE.................................830 203-5210
EMP: 59
SALES (corp-wide): 422.8MM **Privately Held**
WEB: www.gravityoilfieldservices.com
SIC: 1389 Oil field services
HQ: Gravity Oilfield Services Llc
3300 N A St Bldg 4-100
Midland TX 79705

(G-7754)
GUADALUPE VALLEY PUBLISHING CO
Also Called: Gonzales Inquirer
622 Saint Paul St (78629-3552)
P.O. Box 616 (78629-0616)
PHONE.................................830 672-2861
James Chionsini, *President*
Susie Bernd, *Advt Staff*
EMP: 9 EST: 1853
SQ FT: 6,400
SALES (est): 521.3K **Privately Held**
WEB: www.gonzalesinquirer.com
SIC: 2711 Commercial printing & newspaper publishing combined

(G-7755)
HOLMES FOODS INC
Also Called: Feedmill
2170 Fm 108 S (78629-6529)
PHONE.................................830 437-5555
Roger Crouch, *Manager*
EMP: 11
SALES (corp-wide): 64.9MM **Privately Held**
WEB: www.holmesfoods.com
SIC: 2015 Poultry, processed; poultry, slaughtered & dressed
PA: Holmes Foods, Inc.
101 S Liberty Ave
Nixon TX 78140
830 582-1551

(G-7756)
HOLMES FOODS INC
108 South St (78629-3430)
PHONE.................................830 437-2555
Phillip Morris, *President*
Roger Crouch, *Manager*
EMP: 11
SALES (corp-wide): 64.9MM **Privately Held**
WEB: www.holmesfoods.com
SIC: 2015 Poultry slaughtering & processing
PA: Holmes Foods, Inc.
101 S Liberty Ave
Nixon TX 78140
830 582-1551

(G-7757)
INGRAM READYMIX INC
307 Theo St (78629-2008)
PHONE.................................830 672-6420
Joe Blanco, *Manager*
EMP: 21
SALES (corp-wide): 125.6MM **Privately Held**
WEB: www.ingramreadymixinc.com
SIC: 3273 Ready-mixed concrete
PA: Ingram Readymix, Inc.
3580 Farm Market 482
New Braunfels TX 78132
830 625-9156

(G-7758)
KIXX RENTALS & SERVICES LLC
77 County Road 312 (78629-6596)
PHONE.................................830 437-2959
Sue Lynn Lester,
EMP: 20
SQ FT: 217,800
SALES (est): 1.1MM **Privately Held**
SIC: 1389 Oil field services

(G-7759)
MERCO SOLUTIONS CORPORATION
1078 Highway 304 (78629-2883)
PHONE.................................830 519-4260
Amy Mertz, *Principal*
EMP: 22
SALES (est): 728.6K **Privately Held**
SIC: 1389 Oil & gas field services

(G-7760)
ONE GAS INC
Also Called: Texas Gas Service Company
619 N Saint Joseph St (78629-3504)
PHONE.................................830 672-2921
Larry Schuenemaman, *Branch Mgr*
EMP: 48
SALES (corp-wide): 1.6B **Publicly Held**
WEB: www.onegas.com
SIC: 1311 Natural gas production
PA: One Gas, Inc.
15 E 5th St
Tulsa OK 74103
918 947-7000

(G-7761)
ONE GAS INC
Also Called: Texas Gas Service Company
225 Commerce Ct (78629-6783)
PHONE.................................830 672-2256
EMP: 48
SALES (corp-wide): 1.6B **Publicly Held**
WEB: www.onegas.com
SIC: 1311 Natural gas production
PA: One Gas, Inc.
15 E 5th St
Tulsa OK 74103
918 947-7000

(G-7762)
PURINA ANIMAL NUTRITION LLC
1402 E Sarah Dewitt Dr (78629-2519)
PHONE.................................830 672-6565
Martyn Hafley, *Sales Staff*
Barry Fisher, *Manager*
EMP: 35
SALES (corp-wide): 6.1B **Privately Held**
WEB: www.purinamills.com
SIC: 2048 Prepared feeds
HQ: Purina Animal Nutrition Llc
100 Danforth Dr
Gray Summit MO 63039

(G-7763)
PURINA MILLS LLC
1402 E Sarah Dewitt Dr (78629-2519)
PHONE.................................830 672-6565
Barry Fisher, *General Mgr*
EMP: 60
SALES (corp-wide): 6.1B **Privately Held**
WEB: www.purinamills.com
SIC: 2048 Prepared feeds
HQ: Purina Mills, Llc
555 Maryvle Univ Dr 200
Saint Louis MO 63141

(G-7764)
SEGURO WELL SERVICE INC
183 South St (78629-3429)
P.O. Box 1642 (78629-1142)
PHONE.................................830 672-8025
Leonardo Reyna, *President*
Cantley Kennon, *Vice Pres*
EMP: 10
SALES (est): 1MM **Privately Held**
SIC: 1389 Servicing oil & gas wells; well plugging & abandoning, oil & gas

(G-7765)
TROPICAL FUSIONS INC
2712 Harwood Rd (78629-6019)
PHONE.................................830 203-5116
Norman Burns, *Director*
Robert Lee, *Director*
EMP: 23
SALES (est): 4.3MM **Privately Held**
SIC: 2086 Fruit drinks (less than 100% juice): packaged in cans, etc.

(G-7766)
TYSON FOODS INC
2504 Church St (78629-2100)
P.O. Box 697 (78629-0697)
PHONE.................................830 672-6548
Steve Willman, *Manager*

EMP: 130
SALES (corp-wide): 43.1B Publicly Held
WEB: www.tysonfoods.com
SIC: 2015 Poultry slaughtering & processing
PA: Tyson Foods, Inc.
    2200 W Don Tyson Pkwy
    Springdale AR 72762
    479 290-4000

(G-7767)
XL OILFIELD SERVICES LLC
530 Seydler St (78629-3750)
P.O. Box 526 (78629-0526)
PHONE..................................830 672-6644
Paul L Prove, President
Melissa L Prove, Vice Pres
Cherry D Prove, Treasurer
EMP: 35 EST: 2011
SQ FT: 1,500
SALES (est): 4.6MM Privately Held
WEB: www.xloilfield.com
SIC: 1389 Oil field services

Goodrich
Polk County

(G-7768)
AMERICAN RAILCAR INDS INC
Also Called: American Rail Car Coatings
1718 State Hwy Loop 393 (77335-8344)
P.O. Box 501 (77335-0501)
PHONE..................................936 365-2679
Oscar Guerra, Opers Staff
Jerry Kelley, Manager
EMP: 70
SALES (corp-wide): 476.8MM Privately Held
WEB: www.americanrailcar.com
SIC: 3743 2675 5088 Railroad equipment; liners for freight car doors: reinforced with metal strip; railroad equipment & supplies
HQ: American Railcar Industries, Inc.
    100 Clark St
    Saint Charles MO 63301

Gordon
Palo Pinto County

(G-7769)
RAIDER SERVICES LP
6215 County Road 120 (76453-5816)
PHONE..................................830 996-0016
Mark McKelvey, Owner
EMP: 120 EST: 2010
SQ FT: 217,800
SALES (est): 10.1MM Privately Held
SIC: 7389 1389 7331 Packaging & labeling services; oil field services; mailing service

Gordonville
Grayson County

(G-7770)
MAHARD FEED MILL INC
27019 Us Highway 377 (76245-4512)
PHONE..................................903 523-4455
EMP: 9
SALES (corp-wide): 6.1MM Privately Held
WEB: www.mahard.com
SIC: 2048 Livestock feeds
PA: Mahard Feed Mill, Inc.
    410 E 1st St
    Prosper TX 75078
    972 346-3074

Gorman
Eastland County

(G-7771)
BIRDSONG CORPORATION
Birdsong Peanuts Div
601 Mc Call St (76454)
P.O. Box 698 (76454-0698)
PHONE..................................254 734-2266
G M Grice, Manager
EMP: 21
SALES (corp-wide): 68.3MM Privately Held
WEB: www.birdsongpeanuts.com
SIC: 5159 5441 2099 2068 Peanuts (bulk), unroasted; nuts; food preparations; salted & roasted nuts & seeds
PA: Birdsong Corporation
    612 Madison Ave
    Suffolk VA 23434
    757 539-3456

(G-7772)
GORMAN MILLING CO INC (PA)
502 E Lubbock St (76454-3066)
P.O. Box 276 (76454-0276)
PHONE..................................254 734-2252
John Fritts, President
Robert Fritts, Treasurer
EMP: 86 EST: 1969
SQ FT: 20,000
SALES (est): 35MM Privately Held
WEB: www.redchainfeeds.com
SIC: 2048 Livestock feeds

Graford
Palo Pinto County

(G-7773)
SOLID ROCKS PROPERTIES LLC
20115 State Highway 337 (76449-3316)
PHONE..................................940 779-3700
Scott Herring, Mng Member
EMP: 15
SALES (est): 892.1K Privately Held
SIC: 1442 Construction sand & gravel

Graham
Young County

(G-7774)
1954 MANUFACTURING INC
4688 State Highway 16 S (76450-6664)
P.O. Box 1688 (76450-7688)
PHONE..................................760 524-1378
EMP: 14
SALES (est): 1.7MM Privately Held
WEB: www.1954manufacturing.com
SIC: 3999 Manufacturing industries

(G-7775)
ALLAR COMPANY
735 Elm St (76450-3018)
P.O. Box 1567 (76450-7567)
PHONE..................................940 549-0077
John C Graham, President
EMP: 9
SQ FT: 4,400
SALES (est): 1.5MM Privately Held
WEB: www.echoproduction.com
SIC: 6792 1311 Oil leases, buying & selling on own account; crude petroleum production; natural gas production

(G-7776)
ARCOOIL CORP
471 State Highway 67 (76450-7046)
PHONE..................................940 549-4444
Harprit Sahota, Mng Member
EMP: 30
SQ FT: 4,000
SALES (est): 571.1K Privately Held
WEB: www.arcooil.com
SIC: 1382 2911 Oil & gas exploration services; gases & liquefied petroleum gases

(G-7777)
BETTIS BOYLE & STOVALL INC
505 5th St (76450-2506)
P.O. Box 1240 (76450-1240)
PHONE..................................940 549-0780
Harry M Bettis, President
Brint Albritton, Vice Pres
Weldon T Boyle, Vice Pres
Norman D Stovall Jr, Vice Pres
Spencer B Street, Shareholder
EMP: 35
SQ FT: 8,000
SALES (est): 3.9MM Privately Held
SIC: 1311 Crude petroleum production; natural gas production

(G-7778)
CORPORATE TEXAS CO LLC
Also Called: Street Cos,
901 4th St (76450-3115)
P.O. Box 1101 (76450-1101)
PHONE..................................940 549-1400
EMP: 10 EST: 1967
SQ FT: 800
SALES (est): 780.5K Privately Held
SIC: 1311 Crude petroleum production

(G-7779)
DAVID R ROGERS CNSTR INC
2811 State Highway 16 S (76450-5105)
P.O. Box 1019 (76450-1019)
PHONE..................................940 549-6374
David R Rogers, President
EMP: 120
SALES (est): 13.4MM Privately Held
SIC: 1389 Oil field services

(G-7780)
DOYLES CONSTRUCTION & MFG INC
624 6th St (76450-2631)
P.O. Box 451 (76450-0451)
PHONE..................................940 549-5517
Steve Doyle, President
EMP: 10
SALES (est): 2.6MM Privately Held
WEB: www.doyles-construction.com
SIC: 3448 1521 Buildings, portable: prefabricated metal; new construction, single-family houses

(G-7781)
E & H DRILLING CO
New Castle Hwy (76450)
P.O. Box 1058 (76450-1058)
PHONE..................................940 549-0370
Ray Herring, President
Earlene Rogers, Corp Secy
Ronnie Robertson, Vice Pres
EMP: 50 EST: 1953
SQ FT: 3,700
SALES (est): 10.1MM Privately Held
SIC: 1381 1311 Drilling oil & gas wells; crude petroleum production

(G-7782)
GRAHAM CUSTOM CABINETS LLC
Hc 60 Box 260 (76450-9517)
PHONE..................................940 549-4311
Chris Hall, Mng Member
Moni Hall,
Richard Hall,
Theresa Stewart,
EMP: 12
SALES (est): 600K Privately Held
WEB: www.grahamtexas.net
SIC: 2434 1799 1751 Wood kitchen cabinets; kitchen & bathroom remodeling; cabinet & finish carpentry

(G-7783)
HAMM WELL SERVICE CO
652 State Highway 67 (76450-6739)
P.O. Box 592 (76450-0592)
PHONE..................................940 549-4769
Coye Hamm, Owner
EMP: 10
SQ FT: 2,000
SALES (est): 1.1MM Privately Held
SIC: 1389 Servicing oil & gas wells; oil field services

(G-7784)
HUB MACHINE & TOOL INC
800 380 Byp (76450-2145)
P.O. Box 1508 (76450-7508)
PHONE..................................940 549-0155
Sherrill I Pettus, President
Joann Pettus, Corp Secy
EMP: 35 EST: 1954
SQ FT: 30,000
SALES (est): 2MM Privately Held
WEB: www.hubmachineandtool.com
SIC: 7692 3599 Welding repair; machine shop, jobbing & repair

(G-7785)
KARPER OIL & GAS CORPORATION
407 Elm St (76450-2515)
P.O. Box 149 (76450-0149)
PHONE..................................940 549-0606
Ed Kapper Jr, President
Philip Karper, Corp Secy
Gene Karper, Vice Pres
Ed A Karper Sr, Director
EMP: 10
SQ FT: 3,000
SALES (est): 2.2MM Privately Held
SIC: 1311 Crude petroleum production; natural gas production

(G-7786)
MASH OILFIELD SERVICES LP
3015 State Highway 16 S (76450-5109)
P.O. Box 926 (76450-0926)
PHONE..................................940 549-6152
Mason Shierry, General Ptnr
EMP: 10
SALES (est): 526K Privately Held
WEB: www.mashoilfieldservices.com
SIC: 1389 4789 Oil field services; pipeline terminal facilities, independently operated

(G-7787)
N D STOVALL & SON
605 3rd St Ste 200 (76450-3154)
P.O. Box 10 (76450-0010)
PHONE..................................940 549-2616
Norman D Stovall Jr, Partner
Martha Stovall Bennett, Partner
Malinda Stovall Guinn, Partner
EMP: 9 EST: 1930
SQ FT: 500
SALES (est): 930.7K Privately Held
SIC: 1311 Crude petroleum production

(G-7788)
PITCOCK INC (PA)
166 Elm St (76450-2010)
P.O. Box 1747 (76450-7747)
PHONE..................................940 549-3344
Roy Pitcock, President
Roy T Pitcock, President
J Duff Pitcock, Treasurer
Louis Pitcock Jr, Treasurer
EMP: 13
SQ FT: 4,600
SALES (est): 2.3MM Privately Held
WEB: www.pitcockinc.com
SIC: 1311 0212 Crude petroleum production; natural gas production; beef cattle except feedlots

(G-7789)
SOUTHERN BLEACHER COMPANY INC
801 5th St (76450-2637)
P.O. Box 1 (76450-0001)
PHONE..................................940 549-0733
Jo Ann Geurin Pettus, President
Garrett Pettus, Vice Pres
Wyatt Pettus, Vice Pres
Ben Zudell, Project Mgr
Corey Gober, Engineer
▲ EMP: 175
SQ FT: 27,650
SALES (est): 40.1MM Privately Held
WEB: www.southernbleacher.com
SIC: 2531 Public building & related furniture

(G-7790)
TEXAS MRI LP (PA)
510 Corporate Dr (76450-2923)
P.O. Box 1407 (76450-7407)
PHONE..................................940 549-5462

G
E
O
G
R
A
P
H
I
C

Gerard Smith, *Partner*
Juergen Van Beekum, *Representative*
EMP: 150
SALES (est): 16.2MM **Privately Held**
WEB: www.spotsee.io
SIC: 2759 3679 Labels & seals: printing;
electronic circuits

Granbury
Hood County

(G-7791)
A & A WELDING INC
333 Liberty Rd (76049-5958)
PHONE.................................817 910-9700
Poggie Ames, *President*
Dan Ames,
EMP: 17
SALES (est): 2MM **Privately Held**
WEB: www.aaweldtx.com
SIC: 7692 Welding repair

(G-7792)
ACCENT MERCANTILE INC
440 E Pearl St (76048-2216)
P.O. Box 1521 (76048-8521)
PHONE.................................817 579-6076
EMP: 19 **Privately Held**
SIC: 2679 Mfg Converted Paper Products
PA: Accent Mercantile, Inc.
1663 W Henderson St # 189
Cleburne TX 76033

(G-7793)
BIONIC WELDER LLC
Also Called: T B W
2080 Miller Ct (76049-1845)
PHONE.................................817 579-5080
Michael H Melton, *Mng Member*
Debbie Melton,
EMP: 30
SQ FT: 16,000
SALES (est): 4MM **Privately Held**
SIC: 3449 Miscellaneous metalwork

(G-7794)
C&J WELL SERVICES INC
4801 Glen Rose Hwy (76048-6214)
PHONE.................................817 573-3550
John Lewis, *General Mgr*
EMP: 39
SALES (corp-wide): 567.2MM **Publicly
Held**
WEB: www.nabors.com
SIC: 1389 Mud service, oil field drilling
HQ: C&J Well Services, Inc.
3990 Rogerdale Rd
Houston TX 77042

(G-7795)
COUNTER CLUB INC (PA)
Also Called: Umps
701 N Houston St (76048-1540)
PHONE.................................817 573-5040
Todd Riley, *Principal*
EMP: 9 **EST:** 2009
SALES (est): 2MM **Privately Held**
WEB: www.grumpsburgers.com
SIC: 3131 Counters

(G-7796)
**EQUIBRAND PRODUCTS
GROUP LP (DH)**
3500 W Us Highway 377 (76048-1103)
PHONE.................................817 573-1884
Ken Bray, *Partner*
Craig Bray, *Partner*
Ed Pinder, *Partner*
Clay Bearden, *Warehouse Mgr*
Nikki Callahan, *Controller*
▲ **EMP:** 100
SALES (est): 25.3MM
SALES (corp-wide): 37MM **Privately
Held**
WEB: www.equibrand.com
SIC: 2298 Hard fiber cordage & twine
HQ: Equibrand Corporation
1301 Weatherford Hwy
Granbury TX 76048
817 573-1884

(G-7797)
FABRICATION SPECIALTY INC
6530 Smoky Hill Ct (76049-7042)
PHONE.................................214 742-3571
Jon Lewis, *President*
Judy G Lewis, *Corp Secy*
Joe Lewis, *VP Admin*
G Joe Lewis, *Vice Pres*
Peggy Lewis, *IT Executive*
EMP: 12
SQ FT: 30,000
SALES (est): 2.5MM **Privately Held**
WEB: www.fabspec.com
SIC: 3795 3452 3429 3451 Tanks & tank
components; bolts, nuts, rivets & wash-
ers; aircraft & marine hardware, inc. pul-
leys & similar items; aircraft hardware;
screw machine products

(G-7798)
FAST BACK ROPE MFG
3721 Tin Top Hwy (76048-3706)
PHONE.................................817 279-1851
Derk Suitt, *Partner*
Allan Benson, *Partner*
Donna Garland, *Partner*
▲ **EMP:** 10
SQ FT: 960
SALES (est): 1.2MM **Privately Held**
WEB: www.fastbackropes.com
SIC: 2298 Rope, except asbestos & wire

(G-7799)
HARRIS COMPOSITES INC
600 Holmes Dr (76048-5644)
PHONE.................................817 279-9546
Debra Harris, *CEO*
Vernon Harris, *Vice Pres*
EMP: 20
SQ FT: 40,000
SALES (est): 4.3MM **Privately Held**
WEB: www.harriscomposites.com
SIC: 3721 7699 Aircraft; aircraft & heavy
equipment repair services

(G-7800)
HOOD COUNTY NEWS INC
Also Called: Os Hood County News
1501 S Morgan St (76048-2791)
P.O. Box 879 (76048-0879)
PHONE.................................817 573-7066
Jerry Tidwell, *President*
Walter Buckle, *Corp Secy*
Larry Crabtree, *Vice Pres*
Karen Chandler, *Advt Staff*
Penny Holloway, *Advt Staff*
EMP: 65 **EST:** 1953
SQ FT: 14,000
SALES (est): 1.1MM **Privately Held**
WEB: www.hcnews.com
SIC: 2711 4813 Newspapers: publishing
only, not printed on site; telephone com-
munication, except radio

(G-7801)
JK RED DIRT RENTALS LLC
100 Gteway Hills Ln Ste A (76049)
P.O. Box 5006 (76049-0006)
PHONE.................................214 530-3922
John Moore III, *President*
Don Peters, *Principal*
Aaron Lewallen, *Vice Pres*
Kyle Lewis, *Vice Pres*
EMP: 70
SQ FT: 1,200
SALES (est): 16.9MM **Privately Held**
WEB: www.reddirtinc.com
SIC: 1389 Oil field services

(G-7802)
NORTH TEXAS CORING INC
315 Sun Valley Ct (76049-7722)
P.O. Box 1380 (76048-8380)
PHONE.................................817 279-8930
Eddie Steel II, *President*
Shelly Steel, *Vice Pres*
EMP: 12
SALES (est): 1.9MM **Privately Held**
SIC: 3272 1795 Concrete products; con-
crete breaking for streets & highways

(G-7803)
OTA COMPRESSION LLC
120 Industrial Ave (76049-7809)
P.O. Box 5307 (76049-0307)
PHONE.................................817 326-8250

EMP: 10
SALES (corp-wide): 31.1MM **Privately
Held**
WEB: www.otacompression.com
SIC: 3585 Evaporative condensers, heat
transfer equipment
PA: Ota Compression Llc
102 Decker Ct Ste 204
Irving TX 75062
972 831-1300

(G-7804)
**PARAGON DIRECTIONAL DRLG
LLC**
3501 Old Granbury Rd (76049-7446)
PHONE.................................903 880-7398
Kenneth Kines, *Mng Member*
Josh Tucker,
EMP: 10
SALES (est): 261.7K **Privately Held**
SIC: 1389 7389 Oil field services; busi-
ness services

(G-7805)
PREMIERE INC
215 Industrial Ave (76049-7842)
PHONE.................................817 326-3500
Gary Cherry, *Manager*
EMP: 29 **Privately Held**
WEB: www.premiereinc.com
SIC: 1389 Oil field services
PA: Premiere, Inc.
615 N Landry Dr
New Iberia LA 70563

(G-7806)
PROPELL AMERICAN LLC
4801 Glen Rose Hwy (76048-6214)
PHONE.................................817 573-3550
Gary Teichrob, *Mng Member*
Steven Baker,
Scott Mason,
EMP: 66
SQ FT: 93,000
SALES (est): 30MM
SALES (corp-wide): 194.6MM **Privately
Held**
WEB: www.propell.com
SIC: 3533 Oil & gas field machinery
PA: Ty-Crop Manufacturing Ltd
9880 Mcgrath Rd
Rosedale BC
604 794-7078

(G-7807)
**RENEGADE WELL SERVICES
LLC (HQ)**
3301 E Us Highway 377 # 202
(76049-3414)
P.O. Box 7180 (76049-0138)
PHONE.................................682 936-4466
Jacob Percifull, *CEO*
Tina Zuniga, *Office Mgr*
EMP: 50
SALES (est): 52.6MM **Privately Held**
WEB: www.renegadewellservices.com
SIC: 1389 Building oil & gas well founda-
tions on site

(G-7808)
SALES R UP MEDIA INC
Also Called: Texas Real Estate Magazine
3609 Acton Hwy Ste 24 (76049-7536)
P.O. Box 5159 (76049-0159)
PHONE.................................817 326-3282
Steve Haines, *President*
EMP: 10
SALES (est): 1.2MM **Privately Held**
WEB: www.texasrealestatemagazine.com
SIC: 2731 2721 Books: publishing only;
magazines: publishing & printing; trade
journals: publishing & printing

(G-7809)
**SCOTT MEASUREMENT
SERVICE INC (PA)**
5718 Acton Cir (76049-7808)
P.O. Box 5247 (76049-0247)
PHONE.................................817 326-2361
Ronnie Scott, *President*
Patti Scott, *Corp Secy*
Carey Balentine, *Supervisor*
Brady Lunceford, *Technician*
EMP: 23
SQ FT: 9,000

SALES (est): 4.2MM **Privately Held**
WEB: www.scottmeasurement.com
SIC: 1389 Oil field services

(G-7810)
SKY TEC LTD
350 Howard Clemmons Rd (76048-5703)
PHONE.................................817 573-2250
Leven Staples, *Partner*
▲ **EMP:** 10
SQ FT: 6,000
SALES (est): 1.7MM **Privately Held**
SIC: 3728 5088 Aircraft parts & equip-
ment; transportation equipment & sup-
plies

(G-7811)
TE&S LIMITED (PA)
Also Called: Total Equipment and Service
4801 Glen Rose Hwy (76048-6214)
PHONE.................................817 573-3550
Barry Beadle, *President*
Luke A Phenicle, *Admin Sec*
▲ **EMP:** 70
SQ FT: 30,000
SALES (est): 35.3MM **Privately Held**
WEB: www.total-equipment.com
SIC: 3533 Oil field machinery & equipment

(G-7812)
TEXAS TANK TRUCKS CO
4500 Blue Heron Ct (76049-1745)
PHONE.................................254 559-5404
Jeff Rogers, *Owner*
Rusty Martin, *Sales Executive*
EMP: 20
SALES (est): 2MM **Privately Held**
SIC: 4212 1389 Local trucking, without
storage; haulage, oil field

(G-7813)
TRACY AND ASSOCIATES
3408 Sundance Ct (76049-5442)
PHONE.................................817 559-9274
Sandy Tracy, *Partner*
EMP: 10
SALES (est): 50K **Privately Held**
SIC: 3812 Search & navigation equipment

(G-7814)
TRITEX GRASS LLC
5901 E Us Highway 377 (76049-7834)
PHONE.................................817 573-6676
Randy Price,
EMP: 35
SALES (est): 3.5MM **Privately Held**
WEB: www.tritexgrass.com
SIC: 3645 0782 Garden, patio, walkway &
yard lighting fixtures: electric; turf installa-
tion services, except artificial

(G-7815)
TWILIGHT SERVICES LLC (PA)
5401 Old Granbury Rd (76049-7747)
P.O. Box 7160 (76049-0138)
PHONE.................................817 326-4806
John Coonce, *Superintendent*
Melissa Singleton, *Vice Pres*
Kendra James, *Sales Staff*
Danny Singleton, *Mng Member*
Donnie Storey, *Director*
EMP: 10
SQ FT: 6,000
SALES (est): 11.2MM **Privately Held**
WEB: www.twilightservicesinc.com
SIC: 7353 1382 Oil field equipment, rental
or leasing; oil & gas exploration services

Grand Prairie
Dallas County

(G-7816)
A E S CUSTOM WOOD INC
3118 E Main St (75050-4735)
PHONE.................................972 262-0755
Glen Smallwood, *President*
Diane Smallwood, *Corp Secy*
EMP: 9
SQ FT: 5,000
SALES (est): 1.1MM **Privately Held**
WEB: www.aescustomwood.com
SIC: 2431 2521 Moldings, wood: unfin-
ished & prefinished; mantels, wood; wood
office furniture

(G-7817)
A ZAHNER COMPANY
2860 Alouette Dr (75052-7678)
PHONE..................................469 348-2000
Eric Steele, *General Mgr*
Patrick Glunt, *Foreman/Supr*
Nathan Barnes, *Project Engr*
Robert Zahner, *Manager*
EMP: 10
SALES (corp-wide): 360MM **Privately Held**
WEB: www.azahner.com
SIC: 1799 1761 3446 3444 Ornamental metal work; architectural sheet metal work; architectural metalwork; sheet metalwork
PA: A. Zahner Company
1400 E 9th St
Kansas City MO 64106
816 474-8882

(G-7818)
ABC COMPOUNDING CO TEXAS INC
1102 E Avenue J (75050-2624)
P.O. Box 16247, Atlanta GA (30321-0247)
PHONE..................................972 988-9200
Stephen Walker, *President*
Douglas Armstead, *Vice Pres*
Ian Englefield, *Sales Staff*
▲ **EMP:** 150 **EST:** 1965
SQ FT: 50,000
SALES (est): 22.5MM
SALES (corp-wide): 33.6MM **Privately Held**
SIC: 2842 Specialty cleaning, polishes & sanitation goods
PA: A.B.C. Compounding Company, Inc.
2600 Dogwood Dr Se
Conyers GA 30013
770 968-9222

(G-7819)
ABC INGREDIENTS CORP
1179 109th St (75050-2604)
PHONE..................................972 602-2427
Javier Acevedo, *President*
Jose Acevedo, *Vice Pres*
Jose Francisco Acevedo, *Treasurer*
EMP: 11
SQ FT: 10,000
SALES (est): 2.8MM **Privately Held**
WEB: www.abcingredients.com
SIC: 2052 Bakery products, dry

(G-7820)
ACCENT GRAPHICS INC
523 E Rock Island Rd (75050-6510)
PHONE..................................972 399-0333
John Muldoon, *President*
Danielle Manion, *Project Mgr*
Jeff Cope, *Opers Staff*
Alex Teator, *Accounts Exec*
Kimberly Goodwin, *Office Mgr*
EMP: 40
SQ FT: 24,000
SALES (est): 5.6MM **Privately Held**
WEB: www.accentgraphicsinc.com
SIC: 3993 1799 Electric signs; neon signs; sign installation & maintenance

(G-7821)
ACE AERONAUTICS LLC
2985 Red Hawk Dr (75052-7622)
PHONE..................................972 641-0835
Katrina Fisk, *Controller*
EMP: 11
SALES (corp-wide): 7.1MM **Privately Held**
WEB: www.aceaero.com
SIC: 3721 Motorized aircraft
PA: Ace Aeronautics, Llc
105 Buck Island Rd
Guntersville AL 35976
256 705-0250

(G-7822)
ADVANCED INTEGRATION TECH GP
Also Called: Ait Aerospace Components Svcs
901 Avenue S (75050-1134)
PHONE..................................972 522-6363
Edward J Chalupa, *Managing Prtnr*
Erich Wiener, *Engineer*
Anne Andresen, *Manager*
EMP: 31
SQ FT: 96,000
SALES (est): 4MM
SALES (corp-wide): 13.3MM **Privately Held**
WEB: www.aint.com
SIC: 3728 Aircraft parts & equipment
PA: Advanced Integration Technology, Lp
2805 E Plano Pkwy Ste 300
Plano TX 75074
972 423-8354

(G-7823)
ADVANCED RUBBER MOLDING INC
1202 E Avenue J (75050-2626)
PHONE..................................972 647-4040
Rocky Rossellini, *President*
Elaine Warren Richardson, *Vice Pres*
EMP: 25
SALES (est): 4.2MM **Privately Held**
WEB: www.advancedrubber.com
SIC: 3069 Bags, rubber or rubberized fabric; molded rubber products

(G-7824)
AIRBUS HELICOPTERS INC (DH)
2701 N Forum Dr (75052-8927)
PHONE..................................972 641-0000
Marc Paganini, *CEO*
Romain Trapp, *President*
Mark C Jones, *Principal*
John Burke, *Vice Pres*
Kevin Cabaniss, *Vice Pres*
◆ **EMP:** 251
SALES (est): 241MM
SALES (corp-wide): 77.9B **Privately Held**
WEB: www.airbus.com
SIC: 5088 7699 3721 Helicopter parts; aircraft & heavy equipment repair services; helicopters

(G-7825)
AIRGAS USA LLC
801 W North Carrier Pkwy (75050)
PHONE..................................972 660-0500
Jay Goldman, *Sales/Mktg Mgr*
Melody Huddleston, *Administration*
EMP: 30
SQ FT: 53,698
SALES (corp-wide): 129.8MM **Privately Held**
WEB: www.airgas.com
SIC: 5084 5169 5099 2813 Welding machinery & equipment; industrial gases; safety equipment & supplies; industrial gases
HQ: Airgas Usa, Llc
259 N Radnor Chester Rd
Radnor PA 19087
216 642-6600

(G-7826)
ALEX ORTHOPEDIC INC
510 Fountain Pkwy (75050-1405)
P.O. Box 201442, Arlington (76006-1442)
PHONE..................................972 641-9680
Ebrahim Lavi, *President*
Linda Lavi, *Vice Pres*
▲ **EMP:** 20
SQ FT: 65,000
SALES (est): 1.5MM **Privately Held**
WEB: www.alexorthopedic.com
SIC: 3842 5047 Orthopedic appliances; medical equipment & supplies

(G-7827)
ALL-SPEC SALES INC
2125 109th St (75050-1128)
PHONE..................................972 641-4053
Doug Zadow, *President*
Cheryl Fox,
EMP: 12
SALES (est): 1.6MM **Privately Held**
WEB: www.allspecsales.com
SIC: 3452 Bolts, metal; nuts, metal

(G-7828)
AMERICAN ANIMAL HEALTH INC (PA)
Also Called: American Embryo Systems
2619 Skyway Dr (75052-7610)
PHONE..................................817 293-6363
Jerry B Payne, *President*
H T Tung, *Vice Pres*
Ginger Hamrick, *Manager*
Cathy Abel, *Executive*
EMP: 15
SALES (est): 7.4MM **Privately Held**
WEB: www.ampharmco.com
SIC: 2836 Vaccines

(G-7829)
AMERICAN ANIMAL HEALTH INC
2619 Skyway Dr (75052-7610)
PHONE..................................972 641-5420
Hsi-Tang Tung Dv, *Exec VP*
Vanessa Kelly, *Office Mgr*
Ginger Hamrick, *Manager*
EMP: 13
SALES (corp-wide): 7.4MM **Privately Held**
WEB: www.ampharmco.com
SIC: 2836 Biological products, except diagnostic
PA: American Animal Health, Inc.
2619 Skyway Dr
Grand Prairie TX 75052
817 293-6363

(G-7830)
AMERICAN STEEL & ALUM CO INC
3545 E Main St (75050-4505)
PHONE..................................972 264-1533
Wayne Beason, *President*
Rob Beason, *Exec VP*
Larry Rogers, *Purchasing*
Eli Florido, *Engineer*
Matthew Graham, *Engineer*
EMP: 75
SQ FT: 100,000
SALES (est): 22.2MM **Privately Held**
WEB: www.asafab.com
SIC: 3441 Fabricated structural metal

(G-7831)
AMMERAAL BELTECH INC
Also Called: Burrell-Leder Beltech
1014 Santerre St (75050-1937)
PHONE..................................972 647-8996
Bob Heinl, *Engineer*
John Gapley, *Branch Mgr*
EMP: 16
SQ FT: 10,000
SALES (corp-wide): 814.6MM **Privately Held**
WEB: www.ammeraalbeltech.com
SIC: 5084 3535 Conveyor systems; conveyors & conveying equipment
HQ: Ammeraal Beltech, Inc.
7501 Saint Louis Ave
Skokie IL 60076
847 673-6720

(G-7832)
AQUACUT INC
Also Called: Aqua Cut
1249 Avenue R (75050-1602)
PHONE..................................972 247-6288
Steve Hill, *President*
EMP: 50 **EST:** 1998
SQ FT: 30,000
SALES (est): 7.8MM **Privately Held**
SIC: 3315 Steel wire & related products

(G-7833)
AQUAMARINE POWER USA LLC
2005 Westfield St (75050-1754)
PHONE..................................972 606-2912
John M Fedorko,
EMP: 10
SALES (est): 833.8K **Privately Held**
WEB: www.aquamarinepower.com
SIC: 3499 Fabricated metal products

(G-7834)
ARCH ALUMINUM AND GL CO TEXAS (PA)
930 W N Carrier Pkwy (75050-1101)
PHONE..................................972 647-9230
Raymond London, *President*
Irene London, *Vice Pres*
EMP: 15
SQ FT: 22,000
SALES (est): 2.3MM **Privately Held**
SIC: 3442 Sash, door or window: metal

(G-7835)
ARLINGTON MACHINE & HYDRAULICS
2413 Arkansas Ln (75052-7204)
PHONE..................................972 988-6644
Jmaes Blanton, *Partner*
James Blanton, *Partner*
EMP: 30
SQ FT: 15,000
SALES (est): 5MM **Privately Held**
WEB: www.arlmachyd.com
SIC: 3599 Machine shop, jobbing & repair

(G-7836)
ARLINGTON PRTG PLYING CARD LLC
202 N Great Sw Pkwy (75050-4813)
P.O. Box 200102, Arlington (76006-0102)
PHONE..................................817 275-2731
M Kamal, *Owner*
▲ **EMP:** 10
SQ FT: 6,400
SALES (est): 1.8MM **Privately Held**
SIC: 2752 Commercial printing, offset

(G-7837)
ASTRO SHEET METAL CO INC
1906 S Great Sw Pkwy (75051-3503)
PHONE..................................972 438-1110
Warren Hankammer, *President*
Steven Paxton, *President*
Allen Paxton, *Vice Pres*
Arthur Paxton, *Vice Pres*
John Paxton, *Vice Pres*
EMP: 27 **EST:** 1966
SQ FT: 20,000
SALES (est): 5MM **Privately Held**
WEB: www.astrosheetmetal.com
SIC: 3444 Sheet metalwork

(G-7838)
AVCOR HEALTH CARE PRODUCTS INC
2750 113th St Ste 300 (75050-0633)
PHONE..................................817 551-0595
Richard Manley, *President*
Charles Bowman, *President*
Carter Smith, *President*
Bruce Cheatham, *COO*
Bruce N Chetham Jr, *COO*
◆ **EMP:** 27
SQ FT: 10,000
SALES: 6.3MM **Privately Held**
WEB: www.avcorhealth.com
SIC: 3842 Dressings, surgical

(G-7839)
BATCHELOR STEEL RULE DIES INC
2121 Galveston St (75051-1239)
PHONE..................................972 263-2263
Bobby J Batchelor, *President*
Shaw Batchelor, *President*
EMP: 13
SQ FT: 4,000
SALES (est): 1.1MM **Privately Held**
WEB: www.batchelorsteelruledies.com
SIC: 3544 Dies, steel rule

(G-7840)
BAUMANN SPRINGS TEXAS LTD
3075 N Great Sw Pkwy 10 (75050-7821)
PHONE..................................972 641-7272
URS Schaffmetzel, *Principal*
Tim Trame, *Manager*
Shonda Davis, *Executive*
▲ **EMP:** 23
SALES (est): 5MM
SALES (corp-wide): 494.2K **Privately Held**
WEB: www.baumann-springs.com
SIC: 3469 3495 3496 3493 Metal stampings; mechanical springs, precision; miscellaneous fabricated wire products; steel springs, except wire
PA: Baugeschaft Spring Ag
Grabemattweg 8
Niederrohrdorf AG
796 637-127

(G-7841)
BAUMANN SPRINGS USA INC (HQ)
3075 N Great Sw Pkwy (75050-7821)
P.O. Box 730516, Dallas (75373-0516)
PHONE..............................972 641-7272
T Ruegg, *President*
Thomas Ruegg, *President*
Chris Skinner, *COO*
URS Schaffluetzel, *Vice Pres*
Toni Kaelin, *Prdtn Mgr*
▲ EMP: 65
SQ FT: 50,000
SALES (est): 20.2MM
SALES (corp-wide): 187.1MM **Privately Held**
WEB: www.baumann-springs.com
SIC: 3469 3495 3496 3493 Metal stampings; mechanical springs, precision; miscellaneous fabricated wire products; steel springs, except wire
PA: Baumann Federn Ag
Speerstrasse 6
RUti ZH 8630
552 868-111

(G-7842)
BAUMANN SPRNG TXAS HLDINGS LLC
3075 N Great Sw Pkwy (75050-7821)
PHONE..............................972 641-7272
Frank Mauro,
▲ EMP: 50
SALES (est): 6.1MM
SALES (corp-wide): 187.1MM **Privately Held**
WEB: www.baumann-springs.com
SIC: 3495 3496 3469 Wire springs; miscellaneous fabricated wire products; metal stampings
HQ: Baumann Springs Usa, Inc.
3075 N Great Sw Pkwy
Grand Prairie TX 75050
972 641-7272

(G-7843)
BDM GROUP LLC
Also Called: Logan Graphics
1017 Santerre St (75050-1938)
PHONE..............................214 412-2291
Marcos Felan, *Mng Member*
David Laskowski,
Bob Taggart,
EMP: 12 EST: 2016
SALES (est): 915K **Privately Held**
SIC: 2752 Commercial printing, lithographic

(G-7844)
BELL SPORTS INC
602 Fountain Pkwy (75050-1440)
PHONE..............................972 343-1000
Nancy Edge, *Branch Mgr*
EMP: 30
SALES (corp-wide): 1.7B **Publicly Held**
WEB: www.bellhelmets.com
SIC: 3949 Sporting & athletic goods
HQ: Bell Sports, Inc.
5550 Scotts Valley Dr
Scotts Valley CA 95066
469 417-6600

(G-7845)
BELL TEXTRON INC
Also Called: Bell Helicopter Plant 5
1700 N Hwy 360 (75050-1926)
P.O. Box 482, Fort Worth (76101-0482)
PHONE..............................817 280-2011
Aron Jones, *Mfg Staff*
Mike Redenbaugh, *Branch Mgr*
Gregory Stiborek, *Technical Staff*
Brendan Salka, *IT/INT Sup*
EMP: 75
SALES (corp-wide): 13.6B **Publicly Held**
WEB: www.bellflight.com
SIC: 3728 Aircraft parts & equipment
HQ: Bell Textron Inc.
3255 Bell Flight Blvd
Fort Worth TX 76118
817 280-2011

(G-7846)
BEXTER ENTERPRISES LLC
Also Called: Rainfost
734 Greenview Dr (75050-2407)
PHONE..............................972 647-4700
Susan Curie, *Mng Member*
EMP: 50
SALES (est): 4.1MM **Privately Held**
SIC: 3589 Water treatment equipment, industrial

(G-7847)
BMC STOCK HOLDINGS INC
Also Called: Texas Plywood and Lumber Co
1001 E Avenue K (75050-2638)
PHONE..............................972 606-6200
S Ledbetter, *General Mgr*
Chris Jacobs, *Opers Staff*
Dexter Chitwood, *Sales Staff*
Paul Evans, *Sales Staff*
EMP: 131
SALES (corp-wide): 7.2B **Publicly Held**
WEB: www.buildwithbmc.com
SIC: 2431 Doors, wood
HQ: Bmc Stock Holdings, Inc.
4800 Falls Of Neuse Rd # 400
Raleigh NC 27609

(G-7848)
BREG INC
2601 Pinewood Dr (75051-3516)
PHONE..............................972 647-0884
Gary Bledsoe, *Vice Pres*
Dale Davidson, *Technician*
EMP: 11 **Privately Held**
WEB: www.breg.com
SIC: 3841 Surgical & medical instruments
HQ: Breg, Inc.
2885 Loker Ave E
Carlsbad CA 92010

(G-7849)
CAMCARA INC
Also Called: AST Waterjet
1000 Avenue N (75050-1920)
PHONE..............................800 532-0383
Anthony J Woodall, *President*
Val Woodall, *Vice Pres*
Valerie A Woodall, *Admin Sec*
EMP: 9
SQ FT: 10,000
SALES (est): 1.9MM **Privately Held**
WEB: www.astwaterjet.com
SIC: 3541 Drilling machine tools (metal cutting)

(G-7850)
CAPITOL FOOD & BEVERAGE INC
Also Called: Capitol Manufacturing
2430 January Ln (75050-2913)
PHONE..............................972 660-4450
Keith White, *President*
EMP: 12
SQ FT: 25,000
SALES (est): 2.3MM **Privately Held**
WEB: www.capitolfb.com
SIC: 3585 3444 Soda fountain & beverage dispensing equipment & parts; sheet metalwork

(G-7851)
CARLSTAR GROUP LLC
1504 W North Carrier Pkwy (75050)
PHONE..............................972 606-2126
Ed Mills, *Branch Mgr*
EMP: 165 **Privately Held**
WEB: www.carlstargroup.com
SIC: 3011 Industrial tires, pneumatic
PA: The Carlstar Group Llc
725 Cool Springs Blvd
Franklin TN 37067

(G-7852)
CFC PRINT SOLUTIONS LLC
2800 112th St Ste 300 (75050-6495)
PHONE..............................972 890-9248
Jamie Hughes, *Sales Mgr*
Keven Webb, *Info Tech Mgr*
Kristen Williams, *Director*
Brett Gillis, *Business Dir*
John T Gillis Jr,
EMP: 15 EST: 2008
SALES (est): 4.5MM **Privately Held**
WEB: www.cfcprint.com
SIC: 2752 Commercial printing, offset

(G-7853)
CLIMATIC SYSTEMS INC
Also Called: Enviromatic Systems
2337 W Warrior Trl (75052-7255)
PHONE..............................972 206-2590
Bruce L Rummans, *President*
Bruce Rummans, *Vice Pres*
EMP: 13 EST: 1974
SQ FT: 2,200
SALES (est): 1.5MM **Privately Held**
WEB: www.enviromaticsystems.com
SIC: 3822 Temperature controls, automatic

(G-7854)
CMCS GROUP LLC
Also Called: Commercial Millwork
2457 Nw Dallas St (75050-4907)
PHONE..............................972 647-6260
Michael Berry,
EMP: 15
SQ FT: 12,000
SALES (est): 1.7MM **Privately Held**
WEB: www.performancemillwork.com
SIC: 2431 Millwork

(G-7855)
CMP EXPRESS LLC
901 Avenue M (75050-1915)
PHONE..............................469 348-2272
W E Dries III, *Mng Member*
William Elijah Dries III, *Mng Member*
EMP: 14
SALES (est): 1.3MM **Privately Held**
SIC: 2514 Household furniture: upholstered on metal frames

(G-7856)
CO WAGGONER INC
2100 S Great Southwest Pk (75051-5130)
PHONE..............................972 641-8888
Brian C Waggoner, *President*
Kim Waggoner, *Vice Pres*
EMP: 10 EST: 2007
SALES (est): 1.5MM **Privately Held**
WEB: www.cowaggoner.com
SIC: 3599 Machine shop, jobbing & repair

(G-7857)
COATINGS GROUP INC (PA)
Also Called: Cgi Commercial Accounts
616 E Avenue J (75050-2562)
PHONE..............................817 633-7383
Mark Stambaugh, *President*
Bert Hendren, *Director*
EMP: 110 EST: 1999
SALES (est): 3.6MM **Privately Held**
WEB: www.thecoatingsgroup.com
SIC: 2952 Coating compounds, tar

(G-7858)
CONTROL PRODUCTS CORPORATION (PA)
1513 W Jefferson St (75051-1443)
PHONE..............................972 264-0368
H Wayne Hanks, *CEO*
Ron Jensen, *President*
Eric Jensen, *Exec VP*
Brad Davidson, *Vice Pres*
Chet Pieroway, *Vice Pres*
EMP: 122 EST: 1963
SQ FT: 70,000
SALES (est): 24.3MM **Privately Held**
WEB: www.cpctexas.com
SIC: 3648 3823 Lighting equipment; industrial instrmnts msrmnt display/control process variable

(G-7859)
CURTISS-WRIGHT SURFC TECH LLC
1450 Avenue S (75050-1242)
PHONE..............................972 641-8011
Michael Cummings, *Manager*
EMP: 16
SALES (corp-wide): 2.4B **Publicly Held**
WEB: www.cwst.com
SIC: 3398 Shot peening (treating steel to reduce fatigue)
HQ: Curtiss-Wright Surface Technologies Llc
80 E Rte 4 Ste 310
Paramus NJ 07652
201 843-7800

(G-7860)
CUSTOM BUILDING PRODUCTS INC
1795 109th St (75050-1908)
PHONE..............................972 641-6996
Dian Shipberg, *Principal*
Gladys Johnson, *Sales Staff*
Tim Spencer, *Branch Mgr*
EMP: 100
SQ FT: 10,000 **Privately Held**
WEB: www.custombuildingproducts.com
SIC: 5039 3255 3241 2899 Prefabricated buildings; clay refractories; cement, hydraulic; chemical preparations
HQ: Custom Building Products
7711 Center Ave Ste 500
Huntington Beach CA 92647
800 272-8786

(G-7861)
CYLINDER HEADS INTERNATIONAL
3900 E Jefferson St (75051-2428)
PHONE..............................972 264-3449
Glen R Nied, *President*
Ed Nied, *Vice Pres*
Mike Hunt, *Chief Engr*
EMP: 30
SQ FT: 4,000
SALES (est): 4.6MM **Privately Held**
WEB: www.headsonly.com
SIC: 3714 Motor vehicle parts & accessories

(G-7862)
DCM MANUFACTURING INC
2800 112th St Ste 200 (75050-6495)
PHONE..............................817 428-3636
Pat Hennessy, *Chief Mktg Ofcr*
Theodore J Beger, *Branch Mgr*
▲ EMP: 24
SALES (corp-wide): 49.5MM **Privately Held**
WEB: www.dcm-mfg.com
SIC: 3089 Injection molding of plastics
HQ: Dcm Manufacturing, Inc.
4540 W 160th St
Cleveland OH 44135

(G-7863)
DELTA GROUP ELECTRONICS INC
2920 N State Highway 360 # 100 (75050-1054)
PHONE..............................972 606-2102
Sandy Olive, *Manager*
EMP: 60
SALES (corp-wide): 145.8MM **Privately Held**
WEB: www.deltagroupinc.com
SIC: 3679 3577 3672 Electronic circuits; computer peripheral equipment; printed circuit boards
PA: Delta Group Electronics, Inc.
4521a Osuna Rd Ne
Albuquerque NM 87109
505 883-7674

(G-7864)
DFM PRINT PAK LLC
1350 Avenue S Ste 23 (75050-1220)
PHONE..............................817 385-0600
Dan Moody, *President*
Rick Davis, *Exec VP*
EMP: 15
SQ FT: 28,000
SALES (est): 4.4MM **Privately Held**
WEB: www.dfmprintpak.com
SIC: 2752 Commercial printing, lithographic

(G-7865)
DN TANKS INC
410 E Trinity Blvd (75050-8033)
PHONE..............................972 823-3300
Sean Sudol, *Regional Mgr*
Bob Walsh, *Vice Pres*
Chris Brown, *Project Mgr*
Andrew Christy, *Project Mgr*
Adam Blaser, *Engineer*
EMP: 20 **Privately Held**
WEB: www.dntanks.com
SIC: 3272 Tanks, concrete

▲ = Import ▼=Export
◆ =Import/Export

PA: Dn Tanks, Inc.
11 Teal Rd
Wakefield MA 01880

(G-7866)
EPIROC DRILLING TOOLS LLC (HQ)
1600 S Great Sw Pkwy (75051-2516)
P.O. Box 271, Fort Loudon PA (17224-0271)
PHONE..................................844 437-4762
Keith Mackling, *President*
Timothy Sturm, *Vice Pres*
Roger Goransson, *Treasurer*
▲ **EMP:** 161
SALES (est): 36.9MM
SALES (corp-wide): 4.2B **Privately Held**
WEB: www.us.atlascopco.com
SIC: 3545 Drill bits, metalworking
PA: Epiroc Ab
Sickla Industrivag 19
Nacka 131 5
107 550-000

(G-7867)
EXEL N AMERCN LOGISTICS INC
Also Called: Power Packaging of Texas
802 W North Carrier Pkwy (75050)
PHONE..................................972 647-1101
Christopher Barajas, *Opers Spvr*
Mike Harston, *Manager*
Patricia Cruz, *Supervisor*
EMP: 350
SALES (corp-wide): 70B **Privately Held**
WEB: www.exel.com
SIC: 2099 Ready-to-eat meals, salads & sandwiches
HQ: Exel North American Logistics, Inc.
570 Players Pkwy
Westerville OH 43081

(G-7868)
FAB-TEX FIXTURE & MFG CO
2353 Nw Dallas St (75050-4904)
PHONE..................................972 660-6304
Robert B Brueggmeyer, *President*
Fred A King, *Vice Pres*
EMP: 50
SQ FT: 20,000
SALES (est): 4.7MM **Privately Held**
SIC: 2542 Counters or counter display cases: except wood

(G-7869)
FAIRBANKS PACKAGING LLC
608 E Avenue K (75050-2404)
P.O. Box 683, Colleyville (76034-0683)
PHONE..................................817 849-1366
Linda Fairbanks, *President*
EMP: 9
SALES (est): 52.4K **Privately Held**
WEB: www.fairbankspackaging.com
SIC: 5199 3086 2653 5113 Packaging materials; plastics foam products; packaging & shipping materials, foamed plastic; corrugated boxes, partitions, display items, sheets & pad; corrugated & solid fiber boxes

(G-7870)
FENNER TECHNOLOGIES INC
1513 W Jefferson St (75051-1443)
P.O. Box 531109 (75053-1109)
PHONE..................................972 264-0368
H Wayne Hanks, *President*
Ron Jensen, *Vice Pres*
Rhea Wallace, *Treasurer*
EMP: 115
SQ FT: 30,000
SALES (est): 6.7MM
SALES (corp-wide): 24.3MM **Privately Held**
SIC: 3646 3647 Ornamental lighting fixtures, commercial; aircraft lighting fixtures
PA: Control Products Corporation
1513 W Jefferson St
Grand Prairie TX 75051
972 264-0368

(G-7871)
FGS - DALLAS INC
Also Called: A Freedom Graphic Systems
1040 N State Highway 161 # 105 (75051-1437)
PHONE..................................972 375-0253

Lonnie Eager, *President*
Martin Liebert, *Director*
EMP: 30
SALES (est): 17.7MM **Privately Held**
SIC: 2752 7331 Commercial printing, lithographic; direct mail advertising services

(G-7872)
FIRSTEX INDUSTRIES INC
Also Called: Wiscast
111 Ne 11th St (75050-5913)
PHONE..................................972 602-1478
Tracy Lee, *President*
Morgan Lee, *Sales Staff*
▲ **EMP:** 10
SQ FT: 10,000
SALES (est): 1.8MM **Privately Held**
WEB: www.firstexind.com
SIC: 3429 5051 8741 Locks or lock sets; castings, rough: iron or steel; management services

(G-7873)
FLEMING & SON CORPORATION
Also Called: Metal Specialties Mfg Co
1950 E Main St (75050-6135)
PHONE..................................972 263-1713
EMP: 20 **EST:** 1979
SQ FT: 80,000
SALES (est): 4.3MM **Privately Held**
WEB: www.metalspecialtiesmfg.com
SIC: 3499 2531 3444 3469 Automobile seat frames, metal; seats, automobile; sheet metalwork; metal stampings

(G-7874)
FLEX-N-GATE TEXAS LLC
823-841 Heinz Way (75051)
PHONE..................................817 652-3400
Don Cumming, *Branch Mgr*
EMP: 50
SALES (corp-wide): 3.2B **Privately Held**
SIC: 3714 Motor vehicle parts & accessories
HQ: Flex-N-Gate Texas, Llc
2150 Bardin Rd
Grand Prairie TX 75052
817 652-3400

(G-7875)
FLEX-N-GATE TEXAS LLC (HQ)
2150 Bardin Rd (75052-1602)
PHONE..................................817 652-3400
Shahid R Khan, *President*
Tom Clarkson, *CFO*
David Ekblad, *CFO*
Lindsey Desjardins, *Accounts Mgr*
Tim Graham, *Admin Sec*
▲ **EMP:** 37
SQ FT: 200,000
SALES (est): 200MM
SALES (corp-wide): 3.2B **Privately Held**
SIC: 3714 Motor vehicle parts & accessories
PA: Flex-N-Gate Llc
1306 E University Ave
Urbana IL 61802
217 384-6600

(G-7876)
FLOWERS BAKING CO DENTON LLC
180 W Pioneer (75051)
PHONE..................................972 263-3363
Mark Rhodes, *Vice Pres*
EMP: 20
SALES (corp-wide): 4.1B **Publicly Held**
WEB: www.flowersfoods.com
SIC: 2051 Bakery: wholesale or wholesale/retail combined
HQ: Flowers Baking Co. Of Denton, Llc
4210 Edwards Rd
Denton TX 76208
940 383-5280

(G-7877)
FORTERRA PIPE & PRECAST LLC
1000 Macarthur Blvd (75050-7942)
PHONE..................................972 263-2181
Brian Gregory, *Plant Mgr*
Chris Lingemann, *Opers Mgr*
Anthony Carahesio, *Manager*
Dan Dunegan, *Analyst*
EMP: 250

SALES (corp-wide): 1.5B **Publicly Held**
WEB: www.forterrabp.com
SIC: 3272 Concrete products
HQ: Forterra Pipe & Precast, Llc
511 E John Carpenter Fwy
Irving TX 75062
469 458-7973

(G-7878)
FORTERRA PIPE & PRECAST LLC
Also Called: Forterra Pressure Pipe
1004 Macarthur Blvd (75050-7942)
PHONE..................................972 262-1571
Darren Dunker, *Branch Mgr*
EMP: 300
SALES (corp-wide): 1.5B **Publicly Held**
WEB: www.forterrabp.com
SIC: 3272 Concrete products
HQ: Forterra Pipe & Precast, Llc
511 E John Carpenter Fwy
Irving TX 75062
469 458-7973

(G-7879)
FRONT END SERVICES
1100 Fountain Pkwy (75050-1513)
PHONE..................................214 672-0600
George Jensen, *President*
EMP: 30
SQ FT: 50,000
SALES (est): 3.3MM **Privately Held**
SIC: 3663 4813 Cellular radio telephone; telephone communications broker

(G-7880)
FRUIT OF EARTH INC (PA)
3325 W Trinity Blvd (75050-6716)
PHONE..................................817 510-1600
Thomas E McCurry Sr, *CEO*
Thomas E McCurry Jr, *President*
Faye McCurry, *Corp Secy*
Thomas Kramka, *Plant Mgr*
Pete Rodriguez, *Purch Agent*
◆ **EMP:** 40
SQ FT: 120,000
SALES (est): 165MM **Privately Held**
WEB: www.fote.com
SIC: 5122 2844 Cosmetics; toilet soap; face creams or lotions; suntan lotions & oils; toilet preparations

(G-7881)
GAJESKE INC
1314 W Oakdale Rd (75050-7316)
PHONE..................................972 314-8100
Rick White, *Principal*
Jeff Ehresmann, *Warehouse Mgr*
Kelly Burns, *Purchasing*
Cody Pattison, *Sales Staff*
EMP: 10
SALES (est): 1.5MM **Privately Held**
WEB: www.gajeske.com
SIC: 3089 Plastic containers, except foam

(G-7882)
GEORGE HALL
Also Called: Maverick Hydraulics Machining
2226 E Main St (75050-6141)
PHONE..................................972 266-2700
George Hall, *Owner*
EMP: 20
SALES (est): 2.9MM **Privately Held**
SIC: 3593 3599 Fluid power cylinders, hydraulic or pneumatic; machine shop; jobbing & repair

(G-7883)
GOELZER INDUSTRIES INC
201 E Trinity Blvd (75050-8048)
PHONE..................................214 524-6700
Paul Goelzer Jr, *President*
▲ **EMP:** 70
SQ FT: 120,000
SALES (est): 23.7MM **Privately Held**
WEB: www.goelzerind.com
SIC: 2677 Envelopes

(G-7884)
GRANUTCH-STURN SYSTEMS CORP AM (PA)
Also Called: Saturn Shredders
201 E Shady Grove Rd (75050-6647)
PHONE..................................972 790-7800
Glen Newton, *President*
Roy E Townsdin, *Chairman*

Jack West, *Vice Pres*
Chip Dillard, *Human Res Mgr*
A E Chaffin, *Director*
◆ **EMP:** 60
SQ FT: 45,000
SALES (est): 20.3MM **Privately Held**
WEB: www.granutech.com
SIC: 3589 3549 Shredders, industrial & commercial; metalworking machinery

(G-7885)
HAGANS PLASTICS CO INC
121 W Rock Island Rd (75050-6514)
P.O. Box 153986, Irving (75015-3986)
PHONE..................................972 790-9001
Konnie Hagan, *Ch of Bd*
Dennis Hagan, *President*
Jim Arnet, *Sales Staff*
EMP: 28
SQ FT: 21,000
SALES (est): 10MM **Privately Held**
WEB: www.hagansus.com
SIC: 3089 Injection molding of plastics

(G-7886)
HANGAR R LLC
2550 N Great Sw Pkwy (75050-6428)
PHONE..................................469 865-2110
Rayando Alicea, *President*
Alexander Schmidt, *Principal*
EMP: 12
SALES (est): 746.7K **Privately Held**
WEB: www.hangar-r.com
SIC: 3999 Manufacturing industries

(G-7887)
HANSON AGGREGATES LLC
1000 Macarthur Blvd (75050-7942)
PHONE..................................972 263-2181
Greg Minteer, *Manager*
EMP: 19
SALES (corp-wide): 20.8B **Privately Held**
WEB: www.heidelbergcement.com
SIC: 3273 Ready-mixed concrete
HQ: Hanson Aggregates Llc
8505 Freport Pkwy Ste 500
Irving TX 75063
469 417-1200

(G-7888)
HAYDON CORPORATION
1139 W N Carrier Pkwy (75050)
PHONE..................................972 641-6400
Patricia McDonough, *Sales Staff*
Tom Armour, *Manager*
EMP: 15
SALES (corp-wide): 55.9MM **Privately Held**
WEB: www.haydoncorp.com
SIC: 3449 3634 3567 3498 Miscellaneous metalwork; heating units, electric (radiant heat): baseboard or wall; industrial furnaces & ovens; fabricated pipe & fittings; sheet metalwork; fabricated plate work (boiler shop)
PA: Haydon Corporation
415 Hamburg Tpke Ste 1
Wayne NJ 07470
973 904-0800

(G-7889)
HERITAGE FMLY SPCLTY FOODS INC
Also Called: HFS Foods
901 Santerre St (75050-1939)
PHONE..................................972 660-6511
Daniel L Brackeen, *President*
Cheryl Brackeen, *Exec VP*
Philippe Lecoq, *Research*
Ardeshir Mistry, *Research*
Sledge Thomas, *CFO*
◆ **EMP:** 50
SQ FT: 52,000
SALES (est): 11.3MM **Privately Held**
WEB: www.hfsfoods.com
SIC: 2035 Dressings, salad: raw & cooked (except dry mixes); seasonings, meat sauces (except tomato & dry); seasonings, seafood sauces (except tomato & dry); seasonings, vegetable sauces (except tomato & dry)

(G-7890)
HG TSHIRT DESIGN COMPANY
320 S Center St Apt 114 (75051-1780)
PHONE..................................469 776-4995

Landon Hurd,
EMP: 10
SALES (est): 376.2K **Privately Held**
SIC: 2253 T-shirts & tops, knit

(G-7891)
HHBODU LLC
945 Bloomfield Dr (75052-0002)
PHONE...................210 464-2669
Humphrey Klobodu,
EMP: 10 **EST:** 2017
SALES (est): 283.1K **Privately Held**
SIC: 3999 Manufacturing industries

(G-7892)
HLCL CAPITAL CORPORATION
2113 109th St (75050-1128)
PHONE...................972 660-4096
George Samuel, *President*
Hy D Le, *President*
Kartick Kudtarkar, *Vice Pres*
Timothy Pritchard, *Vice Pres*
EMP: 50
SALES (est): 7.7MM **Privately Held**
WEB: www.hlelectronics.com
SIC: 3699 5084 Electrical equipment &
supplies; industrial machinery & equip-
ment

(G-7893)
**INNOVTIVE CNVEYOR
CONCEPTS INC**
910 Fountain Pkwy (75050-1509)
P.O. Box 535009 (75053-5009)
PHONE...................972 323-0797
Gregory S Terry, *President*
Michael T Terry, *Vice Pres*
Richard Hill, *Sales Staff*
Colin Muncy, *Sales Staff*
EMP: 10
SQ FT: 850
SALES (est): 5MM **Privately Held**
WEB: www.iccconveyors.com
SIC: 3535 Conveyors & conveying equip-
ment

(G-7894)
INTERMEX PRODUCTS USA LTD
1375 Avenue S Ste 300 (75050-1293)
P.O. Box 535461 (75053-5461)
PHONE...................972 660-2071
Juan Carlos Lorenzo, *President*
Sandy Eastep, *Corp Secy*
David Hagli, *Vice Pres*
Jacqui Ortega, *Manager*
Beth Faulks,
▲ **EMP:** 50
SQ FT: 63,500
SALES (est): 12.6MM **Privately Held**
WEB: www.intermexproducts.com
SIC: 2099 Food preparations

(G-7895)
**INTERNATIONAL PAPER
COMPANY**
1200 W North Carrier Pkwy (75050)
PHONE...................972 602-9880
Mary Orozco, *Accounts Mgr*
Roger Konka, *Manager*
EMP: 100
SALES (corp-wide): 22.3B **Publicly Held**
WEB: www.internationalpaper.com
SIC: 2621 Paper mills
PA: International Paper Company
6400 Poplar Ave
Memphis TN 38197
901 419-9000

(G-7896)
**INTERNATIONAL PAPER
COMPANY**
1302 W North Carrier Pkwy (75050)
PHONE...................972 641-2972
Kevin Brooks, *Manager*
EMP: 133
SALES (corp-wide): 22.3B **Publicly Held**
WEB: www.internationalpaper.com
SIC: 2621 2653 Paper mills; corrugated &
solid fiber boxes
PA: International Paper Company
6400 Poplar Ave
Memphis TN 38197
901 419-9000

(G-7897)
**ITW BLDING CMPONENTS
GROUP INC**
Alpine Engineered Products
2820 N Great Sw Pkwy (75050-6472)
PHONE...................972 660-4422
Michael Schwitter, *General Mgr*
Chris Cronje, *Branch Mgr*
Brian Westfall, *Info Tech Dir*
EMP: 48
SALES (corp-wide): 14.1B **Publicly Held**
WEB: www.alpineacademyitw.com
SIC: 8711 3499 3089 Engineering serv-
ices; strapping, metal; injection molded
finished plastic products
HQ: Itw Building Components Group, Inc.
13389 Lakefront Dr
Earth City MO 63045
314 344-9121

(G-7898)
J LEALS FOOD INC
Also Called: Leal Foods
2515 W Jefferson St # 128 (75051-1063)
PHONE...................214 412-3158
Joel Leal, *President*
EMP: 29
SQ FT: 18,000
SALES (est): 2MM **Privately Held**
SIC: 2099 Tortillas, fresh or refrigerated

(G-7899)
J M H PRINTING COMPANY
721 W Tarrant Rd (75050-3445)
P.O. Box 530797 (75053-0797)
PHONE...................972 263-1226
James M Highfill, *President*
James M Highfill III, *President*
John M Highfill, *Vice Pres*
Linda Highfill, *Treasurer*
EMP: 40
SQ FT: 6,000
SALES (est): 7.8MM **Privately Held**
WEB: www.jmhprinting.com
SIC: 2752 2791 2789 Commercial print-
ing, offset; typesetting; bookbinding & re-
lated work

(G-7900)
J V PLASTICS INC
2723 S Great Sw Pkwy (75052-7231)
P.O. Box 532071 (75053-2071)
PHONE...................972 606-0500
Khem Nangrani, *President*
▲ **EMP:** 10
SQ FT: 20,000
SALES (est): 2.3MM **Privately Held**
WEB: www.jvplastics.com
SIC: 3089 Molding primary plastic; plastic
containers, except foam

(G-7901)
JAYCO MANUFACTURING LLC
1470 Avenue T (75050-1222)
PHONE...................972 623-2004
Kevin Maynard, *CEO*
Ray Luedecke, *Info Tech Mgr*
▲ **EMP:** 100
SQ FT: 120,000
SALES (est): 2MM **Privately Held**
WEB: www.jaycomfg.com
SIC: 3469 Stamping metal for the trade

(G-7902)
JELD-WEN INC
2510 W Main St Ste 300 (75050-4939)
PHONE...................972 623-1727
Richard L Wendt, *Chairman*
EMP: 80 **Publicly Held**
WEB: www.jeld-wen.com
SIC: 2431 Doors, wood
HQ: Jeld-Wen, Inc.
2645 Silver Crescent Dr
Charlotte NC 28273
800 535-3936

(G-7903)
JIM DANDY BOXES INC
1750 Westpark Dr Ste 110 (75050-1948)
PHONE...................817 608-9180
C Daniel Cordrey, *President*
Virginia Cordrey, *Vice Pres*
EMP: 23 **EST:** 1967
SQ FT: 31,000

SALES (est): 4.2MM **Privately Held**
WEB: www.jimdandyboxes.com
SIC: 2653 3993 2542 Boxes, corrugated:
made from purchased materials; signs &
advertising specialties; partitions & fixtures, except wood

(G-7904)
K & N ENGINEERING INC
741 Refuge Way (75050)
PHONE...................951 826-0000
Kevin Nahin, *Controller*
EMP: 43
SALES (corp-wide): 140.5MM **Privately
Held**
WEB: www.knfilters.com
SIC: 3714 Motor vehicle parts & acces-
sories
PA: K & N Engineering, Inc.
1455 Citrus St
Riverside CA 92507
951 826-4000

(G-7905)
KITCHEN CABINETS INC
Also Called: Kci
2330 Nw Dallas St (75050-4903)
PHONE...................972 660-6304
Robert Brueggemeyer, *President*
Dennis Brueggemeyer, *Vice Pres*
EMP: 68
SALES (est): 12.9MM **Privately Held**
WEB: www.kcicabs.com
SIC: 2541 Cabinets, except refrigerated:
show, display, etc.: wood

(G-7906)
KOHLER CO
1820 High Prairie Rd (75050-4241)
PHONE...................920 457-4441
Matt Hopper, *Manager*
EMP: 51
SALES (corp-wide): 9B **Privately Held**
WEB: www.us.kohler.com
SIC: 3431 Metal sanitary ware
PA: Kohler Co.
444 Highland Dr
Kohler WI 53044
920 457-4441

(G-7907)
KOMPLETE GROUP INC
Also Called: Adampac
202 N Great Sw Pkwy (75050-4813)
P.O. Box 200102, Arlington (76006-0102)
PHONE...................214 252-8100
Mohammad Kamal, *President*
Trudy Lambert, *Business Mgr*
Senad Rasidovic, *Marketing Mgr*
▲ **EMP:** 53
SQ FT: 92,000
SALES (est): 11.8MM **Privately Held**
WEB: www.kpak.com
SIC: 3081 5199 Packing materials, plastic
sheet; packaging materials

(G-7908)
LASELEC INC
2605 N Forum Dr (75052-8925)
PHONE...................817 460-7830
Eric Dupont, *President*
Justin Clements, *Marketing Staff*
Penny Culran, *Manager*
Dina Clayburn, *Technical Staff*
Guillermo Casas, *Technician*
EMP: 10
SQ FT: 6,200
SALES (est): 1.8MM **Privately Held**
WEB: www.laselec.com
SIC: 3699 Laser systems & equipment;
laser welding, drilling & cutting equipment

(G-7909)
**LATICRETE INTERNATIONAL
INC**
1710 111th St (75050-1913)
PHONE...................972 641-3266
Steven Fine, *Research*
George Wylie, *Branch Mgr*
Kathleen Kinsella, *Manager*
Kevin Rinaldi, *Technical Staff*
Christine Cafferty, *Director*
EMP: 50
SQ FT: 40,000

SALES (corp-wide): 146.9MM **Privately
Held**
WEB: www.laticrete.com
SIC: 2891 2899 Sealing compounds, synthetic rubber or plastic; adhesives, plastic;
cement, except linoleum & tile; chemical
preparations
PA: Laticrete International, Inc.
1 Laticrete Park N
Bethany CT 06524
203 393-0010

(G-7910)
LEAR CORPORATION
3120 N Great Sw Pkwy (75050-6422)
PHONE...................817 419-3000
Laura Finley, *Senior Buyer*
Kirk Mac Lennan, *Branch Mgr*
EMP: 300
SALES (corp-wide): 17B **Publicly Held**
WEB: www.lear.com
SIC: 3714 Motor vehicle parts & acces-
sories
PA: Lear Corporation
21557 Telegraph Rd
Southfield MI 48033
724 248-1500

(G-7911)
LIBERTY FLUID POWER INC
214 Nw 25th St (75050-4803)
PHONE...................972 623-0927
Mario Villegas, *President*
Francisco Villegas, *Vice Pres*
Bill Manning, *Sales Mgr*
EMP: 25
SQ FT: 56,000
SALES (est): 4.2MM **Privately Held**
WEB: www.libertyhydraulics.com
SIC: 7699 3441 3599 Hydraulic equip-
ment repair; fabricated structural metal;
custom machinery

(G-7912)
LIBERTY PLAYING CARDS LP
1100 Avenue T (75050-1118)
PHONE...................214 252-8175
▲ **EMP:** 14
SALES (est): 114.7K **Privately Held**
WEB: www.libertyplayingcards.com
SIC: 2754 Gravure Commercial Printing

(G-7913)
**LMT RUSTIC & WESTERN
IMPORTS**
2920 N State Highway 360 # 200
(75050-1051)
PHONE...................972 641-6700
Peter J Clark, *CEO*
Lilia Lopez, *Opers Staff*
Brent Tims, *Opers Staff*
▲ **EMP:** 13 **EST:** 2009
SALES (est): 1.9MM **Privately Held**
WEB: www.lmtrustic.com
SIC: 2599 Boards: planning, display, notice

(G-7914)
**LOCKHEED MARTIN
CORPORATION**
Also Called: Lockheed Martin Missiles
1902 W Freeway St (75051)
P.O. Box 650003, Dallas (75265-0003)
PHONE...................972 603-1000
Jim Berry, *President*
Frances Sandlin, *Opers Staff*
Melissa Gonzales, *Buyer*
Mike Burns, *Engineer*
James Duppstadt, *Engineer*
EMP: 4000
WEB: www.lockheedmartin.com
SIC: 3812 3721 3769 3489 Search &
navigation equipment; aircraft; guided
missile & space vehicle parts & auxiliary
equipment; ordnance & accessories
PA: Lockheed Martin Corporation
6801 Rockledge Dr
Bethesda MD 20817

(G-7915)
**LOCKHEED MARTIN
CORPORATION**
Lockheed Martin Mis Fire Ctrl
1701 W Marshall Dr (75051-2704)
PHONE...................972 603-1000
Annie Hale, *Opers Staff*

John Brozovic, *Engineer*
Steven Klekar, *Engineer*
Tyler Lynch, *Engineer*
Clint Madewell, *Engineer*
EMP: 2600 **Publicly Held**
WEB: www.lockheedmartin.com
SIC: 3812 Search & navigation equipment
PA: Lockheed Martin Corporation
6801 Rockledge Dr
Bethesda MD 20817

(G-7916)
LOFTWALL INC
2617 N Great Southwest Pk (75050-6432)
PHONE..................214 239-3162
Steven Kinder, *Principal*
Dari Esfahani, *Sales Staff*
Derek Andreas, *Manager*
Rose Chavez, *Manager*
Sue Madrid, *Administration*
▲ **EMP:** 14
SALES (est): 250K **Privately Held**
WEB: www.loftwall.com
SIC: 2542 5211 Partitions & fixtures, except wood; wallboard (composition) & paneling

(G-7917)
LOGO FACTORY
116 Nw 15th St (75050-5239)
PHONE..................972 642-4222
Hugo Serrato, *Principal*
EMP: 11
SALES (est): 1.1MM **Privately Held**
WEB: www.logofactoryco.com
SIC: 2759 Screen printing

(G-7918)
LONGHORN PAPER CONVERTING LLC
1123 W North Carrier Pkwy (75050)
PHONE..................214 988-3251
Frederic Martel, *Mng Member*
EMP: 21 **EST:** 2012
SALES (est): 6.6MM **Privately Held**
WEB: www.longhornpaper.com
SIC: 2621 Paper mills

(G-7919)
M G BRYAN EQUIPMENT CO LP
1906 S Great Sw Pkwy (75051-3503)
PHONE..................972 623-4300
Matt Bryan, *President*
Mike Bryan, *General Ptnr*
Jayson Aparicio, *Engineer*
Elizabeth Altimore, *Human Res Dir*
Brandy Smith, *Human Res Mgr*
▲ **EMP:** 19
SQ FT: 20,000
SALES (est): 18.1MM **Privately Held**
WEB: www.mgbryan.com
SIC: 5084 3561 5082 3531 Engines & parts, diesel; industrial pumps & parts; cranes, construction; backhoes, tractors, cranes, plows & similar equipment

(G-7920)
M2L SYSTEMS LLC
Also Called: Intelligent Package Systems
2122 113th St (75050-1240)
P.O. Box 1693, Arlington (76004-1693)
PHONE..................214 412-1400
Morteza Langrodi, *Mng Member*
EMP: 16
SQ FT: 10,000
SALES (est): 966.3K **Privately Held**
WEB: www.qcon-24.com
SIC: 3535 Conveyors & conveying equipment

(G-7921)
MAC MACHINE AND GEAR CORP
201 E Shady Grove Rd (75050-6647)
PHONE..................972 790-7800
Glen E Newton, *President*
EMP: 17
SQ FT: 18,000
SALES (est): 2.3MM **Privately Held**
WEB: www.granutech.com
SIC: 3599 Machine shop, jobbing & repair

(G-7922)
MBK-WI INC
Also Called: Freedom Graphic Systems
1050 S State Highway 161 (75051-1437)
PHONE..................972 375-0253
Lonnie Eager, *General Mgr*
EMP: 550
SALES (corp-wide): 121MM **Privately Held**
WEB: www.fgs.com
SIC: 2752 Commercial printing, offset
PA: Mbk-Wi, Inc.
1101 S Janesville St
Milton WI 53563
608 373-6500

(G-7923)
MDS PRINTGRAPHICS INC
Also Called: Print Graphics
2641 N Forum Dr (75052-8925)
PHONE..................972 647-0043
Edwin Stracener, *President*
Darrell Canright, *Manager*
EMP: 17
SALES (est): 2.1MM **Privately Held**
WEB: www.printeddata.com
SIC: 2752 Commercial printing, offset

(G-7924)
MEDICAL TECHNOLOGY INC
Also Called: Bledsoe Brace Systems
2601 Pinewood Dr (75051-3516)
PHONE..................972 647-0884
Greg Nelson, *Ch of Bd*
Gary Henley, *President*
Gary Bledsoe, *President*
Gregory R Nelson, *Vice Pres*
Timothy Perison, *Vice Pres*
▲ **EMP:** 250
SQ FT: 67,000
SALES (est): 53.3MM **Privately Held**
SIC: 3842 8011 Orthopedic appliances; offices & clinics of medical doctors

(G-7925)
MERCER METALS LP
1249 Avenue R (75050-1602)
PHONE..................214 905-9915
Robert Mercer, *Partner*
Myrna Mercer, *Partner*
Joey Carter, *Engineer*
EMP: 24 **EST:** 2005
SALES (est): 5.7MM **Privately Held**
WEB: www.mercermetals.com
SIC: 3441 3549 Fabricated structural metal; metalworking machinery

(G-7926)
METAL IMPROVEMENT COMPANY LLC
1450 Avenue S (75050-1242)
PHONE..................972 660-3692
EMP: 21
SQ FT: 10,000
SALES (corp-wide): 2.2B **Publicly Held**
SIC: 3398 Metal Heat Treating
HQ: Metal Improvement Company, Llc
80 E Rte 4 Ste 310
Paramus NJ 07652
201 843-7800

(G-7927)
METRO COFFEE GROUPPE INC
320 Se 26th St (75050-6203)
P.O. Box 531408 (75053-1408)
PHONE..................972 263-8744
Don Noe, *CEO*
Tim Noe, *Vice Pres*
Thomas J Gingerich, *VP Finance*
Kay Nichols, *Cust Mgr*
EMP: 18
SQ FT: 25,000
SALES (est): 2MM **Privately Held**
WEB: www.metrocoffeegrouppe.com
SIC: 2095 5046 7389 Roasted coffee; coffee brewing equipment & supplies; coffee service

(G-7928)
MIDWEST INDUSTRIAL RUBBER INC
Also Called: Mir
1330 Post & Paddock Rd St (75050)
PHONE..................972 988-6700
Terry Ohearn, *Branch Mgr*

EMP: 12
SQ FT: 14,640
SALES (corp-wide): 49MM **Privately Held**
WEB: www.mir-belting.com
SIC: 5085 3535 3061 3053 Hose, belting & packing; conveyors & conveying equipment; mechanical rubber goods; gaskets, packing & sealing devices
PA: Midwest Industrial Rubber Inc
10431 Midwest Indus Dr
Saint Louis MO 63132
314 890-0070

(G-7929)
MILLER PRODUCTS INC
Also Called: M P I Label Systems of Texas
916 Avenue N (75050-1918)
PHONE..................972 988-0983
Phill Henning, *Manager*
Phil Henning, *Director*
EMP: 38
SALES (corp-wide): 39.9MM **Privately Held**
WEB: www.mpilabels.com
SIC: 2672 2679 Labels (unprinted), gummed: made from purchased materials; tape, pressure sensitive: made from purchased materials; labels, paper: made from purchased material
PA: Miller Products, Inc.
450 Courtney Rd
Sebring OH 44672
330 938-2134

(G-7930)
NATIONAL STONE LTD
Also Called: National Stone TX
804 W Shady Grove Rd (75050-6920)
PHONE..................214 651-7667
Stephen Broussard, *President*
EMP: 20
SALES (est): 1.5MM **Privately Held**
WEB: www.nationalstone.com
SIC: 3281 Cut stone & stone products

(G-7931)
NEOS THERAPEUTICS INC (PA)
2940 N Highway 360 (75050)
PHONE..................972 408-1300
Jerry McLaughlin, *CEO*
Alan Heller, *Ch of Bd*
Vipin Garg, *President*
Jeff Swalley, *General Mgr*
Margaret Cabano, *Vice Pres*
EMP: 36 **EST:** 1994
SQ FT: 97,282
SALES: 64.6MM **Publicly Held**
WEB: www.neostx.com
SIC: 2834 Pharmaceutical preparations

(G-7932)
NEOS THERAPEUTICS LP
2940 N State Highway 360 (75050-6425)
PHONE..................972 408-1300
Mark Tengler, *President*
Ellen Hoffing, *COO*
Margaret Cabano, *Vice Pres*
Russ McMahen, *Vice Pres*
Asif Mughal, *Vice Pres*
EMP: 70
SQ FT: 110,000
SALES (est): 15.5MM
SALES (corp-wide): 64.6MM **Publicly Held**
WEB: www.neostx.com
SIC: 2834 Vitamin, nutrient & hematinic preparations for human use
PA: Neos Therapeutics, Inc.
2940 N Highway 360
Grand Prairie TX 75050
972 408-1300

(G-7933)
NETFIRES LLC
2400 W Marshall Dr (75051-3511)
PHONE..................972 603-2702
Jim Riley, *Chairman*
EMP: 10
SALES (est): 640.5K **Privately Held**
WEB: www.lmco.com
SIC: 3324 3552 Aerospace investment castings, ferrous; warping machines, textile

(G-7934)
NEXT GEN COMPOUNDING LLC
2901 Eagle Dr (75052-8191)
PHONE..................972 602-9717
Mike Chase, *CEO*
Steve Chase, *Vice Pres*
Jake Tansey, *Technology*
EMP: 22 **EST:** 2014
SALES (est): 4.3MM **Privately Held**
WEB: www.nextgencompounding.com
SIC: 3069 Custom compounding of rubber materials

(G-7935)
NG OPERATIONS LLC
1502 W North Carrier Pkwy (75050)
PHONE..................972 660-7140
EMP: 13
SALES (corp-wide): 478MM **Privately Held**
WEB: www.nationalgypsum.com
SIC: 3275 2899 Mfg Gypsum Products Mfg Chemical Preparation
HQ: Proform Finishing Products, Llc
2001 Rexford Rd
Charlotte NC 28211

(G-7936)
NORTH AMERICAN ATK CORPORATION (HQ)
Also Called: Atk North America
1102 W N Carrier (75050)
PHONE..................972 647-1400
Peter Butterfield, *President*
Juan Luis Bernal Blanco, *Vice Pres*
Shannon Empting, *Vice Pres*
Orjan Kers, *Vice Pres*
Scott Miller, *Vice Pres*
▲ **EMP:** 88
SALES (est): 30.1MM
SALES (corp-wide): 12.5B **Publicly Held**
WEB: www.atkvege.com
SIC: 3714 Motor vehicle parts & accessories
PA: Lkq Corporation
500 W Madison St Ste 2800
Chicago IL 60661
312 621-1950

(G-7937)
NORTH TEXAS PACKING INC
1350 Avenue S Ste 110 (75050-1256)
PHONE..................972 660-2800
Jeffrey Sedacca, *President*
Richard Reeder, *Vice Pres*
EMP: 13
SQ FT: 10,000
SALES (est): 3.2MM **Privately Held**
SIC: 2092 Seafoods, frozen: prepared

(G-7938)
NORTH TXAS HLTH CARE LDRY COOP
Also Called: North Texas Health Care Ldry
1080 Post And Paddock St (75050-1139)
PHONE..................469 916-1150
Lynn Dunning, *President*
Alan Bonds, *General Mgr*
Kurt Koenig, *General Mgr*
Jennifer M Chege, *CFO*
Kimberly Dispagna, *Controller*
▲ **EMP:** 300
SQ FT: 106,236
SALES (est): 6.3MM **Privately Held**
WEB: www.nthcl.org
SIC: 3582 Extractors, commercial laundry

(G-7939)
NW SIGN INDUSTRIES INC
1170 109th St (75050-2603)
PHONE..................972 602-9434
EMP: 77 **Privately Held**
SIC: 3993 Mfg Signs/Advertising Specialties
PA: Nw Sign Industries, Inc.
360 Crider Ave
Moorestown NJ 08057

(G-7940)
OLDCASTLE BUILDING ENVELOPE
1101 Fountain Pkwy (75050-1514)
PHONE..................972 647-4028
Ed Swift, *Manager*
Freddie Warren, *Manager*

GEOGRAPHIC

EMP: 50
SALES (est): 3.5MM **Privately Held**
WEB: www.obe.com
SIC: 3231 5039 Industrial glassware: made from purchased glass; glass construction materials

(G-7941)
OMNIMAX INTERNATIONAL INC
Amerimax Home Products
3125 N Grt Sw Pkwy 300 (75050-6462)
PHONE.....................972 522-0148
Mitchell B Lewis, *CEO*
EMP: 12
SQ FT: 30,000 **Privately Held**
WEB: www.omnimax.com
SIC: 3444 Sheet metalwork
HQ: Omnimax International, Inc.
　30 Technology Pkwy S # 400
　Peachtree Corners GA 30092

(G-7942)
ORIGIN INSTRUMENTS CORP
Also Called: Hme
854 Greenview Dr (75050-2438)
PHONE.....................972 606-8740
George S Bain, *President*
Melvin Dashner, *Vice Pres*
Pam Gee, *Mfg Mgr*
Joel Watson, *Research*
Edie Moore, *Office Mgr*
EMP: 10
SALES (est): 1.6MM **Privately Held**
WEB: www.orin.com
SIC: 3827 7371 8731 Optical instruments & lenses; custom computer programming services; electronic research

(G-7943)
P&G MINING LLC
2860 N Hwy (75050-6411)
PHONE.....................682 500-8986
Bonnie Melton, *Accountant*
George R Parra,
EMP: 10
SALES (est): 220.2K **Privately Held**
WEB: www.pandgminingllc.com
SIC: 1241 Mining services: anthracite

(G-7944)
PALLET DEPOT
2501 Dalworth St Ste B (75050-4802)
PHONE.....................972 336-0006
Mike Flanagan, *Owner*
EMP: 10
SALES (est): 750K **Privately Held**
WEB: www.thepalletdepot.net
SIC: 2448 Pallets, wood

(G-7945)
PEPSI COLA SALES & DIST
Also Called: Pepsico
735 E Trinity Blvd # 100 (75050-8069)
PHONE.....................909 472-4060
Bob Hoch, *Principal*
▲ **EMP:** 9
SALES (est): 727.5K **Privately Held**
SIC: 2086 Carbonated soft drinks, bottled & canned

(G-7946)
PLANO SYNERGY HOLDING INC (PA)
602 Fountain Pkwy Ste C (75050-1441)
PHONE.....................469 733-1868
David E Dudick, *CEO*
Ryan Busbice, *President*
Ben Harvey, *Exec VP*
John Klossing, *Plant Mgr*
Mark Tripp, *CFO*
EMP: 21
SALES (est): 99.6MM **Privately Held**
WEB: www.planosynergy.com
SIC: 2426 5941 Gun stocks, wood; hunting equipment

(G-7947)
POLK MECHANICAL COMPANY LLC (PA)
Also Called: PMC Service Company
2425 Dillard St (75051-1004)
PHONE.....................972 339-1200
Fran McCann, *CEO*
Ken Polk, *Ch of Bd*
Ed Bray, *Superintendent*
Thomas Garrison, *Superintendent*

Steven Grady, *Superintendent*
EMP: 225
SALES (est): 92.3MM **Privately Held**
WEB: www.polkmechanical.com
SIC: 1711 3444 3498 3599 Mechanical contractor; pipe, sheet metal; fabricated pipe & fittings; hose, flexible metallic; cleaners, pipe & cigarette holder

(G-7948)
POLY-AMERICA LP (PA)
Also Called: Pol-Tex International Division
2000 W Marshall Dr (75051-2795)
PHONE.....................972 337-7100
Michael Ross, *Managing Prtnr*
George Hall, *COO*
Christopher Hailey, *Buyer*
Kelly Karlik, *Credit Mgr*
Michael Deal, *Department Mgr*
◆ **EMP:** 1700 **EST:** 1976
SQ FT: 780,000
SALES (est): 561.6MM **Privately Held**
WEB: www.poly-america.com
SIC: 3081 2673 Polyethylene film; trash bags (plastic film): made from purchased materials

(G-7949)
POLY-AMERICA LP
1350 S State Highway 161 (75051-2724)
PHONE.....................972 337-7107
EMP: 180
SALES (corp-wide): 561.6MM **Privately Held**
WEB: www.poly-america.com
SIC: 3081 Polyethylene film
PA: Poly-America, L.P.
　2000 W Marshall Dr
　Grand Prairie TX 75051
　972 337-7100

(G-7950)
POLY-FLEX CONSTRUCTION INC
Also Called: Poly America
2000 W Marshall Dr (75051-2709)
PHONE.....................972 647-4374
George Hall, *President*
Morris Jett, *Corp Secy*
Andrew Richards, *Site Mgr*
Brandon Beasley, *Buyer*
Michael Hay, *Engineer*
EMP: 15
SALES (est): 6.3MM **Privately Held**
WEB: www.poly-americarecycling.com
SIC: 2821 Plastics materials & resins

(G-7951)
PRAIRIE DOG PET PRODUCTS LLC
907 Avenue R (75050-1504)
PHONE.....................972 606-9050
Ted Mischaikov, *CEO*
Scott Gordon, *CFO*
Jeff Camosci, *Risk Mgmt Dir*
EMP: 280
SALES (est): 6MM **Privately Held**
WEB: www.prairiedogpetproducts.com
SIC: 2047 Dog food

(G-7952)
PRATT & WHITNEY ENG SVCS INC
1177 N Great Sw Pkwy (75050-2696)
PHONE.....................972 343-1300
Ed Perret, *Engineer*
Tom Vetere, *Engineer*
Kathy Clark, *Human Resources*
Jack Planchak, *Manager*
Tony Graziano, *Manager*
EMP: 500
SALES (corp-wide): 56.5B **Publicly Held**
WEB: www.rtx.com
SIC: 7699 3724 Aviation propeller & blade repair; aircraft engines & engine parts
HQ: Pratt & Whitney Engine Services, Inc.
　1525 Midway Park Rd
　Bridgeport WV 26330
　304 842-5421

(G-7953)
PRC - DESOTO INTERNATIONAL INC
Also Called: PPG Aerospace
2750 114th St Ste 400 (75050-8735)
PHONE.....................817 640-1067
Patrick Raffa, *Sales & Mktg St*
La Donna Hyatt, *Office Mgr*
EMP: 40
SALES (corp-wide): 15.3B **Publicly Held**
WEB: www.ppgaerospace.com
SIC: 2891 Adhesives
HQ: Prc - Desoto International, Inc.
　24811 Ave Rockefeller
　Valencia CA 91355
　661 678-4209

(G-7954)
PRINTEDD PRODUCTS & SVCS LTD (PA)
Also Called: Laser Graphics Arlington
2641 N Forum Dr (75052-8925)
P.O. Box 40, Arlington (76004-0040)
PHONE.....................972 660-3800
Mark Carter, *President*
Edwin E Stracener, *General Ptnr*
Roland Ramos, *Prdtn Mgr*
Darrell Stracener, *Administration*
▲ **EMP:** 85 **EST:** 1982
SQ FT: 30,000
SALES (est): 12.2MM **Privately Held**
WEB: www.printedd.com
SIC: 2759 Business forms: printing; bank notes: engraved

(G-7955)
PRINTPACK INC
2006 Great Southwest Pkwy (75051-3507)
PHONE.....................972 602-8421
Terry Eicher, *Human Resources*
Debra Green, *Branch Mgr*
James Tate, *Manager*
Shirley Armstrong EXT, *Executive*
Lori Morgan, *Administration*
EMP: 225
SQ FT: 24,000
SALES (corp-wide): 1.3B **Privately Held**
WEB: www.printpack.com
SIC: 2673 5199 2671 Bags: plastic, laminated & coated; packaging materials; packaging paper & plastics film, coated & laminated
HQ: Printpack, Inc.
　2800 Overlook Pkwy Ne
　Atlanta GA 30339
　404 460-7000

(G-7956)
PRINTPACK INC
2005 S Great Sw Pkwy (75051-3508)
PHONE.....................972 641-4421
Larry Kyle, *General Mgr*
Bryan Philpot, *Purch Agent*
Denise Kirmse, *Manager*
EMP: 22
SALES (corp-wide): 1.3B **Privately Held**
WEB: www.printpack.com
SIC: 2673 3081 Bags: plastic, laminated & coated; plastic film & sheet
HQ: Printpack, Inc.
　2800 Overlook Pkwy Ne
　Atlanta GA 30339
　404 460-7000

(G-7957)
PROLUX LLC
Also Called: Bathcrest Prolux Mfg
3125 N Great Southwest Pk (75050-6492)
PHONE.....................801 955-7070
Craig Peterson, *Mng Member*
Aaron L Peterson,
Brad Peterson,
Marge Peterson,
EMP: 18
SQ FT: 54,000
SALES (est): 2.7MM **Privately Held**
WEB: www.proluxmfg.com
SIC: 3088 Tubs (bath, shower & laundry), plastic

(G-7958)
PROSOURCE INDUSTRIES INC
1700 111th St (75050-1913)
PHONE.....................972 660-1400
Tim Hissam, *President*

Brandon Burgess, *Controller*
EMP: 40
SQ FT: 35,000
SALES (est): 13.5MM **Privately Held**
WEB: www.prosourceind.com
SIC: 3643 Current-carrying wiring devices

(G-7959)
PROTECH DIAMOND USA INC
1600 109th St (75050-1905)
PHONE.....................972 602-0080
David Young Liao, *President*
David Liao, *General Mgr*
▲ **EMP:** 17
SALES (est): 3.1MM
SALES (corp-wide): 955.2K **Privately Held**
WEB: www.protechdiamondusa.com
SIC: 3531 Construction machinery
PA: Protech Diamond Tools Inc
　4639 6 St Ne Suite 2
　Calgary AB T2E 3
　403 230-8826

(G-7960)
QUALITY CUSTOM FABRICATORS
1750 Westpark Dr Ste 100 (75050-1944)
PHONE.....................817 649-8020
D L West, *Partner*
Vince Adams, *Partner*
Wanda Adams, *Partner*
Linda McCarley, *Partner*
Betty Stayton, *Partner*
EMP: 100
SQ FT: 111,000
SALES (est): 10.4MM **Privately Held**
WEB: www.vinceadams.biz
SIC: 5084 3556 Food industry machinery; food products machinery

(G-7961)
R & B ELECTRONICS INC
2358 Nw Dallas St (75050-4903)
PHONE.....................906 632-1542
Ron Ledbetter, *Manager*
Karlie Laitinen, *IT/INT Sup*
EMP: 20
SALES (corp-wide): 4.4MM **Privately Held**
WEB: www.randbelectronics.com
SIC: 3728 3721 3644 Aircraft assemblies, subassemblies & parts; aircraft; noncurrent-carrying wiring services
PA: R & B Electronics, Inc.
　1520 Industrial Park Dr
　Sault Sainte Marie MI 49783
　906 632-1542

(G-7962)
RAMSES LUBR REPACKAGING LLC
861 S Great Sw Pkwy (75051-1013)
PHONE.....................972 672-8717
Munir Hindi, *Mng Member*
EMP: 10
SALES (est): 450.6K **Privately Held**
SIC: 2992 Lubricating oils & greases

(G-7963)
RED THE UNIFORM TAILOR (PA)
1630 111th St (75050-1911)
PHONE.....................972 660-8433
Gwyn Prater, *General Mgr*
Randy Clark, *Manager*
EMP: 26
SALES (est): 2.1MM **Privately Held**
WEB: www.rtut.com
SIC: 2311 Firemen's uniforms: made from purchased materials; policemen's uniforms: made from purchased materials

(G-7964)
REYCOMP INC
2525 Dalworth St (75050-4812)
PHONE.....................972 606-4600
George Rey, *President*
Philipp Rey, *Vice Pres*
Eva Rey, *CFO*
EMP: 12
SQ FT: 13,000
SALES (est): 2.1MM **Privately Held**
WEB: www.reycomp.com
SIC: 3672 Printed circuit boards

▲ = Import ▼=Export
◆ =Import/Export

(G-7965)
RHEACO INC
1801 W Jefferson St (75051-1328)
P.O. Box 530531 (75053-0531)
PHONE...............................972 264-4748
Ron Jensen, *President*
EMP: 100 **EST:** 2000
SALES (est): 12.6MM
SALES (corp-wide): 24.3MM **Privately Held**
WEB: www.rheaco.com
SIC: 3599 3444 Machine shop, jobbing & repair; sheet metalwork
PA: Control Products Corporation
1513 W Jefferson St
Grand Prairie TX 75051
972 264-0368

(G-7966)
RICHARD PHILLIPS INC
Also Called: Phillips Signs
116 Ne 6th St (75050-5813)
PHONE...............................972 264-5315
Salvacion Phillips, *President*
Richard Phillips, *Vice Pres*
EMP: 28
SQ FT: 28,000
SALES (est): 3MM **Privately Held**
WEB: www.phillipssigns.net
SIC: 1799 3448 1791 Sign installation & maintenance; trusses & framing: prefabricated metal; building front installation metal

(G-7967)
ROAD KARE INTERNATIONAL LP
530 Jesse St (75051-1142)
PHONE...............................972 647-8300
Foy Barratt, *Partner*
▲ **EMP:** 30
SALES (est): 3.7MM **Privately Held**
WEB: www.rubberform.com
SIC: 3714 Bumpers & bumperettes, motor vehicle

(G-7968)
SAFRAN ELEC DEF AVNICS USA LLC (DH)
2802 Safran Dr (75052-8187)
PHONE...............................972 314-3600
Trice Smith III, *President*
Patrick Prulhiere, *President*
Adaora Nelson, *COO*
George Davis, *Facilities Mgr*
Eric Fernandes, *Engineer*
▲ **EMP:** 120
SQ FT: 60,000
SALES (est): 74.1MM
SALES (corp-wide): 799.9MM **Privately Held**
WEB: www.safran-electronics-defense.com
SIC: 3728 Aircraft parts & equipment

(G-7969)
SAFRAN HELICOPTER ENGINES USA
2709 N Forum Dr (75052-8927)
PHONE...............................972 606-7600
Thierry Derrien, *CEO*
Michael Martin, *Business Mgr*
Keith Marshall, *COO*
Jean-Marc Domergue, *Vice Pres*
Martin Boyles, *Opers Mgr*
EMP: 370
SQ FT: 30,000
SALES (est): 47.9MM
SALES (corp-wide): 799.9MM **Privately Held**
SIC: 7699 3724 Engine repair & replacement, non-automotive; aircraft engines & engine parts
HQ: Safran Usa, Inc.
700 S Washington St # 320
Alexandria VA 22314
703 351-9898

(G-7970)
SAFRAN POWER UNITS DALLAS INC
2709 N Forum Dr (75052-8927)
PHONE...............................972 606-7681
Parel Francois, *CEO*
Lindsay Adams, *Vice Pres*
Vanessa Lecacheux, *CFO*

Rich Fullmer, *Representative*
EMP: 11 **EST:** 1992
SQ FT: 32,000
SALES (est): 1.8MM
SALES (corp-wide): 799.9MM **Privately Held**
WEB: www.safran-power-units.com
SIC: 7699 3511 Aircraft & heavy equipment repair services; gas turbines, mechanical drive
HQ: Safran Power Units
8 Chemin Du Pont De Rupe
Toulouse 31200
561 701-651

(G-7971)
SAGE INTERNATIONAL INC (PA)
Also Called: Jayco Manufacturing
1470 Avenue T Ste 1222 (75050-1222)
PHONE...............................972 623-2004
Ramakrishnan Krishnan, *Mng Member*
Satish Kumar, *Admin Sec*
EMP: 57
SALES (est): 16.6MM **Privately Held**
WEB: www.tridentcomponents.com
SIC: 3469 3431 3444 Stamping metal for the trade; plumbing fixtures: enameled iron cast iron or pressed metal; metal roofing & roof drainage equipment

(G-7972)
SEALED AIR CORPORATION
Packaging Products Div
2401 Dillard St (75051-1090)
PHONE...............................817 540-2020
EMP: 70
SALES (corp-wide): 4.7B **Publicly Held**
WEB: www.sealedair.com
SIC: 3086 5199 2671 Packaging & shipping materials, foamed plastic; packaging materials; packaging paper & plastics film, coated & laminated
PA: Sealed Air Corporation
2415 Cascade Pointe Blvd
Charlotte NC 28208
980 221-3235

(G-7973)
SIEMENS INDUSTRY INC
501 Fountain Pkwy (75050-1411)
PHONE...............................817 633-4430
Bob Bacchus, *Engineer*
Dan Avitua, *VP Sales*
Roger Langston, *Branch Mgr*
Christine Anderson, *Meeting Planner*
EMP: 50
SALES (corp-wide): 67.4B **Privately Held**
WEB: www.new.siemens.com
SIC: 3625 5084 3672 3613 Motor controls, electric; conveyor systems; printed circuit boards; switchgear & switchboard apparatus
HQ: Siemens Industry, Inc.
1000 Deerfield Pkwy
Buffalo Grove IL 60089
847 215-1000

(G-7974)
SOUTHWEST INDUS SURFACES INC (PA)
Also Called: SIS
1165 111th St (75050-2608)
PHONE...............................972 641-4393
Jerold R Baker, *President*
Nicole Foster, *Vice Pres*
Vicki Baker, *Treasurer*
EMP: 23
SQ FT: 12,000
SALES (est): 3.7MM **Privately Held**
SIC: 1752 1771 3398 Floor laying & floor work; concrete work; shot peening (treating steel to reduce fatigue)

(G-7975)
SPECILTY ADHESIVES COATING INC
1164 N Great Sw Pkwy (75050-2628)
PHONE...............................972 641-7600
Kenneth Patton, *Branch Mgr*
EMP: 18
SALES (corp-wide): 49.5MM **Privately Held**
WEB: www.specialtyadhesivesinc.com
SIC: 2891 Adhesives

PA: Specialty Adhesives & Coating, Inc.
3791 Air Park St
Memphis TN 38118
800 728-9171

(G-7976)
STRAIGHT LINE SAWING & SEALING
114 Ne 28th St (75050-6219)
PHONE...............................972 590-8922
Eric M Johnson, *President*
EMP: 11 **EST:** 2015
SALES (est): 161.9K **Privately Held**
WEB: www.slssTexas.com
SIC: 3546 3579 Saws & sawing equipment; letter folding, stuffing & sealing machines

(G-7977)
SUN CHEMICAL CORPORATION
1505 109th St (75050-1904)
PHONE...............................972 647-1641
Renaldo Ramirez, *Cust Svc Dir*
Christopher Rice, *Accounts Mgr*
Frank Hester, *Manager*
Moe Rahmeh, *Manager*
EMP: 30 **Privately Held**
WEB: www.sunchemical.com
SIC: 2893 2899 3952 Printing ink; chemical preparations; lead pencils & art goods
HQ: Sun Chemical Corporation
35 Waterview Blvd Ste 100
Parsippany NJ 07054
973 404-6000

(G-7978)
SUPER STRONG PRODUCTS INC
Also Called: A A A Super Strong Products
601 E Rock Island Rd (75050-6512)
PHONE...............................972 342-6921
David Flores, *President*
Jorge D Flores, *Vice Pres*
Luz C Diaz, *Treasurer*
EMP: 10
SQ FT: 3,000 **Privately Held**
SIC: 3579 5084 Binding machines, plastic & adhesive; printing trades machinery, equipment & supplies

(G-7979)
SWECO
Also Called: Surfrac
1850 Westpark Dr (75050-1924)
PHONE...............................817 202-0350
Josepg Berrones, *Branch Mgr*
Joseph Berrones, *Branch Mgr*
▲ **EMP:** 10
SALES (est): 2.5MM **Privately Held**
SIC: 5084 1389 Petroleum industry machinery; oil field services

(G-7980)
TECH-LAB INDUSTRIES INC
2371 Nw Dallas St Ste 400 (75050-4970)
P.O. Box 6217, Arlington (76005-6217)
PHONE...............................972 660-1111
Raleigh Simmons, *President*
EMP: 15
SQ FT: 10,000
SALES (est): 2.3MM **Privately Held**
WEB: www.tech-lab.com
SIC: 3821 5049 Laboratory equipment: fume hoods, distillation racks, etc.; laboratory equipment, except medical or dental

(G-7981)
TEXAS STARWARES INC
2606 Aviation Pkwy (75052-8917)
PHONE...............................972 641-2100
Debra K Wolcott, *President*
Kay Walcott, *General Mgr*
Jim Wolcott, *Vice Pres*
Josh Scheer, *Technology*
▲ **EMP:** 14
SQ FT: 15,000
SALES (est): 3.1MM **Privately Held**
WEB: www.starwaresww.com
SIC: 3429 3728 Manufactured hardware (general); military aircraft equipment & armament

(G-7982)
THOM-BAT-LER ENTERPRISES
2622 Skyway Dr Ste 3d (75052-8919)
PHONE...............................972 660-4056
Frank Batts, *Managing Prtnr*
Larry Thompson, *Partner*
▲ **EMP:** 13
SQ FT: 15,000
SALES (est): 1.9MM **Privately Held**
SIC: 2542 5046 2434 Cabinets: show, display or storage: except wood; store fixtures & display equipment; wood kitchen cabinets

(G-7983)
THREE CHIEFS & NO INDIANS LLC
Also Called: California Sample Services
2800 112th St Ste 100 (75050-6495)
PHONE...............................909 465-6314
Lee Hein, *General Mgr*
Donna Garcia, *Accounts Mgr*
Raymond Paul Gaytan,
Andrew Kallman,
◆ **EMP:** 190
SALES (est): 27MM **Privately Held**
WEB: www.americansample.com
SIC: 2789 Swatches & samples

(G-7984)
TPG PRESSURE INC
Also Called: Thompson Pipe Group - Pressure
1004 Macarthur Blvd (75050-7942)
PHONE...............................972 262-3600
Ashley Payne, *Asst Controller*
Jennifer Monk, *Sales Staff*
Ken Thompson, *Branch Mgr*
Thomas Thornton, *Manager*
EMP: 200
SALES (corp-wide): 54.3MM **Privately Held**
WEB: www.thompsonpipegroup.com
SIC: 3498 Fabricated pipe & fittings
PA: Tpg Pressure, Inc.
1003 Macarthur Blvd
Grand Prairie TX 75050
972 262-3600

(G-7985)
TPG PRESSURE INC (PA)
Also Called: Thompson Pipe Group - Pressure
1003 Macarthur Blvd (75050-7943)
P.O. Box 3007, Conroe (77305-3007)
PHONE...............................972 262-3600
Kenneth D Thompson, *CEO*
Mike Leather, *President*
Monty Harrup, *Regl Sales Mgr*
EMP: 74
SQ FT: 1,000
SALES (est): 54.3MM **Privately Held**
WEB: www.thompsonpipegroup.com
SIC: 3272 Pipe, concrete or lined with concrete

(G-7986)
TRIUMPH ACCSSORY SVCS - GRND P
Also Called: Triump Group
1038 Santerre St (75050-1937)
PHONE...............................972 623-9300
Kevin Murphy, *President*
Nancy Lira, *Business Mgr*
Jason Loman, *Engineer*
Joe O'Brien, *Engineer*
Brian Causer, *Sales Staff*
EMP: 99
SALES (est): 39.4MM **Publicly Held**
WEB: www.triumphgroup.com
SIC: 3728 3724 Aircraft parts & equipment; aircraft engines & engine parts
PA: Triumph Group, Inc.
899 Cassatt Rd Ste 210
Berwyn PA 19312

(G-7987)
TRIUMPH AEROSTRUCTURES LLC
Also Called: Vought Commercial Division
1601 W Marshall Dr (75051-2801)
PHONE...............................972 595-9900
Ron Muckley, *Branch Mgr*
Steve Downen, *Manager*
EMP: 250 **Publicly Held**

WEB: www.triumphgroup.com
SIC: 3728 Aircraft parts & equipment
HQ: Triumph Aerostructures, Llc
300 Austin Blvd
Red Oak TX 75154

(G-7988)
TURNER SIGN SYSTEMS INC
1302 Avenue R (75050-1603)
PHONE.................................817 222-0033
Greg Turner, *President*
EMP: 15
SALES (est): 2.2MM **Privately Held**
WEB: www.turnersignsystems.com
SIC: 3993 Electric signs

(G-7989)
ULTRA SEATING COMPANY (HQ)
602 Fountain Pkwy Ste B (75050-1442)
P.O. Box 535543 (75053-5543)
PHONE.................................469 865-2010
Robert Rishel, *President*
Vivek Naik, *Vice Pres*
Donna Rishel, *Vice Pres*
▲ **EMP:** 18 **EST:** 1978
SQ FT: 150,000
SALES (est): 3.6MM
SALES (corp-wide): 752.6MM **Publicly Held**
WEB: www.ultraseating.com
SIC: 2531 5013 2521 Seats, automobile; truck parts & accessories; wood office furniture
PA: Vse Corporation
6348 Walker Ln
Alexandria VA 22310
703 960-4600

(G-7990)
UNIQUE STAINLESS DESIGNS LLC
259 Gilbert Cir (75050-6528)
P.O. Box 153049, Irving (75015-3049)
PHONE.................................972 254-8424
Jordan J Johnson, *President*
Darrell Johnson, *Vice Pres*
Spencer Johnson, *Manager*
EMP: 12
SQ FT: 10,000
SALES (est): 1.4MM **Privately Held**
WEB: www.uniquestainlessdesigns.com
SIC: 3448 1796 Prefabricated metal buildings; installing building equipment

(G-7991)
VIP SAMPLES INCORPORATED
2800 112th St Ste 100 (75050-6499)
PHONE.................................972 647-8888
▲ **EMP:** 180
SQ FT: 135,000
SALES (est): 32.2MM **Privately Held**
WEB: www.vipsamples.com
SIC: 2782 Sample books

(G-7992)
WEYERHAEUSER COMPANY
Willametteindustries
1200 W N Carrier Pkwy (75050-1201)
P.O. Box 539501 (75053-9501)
PHONE.................................972 641-3891
Roger P Kionka, *Sales Mgr*
Thomas J Reilly, *Manager*
Thomas R Milton, *Admin Mgr*
EMP: 143
SALES (corp-wide): 6.5B **Publicly Held**
WEB: www.weyerhaeuser.com
SIC: 2653 5113 3412 Boxes, corrugated: made from purchased materials; corrugated & solid fiber boxes; metal barrels, drums & pails
PA: Weyerhaeuser Company
220 Occidental Ave S
Seattle WA 98104
206 539-3000

(G-7993)
WGI INNOVATIONS LTD
602 Fountain Pkwy (75050-1440)
PHONE.................................469 733-1868
Chris Barley, *Branch Mgr*
EMP: 42
SALES (corp-wide): 59.9MM **Privately Held**
WEB: www.wildgameinnovations.com
SIC: 3625 Relays & industrial controls

HQ: Wgi Innovations, Ltd.
3849 Plaza Tower Dr
Baton Rouge LA 70816
972 352-6600

(G-7994)
WIKOFF COLOR CORPORATION
1710 Robinson Rd (75051-2848)
P.O. Box 532337 (75053-2337)
PHONE.................................972 647-1371
David Drake, *Prdtn Mgr*
Randy Jeffries, *Manager*
Robyn Farris, *Manager*
EMP: 10
SQ FT: 8,500
SALES (corp-wide): 173.8MM **Privately Held**
WEB: www.wikoff.com
SIC: 2893 5085 Printing ink; ink, printers'
PA: Wikoff Color Corporation
1886 Merritt Rd
Fort Mill SC 29715
803 548-2210

(G-7995)
WIN-HOLT EQUIPMENT CORP
Also Called: Win-Holt Equipment Inc S W
1169 N Great Sw Pkwy (75050-2629)
PHONE.................................972 641-4658
Courtney Guerrero, *General Mgr*
Todd Gilleland, *Engineer*
Dennis Salcedo, *Engineer*
Dana Jimenez, *Controller*
Brett Taylor, *Branch Mgr*
EMP: 138
SQ FT: 72,000
SALES (corp-wide): 67.6MM **Privately Held**
WEB: www.winholt.com
SIC: 3499 5046 3556 3537 Machine bases, metal; commercial cooking & food service equipment; food products machinery; industrial trucks & tractors
PA: Win-Holt Equipment Corp.
20 Crossways Park Dr N # 2
Woodbury NY 11797
516 222-0335

(G-7996)
WINSYSTEMS INC
2890 112th St Ste 100 (75050-0635)
P.O. Box 121361, Arlington (76012-1361)
PHONE.................................817 274-7553
Jerry Winfield, *President*
Sandra Winfield, *Corp Secy*
Robert A Burckle, *Vice Pres*
Keith Thomas, *Opers Mgr*
Suzanne Thomas, *Purch Mgr*
▲ **EMP:** 50 **EST:** 1982
SALES (est): 17.5MM **Privately Held**
WEB: www.winsystems.com
SIC: 3571 Electronic computers

Grand Saline
Van Zandt County

(G-7997)
B&B CUSTOM FABRICATION LLC
915 Vz County Road 1818 (75140-4394)
PHONE.................................214 773-9240
EMP: 20 **EST:** 2012
SALES (est): 277.3K **Privately Held**
WEB: www.bbcustomfab.com
SIC: 3999 Atomizers, toiletry

(G-7998)
PARKER PETROLEUM PROS INC
526 Springcreek Rd (75140-1943)
PHONE.................................903 360-5450
Herschel Eugene Parker, *President*
Vicki Parker, *Corp Secy*
EMP: 19
SALES (est): 3.8MM **Privately Held**
WEB: www.parkerpetroleumpros.com
SIC: 2813 8711 Industrial gases; petroleum engineering

(G-7999)
PLASKOLITE TEXAS LLC
5300 Us Hwy 80 (75140)
P.O. Box 429 (75140-0429)
PHONE.................................903 962-7573
▲ **EMP:** 90
SALES (est): 13.3MM
SALES (corp-wide): 307.8MM **Privately Held**
WEB: www.plaskolite.com
SIC: 2821 Plastics materials & resins
PA: Plaskolite, Llc
400 W Nationwide Blvd # 400
Columbus OH 43215
614 294-3281

Grandfalls
Ward County

(G-8000)
ROYALTY WELL SERVICE INC (PA)
Also Called: Royalty Supply
Fm 1219 (79742)
PHONE.................................432 547-2926
Jeffery E Kester, *President*
Otho Pierce, *Partner*
Toni D Kester, *Treasurer*
EMP: 70
SQ FT: 6,750
SALES (est): 14MM **Privately Held**
WEB: www.royaltywellservice.com
SIC: 1389 1311 Oil field services; crude petroleum production

Grandview
Johnson County

(G-8001)
ACCU-LOCK INC
Also Called: Acculock
9901 S Interstate 35 W (76050-3250)
PHONE.................................866 222-8562
Rick Segerstron, *President*
Debbie Segerstron, *Vice Pres*
Saundra Cawvey, *CFO*
Robert Wright, *Sales Staff*
▲ **EMP:** 37
SQ FT: 5,000
SALES (est): 1.1MM **Privately Held**
WEB: www.acculock.com
SIC: 3429 5099 5251 Door locks, bolts & checks; safety equipment & supplies; locks & lock sets; door locks & lock sets

(G-8002)
NOLTEX TRUSS DFW INC
8800 E Fm 916 (76050-4724)
P.O. Box 1060 (76050-1060)
PHONE.................................817 866-3333
EMP: 50
SALES (est): 879.1K **Privately Held**
WEB: www.noltextruss.com
SIC: 2439 Trusses, wooden roof

(G-8003)
WHM CUSTOM SERVICES INC (PA)
8720 County Road 421 (76050-3728)
PHONE.................................254 854-2111
William S Martin, *President*
Steve Wehlmann, *Manager*
James Woods, *Supervisor*
Elisabeth Frazier, *Analyst*
EMP: 68
SQ FT: 9,000
SALES (est): 16.3MM **Privately Held**
WEB: www.turn2sc.com
SIC: 2819 7692 Catalysts, chemical; welding repair

(G-8004)
WIND CLEAN CORP
8465 E Fm 916 (76050-3890)
PHONE.................................325 625-1899
James Hartley, *President*
Ken Davis, *Vice Pres*
▲ **EMP:** 39

SALES (est): 6.3MM **Privately Held**
WEB: www.colemantexas.org
SIC: 3441 Building components, structural steel

Grapeland
Houston County

(G-8005)
GEORGE BARTEE CNSTR CO INC
13363 U S Hwy 287 N (75844)
P.O. Box 372 (75844-0372)
PHONE.................................936 687-4811
Jason Bridges, *President*
George M Bartee, *President*
Linda Meador, *Admin Sec*
George Bartee, *Associate*
EMP: 22
SQ FT: 2,000
SALES (est): 4.8MM **Privately Held**
WEB: www.barteeconstruction.com
SIC: 1623 1389 1629 Oil & gas pipeline construction; oil field services; earthmoving contractor

(G-8006)
MICO GROUP LTD
630 An County Road 1215 (75844-4908)
P.O. Box 1784, Tomball (77377-1784)
PHONE.................................713 460-3172
Gregorey T Smith, *President*
Debbie Harton, *Vice Pres*
Gloria Tobias, *Vice Pres*
EMP: 18
SALES (est): 4MM **Privately Held**
SIC: 3613 Control panels, electric

(G-8007)
NUCOR CORPORATION
Vulcraft Div
175 County Road 2345 (75844-5886)
P.O. Box 186 (75844-0186)
PHONE.................................936 687-4665
Rick Wilcox, *Safety Mgr*
Donnis Collins, *Maint Spvr*
Leona Smith, *Buyer*
John Grayson, *Sales Mgr*
Jeff Jeffcoat, *Manager*
EMP: 110
SALES (corp-wide): 22.5B **Publicly Held**
WEB: www.nucor.com
SIC: 3441 3444 Expansion joints (structural shapes), iron or steel; sheet metalwork
PA: Nucor Corporation
1915 Rexford Rd Ste 400
Charlotte NC 28211
704 366-7000

(G-8008)
VULCRAFT CARRIER CORPORATION
N Main St Ext (75844)
P.O. Box 188 (75844-0188)
PHONE.................................936 687-4665
Donald J Bromley, *President*
John P Garniewski Jr, *Vice Pres*
Terry S Lisenby, *VP Finance*
Elizabeth W Bowers, *Admin Sec*
Christopher S Cox, *Asst Sec*
EMP: 25
SALES (est): 6.7MM
SALES (corp-wide): 22.5B **Publicly Held**
SIC: 3441 Fabricated structural metal
PA: Nucor Corporation
1915 Rexford Rd Ste 400
Charlotte NC 28211
704 366-7000

Grapevine
Tarrant County

(G-8009)
1A SMART START LLC (PA)
500 E Dallas Rd Ste 100 (76051-7658)
PHONE.................................972 621-0252
Matt Strausz, *CEO*
Jim Ballard, *President*
Jackie Maxwell, *General Mgr*
Larry Wible, *Principal*

▲ = Import ▼ =Export
◆ =Import/Export

Ian Marples, *Vice Pres*
▲ EMP: 15
SQ FT: 20,000
SALES (est): 26.8MM **Privately Held**
WEB: www.smartstartinc.com
SIC: 3694 Engine electrical equipment

(G-8010)
A & W INDUSTRIES INC
Also Called: Wilbert of North Texas
827 Dawn Ln (76051-4124)
P.O. Box 130 (76099-0130)
PHONE..............................817 481-3577
Bert George, *President*
Sherry Rountree, *Vice Pres*
Patricia Zubritski, *Info Tech Mgr*
EMP: 25
SQ FT: 11,888
SALES (est): 2.7MM **Privately Held**
WEB: www.wilbertntx.com
SIC: 3272 Burial vaults, concrete or pre-
cast terrazzo

(G-8011)
AMERICAN POS ALLIANCE LLC
715 N Dove Rd (76051-3110)
P.O. Box 3063 (76099-3063)
PHONE..............................817 350-4714
M S Winslow, *Mng Member*
Melinda Steapp Winslow,
EMP: 13
SALES (est): 1MM **Privately Held**
SIC: 3578 Automatic teller machines (ATM)

(G-8012)
ARGOS USA LLC
1968 Brumlow Ave (76092-9733)
PHONE..............................817 329-8550
Garry Putnam, *Safety Mgr*
John Thompson, *Manager*
Jennifer Warner, *Manager*
EMP: 70 **Privately Held**
WEB: www.argos-us.com
SIC: 3273 Ready-mixed concrete
HQ: Argos Usa Llc
3015 Windward Plz Ste 300
Alpharetta GA 30005
678 368-4300

(G-8013)
AUTOMATIZE LOGISTICS LLC
1123 S Main St (76051-7533)
PHONE..............................817 221-8106
Bradley Nichols,
EMP: 25
SALES (est): 5.9MM **Privately Held**
WEB: www.automatizelogistics.com
SIC: 7372 7371 Application computer soft-
ware; computer software development &
applications

(G-8014)
BIG BUCK BREWERY & STEAKHOUSE
2501 Bass Pro Dr Ste 100 (76051-2009)
PHONE..............................972 691-5100
Cloeaon Convers, *Manager*
EMP: 100 **Privately Held**
WEB: www.bigbuckbrewery.com
SIC: 7389 5921 5813 5812 Restaurant
reservation service; liquor stores; drinking
places; eating places; malt beverages
PA: Big Buck Brewery & Steakhouse, Inc.
550 S Wisconsin Ave
Gaylord MI 49735

(G-8015)
BOBBY G SMITH DO
Also Called: Labuena Vida Vineyards
416 E College St (76051-5468)
PHONE..............................817 481-9463
Bobby Smith, *Branch Mgr*
EMP: 12
SALES (corp-wide): 886.2K **Privately
Held**
WEB: www.umbrawinery.com
SIC: 2084 Wines
PA: Bobby G Smith Do
600 W Park Row Dr Ste A
Arlington TX 76010
817 265-1551

(G-8016)
BUYERS BARRICADES INC (PA)
1024 Texan Trl (76051-3703)
PHONE..............................817 535-3939

Shelba Buyers, *President*
Blake Buyers, *COO*
Steven W Buyers, *Vice Pres*
Jason Garrett, *Vice Pres*
Miles Britt, *Opers Dir*
EMP: 50
SALES (est): 12.9MM **Privately Held**
WEB: www.buyersbarricades.com
SIC: 3499 7359 Barricades, metal; work
zone traffic equipment (flags, cones, bar-
rels, etc.)

(G-8017)
BUYERS BARRICADES HOUSTON LLC
1024 Texan Trl (76051-3703)
P.O. Box 7498, Fort Worth (76111-0498)
PHONE..............................817 535-3939
Robert Tuggle, *Mng Member*
Darcy Brown, *Manager*
EMP: 20
SALES (est): 3MM
SALES (corp-wide): 12.9MM **Privately
Held**
WEB: www.buyersbarricades.com
SIC: 8748 3669 Traffic consultant; pedes-
trian traffic control equipment
PA: Buyers Barricades, Inc.
1024 Texan Trl
Grapevine TX 76051
817 535-3939

(G-8018)
C PEARSON PLUMBING INC
910 S Pine St (76051-5567)
PHONE..............................817 488-0490
Carey Pearson, *President*
Kelly Pearson, *Vice Pres*
EMP: 10
SALES (est): 1.5MM **Privately Held**
SIC: 3432 Plumbing fixture fittings & trim

(G-8019)
C2 INTERNATIONAL USA LLC
801 Hanover Dr Ste 500 (76051-7684)
PHONE..............................405 473-7144
Shuang Zhang, *Mng Member*
EMP: 11 EST: 2014
SALES (est): 852K **Privately Held**
SIC: 3559 Automotive related machinery

(G-8020)
CCT PLASTICS INC
804 Port America Pl Ste B (76051-7613)
PHONE..............................817 410-1222
Greg Mince, *President*
Marshall Dunn, *Exec VP*
Neil M Dunn Jr, *Vice Pres*
Louis Kemp, *Vice Pres*
Aaron Sharp, *Sales Dir*
EMP: 35
SQ FT: 19,500
SALES (est): 6.5MM **Privately Held**
WEB: www.cctprecision.com
SIC: 3599 Machine shop, jobbing & repair;
machine & other job shop work

(G-8021)
CCT PRECISION MACHINING LLC
804 Port America Pl (76051-7613)
PHONE..............................817 410-1222
Israel Bernal,
EMP: 37
SALES (est): 1.1MM **Privately Held**
WEB: www.cctprecision.com
SIC: 3599 Custom machinery

(G-8022)
CLARKE HARLAND CORP
4055 Corporate Dr Ste 100 (76051-2307)
PHONE..............................817 329-7113
Keith Knicely, *Manager*
EMP: 551 **Publicly Held**
WEB: www.harlandclarke.com
SIC: 2782 Checkbooks
HQ: Harland Clarke Corp.
15955 La Cantera Pkwy
San Antonio TX 78256
830 609-5500

(G-8023)
CONCEPT LASER INC
1000 Texan Trl Ste 150 (76051-3780)
PHONE..............................817 328-6500
John Murray, *CEO*

EMP: 25
SQ FT: 7,500
SALES (est): 2.3MM
SALES (corp-wide): 95.2B **Publicly Held**
WEB: www.ge.com
SIC: 3542 Machine tools, metal forming
type
HQ: Concept Laser Gmbh
An Der Zeil 8
Lichtenfels 96215
957 116-790

(G-8024)
CROSSROADS WINERY
Also Called: Umbra Winery
415 S Main St (76051-5328)
P.O. Box 399, Springtown (76082-0399)
PHONE..............................817 421-2999
EMP: 9
SALES (corp-wide): 1.3MM **Privately
Held**
WEB: www.umbrawinery.com
SIC: 2084 Wines
PA: Crossroads Winery
404 Rose Hill Ln
Frisco TX 75034
972 294-4144

(G-8025)
DAIRY FARMERS AMERICA INC
3500 William D Tate Ave # 100
(76051-8734)
PHONE..............................817 410-4500
Tim Theisner, *Opers Mgr*
David Jones, *Manager*
Brandon Meiwes, *Manager*
Sandra Sackville, *Administration*
EMP: 35
SALES (corp-wide): 15.8B **Privately Held**
WEB: www.dfamilk.com
SIC: 2026 8734 Fluid milk; testing labora-
tories
PA: Dairy Farmers Of America, Inc.
1405 N 98th St
Kansas City KS 66111
816 801-6455

(G-8026)
DBS GROUP INC
Also Called: Tiger Tails
242 Churchill Loop (76051-8002)
PHONE..............................817 453-8386
Brenda Scarborough, *President*
David Scarborough, *Vice Pres*
EMP: 11
SALES (est): 841.9K **Privately Held**
WEB: www.dbstigertails.com
SIC: 2395 Embroidery products, except
schiffli machine

(G-8027)
DEEPWELL ENERGY SERVICES LLC
1065 Texan Trl Ste 300 (76051-3740)
PHONE..............................817 796-9970
EMP: 21
SALES (corp-wide): 254.8MM **Privately
Held**
WEB: www.dwservices.com
SIC: 1381 Drilling oil & gas wells
PA: Deepwell Energy Services, Llc
4025 Highway 35 N
Columbia MS 39429
800 477-2855

(G-8028)
DELANEY VINEYARDS INC (PA)
2000 Champagne Blvd (76051-7354)
PHONE..............................817 421-0950
Jerry Delaney, *President*
EMP: 10
SALES (est): 1.6MM **Privately Held**
WEB: www.delaneyvineyards.com
SIC: 2084 7299 5921 Wines; banquet hall
facilities; wine

(G-8029)
DELL SOFTWARE INC
2417 Bonham Trl (76051-8011)
PHONE..............................469 221-4335
EMP: 30
SALES (corp-wide): 23.2B **Publicly Held**
SIC: 7372 Prepackaged Software Services

HQ: Dell Software, Inc.
5 Polaris Way
Aliso Viejo CA 92656
949 754-8000

(G-8030)
ECOLAB INC
Kay Checmical
4050 Corporate Dr (76051-2326)
PHONE..............................800 532-7732
Tom Aubrey, *Branch Mgr*
Megan Ginn, *Manager*
Lori Reyes, *Supervisor*
EMP: 38
SALES (corp-wide): 14.9B **Publicly Held**
WEB: www.ecolab.com
SIC: 2842 Specialty cleaning, polishes &
sanitation goods
PA: Ecolab Inc.
1 Ecolab Pl
Saint Paul MN 55102
800 232-6522

(G-8031)
ENTECH SOLAR INC (PA)
641 Industrial Blvd (76051-3915)
P.O. Box 742, Krum (76249-0742)
PHONE..............................817 421-4658
David Gelbaum, *Ch of Bd*
Aj McDanal, *COO*
Douglas L Washington, *Vice Pres*
Shelley Hollingsworth, *CFO*
▲ EMP: 18
SQ FT: 71,000
SALES (est): 2.8MM **Privately Held**
SIC: 3674 Solar cells

(G-8032)
EREPLACEMENTS LLC (PA)
600 E Dallas Rd Ste 200 (76051-4191)
PHONE..............................214 935-3591
Alicia Arduini, *Marketing Staff*
Thomas M Peck, *Mng Member*
Kyle Jundt,
▲ EMP: 15
SALES (est): 4.7MM **Privately Held**
WEB: www.ereplacements.com
SIC: 3691 Storage batteries

(G-8033)
EXECUTIVE VOICE MAIL SYSTEMS
226 N Dove Rd (76051-3105)
P.O. Box 92885, Southlake (76092-0885)
PHONE..............................817 329-9788
Mary Ann Holliday, *President*
EMP: 15
SQ FT: 6,500
SALES (est): 1.6MM **Privately Held**
WEB: www.executivetelephony.com
SIC: 3661 5731 4813 Message concen-
trators; radio, television & electronic
stores; telephone communication, except
radio

(G-8034)
FGL GROUP LLC
1901 N Port Ct (76051-7135)
PHONE..............................817 481-7857
Peter Zehr, *President*
EMP: 19
SALES (est): 2.3MM **Privately Held**
SIC: 2899 Chemical preparations

(G-8035)
FIVEPAYNE LLC (PA)
Also Called: Greentree Packaging and Lum-
ber
818 S Main St Ste 200 (76051-7534)
PHONE..............................817 310-0147
Enrique Castruita, *Vice Pres*
Adolfo Castruita, *VP Opers*
Keith Smith, *Purchasing*
Barbara Gallup, *Sales Staff*
Larry Tubbs, *Sales Staff*
EMP: 85
SQ FT: 1,000
SALES (est): 14MM **Privately Held**
WEB: www.greentreepackaging.com
SIC: 2448 5031 Pallets, wood; lumber,
plywood & millwork

(G-8036)
FLEETPRIDE INC
P D C
4050 Corporate Dr Ste 400 (76051-2308)
PHONE....................................800 549-7278
Greg Wagner, *Branch Mgr*
EMP: 45 **Privately Held**
WEB: www.fleetpride.com
SIC: **5013** 3711 Truck parts & accessories;
truck & tractor truck assembly
HQ: Fleetpride, Inc.
600 Las Colinas Blvd E # 400
Irving TX 75039
469 249-7500

(G-8037)
GAME DAY SPORTS APPAREL
LLC
Also Called: Gsa
2140 Hall Johnson Rd # 1 (76051-8753)
PHONE....................................214 499-0028
Rohan Amrstrong, *President*
Rohan Armstrong, *President*
Scot Whaley, *Vice Pres*
Blake Armstrong, *Finance*
EMP: 50
SALES (est): 1MM **Privately Held**
SIC: **2389** Apparel & accessories

(G-8038)
GAMESTOP CORP (PA)
625 Westport Pkwy (76051-6740)
PHONE....................................817 424-2000
George E Sherman, *CEO*
Daniel A Dematteo, *Ch of Bd*
Cathy Preston, *Publisher*
Isaias Quintana, *General Mgr*
Todd Andresen, *District Mgr*
▲ EMP: 120
SQ FT: 519,000
SALES: 6.4B **Publicly Held**
WEB: www.gamestop.com
SIC: **5734** 5932 2721 5945 Computer &
software stores; software, computer
games; computer software & accessories;
used merchandise stores; computers &
accessories, secondhand; magazines:
publishing only, not printed on site; dolls &
accessories

(G-8039)
GAMESTOP HOLDINGS CORP
625 Westport Pkwy (76051-6740)
PHONE....................................817 424-2159
R Richard Fontaine, *CEO*
Daniel De Matteo, *Ch of Bd*
David W Carlson, *CFO*
Michael N Rosen, *Admin Sec*
EMP: 279
SQ FT: 250,000
SALES (est): 32.3MM **Publicly Held**
WEB: www.gamestop.com
SIC: **5961** 5734 5932 2721 Computer
software, mail order; computer & software
stores; used merchandise stores; maga-
zines: publishing only, not printed on site;
video games
HQ: Electronics Boutique America, Inc
625 Westport Pkwy
Grapevine TX 76051
817 424-2000

(G-8040)
GEM-TECH INC (PA)
Also Called: G T Products
501 Industrial Blvd (76051-3913)
PHONE....................................817 329-3586
Gary Mellema, *President*
Lari Ann Mellema, *Vice Pres*
Kimbelry Adams, *Personnel*
▲ EMP: 29
SQ FT: 55,000
SALES (est): 15.5MM **Privately Held**
WEB: www.gtproducts.com
SIC: **5162** 2821 Plastics products; plastics
materials & resins

(G-8041)
GRIFFITHS CORPORATION
Also Called: Wrico Stamping of Texas
650 Industrial Blvd (76051-3916)
PHONE....................................817 488-6547
David Wall, *Plant Supt*
Carole Fotoiuhi, *Office Mgr*
Kenton Kirkpatrick, *Manager*
Joyce Price, *Executive*

Jody Harper, *Administration*
EMP: 70
SALES (corp-wide): 147.9MM **Privately**
Held
WEB: www.griffithscorp.com
SIC: **3469** Stamping metal for the trade
HQ: Griffiths Corporation
2717 Niagara Ln N
Minneapolis MN 55447
763 557-8935

(G-8042)
GT PRODUCTS INC
501 Industrial Blvd (76051-3913)
PHONE....................................817 481-7113
Gary Mellema, *President*
Lari Ann Mellema, *Vice Pres*
EMP: 20
SQ FT: 12,500
SALES (est): 3.1MM
SALES (corp-wide): 15.5MM **Privately**
Held
WEB: www.gtproducts.com
SIC: **2869** Silicones
PA: Gem-Tech, Inc.
501 Industrial Blvd
Grapevine TX 76051
817 329-3586

(G-8043)
INTERNATIONAL AIRMOTIVE
HOLDG (HQ)
900 Nolen Dr Ste 100 (76051-8641)
PHONE....................................214 956-3000
Hugh McElory, *President*
Douglas Meador, *CFO*
EMP: 12
SALES (est): 18.4MM
SALES (corp-wide): 2.2B **Privately Held**
WEB: www.dallasairmotive.com
SIC: **7699** 3724 Aircraft & heavy equip-
ment repair services; aircraft engines &
engine parts
PA: Signature Aviation Plc
105 Wigmore Street
London W1U 1
207 514-3999

(G-8044)
INTERTECH FLUID POWER INC
151 Central Ave (76051-6229)
P.O. Box 3018 (76099-3018)
PHONE....................................817 329-9733
William Buhrkuhl, *President*
EMP: 9
SQ FT: 7,200
SALES (est): 2.3MM **Privately Held**
WEB: www.intertechfluidpower.com
SIC: **3594** 5084 Pumps, hydraulic, aircraft;
pumps, hydraulic power transfer; indus-
trial machinery & equipment

(G-8045)
KMT WIRELESS LLC
Also Called: Cynergy
4055 Corporate Dr Ste 400 (76051-2307)
PHONE....................................817 591-4600
Darin Mickel, *CEO*
John Maeng, *Human Resources*
Rachael Webb, *Human Resources*
Justin Chastang, *Manager*
EMP: 350
SQ FT: 99,000
SALES (est): 59MM **Privately Held**
WEB: www.cynergyus.com
SIC: **3663** Radio & TV communications
equipment

(G-8046)
N 2 THE WORLD
3510 Hightimber Dr (76051-6824)
PHONE....................................817 424-0799
Melodie L Hrabak, *Owner*
Melodie Hrabak, *Owner*
EMP: 25
SALES (est): 1.1MM **Privately Held**
SIC: **2211** Apparel & outerwear fabrics,
cotton

(G-8047)
OFFSHORE WIND POWER
SYSTEMS OF
1210 Woodmoor Ct (76051-5073)
PHONE....................................682 367-0652
Douglas Hines, *President*
John Knouse, *Vice Pres*

Gene Niswander, *CFO*
EMP: 10
SALES (est): 598.7K **Privately Held**
WEB: www.offshorewindpowersystemsoft-
exas.com
SIC: **3531** Marine related equipment

(G-8048)
OLD CASTLE APG WEST
Also Called: Jewell, An Oldcastle Company
2561 Sw Grapevine Pkwy # 200
(76051-1002)
PHONE....................................844 576-1364
Dan Hamblen, *Principal*
EMP: 100
SALES (est): 6.9MM **Privately Held**
SIC: **3241** Masonry cement

(G-8049)
OLDCASTLE APG TEXAS INC
(DH)
Also Called: Jewell Concrete Products
2561 Sw Grapevine Pkwy # 200
(76051-1005)
PHONE....................................817 545-8325
Joe Mc Cullough, *Ch of Bd*
Wade Ficklin, *President*
Russell Rumley, *CFO*
Keith A Haas, *Director*
▲ EMP: 40
SALES (est): 17.6MM
SALES (corp-wide): 30.6B **Privately Held**
WEB: www.jewellcp.com
SIC: **3271** 5031 Blocks, concrete or cin-
der: standard; metal doors, sash & trim
HQ: Crh Americas, Inc.
900 Ashwood Pkwy Ste 600
Atlanta GA 30338
770 804-3363

(G-8050)
ORORA NORTH AMERICA
Also Called: Landsberg Dallas Div 1053
4151 State Hwy 121 N (76051)
PHONE....................................972 724-2828
Matt Jones, *Division Mgr*
Lesa Alexander, *Opers Mgr*
Michael Reid, *Warehouse Mgr*
John Demmer, *Buyer*
Jai Iyengar, *Buyer*
EMP: 50 **Privately Held**
WEB: www.ororagroup.com
SIC: **5113** 2653 Paper & products, wrap-
ping or coarse; boxes, corrugated: made
from purchased materials
HQ: Orora Packaging Solutions
6600 Valley View St
Buena Park CA 90620
714 562-6000

(G-8051)
PAVESTONE LLC
3215 State Highway 360 (76051-4338)
P.O. Box 1868 (76099-1868)
PHONE....................................817 481-5802
Tom Davis, *Manager*
EMP: 75 **Privately Held**
WEB: www.pavestone.com
SIC: **3272** Concrete products, precast
HQ: Pavestone, Llc
5 Concourse Pkwy Ste 1900
Atlanta GA 30328
404 926-3167

(G-8052)
ROCKWELL MEDICAL TECH INC
4051 Freport Pkwy Ste 100 (76051)
PHONE....................................972 874-2130
Robert Chioini, *CEO*
Tom Kleema, *CFO*
▼ EMP: 20
SALES (est): 3.3MM **Privately Held**
SIC: **3841** Surgical & medical instruments

(G-8053)
SAM GROUP INC
Also Called: Valley View Productions
213 E Northwest Hwy (76051-3332)
PHONE....................................817 481-1968
Stan Maddox, *President*
Alice Maddox, *Vice Pres*
Nathan Dimiceli, *Prdtn Mgr*
Daniel Dehart, *Graphic Designe*
EMP: 11
SQ FT: 4,000

SALES (est): 1.4MM **Privately Held**
WEB: www.thetshirtguys.com
SIC: **2261** 7389 5199 Screen printing of
cotton broadwoven fabrics; embroidering
of advertising on shirts, etc.; advertising
specialties

(G-8054)
SOFT AIR USA INC
4265 Trade Center Dr # 130 (76051-2336)
PHONE....................................817 717-4300
Joseph C Huston, *CEO*
John S Steele, *President*
Kevin Franklin, *Vice Pres*
Will Kilgore, *Opers-Prdtn-Mfg*
▲ EMP: 11
SQ FT: 3,600
SALES (est): 20.6MM **Privately Held**
WEB: www.unitedstatesairsoft.com
SIC: **3944** Toy guns

(G-8055)
SSB MANUFACTURING
COMPANY
4255 Patriot Dr Ste 100 (76051-2304)
P.O. Box 619062, Dallas (75261-9062)
PHONE....................................972 874-9666
Jim Vanlear, *Manager*
EMP: 300 **Privately Held**
WEB: www.simmons.com
SIC: **5172** 2515 Gases, liquefied petro-
leum (propane); mattresses & bedsprings
HQ: Ssb Manufacturing Company
2451 Industry Ave
Doraville GA 30360
770 512-7700

(G-8056)
TAHWAHKARO DISTILLING CO
LLC
541 Industrial Blvd Ste C (76051-8636)
PHONE....................................479 871-2565
Justin Jackson, *Manager*
EMP: 9 EST: 2018
SALES (est): 879.3K **Privately Held**
SIC: **2085** Bourbon whiskey

(G-8057)
THIEL CO
531 Industrial Blvd (76051-3913)
PHONE....................................817 310-3110
Jesse Perez, *General Mgr*
EMP: 10 **Privately Held**
SIC: **3699** 1731 Electrical equipment &
supplies; electrical work
PA: Thiel Co
2470 Gray Falls Dr # 170
Houston TX 77077

(G-8058)
TRESU ROYSE INC
Also Called: Tresu Americas
635 Westport Pkwy Ste 300 (76051-6747)
PHONE....................................214 631-2844
Harry Royse, *Ch of Bd*
Kurt Jensen, *President*
Steffan Rasmussen, *Business Mgr*
Clint Craig, *Purch Mgr*
Jan Larsen, *Technical Mgr*
▲ EMP: 43
SALES (est): 9.7MM **Privately Held**
WEB: www.tresuroyse-webshop.com
SIC: **3555** 3585 Printing trades machinery;
refrigeration & heating equipment
HQ: Tresu A/S
Venusvej 44
Kolding
763 235-00

(G-8059)
VIEWCASTCOM INC (PA)
756 Port America Pl # 400 (76051-7655)
PHONE....................................972 488-7200
Lance E Ouellette, *Ch of Bd*
Jeffrey A Kopang, *VP Mktg*
Adrian Guihat, *Officer*
EMP: 37
SQ FT: 18,676
SALES: 12.1MM **Publicly Held**
WEB: www.viewcast.com
SIC: **3577** 3572 7372 Computer periph-
eral equipment; computer storage de-
vices; disk drives, computer; prepackaged
software

(G-8060)
WILBERT BURIAL VAULT CORP
Also Called: A and W Industry
827 Dawn Ln (76051-4124)
P.O. Box 130 (76099-0130)
PHONE..............................817 481-3577
George Humberto, *President*
EMP: 30
SALES (est) 2MM **Privately Held**
SIC: 3272 Burial vaults, concrete or pre-cast terrazzo

Greenville
Hunt County

(G-8061)
AB MAURI FOOD INC
Also Called: Fleishmanns Yeast
6311 Industrial Dr (75402-5718)
P.O. Box 1052 (75403-1052)
PHONE..............................903 454-3891
Carolyn Coopland, *Branch Mgr*
EMP: 38
SALES (corp-wide): 18.2B **Privately Held**
WEB: www.abmna.com
SIC: 2051 2099 Bread, cake & related products; food preparations
HQ: Ab Mauri Food Inc.
4240 Duncan Ave Ste 150
Saint Louis MO 63110
314 392-0800

(G-8062)
ATRIUM EXTRUSION SYSTEMS INC
1001 Ed Rutherford Dr (75402-5701)
PHONE..............................903 455-8560
Kevin P O'Meara, *Director*
Wayne C Terry, *Director*
EMP: 3875
SALES (est): 221.7K
SALES (corp-wide): 459.8MM **Privately Held**
SIC: 3089 Injection molded finished plastic products
PA: Atrium Corporation
959 Profit Dr
Dallas TX 75247
214 583-1543

(G-8063)
BALFOUR SCHOLASTIC SCHOOL SUP
2511 Ridgecrest Rd (75402-6457)
P.O. Box 8429 (75404-8429)
PHONE..............................903 455-4556
Donald Barker, *Owner*
EMP: 10
SALES (est): 715.2K **Privately Held**
WEB: www.balfour4u.com
SIC: 3911 Jewelry, precious metal

(G-8064)
BARMAC LLC
8916 Wesley St (75402-3836)
PHONE..............................903 454-3166
Jennifer Barrow, *Principal*
EMP: 9 EST: 2011
SALES (est): 796.8K **Privately Held**
WEB: www.barrowmotors.com
SIC: 2085 Cocktails, alcoholic

(G-8065)
BONUS CROP FERTILIZER INC
Also Called: B C F Products
5903 Hwy 66 (75402-5907)
P.O. Box 1062 (75403-1062)
PHONE..............................903 455-9439
W D Barton Jr, *CEO*
H S Barton, *President*
Steve Barton, *President*
Bruce C Richardson, *Vice Pres*
Bruce Richardson, *Vice Pres*
EMP: 45 EST: 1973
SQ FT: 3,000
SALES (est): 8.4MM **Privately Held**
WEB: www.bcfproducts.com
SIC: 2875 5191 Fertilizers, mixing only; chemicals, agricultural

(G-8066)
CASSCOM MEDIA LP
6000 Industrial Dr (75402-5709)
PHONE..............................903 455-2555
Dwain Moyer, *Partner*
Ollie Moyer, *General Ptnr*
▲ EMP: 13
SALES (est): 2.3MM **Privately Held**
WEB: www.casscommedia.com
SIC: 3652 Compact laser discs, prere-corded

(G-8067)
COMPASS METERING SOLUTIONS
5217 County Road 2208 (75402-5024)
PHONE..............................972 834-5479
Bob Asmondy, *President*
Alex Wright, *Vice Pres*
Robert C Asmondy, *Exec Dir*
EMP: 40
SALES (est): 5.7MM **Privately Held**
WEB: www.cmsmeter.com
SIC: 3825 Instruments to measure electricity

(G-8068)
CYTEC ENGINEERED MATERIALS INC
4300 Jackson St (75402-5721)
PHONE..............................903 457-8500
Robin Prokop, *Branch Mgr*
EMP: 225
SQ FT: 140,000
SALES (corp-wide): 13.8MM **Privately Held**
WEB: www.solvay.com
SIC: 3365 2821 Aerospace castings, aluminum; plastics materials & resins
HQ: Cytec Engineered Materials Inc.
2085 E Tech Cir Ste 102
Tempe AZ 85284

(G-8069)
CYTEC INDUSTRIES INC
Also Called: Cytec Aerospace Materials
4300 Jackson St (75402-5721)
PHONE..............................903 454-2004
James Gumpert, *Plant Mgr*
Jeffrey Scott, *Plant Mgr*
Eric Cui, *Engineer*
Robert Doggett, *Engineer*
Randy Inwood, *Engineer*
EMP: 1350
SALES (corp-wide): 13.8MM **Privately Held**
WEB: www.solvay.com
SIC: 2899 Chemical preparations
HQ: Cytec Industries Inc.
4500 Mcginnis Ferry Rd
Alpharetta GA 30005

(G-8070)
DAL-TEX SPECIALTY & MFG CO
174 County Road 3318 (75402-5242)
PHONE..............................903 883-3689
James Carr, *Manager*
EMP: 10
SALES (corp-wide): 3.1MM **Privately Held**
WEB: www.dallasspecialty.com
SIC: 3088 3432 Plastics plumbing fixtures; plumbing fixture fittings & trim
PA: Dal-Tex Specialty & Manufacturing Co.
1161 Ruggles St
Grand Prairie TX 75050
972 641-8444

(G-8071)
DVE MANAGEMENT INC
Also Called: One Source Energy Services
2824 Terrell Rd Ste 406 (75402-5571)
P.O. Box 9226 (75404-9226)
PHONE..............................214 957-1095
David Carr, *President*
EMP: 45
SQ FT: 3,200
SALES (est): 10MM **Privately Held**
WEB: www.onesourcees.com
SIC: 1389 Pipe testing, oil field service

(G-8072)
FIBERGRATE COMPOSITE
900 Fm 205 (75401)
PHONE..............................254 965-3148

William C Coonrod, *Branch Mgr*
EMP: 78
SALES (corp-wide): 5.5B **Publicly Held**
WEB: www.fibergrate.com
SIC: 3089 Plastic & fiberglass tanks
HQ: Fibergrate Composite Structures Incorporated
5151 Belt Line Rd Ste 700
Dallas TX 75254

(G-8073)
FLIP MANUFACTURING
4410 Ed Rutherford Rd (75402-5702)
PHONE..............................903 454-1538
Dylan Knight, *Managing Prtnr*
Daniel Gill, *Principal*
▲ EMP: 9 EST: 2012
SALES (est): 563.5K **Privately Held**
WEB: www.flipmfg.com
SIC: 3999 Manufacturing industries

(G-8074)
FREEMAN METAL PRODUCTS INC
Also Called: F & F Metal Products
4410 Ed Rutherford Rd (75402-5702)
PHONE..............................877 278-2275
Fax: 903 454-4554
EMP: 30
SALES (corp-wide): 6.8MM **Privately Held**
SIC: 3995 Manufactures Caskets
PA: Freeman Metal Products, Inc.
2124 Us Highway 13 S
Ahoskie NC 27910
252 332-5390

(G-8075)
FRITZ INDUSTRIES INC
6902 Hwy 66 (75402-5817)
PHONE..............................214 244-7822
EMP: 178
SALES (corp-wide): 136.4MM **Privately Held**
SIC: 2899 Mfg Chemical Preparations
PA: Fritz Industries, Inc.
500 N Sam Houston Rd
Mesquite TX 75149
972 285-5471

(G-8076)
GREENVILLE TRANSFORMER CO
1807 Church St (75401-3519)
P.O. Box 845 (75403-0845)
PHONE..............................903 455-1610
Billie Pickens, *President*
Kelly E Pickens, *Corp Secy*
Steve Pickens, *Exec VP*
EMP: 21
SQ FT: 14,000
SALES (est): 4.6MM **Privately Held**
WEB: www.greenvilletransformer.com
SIC: 3612 7629 Voltage regulating transformers, electric power; electrical equipment repair, high voltage

(G-8077)
INTERNTIONAL GRAINS CEREAL LLC
6902 Hwy 66 (75402-5817)
PHONE..............................903 554-1003
Jose Anzola, *Mng Member*
◆ EMP: 50
SALES: 34.6MM **Privately Held**
SIC: 2046 Corn milling by-products
HQ: Alimentos Polar International Inc.
6902 Hwy 66
Greenville TX 75402
903 456-6613

(G-8078)
JARDEN LLC
7000 Industrial Dr (75402-5713)
PHONE..............................903 455-0691
Mike Day, *Branch Mgr*
EMP: 165
SALES (corp-wide): 9.7B **Publicly Held**
WEB: www.newellbrands.com
SIC: 3221 Food containers, glass
HQ: Jarden Llc
221 River St
Hoboken NJ 07030

(G-8079)
JOE ROSS
Also Called: Cleanroom Certification Cnstr
5430 Fm 118 (75401-6162)
PHONE..............................903 450-9960
Joe Ross, *Owner*
EMP: 15
SALES (est): 1.7MM **Privately Held**
SIC: 3826 7532 Environmental testing equipment; top & body repair & paint shops

(G-8080)
L3 TECHNOLOGIES INC
CSB Sector
10001 Jack Finney Blvd (75402-3119)
PHONE..............................903 457-4100
John McNellis, *President*
Claude Tignor, *Project Engr*
Keith Winters, *Accounting Mgr*
Angela Lassiter, *Manager*
Christin Campbell, *Director*
EMP: 4627
SALES (corp-wide): 11.3B **Publicly Held**
WEB: www.l3t.com
SIC: 8732 3812 3699 8711 Business economic service; navigational systems & instruments; electrical equipment & supplies; engineering services
HQ: L3 Technologies, Inc.
600 3rd Ave Fl 34
New York NY 10016
212 805-5234

(G-8081)
L3HARRIS TECHNOLOGIES INC
10001 Jack Finney Blvd (75402-3119)
PHONE..............................903 457-7461
Mark Von Schwarz, *Branch Mgr*
EMP: 4627
SALES (corp-wide): 11.3B **Publicly Held**
WEB: www.l3t.com
SIC: 3663 3812 3699 8711 Telemetering equipment, electronic; aircraft/aerospace flight instruments & guidance systems; electrical equipment & supplies; engineering services
PA: L3harris Technologies, Inc.
1025 W Nasa Blvd
Melbourne FL 32919
321 727-9100

(G-8082)
LEKTROTECH INC
Also Called: Williams & Davis Boilers
6800 Highway 66 (75402-5816)
PHONE..............................972 225-2356
Jimmie Caradine, *CEO*
Jarvis Caradine, *President*
Jim Caradine, *Owner*
EMP: 12 EST: 2011
SALES (est): 1.8MM **Privately Held**
WEB: www.w-dboilers.com
SIC: 3443 Finned tubes, for heat transfer; boiler & boiler shop work; economizers (boilers); heat exchangers: coolers (after, inter), condensers, etc.

(G-8083)
LONGHORN LEATHER CO
1909 Interstate Hwy 30 W (75402-4665)
PHONE..............................903 454-4866
Thomas Major, *Manager*
EMP: 34
SALES (est): 1.4MM **Privately Held**
SIC: 5941 3172 Saddlery & equestrian equipment; personal leather goods

(G-8084)
MASONITE INTERNATIONAL CORP
6308 Industrial Dr (75402-5712)
P.O. Box 1887 (75403-1887)
PHONE..............................903 454-9500
James Walters, *Mktg Dir*
Steve Maulsby, *Manager*
EMP: 40
SALES (corp-wide): 2.1B **Publicly Held**
WEB: www.masonite.com
SIC: 2431 Doors, wood
PA: Masonite International Corporation
1242 E 5th Ave
Tampa FL 33605
800 895-2723

(G-8085)
NEWSPAPER HOLDING INC
Also Called: Herald Banner
2305 King St (75401-3257)
P.O. Box 6000 (75403-6000)
PHONE..........................903 455-4220
David Claybourn, *Editor*
Cliff Gibson, *Editor*
Warren Morrison, *Editor*
Daniel Walker, *Editor*
Deneen Lopez, *Advt Staff*
EMP: 35
SQ FT: 22,000
SALES (corp-wide): 23.7B **Privately Held**
WEB: www.oskaloosa.com
SIC: 2711 Newspapers, publishing & printing
HQ: Newspaper Holding, Inc.
425 Locust St
Johnstown PA 15901
814 532-5102

(G-8086)
POLARA ENGINEERING INC
1497 County Road 2178 (75402-4941)
PHONE..........................951 547-5500
▲ **EMP:** 65 **EST:** 1963
SALES (est): 16.2MM **Privately Held**
WEB: www.polara.com
SIC: 3679 3677 Electronic circuits; electronic coils, transformers & other inductors

(G-8087)
POLARA ENTERPRISES LLC
1497 County Road 2178 (75402-4941)
PHONE..........................903 366-0300
John McGaffey, *President*
Cindy McGaffey, *Vice Pres*
Rkrista Pietersma, *Treasurer*
EMP: 10 **EST:** 2014
SALES (est): 1.8MM **Privately Held**
WEB: www.polara.com
SIC: 3679 Electronic circuits

(G-8088)
RACK SOLUTIONS INC
6725 Fm 1570 W (75402-3605)
PHONE..........................903 453-0800
Lawrence A Harris, *President*
Dennis Feeney, *Vice Pres*
Warren Weeks, *Vice Pres*
James Tonthat, *Engineer*
Carlos Valles, *Engineer*
▼ **EMP:** 15
SQ FT: 20,000
SALES (est): 3MM
SALES (corp-wide): 12.3MM **Privately Held**
WEB: www.racksolutions.com
SIC: 2511 Racks, book & magazine: wood
PA: Innovation First International, Inc.
6725 Fm 1570 W
Greenville TX 75402
903 453-0800

(G-8089)
ROCKING T SADDLERY
2210 Highway 34 N (75401-1751)
P.O. Box 8813 (75404-8813)
PHONE..........................903 455-6629
Sergio Lomeli, *Owner*
EMP: 10
SALES (est): 765.3K **Privately Held**
WEB: www.rockingtsaddlery.com
SIC: 3199 Saddles or parts

(G-8090)
ROYAL OAK ENTERPRISES LLC
7000 Industrial Dr (75402-5713)
PHONE..........................903 455-5803
Mike Day, *Plant Mgr*
EMP: 75
SALES (corp-wide): 262.3MM **Privately Held**
WEB: www.royaloak.com
SIC: 2899 Lighter fluid
PA: Royal Oak Enterprises, Llc
1 Royal Oak Ave
Roswell GA 30076
678 461-3200

(G-8091)
SHELBIS STUFF INC
Also Called: Luv Stuff
2310 Stonewall St (75401-3348)
P.O. Box 1376 (75403-1376)
PHONE..........................903 450-1300
Suzan Bjork, *President*
Pauline O'Neal, *Vice Pres*
EMP: 18 **EST:** 1978
SQ FT: 6,800
SALES (est): 1.5MM **Privately Held**
WEB: www.simplestuffbaby.com
SIC: 2392 5641 5719 Blankets, comforters & beddings; infants' wear; beddings & linens

(G-8092)
STROMBERG ARCHITECTURAL PRODUC
2142 County Road 3124 (75402-4030)
PHONE..........................903 454-0904
Lyndon D Stromberg, *Branch Mgr*
EMP: 59
SALES (corp-wide): 12.8MM **Privately Held**
WEB: www.strombergarchitectural.com
SIC: 3272 Concrete products
PA: Stromberg Architectural Products Southeast Inc.
4400 Oneal St
Greenville TX 75401
903 454-8682

(G-8093)
STROMBERG ARCHTCTRAL PDTS STHA (PA)
Also Called: Strombergs Architectural Pdts
4400 Oneal St (75401-7018)
P.O. Box 8036 (75404-8036)
PHONE..........................903 454-8682
Phyllis Stromberg, *President*
Marta Blackwell, *Finance Mgr*
Julie Schuessler, *Sr Project Mgr*
Phillip Stromberg, *Info Tech Dir*
Lyndon Stromberg, *Director*
◆ **EMP:** 40
SQ FT: 45,000
SALES (est): 12.8MM **Privately Held**
WEB: www.strombergarchitectural.com
SIC: 3272 Concrete products

(G-8094)
TEXAS INDUSTRIES INC
Also Called: T X I
6500 Fm 1570 W (75402-3649)
P.O. Box 595, Wills Point (75169-0595)
PHONE..........................903 454-2029
Jerry Mills, *Manager*
EMP: 14 **Publicly Held**
WEB: www.martinmarietta.com
SIC: 3273 3271 Ready-mixed concrete; blocks, concrete or cinder: standard
HQ: Texas Industries, Inc.
1503 Lyndon B Johnson Fwy
Dallas TX 75234
972 647-6700

(G-8095)
WEATHERFORD INTERNATIONAL LLC
6325 Highway 380 W (75401-9407)
PHONE..........................661 589-2146
Daniel Erbs, *Branch Mgr*
EMP: 40 **Privately Held**
WEB: www.weatherford.com
SIC: 1389 Oil field services
HQ: Weatherford International, Llc
2000 Saint James Pl
Houston TX 77056
713 693-4000

(G-8096)
WESTROCK RKT LLC
Also Called: Rock-Tenn Folding Carton
6702 Hwy 66 (75402-5815)
PHONE..........................903 455-0147
Jim Rubright, *Branch Mgr*
EMP: 120
SALES (corp-wide): 17.5B **Publicly Held**
WEB: www.westrock.com
SIC: 2631 2657 Container board; folding paperboard boxes

HQ: Westrock Rkt, Llc
1000 Abernathy Rd Ste 125
Atlanta GA 30328
770 448-2193

(G-8097)
WHITEHAWK MACHINE & TOOLS INC
6008 Hwy 66 (75402-5808)
PHONE..........................903 450-1060
Olyn Whitaker, *President*
Loyal H Whitaker, *Vice Pres*
EMP: 9
SQ FT: 9,500
SALES (est): 500K **Privately Held**
SIC: 3599 Machine shop, jobbing & repair

Gregory
San Patricio County

(G-8098)
ALLIED ALUMINA GROUP INC
Also Called: Sherwin Alumina Company Div
4633 Hwy 361 (78359)
PHONE..........................361 777-2400
Houshang Shams, *CEO*
Peter Bailey, *President*
▲ **EMP:** 170 **EST:** 2000
SALES (est): 44MM
SALES (corp-wide): 215.1B **Privately Held**
WEB: www.sherwinalumina.com
SIC: 3444 Sheet metal specialties, not stamped
HQ: Glencore Ag
Baarermattstrasse 3
Baar ZG 6340
417 092-000

(G-8099)
BRADLEYS INC
600 E Hwy 35 (78359)
P.O. Box 308 (78359-0308)
PHONE..........................361 643-0100
Jimmie L Williams Jr, *President*
Gary Castle, *Electrical Engi*
Alex Trevino, *Sales Mgr*
Lola Williams, *Marketing Mgr*
▲ **EMP:** 60
SQ FT: 90,000
SALES (est): 15.6MM **Privately Held**
WEB: www.bradleysinc.com
SIC: 7694 Electric motor repair

(G-8100)
CORPUS CHRISTI PIPELINE GP LLC
554 Hwy 35 (78359)
PHONE..........................713 375-5000
Stanley C Horton,
EMP: 200
SALES (est): 100.4K
SALES (corp-wide): 9.7B **Publicly Held**
WEB: www.cheniere.com
SIC: 1321 Liquefied petroleum gases (natural) production
PA: Cheniere Energy, Inc.
700 Milam St Ste 1900
Houston TX 77002
713 375-5000

(G-8101)
MERRELL LEASE SERVICE INC
610 N Ave D (78359)
P.O. Box 404 (78359-0404)
PHONE..........................361 643-6911
Gary Merrell, *President*
Debra E Harris, *Corp Secy*
EMP: 53
SQ FT: 2,400
SALES (est): 9.6MM **Privately Held**
SIC: 1389 1623 1611 Oil & gas wells: building, repairing & dismantling; oil field services; oil & gas pipeline construction; highway & street construction

(G-8102)
NASHTEC LLC
4633 Hwy 361 (78359)
PHONE..........................361 777-2280
Robert Barnes, *President*
▼ **EMP:** 22

SALES (est): 131.2MM
SALES (corp-wide): 202.3MM **Privately Held**
SIC: 2819 Industrial inorganic chemicals
PA: Nabaltec Ag
Alustr. 50-52
Schwandorf 92421
943 153-0

(G-8103)
OCCIDENTAL CHEMICAL CORP
4133 Hwy 361 (78359)
PHONE..........................361 776-6000
David Crawford, *Branch Mgr*
EMP: 12
SALES (corp-wide): 21.2B **Publicly Held**
WEB: www.oxy.com
SIC: 2812 Chlorine, compressed or liquefied
HQ: Occidental Chemical Corporation
14555 Dallas Pkwy Ste 400
Dallas TX 75254
972 404-3800

(G-8104)
REYNOLDS METALS COMPANY LLC
Also Called: Alcoa
4633 Hwy 361 (78359)
PHONE..........................361 777-2200
Frank Newchurch, *Manager*
EMP: 656
SALES (corp-wide): 10.4B **Publicly Held**
SIC: 3411 Aluminum cans
HQ: Reynolds Metals Company, Llc
390 Park Ave
New York NY 10022
212 518-5400

(G-8105)
SHERWIN ALUMINA COMPANY LLC
4633 Hwy 361 (78359)
PHONE..........................361 777-2200
Tom Russell,
◆ **EMP:** 550
SALES (est): 205.9MM **Privately Held**
WEB: www.sherwinalumina.com
SIC: 2819 Aluminum oxide

(G-8106)
TEDA TPCO AMERICA CORPORATION
Also Called: Blessings Womans Care
5431 Highway 35 (78359-2003)
PHONE..........................361 826-2610
Daryl Downs, *General Mgr*
Barnabus Chen, *Accountant*
Justin Cook, *Administration*
Mauro Rodriguez, *Assistant*
EMP: 20 **Privately Held**
WEB: www.tpcoamerica.com
SIC: 3317 Tubes, seamless steel
HQ: Teda Tpco America Corporation
10700 Richmond Ave # 302
Houston TX 77042
361 704-8101

Groesbeck
Limestone County

(G-8107)
DUGAN TRAILER
1326 Highway 164 W (76642-3540)
PHONE..........................254 729-3253
James Dugan, *Owner*
EMP: 18
SQ FT: 800
SALES (est): 172.4K **Privately Held**
SIC: 3523 Trailers & wagons, farm

(G-8108)
S & S MCHINING FABRICATION INC
1331 N Highway 14 (76642-2567)
P.O. Box 637 (76642-0637)
PHONE..........................254 729-3685
Tracey Sims, *President*
Ronnie Sims, *Vice Pres*
EMP: 20
SQ FT: 8,650

▲ = Import ▼=Export
◆ =Import/Export

SALES (est): 3.3MM **Privately Held**
WEB: www.sandsmachining.com
SIC: 3599 Machine shop, jobbing & repair

Groves
Jefferson County

(G-8109)
LINDE INC
Also Called: Praxair
6710 Hogaboom Rd (77619-6039)
PHONE..........................409 963-0141
David Droste, *Engineer*
Ross Vaughn, *Branch Mgr*
EMP: 17 **Privately Held**
WEB: www.praxair.com
SIC: 2813 Industrial gases
HQ: Linde Inc.
10 Riverview Dr
Danbury CT 06810
203 837-2000

(G-8110)
**SOUTHERN MANUFACTURING
CO LLC**
6287 Gulfway Dr (77619-4220)
P.O. Box 790 (77619-0790)
PHONE..........................409 962-4501
Valeri Chelette,
EMP: 20
SQ FT: 22,500
SALES (est): 172.9K **Privately Held**
SIC: 3089 Septic tanks, plastic

(G-8111)
SUPERIOR ENERGIES INC (PA)
3115 Main Ave (77619-4410)
P.O. Box 386 (77619-0386)
PHONE..........................409 962-8549
Sean A Scott, *President*
Betty Scott Washenfelder, *Vice Pres*
Brenda McKee, *Office Mgr*
◆ EMP: 50
SQ FT: 50,000
SALES (est): 9.9MM **Privately Held**
WEB: www.insulationsei.com
SIC: 3296 1742 Fiberglass insulation; insulation, buildings

Groveton
Trinity County

(G-8112)
DEAN DUE LOGGING INC
1180 Rainey Ave (75845-2400)
P.O. Box 1155 (75845-1155)
PHONE..........................936 642-2782
Dean Due, *President*
EMP: 15
SALES (est): 1.4MM **Privately Held**
SIC: 2411 Logging camps & contractors

(G-8113)
**TEXAS CONCRETE CHEMICAL
INC**
Also Called: Tcc
7780 Grvton Flat Prrie Rd (75845-3628)
PHONE..........................936 638-4273
EMP: 20 EST: 1980
SQ FT: 60,000
SALES (est): 1.1MM **Privately Held**
SIC: 3272 5169 Mfg Concrete Products

Gun Barrel City
Henderson County

(G-8114)
FORM AND FIBER INC
538 Welch Ln (75156-4159)
PHONE..........................888 314-8852
EMP: 12
SALES (est): 1.2MM **Privately Held**
WEB: www.formandfiber.com
SIC: 3499 3272 Concrete work

Gunter
Grayson County

(G-8115)
**GUNTER LUMBER COMPANY
INC**
Also Called: Gunter Lumber & Mill
520 N Preston Rd (75058-4713)
PHONE..........................903 433-1303
Mark D Plumb, *President*
EMP: 21
SQ FT: 4,000
SALES (est): 2.6MM **Privately Held**
WEB: www.guntercabinets.com
SIC: 2431 5211 Millwork; millwork & lumber

(G-8116)
SMITH DESIGN AND MFG INC
208 E College St (75058-9726)
P.O. Box 187 (75058-0187)
PHONE..........................903 433-4444
Fax: 903 433-1111
EMP: 19 EST: 1999
SQ FT: 20,000
SALES: 2.1MM **Privately Held**
SIC: 2499 Mfg Wood Products

(G-8117)
STARTKLEEN LEGACY LLC
193 Wall Street Rd (75058-2031)
P.O. Box 302 (75058-0302)
PHONE..........................903 207-1079
Rebec: a Hudson, *Principal*
Jason Holcombe, *VP Bus Dvlpt*
EMP: 14
SALES (est): 2.9MM **Privately Held**
SIC: 2841 Soap & other detergents

Hale Center
Hale County

(G-8118)
**DELTA AND PINE LAND
COMPANY**
1596 I H 27 87 (79041-3804)
P.O. Box 60 (79041-0060)
PHONE..........................806 839-2491
Richard Sheets, *Manager*
EMP: 10
SALES (corp-wide): 48.1B **Privately Held**
WEB: www.dplmgtllc.com
SIC: 5191 2074 Seeds & bulbs; cottonseed oil, cake or meal
HQ: Delta And Pine Land Company
1 Cotton Row
Scott MS 38772
662 742-4000

Hallettsville
Lavaca County

(G-8119)
BLUDAU FABRICATION INC
431 County Rd 187 (77964)
P.O. Box 255 (77964-0255)
PHONE..........................361 798-4339
Anthony Bludau, *President*
Steve Bludau, *Vice Pres*
Frank Bludau, *Treasurer*
EMP: 33
SQ FT: 48,000
SALES (est): 14.7MM **Privately Held**
WEB: www.bludaufab.com
SIC: 3441 Building components, structural steel

(G-8120)
**CHANNL-TRACK TUBE-WAY
INDS INC**
Also Called: Fair-West Trailers
1411 Us Highway 90a W (77964-5730)
P.O. Box 345 (77964-0345)
PHONE..........................361 798-4979
Laurie Janak, *Manager*
EMP: 19

SALES (corp-wide): 21.4MM **Privately Held**
WEB: www.channel-track.com
SIC: 8611 3743 5599 3537 Trade associations; freight cars & equipment; utility trailers; industrial trucks & tractors
PA: Channel-Track & Tube-Way Industries, Inc.
1209 W 17th St
Houston TX 77008
713 864-2551

(G-8121)
**DUKE ENERGY NATURAL GAS
CORP**
404 Private Road 1045 (77964-4614)
P.O. Box Rr1 97 (77964)
PHONE..........................361 579-4600
Mim McClain, *Branch Mgr*
Dawn Jansky, *Manager*
EMP: 20 **Publicly Held**
SIC: 4922 2813 Pipelines, natural gas; industrial gases
HQ: Duke Energy Natural Gas Corporation
5400 Westheimer Ct
Houston TX 77056

(G-8122)
GLENS PACKING COMPANY INC
200 E 1st St (77964-2716)
P.O. Box 244 (77964-0244)
PHONE..........................361 798-2601
Harold Dolezal, *President*
Dolezal Glen H Jr, *Vice Pres*
EMP: 16
SQ FT: 5,000
SALES (est): 1.3MM **Privately Held**
WEB: www.glenspacking.com
SIC: 5421 2011 Meat markets, including freezer provisioners; meat packing plants

(G-8123)
JANAK PACKING INC
3116 Us Highway 90a W (77964-5756)
PHONE..........................361 798-2985
Leroy R Janak, *President*
Paul L Janak, *Vice Pres*
Magdalen Rehm, *Vice Pres*
Edna Janak, *Shareholder*
Mary Jane Rehm, *Admin Sec*
EMP: 9 EST: 1938
SQ FT: 4,800
SALES (est): 750K **Privately Held**
WEB: www.janakscountrymarket.com
SIC: 2011 5812 Bacon, slab & sliced from meat slaughtered on site; sausages from meat slaughtered on site; hams & picnics from meat slaughtered on site; cured meats from meat slaughtered on site; eating places

(G-8124)
**PEPSI-COLA METRO BTLG CO
INC**
Also Called: Pepsico
1415 Us Highway 90a E (77964)
PHONE..........................361 798-3651
Sam Bandana, *Manager*
EMP: 30
SALES (corp-wide): 67.1B **Publicly Held**
WEB: www.pepsico.com
SIC: 2086 5149 Soft drinks: packaged in cans, bottles, etc.; soft drinks
HQ: Pepsi-Cola Metropolitan Bottling Company, Inc.
1111 Westchester Ave
White Plains NY 10604
914 767-6000

(G-8125)
PRO FIELD SERVICES INC (PA)
212 E 2nd St (77964-2738)
P.O. Box 525 (77964-0525)
PHONE..........................361 798-5552
John A Davenport, *President*
Jess T Davenport, *Vice Pres*
Evelyn M Jansky, *Treasurer*
EMP: 30
SALES (est): 29.6MM **Privately Held**
WEB: www.profieldservices.com
SIC: 1389 Oil field services

Hallsville
Harrison County

(G-8126)
AUDEX INC (PA)
332 W Main St (75650-5256)
P.O. Box 1375 (75650-1375)
PHONE..........................903 757-4083
Charles W Beatty Jr, *President*
Vickie Beatty, *Marketing Staff*
EMP: 10 EST: 1950
SQ FT: 8,200
SALES (est): 783.8K **Privately Held**
WEB: www.audex.com
SIC: 3674 5999 Infrared sensors, solid state; hearing aids

(G-8127)
**BP AMERICA PRODUCTION
COMPANY**
Also Called: BP America East Texas
886 Finklea Rd (75650-7752)
PHONE..........................903 927-8999
Dick Moritz, *Manager*
EMP: 15
SALES (corp-wide): 278.4B **Privately Held**
WEB: www.bp.com
SIC: 1311 1321 Crude petroleum production; natural gas production; natural gas liquids
HQ: Bp America Production Company
501 Westlake Park Blvd
Houston TX 77079
281 366-2000

(G-8128)
**CHURCHILL MANUFACTURING
INC**
Also Called: Texas Marble Manufacturing
13062 I H 20 N Service Rd (75650-6358)
P.O. Box 749 (75650-0749)
PHONE..........................903 660-4585
Mark Churchill, *President*
Leslie Churchill, *Corp Secy*
Joan Copeland, *Vice Pres*
EMP: 13 EST: 1998
SQ FT: 2,000
SALES (est): 1.3MM **Privately Held**
WEB: www.texasmarble.com
SIC: 3281 Marble, building: cut & shaped

(G-8129)
MERIT ENERGY COMPANY LLC
886 Finklea Rd (75650-7752)
PHONE..........................903 923-7300
EMP: 15 **Privately Held**
WEB: www.meritenergy.com
SIC: 1311 Crude petroleum production
PA: Merit Energy Company, Llc
13737 Noel Rd Ste 1200
Dallas TX 75240

(G-8130)
SABINE MINING COMPANY
6501 Fm 968 W (75650-7800)
PHONE..........................903 660-4200
Clifford Miercort, *Ch of Bd*
Rick J Ziegler, *President*
K Donald Grischow, *Treasurer*
Thomas Koza, *Admin Sec*
John D Neumann, *Admin Sec*
▲ EMP: 163
SQ FT: 68,000
SALES: 154.6MM
SALES (corp-wide): 140.9MM **Publicly Held**
SIC: 1241 8711 1221 Mining services: lignite; engineering services; bituminous coal & lignite-surface mining
HQ: The North American Coal Corporation
5340 Legacy Dr Ste 300
Plano TX 75024
972 448-5400

Haltom City
Tarrant County

(G-8131)
A O SMITH WTR TRTMNT N AMER (HQ)
Also Called: Aquasana, Inc.
6310 Midway Rd (76117-5344)
PHONE....................817 536-5250
Todd Bartee, *CEO*
D Samuel Karge, *President*
Jay Martin, *COO*
Darrell Dreibrodt, *CFO*
Kate Kyle, *Marketing Staff*
◆ **EMP: 78 EST: 1997**
SQ FT: 50,000
SALES (est): 44MM
SALES (corp-wide): 2.9B Publicly Held
WEB: www.aquasana.com
SIC: 3589 Water filters & softeners, household type
PA: A. O. Smith Corporation
　11270 W Park Pl Ste 1200
　Milwaukee WI 53224
　414 359-4000

(G-8132)
ATS DRILLING LP
6559 Midway Rd (76117-5351)
P.O. Box 14633 (76117-0633)
PHONE....................817 498-0040
Fred S Shin, *Partner*
Bill Driesslein, *Partner*
Dave Hoag P E, *Partner*
Brent Lawler, *Partner*
Michael Martin, *Partner*
▲ **EMP: 75 EST: 2000**
SQ FT: 6,500
SALES (est): 15.2MM Privately Held
WEB: www.atsdrilling.com
SIC: 1771 1381 Foundation & footing contractor; drilling oil & gas wells; drilling water intake wells

(G-8133)
C & L MILLWORK INC
4237 Janada St (76117-1231)
PHONE....................817 605-0002
Chip Boelkins, *President*
Charles Boelkins, *President*
EMP: 9
SALES (est): 1.4MM Privately Held
WEB: www.clmillwork.com
SIC: 2426 5021 Furniture stock & parts, hardwood; furniture

(G-8134)
CARL KISABETH CO INC (PA)
Also Called: Kisabeth Furniture
5320 Glenview Dr (76117-1401)
PHONE....................817 281-7560
Keith Webster, *President*
Alan Novikoff, *General Mgr*
Mitchell Parr, *Director*
Laurel McEuen, *Creative Dir*
EMP: 35
SQ FT: 40,000
SALES (est): 5.8MM Privately Held
WEB: www.kisabethfurniture.com
SIC: 2512 5021 5131 Upholstered household furniture; household furniture; upholstery fabrics, woven

(G-8135)
CSB ENERGY TECH AMERICAS LTD
4008 Clay Ave Ste 210 (76117-1726)
PHONE....................817 244-7777
Wuihan Cheah, *Vice Pres*
Jackie Stanton, *Vice Pres*
Peggy Villagomez, *Director*
Jessica Pendleton, *Administration*
◆ **EMP: 28**
SQ FT: 30,000
SALES (est): 11.3MM Privately Held
WEB: www.hitachi-chem-en.com
SIC: 5063 3692 Batteries, dry cell; primary batteries, dry & wet
HQ: Csb Energy Technology Co., Ltd.
　11f, No. 150, Chengde Rd., Sec. 4
　Taipei City TAP 11167

(G-8136)
DAL-TILE CORPORATION
6323 Airport Fwy Ste A (76117-5304)
PHONE....................817 831-6935
Ben Redding, *Branch Mgr*
EMP: 11 Publicly Held
WEB: www.daltile.com
SIC: 2824 5032 Organic fibers, noncellulosic; ceramic wall & floor tile
HQ: Dal-Tile Corporation
　7834 C F Hawn Fwy
　Dallas TX 75217
　214 398-1411

(G-8137)
DALPACK
4400 Glenview Dr (76117-1819)
PHONE....................972 446-8101
Glenn Farkas, *Principal*
EMP: 10
SALES (est): 1.3MM Privately Held
SIC: 2671 Packaging paper & plastics film, coated & laminated

(G-8138)
ECOLAB INC
Also Called: Johnson Contrls Authorized Dlr
2121 Solona St (76117-5338)
PHONE....................817 916-9600
Keith Tadlock, *Branch Mgr*
EMP: 34
SALES (corp-wide): 14.9B Publicly Held
WEB: www.ecolab.com
SIC: 2841 5075 Soap & other detergents; warm air heating & air conditioning
PA: Ecolab Inc.
　1 Ecolab Pl
　Saint Paul MN 55102
　800 232-6522

(G-8139)
EMERGENCY VEHICLES TEXAS INC
6000 Huddleston St (76137-2214)
PHONE....................817 281-4172
Ed Beene, *President*
Patricia Beene, *Admin Sec*
EMP: 12
SQ FT: 13,000
SALES (est): 1.7MM Privately Held
WEB: www.evotexas.com
SIC: 5012 5013 3569 Ambulances; fire trucks; automotive supplies & parts; fire-fighting apparatus & related equipment

(G-8140)
F W PROMO
Also Called: Just Right Products
5941 Posey Ln (76117-5238)
PHONE....................817 231-8040
Marc E Johnson, *CEO*
John Howard, *Sales Staff*
EMP: 25 EST: 2010
SALES (est): 3.8MM Privately Held
WEB: www.fwpromo.com
SIC: 2759 Screen printing

(G-8141)
FORE MACHINE LLC
5933 Eden Dr (76117-6122)
PHONE....................817 834-6251
Stan Fore, *General Mgr*
Bill Foust, *Mfg Mgr*
Greg Bennett, *QC Mgr*
Gary Fore, *Financial Exec*
Dustin Ragsdale, *Manager*
EMP: 99
SALES (est): 3.7MM Privately Held
WEB: www.foreaero.com
SIC: 3724 3728 3364 Aircraft engines & engine parts; aircraft parts & equipment; nonferrous die-castings except aluminum

(G-8142)
GOODRICH CORPORATION
Also Called: Part of Collins Aerospace, A
4630 N Beach St Ste 104 (76137-3201)
PHONE....................682 730-4270
Karen Crawford, *Manager*
EMP: 198
SALES (corp-wide): 56.5B Publicly Held
WEB: www.collinsaerospace.com
SIC: 3728 Aircraft parts & equipment

HQ: Goodrich Corporation
　2730 W Tyvola Rd
　Charlotte NC 28217
　704 423-7000

(G-8143)
GP RUBBER LP
2211 Moneda St (76117-5311)
PHONE....................817 838-8222
David E Walstad, *Managing Prtnr*
Rob Harris, *General Mgr*
GP Rubber Mgmt LLC, *General Ptnr*
Nick Webster, *Design Engr*
EMP: 30
SQ FT: 10,000
SALES (est): 4.8MM Privately Held
WEB: www.gprubber.com
SIC: 3069 Rubber coated fabrics & clothing

(G-8144)
GREIF INC
Western Division
3800 N Beach St (76137-3203)
PHONE....................817 834-6333
George N Peterson, *Opers-Prdtn-Mfg*
EMP: 45
SQ FT: 64,924
SALES (corp-wide): 4.5B Publicly Held
WEB: www.deltacogroup.com
SIC: 2655 Drums, fiber: made from purchased material
PA: Greif, Inc.
　425 Winter Rd
　Delaware OH 43015
　740 549-6000

(G-8145)
GREIF INC
Greif Bros Eastern Division
3800 N Beach St (76137-3203)
PHONE....................817 222-0413
Richard Ledbetter, *Manager*
EMP: 30
SQ FT: 60,000
SALES (corp-wide): 4.5B Publicly Held
WEB: www.deltacogroup.com
SIC: 2655 Drums, fiber: made from purchased material
PA: Greif, Inc.
　425 Winter Rd
　Delaware OH 43015
　740 549-6000

(G-8146)
GST MANUFACTURING LTD
4201 Janada St (76117-1231)
PHONE....................817 335-1401
George Lamberth, *Partner*
Sharrian Lamberth, *Partner*
EMP: 124
SQ FT: 128,000
SALES (est): 399.7K Privately Held
WEB: www.gstmanufacturing.com
SIC: 1761 3444 Sheet metalwork; sheet metalwork

(G-8147)
GST MANUFACTURING LTD (PA)
Also Called: Clemens Sheet Metal Works
4201 Janada St (76117-1231)
PHONE....................817 520-2320
George Lamberth, *CEO*
Sherri Lamberth, *President*
Lamberth Sharrian, *Managing Prtnr*
David Nevins, *Superintendent*
Samuel Kerbel, *Vice Pres*
EMP: 30
SALES (est): 33.1MM Privately Held
WEB: www.gstmanufacturing.com
SIC: 3441 Fabricated structural metal

(G-8148)
HARRIS PACKAGING CORPORATION (PA)
1600 Carson St (76117-6188)
P.O. Box 14437 (76117-0437)
PHONE....................817 429-6262
Jana M Harris, *CEO*
Jenise R Cox, *Chairman*
Joe G Harris, *Exec VP*
Gerald Adams, *Vice Pres*
Harrell Bivens, *Vice Pres*
EMP: 100 EST: 1976
SQ FT: 164,000

SALES (est): 34.6MM Privately Held
WEB: www.harrispackaging.com
SIC: 2653 3086 Boxes, corrugated: made from purchased materials; packaging & shipping materials, foamed plastic

(G-8149)
KENNYS KUSTOM KARDS INC
5400 Airport Fwy Ste G (76117-5928)
PHONE....................817 332-8639
Kenny Line, *President*
John W Line, *Vice Pres*
EMP: 14
SQ FT: 8,000
SALES (est): 1.3MM Privately Held
WEB: www.kennyskustomkards.com
SIC: 2752 Commercial printing, offset

(G-8150)
LEWIS & LAMBERT LLLP
5936 Eden Dr (76117-6121)
P.O. Box 14439 (76117-0439)
PHONE....................817 834-7146
Alfred Leidner, *President*
Larry Brady, *Vice Pres*
Dennis Hacic, *Vice Pres*
Bill Morrow, *Vice Pres*
Mike Tankersley, *CFO*
EMP: 150
SQ FT: 77,500
SALES (est): 37.3MM Privately Held
WEB: www.lewisandlambert.com
SIC: 1711 3444 3545 Ventilation & duct work contractor; ducts, sheet metal; angle rings

(G-8151)
LIBERTY CARTON CO - TEXAS
Also Called: Liberty Packaging
5100 Glenview Dr (76117-1304)
PHONE....................817 577-6100
Michael Fiterman, *CEO*
Daniel Zdon, *COO*
David Lenzen, *Exec VP*
Ronda Bayer, *Vice Pres*
Byron Wieberdink, *CFO*
▲ **EMP: 200**
SQ FT: 191,000
SALES (est): 54.3MM
SALES (corp-wide): 382.4MM Privately Held
WEB: www.libertycartontx.com
SIC: 2653 Boxes, corrugated: made from purchased materials
PA: Liberty Diversified International, Inc.
　5600 Highway 169 N
　New Hope MN 55428
　763 536-6600

(G-8152)
LONGHORN POWDER COATING I
2516 Minnis Dr Ste 180 (76117-4890)
PHONE....................817 759-2224
Blake Behringer, *Principal*
EMP: 9
SALES (est): 888.5K Privately Held
WEB: www.longhornpowdercoating.com
SIC: 3479 Coating of metals & formed products

(G-8153)
MEDTRONIC PS MEDICAL INC
4620 N Beach St (76137-3219)
PHONE....................817 788-6400
Doug Hosea, *District Mgr*
Roy Galvin, *Vice Pres*
Chris Lee, *Vice Pres*
Milton Barnes, *Engineer*
Kim Hernandez, *Engineer*
EMP: 250 Privately Held
WEB: www.medtronic.com
SIC: 3841 Surgical & medical instruments
HQ: Medtronic Ps Medical, Inc.
　5290 California Ave # 100
　Irvine CA 92617
　805 571-3769

(G-8154)
MICA STEELWORKS INC
4201 Old Denton Rd (76117-2208)
PHONE....................817 581-9500
Joel Flint, *Branch Mgr*
EMP: 124

SALES (corp-wide): 93.4MM **Privately Held**
WEB: www.micacorporation.com
SIC: 3312 Blast furnaces & steel mills
PA: Mica Steelworks, Inc.
　5750 N Riverside Dr
　Fort Worth TX 76137
　817 529-5000

(G-8155)
NURSE ASSIST LLC
4409 Haltom Rd (76117-1207)
PHONE....................................800 649-6800
Kevin Seifert, *CEO*
Jaye Martin, *Vice Pres*
Matt Picha, *Vice Pres*
Robert Snirch, *Mfg Mgr*
Courtni Bragg, *Purch Mgr*
▲ EMP: 130
SQ FT: 132,000
SALES (est): 29.1MM **Privately Held**
WEB: www.stericaresolutions.com
SIC: 3841 Surgical & medical instruments
PA: Tower Three Partners Llc
　2 Sound View Dr Ste 4
　Greenwich CT 06830

(G-8156)
PB UNLIMITED LLC
1659 Hickory Dr Ste H (76117-6033)
PHONE....................................817 831-4336
Bryan A Benton, *President*
Brian Cross, *Prdtn Mgr*
Ryan A Benton, *Treasurer*
EMP: 12
SQ FT: 7,500
SALES (est): 1.7MM **Privately Held**
WEB: www.pbunlimited.com
SIC: 3993 2396 Advertising novelties;
　screen printing on fabric articles

(G-8157)
RF MANUFACTURING LLC
4212 Glenview Dr (76117-1006)
PHONE....................................817 479-1950
Ryan Fitzgerald, *President*
EMP: 24
SALES (est): 988.5K **Privately Held**
WEB: www.rfmanufacturing.net
SIC: 3429 3728 3721 Aircraft hardware;
　aircraft parts & equipment; aircraft

(G-8158)
SOUTHWEST FENTER INC
Also Called: Lanbert's Ornamental Iron
4201 Hahn Blvd (76117-1712)
PHONE....................................817 577-3837
Chris Gruensfeldr, *President*
EMP: 36
SALES (est): 4.2MM **Privately Held**
SIC: 3446 Ornamental metalwork

(G-8159)
TWO OLD GOATS LLC (PA)
4117 Murray Ave (76117-1714)
PHONE....................................817 520-4230
Richard Snyder, *President*
EMP: 9
SQ FT: 8,400
SALES (est): 2.7MM **Privately Held**
WEB: www.twooldgoats.com
SIC: 2844 2841 Face creams or lotions;
　soap & other detergents

(G-8160)
UNIFIRST CORPORATION
2900 N Beach St (76111-6203)
P.O. Box 7580, Fort Worth (76111-0580)
PHONE....................................817 834-7386
Rj Jacobs, *District Mgr*
Kevin B Garrett, *Branch Mgr*
EMP: 70
SALES (corp-wide): 1.8B **Publicly Held**
WEB: www.unifirst.com
SIC: 7218 7213 2392 Industrial uniform
　supply; uniform supply; mops, floor & dust
PA: Unifirst Corporation
　68 Jonspin Rd
　Wilmington MA 01887
　978 658-8888

(G-8161)
USA EAGLE CARPORTS INC
Also Called: Texas Eagle Construction
5700 E Belknap St (76117-4139)
P.O. Box 162021, Fort Worth (76161-2021)
PHONE....................................817 788-5395
Dave Murphy, *President*
Kevin Boyer, *General Mgr*
Julie Zuefeldt, *General Mgr*
Tommy Linamen, *Superintendent*
Thomas Linamen Jr, *Treasurer*
EMP: 11
SALES (est): 4.8MM **Privately Held**
WEB: www.usaeaglecarports.com
SIC: 3448 Carports: prefabricated metal

(G-8162)
WMK LLC
Also Called: Mobility Works of Texas
2110 N Beach St (76111-6812)
PHONE....................................817 429-1273
Andrew Blumberg, *General Mgr*
EMP: 12
SALES (corp-wide): 564.6MM **Privately Held**
WEB: www.mobilityworks.com
SIC: 5999 7532 7514 5531 Medical ap-
　paratus & supplies; van conversion; rent-
　a-car service; automotive accessories;
　wheelchair lifts
PA: Wmk, Llc
　4199 Kinross Lakes Pkwy
　Richfield OH 44286
　234 312-2000

(G-8163)
WORKSITE LIGHTING LLC
4109 Murray Ave (76117-1714)
PHONE....................................225 313-3711
Carla Matthews, *Controller*
William A Matthews II, *Mng Member*
Alex Robeau,
EMP: 25 EST: 2007
SQ FT: 40,000
SALES (est): 8.7MM **Privately Held**
WEB: www.worksitelighting.com
SIC: 3648 Lighting equipment

Hamilton
Hamilton County

(G-8164)
ALEXANDER MOULDING MILL CO
Hwy 281 S (76531)
PHONE....................................254 386-3187
Richard Wheeler, *Vice Pres*
Christine Winter, *Comms Dir*
Victoria Stevens, *Director*
EMP: 92
SQ FT: 100,000
SALES (est): 4MM **Privately Held**
WEB: www.cancer.org
SIC: 2431 Moldings, wood: unfinished &
　prefinished

(G-8165)
C & F STEEL COMPANY INC
91 State Hwy 36 W (76531)
P.O. Box 72 (76531-0072)
PHONE....................................254 386-8847
Warner Fox, *President*
Bill Barrett, *Vice Pres*
Reed Smith, *Project Mgr*
Sheldon Blackwell, *Opers Mgr*
John Loden, *Prdtn Mgr*
EMP: 30
SQ FT: 30,000
SALES (est): 10.1MM **Privately Held**
WEB: www.candfsteel.com
SIC: 3441 1791 Building components,
　structural steel; structural steel erection

(G-8166)
K-6 MACHINE INC (PA)
800 N Rice St (76531-1251)
P.O. Box 349 (76531-0349)
PHONE....................................254 386-3491
Richard Kirkham, *President*
Debbie Kirkham, *Office Mgr*
EMP: 14
SQ FT: 1,200

SALES (est): 1.6MM **Privately Held**
WEB: www.k6machine.com
SIC: 3599 Machine shop, jobbing & repair

(G-8167)
K-6 MACHINE INC
800 N Rice St (76531-1251)
P.O. Box 349 (76531-0349)
PHONE....................................254 386-3491
Richard Kirkham, *President*
EMP: 9
SALES (corp-wide): 1.6MM **Privately Held**
WEB: www.k6machine.com
SIC: 3599 Machine shop, jobbing & repair
PA: K-6 Machine, Inc.
　800 N Rice St
　Hamilton TX 76531
　254 386-3491

(G-8168)
PEDERSON KRONSEDER LLC
1207 S Rice St (76531-9613)
PHONE....................................254 386-4790
Harold Kroneder, *Owner*
EMP: 35 EST: 2002
SALES (est): 3.3MM **Privately Held**
SIC: 2013 Prepared pork products from
　purchased pork

(G-8169)
PEDERSON NATURAL FARMS INC
1207 S Rice St (76531-9613)
PHONE....................................254 386-4790
Cody Lane, *President*
Scott Cooney, *Vice Pres*
Neil Dudley, *Vice Pres*
Stacy Dudley, *Vice Pres*
Chad Ondrusek, *Plant Mgr*
EMP: 25
SQ FT: 13,000
SALES (est): 5.9MM **Privately Held**
WEB: www.pedersonsfarms.com
SIC: 2011 Pork products from pork slaugh-
　tered on site

Hamlin
Jones County

(G-8170)
HAMLIN PET WORX LLC
701 E Lake Dr (79520-3503)
PHONE....................................855 430-9888
EMP: 18
SALES (est): 676.9K **Privately Held**
SIC: 2048 Mfg Prepared Feeds

Hargill
Hidalgo County

(G-8171)
US CITRUS LLC
30232 Fm 493 (78549)
P.O. Box 258 (78549-0258)
PHONE....................................956 252-3101
Mani Skaria, *CEO*
Christopher W James,
Robert A Needham,
EMP: 21
SALES (est): 1.1MM **Privately Held**
WEB: www.uscitrus.com
SIC: 0174 2099 Citrus fruits; salads, fresh
　or refrigerated

Harker Heights
Bell County

(G-8172)
MILITARY CUSTOMS LLC
Also Called: Logos In Thread
229 Cox Dr (76548-2406)
PHONE....................................254 699-8106
Brandon McKinniss,
Al Contreras,
EMP: 12

SALES (est): 600.1K **Privately Held**
SIC: 2396 2399 5699 Fabric printing &
　stamping; screen printing on fabric arti-
　cles; tip printing & stamping on fabric; mil-
　itary insignia, textile; customized clothing
　& apparel

(G-8173)
SHELL RAPID LUBE LONESTAR AUTO
Also Called: Lonestar Recreational Vhcl Ctr
611 E Central Texas Expy (76548-1385)
PHONE....................................254 953-4360
Iris Bowyer, *Owner*
EMP: 12
SALES (est): 980.2K **Privately Held**
WEB: www.lonestarrvs.com
SIC: 2992 Lubricating oils

Harlingen
Cameron County

(G-8174)
AIM MEDIA TEXAS OPERATING LLC
Also Called: Valley Morning Star
1310 S Commerce St (78550-7711)
PHONE....................................956 430-6200
Ed Asher, *Editor*
Ernie Garrido, *Editor*
Diana E Maldonado, *Editor*
Doug Hardie, *Branch Mgr*
Rusty Hall, *Manager*
EMP: 154
SQ FT: 32,277
SALES (corp-wide): 98.1MM **Privately Held**
WEB: www.digitalaimmedia.com
SIC: 2711 Newspapers, publishing & print-
　ing
PA: Aim Media Texas Operating, Llc
　1400 E Nolana Ave
　Mcallen TX 78504
　956 683-4000

(G-8175)
ALAMO CONCRETE PRODUCTS LTD
Also Called: Pipe Division
2301 Industrial Crossway (78550)
P.O. Box 531808 (78553-1808)
PHONE....................................956 423-6388
Luis Martinez, *Branch Mgr*
EMP: 30 **Privately Held**
SIC: 3272 Concrete products
PA: Alamo Concrete Products, Ltd.
　6055 W Green Mountain Rd
　Austin TX 78744

(G-8176)
ALAMO CONCRETE PRODUCTS LTD
Also Called: Varmicon Industries
2301 Industrial Crossway (78550)
PHONE....................................956 423-6380
Veronico Ramos, *Branch Mgr*
EMP: 27 **Privately Held**
SIC: 3272 Concrete products
PA: Alamo Concrete Products, Ltd.
　6055 W Green Mountain Rd
　Austin TX 78744

(G-8177)
ALOE FARMS INC (PA)
3102 Wilson Rd (78552-5011)
PHONE....................................956 425-1289
Mark Elliott Berry, *President*
Elvia Berry, *Vice Pres*
Catherine Berry, *Treasurer*
▼ EMP: 10
SQ FT: 1,056
SALES (est): 1.7MM **Privately Held**
WEB: www.aloeverafarms.com
SIC: 5261 2033 Nursery stock, seeds &
　bulbs; vegetable juices: packaged in
　cans, jars, etc.; jellies, edible, including
　imitation: in cans, jars, etc.

(G-8178)
ALOE LABORATORIES INC
5821 E Harrison Ave (78550-1811)
P.O. Box 831 (78551-0831)
PHONE....................................956 428-8416

GEOGRAPHIC

Luis Rodriguez, *Principal*
Hide Aragaki, *Senior VP*
Kosuke Baba, *Vice Pres*
Luis Rodriguez, *Vice Pres*
Willyan Kmetz,
EMP: 60
SQ FT: 40,000
SALES (est): 11.8MM **Privately Held**
WEB: www.aloelabs.com
SIC: 2087 2834 Concentrates, drink; extracts of botanicals: powdered, pilular, solid or fluid
HQ: Harmony Green Co., Ltd.
1-8-2, Marunouchi
Chiyoda-Ku TKY 100-0

(G-8179)
ALTECA LLC
Also Called: Hilco
25691 Altas Palmas Rd (78552-6370)
PHONE................956 423-1885
Terrie Crockett, *Info Tech Mgr*
Allan Crockett,
▲ **EMP:** 10
SQ FT: 16,000
SALES (est): 375K **Privately Held**
WEB: www.hilsport.com
SIC: 2211 Canvas & other heavy coarse fabrics: cotton

(G-8180)
AMERICAN BOTTLING COMPANY
Also Called: 7up/Rc/Bigred of Harlingen
915 N Ed Carey Dr (78550-9203)
PHONE................956 423-2705
Mario Ortiz, *Manager*
EMP: 80 **Publicly Held**
WEB: www.keurigdrpepper.com
SIC: 2086 5149 Bottled & canned soft drinks; groceries & related products
HQ: The American Bottling Company
5301 Legacy Dr
Plano TX 75024

(G-8181)
ASPHALT PRODUCTS INC
Also Called: Transformer Components
5809 Progress Dr (78550-1760)
P.O. Box 132, Kosciusko MS (39090-0132)
PHONE................956 423-8315
Billy Atwood, *President*
Rosemary Atwood, *Vice Pres*
Bobby Mathews, *Admin Sec*
▼ **EMP:** 16
SQ FT: 3,200
SALES (est): 1.5MM **Privately Held**
SIC: 2952 Asphalt felts & coatings

(G-8182)
ATLANTIC DURANT TECHNOLOGY INC
Also Called: Adtech
5801 Progress Dr (78550-1760)
PHONE................956 440-8005
Paul Durant, *Manager*
Durant Paul, *Manager*
EMP: 42
SALES (corp-wide): 149MM **Privately Held**
WEB: www.atlantictool.com
SIC: 3469 3544 3542 Stamping metal for the trade; special dies, tools, jigs & fixtures; machine tools, metal forming type
HQ: Atlantic Durant Technology, Inc.
19963 Progress Dr
Strongsville OH 44149

(G-8183)
C & M GRAPHICS & SIGNS
1149 S Commerce St (78550-7706)
PHONE................956 421-2114
Miguel A Plata, *Principal*
EMP: 13
SALES (est): 1.3MM **Privately Held**
WEB: www.cm-graphics.net
SIC: 3993 Signs & advertising specialties

(G-8184)
CAREY SHEET METAL SHOP INC
14392 W Expressway 83 (78552-6758)
P.O. Box 586 (78551-0586)
PHONE................956 423-1394
John Carey Jr, *CEO*

Ree Lyons, *Corp Secy*
John B Carey Jr, *Vice Pres*
John B Carey III, *Shareholder*
EMP: 10
SQ FT: 54,500
SALES (est): 1.4MM **Privately Held**
SIC: 3444 Sheet metalwork

(G-8185)
CIRCLE A XPRESS INC
27283 S Altas Palmas Rd (78552-3703)
PHONE................956 547-9393
Andres Garica Jr, *President*
EMP: 10
SALES (est): 979.5K **Privately Held**
SIC: 2741 Miscellaneous publishing

(G-8186)
ELIAS & ASSOCIATES LLC
1327 E Washington Ave # 138
(78550-5684)
PHONE................956 244-6552
Jesus Ruben Elias,
Yamile Elias,
Ruben Elias Valencia,
◆ **EMP:** 30
SALES (est): 3MM **Privately Held**
SIC: 3578 Point-of-sale devices

(G-8187)
EMERSON ATMTN SLTONS FNAL CTRL
5801 E Harrison Ave (78550-1811)
PHONE................956 430-2500
Jim Dennis, *Engineer*
Ryan O'Reilly, *Human Res Mgr*
Servando Galman, *Branch Mgr*
EMP: 105
SQ FT: 78,288
SALES (corp-wide): 16.7B **Publicly Held**
WEB: www.pentair.com
SIC: 3491 Industrial valves
HQ: Emerson Automation Solutions Final Control Us Lp
10707 Clay Rd
Houston TX 77041

(G-8188)
FAVELLE FAVCO CRANES USA INC
26360 Fm 106 (78550-1897)
P.O. Box 3049 (78551-3049)
PHONE................956 428-7488
Lee Poh Kwee, *President*
Kok Eng Khoo, *Admin Sec*
▲ **EMP:** 65 **EST:** 1997
SQ FT: 80
SALES (est): 15.6MM **Privately Held**
WEB: www.favcousa.com
SIC: 3531 3536 Cranes; hoists, cranes & monorails
PA: Favelle Favco Berhad
Lot 586 2nd Mile
Klang SLG

(G-8189)
FOX VALLEY MOLDING INC
5506 E Grimes St (78550-1854)
PHONE................956 428-2506
Dave Blackburn, *Branch Mgr*
EMP: 35
SALES (corp-wide): 32.1MM **Privately Held**
WEB: www.foxvalleymolding.com
SIC: 3089 5031 Injection molded finished plastic products; molding, all materials
PA: Fox Valley Molding, Inc.
113 S Center St
Plano IL 60545
630 552-3176

(G-8190)
INDUSTRIAL TOOL & DIE CO INC
818 N Fm 509 (78550-1855)
PHONE................956 440-9960
Joseph Scott Hayes, *Manager*
EMP: 13
SALES (corp-wide): 9.1MM **Privately Held**
WEB: www.itdprecision.com
SIC: 3469 3599 Stamping metal for the trade; machine shop, jobbing & repair
PA: Industrial Tool & Die Co., Inc.
9719 Telge Rd
Houston TX 77095
281 859-4499

(G-8191)
ITD PRECISION
818 N Fm 509 (78550-1855)
PHONE................956 440-9960
Mike Tofte, *Owner*
EMP: 40
SQ FT: 38,600
SALES (est): 4.7MM **Privately Held**
WEB: www.itdprecision.com
SIC: 3469 Stamping metal for the trade

(G-8192)
JF FILTRATION INC
2810 N Expwy 77 Ste C (78552-2774)
PHONE................956 412-3234
Adrian Cortez, *Manager*
EMP: 15 **Privately Held**
WEB: www.joeflyco.com
SIC: 5075 3564 Air filters; filters, air: furnaces, air conditioning equipment, etc.
PA: Jf Filtration, Inc.
4820 Memphis St
Dallas TX 75207

(G-8193)
LOCKHEED MARTIN CORPORATION
2800 Airport Dr (78550-3664)
PHONE................956 425-4447
Steve Metana, *Manager*
EMP: 164 **Publicly Held**
WEB: www.lockheedmartin.com
SIC: 3721 3761 8711 3769 Aircraft; space vehicles, complete; aviation &/or aeronautical engineering; guided missile & space vehicle parts & auxiliary equipment
PA: Lockheed Martin Corporation
6801 Rockledge Dr
Bethesda MD 20817

(G-8194)
LONE STAR PRINTING
2004 W Jefferson Ave D (78550-5212)
PHONE................956 535-2194
Robert Gonzales, *Owner*
EMP: 10 **EST:** 2011
SALES (est): 776K **Privately Held**
SIC: 2752 Commercial printing, lithographic

(G-8195)
MEXICAN SNACKS INC
Also Called: MSI
826 N Fm 509 (78550-1855)
PHONE................956 440-9127
Pedro Sepulveda Salinas, *President*
Jorge Elizondo Margain, *Director*
Oscar Martinez Trevino, *Director*
▼ **EMP:** 20
SQ FT: 43,108
SALES (est): 4.1MM **Privately Held**
SIC: 2096 Potato chips & similar snacks

(G-8196)
NEW CORE INC
22673 Hand Rd (78552-5810)
PHONE................956 421-2446
Robert Ross, *President*
Elvia Mata, *Office Mgr*
Valentin Olvera, *Manager*
EMP: 12
SALES (est): 1.9MM **Privately Held**
WEB: www.newcoreinc.com
SIC: 3621 7694 5063 Electric motor & generator auxillary parts; electric motor repair; motors, electric

(G-8197)
PRIMERA FABRICATION INC
15671 Primera Rd (78552-0018)
PHONE................956 367-8690
Sean Lavergne, *President*
EMP: 30
SQ FT: 10,000
SALES (est): 300K **Privately Held**
SIC: 3498 Fabricated pipe & fittings

(G-8198)
PRISM INDUSTRIES LLC
2901 N Expressway 77 (78552-2566)
PHONE................956 425-3300
Jerry Williams, *Owner*
Rodney Dricker, *Owner*
Jerry Phillips, *Owner*

EMP: 30
SQ FT: 30,000
SALES (est): 3.8MM **Privately Held**
SIC: 3089 Molding primary plastic

(G-8199)
REDDY ICE CORPORATION
1409 N 28th St (78550-4551)
PHONE................956 428-6666
Fadi Raad, *Branch Mgr*
EMP: 26 **Privately Held**
WEB: www.reddyice.com
SIC: 2097 5999 Manufactured ice; ice
HQ: Reddy Ice Corporation
5710 Lbj Fwy Ste 300
Dallas TX 75240
214 526-6740

(G-8200)
SANCHEZ TIRE SHOP 5
622 S F St (78550-6574)
PHONE................956 423-0047
Robert Sanchez, *Principal*
EMP: 11 **EST:** 2011
SALES (est): 1.5MM **Privately Held**
SIC: 3011 5014 Tires & inner tubes; tires & tubes

(G-8201)
SON AND DAUGHTERS INC
Also Called: Godwin & Son Sign Co
313 Hanmore Indus Pkwy (78550-7674)
PHONE................956 423-2689
Linda L Pullin, *President*
Dennis Pullin, *Corp Secy*
Mary Ann Thomas, *Vice Pres*
Mary Thomas, *Vice Pres*
EMP: 17 **EST:** 1917
SQ FT: 8,000
SALES (est): 950K **Privately Held**
WEB: www.godwinsigns.com
SIC: 7629 3993 Electrical repair shops; electric signs; neon signs

(G-8202)
SORT-RITE INTERNATIONAL INC
825 W Jefferson Ave (78550-5316)
P.O. Box 1805 (78551-1805)
PHONE................956 423-2427
Willam Capt, *Ch of Bd*
Linda L Capt, *President*
Pat Holley, *Corp Secy*
George Daily, *Vice Pres*
◆ **EMP:** 23 **EST:** 1978
SQ FT: 45,100 **Privately Held**
WEB: www.sort-rite.com
SIC: 3556 Fish & shellfish processing machinery

(G-8203)
STITCH GALLERY INC
Also Called: Hhey Hay Farm
113 S 77 Sunshinestrip (78550-7337)
P.O. Box 2729 (78551-2729)
PHONE................956 412-3087
Eduardo Diaz, *Owner*
EMP: 12
SALES (est): 852.4K **Privately Held**
WEB: www.stitchgallery.net
SIC: 2395 Embroidery products, except schiffli machine

(G-8204)
SUNCOAST A/C & RFRGN INC
28020 S Dilworth Rd (78552-1762)
P.O. Box 1031 (78551-1031)
PHONE................956 428-1190
Larry Fitting, *President*
Cindy Kratzer, *Office Mgr*
Troy Fitting, *Manager*
EMP: 15
SQ FT: 17,000
SALES (est): 2.8MM **Privately Held**
WEB: www.suncoastrgv.com
SIC: 7623 3585 4961 5078 Air conditioning repair; refrigeration repair service; air conditioning equipment, complete; compressors for refrigeration & air conditioning equipment; air conditioning supply services; commercial refrigeration equipment

▲ = Import ▼=Export
◆ =Import/Export

(G-8205)
TEXAS GAS SERVICE COMPANY
5602 E Grimes St (78550-1818)
P.O. Box 531827 (78553-1827)
PHONE.....................956 444-3900
EMP: 1574
SALES (est): 57.6MM
SALES (corp-wide): 1.6B **Publicly Held**
WEB: www.texasgasservice.com
SIC: 1311 Natural gas production
PA: One Gas, Inc.
15 E 5th St
Tulsa OK 74103
918 947-7000

(G-8206)
TEXAS THREAD MANUFACTURING CO
2222 Wilson Rd (78552-2905)
PHONE.....................956 412-4999
Kavanaugh Francis, *President*
T H Francis, *Corp Secy*
Francis Tom H, *Vice Pres*
Susan Francis, *Manager*
EMP: 9
SQ FT: 24,000
SALES (est): 1MM **Privately Held**
SIC: 2284 Thread from manmade fibers

(G-8207)
TRI-PAK MACHINERY INC
1102 N Commerce St (78550-4814)
P.O. Box 1228 (78551-1228)
PHONE.....................956 423-5140
David A Fitzgerald, *President*
Charles M Kilbourn, *Vice Pres*
Wayne Allison, *Plant Mgr*
Robert Fitzgerald, *Sales Staff*
Daniel J Groves, *Director*
EMP: 31 EST: 1934
SQ FT: 7,000
SALES (est): 6MM **Privately Held**
WEB: www.tri-pak.com
SIC: 3556 Packing house machinery

(G-8208)
UNITED LAUNCH ALLIANCE LLC
2800 Airport Dr (78550-3664)
PHONE.....................956 425-4447
Raul Garza, *Opers Staff*
Emily Ehrle, *Engineer*
Barbara West, *Design Engr*
Mais Korniyenko, *Financial Analy*
Jim Hardin, *Branch Mgr*
EMP: 99 **Privately Held**
WEB: www.ulalaunch.com
SIC: 3761 Rockets, space & military, complete
PA: United Launch Alliance, L.L.C.
9501 E Panorama Cir
Centennial CO 80112

Harper
Gillespie County

(G-8209)
GOLD BOND BUILDING PDTS LLC
5124 Gypsum Mine Rd (78631)
PHONE.....................830 864-4100
EMP: 18
SALES (corp-wide): 54.2MM **Privately Held**
SIC: 2621 Paper Mills
PA: Gold Bond Building Products, Llc
2001 Rexford Rd
Charlotte NC

(G-8210)
NG OPERATIONS LLC
Also Called: National Gypsum Company
5124 Gypsum Mine Rd (78631)
P.O. Box 128 (78631-0128)
PHONE.....................830 864-4100
Doug Bergquist, *Manager*
Drew Gilson, *Manager*
EMP: 92
SALES (corp-wide): 478MM **Privately Held**
WEB: www.nationalgypsum.com
SIC: 3275 Gypsum products

HQ: Proform Finishing Products, Llc
2001 Rexford Rd
Charlotte NC 28211

Hartley
Hartley County

(G-8211)
HELENA AGRI-ENTERPRISES LLC
410 4th St (79044)
P.O. Box 109 (79044-0109)
PHONE.....................806 365-4433
Trent Truler, *Branch Mgr*
EMP: 9 **Privately Held**
WEB: www.helenaagri.com
SIC: 5191 2879 Chemicals, agricultural; pesticides; fertilizer & fertilizer materials; seeds & bulbs; pesticides, agricultural or household
HQ: Helena Agri-Enterprises, Llc
255 Schilling Blvd # 300
Collierville TN 38017
901 761-0050

Harwood
Gonzales County

(G-8212)
SIERRA DUST CONTROL LLC
8197 Fm 794 (78632)
PHONE.....................903 836-4642
EMP: 19
SALES (corp-wide): 4.2MM **Privately Held**
WEB: www.sierrafracsand.com
SIC: 2865 2869 Cyclic crudes & intermediates; industrial organic chemicals
PA: Sierra Dust Control, L.L.C.
1155 E Johnson St
Tatum TX 75691
903 836-4642

Haskell
Haskell County

(G-8213)
LANGFORD ROUSTABOUT SVCS LLC
8348 Bus Us Hwy 277 N (79521)
PHONE.....................940 864-3490
Terry Scott Langford,
EMP: 13
SALES (est): 1.6MM **Privately Held**
SIC: 1389 Roustabout service

(G-8214)
STRICKLAND BRIDGE INC
175 Business Us Highway 2 (79521-9036)
P.O. Box 123 (79521-0123)
PHONE.....................940 864-2677
Fax: 940 864-2969
EMP: 10
SQ FT: 2,800
SALES: 700K **Privately Held**
SIC: 3273 1622 Mfg Ready Mix Concrete & Bridge Construction

Haslet
Tarrant County

(G-8215)
AMERICAN COOLING TECH INC
6630 E State Highway 114 (76052-2054)
PHONE.....................717 767-2775
Mark Smith, *President*
Andy Beard, *Vice Pres*
J R Lucas, *Vice Pres*
Benjamin Hauer, *Plant Mgr*
Howard Fisher, *Purch Mgr*
▲ EMP: 16
SALES (est): 6.3MM
SALES (corp-wide): 62.6MM **Privately Held**
WEB: www.actusa.us.com
SIC: 3585 5075 Air conditioning, motor vehicle; automotive air conditioners

HQ: Proair Holdings Corporation
6630 E State Highway 114
Haslet TX 76052
817 636-2308

(G-8216)
BLADE LAB INC
791 Westport Pkwy (76052)
P.O. Box 376 (76052-0376)
PHONE.....................817 491-6755
James Randy Stevens, *CEO*
EMP: 15
SALES (est): 850.8K **Privately Held**
SIC: 3599 Air intake filters, internal combustion engine, except auto

(G-8217)
BUS AIR LLC
6630 E State Highway 114 (76052-2054)
PHONE.....................817 636-2308
Mark L Smith, *President*
Rodney Roderick, *CFO*
EMP: 50
SALES (est): 1.6MM
SALES (corp-wide): 62.6MM **Privately Held**
WEB: www.proairllc.com
SIC: 3585 5531 Air conditioning, motor vehicle; automobile air conditioning equipment, sale, installation
HQ: Proair Holdings Corporation
6630 E State Highway 114
Haslet TX 76052
817 636-2308

(G-8218)
CONSOLIDATED WELLSITE SVCS LLC
104 Metrotex Dr (76052-2081)
PHONE.....................903 983-9811
EMP: 26 EST: 2014
SALES (est): 8MM **Privately Held**
WEB: www.consolidatedwellsite.com
SIC: 1389 Oil field services

(G-8219)
KENNEDY MACHINE & MFG INC
13112 Maida Vale Ln (76052-5116)
PHONE.....................972 241-7610
Hubert Kennedy, *President*
Ruth Kennedy, *Treasurer*
Gary Harris, *Director*
EMP: 22
SQ FT: 26,000
SALES (est): 3MM **Privately Held**
SIC: 3599 7692 7629 Machine shop, jobbing & repair; welding repair; electrical repair shops

(G-8220)
KSH ENTERPRISES INC
Also Called: Iwire
233 Ashmore Pl (76052-3811)
P.O. Box 54551, Hurst (76054-4551)
PHONE.....................817 313-0926
Kirtis J Hill, *President*
EMP: 14
SALES (est): 1.2MM **Privately Held**
WEB: www.iwireinc.com
SIC: 3651 7539 Audio electronic systems; electrical services

(G-8221)
ONE FOCUS INC (PA)
Also Called: Express Signs Plus
900 Blue Mound Rd E (76052-4056)
PHONE.....................817 750-7667
Steven D Helling, *President*
Joan Rawrson, *Manager*
EMP: 10
SQ FT: 3,000
SALES (est): 944.9K **Privately Held**
WEB: www.esignsplus.com
SIC: 3993 Signs & advertising specialties

(G-8222)
PRODUCT HANDLING DESIGN INC (PA)
Also Called: PHD Crane Systems
6650 E State Highway 114 (76052-2054)
P.O. Box 1009, Rhome (76078-1009)
PHONE.....................972 231-4628
Mark A Scott, *President*
Ron Walker, *General Mgr*
Morgan Riling, *Project Mgr*
Mary A Scott, *Treasurer*

Jeff Porter, *Finance Dir*
▲ EMP: 10
SQ FT: 3,060
SALES (est): 19.9MM **Privately Held**
WEB: www.producthandling.com
SIC: 5084 3536 Materials handling machinery; hoists, cranes & monorails

(G-8223)
STEPHENS PNEUMATICS INC
147 County Road 4840 (76052-2026)
PHONE.....................817 636-9004
Jerry Stephens, *Ch of Bd*
Stan Stephens, *President*
June Stephens, *Vice Pres*
Rich White, *Opers Mgr*
Jerry Fonville, *QC Mgr*
EMP: 50
SQ FT: 45,000
SALES (est): 15.1MM **Privately Held**
WEB: www.stephenstankproducts.com
SIC: 3443 Tanks for tank trucks, metal plate

(G-8224)
TANKHEADS INC
147 County Road 4840 (76052-2026)
PHONE.....................817 636-2085
Jerry Stephens, *Ch of Bd*
Stan Stephens, *President*
Rich White, *Opers Mgr*
James Darnell, *Shareholder*
Wayne Gilaum, *Shareholder*
EMP: 9
SQ FT: 13,200
SALES (est): 1.7MM **Privately Held**
WEB: www.tankheadsinc.com
SIC: 3441 Fabricated structural metal

(G-8225)
TEXSTAR INTERNATIONAL LLC
1624 Intermodal Pkwy (76052-2735)
PHONE.....................817 740-9072
Sylvia Clark,
▲ EMP: 12
SALES (est): 1.2MM **Privately Held**
WEB: www.motivatinggraphics.com
SIC: 2741 Business service newsletters: publishing & printing

(G-8226)
TRIPLE - C FENCE LLC
1803 Avondale Haslet Rd (76052-3209)
PHONE.....................817 439-9500
Michael McDonald, *Mng Member*
Jill McDonald, *Manager*
EMP: 23
SALES (est): 2.5MM **Privately Held**
WEB: www.triple-cfence.com
SIC: 1799 3446 Fence construction; fences, gates, posts & flagpoles

(G-8227)
WILLOW CREEK SIGNS INC
2633 Blue Mound Rd W (76052-3289)
PHONE.....................817 847-0571
Tim Dennis, *Principal*
EMP: 32
SQ FT: 19,600
SALES (est): 5.7MM **Privately Held**
WEB: www.willowcreeksigns.com
SIC: 3993 Signs & advertising specialties

Hawkins
Wood County

(G-8228)
BOBBITT CONSTRUCTION INC
599 E Blackbourn St (75765-2971)
P.O. Box 540 (75765-0540)
PHONE.....................903 769-4513
Bobby Bobbitt, *President*
Corey Bobbitt, *Vice Pres*
Harold Bobbitt, *Vice Pres*
Lisa Bailey, *Treasurer*
Brad Cox, *Director*
▲ EMP: 21
SALES (est): 2.5MM **Privately Held**
WEB: www.bobbittconstruction.com
SIC: 1389 Lease tanks, oil field: erecting, cleaning & repairing

(G-8229)
FABCO PRODUCTS INC
2521 S Fm 2869 (75765-4727)
P.O. Box 489 (75765-0489)
PHONE.............................903 769-3707
Charles McLenden, *President*
Michael Cates, *Sr Project Mgr*
Jamie McLendon, *Administration*
Rachael Kiowski, *Receptionist*
▲ EMP: 24 EST: 1989
SQ FT: 10,000
SALES (est): 5.5MM **Privately Held**
WEB: www.fabcoproducts.com
SIC: 3491 Gas valves & parts, industrial

Hawley
Jones County

(G-8230)
COYOTE ROUSTABOUT LLC
13000 Fm 707 (79525-2416)
P.O. Box 7091, Abilene (79608-7091)
PHONE.............................325 455-0090
Jeremiah G Thompson, *Owner*
George E Sellers, *Mng Member*
EMP: 11
SQ FT: 2,400
SALES (est): 670K **Privately Held**
SIC: 1389 Oil field services

Hearne
Robertson County

(G-8231)
GENEMCO INC
3385 S San Gabriel St (77859-2664)
PHONE.............................979 268-7447
Mark McMillan, *Principal*
EMP: 25 **Privately Held**
WEB: www.genemco.com
SIC: 3556 Dehydrating equipment, food
   processing
PA: Genemco, Inc.
   3385 S San Gabriel St
   Hearne TX 77859

(G-8232)
HEARNE STEEL COMPANY
Also Called: Hearne Steel Company, Inc.
1011 Vaughn Ln (77859-4046)
P.O. Box 1239 (77859-1239)
PHONE.............................979 279-3464
Rodney Wayne Amos, *President*
Cannon Ray Amos, *Treasurer*
Acey Chappell, *Sales Staff*
Connie Ricks, *Admin Sec*
EMP: 55 EST: 1957
SQ FT: 85,000
SALES (est): 17.8MM **Privately Held**
WEB: www.hearnesteel.com
SIC: 3315 3496 3312 Chain link fencing;
   miscellaneous fabricated wire products;
   blast furnaces & steel mills

(G-8233)
WILBUR-ELLIS COMPANY LLC
1100 W Brown St (77859-3065)
P.O. Box 572, Rosebud (76570-0572)
PHONE.............................979 279-3486
Fax: 979 279-6576
EMP: 13
SALES (corp-wide): 1.1B **Privately Held**
SIC: 2875 Mfg Fertilizers-Mix Only
HQ: Wilbur-Ellis Company Llc
   345 California St Fl 27
   San Francisco CA 94104
   415 772-4000

Hebbronville
Jim Hogg County

(G-8234)
GRAY SALES INC
Also Called: Lone Star Sales
57 E State Highway 359 (78361-4428)
P.O. Box 188 (78361-0188)
PHONE.............................361 527-4460
John Gray, *CEO*
EMP: 9

SALES (est): 2.5MM **Privately Held**
WEB: www.lonestarindustries.com
SIC: 3082 5999 Unsupported plastics pro-
file shapes; feed & farm supply

(G-8235)
**KATCO VACUUM TRUCK
SERVICE LP**
809 E Galbraith St (78361-3418)
P.O. Box 399 (78361-0399)
PHONE.............................361 527-4421
Gilbert Troell, *President*
EMP: 32
SQ FT: 400
SALES (est): 3.7MM **Privately Held**
WEB: www.katcovacuum.com
SIC: 1389 Oil field services

Helotes
Bexar County

(G-8236)
**DERMATECH INTERNATIONAL
INC**
11844 Bandera Rd Ste 105 (78023-4132)
PHONE.............................210 558-1387
Elizabeth Baile, *Director*
Kimberly Dalton,
EMP: 38
SALES (corp-wide): 2.8MM **Privately
Held**
WEB: www.dermatecinternational.com
SIC: 3841 Surgical lasers
PA: Dermatech International, Inc.
   3155 E Patrick Ln Ste 1
   Las Vegas NV

(G-8237)
**GAVIN STEEL FABRICATING
INC**
18593 Bandera Rd (78023-2912)
PHONE.............................210 695-9672
Raul Morales, *President*
Sandi C Morales, *Vice Pres*
Sandi Morales, *Vice Pres*
EMP: 20
SQ FT: 10,000
SALES (est): 6.5MM **Privately Held**
WEB: www.gavinsteel.com
SIC: 3441 Building components, structural
   steel

(G-8238)
HEMAQ AMERICA LLC
342 Santa Domingo (78023-4638)
P.O. Box 1658 (78023-1658)
PHONE.............................877 700-5060
Enrique Gritzewsky,
Benito Gritzewsky,
EMP: 100
SALES (est): 13.8MM **Privately Held**
SIC: 3541 Machine tools, metal cutting
   type

(G-8239)
JR PETERSON INC
Also Called: Hill County Animal Hospital
12410 Bandera Rd (78023-4794)
PHONE.............................210 695-4455
James Peterson, *President*
EMP: 22
SALES (est): 142.8K **Privately Held**
WEB: www.hillcountryanimalhospital.com
SIC: 0742 7372 Animal hospital services,
   pets & other animal specialties; applica-
   tion computer software

(G-8240)
KADY INTERNATIONAL LLC
306 Pueblo Pintado (78023-4724)
PHONE.............................210 860-1637
Fernando Franco, *President*
EMP: 25
SALES (est): 2.9MM **Privately Held**
SIC: 2026 Fluid milk

(G-8241)
KAMAL INCORPORATED (PA)
Also Called: Venetian Marble of San Antonio
13310 Western Oak Dr (78023-2904)
PHONE.............................210 695-2678
Harnek S Gill, *CEO*
Anthony J Frankowiak, *President*

Margaret Siress, *Office Mgr*
Brenda M Frankowiak, *Director*
Malkit Gill, *Admin Sec*
EMP: 64
SQ FT: 26,000
SALES (est): 12.4MM **Privately Held**
WEB: www.venetiancountertops.com
SIC: 3281 3231 3229 2541 Marble, build-
   ing: cut & shaped; products of purchased
   glass; pressed & blown glass; wood parti-
   tions & fixtures

(G-8242)
MEGA SYSTEMS INC (PA)
Also Called: Mega-Lite
18668 Hwy 16 N (78023)
PHONE.............................210 684-2600
Guillermo Cabada, *President*
Guillermp Cabada, *Engineer*
Arturo Cabada, *Treasurer*
Marisol Gamboa, *Accounting Dir*
Isabel Cabada, *Accounts Mgr*
▲ EMP: 24
SQ FT: 11,000
SALES (est): 4.5MM **Privately Held**
WEB: www.megasystemsinc.com
SIC: 3651 5063 Audio electronic systems;
   electrical apparatus & equipment

(G-8243)
METRIC MEDICAL DEVICES INC
846 Silver Spgs (78023-2530)
P.O. Box 63389, Pipe Creek (78063-3389)
PHONE.............................830 535-6300
W Casey Fox, *President*
Stephen Erdner, *Vice Pres*
Nancy Fox, *Treasurer*
Chris Hauser, *Natl Sales Mgr*
Rhonda Unser, *Marketing Staff*
EMP: 9
SALES (est): 1.1MM **Privately Held**
WEB: www.metricmd.com
SIC: 3841 Surgical & medical instruments

(G-8244)
VULCAN MATERIALS COMPANY
11602 Rainbow Rdg (78023-4405)
P.O. Box 992 (78023-0992)
PHONE.............................210 695-3081
Eva Alarcon, *Controller*
EMP: 10 **Publicly Held**
WEB: www.vulcanmaterials.com
SIC: 3273 Ready-mixed concrete
PA: Vulcan Materials Company
   1200 Urban Center Dr
   Vestavia AL 35242

Hemphill
Sabine County

(G-8245)
BIG 4 INC
Also Called: Big 4 Services
301 Worth St (75948-7278)
PHONE.............................409 787-2733
Billy McGee, *CEO*
Melissa J McGee, *Vice Pres*
Herbert Ray Wood, *Vice Pres*
Linda A McGee, *CFO*
Linda McGee, *CFO*
EMP: 40
SQ FT: 1,500
SALES (est): 3.4MM **Privately Held**
WEB: www.big4inc.com
SIC: 1799 1611 1389 1499 Building site
   preparation; concrete construction: roads,
   highways, sidewalks, etc.; oil field serv-
   ices; greensand mining; pipeline & power
   line inspection service

(G-8246)
G D EDGAR LUMBER CO INC
379 Sawmill Dr (75948-9866)
P.O. Box 1067 (75948-1067)
PHONE.............................409 787-2452
George D Edgar, *President*
Robert D Edgar, *Corp Secy*
EMP: 17
SQ FT: 50,000
SALES (est): 3.6MM **Privately Held**
SIC: 2421 2426 Specialty sawmill prod-
   ucts; kiln drying of lumber; hardwood di-
   mension & flooring mills

(G-8247)
PROCELLA LOGGING
1440 Hwy 184 (75948)
P.O. Box 598 (75948-0598)
PHONE.............................409 787-2325
Eugene Procella, *Principal*
EMP: 10 EST: 2010
SALES (est): 928K **Privately Held**
SIC: 2411 Logging

Hempstead
Waller County

(G-8248)
**ADVANCED CEMENTING SVCS
INC**
40466 Fm 1488 Rd (77445-9304)
PHONE.............................979 921-0356
Shannon McConnell, *President*
Jerry McConnell, *Director*
EMP: 12 EST: 2014
SALES (est): 1MM **Privately Held**
WEB: www.advancedcementing.com
SIC: 1389 Oil field services

(G-8249)
**BAKER HUGHES A GE
COMPANY LLC**
Also Called: Baker Atlas
35372 Betka Rd (77445-8588)
PHONE.............................979 826-3621
John Loehr, *Plant Mgr*
George Bartges, *Manager*
Mary Martinez, *Administration*
Darren Ochsner, *Maintence Staff*
EMP: 65
SQ FT: 34,757
SALES (corp-wide): 23.8B **Publicly Held**
WEB: www.bhge.com
SIC: 1389 1382 Oil field services; well log-
   ging; seismograph surveys
HQ: Baker Hughes Holdings Llc
   17021 Aldine Westfield Rd
   Houston TX 77073
   713 439-8600

(G-8250)
**BRUMLEY MANUFACTURING
INC**
Also Called: Brumley, LLC
22840 Mack Washington Ln (77445-8051)
P.O. Box 883 (77445-0883)
PHONE.............................979 826-4222
Elizabeth Puryear, *Principal*
Jessie Flores, *Opers Mgr*
John Garza, *QC Mgr*
Johnny Salazar, *Manager*
Beth Brumley,
EMP: 100
SQ FT: 36,000
SALES (est): 20.4MM
SALES (corp-wide): 6MM **Privately Held**
WEB: www.brumleymfg.com
SIC: 3533 Oil field machinery & equipment
PA: Canerector Inc
   1 Sparks Ave
   North York ON M2H 2
   416 225-6240

(G-8251)
**DIAMOND DOOR PRODUCTS
LTD (PA)**
52294 Highway 290 (77445-9107)
PHONE.............................979 826-0238
Steve F Curry, *Partner*
EMP: 39
SALES (est): 8MM **Privately Held**
WEB: www.diamonddoorltd.com
SIC: 3448 Prefabricated metal buildings

(G-8252)
**EAST TEXAS PRECAST
COMPANY**
44855 Old Houston Hwy (77445-2006)
P.O. Box 579, Waller (77484-0579)
PHONE.............................281 463-0654
James B Harlow, *President*
Dale Stites, *Vice Pres*
Brian Nance, *Sr Project Mgr*
EMP: 170
SQ FT: 500

SALES (est): 53.3MM **Privately Held**
WEB: www.easttexasprecast.net
SIC: **3272** Concrete products, precast

(G-8253)
JR SIMPLOT COMPANY
Also Called: Simplot Growers Solutions
1275 Zach Rd (77445-7048)
PHONE................................979 826-8063
Howard West, *Branch Mgr*
Yolanda Colquitt, *Executive*
EMP: 54
SALES (corp-wide): 4.8B **Privately Held**
WEB: www.simplot.com
SIC: **2037** 2874 2873 2879 Potato products, quick frozen & cold pack; vegetables, quick frozen & cold pack, excl. potato products; fruits, quick frozen & cold pack (frozen); phosphatic fertilizers; ammonium phosphate; nitrogenous fertilizers; agricultural chemicals; beef cattle feedlots
PA: J. R. Simplot Company
 1099 W Front St
 Boise ID 83702
 208 336-2110

(G-8254)
PARISH INTERNATIONAL INC
1100 Zach Rd (77445-6060)
P.O. Box 468 (77445-0468)
PHONE................................281 463-9233
Raymond Mohn, *Ch of Bd*
E W McSwain, *Shareholder*
James E Parish, *Shareholder*
▲ EMP: 31
SQ FT: 11,000
SALES (est): 5.1MM **Privately Held**
WEB: www.parishforge.com
SIC: **3462** Iron & steel forgings

(G-8255)
PLASTIC TUBING INDS TEXAS INC
18121 Cochran Rd (77445-9373)
PHONE................................979 921-9990
Michael Maroshak, *President*
▲ EMP: 15
SQ FT: 10,000
SALES (est): 2.8MM **Privately Held**
SIC: **3084** Plastics pipe

(G-8256)
VF INDUSTRIAL PARK INC
805 Factory Outlet Dr (77445-5604)
PHONE................................979 826-8277
Oscar Molina, *Branch Mgr*
EMP: 25
SALES (corp-wide): 10.4B **Publicly Held**
SIC: **2325** Men's & boys' trousers & slacks
HQ: Vf Industrial Park, Inc.
 801 Hill Ave Ofc
 Reading PA 19610
 610 378-0408

Henderson
Rusk County

(G-8257)
BASIC ENERGY SERVICES LP
3139 County Road 205 N (75652-9309)
PHONE................................903 657-8171
EMP: 17
SALES (corp-wide): 1.4B **Publicly Held**
SIC: **4212** 1389 Local Trucking Operator Oil/Gas Field Services
HQ: Basic Energy Services, L.P.
 801 Cherry St Unit 2
 Fort Worth TX 76102
 817 334-4100

(G-8258)
BOWMANS OILFIELD SERVICE LLC
608 E Main St Ste 102 (75652-2617)
P.O. Box 421 (75653-0421)
PHONE................................903 657-0698
Tracie Bowman, *Manager*
Jim Bowman,
EMP: 25
SQ FT: 2,000
SALES (est): 2MM **Privately Held**
SIC: **1382** Oil & gas exploration services

(G-8259)
BRYAN & BRYAN ASP RD OIL CO
8621 Fm 2276 N (75652-4002)
P.O. Box 625 (75653-0625)
PHONE................................903 657-2391
Billy Todd Bryan, *President*
Tim Brittain, *General Mgr*
Charlotte Bryan, *Vice Pres*
Angela Ybarra, *Associate*
EMP: 45
SQ FT: 1,200
SALES (est): 8.9MM **Privately Held**
WEB: www.bryanasphalt.net
SIC: **2951** Asphalt & asphaltic paving mixtures (not from refineries)

(G-8260)
CASE HILL GROUP INC
700 Kilgore Dr (75652-5224)
P.O. Box 817 (75653-0817)
PHONE................................903 657-7000
Donnie Powers, *President*
EMP: 12 EST: 1995
SALES (est): 165K **Privately Held**
SIC: **2439** Trusses, wooden roof

(G-8261)
COLDVAULT LLC (PA)
100 Millard Dr (75652-5034)
P.O. Box 1690 (75653-1690)
PHONE................................903 657-2377
Robert N Zintgraff,
EMP: 9
SALES (est): 1.3MM **Privately Held**
WEB: www.coldvault.com
SIC: **3585** 3632 Refrigeration & heating equipment; freezers, home & farm

(G-8262)
FIBERGLASS CREATIONS INC
1601 Hamlett St (75652-5017)
P.O. Box 2042 (75653-2042)
PHONE................................903 657-6616
Kelly S Hall, *President*
Beverly Hall, *Admin Sec*
EMP: 20
SQ FT: 24,000 **Privately Held**
WEB: www.fiberglasscreations.com
SIC: **3229** 3231 Glass fiber products; aquariums & reflectors, glass

(G-8263)
FIBERGLASS SPECIALTIES INC
500 Austin Ave (75652-0101)
P.O. Box 1340 (75653-1340)
PHONE................................903 657-6522
Rocky Hall, *President*
EMP: 90
SQ FT: 42,000
SALES (est): 12.1MM **Privately Held**
WEB: www.fiberglassspecialties.com
SIC: **2221** 3585 Fiberglass fabrics; heat pumps, electric

(G-8264)
HACKER INTERNATIONAL LLC
1601 N Frisco St (75652-6919)
P.O. Box 1208 (75653-1208)
PHONE................................903 657-3546
Jennifer Young, *QC Mgr*
Karen Jimerson, *Finance Mgr*
Josh Stampley, *Supervisor*
Thomas Lortz, *Director*
John Hacker,
▲ EMP: 15
SALES (est): 3.4MM **Privately Held**
WEB: www.hackerinternational.com
SIC: **3532** Drills, bits & similar equipment

(G-8265)
HENDERSON NEWSPAPERS INC
Also Called: Henderson Daily News
1711 Us Highway 79 S (75654-4509)
P.O. Box 30 (75653-0030)
PHONE................................903 657-2501
Noble Welch, *President*
Les Linebarger, *General Mgr*
Sherry Price, *Editor*
King Clyde C Jr, *Vice Pres*
EMP: 30
SQ FT: 11,500
SALES (est): 1.7MM **Privately Held**
WEB: www.thehendersonnews.com
SIC: **2711** 2791 2752 Newspapers, publishing & printing; typesetting; commercial printing, lithographic

(G-8266)
K&B OILFIELD SERVICES INC (PA)
120 Taylor St (75652-5267)
P.O. Box 2384 (75653-2384)
PHONE................................903 392-8213
Anthony King, *President*
Joel Bisnett, *Vice Pres*
EMP: 13
SALES (est): 13MM **Privately Held**
WEB: www.kandboilfieldservices.com
SIC: **1389** 1799 Servicing oil & gas wells; hydraulic equipment, installation & service

(G-8267)
MANSFIELD PLUMBING PDTS LLC
1505 Industrial Dr (75652-5027)
PHONE................................903 657-1436
Dan Butler,
EMP: 84 **Privately Held**
WEB: www.mansfieldplumbing.com
SIC: **3088** 3949 3431 Tubs (bath, shower & laundry), plastic; sporting & athletic goods; metal sanitary ware
HQ: Mansfield Plumbing Products Llc
 150 E 1st St
 Perrysville OH 44864
 419 938-5211

(G-8268)
OIL SCHOOL SERVICES LLC
800 Industrial Dr (75652-5024)
P.O. Box 1598 (75653-1598)
PHONE................................903 657-7600
EMP: 11
SQ FT: 22,000
SALES (est): 950K **Privately Held**
SIC: **3498** Mfg Coil Pipes

(G-8269)
PALMETTO SERVICES LLC
2905 County Road 205 N (75652-9320)
PHONE................................903 655-0900
James Roberts, *CPA*
Ron Stringer, *Mng Member*
Jeffrey T Goldsby,
EMP: 100
SQ FT: 3,500
SALES (est): 16.3MM **Privately Held**
SIC: **1623** 1389 Oil & gas pipeline construction; oil & gas wells: building, repairing & dismantling

(G-8270)
PANEL TRUSS OF LONGVIEW INC
700 Kilgore Dr (75652-5224)
P.O. Box 817 (75653-0817)
PHONE................................903 657-7000
Donnie Powers, *President*
Maline Young, *Principal*
James T Powers, *Vice Pres*
Matt Cummings, *Project Mgr*
Bob Cincar, *Design Engr*
EMP: 15
SALES (est): 2.6MM **Privately Held**
WEB: www.paneltruss.com
SIC: **2439** Trusses, wooden roof

(G-8271)
PANEL TRUSS TEXAS INC
700 Kilgore Dr (75652-5224)
P.O. Box 817 (75653-0817)
PHONE................................903 657-7000
Donnie Powers, *President*
Ron Reid, *General Mgr*
Dickie Vail, *General Mgr*
Bo Powers, *Vice Pres*
Joshua McClanahan, *Plant Mgr*
EMP: 100 EST: 1970
SALES (est): 36.5MM **Privately Held**
WEB: www.paneltruss.com
SIC: **2439** Trusses, wooden roof; trusses, except roof: laminated lumber

(G-8272)
RUNNELS CARPET AND TILE INC
414 Us Highway 79 N (75652-2650)
PHONE................................903 392-8026
Wes Phillips, *President*
Karen Phillips, *Vice Pres*
EMP: 10
SQ FT: 16,000

SALES (est): 1.4MM **Privately Held**
WEB: www.runnelscarpets.com
SIC: **3253** Ceramic wall & floor tile

(G-8273)
SAULSBURY INDUSTRIES INC
2800 County Road 205 N (75652-9301)
PHONE................................903 392-2248
Darwin Witaker, *Branch Mgr*
EMP: 30
SALES (corp-wide): 718.7MM **Privately Held**
WEB: www.saulsbury.com
SIC: **3599** 7692 3441 Machine & other job shop work; welding repair; fabricated structural metal
PA: Saulsbury Industries, Inc.
 2951 E Interstate 20
 Odessa TX 79766
 432 366-3686

(G-8274)
SWC INDUSTRIES INC
Also Called: Swirl-Way
1505 Industrial Dr (75652-5027)
PHONE................................903 657-1436
Larry Rohs, *President*
EMP: 84
SQ FT: 190,000
SALES (est): 7.8MM **Privately Held**
SIC: **3088** Tubs (bath, shower & laundry), plastic
HQ: Mansfield Plumbing Products Llc
 150 E 1st St
 Perrysville OH 44864
 419 938-5211

(G-8275)
TRINITY ASPHALT INC
8621 Hwy 2276 (75652)
PHONE................................903 657-2391
Charles Moore, *President*
Billy Todd Bryan, *Vice Pres*
John Taylor, *Controller*
EMP: 24
SQ FT: 6,500
SALES (est): 9.9MM **Privately Held**
WEB: www.bryanasphalt.net
SIC: **2951** Asphalt paving mixtures & blocks

(G-8276)
TRUSS OPS NORTH LLC
700 Kilgore Dr (75652-5224)
PHONE................................479 824-8787
James Powers, *Principal*
Rich Ackley, *Sales Staff*
EMP: 9
SALES (est): 811.4K **Privately Held**
WEB: www.trussops.com
SIC: **2439** Trusses, wooden roof

(G-8277)
WEST FRASER INC
609 Industrial Dr (75652-5527)
P.O. Box 460 (75653-0460)
PHONE................................903 657-4575
Raymond Mitchell, *Superintendent*
Bill White, *Sales Staff*
Kathy Collvins, *Clerk*
EMP: 135
SQ FT: 9,000
SALES (corp-wide): 3.6B **Privately Held**
WEB: www.westfraser.com
SIC: **2421** Sawmills & planing mills, general
HQ: West Fraser, Inc.
 1900 Exeter Rd Ste 105
 Germantown TN 38138
 901 620-4200

(G-8278)
WILLIAM GRANT TANK VESSEL INC
915 Cr 201 W W (75652)
PHONE................................903 657-6100
William Gary Kappen, *President*
William C Kappen, *Vice Pres*
Kelly G Poe, *Vice Pres*
Mike Brandl, *Materials Mgr*
EMP: 16
SQ FT: 9,900
SALES (est): 6.6MM **Privately Held**
WEB: www.wgt-v.com
SIC: **3443** Tanks, standard or custom fabricated: metal plate

Henrietta
Clay County

(G-8279)
CLAYTEX TROPHIES INC (PA)
Highway 287 W (76365)
P.O. Box 509 (76365-0509)
PHONE..............................940 538-6521
Jack Ellis, *President*
John Belcher, *Vice Pres*
Bill M Holman, *Vice Pres*
▲ EMP: 110
SALES (est): 13MM **Privately Held**
WEB: www.claytex.net
SIC: 3499 3993 3366 2431 Trophies,
metal, except silver; signs & advertising
specialties; copper foundries; millwork

(G-8280)
EXTECH CONSULTING LLC
115 N Main St (76365-2847)
P.O. Box 1 (76365-0001)
PHONE..............................940 613-6461
Adam Gonbenbach, *Mng Member*
Josh Lewig, *Mng Member*
EMP: 50
SALES (est): 1.2MM **Privately Held**
SIC: 1389 Oil consultants

(G-8281)
KERR FEED & GRAIN COMPANY
903 E Omega St (76365-3006)
P.O. Box 226 (76365-0226)
PHONE..............................940 538-4354
Bill Bryant, *President*
William Wade Bryant, *Vice Pres*
Kerri Beaver, *Director*
EMP: 11
SQ FT: 5,000
SALES (est): 710K **Privately Held**
WEB: www.kerrfeed.com
SIC: 0212 3999 3432 5211 Beef cattle
except feedlots; pet supplies; plumbing
fixture fittings & trim; fencing; lawn & gar-
den equipment

(G-8282)
PIERCE ARROW INC
Also Called: Pierce Sales
549 Us Highway 287 S (76365-7006)
PHONE..............................940 538-5643
Jeff Pierce, *President*
Wade Pierce, *Opers Mgr*
Chris Claeys, *Parts Mgr*
Tyler Coleman, *Engineer*
Ginger Schaffner, *Accounting Mgr*
◆ EMP: 16
SQ FT: 14,000
SALES (est): 4MM **Privately Held**
WEB: www.piercesales.com
SIC: 3711 3531 5072 3523 Wreckers
(tow truck), assembly of; winches; hard-
ware; farm machinery & equipment;
pumps & pumping equipment; motor vehi-
cle parts & accessories

Hereford
Deaf Smith County

(G-8283)
ARCHER-DANIELS-MIDLAND COMPANY
Also Called: ADM
3746 S Progressive Rd (79045-8515)
PHONE..............................806 364-4732
Mona Klein, *Branch Mgr*
Randy Paetzold, *Manager*
EMP: 10
SALES (corp-wide): 64.6B **Publicly Held**
WEB: www.adm.com
SIC: 2041 Flour & other grain mill products
PA: Archer-Daniels-Midland Company
77 W Wacker Dr Ste 4600
Chicago IL 60601
312 634-8100

(G-8284)
BRANDON & CLARK INC
Also Called: Hereford Division
501 E 1st St (79045-5603)
PHONE..............................806 364-5470
Jody Lawrence, *Sales Staff*
Keith Kelso, *Branch Mgr*
EMP: 13
SALES (corp-wide): 49.3MM **Privately Held**
WEB: www.brandonclark.com
SIC: 7694 5063 Electric motor repair;
power transmission equipment, electric
PA: Brandon & Clark, Inc.
3623 Interstate 27
Lubbock TX 79404
806 771-5600

(G-8285)
CARGILL INCORPORATED
3537 S Progressive Rd (79045-7566)
PHONE..............................806 364-3891
Derek McChesney, *Manager*
EMP: 18
SALES (corp-wide): 113.4B **Privately Held**
WEB: www.peterschocolate.com
SIC: 2048 Prepared feeds
PA: Cargill, Incorporated
15407 Mcginty Rd W
Wayzata MN 55391
952 742-7575

(G-8286)
CAVINESS PACKING COMPANY INC
3255 Hwy 60 (79045)
P.O. Box 790 (79045-0790)
PHONE..............................806 357-2443
Trevor Caviness, *Vice Pres*
Israel Martinez, *Purchasing*
Jorge Aleman, *QC Mgr*
Allen Hare, *Sales Staff*
Steve Anthony, *Director*
EMP: 240
SALES (est): 25.4MM **Privately Held**
WEB: www.cavinessbeefpackers.com
SIC: 2011 Beef products from beef slaugh-
tered on site

(G-8287)
COLLIERS TOP OF TEXAS INC
715 E New York St (79045-5805)
P.O. Box 233 (79045-0233)
PHONE..............................806 363-2867
Matt J Collier, *President*
Robbie Collier, *Vice Pres*
Kathleen J Collier, *Admin Sec*
Kathleen Collier, *Admin Sec*
EMP: 30
SQ FT: 32,500
SALES (est): 4.6MM **Privately Held**
WEB: www.topoftx.com
SIC: 1796 7692 Millwright; welding repair

(G-8288)
FERRELL-ROSS ROLL MFG INC
3690 Fm 2856 (79045-7463)
PHONE..............................806 364-9051
David C Ibach Jr, *CEO*
Jim Cwelich, *Vice Pres*
Angela Friemel, *Buyer*
Wade Carrol, *Sales Staff*
Jake Mendoza, *Sales Staff*
◆ EMP: 65
SALES (est): 16.3MM **Privately Held**
WEB: www.ferrellross.com
SIC: 3556 3499 3533 Food products ma-
chinery; machine bases, metal; oil & gas
field machinery

(G-8289)
GREEN PLAINS HEREFORD LLC
4300 County Road 6 (79045-7548)
P.O. Box 7000, El Dorado AR (71731-
7000)
PHONE..............................806 258-7800
R Andrew Clyde, *President*
Marn Cheng, *President*
L W Stutts III, *Vice Pres*
T Stutts, *Vice Pres*
J Ford, *Treasurer*
EMP: 59
SALES (est): 16.6MM
SALES (corp-wide): 2.4B **Publicly Held**
WEB: www.herefordbrand.com
SIC: 2869 Ethyl alcohol, ethanol
PA: Green Plains Inc.
1811 Aksarben Dr
Omaha NE 68106
402 884-8700

(G-8290)
H & R BLACK MFG CO LLC
Also Called: Www.wtrt.net/Handrmfg
210 Ross Ave (79045-5149)
P.O. Box 1411 (79045-1411)
PHONE..............................806 364-2040
Ruth Black, *Owner*
Carey Black, *Purch Dir*
Tanner Black, *Engineer*
Phil Martin, *Sales Staff*
Herschel Black, *Mng Member*
EMP: 10
SQ FT: 16,000
SALES (est): 1MM **Privately Held**
WEB: www.hrmfgco.com
SIC: 2395 2329 Embroidery products, ex-
cept schiffli machine; jackets (suede,
leatherette, etc.), sport: men's & boys';
windbreakers: men's, youths' & boys'

(G-8291)
HEREFORD BRAND INC
Also Called: Hereford Brand, The
506 S 25 Mile Ave (79045-5004)
P.O. Box 673 (79045-0673)
PHONE..............................806 364-2030
James Roberts, *Ch of Bd*
Mauri Montgomery, *President*
Walter Buckel, *Corp Secy*
Robert Brown, *Vice Pres*
EMP: 20
SQ FT: 11,750
SALES (est): 1.1MM **Privately Held**
WEB: www.herefordbrand.com
SIC: 2711 Newspapers: publishing only,
not printed on site

(G-8292)
K P A N BROADCASTERS
Also Called: Kpan Am/FM
218 E 5th St (79045-5404)
P.O. Box 1757 (79045-1757)
PHONE..............................806 364-1860
Chip Formby, *General Mgr*
EMP: 10
SQ FT: 2,200
SALES (est): 411.7K **Privately Held**
WEB: www.kpanradio.com
SIC: 4832 2711 Radio broadcasting sta-
tions, music format; newspapers

(G-8293)
MARCO SERVICES INC
222 Northwest Dr (79045-4126)
P.O. Box 1006 (79045-1006)
PHONE..............................806 344-4784
Jerry Marquez, *President*
EMP: 10 EST: 2014
SQ FT: 4,000
SALES (est): 719.3K **Privately Held**
SIC: 1389 Haulage, oil field

(G-8294)
NUTRI-FEEDS INC
Us 60 Rd I (79045)
P.O. Box 2257 (79045-2257)
PHONE..............................806 357-2288
Brady Jones, *Manager*
EMP: 30
SALES (corp-wide): 2.7MM **Privately Held**
SIC: 2077 2048 Rendering; prepared
feeds
PA: Nutri-Feeds Inc
W Hwy 60 Rd I
Hereford TX
806 364-0951

(G-8295)
TEJAS INDUSTRIES INC
3783 Fm 2943 (79045-7585)
PHONE..............................806 322-2822
Garth Merrick, *President*
EMP: 20
SALES (corp-wide): 93.5B **Privately Held**
WEB: www.merrickpetcare.com
SIC: 2047 Dog food
HQ: Tejas Industries, Inc.
101 Se 11th Ave Ste 200
Amarillo TX 79101
806 322-2800

(G-8296)
VALLEY FARM SERVICE INC
3510 Us Highway 385 (79045-7414)
P.O. Box 110 (79045-0110)
PHONE..............................806 364-6900
Tim Gearn, *CEO*
EMP: 10 EST: 1976
SQ FT: 5,200
SALES (est): 2.1MM **Privately Held**
SIC: 3523 3498 Fertilizing, spraying, dust-
ing & irrigation machinery; fabricated pipe
& fittings

(G-8297)
WE HEREFORD LLC
Also Called: White Energy Hereford
3748 S Progressive Rd (79045-8515)
PHONE..............................806 360-7400
Don Gales, *CEO*
EMP: 42
SALES (est): 6.2MM
SALES (corp-wide): 17.1MM **Privately Held**
WEB: www.white-energy.com
SIC: 2869 Ethyl alcohol, ethanol
PA: White Energy Holding Company, Llc
2595 Dallas Pkwy Ste 310
Frisco TX 75034
972 715-6490

(G-8298)
WESTWAY FEED PRODUCTS LLC
Shur-Gro Liquid Feed Division
3588 County Road H (79045-7393)
PHONE..............................806 364-5200
Troy Miller, *Regional Mgr*
Harold Mnnutt, *Manager*
EMP: 18
SQ FT: 3,000
SALES (corp-wide): 7.7B **Privately Held**
WEB: www.contanda.com
SIC: 2048 5191 Feed supplements; ani-
mal feeds
HQ: Westway Feed Products Llc
365 Canal St Ste 2929
New Orleans LA 70130
504 934-1850

Hewitt
Mclennan County

(G-8299)
DAVIS IRON WORKS INC
Also Called: Davis Steel Services
224 N Hewitt Dr (76643-3044)
P.O. Box 99 (76643-0099)
PHONE..............................254 666-1000
J E Williams, *President*
Frank Ramos, *Senior VP*
Bailey Rogers, *CFO*
Beverly Reinke, *Admin Sec*
EMP: 74
SQ FT: 140,000
SALES (est): 22.6MM **Privately Held**
WEB: www.davisiron.com
SIC: 3441 Fabricated structural metal

(G-8300)
SCHULTZ INDUSTRIES INC (PA)
Also Called: Sturdisteel Company
131 Ava Dr (76643-2906)
P.O. Box 2655, Waco (76702-2655)
PHONE..............................254 666-5155
Fred J Schultz, *CEO*
Johnny Bledsoe, *President*
Roger Mills, *Purch Mgr*
Kevin Warapius, *Engineer*
Cynthia Peterson, *Controller*
EMP: 92
SQ FT: 46,000
SALES: 33.2MM **Privately Held**
WEB: www.sturdisteel.com
SIC: 2531 Bleacher seating, portable; sta-
dium seating; picnic tables or benches,
park

(G-8301)
SURE TRAC INC
Also Called: Sure Trac of Texas
1037 Industrial Blvd (76643-4102)
PHONE..............................254 666-6732
Pat Boney, *Branch Mgr*

▲ = Import ▼=Export
◆ =Import/Export

EMP: 20
SALES (corp-wide): 2MM **Privately Held**
WEB: www.suretracaxle.com
SIC: 3462 Automotive forgings, ferrous: crankshaft, engine, axle, etc.
PA: Sure Trac Inc
635 Highway 9 Byp W
Loris SC 29569
843 756-5544

Hico
Hamilton County

(G-8302)
CARPENTER WELDING & MACHINE
Hwy 281 N (76457)
P.O. Box 620 (76457-0620)
PHONE.....................254 796-2114
Billy L Carpenter, *President*
Brandon Carpenter, *Vice Pres*
St Clare Carpenter, *Treasurer*
EMP: 10
SQ FT: 9,000
SALES (est): 1.4MM **Privately Held**
SIC: 3599 Machine shop, jobbing & repair

(G-8303)
WISEMAN HOUSE COMPANIES INC (PA)
Also Called: Wiseman House Chocolates
406 W Grubbs St (76457)
P.O. Box 583 (76457-0583)
PHONE.....................254 796-2565
Ladonne Wenzel, *President*
Kevin Wenzel, *Vice Pres*
EMP: 11
SQ FT: 2,700
SALES (est): 907.2K **Privately Held**
WEB: www.wisemanhousechocolates.com
SIC: 2066 5441 5932 Chocolate; candy, nut & confectionery stores; antiques

Hidalgo
Hidalgo County

(G-8304)
BSN MEDICAL INC
400 Olmos (78557-2554)
PHONE.....................956 926-4400
Coleen Thompson, *Partner*
Brian Cooper, *Business Mgr*
Laney Gonzalez, *Business Mgr*
Marc Hatch, *Business Mgr*
Marc Jones, *Business Mgr*
EMP: 20
SALES (est): 13.3B **Privately Held**
WEB: www.bsnmedical.us
SIC: 3842 Surgical appliances & supplies
HQ: Bsn Medical, Inc.
5825 Carnegie Blvd
Charlotte NC 28209
704 554-9933

(G-8305)
DURO BAG MANUFACTURING COMPANY
410 N 4th St (78557-2559)
PHONE.....................956 843-6607
Roberto Castill, *Branch Mgr*
EMP: 175
SALES (corp-wide): 797.8MM **Privately Held**
WEB: www.novolex.com
SIC: 2621 Bags: uncoated paper & multi-wall
PA: Duro Bag Manufacturing Company
7600 Empire Dr
Florence KY 41042
859 371-2150

(G-8306)
EATON CORPORATION
Also Called: Corning
300 E Olmos Dr Ste B (78557)
PHONE.....................956 843-3450
EMP: 11 **Privately Held**
WEB: www.eatonelectrical.com
SIC: 3511 Hydraulic turbine generator set units, complete

HQ: Eaton Corporation
1000 Eaton Blvd
Cleveland OH 44122
440 523-5000

(G-8307)
FERZA COMPANY LLC
1314 E Ramon Ayala Dr 4 (78557-2621)
PHONE.....................956 686-7100
EMP: 9
SALES (est): 1MM **Privately Held**
SIC: 1381 Oil/Gas Well Drilling

(G-8308)
GEMINI INCORPORATED
600 E Produce Rd (78557-4324)
PHONE.....................507 263-3957
EMP: 10
SALES (corp-wide): 94.6MM **Privately Held**
WEB: www.geminisignproducts.com
SIC: 3089 Injection molding of plastics
PA: Gemini, Incorporated
103 Mensing Way
Cannon Falls MN 55009
507 263-3957

(G-8309)
SANTRE EXPORT USA LLC
319 E Coma Ave Ste 844 (78557-2506)
PHONE.....................811 053-1165
Javier Santisteban,
EMP: 30
SALES (est): 707.6K **Privately Held**
SIC: 3999 Manufacturing industries

(G-8310)
TST NA TRIM LLC
401 E Olmos Ave (78557)
PHONE.....................956 843-3500
Masahito Iida, *President*
Yasuo Kibe, *Treasurer*
Jason MA, *Admin Sec*
Kiyohiko Hamaguchi,
▲ **EMP:** 3000 **EST:** 2010
SQ FT: 12,486
SALES (est): 228.8MM **Privately Held**
WEB: www.tstech.co.jp
SIC: 2396 Automotive trimmings, fabric
HQ: Ts Tech Americas, Inc.
8458 E Broad St
Reynoldsburg OH 43068
614 575-4100

Highlands
Harris County

(G-8311)
AHA PROCESS INC (PA)
421 Jones Rd (77562-4215)
P.O. Box 727 (77562-0727)
PHONE.....................281 426-5300
Ruby K Payne, *CEO*
T Hardie Bowman IV, *COO*
Peg Conrad, *Vice Pres*
Alecia Chapman, *Project Mgr*
Susie Spurgeon, *Controller*
EMP: 20
SQ FT: 18,000
SALES (est): 3.3MM **Privately Held**
WEB: www.ahaprocess.com
SIC: 2731 Books: publishing only

(G-8312)
INDUSTRIAL SAND PRODUCTS LLC
11501 Crosby Rd (77562)
P.O. Box 656 (77562-0656)
PHONE.....................832 838-8095
EMP: 10
SALES (corp-wide): 1.9MM **Privately Held**
SIC: 1446 Industrial sand
PA: Industrial Sand Products, Llc
11501 Crosby Lynchburg Rd
Crosby TX 77532
281 843-7263

(G-8313)
MINERALTECH GULF COAST ABR LLC (PA)
Also Called: Mineraltechllc.com
11501 Crosby Lynchburg (77562)
P.O. Box 1027 (77562-1027)
PHONE.....................832 838-8623
Glenn McClain, *President*
Randy Barnes, *Plant Mgr*
Warde Liesmann, *Plant Mgr*
Rick Pierson, *Plant Mgr*
Shawn Barnes, *Admin Sec*
EMP: 31 **EST:** 2011
SALES (est): 19MM **Privately Held**
WEB: www.mineraltechllc.com
SIC: 3312 Blast furnace & related products

(G-8314)
RECONDITIONED COUPLINGS INC
102 Whites Lk Estates Dr (77562-4251)
PHONE.....................832 878-6255
Kathy Meek, *President*
EMP: 12
SALES (corp-wide): 2MM **Privately Held**
WEB: www.reconditioncouplings.com
SIC: 3498 4731 Couplings, pipe: fabricated from purchased pipe; freight transportation arrangement
PA: Reconditioned Couplings Inc
7415 Miller Road 2
Houston TX 77049
281 457-6622

(G-8315)
TUBULAR MAKEUP TECHNOLOGY INC
Also Called: T M T
1105 N Main St (77562-2631)
P.O. Box 931, Crosby (77532-0931)
PHONE.....................281 452-5211
Earl L Magee, *President*
Donny Wade, *Plant Mgr*
Philip Handley, *Maint Spvr*
Blake Thomas, *Treasurer*
Grant Thomas, *Sales Mgr*
EMP: 20
SALES (est): 4.7MM **Privately Held**
WEB: www.tmtusa.net
SIC: 1389 Oil field services

(G-8316)
ZXP TECHNOLOGIES LLC
409 E Wallisville Rd (77562-3827)
PHONE.....................281 426-8800
EMP: 200
SALES (est): 5.7MM **Privately Held**
SIC: 2899 Mfg Chemical Preparations

(G-8317)
ZXP TECHNOLOGIES LLC
409 Wallisville Rd (77562)
PHONE.....................281 426-8800
James Taylor, *CEO*
Steve Davis, *COO*
Patric Elders, *Vice Pres*
Jayna Mull, *Vice Pres*
Mike Standley, *Vice Pres*
◆ **EMP:** 259
SQ FT: 375,000
SALES (est): 77.9MM **Privately Held**
WEB: www.zxptech.com
SIC: 2992 7549 2879 Oils & greases, blending & compounding; lubrication service, automotive; agricultural chemicals

Hillister
Tyler County

(G-8318)
DAVID HATTON LOGGING INC
601 County Road 4390 (77624-5195)
PHONE.....................409 656-8535
David Hatton, *President*
Brad Hatton, *Vice Pres*
Pamela Hatton, *Admin Sec*
EMP: 9
SALES (est): 2MM **Privately Held**
SIC: 2411 Timber, cut at logging camp

(G-8319)
EAST TEXAS TRUSS LLC
532 Fm 1013 Rd (77624-5271)
P.O. Box 80 (77624-0080)
PHONE.....................409 283-3728
Ronald Poindexter,
EMP: 10 **EST:** 2006
SALES (est): 1.4MM **Privately Held**
WEB: www.easttexastruss.com
SIC: 2439 Trusses, wooden roof

Hillsboro
Hill County

(G-8320)
ACE MACHINING TECHNOLOGIES
110 Private Road 435 (76645-7263)
PHONE.....................254 632-4250
EMP: 15
SQ FT: 33,000
SALES (est): 2.4MM **Privately Held**
WEB: www.acemachining.com
SIC: 3599 Machine shop, jobbing & repair

(G-8321)
ASCOT ENTERPRISES INC
304 Coke Ave (76645-2655)
P.O. Box 165, Nappanee IN (46550-0165)
PHONE.....................254 582-1970
EMP: 15
SALES (corp-wide): 102.7MM **Privately Held**
SIC: 2391 Manufacturer Of Window Treatments
PA: Ascot Enterprises Inc
503 S Main St
Nappanee IN 46550
877 773-7751

(G-8322)
BOBCAT CONTRACTING LLC (PA)
1721 Hcr 3106 (76645-4092)
P.O. Box 663 (76645-0663)
PHONE.....................254 582-0205
Roy M Young, *President*
Lance Kettler, *Superintendent*
Jay Mackey, *Superintendent*
Tony White, *Safety Dir*
Ryan King, *Project Mgr*
EMP: 152
SQ FT: 5,000
SALES (est): 169.7MM **Privately Held**
WEB: www.bobcatcontracting.com
SIC: 1389 Construction, repair & dismantling services

(G-8323)
BRANDOM HOLDINGS LLC
Also Called: Brandom Cabinets
404 Hawkins St (76645-3224)
PHONE.....................800 366-8001
Dwayne Warren, *Mng Member*
Ben Hinterlong, *Mng Member*
William Montgomery, *Mng Member*
EMP: 140
SQ FT: 150,000
SALES (est): 12MM **Privately Held**
WEB: www.wisenbaker.com
SIC: 2434 Vanities, bathroom: wood

(G-8324)
COLLINGWOOD GRAIN INC
Also Called: ADM
221 Chestnut St (76645-3209)
PHONE.....................254 582-5344
Fax: 254 582-3066
EMP: 10
SALES (corp-wide): 81.2B **Publicly Held**
SIC: 2041 5261 Grain Marketing & Retails Feed Fertilizer
HQ: Collingwood Grain Inc
17 Wyoming
Goodland KS 67735
785 899-3636

(G-8325)
GATE PRECAST COMPANY
1220 N Highway 77 (76645-3605)
P.O. Box 1305 (76645-1305)
PHONE.....................254 582-7200
Bill Dohrwardt, *Design Engr*

Scott Robinson, *Sales Staff*
EMP: 120
SALES (corp-wide): 708.1K **Privately Held**
WEB: www.gateprecast.com
SIC: 3272 Concrete products
HQ: Gate Precast Company
　9540 San Jose Blvd
　Jacksonville FL 32257
　904 732-7668

(G-8326)
HANESBRANDS INC
Also Called: L'Eggs - Hnes - Bali - Playtex
104 I 35 Hwy Se Ste 138b (76645-2709)
PHONE......................254 582-7541
Paula Wheeler, *Branch Mgr*
EMP: 10 **Publicly Held**
WEB: www.hanes.com
SIC: 2342 5632 Bras, girdles & allied garments; hosiery
PA: Hanesbrands Inc.
　1000 E Hanes Mill Rd
　Winston Salem NC 27105

(G-8327)
HILL COUNTY PRESS INC (PA)
Also Called: Business Supply Center
335 Country Club Dr (76645-2374)
P.O. Box 569 (76645-0569)
PHONE......................254 582-3431
Roger W Galle, *President*
David Kolar, *Corp Secy*
Richard D Bailey Jr, *Vice Pres*
Dave Kolar, *Treasurer*
Mary Ann Johnson, *Admin Sec*
EMP: 19
SQ FT: 9,500
SALES (est): 1.5MM **Privately Held**
WEB: www.bschillsboro.net
SIC: 2711 5943 5112 Newspapers, publishing & printing; office forms & supplies; office supplies

(G-8328)
HILLSBORO REPORTER INC
335 Country Club Dr (76645-2374)
P.O. Box 569 (76645-0569)
PHONE......................254 582-3431
Roger Galle, *President*
Nelson Galle, *Vice Pres*
Richard Ray Galle, *Vice Pres*
EMP: 15
SQ FT: 10,000
SALES (est): 846.9K **Privately Held**
WEB: www.hillsbororeporter.com
SIC: 2711 2752 Newspapers, publishing & printing; commercial printing, lithographic

(G-8329)
L B FOSTER COMPANY
Also Called: Foster Geotechnical
901 N Highway 77 (76645-3600)
PHONE......................254 296-6100
Jason Busby, *Plant Mgr*
Kerry Moore, *Sales Staff*
EMP: 55
SALES (corp-wide): 655MM **Publicly Held**
WEB: www.lbfoster.com
SIC: 3441 Fabricated structural metal
PA: L. B. Foster Company
　415 Holiday Dr Ste 1
　Pittsburgh PA 15220
　412 928-3400

(G-8330)
MCGILL AIRFLOW LLC
206 Pecos St (76645-3050)
PHONE......................254 580-1680
John Montell, *Managing Dir*
Bill Perry, *Branch Mgr*
Trey Fitzgerald, *Manager*
EMP: 25
SQ FT: 30,000
SALES (corp-wide): 72.8MM **Privately Held**
WEB: www.mcgillairflow.com
SIC: 3444 Ducts, sheet metal
HQ: Mcgill Airflow Llc
　1 Mission Park
　Groveport OH 43125
　614 829-1200

(G-8331)
THERMAFOAM OPERATING LLC
1240 N Highway 77 (76645-3605)
PHONE......................254 582-2730
Mike Power, *President*
Michael Janek, *Plant Mgr*
Cindy Gebbia, *Sales Staff*
Dennis Shannon, *Manager*
Richard Davidovich,
EMP: 33
SALES (est): 11MM **Privately Held**
WEB: www.thermafoam.com
SIC: 3086 Insulation or cushioning material, foamed plastic; ice chests or coolers (portable), foamed plastic

(G-8332)
VESUVIUS U S A CORPORATION
210 Pecos St (76645-3050)
PHONE......................903 597-7237
David McPherson, *Manager*
EMP: 112
SALES (corp-wide): 2.2B **Privately Held**
WEB: www.vesuvius.com
SIC: 3297 Graphite refractories: carbon bond or ceramic bond
HQ: Vesuvius U S A Corporation
　1404 Newton Dr
　Champaign IL 61822
　217 351-5000

Hitchcock
Galveston County

(G-8333)
AMERICAN WELDING SERVICES
5923 Delany Rd (77563-1716)
P.O. Box 65 (77563-0065)
PHONE......................409 440-8143
Christopher T Gray, *President*
Chris Gray, *Business Mgr*
Karen Kiddie, *Executive*
EMP: 38
SALES (est): 6.9MM **Privately Held**
WEB: www.aws-corp.com
SIC: 7692 Welding repair

(G-8334)
C BAR CONTRACTORS I LTD
5757 Ghinaudo Rd (77563-4670)
PHONE......................409 925-5757
Chad Childress, *Partner*
EMP: 10
SALES (est): 950K **Privately Held**
WEB: www.cbarcontractors.com
SIC: 1522 3499 Residential construction; fabricated metal products

(G-8335)
CHRISS WELDING & FABRICATING
Also Called: Chriss Welding & Sign Erection
5930 Delany Rd (77563-1717)
PHONE......................409 986-6094
Chris Ray, *Owner*
EMP: 10 **EST:** 1981
SQ FT: 2,400
SALES (est): 200K **Privately Held**
SIC: 7692 Welding repair

(G-8336)
DAVID KEELS
Also Called: D & A Welding & Fabrication Co
7610 Fm 2004 Rd (77563-3860)
PHONE......................409 316-9265
David Keels, *Owner*
Roy Buchan, *Principal*
Ashley Cantrell, *Principal*
EMP: 21
SALES (est): 1.4MM **Privately Held**
WEB: www.dawelding.com
SIC: 3731 3732 3089 2899 Offshore supply boats, building & repairing; crew boats, building & repairing; motorized boat, building & repairing; plastic boats & other marine equipment; fluxes: brazing, soldering, galvanizing & welding; construction, repair & dismantling services; crane & aerial lift service

(G-8337)
DIAMOND HYDRAULICS INC
6776 Fm 2004 Rd (77563-3039)
PHONE......................409 440-8032
Debra Gibson, *CEO*
Robert C Drenth, *President*
William Paul Gibson, *Corp Secy*
▲ **EMP:** 46
SQ FT: 33,000
SALES (est): 10MM **Privately Held**
WEB: www.diamondhydraulics.com
SIC: 7699 3594 Hydraulic equipment repair; pumps, hydraulic power transfer; motors: hydraulic, fluid power or air

(G-8338)
JOHNNY BAULCH
Also Called: Baulch's Sandpit
5305 Highway 6 (77563-2310)
P.O. Box 1143, Texas City (77592-1143)
PHONE......................409 938-8971
Johnny Baulch, *Owner*
EMP: 10
SALES (est): 829.3K **Privately Held**
SIC: 1629 1442 Dredging contractor; earthmoving contractor; common sand mining; construction sand mining

(G-8339)
PARKLINE INC
Also Called: Bebco Industries
5235 Delany Rd (77563-1855)
P.O. Box 128 (77563-0128)
PHONE......................409 935-5743
Rolo Philips, *President*
Joseph Downey, *Business Mgr*
EMP: 70
SALES (corp-wide): 41.9MM **Privately Held**
WEB: www.parkline.com
SIC: 3448 3822 3444 3613 Prefabricated metal buildings; pneumatic relays, air-conditioning type; sheet metal specialties, not stamped; control panels, electric
PA: Parkline, Inc.
　328 Eleanor Indus Pk Dr
　Eleanor WV 25070
　800 786-4855

(G-8340)
TOM DAENEN INC
Also Called: Design Power International
7531 Fm 2004 Rd (77563-4588)
P.O. Box 86 (77563-0086)
PHONE......................409 978-2132
Tom Daenen, *President*
Jan Daenen, *Vice Pres*
◆ **EMP:** 27
SQ FT: 30,000
SALES (est): 3.5MM **Privately Held**
SIC: 3519 5084 Diesel engine rebuilding; engines & parts, diesel

---

Hockley
Harris County

(G-8341)
BALLISTICS SYSTEMS INC
26200 Lakeview Dr (77447-6450)
PHONE......................713 939-1160
EMP: 14
SALES (est): 1MM **Privately Held**
SIC: 3211 Manufacturer Security Windows Specializing In Bullet Proof Windows

(G-8342)
CEMEX CONSTRUCTION MTLS S LLC
17919 Kermier Rd (77447-9131)
PHONE......................936 372-0493
Mike Reid, *Branch Mgr*
EMP: 14 **Privately Held**
WEB: www.cemexusa.com
SIC: 3241 1771 Cement, hydraulic; concrete work
HQ: Cemex Construction Materials South, Llc
　2088 E 20th St
　Yuma AZ 85365
　928 343-4100

(G-8343)
EXQUIP USA LLC (PA)
31975 Joseph Rd (77447-6164)
P.O. Box 925750, Houston (77292-5750)
PHONE......................936 372-3002
Peter Kroll, *President*
◆ **EMP:** 15
SQ FT: 1,200
SALES (est): 3.3MM **Privately Held**
WEB: www.exquip.de
SIC: 3084 8742 Plastics pipe; manufacturing management consultant

(G-8344)
FISHER INDUSTRIES INC
Also Called: Fisherpump
26091 Pine Shadows Dr (77447-6398)
P.O. Box 41026, Houston (77241-1026)
PHONE......................713 937-6838
Raymond Fisher, *President*
◆ **EMP:** 11
SQ FT: 30,000
SALES (est): 4.1MM **Privately Held**
WEB: www.fisher-energy.com
SIC: 5084 3599 3443 Pumps & pumping equipment; machine shop, jobbing & repair; industrial vessels, tanks & containers

(G-8345)
FOSTER FARM & EQUIPMENT SUPPLY
Also Called: John Deere Authorized Dealer
33402 Highway 290 (77447-7885)
P.O. Box 11050, Liberty (77575-7980)
PHONE......................281 256-6900
David Foster, *Principal*
EMP: 15
SALES (est): 1.7MM **Privately Held**
WEB: www.generalimp.com
SIC: 3523 5082 Farm machinery & equipment; construction & mining machinery

(G-8346)
H & H LANDSCAPE SERVICES LLC
35514 Old Highway 290 (77447-7916)
PHONE......................832 831-9133
Brandon J Holladay, *Principal*
Ray Goldbeck, *Sales Staff*
EMP: 12 **EST:** 2012
SALES (est): 509.9K **Privately Held**
WEB: www.handhlandscapeservices.com
SIC: 0781 1611 3523 1711 Landscape services; concrete construction: roads, highways, sidewalks, etc.; fertilizing, spraying, dusting & irrigation machinery; irrigation sprinkler system installation; irrigation system construction; irrigation systems

(G-8347)
ROWE EQUIPMENT INC
19534 Bauer Rd (77447-9639)
P.O. Box 1716, Cypress (77410-1716)
PHONE......................281 255-0555
Jeffrey Rowe, *President*
Sue Lynn Hattan, *Vice Pres*
John Williams, *Controller*
▲ **EMP:** 15
SQ FT: 5,000
SALES (est): 1MM **Privately Held**
WEB: www.roweequipment.com
SIC: 3496 Fabrics, woven wire

(G-8348)
SCHULTE BUILDING SYSTEMS INC (PA)
17600 Badtke Rd (77447-7818)
P.O. Box 609 (77447-0609)
PHONE......................281 304-6111
Fred Koetting, *President*
Sam Thompson, *Regional Mgr*
Joe Arnold, *District Mgr*
Jeff Cheyne, *District Mgr*
Wil Cheyne, *District Mgr*
EMP: 84
SQ FT: 12,000
SALES (est): 150MM **Privately Held**
WEB: www.sbslp.com
SIC: 3448 Buildings, portable: prefabricated metal

(G-8349)
TRIPLE C INDUSTRIES INC
36296 1/2 Old Highway 290 (77447-7907)
PHONE....................................936 931-1171
J G Carlton, *President*
M B Carlton, *Vice Pres*
Curtis Carlton, *Opers Mgr*
EMP: 24
SQ FT: 10,000
SALES (est): 3.9MM **Privately Held**
WEB: www.triplecindustries.com
SIC: 3444 1799 1721 7692 Sheet metal specialties, not stamped; sandblasting of building exteriors; industrial painting; welding repair

(G-8350)
UNITED SALT BAYTOWN LLC
14002 Warren Ranch Rd (77447-9111)
PHONE....................................936 372-3931
Dennis Bradley, *Manager*
Chris Du Plooy, *Administration*
EMP: 46
SALES (corp-wide): 247.1MM **Privately Held**
WEB: www.unitedsalt.com
SIC: 1479 2899 Salt (common) mining; chemical preparations
HQ: United Salt Baytown Llc
    4800 San Felipe St # 100
    Houston TX 77056
    713 877-2600

(G-8351)
UNITED SALT HOCKLEY LLC
14002 Warren Ranch Rd (77447-9111)
PHONE....................................713 877-2781
Mark Wiggins, *President*
Stacey Owens, *Treasurer*
Cathy Gillies, *Admin Sec*
EMP: 50
SALES (est): 9MM **Privately Held**
WEB: www.unitedsalt.com
SIC: 1479 Mineral pigment mining

Holliday
Archer County

(G-8352)
LEWIS OPERATING CO
Also Called: Lewis, Larry
105 S E Ave (76366)
P.O. Box 10 (76366-0010)
PHONE....................................940 723-0266
Mark A Lewis, *President*
Casey Barham, *Vice Pres*
EMP: 16
SQ FT: 6,000
SALES (est): 3.1MM **Privately Held**
SIC: 1311 Crude petroleum production; natural gas production

Hondo
Medina County

(G-8353)
ASSOCIATED TEXAS NEWSPAPERS
Also Called: Hondo Anvil Herald, The
1601 Avenue K (78861-1838)
P.O. Box 400 (78861-0400)
PHONE....................................830 426-3346
William E Berger, *President*
Cathy Walton, *Principal*
Jerry Berger, *Corp Secy*
Jeff Berger, *Vice Pres*
Kaye Langford, *Vice Pres*
EMP: 15 EST: 1886
SQ FT: 4,000
SALES (est): 1MM **Privately Held**
WEB: www.hondoanvilherald.com
SIC: 2711 2752 Newspapers: publishing only, not printed on site; commercial printing, offset

(G-8354)
C & W FUELS INC (PA)
670 Fm 462 N (78861-5028)
P.O. Box 40 (78861-0040)
PHONE....................................830 426-4301
Ryan Wiemers, *President*

EMP: 12 EST: 2008
SALES (est): 1.6MM **Privately Held**
WEB: www.wjgcpa.com
SIC: 2869 Fuels

(G-8355)
MARTIN MARIETTA MATERIALS INC
4670 State Highway 173 N (78861-6576)
PHONE....................................830 741-8227
EMP: 20 **Publicly Held**
WEB: www.martinmarietta.com
SIC: 3273 Crushed & broken limestone
PA: Martin Marietta Materials Inc
    2710 Wycliff Rd
    Raleigh NC 27607

(G-8356)
T HANGERS INC
3095 County Road 251 (78861-6873)
P.O. Box 7 (78861-0007)
PHONE....................................830 741-8383
Bill Tinert, *President*
▲ EMP: 12
SALES (est): 1MM **Privately Held**
WEB: www.t-hangers.com
SIC: 3949 Hunting equipment

Honey Grove
Fannin County

(G-8357)
NATIONAL BANNER COMPANY INC
300 E Main St (75446-1334)
PHONE....................................903 378-2761
Abraham Goldfarb, *Owner*
Kari Perkins, *Plant Mgr*
EMP: 46
SALES (corp-wide): 24.7MM **Privately Held**
WEB: www.nationalbanner.com
SIC: 3993 Signs & advertising specialties
PA: National Banner Company, Inc.
    11938 Harry Hines Blvd
    Dallas TX 75234
    972 241-2131

(G-8358)
R K TEXAS LEATHER MFG INC
Also Called: Rebirth Leathers
104 E Main St (75446-1346)
P.O. Box 148 (75446-0148)
PHONE....................................903 378-2100
Richard Ohr, *President*
Morris Cynthia, *Vice Pres*
▲ EMP: 9
SQ FT: 10,000
SALES (est): 1.5MM **Privately Held**
WEB: www.texasleather.com
SIC: 3172 5948 5199 Personal leather goods; leather goods, except luggage & shoes; leather, leather goods & furs

(G-8359)
WISE PRODUCTS CO INC (PA)
400 Commerce St E (75446-1329)
P.O. Box 67 (75446-0067)
PHONE....................................903 378-2233
Gary L Beavers, *President*
Gary Beavers, *President*
EMP: 17 EST: 1969
SQ FT: 72,500
SALES (est): 8.4MM **Privately Held**
WEB: www.wiseproductsinc.com
SIC: 5087 3995 3272 Caskets; grave vaults, metal; concrete products

Hooks
Bowie County

(G-8360)
AMERICAN DEHYDRATED FOODS INC
Lone Star Army Amntn Plnt (75561)
P.O. Box 1359 (75561-1359)
PHONE....................................903 838-0366
Mark Dunn, *Manager*
EMP: 9

SALES (corp-wide): 47.1MM **Privately Held**
WEB: www.adf.com
SIC: 2048 Prepared feeds
PA: American Dehydrated Foods, Llc
    3801 E Sunshine St
    Springfield MO 65809
    417 881-7755

Horizon City
El Paso County

(G-8361)
AGE INDUSTRIES LTD
491 S Darrington Rd (79928-7449)
PHONE....................................915 852-9099
Bobby Ortiz, *Prdtn Mgr*
Robert Ortiz, *Safety Mgr*
Ralph Roman, *Manager*
Rosie Ocegueda, *Executive*
EMP: 34
SQ FT: 25,000
SALES (corp-wide): 140.8MM **Privately Held**
WEB: www.ageindustries.com
SIC: 2653 2448 2655 2657 Boxes, corrugated: made from purchased materials; pallets, wood; tubes, fiber or paper: made from purchased material; folding paperboard boxes; paperboard mills
PA: Age Industries, Ltd.
    3601 County Road 316c
    Cleburne TX 76031
    817 477-5266

(G-8362)
AIR SYSTEM COMPONENTS INC
Also Called: Titus
12504 Weaver Rd (79928-7335)
PHONE....................................915 852-1358
Oscar Montez, *Manager*
EMP: 300 **Privately Held**
WEB: www.airsysco.com
SIC: 3585 Air conditioning equipment, complete; heating equipment, complete
HQ: Air System Components, Inc.
    605 Shiloh Rd
    Plano TX 75074
    972 212-4888

(G-8363)
CHASE TRANSPORTATION LLC
16005 Darley Dr (79928-6500)
PHONE....................................915 307-5488
Adrian Prieto, *President*
EMP: 21
SALES (est): 4.9K **Privately Held**
WEB: www.chasetransportationllc.business.site
SIC: 3715 Truck trailers

(G-8364)
DMD CUSTOM CRATES & BXS INC
12570 Weaver Rd (79928-7335)
PHONE....................................915 849-1744
Daniel Minjares, *President*
Juan Francisco Barraza, *Treasurer*
◆ EMP: 10 EST: 2000
SQ FT: 43,560
SALES (est): 3.4MM **Privately Held**
SIC: 2449 Rectangular boxes & crates, wood
PA: Proveedora De Material Industrial, S.A. De C.V.
    Prol. Ortiz Rubio No. 5050
    Ciudad Juarez CHIH.

(G-8365)
HART & COOLEY INC
12504 Weaver Rd (79928-7335)
PHONE....................................915 852-9111
Oscar Montez, *Manager*
EMP: 300
SALES (corp-wide): 650.5MM **Privately Held**
WEB: www.hartandcooleyinc.com
SIC: 3446 Grillwork, ornamental metal
PA: Hart & Cooley Inc
    5030 Corp Exch Blvd Se
    Grand Rapids MI 49512
    616 656-8200

Horseshoe Bay
Llano County

(G-8366)
DBLJS7 INC (PA)
Also Called: La-Z-Boy Furniture Galleries
106 Mason Ct (78657-5963)
PHONE....................................440 746-1200
Peter D Brosse, *President*
▲ EMP: 15
SQ FT: 51,289
SALES (est): 9.1MM **Privately Held**
SIC: 2512 Upholstered household furniture

(G-8367)
E-Z HEAT CORPORATION
7375 A Highway 281 S (78657)
PHONE....................................830 693-4005
Tyler Cozby, *General Mgr*
Michele Cozby, *Exec Dir*
EMP: 13
SALES (est): 2.7MM **Privately Held**
WEB: www.ezheat.com
SIC: 3567 Heating units & devices, industrial: electric

(G-8368)
JAFFE GROUP LTD
1449 Airpark (78657-5703)
PHONE....................................830 598-2413
Justin P Jaffe, *President*
Justin Jaffe, *President*
EMP: 30
SALES (est): 159.8K **Privately Held**
SIC: 7389 3721 7359 Design services; aircraft; aircraft & industrial truck rental services

Houston
Fort Bend County

(G-8369)
ACS INDUSTRIES LP
14211 Industry St (77053-2526)
PHONE....................................713 434-0934
Peter Botvin, *General Ptnr*
Mike Thompson, *VP Opers*
Donato Saldana, *Plant Mgr*
Patricia Bareis, *Sales Dir*
Jessica Grindstaff, *Sales Staff*
◆ EMP: 70
SALES (est): 11.2MM
SALES (corp-wide): 1.1B **Privately Held**
WEB: www.amacs.com
SIC: 3496 Miscellaneous fabricated wire products
PA: Acs Industries, Inc.
    1 New England Way Unit 1 # 1
    Lincoln RI 02865
    401 769-4700

(G-8370)
AKZO NOBEL INC
15200 Almeda Rd (77053-4920)
PHONE....................................713 433-7289
Christopher Dickson, *Safety Mgr*
Kevin Foster, *Production*
David McDaniel, *Production*
Anders Hagg, *Sales Staff*
Cliff Barr, *Branch Mgr*
EMP: 23
SQ FT: 78,746
SALES (corp-wide): 10.2B **Privately Held**
WEB: www.akzonobel.com
SIC: 2865 2899 Cyclic crudes & intermediates; chemical preparations
HQ: Akzo Nobel Inc.
    535 Marriott Dr Ste 500
    Nashville TN 37214

(G-8371)
ALL-STATE BELTING LLC
3939 Anderson Rd (77053-2407)
PHONE....................................713 433-1272
Bill Duecker, *Branch Mgr*
EMP: 17 **Privately Held**
WEB: www.all-statebelting.com
SIC: 3535 3496 3069 Conveyors & conveying equipment; conveyor belts; rubber rolls & roll coverings

HQ: All-State Belting, Llc
520 S 18th St
West Des Moines IA 50265
515 645-6959

(G-8372)
**AMACS PROCESS TOWER
INTERNALS**
14211 Industry St (77053-2526)
PHONE..............................713 434-0934
Bruce Taylor, *CEO*
Tracie Charleville, *Manager*
EMP: 13
SALES (est): 2MM
SALES (corp-wide): 1.1B **Privately Held**
WEB: www.amacs.com
SIC: 3823 8711 Industrial process control
instruments; engineering services
PA: Acs Industries, Inc.
1 New England Way Unit 1 # 1
Lincoln RI 02865
401 769-4700

(G-8373)
**AMISTCO SEPARATION PDTS
INC**
Also Called: Amacs
14211 Industry St (77053-2526)
PHONE..............................281 331-5956
Christa Boyd, *CEO*
Lee Boyd, *President*
Blanca Gonzalez, *Project Mgr*
Kien Ong, *Mfg Staff*
Andrea Cook, *Sales Staff*
◆ **EMP:** 100
SQ FT: 65,000
SALES (est): 62MM **Privately Held**
WEB: www.amacs.com
SIC: 3496 Mesh, made from purchased
wire

(G-8374)
**B & B PIPE & INDUSTRIAL
TOOLS**
Also Called: B&B Steel Products
4433 South Dr (77053-4835)
P.O. Box 12749 (77217-2749)
PHONE..............................832 581-3179
Carol H Barwick, *President*
Tom Broach, *Vice Pres*
Jack Bush, *Vice Pres*
Travis Newman, *Bookkeeper*
Elizabeth Gay, *Sales Staff*
EMP: 10
SALES (est): 2.2MM **Privately Held**
WEB: www.bbpipetools.com
SIC: 3441 Fabricated structural metal

(G-8375)
CIERRA TANK SERVICES LLC
4322 South Dr (77053-4819)
PHONE..............................713 568-4028
Oni Jackson, *Principal*
EMP: 30
SALES (est): 2.3MM **Privately Held**
WEB: www.cierratankservices.com
SIC: 1389 Lease tanks, oil field: erecting,
cleaning & repairing

(G-8376)
CUMMINGS INV BANKERS INC
Also Called: Sierra Chemical
4202 Bluebonnet Dr (77053-4803)
PHONE..............................281 416-3007
Ray Cummings, *President*
Paul Shinsky Jr, *Principal*
Vonda Cummings, *Vice Pres*
Adrian Carrizales, *Regl Sales Mgr*
EMP: 15
SQ FT: 4,000
SALES (est): 4.3MM **Privately Held**
WEB: www.sierra-chemical.com
SIC: 5087 3589 Janitors' supplies; com-
mercial cleaning equipment

(G-8377)
DEMARCO MACHINE LTD
6750 Mchard Rd (77053-5231)
PHONE..............................832 230-0850
EMP: 67
SALES (corp-wide): 2.5MM **Privately
Held**
SIC: 3545 Machine tool accessories

PA: Demarco Machine, Ltd.
1011 Buffalo Run
Missouri City TX

(G-8378)
DETERLING COMPANY INC
Also Called: Southwest Formseal
4323 South Dr (77053-4820)
PHONE..............................832 399-9393
John Deterling, *President*
Paul Felan, *General Mgr*
Mike Evans, *Engineer*
EMP: 45
SQ FT: 24,000
SALES (est): 6.9MM **Privately Held**
WEB: www.deterling.com
SIC: 3599 Machine shop, jobbing & repair

(G-8379)
EXCELL 7 MACHINE SHOP INC
4206 Bluebonnet Dr (77053-4803)
PHONE..............................281 416-0001
Lee Roy Ivey, *President*
EMP: 10
SALES (est): 2.3MM **Privately Held**
WEB: www.machinelist.us
SIC: 3533 Oil & gas field machinery

(G-8380)
FLAME SEAL PRODUCTS INC
15200 West Dr (77053-4831)
PHONE..............................713 668-4291
Michael D Kiser, *President*
Craig Keyser, *Principal*
Craig Keysar, *Vice Pres*
Judy Davison, *Accountant*
Adam Attayi, *Natl Sales Mgr*
EMP: 10
SQ FT: 15,000
SALES (est): 3.3MM **Privately Held**
WEB: www.flameseal.com
SIC: 2899 Fire retardant chemicals

(G-8381)
FLEXICORE OF TEXAS INC
8634 Mchard Rd (77053-4827)
P.O. Box 450049 (77245-0049)
PHONE..............................281 437-5700
Joseph Phillips, *President*
William Fellers, *Plant Mgr*
Gordon Koepp, *Facilities Mgr*
Joe Zapata, *Sales Staff*
Don Edsall, *Manager*
▲ **EMP:** 209 **EST:** 1953
SQ FT: 3,200
SALES (est): 43.1MM **Privately Held**
WEB: www.flexicoreoftexas.com
SIC: 3272 Concrete products, precast

(G-8382)
GADUTEX INC (PA)
5710 Arthington St (77053-3002)
PHONE..............................713 413-0006
Maria Banuelos, *President*
EMP: 15 **EST:** 2009
SALES (est): 5.4MM **Privately Held**
WEB: www.gadutex.com
SIC: 3441 Fabricated structural metal

(G-8383)
GLORI ENERGY INC
4315 South Dr (77053-4820)
PHONE..............................713 237-8880
Kevin Guilbeau, *CEO*
Eric C Neuman, *Co-COB*
Thomas Holland, *Senior VP*
Kenneth E Nimitz, *Senior VP*
Victor M Perez, *CFO*
EMP: 35
SQ FT: 7,800
SALES: 9MM **Privately Held**
WEB: www.glorienergy.com
SIC: 1382 1311 Oil & gas exploration serv-
ices; crude petroleum & natural gas

(G-8384)
**HOUMA ARMTURE WRKS
HOUSTON LLC**
Also Called: Ward Leonard
8100 Mchard Rd (77053-5259)
PHONE..............................713 748-0702
Kevin Wiemann, *General Mgr*
EMP: 30

SALES (est): 1.2MM **Privately Held**
WEB: www.wardleonard.com
SIC: 1731 7694 Electrical work; armature
rewinding shops

(G-8385)
HOUSTON THERMOSEAL INC
Also Called: Klinger
3803 S Sam Houston Pkwy W
(77053-2603)
PHONE..............................713 997-8111
D Vanderwalph, *General Mgr*
Deon Vanderwalph, *General Mgr*
EMP: 10
SALES (est): 911.5K **Privately Held**
WEB: www.thermosealinc.com
SIC: 3053 Gaskets, packing & sealing de-
vices

(G-8386)
HUNT & HUNT LTD (PA)
14441 Almeda Rd (77053-2555)
PHONE..............................713 413-2500
David L Hunt, *CEO*
Michael Bowman, *President*
Sergio Valdez, *QC Mgr*
Jodi Osterhout, *Accounting Mgr*
EMP: 110 **EST:** 1954
SQ FT: 18,000
SALES (est): 20.4MM **Privately Held**
WEB: www.huntandhunt.com
SIC: 3599 Machine shop, jobbing & repair

(G-8387)
LS ENERGY FABRICATION LLC
Also Called: Lonestar Energy Fabrication
8120 Mchard Rd (77053-5259)
PHONE..............................281 573-9500
Darryl A Schroeder,
EMP: 100
SALES (corp-wide): 45.2MM **Privately
Held**
WEB: www.lsenergyfabrication.com
SIC: 3533 Oil & gas field machinery
PA: Ls Energy Fabrication, Llc
2050 Fm 1405 Rd
Baytown TX 77523
281 573-9500

(G-8388)
**LUBRICATION SYSTEMS TEXAS
LLC (HQ)**
Also Called: Total Lubrication MGT Co
15150 West Dr (77053-4817)
PHONE..............................713 464-6266
Clay H Kiefaber, *CEO*
William Flexon, *Vice Pres*
C Scott Brannan, *CFO*
Janette Cock, *Personnel*
A Lynne Puckett, *Admin Sec*
▼ **EMP:** 80 **EST:** 2007
SQ FT: 25,000
SALES (est): 21.2MM
SALES (corp-wide): 3.3B **Publicly Held**
WEB: www.reladyne.com
SIC: 1796 3569 Machinery installation; lu-
bricating systems, centralized; filters
PA: Colfax Corporation
420 Natl Bus Pkwy Ste 500
Annapolis Junction MD 20701
301 323-9000

(G-8389)
MICRO-SMART SYSTEMS INC
5355 Anderson Rd (77053-2137)
PHONE..............................713 433-2277
Otis Anderson, *President*
Sylvia Brady, *Accountant*
Celene Trujillo, *Admin Asst*
EMP: 11
SQ FT: 8,000
SALES (est): 2.4MM **Privately Held**
WEB: www.micro-smart.com
SIC: 3571 Computers, digital, analog or
hybrid

(G-8390)
**PANTEX ENNERFLO SYSTEMS
INC**
8110 Mchard Rd (77053-5259)
PHONE..............................832 861-7700
Anand M Bhagavatula, *President*
Shawn Stafford, *Production*
Elissa Rogers, *Purchasing*
Jason Gamble, *Engineer*
Deedra Hodrick, *Human Resources*

▲ **EMP:** 35
SQ FT: 18,000
SALES (est): 32.8MM **Privately Held**
WEB: www.pantexennerflo.com
SIC: 3511 3593 3492 3724 Hydraulic turbines; fluid power actuators, hydraulic or
pneumatic; control valves, fluid power: hydraulic & pneumatic; turbines, aircraft
type

(G-8391)
PEARLAND INDUSTRIES INC
Also Called: Pearland American Door
14510 Almeda Rd (77053-3805)
P.O. Box 55187 (77255-5187)
PHONE..............................713 434-9898
Dave Popa, *President*
Becky Brown, *Manager*
EMP: 83
SQ FT: 16,000
SALES (est): 9.1MM
SALES (corp-wide): 23.5MM **Privately
Held**
WEB: www.pearlandindustries.com
SIC: 3442 Window & door frames; metal
doors
PA: American Door Products, Inc.
7967 Blankenship Dr
Houston TX 77055
713 681-8047

(G-8392)
SOUTHWEST FORMSEAL INC
4323 South Dr (77053-4820)
PHONE..............................832 399-3900
John Deterling, *Principal*
EMP: 30
SALES (est): 2.1MM **Privately Held**
WEB: www.swformseal.com
SIC: 3599 Machine shop, jobbing & repair

(G-8393)
TBC-BRINADD LLC
Also Called: Tbc Brinadd
5035 Mchard Rd (77053-4231)
PHONE..............................281 438-2565
Henry Largo, *Research*
Jennifer Hennig, *Cust Mgr*
Rick Warmack, *Manager*
EMP: 19
SALES (corp-wide): 17.1MM **Privately
Held**
WEB: www.tbc-brinadd.com
SIC: 2819 Industrial inorganic chemicals
HQ: Tbc-Brinadd, Llc
4800 San Felipe St
Houston TX 77056
713 877-2600

(G-8394)
**WARD VESSEL AND
EXCHANGER CORP**
6900 Mchard Rd (77053-5235)
PHONE..............................713 413-8416
Richard Shepperd, *Branch Mgr*
EMP: 30
SQ FT: 13,800
SALES (corp-wide): 21.5MM **Privately
Held**
WEB: www.wardvesselandexchanger.com
SIC: 3444 Sheet metalwork
PA: Ward Vessel And Exchanger Corpora-
tion
6670 E W T Harris Blvd
Charlotte NC 28215
704 568-3001

(G-8395)
**WELDFORCE FABRICATORS
LLC**
14875 Waterloo Dr (77053-1617)
PHONE..............................713 270-7733
Karem Dehoyos, *Mng Member*
EMP: 25
SALES (est): 3.3MM **Privately Held**
WEB: www.weldforcesolutions.com
SIC: 3411 3444 Metal cans; sheet metal-
work

(G-8396)
WEST UNIVERSITY MARBLE CO
Also Called: West U Marble Company
14715 Almeda Rd (77053-4929)
PHONE..............................713 433-2240
William J Munoz,
EMP: 15

SALES (est): 1MM **Privately Held**
WEB: www.westumarble.com
SIC: 3281 1743 Marble, building: cut & shaped; terrazzo, tile, marble, mosaic work

(G-8397)
WESTFIELD ENGRG & SVCS INC
8310 Mchard Rd (77053-4821)
PHONE..................................281 438-2047
Ulhas V Sardesai, *President*
EMP: 36
SQ FT: 50,000
SALES (est): 12.3MM **Privately Held**
WEB: www.westfieldengineering.com
SIC: 3533 3443 8711 Oil field machinery & equipment; gas field machinery & equipment; vessels, process or storage (from boiler shops): metal plate; chemical engineering

Houston
Harris County

(G-8398)
1 TO 1 PRINTERS LLC
15031 Woodham Dr Ste 370 (77073-5906)
PHONE..................................281 821-4400
Maria Ballina, *Mng Member*
Albert Campos,
Axel Krayer,
Jose Martinez,
EMP: 9
SQ FT: 6,000
SALES (est): 2.1MM **Privately Held**
WEB: www.1to1printers.com
SIC: 3552 2759 Printing machinery, textile; publication printing

(G-8399)
10-4 TUBULAR INC
9025 Pineland Rd (77044-6155)
PHONE..................................281 436-0380
Gladys Bishop, *President*
Murray E Taylor, *CFO*
EMP: 23
SQ FT: 910
SALES (est): 2.1MM **Privately Held**
SIC: 3444 3599 Casings, sheet metal; tubing, flexible metallic

(G-8400)
101 PRODUCTS LLC
Also Called: Platform Group Gallery , The
2400 Central Pkwy Ste D (77092-7712)
PHONE..................................832 247-7979
Jacquelynne S Sedgwick, *Controller*
Allison Gower, *Mng Member*
Jeremy Konko,
EMP: 15
SQ FT: 9,000
SALES (est): 3.4MM **Privately Held**
WEB: www.101products.com
SIC: 2653 Corrugated & solid fiber boxes

(G-8401)
146 BUSINESS PARK INC
Also Called: Hitech Truck Rigging
13531 W Hardy Rd (77060-5608)
P.O. Box 111535 (77293-0535)
PHONE..................................281 260-0617
Ben Baty Jr, *President*
Byron Baty, *Vice Pres*
Diane McDougal, *Manager*
EMP: 22
SQ FT: 65,000
SALES (est): 4.8MM **Privately Held**
WEB: www.hi-techtruckrigging.com
SIC: 3713 Specialty motor vehicle bodies; utility truck bodies

(G-8402)
14703 PARTNERS INDUSTRIES LLC
Also Called: Garfam Industries
14703 W Hardy Rd (77060-4605)
PHONE..................................281 847-0788
Julian Garcia, *President*
Luis Garcia, *General Mgr*
Olga Garcia, *Admin Sec*
EMP: 15
SQ FT: 8,250

SALES (est): 1.8MM **Privately Held**
WEB: www.garfam.com
SIC: 3469 3599 Electronic enclosures, stamped or pressed metal; machine shop, jobbing & repair

(G-8403)
2 K MACHINE WORKS INC
1716 Townhurst Dr (77043-2811)
PHONE..................................713 467-6921
Luyen Nguyen, *President*
EMP: 9
SALES (est): 528K **Privately Held**
WEB: www.2kmachine.com
SIC: 3599 Machine shop, jobbing & repair

(G-8404)
212 RESOURCES LLC
450 Gears Rd Ste 212 (77067-4513)
PHONE..................................303 892-5616
Stephen Hester, *CEO*
Dan Owen, *Vice Pres*
Michael Vitek, *CFO*
Jane Gaul, *Asst Controller*
Janette Martinez, *Human Res Dir*
EMP: 57
SALES (est): 6.3MM **Privately Held**
WEB: www.212resources.com
SIC: 1389 Oil field services

(G-8405)
2D INC
Also Called: Allegra Print & Imaging
15020 Mintz Ln (77014-1404)
PHONE..................................281 893-3366
John Dawson, *President*
Kim Dawson, *Office Mgr*
EMP: 10
SQ FT: 11,000
SALES (est): 1.6MM **Privately Held**
WEB: www.allegramarketingprint.com
SIC: 2752 Commercial printing, offset

(G-8406)
2DA ANALYTICS INCORPORATED
945 Mckinney St (77002-6308)
PHONE..................................832 472-2093
EMP: 10
SALES (est): 739.1K **Privately Held**
WEB: www.2da.us
SIC: 7372 Prepackaged software

(G-8407)
3C METAL USA INC
5100 Westheimer Rd # 595 (77056-5521)
PHONE..................................713 808-9651
Iris Braggs, *Administration*
EMP: 10
SALES (est): 134.3K **Privately Held**
WEB: www.3cmetal.com
SIC: 3471 Plating & polishing

(G-8408)
3D PRINT BUREAU OF TEXAS LLC
3923 Artdale St (77063-5247)
P.O. Box 630887 (77263-0887)
PHONE..................................713 357-4700
William J Dore Jr,
EMP: 9
SQ FT: 3,400
SALES (est): 323.9K **Privately Held**
WEB: www.3dprinttexas.com
SIC: 2752 Commercial printing, lithographic

(G-8409)
3F INVESTMENTS CO
Also Called: Minute Man Press Southwest
9000 Suthwest Fwy Ste 100 (77074)
PHONE..................................713 541-2258
Fahd Abouabsi, *President*
Faisal Abouabsi, *Vice Pres*
Terry Abouabsi, *CFO*
EMP: 11
SQ FT: 6,500
SALES (est): 2MM **Privately Held**
WEB: www.minutemansw.com
SIC: 2752 Commercial printing, lithographic

(G-8410)
3P PERFORMANCE PLASTICS PDTS
12317 Cutten Rd (77066-1807)
PHONE..................................281 537-8816
Alain Delion, *President*
Benita Austin, *Purch Mgr*
Nick Sazziri, *Finance Mgr*
▲ EMP: 13
SALES (est): 2.3MM **Privately Held**
WEB: www.3pcorporate.com
SIC: 3089 Injection molding of plastics

(G-8411)
3S BUSINESS CORPORATION
11271 Richmond Ave Ste H1 (77082-6660)
PHONE..................................281 823-9222
Anil Kumar Sunkara, *President*
Rakesh Kumar, *Business Mgr*
Satya Athi, *Vice Pres*
Sunil Paleru, *Vice Pres*
SRI Nagendra Tayi, *Marketing Staff*
EMP: 87
SQ FT: 3,700
SALES (est): 1.3MM **Privately Held**
WEB: www.3sbc.com
SIC: 7372 Application computer software

(G-8412)
4D SIGNWORX LLC
Also Called: Gaitz Memorials
2022 Pech Rd (77055-1428)
PHONE..................................713 984-2010
Sanford P Gaitz, *President*
Richard Allison, *Partner*
Andrea Gaitz, *Vice Pres*
Jason Gaitz, *Vice Pres*
John Blue, *Sales Executive*
▲ EMP: 27
SQ FT: 30,000
SALES (est): 657.8K **Privately Held**
WEB: www.gaitzmemorials.com
SIC: 3993 Signs & advertising specialties

(G-8413)
5 ELEMENTS DRILLING LLC
12650 Crossroads Park Dr (77065-3371)
PHONE..................................281 203-0405
June Ressler,
Michael Bloch,
Lyn Oakes,
EMP: 26
SALES (est): 1.5MM **Privately Held**
WEB: www.5elementsdrilling.com
SIC: 1381 Drilling oil & gas wells

(G-8414)
750 LOGISTICS LLC
2207 Blodgett St (77004-5217)
PHONE..................................214 433-2615
Eddie Brown,
EMP: 20
SALES (est): 980K **Privately Held**
SIC: 3743 Freight cars & equipment

(G-8415)
81 TRUCKING SERVICES LLC
11811 North Fwy Ste 500 (77060-3287)
PHONE..................................713 259-1076
Jerome Moore, *Mng Member*
EMP: 15
SALES (est): 1.7MM **Privately Held**
WEB: www.81truckingservicesllc.com
SIC: 3715 4231 4213 Truck trailers; trucking terminal facilities; trucking, except local

(G-8416)
820 HYDRAULICS LLC
Also Called: Hurst Hydraulics
3714 Pinemont Dr (77018-1220)
PHONE..................................713 863-0340
David Schmidt, *President*
Mary Schmidt, *Vice Pres*
EMP: 13
SALES (est): 560.3K **Privately Held**
WEB: www.hursthydraulics.com
SIC: 3599 Machine shop, jobbing & repair

(G-8417)
8228 CORPORATION
Also Called: Hot Line
1141 A Half Brittmoore Rd (77043)
PHONE..................................713 465-1303
Allen Brill, *President*

Sara Brill, *Vice Pres*
EMP: 23
SQ FT: 6,000
SALES (est): 100K **Privately Held**
WEB: www.hotlinemfg.com
SIC: 2329 2339 2395 Men's & boys' sportswear & athletic clothing; athletic (warmup, sweat & jogging) suits: men's & boys'; bathing suits & swimwear: men's & boys'; women's & misses' athletic clothing & sportswear; bathing suits: women's, misses' & juniors'; sportswear, women's; embroidery & art needlework

(G-8418)
9650 NF LTD
Also Called: Team Mncuso Pwrsports Gulf Fwy
11415 Gulf Fwy (77034-3548)
PHONE..................................281 486-4604
John Thompson, *President*
EMP: 13
SALES (est): 1.6MM **Privately Held**
WEB: www.tmpgf.com
SIC: 3711 Motor vehicles & car bodies

(G-8419)
A & A GENPRO INC
Also Called: Aa Genpro Electric
2870 Gessner Rd Ste C14 (77080-2556)
PHONE..................................713 830-3280
Ashton Tennant, *President*
Andrew Spitzmueller, *COO*
John Crockett, *CFO*
Carroll Tennant, *Advisor*
EMP: 20
SQ FT: 8,000
SALES (est): 1.1MM **Privately Held**
WEB: www.aagenpro.com
SIC: 3621 Motors & generators

(G-8420)
A & A PALLET AND LUMBER CO
10350 W Montgomery Rd (77088-3023)
PHONE..................................713 462-4575
Ae Suk Kim, *President*
EMP: 11
SALES (est): 1.5MM **Privately Held**
WEB: www.anapallet.com
SIC: 2448 Pallets, wood

(G-8421)
A & A PALLET CO
1028 Candlelight Ln (77018-2004)
PHONE..................................713 480-9861
EMP: 20 EST: 2014
SALES (est): 320.2K **Privately Held**
WEB: www.anapallet.com
SIC: 2448 Pallets, wood

(G-8422)
A & B AUTO ELECTRIC INC
Also Called: Ace Houston Warehouse
9225 Manchester St (77012-2297)
P.O. Box 624, Pearland (77588-0624)
PHONE..................................713 928-3219
R H Spencer, *President*
Joyce Schroeder, *President*
Victor Wenzel, *Vice Pres*
EMP: 17 EST: 1948
SQ FT: 9,800
SALES (est): 3.2MM **Privately Held**
WEB: www.abautoelectric.trustab.org
SIC: 5013 5531 3694 3625 Automotive supplies & parts; alternators; automotive parts; ignition apparatus & distributors; alternators, automotive; relays & industrial controls; nonferrous wiredrawing & insulating

(G-8423)
A & C PLASTIC PRODUCTS INC (PA)
Also Called: A&C Plastics
6135 Northdale St (77087-5095)
PHONE..................................713 645-4915
◆ EMP: 37
SQ FT: 75,000
SALES (est): 20.4MM **Privately Held**
WEB: www.acplasticsinc.com
SIC: 2821 Plastics materials & resins

(G-8424)
A B C PLASTIC MOLDING INC
501 E Parker Rd (77076-3120)
PHONE..................................713 692-9122

Melvin Cross, *President*
▼ **EMP:** 20
SQ FT: 12,000 **Privately Held**
SIC: 3089 Injection molding of plastics

(G-8425)
A C N MILLWORK CORP
5711 Ransom St (77087-4103)
PHONE................................713 649-6015
Andreas Nicolaou, *President*
EMP: 14
SQ FT: 13,000
SALES (est): 1.6MM **Privately Held**
SIC: 2431 Millwork

(G-8426)
A G H MACHINE INC
13610 Reeveston Rd (77039-2908)
PHONE................................281 372-1200
Leopoldo Alanis, *President*
Guillermo Alanis, *Vice Pres*
EMP: 9
SQ FT: 2,000
SALES (est): 1.4MM **Privately Held**
WEB: www.aghmachine.com
SIC: 3599 Machine shop, jobbing & repair

(G-8427)
A LAKHANY INTERNATIONAL INC
Also Called: Excel Linen Company
10190 Katy Fwy Ste 350 (77043-5239)
PHONE................................713 266-8799
Hashim Lakhany, *Ch of Bd*
Salma Lakhany, *Admin Sec*
▲ **EMP:** 152
SALES (est): 15.1MM **Privately Held**
WEB: www.excellinencompany.com
SIC: 2211 Surgical fabrics, cotton

(G-8428)
A TRACE MATIC CORPORATION
7210 Empire Central Dr (77040-3210)
PHONE................................713 538-1370
Mark Ritter, *Prdtn Mgr*
Darren Hoyland, *Maintence Staff*
EMP: 42
SALES (corp-wide): 28.4MM **Privately Held**
WEB: www.traceamatic.com
SIC: 3531 Construction machinery
PA: A Trace Matic Corporation
　　21125 Enterprise Ave
　　Brookfield WI 53045
　　877 375-0217

(G-8429)
A VARCO SHAFFER CO
Also Called: Varco BJ Oil Tools
6390 N Eldridge Pkwy (77041-3504)
PHONE................................713 937-5500
John Lauletta, *President*
Greg Hottle, *Vice Pres*
Toby Zyroll, *Vice Pres*
◆ **EMP:** 91
SALES (est): 16.3MM
SALES (corp-wide): 8.4B **Publicly Held**
SIC: 3533 Oil field machinery & equipment
PA: National Oilwell Varco, Inc.
　　7909 Parkwood Circle Dr
　　Houston TX 77036
　　713 346-7500

(G-8430)
A&S INTERESTS INC
Also Called: Metal Specialties
8321 Bauman Rd (77022-3205)
PHONE................................713 695-0000
Anthony Vento, *President*
Mike Deaton, *Purchasing*
David Kotch, *Sales Staff*
EMP: 20
SQ FT: 4,000
SALES (est): 6MM **Privately Held**
WEB: www.metalspecialties.co
SIC: 3446 Architectural metalwork

(G-8431)
A-1 FUEL STOP INC
Also Called: Gulf
9161 Wallisville Rd (77029-1323)
PHONE................................713 674-3683
Mushtaq Khan, *Principal*
EMP: 9
SALES (est): 1MM **Privately Held**
SIC: 2869 Fuels

(G-8432)
A1 CHROME SHOP INC
Also Called: Chrome Stop, The
4520 N Mccarty St (77013-3634)
PHONE................................713 885-1727
Daniel Estivel, *Principal*
Les Compton, *Sales Engr*
Mark Little, *Director*
Alex Leal, *Representative*
EMP: 10
SQ FT: 2,700
SALES (est): 600K **Privately Held**
WEB: www.chrome-stop.com
SIC: 2816 Chrome pigments: chrome green, chrome yellow, zinc yellow

(G-8433)
A3IM INC
8866 Gulf Fwy Ste 550 (77017-6518)
PHONE................................713 378-7600
Pam Trepagnier, *President*
Tanya Herford, *Vice Pres*
Gina Miramontes, *Accounts Mgr*
Debra Jimenez, *Manager*
Elizabeth Morris, *Manager*
EMP: 15
SALES (est): 347.2K
SALES (corp-wide): 145.2MM **Privately Held**
WEB: www.a3im.com
SIC: 3699 Electrical equipment & supplies
HQ: A3im, Inc.
　　6655 Exchequer Dr
　　Baton Rouge LA 70809

(G-8434)
A9 MANUFACTURING INC
14401 Interdrive W (77032-3335)
PHONE................................832 554-2464
Brad Long, *President*
EMP: 9
SQ FT: 13,000
SALES (est): 1.5MM **Privately Held**
WEB: www.a9mfg.com
SIC: 3533 Oil & gas drilling rigs & equipment

(G-8435)
AAA FLAME CUT STEEL INC
1015 Judiway St (77018-5220)
P.O. Box 924947 (77292-4947)
PHONE................................713 868-2337
Timothy P McConnell, *President*
Barbara Daily, *Controller*
Mary B Parish, *Admin Sec*
EMP: 11
SQ FT: 30,000
SALES (est): 3.1MM **Privately Held**
WEB: www.aaaflamecutsteel.com
SIC: 3312 Plate, steel

(G-8436)
AAA TECHNOLOGY AND SPC CO INC (PA)
6219 Brittmoore Rd (77041-5114)
PHONE................................713 849-3366
▲ **EMP:** 37
SQ FT: 12,000
SALES (est): 6.1MM **Privately Held**
WEB: www.aaatech.com
SIC: 3498 Fabricated pipe & fittings

(G-8437)
AAA WOODWORK
9817 Honeywell St (77074-1316)
PHONE................................713 935-0002
Nelson Alehenbre, *President*
Nelson Alexandre, *Vice Pres*
EMP: 10
SALES (est): 867.8K **Privately Held**
WEB: www.aaawoodwork.com
SIC: 2431 Millwork

(G-8438)
AAB MFG HOLDINGS LP
13913 Buxley St (77045-5303)
PHONE................................281 438-1599
Myrna Tucker, *President*
Matt Flajnik, *General Mgr*
Joe Ackman, *Buyer*
EMP: 25
SQ FT: 17,000
SALES (est): 5.4MM **Privately Held**
WEB: www.americananchorbolt.com
SIC: 3452 Bolts, metal

(G-8439)
AAP METALS LLC
8411 Irvington Blvd (77022-3449)
PHONE................................800 231-8890
Bill Leavelle, *Manager*
EMP: 10
SALES (corp-wide): 640.1MM **Privately Held**
WEB: www.metalsinc.com
SIC: 3312 Stainless steel
HQ: Aap Metals, Llc
　　1010 W 37th Pl
　　Tulsa OK 74107
　　918 446-1458

(G-8440)
AB BELLCO CORPORATION
Also Called: Scientific Climate Systems
6650 W Sam Houston Pkwy N (77041-5151)
PHONE................................713 781-6447
Arthur Bell, *Ch of Bd*
Ben Bell, *President*
David Parkman, *Project Engr*
▲ **EMP:** 26
SQ FT: 20,000
SALES (est): 10MM **Privately Held**
WEB: www.scs-usa.com
SIC: 3569 3443 3821 Testing chambers for altitude, temperature, ordnance, power; chambers & caissons; laboratory apparatus & furniture

(G-8441)
ABACO DRILLING TECH LLC (HQ)
Also Called: Basintek LLC
713 Northpark Central Dr # 400 (77073-6347)
PHONE................................281 869-0700
Dan O'Sullivan, *President*
Alberto Paredes, *General Mgr*
Peter Cariveau, *Vice Pres*
John Jenkins, *Vice Pres*
Shannon Critchley, *VP Opers*
▲ **EMP:** 125
SALES (est): 52.3MM
SALES (corp-wide): 26.1MM **Privately Held**
WEB: www.abacodrilling.com
SIC: 3621 7694 Rotors, for motors; rewinding stators

(G-8442)
ABACUS COMPUTER CO INC
11111 Katy Fwy Ste 725 (77079-2175)
PHONE................................713 467-2136
Bob Leared, *President*
Deborah Grosso, *Principal*
Shirley McLennan, *Vice Pres*
EMP: 25
SALES (est): 1.2MM **Privately Held**
SIC: 7372 7378 Prepackaged software; computer maintenance & repair

(G-8443)
ABB INC
Also Called: Total Flow Products Div
3700 W Sam Houston Pkwy S # 600 (77042-5120)
PHONE................................713 587-8000
James Kan, *Principal*
Libby Smith, *Vice Pres*
Oscar Tillberg, *Vice Pres*
Kjetil Wold, *Vice Pres*
Michael Balentine, *Opers Staff*
EMP: 97
SALES (corp-wide): 27.9B **Privately Held**
WEB: www.new.abb.com
SIC: 3823 Industrial instrmnts msrmnt display/control process variable
HQ: Abb Inc.
　　305 Gregson Dr
　　Cary NC 27511

(G-8444)
ABB INSTALLATION PRODUCTS INC
8700 Fairbanks N Houston (77064-6808)
PHONE................................713 466-6761
David Fortune, *Manager*
EMP: 250

SALES (corp-wide): 27.9B **Privately Held**
WEB: www.elastimoldswitchgear.com
SIC: 3312 3317 Structural shapes & pilings, steel; steel pipe & tubes
HQ: Abb Installation Products Inc.
　　860 Ridge Lake Blvd
　　Memphis TN 38120
　　901 252-5000

(G-8445)
ABC IMAGING OF WASHINGTON
4902 Richmond Ave Ste C (77027-6613)
PHONE................................832 426-5815
EMP: 11
SALES (corp-wide): 144.4MM **Privately Held**
WEB: www.abcimaging.com
SIC: 2759 Commercial printing
PA: Abc Imaging Of Washington, Inc
　　5290 Shawnee Rd Ste 300
　　Alexandria VA 22312
　　202 429-8870

(G-8446)
ABCD PRECISION INC
7045 Satsuma Dr (77041-1903)
PHONE................................832 230-5729
EMP: 9
SALES (est): 1.1MM **Privately Held**
WEB: www.abcdprecision.com
SIC: 3599 Machine shop, jobbing & repair

(G-8447)
ABCO PRODUCTS INC
Also Called: Abco Subsea
7108 W Little York Rd (77040-4814)
PHONE................................713 871-8020
William Simms, *President*
Andrew Boyd, *Principal*
Mary Boyd, *Corp Secy*
Canion Boyd, *Human Resources*
Andrew Nyberg, *Info Tech Mgr*
▲ **EMP:** 48
SQ FT: 3,000
SALES (est): 10MM **Privately Held**
WEB: www.abcosubsea.com
SIC: 3533 Oil field machinery & equipment

(G-8448)
ABLE SUPPLY CO
Also Called: Able Refractory Products
5220 Texas St (77011-4295)
P.O. Box 912 (77001-0912)
PHONE................................713 926-9623
Wayne Pratt, *Ch of Bd*
Tom J Daubner, *President*
Brenda Pratt, *Office Mgr*
EMP: 16
SQ FT: 50,000
SALES (est): 2.3MM **Privately Held**
WEB: www.ablerefractory.com
SIC: 3297 5085 Brick, bauxite; dolomite or dolomite-magnesite brick & shapes; pyrolytic graphite; industrial supplies

(G-8449)
ABSOLUTE COLOR LTD
11101 Ella Blvd (77067-4234)
PHONE................................713 996-0202
Christy Nguyen, *Partner*
Hugh Nguyen, *General Ptnr*
Robert Weathers, *Opers Mgr*
Randy Wrench, *Accounts Mgr*
EMP: 15
SALES (est): 3.7MM **Privately Held**
WEB: www.absolutecolor.com
SIC: 2759 Commercial printing

(G-8450)
ABSOLUTE FABRICATION LLC (PA)
Also Called: Absolute Enrgy Field Pdts Svcs
7218 Clinton Dr (77020-7548)
PHONE................................832 226-3345
Ravinder Singh, *Mng Member*
Anupam Singh,
EMP: 20
SALES (est): 3MM **Privately Held**
WEB: www.absoluteenergyfield.com
SIC: 3533 Oil & gas drilling rigs & equipment

▲ = Import ▼ = Export
◆ = Import/Export

(G-8451)
ABSOLUTE METAL PRODUCTS LLC
7208 Gessner Rd (77040-3142)
PHONE................................713 340-5990
Richard Rose, *President*
Travis Tedrow, *Sales Executive*
EMP: 15 EST: 2015
SQ FT: 155,000
SALES (est): 988.3K **Privately Held**
WEB: www.absolutemetalusa.com
SIC: 3444 Sheet metalwork

(G-8452)
ACACIA ENERGY INC
11011 Brooklet Dr Ste 220 (77099-3573)
PHONE................................877 997-2946
Debbie Wernet, *President*
Alyson Beicker, *Exec VP*
EMP: 20
SALES (est): 3.3MM **Privately Held**
WEB: www.acaciaenergy.com
SIC: 2813 Industrial gases

(G-8453)
ACCELERATED PROCESS SYSTEMS
7227 Wright Rd (77041-2417)
PHONE................................713 937-6838
Brad Goebel, *CEO*
Mitchell K Ulrey, *Principal*
David Zachariah, *Principal*
Mitch Ulrey, *CFO*
Tim Burke, *Director*
▲ EMP: 122
SQ FT: 60,000
SALES (est): 25.2MM
SALES (corp-wide): 7.1B **Publicly Held**
WEB: www.distributionnow.com
SIC: 3441 3443 Fabricated structural
metal; fabricated plate work (boiler shop)
PA: Dover Corporation
3005 Highland Pkwy # 200
Downers Grove IL 60515
630 541-1540

(G-8454)
ACCENT SCREEN PRINTING INC
10400 Wstfice Dr Ste 110 (77042)
PHONE................................713 782-6683
Paula Sidler, *President*
EMP: 9
SQ FT: 2,600
SALES (est): 1.2MM **Privately Held**
WEB: www.accentscreenprint.com
SIC: 2759 Screen printing

(G-8455)
ACCENT SIGN & AWNING CO LLC
Also Called: Accent Signs & Graphics
6015 Skyline Dr (77057-7003)
PHONE................................713 780-1151
Jay Shaw, *Production*
Debi Poindexter, *Controller*
Nathan Niemeyer, *Accounts Exec*
Jason Rodriguez, *Accounts Exec*
Dimitri Giannukos, *Sales Staff*
EMP: 15
SALES (est): 2.3MM **Privately Held**
WEB: www.accentsignco.com
SIC: 1799 3993 Sign installation & mainte-
nance; signs & advertising specialties

(G-8456)
ACCESS ATM INC (PA)
10801 Hammerly Blvd # 238 (77043-1924)
PHONE................................713 463-9033
David Hardy, *President*
Nasir Khan, *Vice Pres*
Chris Schneider, *Vice Pres*
EMP: 10 EST: 1999
SQ FT: 6,000
SALES (est): 914.8K **Privately Held**
WEB: www.accessatm.com
SIC: 7699 3578 Automated teller machine
(ATM) repair; automatic teller machines
(ATM)

(G-8457)
ACCESS CHEMICALS & SVCS LLC
7322 Southwest Fwy # 2000 (77074-2010)
PHONE................................713 270-7215
Richard Raymond, *Corp Secy*

Vanessa Moore, *Accounts Mgr*
Ron Treece, *Mng Member*
▲ EMP: 12
SQ FT: 4,000
SALES (est): 2.1MM **Privately Held**
WEB: www.access-chemicals.com
SIC: 2819 2869 Industrial inorganic chem-
icals; industrial organic chemicals

(G-8458)
ACCESS INTELLIGENCE EVENTS LLC
11000 Richmond Ave # 690 (77042-4776)
PHONE................................832 242-1969
Don Pazour, *CEO*
Carey Buchholtz, *Marketing Staff*
Mary P Bailey, *Assoc Editor*
Joe Flowers, *Technology*
Kayla Sparks, *Director*
▲ EMP: 100
SALES (est): 5.3MM
SALES (corp-wide): 66.7MM **Privately
Held**
WEB: www.accessintel.com
SIC: 2741 Miscellaneous publishing
PA: Access Intelligence Llc
9211 Corporate Blvd Fl 4
Rockville MD 20850
301 354-2000

(G-8459)
ACCUMED BIOTECH LLC
16727 Park Row (77084-5020)
PHONE................................315 790-0466
Abdurahman Ravat, *Mng Member*
EMP: 10
SALES (est): 500K **Privately Held**
SIC: 3841 5047 Surgical & medical instru-
ments; medical & hospital equipment

(G-8460)
ACCUMULATORS INC
Also Called: Accumulators.com
18435 Morton Rd (77084-7796)
P.O. Box 660828, Dallas (75266-0828)
PHONE................................713 465-0202
Jeff Schneider, *President*
Scott J Schneider, *COO*
Richard T Kendall, *Vice Pres*
Dean Bauchelle, *Production*
Dwayne Lister, *Chief Engr*
◆ EMP: 35
SQ FT: 50,000
SALES (est): 8.4MM **Privately Held**
WEB: www.accumulators.com
SIC: 3491 Pressure valves & regulators,
industrial

(G-8461)
ACCURATE CONTROL COMPANY LLC (PA)
6526 Petropark Dr (77041-4923)
PHONE................................713 699-3799
Manuel Haro, *CEO*
Dawn Kopa, *Opers Staff*
Frank D Agostino, *CFO*
Frank Agostino, *CFO*
Wendy Mechelle, *Mktg Dir*
EMP: 25
SALES (est): 8.5MM **Privately Held**
WEB: www.accuratecontrol.com
SIC: 3613 3625 8711 Control panels,
electric; motor control centers; engineer-
ing services

(G-8462)
ACCURATE FLAMECUTTING STL LLC
Also Called: Accurate Flame Cutting and Stl
842 Buschong St (77039-1002)
PHONE................................281 987-9100
Danny Doron, *President*
EMP: 9
SQ FT: 40,000
SALES (est): 988.9K **Privately Held**
SIC: 3312 Blast furnaces & steel mills

(G-8463)
ACCURATE PRECISION PLATING LLC
1506 Lone Oak Rd (77093-3240)
PHONE................................281 598-8835
Alberto Mani, *Mng Member*
EMP: 25
SQ FT: 11,200

SALES (est): 3MM **Privately Held**
WEB: www.accurateprecisionplating.com
SIC: 3471 Electroplating of metals or
formed products

(G-8464)
ACCUTURN MANUFACTURING INC
845 Buschong St (77039-1001)
PHONE................................281 449-9000
Gerald Chandler, *President*
Wetona Lorraine Chandler, *Vice Pres*
EMP: 14
SALES (est): 2.3MM **Privately Held**
WEB: www.accuturnmfgtx.com
SIC: 3599 Machine shop, jobbing & repair

(G-8465)
ACCUWELD INC
845 Buschong St (77039-1001)
PHONE................................281 442-5900
Gerald Chandler, *President*
Glenndel Cotie, *Business Mgr*
Wetona Lorraine Chandler, *Vice Pres*
Estee Adame, *Opers Mgr*
Glenn Moody, *Prdtn Mgr*
EMP: 22
SQ FT: 37,524
SALES (est): 4.1MM **Privately Held**
WEB: www.accuweldtx.com
SIC: 7692 Welding repair

(G-8466)
ACE FABRICATORS INC
7010 Furay Rd (77016-1508)
PHONE................................281 442-0992
Miguel Acevedo, *President*
Minnie Acevedo, *Vice Pres*
Melinda Acevedo, *Admin Sec*
EMP: 85
SQ FT: 17,000
SALES (est): 32.5MM **Privately Held**
WEB: www.acefabricatorsinc.com
SIC: 3441 Fabricated structural metal

(G-8467)
ACENTUM INC
3752 Darcus St (77005-3704)
PHONE................................713 668-8742
Kalpana Visweswaran, *CFO*
EMP: 11 **Privately Held**
SIC: 2869 Fuels

(G-8468)
ACG QUALITY ELECTRIC INC
1004 Collingsworth St (77009-4903)
PHONE................................713 225-6531
Charles Garcia Sr, *President*
Charles Garcia II, *Vice Pres*
Dorothy Garcia, *Treasurer*
▲ EMP: 10
SQ FT: 25,000
SALES (est): 1.4MM **Privately Held**
WEB: www.qualityelectrichouston.com
SIC: 7694 5999 Electric motor repair; re-
building motors, except automotive; mo-
tors, electric

(G-8469)
ACTION BOX CO INC
6207 N Houston Rosslyn Rd (77091-3409)
PHONE................................713 869-7701
Terry J Malloy, *President*
Marcelene Malloy, *Corp Secy*
Eric Malloy, *Vice Pres*
Daniel Brandt, *Purch Mgr*
Brent Camp, *Purch Mgr*
▲ EMP: 109
SQ FT: 155,000
SALES (est): 35.8MM **Privately Held**
WEB: www.actionboxinc.com
SIC: 2653 5199 Boxes, corrugated: made
from purchased materials; packaging ma-
terials

(G-8470)
ACTION1 CORPORATION
12333 Sowden Rd B36066 (77080-2058)
PHONE................................346 444-8530
Alex Vovk, *CEO*
EMP: 10
SALES (est): 1MM **Privately Held**
WEB: www.action1.com
SIC: 7372 Prepackaged software

(G-8471)
ACTIUM BIOSYSTEMS
11777 Katy Fwy Ste 120s (77079-1705)
PHONE................................832 379-4222
George Kauss, *Owner*
EMP: 10
SALES (est): 436.1K **Privately Held**
WEB:
SIC: 3845 Electromedical equipment

(G-8472)
ACTUAL SEO MEDIA INC
1880 S Dairy Ashford Rd # 682
(77077-4705)
PHONE................................832 834-0661
Jamin Mootz, *Owner*
EMP: 25
SALES (est): 560.4K **Privately Held**
WEB: www.actualseomedia.com
SIC: 2741

(G-8473)
ACUTE TECHNOLOGICAL SVCS INC
11925 Brittmoore Park Dr (77041-7226)
PHONE................................713 983-9353
John B Mitchell, *CEO*
Thomas A Nevitt, *CEO*
Michael D Hayes, *President*
Richard A Zelko, *Vice Pres*
Juan Cavazos, *Project Mgr*
EMP: 90
SQ FT: 26,000
SALES (est): 23.3MM
SALES (corp-wide): 1B **Publicly Held**
WEB: www.oilstates.com
SIC: 8711 3441 Consulting engineer; fab-
ricated structural metal
PA: Oil States International, Inc.
333 Clay St Ste 4620
Houston TX 77002
713 652-0582

(G-8474)
AD VALOREM RECORDS INC
Also Called: Avr
12332 Cutten Rd (77066-1808)
PHONE................................713 523-1623
Ron Emberg, *CEO*
Francis Leong, *President*
Susan Emberg, *COO*
Ana Villarreal, *CFO*
Ren Nelson, *Client Mgr*
EMP: 49
SQ FT: 15,988
SALES: 8.6MM
SALES (corp-wide): 150.1MM **Publicly
Held**
WEB: www.avrub.com
SIC: 7372 Business oriented computer
software; utility computer software
PA: I3 Verticals, Inc.
40 Burton Hills Blvd # 415
Nashville TN 37215
615 465-4487

(G-8475)
ADAMS RESOURCES & ENERGY INC (PA)
17 S Briar Hollow Ln # 100 (77027-3156)
P.O. Box 844 (77001-0844)
PHONE................................713 881-3600
EMP: 37
SQ FT: 27,932
SALES: 1.8B **Publicly Held**
WEB: www.adamsresources.com
SIC: 5172 4212 1382 1311 Crude oil; pe-
troleum haulage, local; oil & gas explo-
ration services; crude petroleum & natural
gas production

(G-8476)
ADAMS RESOURCES MARKETING LTD (HQ)
16800 Imperial Valley Dr # 2 (77060-3159)
P.O. Box 844 (77001-0844)
PHONE................................281 902-4100
Richard Abshire, *Partner*
▼ EMP: 14 EST: 1999
SALES (est): 2.6MM
SALES (corp-wide): 1.8B **Publicly Held**
WEB: www.adamsresources.com
SIC: 1382 Oil & gas exploration services

GEOGRAPHIC

PA: Adams Resources & Energy, Inc.
17 S Briar Hollow Ln # 100
Houston TX 77027
713 881-3600

(G-8477)
ADDAX PETRO CAMEROON CO LLC
910 Louisiana St (77002-4916)
PHONE..................................713 245-1263
Dan Schram, *President*
▲ EMP: 180
SALES (est): 6.9MM **Privately Held**
SIC: 1382 1311 Oil & gas exploration services; crude petroleum production
HQ: Addax Petroleum Us Services Corporation
1301 Mckinney St Ste 2050
Houston TX 77010

(G-8478)
ADEM RUMAN INC
Also Called: Pain Du Jour French Bakery
3700 Crossview Dr A (77063-5709)
PHONE..................................713 266-8584
Mommhomad Adam, *President*
EMP: 9 EST: 1982
SQ FT: 6,500
SALES (est): 794.1K **Privately Held**
SIC: 2051 Bakery: wholesale or wholesale/retail combined

(G-8479)
ADEMCO INC
Also Called: ADI Global Distribution
7425 Pinemont Dr Ste 100 (77040-6437)
PHONE..................................713 861-9418
Vince Lasota, *Branch Mgr*
EMP: 11
SQ FT: 4,000
SALES (corp-wide): 4.9B **Publicly Held**
WEB: www.honeywell.com
SIC: 5063 3669 3822 Electrical apparatus & equipment; emergency alarms; air conditioning & refrigeration controls
HQ: Ademco Inc.
1985 Douglas Dr N
Golden Valley MN 55422
800 468-1502

(G-8480)
ADMP LLC
6401 Long Point Rd # 506 (77055-2612)
PHONE..................................832 519-9746
EMP: 16 EST: 2012
SALES (est): 3.4MM **Privately Held**
WEB: www.admp.us
SIC: 3444 Metal ventilating equipment

(G-8481)
ADVANCE ENERGY PARTNERS LLC
11490 Westheimer Rd # 950 (77077-6841)
PHONE..................................832 672-4700
Peter Lellis, *President*
Edward Caamano, *Vice Pres*
David Harwell, *Vice Pres*
David Scott, *Vice Pres*
Kevin Hays, *CFO*
EMP: 18
SQ FT: 17,000
SALES (est): 53MM **Privately Held**
WEB: www.advanceenergypartners.com
SIC: 1382 Oil & gas exploration services

(G-8482)
ADVANCE FBRCTION MSUREMENT LLC
Also Called: Afm
1223 Brittmoore Rd (77043-4001)
P.O. Box 60112 (77205-0112)
PHONE..................................713 468-9581
Don Ray, *Principal*
Kyle Phillips,
EMP: 21
SQ FT: 15,000
SALES (est): 4.2MM **Privately Held**
SIC: 4932 3533 Gas & other services combined; oil & gas field machinery

(G-8483)
ADVANCE HYDROCARBON CORP (DH)
10343 Sam Houston Park Dr # 325 (77064-1360)
PHONE..........................979 690-2226
Don Parkerson, *President*
Josh Parkerson, *Vice Pres*
John Kiger, *Manager*
EMP: 12
SALES (est): 61.3MM
SALES (corp-wide): 7.4MM **Privately Held**
WEB: www.ahcus.com
SIC: 1389 Impounding & storing salt water, oil & gas field
HQ: Aqua Terra Water Management, L.P.
301 58th St W Ste 332
Williston ND 58801
307 321-3525

(G-8484)
ADVANCE TECHNOLOGY PRODUCTS
14123 Market Street Rd (77015-6460)
PHONE..................................713 450-5990
▼ EMP: 10
SQ FT: 20,000
SALES (est): 970K **Privately Held**
SIC: 3589 3295 Mfg Fuel Filtration Equipment & Moisture Control Products

(G-8485)
ADVANCED ARCHTECTURAL MTLS INC
6100 Brittmoore Rd Ste S (77041-5647)
PHONE..................................713 983-9979
Stuart Campbell, *President*
EMP: 13
SQ FT: 10,000
SALES (est): 1.9MM **Privately Held**
WEB: www.advanced-metals.com
SIC: 3441 Fabricated structural metal

(G-8486)
ADVANCED CNTINMENT SYSTEMS INC
Also Called: Acsi
8720 Lambright Rd (77075-3123)
PHONE..................................713 987-0336
Phil J Dunne, *President*
Susan I Dunne, *Corp Secy*
Rick Stapleton, *Vice Pres*
Robert Vela, *Prdtn Mgr*
Sara Jenkins, *Marketing Staff*
◆ EMP: 210
SALES (est): 71.4MM **Privately Held**
WEB: www.acsi-us.com
SIC: 3589 Asbestos removal equipment

(G-8487)
ADVANCED CONTROL SYSTEMS LLC
4903 W Sam Houston Pkwy N B (77041-8231)
PHONE..........................832 529-2234
Marvin Callies, *General Mgr*
Allan Olsen, *Electrical Engi*
Josefina Bordallo, *Controller*
Jeremi Ball, *Mng Member*
Keith Kostelnik,
EMP: 35 EST: 2012
SALES (est): 5.3MM **Privately Held**
WEB: www.acsoilfield.com
SIC: 7389 1731 3612 3625 Personal service agents, brokers & bureaus; electric power systems contractors; generator voltage regulators; motor controls & accessories

(G-8488)
ADVANCED INDICATORS AND MFG
Also Called: Advanced Flow Products
1463 Brittmoore Rd (77043-4005)
PHONE..................................713 932-6464
Hans Karani, *President*
Tushpa Karani, *Admin Sec*
EMP: 12
SQ FT: 15,400

SALES (est): 3.1MM **Privately Held**
WEB: www.advflow.com
SIC: 5084 3533 Oil well machinery, equipment & supplies; oil field machinery & equipment

(G-8489)
ADVANCED OCEAN SHIPPING
Also Called: Greenway Textile Products
323 S Cesar Chavez Blvd (77011-4448)
PHONE..................................281 300-0191
Gibson Oluyigan, *President*
EMP: 22
SALES (est): 180K **Privately Held**
SIC: 2299 Fibers, textile: recovery from textile mill waste & rags

(G-8490)
ADVANCED PIPING PRODUCTS INC
5611 Guhn Rd Ste A1 (77040-6143)
PHONE..................................713 956-2922
Caroline Reese, *President*
Bill Godsey, *General Mgr*
William Godsey, *General Mgr*
Yulman Flores, *Business Mgr*
Matthew Reese, *COO*
▼ EMP: 14
SALES (est): 4.2MM **Privately Held**
WEB: www.appmfg.com
SIC: 3498 Fabricated pipe & fittings

(G-8491)
ADVANCED RET MGT SYSTEMS INC (PA)
Also Called: Arm Systems
2555 Westhollow Dr (77082-1844)
PHONE..................................303 738-1800
Bruce Klepper, *President*
EMP: 32
SQ FT: 7,000
SALES (est): 2.4MM **Privately Held**
SIC: 3578 Point-of-sale devices

(G-8492)
ADVANCED TRACKING TECH INC
6001 Savoy Dr Ste 301 (77036-3322)
P.O. Box 168, Sugar Land (77487-0168)
PHONE..................................800 279-0035
Paul Glass, *President*
David Koonce, *Prdtn Mgr*
Larry Shepperd, *CFO*
Adam Howard, *Natl Sales Mgr*
Tony O'Brien, *Natl Sales Mgr*
▲ EMP: 45
SQ FT: 21,000
SALES (est): 8.5MM **Privately Held**
WEB: www.advantrack.com
SIC: 3577 7371 Computer peripheral equipment; custom computer programming services

(G-8493)
ADVANCED WELDING SERVICES INC
Also Called: Aws
9840 Windmill Park Ln (77064-3301)
PHONE..................................713 933-2626
Raymond Knight, *President*
Henry Gammon, *President*
Billy Kopech, *General Mgr*
Tom Mace, *Sales Staff*
Eddie Davila, *Supervisor*
EMP: 19
SALES (est): 2.5MM **Privately Held**
WEB: www.awsinc.us
SIC: 7692 3498 Welding repair; fabricated pipe & fittings

(G-8494)
ADVANTAGE INTERESTS INC
Also Called: Advantage Fire SEC Integration
7840 W Little York Rd (77040-5310)
PHONE..................................713 983-7253
Carter White, *Business Mgr*
Michael P Staley, *Vice Pres*
Michael Staley, *Vice Pres*
Curtis Laird, *Project Mgr*
Darrell Rich, *Project Mgr*
▲ EMP: 82

SALES (est): 17.4MM **Privately Held**
WEB: www.advantagefireprotection.com
SIC: 1711 3499 Fire sprinkler system installation; fire- or burglary-resistive products

(G-8495)
ADVENT GLOBAL SOLUTIONS INC (PA)
12777 Jones Rd Ste 445 (77070-4950)
PHONE..................................281 970-3000
Raj Chappidi, *CEO*
Shashi Kulkarni, *Business Mgr*
Kishore Reddy, *Business Mgr*
Dev Anand, *Finance Mgr*
Jay Kumar, *Accountant*
EMP: 16
SQ FT: 5,540
SALES: 30.5MM **Privately Held**
WEB: www.adventglobal.com
SIC: 7379 7371 7372 Computer related consulting services; computer software development & applications; computer software development; application computer software

(G-8496)
ADVENTURE PLYGRUND SYSTEMS INC
10845 Church Ln (77043-4007)
PHONE..................................713 935-9684
Toll Free:..................................888 -
James Contreras, *President*
Tom Corcoran, *Vice Pres*
Christian Cordero, *VP Opers*
Linda Contreras, *Sales Mgr*
EMP: 12 EST: 1997
SQ FT: 6,000
SALES: 2MM **Privately Held**
WEB: www.adventureplaysystems.com
SIC: 3949 Playground equipment

(G-8497)
AEGIS CHEMICAL SOLUTIONS LLC (PA)
4560 Kendrick Plaza Dr (77032-2675)
PHONE..................................281 258-4095
Gary Cooper, *CEO*
Steve Clark, *District Mgr*
Jeff West, *District Mgr*
Darin Cottrell, *Area Mgr*
Rick Braddock, *Vice Pres*
EMP: 74
SQ FT: 15,000
SALES (est): 8MM **Privately Held**
WEB: www.aegischemical.com
SIC: 1382 Oil & gas exploration services

(G-8498)
AERODYNMIC PRCSION MCHNING INC
6627 Theall Rd (77066-1213)
PHONE..................................713 856-9990
Steven Anderson, *President*
EMP: 14
SQ FT: 23,000
SALES (est): 2.1MM **Privately Held**
SIC: 3599 Machine shop, jobbing & repair

(G-8499)
AES DRILLING FLUIDS LLC (HQ)
11767 Katy Fwy Ste 230 (77079-1711)
PHONE..................................888 556-4533
Richard Baxter, *President*
Sean Pond, *Division Mgr*
Kristopher Megahan, *Vice Pres*
Nathan Castaneda, *Opers Mgr*
Mike Hughes, *Opers Mgr*
◆ EMP: 125
SALES (est): 402.4MM
SALES (corp-wide): 959.2MM **Privately Held**
WEB: www.aesfluids.com
SIC: 1381 Drilling oil & gas wells
PA: Ces Energy Solutions Corp
332 6 Ave Sw Suite 1400
Calgary AB T2P 0
403 269-2800

(G-8500)
AFTON PUMPS INC
7335 Avenue N (77011-1709)
P.O. Box 9426 (77261-9426)
PHONE..................................713 923-9731
Michael L Derr, *President*

▲ = Import ▼=Export
◆ =Import/Export

Jorge Delatorre, *District Mgr*
David Derr, *Exec VP*
Sam Bailey, *Buyer*
Terry Wold, *Engineer*
◆ **EMP:** 54 **EST:** 1957
SQ FT: 50,000
SALES (est): 18MM **Privately Held**
WEB: www.aftonpumps.com
SIC: 3561 7699 Industrial pumps & parts; pumps & pumping equipment repair

(G-8501)
AGAR CORPORATION INC (HQ)
5150 Tacoma Dr (77041-7034)
PHONE.................................832 476-5100
Joram Agar, *President*
Rafael Carbajal, *Vice Pres*
David Farchi, *Vice Pres*
David Shelef, *Project Mgr*
Linda Shelvin, *Purch Mgr*
◆ **EMP:** 70
SQ FT: 22,000
SALES (est): 14.8MM **Privately Held**
WEB: www.agarcorp.com
SIC: 3823 Industrial flow & liquid measuring instruments; flow instruments, industrial process type

(G-8502)
AGE INDUSTRIES LTD
7001 Barney Rd (77092-4440)
PHONE.................................713 460-3060
Barbara Lawrence, *Accountant*
Charlie Fry, *Sales Staff*
Jeff Eshleman, *Branch Mgr*
EMP: 35
SQ FT: 33,000
SALES (corp-wide): 140.8MM **Privately Held**
WEB: www.ageindustries.com
SIC: 2653 Boxes, corrugated: made from purchased materials
PA: Age Industries, Ltd.
3601 County Road 316c
Cleburne TX 76031
817 477-5266

(G-8503)
AGM TOOLS INC
5074 Steadmont Dr (77040-6524)
PHONE.................................832 499-6090
Alejandro E Garcia, *President*
Rocia Soria Gerardo, *Vice Pres*
EMP: 13
SQ FT: 5,600
SALES (est): 535.9K **Privately Held**
WEB: www.agmtools.com
SIC: 5085 3545 Tools; machine tool accessories

(G-8504)
AGRIBAG INC
8830 Market St (77029-3420)
PHONE.................................713 847-8008
Chris Liang, *Manager*
Cynthia Wang, *Manager*
▲ **EMP:** 10
SALES (est): 2.1MM **Privately Held**
WEB: www.agribag.com
SIC: 2673 Plastic bags: made from purchased materials

(G-8505)
AIR DRILLING ASSOCIATES INC (PA)
Also Called: Ada Energy Services
18155 Chisholm Trl (77060-1101)
PHONE.................................832 957-6093
Tommy Ramsay, *CEO*
Donald Wells, *President*
Chaman Malhotra, *Chairman*
Devin Crisanti, *Counsel*
Dennis E Wood, *Senior VP*
EMP: 10
SALES (est): 14MM **Privately Held**
WEB: www.airdrilling.com
SIC: 7353 1781 1381 Oil field equipment, rental or leasing; geothermal drilling; service well drilling

(G-8506)
AIR DUCT SYSTEMS MFG CO
Also Called: ADS Manufacturing Co
6401 Long Point Rd # 506 (77055-2631)
PHONE.................................832 519-9746
Mahmood A Khawaja, *President*

Jamal Khawaja, *Vice Pres*
EMP: 25
SQ FT: 25,000
SALES (est): 3.5MM **Privately Held**
WEB: www.texasductsystems.com
SIC: 3444 Sheet metalwork

(G-8507)
AIR FILTERS INC
8282 Warren Rd (77040-2602)
PHONE.................................713 896-8901
Anthony Dimicelli, *President*
Brandy Sadler, *Finance*
Soraya Garcia, *Supervisor*
▲ **EMP:** 45
SQ FT: 50,000
SALES (est): 10MM **Privately Held**
WEB: www.airfilterusa.com
SIC: 3564 Filters, air: furnaces, air conditioning equipment, etc.

(G-8508)
AIR FLOW PRODUCTS LP
Also Called: Cool-A-Zone
5310 Glenmont Dr Ste C (77081-2008)
PHONE.................................713 305-0258
Hillary Hobbs, *Partner*
EMP: 10
SALES (est): 641.5K **Privately Held**
WEB: www.coolazone.com
SIC: 3585 Evaporative condensers, heat transfer equipment

(G-8509)
AIR LIQUIDE ADVANCED MTLS INC (HQ)
9811 Katy Fwy Ste 100 (77024-1274)
PHONE.................................713 624-8000
Paul Burlingame, *President*
Richard Hallett, *CFO*
Ann Marie Hansen, *Finance Dir*
◆ **EMP:** 20
SQ FT: 16,700
SALES (est): 58.8MM
SALES (corp-wide): 129.8MM **Privately Held**
WEB: www.industry.airliquide.us
SIC: 2813 Industrial gases
PA: L'air Liquide Societe Anonyme Pour L'etude Et L'exploitation Des Procedes Georges Claude
75 Quai D Orsay
Paris 75007
140 625-555

(G-8510)
AIR LIQUIDE AMERICA LP
12800 W Little York Rd (77041-4218)
P.O. Box 3047 (77253-3047)
PHONE.................................713 896-2100
Carl A Davis, *Plant Mgr*
Bill Clinton, *Manager*
Ray Sidenblad, *Manager*
Nicole McDowell, *Supervisor*
John H Hoover, *Director*
EMP: 240
SALES (corp-wide): 129.8MM **Privately Held**
WEB: www.industry.airliquide.us
SIC: 2813 Industrial gases
HQ: Air Liquide America L.P.
9811 Katy Fwy Ste 100
Houston TX 77024
713 624-8000

(G-8511)
AIR LIQUIDE LARGE INDS US LP (DH)
9811 Katy Fwy Ste 100 (77024-1274)
PHONE.................................713 624-8000
Roger Perreault, *Managing Prtnr*
Gb Alexander, *Partner*
Kevin Feeney, *Partner*
Rose Dubiel, *Manager*
Patti Hess, *Manager*
▲ **EMP:** 259
SALES (est): 232.2MM
SALES (corp-wide): 129.8MM **Privately Held**
WEB: www.airliquide.com
SIC: 2813 Industrial gases
HQ: American Air Liquide Holdings, Inc.
2700 Post Oak Blvd
Houston TX 77056
713 624-8000

(G-8512)
AIR LIQUIDE USA LLC
9811 Katy Fwy Ste 100 (77024-1274)
P.O. Box 460149 (77056-8149)
PHONE.................................713 402-2221
Susan Ellerbusch, *CEO*
Gregory B Alexander, *Vice Pres*
Ann Attaway, *Manager*
Richard Davis, *Technical Staff*
Kevin M Feeney, *Admin Sec*
EMP: 600
SALES (est): 1.9MM
SALES (corp-wide): 129.8MM **Privately Held**
WEB: www.airliquide.com
SIC: 2813 Industrial gases
HQ: Air Liquide America L.P.
9811 Katy Fwy Ste 100
Houston TX 77024
713 624-8000

(G-8513)
AIR LQIDE ADVANCED TECH US LLC (DH)
9807 Katy Fwy (77024-1275)
PHONE.................................713 624-8000
Ole Hoefelmann, *CEO*
Michael F Smith, *President*
Sabrina Kristobak, *Principal*
David W Smith, *Controller*
▲ **EMP:** 500
SALES (est): 847.4MM
SALES (corp-wide): 129.8MM **Privately Held**
WEB: www.industry.airliquide.us
SIC: 2813 Industrial gases
HQ: American Air Liquide Holdings, Inc.
2700 Post Oak Blvd
Houston TX 77056
713 624-8000

(G-8514)
AIR LQIDE AMER SPCLTY GSES LLC (DH)
2700 Post Oak Blvd (77056-5784)
PHONE.................................800 217-2688
David Meneses, *CEO*
Matt Wigle, *President*
Johnnye Wozniak, *President*
Paul Chabot, *Business Mgr*
Stephen Dziak, *Vice Pres*
◆ **EMP:** 30
SQ FT: 72,320
SALES (est): 69.4MM
SALES (corp-wide): 129.8MM **Privately Held**
WEB: www.airgas.com
SIC: 2911 2813 Petroleum refining; industrial gases
HQ: American Air Liquide Holdings, Inc.
2700 Post Oak Blvd
Houston TX 77056
713 624-8000

(G-8515)
AIR LQIDE HYDRGEN ENRGY US LLC
9811 Katy Fwy Ste 100 (77024-1274)
PHONE.................................346 971-3051
Karine Boissy-Rousseau,
EMP: 22
SALES (est): 1MM **Privately Held**
SIC: 2813 Industrial gases

(G-8516)
AIRGAS INC
14833 Tomball Pkwy (77086-1601)
PHONE.................................281 893-9353
Troy Sands, *Principal*
Kathy Russell, *Sales Staff*
EMP: 34
SALES (corp-wide): 129.8MM **Privately Held**
WEB: www.airgas.com
SIC: 2813 5169 Industrial gases; gases, compressed & liquefied
HQ: Airgas, Inc.
259 N Radnor Chester Rd # 100
Radnor PA 19087
610 687-5253

(G-8517)
AIRLINE PLATING INC
6901 Airline Dr (77076-2429)
PHONE.................................713 692-6369

Joe Olivares, *President*
Graciela Olivares, *Vice Pres*
EMP: 12 **EST:** 1979
SQ FT: 2,300
SALES (est): 1.2MM **Privately Held**
WEB: www.airlinechromeplating.com
SIC: 3471 Plating of metals or formed products

(G-8518)
AIRTECH SPRAY SYSTEMS INC
4303 Pinemont Dr (77018-1041)
PHONE.................................713 681-0013
Joe A Acosta, *President*
Ronald Cradit, *Vice Pres*
John Weems Jr, *Vice Pres*
Sam Hertenberger, *Purch Mgr*
Bill Van Buren, *Natl Sales Mgr*
EMP: 32
SQ FT: 12,400
SALES (est): 8.4MM **Privately Held**
WEB: www.airtechspraysystems.com
SIC: 3441 5084 Fabricated structural metal; paint spray equipment, industrial

(G-8519)
AKER SOLUTIONS INC (HQ)
2103 Citywest Blvd # 800 (77042-2833)
PHONE.................................713 685-5700
Neil Holder, *CEO*
Erik Wiik, *President*
Cheryl Fisher, *Engineer*
▲ **EMP:** 150
SQ FT: 200,000
SALES (est): 154.2MM
SALES (corp-wide): 3.2B **Privately Held**
WEB: www.akersolutions.com
SIC: 3533 1389 8711 Oil field machinery & equipment; construction, repair & dismantling services; engineering services

(G-8520)
AKZO NOBEL COATINGS INC
6001 Antoine Dr (77091-3503)
PHONE.................................713 684-1324
Courtney Kincaid, *Engineer*
Martin Rodriguez, *Sales Mgr*
Matthew Anzardo, *Marketing Staff*
Christopher McMillan, *Marketing Staff*
James Hohertz, *Manager*
EMP: 14
SALES (corp-wide): 10.2B **Privately Held**
WEB: www.akzonobel.com
SIC: 2851 Paints: oil or alkyd vehicle or water thinned
HQ: Akzo Nobel Coatings Inc.
8220 Mohawk Dr
Strongsville OH 44136
440 297-5100

(G-8521)
AKZO NOBEL INC
Also Called: ICI Paints Store
14502 Richmond Ave (77082-1725)
PHONE.................................281 584-0093
EMP: 34
SALES (corp-wide): 10.2B **Privately Held**
WEB: www.akzonobel.com
SIC: 2869 Industrial organic chemicals
HQ: Akzo Nobel Inc.
535 Marriott Dr Ste 500
Nashville TN 37214

(G-8522)
ALAMO CONCRETE PRODUCTS CO
18880 E Hardy Rd (77073-3504)
PHONE.................................281 443-2644
EMP: 13
SALES (corp-wide): 345.6K **Privately Held**
SIC: 3272 Concrete products
PA: Alamo Concrete Products Company
6981 E Evans Rd
San Antonio TX 78266
210 208-1500

(G-8523)
ALAMO READY MIX LLC
1818 Federal Rd (77015-6710)
PHONE.................................713 330-3000
Babu George, *Mng Member*
EMP: 35 **EST:** 2013
SALES (est): 12.9MM **Privately Held**
WEB: www.smyrnareadymix.com
SIC: 3273 Ready-mixed concrete

(G-8524)
ALAMO RESOURCES LLC
820 Gessner Rd Ste 1650 (77024-4279)
PHONE....................................281 398-9500
Carl Campbell, COO
Christa Fitzgibbons, Vice Pres
Antonio Pelletier,
Joan Robilio, Executive Asst
Tony Pelletier,
EMP: 15
SALES (est): 1.5MM Privately Held
WEB: www.alamoresources.com
SIC: 1382 Oil & gas exploration services

(G-8525)
ALAMO TAMALE COMPANY LP
809 Berry Rd (77022-3307)
PHONE....................................713 228-6445
Louis M Webster, CEO
Vicky Hinajosa, Prdtn Mgr
EMP: 80 EST: 1960
SALES (est): 3.6MM Privately Held
WEB: www.alamotamale.net
SIC: 2099 Tortillas, fresh or refrigerated

(G-8526)
**ALAMO TRANSFORMER
SUPPLY CO**
Also Called: Atsco
10220 Mykawa Rd (77048-1326)
PHONE....................................713 991-6060
Susan Peter, CFO
Tom Langley, Branch Mgr
EMP: 20
SQ FT: 31,480
SALES (corp-wide): 16.5MM Privately
Held
WEB: www.alamotransformer.com
SIC: 7629 5063 3612 Electrical equip-
ment repair, high voltage; transformers,
electric; transformers, except electric
PA: Alamo Transformer Supply Company
4931 Space Center Dr
San Antonio TX 78218
210 661-8411

(G-8527)
ALART TOOL & DIE CORP
37 Berry Rd (77022-3058)
PHONE....................................713 691-0434
Arthur J Speetzen, President
Scott Speetzen, General Mgr
Patricia Speetze, Vice Pres
Sarah Redding, Office Mgr
EMP: 15
SQ FT: 7,500
SALES (est): 2.4MM Privately Held
WEB: www.alartmachine.com
SIC: 3544 3599 Special dies & tools; cus-
tom machinery

(G-8528)
ALBAS CUSTOM IRON INC
Also Called: A.C.I. Metal Works
7105 Fulton St (77022-4459)
P.O. Box 130501, Spring (77393-0501)
PHONE....................................281 401-9797
Samuel Alba Sr, President
Paul Alba, Vice Pres
Juanita Alba, Treasurer
EMP: 10 EST: 1968
SQ FT: 13,200
SALES (est): 1.6MM Privately Held
WEB: www.acimetals.com
SIC: 3446 3441 Fences or posts, orna-
mental iron or steel; stairs, staircases,
stair treads: prefabricated metal; fabri-
cated structural metal

(G-8529)
ALBEMARLE CORPORATION
13100 Space Center Blvd # 400
(77059-3654)
PHONE....................................281 480-4747
Jeff Mason, Research
Adondria Parker, Supervisor
Tom Perry, Info Tech Mgr
Wally Bigler, Director
Steve Murff, Admin Sec
EMP: 45 Publicly Held
WEB: www.albemarle.com
SIC: 2821 2819 Plastics materials &
resins; bromine, elemental
PA: Albemarle Corporation
4250 Congress St Ste 900
Charlotte NC 28209

(G-8530)
ALBEMARLE CORPORATION
2625 Bay Area Blvd # 250 (77058-1523)
PHONE....................................281 480-4747
David Leach, Business Mgr
Fred Cannon, Manager
Bruce Adkins, Manager
Robert Haseltine, Manager
Jason Mejia, Manager
EMP: 14 Publicly Held
WEB: www.albemarle.com
SIC: 2819 Catalysts, chemical
PA: Albemarle Corporation
4250 Congress St Ste 900
Charlotte NC 28209

(G-8531)
ALCON MANUFACTURING LTD
9965 Buffalo Speedway (77054-1309)
PHONE....................................713 668-9100
David Valdos, Engineer
EMP: 33
SALES (corp-wide): 2.1MM Privately
Held
WEB: www.alcon.com
SIC: 2834 Veterinary pharmaceutical
preparations
PA: Alcon Manufacturing, Ltd.
15800 Alton Pkwy
Irvine CA 92618
949 753-1393

(G-8532)
ALCON VISION LLC
2650 W Belford St (77002)
PHONE....................................713 668-9100
Timothy R Sear, President
EMP: 26
SALES (corp-wide): 7.5B Privately Held
WEB: www.alcon.com
SIC: 2834 3841 Pharmaceutical prepara-
tions; surgical & medical instruments
HQ: Alcon Vision, Llc
6201 South Fwy
Fort Worth TX 76134
817 293-0450

(G-8533)
ALCON VISION LLC
Also Called: Alcon Surgical
9965 Buffalo Speedway (77054-1309)
PHONE....................................713 668-9100
Jeffery Wagen, Purch Mgr
Ian Karle, Engineer
Jhonny Jaimes, Human Resources
Rebekah Lilly, Manager
Lindsey Brown, Analyst
EMP: 1000
SALES (corp-wide): 7.5B Privately Held
WEB: www.alcon.com
SIC: 3851 Ophthalmic goods
HQ: Alcon Vision, Llc
6201 South Fwy
Fort Worth TX 76134
817 293-0450

(G-8534)
ALERT TECHNOLOGIES INC
16875 Diana Ln (77058-2526)
PHONE....................................281 326-9900
Marjorie A Laney, President
Frank Giuliano, Vice Pres
Scott Magee, Vice Pres
Rick Vaughn, Vice Pres
Isidore Trevino, Engineer
EMP: 21
SALES (est): 4.8MM Privately Held
WEB: www.alerttech.net
SIC: 3663 7371 3826 Radio broadcasting
& communications equipment; custom
computer programming services; analyti-
cal instruments

(G-8535)
ALFA LAVAL INC
Also Called: Alfa Laval Thermal
10470 Deer Trail Dr (77038-3131)
PHONE....................................713 329-1270
Taha Suria, Business Mgr
Kathy Manning, Purch Mgr
Carl Lemke, Technical Mgr
Randy Herrell, Manager
EMP: 10 Privately Held
SIC: 3443 Fabricated plate work (boiler
shop)

HQ: Alfa Laval Inc.
5400 Intl Trade Dr
Richmond VA 23231
866 253-2528

(G-8536)
ALFA LAVAL US HOLDING INC
11600 E Hardy Rd (77093-1021)
PHONE....................................281 449-0322
Cecilie Ogara, Business Mgr
EMP: 175 Privately Held
WEB: www.alfalaval.com
SIC: 3589 Water treatment equipment, in-
dustrial
HQ: Alfa Laval U.S. Holding Inc.
5400 Intl Trade Dr
Richmond VA 23231

(G-8537)
ALGAE PRODUCTION SYSTEMS
9337b Katy Fwy Ste 193 (77024-1515)
PHONE....................................832 515-9670
Richard A Fortune, President
Glen Cook, Sls & Mktg Exec
EMP: 10
SALES (est): 743.1K Privately Held
WEB: www.algaeproductionsystems.com
SIC: 2819 Nuclear fuel & cores, inorganic

(G-8538)
ALIG LLC (DH)
Also Called: Mg Industries
2700 Post Oak Blvd (77056-5784)
PHONE....................................212 626-4936
Benot Potier, Ch of Bd
▲ EMP: 100
SALES (est): 76.4MM
SALES (corp-wide): 129.8MM Privately
Held
SIC: 2813 5169 5085 Oxygen, com-
pressed or liquefied; industrial gases;
tanks, pressurized
HQ: Air Liquide America L.P.
9811 Katy Fwy Ste 100
Houston TX 77024
713 624-8000

(G-8539)
ALKOTE INC
13 Farrell St (77022-2699)
PHONE....................................713 695-3609
J Wayne Dyer, President
Nina Dyer, Treasurer
Brian Dyer, Manager
EMP: 24
SQ FT: 15,000
SALES (est): 2.1MM Privately Held
WEB: www.alkoteinc.com
SIC: 3471 3479 Anodizing (plating) of met-
als or formed products; coloring & finish-
ing of aluminum or formed products;
finishing, metals or formed products;
painting of metal products

(G-8540)
**ALL POINTS EQUIPMENT CO
LLC**
9710 Telge Rd (77095-5004)
P.O. Box 1786, Cypress (77410-1786)
PHONE....................................337 369-6314
Mary Thomas, Mng Member
◆ EMP: 10
SALES (est): 1.2MM Privately Held
WEB: www.afglobalcorp.com
SIC: 1389 Servicing oil & gas wells

(G-8541)
ALL-RITE SHEET METAL INC
5718 Broom St (77091-4908)
PHONE....................................713 680-0515
Larry Bailey, CEO
EMP: 28
SQ FT: 10,000
SALES (est): 5.3MM Privately Held
SIC: 3444 Sheet metalwork

(G-8542)
**ALLCHEM SERVICES
INCORPORATED**
9011 E Almeda St (77054-4515)
P.O. Box 7746, Pasadena (77508-7746)
PHONE....................................713 796-8000
Richard Robinson, President
Donna Tylka, Corp Secy
Charles Tylka, Vice Pres
◆ EMP: 50

SQ FT: 125,000
SALES (est): 22.2MM Privately Held
WEB: www.allchem.net
SIC: 5169 2899 Industrial chemicals;
chemical preparations

(G-8543)
**ALLENDALE MACHINE CO INC
(PA)**
10014 Lucore St (77017-3428)
P.O. Box 12907 (77217-2907)
PHONE....................................713 477-8776
Weldon Settle, President
Profirio Flores, Foreman/Supr
EMP: 14 EST: 1971
SQ FT: 13,500
SALES (est): 2.6MM Privately Held
WEB: www.allendalemachine.com
SIC: 3533 Oil field machinery & equipment

(G-8544)
ALLENDALE MACHINE CO INC
10017 Steelman St (77017-3439)
P.O. Box 12907 (77217-2907)
PHONE....................................713 477-8776
Weldon Settle, Manager
EMP: 15
SALES (corp-wide): 2.6MM Privately
Held
WEB: www.allendalemachine.com
SIC: 3533 Oil field machinery & equipment
PA: Allendale Machine Co, Inc
10014 Lucore St
Houston TX 77017
713 477-8776

(G-8545)
**ALLIANCE ENERGY
CORPORATION**
3 Riverway Ste 825 (77056-1941)
PHONE....................................713 333-4000
Chris Dittmar, CEO
EMP: 14
SALES (est): 830.1K Privately Held
SIC: 1382 Oil & gas exploration services

(G-8546)
ALLIANCE PRESS LEASING INC
5225 Hollister St (77040-6205)
PHONE....................................713 957-3349
Jeff Birmingham, President
EMP: 23
SALES (est): 2.1MM Privately Held
WEB: www.alliancegraphicsprinting.com
SIC: 2752 2791 2789 Commercial print-
ing, offset; typesetting; bookbinding & re-
lated work

(G-8547)
ALLIANCE PRINTING LP
Also Called: Alliance Graphics & Printing
5225 Hollister St (77040-6205)
PHONE....................................713 957-3349
Jeff Birmingham, Partner
Eduardo Caballero, Project Mgr
Paul Quin, VP Bus Dvlpt
Chris Hawkinson, Accounts Exec
Justin Shillings, Manager
EMP: 50 EST: 2001
SQ FT: 22,000
SALES (est): 13.2MM Privately Held
WEB: www.alliancegp.net
SIC: 2752 7336 Commercial printing, off-
set; graphic arts & related design

(G-8548)
ALLIED ASSETS CORPORATION
Also Called: Arcot Manufacturing
2950 Mowery Rd (77045-4855)
PHONE....................................713 413-9700
Mehdi Banijamali, President
Mahmood Banijamali, Opers Mgr
EMP: 30
SQ FT: 40,000
SALES (est): 5MM Privately Held
WEB: www.arcotmanufacturing.com
SIC: 2842 Cleaning or polishing prepara-
tions

(G-8549)
ALLIED IMAGING GROUP LLC
2519 Fairway Park Dr # 310 (77092-7600)
PHONE....................................713 812-8100
Fax: 713 812-8210
EMP: 30
SQ FT: 8,600

SALES (est): 2.6MM **Privately Held**
SIC: 3299 Mfg Nonmetallic Mineral Products

(G-8550)
ALLIED NATURAL GAS CORPORATION
1001 Fannin St Ste 900 (77002-6706)
PHONE...................................713 658-1144
Charles A Sherman, *President*
Melinda A Faust, *Business Mgr*
Mac Mullan Energy, *Shareholder*
EMP: 16
SQ FT: 2,100
SALES (est): 10MM **Privately Held**
SIC: 1311 Crude petroleum & natural gas

(G-8551)
ALLIED PALLET & EQP CO LLC
16760 Beaumont Hwy (77049-2024)
P.O. Box 215, Crosby (77532-0215)
PHONE...................................281 850-8090
Jerry Friday, *President*
Michael Friday, *Owner*
EMP: 15
SQ FT: 32,000
SALES (est): 5MM **Privately Held**
SIC: 2448 Pallets, wood

(G-8552)
ALLIED PROD SOLUTIONS GP LLC (PA)
10344 Sam Houston Park Dr # 300 (77064-4665)
PHONE...................................405 224-5779
John D Schmitz, *President*
Kellie Holt, *Human Res Dir*
Wendell Brooks, *Director*
Steve M Schmitz, *Director*
Adam Zylman, *Director*
EMP: 150
SALES (est): 17.2MM **Privately Held**
WEB: www.f-e-t.com
SIC: 3533 Oil & gas drilling rigs & equipment

(G-8553)
ALLIED THREADED MTLS & MCHY CO
8918 Spring Branch Dr A (77080-7446)
PHONE...................................713 464-3594
EMP: 9 EST: 1966
SQ FT: 8,000
SALES (est): 810K **Privately Held**
WEB: www.alliedthreadedmetals.com
SIC: 3599 Machine shop, jobbing & repair

(G-8554)
ALLIED TOOLS OF TEXAS CORP
5230 Galveston Rd (77017-6146)
PHONE...................................713 943-8500
EMP: 9
SQ FT: 8,000
SALES (est): 159.5K **Privately Held**
WEB: www.alliedtoolsoftexas.com
SIC: 3469 3599 Stamping metal for the trade; machine shop, jobbing & repair

(G-8555)
ALLIED WIRELINE SERVICES LLC (PA)
Also Called: Allied-Hrizontal Wireline Svcs
3200 Wilcrest Dr Ste 170 (77042-3366)
PHONE...................................713 343-7280
Larry Albert, *President*
Joshua Atkins, *District Mgr*
Robert Moneypenny, *District Mgr*
Jeff Barron, *Vice Pres*
Laura Miller, *Vice Pres*
EMP: 15
SQ FT: 3,000
SALES (est): 142.8MM **Privately Held**
WEB: www.alliedhorizontal.com
SIC: 1389 Oil field services

(G-8556)
ALLOY CARBIDE COMPANY (PA)
7827 Avenue H (77012-1196)
P.O. Box 5368 (77262-5368)
PHONE...................................713 923-2700
Robert Perez, *President*
Walter J McCaine, *President*
Tony Gonzalez, *Facilities Mgr*
Ron Beshears, *Engrg Mgr*
Randy Manuel, *Engrg Mgr*

EMP: 50 EST: 1956
SQ FT: 50,000
SALES (est): 15MM **Privately Held**
WEB: www.alloycarbide.com
SIC: 3599 3313 3545 Machine shop, jobbing & repair; electrometallurgical products; machine tool accessories

(G-8557)
ALLOY CARBIDE COMPANY
7820 Avenue I (77012-1136)
PHONE...................................713 923-2700
Robert Perez, *Branch Mgr*
EMP: 47
SQ FT: 1,200
SALES (corp-wide): 15MM **Privately Held**
WEB: www.alloycarbide.com
SIC: 1382 Oil & gas exploration services
PA: Alloy Carbide Company
   7827 Avenue H
   Houston TX 77012
   713 923-2700

(G-8558)
ALLPOINTS OILFIELD SVCS LLC
945 Bunker Hill Rd # 500 (77024-1358)
PHONE...................................713 393-4200
Brian Fontana, *Vice Pres*
Thomas Giles, *Vice Pres*
Curtis Samford,
Michael L Tiner,
EMP: 14
SALES (est): 1.4MM
SALES (corp-wide): 252.3MM **Privately Held**
WEB: www.afglobalcorp.com
SIC: 1389 Servicing oil & gas wells
HQ: Afg Louisiana Holdings Inc.
   945 Bunker Hill Rd # 500
   Houston TX

(G-8559)
ALLTRANS PORT TRUCKING INC
Also Called: All Transportation Services
9640 Clinton Dr (77029-4324)
P.O. Box 143, Galena Park (77547-0143)
PHONE...................................713 673-3844
Donna Rains, *CEO*
Benny R Rains, *President*
EMP: 20
SALES (est): 3.8MM **Privately Held**
WEB: www.alltransportservices.com
SIC: 4213 3537 7389 Trucking, except local; trucks, tractors, loaders, carriers & similar equipment;

(G-8560)
ALPA PRECISION LLP
1819 Antoine Dr (77055-1801)
PHONE...................................713 680-8556
Patricia Lozano, *Partner*
EMP: 52
SALES (est): 8MM **Privately Held**
WEB: www.alpaprecision.com
SIC: 3823 Industrial flow & liquid measuring instruments

(G-8561)
ALPA PRECISION MCH WORKS INC
1819 Antoine Dr (77055-1801)
PHONE...................................713 680-8556
Alberto A Lozano, *President*
EMP: 33
SQ FT: 15,000
SALES (est): 5.6MM **Privately Held**
WEB: www.alpaprecision.com
SIC: 3823 Industrial flow & liquid measuring instruments

(G-8562)
ALPHA LASER RECHARGE INC
821 Hodgkins St Ste B (77032-2733)
PHONE...................................713 861-2425
Mark Fulmer, *President*
Kevin Dedmon, *General Mgr*
Lynette Fulmer, *Treasurer*
Al Koch, *Technician*
EMP: 14
SQ FT: 3,767

SALES (est): 1.9MM **Privately Held**
WEB: www.alphalaser.net
SIC: 5044 7378 3955 3861 Copying equipment; adding machines; computer maintenance & repair; print cartridges for laser & other computer printers; photographic equipment & supplies

(G-8563)
ALPHA MASUREMENT SOLUTIONS LLC (PA)
10540 Rockley Rd (77099-3545)
PHONE...................................832 456-4100
Drew Hall, *CEO*
Steve Krebs, *COO*
Julius Ivancsits, *CFO*
EMP: 240
SALES (est): 28.3MM **Privately Held**
SIC: 3826 Thermal analysis instruments, laboratory type

(G-8564)
ALTA MARCELLUS DEVELOPMENT LLC
500 Dallas St Ste 2930 (77002-4701)
PHONE...................................713 759-1155
Joseph Greenberg, *Mng Member*
Jennifer McCarthy, *Manager*
EMP: 11 EST: 2016
SQ FT: 6,500
SALES (est): 370.2K **Privately Held**
WEB: www.alta-resources.com
SIC: 1382 Oil & gas exploration services
PA: Alta Resources, L.L.C.
   500 Dallas St Ste 2920
   Houston TX 77002

(G-8565)
ALTA MESA HOLDINGS LP (HQ)
4119 Montrose Blvd # 230 (77006-4964)
PHONE...................................281 530-0991
James Hackett, *Ch of Bd*
Harlan H Chappelle, *President*
Michael Ellis, *COO*
Homer Cole, *Vice Pres*
David Murrell, *Vice Pres*
EMP: 9
SALES (est): 79.3MM
SALES (corp-wide): 100MM **Privately Held**
WEB: www.altamesa.net
SIC: 1382 Oil & gas exploration services
PA: Bce - Mach Iii Llc
   14201 Wireless Way # 300
   Oklahoma City OK 73134
   405 252-8100

(G-8566)
ALTA RESOURCES LLC (PA)
Also Called: Alta Operating
500 Dallas St Ste 2920 (77002-4701)
PHONE...................................713 759-1155
Joe Greenberg,
EMP: 11
SALES (est): 5MM **Privately Held**
WEB: www.alta-resources.com
SIC: 1382 Oil & gas exploration services

(G-8567)
ALTA RESOURCES DEVELOPMENT LLC
1 Allen Ctr 500 Dllas S (77002)
PHONE...................................713 759-1155
Joseph Greenberg, *CEO*
Jennifer McCarthy, *President*
Richard Steet, *CFO*
EMP: 20
SALES (est): 1MM **Privately Held**
WEB: www.alta-resources.com
SIC: 1382 Oil & gas exploration services

(G-8568)
ALTEC INDUSTRIES INC
6902 E Orem Dr (77075-5326)
PHONE...................................713 336-6230
Mack Kinnamon, *General Mgr*
EMP: 13
SALES (corp-wide): 1.1B **Privately Held**
WEB: www.altec.com
SIC: 3531 Construction machinery
HQ: Altec Industries, Inc.
   210 Inverness Center Dr
   Birmingham AL 35242
   205 991-7733

(G-8569)
ALTIUM PACKAGING LP
Packaging-Plastic Div
6831 Silsbee St (77033-1114)
PHONE...................................678 742-4600
Dawson Stertan, *Manager*
EMP: 140
SALES (corp-wide): 728.4MM **Privately Held**
WEB: www.altiumpkg.com
SIC: 3089 Plastic containers, except foam
PA: Altium Packaging Lp
   2500 Windy Ridge Pkwy Se # 1400
   Atlanta GA 30339
   678 742-4600

(G-8570)
ALTIVIA CHEMICALS LLC (PA)
1100 La St Ste 4800 (77002)
PHONE...................................713 658-9000
J Michael Jusbasche, *CEO*
Louie Huey, *COO*
Kevin Reehling, *Production*
Frank Hayes, *CFO*
Fred Stahelin, *CFO*
▲ EMP: 25 EST: 2012
SQ FT: 4,000
SALES (est): 34MM **Privately Held**
WEB: www.altivia.com
SIC: 2819 Industrial inorganic chemicals

(G-8571)
ALTIVIA CORPORATION (DH)
1100 La St Ste 4800 (77002)
PHONE...................................713 658-9000
J Michael Jusbasche, *CEO*
James Taylor, *President*
Davey Pearson, *Business Mgr*
Louis G Huey, *COO*
Donny P Clark, *Vice Pres*
▲ EMP: 15
SQ FT: 10,000
SALES (est): 57.7MM
SALES (corp-wide): 14.1B **Privately Held**
WEB: www.altivia.com
SIC: 2819 7389 4971 Industrial inorganic chemicals; water softener service; water distribution or supply systems for irrigation
HQ: Brenntag Southwest, Inc.
   610 Fisher Rd
   Longview TX 75604
   972 218-3500

(G-8572)
ALTIVIA SPECIALTY CHEM LLC (HQ)
1100 La St Ste 4800 (77002)
PHONE...................................713 658-9000
J Michael Jusbasche, *CEO*
Louis G Huey, *COO*
Fred Stahelin, *CFO*
◆ EMP: 65
SQ FT: 7,118
SALES (est): 34MM **Privately Held**
WEB: www.altivia.com
SIC: 2819 Industrial inorganic chemicals
PA: Altivia Chemicals Llc
   1100 La St Ste 4800
   Houston TX 77002
   713 658-9000

(G-8573)
ALTUS INTERVENTION USA INC (HQ)
15150 Sommermeyer St (77041-5374)
PHONE...................................346 231-0060
Sean O Shaughnessy, *President*
Olav Lindtjorn, *Vice Pres*
Louis Leggett, *Treasurer*
Carter Bolt, *Accountant*
Matt Peoples, *Accounts Mgr*
EMP: 44
SALES (est): 18.8MM **Privately Held**
WEB: www.competentia.com
SIC: 1389 Servicing oil & gas wells

(G-8574)
ALUMINUM MINT SYSTEMS TXAS INC
Also Called: Amst
7777 Parnell St (77021-6008)
PHONE...................................713 522-8925
Larue Coleman, *President*
Dustin Mattison, *Safety Dir*

EMP: 200
SQ FT: 38,000
SALES (est): 22.9MM **Privately Held**
WEB: www.jobs-amst.com
SIC: 3479 Painting, coating & hot dipping

(G-8575)
ALVAREZ & MARSAL INC
700 Louisiana St Ste 3300 (77002-2823)
PHONE................................212 759-4433
Leonid Afendikov, *Managing Dir*
Asad Ahmed, *Managing Dir*
Phil Beckett, *Managing Dir*
Adriano Bianchi, *Managing Dir*
Chandu Chilakapati, *Managing Dir*
EMP: 175
SALES (corp-wide): 207.5MM **Privately
Held**
WEB: www.alvarezandmarsal.com
SIC: 8742 3523 3448 Financial consult-
ant; farm machinery & equipment; prefab-
ricated metal buildings
HQ: Alvarez & Marsal, Inc.
　　600 Madison Ave Fl 8
　　New York NY 10022
　　212 759-4433

(G-8576)
AMBAR INC
16825 Northchase Dr # 16 (77060-6024)
PHONE................................281 873-7600
Anthony Caridi, *President*
Mike De Carlo, *COO*
Ron Brazzel, *Vice Pres*
J Travis Kieffer, *Vice Pres*
Dick Mac Dougal, *Purchasing*
EMP: 200
SQ FT: 9,000
SALES (est): 60MM **Privately Held**
WEB: www.cri-catalysts.com
SIC: 5169 2819 4953 7359 Drilling mud;
calcium chloride & hypochlorite; haz-
ardous waste collection & disposal; equip-
ment rental & leasing

(G-8577)
AMBER/BOOTH INC
Also Called: Vmc Group, The
11930 Brittmoore Park Dr (77041-7225)
PHONE................................713 466-0003
John Wilson, *CEO*
John B Burum, *Vice Pres*
Warner Stebner, *Vice Pres*
E Kimball Salls III, *Treasurer*
▼ **EMP:** 90
SQ FT: 49,050
SALES (est): 26.7MM
SALES (corp-wide): 35MM **Privately
Held**
WEB: www.thevmcgroup.com
SIC: 3531 5075 Vibrators for concrete
construction; air conditioning equipment,
except room units; electrical heating
equipment
PA: Vibration Mountings & Controls, Inc.
　　113 Main St
　　Bloomingdale NJ 07403
　　800 569-8423

(G-8578)
**AMEC FOSTER WHEELER USA
CORP (DH)**
17325 Park Row (77084-4932)
PHONE................................713 929-5000
Robin Watson, *CEO*
Ron Platt, *Superintendent*
Mark Bartus, *Project Mgr*
Michael McGrath, *Director*
Jennifer Ritchie,
▲ **EMP:** 29
SALES (est): 277.5MM
SALES (corp-wide): 12.7B **Privately Held**
WEB: www.woodplc.com
SIC: 8711 3443 1629 Engineering serv-
ices; boilers: industrial, power, or marine;
chemical plant & refinery construction; oil
refinery construction
HQ: Amec Foster Wheeler Limited
　　23rd Floor
　　London E14 5
　　207 429-7500

(G-8579)
AMERIBOLT INC
9506 Bamboo Rd (77041-7706)
PHONE................................713 580-4997

James Province, *Branch Mgr*
Michael Jones, *Director*
EMP: 20 **Privately Held**
SIC: 5072 3462 Miscellaneous fasteners;
iron & steel forgings
HQ: Ameribolt, Inc.
　　18060 Al Hwy 21
　　Sycamore AL 35149
　　256 249-6979

(G-8580)
**AMERICA INDUSTRIAL PDTS
LLC**
3880 Grnhse Rd Ste 427 (77084)
PHONE................................832 974-4153
Lempira F Moran, *Mng Member*
EMP: 10
SALES (est): 3MM **Privately Held**
SIC: 5084 3599 7699 Food industry ma-
chinery; amusement park equipment; in-
dustrial machinery & equipment repair

(G-8581)
**AMERICAN A LQUIDE
HOLDINGS INC (HQ)**
2700 Post Oak Blvd (77056-5784)
PHONE................................713 624-8000
Bob Collier, *Plant Mgr*
Perry Page, *Plant Mgr*
Brett Phillips, *Plant Mgr*
Shawn Riehle, *Plant Mgr*
Julie Heil, *Project Mgr*
EMP: 50
SALES (est): 4.5B
SALES (corp-wide): 129.8MM **Privately
Held**
WEB: www.industry.airliquide.us
SIC: 2813 6719 Industrial gases; invest-
ment holding companies, except banks
PA: L'air Liquide Societe Anonyme Pour
　　L'etude Et L'exploitation Des Procedes
　　Georges Claude
　　75 Quai D Orsay
　　Paris 75007
　　140 625-555

(G-8582)
AMERICAN AIR LIQUIDE INC
9811 Katy Fwy Ste 100 (77024-1274)
PHONE................................877 855-9533
Michael J Graff, *President*
Adam Peters, *Vice Pres*
Augustin Roubin, *Vice Pres*
Guy Salzgeber, *Vice Pres*
Mok Weng, *Vice Pres*
◆ **EMP:** 35 **EST:** 2013
SALES (est): 6.6MM
SALES (corp-wide): 129.8MM **Privately
Held**
WEB: www.industry.airliquide.us
SIC: 2813 3519 Industrial gases; gasoline
engines
PA: L'air Liquide Societe Anonyme Pour
　　L'etude Et L'exploitation Des Procedes
　　Georges Claude
　　75 Quai D Orsay
　　Paris 75007
　　140 625-555

(G-8583)
AMERICAN AIR SERVICES LLC
10925 Grant Rd 435 (77070-4446)
PHONE................................832 715-8025
Monica Barger,
EMP: 10
SALES (est): 325K **Privately Held**
WEB: www.americanairservices.com
SIC: 3585 Air conditioning equipment,
complete

(G-8584)
**AMERICAN ALLOY STEEL INC
(PA)**
6230 N Houston Rosslyn Rd (77091-3410)
P.O. Box 40469 (77240-0469)
PHONE................................713 462-8081
Arthur Moore, *President*
James Moore, *Exec VP*
Anne Haynes, *Senior VP*
Al Acock Jr, *Vice Pres*
Stephen Kibling, *Vice Pres*
◆ **EMP:** 135
SQ FT: 166,000

SALES: 192.6MM **Privately Held**
WEB: www.aasteel.com
SIC: 3443 Fabricated plate work (boiler
shop)

(G-8585)
**AMERICAN ARMTIVE
CMPONENTS INC**
1733 Lauder Rd (77039-3027)
PHONE................................281 442-7791
James Carroll, *President*
Jay Carroll, *Opers Mgr*
EMP: 30
SALES (est): 3.9MM **Privately Held**
WEB: www.americanaeromotive.com
SIC: 3728 Aircraft parts & equipment

(G-8586)
AMERICAN ASSN NOTARIES INC
8027 Gulf Fwy (77017-3644)
P.O. Box 630601 (77263-0601)
PHONE................................713 644-2299
Kal Tabbara, *President*
EMP: 10
SALES (est): 1MM **Privately Held**
WEB: www.texasnotary.com
SIC: 3953 6351 Seal presses, notary &
hand; fidelity or surety bonding

(G-8587)
AMERICAN BLOCK COMPANY
5900 Bingle Rd (77092-1302)
PHONE................................281 820-5332
Robert Acuna, *Branch Mgr*
EMP: 62
SALES (corp-wide): 152.8MM **Privately
Held**
WEB: www.americanblock.com
SIC: 3441 Fabricated structural metal
PA: American Block Company
　　6311 Breen Dr
　　Houston TX 77086
　　800 572-9087

(G-8588)
**AMERICAN BLOCK COMPANY
(PA)**
Also Called: American Block Mfg Co
6311 Breen Dr (77086-3836)
P.O. Box 38266 (77238-8266)
PHONE................................800 572-9087
Rajani K Shah, *President*
Robert Acuna, *Division Mgr*
Randy Little, *Division Mgr*
Jack Franklin, *General Mgr*
Darshana Shah, *Corp Secy*
◆ **EMP:** 120 **EST:** 1980
SQ FT: 38,000
SALES (est): 152.8MM **Privately Held**
WEB: www.americanblock.com
SIC: 3441 3599 3533 3496 Fabricated
structural metal; machine & other job
shop work; oil & gas field machinery; mis-
cellaneous fabricated wire products;
sheet metalwork; manufactured hardware
(general)

(G-8589)
AMERICAN BLOCK COMPANY
7903 Breen Dr (77064-8420)
PHONE................................281 820-5332
Reina Caballero, *Branch Mgr*
EMP: 62
SALES (corp-wide): 152.8MM **Privately
Held**
WEB: www.americanblock.com
SIC: 3441 Fabricated structural metal
PA: American Block Company
　　6311 Breen Dr
　　Houston TX 77086
　　800 572-9087

(G-8590)
**AMERICAN BOTTLING
COMPANY**
Also Called: Southwest Fountain Supply Co
2400 Holly Hall St (77054-3904)
P.O. Box 4262 (77210-4262)
PHONE................................713 799-1024
Dave Lenier, *Principal*
EMP: 100 **Publicly Held**
WEB: www.keurigdrpepper.com
SIC: 2086 2087 Soft drinks: packaged in
cans, bottles, etc.; flavoring extracts &
syrups

HQ: The American Bottling Company
　　5301 Legacy Dr
　　Plano TX 75024

(G-8591)
**AMERICAN BRONZE ALUM
CAST CORP**
Also Called: Dee Foundries
2408 Everett St (77009-7806)
P.O. Box 8727 (77249-8727)
PHONE................................713 222-0236
Robert E Wolf, *President*
Nate McClain, *Production*
EMP: 20
SQ FT: 70,000
SALES (est): 5.1MM **Privately Held**
WEB: www.deefoundries.com
SIC: 3366 Copper foundries

(G-8592)
**AMERICAN COMPLETION
TOOLS INC**
1255 Grand Plaza Dr (77067-4330)
PHONE................................281 894-5213
Deb Sinha, *Manager*
EMP: 12 **Privately Held**
WEB: www.acthammerunion.com
SIC: 3545 Machine tool accessories
HQ: American Completion Tools, Inc.
　　3084 S Burleson Blvd
　　Burleson TX 76028

(G-8593)
AMERICAN DAWN INC
8505 North Loop E Ste 103 (77029-1245)
PHONE................................713 670-8505
Mona Pearl, *Principal*
Scott Furr, *Opers Mgr*
Joe Valdez, *Facilities Mgr*
EMP: 9
SALES (corp-wide): 25MM **Privately
Held**
WEB: www.americandawninc.com
SIC: 2392 Household furnishings
PA: American Dawn, Inc.
　　401 W Artesia Blvd
　　Compton CA 90220
　　800 821-2221

(G-8594)
**AMERICAN DOOR PRODUCTS
INC (PA)**
Also Called: Versatrac
7967 Blankenship Dr (77055-1005)
P.O. Box 55187 (77255-5187)
PHONE................................713 681-8047
David L Popa, *President*
Paul Jamison, *General Mgr*
Don R Dean, *Chairman*
Dave Popa, *Dean*
Marissa Douglas, *Project Mgr*
▼ **EMP:** 93 **EST:** 1938
SQ FT: 50,000
SALES (est): 23.5MM **Privately Held**
WEB: www.americandoorproducts.com
SIC: 3442 Weather strip, metal

(G-8595)
**AMERICAN ENGINE & GRINDING
CO**
100 N Jackson St (77002-1308)
P.O. Box 849, Columbus (78934-0849)
PHONE................................713 224-5326
Franklin Hudec, *President*
Gilbert M Turner, *President*
EMP: 11
SQ FT: 7,505
SALES (est): 1.5MM **Privately Held**
WEB: www.americaneg.com
SIC: 3599 5013 Machine shop, jobbing &
repair; automotive supplies & parts

(G-8596)
**AMERICAN EXTRUSION
COMPANY**
9210 Emmott Rd (77040-3328)
PHONE................................713 869-9551
Norman D Feil III, *President*
Lexuan Huynh, *CFO*
Elizangela Loredo, *Assistant*
▲ **EMP:** 10
SQ FT: 45,094
SALES: 2.4MM **Privately Held**
SIC: 3354 Aluminum extruded products

(G-8597)
AMERICAN GILSONITE COMPANY
16200 Park Row Ste 250 (77084-7652)
PHONE................................713 400-7600
Craig Mueller, *Officer*
EMP: 19
SALES (corp-wide): 19.8MM **Privately Held**
WEB: www.americangilsonite.com
SIC: 1499 Gilsonite mining
PA: American Gilsonite Company
29950 Bonanza Hwy
Bonanza UT 84008
435 789-1921

(G-8598)
AMERICAN GREEN TECHNOLOGY INC
1301 Mckinney St Ste 5100 (77010-3095)
PHONE................................269 340-9975
Danny Bogar, *CEO*
Gordon Norquist, *Exec VP*
Larry Seurynck, *Vice Pres*
Chuck Weiser, *CFO*
Jean Verteramo, *Accounting Mgr*
▲ **EMP:** 43
SALES (est): 16.1MM **Privately Held**
WEB: www.agtus.org
SIC: 5063 3564 Lighting fixtures, commercial & industrial; air purification equipment
PA: Ushio Inc.
1-6-5, Marunouchi
Chiyoda-Ku TKY 100-0

(G-8599)
AMERICAN JEREH INTL CORP
7501 Miller Rd Ste 2 (77049)
PHONE................................432 288-2431
Weijie Sun, *President*
Chengcheng Yu, *General Mgr*
Ying Zhou, *Principal*
LI Yang, *Vice Pres*
Mike Spann, *Purch Mgr*
EMP: 40
SALES (est): 11.4MM **Privately Held**
WEB: www.americanjereh.com
SIC: 3533 Oil & gas field machinery
PA: Yantai Jereh Oilfield Services Group Co., Ltd.
No.5, Jierui Road, Laishan District
Yantai 26400

(G-8600)
AMERICAN MARBLE MOSAIC COMPANY
6314 Saint Augustine St (77021-2615)
PHONE................................713 747-7634
Robert J Bertin, *President*
Gabriel Baldazo, *Project Mgr*
David Gassert, *Opers Mgr*
Donald Roventini, *Treasurer*
Irene Lopez, *Accountant*
EMP: 40
SQ FT: 15,000
SALES (est): 6.7MM **Privately Held**
SIC: 1743 3281 1752 Terrazzo work; marble installation, interior; tile installation, ceramic; cut stone & stone products; floor laying & floor work

(G-8601)
AMERICAN MAST INC (PA)
Also Called: American Gear
5400 Cedar Crest St (77087-3218)
PHONE................................713 643-4321
Phil R Hampton, *President*
▲ **EMP:** 30
SQ FT: 30,000
SALES (est): 3.7MM **Privately Held**
SIC: 3568 Power transmission equipment

(G-8602)
AMERICAN MATERIALS TECH I LLC
15821 Fm 529 Rd Ste 282 (77095-2503)
PHONE................................281 345-0169
Diana Conroy,
▲ **EMP:** 12
SALES (est): 1.3MM **Privately Held**
SIC: 3317 Steel pipe & tubes

(G-8603)
AMERICAN NATURAL RESOURCES CO (HQ)
717 Texas St Ste 2400 (77002-2834)
PHONE................................832 320-5000
Gregory A Lohnes, *President*
Rodney Savely, *Area Mgr*
Brandy Earl, *Accountant*
Paul Oliver, *Manager*
Hugo Palacios, *Manager*
EMP: 25 EST: 1901
SALES (est): 839.1MM
SALES (corp-wide): 9.9B **Privately Held**
WEB: www.shaleexperts.com
SIC: 4922 1311 1222 Pipelines, natural gas; storage, natural gas; natural gas production; underground mining, semi-anthracite
PA: Tc Energy Corporation
450 1 St Sw
Calgary AB T2P 5
403 920-2000

(G-8604)
AMERICAN PLATING CO TEXAS LTD
2421 Wadsworth St (77015-6516)
P.O. Box 9939 (77213-0939)
PHONE................................281 452-4241
Gary Minter, *President*
EMP: 45
SQ FT: 25,000
SALES (est): 5MM **Privately Held**
WEB: www.americanplating.com
SIC: 3471 Electroplating of metals or formed products

(G-8605)
AMERICAN PRTG & PROMOTIONS INC
Also Called: American Zebra Line, The
6100 Skyline Dr Ste M (77057-7021)
PHONE................................713 645-1991
▲ **EMP:** 20
SQ FT: 12,000
SALES (est): 2.7MM **Privately Held**
WEB: www.americanzebra.com
SIC: 3993 2752 Signs & advertising specialties; transfers, decalcomania or dry: lithographed

(G-8606)
AMERICAN RICE INC (DH)
Also Called: ARI
10700 North Fwy Ste 800 (77037-1158)
PHONE................................281 272-8800
Bastiaan G Dezeeuw, *President*
Lee Adams, *President*
John Carroll, *Vice Pres*
Paul A Galvani, *Vice Pres*
Keith Gray, *Vice Pres*
◆ **EMP:** 40 EST: 1901
SQ FT: 16,000
SALES (est): 35.3MM **Privately Held**
SIC: 2044 Rice milling
HQ: Riviana Foods Inc.
2777 Allen Pkwy Fl 15
Houston TX 77019
713 529-3251

(G-8607)
AMERICAN ROLLER COMPANY LLC
Also Called: Houston Plant
14100 Westfair East Dr (77041-1104)
PHONE................................262 878-2445
EMP: 14
SALES (corp-wide): 94.2MM **Privately Held**
WEB: www.americanroller.com
SIC: 3479 2816 2851 Coating of metals & formed products; inorganic pigments; paints & allied products
PA: American Roller Company, Llc
1440 13th Ave
Union Grove WI 53182
262 878-8665

(G-8608)
AMERICAN ROLLER COMPANY LLC
Also Called: Scs Machine & Fabricating
14100 Westfair East Dr (77041-1104)
PHONE................................713 466-0550
Mike Chirpich, *Branch Mgr*

EMP: 24
SALES (corp-wide): 94.2MM **Privately Held**
WEB: www.americanroller.com
SIC: 3479 Coating of metals & formed products
PA: American Roller Company, Llc
1440 13th Ave
Union Grove WI 53182
262 878-8665

(G-8609)
AMERICAN SCREEN GRAPHICS & EMB
1701 Park St Ste 15 (77019-5705)
PHONE................................281 354-2581
Jackie Todaro, *Owner*
EMP: 12
SALES (est): 298.8K **Privately Held**
WEB: www.americanscreengraphics.com
SIC: 5699 5949 2759 2395 Sports apparel; needlework goods & supplies; screen printing; embroidery products, except schiffli machine

(G-8610)
AMERICAN SHEET METAL INC
1110 Blue Bell Rd (77038-3220)
P.O. Box 38197 (77238-8197)
PHONE................................281 999-5210
Jodie Born, *President*
EMP: 15
SALES (est): 1.4MM **Privately Held**
SIC: 3444 Sheet metalwork

(G-8611)
AMERICAN THERMOPLASTICS CORP
1235 Kress St (77020-7499)
PHONE................................713 671-6900
L W Brenek, *President*
EMP: 85
SALES (est): 14.1MM
SALES (corp-wide): 36.6B **Publicly Held**
SIC: 2821 Plastics materials & resins
HQ: Conocophillips Company
925 N Eldridge Pkwy
Houston TX 77079
281 293-1000

(G-8612)
AMERICAN TIRE DISTRIBUTORS INC
860 Greens Pkwy Ste 100 (77067-4433)
PHONE................................281 872-0397
Don Cocker, *Manager*
Jeff Boyd, *Manager*
Jose Garcia, *Manager*
EMP: 19
SALES (corp-wide): 170.8MM **Privately Held**
WEB: www.atd-us.com
SIC: 5531 3011 Truck equipment & parts; tires & inner tubes
HQ: American Tire Distributors Inc.
12200 Herbert Wayne Ct # 150
Huntersville NC 28078
704 992-2000

(G-8613)
AMERICAN TRUSS SYSTEMS INC
1502 Strawn Rd (77039-2022)
PHONE................................281 442-4584
John Dermer, *President*
EMP: 30
SQ FT: 50,000
SALES (est): 5.8MM **Privately Held**
WEB: www.americantrusssystems.com
SIC: 2439 Trusses, wooden roof

(G-8614)
AMERICO ENERGY RESOURCES LLC
7575 San Felipe St 200a (77063-1778)
PHONE................................713 984-9700
Ardeshir Tajvari,
Mostafa Alavi,
Asghar Nostrati,
EMP: 35 EST: 1998
SALES (est): 13.7MM **Privately Held**
WEB: www.americoenergy.com
SIC: 1382 Oil & gas exploration services

(G-8615)
AMERIFORGE CORPORATION (HQ)
Also Called: Pk Manufacturing
945 Bunker Hill Rd # 500 (77024-1358)
PHONE................................713 393-4200
Gean B Stalcup, *President*
Guenter Karhut, *COO*
Brian Fontana, *Vice Pres*
Gabriel Faimann, *CFO*
Perry Ewing, *Treasurer*
▲ **EMP:** 17
SQ FT: 800,000
SALES (est): 76.9MM
SALES (corp-wide): 252.3MM **Privately Held**
WEB: www.afglobalcorp.com
SIC: 3462 Automotive forgings, ferrous: crankshaft, engine, axle, etc.
PA: Ameriforge Group Inc.
945 Bunker Hill Rd # 500
Houston TX 77024
713 393-4200

(G-8616)
AMERIFORGE GROUP INC (PA)
Also Called: AF Global
945 Bunker Hill Rd # 500 (77024-1358)
PHONE................................713 393-4200
Curtis Sanford, *President*
John Rizzotti, *Principal*
Gean Stalcup, *COO*
Thomas Giles, *Exec VP*
Harold Catlett, *Vice Pres*
◆ **EMP:** 40
SALES (est): 252.3MM **Privately Held**
WEB: www.afglobalcorp.com
SIC: 3462 Flange, valve & pipe fitting forgings, ferrous

(G-8617)
AMERIG SOLUTIONS LLC
4265 San Felipe St (77027-2920)
PHONE................................713 960-6606
Yongan Wang, *President*
Rebecca Su, *Vice Pres*
EMP: 15 EST: 2010
SALES (est): 1.1MM **Privately Held**
WEB: www.amerig.us
SIC: 1389 5084 Oil field services; oil field tool joints

(G-8618)
AMERIMEX MOTOR & CONTROLS LLC (HQ)
610 N Milby St (77003-1369)
P.O. Box 1549 (77251-1549)
PHONE................................713 225-4300
V Wayne Stockstill, *President*
Wade Stockstill, *Senior VP*
James McGuane, *Vice Pres*
Alan Birkelbach, *Foreman/Supr*
Jim French, *Engineer*
▲ **EMP:** 64
SQ FT: 150,000
SALES (est): 65.5MM **Privately Held**
WEB: www.amerimexinc.com
SIC: 5063 3625 7694 Motors, electric; generators; motor control centers; armature rewinding shops

(G-8619)
AMERIMEX POWER SYSTEMS INC
11902 Rockville Dr (77064-2015)
P.O. Box 1549 (77251-1549)
PHONE................................832 678-3520
Virgil W Stockstill, *President*
EMP: 13
SQ FT: 25,000
SALES (est): 10MM
SALES (corp-wide): 65.5MM **Privately Held**
SIC: 3613 Generator control & metering panels
HQ: Amerimex Motor & Controls, Llc
610 N Milby St
Houston TX 77003
713 225-4300

(G-8620)
AMERIPRO PARTNERSHIP LP (PA)
Also Called: Gilson/Stanley-Ameripro
6566 Mcgrew St (77087-3430)
P.O. Box 2130, New Caney (77357-2130)
PHONE..................713 526-3936
Richard Berry, *Partner*
Cynthia Fore Berry, *Partner*
▲ EMP: 10
SQ FT: 8,000
SALES (est): 2MM **Privately Held**
WEB: www.pflowerpress.com
SIC: 2426 4225 Hardwood dimension & flooring mills; general warehousing & storage

(G-8621)
AMERITEK DESIGN INC
14203 Luthe Rd (77039-1409)
PHONE..................281 442-7767
Kadar Maharaj, *President*
Joe Bogdanski, *Project Mgr*
EMP: 21
SQ FT: 15,000
SALES (est): 3.3MM **Privately Held**
WEB: www.ameritekdesign.com
SIC: 2541 Counter & sink tops

(G-8622)
AMERON INTERNATIONAL CORP
Ameron Fiberglass & Pipe
400 N Sam Houston Pkwy E (77060-3548)
PHONE..................940 569-1471
Fax: 832 912-9393
EMP: 9
SQ FT: 3,000
SALES (corp-wide): 14.7B **Publicly Held**
SIC: 8743 3317 Public Relations Services Mfg Steel Pipe/Tubes
HQ: Ameron International Corporation
245 S Los Robles Ave
Pasadena CA 77036
626 683-4000

(G-8623)
AMERON INTERNATIONAL CORP (HQ)
7909 Parkwood Circle Dr (77036-6565)
P.O. Box 4888 (77210-4888)
PHONE..................713 375-3700
Clay C Williams, *CEO*
Craig C Goss, *Vice Pres*
Alexandr Gorbanev, *Engineer*
Manuel Ramirez, *Engineer*
Jeremy Thigten, *CFO*
◆ EMP: 39
SALES (est): 439MM
SALES (corp-wide): 8.4B **Publicly Held**
SIC: 3272 3317 3273 Cylinder pipe, prestressed or pretensioned concrete; steel pipe & tubes; ready-mixed concrete
PA: National Oilwell Varco, Inc.
7909 Parkwood Circle Dr
Houston TX 77036
713 346-7500

(G-8624)
AMGIS LLC
Also Called: Affilate Amran Instr Trnsfrmer
10899 Kinghurst Dr # 220 (77099-3465)
PHONE..................832 775-1319
Jakob Jakobsson, *President*
Mary Brown, *Info Tech Mgr*
▲ EMP: 27
SALES (est): 2.2MM **Privately Held**
WEB: www.amgistoroids.com
SIC: 3699 Electrical equipment & supplies

(G-8625)
AMMANN AMERICA INC
1900 West Loop S Ste 1550 (77027-3379)
PHONE..................253 266-4023
Hans-Christian Schneider, *CEO*
Bill Bernard, *Controller*
Jason Debois, *Manager*
◆ EMP: 10
SALES (est): 1.6MM
SALES (corp-wide): 907MM **Privately Held**
WEB: www.ammann.com
SIC: 3531 Bituminous, cement & concrete related products & equipment

PA: Ammann Group Holding Ag
C/O Walder Wyss Ag
Bern BE 3011
629 166-161

(G-8626)
AMMR SERVICES INC
Also Called: Advanced Machine Maintenance
14410 Luthe Rd Ste 106 (77039-1421)
PHONE..................281 449-7162
Stephen Hill, *President*
Stanley Christiansen, *Vice Pres*
Ricahard Sandifer, *Treasurer*
▲ EMP: 13
SQ FT: 3,500
SALES (est): 1.5MM **Privately Held**
SIC: 3599 Machine shop, jobbing & repair

(G-8627)
AMPCO SERVICES LLC
16945 Northchase Dr # 1950 (77060-2135)
PHONE..................281 872-8324
Paul Moschell, *President*
Marcus Allen, *Chairman*
Jim O Casek, *Vice Pres*
Edson S Jones, *Vice Pres*
Jeff Schultz, *Vice Pres*
▼ EMP: 500 EST: 1998
SQ FT: 6,800
SALES (est): 376.9MM **Privately Held**
WEB: www.atlanticmethanol.com
SIC: 2869 Methyl alcohol, synthetic methanol

(G-8628)
AMPLIFY ACQUISITIONCO INC
500 Dallas St Ste 1700 (77002-4732)
PHONE..................713 490-8900
EMP: 31
SALES (est): 118.9K
SALES (corp-wide): 275.5MM **Publicly Held**
WEB: www.amplifyenergy.com
SIC: 1311 Crude petroleum & natural gas
HQ: Amplify Energy Holdings Llc
500 Dallas St Ste 1600
Houston TX 77002
713 490-8900

(G-8629)
AMPLIFY ENERGY CORP (PA)
500 Dallas St Ste 1700 (77002-4732)
PHONE..................713 490-8900
Martyn Willsher, *CEO*
Richard P Smiley, *Senior VP*
Eric M Willis, *Senior VP*
Tony Lopez, *Vice Pres*
Denise Dubard, *Officer*
EMP: 27
SALES: 275.5MM **Publicly Held**
WEB: www.amplifyenergy.com
SIC: 1382 Oil & gas exploration services

(G-8630)
AMPLIFY ENERGY HOLDINGS LLC (HQ)
500 Dallas St Ste 1600 (77002-4729)
PHONE..................713 490-8900
William J Scarff, *President*
Jason M Childress, *Senior VP*
Tony Lopez, *Vice Pres*
Martyn Willsher, *CFO*
Matthew J Hoss, *VP Accounting*
EMP: 19 EST: 2011
SALES (est): 340.1MM
SALES (corp-wide): 275.5MM **Publicly Held**
WEB: www.amplifyenergy.com
SIC: 1311 Crude petroleum & natural gas
PA: Amplify Energy Corp.
500 Dallas St Ste 1700
Houston TX 77002
713 490-8900

(G-8631)
AMY FOOD INC
Also Called: Amy's
3324 S Richey St (77017-6259)
PHONE..................713 910-5860
Phyllis Hsu, *President*
Terry Bohr, *Vice Pres*
Jay Tsai, *Vice Pres*
Frank Benso, *VP Sales*
Kammy Li, *Manager*
◆ EMP: 87

SALES (est): 16.8MM **Privately Held**
WEB: www.amyfood.com
SIC: 2038 Frozen specialties

(G-8632)
AMZG PRODUCTS LLC
Also Called: Amazing Wristbands
4025 Willowbend Blvd (77025-5726)
PHONE..................713 628-5504
Michael H Leitner, *Principal*
Billie Bateson, *Manager*
EMP: 11
SALES (est): 1.2MM **Privately Held**
WEB: www.amazingwristbands.com
SIC: 2752 Commercial printing, lithographic

(G-8633)
ANADARKO HOLDING COMPANY (DH)
17001 Northchase Dr (77060-2141)
P.O. Box 1330 (77251-1330)
PHONE..................832 636-7200
Robert J Allison Jr, *Ch of Bd*
John N Seitz, *President*
George Lindahl, *Principal*
James R Larson, *Senior VP*
J Stephen Martin, *Vice Pres*
▲ EMP: 14
SALES (est): 397.8MM
SALES (corp-wide): 21.2B **Publicly Held**
WEB: www.oxy.com
SIC: 1311 1321 5172 4922 Crude petroleum production; natural gas production; natural gas liquids; petroleum products; pipelines, natural gas
HQ: Anadarko Petroleum Corporation
1201 Lake Robbins Dr
The Woodlands TX 77380
832 636-1000

(G-8634)
ANADRILL DIRECTIONAL SVCS INC
11757 Katy Fwy Ste 1300 (77079-1725)
PHONE..................281 745-6983
Patrick McKinley, *CEO*
Patrick Connors, *COO*
EMP: 10
SALES (est): 150K **Privately Held**
SIC: 1389 Oil field services

(G-8635)
ANALYTCAL APPLIED SLUTIONS LLC
Also Called: Analytical Systems Intl
9515 Windfern Rd (77064-7722)
PHONE..................281 255-6537
EMP: 19
SALES (est): 3.7MM **Privately Held**
WEB: www.liquidgasanalyzers.com
SIC: 3826 Analytical instruments

(G-8636)
ANALYTICAL SENSORS INSTRS LLC (HQ)
10540 Rockley Rd Ste 100 (77099-3530)
PHONE..................281 565-8818
Drew Hall, *CEO*
Peter Cai, *President*
John Pham, *Vice Pres*
Dave Ruane, *Vice Pres*
Frank Zheng, *Vice Pres*
▲ EMP: 65
SALES (est): 11.9MM
SALES (corp-wide): 28.3MM **Privately Held**
WEB: www.asi-sensors.com
SIC: 3823 3629 5065 3826 Electrodes used in industrial process measurement; electrochemical generators (fuel cells); paging & signaling equipment; analytical instruments; search & navigation equipment; semiconductors & related devices
PA: Alpha Measurement Solutions, Llc
10540 Rockley Rd
Houston TX 77099
832 456-4100

(G-8637)
ANALYTICAL SYSTEMS KECO LLC
9515 Windfern Rd (77064-7722)
PHONE..................281 255-6537
Wes Kimbell,

EMP: 17
SALES (est): 778.1K **Privately Held**
WEB: www.liquidgasanalyzers.com
SIC: 3823 Analyzers, industrial process type

(G-8638)
ANC ION COATING INC
Also Called: A N C Iron Coating
12823 Trinity St (77036)
PHONE..................281 207-0300
Xuan Gao, *President*
Jessi Xi, *Accountant*
Sam Shu, *Manager*
▲ EMP: 12
SALES (est): 2.2MM **Privately Held**
WEB: www.anccoating.com
SIC: 2851 5251 Epoxy coatings; tools

(G-8639)
ANCHOR INDUSTRIAL SERVICES LLC
2707 Wadsworth St (77015-5931)
PHONE..................281 385-0607
James Harrell, *Principal*
Frances Kerneckel, *Manager*
Alton W Pruitt,
Wyne Pruitt,
Mark Schimming,
EMP: 95
SALES (est): 19.1MM **Privately Held**
WEB: www.anchorteams.com
SIC: 3446 1742 Scaffolds, mobile or stationary: metal; plastering, drywall & insulation

(G-8640)
ANCHOR MACHINE WORKS INC
6211 Evergreen St (77081-6813)
PHONE..................713 988-0400
Don Johnston, *President*
Gail Johnston, *Corp Secy*
▼ EMP: 10
SQ FT: 6,000
SALES (est): 1.7MM **Privately Held**
WEB: www.anchor-machine.com
SIC: 3599 3441 7692 Machine shop, jobbing & repair; fabricated structural metal; welding repair

(G-8641)
ANDERSON OIL LTD (PA)
5005 Woodway Dr Ste 300 (77056-1784)
PHONE..................713 652-5746
Jacqueline Anderson, *President*
Craig Anderson, *Vice Pres*
Kevin Anderson, *Vice Pres*
Neal Anderson, *Vice Pres*
Scott Anderson, *Vice Pres*
EMP: 12 EST: 1948
SQ FT: 6,000
SALES (est): 4.5MM **Privately Held**
WEB: www.andersonoilltd.com
SIC: 1311 6799 Crude petroleum production; natural gas production; real estate investors, except property operators

(G-8642)
ANDREW & ASSOCIATES
5103 Heathercrest St (77045-5225)
P.O. Box 450714 (77245-0714)
PHONE..................713 471-0922
Andrew Ybarra, *Owner*
Andrew E Ybarra, *Owner*
EMP: 55
SALES (est): 5.7MM **Privately Held**
SIC: 3663 7389 Radio & TV communications equipment;

(G-8643)
ANDREWS FABRICATION INC
1528 Mooney Rd (77093-1823)
PHONE..................281 372-0440
Mark Thomas, *President*
EMP: 9
SALES (est): 2.1MM **Privately Held**
WEB: www.andrewsfabrication.com
SIC: 3699 Electrical equipment & supplies

(G-8644)
ANHEUSER-BUSCH LLC
775 Gellhorn Dr (77029-1496)
PHONE..................713 670-1629
Steve Ghiglieri, *General Mgr*
Gene Thompson, *Area Mgr*
Brian Mayer, *Opers Mgr*

Scott Preston, *Safety Mgr*
Gary Roberson, *Production*
EMP: 162
SALES (corp-wide): 1.4B **Privately Held**
WEB: www.budweisertours.com
SIC: 2082 Beer (alcoholic beverage)
HQ: Anheuser-Busch, Llc
  1 Busch Pl
  Saint Louis MO 63118
  800 342-5283

(G-8645)
ANHEUSER-BUSCH LLC
8657 Market St (77029-2429)
PHONE 713 675-2311
Steve Ghigleri, *Manager*
EMP: 162
SALES (corp-wide): 1.4B **Privately Held**
WEB: www.budweisertours.com
SIC: 2082 Beer (alcoholic beverage)
HQ: Anheuser-Busch, Llc
  1 Busch Pl
  Saint Louis MO 63118
  800 342-5283

(G-8646)
ANNAPURNA SOLUTIONS LLC
5000 Gulf Fwy (77023-4634)
PHONE 916 905-3144
Ashok Naidu, *CEO*
EMP: 16
SALES (est): 410.6K **Privately Held**
SIC: 7373 7371 7372 7379 Computer in-
  tegrated systems design; custom com-
  puter programming services;
  prepackaged software; computer related
  services

(G-8647)
ANODICO CORPORATION
5900 Frbanks N Houston Rd (77040-5102)
PHONE 713 690-6100
Agustin Navarro, *President*
EMP: 15
SQ FT: 78,400
SALES (est): 421.7K **Privately Held**
WEB: www.anodico.com
SIC: 3369 3365 Zinc & zinc-base alloy
  castings, except die-castings; machinery
  castings, aluminum

(G-8648)
ANTELOPE REFINING LLC
919 Milam St Ste 2100 (77002-5417)
PHONE 713 860-2746
Grant Sims, *CEO*
EMP: 20
SQ FT: 2,000
SALES (est): 1.8MM **Publicly Held**
SIC: 2911 Petroleum refining
PA: Genesis Energy, L.P.
  919 Milam St Ste 2100
  Houston TX 77002

(G-8649)
ANTHERA PHARMACEUTICALS INC
700 Milam St Ste 1300 (77002-2736)
PHONE 510 856-5600
Paul F Truex, *Ch of Bd*
Craig Thompson, *President*
May Liu, *Senior VP*
Renee Martin, *Senior VP*
William R Shanahan, *Chief Mktg Ofcr*
EMP: 33
SALES (est): 175.4K **Privately Held**
WEB: www.anthera.com
SIC: 2834 Druggists' preparations (phar-
  maceuticals)

(G-8650)
APACHE CORPORATION (PA)
2000 Post Oak Blvd Ste 10 (77056-4499)
PHONE 713 296-6000
John E Lowe, *Ch of Bd*
John J Christmann IV, *President*
James Pyle, *Superintendent*
Andrew Friedberg, *Counsel*
Joshua Nix, *Counsel*
▲ **EMP:** 507 **EST:** 1954
SALES: 6.4B **Publicly Held**
WEB: www.apachecorp.com
SIC: 1311 Crude petroleum production;
  natural gas production

(G-8651)
APACHE CORPORATION
Also Called: Apache Offshore
2000 Post Oak Blvd # 100 (77056-4400)
PHONE 800 272-2434
Ron Garber, *Manager*
EMP: 50
SALES (corp-wide): 6.4B **Publicly Held**
WEB: www.apachecorp.com
SIC: 1311 Crude petroleum production
PA: Apache Corporation
  2000 Post Oak Blvd Ste 10
  Houston TX 77056
  713 296-6000

(G-8652)
APACHE CORPORATION
Also Called: Apache Drilling
2000 Post Oak Blvd # 100 (77056-4400)
PHONE 713 296-6000
Bradley Orr, *Branch Mgr*
EMP: 15
SALES (corp-wide): 6.4B **Publicly Held**
WEB: www.apachecorp.com
SIC: 1311 Crude petroleum production
PA: Apache Corporation
  2000 Post Oak Blvd Ste 10
  Houston TX 77056
  713 296-6000

(G-8653)
APACHE CRUDE OIL MARKETING
2000 Post Oak Blvd # 100 (77056-4499)
PHONE 713 296-6000
Raymond Plank, *Ch of Bd*
Roger B Plank, *Vice Pres*
EMP: 10
SALES (est): 687.5K
SALES (corp-wide): 6.4B **Publicly Held**
WEB: www.apachecorp.com
SIC: 1311 Crude petroleum & natural gas
PA: Apache Corporation
  2000 Post Oak Blvd Ste 10
  Houston TX 77056
  713 296-6000

(G-8654)
APACHE DEEPWATER LLC
2000 Post Oak Blvd Ste 10 (77056-4499)
PHONE 713 296-6000
Alfonso Leon, *CFO*
EMP: 43
SALES (est): 1MM
SALES (corp-wide): 6.4B **Publicly Held**
WEB: www.apachecorp.com
SIC: 1311 Crude petroleum production;
  natural gas production
PA: Apache Corporation
  2000 Post Oak Blvd Ste 10
  Houston TX 77056
  713 296-6000

(G-8655)
APACHE FABRICATORS LLC
8101 E Houston Rd (77028-2022)
PHONE 832 804-6236
Christian Gonzalez, *Vice Pres*
Mario Villalva,
EMP: 22 **EST:** 2014
SALES (est): 4.5MM **Privately Held**
WEB: www.apachefabricators.com
SIC: 3441 Machine shop, jobbing & repair

(G-8656)
APACHE FOUNDATION
2000 Post Oak Blvd B100 (77056-4499)
P.O. Box 721950 (77272-1950)
PHONE 713 296-6000
G Steven Farris, *President*
EMP: 34
SALES (est): 2MM
SALES (corp-wide): 6.4B **Publicly Held**
WEB: www.apachecorp.com
SIC: 1382 Oil & gas exploration services
PA: Apache Corporation
  2000 Post Oak Blvd Ste 10
  Houston TX 77056
  713 296-6000

(G-8657)
APACHE GATHERING COMPANY
2000 Post Oak Blvd # 100 (77056-4499)
PHONE 713 296-6000
Raymond Plank, *Ch of Bd*
G Steven Farris, *President*

EMP: 1000
SALES (est): 18MM
SALES (corp-wide): 6.4B **Publicly Held**
WEB: www.apachecorp.com
SIC: 1311 Crude petroleum production
PA: Apache Corporation
  2000 Post Oak Blvd Ste 10
  Houston TX 77056
  713 296-6000

(G-8658)
APACHE GLOBAL PAINTING INC (PA)
Also Called: Apache Industrial Painting
9011 Sheldon Rd (77049-1810)
P.O. Box 670369 (77267-0369)
PHONE 713 450-9307
Michael J Knigin, *CEO*
Douglas B Lee, *President*
Inocente Ladislao, *Superintendent*
David Franey, *Vice Pres*
Miguel Garcia, *Project Mgr*
◆ **EMP:** 120
SQ FT: 43,000
SALES (est): 22.1MM **Privately Held**
WEB: www.apacheip.com
SIC: 3479 Coating of metals & formed
  products

(G-8659)
APACHE INTERNATIONAL LLC
2000 Post Oak Blvd Ste 10 (77056-4499)
PHONE 713 296-6000
Raymond Plank, *Ch of Bd*
G Steven Farris, *President*
William J Johnson, *Vice Chairman*
Carolyn E Lucas, *Vice Pres*
Michael W Stewart, *Vice Pres*
EMP: 25
SQ FT: 5,000
SALES (est): 1.4MM
SALES (corp-wide): 6.4B **Publicly Held**
WEB: www.apachecorp.com
SIC: 1311 Crude petroleum production
PA: Apache Corporation
  2000 Post Oak Blvd Ste 10
  Houston TX 77056
  713 296-6000

(G-8660)
APACHE SIGN & SERVICE INC
4125 Hollister St (77080-3044)
PHONE 713 462-3220
George Ocanas, *President*
EMP: 15
SALES (est): 2.1MM **Privately Held**
SIC: 3993 Signs & advertising specialties

(G-8661)
APACHE STEEL WORKS LLC
7410 Apache St (77028-3908)
P.O. Box 21169 (77226-1169)
PHONE 832 473-4525
Mario Villalva, *President*
Melina Deflores, *Sales Staff*
EMP: 15 **EST:** 2014
SQ FT: 26,000
SALES (est): 4.6MM **Privately Held**
WEB: www.apachesteelworks.com
SIC: 3441 Fabricated structural metal

(G-8662)
APERGY ARTFL LIFT INTL LLC
Dover Energy
11122 W Little York Rd (77041-5016)
PHONE 713 466-3552
Robert Funk, *Branch Mgr*
EMP: 100
SALES (corp-wide): 1.1B **Publicly Held**
WEB: www.apergy.com
SIC: 3533 3822 3625 3494 Oil field ma-
  chinery & equipment; auto controls regu-
  lating residntl & coml environmt &
  applncs; relays & industrial controls;
  valves & pipe fittings; fluid power valves &
  hose fittings; industrial valves
HQ: Apergy Artificial Lift International, Llc
  2445 Tech Frest Blvd Ste
  Spring TX 77381
  281 403-5742

(G-8663)
APEX INTL ENRGY MGT LLC
1300 Post Oak Blvd (77056-3043)
PHONE 832 770-6900
Roger B Plank, *CEO*

Thomas M Maher, *President*
Michael Leblanc, *Controller*
Dalal Hanno, *Human Resources*
David Pivnik, *Executive*
EMP: 13
SALES (est): 99.1K **Privately Held**
WEB: www.apexintl.com
SIC: 1382 Oil & gas exploration services

(G-8664)
APOLLO SEPARATION TECH USA INC
1111 Goodnight Trl (77060-1112)
P.O. Box 681476 (77268-1476)
PHONE 281 233-9600
Philip Y Lau, *President*
Samuel Chan, *Office Mgr*
EMP: 25
SQ FT: 12,500
SALES (est): 5MM **Privately Held**
WEB: www.apollogreenzyme.com
SIC: 3589 Water treatment equipment, in-
  dustrial

(G-8665)
APPLETON GRP LLC
Appleton Electric Division
13639 Aldine Westfield Rd (77039-3007)
PHONE 281 774-3700
Theodor Cojocaru, *Vice Pres*
Jeff Philippe, *Manager*
Guillermo Ruiz, *Director*
EMP: 110
SQ FT: 41,400
SALES (corp-wide): 16.7B **Publicly Held**
WEB: www.emersonindustrial.com
SIC: 3644 3699 3444 Electric conduits &
  fittings; electrical equipment & supplies;
  sheet metalwork
HQ: Appleton Grp Llc
  9377 W Higgins Rd
  Rosemont IL 60018
  847 268-6000

(G-8666)
APPLIED CRYO TECHNOLOGIES INC (PA)
7150 Almeda Genoa Rd (77075-2810)
PHONE 281 888-3884
Bob Ernull, *CEO*
Jack Smith, *COO*
Keith Hall, *Vice Pres*
Tim Lowrey, *Vice Pres*
Alberto Gonzalez, *Project Mgr*
EMP: 100
SALES (est): 91.2MM **Privately Held**
WEB: www.appliedcryotech.com
SIC: 3443 3559 Cryogenic tanks, for liq-
  uids & gases; cryogenic machinery, in-
  dustrial

(G-8667)
APPLIED DRILLING TECH INC
1311 Brdfeld Blvd Ste 110 (77084)
P.O. Box 4509 (77210-4509)
PHONE 281 925-7100
Stephen E Morrison, *President*
Michael R Dawson, *President*
Robert L Herrin Jr, *President*
Richard J Hoffman, *President*
Roger B Hunt, *President*
▲ **EMP:** 100
SQ FT: 4,853
SALES (est): 6.5MM
SALES (corp-wide): 4.1B **Privately Held**
SIC: 1381 Drilling oil & gas wells
HQ: Global Marine Inc
  4 Greenway Plz Ste 100
  Houston TX 77046
  713 232-7500

(G-8668)
APPLIED GEOPHYSICAL SERVICES
Also Called: AGS
11490 Westheimer Rd # 800 (77077-6847)
PHONE 832 327-3408
Daniel Heinze, *President*
John Sherwood, *President*
EMP: 12
SQ FT: 7,000
SALES (corp-wide): 896MM **Privately Held**
SIC: 7372 Prepackaged software

PA: Pgs Asa
Lilleakerveien 4c
Oslo 0283
675 264-00

(G-8669)
APPLIED US ENERGY INC
Also Called: Reliance Industrial Products
8790 West Rd Ste 100 (77064-1451)
PHONE......................713 466-1538
Mike Sirois, *Branch Mgr*
EMP: 23
SALES (corp-wide): 3.2B **Publicly Held**
WEB: www.relianceindustrial.com
SIC: 1389 Pipe testing, oil field service
HQ: Applied Us Energy, Inc.
1 Applied Plz
Cleveland OH 44115
325 227-8915

(G-8670)
APS BUILDING SERVICES INC
11050 W Little York Rd P (77041-5056)
PHONE......................713 979-0720
EMP: 100
SALES (est): 3.8MM **Privately Held**
SIC: 3822 Building services monitoring
controls, automatic

(G-8671)
AQSEPTENCE GROUP INC
515 Post Oak Blvd (77027-9482)
PHONE......................651 636-3900
John Ollech, *CEO*
EMP: 200
SALES (est): 5MM **Privately Held**
WEB: www.aqseptence.com
SIC: 3543 3069 Foundry patternmaking;
hard rubber products

(G-8672)
AQUA/PROCESS INC
125 Southbelt Indus Dr (77047-7020)
PHONE......................713 910-2977
▲ **EMP:** 25
SQ FT: 20,000
SALES (est): 6.7MM **Privately Held**
WEB: www.aquaprocessinc.com
SIC: 2869 2819 Industrial organic chemi-
cals; industrial inorganic chemicals

(G-8673)
AQUASOL CONTROLLERS INC
(PA)
Also Called: Commercial Chemical
1707 Townhurst Dr (77043-2810)
PHONE......................713 683-6406
Alan Falik, *CEO*
John L Falik, *CEO*
Anthony Haynes, *Prdtn Mgr*
Nancy Wharton, *Purch Agent*
Kevin Boyer, *Research*
▼ **EMP:** 50
SQ FT: 11,000
SALES (est): 25.5MM **Privately Held**
WEB: www.aquasol.com
SIC: 3823 Water quality monitoring & con-
trol systems

(G-8674)
ARAVIVE INC (PA)
3730 Kirby Dr Ste 1200 (77098-3985)
PHONE......................936 355-1910
Gail McIntyre, *CEO*
Fred Eshelman, *Ch of Bd*
Randy Anderson, *Senior VP*
Elisabeth Gardiner, *Vice Pres*
Patrick Simms, *Vice Pres*
EMP: 16
SALES: 4.7MM **Publicly Held**
WEB: www.aravive.com
SIC: 2834 8731 Pharmaceutical prepara-
tions; biotechnical research, commercial

(G-8675)
ARAVIVE BIOLOGICS INC
3730 Kirby Dr Ste 1200 (77098-3985)
PHONE......................936 355-1910
Stephen L Eck, *President*
Gail McIntyre, *Senior VP*
Laura Bonifacio, *Vice Pres*
EMP: 17
SALES (est): 181.3K
SALES (corp-wide): 4.7MM **Publicly Held**
WEB: www.aravive.com
SIC: 2834 Pharmaceutical preparations

PA: Aravive, Inc.
3730 Kirby Dr Ste 1200
Houston TX 77098
936 355-1910

(G-8676)
ARBOR RENEWABLE GAS LLC
1800 Bering Dr Ste 510 (77057-3158)
PHONE......................281 849-9834
Vail Timothy, *CEO*
EMP: 10
SALES (est): 259.7K **Privately Held**
SIC: 1321 Natural gasoline production

(G-8677)
ARC DESIGNS INC
11957 Fm 529 Rd (77041-3017)
P.O. Box 1012, Cypress (77410-1012)
PHONE......................281 940-0430
Josh Norris, *President*
▲ **EMP:** 35
SQ FT: 34,000
SALES (est): 8.9MM **Privately Held**
WEB: www.arcdesignsinc.com
SIC: 3441 Fabricated structural metal

(G-8678)
ARC DOCUMENT SOLUTIONS
LLC (HQ)
6300 Gulfton St (77081-1108)
P.O. Box 218629 (77218-8629)
PHONE......................713 988-9200
K Suriyakumar, *President*
EMP: 256 **EST:** 2008
SQ FT: 52,000
SALES (est): 105.5MM
SALES (corp-wide): 382.4MM **Publicly
Held**
WEB: www.riotcolor.com
SIC: 7334 2752 5049 2791 Blueprinting
service; commercial printing, lithographic;
scientific & engineering equipment & sup-
plies; typesetting; bookbinding & related
work; commercial printing
PA: Arc Document Solutions, Inc.
12657 Alcosta Blvd # 200
San Ramon CA 94583
925 949-5100

(G-8679)
ARC DOCUMENT SOLUTIONS
LLC
16840 Barker Springs Rd (77084-5066)
PHONE......................713 787-1244
John J Zulli III, *Manager*
EMP: 17
SALES (corp-wide): 382.4MM **Publicly
Held**
WEB: www.riotcolor.com
SIC: 7334 2752 5049 2791 Blueprinting
service; commercial printing, lithographic;
offset & photolithographic printing; scientific & engineering equipment & supplies;
engineers' equipment & supplies; typesetting; bookbinding & related work; commercial printing
HQ: Arc Document Solutions, Llc
6300 Gulfton St
Houston TX 77081
713 988-9200

(G-8680)
ARC SPECIALTIES INC
1730 Stebbins Dr (77043-2807)
PHONE......................713 631-7575
Daniel W Allford, *President*
John Martin, *Vice Pres*
Randy Ellington, *Project Mgr*
Daryl Pope, *Project Mgr*
Kevin Sevcik, *Project Mgr*
▲ **EMP:** 47
SQ FT: 18,000
SALES (est): 8.5MM **Privately Held**
WEB: www.arcspecialties.com
SIC: 3569 Robots, assembly line: industrial
& commercial

(G-8681)
ARCHER PROD CMPLETION
SVCS LLC
911 Regional Park Dr (77060-3942)
PHONE......................281 951-4038
EMP: 50
SALES (est): 2.8MM **Privately Held**
SIC: 1389 Oil/Gas Field Services

PA: Archer Limited
14 Par-La-Ville Road
Hamilton HM 08

(G-8682)
ARCHER WELL COMPANY INC
(DH)
Also Called: Archer The Well Company
5510 Clara Rd (77041-7204)
PHONE......................713 856-4222
David King, *CEO*
Max Bouthillette, *President*
Jim Archer, *Principal*
Ernie Turner, *Principal*
Robin Brice, *Vice Pres*
▲ **EMP:** 51
SALES (est): 629.5MM **Privately Held**
WEB: www.archerwell.com
SIC: 1381 Drilling oil & gas wells
HQ: Archer Assets Uk Limited
25 Knightsbridge
London SW1X
207 838-2222

(G-8683)
ARCHITECTURAL GRAPHIC
PRODUCTS
Also Called: Agp
10616 Hempstead Rd Ste E (77092-8404)
PHONE......................713 683-8942
Tony Avery, *President*
EMP: 9
SQ FT: 6,000
SALES (est): 963.8K **Privately Held**
WEB: www.agpsignsonline.com
SIC: 3993 Signs, not made in custom sign
painting shops

(G-8684)
ARCHITECTURAL METAL
CRAFTS
14320 1/2 Luthe Rd (77039-1412)
PHONE......................281 449-1881
EMP: 17
SQ FT: 36,000
SALES (est): 3.7MM **Privately Held**
WEB: www.archmetalcrafts.com
SIC: 3446 Architectural metalwork

(G-8685)
ARCHROCK INC (PA)
9807 Katy Fwy Ste 100 (77024-1276)
PHONE......................281 836-8000
Gordon T Hall, *Ch of Bd*
D Bradley Childers, *President*
Eric Estell, *Area Mgr*
Stephanie C Hildebrandt, *Senior VP*
Jason G Ingersoll, *Senior VP*
EMP: 200
SQ FT: 77,000
SALES (est): 965.4MM **Publicly Held**
WEB: www.archrock.com
SIC: 1389 Gas compressing (natural gas)
at the fields; gas field services; oil field
services

(G-8686)
ARCTIC PIPE INSPTN INC
TEXAS
Also Called: Arctic Pipe Inspection Houston
9500 Sheldon Rd (77049-1256)
P.O. Box 1258, Channelview (77530-1258)
PHONE......................281 456-8300
Jim Hildebrandt, *Vice Pres*
Leon Elliot, *Manager*
EMP: 60
SALES (corp-wide): 9.8MM **Privately
Held**
SIC: 1389 Oil field services
PA: Arctic Pipe Inspection Inc Of Texas
Mi 18 5 Kenai Spur Rd Mi St
Kenai AK 99611
907 283-4471

(G-8687)
ARD OPERATING LLC (PA)
Also Called: Alta Resources
500 Dallas St Ste 2700 (77002-4701)
PHONE......................713 759-1155
Joseph Greenberg, *CEO*
Jennifer McCarthy, *President*
Richard Steeg, *CFO*
EMP: 40
SQ FT: 7,000

SALES (est): 42.7MM **Privately Held**
WEB: www.alta-resources.com
SIC: 1382 Oil & gas exploration services

(G-8688)
ARES ROBOTICS LLC
4807 Cripple Creek Dr (77017-5935)
P.O. Box 87749 (77287-7749)
PHONE......................713 320-4690
Michael Harris,
Richard Starr,
EMP: 30 **EST:** 1998
SALES (est): 3.9MM **Privately Held**
SIC: 3563 Robots for industrial spraying,
painting, etc.

(G-8689)
ARGOS USA LLC
302 Bennington St (77022-4820)
PHONE......................713 692-4408
Nick Hinze, *Manager*
EMP: 9 **Privately Held**
WEB: www.argos-us.com
SIC: 3273 Ready-mixed concrete
HQ: Argos Usa Llc
3015 Windward Plz Ste 300
Alpharetta GA 30005
678 368-4300

(G-8690)
ARGOS USA LLC
Also Called: Southern Star Concrete
10715 Highway 3 (77034-4818)
PHONE......................713 273-2800
EMP: 15 **Privately Held**
WEB: www.argos-us.com
SIC: 3273 Ready-mixed concrete
HQ: Argos Usa Llc
3015 Windward Plz Ste 300
Alpharetta GA 30005
678 368-4300

(G-8691)
ARGUS MEDIA INC (DH)
2929 Allen Pkwy Ste 700 (77019-7123)
P.O. Box 841084 (77284-1084)
PHONE......................713 968-0000
Neil Bradford, *CEO*
Euan Craik, *CEO*
Daniel Massey, *President*
Mark Babineck, *Editor*
Charlotte Blum, *Editor*
EMP: 39
SALES (est): 10.5MM
SALES (corp-wide): 257.9MM **Privately
Held**
WEB: www.argusmediagroup.com
SIC: 2741 Miscellaneous publishing
HQ: Argus Media Limited
Lacon House
London WC1X
207 780-4200

(G-8692)
ARGUS SOFTWARE INC (HQ)
750 Town And Country Blvd # 800
(77024-3980)
PHONE......................713 621-4343
Mark P Kingston, *President*
Paul Broadley, *Principal*
Michael Verma, *COO*
Larry Oglesby, *Senior VP*
Jeff Hayward, *Vice Pres*
EMP: 75
SALES (est): 36.5MM
SALES (corp-wide): 426.1MM **Privately
Held**
WEB: www.altusgroup.com
SIC: 7372 Prepackaged software
PA: Altus Group Limited
33 Yonge St Suite 500
Toronto ON M5E 1
416 641-9500

(G-8693)
ARIEL KENNARD
Also Called: Xplicit Treasure
12639 Ashford Pine Dr (77082-3658)
PHONE......................832 997-4537
Ariel Kennard, *Owner*
EMP: 10
SALES (est): 369.4K **Privately Held**
SIC: 3944 Board games, children's &
adults'

▲ = Import ▼=Export
◆ =Import/Export

(G-8694)
ARIES BUILDING SYSTEMS LLC (PA)
12621 Featherwood Dr # 300 (77034-4905)
PHONE..................254 938-0800
Michael Bollero, *President*
Michael I Roman, *Vice Pres*
Adam Bragg, *Project Mgr*
Ashley Harris, *Human Res Mgr*
Traci Prater, *Accounts Mgr*
EMP: 12 EST: 2012
SALES (est): 24.6MM Privately Held
WEB: www.ariesbuildings.com
SIC: 2452 Modular homes, prefabricated, wood

(G-8695)
ARIES ONE LLC
2416 W Main St (77098-3221)
PHONE..................832 564-3628
Armando Gonzalez,
EMP: 11
SALES (est): 278.1K Privately Held
SIC: 1381 Drilling oil & gas wells

(G-8696)
ARIZONA TILE LLC
10811 S Westview Circle D (77043-2748)
PHONE..................713 292-1001
John Himelrick, *Manager*
Pamela Behrend, *Manager*
Leyla Beltran, *Manager*
Sarah Perez, *Asst Mgr*
EMP: 28
SALES (corp-wide): 263MM Privately Held
WEB: www.arizonatile.com
SIC: 5211 5032 3253 1743 Tile, ceramic; ceramic wall & floor tile; ceramic wall & floor tile; tile installation, ceramic
PA: Arizona Tile, L.L.C.
8829 S Priest Dr
Tempe AZ 85284
480 893-9393

(G-8697)
ARK-CONCRETE SPECIALTIES INC
Also Called: Ark, The
713 Lehman St (77018-1513)
PHONE..................713 692-6736
Brian Penso, *President*
Sandra Moatz, *Manager*
Harry Durham, *Shareholder*
EMP: 30
SQ FT: 10,000
SALES (est): 5.4MM Privately Held
WEB: www.arkconcrete.com
SIC: 3272 Concrete products, precast

(G-8698)
ARKEMA INC
Also Called: Houston Plant
2231 Haden Rd (77015-6449)
PHONE..................713 455-1211
Cameron Laird, *Production*
Leon Connor, *Opers-Prdtn-Mfg*
Austin Owens, *Engineer*
Marianne Bullock, *Manager*
Dave Selter, *Technical Staff*
EMP: 55
SALES (corp-wide): 120.6MM Privately Held
WEB: www.arkema-americas.com
SIC: 2869 2819 Industrial organic chemicals; industrial inorganic chemicals
HQ: Arkema Inc.
900 First Ave
King Of Prussia PA 19406
610 205-7000

(G-8699)
ARMSTEAD OIL
7825 Creekbend Dr (77071-1713)
PHONE..................713 454-3866
M Armstead, *President*
EMP: 25 EST: 2009
SQ FT: 2,500
SALES (est): 3.4MM Privately Held
SIC: 2911 Oils, fuel

(G-8700)
ARNE DISTRIBUTORS INC
Also Called: Arne's Wholesale
2830 Hicks St (77007-3812)
P.O. Box 7721 (77270-7721)
PHONE..................713 869-8321
Arnold M Grossman, *President*
Alan Grossman, *Vice Pres*
Terri Sallack, *Business Dir*
Alejandra Arellano, *Admin Sec*
▲ EMP: 15
SQ FT: 15,000
SALES (est): 7.1MM Privately Held
WEB: www.arneswarehouse.com
SIC: 5023 3499 2499 7359 Pottery; giftware, brass goods; kitchen, bathroom & household ware: wood; party supplies rental services; pet supplies

(G-8701)
ARNS HOLDINGS LTD
2611 El Camino St (77054-4114)
PHONE..................713 863-0600
Gregg Hollenberg, *Principal*
Danae Stephenson, *Vice Pres*
Amanda Tanner, *Controller*
Brandon Yannerella, *Manager*
EMP: 60
SQ FT: 60,000
SALES (est): 11MM Privately Held
WEB: www.nationalsigns.com
SIC: 3993 1731 Electric signs; general electrical contractor

(G-8702)
AROC INC
1000 La St Ste 6700 (77002)
PHONE..................832 538-0300
Frank Lodzinski, *President*
Jerry M Crews, *Vice Pres*
Howard Ehler, *Vice Pres*
Francis M Mury, *Vice Pres*
Peggy C Simpson, *Vice Pres*
EMP: 60
SQ FT: 2,100
SALES (est): 3MM Privately Held
SIC: 1311 Crude petroleum & natural gas
HQ: Mpac Llc
1100 Louisiana St # 3150
Houston TX 77002
713 659-6100

(G-8703)
ARRAY COATING TECHNOLOGY LLC
11987 Fm 529 Rd (77041-3011)
PHONE..................936 321-7000
Rick Bridges, *Owner*
Yvonne Goodnight, *Office Mgr*
EMP: 28
SALES (est): 5MM Privately Held
WEB: www.subseacoat.com
SIC: 1389 Oil field services

(G-8704)
ARRAY HOLDINGS INC (PA)
Also Called: Sigma Valves
15900 Morales Rd (77032-2126)
PHONE..................281 260-8366
Jerry Skweres, *CEO*
Mike McGovern, *President*
David Deslatte, *Treasurer*
◆ EMP: 45
SALES (est): 25.6MM Privately Held
WEB: www.cactusflowproducts.com
SIC: 3491 Valves, automatic control

(G-8705)
ARROW MARBLE LLC
Also Called: Luxury Baths By Arrow
12306 Shiloh Church Rd (77066-2002)
P.O. Box 40592 (77240-0592)
PHONE..................832 467-4345
Kevin Sweeney, *Sales Staff*
Joseph Kinsella, *Mng Member*
Tiffany Edmond, *Manager*
Monica Orozco, *Manager*
Thomas Moore,
EMP: 80
SALES (est): 7.9MM Privately Held
WEB: www.arrowglassindustries.com
SIC: 3261 Bathroom accessories/fittings, vitreous china or earthenware

(G-8706)
ARROW MIRROR & GLASS INC (PA)
12306 Shiloh Church Rd (77066-2002)
P.O. Box 40592 (77240-0592)
PHONE..................832 467-4345
Joe Kinsella, *President*
Miguel Torres, *Purchasing*
Ana Nieto, *Supervisor*
▲ EMP: 148
SQ FT: 9,000
SALES (est): 21MM Privately Held
WEB: www.arrowglassindustries.com
SIC: 1793 3431 Glass & glazing work; metal sanitary ware

(G-8707)
ARROW STEEL PROCESSORS INC
8710 Clinton Dr (77029-4304)
PHONE..................713 670-0160
Dieter Scherfenberg, *President*
Shelly Bridges, *Office Mgr*
EMP: 16
SQ FT: 80,000
SALES (est): 2.4MM Privately Held
SIC: 3312 Blast furnaces & steel mills

(G-8708)
ART MIX LLC
3701 W Alabama St Ste 250 (77027-5264)
PHONE..................713 552-9028
Jacqueline Kenneally, *Principal*
EMP: 9
SALES (est): 1MM Privately Held
WEB: www.artmixlearning.com
SIC: 3273 Ready-mixed concrete

(G-8709)
ART&QUILT MAGAZINE
9502 Meadowbriar Ln (77063-3813)
PHONE..................713 975-7140
EMP: 9
SALES (est): 343.6K Privately Held
SIC: 2721 Periodicals-Publishing/Printing

(G-8710)
ARTESIA ECOSCIENCE LLC
15 River Cir (77063-1502)
PHONE..................281 978-2521
Enrico J Termine, *COO*
Dennis Naeger, *Vice Pres*
EMP: 12 EST: 2016
SALES (est): 604K Privately Held
WEB: www.artesia-ecoscience.com
SIC: 1389 3589 Oil field services; water treatment equipment, industrial

(G-8711)
ARTISTIC PLATING INC
1231 W 34th St Ste B (77018-6207)
PHONE..................713 864-1352
John Barreiro, *President*
EMP: 15
SQ FT: 60,000
SALES (est): 1.8MM Privately Held
SIC: 3471 Gold plating; electroplating of metals or formed products; plating of metals or formed products

(G-8712)
ASAP MACHINE INC
Also Called: ASAP Precision Machine
9026 Sweetwater Ln (77037-1740)
PHONE..................281 448-4800
Michael Brock, *President*
Peter Dao, *Vice Pres*
Tony Nguyen, *Treasurer*
EMP: 11 EST: 2001
SALES (est): 2.1MM Privately Held
WEB: www.asapmachine.com
SIC: 3599 Machine shop, jobbing & repair

(G-8713)
ASCEND PERFORMANCE MTLS INC (DH)
1010 Travis St Ste 900 (77002-2111)
PHONE..................713 315-5700
Phil McDivitt, *President*
Marjorie Sims, *Managing Dir*
John Slaven, *Business Mgr*
Dan Burke, *Counsel*
Dale Borths, *Vice Pres*
◆ EMP: 11 EST: 2012

SALES (est): 3.3MM
SALES (corp-wide): 992.8MM Privately Held
WEB: www.ascendmaterials.com
SIC: 2299 2821 Batting, wadding, padding & fillings; nylon resins
HQ: Ascend Performance Materials Holdings Inc.
1010 Travis St Ste 900
Houston TX 77002
713 315-5700

(G-8714)
ASCEND PRFMCE MTLS HLDINGS INC (DH)
1010 Travis St Ste 900 (77002-5928)
PHONE..................713 315-5700
J Timothy Strehl, *President*
Phil McDivitt, *President*
Dale Borths, *Vice Pres*
Gustavo Nechar, *Vice Pres*
Malcolm Oneal, *Vice Pres*
◆ EMP: 26 EST: 2009
SALES (est): 413MM
SALES (corp-wide): 992.8MM Privately Held
WEB: www.ascendmaterials.com
SIC: 2821 2299 Nylon resins; batting, wadding, padding & fillings
HQ: Sk Titan Holdings Llc
400 Park Ave
New York NY 10022
212 826-2700

(G-8715)
ASCEND PRFMCE MTLS OPRTONS LLC (DH)
1010 Travis St Ste 900 (77002-5928)
PHONE..................713 315-5700
Barry Siadat, *Ch of Bd*
J Timothy Strehl, *President*
Joe Menner, *Business Mgr*
Dale Borths, *Vice Pres*
Jamshid Keynejad, *Vice Pres*
◆ EMP: 50
SALES (est): 698.3MM
SALES (corp-wide): 992.8MM Privately Held
WEB: www.ascendmaterials.com
SIC: 2821 Plastics materials & resins
HQ: Ascend Performance Materials Holdings Inc.
1010 Travis St Ste 900
Houston TX 77002
713 315-5700

(G-8716)
ASCENT BUSINESS SYSTEMS INC
Also Called: Automated Service Systems
1880 S Dairy Ashford Rd # 535 (77077-4851)
PHONE..................281 497-8882
Michael Hutar, *President*
Tom Irick, *Opers Staff*
Christopher Esselborn, *Marketing Mgr*
Julian Bartle, *Info Tech Mgr*
EMP: 12
SQ FT: 2,500
SALES (est): 1.5MM Privately Held
WEB: www.ascent-sys.com
SIC: 7372 5045 Prepackaged software; computers, peripherals & software

(G-8717)
ASH GROVE CEMENT COMPANY
9550 Clinton Dr (77029-4323)
PHONE..................713 674-4100
Kelly McDonald, *Regl Sales Mgr*
Daniel Douglas, *Branch Mgr*
Cindy Whatley, *Admin Asst*
EMP: 36
SALES (corp-wide): 30.6B Privately Held
WEB: www.ashgrove.com
SIC: 3241 Masonry cement
HQ: Ash Grove Cement Company
11011 Cody St Ste 300
Overland Park KS 66210
913 451-8900

(G-8718)
ASHBURN INDUSTRIES
Also Called: Fluid Service Technologies
7403 Wright Rd (77041-2421)
P.O. Box 41345 (77241-1345)
PHONE..................832 399-1000

Steven Madden, *President*
Kacey Noland, *VP Finance*
JD Bermudez, *Sales Staff*
Krista Trimmer,
EMP: 30
SQ FT: 30,000
SALES (est): 9.8MM **Privately Held**
WEB: www.ashburnchemical.com
SIC: 2899 2992 Chemical preparations;
cutting oils, blending: made from pur-
chased materials

(G-8719)
ASHLEY DONUTS & ICE CREAM INC
Also Called: Ashley's Donuts
2160 Bay Area Blvd (77058-2006)
PHONE....................................281 486-5644
Stephan I Robinson, *President*
Robinson Frieda, *Vice Pres*
EMP: 12
SALES (est): 479.6K **Privately Held**
SIC: 5461 5812 2051 Doughnuts; ice
cream stands or dairy bars; doughnuts,
except frozen

(G-8720)
ASI INDUSTRIAL SERVICES LLC
8412 Mosley Rd (77075-1114)
PHONE....................................713 378-9200
Gary McGregor, *President*
EMP: 15
SALES (est): 1.6MM **Privately Held**
SIC: 3297 Nonclay refractories

(G-8721)
ASIA CHEMICAL CORPORATION INC
1417 Kress St (77020-7422)
PHONE....................................713 673-4100
Lain Wu, *Branch Mgr*
EMP: 16
SALES (corp-wide): 83.5MM **Privately Held**
WEB: www.asiachem-tx.com
SIC: 2821 Plastics materials & resins
PA: Asia Chemical Corporation Inc
11950 Airline Dr Ste 300
Houston TX 77037
281 445-1793

(G-8722)
ASINNI 2000 RECORDS INC
14601 Bellaire Blvd 308-A (77083-2505)
PHONE....................................281 564-4111
J Ward, *CEO*
Mout Ward, *President*
Phillis Ward, *CFO*
EMP: 45
SALES (est): 3.6MM **Privately Held**
SIC: 3652 Pre-recorded records & tapes

(G-8723)
ASP WESTWARD LP (PA)
Also Called: Houston Community Newspaper
523 N Sam Houston Pkwy E (77060-4036)
P.O. Box 609, Conroe (77305-0609)
PHONE....................................713 256-0953
James W Hopson, *CEO*
Vanesa Brashier, *Editor*
Jon Poorman, *Editor*
Brian Cope, *Sales Staff*
Kari Carlson, *Advt Staff*
EMP: 60
SQ FT: 13,000
SALES (est): 91.3MM **Privately Held**
WEB: www.thewoodcountydemocrat.com
SIC: 2711 Newspapers, publishing & print-
ing

(G-8724)
ASSA ABLOY DOOR GROUP LLC
Also Called: Dominion Building Products
550 Greens Pkwy Ste 100 (77067-4538)
PHONE....................................713 466-6790
Robert Mushinski, *Principal*
Anna Adeniran, *Controller*
Adolf Flores, *Sr Project Mgr*
EMP: 15
SALES (corp-wide): 9.7B **Privately Held**
WEB: www.cecodoor.com
SIC: 3499 3442 Doors, safe & vault:
metal; metal doors, sash & trim

HQ: Assa Abloy Door Group, Llc
9159 Telecom Dr
Milan TN 38358
731 686-8345

(G-8725)
ASSA ABLOY ENTRANCE SYSTEMS US
Also Called: Besam Entrance Solutions
9001 Jameel Rd Ste 190 (77040-5092)
PHONE....................................713 934-9095
Chris Harris, *Branch Mgr*
EMP: 11
SALES (corp-wide): 9.7B **Privately Held**
WEB: www.assaabloyentrance.us
SIC: 3699 1796 3442 Door opening &
closing devices, electrical; installing build-
ing equipment; metal doors
HQ: Assa Abloy Entrance Systems Us Inc.
1900 Airport Rd
Monroe NC 28110
704 290-5520

(G-8726)
ASSOCIATED TIME INSTRS CO INC
Also Called: Associated Time & Prkg Contrls
6699 Portwest Dr Ste 160 (77024-8078)
PHONE....................................713 263-1366
Glenn Rodriguez, *Branch Mgr*
EMP: 10
SALES (corp-wide): 19MM **Privately Held**
WEB: www.associatedtime.com
SIC: 3579 5046 5072 Time clocks & time
recording devices; parking meters; secu-
rity devices, locks
PA: Associated Time Instruments Com-
pany, Inc.
9104 Diplomacy Row
Dallas TX 75247
214 637-2763

(G-8727)
ASSOCTED BLDRS CNTRS GRTER HST
Also Called: Assocted Bldrs Cntrs Grter Hst
4910 Dacoma St (77092-7736)
PHONE....................................713 523-6222
Russell Hamley, *President*
Roger Berry, *Chairman*
Rodney Page, *Chairman*
Charles Holley, *Vice Pres*
Rusty Bay, *Treasurer*
EMP: 12
SALES: 1.8MM **Privately Held**
WEB: www.abchouston.org
SIC: 8611 2711 1522 Contractors' associ-
ation; newspapers: publishing only, not
printed on site; residential construction

(G-8728)
ASSURE LABS INC
5250 Gulfton St Ste 2c (77081-2936)
PHONE....................................713 561-5529
Hongqiao Di, *President*
Zhenguo Luo, *Director*
EMP: 100
SALES (est): 219.3K **Privately Held**
WEB: www.assurelabs.com
SIC: 8734 8731 2836 Testing laborato-
ries; biotechnical research, commercial;
biological products, except diagnostic

(G-8729)
ASTRIMAR CONSULTANTS LLC
1400 Brdfeld Blvd Ste 200 (77084)
PHONE....................................281 994-7816
John Strutt, *President*
Elizabeth Garry, *Director*
Caroline Roberts-Haritonov, *Director*
EMP: 20 EST: 2012
SALES (est): 572.4K **Privately Held**
SIC: 1389 8331 Oil consultants; job train-
ing & vocational rehabilitation services

(G-8730)
ASTRIMAR CONSULTANTS LLC
1400 Brdfeld Blvd Ste 200 (77084)
PHONE....................................281 994-7816
John Strutt, *President*
EMP: 20
SALES (est): 593.1K **Privately Held**
SIC: 1389 8331 Oil consultants; job train-
ing & vocational rehabilitation services

(G-8731)
ASTRO TECHNOLOGY INC
Also Called: ATI
15255 Gulf Fwy Ste 116f (77034-5379)
PHONE....................................281 464-0100
Robyn H Brower, *CEO*
David V Brower, *President*
EMP: 15
SALES (est): 2.4MM **Privately Held**
WEB: www.astrotechnology.com
SIC: 3812 8711 8731 Search & navigation
equipment; engineering services; com-
mercial physical research

(G-8732)
ATCO RUBBER PRODUCTS INC
9222 Wood Forest Blvd (77013-6108)
PHONE....................................713 674-6665
Jack Willis, *Manager*
Debbie Conover, *Admin Asst*
EMP: 40
SQ FT: 51,300 **Publicly Held**
WEB: www.atcoflex.com
SIC: 3084 3443 3585 3444 Plastics pipe;
ducting, metal plate; refrigeration & heat-
ing equipment; sheet metalwork
HQ: Atco Rubber Products, Inc.
7101 Atco Dr
Fort Worth TX 76118
817 595-2894

(G-8733)
ATHENA OILFIELD SERVICES LLC
601 Sawyer St Ste 200 (77007-7560)
P.O. Box 130502 (77219-0502)
PHONE....................................713 426-1969
EMP: 10
SALES: 5MM **Privately Held**
SIC: 5084 3533 Whol Industrial Equip-
ment Mfg Oil/Gas Field Machinery

(G-8734)
ATHLETIC DECALS INC
8800 Bissonnet St Ste N (77074-2435)
PHONE....................................713 774-0663
William R Stuck, *President*
Chris Willis, *General Mgr*
Chris Wills, *Admin Sec*
EMP: 13 EST: 1999
SQ FT: 5,600
SALES (est): 1.7MM **Privately Held**
WEB: www.athleticdecals.com
SIC: 2759 Screen printing

(G-8735)
ATHLON SOLUTIONS LLC (HQ)
Also Called: Athlon, A Halliburton Service
5500 N Sam Houston Pkwy W # 800
(77086-1573)
P.O. Box 27727 (77227-7727)
PHONE....................................713 457-2400
Anthony Maciejewski, *Area Mgr*
George Kraus, *Plant Mgr*
Jorge Bedoya, *Project Mgr*
Chip Aloisio, *Site Mgr*
Derick Krutsinger, *Site Mgr*
EMP: 160
SQ FT: 15,000
SALES (est): 42MM **Publicly Held**
WEB: www.athlonsolutions.com
SIC: 2899 Chemical preparations

(G-8736)
ATKORE INTERNATIONAL GROUP INC
11539 N Huston Rosslyn Rd (77088-1414)
PHONE....................................708 339-1610
Robert Ashford, *Branch Mgr*
EMP: 68 **Publicly Held**
WEB: www.atkore.com
SIC: 3441 Fabricated structural metal
PA: Atkore International Group Inc.
16100 Lathrop Ave
Harvey IL 60426

(G-8737)
ATLANTIA OFFSHORE LIMITED
1255 Enclave Pkwy Ste 600 (77077-1999)
PHONE....................................281 899-4300
Joseph W Blandford, *Partner*
Patricia Blandford, *Partner*
Esther Bishop, *General Mgr*
Steven Leverette, *Manager*
Peter Lunde, *Info Tech Mgr*

EMP: 80
SALES (est): 5.8MM **Privately Held**
WEB: www.sbmoffshore.com
SIC: 8711 3731 5084 Petroleum engineering; drilling & production platforms,
floating (oil & gas); oil well machinery,
equipment & supplies

(G-8738)
ATLANTIC COF INDUS SLTIONS LLC
Also Called: Atlantic Coffee Solutions
3900 Harrisburg Blvd (77003-2638)
PHONE....................................713 228-9501
Jorge Esteve, *President*
David Martinez, *President*
Cindy Parrish, *Treasurer*
Carlos Aldecoa Bueno,
◆ **EMP:** 350
SALES (est): 119.8MM **Privately Held**
SIC: 2095 Roasted coffee

(G-8739)
ATLANTIC MARITIME SERVICES LLC
2800 Post Oak Blvd Fl 54 (77056-6168)
PHONE....................................713 621-7800
Aric Wilbanks, *Superintendent*
Mark Holleman, *Counsel*
Brian Jackson, *Engineer*
Jeramy Montgomery, *Senior Mgr*
Scott Morain, *Supervisor*
EMP: 14
SALES (est): 1.8MM
SALES (corp-wide): 67.2MM **Privately Held**
SIC: 3533 1381 Oil & gas drilling rigs &
equipment; drilling oil & gas wells
HQ: Rowan Companies, Llc
5847 San Felipe St # 330
Houston TX 77057
713 621-7800

(G-8740)
ATLANTIC PACIFIC MARINE CORP
Also Called: Moller Supply Services
2500 City W Blvd Ste 1850 (77042)
PHONE....................................713 346-4300
Andrea Jones, *President*
Gregory Shelli, *Manager*
Russell Bruner, *Admin Sec*
Brent M Taylor, *Admin Sec*
◆ **EMP:** 10 EST: 1971
SALES (est): 100MM
SALES (corp-wide): 1.9MM **Privately Held**
WEB: www.maerskdrilling.com
SIC: 1389 Oil & gas wells: building, repair-
ing & dismantling
HQ: Maersk Inc.
180 Park Ave Ste 105
Florham Park NJ 07932
703 351-9200

(G-8741)
ATLANTICA MANAGEMENT USA INC
515 Post Oak Blvd Ste 120 (77027-9407)
PHONE....................................832 494-2200
Kerry Kunz, *President*
Christian Delater, *Area Mgr*
Eric Hoegg, *Vice Pres*
Stratton Keith, *Vice Pres*
Christian Wood, *Vice Pres*
▲ **EMP:** 43
SALES (est): 13.5MM **Privately Held**
WEB: www.atlanticatd.com
SIC: 1381 Drilling oil & gas wells
HQ: Atlantica Tender Drilling Ltd
C/O Appleby
Hamilton HM 12

(G-8742)
ATLANTIS PLASTIC COMPANY
5705 Hogue St (77087-4013)
PHONE....................................713 643-8387
Larry Walters, *President*
Darlene Walters, *Treasurer*
EMP: 10
SQ FT: 12,800
SALES (est): 1.8MM **Privately Held**
WEB: www.atlantisplasticscompany.com
SIC: 3089 Injection molding of plastics

(G-8743)
ATLAS COPCO COMPRESSORS LLC
15045 Lee Rd (77032-4001)
PHONE....................281 453-6800
Rob Ryan, *Branch Mgr*
Kevin Martin, *Sr Project Mgr*
EMP: 12
SALES (corp-wide): 10.7B **Privately Held**
WEB: www.atlascopco.us
SIC: 3563 Air & gas compressors
HQ: Atlas Copco Compressors Llc
300 Technology Center Way # 5
Rock Hill SC 29730
866 472-1015

(G-8744)
ATLAS COPCO COMPRESSORS LLC
6755a Willow Brook Park (77066-3011)
PHONE....................281 453-6800
Rob Ryan, *Manager*
EMP: 23
SALES (corp-wide): 10.7B **Privately Held**
WEB: www.atlascopco.us
SIC: 3563 Air & gas compressors
HQ: Atlas Copco Compressors Llc
300 Technology Center Way # 5
Rock Hill SC 29730
866 472-1015

(G-8745)
ATLAS PTRO EXPLRTION WORLDWIDE
Also Called: Apex
16600 Park Row (77084-5019)
PHONE....................281 579-5200
EMP: 40
SALES (est): 2.9MM **Privately Held**
SIC: 1381 Oil/Gas Well Drilling

(G-8746)
ATLAS SIGN SERVICES INC
Also Called: Atlas Sign Co
6411 Airline Dr (77076-3507)
PHONE....................713 699-1121
Stan Titlow, *Ch of Bd*
Linda Ann Titlow, *Treasurer*
Michael Johnson, *Sales Staff*
EMP: 19
SQ FT: 6,700
SALES (est): 2.4MM **Privately Held**
WEB: www.atlassigns.com
SIC: 3993 Electric signs

(G-8747)
ATWOOD OCEANICS MANAGEMENT LLC
5847 San Felipe St # 3300 (77057-3195)
P.O. Box 570788 (77257-0788)
PHONE....................281 749-7800
Rob Saltiel, *President*
Mark L Mey, *Senior VP*
Stuart Allen, *Vice Pres*
Mike Campbell, *Controller*
▲ EMP: 13
SALES (est): 2.3MM
SALES (corp-wide): 2B **Privately Held**
WEB: www.valaris.com
SIC: 1381 Drilling oil & gas wells
HQ: Atwood Oceanics, Llc
5847 San Felipe St # 3300
Houston TX 77057

(G-8748)
AUC MANAGEMENT LLC
Also Called: Auc Group
1800 Augusta Dr Ste 108 (77057-3130)
PHONE....................713 983-3255
Todd Mueller, *Mng Member*
EMP: 10
SQ FT: 2,107
SALES (est): 2.9MM
SALES (corp-wide): 14.4MM **Privately Held**
WEB: www.aucgroup.net
SIC: 2819 Nuclear fuels, uranium slug (radioactive)
PA: Argosy Investment Partners Iv, L.P.
950 W Valley Rd Ste 2900
Wayne PA 19087
610 971-9685

(G-8749)
AUSTIN COCA-COLA BOTTLING CO
1700 Crosspoint Ave (77054-3708)
PHONE....................713 799-7296
Perry Bradburn, *Manager*
EMP: 50
SALES (corp-wide): 309.5MM **Privately Held**
SIC: 2086 Bottled & canned soft drinks
PA: Austin Coca-Cola Bottling Company
1 Coca Cola Pl
San Antonio TX 78219
210 225-2601

(G-8750)
AUSTIN COCA-COLA BOTTLING CO
1722 Brittmoore Rd (77043-2711)
PHONE....................713 805-9722
Lonell Truscott, *Manager*
EMP: 75
SQ FT: 107,377
SALES (corp-wide): 309.5MM **Privately Held**
WEB: www.coca-cola.com
SIC: 2086 Bottled & canned soft drinks
PA: Austin Coca-Cola Bottling Company
1 Coca Cola Pl
San Antonio TX 78219
210 225-2601

(G-8751)
AUSTINS CABINETS & CNSTR
Also Called: Austin Cabinets
2622 Lakemont Dr (77039-2116)
PHONE....................281 987-3308
Mitch Austin, *President*
Aiden Forsythe, *Corp Secy*
EMP: 14
SQ FT: 4,000
SALES (est): 1.4MM **Privately Held**
SIC: 2431 Millwork

(G-8752)
AUTO FIT INC (PA)
Also Called: Auto Fit Company
6969 North Fwy (77076-2031)
PHONE....................713 696-9000
Mahmoud Emadi, *President*
Fakhredin Emadi, *Vice Pres*
Julie Emadi, *CFO*
Lupina Martinez, *Admin Sec*
▲ EMP: 11
SQ FT: 20,000
SALES (est): 9.5MM **Privately Held**
WEB: www.autofitparts.com
SIC: 5013 5599 3999 Automotive supplies & parts; dunebuggies; atomizers, toiletry

(G-8753)
AUTOMATIC SWITCH COMPANY
16203 Park Row (77084-5136)
PHONE....................281 829-2900
Mark Robins, *Branch Mgr*
EMP: 601
SALES (corp-wide): 16.7B **Publicly Held**
WEB: www.asco.com
SIC: 3491 Solenoid valves
HQ: Automatic Switch Company
50-60 Hanover Rd
Florham Park NJ 07932
973 966-2000

(G-8754)
AUTOMATION SOLUTIONS LP (PA)
Also Called: Autosol
16055 Space Center Blvd # 45 (77062-6251)
PHONE....................281 286-6017
Douglas Osburn, *President*
Arthur Hester, *Engineer*
Julie Cannoy, *CFO*
Lynn Spencer, *Regl Sales Mgr*
Melissa Ferstl, *Marketing Staff*
EMP: 40
SQ FT: 5,000
SALES (est): 5.8MM **Privately Held**
WEB: www.autosoln.com
SIC: 7373 8711 3577 Systems integration services; computer systems analysis & design; professional engineer; computer peripheral equipment

(G-8755)
AVANGARD INNOVATIVE LP (PA)
11906 Brittmoore Park Dr A (77041-7345)
PHONE....................281 582-0700
Rick Perez, *Partner*
Walker Chan, *Partner*
Javier Pena, *Partner*
Reece Hammer, *Regional Mgr*
Ali Conrad, *Business Mgr*
◆ EMP: 24
SQ FT: 40,000
SALES (est): 19.7MM **Privately Held**
WEB: www.avaicg.com
SIC: 2821 Plastics materials & resins

(G-8756)
AXALT POWDE COATI SYSTE USA I (DH)
Also Called: Dupont Coating Solutions
9800 Genard Rd (77041-7624)
PHONE....................800 247-3886
Florian Girthofer, *President*
Nathan Rotter, *Business Mgr*
Adalberto Garza, *Engineer*
Ines Taboada, *Treasurer*
Robert Robbins, *Sales Mgr*
▲ EMP: 192
SQ FT: 170,000
SALES (est): 95.7MM
SALES (corp-wide): 4.4B **Publicly Held**
WEB: www.axalta.com
SIC: 2851 Paints & allied products
HQ: Axalta Coating Systems Belgium
Geerdegem-Schonenberg 248
Mechelen 2800
154 214-13

(G-8757)
AXALTA PWDR CATING SYSTEMS INC
9800 Genard Rd (77041-7624)
PHONE....................832 955-0201
Gilles Georges, *Director*
◆ EMP: 250
SALES (est): 24.1K
SALES (corp-wide): 4.4B **Publicly Held**
SIC: 2851 Paints & allied products
HQ: Axalta Coating Systems Belgium
Geerdegem-Schonenberg 248
Mechelen 2800
154 214-13

(G-8758)
AXESS NORTH AMERICA INC
15915 Katy Fwy (77094-1708)
PHONE....................281 994-0364
Hughie Watson, *Principal*
Erik Aalde, *Business Mgr*
Trond Stokke, *Department Mgr*
Christian Nerland, *Director*
EMP: 20
SALES (est): 1MM **Privately Held**
WEB: www.axessgroup.com
SIC: 1311 1382 Crude petroleum production; oil & gas exploration services

(G-8759)
AXIOM SPACE INC
1290 Hercules Ave Ste 120 (77058-2769)
PHONE....................346 293-7045
Kamal Ghaffarian, *CEO*
EMP: 40
SALES (est): 133.5K **Privately Held**
WEB: www.axiomspace.com
SIC: 3761 Space vehicles, complete

(G-8760)
AXIOM TECHNOLOGIES LLC
255 Pennbright Dr Ste 220 (77090-5908)
P.O. Box 773, Spring (77383-0773)
PHONE....................281 931-0907
Miquel A Timm, *President*
Jason Savoie, *Vice Pres*
▼ EMP: 20
SQ FT: 10,000
SALES (est): 1.7MM **Privately Held**
WEB: www.axiomsafety.com
SIC: 1389 Oil field services

(G-8761)
AXIS PIPE AND TUBE LLC (PA)
770 S Post Oak Ln Ste 200 (77056-1913)
PHONE....................281 494-0900
Allen McMillan, *Prdtn Mgr*
Nancy Cabrera, *Sales Staff*
Jorge Montemayor, *Director*
Andres Montalvo, *Director*
Jose Montemayor, *Director*
EMP: 117
SALES (est): 38.3MM **Privately Held**
WEB: www.axispipeandtube.com
SIC: 3312 Pipes & tubes

(G-8762)
AXON EP INC (HQ)
Also Called: Axon Energy Products
12606 N Huston Rosslyn Rd (77086-3156)
PHONE....................281 855-3200
Gary Stratulate, *CEO*
Jeff Justice, *General Mgr*
Jordan Strouse, *Principal*
Randall Stockton, *Vice Pres*
Craig Taylor, *Vice Pres*
EMP: 40
SALES (est): 18.5MM **Privately Held**
WEB: www.axonep.com
SIC: 1381 3533 Directional drilling oil & gas wells; oil & gas field machinery

(G-8763)
AXON PRESSURE PRODUCTS INC (HQ)
Also Called: Axon Energy Services
12606 N Huston Rosslyn Rd (77086-3156)
PHONE....................281 855-3200
Keith Klopfenstein, *CEO*
Okan Gurbuz, *Vice Pres*
Lane Westerman, *Warehouse Mgr*
Travis Stehling, *Engineer*
Jeff Merecka, *CFO*
▲ EMP: 75
SALES (est): 17.4MM
SALES (corp-wide): 17.1MM **Privately Held**
WEB: www.axonpp.com
SIC: 3533 Oil field machinery & equipment
PA: Pelican Energy Partners Lp
2050 W Sam Houston Pkwy S # 1550
Houston TX 77042
713 559-7110

(G-8764)
AXON PRESSURE PRODUCTS INC
Also Called: Axon Well Intervention Pdts
12606 N Huston Rosslyn Rd (77086-3156)
PHONE....................713 478-8007
Ashley Schubert, *Branch Mgr*
EMP: 13
SALES (corp-wide): 17.1MM **Privately Held**
WEB: www.axonpp.com
SIC: 3533 Oil field machinery & equipment
HQ: Axon Pressure Products, Inc.
12606 N Huston Rosslyn Rd
Houston TX 77086

(G-8765)
AXXIS DRILLING INC
15015 Vickery Dr (77032-2554)
PHONE....................985 868-6969
Robert Dunn, *President*
Brent Conway, *President*
Lynn Poche, *President*
Lisa Gonsuron, *Finance*
Rene Borel, *Sales Dir*
EMP: 35 EST: 2007
SALES (est): 40MM **Privately Held**
SIC: 1381 Drilling oil & gas wells

(G-8766)
AZ PALLET EXCHANGE
13100 Northwest Fwy (77040-6310)
PHONE....................713 332-6145
EMP: 21
SALES (est): 2.3MM **Privately Held**
SIC: 2448 Pallets, wood & wood with metal

(G-8767)
AZURE MIDSTREAM COMPANY LLC (HQ)
12121 Wickchester Ln # 750 (77079-1230)
PHONE....................281 680-4300
Chip Berthelot, *President*
Dennie Dixon, *Vice Pres*
David Garrett, *Vice Pres*
EMP: 10
SALES (est): 14.2MM **Privately Held**
WEB: www.azuremidstream.com
SIC: 1311 Natural gas production

GEOGRAPHIC

PA: Azure Midstream Holdings Llc
12121 Wickchester Ln # 750
Houston TX 77079
281 680-4300

(G-8768)
AZZ ENCLOSURE SYSTEMS
1318 Bammel Rd (77073-2106)
PHONE..................................832 295-1200
Brian Fine, *President*
Mark Arms, *Manager*
EMP: 214
SQ FT: 110,000
SALES (corp-wide): 1B **Publicly Held**
SIC: 3444 Metal housings, enclosures,
casings & other containers
HQ: Azz Enclosure Systems - Chattanooga
Llc
1919 W Polymer Dr
Chattanooga TN 37421
423 894-9268

(G-8769)
AZZ INC
Aztec Manufacturing
7407 C E King Pkwy (77044-2810)
P.O. Box 24720 (77229-4720)
PHONE..................................281 458-1550
Evan Randall, *Office Mgr*
EMP: 31
SALES (corp-wide): 1B **Publicly Held**
WEB: www.azz.com
SIC: 3699 3479 Electrical equipment &
supplies; galvanizing of iron, steel or end-
formed products
PA: Azz Inc.
3100 W 7th St Ste 500
Fort Worth TX 76107
817 810-0095

(G-8770)
AZZ INC
Also Called: Azz Rig-A-Lite Product
8500 Hansen Rd (77075-1006)
PHONE..................................713 943-0340
Brent Gathright, *Engineer*
Dave Nark, *VP Mktg*
EMP: 50
SALES (corp-wide): 1B **Publicly Held**
WEB: www.azz.com
SIC: 3646 Electrical equipment & supplies
PA: Azz Inc.
3100 W 7th St Ste 500
Fort Worth TX 76107
817 810-0095

(G-8771)
AZZ INC
9103 Frbanks N Houston Rd (77064-6204)
PHONE..................................832 467-3772
Park Whitington, *Sales/Mktg Mgr*
EMP: 50
SALES (corp-wide): 1B **Publicly Held**
WEB: www.azz.com
SIC: 3479 Hot dip coating of metals or
formed products; galvanizing of iron, steel
or end-formed products
PA: Azz Inc.
3100 W 7th St Ste 500
Fort Worth TX 76107
817 810-0095

(G-8772)
B & G INC
11460 Gulf Fwy (77034-3549)
PHONE..................................713 944-1200
Issa Baba, *President*
Haitham Baba, *President*
Jad Baba, *Vice Pres*
Abraham Ganim, *Treasurer*
EMP: 13
SQ FT: 20,000
SALES (est): 1.7MM **Privately Held**
WEB: www.bngdist.com
SIC: 2064 Candy & other confectionery
products

(G-8773)
B BAD SPORTS INC
5325 Glenmont Dr Ste E (77081-2050)
PHONE..................................713 664-3838
Ann Cramer, *President*
EMP: 26 **EST:** 2002

SALES (est): 2MM **Privately Held**
WEB: www.bbadsports.com
SIC: 2339 Women's & misses' acces-
sories; sportswear, women's

(G-8774)
B C O BLACK CANE ORIGINAL
5720 Wayne St (77026-2354)
PHONE..................................832 883-5774
Brian Smith, *Owner*
EMP: 9
SALES (est): 20MM **Privately Held**
SIC: 3842 Surgical appliances & supplies

(G-8775)
B J SERVICES COMPANY USA
17015 Aldine Westfield Rd (77073-5101)
PHONE..................................713 625-4200
EMP: 1532
SALES (corp-wide): 482.7MM **Privately
Held**
SIC: 1389 Oil/Gas Field Services
PA: B J Services Company, U.S.A.
5500 Nw Central Dr # 100
Houston TX 77092

(G-8776)
B J SERVICES COMPANY USA
17021 Aldine Westfield Rd (77073-5101)
PHONE..................................713 879-1727
EMP: 880
SALES (corp-wide): 482.7MM **Privately
Held**
SIC: 1389 Oil/Gas Field Services
PA: B J Services Company, U.S.A.
5500 Nw Central Dr # 100
Houston TX 77092

(G-8777)
B J SERVICES COMPANY USA
2929 Allen Pkwy Ste 2100 (77019-7111)
PHONE..................................713 439-8600
EMP: 868
SALES (corp-wide): 482.7MM **Privately
Held**
SIC: 1389 Oil/Gas Field Services
PA: B J Services Company, U.S.A.
5500 Nw Central Dr # 100
Houston TX 77092

(G-8778)
B M HIGGINBTHAMS MCH WORKS INC
Also Called: B&M Machine Works
8353 Mosley Rd (77075-1111)
PHONE..................................713 941-1854
Joe Higginbotham, *President*
Connie Higginbotham, *Corp Secy*
Scott Higginbotham, *Vice Pres*
EMP: 23 **EST:** 1962
SQ FT: 26,600
SALES: 5MM **Privately Held**
WEB: www.b-mmachineworks.com
SIC: 3599 Machine shop, jobbing & repair

(G-8779)
B&G FOODS INC
Also Called: B & G Foods
14700 North Fwy (77090-6504)
PHONE..................................281 821-6680
EMP: 11
SALES (corp-wide): 1.6B **Publicly Held**
WEB: www.bgfoods.com
SIC: 2013 Sausages & other prepared
meats
PA: B&G Foods, Inc.
4 Gatehall Dr Ste 110
Parsippany NJ 07054
973 401-6500

(G-8780)
B&L PIPECO SERVICES INC (DH)
20465 Sh 249 Ste 200 (77070)
PHONE..................................281 955-3500
Steve Tait, *President*
Craig Wilkins, *CFO*
Brad Berlin, *Sales Staff*
Gene Hunt, *Sales Staff*
Blake Bourgeois, *Sales Executive*
EMP: 12
SALES (est): 17.3MM **Privately Held**
WEB: www.blpipeco.com
SIC: 3317 Welded pipe & tubes

HQ: Sumitomo Corporation Of Americas
300 Madison Ave
New York NY 10017
212 207-0700

(G-8781)
B&P LITTLEFORD LLC
13135 South Fwy (77047-1927)
PHONE..................................713 433-3304
Jim Fletcher, *Manager*
EMP: 12
SQ FT: 23,071
SALES (corp-wide): 19.1MM **Privately
Held**
WEB: www.bplittleford.com
SIC: 3559 3542 Chemical machinery &
equipment; machine tools, metal forming
type
PA: B&P Littleford Llc
1000 Hess Ave
Saginaw MI 48601
989 757-1300

(G-8782)
B-W GRINDING SERVICE INC
5807 Nunn St (77087-4137)
PHONE..................................713 641-0888
William T Hargrave, *President*
Dodie L Hargrave, *Corp Secy*
David Hargrave, *Vice Pres*
Wanda T Hargrave, *Vice Pres*
Pat Scott, *Plant Mgr*
▲ **EMP:** 62 **EST:** 1970
SQ FT: 20,600
SALES (est): 12.2MM **Privately Held**
WEB: www.bwgrinding.com
SIC: 3599 3549 Machine shop, jobbing &
repair; metalworking machinery

(G-8783)
BAART INDUSTRIAL GROUP (PA)
4660 Pine Timbers St # 165 (77041-9322)
P.O. Box 16528, Boise ID (83715-6528)
PHONE..................................713 690-1690
EMP: 11 **EST:** 2014
SALES (est): 4.1MM **Privately Held**
WEB: www.baartgroup.com
SIC: 3366 3568 Bushings & bearings;
bearings, bushings & blocks

(G-8784)
BABCOCK & WILCOX COMPANY
363 N Sam Houston Pkwy E # 600
(77060-2480)
PHONE..................................281 405-6800
Mike Nickey, *Branch Mgr*
EMP: 10
SALES (corp-wide): 859.1MM **Publicly
Held**
WEB: www.babcock.com
SIC: 3511 Steam turbines
HQ: The Babcock & Wilcox Company
1200 E Market St Ste 650
Akron OH 44305
330 753-4511

(G-8785)
BAC PRODUCTS INC
10197 Windfern Rd (77064-5813)
PHONE..................................832 230-1463
Ron Hahn, *Ch of Bd*
Stephen C Foust, *President*
Maria D Foust, *Admin Sec*
▲ **EMP:** 24 **EST:** 2005
SALES (est): 5.7MM **Privately Held**
WEB: www.bacproductsinc.com
SIC: 2542 Cabinets: show, display or stor-
age: except wood

(G-8786)
BACE MANUFACTURING INC
Also Called: Spm Division
7131 Perimeter Park Dr (77041-4020)
PHONE..................................713 329-8954
Freddy Venegas, *Business Mgr*
Royal Smith, *Manager*
EMP: 200
SALES (corp-wide): 456.1MM **Privately
Held**
SIC: 3089 Injection molding of plastics
HQ: Bace Manufacturing, Inc.
3125 E Coronado St
Anaheim CA 92806
714 630-6002

(G-8787)
BACE MANUFACTURING INC
Also Called: Spm
7131 Perimeter Park Dr (77041-4020)
PHONE..................................713 466-5563
Royal Smith, *Manager*
EMP: 125
SALES (corp-wide): 456.1MM **Privately
Held**
SIC: 3089 Molding primary plastic
HQ: Bace Manufacturing, Inc.
3125 E Coronado St
Anaheim CA 92806
714 630-6002

(G-8788)
BADGER MIDSTREAM ENERGY LP
919 Milam St Ste 2300 (77002-5418)
PHONE..................................713 395-6111
Alex A Bucher, *CEO*
Joan A W Schnepp, *COO*
David Markle, *Vice Pres*
Ralph W Neumann, *Vice Pres*
Drew Hardy, *Plant Mgr*
EMP: 36
SQ FT: 6,000
SALES (est): 13.1MM **Privately Held**
WEB: www.badgermidstream.com
SIC: 1311 Natural gas production

(G-8789)
BAE SYSTEMS RESOLUTION INC (DH)
1000 La St Ste 4950 (77002)
PHONE..................................713 868-7700
Howard Wolf, *Ch of Bd*
Max L Lukens, *President*
Ian T Graham, *President*
Carl B King, *Senior VP*
Britt Davis, *Vice Pres*
◆ **EMP:** 38 **EST:** 1902
SQ FT: 30,500
SALES (est): 161.9MM
SALES (corp-wide): 2.8B **Publicly Held**
WEB: www.stewartandstevenson.com
SIC: 3713 5084 3711 7699 Van bodies;
dump truck bodies; industrial machinery &
equipment; scout cars (motor vehicles),
assembly of; universal carriers, military,
assembly of; industrial equipment services;
nautical repair services; construction
equipment repair; tubing, copper & cop-
per alloy; seismographs

(G-8790)
BAILY INTERNATIONAL INC
5600 Harvey Wilson Dr (77020-8019)
PHONE..................................713 673-0080
Curtis Cronkite, *Branch Mgr*
EMP: 150 **Privately Held**
WEB: www.bailyfoods.com
SIC: 2098 Noodles (e.g. egg, plain &
water), dry
PA: Baily International, Inc.
2501 W 20th St
Granite City IL 62040

(G-8791)
BAIRDS MRS BAKERIES BUS TR
Also Called: Mrs Baird's Baking Co
6650 N Houston Rosslyn Rd (77091-1009)
P.O. Box 924227 (77292-4227)
PHONE..................................713 996-5000
Rafael Quevedo, *Branch Mgr*
EMP: 411
SQ FT: 45,000
SALES (corp-wide): 240.9MM **Privately
Held**
WEB: www.mrsbairds.com
SIC: 2051 5461 Bakery: wholesale or
wholesale/retail combined; bakeries
PA: Baird's, Mrs Bakeries Business Trust
7301 South Fwy
Fort Worth TX 76134
817 615-3100

(G-8792)
BAKER HGHES OLFLD OPRTIONS LLC
Also Called: Baker Hughes Drilling Fluids
9902 Sheldon Rd (77049-1247)
PHONE..................................281 456-5300
Jim Vernon, *Branch Mgr*

EMP: 15 **Privately Held**
WEB: www.bakerhughes.com
SIC: **1389** Oil field services
PA: Baker Hughes Oilfield Operations Llc
2001 Rankin Rd
Houston TX 77073

(G-8793)
BAKER HGHES OLFLD OPRTIONS LLC
Also Called: Baker Oil Tool
1902 Cypress Station Dr B (77090-4038)
PHONE...................................713 879-3760
Carlton Efird, *Manager*
EMP: 17
SQ FT: 1,746 **Privately Held**
WEB: www.bakerhughes.com
SIC: **1389** 1382 Oil field services; oil & gas exploration services
PA: Baker Hughes Oilfield Operations Llc
2001 Rankin Rd
Houston TX 77073

(G-8794)
BAKER HGHES OLFLD OPRTIONS LLC
Baker Oil Tools
14990 Yorktown Plaza Dr (77040-4026)
P.O. Box 3048 (77253-3048)
PHONE...................................713 923-9351
Steven Graham, *Branch Mgr*
EMP: 150 **Privately Held**
WEB: www.bakerhughes.com
SIC: **1389** Oil field services
PA: Baker Hughes Oilfield Operations Llc
2001 Rankin Rd
Houston TX 77073

(G-8795)
BAKER HGHES OLFLD OPRTIONS LLC
Baker Oil Tools
9100 Emmott Rd (77040-3514)
P.O. Box 40129 (77240-0129)
PHONE...................................713 466-1322
Doug Wall, *President*
Derek Hardie, *Business Mgr*
James Fraser, *Project Mgr*
Liz Williams, *Senior Buyer*
Halit Dilber, *Engineer*
EMP: 51 **Privately Held**
WEB: www.bakerhughes.com
SIC: **1389** Oil field services
PA: Baker Hughes Oilfield Operations Llc
2001 Rankin Rd
Houston TX 77073

(G-8796)
BAKER HGHES OLFLD OPRTIONS LLC (PA)
Also Called: Baker Hughes Solutions
2001 Rankin Rd (77073-5114)
PHONE...................................713 879-1000
Martin Craighead, *CEO*
Maria Claudia Borras, *President*
Belgacem Chariag, *President*
Alan Crain, *Senior VP*
Didier Charreton, *Vice Pres*
◆ EMP: 15
SALES (est): 6.2B **Privately Held**
WEB: www.bakerhughes.com
SIC: **1381** 1311 1389 2899 Drilling oil & gas wells; crude petroleum & natural gas production; servicing oil & gas wells; chemical preparations

(G-8797)
BAKER HGHES OLFLD OPRTIONS LLC
4101 Oates Rd (77013-4111)
P.O. Box 23656 (77228-3656)
PHONE...................................832 519-2000
Martyn Bates, *Branch Mgr*
EMP: 42 **Privately Held**
WEB: www.bakerhughes.com
SIC: **1389** Oil field services
PA: Baker Hughes Oilfield Operations Llc
2001 Rankin Rd
Houston TX 77073

(G-8798)
BAKER HGHES PRCESS PPLINE SVCS
4101 Oates Rd (77013-4111)
PHONE...................................832 519-2000

EMP: 9 EST: 2014
SALES (est): 736.8K **Privately Held**
SIC: **1389** Oil field services

(G-8799)
BAKER HUGHES A GE COMPANY LLC
2001 Rankin Rd (77073-5114)
PHONE...................................713 580-9700
EMP: 87
SALES (corp-wide): 122B **Publicly Held**
SIC: **1389** Oil/Gas Field Services
HQ: Baker Hughes, A Ge Company, Llc
17021 Aldine Westfield Rd
Houston TX 77073
713 439-8600

(G-8800)
BAKER HUGHES A GE COMPANY LLC
Baker Hughes Inteq Div
2001 Rankin Rd (77073-5114)
P.O. Box 1407 (77251-1407)
PHONE...................................713 625-4200
Christopher Rose, *Project Mgr*
James Cessar, *Opers Staff*
Asam Nadeem, *Purch Mgr*
Debbie Plitt, *Buyer*
Marlene Bray, *Engineer*
EMP: 230
SQ FT: 1,388
SALES (corp-wide): 23.8B **Publicly Held**
WEB: www.bhge.com
SIC: **1389** Oil field services
HQ: Baker Hughes Holdings Llc
17021 Aldine Westfield Rd
Houston TX 77073
713 439-8600

(G-8801)
BAKER HUGHES A GE COMPANY LLC
15355 Vantage Pkwy W # 300 (77032-1973)
PHONE...................................713 625-4200
Craig Mueller, *VP Sales*
Jason Davis, *Business Anlyst*
Iain McIntosh, *Manager*
Russell Hawbaker, *Manager*
Ernest Perez, *Technology*
EMP: 300
SALES (corp-wide): 23.8B **Publicly Held**
WEB: www.bakerhughes.com
SIC: **3533** 2899 2865 1381 Oil & gas field machinery; chemical preparations; cyclic crudes & intermediates; drilling oil & gas wells; fishing for tools, oil & gas field; pumps & pumping equipment
HQ: Baker Hughes Holdings Llc
17021 Aldine Westfield Rd
Houston TX 77073
713 439-8600

(G-8802)
BAKER HUGHES COMPANY (PA)
17021 Aldine Westfield Rd (77073-5101)
PHONE...................................713 439-8600
Lorenzo Simonelli, *Ch of Bd*
Thomas Dowell, *District Mgr*
Shelly Cory, *Business Mgr*
Nikolay Rotar, *Business Mgr*
Scott Stapleton, *Business Mgr*
EMP: 119
SALES (est): 23.8B **Publicly Held**
WEB: www.bakerhughes.com
SIC: **3533** 3561 Oil & gas field machinery; oil field machinery & equipment; gas field machinery & equipment; bits, oil & gas field tools: rock; pumps, oil well & field

(G-8803)
BAKER HUGHES ENERGY SVCS LLC (HQ)
17021 Aldine Westfield Rd (77073-5101)
P.O. Box 2291 (77252-2291)
PHONE...................................713 439-8600
Lorenzo Simonelli, *President*
Eugene Borak, *Principal*
Mark E Buchanan, *Vice Pres*
Barbara A Cameron, *Vice Pres*
Jose Dumenigo, *Vice Pres*
EMP: 99

SALES (est): 29MM
SALES (corp-wide): 95.2B **Publicly Held**
WEB: www.bhge.com
SIC: **3563** Air & gas compressors
PA: General Electric Company
5 Necco St
Boston MA 02210
617 443-3000

(G-8804)
BAKER HUGHES FINANCING LLC (DH)
2001 Rankin Rd (77073-5114)
P.O. Box 4740 (77210-4740)
PHONE...................................713 439-8600
G F Finley, *CEO*
Chad Deaton, *Ch of Bd*
Mark Lewis, *President*
Sandy Olfer, *Admin Sec*
EMP: 54
SALES (est): 43.4MM
SALES (corp-wide): 23.8B **Publicly Held**
WEB: www.bakerhughes.com
SIC: **1389** Oil field services
HQ: Baker Hughes Holdings Llc
17021 Aldine Westfield Rd
Houston TX 77073
713 439-8600

(G-8805)
BAKER HUGHES HOLDINGS LLC
Also Called: Global Business Services
17021 Aldine Westfield Rd (77073-5101)
PHONE...................................713 625-4200
Craig Mueller, *Vice Pres*
Tariq Khan, *Technical Mgr*
Bradley Ingham, *Senior Engr*
Angie McPherson, *Human Res Dir*
Daniel Funes, *Accounts Mgr*
EMP: 10
SALES (corp-wide): 23.8B **Publicly Held**
WEB: www.bhge.com
SIC: **1389** Oil field services
HQ: Baker Hughes Holdings Llc
17021 Aldine Westfield Rd
Houston TX 77073
713 439-8600

(G-8806)
BAKER HUGHES HOLDINGS LLC (HQ)
17021 Aldine Westfield Rd (77073-5101)
P.O. Box 4740 (77210-4740)
PHONE...................................713 439-8600
Lorenzo Simonelli, *Ch of Bd*
Maria Claudia Borras, *President*
Roderick Christie, *President*
Matthias Heilmann, *President*
Neil Saunders, *President*
◆ EMP: 130
SALES (est): 23.8B **Publicly Held**
WEB: www.bhge.com
SIC: **3533** 3561 Oil & gas field machinery; oil field machinery & equipment; gas field machinery & equipment; bits, oil & gas field tools: rock; pumps, oil well & field
PA: Baker Hughes Company
17021 Aldine Westfield Rd
Houston TX 77073
713 439-8600

(G-8807)
BAKER HUGHES HOLDINGS LLC
Baker Hughes Production Quest
7000 Hollister St Ste 300 (77040-5618)
PHONE...................................281 231-1000
Steve Hester, *Branch Mgr*
Bernardo Maldonado, *Director*
EMP: 70
SQ FT: 145,714
SALES (corp-wide): 23.8B **Publicly Held**
WEB: www.bhge.com
SIC: **3533** Oil & gas field machinery
HQ: Baker Hughes Holdings Llc
17021 Aldine Westfield Rd
Houston TX 77073
713 439-8600

(G-8808)
BAKER HUGHES HOLDINGS LLC
1999 Rankin Rd (77073-5109)
PHONE...................................713 439-8600

Aravind Tarigopula, *Opers Mgr*
Melancon Carleen, *Buyer*
Hlavacek Holland, *Buyer*
Long Ryan, *Buyer*
Russell Craig, *Engineer*
EMP: 87
SALES (corp-wide): 23.8B **Publicly Held**
WEB: www.bhge.com
SIC: **1389** Oil field services
HQ: Baker Hughes Holdings Llc
17021 Aldine Westfield Rd
Houston TX 77073
713 439-8600

(G-8809)
BAKER PETROLITE LLC
3900 Essex Ln Ste 1200 (77027-5486)
PHONE...................................713 599-7400
Mg Bassett, *Manager*
EMP: 270 **Privately Held**
WEB: www.bakerhughesdirect.lookchem.com
SIC: **2899** Water treating compounds
HQ: Baker Petrolite Llc
12645 W Airport Blvd
Sugar Land TX 77478
281 276-5400

(G-8810)
BALLARD EXPLORATION CO INC (PA)
1021 Manor St Ste 2310 (77015-5460)
PHONE...................................713 651-0181
A L Ballard, *President*
Jane Bortoni, *Production*
Mallory Boyd, *Production*
Janie Uresti, *Accountant*
Randy Jennings, *Info Tech Mgr*
EMP: 24 EST: 1976
SQ FT: 10,000
SALES (est): 25.2MM **Privately Held**
WEB: www.ipglobal.net
SIC: **1382** 1311 Oil & gas exploration services; crude petroleum production

(G-8811)
BAMBERGER POLYMERS INC
12600 N Featherwood Dr # 300 (77034-4444)
PHONE...................................281 481-9100
Veronica Christensen, *Principal*
Lynnette Russo, *Sales Staff*
Lori Brustowicz, *Office Mgr*
EMP: 10 **Privately Held**
WEB: www.bambergerpolymers.com
SIC: **2821** Plastics materials & resins
HQ: Bamberger Polymers, Inc.
2 Jericho Plz Ste 109
Jericho NY 11753

(G-8812)
BAMBERGER POLYMERS CORP
11550 Fuqua St Ste 205 (77034-4537)
PHONE...................................281 481-9100
Dennis Don, *Manager*
EMP: 20 **Privately Held**
WEB: www.bambergerpolymers.com
SIC: **2821** Plastics materials & resins
PA: Bamberger Polymers Corp.
2 Jericho Plz Ste 109
Jericho NY 11753

(G-8813)
BAMSCH ENTERPRISES INTL LTD
7113 Chippewa Blvd (77086-3226)
P.O. Box 1608, Tomball (77377-1608)
PHONE...................................281 448-5925
Neil Bamsch, *President*
EMP: 10
SALES (est): 1.3MM **Privately Held**
WEB: www.beioil.com
SIC: **3599** Machine & other job shop work

(G-8814)
BANNER SUPPLY INC
4800 W 34th St Ste D1 (77092-6664)
PHONE...................................713 802-2225
Frank Novelli, *Treasurer*
Frank J Novelli Jr, *Admin Sec*
EMP: 14
SQ FT: 12,000
SALES (est): 1.5MM **Privately Held**
WEB: www.banner-supply-inc.business.site
SIC: **2399** Banners, made from fabric

(G-8815)
BANNER TECHNOLOGY INC
Also Called: Chem Organics
959 Pleasantville Dr (77029-2431)
PHONE.....................713 675-3100
David Swallow, *President*
Tom Swallow, *Opers Spvr*
▲ EMP: 12
SQ FT: 24,000
SALES (est): 3.3MM **Privately Held**
WEB: www.chemorganics.com
SIC: 2899 Chemical preparations

(G-8816)
BAR YAM ENGINEERING INC
Also Called: Scorpion Hydraulic
13911 Faber St (77037-1921)
PHONE.....................281 999-8664
Avram Bar-Yam, *President*
EMP: 9
SQ FT: 4,000
SALES (est): 1MM **Privately Held**
WEB: www.scorpion.com
SIC: 3533 Oil & gas drilling rigs & equipment

(G-8817)
BARMALCO INC
Also Called: Barmalco Prcision Mch Tls Dies
12943 Old Richmond Rd (77099-2246)
PHONE.....................281 933-9128
Miguel Leanes, *President*
Monica Leanes, *Vice Pres*
EMP: 10
SQ FT: 12,000
SALES (est): 800K **Privately Held**
SIC: 3599 Machine shop, jobbing & repair

(G-8818)
BARRPORT PROPERTIES INC
(HQ)
Also Called: Reflection Printing
6131 Corporate Dr (77036-3409)
PHONE.....................713 271-2253
Mike Hensley, *President*
Jim White, *Opers Mgr*
◆ EMP: 12
SALES (est): 1.1MM
SALES (corp-wide): 2.4MM **Privately Held**
WEB: www.reflectionprint.com
SIC: 2752 Commercial printing, offset
PA: Arching Oaks Investments Ltd
6131 Corporate Dr
Houston TX 77036
713 271-2253

(G-8819)
BARTEC US CORPORATION
650 Century Plaza Dr # 120 (77073-6135)
PHONE.....................281 214-8542
Stefan Schaffer, *President*
Edgar Geissler, *CFO*
▲ EMP: 17
SALES (est): 4.1MM
SALES (corp-wide): 7.5MM **Privately Held**
WEB: www.bartecus.com
SIC: 3842 3644 Personal safety equipment; noncurrent-carrying wiring services
PA: Capvis Ag
Grabenstrasse 17
Baar ZG 6340
433 005-858

(G-8820)
BASE BASE CORPORATION
2746 Clay St (77003-4519)
PHONE.....................832 236-9801
G G Wu, *Principal*
EMP: 10
SALES (est): 941K **Privately Held**
SIC: 7372 Prepackaged software

(G-8821)
BASF CORPORATION
3120 Hayes Rd Ste 200 (77082-3180)
PHONE.....................800 794-1019
Andre Wehrmann, *Vice Pres*
David Armentor, *Project Mgr*
Santiago Gonzalez, *Project Mgr*
Brock Zauderer, *Opers Staff*
Sharon Scope, *Engineer*
EMP: 117
SALES (corp-wide): 65.6B **Privately Held**
WEB: www.basf.com
SIC: 2869 2819 2899 2843 Industrial organic chemicals; industrial inorganic chemicals; antifreeze compounds; surface active agents; pharmaceutical preparations; vitamin preparations; agricultural chemicals
HQ: Basf Corporation
100 Park Ave
Florham Park NJ 07932
973 245-6000

(G-8822)
BASF CORPORATION
1703 Crosspoint Ave (77054-3707)
PHONE.....................713 383-4500
Dennis Holbert, *President*
Steve Voller, *General Mgr*
Melinda Holbert, *Principal*
Javier Cuellar, *Opers Staff*
Muhammed Abbas, *Engineer*
EMP: 80
SALES (corp-wide): 65.6B **Privately Held**
WEB: www.basf.com
SIC: 2869 Industrial organic chemicals
HQ: Basf Corporation
100 Park Ave
Florham Park NJ 07932
973 245-6000

(G-8823)
BASTION TECHNOLOGIES INC
(PA)
17625 El Cmino Real Ste 3 (77058)
PHONE.....................281 283-9330
EMP: 25
SQ FT: 11,000
SALES (est): 37.6MM **Privately Held**
WEB: www.bastiontechnologies.com
SIC: 8711 1389 8733 Aviation &/or aeronautical engineering; construction, repair & dismantling services; physical research, noncommercial

(G-8824)
BATES AC & SVC CO INC
Also Called: Honeywell Authorized Dealer
620 Rankin Cir N (77073-4308)
PHONE.....................713 869-5521
Andrew Mahoney, *President*
Ann Mahoney, *Vice Pres*
Bill Sheppard, *Project Mgr*
Ann Mahony, *Office Mgr*
Ronnie Gill, *Manager*
EMP: 49
SQ FT: 28,800
SALES (est): 11MM **Privately Held**
WEB: www.batesac.com
SIC: 1711 3444 7623 Warm air heating & air conditioning contractor; ducts, sheet metal; refrigeration service & repair

(G-8825)
BATHSYSTEM AMERICA LLC
5301 Polk St Bldg 20 (77023-1453)
PHONE.....................713 382-8585
Riccardo Scionti,
EMP: 50
SALES (est): 96.8K **Privately Held**
SIC: 3448 Buildings, portable: prefabricated metal

(G-8826)
BATTALION OIL CORPORATION
(PA)
1000 La St Ste 6700 (77002)
PHONE.....................832 538-0300
Richard H Little, *CEO*
Laura Platon, *CEO*
Daniel P Rohling, *COO*
Daniel Rohling, *COO*
Jon C Wright, *COO*
EMP: 40
SALES: 65.5MM **Privately Held**
WEB: www.battalionoil.com
SIC: 1311 Crude petroleum production

(G-8827)
BATTERIES CONCORD
5875 W 34th St (77092-6401)
PHONE.....................281 931-4488
Solomon Sanchez, *Owner*
Osmond Padilla, *Opers Mgr*
EMP: 10
SALES (est): 605.4K **Privately Held**
WEB: www.concordbatterytex.com
SIC: 5063 3694 3537 Storage batteries, industrial; battery charging alternators & generators; forklift trucks

(G-8828)
BATTERSON IRON WORKS L L P
6800 Dixie Dr (77087-5135)
PHONE.....................713 688-5433
Erick Tiscareno, *Purch Mgr*
Bryan Duncan, *Controller*
Carlos Gonzales, *Manager*
David Hernandez, *Manager*
Scott Lewis, *Manager*
EMP: 100
SALES (est): 13.3MM **Privately Held**
WEB: www.batterson.com
SIC: 3441 1721 Fabricated structural metal; painting & paper hanging

(G-8829)
BATTERSON TRUCK EQUIPMENT LLC
5430 Killough St (77086-4012)
PHONE.....................281 598-6588
Dan Batterson,
Paula Mittelstedt,
EMP: 15
SALES (est): 4.9MM **Privately Held**
WEB: www.battersontruck.com
SIC: 5012 5013 3465 Truck bodies; truck parts & accessories; body parts, automobile: stamped metal

(G-8830)
BATTLE MOUNTAIN DOMINIAN REPUB
333 Clay St Fl 42 (77002-4000)
PHONE.....................713 655-1742
Eian Bayer, *President*
EMP: 50
SALES (est): 2.5MM
SALES (corp-wide): 9.7B **Publicly Held**
SIC: 1041 1044 Gold ores mining; gold ores processing; silver ores mining; silver ores processing
PA: Newmont Corporation
6900 E Layton Ave Ste 700
Denver CO 80237
303 863-7414

(G-8831)
BAUMANN PROPELLERS LLC
2309 Ssgt Mcrio Grcia Dr (77011-1207)
PHONE.....................713 714-5573
EMP: 12 EST: 2017
SALES (est): 69.7K **Privately Held**
WEB: www.baumannprops.com
SIC: 3366 Propellers

(G-8832)
BAWCO FABRICATORS INC
1159 Aldine Bender Rd (77032-2900)
P.O. Box 8, Broaddus (75929-0008)
PHONE.....................281 449-0171
Hallie R Barber, *President*
H E Barber, *Consultant*
Betty Barber, *Admin Sec*
EMP: 20
SQ FT: 14,200
SALES (est): 5.7MM **Privately Held**
WEB: www.bawcofab.com
SIC: 3441 Fabricated structural metal

(G-8833)
BAYOU BOUILLON OPERATING LLC
5120 Woodway Dr Ste 1014 (77056-1742)
PHONE.....................346 802-3134
Stacy Reeves, *Office Mgr*
Majid Jourabchi, *Mng Member*
EMP: 10
SALES (est): 744.2K **Privately Held**
SIC: 1382 Oil & gas exploration services

(G-8834)
BAYOU CITY LUMBER COMPANY
11106 Telephone Rd (77075-4524)
P.O. Box 41027 (77241-1027)
PHONE.....................713 991-2377
Jim Tingle, *General Mgr*
Warren Spencer, *Principal*
Randy Vaughn, *Vice Pres*
EMP: 18
SQ FT: 500
SALES (est): 8.8MM **Privately Held**
WEB: www.bayoucitylumber.com
SIC: 5031 2491 Lumber: rough, dressed & finished; structural lumber & timber, treated wood

(G-8835)
BAYOU IMAGING PRODUCTS LLC
829 S 75th St (77023-4301)
P.O. Box 9340 (77261-9340)
PHONE.....................713 923-8300
Francisco Cornejo, *Plant Mgr*
Chris Thompson, *Opers Mgr*
W Yandell Rogers Jr,
EMP: 18
SALES (est): 5MM **Privately Held**
WEB: www.bayouimaging.com
SIC: 2671 7389 Packaging paper & plastics film, coated & laminated; packaging & labeling services; design services

(G-8836)
BAYOU PROCESSING & STORAGE LP
13925 Industrial Rd (77015-6824)
P.O. Box 24127 (77229-4127)
PHONE.....................713 450-8401
Alberto Maldonado, *General Mgr*
John Shipley, *Supervisor*
EMP: 22
SQ FT: 125,000
SALES (est): 2.7MM **Privately Held**
WEB: www.bayoups.com
SIC: 4225 7694 General warehousing; coil winding service

(G-8837)
BAYPORT LABORATORIES LLC
(PA)
15864 W Hardy Rd Ste 710 (77060-3150)
PHONE.....................832 230-0480
Angie D Camacho, *Mng Member*
▲ EMP: 30 EST: 2010
SQ FT: 15,000
SALES (est): 2.3MM **Privately Held**
WEB: www.bayportlab.com
SIC: 2844 Face creams or lotions; hair coloring preparations; hair preparations, including shampoos

(G-8838)
BAYSIDE PRINTING INC
160 Lockhaven Dr (77073-5500)
P.O. Box 73687 (77273-3687)
PHONE.....................281 209-9500
Rose Mary Bundscho, *President*
Joe Bundscho, *General Mgr*
Terry Bundscho, *Vice Pres*
Josh Pedraza, *Purchasing*
Ray Rios, *Accounts Exec*
EMP: 30 EST: 1973
SQ FT: 25,000
SALES (est): 5MM **Privately Held**
WEB: www.baysideprinting.com
SIC: 2752 2791 Business form & card printing, lithographic; promotional printing, lithographic; typesetting

(G-8839)
BAYTEK INTERNATIONAL INC
16902 El Cam (77058)
PHONE.....................281 218-8880
Dan Richter, *CEO*
Patricia Richter, *Admin Sec*
EMP: 27
SQ FT: 25,000
SALES (est): 4.5MM **Privately Held**
WEB: www.baytekinternational.com
SIC: 7372 Prepackaged software

(G-8840)
BAYTEX ENERGY (USA) INC
5444 Westheimr Rd # 1000 (77056-5318)
PHONE.....................713 402-1920
Michael Berm, *President*
Raymond T Chan, *Chairman*
EMP: 34
SALES (est): 6.9MM
SALES (corp-wide): 1.1B **Privately Held**
SIC: 1382 Oil & gas exploration services

PA: Baytex Energy Corp
520 3 Ave Sw Suite 2800
Calgary AB T2P 0
587 952-3000

(G-8841)
BC JOHNSON ASSOC LLC
1080 Eldridge Pkwy # 1200 (77077-2576)
PHONE..................281 489-4894
Steven Butler, *Vice Pres*
Bob Kachnik, *Vice Pres*
Bruce French, *Project Mgr*
Bryan Johnson, *Manager*
Brian Johnson,
EMP: 9
SALES (est): 636.1K Privately Held
WEB: www.yorkrisk.com
SIC: 1389 Oil consultants

(G-8842)
BCS SYSTEMS INC
10300 Town Park Dr Se1 (77072-5236)
PHONE..................713 978-6511
Jonathan Gibson, *President*
Aditya Damera, *Associate*
EMP: 16
SQ FT: 8,000
SALES (est): 2.8MM Privately Held
WEB: www.bcssys.com
SIC: 7372 Prepackaged software

(G-8843)
BD ENERGY SYSTEMS LLC (PA)
1001 S Dar Ashford Ste 41 (77077)
PHONE..................281 407-9812
David Hawkins, *Chairman*
Andy Castell, *COO*
Greg Cargle, *Vice Pres*
John Drews, *Engineer*
Joe Price, *Engineer*
EMP: 34
SALES: 43.2MM Privately Held
WEB: www.bdenergysystems.com
SIC: 3559 Refinery, chemical processing &
similar machinery

(G-8844)
BDM METAL COATERS LLC
Also Called: Bdm Coil Coaters
13855 Industrial Rd (77015-6822)
P.O. Box 24745 (77229-4745)
PHONE..................713 400-2300
Stanley Katz, *Mng Member*
EMP: 82
SALES (est): 153.4K
SALES (corp-wide): 50.4B Privately Held
WEB: www.bdm-coilcoaters.com
SIC: 3479 Coating of metals & formed
products
HQ: Duferco Steel Inc.
100 Matawan Rd Ste 400
Matawan NJ 07747

(G-8845)
BEACON OFFSHORE ENRGY OPER LLC
333 Clay St Ste 4200 (77002-4006)
PHONE..................346 867-0509
Mark Hensel, *Mng Member*
EMP: 9
SALES (est): 114K Privately Held
WEB: www.beaconoffshore.com
SIC: 1382 Oil & gas exploration services

(G-8846)
BEAR PUMP & EQUIPMENT INC
9616 Telge Rd (77095-5113)
PHONE..................281 200-1000
Randall C Hinson, *President*
June Hinson, *Corp Secy*
▲ EMP: 10
SQ FT: 32,000
SALES (corp-wide): 8.4B Publicly Held
WEB: www.21925-us.all.biz
SIC: 5084 3586 Oil well machinery, equip-
ment & supplies; oil pumps, measuring or
dispensing
PA: National Oilwell Varco, Inc.
7909 Parkwood Circle Dr
Houston TX 77036
713 346-7500

(G-8847)
BEAUTY ELITE GROUP INC
Also Called: Blowpro
20411 Imperial Valley Dr (77073-5504)
PHONE..................800 619-1333
Basim Shami, *President*
Tony Rahmoun, *Vice Pres*
▲ EMP: 32
SQ FT: 67,000
SALES (est): 8.2MM Privately Held
WEB: www.beautyelitegroup.com
SIC: 2844 5122 Hair coloring prepara-
tions; cosmetics, perfumes & hair prod-
ucts

(G-8848)
BECKER INDUSTRIES INC
2712 Frank Rd (77032-3206)
PHONE..................281 590-4900
EMP: 10
SQ FT: 18,800
SALES (est): 1.6MM Privately Held
SIC: 3561 Mfg Pumps

(G-8849)
BECTON DICKINSON AND COMPANY
6428 Community Dr (77005-3519)
PHONE..................713 839-0753
Laura Sarlin, *Principal*
EMP: 379
SALES (corp-wide): 17.1B Publicly Held
WEB: www.bd.com
SIC: 3841 Hypodermic needles & syringes
PA: Becton, Dickinson And Company
1 Becton Dr
Franklin Lakes NJ 07417
201 847-6800

(G-8850)
BEDROCK PRODUCTION LLC
Also Called: Bedrock Energy Partners
820 Gessner Rd Ste 1100 (77024-4265)
PHONE..................281 786-0220
EMP: 44
SALES (est): 154.2K Privately Held
WEB: www.bedrockep.com
SIC: 1389 Oil field services

(G-8851)
BEECO MOTORS & CONTROLS INC
5630 Guhn Rd Ste 110 (77040-6144)
PHONE..................832 320-3100
Jennifer M Claridg, *President*
Gary H Muslin, *Principal*
Eilleen Muslin, *Corp Secy*
Danny Muslin, *Opers Mgr*
William Sheats, *Engineer*
▲ EMP: 25
SQ FT: 40,000
SALES (est): 15.7MM Privately Held
WEB: www.beecomc.com
SIC: 5063 3613 Electrical supplies;
switchgear & switchboard apparatus

(G-8852)
BEICIP INC
1880 S Dairy Ashford Rd # 630
(77077-4781)
PHONE..................281 293-8550
Jean-Louis Gelot, *President*
Pierre Yves Chenet, *President*
EMP: 13
SQ FT: 4,500
SALES (est): 5MM
SALES (corp-wide): 45.4MM Privately
Held
WEB: www.beicip.com
SIC: 7372 7379 Prepackaged software;
computer related consulting services
HQ: Beicip-Franlab
232 Avenue Napoleon Bonaparte
Rueil Malmaison 92500
141 390-715

(G-8853)
BELLICUM PHARMACEUTICALS INC (PA)
2710 Reed Rd Ste 160 (77051-2558)
PHONE..................832 384-1100
James F Brown, *Ch of Bd*
Richard A Fair, *President*
Aaron A Foster, *Senior VP*
Aaron Foster, *Vice Pres*

Ken Roberts, *Project Mgr*
EMP: 79
SALES: 7.1MM Publicly Held
WEB: www.bellicum.com
SIC: 2834 2836 Pharmaceutical prepara-
tions; biological products, except diagnos-
tic

(G-8854)
BELLOWS SYSTEMS INC
Also Called: BSI
11981 Fm 529 Rd (77041-3017)
PHONE..................281 721-2947
Ronald Smith, *Manager*
EMP: 14
SALES (corp-wide): 4.4MM Privately
Held
WEB: www.bellows-systems.com
SIC: 3441 3599 Fabricated structural
metal; bellows, industrial: metal
PA: Bellows Systems, Inc.
701 W Murphy St
Odessa TX 79763
432 333-4600

(G-8855)
BELTRAN BROTHERS FABRICATION
11826 Connor St (77039-6304)
PHONE..................281 987-2331
Jesus Martinez, *Owner*
EMP: 25
SALES (est): 3.1MM Privately Held
WEB: www.beltranbros.com
SIC: 3441 Fabricated structural metal

(G-8856)
BEND-IT INC
6120 Nunn St (77087-5125)
PHONE..................713 991-0745
Thomas Young, *President*
EMP: 14
SQ FT: 21,000
SALES (est): 2.5MM Privately Held
WEB: www.benditinc.com
SIC: 3441 Fabricated structural metal

(G-8857)
BENNINGFELD STL FBRICATION LLC
901 Marcella St (77091-5647)
PHONE..................832 831-3691
Keith Benningfield, *Mng Member*
Glenn Benningfield,
EMP: 11 EST: 2012
SALES (est): 2.5MM Privately Held
SIC: 3441 Fabricated structural metal

(G-8858)
BENTONITE PERFORMANCE MNRL LLC (HQ)
Also Called: Bet Minerals
3000 N Sam Houston Pkwy E
(77032-3219)
PHONE..................281 871-7900
Jeffrey Allen Miller, *President*
Charles A Geer, *Vice Pres*
Christian A Garcia, *CFO*
Bruce A Metzinger, *Admin Sec*
◆ EMP: 15
SALES (est): 45.9MM Publicly Held
WEB: www.bentonite.com
SIC: 3295 Clay, ground or otherwise
treated

(G-8859)
BEP OILFIELD LTD
12941 North Fwy Ste 520 (77060-1243)
PHONE..................281 873-9100
Larry J Karambis, *Mng Member*
EMP: 15
SALES (est): 5.4MM Privately Held
SIC: 1389 Oil field services
PA: Bison Energy Partners, Inc.
13700 Veterans Mem Dr 4
Houston TX 77014
281 873-9100

(G-8860)
BERGER IRON WORKS INC
8107 W Little York Rd (77040-5315)
PHONE..................713 869-7386
Joseph J Rigano, *President*
Belk Null, *General Mgr*
Todd Dawson, *Superintendent*

William N Carbery, *Corp Secy*
G W Eckhardt, *Vice Pres*
EMP: 45 EST: 1893
SQ FT: 37,200
SALES (est): 6.9MM Privately Held
WEB: www.bergeriron.com
SIC: 3211 3446 Skylight glass; stairs, fire
escapes, balconies, railings & ladders

(G-8861)
BERRIDGE MANUFACTURING COMPANY
1720 Maury St (77026-7199)
PHONE..................713 223-4971
Todd Baker, *COO*
Mark Tice, *Regl Sales Mgr*
Glenn Antle, *Branch Mgr*
Stacy Canales, *Manager*
Cathy Lane, *Coordinator*
EMP: 13
SALES (corp-wide): 59.5MM Privately
Held
WEB: www.berridge.com
SIC: 3479 3444 Coating of metals &
formed products; metal roofing & roof
drainage equipment
PA: Berridge Manufacturing Company, Inc
6515 Fratt Rd
San Antonio TX 78218
210 650-7056

(G-8862)
BEST DRILLING SERVICES (BDS)
925 W 20th St (77008-3309)
PHONE..................713 864-3900
Doreen Firouzbakht, *President*
EMP: 20 Privately Held
WEB: www.bestdrilling.com
SIC: 3731 8748 Drilling & production plat-
forms, floating (oil & gas); environmental
consultant
PA: Best Drilling Services (Bds), Inc
925 W 20th St
Houston TX 77008

(G-8863)
BEST LETTER PRESS INC
5853 W 34th St (77092-6401)
PHONE..................713 123-4567
Ernie Salazar, *President*
EMP: 9
SQ FT: 6,500
SALES (est): 560K Privately Held
WEB: www.bestletterpress.com
SIC: 2759 Commercial printing

(G-8864)
BETA OPERATING COMPANY LLC (DH)
Also Called: Beta Offshore
500 Dallas St Ste 1600 (77002-4729)
PHONE..................562 628-8900
Dickie Hunter,
EMP: 24
SQ FT: 15,000
SALES: 20.4MM
SALES (corp-wide): 275.5MM Publicly
Held
WEB: www.betaoffshore.com
SIC: 1311 Crude petroleum production
HQ: Amplify Energy Holdings Llc
500 Dallas St Ste 1600
Houston TX 77002
713 490-8900

(G-8865)
BETA TECHNOLOGY INC
16810 Barker Springs Rd (77084-5094)
P.O. Box 218686 (77218-8686)
PHONE..................281 647-9700
Michael Quammen, *CEO*
EMP: 45
SQ FT: 13,000
SALES (est): 8.2MM Privately Held
WEB: www.betatechnologyinc.com
SIC: 2842 Specialty cleaning, polishes &
sanitation goods

(G-8866)
BETTER BAGS INC
Also Called: Bbi
6419 Toledo St (77008-6226)
PHONE..................713 864-8200
Rafael Alvarado, *President*

Pedro Monterrosa, *Maint Spvr*
Albert Strausser, *Info Tech Mgr*
Charles Weller, *Director*
Christine Marlett, *Admin Sec*
▲ EMP: 25
SQ FT: 61,000
SALES (est): 6.1MM **Privately Held**
WEB: www.betterbags.com
SIC: 2673 Plastic bags: made from purchased materials

(G-8867)
BETTER BURGLAR BARS INC
Also Called: Ross Metal Works
1910 Turner Dr Apt C (77093-6146)
PHONE......................................713 699-9543
Barry D Ross, *President*
EMP: 30
SALES (est): 2.4MM **Privately Held**
WEB: www.rossmetalworks.com
SIC: 1799 3462 Screening contractor: window, door, etc.; iron & steel forgings

(G-8868)
BG BRASILIA LLC
Also Called: Bg Group
910 Louisiana St (77002-4916)
PHONE......................................713 599-4000
Chris Finlayson, *CEO*
John Fontenot, *Opers Mgr*
Chris Hill, *Opers Staff*
◆ EMP: 10
SALES (est): 1.3MM
SALES (corp-wide): 344.8B **Privately Held**
WEB: www.bggroupplace.com
SIC: 1311 Crude petroleum & natural gas production
HQ: Bg Group Limited
Shell Centre
London SE1 7

(G-8869)
BG ENERGY MERCHANTS LLC
Also Called: Bgem
811 Main St Ste 3400 (77002-6131)
PHONE......................................713 599-4000
Elizabeth Spomer, *President*
Barbara Heim, *Vice Pres*
Ryan Hodgkinson, *Vice Pres*
Michael Mott, *Vice Pres*
Sameh Serour, *Prdtn Mgr*
▲ EMP: 400
SALES (est): 17.7MM
SALES (corp-wide): 344.8B **Privately Held**
SIC: 1321 Natural gas liquids
HQ: Bg Group Limited
Shell Centre
London SE1 7

(G-8870)
BG LNG SERVICES LLC
Also Called: Bg LNG Trading
811 Main St Ste 2100 (77002-6128)
PHONE......................................713 599-4000
Renee Klimczak, *Mng Member*
John Boardman,
Martin Houston,
Christopher Micklas,
Anita Odedra,
▲ EMP: 100
SALES (est): 7.8MM
SALES (corp-wide): 344.8B **Privately Held**
WEB: www.811main.com
SIC: 1321 Natural gas liquids
HQ: Bg Group Limited
Shell Centre
London SE1 7

(G-8871)
BGRS INC
9318 Reid Lake Dr (77064-7750)
PHONE......................................281 890-6862
Frank Cmajdalka, *President*
Peter Berveiler, *President*
J R Quisenberry, *Vice Pres*
Marty Boros, *Manager*
EMP: 17
SQ FT: 25,500
SALES (est): 4.8MM **Privately Held**
WEB: www.bgrsinc.com
SIC: 3444 Sheet metalwork

(G-8872)
BGS INDUSTRIES INC
11155 Windfern Rd (77064-4807)
P.O. Box 272922 (77277-2922)
PHONE......................................281 970-4118
Clifford Shedd, *President*
Bob Burke, *Partner*
John Keife, *Partner*
Adolph B Wischnewsky, *Partner*
EMP: 22
SQ FT: 15,000
SALES: 6.5MM **Privately Held**
WEB: www.bgsindustries.com
SIC: 3599 Machine shop, jobbing & repair

(G-8873)
BHI LLC
11111 Forbes Rd (77075-2817)
PHONE......................................713 644-2431
David Brader,
EMP: 10
SALES (est): 374.3K **Privately Held**
WEB: www.bhicorporation.com
SIC: 3599 Machine & other job shop work

(G-8874)
BHL INTERNATIONAL INC
5223 Hopper Rd (77093-2243)
PHONE......................................281 449-5762
Reuel Lataquin, *President*
Lorna A Lataquin, *Principal*
Lataquin Barron, *Vice Pres*
David Drown, *Vice Pres*
Barron H Lataquin, *Vice Pres*
EMP: 45
SALES (est): 20.8MM **Privately Held**
WEB: www.bhlinternational.com
SIC: 3546 3499 Drills & drilling tools; fire- or burglary-resistive products

(G-8875)
BHP BILLITON PETRO N AMER INC (HQ)
1500 Post Oak Blvd (77056-3004)
PHONE......................................713 961-8500
Mr Chip Goodyear, *CEO*
J Michael Yeager, *President*
Lisa Haskell, *Vice Pres*
Julye Nugent, *Vice Pres*
James Wear, *Vice Pres*
▲ EMP: 225
SQ FT: 90,000
SALES (est): 2.2B **Privately Held**
WEB: www.bhp.com
SIC: 1311 4922 Crude petroleum production; natural gas production; pipelines, natural gas

(G-8876)
BHP BLLTON PETRO DEEPWATER INC
1500 Post Oak Blvd (77056-3004)
PHONE......................................713 961-8500
James Michael Yeager, *CEO*
Malcolm Brinded, *Principal*
Malcolm Broomhead, *Principal*
Jac Nasser, *Chairman*
Douglas Dale Handyside, *Vice Pres*
▲ EMP: 11
SALES (est): 8.9MM **Privately Held**
WEB: www.bhp.com
SIC: 1382 Oil & gas exploration services
PA: Bhp Group Limited
L 18 171 Collins St
Melbourne VIC 3000

(G-8877)
BHP MINERAL RESOURCES INC
1360 Post Oak Blvd # 150 (77056-3030)
PHONE......................................713 961-8500
Paul Anderson, *CEO*
EMP: 79
SALES (est): 519.3K **Privately Held**
SIC: 1222 Bituminous coal-underground mining
HQ: Bhp Billiton Petroleum (North America) Inc.
1500 Post Oak Blvd
Houston TX 77056
713 961-8500

(G-8878)
BHP MINERALS INTERNATIONAL LLC (HQ)
1500 Post Oak Blvd (77056-3004)
PHONE......................................713 961-8500
Earl K Moore, *President*
Daivd Braley, *Treasurer*
James Bowling, *Manager*
Vandita Pant, *Officer*
Athalie Williams, *Officer*
◆ EMP: 300 EST: 1956
SALES (est): 1B **Privately Held**
WEB: www.bhp.com
SIC: 1222 1011 1021 Bituminous coal-underground mining; underground iron ore mining; copper ores

(G-8879)
BICO DRILLING TOOLS INC (DH)
4667 Kennedy Commerce Dr (77032-3432)
PHONE......................................832 598-9200
Sam Claytor, *President*
Steven Robinson, *Business Mgr*
Mike Watson, *Business Mgr*
Rocky Seale, *Vice Pres*
Paul Stoll, *Vice Pres*
▲ EMP: 30
SQ FT: 18,792
SALES (est): 42.1MM
SALES (corp-wide): 2.6MM **Privately Held**
WEB: www.bicodrillingtools.com
SIC: 1389 Oil field services
HQ: Schoeller-Bleckmann Oilfield Equipment Aktiengesellschaft
HauptstraBe 2
Ternitz 2630
263 031-50

(G-8880)
BIG 6 DRILLING COMPANY
7500 San Felipe St # 250 (77063-1700)
PHONE......................................713 783-2300
Chester B Benge Jr, *President*
Jack Burnett, *Superintendent*
Michael Stone, *Principal*
M D Stone, *Vice Pres*
Mike Stone, *Vice Pres*
EMP: 40 EST: 1945
SQ FT: 3,200
SALES (est): 9.4MM **Privately Held**
WEB: www.big6drilling.com
SIC: 1381 Directional drilling oil & gas wells

(G-8881)
BIG CITY MANUFACTURING INC
7561 Morley St (77061-2828)
P.O. Box 262553 (77207-2553)
PHONE......................................713 649-7769
M Wayne Brueggeman, *President*
Kevin Brueggeman, *Production*
David Brueggeman, *Treasurer*
EMP: 18 EST: 1976
SQ FT: 10,000
SALES (est): 3.1MM **Privately Held**
WEB: www.metaltags.com
SIC: 3999 Identification badges & insignia

(G-8882)
BIG LAKE FUELS LLC
600 Travis St Ste 3680 (77002-2995)
PHONE......................................713 943-2200
Tim Vail, *CEO*
EMP: 26
SALES (est): 3.3MM
SALES (corp-wide): 533.7K **Privately Held**
WEB: www.g2xenergy.com
SIC: 2899 Chemical preparations
HQ: Proman Usa, Inc.
600 Travis St Ste 3680
Houston TX 77002
713 943-2200

(G-8883)
BIG M CONSTRUCTORS INC
10200 Windfern Rd (77064-5815)
PHONE......................................281 469-9770
B J Maciejeski, *President*
Pat A Maciejeski, *Corp Secy*
EMP: 49 EST: 1979

SALES (est): 15MM **Privately Held**
WEB: www.bigmconstructorsinc.trustab.org
SIC: 1541 3441 1731 Industrial buildings, new construction; renovation, remodeling & repairs: industrial buildings; fabricated structural metal; electrical work

(G-8884)
BIG RED INC
2400 Holly Hall St (77054-3904)
PHONE......................................713 791-9886
Nancy Albitar, *Supervisor*
EMP: 9
SALES (corp-wide): 57.5MM **Privately Held**
WEB: www.bigred.com
SIC: 2086 Soft drinks: packaged in cans, bottles, etc.
PA: Big Red, Inc.
7208 Cielo Azul Pass
Austin TX 78732
512 501-3890

(G-8885)
BILL WEST PROPERTIES INC
11800 Fairmont St (77035-6556)
P.O. Box 31729 (77231-1729)
PHONE......................................713 726-0151
Bill West, *President*
Wanda West, *Vice Pres*
Wynette Stone, *Treasurer*
Randy West, *Admin Sec*
EMP: 20
SQ FT: 13,000
SALES (est): 2.2MM **Privately Held**
SIC: 3564 3533 5084 Blowers & fans; drill rigs; industrial machinery & equipment

(G-8886)
BIOGENIX LLC
2800 Post Oak Blvd (77056-6100)
PHONE......................................888 418-7172
Abey Gideon, *Manager*
EMP: 20
SALES (est): 1.5MM **Privately Held**
WEB: www.biogenix.com
SIC: 3069 Medical & laboratory rubber sundries & related products

(G-8887)
BIOTOOL LLC
9330 Kirby Dr Ste 200 (77054-2595)
P.O. Box 300287 (77230-0287)
PHONE......................................713 732-2181
Graham Dong, *Vice Pres*
EMP: 10
SQ FT: 2,900
SALES (est): 951.7K **Privately Held**
WEB: www.bimake.com
SIC: 2834 7389 Pharmaceutical preparations; business services

(G-8888)
BIRACTUAL LLC
10700 Richmond Ave # 310 (77042-4925)
PHONE......................................713 623-5099
Justin Dennis,
EMP: 10
SALES (est): 404.7K **Privately Held**
SIC: 7372 Prepackaged software

(G-8889)
BIRCH B LLC
Also Called: Deluxe Honeydrop
1223 Wynden Commons Ln (77056-2538)
PHONE......................................646 942-8058
David Luks,
▼ EMP: 16
SALES (est): 1.7MM **Privately Held**
SIC: 2086 Carbonated beverages, nonalcoholic: bottled & canned

(G-8890)
BIRCH OPERATIONS INC (PA)
909 Fannin St Ste 1350 (77010-1042)
PHONE......................................832 701-1776
Kyle R Miller, *CEO*
Jason R Cansler, *President*
David M Frazier, *Vice Pres*
Brian F Harper, *Vice Pres*
Julien R Smythe, *Vice Pres*
EMP: 12
SALES (est): 3.3MM **Privately Held**
SIC: 1389 Cementing oil & gas well casings

(G-8891)
BIRCH PLASTICS INC
5957 South Loop E (77033-1017)
PHONE................................713 433-1898
Robert J Lang, *President*
Brandon Cleary, *Vice Pres*
Collin Howell, *Accounts Mgr*
Paul Wilson, *Manager*
◆ EMP: 25
SQ FT: 33,000
SALES (est): 10MM **Privately Held**
WEB: www.birchplastics.com
SIC: 2821 Plastics materials & resins

(G-8892)
BISE WELDING & FABRICATING INC
1900 De Soto St (77091-3927)
PHONE................................713 681-0958
Kelly Bise, *President*
Mike Marsh, *Vice Pres*
Sue Lee, *Human Resources*
Tammy Marsh, *Admin Sec*
EMP: 80
SQ FT: 65,000
SALES (est): 18.1MM **Privately Held**
WEB: www.bisewelding.com
SIC: 3547 7692 5051 3444 Plate rolling mill machinery; welding repair; pipe & tubing, steel; pipe, sheet metal; pipe, large diameter; metal plate

(G-8893)
BISN OIL TOOLS LLC (PA)
4514 Brittmoore Rd (77041-8006)
PHONE................................832 919-7500
Paul Deutch, *President*
Denna Gatewood, *QC Mgr*
Subhra Dey, *Engineer*
Dawn Carragher, *Controller*
Carragher Dawn, *Controller*
EMP: 32 EST: 2014
SALES (est): 15.4MM **Privately Held**
WEB: www.bisn.com
SIC: 1389 Oil field services

(G-8894)
BISON ENERGY PARTNERS INC (PA)
13700 Veterans Mem Dr 4 (77014-1026)
PHONE................................281 873-9100
Larry J Karambis, *President*
R M Rayburn Sr, *Vice Pres*
EMP: 17
SALES (est): 5.4MM **Privately Held**
WEB: www.bisonenergy.com
SIC: 1389 Gas field services

(G-8895)
BITCOIN CRYPTO CRRNCY EXCH COR
Also Called: Amsr
19 Briar Hollow Ln # 125 (77027-2819)
PHONE................................713 465-1001
Frank Neukomm, *Ch of Bd*
Robert C Farr, *President*
Ben Schafer, *President*
Mike Cherry, *Vice Pres*
Randall Newton, *CFO*
EMP: 12 EST: 2004
SQ FT: 1,600
SALES (est): 1.3MM **Privately Held**
SIC: 3629 Electrochemical generators (fuel cells)

(G-8896)
BIZTEL LP
1235 North Loop W Ste 400 (77008-4702)
PHONE................................713 600-2600
EMP: 12
SALES (est): 368.3K **Privately Held**
SIC: 4911 3679 7389 Mfg Electronic Components Business Services

(G-8897)
BK CORROSION LLC
4411 Navigation Blvd (77011-1035)
PHONE................................713 225-6661
Jagdish Desai, *Ch of Bd*
Brent Bertrand, *President*
Brenda Renteria, *Controller*
▼ EMP: 33
SQ FT: 38,347

SALES (est): 20MM **Privately Held**
WEB: www.bkcorrosion.com
SIC: 3549 Wiredrawing & fabricating machinery & equipment, ex. die

(G-8898)
BK POWER SYSTEMS LLC
601 Century Plaza Dr (77073-6008)
PHONE................................713 225-6661
Dale Betz, *Vice Pres*
EMP: 10
SALES (est): 2.2MM
SALES (corp-wide): 11.1MM **Privately Held**
WEB: www.bkpowersystems.com
SIC: 3568 Clutches, except vehicular
PA: Integrated Corrosion Companies, Inc.
601 Century Plaza Dr
Houston TX 77073
713 789-9181

(G-8899)
BLACK & DECKER CORPORATION
10245 W Little York Rd # 300 (77040-2937)
PHONE................................713 466-1194
Scott Newman, *Manager*
EMP: 21
SQ FT: 8,000
SALES (corp-wide): 14.4B **Publicly Held**
WEB: www.blackanddecker.com
SIC: 3546 Power-driven handtools
HQ: The Black & Decker Corporation
701 E Joppa Rd
Towson MD 21286
410 716-3900

(G-8900)
BLACK BOX CORPORATION
5959 Corp Dr Ste 250ll (77036)
P.O. Box 4516 (77210-4516)
PHONE................................713 307-4000
Zelda Howell, *Principal*
Sheila Fresquez, *Human Res Mgr*
Randy Philips, *Manager*
Catherine McCallum, *Supervisor*
Rigo Ramirez, *Analyst*
EMP: 11 **Privately Held**
WEB: www.blackbox.com
SIC: 3577 Computer peripheral equipment
HQ: Black Box Corporation
1000 Park Dr
Lawrence PA 15055
724 746-5500

(G-8901)
BLACK DIAMOND MINERALS LLC
500 Dallas St Ste 1800 (77002-2067)
PHONE................................720 341-2212
Scott D Hall, *CEO*
Jamey Brumley, *Vice Pres*
Shirley Kovar, *Vice Pres*
Ward Giltner, *CFO*
EMP: 9
SALES (est): 727.7K **Privately Held**
WEB: www.blackstoneminerals.com
SIC: 1382 Oil & gas exploration services

(G-8902)
BLACK ELK ENERGY LLC (PA)
3100 S Gessner Rd Ste 215 (77063-3744)
PHONE................................281 507-7652
Bernard Huizenga, *Business Mgr*
Bruce Koch, *CFO*
John Hoffman, *Mng Member*
James Hagemeier, *Mng Member*
John Haufman,
EMP: 25
SQ FT: 5,000
SALES (est): 6MM **Privately Held**
WEB: www.blackelkenergy.com
SIC: 1389 Gas compressing (natural gas) at the fields

(G-8903)
BLACK ELK ENERGY OFFSHORE OPER
842 W Sam Houston Pkwy N # 500 (77024-4591)
PHONE................................832 973-4230
John Hoffman, *CEO*
Terry Clark, *Exec VP*
James Hagemeier, *CFO*

EMP: 10
SALES: 258MM **Privately Held**
WEB: www.blackelkenergy.com
SIC: 1389 Oil field services; gas field services

(G-8904)
BLACK HORSE LLC
9950 W Gulf Bank Rd (77040-3118)
P.O. Box 40249 (77240-0249)
PHONE................................281 598-8100
Frank Wierengo, *General Mgr*
Brian Lenhart, *Buyer*
Beth Moniuszko, *Purchasing*
Douglas Oberhelman, *Mng Member*
Matthew Morse, *Manager*
EMP: 15
SALES (est): 7.5MM **Privately Held**
WEB: www.blackhorsepumps.com
SIC: 3533 Oil & gas field machinery

(G-8905)
BLACK LEMON MEDIA INC
3702 Cypress Creek Steo (77068)
P.O. Box 130144, Spring (77393-0144)
PHONE................................832 666-6600
Jesse Black, *CEO*
EMP: 10
SALES (est): 420.4K **Privately Held**
SIC: 2741

(G-8906)
BLACK STONE ENERGY COMPANY LLC
Also Called: Black Stone Holdings Partnr
1001 Fannin St Ste 2020 (77002-6715)
PHONE................................713 658-0647
Mark Robinson, *Vice Pres*
Randi Collins, *Director*
Thomas L Carter Jr,
Marshall Eubank,
Joseph Mills,
EMP: 30
SALES (est): 5.1MM
SALES (corp-wide): 487.8MM **Publicly Held**
WEB: www.blackstoneminerals.com
SIC: 1311 1382 Crude petroleum production; oil & gas exploration services
PA: Black Stone Minerals, L.P.
1001 Fannin St Ste 2020
Houston TX 77002
713 445-3200

(G-8907)
BLACK STONE MINERALS LP (PA)
1001 Fannin St Ste 2020 (77002-6715)
PHONE................................713 445-3200
Thomas L Carter Jr, *Ch of Bd*
Jeffrey P Wood, *President*
Jeff Wood, *Partner*
Black Stone Minerals GP, *General Ptnr*
Luke Putman, *General Ptnr*
EMP: 25
SQ FT: 55,862
SALES: 487.8MM **Publicly Held**
WEB: www.blackstoneminerals.com
SIC: 1382 Oil & gas exploration services

(G-8908)
BLACK STONE MINERALS CO LP (PA)
1001 Fannin St Ste 2020 (77002-6715)
PHONE................................713 658-0647
Thomas Carter Jr, *Managing Prtnr*
Marc Carroll, *Partner*
Samuel Crabb, *Partner*
Hallie Vanderhider, *Partner*
Mark Harmon, *Senior VP*
EMP: 13 EST: 1956
SQ FT: 1,500
SALES (est): 3.9MM **Privately Held**
WEB: www.blackstoneminerals.com
SIC: 1382 Oil & gas exploration services

(G-8909)
BLACK STONE NTRAL RSOURCES MGT
1001 Fannin St Ste 2020 (77002-6715)
PHONE................................713 445-3241
EMP: 12

EMP: 10
SALES (est): 331.1K
SALES (corp-wide): 487.8MM **Publicly Held**
WEB: www.blackstoneminerals.com
SIC: 1382 Oil & gas exploration services
PA: Black Stone Minerals, L.P.
1001 Fannin St Ste 2020
Houston TX 77002
713 445-3200

(G-8910)
BLACKBURN MACHINE & FAB LLC
7525 Wynlea St (77061-2833)
PHONE................................713 644-2386
Jerry S O Brien, *President*
John Tonsall, *General Mgr*
EMP: 23
SQ FT: 17,890
SALES (est): 4.5MM **Privately Held**
SIC: 3444 7692 3599 Sheet metal specialties, not stamped; welding repair; machine shop, jobbing & repair

(G-8911)
BLACKSTAR ENVMTL INDUS SVCS LL
505 N Sam Houston Pkwy E (77060-4018)
PHONE................................713 280-0590
Jason Miller,
EMP: 15
SALES (est): 266.3K **Privately Held**
SIC: 1389 Oil consultants

(G-8912)
BLACKWELL PLASTICS LP
5606 Cavanaugh St (77021-3802)
PHONE................................713 643-6577
Karen Blackwell, *Owner*
Jeff Applegate,
Ld Blackwell,
Scott Kelley,
▲ EMP: 50 EST: 1939
SQ FT: 90,000
SALES (est): 9.5MM **Privately Held**
WEB: www.blackwellplastics.com
SIC: 3089 3544 Injection molded finished plastic products; special dies, tools, jigs & fixtures

(G-8913)
BLAZE SALES AND SERVICE INC
7824 Scott St (77051-1644)
PHONE................................713 828-1685
Paul Abad, *Principal*
EMP: 10 EST: 2018
SALES (est): 824.7K **Privately Held**
WEB: www.blazess.com
SIC: 1389 4922 Pipe testing, oil field service; natural gas transmission

(G-8914)
BLENTECH CORPORATION
1305 Rye St (77029-3199)
PHONE................................713 673-3436
George A Hahn, *President*
Nancy Hahn, *Treasurer*
▲ EMP: 30 EST: 1977
SQ FT: 40,000
SALES (est): 7MM **Privately Held**
WEB: www.blentech.org
SIC: 2899 Chemical preparations

(G-8915)
BLESS OILFIELD SERVICES INC (PA)
6301 Mount Houston Rd (77050-5513)
P.O. Box 23716 (77228-3716)
PHONE................................281 227-3300
Ramiro B Garza Jr, *CEO*
EMP: 23
SALES: 5.9MM **Privately Held**
WEB: www.blessoilfield.com
SIC: 1389 Oil field services

(G-8916)
BLP SETTLEMENT COMPANY (DH)
125 Mccarty St (77029-1135)
PHONE................................713 674-2266
Jeff Bishop, *President*
Rebecca Bishop Piro, *Corp Secy*
Derrick J Deakins, *Vice Pres*
Armando Pineda, *Opers Mgr*

◆ **EMP:** 100
SQ FT: 46,000
SALES (est): 202.9MM
SALES (corp-wide): 3.1B **Privately Held**
WEB: www.lifting.com
SIC: 5085 3496 Industrial supplies; slings, lifting: made from purchased wire
HQ: Sbp Holding Lp
    125 Mccarty St
    Houston TX 77029
    713 953-1113

(G-8917)
BLUE BELL ENERGY LLC
8955 Katy Fwy Ste 310 (77024-1678)
PHONE.................................713 661-1040
James Trippon, *Mng Member*
EMP: 10 **EST:** 2014
SALES (est): 593.3K **Privately Held**
SIC: 1311 Crude petroleum & natural gas

(G-8918)
BLUE CHIP MANUFACTURING INC
2330 Wirtcrest Ln (77055-1338)
PHONE.................................713 683-1555
Albert Kopesky, *President*
Robert Henkhaus, *Vice Pres*
EMP: 10
SQ FT: 10,000
SALES (est): 1.5MM **Privately Held**
SIC: 3599 Machine shop, jobbing & repair

(G-8919)
BLUE MOUNTAIN MIDSTREAM LLC (HQ)
717 Texas St Ste 2000 (77002-2854)
PHONE.................................281 377-8770
Mark E Ellis, *CEO*
Arden L Walker Jr, *COO*
Thomas Emmons, *Vice Pres*
Jamin McNeil, *Vice Pres*
Candice J Wells, *Vice Pres*
EMP: 15 **EST:** 1991
SALES (est): 9.8MM
SALES (corp-wide): 479.7MM **Publicly Held**
WEB: www.bluemountainmidstream.com
SIC: 1311 Crude petroleum & natural gas
PA: Riviera Resources, Inc.
    717 Texas St Ste 2000
    Houston TX 77002
    281 840-4000

(G-8920)
BLUE STAR LTD
15603 Kuykendahl Rd # 219 (77090-3654)
PHONE.................................281 893-6035
EMP: 20
SQ FT: 1,300
SALES (est): 1.7MM **Privately Held**
SIC: 1311 Crude Petroleum/Natural Gas Production

(G-8921)
BLUE THUMB INC
Also Called: Houston House & Home
2414 Woodhead St (77019-6740)
P.O. Box 131845 (77219-1845)
PHONE.................................713 523-6523
Mike Harrison, *Publisher*
Tim Beeson, *Principal*
Christina Garza, *Accounts Exec*
Michael Harrison, *Admin Sec*
EMP: 22
SQ FT: 3,000
SALES (est): 550K **Privately Held**
WEB: www.houstonhouseandhome.net
SIC: 2721 Magazines: publishing only, not printed on site

(G-8922)
BLUEBONNET INDUSTRIAL BRUSH CO
8302 La Porte Rd (77012-3795)
P.O. Box 5452 (77262-5452)
PHONE.................................713 923-2855
Jerry S O'Brien, *President*
Jerry O'Brien, *Safety Mgr*
EMP: 13
SQ FT: 7,100
SALES (est): 1.2MM **Privately Held**
SIC: 3991 Brushes, household or industrial

(G-8923)
BLUMENTHAL INC
Also Called: Blumenthal Sheet Metal Company
1710 Burnett St (77026-7213)
PHONE.................................713 228-6432
William C Lipscomb, *President*
EMP: 35 **EST:** 1905
SQ FT: 85,000
SALES (est): 7.4MM **Privately Held**
WEB: www.blumenthalsheetmetal.com
SIC: 3444 Sheet metal specialties, not stamped

(G-8924)
BMC SOFTWARE INC (PA)
2103 Citywest Blvd # 2100 (77042-2857)
PHONE.................................713 918-8800
Ayman Sayed, *CEO*
Jim Schaper, *Ch of Bd*
Bill Berutti, *President*
Michelle Carbone, *President*
Terry Gast, *President*
▲ **EMP:** 1464
SQ FT: 570,000
SALES (est): 1.4B **Privately Held**
WEB: www.bmc.com
SIC: 7372 7371 Business oriented computer software; custom computer programming services

(G-8925)
BMC SOFTWARE FEDERAL LLC
2103 Citywest Blvd # 2100 (77042-2857)
PHONE.................................713 918-8800
Brian Trevor, *President*
Cuong Nguyen, *Regional Mgr*
Brian Marvin, *Vice Pres*
Robert Mosley, *Vice Pres*
Chris Stauber, *Vice Pres*
EMP: 10 **EST:** 2013
SALES (est): 1MM
SALES (corp-wide): 1.4B **Privately Held**
WEB: www.bmc.com
SIC: 7372 Prepackaged software
PA: Bmc Software, Inc.
    2103 Citywest Blvd # 2100
    Houston TX 77042
    713 918-8800

(G-8926)
BMF OIL & GAS SERVICES INC
9006 Fawnshadow Ct (77064-7757)
PHONE.................................832 443-2089
David A Flores, *CFO*
EMP: 12 **EST:** 2014
SALES (est): 302K **Privately Held**
SIC: 1389 1711 1721 1731 Gas field services; oil field services; mechanical contractor; painting & paper hanging; electrical work; insulation, buildings

(G-8927)
BMP & ASSOCIATES INC
Also Called: Craftmasters Countertops
1707 Hartwick Rd (77093-1030)
PHONE.................................713 779-8677
Juan Mireles III, *CEO*
Wayne D Lucas, *Vice Pres*
Todd Mann, *Sales Staff*
Ismael S Padron, *Admin Sec*
EMP: 23
SQ FT: 13,000
SALES (est): 3.4MM **Privately Held**
WEB: www.craftmasters.us.com
SIC: 1799 1752 2541 Counter top installation; kitchen cabinet installation; floor laying & floor work; wood floor installation & refinishing; counter & sink tops

(G-8928)
BMP PAPER & PRINTING INC
4923 W 34th St (77092-6605)
PHONE.................................713 228-9191
James E Stewart, *President*
Frank Moscariello, *Manager*
▲ **EMP:** 36
SALES (est): 4.1MM **Privately Held**
WEB: www.bmpdirect.com
SIC: 2752 Commercial printing, lithographic

(G-8929)
BMS SOLUTIONS USA INC
10375 Richmond Ave # 290 (77042-4143)
PHONE.................................713 954-4970

Neil Eddy, *President*
EMP: 65
SQ FT: 4,000
SALES (est): 3.3MM **Privately Held**
SIC: 7372 Prepackaged software

(G-8930)
BNX CONVERTING LLC
16727 Park Row (77084-5020)
PHONE.................................713 936-2726
Abdulraman Ravat, *Mng Member*
EMP: 10
SALES (est): 2MM **Privately Held**
WEB: www.bnx.com
SIC: 3842 3821 Personal safety equipment; incubators, laboratory

(G-8931)
BOARDWALK MIDSTREAM LLC
9 Greenway Plz Ste 2800 (77046-0926)
PHONE.................................888 315-5005
Stan Horton, *CEO*
EMP: 10 **EST:** 2010
SALES (est): 1.5MM
SALES (corp-wide): 12.5B **Publicly Held**
WEB: www.boardwalkfs.com
SIC: 3317 Steel pipe & tubes
HQ: Boardwalk Pipeline Partners Lp
    9 Greenway Plz Ste 2800
    Houston TX 77046

(G-8932)
BOATMAN INDUSTRIES INC
7355 Airport Blvd (77061-3915)
PHONE.................................713 641-6006
Marvin C Boatman, *President*
Eric Boatman, *Vice Pres*
Mike Hensley, *Sales Dir*
Thomas Boatman, *Mktg Dir*
EMP: 20
SQ FT: 2,300
SALES (est): 4MM **Privately Held**
WEB: www.boatmanind.com
SIC: 7359 7699 3443 5084 Equipment rental & leasing; industrial equipment cleaning; plate work for the metalworking trade; hydraulic systems equipment & supplies; machine tools & metalworking machinery; machine shop, jobbing & repair

(G-8933)
BOCCARD LIFE SCIENCES INC (HQ)
2500 Galveston Rd (77017-1925)
PHONE.................................281 269-6020
Fabricio Braga, *CEO*
Alain Boccard, *President*
Marc Dagues, *President*
Bruno Boccard, *Vice Pres*
Rick Moreau, *Mfg Dir*
▲ **EMP:** 25
SQ FT: 3,500
SALES (est): 44.9MM
SALES (corp-wide): 228.1MM **Privately Held**
WEB: www.boccard.com
SIC: 2834 3556 Emulsions, pharmaceutical; beverage machinery
PA: Boccard
    158 Avenue Roger Salengro
    Villeurbanne 69100
    437 281-200

(G-8934)
BOCCARD PIPE FABRICATORS INC
Also Called: Boccard USA
2500 Galveston Rd (77017-1925)
PHONE.................................713 643-0681
Bruno Boccard, *Ch of Bd*
Larry Fulcher, *Vice Pres*
Pascal Riu, *Vice Pres*
Edouard Villaret, *Project Mgr*
Floyd Martin, *Safety Mgr*
◆ **EMP:** 300
SQ FT: 220,000
SALES (est): 95.9MM
SALES (corp-wide): 228.1MM **Privately Held**
WEB: www.boccard.com
SIC: 3498 Pipe sections fabricated from purchased pipe

PA: Boccard
    158 Avenue Roger Salengro
    Villeurbanne 69100
    437 281-200

(G-8935)
BODY BROTHER INC
10355 Harwin Dr Unit B (77036-1501)
PHONE.................................713 487-8227
Hang Yu, *Principal*
EMP: 10
SALES (est): 692.9K **Privately Held**
WEB: www.ootorihousehold.com
SIC: 3634 Massage machines, electric, except for beauty/barber shops

(G-8936)
BODY LANGUAGE FASHIONS INC
9931 Harwin Dr Ste 152 (77036-1695)
PHONE.................................713 974-0960
Nicholas Abdouche, *President*
EMP: 17
SQ FT: 2,500
SALES (est): 1.7MM **Privately Held**
WEB: www.bodylanguagefashions.com
SIC: 2341 2253 Nightgowns & negligees: women's & children's; bathing suits & swimwear, knit

(G-8937)
BODYCOTE K-TECH INC
Also Called: Bodycote Houston Thermal Spray
5151 World Houston Pkwy # 150 (77032-2658)
PHONE.................................281 227-8222
George Landa, *Branch Mgr*
EMP: 10
SALES (corp-wide): 929.6MM **Privately Held**
SIC: 3398 Metal heat treating
HQ: Bodycote K-Tech, Inc.
    12750 Merit Dr Ste 1400
    Dallas TX 75251
    214 904-2420

(G-8938)
BODYCOTE THERMAL PROC INC
1301 Hays St (77009-6442)
PHONE.................................713 225-6050
Jeff Bell, *Branch Mgr*
EMP: 36
SALES (corp-wide): 929.6MM **Privately Held**
WEB: www.bodycote.com
SIC: 3398 Metal heat treating
HQ: Bodycote Thermal Processing, Inc.
    12750 Merit Dr Ste 1400
    Dallas TX 75251
    214 904-2420

(G-8939)
BOEING COMPANY
3700 Bay Area Blvd # 150 (77058-1160)
PHONE.................................281 226-4000
Lauri Zuchlewski, *Project Mgr*
Edward Burnett, *Engineer*
Michael Macomber, *Technology*
Michelle Chang, *Programmer Anys*
EMP: 2000
SALES (corp-wide): 58.1B **Publicly Held**
WEB: www.boeing.com
SIC: 3721 Airplanes, fixed or rotary wing
PA: The Boeing Company
    100 N Riverside Plz
    Chicago IL 60606
    312 544-2000

(G-8940)
BOEING COMPANY
5122 Huckleberry Cir (77056-2414)
PHONE.................................281 226-4057
Matthew J Jurick, *Principal*
Scott Whitehead, *Manager*
EMP: 895
SALES (corp-wide): 58.1B **Publicly Held**
WEB: www.boeing.com
SIC: 3721 Aircraft
PA: The Boeing Company
    100 N Riverside Plz
    Chicago IL 60606
    312 544-2000

▲ = Import ▼=Export
◆ =Import/Export

(G-8941)
BOEING COMPANY
1600 Smith St (77002-7362)
P.O. Box 580605 (77258-0605)
PHONE....................................713 658-0831
Melvin B Greenberg, *Principal*
EMP: 258
SALES (corp-wide): 58.1B **Publicly Held**
WEB: www.boeing.com
SIC: 3721 Aircraft
PA: The Boeing Company
100 N Riverside Plz
Chicago IL 60606
312 544-2000

(G-8942)
BOEING COMPANY
3700 Bay Area Blvd (77058-1160)
PHONE....................................281 244-4000
Steven Boes, *Project Mgr*
Sunit Kaur, *Project Mgr*
Pamela Brown, *Engineer*
James Davis, *Engineer*
Russell Graves, *Engineer*
EMP: 530
SALES (corp-wide): 58.1B **Publicly Held**
WEB: www.boeing.com
SIC: 8711 3769 3761 3663 Aviation &/or
aeronautical engineering; guided missile
& space vehicle parts & auxiliary equip-
ment; guided missiles & space vehicles;
radio & TV communications equipment
PA: The Boeing Company
100 N Riverside Plz
Chicago IL 60606
312 544-2000

(G-8943)
BOEING COMPANY
· 3700 Bay Area Blvd (77058-1160)
PHONE....................................281 244-3056
Stan Van Derbrink, *Manager*
Sherry Littlefield, *Analyst*
EMP: 300
SALES (corp-wide): 58.1B **Publicly Held**
WEB: www.boeing.com
SIC: 3721 7389 Airplanes, fixed or rotary
wing; inspection & testing services
PA: The Boeing Company
100 N Riverside Plz
Chicago IL 60606
312 544-2000

(G-8944)
BOEING COMPANY
3700 Bay Area Blvd # 150 (77058-1160)
PHONE....................................281 226-4000
John North, *Manager*
EMP: 99
SALES (corp-wide): 58.1B **Publicly Held**
WEB: www.boeing.com
SIC: 3721 Aircraft
PA: The Boeing Company
100 N Riverside Plz
Chicago IL 60606
312 544-2000

(G-8945)
**BOLD PRODUCTION SERVICES
LLC**
10880 Alcott Dr Unit A (77043-2040)
PHONE....................................281 615-6799
EMP: 9 EST: 2013
SALES (est): 6.1MM **Privately Held**
WEB: www.bps-llc.com
SIC: 1389 Construction, repair & disman-
tling services

(G-8946)
BOLDWALL LLC
17350 State Highway 249 # 2
(77064-1147)
PHONE....................................312 898-9460
EMP: 10
SALES (est): 500K **Privately Held**
SIC: 3537 Industrial Trucks And Tractors,
Nsk

(G-8947)
**BOLTEX MANUFACTURING CO
LP**
Also Called: Boltex Mfg Forge Plant
13609 Industrial Rd (77015-6835)
PHONE....................................713 451-2180
Franco Bernobich, *General Mgr*

EMP: 100
SALES (corp-wide): 35.8MM **Privately
Held**
WEB: www.boltexmfg.com
SIC: 3462 3494 Flange, valve & pipe fit-
ting forgings, ferrous; valves & pipe fit-
tings
PA: Boltex Manufacturing Company, L.P.
4901 Oates Rd
Houston TX 77013
713 675-9433

(G-8948)
BONANZA INDUSTRIES INC
Also Called: Bonanza Marble Company
7043 Satsuma Dr Ste C (77041-1895)
P.O. Box 801585 (77280-1585)
PHONE....................................713 466-7900
Stephen Mitchell, *President*
EMP: 90
SQ FT: 40,000
SALES (est): 9.3MM **Privately Held**
SIC: 3281 Cut stone & stone products

(G-8949)
BOND CLOTHIER INC
9311 Summerbell Ln (77074-1342)
PHONE....................................713 784-7121
▲ EMP: 30
SQ FT: 1,080
SALES (est): 2.6MM **Privately Held**
WEB: www.bondclothiers.com
SIC: 2321 5699 Men's & boys' dress
shirts; shirts, custom made

(G-8950)
BONNEY FORGE CORPORATION
Wfi International
4404 Haygood St (77022-3506)
PHONE....................................713 695-3633
John Leone, *Branch Mgr*
EMP: 100
SALES (corp-wide): 71.6MM **Privately
Held**
WEB: www.bonneyforge.com
SIC: 3462 3498 3494 3451 Flange, valve
& pipe fitting forgings, ferrous; fabricated
pipe & fittings; valves & pipe fittings;
screw machine products
PA: Bonney Forge Corporation
14496 Croghan Pike
Mount Union PA 17066
814 542-2545

(G-8951)
**BONNEY FORGE TEXAS LP
(HQ)**
Also Called: Wfi International
4404 Haygood St (77022-3506)
P.O. Box 7303 (77248-7303)
PHONE....................................713 695-3633
John Leone, *President*
Philip Cazayoux, *Business Mgr*
Matthew Daniels, *Business Mgr*
Kyle Gerardi, *Business Mgr*
Michael Pieper, *Business Mgr*
▲ EMP: 40
SQ FT: 10,000
SALES (est): 27.5MM
SALES (corp-wide): 71.6MM **Privately
Held**
WEB: www.wfi-intl.com
SIC: 3494 Pipe fittings
PA: Bonney Forge Corporation
14496 Croghan Pike
Mount Union PA 17066
814 542-2545

(G-8952)
BOOMERANG TUBE LLC
13500 Industrial Rd (77015-6817)
PHONE....................................713 231-2929
Martin Johnson, *Opers Mgr*
EMP: 133
SALES (corp-wide): 277.8MM **Privately
Held**
WEB: www.boomerangtube.com
SIC: 3317 Steel pipe & tubes
PA: Boomerang Tube, Llc
14567 North Outer 40 Rd # 50
Chesterfield MO 63017
636 534-5555

(G-8953)
BOOTS & COOTS LLC
7908 N Sam Houston Pkwy W # 300
(77064-3508)
PHONE....................................281 931-8884
Jerry Winchester, *Manager*
EMP: 40 **Publicly Held**
WEB: www.halliburton.com
SIC: 1389 Oil field services
HQ: Boots & Coots, Llc
3000 N Sam Houston Pkwy E
Houston TX 77032

(G-8954)
BOOTS & COOTS LLC (HQ)
3000 N Sam Houston Pkwy E
(77032-3219)
PHONE....................................281 871-2699
Jerry L Winchester, *CEO*
Dewitt Edwards, *COO*
Allen Duke, *Senior VP*
John Hebert, *Senior VP*
Cary Baetz, *CFO*
◆ EMP: 21
SALES (est): 273.7MM **Publicly Held**
WEB: www.halliburton.com
SIC: 1389 Oil field services

(G-8955)
**BOOTS & COOTS SERVICES
LLC (DH)**
7908 N Sam Houston Pkwy W # 300
(77064-3508)
PHONE....................................281 931-8884
Jerry Winchester, *CEO*
Brian Krause, *President*
EMP: 35
SQ FT: 17,436
SALES (est): 5.5MM **Publicly Held**
WEB: www.halliburton.com
SIC: 1389 Oil field services

(G-8956)
**BOOTS & COOTS SERVICES INC
(DH)**
7908 N Sam Houston Pkwy W # 300
(77064-3508)
PHONE....................................281 931-8884
Marc Edwards, *Senior VP*
Jerry Winchester, *Vice Pres*
EMP: 10
SALES (est): 4.4MM **Publicly Held**
WEB: www.halliburton.com
SIC: 1389 Oil field services

(G-8957)
BOP PRODUCTS LLC (PA)
9118 Sweetbrush Dr (77064-1415)
P.O. Box 692172 (77269-2172)
PHONE....................................281 955-6321
Lisa Bordavsky, *General Mgr*
Floyd Estay, *Business Mgr*
Gary Argabright, *Sales Staff*
Renee Wade, *Sales Staff*
Clifton R Broughton, *Mng Member*
◆ EMP: 15
SQ FT: 10,000
SALES (est): 14.5MM **Privately Held**
WEB: www.bop-products.com
SIC: 1389 3533 Oil field services; gas field
machinery & equipment; oil field machin-
ery & equipment

(G-8958)
BORETS US INC
Also Called: Borets Worldwide
10497 Town And Country Wa (77024-1122)
PHONE....................................713 980-4530
Obran Lekic, *CEO*
Lev Stulberg, *CEO*
Christopher Mackenzie, *Chairman*
Ernest Harris, *VP Opers*
Nicholas Naik, *Senior Buyer*
EMP: 20
SALES (est): 4.4MM **Privately Held**
WEB: www.borets.com
SIC: 3561 3714 Pumps, oil well & field;
fuel pumps, motor vehicle; oil pump,
motor vehicle

(G-8959)
**BORO PARK MARKETING AND
MFG CO**
10435 Woodedge Dr (77070-5333)
PHONE....................................281 890-3848

Raymond Gama, *President*
Camille Gama, *Treasurer*
EMP: 40
SALES (est): 2.6MM **Privately Held**
WEB: www.boroparkmfg.com
SIC: 3444 Sheet metalwork

(G-8960)
**BORUSAN MANNESMANN PIPE
US INC (DH)**
363 N Sam H Pkwy E Ste 63 (77060)
PHONE....................................832 399-6000
Joel Johnson, *CEO*
Hakan Duman, *COO*
Zafer Atabey, *Exec VP*
Mustafa Esen, *Project Engr*
Eric Diehl, *CFO*
▲ EMP: 121
SQ FT: 545,000
SALES (est): 161.7MM **Privately Held**
WEB: www.borusan.com
SIC: 3317 Steel pipe & tubes

(G-8961)
BOSS & HUGHES LLC
10200 Hempstead Rd Ste 2g (77092-8400)
P.O. Box 838, Bellaire (77402-0838)
PHONE....................................713 664-9829
Gaurav Sood, *President*
EMP: 15
SQ FT: 8,000
SALES (est): 2.9MM **Privately Held**
WEB: www.bosshughes.com
SIC: 2752 7334 5112 Offset & photolitho-
graphic printing; photocopying & duplicat-
ing services; stationery & office supplies

(G-8962)
**BOWERS EQUIPMENT
COMPANY INC**
10303 Pineland Rd (77044-5765)
P.O. Box 936, Humble (77347-0936)
PHONE....................................281 458-8891
Doyle Bowers Jr, *President*
Ricky Trevathan, *Superintendent*
Patsy Bowers, *Treasurer*
◆ EMP: 10
SQ FT: 33,900
SALES (est): 2MM **Privately Held**
WEB: www.bowerseq.com
SIC: 3544 3548 Welding positioners (jigs);
welding & cutting apparatus & acces-
sories

(G-8963)
**BOX GANG MANUFACTURING
LLC**
16736 E Hardy Rd (77032-1125)
PHONE....................................713 742-5555
Rafael Marrero,
EMP: 25
SQ FT: 217,800
SALES: 7.1MM **Privately Held**
WEB: www.boxgangmfg.com
SIC: 3291 Abrasive metal & steel products

(G-8964)
**BOXER PARENT COMPANY INC
(PA)**
2103 Citywest Blvd (77042-2833)
PHONE....................................713 918-8800
Lan Loring, *President*
Prescott Ashe, *Vice Pres*
Matt Howell, *Vice Pres*
David Humphrey, *Vice Pres*
Kyle Yarborough, *Vice Pres*
EMP: 46
SALES (est): 462.2MM **Privately Held**
WEB: www.ncsu.edu
SIC: 7372 Prepackaged software

(G-8965)
**BP CORPORATION NORTH
AMER INC (DH)**
Also Called: B P Amoco Business Services
501 Westlake Park Blvd (77079-2604)
PHONE....................................281 366-2000
John C Minge, *President*
John Mummery, *Area Mgr*
Donette Dewar, *Vice Pres*
Michael C Mroz, *Treasurer*
Scott Walker, *Credit Staff*
◆ EMP: 1900 EST: 1889

SALES (est): 17.2B
SALES (corp-wide): 278.4B **Privately Held**
WEB: www.bp.com
SIC: 5541 5171 1311 4613 Filling stations, gasoline; petroleum bulk stations & terminals; crude petroleum production; refined petroleum pipelines; crude petroleum pipelines; gasoline
HQ: Bp America Inc
4101 Winfield Rd Ste 200
Warrenville IL 60555
630 420-5111

(G-8966)
BP CORPORATION NORTH AMER INC
200 Westlake Park Blvd (77079-2663)
P.O. Box 4587 (77210-4587)
PHONE................................281 366-3988
Sampat Rampuria, *Branch Mgr*
EMP: 700
SALES (corp-wide): 278.4B **Privately Held**
WEB: www.bp.com
SIC: 2911 Gasoline
HQ: Bp Corporation North America Inc.
501 Westlake Park Blvd
Houston TX 77079
281 366-2000

(G-8967)
BP CORPORATION NORTH AMER INC
Also Called: BP Energy Company
201 Helios Way (77079-2678)
PHONE................................281 366-2000
EMP: 729
SALES (corp-wide): 278.4B **Privately Held**
WEB: www.bp.com
SIC: 5541 5171 1311 4613 Filling stations, gasoline; petroleum bulk stations & terminals; crude petroleum production; refined petroleum pipelines; crude petroleum pipelines; gasoline
HQ: Bp Corporation North America Inc.
501 Westlake Park Blvd
Houston TX 77079
281 366-2000

(G-8968)
BP ENERGY COMPANY (DH)
Also Called: B P Upstream Technology, Div
501 Westlake Park Blvd (77079-2604)
P.O. Box 3092 (77253-3092)
PHONE................................281 366-2000
Bob Dudley, *CEO*
Brian Frank, *President*
Karen Wheatley, *Managing Dir*
John McNamara, *Vice Pres*
Greg Sharp, *Vice Pres*
◆ **EMP:** 101
SALES (est): 642.8MM
SALES (corp-wide): 278.4B **Privately Held**
WEB: www.bp.com
SIC: 1382 Oil & gas exploration services
HQ: Bp America Production Company
501 Westlake Park Blvd
Houston TX 77079
281 366-2000

(G-8969)
BP EXPLORATION & PROD INC
501 Westlake Park Blvd (77079-2604)
PHONE................................800 333-3991
Robert Dudley, *CEO*
Bernard Looney, *CEO*
Andy Hopwood, *COO*
Brian Centeno, *Counsel*
Bob Fryar, *Exec VP*
◆ **EMP:** 28
SALES (est): 11MM
SALES (corp-wide): 278.4B **Privately Held**
WEB: www.bp.com
SIC: 1311 1382 Crude petroleum & natural gas production; oil & gas exploration services
PA: Bp P.L.C.
1 St. James's Square
London SW1Y
207 496-4000

(G-8970)
BP INTERNATIONAL LTD
501 Westlake Park Blvd (77079-2604)
PHONE................................281 366-2000
Lamar McKay, *CEO*
EMP: 116
SALES (est): 11.2MM
SALES (corp-wide): 278.4B **Privately Held**
WEB: www.bp.com
SIC: 1382 Geological exploration, oil & gas field
PA: Bp P.L.C.
1 St. James's Square
London SW1Y
207 496-4000

(G-8971)
BP WIND ENERGY NORTH AMER INC (DH)
700 Louisiana St Fl 33 (77002-2700)
PHONE................................713 354-2100
Robert Lukefahr, *President*
Erika Stachowiak, *Project Mgr*
Rodney McAtee, *Manager*
EMP: 100
SQ FT: 40,000
SALES (est): 26.8MM
SALES (corp-wide): 278.4B **Privately Held**
WEB: www.bp.com
SIC: 3612 Transformers, except electric

(G-8972)
BPM MICROSYSTEMS INC
15000 Northwest Fwy (77040-3220)
PHONE................................713 688-4600
William H White, *CEO*
Don McMahan, *Vice Pres*
Calvin Tang, *CFO*
Armando Garcia, *Sales Mgr*
James Holava, *Sales Staff*
EMP: 58
SQ FT: 35,000
SALES (est): 3.2MM **Privately Held**
WEB: www.bpmmicro.com
SIC: 3825 Semiconductor test equipment

(G-8973)
BPZ RESOURCES INC
Also Called: Bpz Energy
10497 Town And Cntry Way (77024-1117)
PHONE................................281 556-6200
James B Taylor, *Ch of Bd*
Manuel Pablo Zuniga-Pflucker, *President*
Manuel Zuniga-Pflucker, *Principal*
Richard S Menniti, *CFO*
J Durkin Ledgard, *Administration*
EMP: 25
SQ FT: 13,300
SALES: 83.9MM **Privately Held**
SIC: 1311 Crude petroleum production

(G-8974)
BRADEN AND PREWITT INC
Also Called: Fuller-Phnix Architectual Pdts
2525 Vaughn St (77093-8600)
PHONE................................713 699-2262
Mackie Braden, *President*
Douglas W Petitt, *Vice Pres*
Don Johnson Fuller, *IT/INT Sup*
EMP: 10
SQ FT: 26,000
SALES (est): 2MM **Privately Held**
WEB: www.fullerphoenix.com
SIC: 3448 Panels for prefabricated metal buildings

(G-8975)
BRADMARK TECHNOLOGIES INC (PA)
4265 San Felipe St # 700 (77027-2926)
PHONE................................713 621-2808
C Bradley Tashenberg, *CEO*
Steve Capelli, *Ch of Bd*
Aurelio B Madrazo, *Chairman*
Brad Tashenberg Jr, *Exec VP*
Bradley Tashenberg, *Exec VP*
EMP: 30
SQ FT: 10,000
SALES (est): 4.2MM **Privately Held**
WEB: www.bradmark.com
SIC: 7372 7371 Utility computer software; custom computer programming services

(G-8976)
BRASKEM AMERICA INC
5100 Westheimer Rd # 495 (77056-5520)
PHONE................................713 255-4747
Walmir Soller, *Director*
Almir Filho, *Planning*
EMP: 106 **Privately Held**
WEB: www.braskem.com
SIC: 2821 2865 2869 Polypropylene resins; polyesters; acrylic resins; plasticizer/additive based plastic materials; cyclic crudes & intermediates; phenol, alkylated & cumene; aniline, nitrobenzene; diphenylamines; acetone, synthetic; alcohols, non-beverage
HQ: Braskem America, Inc.
1735 Market St Fl 28
Philadelphia PA 19103
215 841-3100

(G-8977)
BRAVELETS LLC
337 Garden Oaks Blvd (77018-5501)
PHONE................................800 780-9227
Stephanie Hansen, *President*
EMP: 12 EST: 1964
SALES (est): 1.6MM **Privately Held**
WEB: www.bravelets.com
SIC: 5944 3911 Jewelry stores; bracelets, precious metal

(G-8978)
BRAY INTERNATIONAL INC
Also Called: Bray Sales-Texas
13788 West Rd Ste 200 (77041-1139)
PHONE................................281 517-5400
Debbie Koon, *Human Resources*
Todd Griffin, *Manager*
Scott Souders, *Technology*
EMP: 15
SALES (corp-wide): 174.4MM **Privately Held**
WEB: www.bray.com
SIC: 3592 5999 Valves; farm machinery
PA: Bray International, Inc.
13333 Westland East Blvd
Houston TX 77041
281 894-7979

(G-8979)
BRAY INTERNATIONAL INC (PA)
Also Called: Bray Controls USA
13333 Westland East Blvd (77041-1219)
PHONE................................281 894-7979
Craig C Brown, *CEO*
Ronald J Warren, *President*
Steve Drollinger, *General Mgr*
Bruce McGriff, *General Mgr*
Nick Smith, *General Mgr*
◆ **EMP:** 250
SQ FT: 100,000
SALES (est): 174.4MM **Privately Held**
WEB: www.bray.com
SIC: 5085 3491 Valves & fittings; industrial valves

(G-8980)
BREAKWATER ENERGY PARTNERS LLC (PA)
8 Greenway Plz Ste 1005 (77046-0830)
PHONE................................281 648-1268
Richard Kinsel, *Managing Prtnr*
Robert Bailey, *Partner*
Kyle Kinsel, *Partner*
John Ncgillis, *Partner*
EMP: 55 EST: 2012
SALES (est): 32.5MM **Privately Held**
WEB: www.breakwaterenergy.com
SIC: 1389 Oil field services

(G-8981)
BRECO INTERNATIONAL LLC (DH)
6830 La Paseo St (77087-5113)
PHONE................................713 641-6073
George Whittier, *CEO*
▲ **EMP:** 15
SQ FT: 26,840
SALES (est): 4.2MM
SALES (corp-wide): 95.8MM **Privately Held**
WEB: www.brecointernational.com
SIC: 5084 3621 Engines & parts, diesel; motors & generators

HQ: Fairbanks Morse, Llc
701 White Ave
Beloit WI 53511
800 356-6955

(G-8982)
BREDERO SHAW LLC (DH)
Also Called: Shawcor Company
3838 N S Houston Pkwy E (77032)
PHONE................................281 886-2350
John D Tikkanen, *President*
William P Buckley, *Vice Pres*
Michael Cockrell, *Vice Pres*
Timothy L Hutzul, *Vice Pres*
Doris Mardesic, *Opers Mgr*
◆ **EMP:** 45
SALES (est): 14MM
SALES (corp-wide): 1.1B **Privately Held**
WEB: www.shawcor.com
SIC: 3479 Coating or wrapping steel pipe
HQ: Shawcor Inc.
5875 N Sam Houston Pkwy W # 200
Houston TX 77086
281 886-2350

(G-8983)
BRI CONSULTING GROUP INC
1616 S Voss Rd Ste 845 (77057-2638)
PHONE................................713 468-6813
Keith R McCarthy, *President*
Keith McCarthy, *President*
Meredith McCarthy, *Admin Sec*
EMP: 12
SQ FT: 2,000
SALES (est): 10MM **Privately Held**
WEB: www.bri-consultants.com
SIC: 1382 Oil & gas exploration services

(G-8984)
BRIDON-AMERICAN CORPORATION
Also Called: Universal Lifting Products
1110 Lockwood Dr (77020-7322)
PHONE................................713 921-4101
Chris Black, *Branch Mgr*
EMP: 35
SQ FT: 16,000
SALES (corp-wide): 353.3MM **Privately Held**
WEB: www.bridon-bekaert.com
SIC: 3496 5051 Cable, uninsulated wire: made from purchased wire; rope, wire (not insulated)
HQ: Bridon-American Corporation
280 New Commerce Blvd
Hanover Township PA 18706
570 822-3349

(G-8985)
BRISCO PLASTICS AND CHEM LLC
16225 Park Ten Pl Ste 500 (77084-5152)
PHONE................................713 395-7081
Guillermo Castillo, *Mng Member*
Francisco Domingos,
◆ **EMP:** 10
SALES (est): 1.2MM **Privately Held**
WEB: www.briscopc.com
SIC: 5162 2821 Plastics materials; plastics materials & resins
PA: Brisco Do Brasil Industria Quimica E Comercio Ltda
Rua Joao Ranieri 1077
Guarulhos SP 07177

(G-8986)
BRISTOL-MYERS SQUIBB COMPANY
1034 Hercules Ave (77058-2722)
PHONE................................212 546-4000
Jane Yonish, *Director*
EMP: 40
SALES (corp-wide): 42.5B **Publicly Held**
WEB: www.bms.com
SIC: 2023 2834 Baby formulas; drugs acting on the cardiovascular system, except diagnostic
PA: Bristol-Myers Squibb Company
430 E 29th St Fl 14
New York NY 10016
212 546-4000

(G-8987)
BRM CONCRETE
1731 Peach Leaf St (77039-1229)
PHONE..................................346 570-2975
Arnold Baker, *Vice Pres*
Whitney Larale Baker, *Mng Member*
EMP: 15
SALES (est): 133.7K **Privately Held**
WEB: www.bakerreadymix.com
SIC: 3273 Ready-mixed concrete

(G-8988)
BROADCAST TECHNICAL SVCS INC
7219 Gessner Rd (77040-3143)
P.O. Box 40187 (77240-0187)
PHONE..................................832 467-0002
William McKee, *CEO*
Shelly Harper, *COO*
Russell Steele, *Vice Pres*
Michael Hobart, *VP Sales*
Travis Carter, *Accounts Mgr*
EMP: 11
SQ FT: 6,500
SALES (est): 3.5MM **Privately Held**
WEB: www.btshouston.com
SIC: 7373 7389 4899 8711 Systems integration services; music & broadcasting services; data communication services; engineering services; studio equipment; radio & television broadcasting

(G-8989)
BROADSPECTRUM DOWNSTREAM SERVI
Also Called: Transfield Services
1330 Post Oak Blvd # 1250 (77056-3031)
PHONE..................................713 964-2800
Phil Wratt, *President*
Steve Whitman, *CFO*
Paul Garrison, *Admin Sec*
EMP: 2000
SALES (est): 57.6MM **Privately Held**
WEB: www.transfieldservices.com
SIC: 1382 Oil & gas exploration services
HQ: Broadspectrum Pty Ltd
L 8 80 Pacific Hwy
North Sydney NSW 2060

(G-8990)
BROCK ENTERPRISES INC
Also Called: Brock Specialty Services
10343 Sam Houston Park Dr # 200
(77064-4656)
PHONE..................................281 870-8200
Roger Gossett, *President*
EMP: 15
SALES (est): 1.8MM **Privately Held**
WEB: www.brockgroup.com
SIC: 3944 Craft & hobby kits & sets

(G-8991)
BROCK SERVICES LLC (DH)
Also Called: United Scaffolding
10343 Sam Houston Park Dr # 200
(77064-4656)
PHONE..................................281 807-8200
Jim Dreyer, *President*
Marco Diaz, *Superintendent*
Terry Lester, *Superintendent*
Kenneth Harold, *Vice Pres*
Jamie Moncur, *Vice Pres*
EMP: 151 EST: 1995
SQ FT: 6,200
SALES (est): 889.1MM **Privately Held**
WEB: www.brockgroup.com
SIC: 1721 1799 3441 Industrial painting; fireproofing buildings; fabricated structural metal
HQ: Brock Holdings Iii, Llc
10343 Sam Houston Park Dr
Houston TX 77064
281 807-8200

(G-8992)
BROKEN HILL PROPTY USA INC (DH)
Also Called: BHP Billiton
1360 Post Oak Blvd Ste 15 (77056-3030)
PHONE..................................713 961-8500
Michael Yeager, *CEO*
EMP: 99

SALES: 57.2MM **Privately Held**
WEB: www.bhp.com
SIC: 1311 4922 Crude petroleum production; pipelines, natural gas
HQ: Bhp Holdings (Resources) Inc.
1360 Post Oak Blvd Ste 15
Houston TX 77056
713 961-8500

(G-8993)
BRONCO MANUFACTURING LLC
Supply Services Division
12502 Mosielee St (77086-3408)
PHONE..................................918 446-7196
Paul Humphries, *General Mgr*
Joe West, *Sales Staff*
EMP: 30
SALES (corp-wide): 35MM **Privately Held**
WEB: www.broncomfg.com
SIC: 5084 3533 Oil well machinery, equipment & supplies; oil field machinery & equipment
PA: Bronco Manufacturing, Llc
4953 S 48th West Ave
Tulsa OK 74107
918 446-7196

(G-8994)
BRONX INDUSTRIES INC
Also Called: Perfect Quilt
8566 Katy Fwy Ste 128 (77024-1811)
PHONE..................................713 467-6155
Carol Addiego, *President*
EMP: 9
SQ FT: 8,750
SALES (est): 450K **Privately Held**
SIC: 2392 2395 Bedspreads & bed sets: made from purchased materials; quilted fabrics or cloth

(G-8995)
BROOK SARA ENTERPRISES INC (PA)
Also Called: Dessert Gallery, The
3600 Kirby Dr Ste D (77098-3941)
P.O. Box 981034 (77098-8034)
PHONE..................................713 522-9999
Sara Brook, *Owner*
Nicole Morris, *COO*
Christopher Posey, *Sales Staff*
EMP: 15
SALES (est): 1.9MM **Privately Held**
WEB: www.dessertgallery.com
SIC: 2087 5812 Syrups, flavoring (except drink); eating places

(G-8996)
BROUGHER INC
Also Called: Forge USA
8881 Hempstead Rd (77008-6017)
PHONE..................................713 869-7577
Wade Brougher, *President*
Jerry W Brougher, *Chairman*
Michelle Baker, *CFO*
John Deveau, *CFO*
Brenda Meekins, *Human Res Mgr*
▲ EMP: 100
SQ FT: 88,000
SALES (est): 26MM **Privately Held**
WEB: www.forgeusa.com
SIC: 3449 3462 Miscellaneous metalwork; iron & steel forgings

(G-8997)
BRUEGMANN USA INC
589 Garden Oaks Blvd (77018-5505)
P.O. Box 924283 (77292-4283)
PHONE..................................713 742-0788
Malte Bruegmann, *President*
Joel Linton, *Vice Pres*
Carol Andrews, *Comptroller*
Clay Bibb, *Sales Staff*
Hilary Scullane, *Sales Staff*
◆ EMP: 50
SQ FT: 55,000
SALES (corp-wide): 1MM **Privately Held**
WEB: www.avalair.net
SIC: 5162 2821 Plastics products; plastics materials & resins
HQ: Bruegmann Verwaltungsges. Mbh
Werkzeugstr. 18
Hagen
233 195-980

(G-8998)
BRUIN E&P OPERATING LLC
602 Sawyer St Ste 710 (77007-7510)
PHONE..................................713 456-3000
Charlie Kinard, *President*
Kennon Doyal, *Vice Pres*
Tyler Crabtree, *CFO*
Nader Daylami, *Finance*
Matthew Steele,
EMP: 140 EST: 2015
SALES (est): 212.5K
SALES (corp-wide): 522.1MM **Privately Held**
WEB: www.bruinep.com
SIC: 1382 Oil & gas exploration services
PA: Bruin E&P Partners Llc
602 Sawyer St Ste 710
Houston TX 77007
713 456-3000

(G-8999)
BRUIN E&P PARTNERS LLC (PA)
602 Sawyer St Ste 710 (77007-7510)
PHONE..................................713 456-3000
Charlie Kinard, *President*
Kirk Osborne, *Engineer*
Tyler Crabtree, *CFO*
Dusty Grosulak, *Manager*
Ali Kazemi, *Manager*
EMP: 14
SALES (est): 522.1MM **Privately Held**
WEB: www.bruinep.com
SIC: 1382 Oil & gas exploration services

(G-9000)
BRUNSWICK PRESS INC
9430 Baythorne Dr (77041-7797)
PHONE..................................713 462-0600
James A Wickman, *President*
Friedrich Bubeck, *Vice Pres*
Barbara Wickman, *Manager*
Tom Wickman, *Admin Sec*
EMP: 30 EST: 1970
SQ FT: 19,000
SALES (est): 7.2MM **Privately Held**
WEB: www.brunswickpress.net
SIC: 5112 2752 2791 2789 Business forms; commercial printing, lithographic; typesetting; bookbinding & related work; commercial printing

(G-9001)
BT5 TECHNOLOGIES LLC
433 North Loop W (77008-2029)
PHONE..................................832 727-5214
Luis Bustamante,
Claudia Ramirez,
EMP: 10
SALES (est): 94.5K **Privately Held**
SIC: 3577 3949 Computer peripheral equipment; exercise equipment

(G-9002)
BTEC TURBINES LP
Also Called: B-TEC
6755 Willow Brook Park (77066-3011)
P.O. Box 27556 (77227-7556)
PHONE..................................281 864-9122
Phiroz Mike Boyce, *CEO*
Alan Wormuth, *Opers Mgr*
Kirk Jensen, *Design Engr*
Sharon Moran, *Sales Staff*
Mike Boyce,
▲ EMP: 65
SQ FT: 956,719
SALES (est): 22.6MM **Privately Held**
WEB: www.btecturbines.com
SIC: 3511 Gas turbine generator set units, complete
PA: The Sterling Group L P
9 Greenway Plz Ste 2400
Houston TX 77046

(G-9003)
BTIC AMERICA CORPORATION (PA)
Also Called: BAC and Btic America
6600 Sands Point Dr # 121 (77074-3711)
PHONE..................................713 779-8882
Guoxiang Zheng, *CEO*
Ned Chen, *Vice Pres*
John Tilley, *Warehouse Mgr*
▲ EMP: 12
SALES (est): 1.6MM **Privately Held**
WEB: www.btic-america.com
SIC: 3491 Compressed gas cylinder valves

(G-9004)
BTM SERVICES LLC
4637 Orange Grove Dr (77039-6321)
PHONE..................................281 773-6060
Debra Stubbe,
Bubba McGee,
EMP: 28 EST: 2015
SQ FT: 174,240
SALES (est): 500K **Privately Held**
WEB: www.btmservicesllc.com
SIC: 1731 3545 Fiber optic cable installation; boring machine attachments (machine tool accessories)

(G-9005)
BTU RESEARCH LLC
3030 Post Oak Blvd Unit 6 (77056-6559)
PHONE..................................713 542-6228
Michael Kanarellis, *CEO*
Thomas Darr, *Principal*
Nance Curtis, *VP Bus Dvlpt*
EMP: 13
SALES (est): 1.3MM **Privately Held**
WEB: www.bturesearch.com
SIC: 3679 Power supplies, all types: static

(G-9006)
BUCKEYE CORRUGATED INC
1401 Greengrass Dr (77008-5005)
PHONE..................................713 869-9121
Gary Ames, *Branch Mgr*
EMP: 100
SALES (corp-wide): 196.6MM **Privately Held**
WEB: www.bcipkg.com
SIC: 2653 Boxes, corrugated: made from purchased materials
PA: Buckeye Corrugated, Inc
822 Kumho Dr Ste 400
Fairlawn OH 44333
330 576-0590

(G-9007)
BUCKEYE INTERNATIONAL INC
Also Called: Buckeye Cleaning Center
16420 W Hardy Rd Ste 150 (77060-6243)
PHONE..................................281 873-4200
Wayne Minor, *Sales Staff*
Craig Place, *Sales Staff*
Christine Chambers, *Office Mgr*
Reagan Lapoint, *Manager*
EMP: 10
SALES (corp-wide): 158.4MM **Privately Held**
WEB: www.buckeyeinternational.com
SIC: 2842 2841 2899 2812 Specialty cleaning preparations; detergents, synthetic organic or inorganic alkaline; chemical preparations; alkalies & chlorine
PA: Buckeye International, Inc.
2700 Wagner Pl
Maryland Heights MO 63043
314 291-1900

(G-9008)
BUCKHEAD MIDSTREAM LLC
109 N Post Oak Ln Ste 520 (77024-7791)
PHONE..................................832 752-4526
Martin Tilson, *COO*
Steven M McNear,
EMP: 50
SALES (est): 335.6K **Privately Held**
WEB: www.buckheadmidstream.com
SIC: 1382 Oil & gas exploration services

(G-9009)
BUCKHEAD MT SAFOOD HOUSTON INC (HQ)
Also Called: Buckhead Meats Houston
10310 Grens Crossing Blvd (77038)
PHONE..................................281 405-3201
Bruce Daley, *President*
Ken Cable, *President*
Julia Lopez, *Principal*
Frank Quant, *Principal*
Barbara B Green, *Vice Pres*
EMP: 93 EST: 1976
SALES (est): 51.8MM
SALES (corp-wide): 52.8B **Publicly Held**
WEB: www.freedmanfoods.com
SIC: 2011 Meat packing plants
PA: Sysco Corporation
1390 Enclave Pkwy
Houston TX 77077
281 584-1390

(G-9010)
BUDGET READY MIX LLC
Also Called: Pete Sanchez
14915 Market Street Rd (77015-6473)
PHONE...................................281 452-5233
Pete Sanchez, *Owner*
EMP: 20
SALES (est): 4MM **Privately Held**
WEB: www.budgetreadymixx.com
SIC: 3273 Ready-mixed concrete

(G-9011)
BUFFALO SEAL AND GASKET CO
3780 Yale St (77018-6564)
PHONE...................................713 694-9003
Paul Leggett, *President*
▲ EMP: 11
SALES (est): 4.2MM **Privately Held**
WEB: www.buffalosealandgasket.com
SIC: 5085 3053 Gaskets; gaskets, packing & sealing devices

(G-9012)
BUILDERS DEPOT DIRECT LLC
Also Called: Builders Direct Depot
7830 Westglen Dr (77063-6408)
PHONE...................................832 384-7272
Gagan Dhall, *Mng Member*
EMP: 10
SALES (est): 1.4MM **Privately Held**
WEB: www.bddllc.com
SIC: 3272 5064 5211 3281 Electrical appliances, major; washing machines; floor slabs & tiles, precast concrete; stone, cast concrete

(G-9013)
BUILDERS EQUIPMENT & TOOL CO (HQ)
Also Called: B E T C O
1617 Enid St (77009-2503)
P.O. Box 8508 (77249-8508)
PHONE...................................713 869-3491
Stavis Gilbreath, *Ch of Bd*
Jay H Rosen, *President*
Randy Goss, *COO*
Melissa Rodriguez, *Production*
Travis Doyle, *Sales Staff*
EMP: 100
SQ FT: 9,500
SALES (est): 18.3MM
SALES (corp-wide): 21MM **Privately Held**
WEB: www.scaffold.com
SIC: 3446 7353 Scaffolds, mobile or stationary: metal; heavy construction equipment rental
PA: Bleacher Sales Company
1617 Enid St
Houston TX 77009
713 869-3491

(G-9014)
BUILDERS POST-TENSION INC (PA)
403 Richey Rd (77090-5713)
PHONE...................................281 873-9500
Greg N Tomlinson, *President*
Brian Conley, *Vice Pres*
Larry Cupit, *Opers Staff*
Marta Greer, *Accounting Mgr*
Cody Cornell, *Sales Staff*
▲ EMP: 40
SQ FT: 18,500
SALES (est): 18.6MM **Privately Held**
WEB: www.builderspt.com
SIC: 1771 3199 2951 3292 Concrete work; stirrups, wood or metal; mastic floor composition; tape, asbestos

(G-9015)
BUILDING PLASTICS INC
Also Called: B P I Texas
10375 Tanner Rd (77041-7401)
PHONE...................................713 896-9001
Mickey Pierson, *General Mgr*
John Lovelace, *Regl Sales Mgr*
Jim Frasier, *Branch Mgr*
Shelia Murrell, *Manager*
EMP: 20
SALES (corp-wide): 217.8MM **Privately Held**
WEB: www.bpiteam.com
SIC: 2426 Flooring, hardwood

PA: Building Plastics, Inc.
3263 Sharpe Ave
Memphis TN 38111
901 744-6200

(G-9016)
BUILDING PRODUCTS PLUS LLC
Also Called: American Pole and Timber
12317 Almeda Rd (77045-4742)
PHONE...................................713 946-7939
Dorian Benn, *Accountant*
Linda Frnklin, *Accountant*
Holoy Jackson, *Accountant*
Ronda Catlett, *Mktg Dir*
William Plant, *Mng Member*
▼ EMP: 30
SALES (est): 12.1MM **Privately Held**
WEB: www.buildingproductsplus.com
SIC: 5031 2491 Lumber: rough, dressed & finished; wood preserving

(G-9017)
BULLEN PUMP INC
12305 Kurland Dr (77034-4811)
PHONE...................................281 274-1800
Randy Barrios, *Sales Staff*
Theresa Palmer, *Sales Staff*
Leah May, *Assistant*
◆ EMP: 21
SALES (est): 6.3MM **Privately Held**
WEB: www.bullenpump.com
SIC: 3564 Blowers & fans

(G-9018)
BURGESS SPECIALTY FABG INC
8222 Fawndale Ln (77040-5510)
P.O. Box 40528 (77240-0528)
PHONE...................................713 462-0293
William G Burgess, *President*
Richard Roy, *President*
Jim Deasy, *Plant Mgr*
Ronny Lisenbe, *Production*
Tom Deasy, *Purch Mgr*
EMP: 75
SQ FT: 22,000
SALES (est): 10.5MM **Privately Held**
WEB: www.burgessfab.com
SIC: 3599 3444 Machine & other job shop work; sheet metalwork

(G-9019)
BURKHEAD MANUFACTURING COMPANY
Also Called: Redi Smok Electric Cookers
1620 Maury St (77026-7249)
P.O. Box 4 (77001-0004)
PHONE...................................713 227-5248
Bruce K Jamison, *President*
Bryan W Jamison, *Chairman*
▲ EMP: 20 EST: 1923
SQ FT: 80,000
SALES (est): 3.8MM **Privately Held**
WEB: www.oldsmokey.com
SIC: 3631 5719 3634 Barbecues, grills & braziers (outdoor cooking); cookware, except aluminum; electric housewares & fans

(G-9020)
BURLINGTON RESOURCES LLC (HQ)
600 N Dairy Ashford Rd (77079-1100)
P.O. Box 2197 (77252-2197)
PHONE...................................281 293-1000
Randy L Limbacher, *COO*
L David Hanower, *Senior VP*
John A Williams, *Senior VP*
Steven J Shapiro, *CFO*
▲ EMP: 220
SQ FT: 129,000
SALES (est): 229.5MM
SALES (corp-wide): 36.6B **Publicly Held**
SIC: 1311 5172 4922 4612 Crude petroleum production; petroleum products; pipelines, natural gas; crude petroleum pipelines
PA: Conocophillips
925 N Eldridge Pkwy
Houston TX 77079
281 293-1000

(G-9021)
BUSINESS EXT BUR TEXAS INC
Also Called: Beb Data
4802 Travis St (77002-9740)
P.O. Box 66273 (77266-6273)
PHONE...................................713 528-5568
Robert L Royall, *Ch of Bd*
Richard Vidock, *Vice Pres*
James R Tardy, *CFO*
Walter Barnes, *Officer*
Jim Tardy, *Executive*
EMP: 25 EST: 1949
SQ FT: 25,000
SALES (est): 4.8MM **Privately Held**
WEB: www.bebtexas.com
SIC: 7331 2752 Mailing service; mailing list compilers; commercial printing, offset

(G-9022)
BUTTERWORTH INC
16737 W Hardy Rd (77060-6241)
PHONE...................................281 821-7300
George Sherman, *President*
Grace Sanders, *General Mgr*
Catherine Sherman, *Prdtn Mgr*
Darryl Kee, *Purchasing*
Vernon Kohut, *Accounting Mgr*
▲ EMP: 15
SQ FT: 8,500
SALES (est): 4.5MM **Privately Held**
WEB: www.butterworth.com
SIC: 3569 Lubricating equipment

(G-9023)
BWFS INDUSTRIES LLC
Also Called: Butchers Welding & Fabg Svc
5637 Etheline Dr (77039-3911)
PHONE...................................281 590-9391
Aaron Anderson, *Project Mgr*
Mike Books, *Project Mgr*
Rick Carden, *Sales Staff*
Steve Rice, *Manager*
Jason Jaeger, *Info Tech Mgr*
▲ EMP: 75
SQ FT: 1,000
SALES (est): 20.8MM **Privately Held**
WEB: www.bwfsindustries.com
SIC: 3441 Fabricated structural metal

(G-9024)
BWT LLC
1733 Lauder Rd (77039-3027)
PHONE...................................281 442-6694
Michael Wellham, *President*
EMP: 25 **Privately Held**
SIC: 3398 Metal heat treating
HQ: Bwt Llc
201 Brookfield Pkwy
Greenville SC 29607

(G-9025)
C & K MANAGEMENT CO INC (PA)
Also Called: Shipley's Do-Nut Shop
6545 Bissonnet St (77074-6521)
P.O. Box 96696 (77213-6696)
PHONE...................................713 774-7429
James Kirk Holt, *President*
EMP: 14
SALES (est): 3.6MM **Privately Held**
SIC: 8742 2051 Management consulting services; doughnuts, except frozen

(G-9026)
C AUTOMATION INC (PA)
10535 Fisher Rd (77041-4083)
P.O. Box 40267 (77240-0267)
PHONE...................................832 467-4644
Avilia Gould, *President*
Jason Kovarik, *General Mgr*
Tim Plasek, *Prdtn Mgr*
Jason Dunn, *Controller*
Ruthe Locklear, *Finance Mgr*
EMP: 39
SQ FT: 3,200
SALES (est): 15.2MM **Privately Held**
WEB: www.c-automation.com
SIC: 1389 Oil field services

(G-9027)
C D STEEL & SERVICE INC
6318 Deihl Rd (77092-1310)
PHONE...................................713 957-3604
Garrett Stone, *President*
Mary Brymer, *Sales Mgr*
EMP: 9

SQ FT: 10,000
SALES (est): 1.7MM **Privately Held**
WEB: www.cdsteelservice.com
SIC: 3312 Blast furnaces & steel mills

(G-9028)
C E SHEPHERD COMPANY LP (PA)
2221 Canada Dry St (77023-4503)
PHONE...................................713 924-4300
G Maury Shepherd, *President*
Philip Tweeton, *Vice Pres*
Walt Jonischkies, *Purchasing*
Duncan Hasell, *Plant Engr*
Mary Ann Anaya, *Human Res Mgr*
◆ EMP: 75 EST: 1957
SQ FT: 60,000
SALES (est): 23.2MM **Privately Held**
WEB: www.ceshepherd.com
SIC: 3479 3081 3089 3354 Coating of metals with plastic or resins; plastic film & sheet; injection molded finished plastic products; aluminum extruded products; manufactured hardware (general); metals service centers & offices

(G-9029)
C H V CORPORATION
Also Called: Hill, W K Awning & Tent Co
1111 W Drew St (77006-1221)
P.O. Box 66086 (77266-6086)
PHONE...................................713 526-1347
Alice Venable, *President*
Joe Venable, *Vice Pres*
Robert Venable Jr, *Vice Pres*
EMP: 14 EST: 1894
SQ FT: 10,000
SALES (est): 1.4MM **Privately Held**
WEB: www.wkhillawning.com
SIC: 2394 Awnings, fabric: made from purchased materials; canopies, fabric: made from purchased materials; canvas covers & drop cloths

(G-9030)
C K KELLEY & SONS INC
Also Called: Mercury Companies
10651 Harwin Dr Ste 700 (77036-1547)
PHONE...................................713 778-9232
Karen Packard, *President*
Michael J Kelley, *Vice Pres*
Donald G Kelley, *Treasurer*
EMP: 20 EST: 1959
SQ FT: 23,000
SALES (est): 3.7MM **Privately Held**
WEB: www.mermetals.com
SIC: 3444 Metal housings, enclosures, casings & other containers

(G-9031)
C M C STEEL FABRICATORS INC
777 N Eldridge Pkwy # 500 (77079-4425)
PHONE...................................713 799-1150
Anna Olivars, *Branch Mgr*
EMP: 72
SALES (corp-wide): 5.4B **Publicly Held**
WEB: www.cmc.com
SIC: 3441 Fabricated structural metal
HQ: C M C Steel Fabricators, Inc.
1 Steel Mill Dr
Seguin TX 78155
830 372-8200

(G-9032)
C M C STEEL FABRICATORS INC
Also Called: CMC Texas Cold Finished Steel
235 Portwall St (77029-1307)
PHONE...................................713 225-4446
Randy Hunt, *Branch Mgr*
Jim Eisele, *Manager*
EMP: 100
SQ FT: 61,622
SALES (corp-wide): 5.4B **Publicly Held**
WEB: www.cmc.com
SIC: 3441 3452 3444 Fabricated structural metal; bolts, nuts, rivets & washers; sheet metalwork
HQ: C M C Steel Fabricators, Inc.
1 Steel Mill Dr
Seguin TX 78155
830 372-8200

▲ = Import ▼ =Export
◆ =Import/Export

(G-9033)
C M C STEEL FABRICATORS INC
Also Called: CMC Alamo Steel
15990 N Barkers Landing R (77079-2468)
PHONE..............................877 297-9111
Fax: 281 597-5402
EMP: 100
SALES (corp-wide): 4.6B **Publicly Held**
SIC: 3441 Structural Metal Fabrication
HQ: C M C Steel Fabricators, Inc.
1 Steel Mill Dr
Seguin TX 78155
830 372-8200

(G-9034)
C T GASKET & POLYMER CO INC
Also Called: C T G
12308 Cutten Rd (77066-1808)
PHONE..............................713 856-8667
Joe Jackson, *President*
Cory Jackson, *Vice Pres*
EMP: 45
SQ FT: 36,000
SALES (est): 11.4MM **Privately Held**
WEB: www.ctgasket.com
SIC: 3053 5085 Gaskets, all materials;
gaskets

(G-9035)
C VILLANUEVA COMPANY LLC
Also Called: Quality Brewers
2909 Hillcroft St Ste 255 (77057-5848)
PHONE..............................281 974-2361
Celia Villanueva,
EMP: 12
SALES (est): 618.9K **Privately Held**
SIC: 2082 2085 5182 Beer (alcoholic bev-
erage); malt beverage products; distilled
& blended liquors; wine & distilled bever-
ages

(G-9036)
C W PRECISION FABRICATION WLDG
13118 Sundale Rd (77038-1639)
PHONE..............................281 820-4224
Kenneth L Wagner, *President*
Lynn Wagner, *Treasurer*
Jennifer Wagner, *Senior Mgr*
EMP: 15
SQ FT: 15,000
SALES (est): 2.5MM **Privately Held**
WEB: www.cwprecision.com
SIC: 3441 Fabricated structural metal

(G-9037)
C&A MACHINE AND REPAIR SVC INC
6227 Nyoka St (77041-5311)
PHONE..............................713 937-3426
Darrell Rittiman, *President*
Darrell W Rittiman, *Vice Pres*
Dennis J Rittiman Sr, *Shareholder*
EMP: 32
SQ FT: 13,000
SALES (est): 4.8MM **Privately Held**
SIC: 3599 3441 Machine shop, jobbing &
repair; fabricated structural metal

(G-9038)
C&C INDUSTRIES INC
Cnc Flow Control
10350 Clay Rd Ste 150 (77041-8760)
PHONE..............................832 631-2687
EMP: 14 **Privately Held**
WEB: www.cncflowcontrol.com
SIC: 3491 Industrial valves
HQ: C&C Industries, Inc.
10350 Clay Rd Ste 250
Houston TX 77041
713 466-1644

(G-9039)
C&J CLADDING LLC
Also Called: C & J
6611 Willow Brook Park (77066-3013)
PHONE..............................281 987-2383
Jim Gray,
Jeff Hoye,
Bill Lawrence,
EMP: 26

SALES (est): 9MM
SALES (corp-wide): 586MM **Privately Held**
WEB: www.cjcladding.com
SIC: 1799 7692 Welding on site; welding
repair
PA: Ellwood Group, Inc.
600 Commercial Ave
Ellwood City PA 16117
724 752-3680

(G-9040)
C-B-GEAR & MACHINE INC
4232 Mooney Rd (77093-2813)
P.O. Box 111278 (77293-0278)
PHONE..............................281 449-0777
Jack Nowlin, *President*
Jack L Nowlin, *Treasurer*
Jed Nowlin, *Sales Staff*
Roger Patton, *Sales Staff*
Debbie Brown, *Office Mgr*
▲ EMP: 46 EST: 1952
SQ FT: 50,000
SALES (est): 8.9MM **Privately Held**
WEB: www.cbgear.com
SIC: 3599 3625 3462 Machine shop, job-
bing & repair; relays & industrial controls;
iron & steel forgings

(G-9041)
CABOT OIL & GAS CORPORATION (PA)
840 Gessner Rd Ste 1400 (77024-4152)
PHONE..............................281 589-4600
Dan O Dinges, *Ch of Bd*
Jeffrey W Hutton, *Senior VP*
Todd L Liebl, *Senior VP*
Steven W Lindeman, *Senior VP*
Phillip L Stalnaker, *Senior VP*
EMP: 183
SALES (est): 2B **Publicly Held**
WEB: www.cabotog.com
SIC: 1311 Crude petroleum & natural gas;
crude petroleum production; natural gas
production

(G-9042)
CACO MANUFACTURING CORPORATION (PA)
5816 Heiser St (77087-4122)
P.O. Box 263129 (77207-3129)
PHONE..............................713 644-0170
Tina C Jou, *President*
Randall Chaffee, *General Mgr*
Shirene Feiz, *Sales Staff*
▲ EMP: 12 EST: 1964
SQ FT: 10,000
SALES (est): 2.4MM **Privately Held**
WEB: www.solomatic.com
SIC: 2522 Chairs, office: padded or plain,
except wood

(G-9043)
CACTUS INC (PA)
920 Mmrial Cy Way Ste 300 (77024)
PHONE..............................713 626-8800
Bruce Rothstein, *Ch of Bd*
Scott Bender, *President*
Joel Bender, *COO*
Steven Bender, *Vice Pres*
David Isaac, *Vice Pres*
EMP: 21 EST: 2011
SALES: 628.4MM **Publicly Held**
WEB: www.cactuswhd.com
SIC: 3533 Drilling tools for gas, oil or water
wells

(G-9044)
CACTUS WELLHEAD LLC (HQ)
920 Mmrial Cy Way Ste 300 (77024)
PHONE..............................713 626-8800
Clayton Dickerson, *Regional Mgr*
Randy Brazeau, *Business Mgr*
Steven Bender, *Vice Pres*
Greg Richard, *Opers Mgr*
Pam Crossan, *Purch Mgr*
◆ EMP: 133
SALES (est): 483.3MM
SALES (corp-wide): 628.4MM **Publicly Held**
WEB: www.cactuswhd.com
SIC: 1389 Oil field services
PA: Cactus, Inc.
920 Mmrial Cy Way Ste 300
Houston TX 77024
713 626-8800

(G-9045)
CADILLAC FABRICATION
8980 Scranton St (77075-1135)
PHONE..............................713 910-2200
Gary Mills, *Principal*
Jeff Brown, *Supervisor*
EMP: 13
SALES (est): 2MM **Privately Held**
WEB: www.cadillacfab.com
SIC: 3089 Plastics products

(G-9046)
CAILIP GAS MARKETING LLC
1980 Post Oak Blvd # 2000 (77056-3899)
PHONE..............................281 833-4217
Young Don Cho, *Accounts Mgr*
Sijong Lim,
Ho Sik Lee, *Admin Sec*
EMP: 20
SQ FT: 6,000
SALES (est): 484.3K **Privately Held**
SIC: 1321 Natural gas liquids
HQ: Sk E&S Americas, Inc.
1980 Post Oak Blvd # 2000
Houston TX 77056
281 833-4200

(G-9047)
CAL SIERRA INTERNATIONAL LLC
6333 Rothway St (77040-5040)
PHONE..............................832 615-6002
Felix Ho, *Mng Member*
▲ EMP: 12
SALES (est): 2MM **Privately Held**
SIC: 3085 Plastics bottles

(G-9048)
CALCO TAIWAN MARKETING SERVICE
Also Called: Zesty-Calco Marketing Service
3988 Clay St (77023-1700)
PHONE..............................713 247-9918
Karen Chang, *Manager*
▲ EMP: 15
SQ FT: 40,000
SALES (est): 2.2MM **Privately Held**
SIC: 5084 5191 0119 2099 Food product
manufacturing machinery; fertilizer & fer-
tilizer materials; bean (dry field & seed)
farm; packaged combination products:
pasta, rice & potato

(G-9049)
CALDWELL UPFITTERS LLC
4909 Fulton St (77009-2604)
PHONE..............................832 203-5658
Marissa Rosado, *General Mgr*
Tim Rainwater, *Sales Staff*
Chris Belk, *Manager*
Brandon Kloss, *Manager*
EMP: 10
SALES (corp-wide): 1.6MM **Privately Held**
WEB: www.capfleetupfitters.com
SIC: 3465 Body parts, automobile:
stamped metal
PA: Caldwell Upfitters, Llc
4715 S General Bruce Dr
Temple TX 76502
254 773-1959

(G-9050)
CALKINS AERO SERVICE INC
18000 Groschke Rd Ste 3e (77084-5677)
PHONE..............................281 579-6674
Forrest Colditz, *President*
Heather Mitchell, *Principal*
EMP: 10
SALES (est): 1.4MM **Privately Held**
WEB: www.calkins.aero
SIC: 3728 Aircraft & heavy equipment re-
pair services

(G-9051)
CALLON PETROLEUM COMPANY (PA)
2000 W Sam Houston Pkwy S # 2000
(77042-3622)
PHONE..............................281 589-5200
L Richard Flury, *Ch of Bd*
Joseph C Gatto Jr, *President*
Jeffrey S Balmer, *COO*
Jeffrey Balmer, *COO*
Michol L Ecklund, *Senior VP*

EMP: 85
SALES: 671.5MM **Publicly Held**
WEB: www.callon.com
SIC: 1311 Crude petroleum & natural gas
production

(G-9052)
CALLON PETROLEUM COMPANY
500 Dallas St Ste 2300 (77002-4724)
PHONE..............................713 328-1000
EMP: 75
SALES (corp-wide): 671.5MM **Publicly Held**
WEB: www.callon.com
SIC: 1382 Oil & gas exploration services
PA: Callon Petroleum Company
2000 W Sam Houston Pkwy S # 2000
Houston TX 77042
281 589-5200

(G-9053)
CALLON PETROLEUM OPERATING CO (HQ)
Also Called: Callon Petroleum Company
2000 W Sam Houston Pkwy S # 2000
(77042-3622)
PHONE..............................601 442-1601
Joseph C Gatto Jr, *CEO*
Gary A Newberry, *COO*
Mitzi P Conn, *Vice Pres*
Michol L Ecklund, *Vice Pres*
Michael J O'Connor, *Vice Pres*
▲ EMP: 46
SALES (est): 178.7MM
SALES (corp-wide): 671.5MM **Publicly Held**
WEB: www.callon.com
SIC: 1311 Crude petroleum production;
natural gas production
PA: Callon Petroleum Company
2000 W Sam Houston Pkwy S # 2000
Houston TX 77042
281 589-5200

(G-9054)
CALROCK MUSIC
Also Called: Calrock Records
1321 Upland Dr (77043-4718)
PHONE..............................432 213-8822
Cal Sanders, *President*
▲ EMP: 55
SALES (est): 3.1MM **Privately Held**
SIC: 3577 3695 7313 Data conversion
equipment, media-to-media: computer;
magnetic & optical recording media;
printed media advertising representatives

(G-9055)
CALYX CULTIVATION TECH CORP (PA)
14340 Torrey Chase Blvd (77014-1021)
PHONE..............................281 227-2208
John Higgins, *CEO*
Mark Sam, *COO*
EMP: 11
SALES (est): 120K **Privately Held**
WEB: www.calyxcultivation.com
SIC: 3641 Electric lamps & parts for gener-
alized applications

(G-9056)
CALYX ENERGY LLC
4544 Post Ok Pl Dr Ste 37 (77027)
PHONE..............................918 949-4224
James F Stephenson Jr, *CFO*
EMP: 24
SALES (corp-wide): 15.6MM **Privately Held**
WEB: www.calyxenergy.com
SIC: 1382 Oil & gas exploration services
PA: Calyx Energy, Llc
6120 S Yale Ave Ste 1480
Tulsa OK 74136

(G-9057)
CAM FIELD SOLUTIONS LLC
1700 Katy Fwy (77094)
PHONE..............................832 533-2706
David Stroble,
EMP: 20
SALES (est): 327.3K **Privately Held**
SIC: 1389 Oil & gas field services

(G-9058)
CAM SPECIALTY PRODUCTS INC
10810 Katy Fwy Ste 100 (77043-5013)
PHONE..............................936 228-0824
Michael P Balas, *CEO*
James M Blake, *President*
James Craig Campagna, *President*
Gordon Hammett, *Vice Pres*
Chuck Rankin, *Vice Pres*
▲ EMP: 50
SQ FT: 30,000
SALES (est): 8.4MM
SALES (corp-wide): 164.4MM **Privately Held**
SIC: 2821 Plastics materials & resins
HQ: Cam Specialty Intermediate Holdings, Inc.
    10810 Katy Fwy Ste 100
    Houston TX

(G-9059)
CAMAC INTERNATIONAL CORP (PA)
1330 Post Oak Blvd Ste 22 (77056-3031)
PHONE..............................713 965-5100
Kamoru A Lawal, *President*
Kase Lawal, *Chairman*
J Alex Loftus, *Exec VP*
Daniel Ogbonna, *Exec VP*
Fisoye Delano, *Senior VP*
EMP: 35
SQ FT: 100,000
SALES (est): 1.4B **Privately Held**
WEB: www.camac.com
SIC: 8711 6552 1382 8741 Engineering services; subdividers & developers; oil & gas exploration services; construction management; oil consultants

(G-9060)
CAMEO FABRICATORS INC
13835 Chrisman Rd (77039-1997)
PHONE..............................281 449-6207
Larry Coleman, *President*
Kathleen Coleman, *Treasurer*
EMP: 20
SQ FT: 44,000
SALES (est): 4MM **Privately Held**
WEB: www.cameofab.com
SIC: 3494 3498 3441 Valves & pipe fittings; pipe fittings, fabricated from purchased pipe; fabricated structural metal

(G-9061)
CAMERON INTERNATIONAL CORP
Also Called: Cameron Process Valves
8820 Meldrum Ln (77075-2218)
PHONE..............................713 946-2122
Jeoff Johnson, *Manager*
EMP: 63 **Publicly Held**
WEB: www.products.slb.com
SIC: 5085 7699 3494 Valves & fittings; valve repair, industrial; valves & pipe fittings
HQ: Cameron International Corporation
    4646 W Sam Houston Pkwy N
    Houston TX 77041

(G-9062)
CAMERON INTERNATIONAL CORP
11210 Equity Dr (77041-8241)
PHONE..............................713 849-7789
Matt Bajmanlou, *Engineer*
Carthy Patrick, *Branch Mgr*
EMP: 58 **Publicly Held**
WEB: www.products.slb.com
SIC: 3533 Oil field machinery & equipment
HQ: Cameron International Corporation
    4646 W Sam Houston Pkwy N
    Houston TX 77041

(G-9063)
CAMERON INTERNATIONAL CORP
Also Called: Cameron Drilling Systems
4601 Westway Park Blvd (77041-2037)
PHONE..............................713 939-2211
Eric Polansky, *District Mgr*
Janet Gonyer, *Project Mgr*
Kitty Harvey, *Engineer*
Bruce Boulanger, *Senior Engr*
Charles Curtis, *Manager*

EMP: 13 **Publicly Held**
WEB: www.products.slb.com
SIC: 3533 Oil & gas field machinery
HQ: Cameron International Corporation
    4646 W Sam Houston Pkwy N
    Houston TX 77041

(G-9064)
CAMERON INTERNATIONAL CORP
Cameron Measurement Systems
3600 Briarpark Dr (77042-5206)
PHONE..............................281 582-9500
Celine Gerson, *Vice Pres*
Christopher Krummel, *Vice Pres*
Josh Stanford, *Vice Pres*
Elaine Good, *Engineer*
Giuseppe Biasco, *VP Finance*
EMP: 90 **Publicly Held**
WEB: www.products.slb.com
SIC: 3563 3491 3533 Air & gas compressors; automatic regulating & control valves; oil field machinery & equipment
HQ: Cameron International Corporation
    4646 W Sam Houston Pkwy N
    Houston TX 77041

(G-9065)
CAMERON INTERNATIONAL CORP
Also Called: Cameron A Schlumberger Company
4800 W Greens Rd Ste 400 (77066-4866)
PHONE..............................281 716-1000
Milton Sheppard, *Manager*
EMP: 17 **Publicly Held**
WEB: www.products.slb.com
SIC: 3533 Oil & gas field machinery
HQ: Cameron International Corporation
    4646 W Sam Houston Pkwy N
    Houston TX 77041

(G-9066)
CAMERON INTERNATIONAL CORP
6500 Brittmoore Rd (77041-5109)
PHONE..............................601 629-3300
Jesse Picard, *Plant Mgr*
Donald Cross, *Sales/Mktg Mgr*
EMP: 850 **Publicly Held**
WEB: www.products.slb.com
SIC: 3531 3541 3533 Construction machinery; machine tools, metal cutting type; oil & gas field machinery
HQ: Cameron International Corporation
    4646 W Sam Houston Pkwy N
    Houston TX 77041

(G-9067)
CAMERON INTERNATIONAL CORP
Cameron Engineered Valves
4646 W Sam Houston Pkwy N (77041-8214)
P.O. Box 1212 (77251-1212)
PHONE..............................713 939-2211
Hakan Eser, *Vice Pres*
Reese Sparacino, *Project Mgr*
Quang Nguyen, *Buyer*
Matthew Butler, *Purchasing*
Marla Oquinn, *Purchasing*
EMP: 800
SQ FT: 40,000 **Publicly Held**
WEB: www.products.slb.com
SIC: 1389 Oil field services
HQ: Cameron International Corporation
    4646 W Sam Houston Pkwy N
    Houston TX 77041

(G-9068)
CAMERON INTERNATIONAL CORP
Also Called: Cameron Energy Services
16250 Port Nw Ste 100 (77041-2667)
PHONE..............................713 354-1900
John Bartos, *President*
Robert Rajeski, *Manager*
EMP: 250 **Publicly Held**
WEB: www.products.slb.com
SIC: 3511 3563 3519 3491 Turbines & turbine generator sets; gas turbines, mechanical drive; air & gas compressors; internal combustion engines; automatic regulating & control valves; oil field machinery & equipment

HQ: Cameron International Corporation
    4646 W Sam Houston Pkwy N
    Houston TX 77041

(G-9069)
CAMERON INTERNATIONAL CORP
Also Called: Cameron's Valves & Measurement
8820 Meldrum Ln (77075-2218)
PHONE..............................713 946-2122
John Grady, *Manager*
EMP: 25 **Publicly Held**
WEB: www.products.slb.com
SIC: 1389 Oil field services
HQ: Cameron International Corporation
    4646 W Sam Houston Pkwy N
    Houston TX 77041

(G-9070)
CAMERON INTERNATIONAL CORP
Cameron Subsea Manifolds US
4646 W Sam Houston Pkwy N (77041-8214)
PHONE..............................713 939-2650
Mike Cote, *Branch Mgr*
EMP: 413 **Publicly Held**
WEB: www.products.slb.com
SIC: 1389 Oil field services
HQ: Cameron International Corporation
    4646 W Sam Houston Pkwy N
    Houston TX 77041

(G-9071)
CAMERON INTERNATIONAL CORP
Also Called: Cameron Process Systems
4901 W Sam Houston Pkwy N (77041-8218)
PHONE..............................713 849-7500
Jimmy Lewis, *Branch Mgr*
EMP: 49 **Publicly Held**
WEB: www.products.slb.com
SIC: 1389 Oil field services
HQ: Cameron International Corporation
    4646 W Sam Houston Pkwy N
    Houston TX 77041

(G-9072)
CAMERON INTERNATIONAL CORP (DH)
4646 W Sam Houston Pkwy N (77041-8214)
PHONE..............................713 939-2282
R Scott Rowe, *President*
Jesse Jones, *General Mgr*
Mike Hintz, *District Mgr*
Chris Shea, *District Mgr*
Daniel Garcia, *Business Mgr*
◆ EMP: 40
SALES (est): 4.7B **Publicly Held**
WEB: www.slb.com
SIC: 3563 3491 3533 Air & gas compressors; automatic regulating & control valves; oil field machinery & equipment
HQ: Schlumberger Limited
    5599 San Felipe St Fl 17
    Houston TX 77056
    713 513-2000

(G-9073)
CAMERON INTERNATIONAL CORP
Cameron Drilling Systems
4646 W Sam Houston Pkwy N (77041-8214)
PHONE..............................281 901-3100
Lance Westcott, *Branch Mgr*
Brad Johnson, *Manager*
EMP: 413 **Publicly Held**
WEB: www.products.slb.com
SIC: 3533 Oil & gas field machinery
HQ: Cameron International Corporation
    4646 W Sam Houston Pkwy N
    Houston TX 77041

(G-9074)
CAMERON INTERNATIONAL HOLDING (DH)
4646 W Sam Houston Pkwy N (77041-8214)
PHONE..............................713 513-3300
Mark Prickett, *Principal*
Charles Sledge, *Vice Pres*

Chintan Barbhaya, *Plant Mgr*
Maria Gutierrez, *Project Mgr*
Yolanda Wright, *Buyer*
▼ EMP: 10
SALES (est): 82.7MM **Publicly Held**
WEB: www.products.slb.com
SIC: 1389 Oil field services

(G-9075)
CAMERON LNG HOLDINGS LLC
2925 Briarpark Dr # 1000 (77042-3720)
P.O. Box 439, Hackberry LA (70645-0439)
PHONE..............................832 783-5500
Farhad Ahrabi, *CEO*
John O'Leary, *COO*
Farid Bogani, *Vice Pres*
Andre Bruce, *Opers Staff*
Anne Leblanc, *Senior Buyer*
◆ EMP: 25 EST: 2013
SALES (est): 6.8MM **Privately Held**
WEB: www.cameronlng.com
SIC: 1311 1321 Natural gas production; natural gas liquids production

(G-9076)
CAMERON RIG SOLUTIONS LLC (DH)
Also Called: Cameron Rig Solutions, Inc.
6500 Brittmoore Rd (77041-5109)
PHONE..............................832 782-6500
William C Lemmer, *President*
Glenn Jude Chiasson, *President*
Dan C Eckermann, *President*
R G Croyle, *Vice Pres*
Christopher A Krummel, *Vice Pres*
◆ EMP: 83
SALES (est): 30.7MM **Publicly Held**
SIC: 3532 Drills & drilling equipment, mining (except oil & gas)

(G-9077)
CAMERON SOLUTIONS INC
4901 W Sam Houston Pkwy N (77041-8218)
PHONE..............................713 896-3600
Gary Sams, *Manager*
EMP: 20 **Publicly Held**
SIC: 8732 8731 3533 Research services, except laboratory; commercial physical research; oil & gas field machinery
HQ: Cameron Solutions Inc.
    3600 Briarpark Dr
    Houston TX 77042
    713 849-7500

(G-9078)
CAMERON SOLUTIONS INC
10810 Train Ct (77041-7041)
PHONE..............................713 849-6556
EMP: 55 **Publicly Held**
SIC: 3533 Gas field machinery & equipment
HQ: Cameron Solutions Inc.
    3600 Briarpark Dr
    Houston TX 77042
    713 849-7500

(G-9079)
CAMERON SOLUTIONS INC (DH)
Also Called: Natco
3600 Briarpark Dr (77042-5206)
PHONE..............................713 849-7500
John U Clarke, *Ch of Bd*
William C Lemmer, *President*
Stuart Taylor, *Vice Pres*
Jaime Ledergerber, *Treasurer*
Katherine Ellis, *Admin Sec*
◆ EMP: 200
SQ FT: 65,000
SALES (est): 362.3MM **Publicly Held**
SIC: 3533 3569 3533 Gas field machinery & equipment; oil & gas wells: building, repairing & dismantling; separators for steam, gas, vapor or air (machinery)

(G-9080)
CAMP LOGAN CEMENT WORKS INC
1212 Asbury St (77007-3194)
P.O. Box 70126 (77270-0126)
PHONE..............................713 869-3385
Larry W Huseman, *President*
Martha A Huseman, *Corp Secy*
EMP: 40 EST: 1923
SQ FT: 800

SALES (est): 5.9MM **Privately Held**
WEB: www.camplogancement.com
SIC: 3272 3271 3446 Steps, prefabricated concrete; blocks, concrete or cinder: standard; brick, concrete; architectural metalwork

(G-9081)
CAMPBELL CONCRETE & MTLS LP
Also Called: Campbell Contrete & Materials
3935 Schurmier Rd (77047-4803)
PHONE................................713 734-6600
Paul Bundic, *Manager*
EMP: 14
SALES (corp-wide): 20.8B **Privately Held**
WEB: www.michaeljames.com
SIC: 3273 Ready-mixed concrete
HQ: Campbell Concrete & Materials, L.P.
16155 Park Row Ste 120
Houston TX 77084
281 592-5201

(G-9082)
CAMPBELL CONCRETE & MTLS LP (DH)
Also Called: Gulf Caost Stabilized Mtls
16155 Park Row Ste 120 (77084-6971)
PHONE................................281 592-5201
Scott Ducoff, *Managing Prtnr*
Doug Lilley, *Office Mgr*
▲ EMP: 50
SQ FT: 8,000
SALES (est): 136.1MM
SALES (corp-wide): 20.8B **Privately Held**
WEB: www.michaeljames.com
SIC: 3273 Ready-mixed concrete

(G-9083)
CAMPBELL CONCRETE & MTLS LP
9500 Harwin Dr (77036-1704)
PHONE................................713 783-4761
Richard Saenz, *Manager*
EMP: 9
SALES (corp-wide): 20.8B **Privately Held**
WEB: www.michaeljames.com
SIC: 3273 Ready-mixed concrete
HQ: Campbell Concrete & Materials, L.P.
16155 Park Row Ste 120
Houston TX 77084
281 592-5201

(G-9084)
CAN-AM AERO SUPPORT LLC
Also Called: Intech Aerospace
4750 World Hstn Pkwy (77032-2588)
PHONE................................281 810-4400
Salley Siau Mee Chung, *Managing Prtnr*
Sally Chung,
Todd Wilkinson,
EMP: 85 EST: 2012
SALES (est): 8.6MM **Privately Held**
WEB: www.intechaero.com
SIC: 3728 4581 Aircraft parts & equipment; aircraft servicing & repairing

(G-9085)
CANRIG DRILLING TECHNOLOGY LTD
19510 Oil Center Blvd (77073-3355)
PHONE................................281 443-1414
Kevin Harsy, *Vice Pres*
Rob Guillory, *Vice Pres*
Anthony Korzeniewski, *Electrical Engi*
Zachary Parrott, *Sales Staff*
Randy Clark, *VP Mktg*
EMP: 13
SALES (est): 1.1MM **Privately Held**
WEB: www.nabors.com
SIC: 1389 Oil field services

(G-9086)
CANYON MANUFACTURING SVCS INC
523 Rankin Cir N (77073-4311)
PHONE................................281 876-7105
Michael J Henn, *President*
Susan Henn, *Vice Pres*
JP Zuehlke, *Production*
Renee Somers, *Purch Mgr*
Richard Back, *Engineer*
EMP: 30
SQ FT: 12,000

SALES (est): 8.7MM **Privately Held**
WEB: www.canyon-mfg.com
SIC: 3672 Circuit boards, television & radio printed

(G-9087)
CANYON MIDSTREAM PARTNERS LLC (PA)
1331 Lamar St Ste 1675 (77010-3133)
PHONE................................713 655-9500
Michael Walsh, *President*
Mark Fuqua, *Senior VP*
Dale Harper, *Senior VP*
Bret Shapot, *Engineer*
Jocelyn Orellana, *Assistant*
EMP: 20
SQ FT: 11,000
SALES (est): 6.9MM **Privately Held**
WEB: www.canyonmidstream.com
SIC: 1382 Oil & gas exploration services

(G-9088)
CANYON OFFSHORE INC (HQ)
5212 Brittmoore Rd (77041-7108)
PHONE................................713 856-6010
David Tucker, *President*
Doug Stroud, *Senior VP*
Kevin Brennan, *Vice Pres*
Jeremiah Hebert, *Vice Pres*
▲ EMP: 55
SQ FT: 15,000
SALES (est): 70.3MM
SALES (corp-wide): 751.9MM **Publicly Held**
SIC: 1389 Construction, repair & dismantling services; oil field services
PA: Helix Energy Solutions Group, Inc.
3505 W Sam Houston Pkwy N S
Houston TX 77043
281 618-0400

(G-9089)
CARBER HOLDINGS INC (PA)
Also Called: Car-Ber Testing Services
12600 N Featherwood Dr # 450 (77034-4451)
PHONE................................713 797-2859
Jim Nattier, *CEO*
John Tucci, *President*
Joseph Kring, *Opers Mgr*
Joel Troyer, *Opers Staff*
Hank Winfield, *CFO*
EMP: 20
SQ FT: 7,000
SALES (est): 150.7MM **Privately Held**
WEB: www.hydrochempsc.com
SIC: 1389 7389 Testing, measuring, surveying & analysis services; pipe testing, oil field service; surveying wells; petroleum refinery inspection service

(G-9090)
CARBIDE GRINDING INC
9317 Gamebird Ln (77034-3591)
PHONE................................713 944-0015
Philip D Sanders, *President*
Robin Boyd, *General Mgr*
Lee Lefforge, *Admin Sec*
EMP: 16
SQ FT: 5,700
SALES (est): 3.1MM **Privately Held**
WEB: www.carbidegrinding.com
SIC: 2819 3545 3541 Carbides; machine tool accessories; machine tools, metal cutting type

(G-9091)
CARBO CERAMICS INC (PA)
575 N Dairy Ashford Rd # 300 (77079-1121)
PHONE................................281 921-6400
Shelly Rosen, *CEO*
Gary A Kolstad, *Ch of Bd*
Michael Carbo, *Managing Prtnr*
Daniel Hunter, *Principal*
Don Conkle, *Vice Pres*
EMP: 277
SALES: 161.7MM **Privately Held**
WEB: www.carboceramics.com
SIC: 3291 5945 8742 7371 Abrasive products; ceramics supplies; management consulting services; custom computer programming services

(G-9092)
CARGO CRATING COMPANY LTD
Also Called: Cargo Forwarding International
15370 Vantage Pkwy W (77032-1926)
PHONE................................713 699-0172
Michael Gallagher,
Alex Gallagher,
EMP: 14
SALES (est): 2.1MM **Privately Held**
WEB: www.cargocratingco.com
SIC: 4783 4212 4225 2449 Crating goods for shipping; local trucking, without storage; general warehousing & storage; wood containers; wood pallets & skids

(G-9093)
CARLTON FOODS CORP (HQ)
2030 North Loop W Ste 100 (77018-8107)
PHONE................................830 625-7583
Randy Rust, *President*
Thomas M Dalton, *President*
Randy Rust, *President*
Tom Wippman, *Admin Sec*
EMP: 84 EST: 1996
SQ FT: 2,000
SALES (est): 13.1MM
SALES (corp-wide): 84.7MM **Privately Held**
WEB: www.carltonfoods.com
SIC: 2013 5812 Smoked meats from purchased meat; eating places
PA: Atlantic Beverage Company, Inc.
1033 Skokie Blvd Ste 600
Northbrook IL 60062
847 412-6200

(G-9094)
CARPORTS CHILDERS & STRUCTURES
11711 Brittmoore Park Dr (77041-6923)
P.O. Box 800397 (77280-0397)
PHONE................................713 460-2181
Morris Babin, *President*
Tod M Babin, *Vice Pres*
Everardo Rodriguez, *Engineer*
Tod Babin, *Info Tech Mgr*
EMP: 11
SQ FT: 46,000
SALES (est): 2.2MM **Privately Held**
WEB: www.childersonline.com
SIC: 3448 3444 3312 2394 Carports: prefabricated metal; docks: prefabricated metal; canopies, sheet metal; blast furnaces & steel mills; canvas & related products

(G-9095)
CAST FIREPLACES (PA)
10425 Tanner Rd (77041-7439)
PHONE................................713 937-1080
Robert W Milner, *Owner*
EMP: 11
SQ FT: 30,000
SALES (est): 2.5MM **Privately Held**
WEB: www.castfireplaces.com
SIC: 3272 1799 Cast stone, concrete; home/office interiors finishing, furnishing & remodeling

(G-9096)
CASTEX ENERGY INC
333 Clay St Ste 2000 (77002-2569)
PHONE................................281 447-8601
John Stoika, *President*
Joe Melnyk, *Vice Pres*
Virginia Averill, *Production*
Mark Johnson, *Engineer*
George Payne, *Asst Controller*
EMP: 35
SALES (est): 41.6MM **Privately Held**
WEB: www.castexenergy.com
SIC: 1382 Oil & gas exploration services

(G-9097)
CASTRO CHEESE COMPANY INC
Also Called: La Vakita
4006 Campbell Rd (77080-1325)
PHONE................................713 460-0329
Mark Korsmeyer, *President*
Joel Clark, *Corp Secy*
David Meyer, *Vice Pres*
Saul Yabarra, *Director*
EMP: 50

SQ FT: 35,000
SALES (est): 11.7MM
SALES (corp-wide): 15.8B **Privately Held**
WEB: www.lavaquitacheese.com
SIC: 2022 Processed cheese
PA: Dairy Farmers Of America, Inc.
1405 N 98th St
Kansas City KS 66111
816 801-6455

(G-9098)
CASTRONICS INC
7814 Miller Road 3 (77049-1734)
PHONE................................308 235-4881
Perry Van Newkirk, *President*
Kori Hrbek, *Manager*
EMP: 108
SALES (est): 16.2MM
SALES (corp-wide): 655MM **Publicly Held**
SIC: 3498 3599 Tube fabricating (contract bending & shaping); machine shop, jobbing & repair
HQ: Castronics Holding Co., Llc
4386 E Highway 30
Kimball NE 69145
308 235-4881

(G-9099)
CATEC AMERICAS INC
1400 Brdfeld Blvd Ste 200 (77084)
PHONE................................281 398-8806
Jie Cai, *President*
Cathy Cai, *Vice Pres*
EMP: 10
SQ FT: 1,000
SALES (est): 2.4MM **Privately Held**
WEB: www.catecamericas.com
SIC: 3533 Oil field machinery & equipment

(G-9100)
CATERPILLAR INC
13105 Nw Fwy Ste 1010 (77040-6354)
PHONE................................713 895-2316
Richard Barber, *Project Mgr*
Jim Bileenberg, *Branch Mgr*
Jennifer Shafer, *Manager*
Mark Kingsley, *Director*
EMP: 355
SALES (corp-wide): 53.8B **Publicly Held**
WEB: www.caterpillar.com
SIC: 3531 Construction machinery
PA: Caterpillar Inc.
510 Lake Cook Rd Ste 100
Deerfield IL 60015
224 551-4000

(G-9101)
CATERPILLAR INC
10203 Sam Houston Park Dr (77064-4670)
PHONE................................713 895-2300
Ricardo Rodriguez, *Accounts Mgr*
Donal Gavagan, *Director*
EMP: 17
SALES (corp-wide): 53.8B **Publicly Held**
WEB: www.caterpillar.com
SIC: 3531 Construction machinery
PA: Caterpillar Inc.
510 Lake Cook Rd Ste 100
Deerfield IL 60015
224 551-4000

(G-9102)
CATHEDRAL ENERGY SERVICES INC (PA)
6622 Willow Brook Park (77066-3012)
PHONE................................303 825-1001
P Scott Macfarlane, *President*
Randy Pustanyk, *COO*
Michael Hill, *CFO*
Peter Blazek, *Manager*
Nancy Barrett, *Office Admin*
EMP: 26
SALES (est): 13.2MM **Privately Held**
WEB: www.cathedralenergyservices.com
SIC: 1381 Directional drilling oil & gas wells

(G-9103)
CAVERN SOLUTIONS INC
2515 Texas St (77003-3240)
P.O. Box 1717, Clute (77531-1717)
PHONE................................713 393-7733
John Kyle, *CEO*
EMP: 13 EST: 2014
SQ FT: 10,000

SALES: 13.2MM **Privately Held**
WEB: www.cavernsolutions.com
SIC: 8711 1389 1381 7389 Petroleum, mining & chemical engineers; oil consultants; drilling oil & gas wells; reworking oil & gas wells;

(G-9104)
CB&I LLC
CB&i Constructors
3600 W Sam Houston Pkwy S (77042-5096)
P.O. Box 12210, San Luis Obispo CA (93406-2210)
PHONE....................832 513-1848
Steven W Knott, *Vice Pres*
Brad Smith, *Human Res Dir*
Brian M Sherman, *Sales Staff*
Mike Keller, *Manager*
Jennifer Hessels, *Manager*
EMP: 78
SALES (corp-wide): 8.4B **Privately Held**
WEB: www.cbi.com
SIC: 3443 1721 Tanks, standard or custom fabricated: metal plate; industrial painting
HQ: Cb&i Llc
915 N Eldridge Pkwy # 10
Houston TX 77079
281 870-5000

(G-9105)
CB&I LLC
Also Called: McDermott International
9803 Sheldon Rd (77049-1299)
PHONE....................281 456-5700
Duncan Wigney, *Principal*
EMP: 37
SALES (corp-wide): 8.4B **Privately Held**
WEB: www.cbi.com
SIC: 3443 1791 3312 Fabricated plate work (boiler shop); structural steel erection; blast furnaces & steel mills
HQ: Cb&i Llc
915 N Eldridge Pkwy # 10
Houston TX 77079
281 870-5000

(G-9106)
CB&I LLC
7330 Neuhaus St (77061-4612)
PHONE....................713 649-4277
Ken Rowley, *Branch Mgr*
EMP: 194
SALES (corp-wide): 8.4B **Privately Held**
WEB: www.cbi.com
SIC: 3443 3312 1791 Fabricated plate work (boiler shop); blast furnaces & steel mills; storage tanks, metal: erection
HQ: Cb&i Llc
915 N Eldridge Pkwy # 10
Houston TX 77079
281 870-5000

(G-9107)
CB&I LLC
Also Called: Chicago Bridge & Iron Company
3600 W Sam Houston Pkwy S (77042-5096)
PHONE....................713 375-8000
Carla Aguilar, *General Mgr*
Andrew Brock, *Business Mgr*
Regina Verducci, *Counsel*
Frank Mulcahey, *Project Mgr*
Angelo Yoder, *Opers Staff*
EMP: 216
SALES (corp-wide): 8.4B **Privately Held**
WEB: www.cbi.com
SIC: 3443 3312 1791 Fabricated plate work (boiler shop); blast furnaces & steel mills; storage tanks, metal: erection
HQ: Cb&i Llc
915 N Eldridge Pkwy # 10
Houston TX 77079
281 870-5000

(G-9108)
CB&I LLC
5850 Rogerdale Rd Ste 150 (77072-1666)
PHONE....................713 485-1000
Peter Olson, *Branch Mgr*
EMP: 216

SALES (corp-wide): 8.4B **Privately Held**
WEB: www.cbi.com
SIC: 3443 3312 1791 Fabricated plate work (boiler shop); blast furnaces & steel mills; storage tanks, metal: erection
HQ: Cb&i Llc
915 N Eldridge Pkwy # 10
Houston TX 77079
281 870-5000

(G-9109)
CCI THERMAL TECH TEXAS INC
15550 Vickery Dr Ste 100 (77032-2583)
PHONE....................855 219-2101
Harold A Roozen, *CEO*
Cathy Roozen, *Admin Sec*
EMP: 12
SQ FT: 1,700
SALES (est): 6.5MM **Publicly Held**
WEB: www.ccithermal.com
SIC: 3433 3569 Heating equipment, except electric; filters
HQ: Thermon Heating Systems, Inc
5918 Roper Rd Nw
Edmonton AB T6B 3
780 466-3178

(G-9110)
CCPJV INC
Also Called: Complete Curb Products
7229 Fairview St (77041-2103)
PHONE....................713 690-1622
John Boger, *President*
Sherman Law, *Vice Pres*
EMP: 30
SQ FT: 25,000
SALES (est): 7.2MM **Privately Held**
WEB: www.completecurbs.com
SIC: 3444 Sheet metal specialties, not stamped

(G-9111)
CCT CORPORATION
300 N Palmer St (77003-1219)
PHONE....................713 223-2521
Chris Lin, *President*
EMP: 10
SALES (est): 1.1MM **Privately Held**
SIC: 2821 Plastics materials & resins

(G-9112)
CDB SOFTWARE INC (PA)
10011 Meadowglen Ln # 110 (77042-3760)
P.O. Box 420789 (77242-0789)
PHONE....................713 588-1778
Richard E Barry, *President*
EMP: 18
SALES (est): 5MM **Privately Held**
WEB: www.cdbsoftware.com
SIC: 7372 Application computer software

(G-9113)
CDI VESSEL HOLDINGS LLC
2500 Citywest Blvd # 2200 (77042-3000)
PHONE....................713 361-2600
EMP: 657
SALES (est): 612.9K
SALES (corp-wide): 516.9MM **Privately Held**
SIC: 1389 Oil/Gas Field Services
PA: Cal Dive International, Inc.
2500 Citywest Blvd # 2200
Houston TX 77042
713 361-2600

(G-9114)
CDM RESOURCE MANAGEMENT LLC (HQ)
20405 State Hwy (77070)
PHONE....................281 376-2980
Paul Ludwick, *President*
Kenny Callihan, *Area Mgr*
Randy Garcia, *Area Mgr*
Kenneth Smith, *Counsel*
Trey Shaddox, *Vice Pres*
EMP: 70
SQ FT: 39,158
SALES (est): 251MM
SALES (corp-wide): 698.3MM **Publicly Held**
WEB: www.cdmrm.com
SIC: 1389 Oil field services
PA: Usa Compression Partners, Lp
111 Congress Ave Ste 2400
Austin TX 78701
512 473-2662

(G-9115)
CEDAR CREEK II
700 Louisiana St Fl 33 (77002-2700)
PHONE....................713 354-2100
Matthew Sakurada, *Principal*
Carla Bayer, *Principal*
EMP: 27
SALES (est): 6.1MM **Privately Held**
SIC: 3621 Motors & generators

(G-9116)
CEDAR MILL CO INC
2121 Brittmoore Rd # 200 (77043-2236)
PHONE....................713 984-2600
Stephen Blalock, *President*
Aimee Blalock, *Admin Sec*
EMP: 32 **EST:** 2009
SQ FT: 15,000
SALES (est): 4.5MM **Privately Held**
WEB: www.cedarmillco.com
SIC: 5031 2431 Doors & windows; window shutters, wood

(G-9117)
CEDRA PHARMACY HOUSTON LLC
1607 S Post Oak Ln (77056-2807)
PHONE....................713 621-0621
Jennifer Fullbright, *Mng Member*
EMP: 20
SQ FT: 1,500
SALES (est): 319K **Privately Held**
WEB: www.cedrapharmacy.com
SIC: 5912 2542 Drug stores; locker boxes, postal service: except wood

(G-9118)
CEE-SAN MCH & FABRICATION CO
5609 Clara Rd (77041-7208)
PHONE....................713 466-4586
Charles Sherretts, *President*
Kurt Sherretts, *General Mgr*
David Winkelman, *Foreman/Supr*
EMP: 12
SQ FT: 10,000
SALES (est): 2MM **Privately Held**
WEB: www.ceesan.com
SIC: 3533 3599 Oil field machinery & equipment; machine shop, jobbing & repair

(G-9119)
CELLTEX THERAPEUTICS CORP (PA)
2401 Ftn View Dr Ste 416 (77057)
PHONE....................713 590-1000
David G Eller, *CEO*
Madison Mauze, *President*
Glenn McGee, *President*
Andrea Ferrenz, *Exec VP*
Candy Eller, *Vice Pres*
EMP: 21
SALES (est): 4.2MM **Privately Held**
WEB: www.celltexbank.com
SIC: 2834 Pharmaceutical preparations

(G-9120)
CEMEX INC (HQ)
10100 Katy Fwy Ste 300 (77043-5267)
P.O. Box 24731, West Palm Beach FL (33416-4731)
PHONE....................713 650-6200
Ignacio Madridejos, *President*
Gonzalo Galindo, *President*
Andrew Tate, *Vice Chairman*
Juan San Agustin, *Exec VP*
Robert F Craddock, *Exec VP*
◆ **EMP:** 400
SQ FT: 9,000
SALES (est): 5.7B **Privately Held**
WEB: www.cemex.com
SIC: 3273 3271 3272 5032 Ready-mixed concrete; concrete block & brick; concrete products; cement

(G-9121)
CEMEX CEMENT INC (DH)
10100 Katy Fwy Ste 300 (77043-5267)
PHONE....................713 650-6200
Thomas Edgeller, *Corp Secy*
Thomas Damon, *Vice Pres*
Doug Augeri, *Vice Pres*
Cheryl Ellis, *Opers Staff*
Rafe Allen, *Accounts Mgr*

◆ **EMP:** 500
SQ FT: 125,000
SALES (est): 996.1MM **Privately Held**
WEB: www.cemexusa.com
SIC: 3273 3241 Ready-mixed concrete; portland cement
HQ: Cemex, Inc.
10100 Katy Fwy Ste 300
Houston TX 77043
713 650-6200

(G-9122)
CEMEX CONSTRUCTION MTLS LP (PA)
929 Gessner Rd Ste 1900 (77024-2317)
PHONE....................713 650-6200
Clarence C Comer, *CEO*
Mike Egan, *Exec VP*
▲ **EMP:** 10
SALES (est): 162MM **Privately Held**
WEB: www.cemexusa.com
SIC: 3273 Ready-mixed concrete

(G-9123)
CEMEX CONSTRUCTION MTLS S LLC
Also Called: Admin - South Cement Const Pro
929 Gessner Rd Ste 1900 (77024-2317)
PHONE....................713 650-6200
James Lane, *Vice Pres*
Lucas Mooney, *Business Anlyst*
Karl Watson, *Branch Mgr*
Joshua Hernandez, *Manager*
Josue Rodriguez, *Technology*
EMP: 27 **Privately Held**
WEB: www.cemexusa.com
SIC: 3273 Ready-mixed concrete
HQ: Cemex Construction Materials South, Llc
2088 E 20th St
Yuma AZ 85365
928 343-4100

(G-9124)
CEMEX CONSTRUCTION MTLS S LLC
Also Called: Cem - Houston Terminal
6203 Industrial Way (77011-1125)
PHONE....................713 967-5416
Clifford Scrivener, *Branch Mgr*
EMP: 36
WEB: www.cemexusa.com
SIC: 3273 Ready-mixed concrete
HQ: Cemex Construction Materials South, Llc
2088 E 20th St
Yuma AZ 85365
928 343-4100

(G-9125)
CEMEX CONSTRUCTION MTLS S LLC
Also Called: Mosielee Rm Dual
12132 Mosielee St (77086-3500)
PHONE....................281 260-9651
EMP: 36 **Privately Held**
WEB: www.cemexusa.com
SIC: 3273 Ready-mixed concrete
HQ: Cemex Construction Materials South, Llc
2088 E 20th St
Yuma AZ 85365
928 343-4100

(G-9126)
CEMEX CONSTRUCTION MTLS S LLC
Also Called: Holmes Rm
202 Holmes Rd (77045-1502)
EMP: 36
SALES (corp-wide): 14.9B **Privately Held**
SIC: 3241 Mfg Hydraulic Cement
HQ: Cemex Construction Materials South, Llc
2088 E 20th St
Yuma AZ 85365
928 343-4100

▲ = Import ▼=Export
◆ =Import/Export

(G-9127)
CEMEX CONSTRUCTION MTLS S LLC
Also Called: Cutten Road Rm Dual
11331 Cutten Rd (77066-3705)
PHONE..................................281 444-8306
Fructuoso Irigoyen, *Manager*
EMP: 30 **Privately Held**
WEB: www.cemexusa.com
SIC: 3273 Ready-mixed concrete
HQ: Cemex Construction Materials South, Llc
2088 E 20th St
Yuma AZ 85365
928 343-4100

(G-9128)
CEMEX CONSTRUCTION MTLS S LLC
920 Mmrial Cy Way Ste 100 (77024)
PHONE..................................713 650-6200
Gilberto Perez,
David Berger,
EMP: 2600
SALES (est): 136.1MM **Privately Held**
WEB: www.cemex.com
SIC: 3271 3273 3272 1422 Blocks, concrete or cinder: standard; ready-mixed concrete; pipe, concrete or lined with concrete; crushed & broken limestone
HQ: Cemex Materials Llc
1501 Belvedere Rd
West Palm Beach FL 33406
561 833-5555

(G-9129)
CEMEX CONSTRUCTION MTLS S LLC
Also Called: Navigation Rm Dual
5303 Navigation Blvd (77011-1025)
PHONE..................................713 767-7983
Craig McGaugsy, *Branch Mgr*
Brian Richie, *Manager*
EMP: 9 **Privately Held**
WEB: www.cemexusa.com
SIC: 3273 Ready-mixed concrete
HQ: Cemex Construction Materials South, Llc
2088 E 20th St
Yuma AZ 85365
928 343-4100

(G-9130)
CEMEX INTERNATIONAL TRDG LLC
10100 Katy Fwy Ste 3000 (77043-5267)
PHONE..................................713 650-6200
Fernando A Gonzalez, *CEO*
Jaime Elizondo, *President*
Joaqun Estrada, *President*
Maher Al-Haffar, *Exec VP*
Mauricio Doehner, *Exec VP*
EMP: 50
SALES (est): 170.2K **Privately Held**
SIC: 3273 Ready-mixed concrete

(G-9131)
CEMEX MATERIALS LLC
Also Called: Houston Shared Services
929 Gessner Rd Ste 1900 (77024-2317)
PHONE..................................713 650-6200
EMP: 42 **Privately Held**
SIC: 3273 Ready-mixed concrete
HQ: Cemex Materials Llc
1501 Belvedere Rd
West Palm Beach FL 33406
561 833-5555

(G-9132)
CEMEX MATERIALS LLC
6560 Langfield Rd Bldg 3 (77092-1008)
P.O. Box 55309 (77255-5309)
PHONE..................................832 590-5400
Claire Branch, *Regional Mgr*
Marge Harper, *Manager*
EMP: 100 **Privately Held**
SIC: 3273 Ready-mixed concrete
HQ: Cemex Materials Llc
1501 Belvedere Rd
West Palm Beach FL 33406
561 833-5555

(G-9133)
CEMEX SOUTHEAST LLC (HQ)
840 Gessner Rd Ste 1400 (77024-4152)
PHONE..................................713 722-5818
Luis Gonzalez, *Human Res Mgr*
David B Rumsey, *Sales Staff*
EMP: 104
SALES (est): 84.1MM **Privately Held**
WEB: www.cemex.com
SIC: 3273 Ready-mixed concrete

(G-9134)
CEMEX TRADING LLC (DH)
920 Mmrial Cy Way Ste 100 (77024)
PHONE..................................713 650-6200
Fernando A Gonz Lez, *CEO*
Guillermo Martinez, *Exec VP*
Laura Lee, *Director*
EMP: 10
SALES (est): 2.2MM **Privately Held**
WEB: www.cemex.com
SIC: 3273 Ready-mixed concrete

(G-9135)
CENSORED SOLES
10222 Royal Oaks Dr (77016-3339)
PHONE..................................832 443-4365
Benard Lewis, *Owner*
EMP: 12
SALES (est): 406.8K **Privately Held**
SIC: 2211 Apparel & outerwear fabrics, cotton

(G-9136)
CENTERLINE MANUFACTURING LTD
5711 Campbell Rd (77041-6201)
PHONE..................................713 329-9070
Clint Pargmann, *CEO*
Tim Rueter, *COO*
Ken Lee, *Controller*
Vanessa Rendon, *Sales Associate*
Mike Phillips, *Manager*
▲ EMP: 60
SQ FT: 19,000
SALES (est): 11MM **Privately Held**
WEB: www.centerlinemanufacturingltd.com
SIC: 3599 Machine shop, jobbing & repair

(G-9137)
CENTRAL ADMXTURE PHRM SVCS INC
Also Called: C A P S
1000 S Loop W Ste 115 (77054-4637)
PHONE..................................713 748-2200
Cole Knutson, *Manager*
EMP: 29
SALES (corp-wide): 2.6MM **Privately Held**
WEB: www.capspharmacy.com
SIC: 2834 5122 Pharmaceutical preparations; pharmaceuticals
HQ: Central Admixture Pharmacy Services, Inc.
2525 Mcgaw Ave
Irvine CA 92614

(G-9138)
CENTRAL MANAGEMENT INC (PA)
Also Called: C M I Brokerage
820 Gessner Rd Ste 1525 (77024-4472)
PHONE..................................713 961-9777
Vic Vacek, *President*
Jan Echard, *Vice Pres*
Becky Edmonson, *Vice Pres*
Dianne Vacek, *Treasurer*
Lynn Blevins, *Controller*
EMP: 19
SALES (est): 3.4MM **Privately Held**
WEB: www.cmirealestate.com
SIC: 6798 1382 Real estate investment trusts; oil & gas exploration services

(G-9139)
CENTRAL TAPE & LABEL CO
5525 Bingle Rd (77092-2106)
PHONE..................................713 462-8585
Albert W Little, *CEO*
Darrell Little, *Vice Pres*
Dolores Little, *Treasurer*
EMP: 21
SQ FT: 15,000

SALES (est): 3MM **Privately Held**
WEB: www.centraltapeandlabel.com
SIC: 2752 Commercial printing, offset

(G-9140)
CENTURION PIPELINE LP (HQ)
5 Greenway Plz Ste 110 (77046-0521)
PHONE..................................713 215-7000
Bryan D Humphries, *President*
Jesse Mitchell, *Manager*
Margie Petrusek, *IT/INT Sup*
EMP: 25
SQ FT: 5,000
SALES: 275.2MM **Privately Held**
WEB: www.centurionpipeline.com
SIC: 1311 Crude petroleum & natural gas
PA: Lotus Midstream, Llc
2150 Town Square Pl # 395
Sugar Land TX 77479
713 234-7865

(G-9141)
CENTURY INSTR & MCH CO INC
3601 Bacor Rd (77084-7229)
PHONE..................................281 587-5333
Tammy Leared, *Treasurer*
EMP: 13
SQ FT: 6,000
SALES (est): 2.3MM **Privately Held**
WEB: www.cimco-us.com
SIC: 3599 Machine shop, jobbing & repair

(G-9142)
CENTURY MILLWORK LLC
18927 Aldine Westfield Rd (77073-3817)
PHONE..................................281 821-0191
Mike Kelly, *Info Tech Dir*
Herbert L Walpole,
Herb Walpole,
EMP: 50
SQ FT: 35,000
SALES (est): 7.8MM **Privately Held**
WEB: www.centurymillwork.com
SIC: 2435 2431 Hardwood veneer & plywood; millwork

(G-9143)
CEO PERFORMANCE CHEM LLC
Also Called: Chemstation Texas Gulf Coast
2701 Appelt Dr (77015-6553)
PHONE..................................281 457-2020
Edward Cocetti, *Mng Member*
Daniel Curnock,
EMP: 20
SALES (est): 5.4MM **Privately Held**
WEB: www.ceoperformancechemicals.com
SIC: 5169 2899 Chemical additives; chemical preparations

(G-9144)
CERAMETALS CARBIDE LLC
7425 Carbide Cir (77040-2505)
P.O. Box 5368 (77262-5368)
PHONE..................................713 937-3801
Michael O Babcock,
▼ EMP: 35
SQ FT: 16,000
SALES (est): 3.8MM
SALES (corp-wide): 15MM **Privately Held**
WEB: www.cerametals.com
SIC: 3291 Tungsten carbide abrasive
PA: Alloy Carbide Company
7827 Avenue H
Houston TX 77012
713 923-2700

(G-9145)
CERDA INDUSTRIES INC
7600 S Santa Fe Dr B-W (77061-4508)
PHONE..................................713 242-7700
Victor Cerda, *President*
Keri Cerda, *Admin Sec*
EMP: 115
SALES (est): 45.7MM **Privately Held**
WEB: www.cerdaindustries.com
SIC: 3441 Fabricated structural metal

(G-9146)
CERTOPLAST NORTH AMERICA INC
1900 West Loop S (77027-3214)
PHONE..................................832 384-1244
EMP: 20 EST: 2012

SALES (est): 1.2MM **Privately Held**
WEB: www.certoplast.com
SIC: 3842 Tape, adhesive: medicated or non-medicated

(G-9147)
CETCO ENERGY SERVICES CO LLC
Cetco Offshore
16350 Park Ten Pl Ste 217 (77084-5196)
PHONE..................................281 578-8911
Melissa Vasquez, *Accounts Mgr*
David Sellers, *Branch Mgr*
EMP: 85 **Publicly Held**
WEB: www.mineralstech.com
SIC: 1389 Oil field services; lease tanks, oil field: erecting, cleaning & repairing
HQ: Cetco Energy Services Company Llc
1001 Ochsner Blvd Ste 425
Covington LA 70433

(G-9148)
CGG MARINE (US) INC
Also Called: Fugro-Geoteam, Inc.
6100 Hillcroft St Ste 100 (77081-1012)
PHONE..................................713 369-5600
Hans Christian Vaage, *President*
W Scott Rainey, *Chairman*
Hans Meyer, *Director*
Paul Van Riel, *Director*
EMP: 15
SQ FT: 5,904
SALES (est): 339.5K
SALES (corp-wide): 1B **Privately Held**
WEB: www.fugro.com
SIC: 8999 1382 Geophysical consultant; geophysical exploration, oil & gas field; seismograph surveys
HQ: Fugro (Usa) Holdings Inc.
6100 Hillcroft St Ste 700
Houston TX 77081
713 772-3700

(G-9149)
CGG SERVICES (US) INC (HQ)
Also Called: C G G
10300 Town Park Dr (77072-5236)
PHONE..................................832 351-8300
Jean Georges Malcor, *CEO*
Colin Murdoch, *President*
Jacques Micaelli, *President*
Vincent M Thielen, *President*
Bob Vivian, *President*
◆ EMP: 500
SQ FT: 218,151
SALES (est): 921.2MM
SALES (corp-wide): 29.2MM **Privately Held**
WEB: www.cgg.com
SIC: 1382 Seismograph surveys
PA: Cgg
27 Avenue Carnot
Massy
164 473-000

(G-9150)
CGI TECHNOLOGIES SOLUTIONS INC
Also Called: Logica North America
3700 W Sam Houston Pkwy S (77042-5118)
PHONE..................................866 344-3221
Derek Jarrell, *Project Mgr*
Dick Kuan, *Branch Mgr*
EMP: 277
SALES (corp-wide): 9.2B **Privately Held**
WEB: www.cgi.com
SIC: 7372 5045 7379 Prepackaged software; computer software; computer related consulting services
HQ: Cgi Technologies And Solutions Inc.
11325 Random Hills Rd
Fairfax VA 22030
703 267-8000

(G-9151)
CGJ ENTERPRISES INC
Also Called: Banyan Foods Company
10940 S Wilcrest Dr (77099-3523)
PHONE..................................281 575-8801
Carol Sue Chiu, *President*
Jimmy Chiu, *VP Opers*
▲ EMP: 15
SQ FT: 20,000

SALES (est): 1MM **Privately Held**
SIC: 2032 5149 5153 Chinese foods: packaged in cans, jars, etc.; groceries & related products; soybeans

(G-9152)
CGP MANUFACTURING INC
8363 Market St (77029-2417)
PHONE..................713 641-5544
Michelle Becker, *President*
Jorge Garcia, *Vice Pres*
Connie Vara, *Sales Staff*
EMP: 35
SQ FT: 25,000
SALES (est): 8.1MM **Privately Held**
WEB: www.cgpfittings.com
SIC: 3494 Pipe fittings

(G-9153)
CHALKS TRUCK PARTS INC (PA)
Also Called: Randy's Drive Shaft Service
818 Mc Carty Dr (77029)
P.O. Box 15675 (77220-5675)
PHONE..................713 672-6344
Robert A Chalk, *Ch of Bd*
Randall A Chalk, *Vice Pres*
Mark Limmlagrone, *Controller*
Cherie L Chalk, *Director*
Barbara Chalk, *Admin Sec*
▼ **EMP:** 38 **EST:** 1957
SQ FT: 39,000
SALES (est): 7.3MM **Privately Held**
WEB: www.chalks.com
SIC: 3714 5013 Drive shafts, motor vehicle; truck parts & accessories

(G-9154)
CHALKS TRUCK PARTS INC
Also Called: Randy Drive Shaft Service
8025 Market St (77029-2411)
PHONE..................713 672-6344
Dante Medrano, *General Mgr*
Randy Chalk, *Manager*
EMP: 10
SALES (corp-wide): 7.3MM **Privately Held**
WEB: www.chalks.com
SIC: 5013 3714 Truck parts & accessories; drive shafts, motor vehicle
PA: Chalk's Truck Parts, Inc.
818 Mc Carty Dr
Houston TX 77029
713 672-6344

(G-9155)
CHAMMAS CUTTERS INC
11320 Fm 529 Rd Ste I (77041-3222)
PHONE..................713 856-8777
Michel E Chammas, *President*
Mirna Chammas, *Vice Pres*
▲ **EMP:** 9
SQ FT: 7,700
SALES (est): 2.2MM **Privately Held**
WEB: www.chammascutters.com
SIC: 3533 Bits, oil & gas field tools: rock

(G-9156)
CHAMPION DRILLING FLUIDS INC
Also Called: AES Drilling Fluid
11767 Katy Fwy Ste 230 (77079-1711)
PHONE..................580 225-3450
EMP: 12
SALES (est): 849.2K
SALES (corp-wide): 806.7MM **Privately Held**
SIC: 1389 Oil/Gas Field Services
PA: Ces Energy Solutions Corp
700 4 Ave Sw Suite 1400
Calgary AB T2P 0
403 269-2800

(G-9157)
CHAMPION GROUP INC (PA)
5565 Maudlin St (77087-3341)
P.O. Box 262427 (77207-2427)
PHONE..................713 644-2181
F John Burton, *President*
Wade S Medlin, *Admin Sec*
EMP: 25
SQ FT: 25,000

SALES (est): 7.4MM **Privately Held**
WEB: www.championgroup.com
SIC: 3053 7699 5085 Gaskets, packing & sealing devices; industrial machinery & equipment repair; seals, industrial

(G-9158)
CHAMPION INDUSTRIAL SALES CO (PA)
Also Called: Cisco
6420 Navigation Blvd (77011-1140)
P.O. Box 9130 (77261-9130)
PHONE..................713 921-7183
Mike Kegg, *President*
Ron Pyle, *Executive*
Patty White, *Admin Sec*
Donna Allen, *Representative*
◆ **EMP:** 9 **EST:** 1944
SQ FT: 20,000
SALES (est): 5.8MM **Privately Held**
WEB: www.championindustrialsales.com
SIC: 5084 3699 Welding machinery & equipment; electrical welding equipment

(G-9159)
CHAMPION PROCESS INC
5171 Ashley Ct (77041-6914)
PHONE..................281 953-9000
James Allen Howard Jr, *President*
Mark Meyer, *Vice Pres*
Hailey Shipman, *Admin Sec*
EMP: 13
SQ FT: 26,000
SALES (est): 49.5MM **Privately Held**
WEB: www.championprocess.com
SIC: 5085 5084 5082 7353 Filters, industrial; pumps & pumping equipment; oil field equipment; oil field equipment, rental or leasing; filters & strainers, pipeline

(G-9160)
CHAMPIONS PRINTING & PUBG INC
6608 Fm 1960 Rd W Ste G (77069-3910)
PHONE..................281 583-7661
Jim Callahan, *President*
Shelly L Callahan, *Corp Secy*
Cathy Castillo, *Production*
Shelly Callahan, *Treasurer*
Lori Short, *Creative Dir*
EMP: 30
SQ FT: 1,610
SALES (est): 2.4MM **Privately Held**
WEB: www.championsprinting.com
SIC: 2741 2752 2791 Directories: publishing & printing; newsletter publishing; commercial printing, offset; typesetting

(G-9161)
CHANNEL BRFINERY TERMINALS LLC
13605 Industrial Rd (77015-6818)
PHONE..................713 965-4150
James Driscoll, *CEO*
Ronald Ehlinger, *CFO*
EMP: 12
SALES (est): 6.6MM **Privately Held**
SIC: 1311 Natural gas production

(G-9162)
CHANNL-TRACK TUBE-WAY INDS INC (PA)
Also Called: Channel-Track Tubeway
1209 W 17th St (77008-3439)
P.O. Box 70067 (77270-0067)
PHONE..................713 864-2551
Max West, *CEO*
Darin West, *President*
Patrick Green, *Marketing Staff*
Nancy Gutranski, *Executive*
Lauren Gutfranski, *Admin Asst*
EMP: 33
SQ FT: 20,000
SALES (est): 21.4MM **Privately Held**
WEB: www.channel-track.com
SIC: 5251 3694 3643 3357 Hardware; engine electrical equipment; current-carrying wiring devices; nonferrous wire-drawing & insulating

(G-9163)
CHARBONNEAU INDUSTRIES INC (PA)
Also Called: C.I. Actuation
1619 E Richey Rd (77073-3512)
PHONE..................770 664-4319
Steven R Charbonneau, *President*
Don Dean, *General Mgr*
Bob Hamilton, *Business Mgr*
Bryan Mong, *Opers Staff*
Nicholas Borrego, *Production*
EMP: 15
SQ FT: 12,900
SALES (est): 12.1MM **Privately Held**
WEB: www.cioilandgas.com
SIC: 5074 5085 3498 Pipes & fittings, plastic; valves & fittings; fabricated pipe & fittings

(G-9164)
CHARLES DE VUAE INC
6100 Richmond Ave Ste 216 (77057-6219)
PHONE..................713 789-8485
Charles Omadevuae, *President*
▼ **EMP:** 11
SALES (est): 7MM **Privately Held**
SIC: 2339 Women's & misses' outerwear

(G-9165)
CHART INC
Also Called: Chart Dist & Stor Group
55 Southbelt Indus Dr (77047-7011)
PHONE..................713 413-3000
Joe Walters, *General Mgr*
EMP: 25 **Publicly Held**
WEB: www.chartindustries.com
SIC: 3443 Fabricated plate work (boiler shop)
HQ: Chart Inc.
407 7th St Nw
New Prague MN 56071
952 758-4484

(G-9166)
CHAS P YOUNG COMPANY
Also Called: Cpy
1645 W Sam Houstorl Pkwy N (77043-3114)
P.O. Box 2622 (77252-2622)
PHONE..................713 652-2100
Joe R Davis, *CEO*
James Hill, *President*
Ryan Mayo, *Accounts Exec*
Samir Parikh, *Sales Staff*
Mike Wall, *Sales Staff*
EMP: 70
SALES (est): 16MM
SALES (corp-wide): 6.2B **Publicly Held**
WEB: www.cpy.com
SIC: 2752 Commercial printing, offset
HQ: Consolidated Graphics, Inc.
5858 Westheimer Rd # 200
Houston TX 77057
713 787-0977

(G-9167)
CHECKFREE CORPORATION
Also Called: Aphelion Checkfree
1100 Nasa Pkwy Ste 606 (77058-3325)
PHONE..................281 333-9800
Kevin Horner, *Finance*
Paul Bunting, *Branch Mgr*
EMP: 77
SALES (corp-wide): 10.1B **Publicly Held**
WEB: www.fiserv.com
SIC: 7371 7372 Computer software development; business oriented computer software
HQ: Checkfree Corporation
2900 Westside Pkwy
Alpharetta GA 30004
678 375-3000

(G-9168)
CHEERS HEALTH INC
1334 Brittmoore Rd # 1003 (77043-4033)
PHONE..................518 379-6133
Brooks Powell, *President*
EMP: 20
SALES (est): 671.8K **Privately Held**
WEB: www.cheershealth.com
SIC: 2023 Dietary supplements, dairy & non-dairy based

(G-9169)
CHEF UNITS LLC (PA)
2501 Karbach St Ste C (77092-8042)
PHONE..................713 589-2613
Marco Novo,
EMP: 18
SQ FT: 10,000
SALES (est): 1.5MM **Privately Held**
WEB: www.chefunits.com
SIC: 2599 Carts, restaurant equipment

(G-9170)
CHEMICAL DATA LLC
3355 W Alabama St Ste 700 (77098-1789)
PHONE..................713 683-3900
Jason Brown, *President*
EMP: 10
SALES (est): 1.8MM
SALES (corp-wide): 10.1B **Privately Held**
WEB: www.chemicaldata.com
SIC: 8748 2721 Business consulting; periodicals: publishing only
HQ: Relx Inc.
230 Park Ave Ste 700
New York NY 10169
212 309-8100

(G-9171)
CHEMSTATION INTERNATIONAL INC
2701 Appelt Dr (77015-6553)
PHONE..................281 457-2020
Lesley Branham, *Branch Mgr*
EMP: 10
SALES (corp-wide): 24.3MM **Privately Held**
WEB: www.chemstation.com
SIC: 5169 2899 2841 Chemical additives; chemical preparations; soap & other detergents
PA: Chemstation International Inc.
3400 Encrete Ln
Moraine OH 45439
937 294-8265

(G-9172)
CHEMSYSTEMS INC
Also Called: Houston Building Supply
10101 Genard Rd (77041-7529)
PHONE..................713 329-9066
Nancy B Meikle, *President*
Bruce Meikle, *President*
Jessica Davis, *Vice Pres*
Christopher Sullivan, *Vice Pres*
▲ **EMP:** 10
SQ FT: 35,000
SALES (est): 3MM **Privately Held**
WEB: www.chemsystemsinc.net
SIC: 2899 Chemical preparations

(G-9173)
CHEMTRUSION INC (PA)
7115 Clinton Dr (77020-8135)
PHONE..................713 675-1616
Scott Owens, *President*
Edward Bourbonais, *Vice Pres*
Kenneth W Owens, *Vice Pres*
Dave Wilson, *Vice Pres*
John S Sutjar, *CFO*
▲ **EMP:** 60
SQ FT: 98,000
SALES (est): 22MM **Privately Held**
WEB: www.chemtrusion.com
SIC: 2821 8742 3087 Molding compounds, plastics; management consulting services; custom compound purchased resins

(G-9174)
CHENIERE CCH HOLDCO II LLC (HQ)
700 Milam St Ste 1900 (77002-2835)
PHONE..................713 375-5000
Michael J Wortley, *President*
EMP: 1530
SALES (est): 62.8K
SALES (corp-wide): 9.7B **Publicly Held**
SIC: 1321 Liquefied petroleum gases (natural) production
PA: Cheniere Energy, Inc.
700 Milam St Ste 1900
Houston TX 77002
713 375-5000

▲ = Import ▼ =Export
◆ =Import/Export

(G-9175)
CHENIERE ENERGY INC (PA)
700 Milam St Ste 1900 (77002-2835)
PHONE..................713 375-5000
G Andrea Botta, *Ch of Bd*
Jack A Fusco, *President*
Douglas D Shanda, *Senior VP*
Julie Nelson, *Vice Pres*
Mitch Price, *Vice Pres*
EMP: 100
SALES: 9.7B **Publicly Held**
WEB: www.cheniere.com
SIC: 1321 4925 4922 Liquefied petroleum gases (natural) production; liquefied petroleum gas, distribution through mains; pipelines, natural gas

(G-9176)
CHEVAS COMPANY LLC
1927 Edmundson St (77003-5511)
P.O. Box 230061 (77223-0061)
PHONE..................713 225-6595
Michael Holden, *President*
Charles Thrasher, *Chairman*
M W Beal, *Director*
EMP: 19 EST: 1936
SQ FT: 30,000
SALES (est): 6.9MM **Privately Held**
SIC: 3823 3599 3451 3541 Industrial instrmnts msrmnt display/control process variable; machine shop, jobbing & repair; screw machine products; machine tools, metal cutting type

(G-9177)
CHEVRON CORPORATION
Also Called: Unocal
1400 Smith St Ste 3600 (77002-7342)
PHONE..................907 276-7600
Chuck Paris, *Vice Pres*
Don Mrla, *Project Mgr*
Elizabeth Jensen, *Engineer*
Andy Lucena, *Contract Mgr*
Esmeralda Roberts, *Legal Staff*
EMP: 120
SALES (corp-wide): 146.5B **Publicly Held**
WEB: www.chevron.com
SIC: 1382 1311 Oil & gas exploration services; crude petroleum & natural gas
PA: Chevron Corporation
6001 Bollinger Canyon Rd
San Ramon CA 94583
925 842-1000

(G-9178)
CHEVRON CORPORATION
1600 Smith St Ste 3895 (77002-7512)
PHONE..................713 754-3998
John Welch, *Counsel*
MBA R Stuart Pmp, *Project Mgr*
WEI Kaihong, *Research*
Bechir Abbassi, *Branch Mgr*
Sandra P Medina, *Technology*
EMP: 391
SALES (corp-wide): 146.5B **Publicly Held**
WEB: www.chevron.com
SIC: 5541 1311 1382 1321 Filling stations, gasoline; crude petroleum production; oil & gas exploration services; natural gas liquids
PA: Chevron Corporation
6001 Bollinger Canyon Rd
San Ramon CA 94583
925 842-1000

(G-9179)
CHEVRON MARINE PRODUCTS LLC (HQ)
1500 Louisiana St (77002-7308)
PHONE..................832 854-2767
C Michael Bandy, *President*
Peter M Meade, *CFO*
◆ EMP: 75
SALES (est): 524.6MM
SALES (corp-wide): 146.5B **Publicly Held**
WEB: www.chevronmarineproducts.com
SIC: 5172 2992 2869 Engine fuels & oils; lubricating oils & greases; lubricating oils & greases; fuels
PA: Chevron Corporation
6001 Bollinger Canyon Rd
San Ramon CA 94583
925 842-1000

(G-9180)
CHEVRON ORONITE COMPANY LLC
4800 Fournace Place Bella (77001)
P.O. Box 285 (77001-0285)
PHONE..................713 432-2500
Yvonne Rocha, *Manager*
EMP: 50
SALES (corp-wide): 146.5B **Publicly Held**
WEB: www.oronite.com
SIC: 2821 Plastics materials & resins
HQ: Chevron Oronite Company Llc
6001 Bollinger Canyon Rd
San Ramon CA 94583

(G-9181)
CHEVRON USA INC
1301 Mckinney St Ste 900 (77010-8001)
PHONE..................925 842-1000
John Long, *Project Mgr*
Kimchi Pham, *Info Tech Dir*
Willy George, *Info Tech Mgr*
Ken Morris, *Technology*
Marilyn Stanton, *Analyst*
EMP: 235
SALES (corp-wide): 146.5B **Publicly Held**
WEB: www.chevron.com
SIC: 2911 5511 5541 5171 Gasoline blending plants; automobiles, new & used; filling stations, gasoline; petroleum bulk stations
HQ: Chevron U.S.A. Inc.
6001 Bollinger Canyon Rd D1248
San Ramon CA 94583
925 842-1000

(G-9182)
CHEYENNE SERVICES INC
12206 Fm 529 Rd (77041-2806)
PHONE..................713 937-7733
EMP: 20
SQ FT: 10,000
SALES (est): 868K **Privately Held**
SIC: 1389 Oil & Gas Field Services

(G-9183)
CHICAGO BRIDGE & IRON CO DEL (DH)
915 N Eldridge Pkwy (77079-2703)
PHONE..................832 513-1000
Rick L Gorder, *Senior VP*
Luciano Reyes, *Treasurer*
David A Delman, *Officer*
◆ EMP: 125 EST: 1979
SALES (est): 3.7B
SALES (corp-wide): 8.4B **Privately Held**
WEB: www.mcdermott.com
SIC: 3325 3462 8711 Steel foundries; iron & steel forgings; industrial engineers
HQ: Chicago Bridge & Iron Company
757 N Eldridge Pkwy
Houston TX 77079
281 870-5000

(G-9184)
CHOCTAW II OIL & GAS LTD (PA)
815 Walker St Ste 1040 (77002-5776)
PHONE..................713 632-0222
Blake Liedtke, *CEO*
Russell Brown, *President*
Carl Herkert, *Vice Pres*
EMP: 15
SQ FT: 13,220
SALES (est): 1.1MM **Privately Held**
SIC: 1311 6519 Crude petroleum production; real property lessors

(G-9185)
CHOICE CAP INC (PA)
8000 Harwin Dr Ste 165 (77036-1817)
PHONE..................832 251-9551
Sung Su Park, *President*
▲ EMP: 15 EST: 2005
SQ FT: 6,500
SALES (est): 1.3MM **Privately Held**
WEB: www.mychoicecap.com
SIC: 2353 Uniform hats & caps

(G-9186)
CHUNGS PRODUCTS LP
Also Called: Chung's Gourmet Foods
777 Post Oak Blvd Ste 250 (77056-3236)
PHONE..................713 741-2118
Rick Harris, *President*
Joe Mason, *Vice Pres*
Vicente Cortez, *Opers Mgr*
Vernon Fowler, *Opers Mgr*
Robert Huddow, *Controller*
▲ EMP: 130
SALES (est): 59.3MM **Privately Held**
WEB: www.chungsfoods.com
SIC: 5142 2038 Packaged frozen goods; frozen specialties

(G-9187)
CHURCH ENERGY SERVICES LTD
2810 Washington Dr (77038-3319)
PHONE..................281 931-1400
Richard Church Jr, *Partner*
Dan Church, *General Ptnr*
▲ EMP: 25
SQ FT: 29,174
SALES (est): 4.2MM
SALES (corp-wide): 17.1MM **Privately Held**
WEB: www.axonpp.com
SIC: 3533 Oil field machinery & equipment
HQ: Axon Pressure Products, Inc.
12606 N Huston Rosslyn Rd
Houston TX 77086

(G-9188)
CHURCH HILL DRILLING TOOLS US
5440 Guhn Rd (77040-6211)
PHONE..................281 893-0233
Andy Churchill, *Owner*
▲ EMP: 10
SALES (est): 1.5MM **Privately Held**
WEB: www.coretrax.com
SIC: 3546 Drills & drilling tools

(G-9189)
CIMARRON ENERGY HOLDING CO LLC
Also Called: Diverse Energy Systems
11025 Equity Dr Ste 200 (77041-8247)
PHONE..................701 352-9620
Chet Erwin, *CEO*
Andrew Leeser, *Vice Pres*
Gauthier Pierozak, *Vice Pres*
Jason Templeton, *Project Mgr*
EMP: 84
SALES (corp-wide): 416.9MM **Privately Held**
WEB: www.cimarron-energy.com
SIC: 1389 Oil field services
HQ: Cimarron Energy Holding Company, Llc
4190 S Harvey Ave
Norman OK 73072
405 928-7373

(G-9190)
CIMARRON SOFTWARE SERVICES INC (PA)
18050 Saturn Ln Ste 280 (77058-4502)
PHONE..................281 226-5100
Jeanie Crowell, *CEO*
Jeannie Crowell, *CEO*
Darren Crowell, *President*
Laurie Nasta, *Engineer*
Walter Medsger, *CFO*
EMP: 30 EST: 1981
SQ FT: 6,000
SALES (est): 20.1MM **Privately Held**
WEB: www.cimarroninc.com
SIC: 7371 8711 5045 8741 Computer software development; engineering services; computer software; management services; prepackaged software

(G-9191)
CINA PHARMACEUTICAL INC
21602 E Hardy Rd (77073)
PHONE..................281 602-3491
Samira Sanchez, *Principal*
EMP: 9
SALES (est): 1.4MM **Privately Held**
WEB: www.cinapharma.com
SIC: 2834 Pharmaceutical preparations

(G-9192)
CINCO ENERGY MGT GROUP LLC (PA)
Also Called: Cinco Energy Services
1616 S Voss Rd Ste 100 (77057-2634)
PHONE..................713 463-6009
Randall H Nichols, *President*
EMP: 18
SALES (est): 3.7MM **Privately Held**
WEB: www.cincoland.com
SIC: 1382 Oil & gas exploration services

(G-9193)
CIPHERWASTE POLYMERS LP
1130 Enclave Pkwy (77077-1606)
PHONE..................281 946-8090
Arturo Turlan, *Managing Prtnr*
Richard Bourne, *Opers Mgr*
◆ EMP: 9
SQ FT: 3,000
SALES (est): 7MM **Privately Held**
WEB: www.cipherwaste.com
SIC: 2821 Plastics materials & resins

(G-9194)
CIRCOR ENERGY PRODUCTS LLC (HQ)
Also Called: Circor Energy Products, Inc.
11331 Tanner Rd (77041-6901)
P.O. Box 945 (77001-0945)
PHONE..................713 400-2200
Mahesh Joshi, *CEO*
Chaz Burgs, *Controller*
Barry Abel, *Manager*
Mike Savoie, *Technology*
Anupama Nagasimha, *Analyst*
◆ EMP: 162 EST: 1972
SQ FT: 148,000
SALES (est): 52.1MM
SALES (corp-wide): 1.1B **Publicly Held**
WEB: www.circor.com
SIC: 3491 Industrial valves
PA: Circor International, Inc.
30 Corporate Dr Ste 200
Burlington MA 01803
781 270-1200

(G-9195)
CIRCUIT SERVICES INC
Also Called: Niltronix Circuits
1765 Upland Dr (77043-3506)
PHONE..................713 465-4216
Bharat Karsaliya, *President*
Mehul Patel, *Opers Mgr*
EMP: 15 EST: 2016
SQ FT: 15,000
SALES (est): 3MM **Privately Held**
WEB: www.niltronix.com
SIC: 3672 Circuit boards, television & radio printed

(G-9196)
CISCO BOILER SERVICE CO INC
2403 Appelt Dr (77015-6591)
PHONE..................713 928-5700
Steve Peddicord, *President*
David Pederson, *President*
Roger Stephen, *Vice Pres*
Chuck Thrall, *Vice Pres*
Jackie Greer, *Admin Sec*
▼ EMP: 20
SQ FT: 12,500
SALES (est): 3.4MM **Privately Held**
WEB: www.cbservice.com
SIC: 3433 3443 7699 5074 Boilers, low-pressure heating: steam or hot water; boiler & boiler shop work; boiler repair shop; boilers, hot water heating; boilers, power (industrial); boilers, steam

(G-9197)
CISCO SYSTEMS INC
10650 Okanella St (77041-5398)
PHONE..................972 393-0874
Christopher Avalos, *Engineer*
Eric Kalisek, *Engineer*
Brad White, *Sales Staff*
EMP: 691
SALES (corp-wide): 49.3B **Publicly Held**
WEB: www.cisco.com
SIC: 3577 Computer peripheral equipment

PA: Cisco Systems, Inc.
170 W Tasman Dr
San Jose CA 95134
408 526-4000

(G-9198)
CITATION 2002 INV LTD PARTNR
Also Called: Citation Oil & Gas
14077 Cutten Rd (77069-2212)
PHONE..................281 891-1000
C F Harrell, *President*
EMP: 10
SALES (est): 1.3MM **Privately Held**
WEB: www.cogc.com
SIC: 3533 Oil & gas field machinery

(G-9199)
CITATION OIL & GAS CORP (PA)
14077 Cutten Rd (77069-2212)
PHONE..................281 891-1000
Forrest E Harrell, *Ch of Bd*
C F Harrell, *President*
Curtis Harrell, *COO*
Steve Anna, *Senior VP*
Mark Anchondo, *Vice Pres*
EMP: 170
SQ FT: 55,000
SALES (est): 283.5MM **Privately Held**
WEB: www.cogc.com
SIC: 1311 1382 Crude petroleum production; natural gas production; oil & gas exploration services

(G-9200)
CITGO HOLDING TERMINALS LLC
1293 Eldridge Pkwy (77077-1670)
P.O. Box 4689 (77210-4689)
PHONE..................832 486-4000
Nelson P Martinez, *CEO*
EMP: 453
SALES (est): 133.9MM **Privately Held**
WEB: www.citgo.com
SIC: 5171 4213 4612 2911 Petroleum bulk stations & terminals; trucking, except local; crude petroleum pipelines; gasoline
HQ: Pdv America, Inc.
1293 Eldridge Pkwy
Houston TX 77077

(G-9201)
CITGO PETROLEUM CORPORATION (DH)
1293 Eldridge Pkwy (77077-1670)
P.O. Box 4689 (77210-4689)
PHONE..................832 486-4000
Judy Berckman, *General Mgr*
Rafael Gomez Abreu, *Principal*
Wladimir Noriega, *Principal*
Luisa Palacios, *Chairman*
Richard Bowman, *Business Mgr*
◆ **EMP:** 940
SQ FT: 350,000
SALES (est): 26.7B **Privately Held**
WEB: www.citgolubes.com
SIC: 5171 4213 4612 2911 Petroleum bulk stations & terminals; trucking, except local; crude petroleum pipelines; gasoline

(G-9202)
CITROLIM INC
14405 Walters Rd Ste 600 (77014-1344)
PHONE..................281 453-5150
James M Readhimer, *President*
Marvin Readhimer, *Vice Pres*
EMP: 13
SALES (est): 1.5MM **Privately Held**
WEB: www.citrolim.com
SIC: 2037 Citrus pulp, dried

(G-9203)
CITY OF HOUSTON
Also Called: Building Services Dept
900 Bagby St Fl 2 (77002-2533)
P.O. Box 61189 (77208-1189)
PHONE..................713 221-0404
Issa Z Dadoush, *Principal*
EMP: 250
SALES (corp-wide): 3.3B **Privately Held**
WEB: www.hfdcareers.org
SIC: 3822 9532 Building services monitoring controls, automatic; liquid level controls, residential or commercial heating; urban & community development

PA: City Of Houston
901 Bagby St
Houston TX 77002
832 393-1000

(G-9204)
CL&F OFFSHORE LLC (HQ)
16945 Northchase Dr # 15 (77060-2135)
PHONE..................281 873-9378
R Paul Loveless,
EMP: 13
SALES (est): 4.5MM
SALES (corp-wide): 14.1MM **Privately Held**
WEB: www.clfoperating.com
SIC: 1382 1389 Oil & gas exploration services; pumping of oil & gas wells
PA: Cl&f Operating Llc
16945 Northchase Dr # 15
Houston TX 77060
281 873-9378

(G-9205)
CL&F OPERATING LLC (PA)
16945 Northchase Dr # 15 (77060-2135)
PHONE..................281 873-9378
R Paul Loveless, *President*
EMP: 14 **EST:** 2008
SALES: 14.1MM **Privately Held**
WEB: www.clfoperating.com
SIC: 1389 1382 Pumping of oil & gas wells; oil & gas exploration services

(G-9206)
CL&F RESOURCES LP (PA)
16945 Nrthchase D Ste 150 (77060)
PHONE..................281 873-9378
R Paul Loveless, *CEO*
Charles Bolt, *President*
Mark K Stover, *Senior VP*
Gary A Dobbs, *Vice Pres*
George A Strain, *Vice Pres*
EMP: 34
SQ FT: 6,000
SALES (est): 6.9MM **Privately Held**
WEB: www.clf-co.com
SIC: 1382 Oil & gas exploration services

(G-9207)
CLARION EVENTS INC
Also Called: Pennwell C & E
1700 West Loop S Ste 1000 (77027-3007)
P.O. Box 3448 (77253-3448)
PHONE..................713 963-6220
Roy Markum, *Vice Pres*
Brian Vass, *Branch Mgr*
EMP: 147 **Privately Held**
WEB: www.pennwell.com
SIC: 2721 2731 Periodicals: publishing only; books: publishing only
HQ: Clarion Events, Inc.
110 S Hartford Ave # 200
Tulsa OK 74120
918 835-3161

(G-9208)
CLARIOS
Also Called: Johnson Controls
20555 State Highway 249 (77070-2607)
PHONE..................281 518-8053
Gary Hall, *Manager*
EMP: 110 **Privately Held**
WEB: www.johnsoncontrols.com
SIC: 7349 2531 Building maintenance services; seats, automobile
HQ: Johnson Controls, Inc.
5757 N Green Bay Ave
Glendale WI 53209
800 382-2804

(G-9209)
CLARK FIRE EQUIPMENT INC
1838 Federal Rd (77015-6710)
PHONE..................713 453-3778
John R Clark, *President*
Steve Thompson, *Manager*
Bobbie Clark, *Shareholder*
EMP: 15 **EST:** 1980
SQ FT: 12,000
SALES (est): 2.1MM **Privately Held**
WEB: www.clarkfireequipment.com
SIC: 5099 3993 Safety equipment & supplies; signs, not made in custom sign painting shops

(G-9210)
CLARKE HARLAND CORP
1713 Townhurst Dr (77043-2810)
P.O. Box 460, San Antonio (78292-0460)
PHONE..................210 697-8888
Allen Bo, *General Mgr*
Michael Davis, *COO*
Peter A Fera, *Senior VP*
Kevin Elms, *CFO*
Peter Fera, *CFO*
EMP: 100 **Publicly Held**
WEB: www.harlandclarke.com
SIC: 2752 2782 Commercial printing, lithographic; blankbooks & looseleaf binders
HQ: Harland Clarke Corp.
15955 La Cantera Pkwy
San Antonio TX 78256
830 609-5500

(G-9211)
CLARKS HARDWOOD LUMBER CO LP
700 E 5 And A Half St (77007)
P.O. Box 7793 (77270-7793)
PHONE..................713 862-6628
Wayne Clark, *Partner*
Johnie Cates, *General Mgr*
Christine Tyson, *Accounting Mgr*
Steve Cranford, *Sales Staff*
Ernie Sonderegger, *Sales Staff*
EMP: 16 **EST:** 1946
SQ FT: 40,000
SALES (est): 4.8MM **Privately Held**
WEB: www.clarkshardwood.com
SIC: 5031 5023 5211 2431 Lumber: rough, dressed & finished; wood flooring; lumber & other building materials; millwork; hardwood dimension & flooring mills

(G-9212)
CLASSIC PROTECTION SYSTEMS
1648 W Sam Houston Pkwy N (77043-3115)
PHONE..................713 468-3573
Curtis Carsey, *President*
Cathy Carsey, *Vice Pres*
Guadalupe Brown, *Manager*
EMP: 30
SQ FT: 10,000
SALES (est): 9.6MM **Privately Held**
WEB: www.classicprotectionsys.com
SIC: 5063 3999 5999 7382 Fire alarm systems; fire extinguishers, portable; fire extinguishers; banners; fire alarm maintenance & monitoring

(G-9213)
CLEARLY PETROLEUM OPCO LLC
5825 N Houston Pkwy Ste 5 (77086)
PHONE..................281 781-0412
Rachel Rangel, *Controller*
Tom Wilker,
EMP: 45
SQ FT: 12,000
SALES (est): 512.9K **Privately Held**
WEB: www.clearlypetroleum.com
SIC: 1382 Oil & gas exploration services

(G-9214)
CLEARMEDIAONE INC (PA)
19 Briar Hollow Ln # 235 (77027-2819)
PHONE..................713 622-9393
Wesley M Jaynes, *Officer*
Robert F Strange, *Officer*
Elmer C Gardner, *Shareholder*
▲ **EMP:** 20
SALES (est): 20.3MM **Privately Held**
SIC: 2517 Home entertainment unit cabinets, wood

(G-9215)
CLOCK SPRING COMPANY INC (PA)
621 Lockhaven Dr (77073-5506)
PHONE..................281 590-8491
Matt Boucher, *President*
Pipe R LP, *Partner*
Vikki Dunn, *Exec VP*
Andrew Patrick, *Exec VP*
Emily Robertson, *Exec VP*
▼ **EMP:** 71
SQ FT: 15,000

SALES (est): 35.1MM **Privately Held**
WEB: www.cs-nri.com
SIC: 3317 Steel pipe & tubes

(G-9216)
CLOROX MANUFACTURING COMPANY
5822 Armour Dr (77020-8199)
PHONE..................713 674-5042
Joseph Rutter, *Engineer*
Steve Stewart, *Manager*
EMP: 59
SQ FT: 56,000
SALES (corp-wide): 6.7B **Publicly Held**
WEB: www.thecloroxcompany.com
SIC: 2842 Bleaches, household: dry or liquid
HQ: Clorox Manufacturing Company
1221 Broadway
Oakland CA 94612

(G-9217)
CLOUD NINJAS LLC
Also Called: Techtrade Solutions
10757 Cutten Rd Bldg 5 (77066-5026)
PHONE..................832 478-9158
Lizann Flowers, *COO*
Scott Flowers, *Mng Member*
EMP: 15
SALES (est): 5MM **Privately Held**
WEB: www.techtradesolutions.com
SIC: 3679 Antennas, receiving

(G-9218)
CME PRINTING INC
8181 Commerce Park Dr # 708 (77036-7424)
PHONE..................713 271-7700
Cynthia Davison, *President*
Kristen D Malone, *Vice Pres*
Kristen Malone, *Vice Pres*
▲ **EMP:** 22 **EST:** 2001
SQ FT: 15,000
SALES (est): 4.3MM **Privately Held**
WEB: www.cmeprinting.com
SIC: 2759 7374 7371 Commercial printing; computer graphics service; computer software development

(G-9219)
CNH GROUP INCORPORATED
Also Called: Caisson Fabrication Co
12227 Fm 529 Rd (77041-2800)
PHONE..................832 453-9977
Edmundo Hurtado, *President*
EMP: 17
SALES (est): 1.4MM **Privately Held**
SIC: 3441 Fabricated structural metal

(G-9220)
CNOOC ENERGY HOLDINGS USA INC
945 Bunker Hill Rd # 1000 (77024-1358)
PHONE..................713 380-4800
Rick L Sumrall, *President*
EMP: 50
SALES (est): 1.4MM **Privately Held**
WEB: www.cnoocinternational.com
SIC: 1311 Crude petroleum & natural gas

(G-9221)
CNOOC MARKETING USA INC
Also Called: Nexen Energy Marketing USA Inc
945 Bunker Hill Rd # 1000 (77024-1358)
PHONE..................713 380-4800
Corey D Riley, *President*
Douglas R Dreisinger, *Chairman*
Gregg E Redetsky, *Vice Pres*
Shirley Whitfield, *Analyst*
EMP: 100
SALES (est): 3.9MM **Privately Held**
WEB: www.cnoocinternational.com
SIC: 1389 Oil consultants
HQ: Cnooc Petroleum North America Ulc
500 Centre St Se Suite 2300
Calgary AB T2G 1
403 699-4000

(G-9222)
CNPC USA CORPORATION (DH)
2901 Wilcrest Dr Fl 3 (77042-3399)
PHONE..................713 465-7382
Gordon Zhang, *President*
Jack Shoemaker, *Vice Pres*
Xu Wang, *Vice Pres*

Jack Robbins, *Mfg Staff*
RC Smith, *Engineer*
▲ **EMP:** 25
SALES (est): 12.7MM **Privately Held**
WEB: www.cnpc-usa.com
SIC: 1382 Aerial geophysical exploration oil & gas

(G-9223)
COASTAL CASTING SERVICE (PA)
2903 Gano St (77009-6999)
P.O. Box 16105 (77222-6105)
PHONE..............................713 223-4439
Coral Eichenour, *President*
R Eichenou, *President*
Robert L Eichenour, *Vice Pres*
Dan Eichenour, *Sales Staff*
◆ **EMP:** 55 **EST:** 1953
SALES (est): 9.5MM **Privately Held**
WEB: www.coastalcasting.com
SIC: 3599 3369 Machine shop, jobbing & repair; nonferrous foundries

(G-9224)
COASTAL CRUSHED CONCRETE LLC (PA)
Also Called: C C C
9026 Lambright Rd (77075-3208)
PHONE..............................713 941-3232
Cindy L Bulgier,
EMP: 50
SQ FT: 75,000
SALES (est): 5.1MM **Privately Held**
SIC: 3273 Ready-mixed concrete

(G-9225)
COASTAL FLOW MEASUREMENT INC (HQ)
2525 Bay Area Blvd # 500 (77058-1556)
P.O. Box 58965 (77258-8965)
PHONE..............................713 477-1956
Stephen Whitman, *President*
Steve Whitman, *President*
Curtis Fillman, *Principal*
Curtis R Fillman, *Principal*
Mark Fillman, *COO*
EMP: 58 **EST:** 1975
SALES (est): 24.9MM
SALES (corp-wide): 60.9MM **Privately Held**
WEB: www.coastalflow.com
SIC: 3829 1389 3823 Measuring & controlling devices; testing, measuring, surveying & analysis services; measurement of well flow rates, oil & gas; industrial instrmnts msrmnt display/control process variable
PA: Quorum Business Solutions, Inc.
811 Main St Ste 2200
Houston TX 77002
214 630-6442

(G-9226)
COASTAL FOUNDRY COMPANY
506 Rosamond St (77076-3399)
PHONE..............................713 695-4008
Harold L Gluckman, *President*
Leonard P Rigamonti, *Treasurer*
EMP: 27 **EST:** 1970
SQ FT: 16,000
SALES (est): 5.3MM **Privately Held**
WEB: www.coastalfoundry.com
SIC: 3364 3363 3369 Brass & bronze die-castings; aluminum die-castings; nonferrous foundries

(G-9227)
COASTAL MECHANICS COMPANY INC
7660 Woodway Dr Ste 510 (77063-1538)
PHONE..............................713 784-0111
▼ **EMP:** 200 **EST:** 1973
SALES (est): 33.6MM **Privately Held**
WEB: www.coastalmechanics.com
SIC: 3728 Aircraft parts & equipment

(G-9228)
COASTAL MECHANICS TL & MCH INC
Also Called: Major Metals Machining
14375 Luthe Rd (77039-1411)
PHONE..............................281 987-2530
Ed Levy, *Principal*
Oren Levy, *Principal*

Robert Jewell, *Treasurer*
EMP: 30
SQ FT: 9,000
SALES (est): 4.6MM **Privately Held**
SIC: 3599 Machine shop, jobbing & repair

(G-9229)
COASTLINE PETROLEUM LLC
5601 Irvington Blvd (77009-1926)
PHONE..............................281 844-4272
Mohammad Motaghi, *Mng Member*
Sean Kramer,
EMP: 10
SALES (est): 5.6MM **Privately Held**
SIC: 1311 Crude petroleum & natural gas

(G-9230)
COATING INDUSTRIES INC
6414 Thomas Rd (77041-4915)
PHONE..............................713 937-8581
Aban Rustomji, *President*
Amadeo Rodas, *Superintendent*
Arish Rustomji, *Vice Pres*
Vincent Garcia, *Supervisor*
EMP: 50 **EST:** 1982
SQ FT: 28,000
SALES (est): 7MM **Privately Held**
WEB: www.coatingindustries.com
SIC: 3479 Coating of metals & formed products

(G-9231)
COBALT INTERNATIONAL ENERGY LP (HQ)
920 Mmrial Cy Way Ste 100 (77024)
PHONE..............................713 452-2322
Joe Bryant, *Partner*
James Farnsworth, *Partner*
Sam Gillespie, *Partner*
James Painter, *Partner*
▼ **EMP:** 61
SQ FT: 5,000
SALES (est): 15.3MM **Privately Held**
WEB: www.cobaltintl.com
SIC: 1382 Oil & gas exploration services

(G-9232)
COBALT INTERNATIONAL ENRGY INC (PA)
920 Mmrial Cy Way Ste 100 (77024)
PHONE..............................713 579-9100
Timothy J Cutt, *CEO*
William P Utt, *Ch of Bd*
Rodney M Skaufel, *President*
Jeffrey A Starzec, *Exec VP*
Richard A Smith, *Senior VP*
EMP: 48
SALES (est): 53.8MM **Privately Held**
WEB: www.cobaltintl.com
SIC: 1382 Oil & gas exploration services

(G-9233)
COBURN SUPPLY COMPANY INC
5910 Gardendale Dr (77092-7020)
PHONE..............................409 838-6363
Larry Oneil, *Principal*
EMP: 203
SALES (corp-wide): 404.4MM **Privately Held**
WEB: www.coburns.com
SIC: 5075 3585 Air conditioning equipment, except room units; air conditioning equipment, complete
PA: Coburn Supply Company, Inc.
350 Pine St Ste 850
Beaumont TX 77701
409 838-6363

(G-9234)
COCA-COLA COMPANY
9300 Center Point Dr (77054-3704)
PHONE..............................713 799-7332
Fax: 713 799-7324
EMP: 200
SQ FT: 187,491
SALES (corp-wide): 35.4B **Publicly Held**
SIC: 2086 Carb Sft Drnkbtlcn
PA: The Coca-Cola Company
1 Coca Cola Plz Nw
Atlanta GA 30313
404 676-2121

(G-9235)
COCKRELL OIL CORPORATION
Also Called: Cockrell Foundation
1600 Smith St Ste 4600 (77002-7362)
PHONE..............................713 209-7300
Ernest H Cockrell, *Ch of Bd*
Ronald D Christie, *President*
Charles Hubbard, *Vice Pres*
Milton Graves, *CFO*
E Lynn Johnson, *Treasurer*
EMP: 45 **EST:** 1948
SQ FT: 17,000
SALES (est): 11.6MM **Privately Held**
WEB: www.graves-co.com
SIC: 1311 1382 Crude petroleum production; oil & gas exploration services

(G-9236)
COCKRELL RESOURCES INC
8620 W Monroe Rd Ste 200 (77061-4821)
PHONE..............................713 454-1400
Alberto Castro, *President*
Wayne Shellenberg, *Director*
EMP: 30 **EST:** 1970
SALES (est): 4.7MM **Privately Held**
WEB: www.cockrellresources.com
SIC: 3721 Airplanes, fixed or rotary wing; helicopters

(G-9237)
COEN FURNITURE INC
Also Called: Environment
10506 Kinghurst Dr (77099-3506)
PHONE..............................281 983-0100
Greg Mesler, *President*
John Rivera, *Project Mgr*
Tim Coen, *Treasurer*
EMP: 30
SQ FT: 50,000
SALES (est): 3.6MM **Privately Held**
WEB: www.environmentmillwork.com
SIC: 2431 Store & office display cases & fixtures

(G-9238)
COGENT ENERGY SERVICES LLC
Also Called: Animas Well Services
919 Milam St Ste 2480 (77002-5338)
PHONE..............................713 554-1200
David Gutierrez, *CFO*
Braden Norris, *Manager*
Charles Erwin,
EMP: 40 **EST:** 2016
SQ FT: 4,000
SALES (est): 1.9MM **Privately Held**
WEB: www.cogentenergyservices.com
SIC: 1389 Oil & gas wells: building, repairing & dismantling

(G-9239)
COGNITE INC
1000 N Post Oak Rd Ste 22 (77055-7232)
PHONE..............................512 593-7120
Trygve Ronningen, *COO*
EMP: 15
SALES (est): 305.2K **Privately Held**
SIC: 7372 Prepackaged software

(G-9240)
COIL TUBING TECHNOLOGY INC (PA)
Also Called: CTT
3002 Farrell Rd (77073-3007)
PHONE..............................281 651-0200
Richard R Royall, *CFO*
Courtney Quarles, *Office Mgr*
EMP: 18
SQ FT: 6,000
SALES: 6.8MM **Publicly Held**
WEB: www.coiltubingtechnology.com
SIC: 1389 Oil field services

(G-9241)
COILING TECHNOLOGIES INC (PA)
7777 Wright Rd (77041-2427)
PHONE..............................713 849-4000
Roger Hohman, *President*
▲ **EMP:** 75 **EST:** 1976
SQ FT: 100,000 **Privately Held**
WEB: www.coilingtech.com

SIC: 3495 3469 3479 3493 Wire springs; stamping metal for the trade; coating of metals & formed products; steel springs, except wire

(G-9242)
COKINOS OIL COMPANY
5718 Westheimer Rd # 900 (77057-5745)
PHONE..............................713 974-0101
Michael Evan Cokinos, *Principal*
Kathleen Freece, *Corp Secy*
Kevin Cokinos, *Vice Pres*
EMP: 11
SALES (est): 943.7K
SALES (corp-wide): 1B **Privately Held**
WEB: www.cokinosenergy.com
SIC: 1389 Oil field services
PA: Cokinos Energy, L.L.C.
5718 Westheimer Rd # 900
Houston TX 77057
713 974-0101

(G-9243)
COLE & ASHCROFT LP
Also Called: Flora International
5631 Brystone Dr (77041-7014)
PHONE..............................713 937-8657
Paul Wagner, *Partner*
John Lines, *Partner*
Gerald McAdams, *Partner*
Gina Hightower,
◆ **EMP:** 40
SQ FT: 70,000
SALES (est): 5.5MM **Privately Held**
WEB: www.coleandashcroft.com
SIC: 2679 Gift wrap & novelties, paper

(G-9244)
COLEMN-HNNA CRWASH SYSTEMS LLC
5842 W 34th St (77092-6402)
PHONE..............................713 683-9878
Neil Johnson, *Purch Mgr*
Tony Cruz, *Inv Control Mgr*
Kathleen Coleman, *Marketing Staff*
Edward J O'Hanrahan, *Mng Member*
Russell Coleman, *Mng Member*
◆ **EMP:** 45 **EST:** 1960
SALES (est): 12.9MM **Privately Held**
WEB: www.colemanhanna.com
SIC: 3589 Car washing machinery

(G-9245)
COLONIAL ART INC
5701 Cochran St (77009-1426)
PHONE..............................713 697-8407
Gerardo P Rivera, *President*
EMP: 10
SALES (est): 1.3MM **Privately Held**
WEB: www.colonialart.net
SIC: 3446 2514 Ornamental metalwork; metal household furniture

(G-9246)
COLORSTONE MFG
9707 Clay Rd (77080-1221)
PHONE..............................713 690-3100
Mahmoud Mirzakhani, *President*
EMP: 15
SALES (est): 1.7MM **Privately Held**
WEB: www.colorstonemfg.com
SIC: 3996 Hard surface floor coverings

(G-9247)
COMET SIGNS LLC
7630 Hansen Rd (77061-3410)
PHONE..............................281 492-6581
Tommy Reynolds, *Branch Mgr*
EMP: 37
SALES (corp-wide): 38MM **Privately Held**
WEB: www.cometsigns.com
SIC: 3993 1799 Neon signs; sign installation & maintenance
PA: Comet Signs, Llc
5003 Stout Dr
San Antonio TX 78219
210 341-7244

(G-9248)
COMMERCIAL ARMATURE WORKS
10029 Market St (77029-2314)
PHONE..............................713 672-7873
▲ **EMP:** 10
SQ FT: 8,000

SALES (est): 547.8K **Privately Held**
SIC: 7694 1731 Electric motor repair; electrical work

(G-9249)
COMMERCIAL BEV CONCEPTS LLC
Also Called: Modern Chemical
2408 Karbach St (77092-8006)
PHONE.................................713 554-4569
John Zotos, *Mng Member*
EMP: 35
SALES (est): 5.1MM **Privately Held**
SIC: 5149 2842 5047 Coffee & tea; specialty cleaning, polishes & sanitation goods; industrial safety devices: first aid kits & masks

(G-9250)
COMMERCIAL KITCHENS INC
Also Called: Mod-U-Serve
2320 Peyton Rd (77032-2018)
PHONE.................................281 442-8001
David Calfee, *President*
Carla Calfee, *Corp Secy*
Lindsay Clark, *Vice Pres*
Mike McKinney, *Vice Pres*
Billy Smith, *Mfg Spvr*
EMP: 69
SQ FT: 50,000
SALES (est): 17.1MM **Privately Held**
WEB: www.mod-u-serve.com
SIC: 3469 3556 Kitchen fixtures & equipment: metal, except cast aluminum; food products machinery

(G-9251)
COMMERCIAL METALS COMPANY
Also Called: CMC Recycling
2015 Quitman St (77026-6744)
PHONE.................................713 226-0100
James Jarvis, *Sales Mgr*
Joe Sellers, *Sales Staff*
Carlos Breeden, *Branch Mgr*
Wire Rod, *Products*
EMP: 100
SALES (corp-wide): 5.4B **Publicly Held**
WEB: www.cmc.com
SIC: 5093 3341 Ferrous metal scrap & waste; nonferrous metals scrap; secondary nonferrous metals
PA: Commercial Metals Company
6565 N Macarthur Blvd # 800
Irving TX 75039
214 689-4300

(G-9252)
COMMERCIAL METALS COMPANY
Also Called: CMC Sterling Steel
2001 Brittmoore Rd (77043-2208)
PHONE.................................713 690-0347
Jeff Garrelts, *Branch Mgr*
Diane Bernard, *Manager*
Michelle Thomas, *Clerk*
EMP: 69
SALES (corp-wide): 5.4B **Publicly Held**
WEB: www.cmc.com
SIC: 3441 Expansion joints (structural shapes), iron or steel
PA: Commercial Metals Company
6565 N Macarthur Blvd # 800
Irving TX 75039
214 689-4300

(G-9253)
COMMON SOURCE LP
14500 North Fwy (77090-6808)
PHONE.................................281 443-7575
Ann Zdansky, *Partner*
Shannon Reed, *COO*
EMP: 10
SALES (est): 1.1MM **Privately Held**
WEB: www.commonsource.com
SIC: 8111 7374 7372 Legal services; optical scanning data service; prepackaged software

(G-9254)
COMMONWEALTH UROLOGY
4720 Aldine Mail Rte (77039-5966)
PHONE.................................281 372-1112
EMP: 36 **Privately Held**
WEB: www.lexingtonclinic.com

SIC: 2099 Tortillas, fresh or refrigerated
PA: Commonwealth Urology
2444 Harrodsburg Rd
Lexington KY 40503

(G-9255)
COMPASS DRCTIONAL GUIDANCE INC
14230 Interdrive E (77032-3314)
P.O. Box 9863, Spring (77387-6863)
PHONE.................................281 442-7484
Gary Long, *President*
Wayne Pace, *Engineer*
Jen Bass, *Controller*
EMP: 10 EST: 2011
SALES (est): 1.7MM **Privately Held**
WEB: www.compass-mwd.com
SIC: 1389 Oil field services

(G-9256)
COMPASS DRCTIONAL GUIDANCE INC
14427 Interdrive W (77032-3335)
PHONE.................................281 442-7484
Gary Long, *President*
Terry Redell, *CFO*
Vickie Long, *Admin Sec*
EMP: 25
SQ FT: 5,000
SALES (est): 4.5MM **Privately Held**
WEB: www.compass-mwd.com
SIC: 1389 Oil field services

(G-9257)
COMPASS ORTHOPEDIC TECH & PDTS
6776 Suthwest Fwy Ste 160 (77074)
P.O. Box 4346 (77210-4346)
PHONE.................................713 995-7010
Dinker Anatya, *President*
EMP: 10
SALES (est): 1MM **Privately Held**
WEB: www.compassdmehouston.com
SIC: 3841 8011 Medical instruments & equipment, blood & bone work; orthopedic physician

(G-9258)
COMPASS SERVICES INC
11620 Brittmoore Park Dr # 200 (77041-6917)
PHONE.................................713 937-9538
Adriana Pineda, *Exec VP*
EMP: 50
SQ FT: 22,400
SALES (est): 7.2MM **Privately Held**
SIC: 2899 Metal treating compounds

(G-9259)
COMPLETE PLASTIC FABRICATORS
8533 Market St (77029-2421)
P.O. Box 15465 (77220-5465)
PHONE.................................713 674-7686
Bryan Sandow, *President*
EMP: 12
SQ FT: 40,000
SALES (est): 1.8MM **Privately Held**
WEB: www.completeplastic.com
SIC: 3089 Injection molding of plastics; plastic processing

(G-9260)
COMPLETE PRODUCTION SVCS INC (HQ)
1001 Louisiana St (77002-5089)
PHONE.................................281 372-2300
Joseph C Winkler, *President*
Brian K Moore, *President*
Ronald L Boyd, *Vice Pres*
David Hightower, *Vice Pres*
Jeff Kaufmann, *Vice Pres*
◆ **EMP:** 25
SALES (est): 1.3B **Publicly Held**
WEB: www.completeproduction.com
SIC: 1389 Oil field services

(G-9261)
COMPRESSOR PRODUCTS INTL LLC
14028 Aston St (77040-5406)
PHONE.................................713 462-1061
EMP: 52

SALES (corp-wide): 1.2B **Publicly Held**
WEB: www.cpicompression.com
SIC: 3569 Lubricating systems, centralized
HQ: Compressor Products International Llc
4410 Greenbriar Dr
Stafford TX 77477
281 207-4600

(G-9262)
COMPRSSION/GENERATION SVCS LLC (PA)
Also Called: C G S
15502 Stone Gables Ln (77044-5364)
PHONE.................................281 209-3616
Kalu Guasco, *Electrical Engi*
John Pauk,
EMP: 67
SALES (est): 12.1MM **Privately Held**
WEB: www.compgenservices.com
SIC: 3621 Power generators

(G-9263)
COMPU-DATA INTERNATIONAL LLC
14610 Falling Creek Dr (77068-2938)
PHONE.................................281 292-1333
Carlos Gutierrez, *Marketing Staff*
Juan Celaya, *Mng Member*
Jan Klatt, *Technical Staff*
William Knapp, *Director*
EMP: 45
SALES (est): 1.3MM **Privately Held**
WEB: www.cdlac.com
SIC: 7371 7372 7379 7373 Software programming applications; computer software development & applications; prepackaged software; application computer software; computer related consulting services; computer integrated systems design; optical scanning data service

(G-9264)
COMPUINK
10007 Lynette Falls Dr (77095-2377)
PHONE.................................281 705-0758
Terrance Hollie, *Owner*
EMP: 15
SALES (est): 855K **Privately Held**
WEB: www.houstonhomesdirect.com
SIC: 3699 Security control equipment & systems

(G-9265)
COMPUTERIZED MILLWORK SVCS INC
10855 Seaboard Loop (77099-3402)
PHONE.................................281 575-1699
Sunardjo Sumargono, *President*
EMP: 15
SALES (est): 2MM **Privately Held**
SIC: 2431 5211 Millwork; millwork & lumber

(G-9266)
CON-TEX BUILDERS INC
Also Called: Con-Tex Roofing
820 Turney Dr (77038-3922)
PHONE.................................281 847-3336
Harold Parkinson, *President*
Stephen W Connolly, *Vice Pres*
Sandra Kline, *Treasurer*
Carol Parkinson, *Admin Sec*
EMP: 20
SQ FT: 2,200
SALES (est): 2.6MM **Privately Held**
WEB: www.houtexsheetmetal.com
SIC: 1761 3444 Roofing contractor; sheet metalwork

(G-9267)
CONCHO RESOURCES INC
1001 Fannin St (77002-6706)
PHONE.................................713 739-7561
Brenda R Schroer, *Vice Pres*
Jeff Gasch, *Vice Pres*
Megan P Hays, *Vice Pres*
Ira Clark, *Branch Mgr*
Young Choi, *Senior Mgr*
EMP: 58 **Privately Held**
WEB: www.concho.com
SIC: 1382 Oil & gas exploration services
PA: Concho Resources Inc.
600 W Illinois Ave
Midland TX 79701

(G-9268)
CONCRETE ASAP LLC
2918 Elysian St (77009-7038)
PHONE.................................713 222-6216
Camilo Munoz,
EMP: 17
SALES (est): 2.5MM **Privately Held**
WEB: www.concreteasap.com
SIC: 3272 Concrete products

(G-9269)
CONFEDERATE STEEL CORPORATION
4507 Cypress Pond Ct (77059-3279)
P.O. Box 266386 (77207-6386)
PHONE.................................713 643-8526
B A Wingate, *President*
Robert N Bosworth, *Vice Pres*
EMP: 10 EST: 1960
SALES (est): 1.7MM **Privately Held**
WEB: www.cscrebar.com
SIC: 3316 Bars, steel, cold finished, from purchased hot-rolled

(G-9270)
CONNER INDUSTRIES INC
5707 Mitchelldale St (77092-7029)
PHONE.................................713 944-6766
EMP: 19
SALES (corp-wide): 125MM **Privately Held**
SIC: 2448 Mfg Wood Pallets/Skids
PA: Conner Industries, Inc.
3800 Sandshell Dr Ste 235
Fort Worth TX 76137
800 413-8006

(G-9271)
CONNER STEEL PRODUCTS INC
9224 Beechnut St (77036-6674)
PHONE.................................325 655-8225
Joseph Fiamingo, *President*
Brian Minzenmayer, *Vice Pres*
Wesley Dehaven, *CFO*
Aubrey R Conner, *Shareholder*
Hollie Conner, *Admin Sec*
EMP: 260
SQ FT: 103,000
SALES (est): 49.6MM
SALES (corp-wide): 8.4B **Publicly Held**
WEB: www.oilfieldpros.com
SIC: 3443 3312 Tanks, standard or custom fabricated: metal plate; bars, iron: made in steel mills
PA: National Oilwell Varco, Inc.
7909 Parkwood Circle Dr
Houston TX 77036
713 346-7500

(G-9272)
CONOCOPHILLIPS (PA)
925 N Eldridge Pkwy (77079-2703)
Rural Route 2197 (77252)
PHONE.................................281 293-1000
Ryan M Lance, *Ch of Bd*
William L Bullock Jr, *President*
Michael D Hatfield, *President*
David Forbes, *General Mgr*
Steve Autry, *Superintendent*
EMP: 3000
SALES: 36.6B **Publicly Held**
WEB: www.conocophillips.com
SIC: 1311 1382 Crude petroleum & natural gas; oil & gas exploration services

(G-9273)
CONOCOPHILLIPS COMPANY (HQ)
925 N Eldridge Pkwy (77079-2703)
P.O. Box 2197 (77252-2197)
PHONE.................................281 293-1000
Ryan M Lance, *CEO*
J J Mulva, *Ch of Bd*
Karl Herzog, *Principal*
Nancy McSmith, *Principal*
Billy Sigman, *Principal*
◆ **EMP:** 3700 **EST:** 1917
SQ FT: 268,286
SALES (est): 11.9B
SALES (corp-wide): 36.6B **Publicly Held**
WEB: www.conocophillips.com
SIC: 1382 2911 5171 5541 Oil & gas exploration services; gasoline; petroleum bulk stations; filling stations, gasoline

▲ = Import ▼ =Export
◆ =Import/Export

PA: Conocophillips
925 N Eldridge Pkwy
Houston TX 77079
281 293-1000

(G-9274)
CONOCOPHILLIPS HOLDING COMPANY (HQ)
600 N Dairy Ashford Rd (77079-1100)
P.O. Box 2197 (77252-2197)
PHONE..............................281 293-1000
J J Mulva, *President*
John Schuelke, *Superintendent*
J A Carrig, *CFO*
Ralph Burch, *General Counsel*
Stephen F Gates, *General Counsel*
▲ EMP: 100
SQ FT: 1,200,000
SALES (est): 302.5MM
SALES (corp-wide): 36.6B **Publicly Held**
WEB: www.conocophillips.com
SIC: 5541 2911 Gasoline service stations; gasoline
PA: Conocophillips
925 N Eldridge Pkwy
Houston TX 77079
281 293-1000

(G-9275)
CONSOLIDATED GRAPHICS INC (HQ)
Also Called: Westland Printers
5858 Westheimer Rd # 200 (77057-5643)
PHONE..............................713 787-0977
Joe R Davis, *CEO*
Kurt Johnson, *General Mgr*
Bruce Wasdin, *Purchasing*
Jon C Biro, *CFO*
Robert Smith, *Controller*
◆ EMP: 17
SQ FT: 6,200,000
SALES (est): 1.2B
SALES (corp-wide): 6.2B **Publicly Held**
WEB: www.cgx.com
SIC: 2752 Commercial printing, offset
PA: R. R. Donnelley & Sons Company
35 W Wacker Dr
Chicago IL 60601
312 326-8000

(G-9276)
CONSOLIDATED MILLS INC
7190 Brittmoore Rd # 150 (77041-3233)
PHONE..............................713 896-4196
Scott K Vrana, *President*
Charles Ordner, *President*
Keith E Vrana, *Exec VP*
EMP: 30
SQ FT: 25,000
SALES (est): 10.6MM **Privately Held**
WEB: www.consolidatedmills.com
SIC: 2099 2087 5149 Spices, including grinding; flavoring extracts & syrups; spices & seasonings

(G-9277)
CONSTELLATION LIGHTING LTD
21175 State Highway 249 (77070-1655)
PHONE..............................832 717-5750
John Banks, *President*
Angela Banks, *Admin Sec*
▲ EMP: 9
SALES (est): 1MM **Privately Held**
WEB: www.constellationlighting.us
SIC: 3646 Commercial indusl & institutional electric lighting fixtures

(G-9278)
CONSTRUCT CAPITAL LLC
Also Called: Perma-Pier Foundation Repair O
10912 Metronome Dr (77043-2202)
PHONE..............................713 322-6714
EMP: 74
SALES (corp-wide): 64.4MM **Privately Held**
WEB: www.permapier.com
SIC: 1629 1741 1381 Drainage system construction; foundation & retaining wall construction; service well drilling
PA: Construct Capital, Llc
2821 E Randol Mill Rd
Arlington TX 76011
214 637-1444

(G-9279)
CONSUMER ENERGY ALLIANCE
2211 Norfolk St Ste 610 (77098-4064)
PHONE..............................713 337-8800
Brett Vassey, *Ch of Bd*
Wyatt Boutwell, *President*
David Holt, *Principal*
Paul Looney, *Exec VP*
Bryson Hull, *Vice Pres*
EMP: 13
SALES: 4.6MM **Privately Held**
WEB: www.consumerenergyalliance.org
SIC: 3494 Plumbing & heating valves

(G-9280)
CONSUMER GUIDE INC
9894 Bissonnet St Ste 900 (77036-8272)
PHONE..............................713 417-6152
EMP: 11
SALES: 2.7MM **Privately Held**
SIC: 2791 Typesetting Services

(G-9281)
CONTANDA LLC (PA)
Also Called: Westway Group
1111 Bagby St Ste 1800 (77002-2548)
PHONE..............................832 699-4001
Gene McClain, *CEO*
Eric Gadd, *Principal*
Robert H Lewis, *Senior VP*
Jim Keller, *VP Legal*
Tim McDavid, *Vice Pres*
◆ EMP: 25
SALES (est): 90.2MM **Privately Held**
WEB: www.contanda.com
SIC: 4226 2048 Liquid storage; feed supplements

(G-9282)
CONTANGO OIL & GAS COMPANY (PA)
717 Texas St Ste 2900 (77002-2836)
PHONE..............................713 236-7400
John C Goff, *Ch of Bd*
Wilkie S Colyer Jr, *President*
Farley Dakan, *President*
Chad Roller, *COO*
Chad McLawhorn, *Senior VP*
EMP: 27
SALES: 76.5MM **Publicly Held**
WEB: www.contango.com
SIC: 1311 1382 Crude petroleum & natural gas; oil & gas exploration services

(G-9283)
CONTINENTAL CARBON COMPANY (DH)
16850 Park Row (77084-5023)
PHONE..............................281 647-3700
Leslie C Y Koo, *Ch of Bd*
Dennis Hetu, *President*
Phillip Burton, *General Mgr*
Greg Johnstone, *General Mgr*
Deepak Malik, *Managing Dir*
◆ EMP: 70 EST: 1936
SQ FT: 28,000
SALES (est): 114.5MM **Privately Held**
WEB: www.continentalcarbon.com
SIC: 2895 3624 Carbon black; carbon & graphite products

(G-9284)
CONTINENTAL CARBON COMPANY
10655 Richmond Ave # 100 (77042-4909)
PHONE..............................281 647-3728
Tom Carroll, *CFO*
Susan Ball, *Human Res Dir*
Todd N Miller, *Director*
EMP: 11 **Privately Held**
WEB: www.continentalcarbon.com
SIC: 2819 Industrial inorganic chemicals
HQ: Continental Carbon Company
16850 Park Row
Houston TX 77084
281 647-3700

(G-9285)
CONTINENTAL LABORATORIES INC
6600 Frbanks N Houston Rd (77040-4309)
PHONE..............................713 460-0780
Patrick Remmers, *President*
Craig Macleod, *Vice Pres*
Tony Welka, *Vice Pres*
John Mumford, *Personnel*
EMP: 50 EST: 1954
SQ FT: 6,000
SALES (est): 4.1MM **Privately Held**
WEB: www.continentallabs.com
SIC: 1389 3533 Well logging; oil & gas field machinery; well logging equipment

(G-9286)
CONTINENTAL LAND & FUR CO INC
16945 Northchase Dr # 1500 (77060-2135)
PHONE..............................281 873-9378
R Paul Loveless, *President*
Kerri Battaglia, *Vice Pres*
Mark Stover, *Vice Pres*
Mark Parrott, *Exploration*
EMP: 18
SALES (corp-wide): 1MM **Privately Held**
WEB: www.clf-co.com
SIC: 1382 Oil & gas exploration services
PA: Continental Land & Fur Co Inc
111 Veterans Memorial Blv
Metairie LA 70005
504 378-9378

(G-9287)
CONTINENTAL OPERATING CO
9805 Katy Fwy Ste 500 (77024-1271)
PHONE..............................713 209-1110
Peter D Huddleston, *Ch of Bd*
Peter Curry, *Vice Pres*
Glenda Dole, *Executive*
EMP: 15
SALES (est): 2.6MM **Privately Held**
WEB: www.continentaloperating.com
SIC: 1311 Crude petroleum production; natural gas production

(G-9288)
CONTINENTAL PROD SVCS INC
5124 Polk St (77023-1420)
P.O. Box 231287 (77223-1287)
PHONE..............................281 431-0502
Craig Corbell II, *President*
Grant Richardson, *Vice Pres*
Dan McGookey, *Consultant*
EMP: 21 EST: 1981
SQ FT: 4,800
SALES (est): 2.6MM **Privately Held**
WEB: www.continentalproductionservices.com
SIC: 1389 Oil field services

(G-9289)
CONTINENTAL STONE LLC (PA)
Also Called: Earthstone
8758 Clay Rd Ste 400 (77080-8107)
PHONE..............................713 462-5700
Masoud Ladjevardian, *President*
Mary Nguyen, *Comptroller*
Bob Jameson, *VP Sales*
Yolanda Gonzalez, *Sales Staff*
Michelle Zullinger, *Sales Staff*
▲ EMP: 24 EST: 2007
SQ FT: 90,000
SALES (est): 7.7MM **Privately Held**
WEB: www.earthstonetexas.com
SIC: 5032 3272 Building stone; granite building stone; marble building stone; roofing tile & slabs, concrete

(G-9290)
CONTINENTAL TURBINE SERVICES
Also Called: Power Generation
430 E Helms Rd Ste D2 (77037-1600)
PHONE..............................281 541-6060
Juan Cantu, *President*
EMP: 10
SALES (est): 1.7MM **Privately Held**
WEB: www.continentalturbine.com
SIC: 3511 Turbines & turbine generator sets

(G-9291)
CONTINNTAL SILVERLINE PDTS LLC
Also Called: Restonic-Houston
710 N Drennan St (77003-1321)
P.O. Box 7072 (77248-7072)
PHONE..............................713 222-7394
◆ EMP: 80
SQ FT: 200,000

SALES (est): 20MM **Privately Held**
WEB: www.restonic.com
SIC: 2515 5021 Mattresses, innerspring or box spring; bedsprings

(G-9292)
CONTRACT FABRICATING SVCS LLC
801 E Whitney St (77022-3539)
PHONE..............................281 501-8664
Doug Evans, *President*
EMP: 20
SQ FT: 3,000
SALES (est): 3.4MM **Privately Held**
WEB: www.contractfabricatingservices.com
SIC: 3441 Fabricated structural metal

(G-9293)
CONTRACTORS METAL WORKS INC
8707 Frbanks N Houston Rd (77064-6801)
P.O. Box 41342 (77241-1342)
PHONE..............................713 856-6600
Michael G Broome, *President*
EMP: 14 EST: 1974
SQ FT: 25,400
SALES (est): 3.7MM **Privately Held**
WEB: www.contractorsmetalworks.com
SIC: 3441 Building components, structural steel

(G-9294)
CONTROL COMPONENTS INC
Also Called: C C I Valve
4525 Kennedy Commerce Dr (77032-3425)
PHONE..............................832 467-7200
Paula Madden, *Finance Mgr*
David Nguyen, *Credit Staff*
Jay Giffen, *Sales Staff*
Mike Yancey, *Branch Mgr*
Arlene Dzura, *Manager*
EMP: 15
SALES (corp-wide): 2.4B **Privately Held**
WEB: www.controlcomponentsinc.com
SIC: 3491 7699 Process control regulator valves; valve repair, industrial
HQ: Control Components Inc.
22591 Avenida Empresa
Rcho Sta Marg CA 92688
949 858-1877

(G-9295)
CONTROL FLOW INC (PA)
Also Called: Westech Heavy Machinery Div
9201 Frbanks N Houston Rd (77064-6206)
P.O. Box 40788 (77240-0788)
PHONE..............................281 890-8300
◆ EMP: 120 EST: 1975
SQ FT: 20,000
SALES (est): 33.6MM **Privately Held**
WEB: www.controlflow.com
SIC: 3533 7361 Oil field machinery & equipment; ship crew agency

(G-9296)
CONVERGENT PERFORMANCE LLC
13719 Chelwood Pl (77069-2707)
PHONE..............................713 398-8496
William P Daily, *Branch Mgr*
EMP: 9
SALES (corp-wide): 2.8MM **Privately Held**
WEB: www.convergentperformance.com
SIC: 3674 Semiconductors & related devices
PA: Convergent Performance, Llc
7150 Campus Dr Ste 275
Colorado Springs CO
719 481-0530

(G-9297)
CONVERGENTZ BLDG SYSTEMS LLC
10555 Westpark Dr (77042-5232)
P.O. Box 4591 (77210-4591)
PHONE..............................713 266-3900
Mike Jordan, *Project Mgr*
Christopher Rose, *Project Mgr*
Jeff Crook, *Sales Mgr*
Richard Hunton,
Crystal Gekler, *Administration*
EMP: 25
SQ FT: 52,000

SALES (est): 2.4MM **Privately Held**
WEB: www.convergentz.com
SIC: 8711 1711 3822 Heating & ventilation engineering; heating systems repair & maintenance; refrigeration controls (pressure); refrigeration thermostats

(G-9298)
CONVERGEPOINT INC
Also Called: Care Converge
1011 Highway 6 S Ste 105 (77077-1031)
PHONE.................................347 948-4258
Steven Moore, *Manager*
Aju Koshy, *Director*
EMP: 15
SALES (est): 1.3MM **Privately Held**
WEB: www.convergepoint.com
SIC: 7371 7372 Computer software systems analysis & design, custom; prepackaged software

(G-9299)
CONVEYOR AGGREGATE PDTS CORP
Also Called: Cap
5131 Steadmont Dr (77040-6525)
PHONE.................................713 856-5600
Bob Pervis, *President*
Bill Nungesser, *Branch Mgr*
Jack Paige, *Manager*
EMP: 15
SALES (est): 1.9MM **Privately Held**
WEB: www.purvisindustries.com
SIC: 3535 Conveyors & conveying equipment

(G-9300)
COOK CMPRSSN-PARLAND OPERATION
11951 Spectrum Blvd (77047-7803)
PHONE.................................713 433-2002
Raj Subramanian, *Principal*
EMP: 44
SQ FT: 32,400
SALES (est): 10MM **Privately Held**
WEB: www.cookcompression.com
SIC: 3549 Metalworking machinery

(G-9301)
COOK COMPRESSION (HQ)
11951 Spectrum Blvd (77047-7803)
PHONE.................................713 433-2002
Frank Wierengo, *President*
Don York, *Principal*
Marc Edmonson, *Regional Mgr*
Wade Calk, *Opers Mgr*
Raj Subramanian, *Opers Mgr*
EMP: 41
SALES (est): 16.7MM
SALES (corp-wide): 7.1B **Publicly Held**
WEB: www.cookcompression.com
SIC: 2821 Thermoplastic materials
PA: Dover Corporation
3005 Highland Pkwy # 200
Downers Grove IL 60515
630 541-1540

(G-9302)
COOLE SCHOOL INC
1213 West Loop N Ste 100 (77055-7242)
PHONE.................................713 552-1600
James W Ogg, *President*
Steven G Hassenmiller, *COO*
Cathy Theiss, *Accounts Mgr*
Heather Lochhead, *Sales Staff*
▲ **EMP:** 9
SQ FT: 5,000
SALES (est): 3.1MM **Privately Held**
WEB: www.cooleschool.com
SIC: 2741 8322 Miscellaneous publishing; individual & family services

(G-9303)
COOPER B-LINE INC
7106 Cavalcade St (77028-5902)
PHONE.................................713 678-4460
Brandon Sitterle, *Branch Mgr*
EMP: 20 **Privately Held**
WEB: www.eaton.com
SIC: 3674 Semiconductors & related devices
HQ: Cooper B-Line, Inc.
509 W Monroe St
Highland IL 62249
618 654-2184

(G-9304)
COOPER CROUSE HINDS LLC
Also Called: Industrial Control Instruments
3413 N Sam Houston Pkwy W # 212 (77086-1490)
PHONE.................................713 280-3400
Grant L Gawronski, *President*
Pat Davin, *Vice Pres*
Tyler W Johnson, *Treasurer*
Terrance V Helz, *Admin Sec*
EMP: 27 EST: 2004
SALES (est): 4.6MM **Privately Held**
SIC: 3999 Identification plates

(G-9305)
COOPER CROUSE-HINDS LLC
Also Called: Cooper Crouse Hinds Pauluhn
3530 S Sam Houston Pkwy E (77047-6536)
PHONE.................................832 390-3858
James Wilkinson, *Engineer*
Teresa Young, *Clerk*
EMP: 15 **Privately Held**
WEB: www.cooperindustries.com
SIC: 3699 Fire control or bombing equipment, electronic
HQ: Cooper Crouse-Hinds, Llc
1201 Wolf St
Syracuse NY 13208
315 477-7000

(G-9306)
COOPER CROUSE-HINDS MTL INC
3413 N Sam Houston Pkwy W # 212 (77086-1490)
PHONE.................................281 571-8065
Sandy Cutler, *CEO*
Zeb Hughey, *Sales Staff*
EMP: 150
SALES (est): 18.8MM **Privately Held**
WEB: www.azonix.com
SIC: 3629 Battery chargers, rectifying or nonrotating
HQ: Cooper Crouse-Hinds, Llc
1201 Wolf St
Syracuse NY 13208
315 477-7000

(G-9307)
COOPER LIGHTING LLC
600 Travis St Ste 5600 (77002-2909)
PHONE.................................770 486-4800
Ted Brickenden, *President*
Bart Ideker, *VP Engrg*
Rafael Doria, *QC Mgr*
Bryan Dumler, *Engineer*
Rodney Jacobs, *Engineer*
EMP: 10
SALES (corp-wide): 6.9B **Privately Held**
WEB: www.cooperlighting.com
SIC: 3648 Lighting equipment
HQ: Cooper Lighting, Llc
1121 Highway 74 S
Peachtree City GA 30269
770 486-4800

(G-9308)
COORDNATED DESIGNS CONTRLS INC
601 Mcfarland St Ste 1 (77011-1100)
PHONE.................................713 921-0220
John J Colvin, *President*
Craig P Collins, *Vice Pres*
Tim Torrico, *Purchasing*
Donnea Moon, *Financial Exec*
EMP: 15
SQ FT: 12,000
SALES (est): 4.4MM **Privately Held**
WEB: www.coordinateddesigns.com
SIC: 3613 Control panels, electric

(G-9309)
COPERION CORPORATION
Also Called: Werner & Pfleiderer
5825 N Sam Houston Pkwy W # 250 (77086-1549)
PHONE.................................281 449-9944
Doug Wilson, *Project Engr*
Al Wetzel, *Sales Engr*
Robert Reischl, *Branch Mgr*
Suzanne Vides, *Admin Asst*
EMP: 12 **Publicly Held**
WEB: www.zsk101.com

SIC: 3559 8711 3535 8734 Plastics working machinery; rubber working machinery, including tires; structural engineering; bulk handling conveyor systems; testing laboratories; rolling mill machinery
HQ: Coperion Corporation
590 Woodbury Glassboro Rd
Sewell NJ 08080

(G-9310)
COPPERLOGIC INC (DH)
Also Called: Moller Electric
4140 World Houston Pkwy (77032-2489)
PHONE.................................713 933-0999
John W Hamm, *President*
▲ **EMP:** 30
SQ FT: 35,000
SALES (est): 4.7MM **Privately Held**
SIC: 3625 Relays & industrial controls
HQ: Eaton Corporation
1000 Eaton Blvd
Cleveland OH 44122
440 523-5000

(G-9311)
COR THERMOTICS LLC
15995 N Barkers Lndg (77079-2467)
PHONE.................................832 308-5151
EMP: 18
SQ FT: 50,000
SALES (est): 2.2MM **Privately Held**
WEB: www.cbac.com
SIC: 3511 3589 Steam turbine generator set units, complete; water treatment equipment, industrial

(G-9312)
COR-PRO SYSTEMS INC
10555 W Little York Rd (77041-4043)
PHONE.................................713 896-1091
Edward G Mann, *President*
Eddie Mann, *Managing Dir*
Arnold Navarro, *Buyer*
Charles Haymaker, *Officer*
Art Travis, *Officer*
EMP: 40
SQ FT: 40,000
SALES (est): 6.1MM **Privately Held**
WEB: www.cor-pro.com
SIC: 1799 3471 Sandblasting of building exteriors; coating of concrete structures with plastic; coating of metal structures at construction site; plating & polishing

(G-9313)
CORDYNE INC (PA)
Also Called: Cordyne Electrical Mfg & Dist
9820 Drysdale Ln (77041-6211)
PHONE.................................713 460-5151
Benjamin L Devine, *President*
Justin A Morgan, *Vice Pres*
Justin Morgan, *Vice Pres*
Richard Ebey, *Engineer*
Stephen Mathews, *Engineer*
◆ **EMP:** 99
SQ FT: 30,000
SALES (est): 21.2MM **Privately Held**
WEB: www.cordyne.com
SIC: 3612 3613 3629 3621 Transformers, except electric; switchgear & switchboard apparatus; capacitors & condensers; motors & generators; electronic circuits; electronic crystals; electrical equipment & supplies

(G-9314)
CORE INTERNATIONAL LLC (HQ)
Also Called: Core Rubber Resources
10540 Bissonnet St # 100 (77099-2268)
PHONE.................................281 880-0200
Julius Lyons, *General Mgr*
Chad Myers, *Vice Pres*
Rachel Jones, *Engineer*
Dwayne Kimball, *Director*
Lance Reed,
◆ **EMP:** 12
SALES (est): 3MM
SALES (corp-wide): 1.2MM **Privately Held**
WEB: www.coreintlgroup.com
SIC: 3069 Castings, rubber
PA: Core Javelina Holdings, Llc
9774 Whithorn Dr
Houston TX 77095
281 880-0200

(G-9315)
CORE LABORATORIES (TEXAS) LLC
6316 Windfern Rd (77040-4950)
PHONE.................................713 328-2673
David Demshur, *CEO*
Larry Bruno, *President*
Brian Qualls, *Mng Member*
Shirley McMillan, *Representative*
EMP: 400
SALES (est): 2.8MM
SALES (corp-wide): 668.2MM **Privately Held**
WEB: www.corelab.com
SIC: 1389 Oil field services
PA: Core Laboratories N.V.
Van Heuven Goedhartlaan 7 B
Amstelveen
204 203-191

(G-9316)
CORE LABORATORIES HOLDING INC
6316 Windfern Rd (77040-4950)
PHONE.................................713 328-2673
David M Demshur, *President*
Gina Escalante, *Owner*
Craig Merritt, *Regional Mgr*
Virgil Alexander, *District Mgr*
Frank Isbell, *District Mgr*
EMP: 400
SALES (est): 11.2MM **Privately Held**
WEB: www.corelab.com
SIC: 1389 7382 Pipe testing, oil field service; surveying wells; confinement surveillance systems maintenance & monitoring

(G-9317)
CORE LABORATORIES LP (HQ)
6316 Windfern Rd (77040-4950)
PHONE.................................713 328-2673
David M Demshur, *President*
Ruben Lopez, *General Mgr*
Craig Merritt, *Regional Mgr*
Brent Bolin, *District Mgr*
Ricky Kent, *District Mgr*
◆ **EMP:** 480
SQ FT: 190,000
SALES (est): 1.9B
SALES (corp-wide): 668.2MM **Privately Held**
WEB: www.corelab.com
SIC: 1389 Oil field services; gas field services
PA: Core Laboratories N.V.
Van Heuven Goedhartlaan 7 B
Amstelveen
204 203-191

(G-9318)
CORE PACIFIC INC
4000 Leeland St (77023-3012)
PHONE.................................800 860-1637
Sean Moore, *President*
Dan Anend, *Vice Pres*
Patrick Gwen, *Vice Pres*
Brad Borden, *VP Sls/Mktg*
Cathy Teng, *CFO*
▲ **EMP:** 25 EST: 2013
SQ FT: 30,000
SALES (est): 8MM **Privately Held**
WEB: www.corepacificinc.com
SIC: 5162 3089 Plastics products; plastic containers, except foam

(G-9319)
COREV AMERICA INC (PA)
Also Called: Perma Tone
11620 Brittmoore Park Dr (77041-6917)
PHONE.................................713 849-3671
Mauricio Pineda, *President*
Adriana Pineda, *Exec VP*
Sergio Pineda, *Vice Pres*
Toni Darnell, *CFO*
Nathalie Palacios,
▼ **EMP:** 20
SQ FT: 22,400
SALES (est): 2.1MM **Privately Held**
WEB: www.corev.com
SIC: 2899 2891 2851 3479 Metal treating compounds; sealants; paints & paint additives; coating of metals & formed products

(G-9320)
CORNERSTONE BLDG BRANDS INC
Star Building Systems
10943 Sam Houston Pkwy W
(77064-5758)
P.O. Box 692055 (77269-2055)
PHONE....................281 897-7788
EMP: 142
SALES (corp-wide): 4.8B **Publicly Held**
WEB: www.cornerstonebuildingbrands.com
SIC: 3448 Prefabricated metal buildings
PA: Cornerstone Building Brands, Inc.
5020 Weston Pkwy Ste 400
Cary NC 27513
866 419-0042

(G-9321)
CORNERSTONE BLDG BRANDS INC
Also Called: N C I
10943 N Sam Huston Pkwy W
(77064-5758)
P.O. Box 840435, Dallas (75284-0435)
PHONE....................281 897-7726
Jeffrey Feaster, *President*
Trevis Lipsey, *Vice Pres*
Brian Bailey, *Plant Mgr*
Paul Stevens, *Plant Mgr*
Vanessa Van Pelt, *Facilities Mgr*
EMP: 9
SALES (corp-wide): 4.8B **Publicly Held**
WEB: www.cornerstonebuildingbrands.com
SIC: 3448 Prefabricated metal buildings
PA: Cornerstone Building Brands, Inc.
5020 Weston Pkwy Ste 400
Cary NC 27513
866 419-0042

(G-9322)
CORNERSTONE BLDG BRANDS INC
Also Called: Chico Building System
7301 Fairview St (77041-2105)
PHONE....................713 466-0712
Mitch Kowen, *Vice Pres*
Trey Ohl, *Sales Staff*
Bob Gallaway, *Info Tech Dir*
EMP: 85
SALES (corp-wide): 4.8B **Publicly Held**
WEB: www.cornerstonebuildingbrands.com
SIC: 3448 Buildings, portable: prefabricated metal
PA: Cornerstone Building Brands, Inc.
5020 Weston Pkwy Ste 400
Cary NC 27513
866 419-0042

(G-9323)
CORRELOG INC
2103 Citywest Blvd # 2100 (77042-2857)
PHONE....................239 514-3331
George Faucher, *CEO*
Peter Mills, *Vice Pres*
EMP: 11 **EST:** 2008
SALES (est): 1.3MM **Privately Held**
WEB: www.correlog.com
SIC: 7371 7372 Computer software development; prepackaged software

(G-9324)
CORROSION PRTCTION PRCSSES OF
340 W 26th St (77008-2049)
P.O. Box 7435 (77248-7435)
PHONE....................713 869-9454
Ken Kleinmann, *President*
Jen Lahad, *General Mgr*
Josey Rae A, *Vice Pres*
EMP: 16
SQ FT: 5,000
SALES (est): 1.8MM **Privately Held**
WEB: www.corrosionpp.com
SIC: 3479 Coating of metals & formed products

(G-9325)
CORRPRO COMPANIES INC
7000 Hollister St Bldg B (77040-5650)
PHONE....................713 460-6000
Jimmy Granger, *Superintendent*
Greg Patton, *Business Mgr*
David Bruhn, *Project Mgr*
Hector Hernandez, *Engineer*
Jeff Hislop, *Accounts Exec*

EMP: 106
SALES (corp-wide): 1.2B **Publicly Held**
WEB: www.aegion.com
SIC: 7389 8711 3317 2899 Copyright protection service; engineering services; steel pipe & tubes; chemical preparations; paints & allied products
HQ: Corrpro Companies, Inc.
1055 W Smith Rd
Medina OH 44256
330 723-5082

(G-9326)
CORRUGATED CONCEPTS PACKG INC
Also Called: C C P I
5050 Campbell Rd Ste C (77041-7657)
PHONE....................713 462-5600
Pamela J Hoffman, *President*
Randy Cox, *General Mgr*
Karie Hoffman, *Vice Pres*
Shaun Hoffman, *VP Mfg*
Diana Perez, *Administration*
EMP: 50
SQ FT: 121,000
SALES (est): 25.6MM **Privately Held**
WEB: www.corrcon.com
SIC: 2653 Boxes, corrugated: made from purchased materials

(G-9327)
COSA XENTAUR CORPORATION (PA)
Also Called: Alpha Omega Intruments
4140 World Houston Pkwy # 180
(77032-2490)
PHONE....................713 947-9591
Gary Astle, *President*
Thomas Bowden, *Engineer*
Lena Pickett, *CFO*
Paul Phelps, *Human Res Mgr*
Michael Surgeary, *Sales Mgr*
◆ **EMP:** 30
SQ FT: 24,000
SALES (est): 20MM **Privately Held**
WEB: www.cosaxentaur.com
SIC: 3823 Coulometric analyzers, industrial process type

(G-9328)
COSA XENTAUR CORPORATION
4140 World Hstn Pkwy # 180 (77032-2490)
PHONE....................631 345-3434
Richard Noone, *Manager*
EMP: 50
SALES (corp-wide): 20MM **Privately Held**
WEB: www.cosaxentaur.com
SIC: 3823 Measuring tools & machines, machinists' metalworking type
PA: Cosa Xentaur Corporation
4140 World Houston Pkwy # 180
Houston TX 77032
713 947-9591

(G-9329)
COSINE ADDITIVE INC
8181 W Hardy Rd (77022-3469)
PHONE....................832 519-8441
Jason Miller, *CEO*
Geoffrey Nordloh, *CFO*
Jacob Jacobson, *Manager*
John O'Connell, *Director*
John Balena,
EMP: 17
SALES (est): 867.8K **Privately Held**
WEB: www.cosineadditive.com
SIC: 3559 Robots, molding & forming plastics

(G-9330)
COUGAR PALLET INC
13417 Aldine Westfield Rd (77039-3003)
PHONE....................281 442-1177
C J Bruley, *President*
Jerry Bruley, *Vice Pres*
Jo Ann Bruley, *Treasurer*
Billie Bruley, *Admin Sec*
EMP: 65
SALES (est): 11.8MM **Privately Held**
WEB: www.cougarpallet.com
SIC: 2449 2448 Boxes, wood: wirebound; wood pallets & skids

(G-9331)
COVALNCE SPCALTY ADHESIVES LLC
Also Called: Covalence Adhesives
13835 Beaumont Hwy (77049-1417)
PHONE....................713 676-0085
Ricardo Gonzalez, *Manager*
EMP: 20 **Publicly Held**
WEB: www.berryglobal.com
SIC: 3089 Bottle caps, molded plastic
HQ: Covalence Specialty Adhesives Llc
101 Oakley St
Evansville IN 47710

(G-9332)
CPFD LLC
Also Called: Cpfd Software
1255 Enclave Pkwy Ste E (77077-1846)
PHONE....................713 429-1252
Peter Blaser, *Vice Pres*
Pinghua Zhao, *Research*
Sam Clark, *Engineer*
Matthew Hamilton, *Project Engr*
James Parker, *CTO*
EMP: 16
SALES (est): 1MM **Privately Held**
WEB: www.cpfd-software.com
SIC: 7372 Prepackaged software

(G-9333)
CRAIG INSTRUMENTS INC
6333 Guhn Rd (77040-5209)
P.O. Box 41560 (77241-1560)
PHONE....................713 690-6904
Ronald C Buchtien, *President*
Karen M Buchtien, *Admin Sec*
EMP: 36
SQ FT: 2,000
SALES (est): 6.9MM **Privately Held**
WEB: www.craiginst.com
SIC: 3599 Machine shop, jobbing & repair

(G-9334)
CRANEWORKS INC (PA)
7795 Little York Rd (77016-2468)
PHONE....................281 219-7779
David W Collis, *President*
Keith Ayers, *President*
Bob Maze, *General Mgr*
Jeff Aicard, *Opers Mgr*
Brandon Bryan, *Parts Mgr*
EMP: 45
SQ FT: 700,000
SALES (est): 22.6MM **Privately Held**
WEB: www.crane-works.com
SIC: 3537 7353 Cranes, industrial truck; cranes & aerial lift equipment, rental or leasing

(G-9335)
CRAWFORD ENERGY INC
770 S Post Oak Ln Ste 520 (77056-1938)
PHONE....................713 626-2637
A Gail Crawford, *President*
Dan Crawford, *Vice Pres*
EMP: 15
SQ FT: 1,000
SALES (est): 2.6MM **Privately Held**
WEB: www.crawfordenergy.com
SIC: 1311 1382 Crude petroleum production; oil & gas exploration services

(G-9336)
CRC-EVANS INTL HOLDINGS INC (HQ)
Also Called: CRC-Evans Pipeline Intl
7011 High Life Dr (77066-3717)
PHONE....................832 249-3100
Timothy Carey, *CEO*
James Cannon, *President*
Brian S Laing, *President*
James F Reed, *Vice Pres*
Greg Laake, *CFO*
▲ **EMP:** 33
SALES (est): 34.8MM
SALES (corp-wide): 14.4B **Publicly Held**
WEB: www.crc-evans.com
SIC: 3531 Construction machinery
PA: Stanley Black & Decker, Inc.
1000 Stanley Dr
New Britain CT 06053
860 225-5111

(G-9337)
CRC-EVANS PIPELINE INTL INC (DH)
7011 High Life Dr (77066-3717)
PHONE....................800 664-9224
M Timothy Carey, *President*
C Paul Evans, *Chairman*
Michael P Smith, *COO*
Mark Biggers, *CFO*
▲ **EMP:** 110
SALES (est): 34.2MM
SALES (corp-wide): 14.4B **Publicly Held**
WEB: www.crc-evans.com
SIC: 3699 3531 3541 Welding machines & equipment, ultrasonic; construction machinery; machine tools, metal cutting type
HQ: Crc-Evans International Holdings, Inc.
7011 High Life Dr
Houston TX 77066
832 249-3100

(G-9338)
CRC/MASTERCRAFT INC
11350 Fm 1960 Rd W (77065-3605)
PHONE....................281 897-8880
Richard Wilson Jr, *President*
Charles Cowher, *Vice Pres*
David Crossland, *Vice Pres*
Daryl Bracht, *Project Mgr*
Candi Graves, *Bookkeeper*
EMP: 30
SQ FT: 31,500
SALES (est): 8.1MM **Privately Held**
WEB: www.crcmastercraft.com
SIC: 2431 Moldings, wood: unfinished & prefinished

(G-9339)
CREATIONS UNLIMTED INC
18927 Aldine Westfield Rd (77073-3817)
PHONE....................281 821-1382
Herb Walpole, *President*
Vivian D Walpole, *Treasurer*
EMP: 32 **Privately Held**
SIC: 3299 Architectural sculptures: gypsum, clay, papier mache, etc.

(G-9340)
CREATIVE SOUND PRODUCTIONS
8383 Commerce Park Dr # 604
(77036-7435)
P.O. Box 720941 (77272-0941)
PHONE....................713 777-9975
Edward B Smith, *President*
Marian Smith, *Vice Pres*
EMP: 14
SQ FT: 12,200
SALES (est): 1.4MM **Privately Held**
SIC: 3652 7819 5099 Magnetic tape (audio): prerecorded; video tape or disk reproduction; video & audio equipment

(G-9341)
CREATIVE SPCLTY FD SLTIONS LLC
3713 Jensen Dr (77026-3215)
PHONE....................713 864-7777
Donald Vaugn, *CEO*
James Baxter, *Partner*
EMP: 100
SALES (est): 17MM **Privately Held**
WEB: www.45foods.com
SIC: 2032 Mexican foods: packaged in cans, jars, etc.

(G-9342)
CRESCENT DIRECTIONAL DRLG LP (PA)
2040 Aldine Western Rd (77038-1208)
PHONE....................281 668-9500
Carol Owsley, *CEO*
Carol McFadden, *President*
Sally Beers, *Vice Pres*
Jennifer Whitley, *Vice Pres*
Danny Greene, *Engineer*
EMP: 96
SQ FT: 40,312
SALES (est): 60MM **Privately Held**
WEB: www.crescentdirectional.com
SIC: 1381 Directional drilling oil & gas wells

(G-9343)
**CRESCENT REEL
MANUFACTURING CO**
201 Burbank St (77076-5004)
P.O. Box 16063 (77222-6063)
PHONE.................................713 695-4587
William E Martin, *President*
Kimarie Inman, *Treasurer*
EMP: 15
SQ FT: 25,000
SALES (est): 135K **Privately Held**
SIC: 2499 Reels, plywood

(G-9344)
**CRIMSON EXPLORATION INC
(HQ)**
717 Texas St Ste 2900 (77002-2836)
PHONE.................................713 236-7400
Thomas H Atkins, *Senior VP*
A Carl Isaac, *Senior VP*
Jay S Mengle, *Senior VP*
E Joseph Grady, *CFO*
Jim La Fevers, *Manager*
EMP: 44
SQ FT: 54,939
SALES (est): 114.7MM **Publicly Held**
SIC: 1311 1382 1381 Crude petroleum
production; oil & gas exploration services;
drilling oil & gas wells

(G-9345)
CRISTACURVA LLC
13105 Nw Fwy Ste 800 (77040-6313)
PHONE.................................713 353-5800
Joanna Smith, *Mfg Staff*
Patrisia Yanez, *Regl Sales Mgr*
Vanessa Violante, *Sales Staff*
Shandi Cowan, *Manager*
Carl Frey, *Manager*
▲ EMP: 9
SALES (est): 1.8MM **Privately Held**
WEB: www.cristacurva.com
SIC: 3211 Laminated glass

(G-9346)
**CROWN CASTLE INTL CORP
(PA)**
1220 Augusta Dr Ste 600 (77057-6801)
PHONE.................................713 570-3000
J Landis Martin, *Ch of Bd*
Jay A Brown, *President*
Kevin Forte, *District Mgr*
Robert C Ackerman, *COO*
James D Young, *COO*
EMP: 11
SALES (est): 5.7B **Publicly Held**
WEB: www.crowncastle.com
SIC: 3663 4899 4812 7622 Satellites,
communications; data communication
services; radio telephone communication;
antenna repair & installation

(G-9347)
**CROWN ENERGY
TECHNOLOGIES INC (DH)**
1617 E Richey Rd (77073-3512)
PHONE.................................403 215-5300
Rance E Fisher, *Ch of Bd*
Todd E Fisher, *President*
Ross Clements, *Vice Pres*
Paul Hadris, *Opers Dir*
◆ EMP: 12
SQ FT: 25,000
SALES (est): 15.1MM
SALES (corp-wide): 2.8B **Publicly Held**
WEB: www.crownhouse.com
SIC: 5082 1389 5084 Oil field equipment;
oil field services; industrial machinery &
equipment

(G-9348)
**CROWN EQUIPMENT
CORPORATION**
Also Called: Crown Lift Trucks
1650 N Sam Houston Pkwy E
(77032-3032)
PHONE.................................281 985-0300
Chris Fogt, *Sales/Mktg Mgr*
Jennifer Adam, *Sales Staff*
EMP: 75
SALES (corp-wide): 3.7B **Privately Held**
WEB: www.crown.com
SIC: 3537 Lift trucks, industrial: fork, plat-
form, straddle, etc.

PA: Crown Equipment Corporation
44 S Washington St
New Bremen OH 45869
419 629-2311

(G-9349)
**CRYOGNIC INDS SVC CMPANIES
LLC**
14014 Interdrive E (77032-3313)
PHONE.................................281 590-4800
EMP: 14 **Privately Held**
WEB: www.acdllc.com
SIC: 3561 Industrial pumps & parts
HQ: Cryogenic Industries Service Compa-
nies, Llc
1851 Kaiser Ave
Irvine CA 92614
949 261-7533

(G-9350)
**CRYOGNIC VSSEL
ALTRNATIVES INC**
952 Echo Ln Ste 250 (77024-2826)
PHONE.................................713 357-9714
Hector Villarreal, *Exec VP*
Siddarth Jain, *Director*
Deepak Acharya, *Director*
Parag Kulkarni, *Director*
◆ EMP: 1003
SQ FT: 44,000
SALES: 17.4MM **Privately Held**
WEB: www.twcryo.com
SIC: 3559 Cryogenic machinery, industrial

(G-9351)
**CRYOTECH PRECISION
MACHINE LLC**
10029 Tanner Rd (77041-7551)
PHONE.................................713 690-2796
Paul Barr, *Principal*
EMP: 16
SALES (est): 2.5MM **Privately Held**
WEB: www.houstoncryotech.com
SIC: 3599 Machine shop, jobbing & repair

(G-9352)
**CRYSTAPHASE PRODUCTS INC
(PA)**
16945 North Fwy Ste 1610 (77090-5001)
PHONE.................................281 874-2110
John Glover, *President*
Chris Alexander, *COO*
Jerry Czubinski, *Opers Staff*
Brad Glover, *CFO*
Larry Bohannon, *Controller*
▲ EMP: 25
SQ FT: 7,500
SALES (est): 5.7MM **Privately Held**
WEB: www.crystaphase.com
SIC: 2911 Oils, partly refined: sold for re-
running

(G-9353)
CS MANUFACTURING INC
14635 Chrisman Rd (77039-1116)
PHONE.................................281 442-3400
EMP: 9
SALES (est): 322.4K **Privately Held**
WEB: www.csmanufacturing.us
SIC: 3089 Injection molding of plastics

(G-9354)
CTCI AMERICAS INC
11490 Westheimer Rd # 200 (77077-6855)
PHONE.................................281 870-9998
EMP: 10 EST: 2016
SALES (est): 1.7MM **Privately Held**
SIC: 2819 Sulfur, recovered or refined, incl.
from sour natural gas

(G-9355)
**CUATRO CINCO ENTERPRISES
LLC**
Also Called: Papa Jose
3715 Jensen Dr (77026-3215)
PHONE.................................713 647-2846
Donald E Vaughn,
EMP: 20
SQ FT: 750
SALES (est): 2.7MM **Privately Held**
WEB: www.45foods.com
SIC: 2032 Mexican foods: packaged in
cans, jars, etc.

(G-9356)
CUBECO INC
1415 Harris St (77020-7538)
PHONE.................................713 671-2466
EMP: 39 EST: 1973
SQ FT: 44,000
SALES (est): 4.5MM **Privately Held**
WEB: www.cubecoinc.com
SIC: 3446 3441 3444 3353 Ladders, for
permanent installation: metal; fabricated
structural metal; sheet metalwork; alu-
minum sheet, plate & foil

(G-9357)
CUBELOGIC LLC
Also Called: Cubelogic Software
4004 Rice Blvd (77005-2742)
PHONE.................................832 498-6374
Roderick Austin,
Lee Campbell,
Riyazahmad Mulla,
David Priestley,
EMP: 31 EST: 2016
SQ FT: 1,500
SALES (est): 653.9K **Privately Held**
WEB: www.cubelogic.com
SIC: 7372 Business oriented computer
software

(G-9358)
**CUMMINS SOUTHERN PLAINS
LLC**
7045 North Loop E 610 (77028-5946)
PHONE.................................713 679-2220
Christopher Baca, *Parts Mgr*
John Mikolaitis, *Manager*
EMP: 115
SALES (corp-wide): 19.8B **Publicly Held**
WEB: www.cummins.com
SIC: 5063 3519 Generators; internal com-
bustion engines
HQ: Cummins Southern Plains Llc
600 N Watson Rd
Arlington TX 76011
817 640-6801

(G-9359)
**CURRENT POWER SOLUTIONS
INC**
Also Called: Cpsi
5050 W Greens Rd (77066-4860)
PHONE.................................281 943-7700
Greg Germenis, *President*
John Franks, *COO*
Gerardo Guerra, *Buyer*
John Malek, *CFO*
Jay Pennison, *Sales Staff*
◆ EMP: 55
SQ FT: 37,000
SALES (est): 22MM
SALES (corp-wide): 1.1B **Publicly Held**
WEB: www.currentpsi.com
SIC: 1382 7699 3532 Oil & gas explo-
ration services; marine engine repair;
mining machinery
PA: Patterson-Uti Energy, Inc.
10713 W Sam Houston Pkwy
Houston TX 77064
281 765-7100

(G-9360)
CURRID & COMPANY
11152 Westheimer Rd # 883 (77042-3208)
PHONE.................................713 893-8401
Cheryl Currid, *President*
EMP: 19
SQ FT: 9,000
SALES (est): 2.6MM **Privately Held**
WEB: www.currid.com
SIC: 8731 2731 2721 Commercial physi-
cal research; book publishing; television
schedules: publishing only, not printed on
site

(G-9361)
**CURTISS-WRIGHT
CORPORATION**
13805 Industrial Rd (77015-6822)
PHONE.................................713 581-3400
John Garcia, *Purch Mgr*
Mike King, *Branch Mgr*
EMP: 11
SALES (corp-wide): 2.4B **Publicly Held**
WEB: www.curtisswright.com
SIC: 3491 Industrial valves

PA: Curtiss-Wright Corporation
130 Harbour Place Dr # 300
Davidson NC 28036
704 869-4600

(G-9362)
CUSTOM ABRASIVES LLC (PA)
2525 Bay Area Blvd # 290 (77058-1571)
PHONE.................................281 286-7200
William A Keckley,
EMP: 14
SALES (est): 8.5MM **Privately Held**
WEB: www.customabrasivesllc.com
SIC: 1446 3291 Industrial sand; abrasive
products

(G-9363)
CUSTOM AC & SHTMTL
Also Called: Custom Duct
1729 Stebbins Dr 100 (77043-2842)
PHONE.................................713 868-5557
Thomas M Transou, *President*
Adam Transou, *Vice Pres*
EMP: 11
SQ FT: 20,000
SALES (est): 1.9MM **Privately Held**
SIC: 3444 Sheet metalwork

(G-9364)
**CUSTOM AIR PRODUCTS &
SVCS INC**
16635 Buffalo Speedway (77047-7009)
PHONE.................................713 434-1192
John S Boger, *Branch Mgr*
Vicki Hafner, *Administration*
Linda Shewell, *Receptionist*
EMP: 100 **Privately Held**
WEB: www.customairproducts.com
SIC: 3599 3441 Machine shop, jobbing &
repair; fabricated structural metal
PA: Custom Air Products & Services, Inc.
35 Southbelt Indus Dr
Houston TX 77047

(G-9365)
**CUSTOM AIR PRODUCTS &
SVCS INC (PA)**
Also Called: Honeywell Authorized Dealer
35 Southbelt Indus Dr (77047-7011)
PHONE.................................281 802-7419
John S Boger, *CEO*
James T Norris, *President*
Brad Chaykoski, *General Mgr*
Luke Boger, *Project Mgr*
Mark Browne, *Project Mgr*
▲ EMP: 59
SALES (est): 36MM **Privately Held**
WEB: www.customairproducts.com
SIC: 3599 3441 3564 Machine shop, job-
bing & repair; fabricated structural metal;
blowers & fans

(G-9366)
CUSTOM BOX SOLUTIONS LLC
10685 Hazelhurst Dr Ste B (77043-3261)
PHONE.................................888 376-8061
Sammy Jane,
EMP: 12
SALES (est): 524.6K **Privately Held**
WEB: www.customboxsolutions.com
SIC: 2631 Container, packaging &
boxboard

(G-9367)
**CUSTOM CMPNENTS
ASSEMBLIES INC**
3347 Frick Rd (77086-2913)
PHONE.................................713 937-6225
Mark Cruze, *President*
Greg Toellner, *Purchasing*
Leslie Cruze, *Manager*
EMP: 33
SQ FT: 20,000
SALES (est): 4.9MM **Privately Held**
WEB: www.customcomponentsinc.com
SIC: 3599 Machine shop, jobbing & repair

(G-9368)
CUSTOM CONTROLS COMPANY
5712 Yale St (77076-4524)
P.O. Box 16668 (77222-6668)
PHONE.................................713 666-3258
Timothy I Rodwell, *President*
Shannahan Byargeon, *Opers Mgr*
Eileen Byargeon, *Purchasing*

Al Boesdorfer, *Sales Staff*
Teresa Orlando, *Sales Staff*
EMP: 20 **EST:** 1960
SQ FT: 15,000
SALES (est): 4.8MM **Privately Held**
WEB: www.customcontrolsco.com
SIC: 3585 3613 Air conditioning equipment, complete; control panels, electric

(G-9369)
CUSTOM CRETE INC
4523 Brittmoore Rd (77041-8005)
PHONE................................713 937-3966
Denis Atwood, *Manager*
EMP: 15
SALES (corp-wide): 1.4B **Publicly Held**
WEB: www.custom-crete.com
SIC: 5023 3281 3273 3272 Floor coverings; cut stone & stone products; ready-mixed concrete; concrete products; dimension stone
HQ: Custom Crete, Inc.
2624 Joe Field Rd
Dallas TX 75229
972 243-4466

(G-9370)
CUSTOM DRAPERY COMPANY INC
Also Called: Custom Drapery Blinds & Carpet
3402 E T C Jester Blvd (77018-6022)
PHONE................................713 225-9221
Allan R Klein, *President*
Mark Garrison, *Corp Secy*
Jason Thumann, *Sales Mgr*
Lucy Vences, *Consultant*
EMP: 95
SQ FT: 80,000
SALES (est): 15.1MM **Privately Held**
SIC: 5023 2391 2591 Floor coverings; curtains & draperies; window blinds; window shades

(G-9371)
CUSTOM FILTER SUPPLY INC
8581 Mosley Rd 17 (77075-1115)
PHONE................................713 947-8147
EMP: 11 **EST:** 1974
SQ FT: 6,000
SALES (est): 1.5MM **Privately Held**
WEB: www.customfiltersupplyinc.com
SIC: 2211 Filter cloth, cotton

(G-9372)
CUSTOM FLOORS UNLIMITED INC
12405 Sowden Rd (77080-2032)
PHONE................................713 861-4139
▲ **EMP:** 65
SALES (est): 5MM **Privately Held**
SIC: 2426 Flooring, hardwood

(G-9373)
CUSTOM PIPE COATING INC
7177 Cavalcade St (77028-5901)
PHONE................................713 675-2324
Jerry Brock, *Ch of Bd*
O Bryan Rabon, *President*
Larry Ducharme, *Corp Secy*
EMP: 28
SQ FT: 41,000
SALES (est): 2.9MM **Privately Held**
SIC: 1799 1721 2851 Coating of metal structures at construction site; industrial painting; paints & allied products
HQ: Brock Enterprises Llc
10343 Sam Houston Park Dr # 200
Houston TX 77064
281 807-8200

(G-9374)
CUSTOM PRECISION SHTMTL INC
8913 Elsie Ln (77064-7703)
P.O. Box 41206 (77241-1206)
PHONE................................713 856-9997
C R Reyes Vasquez, *President*
Maria Reyes, *Corp Secy*
EMP: 20
SQ FT: 14,500
SALES (est): 3.6MM **Privately Held**
WEB: www.cpsminc.com
SIC: 3444 Sheet metalwork

(G-9375)
CUSTOM SEC FENCE IR WORKS LLC
13824 E Hardy Rd (77039-1801)
PHONE................................281 219-1400
Diego Lozano, *Sales Staff*
Emilio Lozano,
EMP: 10
SQ FT: 4,176
SALES (est): 1.5MM **Privately Held**
WEB: www.customsecurityfence.com
SIC: 3446 Ornamental metalwork

(G-9376)
CUSTOM THREADING INC
5835 Cheswood St (77087-4003)
PHONE................................713 645-8422
James Ward, *President*
Stephen Carter, *Opers Staff*
Dora Samwel, *Manager*
EMP: 13
SQ FT: 10,000
SALES (est): 2.6MM **Privately Held**
WEB: www.ctithread.com
SIC: 3599 Machine shop, jobbing & repair

(G-9377)
CUSTOM-BUILT EQUIPMENT CO INC
1400 Rothwell St (77002-1136)
PHONE................................713 222-0342
Louis Hoffert, *President*
Susan Hoffert, *Vice Pres*
EMP: 12
SQ FT: 14,000
SALES (est): 1.8MM **Privately Held**
SIC: 3589 Commercial cooking & food-warn.ng equipment

(G-9378)
CUTTING SOURCE PRECISION INC
7951 Fairview St (77041-2117)
PHONE................................281 859-2900
Amber Stoltz, *President*
James Barnhill, *General Mgr*
Eric Cormick, *Administration*
EMP: 18 **EST:** 2000
SALES (est): 3.9MM **Privately Held**
WEB: www.cspmachine.com
SIC: 3599 Machine shop, jobbing & repair

(G-9379)
CW SEHORN ENTERPRISES LTD
Also Called: Circle D Specialties
14105 Packard St (77040-5431)
PHONE................................713 895-8834
Christopher W Sehorn, *President*
EMP: 50
SQ FT: 2,500
SALES (est): 1.1MM **Privately Held**
WEB: www.circledspecialties.com
SIC: 3465 Body parts, automobile: stamped metal

(G-9380)
CWS ROAD PLATE LLC
Also Called: Cerda Industries
8411 Villa Dr (77061-4601)
PHONE................................713 242-7711
Victor Cerda,
Daniel Williamson,
EMP: 62
SALES (est): 9.6MM **Privately Held**
WEB: www.cwsroadplate.com
SIC: 3312 Plate, steel

(G-9381)
CYBER MANUFACTURING LLC
10060 W Gulf Bank Rd (77040-3160)
PHONE................................713 946-4903
Tiffany Vu, *Purch Mgr*
Andrew George, *Mng Member*
Peter Dinh,
▼ **EMP:** 19 **EST:** 2012
SQ FT: 3,000
SALES (est): 4.5MM **Privately Held**
WEB: www.cybermfg.com
SIC: 3441 Fabricated structural metal

(G-9382)
CYCLONE BOLT INCORPORATED
Also Called: Cyclone Bolt and Gasket
5258 N Sam Houston Pkwy E (77032-4009)
PHONE................................281 372-6050
EMP: 10
SALES (est): 1.5MM **Privately Held**
WEB: www.cyclonebolt.com
SIC: 3965 Fasteners

(G-9383)
CYCLONE COTTON CANDY LLC
142 Knobcrest Dr (77060-1213)
PHONE................................281 748-9163
Jacque Mendenhall, *Mng Member*
Michael Mendenhall, *Mng Member*
EMP: 20
SALES (est): 500K **Privately Held**
SIC: 2064 5145 Candy & other confectionery products; candy

(G-9384)
CYCLONE PRODUCTION INC
6102 Brittmoore Rd Ste C (77041-5645)
PHONE................................713 979-1101
Carlos Martin Pedraza, *President*
Gene Carson, *Exec VP*
Jose Pedraza, *VP Mktg*
EMP: 10
SQ FT: 500
SALES (est): 1.4MM **Privately Held**
WEB: www.cycloneproduction.com
SIC: 3555 2732 2754 7389 Printing presses; pamphlets: printing only, not published on site; business form & card printing, gravure; embroidering of advertising on shirts, etc.

(G-9385)
CYCLONE STEEL SERVICES LLC
4950 W Greens Rd (77066-4852)
P.O. Box 682017 (77268-2017)
PHONE................................713 635-5555
Steve Lesikar, *CEO*
Ladonna Lesikar, *CFO*
EMP: 40 **EST:** 2008
SALES (est): 11MM **Privately Held**
WEB: www.cyclonesteel.com
SIC: 5051 3312 Steel

(G-9386)
D & D DRAPERY COMPANY
5000 San Jacinto St (77004-5793)
PHONE................................713 522-1643
David M Ferley, *President*
Monica Ferley, *Vice Pres*
Scott Ferley, *Treasurer*
Dorothy Ferley, *Admin Sec*
EMP: 19 **EST:** 1957
SQ FT: 14,800
SALES (est): 2.8MM **Privately Held**
WEB: www.dddrapery.com
SIC: 5714 2391 Draperies; draperies, plastic & textile: from purchased materials

(G-9387)
D & L QUALITY PAINTING INC
12212 Green River Dr (77044-2213)
PHONE................................281 458-3588
David Berryhill, *President*
Kenneth S Berrhyill, *Vice Pres*
EMP: 40
SQ FT: 20,000
SALES (est): 5.6MM **Privately Held**
WEB: www.dlpainting.com
SIC: 1623 3441 7699 1721 Water, sewer & utility lines; fabricated structural metal; industrial equipment services; industrial painting; fireproofing buildings; sandblasting of building exteriors

(G-9388)
D & S MACHINE WORKS INC
Also Called: D&S
4136 Pinemont Dr (77018-1106)
PHONE................................713 686-4222
John S Stanfield, *President*
Emily C Stanfield, *Principal*
EMP: 20
SQ FT: 16,000

SALES (est): 2.8MM **Privately Held**
WEB: www.dsmachineworks.com
SIC: 3599 Machine shop, jobbing & repair

(G-9389)
D & W NAMEPLATE SERVICE INC
5200 Mitchelldale St E19 (77092-7222)
P.O. Box 920743 (77292-0743)
PHONE................................713 681-6616
Mathew White, *President*
Dennis White, *President*
White Dennis R, *Vice Pres*
EMP: 10
SALES (est): 1.1MM **Privately Held**
WEB: www.dwnameplate.com
SIC: 3999 Identification badges & insignia

(G-9390)
DACO ABRASIVES
7030 Avenue C (77011-3734)
P.O. Box 9523 (77261-9523)
PHONE................................713 923-4664
Russell Eddinton, *President*
Russell Eddington, *President*
W L Eddington, *Treasurer*
EMP: 23
SQ FT: 70,000
SALES (est): 3.2MM **Privately Held**
WEB: www.dacoabrasives.com
SIC: 3545 5085 Cutting tools for machine tools; industrial tools

(G-9391)
DADEKS MACHINE WORKS CORP
150 Raymac St (77037-1410)
PHONE................................281 447-4723
Janis Dadeks, *President*
Debbien Sharpoffc, *Manager*
Nora Sustaita, *Assistant*
EMP: 10
SQ FT: 3,800
SALES (est): 500K **Privately Held**
SIC: 3599 Machine shop, jobbing & repair

(G-9392)
DAHILL OFFICE TECHNOLOGY CORP
2100 West Loop S Ste 1300 (77027-3577)
PHONE................................713 329-9909
Kathy Reynolds, *Sales Mgr*
EMP: 26
SALES (corp-wide): 9B **Publicly Held**
WEB: www.southwest.xeroxbusinesssolutions.com
SIC: 5999 3861 2759 Business machines & equipment; photocopy machines; facsimile equipment; photographic equipment & supplies; commercial printing
HQ: Dahill Office Technology Corporation
8200 W Interstate 10 # 4
San Antonio TX 78230
210 805-8200

(G-9393)
DAIKIN MANUFACTURING CO LP
5151 San Felipe St # 500 (77056-3650)
PHONE................................972 245-1510
Kimberly Fields, *Principal*
Jacky Cruz, *Regional Mgr*
Peter Vanbooven, *Regional Mgr*
Jon Steadman, *Area Mgr*
Ian Herrod, *Exec VP*
EMP: 10
SALES (est): 100MM **Privately Held**
WEB: www.daikin.com
SIC: 3585 Heating & air conditioning combination units

(G-9394)
DAILY COURT REVIEW INC
8 Greenway Plz Ste 101 (77046-0830)
P.O. Box 1889 (77251-1889)
PHONE................................713 869-5434
Thomas Morin Jr, *President*
Sarah Morin, *President*
Jennifer Hassan, *Executive Asst*
EMP: 15 **EST:** 1889
SQ FT: 5,000

SALES (est): 1MM **Privately Held**
WEB: www.dailycourtreview.com
SIC: 2711 2752 Newspapers: publishing only, not printed on site; commercial printing, lithographic

(G-9395)
DAILY INSTRUMENTS CORPORATION (PA)
Also Called: Daily Thermetrics
5700 Hartsdale Dr (77036-2112)
PHONE..........................713 780-8600
Anabel L Daily, *CEO*
Walter Tijmes, *Vice Pres*
Larry Welch, *Vice Pres*
Don Fulton, *CFO*
Evan Blumfield, *Accountant*
▼ **EMP:** 20
SQ FT: 32,000
SALES (est): 25.3MM **Privately Held**
WEB: www.dailyinst.com
SIC: 3829 Thermocouples

(G-9396)
DAIRY QUEEN
12930 Scarsdale Blvd (77089-6226)
PHONE..........................281 481-8505
Asmael Catrrez, *Owner*
Tom To, *Owner*
EMP: 15
SALES (est): 274.8K **Privately Held**
WEB: www.dairyqueen.com
SIC: 5812 2024 Ice cream stands or dairy bars; ice cream & ice milk

(G-9397)
DAKOTA CABINETS INC
13519 Sundale Rd (77038-1031)
PHONE..........................281 741-7695
Gary Henry, *President*
EMP: 10
SQ FT: 10,000
SALES (est): 1MM **Privately Held**
SIC: 2522 Panel systems & partitions, office: except wood; cabinets, office: except wood

(G-9398)
DALE COMPANY INC
6216 Navigation Blvd (77011-1136)
PHONE..........................713 928-3437
E R Leggett, *President*
Donald Russell, *Vice Pres*
Sandy Hernandez, *Sales Staff*
◆ **EMP:** 15 **EST:** 1959
SQ FT: 17,000
SALES (est): 3.3MM **Privately Held**
WEB: www.dalecompany.com
SIC: 3452 5085 Bolts, nuts, rivets & washers; fasteners, industrial: nuts, bolts, screws, etc.

(G-9399)
DAN-LOC GROUP LLC (PA)
Also Called: Dan-Loc Drennan
725 N Drennan St (77003-1320)
P.O. Box 292 (77001-0292)
PHONE..........................713 356-3500
Brad Jones, *Vice Pres*
Johnny Johnson, *Sales Staff*
Jill McKenzie, *Sales Staff*
Jose Ruiz, *Supervisor*
Pat Garrett, *Director*
EMP: 68
SALES (est): 51.4MM **Privately Held**
WEB: www.danlocgroup.com
SIC: 3452 3053 3462 Bolts, metal; gaskets & sealing devices; flange, valve & pipe fitting forgings, ferrous

(G-9400)
DAN-LOC, LLC (PA)
Also Called: Dan-Loc Group
725 N Drennan St (77003-1320)
PHONE..........................713 356-3500
◆ **EMP:** 122 **Privately Held**
WEB: www.danlocgroup.com
SIC: 3452 3053 3462 Bolts, metal; gaskets & sealing devices; flange, valve & pipe fitting forgings, ferrous

(G-9401)
DANIEL INDUSTRIES INC (HQ)
11100 Brittmoore Park Dr (77041-6930)
P.O. Box 19097 (77224-9097)
PHONE..........................713 467-6000

Dennis G Perkins, *CEO*
Shane Hale, *Business Mgr*
Jan Bendfeldt, *Marketing Staff*
Dave Seiler, *Executive*
EMP: 30 **EST:** 1999
SALES (est): 381.7MM
SALES (corp-wide): 16.7B **Publicly Held**
WEB: www.emerson.com
SIC: 3823 3824 3494 3829 Industrial flow & liquid measuring instruments; turbine flow meters, industrial process type; flow instruments, industrial process type; turbine meters; positive displacement meters; plumbing & heating valves; measuring & controlling devices; analytical instruments; electronic computers
PA: Emerson Electric Co.
8000 West Florissant Ave
Saint Louis MO 63136
314 553-2000

(G-9402)
DANIEL MEASUREMENT & CTRL LLC (DH)
Also Called: Daniel Measurement & Ctrl Inc
5650 Brittmoore Rd (77041-5613)
PHONE..........................713 827-5033
Jon Stokes, *President*
Greg Schirm, *Business Mgr*
Mike Mason, *Exec VP*
John J Kadera, *Vice Pres*
Robin C Palmer, *Vice Pres*
◆ **EMP:** 448
SALES (est): 240.6MM
SALES (corp-wide): 16.7B **Publicly Held**
WEB: www.emerson.com
SIC: 3824 3498 3499 3823 Gas meters, domestic & large capacity: industrial; turbine meters; pipe sections fabricated from purchased pipe; machine bases, metal; industrial instrmnts msrmnt display/control process variable; electronic computers; industrial valves
HQ: Daniel Industries Inc
11100 Brittmoore Park Dr
Houston TX 77041
713 467-6000

(G-9403)
DAPHANY BROUSSARD
Also Called: Butterfly Effect Hair
17522 Stonebelt Dr (77073-2770)
PHONE..........................832 229-0999
EMP: 10
SALES (est): 283.1K **Privately Held**
SIC: 3999 Mfg Misc Products

(G-9404)
DARLING INGREDIENTS INC
3701 Schalker Dr (77026-3227)
P.O. Box 21183 (77226-1183)
PHONE..........................713 224-0438
Richard Shewmake, *General Mgr*
Scott Sargent, *General Mgr*
Rusty Wilbourn, *General Mgr*
Mitch Coleman, *Plant Supt*
Jocelyne Gilbert, *Opers Staff*
EMP: 50
SALES (corp-wide): 3.3B **Publicly Held**
WEB: www.darlingii.com
SIC: 2077 2992 Grease rendering, inedible; tallow rendering, inedible; bone meal, except as animal feed; meat meal & tankage, except as animal feed; lubricating oils & greases
PA: Darling Ingredients Inc.
5601 N Macarthur Blvd
Irving TX 75038
972 717-0300

(G-9405)
DATAGRATION SOLUTIONS INC
Also Called: Petrovisor
5555 San Felipe St # 2100 (77056-2701)
PHONE..........................713 568-4580
Ike Epley, *CEO*
John Isaac Epley, *Ch of Bd*
Peter Bernard, *Chairman*
Jorge Machnizh, *COO*
David Freer, *CFO*
EMP: 20
SALES (est): 742.4K **Privately Held**
WEB: www.datagration.com
SIC: 1382 7372 Oil & gas exploration services; prepackaged software

(G-9406)
DATASEISMIC CORPORATION
Also Called: Dataseismic Geophysical Svcs
1001 Texas St Ste 1020 (77002-3128)
PHONE..........................713 650-3200
Raul Stolarza, *President*
Santiago Luis Juranovic, *Vice Pres*
Alejandro Azadte, *Technology*
Alejandro Juranovic, *Admin Sec*
EMP: 31
SALES (est): 2.8MM **Privately Held**
WEB: www.dataseismic.com
SIC: 1382 Geological exploration, oil & gas field

(G-9407)
DAVID
Also Called: Jaymaran Wholesale and Dist
9950 Westpark Dr (77063-5138)
PHONE..........................713 357-6393
EMP: 30
SALES (est): 942.1K **Privately Held**
SIC: 2051 Bakery: wholesale or wholesale/retail combined

(G-9408)
DAVID W ARNOLD
Also Called: Ace Machine Works
2001 Lyons Ave (77020-2027)
P.O. Box 15178 (77220-5178)
PHONE..........................713 227-7869
David W Arnold, *Owner*
Phillip Roten, *General Mgr*
EMP: 10
SQ FT: 20,000
SALES (est): 1.9MM **Privately Held**
WEB: www.acemachineworks.com
SIC: 3599 Machine shop, jobbing & repair

(G-9409)
DAVIS OFFSHORE LP
1360 Post Oak Blvd # 2400 (77056-3030)
PHONE..........................713 933-0064
Greg Davis, *President*
EMP: 10 **EST:** 2000
SALES (est): 25MM **Privately Held**
WEB: www.davisoffshore.com
SIC: 1382 Oil & gas exploration services

(G-9410)
DAWSON GEOPHYSICAL COMPANY
10333 Richmond Ave # 800 (77042-4244)
PHONE..........................713 917-6772
Mark Pruitt, *Vice Pres*
EMP: 13
SALES (corp-wide): 145.7MM **Publicly Held**
WEB: www.dawson3d.com
SIC: 1382 Seismograph surveys
HQ: Dawson Operating Llc
508 W Wall St Ste 800
Midland TX 79701
432 684-3000

(G-9411)
DAXWELL LLC (PA)
2825 Wilcrest Dr Ste 500 (77042-6040)
PHONE..........................281 669-0622
Mike McGoogan, *Sales Staff*
Brad Ottosen, *Marketing Staff*
Frank D Zhang, *Mng Member*
Helen Y Zhang,
Samuel Zhang,
◆ **EMP:** 40
SQ FT: 148,000
SALES (est): 20.2MM **Privately Held**
WEB: www.daxwell.com
SIC: 5162 3089 Plastics products; work gloves, plastic; plastic kitchenware, tableware & houseware

(G-9412)
DAYTECH INSTRUMENTS INC
6102 Brittmoore Rd Ste G (77041-5645)
PHONE..........................713 856-6555
Phil Dehmer, *President*
Nanette Dehmer, *Vice Pres*
Cori Dehmer, *Project Mgr*
Chris Dehmer, *QC Mgr*
EMP: 11
SQ FT: 8,000
SALES (est): 1.3MM **Privately Held**
WEB: www.daytechinstruments.com
SIC: 3599 Machine shop, jobbing & repair

(G-9413)
DAYTON-PHOENIX GROUP INC
3340b Greens Rd (77032-2331)
PHONE..........................281 372-0685
EMP: 13 **Privately Held**
WEB: www.dayton-phoenix.com
SIC: 3621 Motors & generators
PA: Dayton-Phoenix Group, Inc.
250 Northwoods Blvd
Vandalia OH 45377

(G-9414)
DB PRECISION CO
6207 W Little York Rd (77091-1105)
P.O. Box 38553 (77238-8553)
PHONE..........................713 681-6400
David Bigelow, *President*
Ben Jacobs, *Sales Staff*
EMP: 12
SQ FT: 15,000
SALES (est): 1.6MM **Privately Held**
WEB: www.dbprecisionco.com
SIC: 3599 Machine shop, jobbing & repair

(G-9415)
DBZ GUITARS LLC
8637 Windfern Rd (77064-7804)
PHONE..........................713 934-0110
▲ **EMP:** 11
SALES (est): 2MM **Privately Held**
SIC: 3931 Mfg Musical Instruments

(G-9416)
DCP NGL SERVICES LP (DH)
5718 Westheimer Rd # 2000 (77057-5745)
PHONE..........................713 735-3600
Jim Mogg, *Partner*
Gary Lyon, *Senior Buyer*
Aaron Titus, *Director*
◆ **EMP:** 12 **EST:** 1997
SALES (est): 43MM **Publicly Held**
WEB: www.dcpmidstream.com
SIC: 1321 1311 Natural gas liquids; crude petroleum & natural gas
HQ: Dcp Operating Company, Lp
370 17th St Ste 2500
Denver CO 80202
303 595-3331

(G-9417)
DE WALCH ENTERPRISE INC
6850 Wynnwood Ln (77008-5024)
PHONE..........................713 861-8993
Don P De Walch, *President*
Gladys K De Walch, *Vice Pres*
EMP: 99
SALES (est): 8.9MM **Privately Held**
WEB: www.dewalch.com
SIC: 3446 Flagpoles, metal

(G-9418)
DEACERO USA INC (HQ)
Also Called: D W R Strl Con Reinforcing
8411 Irvington Blvd (77022-3449)
PHONE..........................713 697-1500
Sergio Gutierrez Muguerz, *President*
David M Gutierrez, *COO*
Raul Manuel Gutierrez, *Vice Pres*
Javier Manuel Gutierrez, *Treasurer*
Dan Hayes, *Sales Staff*
▲ **EMP:** 168
SALES (est): 74.6MM **Privately Held**
WEB: www.deacero.com
SIC: 3312 Rods, iron & steel: made in steel mills

(G-9419)
DEAN-CHEM INC
Also Called: Dean Chem Co
5616 Corl St (77087-4108)
P.O. Box 740023 (77274-0023)
PHONE..........................713 644-3882
Edgar L Dean Jr, *President*
EMP: 10
SQ FT: 5,000
SALES (est): 1.1MM **Privately Held**
WEB: www.alliedpowder.com
SIC: 3479 3471 Coating of metals & formed products; plating of metals or formed products

(G-9420)
DEEP DOWN INC (PA)
Also Called: DEEP DOWN
18511 Beaumont Hwy (77049-1220)
PHONE..........................281 517-5000

▲ = Import ▼ =Export
◆ =Import/Export

Mark Carden, *Ch of Bd*
Charles K Njuguna, *President*
EMP: 72
SALES: 18.9MM **Publicly Held**
WEB: www.deepdowninc.com
SIC: 3533 8711 3531 Oil & gas field machinery; marine engineering; marine related equipment

(G-9421)
DEEP GULF ENERGY II LLC
15011 Katy Fwy Ste 800 (77094-0011)
PHONE...............................281 596-0933
Richard Clark, *President*
EMP: 90 **EST:** 2007
SALES (est): 19.8MM
SALES (corp-wide): 27.6MM **Privately Held**
WEB: www.kosmosenergy.com
SIC: 1382 Oil & gas exploration services
PA: Kosmos Energy Gulf Of Mexico, Llc
    8176 Park Ln Ste 500
    Dallas TX 75231
    214 445-9600

(G-9422)
DEEP GULF ENERGY LP
Also Called: Dge
15011 Katy Fwy Ste 800 (77094-0011)
PHONE...............................281 596-0933
Richard Clarke, *Partner*
Dave Huber, *Partner*
Ray Nelson, *Partner*
Jere Overdyke, *Partner*
Tom Young, *Partner*
▲ **EMP:** 16
SALES (est): 8MM
SALES (corp-wide): 27.6MM **Privately Held**
WEB: www.kosmosenergy.com
SIC: 1382 Oil & gas exploration services
PA: Kosmos Energy Gulf Of Mexico, Llc
    8176 Park Ln Ste 500
    Dallas TX 75231
    214 445-9600

(G-9423)
DEEPHOLE SOLUTIONS INC
9802 Windmill Park Ln (77064-3301)
PHONE...............................713 896-1121
Don Perrin, *President*
Michael Phillips, *Vice Pres*
EMP: 12
SQ FT: 17,000
SALES (est): 500K **Privately Held**
WEB: www.deepholesolutions.com
SIC: 3599 Machine shop, jobbing & repair

(G-9424)
DEEPSEA TECHNOLOGIES INC
7807 Fairview St (77041-2115)
PHONE...............................713 849-5555
Sanjay K Reddy, *President*
Rory Satterfield, *General Mgr*
Marcos Caldera, *Project Mgr*
CJ Danchak, *Mfg Mgr*
Srinivas Changalpet, *Engineer*
▲ **EMP:** 16 **EST:** 2001
SQ FT: 1,500
SALES (est): 7.3MM **Privately Held**
WEB: www.deepsea-tech.com
SIC: 1389 Oil field services

(G-9425)
DEEPWATER MFG USA INC
13813 Fm 529 Rd (77041-2520)
PHONE...............................713 983-7117
Bryan Long, *Manager*
EMP: 25
SALES (est): 5.6MM **Publicly Held**
WEB: www.stoprust.com
SIC: 3331 Cathodes (primary), copper
HQ: Deepwater Corrosion Services, Inc.
    13813 Fm 529 Rd
    Houston TX 77041
    713 983-7117

(G-9426)
DELATORRE INC
Also Called: Custom Creations Furniture
1200 Missouri St (77006-2711)
PHONE...............................713 522-5833
Steven Delatorre, *President*
Ceci Delatorre, *Vice Pres*
Jenny Farris, *Manager*
Kristen Halstead, *Creative Dir*

EMP: 19 **EST:** 1964
SQ FT: 13,500
SALES: 1.4MM **Privately Held**
WEB: www.ccftexas.com
SIC: 2512 7641 Living room furniture: upholstered on wood frames; reupholstery & furniture repair

(G-9427)
DELMAR SYSTEMS INC
900 Town And Country Ln # 400
(77024-2226)
PHONE...............................832 252-7100
Matthew Smith, *Vice Pres*
EMP: 20
SALES (corp-wide): 82.3MM **Privately Held**
WEB: www.delmarsystems.com
SIC: 1389 Oil field services
PA: Delmar Systems, Inc.
    8114 Highway 90 E
    Broussard LA 70518
    337 365-0180

(G-9428)
DELS PLATING INDUSTRIES CORP
Also Called: Del's Plating Works
8736 Schumacher Ln (77063-5621)
PHONE...............................713 785-4955
William Lee, *President*
Bill Lee, *General Mgr*
Travis Lee, *General Mgr*
Susan Lee, *Treasurer*
Yahn Lee, *Office Mgr*
EMP: 15
SQ FT: 10,000
SALES (est): 2.3MM **Privately Held**
WEB: www.delsplating.com
SIC: 3471 Electroplating of metals or formed products

(G-9429)
DELSTAR METAL FINISHING INC
11501 Brittmoore Park Dr (77041-6916)
P.O. Box 840128 (77284-0128)
PHONE...............................713 849-2090
Calvin Riggs, *President*
Charlie Sturm, *Prdtn Mgr*
Arnie Sturm, *Technology*
EMP: 26
SALES (est): 3.9MM **Privately Held**
WEB: www.delstar.com
SIC: 3471 Electroplating of metals or formed products

(G-9430)
DELTA COMPOSITES LLC
1617 Peach Leaf St (77039-2028)
PHONE...............................281 907-0619
Jason Huechtker, *General Mgr*
Dean Halbirt,
Rodney Masters,
▲ **EMP:** 57
SQ FT: 24,000
SALES (est): 11.5MM **Privately Held**
WEB: www.aimscomposites.com
SIC: 2519 Fiberglass & plastic furniture

(G-9431)
DELTA FLANGE & MFG INC
3807 Pinemont Dr (77018-1221)
P.O. Box 920942 (77292-0942)
PHONE...............................713 686-9702
Kenneth Battarbee, *President*
Janet Battarbee, *Treasurer*
▲ **EMP:** 12 **EST:** 1978
SQ FT: 20,500
SALES (est): 2.5MM **Privately Held**
WEB: www.deltaflange.com
SIC: 3462 Flange, valve & pipe fitting forgings, ferrous

(G-9432)
DELTA MILLWORK
Also Called: Delta Doors
5210 Ashley Ct (77041-6926)
PHONE...............................713 849-2281
Thomas R Hohl, *Owner*
EMP: 20
SQ FT: 12,000
SALES (est): 2.4MM **Privately Held**
WEB: www.deltamillwork.com
SIC: 2431 2434 5031 Doors, wood; wood kitchen cabinets; lumber, plywood & millwork

(G-9433)
DELTA RIGGING & TOOLS INC (DH)
125 Mccarty St (77029-1135)
PHONE...............................713 512-1700
Derrick Deakins, *President*
Mike Lindsey, *Vice Pres*
Sabrina Martinez, *Purch Agent*
Tom Maslyk, *Purch Agent*
Michael Terry, *Purchasing*
◆ **EMP:** 148
SALES (est): 67.1MM
SALES (corp-wide): 3.1B **Privately Held**
WEB: www.deltarigging.com
SIC: 7359 2298 3496 Equipment rental & leasing; slings, rope; slings, lifting: made from purchased wire
HQ: Bishop Lifting Products, Inc.
    125 Mccarty St
    Houston TX
    713 674-2266

(G-9434)
DELTA SCREEN & FILTRATION LLC
6649 N Eldridge Pkwy (77041-3509)
P.O. Box 842397 (77284-2397)
PHONE...............................713 856-0300
Richard Grifno, *President*
Wren Munsterman, *Business Mgr*
Carl Cooper, *Mfg Mgr*
Teresa Kaminski, *QC Mgr*
Phong Vu, *Engineer*
◆ **EMP:** 75
SQ FT: 79,000
SALES (est): 14.8MM **Privately Held**
WEB: www.deltascreens.com
SIC: 3496 3569 Miscellaneous fabricated wire products; filters & strainers, pipeline; filters, general line: industrial

(G-9435)
DELTA SEABOARD LLC (PA)
1212 W Sam Houston Pkwy N
(77043-4009)
PHONE...............................713 782-1468
Robert Derrick Jr,
Ron Burleigh,
▲ **EMP:** 9
SALES (est): 5.2MM **Privately Held**
SIC: 1389 Well plugging & abandoning, oil & gas

(G-9436)
DELTA TECHNOLOGY CORPORATION
1602 Townhurst Dr (77043-3283)
PHONE...............................713 464-7407
Lorne S Libin, *Chairman*
Eduardo Libin, *Vice Pres*
Irwin Eduardo Libin, *Vice Pres*
Francisco Hernandez, *Manager*
Mitchell Glassman, *Admin Sec*
▲ **EMP:** 25
SQ FT: 13,000
SALES (est): 5.4MM **Privately Held**
WEB: www.deltatechnology.com
SIC: 3523 Grading, cleaning, sorting machines, fruit, grain, vegetable

(G-9437)
DENSO NORTH AMERICA USA INC
Also Called: Premier Coatings
9710 Telge Rd (77095-5004)
PHONE...............................281 821-3355
Lucian Williams, *President*
Rick Lujano, *Technical Staff*
Christopher Paul Winn, *Director*
David L Winn, *Director*
◆ **EMP:** 20
SALES (est): 36MM
SALES (corp-wide): 75.7MM **Privately Held**
WEB: www.densona.com
SIC: 2899 Corrosion preventive lubricant
HQ: Winn & Coales (Denso) Limited
    Denso House
    London SE27
    208 670-7511

(G-9438)
DEQ COATINGS INC
8532 South Loop E (77017-1934)
PHONE...............................713 645-1777

Heron Garcia, *President*
EMP: 10
SALES (est): 1.1MM **Privately Held**
WEB: www.deqcoatings.com
SIC: 3479 2759 Coating of metals & formed products; engraving

(G-9439)
DERBEC ENTERPRISES LTD
Also Called: Hamiltn-Steele Outdoor Accents
10800 Northwest Fwy (77092-7304)
PHONE...............................713 533-9059
David Fuentes, *Opers Staff*
Derek Dooley,
Deneige Soileau,
▲ **EMP:** 32
SALES (est): 5.8MM **Privately Held**
WEB: www.hamilton-steele.com
SIC: 3315 Steel wire & related products

(G-9440)
DERRICK CORPORATION
Also Called: Derrick Equipment Company
15630 Export Plaza Dr (77032-2517)
P.O. Box 221 (77001-0221)
PHONE...............................281 590-3003
Joelle Derrick, *Area Mgr*
Greg Gulledge, *Area Mgr*
Quan Luu, *Vice Pres*
Cynthia Putt, *Sales Staff*
Ron Rice, *Manager*
EMP: 50
SALES (corp-wide): 226.8MM **Privately Held**
WEB: www.derrick.com
SIC: 3532 3533 Crushing, pulverizing & screening equipment; oil & gas field machinery
PA: Derrick Corporation
    590 Duke Rd
    Buffalo NY 14225
    716 683-9010

(G-9441)
DESERT NDT LLC
5875 N Sam Houston Pkwy W # 200
(77086-1578)
P.O. Box 748, Elk City OK (73648-0748)
PHONE...............................580 225-2108
Dennis Ezzell, *Manager*
EMP: 20
SALES (corp-wide): 1.1B **Privately Held**
WEB: www.shawcor.com
SIC: 1389 Oil field services; surveying wells
HQ: Desert Ndt, Llc
    4250 N Sam Houston Pkwy E # 180
    Houston TX 77032
    713 568-3513

(G-9442)
DESHAZO LLC
Also Called: Deshazo Crane
14223 Interdrive E (77032-3315)
PHONE...............................281 227-6200
David Tackett, *Manager*
Crystal Copeland, *Manager*
Ken Dallas, *Technician*
EMP: 23
SALES (corp-wide): 117.3MM **Privately Held**
WEB: www.deshazo.com
SIC: 3536 Cranes, overhead traveling
PA: Deshazo, Llc
    200 Kilsby Cir
    Bessemer AL 35022
    205 664-2006

(G-9443)
DESIGNER STONE CENTER INC
11811 Brittmoore Park Dr (77041-7224)
PHONE...............................713 862-0120
Jorge E Lefebvre, *President*
Dennys Lagos, *Project Mgr*
Ernesto Rubeis, *Project Mgr*
Elena Lefebvre, *CFO*
Hugo Gonzalez, *Sales Mgr*
▲ **EMP:** 45
SQ FT: 37,000
SALES (est): 6.9MM **Privately Held**
WEB: www.designerstonecenter.com
SIC: 3281 Marble, building: cut & shaped

(G-9444)
DETAIL DESIGN INC
Also Called: Ddi
12125 Ann Ln (77064-1225)
PHONE..........................281 890-4715
Art Jones, *President*
Mary C Curl, *Vice Pres*
Matthew F Curl, *Admin Sec*
▲ EMP: 50
SQ FT: 2,000
SALES (est): 7.1MM **Privately Held**
WEB: www.detaildesigninc.com
SIC: 8711 3533 Professional engineer; oil
field machinery & equipment

(G-9445)
DETECHTION USA INC
8 Greenway Plz Ste 1300 (77046-0802)
PHONE..........................713 357-4775
Christopher Smith, *CEO*
EMP: 20
SALES (est): 1.6MM **Privately Held**
WEB: www.detechtion.com
SIC: 7372 Business oriented computer
software

(G-9446)
**DETERING COMPANY OF
HOUSTON LP**
Also Called: Detering Company, The
6800 Helmers St (77022-4918)
P.O. Box 7766 (77270-7766)
PHONE..........................713 869-3761
Carl A Detering Jr, *President*
Shelby Wallace, *Purch Agent*
Shelby Wunsch, *Purchasing*
Christina Gonzalez, *Sales Mgr*
Cheryl Burns, *Sales Staff*
EMP: 140 EST: 1925
SQ FT: 125,000
SALES (est): 52.1MM **Privately Held**
WEB: www.detering.com
SIC: 5031 5032 2431 Building materials,
exterior; doors & windows; windows; mill-
work; brick, except refractory; millwork

(G-9447)
DEVRIES INSTRUMENTS INC
5510 Brystone Dr (77041-7011)
PHONE..........................281 506-9100
James G Devries, *President*
EMP: 14
SQ FT: 5,000
SALES (est): 2.3MM **Privately Held**
SIC: 3599 Machine shop, jobbing & repair

(G-9448)
DFA DAIRY BRANDS FLUID LLC
Also Called: Oak Farms Dairy
3417 Leeland St (77003-5411)
P.O. Box 1270 (77251-1270)
PHONE..........................713 223-5296
Bill Murphy, *Branch Mgr*
EMP: 362
SALES (corp-wide): 15.8B **Privately Held**
SIC: 2026 2033 Milk processing (pasteur-
izing, homogenizing, bottling); canned
fruits & specialties
HQ: Dfa Dairy Brands Fluid, Llc
1405 N 98th St
Kansas City KS 66111
816 801-6455

(G-9449)
**DFM TECHNOLOGY PVT USA
INC**
3119 Canal St (77003-1628)
PHONE..........................713 547-0114
Sandeep Ramakrishna, *Principal*
EMP: 10
SALES (est): 1.5MM **Privately Held**
SIC: 3679 Electronic circuits

(G-9450)
DIAL ELECTRICAL OF HOUSTON
Also Called: Dial Electrical Controls
60 Rittenhouse St (77076-2408)
PHONE..........................713 691-4666
Lynn Hawkins-Vines, *President*
EMP: 9 EST: 1966
SQ FT: 20,000
SALES (est): 1.5MM **Privately Held**
SIC: 3613 Switchgear & switchboard appa-
ratus

(G-9451)
**DIAMOND MODERN FURNITURE
LLC**
9524 Westheimer Rd (77063-3308)
PHONE..........................877 349-5003
Maurice Hill, *Mng Member*
EMP: 9
SALES (est): 295.7K **Privately Held**
WEB: www.3roompackages.com
SIC: 2512 Living room furniture: uphol-
stered on wood frames

(G-9452)
**DIAMOND OFFSHORE
COMPANY (DH)**
15415 Katy Fwy Ste 100 (77094-1810)
P.O. Box 4558 (77210-4558)
PHONE..........................281 492-5300
Lawrence R Dickerson, *CEO*
Andy Breaux, *Superintendent*
John Carter, *Chief*
Weldon Knight, *Chief*
Drew Ryser, *Chief*
◆ EMP: 131 EST: 1985
SQ FT: 60,000
SALES (est): 576.8MM
SALES (corp-wide): 12.5B **Publicly Held**
WEB: www.diamondoffshore.com
SIC: 1381 Drilling oil & gas wells
HQ: Diamond Offshore Finance Company
15415 Katy Fwy Ste 100
Barker TX 77413
281 492-5300

(G-9453)
**DIAMOND OFFSHORE DRILLING
INC (HQ)**
Also Called: LOEWS
15415 Katy Fwy Ste 100 (77094-1810)
PHONE..........................281 492-5300
James S Tisch, *Ch of Bd*
Marc Edwards, *President*
David L Roland, *Senior VP*
Thomas Roth, *Senior VP*
Beth G Gordon, *Vice Pres*
◆ EMP: 116
SALES: 733.6MM
SALES (corp-wide): 12.5B **Publicly Held**
WEB: www.diamondoffshore.com
SIC: 1381 Drilling oil & gas wells
PA: Loews Corporation
667 Madison Ave Fl 7
New York NY 10065
212 521-2000

(G-9454)
**DIAMOND OFFSHORE DRLG
SVCS INC**
15415 Katy Fwy Ste 400 (77094-1812)
P.O. Box 4558 (77210-4558)
PHONE..........................281 492-5300
Lawrence Dickerson, *President*
Lester L Thomas, *Treasurer*
EMP: 50
SQ FT: 50,000
SALES (est): 281K
SALES (corp-wide): 12.5B **Publicly Held**
WEB: www.diamondoffshore.com
SIC: 1381 Drilling oil & gas wells
HQ: Diamond Offshore Drilling Inc
15415 Katy Fwy Ste 100
Houston TX 77094

(G-9455)
**DIAMOND OFFSHORE GENERAL
CO**
15415 Katy Fwy Ste 100 (77094-1810)
PHONE..........................281 492-5300
Lawrence R Dickerson, *President*
Robert Dickerson, *President*
David Willams, *Vice Pres*
Lester L Thomas, *Treasurer*
EMP: 300
SQ FT: 50,000
SALES (est): 89.8K
SALES (corp-wide): 12.5B **Publicly Held**
WEB: www.diamondoffshore.com
SIC: 1381 Drilling oil & gas wells
HQ: Diamond Offshore Company
15415 Katy Fwy Ste 100
Houston TX 77094
281 492-5300

(G-9456)
**DIAMOND OFFSHORE
MANAGEMENT CO**
15415 Katy Fwy Ste 100 (77094-1810)
P.O. Box 4558 (77210-4558)
PHONE..........................281 492-5300
Larry Dickerson, *President*
Mark F Baudoin, *Vice Pres*
David W Williams, *Vice Pres*
Lester L Thomas, *Treasurer*
Debbie Mc Cauley, *Accounting Mgr*
EMP: 300 EST: 1990
SALES (est): 9.7MM
SALES (corp-wide): 12.5B **Publicly Held**
WEB: www.diamondoffshore.com
SIC: 8741 1381 Management services;
drilling oil & gas wells
HQ: Diamond Offshore Finance Company
15415 Katy Fwy Ste 100
Barker TX 77413
281 492-5300

(G-9457)
**DIAMOND OFFSHORE
NTHRLANDS B U**
15415 Katy Fwy Ofc (77094-1811)
PHONE..........................281 492-5300
Jim Tish, *CEO*
David W Williams, *President*
Lawrence Dickerson, *COO*
EMP: 375
SQ FT: 60,000
SALES (est): 4.9MM
SALES (corp-wide): 12.5B **Publicly Held**
WEB: www.diamondoffshore.com
SIC: 1381 Drilling oil & gas wells
HQ: Diamond Offshore Drilling Inc
15415 Katy Fwy Ste 100
Houston TX 77094

(G-9458)
**DIAMOND REFRACTORY SVCS
LLC**
8412 Mosley Rd (77075-1114)
PHONE..........................713 378-9200
EMP: 42 EST: 1999
SQ FT: 25,000
SALES (est): 16.3MM
SALES (corp-wide): 9.1B **Publicly Held**
WEB: www.diamondrefractory.com
SIC: 1389 Oil & gas wells: building, repair-
ing & dismantling
PA: Emcor Group, Inc.
301 Merritt 7 Fl 6
Norwalk CT 06851
203 849-7800

(G-9459)
**DIAMOND-USA PRCSN-
MCHINING LTD**
Also Called: Diamond USA Precision
4004 Westhollow Pkwy (77082-2604)
PHONE..........................281 596-9300
Dafie Vo, *General Ptnr*
Larry Uren, *Info Tech Mgr*
EMP: 20
SQ FT: 10,000
SALES (est): 2.6MM **Privately Held**
SIC: 3599 Machine shop, jobbing & repair

(G-9460)
DIAPAC LLC
283 Lockhaven Dr Ste 300 (77073-5519)
PHONE..........................713 715-6300
Robert D Horswell, *Principal*
▲ EMP: 20 EST: 2010
SALES (est): 2.9MM **Privately Held**
SIC: 2819 Tungsten carbide powder, ex-
cept abrasive or metallurgical

(G-9461)
**DIBELLA BAKING COMPANY
LLC**
14212 Interdrive W (77032-3322)
PHONE..........................281 987-8985
Mark Martin, *CEO*
Aman Dhuka, *CFO*
EMP: 18
SALES (est): 4.7MM
SALES (corp-wide): 13.5MM **Privately
Held**
WEB: www.dibellafamiglia.com
SIC: 2051 Bread, cake & related products

HQ: Bakery Warehouse Llc
14212 Interdrive W
Houston TX 77032
281 987-8985

(G-9462)
**DIBELLOS DYNAMIC
ORTHOTICS (DH)**
Also Called: Dynamic Orthotics Prosthetics
11155 Main St (77025-5600)
PHONE..........................713 747-4171
Thomas Dibello, *President*
Dennis W Treffry, *CFO*
Ralph Parman, *Controller*
EMP: 44
SQ FT: 25,195
SALES (est): 6.2MM
SALES (corp-wide): 1.1B **Publicly Held**
WEB: www.hangerclinic.com
SIC: 3842 Orthopedic appliances; pros-
thetic appliances
HQ: Hanger Prosthetics & Orthotics, Inc.
10910 Domain Dr Ste 300
Austin TX 78758
512 777-3800

(G-9463)
**DICKSON FURNITURE MFRS
LLC (PA)**
Also Called: Dickson Furniture Industries
6900 Overmyer Dr (77008-5016)
PHONE..........................713 747-0341
Douglas Mueller, *CEO*
Richard Dixon, *Vice Pres*
EMP: 16
SQ FT: 100,000
SALES (est): 5MM **Privately Held**
WEB: www.dicksonstudenthousing.com
SIC: 2511 2514 2599 2531 Wood house-
hold furniture; metal household furniture;
hotel furniture; public building & related
furniture

(G-9464)
**DICKSON FURNITURE MFRS
LLC**
1502 Greengrass Dr (77008-5008)
PHONE..........................281 299-6197
Bret Baker, *Principal*
EMP: 45
SALES (corp-wide): 5MM **Privately Held**
WEB: www.dicksonfurniture.com
SIC: 2511 Wood household furniture
PA: Dickson Furniture Manufacturers, Llc
6900 Overmyer Dr
Houston TX 77008
713 747-0341

(G-9465)
DICQIE M FULLER LOONEY
Also Called: Transformation Enzyme
2900 Wilcrest Dr Ste 220 (77042-6008)
PHONE..........................713 266-2117
EMP: 12
SALES (est): 1.8MM **Privately Held**
SIC: 2869 2835 Mfg Industrial Organic
Chemicals Mfg Diagnostic Substances

(G-9466)
**DIESEL ENGINE AND PARTS CO
LLC**
Also Called: Depco
8123 Hillsboro St (77029-1330)
PHONE..........................713 675-6100
Dick A Davis, *President*
Tim Felty, *President*
Tadd Stickler, *Vice Pres*
Jim Wanner, *Controller*
Luis Vazquez, *Sales Staff*
◆ EMP: 30
SQ FT: 18,000
SALES (est): 6MM **Privately Held**
WEB: www.depco.com
SIC: 5261 3621 Hydroponic equipment &
supplies; generators & sets, electric

(G-9467)
DIETZGEN CORPORATION
15080 Sommermeyer St # 100
(77041-5324)
PHONE..........................713 937-1632
Darren A Letang, *President*
EMP: 10 **Privately Held**
WEB: www.dietzgen.com
SIC: 2679 Paper products, converted

▲ = Import ▼=Export
◆ =Import/Export

PA: Dietzgen Corporation
121 Kelsey Ln Ste G
Tampa FL 33619

(G-9468)
DIGCO UTILITY CONSTRUCTION LP
8706 E Hardy Rd (77093-7226)
PHONE.................................281 833-2000
Derrell Isenberg, *Principal*
EMP: 10
SALES (corp-wide): 12.1B **Publicly Held**
WEB: www.digco.com
SIC: 1389 Construction, repair & dismantling services
HQ: Digco Utility Construction, L.P.
1608 Margaret St
Houston TX 77093

(G-9469)
DIGIMAGINATION LLC
Also Called: Esigns
10115 Sweetwater Ln (77037-1238)
P.O. Box 8367 (77288-8367)
PHONE.................................281 445-6671
Robert Marsh, *CEO*
Roy Marsh, *CFO*
Shay Luedeke, *Technology*
Fouzia Mahtab, *Software Dev*
EMP: 18
SALES (est): 2.3MM **Privately Held**
WEB: www.esigns.com
SIC: 3993 Signs & advertising specialties

(G-9470)
DIGIOP TECHNOLOGIES LTD
5902 Sovereign Dr (77036-2310)
PHONE.................................713 333-4900
Mark Rome, *CEO*
Charles Schwarz, *Partner*
James D Story, *Partner*
Heather Probala, *Marketing Staff*
Ryan Schalk, *Officer*
▼ EMP: 50
SQ FT: 30,000
SALES (est): 5.7MM **Privately Held**
WEB: www.digiop.com
SIC: 3699 Security control equipment & systems

(G-9471)
DIGITAL AIR CONTROL INC (PA)
Also Called: Dac
11251 Northwest Fwy # 200 (77092-6529)
PHONE.................................713 975-8160
Peter J Kurtz, *President*
Scott Hagan, *Business Mgr*
Clayton S King, *Project Mgr*
John Lloyd, *Project Mgr*
Dave Opper, *Project Mgr*
EMP: 26
SQ FT: 6,400
SALES: 21MM **Privately Held**
WEB: www.dac-inc.com
SIC: 3822 Auto controls regulating residntl & coml environmt & applncs

(G-9472)
DIGITAL I M
6615 Stonechase (77084-1254)
PHONE.................................281 855-4933
Vernon Nielson, *Owner*
EMP: 10 EST: 2001
SALES (est): 493.7K **Privately Held**
SIC: 8748 2791 Telecommunications consultant; photocomposition, for the printing trade

(G-9473)
DILLY LETTER JACKETS
1221 Lumpkin Rd (77043-4101)
PHONE.................................713 334-3232
David Dillingham, *Owner*
EMP: 18
SALES (est): 1.5MM **Privately Held**
WEB: www.dillyletterjackets.com
SIC: 2329 Jackets (suede, leatherette, etc.), sport: men's & boys'

(G-9474)
DIMENSIONAL CNC LLC
Also Called: HI Tech Designers
6920 San Antonio St (77040-4144)
PHONE.................................713 329-9711
Tu Vu, *Controller*
Nguyen, *Mng Member*

EMP: 25
SALES (est): 4MM **Privately Held**
WEB: www.dimensional.us
SIC: 3533 Oil & gas field machinery

(G-9475)
DINACO INC (PA)
11275 S Sm Hustn Pyww 3 (77031)
PHONE.................................281 848-3600
EMP: 22 EST: 1969
SALES (est): 1.6MM **Privately Held**
WEB: www.dinaco.com
SIC: 3993 Displays & cutouts, window & lobby

(G-9476)
DINAMICA INC
Also Called: Dynamax
10808 Fallstone Rd # 350 (77099-3474)
PHONE.................................281 564-5100
Michael Van Bavel, *President*
Claudio Lopez, *Principal*
Cornelius Bavel, *Vice Pres*
Megan Tucker, *Engineer*
Martha Casillas, *Sales Staff*
◆ EMP: 21
SQ FT: 5,700
SALES (est): 4.3MM **Privately Held**
WEB: www.dynamax.com
SIC: 3572 Computer storage devices

(G-9477)
DISC PRO GRAPHICS INC
339 Greens Landing Dr (77038-2645)
PHONE.................................281 999-2717
Dale Morris, *President*
Jerry Bass, *Vice Pres*
Ed Dexter, *Vice Pres*
Sergio Artiga, *Foreman/Supr*
Krista Richter, *Finance Mgr*
EMP: 54 EST: 1997
SQ FT: 22,000
SALES (est): 12.1MM **Privately Held**
WEB: www.discpro.com
SIC: 2752 Commercial printing, offset

(G-9478)
DISCOVERY GREEN CONSERVANCY
1500 Mckinney St (77010-4011)
PHONE.................................713 400-7336
Barry Mandel, *President*
Larry Faulkner, *Chairman*
Clark Curry, *Opers Dir*
◆ EMP: 35
SALES: 6.3MM **Privately Held**
WEB: www.discoverygreen.com
SIC: 2531 Picnic tables or benches, park

(G-9479)
DISCOVERY GREEN CONSERVANCY
1500 Mckinney St (77010-4011)
P.O. Box 130646 (77219-0646)
PHONE.................................713 529-5534
Brady F Carruth, *Ch of Bd*
Jacqueline S Martin, *Ch of Bd*
Nancy G Kinder, *Treasurer*
EMP: 25
SQ FT: 2,000
SALES: 4.9MM **Privately Held**
WEB: www.discoverygreen.com
SIC: 2531 Picnic tables or benches, park

(G-9480)
DISPLAY GRAPHICS INC
9227 Alberene Dr (77074-1301)
PHONE.................................713 977-7888
Lynn Creel, *President*
Diane Creel, *Vice Pres*
EMP: 10
SQ FT: 6,500
SALES (est): 1.6MM **Privately Held**
WEB: www.displaygraphics.com
SIC: 3993 2759 7389 7336 Signs, not made in custom sign painting shops; decals: printing; posters, including billboards: printing; sign painting & lettering shop; graphic arts & related design; signs, except electric

(G-9481)
DIVERSIFIED BUS CONSULTING LLC
10311 Urban Oak Trl (77044-1685)
P.O. Box 671641 (77267-1641)
PHONE.................................713 677-9282
Tamika Scott, *Mng Member*
EMP: 10
SALES (est): 222.3K **Privately Held**
WEB:
www.diversifiedbusinessconsulting.net
SIC: 7291 7389 7349 3537 Tax return preparation services; notary publics; janitorial service, contract basis; trucks, tractors, loaders, carriers & similar equipment; bermuda sprigging services

(G-9482)
DIVERSIFIED DIAGNOSTIC PDTS
Also Called: Diversified Diagnostic Pdts
11603 Windfern Rd (77064-4866)
PHONE.................................281 955-5323
Gerald Timpe, *President*
James Whalen, *CFO*
Terry Deville, *Treasurer*
EMP: 15 EST: 1981
SQ FT: 12,000
SALES (est): 2MM **Privately Held**
WEB: www.ddpixray.com
SIC: 3841 3844 Surgical & medical instruments; X-ray apparatus & tubes

(G-9483)
DIXIE ELECTRO PLATING COMPANY
3001 Engelke St (77003-1293)
PHONE.................................713 224-1826
Andrew Schumacher, *President*
Hazel M Smith, *President*
Jim Hollingsworth, *Vice Pres*
Donna J Parks, *Admin Sec*
▲ EMP: 32 EST: 1928
SQ FT: 45,000
SALES (est): 3.7MM
SALES (corp-wide): 15.6MM **Privately Held**
SIC: 3471 Anodizing (plating) of metals or formed products; chromium plating of metals or formed products; electroplating of metals or formed products
PA: Schumacher International, Inc.
5610 Polk St
Houston TX 77023
713 923-5548

(G-9484)
DIXIE FREIGHT SOLUTIONS LP
Also Called: Dfs Worldwide
15600 W Hardy Rd (77060-3102)
P.O. Box 62165 (77205-2165)
PHONE.................................281 447-7500
Fred Fontana, *General Ptnr*
Jon Fontana, *Vice Pres*
Melinda Ardoin, *Opers Mgr*
EMP: 28
SALES (est): 3.7MM **Privately Held**
WEB: www.dfsworldwide.us.com
SIC: 8742 2741 Transportation consultant; miscellaneous publishing

(G-9485)
DJH SERVICES LLC (PA)
Also Called: Arrow S Ranch
712 Main St Ste 1900 (77002-3220)
PHONE.................................713 228-5911
Rebecca Gonzales Cook, *Partner*
Rosemary J Harrison, *General Mgr*
Dan J Harrison III, *General Ptnr*
EMP: 50 EST: 1979
SQ FT: 15,000
SALES (est): 9.8MM **Privately Held**
SIC: 0212 1311 1381 0752 Beef cattle except feedlots; crude petroleum production; natural gas production; drilling oil & gas wells; breeding services, horses: racing & non-racing

(G-9486)
DJMW INVESTMENTS LLC
19255 Aldine Westfield Rd (77073-3811)
PHONE.................................281 821-0010
Danny Thornhill,
EMP: 35
SQ FT: 27,000

SALES (est): 4MM **Privately Held**
SIC: 3533 Oil & gas field machinery

(G-9487)
DLT PRINTING INC
Also Called: Dlt Envelopes
6618 Gant Rd (77066-1912)
PHONE.................................281 880-8883
Eddie L Taylor, *President*
Debra Taylor, *Vice Pres*
Michael Lalor,
EMP: 14
SQ FT: 3,000
SALES (est): 2.2MM **Privately Held**
WEB: www.dltenvelopes.com
SIC: 2759 Commercial printing

(G-9488)
DMV WICKS INC
Also Called: The Hot Bagel Shop
2015 S Shepherd Dr (77019-7007)
PHONE.................................713 520-0340
Don Wicks, *President*
Virginia Wicks, *Treasurer*
Mark Wicks, *Admin Sec*
EMP: 10
SQ FT: 1,200
SALES (est): 461.4K **Privately Held**
SIC: 5461 2051 Bagels; breads, rolls & buns; bakery: wholesale or wholesale/retail combined

(G-9489)
DNATRIX INC
2450 Holcombe Blvd Ste X2 (77021-2039)
PHONE.................................832 930-2401
Frank Tufaro PHD, *CEO*
Imran Alibhai, *Senior VP*
Brett Ewald, *Vice Pres*
Erin Mitchell, *VP Mfg*
Imre Kovesdi PHD, *Officer*
EMP: 10
SALES (est): 690.3K **Privately Held**
WEB: www.dnatrix.com
SIC: 2836 Biological products, except diagnostic

(G-9490)
DOCS ON DEMAND INC
1500 Citywest Blvd # 700 (77042-2300)
PHONE.................................713 980-9500
James L Robertson, *President*
Everett L Anschutz Jr, *Vice Pres*
EMP: 45
SQ FT: 10,000
SALES (est): 5MM **Privately Held**
WEB: www.docsondemand.com
SIC: 7372 Business oriented computer software

(G-9491)
DOF SUBSEA USA INC
5365 W Sam Houston Pkwy N # 400 (77041-5243)
PHONE.................................713 896-2500
Marco Sclocchi, *President*
Scott Shults, *Chief*
Allen Bishop, *Vice Pres*
Brent Boyce, *Vice Pres*
Andrew Duncan, *Vice Pres*
◆ EMP: 200
SQ FT: 18,698
SALES (est): 36MM
SALES (corp-wide): 686.4MM **Privately Held**
WEB: www.dofsubsea.com
SIC: 1389 1382 Oil field services; oil & gas exploration services
PA: Dof Asa

Storebo
561 810-00

(G-9492)
DOLPHIN GRAPHICS INC
5601 Bintliff Dr Ste 530 (77036-2120)
PHONE.................................713 789-7474
Joseph Baden, *President*
Cathy Cooney, *Controller*
Mike Boydstun, *Sales Dir*
Ken Fitzhenry, *Sales Mgr*
Joyce Graphics, *Accounts Mgr*
EMP: 41
SQ FT: 12,500

SALES (est): 6.9MM **Privately Held**
WEB: www.dolphingraphicsinc.com
SIC: 2752 Commercial printing, offset

(G-9493)
DOMATEX INC
842 Buschong St (77039-1002)
PHONE.....................................281 219-1800
Daniel A Doran, *President*
▲ **EMP:** 60
SQ FT: 36,766
SALES (est): 8MM **Privately Held**
WEB: www.domatex.net
SIC: 3531 3799 Mixers, concrete; trailers
  & trailer equipment

(G-9494)
DOME ENERGY INC (HQ)
6363 Woodway Dr Ste 715 (77057-1747)
PHONE.....................................281 558-8585
Paul Morch, *CEO*
Victoria Allen, *Vice Pres*
Susanna Helgesen, *CFO*
EMP: 9
SALES (est): 4.5MM **Privately Held**
WEB: www.domeenergy.com
SIC: 1382 Oil & gas exploration services

(G-9495)
DOMINION MACHINING & MFG INC
9140 Meadow Vista Blvd (77064-2010)
PHONE.....................................281 477-7355
Donald W Martin, *President*
EMP: 10
SQ FT: 5,000
SALES (est): 1.3MM **Privately Held**
SIC: 3599 Machine shop, jobbing & repair

(G-9496)
DONS GRINDING LAPPING SVC INC
8700 Tweed Dr (77061-5022)
PHONE.....................................713 643-7928
▲ **EMP:** 35
SQ FT: 9,000
SALES (est): 888.6K **Privately Held**
WEB: www.donsgrinding.com
SIC: 3599 Machine shop, jobbing & repair;
  grinding castings for the trade

(G-9497)
DOOR CENTER
Also Called: Door Masters Woodworks
1843 Bingle Rd (77055-2334)
PHONE.....................................713 932-9343
Ana Villanueva, *Owner*
EMP: 10 EST: 2011
SALES (est): 1.2MM **Privately Held**
WEB: www.doormastershouston.com
SIC: 2431 Millwork

(G-9498)
DOOSAN MECATEC AMERICA CO LTD
4900 Woodway Dr Ste 725 (77056-2820)
PHONE.....................................713 961-4646
Yong Man Kim, *President*
Bruce Collins, *Vice Pres*
Bruce Stephens, *Purchasing*
John Gunn, *Engineer*
Doug Kempel, *Engineer*
EMP: 10
SALES (est): 1.2MM **Privately Held**
WEB: www.doosan.com
SIC: 3443 Heat exchangers, condensers &
  components

(G-9499)
DORF KETAL CHEMICALS LLC
11200 Westheimer Rd # 400 (77042-3234)
PHONE.....................................713 343-2377
Subodh Menon, *President*
James Noland, *General Mgr*
Parag Shah, *General Mgr*
Sudhir Menon, *Chairman*
Dane Roth, *Area Mgr*
▲ **EMP:** 49
SQ FT: 4,000
SALES: 87.6MM **Privately Held**
WEB: www.dorfketal.com
SIC: 2899 Chemical preparations

PA: Dorf-Ketal Chemicals India Private Limited
  No. 1, Dorf Ketal Towers, D'monte Street,
  Mumbai MH 40006

(G-9500)
DORIS USA INC
840 Gessner Rd Ste 400 (77024-4142)
PHONE.....................................713 973-2520
Jim Fairbairn, *President*
Loic Des Deserts, *Chairman*
Rick Haun, *Vice Pres*
Nicholas Parsole, *Vice Pres*
Joaquin Serrano, *Vice Pres*
EMP: 40
SALES (est): 7.6MM
SALES (corp-wide): 29MM **Privately Held**
WEB: www.dorisgroup.com
SIC: 1389 Oil field services; gas field services
PA: Doris Group
  58 A
  Paris 75013
  144 061-000

(G-9501)
DOUBLE BARREL DOWNHOLE TECH
10511 Fallstone Rd (77099-4301)
PHONE.....................................281 495-1200
Roney Nazarian, *President*
Dave Macneill, *Owner*
▲ **EMP:** 11
SQ FT: 15,000
SALES (est): 1.2MM **Privately Held**
WEB: www.doublebarrelrss.com
SIC: 1389 Nonclassified Establishment

(G-9502)
DOUBLE R BRAND FOODS LLC (PA)
Also Called: Holmes Smokehouse
6633 Portwest Dr Ste 110 (77024-8001)
PHONE.....................................713 868-0030
Rodney Roth, *President*
EMP: 25
SQ FT: 10,000
SALES (est): 13.2MM **Privately Held**
WEB: www.holmessmokehouse.com
SIC: 2013 Sausages from purchased meat

(G-9503)
DOUGLAS PADS & SPORTS INC
12325 Cutten Rd (77066-1807)
PHONE.....................................713 697-9787
Rogers Douglas Sr, *President*
Jeff Cook, *Warehouse Mgr*
Bob Logan, *CFO*
Gary Montgomery, *Sr Project Mgr*
Ryan Huntsman, *Officer*
▲ **EMP:** 30
SALES (est): 4.3MM **Privately Held**
WEB: www.douglaspads.com
SIC: 3949 5941 7699 Protectors: baseball, basketball, hockey, etc.; specialty sport supplies; recreational sporting equipment repair services

(G-9504)
DOVER EQUIPMENT INC (PA)
5829 W S Houston Pky N407 (77041)
P.O. Box 8, Inman SC (29349-0008)
PHONE.....................................713 690-5200
Mark Weissenbberger, *President*
George Weissenberger, *Vice Pres*
Donn D Huot, *Shareholder*
EMP: 25
SQ FT: 20,000
SALES (est): 4.8MM **Privately Held**
WEB: www.doverequipment.com
SIC: 3535 5084 Pneumatic tube conveyor systems; industrial machinery & equipment

(G-9505)
DOW CHEMICAL COMPANY
16717 Jacintoport Blvd (77015-6544)
PHONE.....................................281 452-5951
Michael Parker, *President*
Jason Giles, *Technology*
EMP: 200
SALES (corp-wide): 38.5B **Publicly Held**
WEB: www.dow.com
SIC: 2869 Industrial organic chemicals

HQ: The Dow Chemical Company
  2211 H H Dow Way
  Midland MI 48642
  989 636-1000

(G-9506)
DOW CHEMICAL COMPANY
1254 Enclave Pkwy (77077-2564)
P.O. Box 4269 (77210-4269)
PHONE.....................................713 826-5234
Doug Wargo, *Production*
Nermeen Aboelella, *Research*
Colleen Grinham, *Engineer*
Kim Kincannon, *Engineer*
Lee Kittleson, *Engineer*
EMP: 9
SALES (corp-wide): 38.5B **Publicly Held**
WEB: www.dow.com
SIC: 2819 Industrial inorganic chemicals
HQ: The Dow Chemical Company
  2211 H H Dow Way
  Midland MI 48642
  989 636-1000

(G-9507)
DOW MACHINERY CORPORATION
12530 Taylor Rd (77041-1232)
PHONE.....................................832 467-0600
Gary Dowling, *President*
Pat Dowling, *Vice Pres*
Rick Dowling, *Treasurer*
EMP: 50
SALES (est): 10.4MM **Privately Held**
SIC: 3533 Oil field machinery & equipment

(G-9508)
DOWNHOLE INNOVATIONS LLC
6807 Willow Brook Park (77066-3015)
PHONE.....................................936 537-4640
Joe Jordan, *President*
Ryan Ward, *Engineer*
Chuck Wintill, *Engineer*
Khai Tran, *Technology*
EMP: 14 EST: 2013
SALES (est): 2.1MM **Privately Held**
WEB: www.downholeinnovations.com
SIC: 1389 Construction, repair & dismantling services

(G-9509)
DOWNHOLE TECHNOLOGY LLC
Also Called: Boss Hog Energy Services
12450 Cutten Rd (77066-1806)
PHONE.....................................281 820-2545
▼ **EMP:** 58 EST: 2012
SALES (est): 37.6MM
SALES (corp-wide): 2.6MM **Privately Held**
WEB: www.downholetechnology.com
SIC: 1389 Construction, repair & dismantling services
HQ: Schoeller-Bleckmann Oilfield Equipment Aktiengesellschaft
  HauptstraBe 2
  Ternitz 2630
  263 031-50

(G-9510)
DOWNUNDER GOSOLUTIONS AMER LLC
16200 Park Row Ste 100 (77084-7346)
PHONE.....................................832 582-3221
Matthew Lamont, *President*
Lorraine Taylor,
Troy Thompson,
EMP: 9 EST: 2012
SALES (est): 1MM **Privately Held**
WEB: www.dug.com
SIC: 1382 Geological exploration, oil & gas field
HQ: Downunder Geosolutions Pty Ltd
  76 Kings Park Rd
  West Perth WA 6005

(G-9511)
DPC ENTERPRISES LP
300 Jackson Hill St (77007-7430)
PHONE.....................................713 863-1947
S Reed Morian, *Chairman*
Chuck King, *Plant Mgr*
Chad Vermillion, *Plant Mgr*
Ron Rech, *Opers Mgr*
Cooper Davis, *Sales Mgr*
EMP: 40

SALES (est): 7.1MM **Privately Held**
WEB: www.dxgroup.com
SIC: 2869 2819 Industrial organic chemicals; industrial inorganic chemicals
HQ: Dx Service Company, Inc.
  300 Jackson Hill St
  Houston TX 77007
  713 863-1947

(G-9512)
DRACO SPRING MANUFACTURING CO (PA)
7042 Long Dr (77087-4204)
PHONE.....................................713 645-4973
Barry L Drager, *President*
Keith Jones, *Engineer*
Daryl Deloney, *Sales Staff*
Arlan Walters, *Manager*
Derek Hall, *Info Tech Mgr*
EMP: 84
SQ FT: 120,000
SALES (est): 18.6MM **Privately Held**
WEB: www.dracospring.com
SIC: 3493 3495 Steel springs, except wire; wire springs

(G-9513)
DRACO SPRING MANUFACTURING CO
7143 Edna St (77087-4209)
PHONE.....................................713 645-4973
Barry L Drager, *Branch Mgr*
EMP: 71
SALES (corp-wide): 18.6MM **Privately Held**
WEB: www.dracospring.com
SIC: 3493 3495 Steel springs, except wire; wire springs
PA: Spring Draco Manufacturing Company
  7042 Long Dr
  Houston TX 77087
  713 645-4973

(G-9514)
DRAKE ALLIANCE CORPORATION (HQ)
Also Called: Drake Company, The
10343 Ella Blvd (77038-2327)
PHONE.....................................713 869-9121
John Carrico, *CEO*
Dave Gaidousek, *President*
Darlene Bassi, *Project Mgr*
John Davison, *Production*
Shirley Golden, *CFO*
▲ **EMP:** 64
SALES (est): 14.1MM
SALES (corp-wide): 196.6MM **Privately Held**
WEB: www.thedrakecompany.com
SIC: 7361 3993 Employment agencies; signs & advertising specialties
PA: Buckeye Corrugated, Inc
  822 Kumho Dr Ste 400
  Fairlawn OH 44333
  330 576-0590

(G-9515)
DRAKE CONTROLS LLC
8731 Fallbrook Dr (77064-3322)
PHONE.....................................713 996-0190
Joshua F Gore, *President*
Anton Gale, *VP Engrg*
Rodolfo Bermudez, *Sales Staff*
George Gore, *Sales Staff*
Dan Kovar, *Sales Staff*
▲ **EMP:** 14
SQ FT: 10,000
SALES (est): 8.2MM **Privately Held**
WEB: www.drakecontrols.com
SIC: 3491 Gas valves & parts, industrial

(G-9516)
DRECO INC
Also Called: Dreco Channelview
16730 Jacintoport Blvd (77015-6543)
PHONE.....................................281 452-7900
Joel Staff, *CEO*
James J Fasnacht, *Vice Pres*
W Douglass Frame, *Vice Pres*
Merrill A Miller, *Vice Pres*
Frederick W Pheasey, *Vice Pres*
EMP: 500
SALES (est): 95.4MM
SALES (corp-wide): 8.4B **Publicly Held**
SIC: 3533 Oil field machinery & equipment

▲ = Import ▼ =Export
◆ =Import/Export

PA: National Oilwell Varco, Inc.
7909 Parkwood Circle Dr
Houston TX 77036
713 346-7500

(G-9517)
DRESSER LLC (HQ)
4425 Westway Park Blvd (77041-2001)
PHONE....................262 549-2626
◆ **EMP:** 150 **EST:** 1998
SALES (est): 1B
SALES (corp-wide): 95.2B **Publicly Held**
WEB: www.dressergs.com
SIC: 3491 3825 3594 3593 Industrial
valves; instruments to measure electricity;
fluid power pumps & motors; fluid power
cylinders & actuators; pumps & pumping
equipment; valves & pipe fittings
PA: General Electric Company
5 Necco St
Boston MA 02210
617 443-3000

(G-9518)
DRESSER LLC
Also Called: Industrial Products Group
16240 Port Nw Ste 100 (77041-2668)
PHONE....................832 590-2306
EMP: 27
SALES (corp-wide): 122B **Publicly Held**
SIC: 3625 Mfg Relays/Industrial Controls
HQ: Dresser, Llc
601 Shiloh Rd
Plano TX 77041
262 549-2626

(G-9519)
DRESSER-RAND COMPANY
1415 Lumpkin Rd (77043-4105)
PHONE....................713 346-2257
Ken Delooze, Branch Mgr
EMP: 80
SQ FT: 68,414
SALES (corp-wide): 67.4B **Privately Held**
WEB: www.new.siemens.com
SIC: 3563 Spraying & dusting equipment
HQ: Dresser-Rand Company
500 Paul Clark Dr
Olean NY 14760
716 375-3000

(G-9520)
DRESSER-RAND COMPANY
1210 W Sam Houston Pkwy N
(77043-4009)
PHONE....................713 354-6100
EMP: 12
SALES (corp-wide): 67.4B **Privately Held**
WEB: www.new.siemens.com
SIC: 3563 Air & gas compressors
HQ: Dresser-Rand Company
500 Paul Clark Dr
Olean NY 14760
716 375-3000

(G-9521)
DRESSER-RAND COMPANY
1200 W Sam Houston Pkwy N
(77043-4009)
PHONE....................713 468-4210
Dan Lowry, Vice Pres
Brian Guske, Project Mgr
William Swinton, Project Mgr
Timothy Benson, QC Mgr
Gabriel Gonzalez, Engineer
EMP: 66
SALES (corp-wide): 67.4B **Privately Held**
WEB: www.new.siemens.com
SIC: 3563 Air & gas compressors
HQ: Dresser-Rand Company
500 Paul Clark Dr
Olean NY 14760
716 375-3000

(G-9522)
DRESSER-RAND GROUP INC
(HQ)
Also Called: Dresser-Rand Company
15375 Memorial Dr Ste 600 (77079-4139)
PHONE....................713 354-6100
Paulo Ruiz Sternadt, CEO
Vijay Phatarphekar, Managing Dir
Pascal Lardy, Exec VP
Luciano Mozzato, Exec VP
Christopher Rossi, Exec VP
▲ **EMP:** 233

SALES (est): 2.3B
SALES (corp-wide): 67.4B **Privately Held**
WEB: www.new.siemens.com
SIC: 3563 Air & gas compressors;
steam turbines; turbo-generators
PA: Siemens Ag
Werner-Von-Siemens-Str. 1
Munchen 80333
896 360-0

(G-9523)
DRESSER-RAND LLC
Also Called: Dresser-Rand Control Systems
1202 W Sam Houston Pkwy N
(77043-4009)
PHONE....................713 467-2221
Jeffrey Moshier, Branch Mgr
Trevor Burt, Analyst
EMP: 24
SALES (corp-wide): 67.4B **Privately Held**
WEB: www.new.siemens.com
SIC: 3563 3511 Air & gas compressors;
steam turbines; turbo-generators
HQ: Dresser-Rand Llc
1200 W Sam Houston Pkwy N
Houston TX 77043

(G-9524)
DRESSER-RAND LLC (DH)
1200 W Sam Houston Pkwy N
(77043-4009)
PHONE....................713 354-6100
Vincent R Volpe Jr, President
Ann Ackerson, Vice Pres
Sammy Antoun, Vice Pres
James Brown, Engineer
Mark E Baldwin, CFO
▲ **EMP:** 900
SALES (est): 827.2MM
SALES (corp-wide): 67.4B **Privately Held**
WEB: www.new.siemens.com
SIC: 3563 Air & gas compressors

(G-9525)
DRIL-QUIP INC (PA)
6401 N Eldridge Pkwy (77041-3505)
PHONE....................713 939-7711
John V Lovoi, Ch of Bd
Blake T Deberry, President
Jeffrey J Bird, President
Steven Landes, Superintendent
James A Gariepy, COO
◆ **EMP:** 759
SQ FT: 1,731,000
SALES: 414.8MM **Publicly Held**
WEB: www.dril-quip.com
SIC: 3533 Oil field machinery & equipment;
drilling tools for gas, oil or water wells;
gas field machinery & equipment

(G-9526)
DRIL-QUIP INC
13550 Hempstead Rd (77040-5849)
PHONE....................713 939-7711
Ian Duncan, Buyer
Judy Enloe, Purchasing
John Mastren, Purchasing
John Cullion, Engineer
Gary Hurta, Engineer
EMP: 30
SALES (corp-wide): 414.8MM **Publicly Held**
WEB: www.dril-quip.com
SIC: 3533 Drilling tools for gas, oil or water
wells
PA: Dril-Quip, Inc.
6401 N Eldridge Pkwy
Houston TX 77041
713 939-7711

(G-9527)
DRILEX CORPORATION
16311 Aldine Westfield Rd (77032-1309)
P.O. Box 60460 (77205-0460)
PHONE....................281 821-3360
▲ **EMP:** 32 **EST:** 1982
SQ FT: 45,000
SALES (est): 5.2MM **Privately Held**
WEB: www.drilex.com
SIC: 3599 Machine shop, jobbing & repair

(G-9528)
DRILFORMANCE LLC (PA)
15815 Waverly Dr (77032-1905)
PHONE....................832 772-7808
Lane Dyer, Accounts Mgr

Jenny Wilson, Mktg Coord
Rusty Petree, Mng Member
EMP: 37
SALES (est): 7.1MM **Privately Held**
WEB: www.drilformance.com
SIC: 3532 Drills, bits & similar equipment

(G-9529)
DRILLING & PROD RESOURCES
LLC
Also Called: Dpr
9455 Baythorne Dr (77041-7709)
PHONE....................713 996-7600
David Cox, Mng Member
◆ **EMP:** 12
SALES (est): 683.7K **Privately Held**
WEB: www.dprhou.com
SIC: 3533 Oil & gas drilling rigs & equip-
ment

(G-9530)
DRILLING STRUCTURES INTL
INC
2431 Kelly Ln (77066-4401)
P.O. Box 680207 (77268-0207)
PHONE....................281 880-8833
Phillip Rivera, President
P J Rivera, Vice Pres
Luisfer Angarita, Chief Engr
Julian Gotay, Executive
◆ **EMP:** 100
SALES (est): 50MM **Privately Held**
WEB: www.drillingstructuresintl.com
SIC: 3441 Fabricated structural metal

(G-9531)
DRILLTEC TECHNOLOGIES INC
10875 Kempwood Dr Ste 2 (77043-1416)
PHONE....................713 895-9852
Bryan C Baker, President
Peter Hudson, Vice Pres
Tim O'Grady, Opers Mgr
Steve Hammonds, Prdtn Mgr
Bianca Huynh, Purchasing
▲ **EMP:** 81 **EST:** 1981
SQ FT: 64,000
SALES (est): 16.1MM **Privately Held**
WEB: www.drilltec.com
SIC: 2655 Fiber cans, drums & similar
products
PA: Dtc P&T Liquidating Co.
10875 Kempwood Dr Ste 2
Houston TX 77043

(G-9532)
DROUBIS BAKERY & DELI INC
(PA)
7333 Hillcroft St (77081-6203)
PHONE....................713 988-5897
A J Droubi, President
Sharon Droubi, Vice Pres
▲ **EMP:** 18
SQ FT: 10,200
SALES (est): 2.6MM **Privately Held**
WEB: www.jdroubert416.tripod.com
SIC: 2051 5149 5141 5461 Bakery:
wholesale or wholesale/retail combined;
bakery products; groceries, general line;
bakeries; delicatessens

(G-9533)
DS SERVICES OF AMERICA INC
Also Called: Sparkletts
8206 1/2 Mosley Rd (77075-1110)
PHONE....................713 947-1900
Scott Warner, Branch Mgr
EMP: 21
SALES (corp-wide): 41.7MM **Privately**
Held
WEB: www.water.com
SIC: 2086 5499 Mineral water, carbon-
ated: packaged in cans, bottles, etc.;
water: distilled mineral or spring
HQ: Ds Services Of America, Inc.
2300 Windy Ridge Pkwy Se
Atlanta GA 30339
770 933-1400

(G-9534)
DTC P&T LIQUIDATING CO (PA)
Also Called: Drilltec
10875 Kempwood Dr Ste 2 (77043-1416)
PHONE....................713 996-8802
Bryan C Baker, President
David Clem, COO

Peter Hudson, Vice Pres
Tim E Ogrady, Vice Pres
Kerry Liles, QC Mgr
▼ **EMP:** 30
SALES (est): 16.1MM **Privately Held**
WEB: www.drilltec.com
SIC: 2655 Fiber cans, drums & similar
products

(G-9535)
DTN LLC
Also Called: Wilkens Weather Technologies
2925 Briarpark Dr Ste 710 (77042-3770)
PHONE....................713 430-7100
Ryan Folton, Branch Mgr
Jacob Banitt, Manager
EMP: 28
SALES (corp-wide): 500.3K **Privately**
Held
WEB: www.dtn.com
SIC: 1382 Geological exploration, oil & gas
field
HQ: Dtn, Llc
9110 W Dodge Rd Ste 100
Omaha NE 68114
402 390-2328

(G-9536)
DUALCO INC
8404 Braniff St (77061-5224)
PHONE....................713 644-1164
D Whitney Reed, President
Brian K Reed, Vice Pres
EMP: 20
SQ FT: 15,000
SALES (est): 4.7MM **Privately Held**
WEB: www.dualco-inc.com
SIC: 3586 5093 Grease guns (lubricators);
ferrous metal scrap & waste

(G-9537)
DUBAI PETROLEUM COMPANY
600 N Dairy Ashford Rd (77079-1100)
P.O. Box 4569 (77210-4569)
PHONE....................281 293-1000
R E Rutherford, President
D A Jenkins, Vice Pres
Mike Espinosa, Treasurer
L B Cobb, Admin Sec
▲ **EMP:** 850
SALES (est): 16.9MM
SALES (corp-wide): 36.6B **Publicly Held**
SIC: 1311 Crude petroleum production
HQ: Conocophillips Company
925 N Eldridge Pkwy
Houston TX 77079
281 293-1000

(G-9538)
DUPR ENERGY SERVICES LLC
(PA)
510 Bering Dr Ste 455 (77057-1451)
PHONE....................713 231-9000
Donna Kibler, Controller
Eric Patterson, Executive
Cornelius Dupre II,
Frank Weise,
EMP: 11
SALES (est): 46.3MM **Privately Held**
WEB: www.airiswellsite.com
SIC: 1389 Oil field services

(G-9539)
DURON SYSTEMS INC
9110 Taub Rd (77064-6618)
PHONE....................281 469-0040
Joseph D Lower, President
J Donald Lower, President
Phillip M Lower, Vice Pres
Thomas D Lower, Vice Pres
EMP: 160 **EST:** 1980
SQ FT: 27,500
SALES (est): 31.6MM **Privately Held**
WEB: www.durontech.com
SIC: 3533 Oil field machinery & equipment

(G-9540)
DX HOLDING COMPANY INC
(PA)
300 Jackson Hill St (77007-7430)
P.O. Box 130410 (77219-0410)
PHONE....................713 863-1947
S Reed Morian, Ch of Bd
Camilo Garcia, Plant Mgr
Chad Ayers, Foreman/Supr
Cristian Hunt, Opers Staff

Bill Ingram, *CFO*
EMP: 50
SALES (est): 163.6MM **Privately Held**
WEB: www.dxgroup.com
SIC: 2869 2819 5169 Industrial organic chemicals; industrial inorganic chemicals; drilling mud; industrial gases

(G-9541)
DX OILFIELD PRODUCTS LLC
300 Jackson Hill St (77007-7430)
PHONE..................713 863-1947
S R Morian,
Sara Morian Wadstrom,
EMP: 40
SQ FT: 20,000
SALES (est): 6.6MM **Privately Held**
WEB: www.dxoilfield.com
SIC: 3533 Oil & gas field machinery

(G-9542)
DX SERVICE COMPANY INC
Also Called: D X Distributors
1919 Jacintoport Blvd (77015-6585)
P.O. Box 24600 (77229-4600)
PHONE..................281 457-4888
Rick Karm, *President*
Jason Wisdom, *Plant Mgr*
Den Kieta, *Manager*
EMP: 40 **Privately Held**
SIC: 5169 2819 Industrial chemicals; industrial inorganic chemicals
HQ: Dx Service Company, Inc.
300 Jackson Hill St
Houston TX 77007
713 863-1947

(G-9543)
DYNA TORQUE TECHNOLOGIES INC
11050 W Little York Rd F (77041-5056)
PHONE..................713 937-6699
Andrew Scherfenberg, *President*
▲ **EMP:** 10 **EST:** 1998
SQ FT: 200,000
SALES (est): 2.7MM **Privately Held**
WEB: www.dyna-torque.com
SIC: 3548 1623 Electric welding equipment; pipeline construction

(G-9544)
DYNAENERGETICS US INC (HQ)
Also Called: Aeco
2050 W Sam Houston Pkwy S # 1750 (77042-2079)
PHONE..................512 327-2043
Herbert Zinsmeyer, *President*
Achim Pabst, *General Mgr*
Jeffrey Parsons, *Business Mgr*
Ron Berger, *Vice Pres*
Liam McNelis, *Vice Pres*
▲ **EMP:** 54 **EST:** 2012
SALES (est): 98MM
SALES (corp-wide): 326.4MM **Publicly Held**
WEB: www.dynaenergetics.com
SIC: 1389 Oil field services
PA: Dmc Global Inc.
11800 Ridge Pkwy Ste 300
Broomfield CO 80021
303 665-5700

(G-9545)
DYNALLOY INDUSTRIES INC
6103 Brittmoore Rd (77041-5610)
PHONE..................713 856-9377
Christopher Leija, *VP Sales*
Chris Leija, *Branch Mgr*
Michael Crites, *Manager*
Todd Fry, *Manager*
EMP: 15
SALES (corp-wide): 6.3MM **Privately Held**
WEB: www.dynalloyinc.com
SIC: 3291 Tungsten carbide abrasive
PA: Dynalloy Industries, Inc.
25880 State Highway 6 S
Navasota TX 77868
936 825-2532

(G-9546)
DYNALYST MANUFACTURING CORP (PA)
Also Called: Ate Group
738 Highway 6 S Ste 230 (77079-4037)
PHONE..................281 293-7980

EMP: 50
SALES (est): 6.1MM **Privately Held**
SIC: 3672 Mfg Printed Circuit Boards

(G-9547)
DYNAMIC CRANE SVC FBRCTION INC
Also Called: Dynamic Lifting Solutions
5512 Clara Rd (77041-7204)
PHONE..................713 849-1341
Derrick Deakins, *President*
Kyle Eilers, *CFO*
EMP: 22
SALES (est): 2.7MM **Privately Held**
WEB: www.dynamiclifting.com
SIC: 1796 3441 Machine moving & rigging; fabricated structural metal

(G-9548)
DYNAMIC PRECISION MCH TLS INC
5852 Thomas Rd (77041-4903)
PHONE..................713 466-4545
Dennis Nguyen, *President*
EMP: 30
SQ FT: 10,000
SALES (est): 10MM **Privately Held**
SIC: 3599 Machine shop, jobbing & repair

(G-9549)
DYNAMIC PRECISION MFG LLC
5852 Thomas Rd (77041-4903)
PHONE..................713 466-4545
Dennis Nguyen,
EMP: 20 **EST:** 2017
SALES (est): 1MM **Privately Held**
SIC: 3541 Boring mills

(G-9550)
DYNAMIC PRODUCTS INC
16520 Peninsula St (77015-6504)
PHONE..................281 457-3500
Ronald N Lindquist, *President*
◆ **EMP:** 95 **EST:** 1969
SQ FT: 175,000
SALES (est): 25.7MM **Privately Held**
WEB: www.dynamicproducts.net
SIC: 3494 3498 Valves & pipe fittings; tube fabricating (contract bending & shaping)

(G-9551)
DYOPATH LLC (PA)
13430 Nw Fwy Ste 1000 (77040-6051)
PHONE..................855 749-6758
Charles Orrico, *CEO*
Patrick Clary, *Principal*
EMP: 55
SALES (est): 27MM **Privately Held**
WEB: www.dyopath.com
SIC: 7372 Prepackaged software

(G-9552)
E AND H ORIGINALS IN WOOD INC
Also Called: E & H
10902 Kingspoint Rd (77075-4120)
PHONE..................832 203-7629
Shawn Hamilton, *President*
EMP: 13
SALES (est): 1.5MM **Privately Held**
SIC: 2541 Cabinets, except refrigerated: show, display, etc.: wood

(G-9553)
E I DU PONT DE NEMOURS & CO
12701 Almeda Rd (77045-5807)
PHONE..................713 413-0000
Randy Divalerio, *Plant Engr*
EMP: 9
SALES (corp-wide): 14.2B **Publicly Held**
WEB: www.dupont.com
SIC: 2879 Agricultural chemicals
HQ: E. I. Du Pont De Nemours And Company
974 Centre Rd Bldg 735
Wilmington DE 19805
302 485-3000

(G-9554)
E-CEPTIONIST INC
Also Called: Profitgarden
405 Main St Ste 800 (77002-1822)
PHONE..................713 520-6688
Dirk Voorhees, *Principal*

Milton Havlick III, *Principal*
Jody Bare, *Sales Staff*
Andrew Stroud, *Manager*
EMP: 20
SALES (est): 620K **Privately Held**
WEB: www.eceptionist.com
SIC: 7372 7373 Application computer software; computer integrated systems design

(G-9555)
EADS COOLING SOLUTIONS LLC
3914 Fairhill Dr Ste 200 (77063-6430)
PHONE..................713 780-1551
Michael Garner, *Mng Member*
EMP: 15
SALES (est): 628.8K **Privately Held**
SIC: 3443 Heat exchangers: coolers (after, inter), condensers, etc.

(G-9556)
EAGLE FABRICATORS INC (PA)
5522 Shirley Ln Houston (77032)
PHONE..................281 442-8787
Pablo Elizondo, *President*
Judge Noe Gonzalez, *Chairman*
Cameron Britten, *Project Mgr*
EMP: 65
SQ FT: 30,000
SALES (est): 29.2MM **Privately Held**
WEB: www.eaglefabsteel.com
SIC: 3441 Building components, structural steel

(G-9557)
EAGLE GEOPHYSICAL INC (PA)
520 Post Oak Blvd Ste 320 (77027-9498)
PHONE..................713 881-2800
Douglas B Thompson, *Ch of Bd*
Samuel T Sloan III, *President*
Rob Wood, *President*
John Pearce, *CFO*
EMP: 20
SQ FT: 800
SALES (est): 23.4MM **Privately Held**
SIC: 1382 Oil & gas exploration services

(G-9558)
EAGLE HYDROCARBONS LLC
Also Called: Eagle Energy Acquisitions
11750 Katy Fwy Ste 830 (77079-1219)
P.O. Box 440414 (77244-0414)
PHONE..................713 300-3245
Greg Roberts, *President*
Dusty Dumas, *Principal*
Jo-Anne Bund, *Admin Sec*
EMP: 25 **EST:** 2010
SALES (est): 6.7MM **Privately Held**
WEB: www.eagleenergytrust.com
SIC: 2911 Fractionation products of crude petroleum, hydrocarbons

(G-9559)
EAGLE MOLDED PRODUCTS
12018 Palmerton Dr Ste A (77064-1437)
P.O. Box 41326 (77241-1326)
PHONE..................281 894-4995
John Johnson, *President*
William Noel, *Vice Pres*
▲ **EMP:** 11
SALES (est): 720K **Privately Held**
SIC: 3069 Molded rubber products

(G-9560)
EAGLE PIPE LLC
9525 Katy Fwy Ste 306 (77024-1468)
PHONE..................713 464-7473
Monique Ybarra, *General Mgr*
Jared Light, *COO*
Chris Lagasse, *Vice Pres*
Adam Tesanovich, *Vice Pres*
Emily Carruth, *Opers-Prdtn-Mfg*
EMP: 11
SQ FT: 20,000
SALES (est): 118.1MM **Privately Held**
WEB: www.eaglepipe.net
SIC: 3533 5082 Oil & gas drilling rigs & equipment; oil field equipment

(G-9561)
EAGLE ROCK ENERGY G&P LLC
1415 La St Ste 2700 (77002)
P.O. Box 2968 (77252-2968)
PHONE..................281 408-1200

Joseph A Mills, *CEO*
Jeffrey Wood, *CFO*
EMP: 13 **EST:** 2005
SALES (est): 834.4K
SALES (corp-wide): 460.2MM **Publicly Held**
SIC: 1311 Crude petroleum & natural gas
HQ: Eagle Rock Energy Partners, Lp
5847 San Felipe St # 3000
Houston TX 77057

(G-9562)
EAGLE ROCK ENERGY PARTNERS LP (HQ)
5847 San Felipe St # 3000 (77057-3399)
PHONE..................281 408-1200
Britt Pence, *Exec VP*
Robert D Hallett, *Senior VP*
Richard A Robert, *CFO*
EMP: 53
SALES (est): 205MM
SALES (corp-wide): 460.2MM **Publicly Held**
WEB: www.eaglerockfund.com
SIC: 1311 1321 Natural gas production; liquefied petroleum gases (natural) production
PA: Grizzly Energy, Llc
5847 San Felipe St # 3000
Houston TX 77057
832 327-2255

(G-9563)
EAGLE ROCK FIELD SERVICES LP (DH)
1415 La St Ste 2700 (77002)
PHONE..................281 408-1200
Alex A Bucher, *Partner*
William Puckett Sr, *Partner*
Joan A W Schnepp, *Partner*
Adam Altsuler, *Vice Pres*
Jeff Wood, *CFO*
EMP: 47
SALES (est): 31.3MM
SALES (corp-wide): 460.2MM **Publicly Held**
SIC: 1321 Natural gas liquids production

(G-9564)
EAGLE ROCK OPERATING LP (DH)
1415 La St Ste 2700 (77002)
PHONE..................281 408-1200
Joan Schnepp, *Partner*
Alex A Bucher, *Partner*
William Puckett Sr, *Partner*
EMP: 15
SALES (est): 2.5MM
SALES (corp-wide): 460.2MM **Publicly Held**
SIC: 1321 Natural gas liquids production

(G-9565)
EAGLE ROCK PIPELINE LP
Also Called: Eagle Rock Energy
5847 San Felipe St # 3000 (77057-3399)
PHONE..................281 408-1200
Joseph Mills, *Mng Member*
Alfredo Garica,
EMP: 30
SALES (est): 5.8MM
SALES (corp-wide): 460.2MM **Publicly Held**
WEB: www.eaglerockenergy.com
SIC: 1311 Crude petroleum production
HQ: Eagle Rock Energy Partners, Lp
5847 San Felipe St # 3000
Houston TX 77057

(G-9566)
EAGLE TRAFFIC SIGNS SAFETY LLC
10800 Telephone Rd (77075-4518)
P.O. Box 750187 (77275-0187)
PHONE..................713 987-9178
Lori Clarac, *Sales Staff*
Anthony Vowell, *Sales Staff*
Betty Patterson,
William Patterson,
EMP: 9
SQ FT: 3,200
SALES (est): 1.3MM **Privately Held**
WEB: www.eagletrafficsigns.com
SIC: 3993 Signs, not made in custom sign painting shops

▲ = Import ▼=Export
◆ =Import/Export

(G-9567)
EAGLEBURGMANN INDUSTRIES LP (DH)
Also Called: Eagle Burgmann Industries
10035 Brookriver Dr (77040-3193)
PHONE.................................713 939-9515
Jack Fountain, *CEO*
Anup Desai, *President*
Marcus Pillion, *President*
Wes Bush, *General Mgr*
Su Das, *Regional Mgr*
▲ EMP: 40 EST: 1977
SQ FT: 20,000
SALES (est): 46.6MM
SALES (corp-wide): 10.5B **Privately Held**
WEB: www.eagleburgmann.us
SIC: 3053 5085 Gaskets, packing & sealing devices; seals, industrial; valves & fittings
HQ: Eagleburgmann Germany Gmbh & Co. Kg
Sauerlacher Str. 6-10
Wolfratshausen 82515
817 123-0

(G-9568)
EAGLEHAWK FIELD SERVICES LLC
1000 La St Ste 5600 (77002)
PHONE.................................832 204-2700
Stephen W Herod, *Principal*
David S Elkouri, *Principal*
EMP: 106
SALES (est): 1.6MM **Privately Held**
SIC: 1311 Crude petroleum & natural gas
HQ: Bhp Billiton Petroleum (North America) Inc.
1500 Post Oak Blvd
Houston TX 77056
713 961-8500

(G-9569)
EARTH COLOR HOUSTON INC
7021 Portwest Dr Ste 190 (77024-8084)
PHONE.................................713 861-8158
Robert Kashan, *President*
Dennis Ganzak, *Vice Pres*
EMP: 65 EST: 1982
SQ FT: 16,000
SALES (est): 14MM
SALES (corp-wide): 275.5MM **Privately Held**
WEB: www.mittera.com
SIC: 2752 Commercial printing, offset
HQ: Earth Color New York, Inc.
249 Pomeroy Rd
Parsippany NJ 07054
973 884-1300

(G-9570)
EASTERN OIL WELL SERVICE CORP (HQ)
9821 Katy Fwy Ste 1050 (77024-1218)
PHONE.................................203 358-5700
Charles E Drimal Jr, *President*
Beverly A Cummings, *Vice Pres*
James Gilbert, *Admin Sec*
Lynn Pizor, *Admin Sec*
EMP: 27
SALES (est): 6.8MM
SALES (corp-wide): 104.8MM **Publicly Held**
SIC: 1389 Construction, repair & dismantling services
PA: Primeenergy Corporation
9821 Katy Fwy Ste 1050
Houston TX 77024
713 735-0000

(G-9571)
EASTON ENERGY LLC
15375 Memorial Dr (77079-4138)
PHONE.................................214 712-2141
Joel McComas, *President*
EMP: 15
SALES (est): 420.3K **Privately Held**
WEB: www.easton.energy
SIC: 1382 Oil & gas exploration services

(G-9572)
EATON CORPORATION
14825 Nw Fwy Ste 100 (77040-4083)
PHONE.................................713 849-1600
Wilson Dimarcus, *Project Mgr*
Derrick Arrington, *Engineer*

Matthew Soble, *Sales Engr*
Patrick Bawer, *Sales Staff*
Tyler Evans, *Sales Staff*
EMP: 30 **Privately Held**
WEB: www.eatonelectrical.com
SIC: 5063 3699 3613 Electrical supplies; electrical equipment & supplies; switchgear & switchboard apparatus
HQ: Eaton Corporation
1000 Eaton Blvd
Cleveland OH 44122
440 523-5000

(G-9573)
EBROFROST NORTH AMERICA INC
2777 Allen Pkwy Ste 1600 (77019-2141)
P.O. Box 2636 (77252-2636)
PHONE.................................281 727-8139
Michael Slavin, *CFO*
Stephan Keck, *Director*
Gregory S Richardson, *Director*
Pablo Albendea Solis, *Director*
EMP: 25 EST: 2017
SALES (est): 1.2MM **Privately Held**
WEB: www.ebrofrostna.com
SIC: 2044 Rice milling

(G-9574)
ECM BIOSURGERY INC
4235 Oberlin St (77005-3524)
PHONE.................................281 229-0348
Magnus Hook, *Principal*
Brooke Russell, *Principal*
David McQuillan, *Opers Staff*
EMP: 15
SALES (est): 1.1MM **Privately Held**
WEB: www.ecmbiosurgery.com
SIC: 2836 Biological products, except diagnostic

(G-9575)
ECMM SERVICES INC
10305 Round Up Ln Ste 400 (77064-5560)
PHONE.................................909 979-4526
EMP: 9
SALES (corp-wide): 2.2MM **Privately Held**
SIC: 3955 Print cartridges for laser & other computer printers
PA: Ecmm Services Inc.
8801 Fallbrook Dr
Houston TX 77064
281 668-1678

(G-9576)
ECO SERVICES OPERATIONS CORP
8615 Manchester St (77012-2142)
PHONE.................................713 924-1401
Daniel Tate, *Plant Mgr*
Ross Denicola, *Opers Mgr*
Lesley Kirkland, *Senior Buyer*
Landry Garcia, *Purchasing*
John Willis, *Engineer*
EMP: 122
SALES (corp-wide): 1.5B **Publicly Held**
SIC: 2819 Sulfuric acid, oleum
HQ: Eco Services Operations Corp.
300 Lindenwood Dr
Malvern PA 19355
610 251-9118

(G-9577)
ECODYNE HEAT EXCHANGER LLC (DH)
Also Called: O& M Manufacturing
4847 Homestead Rd Ste 416 (77028-5808)
PHONE.................................713 675-3511
John Heeney, *President*
Mark P Oppenheim, *Principal*
Greg Cash, *Vice Pres*
Larry Arndt, *VP Finance*
◆ EMP: 67 EST: 2007
SQ FT: 141,000
SALES (est): 10MM
SALES (corp-wide): 254.6B **Publicly Held**
WEB: www.ecodyne-heatexchangers.com
SIC: 3443 Heat exchangers, condensers & components

(G-9578)
ECOLAB INC
8150 Westpark Dr (77063-6316)
PHONE.................................281 908-4877
Guy Lamonica, *Manager*
Guillermo Avalis, *Director*
Beth Ballard, *Director*
EMP: 17
SALES (corp-wide): 14.9B **Publicly Held**
WEB: www.ecolab.com
SIC: 2841 Soap & other detergents
PA: Ecolab Inc.
1 Ecolab Pl
Saint Paul MN 55102
800 232-6522

(G-9579)
ECOLAB INC
20465 State Highway 249 # 200 (77070-2759)
PHONE.................................800 325-1671
Craig Goulding, *Principal*
Michael Jerla, *Senior Mgr*
Kimberly Holloman, *Supervisor*
EMP: 100
SALES (corp-wide): 14.9B **Publicly Held**
WEB: www.ecolab.com
SIC: 2841 Soap & other detergents
PA: Ecolab Inc.
1 Ecolab Pl
Saint Paul MN 55102
800 232-6522

(G-9580)
ECONOMY MUD PRODUCTS COMPANY (PA)
Also Called: Economy Polymers & Chemical
435 E Anderson Rd (77047-5016)
P.O. Box 450246 (77245-0246)
PHONE.................................800 231-2066
Lawrence E Walton, *President*
Walter M White, *Treasurer*
Jim Irsik, *Sales Mgr*
Gordon Zimmerman, *Sales Mgr*
Arnold Adame, *Sales Staff*
◆ EMP: 98 EST: 1951
SQ FT: 20,000
SALES (est): 150MM **Privately Held**
WEB: www.economypolymers.com
SIC: 2869 2899 Hydraulic fluids, synthetic base; chemical preparations

(G-9581)
ECOPETROL AMERICA INC
2800 Post Oak Blvd (77056-6100)
PHONE.................................713 634-3800
Gabriel Osorio, *President*
Tulio Di Renzo, *Buyer*
Christina Rosiello, *Buyer*
Mayra Solarte, *Buyer*
Wilbert Bernard, *Engineer*
◆ EMP: 60
SQ FT: 19,000
SALES (est): 57.6MM **Privately Held**
WEB: www.ecopetrol-america.com
SIC: 1382 Oil & gas exploration services
PA: Ecopetrol S A
Carrera 13 36 24 Piso 12
Bogota

(G-9582)
EDELHOFF TECHNOLOGIES USA LLC
Also Called: Edelhoff U.S.a
9361 Winkler Dr Ste A (77017-6090)
PHONE.................................713 947-6469
Robert Cantu, *President*
Pat Latona, *Engineer*
EMP: 14
SALES (est): 2.5MM **Privately Held**
WEB: www.edelhoff-technologies.com
SIC: 3535 Bulk handling conveyor systems

(G-9583)
EDS PRECISION MFG LLC
6061 Thomas Rd (77041-4906)
PHONE.................................713 956-1112
Allan Bolton, *COO*
Jim Groves, *Prdtn Mgr*
Allie Pavel, *Sales Staff*
Larry Shuler, *Sales Staff*
Edwin Decora,
EMP: 60

SALES (est): 8.3MM **Privately Held**
WEB: www.edsprecision.com
SIC: 3599 Machine shop, jobbing & repair

(G-9584)
EFFECTIVE METAL SERVICES LLC
14173 Nw Fwy 147 (77040-5013)
PHONE.................................832 962-8626
Ken Odom, *CFO*
Chris R Ewing, *Mng Member*
Sean Easton, *Mng Member*
EMP: 10
SALES (est): 1.5MM **Privately Held**
SIC: 3449 Bars, concrete reinforcing: fabricated steel
PA: E4 Holdings, Inc.
2000 Airport Rd
Terrell TX 75160

(G-9585)
EL PASO CGP COMPANY LLC (DH)
1001 Louisiana St (77002-5089)
P.O. Box 2511 (77252-2511)
PHONE.................................713 420-2600
Ronald L Kuehn Jr, *Ch of Bd*
H Brent Austin, *President*
Peggy A Heeg, *Exec VP*
H Austin, *Vice Pres*
D Dwight Scott, *CFO*
◆ EMP: 35
SALES (est): 478.6MM **Publicly Held**
SIC: 2911 1311 4613 4612 Petroleum refining; crude petroleum & natural gas; refined petroleum pipelines; crude petroleum pipelines; gasoline service stations; natural gas transmission
HQ: El Paso Llc
1001 Louisiana St
Houston TX 77002
713 420-2600

(G-9586)
EL PASO CNG COMPANY LLC (DH)
9 Greenway Plz (77046-0905)
PHONE.................................713 420-2600
O S Wyatt Jr, *Vice Ch Bd*
James R Paul, *President*
James F Cordes, *Exec VP*
Coby C Hesse, *Senior VP*
Austin A O'Toole, *Senior VP*
EMP: 12
SALES (est): 2.4MM **Publicly Held**
SIC: 4922 1382 1311 1221 Pipelines, natural gas; oil & gas exploration services; crude petroleum production; bituminous coal & lignite-surface mining; trucking, except local; local trucking, without storage
HQ: El Paso Llc
1001 Louisiana St
Houston TX 77002
713 420-2600

(G-9587)
EL VENADO FOODS
3919 Eastex Fwy (77026-3214)
PHONE.................................713 692-0688
Salvador Rommo, *Owner*
Josh Romo, *Marketing Staff*
▲ EMP: 30 EST: 2004
SQ FT: 35,000
SALES (est): 10.8MM **Privately Held**
WEB: www.elvenadofoods.com
SIC: 2099 5499 Seasonings & spices; spices & herbs

(G-9588)
ELDRED SHEET METAL WORKS LP
3119 Chapman St (77009-6411)
P.O. Box 8725 (77249-8725)
PHONE.................................713 227-3251
Milton Smoot, *Partner*
George Alan Lever, *Partner*
Buddy Smoot, *Partner*
Jason Jones, *Accounts Mgr*
Laura Alexander, *Office Mgr*
EMP: 20
SQ FT: 12,000

GEOGRAPHIC

SALES (est): 3.9MM **Privately Held**
WEB: www.eldredsheetmetal.com
SIC: 7692 3441 3444 Welding repair; fabricated structural metal; sheet metalwork

(G-9589)
ELECTRICAL SIGN DISPLAYS INC
Also Called: E S D Sign Services
6537 Rupley Cir (77087-3441)
P.O. Box 266842 (77207-6842)
PHONE..................................713 644-8081
Mardell Greenan, *President*
Shawn Greenan, *Vice Pres*
EMP: 10
SQ FT: 11,200
SALES (est): 1.4MM **Privately Held**
WEB: www.esdsignservices.com
SIC: 3993 Signs & advertising specialties

(G-9590)
ELECTRO TECHNICAL INDS INC
Also Called: Electro Tech Industries
303 Little York Rd (77076-1122)
PHONE..................................713 691-5182
George Houche, *President*
Cheryl A Houche, *President*
Sam Saliba, *General Mgr*
Raji Hakam, *Project Mgr*
Adel RAD, *Project Mgr*
▲ **EMP:** 60
SALES (est): 24.7MM **Privately Held**
WEB: www.etii.us
SIC: 3699 Electrical equipment & supplies

(G-9591)
ELECTRO-COATINGS TEXAS INC
216 Baywood St (77011-2399)
PHONE..................................210 798-3460
Jeff Garvens, *President*
Mark S Freer, *President*
Chuck McShane, *Controller*
Robert Lee, *Manager*
Tim Foster, *Maintence Staff*
EMP: 27
SQ FT: 13,000
SALES (est): 3.3MM **Privately Held**
WEB: www.electro-coatings.com
SIC: 3471 Electroplating of metals or formed products; chromium plating of metals or formed products; finishing, metals or formed products
HQ: Electro-Coatings, Inc.
216 Baywood St
Houston TX 77011
713 923-5935

(G-9592)
ELECTRO-MECHANICAL INDS INC
Also Called: E M I
11230 Neeshaw Dr (77065-4472)
P.O. Box 690648 (77269-0648)
PHONE..................................281 894-1600
Fallon Egan, *President*
Patrick Weisbrod, *Engineer*
Michele Johnson, *Controller*
Earl Simon, *Manager*
▲ **EMP:** 40
SQ FT: 4,700
SALES (est): 28.1MM **Privately Held**
WEB: www.emiproducts.com
SIC: 3533 3443 Oil & gas field machinery; chutes & troughs; cable trays, metal plate

(G-9593)
ELECTRO-QUIP SERVICE INC
8145 Miller Road 2 (77049-1958)
P.O. Box 729, Channelview (77530-0729)
PHONE..................................281 456-8600
Albert L Anderson, *President*
Adrian A Contreras, *President*
Jeanne A Anderson, *Corp Secy*
Haron Moreno, *Vice Pres*
Aaron Jonas, *CFO*
EMP: 55
SQ FT: 125,800
SALES (est): 50MM **Privately Held**
WEB: www.electroquip.homestead.com
SIC: 1731 3625 5063 Electronic controls installation; motor control accessories, including overload relays; panelboards

(G-9594)
ELECTRONIC ASSEMBLY SVCS INC
4501 S Pinemont Dr # 108 (77041-9346)
PHONE..................................713 686-4390
Evelyn Fletcher, *President*
EMP: 15
SALES (est): 2.7MM **Privately Held**
WEB: www.electronicassemblyservicesinc.com
SIC: 3679 Harness assemblies for electronic use: wire or cable

(G-9595)
ELECTRONIC MED RESOURCES LL C
333 N Sam Houston Pkwy E (77060-2414)
PHONE..................................832 456-2600
Larry Wedekind, *CEO*
EMP: 12
SQ FT: 10,000
SALES (est): 911.9K **Privately Held**
SIC: 7372 Operating systems computer software

(G-9596)
ELECTRONIC POWER DESIGN INC
Also Called: Epd
15200 North Fwy (77090-6306)
PHONE..................................713 923-1191
John Janik, *President*
Carla Leblanc, *General Mgr*
Amber Allen, *Editor*
John Norwood, *VP Bus Dvlpt*
Zhang Zhenhua, *CTO*
◆ **EMP:** 96
SQ FT: 18,000
SALES (est): 34.6MM **Privately Held**
WEB: www.electronicpowerdesign.com
SIC: 3621 3625 3825 3613 Motors, electric; control equipment, electric; instruments to measure electricity; switchgear & switchboard apparatus; fluid power pumps & motors

(G-9597)
ELECTRONIC SERVICES UNLIMITED
1906 Johanna Dr Ste A (77055-2470)
P.O. Box 802012 (77280-2012)
PHONE..................................713 683-0601
John Lankford Sr, *President*
Jessica Garza, *Treasurer*
EMP: 10
SQ FT: 12,000
SALES (est): 1.9MM **Privately Held**
WEB: www.esuinc.com
SIC: 3672 Printed circuit boards

(G-9598)
ELEMENT MARKETS LLC (HQ)
3200 Southwest Fwy # 1310 (77027-7589)
PHONE..................................281 207-7200
Angela Schwarz, *President*
Randall Lack, *Principal*
Ken Nelson, *Senior VP*
Mike Taylor, *Senior VP*
Tiffany Grigsby, *Vice Pres*
EMP: 38
SALES (est): 18.9MM
SALES (corp-wide): 1.7MM **Privately Held**
WEB: www.elementmarkets.com
SIC: 1382 8741 Geological exploration, oil & gas field; industrial management
PA: The Rise Fund
345 California St
San Francisco CA 94104
415 743-1500

(G-9599)
ELEVATE MIDSTREAM PARTNERS LLC
1415 La St Ste 3400 (77002)
PHONE..................................214 215-9298
Roger Fox, *CEO*
Roger Ondreko, *CFO*
Chris Wu, *Manager*
EMP: 13
SALES (est): 733.2K **Privately Held**
WEB: www.elevatemidstream.com
SIC: 1382 Oil & gas exploration services

(G-9600)
ELG METALS INC
15135 Jacintoport Blvd (77015-6530)
P.O. Box 1319, Channelview (77530-1319)
PHONE..................................281 457-2100
Andres Montes, *General Mgr*
Shawn Morrow, *Warehouse Mgr*
Paige Allen, *Accounts Mgr*
EMP: 20
SALES (corp-wide): 5.3B **Privately Held**
WEB: www.elg.de
SIC: 5093 3341 Nonferrous metals scrap; secondary nonferrous metals
HQ: Elg Metals, Inc.
369 River Rd
Mckeesport PA 15132
412 672-9200

(G-9601)
ELI-SHIR LTD
11550 Fuqua St Ste 250 (77034-4200)
PHONE..................................281 464-9616
William Lipsky, *Med Doctor*
Shaena Choi, *Med Doctor*
Nancy Stephens,
EMP: 9 **EST:** 1989
SALES (est): 25.2K **Privately Held**
WEB: www.advancedlaservision.com
SIC: 3841 Ophthalmic lasers

(G-9602)
ELITE PUBLICATIONS INC
4520 W 34th St Ste E (77092-5938)
PHONE..................................713 263-9476
Vanee M Biering, *President*
EMP: 12
SQ FT: 1,800
SALES (est): 910K **Privately Held**
SIC: 2721 Trade journals: publishing & printing

(G-9603)
ELITE UPSTREAM LLC
16610 Crystal View Cir (77095-4391)
PHONE..................................832 674-3050
Binh Thai,
EMP: 14 **EST:** 2017
SALES (est): 351.4K **Privately Held**
SIC: 1389 Oil consultants

(G-9604)
ELLINGER MATERIALS LLC
14508 Chrisman Rd Ste 200 (77039-1115)
PHONE..................................281 227-6233
EMP: 15
SALES (est): 594.1K **Privately Held**
SIC: 1442 Construction sand & gravel

(G-9605)
ELLWOOD TEXAS FORGE LP
Also Called: Ecdg
12500 Amelia Dr (77045-4818)
PHONE..................................713 434-5100
Richard Allender, *President*
Dale Gantt, *Vice Pres*
Jim Harrison, *Vice Pres*
Valli Senthilnathan, *Vice Pres*
Wayne Thompson, *Vice Pres*
◆ **EMP:** 130
SQ FT: 180,000
SALES (est): 33.2MM
SALES (corp-wide): 586MM **Privately Held**
WEB: www.ellwoodcloseddiegroup.com
SIC: 3462 3463 3398 Iron & steel forgings; nonferrous forgings; metal heat treating
PA: Ellwood Group, Inc.
600 Commercial Ave
Ellwood City PA 16117
724 752-3680

(G-9606)
ELMAR SERVICES INC
Also Called: Nov Asep Elmar
11993 Fm 529 Rd (77041-3011)
PHONE..................................713 983-9281
Fax: 713 983-9282
◆ **EMP:** 56
SALES (est): 18.3MM
SALES (corp-wide): 21.4B **Publicly Held**
SIC: 3533 Mfg Oil/Gas Field Machinery
PA: National Oilwell Varco, Inc.
7909 Parkwood Circle Dr
Houston TX 77036
713 346-7500

(G-9607)
EMAS CHIYODA SUBSEA INC (HQ)
Also Called: Emas AMC
17220 Katy Fwy Ste 100 (77094-1485)
PHONE..................................832 487-7300
Lionel Lee, *Chairman*
Richard Riopel, *Business Mgr*
Daniel Sack, *COO*
Kenny Campbell, *Vice Pres*
Dale Rice, *Vice Pres*
◆ **EMP:** 52
SALES (est): 139.4MM **Privately Held**
WEB: www.ezraholdings.com
SIC: 1381 Drilling oil & gas wells

(G-9608)
EMBOSSED GRAPHICS INC
5325 Glenmont Dr Ste D (77081-2098)
PHONE..................................713 667-0034
Kenny Guinn, *Vice Pres*
EMP: 10
SQ FT: 6,000
SALES (est): 1MM **Privately Held**
WEB: www.embossedgraphics.com
SIC: 2754 2759 2711 Imprinting, gravure; embossing on paper; newspapers

(G-9609)
EMC CORPORATION
1 Riverway Ste 1700 (77056-1997)
PHONE..................................713 621-9800
EMP: 50
SALES (corp-wide): 78.6B **Publicly Held**
SIC: 3572 Mfg Computer Storage Devices
HQ: Emc Corporation
176 South St
Hopkinton MA 01748
508 435-1000

(G-9610)
EMCO PRESS CORPORATION
Also Called: Emco Envelopes
4935 Milwee St (77092-6614)
P.O. Box 40335 (77240-0335)
PHONE..................................713 956-6055
Steve Emmott, *President*
Russell Emmott, *Vice Pres*
Gary Emmott, *Accounts Exec*
Billy Amuny, *Sales Staff*
Jenson Kerr, *Sales Executive*
EMP: 30
SQ FT: 17,500
SALES (est): 3.4MM **Privately Held**
WEB: www.emcopress.com
SIC: 2759 2752 Business forms: printing; commercial printing, lithographic

(G-9611)
EMERALD GATHERING & TRNSP LLC
9801 Westheimer Rd # 1060 (77042-3977)
PHONE..................................713 621-2242
Douglas Shaefer, *Opers Staff*
Richard Blakey, *Mng Member*
EMP: 15
SQ FT: 3,600
SALES (est): 1.4MM **Privately Held**
SIC: 1311 Crude petroleum & natural gas

(G-9612)
EMERSON ATMTN SLTONS FNAL CTRL (HQ)
10707 Clay Rd (77041-6145)
PHONE..................................713 986-4665
Randall J Hogan, *CEO*
Thomas Boty, *Business Mgr*
Sandra Castro, *Counsel*
Frederick S Koury, *Senior VP*
Angela D Lageson, *Senior VP*
◆ **EMP:** 350
SQ FT: 41,000
SALES (est): 489.1MM
SALES (corp-wide): 16.7B **Publicly Held**
WEB: www.pentair.com
SIC: 3491 3625 3494 Industrial valves; relays & industrial controls; valves & pipe fittings
PA: Emerson Electric Co.
8000 West Florissant Ave
Saint Louis MO 63136
314 553-2000

▲ = Import ▼=Export
◆ =Import/Export

(G-9613)
EMERSON ELECTRIC CO
10241 W Little York Rd (77040-3228)
PHONE....................713 447-2839
Indy Chakrabarti, *Vice Pres*
Charlene Davis, *Opers Staff*
Richard Upton, *Engineer*
Damian Trujillo, *Natl Sales Mgr*
Paul Capistran, *Regl Sales Mgr*
EMP: 9
SALES (corp-wide): 16.7B **Publicly Held**
WEB: www.emerson.com
SIC: 3823 Industrial instrmnts msrmnt display/control process variable
PA: Emerson Electric Co.
8000 West Florissant Ave
Saint Louis MO 63136
314 553-2000

(G-9614)
EMERSON PROCESS MANAGEMENT
6005 Rogerdale Rd (77072-1656)
PHONE....................281 879-2300
Ken Atkins, *Manager*
EMP: 30
SALES (corp-wide): 16.7B **Publicly Held**
WEB: www.emerson.com
SIC: 3823 Industrial instrmnts msrmnt display/control process variable
HQ: Emerson Process Management Power & Water Solutions, Inc.
200 Beta Dr
Pittsburgh PA 15238
412 963-4000

(G-9615)
EMGS AMERICAS INC (HQ)
16285 Park Ten Pl Ste 410 (77084-5092)
PHONE....................281 920-5601
Dave Ridyard, *President*
Svein Ellingsrud, *Vice Pres*
Carl Hutchins, *Vice Pres*
Stale E Johansn, *Vice Pres*
Michael A Vigeant, *Vice Pres*
EMP: 50
SQ FT: 17,500
SALES (est): 7.6MM
SALES (corp-wide): 86MM **Privately Held**
WEB: www.emgs.com
SIC: 2911 Fractionation products of crude petroleum, hydrocarbons
PA: Electromagnetic Geoservices Asa
Karenslyst Alle 4
Oslo 0278
735 688-10

(G-9616)
EMISSIONS TECHNOLOGY INC
360 Garden Oaks Blvd (77018-5502)
P.O. Box 10965 (77206-0965)
PHONE....................713 691-1211
Mark Spoon, *President*
Ric Porter, *Principal*
Gary Lawson, *Vice Pres*
Steve Kelly, *Mfg Staff*
Steve Porter, *CFO*
EMP: 10
SALES (est): 684K **Privately Held**
WEB: www.ultraburnccs.com
SIC: 3714 Motor vehicle parts & accessories

(G-9617)
EML MANUFACTURING LLC
14315 Beacons Trace Ct (77069-1439)
P.O. Box 41935 (77241-1935)
PHONE....................281 880-7517
Yuet Ming Yong, *President*
Edmond Loh,
EMP: 20
SALES (est): 5.6MM **Privately Held**
WEB: www.emlmanufacturing.com
SIC: 3822 3533 Electric heat controls; oil field machinery & equipment

(G-9618)
EMMA GRACE SIGN CO
5660 Allen St (77007-4313)
P.O. Box 7387 (77248-7387)
PHONE....................713 864-4644
EMP: 16
SALES (est): 583.2K **Privately Held**
SIC: 3993 Signs And Advertising Specialties

(G-9619)
EMPIRE ELECTRIC INC
944 Fisher St (77018-5306)
P.O. Box 11662, Spring (77391-1662)
PHONE....................713 688-0151
Larry Womack, *President*
Tom Amarouso, *President*
EMP: 25
SQ FT: 250,000
SALES (est): 2.2MM **Privately Held**
SIC: 2542 Shelving, office & store: except wood

(G-9620)
EMPIRICA LLC
Also Called: Als Empirica
6360 W Sam Houston Pkwy N # 100 (77041-5165)
PHONE....................713 466-7400
Michal Rozanski, *CEO*
George Drewry, *Vice Pres*
Larry Krystosek, *Engineer*
EMP: 25
SALES (est): 3.1MM **Privately Held**
WEB: www.empirica-logging.com
SIC: 1389 Oil field services

(G-9621)
EMPOWER CLINIC SERVICES LLC
Also Called: Empower Pharmacy
5980 W Sam Houston Pkwy N S (77041-5252)
PHONE....................832 678-4417
Gilberto Iracheta, *Controller*
Stacy Germano, *Human Res Mgr*
Gabbi Nguyen, *Sales Staff*
Shaun Noorian, *Mng Member*
Daniel Royster, *Manager*
▲ EMP: 200
SQ FT: 15,000
SALES (est): 26MM **Privately Held**
WEB: www.empowerpharmacy.com
SIC: 5912 2834 Drug stores; pharmaceutical preparations

(G-9622)
EN PLAST TECHNOLOGY LLC
17510 Carlsway (77073-1438)
PHONE....................832 730-4606
Giovanni Capra, *Mng Member*
▲ EMP: 10
SQ FT: 30,000
SALES (est): 5MM **Privately Held**
WEB: www.en-plast.us
SIC: 3069 3011 3262 Medical & laboratory rubber sundries & related products; pneumatic tires, all types; bone china

(G-9623)
EN-FAB INC (PA)
3905 Jensen Dr (77026-3200)
PHONE....................713 225-4913
Chandra S Tripathy, *President*
Rick Smart, *Project Engr*
Shivani Tripathy, *CFO*
Dane Anderson, *Manager*
Roxana Mora, *Executive*
◆ EMP: 79
SQ FT: 100,000
SALES (est): 18.4MM **Privately Held**
WEB: www.en-fabinc.com
SIC: 1389 Oil field services

(G-9624)
ENCINO ENERGY LLC (PA)
5847 San Felipe St # 300 (77057-3426)
PHONE....................281 254-7070
Sheena Rizvi, *Production*
Anangela Gonzalez, *Engineer*
Preston Peeples, *Engineer*
Bonnie Furlough, *Accountant*
Ashley Barela, *Office Mgr*
EMP: 30 EST: 2011
SALES (est): 24.6MM **Privately Held**
WEB: www.encinoenergy.com
SIC: 1382 Oil & gas exploration services

(G-9625)
ENCORE WELLHEAD SYSTEMS LLC (PA)
3403 Marquart St (77027-6505)
PHONE....................832 742-1350
J Kelly Joy, *CEO*
Kenneth Bean, *President*

Jennifer A Duncan, *Vice Pres*
Max Bush, *Sales Mgr*
EMP: 19
SALES (est): 37.9MM **Privately Held**
WEB: www.encorewellhead.com
SIC: 1389 Bailing, cleaning, swabbing & treating of wells

(G-9626)
ENDEAVOR NATURAL GAS LLC
1201 La St Ste 3350 (77002)
PHONE....................713 658-8555
Bill Russ, *Principal*
William E Russ,
Richard C Jenner,
David Stevens,
EMP: 22
SALES (est): 37.9K **Privately Held**
WEB: www.endeavorgas.com
SIC: 1382 Oil & gas exploration services

(G-9627)
ENDEAVOUR INTERNATIONAL CORP (PA)
811 Main St Ste 2100 (77002-6128)
PHONE....................713 307-8700
William L Transier, *Ch of Bd*
John N Seitz, *Vice Ch Bd*
John Seitz, *COO*
James J Emme, *Exec VP*
Carl Grenz, *Exec VP*
▲ EMP: 24
SALES (est): 316MM **Privately Held**
WEB: www.endeavourcorp.com
SIC: 1311 Crude petroleum & natural gas

(G-9628)
ENDICOTT BIOFUELS II LLC (PA)
305 Wells Fargo Dr Ste A8 (77090-4068)
PHONE....................281 598-2180
David M Robinson, *CEO*
Stephen W Brown, *Principal*
Christopher J Frantz, *Principal*
Robert J Ireland, *Principal*
Richard G Allen, *Vice Pres*
EMP: 10
SQ FT: 3,336
SALES (est): 1.5MM **Privately Held**
SIC: 2869 Fuels

(G-9629)
ENDRESS + HAUSER INC
4333 W Sam Houston Pkwy N # 190 (77043-1222)
PHONE....................713 300-6200
Santosh Kumar, *Finance*
Steven Spangler, *Regl Sales Mgr*
Chris Ewart, *Sales Staff*
David Hall, *Manager*
Monica Donahue, *Manager*
EMP: 12
SALES (corp-wide): 291.8MM **Privately Held**
WEB: www.us.endress.com
SIC: 3823 Industrial instrmnts msrmnt display/control process variable
HQ: Endress + Hauser Inc
2350 Endress Pl
Greenwood IN 46143
317 535-7138

(G-9630)
ENDURO COMPOSITES INC (PA)
16602 Central Green Blvd (77032-5131)
P.O. Box 728 (77001-0728)
PHONE....................713 358-4000
Walter C Greig, *Ch of Bd*
Wallace Woodlief, *President*
Kyle Montgomery, *Managing Dir*
Bill Knox, *Regional Mgr*
Flavio Ortiz, *Vice Pres*
▲ EMP: 100
SALES (est): 76.4MM **Privately Held**
WEB: www.endurocomposites.com
SIC: 3089 Plastic containers, except foam

(G-9631)
ENERFLEX ENERGY SYSTEMS INC (HQ)
10815 Telge Rd (77095-5038)
PHONE....................281 345-9300
Greg Stewart, *President*
Craig Hughes, *Vice Pres*
Mauricio Meineri, *Vice Pres*

Jerry Crockett, *Project Mgr*
David Smith, *Purchasing*
◆ EMP: 296
SQ FT: 17,000
SALES (est): 453MM
SALES (corp-wide): 1.5B **Privately Held**
WEB: www.enerflex.com
SIC: 3585 7623 7699 3563 Refrigeration equipment, complete; compressors for refrigeration & air conditioning equipment; refrigeration repair service; compressor repair; air & gas compressors
PA: Enerflex Ltd
1331 Macleod Trl Se Suite 904
Calgary AB T2G 0
403 387-6377

(G-9632)
ENERFLEX INC (HQ)
10815 Telge Rd (77095-5038)
PHONE....................801 292-0493
Jerry Duncan, *Principal*
Anna M Paravi, *Corp Secy*
Chuck Galey, *Vice Pres*
Anna Paravi, *Vice Pres*
Kyle Turney, *Vice Pres*
EMP: 150
SQ FT: 74,000
SALES (est): 67.7MM
SALES (corp-wide): 1.5B **Privately Held**
WEB: www.enerflex.com
SIC: 3585 1711 3444 Refrigeration equipment, complete; refrigeration contractor; sheet metalwork
PA: Enerflex Ltd
1331 Macleod Trl Se Suite 904
Calgary AB T2G 0
403 387-6377

(G-9633)
ENERFLEX SERVICES INC
711 Louisiana St Fl 17 (77002-2719)
PHONE....................281 345-9300
Danny Aguilar, *General Mgr*
Santosh Yarlagadda, *Engineer*
Daniel Van Praag, *Sales Staff*
Peter Kourkoubes, *Director*
Dale Grisso, *Director*
◆ EMP: 42
SALES (est): 8.9MM
SALES (corp-wide): 1.5B **Privately Held**
WEB: www.enerflex.com
SIC: 7699 8711 3999 Industrial equipment services; industrial engineers; atomizers, toiletry
PA: Enerflex Ltd
1331 Macleod Trl Se Suite 904
Calgary AB T2G 0
403 387-6377

(G-9634)
ENERGY FACILITY SERVICES INC
Also Called: Efsi
15255 Gulf Fwy Ste 140d (77034-5375)
PHONE....................281 286-8500
Garland Faulk, *President*
Mary Roberts, *Corp Secy*
James Moore, *COO*
EMP: 12
SQ FT: 4,841
SALES (est): 895.1K **Privately Held**
SIC: 1389 8711 Testing, measuring, surveying & analysis services; engineering services

(G-9635)
ENERGY FISHING RENTL SVCS INC
6925 Burkett St (77021-4605)
PHONE....................713 433-5506
Tim Lange, *Branch Mgr*
EMP: 10 **Privately Held**
WEB: www.energyfrs.com
SIC: 1389 Equipment rental & leasing
PA: Energy Fishing & Rental Services, Inc.
10235 W Little York Rd
Houston TX 77040

(G-9636)
ENERGY RESERVES GROUP LLC
333 Clay St Ste 4400 (77002-4105)
P.O. Box 721380 (77272-1380)
PHONE....................713 659-7800
Jonathan Godwin, *Client Mgr*

Reed Barrett, *Accounts Exec*
Bridget Silva, *Sales Staff*
Scott Wood, *Mng Member*
Matt Johnson, *Officer*
EMP: 25
SQ FT: 10,000
SALES (est): 4.4MM **Privately Held**
WEB: www.ergresources.com
SIC: 1381 Drilling oil & gas wells

(G-9637)
ENERGY TECHNOLOGY MANUFA
15438 Miller 1 Rd Lot B Lot B 1st (77049)
PHONE..................................281 862-2829
Octavio Morales, *Manager*
EMP: 15
SALES (corp-wide): 7.5MM **Privately Held**
WEB:
www.energytechnologythreading.com
SIC: 3317 Steel pipe & tubes
PA: Energy Technology Manufacturing & Threading, Llc
1200 N Airport Rd
Abbeville LA 70510
337 984-2199

(G-9638)
ENERGY VALVE & SUPPLY CO LLC
Also Called: Envasco
8207 North Loop E Ste 400 (77029-1261)
PHONE..................................713 675-7525
Sondra Brannan, *Purchasing*
Brenda Johnson, *Accounting Mgr*
Don Arlington, *Sales Staff*
James R Lyons,
Bryan Dedman,
▲ **EMP:** 13
SALES (est): 6.3MM **Privately Held**
WEB: www.envasco.com
SIC: 3491 5085 Industrial valves; industrial supplies

(G-9639)
ENERGY XXI GOM LLC
1021 Main St Ste 2626 (77002-6516)
PHONE..................................713 659-2100
Steve Weyel, *President*
Antonio De Pinho, *COO*
Rodney Dykes, *COO*
Vincent Devito, *Exec VP*
Hugh Menown, *Exec VP*
EMP: 50
SALES (est): 24.9MM
SALES (corp-wide): 658.8MM **Privately Held**
WEB: www.energyxxi.com
SIC: 1382 Oil & gas exploration services
HQ: Energy Xxi Gulf Coast, Inc.
1021 Main St Ste 2626
Houston TX 77002

(G-9640)
ENERGY XXI GULF COAST INC (HQ)
1021 Main St Ste 2626 (77002-6516)
PHONE..................................713 351-3000
Douglas E Brooks, *President*
Scott M Heck, *COO*
Greg Smith, *Vice Pres*
Tiffany J Thom, *CFO*
Charles Wampler, *Bd of Directors*
EMP: 11
SALES (est): 654.1MM
SALES (corp-wide): 658.8MM **Privately Held**
WEB: www.energyxxi.com
SIC: 1311 Crude petroleum & natural gas production
PA: Cexxi, Inc.
4514 Cole Ave Ste 1175
Dallas TX 75205
214 420-7710

(G-9641)
ENERGY XXI LTD
1021 Main St Ste 2626 (77002-6516)
PHONE..................................713 351-3000
Bruce W Busmire, *Principal*
Terry Norris, *Manager*
Lisa Tivet, *Clerk*
EMP: 30

SALES (est): 1.5MM **Privately Held**
WEB: www.energyxxi.com
SIC: 1311 Crude petroleum & natural gas

(G-9642)
ENERGY XXI USA INC
1021 Main St Ste 2626 (77002-6516)
PHONE..................................713 351-3000
Ben Marchive, *CEO*
Granger Anderson, *President*
Steve Nelson, *Vice Pres*
Glen Priestley, *Vice Pres*
David Edwards, *Purchasing*
EMP: 200
SQ FT: 70,000
SALES (est): 42.5MM
SALES (corp-wide): 658.8MM **Privately Held**
WEB: www.energyxxi.com
SIC: 1382 Oil & gas exploration services
HQ: Energy Xxi Gulf Coast, Inc.
1021 Main St Ste 2626
Houston TX 77002

(G-9643)
ENERVEST LTD (PA)
1001 Fannin St Ste 800 (77002-6707)
PHONE..................................713 659-3500
John B Walker, *CEO*
Ken Mariani, *President*
Judson B Walker, *President*
Kevin M Miller, *Managing Dir*
Mike Angus, *Superintendent*
EMP: 58
SQ FT: 11,500
SALES (est): 524.2MM **Privately Held**
WEB: www.enervest.net
SIC: 1311 1382 Crude petroleum & natural gas production; oil & gas exploration services

(G-9644)
ENERVEST OPERATING LLC (HQ)
1001 Fannin St Ste 800 (77002-6707)
PHONE..................................713 659-3500
John B Walker, *CEO*
Mark Houser, *Vice Pres*
Josh Price, *Foreman/Supr*
L Todd Guest,
James M Vanderhider,
EMP: 20
SALES (est): 159MM **Privately Held**
WEB: www.enervest.net
SIC: 1382 Oil & gas exploration services

(G-9645)
ENGIE RETAIL LLC
Also Called: Think Energy
11807 Westheimer Rd # 550 (77077-6790)
PHONE..................................713 636-1127
Greg Chapman, *Manager*
Michael Petrini, *Manager*
Sayun Sukduang,
Jason Austin,
David Coffman,
EMP: 33
SALES (est): 4.7MM
SALES (corp-wide): 19.1B **Privately Held**
WEB: www.mythinkenergy.com
SIC: 3825 Digital panel meters, electricity measuring
HQ: Engie North America Inc.
1360 Post Oak Blvd # 400
Houston TX 77056
713 636-0000

(G-9646)
ENGINEERED CSTM SOLUTIONS LLC
Also Called: E C S
13720 Fm 529 Rd Ste 200 (77041-2691)
PHONE..................................832 598-2083
Chau M Nguyen,
EMP: 13
SALES (est): 3.2MM **Privately Held**
WEB:
www.engineeredcustomsolutions.com
SIC: 3533 Oil field machinery & equipment

(G-9647)
ENGLOBAL CONSTANT POWER INC
1400 N Sam Houston Pkwy E S (77032-2966)
PHONE..................................713 880-6200
William Coskey, *CEO*
Frank Ivester, *President*
James Dorsey, *Senior VP*
EMP: 200 **EST:** 1986
SQ FT: 32,000
SALES (est): 44.8MM
SALES (corp-wide): 56.4MM **Publicly Held**
WEB: www.englobal.com
SIC: 3629 3694 Battery chargers, rectifying or nonrotating; engine electrical equipment
PA: Englobal Corporation
654 N Sam Houston Pkwy E # 400
Houston TX 77060
281 878-1000

(G-9648)
ENI PETROLEUM US LLC
1201 La St Ste 3500 (77002)
PHONE..................................713 393-6100
Robert White,
EMP: 150
SALES (est): 8.3MM
SALES (corp-wide): 31.5B **Privately Held**
SIC: 1311 Crude petroleum & natural gas
HQ: Eni Petroleum Co. Inc.
1201 La St Ste 3500
Houston TX 77002
713 393-6100

(G-9649)
ENI USA INC
1200 Smith St Ste 1700 (77002-4372)
PHONE..................................713 393-6100
Lucianio Vasques, *President*
Fabrizio Trilli, *Managing Dir*
Corinna Carbone, *Vice Pres*
Gary Clifford, *Vice Pres*
Andrew Lees, *Vice Pres*
▲ **EMP:** 300
SALES (est): 10.2MM
SALES (corp-wide): 31.5B **Privately Held**
WEB: www.eni.com
SIC: 1382 Oil & gas exploration services
PA: Eni Spa
Piazzale Enrico Mattei 1
Roma RM 00144
064 123-581

(G-9650)
ENPRO INDUSTRIES INC
Also Called: Texolon
6455 Clara Rd Ste 300 (77041-5389)
PHONE..................................713 983-4222
Maya Ramachandran, *Engineer*
Joe Mattingly, *Branch Mgr*
Paul Vaut, *Planning Mgr*
Mark De Guia, *Technical Staff*
EMP: 40
SALES (corp-wide): 1.2B **Publicly Held**
WEB: www.safety-culture-training.com
SIC: 3053 Gaskets & sealing devices
PA: Enpro Industries, Inc.
5605 Carnegie Blvd # 500
Charlotte NC 28209
704 731-1500

(G-9651)
ENPRO INDUSTRIES INC
10633 W Little York Rd # 300 (77041-4052)
PHONE..................................713 983-4200
Mohsin Syed, *Controller*
Woody Woodworth, *Branch Mgr*
EMP: 10
SALES (corp-wide): 1.2B **Publicly Held**
WEB: www.safety-culture-training.com
SIC: 3053 Gaskets & sealing devices
PA: Enpro Industries, Inc.
5605 Carnegie Blvd # 500
Charlotte NC 28209
704 731-1500

(G-9652)
ENSCO INTERNATIONAL INC (HQ)
Also Called: Valaris Hereunder Ensco Intl
5847 San Felipe St # 330 (77057-3000)
PHONE..................................800 423-8006
Daniel W Rabun, *Ch of Bd*
Carl Trowll, *President*
William Chadwick, *COO*
Jonathan Baksht, *Exec VP*
Christopher Johnston, *Vice Pres*
◆ **EMP:** 81
SALES (est): 1.2B
SALES (corp-wide): 2B **Privately Held**
WEB: www.valaris.com
SIC: 1381 Drilling oil & gas wells
PA: Valaris Plc
78 Cannon Street Cannon Place
London EC4N
207 659-4660

(G-9653)
ENSEMBLE THEATRE
3535 Main St (77002-9529)
PHONE..................................713 520-0055
Argentina M James, *Ch of Bd*
Hasting Stuart, *President*
Janette L Cosley, *Exec Dir*
Kassandra Campbell, *Director*
Emma Williams, *Executive Asst*
EMP: 12 **EST:** 1976
SQ FT: 3,000
SALES: 2.2MM **Privately Held**
WEB: www.ensemblehouston.com
SIC: 7922 2337 Theatrical companies; women's & misses' suits & coats

(G-9654)
ENSERCO MIDSTREAM LLC
8847 W Sam Houston Pkwy N (77040-5668)
PHONE..................................713 341-7378
Craig Kelbel, *Principal*
EMP: 10
SALES (est): 1.2MM **Privately Held**
WEB: www.twineagle.com
SIC: 1389 Oil field services

(G-9655)
ENSIGN INTL ENRGY SVCS INC
450 Gears Rd Ste 777 (77067-4522)
PHONE..................................281 872-7770
Robert Geddes, *President*
Robert H Geddes, *President*
Brenda Rodriguez, *Buyer*
Timothy Lemke, *Treasurer*
Crystal Milsaps, *Chief Acct*
EMP: 40
SALES (est): 8.5MM **Privately Held**
SIC: 1389 Oil field services

(G-9656)
ENSIGN MANAGEMENT LLC
5875 N Sam Houston Pkwy W (77086-1561)
PHONE..................................281 403-6304
Brett Pennington, *CEO*
Stephen Goldfarb, *CFO*
EMP: 33
SQ FT: 161,000
SALES (est): 2MM
SALES (corp-wide): 12.2MM **Privately Held**
SIC: 1389 Gas field services; oil field services
PA: Ensign Natural Resources Llc
5875 N Sam Houston Pkwy W # 600
Houston TX 77086
281 800-3400

(G-9657)
ENSIGN UNITED STATES DRLG INC (HQ)
15015 Vickery Dr (77032-2554)
P.O. Box 17805, Denver CO (80217-0805)
PHONE..................................303 292-1206
Edward D Kautz, *President*
Jackie Crader, *Superintendent*
Blake N Barson, *Principal*
Selby W Porter, *Principal*
N Murray Edwards, *Chairman*
▼ **EMP:** 40
SALES (est): 1.1B
SALES (corp-wide): 1.2B **Privately Held**
SIC: 1381 Drilling oil & gas wells

PA: Ensign Energy Services Inc
400 5 Ave Sw Suite 1000
Calgary AB T2P 0
403 262-1361

(G-9658)
ENSIGN US SOUTHERN DRLG LLC
15015 Vickery Dr (77032-2554)
PHONE..................................303 292-1206
Robert Geddes, *Mng Member*
Glenn Dagenais,
Suzanne Davies,
Edwart Kautz,
Michael Nuss,
EMP: 14 **EST:** 2011
SALES (est): 1.7MM **Privately Held**
SIC: 1381 Drilling oil & gas wells

(G-9659)
ENSINGER SPECIAL POLYMERS INC
12331 Cutten Rd (77066-1807)
P.O. Box 691728 (77269-1728)
PHONE..................................281 580-3600
Christian Ranallo, *CEO*
Anthony Scanlin, *President*
Tony Scanlin, *General Mgr*
Tracy Muong, *Purchasing*
EMP: 47
SQ FT: 26,000
SALES (est): 10MM
SALES (corp-wide): 533.1MM **Privately Held**
WEB: www.ensingerspi.com
SIC: 3089 Injection molding of plastics
HQ: Ensinger Industries, Inc.
365 Meadowlands Blvd
Washington PA 15301
724 746-6050

(G-9660)
ENSOSOFT LLC
16307 S Temple Dr (77095-5919)
PHONE..................................713 360-4841
Michael T Letan,
Noor Alnahhas,
EMP: 17
SALES (est): 82.4K **Privately Held**
WEB: www.ensosoft.com
SIC: 7373 1382 Systems software development services; oil & gas exploration services

(G-9661)
ENTERPRISE GAS PROCESSING LLC
2727 North Loop W Ste 700 (77008-1060)
P.O. Box 4324 (77210-4324)
PHONE..................................713 381-4068
Michael A Creel, *President*
A James Teague, *COO*
William Ordemann, *Exec VP*
Jesse Radvansky, *Exec VP*
Kevin C Bodenhamer, *Senior VP*
EMP: 40
SALES (est): 3.7MM
SALES (corp-wide): 32.7B **Publicly Held**
WEB: www.enterpriseproducts.com
SIC: 1321 Natural gas liquids
HQ: Enterprise Products Operating Llc
1100 La St Ste Ste 1000
Houston TX 77002

(G-9662)
ENTERPRISE OFFSHORE DRLG LLC
11700 Katy Fwy Ste 550 (77079-1263)
PHONE..................................832 399-6500
Brad James, *President*
Mike Roth, *Vice Pres*
David Hatcher, *CFO*
Judy Ammann, *Controller*
James Aday, *Manager*
EMP: 300
SQ FT: 2,500
SALES (est): 18.9MM **Privately Held**
WEB: www.enterpriseoffshore.com
SIC: 1381 Drilling oil & gas wells

(G-9663)
ENTERPRISE PRODUCTS COMPANY (HQ)
1100 Louisiana St (77002-5227)
P.O. Box 4324 (77210-4324)
PHONE..................................713 381-6500
Michael J Knesek, *CEO*
Richard H Bachmann, *President*
Randa L Duncan, *President*
Michelle George, *General Mgr*
Kimberly Chesler, *Principal*
◆ **EMP:** 188
SQ FT: 98,110
SALES (est): 2.5B
SALES (corp-wide): 32.7B **Publicly Held**
WEB: www.enterpriseproducts.com
SIC: 1321 4925 Natural gas liquids; gas production and/or distribution
PA: Enterprise Products Partners L.P.
1100 Louisiana St Fl 10
Houston TX 77002
713 381-6500

(G-9664)
ENTERPRISE SVCS LTIN AMER CORP (HQ)
Also Called: Compaq
20555 State Highway 249 (77070-2607)
PHONE..................................703 245-9675
Michael Lawrie, *President*
EMP: 20
SALES (est): 21.5MM
SALES (corp-wide): 19.5B **Publicly Held**
WEB: www.hp.com
SIC: 3571 Personal computers (microcomputers)
PA: Dxc Technology Company
1775 Tysons Blvd Fl 8
Tysons VA 22102
703 245-9675

(G-9665)
ENTRANS INTERNATIONAL LLC
Also Called: Polar Service Centers
7600 E Sam Houston Pkwy N (77049-3000)
P.O. Box 9201, Minneapolis MN (55480-9201)
PHONE..................................281 459-5350
Brian Watson, *Manager*
EMP: 50 **Privately Held**
WEB: www.entransinternational.com
SIC: 3443 5012 7699 Bins, prefabricated metal plate; trailers for trucks, new & used; tank repair
HQ: Entrans International, Llc
1145 Congress Pkwy N
Athens TN 37303
404 845-0083

(G-9666)
ENVEN ENERGY VENTURES LLC
609 Main St Ste 3200 (77002-3276)
PHONE..................................713 335-7000
Andrew Schaefer, *Vice Pres*
Eddie Stanton, *Foreman/Supr*
Jonathan C Garrett, *Mng Member*
Nicholas Gibbens, *Manager*
Kayla Baird, *Officer*
EMP: 23
SALES (est): 34MM **Privately Held**
WEB: www.enven.com
SIC: 1382 Oil & gas exploration services

(G-9667)
ENVIROCAL INC
4006 Windsong Trl (77084-3218)
PHONE..................................832 296-4205
Vikraman Raghavan, *President*
Anid Johnson, *Principal*
Danny Williams, *Director*
EMP: 11
SALES (est): 2.5MM **Privately Held**
WEB: www.ipigs.net
SIC: 3533 Oil field machinery & equipment

(G-9668)
ENVIROKIND INC
Also Called: Preservo Pnt & Coatings Mfg Co
75 Southbelt Indus Dr (77047-7011)
P.O. Box 20125 (77225-0125)
PHONE..................................713 434-9900
Robert Schneider, *President*
Pamela Clark, *Corp Secy*
▼ **EMP:** 10 **EST:** 1946
SQ FT: 16,000
SALES (est): 1.7MM **Privately Held**
WEB: www.preservo.com
SIC: 2851 Paints & paint additives

(G-9669)
ENVIROSENSE LLC (PA)
18527 Berry Leaf Ct (77084-5644)
PHONE..................................281 828-8989
EMP: 23
SQ FT: 2,100 **Privately Held**
SIC: 3825 Instruments to measure electricity

(G-9670)
ENVIROTECH DRILLING SERVICES
4214 Creekmont Dr (77091-5328)
P.O. Box 19064 (77224-9064)
PHONE..................................832 493-8063
David Dreybuck, *President*
Jaime Vasquez, *Vice Pres*
EMP: 18
SALES (est): 1.6MM **Privately Held**
SIC: 1381 Service well drilling

(G-9671)
EOG RESOURCES INC (PA)
1111 Bagby Sky Lbby 2 (77002)
P.O. Box 4362 (77210-4362)
PHONE..................................713 651-7000
William R Thomas, *Ch of Bd*
Ezra Y Yacob, *President*
Kande Lewis, *Chairman*
Lloyd W Helms Jr, *COO*
Kit Reynolds, *Counsel*
EMP: 188
SALES (est): 17.3B **Publicly Held**
WEB: www.eogresources.com
SIC: 1311 Crude petroleum production; natural gas production

(G-9672)
EOG RESOURCES INVESTMENTS INC
333 Clay St Ste 4200 (77002-4006)
PHONE..................................713 651-6914
EMP: 11
SALES (est): 855.6K
SALES (corp-wide): 17.2B **Publicly Held**
SIC: 1382 Oil And Gas Exploration Services
PA: Eog Resources, Inc.
1111 Bagby Sky Lbby 2
Houston TX 77002
713 651-7000

(G-9673)
EP ENERGY CORPORATION (PA)
601 Travis St Ste 1400 (77002-3253)
P.O. Box 4660 (77210-4660)
PHONE..................................713 997-1000
Alan R Crain Jr, *Ch of Bd*
Russell E Parker, *President*
Susan Grantham, *Counsel*
Raymond J Ambrose, *Senior VP*
Chad D England, *Senior VP*
EMP: 17 **EST:** 2012
SALES (est): 820MM **Privately Held**
WEB: www.epenergy.com
SIC: 1311 Crude petroleum production; natural gas production

(G-9674)
EP ENERGY E&P COMPANY LP (DH)
601 Travis St Ste 1400 (77002-3253)
P.O. Box 4660 (77210-4660)
PHONE..................................713 997-1200
Clayton A Carrell, *Exec VP*
John D Jensen, *Exec VP*
Joan M Gallagher, *Senior VP*
Dane E Whitehead, *CFO*
Greg Beard, *Mng Member*
EMP: 54
SALES (est): 526.6MM
SALES (corp-wide): 820MM **Privately Held**
WEB: www.epenergy.com
SIC: 1382 Oil & gas exploration services

(G-9675)
EP ENERGY LLC (HQ)
601 Travis St Ste 1400 (77002-3253)
P.O. Box 4660 (77210-4660)
PHONE..................................713 997-1200
Patricia Francis, *Counsel*
Frank Falleri, *Vice Pres*
Kyle McCuen, *Vice Pres*
Jnmes Gallyer, *Production*
Steve Watson, *Production*
EMP: 19 **EST:** 2012
SALES (est): 820MM **Privately Held**
WEB: www.epenergy.com
SIC: 1311 Crude petroleum & natural gas; crude petroleum production
PA: Ep Energy Corporation
601 Travis St Ste 1400
Houston TX 77002
713 997-1000

(G-9676)
EP ENERGY MANAGEMENT LLC (HQ)
601 Travis St Ste 1400 (77002-3253)
P.O. Box 2511 (77252-2511)
PHONE..................................713 997-1000
William Griffin, *Senior VP*
Thomas Hart, *Senior VP*
William Smolik, *Senior VP*
Dane Whitehead, *CFO*
Margaret Roark, *Admin Sec*
EMP: 21
SALES (est): 61.1MM
SALES (corp-wide): 820MM **Privately Held**
WEB: www.epenergy.com
SIC: 4922 1321 Natural gas transmission; natural gas liquids production
PA: Ep Energy Corporation
601 Travis St Ste 1400
Houston TX 77002
713 997-1000

(G-9677)
EP ENERGY RESALE COMPANY LLC (DH)
601 Travis St Ste 1400 (77002-3253)
P.O. Box 4660 (77210-4660)
PHONE..................................713 997-1000
Ralph Alexander, *Director*
EMP: 12
SALES (est): 61.1MM
SALES (corp-wide): 820MM **Privately Held**
SIC: 2911 Petroleum refining

(G-9678)
EPD INTERNATIONAL LTD
15200 North Fwy (77090-6306)
PHONE..................................713 923-1191
John Janik, *Partner*
▲ **EMP:** 70
SQ FT: 18,000
SALES (est): 11.4MM **Privately Held**
WEB: www.electronicpowerdesign.com
SIC: 3621 Motors & generators

(G-9679)
EPE INDUSTRIES USA INC
Also Called: Epe USA
6615 Roxburgh Dr Ste 200 (77041-5211)
PHONE..................................800 315-0336
Darryl Lambert, *Branch Mgr*
EMP: 9 **Privately Held**
WEB: www.epeusa.com
SIC: 3086 Packaging & shipping materials, foamed plastic
HQ: Epe Industries Usa, Inc.
17835 Newhope St Ste G
Fountain Valley CA 92708

(G-9680)
EPIC DISTRIBUTION LLC
9260 Bryant St (77075-1104)
PHONE..................................346 308-6038
EMP: 10
SALES (corp-wide): 826.1K **Privately Held**
WEB: www.epicpiping.com
SIC: 3498 Fabricated pipe & fittings
HQ: Epic Distribution, Llc
1395 Horse Creek Dr
Frisco TX 75036
214 733-2887

G E O G R A P H I C

(G-9681)
EPIC ENERGY RESOURCES INC
10330 Lake Rd Ste D (77070-1696)
PHONE....................281 419-3742
Alan Carnrite, *President*
W Robert Eissler, *Principal*
Robert Ferguson, *Principal*
Martin Lipper, *Principal*
Jack W Schanck, *Principal*
EMP: 133
SQ FT: 4,150
SALES (est): 10.6MM **Privately Held**
WEB: www.1epic.com
SIC: 8742 1381 Business planning & organizing services; drilling oil & gas wells

(G-9682)
EPL OIL & GAS INC
919 Milam St Ste 1650 (77002-5360)
PHONE....................713 228-0711
EMP: 17 **Privately Held**
SIC: 1382 Exploration/Production Gas & Oil
HQ: Epl Oil & Gas, Inc.
919 Milam St Ste 1650
Houston TX 77002
713 228-0711

(G-9683)
EPOCHTIMES PUBLIC MEDIA INC
Also Called: Epoch Mdia Group Suthern Texas
7001 Corporate Dr Ste 206 (77036-5115)
PHONE....................713 790-0815
Shaoling Huang, *President*
Xuewei Chen, *Principal*
Michael Hwang, *Treasurer*
EMP: 10
SALES: 941.1K **Privately Held**
WEB: www.epochtimes.com
SIC: 2711 Newspapers: publishing only, not printed on site

(G-9684)
EPSILON ENERGY USA INC
16945 Northchase Dr # 1610 (77060-2152)
PHONE....................281 670-0002
Michael Raleigh, *CEO*
B Lane Bond, *CFO*
Aerayna Flores, *Finance*
Paul Atwood, *Director*
Lane Bond, *Officer*
EMP: 10
SALES: 52.7MM **Privately Held**
WEB: www.epsilonenergyltd.com
SIC: 1382 Oil & gas exploration services

(G-9685)
EQUILON ENTERPRISES LLC (HQ)
Also Called: Shell Oil Products U S
910 Louisiana St Ste 2 (77002-4906)
PHONE....................713 767-5337
Lynn Elsenhans, *President*
Lisa A Davis, *President*
R R Caplan, *Vice Pres*
S P Methvin, *Vice Pres*
D J Pirret, *Vice Pres*
◆ **EMP:** 500 **EST:** 1998
SALES (est): 702.5MM
SALES (corp-wide): 344.8B **Privately Held**
WEB: www.equilonmotivaequiva.com
SIC: 2911 4612 2992 5172 Petroleum refining; crude petroleum pipelines; lubricating oils; petroleum products
PA: Royal Dutch Shell Plc
Shell Centre
London SE1 7
207 934-1234

(G-9686)
EQUINOR GULF OF MEXICO LLC (DH)
2107 Citywest Blvd # 100 (77042-2827)
PHONE....................713 918-8200
Carri Lockhart, *CEO*
EMP: 14 **EST:** 2004
SALES (est): 54.7MM **Privately Held**
SIC: 1382 5172 Oil & gas exploration services; crude oil

HQ: Equinor Us Holdings Inc.
120 Long Ridge Rd 3eo1
Stamford CT 06902
203 978-6900

(G-9687)
EQUINOR US OPERATIONS LLC (DH)
2107 Citywest Blvd # 100 (77042-2827)
PHONE....................713 918-8200
Bent Rune Solheim, *CEO*
Kevin Ford, *Opers Staff*
Mark Miller, *Opers Staff*
Kim Soika, *Opers Staff*
Irfan Ahmed, *Engineer*
▲ **EMP:** 39
SALES (est): 9.4MM **Privately Held**
SIC: 1382 Oil & gas exploration services
HQ: Equinor Us Holdings Inc.
120 Long Ridge Rd 3eo1
Stamford CT 06902
203 978-6900

(G-9688)
EQUINOR USA E&P INC (DH)
Also Called: Statoil USA E&P, Inc.
2107 Citywest Blvd # 100 (77042-2827)
PHONE....................713 918-8200
Carri Lockhart, *CEO*
John Knight, *Exec VP*
Morten Loktu, *Exec VP*
Irene Rummelhoff, *Exec VP*
Ivar Aasheim, *Vice Pres*
▲ **EMP:** 28
SALES (est): 54.7MM **Privately Held**
WEB: www.equinor.com
SIC: 1382 Oil & gas exploration services
HQ: Equinor Gulf Of Mexico Llc
2107 Citywest Blvd # 100
Houston TX 77042
713 918-8200

(G-9689)
EQUISTAR CHEMICALS LP (DH)
Also Called: Lyondellbasell
1221 Mckinney St Ste 300 (77010-2036)
P.O. Box 3448 (77253-3448)
PHONE....................713 309-7200
Bhavesh V Patel, *CEO*
Dan Smith, *General Mgr*
Thea N Bullard, *Principal*
Dave Balderston, *Vice Pres*
Calvin Collard, *Vice Pres*
◆ **EMP:** 800
SALES (est): 986.9MM
SALES (corp-wide): 34.9B **Privately Held**
WEB: www.lyondellbasell.com
SIC: 2869 2822 Olefins; ethylene; butadiene (industrial organic chemical); ethylene oxide; polyethylene, chlorosulfonated (hypalon)
HQ: Lyondell Chemical Company
1221 Mckinney St Ste 300
Houston TX 77010
713 309-7200

(G-9690)
ERG RESOURCES LLC
333 Clay St Ste 4400 (77002-4105)
PHONE....................713 812-1800
Scott Y Wood, *President*
Kathy Friesen, *Accountant*
Phillip Jewett, *Exploration*
EMP: 23
SQ FT: 5,000
SALES (est): 3.6MM **Privately Held**
WEB: www.ergresources.com
SIC: 1382 Oil & gas exploration services

(G-9691)
ERHC ENERGY INC (PA)
5444 Westheimr Rd # 1440 (77056-5306)
PHONE....................713 626-4700
Peter C Ntephe, *President*
Gwen Hambrick, *VP Admin*
EMP: 9
SALES (est): 1.6MM **Privately Held**
WEB: www.erhc.com
SIC: 1382 1389 Oil & gas exploration services; oil field services; gas field services

(G-9692)
ERIN ENERGY CORPORATION
1330 Post Oak Blvd # 2250 (77056-3031)
PHONE....................713 797-2940

EMP: 64
SQ FT: 13,200
SALES (est): 101.1MM **Privately Held**
WEB:
SIC: 1381 Drilling oil & gas wells

(G-9693)
ERNMEX INTERNTATIONAL INC
12543 Unison Rd (77044-2323)
PHONE....................281 458-0152
Edgar Papilla, *President*
Bruce Partin, *President*
EMP: 20
SQ FT: 40,000
SALES (est): 3.5MM **Privately Held**
WEB: www.enermex.us
SIC: 3441 3533 Building components, structural steel; oil & gas field machinery

(G-9694)
ERSKINE ENERGY LLC
Also Called: Erskine Energy Prod Companies
11700 Katy Fwy Ste 1200 (77079-1231)
PHONE....................281 225-7223
Jorge Dimopulos, *CFO*
Gregory W Hutson, *Principal*
EMP: 27
SQ FT: 4,000
SALES (est): 3.2MM **Privately Held**
SIC: 1382 Oil & gas exploration services

(G-9695)
ESBEE SIGNS INC
Also Called: Esbee Sign Sysyems
5322 Addicks Satsuma Rd B (77084-6874)
P.O. Box 842083 (77284-2083)
PHONE....................281 550-4577
Saifudin Karimjee, *President*
Saif Karimjee, *Engineer*
EMP: 10
SQ FT: 10,000
SALES (est): 300K **Privately Held**
WEB: www.esbee.com
SIC: 3993 Electric signs

(G-9696)
ESEIS INC
Also Called: E Seis
12012 Wickchester Ln # 60 (77079-1229)
PHONE....................281 531-1447
Robert Loticcolo, *President*
Dan Morris, *President*
Tammy Price, *Manager*
EMP: 15
SQ FT: 9,000
SALES (est): 1.9MM **Privately Held**
WEB: www.e-seis.com
SIC: 1382 Oil & gas exploration services

(G-9697)
ESP ENTERPRISES INC
Also Called: ESP Services
13161 Misty Willow Dr (77070-5635)
PHONE....................281 444-2377
Steve Phelan, *President*
Roland Sierra, *Opers Mgr*
Conor Stanley, *Sr Project Mgr*
Richard Torres, *Manager*
EMP: 75
SQ FT: 3,000
SALES (est): 4MM **Privately Held**
WEB: www.espenterprisesinc.com
SIC: 4011 1731 3829 Railroads, line-haul operating; electrical work; electronic controls installation; voice, data & video wiring contractor; measuring & controlling devices

(G-9698)
ESP SAFETY INC
4001 W Sam Houston Pkwy N # 150 (77043-1237)
PHONE....................972 310-0754
Ivan Lukitsa, *CEO*
EMP: 35 **EST:** 2007
SALES (est): 2.6MM **Privately Held**
WEB: www.espsafetyinc.com
SIC: 3842 Personal safety equipment

(G-9699)
ESPITIAS CABINET & DOOR MAKERS
8529 Rannie Rd (77080-2024)
PHONE....................713 329-9515
Fillmeno Espitia, *President*
Clemente Espitias, *Director*

EMP: 24
SALES (est): 2.9MM **Privately Held**
WEB: www.classiccabinetdoors.com
SIC: 2434 Wood kitchen cabinets

(G-9700)
ESSA PHARMACEUTICALS
2130 W Holcombe Blvd # 900 (77030-3310)
PHONE....................832 831-5958
David Parkinson, *CEO*
Peter Virsik, *Exec VP*
EMP: 20
SALES (est): 1.5MM **Privately Held**
WEB: www.essapharma.com
SIC: 2834 Pharmaceutical preparations

(G-9701)
ESSER CASKET CO LLC
Also Called: Esser Caskets
7100 Cavalcade St (77028-5902)
PHONE....................713 225-5548
E Fred Esser III,
EMP: 40 **EST:** 1949
SQ FT: 30,000
SALES (est): 4MM **Privately Held**
WEB: www.essermfg.com
SIC: 3995 Burial caskets

(G-9702)
ESSILOR LABORATORIES AMER INC
Also Called: Duffens Optical
3625 Willowbend Blvd # 110 (77054-1118)
P.O. Box 20545 (77225-0545)
PHONE....................713 663-3000
Sanya Helguero, *Branch Mgr*
Michelle Rivera, *Manager*
EMP: 50
SQ FT: 6,000
SALES (corp-wide): 1.7MM **Privately Held**
WEB: www.essilorusa.com
SIC: 3851 Eyeglasses, lenses & frames
HQ: Essilor Laboratories Of America, Inc.
13515 N Stemmons Fwy
Dallas TX 75234
972 241-4141

(G-9703)
ETC INTRASTATE PROCUREMENT LLC
Also Called: Energy Transfer Company
1300 Main St (77002-6803)
PHONE....................713 989-2688
EMP: 1200
SALES (est): 8MM
SALES (corp-wide): 42.1B **Publicly Held**
SIC: 1311 Crude Petroleum/Natural Gas Production
PA: Energy Transfer Equity, L.P.
3738 Oak Lawn Ave
Dallas TX 75225
214 981-0700

(G-9704)
ETHOS ENERGY LP
2800 North Loop W # 1100 (77092-8825)
PHONE....................713 336-1300
Mark Dobler, *CEO*
George Gaudette, *President*
Tom Watson, *General Mgr*
Bill Scott, *Business Mgr*
Katrina Papetti, *Counsel*
EMP: 141
SALES (est): 44.2MM **Privately Held**
WEB: www.ethosenergygroup.com
SIC: 3511 Turbines & turbine generator sets

(G-9705)
ETHOSENERGY (USA) LLC (DH)
2800 North Loop W (77092-8838)
PHONE....................713 812-2300
Bob Keiller, *CEO*
George Gaudette, *President*
Eric Roy, *Business Mgr*
Steve Kaczmarek, *Counsel*
Randall Miller, *Vice Pres*
EMP: 34
SALES (est): 14.9MM
SALES (corp-wide): 12.7B **Privately Held**
WEB: www.ethosenergygroup.com
SIC: 3511 Turbines & turbine generator sets

(G-9706)
ETHOSENERGY FIELD SERVICES LLC
6225 W Sam Houston Pkwy N A
(77041-5196)
PHONE...................713 849-8835
Jeffrey Daun, *Regl Sales Mgr*
Ricki Barnstable, *Manager*
EMP: 10
SALES (corp-wide): 12.7B **Privately Held**
WEB: www.ethosenergyfs.com
SIC: 3511 Turbines & turbine generator sets
HQ: Field Ethosenergy Services Llc
10455 Slusher Dr Bldg 12
Santa Fe Springs CA 90670

(G-9707)
ETHOSENERGY LIGHT TURBINES LLC (DH)
6225 W Sam Houston Pkwy N
(77041-5196)
PHONE...................713 849-8800
Kevin Seitzer, *General Mgr*
Virginia Duron, *Mfg Staff*
Julio Vazquez, *Production*
Tyler Clayton, *Project Engr*
Sammy Averett, *Design Engr*
▲ EMP: 82
SALES (est): 13.9MM
SALES (corp-wide): 12.7B **Privately Held**
WEB: www.ethosenergygroup.com
SIC: 3511 Turbines & turbine generator sets

(G-9708)
ETHOSENERGY TC INC
Also Called: Houston Operations
3100 S Sam Houston Pkwy E
(77047-6508)
PHONE...................713 336-1300
Keith Stewart, *Mfg Staff*
Larry Sims, *Branch Mgr*
EMP: 38
SALES (corp-wide): 12.7B **Privately Held**
WEB: www.ethosenergygroup.com
SIC: 3511 Turbines & turbine generator sets
HQ: Ethosenergy Tc, Inc.
2140 Westover Rd
Chicopee MA 01022
802 257-2721

(G-9709)
ETHOSIQ LLC
17121 W Rd Ste 201 Huston (77095)
PHONE...................281 616-5711
Scott Walker, *Mng Member*
Steven Langley, *CTO*
Justin Staley, *Software Engr*
Matthew Allen, *Software Dev*
EMP: 10
SQ FT: 2,000
SALES (est): 1MM **Privately Held**
WEB: www.ethosiq.com
SIC: 7372 Business oriented computer software

(G-9710)
EURECAT U S INCORPORATED (HQ)
1331 Gemini St Ste 310 (77058-2794)
PHONE...................281 218-0669
Frederic Jardin, *President*
Rodrigo Pinto, *Exec VP*
Bruce Cassidy, *Plant Engr*
Rene Perez, *Controller*
Sheila Whiten, *Human Res Dir*
▲ EMP: 12
SQ FT: 69,400
SALES (est): 13.6MM
SALES (corp-wide): 2MM **Privately Held**
WEB: www.eurecat.com
SIC: 2819 Catalysts, chemical
PA: Eurecat Sa
Zone Industrielle Jean Jaures
La Voulte-Sur-Rhone 07800
475 620-402

(G-9711)
EUREKA MIDSTREAM LLC
1111 La St Ste 4520 (77002)
PHONE...................832 203-4544
Gary C Evans, *CEO*
Christopher T Akers, *COO*

Paul Layne, *Senior Engr*
Ryan Crowe, *Planning*
EMP: 36 EST: 2010
SALES (est): 6.5MM **Privately Held**
WEB: www.eurekamidstream.com
SIC: 1382 Oil & gas exploration services
HQ: Eureka Midstream Holdings, Llc
1111 La St Ste 4520
Houston TX 77002
732 203-4544

(G-9712)
EUROTECH INDUSTRIES INC
11701 Brittmoore Park Dr (77041-6923)
PHONE...................713 937-1730
Christopher Mealey, *President*
Gunther Schmitzberger, *Vice Pres*
Valerie Mealey, *Admin Sec*
EMP: 13
SQ FT: 15,000
SALES (est): 1.8MM **Privately Held**
WEB: www.eurotechindustries.com
SIC: 3599 Machine shop, jobbing & repair

(G-9713)
EUTSLER TECHNICAL PRODUCTS INC
3718 Creekmont Dr (77091-5412)
P.O. Box 920818 (77292-0818)
PHONE...................713 686-8209
M T Borski, *President*
Jeff Borski, *Vice Pres*
Ann Eutsler, *Vice Pres*
Jeremy Green, *QC Mgr*
Ken Borski, *Sales Mgr*
EMP: 52 EST: 1964
SQ FT: 45,000
SALES (est): 8.5MM **Privately Held**
WEB: www.eutsler-rubber.com
SIC: 3069 Custom compounding of rubber materials

(G-9714)
EV ENERGY PARTNERS LP (PA)
1001 Fannin St Ste 800 (77002-6707)
PHONE...................713 659-3500
Steven J Pully, *Ch of Bd*
John B Walker, *Ch of Bd*
Michael E Mercer, *President*
Phil Delozier, *Exec VP*
Ryan Flory, *Senior VP*
EMP: 13
SALES: 113.8MM **Publicly Held**
WEB: www.hvstog.com
SIC: 1382 Oil & gas exploration services

(G-9715)
EVANS - HAMILTON INC (PA)
411 N Sam Houston Pkwy E (77060-3543)
PHONE...................281 448-6188
EMP: 32
SQ FT: 5,600
SALES (est): 12.7MM **Privately Held**
WEB: www.evanshamilton.com
SIC: 8748 3577 Environmental consultant; data conversion equipment, media-to-media: computer

(G-9716)
EVEREST SYSTEMS LLC (PA)
16601 Central Green Blvd # 100
(77032-5143)
P.O. Box 458, Spring (77383-0458)
PHONE...................800 575-8966
John Linnell, *President*
Guy Glenn, *Manager*
EMP: 22
SALES (est): 10.8MM **Privately Held**
WEB: www.everestsystemsco.com
SIC: 3444 Sheet metalwork

(G-9717)
EVEREST VALVE COMPANY INC
6612 Avenue U (77011-1236)
P.O. Box 24295 (77229-4295)
PHONE...................713 923-8696
Phillip R Blest, *President*
Braja B Das, *Vice Pres*
David Taylor, *Opers Mgr*
Phillip Das, *Prdtn Mgr*
Felix Sanchez, *Purch Agent*
◆ EMP: 32 EST: 1978
SQ FT: 20,000
SALES (est): 7.2MM **Privately Held**
WEB: www.everestvalveusa.com
SIC: 3491 Industrial valves

(G-9718)
EVERYTHING ENERGY LLC
1201 Fannin St (77002-6929)
PHONE...................713 537-3000
Sheila Dixon, *Credit Mgr*
EMP: 50
SALES (est): 1.8MM **Publicly Held**
WEB: www.everythingenergytx.com
SIC: 8748 3825 Energy conservation consultant; instruments to measure electricity
HQ: Nrg Texas Power Llc
1201 Fannin St
Houston TX 77002
713 537-3000

(G-9719)
EVOLEAP LLC
10333 Richmond Ave # 450 (77042-4244)
PHONE...................832 371-6677
Michael Zaldivar, *CEO*
Prasanna Parthasarathy,
EMP: 11
SALES (est): 459.1K **Privately Held**
WEB: www.evoleap.com
SIC: 8711 7373 7372 Engineering services; computer integrated systems design; prepackaged software

(G-9720)
EVOLVE HOLDINGS INC (PA)
10555 Cossey Rd (77070-6407)
PHONE...................832 375-0099
Tye A Johnson, *President*
Doug Herron, *Division Mgr*
Lindy Devitt, *General Mgr*
Todd Bermont, *Marketing Staff*
Tyndall Overby, *Director*
EMP: 45
SALES (est): 8.6MM **Privately Held**
WEB: www.evolveincorporated.com
SIC: 8711 8741 1796 1629 Engineering services; management services; power generating equipment installation; power plant construction; power generators; building services monitoring controls, automatic

(G-9721)
EVOSITE LLC
7240 Brittmoore Rd # 100 (77041-3225)
PHONE...................713 365-3900
Gabriel Hinchliffe, *Project Mgr*
Andrew Weibust, *Sales Dir*
Edward Diaz, *Sales Staff*
Emma Galvez, *Sales Staff*
Steve Will, *Mng Member*
◆ EMP: 21
SQ FT: 15,000
SALES (est): 3.5MM **Privately Held**
WEB: www.evosite.com
SIC: 2521 2522 Wood office furniture; office furniture, except wood

(G-9722)
EXAMINER NEWSPAPER GROUP INC
4635 Southwest Fwy Ste 320 (77027)
PHONE...................713 526-3617
Ben Rubio, *Manager*
EMP: 15
SALES (est): 602.5K **Privately Held**
SIC: 2711 Newspapers

(G-9723)
EXHIBITCO INC (PA)
1421 Preston St (77002-2129)
PHONE...................713 830-8989
Kevin Adley, *President*
▲ EMP: 15
SALES (est): 1.3MM **Privately Held**
SIC: 2752 7338 7334 Commercial printing, offset; court reporting service; photocopying & duplicating services

(G-9724)
EXIDE TECHNOLOGIES LLC
Also Called: Exide Batteries
14820 North Fwy (77090-6649)
PHONE...................281 443-0382
Neil Ruse, *Manager*
EMP: 20
SALES (corp-wide): 2.1B **Privately Held**
WEB: www.exide.com
SIC: 5013 3629 Automotive batteries; battery chargers, rectifying or nonrotating

PA: Exide Technologies, Llc
13000 Drfeld Pkwy Bldg 20
Milton GA 30004
678 566-9000

(G-9725)
EXILE TECHNOLOGIES CORPORATION (HQ)
7007 Pinemont Dr (77040-6601)
PHONE...................713 343-5662
Robbin B Adams, *Exec VP*
Walter R Wheeler, *Exec VP*
Lance Heap, *Vice Pres*
Chung Tan, *Vice Pres*
Chung-L Tan, *Research*
▲ EMP: 29
SQ FT: 42,000
SALES (est): 4.7MM
SALES (corp-wide): 87.8MM **Publicly Held**
WEB: www.exiletech.com
SIC: 3829 Geophysical & meteorological testing equipment
PA: Geospace Technologies Corporation
7007 Pinemont Dr
Houston TX 77040
713 986-4444

(G-9726)
EXOTHERM CORPORATION
888 Wilcrest Dr (77042-1350)
PHONE...................713 981-9100
Hubert E Magee Jr, *President*
H E Magee Jr, *President*
John Pendergraff, *Engineer*
Jeffrey Adams, *Controller*
EMP: 11
SALES (est): 10MM **Privately Held**
WEB: www.exotherm.com
SIC: 3433 3567 Heating equipment, except electric; industrial furnaces & ovens

(G-9727)
EXPLOITATION COMPANY LLP
Also Called: Energy Xxi
1021 Main St Ste 2626 (77002-6516)
PHONE...................713 351-3000
John Schiller, *Partner*
West Griffin, *Partner*
Rickey Giroir, *Superintendent*
Joel Guichard, *Superintendent*
Michael Renken, *Superintendent*
EMP: 130
SQ FT: 5,000
SALES (est): 17.5MM
SALES (corp-wide): 658.8MM **Privately Held**
WEB: www.energyxxi.com
SIC: 1382 Oil & gas exploration services
HQ: Energy Xxi Gulf Coast, Inc.
1021 Main St Ste 2626
Houston TX 77002

(G-9728)
EXPOTECH USA INC
10700 Rockley Rd (77099-3516)
P.O. Box 821172 (77282-1172)
PHONE...................281 879-8998
Vijay Dhingra, *President*
Abhishek Dhingra, *Vice Pres*
Ash Dhingra, *Human Res Mgr*
Hassan Alizadeh, *Info Tech Dir*
▼ EMP: 22
SQ FT: 46,000
SALES (est): 8MM **Privately Held**
WEB: www.expotechusa.com
SIC: 3826 5049 Analytical instruments; scientific instruments; laboratory equipment, except medical or dental

(G-9729)
EXPRESS ENERGY SERVICES GP LLC
9800 Richmond Ave Ste 700 (77042-4685)
PHONE...................713 625-7400
Tyler Krimm, *District Mgr*
Harry Lehman, *District Mgr*
Hector Garcia, *Business Mgr*
Jeff Bratcher, *Vice Pres*
Justin Morgan, *Project Mgr*
EMP: 693
SALES (est): 37.4MM
SALES (corp-wide): 770.4MM **Privately Held**
WEB: www.eeslp.com
SIC: 1389 Oil field services

PA: Express Energy Services Operating, Lp
9800 Richmond Ave Ste 500
Houston TX 77042
713 625-7400

(G-9730)
EXPRESS ENERGY SVCS OPER LP (PA)
9800 Richmond Ave Ste 500 (77042-4853)
PHONE....................................713 625-7400
Stuart Bodden, *CEO*
Donnie Goodwin, *Partner*
Mary Collins, *General Mgr*
Darron Anderson, *General Ptnr*
Mathew Garcia, *District Mgr*
EMP: 12
SALES (est): 770.4MM **Privately Held**
WEB: www.eeslp.com
SIC: 1389 Oil field services

(G-9731)
EXPRESS FREIGHT SYSTEMS INC
Also Called: Central Plastics
1215 Seamist Dr (77008-6145)
P.O. Box 87218 (77287-7218)
PHONE....................................713 861-1888
Edwin Sy, *President*
Robert Burratt, *Vice Pres*
◆ **EMP:** 10
SQ FT: 50,000
SALES (est): 2.6MM **Privately Held**
WEB: www.expfreight.com
SIC: 2821 Plastics materials & resins

(G-9732)
EXPRESS PLASTIC CORPORATION
11500 Main St Ste 144 (77025-5914)
PHONE....................................713 664-9588
Zhijian Mao, *Director*
Sheree H Lee, *Director*
Wen Cheih Liu, *Director*
Wayne Wang, *Director*
▲ **EMP:** 10
SALES (est): 1.7MM **Privately Held**
SIC: 2673 Bags: plastic, laminated & coated

(G-9733)
EXPRO AMERICAS LLC
10815 Huffmeister Rd (77065-3105)
PHONE....................................281 977-2600
Austin Smedley, *District Mgr*
Jet Shelton, *Project Mgr*
Travis Stone, *Project Mgr*
Chad Castille, *Opers Spvr*
James Latiolais, *Opers Staff*
EMP: 30 **Privately Held**
WEB: www.exprogroup.com
SIC: 1389 Oil field services
HQ: Expro Americas, Llc
1311 Brdfeld Blvd Ste 400
Houston TX 77084

(G-9734)
EXPRO AMERICAS LLC (DH)
Also Called: Expo Group
1311 Brdfeld Blvd Ste 400 (77084)
PHONE....................................713 463-9776
Michael Jardon, *President*
Chance Knight, *Business Mgr*
Tony Vaughn, *COO*
Alistair Geddes, *Exec VP*
Jean Moritz, *Vice Pres*
◆ **EMP:** 30
SALES (est): 55.4MM **Privately Held**
WEB: www.exprogroup.com
SIC: 7353 3533 Oil equipment rental services; oil & gas drilling rigs & equipment

(G-9735)
EXTERRAN CORPORATION (PA)
11000 Equity Dr Ste 100 (77041-8235)
PHONE....................................281 836-7000
Mark R Sotir, *Ch of Bd*
Andrew J Way, *President*
Mike Redding, *Business Mgr*
Girish K Saligram, *COO*
Stephan Selinidis, *Counsel*
EMP: 43
SQ FT: 58,857

SALES: 1.3B **Publicly Held**
WEB: www.exterran.com
SIC: 1311 1389 4923 Natural gas production; gas compressing (natural gas) at the fields; gas transmission & distribution

(G-9736)
EXTERRAN ENERGY SOLUTIONS LP (HQ)
11000 Equity Dr (77041-8234)
PHONE....................................281 836-7000
Andrew Way, *Managing Prtnr*
Kory Martin, *Materials Mgr*
◆ **EMP:** 148
SQ FT: 35,000
SALES (est): 344.4MM
SALES (corp-wide): 1.3B **Publicly Held**
WEB: www.exterran.com
SIC: 7353 1389 3569 3589 Oil equipment rental services; oil field services; gas field services; gas producers (machinery); water treatment equipment, industrial; engineering services
PA: Exterran Corporation
11000 Equity Dr Ste 100
Houston TX 77041
281 836-7000

(G-9737)
EXTERRAN TRINIDAD LLC (DH)
Also Called: Exterran Energy
12001 N Huston Rosslyn Rd (77086-3212)
PHONE....................................281 921-9337
Andrew J Way, *President*
Girish K Saligram, *President*
Valerie L Banner, *Vice Pres*
Ray Carney, *Vice Pres*
Jon C Biro, *CFO*
▲ **EMP:** 300
SQ FT: 67,937
SALES (est): 209.8MM
SALES (corp-wide): 1.3B **Publicly Held**
SIC: 7353 5084 1389 Oil field equipment, rental or leasing; petroleum industry machinery; gas compressing (natural gas) at the fields
HQ: Exterran Energy Solutions, L.P.
11000 Equity Dr
Houston TX 77041
281 836-7000

(G-9738)
EXTREME FAB INC
12889 Market Street Rd (77015-6017)
PHONE....................................713 637-0001
EMP: 82
SQ FT: 165,000
SALES (est): 20.3MM **Privately Held**
WEB: www.extremefab.com
SIC: 3441 Fabricated structural metal

(G-9739)
EXXON MOBIL CORPORATION
Exxonmobil Refining & Sup Co
800 Bell St (77002-7497)
P.O. Box 273, Franklinton NC (27525-0273)
PHONE....................................713 656-3636
Joshua Swanson, *General Mgr*
Gregory Hodgdon, *Superintendent*
Harry Janke, *Business Mgr*
Mac Oparakum, *Business Mgr*
Casey Rand, *Business Mgr*
EMP: 476
SALES (corp-wide): 264.9B **Publicly Held**
WEB: www.exxonmobilchemical.com
SIC: 5541 5171 2911 Filling stations, gasoline; petroleum bulk stations & terminals; light distillates
PA: Exxon Mobil Corporation
5959 Las Colinas Blvd
Irving TX 75039
972 940-6000

(G-9740)
EXXONMOBIL DEVELOPMENT COMPANY
Also Called: Exxonmobil Abu Dhabi Gas Ventr
12450 Greenspoint Dr # 1000 (77060-1909)
PHONE....................................713 656-3636
Neil W Duffin, *President*
Jerry J Wolahan, *Exec VP*
Don S Bagley, *Vice Pres*

Kim M Bates, *Vice Pres*
John P Chaplin, *Vice Pres*
▼ **EMP:** 50
SALES: 8.9MM
SALES (corp-wide): 264.9B **Publicly Held**
WEB: www.corporate.exxonmobil.com
SIC: 1381 Drilling oil & gas wells
PA: Exxon Mobil Corporation
5959 Las Colinas Blvd
Irving TX 75039
972 940-6000

(G-9741)
EYESYS VISION INC
16720 Hedgecroft Dr # 208 (77060-3643)
PHONE....................................281 885-3800
Alain Magro, *President*
Joe S Wakil, *Director*
▲ **EMP:** 9
SALES (est): 1.3MM **Privately Held**
WEB: www.eyesys.com
SIC: 3841 Ophthalmic instruments & apparatus

(G-9742)
EZZI SIGNS INC
16611 W Little York Rd (77084-6518)
PHONE....................................713 232-0771
Hussain Contractor, *President*
EMP: 39
SALES (est): 157K **Privately Held**
WEB: www.ezzisigns.com
SIC: 3993 Signs & advertising specialties

(G-9743)
F C DESIGNS INC
11440 Brittmoore Park Dr (77041-6900)
PHONE....................................713 462-1442
Omar Falero, *President*
Omar Filero, *Owner*
Gladys Falero, *Vice Pres*
EMP: 17
SQ FT: 22,000
SALES (est): 2.5MM **Privately Held**
WEB: www.fcdesigns.com
SIC: 2541 Cabinets, except refrigerated: show, display, etc.: wood; store fixtures, wood

(G-9744)
F F FOSTER & ASSOCIATES INC
675 Bering Dr Ste 800 (77057-2129)
PHONE....................................713 266-2883
Larry D Corbin, *President*
L M Atkins, *Vice Pres*
Leonard M Atkins, *Vice Pres*
Angela Posey, *Admin Sec*
EMP: 9
SALES (est): 1.8MM **Privately Held**
WEB: www.justdrillit.com
SIC: 1382 Oil & gas exploration services

(G-9745)
FABCO LLC (PA)
13835 Beaumont Hwy (77049-1417)
PHONE....................................713 633-6500
Edgar Salgado, *Production*
Laura Butler, *Human Res Dir*
Brandy Buzzelli, *Human Resources*
Travis Nelson, *Sales Mgr*
Brandon King, *Sales Staff*
▲ **EMP:** 85
SQ FT: 110,000
SALES (est): 71.5MM **Privately Held**
WEB: www.fabcous.com
SIC: 3441 8741 8711 Fabricated structural metal; management services; building construction consultant

(G-9746)
FABCORP INC (PA)
6951 W Little York Rd (77040-4809)
PHONE....................................713 466-3962
J Allan Hohman, *CEO*
Marianne K Hohman, *President*
Denise Voelkel, *Executive Asst*
EMP: 40
SQ FT: 69,000
SALES (est): 48.5MM **Privately Held**
WEB: www.fabcorp.com
SIC: 3443 3444 3441 Bins, prefabricated metal plate; hoppers, metal plate; sheet metalwork; fabricated structural metal

(G-9747)
FABENCO INC
2002 Karbach St (77092-8406)
PHONE....................................713 686-6620
Scott Friedman, *President*
Martha Matlock, *Sales Staff*
Robert Menn, *Admin Sec*
▼ **EMP:** 33
SQ FT: 21,000
SALES (est): 8.1MM **Privately Held**
WEB: www.tractel.com
SIC: 3312 Structural shapes & pilings, steel

(G-9748)
FABER CNK
6500 Long Point Rd # 304 (77055-2626)
PHONE....................................832 831-7222
EMP: 13
SALES (est): 1.9MM **Privately Held**
WEB: www.fabercnkstone.com
SIC: 3531 3251 Pavers; building tile, clay

(G-9749)
FABRICATING SPECIALTIES LTD
Also Called: FSI
11505 Todd St (77055-1305)
PHONE....................................281 405-2010
William Bean, *CEO*
Kim Ballou, *CFO*
Natasha Valdez, *Human Resources*
Raymond Hartis, *Sales Mgr*
Jesse Trubia, *Planning*
▲ **EMP:** 150
SQ FT: 45,000
SALES (est): 20MM **Privately Held**
WEB: www.fsihou.com
SIC: 3441 Fabricated structural metal

(G-9750)
FABRICATION UNLIMITED INC
5410 Trafalgar Dr (77045-6034)
P.O. Box 450287 (77245-0287)
PHONE....................................713 433-6401
Karl Wagner, *President*
Roswita Wagner, *Vice Pres*
EMP: 21
SQ FT: 70,000
SALES (est): 3MM **Privately Held**
WEB: www.waterstandard.com
SIC: 3443 8711 3441 Metal parts; engineering services; fabricated structural metal

(G-9751)
FAIRBANKS MORSE LLC
12253 Fm 529 Rd (77041-2805)
PHONE....................................713 896-9455
Dennis Mowry, *Vice Pres*
Barb Hellegers, *Buyer*
Margaret Larson, *Buyer*
Steven Wyatt, *Engineer*
Dave Parks, *Director*
EMP: 45
SALES (corp-wide): 95.8MM **Privately Held**
WEB: www.fairbanksmorse.com
SIC: 3519 Diesel, semi-diesel or duel-fuel engines, including marine
HQ: Fairbanks Morse, Llc
701 White Ave
Beloit WI 53511
800 356-6955

(G-9752)
FAIRFIELD INDUSTRIES INC (HQ)
Also Called: Fairfieldnodal
9811 Katy Fwy (77024-1273)
PHONE....................................281 275-7500
Chris Sugahara, *CEO*
Walter D Pharris, *Ch of Bd*
Joe Dryer, *President*
Reagan Woodard, *Division Mgr*
Nick Shilcock, *General Mgr*
◆ **EMP:** 205

SALES (est): 92.1MM
SALES (corp-wide): 111.7MM **Privately Held**
WEB: www.fairfieldgeo.com
SIC: 7374 3829 1382 3429 Data processing service; geophysical or meteorological electronic equipment; geophysical exploration, oil & gas field; manufactured hardware (general)
PA: Fairfield-Maxwell Ltd.
60 E 42nd St Fl 55
New York NY 10165
212 297-9030

(G-9753)
FAIRWAYS EXPLORATION PROD LLC
Also Called: Fairways Resources
1800 Bering Dr Ste 935 (77057-3172)
PHONE..................................713 622-3492
William M Kallop, *CEO*
Dwayne T Stewart, *President*
W Garret Holt, *Senior VP*
Tammy T Naron, *Vice Pres*
J Breck Selman, *Vice Pres*
EMP: 15
SALES (est): 4MM **Privately Held**
SIC: 1382 Oil & gas exploration services

(G-9754)
FAIRWAYS OFFSHORE EXPL
20445 State Highway 249 # 280
(77070-2624)
PHONE..................................713 622-3492
William M Kallop, *CEO*
Dwayne T Stewart, *President*
Matthew Brogden, *President*
J Breck Selman, *Vice Pres*
Craig Townsend, *Vice Pres*
EMP: 22
SQ FT: 9,300
SALES (est): 3.7MM **Privately Held**
SIC: 1382 Oil & gas exploration services
PA: Offshore Specialty Fabricators, Llc
20445 State Highway 249 # 280
Houston TX 77070

(G-9755)
FALCON SEABOARD HOLDINGS LLC (PA)
3 Homewood Row Ln (77056-2198)
PHONE..................................713 622-0055
Howard Wolf, *Ch of Bd*
Curt E Beck, *Vice Pres*
Curt Beck, *Vice Pres*
Gene Dewhurst, *Vice Pres*
Martin H Young Jr, *CFO*
EMP: 45
SALES (est): 33.8MM **Privately Held**
WEB: www.falconseaboard.com
SIC: 4911 1382 1311 4923 Generation, electric power; geological exploration, oil & gas field; crude petroleum production; gas transmission & distribution

(G-9756)
FALCON SEABOARD OIL & GAS LLC
1224 N Post Oak Rd Ste 10 (77055-7277)
PHONE..................................713 622-0055
Howard Wolf, *Ch of Bd*
Curt E Beck, *Vice Pres*
Martin H Young Jr, *CFO*
E H Dewhurst, *Treasurer*
Edna P Tyler, *Admin Sec*
EMP: 16 EST: 1996
SALES (est): 751.1K **Privately Held**
SIC: 1381 Drilling oil & gas wells
PA: Falcon Seaboard Holdings, Llc
3 Homewood Row Ln
Houston TX 77056

(G-9757)
FALCON STEEL FABRICATOR INC
13411 Reeveston Rd (77039-2903)
PHONE..................................281 227-2766
Daniel Morua Sr, *President*
Ana Morua, *Office Mgr*
EMP: 40 EST: 2001
SALES (est): 6.7MM **Privately Held**
WEB: www.falconsteelfab.com
SIC: 3441 Fabricated structural metal

(G-9758)
FALCON-AUGER INC (PA)
Also Called: F A I
4802 Blalock Rd (77041-7714)
PHONE..................................713 690-2761
Michael C Dietrich, *President*
Dona Hebert, *Principal*
EMP: 10
SALES (est): 1MM **Privately Held**
WEB: www.hawksawblades.com
SIC: 3425 Saw blades & handsaws

(G-9759)
FALCONVIEW ENERGY PROD'JCTS LLC
6834 Bourgeois Rd (77066-3107)
PHONE..................................832 665-2850
EMP: 15 EST: 2014
SALES (est): 10MM **Privately Held**
WEB: www.falconep.com
SIC: 3533 Oil field machinery & equipment

(G-9760)
FAMCO
Also Called: Famco Machine Shop
14823 Hooper Rd (77047-7316)
PHONE..................................713 433-2723
Sterling Mc Queen, *Owner*
Ashley Scroggins, *Office Mgr*
EMP: 10
SQ FT: 10,725
SALES (est): 813.6K **Privately Held**
WEB: www.famcomachineshop.com
SIC: 3599 Machine shop, jobbing & repair

(G-9761)
FAR EAST ENERGY (BERMUDA) LTD
333 N Sam Houston Pkwy E (77060-2414)
PHONE..................................832 598-0470
EMP: 11
SALES (est): 517.1K
SALES (corp-wide): 1.5MM **Publicly Held**
SIC: 3569 Mfg General Industrial Machinery
PA: Far East Energy Corporation
333 N Sam Houston Pkwy E # 230
Houston TX 77060
832 598-0470

(G-9762)
FAR EAST ENERGY CORPORATION (PA)
333 N Sam Houston Pkwy E # 230
(77060-2498)
PHONE..................................832 598-0470
Fax: 832 598-0479
▼ EMP: 10
SQ FT: 2,200
SALES: 1.5MM **Publicly Held**
SIC: 1241 1382 1311 Oil/Gas Exploration Services

(G-9763)
FARMER BROS CO
Also Called: Farmers Brothers Coffee
6300 W By Northwest Blvd # 400
(77040-4967)
PHONE..................................713 864-1487
Cliff Shearow, *Branch Mgr*
EMP: 10
SALES (corp-wide): 501.3MM **Publicly Held**
WEB: www.farmerbros.com
SIC: 2095 5812 Coffee roasting (except by wholesale grocers); coffee shop
PA: Farmer Bros. Co.
1912 Farmer Brothers Dr
Northlake TX 76262
682 549-6767

(G-9764)
FARMERS OIL CO
Also Called: Madison Pipeline
211 Highland Cross Dr (77073-1733)
PHONE..................................281 874-2101
John R Parten, *President*
Robert F Pratka, *Vice Pres*
Virginia O Cortinas, *Admin Sec*
Virginia Cortinas, *Admin Sec*
EMP: 20
SQ FT: 10,000
SALES (est): 1.3MM **Privately Held**
WEB: www.farmersoilcoinc.com
SIC: 1311 Crude petroleum & natural gas

(G-9765)
FAROUK SYSTEMS INC (PA)
250 Pennbright Dr (77090-5905)
PHONE..................................281 876-2000
Rami Shami, *CEO*
Farouk Shami, *Ch of Bd*
Lisa Marie Garcia, *President*
Shauky Gulamani, *President*
John McCall, *Principal*
◆ EMP: 276
SQ FT: 130,000
SALES (est): 423.7MM **Privately Held**
WEB: www.farouk.com
SIC: 2844 Hair preparations, including shampoos; hair coloring preparations

(G-9766)
FAROUK SYSTEMS INC
20805 Fernbush Dr (77073-3599)
PHONE..................................281 443-0715
Farouk Hami, *Branch Mgr*
EMP: 10
SALES (corp-wide): 423.7MM **Privately Held**
WEB: www.farouk.com
SIC: 2844 Hair preparations, including shampoos
PA: Farouk Systems, Inc.
250 Pennbright Dr
Houston TX 77090
281 876-2000

(G-9767)
FC DSIGNS QULTY WD WORK CORP
12218 Jones Rd Ste D117 (77070-5267)
PHONE..................................713 462-1442
Santos O Falero, *Principal*
EMP: 10
SALES (est): 1.5MM **Privately Held**
SIC: 2431 Millwork

(G-9768)
FEDERAL FLANGE INC (PA)
4014 Pinemont Dr (77018-1104)
P.O. Box 925097 (77292-5097)
PHONE..................................713 681-0606
Charles Lyons, *President*
Kevin Lyons, *Vice Pres*
Dennis Vine, *CFO*
Eliseo Acevedo, *Sales Staff*
Will McKelvain, *Sales Staff*
▲ EMP: 51 EST: 1975
SQ FT: 43,500
SALES (est): 15.9MM **Privately Held**
WEB: www.federalflange.com
SIC: 3463 3494 Flange, valve or pipe fitting forgings, nonferrous; valves & pipe fittings

(G-9769)
FEDERAL FLANGE INC
3945 Creekmont Dr (77091-5321)
PHONE..................................713 681-0606
Charles Lyons, *Branch Mgr*
EMP: 109
SALES (corp-wide): 15.9MM **Privately Held**
WEB: www.federalflange.com
SIC: 3463 3494 Flange, valve or pipe fitting forgings, nonferrous; valves & pipe fittings
PA: Federal Flange, Inc.
4014 Pinemont Dr
Houston TX 77018
713 681-0606

(G-9770)
FEDERAL FLANGE & FITTING CO
Also Called: Federal Connects
4014 Pinemont Dr (77018-1104)
P.O. Box 925097 (77292-5097)
PHONE..................................713 681-0606
Kirk Luomala, *CEO*
Thomas N Lyons Jr, *President*
◆ EMP: 65
SALES (est): 10.9MM **Privately Held**
WEB: www.federalflange.com
SIC: 3463 Flange, valve or pipe fitting forgings, nonferrous

(G-9771)
FEDERAL ROYALTY PARTNERS LTD
2001 Kirby Dr Ste 1210 (77019-6081)
PHONE..................................713 529-3729
Daniel F Flowers, *Partner*
EMP: 34
SALES (est): 1.6MM **Privately Held**
SIC: 1311 Crude petroleum & natural gas production

(G-9772)
FEDEX OFFICE & PRINT SVCS INC
2455 Rice Blvd (77005-3202)
PHONE..................................713 521-9465
EMP: 15
SALES (corp-wide): 69.2B **Publicly Held**
WEB: www.fedex.com
SIC: 7334 2791 2789 2759 Photocopying & duplicating services; typesetting; bookbinding & related work; commercial printing; commercial printing, lithographic; coated & laminated paper
HQ: Fedex Office And Print Services, Inc.
7900 Legacy Dr
Plano TX 75024
800 463-3339

(G-9773)
FEDEX OFFICE & PRINT SVCS INC
12121 Westheimer Rd # 201 (77077-6682)
PHONE..................................713 977-2666
Ladell Udoh, *Manager*
EMP: 20
SALES (corp-wide): 69.2B **Publicly Held**
WEB: www.fedex.com
SIC: 7334 2789 2752 Photocopying & duplicating services; bookbinding & related work; commercial printing, lithographic
HQ: Fedex Office And Print Services, Inc.
7900 Legacy Dr
Plano TX 75024
800 463-3339

(G-9774)
FEDEX OFFICE & PRINT SVCS INC
10670 Northwest Fwy (77092-8207)
PHONE..................................713 956-2366
EMP: 15
SALES (corp-wide): 69.2B **Publicly Held**
WEB: www.fedex.com
SIC: 7334 2759 Photocopying & duplicating services; commercial printing
HQ: Fedex Office And Print Services, Inc.
7900 Legacy Dr
Plano TX 75024
800 463-3339

(G-9775)
FEDEX OFFICE & PRINT SVCS INC
7700 Highway 6 N Ste 103 (77095-2672)
PHONE..................................281 463-8433
EMP: 15
SALES (corp-wide): 69.2B **Publicly Held**
WEB: www.fedex.com
SIC: 7334 2789 Photocopying & duplicating services; bookbinding & related work
HQ: Fedex Office And Print Services, Inc.
7900 Legacy Dr
Plano TX 75024
800 463-3339

(G-9776)
FENCECRETE AMERICA INC
15100 West Rd (77095-3019)
PHONE..................................281 438-1444
Rene Narvaiz, *Principal*
Valerie Davis, *Office Mgr*
EMP: 125
SALES (corp-wide): 32.8MM **Privately Held**
WEB: www.fencecrete.com
SIC: 3272 1741 1799 Concrete products, precast; concrete block masonry laying; fence construction
PA: Fencecrete America, Inc.
15089 Tradesman
San Antonio TX 78249
210 492-7911

GEOGRAPHIC

(G-9777)
FERPA PRECISION MACHINE INC
1402 Hugh Rd (77067-1404)
P.O. Box 672714 (77267-2714)
PHONE..........................281 874-9747
Antonio Patino, *President*
EMP: 40
SALES (est): 2MM **Privately Held**
WEB: www.ferpa-pmi.com
SIC: 3053 Gaskets, packing & sealing devices

(G-9778)
FERUS LP
20445 State Highway 249 # 250
(77070-2628)
PHONE..........................832 709-0750
Dick Brown, *President*
Sara Jaremko, *Partner*
EMP: 40
SALES (est): 7MM
SALES (corp-wide): 1.3MM **Privately Held**
WEB: www.ferus.com
SIC: 1382 Oil & gas exploration services
HQ: Ferus Inc
    401 9 Ave Sw Suite 1220
    Calgary AB T2P 3
    403 517-8777

(G-9779)
FERVID GROUP LLC
11222 Richmond Ave # 120 (77082-2646)
PHONE..........................713 364-3378
Dhimant Desai, *Mng Member*
Abhijeet Narvekar,
EMP: 14
SQ FT: 2,400
SALES (est): 1.5MM **Privately Held**
WEB: www.thefervidgroup.com
SIC: 1382 8742 Geological exploration, oil & gas field; human resource consulting services

(G-9780)
FESTIVE TENTS LP
3302 Chartreuse Way (77082-6857)
PHONE..........................713 468-3687
Timothy Aaron Bolton, *General Ptnr*
EMP: 15
SQ FT: 26,000
SALES (est): 2MM **Privately Held**
WEB: www.festivetents.com
SIC: 7359 2394 Tent & tarpaulin rental; tents: made from purchased materials

(G-9781)
FESTONI INC
1291 N Post Oak Rd # 100 (77055-7268)
PHONE..........................713 830-1077
Sissy Fenoglio, *President*
Bill Fenoglio, *Vice Pres*
▲ **EMP:** 10
SALES (est): 1.5MM **Privately Held**
WEB: www.festoni.com
SIC: 3646 Commercial indusl & institutional electric lighting fixtures

(G-9782)
FGI ACQUISITION CORP (HQ)
Also Called: Flexitallic
4150 N Sam Houston Pkwy E
(77032-3893)
PHONE..........................281 604-2400
Jon Stokes, *CEO*
Richard Rodgers, *Engineer*
Gerry Maters, *CFO*
Jerry Maters, *CFO*
EMP: 27
SQ FT: 14,625
SALES (est): 153MM
SALES (corp-wide): 5.2MM **Privately Held**
WEB: www.flexitallic.com
SIC: 3053 Gaskets & sealing devices

(G-9783)
FIBERSPAR CORPORATION
W12239 Fm 529 (77041)
PHONE..........................713 849-2609
Mark Gardner, *President*
EMP: 100

SALES (corp-wide): 8.4B **Publicly Held**
WEB: www.nov.com
SIC: 3069 7389 Tubing, rubber; design, commercial & industrial
HQ: Fiberspar Corporation
    12239 Fm 529 Rd
    Houston TX 77041
    713 849-2609

(G-9784)
FIBERSPAR CORPORATION (HQ)
Also Called: Fiber Glass Systems
12239 Fm 529 Rd (77041-2805)
PHONE..........................713 849-2609
Peter Quigley, *CEO*
Michael S Zavell, *Admin Sec*
◆ **EMP:** 11
SQ FT: 35,000
SALES (est): 34.3MM
SALES (corp-wide): 8.4B **Publicly Held**
WEB: www.nov.com
SIC: 3084 Plastics pipe
PA: National Oilwell Varco, Inc.
    7909 Parkwood Circle Dr
    Houston TX 77036
    713 346-7500

(G-9785)
FILECONTROL PARTNERS LTD (PA)
1300 Texas St (77002-3509)
PHONE..........................713 355-1111
Ahmad Mian, *President*
Chris Fernelius, *Managing Dir*
Shawn Edwards, *Vice Pres*
Leslie Rogers, *Vice Pres*
EMP: 10
SALES (est): 1.3MM **Privately Held**
WEB: www.filecontrol.com
SIC: 3572 7372 7371 Computer storage devices; prepackaged software; custom computer programming services

(G-9786)
FILTER MAINTENANCE COMPANY INC (PA)
Also Called: Filter Warehouse
8278 Warren Rd (77040-2602)
P.O. Box 218449 (77218-8449)
PHONE..........................713 432-7969
Faye Carroll, *President*
Robert Felton, *Shareholder*
Linda Migil, *Shareholder*
EMP: 20
SQ FT: 3,000
SALES (est): 2MM **Privately Held**
WEB: www.airfilterusa.com
SIC: 7699 7349 3564 Filter cleaning; air duct cleaning; filters, air: furnaces, air conditioning equipment, etc.

(G-9787)
FIN-TECH INC
5225 Milwee St (77092-6619)
PHONE..........................713 680-3777
Michael Martin, *President*
Timothy P Daly, *Admin Sec*
▲ **EMP:** 30
SQ FT: 19,500
SALES (est): 4.1MM **Privately Held**
WEB: www.fin-techinc.com
SIC: 3471 Polishing, metals or formed products

(G-9788)
FINLEY INVESTMENTS INC
Also Called: Mirror Industries
11510 Kilburn Rd (77055-1324)
P.O. Box 55328 (77255-5328)
PHONE..........................713 686-4629
Sam H Finley Jr, *President*
Les Armstrong, *Vice Pres*
EMP: 35
SQ FT: 36,000
SALES (est): 4.1MM **Privately Held**
WEB: www.mirrorindustries.com
SIC: 3471 3599 Chromium plating of metals or formed products; machine shop, jobbing & repair

(G-9789)
FIREPLACE INSTALLERS INC
Also Called: Perfection Wholesale Supply
6742 N Eldridge Pkwy (77041-2695)
PHONE..........................713 937-4575
Salvatore Frusco Jr, *President*

Caroline Frusco, *Corp Secy*
Mike Garcia, *Purchasing*
Laura Collins, *Human Resources*
Cassie Baker, *Sales Staff*
EMP: 75
SQ FT: 84,000
SALES (est): 5.9MM **Privately Held**
WEB: www.perfectionsupply.com
SIC: 3089 Plastic hardware & building products

(G-9790)
FIRST CAPITAL INTL INC (PA)
5120 Woodway Dr Ste 9004 (77056-1765)
PHONE..........................713 629-4866
Alex Genin, *Ch of Bd*
James Gooch Sr, *VP Engrg*
Daniel Genin, *Manager*
Edward Genin, *Officer*
EMP: 9
SQ FT: 2,123
SALES (est): 6.9MM **Privately Held**
WEB: www.firstcap.net
SIC: 3826 Integrators (mathematical instruments)

(G-9791)
FIRST NATIONAL TRADING CO LLC
Also Called: Minuteman Press Houston
2117 Chenevert St (77003-5848)
PHONE..........................713 771-3600
George Liu, *Branch Mgr*
EMP: 9
SALES (corp-wide): 141K **Privately Held**
WEB: www.minutemanpress.com
SIC: 2752 Commercial printing, lithographic
PA: First National Trading Company Llc
    2604 Orchid Creek Dr
    Pearland TX 77584
    713 261-0708

(G-9792)
FISHER ENERGY PARTNERS LLC
7227 Wright Rd (77041-2417)
PHONE..........................713 937-6838
Andrew Martin,
EMP: 29
SALES (est): 1.5MM **Privately Held**
SIC: 3594 7389 Fluid power pumps; personal service agents, brokers & bureaus

(G-9793)
FISK/MEI INSPECTION SVCS INC (PA)
2 Northpoint Dr Ste 700 (77060-3200)
PHONE..........................281 436-5500
Johnnie Fisk, *President*
Bob Logan, *Vice Pres*
Brad Peacock, *Vice Pres*
EMP: 129
SQ FT: 2,400
SALES (est): 3.6MM **Privately Held**
SIC: 1389 Oil field services

(G-9794)
FIVES CRYO INC
17314 State Highway 249 # 108
(77064-1100)
PHONE..........................281 820-6990
Brent West, *President*
◆ **EMP:** 10 **EST:** 2015
SALES (est): 16MM
SALES (corp-wide): 2.1MM **Privately Held**
WEB: www.htstx.com
SIC: 3559 Cryogenic machinery, industrial
HQ: Fives Inc.
    23400 Halsted Rd
    Farmington Hills MI 48335
    248 477-0800

(G-9795)
FIVES N AMERCN COMBUSTN INC
11507 Orchard Mountain Dr (77059-5587)
PHONE..........................281 488-2667
Ron Henry, *Sales Engr*
Ron Hypes, *Manager*
EMP: 43

SALES (corp-wide): 2.1MM **Privately Held**
WEB: www.combustion.fivesgroup.com
SIC: 3433 Heating equipment, except electric
HQ: Fives North American Combustion, Inc.
    4455 E 71st St
    Cleveland OH 44105
    216 271-6000

(G-9796)
FLAMEOUT LLC
1701 Brittmoore Rd (77043-2799)
PHONE..........................713 984-8310
Michael Moore, *Mng Member*
EMP: 10
SALES (est): 2MM **Privately Held**
WEB: www.fdfeng.com
SIC: 8711 3569 5087 Engineering services; firefighting apparatus & related equipment; firefighting equipment

(G-9797)
FLARE WELL TESTERS INC (PA)
16000 Barkers Point Ln # 150
(77079-4043)
PHONE..........................281 741-9335
Rick Hall, *President*
Tommy Yocham, *Vice Pres*
Charles Shook, *CFO*
Allan Green, *Manager*
Aaron Hammack, *Manager*
EMP: 39 **EST:** 2008
SALES (est): 13.6MM **Privately Held**
WEB: www.flarewelltesters.com
SIC: 2899 Flares

(G-9798)
FLATROCK COMPRESSION LTD (PA)
17350 State Hwy Ste 249 (77064)
PHONE..........................:..281 517-3680
Brian McDonald, *President*
Joe Baker, *Vice Pres*
Mark Riley, *Opers Staff*
BJ Ellis, *Sales Staff*
Kim Andrews, *Manager*
EMP: 34
SQ FT: 6,235
SALES (est): 19.7MM **Privately Held**
WEB: www.flatrockcompression.com
SIC: 1389 Oil field services

(G-9799)
FLEXITALLIC GROUP INC (DH)
201 Kngwood Med Dr Ste B2 (77067)
PHONE..........................281 604-2525
Jon Stokes, *CEO*
Lee Harn, *Senior VP*
Steve Bond, *Vice Pres*
Matt Dobson, *Vice Pres*
Greg English, *CFO*
▼ **EMP:** 23
SQ FT: 2,500
SALES (est): 89.2MM
SALES (corp-wide): 5.2MM **Privately Held**
WEB: www.flexitallic.com
SIC: 3053 3533 3463 3965 Gaskets, all materials; oil field machinery & equipment; flange, valve or pipe fitting forgings, nonferrous; fasteners
HQ: Fgi Acquisition Corp.
    4150 N Sam Houston Pkwy E
    Houston TX 77032
    281 604-2400

(G-9800)
FLEXITALLIC INVESTMENTS INC (DH)
4660 N Sam Houston Pkwy E
(77032-3850)
PHONE..........................281 604-2525
Jon Stokes, *CEO*
Gerry Matters, *CFO*
EMP: 11
SQ FT: 3,000
SALES (est): 1.5MM
SALES (corp-wide): 5.2MM **Privately Held**
WEB: www.flexitallic.com
SIC: 3053 Gaskets, packing & sealing devices

HQ: Fgi Acquisition Corp.
4150 N Sam Houston Pkwy E
Houston TX 77032
281 604-2400

(G-9801)
FLEXMASTER USA INC
5235 Ted St (77040-6209)
PHONE..................................713 462-7694
Michael Jakobs, *President*
Phyllis Beer, *Vice Pres*
John B Bembenick, *Vice Pres*
Neil Silverman, *Vice Pres*
Michael Thompson, *Vice Pres*
▲ **EMP:** 60
SQ FT: 53,000
SALES (est): 14.3MM
SALES (corp-wide): 88.4MM **Privately Held**
WEB: www.flexmasterusa.com
SIC: 3052 3444 Rubber hose; ducts, sheet metal
PA: Masterflex Se
Willy-Brandt-Allee 300
Gelsenkirchen 45891
209 970-770

(G-9802)
FLIGHTAWARE LLC (PA)
11 Greenway Plz Ste 2900 (77046-1111)
PHONE..................................713 877-9010
Daniel Baker, *CEO*
Max Tribolet, *Business Mgr*
Tamara Elles, *Engineer*
Kim Hickok, *Human Res Dir*
Sara Orsi, *Marketing Staff*
EMP: 57
SALES (est): 14.9MM **Privately Held**
WEB: www.flightaware.com
SIC: 7372 Business oriented computer software

(G-9803)
FLINT HLLS RSRCES HSTON CHEM L
9822 La Porte Fwy (77017-2721)
PHONE..................................713 740-3900
Jeffrey P Ramsey, *President*
David Lumpkins, *Mng Member*
John Holtan, *Manager*
Nathan Ticatch,
▲ **EMP:** 70
SALES (est): 30.1MM
SALES (corp-wide): 36.8B **Privately Held**
WEB: www.petrologistics.com
SIC: 2911 Petroleum refining
HQ: Flint Hills Resources, Llc
8415 E 21st St N Ste 200
Wichita KS 67206
316 828-5500

(G-9804)
FLO TREND SYSTEMS INC
1400 Kowis St (77093-3202)
PHONE..................................713 699-0152
Martin Kroesche, *COO*
Rick Hicks, *Natl Sales Mgr*
Michael Self, *Mktg Coord*
Lance Kothmann, *Associate*
EMP: 20
SQ FT: 10,000
SALES (est): 5.8MM **Privately Held**
WEB: www.flotrend.com
SIC: 1389 4959 7353 Oil field services; toxic or hazardous waste cleanup; oil field equipment, rental or leasing

(G-9805)
FLORES PALLETS LLC
6101 Dixie Dr (77087-5001)
PHONE..................................713 645-1022
Lazaro S Flores, *President*
EMP: 10
SQ FT: 217,800
SALES (est): 4MM **Privately Held**
SIC: 2448 Pallets, wood

(G-9806)
FLOTEK INDUSTRIES INC (PA)
8846 N Sam Houston Pkwy W # 150 (77064-2305)
PHONE..................................713 849-9911
John W Chisholm, *Ch of Bd*
James A Silas, *Exec VP*
Nick Bigney, *Senior VP*
Sally Cheadle, *Vice Pres*

Gary Flock, *Vice Pres*
▲ **EMP:** 20
SALES: 119.3MM **Publicly Held**
WEB: www.flotekind.com
SIC: 2087 2869 2899 3533 Flavoring extracts & syrups; flavors or flavoring materials, synthetic; chemical preparations; drilling tools for gas, oil or water wells; gas field machinery & equipment; industrial valves

(G-9807)
FLOW CONTROL DIVISION CAMERON
6213 W Sam Houston Pkwy N (77041-5145)
PHONE..................................713 513-3300
EMP: 11
SALES (est): 952.6K **Privately Held**
SIC: 1382 Oil/Gas Exploration Services

(G-9808)
FLOW-CAL INC
2525 Bay Area Blvd # 500 (77058-1556)
P.O. Box 58965 (77258-8965)
PHONE..................................832 240-4800
Michael Squyres, *President*
JD Brookes, *Sales Dir*
Byron Saunders, *Sales Executive*
Rose Asimakis, *Marketing Mgr*
Sophie Kim, *Business Anlyst*
EMP: 26 **EST:** 1991
SALES: 16.1MM
SALES (corp-wide): 60.9MM **Privately Held**
WEB: www.flowcal.com
SIC: 7372 Prepackaged software
HQ: Coastal Flow Measurement, Inc.
2525 Bay Area Blvd # 500
Houston TX 77058
713 477-1956

(G-9809)
FLOW-TEK INC
8323 N Eldridge Pkwy 100b (77041-1299)
PHONE..................................832 912-2300
Frank J Raymond, *Ch of Bd*
Craig C Brown, *President*
John Giordano, *Vice Pres*
Greg Filipowicz, *Engineer*
Gregory Filipowicz, *Engineer*
▲ **EMP:** 54
SQ FT: 30,000
SALES (est): 19MM
SALES (corp-wide): 174.4MM **Privately Held**
WEB: www.bray.com
SIC: 5085 3494 Valves & fittings; valves & pipe fittings
PA: Bray International, Inc.
13333 Westland East Blvd
Houston TX 77041
281 894-7979

(G-9810)
FLOWCO PROD SOLUTIONS LLC (PA)
20405 State Highway 249 # 600 (77070-2618)
PHONE..................................281 528-6298
Jobie Petersen, *District Mgr*
Jake Rodstrom, *District Mgr*
Phillip Ferguson, *Mfg Mgr*
Susan Horton, *CFO*
Ryan Hubbell, *Accounts Mgr*
EMP: 15
SQ FT: 6,000
SALES (est): 49.5MM **Privately Held**
WEB: www.flowcosolutions.com
SIC: 3533 Oil & gas field machinery

(G-9811)
FLOWCO PROD SOLUTIONS LLC
6825 Theall Rd (77066-1115)
PHONE..................................281 528-6298
EMP: 39
SALES (corp-wide): 49.5MM **Privately Held**
WEB: www.flowcosolutions.com
SIC: 3533 Oil & gas field machinery
PA: Flowco Production Solutions L.L.C
20405 State Highway 249 # 600
Houston TX 77070
281 528-6298

(G-9812)
FLOWERS BAKING CO HOUSTON LLC (DH)
Also Called: Flowers Bakery
3000 Washington Ave (77007-6029)
PHONE..................................713 869-5701
Michael Lawson, *Vice Pres*
Andy Brown,
EMP: 48 **EST:** 1893
SQ FT: 111,000
SALES (est): 17MM
SALES (corp-wide): 4.1B **Publicly Held**
WEB: www.flowersfoods.com
SIC: 2051 5149 5461 Bakery: wholesale or wholesale/retail combined; bakery products; bakeries

(G-9813)
FLOWSERVE CORPORATION
6840 Wynnwood Ln (77008-5024)
PHONE..................................832 375-0807
Gabriel Bernal, *Mfg Mgr*
Oscar Bermudez, *Engineer*
Frenika Roberts, *Controller*
Robert Lowe, *Regl Sales Mgr*
Montgomery Chuck, *Sales Staff*
EMP: 25
SALES (corp-wide): 3.9B **Publicly Held**
WEB: www.flowserve.com
SIC: 3561 3491 3494 3463 Pumps & pumping equipment; industrial valves; pressure valves & regulators, industrial; regulators (steam fittings); valves, nuclear; valves & pipe fittings; pump & compressor forgings, nonferrous; engineering help service
PA: Flowserve Corporation
5215 N Ocnnor Blvd Ste 23 Connor
Irving TX 75039
972 443-6500

(G-9814)
FLOWSERVE CORPORATION
3993 W Sam Houston Pkwy N # 100 (77043-1238)
P.O. Box 4628 (77210-4628)
PHONE..................................713 863-9180
Hector Hinojosa, *General Mgr*
Artur Czarnecki, *Vice Pres*
Kim Millin, *Production*
Oscar Bermudez, *Engineer*
Patricia Fore, *Engineer*
EMP: 45
SALES (corp-wide): 3.9B **Publicly Held**
WEB: www.flowserve.com
SIC: 3561 Pumps & pumping equipment
PA: Flowserve Corporation
5215 N Ocnnor Blvd Ste 23 Connor
Irving TX 75039
972 443-6500

(G-9815)
FLUENTA INC (PA)
1155 Dairy Ashford Rd # 211 (77079-3021)
PHONE..................................832 456-2021
Dag S Johansen, *President*
Tom Pugliese, *Vice Pres*
▲ **EMP:** 11
SQ FT: 2,500
SALES (est): 1.7MM **Privately Held**
WEB: www.fluenta.com
SIC: 3824 3211 Gas meters, domestic & large capacity: industrial; window glass, clear & colored

(G-9816)
FLUID SEALING PRODUCTS INC
155 Southbelt Indus Dr (77047-7020)
PHONE..................................713 910-1028
David Massie, *President*
John Blake, *Vice Pres*
Bruce Sudano, *Accounts Mgr*
Michelle McCallick, *Admin Sec*
▲ **EMP:** 75
SQ FT: 20,000
SALES (est): 16.9MM **Privately Held**
WEB: www.fluidsealingproducts.com
SIC: 3965 3492 3452 5085 Fasteners; control valves, fluid power: hydraulic & pneumatic; bolts, nuts, rivets & washers; packing, industrial; gasket materials

(G-9817)
FLUTURA BUSINESS SOLUTIONS LLC
5858 Westheimer Rd # 405 (77057-5650)
PHONE..................................832 265-9172
Greg Slater, *General Mgr*
Rick Harlow, *Mng Member*
Srivatsa Kondapalli, *Manager*
EMP: 10
SQ FT: 8,000
SALES (est): 2.5MM **Privately Held**
WEB: www.flutura.com
SIC: 7372 Business oriented computer software

(G-9818)
FLUXMETALS LLC
650 N Sam Houston Pkwy E (77060-5906)
PHONE..................................832 948-4307
Javier Suarez, *President*
Javier Canedo, *Vice Pres*
EMP: 53
SALES (est): 2.9MM **Privately Held**
WEB: www.fluxmetals.sitey.me
SIC: 3563 3561 3599 3443 Air & gas compressors; pumps & pumping equipment; machine & other job shop work; metal parts; fabricated structural metal

(G-9819)
FMC CORPORATION
1777 Gears Rd (77067-4099)
PHONE..................................281 591-4470
Rick Kesler, *Business Mgr*
John Bright, *Senior Buyer*
Ronald Mambu, *Branch Mgr*
Donald Burleiogh, *Manager*
William Thomas, *Manager*
EMP: 61
SALES (corp-wide): 4.6B **Publicly Held**
WEB: www.fmc.com
SIC: 2812 Soda ash, sodium carbonate (anhydrous)
PA: Fmc Corporation
2929 Walnut St
Philadelphia PA 19104
215 299-6000

(G-9820)
FMC TECHNOLOGIES INC (HQ)
Also Called: Technipfmc
11740 Katy Fwy Enrgy Twr (77079)
PHONE..................................281 591-4000
Douglas Pferdehirt, *President*
Dana Carte, *Superintendent*
Doug Pferdehirt, *COO*
Arnaud Pieton, *Exec VP*
Ronald Birkhoff, *Vice Pres*
◆ **EMP:** 50
SALES (est): 5.6B
SALES (corp-wide): 13.4B **Privately Held**
WEB: www.fmctechnologies.com
SIC: 3533 Oil field machinery & equipment
PA: Technipfmc Plc
One St. Paul's Churchyard
London EC4M
203 429-3950

(G-9821)
FMC TECHNOLOGIES INC
1803 Gears Rd (77067-4097)
PHONE..................................281 260-2190
Victor Van Asperen, *General Mgr*
Coy Dever, *District Mgr*
Wendy Schneider, *Counsel*
Bradley Beitler, *Vice Pres*
Sanjay Bhatia, *Vice Pres*
EMP: 11
SALES (corp-wide): 13.4B **Privately Held**
WEB: www.technipfmc.com
SIC: 3533 Oil & gas field machinery
HQ: Fmc Technologies, Inc.
11740 Katy Fwy Enrgy Twr
Houston TX 77079
281 591-4000

(G-9822)
FMC TECHNOLOGIES INC
16700 E Hardy Rd (77032-1193)
PHONE..................................281 821-2355
Cory Ormsby, *Project Mgr*
Andy Baker, *Engineer*
Jeremiah Johnson, *Engineer*
Edwin Rendon, *Engineer*
Blake Sutter, *Engineer*
EMP: 15

SALES (corp-wide): 13.4B **Privately Held**
WEB: www.technipfmc.com
SIC: 3533 Oil field machinery & equipment
HQ: Fmc Technologies, Inc.
　11740 Katy Fwy Enrgy Twr
　Houston TX 77079
　281 591-4000

(G-9823)
FMC TECHNOLOGIES INC
Also Called: Subsea Services Western Region
11220 Tc Gester (77067)
PHONE.....................281 591-4106
Robert Douglas, *President*
Craig Hamilton-Smith, *Engineer*
Gabriel Silva, *Manager*
EMP: 13
SALES (corp-wide): 13.4B **Privately Held**
WEB: www.technipfmc.com
SIC: 3556 Food products machinery
HQ: Fmc Technologies, Inc.
　11740 Katy Fwy Enrgy Twr
　Houston TX 77079
　281 591-4000

(G-9824)
FMC TECHNOLOGIES INC
1777 Gears Rd (77067-4099)
PHONE.....................281 591-4000
Richard Clark, *General Mgr*
Frode Nilsen, *Managing Dir*
Aneet Nehra, *Vice Pres*
Robert Houlgrave, *Plant Mgr*
Matt Dossey, *Project Mgr*
EMP: 29
SALES (corp-wide): 13.4B **Privately Held**
WEB: www.technipfmc.com
SIC: 3533 Oil field machinery & equipment
HQ: Fmc Technologies, Inc.
　11740 Katy Fwy Enrgy Twr
　Houston TX 77079
　281 591-4000

(G-9825)
FMC TECHNOLOGIES INC
13460 Lockwood Rd S01 (77044-6444)
PHONE.....................281 569-6194
Keith Haynes, *Opers Mgr*
Paul Leslie, *Opers Mgr*
Oscar Morales, *Engineer*
Derek Smith, *Engineer*
Qiaoyan Borth, *Project Engr*
EMP: 9
SALES (corp-wide): 13.4B **Privately Held**
WEB: www.technipfmc.com
SIC: 3533 Oil field machinery & equipment
HQ: Fmc Technologies, Inc.
　11740 Katy Fwy Enrgy Twr
　Houston TX 77079
　281 591-4000

(G-9826)
FMC TECHNOLOGIES INC
500 N Sam Houston Pkwy E (77060-4002)
PHONE.....................281 260-2121
Toan Tang, *Engineer*
David Oskins, *Controller*
Joseiv Figueroa, *Manager*
Donye Robison, *Manager*
EMP: 15
SALES (corp-wide): 13.4B **Privately Held**
WEB: www.technipfmc.com
SIC: 3533 Oil field machinery & equipment
HQ: Fmc Technologies, Inc.
　11740 Katy Fwy Enrgy Twr
　Houston TX 77079
　281 591-4000

(G-9827)
FMC TECHNOLOGIES INC
Also Called: Shipping Department
16736 E Hardy Rd (77032-1125)
PHONE.....................281 405-7927
Brian Dewitter, *Branch Mgr*
EMP: 15
SALES (corp-wide): 13.4B **Privately Held**
WEB: www.technipfmc.com
SIC: 3533 Oil & gas field machinery
HQ: Fmc Technologies, Inc.
　11740 Katy Fwy Enrgy Twr
　Houston TX 77079
　281 591-4000

(G-9828)
FMC TECHNOLOGIES OFFSHORE LLC
Also Called: Fto Services
2000 W Sam Houston Pkwy S
(77042-3615)
PHONE.....................713 341-7742
John Griffin, *President*
EMP: 40
SALES (est): 2.8MM **Privately Held**
WEB: www.technipfmc.com
SIC: 1389 Servicing oil & gas wells

(G-9829)
FOAM PAK US LP
1103 S Dr (77099)
PHONE.....................832 212-8896
Henry Vo, *Ltd Ptnr*
Vay M Vo, *Ltd Ptnr*
EMP: 52
SALES (est): 5.2MM **Privately Held**
SIC: 3086 Plastics foam products

(G-9830)
FOCUS EXPLORATION LLC
10333 Richmond Ave # 750 (77042-4172)
PHONE.....................713 435-0021
Michael Sherrer, *Partner*
Donald Crider, *Partner*
EMP: 10
SALES (est): 780K **Privately Held**
WEB: www.focusexploration.com
SIC: 1382 Oil & gas exploration services

(G-9831)
FOOTHILLS RESOURCES INC (PA)
2450 Fondren Rd Ste 200 (77063-2320)
P.O. Box 690006 (77269-0006)
PHONE.....................713 621-9408
Dennis B Tower, *Ch of Bd*
John L Moran, *President*
Perry Dragon, *COO*
James H Drennan, *Vice Pres*
John Garber, *Vice Pres*
EMP: 10
SQ FT: 4,500
SALES (est): 2MM **Privately Held**
WEB: www.foothills-resources.com
SIC: 1311 1382 Crude petroleum production; oil & gas exploration services

(G-9832)
FOR SALE BY OWNER MAGAZINE
10560 Northwest Fwy (77092-8205)
PHONE.....................713 457-0181
Fax: 713 683-0235
EMP: 12
SALES (est): 1.1MM **Privately Held**
SIC: 2759 Commercial Printing

(G-9833)
FORGED PRODUCTS INC
6505 N Houston Rosslyn Rd (77091-1006)
PHONE.....................713 462-3416
Kevin Crowley, *President*
Richard M Hamlin Jr, *Vice Pres*
Ivan Dupont, *CFO*
Pamela Woodson, *Manager*
Marc Sexton, *Asst Mgr*
EMP: 92
SALES (est): 19MM **Privately Held**
WEB: www.fpitx.com
SIC: 3462 Iron & steel forgings

(G-9834)
FORMERS BY ERNIE INC
7905 Almeda Genoa Rd A (77075-2007)
PHONE.....................713 991-3455
Ernie Sanchez Sr, *President*
Teresa Sanchez, *Corp Secy*
Lore Bass, *Vice Pres*
Eric Sanchez, *Vice Pres*
Ernie Sanchez Jr, *Vice Pres*
EMP: 17
SQ FT: 2,925
SALES (est): 2MM **Privately Held**
WEB: www.formersbyernie.com
SIC: 3542 Machine tools, metal forming type

(G-9835)
FORMS & PRINTING SERVICE INC
3737 Westcenter Dr (77042-5217)
PHONE.....................713 266-4201
Brent Peterson, *President*
Linda Peterson, *Treasurer*
EMP: 10
SQ FT: 17,000
SALES (est): 1MM **Privately Held**
WEB: www.formsandprinting.com
SIC: 2752 Commercial printing, offset

(G-9836)
FORMTEX PLASTICS CORPORATION
6817 Wynnwood Ln (77008-5023)
PHONE.....................713 493-6628
Frank A Yerich, *President*
Wilson Thibodeaux, *Vice Pres*
Elizabeth Macgowan, *Purchasing*
Mark Anselmo, *Shareholder*
Rocky Chan, *Shareholder*
▼ **EMP:** 32
SQ FT: 50,000
SALES (est): 10MM **Privately Held**
WEB: www.formtex.com
SIC: 3089 2671 Injection molding of plastics; plastic containers, except foam; packaging paper & plastics film, coated & laminated

(G-9837)
FORREST MFG CO
2825 W 11th St (77008-6210)
PHONE.....................713 864-2545
Stephen Sykes, *President*
Charles Gregory, *Vice Pres*
Jennifer Rex, *Vice Pres*
▲ **EMP:** 10
SQ FT: 13,500
SALES (est): 1.9MM **Privately Held**
WEB: www.forrestmfg.com
SIC: 3541 Numerically controlled metal cutting machine tools

(G-9838)
FORTERRA PIPE & PRECAST LLC
11201 Fm 529 Rd (77041-3205)
PHONE.....................713 466-6324
Roderick Honea, *Sales Mgr*
Raul Ortiz, *Branch Mgr*
Mike Haddy, *Manager*
EMP: 100
SALES (corp-wide): 1.5B **Publicly Held**
WEB: www.forterrabp.com
SIC: 1771 3732 Concrete work; boat building & repairing
HQ: Forterra Pipe & Precast, Llc
　511 E John Carpenter Fwy
　Irving TX 75062
　469 458-7973

(G-9839)
FORTITUDE SPECIALTY MFG LLC
Also Called: Economy Metal Works
8400 Villa Dr (77061-4602)
PHONE.....................713 465-3370
Richard E Agee,
Bart Agee,
EMP: 56
SQ FT: 70,000
SALES (est): 9.8MM **Privately Held**
WEB: www.fortitudespecialtymfg.com
SIC: 3446 3449 Channels, louvers & registers; bars, concrete reinforcing: fabricated steel

(G-9840)
FORTUNE ONE FOODS INC
935 W 18th St (77008-3336)
PHONE.....................713 426-1133
Jonathan C Lin, *President*
Jim Zhang, *Vice Pres*
EMP: 45
SALES (est): 23.5MM **Privately Held**
SIC: 5141 2032 Food brokers; Chinese foods: packaged in cans, jars, etc.

(G-9841)
FORUM ENERGY TECHNOLOGIES INC
Also Called: Forum Production Equipment
10344 Sam Houston Park Dr # 300
(77064-4666)
PHONE.....................940 612-5890
Richard Grant, *Plant Mgr*
Nick Clark, *Engineer*
Martha Amezcua, *Sales Staff*
Rex Haynes, *Sales Staff*
Angie Jimenez, *Admin Asst*
EMP: 140 **Publicly Held**
WEB: www.f-e-t.com
SIC: 3533 Oil & gas field machinery
PA: Forum Energy Technologies, Inc.
　10344 Sam Houston Park Dr # 300
　Houston TX 77064

(G-9842)
FORUM ENERGY TECHNOLOGIES INC
10344 Sam Houston Park Dr # 300
(77064-4666)
PHONE.....................713 329-8730
Rodrigo Villarreal, *Manager*
EMP: 82 **Publicly Held**
WEB: www.f-e-t.com
SIC: 3533 Oil field machinery & equipment
PA: Forum Energy Technologies, Inc.
　10344 Sam Houston Park Dr # 300
　Houston TX 77064

(G-9843)
FORUM ENERGY TECHNOLOGIES INC (PA)
10344 Sam Houston Park Dr # 300
(77064-4666)
PHONE.....................281 949-2500
C Christopher Gaut, *Ch of Bd*
John Hebert, *Business Mgr*
Michael D Danford, *Senior VP*
John C Ivascu, *Senior VP*
D Lyle Williams Jr, *Senior VP*
◆ **EMP:** 229
SALES: 956.5MM **Publicly Held**
WEB: www.f-e-t.com
SIC: 3533 Oil field machinery & equipment

(G-9844)
FORUM US INC (HQ)
Also Called: Forum-Valve Solutions
10344 Sam Houston Park Dr # 300
(77064-4666)
PHONE.....................713 351-7900
Tylar Schmitt, *President*
Robert Fontenot, *Engineer*
Glen Smeal, *Engineer*
Chris Arthur, *Sales Staff*
▲ **EMP:** 149 **EST:** 2008
SALES (est): 288MM **Publicly Held**
WEB: www.f-e-t.com
SIC: 1382 Oil & gas exploration services

(G-9845)
FORWARD TIMES PUBLISHING CO
4411 Almeda Rd (77004-4999)
P.O. Box 8346 (77288-8346)
PHONE.....................713 526-4727
Lenora Carter, *President*
Karen C Richards, *Publisher*
Patsy Hunter, *Manager*
Grace Boateng, *Graphic Designe*
EMP: 20 **EST:** 1947
SQ FT: 10,000
SALES (est): 1.3MM **Privately Held**
WEB: www.forwardtimes.com
SIC: 2711 2752 Newspapers: publishing only, not printed on site; commercial printing, offset

(G-9846)
FOUR POINT PUBLISHING LLC
1440 S Creek Dr (77084-4906)
PHONE.....................281 228-6237
Tony Keane, *Admin Sec*
EMP: 20
SALES (est): 1.1MM **Privately Held**
SIC: 2741 Miscellaneous publishing

(G-9847)
FOUR WAY PALLET CO
7911 Richards St (77029-3851)
P.O. Box 202, Galena Park (77547-0202)
PHONE...........................713 675-7788
Antonio Membreno, *Owner*
EMP: 10
SALES (est): 1.1MM **Privately Held**
WEB: www.palletsinhouston.com
SIC: 2448 Pallets, wood

(G-9848)
FOXCONN ASSEMBLY LLC
8801 Fallbrook Dr (77064-4856)
PHONE...........................281 668-1668
Henry Jong Hwang Cheng, *CEO*
Benjamin Chuang, *Program Mgr*
Amy So, *Manager*
Foo Ming Fu,
Ching Hui Hsu,
▲ EMP: 85
SALES (est): 27.3MM **Privately Held**
WEB: www.foxconn.com
SIC: 3571 Electronic computers
PA: Hon Hai Precision Industry Co., Ltd.
No. 66, Zhongshan Rd.
New Taipei City TAP 23680

(G-9849)
FOXCONN CORPORATION (HQ)
8801 Fallbrook Dr (77064-4856)
PHONE...........................281 668-1668
Henry Hwang Cheng, *CEO*
Jim Chang, *President*
Kirk Fleischhauer, *President*
Miles Hsiao, *President*
Mark Aguirre, *Vice Pres*
◆ EMP: 40
SQ FT: 94,000
SALES (est): 26.5MM **Privately Held**
WEB: www.foxconn.com
SIC: 3571 Electronic computers

(G-9850)
FOXXE ENERGY SERVICES LLC
2121 Sage Rd Ste 370 (77056-4338)
PHONE...........................713 960-0381
James C Stewart,
James W Clancy,
Jean T Shepherd,
EMP: 70
SALES (est): 2.8MM **Privately Held**
SIC: 1381 Drilling oil & gas wells

(G-9851)
FRAC SAND SERVICES LLC
5419 Ariel St (77096-2201)
PHONE...........................713 668-6766
EMP: 14 EST: 2009
SQ FT: 19,000
SALES (est): 750K **Privately Held**
SIC: 1446 Industrial Sand

(G-9852)
FRAMECRAFTERS INC
1410 Campbell Rd (77055-4604)
PHONE...........................713 973-1333
Raymond Munk, *President*
Debbie Munk, *Vice Pres*
▲ EMP: 25
SQ FT: 24,000
SALES (est): 4.1MM **Privately Held**
WEB: www.framecraftersinc.com
SIC: 2499 Picture frame molding, finished;
picture & mirror frames, wood

(G-9853)
FRAMEWORKS MANUFACTURING LLC
1910 Cypress Station Dr # 100
(77090-4038)
P.O. Box 90849 (77290-0849)
PHONE...........................713 692-5222
Dale Waite, *President*
Chris Howard, *President*
Kenny Webb, *Vice Pres*
Pamela Decker, *Project Mgr*
Adolf Flores, *Project Mgr*
EMP: 32
SQ FT: 40,000
SALES (est): 6.3MM **Privately Held**
WEB: www.frameworks.com
SIC: 3442 Metal doors

(G-9854)
FRANK WHITE
6927 Brittmoore Rd (77041-3807)
PHONE...........................713 937-3800
Frank White, *President*
EMP: 26
SALES (est): 1.7MM **Privately Held**
SIC: 3533 Oil & gas field machinery

(G-9855)
FRANKLIN COVEY CO
Also Called: Franklin Quest Store
2611 S Shepherd Dr # 140 (77098-1561)
PHONE...........................713 527-9494
Addie Ward, *Manager*
EMP: 9
SALES (corp-wide): 198.4MM **Publicly
Held**
WEB: www.shop.franklinplanner.com
SIC: 2741 Miscellaneous publishing
PA: Franklin Covey Co.
2200 W Parkway Blvd
Salt Lake City UT 84119
801 817-1776

(G-9856)
FRANKLIN HOWARD INTL LLC
777 S Post Oak Ln 1700 (77056)
PHONE...........................281 815-1527
Obinna Nwadike, *President*
Rauny Baez, *Vice Pres*
◆ EMP: 10
SALES (est): 862.3K **Privately Held**
WEB: www.franklinhoward.com
SIC: 4932 1389 5084 Gas & other serv-
ices combined; construction, repair & dis-
mantling services; oil well machinery,
equipment & supplies

(G-9857)
FRANKS INTERNATIONAL LLC (HQ)
Also Called: Franks International
10260 Westheimer Rd (77042-3110)
P.O. Box 51729, Lafayette LA (70505-
1729)
PHONE...........................281 966-7300
Donald Keith Mosing, *Ch of Bd*
Douglas Stephens, *President*
Troy Matherne, *Vice Pres*
Robert R Rader, *Vice Pres*
Steve Russell, *Vice Pres*
◆ EMP: 75
SQ FT: 15,642
SALES (est): 762.6MM
SALES (corp-wide): 581MM **Privately
Held**
SIC: 1382 7353 Oil & gas exploration
services; heavy construction equipment
rental
PA: Frank's International N.V.
Mastenmakersweg 1
Den Helder 1786
223 670-000

(G-9858)
FRAZER LTD
Also Called: Frazerbilt
7219 Rampart St (77081-6403)
PHONE...........................713 772-5511
John Griffin Sr, *Partner*
John Griffin Jr, *Partner*
Laura G Richardson, *Partner*
Janice Frazer Griffin, *General Ptnr*
Bert Jones, *Vice Pres*
EMP: 135 EST: 1956
SQ FT: 25,000
SALES (est): 51.9MM **Privately Held**
WEB: www.frazerbilt.com
SIC: 3711 Ambulances (motor vehicles),
assembly of

(G-9859)
FREEDOM OIL & GAS INC (HQ)
1010 Nantucket Dr Unit E (77057-2095)
PHONE...........................832 783-5700
J Michael Yeager, *President*
Randy Rutledge, *Manager*
Joan Robilio, *Executive Asst*
EMP: 11 EST: 2007
SALES (est): 5.8MM **Privately Held**
WEB: www.freedomog.com
SIC: 1311 Crude petroleum & natural gas

(G-9860)
FREEDOM WHEELS INC (PA)
Also Called: Balder USA
580 T C Jester Blvd (77007-1127)
P.O. Box 842065 (77284-2065)
PHONE...........................713 864-1460
Carlos Saez, *President*
▲ EMP: 15
SQ FT: 25,000
SALES (est): 2.1MM **Privately Held**
WEB: www.freedomwheels.com
SIC: 7532 3842 7538 Customizing serv-
ices, non-factory basis; wheelchairs; gen-
eral automotive repair shops

(G-9861)
FREEMAN & CURIEL ENGINEERS LLP
13101 Nw Fwy Ste 320 (77040-6316)
PHONE...........................713 895-8668
Ivan Curiel, *Managing Prtnr*
Michael A Freeman, *Partner*
Ivan A Curiel Pe, *Partner*
Craig Stewart, *Business Mgr*
Todd Blum, *Engineer*
EMP: 40
SQ FT: 11,500
SALES (est): 27MM **Privately Held**
WEB: www.fcengr.com
SIC: 1382 8711 Oil & gas exploration serv-
ices; engineering services

(G-9862)
FREEPORT-MCMORAN OIL & GAS LLC (HQ)
700 Milam St Ste 3100 (77002-2764)
PHONE...........................713 579-6000
Tom Batsche, *Asst Controller*
James C Flores,
▲ EMP: 169
SALES (est): 666.1MM
SALES (corp-wide): 14.4B **Publicly Held**
WEB: www.fcx.com
SIC: 1382 Aerial geophysical exploration
oil & gas
PA: Freeport-Mcmoran Inc.
333 N Central Ave
Phoenix AZ 85004
602 366-8100

(G-9863)
FRENCHYS SAUSAGE CO INC
4220 Pine Mt (77018)
PHONE...........................713 862-2299
Percy Creuzot III, *President*
Gloria Hawkins, *Finance*
EMP: 13
SQ FT: 10,000
SALES (est): 6.4MM **Privately Held**
WEB: www.frenchyscreole.com
SIC: 5147 2013 Meats & meat products;
sausages from purchased meat

(G-9864)
FRESH BREW GROUP USA LP
11600 Big John St (77038-3334)
PHONE...........................281 847-2222
Dari Ansari, *CEO*
Al Ansari, *President*
Kevin Miller, *District Mgr*
Steven Weyel, *COO*
Fenton Allen, *Vice Pres*
▲ EMP: 50
SQ FT: 110,000
SALES: 34.4MM **Privately Held**
WEB: www.freshbrewgroup.com
SIC: 2095 Coffee roasting (except by
wholesale grocers)

(G-9865)
FRESH MEADOWS INDUSTRIES INC
Also Called: G & S Custom Draperies
8570 Katy Fwy Ste 119 (77024-1832)
PHONE...........................713 464-9554
Steve Addiego, *President*
EMP: 25
SQ FT: 9,000
SALES (est): 3.3MM **Privately Held**
WEB: www.gandscustomdraperies.com
SIC: 2211 5023 2391 Draperies & drap-
ery fabrics, cotton; venetian blinds; cur-
tains & draperies

(G-9866)
FRESH-PAK CORP
16240 Port Nw Ste 200 (77041-2668)
PHONE...........................713 690-8742
John Bazbaz, *President*
Kathy Beezley, *General Mgr*
Donna Smith, *Accountant*
Bill Keating, *CPA*
Rudy Macdonel, *Sales Staff*
▼ EMP: 110
SALES (est): 800K **Privately Held**
WEB: www.freshpakcorp.com
SIC: 3081 Packing materials, plastic sheet

(G-9867)
FREUDENBERG OIL & GAS LLC (HQ)
10035 Brookriver Dr # 400 (77040-3193)
P.O. Box 2032 (77252-2032)
PHONE...........................281 233-1400
Ralf Krieger, *President*
Mike Long, *Vice Pres*
Kay Tanner, *Vice Pres*
Barry Tate, *Vice Pres*
Ryan Fitzgerald, *Project Mgr*
▲ EMP: 74
SALES (est): 122.2MM
SALES (corp-wide): 10.5B **Privately Held**
WEB: www.fogt.com
SIC: 1389 Crude oil
PA: Freudenberg & Co. Kg
Hohnerweg 2-4
Weinheim 69469
620 180-0

(G-9868)
FRONTERA RESOURCES CORPORATION (PA)
3040 Post Oak Blvd # 1100 (77056-6540)
PHONE...........................713 585-3200
Steve Nicandros, *CEO*
Jesse Jefferies, *CEO*
Lan C Bentsen, *Exec VP*
Reg Spiller, *Senior VP*
Levan Bakhutashvili, *Vice Pres*
▼ EMP: 12
SQ FT: 8,571
SALES (est): 21.8MM **Privately Held**
WEB: www.fronteraresources.com
SIC: 1381 8748 Drilling oil & gas wells;
business consulting

(G-9869)
FRONTIER PETROLEUM RESOURCES
6200 Savoy Dr Ste 650 (77036-3384)
PHONE...........................832 242-1510
Olatunji Odusola, *President*
Morakinyo C Akinrinlola, *Director*
Kolawole Akosile, *Director*
Olumide Mayungbe, *Director*
Stanley A Reid, *Director*
EMP: 50
SQ FT: 3,000
SALES (est): 100MM **Privately Held**
WEB: www.fronterapetroleum.com
SIC: 2911 5172 Petroleum refining; gaso-
line

(G-9870)
FRONTLINE ENERGY INC
1716 Lubbock St (77007-7718)
P.O. Box 2649, Conway AR (72033-2649)
PHONE...........................713 228-3577
Justin G Despot, *Principal*
EMP: 12
SALES (est): 763.6K **Privately Held**
WEB: www.frontlineenergy.com
SIC: 1389 Oil & gas field services

(G-9871)
FROSTWOOD ENERGY LLC
8558 Katy Fwy Ste 320 (77024-1839)
PHONE...........................713 623-7133
Jason Eubanks, *President*
Steve Knowles, *Opers Staff*
Nicole Richard, *Technician*
EMP: 9
SALES (est): 2.9MM **Privately Held**
WEB: www.frostwoodenergy.com
SIC: 1311 Crude petroleum & natural gas
production

(G-9872)
FSI HOLDINGS LLC (PA)
Also Called: Fluid Systems
18720 Intrcntnntal Crssin (77073-5010)
PHONE....................................832 467-9898
Ben Hiltl, *President*
Pete Hoffmann, *Exec VP*
Peter Hoffman, *Vice Pres*
Romiel William, *Mfg Mgr*
Keith Anderson, *Purchasing*
◆ EMP: 20
SALES (est): 7.8MM **Privately Held**
WEB: www.fluidsystems.com
SIC: 3533 Oil field machinery & equipment

(G-9873)
FULKRUM TCHNICAL RESOURCES INC
1415 North Loop W Ste 800 (77008-1683)
PHONE....................................713 485-4519
Owen Gibbons, *Exec Dir*
Andrew Bethel, *Director*
EMP: 53
SALES (est): 259.9K
SALES (corp-wide): 5.4MM **Privately Held**
WEB: www.fulkrum.com
SIC: 1389 Oil field services
PA: Fulkrum Technical Resources Ltd
    Office 4
    London W8 6B
    845 519-8535

(G-9874)
FUN DA MENTALS FOR EDUCATN LLC
Also Called: Fun Da Mentals For Contruction
5330 Griggs Rd Ste F104 (77021-3713)
P.O. Box 865, Richmond (77406-0022)
PHONE....................................832 368-3345
Malika Martin, *Administration*
Terrian Shackelford,
EMP: 45
SALES (est): 1.8MM **Privately Held**
WEB: www.fun4education.com
SIC: 6732 1799 1389 8741 Educational trust management; construction site cleanup; construction, repair & dismantling services; construction management; construction sand & gravel

(G-9875)
FUNSOURCE PARTNERS
Also Called: Funtastic
3244 Locke Ln (77019-6208)
PHONE....................................713 864-3412
Carolyn Almstedt, *Partner*
Tom Almstedt, *Partner*
Toy Novelty Merchandisers In, *Partner*
John Christoffel, *General Mgr*
Irma Christoffel, *Controller*
▲ EMP: 25
SQ FT: 17,000
SALES (est): 3.4MM **Privately Held**
SIC: 3069 5092 Toys, rubber; toys

(G-9876)
FURMANITE AMERICA INC
6330 Dixie Dr (77087-5052)
PHONE....................................713 844-7656
Eric Moore Ctp, *Asst Treas*
Gerald Blackwell, *Manager*
Robert Quinones, *Supervisor*
EMP: 30
SALES (corp-wide): 1.1B **Publicly Held**
WEB: www.teaminc.com
SIC: 2891 Sealing compounds for pipe threads or joints
HQ: Furmanite America, Inc.
    10370 Richmond Ave # 600
    Houston TX 77042
    713 634-7777

(G-9877)
FUSION LED INC
Also Called: Sign Express
1924 Rankin Rd Ste 300 (77073-5117)
PHONE....................................281 990-6011
Darick Endecott, *President*
Karrie Endecott, *Vice Pres*
EMP: 12
SQ FT: 6,000

SALES (est): 1.8MM **Privately Held**
WEB: www.sign-express.com
SIC: 7389 3993 Design services; electric signs

(G-9878)
FUSION OPERATIONS LP
6911 Fulton St (77022-4834)
PHONE....................................713 691-6547
Stratton Gillis, *Partner*
Al Wade, *Partner*
Reese Chesnut, *General Mgr*
Bob Curd, *Engineer*
Jeff Fenner, *Mktg Dir*
▲ EMP: 54
SQ FT: 65,000
SALES (est): 7.5MM **Privately Held**
WEB: www.fusionhouston.com
SIC: 3479 2851 3541 Coating of metals & formed products; paints & allied products; grinding, polishing, buffing, lapping & honing machines

(G-9879)
FUTURE PIPE INDUSTRIES INC (DH)
11811 Proctor St (77038-2701)
PHONE....................................281 847-2987
Gradi Harrison, *President*
Saad Elkhadem, *President*
Mounib Hatab, *Vice Pres*
Lawrence P Moore, *Vice Pres*
Walaa Mohamed, *Prdtn Mgr*
◆ EMP: 150
SALES (est): 28MM **Privately Held**
WEB: www.futurepipe.com
SIC: 3084 3089 3498 3494 Plastics pipe; fittings for pipe, plastic; synthetic resin finished products; fabricated pipe & fittings; valves & pipe fittings; organic fibers, non-cellulosic
HQ: Future Pipe Industries, Inc.
    1200 G St Nw Ste 600
    Washington DC 20005
    281 847-2987

(G-9880)
FXM INTERNATIONAL LLC
800 Town And Country Blvd # 300 (77024-4552)
PHONE....................................832 886-0003
Ruth Morales Mercado,
EMP: 10 EST: 2009
SALES (est): 321.1K **Privately Held**
WEB: www.fxm.com.mx
SIC: 2051 2052 Bakery: wholesale or wholesale/retail combined; bakery products, dry
PA: F.X. Morales Y Asociados, S.A.P.I. De C.V.
    Jardines Del Cerro No. 149-3
    Monterrey N.L.

(G-9881)
G & A PALLET LLC
8827 Clinton Dr (77029-4305)
PHONE....................................713 670-8118
Maria Moreno, *President*
EMP: 22
SALES (est): 4MM **Privately Held**
SIC: 7699 2448 Pallet repair; pallets, wood

(G-9882)
G & A PALLET CO
8827 Clinton Dr (77029-4305)
P.O. Box 202, Galena Park (77547-0202)
PHONE....................................713 670-8118
EMP: 16 EST: 2009
SALES (est): 960K **Privately Held**
SIC: 2448 Mfg Wood Pallets/Skids

(G-9883)
G & H DIVERSIFIED MFG LP (PA)
11660 Brittmoore Park Dr (77041-6917)
PHONE....................................713 856-1600
Edward Kash, *Partner*
Jimmy Cash, *Partner*
Danny Kash, *Partner*
Janan Kash, *Partner*
Bobby McIntire, *Partner*
EMP: 77 EST: 1958
SQ FT: 20,000

SALES (est): 116.7MM **Privately Held**
WEB: www.ghdiv.com
SIC: 3544 3441 3469 Special dies & tools; die sets for metal stamping (presses); fabricated structural metal; metal stampings

(G-9884)
G & S ENTERPRISES INCORPORATED
Also Called: G S L
10863 Rockley Rd (77099-3405)
PHONE....................................281 530-3077
John W Shadle, *President*
Lindley Cates, *Vice Pres*
Jerome Lewis, *Admin Sec*
EMP: 40
SQ FT: 22,000
SALES (est): 6.7MM **Privately Held**
SIC: 2834 Dermatologicals; ointments

(G-9885)
G B MANUFACTURING INC
1919 Antoine Dr (77055-1803)
PHONE....................................713 681-5837
Greg Miller, *CEO*
Al Simon, *COO*
EMP: 25
SALES (est): 1.7MM **Privately Held**
SIC: 3084 Plastics pipe

(G-9886)
G E OIL TECHNOLOGY INC
6407b Hillcroft St Ste B (77081-3101)
PHONE....................................713 774-0340
Alfredo Belledonne, *President*
EMP: 25
SALES (est): 700K **Privately Held**
SIC: 1389 Oil consultants

(G-9887)
G&C COATINGS & INDUSTRIAL SERV
7450 Miller Road 2 (77049-4818)
PHONE....................................832 916-6070
EMP: 9
SALES (est): 1.3MM **Privately Held**
WEB: www.gandccoatings.com
SIC: 3479 Paints & allied products

(G-9888)
GA STEEL LLC
11117 N Huston Rosslyn Rd (77088-1406)
PHONE....................................281 741-7284
Baltazar Dera, *Manager*
EMP: 16 EST: 2011
SALES (est): 4.1MM **Privately Held**
WEB: www.ga-steel.com
SIC: 3441 Fabricated structural metal

(G-9889)
GADUTEX INC
14023 S Post Oak Rd Ste B (77045-5169)
PHONE....................................713 413-0006
Maria Banuelos, *President*
EMP: 31
SALES (corp-wide): 5.4MM **Privately Held**
WEB: www.gadutex.com
SIC: 3441 Fabricated structural metal
PA: Gadutex Inc.
    5710 Arthington St
    Houston TX 77053
    713 413-0006

(G-9890)
GADUTEX INC
3930 Fuqua St (77047-4820)
PHONE....................................713 413-0006
EMP: 12
SALES (corp-wide): 5.4MM **Privately Held**
WEB: www.gadutex.com
SIC: 3441 Fabricated structural metal
PA: Gadutex Inc.
    5710 Arthington St
    Houston TX 77053
    713 413-0006

(G-9891)
GAINES GROUP LLC (PA)
2901 W Sam Houston Pkwy N A100 (77043-1629)
PHONE....................................713 467-4774
Tom Gaines,

EMP: 53
SALES (est): 1.7MM **Privately Held**
SIC: 3999 Candles

(G-9892)
GAITHER PETROLEUM CORPORATION
16600 Park Row (77084-5019)
PHONE....................................281 579-5200
Orville Duane Gaither II P E, *CEO*
Orville Duane Gaither II, *CEO*
Douglas W Gaither, *President*
Louis Doublet, *Vice Pres*
James Hammelman, *Vice Pres*
EMP: 30
SALES (est): 11.2MM **Privately Held**
WEB: www.gpcoil.co
SIC: 1382 Oil & gas exploration services
PA: Quantum Investment Group, Inc.
    16600 Park Row
    Houston TX 77084
    281 994-5400

(G-9893)
GALAM METALS LLC
Also Called: Metal Supermarkets
13240 Hempstead Rd (77040-6531)
PHONE....................................713 934-8528
Clement Njowo, *President*
EMP: 13
SALES (est): 4.7MM **Privately Held**
WEB: www.metalsupermarkets.com
SIC: 5051 3542 7389 Metals service centers & offices; punching, shearing & bending machines; metal slitting & shearing

(G-9894)
GALLOP CONTRACTING GROUP INC
1602 Mooney Rd (77093-1825)
PHONE....................................281 449-1051
Michael Mitchell, *President*
Tim Rebeau, *Vice Pres*
Paul Moeder, *Project Mgr*
Sean Moore, *Manager*
EMP: 39
SQ FT: 15,000
SALES (est): 11.9MM **Privately Held**
WEB: www.gallopcgi.com
SIC: 3441 Fabricated structural metal

(G-9895)
GALPERTI INC
160 Southbelt Indus Dr (77047-7012)
PHONE....................................713 433-0700
Glenn Fremont, *Vice Pres*
Stephen Bouline, *Controller*
Joyce Willeford, *Credit Staff*
Gerardo Sorola, *Supervisor*
◆ EMP: 111
SALES (est): 45MM
SALES (corp-wide): 1.7MM **Privately Held**
WEB: www.galperti-am.com
SIC: 3462 Flange, valve & pipe fitting forgings, ferrous
HQ: Officine Nicola Galperti E Figlio Spa
    Via Trivio Di Fuentes 4
    Gera Lario CO 22010
    034 193-0186

(G-9896)
GALVESTON BAY GATHERING LLC
1415 La St Ste 2700 (77060)
PHONE....................................281 408-1200
Joseph A Mills, *Principal*
EMP: 14 EST: 2010
SALES (est): 104.6K **Publicly Held**
SIC: 1311 Crude petroleum & natural gas
HQ: Etp Legacy Lp
    8111 Westchester Dr # 600
    Dallas TX 75225
    214 981-0700

(G-9897)
GARDNER DENVER INC
Also Called: Gardner Denver Pumps
785 Greens Pkwy Ste 225 (77067-4466)
PHONE....................................281 873-1200
Peter Wallaco, *CEO*
Jeremy Holberg, *Vice Pres*
Kevin Burt, *Regl Sales Mgr*
Brandon Janda, *Manager*
EMP: 10

SALES (corp-wide): 2.4B **Publicly Held**
WEB: www.gardnerdenver.com
SIC: 3564 Purification & dust collection equipment
HQ: Gardner Denver, Inc.
800 Beaty St
Davidson NC 28036

(G-9898)
GARDNER DNVER WTR JTTING SYSTE
785 Greens Pkwy Ste 225 (77067-4466)
PHONE.................................281 448-5800
Helen W Cornell, *President*
Duane Morgan, *Vice Pres*
Brent A Walters, *Vice Pres*
Thomas Bannon, *Prdtn Mgr*
◆ EMP: 101
SALES (est): 22MM
SALES (corp-wide): 2.4B **Publicly Held**
WEB: www.gardnerdenver.com
SIC: 3561 3829 Pumps & pumping equipment; measuring & controlling devices
HQ: Gardner Denver, Inc.
800 Beaty St
Davidson NC 28036

(G-9899)
GARDNER-GIBSON INCORPORATED
Gardner Asphalt Division
6733 Silsbee St (77033-1113)
PHONE.................................832 288-4111
Orlando Quesada, *Export Mgr*
Ronnie Parker, *Opers-Prdtn-Mfg*
EMP: 10
SQ FT: 36,000
SALES (corp-wide): 424.6MM **Privately Held**
WEB: www.gardner-gibson.com
SIC: 2851 2899 2952 Paints, asphalt or bituminous; waterproofing compounds; roofing felts, cements or coatings
HQ: Gardner-Gibson, Incorporated
4161 E 7th Ave
Tampa FL 33605
813 248-2101

(G-9900)
GARDNER-GIBSON MFG INC
919 Crosstimbers St (77022-3903)
PHONE.................................713 637-4791
Steve Ullery, *Branch Mgr*
EMP: 25
SALES (corp-wide): 424.6MM **Privately Held**
WEB: www.gardner-gibson.com
SIC: 2891 Caulking compounds
HQ: Gardner-Gibson Manufacturing, Inc.
4161 E 7th Ave
Tampa FL 33605
813 248-2101

(G-9901)
GARLOCK SEALING TECH LLC
Also Called: Garlock Metallic Gasket Div
250 Portwall St Ste 300 (77029-1354)
PHONE.................................281 840-4853
Rachael Shulla, *General Mgr*
Adriana Sigaran, *General Mgr*
Matt Miller, *Area Mgr*
Danielle Phillips, *Vice Pres*
Irvin Eshelman, *Research*
EMP: 150
SALES (corp-wide): 1.2B **Publicly Held**
WEB: www.garlock.com
SIC: 3053 Gaskets & sealing devices
HQ: Garlock Sealing Technologies Llc
1666 Division St
Palmyra NY 14522
315 597-4811

(G-9902)
GAS SENSING TECHNOLOGY CORP (PA)
Also Called: Welldog
1415 N Loop W Messanine A (77008)
PHONE.................................307 742-6340
John Pope, *President*
James Walker, *COO*
Bob Rees, *Opers Staff*
Dalton Betts, *Engineer*
Trenton Thornock, *CFO*
EMP: 33 EST: 2007

SALES (est): 18.2MM **Privately Held**
WEB: www.welldog.com
SIC: 1382 Oil & gas exploration services

(G-9903)
GAS VENTURES LTD LIABILITY CO
6363 Woodway Dr Ste 1025 (77057-1757)
PHONE.................................307 864-3754
Ted Knapp,
EMP: 9
SALES (est): 1.7MM **Privately Held**
WEB: www.domeenergy.com
SIC: 1382 Oil & gas exploration services

(G-9904)
GASTAR EXPLORATION INC (PA)
1331 Lamar St Ste 650 (77010-3131)
PHONE.................................713 739-1800
Jerry R Schuyler, *Ch of Bd*
Stephen P Roberts, *COO*
Henry J Hansen, *Vice Pres*
Henry Hansen, *Vice Pres*
Alicia Norton, *Production*
EMP: 20
SALES: 72.1MM **Privately Held**
WEB: www.gastar.com
SIC: 1382 Oil & gas exploration services

(G-9905)
GAUMER COMPANY INC
Also Called: Gaumer Process
13616 Hempstead Rd (77040-5816)
PHONE.................................713 460-5200
EMP: 110
SQ FT: 100,000
SALES (est): 40.2MM
SALES (corp-wide): 2.6B **Privately Held**
WEB: www.gaumer.com
SIC: 3533 3433 Gas field machinery & equipment; heating equipment, except electric
PA: Nibe Industrier Ab
Jarnvagsgatan 40
Markaryd 285 3
433 730-00

(G-9906)
GAUS ANODES INTERNATIONAL LLC
Also Called: Houston Anodes Intl LLC
6425 Cunningham Rd (77041-4713)
PHONE.................................832 243-0700
Antonio Galvan, *President*
Juan Antonio Galvan, *President*
Rodrigo Himiob, *COO*
Roberto Valencia, *Exec VP*
Jaime Galvan, *Vice Pres*
EMP: 25
SALES (est): 3MM **Privately Held**
WEB: www.gausanodes.com
SIC: 3364 3365 Zinc & zinc-base alloy die-castings; aluminum & aluminum-based alloy castings

(G-9907)
GAYLA INDUSTRIES INC (PA)
Also Called: Gayla International
6401 Antoine Dr (77091-1201)
P.O. Box 920800 (77292-0800)
PHONE.................................713 681-2411
Douglas Phillips, *President*
Chris Phillips, *Safety Mgr*
Jeff Phillips, *Sales Mgr*
Andy Reese, *Manager*
D R Phillips, *Director*
▲ EMP: 85 EST: 1954
SQ FT: 85,000
SALES (est): 11.1MM **Privately Held**
WEB: www.gaylainc.com
SIC: 3069 3944 Balloons, advertising & toy: rubber; games, toys & children's vehicles; kites

(G-9908)
GB BIOSCIENCES LLC
2239 Haden Rd (77015-6449)
PHONE.................................713 453-7281
Ronnie Mullins, *Production*
Howard Peters, *Branch Mgr*
Dawn Morris, *Manager*
EMP: 10 **Privately Held**
WEB: www.syngenta.com
SIC: 2879 Pesticides, agricultural or household

HQ: Gb Biosciences Llc
410 S Swing Rd
Greensboro NC 27409
336 632-6000

(G-9909)
GC3 SPECIALTY CHEMICALS INC
Also Called: G C 3
733 Heights Blvd (77007-1539)
PHONE.................................713 802-1761
Elisa Press, *President*
Steven Press, *Treasurer*
EMP: 15 EST: 1994
SQ FT: 4,000
SALES (est): 3.3MM **Privately Held**
WEB: www.gc3.com
SIC: 2899 5169 Corrosion preventive lubricant; water treating compounds; antiscaling compounds, boiler; industrial chemicals

(G-9910)
GDS INTERNATIONAL LLC
Also Called: Global Drilling Support
9841 Windml Lks Blvd (77075-3365)
PHONE.................................713 623-1449
Keith G Holliday, *President*
Les Stewart, *Partner*
Paul A Nicholson, *Vice Pres*
Jessica Salas, *Vice Pres*
Oliver Smart, *Vice Pres*
EMP: 26
SALES (est): 23.4MM **Privately Held**
WEB: www.globaldrillingsupport.com
SIC: 1389 Oil & gas wells: building, repairing & dismantling

(G-9911)
GDS REALTY LLC
Also Called: Global Drilling Support
9841 Windmill Park Ln (77064-3300)
PHONE.................................713 623-1449
Keith G Holliday, *President*
Paul A Nicholson, *Vice Pres*
Juan Valdez, *CFO*
EMP: 17
SALES (est): 6.4MM **Privately Held**
WEB: www.globaldrillingsupport.com
SIC: 3545 Drilling machine attachments & accessories

(G-9912)
GDSWARE
15603 Kuykendahl Rd # 114 (77090-3654)
PHONE.................................832 350-1166
Babar Chaudhary, *Owner*
EMP: 12 EST: 2014
SALES (est): 486.6K **Privately Held**
WEB: www.gdsware.com
SIC: 1389 Oil & gas field services

(G-9913)
GE ENERGY MANUFACTURING INC (HQ)
Also Called: GE Aero Energy Products
1333 West Loop S Ste 700 (77027-9117)
PHONE.................................713 803-0900
Charles Blakenship, *President*
Richard Kasson, *CFO*
Michael Gregory, *Admin Sec*
◆ EMP: 80
SQ FT: 60,000
SALES (est): 1.3B
SALES (corp-wide): 95.2B **Publicly Held**
WEB: www.ge.com
SIC: 3621 3568 5084 Power generators; power transmission equipment; power plant machinery
PA: General Electric Company
5 Necco St
Boston MA 02210
617 443-3000

(G-9914)
GE ENERGY MANUFACTURING INC
16415 Jacintoport Blvd (77015-6589)
PHONE.................................281 864-2669
Jim Wilkinson, *Principal*
Travis Schega, *Opers Staff*
Joe F Schornick, *Engineer*
Lance Hall, *Branch Mgr*
EMP: 53

SALES (corp-wide): 95.2B **Publicly Held**
WEB: www.ge.com
SIC: 3621 3568 3511 Power generators; power transmission equipment; turbines & turbine generator sets
HQ: Ge Energy Manufacturing, Inc.
1333 West Loop S Ste 700
Houston TX 77027
713 803-0900

(G-9915)
GE OIL & GAS PRESSURE CTRL LP (DH)
4424 W Sam Houston Pkwy N S (77041-8243)
P.O. Box 2291 (77252-2291)
PHONE.................................281 398-8901
Daniel C Heintzelman, *CEO*
Ian Milne, *President*
Thomas Adams, *Partner*
Joel Bender, *Partner*
Wendell Brooks, *Partner*
◆ EMP: 100 EST: 2001
SQ FT: 50,000
SALES (est): 313.9MM
SALES (corp-wide): 95.2B **Publicly Held**
WEB: www.woodplc.com
SIC: 3491 Industrial valves
HQ: Ge Energy Manufacturing, Inc.
1333 West Loop S Ste 700
Houston TX 77027
713 803-0900

(G-9916)
GE OIL GAS CMPRSSION SYSTEMS L (PA)
16250 Port Nw (77041-2667)
PHONE.................................713 354-1900
John Sargent, *CEO*
Rudy Kusak, *President*
David Brooks,
▲ EMP: 282
SQ FT: 372,000
SALES (est): 178.9MM **Privately Held**
WEB: www.products.slb.com
SIC: 3463 Pump, compressor, turbine & engine forgings, except auto

(G-9917)
GE PACKAGED POWER LLC (DH)
1330 West Loop S Ste 1000 (77027-9102)
PHONE.................................713 803-0900
Darryl L Wilson, *President*
Bryan Kay, *Counsel*
Mark E Buchanan, *Vice Pres*
Barbara A Cameron, *Vice Pres*
◆ EMP: 200
SALES (est): 121.6MM
SALES (corp-wide): 95.2B **Publicly Held**
SIC: 3511 Turbines & turbine generator sets
HQ: Ge Energy Manufacturing, Inc.
1333 West Loop S Ste 700
Houston TX 77027
713 803-0900

(G-9918)
GE PACKAGED POWER LP (HQ)
Also Called: GE Energy
16415 Jacintoport Blvd (77015-6589)
PHONE.................................281 452-3610
Ryan A Brown, *Partner*
▼ EMP: 67
SALES (est): 102.4MM
SALES (corp-wide): 95.2B **Publicly Held**
WEB: www.ge.com
SIC: 3511 Turbines & turbine generator sets
PA: General Electric Company
5 Necco St
Boston MA 02210
617 443-3000

(G-9919)
GELU ITALIAN ICE LLC
9809 Rowlett Rd Ste G (77075-3439)
PHONE.................................970 986-9535
Karin Gookin, *Mng Member*
EMP: 10
SALES (est): 250K **Privately Held**
WEB: www.lovegelu.com
SIC: 2024 Ices, flavored (frozen dessert)

(G-9920)
GENERAL BODY MANUFACTURING CO (PA)
Also Called: General Truck Body
7110 Jensen Dr (77093-8703)
PHONE...................................713 692-5177
Barbara L Paull, *President*
Barbara Paull, *President*
EMP: 61
SQ FT: 70,000
SALES (est): 39.4MM **Privately Held**
WEB: www.generalbody.com
SIC: 3713　3715　3711　Truck bodies (motor vehicles); truck trailers; motor vehicles & car bodies

(G-9921)
GENERAL CRANE SERVICE INC (PA)
Also Called: Bay Area/General Crane Svc Co
4206 Weslow St (77087-2206)
PHONE...................................713 649-4088
EMP: 40 EST: 1976
SQ FT: 20,000
SALES (est): 21MM **Privately Held**
WEB: www.bayareacrane.com
SIC: 5084　3536　7389　Lift trucks & parts; cranes, overhead traveling; crane & aerial lift service

(G-9922)
GENERAL ELECTRIC COMPANY
11330 Clay Rd (77041-5587)
PHONE...................................281 921-2850
Jeffrey Immelt, *CEO*
Jennifer Ramirez, *Engineer*
Javeed Shah, *Engineer*
Simon Jenkins, *Senior Engr*
Bill Mohr, *Manager*
EMP: 25
SALES (corp-wide): 95.2B **Publicly Held**
WEB: www.ge.com
SIC: 6159　3511　Equipment & vehicle finance leasing companies; turbines & turbine generator sets
PA: General Electric Company
　　5 Necco St
　　Boston MA 02210
　　617 443-3000

(G-9923)
GENERAL ELECTRIC COMPANY
2707 North Loop W Ste 9 (77008-1048)
PHONE...................................713 803-0437
Rick Stewart, *President*
EMP: 500
SALES (corp-wide): 95.2B **Publicly Held**
WEB: www.ge.com
SIC: 3511　Turbines & turbine generator sets
PA: General Electric Company
　　5 Necco St
　　Boston MA 02210
　　617 443-3000

(G-9924)
GENERAL METAL FABRICATING INC
6495 Dixie Dr (77087-5007)
PHONE...................................713 641-5509
Arnold Curry, *President*
Janet Curry, *Admin Sec*
EMP: 10
SQ FT: 11,000
SALES (est): 1.9MM **Privately Held**
SIC: 3441　Fabricated structural metal

(G-9925)
GENERAL MILLS INC
7525 Fm 1960 Rd W (77070-5805)
PHONE...................................281 890-0784
Ester Herrerra, *Branch Mgr*
Wade Jones, *Manager*
EMP: 100
SALES (corp-wide): 17.6B **Publicly Held**
WEB: www.generalmills.com
SIC: 2043　Cereal breakfast foods
PA: General Mills, Inc.
　　1 General Mills Blvd
　　Minneapolis MN 55426
　　763 764-7600

(G-9926)
GENERAL PACKAGING EQUIPMENT CO
6048 Westview Dr (77055-5499)
PHONE...................................713 686-4331
Robert C Kelly, *President*
Geoff Knowers, *Vice Pres*
Sandra G Frieden, *Director*
◆ EMP: 20 EST: 1954
SQ FT: 77,000
SALES (est): 3MM **Privately Held**
WEB: www.generalpackaging.com
SIC: 3565　Bag opening, filling & closing machines

(G-9927)
GENERAL PLAS & COMPOSITES LP
Also Called: GP&c
6910 E Orem Dr (77075-5326)
PHONE...................................713 644-1449
David Walstad, *CEO*
Simon Lawrie, *President*
Edgar Castro, *Mfg Mgr*
Max Stormo, *Mfg Mgr*
Krista Vaughn, *Purch Mgr*
▼ EMP: 150 EST: 1967
SQ FT: 120,000
SALES (est): 47.6MM **Privately Held**
WEB: www.genplastics.com
SIC: 2821　Plastics materials & resins

(G-9928)
GENERON IGS INC
16250 Tomball Pkwy (77086-1014)
PHONE...................................713 937-5200
EMP: 20
SALES (corp-wide): 35MM **Privately Held**
WEB: www.generon.com
SIC: 3569　3443　2813　Separators for steam, gas, vapor or air (machinery); fabricated plate work (boiler shop); nitrogen
HQ: Generon Igs, Inc.
　　16250 State Highway 249
　　Houston TX 77086
　　713 937-5200

(G-9929)
GENERON IGS INC (HQ)
16250 State Highway 249 (77086-1014)
PHONE...................................713 937-5200
Tom Jeffers, *President*
Edward J Devine, *CFO*
John Gallo, *Sales Mgr*
Bob Taylor, *Sales Staff*
Russ Granger, *Manager*
◆ EMP: 100
SQ FT: 20,000
SALES (est): 37.5MM
SALES (corp-wide): 35MM **Privately Held**
SIC: 3569　Separators for steam, gas, vapor or air (machinery)
PA: Innovative Gas Systems, Inc.
　　16250 State Highway 249
　　Houston TX 77086
　　713 937-5200

(G-9930)
GENESIS ALKALI LLC (HQ)
919 Milam St Ste 2100 (77002-5417)
PHONE...................................713 860-2500
Grant Sims, *CEO*
Edward Flynn, *President*
Robert Deere, *CFO*
Terry Harding, *VP Finance*
▼ EMP: 60
SALES (est): 238.7MM **Publicly Held**
WEB: www.genesisenergy.com
SIC: 2812　Sodium bicarbonate

(G-9931)
GENESIS CRUDE OIL LP (HQ)
919 Milam St Ste 2100 (77002-5417)
PHONE...................................713 860-2500
Grant E Sims, *CEO*
Steve Nathanson, *President*
Mark Gorman, *Partner*
Karen N Pape, *Senior VP*
Robert V Deere, *CFO*
▲ EMP: 127
SQ FT: 25,000

SALES (est): 244MM **Publicly Held**
WEB: www.genesiscrudeoil.com
SIC: 1382　Oil & gas exploration services

(G-9932)
GEO HALCON HOLDINGS LLC
1000 La St Ste 6700 (77002)
PHONE...................................832 538-0300
Stephen W Herod, *President*
Robert J Anderson, *Exec VP*
David S Elkouri, *Exec VP*
Joseph Rinando, *Vice Pres*
Mark J Mize, *CFO*
EMP: 77
SALES (est): 1.9MM **Privately Held**
WEB: www.battalionoil.com
SIC: 1311　Crude petroleum production
PA: Battalion Oil Corporation
　　1000 La St Ste 6700
　　Houston TX 77002

(G-9933)
GEO SPACE LP
Also Called: Geo Space Offshore
7334 Gessner Rd (77040-3144)
PHONE...................................713 939-7093
Gary D Owens, *Partner*
James Y'Barbo, *Partner*
Thomas T McEntire, *Partner*
EMP: 11
SALES (est): 2.1MM
SALES (corp-wide): 87.8MM **Publicly Held**
WEB: www.geospace.com
SIC: 3357　3315　Shipboard cable, nonferrous; cable, steel: insulated or armored
PA: Geospace Technologies Corporation
　　7007 Pinemont Dr
　　Houston TX 77040
　　713 986-4444

(G-9934)
GEOKINETICS ACQUISITION CO (HQ)
Also Called: Pgs Onshore
15150 Memorial Dr # 1009 (77079-4304)
PHONE...................................281 509-8000
Eric Wersich, *President*
Sven O Havig, *President*
Jerry Courtney, *Vice Pres*
Susan Gair, *Controller*
James Brasher, *Admin Sec*
▲ EMP: 140 EST: 1997
SALES (est): 26MM
SALES (corp-wide): 896MM **Privately Held**
SIC: 1382　Seismograph surveys
PA: Pgs Asa
　　Lilleakerveien 4c
　　Oslo 0283
　　675 264-00

(G-9935)
GEOKINETICS INC (HQ)
1500 Citywest Blvd # 800 (77042-2300)
PHONE...................................713 850-7600
◆ EMP: 32
SALES (est): 3.7B **Privately Held**
WEB: www.geokineticsinc.com
SIC: 1382　7374　Geophysical exploration, oil & gas field; data processing service
PA: Saexploration Acquisitions (U.S.), Llc
　　1160 Dairy Ashford Rd
　　Houston TX 77079
　　281 258-4400

(G-9936)
GEOLOG AMERICAS INC
10402 Valley Forge Dr (77042-1911)
PHONE...................................281 984-7078
Richard Calleri, *President*
Joseph Kerherve, *Vice Pres*
Samuel Bernstein, *Admin Sec*
▲ EMP: 11
SQ FT: 4,200
SALES (est): 2MM
SALES (corp-wide): 177.9K **Privately Held**
WEB: www.geolog.com
SIC: 1382　Oil & gas exploration services
HQ: Geolog International B.V.
　　Herikerbergweg 282
　　Amsterdam 1101
　　203 420-620

(G-9937)
GEOMECHANICS INTERNATIONAL INC (DH)
5444 Westheimer Rd (77056-5397)
P.O. Box 670968 (77267-0968)
PHONE...................................713 599-0373
Patrick Keenan, *President*
Martin Brudy, *President*
Dennis Dwulet, *CFO*
EMP: 13
SALES (est): 8.3MM
SALES (corp-wide): 23.8B **Publicly Held**
SIC: 4961　7372　Steam supply systems, including geothermal; business oriented computer software
HQ: Baker Hughes Holdings Llc
　　17021 Aldine Westfield Rd
　　Houston TX 77073
　　713 439-8600

(G-9938)
GEOMETRIS LP
Also Called: Geometrics
16125 Timber Creek Place (77084-6901)
PHONE...................................281 856-9600
Manish Desai, *Partner*
EMP: 12
SQ FT: 7,000
SALES: 5MM **Privately Held**
WEB: www.geometris.com
SIC: 3812　Altimeters, standard & sensitive

(G-9939)
GEOPHYSCAL EXPLRTION TECHNOLGY
Also Called: Getech
3000 Wilcrest Dr Ste 155 (77042-3498)
PHONE...................................713 979-9900
James D Fairhead, *President*
Graham Gifford, *Vice Pres*
EMP: 100
SQ FT: 2,204
SALES (est): 5.6MM **Privately Held**
WEB: www.getech.com
SIC: 1382　Geophysical exploration, oil & gas field
PA: Getech Group Plc
　　Kitson House
　　Leeds LS8 2

(G-9940)
GEORESOURCES INC (HQ)
1000 La St Ste 6700 (77002)
PHONE...................................832 538-0300
Frank A Lodzinski, *CEO*
Robert J Anderson, *Exec VP*
Timothy D Merrifield, *Exec VP*
Francis M Mury, *Exec VP*
Leah Kasparek, *Vice Pres*
EMP: 10
SQ FT: 15,800
SALES (est): 12MM **Privately Held**
WEB: www.georesourcesinc.com
SIC: 1311　Natural gas production

(G-9941)
GEORGE MYER COMPANY INC
Also Called: Gmco
2619 Lidstone St (77023-5298)
P.O. Box 230014 (77223-0014)
PHONE...................................713 928-2606
Gardner T Baldwin, *President*
Steven Spuler, *QC Mgr*
Lane Alexander, *Engineer*
Edward M Loke, *Treasurer*
Ryan Goetz, *Sales Staff*
◆ EMP: 13 EST: 1953
SQ FT: 15,600
SALES (est): 3.5MM **Privately Held**
WEB: www.georgemyerco.com
SIC: 3492　Hose & tube fittings & assemblies, hydraulic/pneumatic

(G-9942)
GEORGE R BROWN PARTNERSHIP (PA)
1001 Fannin St Ste 4700 (77002-6798)
PHONE...................................713 652-4901
Nancy Brown Negley, *Partner*
Maconda Brown O'Connor, *Partner*
Louisa Sarofim, *Partner*
Mike S Stude, *Partner*
Isabel Brown Wilson, *Partner*
EMP: 35

▲ = Import ▼=Export
◆ =Import/Export

SQ FT: 21,000
SALES (est) 9.5MM **Privately Held**
SIC: 1311 Crude petroleum production; natural gas production

(G-9943)
GEORGE WOOD AND COMPANY INC
Also Called: A-1 Public Scales
773 Mccarty St (77029-1147)
P.O. Box 1261 (77251-1261)
PHONE.................................713 672-7270
EMP: 50
SQ FT: 2,000
SALES (est) 14.8MM **Privately Held**
WEB: www.a-1scales.com
SIC: 3822 Pressure controllers, air-conditioning system type

(G-9944)
GEOSERVICES INCORPORATED
Also Called: Schlumberger
3600 Briarpark Dr (77042-5206)
PHONE.................................281 443-3370
Chris Platt, *Manager*
Eeksha Kohli, *Manager*
Iriana Pedrero, *Manager*
Leo Leon, *Project Leader*
EMP: 11 **Publicly Held**
WEB: www.geoservices.com
SIC: 1389 Oil field services; mud service, oil field drilling
HQ: Geoservices Incorporated
1325 S Dairy Ashford Rd
Houston TX 77077

(G-9945)
GEOSPACE TECHNOLOGIES CORP (PA)
7007 Pinemont Dr (77040-6601)
PHONE.................................713 986-4444
Gary D Owens, *Ch of Bd*
Walter R Wheeler, *President*
Robbin B Adams, *Exec VP*
Michael J Sheen, *Senior VP*
Robert L Curda, *CFO*
◆ **EMP:** 627
SQ FT: 387,000
SALES: 87.8MM **Publicly Held**
WEB: www.geospace.com
SIC: 3829 3826 Seismographs; seismometers; seismoscopes; thermal analysis instruments, laboratory type

(G-9946)
GESTAMP WIND ENERGY N AMER INC
5120 Woodway Dr Ste 9004 (77056-1765)
PHONE.................................713 263-8166
Alejandor Burgaleta, *CFO*
Tom Roots, *Office Mgr*
Jeremiah Yates, *Office Mgr*
Aday Magec, *Technology*
EMP: 10 **EST:** 2010
SQ FT: 1,500
SALES (est) 1.2MM **Privately Held**
WEB: www.gestampren.com
SIC: 3621 Windmills, electric generating

(G-9947)
GFK INTERESTS LTD
Also Called: F. W. Gartner Therman Spraying
25 Southbelt Indus Dr (77047-7011)
P.O. Box 451509 (77245-1509)
PHONE.................................713 225-0010
Larry Peach, *President*
Michele Falzon, *President*
Jimmy Walker, *Corp Secy*
Tony Carroll, *Opers Mgr*
Richard McCullough, *Opers Mgr*
▲ **EMP:** 90
SQ FT: 90,000
SALES (est) 13MM **Privately Held**
WEB: www.fwgts.com
SIC: 3479 Coating of metals & formed products

(G-9948)
GGS WIPING PRODUCTS LLC
13327 Wallisville Rd (77049-3901)
PHONE.................................713 672-7200
Sunny Khatra, *President*
Devinder Khatra, *Vice Pres*
Iqet Singh Khatra, *Treasurer*
▼ **EMP:** 50 **EST:** 2008

SALES (est) 5.9MM **Privately Held**
SIC: 2211 Scrub cloths

(G-9949)
GHASHIM CAPITAL VENTURES CORP
Also Called: Wearform
11321 Richmond Ave M10 (77082-6668)
PHONE.................................713 266-1888
Mazen Ghashim, *President*
EMP: 10
SQ FT: 4,600
SALES (est) 1MM **Privately Held**
WEB: www.wearform.com
SIC: 7213 5699 5136 2395 Uniform supply; uniforms; uniforms, men's & boys'; embroidery & art needlework; screen printing on fabric articles

(G-9950)
GHX INDUSTRIAL LLC (HQ)
Also Called: G H X Indl
13311 Lockwood Rd (77044-1784)
PHONE.................................713 341-3407
Daniel Ahuero, *CEO*
Richard Harrison, *President*
Titus Jumper, *Business Mgr*
Brad Hoffman, *Vice Pres*
Tom Livesay, *Vice Pres*
◆ **EMP:** 40 **EST:** 2007
SQ FT: 60,500
SALES (est) 189.6MM
SALES (corp-wide): 366.9MM **Privately Held**
WEB: www.ghxinc.com
SIC: 3053 3052 3061 Gaskets & sealing devices; rubber hose; oil & gas field machinery rubber goods (mechanical)
PA: United Distributors Group, Inc.
1241 Vlntr Pkwy Ste 1000
Bristol TN 37620
423 573-7300

(G-9951)
GHX INDUSTRIAL LLC
Also Called: G H X West
6507 W Little York Rd (77040-4801)
PHONE.................................713 939-7423
Rick Clapie, *Branch Mgr*
EMP: 15
SALES (corp-wide): 366.9MM **Privately Held**
WEB: www.ghxinc.com
SIC: 3053 3052 3061 Gaskets & sealing devices; rubber hose; oil & gas field machinery rubber goods (mechanical)
HQ: Ghx Industrial, Llc
13311 Lockwood Rd
Houston TX 77044
713 341-3407

(G-9952)
GHX INDUSTRIAL LLC
Also Called: Ghx Houston
13311 Lockwood Rd (77044-1784)
PHONE.................................713 222-2231
Andrew Martin, *Regional Mgr*
Rick Clapie, *Project Mgr*
Tim Alexander, *Opers Mgr*
Bryce Dolin, *Opers Mgr*
Finlay Drummond, *Opers Mgr*
EMP: 44
SALES (corp-wide): 366.9MM **Privately Held**
WEB: www.ghxinc.com
SIC: 3053 3052 3061 Gaskets & sealing devices; rubber hose; oil & gas field machinery rubber goods (mechanical)
HQ: Ghx Industrial, Llc
13311 Lockwood Rd
Houston TX 77044
713 341-3407

(G-9953)
GIANT CEMENT COMPANY (HQ)
396 W Greens Rd Ste 300 (77067-4530)
P.O. Box 352, Harleyville SC (29448-0352)
PHONE.................................843 851-9898
Duncan Gage, *CEO*
Gary Pechota, *Chairman*
Robert B Thompson, *Vice Pres*
▲ **EMP:** 15
SQ FT: 5,600

SALES (est) 55.8MM **Privately Held**
WEB: www.giantcement.com
SIC: 3241 Masonry cement; portland cement

(G-9954)
GIANT CEMENT HOLDING INC (HQ)
396 W Greens Rd Ste 300 (77067-4530)
PHONE.................................571 302-7150
Jose A Llontop, *CEO*
F William Biddix, *Vice Pres*
Fernando R Saenz, *CFO*
Erin K Cannon, *Admin Sec*
▲ **EMP:** 50
SQ FT: 12,000
SALES (est) 166.1MM **Privately Held**
WEB: www.ensembleiq.com
SIC: 3241 4953 Cement, hydraulic; recycling, waste materials

(G-9955)
GIBRALTAR MONEX CENTURION SVC
5100 Westheimer Rd # 200 (77056-5596)
PHONE.................................800 409-2674
V L Eason, *CEO*
EMP: 9
SALES (est) 308.6K **Privately Held**
WEB: www.centurionmediasolutions.com
SIC: 7372 8741 Prepackaged software; business management

(G-9956)
GIBRALTAR TRADING INC
6885 Harwin Dr Ste K (77036-2247)
PHONE.................................281 777-6786
Muhammad Atiq Ur Rehman, *CEO*
EMP: 15
SALES (est) 587.6K **Privately Held**
SIC: 3612 Distribution transformers, electric

(G-9957)
GIL AUTOMATIONS LLC
Also Called: Test Equipment USA
16840 Barker Springs Rd # 306 (77084-5039)
PHONE.................................713 904-4600
Gbolahan Lawal, *Principal*
Philip Adebo, *Engineer*
Chibuzor Muoka, *Engineer*
Sola Alo, *Manager*
Omotayo Fisuyi, *Technology*
EMP: 10
SQ FT: 5,000
SALES: 2.5MM **Privately Held**
WEB: www.gilautomation.com
SIC: 3613 7629 8734 Control panels, electric; electrical measuring instrument repair & calibration; calibration & certification

(G-9958)
GILMORE-GLOBAL INSTRS CO INC
9195 Winkler Dr Ste D (77017-5090)
PHONE.................................713 946-9133
Ron Juren, *President*
Jason Juren, *Counsel*
George Winsted, *Prdtn Mgr*
Joanne Juren, *Treasurer*
Jay Woodruff, *Sales Mgr*
▲ **EMP:** 14 **EST:** 1950
SQ FT: 15,000
SALES (est) 5.5MM **Privately Held**
WEB: www.gilmore-global.com
SIC: 5063 3679 Electronic wire & cable; harness assemblies for electronic use; wire or cable

(G-9959)
GIP II BLUE HOLDING PARTNR LP
1501 Mckinney St (77010-4010)
PHONE.................................713 496-4200
John B Hess, *Ch of Bd*
EMP: 170
SALES (est) 1.9MM **Privately Held**
SIC: 1311 Crude petroleum & natural gas

(G-9960)
GLASS BEVELING COMPANY INC (PA)
5214 Brittmoore Rd (77041-7108)
PHONE.................................713 466-5262
Alex Epley, *President*
EMP: 20
SQ FT: 15,000
SALES (est) 3MM **Privately Held**
SIC: 3231 Furniture tops, glass: cut, beveled or polished

(G-9961)
GLASS WHOLESALERS LTD (PA)
Also Called: Craftsman Awards
13105 Nw Fwy Ste 800 (77040-6313)
P.O. Box 7465 (77248-7465)
PHONE.................................713 353-5800
Charles R Lawrence, *President*
◆ **EMP:** 10
SALES (est) 2.6MM **Privately Held**
WEB: www.craftsmanfab.com
SIC: 3229 Pressed & blown glass

(G-9962)
GLASSCRAFT DOOR MFG CORP
2002 Brittmoore Rd (77043-2209)
PHONE.................................713 690-8282
John Plummer, *President*
Eric Eilers, *Vice Pres*
John M Hart, *Vice Pres*
David Miller, *Vice Pres*
Mark O'Neil, *Vice Pres*
▲ **EMP:** 128
SQ FT: 135,000
SALES (est) 21MM
SALES (corp-wide): 23.4MM **Privately Held**
WEB: www.glasscraftdirect.com
SIC: 3231 5031 5039 2431 Products of purchased glass; doors; glass construction materials; millwork
PA: Glass & Door International I, Llc
2002 Brittmoore Rd
Houston TX 77043
713 690-8282

(G-9963)
GLEN KAMMERMAN ENTERPRISES INC
Also Called: Gourmet Table Skirts & Linens
9415 W Bellfort Ave (77031-2308)
PHONE.................................713 666-0602
Glen Kammerman, *President*
Roselle Kammerman, *Vice Pres*
Karolyn Wallace-Meuth, *Executive*
Hilda Sternberg, *Admin Sec*
◆ **EMP:** 100 **EST:** 1971
SQ FT: 40,000
SALES (est) 10.9MM **Privately Held**
WEB: www.tableskirts.com
SIC: 2392 Tablecloths: made from purchased materials

(G-9964)
GLEN ROSE PETROLEUM CORP (PA)
1210 W Clay St Ste 5 (77019-4174)
PHONE.................................832 437-0701
Andrew Taylor-Kimmins, *Ch of Bd*
Cliff M West Jr, *COO*
Theodore D Williams, *CFO*
▼ **EMP:** 11
SALES (est) 739.6K **Publicly Held**
SIC: 1311 Crude petroleum production

(G-9965)
GLEX INC
12900 Fm 529 Rd (77041-2629)
PHONE.................................713 849-4985
Elba Larco, *President*
Larco Guillermo, *Vice Pres*
William Larco, *Vice Pres*
Thomas Boyd, *Project Mgr*
Bobby Charles, *Purchasing*
EMP: 20
SQ FT: 36,000
SALES (est) 5.1MM **Privately Held**
WEB: www.glexinc.com
SIC: 8711 3823 Industrial engineers; industrial process measurement equipment

(G-9966)
GLOBAL CARDIAC MONITORS LLC
2002 Norfolk St Apt B (77098-4255)
PHONE..................................281 788-7269
Karim Alhussiny, *President*
EMP: 11
SALES (est): 826.5K **Privately Held**
SIC: 3845 Electromedical equipment

(G-9967)
GLOBAL CATHODIC PROTECTION INC
9300 Lawndale St Ste A (77012-2705)
P.O. Box 5189 (77262-5189)
PHONE..................................713 784-9588
Bruce Ellis, *Manager*
EMP: 15
SQ FT: 25,000
SALES (est): 395.5K
SALES (corp-wide): 16.1MM **Privately Held**
WEB: www.globalcorrosion.com
SIC: 2899 Corrosion preventive lubricant
PA: Aps-Materials, Inc.
    4011 Riverside Dr
    Dayton OH 45405
    937 278-6547

(G-9968)
GLOBAL CHEMLIQUIDATIONS LLC
198 Hirsch Rd (77020-6334)
PHONE..................................832 539-3969
Kenneth Yellowe, *Principal*
Gaddy Fankeng,
Prince Yellowe,
EMP: 32
SQ FT: 30,000
SALES (est): 3MM **Privately Held**
WEB:
www.globalchemliquid.lookchem.com
SIC: 2879 2261 2819 Agricultural chemicals; chemical coating or treating of cotton broadwoven fabrics; industrial inorganic chemicals

(G-9969)
GLOBAL COMPRESSOR LP
13415 Emmett Rd (77041-2555)
PHONE..................................713 983-8773
Sarah Jackson, *Partner*
Dennis A Wheatley, *Partner*
Shanna House, *Accounting Mgr*
Dawn Burton, *Sales Staff*
America Galvan, *Sales Staff*
EMP: 31
SALES (est): 10.6MM **Privately Held**
WEB: www.globalcompressorparts.com
SIC: 3563 Air & gas compressors including vacuum pumps

(G-9970)
GLOBAL CRANE SALES
14702 Jersey Shore Dr (77047-7001)
PHONE..................................832 364-8301
Uri Toudjarov, *President*
Mike Liu, *Admin Mgr*
EMP: 14
SALES (est): 3MM **Privately Held**
WEB: www.globalcranes.com
SIC: 3531 Cranes

(G-9971)
GLOBAL EMPIRE INCORPORATED
4023 Westhollow Pkwy (77082-4600)
P.O. Box 901 (77001-0901)
PHONE..................................713 503-5545
Nhan Tran, *CEO*
Tuyen Tran, *Director*
EMP: 10
SQ FT: 40,000
SALES (est): 10MM **Privately Held**
SIC: 2673 Plastic & pliofilm bags

(G-9972)
GLOBAL ENTP WORLDWIDE LLC
10777 Westheimer Rd # 1100
(77042-3462)
PHONE..................................713 260-9687
Muhammad Iqbal, *Branch Mgr*
EMP: 18 **Privately Held**

WEB: www.tektraglobal.com
SIC: 2673 5031 Bags: plastic, laminated & coated; lumber, plywood & millwork
PA: Global Enterprise Worldwide, Llc
    1201 N Orange St Ste 700
    Wilmington DE 19801

(G-9973)
GLOBAL FABRICATION SVCS INC
Also Called: Global Stl & Flamecutting Svcs
14460 Wagg Way Rd (77041-1896)
P.O. Box 9716, Spring (77387-6716)
PHONE..................................281 367-9333
Karl W Oswald, *CEO*
Ron Borg, *President*
Larry Keeler, *CFO*
Jessica Little, *Sales Staff*
Stefani Watson, *Sales Staff*
◆ **EMP:** 110
SQ FT: 120,000
SALES (est): 25.1MM **Privately Held**
WEB: www.globalsteel.net
SIC: 3441 Fabricated structural metal for ships

(G-9974)
GLOBAL MARINE INC (DH)
Also Called: Transocean
4 Greenway Plz Ste 100 (77046-0403)
PHONE..................................713 232-7500
Steven L Newman, *CEO*
Gregory L Cauthen, *President*
John Stobart, *COO*
ESA Ikheimonen, *Exec VP*
Ramon Yi, *Treasurer*
EMP: 52 **EST:** 1955
SALES (est): 292.5MM
SALES (corp-wide): 4.1B **Privately Held**
WEB: www.deepwater.com
SIC: 1381 1311 Drilling oil & gas wells; crude petroleum production; natural gas production
HQ: Transocean Inc.
    4 Greenway Plz Ste 700
    Houston TX 77046
    713 232-7500 .

(G-9975)
GLOBAL NUCLEONICS LLC
16203 Park Row Ste 110 (77084-5136)
PHONE..................................281 578-7900
Kyriakos Tsorbatzoglou, *President*
Dennis Lappert, *Engineer*
Yanis Barela, *Manager*
EMP: 15
SALES (est): 4MM **Privately Held**
WEB: www.globalnucleonics.com
SIC: 3829 3674 Measuring & controlling devices; radiation sensors

(G-9976)
GLOBAL SANTA FE DRILLING CO (DH)
4 Greenway Plz Ste 100 (77046-0403)
PHONE..................................281 925-6821
Charles M Striedel, *President*
Steven J Gangelhoff, *Vice Pres*
Mark E Monroe, *Vice Pres*
L Craig Williams, *Treasurer*
Margaret C Fitzgerald, *Admin Sec*
EMP: 58 **EST:** 1970
SQ FT: 50,000
SALES (est): 43.7MM
SALES (corp-wide): 4.1B **Privately Held**
WEB: www.deepwater.com
SIC: 1381 Drilling oil & gas wells
HQ: Global Marine Inc
    4 Greenway Plz Ste 100
    Houston TX 77046
    713 232-7500

(G-9977)
GLOBAL SANTA FE INC
4 Greenway Plz Ste 100 (77046-0403)
P.O. Box 4379 (77210-4379)
PHONE..................................281 925-6000
Jon Marshall, *President*
Steve Gangelhoff, *President*
EMP: 485
SQ FT: 100,000
SALES (est): 20.2MM
SALES (corp-wide): 4.1B **Privately Held**
WEB: www.deepwater.com
SIC: 1381 Drilling oil & gas wells

HQ: Global Marine Inc
    4 Greenway Plz Ste 100
    Houston TX 77046
    713 232-7500

(G-9978)
GLOBAL TEKNICIANS INC
2016 Main St Ste 101 (77002-8842)
PHONE..................................407 504-9087
Letitia Poleon, *Vice Pres*
Marc S Poleon, *Director*
EMP: 24 **EST:** 2015
SQ FT: 600
SALES (est): 300.3K **Privately Held**
SIC: 3357 Fiber optic cable (insulated)

(G-9979)
GLOBAL VAPOR CONTROL INC
12600 N Featherwood Dr # 330
(77034-4449)
PHONE..................................713 463-9200
Alan Finley, *Principal*
Maria Leal, *Opers Staff*
EMP: 25
SALES (est): 5MM **Privately Held**
WEB: www.gvcontrol.com
SIC: 3559 Sewing machines & hat & zipper making machinery

(G-9980)
GLOBAL WELDING SERVICES INC
7931 Hall Rd (77075-4618)
PHONE..................................713 991-3555
Miguel Monteiro, *President*
Raul Rodriguez, *Admin Sec*
EMP: 87 **EST:** 2003
SQ FT: 32,000
SALES (est): 8.6MM **Privately Held**
WEB: www.weldingglobalservices.com
SIC: 7692 Welding repair

(G-9981)
GLOBAL WSTEWATER SOLUTIONS INC
Also Called: Energy Specialties Intl
6766 Bourgeois Rd (77066-3105)
PHONE..................................832 286-4600
Jason E Bramlett, *President*
Kendell H Bramlett, *Vice Pres*
Kendell Hill, *Controller*
EMP: 9
SALES (est): 742.4K **Privately Held**
WEB: www.energyspecialties.com
SIC: 2899 Water treating compounds

(G-9982)
GLOBALOGIX INC (PA)
7840 N Sam Houston Pkwy W # 300
(77064-3505)
PHONE..................................713 987-7630
Charles Drobny Jr, *CEO*
Jim Fererro, *Senior VP*
Wayne Salsiccia, *Vice Pres*
Kristopher Klug, *CFO*
EMP: 30
SALES (est): 19.4MM **Privately Held**
WEB: www.globlx.com
SIC: 1389 Construction, repair & dismantling services

(G-9983)
GLOBALPETROCHEM LLC
Also Called: Lotus Lubes
10301 Northwest Fwy # 312 (77092-8225)
PHONE..................................832 788-3952
Sanjeev Jaiswal, *CEO*
EMP: 10
SALES (est): 545.3K **Privately Held**
WEB: www.lotuslubes.com
SIC: 2992 Lubricating oils

(G-9984)
GLOBALTECH MOTOR & CONTRLS INC
525 Mccarty St (77029-1157)
PHONE..................................281 487-9300
Fernando Osornia, *President*
Frank T Stockstill, *Vice Pres*
Frank Stockstill, *Vice Pres*
Monica Luna, *Purchasing*
▲ **EMP:** 40
SALES (est): 9.1MM **Privately Held**
WEB: www.globaltechmotors.com
SIC: 7694 Electric motor repair

(G-9985)
GLOBE INDUSTRIES INC
3303 Cypress Creek Pkwy # 250
(77068-3615)
PHONE..................................281 440-3999
Mark Gornall, *President*
Pamela Gu, *Vice Pres*
▲ **EMP:** 35
SALES (est): 5.4MM **Privately Held**
WEB: www.globecorp.com
SIC: 3559 3089 Plastics working machinery; injection molding of plastics

(G-9986)
GLYCOL TECHNOLOGIES LLC
1502 Augusta Dr Ste 120 (77057-2454)
PHONE..................................281 779-4753
Richard Heien,
EMP: 10
SALES (est): 283.1K **Privately Held**
WEB: www.glycoltech.com
SIC: 3999 Manufacturing industries

(G-9987)
GMP ENERGY LLC
1700 Post Oak Blvd (77056-3963)
PHONE..................................713 963-4600
EMP: 10
SALES (est): 356.2K **Privately Held**
SIC: 1389 Oil/Gas Field Services

(G-9988)
GMT EXPLORATION CO TEXAS LLC
10260 Westheimer Rd # 460 (77042-3110)
PHONE..................................713 334-6001
William Lancaster, *President*
Guy Bradfield, *CFO*
EMP: 15
SQ FT: 3,500
SALES (est): 11.5MM **Privately Held**
WEB: www.gmtexploration.com
SIC: 1311 1382 Crude petroleum & natural gas production; oil & gas exploration services

(G-9989)
GODS WORD IN TIME INC
9777 W Gulf Bank Rd # 300 (77040-3132)
P.O. Box 1290, Elgin (78621-8290)
PHONE..................................713 466-6799
Gail Rawlings, *President*
Doris Theiss, *Vice Pres*
▲ **EMP:** 16
SQ FT: 2,500
SALES (est): 1MM **Privately Held**
WEB: www.scriptureplanners.com
SIC: 2731 Books: publishing only

(G-9990)
GOENGINEER INC
13105 Nw Fwy Ste 700 (77040-6313)
PHONE..................................713 735-3295
Mike Zaworski, *Principal*
Ross Phillips, *Engineer*
Rozlyn Veteto, *Sales Staff*
EMP: 16
SALES (corp-wide): 48.5MM **Privately Held**
WEB: www.goengineer.com
SIC: 7372 Prepackaged software
PA: Goengineer, Inc.
    1787 E Fort Union Blvd # 100
    Salt Lake City UT 84121
    801 359-6100

(G-9991)
GOLD TASTE FOODS INC
10765 Kingspoint Rd (77075-4115)
PHONE..................................713 378-0198
Kenny Chiu, *President*
Hung B Trieu, *President*
EMP: 60
SALES (est): 8.2MM **Privately Held**
SIC: 2015 Chicken slaughtering & processing

(G-9992)
GOLDEN DUCK INC
2619 Texas St (77003-3242)
PHONE..................................713 222-9262
Binh Vo, *President*
Luong Hong, *Vice Pres*
EMP: 20
SQ FT: 8,000

SALES (est): 3.2MM **Privately Held**
WEB: www.goldenduck.com
SIC: 2015 Poultry slaughtering & processing

(G-9993)
GOLDEN OIL COMPANY
2000 Bering Dr Ste 255 (77057-3730)
PHONE...................................713 626-1110
Ralph T Mc Elvenny Jr, *President*
A M Alloway, *Principal*
EMP: 21
SQ FT: 4,000
SALES (est): 3.6MM **Privately Held**
SIC: 1311 Crude petroleum production

(G-9994)
GOLDEN STONES LP
7902 Hillmont St (77040-6110)
PHONE...................................713 934-7887
Hank Vu, *Partner*
Randy Skinner, *Sales Mgr*
▲ EMP: 46
SQ FT: 12,500
SALES (est): 20MM **Privately Held**
WEB: www.goldenstones.com
SIC: 5211 3281 5032 Counter tops; table tops, marble; marble building stone

(G-9995)
GOLDSTON OIL CORPORATION
1819 Saint James Pl (77056-4110)
P.O. Box 570365 (77257-0365)
PHONE...................................713 355-3408
Jack H Mayfield Jr, *CEO*
Walter G Mayfield, *President*
John Mitchell, *Senior VP*
Rodney Henckel, *Vice Pres*
Edgar Graham, *Production*
EMP: 27
SQ FT: 30,000
SALES (est): 10.4MM **Privately Held**
WEB: www.goldstonoil.com
SIC: 1382 1311 Geological exploration, oil & gas field; crude petroleum production; natural gas production

(G-9996)
GOLIATH MANUFACTURING INC
13942 Chrisman Rd (77039-1918)
PHONE...................................713 641-6979
Bany Gallegos, *President*
EMP: 27
SALES (est): 5MM **Privately Held**
WEB: www.goliathmfg.com
SIC: 3599 Machine shop, jobbing & repair

(G-9997)
GOODCRANE CORPORATION
Also Called: Triyards
12221 Almeda Rd (77045-3725)
PHONE...................................713 434-3322
Levi Romero, *President*
EMP: 80
SQ FT: 20,000
SALES (est): 23.6MM **Privately Held**
WEB: www.goodcrane.com
SIC: 3531 Cranes, locomotive

(G-9998)
GOODMAN MANUFACTURING CO LP
2727 W 18th St Apt 250 (77008-1074)
PHONE...................................713 263-5556
EMP: 267 **Privately Held**
WEB: www.goodmanmfg.com
SIC: 3585 Air conditioning units, complete: domestic or industrial
HQ: Goodman Manufacturing Company, Lp
19001 Kermier Rd
Waller TX 77484
713 861-2500

(G-9999)
GOODMAN MANUFACTURING CO LP
6751 N Eldridge Pkwy (77041-2606)
PHONE...................................713 263-5416
EMP: 13 **Privately Held**
WEB: www.goodmanmfg.com
SIC: 3585 Air conditioning units, complete: domestic or industrial
HQ: Goodman Manufacturing Company, Lp
19001 Kermier Rd
Waller TX 77484
713 861-2500

(G-10000)
GOODRICH DRILLERS LLC
1001 Fannin St Ste 4670 (77002-6721)
P.O. Box 1148 (77251-1148)
PHONE...................................713 659-3680
Hugh R Goodrich, *President*
EMP: 10 EST: 1994
SQ FT: 9,000
SALES (est): 641.7K **Privately Held**
WEB: www.goodrichpetroleum.com
SIC: 1381 Drilling oil & gas wells

(G-10001)
GOODRICH PETROLEUM CO LA LLC
801 Louisiana St Ste 700 (77002-4936)
PHONE...................................713 780-9494
Gil Goodrich,
EMP: 85 EST: 1995
SALES (est): 5.4MM **Privately Held**
WEB: www.goodrichpetroleum.com
SIC: 1382 Oil & gas exploration services

(G-10002)
GOODRICH PETROLEUM COMPANY LLC
801 Louisiana St Ste 700 (77002-4936)
PHONE...................................713 780-9494
Robert C Turnham Jr,
EMP: 70
SALES (est): 7.2MM **Publicly Held**
WEB: www.goodrichpetroleum.com
SIC: 1311 Crude petroleum & natural gas production
PA: Goodrich Petroleum Corporation
801 Louisiana St Ste 700
Houston TX 77002

(G-10003)
GOODRICH PETROLEUM CORPORATION (PA)
801 Louisiana St Ste 700 (77002-4936)
PHONE...................................713 780-9494
Walter G Goodrich, *Ch of Bd*
Robert C Turnham Jr, *President*
Mark E Ferchau, *Exec VP*
Michael J Killelea, *Exec VP*
Robert T Barker, *CFO*
▲ EMP: 121
SALES: 118.3MM **Publicly Held**
WEB: www.goodrichpetroleumcorp.investorroom.com
SIC: 1311 1382 Crude petroleum & natural gas; oil & gas exploration services

(G-10004)
GORDY GAS CORPORATION
Also Called: Sg Interest
100 Waugh Dr Ste 400 (77007-5962)
PHONE...................................979 922-1313
Russell Gordy, *President*
Michael Irey, *Managing Dir*
Bud Guffey, *Superintendent*
Tom Speck, *Vice Pres*
Sharin Scott, *CFO*
EMP: 30
SQ FT: 10,000
SALES (est): 4.7MM **Privately Held**
SIC: 1382 Oil & gas exploration services

(G-10005)
GORDY OIL COMPANY
Also Called: Sg Interests
100 Waugh Dr Ste 400 (77007-5962)
PHONE...................................713 951-0100
Russell Gordy, *President*
Tom Speck, *Vice Pres*
EMP: 20
SALES (est): 2.7MM **Privately Held**
WEB: www.gordyandsons.com
SIC: 1382 Oil & gas exploration services

(G-10006)
GORMANS UNIFORM RENTAL INC
Also Called: Gorman Mat Specialists
9021 Katy Fwy (77024-1601)
PHONE...................................713 467-5424
EMP: 60 EST: 1973
SQ FT: 10,000
SALES (est): 5.2MM **Privately Held**
WEB: www.gormanuniform.com
SIC: 7299 7213 2273 Clothing rental services; uniform supply; mats & matting

(G-10007)
GOWELL INTERNATIONAL LLC
10642 W Little York Rd (77041-4014)
PHONE...................................713 909-2555
Werthmuller Ernst, *Principal*
Widyanto Andono, *Business Mgr*
Bernardo Bur, *Vice Pres*
Nicholas Boggs, *Research*
Yanxiang Yu, *Research*
▲ EMP: 45 EST: 2012
SALES: 3.9MM
SALES (corp-wide): 4.4MM **Privately Held**
WEB: www.gowellpetro.com
SIC: 1389 Well logging; oil field services
PA: Xi'an Gowell Petroleum Equipment Co., Ltd.
Building 3, No.70 Jinye Rd., Hi-Tech Zone
Xian 71008
298 888-8916

(G-10008)
GPS-GLOBAL PALLETS SVCS LLC
7215 Miller Road 2 (77049-4821)
PHONE...................................281 862-9244
Vianney Roger,
◆ EMP: 21
SALES (est): 4.3MM **Privately Held**
WEB: www.fr-gps.com
SIC: 2448 Pallets, wood
HQ: Global Pallets And Packaging Services
160 Avenue Des Pyrenees
Villenave D Ornon 33140

(G-10009)
GRACE INSTRUMENT COMPANY
10770 Moss Ridge Rd (77043-1175)
PHONE...................................713 783-1560
Hongfeng Bi, *President*
Richard Head, *Mfg Staff*
Robert Thibeaux, *Engineer*
Antonio Colorado, *Sales Staff*
Lee Bentley, *Webmaster*
EMP: 30
SQ FT: 1,000
SALES (est): 8.3MM **Privately Held**
WEB: www.graceinstrument.com
SIC: 3823 Viscosimeters, industrial process type

(G-10010)
GRACO INTERESTS INC (PA)
5910 Schumacher Ln (77057-7124)
PHONE...................................713 978-7000
James R Graves Sr, *President*
Rob Miller, *Opers Mgr*
Rodney Schuster, *Opers Staff*
Charles Flynn, *Sales Staff*
Johnny Kanouff, *Sales Staff*
EMP: 280
SQ FT: 30,000
SALES (est): 20.3MM **Privately Held**
WEB: www.gracomechanical.com
SIC: 1711 3444 Plumbing contractors; warm air heating & air conditioning contractor; sheet metal specialties, not stamped

(G-10011)
GRACO MECHANICAL INC
5910 Schumacher Ln (77057-7188)
PHONE...................................713 978-7000
James R Graves Sr, *President*
Bryant See, *Vice Pres*
Randy Allen, *Project Mgr*
Rob Miller, *Sales Staff*
David Bittner, *Manager*
EMP: 60 EST: 1958
SQ FT: 14,800
SALES (est): 14.9MM
SALES (corp-wide): 20.3MM **Privately Held**
WEB: www.gracomechanical.com
SIC: 1711 3444 Heating & air conditioning contractors; ducts, sheet metal
PA: Graco Interests, Inc.
5910 Schumacher Ln
Houston TX 77057
713 978-7000

(G-10012)
GRAFIKSHOP CORPORATION
Also Called: Falcon Fast Print
5906 Star Ln (77057-7118)
PHONE...................................713 977-2555
Gilbert Hoffman, *President*
MEI-Ing Liu, *Corp Secy*
▲ EMP: 20 EST: 1978
SQ FT: 9,000
SALES (est): 2.5MM **Privately Held**
WEB: www.grafikshophouston.com
SIC: 2752 7336 2791 2789 Commercial printing, offset; graphic arts & related design; typesetting; bookbinding & related work; commercial printing; automotive & apparel trimmings

(G-10013)
GRAHAM PACKAGING COMPANY LP
3833 W 11th St (77055-7301)
PHONE...................................713 869-5471
Robert Roos, *Dir Ops-Prd-Mfg*
Corey Tracey, *Manager*
EMP: 120
SQ FT: 52,500 **Publicly Held**
WEB: www.grahampackaging.com
SIC: 3089 3085 Plastic containers, except foam; plastics bottles
HQ: Graham Packaging Company, L.P.
700 Indian Springs Dr # 100
Lancaster PA 17601
717 849-8500

(G-10014)
GRAND COFFEES OF TEXAS LLC
Also Called: Dunn Bros Coffee
6915 La Granada Dr (77083-2405)
PHONE...................................281 530-8321
EMP: 11
SALES: 400K **Privately Held**
SIC: 2095 Mfg Roasted Coffee

(G-10015)
GRANITI VICENTIA LLC (PA)
1075 W Sam Houston Pkwy N # 214 (77043-5018)
PHONE...................................713 869-0800
Michael Robinson, *Vice Pres*
Brian Dirden, *Purchasing*
Belen Perez, *Comptroller*
Megha Raja, *Human Res Mgr*
Debbie Marks, *VP Sales*
◆ EMP: 41
SALES: 30.7MM **Privately Held**
WEB: www.granitivicentia.com
SIC: 3253 Floor tile, ceramic

(G-10016)
GRANT & GERHARDT MACHINE & MFG
3631 Deal St (77025-3606)
P.O. Box 751054 (77275-1054)
PHONE...................................713 946-4664
Harper Gerhardt, *Partner*
EMP: 12
SALES (est): 1MM **Privately Held**
WEB: www.grantmachineco.com
SIC: 3312 Blast furnaces & steel mills

(G-10017)
GRANT PRIDECO INC (HQ)
Also Called: Atlas Bradford Division
10100 Houston Oaks Dr (77064-3514)
PHONE...................................281 878-8000
John D Deane, *President*
David R Black, *President*
Jim Breihan, *President*
Greg L Boane, *Vice Pres*
Philip Choyce, *Vice Pres*
◆ EMP: 85
SQ FT: 42,534
SALES (est): 506.1MM
SALES (corp-wide): 8.4B **Publicly Held**
SIC: 3533 Oil & gas drilling rigs & equipment
PA: National Oilwell Varco, Inc.
7909 Parkwood Circle Dr
Houston TX 77036
713 346-7500

(G-10018)
GRANT PRIDECO LP
400 N Sam Houston Pkwy E # 900
(77060-3548)
PHONE..................................281 878-8000
Brett Chandler, *President*
EMP: 150
SALES (est): 28.6MM
SALES (corp-wide): 8.4B **Publicly Held**
SIC: 3533 5084 Oil & gas field machinery;
petroleum industry machinery
PA: National Oilwell Varco, Inc.
7909 Parkwood Circle Dr
Houston TX 77036
713 346-7500

(G-10019)
GRAPHTEC INC
6209 Windfern Rd (77040-4913)
PHONE..................................713 690-9999
Dillard Grasty, *President*
Carmen Poehler, *Principal*
Angus M Brown, *Vice Pres*
Angus Brown, *Vice Pres*
Scott Dunn, *Opers Staff*
EMP: 50
SQ FT: 25,000
SALES (est): 8.1MM **Privately Held**
WEB: www.graphtecinc.com
SIC: 3993 8712 7336 3944 Electric
signs; architectural services; graphic arts
& related design; craft & hobby kits &
sets; interior design services; design serv-
ices

(G-10020)
GRAVITY MIDSTREAM LLC
1990 Post Oak Blvd # 2400 (77056-3847)
PHONE..................................832 426-3302
Arthur J Brass, *CEO*
Jason Goldstein, *COO*
J David Hubenak, *Vice Pres*
Kenny Hucker, *Vice Pres*
Craig Peus, *CFO*
EMP: 16
SALES: 610K **Privately Held**
WEB: www.gravitymidstream.com
SIC: 1382 Oil & gas exploration services

(G-10021)
GRAYLOC PRODUCTS LLC (HQ)
9342 Telge Rd (77095-5107)
PHONE..................................713 466-8853
Kevin McEvoy, *President*
Gerald Marsh,
▲ EMP: 40
SQ FT: 12,000
SALES (est): 4.9MM
SALES (corp-wide): 2B **Publicly Held**
WEB: www.oceaneering.com
SIC: 3494 3589 Valves & pipe fittings; high
pressure cleaning equipment
PA: Oceaneering International Inc
11911 Fm 529 Rd
Houston TX 77041
713 329-4500

(G-10022)
GRAYSON MILL ENERGY LLC
1160 Dar Ashford Ste 140 (77079)
PHONE..................................832 271-8050
Matt Ultis,
EMP: 10
SALES (est): 259.7K **Privately Held**
WEB: www.graysonmillenergy.com
SIC: 1382 Oil & gas exploration services

(G-10023)
GRAZCO LLC (PA)
Also Called: Precision Wldg & Fabrication
10002 Sweetwater Ln (77037-1200)
PHONE..................................281 252-0151
John T Graziano, *President*
Stacy Graziano, *Treasurer*
EMP: 18
SQ FT: 100,000
SALES (est): 2.4MM **Privately Held**
WEB: www.weweld.com
SIC: 7692 Welding repair

(G-10024)
GREAT AMERICAN MARKETING CO
1224 N Post Oak Rd 160b (77055-7231)
PHONE..................................713 682-6471
Dennis Gleason, *President*

Bill Welch, *Vice Pres*
EMP: 55
SALES (est): 8MM **Privately Held**
WEB: www.greatamericanmktco.com
SIC: 2099 Sandwiches, assembled &
packaged: for wholesale market

(G-10025)
GREAT DANE LLC
Also Called: Great Dane Trailers
10030 Wallisville Rd (77013-4616)
P.O. Box 96666 (77213-6666)
PHONE..................................713 675-6577
H-Glen Williams, *Manager*
Eric Peterson, *Manager*
EMP: 28
SQ FT: 22,455
SALES (corp-wide): 811.6MM **Privately
Held**
WEB: www.greatdane.com
SIC: 3715 5511 7538 Semitrailers for
truck tractors; trucks, tractors & trailers:
new & used; general automotive repair
shops
HQ: Great Dane Llc
222 N Lasalle St Ste 920
Chicago IL 60601

(G-10026)
GREAT HOST INTERNATIONAL INC (PA)
Also Called: Andalucia Nuts
3505 Bering Dr (77057-7103)
PHONE..................................713 977-9090
Ali Zeini, *President*
Sal Zeini, *Vice Pres*
Amar Patel, *Plant Mgr*
Zach Zeny, *Executive*
◆ EMP: 56
SQ FT: 140,000
SALES (est): 4.8MM **Privately Held**
WEB: www.andalucianuts.com
SIC: 2068 Nuts: dried, dehydrated, salted
or roasted

(G-10027)
GREAT LAKES TEXTILES INC
Also Called: Glt Products
2902 E 13th St Ste 200 (77029)
PHONE..................................713 670-9700
Steven Wake, *Branch Mgr*
EMP: 10
SALES (corp-wide): 14.2MM **Privately
Held**
WEB: www.gltproducts.com
SIC: 3086 Insulation or cushioning mate-
rial, foamed plastic
PA: Great Lakes Textiles, Inc.
6810 Cochran Rd
Solon OH 44139
440 914-1122

(G-10028)
GREAT RUG COMPANY (PA)
3001 Fondren Rd Ste L (77063-4900)
PHONE..................................713 789-3666
Wilma Friedman, *Ch of Bd*
Lois Snider, *President*
John Snider, *Vice Pres*
▲ EMP: 13
SALES (est): 2.2MM **Privately Held**
WEB: www.greatrug.com
SIC: 5713 2273 Rugs; carpets; rugs, hand
& machine made

(G-10029)
GREEN LINKS
1624 Van Buren St (77006-1228)
P.O. Box 19136 (77224-9136)
PHONE..................................713 205-6629
Terry Westbrook, *COO*
EMP: 11
SALES (est): 1.7MM **Privately Held**
WEB: www.greenlinksinc.com
SIC: 2822 Synthetic rubber

(G-10030)
GREEN STREAM SOLUTIONS LLC
7941 Katy Fwy Ste 153 (77024-1924)
PHONE..................................832 404-2436
Denise Christianson, *President*
Justin Carter, *CFO*
Kevin Schuldes,
Georgeanna Fischer,
EMP: 60

SQ FT: 6,000
SALES (est): 1.7MM **Privately Held**
WEB: www.greenstreamsolutions.com
SIC: 2899 Chemical preparations

(G-10031)
GREEN VLY OIL SVCS FREE ZONE
5821 Southwest Fwy (77057-7529)
PHONE..................................936 242-0603
Mahmoud Ramadan, *Business Mgr*
EMP: 10 **Privately Held**
WEB: www.gvosgroup.com
SIC: 1382 Oil & gas exploration services

(G-10032)
GREENAMERICA BIOFUELS LLC
20 Greenway Plz Ste 310 (77046-2001)
PHONE..................................865 474-4086
Brad Jenkins, *President*
Shameek Konar, *Vice Pres*
Kristine K Seabrook, *Vice Pres*
Steven Hollerbach, *Treasurer*
EMP: 20
SALES (est): 931.5K
SALES (corp-wide): 5B **Privately Held**
SIC: 2869 Fuels
HQ: Pilot Travel Centers Llc
5508 Lonas Dr
Knoxville TN 37909
877 866-7378

(G-10033)
GREENE TWEED & CO INC
Also Called: Greene Tweed Fluid Group
1930 Rankin Rd Ste 100 (77073-5110)
PHONE..................................281 821-8337
Girish Hedge, *General Mgr*
Tammy Schiferl, *General Mgr*
Ryan Aulenbach, *Engineer*
Sean Brysch, *Engineer*
Jose Cabrera, *Engineer*
EMP: 350
SQ FT: 27,440
SALES (corp-wide): 284.9MM **Privately
Held**
WEB: www.gtweed.com
SIC: 2821 3053 Plastics materials &
resins; gaskets, packing & sealing de-
vices
PA: Tweed Greene & Co Inc
2075 Detwiler Rd
Kulpsville PA 19443
215 256-9521

(G-10034)
GREENE TWEED & CO LLC
1930 Rankin Rd (77073-5110)
PHONE..................................281 765-4500
Seema Gangatirkar, *Vice Pres*
Melanie Kern, *Senior Engr*
Buryl NYCE, *Sales Staff*
Dan Lazas, *Manager*
Charles Burke, *Manager*
EMP: 23 EST: 2014
SALES (est): 4.1MM **Privately Held**
WEB: www.gtweed.com
SIC: 2824 2821 Elastomeric fibers; ther-
moplastic materials

(G-10035)
GREENES ENERGY GROUP LLC (PA)
11757 Katy Fwy Ste 700 (77079-0011)
P.O. Box 80129, Lafayette LA (70598-
0129)
PHONE..................................337 232-1830
Frank Mathews, *President*
Maury Dumba, *Senior VP*
Eugene Garber, *Senior VP*
Gene Garber, *Senior VP*
Minna Tuomi, *Engineer*
▲ EMP: 24
SALES (est): 51.2MM **Privately Held**
WEB: www.greenesenergy.com
SIC: 1389 Oil field services

(G-10036)
GREENSTAR NORTH AMER HOLDINGS
3411 Richmond Ave Ste 700 (77046-3417)
PHONE..................................713 965-0005
Matt Delnick, *CEO*
Dan Crociata, *CFO*
EMP: 600

SQ FT: 90,000
SALES (est): 31.5MM **Privately Held**
WEB: www.greenstarrecycling.com
SIC: 4953 3229 8741 2611 Recycling,
waste materials; glassware, industrial;
management services; pulp mills
PA: Altas Investments Public Limited Com-
pany
Burton Court
Dublin D18 Y

(G-10037)
GREENWELL ENERGY SOLUTIONS LLC (PA)
2000 Edwards St Unit B (77007-4433)
PHONE..................................713 993-7772
Peter Shaper, *CEO*
Ron Wagnon, *President*
Gary McAnally, *District Mgr*
Ron Long, *Vice Pres*
Parel Patel, *Vice Pres*
EMP: 10 EST: 2012
SQ FT: 10,000
SALES (est): 59.6MM **Privately Held**
WEB: www.greenwellsolutions.com
SIC: 1389 Oil field services

(G-10038)
GREENWOOD MANUFACTURING INC
Also Called: Tech Fab
7450 Miller Road 2 (77049-4818)
P.O. Box 1030, Channelview (77530-1030)
PHONE..................................281 862-9001
Clayton Greenwood, *President*
Jeffrey S Greenwood, *Corp Secy*
Shain Bearden, *Project Mgr*
Heather Smith, *Purch Mgr*
EMP: 19
SQ FT: 20,000
SALES (est): 5MM **Privately Held**
WEB: www.tech-fab.com
SIC: 3441 Fabricated structural metal

(G-10039)
GREIF INC
9280 Baythorne Dr (77041-7736)
PHONE..................................713 462-0073
Brian Sherrod, *Plant Supt*
Tom Meyer, *Manager*
EMP: 50
SQ FT: 50,262
SALES (corp-wide): 4.5B **Publicly Held**
WEB: www.deltacogroup.com
SIC: 2655 Fiber cans, drums & similar
products
PA: Greif, Inc.
425 Winter Rd
Delaware OH 43015
740 549-6000

(G-10040)
GREIF FLEXIBLES USA INC
Also Called: Greif Flexible Products & Svcs
7111 Perimeter Park Dr # 300
(77041-4022)
PHONE..................................713 461-0840
Bruce A Boyd, *CEO*
Michael Mapes, *President*
Alf Knutar, *Sales Staff*
Gary Martz, *Admin Sec*
▲ EMP: 16
SQ FT: 61,000
SALES (est): 4.9MM
SALES (corp-wide): 4.5B **Publicly Held**
SIC: 5199 2671 3086 Packaging materi-
als; plastic film, coated or laminated for
packaging; packaging & shipping materi-
als, foamed plastic
HQ: Greif Packaging Llc
366 Greif Pkwy
Delaware OH 43015

(G-10041)
GRETNA MACHINE SHOP INC
3450 Lang Rd (77092-6104)
PHONE..................................713 690-7328
Ninfa Perez, *President*
Jose Benjamin Perez, *Principal*
Nubia Perez, *Vice Pres*
Rosa Ramoz, *Bookkeeper*
Debbie Dostalik, *Office Mgr*
EMP: 40 EST: 1980
SQ FT: 1,500

▲ = Import ▼=Export
◆ =Import/Export

SALES (est): 7.8MM **Privately Held**
WEB: www.gretnamachine.com
SIC: 3599 Machine shop, jobbing & repair

(G-10042)
GRIERSON SPRINGS
MIDSTREAM LLC
1331 Lamar St Ste 1675 (77010-3133)
PHONE..........................713 655-9500
Michael Walsh, *President*
EMP: 50
SQ FT: 7,000
SALES (est): 1.6MM
SALES (corp-wide): 6.9MM **Privately Held**
WEB: www.canyonmidstream.com
SIC: 1382 Oil & gas exploration services
PA: Canyon Midstream Partners, Llc
1331 Lamar St Ste 1675
Houston TX 77010
713 655-9500

(G-10043)
GRIFFIN BARGE LINE LLC
4265 San Felipe St (77027-2920)
PHONE..........................713 560-6874
Edgar C Griffin Jr,
EMP: 23
SALES (est): 3MM **Privately Held**
WEB: www.griffinbarge.com
SIC: 3731 Barges, building & repairing

(G-10044)
GRIFFIN DEWATERING LLC (HQ)
5306 Clinton Dr (77020-7912)
PHONE..........................713 676-8000
Kazem Khonsari, *President*
Parker Harrell, *Business Mgr*
Daisy Suit, *Exec VP*
Alon Najer, *Vice Pres*
Bronson Gerken, *Project Mgr*
▲ EMP: 22
SALES (est): 46.5MM
SALES (corp-wide): 67.4MM **Privately Held**
WEB: www.griffindewatering.com
SIC: 1799 7359 3561 Dewatering; equipment rental & leasing; pumps & pumping equipment
PA: Griffin Holdco, Llc
5306 Clinton Dr
Houston TX 77020
713 671-7000

(G-10045)
GRIFFIN PUMP & EQUIPMENT INC (HQ)
Also Called: Griffin Dewatering
5306 Clinton Dr (77020-7912)
PHONE..........................866 770-8100
David Singleton, *President*
Josh Nabb, *Vice Pres*
Michael Sherraden, *Vice Pres*
Jerry Suto, *Vice Pres*
Michael Bilski, *CFO*
▲ EMP: 20
SQ FT: 50,000
SALES (est): 15MM
SALES (corp-wide): 67.4MM **Privately Held**
WEB: www.griffindewatering.com
SIC: 3561 Pumps & pumping equipment
PA: Griffin Holdco, Llc
5306 Clinton Dr
Houston TX 77020
713 671-7000

(G-10046)
GRIFFITH LAND SERVICES INC
11060 Timberline Rd (77043-3804)
PHONE..........................713 465-3273
Marty Griffith, *President*
Sid Beaumier, *Vice Pres*
EMP: 9
SALES (est): 944.8K **Privately Held**
WEB: www.griffithlandservices.com
SIC: 1382 Oil & gas exploration services

(G-10047)
GRIZZLY ENERGY LLC (PA)
5847 San Felipe St # 3000 (77057-3000)
PHONE..........................832 327-2255
Jonathan C Curth, *CEO*
Joseph Citarrella, *Ch of Bd*
Britt Pence, *Exec VP*
Russell Haseloff, *Foreman/Supr*

Al Abeyta, *Engineer*
EMP: 23
SALES (est): 460.2MM **Publicly Held**
WEB: www.grizzlyenergyllc.com
SIC: 1382 1311 Oil & gas exploration services; crude petroleum production

(G-10048)
GROGAN-HAZEL STEEL INC
10547 Fisher Rd (77041-4083)
P.O. Box 40068 (77240-0068)
PHONE..........................713 466-7501
Kirby Clark, *President*
Kent Rump, *President*
David Grogan, *Principal*
Gene A Grogan, *Principal*
Cathy Messerly, *Corp Secy*
EMP: 25
SQ FT: 15,000
SALES (est): 8.3MM **Privately Held**
SIC: 3441 Fabricated structural metal

(G-10049)
GRON FUELS LLC
109 N Post Oak Ln Ste 440 (77024-7773)
PHONE..........................813 220-3331
EMP: 10
SALES (est): 450.6K **Privately Held**
SIC: 2911 Petroleum Refiner

(G-10050)
GRUMA CORPORATION
Also Called: Mission Foods
12600 Wallisville Rd (77013-4238)
PHONE..........................832 441-5982
Edgar Peral, *Sales Staff*
Alejandro Vambrenal, *Manager*
EMP: 100 **Privately Held**
WEB: www.missionfoods.com
SIC: 4226 2099 Special warehousing & storage; food preparations
HQ: Gruma Corporation
5601 Executive Dr Ste 800
Irving TX 75038
972 232-5000

(G-10051)
GRYPHON OILFIELD SOLUTIONS LLC (PA)
11300 Windfern Rd (77064-4812)
PHONE..........................281 738-3110
Benjamin Weber, *President*
Cesar Casallas, *Business Mgr*
Steve Soileau, *VP Mktg*
Christi Cheramie, *Office Mgr*
Amy Cornutt, *Office Mgr*
EMP: 15
SQ FT: 59,600
SALES (est): 11MM **Privately Held**
WEB: www.gryphonoilfield.com
SIC: 1389 Oil field services

(G-10052)
GS-HYDRO US INC
16405 A Ctr Blvd Ste 400 (77032)
PHONE..........................281 209-1000
Scot Wilkerson, *President*
Sharla Grossie, *Accounts Mgr*
▲ EMP: 20
SQ FT: 32,000
SALES (est): 7MM
SALES (corp-wide): 109.4MM **Privately Held**
WEB: www.gshydro.com
SIC: 3494 3441 5084 Pipe fittings; fabricated structural metal; hydraulic systems equipment & supplies
HQ: Interpump Piping Gs Srl
Via Giambattista Vico 2
Reggio Emilia RE

(G-10053)
GSE ENVIRONMENTAL INC (DH)
19103 Gundle Rd (77073-3515)
PHONE..........................281 443-8564
Charles A Sorrentino, *CEO*
Daniel J Hennessy, *Ch of Bd*
Mark Arnold, *President*
C W Case, *Counsel*
Jeffrey Nigh, *Exec VP*
◆ EMP: 81
SQ FT: 31,400

SALES (est): 230.7MM
SALES (corp-wide): 2.1MM **Privately Held**
WEB: www.gseworld.com
SIC: 3081 1799 Plastic film & sheet; protective lining installation, underground (sewage, etc.)
HQ: Gse Holding, Inc.
19103 Gundle Rd
Houston TX 77073
281 443-8564

(G-10054)
GSE HOLDING INC (DH)
Also Called: GSE Environmental
19103 Gundle Rd (77073-3515)
PHONE..........................281 443-8564
Robert Preston, *President*
Cody Huff, *Regional Mgr*
Jeffery D Nigh, *Exec VP*
Daniel C Storey, *CFO*
Cort Cacicio, *Accountant*
▼ EMP: 150
SQ FT: 149,400
SALES (est): 395MM
SALES (corp-wide): 2.1MM **Privately Held**
WEB: www.gseworld.com
SIC: 3081 6719 Polyethylene film; investment holding companies, except banks
HQ: Groupe Solmax Inc
2801 Rte Marie-Victorin
Varennes QC J3X 1
450 929-1234

(G-10055)
GSE INTERNATIONAL INC (DH)
19103 Gundle Rd (77073-3515)
PHONE..........................281 443-8564
Samir T Badawi, *CEO*
EMP: 11
SALES (est): 45.5MM
SALES (corp-wide): 2.1MM **Privately Held**
WEB: www.gseworld.com
SIC: 3081 1799 Plastic film & sheet; protective lining installation, underground (sewage, etc.)
HQ: Gse Environmental, Inc.
19103 Gundle Rd
Houston TX 77073
281 443-8564

(G-10056)
GUIDANT SALES LLC
Also Called: Guidant/C P I
8934 Kirby Dr (77054-2829)
PHONE..........................713 218-4069
Ryan Mearns, *Sales Staff*
Richard Calfee, *Branch Mgr*
EMP: 55
SALES (corp-wide): 10.7B **Publicly Held**
WEB: www.bostonscientific.com
SIC: 3841 Surgical & medical instruments
HQ: Guidant Sales Llc
4100 Hamline Ave N
Saint Paul MN 55112

(G-10057)
GULF COAST BAG INC (PA)
Also Called: Gulf Coast Bag & Bagging Co
4422 W 12th St (77055-7203)
PHONE..........................281 556-8500
Roger Rochman, *President*
Edward Rochman, *Vice Pres*
Jerry Rochman, *Vice Pres*
Don Long, *Treasurer*
▲ EMP: 10 EST: 1988
SQ FT: 26,500
SALES (est): 10MM **Privately Held**
WEB: www.gulfcoastbag.com
SIC: 3111 2393 Bag leather; textile bags

(G-10058)
GULF COAST BEARING & SEAL INC
8730 Meldrum Ln (77075-2216)
PHONE..........................832 399-4227
Larry Fisher, *CEO*
EMP: 19
SALES (est): 83.5K **Privately Held**
WEB: www.indservllc.com
SIC: 3562 Ball & roller bearings

(G-10059)
GULF COAST DOWNHOLE TECH LLC
Also Called: Gcdt
1610 Greens Rd Ste 300 (77032-1189)
PHONE..........................713 667-4238
◆ EMP: 10
SALES (est): 3.2MM **Privately Held**
WEB: www.gcdt.com
SIC: 3533 Oil & gas field machinery
PA: Prysmian Spa
Via Chiese 6
Milano MI

(G-10060)
GULF COAST MODIFICATION LP
22806 Nw Lake Dr (77095-5374)
PHONE..........................713 896-3000
Ryan Loving, *General Mgr*
EMP: 79
SALES (est): 17MM **Privately Held**
WEB: www.gulfcoastmod.com
SIC: 3599 Machine shop, jobbing & repair

(G-10061)
GULF COAST OIL & GAS INDS LLC
Also Called: Carbide Fabricators
1204 Hays St (77009-6318)
PHONE..........................713 236-1158
Gaylon B Hale, *Principal*
John W Hale, *Vice Pres*
John Hale, *Vice Pres*
Duane Hale, *Production*
Duane W Hale, *Production*
▲ EMP: 85 EST: 1974
SQ FT: 10,000
SALES (est): 23.5MM **Privately Held**
WEB: www.gcivalves.com
SIC: 3533 3494 Oil & gas field machinery; valves & pipe fittings

(G-10062)
GULF COAST SPRING CO INC
9125 Spring Branch Dr (77080-7409)
P.O. Box 430938 (77243-0938)
PHONE..........................713 461-5092
Donald R Byrd, *President*
Charles W Mills, *Vice Pres*
Linda Byrd, *Treasurer*
EMP: 10
SQ FT: 10,000
SALES (est): 1.1MM **Privately Held**
WEB: www.gulfcoastspring.com
SIC: 3495 Wire springs

(G-10063)
GULF COAST STEEL INC
403 S Loop W (77054-4701)
P.O. Box 451147 (77245-1147)
PHONE..........................281 768-8392
Benjamin Ewing, *Principal*
EMP: 30
SALES (est): 11MM **Privately Held**
WEB: www.gulfcoaststeelinc.com
SIC: 3441 Fabricated structural metal

(G-10064)
GULF COAST WELDING LLC
4133 Southerland Rd (77092-4416)
PHONE..........................713 460-3700
Steven Madden, *President*
Kassandra Noland, *VP Finance*
EMP: 40
SALES (est): 6.4MM **Privately Held**
WEB: www.weldfit.com
SIC: 3441 Fabricated structural metal

(G-10065)
GULF ISLAND FABRICATION INC (PA)
16225 Park Ten Pl Ste 300 (77084-5183)
P.O. Box 310, Houma LA (70361-0310)
PHONE..........................713 714-6100
John P Laborde, *Ch of Bd*
Kirk J Meche, *President*
Todd F Ladd, *COO*
Donald Mackay, *Exec VP*
Christian Vaccari, *Exec VP*
▲ EMP: 400
SQ FT: 8,000

SALES: 303.3MM **Publicly Held**
WEB: www.gulfisland.com
SIC: 3441 1389 Fabricated structural metal; construction, repair & dismantling services; oil field services

(G-10066)
GULF PACIFIC RICE CO INC
12010 Taylor Rd (77041-1239)
PHONE..................713 464-0606
Christian Brenckmann, *CEO*
Patrick Casserly, *President*
Friedrich Brenckmann, *Chairman*
◆ **EMP:** 27
SQ FT: 6,500
SALES (est): 3.9MM
SALES (corp-wide): 87MM **Privately Held**
WEB: www.gulfpac.com
SIC: 2044 Rice milling
PA: Gulf Pacific, Inc.
　　12010 Taylor Rd
　　Houston TX 77041
　　713 464-0606

(G-10067)
GULF PUBLISHING COMPANY (PA)
2 Greenway Plz Ste 1020 (77046-0208)
P.O. Box 2608 (77252-2608)
PHONE..................713 529-4301
John T Royall, *President*
Andy McDowell, *Publisher*
Hortensia Barroso, *Business Mgr*
Ron Higgins, *Vice Pres*
Catherine Watkins, *Vice Pres*
EMP: 25 **EST:** 1916
SQ FT: 10,000
SALES (est): 13.7MM **Privately Held**
WEB: www.store.gulfenergyinfo.com
SIC: 2741 2721 Catalogs: publishing only, not printed on site; trade journals: publishing only, not printed on site

(G-10068)
GULF PUBLISHING COMPANY
3 Greenwood St 1020 (77011-3336)
PHONE..................713 529-4301
Rusty Meador, *Principal*
Deborah Hallene, *Controller*
EMP: 50
SALES (corp-wide): 13.7MM **Privately Held**
WEB: www.store.gulfenergyinfo.com
SIC: 2731 2741 2721 Books: publishing only; miscellaneous publishing; periodicals
PA: Gulf Publishing Company
　　2 Greenway Plz Ste 1020
　　Houston TX 77046
　　713 529-4301

(G-10069)
GULF REDUCTION CORPORATION
6020 Esperson St (77011-2330)
PHONE..................713 926-1705
Shawn Bradley, *President*
Sean M Stack, *President*
Barry Hamilton, *Vice Pres*
Scott A McKinley, *Treasurer*
Christopher R Clegg, *Admin Sec*
▲ **EMP:** 135 **EST:** 1949
SQ FT: 225,000
SALES (est): 19.9MM **Privately Held**
WEB: www.uszinc.com
SIC: 3341 2816 Zinc smelting & refining (secondary); zinc pigments: zinc oxide, zinc sulfide
PA: U.S. Zinc Corporation
　　2727 Allen Pkwy Ste 800
　　Houston TX 77019

(G-10070)
GULF RICE MILLING INC
12010 Taylor Rd (77041-1239)
PHONE..................713 464-0606
Christian Brenckmann, *CEO*
Patrick Casserly, *CEO*
Friedrich Brenckmann, *Ch of Bd*
John Poole, *Vice Pres*
◆ **EMP:** 75
SQ FT: 4,500

SALES (est): 19.5MM
SALES (corp-wide): 87MM **Privately Held**
WEB: www.gulfpac.com
SIC: 2044 Flour, rice
PA: Gulf Pacific, Inc.
　　12010 Taylor Rd
　　Houston TX 77041
　　713 464-0606

(G-10071)
GULF STATES LABEL COMPANY LLC
4537 Brittmoore Rd (77041-8005)
PHONE..................713 812-8390
Mike Williams, *Principal*
Robert Niolosi,
EMP: 19
SALES (est): 2.2MM **Privately Held**
WEB: www.gulfstateslabel.com
SIC: 2759 Labels & seals: printing

(G-10072)
GULFCO FORGE COMPANY LLC
12500 Amelia Dr (77045-4818)
PHONE..................409 842-1311
Richard Allendar, *President*
Mark Miller, *Vice Pres*
George Siller, *CFO*
Jeremy Kaufman, *Sales Mgr*
Brian Shoaf, *Accounts Mgr*
EMP: 125
SALES (est): 6.4MM
SALES (corp-wide): 586MM **Privately Held**
WEB: www.elwd.com
SIC: 3462 Iron & steel forgings
PA: Ellwood Group, Inc.
　　600 Commercial Ave
　　Ellwood City PA 16117
　　724 752-3680

(G-10073)
GULFSTREAM HOLDINGS INC
331 Garden Oaks Blvd (77018-5501)
PHONE..................713 696-9996
William Mark Rand, *President*
Julia Rand, *Corp Secy*
EMP: 64 **EST:** 2000
SQ FT: 27,447
SALES (est): 7.2MM **Privately Held**
WEB: www.gulfstream.com
SIC: 2752 Commercial printing, lithographic

(G-10074)
GULL INDUSTRIES INC (PA)
Also Called: Armoloy of Texas
3233 Gano St (77009-6398)
PHONE..................713 224-2430
Kelly Mowry, *President*
J Kelly Mowry, *President*
David Hannah, *General Mgr*
◆ **EMP:** 28
SQ FT: 27,000
SALES (est): 5.7MM **Privately Held**
WEB: www.armoloy-tx.com
SIC: 3479 Coating of metals & formed products

(G-10075)
GUNNS RESTORATION
2423 Greens Rd (77032-1300)
PHONE..................281 645-2260
Katy Link, *Owner*
EMP: 23 **Privately Held**
WEB: www.gunnsrestoration.com
SIC: 2273 Floor coverings, textile fiber
PA: Gunns Restoration
　　2209 8th Ave
　　Fort Worth TX 76110

(G-10076)
GURU GARMENTS
2411 Karbach St Ste 4 (77092-8027)
PHONE..................832 674-0990
Daniel Gonzalez, *Partner*
EMP: 9
SALES (est): 300K **Privately Held**
SIC: 2759 Letterpress & screen printing

(G-10077)
GW MARINE (USA) LLC
430 Highway 6 S Ste 212 (77079-2339)
PHONE..................281 809-6213
Dave Goodman, *Opers Mgr*

EMP: 31
SQ FT: 1,500
SALES (est): 1.5MM **Privately Held**
WEB: www.gwmarine.com.au
SIC: 8711 8999 1389 Consulting engineer; geophysical consultant; oil consultants

(G-10078)
GYRODATA INCORPORATED (PA)
23000 Nw Lake Dr (77095-5344)
PHONE..................713 461-3146
Steve Klopp, *CEO*
Bob McMahan, *President*
David Braquet, *District Mgr*
Donny Dettlaff, *District Mgr*
Dustin Heard, *District Mgr*
◆ **EMP:** 100
SQ FT: 10,000
SALES (est): 394.1MM **Privately Held**
WEB: www.gyrodata.com
SIC: 1389 8713 Oil field services; surveying services

(G-10079)
H & M BAKING LLC
9330 W Arprt Blvd Ste 100 (77031)
PHONE..................713 568-5674
Heath E Wendell, *Principal*
EMP: 9
SALES (est): 1.6MM **Privately Held**
SIC: 2051 Bread, cake & related products

(G-10080)
H & M PLATING COMPANY INC
6804 La Paseo St (77087-5113)
PHONE..................713 643-6516
Gary Hamby, *President*
Deborah Crenshaw, *Treasurer*
Greg Palma, *Sales Dir*
▲ **EMP:** 68 **EST:** 1971
SQ FT: 50,000
SALES (est): 11MM **Privately Held**
WEB: www.hmplating.com
SIC: 3471 Electroplating of metals or formed products

(G-10081)
H & S ENTERPRISES
10523 Mills Cove St (77070-4416)
PHONE..................281 955-1652
Jesse L Stockard Jr, *President*
Stanley Lamar, *Vice Pres*
Macy Stockard, *Vice Pres*
EMP: 10 **EST:** 1953
SQ FT: 7,200
SALES (est): 954.9K **Privately Held**
SIC: 3599 Machine shop, jobbing & repair

(G-10082)
H AND H BINDERY SERVICES INC
6504 Mcgrew St (77087-3430)
PHONE..................713 641-1831
Donald Ray Hailey, *President*
Clara Hailey, *Treasurer*
EMP: 9
SQ FT: 4,000
SALES (est): 500K **Privately Held**
SIC: 2789 Binding only: books, pamphlets, magazines, etc.

(G-10083)
H E & D OPERATING INC
1415 La St Ste 2150 (77002)
PHONE..................713 650-8008
Ronald E Neal, *President*
Frank W Harrison III, *Vice Pres*
EMP: 40
SALES (est): 2.5MM **Privately Held**
SIC: 1382 Oil & gas exploration services

(G-10084)
H K SPECIALTIES CO INC
4711 Steffani Ln (77041-7813)
P.O. Box 886, Katy (77492-0886)
PHONE..................713 466-1567
EMP: 10 **EST:** 1975
SQ FT: 4,000
SALES (est): 1.5MM **Privately Held**
SIC: 3053 Mfg Gaskets

(G-10085)
H ROSEN USA LLC
14120 Interdrive E (77032-3324)
PHONE..................281 442-8282
Hermann Rosen, *President*
Bryce Brown, *Sales Mgr*
Yesenia Gonzalez, *Sales Staff*
Ricky Ramon, *Sr Project Mgr*
Jim Stimson, *Technical Staff*
EMP: 400
SALES (est): 1.1MM **Privately Held**
WEB: www.rosen-group.com
SIC: 3999 5734 Atomizers, toiletry; software, business & non-game

(G-10086)
H&A MACHINE & WELDING LLC
11666 Gulf Pointe Dr (77089-2635)
PHONE..................832 857-8505
Ivan Humbria, *Principal*
Luis Quezada, *Principal*
EMP: 10
SALES (est): 159.7K **Privately Held**
SIC: 7692 Welding repair

(G-10087)
H2ECO BULK LLC
16310 Aldine Westfield Rd (77032-1310)
P.O. Box 7567 (77270-7567)
PHONE..................713 812-8400
EMP: 12 **EST:** 2014
SALES (est): 2MM **Privately Held**
WEB: www.h2ecowater.com
SIC: 2086 Bottled & canned soft drinks

(G-10088)
HAGER MACHINE AND TOOL INC
1303 Hugh Rd (77067-1503)
P.O. Box 672402 (77267-2402)
PHONE..................281 872-6393
William Hager, *President*
Nancy Hager, *President*
Greg Anspach, *General Mgr*
George Torres, *Vice Pres*
EMP: 30
SQ FT: 7,600
SALES (est): 5.2MM **Privately Held**
WEB: www.hagermachine.com
SIC: 3599 Machine shop, jobbing & repair

(G-10089)
HAHN & CLAY LTD
5100 Clinton Dr (77020-7998)
P.O. Box 15521 (77220-5521)
PHONE..................713 672-1671
Don B Sheffield, *President*
Ron Herbanek, *Engineer*
Robby Bowerman, *Sales Staff*
Todd Kokott, *Sales Staff*
Joe Heindl, *Manager*
▲ **EMP:** 200 **EST:** 1890
SQ FT: 250,000
SALES (est): 65.5MM **Privately Held**
WEB: www.hahnclay.com
SIC: 3443 3599 3444 Fabricated plate work (boiler shop); machine shop, jobbing & repair; sheet metalwork

(G-10090)
HALCO LIGHTING TECH LLC
6323 Brookhill Dr (77087-1103)
PHONE..................713 644-6073
Shame Moore, *Branch Mgr*
EMP: 23 **Privately Held**
WEB: www.halcolighting.com
SIC: 3641 Electric lamps
PA: Halco Lighting Technologies Llc
　　2940 Pacific Dr
　　Norcross GA 30071

(G-10091)
HALCON GULF STATES LLC
1000 Louisiana St # 6700 (77002-5005)
PHONE..................832 538-0300
Robert Gainey, *Superintendent*
Warren Overgaard, *Foreman/Supr*
Crystal Huegele, *Human Resources*
Anthony Amoroso, *Marketing Staff*
Andy Hill, *Compensation Mg*
EMP: 19 **EST:** 1997
SALES (est): 1.3MM **Privately Held**
WEB: www.battalionoil.com
SIC: 1311 6792 Crude petroleum production; oil leases, buying & selling on own account

▲ = Import ▼=Export
◆ =Import/Export

HQ: Halcon Holdings, Inc.
1000 La St Ste 6700
Houston TX 77002
832 538-0300

(G-10092)
HALCON HOLDINGS INC (HQ)
1000 La St Ste 6700 (77002)
PHONE...................................832 538-0300
Floyd C Wilson, *CEO*
Stephen Herod, *President*
David S Elkouri, *Exec VP*
Jason Brown, *Vice Pres*
Leah Kasparek, *Vice Pres*
EMP: 35
SQ FT: 19,000
SALES (est): 13.2MM **Privately Held**
WEB: www.battalionoil.com
SIC: 6792 1311 Oil leases, buying & selling on own account; crude petroleum production

(G-10093)
HALCON OPERATING CO INC
Also Called: Hunt Oilfield Supply
1000 La St Ste 6700 (77002)
P.O. Box 1232, Electra (76360-1232)
PHONE...................................832 538-0300
Stephen W Herod, *Exec VP*
Mark J Mize, *CFO*
EMP: 72
SALES (est): 5.2MM **Privately Held**
WEB: www.battalionoil.com
SIC: 1311 Crude petroleum production
PA: Battalion Oil Corporation
1000 La St Ste 6700
Houston TX 77002

(G-10094)
HALDOR TOPSOE INC (DH)
17629 El Cmino Real Ste 3 (77058)
PHONE...................................281 228-5000
Bjerne S Clausen, *CEO*
Anders N Olsen, *CEO*
Haldor Topsoe, *Ch of Bd*
Mark Daniel, *Business Mgr*
Morten Schaldemose, *Exec VP*
◆ **EMP:** 168
SQ FT: 29,354
SALES (est): 63.6MM
SALES (corp-wide): 878MM **Publicly Held**
WEB: www.topsoe.com
SIC: 2819 8711 Catalysts, chemical; chemical engineering
HQ: Haldor Topsoe A/S
Haldor Topsoes Alle 1
Kongens Lyngby 2800
452 720-00

(G-10095)
HALL-HOUSTON EXPLORATION LP
4605 Post Oak Place Dr # 100 (77027-9732)
PHONE...................................713 333-0975
Gary Hall, *Partner*
Brad Bynum, *General Ptnr*
EMP: 9
SALES (est): 1.5MM **Privately Held**
SIC: 1382 7389 Oil & gas exploration services;

(G-10096)
HALL-HOUSTON EXPLORATION II LP
4605 Post Oak Place Dr # 100 (77027-9732)
PHONE...................................713 333-0930
Gary L Hall, *Partner*
Gary Hall, *Partner*
Lynn Rutherford, *Marketing Mgr*
EMP: 10
SALES (est): 595.5K **Privately Held**
SIC: 1382 Oil & gas exploration services

(G-10097)
HALLIBURTON COMPANY
10200 Bellaire Blvd (77072-5206)
P.O. Box 60087 (77205-0087)
PHONE...................................281 575-3000
Bob Dodson, *Opers Staff*
David Lee, *Opers Staff*
David Prather, *VP Bus Dvlpt*
Maria Rabelo, *Finance Mgr*
James McGinty, *Manager*

EMP: 20 **Publicly Held**
WEB: www.halliburton.com
SIC: 1389 Oil field services
PA: Halliburton Company
3000 N Sam Houston Pkwy E
Houston TX 77032

(G-10098)
HALLIBURTON COMPANY
Also Called: Unity Lab Services
15081 Milner Rd (77032-2207)
PHONE...................................281 871-6875
Stephanie Holzhauser, *Finance*
Nicole Shelton, *Branch Mgr*
EMP: 23 **Publicly Held**
WEB: www.halliburton.com
SIC: 1389 Oil field services
PA: Halliburton Company
3000 N Sam Houston Pkwy E
Houston TX 77032

(G-10099)
HALLIBURTON COMPANY
Also Called: Halliburton Technology Center
15081 1/2 Milner Rd Gate3 (77032-2207)
PHONE...................................281 871-2908
Kiattisak Petpisit, *Business Mgr*
Jason Tawse, *Business Mgr*
Deandre Grant, *Warehouse Mgr*
David Lyle, *Technical Mgr*
Allan Rennie, *Technical Mgr*
EMP: 2000 **Publicly Held**
WEB: www.halliburton.com
SIC: 1389 Oil field services
PA: Halliburton Company
3000 N Sam Houston Pkwy E
Houston TX 77032

(G-10100)
HALLIBURTON COMPANY
14524 Hthrow Forrest Pkwy (77032-5400)
PHONE...................................281 297-1200
David Swiderski, *Branch Mgr*
EMP: 170 **Publicly Held**
WEB: www.halliburton.com
SIC: 1389 1382 1381 8711 Oil field services; cementing oil & gas well casings; well logging; perforating well casings; oil & gas exploration services; drilling oil & gas wells; petroleum, mining & chemical engineers
PA: Halliburton Company
3000 N Sam Houston Pkwy E
Houston TX 77032

(G-10101)
HALLIBURTON COMPANY
Also Called: Halliburton Energy Services
3000 N Sam Houston Pkwy E (77032-3299)
P.O. Box 4960, Portland OR (97208-4960)
PHONE...................................281 871-4000
EMP: 184 **Publicly Held**
WEB: www.halliburton.com
SIC: 1389 Oil field services
PA: Halliburton Company
3000 N Sam Houston Pkwy E
Houston TX 77032

(G-10102)
HALLIBURTON COMPANY
13609 Industrial Rd (77015-6835)
PHONE...................................713 455-9547
Charles Beauchamp, *Manager*
EMP: 15 **Publicly Held**
WEB: www.halliburton.com
SIC: 1389 Oil field services
PA: Halliburton Company
3000 N Sam Houston Pkwy E
Houston TX 77032

(G-10103)
HALLIBURTON COMPANY
2101 City West Blvd (77042)
PHONE...................................713 839-2000
Mark Jennings, *Project Mgr*
Jose Abigail, *Opers Staff*
Sinisa Iliskovic, *Opers Staff*
Tim Presley, *Engineer*
Drew Plasek, *Controller*
EMP: 9 **Publicly Held**
WEB: www.halliburton.com
SIC: 1389 Oil field services
PA: Halliburton Company
3000 N Sam Houston Pkwy E
Houston TX 77032

(G-10104)
HALLIBURTON COMPANY
3950 Interwood S Pkwy (77032-3873)
PHONE...................................281 986-4400
Noreen Sanderson, *Branch Mgr*
Rena Candelaria, *Technician*
EMP: 11 **Publicly Held**
WEB: www.halliburton.com
SIC: 1389 Oil field services
PA: Halliburton Company
3000 N Sam Houston Pkwy E
Houston TX 77032

(G-10105)
HALLIBURTON COMPANY
Also Called: Fann Instrument Company
15112 Morales Rd Fl 4 (77032-3210)
P.O. Box 4350 (77210-4350)
PHONE...................................281 871-4482
Shaokun Liu, *Sales Staff*
Dave Lazar, *Marketing Staff*
Carol Woods, *Supervisor*
EMP: 20 **Publicly Held**
WEB: www.halliburton.com
SIC: 1389 Oil field services
PA: Halliburton Company
3000 N Sam Houston Pkwy E
Houston TX 77032

(G-10106)
HALLIBURTON COMPANY
3000 N Sam Houston Pkwy E (77032-3299)
PHONE...................................281 871-4000
Federico Lucas, *Principal*
Michael Hillman, *Vice Pres*
William Rountree, *Production*
Brian Doud, *Engineer*
Travis Honeycutt, *Engineer*
EMP: 20 **Publicly Held**
WEB: www.halliburton.com
SIC: 1389 Oil field services
PA: Halliburton Company
3000 N Sam Houston Pkwy E
Houston TX 77032

(G-10107)
HALLIBURTON COMPANY (PA)
3000 N Sam Houston Pkwy E (77032-3299)
PHONE...................................281 871-2699
Jeffrey A Miller, *Ch of Bd*
Joe D Rainey, *President*
Mark J Richard, *President*
Sheila Gibbs, *Principal*
Tom Coleman, *District Mgr*
◆ **EMP:** 30
SALES: 14.4B **Publicly Held**
WEB: www.halliburton.com
SIC: 1389 1382 1381 8711 Oil field services; cementing oil & gas well casings; well logging; perforating well casings; oil & gas exploration services; drilling oil & gas wells; petroleum, mining & chemical engineers

(G-10108)
HALLIBURTON DELAWARE INC (HQ)
3000 Houston Ave (77009-6735)
PHONE...................................713 759-2600
David J Lesar, *President*
Lester L Colma, *President*
Garry H Dlaurton, *President*
Robert F Heinemann, *President*
Susan S Keith, *President*
▲ **EMP:** 100
SQ FT: 55,000
SALES (est): 2.9B **Publicly Held**
WEB: www.halliburton.com
SIC: 1629 1611 1622 8711 Power plant construction; chemical plant & refinery construction; oil refinery construction; marine construction; highway & street paving contractor; bridge, tunnel & elevated highway; bridge construction; engineering services; consulting engineer; sanitary engineers; pollution control engineering; oil field services; cementing oil & gas well casings; well logging; perforating well casings

(G-10109)
HALLIBURTON ENERGY SVCS INC (HQ)
3000 N Sam Houston Pkwy E (77032)
P.O. Box 60087 (77205-0087)
PHONE...................................281 871-4000
Jeffrey Allen Miller, *President*
Tim McKeon, *President*
John Fronczak, *Principal*
Lawrence J Pope, *Exec VP*
Joel Walden, *Sales Staff*
◆ **EMP:** 50 **EST:** 1924
SALES (est): 13.1MM **Publicly Held**
WEB: www.halliburton.com
SIC: 1389 Oil field services; cementing oil & gas well casings; well logging; perforating well casings

(G-10110)
HALLIBURTON ENERGY SVCS INC
Also Called: Fann Instrument Company
14851 Milner Rd Gate5a (77032-3401)
PHONE...................................281 871-4482
EMP: 86 **Publicly Held**
WEB: www.halliburton.com
SIC: 1389 Oil field services
HQ: Halliburton Energy Services, Inc.
3000 N Sam Houston Pkwy E
Houston TX 77032
281 871-4000

(G-10111)
HALRES LLC
1000 La St Ste 6700 (77002)
PHONE...................................832 538-0300
Stephen W Herod, *President*
Floyd C Wilson, *Chairman*
Robert J Anderson, *Exec VP*
David S Elkouri, *Exec VP*
Mark J Mize, *Exec VP*
EMP: 206 **EST:** 2011
SALES (est): 18.7MM **Privately Held**
WEB: www.battalionoil.com
SIC: 1311 Crude petroleum production

(G-10112)
HAMILL RESOURCES INC
Also Called: Hamill, Claud B Estate
1160 Dairy Ashford Rd # 250 (77079-3022)
PHONE...................................281 556-9581
Charles D Mc Murrey, *President*
Tom H Brown, *Vice Pres*
Brown Thomas H, *Vice Pres*
Charles W Snider, *Vice Pres*
Charlie H Read, *VP Finance*
▲ **EMP:** 13
SQ FT: 10,000
SALES (est): 1.1MM **Privately Held**
SIC: 1382 1311 Oil & gas exploration services; crude petroleum production; natural gas production

(G-10113)
HAMILTON SHIRT INTERESTS LTD
Also Called: Hamilton Shirts
5700 Richmond Ave (77057-6313)
P.O. Box 37113 (77237-7113)
PHONE...................................713 780-8222
James B Hamilton, *President*
Sarah Sadka, *Sales Dir*
Elizabeth Wallace, *Director*
James Hamilton, *Executive*
Jaime Ball, *Retailers*
EMP: 25
SQ FT: 4,700
SALES (est): 3MM **Privately Held**
WEB: www.hamiltonshirts.com
SIC: 5699 2321 Custom tailor; men's & boys' furnishings

(G-10114)
HAMMER INDUSTRIESS LLC
21430 Springbridge Dr (77073-2365)
P.O. Box 8235, Bacliff (77518-8235)
PHONE...................................281 763-2189
Michael Adkins, *Principal*
EMP: 30
SALES (est): 3.1MM **Privately Held**
WEB: www.hammer-ind.com
SIC: 3999 Manufacturing industries

(G-10115)
HAMMONDS TECHNICAL SVCS INC
6807 W Little York Rd (77040-4807)
PHONE..................................281 999-2900
J Allan Hohman, *CEO*
Carl Hammonds, *President*
Marianne K Hohman, *Vice Pres*
Rick Richardson, *Vice Pres*
Norman Ganslen, *Treasurer*
EMP: 35
SQ FT: 106,000
SALES (est): 3.5MM **Privately Held**
WEB: www.hammondscos.com
SIC: 3569 3561 Liquid automation machinery & equipment; pumps & pumping equipment
HQ: Hammonds Technologies, Llc
6951 W Little York Rd
Houston TX 77040

(G-10116)
HANNON HYDRAULICS INC
11550 Brittmoore Park Dr (77041-6915)
PHONE..................................713 849-4445
Donald Mullins, *Exec VP*
Don Mullins, *Vice Pres*
Lou Moyer, *Opers-Prdtn-Mfg*
EMP: 25
SALES (corp-wide): 25.5MM **Privately Held**
WEB: www.hannonoffshore.com
SIC: 7629 3593 3594 Electrical equipment repair services; fluid power cylinders & actuators; fluid power pumps & motors
PA: Hannon Hydraulics, Inc.
625 N Loop 12
Irving TX 75061
972 438-2870

(G-10117)
HANSEN MANUFACTURING INC
Also Called: Hansen Metal Processing
4807 Ramus St (77092-8037)
PHONE..................................713 682-1075
David Hansen, *President*
EMP: 21 **EST:** 1994
SALES (est): 4.8MM **Privately Held**
WEB: www.hmitexas.com
SIC: 3469 3544 Stamping metal for the trade; die sets for metal stamping (presses)

(G-10118)
HANSON AGGREGATES LLC
302 Bennington St A (77022-4820)
PHONE..................................713 692-4408
Jim Norakowski, *Principal*
EMP: 20
SALES (corp-wide): 20.8B **Privately Held**
WEB: www.heidelbergcement.com
SIC: 3273 Ready-mixed concrete
HQ: Hanson Aggregates Llc
8505 Freport Pkwy Ste 500
Irving TX 75063
469 417-1200

(G-10119)
HANSON AGGREGATES LLC
7641 Wright Rd (77041-2425)
PHONE..................................713 937-7405
Nick Hinez, *Opers-Prdtn-Mfg*
EMP: 23
SALES (corp-wide): 20.8B **Privately Held**
WEB: www.heidelbergcement.com
SIC: 3273 Ready-mixed concrete
HQ: Hanson Aggregates Llc
8505 Freport Pkwy Ste 500
Irving TX 75063
469 417-1200

(G-10120)
HANSON LEHIGH INC
16155 Park Row (77084-6972)
PHONE..................................281 616-0700
Kalli Vanderbilt, *General Mgr*
Tom Chizmadia, *Vice Pres*
Michael Milby, *Foreman/Supr*
James Hopper, *Opers Staff*
Jmichael Lau, *Engineer*
EMP: 40

SALES (corp-wide): 20.8B **Privately Held**
WEB: www.lehighhanson.com
SIC: 1442 1422 1423 3297 Sand mining; crushed & broken limestone; crushed & broken granite; cement refractories; concrete products used to facilitate drainage; ready-mixed concrete
HQ: Hanson Lehigh Inc
300 E John Carpenter Fwy
Irving TX 75062

(G-10121)
HANWHA PWR SYSTEMS AMRICAS INC
11700 Katy Fwy (77079-1216)
PHONE..................................281 599-3377
Karl Wygant, *CEO*
Jonathan Bygrave, *Vice Pres*
◆ **EMP:** 14
SQ FT: 4,000
SALES (est): 5.9MM **Privately Held**
WEB: www.hanwhapowersystems.com
SIC: 3564 Turbo-blowers, industrial; purification & dust collection equipment
HQ: Hanwha Power Systems Co., Ltd.
1204 Changwon-Daero, Seongsan-Gu
Changwon 51542

(G-10122)
HAPPY SHOPPER INC
13700 Veterans Memorial D (77014-1026)
P.O. Box 682374 (77268-2374)
PHONE..................................281 751-7138
Lan Nguyen, *CEO*
EMP: 10
SALES (est): 80K **Privately Held**
WEB: www.happyshopper.com
SIC: 7371 7372 Computer software development & applications; application computer software

(G-10123)
HARBISONWALKER INTL INC
4845 Homestead Rd Ste 500 (77028-5835)
PHONE..................................713 635-3200
Ray Deldon, *Branch Mgr*
EMP: 22
SALES (corp-wide): 688.4MM **Privately Held**
WEB: www.thinkhwi.com
SIC: 3255 Clay refractories
HQ: Harbisonwalker International, Inc.
1305 Cherrington Pkwy # 1
Moon Township PA 15108

(G-10124)
HARDMAN SIGNS LP (PA)
9980 Bammel N Houston Rd (77086-2970)
PHONE..................................713 957-2324
Clay Hardman, *President*
EMP: 63
SALES (est): 13MM **Privately Held**
WEB: www.hardmansigns.com
SIC: 3993 Electric signs

(G-10125)
HARDY MACHINE & DESIGN INC
5737 Windfern Rd (77041-6209)
PHONE..................................713 690-3335
Ravinder K Goel, *President*
Aruna Goel, *Corp Secy*
Ankur Goel, *Vice Pres*
Harpreet Dhiman, *Project Mgr*
Roger Swetnam, *Info Tech Mgr*
EMP: 60
SQ FT: 25,000
SALES (est): 12.7MM **Privately Held**
WEB: www.hardymachine.com
SIC: 3599 Machine shop, jobbing & repair

(G-10126)
HARRISON ELECTROPOLISHING LP
13002 Brittmoore Park Dr (77041-7231)
PHONE..................................832 467-3100
Sterling T Harrison, *Partner*
Gustavo Guzman, *Prdtn Mgr*
Ginger Happacher, *Office Mgr*
EMP: 30
SQ FT: 18,500
SALES (est): 3.5MM **Privately Held**
WEB: www.harrisonep.com
SIC: 3471 Electroplating of metals or formed products

(G-10127)
HARRISON HYDRA-GEN LTD
14233 W Road Houston (77041)
PHONE..................................281 807-4420
James L Otwell, *President*
Dan Clarke, *Business Mgr*
Jeff Brock, *Director*
▲ **EMP:** 31
SQ FT: 40,000
SALES (est): 7.3MM **Privately Held**
WEB: www.harrisonhydragen.com
SIC: 3694 Generators, automotive & aircraft

(G-10128)
HARRISON MULLANE INC
Also Called: Right Machine Company
10938 Lucerne St (77016-1918)
PHONE..................................281 449-4846
George W Mullane, *President*
Wilma Mullane, *Vice Pres*
EMP: 120
SQ FT: 35,600
SALES (est): 10MM **Privately Held**
WEB: www.usarightmachine.com
SIC: 3599 3533 3544 Machine shop, jobbing & repair; oil field machinery & equipment; special dies, tools, jigs & fixtures

(G-10129)
HARSCO CORPORATION
Harsco Industrial Ikg
15635 Jacintoport Blvd # 203 (77015-6534)
PHONE..................................281 452-6637
EMP: 52
SALES (corp-wide): 1.5B **Publicly Held**
WEB: www.harsco.com
SIC: 3446 Gratings, open steel flooring
PA: Harsco Corporation
350 Poplar Church Rd
Camp Hill PA 17011
717 763-7064

(G-10130)
HART ENERGY PUBLISHING LLC (PA)
1616 S Voss Rd Ste 1000 (77057-2641)
PHONE..................................713 993-9320
EMP: 55 **EST:** 1973
SQ FT: 50,000
SALES (est): 42.2MM **Privately Held**
WEB: www.hartenergy.com
SIC: 2721 8748 2741 8742 Magazines: publishing only, not printed on site; business consulting; directories: publishing only, not printed on site; newsletter publishing; business planning & organizing services

(G-10131)
HART ENERGY PUBLISHING LLLP
2424 Wilcrest Dr Ste 100 (77042-2753)
PHONE..................................713 952-9500
Richard A Eichler, *Branch Mgr*
George Popps, *Analyst*
EMP: 10
SALES (corp-wide): 42.2MM **Privately Held**
WEB: www.hartenergy.com
SIC: 2741 8742 Miscellaneous publishing; management consulting services
PA: Hart Energy Publishing Llc
1616 S Voss Rd Ste 1000
Houston TX 77057
713 993-9320

(G-10132)
HART ENERGY PUBLISHING LLLP
4545 Postoak Pl (77027)
PHONE..................................713 993-9320
Chris Arndt, *CFO*
Gina Acosta, *Branch Mgr*
Emily Patsy, *Assoc Editor*
Katia Mirkovic, *Analyst*
Jiangtao Sun, *Analyst*
EMP: 55
SALES (corp-wide): 42.2MM **Privately Held**
WEB: www.hartenergy.com
SIC: 2741 2721 Newsletter publishing; magazines: publishing only, not printed on site

PA: Hart Energy Publishing Llc
1616 S Voss Rd Ste 1000
Houston TX 77057
713 993-9320

(G-10133)
HART HEAT TRANSFER PDTS INC
Also Called: Hart Radiators
8226 Kerr St (77029-3908)
PHONE..................................713 675-9848
John E Hart Sr, *Chairman*
Gerry L Hart, *Vice Pres*
John E Hart Jr, *Vice Pres*
Maurice Hart Jr, *Vice Pres*
Mike Contreras, *Manager*
◆ **EMP:** 75
SQ FT: 70,000
SALES (est): 14.3MM **Privately Held**
WEB: www.hartheat.com
SIC: 3443 3732 3714 3585 Heat exchangers, condensers & components; air coolers, metal plate; boat building & repairing; motor vehicle parts & accessories; refrigeration & heating equipment; heating equipment, except electric

(G-10134)
HARTWELL INDUSTRIES INC
8930 Bissonnet St (77074-2496)
P.O. Box 36589 (77236-6589)
PHONE..................................713 771-4311
Charles G Hartwell, *President*
Dana Hartwell, *Treasurer*
▲ **EMP:** 25 **EST:** 1955
SQ FT: 5,000
SALES (est): 4.6MM **Privately Held**
WEB: www.hartwelldrillingproducts.com
SIC: 3291 Abrasive products

(G-10135)
HARVEST PIPELINE COMPANY
1111 Travis St (77002-5924)
P.O. Box 61229 (77208-1229)
PHONE..................................830 334-3280
William P Swenson, *Principal*
EMP: 17
SALES (est): 1.9MM **Privately Held**
WEB: www.harvestmidstream.com
SIC: 1382 Oil & gas exploration services

(G-10136)
HAULING & EXCAVATING CASCO
Also Called: Action Trucking Co
1306 E Anderson Rd (77047-5226)
PHONE..................................713 433-6209
Richard H Martini, *President*
Richard A Martini, *Vice Pres*
Robert Cowan, *Treasurer*
EMP: 35 **EST:** 1975
SQ FT: 1,000
SALES (est): 3.4MM **Privately Held**
WEB: www.actiontrucking.com
SIC: 1794 4212 1446 Excavation & grading, building construction; dump truck haulage; industrial sand

(G-10137)
HAVERHILL CHEMICALS LLC
16800 Imperial Valley Dr # 499 (77060-3159)
PHONE..................................281 885-8900
Alberto Spera, *CEO*
Suresh Gehi, *CFO*
Elizabeth Labarbara, *CFO*
▼ **EMP:** 178
SALES (est): 135.1MM **Privately Held**
SIC: 2899 Chemical preparations

(G-10138)
HAYNES INTERNATIONAL INC
12241 Fm 529 Rd (77041-2805)
PHONE..................................713 937-7597
Robert Pedrick, *Sales/Mktg Mgr*
EMP: 13
SQ FT: 2,300
SALES (corp-wide): 380.5MM **Publicly Held**
WEB: www.haynesintl.com
SIC: 1311 Crude petroleum production; natural gas production
PA: Haynes International, Inc.
1020 W Park Ave
Kokomo IN 46901
765 456-6000

▲ = Import ▼ =Export
◆ =Import/Export

(G-10139)
HB FULLER CNSTR PDTS INC
6107 Industrial Way (77011-1123)
PHONE..............................713 926-3125
Joe Karan, *Opers-Prdtn-Mfg*
EMP: 26
SALES (corp-wide): 2.7B **Publicly Held**
WEB: www.hbfuller-cp.com
SIC: 2891 Adhesives
HQ: H.B. Fuller Construction Products Inc.
    1105 S Frontenac St
    Aurora IL 60504

(G-10140)
HB2 ENERGY INC (PA)
2777 Allen Pkwy Ste 600 (77019-2166)
PHONE..............................713 377-9860
Michael Bertuccio, *CEO*
EMP: 25
SALES (est): 1MM **Privately Held**
SIC: 1381 1382 Drilling oil & gas wells; oil
    & gas exploration services

(G-10141)
HDD ROTARY SALES LLC
1221 Mckinney St Ste 2850 (77010-2028)
PHONE..............................936 446-1200
Gary L Haub, *President*
Steven Bart Powell, *Vice Pres*
EMP: 36
SQ FT: 10,000
SALES (est): 2.8MM **Privately Held**
WEB: www.hddrotary.com
SIC: 1381 Drilling oil & gas wells

(G-10142)
HDI INSTRUMENTS LLC (PA)
Also Called: Houston Digital Instruments
7240 Brittmoore Rd # 119 (77041-3200)
PHONE..............................713 688-8555
William S Condon, *Owner*
Will Condon, *COO*
Rohit Patel, *Admin Sec*
EMP: 23
SALES (est): 4MM **Privately Held**
WEB: www.hdigauges.com
SIC: 3533 3825 3823 Drilling tools for
    gas, oil or water wells; instruments to
    measure electricity; industrial instrmnts
    msrmnt display/control process variable

(G-10143)
HEALTH CARE TEMPORARIES INC
Also Called: H C T
8926 Sherbourne St Ste D (77016-4900)
PHONE..............................713 631-7106
Arthur Woods, *President*
D'Anne Woods, *Corp Secy*
Bonita Woods, *Vice Pres*
EMP: 1100
SQ FT: 5,000
SALES (est): 19.8MM **Privately Held**
WEB: www.healthcaretemporaries.com
SIC: 8082 1542 1522 1081 Home health
    care services; commercial & office build-
    ing contractors; remodeling, multi-family
    dwellings; metal mining services; general
    construction machinery & equipment

(G-10144)
HEARST NEWSPAPERS LLC (PA)
Also Called: Houston Chronicle
4747 Southwest Fwy (77027-6901)
P.O. Box 4260 (77210-4260)
PHONE..............................713 220-7171
Don Bricker, *President*
John T O'Loughlin, *President*
Melissa Bech, *Editor*
Diane Cowen, *Editor*
Charlie Crixell, *Editor*
EMP: 193
SQ FT: 75,000
SALES (est): 252.7MM **Privately Held**
WEB: www.chron.com
SIC: 2711 Newspapers, publishing & print-
    ing

(G-10145)
HEARST NEWSPAPERS LLC
4747 Southwest Fwy (77027-6901)
P.O. Box 4260 (77210-4260)
PHONE..............................713 220-7171
EMP: 224

SALES (corp-wide): 284MM **Privately
Held**
SIC: 2711 Newspapers-Publishing/Printing
PA: Hearst Newspapers, Llc
    801 Texas St
    Houston TX 77027
    713 220-7171

(G-10146)
HEATH CONSULTANTS INCORPORATED (PA)
9030 W Monroe Rd (77061-5212)
PHONE..............................713 844-1300
Carolyn Haag, *President*
Paul Wehnert, *Exec VP*
James Rutherford, *Senior VP*
Kenneth Cowher, *Vice Pres*
Dan Davis, *Vice Pres*
▲ EMP: 148
SQ FT: 34,500
SALES (est): 213.8MM **Privately Held**
WEB: www.heathus.com
SIC: 3826 3812 8711 Analytical instru-
    ments; search & navigation equipment;
    consulting engineer

(G-10147)
HEIGHTS ARMATURE WORKS INC
12250 Taylor Rd (77041-1226)
PHONE..............................713 937-7676
N Jack Segal Jr, *President*
Barbara Segal, *President*
Larry Payne, *General Mgr*
Howard Segal, *Vice Pres*
Ralph Valadez, *Engineer*
EMP: 15
SQ FT: 25,000
SALES (est): 7.5MM **Privately Held**
WEB: www.hawtx.com
SIC: 5063 7694 Motors, electric; armature
    rewinding shops

(G-10148)
HEITMAN COMPANY INC
1422 Mccarty St (77029-4153)
P.O. Box 15588 (77220-5588)
PHONE..............................713 675-9001
Roger W Dickey, *President*
Landy Dickey, *Vice Pres*
Bill Collazo, *Executive*
EMP: 15
SQ FT: 5,000
SALES (est): 2.7MM **Privately Held**
WEB: www.heitmancompany.com
SIC: 7539 3493 3499 Brake repair, auto-
    motive; leaf springs: automobile, locomo-
    tive, etc.; friction material, made from
    powdered metal

(G-10149)
HELEN GORDON INTERESTS LTD (PA)
Also Called: Greensheet
2020 North Loop W Ste 220 (77018-8103)
PHONE..............................713 371-3500
Kathy Douglass, *CEO*
Leo Kissner, *Partner*
Frank Vasquez, *COO*
Ronald Smarrella, *Maint Spvr*
Beth Dill, *CFO*
EMP: 225
SQ FT: 45,000
SALES (est): 62.3MM **Privately Held**
WEB: www.thegreensheet.com
SIC: 2711 Newspapers: publishing only,
    not printed on site

(G-10150)
HELIX ENRGY SLUTIONS GROUP INC (PA)
3505 W Sam Houston Pkwy N S
(77043-1252)
PHONE..............................281 618-0400
William L Transier, *Ch of Bd*
Owen Kratz, *President*
Mark Sanders, *Superintendent*
Scotty Sparks, *COO*
Johnny Edwards, *Exec VP*
◆ EMP: 200
SALES: 751.9MM **Publicly Held**
WEB: www.helixesg.com
SIC: 1629 1389 1311 Marine construc-
    tion; well logging; crude petroleum pro-
    duction; natural gas production

(G-10151)
HELMERICH & PAYNE INTL DRLG CO
2930 W Sam Houston Pkwy N # 250
(77043-1636)
P.O. Box 1429 (77251-1429)
PHONE..............................832 782-6800
Chris Gallio, *Accounts Mgr*
David Moyer, *Branch Mgr*
EMP: 300
SALES (corp-wide): 1.7B **Publicly Held**
WEB: www.hpinc.com
SIC: 1381 Drilling oil & gas wells
HQ: Helmerich & Payne International
    Drilling Co Inc
    1437 S Boulder Ave # 1400
    Tulsa OK 74119
    918 742-5531

(G-10152)
HEMCO INDUSTRIES INC
9318 Reid Lake Dr (77064-7750)
PHONE..............................713 681-2426
Richard M Bevis, *President*
Stephen Nunes, *Vice Pres*
Ryan Barnes, *Accounts Mgr*
Jared Williams, *Marketing Mgr*
EMP: 28 EST: 1968
SALES (est): 7.4MM **Privately Held**
WEB: www.hemcoind.com
SIC: 3446 3534 3441 Architectural metal-
    work; walkways, moving; fabricated struc-
    tural metal

(G-10153)
HENDEE ENTERPRISES INC
9350 S Point Dr (77054-3724)
PHONE..............................713 796-2322
A Kelly Williams, *CEO*
Robert Veasey, *President*
Matt Ranieri, *Opers Mgr*
◆ EMP: 85
SQ FT: 96,000
SALES (est): 18.6MM **Privately Held**
WEB: www.hendee.com
SIC: 2394 Awnings, fabric: made from pur-
    chased materials

(G-10154)
HENDRIX SPCLTY FABRICATION INC
9840 Windmill Park Ln (77064-3301)
PHONE..............................713 466-6888
Philip Barns, *President*
Margaret E Hendrix Salazar, *Corp Secy*
Connie Adams, *Vice Pres*
▼ EMP: 33
SALES (est): 8.1MM **Privately Held**
WEB: www.hendrixfabrication.com
SIC: 3441 Fabricated structural metal

(G-10155)
HENKEL CONSUMER GOODS INC
1110 Nasa Pkwy Ste 470 (77058-3351)
PHONE..............................832 261-2000
EMP: 210
SALES (corp-wide): 22.2B **Privately Held**
WEB: www.henkel-northamerica.com
SIC: 2841 Detergents, synthetic organic or
    inorganic alkaline
HQ: Henkel Consumer Goods Inc.
    200 Elm St
    Stamford CT 06902

(G-10156)
HEP SERVICES LLC
9805 Katy Fwy Ste 900 (77024-1284)
PHONE..............................210 278-1563
EMP: 14
SALES (corp-wide): 1.2MM **Privately
Held**
WEB: www.howardenergypartners.com
SIC: 1382 Oil & gas exploration services
PA: Hep Services, Llc
    16211 La Cantera Pkwy
    San Antonio TX 78256
    210 298-2222

(G-10157)
HERCULES DRILLING COMPANY LLC
Also Called: Hercules International Drlg
9 Greenway Plz Ste 2200 (77046-0931)
P.O. Box 6809 (77265-6809)
PHONE..............................713 350-5100
Stephen M Butz, *Exec VP*
James W Noe, *Exec VP*
Terry L Carr, *Senior VP*
Troy L Carson, *Senior VP*
Richard E McClaine, *Vice Pres*
EMP: 1800
SQ FT: 10,188
SALES (est): 47.1MM **Publicly Held**
WEB: www.herculesoffshore.com
SIC: 1381 Oil & gas exploration services
PA: Hercules Offshore, Inc.
    9 Greenway Plz Ste 2300
    Houston TX 77046

(G-10158)
HERCULES OFFSHORE INC (PA)
9 Greenway Plz Ste 2300 (77046-0941)
PHONE..............................713 350-5100
Lawrence Dickerson, *Ch of Bd*
John T Rynd, *President*
Claus E Feyling, *President*
Beau M Thompson, *Senior VP*
Troy L Carson, *CFO*
◆ EMP: 1000
SALES (est): 63.2MM **Publicly Held**
WEB: www.herculesoffshore.com
SIC: 1381 1389 Drilling oil & gas wells;
    construction, repair & dismantling serv-
    ices; derrick building, repairing & disman-
    tling

(G-10159)
HERMAN PACKAGING CO INC
12822 Hempstead Rd Ste C (77092-4534)
PHONE..............................713 462-0228
Jose G Rivas, *President*
Richard Wininhan, *Sales Mgr*
EMP: 21
SALES (est): 9.6MM **Privately Held**
WEB: www.hermanpackaging.com
SIC: 2653 Boxes, corrugated: made from
    purchased materials

(G-10160)
HERMES CONSOLIDATED LLC (HQ)
Also Called: Wyoming Refining Company
825 Town And Country Ln # 1500
(77024-2235)
PHONE..............................303 894-9966
Anthony Lewis, *CEO*
James Runyan, *President*
Terry Perardi, *CFO*
▲ EMP: 11
SQ FT: 5,500
SALES (est): 32.6MM
SALES (corp-wide): 5.4B **Publicly Held**
WEB: www.parpacific.com
SIC: 2911 4612 Petroleum refining; crude
    petroleum pipelines
PA: Par Pacific Holdings, Inc.
    825 Town And Country Ln # 1500
    Houston TX 77024
    281 899-4800

(G-10161)
HERMITAGE OPERATING LLC
Also Called: Endurance Sands
720 Rusk St Ste 306 (77002-2713)
PHONE..............................337 852-0001
Dale Behan,
EMP: 10 EST: 2013
SALES (est): 238K **Privately Held**
SIC: 1446 Industrial sand

(G-10162)
HERRING ENTERPRISES INC
Also Called: Herring Construction Co
1122 W 20th St (77008-3314)
PHONE..............................713 862-3614
Arthur Allen Herring, *President*
D M Ehley, *Vice Pres*
Paul Westfall, *Vice Pres*
Carol Herring, *Admin Sec*
EMP: 12 EST: 1976
SQ FT: 7,000

SALES (est): 3.6MM **Privately Held**
WEB: www.herringconstruction.com
SIC: 1542 3443 Commercial & office building, new construction; fabricated plate work (boiler shop)

(G-10163)
HESS CORPORATION
1501 Mckinney St (77010-4010)
P.O. Box 2040 (77252-2040)
PHONE....................................713 496-4000
Trey Cleveland, *General Mgr*
Bill Drennen, *Senior VP*
Barbara Lowery-Yilmaz, *Vice Pres*
Brian Truelove, *Vice Pres*
Ken Larson, *Project Mgr*
EMP: 10
SALES (corp-wide): 6.5B **Publicly Held**
WEB: www.hess.com
SIC: 1382 Oil & gas exploration services
PA: Hess Corporation
1185 Ave Of The Amrcas Fl
New York NY 10036
212 997-8500

(G-10164)
HESS INVESTMENTS ND LLC
1501 Mckinney St (77010-4010)
PHONE....................................713 496-4000
John B Hess,
EMP: 170
SALES (est): 180.4K
SALES (corp-wide): 6.5B **Publicly Held**
WEB: www.hess.com
SIC: 1382 Oil & gas exploration services
PA: Hess Corporation
1185 Ave Of The Amrcas Fl
New York NY 10036
212 997-8500

(G-10165)
HESS MIDSTREAM GP LP
1501 Mckinney St (77010-4010)
PHONE....................................713 496-4200
John B Hess, *Ch of Bd*
EMP: 170
SALES (est): 1.9MM
SALES (corp-wide): 5.8MM **Privately Held**
SIC: 1311 Crude petroleum & natural gas
PA: Hess Infrastructure Partners Gp Llc
1501 Mckinney St
Houston TX 77010
713 496-4200

(G-10166)
HEWLETT PACKARD ENTERPRISE CO (PA)
Also Called: Hpe
11445 Compaq Center W Dr (77070-1433)
PHONE....................................650 687-5817
Patricia F Russo, *Ch of Bd*
Antonio Neri, *President*
Keerti Melkote, *President*
Tom Black, *Senior VP*
Neil Macdonald, *Senior VP*
EMP: 148 EST: 1939
SALES: 26.9B **Publicly Held**
WEB: www.hpe.com
SIC: 7372 7379 3572 Business oriented computer software; computer related maintenance services; computer storage devices

(G-10167)
HF GUYTON INC
Also Called: Prime Source Office Solutions
6131 Corporate Dr (77036-3409)
PHONE....................................713 869-6483
Harry F Guyton, *CEO*
Kendra G Williams, *President*
EMP: 30
SQ FT: 16,000
SALES (est): 3.5MM **Privately Held**
WEB: www.primesos.com
SIC: 2759 5943 Commercial printing; office forms & supplies

(G-10168)
HFJ GROUP LLC
Also Called: Lone Star Emergency Group
4553 Aldine Bender Rd (77032-4112)
PHONE....................................833 777-3473
EMP: 45 EST: 2017

SALES (est): 5MM **Privately Held**
WEB: www.lonestareg.com
SIC: 5013 4119 3711 5012 Automotive supplies & parts; ambulance service; ambulances (motor vehicles), assembly of; ambulances

(G-10169)
HH OIL TOOLS INC
5322 Addicks Satsuma Rd A (77084-6874)
P.O. Box 397, Barker (77413-0397)
PHONE....................................281 550-0633
Lance Pattillo, *President*
EMP: 12
SALES (est): 1.4MM **Privately Held**
WEB: www.hot-hed.com
SIC: 5015 2911 Tools & equipment, used: automotive; petroleum refining

(G-10170)
HI-CRUSH INC (PA)
1330 Post Oak Blvd # 600 (77056-3166)
PHONE....................................713 980-6200
Dirk Hallen, *CEO*
Hi-Crush P LP, *General Ptnr*
Stephen White, *COO*
Phil McCormick, *Vice Pres*
Alan Oehlert, *Vice Pres*
▲ **EMP:** 47
SALES: 636.3MM **Privately Held**
WEB: www.hicrushinc.com
SIC: 1442 1481 Sand mining; mine & quarry services, nonmetallic minerals; mine exploration, nonmetallic minerals

(G-10171)
HI-CRUSH WYEVILLE OPER LLC (HQ)
1330 Post Oak Blvd # 600 (77056-3166)
PHONE....................................608 372-4705
James Whipkey, *CEO*
J Philip McCormick Jr, *President*
Jay Alston, *COO*
William Fehr, *Exec VP*
Stephen Klein, *Vice Pres*
EMP: 50
SQ FT: 6,000
SALES (est): 8.5MM **Privately Held**
WEB: www.hicrushinc.com
SIC: 1442 Sand mining

(G-10172)
HI-TECH CHAMPION MANUFACTURING (HQ)
5565 Maudlin St (77087-3341)
P.O. Box 262427 (77207-2427)
PHONE....................................713 644-2181
F John Burton, *President*
Kc Grier, *Controller*
Juan Balderas, *Sales Staff*
Dona Sharbeno, *Sales Staff*
Kara Gardner, *Manager*
◆ **EMP:** 22
SQ FT: 25,000
SALES (est): 5.5MM
SALES (corp-wide): 7.4MM **Privately Held**
WEB: www.chmpgrp.com
SIC: 3053 7699 Gaskets, all materials; industrial machinery & equipment repair
PA: The Champion Group Inc
5565 Maudlin St
Houston TX 77087
713 644-2181

(G-10173)
HIBERNIA ENERGY III LLC
5599 San Felipe St # 1200 (77056-2724)
PHONE....................................713 728-7911
P Embry Canterbury, *CEO*
John Blevins III, *COO*
Sean Keenan, *CFO*
Holly Blair, *Admin Sec*
EMP: 10
SQ FT: 10,000
SALES (est): 285.7K **Privately Held**
WEB: www.hiberniaresources.com
SIC: 1382 Geological exploration, oil & gas field

(G-10174)
HICOR TECHNOLOGIES INC (PA)
4140 World Hstn Pkwy # 100 (77032-2489)
PHONE....................................281 727-0250

William Sayre, *CEO*
Mark Glaze, *Opers Mgr*
Andrei Strikovski, *Chief Engr*
Philip Nelson, *Engineer*
David Freer, *CFO*
EMP: 44
SALES (est): 12.4MM **Privately Held**
WEB: www.hicor.com
SIC: 3563 Air & gas compressors

(G-10175)
HIGH STANDARD MANUFACTURING CO
Also Called: Hs
5151 Mitchelldale St B14 (77092-7201)
PHONE....................................713 462-4200
Allan Aronstein, *President*
Brent Whiteley, *Admin Sec*
EMP: 12
SQ FT: 6,000
SALES (est): 2.3MM **Privately Held**
WEB: www.highstandardfirearmsusa.com
SIC: 3484 Pistols or pistol parts, 30 mm. & below

(G-10176)
HIGH TECH MACHINE II CO LLC
6518 Wesco Way (77041-3401)
PHONE....................................832 467-2806
Melinda Bodukoglu, *President*
Gary Bodukoglu, *Admin Sec*
EMP: 43
SQ FT: 20,000
SALES (est): 6.4MM **Privately Held**
WEB: www.hightechmach.com
SIC: 3599 Machine shop, jobbing & repair

(G-10177)
HIGHMOUNT EXPLORATION PROD LLC (HQ)
1001 Fannin St Ste 800 (77002-6707)
PHONE....................................281 873-1500
Steven B Hinchman, *CEO*
Malcolm Johns, *President*
Dennis G Millet, *CFO*
EMP: 200
SALES (est): 131.7MM **Privately Held**
SIC: 1382 Oil & gas exploration services

(G-10178)
HIGHTOWER COMPANY
11111 Pleast Colny Dr 9 Apt 902 (77065)
PHONE....................................972 874-2419
EMP: 9
SALES (corp-wide): 1.2MM **Privately Held**
SIC: 3089 Mfg Plastic Products
PA: Hightower Company
1400 Harvest Glen Dr
Flower Mound TX 75028
972 874-1487

(G-10179)
HIGHTOWER METAL WORKS INC
9001 Taub Rd (77064-6610)
P.O. Box 691207 (77269-1207)
PHONE....................................713 937-7181
EMP: 10
SQ FT: 4,000
SALES (est): 1.3MM **Privately Held**
SIC: 3444 Sheet metalwork

(G-10180)
HILAND GP LLC
1001 Louisiana St # 1000 (77002-5089)
PHONE....................................713 369-9000
Joseph L Griffin, *President*
EMP: 34
SALES (est): 145.1K **Publicly Held**
WEB: www.kindermorgan.com
SIC: 1321 Natural gas liquids production
HQ: Hiland Partners Holdings, Llc
1001 Louisiana St # 1000
Houston TX 77002
713 369-9000

(G-10181)
HILAND PARTNERS HOLDINGS LLC (HQ)
1001 Louisiana St # 1000 (77002-5089)
PHONE....................................713 369-9000
Joseph L Griffin, *President*
Jim Suttle, *Senior VP*
Derek Gipson, *CFO*

EMP: 55
SQ FT: 12,358
SALES (est): 231.9MM **Publicly Held**
WEB: www.kindermorgan.com
SIC: 1321 5169 6719 Natural gas liquids; industrial gases; investment holding companies, except banks

(G-10182)
HILCORP ENERGY COMPANY (PA)
1111 Travis St (77002-5924)
P.O. Box 61529 (77208-1529)
PHONE....................................713 209-2400
Greg Lalicker, *CEO*
▲ **EMP:** 18
SALES (est): 179.6MM **Privately Held**
WEB: www.hilcorp.com
SIC: 1311 1382 Crude petroleum production; oil & gas exploration services

(G-10183)
HILCORP ENERGY I LP
1111 Travis St (77002-5924)
PHONE....................................713 209-2400
Jeffery Hildebrand, *Partner*
Greg Lalicker, *Partner*
EMP: 14
SALES (est): 109K **Privately Held**
WEB: www.hilcorp.com
SIC: 1382 Oil & gas exploration services

(G-10184)
HILCORP ENERGY I LP
1201 Louisiana St # 1400 (77002-5606)
PHONE....................................713 209-2400
Jeffery D Hildebrand, *CEO*
Greg R Lalicker, *President*
Jason C Rebrook, *Vice Pres*
EMP: 11
SALES (est): 3MM **Privately Held**
WEB: www.hilcorp.com
SIC: 1382 Oil & gas exploration services

(G-10185)
HILCORP FINANCE COMPANY
1201 La St Ste 1400 (77002)
PHONE....................................713 209-2400
EMP: 115
SALES (est): 121.1K **Privately Held**
WEB: www.hilcorp.com
SIC: 1382 Oil & gas exploration services
PA: Hilcorp Energy Company
1111 Travis St
Houston TX 77002

(G-10186)
HILLSHIRE BRANDS COMPANY
Also Called: Sara Lee Coffee & Tea
235 N Norwood St (77011-2311)
P.O. Box 9389 (77261-9389)
PHONE....................................713 928-6281
EMP: 175
SQ FT: 8,800
SALES (corp-wide): 43.1B **Publicly Held**
WEB: www.sterlingbay.com
SIC: 2095 2099 Roasted coffee; food preparations
HQ: The Hillshire Brands Company
400 S Jefferson St Ste 1n
Chicago IL 60607
312 614-6000

(G-10187)
HIS COMPANY INC
Adhesive Materials Group
10803 Vinecrest Dr # 190 (77086-1792)
PHONE....................................713 934-1600
Will Rinehart, *Sales Executive*
Chris Irwin, *Branch Mgr*
EMP: 11
SALES (corp-wide): 250.3MM **Privately Held**
WEB: www.hisco.com
SIC: 2672 2891 Adhesive backed films, foams & foils; epoxy adhesives
PA: His Company, Inc.
6650 Concord Park Dr
Houston TX 77040
713 934-1600

(G-10188)
HK ENERGY OPERATING LLC
1000 La St Ste 6700 (77002)
PHONE....................................281 537-9920
Floyd C Wilson, *CEO*

Martin Aguero, *Administration*
EMP: 150
SALES (est): 9.1MM **Privately Held**
SIC: 1382 Oil & gas exploration services

(G-10189)
HMC INSTRUMENT & MCH WORKS LTD
2325 Blalock Rd (77080-5409)
PHONE.................713 468-1426
Howard Chong, *Partner*
Susie Chong, *Partner*
Allan Bolton, *General Mgr*
Won Shin, *Vice Pres*
Marty Reid, *Opers Mgr*
▲ **EMP:** 40
SQ FT: 35,000
SALES (est): 10.8MM **Privately Held**
WEB: www.hmcmachine.com
SIC: 3533 3841 Oil & gas field machinery; surgical & medical instruments

(G-10190)
HOBAS PIPE USA INC
1413 E Richey Rd (77073-3508)
PHONE.................281 821-2200
Martin W Dana, *President*
Russell Beasley, *Vice Pres*
Martin Dana, *Vice Pres*
Rene R Garcia, *Vice Pres*
Kimberly Paggioli, *Vice Pres*
▲ **EMP:** 110
SQ FT: 82,000
SALES (est): 34.8MM
SALES (corp-wide): 204.7MM **Privately Held**
WEB: www.hobaspipe.com
SIC: 3084 Plastics pipe
PA: Amiblu Holding Gmbh
SterneckstraBe 19
Klagenfurt 9020
463 482-4240

(G-10191)
HOERBIGER SERVICE INC
5405 Consulate Plaza Dr (77032-2533)
PHONE.................281 442-2497
CJ Sulik, *Project Mgr*
Bryan Stewart, *Branch Mgr*
EMP: 25
SQ FT: 18,281
SALES (corp-wide): 114.7MM **Privately Held**
WEB: www.hoerbiger.com
SIC: 7699 3491 5085 Valve repair, industrial; industrial valves; valves & fittings
HQ: Hoerbiger Service Inc.
1191 E Nwport Ctr Dr Ste
Deerfield Beach FL 33442
281 955-5888

(G-10192)
HOFFA INC
4106 Campbell Rd (77080-1327)
P.O. Box 801287 (77280-1287)
PHONE.................713 460-9000
Steve Hoffa, *President*
Pat Bond, *Vice Pres*
EMP: 15
SQ FT: 15,000
SALES (est): 2.6MM **Privately Held**
WEB: www.hoffainc.com
SIC: 3446 Architectural metalwork

(G-10193)
HOLCIM INC
9600 Clinton Dr (77029-4324)
P.O. Box 122 (77001-0122)
PHONE.................713 672-4316
Mike Ridenour, *Manager*
Nacho Cervera, *Risk Mgmt Dir*
EMP: 9
SALES (est): 510.8K
SALES (corp-wide): 1.7B **Privately Held**
WEB: www.lafargeholcim.com
SIC: 3241 Cement, hydraulic
PA: Lafargeholcim Ltd
Zurcherstrasse 156
Jona SG 8645
588 585-858

(G-10194)
HOLLOMAN CORPORATION (PA)
333 N Sam Houston Pkwy E (77060-2414)
PHONE.................281 878-2600
Sam E Holloman, *Ch of Bd*

Mark Stevenson, *President*
Charlie Brannon, *Division Mgr*
Dean Burns, *Division Mgr*
Coy Harris, *Division Mgr*
EMP: 30 **EST:** 1967
SQ FT: 40,000
SALES (est): 643MM **Privately Held**
WEB: www.hollomancorp.com
SIC: 1541 1623 1389 Industrial buildings, new construction; oil & gas pipeline construction; roustabout service

(G-10195)
HOLLOWAY COMPANY INC
Also Called: Gemini Contracting
12660 La Rochelle Dr (77015-3312)
P.O. Box 96408 (77213-6408)
PHONE.................713 453-4691
Jim Van Schuyver, *Vice Pres*
EMP: 14
SALES (corp-wide): 5.4MM **Privately Held**
WEB: www.hollowaycompanyinc.com
SIC: 1791 3443 Storage tanks, metal: erection; tanks, standard or custom fabricated: metal plate
PA: Holloway Company, Inc.
1200 Jarvis Rd
Saginaw TX 76179
817 232-8663

(G-10196)
HOLLYWOOD STEEL INC
6322 W 34th St (77092-6399)
PHONE.................713 686-4325
M D Jolly, *President*
Kelley Bitner, *Vice Pres*
Kelly Bitner, *Executive*
EMP: 29
SQ FT: 50,000
SALES (est): 5.7MM **Privately Held**
WEB: www.hollywoodsteel.com
SIC: 3441 1791 Building components, structural steel; structural steel erection

(G-10197)
HOME FRAGRANCE HOLDINGS INC (PA)
Also Called: Flintlock
411 N Sam Houston Pkwy E # 300 (77060-3543)
PHONE.................718 641-3759
◆ **EMP:** 390
SQ FT: 200,000
SALES (est): 24.1MM **Privately Held**
SIC: 3999 Mfg Misc Products

(G-10198)
HOME TREASURES INC
5150 Ashley Ct (77041-6913)
PHONE.................713 937-7716
Saeed Taghdisi, *President*
Elahe Faghihi, *Treasurer*
▲ **EMP:** 33
SQ FT: 10,000
SALES (est): 3.9MM **Privately Held**
WEB: www.hometreasureslinens.com
SIC: 2211 2392 Sheets, bedding & table cloths: cotton; household furnishings

(G-10199)
HONEYWELL ENRAF AMERICAS INC
Also Called: Service Center
11201 Grens Crossing Blvd (77067)
PHONE.................281 885-7979
EMP: 13
SALES (corp-wide): 36.7B **Publicly Held**
WEB: www.honeywellprocess.com
SIC: 3724 Aircraft engines & engine parts
HQ: Honeywell Enraf Americas, Inc.
2000 Northfield Ct
Roswell GA 30076
770 475-1900

(G-10200)
HONEYWELL INTERNATIONAL INC
8440 Westglen Dr (77063-6312)
PHONE.................713 780-6500
Joseph Ricca, *Principal*
Mark Allen, *Branch Mgr*
EMP: 275
SQ FT: 10,000

SALES (corp-wide): 36.7B **Publicly Held**
WEB: www.honeywell.com
SIC: 3724 Aircraft engines & engine parts
PA: Honeywell International Inc.
300 S Tryon St
Charlotte NC 28202
704 627-6200

(G-10201)
HONEYWELL INTERNATIONAL INC
1250 W S Houston Pkwy S (77042)
PHONE.................832 252-3500
Jeremy O'Brien, *Vice Pres*
Teddy Onyenaucheya, *Engineer*
David Radtke, *Engineer*
Angela Awoseyi, *Controller*
Pearl Moras, *Finance*
EMP: 46
SALES (corp-wide): 36.7B **Publicly Held**
WEB: www.honeywell.com
SIC: 3812 3823 Aircraft control systems, electronic; aircraft/aerospace flight instruments & guidance systems; space vehicle guidance systems & equipment; temperature instruments: industrial process type
PA: Honeywell International Inc.
300 S Tryon St
Charlotte NC 28202
704 627-6200

(G-10202)
HONEYWELL INTERNATIONAL INC
14503 Bmmel N Hston Rd St (77014-1100)
PHONE.................281 444-2282
Dawn C Eden, *Sales Staff*
Lars Jorgensen, *Manager*
EMP: 24
SALES (corp-wide): 36.7B **Publicly Held**
WEB: www.honeywell.com
SIC: 3724 Aircraft engines & engine parts
PA: Honeywell International Inc.
300 S Tryon St
Charlotte NC 28202
704 627-6200

(G-10203)
HONGHUA AMERICA LLC
Also Called: Hh Rigs and Services
5615 W Fuqua St Bldg A (77085-4079)
PHONE.................832 448-8100
Frank Ao, *President*
Echo Qiao, *Purch Dir*
Mandy Huang, *Purchasing*
Leo Liu, *Engineer*
Feng Yu, *Engineer*
◆ **EMP:** 40
SALES (est): 16.5MM **Privately Held**
WEB: www.hh-america.com
SIC: 3533 Oil & gas field machinery; oil & gas drilling rigs & equipment; drill rigs; drilling tools for gas, oil or water wells
HQ: Honghua International Co., Ltd.
99 East Road, Information Park, Jinniu District,
Chengdu 61003

(G-10204)
HOOVER GROUP INC (PA)
Also Called: Hoover Container Group
2135 Highway 6 S (77077-4319)
PHONE.................800 844-8683
Paul Lewis, *President*
Donald W Young, *Principal*
Adolfo Aguilera, *Vice Pres*
Scott T Meints, *Vice Pres*
Scott Meints, *Vice Pres*
◆ **EMP:** 48
SQ FT: 6,400
SALES (est): 55.3MM **Privately Held**
WEB: www.hooverferguson.com
SIC: 3496 3412 3443 3089 Miscellaneous fabricated wire products; metal barrels, drums & pails; industrial vessels, tanks & containers; tanks, lined: metal plate; tanks, standard or custom fabricated: metal plate; plastic containers, except foam; plastic & fiberglass tanks; equipment rental & leasing; metal cans

(G-10205)
HOOVER MTLS HDLG GROUP INC (HQ)
Also Called: Hoover Container Solutions
2135 Highway 6 S (77077-4319)
PHONE.................800 844-8683
Donald W Young, *CEO*
Paul Lewis, *President*
Conrad A Arnold, *Vice Pres*
Arash Hassanian, *Vice Pres*
Scott T Meints, *Vice Pres*
◆ **EMP:** 90
SQ FT: 20,000
SALES (est): 93MM **Privately Held**
WEB: www.hooverferguson.com
SIC: 5113 3089 Containers, paper & disposable plastic; plastic containers, except foam

(G-10206)
HORIZON PRODUCTION & OPER LLC
2727 Allen Pkwy Ste 1900 (77019-2153)
PHONE.................713 522-5800
R Rothwell Jr, *President*
EMP: 14
SALES (est): 1.2MM **Privately Held**
SIC: 1382 Oil & gas exploration services

(G-10207)
HORIZON RESOURCES LP (PA)
Also Called: Horizon Exploration
2727 Allen Pkwy Ste 1900 (77019-2153)
PHONE.................713 522-5800
Mark Rothwell, *Co-Owner*
EMP: 14
SQ FT: 8,000
SALES (est): 1.7MM **Privately Held**
SIC: 1382 0751 6221 Oil & gas exploration services; breeding services, livestock; commodity traders, contracts

(G-10208)
HORIZON WORLDWIDE CORPORATION
1765 Stebbins Dr (77043-2806)
P.O. Box 79210 (77279-9210)
PHONE.................713 647-7400
Gary Seline, *CEO*
Dorothy Roos, *Accounts Mgr*
Whitney Motley, *Marketing Mgr*
▲ **EMP:** 100
SALES (est): 75MM **Privately Held**
WEB: www.horizonworldwide.com
SIC: 7311 3861 Advertising consultant; printing equipment, photographic

(G-10209)
HORSEPOWER SERVICES LLC
5847 San Felipe St (77057-3000)
PHONE.................713 582-2105
EMP: 41
SALES (corp-wide): 4.2MM **Privately Held**
SIC: 1389 Oil/Gas Field Services
PA: Horsepower Services, Llc
9010 S Eunice Hwy
Hobbs NM

(G-10210)
HORTON DRAPERIES OF TEXAS
6029 Jessamine St (77081-6490)
PHONE.................713 774-7477
Donald L Mc Caleb, *President*
Patricia Mc Caleb, *Treasurer*
EMP: 16 **EST:** 1965
SQ FT: 11,500
SALES (est): 1MM **Privately Held**
SIC: 2391 Draperies, plastic & textile: from purchased materials

(G-10211)
HOSE MASTER LLC
1903 Tellepsen St (77023-4645)
PHONE.................713 926-2288
Anthony Foti, *President*
EMP: 35
SALES (corp-wide): 62MM **Privately Held**
WEB: www.hosemaster.com
SIC: 3441 Fabricated structural metal
PA: Hose Master, Llc
1233 E 222nd St
Cleveland OH 44117
216 481-2020

(G-10212)
HOT HYDRAULICS INC
Also Called: Hydraulics of Texas
6800 Northwinds Dr (77041-3015)
PHONE.................................713 722-7200
Bruce L Buckley Jr, *President*
▲ EMP: 35
SQ FT: 34,000
SALES (est): 8.6MM Privately Held
WEB: www.hydraulicsoftexas.com
SIC: 3593 7699 3594 Fluid power cylinders, hydraulic or pneumatic; hydraulic equipment repair; fluid power pumps & motors

(G-10213)
HOTWELL US LLC (PA)
15905 Waverly Dr (77032-1215)
P.O. Box 672721 (77267-2721)
PHONE.................................281 598-9990
Phil Forbes, *President*
Andres Ospina, *Opers Mgr*
Edith Palos, *CFO*
Mario Danglade, *Analyst*
◆ EMP: 14
SQ FT: 3,000
SALES (est): 1.4MM Privately Held
WEB: www.hotwellus.com
SIC: 1389 Pumping of oil & gas wells; oil field services

(G-10214)
HOU-STONE INC (PA)
Also Called: Olympus Marble & Granite Svc
2142 Ojeman Rd (77080-6206)
PHONE.................................713 827-8700
Raffi Yegyayan, *President*
Manuel Yegyayan, *Vice Pres*
Angelo Bissias, *Admin Sec*
▲ EMP: 52
SQ FT: 20,000
SALES (est): 9.5MM Privately Held
WEB: www.newpatio.com
SIC: 3444 1791 Sheet metal specialties; not stamped; structural steel erection

(G-10215)
HOU-TEX NEWNOM INC
Also Called: Hou-Tex Glass & Mirror
1185 Brittmoore Rd (77043-5003)
PHONE.................................713 777-0748
Rick Newnom, *President*
Linda Newnom, *President*
Richard Newnom, *President*
Elizabeth Bueno, *Manager*
EMP: 72
SALES (est): 8.2MM Privately Held
WEB: www.houtexglass.com
SIC: 3211 1751 Building glass, flat; window & door (prefabricated) installation

(G-10216)
HOUSE OF FORGINGS LLC (PA)
353 Greens Landing Dr (77038-2645)
PHONE.................................281 443-4848
Chris Kamykowski, *Vice Pres*
Patty Harless, *Sales Staff*
Juan Mata, *Sales Staff*
Jennifer Mills, *Sales Staff*
Katie Christian, *Sales Executive*
▲ EMP: 50
SQ FT: 70,000
SALES (est): 11.7MM Privately Held
WEB: www.houseofforgings.net
SIC: 2431 Staircases, stairs & railings; stair railings, wood; staircases & stairs, wood

(G-10217)
HOUSETECH INC
10865 Fallstone Rd (77099-3411)
PHONE.................................281 879-0484
Mike Dennis, *CEO*
EMP: 28
SQ FT: 10,300 Privately Held
WEB: www.houstech.com
SIC: 3672 Printed circuit boards

(G-10218)
HOUSTON BUSINESS & FINCL SVCS
801 Travis St Ste 1900 (77002-5730)
PHONE.................................713 398-6314
Frank H Simonton Jr, *President*
Thomas J Kutac, *Treasurer*
John Q Barnidge, *Admin Sec*

EMP: 15
SALES (est): 740.2K Privately Held
SIC: 1389 Oil consultants

(G-10219)
HOUSTON BUSINESS JOURNALS INC (DH)
Also Called: Dallas Business Journal
5444 Westheimr Rd # 1000 (77056-5397)
PHONE.................................713 688-8811
Ray Shaw, *CEO*
John Beddow, *President*
Giselle Greenwood, *Manager*
April Bruffy, *Executive*
EMP: 40
SQ FT: 8,700
SALES (est): 4.7MM
SALES (corp-wide): 5B Privately Held
WEB: www.discountednewspapers.com
SIC: 2711 Newspapers, publishing & printing
HQ: American City Business Journals, Inc.
120 W Morehead St Ste 400
Charlotte NC 28202
704 973-1000

(G-10220)
HOUSTON CABINETS INC
5902 Royalton St (77081-2921)
PHONE.................................713 349-0848
Richard Keschinger, *President*
EMP: 20
SQ FT: 10,000
SALES (est): 2.8MM Privately Held
WEB: www.houstoncabinetsinc.com
SIC: 2434 Wood kitchen cabinets

(G-10221)
HOUSTON CALCO INC
Also Called: Calco Bean Sprouts Distributor
9903 Daisy Clover Ct (77089-1459)
PHONE.................................713 236-8668
Chien Chun Wang, *President*
Yueh Wu Wang, *Vice Pres*
▲ EMP: 9
SQ FT: 8,000
SALES (est): 1MM Privately Held
WEB: www.houstoncalco.com
SIC: 0182 2099 2032 Bean sprouts grown under cover; tofu, except frozen desserts; canned specialties

(G-10222)
HOUSTON CANVAS AND AWNING CO
Also Called: Houston Uniform & Apparel Co
6015 Skyline Dr (77057-7003)
PHONE.................................713 789-8712
John Giannukos, *President*
Sandra Lam, *Production*
Davis Judy, *Controller*
Karen Smith, *Executive*
Jill Herrold, *Representative*
▲ EMP: 31 EST: 1979
SQ FT: 15,000
SALES (est): 4MM Privately Held
WEB: www.houstonuniform.com
SIC: 2394 Canvas awnings & canopies

(G-10223)
HOUSTON CASING SPECIALITIES
195 Southbelt Indus Dr (77047-7020)
PHONE.................................713 433-3940
EMP: 13
SALES (est): 1.5MM Privately Held
SIC: 1389 Cementing oil & gas well casings

(G-10224)
HOUSTON CEMENT COMPANY LP
9550 Clinton Dr (77029-4323)
PHONE.................................713 754-8000
Mark Clemence, *Branch Mgr*
EMP: 12 Privately Held
WEB: www.texaslehigh.com
SIC: 3241 Masonry cement
PA: Houston Cement Company, L.P.
363 N Sam Houston Pkwy E # 390
Houston TX 77060

(G-10225)
HOUSTON CHRONICLE
10635 Richmond Ave (77042-4989)
PHONE.................................713 362-7171
John T O'Loughlin, *President*
Kevin Pender, *Editor*
Mike Sacks, *Vice Pres*
Jim Jones, *Opers Staff*
Brittany Brinson, *Accounts Exec*
EMP: 698
SALES (est): 16.5MM
SALES (corp-wide): 252.7MM Privately Held
WEB: www.chron.com
SIC: 2711 Newspapers, publishing & printing
PA: Hearst Newspapers, Llc
4747 Southwest Fwy
Houston TX 77027
713 220-7171

(G-10226)
HOUSTON COMPRESSION & SVCS LLC
Also Called: Texas Compression Services
16250 Tomball Pkwy (77086-1014)
PHONE.................................713 550-1556
Adam Busser, *CEO*
Thomas Jeffers, *President*
EMP: 13
SALES (est): 3.1MM Privately Held
WEB: www.texascompressionservices.com
SIC: 3563 Air & gas compressors

(G-10227)
HOUSTON CUSTOM PACKAGING LLC
14109 Lost Meadow Ln (77079-3111)
PHONE.................................713 827-1427
EMP: 24 EST: 2013
SQ FT: 7,000
SALES: 1.5MM Privately Held
SIC: 2673 Mfg Polyethylene Plastic Bag

(G-10228)
HOUSTON D&J INTERNATIONAL INC
5855 Sovereign Dr Ste F (77036-2383)
PHONE.................................713 678-7888
Chien-Ming Lo, *President*
Dinna Lo, *Vice Pres*
▲ EMP: 10 EST: 1994
SQ FT: 50,000
SALES (est): 1.8MM Privately Held
SIC: 2673 Bags: plastic, laminated & coated

(G-10229)
HOUSTON DEFENDER NEWSPAPER INC
3003 S Loop W Ste 320 (77054-1373)
P.O. Box 8005 (77288-8005)
PHONE.................................713 663-6996
Olivia A Messiah, *President*
Sonceria Messiah Jiles, *Treasurer*
Lucille Pervis, *Manager*
Selma Tyler, *Manager*
EMP: 10
SQ FT: 1,000
SALES (est): 69.5K Privately Held
WEB: www.defendernetwork.com
SIC: 2711 Newspapers, publishing & printing

(G-10230)
HOUSTON DYNAMIC SERVICE INC
Also Called: Hds
8150 Lawndale St (77012-3704)
PHONE.................................713 636-5587
EMP: 47 EST: 1976
SQ FT: 35,000
SALES (est): 10.6MM Privately Held
WEB: www.houstondynamic.com
SIC: 3599 Machine shop, jobbing & repair

(G-10231)
HOUSTON ELBOW & NIPPLE CO INC
Also Called: Henco
1714 Hussion St (77003-5622)
P.O. Box 230301 (77223-0301)
PHONE.................................713 225-2257
Richard N Honeycutt, *President*

Cliff Mc Lain, *Vice Pres*
Cliff McLain, *Vice Pres*
Brandon Lehrmann, *Sales Staff*
Susan Mc Lain, *Admin Sec*
EMP: 14
SQ FT: 15,000
SALES (est): 2.7MM Privately Held
WEB: www.houstonelbow.com
SIC: 3498 Tube fabricating (contract bending & shaping)

(G-10232)
HOUSTON ENERGY LP
1200 Smith St Ste 2400 (77002-4315)
PHONE.................................713 650-8008
Ronald E Neal, *Owner*
Frank W Harrison III, *Owner*
Nick Rezvani, *Superintendent*
P David Amend, *Exec VP*
Dale Coulthard, *Vice Pres*
EMP: 42
SALES (est): 23.6MM Privately Held
WEB: www.houstonenergyinc.com
SIC: 1382 Oil & gas exploration services

(G-10233)
HOUSTON FAB TRUCK RIGGING RPS
1124 Keyport Ln (77015-5513)
PHONE.................................713 455-6161
Arturo Garcia, *Owner*
EMP: 20
SALES (est): 4.3MM Privately Held
WEB: www.houstonfab.com
SIC: 3441 7692 3713 Fabricated structural metal; welding repair; truck & bus bodies

(G-10234)
HOUSTON FOAM PLASTICS INC (PA)
2019 Brooks St (77026-7297)
P.O. Box 1615 (77251-1615)
PHONE.................................713 224-3484
Gene Kurtz, *President*
Chris Bueno, *Division Mgr*
Robert Kurtz, *Vice Pres*
Irma Morales, *Plant Mgr*
Nancy Vega, *Purch Mgr*
◆ EMP: 200
SQ FT: 225,000
SALES (est): 76MM Privately Held
WEB: www.houstonfoam.com
SIC: 3086 Insulation or cushioning material, foamed plastic; packaging & shipping materials, foamed plastic

(G-10235)
HOUSTON GRINDING & MFG CO
Also Called: Hgm International
3544 W 12th St (77008-6006)
PHONE.................................713 869-3573
Brian V Lattimer, *President*
Joann Lattimer, *Director*
◆ EMP: 75 EST: 1944
SQ FT: 20,000
SALES (est): 17.5MM Privately Held
SIC: 3561 3511 3599 3569 Pumps & pumping equipment; turbines & turbine generator sets; propellers, ship & boat: machined; lubrication machinery, automatic

(G-10236)
HOUSTON KIK INC
Also Called: Kik Custom Products
2921 Corder St (77054-3401)
P.O. Box 300016 (77230-0016)
PHONE.................................713 747-8710
David Cynamon, *President*
Steven Farris, *Opers Staff*
Roy Pearce, *CFO*
Clarissa Webb, *Regional*
EMP: 114
SQ FT: 250,000
SALES (est): 31.8MM
SALES (corp-wide): 111.1MM Privately Held
WEB: www.kikcorp.com
SIC: 2842 3085 Bleaches, household: dry or liquid; plastics bottles
HQ: Kik International Llc
2921 Corder St
Houston TX
713 747-8710

(G-10237)
HOUSTON MEDICAL TSTG SVCS INC (PA)
Also Called: Houston Medical Testing Svcs
2646 S Loop W Ste 550 (77054-5614)
PHONE....................................713 665-4687
Sherri Vogler, *President*
Jon Vogler, *Vice Pres*
Mohammed Hilal, *Analyst*
Carla Delgado, *Assistant*
EMP: 22
SQ FT: 4,000
SALES (est): 1.8MM **Privately Held**
WEB: www.hmts.com
SIC: 2899 8299   ; educational services

(G-10238)
HOUSTON MFG & FABG CO
4734 Creekmont Dr (77091-5116)
PHONE....................................713 688-8383
Jimmie Naiser, *President*
Jeffrey Naiser, *Vice Pres*
Todd Naiser, *Vice Pres*
Annette Naiser, *Treasurer*
EMP: 9
SQ FT: 14,400 **Privately Held**
WEB: www.houstonmfgfab.com
SIC: 3599 Machine shop, jobbing & repair

(G-10239)
HOUSTON MFG SPECIALTY CO INC
Also Called: H M S
9909 Wallisville Rd (77013-4613)
P.O. Box 24339 (77229-4339)
PHONE....................................281 888-4635
▲ EMP: 30
SQ FT: 28,000
SALES (est): 6.3MM **Privately Held**
WEB: www.houmfg.com
SIC: 3053 3089 3471 7699 Gaskets, all materials; plastic processing; chromium plating of metals or formed products; hydraulic equipment repair

(G-10240)
HOUSTON NORTH SLEEP CENTER
2710 Mangum Rd Ste 300 (77092-7495)
PHONE....................................713 688-3188
Roy Perez, *President*
EMP: 15
SALES (est): 1.3MM **Privately Held**
WEB: www.northhoustonsleep.org
SIC: 2399 5712 Sleeping bags; furniture stores

(G-10241)
HOUSTON NUMISMATIC EXCHANGE
2486 Times Blvd (77005-3223)
P.O. Box 25273 (77265-5273)
PHONE....................................713 528-2135
Pat Johnson, *President*
EMP: 15
SQ FT: 4,000
SALES (est): 2.8MM **Privately Held**
WEB: www.hnex.com
SIC: 5094 3911 5999 Jewelry; jewelry, precious metal; coins

(G-10242)
HOUSTON OPICOIL INC (DH)
3040 Post Oak Blvd # 800 (77056-6590)
PHONE....................................713 840-7171
Ch Chang, *President*
Stacy Sapio, *Admin Sec*
◆ EMP: 11
SALES (est): 1.6MM **Privately Held**
WEB: www.opicoil.com
SIC: 1311 6531 Crude petroleum production; natural gas production; buying agent, real estate; selling agent, real estate

(G-10243)
HOUSTON PIPE BENDERS LLC
14500 E Hardy Rd (77039-1407)
PHONE....................................281 449-8241
Evan Hughes, *President*
Jim Burt, *Vice Pres*
Jeremy Supak, *Opers Mgr*
David Bell, *CFO*
Bret Roper, *CFO*
▲ EMP: 40 EST: 1960

SQ FT: 45,000
SALES (est): 10.8MM **Privately Held**
WEB: www.hpbenders.com
SIC: 3498 Tube fabricating (contract bending & shaping)

(G-10244)
HOUSTON POST TENSION INC
7015 San Antonio St (77040-4109)
PHONE....................................713 937-6990
Ricki J Abney, *President*
David Cooney, *Sales Mgr*
Gordy Saracene, *Sales Staff*
Debbie Abney, *Technology*
Kristen Harshman, *Director*
▲ EMP: 75
SQ FT: 18,000
SALES (est): 16MM **Privately Held**
WEB: www.houstonposttension.com
SIC: 3496 5051 Miscellaneous fabricated wire products; forms, concrete construction (steel)

(G-10245)
HOUSTON POWDER COATERS LLC
14024 E Hardy Rd (77039-1803)
PHONE....................................281 676-3888
Tomas Burkett, *CEO*
Christopher Ranieri, *CEO*
Flaviu Fasie, *Vice Pres*
Steven Wheelock, *Vice Pres*
Chuck Hendee, *Manager*
EMP: 20
SALES (est): 2.6MM **Privately Held**
WEB: www.houstonpowdercoaters.com
SIC: 3479 Coating of metals & formed products

(G-10246)
HOUSTON PRECISION FAS I LP
4923 Cranswick Rd (77041-7723)
PHONE....................................713 462-2227
Mark Hahn III, *President*
Dan Hunt, *Vice Pres*
Craig Steele, *QC Mgr*
Karen Hunt, *Accounting Mgr*
Elizabeth Marshall, *Accounts Mgr*
EMP: 70
SALES (est): 8MM **Privately Held**
WEB: www.hpfasteners.com
SIC: 3965 Fasteners

(G-10247)
HOUSTON PRESS LP
2603 La Branch St (77004-1136)
PHONE....................................713 280-2400
Margaret Downing, *Editor*
Jessica Candler, *Opers Staff*
Shelby Holloway, *Opers Staff*
Juan Rojas, *Sales Dir*
Lisha Abbey, *Accounts Mgr*
EMP: 50 EST: 1996
SQ FT: 8,000
SALES (est): 4.1MM
SALES (corp-wide): 241.4MM **Privately Held**
WEB: www.houstonpress.com
SIC: 2711 Newspapers, publishing & printing
PA: Voice Media Group, Inc.
969 N Broadway
Denver CO 80203
303 296-7744

(G-10248)
HOUSTON R-CO INCORPORATED
Also Called: Gulf Cast Drywall Pnt Svcs Cnt
11840 Gloger St (77039-6310)
PHONE....................................281 987-9909
Carlos Realyvasquez, *President*
Manuel Realyvasquez, *Vice Pres*
Erick W Realyvasquez, *CFO*
EMP: 19
SALES (est): 2.2MM **Privately Held**
WEB: www.houstonrco.com
SIC: 1742 8748 3086 Insulation, buildings; business consulting; insulation or cushioning material, foamed plastic

(G-10249)
HOUSTON ROLL PIPE LLC
4128 Creekmont Dr (77091-5300)
PHONE....................................713 686-8970
EMP: 24 EST: 2012

SALES (est): 4.9MM **Privately Held**
WEB: www.houstonroll.com
SIC: 3498 3494 Fabricated pipe & fittings; pipe fittings

(G-10250)
HOUSTON SERVICE INDUSTRIES INC
Also Called: H S I
15045 Lee Rd (77032-4001)
PHONE....................................713 947-1623
Richard Pearsall, *President*
James Pearsall, *Vice Pres*
◆ EMP: 50
SQ FT: 150,000
SALES (est): 16.3MM
SALES (corp-wide): 10.7B **Privately Held**
WEB: www.hsiblowers.com
SIC: 3564 5084 Blowers & fans; industrial machinery & equipment
HQ: Atlas Copco North America Llc
6 Century Dr Ste 310
Parsippany NJ 07054

(G-10251)
HOUSTON SHUTTERS LLC
Also Called: Rockwood Shutters
7000 Grand Blvd (77054-2206)
PHONE....................................713 723-7100
Jennifer Baur, *CEO*
Mike Blackburn, *General Mgr*
Stephen Baur, *CFO*
Marian Velez, *Human Resources*
Jordan Marr, *Sales Staff*
▲ EMP: 325
SQ FT: 100,000
SALES (est): 110.5MM **Privately Held**
WEB: www.rockwoodshutters.com
SIC: 3089 2431 5039 Shutters, plastic; door shutters, wood; blinds (shutters), wood; doors, sliding

(G-10252)
HOUSTON SIGN & SERVICE INC
Also Called: B & R Sign Company
1536 Hartwick Rd (77093-1027)
P.O. Box 10270 (77206-0270)
PHONE....................................281 442-0175
James Redmond, *President*
Shannon Koheler, *Manager*
Cynthia Santana, *Admin Sec*
EMP: 12
SQ FT: 9,000
SALES (est): 1.4MM **Privately Held**
SIC: 3993 Signs, not made in custom sign painting shops

(G-10253)
HOUSTON SPECIALTIES PRODUCTS
6239 Keyko St (77041-5309)
P.O. Box 608, Hockley (77447-0608)
PHONE....................................936 931-5256
Russell Carlson, *Partner*
Leon Horner, *Partner*
Tommy Salzar, *Partner*
EMP: 12
SQ FT: 1,300
SALES (est): 1.4MM **Privately Held**
WEB: www.hspc.co
SIC: 3061 Oil & gas field machinery rubber goods (mechanical)

(G-10254)
HOUSTON SYSCO INC (HQ)
10710 Grens Crossing Blvd (77038)
PHONE....................................713 672-8080
Bill Delaney, *CEO*
David Devane, *President*
Michael W Green, *President*
Thomas E Lankford, *COO*
Cassandra Petry, *COO*
▲ EMP: 20 EST: 1953
SQ FT: 381,000
SALES (est): 780.8MM
SALES (corp-wide): 52.8B **Publicly Held**
WEB: www.sysco.com
SIC: 5149 5142 5046 5141 Canned goods: fruit, vegetables, seafood, meats, etc.; packaged frozen goods; commercial cooking & food service equipment; groceries, general line; food preparations
PA: Sysco Corporation
1390 Enclave Pkwy
Houston TX 77077
281 584-1390

(G-10255)
HOUSTON TEXCAST INC
706 Lehman St (77018-1514)
PHONE....................................713 697-8006
Gary D Hinds, *President*
Deborah Hinds, *Exec VP*
Tim Budzik, *Supervisor*
EMP: 25
SQ FT: 7,000
SALES (est): 2.5MM **Privately Held**
WEB: www.texcast.com
SIC: 3324 Commercial investment castings, ferrous

(G-10256)
HOUSTON THERMAL PROCESSING LLC
Also Called: Houston Heat Treat
13802 Chrisman Rd (77039-1916)
PHONE....................................281 590-9600
Mark Tate, *General Mgr*
Mark Adamson, *Mng Member*
AMI Hadley, *Director*
EMP: 18
SQ FT: 36,000
SALES (est): 6.6MM **Privately Held**
WEB: www.houstonheattreat.com
SIC: 3398 Metal heat treating

(G-10257)
HOUSTON TRAILER INC
7600 E Sam Houston Pkwy N (77049-3000)
PHONE....................................281 459-5350
Thomas Howell, *CEO*
EMP: 35
SALES (est): 10.6K **Privately Held**
SIC: 3792 Camping trailers & chassis

(G-10258)
HOUSTON TRANSFORMER CO LTD
5725 Braxton Dr (77036-2196)
PHONE....................................713 977-6009
Sara Blair, *Principal*
Suzanne Walkuski, *QC Mgr*
Gholam Arian, *Chief Engr*
Trieu Nguyen, *Info Tech Mgr*
EMP: 80
SQ FT: 35,000
SALES (est): 14.2MM **Privately Held**
WEB: www.houstontransformer.com
SIC: 3612 3677 Specialty transformers; electronic coils, transformers & other inductors

(G-10259)
HOUSTON TRUCK TARPS LLC
3421 Manitou Dr (77013-3605)
PHONE....................................346 571-1832
Marco Gamez,
EMP: 12
SQ FT: 21,535
SALES (est): 338.7K **Privately Held**
WEB: www.houstontrucktarps.com
SIC: 2394 7539 7692 Canvas & related products; trailer repair; automotive welding

(G-10260)
HOUSTON TSM INC
Also Called: Tsm Houston
8026 E Hardy Rd (77093-7913)
PHONE....................................713 691-5271
Randy Pinter, *President*
Mark Pinter, *Corp Secy*
Gregory Baker, *Vice Pres*
EMP: 50 EST: 1953
SQ FT: 16,500
SALES (est): 8.5MM **Privately Held**
WEB: www.rmindustrialservices.com
SIC: 1791 3444 Building front installation metal; sheet metalwork

(G-10261)
HOUSTON VIBRATOR LTD
9921 Tanner Rd Bldg K (77041-7549)
PHONE....................................713 939-0404
Adrienne Lash, *Ltd Ptnr*
Courtaney Lash, *Ltd Ptnr*
▲ EMP: 13
SALES (est): 3MM **Privately Held**
WEB: www.houstonvibrator.com
SIC: 3531 Vibrators for concrete construction

(G-10262)
HOUSTON VIBRATOR MGT INC
9921 Tanner Rd (77041-7549)
P.O. Box 801882 (77280-1882)
PHONE....................................713 939-0404
Richard L Lash, *President*
Adrienne Lash, *Vice Pres*
Courtaney Lash, *Executive*
EMP: 12
SQ FT: 5,800
SALES (est): 3.3MM **Privately Held**
WEB: www.houstonvibrator.com
SIC: 3531 Vibrators for concrete construction

(G-10263)
HOUSTON WELL SCREEN COMPANY
Also Called: Weatherford
11939 Aldine Westfield Rd (77093-1095)
PHONE....................................281 449-7261
Peter Thomas Fontan, *President*
William T Rouse, *Vice Pres*
James M Hudgins, *Treasurer*
Maria Cai, *Manager*
Talgat Ramazanov, *Manager*
◆ EMP: 70 EST: 1944
SALES (est): 4.2MM **Privately Held**
WEB: www.weatherford.com
SIC: 1389 Oil field services
HQ: Weatherford International, Llc
2000 Saint James Pl
Houston TX 77056
713 693-4000

(G-10264)
HOUSTON WIPER & MILL SUPPLY CO
1234 Kress St (77020-7419)
P.O. Box 15128 (77220-5128)
PHONE....................................713 672-0571
Brian McGee, *President*
Letisha McGee, *Vice Pres*
▲ EMP: 17 EST: 1954
SQ FT: 88,000
SALES (est): 2.7MM **Privately Held**
WEB: www.houstonwiper.com
SIC: 2295 2392 Coated fabrics, not rubberized; household furnishings

(G-10265)
HOUSTON WIRE WORKS INC
Also Called: Space Saver Racks
1007 Kentucky St (77087)
PHONE....................................713 946-2920
Barbara Leagler, *CEO*
Ken Leagler, *CEO*
◆ EMP: 15
SQ FT: 70,000
SALES (est): 1.9MM **Privately Held**
WEB: www.houstonwirework.com
SIC: 3315 3496 2542 Wire products, ferrous/iron: made in wiredrawing plants; miscellaneous fabricated wire products; partitions & fixtures, except wood

(G-10266)
HOUTEX HI-TEMP TRANSFORMER LLC
6111 Corporate Dr (77036-3409)
PHONE....................................713 271-8993
Tam Pham, *President*
Vincent Pham,
EMP: 21
SALES (est): 4.1MM **Privately Held**
WEB: www.houtexfmr.com
SIC: 3612 Transformers, except electric

(G-10267)
HOUTEX READY MIX
6262 S Acres Dr (77048-2127)
PHONE....................................713 987-0303
Roberto Melendez, *President*
EMP: 40
SALES (est): 6.8MM **Privately Held**
WEB: www.metroreadymix.net
SIC: 3273 Ready-mixed concrete

(G-10268)
HOWCO METALS MANAGEMENT LLC (DH)
Also Called: Howco Group
9611 Telge Rd (77095-5114)
PHONE....................................281 649-8800
John Ferguson, *President*

Nick Hartle, *President*
Glenn Bilanoski, *General Mgr*
Ingvar Ladsten, *General Mgr*
Dave Davidson, *COO*
◆ EMP: 104
SQ FT: 400,000
SALES (est): 66.7MM **Privately Held**
WEB: www.howcogroup.com
SIC: 5051 3999 8741 Steel; barber & beauty shop equipment; business management
HQ: Howco Group Plc
2nd Floor
Glasgow G3 7U
141 353-7800

(G-10269)
HOWELL PETROLEUM CORPORATION (DH)
1111 Fannin St Ste 1500 (77002-6996)
P.O. Box 1330 (77251-1330)
PHONE....................................281 320-9096
Richard K Hebert, *President*
Robert Moffett, *Vice Pres*
Joseph Small, *Vice Pres*
EMP: 58
SQ FT: 53,000
SALES (est): 8MM
SALES (corp-wide): 21.2B **Publicly Held**
SIC: 1311 Crude petroleum production; natural gas production
HQ: Howell Corporation
1201 Lake Robbins Dr
The Woodlands TX 77380
832 636-1000

(G-10270)
HOYAFAM HOLDINGS LTD
Also Called: Builtrite Reel & Lumber
305 Hambrick Rd (77060-5731)
P.O. Box 19031 (77224-9031)
PHONE....................................281 447-0447
Michael Schieffer, *Partner*
William Barnhart, *Opers Mgr*
EMP: 12
SQ FT: 4,000
SALES (est): 1.9MM **Privately Held**
WEB: www.builtritereels.com
SIC: 2499 Spools, wood

(G-10271)
HP INC
11445 Compaq Center W Dr (77070-1433)
PHONE....................................970 898-0000
David Chappell, *Partner*
David Engler, *Engineer*
Melina McCarty, *Engineer*
Prodpran Suetrong, *Engineer*
Wayne High, *Sales Staff*
EMP: 34
SALES (corp-wide): 56.6B **Publicly Held**
WEB: www.hp.com
SIC: 3571 Personal computers (microcomputers); minicomputers
PA: Hp Inc.
1501 Page Mill Rd
Palo Alto CA 94304
650 857-1501

(G-10272)
HPI LLC (PA)
Also Called: Tgcs
15503 W Hardy Rd (77060-3603)
PHONE....................................713 457-7500
Harold Pontez, *President*
Jhonny Matos, *Business Mgr*
Jeremy Wheelwright, *Vice Pres*
Lillie Rivera, *Purch Mgr*
Leal Deanna, *Bookkeeper*
EMP: 45
SQ FT: 14,000
SALES (est): 10MM **Privately Held**
WEB: www.hpi-llc.com
SIC: 3823 8713 3511 Industrial instrmnts msrmnt display/control process variable; surveying services; steam engines

(G-10273)
HRH DOOR CORP
Also Called: Wayne - Dalton of Houston
419 Century Plaza Dr # 230 (77073-6130)
PHONE....................................281 821-8572
Scott Lee, *Manager*
EMP: 12

SALES (corp-wide): 634.1MM **Privately Held**
WEB: www.wayne-dalton.com
SIC: 3442 5211 Metal doors; garage doors, sale & installation
PA: Hrh Door Corp.
1 Door Dr
Mount Hope OH 44660
850 208-3400

(G-10274)
HUBER CONSTRUCTION COMPANY INC
5220 Texas St (77011-4242)
P.O. Box 912 (77001-0912)
PHONE....................................713 926-9623
Wayne Pratt, *Ch of Bd*
Tom J Daubner, *President*
Wayne PRA, *CTO*
Tony Fiala, *Director*
EMP: 22 EST: 1946
SQ FT: 50,000
SALES (est): 3.5MM **Privately Held**
WEB: www.huberconstruction.com
SIC: 7699 3433 Boiler repair shop; boilers, low-pressure heating: steam or hot water

(G-10275)
HUDSON & HUDSON NEON INC
10500 Windfern Rd (77064-5218)
PHONE....................................281 720-0100
Leonard E Hudson, *President*
Alvin G Hudson, *Vice Pres*
Loren Hudson, *Vice Pres*
EMP: 20
SALES (est): 4.2MM **Privately Held**
SIC: 3354 Aluminum extruded products

(G-10276)
HUDSON ABRASIVE COMPANY
8606 Windswept Ln (77063-5724)
P.O. Box 631442 (77263-1442)
PHONE....................................713 977-0037
Don Hudson, *President*
▲ EMP: 10
SQ FT: 5,450
SALES (est): 1.2MM **Privately Held**
SIC: 3291 Wheels, abrasive

(G-10277)
HUFFCO INDUSTRIES INC
Also Called: Huffco Metals & Machining
1400 W Sam Houston Pkwy N (77043-3129)
PHONE....................................713 827-1248
Robert Huffman, *President*
EMP: 10
SQ FT: 1,000
SALES (est): 1.3MM **Privately Held**
WEB: www.hufco.com
SIC: 3599 Machine shop, jobbing & repair

(G-10278)
HUMATECH INC (PA)
19416 Park Row Ste 170 (77084-7248)
PHONE....................................832 321-3098
David Williams, *President*
John Rottweiler, *CFO*
Landon Bench, *Manager*
▼ EMP: 12
SQ FT: 1,200
SALES (est): 1.2MM **Publicly Held**
WEB: www.humatech.com
SIC: 2879 Agricultural chemicals

(G-10279)
HUNT ENGINE INCORPORATED
14805 Main St (77035-6412)
P.O. Box 35685 (77235-5685)
PHONE....................................713 721-9400
Frank Doonan, *President*
John Biggs, *Corp Secy*
George Granados, *Plant Mgr*
Charles Cook, *Prdtn Mgr*
Britt Keller, *Production*
▲ EMP: 65
SQ FT: 29,135
SALES: 5.5MM **Privately Held**
WEB: www.huntengine.com
SIC: 3533 7699 Oil & gas field machinery; industrial equipment services

(G-10280)
HUNT PETROLEUM CORPORATION
1 Riverway Ste 700 (77056-1988)
P.O. Box 1350 (77251-1350)
PHONE....................................713 871-3400
EMP: 50
SALES (corp-wide): 411.9B **Publicly Held**
SIC: 1382 1311 Oil And Gas Exploration And Production
HQ: Hunt Petroleum Corporation
110 W 7th St
Fort Worth TX 76102
214 880-8400

(G-10281)
HUNTING ENERGY SERVICES INC
1018 Rankin Rd (77073-4606)
PHONE....................................281 821-5577
Donnie Hague, *Opers Mgr*
Rodney Borden, *QC Mgr*
Seth Deutsch, *Sales Staff*
Eddie Johnson, *Manager*
Gina Soto, *Manager*
EMP: 80
SALES (corp-wide): 960MM **Privately Held**
WEB: www.hunting-intl.com
SIC: 1389 3498 Oil field services; fabricated pipe & fittings
HQ: Hunting Energy Services, Llc
16825 Northchase Dr # 600
Houston TX 77060

(G-10282)
HUNTING ENERGY SERVICES INC
4400 N Sam Houston Pkwy W (77086-1471)
PHONE....................................281 569-3620
EMP: 26
SALES (corp-wide): 960MM **Privately Held**
WEB: www.hunting-intl.com
SIC: 8741 1389 Management services; oil field services
HQ: Hunting Energy Services, Llc
16825 Northchase Dr # 600
Houston TX 77060

(G-10283)
HUNTING ENERGY SERVICES LLC (HQ)
Also Called: Hunting Oilfield Services
16825 Northchase Dr # 600 (77060-6005)
PHONE....................................281 820-3838
Bill Cleveland, *General Mgr*
Nathan Schuler, *General Mgr*
Jim Johnson, *Principal*
Nathan Bailey, *Vice Pres*
Andrew Cousins, *Opers Mgr*
◆ EMP: 36
SALES (est): 561.4MM
SALES (corp-wide): 960MM **Privately Held**
WEB: www.hunting-intl.com
SIC: 1389 8741 Oil field services; management services
PA: Hunting Plc
5 Hanover Square
London W1S 1
207 321-0123

(G-10284)
HUNTING INNOVA INC
Also Called: Innova Electronics
8383 N Sam Houston Pkwy W (77064-3452)
PHONE....................................281 653-5500
Dennis Proctor, *CEO*
Leon Chenn, *President*
Rick Smith, *Plant Mgr*
Jay Claybrook, *Facilities Mgr*
Andrew Indihar, *Buyer*
▲ EMP: 350
SQ FT: 101,000
SALES (est): 78MM
SALES (corp-wide): 960MM **Privately Held**
WEB: www.huntinginnova.com
SIC: 3672 3613 8711 Printed circuit boards; power switching equipment; engineering services

▲ = Import ▼=Export
◆ =Import/Export

PA: Hunting Plc
5 Hanover Square
London W1S 1
207 321-0123

(G-10285)
HUNTING TITAN INC
16825 Northchase Dr # 600 (77060-6005)
PHONE....................281 463-5881
Robert Rivet, *Partner*
Sergio Gonzalez, *Sales Staff*
Jeff Skinner, *Sales Staff*
Brad Spisak, *Manager*
William Weems, *Manager*
EMP: 15
SALES (corp-wide): 960MM **Privately Held**
WEB: www.hunting-intl.com
SIC: 1389 Oil field services
HQ: Hunting Titan, Inc.
11785 Highway 152
Pampa TX 79065
806 665-3781

(G-10286)
HUNTON GROUP INC
Also Called: Hunton Distribution Group
16335 Central Green Blvd (77032-5146)
PHONE....................806 788-1100
Norman Gooch, *General Mgr*
Steve Acker, *Vice Pres*
John Edwards, *Credit Mgr*
EMP: 10
SALES (est): 1.2MM **Privately Held**
WEB: www.huntondistribution.com
SIC: 3714 Air conditioner parts, motor vehicle

(G-10287)
HUNTSMAN INTERNATIONAL LLC
101 Concrete St (77012-2443)
PHONE....................713 924-6400
Gary Chapman, *Vice Pres*
Marc Chouinard, *Marketing Staff*
James Machac, *Manager*
Scott Wagaman, *Manager*
EMP: 35
SALES (corp-wide): 6.8B **Publicly Held**
WEB: www.huntsman.com
SIC: 2899 2869 2819 Chemical preparations; industrial organic chemicals; industrial inorganic chemicals
HQ: Huntsman International Llc
10003 Woodloch Forest Dr # 260
The Woodlands TX 77380
281 719-6000

(G-10288)
HURST HYDRAULICS INC
3714 Pinemont Dr (77018-1220)
PHONE....................713 863-0340
Jerry Hurst, *President*
Brian Gerlich, *Vice Pres*
EMP: 15
SQ FT: 12,000
SALES (est): 3.9MM **Privately Held**
WEB: www.hursthydraulics.com
SIC: 3569 7699 Bridge or gate machinery, hydraulic; hydraulic equipment repair

(G-10289)
HUSA ACCURATE MCH WORKS INC
838 Dorchester St (77022-6313)
PHONE....................713 691-0685
Hugo C Sapien, *President*
Fidel Sapien, *Vice Pres*
Rose V Sapien, *Shareholder*
EMP: 14
SQ FT: 14,000
SALES (est): 1.5MM **Privately Held**
SIC: 3599 2821 Machine shop, jobbing & repair; molding compounds, plastics

(G-10290)
HUTCHESON FABRICATING & WLDG
15 N Hutcheson St (77003-1804)
PHONE....................713 224-9703
Daniel Castillo, *Owner*
Cleo Castillo, *Bookkeeper*
EMP: 10 EST: 1992
SQ FT: 10,000

SALES (est): 450K **Privately Held**
SIC: 3356 Nonferrous rolling & drawing

(G-10291)
HUTCHISON HAYES SEPARATION INC
3520 E Sam Houston Pkwy N (77015-3247)
P.O. Box 2965 (77252-2965)
PHONE....................713 455-9600
▲ EMP: 136
SQ FT: 70,000
SALES (est): 22.4MM **Privately Held**
WEB: www.hutch-hayes.com
SIC: 3533 7699 Oil & gas field machinery; professional instrument repair services; mechanical instrument repair
HQ: Alfa Laval U.S. Holding Inc.
5400 Intl Trade Dr
Richmond VA 23231

(G-10292)
HVAC MECHANICAL SVCS OF TEXAS
10555 Westpark Dr (77042-5232)
PHONE....................713 266-3900
Richard Hunton, *President*
EMP: 300
SQ FT: 35,000
SALES (est): 64.5MM **Privately Held**
SIC: 3599 1711 3441 3585 Air intake filters, internal combustion engine, except auto; warm air heating & air conditioning contractor; fabricated structural metal; refrigeration & heating equipment; sheet metalwork

(G-10293)
HWC WIRE & CABLE COMPANY
Also Called: Southwest Wire Rope
8641 Moers Rd (77075-1546)
PHONE....................713 453-8518
James L Pokluda III, *President*
Bill Parrish, *Vice Pres*
Chris Versteeg, *Senior Buyer*
David Sanborn, *Purchasing*
Frank Massaro, *Engineer*
EMP: 112
SALES (corp-wide): 338.2MM **Publicly Held**
WEB: www.houwire.com
SIC: 3496 5051 5251 2298 Miscellaneous fabricated wire products; rope, wire (not insulated); builders' hardware; slings, rope
HQ: Hwc Wire & Cable Company
10201 North Loop E
Houston TX 77029

(G-10294)
HYDRADYNE HYDRAULICS INC (PA)
1019 Rankin Rd (77073-4605)
PHONE....................713 937-8111
Richard Kohl, *President*
EMP: 50 EST: 1960
SQ FT: 21,000
SALES (est): 25.7MM **Privately Held**
WEB: www.hydradynellc.com
SIC: 5084 7699 3441 Hydraulic systems equipment & supplies; hydraulic equipment repair; fabricated structural metal

(G-10295)
HYDRALIFT AMCLYDE INC (HQ)
10353 Richmond Ave Fl 21 (77042-4103)
P.O. Box 3186 (77253-3186)
PHONE....................713 375-3700
◆ EMP: 100
SQ FT: 38,000
SALES (est): 36.6MM
SALES (corp-wide): 8.4B **Publicly Held**
WEB: www.nov.com
SIC: 3536 3533 Cranes & monorail systems; oil field machinery & equipment
PA: National Oilwell Varco, Inc.
7909 Parkwood Circle Dr
Houston TX 77036
713 346-7500

(G-10296)
HYDRAQUIP CUSTOM SYSTEMS INC
Mechatronics & Valve Automtn
16330 Central Green Blvd (77032-5164)
PHONE....................281 822-5000
Ben Parker, *Manager*
EMP: 11 **Privately Held**
WEB: www.hydraquip.com
SIC: 8711 3492 Engineering services; control valves, fluid power: hydraulic & pneumatic
HQ: Hydraquip Custom Systems Incorporated
12311 Cutten Rd
Houston TX 77066

(G-10297)
HYDRAULIC FABRICATION SVCS INC
Also Called: Hydrafab
14490 Wagg Way Rd (77041-1896)
P.O. Box 7249, The Woodlands (77387-7249)
PHONE....................832 844-3724
Karl W Oswald, *CEO*
James Lee, *Mfg Staff*
Nancy Selvidge, *Manager*
Reid Hurt, *Technical Staff*
Yujelis Urdaneta, *Director*
EMP: 50 EST: 1999
SQ FT: 30,000
SALES (est): 25MM **Privately Held**
WEB: www.hydrafabinc.com
SIC: 3441 Fabricated structural metal

(G-10298)
HYDRIL COMPANY (DH)
Also Called: Tenaris Hydril
302 Mccarty St (77029-1140)
PHONE....................713 670-3500
Luca Zanotti, *President*
Ajay Chhabra, *Managing Dir*
Laura Venta, *Admin Sec*
◆ EMP: 680
SALES (est): 124.6MM
SALES (corp-wide): 183.7K **Privately Held**
WEB: www.tenaris.com
SIC: 3533 Oil & gas field machinery
HQ: Maverick Tube Corporation
2200 West Loop S Ste 800
Houston TX 77027
713 767-4400

(G-10299)
HYDRIL COMPANY LP
3300 N Sam Houston Pkwy E (77032-3411)
P.O. Box 60458 (77205-0458)
PHONE....................281 449-2000
Christopher T Seaver, *President*
Fernando Silva, *Production*
Dana Mattiza, *Benefits Mgr*
EMP: 10
SALES (est): 350.3K
SALES (corp-wide): 183.7K **Privately Held**
WEB: www.tenaris.com
SIC: 3533 Derricks, oil or gas field
HQ: Techint Compagnia Tecnica Internazionale Spa
Via Monte Rosa 93
Milano MI 20149
023 593-5001

(G-10300)
HYDRIL USA DISTRIBUTION LLC (DH)
Also Called: Hydril Pressure Control
3300 N Sam Houston Pkwy E (77032-3411)
P.O. Box 671088 (77267-1088)
PHONE....................281 449-2000
Charles Chauvier, *President*
Mat R Castaneda, *General Mgr*
Chuck Chauviere, *Vice Pres*
Cheryl Ballard, *Human Res Mgr*
Neil Russell, *Director*
◆ EMP: 444
SQ FT: 212,000
SALES (est): 361MM
SALES (corp-wide): 95.2B **Publicly Held**
WEB: www.ge.com
SIC: 3533 Oil & gas field machinery

HQ: Ge Energy Manufacturing, Inc.
1333 West Loop S Ste 700
Houston TX 77027
713 803-0900

(G-10301)
HYDRIL USA DISTRIBUTION LLC
5244 N Sam Houston Pkwy E (77032-4009)
PHONE....................832 295-5557
Richard Caine, *Manager*
EMP: 10
SALES (corp-wide): 95.2B **Publicly Held**
WEB: www.ge.com
SIC: 3533 1541 Oil & gas field machinery; industrial buildings & warehouses
HQ: Hydril Usa Distribution Llc
3300 N Sam Houston Pkwy E
Houston TX 77032
281 449-2000

(G-10302)
HYDRIL USA DISTRIBUTION LLC
302 Mccarty St (77029-1140)
PHONE....................713 670-3500
Nick Crowley, *Branch Mgr*
EMP: 61
SALES (corp-wide): 95.2B **Publicly Held**
WEB: www.ge.com
SIC: 3533 Oil & gas field machinery
HQ: Hydril Usa Distribution Llc
3300 N Sam Houston Pkwy E
Houston TX 77032
281 449-2000

(G-10303)
HYDRO CONDUIT OF TEXAS LP
16701 Greenspoint Park Dr (77060-2307)
PHONE....................832 590-5300
Pat Hughes, *Branch Mgr*
EMP: 40 **Privately Held**
WEB: www.rinkerpipe.com
SIC: 5211 8711 3272 Masonry materials & supplies; engineering services; pipe, concrete or lined with concrete
HQ: Hydro Conduit Of Texas, Lp
6560 Langfield Rd 3-H
Houston TX 77092

(G-10304)
HYDRO CONDUIT OF TEXAS LP
Also Called: Houston - Pipe
6560 Langfield Rd Bldg 3 (77092-1008)
PHONE....................832 590-5400
EMP: 34 **Privately Held**
WEB: www.rinkerpipe.com
SIC: 3272 Concrete products
HQ: Hydro Conduit Of Texas, Lp
6560 Langfield Rd 3-H
Houston TX 77092

(G-10305)
HYDRO CONDUIT OF TEXAS LP (DH)
Also Called: Rinker Materials Con Pipe Div
6560 Langfield Rd 3-H (77092-1008)
PHONE....................832 590-5400
David Clarke, *Partner*
Bart Denney, *General Mgr*
Felix Lopez, *General Mgr*
Rick Traylor, *Vice Pres*
Ron Bresette, *Opers Mgr*
EMP: 34
SALES (est): 62.5MM **Privately Held**
WEB: www.rinkerpipe.com
SIC: 3272 Pressure pipe, reinforced concrete
HQ: The Quikrete Companies Llc
5 Concourse Pkwy Ste 1900
Atlanta GA 30328
404 634-9100

(G-10306)
HYDROCRBON EXPLORATION DEV LLC
5825 N Sam Houston Pkwy W (77086-1533)
PHONE....................281 453-5700
EMP: 11
SALES (est): 920K **Privately Held**
SIC: 1382 Oil/Gas Exploration Services

(G-10307)
HYSECO INC
5900 Almeda Genoa Rd (77048-4596)
PHONE....................713 991-4240

▲ **EMP:** 20 **EST:** 1972
SQ FT: 20,000
SALES (est): 4.4MM **Privately Held**
WEB: www.hyseco-hsc.com
SIC: 7699 5084 3593 3561 Hydraulic equipment repair; hydraulic systems equipment & supplies; fluid power cylinders, hydraulic or pneumatic; pumps & pumping equipment

(G-10308)
I & I DESIGN INC
Also Called: Lazio Design
7023 Rampart St (77081-5813)
PHONE...................713 667-6800
Robert Ebik, *President*
▲ **EMP:** 12
SALES (est): 1.6MM **Privately Held**
WEB: www.laziodesign.com
SIC: 3429 5699 Furniture builders' & other household hardware; custom tailor

(G-10309)
I T REMARKETING INC
Also Called: Technocycle
6600 Long Point Rd # 103 (77055-2649)
PHONE...................713 263-8800
Michael Buckles, *President*
Billi Jo Buckles, *Vice Pres*
Barry Aull, *IT/INT Sup*
Marvin Cerritos, *IT/INT Sup*
Kris Girard, *IT/INT Sup*
EMP: 46
SQ FT: 20,000
SALES (est): 5.4MM **Privately Held**
WEB: www.itremarketing.com
SIC: 7373 3559 Value-added resellers; computer systems; recycling machinery

(G-10310)
I W MARKS JEWELERS LP (PA)
3841 Bellaire Blvd (77025-1298)
PHONE...................713 668-5000
Bradley Marks, *Managing Prtnr*
Bradley H Marks, *Managing Prtnr*
Hilda Murphey, *Manager*
Paula Grimes, *CTO*
EMP: 14 **EST:** 1978
SQ FT: 7,500
SALES (est): 2.1MM **Privately Held**
WEB: www.iwmarks.com
SIC: 3911 5944 Jewelry, precious metal; jewelry stores

(G-10311)
IAE INTERNATIONAL INC
Also Called: Sniper Drilling Motors
13300 Stonefield Dr (77014-2923)
PHONE...................281 685-3091
Roxanne Howe, *President*
EMP: 25
SQ FT: 34,000
SALES (est): 4.4MM **Privately Held**
WEB: www.iaeintl.com
SIC: 3546 Drills & drilling tools

(G-10312)
IBERON LLC
10333 Richmond Ave # 500 (77042-4244)
PHONE...................877 559-2140
Richard Ezzeddine, *President*
Jeremy Mattern,
EMP: 13
SALES (est): 1.6MM **Privately Held**
WEB: www.iberon.com
SIC: 7371 3571 Computer software development; computers, digital, analog or hybrid

(G-10313)
ICEE COMPANY
7121 Perimeter Park Dr # 210
(77041-4049)
PHONE...................713 937-9496
Rick Naylor, *Sales/Mktg Mgr*
Jeff Lapilla, *Manager*
Madelyne Terribile, *Manager*
Kay Allen, *Admin Asst*
Julian Robinson, *Technician*
EMP: 18
SALES (corp-wide): 1B **Publicly Held**
WEB: www.icee.com
SIC: 2087 Beverage bases, concentrates, syrups, powders & mixes

HQ: The Icee Company
265 Mason Rd
La Vergne TN 37086
800 426-4233

(G-10314)
IDEAL PRINTERS INC (PA)
Also Called: Idpl
707 West Rd (77038-2505)
PHONE...................713 880-8800
Larry F Vaughn, *President*
Chris Marshall, *Sales Staff*
Mona Schomas, *Sales Staff*
Kevin Wolfley, *Sales Staff*
EMP: 27
SQ FT: 55,000
SALES (est): 5.3MM **Privately Held**
WEB: www.idealprint.com
SIC: 2752 Commercial printing, offset

(G-10315)
IDERA INC (PA)
Also Called: Kiuwan
2950 North Loop W Ste 700 (77092-8806)
PHONE...................713 523-4433
Randy Jacops, *CEO*
Chris Smith, *COO*
Heidi Farris, *Exec VP*
Jerry Morgan, *Vice Pres*
Kristin Dweck, *Project Mgr*
EMP: 78
SALES (est): 137.5MM **Privately Held**
WEB: www.idera.com
SIC: 7371 7372 Computer software development; application computer software

(G-10316)
IES HOLDINGS INC (PA)
5433 Westheimer Rd # 500 (77056-5339)
PHONE...................713 860-1500
Jeffrey L Gendell, *Ch of Bd*
Jeremy Franze, *Division Mgr*
Brian Hartley, *Division Mgr*
Jenny Rich, *Division Mgr*
Mike Lott, *General Mgr*
◆ **EMP:** 60
SALES: 1.1B **Publicly Held**
WEB: www.ies-corporate.com
SIC: 1731 3643 7539 7629 General electrical contractor; communications specialization; voice, data & video wiring contractor; bus bars (electrical conductors); electrical services; electrical equipment repair services

(G-10317)
IES INTERNATIONAL ENERGY SVCS
7224 Lawndale St (77012-2970)
PHONE...................713 928-5311
Eric Counts, *CEO*
Larry Elliott, *General Ptnr*
Patrick Elliott, *General Ptnr*
Robert Schmidt, *General Ptnr*
◆ **EMP:** 53
SQ FT: 40,000
SALES (est): 8.5MM **Privately Held**
WEB: www.intlenergyserv.com
SIC: 3491 Industrial valves

(G-10318)
IFCO SYSTEMS NORTH AMERICA INC
Also Called: Valley Crating & Packaging
6829 Flintlock Rd (77040-4322)
PHONE...................713 937-9311
Fax: 713 332-6146
EMP: 25 **Privately Held**
SIC: 2449 5199 2441 Mfg Wood Containers Whol Nondurable Goods Mfg Wood Boxes/Shook

(G-10319)
IHS GLOBAL INC
Also Called: Ihs Energy
5333 Westheimer Rd # 100 (77056-5411)
PHONE...................713 840-8282
Mark Rose, *Vice Pres*
Sherry Conca, *Manager*
David McCaleb, *Manager*
EMP: 500 **Privately Held**
SIC: 2741 Miscellaneous publishing
HQ: Ihs Global Inc.
15 Inverness Way E
Englewood CO 80112

(G-10320)
IKG USA LLC (PA)
1514 S Sheldon Rd (77015-6650)
P.O. Box 310, Channelview (77530-0310)
PHONE...................281 452-6637
Chad McClendon, *CEO*
Javier Giraldo, *CFO*
EMP: 58
SALES (est): 73.6MM **Privately Held**
WEB: www.ikg.com
SIC: 2431 3444 Staircases, stairs & railings; metal flooring & siding

(G-10321)
ILC DOVER LP
2101 Nasa Pkwy 1 (77058-3607)
PHONE...................281 333-8751
Gonzalez Vanessa, *Engineer*
Don Lacey, *Manager*
Amaya Francisco, *Manager*
EMP: 30
SALES (corp-wide): 114.9MM **Privately Held**
WEB: www.ilcdover.com
SIC: 3842 Personal safety equipment
PA: Ilc Dover Lp
1 Moonwalker Rd
Frederica DE 19946
302 335-3911

(G-10322)
ILI TECHNOLOGIES 2002 USA
4900 Woodway Dr Ste 925 (77056-1835)
PHONE...................713 960-0811
EMP: 10
SALES (est): 385.6K
SALES (corp-wide): 80.2K **Privately Held**
SIC: 1389 Oil/Gas Field Services
PA: Ili Technologies Corp
4760 72 Ave Se
Calgary AB T2C 3
403 543-0060

(G-10323)
ILLINOIS TOOL WORKS INC
Also Called: ITW Global Brand
16200 Park Row Ste 120 (77084-7653)
PHONE...................713 797-2181
James Stone, *Vice Pres*
EMP: 70
SALES (corp-wide): 14.1B **Publicly Held**
WEB: www.itw.com
SIC: 3089 Injection molded finished plastic products
PA: Illinois Tool Works Inc.
155 Harlem Ave
Glenview IL 60025
847 724-7500

(G-10324)
ILLINOIS TOOL WORKS INC
12055 Cutten Rd (77066-1813)
PHONE...................281 580-1589
Maurice Mevissen, *General Mgr*
EMP: 75
SALES (corp-wide): 14.1B **Publicly Held**
WEB: www.itw.com
SIC: 2891 Adhesives & sealants
PA: Illinois Tool Works Inc.
155 Harlem Ave
Glenview IL 60025
847 724-7500

(G-10325)
ILLINOIS TOOL WORKS INC
Also Called: Valron Strength Films
9505 Bamboo Rd (77041-7705)
PHONE...................713 996-4200
Gary Heitzmann, *Regional Mgr*
Chris Gile, *Branch Mgr*
Mike Rancich, *Director*
Diane Zamora, *Assistant*
EMP: 100
SALES (corp-wide): 14.1B **Publicly Held**
WEB: www.itw.com
SIC: 3081 Polyethylene film
PA: Illinois Tool Works Inc.
155 Harlem Ave
Glenview IL 60025
847 724-7500

(G-10326)
ILLINOIS TOOL WORKS INC
Also Called: ITW Futura Coatings
12055 Cutten Rd (77066-1813)
PHONE...................314 733-1110

(G-10327)
ILLINOIS TOOL WORKS INC
ITW Insulation Systems
1370 E 40th St Bldg 71 (77022-4150)
PHONE...................800 231-1024
Larry Keiner, *President*
EMP: 40
SALES (corp-wide): 14.1B **Publicly Held**
WEB: www.itw.com
SIC: 3441 Fabricated structural metal
PA: Illinois Tool Works Inc.
155 Harlem Ave
Glenview IL 60025
847 724-7500

(G-10328)
ILLUMINATE VINTAGE LLC
1121 Delano St (77003-3713)
PHONE...................903 948-1161
Kyle Bostic, *Principal*
EMP: 9
SALES (est): 63.4K **Privately Held**
WEB: www.illuminatevintage.com
SIC: 5719 3645 Lighting, lamps & accessories; residential lighting fixtures

(G-10329)
IMERYS TALC AMERICA INC
17509 Van Rd (77049-1303)
PHONE...................281 272-7200
Masood Khan, *Superintendent*
Dave Matlock, *Branch Mgr*
EMP: 59
SALES (corp-wide): 3.1MM **Privately Held**
WEB: www.imerys-performance-minerals.com
SIC: 3295 Talc, ground or otherwise treated
HQ: Imerys Talc America, Inc.
1732 N 1st St Ste 450
San Jose CA 95112

(G-10330)
IMMATICS US INC
2130 W Holcombe Blvd # 900
(77030-3310)
PHONE...................346 204-5400
Harpreet Singh, *CEO*
Jessica Mosby, *Opers Staff*
Katina Dorton, *CFO*
Carsten Reinhardt, *Chief Mktg Ofcr*
Toni Weinschenk, *CTO*
EMP: 41
SALES (est): 3.2MM
SALES (corp-wide): 310.5K **Privately Held**
WEB: www.immatics.com
SIC: 2899 Chemical preparations
HQ: Immatics Biotechnologies Gmbh
Paul-Ehrlich-Str. 15
Tubingen 72076
707 153-970

(G-10331)
IMMUNOGENESIS INC
909 Fannin St Ste 2000 (77010-1028)
PHONE...................713 276-7600
Michael Curran, *CEO*
EMP: 10
SALES (est): 623.8K **Privately Held**
SIC: 2834 Pharmaceutical preparations

(G-10332)
IMPACT FIRE SERVICES LLC
1285 N Post Oak Rd # 102 (77055-7259)
PHONE...................713 263-7535
John Taylor, *Branch Mgr*
EMP: 52
SALES (corp-wide): 39.8MM **Privately Held**
WEB: www.impactfireservices.com
SIC: 3699 Electric sound equipment
HQ: Impact Fire Services, Llc
103 12th St Ste 200
Pflugerville TX 78660

▲ = Import ▼=Export
◆ =Import/Export

(G-10333)
IMPACT FLUID SOLUTIONS LP (PA)
2800 Post Oak Blvd Ste 20 (77056-6100)
PHONE...................................713 964-7736
Curtis W Huff, *CEO*
Alan Gilmour, *COO*
Harnad Bhat, *CFO*
David Kulakofsky, *Manager*
Andy Bradbury, *CTO*
◆ EMP: 35
SALES: 23.7MM **Privately Held**
WEB: www.impact-fluids.com
SIC: 1381 Drilling oil & gas wells

(G-10334)
IMPERIAL BAG & PAPER CO LLC
Also Called: Imperial Dade
5707 Harvey Wilson Dr (77020-8025)
PHONE...................................713 223-5050
Robert Tillis, *Branch Mgr*
EMP: 40
SALES (corp-wide): 1.4B **Privately Held**
WEB: www.imperialbag.com
SIC: 5113 2679 7349 7389 Paper & products, wrapping or coarse; paper products, converted; janitorial service, contract basis; packaging & labeling services
PA: Imperial Bag & Paper Co. Llc
255 Route 1 And 9
Jersey City NJ 07306
201 437-7440

(G-10335)
IMPREGLON SURFACE TECH INC (DH)
Also Called: Coating Applicators
6421 Calle Lozano Dr (77041-2559)
PHONE...................................713 466-9655
Henning J Claasen, *President*
Philip Nodecker, *Vice Pres*
Marc Zirkle, *CFO*
Lynn Young, *Admin Sec*
EMP: 28
SQ FT: 15,000
SALES (est): 4.4MM
SALES (corp-wide): 3.1B **Privately Held**
WEB:
www.impreglonsurfacetechnologies.us
SIC: 3479 Coating of metals & formed products
HQ: Aalberts Surface Treatment Tamworth Limited
Kingsbury Link Trinity Road
Tamworth STAFFS B78 2
182 787-1400

(G-10336)
INCINERATOR INTERNATIONAL INC
Also Called: International Envmtl Eqp Co
2702 N Main St (77009-6838)
P.O. Box 8617 (77249-8617)
PHONE...................................713 227-1466
Tom M Leervig, *President*
Eunice Leervig, *Corp Secy*
▲ EMP: 12 EST: 1964
SQ FT: 5,500
SALES (est): 3.4MM **Privately Held**
WEB: www.incinerators.com
SIC: 3567 5084 Incinerators, metal: domestic or commercial; waste compactors

(G-10337)
INCLUSIVE PRODUCTS INC
Also Called: Integrated Security Products
1802 Reseda Dr (77062-6019)
P.O. Box 58746, Webster (77598-8746)
PHONE...................................281 650-7057
Annette Mules, *CEO*
Geoff Mules, *Executive*
EMP: 10
SQ FT: 8,000
SALES (est): 813.4K **Privately Held**
SIC: 7372 Prepackaged software

(G-10338)
INDEPENDENCE CONTRACT DRLG INC (PA)
Also Called: Icd
20475 State Highway 249 # 300 (77070-2755)
PHONE...................................281 598-1230
J Anthony Gallegos Jr, *CEO*

Thomas R Bates Jr, *Ch of Bd*
Philip A Dalrymple, *Senior VP*
Scott A Keller, *Senior VP*
Marc S Noel, *Senior VP*
EMP: 99
SQ FT: 18,000
SALES: 203.6MM **Publicly Held**
WEB: www.icdrilling.com
SIC: 1381 Drilling oil & gas wells

(G-10339)
INDEPENDENCE RESOURCES MGT LLC (DH)
11450 Cmpaq Ctr Dr W Bldg (77070)
PHONE...................................832 916-2300
Michael Van Horn, *CEO*
John Nicholas, *COO*
Ricky Chesshire, *Foreman/Supr*
Tyler Guthrie, *Foreman/Supr*
Johnny Allison, *Opers Staff*
EMP: 21
SALES (est): 44.7MM
SALES (corp-wide): 191.2MM **Publicly Held**
WEB: www.independenceresources.com
SIC: 1382 Oil & gas exploration services
HQ: Earthstone Energy Holdings, Llc
1400 Woodloch Forest Dr # 300
The Woodlands TX 77380
281 298-4246

(G-10340)
INDEPENDENT PIPE SERVICES LLC
9025 Pineland Rd (77044-6155)
PHONE...................................281 436-0380
Joe Chandler, *President*
Freddie Alejandro, *Managing Prtnr*
Gilbert Guerra, *General Mgr*
Alfredo Alejandro, *Vice Pres*
Johnny Juarez, *QC Mgr*
▲ EMP: 30
SALES (est): 6.8MM **Privately Held**
SIC: 3312 Pipes & tubes

(G-10341)
INDEPENDENT PLASTIC INC (PA)
6611 Petropark Dr (77041-4924)
PHONE...................................713 329-9955
David Ressler, *President*
Neal Scott, *Vice Pres*
Neil Scott, *Vice Pres*
Austin Miller, *Purch Agent*
Bee Evans, *Sales Staff*
EMP: 12
SQ FT: 28,750
SALES (est): 2.1MM **Privately Held**
WEB: www.independentplastic.com
SIC: 2821 Plastics materials & resins

(G-10342)
INDIGO MINERALS LLC
600 Travis St Ste 5500 (77002-3008)
PHONE...................................713 237-5000
Frank D Tsuru, *CEO*
Frederick Bakun, *President*
Brent Jasper, *Principal*
William E Pritchard III, *Chairman*
Michael G Winsor, *COO*
EMP: 166
SQ FT: 15,000
SALES (est): 56.1MM **Privately Held**
WEB: www.ndgo.com
SIC: 1382 Oil & gas exploration services

(G-10343)
INDOCHINESE CULTURE CENTER (PA)
Also Called: ICC
3333 Fannin St Ste 203 (77004-2954)
PHONE...................................713 522-7799
CHI Do, *President*
Ve Le, *Vice Pres*
Loc Hoang, *Treasurer*
Phung Dong, *Admin Sec*
EMP: 10
SQ FT: 20,000
SALES: 127K **Privately Held**
SIC: 7361 6513 8322 2721 Employment agencies; apartment building operators; senior citizens' center or association; magazines: publishing only, not printed on site; vocational schools; beauty shops

(G-10344)
INDOORMEDIA INC
17015 Park Row (77084-4921)
PHONE...................................281 206-2500
Craig Stevens, *Production*
EMP: 110
SALES (corp-wide): 54.7MM **Privately Held**
WEB: www.rtui.com
SIC: 2752 Promotional printing, lithographic
PA: Indoormedia, Inc.
1445 Langham Creek Dr
Houston TX 77084
800 247-4793

(G-10345)
INDOORMEDIA INC (PA)
Also Called: Rtui
1445 Langham Creek Dr (77084-5012)
PHONE...................................800 247-4793
Edward D Endsley, *President*
Devin Grover, *Regional Mgr*
Frank Iandoli, *Regional Mgr*
Ted Weatherly, *Regional Mgr*
Ashley Mate, *COO*
▲ EMP: 300
SQ FT: 42,000
SALES (est): 54.7MM **Privately Held**
WEB: www.rtui.com
SIC: 7319 2752 Distribution of advertising material or sample services; promotional printing, lithographic

(G-10346)
INDUMAR PRODUCTS INC
Also Called: Stop It Pipe Repair System
2230 W Governors Cir (77092-8732)
PHONE...................................713 977-4100
Ronald P Cuenod Sr, *President*
Angelique Law, *Controller*
Doug Adams, *Sales Staff*
Gary Lacy, *Executive*
EMP: 10
SALES (est): 2.2MM **Privately Held**
WEB: www.indumar.com
SIC: 2891 3429 Sealing compounds for pipe threads or joints; epoxy adhesives; clamps, metal

(G-10347)
INDUSTRIAL CASTINGS CO INC (PA)
6910 Stearns St (77021-4621)
PHONE...................................713 747-5336
Leon G Bujnoch, *President*
David Bujnoch, *Vice Pres*
EMP: 14
SQ FT: 10,360
SALES (est): 1MM **Privately Held**
SIC: 7699 3541 3322 Engine repair & replacement, non-automotive; machine tools, metal cutting type; malleable iron foundries

(G-10348)
INDUSTRIAL CMPONENTS TEXAS LLC (PA)
Also Called: Icotex
2121 W Sam Houston Pkwy N (77043-2305)
PHONE...................................936 755-5697
Reinhild Kuehne, *President*
Quang Nguyen, *Engineer*
Crystal Willis, *CPA*
EMP: 11 EST: 2016
SALES (est): 10K **Privately Held**
WEB: www.ico-tex.com
SIC: 3448 Prefabricated metal components

(G-10349)
INDUSTRIAL CONTROL INC
10808 Alcott Dr (77043-2040)
PHONE...................................713 464-8005
James E Cross, *President*
Pat Cross, *Treasurer*
EMP: 11 EST: 1977
SQ FT: 13,800
SALES (est): 1.9MM **Privately Held**
SIC: 3621 Motors, electric

(G-10350)
INDUSTRIAL DIAMOND PRODUCTS CO (PA)
9925 Moers Rd (77075-3104)
P.O. Box 753167 (77275-3167)
PHONE...................................713 991-1600
Roland K Hayes, *President*
Barbara Jackson, *Treasurer*
Quintin Payne, *Administration*
EMP: 16 EST: 1957
SQ FT: 13,000
SALES (est): 5MM **Privately Held**
WEB: www.idp-tx.com
SIC: 5085 3545 Abrasives; cutting tools for machine tools

(G-10351)
INDUSTRIAL LUMBER AND BOX INC
7710 Bowie St (77012-2537)
PHONE...................................713 928-2096
Samuel O Pitts II, *President*
Joy Pitts, *Corp Secy*
Samuel O Pitts Sr, *Vice Pres*
EMP: 13 EST: 1961
SQ FT: 5,040
SALES: 529.4K **Privately Held**
SIC: 2511 2449 2448 2441 Bed frames, except water bed frames: wood; food containers, wood: wirebound; boxes, wood: wirebound; skids, wood; nailed wood boxes & shook; hardwood dimension & flooring mills

(G-10352)
INDUSTRIAL NEON SIGN CORP
6223 Saint Augustine St (77021-2612)
PHONE...................................713 748-6600
Donald E Jones Jr, *President*
Don Jones, *Owner*
E Lynn Jones, *Vice Pres*
EMP: 10 EST: 1934
SQ FT: 33,000
SALES (est): 568.7K **Privately Held**
WEB: www.ins-corp.com
SIC: 3993 7359 Neon signs; sign rental

(G-10353)
INDUSTRIAL PIPE FITTINGS LLC
Also Called: Tucson Industrial Plastics
6040 Osborn St (77033-1016)
PHONE...................................800 241-4175
Bud Crites, *Manager*
EMP: 15 **Privately Held**
WEB: www.plassonusa.com
SIC: 2679 Pipes & fittings, fiber: made from purchased material
PA: Industrial Pipe Fittings, L.L.C.
10707 Corp Dr Ste 220
Stafford TX 77477

(G-10354)
INDUSTRIAL TAPE & LABEL CORP
7025 W Tidwell Rd Ste 109 (77092-2029)
P.O. Box 14206 (77221-4206)
PHONE...................................713 748-3105
Terrell G Brown, *President*
Charles Smith, *Corp Secy*
EMP: 15 EST: 1952
SQ FT: 6,000
SALES (est): 2.1MM **Privately Held**
WEB: www.itl-labels.com
SIC: 2759 2671 Labels & seals: printing; packaging paper & plastics film, coated & laminated

(G-10355)
INDUSTRIAL TOOL & DIE CO INC (PA)
Also Called: I T D Precision
9719 Telge Rd (77095-5005)
PHONE...................................281 859-4499
Michael A Tofte, *President*
Bill Tofte, *Vice Pres*
William Tofte, *Vice Pres*
Scott Wells, *Vice Pres*
Evelyn Tofte, *Admin Sec*
EMP: 23 EST: 1946
SQ FT: 32,000
SALES (est): 9.1MM **Privately Held**
WEB: www.itdprecision.com
SIC: 3469 3599 Stamping metal for the trade; machine shop, jobbing & repair

(G-10356)
INDUSTRIAL WELDING ACADEMY
11001 Wallisville Rd (77013-4130)
PHONE....................................713 944-0701
Andre Horn, *Principal*
EMP: 10
SALES (est): 435.3K **Privately Held**
WEB: www.iwatraining.com
SIC: 8299 7692 Schools & educational service; welding repair

(G-10357)
INFORMACION PUBLISHING CO INC
Also Called: Informcion-The Spanish Newsppr
6065 Hillcroft St Ste 400 (77081-1005)
PHONE....................................713 272-0100
Emilio Martinez, *CEO*
Lina Martinez, *President*
EMP: 27
SALES (est): 950K **Privately Held**
WEB: www.lainformacion.us
SIC: 2711 Newspapers: publishing only, not printed on site

(G-10358)
INFORMATION STORE INC (PA)
10777 Westheimer Rd # 250 (77042-3476)
PHONE....................................713 787-6798
Barry Irani, *CEO*
Oscar Teoh, *Vice Pres*
EMP: 19
SQ FT: 14,000
SALES (est): 4.5MM **Privately Held**
WEB: www.istore.com
SIC: 7373 7372 7371 8711 Computer integrated systems design; operating systems computer software; computer software systems analysis & design, custom; custom computer programming services; engineering services

(G-10359)
INFOSYS LIMITED
6002 Rogerdale Rd Ste 550 (77072-1669)
PHONE....................................281 454-0300
Abinash Panda, *Consultant*
Karthik Rajagopal, *Technology*
EMP: 10 **Privately Held**
WEB: www.infosys.com
SIC: 7371 7373 7379 7372 Computer software development; systems engineering, computer related; computer related consulting services; prepackaged software
HQ: Infosys Limited
2400 N Glnvlle Dr Ste C15
Richardson TX 75082
214 306-2100

(G-10360)
INFOVINE INC
1100 W 23rd St Ste 100 (77008-1861)
P.O. Box 2706 (77252-2706)
PHONE....................................713 223-9994
EMP: 36 EST: 1999
SQ FT: 20,000
SALES (est): 1.2MM **Privately Held**
WEB: www.infovine.com
SIC: 2759 7331 Commercial printing; direct mail advertising services

(G-10361)
INFRASTRUCTURE NETWORKS INC (PA)
5051 Westheimr Rd # 1700 (77056-5721)
PHONE....................................832 598-6600
Mark Brody, *Vice Pres*
John Nagel, *VP Business*
Scott Crist, *Director*
Stanley Hughey, *Officer*
EMP: 26
SALES (est): 4.6MM **Privately Held**
WEB: www.infrastructurenetworks.com
SIC: 4899 1389 1382 Communication signal enhancement network system; construction, repair & dismantling services; oil & gas exploration services

(G-10362)
INGENIA POLYMERS INC (HQ)
2222 Appelt Dr (77015-6593)
PHONE....................................281 862-2111

John Lefas, *President*
Steve Galland, *President*
Olga Lefas, *Managing Dir*
Maria Lefas, *Exec VP*
Rich Hall, *Vice Pres*
◆ EMP: 90
SQ FT: 135,000
SALES (est): 34MM
SALES (corp-wide): 28.4MM **Privately Held**
WEB: www.ingeniapolymers.com
SIC: 2821 Molding compounds, plastics
PA: Ingenia Polymers Corp
565 Greenwich St
Brantford ON N3T 5
519 758-8941

(G-10363)
INGENIA POLYMERS INC
2222 Appelt Dr (77015-6593)
PHONE....................................281 862-2111
Hoang Dang, *Plant Mgr*
Lowell Pratts, *Production*
Zhehui Liu, *Research*
Mel Dioneda, *Engineer*
Laurence Dreyer, *CFO*
EMP: 27
SALES (corp-wide): 28.4MM **Privately Held**
WEB: www.ingeniapolymers.com
SIC: 2021 Butter oil
HQ: Ingenia Polymers, Inc.
2222 Appelt Dr
Houston TX 77015
281 862-2111

(G-10364)
INHANCE TECHNOLOGIES LLC (HQ)
22008 N Berwick Dr (77095-5053)
PHONE....................................800 929-1743
Mike Coma, *COO*
Diana Muniz, *Plant Mgr*
Mark Torrey, *CFO*
Edwin L Ballard, *Manager*
Jeff Humphrey, *Technology*
▲ EMP: 25
SQ FT: 6,000
SALES (est): 52.4MM
SALES (corp-wide): 19.6MM **Privately Held**
WEB: www.inhanceproducts.com
SIC: 3089 8741 Plastic processing; management services
PA: Inhance Technologies Holdings Llc
22008 N Berwick Dr
Houston TX 77095
800 929-1743

(G-10365)
INHANCE TECHNOLOGIES LLC
Also Called: Houston Plant
9830 East Fwy (77029-1504)
PHONE....................................713 678-7352
Paul Devourchek, *Manager*
Elizabeth Castle, *Director*
EMP: 20
SALES (corp-wide): 19.6MM **Privately Held**
WEB: www.inhancetechnologies.com
SIC: 2819 2851 Industrial inorganic chemicals; paints & allied products
HQ: Inhance Technologies Llc
22008 N Berwick Dr
Houston TX 77095
800 929-1743

(G-10366)
INLAND MACHINE
1917 Highway 6 S (77077-3301)
PHONE....................................281 497-8871
Tom Carroll, *Owner*
EMP: 10
SQ FT: 7,000
SALES (est): 1.2MM **Privately Held**
WEB: www.inlandmachinetx.com
SIC: 3599 Machine shop, jobbing & repair

(G-10367)
INMAN & COMPANY INC
Also Called: Inman Upholstery
2424 Chapman St (77009-7904)
PHONE....................................713 224-4740
Manuel Santillan, *President*
EMP: 15
SQ FT: 1,800

SALES (est): 1.1MM **Privately Held**
SIC: 7641 3429 Furniture upholstery repair; furniture hardware

(G-10368)
INNOSOL INC
12231.5 Fm Rd 529 (77041)
PHONE....................................281 859-4428
Jody Soileau, *President*
EMP: 10
SQ FT: 2,300
SALES (est): 906.8K **Privately Held**
WEB: www.innosolinc.com
SIC: 3545 Drilling machine attachments & accessories

(G-10369)
INNOVA INTGRATED SOLUTIONS INC
6834 Flintlock Rd (77040-4476)
PHONE....................................713 937-9999
Hiep Q Nguyen, *Director*
EMP: 17
SALES (est): 3MM **Privately Held**
SIC: 3533 Oil & gas field machinery

(G-10370)
INNOVATIVE GAS SYSTEMS INC (PA)
16250 State Highway 249 (77086-1014)
PHONE....................................713 937-5200
Tom Jeffers, *President*
E J Devine, *CFO*
◆ EMP: 60
SQ FT: 5,000
SALES (est): 35MM **Privately Held**
WEB: www.generon.com
SIC: 3081 Unsupported plastics film & sheet

(G-10371)
INNOVATIVE GLOVES & SAFETY LLC
11906 Brittmoore Park Dr A (77041-7345)
PHONE....................................281 582-0700
Ricardo J Perez, *President*
Harry Steffen, *Vice Pres*
▲ EMP: 10
SALES (est): 787.4K **Privately Held**
WEB: www.innovativegloves.com
SIC: 2381 3151 Fabric dress & work gloves; leather gloves & mittens

(G-10372)
INNOVATIVE IDM LLC
Also Called: Innovative-Idm
13770 Hollister Dr # 100 (77086-1215)
PHONE....................................281 880-2105
Todd Mueller, *Principal*
Richard Lewis, *Engineer*
Gary Miertschin, *Manager*
Britt Welch, *Executive Asst*
James Bishop, *Technician*
EMP: 35
SALES (corp-wide): 89.7MM **Privately Held**
WEB: www.innovativeidm.com
SIC: 5063 3699 7622 Electrical apparatus & equipment; electrical equipment & supplies; antenna repair & installation
PA: Innovative Idm, Llc
301 W Vsta Rdge Mall Dr S
Lewisville TX 75067
214 574-9500

(G-10373)
INNOVEX DOWNHOLE SOLUTIONS INC (PA)
Also Called: Quick Connectors
4310 N Sam Houston Pkwy E (77032-3807)
PHONE....................................281 602-7815
Adam Anderson, *CEO*
Jeff Kitzman, *Vice Pres*
Mark Reddout, *Vice Pres*
Greg Roger, *Vice Pres*
James Strickland, *Opers Mgr*
EMP: 107 EST: 2016
SALES (est): 206MM **Privately Held**
WEB: www.innovex-inc.com
SIC: 1389 Oil field services

(G-10374)
INPEX CORPORATION
2800 Post Oak Blvd # 2450 (77056-6184)
PHONE....................................713 850-8480
Daphnie Todoroki, *Principal*
Ken P Piatt, *COO*
EMP: 12
SALES (est): 1.6MM **Privately Held**
WEB: www.inpex.com
SIC: 1311 Crude petroleum & natural gas
PA: Inpex Corporation
5-3-1, Akasaka
Minato-Ku TKY 107-0

(G-10375)
INPEX EAGLE FORD LLC
2800 Post Oak Blvd Ste 24 (77056-6100)
PHONE....................................713 850-8480
Ryo Manabe, *President*
Sohei Yamada,
EMP: 90
SALES (est): 5MM **Privately Held**
SIC: 1311 1381 Crude petroleum & natural gas production; drilling oil & gas wells
PA: Inpex Corporation
5-3-1, Akasaka
Minato-Ku TKY 107-0

(G-10376)
INROCK DRILLING SYSTEMS INC
6000 Brittmoore Rd (77041-5622)
PHONE....................................713 690-5600
Brent Lane, *President*
Jim Agnew, *Vice Pres*
Frank McKinney, *Vice Pres*
Jerald Shipley, *Facilities Mgr*
Chad Agnew, *Opers Staff*
▲ EMP: 50
SQ FT: 40,000
SALES (est): 10.7MM **Privately Held**
WEB: www.inrock.com
SIC: 3545 5084 Cutting tools for machine tools; industrial machinery & equipment

(G-10377)
INSERVIO LLC
Also Called: Tts Pediatrics Pdn
7211 Regency Square Blvd # 110 (77036-3138)
PHONE....................................713 344-1214
Risty Durbin, *Co-Owner*
EMP: 20
SALES (est): 1.2MM **Privately Held**
WEB: www.ttspediatrics.com
SIC: 2621 Book, bond & printing papers

(G-10378)
INSITUFORM TECHNOLOGIES INC
7330 Neuhaus St (77061-4612)
PHONE....................................636 530-8020
EMP: 16
SALES (corp-wide): 1.2B **Publicly Held**
WEB: www.aegion.com
SIC: 2299 6794 1623 Felts & felt products; patent buying, licensing, leasing; pipeline construction
HQ: Insituform Technologies, Llc
17988 Edison Ave
Chesterfield MO 63005
636 530-8000

(G-10379)
INSTALLER PRO LLC
3231 Allen Pkwy Apt 6302 (77019-1834)
PHONE....................................713 854-3656
Ana Flores, *Mng Member*
Francisco Pompa, *Mng Member*
EMP: 22
SALES (est): 1.9MM **Privately Held**
SIC: 3496 Grilles & grillework, woven wire

(G-10380)
INSTANT EMBROIDERY
159 Sharpstown Ctr (77036-5031)
PHONE....................................281 888-0485
Yousuf Ghaffar, *Principal*
EMP: 9 EST: 2010
SALES (est): 322.7K **Privately Held**
WEB: www.instantembroidery.net
SIC: 2759 Screen printing

(G-10381)
INSTRUMENT & VALVE SERVICES CO
1133 Bunker Hill Rd (77055-6203)
PHONE..................................713 827-4395
EMP: 18
SALES (corp-wide): 16.7B **Publicly Held**
SIC: 3823 Industrial instrmnts msrmnt display/control process variable
HQ: Instrument & Valve Services Company
205 S Center St
Marshalltown IA 50158

(G-10382)
INSULATION INVESTORS INC
1370 E 40th St Bldg 71 (77022-4150)
PHONE..................................713 691-3661
Jordan Wolf, *President*
▲ EMP: 180
SQ FT: 1,200
SALES (est): 15MM **Privately Held**
WEB: www.jm.com
SIC: 3441 Fabricated structural metal

(G-10383)
INTECH AEROSPACE LLC
4750 World Hstn Pkwy # 100 (77032-2589)
PHONE..................................281 810-4400
Scott Mowery, *President*
Sally Chung, *Managing Prtnr*
Matt McGinnis, *Vice Pres*
Dragan Djordjevic, *CFO*
Jeff Deelsnyder, *Director*
EMP: 50
SALES (est): 7MM **Privately Held**
WEB: www.intechaero.com
SIC: 3728 Aircraft parts & equipment

(G-10384)
INTEGRATED DRIVE SYSTEMS L L C
6754 Willow Brook Park (77066-3010)
PHONE..................................713 462-1400
David Huntington, *General Mgr*
Diann Wilck, *Accountant*
Gregory Ball, *Sales Mgr*
Norman Myers, *Mng Member*
Doug Piper, *Technology*
EMP: 25
SALES (est): 11.9MM **Privately Held**
WEB: www.drivesystems.net
SIC: 3533 Oil field machinery & equipment

(G-10385)
INTEGRATED PRODUCTION SVCS INC (DH)
16800 Greenspt Pk Dr 200s (77060-2304)
PHONE..................................281 774-6700
Jeff Kaufmann, *President*
Jose Bayardo, *President*
Ryan Bridges, *District Mgr*
Robert Copeland, *Vice Pres*
John Graham, *Vice Pres*
EMP: 20
SALES (est): 131.8MM **Publicly Held**
WEB: www.spnws.com
SIC: 1389 3599 Construction, repair & dismantling services; custom machinery
HQ: Complete Production Services, Inc.
1001 Louisiana St
Houston TX 77002
281 372-2300

(G-10386)
INTEGRITY DEFENSE LLC
700 Milam St Ste 1300 (77002-2736)
PHONE..................................832 282-0993
Jeanette Bartholomew, *Principal*
EMP: 15
SALES (est): 716.8K **Privately Held**
SIC: 3812 Defense systems & equipment

(G-10387)
INTEGRITY PLASTICS INC
10215 Landsbury Dr (77099-3447)
PHONE..................................281 575-6688
Donald Duon Ly, *President*
▲ EMP: 22
SALES (est): 10MM **Privately Held**
SIC: 2673 Bags: plastic, laminated & coated

(G-10388)
INTEGRITY PRECISION MCH LLC
6946 Signat Dr (77041-2719)
P.O. Box 842078 (77284-2078)
PHONE..................................832 859-4116
James Schroder,
Warren Fields,
Michael O'Callaghan,
EMP: 20
SQ FT: 12,000
SALES (est): 733.8K **Privately Held**
SIC: 3599 Custom machinery

(G-10389)
INTEGRTED CRRSION CMPANIES INC (PA)
Also Called: Brance-Krachy
601 Century Plaza Dr (77073-6008)
PHONE..................................713 789-9181
Jesse Marion, *President*
Matthew Henning, *Vice Pres*
◆ EMP: 20
SQ FT: 25,000
SALES (est): 11.1MM **Privately Held**
WEB: www.integratedcorrosion.com
SIC: 3471 Electroplating of metals or formed products

(G-10390)
INTEGRTED MLDING SOLUTIONS INC
6703 Theall Rd (77066-1215)
PHONE..................................281 587-9761
Terilynn Jones, *President*
David Jones, *Vice Pres*
Ken Jones, *Vice Pres*
Bobbin Berndt, *Engineer*
Dale Hunt, *Maintence Staff*
EMP: 25
SQ FT: 30,000
SALES (est): 5.3MM **Privately Held**
WEB: www.ims-tex.net
SIC: 3089 Injection molding of plastics

(G-10391)
INTEL CORPORATION
20475 State Highway 249 # 400 (77070-2755)
PHONE..................................281 251-7649
Jenny Wu, *Electrical Engi*
Mike Connally, *Manager*
Shweta Jha, *Software Engr*
Alonzo Williams, *Technician*
EMP: 10
SALES (corp-wide): 77.8B **Publicly Held**
WEB: www.intel.com
SIC: 3577 Computer peripheral equipment
PA: Intel Corporation
2200 Mission College Blvd
Santa Clara CA 95054
408 765-8080

(G-10392)
INTERCOASTAL PAINT CO INC
14029 W Hardy Rd (77060-5304)
PHONE..................................281 448-5258
Tom Ruland, *Vice Pres*
Esther Gonzalez, *Technical Staff*
EMP: 17
SQ FT: 2,500
SALES (est): 4.1MM **Privately Held**
WEB: www.intercoastalpaint.com
SIC: 2851 Paints & paint additives; polyurethane coatings

(G-10393)
INTERCORR INTERNATIONAL INC
14503 Bammel N Houston (77014-1100)
PHONE..................................281 444-2282
Lars Jorgensen, *CEO*
Dr Michael Cayard, *President*
Dr Russell D Kane, *Vice Pres*
EMP: 24
SQ FT: 15,000
SALES (est): 376.6K
SALES (corp-wide): 36.7B **Publicly Held**
WEB: www.intercorr.com
SIC: 3823 8748 8734 Industrial flow & liquid measuring instruments; test development & evaluation service; testing laboratories

PA: Honeywell International Inc.
300 S Tryon St
Charlotte NC 28202
704 627-6200

(G-10394)
INTERCTIVE EXPLRTION SOLUTIONS
Also Called: Inexs
1980 Post Oak Blvd # 2050 (77056-3899)
PHONE..................................713 993-0676
Craig Davis, *President*
Ed Haire, *Vice Pres*
Davis Luke, *Tech Recruiter*
EMP: 10
SQ FT: 8,000
SALES (est): 1.3MM **Privately Held**
WEB: www.inexs.com
SIC: 1382 Oil & gas exploration services

(G-10395)
INTERGLOBAL PLASTICS INC
8451 Market St Ste 138 (77029-2400)
PHONE..................................713 672-6055
Steve Chung, *President*
Henry Chung, *Vice Pres*
Sam Chent, *Manager*
EMP: 15
SQ FT: 31,000
SALES (est): 1.5MM **Privately Held**
SIC: 2673 Bags: plastic, laminated & coated

(G-10396)
INTERMDAL REPR MDFCATION TRCKG
Also Called: Intermodal Repr Sales/Service
11643 Wllsville Rd Unit 2b (77013)
PHONE..................................713 674-2179
Richard Hill, *Owner*
EMP: 11
SALES (est): 954.8K **Privately Held**
WEB: www.shippingcontainermodifications.com
SIC: 7699 2448 4789 Professional instrument repair services; cargo containers, wood & metal combination; cargo loading & unloading services

(G-10397)
INTERMOOR INC
900 Threadneedle St # 300 (77079-2913)
PHONE..................................832 399-5000
Thomas Fulton, *President*
Tom Bauer, *General Mgr*
Afolabi Bolatiwa, *General Mgr*
David Smith, *Managing Dir*
Aaron Bolch, *Business Mgr*
EMP: 17
SALES (est): 2.9MM **Publicly Held**
WEB: www.intermoor.com
SIC: 1382 Oil & gas exploration services
HQ: Acteon Group Limited
Ferry Road
Norwich NR1 1
160 322-7019

(G-10398)
INTERNATIONAL ASSN DRLG CONTRS (PA)
Also Called: I A D C
3657 Briarpark Dr Ste 200 (77042-5267)
PHONE..................................713 292-1945
EMP: 26 EST: 1940
SQ FT: 5,908
SALES (est): 12.4MM **Privately Held**
WEB: www.iadc.org
SIC: 8611 2741 Trade associations; miscellaneous publishing

(G-10399)
INTERNATIONAL BUSINESS PUBLS
Also Called: World Energy Magazine
18719 Ember Trails Dr (77094-2617)
PHONE..................................713 626-5369
Richard Loomis, *President*
EMP: 10 EST: 1997
SQ FT: 2,500
SALES (est): 777.2K **Privately Held**
WEB: www.worldenergysource.com
SIC: 2721 Magazines: publishing & printing

(G-10400)
INTERNATIONAL DAILY NEWS INC
9015 Bellaire Blvd 107a (77036-4625)
PHONE..................................713 270-4855
EMP: 10
SALES (corp-wide): 3.6MM **Privately Held**
SIC: 2711 5192 Newspapers-Publishing/Printing Whol Books/Newspapers
PA: International Daily News, Inc.
870 Monterey Pass Rd
Monterey Park CA 91754
323 265-1317

(G-10401)
INTERNATIONAL DO FOODS IDF INC
Also Called: Le Gourmet
101 Chartres St (77002-2307)
PHONE..................................713 222-0598
Thai D H Do, *President*
EMP: 12
SQ FT: 5,400
SALES (est): 1.8MM **Privately Held**
WEB: www.springkitchen.com
SIC: 2032 Ethnic foods: canned, jarred, etc.

(G-10402)
INTERNATIONAL ENERGY SVCS LLC
10309 Pineland Rd (77044-5765)
P.O. Box 14405, Humble (77347-4405)
PHONE..................................281 973-9462
David Botello, *Vice Pres*
Maurillo Botello, *Vice Pres*
EMP: 49
SALES (est): 953.5K **Privately Held**
WEB: www.intlenergyserv.com
SIC: 1389 1629 1771 Oil field services; heavy construction; concrete work

(G-10403)
INTERNATIONAL PAINT LLC (DH)
6001 Antoine Dr (77091-3503)
PHONE..................................713 682-1711
Chris Birkert, *Business Mgr*
Ian Walton,
Kenneth Frank,
Eifion Jones,
Wallace White,
◆ EMP: 260 EST: 1921
SQ FT: 115,000
SALES (est): 153MM
SALES (corp-wide): 10.2B **Privately Held**
WEB: www.akzonobel.com
SIC: 2851 Enamels; lacquer: bases, dopes, thinner; varnishes

(G-10404)
INTERNATIONAL PAINT LLC
11930 Proctor St (77038-2704)
PHONE..................................713 684-1500
Jeff Whisman, *Branch Mgr*
EMP: 109
SALES (corp-wide): 10.2B **Privately Held**
WEB: www.akzonobel.com
SIC: 2851 3479 5198 Paints & allied products; coating, rust preventive; paints, varnishes & supplies
HQ: International Paint Llc
6001 Antoine Dr
Houston TX 77091
713 682-1711

(G-10405)
INTERNATIONAL PAPER COMPANY
3000 Brittmoore Rd (77043-1023)
PHONE..................................713 996-9877
Sylvia Williams, *Owner*
EMP: 39
SALES (corp-wide): 22.3B **Publicly Held**
WEB: www.internationalpaper.com
SIC: 2621 Paper mills
PA: International Paper Company
6400 Poplar Ave
Memphis TN 38197
901 419-9000

(G-10406)
INTERNTONAL LAMINATING SYSTEMS
7013 Dixie Dr (77087-5217)
PHONE..................................713 645-0383
Douglas E Prasek, *President*
Tom H Moore II, *Vice Pres*
EMP: 11
SQ FT: 12,000
SALES (est): 1.4MM **Privately Held**
SIC: 2521 Panel systems & partitions (free-standing), office: wood

(G-10407)
INTERSHIP SERVICES INC
5630 Northdale St (77087-4028)
PHONE..................................713 645-2666
Tom Labropoulos, *Principal*
Periklis Routsas, *Principal*
▲ EMP: 28
SALES (est): 5.1MM **Privately Held**
WEB: www.intershipservices.com
SIC: 3731 Shipbuilding & repairing

(G-10408)
INTERWELL US LLC
6832 Bourgeois Rd (77066-3107)
PHONE..................................832 461-1500
Torbjorn Buljo, *Engineer*
Ed Vansickle, *VP Bus Dvlpt*
Alex Mal Donnaw, *CFO*
Morten Stevik, *Sales Staff*
Brett Richard, *Mng Member*
▲ EMP: 23
SALES (est): 5.6MM
SALES (corp-wide): 128.8MM **Privately Held**
WEB: www.interwell.com
SIC: 1381 1389 Reworking oil & gas wells; well plugging & abandoning, oil & gas
HQ: Interwell Norway As
　　Kvernevik Ring 177
　　Hafrsfjord 4048

(G-10409)
INTEX UNITED INC
12626 W Bellfort Ave (77099-4803)
PHONE..................................281 568-4000
Tony Moussavi, *President*
Ed Soheili, *Vice Pres*
Masha Kuhns, *Project Mgr*
EMP: 30
SQ FT: 30,000
SALES (est): 3.5MM **Privately Held**
WEB: www.intexunited.com
SIC: 3993 Signs, not made in custom sign painting shops

(G-10410)
INTSEL STEEL DISTRIBUTORS LLC (HQ)
Also Called: Intsel Steel West California
11310 W Little York Rd (77041-4917)
P.O. Box 21119 (77226-1119)
PHONE..................................713 937-9500
Guy Fernandez, *General Mgr*
Craig Peterson, *Vice Pres*
Keith Butkiewicz, *Opers Mgr*
Doug Holden, *Opers Mgr*
George Morris, *Opers Mgr*
◆ EMP: 115
SQ FT: 220,000
SALES (est): 209.8MM
SALES (corp-wide): 640.1MM **Privately Held**
WEB: www.sss-steel.com
SIC: 5051 3312 3444 Steel; blast furnaces & steel mills; sheet metal specialties, not stamped
PA: Triple-S Steel Holdings, Inc.
　　6000 Jensen Dr
　　Houston TX 77026
　　713 697-7105

(G-10411)
INVISISHIELD LLC (PA)
14750 Memorial Dr (77079-5202)
PHONE..................................713 539-6700
David Zamora, *VP Business*
Estevan Perez Jr,
▼ EMP: 12
SQ FT: 11,000
SALES (est): 1.4MM **Privately Held**
WEB: www.invisishield.com
SIC: 2851 Paints & allied products

(G-10412)
IOFFICE LP (PA)
5300 Memorial Dr Ste 300 (77007-8312)
P.O. Box 22243 (77227-2243)
PHONE..................................713 526-1029
Mark Peterson, *Partner*
Renee Hammond, *General Mgr*
Nathan Krichel, *Accounts Mgr*
Tiffany Rivers, *Marketing Staff*
Ozzie Gardner, *Manager*
EMP: 40
SALES (est): 50MM **Privately Held**
WEB: www.iofficecorp.com
SIC: 8744 7372 Facilities support services; application computer software

(G-10413)
ION GEOPHYSICAL CORPORATION (PA)
2105 Citywest Blvd # 100 (77042-2836)
PHONE..................................281 933-3339
James M Lapeyre Jr, *Ch of Bd*
Chris Usher, *President*
Ken Singh, *Managing Dir*
Christopher T Usher, *COO*
Kenneth G Williamson, *COO*
◆ EMP: 200
SQ FT: 226,000
SALES: 180MM **Publicly Held**
WEB: www.iongeo.com
SIC: 7372 3829 Application computer software; geophysical & meteorological testing equipment; seismographs; seismometers; seismoscopes

(G-10414)
IOS/PCI LLC (HQ)
Also Called: Inspection Oilfield Services
7814 Miller Road 3 (77049-1734)
PHONE..................................281 310-5357
Franklin P McLaughlin, *COO*
Jody Arceneaux, *CFO*
EMP: 15
SQ FT: 12,000
SALES (est): 158.5MM
SALES (corp-wide): 655MM **Publicly Held**
WEB: www.iosinspection.com
SIC: 1389 7389 Oil field services; pipeline & power line inspection service; safety inspection service
PA: L. B. Foster Company
　　415 Holiday Dr Ste 1
　　Pittsburgh PA 15220
　　412 928-3400

(G-10415)
IPSCO TUBULARS (KY) INC (DH)
Also Called: Tmk Ipsco
10120 Houston Oaks Dr (77064-3514)
PHONE..................................859 292-6000
Rene J Robichaud, *President*
Mark Patton, *General Mgr*
Thomas J Depenbrock, *Corp Secy*
Prasenjit Adhikari, *Vice Pres*
Frank Corona, *Plant Mgr*
▲ EMP: 179
SALES (est): 38.9MM
SALES (corp-wide): 183.7K **Privately Held**
SIC: 3317 Welded pipe & tubes

(G-10416)
IPSCO TUBULARS INC (DH)
10120 Houston Oaks Dr (77064-3514)
PHONE..................................281 949-1023
Luca Zanotti, *President*
Dhiren Panda, *General Mgr*
Laura Venta, *Vice Pres*
Judy Brannock, *Purch Agent*
Nick Marsalia, *Buyer*
▲ EMP: 36
SALES: 1B
SALES (corp-wide): 183.7K **Privately Held**
WEB: www.ipsco.com
SIC: 3317 3498 Steel pipe & tubes; fabricated pipe & fittings
HQ: Maverick Tube Corporation
　　2200 West Loop S Ste 800
　　Houston TX 77027
　　713 767-4400

(G-10417)
IQ LIFE SCIENCES CORPORATION
16212 State Highway 249 (77086-1014)
PHONE..................................281 444-6454
P Yohanne Gupta, *CEO*
Marty York, *Director*
EMP: 12
SALES: 72K **Privately Held**
WEB: www.iqlsc.org
SIC: 2834 Pharmaceutical preparations

(G-10418)
IQ SCIENTIFIC CORPORATION
16212 State Highway 249 (77086-1014)
PHONE..................................281 444-6454
EMP: 12 EST: 2001
SALES (est): 828.8K **Privately Held**
WEB: www.iqproducts.com
SIC: 2834 Pharmaceutical preparations

(G-10419)
IRON HRSE OLFLED SVC GROUP LLC
16815 Royal Crest Dr (77058-2521)
PHONE..................................832 224-4430
Erik Hanson, *President*
EMP: 12
SQ FT: 3,000
SALES (est): 492.6K **Privately Held**
WEB: www.iron-horsesvc.com
SIC: 1382 Oil & gas exploration services

(G-10420)
IRON SKY
2425 Ftn View Dr Ste 160 (77057)
PHONE..................................281 468-8255
Keith Drummond, *Principal*
EMP: 14
SALES (est): 1.6MM **Privately Held**
WEB: www.ironsky.com
SIC: 7372 Prepackaged software

(G-10421)
IRONFORCE SUPPLY LLC
7075 W 43rd St (77092-4439)
PHONE..................................713 681-5600
Jose Francisco Gonzalez, *Mng Member*
EMP: 10
SQ FT: 10,000
SALES (est): 2.3MM **Privately Held**
WEB: www.ironforcesupply.com
SIC: 3449 Bars, concrete reinforcing: fabricated steel

(G-10422)
IRONROC ENERGY PARTNERS LLC
2777 Allen Pkwy Ste 600 (77019-2166)
PHONE..................................713 377-9860
Michael Bertuccio, *CEO*
Peter Cook,
Samuel Haskell,
David Lewis,
EMP: 25
SALES (est): 1MM
SALES (corp-wide): 1MM **Privately Held**
SIC: 1382 Oil & gas exploration services
PA: Hb2 Energy, Inc
　　2777 Allen Pkwy Ste 600
　　Houston TX 77019
　　713 377-9860

(G-10423)
IRONWOOD OIL & GAS LLC
16945 Northchase Dr # 1500 (77060-2135)
PHONE..................................281 873-9378
C O Bolt, *President*
R Paul Loveless, *COO*
Jeffrey C Pettit, *COO*
Paul C Braun, *Vice Pres*
Kerri D Battaglia, *Treasurer*
EMP: 9
SALES: 25.4MM **Privately Held**
WEB: www.clfoperating.com
SIC: 1382 Oil & gas exploration services

(G-10424)
ISAIAH 49 16 INC
Also Called: Engrave It Houston
9125 Emmott Rd (77040-3513)
PHONE..................................713 896-1765
Lloyd Tomlinson, *President*
Carol Tomlinson, *Vice Pres*
EMP: 12

SQ FT: 5,400
SALES (est): 1.8MM **Privately Held**
SIC: 3499 Novelties & giftware, including trophies

(G-10425)
ISGAS INCORPORATED
5807 Northdale St (77087-4031)
PHONE..................................713 645-5886
Vinh Q Hua, *President*
James Collins, *Vice Pres*
▲ EMP: 9
SALES (est): 1.8MM **Privately Held**
WEB: www.redballoxygen.com
SIC: 3826 Gas testing apparatus

(G-10426)
ISKANDIA ENERGY OPERATING INC
801 Travis St Ste 1818 (77002-5807)
PHONE..................................832 209-8240
Stephane Lamoine, *President*
James Spillane, *CFO*
EMP: 26
SQ FT: 2,722
SALES (est): 9MM **Privately Held**
WEB: www.te-oil.com
SIC: 1382 Oil & gas exploration services

(G-10427)
ISRAMCO INC (DH)
1001 West Loop S Ste 750 (77027-9046)
PHONE..................................713 621-3882
Haim Tsuff, *Ch of Bd*
Edy Francis, *CFO*
Matt Gille, *Controller*
Jin Chua, *Asst Controller*
Max Pridgeon, *Director*
EMP: 13
SALES: 81.3MM **Privately Held**
WEB: www.isramcousa.com
SIC: 1311 Crude petroleum production; crude petroleum & natural gas production

(G-10428)
ISRAMCO ENERGY LLC
1001 West Loop S Ste 750 (77027-9046)
PHONE..................................713 456-7892
Joel M Cutler,
EMP: 25
SALES (est): 1.9MM **Privately Held**
WEB: www.isramcousa.com
SIC: 1382 Oil & gas exploration services
HQ: Isramco, Inc.
　　1001 West Loop S Ste 750
　　Houston TX 77027

(G-10429)
ISSGR INC
Also Called: Imageset
6611 Portwest Dr Ste 190 (77024-8090)
PHONE..................................713 869-7700
Debra Regna Briggs, *President*
Rachel Shepherd, *Senior VP*
Gary Woolsey, *Vice Pres*
Kathi Woolsey, *Vice Pres*
Cliff Rosser, *CFO*
EMP: 36
SQ FT: 6,000
SALES (est): 6.4MM **Privately Held**
WEB: www.imageset.com
SIC: 2752 7374 7336 Commercial printing, offset; computer graphics service; graphic arts & related design

(G-10430)
ITAFOS SERVICES LLC
109 N Post Oak Ln Ste 405 (77024-7792)
PHONE..................................713 242-8446
Brian Zatalan, *CEO*
Wynand Van Dyk, *VP Engrg*
Demian Guthmiller, *Engineer*
Rafael F Rangel, *CFO*
Anthony Cina, *Director*
EMP: 290
SALES (est): 3.7MM **Privately Held**
SIC: 1081 2874 Metal mining services; phosphatic fertilizers

(G-10431)
ITEX PIPING PRODUCTS LLC
13411 West Rd (77041-1109)
PHONE..................................832 604-7900
▲ EMP: 34 EST: 2011

SALES (est): 7.4MM **Privately Held**
WEB: www.itexpp.com
SIC: **3498** Fabricated pipe & fittings

(G-10432)
J & J MACHINING INC (PA)
6520 Springer St (77087-3448)
PHONE..............................713 644-7916
Sara Austin, *President*
Sarah Austin, *President*
EMP: 14
SQ FT: 5,000
SALES (est): 2MM **Privately Held**
WEB: www.jjmachining.com
SIC: **3599** Machine shop, jobbing & repair

(G-10433)
J & L SHEET METAL CO INC
14102 Chrisman Rd (77039-1506)
PHONE..............................713 864-7714
Edward Chisholm, *President*
David Chisholm Jr, *Senior VP*
Ben Chisholm, *Vice Pres*
Stephen Alvarado, *Admin Sec*
EMP: 25 EST: 1955
SQ FT: 20,000
SALES (est): 4.9MM **Privately Held**
WEB: www.jandlsheetmetalhouston.com
SIC: **3444** 1761 Sheet metalwork; sheet
metalwork

(G-10434)
J & R GRINDING LLC
15702 W Hardy Rd Ste 260 (77060-3145)
PHONE..............................281 272-2344
Stephen C Ternois, *CEO*
EMP: 10
SALES (est): 500K **Privately Held**
SIC: **3541** Grinding machines, metalwork-
ing

(G-10435)
J B SMITH MFG CO LLC
6618 Navigation Blvd (77011-1342)
PHONE..............................713 928-5711
Bobby Garza, *Opers Staff*
Tom Fish,
EMP: 70 EST: 1957
SQ FT: 50,000
SALES (est): 17.3MM
SALES (corp-wide): 425.3MM **Privately
Held**
SIC: **3321** Cast iron pipe & fittings
PA: Anvil International, Llc
160 Frenchtown Rd
North Kingstown RI 02852
401 558-2578

(G-10436)
J CONNOR CONSULTING INC
19219 Katy Fwy Ste 200 (77094-1053)
PHONE..............................281 578-3388
Jo Ann Connor, *President*
Williams Jennifer, *President*
Cathy Brock, *Corp Secy*
Pamela Sterling, *Vice Pres*
Lincoln Stroh, *Vice Pres*
EMP: 50
SQ FT: 4,600
SALES (est): 6.2MM **Privately Held**
WEB: www.jccteam.com
SIC: **8742** 1389 Business consultant; oil
consultants

(G-10437)
**J D FIELDS & COMPANY INC
(PA)**
55 Waugh Dr Ste 1250 (77007-5840)
P.O. Box 134401 (77219-4401)
PHONE..............................281 558-7199
Jerry D Fields, *CEO*
Jay D Fields, *President*
J Patrick Burk, *Exec VP*
Steve Fredrich, *CFO*
Steve Friedrich, *CFO*
◆ EMP: 20
SQ FT: 9,800
SALES (est): 92.4MM **Privately Held**
WEB: www.jdfields.com
SIC: **5051** 7359 3443 Steel; equipment
rental & leasing; pipe, standpipe & cul-
verts

(G-10438)
J D RUSH CORPORATION
2 Northpoint Dr Ste 150 (77060-3200)
PHONE..............................281 558-8004
Rick Whitfield, *Senior VP*
James A Varner, *Director*
◆ EMP: 15
SQ FT: 8,000
SALES (est): 100MM **Privately Held**
WEB: www.jdrushcorp.com
SIC: **3498** 5051 Fabricated pipe & fittings;
pipe & tubing, steel

(G-10439)
J E TITUS COMPANY
10425 Moers Rd (77075-3808)
PHONE..............................713 991-1100
Jack E Titus Jr, *President*
William T Gaddis Jr, *Vice Pres*
EMP: 16 EST: 1948
SQ FT: 1,200
SALES (est): 1.3MM **Privately Held**
SIC: **1721** 3471 Industrial painting; com-
mercial painting; plating & polishing

(G-10440)
J HARDING & CO
424 W 19th St (77008-3914)
PHONE..............................713 862-9855
Wendy Drouin, *President*
Loyd Powell, *Sales Mgr*
Deborah Drouin, *Agent*
Lee Kat, *Graphic Designe*
EMP: 12
SQ FT: 4,500
SALES (est): 1.5MM **Privately Held**
WEB: www.jhardingco.com
SIC: **2261** 2395 Screen printing of cotton
broadwoven fabrics; embroidery & art
needlework

(G-10441)
**J L PROLER IRON AND STEEL
CO**
4401 Clinton Dr (77020-7807)
P.O. Box 15357 (77220-5357)
PHONE..............................713 675-3191
L Michael Proler, *President*
Sam H Segal, *Vice Pres*
Sam Segal, *Vice Pres*
Steven Segal, *Vice Pres*
Jose Villagran, *Manager*
▼ EMP: 28 EST: 1926
SQ FT: 5,000
SALES (est): 8.1MM **Privately Held**
WEB: www.jlproler.com
SIC: **5093** 3341 Ferrous metal scrap &
waste; secondary nonferrous metals

(G-10442)
J PAUL HORST & ASSOCIATES
5600 Nw Central Dr (77092-2060)
PHONE..............................713 460-9386
EMP: 19
SQ FT: 6,000
SALES (est): 1.2MM **Privately Held**
SIC: **7372** 7373 Prepackaged Software
Services Computer Systems Design

(G-10443)
J SIMMONS GROUP INC
Also Called: J S G
7207 High Life Dr (77066-3722)
PHONE..............................713 675-5100
James Simmons, *President*
Monica Moss, *Finance Mgr*
EMP: 20
SQ FT: 19,600
SALES (est): 4.8MM **Privately Held**
WEB: www.jsimmonsgroup.com
SIC: **8711** 3317 8741 Consulting engi-
neer; steel pipe & tubes; construction
management

(G-10444)
J T THORPE COMPANY (HQ)
6833 Kirbyville St (77033-1194)
P.O. Box 330407 (77233-0407)
PHONE..............................713 644-1247
John C Schultz, *President*
John Schultz, *Exec VP*
Richard Nowland, *Vice Pres*
Heeth Orr, *Vice Pres*
Keith West, *Vice Pres*
▲ EMP: 108 EST: 1906
SQ FT: 78,600

SALES (est): 35.3MM
SALES (corp-wide): 61.8MM **Privately
Held**
WEB: www.thorpeplantmaintenancean-
dengineering.com
SIC: **1741** 3297 Refractory or acid brick
masonry; nonclay refractories
PA: Thorpe Specialty Services Corporation
6833 Kirbyville St
Houston TX 77033
713 644-1247

(G-10445)
J&F MACHINE SHOP INC
6300 W Little York Rd # 112 (77091-1117)
PHONE..............................713 466-1760
Jose Munoz, *President*
Rafael Munoz, *Vice Pres*
EMP: 32
SQ FT: 12,000
SALES (est): 7.1MM **Privately Held**
SIC: **3533** Oil & gas drilling rigs & equip-
ment; drilling tools for gas, oil or water
wells

(G-10446)
**JACKRABBIT STEEL
PRODUCTS INC**
9009 Jackrabbit Rd (77095-3107)
P.O. Box 7249, The Woodlands (77387-
7249)
PHONE..............................281 550-4551
Karl W Oswald, *CEO*
Michael Jay Fogal, *Exec VP*
Leroy Labelle, *Vice Pres*
Larry Keeler, *CFO*
Ken Brockman, *Sales Staff*
◆ EMP: 23
SALES (est): 5MM **Privately Held**
WEB: www.jackrabbitsteel.com
SIC: **3441** Building components, structural
steel

(G-10447)
**JACKUP STRUCTURES
ALLIANCE INC**
10850 Richmond Ave # 205 (77042-3785)
P.O. Box 7249, The Woodlands (77387-
7249)
PHONE..............................713 910-7556
Karl W Oswald, *CEO*
Michael Jay Fogal, *President*
Harold Denton Jr, *Director*
EMP: 9
SALES (est): 1.5MM **Privately Held**
WEB: www.jackupstructures.com
SIC: **3441** Building components, structural
steel

(G-10448)
JACOB STERN & SONS INC
2104 75th St (77011-1656)
P.O. Box 9359 (77261-9359)
PHONE..............................713 926-8386
Timothy Carmack, *Business Mgr*
Steve Kulchin, *Vice Pres*
Marvin Pierson, *Manager*
EMP: 30
SALES (corp-wide): 123.9MM **Privately
Held**
WEB: www.jacobstern.com
SIC: **2077** Animal & marine fats & oils
PA: Jacob Stern & Sons, Inc.
1464 E Valley Rd # 50740
Santa Barbara CA 93108
805 565-1411

(G-10449)
JAG ENERGY COMPANY
9894 Bissonnet St 100b (77036-8239)
PHONE..............................832 997-0575
Giovanni Prosperi,
EMP: 10
SALES (est): 484.7K **Privately Held**
WEB: www.jagenergycompany.com
SIC: **2911** Petroleum refining

(G-10450)
JAHKUR INTERNATIONAL LLC
Also Called: Jahkur Services
800 W Sam Houston Pkwy N (77024-3920)
PHONE..............................832 431-3232
Darik Jahkur-Muhammad,
EMP: 21
SQ FT: 8,500

SALES (est): 1.7MM **Privately Held**
SIC: **1522** 1542 2844 7349 Residential
construction; commercial & office building
contractors; toilet preparations; cleaning
service, industrial or commercial; perfume
materials, synthetic; entertainment service

(G-10451)
**JAMES FISHER SUBSEA EXCAV
INC**
Also Called: Kdm Marine
6421 Cunningham Rd (77041-4713)
PHONE..............................713 466-1233
Kenneth R Mackie, *CEO*
Keith Douglas, *CFO*
Faisel Chaudry, *Manager*
Richard Beattie, *Director*
Graham Murdoch, *Director*
EMP: 10 EST: 2013
SALES (est): 801.2K **Privately Held**
WEB: www.jfsubseaexcavation.com
SIC: **1382** Oil & gas exploration services

(G-10452)
**JAMESTOWN NORTH AMERICA
LLC**
4550 Homestead Rd (77028-5820)
PHONE..............................713 672-6655
Gina Holt, *VP Sales*
Adrienne Cerf, *Sales Staff*
Charlie Sherling, *Mng Member*
Clyde Sheppard, *Supervisor*
Erika Salazar,
▲ EMP: 9
SQ FT: 18,000
SALES (est): 2.1MM **Privately Held**
WEB: www.jamestownnorthamerica.com
SIC: **3356** Nonferrous rolling & drawing

(G-10453)
**JANUS INTERNATIONAL GROUP
LLC**
1256 Brittmoore Rd (77043-4002)
PHONE..............................713 463-4427
Jerry Clary, *Manager*
EMP: 30
SQ FT: 53,206
SALES (corp-wide): 268.1MM **Privately
Held**
WEB: www.janusintl.com
SIC: **3442** Metal doors
PA: Janus International Group, Llc
135 Janus Intl Blvd
Temple GA 30179
770 562-2850

(G-10454)
**JAPAN AROSPC EXPLORATION
AGCY**
Also Called: Jaxa
18050 Saturn Ln Ste 310 (77058-4502)
PHONE..............................281 333-5999
Keiji Tachikawa, *President*
EMP: 10
SALES (est): 975.8K **Privately Held**
WEB: www.jaxa.jp
SIC: **3761** Guided missiles & space vehi-
cles, research & development
HQ: Japan Aerospace Exploration Agency
7-44-1, Jindaijihigashimachi
Chofu TKY 182-0

(G-10455)
JAR INDUSTRIES LLC
12626 Fuqua St (77034-4629)
PHONE..............................281 484-1777
Jana Blair, *Controller*
Steve Casey,
EMP: 20
SQ FT: 10,500
SALES (est): 2.2MM **Privately Held**
WEB: www.networkcablingservices.com
SIC: **3679** Harness assemblies for elec-
tronic use: wire or cable

(G-10456)
JARCO STEEL INC
1011 Highway 6 S Ste 314 (77077-1040)
P.O. Box 266715 (77207-6715)
PHONE..............................713 644-4900
Joel Ruth, *CEO*
Clifton C Sherrard, *Exec VP*
Faik Ozdogan, *Vice Pres*
EMP: 54

SQ FT: 29,520
SALES (est): 12.7MM **Privately Held**
WEB: www.jarcosteel.com
SIC: 3312 Blast furnaces & steel mills

(G-10457)
JASH USA INC (HQ)
Also Called: Rodney Hunt
6200 Savoy Dr Ste 750 (77036-3357)
PHONE....................281 962-6369
Ranjit Nair, *President*
EMP: 17
SQ FT: 2,000
SALES (est): 9.6MM **Privately Held**
WEB: www.rodneyhunt.com
SIC: 3561 Industrial pumps & parts

(G-10458)
JBD BINDERY INC
Also Called: Sprint Bindery
5800 Corporate Dr Ste A4 (77036-2317)
PHONE....................713 457-4606
John Dreyfus, *President*
EMP: 10
SALES (est): 1.2MM **Privately Held**
WEB: www.sprintbindery.com
SIC: 2789 Binding only: books, pamphlets, magazines, etc.

(G-10459)
JC/FZ HOLDINGS INC
Also Called: Bearings Plus
11951 Spectrum Blvd (77047-7803)
PHONE....................713 948-6000
▲ **EMP:** 45 **EST:** 1997
SALES (est): 11.9MM
SALES (corp-wide): 7.1B **Publicly Held**
WEB: www.bearingsplus.com
SIC: 3366 3568 Bushings & bearings; power transmission equipment
HQ: Waukesha Bearings Corporation
N17w24222 Rivrwood Dr
Waukesha WI 53188
262 506-3000

(G-10460)
JCV MANUFACTURING CORPORATION
131 Eichwurzel Ln Bldg 1 (77009-1832)
PHONE....................281 201-4853
Wenfa Huang, *CEO*
EMP: 10
SALES (est): 1.1MM **Privately Held**
SIC: 3541 Machine tools, metal cutting type

(G-10461)
JDR CABLE SYSTEMS INC
7906 N Sam Houston Pkwy W # 201 (77064-3464)
PHONE....................832 220-4690
Roger Herbert, *CEO*
Richard Turner, *COO*
Paul Gahm, *Exec VP*
John Locke, *Project Mgr*
Chris Norman, *Opers Staff*
◆ **EMP:** 28
SALES (est): 9.5MM
SALES (corp-wide): 411.9MM **Privately Held**
SIC: 5051 3643 5063 Cable, wire; power line cable; wire & cable
HQ: Bi Group Limited
Barlow Road
Coventry W MIDLANDS CV2 2

(G-10462)
JEDCO BUILDING SYSTEMS INC
1645 Hill Rd (77039-5140)
P.O. Box 801467 (77280-1467)
PHONE....................281 591-2860
Shirley J Kindall, *President*
Margaret Duschinski, *Vice Pres*
Clarence Kindall, *Vice Pres*
Tom Duschinski, *Sales Executive*
Shirley Kindall, *Executive*
▼ **EMP:** 40
SQ FT: 1,800
SALES (est): 7.4MM **Privately Held**
WEB: www.jedcohouston.com
SIC: 1541 3441 3448 Steel building construction; fabricated structural metal; prefabricated metal buildings

(G-10463)
JEFFERSON GULF COAST ENERGY (HQ)
811 Louisiana St Ste 2300 (77002-1400)
PHONE....................281 677-4900
Lawrence Waldron, *Principal*
Mark Wilson, *Controller*
Greg Binion, *Mng Member*
Frank Rodriguez,
EMP: 30
SALES (est): 17MM
SALES (corp-wide): 578.7MM **Publicly Held**
WEB: www.jeffersonenergyco.com
SIC: 3822 Energy cutoff controls, residential or commercial types
PA: Fortress Transportation And Infrastructure Investors Llc
1345 Ave Of The Amrcas Fl
New York NY 10105
212 798-6100

(G-10464)
JELEC INC (PA)
16901 Park Row Ste 200 (77084-7162)
PHONE....................713 977-6500
Yuni Paufiques, *General Mgr*
Mike Hanks, *Opers Staff*
Gary Smith, *Sales Executive*
Melissa Yuni Lee,
◆ **EMP:** 50
SQ FT: 210,000
SALES (est): 12.7MM **Privately Held**
WEB: www.jelec.com
SIC: 3695 8711 Instrumentation type tape, blank; engineering services; electrical or electronic engineering

(G-10465)
JENESSCO INDUSTRIES INC
10589 Rockley Rd (77099-3511)
P.O. Box 721434 (77272-1434)
PHONE....................281 498-8833
J Nathanael Essissima, *President*
Nathaniel Essissima, *Finance*
Felix Ess Essissima, *Marketing Staff*
Francine Essissima, *Admin Asst*
▲ **EMP:** 28
SQ FT: 26,000
SALES (est): 5.5MM **Privately Held**
WEB: www.jenessco.com
SIC: 3842 5084 Personal safety equipment; safety equipment

(G-10466)
JERRYCO MCH & BOILER WORKS LP
Also Called: Jerryco Boiler Works
2403 Appelt Dr (77015-6591)
PHONE....................713 224-7900
Jeff L Campbell, *Partner*
1996 Snyder A Family Partnersh, *General Ptnr*
EMP: 55 **EST:** 1977
SQ FT: 111,737
SALES (est): 5MM **Privately Held**
WEB: www.cbservice.com
SIC: 7699 3499 7692 3567 Boiler repair shop; boxes for packing & shipping, metal; welding repair; industrial furnaces & ovens; tubing, metal; machine shop, jobbing & repair

(G-10467)
JESTEX 2 LLC (PA)
8107 E Magnolia St (77012-2118)
P.O. Box 5187 (77262-5187)
PHONE....................713 921-7187
Marty Carnes, *Plant Mgr*
Howard C Palmer,
EMP: 24
SQ FT: 60,000
SALES (est): 1.6MM **Privately Held**
WEB: www.jestex.com
SIC: 3441 Fabricated structural metal

(G-10468)
JET LEARNING LABORATORY INC (PA)
8236 Kirby Dr Ste 190 (77054-1618)
P.O. Box 52190 (77052-2190)
PHONE....................713 524-6284
Rube Williams, *President*
EMP: 9
SQ FT: 2,500

SALES (est): 972.4K **Privately Held**
WEB: www.jetlearninglaboratory.com
SIC: 3724 Research & development on aircraft engines & parts

(G-10469)
JET MACHINE WORKS INC
1107 Aldine Mail Rte (77039-4116)
PHONE....................281 449-0046
Mark A Reneau, *President*
Mark Reneau, *Owner*
Kyle Reneau, *Owner*
Tina Tillman, *Owner*
Danielle R Camp, *Principal*
EMP: 42 **EST:** 1977
SQ FT: 42,000
SALES (est): 7.3MM **Privately Held**
WEB: www.jetmachineworks.com
SIC: 3599 5084 3541 Machine shop, jobbing & repair; industrial machinery & equipment; machine tools, metal cutting type

(G-10470)
JET RUBBER INC
1240 Boyles St (77020-7535)
PHONE....................713 673-5202
EMP: 21 **EST:** 1995
SALES (est): 3.8MM **Privately Held**
WEB: www.jetrubberinc.com
SIC: 3069 Molded rubber products

(G-10471)
JETSTREAM OF HOUSTON LLP (HQ)
Also Called: Fs Solutions
5905 Thomas Rd (77041-4904)
PHONE....................832 590-1300
◆ **EMP:** 89 **EST:** 1976
SQ FT: 20,000
SALES (est): 17.9MM
SALES (corp-wide): 1.2B **Publicly Held**
WEB: www.waterblast.com
SIC: 3589 3491 High pressure cleaning equipment; industrial valves
PA: Federal Signal Corporation
1415 W 22nd St Ste 1100
Oak Brook IL 60523
630 954-2000

(G-10472)
JEWISH HERALD VOICE INC
Also Called: Herald Publishing Co
3403 Audley St (77098-1923)
P.O. Box 153 (77001-0153)
PHONE....................713 630-0391
EMP: 23
SQ FT: 5,900
SALES (est): 1.2MM **Privately Held**
WEB: www.jhvonline.com
SIC: 2711 7336 Newspapers: publishing only, not printed on site; graphic arts & related design

(G-10473)
JGC ENERGY DEVELOPMENT USA INC
3151 Briarpark Dr # 1050 (77042-3804)
PHONE....................832 487-9965
EMP: 11
SALES (est): 2.3MM
SALES (corp-wide): 6.1B **Privately Held**
SIC: 8711 1382 Engineering Services Oil/Gas Exploration Services
PA: Jgc Corporation
2-3-1, Minatomirai, Nishi-Ku
Yokohama KNG 220-0
456 821-111

(G-10474)
JIM COLEMAN COMPANY (PA)
Also Called: Hanna
5842 W 34th St (77092-6402)
PHONE....................713 683-9878
James E Coleman, *Ch of Bd*
Russell Coleman, *Vice Pres*
Randy Coleman, *Vice Pres*
Wayne Coleman, *Treasurer*
Nick Ehrman, *Sales Staff*
◆ **EMP:** 37 **EST:** 1966
SQ FT: 100,000
SALES (est): 39.9MM **Privately Held**
WEB: www.colemanhanna.com
SIC: 3559 5087 Automotive related machinery; carwash equipment & supplies

(G-10475)
JJM OIL & GAS INC
423 N Wayside Dr (77020-7516)
PHONE....................832 740-4606
Jose C Marquez, *President*
Juan H Marquez, *Vice Pres*
Jesus Marquez, *Director*
EMP: 11
SQ FT: 92,000
SALES (est): 3.5MM **Privately Held**
WEB: www.jjmoilandgas.com
SIC: 3441 Fabricated structural metal

(G-10476)
JLK INDUSTRIES INC (PA)
14545 Sommermeyer St (77041-6140)
P.O. Box 40143 (77240-0143)
PHONE....................713 462-7761
Phillip McMahon, *President*
Lanell McMahon, *Admin Sec*
EMP: 25
SQ FT: 30,000
SALES (est): 10.2MM **Privately Held**
WEB: www.jlkind.com
SIC: 5072 5051 3469 Bolts; nuts (hardware); stampings, metal; metal stampings

(G-10477)
JNB MACHINE SHOP INC
20231 Hempstead Rd (77065-5495)
PHONE....................832 237-5000
Juan A Alvarez, *President*
John JC Payne, *Principal*
Frank Vega, *Engineer*
EMP: 14
SQ FT: 1,800
SALES (est): 2.9MM **Privately Held**
WEB: www.jnbmachineshop.net
SIC: 3599 Machine shop, jobbing & repair

(G-10478)
JOANN BAIK
Also Called: Amko International
2777 Jones St Ste 140 (77026-6021)
PHONE....................281 469-1000
Joann Baik, *Owner*
Ho Baik, *Co-Owner*
EMP: 10
SQ FT: 1,850
SALES (est): 920K **Privately Held**
SIC: 3911 5094 Jewelry apparel; jewelry & precious stones

(G-10479)
JOBE SYSTEMS INC
1701 Nance St Ste F&G (77020-5721)
PHONE....................713 344-1292
Jason R Jose, *Branch Mgr*
EMP: 20 **Privately Held**
WEB: www.jobesystems.com
SIC: 3599 Custom machinery
PA: Jobe Systems, Inc.
5452 W Davis St Ste 102
Conroe TX 77304

(G-10480)
JOHN BEAN TECHNOLOGIES CORP
Also Called: Jbt Aerotech
6770 Imperl Vly Dr Ste 12 (77060)
PHONE....................713 875-3735
EMP: 108 **Publicly Held**
WEB: www.jbtc.com
SIC: 3556 3585 3537 Food products machinery; refrigeration & heating equipment; containers (metal); air cargo
PA: John Bean Technologies Corporation
70 W Madison St Ste 4400
Chicago IL 60602

(G-10481)
JOHN H YOUNG INC
4605 Post Oak Place Dr # 250 (77027-9751)
PHONE....................713 236-8303
John H Young, *President*
Gus K Eifler, *Vice Pres*
EMP: 15
SQ FT: 9,000
SALES (est): 1.9MM **Privately Held**
WEB: www.jhyi.com
SIC: 1311 Crude petroleum production; natural gas production

(G-10482)
JOHNSON CONTROLS INC
8323 N Eldridge Pkwy # 120 (77041-1299)
PHONE..................................713 934-2400
Henry Charles, *Opers Staff*
Mike Blankenship, *Manager*
EMP: 94 Privately Held
WEB: www.johnsoncontrols.com
SIC: 2531 Public building & related furniture
HQ: Johnson Controls, Inc.
5757 N Green Bay Ave
Glendale WI 53209
800 382-2804

(G-10483)
JOHNSON CONTROLS INC
2800 N Terminal Rd (77032-5569)
PHONE..................................281 821-0121
Oscar Botello, *Manager*
EMP: 14 Privately Held
WEB: www.johnsoncontrols.com
SIC: 2531 Seats, automobile
HQ: Johnson Controls, Inc.
5757 N Green Bay Ave
Glendale WI 53209
800 382-2804

(G-10484)
JOINT HOLDINGS/BASIC MET INDS (PA)
11921 Fm 529 Rd (77041-3017)
PHONE..................................713 937-7474
Gerald Hodge, *President*
Thomas Viele, *Corp Secy*
EMP: 20
SQ FT: 3,500
SALES (est): 11.1MM Privately Held
SIC: 5051 3441 Steel; fabricated structural metal

(G-10485)
JOVI PRINTING
11177 Katy Fwy Ste C (77079-2127)
PHONE..................................713 467-4980
Jorge Duarte, *Owner*
Sonia Garza, *Accounts Exec*
Mariela Ramirez, *Recruiter*
EMP: 12
SQ FT: 3,400
SALES (est): 918.9K Privately Held
WEB: www.joviprinting.com
SIC: 5699 2395 T-shirts, custom printed; embroidery & art needlework

(G-10486)
JPM EOC OPAL LLC
909 Fannin St Ste 1350 (77010-1042)
PHONE..................................303 861-8140
Kyle R Miller, *CEO*
EMP: 21
SALES (est): 236.9K
SALES (corp-wide): 1.5B Publicly Held
SIC: 1311 Crude petroleum production
PA: Sm Energy Company
1775 N Sherman St # 1200
Denver CO 80203
303 861-8140

(G-10487)
JR MANUFACTURING LP
6485 Thomas Rd (77041-4914)
PHONE..................................713 462-5900
Jerry Cooper Jr, *Partner*
Javier Infante, *Foreman/Supr*
Cherie Vaello, *Office Mgr*
Ryan Grissom, *Manager*
Cathy Torregano, *Contract Law*
EMP: 30
SALES (est): 7.5MM Privately Held
WEB: www.jrmfg.com
SIC: 3498 Fabricated pipe & fittings

(G-10488)
JST GLOBAL LLC (PA)
2104 75th St (77011-1656)
PHONE..................................713 926-8386
EMP: 12
SALES (est): 82.9MM Privately Held
WEB: www.jstg.com
SIC: 2079 Management services

(G-10489)
JT OILFILED MANUFACTURING CO
7443 Fauna St (77061-3906)
PHONE..................................713 947-7006
Shirley Martinez, *Manager*
EMP: 15
SALES (corp-wide): 3.9MM Privately Held
WEB: www.jtoilfield.com
SIC: 3533 Oil field machinery & equipment
PA: Jt Oilfiled Manufacturing Company Inc
1882 Flat Rock St
Friendswood TX 77546
713 947-7006

(G-10490)
JUST ENERGY (US) CORP
5251 Westheimr Rd # 1000 (77056-5412)
PHONE..................................713 850-6784
Deborah Merril, *President*
James Lewis, *President*
Jonah Davids, *Exec VP*
Nancy Cano Nyan, *Project Mgr*
Archana Sukumaran, *Project Mgr*
EMP: 495
SALES (est): 98.2MM
SALES (corp-wide): 2B Privately Held
WEB: www.justenergydeals.com
SIC: 3621 4924 Power generators; natural gas distribution
PA: Just Energy Group Inc
6345 Dixie Rd Suite 400
Mississauga ON L5T 2
905 670-4440

(G-10491)
JVI VIBRATORY EQUIPMENT INC
Also Called: J V I
11929 Brittmoore Park Dr (77041-7226)
P.O. Box 40564 (77240-0564)
PHONE..................................832 467-3720
Mark Neundorfer, *President*
Rob Bishop, *Vice Pres*
Ismael Puga, *Buyer*
Mehmet Temel, *Engineer*
Ann Hutchinson, *Controller*
▼ **EMP: 13**
SQ FT: 10,000
SALES (est): 3.3MM Privately Held
WEB: www.jvivibratoryequipment.com
SIC: 3535 Bulk handling conveyor systems

(G-10492)
JVM MECHANICAL INC
Also Called: Flexelement
8889 W Monroe Rd (77061-5207)
P.O. Box 750635 (77275-0635)
PHONE..................................713 910-3839
Jose Moreno, *CEO*
EMP: 15
SQ FT: 15,000
SALES (est): 460K Privately Held
SIC: 3511 Turbines & turbine generator sets

(G-10493)
K & K MACHINE SHOP INC
2622 Martinville Dr (77017-7307)
P.O. Box 87044 (77287-7044)
PHONE..................................713 947-1705
EMP: 16 EST: 1974
SQ FT: 17,600
SALES (est): 1.9MM Privately Held
SIC: 3599 Mfg Industrial Machinery

(G-10494)
K & T PRINTING INC
10515 Bellaire Blvd Ste D (77072-5235)
PHONE..................................281 988-8088
Peter Pham, *President*
Thanh Huynh, *Vice Pres*
EMP: 20
SQ FT: 34,000
SALES (est): 2.6MM Privately Held
SIC: 2752 2789 2759 Commercial printing, lithographic; bookbinding & related work; commercial printing

(G-10495)
K C CRUSHED CONCRETE INC
909 Pinafore Ln C (77039-1415)
PHONE..................................281 219-0820
EMP: 22 EST: 1997

SALES (est): 2.2MM **Privately Held**
WEB: www.cherrycompanies.com
SIC: 3273 Ready-mixed concrete

(G-10496)
K C FAB INC (PA)
2836 Delafield St (77023-5806)
PHONE..................................713 921-5333
Kenneth Casteel, *President*
Elizabeth Doyle, *Corp Secy*
Mark D Johnston, *Vice Pres*
EMP: 20
SQ FT: 18,000
SALES (est): 4.8MM Privately Held
SIC: 3569 Sprinkler systems, fire: automatic

(G-10497)
K T F INC
Also Called: Speedy Printing K T F
1028 Campbell Rd (77055-7408)
PHONE..................................713 932-6954
Karen Feigley, *President*
Fred Feigley, *Corp Secy*
EMP: 9
SQ FT: 3,000
SALES (est): 1.2MM Privately Held
WEB: www.speedyprintinghouston.com
SIC: 2752 Commercial printing, offset

(G-10498)
K&B MACHINE
Also Called: KB Industries
8500 Miller Road 2 (77049-1951)
PHONE..................................281 456-0293
EMP: 260
SALES (est): 38.1MM Privately Held
SIC: 3561 Pumps, oil well & field

(G-10499)
KAINER EXPORT CRATING INC
6820 Lindbergh St (77087-5119)
P.O. Box 266969 (77207-6969)
PHONE..................................713 641-2345
▼ **EMP: 12**
SQ FT: 30,000
SALES (est): 1.7MM Privately Held
SIC: 2441 Nailed wood boxes & shook

(G-10500)
KAM CONTROLS INC
3939 Ann Arbor Dr (77063-6301)
PHONE..................................713 784-0000
Kim Mohajer, *President*
Eugenio Hinojosa, *Vice Pres*
Vicky Vazquez, *Vice Pres*
Miguel Cano, *Research*
Raquel Gonzales, *Accountant*
EMP: 25
SQ FT: 30,000
SALES (est): 7MM Privately Held
WEB: www.kam.com
SIC: 3823 Flow instruments, industrial process type; moisture meters, industrial process type

(G-10501)
KATCH FILTERS LLC
1414 Sakowitz St (77020-6621)
PHONE..................................713 425-7400
Vince Romeo, *Principal*
EMP: 9
SALES (est): 1.3MM Privately Held
WEB: www.katchfilters.com
SIC: 3569 5075 3511 Filters; air filters; gas turbine generator set units, complete

(G-10502)
KAWASAKI GAS TURBINES-AMERICAS
1200 Smith St Ste 1111 (77002-4310)
PHONE..................................281 970-3255
Ike Takehara, *President*
▲ **EMP: 12**
SALES (est): 3MM Privately Held
WEB: www.kawasakigasturbines.com
SIC: 3511 Gas turbines, mechanical drive
HQ: Kawasaki Motors Corp., U.S.A.
26972 Burbank
Foothill Ranch CA 92610
949 837-4683

(G-10503)
KAWNEER COMPANY INC
6615 Roxburgh Dr Ste 400 (77041-5211)
PHONE..................................713 896-8906

Ray Thompson, *Principal*
EMP: 20
SALES (corp-wide): 7.2B Publicly Held
WEB: www.alcoa.com
SIC: 3446 Architectural metalwork
HQ: Kawneer Company, Inc.
555 Guthridge Ct
Norcross GA 30092
770 449-5555

(G-10504)
KCC CORROSION CONTROL CO LTD
4018 Trey Dr (77084-4042)
PHONE..................................281 550-1199
Thomas G Priest, *Partner*
Barbara Priest, *Executive*
▼ **EMP: 18**
SQ FT: 30,000
SALES (est): 4MM Privately Held
WEB: www.kcccorrosioncontrol.com
SIC: 2899 Corrosion preventive lubricant

(G-10505)
KCS RESOURCES LLC
1000 La St Ste 5600 (77002)
PHONE..................................832 204-2700
EMP: 157
SALES (est): 6.7MM
SALES (corp-wide): 278.4B Privately Held
SIC: 1311 Crude petroleum & natural gas
HQ: Petrohawk Energy Corporation
1360 Post Oak Blvd Ste 15
Houston TX 77056
713 961-8500

(G-10506)
KDH COMPANIES INC
16920 Kuykendahl Rd # 218 (77068-1639)
PHONE..................................281 583-8861
Kevin Holman, *President*
▲ **EMP: 12**
SQ FT: 7,500
SALES (est): 868.5K Privately Held
SIC: 3999 Stage hardware & equipment, except lighting

(G-10507)
KEANE FRAC TX LLC (PA)
2121 Sage Rd (77056-4390)
PHONE..................................713 960-0381
Kevin McDonald, *Exec VP*
EMP: 10
SALES (est): 24.1MM Privately Held
SIC: 1381 8711 Drilling oil & gas wells; engineering services

(G-10508)
KEANE FRAC TX LLC
5825 N Sam Houston Pkwy W # 600 (77086-1551)
PHONE..................................281 929-0370
EMP: 10
SALES (corp-wide): 24.1MM Privately Held
WEB: www.nextierofs.com
SIC: 1389 Oil field services
PA: Keane Frac Tx, Llc
2121 Sage Rd
Houston TX 77056
713 960-0381

(G-10509)
KEANE FRAC TX LLC (PA)
5825 N Sam Houston Pkwy W # 600 (77086-1551)
PHONE..................................281 929-0370
Paul Debonis, *COO*
Jill Arness, *Manager*
Aaron Burleigh, *IT/INT Sup*
EMP: 31 EST: 2009
SALES (est): 31.7MM Privately Held
WEB: www.nextierofs.com
SIC: 1389 Oil field services

(G-10510)
KEANE GROUP HOLDINGS LLC (HQ)
3990 Rogerdale Rd (77042-5142)
PHONE..................................713 960-0381
James Stewart, *CEO*
Paul Debonis, *COO*
Gregory Powell, *CFO*
David Rae, *Manager*
Jason Bedillion, *Supervisor*

EMP: 85
SALES (est): 181.4MM
SALES (corp-wide): 1.8B **Publicly Held**
WEB: www.nextierofs.com
SIC: 1381 7353 4212 Drilling oil & gas wells; oil well drilling equipment, rental or leasing; petroleum haulage, local
PA: Nextier Oilfield Solutions Inc.
3990 Rogerdale Rd
Houston TX 77042
713 325-6000

(G-10511)
KEANE GROUP HOLDINGS LLC
Also Called: Trican Wells Service
20333 State Highway 249 (77070-2617)
PHONE....................................281 716-9152
James Stewart, *Principal*
EMP: 501
SALES (corp-wide): 1.8B **Publicly Held**
WEB: www.nextierofs.com
SIC: 2911 1481 1389 Mineral oils, natural; pumping or draining, nonmetallic mineral mines; oil field services
HQ: Keane Group Holdings, Llc
3990 Rogerdale Rd
Houston TX 77042
713 960-0381

(G-10512)
KELLOGG BROWN & ROOT INTL INC (DH)
601 Jefferson St Ste 7911 (77002-7915)
P.O. Box 4557 (77210-4557)
PHONE....................................713 753-2000
Mary Hawk, *CEO*
Glenn Wong, *Ch of Bd*
Robert R Harl, *President*
Peter W Arbour, *Vice Pres*
J Robert Taylor, *Vice Pres*
◆ **EMP:** 15
SALES (est): 48.3MM **Publicly Held**
WEB: www.kbr.com
SIC: 1389 3441 8711 1629 Oil & gas wells; building, repairing & dismantling; fabricated structural metal; professional engineer; blasting contractor, except building demolition
HQ: Kellogg Brown & Root Llc
601 Jefferson St
Houston TX 77002
713 753-2000

(G-10513)
KELLY B PITTS JR
Also Called: Wce Wholesale Caps, Etc
3703 Reveille St (77087-4501)
PHONE....................................713 923-5555
Kelly B Pitts Jr, *Owner*
EMP: 11 **EST:** 1979
SQ FT: 12,000
SALES (est): 919.6K **Privately Held**
SIC: 7389 2261 Embroidering of advertising on shirts, etc.; screen printing of cotton broadwoven fabrics

(G-10514)
KELMAN TECHNOLOGIES INC
Also Called: Kelman Seismic Processing
10311 Westpark Dr (77042-5312)
PHONE....................................281 529-3204
Kristy Manchul, *Business Mgr*
Thomas Kitchens, *Accounts Mgr*
Shannon Morolez, *Mktg Coord*
Pat Peck, *Branch Mgr*
Garry Voakes, *Manager*
EMP: 35
SALES (corp-wide): 2.1MM **Privately Held**
WEB: www.katalystdm.com
SIC: 1382 1389 Seismograph surveys; gas compressing (natural gas) at the fields
PA: Katalyst Data Holdings Inc
540 5 Ave Sw Suite 1490
Calgary AB
403 294-5274

(G-10515)
KELMSCOTT COMMUNICATIONS LLC (DH)
5858 Westheimer Rd # 410 (77057-5650)
PHONE....................................713 787-0977
Jerry Heitschmidt, *Sales Staff*
Joe R Davis,
◆ **EMP:** 60

SALES (est): 66.2MM
SALES (corp-wide): 6.2B **Publicly Held**
SIC: 2752 Commercial printing, lithographic
HQ: Consolidated Graphics, Inc.
5858 Westheimer Rd # 200
Houston TX 77057
713 787-0977

(G-10516)
KENJER INC (PA)
Also Called: Kenjer Sup-R-Jar
11275 Windfern Rd Ste B (77064-4870)
P.O. Box 693, Humble (77347-0693)
PHONE....................................281 897-8600
Ken Mills, *President*
Jerry L Coker, *Vice Pres*
▲ **EMP:** 15
SQ FT: 7,000
SALES (est): 1.5MM **Privately Held**
WEB: www.kenjer.com
SIC: 1389 Oil field services

(G-10517)
KENNEDY WIRE ROPE & SLING CO
5600 Surrey Square St (77017-5904)
PHONE....................................800 392-5510
EMP: 35
SALES (corp-wide): 48MM **Privately Held**
WEB: www.kwrs.com
SIC: 3496 Miscellaneous fabricated wire products
PA: Kennedy Wire Rope & Sling Co Inc
302 Flato Rd
Corpus Christi TX 78405
361 289-1444

(G-10518)
KEPPEL LETOURNEAU USA INC
5177 Richmond Ave Ste 950 (77056-6729)
PHONE....................................281 677-4482
Chow Yew Yuen, *CEO*
Mark Mascarenhas, *Principal*
Najwa Aejaz, *Human Res Mgr*
Jimmy McDermott, *Sales Mgr*
Bo-D Massey, *Manager*
EMP: 40
SALES (est): 3.2MM **Privately Held**
WEB: www.keppelletourneau.com
SIC: 3533 1381 Oil & gas drilling rigs & equipment; drill rigs; drilling oil & gas wells
HQ: Keppel Offshore & Marine U.S.A., Inc.
5177 Richmond Ave # 1065
Houston TX 77056

(G-10519)
KEPPEL OFFSHORE & MAR USA INC (DH)
5177 Richmond Ave # 1065 (77056-6707)
PHONE....................................713 600-8371
Chow Yew Yuen, *President*
Mohsen Abdelalim, *General Mgr*
George Pritchard, *Engrg Dir*
Tim Saker, *Engineer*
Alex Sibie, *Sales Staff*
EMP: 34
SALES (est): 14MM **Privately Held**
WEB: www.keppelom.com
SIC: 3731 Barges, building & repairing

(G-10520)
KERR ENERGY COMPANIES LLC
258 S Post Oak Ln (77056-1506)
PHONE....................................713 501-9555
Brad Kerr,
EMP: 9 **EST:** 2012
SALES (est): 264.9K **Privately Held**
WEB: www.kerrenergycompanies.com
SIC: 1382 Oil & gas exploration services

(G-10521)
KEY ENERGY DRILLING INC (HQ)
1301 Mckinney St Ste 1800 (77010-3057)
PHONE....................................432 620-0300
Newton W Wilson III, *President*
J Marshall Dodson, *Vice Pres*
Kimberly R Frye, *Vice Pres*
▲ **EMP:** 75

SALES (est): 132.5MM
SALES (corp-wide): 413.8MM **Publicly Held**
WEB: www.keyenergy.com
SIC: 1389 Oil field services
PA: Key Energy Services, Inc.
1301 Mckinney St Ste 1800
Houston TX 77010
713 651-4300

(G-10522)
KEY ENERGY SERVICES INC (PA)
1301 Mckinney St Ste 1800 (77010-3057)
PHONE....................................713 651-4300
Philip E Norment, *Ch of Bd*
Eric Bejaran, *District Mgr*
Mitch Broughton, *District Mgr*
Tony Givens, *District Mgr*
Michael Holloway, *District Mgr*
▼ **EMP:** 150
SALES (est): 413.8MM **Publicly Held**
WEB: www.keyenergy.com
SIC: 1389 1381 1311 Servicing oil & gas wells; drilling oil & gas wells; crude petroleum production; natural gas production

(G-10523)
KEY ENERGY SERVICES INC
12000 W Little York Rd (77041-4503)
PHONE....................................713 651-4300
EMP: 47
SALES (corp-wide): 413.8MM **Publicly Held**
WEB: www.keyenergy.com
SIC: 1389 1381 Servicing oil & gas wells; drilling oil & gas wells
PA: Key Energy Services, Inc.
1301 Mckinney St Ste 1800
Houston TX 77010
713 651-4300

(G-10524)
KEY MAPS INCORPORATED
5922 Richmond Ave Ste C (77057-6343)
PHONE....................................713 522-7949
Jen M Rau, *President*
Robert Abbott, *Vice Pres*
Phillip Cherner, *Treasurer*
EMP: 20 **EST:** 1957
SQ FT: 13,000
SALES (est): 2.7MM **Privately Held**
WEB: www.keymaps.com
SIC: 2741 5199 5999 Maps: publishing only, not printed on site; maps & charts; maps & charts

(G-10525)
KEYS CORPORATION
Also Called: Keys Upholstery
5400 Mitchelldale St A1 (77092-7231)
PHONE....................................713 864-7299
Skip Brown, *President*
EMP: 13
SQ FT: 6,200
SALES (est): 1.3MM **Privately Held**
WEB: www.keysupholstery.com
SIC: 2511 2512 Wood household furniture; upholstered household furniture

(G-10526)
KEYSTON BROS
5250 N Sam Houston Pkwy W # 900 (77086-1475)
PHONE....................................713 692-2132
Shan Breneman, *Branch Mgr*
EMP: 11
SALES (corp-wide): 98.8MM **Privately Held**
WEB: www.keystonbros.com
SIC: 5199 5131 5191 3069 Automobile fabrics; upholstery fabrics, woven; saddlery; film, rubber
HQ: Keyston Bros.
1000 Holcomb Woods Pkwy
Roswell GA 30076
770 587-2555

(G-10527)
KF VALVES LLC
11327 Tanner Rd (77041-6901)
PHONE....................................713 400-2200
Mahesh Joshi, *CEO*
Bhavesh Joshi, *Exec Dir*
EMP: 45

SALES (est): 155K **Privately Held**
SIC: 3491 Industrial valves

(G-10528)
KGGT MANAGEMENT CORP
Also Called: Sir Speedy
13240 Hempstead Rd # 216 (77040-6538)
PHONE....................................713 462-0900
Ted Rice, *President*
EMP: 10
SQ FT: 5,300
SALES (est): 1.8MM **Privately Held**
WEB: www.sirspeedy.com
SIC: 2752 Commercial printing, lithographic

(G-10529)
KHANTY MANSIYSK OIL CORP
5555 San Felipe St (77056-2701)
PHONE....................................713 629-6600
Gerard De Geer, *Ch of Bd*
John Fitzgibbons, *President*
Nikolai V Bogatchev, *Vice Chairman*
Mark C Bilsland, *COO*
Alexander Y Pankov, *Exec VP*
EMP: 900
SALES (est): 16.2MM
SALES (corp-wide): 5.1B **Publicly Held**
WEB: www.marathonoil.com
SIC: 1382 Oil & gas exploration services
PA: Marathon Oil Corporation
5555 San Felipe St
Houston TX 77056
713 629-6600

(G-10530)
KHUDAIRI GROUP INCORPORATED
Also Called: AIN Khudairi Trdg & Contract
1616 S Voss Rd Ste 550 (77057-2620)
PHONE....................................713 782-1080
Aziz S Khudairi, *CEO*
Subhi Khudairi, *President*
Mohammed Khudairi, *Principal*
Paul Gandhi, *Accountant*
Muhanned Hisham, *Sales Staff*
EMP: 40
SALES (est): 3.9MM **Privately Held**
WEB: www.khudairigroup.com
SIC: 5082 1389 4213 Oil field equipment; oil field services; heavy machinery transport

(G-10531)
KICSTAND INC
1631 Mccarty St (77029-3774)
P.O. Box 96242 (77213-6242)
PHONE....................................210 324-0421
Daniel Waits, *CEO*
EMP: 10
SALES (est): 221.8K **Privately Held**
SIC: 7372 Business oriented computer software

(G-10532)
KIGER BROS MCH TL & DIE WORKS
Also Called: Kiger Machine
609 Carby Rd (77037-3302)
P.O. Box 16190 (77222-6190)
PHONE....................................281 447-1315
Gary H Kiger, *President*
Mary Kiger, *Treasurer*
James Kiger, *Consultant*
EMP: 20
SQ FT: 8,864
SALES (est): 3.3MM **Privately Held**
WEB: www.kigermachine.com
SIC: 3544 3599 7692 Special dies & tools; machine shop, jobbing & repair; welding repair

(G-10533)
KING FABRICATION LLC
19300 W Hardy Rd (77073-3500)
PHONE....................................281 209-0811
Vince Rossitto, *Vice Pres*
Erich Thomas, *Project Mgr*
Tim O'Connor, *Controller*
Marc Rossitto, *Mktg Dir*
Louis A Rossitto, *Mng Member*
EMP: 95
SQ FT: 12,000

SALES (est): 31.7MM **Privately Held**
WEB: www.kingfab.com
SIC: **3441** Building components, structural steel

(G-10534)
KING RANCH INC (PA)
3 Riverway Ste 1600 (77056-1967)
PHONE....................................832 681-5700
Robert Underbrink, *President*
James H Clement Jr, *Chairman*
Michael Z Rhyne, *Vice Pres*
Bill Gardiner, *CFO*
William J Gardiner, *CFO*
▼ EMP: 25
SQ FT: 20,000
SALES (est): 189.3MM **Privately Held**
WEB: www.king-ranch.com
SIC: **0212 2711 5083 5948** Beef cattle except feedlots; newspapers, publishing & printing; agricultural machinery; leather goods, except luggage & shoes

(G-10535)
KING RANCH HOLDINGS INC (HQ)
3 Riverway Ste 1600 (77056-1967)
PHONE....................................832 681-5700
Jack Hunt, *President*
EMP: 40
SALES (est): 75MM
SALES (corp-wide): 189.3MM **Privately Held**
WEB: www.king-ranch.com
SIC: **1311 3199 5211 5083** Crude petroleum production; saddles or parts; lumber & other building materials; agricultural machinery
PA: King Ranch, Inc.
    3 Riverway Ste 1600
    Houston TX 77056
    832 681-5700

(G-10536)
KINGSTON I-TEK SOLUTIONS LLC
Also Called: Itek Mobile
9746 Whithorn Dr (77095-5024)
PHONE....................................281 656-4900
Stephen H Joss,
Karen Joss,
Stephen Joss,
George Yax,
EMP: 12
SQ FT: 4,000
SALES: 1.7MM **Privately Held**
SIC: **8742 3663** Business consultant; satellites, communications

(G-10537)
KIT PROFESSIONALS INC
2000 W Sam Houston Pkwy S # 1400 (77042-3626)
PHONE....................................713 783-8700
Sudhakar Kalaga, *President*
Sunil Kommineni, *Vice Pres*
Chetan Vyas, *Vice Pres*
Yongki Shim, *Project Mgr*
Bharath Ramalingam, *Project Engr*
EMP: 13
SALES (est): 1.6MM **Privately Held**
WEB: www.kitprofs.com
SIC: **3999** Manufacturing industries

(G-10538)
KITCHEN EQUIPMENT FABG CO
Also Called: Counter Crast
7007 Stearns St (77021-4622)
P.O. Box 14129 (77221-4129)
PHONE....................................713 747-3611
Alvis L Hartsfield Jr, *President*
Rick Perez, *Project Mgr*
Enrique Salas, *Engineer*
Raymond Calvillo, *Design Engr*
Alyssa Amaya, *Marketing Staff*
EMP: 55 EST: 1958
SQ FT: 31,500 **Privately Held**
WEB: www.countercraftinc.com
SIC: **3469** Kitchen fixtures & equipment: metal, except cast aluminum

(G-10539)
KIZER ENERGY INC
Also Called: Asdfg
1400 Broadfield Blvd # 225 (77084-5679)
PHONE....................................281 712-2047

James Kizer, *President*
Beatriz Trompiz, *Human Res Dir*
Jennifer Vezga, *Administration*
EMP: 25
SQ FT: 3,100
SALES (est): 667.8K **Privately Held**
WEB: www.kizerenergy.com
SIC: **1389** Oil consultants

(G-10540)
KLOECKNER METALS CORPORATION
7400 Mesa Dr (77028-3522)
P.O. Box 23308 (77228-3308)
PHONE....................................713 633-7400
John Ganem, *CEO*
Bryant Smith, *Warehouse Mgr*
Cory Phillips, *Sales Staff*
Eric Platke, *Manager*
EMP: 59
SALES (corp-wide): 6.9B **Privately Held**
WEB: www.kloecknermetals.com
SIC: **5051 3316 3312** Steel; cold finishing of steel shapes; blast furnaces & steel mills
HQ: Kloeckner Metals Corporation
    500 Colonial Center Pkwy # 500
    Roswell GA 30076

(G-10541)
KLOSE CNSTR & FABRICATION
Also Called: Bbq Pits By Klose
1355 Judiway St Ste B (77018-6141)
PHONE....................................713 686-8720
David S Klose, *President*
EMP: 12
SQ FT: 12,000
SALES (est): 2.6MM **Privately Held**
WEB: www.bbqpits.com
SIC: **3631** Barbecues, grills & braziers (outdoor cooking)

(G-10542)
KLX ENERGY SERVICES LLC (HQ)
1415 La St Ste 2900 (77056)
PHONE....................................832 844-1015
Thomas P McCaffrey, *Vice Pres*
Bryan Hall, *Opers Staff*
Bryan Stelly, *Technical Mgr*
Michael Perlman, *Treasurer*
Steven Standridge, *Sales Mgr*
EMP: 65
SALES (est): 110.2MM
SALES (corp-wide): 544MM **Publicly Held**
WEB: www.klxenergy.com
SIC: **1389** Fishing for tools, oil & gas field
PA: Klx Energy Services Holdings, Inc.
    1300 Corporate Center Way
    Wellington FL 33414
    561 383-5100

(G-10543)
KMR GROUP LLC
Also Called: Golden Oolong Tea
1041 Blalock Rd (77055-7424)
PHONE....................................713 932-6988
Shu-Shyan Lin,
EMP: 9
SALES (est): 300K **Privately Held**
WEB: www.kmrgroup.com
SIC: **2046 7389** Tapioca;

(G-10544)
KMT AQUA-DYNE INC
3620 W 11th St (77008-6004)
PHONE....................................713 864-6929
◆ EMP: 30
SQ FT: 90,000
SALES (est): 5.3MM
SALES (corp-wide): 179MM **Privately Held**
WEB: www.aqua-dyne.com
SIC: **3561** Pumps & pumping equipment
HQ: Shape Technologies Group, Inc.
    23500 64th Ave S
    Kent WA 98032
    253 246-3200

(G-10545)
KNG LLC
Also Called: Texas Drect Bndery Letterpress
2127 Harland Dr Ste B (77055-1900)
PHONE....................................713 263-1900
Whitney Amott, *Accounts Mgr*

Nada Koutani, *Mng Member*
Joseph Koutani,
EMP: 9
SQ FT: 11,000
SALES (est): 1MM **Privately Held**
SIC: **2752** Commercial printing, lithographic

(G-10546)
KNIGHT CORPORATION
Also Called: Knight Filter Corporation
10885 Fallstone Rd (77099-3411)
PHONE....................................281 933-5363
Jeff Knight, *Manager*
EMP: 25
SQ FT: 8,035
SALES (corp-wide): 21MM **Privately Held**
WEB: www.knightcorp.com
SIC: **5085 3569 2674** Filters, industrial; filters; bags: uncoated paper & multiwall
PA: The Knight Corporation
    2138 Darby Rd
    Havertown PA 19083
    610 853-2161

(G-10547)
KNIGHT ENERGY HOLDINGS LLC
6003 Cunningham Rd (77041-4705)
P.O. Box 841312 (77284-1312)
PHONE....................................713 466-6660
Britt Sobiesk, *Project Mgr*
Mike Acy, *Manager*
EMP: 30
SALES (corp-wide): 66.3MM **Privately Held**
WEB: www.knightoiltools.com
SIC: **1389** Oil field services
PA: Knight Energy Holdings, Llc
    2727 Se Evangeline Trwy
    Lafayette LA 70508
    337 233-0464

(G-10548)
KNIGHT ENERGY SERVICES LLC (PA)
Also Called: Allis Chalmers
6003 Cunningham Rd (77041-4705)
PHONE....................................832 678-8585
Dwight Gross, *President*
James Griffin, *District Mgr*
Monty Johnston, *Vice Pres*
Roy Trevino, *Opers Mgr*
Tyler Guthrie, *Foreman/Supr*
▲ EMP: 22
SALES (est): 145MM **Privately Held**
WEB: www.irongatees.com
SIC: **1389** Servicing oil & gas wells

(G-10549)
KNIT RAGS LLC
3120 Commerce St (77003-1637)
PHONE....................................713 249-9478
Mustafa Syed, *CEO*
EMP: 16
SALES (est): 625.7K **Privately Held**
SIC: **2299 5093** Fibers, textile: recovery from textile mill waste & rags; waste rags

(G-10550)
KNOLL INC
2800 Post Oak Blvd # 101 (77056-6174)
PHONE....................................713 629-5665
Gerry Fehn, *Division VP*
Jen Graybiel, *Accounts Mgr*
Jaime Brochu, *Sales Staff*
Cindy Cannatella, *Sales Staff*
Susan Quarles, *Sales Staff*
EMP: 13 **Publicly Held**
WEB: www.knoll.com
SIC: **2521** Wood office furniture
PA: Knoll, Inc.
    1235 Water St
    East Greenville PA 18041

(G-10551)
KOCH FILTER CORPORATION
4411 Darien St Ste A (77028-5914)
PHONE....................................502 634-4796
Matt Taylor, *Manager*
EMP: 20 **Privately Held**
WEB: www.kochfilter.com
SIC: **3585** Refrigeration & heating equipment

HQ: Koch Filter Corporation
    8401 Air Commerce Dr
    Louisville KY 40219
    502 634-4796

(G-10552)
KOCH HEAT TRANSFER COMPANY LP (DH)
12602 Fm 529 Rd (77041-2723)
P.O. Box 40082 (77240-0082)
PHONE....................................713 466-3535
John Rosso, *President*
Don Morgan, *Vice Pres*
▲ EMP: 49 EST: 2001
SQ FT: 12,000
SALES (est): 16MM
SALES (corp-wide): 36.8B **Privately Held**
WEB: www.kochheattransfer.com
SIC: **3443** Fabricated plate work (boiler shop)
HQ: Koch-Glitsch, Lp
    4111 E 37th St N
    Wichita KS 67220
    316 828-5000

(G-10553)
KOCH MACHINE TOOL COMPANY
Also Called: Koch Machinery
8500 Westland West Blvd (77041-1214)
PHONE....................................281 720-8500
Michael J Koch, *President*
Steve Lepore, *Admin Sec*
▲ EMP: 12
SQ FT: 4,960
SALES (est): 3.6MM **Privately Held**
WEB: www.kochmachinetool.com
SIC: **3541** Machine tools, metal cutting type

(G-10554)
KOCH PULP & PAPER TRADING LLC
20 Greenway Plz Ste 800 (77046-2019)
PHONE....................................713 544-5070
Steve Kim, *Vice Pres*
Vance Holtzman, *CFO*
EMP: 10
SALES (est): 767.9K
SALES (corp-wide): 36.8B **Privately Held**
WEB: www.kochlumber.com
SIC: **2621** Paper mills
HQ: Koch Mineral Services, Llc
    4111 E 37th St N
    Wichita KS 67220
    316 828-5500

(G-10555)
KOCH SUPPLY & TRADING LP
20 Greenway Plz Ste 850 (77046-2010)
PHONE....................................713 544-4123
Larry Van Horn, *Vice Pres*
Brian Cohen, *Branch Mgr*
EMP: 20
SALES (corp-wide): 36.8B **Privately Held**
WEB: www.ksandt.com
SIC: **2911** Petroleum refining
HQ: Koch Supply & Trading, Lp
    4111 E 37th St N
    Wichita KS 67220
    316 828-5500

(G-10556)
KOCH-GLITSCH LP
Also Called: Koch-Otto York
6611 Killough St (77086-3817)
PHONE....................................281 445-7026
Kevin Alspaw, *Principal*
Duane Martin, *Engineer*
Henry Soto, *Sales Staff*
EMP: 40
SQ FT: 4,951
SALES (corp-wide): 36.8B **Privately Held**
WEB: www.koch-glitsch.com
SIC: **3443** Fabricated plate work (boiler shop)
HQ: Koch-Glitsch, Lp
    4111 E 37th St N
    Wichita KS 67220
    316 828-5000

(G-10557)
KONCEPT SYSTEMS LLC (PA)
11555 Fuqua St (77034-4536)
PHONE....................................800 773-4910

Ryan Martin, *Mng Member*
EMP: 21
SQ FT: 10,000
SALES (est): 3MM **Privately Held**
WEB: www.konceptsystems.com
SIC: 3646 3651 3648 Commercial indusl & institutional electric lighting fixtures; audio electronic systems; speaker systems; stage lighting equipment; arc lighting fixtures

(G-10558)
KONECRANES INC
Also Called: Crane Pro Services
845 Greens Pkwy Ste 300 (77067-4460)
PHONE..............................281 631-0300
Teny Moniaga, *Project Engr*
Sonya Schluens, *Sales Staff*
Erin Carlson, *Branch Mgr*
Jodie Malmay, *Manager*
Charles Perry, *Manager*
EMP: 23
SALES (corp-wide): 3.6B **Privately Held**
WEB: www.konecranes.com
SIC: 3536 Hoists, cranes & monorails
HQ: Konecranes, Inc.
4401 Gateway Blvd
Springfield OH 45502

(G-10559)
KONECRANES INC
Also Called: Crane Pro Parts
845 Greens Pkwy Ste 300 (77067-4460)
P.O. Box 40400 (77240-0400)
PHONE..............................800 486-7278
Nancy Steffan, *Manager*
EMP: 70
SALES (corp-wide): 3.6B **Privately Held**
WEB: www.konecranes.com
SIC: 3536 Hoists, cranes & monorails
HQ: Konecranes, Inc.
4401 Gateway Blvd
Springfield OH 45502

(G-10560)
KONTRACT SFTWR SOLUTIONS LLC
1110 Nasa Pkwy Ste 450 (77058-3346)
PHONE..............................281 994-6104
EMP: 25 **EST:** 2014
SQ FT: 500
SALES (est): 658.1K **Privately Held**
SIC: 7372 Prepackaged Software Services

(G-10561)
KOSMOS CEMENT COMPANY INC (DH)
929 Gessner Rd Ste 1900 (77024-2317)
PHONE..............................713 722-1788
EMP: 14 **EST:** 2015
SALES (est): 2.9MM **Privately Held**
SIC: 3273 Ready-mixed concrete
HQ: Cemex, Inc.
10100 Katy Fwy Ste 300
Houston TX 77043
713 650-6200

(G-10562)
KRAKEN OIL & GAS LLC (PA)
9805 Katy Fwy Ste 300 (77024-1269)
PHONE..............................713 360-7705
Bruce Larsen, *President*
Peter Larsen, *Vice Pres*
Reed Murphy, *Foreman/Supr*
Greg Salveson, *Opers Staff*
Brad Suddarth, *CFO*
EMP: 12
SALES (est): 24.1MM **Privately Held**
WEB: www.krakenoil.com
SIC: 1382 Oil & gas exploration services

(G-10563)
KRATON CORPORATION (PA)
15710 John F Kennedy Blvd # 300 (77032-2347)
PHONE..............................281 504-4700
Dan F Smith, *Ch of Bd*
Kevin M Fogarty, *President*
Marcello C Boldrini, *President*
Holger R Jung, *President*
Melinda S Conley, *Senior VP*
EMP: 104
SQ FT: 105,500

SALES: 1.8B **Publicly Held**
WEB: www.kraton.com
SIC: 2821 2822 Plastics materials & resins; synthetic rubber

(G-10564)
KRATON POLYMERS LLC
700 Milam St (77002-2806)
PHONE..............................832 204-5400
Steven Demetriou, *Principal*
Louis Vitale, *Controller*
EMP: 12 **Publicly Held**
WEB: www.kraton.com
SIC: 2821 Plastics materials & resins
HQ: Kraton Polymers Llc
15710 John F Kennedy Blvd # 300
Houston TX 77032

(G-10565)
KRATON POLYMERS LLC (HQ)
15710 John F Kennedy Blvd # 300 (77032-2347)
PHONE..............................281 504-4700
Kevin M Fogarty, *President*
Robert Newman, *President*
Tammy Gaffney, *Regional Mgr*
Mark Plante, *Business Mgr*
David A Bradley, *COO*
◆ **EMP:** 69
SALES (est): 239.3MM **Publicly Held**
WEB: www.kraton.com
SIC: 2821 Plastics materials & resins

(G-10566)
KRATON POLYMERS US LLC (DH)
15710 John F Kennedy Blvd # 300 (77032-2347)
PHONE..............................281 504-4700
David Bradley, *COO*
Stephen E Tremblay, *Exec VP*
Richard A Ott, *Vice Pres*
Richard Ott, *VP Human Res*
Owen Frawley, *Sales Mgr*
◆ **EMP:** 80
SALES (est): 228.5MM **Publicly Held**
WEB: www.kraton.com
SIC: 2821 Plastics materials & resins

(G-10567)
KRATON POLYMERS US LLC
16400 Park Row (77084-5015)
PHONE..............................281 668-3163
Melinda Conley, *Vice Pres*
Kristin Crawley, *Human Resources*
EMP: 80 **Publicly Held**
WEB: www.kraton.com
SIC: 2821 Plastics materials & resins
HQ: Kraton Polymers U.S. Llc
15710 John F Kennedy Blvd # 300
Houston TX 77032
281 504-4700

(G-10568)
KRENEK PRINTING COMPANY
Also Called: Krenekprinting.com
7102 Glen Chase Ct (77095-2852)
PHONE..............................281 463-8649
John Krenek, *Owner*
Sandra Licarione, *Sales Staff*
Gabe Lukish, *Sales Staff*
Michelle Gray, *Manager*
EMP: 10
SALES (est): 698.7K **Privately Held**
WEB: www.krenekprinting.com
SIC: 2711 Newspapers, publishing & printing

(G-10569)
KSA INDUSTRIES INC (PA)
4400 Post Oak Pkwy Fl 28 (77027-3417)
P.O. Box 844 (77001-0844)
PHONE..............................713 881-3400
Kenneth S Adams Jr, *CEO*
Thomas S Smith, *President*
W R Scofield, *Vice Pres*
Ric Adchire, *CFO*
Steve Underwood, *General Counsel*
EMP: 81 **EST:** 1947
SQ FT: 28,407
SALES (est): 183.5MM **Privately Held**
WEB: www.buick.com
SIC: 1311 0211 5511 6799 Crude petroleum production; natural gas production; beef cattle feedlots; new & used car dealers; investors

(G-10570)
KTX PROPERTIES INC
333 N Sam Houston Pkwy E (77060-2414)
PHONE..............................281 328-3501
Artie McFerrin, *President*
Jeff McFarrin, *Vice Pres*
Kathy Jackson, *CFO*
EMP: 30
SALES (est): 3.2MM **Privately Held**
SIC: 2869 Industrial organic chemicals

(G-10571)
KURARAY AMERICA INC (DH)
Also Called: Kai
2625 Bay Area Blvd Ste 60 (77058-1523)
PHONE..............................800 423-9762
Hitoshi Toyoura, *CEO*
Erich Klein, *Partner*
Seiji Tanimoto, *Division Mgr*
Lisa Ruszkowski, *General Mgr*
Bart Lerman, *Counsel*
◆ **EMP:** 49
SALES (est): 173.6MM **Privately Held**
WEB: www.kuraray.us.com
SIC: 2821 3843 3081 Vinyl resins; glue, dental; polyvinyl film & sheet
HQ: Kuraray Holdings U.S.A., Inc.
2625 Bay Area Blvd Ste 60
Houston TX 77058
713 495-7311

(G-10572)
KW INTERNATIONAL LLC (PA)
11125 Equity Dr Ste 200 (77041-2012)
P.O. Box 19829 (77224-9829)
PHONE..............................713 468-9581
Don Ray, *CEO*
Joe Craft, *COO*
Glen Wind, *Vice Pres*
Laura Golden, *Opers Staff*
Robert Gann, *Mfg Staff*
EMP: 170
SALES (est): 70.1MM **Privately Held**
WEB: www.kwintl.com
SIC: 3533 Oil & gas field machinery

(G-10573)
L J MACHINE WORKS INC
5510 Lawndale St (77023-3899)
PHONE..............................713 928-5786
Fax: 713 928-6132
EMP: 20 **EST:** 1971
SQ FT: 19,500
SALES: 2MM **Privately Held**
SIC: 3533 Mfg Oil/Gas Field Machinery

(G-10574)
L J SMITH INC
6100 W By Northwest Blvd # 110 (77040-4947)
PHONE..............................713 462-4653
EMP: 13
SALES (corp-wide): 238.4MM **Privately Held**
SIC: 2431 Millwork
HQ: L. J. Smith, Inc.
35280 Scio Bowerston Rd
Bowerston OH 44695
740 269-2221

(G-10575)
L L MACHINE WORKS INC
9011 W Little York Rd (77040-4199)
PHONE..............................713 466-7100
Reagan Byrne, *President*
L M Kelley, *Treasurer*
Weldon Byrne, *Admin Sec*
EMP: 13 **EST:** 1964
SQ FT: 10,000
SALES (est): 1.6MM **Privately Held**
SIC: 3599 Machine shop, jobbing & repair

(G-10576)
L V CONTROLS INC
60 Rittenhouse St (77076-2408)
PHONE..............................713 691-4666
Larry L Vines, *President*
Steve Hawkins, *Vice Pres*
EMP: 10
SQ FT: 6,400
SALES (est): 1MM **Privately Held**
WEB: www.lv-controls.com
SIC: 3625 5063 Electric controls & control accessories, industrial; electrical apparatus & equipment

(G-10577)
L&R MIDLAND INC
788 W Sam Houston Pkwy N # 200 (77024-4545)
PHONE..............................713 680-0909
Kenneth Konopka, *Vice Pres*
Shawn Ballard, *Vice Pres*
Wess Johnson, *Broker*
Christopher Rocha, *Broker*
Stephen Willrich, *Marketing Staff*
EMP: 20
SQ FT: 2,500
SALES: 107.9K
SALES (corp-wide): 1.3MM **Privately Held**
WEB: www.lrmidland.com
SIC: 3731 Shipbuilding & repairing
PA: Shipyard Marketing, Inc.
788 W Sam Houston Pkwy N # 200
Houston TX 77024
713 680-0909

(G-10578)
L3 MOBILE-VISION INC
11375 S Sam Hston Pkwy W (77031-2346)
PHONE..............................973 263-1090
Leo Lorenzetti, *President*
▲ **EMP:** 99
SALES: 42.9MM
SALES (corp-wide): 60.9MM **Privately Held**
WEB: www.mobile-vision.com
SIC: 5065 3663 Whol Electronic Parts/Equipment Mfg Radio/Tv Communication Equipment
PA: Safe Fleet Investments Llc
6800 E 163rd St
Belton MO 64012
844 258-8178

(G-10579)
LA BRISA ICE CREAM COMPANY LLC
7842 Canal St (77012-1148)
PHONE..............................713 926-3450
Guadalupe R Flores,
▲ **EMP:** 35
SQ FT: 10,000
SALES (est): 6.7MM **Privately Held**
WEB: www.labrisaicecream.com
SIC: 2024 Juice pops, frozen

(G-10580)
LA ESPIGA DE ORO - GEORGIA INC (PA)
1202 W 15th St (77008-3816)
PHONE..............................713 861-4200
Alfredo S Lira, *President*
Lyvia Lira, *Admin Sec*
EMP: 200 **EST:** 1977
SQ FT: 60,000
SALES (est): 25.7MM **Privately Held**
WEB: www.laespiga.com
SIC: 2099 Tortillas, fresh or refrigerated

(G-10581)
LA PALLET RECYCLERS
9814 Frbanks N Houston Rd (77064-6240)
PHONE..............................281 469-6070
Elmer A Saravia, *Principal*
EMP: 10
SALES (est): 1.1MM **Privately Held**
SIC: 2448 Pallets, wood

(G-10582)
LA RANCHERA INC (PA)
7710 N Shepherd Dr (77088-6343)
PHONE..............................713 699-4400
Veronico Trujillo, *President*
Caesar Zavaleta, *President*
EMP: 10
SQ FT: 4,000
SALES (est): 4.5MM **Privately Held**
WEB: www.larancherainc.com
SIC: 2099 Tortillas, fresh or refrigerated

(G-10583)
LA SUBASTA INCORPORATED (PA)
Also Called: La Subasta Newspaper
6120 Tarnef Dr Ste 100 (77074-3754)
PHONE..............................713 777-1010
Veronica E Budini, *CEO*
Maria R Budini, *President*
Sergio Baldini, *Vice Pres*

▲ = Import ▼=Export
◆ =Import/Export

Marcos Echegaray, *Opers Dir*
Melany Martinez, *Human Resources*
▲ EMP: 35
SQ FT: 15,310
SALES (est): 2.3MM **Privately Held**
WEB: www.lasubasta.com
SIC: 2711 Newspapers, publishing & printing

(G-10584)
LABEL PRODUCTS INC
7511 Langtry St (77040-6630)
P.O. Box 10390 (77206-0390)
PHONE..................................713 869-2959
William Hossley, *President*
Bill Hossley, *General Mgr*
Trish Ricklefsen, *Opers Staff*
Sandy Gonzales, *Human Res Dir*
Becky Mills, *Cust Mgr*
▲ EMP: 33
SALES (est): 7.2MM **Privately Held**
WEB: www.labelproductshouston.com
SIC: 2672 2679 2761 2671 Adhesive papers, labels or tapes: from purchased material; labels, paper: made from purchased material; manifold business forms; packaging paper & plastics film, coated & laminated

(G-10585)
LADISH VALVE COMPANY LLC
7603 Bluff Point Dr (77086-1765)
PHONE..................................281 880-8560
Ryan Scott, *President*
Emily Fraker, *Controller*
Lorena Ibarra, *Sales Staff*
Morgan Mardis, *Sales Staff*
Josh Pfluger, *Manager*
▲ EMP: 65
SQ FT: 44,000
SALES (est): 15MM **Privately Held**
WEB: www.ladishvalves.com
SIC: 5085 3592 3494 3491 Valves & fittings; valves; valves & pipe fittings; industrial valves

(G-10586)
LAGUNA TUBULAR PRODUCTS CORP
16952 Leonard Rd (77049-1800)
PHONE..................................832 734-0044
Eduardo Anaya Kessler, *CEO*
Ignacio Aguirre, *CFO*
Jesus Sebastian Anaya Vera, *Director*
◆ EMP: 75
SQ FT: 4,000
SALES (est): 29.8MM **Privately Held**
WEB: www.lagunatubular.com
SIC: 3399 Laminating steel
HQ: Tuberia Laguna, S.A. De C.V.
Valle Del Guadiana No. 355
Gomez Palacio DGO. 35070

(G-10587)
LAMBDA ENERGY RESOURCES LLC
12012 Wickchester Ln # 300 (77079-1220)
PHONE..................................231 258-6425
Larry Albrecht, *COO*
Jason Ewing, *COO*
Robert Estrada, *CFO*
EMP: 80
SALES (est): 1.1MM **Privately Held**
WEB: www.lambdaenergyllc.com
SIC: 1382 Oil & gas exploration services

(G-10588)
LAMINATE WORKS INC
8600 Telephone Rd (77061-4734)
PHONE..................................713 955-1310
EMP: 49
SALES (corp-wide): 22MM **Privately Held**
WEB: www.laminateworks.com
SIC: 2493 Particleboard, plastic laminated
PA: Laminate Works, Inc.
15900 College Blvd # 200
Lenexa KS 66219
913 800-8263

(G-10589)
LAMONS GASKET COMPANY (HQ)
7300 Airport Blvd (77061-3932)
PHONE..................................713 222-0284

Marc Roberts, *President*
Aaron Patterson, *Business Mgr*
Joshua Sherbin, *Vice Pres*
Robert J Zalupski, *Vice Pres*
Trey Sanchez, *Buyer*
◆ EMP: 300 EST: 1947
SQ FT: 220,000
SALES (est): 182.5MM **Privately Held**
WEB: www.lamons.com
SIC: 3053 5085 Gaskets, all materials; hose, belting & packing
PA: Lgc Us Asset Holdings, Llc
7300 Airport Blvd
Houston TX 77061
713 222-0284

(G-10590)
LAMONT BRANDS INC
920 Gemini St (77058-2704)
PHONE..................................281 286-7553
Melvin Lynn Lamont Jr, *President*
Jerry Lamont, *Principal*
Travis Engler, *Accounts Mgr*
Chris Vassilico, *E-Commerce*
EMP: 9
SQ FT: 2,150
SALES (est): 1MM **Privately Held**
WEB: www.lamontbrands.com
SIC: 2395 7389 Embroidery products, except schiffli machine; embroidering of advertising on shirts, etc.

(G-10591)
LANCASTER FLOW AUTOMATION LLC
14041 West Rd Ste 100 (77041-1132)
PHONE..................................832 237-9444
Jeff Gilgenbach, *President*
Lee Guillis, *President*
Gerardo Harovaldez, *Production*
Nathan Lam, *Purch Mgr*
David Almaraz, *Manager*
EMP: 15 EST: 2008
SALES (est): 4.7MM **Privately Held**
WEB: www.lancasterflow.com
SIC: 3533 Oil field machinery & equipment

(G-10592)
LAND ENTERPRISES INC
Also Called: Texas Electrical Machinery Co
5517 Dorbrandt St (77023-3704)
P.O. Box 230100 (77223-0100)
PHONE..................................713 924-5929
Lance Land, *President*
Daniel Land, *CFO*
Peggy Colsman, *Planning*
EMP: 15
SQ FT: 13,700
SALES (est): 1.9MM **Privately Held**
WEB: www.cpchem.com
SIC: 7694 5063 Rewinding services; electric motor repair; motors, electric

(G-10593)
LANDES INC
4500 S Pinemont Dr (77041-9308)
PHONE..................................713 665-0655
Ralph L De Shong Sr, *Ch of Bd*
Raplh De Shong Jr, *President*
John Harkins, *Opers Mgr*
Michael Mas, *VP Sales*
▲ EMP: 25
SALES (est): 3.2MM **Privately Held**
WEB: www.landesusa.com
SIC: 2393 2396 2759 3993 Duffle bags, canvas: made from purchased materials; bags & containers, except sleeping bags: textile; screen printing on fabric articles; screen printing; signs & advertising specialties

(G-10594)
LANDRETH FASTNER CORPORATION
8700 Scranton St (77075-1008)
PHONE..................................281 414-3103
Thomas C Landreth, *President*
EMP: 12 EST: 1964
SQ FT: 50,000
SALES (est): 1.6MM **Privately Held**
WEB: www.landrethmachining.com
SIC: 3452 3316 Rivets, metal; cold finishing of steel shapes

(G-10595)
LANDRETH PRCSION MACHINING INC
8700 Scranton St (77075-1008)
P.O. Box 262446 (77207-2446)
PHONE..................................713 944-7464
Marlo Landreth, *CEO*
Tom Landreth, *President*
EMP: 10
SALES (est): 871.5K **Privately Held**
WEB: www.landrethmachining.com
SIC: 3599 Machine shop, jobbing & repair

(G-10596)
LANDRY CORPORATION
1518 Hartwick Rd (77093-1027)
PHONE..................................281 449-1052
EMP: 15 EST: 1998
SQ FT: 20,000
SALES (est): 1MM **Privately Held**
WEB: www.landrysinc.com
SIC: 7692 Welding repair

(G-10597)
LANGHAM CREEK MCH WORKS INC
4408 Joyce Blvd Ste D (77084-2418)
PHONE..................................281 550-9587
Mary Jane Boyle, *Principal*
Ricke Karl Boyle Sr, *Vice Pres*
David Rabius, *Plant Supt*
EMP: 70
SQ FT: 20,000
SALES (est): 12.6MM **Privately Held**
WEB: www.lcmw.com
SIC: 3599 Machine shop, jobbing & repair

(G-10598)
LANSA INC
2950 North Loop W Ste 700 (77092-8806)
PHONE..................................630 874-7042
Pete Draney, *CEO*
Alison Henderson, *Vice Pres*
Grant Cooper, *Sales Staff*
Grant Smith, *Sales Staff*
Ali Bolin, *Marketing Mgr*
EMP: 225
SALES (est): 30MM
SALES (corp-wide): 137.5MM **Privately Held**
WEB: www.lansa.com
SIC: 7371 7372 Computer software development; educational computer software
HQ: Lansa Holdings, Inc.
2950 North Loop W Ste 700
Houston TX 77092
630 874-7000

(G-10599)
LAPOLLA INDUSTRIES LLC (DH)
Also Called: Icynene-Lapolla
15402 Vantage Pkwy E # 322 (77032-1966)
PHONE..................................281 219-4100
Douglas J Kramer, *President*
Harvey L Schnitzer, *COO*
Harvey Schnitzer, *COO*
Dave Feitl, *Vice Pres*
Mike Frank, *Mfg Staff*
◆ EMP: 23 EST: 1989
SQ FT: 56,375
SALES (est): 62.9MM
SALES (corp-wide): 11.9MM **Privately Held**
WEB: www.lapolla.com
SIC: 2952 2851 3069 2891 Roofing felts, cements or coatings; paints & paint additives; foam rubber; adhesives & sealants
HQ: Icynene U.S. Holding Corp.
15402 Vantage Pkwy E # 322
Houston TX 77032
281 219-4100

(G-10600)
LAREDO ENERGY IV GP LLC (PA)
840 Houston Ave (77007-7710)
PHONE..................................713 600-6000
Glenn D Hart, *CEO*
Jeremy Fontenot, *Vice Pres*
Steve Jaques, *Vice Pres*
Robert Swanson, *Vice Pres*
Jeff Shyer, *VP Opers*
EMP: 19

SALES (est): 8.3MM **Privately Held**
WEB: www.laredoenergy.com
SIC: 1382 Oil & gas exploration services

(G-10601)
LARK INDUSTRIES INCORPORATED
Also Called: Lark Heat Treating
6640 Mayard Rd (77041-2697)
PHONE..................................713 937-9089
J Frank Clark Sr, *President*
Greg Blackburn, *Corp Secy*
Gene Clark, *COO*
Mark Banas, *Opers Mgr*
Calvin McIver, *Engineer*
EMP: 50
SQ FT: 70,000
SALES (est): 10MM **Privately Held**
WEB: www.larkindustries.com
SIC: 3398 Brazing (hardening) of metal

(G-10602)
LARSON-JUHL US LLC
9232 Baythorne Dr (77041-7736)
PHONE..................................713 895-0296
Mark Nichols, *Opers Mgr*
EMP: 20
SALES (corp-wide): 254.6B **Publicly Held**
WEB: www.larsonjuhl.com
SIC: 2499 3499 Picture frame molding, finished; picture frames, metal
HQ: Larson-Juhl Us Llc
1925 Breckinridge Plz # 200
Duluth GA 30096
770 279-5200

(G-10603)
LASER DRUM PRODUCTS INC
Also Called: Southwestern Laser Charge
6016 Centralcrest St (77092-7010)
PHONE..................................713 263-9050
M J Thompson, *President*
Rory S Thompson, *Vice Pres*
Lance J Thompson, *Treasurer*
EMP: 10
SQ FT: 10,000 **Privately Held**
SIC: 3555 5045 7378 7629 Printing trade parts & attachments; computers, peripherals & software; computer & data processing equipment repair/maintenance; tool repair, electric

(G-10604)
LASER MASTERS INC
6039 Thomas Rd Ste D (77041-4934)
P.O. Box 841846 (77284-1846)
PHONE..................................832 467-4100
Jay Weaver, *CEO*
Steve Doll, *President*
▲ EMP: 26
SALES (est): 5MM **Privately Held**
WEB: www.lmihouston.com
SIC: 3699 Laser welding, drilling & cutting equipment

(G-10605)
LASER WELDING SOLUTIONS LLC
7542 Fairview St (77041-2110)
P.O. Box 550809 (77255-0809)
PHONE..................................713 895-0800
Mike Perkins, *Sales Staff*
Stephan Naegeler, *Mng Member*
Thurman Harrell, *Info Tech Dir*
EMP: 18
SALES (est): 2.7MM **Privately Held**
WEB: www.laserweldingsolutions.com
SIC: 7692 Welding repair

(G-10606)
LASSITER INDUSTRIES INC
321 Century Plaza Dr # 130 (77073-6041)
PHONE..................................281 781-8708
Thomas Lammers, *President*
Tom Lammers, *President*
Patricia Lammers, *Corp Secy*
EMP: 23
SALES (est): 4.5MM **Privately Held**
WEB: www.lassiterindustries.com
SIC: 3993 Signs & advertising specialties

(G-10607)
LASTRAD LLC
Also Called: Lastrad Oil & Gas Pdts & Svcs
1980 Post Oak Blvd (77056-3899)
PHONE..................................713 589-9477
Nicolas Galeano Monsalve, CEO
Carolina Diaz, Vice Pres
▲ EMP: 9
SQ FT: 1,000
SALES (est): 2MM **Privately Held**
WEB: www.lastrad.com
SIC: 3494 3492 3568 Pipe fittings; fluid
power valves & hose fittings; joints & couplings

(G-10608)
LAYLINE PETROLEUM LLC
820 Gessner Rd Ste 1145 (77024-4265)
PHONE..................................713 465-4100
Mukul M Sharma, Mng Member
Christopher J Lewis, Mng Member
EMP: 32
SALES (est): 19MM **Privately Held**
WEB: www.laylinepetroleum.com
SIC: 1382 Oil & gas exploration services

(G-10609)
LAYTON ENERGY INC
2100 West Loop S Ste 1601 (77027-3519)
PHONE..................................713 590-2820
Daniel Layton, CEO
Clarke Legler, CFO
Patricia Mercado, Executive Asst
EMP: 15
SQ FT: 11,000
SALES (est): 1.4MM **Privately Held**
WEB: www.laytoncorporation.com
SIC: 1382 Geophysical exploration, oil &
gas field

(G-10610)
LAZARUS ENERGY LLC
801 Travis St Ste 2100 (77002-5705)
PHONE..................................830 582-3202
Steve Wilson, Site Mgr
Jonathan Carroll, Mng Member
Tommy Bird,
Julie Bogal,
EMP: 9
SALES (est): 665.5K **Publicly Held**
WEB: www.lazarusenergy.com
SIC: 2911 Petroleum refining
PA: Lazarus Energy Holdings Llc
801 Travis St Ste 2100
Houston TX 77002

(G-10611)
**LAZARUS ENERGY HOLDINGS
LLC (PA)**
Also Called: Lazarus Energy Services
801 Travis St Ste 2100 (77002-5705)
PHONE..................................713 850-0500
Jason Heuring, General Mgr
Jonathan Carroll, Mng Member
Gina Carroll, Director
EMP: 16
SQ FT: 2,000
SALES (est): 309.9MM **Publicly Held**
WEB: www.lazarusenergy.com
SIC: 2911 Petroleum refining

(G-10612)
LC SCIENCES
2575 W Bellfort Ave (77054-5025)
PHONE..................................713 664-7087
Chris Hebel, COO
Kyle Navel, Accounts Mgr
Christoph Eicken, Technical Staff
▲ EMP: 13
SALES (est): 1.1MM **Privately Held**
WEB: www.lcsciences.com
SIC: 3944 Science kits: microscopes,
chemistry sets, etc.

(G-10613)
LECOLIFT INC
255 N Wayside Dr (77020-7513)
PHONE..................................713 676-1514
Michael L Pratt, President
Kevin Pratt, Vice Pres
EMP: 15
SQ FT: 32,200
SALES (est): 805.2K **Privately Held**
WEB: www.lecolift.com
SIC: 3713 Truck bodies (motor vehicles)

(G-10614)
LED OEM PARTNERS LLC
11857 Cutten Rd (77066-3003)
PHONE..................................832 769-0593
Nancy Mary Anderson, President
Ike Gamboa, Opers Mgr
Gumaro Ruiz, Art Dir
Regina Cuesta, Graphic Designe
▲ EMP: 11
SQ FT: 21,000
SALES (est): 601.9K **Privately Held**
WEB: www.ledpartners.com
SIC: 3993 Signs & advertising specialties

(G-10615)
LEDI2 INC (PA)
10611 Harwin Dr Ste 402 (77036-1534)
PHONE..................................713 636-9152
Jason Sheng, CEO
Aaron Fu, Vice Pres
Amy Chou, Accountant
Cindy Wang, Sales Mgr
Jared Willis, Sales Staff
▲ EMP: 15
SALES (est): 2MM **Privately Held**
WEB: www.ledi2.com
SIC: 3648 5063 Lighting equipment; light
bulbs & related supplies

(G-10616)
LEE CONTRACTING INC
Also Called: Conveying Techniques
10818 Sheldon Rd (77044-6006)
PHONE..................................281 456-9023
Mark Lee, President
Roy Lee III, Vice Pres
Caron Lee, Treasurer
EMP: 18 EST: 1981
SQ FT: 26,000
SALES (est): 3.6MM **Privately Held**
SIC: 3545 3535 Threading tools (machine
tool accessories); pneumatic tube conveyor systems

(G-10617)
LEE SPECIALTIES (PA)
5119 Hiltonview Rd (77086-1310)
PHONE..................................281 519-1719
EMP: 13
SALES (est): 4.4MM **Privately Held**
WEB: www.leespecialties.com
SIC: 3315 Wire & fabricated wire products

(G-10618)
**LEECO PRECISION SPRING MFG
CO**
Also Called: Leeco Spring International
714 E Burress St (77022-1806)
P.O. Box 16058 (77222-6058)
PHONE..................................713 692-6281
Edgar E Eckert, President
James C Moody II, President
Tamara Couey, Corp Secy
Phillip Lee, Vice Pres
Tami Couey, Treasurer
▼ EMP: 14 EST: 1959
SQ FT: 41,506
SALES (est): 3MM **Privately Held**
WEB: www.leecospring.com
SIC: 3495 3496 3493 3469 Wire springs;
miscellaneous fabricated wire products;
steel springs, except wire; metal stampings

(G-10619)
LEEMAK LP
17171 Park Row Ste 295 (77084-5640)
PHONE..................................281 492-9555
Omer Malik, CFO
Fazil Malik,
EMP: 350 EST: 2006
SALES (est): 53MM **Privately Held**
SIC: 1389 Oil field services

(G-10620)
**LEGACY AUTOMTN PWR
DESIGN INC**
11615 N Huston Rosslyn Rd (77086-3601)
PHONE..................................281 888-5402
EMP: 12 EST: 2009
SQ FT: 36,700
SALES (est): 3.7MM **Privately Held**
SIC: 3533 Mfg Oil/Gas Field Machinery

(G-10621)
LEGANT INTERIOR INC
7914 Westglen Dr (77063-6410)
PHONE..................................713 784-2647
EMP: 35
SQ FT: 400
SALES (est): 1.6MM **Privately Held**
SIC: 7389 2431 Business Services Mfg
Millwork

(G-10622)
LEHIGH HANSON INC
11201 Fm 529 Rd (77041-3205)
PHONE..................................713 466-6306
Thomas Wheelan, Manager
Steven Graham, Analyst
EMP: 99
SALES (corp-wide): 20.8B **Privately Held**
WEB: www.lehighhanson.com
SIC: 3273 Ready-mixed concrete
HQ: Hanson Lehigh Inc
300 E John Carpenter Fwy
Irving TX 75062

(G-10623)
LENGSTON CORPORATION
Also Called: Lengston Personnel
1010 Lamar St Ste 550 (77002-6394)
PHONE..................................713 757-1331
Lisa Leng, President
Janet S Downie, Exec VP
McHahan Betty B, Vice Pres
Patrick Kramer, Vice Pres
EMP: 17
SQ FT: 4,000
SALES (est): 1.4MM **Privately Held**
WEB: www.lengston.com
SIC: 4212 7361 Delivery service,
vehicular; labor contractors (employment
agency); oil field services; gas field services

(G-10624)
LENOIR M JOSEY INC
Also Called: Josey Cypress Ranch
4202 Yoakum Blvd (77006-5418)
PHONE..................................713 526-3844
Lenoir M Josey II, President
Anita Sampson Assist, Admin Sec
Ben P Hooper, Admin Sec
EMP: 9 EST: 1926
SQ FT: 7,000
SALES (est): 1.4MM **Privately Held**
SIC: 1311 0211 0112 0116 Crude petroleum production; beef cattle feedlots; rice;
soybeans

(G-10625)
LEOPARD MEDIA LLC
Also Called: Hart Publication
4545 Post Oak Place Dr # 210
(77027-3164)
PHONE..................................713 993-9320
Rich Eichler, Manager
Richard Eichler, Manager
EMP: 50
SALES (corp-wide): 10.4MM **Privately
Held**
WEB: www.hartenergynetwork.com
SIC: 2721 Periodicals
PA: Leopard Media Llc
9420 Key West Ave Fl 4
Rockville MD
301 279-4200

(G-10626)
LETCO GROUP LLC
Also Called: Living Earth Technology Co
5802 Crawford Rd (77041-5711)
PHONE..................................713 466-7360
Scott Estes, Branch Mgr
EMP: 57
SQ FT: 13,828
SALES (corp-wide): 78.3MM **Privately
Held**
WEB: www.livingearth.net
SIC: 2875 Compost
PA: The Letco Group Llc
1901 Cal Crossing Rd
Dallas TX 75220
972 506-8575

(G-10627)
LETCO GROUP LLC
12202 Cutten Rd (77066-1810)
PHONE..................................281 537-2377

Richard Stamfer, Manager
EMP: 11
SALES (corp-wide): 78.3MM **Privately
Held**
WEB: www.livingearth.net
SIC: 2499 2875 Mulch, wood & bark; potting soil, mixed
PA: The Letco Group Llc
1901 Cal Crossing Rd
Dallas TX 75220
972 506-8575

(G-10628)
LEVAN GROUP I LP
Also Called: High Fshion Decorative Fabrics
3100 Travis St (77006-3634)
PHONE..................................713 528-3838
George Levan, Partner
William Levan, Partner
Lisa Crane, Buyer
Mayra Flores, Buyer
Jeff Le, Buyer
▲ EMP: 18
SQ FT: 20,000
SALES (est): 5.2MM
SALES (corp-wide): 6.9MM **Privately
Held**
WEB: www.highfashionhome.com
SIC: 5714 2211 Drapery & upholstery
stores; broadwoven fabric mills, cotton
PA: Levan Corporation
3101 Louisiana St
Houston TX 77006
713 528-7299

(G-10629)
LFM INDUSTRIES INC
Also Called: Massey Industries
117 N Palmer St (77003-1612)
P.O. Box 1580 (77251-1580)
PHONE..................................713 928-5281
Lisa Faith Massey, President
EMP: 20
SALES (est): 1.9MM **Privately Held**
SIC: 3599 Machine shop, jobbing & repair

(G-10630)
LFT PANELS INC
1606 Crestdale Dr (77080-7202)
PHONE..................................713 984-9878
Luis Torres, President
Willie Fernandez, Vice Pres
EMP: 15
SALES (est): 2.9MM **Privately Held**
SIC: 3613 Control panels, electric

(G-10631)
**LGC US ASSET HOLDINGS LLC
(PA)**
Also Called: Lamons
7300 Airport Blvd (77061-3932)
PHONE..................................713 222-0284
Marc Roberts, CEO
Johnathan Rza, Opers Spvr
Syed Arif, Engineer
Ben Hays, Sales Mgr
Marti Davidson, Sales Staff
EMP: 11
SALES (est): 182.5MM **Privately Held**
SIC: 3452 Bolts, nuts, rivets & washers

(G-10632)
LGC US HOLDINGS LLC
7300 Airport Blvd (77061-3932)
PHONE..................................713 222-0284
Marc Roberts, CEO
EMP: 195 **Privately Held**
SIC: 6719 3452 Investment holding companies, except banks; bolts, nuts, rivets &
washers

(G-10633)
LIBERTY LIFT SOLUTIONS LLC
16420 Park Ten Pl Ste 300 (77084-5692)
PHONE..................................713 575-2300
Bobby Evans, CEO
Cris Bruyere, District Mgr
Don Crow, Vice Pres
Sam Gandee, Vice Pres
Christian Calhoun, Opers Spvr
▲ EMP: 35
SQ FT: 10,936

▲ = Import ▼=Export
◆ =Import/Export

SALES (est): 43.9MM **Privately Held**
WEB: www.libertylift.com
SIC: **1389** 7699 3533 Oil field services;
pumps & pumping equipment repair; oil &
gas field machinery

(G-10634)
LIBERTY PRECISION COMPANY LLC
12715 Fm 529 Rd (77041-2618)
PHONE...................................281 861-5530
Andy Vu, *President*
EMP: 52
SQ FT: 15,000
SALES (est): 13.5MM **Privately Held**
WEB: www.libertypc.com
SIC: **3599** Machine shop, jobbing & repair

(G-10635)
LICHTGITTER USA INC
12818 N Lake Houston Pkwy (77044-6397)
PHONE...................................844 548-7911
Kevin Slawson, *Manager*
◆ EMP: 78
SQ FT: 70,000
SALES (est): 15MM
SALES (corp-wide): 261MM **Privately Held**
WEB: www.lichtgitterusa.com
SIC: **3315** Fence gates posts & fittings:
steel
PA: Lichtgitter Gesellschaft Mit Beschrank-
ter Haftung
Siemensstr. 1
Stadtlohn 48703
256 391-10

(G-10636)
LIFE-TECH INC (PA)
365 Piney Point Rd (77024-6526)
PHONE...................................281 491-6600
Alfred C Coates, *President*
Steve D Crow, *Vice Pres*
Katherine Hoghey Kubena, *Vice Pres*
Louis Lupin III, *Vice Pres*
Geoffrey M Hertel, *Director*
▲ EMP: 54
SQ FT: 35,000
SALES (est): 7.9MM **Privately Held**
SIC: **3841** Diagnostic apparatus, medical

(G-10637)
LIFT MOORE INC
7810 Pinemont Dr (77040-6516)
PHONE...................................713 688-5533
Herb Koenig Jr, *President*
Priscilla Wilkins, *Purch Mgr*
Steve Coffee, *Regl Sales Mgr*
Bill Dunn, *Regl Sales Mgr*
Cylenia Benefield, *Manager*
EMP: 48 EST: 1961
SQ FT: 36,000
SALES (est): 15MM **Privately Held**
WEB: www.liftmoore.com
SIC: **3536** Materials handling machinery

(G-10638)
LIFT-ALL COMPANY INC
16803 Hedgecroft Dr (77060-3195)
PHONE...................................281 445-2256
Andy Wesseler, *Plant Mgr*
Joan Nichols, *Manager*
Marcus Ball, *Data Proc Staff*
EMP: 40
SQ FT: 22,000 **Privately Held**
WEB: www.lift-all.com
SIC: **3496** 2394 Mesh, made from pur-
chased wire; canvas & related products
HQ: Lift-All Company, Inc.
1909 Mcfarland Dr
Landisville PA 17538
717 898-6615

(G-10639)
LIFTEX CORPORATION
7266 Wynnpark Dr (77008-6030)
PHONE...................................713 863-0900
Mark Cowalick, *Owner*
EMP: 25
SALES (corp-wide): 31.1MM **Privately Held**
WEB: www.liftex.com
SIC: **3536** 2221 Hoisting slings; broadwo-
ven fabric mills, manmade

PA: Liftex Corporation
780 Falcon Cir Ste 105
Warminster PA 18974
800 478-4651

(G-10640)
LIGHTHUSE FOR THE BLIND HUSTON (PA)
Also Called: LIGHTHOUSE OF HOUSTON
3602 W Dallas St (77019-1704)
P.O. Box 130435 (77219-0435)
PHONE...................................713 284-8420
Gibson M Duterroil, *President*
Shelagh K Moran, *COO*
Ronda Risley, *Finance*
Will Olivares, *Supervisor*
Pat Von Fricken, *Director*
EMP: 40 EST: 1939
SQ FT: 67,000
SALES: 22.9MM **Privately Held**
WEB: www.houstonlighthouse.org
SIC: **2842** 8331 Disinfectants, household
or industrial plant; vocational rehabilitation
agency

(G-10641)
LILYRAIN JEWELRY LLC (PA)
8820b Wayfarer Ln (77075-3817)
PHONE...................................713 467-5459
Marianne Fazal, *Store Mgr*
Ashley Gray, *Store Mgr*
Kyong Gill, *Mng Member*
Insuk Koo, *
EMP: 13
SALES (est): 4.3MM **Privately Held**
WEB: www.lilyrain.com
SIC: **5944** 3911 Jewelry, precious stones
& precious metals; jewelry, precious metal

(G-10642)
LIME ROCK RESOURCES A LP
1111 Bagby St Ste 4600 (77002-2559)
PHONE...................................713 292-9510
Eric Mullins, *CEO*
Eric D Mullins, *Managing Dir*
Charles Adcock, *Principal*
C Tim Miller, *Principal*
Tim Miller, *COO*
EMP: 30
SALES (est): 40.4MM **Privately Held**
WEB: www.limerockresources.com
SIC: **1382** Oil & gas exploration services

(G-10643)
LIME ROCK RESOURCES IV-A LP
1111 Bagby St Ste 4600 (77002-2559)
PHONE...................................713 292-9500
Eric Mullens, *Partner*
Charles Adcock, *Partner*
Margaret Pollock, *Analyst*
EMP: 150
SALES (est): 5MM **Privately Held**
WEB: www.limerockresources.com
SIC: **6799** 1311 Investors; crude petro-
leum production

(G-10644)
LINCOLN MANUFACTURING INC
5301 Polk St (77023-1455)
PHONE...................................713 514-0059
EMP: 205
SALES (corp-wide): 118.7MM **Privately Held**
WEB: www.lincolnmanufacturing.com
SIC: **3533** 5082 Oil field machinery &
equipment; construction & mining machin-
ery
PA: Lincoln Manufacturing, Inc.
31209 Fm 2978 Rd
Magnolia TX 77354
281 252-9494

(G-10645)
LINDE GAS NORTH AMERICA LLC
Also Called: Lifegas
15150 Nautique Way (77047-7019)
PHONE...................................866 543-3427
EMP: 15 **Privately Held**
WEB: www.praxair.com
SIC: **2813** Nitrogen
HQ: Linde Gas North America Llc
10 Riverview Dr
Danbury CT 06810

(G-10646)
LINDSAYCA INC
Also Called: Lindsyca Oil Gas Int Solutions
1602 Peach Leaf St (77039-1228)
PHONE...................................713 467-9560
Hector Jose Fuentes, *President*
Jorge Santos, *President*
Jesus Rafael Fuentes, *Senior VP*
Jesus Fuentes, *Vice Pres*
Willian Rodriguez, *Vice Pres*
◆ EMP: 96
SQ FT: 192,000
SALES: 17MM **Privately Held**
WEB: www.lindsayca.com
SIC: **1389** 8711 Oil field services; engi-
neering services
PA: Lindsay C.A.
Av. De Enlace Con Ca. 2
Clarines

(G-10647)
LINDSEYS NW OFF FURN INC (PA)
Also Called: Lindsey's Custom Upholstery
12230 Northwest Fwy (77092-4904)
PHONE...................................713 957-2424
David M Lindsey, *President*
Michael Lindsey, *President*
Sharon Lindsey, *Vice Pres*
Preston Smith, *Sales Mgr*
Cassie Guerrero, *Sales Staff*
EMP: 45
SQ FT: 180,000
SALES (est): 10.5MM **Privately Held**
WEB: www.lindseyfurniture.com
SIC: **2426** 2521 5712 7641 Furniture
stock & parts, hardwood; wood office fur-
niture; office furniture; furniture upholstery
repair

(G-10648)
LINN ACQUISITION COMPANY LLC
600 Travis St Ste 4900 (77002-3009)
PHONE...................................281 840-4000
Arden L Walker Jr, *
EMP: 123
SALES (est): 3.2MM
SALES (corp-wide): 517.8MM **Privately Held**
WEB: www.linnenergy.com
SIC: **1382** Oil & gas exploration services
HQ: Linn Energy, Inc.
600 Travis St
Houston TX 77002
281 840-4000

(G-10649)
LINN ENERGY INC (DH)
600 Travis St (77002-3009)
PHONE...................................281 840-4000
Evan Lederman, *Ch of Bd*
Mark E Ellis, *President*
Arden L Walker Jr, *COO*
Thomas E Emmons, *Senior VP*
Jamin B McNeil, *Senior VP*
EMP: 23
SALES (est): 341.1MM
SALES (corp-wide): 517.8MM **Privately Held**
WEB: www.linnenergy.com
SIC: **1382** Oil & gas exploration services
HQ: Pressburg, Llc
14701 Hrtz Qail Sprng Pkw
Oklahoma City OK 73134
405 896-8050

(G-10650)
LINN ENERGY INC
600 Travis St Ste 1400 (77002-3005)
PHONE...................................405 241-2200
Don Davis, *General Mgr*
Donna Benge, *Manager*
EMP: 140
SALES (corp-wide): 517.8MM **Privately Held**
WEB: www.linnenergy.com
SIC: **1382** Oil & gas exploration services
HQ: Linn Energy, Inc.
600 Travis St
Houston TX 77002
281 840-4000

(G-10651)
LINN ENERGY FINANCE CORP
600 Travis St Ste 5100 (77002-3092)
PHONE...................................281 840-4000
Mark E Ellis, *Chairman*
EMP: 46
SALES (est): 242.1K
SALES (corp-wide): 517.8MM **Privately Held**
WEB: www.linnenergy.com
SIC: **1382** Oil & gas exploration services
HQ: Linn Energy, Inc.
600 Travis St
Houston TX 77002
281 840-4000

(G-10652)
LINN ENERGY HOLDINGS LLC (DH)
Jpmorgan Chase Twr 600 Tr (77002)
P.O. Box 305, Borger (79008-0305)
PHONE...................................806 274-3074
Mark Ellis, *President*
Scott Schulte, *Superintendent*
Kyle McKnight, *Vice Pres*
David Alexander, *Foreman/Supr*
Johnnie Wyant, *Foreman/Supr*
EMP: 34 EST: 2008
SALES (est): 65.2MM
SALES (corp-wide): 517.8MM **Privately Held**
WEB: www.linnenergy.com
SIC: **1382** Oil & gas exploration services
HQ: Linn Energy, Inc.
600 Travis St
Houston TX 77002
281 840-4000

(G-10653)
LINNCO LLC (PA)
600 Travis St Ste 5100 (77002-3031)
PHONE...................................281 840-4000
Mark E Ellis, *Ch of Bd*
Arden L Walker Jr, *COO*
Jamin B McNeil, *Senior VP*
Candice J Wells, *Senior VP*
David B Rottino, *CFO*
EMP: 1800
SALES (est): 40.7MM **Publicly Held**
SIC: **1311** Natural gas production

(G-10654)
LION SHARE LLP
213 E Hamilton St (77076-4510)
PHONE...................................281 888-5383
Viet Do, *Managing Prtnr*
EMP: 60
SALES (est): 7.5MM **Privately Held**
SIC: **2015** Eggs, processed: frozen

(G-10655)
LIVANOVA USA INC (HQ)
100 Cyberonics Blvd # 600 (77058-2069)
PHONE...................................281 228-7200
Daniel J Moore, *President*
Julie Leslie, *Partner*
Mark Verratti, *General Mgr*
Emily Gerch, *Regional Mgr*
Matt Melloy, *Regional Mgr*
▲ EMP: 250
SQ FT: 144,000
SALES (est): 262.4MM
SALES (corp-wide): 1B **Privately Held**
WEB: www.vnstherapy.info
SIC: **3845** Transcutaneous electrical nerve
stimulators (TENS)
PA: Livanova Plc
20 Eastbourne Terrace
London W2 6L
203 325-0662

(G-10656)
LLOG EXPLORATION COMPANY LLC
842 W Sam Houston Pkwy N (77024-4591)
PHONE...................................281 752-1100
Tim Lindsey, *Vice Pres*
Lindsey Gordon, *Manager*
Scott Spence, *Manager*
John Doughtie, *Executive*
Donna Bethune, *Technician*
EMP: 93

G
E
O
G
R
A
P
H
I
C

SALES (corp-wide): 298.4MM **Privately Held**
WEB: www.llog.com
SIC: **1382** Oil & gas exploration services
PA: Llog Exploration Company, L.L.C.
1001 Ochsner Blvd Ste 100
Covington LA 70433
985 801-4300

(G-10657)
LLOYD COMPANY
14905 Willis St (77039-1028)
PHONE......................................281 590-8023
Donald L Lloyd, *President*
Lisa Brooks, *Vice Pres*
Mary Lloyd, *Vice Pres*
Steve Teel, *Opers Mgr*
Derek Lloyd, *Buyer*
▲ EMP: 20
SQ FT: 20,000
SALES (est): 4MM **Privately Held**
WEB: www.lloydco.com
SIC: **3599** Machine shop, jobbing & repair

(G-10658)
LLOYDS REGISTER DRILLING INTE
1330 Enclave Pkwy Ste 200 (77077-2578)
PHONE......................................281 675-3100
Paul Huber, *President*
Greg Rockwell, *Program Mgr*
EMP: 276
SALES (est): 7.3MM **Privately Held**
WEB: www.lr.org
SIC: **1389** Servicing oil & gas wells

(G-10659)
LNG FREEPORT DEVELOPMENT L P (PA)
333 Clay St Ste 5050 (77002-4101)
PHONE......................................713 980-2888
Michael S Smith, *CEO*
Charles Reimer, *President*
Wendy Clark, *Vice Pres*
Bill Henry, *Vice Pres*
Christina Browning, *Project Mgr*
▲ EMP: 20
SQ FT: 18,900
SALES (est): 195.4MM **Privately Held**
WEB: www.freeportlng.com
SIC: **1311** Crude petroleum & natural gas

(G-10660)
LOAD SYSTEMS INTERNATIONAL
Also Called: Load Systems Distribution
9633 Zaka Rd (77064-7607)
PHONE......................................281 664-1330
Dave Smith, *Branch Mgr*
Scott Kerr, *Manager*
EMP: 80
SQ FT: 6,000
SALES (corp-wide): 10.2MM **Privately Held**
WEB: www.heavyindustry.trimble.com
SIC: **3596** Weighing machines & apparatus
PA: Load Systems International Inc
2666 Boul Du Parc-Technologique Bureau 190
Quebec QC G1P 4

(G-10661)
LOBUES RUBBER STAMP CO
1228 Mcgowen St (77004-1108)
P.O. Box 52415 (77052-2415)
PHONE......................................713 652-0031
EMP: 11 EST: 1953
SQ FT: 8,075
SALES (est): 1.4MM **Privately Held**
WEB: www.lobuesrubberstampco.com
SIC: **3953** 2759 Cancelling stamps, hand: rubber or metal; seal presses, notary & hand; embossing seals, corporate & official; engraving

(G-10662)
LOCKE INVESTMENTS LLC
Also Called: Locke Solutions
700 Almeda Genoa Rd (77047-4106)
PHONE......................................832 804-7062
Asher Kazmann, *President*
Michael Luck, *Vice Pres*
Joseph Christoferson, *Opers Mgr*
David Ferrel, *Prdtn Mgr*
Carlos Lue, *Prdtn Mgr*

EMP: 58
SQ FT: 27,500
SALES (est): 14.1MM **Privately Held**
WEB: www.lockesolutions.com
SIC: **3272** Precast terrazo or concrete products

(G-10663)
LOCKHEED MARTIN
2625 Bay Area Blvd (77058-1523)
PHONE......................................281 283-4400
EMP: 99 **Publicly Held**
WEB: www.lockheedmartin.com
SIC: **3812** Search & navigation equipment
HQ: Lockheed Martin Integrated Systems, Llc
6801 Rockledge Dr
Bethesda MD 20817

(G-10664)
LOCKHEED MARTIN CORPORATION
18108 Point Lookout Dr A (77058-3506)
PHONE......................................281 283-4400
John Wilkins, *Vice Pres*
Brad Holcomb, *Project Mgr*
Juan Aguilar, *Engineer*
Huong Charles, *Engineer*
Andrew Grant, *Engineer*
EMP: 1500 **Publicly Held**
WEB: www.lockheedmartin.com
SIC: **3812** Search & navigation equipment
PA: Lockheed Martin Corporation
6801 Rockledge Dr
Bethesda MD 20817

(G-10665)
LOCKHEED MARTIN CORPORATION
1300 Hercules Ave Ste 100 (77058-2772)
PHONE......................................281 218-3000
EMP: 435 **Publicly Held**
WEB: www.lockheedmartin.com
SIC: **3812** Search & navigation equipment
PA: Lockheed Martin Corporation
6801 Rockledge Dr
Bethesda MD 20817

(G-10666)
LOCKHEED MARTIN CORPORATION
595 Gemini St (77058-2753)
PHONE......................................281 853-3000
David White, *Research*
Swapnil Patel, *Engineer*
Ron Foster, *Manager*
Wayne Chan, *Post Master*
EMP: 500
SQ FT: 2,785 **Publicly Held**
WEB: www.lockheedmartin.com
SIC: **3812** Search & navigation equipment
PA: Lockheed Martin Corporation
6801 Rockledge Dr
Bethesda MD 20817

(G-10667)
LOCKHEED MARTIN CORPORATION
Also Called: Lockheed Mrtin Space Oprations
2625 Bay Area Blvd 7 (77058-1523)
P.O. Box 57639, Webster (77598-7639)
PHONE......................................281 218-6021
Kevin Repa, *General Mgr*
Richard Hieb, *Vice Pres*
Juan Aguilar, *Engineer*
Huong Charles, *Engineer*
Andrew Grant, *Engineer*
EMP: 232 **Publicly Held**
WEB: www.lockheedmartin.com
SIC: **3812** Search & navigation equipment
PA: Lockheed Martin Corporation
6801 Rockledge Dr
Bethesda MD 20817

(G-10668)
LOCKHEED MARTIN SPACE COMPANY
Also Called: Lockheed Martin Systems Co
2100 Park St (77019-6814)
PHONE......................................281 283-4650
Amanda Rinche, *Principal*
EMP: 1500
SALES (est): 25.7MM **Privately Held**
SIC: **3812** Aircraft/aerospace flight instruments & guidance systems

(G-10669)
LOFTIN EQUIPMENT COMPANY
6113 Brittmoore Rd (77041-5610)
PHONE......................................281 310-6858
Kasey Hoopes, *Project Mgr*
Jim Lambrecht, *Accounts Mgr*
Brandy Bussey, *Sales Staff*
Bryan Dieter, *Manager*
EMP: 25
SALES (corp-wide): 89.5MM **Privately Held**
WEB: www.loftinequip.com
SIC: **5063** 3621 Generators; motors & generators
PA: Loftin Equipment Company
2111 E Highland Ave # 255
Phoenix AZ 85016
800 437-4376

(G-10670)
LOGAN INTERNATIONAL INC
10613 W Sam Houston Pkwy (77064-4663)
PHONE......................................832 386-2500
David Macneill, *President*
Jeff Ferguson, *Vice Pres*
Lawrence Keister, *CFO*
Theresa Sullivan, *Sales Staff*
Doug Smuin, *Manager*
EMP: 170
SALES (est): 1MM
SALES (corp-wide): 108.5MM **Privately Held**
WEB: www.loganinternationalinc.com
SIC: **1381** Drilling oil & gas wells
PA: Rubicon Oilfield International Holdings, Llc
10613 W Sam Hston Pkwy600
Houston TX 77064
832 386-2500

(G-10671)
LOGAN OIL TOOLS INC (PA)
11006 Lucerne St (77016-1920)
PHONE......................................281 219-6613
Gerald Hage, *CEO*
David Barr, *CEO*
Callum Sutherland, *Business Mgr*
Tim Holmes, *Store Mgr*
Randy Bressler, *Warehouse Mgr*
◆ EMP: 250
SQ FT: 130,000
SALES (est): 216.1MM **Privately Held**
WEB: www.loganoiltools.com
SIC: **1389** Oil field services

(G-10672)
LOGIC SERVICES LLC
800 Town And Country Blvd (77024-4552)
PHONE......................................832 617-0805
Eudo Mendez,
Marysabel Villalobos,
EMP: 11 EST: 2011
SQ FT: 2,024
SALES (est): 19.2MM **Privately Held**
WEB: www.logicservicesllc.com
SIC: **1389** Oil field services

(G-10673)
LOGIK PRECISION INC
Also Called: Machine Shop and Water Jet Div
5007 Steffani Ln (77041-7819)
PHONE......................................713 939-0061
Carlos M Sierra, *President*
Eric Frausto, *Project Mgr*
Jaime Sierra, *Mfg Mgr*
Kevin Corcorran, *Buyer*
Abdiel Mejia, *Buyer*
EMP: 40 EST: 1998
SQ FT: 12,000
SALES (est): 15.2MM **Privately Held**
WEB:
www.logikprecisionincwaterjetdiv.blogspot.com
SIC: **3599** Machine shop, jobbing & repair

(G-10674)
LOGITEK ELECTRONIC SYSTEMS
5622 Edgemoor Dr (77081-6116)
PHONE......................................713 664-4470
Tag Borland, *President*
Susan Borland, *CFO*
Frank Grundstein, *Sales Staff*
Elaine Jones, *Pub Rel Staff*
EMP: 12

SQ FT: 7,700 **Privately Held**
WEB: www.logitekaudio.com
SIC: **3663** Radio & TV communications equipment

(G-10675)
LONE STAR CORROSION SVCS INC
9216 Windmill Park Ln (77064-3332)
PHONE......................................281 955-1313
James G Cronin Jr, *President*
Tonya T Cronin, *CFO*
EMP: 80
SQ FT: 40,000
SALES (est): 31MM **Privately Held**
WEB: www.lonestarcorrosion.com
SIC: **5169** 3471 Chemicals & allied products; finishing, metals or formed products

(G-10676)
LONE STAR FACES INC
6100 Chapman St (77022-5713)
PHONE......................................713 706-3223
Troy Crocker, *President*
Steve Matheny, *Principal*
EMP: 30
SALES (est): 2.2MM **Privately Held**
SIC: **3993** Signs & advertising specialties

(G-10677)
LONE STAR GLASS INC (PA)
3804 Bissonnet St (77005-1198)
PHONE......................................713 661-0091
EMP: 18
SQ FT: 8,000
SALES (est): 2.9MM **Privately Held**
WEB: www.lonestarglass.com
SIC: **7536** 1793 5231 3231 Automotive glass replacement shops; glass & glazing work; glass; products of purchased glass

(G-10678)
LONE STAR HEAT TREATING CORP (PA)
3939 Blaffer St (77026-4301)
P.O. Box 15621 (77220-5621)
PHONE......................................713 672-6616
Michael R Van Dorfy Sr, *Partner*
Robert M Gready, *Partner*
Michael R Van Dorfy Jr, *Partner*
Dave Magee, *Vice Pres*
Bud Van Rooyen, *Vice Pres*
▲ EMP: 93 EST: 1945
SQ FT: 44,000
SALES (est): 16.3MM **Privately Held**
WEB: www.lsht.com
SIC: **3398** Metal heat treating

(G-10679)
LONE STAR NGL PIPELINE LP (DH)
1300 Main St 10 (77002-6803)
PHONE......................................210 403-7300
Kelcy L Warren, *Partner*
Marshall S McCrea III, *Partner*
Martin Salinas Jr, *Partner*
EMP: 19
SALES: 1B **Publicly Held**
WEB: www.energytransfer.com
SIC: **4924** 1321 Natural gas distribution; natural gas liquids

(G-10680)
LONE STAR NGL RFINERY SVCS LLC (DH)
1300 Main St (77002-6803)
PHONE......................................210 403-7300
Kelcy L Warren, *CEO*
Marshall S McCrea III, *President*
Martin Salinas Jr, *CFO*
EMP: 19
SALES (est): 14.7MM **Publicly Held**
SIC: **1321** Natural gas liquids

(G-10681)
LONE STAR POULTRY INC
1222 Rutland St (77008-6833)
PHONE......................................713 868-3888
Min Hor, *President*
EMP: 60
SQ FT: 20,000
SALES (est): 6.2MM **Privately Held**
SIC: **2015** Poultry slaughtering & processing

(G-10682)
LONESTAR ALUMINUM SPC LLC
8242 Warren Rd (77040-2602)
PHONE..................................281 617-7177
EMP: 9 **EST:** 2011
SALES (est): 1.3MM **Privately Held**
WEB: www.lsaspecialties.com
SIC: 3355 Aluminum rod & bar

(G-10683)
LONESTAR COUPLINGS INC
8306 Northcourt Rd (77040-4337)
PHONE..................................713 690-1873
Titus Colaco, *President*
EMP: 17
SQ FT: 25,000
SALES (est): 2.2MM **Privately Held**
WEB: www.lonestarcouplings.com
SIC: 3489 3533 3568 Flame throwers
(ordnance); drilling tools for gas, oil or
water wells; power transmission equip-
ment

(G-10684)
LONG PLAN PRINTING INC
Also Called: L P Printing
3029 Crossview Dr (77063-5008)
PHONE..................................713 797-1125
Walter Hudson, *President*
Kelly Luu, *Vice Pres*
Allie Casso, *Prdtn Mgr*
Victor Luu, *Prdtn Mgr*
Joseph Chu, *Opers Staff*
EMP: 40
SQ FT: 15,000
SALES (est): 5MM **Privately Held**
WEB: www.lpprinting.com
SIC: 2752 7389 Commercial printing, off-
set; presorted mail service

(G-10685)
LONGHORN GLASS MFG LP
4202 Fidelity St (77029-3550)
PHONE..................................713 679-7500
Patrick Stokes, *President*
Michael Kurtz, *Human Res Dir*
▲ **EMP:** 150
SALES (est): 38MM
SALES (corp-wide): 1.4B **Privately Held**
WEB: www.anheuser-busch.com
SIC: 3231 Products of purchased glass
HQ: Anheuser-Busch Companies, Llc
1 Busch Pl
Saint Louis MO 63118
314 632-6777

(G-10686)
LONGVIEW DISTRIBUTION I LLC (PA)
Also Called: Gulf Coast Ignition & Controls
6650 Roxburgh Dr Ste 100 (77041-5212)
P.O. Box 924288 (77292-4288)
PHONE..................................832 467-4600
Jack Maley, *CEO*
Tim Smith, *COO*
Mitce Maples, *CFO*
Renee Cravens, *Human Res Mgr*
Aaron Avila, *Sales Staff*
EMP: 25
SQ FT: 2,600
SALES (est): 33.7MM **Privately Held**
WEB: www.res-co.com
SIC: 5084 3625 Instruments & control
equipment; relays & industrial controls

(G-10687)
LOOMIS PUBLISHING SERVICES
18719 Ember Trails Dr (77094-2617)
PHONE..................................281 829-6825
Naomi Loomis, *President*
EMP: 10
SALES (est): 615.3K **Privately Held**
SIC: 2721 Periodicals

(G-10688)
LOPEZ EFRAIN
Also Called: Sierra Blnco Trtlla Fctry Prod
7131 Harrisburg Blvd (77011-4734)
PHONE..................................713 921-0057
Efrain Lopez, *Owner*
George Lopez, *Co-Owner*
EMP: 16
SQ FT: 30,000
SALES (est): 2.3MM **Privately Held**
SIC: 5148 2099 Fresh fruits & vegetables;
tortillas, fresh or refrigerated

(G-10689)
LOUIS HILL KENNON INC
6952 Lawndale St (77023-2549)
P.O. Box 230305 (77223-0305)
PHONE..................................713 926-2623
Joseph H Hugghins, *President*
Kennon H Hugghins, *Vice Pres*
Robert H Hugghins, *Vice Pres*
William R Hugghins, *Vice Pres*
EMP: 25 **EST:** 1930
SQ FT: 16,000
SALES (est): 5.5MM **Privately Held**
WEB: www.lk-ind.com
SIC: 3533 Oil field machinery & equipment

(G-10690)
LOWE OFFSHORE INC
1155 Dairy Ashford Rd # 315 (77079-3021)
PHONE..................................281 894-5454
Vernon Luning, *CEO*
Terry Lowe, *Treasurer*
EMP: 53
SQ FT: 2,200
SALES (est): 1.3MM **Privately Held**
SIC: 1389 1382 Construction, repair & dis-
mantling services; oil & gas exploration
services

(G-10691)
LOWRANCE MACHINE SHOP INC
13510 E Hardy Rd (77039-2893)
PHONE..................................281 449-6524
Ronald W Lowrance, *President*
Matt Lowrance, *Vice Pres*
Peter Maniscalco, *Vice Pres*
Pamela Maniscalco, *Treasurer*
EMP: 30 **EST:** 1964
SQ FT: 2,000
SALES (est): 6MM **Privately Held**
WEB: www.lowrancemachine.com
SIC: 3599 Machine shop, jobbing & repair

(G-10692)
LQC PIPE & TUBE LTD PARTNR
Also Called: Lqc Pipe & Supply
6410 Langfield Rd Ste X (77092-1017)
PHONE..................................832 559-7676
Frank K Spinale, *Partner*
Ashley Arcangeli, *General Mgr*
EMP: 20
SALES (est): 8.2MM **Privately Held**
WEB: www.lqcpipe.com
SIC: 3317 Steel pipe & tubes

(G-10693)
LRR ENERGY LP
1111 Bagby St Ste 4600 (77002-2559)
PHONE..................................713 292-9510
Richard A Robert, *CFO*
EMP: 153
SQ FT: 56,984
SALES (est): 197.2MM
SALES (corp-wide): 460.2MM **Publicly Held**
WEB: www.lrrenergy.com
SIC: 1311 Crude petroleum & natural gas
PA: Grizzly Energy, Llc
5847 San Felipe St # 3000
Houston TX 77057
832 327-2255

(G-10694)
LS PACKAGING DESIGN INC
Also Called: Dsl Forming Collars
6504 Mayfair St (77087-3422)
PHONE..................................713 645-9177
Luis Posada, *President*
Simon Gonzales, *Vice Pres*
EMP: 22
SALES (est): 4.2MM **Privately Held**
WEB: www.dslformers.com
SIC: 3565 Packaging machinery

(G-10695)
LSI INDUSTRIES
14902 Sommermeyer St # 120
(77041-5308)
PHONE..................................513 793-3200
Linda Cooper, *Project Mgr*
Andy Harey, *VP Sales*
David Vrana, *Info Tech Mgr*
Peter Garcia, *Bd of Directors*
Mike Prachar, *Officer*
EMP: 9

SALES (est): 1MM **Privately Held**
WEB: www.lsi-industries.com
SIC: 3999 Manufacturing industries

(G-10696)
LSI INTEGRATED GRAPHICS LP
Also Called: LSI Graphic Solutions Plus
14902 Sommermeyer St # 120
(77041-5306)
PHONE..................................713 744-4100
Randy Hobbs, *Plant Supt*
Shawn Perry, *Project Mgr*
Shane Jelliffe, *Engineer*
Ronald S Stowell, *CFO*
Mike Wallner, *Senior Mgr*
EMP: 200
SQ FT: 200,000
SALES (est): 39.7MM
SALES (corp-wide): 305.5MM **Publicly Held**
WEB: www.lsi-industries.com
SIC: 2759 3993 3613 2851 Screen print-
ing; signs & advertising specialties;
switchgear & switchboard apparatus;
paints & allied products; commercial print-
ing, lithographic; packaging paper & plas-
tics film, coated & laminated
PA: Lsi Industries Inc.
10000 Alliance Rd
Blue Ash OH 45242
513 793-3200

(G-10697)
LT SEAFOOD LP
415 E Hamilton St (77076-4514)
PHONE..................................713 328-1999
Ten Lam, *Partner*
▲ **EMP:** 10
SALES (est): 1.2MM **Privately Held**
SIC: 2091 Canned & cured fish & seafoods

(G-10698)
LTN INDUSTRIES INC
Also Called: Velocity Manufacturing
6829 Flintlock Rd B (77040-4322)
PHONE..................................713 849-1300
Linh Tien Nguyen, *CEO*
Boch Nguyen, *President*
Olivia Balababa, *Buyer*
Long Tien Nguyen, *Director*
EMP: 20
SQ FT: 3,000
SALES (est): 4MM **Privately Held**
WEB: www.velocitymfgcorp.com
SIC: 3541 Machine tools, metal cutting: ex-
otic (explosive, etc.)

(G-10699)
LUFKIN ILS
11050 W Little York Rd (77041-5055)
PHONE..................................281 445-7676
John F Glick, *CEO*
Robert K Raper, *President*
Mike E Woodell, *Admin Sec*
Chris Abide,
Jimmy Broussard,
EMP: 37
SALES (est): 4.7MM
SALES (corp-wide): 1B **Privately Held**
SIC: 1389 Oil field services
PA: Lufkin Gears Llc
409 Ellis Ave
Lufkin TX 75904
936 634-2211

(G-10700)
LUKOIL INTL UPSTREAM W INC (DH)
3200 Southwest Fwy # 3120 (77027-7528)
PHONE..................................713 877-8544
Kevin Black, *CEO*
Edward Hare, *Vice Pres*
Maxim Kobyakov, *CFO*
Eldar Aleskerov, *Supervisor*
Lui Chambers, *General Counsel*
◆ **EMP:** 35 **EST:** 1951
SALES (est): 78.9MM **Privately Held**
SIC: 1382 Oil & gas exploration services
HQ: Lukoil International Upstream Holding
B.V.
Zuidplein 198 H Tower Level 24
Amsterdam
205 788-471

(G-10701)
LULULEMON ATHLETICA
713 Heights Blvd (77007-1539)
PHONE..................................713 863-1280
Susan Denum, *Principal*
EMP: 10
SALES (est): 493K **Privately Held**
SIC: 2329 2339 Men's & boys' sportswear
& athletic clothing; women's & misses'
athletic clothing & sportswear

(G-10702)
LUMINA GLOBAL INC
7115 Belgold St Ste F (77066-1028)
PHONE..................................713 783-7056
Thomas L Kuo, *Principal*
▲ **EMP:** 19
SALES (est): 2.5MM **Privately Held**
SIC: 3211 Flat glass

(G-10703)
LURE CAPITAL CORPORATION
Also Called: Acme Rental Center
11144 S Post Oak Rd (77035-5702)
PHONE..................................713 729-2424
John Loughran, *President*
Uh John, *General Mgr*
Ted L Sewell, *Vice Pres*
Karina Siney, *Research*
Adam Yang, *Marketing Staff*
▲ **EMP:** 20
SQ FT: 20,000
SALES (est): 4.4MM **Privately Held**
WEB: www.acmerental.com
SIC: 3648 7359 Stage lighting equipment;
dishes, silverware, tables & banquet ac-
cessories rental

(G-10704)
LYONDELL CHEMICAL COMPANY
1221 Mckinney St Ste 700 (77010-2045)
PHONE..................................281 597-8935
Tom Kelly, *Manager*
Robert Liebert, *Information Mgr*
Dan Olivarez, *Administration*
EMP: 15
SALES (corp-wide): 34.9B **Privately Held**
WEB: www.lyondellbasell.com
SIC: 2869 Industrial organic chemicals
HQ: Lyondell Chemical Company
1221 Mckinney St Ste 300
Houston TX 77010
713 309-7200

(G-10705)
LYONDELL CHEMICAL COMPANY (DH)
Also Called: Lyondellbasell
1221 Mckinney St Ste 300 (77010-2036)
P.O. Box 3646 (77253-3646)
PHONE..................................713 309-7200
Bhavesh V Patel, *CEO*
Paul Davies, *Vice Pres*
Kim Foley, *Vice Pres*
Charles Hall, *Vice Pres*
Sergey Vasnetsov, *Vice Pres*
◆ **EMP:** 60
SQ FT: 150,000
SALES (est): 2.5B
SALES (corp-wide): 34.9B **Privately Held**
WEB: www.lyondellbasell.com
SIC: 2911 2869 Gasoline blending plants;
oils, fuel; jet fuels; oils, lubricating; olefins

(G-10706)
LYONDELL CHEMICAL COMPANY
14403 Sugar Mill Cir (77095-3418)
PHONE..................................281 291-1488
Phuong Vo, *Accountant*
Dan Smith, *Branch Mgr*
Leslie Davidson, *Executive Asst*
Carolyn Egbert,
EMP: 79
SALES (corp-wide): 34.9B **Privately Held**
WEB: www.lyondellbasell.com
SIC: 2869 Propylene, butylene
HQ: Lyondell Chemical Company
1221 Mckinney St Ste 300
Houston TX 77010
713 309-7200

(G-10707)
LYONDELL-CITGO REFINING LLC
12000 Lawndale St (77017-2740)
P.O. Box 2451 (77252-2451)
PHONE 713 321-4111
Don Hamilton,
▲ **EMP:** 14
SALES (est): 5.9MM **Privately Held**
WEB: www.lyondellbasell.com
SIC: 2911 Petroleum refining
HQ: Petroleos De Venezuela Sa
　　Edf. Petroleos De Venezuela, Torre
　　Este, Piso 9
　　Caracas D.F.

(G-10708)
LYONDELLBASELL ACETYLS LLC
1221 Mckinney St Ste 300 (77010-2036)
P.O. Box 3646 (77253-3646)
PHONE 713 309-7200
James L Gallogly, *President*
Patrick D Quarles, *Senior VP*
Karen M Swindler, *Senior VP*
Paul G Davies, *Vice Pres*
Amber Cobb, *Purch Mgr*
▼ **EMP:** 15
SALES (est): 6.1MM
SALES (corp-wide): 34.9B **Privately Held**
WEB: www.lyondellbasell.com
SIC: 2869 Industrial organic chemicals
HQ: Lyondellbasell Industries Holdings B.V.
　　Delftseplein 27 E
　　Rotterdam 3013
　　102 755-500

(G-10709)
LYONDELLBASELL INDUSTRIES INC (DH)
1221 Mckinney St Ste 300 (77010-2036)
P.O. Box 3646 (77253-3646)
PHONE 713 309-7200
Bob Patele, *Ch of Bd*
Scott Beech, *Counsel*
Dan Coombs, *Exec VP*
Tim Roberts, *Exec VP*
W N Phillips, *Senior VP*
▲ **EMP:** 52
SALES (est): 4.9B
SALES (corp-wide): 34.9B **Privately Held**
WEB: www.lyondellbasell.com
SIC: 2821 Polymethyl methacrylate resins
　　(plexiglass)
HQ: Lyondellbasell Industries Holdings B.V.
　　Delftseplein 27 E
　　Rotterdam 3013
　　102 755-500

(G-10710)
LYONDLLBSELL ADVNCED PLYMERS I (DH)
1221 Mckinney St Ste 300 (77010-2036)
PHONE 713 309-7200
Bhavesh V Patel, *President*
Dennis Smith, *General Mgr*
James Guilfoyle, *Exec VP*
Andreas K Gunther, *Exec VP*
Andrean R Horton, *Exec VP*
◆ **EMP:** 77 **EST:** 1928
SQ FT: 34,000
SALES: 2.4B
SALES (corp-wide): 34.9B **Privately Held**
WEB: www.lyondellbasell.com
SIC: 2821 Molding compounds, plastics

(G-10711)
M & G CHEMICALS (HQ)
Also Called: Corpus Christi Facility
450 Gears Rd Ste 240 (77067-4513)
PHONE 361 500-4747
Marco Toselli, *Principal*
EMP: 11
SALES (est): 3.6MM **Privately Held**
SIC: 2899 Chemical preparations
PA: M & G Usa Holding, Llc
　　27610 Huntington Rd
　　Apple Grove WV 25502
　　304 576-4652

(G-10712)
M & G RESINS USA LLC (HQ)
450 Gears Rd Ste 240 (77067-4513)
PHONE 281 873-5780
Dennis Stogsdill,

EMP: 34
SALES (est): 5.1MM
SALES (corp-wide): 22.5MM **Privately Held**
WEB: www.mgcorpuschristi.com
SIC: 3089 Air mattresses, plastic
PA: M & G Usa Corporation
　　27610 Huntington Rd Stater
　　Apple Grove WV 25502
　　304 576-2041

(G-10713)
M & J VALVE COMPANY (HQ)
Also Called: SPX Flow Control
19191 Hempstead Hwy (77065)
PHONE 281 469-0550
Don Cantra, *President*
▲ **EMP:** 160 **EST:** 1962
SQ FT: 192,000
SALES (est): 37.7MM
SALES (corp-wide): 1.5B **Publicly Held**
WEB: www.spx.com
SIC: 3491 Automatic regulating & control
　　valves
PA: Spx Flow, Inc.
　　13320 Balntyn Corp Pl
　　Charlotte NC 28277
　　704 752-4400

(G-10714)
M & M COASTAL MFG INC
8700 Hirsch Rd (77016-5619)
P.O. Box 112029 (77293-2029)
PHONE 713 472-0700
Mark Fenn, *President*
Spencer Graham, *Corp Secy*
Mark Thompson, *Project Mgr*
Scott Graham, *Prdtn Mgr*
Margaret Blair, *Office Mgr*
EMP: 60
SQ FT: 30,000
SALES (est): 9.5MM **Privately Held**
WEB: www.mandmcoastal.com
SIC: 3291 Abrasive metal & steel products

(G-10715)
M & M LIGHTING LP (PA)
5620 S Rice Ave (77081-2196)
P.O. Box 1027, Bellaire (77402-1027)
PHONE 713 667-5611
Renee Margolin, *Partner*
Allan Margolin, *General Ptnr*
Judy Barrett, *Purchasing*
Daniel Boyd, *Sales Staff*
Randy Ervin, *Sales Staff*
EMP: 58
SQ FT: 41,000
SALES (est): 30MM **Privately Held**
WEB: www.mmlighting.com
SIC: 5063 3646 5719 Lighting fixtures,
　　commercial & industrial; lighting fixtures,
　　residential; commercial indusl & institu-
　　tional electric lighting fixtures; lighting fix-
　　tures

(G-10716)
M & R MACHINE WORKS INC
8511 Rannie Rd (77080-2024)
P.O. Box 431709 (77243-1709)
PHONE 713 462-0746
Marion J Marshall, *President*
Frances Marshall, *Corp Secy*
EMP: 9
SQ FT: 12,000
SALES (est): 1MM **Privately Held**
SIC: 3599 Machine shop, jobbing & repair

(G-10717)
M & R USA (PA)
6420 Richmond Ave Ste 203 (77057-5925)
PHONE 281 497-8973
Claudio Mueller, *CEO*
Marc Bermig, *Project Mgr*
Yanina Rapetti, *Purch Mgr*
Katherine Martin, *Sales Staff*
◆ **EMP:** 10
SQ FT: 1,500
SALES (est): 2.5MM **Privately Held**
SIC: 5085 3469 Industrial supplies; ma-
　　chine parts, stamped or pressed metal

(G-10718)
M A R X STEEL LLC (PA)
11985 Fm 529 Rd (77041-3011)
PHONE 281 679-9700
Nathaniel Marks, *Mng Member*

EMP: 20
SQ FT: 26,000
SALES (est): 10.9MM **Privately Held**
SIC: 3315 Steel wire & related products

(G-10719)
M P ENERGY INC
3100 Weslayan St Ste 375 (77027-5731)
P.O. Box 90610 (77290-0610)
PHONE 281 350-6350
Joseph Martinez, *President*
EMP: 15
SALES (est): 967.6K **Privately Held**
SIC: 1311 1381 Crude petroleum produc-
　　tion; drilling oil & gas wells

(G-10720)
M W WALDROP CO
Also Called: Waldrop Company
8125 Kempwood Dr (77055-1029)
PHONE 713 337-5600
Wayne Waldrop, *President*
Mike Waldrop, *Vice Pres*
David Waldrop, *Engineer*
Joyce Waldrop, *Treasurer*
Chris Waldrop, *Executive*
▲ **EMP:** 20
SQ FT: 37,000
SALES (est): 6.1MM **Privately Held**
WEB: www.waldropco.com
SIC: 3556 3565 Food products machinery;
　　packaging machinery

(G-10721)
M&I ELECTRIC INDUSTRIES INC (HQ)
1250 Wood Branch Park Dr # 600
(77079-1233)
PHONE 832 241-6330
Peter Menikoff, *CEO*
Bill Miller, *COO*
Charles M Dauber, *Senior VP*
Neal T Hare, *Vice Pres*
Ron Nance, *Vice Pres*
◆ **EMP:** 90
SQ FT: 20,000
SALES (est): 43.8MM
SALES (corp-wide): 47MM **Publicly Held**
WEB: www.mielectric.com
SIC: 3613 7694 1731 3825 Switchgear &
　　switchgear accessories; electric motor re-
　　pair; general electrical contractor; instru-
　　ments to measure electricity; relays &
　　industrial controls; transformers, except
　　electric
PA: Stabilis Energy, Inc.
　　10375 Richmond Ave # 700
　　Houston TX 77042
　　832 456-6500

(G-10722)
M&M MANUFACTURING INC
5555 Guhn Rd (77040-6125)
P.O. Box 41066 (77241-1066)
PHONE 713 460-1677
Terry Ward, *Manager*
EMP: 40
SALES (corp-wide): 254.6B **Publicly Held**
WEB: www.mmmfg.com
SIC: 3444 Sheet metalwork
HQ: M&M Manufacturing, Inc.
　　4001 Mark Iv Pkwy
　　Fort Worth TX 76106
　　817 336-2311

(G-10723)
M&P FLANGE PIPE PROTECTION INC
9426 Katy Fwy Bldg 11 (77055-6350)
PHONE 713 463-6339
Gregory A Mattingly, *President*
▲ **EMP:** 12
SQ FT: 15,000
SALES (est): 2.2MM **Privately Held**
WEB: www.m-p.com
SIC: 3463 Flange, valve or pipe fitting forg-
　　ings, nonferrous; pump, compressor, tur-
　　bine & engine forgings, except auto

(G-10724)
M&R MANUFACTURING LLC
15040 Northgreen Blvd (77032-3000)
PHONE 281 590-7200
Mahesh Patel, *Mng Member*
EMP: 10

SQ FT: 10,000
SALES (est): 1.5MM **Privately Held**
WEB: www.mnrmanufacturing.com
SIC: 3999 7539 Barber & beauty shop
　　equipment; machine shop, automotive

(G-10725)
M-I LLC (DH)
Also Called: M-I Swaco A Schlumberger Co
5950 N Course Dr (77072-1626)
P.O. Box 42842 (77242-2842)
PHONE 281 561-1300
Paal Kibsgaard, *CEO*
Joe Bacho, *President*
Simon Ayat, *Exec VP*
Ashok Belani, *Exec VP*
J-F Poupeau, *Exec VP*
◆ **EMP:** 500
SQ FT: 200,000
SALES (est): 5.3B **Publicly Held**
WEB: www.miswaco.com
SIC: 1389 2865 2869 8711 Oil field serv-
　　ices; mud service, oil field drilling; cyclic
　　crudes & intermediates; industrial organic
　　chemicals; engineering services; man-
　　agement services
HQ: Smith International, Inc.
　　1310 Rankin Rd
　　Houston TX 77073
　　281 443-3370

(G-10726)
M-TRIGEN INC
5050 Westway Park Blvd # 175
(77041-2017)
PHONE 713 469-5735
Donald Williams, *CEO*
Randy Erwin, *Vice Pres*
Richard Lee, *Chief Mktg Ofcr*
Maria Sanchez, *Manager*
Erik Rodriguez, *Info Tech Dir*
EMP: 25
SQ FT: 100,000
SALES (est): 1.4MM **Privately Held**
WEB: www.mtrigen.com
SIC: 3621 Power generators

(G-10727)
M3 MIDSTREAM LLC (PA)
600 Travis St Ste 5600 (77002-2909)
PHONE 713 783-3000
Frank Tsuru, *CEO*
Brant Baird, *President*
Bill Pritchard, *Chairman*
Rickey Cooksey, *Vice Pres*
Hondo Hanagan, *Vice Pres*
EMP: 10
SALES (est): 54.6MM **Privately Held**
WEB: www.m3midstream.com
SIC: 1382 Oil & gas exploration services

(G-10728)
M5 LOUISIANA GATHERING LLC
600 Travis St Ste 5600 (77002-2909)
PHONE 713 783-3000
EMP: 31
SALES (est): 7.1MM **Privately Held**
WEB: www.momentummidstream.com
SIC: 1382 Oil & gas exploration services

(G-10729)
MAASS FLANGES CORPORATION (DH)
Also Called: Maas International
6202 Lumberdale Rd (77092-1316)
PHONE 713 329-5500
Alexander Maass, *CEO*
Michael Maass, *President*
Greg Alley, *Corp Secy*
Robert H Burkhardt, *Corp Secy*
David Cook, *Vice Pres*
◆ **EMP:** 45
SQ FT: 4,500
SALES (est): 30.5MM
SALES (corp-wide): 355.8K **Privately Held**
WEB: www.maassflange.com
SIC: 3463 5085 Flange, valve or pipe fit-
　　ting forgings, nonferrous; industrial sup-
　　plies
HQ: Wilhelm Maass Gmbh
　　Zeche Ernestine 18
　　Essen 45141
　　201 294-930

▲ = Import ▼ =Export
◆ =Import/Export

(G-10730)
MACH INDUSTRIAL GROUP LP
6119 Fulton St (77022-5901)
P.O. Box 130630 (77219-0630)
PHONE..............................713 695-6000
Cora Sue Mach, *Partner*
Harry Mach III, *Partner*
Steve P Mach, *Partner*
Thomas Mach, *Partner*
Harry Mach Jr, *General Ptnr*
EMP: 57 **EST:** 1953
SQ FT: 75,000
SALES (est): 13.9MM **Privately Held**
WEB: www.machindustrialgroup.com
SIC: 3599 Machine shop, jobbing & repair

(G-10731)
MACH INTERNATIONAL INC
6119 Fulton St (77022-5901)
P.O. Box 130630 (77219-0630)
PHONE..............................713 695-6000
H E Mach, *CEO*
Butch Mach, *COO*
Steven P Mach, *Vice Pres*
Tony Ballejo, *Purchasing*
S Mach, *CFO*
EMP: 41
SQ FT: 75,000
SALES (est): 7MM **Privately Held**
WEB: www.machindustrialgroup.com
SIC: 3441 Fabricated structural metal

(G-10732)
MADEWELL LLC
1330 Boyles St (77020-7537)
PHONE..............................713 674-1050
Joe Valdez, *President*
Marie Valdez, *Treasurer*
Jesse Villanueva, *Sales Staff*
Irma Valdez, *Admin Sec*
EMP: 26
SQ FT: 8,400
SALES (est): 6.7MM **Privately Held**
WEB: www.madewellcompany.com
SIC: 3441 Fabricated structural metal

(G-10733)
MAERSK DRILLING USA INC (HQ)
800 Town And Country Blvd # 500 (77024-4563)
PHONE..............................713 972-3300
Nils S Andersen, *CEO*
◆ **EMP:** 15
SALES (est): 11.1MM
SALES (corp-wide): 438.6K **Privately Held**
WEB: www.maerskdrilling.com
SIC: 1381 Drilling oil & gas wells
PA: Maersk Drilling Americas A/S
Lyngby Hovedgade 85
Kongens Lyngby
336 333-63

(G-10734)
MAERSK OIL HOUSTON INC
2500 Citywest Blvd # 100 (77042-3038)
PHONE..............................713 346-5800
Jakob Thomasen, *CEO*
Bruce Laws, *President*
Kevin Manser, *COO*
Kenneth Murdoch, *CFO*
Morten K Nicolaisen, *Director*
EMP: 200
SALES (est): 11.7MM
SALES (corp-wide): 7B **Publicly Held**
SIC: 1389 Oil field services
HQ: Total E&P Danmark A/S
Amerika Plads 29, Sal St
KObenhavn 2100
336 340-00

(G-10735)
MAGNETIC FIELD EFFECTS LLC (PA)
Also Called: Micro Tesla Magnetic Field
14149 Westfair East Dr (77041-1105)
PHONE..............................713 856-8111
Jimmy Marek, *Buyer*
Eric Meissner, *Engineer*
Walt Coram, *Mng Member*
Robles Edward, *Info Tech Mgr*
Shawn Trotter, *Technical Staff*
EMP: 14
SQ FT: 15,000
SALES (est): 3.1MM **Privately Held**
WEB: www.microtesla.com
SIC: 3829 Magnetometers

(G-10736)
MAGNOLIA OIL & GAS OPER LLC
9 Greenway Plz Ste 1300 (77046-0922)
PHONE..............................713 842-9050
Stephen Chazen, *CEO*
Christopher Stavros, *CFO*
EMP: 100
SALES (est): 5.2MM
SALES (corp-wide): 936.1MM **Publicly Held**
WEB: www.magnoliaoilgas.com
SIC: 1382 Oil & gas exploration services
PA: Magnolia Oil & Gas Corporation
9 Greenway Plz Ste 1300
Houston TX 77046
713 842-9050

(G-10737)
MAGSEIS FF LLC
9811 Katy Fwy Ste 1100 (77024-1273)
PHONE..............................281 275-7500
Per Christian Grytnes, *CEO*
Tom Henrik Sundby, *CFO*
EMP: 183
SALES (est): 15.5MM **Privately Held**
WEB: www.magseisfairfield.com
SIC: 1382 Geophysical exploration, oil & gas field
PA: Magseis Fairfield Asa
Strandveien 50
Lysaker 1366

(G-10738)
MAIL SERVICES HOUSTON INC
Also Called: Msh Printing
1 N Sampson St (77003-1823)
P.O. Box 15180 (77220-5180)
PHONE..............................713 594-3362
Mitchell K Miller, *President*
Cathy Myers, *Vice Pres*
Lydia C Miller, *Admin Sec*
EMP: 51
SQ FT: 25,000
SALES (est): 6.2MM **Privately Held**
WEB: www.mailservicesofhouston.com
SIC: 7331 2752 Mailing service; commercial printing, offset

(G-10739)
MAIN JEWELL LLC
5005 W 34th St Ste 100a (77092-6712)
PHONE..............................713 623-0499
Larry G Longer,
EMP: 9 **EST:** 2010
SALES (est): 1.1MM **Privately Held**
SIC: 3911 Jewelry, precious metal

(G-10740)
MAIN MARINE REPAIR INC
1714 Broadway St (77012-3308)
PHONE..............................713 645-3553
Alex Rokhsaz, *CEO*
▲ **EMP:** 10
SQ FT: 18,000
SALES (est): 1.5MM **Privately Held**
WEB: www.mmisus.com
SIC: 3731 4491 7359 Commercial cargo ships, building & repairing; ship hold cleaning; equipment rental & leasing

(G-10741)
MAINTENANCE BUILDERS SUP LTD (PA)
Also Called: Mbs Incoporated
1418 Brittmoore Rd (77043-4006)
PHONE..............................713 462-8213
Mark Beatty, *President*
Brett Beatty, *General Mgr*
Cindy Thomas, *Vice Pres*
Dan Canzian, *Sales Staff*
Troy Holt, *Sales Staff*
EMP: 41
SQ FT: 40,000
SALES (est): 23.7MM **Privately Held**
WEB: www.mbssupply.com
SIC: 5099 1751 2431 5031 Locks & lock sets; window & door (prefabricated) installation; doors & door parts & trim, wood; louver doors, wood; door frames, all materials; door opening & closing devices, except electrical

(G-10742)
MAKO OILFIELD SERVICES LLC (PA)
12249-B Northwoods Pk Dr (77041)
PHONE..............................832 680-1300
Mark Provine, *CEO*
Steve Lykins, *President*
Mike Musgrove, *General Mgr*
Keven Harness, *Project Mgr*
Michael Moreland, *Controller*
EMP: 27 **EST:** 2016
SALES (est): 8.8MM **Privately Held**
WEB: www.makooilfield.com
SIC: 1389 Oil field services

(G-10743)
MANAGEMENT CONTROLS INC
15600 Jfk Blvd Ste 850 (77032-2345)
PHONE..............................281 590-5881
Vince Broady, *CEO*
Bob Harrell, *President*
Caleb Caraway, *Accounts Mgr*
Kelly Hall, *Consultant*
David Romney, *Senior Mgr*
EMP: 135
SQ FT: 4,900
SALES (est): 5.2MM **Privately Held**
WEB: www.mccorp.com
SIC: 7372 7371 Business oriented computer software; custom computer programming services

(G-10744)
MANAGEMENT SERVICES INTL
9000 Monroe Rd (77061-5229)
PHONE..............................713 333-0200
John P Emmitte, *President*
EMP: 15
SQ FT: 8,000
SALES (est): 1.9MM **Privately Held**
SIC: 3829 Testing equipment: abrasion, shearing strength, etc.

(G-10745)
MANNING POOL SERVICE INC
2121 Judiway St (77018-5800)
PHONE..............................713 812-9098
Susan O Manning, *Owner*
EMP: 25
SALES (est): 505.7K **Privately Held**
WEB: www.manningpoolservice.com
SIC: 3589 5091 7389 Swimming pool filter & water conditioning systems; swimming pools, equipment & supplies; swimming pool & hot tub service & maintenance

(G-10746)
MANTI RESOURCES INC
2 Riverway Ste 1100 (77056-1940)
P.O. Box 2907, Corpus Christi (78403-2907)
PHONE..............................361 888-7708
Lee Barberito, *President*
Joe Mistich, *Vice Pres*
Kevin Jensen, *Engineer*
Leslie Aymond, *Controller*
Monica Schutz, *Accountant*
EMP: 30
SALES (est): 5.9MM **Privately Held**
WEB: www.mantires.com
SIC: 1382 Oil & gas exploration services

(G-10747)
MANTI TARKA PERMIAN LP
2 Riverway Ste 1100 (77056-1940)
PHONE..............................832 460-0046
EMP: 9
SALES (est): 99.1K **Privately Held**
WEB: www.tarka.com
SIC: 1382 Oil & gas exploration services

(G-10748)
MANTUA MANUFACTURING CO
5534 Armour Dr (77020-8003)
PHONE..............................713 672-9811
Pat Heintz, *Manager*
EMP: 28
SQ FT: 40,536
SALES (corp-wide): 81MM **Privately Held**
WEB: www.bedframes.com
SIC: 2514 Frames for box springs or bedsprings: metal

PA: Mantua Manufacturing Co.
31050 Diamond Pkwy
Solon OH 44139
800 333-8333

(G-10749)
MANUFCTRED COMPONENT PARTS LTD
Also Called: Schill Steel Services
3001 W 11th St (77008-6103)
P.O. Box 70256 (77270-0256)
PHONE..............................713 880-0590
Alfred J Schill, *CEO*
Don Flournoy Jr, *President*
EMP: 35
SQ FT: 185,000
SALES (est): 15MM **Privately Held**
WEB: www.schillsteel.com
SIC: 3441 3312 7692 5051 Fabricated structural metal; plate, steel; welding repair; metals service centers & offices

(G-10750)
MAP OIL TOOLS INC (PA)
7942 Breen Dr (77064-8421)
P.O. Box 11326, New Iberia LA (70562-1326)
PHONE..............................337 560-8559
Glen Holcomb, *President*
Bradley Mayeux, *President*
Jennifer Mair, *Purch Mgr*
Avel Ortiz, *Engineer*
Doris J Holcomb, *Treasurer*
◆ **EMP:** 17
SALES (est): 16MM **Privately Held**
WEB: www.mapoiltools.com
SIC: 1389 Oil field services

(G-10751)
MARALO LLC (PA)
4400 Post Oak Pkwy # 2550 (77027-3421)
PHONE..............................713 622-5420
Geoffrey Perrin, *CFO*
Mary R Lowe, *Mng Member*
EMP: 20 **EST:** 1934
SQ FT: 8,500
SALES (est): 3.6MM **Privately Held**
WEB: www.maralo.com
SIC: 1311 Crude petroleum production; natural gas production

(G-10752)
MARATHON BINDERY SERVICES INC
7511 Langtry St Ste 100 (77040-6630)
PHONE..............................713 690-6040
Kerry Emmott, *President*
Wayne Emmott, *Vice Pres*
James Ward, *Controller*
EMP: 35
SQ FT: 20,000
SALES (est): 2.5MM **Privately Held**
WEB: www.marathonbindery.com
SIC: 2789 Binding only: books, pamphlets, magazines, etc.

(G-10753)
MARATHON INTERNATIONAL OIL CO (DH)
5555 San Felipe St # 2796 (77056-2701)
PHONE..............................713 629-6600
V G Beghini, *President*
D C Gerard, *Vice Pres*
K M Henning, *Vice Pres*
P J Kuntz, *Controller*
Arlene Campbell, *Human Res Dir*
EMP: 60
SALES (est): 155.9MM
SALES (corp-wide): 5.1B **Publicly Held**
WEB: www.marathonoil.com
SIC: 5541 1382 6519 Gasoline service stations; oil & gas exploration services; real property lessors
HQ: Marathon Oil Company
5555 San Felipe St B1
Houston TX 77056
713 629-6600

(G-10754)
MARATHON OIL COMPANY (HQ)
Also Called: Marathon Pipe Line
5555 San Felipe St B1 (77056-2701)
P.O. Box 3128 (77253-3128)
PHONE..............................713 629-6600
Clarence P Cazalot Jr, *President*

Jeffrey L Hayman, *Principal*
Philip E Behrman, *Senior VP*
G D Golder, *Senior VP*
Steven B Hinchman, *Senior VP*
◆ **EMP:** 900 **EST:** 1981
SQ FT: 700,000
SALES (est): 782MM
SALES (corp-wide): 5.1B **Publicly Held**
WEB: www.marathonoil.com
SIC: 5541 1311 4612 4613 Gasoline
service stations; crude petroleum production; natural gas production; crude petroleum pipelines; refined petroleum pipelines; gasoline blending plants
PA: Marathon Oil Corporation
5555 San Felipe St
Houston TX 77056
713 629-6600

(G-10755)
MARATHON OIL COMPANY
5555 San Felipe St (77056-2701)
PHONE.................................713 296-4336
William Schwind Jr, *Manager*
EMP: 27
SALES (corp-wide): 5.1B **Publicly Held**
WEB: www.marathonoil.com
SIC: 2911 Petroleum refining
HQ: Marathon Oil Company
5555 San Felipe St B1
Houston TX 77056
713 629-6600

(G-10756)
MARATHON OIL CORPORATION (PA)
5555 San Felipe St (77056-2701)
P.O. Box 3128 (77253-3128)
PHONE.................................713 629-6600
Lee M Tillman, *President*
Rene Castaneda, *Superintendent*
Albert Jones, *Superintendent*
Steven Gyeszly, *Counsel*
T Mitch Little, *Exec VP*
◆ **EMP:** 1300 **EST:** 1887
SALES (est): 5.1B **Publicly Held**
WEB: www.marathonoil.com
SIC: 1311 2911 5171 5541 Crude petroleum & natural gas; crude petroleum production; natural gas production; petroleum refining; petroleum bulk stations & terminals; gasoline service stations

(G-10757)
MARATHON SPECIAL SERVICES INC
9515 Caraway Ln (77036-5903)
PHONE.................................713 784-4918
Ronny J Cornejo, *President*
Hernan Cornejo, *Vice Pres*
EMP: 13
SQ FT: 4,000
SALES (est): 3.3MM **Privately Held**
SIC: 5085 5049 3491 5084 Valves, pistons & fittings; laboratory equipment, except medical or dental; industrial valves; compressors, except air conditioning

(G-10758)
MARBERRY MACHINE INC
6210 Cunningham Rd (77041-4710)
PHONE.................................713 466-9666
Redgie Marberry, *President*
Larry Shumate, *Business Mgr*
Gary Marberry, *Vice Pres*
Toni Mundy, *QC Mgr*
Donna Martinez, *Accounting Mgr*
▲ **EMP:** 60 **EST:** 1978
SQ FT: 45,000
SALES (est): 9.9MM **Privately Held**
WEB: www.marberrymachine.com
SIC: 3599 Machine shop, jobbing & repair

(G-10759)
MARBLE & GRANITE RESOURCES
3902 Black Locust Dr (77088-6905)
PHONE.................................713 957-2646
Jennie W Kahanek, *President*
EMP: 10
SALES (est): 1MM **Privately Held**
WEB:
www.marbleandgraniteresources.com
SIC: 3281 Marble, building: cut & shaped; benches, cut stone

(G-10760)
MARBLE SLAB CREAMERY NO 152
11430 East Fwy Ste 400 (77029-1993)
PHONE.................................713 455-5786
Nadeem Beg, *President*
EMP: 10
SALES (est): 498K **Privately Held**
WEB: www.marbleslab.com
SIC: 5451 2024 Ice cream (packaged); ice cream & ice milk

(G-10761)
MARC CLIMATIC CONTROLS INC
13415 Emmett Rd (77041-2555)
PHONE.................................713 464-8587
John W Kinsel Jr, *President*
Cheryl Kinsel, *Admin Sec*
▼ **EMP:** 15
SQ FT: 30,000
SALES (est): 3MM **Privately Held**
WEB: www.marcclimatic.com
SIC: 3585 Air conditioning units, complete: domestic or industrial

(G-10762)
MARC JOHNSONUSA INC
7480 Harwin Dr (77036-2008)
PHONE.................................713 780-8486
Jason Yeh, *President*
▲ **EMP:** 15
SALES (est): 439.2K **Privately Held**
WEB: www.marcjohnson-usa.com
SIC: 5099 3161 Luggage; luggage

(G-10763)
MARCH RESOURCES CO
Also Called: Architectural Bldg Components
11625 N Huston Rosslyn Rd (77086-3601)
PHONE.................................281 931-3986
Charles L Smith Jr, *President*
Bill Harris, *Sales Executive*
Don Cherry, *Info Tech Dir*
EMP: 50
SQ FT: 37,000
SALES (est): 8.1MM **Privately Held**
WEB: www.mcelroymetal.com
SIC: 3444 Roof deck, sheet metal; siding, sheet metal

(G-10764)
MARINE COMPUTATION SVCS KENNY
Also Called: MCS Kenny
15115 Park Row Fl 3 (77084-4945)
PHONE.................................281 646-4155
Paul Jukes, *President*
John Conroy, *Admin Sec*
EMP: 60
SALES (est): 5.2MM
SALES (corp-wide): 12.7B **Privately Held**
SIC: 8711 7372 Engineering services; prepackaged software
HQ: John Wood Group Us Holdings Inc
17325 Park Row Ste 500
Houston TX 77084

(G-10765)
MARINE SERVICES LLC
Also Called: NORTHSTAR INDUSTRIES
1714 Broadway St (77012-3308)
PHONE.................................713 923-6688
Kindra A Rokhsaz, *Controller*
Alex Rokhsaz, *Mng Member*
EMP: 30
SALES (est): 3.3MM **Privately Held**
WEB: www.northstarind.net
SIC: 7699 5084 3561 7629 Pumps & pumping equipment repair; industrial machinery & equipment; pumps & pumping equipment; generator repair; electric motor & generator auxillary parts; heat exchangers, condensers & components

(G-10766)
MARINE WELL CONTAINMENT CO LLC (PA)
9807 Katy Fwy Ste 1200 (77024-1277)
PHONE.................................281 820-8800
Don Armijo, *CEO*
Martin Massey, *CEO*
Todd McManus, *Site Mgr*
Brad Fruge, *Foreman/Supr*
Katie Thompson, *Opers Staff*

EMP: 31
SALES (est): 39.4MM **Privately Held**
WEB: www.marinewellcontainment.com
SIC: 1389 Servicing oil & gas wells

(G-10767)
MARINER GULF OF MEXICO LLC
1 Briar Dale Ct Ste 2000 (77027-2904)
PHONE.................................713 954-5500
EMP: 95
SQ FT: 20,000
SALES (est): 3.3MM **Privately Held**
SIC: 1311 1382 Crude Petroleum/Natural Gas Production Oil/Gas Exploration Services

(G-10768)
MARIPOSA CORPORATION
Also Called: National Gasket Company
10893 Shadow Wood Dr (77043-2863)
PHONE.................................713 222-0220
Conover H Able Jr, *President*
Shannon Able, *Corp Secy*
Gary Able, *Vice Pres*
▲ **EMP:** 25
SQ FT: 20,000
SALES (est): 3.9MM **Privately Held**
WEB: www.txgind.com
SIC: 3053 Gaskets, all materials

(G-10769)
MARKET MAKERS INC
Also Called: Mmi Division 7
6846 Theall Rd Ste 400 (77066-1118)
PHONE.................................281 893-9261
Ian Wilson, *President*
Ken Greer, *Sales Staff*
Bart McMurry, *Manager*
Nicole Montalvo, *Manager*
Javier Puerta, *Manager*
EMP: 10
SALES (est): 1.3MM **Privately Held**
WEB: www.marketmakersinc.com
SIC: 2952 1761 1799 3069 Roofing materials; roofing, siding & sheet metal work; roofing contractor; waterproofing; roofing, membrane rubber

(G-10770)
MARKS FLOOR DESIGN INC
9927 Harwin Dr (77036-1609)
PHONE.................................713 974-2300
Akram S El-Jaroudi, *President*
Christopher Jaroudi, *Manager*
EMP: 15
SALES (est): 395.3K **Privately Held**
SIC: 3253 Ceramic wall & floor tile

(G-10771)
MARLINK INC
3327 S Sam Houston Pkwy E # 100
(77047-6548)
PHONE.................................713 910-3352
Anthony Queenan, *CEO*
Steve Birnbaum, *Business Mgr*
Sigrid Lovik, *Project Mgr*
Eric Bakker, *Sales Staff*
EMP: 17 **EST:** 2011
SALES (est): 2.6MM
SALES (corp-wide): 177.9K **Privately Held**
WEB: www.marlink.com
SIC: 3663 Space satellite communications equipment
HQ: Marlink As
Lysaker Torg 45
Lysaker 1366

(G-10772)
MARRONE & CO INC
Also Called: Cold Shot Chillers
14343 Interdrive E (77032-3331)
PHONE.................................281 227-8400
Michael Marrone, *President*
EMP: 24
SALES (est): 8.1MM **Privately Held**
WEB: www.waterchillers.com
SIC: 3585 Refrigeration equipment, complete

(G-10773)
MARS TRANSFORMERS LLC (PA)
83030 Mchard Rd (77067)
PHONE.................................281 648-1600
EMP: 22

SALES (est): 15MM **Privately Held**
SIC: 3612 Power,Distribution And Specilty Trnsfrmrs

(G-10774)
MARSOL TECHNOLOGIES INC
14331 Fm 529 Rd (77095-7510)
PHONE.................................346 701-8268
EMP: 10
SALES (est): 500K **Privately Held**
SIC: 3429 Hardware, Nec

(G-10775)
MARTECH FOODS INC
Also Called: Lenotre Bakery
7070 Allensby St (77022-4322)
PHONE.................................713 692-0077
Alain Lenotre, *President*
EMP: 10 **EST:** 1989
SQ FT: 28,000
SALES (est): 2MM **Privately Held**
WEB: www.gastonlenotrescholarship.org
SIC: 2051 Bakery: wholesale or wholesale/retail combined

(G-10776)
MARTIN MARIETTA MATERIALS INC
Also Called: Melendy Yard
11913 Fm 529 Rd (77041-3000)
PHONE.................................713 896-8683
John Castro, *Manager*
EMP: 20 **Publicly Held**
WEB: www.martinmarietta.com
SIC: 1423 Crushed & broken granite
PA: Martin Marietta Materials Inc
2710 Wycliff Rd
Raleigh NC 27607

(G-10777)
MARTIN PREFERRED FOODS LP (PA)
Also Called: Martin Preferred Logistics
2011 Silver St (77007-2801)
PHONE.................................713 869-6191
Mike Tapick, *Ch of Bd*
Jeffrey Tapick, *President*
Buzz Adcock, *Vice Pres*
Matthew S Boarman, *Vice Pres*
Terry Clayborne, *Vice Pres*
▲ **EMP:** 160 **EST:** 1944
SQ FT: 50,000
SALES (est): 194.4MM **Privately Held**
WEB: www.martinfoods.com
SIC: 5142 2015 2011 5141 Packaged frozen goods; poultry slaughtering & processing; meat packing plants; groceries, general line; poultry: live, dressed or frozen (unpackaged); poultry products; eggs

(G-10778)
MARTIN SPROCKET & GEAR INC
Also Called: Martin Sprocket & Gear 15
9910 Bent Oak Dr (77040-3222)
PHONE.................................817 258-3000
Mark Gniadek, *District Mgr*
Kevin Hornberger, *District Mgr*
Gary C Martin, *Vice Pres*
Hannah Kunnemann, *Sales Staff*
Brad Bowre, *Manager*
EMP: 10
SQ FT: 25,000
SALES (corp-wide): 539MM **Privately Held**
WEB: www.martinsprocket.com
SIC: 3566 3568 Gears, power transmission, except automotive; sprockets (power transmission equipment)
PA: Martin Sprocket & Gear, Inc.
3100 Sprocket Dr
Arlington TX 76015
817 258-3000

(G-10779)
MARTINEZ MILLWORKS INC
8503 Highway 6 S (77083-5710)
PHONE.................................281 988-9334
Santos Martinez, *President*
Maria Martinez, *Vice Pres*
EMP: 13
SQ FT: 12,000

SALES (est): 2.9MM **Privately Held**
WEB: www.martinezmillwork.com
SIC: 2431 Millwork

(G-10780)
MARUBENI AMERICA CORPORATION
2800 Post Oak Blvd # 6000 (77056-6100)
PHONE...................................713 871-5700
Hajime Ichiki, *General Mgr*
Toshihiro Mori, *Vice Pres*
Shigefumi Sam Matsumoto, *Sales Staff*
Sebastian Pedraza, *Sales Staff*
Cathy Wolfe, *Marketing Mgr*
EMP: 20
SQ FT: 12,154 **Privately Held**
WEB: www.marubeni-usa.com
SIC: 2899 5169 Chemical supplies for foundries; chemicals & allied products
HQ: Marubeni America Corporation
375 Lexington Ave
New York NY 10017
212 450-0100

(G-10781)
MARUBENI OIL & GAS (USA) LLC (HQ)
945 Bunker Hill Rd # 700 (77024-1364)
PHONE...................................832 379-1100
Kazuaki Tanaki, *President*
Rose Farmer, *Area Mgr*
Perry Murphree, *COO*
David Barton, *Vice Pres*
Kari Glasco, *Engineer*
▲ EMP: 30
SALES (est): 73.9MM **Privately Held**
WEB: www.mogus.com
SIC: 1311 Natural gas production

(G-10782)
MARYGROVE AWNING LLC
Also Called: Avco
4617 N Shepherd Dr (77018-3315)
P.O. Box 10878 (77206-0878)
PHONE...................................713 697-0156
EMP: 20
SQ FT: 9,600
SALES (est): 2.3MM **Privately Held**
WEB: www.marygrovetexas.com
SIC: 2394 Awnings, fabric: made from purchased materials; canvas covers & drop cloths

(G-10783)
MASCORP LTD
Also Called: Mascoat
4310 Campbell Rd (77041-9116)
PHONE...................................713 465-0304
George More IV, *President*
Aad Dijkshoorn, *Managing Dir*
Gary C Prasher, *COO*
Robert Browning, *Sales Mgr*
Michael Von Schade, *Sales Mgr*
◆ EMP: 30
SQ FT: 45,000
SALES (est): 8.2MM **Privately Held**
WEB: www.mascoat.com
SIC: 2851 Paints & allied products

(G-10784)
MASON ROAD SHEET METAL INC
Also Called: M R Sheet Metal
6450 Clara Rd Ste 190 (77041-5365)
PHONE...................................713 466-5054
Christopher Jinks, *President*
Cleo Jensen, *Project Mgr*
Kelly Stavinoha, *Mfg Staff*
Edward Rangel, *Purch Agent*
Michael Thomas, *Purchasing*
EMP: 100
SQ FT: 12,000
SALES (est): 24.9MM **Privately Held**
WEB: www.mrsheetmetal.com
SIC: 3444 Sheet metal specialties, not stamped

(G-10785)
MASONS MILL & LUMBER CO INC
9885 Tanner Rd (77041-7622)
P.O. Box 430036 (77243-0036)
PHONE...................................713 462-6975
Mason Spellings, *General Mgr*
Michael Spellings, *Principal*

Eric Boer, *Vice Pres*
Barbara Rogers, *QC Mgr*
Anne Spellings, *Treasurer*
EMP: 57
SQ FT: 58,000
SALES (est): 9.2MM **Privately Held**
WEB: www.masonsmillandlumber.com
SIC: 5031 2431 2435 Hardboard; plywood; millwork; hardwood veneer & plywood

(G-10786)
MASTER FABRICATORS
5524 Harvey Wilson Dr (77020-8017)
PHONE...................................832 294-8103
EMP: 10 EST: 2016
SALES (est): 1.1MM **Privately Held**
WEB: www.masterfabricators.com
SIC: 3441 Fabricated structural metal

(G-10787)
MASTER FLO
8726 Fallbrook Dr (77064-3317)
PHONE...................................713 690-2789
Mark McNeill, *President*
German Rubiano, *Regional Mgr*
Walter Emmott, *District Mgr*
EMP: 11
SALES (est): 1.7MM **Privately Held**
WEB: www.masterflo.com
SIC: 2999 Petroleum & coal products

(G-10788)
MASTER MACHINE INC
10101 Chickasaw Ln (77041-6105)
P.O. Box 19791 (77224-9791)
PHONE...................................713 690-3480
Patricia Wolfe, *President*
Richard Chaltry, *Vice Pres*
Destiny Campbell, *Manager*
Nicholas Wolfe, *Admin Sec*
EMP: 15
SQ FT: 7,100
SALES (est): 1.7MM **Privately Held**
WEB: www.mastermachineinc.net
SIC: 3599 3541 Machine shop, jobbing & repair; electrical discharge machining (EDM); grinding machines, metalworking

(G-10789)
MASTERPIECE LITHO INC
7220 Wynnwood Ln (77008-6032)
PHONE...................................713 869-9990
David J Tarnowski Sr, *President*
David J Tarnowski Jr, *Vice Pres*
Tina Dammeyer, *Opers Staff*
Tina Tarnowski, *Treasurer*
EMP: 15
SQ FT: 10,000
SALES (est): 3.1MM **Privately Held**
WEB: www.mlihouston.com
SIC: 2752 Commercial printing, offset

(G-10790)
MATE INC
8910 Point Six Cir (77095-3117)
P.O. Box 40542 (77240-0542)
PHONE...................................281 855-0045
William Paul McWilliam Jr, *President*
Jerry W Collins, *Corp Secy*
Mike Slaid, *Purchasing*
EMP: 20
SQ FT: 15,000
SALES (est): 4.3MM **Privately Held**
WEB: www.matetrailers.com
SIC: 3715 3537 Truck trailers; industrial trucks & tractors

(G-10791)
MATECO TRUCK EQUIPMENT CO (HQ)
8222 North Fwy (77037-3608)
P.O. Box 38775 (77238-8775)
PHONE...................................713 692-3888
Fred Haas, *President*
Jeff Keene, *Director*
EMP: 20
SALES (est): 2.4MM
SALES (corp-wide): 18.8MM **Privately Held**
WEB: www.matecotruck.com
SIC: 3713 Truck bodies (motor vehicles)
PA: Trailer Wheel & Frame Co.
8222 North Fwy
Houston TX 77037
281 931-7777

(G-10792)
MATERIAL DIFFERENCE TECH LLC
Also Called: Mdt Replas
6754 Kirbyville St (77033-1106)
PHONE...................................713 640-2040
Guy Jensen, *Branch Mgr*
EMP: 18
SALES (corp-wide): 10.7MM **Privately Held**
WEB: www.materialdifferencetechnologies.com
SIC: 2821 Plastics materials & resins
PA: Material Difference Technologies Llc
1501 Sarasota Center Blvd
Sarasota FL 34240
888 818-1283

(G-10793)
MATHESON TRI-GAS INC
2018 Houston Ave (77007-2944)
PHONE...................................713 869-7351
EMP: 15 **Privately Held**
WEB: www.mathesongas.com
SIC: 2813 Industrial gases
HQ: Matheson Tri-Gas, Inc.
3 Mountainview Rd Ste 3 # 3
Warren NJ 07059
908 991-9200

(G-10794)
MATHESON TRI-GAS INC
Also Called: Tri Gas
2200 Houston Ave (77007-2948)
PHONE...................................281 471-2544
Rick Phillips, *Vice Pres*
EMP: 45 **Privately Held**
WEB: www.mathesongas.com
SIC: 2813 5084 Industrial gases; welding machinery & equipment
HQ: Matheson Tri-Gas, Inc.
3 Mountainview Rd Ste 3 # 3
Warren NJ 07059
908 991-9200

(G-10795)
MATHEW MARINE INC
4001 Navigation Blvd (77003-1938)
PHONE...................................877 508-4004
Demetrios Halastaras, *President*
Evangelos Halastaras, *Vice Pres*
▲ EMP: 10
SQ FT: 10,000
SALES (est): 3MM **Privately Held**
WEB: www.mathewmarine.com
SIC: 7699 1382 Boat repair; oil & gas exploration services

(G-10796)
MATHIS IRON WORKS INC
6003 Allison Rd (77048-5207)
P.O. Box 450, Pearland (77588-0450)
PHONE...................................713 991-5846
Christopher Mathis, *President*
Ava Mathis, *Treasurer*
EMP: 10
SQ FT: 2,500
SALES (est): 1.4MM **Privately Held**
WEB: www.mathisironworks.com
SIC: 3446 Fences or posts, ornamental iron or steel; fences, gates, posts & flagpoles; railings, bannisters, guards, etc.: made from metal pipe

(G-10797)
MATTHEW WARREN INC
Also Called: Engineered Spring Products
7400 Pinemont Dr (77040-6410)
PHONE...................................800 364-0391
EMP: 77
SALES (corp-wide): 104.6MM **Privately Held**
SIC: 3493 Mfg Steel Springs-Nonwire
HQ: Matthew Warren, Inc.
9501 Tech Blvd Ste 401
Rosemont IL 60018
847 349-5760

(G-10798)
MATTHEWS-DANIEL HOLDINGS INC (PA)
4544 Post Oak Place Dr # 160 (77027-3104)
PHONE...................................713 622-1633
EMP: 72

SALES (est): 7.2MM **Privately Held**
SIC: 6411 4785 1311 Insurance Agent/Broker Motor Freight Fixed Facility Crude Petroleum/Natural Gas Production

(G-10799)
MAUSER USA LLC
4004 Homestead Rd (77028-5810)
PHONE...................................713 670-2332
Joy Butt, *Principal*
Carlos Serrano, *Production*
Ralf Cloud, *Maintence Staff*
EMP: 150
SALES (corp-wide): 1.1B **Privately Held**
WEB: www.mauserpackaging.com
SIC: 3412 3089 Drums, shipping: metal; tubs, plastic (containers)
HQ: Mauser Usa, Llc
35 Cotters Ln Ste C
East Brunswick NJ 08816

(G-10800)
MAVERICK ENTERPRISES
13727 Perry Rd (77070-4259)
PHONE...................................281 444-5010
Tommy Large, *Owner*
Kevin Forster, *Vice Pres*
Ben Ortiz, *Marketing Staff*
Melissa Hoff, *Office Mgr*
EMP: 11
SALES (est): 1.7MM **Privately Held**
WEB: www.maverickenterprises.net
SIC: 3585 5075 Air conditioning equipment, complete; air conditioning & ventilation equipment & supplies

(G-10801)
MAVERICK PRECISION MFG LTD
Also Called: Maverick Machining
13604 Almeda School Rd (77047-4006)
PHONE...................................713 433-3756
Joan Erickson, *Partner*
Roger Regnier, *General Mgr*
EMP: 10 EST: 1997
SQ FT: 10,000
SALES (est): 4MM **Privately Held**
WEB: www.maverickpm.com
SIC: 3599 Machine shop, jobbing & repair

(G-10802)
MAVERICK TUBE CORPORATION (DH)
Also Called: Tenaris
2200 West Loop S Ste 800 (77027-3532)
PHONE...................................713 767-4400
Luca Zanotti, *President*
David Reed, *District Mgr*
Pablo Toy, *Business Mgr*
Ajay Chhabra, *CFO*
Richard Mullings, *Auditor*
◆ EMP: 500
SALES (est): 730.2MM
SALES (corp-wide): 183.7K **Privately Held**
WEB: www.tenaris.com
SIC: 3317 Welded pipe & tubes
HQ: Tenaris S.A.
Boulevard Royal 26
Luxembourg 2449
264 789-78

(G-10803)
MAVERICK TUBE CORPORATION
Also Called: Tenaris
8204 Frbanks N Houston Rd (77064-8406)
PHONE...................................713 937-1800
Jose Torres, *Branch Mgr*
Joel Smith, *Regional*
EMP: 200
SALES (corp-wide): 183.7K **Privately Held**
WEB: www.tenaris.com
SIC: 3541 Machine tools, metal cutting type
HQ: Maverick Tube Corporation
2200 West Loop S Ste 800
Houston TX 77027
713 767-4400

(G-10804)
MAXCO LLC
Also Called: Maxim Silencers
6545 N Eldridge Pkwy (77041-3507)
PHONE...................................832 554-0980
Dennis Nesloney,

◆ **EMP:** 51
SALES (est): 14.6MM
SALES (corp-wide): 21.4MM **Privately Held**
WEB: www.maximsilencers.com
SIC: 3443 Boilers: industrial, power, or marine
PA: Powertherm Co., Inc.
　　6545 N Eldridge Pkwy
　　Houston TX 77041
　　713 682-6777

(G-10805)
MAXISTRUT OF TEXAS INC
1209 W 17th St (77008-3439)
PHONE.....................................713 880-4228
EMP: 50
SQ FT: 30,000
SALES (est): 3.7MM
SALES (corp-wide): 16.7MM **Privately Held**
SIC: 3699 3429 Mfg Electrical Equipment/Supplies Mfg Hardware
PA: Channel-Track & Tube-Way Industries, Inc.
　　1209 W 17th St
　　Houston TX 77008
　　713 864-2551

(G-10806)
MAXUS ENERGY CORPORATION (DH)
10333 Richmond Ave # 1050 (77042-4176)
PHONE.....................................281 681-7200
John Enloe, *President*
Francisco Garcia-Tobar, *CFO*
▲ **EMP:** 25
SALES (est): 15.5MM **Privately Held**
WEB: www.maxuscorp.net
SIC: 1311 Crude petroleum production; natural gas production
HQ: Ypf Holdings, Inc.
　　10333 Richmond Ave
　　Houston TX 77042
　　281 681-7200

(G-10807)
MAYER ENTERPRISES INC
5522 Mitchelldale St (77092-7218)
PHONE.....................................281 498-2600
James W Mayer, *President*
Jeanette R Mayer, *Corp Secy*
Lisa M Lamb, *Vice Pres*
▲ **EMP:** 25
SQ FT: 5,000
SALES (est): 2.9MM **Privately Held**
SIC: 2759 5099 Thermography; rubber stamps

(G-10808)
MB DUSTLESS AIR FILTER CO LLC
6634 Mapleridge St (77081-4612)
PHONE.....................................210 653-6901
Mary Briggle, *President*
EMP: 11
SALES (corp-wide): 1.8MM **Privately Held**
WEB: www.dustlessair.com
SIC: 3585 Parts for heating, cooling & refrigerating equipment
PA: Mb Dustless Air Filter Company Llc
　　11515 N Weidner Rd
　　San Antonio TX 78233
　　210 653-5300

(G-10809)
MC DANIEL METALS INC
1318 Buschong St (77039-1101)
PHONE.....................................281 987-8400
Jim Luke, *President*
William McDaniel, *Principal*
Freda McDaniel, *Corp Secy*
EMP: 140
SQ FT: 85,000
SALES (est): 16MM **Privately Held**
WEB: www.mcdanielmetals.com
SIC: 3444 Metal ventilating equipment

(G-10810)
MCDERMOTT INTERNATIONAL INC (PA)
915 N Eldridge Pkwy (77079-2703)
PHONE.....................................281 588-6600
Gary P Luquette, *Ch of Bd*

David Dickson, *President*
Linh Austin, *Senior VP*
Gentry Brann, *Senior VP*
Mark Coscio, *Senior VP*
EMP: 277
SALES (est): 8.4B **Privately Held**
WEB: www.mcdermott-investors.com
SIC: 3443 1389 1623 8711 Fabricated plate work (boiler shop); construction; repair & dismantling services; oil field services; roustabout service; servicing oil & gas wells; pipeline construction; engineering services

(G-10811)
MCELVY VASQUEZ INC
Also Called: McElvy Media
3500 E T C Jester Blvd (77018-6039)
PHONE.....................................713 686-8494
Jonathan H McElvy, *President*
EMP: 11 **EST:** 2016
SALES (est): 405.2K **Privately Held**
WEB: www.theleadernews.com
SIC: 2741 Miscellaneous publishing

(G-10812)
MCV SALES CO L L C
Also Called: Wristband Connection
7522 Kensico Rd (77036-5722)
PHONE.....................................713 785-0088
Lee Hobson, *Sales Dir*
Victor Rey,
Cliff Adams,
Marcus Stern,
▲ **EMP:** 11 **Privately Held**
WEB: www.wristbandconnection.com
SIC: 2822 Silicone rubbers

(G-10813)
MCWHIRTER WOOD PRODUCTS INC
5815 Schuler St (77007-3055)
PHONE.....................................713 861-1437
EMP: 18
SQ FT: 50,000
SALES (est): 3MM **Privately Held**
WEB: www.mcwwoodreels.com
SIC: 2499 Spools, wood

(G-10814)
MCX GULF OF MEXICO LLC
800 Gessner Rd Ste 800 # 800 (77024-4488)
PHONE.....................................713 953-9292
EMP: 9
SALES: 1MM
SALES (corp-wide): 71B **Privately Held**
SIC: 1382 Oil/Gas Exploration Services
HQ: Mcx Exploration (Usa), Llc
　　5847 San Felipe St # 2525
　　Houston TX
　　713 953-9292

(G-10815)
MEDALLION OIL COMPANY INC
1407 Fannin St (77002-7613)
P.O. Box 1101 (77251-1101)
PHONE.....................................713 654-0144
Robert J Pilegge, *President*
Jereld McQueen, *Senior Partner*
Tony Pilegge, *Managing Dir*
Donald R Mc Lelland, *Vice Pres*
Harry Reay, *Vice Pres*
EMP: 14
SQ FT: 12,000
SALES (est): 1.2MM **Privately Held**
WEB: www.medgrp.com
SIC: 1311 1381 1382 Crude petroleum production; drilling oil & gas wells; oil & gas exploration services

(G-10816)
MEDC INTERNATIONAL
3413 N Sam Houston Pkwy W (77086-1489)
PHONE.....................................713 937-9772
Chris Simms, *Principal*
Martin Knox, *Principal*
Brian Walder, *Principal*
EMP: 99
SALES (est): 10.6MM **Privately Held**
WEB: www.coopermedc.com
SIC: 3669 Emergency alarms

(G-10817)
MEDCALF FABRICATION INC
1703 Hugh Rd (77067-1303)
PHONE.....................................281 893-0775
Ronald Medcalf, *President*
B Jeff Davis, *Treasurer*
EMP: 33
SQ FT: 17,000
SALES (est): 8.8MM **Privately Held**
WEB: www.medcalf-fab.com
SIC: 3441 Fabricated structural metal

(G-10818)
MEDEX SOUTH
8588 Katy Fwy Ste 348 (77024-1822)
PHONE.....................................713 838-1989
Jeremy Kraus,
EMP: 20 **EST:** 2011
SALES (est): 1.8MM **Privately Held**
WEB: www.medexsurgical.com
SIC: 3841 Surgical & medical instruments

(G-10819)
MEDICAL Z
10625 Richmond Ave (77042-4943)
PHONE.....................................210 681-7912
Fax: 210 521-6874
EMP: 18
SQ FT: 1,500
SALES: 130K **Privately Held**
SIC: 3842 Mfg Surgical Appliances/Supplies

(G-10820)
MEDINC OF TEXAS LP
1771 Crosspoint Ave (77054-3707)
PHONE.....................................713 979-4364
Bryan Osterhaus, *Managing Prtnr*
Jay Vaught, *Partner*
Eric White, *Business Mgr*
Roxanne Rico, *Opers Mgr*
Ryan Hubele, *Sales Staff*
EMP: 98
SALES (est): 3.6MM **Privately Held**
WEB: www.medinc.org
SIC: 3841 Surgical instruments & apparatus

(G-10821)
MEDPLAST GROUP INC (PA)
7865 Northcourt Rd # 100 (77040-5615)
PHONE.....................................480 553-6400
David Amrhein, *President*
Sk Tan, *General Mgr*
Carolyn Bourgoyne, *Controller*
▲ **EMP:** 20 **EST:** 1999
SALES (est): 456.1MM **Privately Held**
WEB: www.viantmedical.com
SIC: 3089 Injection molded finished plastic products

(G-10822)
MEGAPOWER INC
Also Called: Mega Compressor
7120 Brittmoore Rd # 410 (77041-3226)
PHONE.....................................832 415-6995
Shi-An Sun, *President*
▲ **EMP:** 9
SQ FT: 15,000
SALES (est): 2MM **Privately Held**
WEB: www.megacompressor.com
SIC: 3531 3559 Construction machinery; automotive related machinery

(G-10823)
MEGATREND DESIGNS INC
1250 Shotwell St (77020-7349)
PHONE.....................................713 675-8838
Michael Harris, *President*
Karen Schrock, *Office Mgr*
EMP: 15
SQ FT: 15,000
SALES (est): 1.9MM **Privately Held**
WEB: www.megatrenddesigns.com
SIC: 2431 Millwork

(G-10824)
MEGATRON INC
Also Called: Ktb USA
11241 Richmond Ave Ste E1 (77082-6657)
PHONE.....................................281 558-0034
Adrian J Guzman, *President*
Maria T Guzman, *Vice Pres*
Karen Licona, *Sales Staff*
Lars B Kitzinger, *Director*
◆ **EMP:** 28

SALES (est): 36.5MM **Privately Held**
SIC: 5063 7694 Motor controls, starters & relays: electric; electric motor repair

(G-10825)
MEL NORTHEY CO INC
303 Gulf Bank Rd (77037-2499)
PHONE.....................................281 445-3485
Melvin Northey, *President*
EMP: 16
SQ FT: 14,000
SALES (est): 2.7MM **Privately Held**
WEB: www.melnorthey.com
SIC: 3648 3444 Street lighting fixtures; mail (post office) collection or storage boxes, sheet metal

(G-10826)
MEMPHIS ELECTRONIC INC
1225 North Loop W Ste 820 (77008-1757)
PHONE.....................................713 600-6080
Peter Nitschke, *President*
Ken Heller, *General Mgr*
Nicholas Urbano, *Sales Staff*
Eden Craig, *Manager*
EMP: 9
SQ FT: 2,400
SALES: 14.5MM
SALES (corp-wide): 177.9K **Privately Held**
WEB: www.memphiselectronic.com
SIC: 3674 5065 Random access memory (RAM); electronic parts
HQ: Memphis Electronic Ag
　　Industriestr. 4-6
　　Oberursel (Taunus) 61440
　　617 290-350

(G-10827)
MEN OF CLOTH LP
Also Called: Champwear
10725 Sagetree Dr (77089-3332)
PHONE.....................................281 464-3141
EMP: 16
SQ FT: 5,000
SALES (est): 188.4K **Privately Held**
SIC: 2759 Commercial Printing

(G-10828)
MENARD INDUSTRIES LLC
Also Called: Menard's Railroad Materials
12052 Homestead Rd (77050-4508)
PHONE.....................................512 628-1058
Manny Scott Menard, *President*
Robert Menard, *Info Tech Mgr*
EMP: 9
SALES (est): 3.2MM **Privately Held**
WEB: www.menardsrail.com
SIC: 5088 2491 Railroad equipment & supplies; railroad cross-ties, treated wood

(G-10829)
MENTOR IMC (USA) INC
3 Riverway Ste 725 (77056-1961)
PHONE.....................................713 425-6307
John Richards, *President*
Georgia Manning, *Opers Staff*
EMP: 20
SALES (est): 1.3MM
SALES (corp-wide): 22.1MM **Privately Held**
WEB: www.mentorimcgroup.com
SIC: 1382 8742 Oil & gas exploration services; management consulting services
HQ: Mentor Imc Group Limited
　　Third Floor Suite E
　　London E14 9
　　207 536-1140

(G-10830)
MEPCO ENTERPRISES INC
11410 Dumas St (77034-3607)
P.O. Box 34340 (77234-4340)
PHONE.....................................713 943-9240
Peter Franks, *President*
EMP: 40
SALES (est): 1.4MM **Privately Held**
WEB: www.mepco-inc.com
SIC: 7699 7692 Industrial equipment services; welding repair

(G-10831)
MERC MEDICAL SUPPLY CO INC
10518 Kipp Way Dr Ste D (77099-2400)
PHONE.....................................713 270-4936

▲ = Import ▼=Export
◆ =Import/Export

George Lising, *President*
EMP: 13
SALES (est): 2MM **Privately Held**
WEB: www.mercmedicalsupply.com
SIC: 3841 5047 Surgical & medical instruments; electro-medical equipment

(G-10832)
MERCURY SIGNS AND DISPLAY LTD
12407 Sowden Rd (77080-2032)
PHONE..................................713 462-1068
Ted Hoffart, *Partner*
Travis S Hoffart, *General Ptnr*
Anton Hoffart, *Director*
EMP: 35 **EST:** 2001
SQ FT: 36,000
SALES (est): 4.5MM **Privately Held**
WEB: www.mercurysigns.com
SIC: 3993 Signs & advertising specialties

(G-10833)
MERICHEM COMPANY (PA)
5455 Old Spanish Trl (77023-5013)
PHONE..................................713 428-5000
Patrick J Hickey, *CEO*
Kenneth F Currie, *Ch of Bd*
Kendra Lee, *Ch of Bd*
Dayong Dong, *General Mgr*
Charles Zhu, *Principal*
◆ **EMP:** 128 **EST:** 1965
SQ FT: 6,000
SALES (est): 83.1MM **Privately Held**
WEB: www.merichem.com
SIC: 2819 Industrial inorganic chemicals

(G-10834)
MERICHEM COMPANY
5450 Old Spanish Trl (77023-5012)
PHONE..................................713 428-5201
John Foresman, *Business Mgr*
Scott Smetters, *Business Mgr*
Allen Thomas, *Engineer*
Maureen Marcon, *Asst Treas*
Barry Norris, *Branch Mgr*
EMP: 50
SALES (corp-wide): 83.1MM **Privately Held**
WEB: www.merichem.com
SIC: 3559 Chemical machinery & equipment
PA: Merichem Company
5455 Old Spanish Trl
Houston TX 77023
713 428-5000

(G-10835)
MERIDIAN BRICK LLC
Also Called: Boral Bricks Studio
1720 N Sam Houston Pkwy E (77032-3034)
PHONE..................................281 442-8400
Steve Young, *Manager*
EMP: 10
SQ FT: 15,000
SALES (corp-wide): 441MM **Privately Held**
WEB: www.meridianbrick.com
SIC: 5211 3251 Brick; brick & structural clay tile
PA: Meridian Brick Llc
6455 Shiloh Rd D
Alpharetta GA 30005
770 645-4500

(G-10836)
MERISOL LP
1914 Haden Rd (77015-6408)
PHONE..................................713 428-5652
Sandie Strickland, *Principal*
Gert Meij, *Project Mgr*
Doug Schwab, *Prdtn Mgr*
Marvin Lee, *Purch Mgr*
Paula Virgadamo, *Buyer*
▲ **EMP:** 28
SALES (est): 6.2MM **Privately Held**
WEB: www.sasolnorthamerica.com
SIC: 2869 Industrial organic chemicals

(G-10837)
MERIT MEDICAL SYSTEMS INC
Also Called: Interventional Products
14646 Kirby Dr (77047-2582)
PHONE..................................832 463-5100
Steven Kraver, *Assoc VP*
David Johnson, *Opers-Prdtn-Mfg*

Joel Marsh, *Engineer*
Peter Vander Wilt, *Engineer*
Spencer Wong, *Engineer*
EMP: 230
SQ FT: 10,000
SALES (corp-wide): 994.8MM **Publicly Held**
WEB: www.merit.com
SIC: 3841 5047 Surgical & medical instruments; hospital equipment & furniture
PA: Merit Medical Systems, Inc.
1600 W Merit Pkwy
South Jordan UT 84095
801 253-1600

(G-10838)
MESA TECHNOLOGIES LLC
5801 Dierker Dr (77041-6214)
PHONE..................................713 895-7000
Allen Shutt, *President*
EMP: 22
SALES (est): 1MM **Privately Held**
WEB: www.mesa-engr.com
SIC: 3577 Computer peripheral equipment

(G-10839)
MESA WIRELINE LLC
11700 Katy Fwy Ste 330 (77079-1218)
P.O. Box 357, Windsor CO (80550-0357)
PHONE..................................970 257-0458
Mark Brown, *CEO*
Kent Brown, *President*
Dan Baker, *CFO*
EMP: 40
SALES (est): 2.8MM
SALES (corp-wide): 221.1MM **Privately Held**
WEB: www.thewirelinegroup.com
SIC: 1389 Removal of condensate gasoline from field (gathering) lines; oil field services
HQ: Cutters Wireline Service Inc
920 S 1500 E
Vernal UT 84078
435 789-5556

(G-10840)
MESQUITE ENERGY INC (PA)
Also Called: Sanchez Energy
700 Milam St Ste 600 (77002-2862)
PHONE..................................713 756-2700
A R Sanchez Jr, *Ch of Bd*
Antonio R Sanchez III, *President*
Gregory B Kopel, *Exec VP*
Patricio D Sanchez, *Exec VP*
Kirsten A Hink, *Senior VP*
EMP: 26
SALES: 1B **Privately Held**
WEB: www.sanchezenergycorp.com
SIC: 1311 Crude petroleum & natural gas

(G-10841)
MET INTERNATIONAL TRDG CO INC
Also Called: Met Company
922 Hill Rd (77037-1808)
PHONE..................................281 445-5005
Sam Osmanagich, *President*
EMP: 100
SQ FT: 12,000
SALES (est): 16.1MM **Privately Held**
WEB: www.metcompany.net
SIC: 3444 Sheet metalwork

(G-10842)
META-TECH INDUSTRIES INC
8916 Spring Branch Dr (77080-7406)
PHONE..................................713 467-6544
Cassandra Khushf, *CEO*
Michael Khushf, *President*
EMP: 13
SQ FT: 9,500
SALES (est): 385K **Privately Held**
WEB: www.metatechinc.com
SIC: 3599 Machine shop, jobbing & repair

(G-10843)
METAL & MATERIALS PROC LLC (PA)
1513 W Dallas St Ste 200 (77019-4545)
PHONE..................................713 664-0050
Jeffrey L Vandersteeg, *Mng Member*
Christopher J Vandersteeg,
EMP: 9

SALES (est): 1.3MM **Privately Held**
WEB: www.metalandmaterials.com
SIC: 3356 Nickel

(G-10844)
METAL COATINGS CORP (PA)
3700 Dunvale Rd (77063-5714)
P.O. Box 630407 (77263-0407)
PHONE..................................713 977-0123
◆ **EMP:** 90
SQ FT: 80,000
SALES (est): 17.1MM **Privately Held**
WEB: www.metcoat.com
SIC: 3479 2851 Coating of metals & formed products; paints & allied products

(G-10845)
METAL CONSTRUCTION MTLS INC
Also Called: McM
7229 Jackrabbit Rd (77095-3515)
PHONE..................................281 550-8383
David B Hatcher II, *President*
Steve Seavall, *Principal*
Kenneth Backus, *Vice Pres*
Jason Seavall, *Vice Pres*
Ron Winans, *Sales Staff*
EMP: 18
SQ FT: 7,000
SALES (est): 12.8MM **Privately Held**
WEB: www.mcmcarport.com
SIC: 5039 3448 Prefabricated buildings; carports: prefabricated metal

(G-10846)
METAL IMPROVEMENT COMPANY LLC
9410 E Hardy Rd (77093-6629)
PHONE..................................713 691-0257
Mike Cummings, *Manager*
EMP: 18
SALES (corp-wide): 2.4B **Publicly Held**
WEB: www.cwst.com
SIC: 3398 Shot peening (treating steel to reduce fatigue)
HQ: Metal Improvement Company, Llc
80 E Rte 4 Ste 310
Paramus NJ 07652
201 843-7800

(G-10847)
METAL KITCHEN FABRICATORS INC
Also Called: Metal Kitchens
5121 April Ln (77092-3402)
PHONE..................................713 683-8375
Bobby Glen Propes, *President*
Sharon Propes, *Treasurer*
EMP: 10 **EST:** 1963
SQ FT: 26,000
SALES (est): 768.9K **Privately Held**
SIC: 3589 Commercial cooking & food-warming equipment

(G-10848)
METAL ZINC LLC
19300 Oil Center Blvd (77073-3353)
PHONE..................................281 449-2787
Ryan Walsh, *President*
EMP: 10
SALES (corp-wide): 3.5MM **Privately Held**
WEB: www.metalzincmfg.com
SIC: 3444 Sheet metalwork
PA: Metal Zinc, Llc
19408 Kenswick Dr
Humble TX 77338
832 252-9116

(G-10849)
METALLIC PRODUCTS CORPORATION
7777 Hollister St (77040-5470)
PHONE..................................713 856-9696
Coy Poret, *CEO*
Daryl Wendt, *Ch of Bd*
Travis Wendt, *President*
Michael Hairston, *Exec VP*
Sam Gray, *Vice Pres*
▼ **EMP:** 60 **EST:** 1968
SQ FT: 40,500
SALES: 9.5MM **Privately Held**
WEB: www.mpvent.com
SIC: 3446 3444 Louvers, ventilating; canopies, sheet metal

(G-10850)
METALLOY INC
5800 Heiser St (77087-4122)
P.O. Box 263107 (77207-3107)
PHONE..................................800 828-0500
Neale Dennis Sullivan, *President*
Sheila McKinney, *Data Proc Staff*
Cecil Griffin, *Admin Sec*
Pete Martinez, *Rector*
EMP: 19
SQ FT: 20,000
SALES (est): 4MM **Privately Held**
WEB: www.metalloyinc.com
SIC: 3356 3312 Nickel & nickel alloy pipe, plates, sheets, etc.; pipes, iron & steel

(G-10851)
METALPLATE GALVANIZING LP
10625 Needham St (77013-3209)
PHONE..................................713 672-9480
Kyle Davis, *Foreman/Supr*
Brett Hirsch, *Foreman/Supr*
Logan Price, *Foreman/Supr*
Marcus Palacios, *Plant Engr*
Olivia Salazar, *Human Res Dir*
EMP: 50
SALES (corp-wide): 95.2MM **Privately Held**
WEB: www.metalplate.com
SIC: 3479 Coating of metals & formed products
PA: Metalplate Galvanizing, L.P.
1120 39th St N
Birmingham AL 35234
205 595-4700

(G-10852)
METALS INCORPORATED
8411 Irvington Blvd (77022-3449)
P.O. Box 1713, Orlando FL (32802-1713)
PHONE..................................713 923-9491
Harry Caldwell, *Manager*
EMP: 15 **EST:** 1982
SALES (est): 3.2MM **Privately Held**
WEB: www.metalsinc.com
SIC: 3469 Metal stampings

(G-10853)
METFAB INC
314 Allen Genoa Rd (77017-3403)
P.O. Box 1804, Deer Park (77536-1804)
PHONE..................................713 472-3900
Sean Casey McGuire, *Principal*
Tracey McGuire, *Vice Pres*
Gene Williams, *Project Mgr*
Glenda G Davis, *Treasurer*
Devin Hanning, *Office Mgr*
EMP: 45
SQ FT: 15,600
SALES (est): 5MM **Privately Held**
WEB: www.metfabusa.com
SIC: 3441 Fabricated structural metal

(G-10854)
METRIX INSTRUMENT CO LP (PA)
8824 Fallbrook Dr (77064-4855)
PHONE..................................281 940-1802
Rob Schulz, *General Ptnr*
Neelima Mungali, *Regional Mgr*
Adriana Romero, *Marketing Staff*
Brandon Van Slyke, *Manager*
Steve Smith, *Director*
EMP: 88
SQ FT: 16,000
SALES (est): 15.5MM **Privately Held**
WEB: www.metrixvibration.com
SIC: 3825 3823 3829 Transducers for volts, amperes, watts, vars, frequency, etc.; industrial instrmnts msrmnt display/control process variable; measuring & controlling devices

(G-10855)
METRIX PMC/BETA (PA)
Also Called: PMC Beta
1711 Townhurst Dr (77043-2810)
PHONE..................................713 461-2131
Tim Winfrey, *CEO*
Ralph S Cass, *Ltd Ptnr*
Alfred A Finocchiaro, *Ltd Ptnr*
F Douglas Stover, *Ltd Ptnr*
EMP: 23
SQ FT: 9,000

SALES (est): 4.3MM **Privately Held**
SIC: 3829 3823 Measuring & controlling devices; industrial instrmnts msrmnt display/control process variable

(G-10856)
METRO READY MIX LTD COMPANY
5421 Schurmier Rd (77048-5715)
PHONE.................................713 991-6466
Felipe Padron,
EMP: 18
SALES (est): 3.5MM **Privately Held**
WEB: www.metroreadymix.net
SIC: 3273 Ready-mixed concrete

(G-10857)
METRO-TEX FABRICATORS INC
5107 Brookglen Dr (77017-5927)
P.O. Box 87705 (77287-7705)
PHONE.................................713 473-3900
Terry Delacerda, *President*
Steve G Lowe, *Vice Pres*
Larry Fischer, *Sales Staff*
Blaine St John, *Sales Staff*
Rachell Bowers, *Admin Asst*
EMP: 23
SQ FT: 12,000
SALES (est): 16.4MM **Privately Held**
WEB: www.metrotexfab.com
SIC: 5085 5084 3498 5051 Valves & fittings; industrial machinery & equipment; fabricated pipe & fittings; pipe & tubing, steel

(G-10858)
METTLE FILTRATION PRODUCTS LLC
8722 Pagewood Ln (77063-5720)
P.O. Box 630145 (77263-0145)
PHONE.................................713 609-9370
Lydia Kelly, *Accounts Mgr*
Michael A Poujol, *Mng Member*
EMP: 30
SALES (est): 118.4K **Privately Held**
WEB: www.mettlefiltration.com
SIC: 3496 Wire cloth & woven wire products; cylinder wire cloth

(G-10859)
MEWBOURNE OIL COMPANY
3303 Fm 1960 Rd W (77068-3615)
PHONE.................................281 580-6608
Jerome Lebo, *Manager*
EMP: 21
SALES (corp-wide): 458.1MM **Privately Held**
WEB: www.mewbourne.net
SIC: 1311 Crude petroleum production; natural gas production
HQ: Mewbourne Oil Company
3620 Old Bullard Rd
Tyler TX 75701
903 561-2900

(G-10860)
MEXICO PACIFIC LIMITED LLC
5444 Westheimr Rd # 1685 (77056-5343)
P.O. Box 19821 (77224-9821)
PHONE.................................713 425-6500
Page Maxson, *Ch of Bd*
Doug Shanda, *President*
Robert Kelly,
EMP: 10
SALES (est): 366.7K **Privately Held**
WEB: www.mexicopacificlimited.com
SIC: 1382 Oil & gas exploration services

(G-10861)
MEXSSUB INTERNATIONAL INC
Also Called: Coastels
7500 San Felipe St # 600 (77063-1790)
PHONE.................................713 278-2175
Jesus L Silva, *CEO*
Bruno Gabuzzi, *President*
Franco Silva, *Vice Pres*
EMP: 200
SQ FT: 2,000
SALES (est): 6MM **Privately Held**
WEB: www.mexssub.com
SIC: 1389 7021 Oil consultants; rooming & boarding houses

PA: Mexicana De Servicios Subacuaticos, S.A. De C.V.
Prol. Paseo De La Reforma No. 61
Piso 9-B-1 Of. 81
Ciudad De Mexico CDMX

(G-10862)
MEYER-SMITH INC (PA)
Also Called: Houston Gate
14239 Sommermeyer St (77041-6202)
PHONE.................................713 862-7339
Walter Meyer, *President*
Joe Ramirez, *Superintendent*
Russell Smith, *Corp Secy*
Sandy McCormack, *Sales Staff*
John Scott, *Sales Executive*
EMP: 19 EST: 1981
SQ FT: 15,000
SALES (est): 7.1MM **Privately Held**
WEB: www.meyersmithinc.com
SIC: 1731 7629 3446 Access control systems specialization; electrical repair shops; gates, ornamental metal

(G-10863)
MGC INC
6800 Sands Point Dr (77074-3730)
PHONE.................................713 800-7300
David Mahood, *CEO*
Wes Furgerson, *President*
EMP: 120
SALES (est): 30MM **Privately Held**
WEB: www.mgcinc.net
SIC: 2431 8734 Millwork; testing laboratories

(G-10864)
MHWIRTH INC
2201 N Sam Houston Pkwy W (77038-1211)
PHONE.................................281 371-2424
Pal L Skogerbo, *CTO*
Dag Stenevik, *Officer*
EMP: 12 **Privately Held**
WEB: www.mhwirth.com
SIC: 1381 Directional drilling oil & gas wells
HQ: Mhwirth Inc.
3010 Briarpark Dr Ste 500
Houston TX 77042
713 988-2002

(G-10865)
MICHAEL RAY
Also Called: Thermo Industrial
17070 Red Oak Dr Ste 211 (77090-2615)
PHONE.................................832 567-2507
Michael Ray, *Owner*
EMP: 9
SALES (est): 499.1K **Privately Held**
SIC: 3541 Machine tools, metal cutting type

(G-10866)
MICHEX INTERNATIONAL INC
3920 Cypress Creek Pkwy # 250 (77068-3533)
PHONE.................................281 397-7770
Ananda V Sagar, *President*
▲ **EMP:** 11
SQ FT: 2,000
SALES (est): 2.1MM **Privately Held**
SIC: 3714 5013 Motor vehicle parts & accessories; motor vehicle supplies & new parts

(G-10867)
MICRO PRECISION OF TEXAS INC (PA)
4413 Campbell Rd (77041-9102)
P.O. Box 40146 (77240-0146)
PHONE.................................713 462-7599
Greg Hummel, *President*
Horst E Hummel, *Chairman*
Chris Hummel, *Vice Pres*
Steven Hummel, *Vice Pres*
EMP: 13 EST: 1965
SQ FT: 9,300
SALES (est): 1.6MM **Privately Held**
WEB: www.microprecisionco.com
SIC: 3599 Machine shop, jobbing & repair

(G-10868)
MICROMED TECHNOLOGY INC
8965 Interchange Dr (77054-2513)
PHONE.................................713 838-9210

Clifford Zur Nieden, *CEO*
Dennis L Winans, *Principal*
Robert Benkowski, *COO*
EMP: 30
SQ FT: 20,000
SALES (est): 3.5MM **Privately Held**
WEB: www.micromedtech.com
SIC: 3841 Surgical & medical instruments
PA: Micromed Cardiovascular, Inc.
8965 Interchange Dr
Houston TX 77054

(G-10869)
MICROSEISMIC INC (PA)
10777 Westheimer Rd # 250 (77042-3455)
PHONE.................................713 781-2323
Gayle Anderson, *CEO*
Jeff Foster, *President*
Peter M Duncan, *Chairman*
Terry Jbeili, *COO*
William B Barker, *Vice Pres*
▲ **EMP:** 53
SALES (est): 27.3MM **Privately Held**
WEB: www.fracrx.com
SIC: 1382 Oil & gas exploration services

(G-10870)
MICROSOFT CORPORATION
2000 W S Houston Pkwy 3 (77042)
PHONE.................................832 252-4300
Mark Lunday, *Project Mgr*
Scott Moody, *Engineer*
John Papadopoulos, *Accounts Exec*
Kim Laursen, *Sales Staff*
Carla Waring, *Office Mgr*
EMP: 100
SALES (corp-wide): 143B **Publicly Held**
WEB: www.microsoft.com
SIC: 7372 Application computer software
PA: Microsoft Corporation
1 Microsoft Way
Redmond WA 98052
425 882-8080

(G-10871)
MIDCOAST ENERGY LLC (HQ)
Also Called: Enbridge Pipelines
1501 Mckinney St Ste 600 (77010-4010)
P.O. Box 128 (77001-0128)
PHONE.................................713 821-2000
Rob Bond, *CEO*
Trey Hall, *General Mgr*
Tommy Stone, *COO*
Terry L McGill, *Vice Pres*
Allan Schneider, *Vice Pres*
EMP: 200
SQ FT: 15,000
SALES (est): 1.2B
SALES (corp-wide): 1.2B **Privately Held**
WEB: www.midcoastenergy.com
SIC: 5172 1389 Gases, liquefied petroleum (propane); processing service, gas; gas field services
PA: Arclight Energy Partners Fund Vi, L.P.
200 Clarendon St Fl 55
Boston MA 02116
617 531-6300

(G-10872)
MIDCOAST ENERGY PARTNERS LP (DH)
1100 La St Ste 3300 (77002)
PHONE.................................713 821-2000
Laura Sayavedra, *President*
Midcoast Holdings, *General Ptnr*
Mark A Maki, *Senior VP*
EMP: 11
SALES: 1.9B
SALES (corp-wide): 3.7B **Privately Held**
WEB: www.midcoastpartners.com
SIC: 1311 4923 Crude petroleum & natural gas; gas transmission & distribution

(G-10873)
MIDSTREAM ENERGY HOLDINGS LLC (PA)
10370 Richmond Ave # 510 (77042-2551)
P.O. Box 421919 (77242-1919)
PHONE.................................713 403-6460
Andy Lang, *Mng Member*
Masoud Karaian,
Paul Oliphant,
Ron Richards,
EMP: 9

SALES (est): 1.9MM **Privately Held**
WEB: www.mehllc.com
SIC: 1382 Oil & gas exploration services

(G-10874)
MIDSTREAM HESS OPERATIONS LP (HQ)
1501 Mckinney St (77010-4010)
PHONE.................................713 496-4200
John B Hess, *Ch of Bd*
Hess M LP, *General Ptnr*
John A Gatling, *COO*
EMP: 18
SALES: 662.4MM
SALES (corp-wide): 848.3MM **Publicly Held**
WEB: www.hess.com
SIC: 4922 1321 Storage, natural gas; natural gas liquids; propane (natural) production
PA: Hess Midstream Lp
1501 Mckinney St
Houston TX 77010
713 496-4200

(G-10875)
MIDSTREAM NOBLE SERVICES LLC (DH)
1001 Noble Energy Way (77070-1435)
PHONE.................................281 872-3100
Terry R Gerhart, *CEO*
EMP: 21
SALES (est): 16.5MM
SALES (corp-wide): 146.5B **Publicly Held**
WEB: www.nblenergy.com
SIC: 1382 Oil & gas exploration services
HQ: Noble Energy, Inc.
1001 Noble Energy Way
Houston TX 77070
281 872-3100

(G-10876)
MIDWESTERN SERVICES INC
8501 South Loop E (77017-1933)
P.O. Box 1395, Snyder (79550-1395)
PHONE.................................325 573-6666
Philip Kimmel, *President*
Rene Beights, *Corp Secy*
Tom Kimmel, *Vice Pres*
EMP: 65
SQ FT: 5,600
SALES (est): 10MM **Privately Held**
WEB: www.midwesternservices.com
SIC: 1389 Oil field services

(G-10877)
MIGHTY WORKS SIGNAGE LLC
7016 Hemlock St (77087-1739)
PHONE.................................713 305-8355
Alex Marin,
Maria Marin,
EMP: 9 EST: 2001
SQ FT: 3,000
SALES (est): 776.5K **Privately Held**
WEB: www.marinsavannah98.wix.com
SIC: 7336 5046 3993 1799 Art design services; signs, electrical; signs & advertising specialties; sign installation & maintenance; sign painting & lettering shop

(G-10878)
MIKADA CABINETS LLC
3724 Creekmont Dr (77091-5412)
PHONE.................................713 681-6116
Kevin Horton, *President*
Bebbie Thompson, *COO*
Karen McGuinn, *Purch Mgr*
Kathleen Boarder, *CFO*
Debbie Thompson, *Human Resources*
EMP: 60 EST: 1965
SQ FT: 50,000
SALES (est): 8.2MM **Privately Held**
WEB: www.mikadacabinets.com
SIC: 2434 Wood kitchen cabinets

(G-10879)
MIL LTD (PA)
Also Called: Myrex Industries
1912 Buschong St (77039-1213)
PHONE.................................713 691-5200
Jim Moffa, *Partner*
R Kelly Boze, *Partner*
Dominic Bangsalud, *Project Mgr*
Jerry Garcia, *Project Mgr*
Donny McCollum, *Project Mgr*

▲ = Import ▼=Export
◆ =Import/Export

▲ **EMP:** 140
SALES (est): 50.2MM **Privately Held**
WEB: www.myrex.com
SIC: 3441 Fabricated structural metal

(G-10880)
MILAGRO EXPLORATION GP LLC
1301 Mckinney St Ste 500 (77010-3089)
PHONE..................713 750-1600
James G Ivey, *President*
Robert Larocque, *Partner*
Gary Mabie, *COO*
Robert Cavnar, *Mng Member*
Richard Piacenti,
EMP: 14
SALES (est): 10.2MM **Privately Held**
WEB: www.milagroexploration.com
SIC: 1382 Oil & gas exploration services

(G-10881)
MILESTONE METALS INC
113 W Lorino St (77037-1515)
PHONE..................281 448-9151
Robert McKee, *President*
Sam Garrett, *Project Mgr*
Edgar Garcia, *Opers Staff*
Samuel Garrett, *Sr Project Mgr*
Macy Archer, *Manager*
◆ **EMP:** 75
SQ FT: 3,000
SALES (est): 25.4MM **Privately Held**
WEB: www.milestonemetals.com
SIC: 3441 Fabricated structural metal

(G-10882)
MILLAR INC (PA)
6001 Gulf Fwy Ste A (77023-5425)
P.O. Box 230227 (77223-0227)
PHONE..................832 667-7000
Craig Thummel, *CEO*
Tim Daugherty, *President*
Huntley Millar, *Chairman*
Simon Malpas, *Vice Chairman*
Anne Stoker, *COO*
EMP: 92
SQ FT: 21,000
SALES (est): 15.2MM **Privately Held**
WEB: www.millar.com
SIC: 3841 Catheters

(G-10883)
MILLSAP WATERPROOFING INC
2414 Mcallister Rd (77092-8023)
PHONE..................713 956-6677
EMP: 68 EST: 1978
SQ FT: 4,000
SALES (est): 11.5MM **Privately Held**
WEB: www.millsapwaterproofing.com
SIC: 1799 3496 Waterproofing; miscellaneous fabricated wire products

(G-10884)
MILLSOURCE INC
4343 Kennedy Commerce Dr
(77032-3429)
PHONE..................281 372-0311
Steve Gatzemeyer, *Branch Mgr*
Marshall Hawkes, *Manager*
▲ **EMP:** 11 **Privately Held**
WEB: www.woodgrain.com
SIC: 2431 Moldings, wood: unfinished & prefinished
HQ: Millsource, Inc.
300 Nw 16th St
Fruitland ID 83619
208 452-3801

(G-10885)
MILSPEC WORKS LLC
11000 Stncliff Rd Ste 160 (77099)
PHONE..................281 530-7002
Michael R Murphy, *President*
Greg Haug, *Opers Mgr*
Michael Hardison, *Prdtn Mgr*
Mike Hardison, *Prdtn Mgr*
Lynne Lanza, *Purch Mgr*
EMP: 20
SQ FT: 15,680
SALES (est): 3.9MM **Privately Held**
WEB: www.milspecworks.com
SIC: 3672 8331 Printed circuit boards; skill training center

(G-10886)
MINERAL RESOURCE TECH INC (DH)
929 Gessner Rd Ste 1900 (77024-2317)
P.O. Box 1500 (77251-1500)
PHONE..................281 362-1060
Juan Carlos Herrera, *Ch of Bd*
John Heffernan, *President*
Hugh Shannonhouse, *President*
Gilberto Perez, *Director*
Leslie S White, *Director*
EMP: 15
SQ FT: 12,000
SALES (est): 25.7MM **Privately Held**
WEB: www.cemexusa.com
SIC: 5169 2819 Concrete additives; non-metallic compounds
HQ: Cemex, Inc.
10100 Katy Fwy Ste 300
Houston TX 77043
713 650-6200

(G-10887)
MINERGY LLC
12000 Westheimer Rd # 303 (77077-6681)
P.O. Box 7941 (77270-7941)
PHONE..................832 800-6336
Steve AMS, *President*
EMP: 612
SALES (est): 8.4MM **Privately Held**
SIC: 1382 Oil & gas exploration services

(G-10888)
MINORITY PRINT MEDIA
Also Called: Houston Style Magazine
2646 S Loop W Ste 600 (77054-2792)
P.O. Box 14035 (77221-4035)
PHONE..................713 748-6300
Francis Page, *Mng Member*
EMP: 14
SALES (est): 950K **Privately Held**
WEB: www.stylemagazine.com
SIC: 2711 Newspapers, publishing & printing

(G-10889)
MIRROR ACQUISITIONS LLC
Also Called: Mirror Industries
11510 Kilburn Rd (77055-1324)
P.O. Box 55328 (77255-5328)
PHONE..................713 686-4435
Gary Hamby,
EMP: 18
SALES (est): 1.1MM **Privately Held**
WEB: www.mirrorindustries.com
SIC: 3471 Chromium plating of metals or formed products

(G-10890)
MISTAWAY SYSTEMS INC
2121 Brittmoore Rd # 5200 (77043-2200)
PHONE..................713 468-6464
James Jackson, *President*
William Maslin, *Exec VP*
Scott Pinkerton, *Vice Pres*
Paul Gilbert, *Sales Staff*
▼ **EMP:** 10
SQ FT: 12,000
SALES (est): 5.3MM **Privately Held**
WEB: www.mistawaysystems.com
SIC: 3524 Lawn & garden equipment

(G-10891)
MITSUBSHI CTRPLLAR FRKLIFT AME (HQ)
Also Called: McFa
2121 W Sam Houston Pkwy N
(77043-2305)
PHONE..................713 365-1000
Kenneth Barina, *President*
Perry Ardito, *General Mgr*
Brett Carsson, *Principal*
Chris Skiba, *Principal*
Diana Urelius, *Principal*
◆ **EMP:** 900
SQ FT: 379,000
SALES: 851.2MM **Privately Held**
WEB: www.mcfa.com
SIC: 3537 5084 Forklift trucks; lift trucks & parts

(G-10892)
MITSUBSHI HVY INDS CMPRSR INTL
14888 Kirby Dr (77047-2589)
PHONE..................713 652-0300
Manabu Saga, *Ch of Bd*
Christopher Morgan, *General Mgr*
Kazuyoshi Tomita, *General Mgr*
Hitoshi Shinohara, *Exec VP*
Lawrence Rominger, *Vice Pres*
EMP: 147
SQ FT: 130,000
SALES (est): 110MM **Privately Held**
WEB: www.mhicompressor.com
SIC: 3511 Turbines & turbine generator sets
HQ: Mitsubishi Heavy Industries Compressor Corporation
4-6-22, Shimmachi, Kan-On, Nishi-Ku
Hiroshima HIR 733-0

(G-10893)
MITSUI E&P USA LLC
Also Called: Mepusa
1300 Post Oak Blvd Ste 18 (77056-3043)
PHONE..................713 960-0023
Kazuhiko Gomi, *President*
Tomohiro Sunada, *COO*
Steven Huddleston, *VP Bus Dvlpt*
Toshiyuki Ishigami, *CFO*
Greg Jallans, *Marketing Staff*
▲ **EMP:** 42
SALES (est): 2.7MM **Privately Held**
WEB: www.mitsui-ep.com
SIC: 1382 Oil & gas exploration services
PA: Mitsui & Co., Ltd.
1-2-1, Otemachi
Chiyoda-Ku TKY 100-0

(G-10894)
MJ STONE LLC
5855 Shurmard Dr (77092-1432)
PHONE..................832 887-3575
EMP: 10
SALES (est): 300K **Privately Held**
SIC: 3281 Mfg Cut Stone/Products

(G-10895)
MJS MANUFACTURING INC
6720 Theall Rd (77066-1216)
PHONE..................832 446-6440
Richard Jeremy Rogers, *Director*
Santiago Gomez Jr, *Director*
EMP: 16
SQ FT: 7,000
SALES: 8.4MM **Privately Held**
WEB: www.mjs-mfg.com
SIC: 3594 Fluid power pumps & motors

(G-10896)
MMLJ INC (PA)
Also Called: Cleanquip
5711 Schurmier Rd (77048-5700)
PHONE..................713 869-2227
Janet Lecompte, *President*
Rhonda Paul, *General Mgr*
Deronr Harrington, *Treasurer*
Jacob Gardner, *Mktg Coord*
Corina Lopez, *Administration*
▼ **EMP:** 14
SQ FT: 13,500
SALES (est): 3.8MM **Privately Held**
WEB: www.mmlj.com
SIC: 3569 Blast cleaning equipment, dustless

(G-10897)
MMS TRADERS LLC
903 Port Houston St (77029-2401)
PHONE..................832 433-7948
Murad Sadruddin, *Principal*
▼ **EMP:** 12 EST: 2012
SALES (est): 1.4MM **Privately Held**
SIC: 3356 Nonferrous rolling & drawing

(G-10898)
MOBIL PRODUCING TEXAS AND NM
9 Greenway Plz 2700 (77046-0905)
PHONE..................713 871-5000
Fines F Martin, *President*
W L Wende, *Controller*
EMP: 2400
SQ FT: 220,000
SALES (est): 25.6MM
SALES (corp-wide): 264.9B **Publicly Held**
SIC: 1311 Crude petroleum & natural gas
PA: Exxon Mobil Corporation
5959 Las Colinas Blvd
Irving TX 75039
972 940-6000

(G-10899)
MOBIL STEEL INTERNATIONAL INC
13830 S Wayside Dr (77048-5210)
PHONE..................713 991-0450
Leonard A Bedell, *President*
Clark A Gunderson, *Principal*
Ray Guillory, *Treasurer*
▲ **EMP:** 41
SQ FT: 80,000
SALES (est): 11.6MM **Privately Held**
WEB: www.mobilsteel.com
SIC: 3441 Fabricated structural metal

(G-10900)
MOBILE MINI INC
7020 Old Katy Rd (77024-2110)
PHONE..................480 894-6311
Jim Brown, *Manager*
EMP: 100
SALES (corp-wide): 1B **Publicly Held**
WEB: www.mobilemini.com
SIC: 3444 3412 Metal housings, enclosures, casings & other containers; metal barrels, drums & pails
HQ: Mobile Mini, Inc.
4646 E Van Buren St # 400
Phoenix AZ 85008
480 894-6311

(G-10901)
MODA MIDSTREAM LLC
1000 Louisiana St # 7100 (77002-5005)
PHONE..................832 930-4838
Bo McCall, *Exec VP*
Bob Headlee, *Vice Pres*
Luis Perez, *Vice Pres*
Ken Owen,
Jonathan Ackerman,
EMP: 14
SALES (est): 7.4MM **Privately Held**
WEB: www.modamidstream.com
SIC: 1382 Oil & gas exploration services

(G-10902)
MODEC INTERNATIONAL INC (DH)
15011 Katy Fwy Ste 500 (77094-0010)
PHONE..................281 529-8100
Yuji Kozai, *President*
Takahiro Osako, *General Mgr*
Puneet Sharma, *General Mgr*
Norihisa Fukuda, *Principal*
Ricky Alan Hall, *Principal*
EMP: 300 EST: 1999
SQ FT: 168,768
SALES (est): 316.1MM **Privately Held**
WEB: www.modec.com
SIC: 8711 3731 Professional engineer; commercial cargo ships, building & repairing

(G-10903)
MODENA OPERATING LLC
2603 Augusta Dr Ste 430 (77057-5677)
PHONE..................713 592-5000
James C Row, *CEO*
Anthony Hamilton, *Ch of Bd*
EMP: 18
SQ FT: 4,380
SALES (est): 1.4MM **Privately Held**
SIC: 1382 Oil & gas exploration services
PA: Cycliq Group Ltd
Suite 1
Subiaco WA 6008

(G-10904)
MODERN PRINT SHOP INC
2728 Columbia St (77008-2234)
PHONE..................713 861-7262
James Q Knetsar, *President*
Ronald B Knetsar, *Vice Pres*
EMP: 9 EST: 1950
SALES (est): 900K **Privately Held**
WEB: www.modernprintshop.com
SIC: 2752 Commercial printing, offset

(G-10905)
MODERN WELDING CO TEXAS INC
715 Sakowitz St (77020-8021)
P.O. Box 15215 (77220-5215)
PHONE.............................713 675-4211
John W Jones, *President*
Wayne Killingsworth, *Vice Pres*
Ronald Ecleberry, *Vice Pres*
Randy Hill, *Vice Pres*
James E Jones, *Vice Pres*
EMP: 38
SALES (est): 8MM
SALES (corp-wide): 131.1MM **Privately Held**
WEB: www.modweldco.com
SIC: 3714 3443 Motor vehicle parts & accessories; tanks, lined: metal plate
PA: Modern Welding Company, Inc.
2880 New Hartford Rd
Owensboro KY 42303
270 685-4400

(G-10906)
MOLECULIN BIOTECH INC
5300 Memorial Dr Ste 950 (77007-8274)
PHONE.............................713 300-5160
Walter V Klemp, *Ch of Bd*
Jonathan P Foster, *CFO*
Joan Smith, *Controller*
Rachel Powalisz, *Accountant*
Cynthia Abbate, *Director*
EMP: 13
SQ FT: 2,333
SALES (est): 1.6MM **Privately Held**
WEB: www.moleculin.com
SIC: 2834 Pharmaceutical preparations

(G-10907)
MOLLOY CORPORATION
Also Called: Printing X-Press
9000 Southwest Fwy Ste 320 (77074)
PHONE.............................713 771-9485
John C Molloy, *President*
Tad Molloy, *Vice Pres*
Dorothy Molloy, *Admin Sec*
EMP: 27 EST: 1980
SQ FT: 8,400
SALES (est): 5MM **Privately Held**
WEB: www.printing-x-press.com
SIC: 2752 8742 2759 2791 Commercial printing, offset; industry specialist consultants; commercial printing; typesetting

(G-10908)
MOMENTUM CHEMICAL LLC
6 Tokeneke Trl (77024-6727)
PHONE.............................713 266-1042
Tamara M Johnson, *Principal*
EMP: 9
SALES (est): 1MM **Privately Held**
WEB: www.momentumchemical.com
SIC: 2869 Laboratory chemicals, organic

(G-10909)
MOMENTUM PLASTICS LLC
5631 Old Clinton Rd (77020-7345)
PHONE.............................713 678-7741
Pi-Chee Chen, *President*
Franky Wong, *Plant Mgr*
John Fresita,
▲ EMP: 150 EST: 1999
SALES (est): 22MM **Privately Held**
WEB: www.momentumplastics.com
SIC: 3089 2673 Plastic containers, except foam; bags: plastic, laminated & coated

(G-10910)
MONDELEZ GLOBAL LLC
Also Called: Nabisco
6803 Almeda Rd (77021-2007)
PHONE.............................713 749-0400
Anthony F Muscarello, *Branch Mgr*
Lelon Ashworth, *Manager*
Greg Hayes, *Manager*
Will Price, *MIS Mgr*
EMP: 700 **Publicly Held**
WEB: www.mondelezinternational.com
SIC: 2052 Cookies & crackers
HQ: Mondelez Global Llc
905 W Fulton Market
Chicago IL 60607
847 943-4000

(G-10911)
MONMOUTH REAL ESTATE INV CORP
16211 Air Center Blvd (77032-5119)
P.O. Box 3186 (77253-3186)
PHONE.............................281 784-4360
Richard Rodriguez, *Manager*
J Sanders, *Info Systems*
EMP: 250
SALES (corp-wide): 167.8MM **Privately Held**
WEB: www.mreic.reit
SIC: 3533 Oil field machinery & equipment
PA: Monmouth Real Estate Investment Corporation
101 Crwfrds Crnr Rd Ste 1
Holmdel NJ 07733
732 577-9996

(G-10912)
MONTEGA LTD
Also Called: Tortilleria La Campera
1370 E 40th St 3 (77022-4150)
PHONE.............................713 692-1400
Rafael Ortega, *Partner*
EMP: 60
SQ FT: 30,000
SALES (est): 7.4MM **Privately Held**
WEB: www.tortillerialacampera.com
SIC: 2099 Tortillas, fresh or refrigerated

(G-10913)
MONTEREY OIL & GAS CORPORATION
3737 Buffalo Speedway (77098-3738)
PHONE.............................832 985-8723
Thomas W Sloop, *President*
EMP: 27
SQ FT: 6,737
SALES (est): 529.5K **Privately Held**
WEB: www.montereyoilandgas.com
SIC: 1311 Crude petroleum & natural gas

(G-10914)
MONTGOMERY MACHINE COMPANY INC
1005 Mae Dr (77015-4806)
PHONE.............................713 453-6381
▲ EMP: 62
SQ FT: 48,000
SALES (est): 9.6MM
SALES (corp-wide): 1B **Publicly Held**
WEB: www.montgomerymachine.com
SIC: 7692 3599 Welding repair; machine shop, jobbing & repair
HQ: Oil States Industries, Inc.
7701 S Cooper St
Arlington TX 76001

(G-10915)
MONTOYA BUILDING SERVICES INC
1400 Brdfeld Blvd Ste 200 (77084)
P.O. Box 752342 (77275-2342)
PHONE.............................713 367-0231
Damarys Montoya, *President*
EMP: 20 EST: 2016
SALES (est): 2.7MM **Privately Held**
SIC: 3523 1799 7349 2842 Cleaning machines for fruits, grains & vegetables; cleaning new buildings after construction; building & office cleaning services; janitorial service, contract basis; specialty cleaning preparations; specialty cleaning & sanitation preparations

(G-10916)
MONUMENT CHEMICAL HOUSTON LLC (HQ)
Also Called: Haltermann Solutions
16717 Jacintoport Blvd (77015-6544)
P.O. Box 429, Channelview (77530-0429)
PHONE.............................281 452-5951
Wayne Petersen, *President*
Dr Rainer Potthast, *Vice Pres*
◆ EMP: 205
SQ FT: 10,000
SALES (est): 83.1MM **Privately Held**
WEB: www.haltermannsolutions.com
SIC: 2824 2869 Organic fibers, noncellulosic; fuels

(G-10917)
MONUMENT CHEMICAL HOUSTON LLC
15635 Jacintoport Blvd (77015-6534)
PHONE.............................832 376-2201
Wayne Peterson, *President*
EMP: 17 **Privately Held**
WEB: www.haltermannsolutions.com
SIC: 2869 2824 Fuels; organic fibers, non-cellulosic
HQ: Monument Chemical Houston, Llc
16717 Jacintoport Blvd
Houston TX 77015
281 452-5951

(G-10918)
MONUMENT CHEMICALS INC
16717 Jacintoport Blvd (77015-6544)
PHONE.............................281 452-5951
Dwight Brown, *Senior Buyer*
Dave Narayan, *Manager*
Christophe Vergote, *Manager*
Nancy Barrientos,
EMP: 14
SALES (est): 2.7MM **Privately Held**
WEB: www.monumentchemical.com
SIC: 2813 Industrial gases

(G-10919)
MOORE FABRICATION INC
901 Bay Area Blvd (77058-2603)
PHONE.............................713 643-7477
Bradford H Freyer, *CEO*
William I Moore III, *President*
Kerry Krumbeck, *Vice Pres*
Cory Legitt, *Production*
Wendell Jolly, *Sales Staff*
EMP: 32
SALES (est): 6.6MM **Privately Held**
WEB: www.moorefabrication.com
SIC: 3089 Injection molding of plastics

(G-10920)
MOREFIELD DEVELOPMENT INC (PA)
Also Called: North Side Electric Motors
2518 Mcallister Rd (77092-8021)
PHONE.............................713 869-2111
William B Morefield III, *President*
Vona C Morefield, *Corp Secy*
William B Morefield IV, *Vice Pres*
William Morefield, *Vice Pres*
Brian Meyers, *Electrical Engi*
▲ EMP: 28
SQ FT: 18,000
SALES (est): 6.6MM **Privately Held**
WEB: www.northsideelectricmotors.com
SIC: 7694 Electric motor repair; rewinding services

(G-10921)
MORGAN KINDER TREATING LP
1001 La St Ste 1000 (77002)
PHONE.............................713 369-8515
Duane Kokinda, *President*
Bill Stokes, *Vice Pres*
EMP: 100
SALES (est): 85.7MM **Publicly Held**
WEB: www.kindermorgantreating.com
SIC: 2911 Gases & liquefied petroleum gases
PA: Kinder Morgan Inc
1001 La St Ste 1000
Houston TX 77002

(G-10922)
MORRIS EXPORT CRATING COMPANY (PA)
Also Called: Morris Export Services
1225 Mccarty St (77029-4141)
P.O. Box 3003 (77253-3003)
PHONE.............................713 675-9101
Terry Moritz, *President*
James M Morris, *Vice Pres*
Jimmy Morris, *Vice Pres*
Ned Sims, *Opers Spvr*
Gary J Baumbach, *CFO*
◆ EMP: 69
SQ FT: 200,000
SALES (est): 10.1MM **Privately Held**
WEB: www.morrisexport.com
SIC: 2441 4783 Nailed wood boxes & shook; packing goods for shipping; crating goods for shipping

(G-10923)
MORRIS MATERIAL HANDLING INC
Also Called: Konecranes America
7300 Chippewa Blvd (77086-3231)
PHONE.............................281 445-2225
Jo Anne Nagel, *General Mgr*
Brett Lawson, *District Mgr*
Antti Vanhatalo, *Vice Pres*
Chuck Harrell, *Site Mgr*
Bing Tian, *Buyer*
EMP: 150
SALES (corp-wide): 3.6B **Privately Held**
WEB: www.konecranes.com
SIC: 3536 Cranes, overhead traveling
HQ: Morris Material Handling, Inc.
4401 Gateway Blvd
Springfield OH 45502
937 525-5520

(G-10924)
MORRISON ENERGY GROUP LLC
16285 Park Ten Pl Ste 100 (77084-5069)
PHONE.............................713 344-9233
Chad Morrison, *Mng Member*
EMP: 1000
SALES (est): 20.4MM **Privately Held**
WEB: www.morrisonenergy.com
SIC: 1389 Oil field services

(G-10925)
MOSELEY MACHINE COMPANY INC (PA)
3608 Polk St (77003-4842)
PHONE.............................713 228-1382
EMP: 15
SQ FT: 13,000
SALES (est): 1.1MM **Privately Held**
SIC: 3599 Machine shop, jobbing & repair

(G-10926)
MOTOROLA SOLUTIONS INC
9800 Richmond Ave (77042-4561)
PHONE.............................713 783-6400
EMP: 15
SALES (corp-wide): 7.8B **Publicly Held**
WEB: www.motorolasolutions.com
SIC: 3663 Radio & TV communications equipment
PA: Motorola Solutions, Inc.
500 W Monroe St Ste 4400
Chicago IL 60661
847 576-5000

(G-10927)
MOUNTAIN PRODUCTS LP (PA)
Also Called: Mountain Commercial Graphics
12922 Hempstead Rd (77040-6508)
PHONE.............................713 895-1350
William M Hartman, *Partner*
Tonja Griffin, *General Mgr*
Randall Norris, *General Ptnr*
Cindy Lerma, *Purch Mgr*
Pat Blair, *VP Sales*
EMP: 67
SALES (est): 17MM **Privately Held**
WEB: www.mountain-cg.com
SIC: 2759 Screen printing

(G-10928)
MOVEMENT INDUSTRIES CORP
6829 Flintlock Rd (77040-4322)
PHONE.............................713 849-1300
Linh Nguyen, *CEO*
Derek Mumford, *Vice Pres*
EMP: 10
SALES (est): 33.8K **Privately Held**
SIC: 7389 3592 3561 3599 Business services

(G-10929)
MPACT STRATEGIC CONSULTING LLC
Also Called: Mpact Construction Services
4635 Suthwest Fwy Ste 700 (77027)
P.O. Box 301248 (77230-1248)
PHONE.............................866 361-7611
EMP: 32

▲ = Import ▼ =Export
◆ =Import/Export

SALES (est): 769.9K **Privately Held**
WEB: www.mpact-consulting.com
SIC: **8748** 8742 1629 1542 Business consulting; management consulting services; dams, waterways, docks & other marine construction; institutional building construction; construction, repair & dismantling services; sidewalk construction; airport runway construction

(G-10930)
MPR PRODUCTS INC (PA)
6124 Highway 6 N 119 (77084-1304)
PHONE....................................713 493-0252
Mufaddal Motiwala, *President*
Aniqua Motiwala, *Admin Sec*
EMP: 10
SALES (est): 764.3K **Privately Held**
WEB: www.mprproducts.com
SIC: **2431** Doors, wood

(G-10931)
MPW CORPORATION
Also Called: Alpha Mar-Imw
5814 Heffernan St (77087-4116)
PHONE....................................713 640-2700
Nikita Papadacos, *President*
◆ EMP: 16
SQ FT: 6,500
SALES (est): 3.1MM **Privately Held**
WEB: www.alphamar.us
SIC: **3731** 3441 4499 Shipbuilding & repairing; fabricated structural metal for ships; ship cleaning

(G-10932)
MPW ENTERPRISES LLC
Also Called: Metro Plex Wood
7501 Schneider St (77093-8527)
P.O. Box 21276 (77226-1276)
PHONE....................................713 671-9560
Steven D Cela, *President*
George Cela,
James F Eubank II,
EMP: 35
SQ FT: 60,000
SALES (est): 5.5MM **Privately Held**
WEB: www.metroplexwood.com
SIC: **2448** Pallets, wood

(G-10933)
MRS JOHN L STRONG & CO LLC
Also Called: Strong Ventures
3245 Ella Lee Ln (77019-5923)
PHONE....................................212 838-3775
Joe Lewis, *President*
Dylan Bergen, *Sales Staff*
Nanette Brown,
EMP: 14
SALES (est): 1.4MM **Privately Held**
WEB: www.mrsstrong.com
SIC: **2754** Stationery: gravure printing

(G-10934)
MUD KING PRODUCTS INC
Also Called: Mud King
15211 Woodham Dr (77073-6035)
PHONE....................................281 645-4158
Djoni L Handoyo, *President*
Nigel Brassington, *Vice Pres*
◆ EMP: 24
SALES (est): 2.1MM **Privately Held**
WEB: www.mudkingproducts.com
SIC: **1389** Oil field services

(G-10935)
MUILENBURG PROSTHETICS INC
3900 La Branch St (77004-4046)
P.O. Box 8313 (77288-8313)
PHONE....................................713 524-3949
Ted Muilenburg, *President*
Paula Marchisio, *General Mgr*
Loretta Muilenburg, *Treasurer*
Amelia S Rosetta,
Mary Torres, *Admin Asst*
EMP: 10 EST: 1948
SQ FT: 10,000
SALES (est): 1.6MM **Privately Held**
WEB: www.mpihouston.com
SIC: **3842** 7699 5999 Limbs, artificial; orthopedic appliances; medical equipment repair, non-electric; artificial limbs

(G-10936)
MULLINS MACHINE & MFG CO
17214 Ash Butte Dr (77090-2202)
PHONE....................................713 672-0451
Allen Caradine, *President*
Myra Luinstra, *Vice Pres*
Dorris Maggio, *Admin Sec*
EMP: 18 EST: 1948
SALES (est): 2.7MM **Privately Held**
SIC: **3599** Machine shop, jobbing & repair

(G-10937)
MULTI-CHEM INC
Also Called: Houston Technology Center
3000 N Sam Houston Pkwy E
(77032-3219)
PHONE....................................281 442-1222
James B Archer, *President*
Randel Paulus, *General Mgr*
Jorge Velarde, *Vice Pres*
Lois Archer, *Admin Sec*
◆ EMP: 60
SALES (est): 1MM **Privately Held**
WEB: www.halliburton.com
SIC: **1389** Oil field services

(G-10938)
MULTI-CHEM GROUP LLC (HQ)
3000 N Sam Houston Pkwy E P
(77032-3219)
PHONE....................................281 871-4000
David J Lesar, *President*
James Archer, *Vice Pres*
Jon Grottis, *Treasurer*
▲ EMP: 40
SQ FT: 64,000
SALES (est): 1.3B **Publicly Held**
WEB: www.halliburton.com
SIC: **1389** Oil field services; servicing oil & gas wells

(G-10939)
MULTISPORTS INC
Also Called: Get Rx'd
2612 Mckinney St (77003-3728)
PHONE....................................713 460-8188
Brucie Chen, *President*
Jong-Shyang Lian, *Manager*
◆ EMP: 10
SQ FT: 20,000
SALES (est): 1.8MM **Privately Held**
WEB: www.getrxd.com
SIC: **3949** 5091 Exercise equipment; exercise equipment

(G-10940)
MUREX PETROLEUM CORPORATION (PA)
363 N Sam Houston Pkwy E # 200
(77060-2437)
P.O. Box 7, Humble (77347-0007)
PHONE....................................281 590-3313
Waldo J Ackerman, *President*
Donald A Kessel, *Senior VP*
Rob Foss, *Vice Pres*
Glenn Kemp, *Vice Pres*
Jason Leeper, *Vice Pres*
EMP: 50
SQ FT: 32,798
SALES: 32.5MM **Privately Held**
WEB: www.murexpetroleum.com
SIC: **1382** Oil & gas exploration services

(G-10941)
MURPHY EXPLORATION & PROD CO
9805 Katy Fwy Ste G200 (77024-1269)
PHONE....................................281 675-9000
EMP: 10
SALES (corp-wide): 2.8B **Publicly Held**
WEB: www.murphyoilcorp.com
SIC: **1382** Oil & gas exploration services
HQ: Murphy Exploration & Production Company
300 E Peach St
El Dorado AR 71730
870 862-6411

(G-10942)
MURPHY EXPLORATION PROD - USA (HQ)
9805 Katy Fwy Ste G200 (77024-1269)
PHONE....................................281 675-9000
R W Jenkins, *President*
Keith Caldwell, *Vice Pres*

Steven A Coss, *Vice Pres*
Miendy K West, *Treasurer*
Bartlett Chris, *Technician*
◆ EMP: 312 EST: 1953
SQ FT: 204,000
SALES (est): 1.4B
SALES (corp-wide): 2.8B **Publicly Held**
WEB: www.murphyoilcorp.com
SIC: **1382** 1311 Oil & gas exploration services; crude petroleum & natural gas production
PA: Murphy Oil Corporation
300 E Peach St
El Dorado AR 71730
870 862-6411

(G-10943)
MURPHY WALL PRODUCTS INTL INC
Also Called: Murco Wall Products
919 E Rittenhouse St (77076-1615)
PHONE....................................713 694-8365
Ron Berno, *Manager*
EMP: 20
SALES (corp-wide): 21.5MM **Privately Held**
WEB: www.murcowall.com
SIC: **3272** 3275 Wall & ceiling squares, concrete; gypsum products
PA: Murphy Wall Products International, Inc.
201 Ne 21st St
Fort Worth TX 76164
800 446-7124

(G-10944)
MURRAY BUILDING & CRANE INDS
Also Called: Murray Building Crane Inds
2218 Pech Rd (77055-1127)
P.O. Box 800334 (77280-0334)
PHONE....................................713 464-6506
EMP: 100
SALES (est): 4.8MM **Privately Held**
SIC: **2452** 3441 Mfg Prefabricated Wood Buildings Structural Metal Fabrication

(G-10945)
MW INDUSTRIES INC
2400 Farrell Rd (77073-4004)
PHONE....................................281 233-0448
Peter Mess, *Principal*
Andy Hees, *Vice Pres*
Scott Solomon, *Vice Pres*
Rick Evangelista, *VP Sales*
Ben Petru, *VP Sales*
EMP: 40
SQ FT: 20,000
SALES (est): 6MM **Privately Held**
WEB: www.mwindustries.com
SIC: **3452** 3544 Bolts, metal; nuts, metal; special dies & tools

(G-10946)
MYKYTYN ENTERPRISE INC
12539 Hammill Path Dr (77066-3450)
PHONE....................................281 866-9263
Rosie Herman, *President*
EMP: 13
SALES (est): 1.4MM **Privately Held**
WEB: www.oneminutemanicure.com
SIC: **3999** 5087 Barber & beauty shop equipment; beauty salon & barber shop equipment & supplies

(G-10947)
N & P SIGN SYSTEM INC
Also Called: Sign System Tech
7590 Fallbrook Dr Ste 1 (77086-2501)
PHONE....................................281 444-9535
Moe Nahidi, *President*
Heidi Nahidi, *Vice Pres*
EMP: 17
SQ FT: 11,846
SALES (est): 1.9MM **Privately Held**
WEB: www.npsign.com
SIC: **3993** Signs & advertising specialties

(G-10948)
N M L INC OF TEXAS
1221 Lamar St Ste 1175 (77010-3051)
PHONE....................................713 753-1448
EMP: 63
SQ FT: 120,000

SALES (est): 3.7MM
SALES (corp-wide): 537.5MM **Privately Held**
SIC: **1311** Crude Petroleum/Natural Gas Production
PA: Torch Energy Advisors Incorporated
1331 Lamar St Ste 1450
Houston TX 77010
713 650-1246

(G-10949)
N-FAB INC
12302 Shiloh Church Rd (77066-2002)
PHONE....................................281 880-6322
William Reminder, *President*
Kelly Kneifl, *COO*
Matt Wautelet, *Plant Mgr*
Jim Bresingham, *CFO*
Maria Zwas, *Admin Sec*
EMP: 12
SALES (est): 3MM
SALES (corp-wide): 280.9MM **Privately Held**
WEB: www.n-fab.com
SIC: **3441** Fabricated structural metal
HQ: Tectum Holdings, Inc.
5400 Data Ct
Ann Arbor MI 48108
734 677-0444

(G-10950)
NABORS CORPORATE SERVICES INC
Also Called: U.S. Completion & Production
515 W Greens Rd Ste 1100 (77067-4511)
PHONE....................................281 874-0035
Anthony G Petrello, *President*
Woody Gros, *President*
Denny Smith, *President*
Arnold Davila, *General Mgr*
Clyde Loll, *General Mgr*
EMP: 200
SQ FT: 50,000
SALES (est): 57.6MM **Privately Held**
WEB: www.nabors.com
SIC: **1389** 1381 Servicing oil & gas wells; drilling oil & gas wells
HQ: Nabors Industries, Inc.
515 W Greens Rd Ste 1200
Houston TX 77067
281 874-0035

(G-10951)
NABORS DRILLING INTERNATIONAL
515 W Greens Rd Ste 1200 (77067-4536)
P.O. Box 672008 (77267-2008)
PHONE....................................281 775-8506
Anthony G Petrello, *CEO*
EMP: 50 EST: 2010
SALES (est): 9.8MM **Privately Held**
WEB: www.nabors.com
SIC: **1389** Oil field services

(G-10952)
NABORS DRILLING TECH USA INC (DH)
515 W Greens Rd Ste 1200 (77067-4536)
PHONE....................................281 874-0035
Randy Clark, *President*
Larry Heidt, *President*
Joe Hudson, *Partner*
Robert Guillory, *Vice Pres*
Clyde Hebert, *Vice Pres*
◆ EMP: 150 EST: 1993
SQ FT: 15,000
SALES (est): 2.1B **Privately Held**
WEB: www.nabors.com
SIC: **1381** Directional drilling oil & gas wells
HQ: Nabors Industries, Inc.
515 W Greens Rd Ste 1200
Houston TX 77067
281 874-0035

(G-10953)
NABORS INDUSTRIES INC (HQ)
515 W Greens Rd Ste 1200 (77067-4599)
PHONE....................................281 874-0035
Eugene M Isenberg, *CEO*
Anthony G Petrello, *Ch of Bd*
Johnny Tudor, *Superintendent*
Murray Nabors, *Principal*
Kenneth Howell, *District Mgr*
◆ EMP: 250
SQ FT: 57,550

SALES (est): 7.6B Privately Held
WEB: www.naborsindustries.com
SIC: 1381 1389 3533 Drilling oil & gas
wells; servicing oil & gas wells; oil field
machinery & equipment

(G-10954)
**NABORS INTERNATIONAL INC
(DH)**
Also Called: Nabors Drilling International
515 W Greens Rd Ste 600 (77067-4510)
PHONE................................281 874-0035
Anthony G Petrello, CEO
Jose Cadena, Vice Pres
Derryl W Cleaveland, Vice Pres
Christopher Papouras, Vice Pres
Bob Supopin, Vice Pres
◆ EMP: 50 EST: 1947
SALES (est): 1.9B Privately Held
WEB: www.nabors.com
SIC: 1381 7353 Drilling oil & gas wells; oil
well drilling equipment, rental or leasing
HQ: Nabors Industries, Inc.
515 W Greens Rd Ste 1200
Houston TX 77067
281 874-0035

(G-10955)
**NABORS OFFSHORE
CORPORATION (DH)**
515 W Greens Rd Ste 1200 (77067-4536)
PHONE................................281 874-0406
Jerry C Shanklin, President
Ronnie L Gaspard, Vice Pres
Daniel McLachlin, Vice Pres
Lonnie Mills, Vice Pres
Earney White, Vice Pres
▲ EMP: 40
SALES (est): 224.9MM Privately Held
WEB: www.nabors.com
SIC: 1381 1389 Reworking oil & gas wells;
directional drilling oil & gas wells; servic-
ing oil & gas wells; oil field services
HQ: Nabors Industries, Inc.
515 W Greens Rd Ste 1200
Houston TX 77067
281 874-0035

(G-10956)
**NABORS WELL SERVICES CO
(DH)**
Also Called: Nabors Oil Tools
515 W Greens Rd Ste 1000 (77067-4536)
PHONE................................281 874-0035
Anthony G Petrello, CEO
Eugene M Isenberg, Chairman
Charlie Davis, Business Mgr
J Gardner, Vice Pres
Frank Labrenz, Vice Pres
▼ EMP: 100
SALES (est): 3.1B Privately Held
WEB: www.nabors.com
SIC: 1389 Oil field services
HQ: Nabors Industries, Inc.
515 W Greens Rd Ste 1200
Houston TX 77067
281 874-0035

(G-10957)
NABORS WELL SERVICES CO
672008 Box (77267)
P.O. Box 671008 (77267-1008)
PHONE................................281 775-8506
EMP: 28 Privately Held
WEB: www.nabors.com
SIC: 1389 Oil field services
HQ: Nabors Well Services Co.
515 W Greens Rd Ste 1000
Houston TX 77067
281 874-0035

(G-10958)
**NABORS WELL SERVICES LTD
(DH)**
515 W Greens Rd Ste 1200 (77067-4536)
PHONE................................281 874-0035
Anthony G Petrello, Ch of Bd
Nicholas Petronio, President
James Sutherland, Opers Mgr
Martha Ditmore, Buyer
Ricky Lee, Manager
EMP: 34

SALES (est): 433MM Privately Held
WEB: www.nabors.com
SIC: 1389 7353 Servicing oil & gas wells;
oil equipment rental services
HQ: Nabors Well Services Co.
515 W Greens Rd Ste 1000
Houston TX 77067
281 874-0035

(G-10959)
NACERO INC
2050 W Sam Houston Pkwy S
(77042-2079)
PHONE................................346 200-7706
Jay McKenna, CEO
EMP: 60
SALES (est): 109K Privately Held
WEB: www.nacero.co
SIC: 1311 Crude petroleum & natural gas

(G-10960)
NAIL THERAPIE HTX
9121a Stella Link Rd (77025-3924)
PHONE................................832 703-4386
Crystal Brunson, CEO
EMP: 10
SALES (est): 45K Privately Held
SIC: 3999 Fingernails, artificial

(G-10961)
**NAILOR INDUSTRIES TEXAS
INC (HQ)**
4714 Winfield Rd (77039-6016)
PHONE................................281 590-1172
Michael Nailor, President
Gus Faris, President
Dennis Gilmore, General Mgr
Lance Nailor, Exec VP
Steven Nailor, Exec VP
▲ EMP: 190
SQ FT: 150,000
SALES (est): 64.8MM
SALES (corp-wide): 67.2MM Privately
Held
WEB: www.nailor.com
SIC: 3822 3444 Hardware for environmen-
tal regulators; thermostats & other envi-
ronmental sensors; sheet metalwork
PA: Nailor Industries Inc
98 Toryork Dr
North York ON M9L 1
416 744-3300

(G-10962)
NAN YA PLASTICS CORP USA
Also Called: Neuma Doors
8989 North Loop E (77029-1217)
PHONE................................713 674-7822
Levi Pirir, Sales Staff
Michelle Bryant, Marketing Staff
Eugene Wu, Branch Mgr
EMP: 65 Privately Held
WEB: www.npcusa.com
SIC: 3089 Plastic containers, except foam
HQ: Nan Ya Plastics Corporation, America
9 Peach Tree Hill Rd
Livingston NJ 07039
973 992-1775

(G-10963)
**NAT G CNG SOLUTIONS LLC
(PA)**
16504 Aldine Westfield Rd A1
(77032-1362)
PHONE................................281 954-4600
Robert Lukefahr, CEO
Balu Balagopal, CEO
John Hearn, Foreman/Supr
Bob Lukefahr
▲ EMP: 15 EST: 2012
SQ FT: 8,000
SALES (est): 6MM Privately Held
WEB: www.nat-g.com
SIC: 3714 7549 Motor vehicle parts & ac-
cessories; fuel system conversion, auto-
motive

(G-10964)
NATCO GROUP INC (DH)
11210 Equity Dr Ste 100 (77041-8239)
PHONE................................713 849-7500
Les Hiller, President
◆ EMP: 18

SALES (est): 496.1MM Publicly Held
WEB: www.natcogroupllc.com
SIC: 1389 3533 Oil field services; gas field
machinery & equipment

(G-10965)
NATIONAL ART SERVICE CO INC
726 Lawrence St (77007-1435)
P.O. Box 70165 (77270-0165)
PHONE................................713 869-5861
EMP: 10 EST: 1970
SALES (est): 1.1MM Privately Held
WEB: www.nationalartservices.net
SIC: 2499 Picture frame molding, finished

(G-10966)
**NATIONAL BEDDING COMPANY
LLC**
Also Called: Serta Mattress
10710 Telge Rd (77095-5002)
PHONE................................281 345-6237
Phillip Walker, Plant Mgr
Mickey Morgan, VP Sales
Andrew Kramer, Regl Sales Mgr
Kelly Hasting, Manager
Thomas Lafleur, Manager
EMP: 95 Privately Held
WEB: www.serta.com
SIC: 2515 5712 Mattresses, innerspring or
box spring; mattresses
HQ: National Bedding Company L.L.C.
2600 Forbs Ave
Hoffman Estates IL 60192

(G-10967)
**NATIONAL ENRGY SVCS RNTED
CORP (PA)**
Also Called: Nesr
777 Post Oak Blvd Ste 730 (77056-3253)
PHONE................................832 925-3777
Sherif Foda, Ch of Bd
Christopher L Boone, CFO
EMP: 9 EST: 2017
SALES (est): 529.5MM Publicly Held
WEB: www.nesr.com
SIC: 1389 1382 Oil field services; oil &
gas exploration services

(G-10968)
**NATIONAL FLANGE & FITTING
CO (PA)**
4420 Creekmont Dr (77091-5227)
P.O. Box 924149 (77292-4149)
PHONE................................713 688-2515
Alois O Keilers, President
Arlis Keilers, Vice Pres
EMP: 50
SQ FT: 40,000
SALES (est): 12.3MM Privately Held
WEB: www.squareflange.com
SIC: 3463 3494 3462 Flange, valve or
pipe fitting forgings, nonferrous; valves &
pipe fittings; flange, valve & pipe fitting
forgings, ferrous

(G-10969)
NATIONAL HEAT TREAT LLC
6923 Brittmoore Rd (77041-3807)
PHONE................................281 809-9840
Robert Gutierrez, President
Jehon Leonce, General Mgr
Michael Pendley, General Mgr
Andrew Duckett, Vice Pres
Kendall Wilkinson, Facilities Dir
EMP: 22 EST: 2012
SQ FT: 50,000
SALES (est): 5MM Privately Held
WEB: www.nationalheattreat.com
SIC: 3398 Metal heat treating

(G-10970)
**NATIONAL MANUFACTURING
LLC**
Also Called: Nelson Machine Products
7131 Jackrabbit Rd (77095-3513)
PHONE................................281 856-7693
Monte Dick, CEO
Betty Dick, CFO
▲ EMP: 13
SQ FT: 10,000

SALES (est): 1.3MM Privately Held
WEB: www.nelson-machine.com
SIC: 3469 3829 3599 Machine parts,
stamped or pressed metal; physical property testing equipment; machine shop,
jobbing & repair

(G-10971)
**NATIONAL OILWELL DHT LP
(HQ)**
Also Called: National Oilwell Varco DHT
10000 Richmond Ave # 100 (77042-4209)
PHONE................................713 346-7500
Richard Legocki, Partner
Jeff Mann, Director
▲ EMP: 51
SALES (est): 29.5MM
SALES (corp-wide): 8.4B Publicly Held
WEB: www.nov.com
SIC: 3533 Oil field machinery & equipment
PA: National Oilwell Varco, Inc.
7909 Parkwood Circle Dr
Houston TX 77036
713 346-7500

(G-10972)
**NATIONAL OILWELL VARCO
INC**
2000 W S Houston Pkwy S (77051)
P.O. Box 808 (77001-0808)
PHONE................................713 799-8198
Hank Smith, President
Marcel Mason, Accounting Dir
David Pitts, Manager
Donna Jones, Personnel Assit
EMP: 10
SALES (corp-wide): 8.4B Publicly Held
WEB: www.nov.com
SIC: 1389 Oil field services
PA: National Oilwell Varco, Inc.
7909 Parkwood Circle Dr
Houston TX 77036
713 346-7500

(G-10973)
**NATIONAL OILWELL VARCO
INC**
7402 N Aldridge Pkwy (77041)
PHONE................................713 466-7999
Larry Dougherty, Manager
Kimberly Russell, Analyst
EMP: 100
SQ FT: 74,114
SALES (corp-wide): 8.4B Publicly Held
WEB: www.nov.com
SIC: 1389 Oil field services
PA: National Oilwell Varco, Inc.
7909 Parkwood Circle Dr
Houston TX 77036
713 346-7500

(G-10974)
**NATIONAL OILWELL VARCO
INC**
Elmar Services Div
8017 Breen Dr (77064-8417)
PHONE................................713 983-9281
Allister Ellis, Manager
Tamara Delton, Assistant
EMP: 60
SALES (corp-wide): 8.4B Publicly Held
WEB: www.nov.com
SIC: 1389 Oil field services
PA: National Oilwell Varco, Inc.
7909 Parkwood Circle Dr
Houston TX 77036
713 346-7500

(G-10975)
**NATIONAL OILWELL VARCO
INC**
1230 W Sam Houston Pkwy N (77043)
PHONE................................713 935-8170
Carlos Kenda, Branch Mgr
EMP: 35
SALES (corp-wide): 8.4B Publicly Held
WEB: www.nov.com
SIC: 3533 Oil field machinery & equipment
PA: National Oilwell Varco, Inc.
7909 Parkwood Circle Dr
Houston TX 77036
713 346-7500

(G-10976)
NATIONAL OILWELL VARCO INC
Nov Monoflo
8708 W Little York Rd # 100 (77040-4155)
PHONE....................281 854-0300
EMP: 19
SALES (corp-wide): 8.4B Publicly Held
WEB: www.nov.com
SIC: 5084 3533 Petroleum industry machinery; oil field machinery & equipment
PA: National Oilwell Varco, Inc.
7909 Parkwood Circle Dr
Houston TX 77036
713 346-7500

(G-10977)
NATIONAL OILWELL VARCO INC
6390 N Eldridge Pkwy (77041-3504)
P.O. Box 1473 (77251-1473)
PHONE....................713 896-9115
Richard Koontz, Engineer
Mike Williams, Branch Mgr
Fortunato Barajas, Manager
Wedell Mendez, Manager
EMP: 28
SALES (corp-wide): 8.4B Publicly Held
WEB: www.nov.com
SIC: 1389 Oil field services
PA: National Oilwell Varco, Inc.
7909 Parkwood Circle Dr
Houston TX 77036
713 346-7500

(G-10978)
NATIONAL OILWELL VARCO INC
9724 Beechnut St Ste 140 (77036-6645)
PHONE....................713 634-3327
Norman Padalino, Vice Pres
Jeff Kriesman, Facilities Mgr
Brian Bennett, Senior Buyer
Laura Sanchez, Buyer
Eloy Sedillo, Buyer
EMP: 23
SALES (corp-wide): 8.4B Publicly Held
WEB: www.nov.com
SIC: 3533 5084 Oil field machinery & equipment; petroleum industry machinery
PA: National Oilwell Varco, Inc.
7909 Parkwood Circle Dr
Houston TX 77036
713 346-7500

(G-10979)
NATIONAL OILWELL VARCO INC
7909 Parkwood Circle Dr (77036-6757)
PHONE....................713 375-3700
Jerri Babin, Vice Pres
Jed Niederer, Vice Pres
Jeff Stolasz, VP Mfg
Conny Krebbekx, Project Mgr
Jomon Kurian, Project Mgr
EMP: 24
SALES (corp-wide): 8.4B Publicly Held
WEB: www.nov.com
SIC: 1389 Oil field services
PA: National Oilwell Varco, Inc.
7909 Parkwood Circle Dr
Houston TX 77036
713 346-7500

(G-10980)
NATIONAL OILWELL VARCO INC
Also Called: National Oil Well
6390 N Eldridge Pkwy (77041-3504)
PHONE....................832 424-6000
EMP: 24
SALES (corp-wide): 8.4B Publicly Held
WEB: www.nov.com
SIC: 3533 Oil & gas field machinery
PA: National Oilwell Varco, Inc.
7909 Parkwood Circle Dr
Houston TX 77036
713 346-7500

(G-10981)
NATIONAL OILWELL VARCO INC
12002 W Little York Rd (77041-4503)
PHONE....................713 237-9793

Dave Teter, President
Julie Timmins, QC Mgr
Eduardo Rodriguez, Chief Engr
Jun Chen, Engineer
Armando Salinas, Master
EMP: 32
SALES (corp-wide): 8.4B Publicly Held
WEB: www.nov.com
SIC: 3533 Oil field machinery & equipment
PA: National Oilwell Varco, Inc.
7909 Parkwood Circle Dr
Houston TX 77036
713 346-7500

(G-10982)
NATIONAL OILWELL VARCO INC
Also Called: Gill Services
650 Aldine Bender Rd (77060-4502)
PHONE....................281 820-5400
Daniel Comalander, Prdtn Mgr
Gay Wathen, Branch Mgr
EMP: 32
SALES (corp-wide): 8.4B Publicly Held
WEB: www.nov.com
SIC: 3533 Oil & gas field machinery
PA: National Oilwell Varco, Inc.
7909 Parkwood Circle Dr
Houston TX 77036
713 346-7500

(G-10983)
NATIONAL OILWELL VARCO INC
Nov Rig Systems
10353 Richmond Ave (77042-4103)
PHONE....................281 854-0537
Joel Staff, Partner
Tahseen Bahmany, Business Anlyst
Monica Doerflinger, Business Anlyst
Puja Malla, Business Anlyst
Barney Nilsen, Manager
EMP: 19
SALES (corp-wide): 8.4B Publicly Held
WEB: www.nov.com
SIC: 3533 Oil & gas field machinery
PA: National Oilwell Varco, Inc.
7909 Parkwood Circle Dr
Houston TX 77036
713 346-7500

(G-10984)
NATIONAL OILWELL VARCO INC
Also Called: Nov Rig Systems
5130 N Sam Houston Pkwy W (77086-1461)
PHONE....................281 943-5948
Hollis Randle, Prdtn Mgr
Odd Aurebekk, Technical Mgr
Anne Grethe Robstad, Accountant
Antonio Ruiz, Administration
EMP: 21
SALES (corp-wide): 8.4B Publicly Held
WEB: www.nov.com
SIC: 3533 Oil & gas field machinery
PA: National Oilwell Varco, Inc.
7909 Parkwood Circle Dr
Houston TX 77036
713 346-7500

(G-10985)
NATIONAL OILWELL VARCO INC
Well Site Services
4310 N Sam Houston Pkwy E (77032-3807)
PHONE....................713 482-0500
Mark Lapeyrouse, Division Mgr
Rudy Soriano, Vice Pres
Michael Bradshaw, Opers Mgr
Shane Olano, Sales Staff
Heather Dulin, Manager
EMP: 50
SALES (corp-wide): 8.4B Publicly Held
WEB: www.nov.com
SIC: 1389 5169 Mud service, oil field drilling; oil additives
PA: National Oilwell Varco, Inc.
7909 Parkwood Circle Dr
Houston TX 77036
713 346-7500

(G-10986)
NATIONAL OILWELL VARCO INC
Fm 529 (77041)
PHONE....................713 849-8011
EMP: 60
SQ FT: 12,792
SALES (corp-wide): 7.3B Publicly Held
SIC: 3533 Mfg Oil/Gas Field Machinery
PA: National Oilwell Varco, Inc.
7909 Parkwood Circle Dr
Houston TX 77036
713 346-7500

(G-10987)
NATIONAL OILWELL VARCO INC
Nov
8018 Breen Dr (77064-8416)
PHONE....................281 599-4700
Ajit Narayan, Mfg Staff
Chris Kitching, Sales Staff
Michelle Klovans, Marketing Staff
Patrick Hughes, Manager
George Fernandez, Manager
EMP: 100
SQ FT: 50,000
SALES (corp-wide): 8.4B Publicly Held
WEB: www.nov.com
SIC: 3533 Oil & gas field machinery
PA: National Oilwell Varco, Inc.
7909 Parkwood Circle Dr
Houston TX 77036
713 346-7500

(G-10988)
NATIONAL OILWELL VARCO INC (PA)
7909 Parkwood Circle Dr (77036-6757)
P.O. Box 4638 (77210-4638)
PHONE....................713 346-7500
Clay C Williams, Ch of Bd
Claus Meyer, General Mgr
Craig L Weinstock, Senior VP
Scott K Duff, Vice Pres
Jeff Lambert, Vice Pres
◆ EMP: 600
SALES (est): 8.4B Publicly Held
WEB: www.nov.com
SIC: 3594 5084 3533 Pumps, hydraulic power transfer; motors: hydraulic, fluid power or air; petroleum industry machinery; oil & gas drilling rigs & equipment

(G-10989)
NATIONAL OILWELL VARCO INC
Also Called: Nov Tuboscope
10222 Sheldon Rd (77049-1250)
PHONE....................281 456-0751
George House, Principal
Jeff Arnold, Opers Staff
Jim Harper, Opers Staff
Epifanio Morales, Opers Staff
Joe Rogers, Opers Staff
EMP: 300
SALES (corp-wide): 8.4B Publicly Held
WEB: www.nov.com
SIC: 1389 Oil field services
PA: National Oilwell Varco, Inc.
7909 Parkwood Circle Dr
Houston TX 77036
713 346-7500

(G-10990)
NATIONAL OILWELL VARCO INC
10011 Madowglen Ste Mg 2a (77042)
PHONE....................713 395-5000
Warren More, Vice Pres
EMP: 15
SALES (corp-wide): 8.4B Publicly Held
WEB: www.nov.com
SIC: 5084 3533 Petroleum industry machinery; oil & gas field machinery
PA: National Oilwell Varco, Inc.
7909 Parkwood Circle Dr
Houston TX 77036
713 346-7500

(G-10991)
NATIONAL OILWELL VARCO INC
8600 Pineland Rd (77044-6132)
P.O. Box 24810 (77229-4810)
PHONE....................281 456-8551
Eddie Offord, Opers Staff
Ruben Cuello, Manager
EMP: 40
SALES (corp-wide): 8.4B Publicly Held
WEB: www.nov.com
SIC: 3479 Hot dip coating of metals or formed products
PA: National Oilwell Varco, Inc.
7909 Parkwood Circle Dr
Houston TX 77036
713 346-7500

(G-10992)
NATIONAL OILWELL VARCO INC
140 Cypress Station Dr # 220 (77090-1633)
PHONE....................281 878-8000
Alan Frial, Division Mgr
Michael McShane, Principal
Robin Macmillan, Vice Pres
Jamey Lebouef, Mktg Dir
Don Schelat, Manager
EMP: 23
SALES (corp-wide): 8.4B Publicly Held
WEB: www.nov.com
SIC: 3533 Oil field machinery & equipment
PA: National Oilwell Varco, Inc.
7909 Parkwood Circle Dr
Houston TX 77036
713 346-7500

(G-10993)
NATIONAL OILWELL VARCO INC
11929 Fm 529 Rd (77041-3017)
PHONE....................713 468-7328
Shannon Bishop, Traffic Mgr
Matthew Stehling, Project Engr
Neil Hieber, Manager
Brian Sommers, Manager
Filiberto Rodriguez, Supervisor
EMP: 250
SALES (corp-wide): 8.4B Publicly Held
WEB: www.nov.com
SIC: 3533 Oil & gas field machinery
PA: National Oilwell Varco, Inc.
7909 Parkwood Circle Dr
Houston TX 77036
713 346-7500

(G-10994)
NATIONAL OILWELL VARCO INC
16211 Air Center Blvd (77032-5119)
PHONE....................281 209-4840
Cindi Cross, Export Mgr
Rodolfo Velazquez, Mfg Spvr
Thurma Beisert, Buyer
Jeff Clausen, Engineer
Jason Crummel, Engineer
EMP: 14
SALES (corp-wide): 8.4B Publicly Held
WEB: www.nov.com
SIC: 1389 Oil field services
PA: National Oilwell Varco, Inc.
7909 Parkwood Circle Dr
Houston TX 77036
713 346-7500

(G-10995)
NATIONAL OILWELL VARCO LP
5100 N Sam Houston Pkwy W (77086-1461)
PHONE....................281 586-2046
EMP: 58
SALES (corp-wide): 7.3B Publicly Held
SIC: 3533 5082 Mfg Oil/Gas Field Machinery Whol Construction/Mining Equipment
HQ: National Oilwell Varco, L.P.
7909 Parkwood Circle Dr
Houston TX 77036
713 960-5100

(G-10996)
NATIONAL OILWELL VARCO LP
10000 Richmond Ave # 100 (77042-4209)
PHONE....................713 346-7500
EMP: 72

SALES (corp-wide): 8.4B **Publicly Held**
WEB: www.nov.com
SIC: 3533 5082 5084 Oil field machinery & equipment; oil field equipment; industrial machinery & equipment
HQ: National Oilwell Varco, L.P.
7909 Parkwood Circle Dr
Houston TX 77036
713 375-3700

(G-10997)
NATIONAL OILWELL VARCO LP
9724 Beechnut St Ste 300 (77036-6655)
PHONE..................................713 375-3700
Gloria Herrera, *Payroll Mgr*
Rona Lyimo, *Technology*
Wayne Clemmer, *Database Admin*
Ruth Posada, *Administration*
EMP: 72
SALES (corp-wide): 8.4B **Publicly Held**
WEB: www.nov.com
SIC: 3533 5082 5084 Oil field machinery & equipment; oil field equipment; industrial machinery & equipment
HQ: National Oilwell Varco, L.P.
7909 Parkwood Circle Dr
Houston TX 77036
713 375-3700

(G-10998)
NATIONAL OILWELL VARCO LP
8018 Breen Dr (77064-8416)
PHONE..................................281 599-4700
EMP: 72
SALES (corp-wide): 7.3B **Publicly Held**
SIC: 3533 5082 5084 Mfg Oil/Gas Field Machinery Whol Construction/Mining Equipment Whol Industrial Equipment
HQ: National Oilwell Varco, L.P.
7909 Parkwood Circle Dr
Houston TX 77036
713 960-5100

(G-10999)
NATIONAL OILWELL VARCO LP
6390 N Eldridge Pkwy (77041-3504)
PHONE..................................713 849-6121
Juan Castro, *QC Mgr*
Tho Nguyen, *Engineer*
Kevin Behrle, *Supervisor*
EMP: 13
SALES (corp-wide): 8.4B **Publicly Held**
WEB: www.nov.com
SIC: 3533 Oil field machinery & equipment
HQ: National Oilwell Varco, L.P.
7909 Parkwood Circle Dr
Houston TX 77036
713 375-3700

(G-11000)
NATIONAL OILWELL VARCO LP (HQ)
7909 Parkwood Circle Dr (77036-6757)
P.O. Box 4638 (77210-4638)
PHONE..................................713 375-3700
Joel Staff, *Partner*
Merrill Miller, *Partner*
Dan Molinaro, *Partner*
Frederick Pheasey, *Partner*
David Brinkley, *Area Mgr*
◆ **EMP:** 310
SQ FT: 115,000
SALES (est): 306.6MM
SALES (corp-wide): 8.4B **Publicly Held**
WEB: www.nov.com
SIC: 3533 5082 5084 Oil field machinery & equipment; oil field equipment; industrial machinery & equipment
PA: National Oilwell Varco, Inc.
7909 Parkwood Circle Dr
Houston TX 77036
713 346-7500

(G-11001)
NATIONAL SIGNS LLC
2611 El Camino St (77054-4114)
PHONE..................................832 433-4957
Cody Johnson, *CEO*
Julius Lyons, *Vice Pres*
Matthew Nicolay, *Vice Pres*
Brandon Yannerella, *Prdtn Mgr*
Nistha Pradhan, *Purchasing*
EMP: 46

SALES (est): 375.5K **Privately Held**
WEB: www.nationalsigns.com
SIC: 5046 3993 Signs, electrical; electric signs

(G-11002)
NATIONAL SPECIALTY ALLOYS INC (HQ)
Also Called: National Specialty Alloys Nsa
18250 Kieth Harrow Blvd (77084-5739)
PHONE..................................281 345-2115
Mark J Russ, *CEO*
Harold Vance, *Assistant VP*
Eileen Casiraghi, *Vice Pres*
Anthony Kosler, *Vice Pres*
Brad Poole, *Vice Pres*
◆ **EMP:** 83
SQ FT: 62,500
SALES (est): 32MM
SALES (corp-wide): 10.9B **Publicly Held**
WEB: www.nsalloys.com
SIC: 5051 3356 Steel; nickel & nickel alloy pipe, plates, sheets, etc.
PA: Reliance Steel & Aluminum Co.
350 S Grand Ave Ste 5100
Los Angeles CA 90071
213 687-7700

(G-11003)
NATIONAL STRAND PRODUCTS LP
12611 Cain Cir (77015-6834)
P.O. Box 96149 (77213-6149)
PHONE..................................713 455-2888
Marty McNair, *Partner*
Angie Davis, *Sales Staff*
▼ **EMP:** 58
SQ FT: 65,000
SALES (est): 17.9MM **Privately Held**
WEB: www.nationalstrand.com
SIC: 3496 Miscellaneous fabricated wire products
PA: The Heico Companies L L C
70 W Madison St Ste 5600
Chicago IL 60602

(G-11004)
NATIONAL VINEGAR COMPANY
5242 Loch Lomond Dr (77096-2511)
PHONE..................................713 223-4214
EMP: 25 **EST:** 1924
SQ FT: 40,000
SALES (est): 3.2MM **Privately Held**
SIC: 2099 Mfg Food Preparations

(G-11005)
NATIONAL WELL SUPPLIES CO INC (PA)
1625 Brittmoore Rd (77043-3107)
PHONE..................................713 467-0462
Barry Wyatt, *President*
Cathy J Wyatt, *CFO*
Cathy Wyatt, *CFO*
Vickie Ross, *Marketing Mgr*
EMP: 16
SQ FT: 10,000
SALES (est): 2.9MM **Privately Held**
WEB: www.nationalwellsupply.com
SIC: 3432 Lawn hose nozzles & sprinklers

(G-11006)
NATURAL COSMECEUTICALS OF AMER
2909 Hillcroft St Ste 250 (77057-5820)
PHONE..................................832 771-0882
Mohamoud Afifi, *Director*
Dr Elbanna Abdulbari, *Director*
Ahmed Al Mallawany, *Director*
EMP: 10
SQ FT: 2,000
SALES (est): 1MM **Privately Held**
WEB: www.nca-usa.com
SIC: 2844 Cosmetic preparations

(G-11007)
NATURAL GAS PIPELINE AMER LLC (HQ)
Also Called: Ngpl
1001 Louisiana St (77002-5089)
PHONE..................................713 369-9000
David Devine, *President*
Steve Kean, *Exec VP*
Fredrik Sultan, *Engineer*
Jim Saunders, *CFO*
Richard D Kinder, *Mng Member*

EMP: 650
SQ FT: 400,000
SALES (est): 763.4MM **Publicly Held**
WEB: www.kindermorgan.com
SIC: 4922 1311 8741 Pipelines, natural gas; storage, natural gas; natural gas production; management services

(G-11008)
NATURAL GAS SLTIONS N AMER LLC
Also Called: Dresser Natural Gas Solutions
16240 Port Nw (77041-2668)
PHONE..................................832 590-2303
David Evans, *CEO*
John Biggs, *COO*
Nelson Rowe, *CFO*
EMP: 529
SQ FT: 138,550
SALES (est): 179MM
SALES (corp-wide): 1.9MM **Privately Held**
WEB: www.dressergs.com
SIC: 1389 Gas field services
HQ: Ngs Us Finco, Llc
290 Harbor Dr Fl 5
Stamford CT 06902
203 661-6601

(G-11009)
NATURAL GRAPHICS INC
6376 Alder Dr (77081-4404)
PHONE..................................713 661-5075
F H Lacy, *President*
Sharon Jackson, *Vice Pres*
Janet Ashbrook, *Project Mgr*
Christie Harrell, *Production*
Anneli Zinser, *Accounts Exec*
EMP: 26
SQ FT: 9,000
SALES (est): 2.6MM **Privately Held**
WEB: www.natgraph.com
SIC: 3299 7389 3993 7336 Art goods: plaster of paris, papier mache & scagliola; design, commercial & industrial; signs & advertising specialties; commercial art & graphic design

(G-11010)
NATURAL RESOURCE PARTNERS LP (PA)
Also Called: Nrp
1201 La St Ste 3400 (77002)
PHONE..................................713 751-7507
Corbin J Robertson Jr, *CEO*
Craig W Nunez, *President*
Nrp LP, *General Ptnr*
Adam Clark, *Regional Mgr*
Patricia Smith, *Vice Pres*
EMP: 47
SALES: 263.9MM **Publicly Held**
WEB: www.nrplp.com
SIC: 1221 1474 Bituminous coal & lignite-surface mining; soda ash (natural) mining

(G-11011)
NATURAL STONE INC
1929 Dorsett St (77029-3742)
PHONE..................................713 678-4407
Roland P St Lawrence, *President*
Rolald P St Lawrence, *President*
Cindy St Lawrence, *Project Mgr*
▲ **EMP:** 15
SQ FT: 40,000
SALES (est): 1.3MM **Privately Held**
WEB: www.naturalstonehouston.com
SIC: 3281 Granite, cut & shaped

(G-11012)
NBL PERMIAN LLC (DH)
1001 Noble Energy Way (77070-1435)
PHONE..................................281 872-3100
Charles J Rimer, *President*
Samuel L Lyssy Jr, *Executive*
EMP: 107
SQ FT: 87,000
SALES (est): 289.4MM
SALES (corp-wide): 146.5B **Publicly Held**
WEB: www.nblenergy.com
SIC: 1382 Oil & gas exploration services
HQ: Nbl Texas, Llc
1001 Noble Energy Way
Houston TX 77070
281 872-3100

(G-11013)
NBL TEXAS LLC (DH)
1001 Noble Energy Way (77070-1435)
PHONE..................................281 872-3100
Charles J Rimer, *CEO*
EMP: 35
SALES (est): 630.1MM
SALES (corp-wide): 146.5B **Publicly Held**
WEB: www.nblenergy.com
SIC: 1382 Oil & gas exploration services
HQ: Noble Energy, Inc.
1001 Noble Energy Way
Houston TX 77070
281 872-3100

(G-11014)
NC GROUP INC
Also Called: NC Millwork
12901 Beaumont Hwy (77049-1446)
PHONE..................................281 459-9418
Daniel Tamez, *President*
EMP: 25
SQ FT: 10,000
SALES (est): 2.9MM **Privately Held**
WEB: www.n-connections.com
SIC: 1731 2431 Voice, data & video wiring contractor; millwork

(G-11015)
NCI GROUP INC
Also Called: Nci Metal Depots Houston Hardy
14031 W Hardy Rd (77060-5304)
P.O. Box 38217 (77238-8217)
PHONE..................................281 897-7788
Kelly Huntsman, *Vice Pres*
Mike Grein, *Branch Mgr*
Anthony Contreras, *Supervisor*
EMP: 30
SALES (corp-wide): 4.8B **Publicly Held**
WEB: www.cornerstonebuildingbrands.com
SIC: 3448 3446 3444 Prefabricated metal buildings; prefabricated metal components; architectural metalwork; sheet metalwork
HQ: Nci Group, Inc.
10943 N Sam Huston Pkwy W
Houston TX 77064
281 897-7788

(G-11016)
NCI GROUP INC (HQ)
Also Called: M B C I
10943 N Sam Huston Pkwy W (77064-5758)
P.O. Box 692055 (77269-2055)
PHONE..................................281 897-7788
Norman C Chambers, *CEO*
John L Kuzdal, *President*
Donald R Riley, *President*
Dianna Lehman, *Regional Mgr*
Jon Lucas, *Business Mgr*
◆ **EMP:** 294
SQ FT: 261,250
SALES (est): 620.3MM
SALES (corp-wide): 4.8B **Publicly Held**
WEB: www.metal-prep.com
SIC: 3448 3446 Buildings, portable: prefabricated metal; prefabricated metal components; architectural metalwork
PA: Cornerstone Building Brands, Inc.
5020 Weston Pkwy Ste 400
Cary NC 27513
866 419-0042

(G-11017)
NCI GROUP INC
Also Called: Doors and Bldg Component Dbci
7311 Fairview St (77041-2105)
PHONE..................................281 302-1900
Larry Miller, *VP Opers*
EMP: 50
SALES (corp-wide): 4.8B **Publicly Held**
WEB: www.metal-prep.com
SIC: 3442 Garage doors, overhead: metal
HQ: Nci Group, Inc.
10943 N Sam Huston Pkwy W
Houston TX 77064
281 897-7788

(G-11018)
NCI GROUP INC
Also Called: Metal-Prep
501 N Greenwood St (77011-1115)
P.O. Box 9329 (77261-9329)
PHONE..................................713 921-7997

▲ = Import ▼ =Export
◆ =Import/Export

Tommy McTaggart, *Engineer*
Michael Stewart, *Sales Staff*
Troy Thomson, *Branch Mgr*
Joseph Gentry, *Manager*
Ruben Batangan, *Supervisor*
EMP: 50
SALES (corp-wide): 4.8B **Publicly Held**
WEB: www.cornerstonebuildingbrands.com
SIC: 3479 3398 Painting of metal products; metal heat treating
HQ: Nci Group, Inc.
10943 N Sam Huston Pkwy W
Houston TX 77064
281 897-7788

(G-11019)
NCI GROUP INC
Also Called: Mid-West Steel Building
7301 Fairview St (77041-2105)
P.O. Box 40220 (77240-0220)
PHONE..............................713 466-7788
Nci O Corp, *General Ptnr*
Jason Grein, *District Mgr*
Kurt Pesch, *District Mgr*
Bob Schlueter, *District Mgr*
A Ginn, *COO*
EMP: 500
SALES (corp-wide): 4.8B **Publicly Held**
WEB: www.cornerstonebuildingbrands.com
SIC: 3448 3444 3443 Buildings, portable: prefabricated metal; sheet metalwork; fabricated plate work (boiler shop)
HQ: Nci Group, Inc.
10943 N Sam Huston Pkwy W
Houston TX 77064
281 897-7788

(G-11020)
NCS MULTISTAGE HOLDINGS INC (PA)
19350 State Highway 249 # 200 (77070-3541)
PHONE..............................281 453-2222
Robert Nipper, *CEO*
Michael McShane, *Ch of Bd*
Marty Stromquist, *President*
Jason Frost, *Regional Mgr*
Donn Hamilton, *Business Mgr*
EMP: 11
SALES: 205.4MM **Publicly Held**
WEB: www.ncsmultistage.com
SIC: 1389 Gas field services; oil field services

(G-11021)
NDSVENTURES LP
Also Called: Imageworks
723 Main St Ste 801 (77002-3318)
PHONE..............................713 395-0461
Stephen Silkwood, *Partner*
Steve Koinis, *Partner*
EMP: 12
SALES (est): 1.1MM **Privately Held**
WEB: www.iwdds.com
SIC: 2759 Commercial printing

(G-11022)
NEMA ENCLOSURE MFG CORP
1118 Pleasantville Dr (77029-3232)
P.O. Box 15669 (77220-5669)
PHONE..............................713 921-2233
James R Bohn Jr, *President*
Antonio Gonzales, *Purch Mgr*
Oscar Gonzales, *Purchasing*
Cheldra Mosemann, *Sales Staff*
Eduardo De, *Technical Staff*
EMP: 83
SQ FT: 20,000
SALES (est): 20.8MM **Privately Held**
WEB: www.nemaenclosures.com
SIC: 3444 Sheet metalwork

(G-11023)
NEON ELECTRIC CORPORATION
Also Called: Nec Signage Architectural Pdts
1122 Lauder Rd (77039-2999)
PHONE..............................281 987-1144
▲ **EMP:** 65
SQ FT: 50,000

SALES (est): 12.5MM **Privately Held**
WEB: www.necsigns.net
SIC: 2531 2452 3089 3993 Picnic tables or benches, park; prefabricated wood buildings; awnings, fiberglass & plastic combination; signs & advertising specialties

(G-11024)
NEOPAL LLC
5100 Cross Continents Dr (77032-1432)
P.O. Box 111759 (77293-0759)
PHONE..............................281 219-9600
Jeffrey Krug, *Mng Member*
EMP: 47 **EST:** 1999
SQ FT: 41,000
SALES (est): 13.3MM **Privately Held**
WEB: www.neopal.com
SIC: 2448 Pallets, wood

(G-11025)
NEOSENSORY INC
1302 Waugh Dr 447 (77019-3908)
PHONE..............................401 257-9460
David Eagleman, *President*
Scott Novich, *Vice Pres*
EMP: 12 **EST:** 2015
SALES (est): 150K **Privately Held**
WEB: www.neosensory.com
SIC: 8711 2311 Designing: ship, boat, machine & product; vests: made from purchased materials

(G-11026)
NESTE OIL SERVICES INC (HQ)
Also Called: Neste Petroleum
3040 Post Oak Blvd Ste 17 (77056-6500)
PHONE..............................713 407-4411
Gerald B Mc Kenna, *President*
Jeffrey Glanz, *Vice Pres*
Simo Honkanen, *Vice Pres*
Hannele Jakosuo-Jansson, *Vice Pres*
ARI Aitolahti, *Plant Mgr*
◆ **EMP:** 11
SALES (est): 10.9MM
SALES (corp-wide): 17.5B **Privately Held**
WEB: www.neste.us
SIC: 1382 Oil & gas exploration services
PA: Neste Oyj
Keilaranta 21
Espoo 02150
104 581-1

(G-11027)
NESTE PETROLEUM INC
3040 Post Oak Blvd # 1700 (77056-6500)
PHONE..............................713 407-4400
Neville Fernandez, *President*
Kim Brown, *Vice Pres*
Carita Nyman, *Maintence Staff*
EMP: 17
SALES (est): 674.3K
SALES (corp-wide): 17.5B **Privately Held**
WEB: www.neste.us
SIC: 1382 Oil & gas exploration services
PA: Neste Oyj
Keilaranta 21
Espoo 02150
104 581-1

(G-11028)
NETIQ CORPORATION (DH)
515 Post Oak Blvd Ste 120 (77027-9407)
PHONE..............................713 548-1700
Jay Gardner, *President*
James Hughes, *General Mgr*
Logan Wray, *General Mgr*
Jeff Hawn, *Chairman*
Marc B Andrews, *COO*
EMP: 60
SALES (est): 90.4MM **Privately Held**
WEB: www.netiq.com
SIC: 7372 7371 Prepackaged software; computer software development & applications
HQ: Attachmate Corporation
1111 3rd Ave Ste 2300
Seattle WA 98101
206 217-7100

(G-11029)
NETTLECOMBE OIL CO INC
3000 Wilcrest Dr Ste 240 (77042-3570)
PHONE..............................713 652-4040
Paul Habermas, *President*
William Ferguson, *Vice Pres*

EMP: 15
SALES (est): 1.7MM **Privately Held**
WEB: www.nettlecombe.net
SIC: 1382 Oil & gas exploration services

(G-11030)
NETWORK INFO SYSTEMS INC (PA)
Also Called: C-Trec
410 Pierce St Ste 303 (77002-8725)
PHONE..............................713 255-4800
Umesh Verma, *CEO*
David Heath, *Principal*
EMP: 50
SALES (est): 16.9MM **Privately Held**
WEB: www.bluelance.com
SIC: 5045 7371 7372 Computer software; computer peripheral equipment; software programming applications; computer software development; prepackaged software

(G-11031)
NEUTEX ADVNCED ENRGY GROUP INC (PA)
14340 Torrey Chase Blvd (77014-1021)
PHONE..............................281 227-2208
John Higgins, *President*
Mark Sam, *CFO*
◆ **EMP:** 20
SALES (est): 3.4MM **Privately Held**
WEB: www.neutexlighting.com
SIC: 3646 Commercial indusl & institutional electric lighting fixtures

(G-11032)
NEUTEX ADVNCED ENRGY GROUP INC
15700 Vickery Dr (77032-2522)
PHONE..............................281 227-2208
EMP: 20
SQ FT: 48,000
SALES (corp-wide): 3.4MM **Privately Held**
WEB: www.neutexlighting.com
SIC: 3646 Commercial indusl & institutional electric lighting fixtures
PA: Neutex Advanced Energy Group, Inc.
14340 Torrey Chase Blvd
Houston TX 77014
281 227-2208

(G-11033)
NEUTREX INC
11119 Jones Rd W (77065-3616)
PHONE..............................281 807-9449
Arthur Haag, *President*
Vivienne Saunders, *Controller*
Austin Watkins, *Manager*
EMP: 13
SQ FT: 3,200
SALES (est): 3.7MM **Privately Held**
WEB: www.purgexonline.com
SIC: 2821 Molding compounds, plastics

(G-11034)
NEW ENGLAND LEAD BURNING INC
Also Called: Nelco of Texas
4600 Homestead Rd (77028-5822)
PHONE..............................713 675-3266
Joey Harrell, *Sales Staff*
Mark Strong, *Branch Mgr*
EMP: 19
SALES (corp-wide): 34MM **Privately Held**
WEB: www.nelcoworldwide.com
SIC: 3295 5051 3444 3356 Lead, black (natural graphite): ground, refined or blended; lead; sheet metalwork; nonferrous rolling & drawing; concrete products
PA: New England Lead Burning Company, Inc.
2 Burlington Woods Dr # 300
Burlington MA 01803
781 933-1940

(G-11035)
NEW PROCESS STEEL LP (HQ)
Also Called: NPS
1322 N Post Oak Rd (77055-5406)
P.O. Box 55205 (77255-5205)
PHONE..............................713 686-9631
Richard E Fant, *CEO*
Steven Swan, *CFO*
Bert Campanelli, *Credit Staff*

◆ **EMP:** 70
SQ FT: 190,000
SALES (est): 331.1MM
SALES (corp-wide): 77.3MM **Privately Held**
WEB: www.nps.cc
SIC: 5051 3469 Metals service centers & offices; metal stampings
PA: New Process Steel Holding Co., Inc.
1322 N Post Oak Rd
Houston TX 77055
713 686-9631

(G-11036)
NEW PURPLE LLC
11152 Wsheimer Rd Ste 804 (77042)
PHONE..............................713 499-0422
Matt Dagli,
EMP: 35
SALES (est): 758.5K **Privately Held**
SIC: 2389 Apparel & accessories

(G-11037)
NEW TK COATINGS LLC
Also Called: Turn-Key Coatings
8411 Rannie Rd (77080-2022)
P.O. Box 800337 (77280-0337)
PHONE..............................713 666-1375
Tim Glanzman,
Natalie A Kirk,
EMP: 33
SALES (est): 3.2MM **Privately Held**
WEB: www.turnkeycoatings.com
SIC: 3471 Electroplating of metals or formed products

(G-11038)
NEW YORK BAGLES INC
Also Called: New York Bagel Shop & Deli
9724 Hillcroft St (77096-3808)
PHONE..............................713 723-5879
Jay Kornhaber, *President*
David Cohen, *Vice Pres*
Edward Gavrila, *Vice Pres*
Ed Gavrila, *Administration*
EMP: 32
SQ FT: 2,000
SALES (est): 1.5MM **Privately Held**
WEB: www.nybagelsandcoffee.com
SIC: 5461 2051 Bagels; bagels, fresh or frozen

(G-11039)
NEWBERRY BAKERS INC
14149 Interdrive W (77032-3326)
PHONE..............................281 987-8985
Mark Navarro, *Manager*
EMP: 55 **Privately Held**
SIC: 2053 Frozen bakery products, except bread
PA: Newberry Bakers, Inc
14212 Interdrive W
Houston TX 77032

(G-11040)
NEWBERRY BAKERS INC (PA)
14212 Interdrive W (77032-3322)
PHONE..............................281 987-8985
W Cecil Ferguson, *President*
William Evans, *Exec VP*
Juan Torres, *Vice Pres*
Linda Sikes, *CFO*
Mark Navarro, *Manager*
EMP: 115
SQ FT: 56,500
SALES (est): 58.5MM **Privately Held**
SIC: 2053 Frozen bakery products, except bread

(G-11041)
NEWHRM LP
8625 Schumacher Ln (77063-5618)
P.O. Box 270923 (77277-0923)
PHONE..............................713 978-7474
EMP: 40
SQ FT: 3,000
SALES (est): 3.2MM **Privately Held**
SIC: 3273 Mfg Ready-Mixed Concrete

(G-11042)
NEWSCO INTL ENRGY SVCS USA INC
Also Called: Newsco USA
12029 Brittmoore Park Dr (77041-7228)
PHONE..............................832 924-4020
Gerard Reumer, *President*

Imran Maniar, *CFO*
Matt McClellan, *Accounts Mgr*
Richard Doncaster, *Manager*
EMP: 26
SALES (est): 11.1MM
SALES (corp-wide): 15.9MM **Privately Held**
WEB: www.newsco-drilling.com
SIC: 3546 Drills & drilling tools
PA: Newsco International Energy Services Inc
4855 102 Ave Se Suite 11
Calgary AB T2C 2
403 243-2331

(G-11043)
NEXA RESOURCES US INC
Also Called: Votorantim Us, Inc.
3200 Southwest Fwy # 3030 (77027-7528)
PHONE..................................832 726-0160
Christian Hunnicutt, *President*
▲ **EMP:** 14 **EST:** 2010
SQ FT: 2,600
SALES (est): 131.2MM **Privately Held**
SIC: 1031 1061 Lead & zinc ores; nickel ore mining
HQ: Nexa Resources
Avenue J.F. Kennedy 37a
Luxembourg 1855
282 637-27

(G-11044)
NEXEN ENERGY SERVICES USA INC
945 Bunker Hill Rd # 1000 (77024-1358)
PHONE..................................832 714-5000
Bradley W Muir, *Ch of Bd*
Allen Smith, *Vice Pres*
EMP: 33 **EST:** 2013
SALES (est): 3.1MM **Privately Held**
WEB: www.cnoocinternational.com
SIC: 1382 Oil & gas exploration services
HQ: China National Offshore Oil Corp.
No.25, Chaoyangmen North St,
Dongcheng District
Beijing 10001

(G-11045)
NEXEN PETROLEUM USA INC (DH)
945 Bunker Hill Rd # 1400 (77024-1361)
PHONE..................................972 450-4600
Peter D Addy, *President*
Douglas B Otten, *President*
Grant W Dreger, *Vice Pres*
Colleen Johnson, *Vice Pres*
Ian W Macleod, *Vice Pres*
EMP: 45
SQ FT: 30,942
SALES (est): 76.3MM **Privately Held**
WEB: www.cnoocinternational.com
SIC: 1311 1382 Crude petroleum production; oil & gas exploration services
HQ: Nexen Petroleum Holdings U.S.A. Inc.
945 Bunker Hill Rd # 1400
Houston TX 77024
832 714-5000

(G-11046)
NEXGEN - ADVNCED FUEL SYSTEMS
2430 Farrell Rd (77073-4004)
PHONE..................................281 789-2000
Mark D Dion, *President*
Nick Dion, *Vice Pres*
James Henry, *VP Mktg*
Sharon Bullock, *Office Mgr*
EMP: 24
SALES (est): 6.8MM **Privately Held**
WEB: www.nexgen-afs.com
SIC: 3511 3599 Turbines & turbine generator sets & parts; machine shop, jobbing & repair
PA: Allied Power Group Llc
10131 Mills Rd
Houston TX 77070

(G-11047)
NEXTDECADE CORPORATION (PA)
1000 Louisiana St # 3900 (77002-5035)
PHONE..................................713 574-1880
Matthew K Schatzman, *CEO*
Brent Wahl, *Senior VP*
Ariel Handler, *Vice Pres*

Patrick Hughes, *Vice Pres*
Nick Verell, *Project Engr*
EMP: 23
SALES (est): 7.4MM **Publicly Held**
WEB: www.next-decade.com
SIC: 4923 1321 Gas transmission & distribution; natural gas liquids

(G-11048)
NEXTIER CMPLTION SOLUTIONS INC (DH)
Also Called: C&J Specialty Rental Tools
3990 Rogerdale Rd (77042-5142)
PHONE..................................713 325-6000
Joshua E Comstock, *CEO*
Lou Lee, *CEO*
Larry Heidt, *President*
Bruce Foster, *Superintendent*
Ken Michalik, *Superintendent*
EMP: 25 **EST:** 1997
SALES (est): 2.1B
SALES (corp-wide): 1.8B **Publicly Held**
WEB: www.cjenergy.com
SIC: 1389 Oil field services
HQ: Kgh Intermediate Holdco Ii, Llc
2121 Sage Rd
Houston TX 77056
713 960-0381

(G-11049)
NEXTIER OILFIELD SOLUTIONS INC (PA)
3990 Rogerdale Rd (77042-5142)
PHONE..................................713 325-6000
Patrick Murray, *Ch of Bd*
Robert W Drummond, *President*
Jeremiah Cornett, *District Mgr*
Gregory L Powell, *Exec VP*
Ian R Henkes, *Senior VP*
EMP: 56
SALES: 1.8B **Publicly Held**
WEB: www.nextierofs.com
SIC: 1389 Oil field services

(G-11050)
NEXUS CAPACITY SERVICES ULC
5400 Westheimer Ct (77056-5353)
PHONE..................................713 627-5040
Eugene Brennan, *President*
William Whaley, *Vice Pres*
EMP: 200 **EST:** 2017
SALES (est): 20MM **Privately Held**
WEB: www.spectraenergy.com
SIC: 1311 Natural gas production

(G-11051)
NIALTI MANUFACTURING LLC
12018 Palmerton Dr (77064-1437)
P.O. Box 1763, Cypress (77410-1763)
PHONE..................................281 894-4995
Alex Stewart, *CEO*
Eddie Stewart, *President*
Asia Lugo, *Manager*
EMP: 11
SALES (est): 81.8K **Privately Held**
WEB: www.nialti.com
SIC: 2821 Polymethyl methacrylate resins (plexiglass)

(G-11052)
NICKLOS DRILLING COMPANY
2229 San Felipe St # 1401 (77019-5666)
PHONE..................................713 224-5959
James M Nicklos, *President*
Jack S Blanton Jr, *Director*
EMP: 100
SQ FT: 3,400
SALES (est): 16.1MM **Privately Held**
WEB: www.nicklosdrilling.com
SIC: 1381 Directional drilling oil & gas wells

(G-11053)
NIGEN INTERNATIONAL LLC
13938 Chrisman Rd (77039-1918)
PHONE..................................713 956-8022
John Gerlach, *Project Engr*
Melanee Hansen, *Human Res Mgr*
Jay James,
Raul Munoz,
EMP: 50
SQ FT: 32,000

SALES (est): 8.4MM **Privately Held**
WEB: www.nigen.com
SIC: 7389 7353 3491 1481 Inspection & testing services; oil field equipment, rental or leasing; pressure valves & regulators, industrial; nonmetallic mineral services

(G-11054)
NIGHT OWLS PRINT SHOP LLC
4303 Southerland Rd (77092-4420)
PHONE..................................281 741-7032
Eric Solomon,
Monika Foglia, *Assistant*
EMP: 17
SALES (est): 2.5MM **Privately Held**
WEB: www.nightowlsprint.com
SIC: 2752 Commercial printing, offset

(G-11055)
NIKKISO PUMPS AMERICA INC
3433 N Sm Hstn Pkwy W 4 (77086)
PHONE..................................281 310-6747
Junichi Takeda, *President*
Ken Deddo, *Vice Pres*
Osamu Watanade, *Vice Pres*
Karla Gomez, *Purchasing*
Leslie Ibikunle, *Engineer*
▲ **EMP:** 26
SQ FT: 16,000
SALES (est): 5.9MM **Privately Held**
SIC: 3561 Pump jacks & other pumping equipment

(G-11056)
NILTRONIX CIRCUITS INC
3715 Artdale St (77063-5243)
PHONE..................................713 465-4216
Bharat Karsaliya, *President*
Jayendra Karsaliya, *Vice Pres*
Larry Karsaliya, *Vice Pres*
Vijay Bunha, *Manager*
EMP: 13
SQ FT: 18,000
SALES (est): 2.4MM **Privately Held**
WEB: www.niltronix.com
SIC: 3672 Circuit boards, television & radio printed

(G-11057)
NIMCO INSTRUMENTS
4301 Town Plaza Dr Ste 1 (77045-2301)
PHONE..................................713 723-5063
Allen T Cook, *Owner*
EMP: 9
SQ FT: 4,000
SALES (est): 400K **Privately Held**
SIC: 3599 Machine shop, jobbing & repair

(G-11058)
NINE ENERGY SERVICE INC (PA)
2001 Kirby Dr Ste 200 (77019-6083)
PHONE..................................281 730-5100
Ernie L Danner, *Ch of Bd*
Ann G Fox, *President*
Edward Bruce Morgan, *President*
Jason Van Hoozen, *Principal*
John Stephenson, *District Mgr*
EMP: 77 **EST:** 2011
SALES: 832.9MM **Publicly Held**
WEB: www.nineenergyservice.com
SIC: 1389 Oil field services

(G-11059)
NIPPLES ELBOWS & COUPLINGS INC
Also Called: Nec
7207 West Rd (77086-3244)
PHONE..................................281 405-8240
Steve Osborne, *President*
▲ **EMP:** 40
SQ FT: 36,000
SALES (est): 12MM **Privately Held**
WEB: www.nec-inc.com
SIC: 3444 3069 3498 3644 Elbows, for air ducts, stovepipes, etc.: sheet metal; nipples, rubber; couplings, pipe: fabricated from purchased pipe; noncurrent-carrying wiring services; valves & pipe fittings

(G-11060)
NITRO-PHOS INC
Also Called: Nitro-Phos Fertilizer
7402 Neuhaus St (77061-4609)
P.O. Box 1356 (77251-1356)
PHONE..................................713 228-1868
Dan E Snyder, *President*
EMP: 20
SQ FT: 30,000
SALES (est): 3.4MM **Privately Held**
WEB: www.nitro-phos.com
SIC: 5261 2874 2873 Fertilizer; phosphatic fertilizers; nitrogenous fertilizers

(G-11061)
NMG WORKSPACE SOLUTIONS LLC
2301 Caroline St (77004-1013)
PHONE..................................281 240-1007
Bassem Nassif, *CEO*
Shannon Schroeder, *Project Mgr*
Ana Danas, *Accountant*
Crystal Lowe, *Sales Staff*
▲ **EMP:** 33
SALES (est): 25MM **Privately Held**
WEB: www.nmg.us.com
SIC: 1731 1771 1799 2431 Electrical work; flooring contractor; office furniture installation; home/office interiors finishing, furnishing & remodeling; millwork

(G-11062)
NOAHS MANUFACTURING INC
Also Called: Texas Mattress Makers
4619 Navigation Blvd (77011-1039)
PHONE..................................713 926-3500
Youval Meicler, *President*
▲ **EMP:** 70
SQ FT: 80,000
SALES (est): 10.6MM **Privately Held**
WEB: www.noahsmfg.com
SIC: 2512 2515 Living room furniture: upholstered on wood frames; mattresses & foundations

(G-11063)
NOBLE ENERGY INC
Onshore US Division
12707 North Fwy Ste 165 (77060-1234)
PHONE..................................800 234-3867
Richard A Peneguy Jr, *Manager*
EMP: 80
SALES (corp-wide): 146.5B **Publicly Held**
WEB: www.nblenergy.com
SIC: 1382 1311 Oil & gas exploration services; crude petroleum & natural gas
HQ: Noble Energy, Inc.
1001 Noble Energy Way
Houston TX 77070
281 872-3100

(G-11064)
NOBLE ENERGY INC (HQ)
1001 Noble Energy Way (77070-1435)
PHONE..................................281 872-3100
Jeff B Gustavson, *President*
Gene Theis, *Superintendent*
Gary Birdwell, *Vice Pres*
Rachel G Clingman, *Vice Pres*
John Elliott, *Vice Pres*
◆ **EMP:** 188 **EST:** 1932
SALES (est): 4.4B
SALES (corp-wide): 146.5B **Publicly Held**
WEB: www.nblenergy.com
SIC: 1311 1382 Crude petroleum & natural gas; crude petroleum & natural gas production; oil & gas exploration services
PA: Chevron Corporation
6001 Bollinger Canyon Rd
San Ramon CA 94583
925 842-1000

(G-11065)
NOEL DUQUE
606 Hill Rd (77037-1717)
PHONE..................................281 447-5789
Noel Duque, *Owner*
EMP: 20
SALES (est): 1.5MM **Privately Held**
SIC: 3272 Copings, concrete

(G-11066)
NOLTEX TRUSS GATESVILLE LP
6247 Navigation Blvd (77011-5500)
PHONE....................................713 926-7715
Joe Nolte, *Partner*
Jason Nolte, *Partner*
Travis Nolte, *Partner*
Nolan Stone, *Opers Staff*
EMP: 70
SALES (est): 15MM **Privately Held**
WEB: www.noltextruss.com
SIC: 2439 Trusses, wooden roof

(G-11067)
NON-FRROUS EXTRSION SCRAP MTLS (PA)
9210 Emmott Rd (77040-3328)
PHONE....................................713 869-9551
Norman D Feil, *President*
Norman D Feil III, *Principal*
Joel Aldaco, *Plant Mgr*
Lexuan Huynh, *CFO*
Oziel Deluna, *Human Res Dir*
▼ EMP: 87
SQ FT: 44,000
SALES (est): 18.9MM **Privately Held**
WEB: www.non-ferrous.com
SIC: 3463 5093 Aluminum forgings; nonferrous metals scrap; ferrous metal scrap & waste

(G-11068)
NORAM DRILLING COMPANY
8400 N Sam Houston Pkwy W # 120 (77064-3462)
PHONE....................................281 598-9200
Marty Jimmerson, *CEO*
Aaron Cannon, *Superintendent*
Ole B Hjertaker, *Chairman*
Thomas Taylor, *COO*
Jesse Hodge, *Manager*
EMP: 50
SALES (est): 7.8MM **Privately Held**
WEB: www.noramdrilling.com
SIC: 1381 Directional drilling oil & gas wells

(G-11069)
NORRISEAL-WELLMARK INC (DH)
Also Called: Norriseal Controls
11122 W Little York Rd (77041-5016)
P.O. Box 40525 (77240-0525)
PHONE....................................713 466-3552
Robert E Funk, *President*
Floyd Weeks, *Plant Mgr*
Jim Denham, *Facilities Mgr*
Calvin Knapp, *Purch Mgr*
Mike Ashworth, *Sales Staff*
▲ EMP: 110
SALES (est): 26.5MM
SALES (corp-wide): 1.1B **Publicly Held**
WEB: www.norrisealwellmark.com
SIC: 3559 Automotive related machinery
HQ: Apergy Artificial Lift International, Llc
2445 Tech Frest Blvd Ste
Spring TX 77381
281 403-5742

(G-11070)
NORSE CUTNG & ABANDONMENT INC
Also Called: N C A
5535 Brystone Dr (77041-7012)
PHONE....................................832 327-3640
Richard Giffhorn, *President*
Jeffery Shulse, *Vice Pres*
EMP: 50
SQ FT: 18,000
SALES (est): 6.4MM
SALES (corp-wide): 2B **Publicly Held**
WEB: www.nca-group.com
SIC: 3541 Pipe cutting & threading machines
PA: Oceaneering International Inc
11911 Fm 529 Rd
Houston TX 77041
713 329-4500

(G-11071)
NORTEX CORPORATION
3009 Post Oak Blvd # 1212 (77056-6599)
PHONE....................................713 658-1142
EMP: 9 EST: 1951

SQ FT: 8,000
SALES (est): 1.3MM **Privately Held**
WEB: www.nortexcorp.com
SIC: 1311 6792 Crude petroleum production; oil royalty traders

(G-11072)
NORTH AMERICAN INTERPIPE INC
1800 West Loop S Ste 1350 (77027-3235)
PHONE....................................713 333-0333
Daniel Valk, *President*
Rod Smith, *President*
Norbert Stadler, *President*
Isaac Villarreal, *Vice Pres*
Olesye Korneva, *Admin Sec*
◆ EMP: 25 EST: 2001
SQ FT: 2,400
SALES (est): 17MM **Privately Held**
WEB: www.interpipe.biz
SIC: 1382 Oil & gas exploration services
HQ: Interpipe Europe Sa
Via San Salvatore 13
Paradiso TI 6900
912 613-900

(G-11073)
NORTH AMERICAN PIPE CORP (HQ)
2801 Post Oak Blvd # 600 (77056-6110)
PHONE....................................855 624-7473
Mike Powell, *Vice Pres*
Renee Havrilla, *Vice Pres*
Jeff Johnson, *Vice Pres*
Michael Mattina, *Vice Pres*
John Stott, *Vice Pres*
◆ EMP: 110
SQ FT: 60,000
SALES (est): 234MM **Publicly Held**
WEB: www.napcopipe.com
SIC: 3084 Plastics pipe

(G-11074)
NORTH HOUSTON ALCOHOL DRG TSTG
440 Benmar Dr Ste 2289 (77060-3077)
PHONE....................................713 816-4990
Angelia Gipson, *Mng Member*
EMP: 20
SALES (est): 913.5K **Privately Held**
SIC: 2899

(G-11075)
NORTH SHORE EXPRESS CLEAN
15119 Wallisville Rd # 1000 (77049-4630)
PHONE....................................832 418-0535
Young Kim, *Owner*
EMP: 13
SALES (est): 100K **Privately Held**
SIC: 3633 Drycleaning machines, household: including coin-operated

(G-11076)
NORTH SHORE SUPPLY COMPANY INC (PA)
Also Called: North Shore Steel
1566 Miles St (77015-6319)
P.O. Box 9940 (77213-0940)
PHONE....................................713 453-3533
Buzzy Bluestone, *President*
Burton L Bluestone, *President*
Bradley Lazard, *General Mgr*
Stanley D Katz, *Vice Pres*
Stephen Beckman, *Sales Staff*
◆ EMP: 204
SQ FT: 400,000
SALES (est): 141.2MM **Privately Held**
WEB: www.nssco.com
SIC: 5051 5085 3441 Pipe & tubing, steel; steel; valves & fittings; fabricated structural metal

(G-11077)
NORTH SHORE SUPPLY COMPANY INC
13935 Industrial Rd (77015-6824)
PHONE....................................713 400-3320
Soth Lambert, *Branch Mgr*
EMP: 70
SALES (corp-wide): 141.2MM **Privately Held**
WEB: www.nssco.com
SIC: 3471 Plating & polishing

PA: North Shore Supply Company, Inc.
1566 Miles St
Houston TX 77015
713 453-3533

(G-11078)
NORTHERN OFFSHORE LTD (HQ)
575 N Dairy Ashford Rd (77079-1117)
PHONE....................................281 649-2600
Gary Casswell, *CEO*
Scott O Keefe, *Chairman*
Maggie Whitaker, *Executive Asst*
◆ EMP: 45
SALES (est): 16.8MM **Privately Held**
WEB: www.northernoffshore.com
SIC: 1381 Drilling oil & gas wells

(G-11079)
NORTHSTAR INTERESTS LC
11 Greenway Plz Ste 2800 (77046-1110)
PHONE....................................713 626-9696
Glynn Roberts,
Gaylon Freeman,
Georgiana Stanley,
Mark Stevens,
EMP: 12
SQ FT: 20,000
SALES (est): 853.4K **Privately Held**
WEB: www.sanarepartners.com
SIC: 1382 Oil & gas exploration services

(G-11080)
NORTHWEST FASTENER AND SUP INC
11320 Fm 529 Rd Ste F (77041-3222)
P.O. Box 681125 (77268-1125)
PHONE....................................281 921-7880
Bassam Tuffaha, *President*
Michael Fitzpatrick, *Business Mgr*
Maribel Ortiz, *Vice Pres*
Shirley Tuffaha, *Vice Pres*
Julio Torres, *Prdtn Mgr*
▲ EMP: 16
SQ FT: 13,500
SALES (est): 7.5MM **Privately Held**
WEB: www.northwestfastener.com
SIC: 5085 3452 Fasteners, industrial: nuts, bolts, screws, etc.; bolts, nuts, rivets & washers

(G-11081)
NORTHWEST MACHINING SVCS LLC
9101 Windmill Park Ln (77064-3119)
PHONE....................................281 894-5388
James Caesar, *Manager*
EMP: 10
SALES (est): 306.2K **Privately Held**
WEB: www.nwmachiningservices.com
SIC: 3599 Machine shop, jobbing & repair

(G-11082)
NORTHWEST METAL AND STEEL INC
6811 Theall Rd Ste A (77066-1120)
PHONE....................................281 444-5269
Arnulfo Rodriguez, *President*
EMP: 9
SALES (est): 1.6MM **Privately Held**
SIC: 5033 3444 Roofing, siding & insulation; metal roofing & roof drainage equipment

(G-11083)
NORTONLIFELOCK INC
Also Called: Symantec
10111 Richmond Ave # 200 (77042-4215)
PHONE....................................650 527-8000
EMP: 54
SALES (corp-wide): 4.7B **Publicly Held**
WEB: www.broadcom.com
SIC: 3674 Prepackaged software
PA: Nortonlifelock Inc.
60 E Rio Salado Pkwy # 1
Tempe AZ 85281
650 527-8000

(G-11084)
NORWOOD EQUIPMENT HOUSTON INC
1812 Mccarty St (77029-3775)
P.O. Box 24306 (77229-4306)
PHONE....................................713 670-1320
Nathan Ralans, *CEO*

Stacey Ewing, *Director*
Thomas Ewing, *Director*
Thomas Graddy, *Director*
Nathan Rawlins, *Director*
EMP: 15
SALES (est): 5.7MM **Privately Held**
SIC: 5084 3713 3711 Materials handling machinery; specialty motor vehicle bodies; chassis, motor vehicle

(G-11085)
NOSHOK INC
12777 Jones Rd Ste 297 (77070-4625)
PHONE....................................281 897-6115
EMP: 17
SALES (corp-wide): 7MM **Privately Held**
WEB: www.noshok.com
SIC: 3823 Industrial instrmnts msrmnt display/control process variable
PA: Noshok, Inc.
1010 W Bagley Rd
Berea OH 44017
440 243-0888

(G-11086)
NOV MSI PIPE PRTCTION TECH INC
Also Called: MSI Oilfield Products
9035 Solon Rd (77064-1214)
P.O. Box 691088 (77269-1088)
PHONE....................................281 890-4595
Brett J York, *CEO*
John Boben, *President*
Richard Reis, *General Mgr*
Mauro Hernandez, *Vice Pres*
Angie Reneau, *Sales Staff*
◆ EMP: 49
SALES (est): 44.7MM
SALES (corp-wide): 1.2B **Privately Held**
WEB: www.msipipeprotection.com
SIC: 2891 Sealing compounds for pipe threads or joints
HQ: Essentra Corp.
2 Westbrook Corp Ctr # 200
Westchester IL 60154
814 899-7671

(G-11087)
NOV TUBOSCOPE
10000 Richmond Ave (77042-4200)
PHONE....................................713 799-5100
Clay C Williams, *Principal*
Katelyn Hoelscher, *Sales Staff*
◆ EMP: 13
SALES (est): 2.2MM **Privately Held**
SIC: 3479 Coating or wrapping steel pipe

(G-11088)
NOVA CONSULTING
Also Called: Nowiczewski, Joe
623 Buffington St (77060-4603)
PHONE....................................281 445-6393
Joe Nowiczewski, *Owner*
EMP: 15
SQ FT: 14,488
SALES (est): 855K **Privately Held**
WEB: www.ternov.com
SIC: 1389 Oil consultants

(G-11089)
NOVA DIRECTIONAL INC
12227 Fm 529 Rd Bldg Ij (77041-2800)
P.O. Box 1619, Cypress (77410-1619)
PHONE....................................281 246-1149
EMP: 42 EST: 2010
SALES (est): 8.4MM **Privately Held**
WEB: www.novadirectional.com
SIC: 1381 Directional drilling oil & gas wells

(G-11090)
NOVA DRILLING TECHNOLOGIES INC
11800 Fairmont St (77035-6556)
P.O. Box 31729 (77231-1729)
PHONE....................................713 726-0151
Bill West, *CEO*
Randy West, *President*
EMP: 15
SQ FT: 12,500
SALES (est): 1.3MM **Privately Held**
WEB: www.decorativemetalart.com
SIC: 1381 Drilling oil & gas wells

(G-11091)
NOW INC (PA)
7402 N Eldridge Pkwy (77041-1902)
PHONE................281 823-4700
Richard J Alario, *CEO*
J Wayne Richards, *Ch of Bd*
Dan Birrer, *Regional Mgr*
Dan Molinaro, *Exec VP*
Daniel L Molinaro, *Exec VP*
EMP: 46
SALES: 2.9B **Publicly Held**
WEB: www.distributionnow.com
SIC: 3533 5084 Oil & gas field machinery;
petroleum industry machinery

(G-11092)
NRP (GP) LP
610 Jefferson St Ste 3600 (77002-7322)
PHONE................713 751-7507
Corbin J Robertson Jr, *Principal*
EMP: 313
SALES (est): 3.6MM **Privately Held**
WEB: www.nrplp.com
SIC: 1221 Bituminous coal & lignite-sur-
face mining

(G-11093)
NRP (OPERATING) LLC
601 Jefferson St Ste 3600 (77002-7906)
PHONE................713 751-7507
Corbin J Robertson Jr, *Ch of Bd*
EMP: 75
SALES (est): 4.5MM
SALES (corp-wide): 263.9MM **Publicly Held**
WEB: www.nrplp.com
SIC: 1221 Bituminous coal & lignite-sur-
face mining
PA: Natural Resource Partners L.P.
1201 La St Ste 3400
Houston TX 77002
713 751-7507

(G-11094)
NS CONTROLS INC
5601 W Sam Houston Pkwy N
(77041-5148)
PHONE................713 465-7591
Beau Senogles, *President*
Noel Senogles, *President*
EMP: 50
SQ FT: 38,600
SALES: 11.3MM **Privately Held**
WEB: www.nscontrols.com
SIC: 3625 3823 Control equipment, elec-
tric; industrial instrmnts msrmnt
display/control process variable

(G-11095)
NSM INDUSTRIES INC
332 Martin St (77018-3306)
PHONE................713 697-2091
Richard H Longmire, *President*
Sidney G Longmire, *President*
James E Longmire Jr, *Vice Pres*
Bill Mosely, *Vice Pres*
Natalie Rivera, *Controller*
EMP: 25 EST: 1943
SQ FT: 38,400
SALES (est): 5.5MM **Privately Held**
WEB: www.nsmindustries.com
SIC: 3443 Industrial vessels, tanks & con-
tainers; vessels, process or storage (from
boiler shops): metal plate

(G-11096)
NUCLEAR SOURCES AND SVCS INC
Also Called: N S S I
5711 Etheridge St (77087-4009)
P.O. Box 34042 (77234-4042)
PHONE................713 641-0391
Robert D Gallagher, *President*
Ivan Mateo, *Business Mgr*
Kimberly Page, *VP Bus Dvlpt*
Robert Gallagher, *CFO*
Maurita Gallagher, *Treasurer*
EMP: 35 EST: 1971
SQ FT: 5,000
SALES (est): 5.3MM **Privately Held**
WEB: www.nssihouston.com
SIC: 8748 2899 Safety training service;
chemical preparations

(G-11097)
NUEVO ENERGY COMPANY
700 Milam St Ste 3100 (77002-2764)
PHONE................713 579-6000
James C Flores, *Ch of Bd*
C Paige Dimaggio, *Treasurer*
EMP: 279
SALES (est): 13.2MM
SALES (corp-wide): 14.4B **Publicly Held**
SIC: 1311 Natural gas production; crude
petroleum production
HQ: Freeport-Mcmoran Oil & Gas Llc
700 Milam St Ste 3100
Houston TX 77002
713 579-6000

(G-11098)
NUKOTE COATING SYSTEMS INTL (PA)
4730 Consulate Plaza Dr # 100
(77032-2677)
P.O. Box 131328 (77219-1328)
PHONE................832 770-7100
Henry Gohlke, *Vice Pres*
Prashant Varshney,
Laxmi Gupta,
Shalesh Gupta,
Michael S Osborne,
▲ EMP: 23
SALES (est): 3.1MM **Privately Held**
WEB: www.nukoteglobal.com
SIC: 2851 2822 Polyurethane coatings;
ethylene-propylene rubbers, EPDM poly-
mers

(G-11099)
NUPI AMERICAS INC
1511 Superior Way (77039-2018)
PHONE................281 590-4471
Marco Genoni, *President*
Guido Zapea, *Vice Pres*
Sara Brunori, *CFO*
John Autry, *Manager*
Robert Jacoby, *Manager*
▲ EMP: 17
SALES (est): 4.3MM **Privately Held**
WEB: www.nupiamericas.com
SIC: 3084 Plastics pipe

(G-11100)
NUT PLACE INC
6605 Gessner Rd (77040-4015)
PHONE................713 462-3147
Denny Pearce, *President*
Vernon Achgill, *Manager*
Ivan Ray, *Supervisor*
EMP: 30
SQ FT: 30,000
SALES (est): 6.9MM **Privately Held**
WEB: www.thenutplace.com
SIC: 3444 3565 5072 Forming machine
work, sheet metal; labeling machines, in-
dustrial; bolts

(G-11101)
NUTECH ENERGY ALLIANCE LTD (PA)
4101 Interwood N Pkwy # 250
(77032-3884)
PHONE................281 812-4030
Alan Howard, *CEO*
Charles R Close, *Partner*
Dewayne Weaver, *Partner*
Bobby Gibson, *Vice Pres*
Greg Jackson, *Vice Pres*
EMP: 97
SALES (est): 13.8MM **Privately Held**
WEB: www.nutechenergy.com
SIC: 1389 Oil field services

(G-11102)
NVENT THERMAL LLC
Also Called: Tyco Thermal Controls
7433 Harwin Dr (77036-2007)
P.O. Box 3608, Harrisburg PA (17105-
3608)
PHONE................800 545-6258
Steve Powell, *Business Mgr*
Allison Riter, *Vice Pres*
J Whitus, *Vice Pres*
Sean McDaniel, *Sales Staff*
Brad Faulconer, *Branch Mgr*
EMP: 400 **Privately Held**
WEB: www.nventthermal.com

SIC: 3571 Computers, digital, analog or
hybrid
HQ: Nvent Thermal Llc
899 Broadway St
Redwood City CA 94063
650 474-7414

(G-11103)
NW FABRICS LLC
8300 Telephone Rd (77061-4737)
PHONE................832 895-1110
Imran Khanji, *President*
Abdul Malik Chunara, *President*
▲ EMP: 10
SALES (est): 1.4MM **Privately Held**
SIC: 2297 Nonwoven fabrics

(G-11104)
NX MEDIA INC
Also Called: Rice Addict
6118 Aletha Ln (77081-6307)
PHONE................713 270-1198
Martina Yang, *President*
Luis Gonzales, *General Mgr*
▲ EMP: 12 EST: 2001
SQ FT: 12,000
SALES (est): 2.2MM **Privately Held**
WEB: www.nxmedia.net
SIC: 2752 Commercial printing, litho-
graphic

(G-11105)
O & I FABRICATION INCORPORATED
6417 Cunningham Rd (77041-4713)
PHONE................281 617-7732
EMP: 45 **Privately Held**
SIC: 3443 Mfg Fabricated Plate Work

(G-11106)
O M C INTERNATIONAL LLC
19302 Whspering Breeze Ln (77094-3072)
P.O. Box 941233 (77094-8233)
PHONE................281 398-4281
David Bingham, *Owner*
Kimberly Bingham, *Owner*
EMP: 25
SALES (est): 3.1MM **Privately Held**
WEB: www.omcintllc.com
SIC: 1389 Oil consultants

(G-11107)
OAKS PRECISION FABRICATING INC
8550 Breen Dr (77064-8407)
PHONE................713 937-9190
Kelli Oaks, *CEO*
Larry Oaks, *President*
EMP: 45
SQ FT: 30,000
SALES (est): 8MM **Privately Held**
WEB: www.oaks.cc
SIC: 3444 Sheet metal specialties, not
stamped

(G-11108)
OASIS MIDSTREAM PARTNERS LP
1001 Fannin St Ste 1500 (77002-6739)
PHONE................281 404-9500
Taylor L Reid, *CEO*
Michael H Lou, *President*
Omp GP LLC, *General Ptnr*
EMP: 105 EST: 2014
SALES: 271.6MM **Publicly Held**
WEB: www.oasismidstream.com
SIC: 1381 Drilling & gas wells
PA: Oasis Petroleum Inc.
1001 Fannin St Ste 1500
Houston TX 77002

(G-11109)
OASIS PETROLEUM INC (PA)
1001 Fannin St Ste 1500 (77002-6739)
PHONE................281 404-9500
Thomas B Nusz, *Ch of Bd*
Taylor L Reid, *President*
Steve Mahanay, *General Mgr*
Nickolas J Lorentzatos, *Exec VP*
Brock Norby, *Foreman/Supr*
EMP: 91
SQ FT: 130,300

SALES: 2B **Publicly Held**
WEB: www.oasispetroleum.com
SIC: 1311 Crude petroleum production;
natural gas production

(G-11110)
OASIS PETROLEUM LLC (HQ)
1001 Fannin St Ste 1500 (77002-6739)
PHONE................281 404-9500
Phillip Krupp, *Engineer*
Taylor L Reid, *Mng Member*
Thomas B Nusz,
EMP: 18
SQ FT: 25,000
SALES (est): 29.2MM **Publicly Held**
WEB: www.oasispetroleum.com
SIC: 1311 Crude petroleum production

(G-11111)
OASIS PETROLEUM NORTH AMER LLC (DH)
1001 Fannin St Ste 1500 (77002-6739)
PHONE................281 404-9500
Thomas B Nusz, *CEO*
Taylor L Reid, *Exec VP*
Nickolas Lorentzatos, *Vice Pres*
Roy W Mace, *Vice Pres*
William J Cassidy, *Director*
EMP: 70
SALES (est): 19.7MM **Publicly Held**
WEB: www.oasispetroleum.com
SIC: 1311 Crude petroleum production

(G-11112)
OBER & SONS INC
7755 Synott Rd (77083-5115)
PHONE................281 879-6760
Ron Ober Sr, *President*
Ryan Ober, *Vice Pres*
Bill Hortness, *Project Mgr*
Mike Ober, *Treasurer*
Kasie Oliver, *Office Mgr*
EMP: 11
SQ FT: 11,000
SALES (est): 1.8MM **Privately Held**
WEB: www.oberandsons.com
SIC: 1799 7692 3441 Welding on site;
welding repair; fabricated structural metal

(G-11113)
OCCIDENTAL ENERGY MKTG INC (HQ)
5 Greenway Plz Ste 110 (77046-0521)
P.O. Box 27570 (77227-7570)
PHONE................713 215-7000
Ronald K Takeuchi, *President*
Michael R Soland, *Exec VP*
Marc Waugh, *Senior VP*
Shayne Buchanan, *Vice Pres*
Gordon E Goodman, *Vice Pres*
▲ EMP: 125
SALES (est): 582.6MM
SALES (corp-wide): 21.2B **Publicly Held**
WEB: www.oxy.com
SIC: 5172 1382 4924 Crude oil; oil & gas
exploration services; natural gas distribu-
tion
PA: Occidental Petroleum Corporation
5 Greenway Plz Ste 110
Houston TX 77046
713 215-7000

(G-11114)
OCCIDENTAL OIL AND GAS CORP (HQ)
Also Called: OXY
5 Greenway Plz Ste 110 (77046-0521)
P.O. Box 27570 (77227-7570)
PHONE................713 215-7000
Vicki A Hollub, *Principal*
Steve Jason, *Principal*
Christopher G Stavros, *Treasurer*
Steve Flynn, *Manager*
William E Albrecht, *Exec Dir*
◆ EMP: 44
SALES (est): 1.7B
SALES (corp-wide): 21.2B **Publicly Held**
WEB: www.oxy.com
SIC: 1311 Crude petroleum production;
natural gas production
PA: Occidental Petroleum Corporation
5 Greenway Plz Ste 110
Houston TX 77046
713 215-7000

▲ = Import ▼=Export
◆ =Import/Export

(G-11115)
OCCIDENTAL PERMIAN LTD (HQ)
5 Greenway Plz Ste 110 (77046-0521)
P.O. Box 27570 (77227-7570)
PHONE..........................713 215-7000
Tom Menges, *President*
◆ EMP: 250
SQ FT: 100,000
SALES (est): 431.5MM
SALES (corp-wide): 21.2B **Publicly Held**
WEB: www.oxy.com
SIC: 1382 1311 Oil & gas exploration services; crude petroleum production
PA: Occidental Petroleum Corporation
5 Greenway Plz Ste 110
Houston TX 77046
713 215-7000

(G-11116)
OCCIDENTAL PETROLEUM CORP (PA)
5 Greenway Plz Ste 110 (77046-0521)
P.O. Box 27757 (77227-7757)
PHONE..........................713 215-7000
Stephen I Chazen, *Ch of Bd*
Vicki Hollub, *President*
Mary Andrews, *Exec VP*
Edward A Lowe, *Exec VP*
Oscar K Brown, *Senior VP*
EMP: 1000
SALES (est): 21.2B **Publicly Held**
WEB: www.oxy.com
SIC: 1311 1382 Crude petroleum production; oil & gas exploration services

(G-11117)
OCCIDENTAL PETROLEUM CORP
17320 Chanute Rd (77032-5559)
PHONE..........................713 640-7500
Jeff F Simmons, *Vice Pres*
Scott Owens, *Branch Mgr*
EMP: 25
SALES (corp-wide): 21.2B **Publicly Held**
WEB: www.oxy.com
SIC: 1311 1382 2819 2869 Crude petroleum production; natural gas production; oil & gas exploration services; potassium compounds or salts, except hydroxide or carbonate; sodium compounds or salts, inorg., ex. refined sod. chloride; sodium silicate, water glass; ethylene; propylene, butylene; ethylene glycols; chlorine, compressed or liquefied; caustic soda, sodium hydroxide
PA: Occidental Petroleum Corporation
5 Greenway Plz Ste 110
Houston TX 77046
713 215-7000

(G-11118)
OCCIDNTAL INTL EXPLRATION PROD (HQ)
5 Greenway Plz Ste 2400 (77046-0532)
PHONE..........................713 215-7600
Dale Lawrence, *President*
John W Morgan, *Exec VP*
EMP: 325 EST: 1973
SQ FT: 300,000
SALES (est): 33.2MM
SALES (corp-wide): 21.2B **Publicly Held**
WEB: www.oxy.com
SIC: 1311 Crude petroleum production
PA: Occidental Petroleum Corporation
5 Greenway Plz Ste 110
Houston TX 77046
713 215-7000

(G-11119)
OCCUPATIONAL MARKETING INC
Also Called: OMI
19424 Park Row Ste 110 (77084-4683)
PHONE..........................281 492-8250
Micky Sullivan, *CEO*
David Rosenfeld, *President*
Claudia Montero, *Technology*
EMP: 9
SALES (est): 1.3MM **Privately Held**
WEB: www.occupational.com
SIC: 8748 7372 5047 Safety training service; prepackaged software; medical equipment & supplies

(G-11120)
OCEAN FREEDOM SHIPPING INC
16211 Park Ten Pl (77084-7016)
PHONE..........................281 579-3700
James P McGregor, *President*
EMP: 32
SALES (est): 1,000K **Privately Held**
WEB: www.oceanshipholdings.com
SIC: 3799 Transportation equipment

(G-11121)
OCEAN SHIP HOLDING INC
16211 Park Ten Pl Ste 200 (77084-7017)
PHONE..........................281 579-3700
Joseph Vaughan, *President*
John A James, *Corp Secy*
John W Morrison, *Vice Pres*
EMP: 31
SQ FT: 12,000
SALES (est): 3MM
SALES (corp-wide): 28.9MM **Privately Held**
WEB: www.oceanshipholdings.com
SIC: 3731 Tankers, building & repairing
PA: Ocean Shipholdings, Inc.
16211 Park Ten Pl
Houston TX 77084
281 579-3700

(G-11122)
OCEAN SHIPHOLDINGS INC (PA)
16211 Park Ten Pl (77084-7016)
PHONE..........................281 579-3700
Joe F Vaughn Jr, *President*
John James, *President*
Delfina Clark, *Buyer*
Jack Welsh, *CFO*
Jake Jacobsen, *Manager*
EMP: 30
SALES (est): 28.9MM **Privately Held**
WEB: www.oceanshipholdings.com
SIC: 3731 4412 Tankers, building & repairing; deep sea foreign transportation of freight

(G-11123)
OCEAN SHIPS INC
16211 Park Ten Pl (77084-7016)
PHONE..........................281 579-3700
Joe F Vaughan Jr, *President*
John James, *Treasurer*
EMP: 31
SQ FT: 12,000
SALES (est): 6.6MM
SALES (corp-wide): 28.9MM **Privately Held**
WEB: www.oceanshipholdings.com
SIC: 4412 3731 Deep sea foreign transportation of freight; shipbuilding & repairing
PA: Ocean Shipholdings, Inc.
16211 Park Ten Pl
Houston TX 77084
281 579-3700

(G-11124)
OCEANEERING INTERNATIONAL INC (PA)
11911 Fm 529 Rd (77041-3000)
PHONE..........................713 329-4500
John R Huff, *Ch of Bd*
Roderick A Larson, *President*
Peter Moles, *Managing Dir*
Jason Charlet, *Superintendent*
Bear Haviland, *Superintendent*
◆ EMP: 188 EST: 1964
SALES: 2B **Publicly Held**
WEB: www.oceaneering.com
SIC: 1389 3731 8711 Oil field services; submersible marine robots, manned or unmanned; engineering services

(G-11125)
OCEANEERING INTERNATIONAL INC
Also Called: Oceaneering Deepwater Tech
11915 Fm 529 Rd (77041-3000)
PHONE..........................713 939-3682
Alejandro Alpizar, *Technician*
EMP: 103
SALES (corp-wide): 2B **Publicly Held**
WEB: www.oceaneering.com
SIC: 1389 Oil field services

(G-11126)
PA: Oceaneering International Inc
11911 Fm 529 Rd
Houston TX 77041
713 329-4500

(G-11126)
OCEANEERING INTERNATIONAL INC
Also Called: Global Data Solutions
11917 Fm 529 Rd (77041-3000)
PHONE..........................713 329-4318
Sam Almerico, *Engineer*
Greg Boyle, *Manager*
Douglas McLeod, *Manager*
Briana Pfeifer, *Supervisor*
EMP: 12
SALES (corp-wide): 2B **Publicly Held**
WEB: www.oceaneering.com
SIC: 1389 3731 8711 Oil field services; submersible marine robots, manned or unmanned; engineering services
PA: Oceaneering International Inc
11911 Fm 529 Rd
Houston TX 77041
713 329-4500

(G-11127)
OCEANEERING INTERNATIONAL INC
Grayloc Products Division
9342 Telge Rd (77095-5107)
PHONE..........................713 466-8853
Gerald Marsh, *Manager*
EMP: 40
SALES (corp-wide): 2B **Publicly Held**
WEB: www.oceaneering.com
SIC: 1389 Oil field services
PA: Oceaneering International Inc
11911 Fm 529 Rd
Houston TX 77041
713 329-4500

(G-11128)
OCEANEERING INTERNATIONAL INC
Oceaneering Space Suit Div
16665 Space Center Blvd (77058-2253)
PHONE..........................281 228-5300
Dave Wallace, *Manager*
EMP: 400
SALES (corp-wide): 2B **Publicly Held**
WEB: www.oceaneering.com
SIC: 3842 Space suits
PA: Oceaneering International Inc
11911 Fm 529 Rd
Houston TX 77041
713 329-4500

(G-11129)
OCEANEERING REFLANGE
Also Called: Reflange Gulf Coast
11911 Fm 529 Rd (77041-3000)
PHONE..........................713 682-5105
EMP: 50
SQ FT: 15,000
SALES (est): 5.9MM **Privately Held**
SIC: 3533 Mfg Oil/Gas Field Machinery

(G-11130)
OCI METHANOL MARKETING LLC (PA)
2800 Post Oak Blvd # 3150 (77056-6181)
PHONE..........................409 723-1900
Bashir Lebada, *President*
Mark Sanders, *Vice Pres*
Amanda Dillon, *Manager*
EMP: 41
SALES (est): 3.4MM **Privately Held**
WEB: www.oci.nl
SIC: 2861 Methanol, natural (wood alcohol)

(G-11131)
ODL INC
Also Called: Americas Odl
17000 Katy Fwy Ste 150 (77094-1446)
PHONE..........................281 647-8300
Derek Blackwood, *President*
William Cochrane, *Vice Pres*
John Lee, *Vice Pres*
Dave McGregor, *Vice Pres*
Des Temple, *Treasurer*
EMP: 9

SALES (est): 944.2K
SALES (corp-wide): 12.7B **Privately Held**
WEB: www.woodplc.com
SIC: 1382 Geological exploration, oil & gas field
HQ: Wood Group Uk Limited
Wellheads Place
Aberdeen AB21
122 450-0400

(G-11132)
ODRILL/MCM INC
Also Called: O'Drill-Mcm Pump & Valve Mfg
5055 Cranswick Rd (77041-7725)
PHONE..........................832 782-6300
Farouk J Saleh, *President*
Ferial Saleh, *Exec VP*
Dilip Shah, *Vice Pres*
Paula Whitfield, *Sales Staff*
Sangita Bhattacharya, *Officer*
◆ EMP: 21
SQ FT: 43,000
SALES (est): 11.6MM **Privately Held**
WEB: www.odrillmcm.com
SIC: 3533 5084 Oil field machinery & equipment; oil well machinery, equipment & supplies

(G-11133)
ODS INTERNATIONAL INC
10375 Richmond Ave # 800 (77042-4477)
PHONE..........................713 782-6767
Richard Hancock, *President*
EMP: 55
SALES (est): 5.1MM **Privately Held**
WEB: www.odsinternational.com
SIC: 8742 1389 Management consulting services; fire fighting, oil & gas field

(G-11134)
ODWALLA INC
Also Called: Coca-Cola
11707 S Sam Houston Pkwy (77031-2345)
PHONE..........................281 925-0189
EMP: 9
SALES (corp-wide): 41.8B **Publicly Held**
SIC: 2086 Carb Sft Drnkbtlcn
HQ: Odwalla, Inc.
1 Coca Cola Plz Nw
Atlanta GA 30313
479 721-6260

(G-11135)
ODYSSEA MARINE HOLDINGS INC
2500 Citywest Blvd (77042-3000)
PHONE..........................713 260-1100
Brad Hopper, *Branch Mgr*
William Gibbens, *General Counsel*
EMP: 864 **Privately Held**
WEB: www.odysseamarine.com
SIC: 1381 Drilling oil & gas wells
PA: Odyssea Marine Holdings, Inc.
11864 Highway 308
Larose LA 70373

(G-11136)
ODYSSEUS HOLDINGS LLC
Also Called: Mgc Electrical Services
5523 Indigo St (77096-1103)
PHONE..........................281 769-2399
Victor Cumagun, *Mng Member*
EMP: 18 EST: 2007
SALES (est): 3MM **Privately Held**
WEB: www.odysseusholdings.com
SIC: 1542 7371 2869 Commercial & office building contractors; custom computer programming services; industrial organic chemicals

(G-11137)
ODYSSEY PRECISION FABRICATING
11669 Brittmoore Park Dr (77041-6918)
PHONE..........................713 849-3043
Jeffrey Sun, *President*
Woody Fu, *Engineer*
EMP: 50
SALES (est): 2.2MM **Privately Held**
WEB: www.odysseyindustrial.com
SIC: 3444 Sheet metalwork

(G-11138)
OEM COMPONENTS INC
14535 Chrisman Rd (77039-1114)
PHONE..........................281 449-6258

EMP: 78
SALES (est): 25.4MM **Privately Held**
WEB: www.oemseals.com
SIC: 3533 Oil field machinery & equipment

(G-11139)
OES OILFIELD SERVICES USA INC
4295 San Felipe St # 250 (77027-2924)
PHONE.....................713 960-1339
Richard Upshall, *President*
Rebecca Reah, *President*
Mark Ashwell, *General Mgr*
M Jay Fogal, *Vice Pres*
Adeel Janjua, *Opers Staff*
EMP: 85
SQ FT: 3,000
SALES (est): 8MM **Privately Held**
WEB: www.oesgroup.com
SIC: 1389 Oil field services
PA: Oes Equipment Llc
　　Palace Tower, 1, S P Oasis Street 2
　　Floor, Office 202 Dubai
　　Dubai

(G-11140)
OFFENHAUSER COMPANY (PA)
Also Called: Structural Glass Division
2201 Telephone Rd (77023-4621)
P.O. Box 230068 (77223-0668)
PHONE.....................713 928-2981
Robert H Dillard, *President*
Tom Cervenka, *Engineer*
Greg Pfohl, *Project Engr*
Ross Ormond, *Producer*
EMP: 54 **EST:** 1933
SQ FT: 120,000
SALES (est): 7.2MM **Privately Held**
WEB: www.offenhauser.com
SIC: 3231 3444 3446 Doors, glass: made from purchased glass; sheet metalwork; ornamental metalwork

(G-11141)
OFFSHORE EXPRESS INC (PA)
20445 State Highway 249 # 280 (77070-2624)
PHONE.....................985 868-1438
Harlan F Belanger, *President*
EMP: 75
SQ FT: 21,000
SALES (est): 28.4MM **Privately Held**
WEB: www.osf-llc.com
SIC: 3731 4492 1389 1382 Drilling & production platforms, floating (oil & gas); towing & tugboat service; oil field services; oil & gas exploration services

(G-11142)
OFFSHORE KINEMATICS INC
16340 Park Ten Pl Ste 200 (77084-5185)
PHONE.....................713 934-7300
Stephen Byle, *CEO*
John Montague, *President*
▲ **EMP:** 12
SQ FT: 25,000
SALES (est): 2MM **Privately Held**
SIC: 3549 Wiredrawing & fabricating machinery & equipment, ex. die

(G-11143)
OFFSHORE SERVICE VESSELS LLC
Also Called: Edison Chouest Offshore
2000 W Sam Houston Pkwy S (77042-3615)
PHONE.....................832 251-6665
Rogerio Lacourt, *Engineer*
Lynn Timmons, *Corp Comm Staff*
George Banos, *Manager*
Louis Schneider, *Director*
John Metcalfe, *Master*
EMP: 9
SALES (corp-wide): 243.2MM **Privately Held**
WEB: www.chouest.com
SIC: 3731 Shipbuilding & repairing
PA: Offshore Service Vessels, L.L.C.
　　16201 E Main St
　　Cut Off LA 70345
　　985 601-4444

(G-11144)
OFFSHORE SPCLTY FBRICATORS LLC (PA)
Also Called: Offshore Domestic Group
20445 State Highway 249 # 280 (77070-2624)
PHONE.....................985 868-1438
Tom Fairley, *CEO*
William Kallop, *President*
Harlan Belanger, *Exec VP*
▲ **EMP:** 150
SQ FT: 21,000
SALES (est): 69.7MM **Privately Held**
WEB: www.osf-llc.com
SIC: 3731 1389 Drilling & production platforms, floating (oil & gas); oil field services

(G-11145)
OFI TESTING EQUIPMENT INC
Also Called: Ofite
11302 Steeplecrest Dr (77065-5649)
PHONE.....................713 880-9885
▼ **EMP:** 75
SQ FT: 35,000
SALES (est): 27.1MM **Privately Held**
WEB: www.ofite.com
SIC: 3533 Oil field machinery & equipment

(G-11146)
OFS INC
17211 Hall Shepperd Rd (77049-1049)
P.O. Box 1390, Harvey LA (70059-1390)
PHONE.....................281 456-0052
Jeff Plost, *District Mgr*
Loretta Shamsey, *District Mgr*
Scott Davis, *Vice Pres*
Matt McCormick, *Vice Pres*
Kyle Rust, *Plant Mgr*
EMP: 20
SQ FT: 3,940
SALES (corp-wide): 19.1MM **Privately Held**
WEB: www.ofsservices.com
SIC: 1389 Oil field services
PA: Ofs, Inc.
　　1120 Engineers Rd
　　Belle Chasse LA 70037
　　504 367-4815

(G-11147)
OFS GLOBAL INC
Also Called: Ensign
5308 Oates Rd (77013-2849)
PHONE.....................832 786-4728
Robert Geddes, *President*
Glenn Dagenais, *Director*
Michael Nuss, *Director*
Thomas Schledwitz, *Director*
Suzanne Davies, *Admin Sec*
EMP: 12
SALES (est): 3.1MM
SALES (corp-wide): 1.2B **Privately Held**
SIC: 1389 Oil field services
PA: Ensign Energy Services Inc
　　400 5 Ave Sw Suite 1000
　　Calgary AB T2P 0
　　403 262-1361

(G-11148)
OFS INTERNATIONAL LLC
7735 Miller Rd Ste 3 (77049)
PHONE.....................281 452-3036
Konstantin Semerikov, *President*
David Green, *COO*
Brandon Case, *Prdtn Mgr*
Gloria Craig, *Production*
Alexey Ratmikov, *CFO*
EMP: 300 **EST:** 2012
SQ FT: 3,659,040
SALES (est): 88.8MM
SALES (corp-wide): 18.6MM **Privately Held**
WEB: www.ofsint.com
SIC: 3533 3498 1389 Oil field machinery & equipment; couplings, pipe: fabricated from purchased pipe; pipe testing, oil field service
HQ: Tmk, Pao
　　D. 40 Str. 2a, Ul. Pokrovka
　　Moscow 10100

(G-11149)
OHS ENERGY CORP
700 Milam St Ste 1300 (77002-2736)
PHONE.....................832 871-5088

Peter Osborne, *President*
Harrison Kordestani, *Treasurer*
Robert Hughes, *Director*
EMP: 9
SALES (est): 240.8K **Privately Held**
WEB: www.ohsenergy.com
SIC: 1311 1382 Crude petroleum & natural gas production; oil & gas exploration services

(G-11150)
OIL DATA INC (PA)
1888 Stebbins Dr (77043-2841)
PHONE.....................713 461-7178
Grant Mackie, *President*
Steve Darnell, *VP Sales*
EMP: 34
SQ FT: 23,000
SALES (est): 4.7MM **Privately Held**
WEB: www.ceooildata.com
SIC: 1382 Seismograph surveys

(G-11151)
OIL FIELD DEV ENGRG LLC
Also Called: Ofd Engineering
12121 Wickchester Ln # 70 (77079-1230)
PHONE.....................281 679-9060
Jay Chen, *President*
James Deaver, *Vice Chairman*
Mike Songer, *Vice Pres*
Cheng-Yo Chen, *Engineer*
Chris Hartmann, *Engineer*
EMP: 64
SALES (est): 6.7MM **Privately Held**
WEB: www.ofdeng.com
SIC: 1389 8711 Oil field services; engineering services

(G-11152)
OIL FIELD SUPPLY PTY LTD
Also Called: Ofs
450 Gears Rd Ste 777 (77067-4522)
PHONE.....................281 877-0049
EMP: 13
SQ FT: 7,000
SALES (corp-wide): 1.2B **Privately Held**
WEB: www.chandelrentals.com
SIC: 5084 1381 Industrial machinery & equipment; drilling oil & gas wells
PA: Ensign Energy Services Inc
　　400 5 Ave Sw Suite 1000
　　Calgary AB T2P 0
　　403 262-1361

(G-11153)
OIL SPILL RESPONSE USA INC (DH)
Citycentre One 800 # 1 (77024)
PHONE.....................832 431-3191
Archibald Smith, *President*
Matt Simmons, *Opers Mgr*
Tony Prest, *CFO*
Gordon Ballard, *Director*
Joel W Conwell, *Director*
EMP: 16
SALES (est): 2.6MM
SALES (corp-wide): 182MM **Privately Held**
WEB: www.oilspillresponse.com
SIC: 1382 Geophysical exploration, oil & gas field

(G-11154)
OIL STATES ENERGY SERVICES LLC (HQ)
333 Clay St Ste 2100 (77002-2570)
PHONE.....................713 425-2400
Cindy B Taylor, *CEO*
Brad Dennis, *District Mgr*
James Jeffrey, *District Mgr*
Brian Sizemore, *District Mgr*
Christopher E Cragg, *Vice Pres*
▲ **EMP:** 50
SALES (est): 629.6MM
SALES (corp-wide): 1B **Publicly Held**
WEB: www.oses.com
SIC: 3533 5082 Oil field machinery & equipment; oil field equipment
PA: Oil States International, Inc.
　　333 Clay St Ste 4620
　　Houston TX 77002
　　713 652-0582

(G-11155)
OIL STATES INDUSTRIES INC
Skagit Smatco Oil Division
13111 Nw Fwy Ste 220 (77040-6318)
PHONE.....................713 510-2200
EMP: 10
SALES (corp-wide): 1B **Publicly Held**
WEB: www.oilstates.com
SIC: 3061 5082 Oil & gas field machinery rubber goods (mechanical); oil field equipment
HQ: Oil States Industries, Inc.
　　7701 S Cooper St
　　Arlington TX 76001

(G-11156)
OIL STATES INDUSTRIES INC
Also Called: Oil Sttes Qlty Conectr Systems
7250 W 43rd St (77092-5731)
PHONE.....................713 920-9800
EMP: 15
SALES (corp-wide): 1B **Publicly Held**
WEB: www.oilstates.com
SIC: 1389 Oil field services
HQ: Oil States Industries, Inc.
　　7701 S Cooper St
　　Arlington TX 76001

(G-11157)
OIL STATES INDUSTRIES INC
6120 E Orem Dr (77048-4429)
PHONE.....................713 445-2200
Ronald Diaz, *President*
Cesar Torres, *Manager*
Stephen Wagema, *Network Enginr*
EMP: 140
SALES (corp-wide): 1B **Publicly Held**
WEB: www.oilstates.com
SIC: 5082 3061 3561 3533 Oil field equipment; oil & gas field machinery rubber goods (mechanical); pumps & pumping equipment; drilling tools for gas, oil or water wells
HQ: Oil States Industries, Inc.
　　7701 S Cooper St
　　Arlington TX 76001

(G-11158)
OIL STATES INDUSTRIES INC
333 Clay St Ste 4620 (77002-4101)
PHONE.....................713 510-2200
Charles Fahrmeier, *Vice Pres*
Amy Callens, *Office Mgr*
EMP: 100
SALES (corp-wide): 1B **Publicly Held**
WEB: www.oilstates.com
SIC: 1389 Oil field services
HQ: Oil States Industries, Inc.
　　7701 S Cooper St
　　Arlington TX 76001

(G-11159)
OIL STATES INDUSTRIES INC
Also Called: Oil Sttes Houston Ship Channel
16730 Jacintoport Blvd (77015-6543)
PHONE.....................281 247-7400
Wyatt Justin, *Engineer*
Joe Canning, *Sales Staff*
Mike Keith, *Branch Mgr*
EMP: 13
SALES (corp-wide): 1B **Publicly Held**
WEB: www.oilstates.com
SIC: 1389 Oil field services
HQ: Oil States Industries, Inc.
　　7701 S Cooper St
　　Arlington TX 76001

(G-11160)
OIL STATES INDUSTRIES INC
5819 Almeda Genoa Rd (77048-4410)
PHONE.....................713 445-2200
Werner Hief, *Branch Mgr*
EMP: 140
SALES (corp-wide): 1B **Publicly Held**
WEB: www.oilstates.com
SIC: 1389 3061 3533 Oil & gas wells: building, repairing & dismantling; oil & gas field machinery rubber goods (mechanical); drilling tools for gas, oil or water wells
HQ: Oil States Industries, Inc.
　　7701 S Cooper St
　　Arlington TX 76001

▲ = Import ▼=Export
◆ =Import/Export

(G-11161)
OIL STATES INTERNATIONAL INC (PA)
333 Clay St Ste 4620 (77002-4101)
PHONE..................................713 652-0582
Robert L Potter, *Ch of Bd*
Cindy B Taylor, *President*
Troy Raicevich, *Superintendent*
Mike Lively, *Area Mgr*
Jacques Leblanc, *Business Mgr*
EMP: 78
SALES: 1B **Publicly Held**
WEB: www.oilstatesintl.com
SIC: 3353 3061 3053 3561 Aluminum sheet, plate & foil; oil & gas field machinery rubber goods (mechanical); gaskets, packing & sealing devices; pumps & pumping equipment; industrial valves

(G-11162)
OIL TECH SERVICES INC
Also Called: All Tech Services
10818 Sheldon Rd (77044-6006)
PHONE..................................281 456-9023
Mark Lee, *Branch Mgr*
EMP: 18
SALES (corp-wide): 2.6MM **Privately Held**
SIC: 3312 Tubes, steel & iron
PA: Oil Tech Services Inc
800 Wilcrest Dr Ste 101
Houston TX 77042
713 789-5144

(G-11163)
OIL TECH SERVICES INC (PA)
800 Wilcrest Dr Ste 101 (77042-1369)
PHONE..................................713 789-5144
Mark S Lee, *President*
Roy Lee Jr, *Vice Pres*
Kathryn M Lee, *Admin Sec*
▼ **EMP:** 15
SQ FT: 1,500
SALES (est): 2.6MM **Privately Held**
SIC: 3312 Tubes, steel & iron

(G-11164)
OILFIELD SERVICES & TECH LLC (PA)
Also Called: Tmk Completions
7735 Miller Road 3 (77049-1737)
PHONE..................................281 452-3036
Konstantin Semerikov, *CEO*
EMP: 14
SALES (est): 14.8MM **Privately Held**
WEB: www.ofsint.com
SIC: 1389 Oil field services

(G-11165)
OILFIELD-ELECTRIC-MARINE INC (HQ)
Also Called: OEM
6500 Brittmoore Rd (77041-5109)
PHONE..................................713 680-9659
Kevin Williams, *President*
John L Buyens Jr, *Vice Pres*
D F McNease, *Vice Pres*
James M Garaghty, *VP Engrg*
Lynda A Aycock, *Treasurer*
▲ **EMP:** 15
SQ FT: 52,000
SALES (est): 8.1MM
SALES (corp-wide): 67.2MM **Privately Held**
WEB: www.acsoilfield.com
SIC: 3825 5063 3612 Electrical power measuring equipment; electrical apparatus & equipment; transformers, except electric

(G-11166)
OKLAHOMA PACIFIC LTD
Also Called: Posse Energy
9805 Katy Fwy Ste 500 (77024-1271)
PHONE..................................713 209-1100
B F Shell, *President*
EMP: 40
SALES (est): 1.7MM **Privately Held**
SIC: 1382 Oil & gas exploration services

(G-11167)
OLAER USA INC (DH)
Also Called: Oil Air Hydraulics
15102 Sommermeyer St # 125 (77041-5307)
PHONE..................................713 937-8900
Klas Bergersen, *President*
Daniel Payton, *Marketing Mgr*
Mike Blenkinsop, *Director*
Tom Hughes, *Director*
Richard Cumberland, *Executive*
▲ **EMP:** 17
SQ FT: 25,000
SALES (est): 3.9MM
SALES (corp-wide): 43.1MM **Privately Held**
SIC: 3569 3443 5085 Filter elements, fluid, hydraulic line; heat exchangers: coolers (after, inter), condensers, etc.; pistons & valves
HQ: Oil Air Holdings Inc.
11505 W Little York Rd
Houston TX
713 937-8900

(G-11168)
OLDCASTLE BUILDINGENVELOPE INC
4822 Southerland Rd (77092-3024)
PHONE..................................800 392-9815
Sheila McDonald, *Office Mgr*
▲ **EMP:** 10
SALES (corp-wide): 30.6B **Privately Held**
WEB: www.obe.com
SIC: 3231 5231 Tempered glass: made from purchased glass; glass
HQ: Oldcastle Buildingenvelope, Inc.
5005 Lyndon B Johnson Fwy # 1050
Dallas TX 75244
214 273-3400

(G-11169)
OLDCASTLE BUILDINGENVELOPE INC
Also Called: H G P Industries
4822 Southerland Rd (77092-3024)
PHONE..................................713 827-1965
Scott Callaway, *General Mgr*
Maggie Walker, *Manager*
EMP: 80
SALES (corp-wide): 30.6B **Privately Held**
WEB: www.obe.com
SIC: 3231 Ornamental glass: cut, engraved or otherwise decorated
HQ: Oldcastle Buildingenvelope, Inc.
5005 Lyndon B Johnson Fwy # 1050
Dallas TX 75244
214 273-3400

(G-11170)
OLDCASTLE INFRASTRUCTURE INC
1606 Greens Rd Ste 100 (77032-1191)
PHONE..................................281 841-9187
EMP: 50
SALES (corp-wide): 30.6B **Privately Held**
WEB: www.oldcastleinfrastructure.com
SIC: 3272 Concrete products, precast
HQ: Oldcastle Infrastructure, Inc.
7000 Central Pkwy Ste 800
Atlanta GA 30328
470 602-2000

(G-11171)
OLIVER EQUIPMENT COMPANY LLC (DH)
Also Called: Nikkiso Pumps
4620 Brittmoore Rd (77041-8008)
P.O. Box 41145 (77241-1145)
PHONE..................................713 856-9206
Scott Jackson, *President*
Zachary Kerstens, *Sales Staff*
Jared Lell, *Sales Staff*
Dana Wetterer, *Sales Staff*
▼ **EMP:** 23 **EST:** 1975
SQ FT: 10,000
SALES (est): 8.4MM
SALES (corp-wide): 403.3MM **Privately Held**
WEB: www.oliverequip.com
SIC: 5084 3564 3561 3511 Hydraulic systems equipment & supplies; pumps & pumping equipment; blowers & fans; pumps & pumping equipment; turbines & turbine generator sets

(G-11172)
OLIVO ENTERPRISES INC
Also Called: Sam & Sons Truck Equipment
9925 Aldine Westfield Rd (77093-5405)
P.O. Box 16155 (77222-6155)
PHONE..................................713 694-3077
Samuel Olivo, *CEO*
Samuel T Olivo Sr, *Chairman*
Olivia Olivo, *Vice Pres*
Sam Olivo Sr, *Vice Pres*
Richard Olivo, *Treasurer*
EMP: 60
SQ FT: 18,000
SALES (est): 13.5MM **Privately Held**
WEB: www.olivocompanies.com
SIC: 3713 7539 Truck bodies (motor vehicles); trailer repair

(G-11173)
OMC AMERICAS INC
14655 Champion Forest Dr # 7 (77069-1400)
PHONE..................................713 893-7413
Louis G Moloer, *President*
EMP: 50
SALES (est): 5.1MM **Privately Held**
SIC: 3491 Automatic regulating & control valves

(G-11174)
OMEGA PROTEIN CORPORATION
1717 Saint James Pl # 550 (77056-3404)
PHONE..................................713 940-6100
Tahnee Evans, *Financial Analy*
Rhonda Coolures, *Branch Mgr*
Becky Thrift, *Technician*
EMP: 143
SALES (corp-wide): 268.6MM **Privately Held**
WEB: www.omegaprotein.com
SIC: 2077 Animal & marine fats & oils
HQ: Omega Protein Corporation
610 Menhaden Rd
Reedville VA 22539
804 453-6262

(G-11175)
OMK TUBE INC (HQ)
8304 Sorrel Leaf Ln (77055-1910)
P.O. Box 732205, Dallas (75373-2205)
PHONE..................................281 609-8150
Joel Johnson, *President*
Thomas Cownan, *CFO*
Lori Johnson, *Credit Staff*
Andy Brooks, *Sales Mgr*
Donald Milam, *Supervisor*
▲ **EMP:** 20 **EST:** 2011
SALES (est): 30.2MM
SALES (corp-wide): 1.5MM **Privately Held**
WEB: www.omksteel.com
SIC: 3317 3398 Steel pipe & tubes; metal heat treating

(G-11176)
OMK TUBE INC
16937 Leonard Rd (77049-1813)
PHONE..................................281 609-8970
Mark Strong, *Branch Mgr*
EMP: 150
SALES (corp-wide): 1.5MM **Privately Held**
WEB: www.omksteel.com
SIC: 3317 Steel pipe & tubes
HQ: Omk Tube, Inc.
8304 Sorrel Leaf Ln
Houston TX 77055
281 609-8150

(G-11177)
OMNI DATA SYSTEMS LTD LLP
11010 Neeshaw Dr Bldg B (77065-5274)
P.O. Box 691828 (77269-1828)
PHONE..................................281 469-4365
Kryill Orellana, *Manager*
Gary F Suttles,
Benjamin Suttles,
Kathy R Suttles,
◆ **EMP:** 10
SQ FT: 7,000

SALES (est): 5MM **Privately Held**
WEB: www.omnidatasys.net
SIC: 5045 7378 3577 Computer peripheral equipment; computer peripheral equipment repair & maintenance; computer peripheral equipment

(G-11178)
OMNI PRECISION INC
3721 Pinemont Dr (77018-1219)
PHONE..................................713 688-3131
Randy Hargrove, *President*
Randy J Hargrove, *President*
Patty McKinley, *Controller*
Michele Hargrove, *Admin Sec*
EMP: 12
SQ FT: 10,500
SALES (est): 1.5MM **Privately Held**
WEB: www.omniprecision.com
SIC: 3599 Machine shop, jobbing & repair; machine & other job shop work

(G-11179)
OMNI USA INC
Also Called: Omni Gear
3620 W 11th St (77008-6004)
PHONE..................................713 635-6331
Jeffrey K Daniel, *President*
Craig L Daniel, *Vice Pres*
Paige Delouche, *Opers Mgr*
▲ **EMP:** 10
SALES (est): 2.4MM **Privately Held**
WEB: www.omnigear.com
SIC: 3566 Gears, power transmission, except automotive

(G-11180)
OMNIDATA SERVICES GROUP LLC
10682 Jones Rd Ste 200 (77065-4214)
P.O. Box 691828 (77269-1828)
PHONE..................................281 469-4365
Gary Suttles, *Mng Member*
Ben Suttles,
EMP: 10 **EST:** 2010
SQ FT: 10,000
SALES (est): 1.5MM **Privately Held**
WEB: www.omnidatasys.net
SIC: 5045 7378 3577 7382 Computer peripheral equipment; printers, computer; computer maintenance & repair; optical scanning devices; input/output equipment, computer; confinement surveillance systems maintenance & monitoring; optical scanning data service

(G-11181)
OMRON ELECTRONICS LLC
Also Called: IDM Control
9510 N Houston Rosslyn Rd (77088-3904)
PHONE..................................713 849-1900
Nancy Lincoln, *Project Mgr*
Nico Silvestri, *Engineer*
Robert Bost, *Branch Mgr*
Sarim Ali, *Manager*
Gerald Allen, *Manager*
EMP: 100 **Privately Held**
WEB: www.omron.com
SIC: 3625 5063 7629 Motor controls, electric; motor controls, starters & relays: electric; electronic equipment repair
HQ: Omron Electronics Llc
2895 Grnspint Pkwy Ste 20
Hoffman Estates IL 60169
847 843-7900

(G-11182)
ONESUBSEA LLC
4646 W Sam Houston Pkwy N (77041-8214)
P.O. Box 3101 (77253-3101)
PHONE..................................713 939-2282
▲ **EMP:** 4265 **EST:** 2013
SALES (est): 228.8MM **Publicly Held**
WEB: www.onesubsea.slb.com
SIC: 3563 3491 3533 Air & gas compressors; automatic regulating & control valves; oil field machinery & equipment
HQ: Cameron International Corporation
4646 W Sam Houston Pkwy N
Houston TX 77041

G
E
O
G
R
A
P
H
I
C

(G-11183)
OPAL RESOURCES LLC
7600 W Tidwell Rd Ste 500 (77040-5792)
P.O. Box 40725 (77240-0725)
PHONE................................713 647-7300
Rick Lester,
EMP: 9
SALES (est): 2.5MM Privately Held
SIC: 1382 Oil & gas exploration services

(G-11184)
OPPORTUNE LP
4424 W Sam Houston Pkwy N # 200
(77041-8244)
PHONE................................713 772-0664
Jim Boney, President
Jeanna Kostak, COO
EMP: 80
SQ FT: 9,600
SALES (est): 4.2MM Privately Held
WEB: www.opportune.com
SIC: 1389 8721 Oil consultants; account-
ing, auditing & bookkeeping
PA: Opportune Llp
711 Louisiana St Ste 3100
Houston TX 77002

(G-11185)
**OPTIMUM CONSULTANCY SVCS
LLC**
9800 Richmond Ave (77042-4561)
PHONE................................713 505-0300
Nooshin Yazhari, President
Ramin Yazhari, Vice Pres
EMP: 10
SALES: 2.3MM Privately Held
WEB: www.optimumcs.com
SIC: 7379 8742 7371 7372 Computer re-
lated consulting services; ; business con-
sultant; computer software systems
analysis & design, custom; computer soft-
ware development & applications; com-
puter software development; business
oriented computer software

(G-11186)
OPULENT TRANSPORT LLC
1430 Wedgewood St (77093-1835)
PHONE................................713 551-1445
Damon Taylor,
Aptil Taylor,
EMP: 25
SALES (est): 3MM Privately Held
SIC: 3715 Truck trailers

(G-11187)
**OQ CHEMICALS CORPORATION
(DH)**
15375 Memorial Dr (77079-4138)
P.O. Box 941548 (77094-8548)
PHONE................................713 830-3135
Robert Gengelbach, President
Martina Flel, Principal
Miguel Mantas, Principal
Cornelius Robertson, Principal
Wolfgang Hackenberg, Vice Pres
◆ EMP: 30
SQ FT: 13,000
SALES (est): 94.4MM
SALES (corp-wide): 1.3B Privately Held
WEB: www.chemicals.oq.com
SIC: 2869 Industrial organic chemicals

(G-11188)
ORACLE CORPORATION
2100 West Loop S Ste 900 (77027-3522)
PHONE................................713 595-7656
Russell Johnson, Manager
EMP: 10
SALES (corp-wide): 39B Publicly Held
WEB: www.oracle.com
SIC: 7372 Prepackaged software
PA: Oracle Corporation
2300 Oracle Way
Austin TX 78741
737 867-1000

(G-11189)
ORACLE GLASS LLC
4927 Cranswick Rd (77041-7723)
PHONE................................713 462-4759
Madalyn Reaves, President
EMP: 10
SALES (est): 110.1K Privately Held
SIC: 7372 Prepackaged software

(G-11190)
**ORBITAL ENERGY GROUP INC
(PA)**
1924 Aldine Western Rd (77038-1204)
PHONE................................832 467-1420
James O'Neil, CEO
William J Clough, President
Paul White, Vice Pres
Daniel N Ford, CFO
Thomas Price, Director
EMP: 26 EST: 1998
SALES: 23.4MM Publicly Held
WEB: www.cuiglobal.com
SIC: 3824 8711 Mechanical & electro-
mechanical counters & devices; electrical
or electronic engineering

(G-11191)
**ORBITAL GAS SYSTEMS N
AMER INC**
Also Called: Ogsna
1924 Aldine Western Rd (77038-1204)
PHONE................................832 467-1420
Nicholas Clough, President
Matthew McKenzie, COO
Judith Howell, Prdtn Mgr
Neil Rudgley, Engineer
Daniel Ford, CFO
▲ EMP: 20
SQ FT: 1,400
SALES (est): 1.4MM
SALES (corp-wide): 23.4MM Publicly
Held
WEB: www.orbitalgas.com
SIC: 3823 Industrial instrmnts msrmnt dis-
play/control process variable
PA: Orbital Energy Group, Inc.
1924 Aldine Western Rd
Houston TX 77038
832 467-1420

(G-11192)
**ORBITAL SCIENCES
CORPORATION**
16055 Space Center Blvd (77062-6251)
PHONE................................281 218-6140
Raul Maldonado, Branch Mgr
EMP: 463 Publicly Held
WEB: www.northropgrumman.com
SIC: 3812 Aircraft/aerospace flight instru-
ments & guidance systems
HQ: Orbital Sciences Llc
45101 Warp Dr
Dulles VA 20166
703 406-5524

(G-11193)
**ORORA PACKAGING
SOLUTIONS**
Landsberg Houston Div 1052
10000 W Sam Huston Pkwy N
(77064-7472)
PHONE................................281 517-8600
Joanne Delaney, Sales Staff
Mindy Macintosh, Manager
Nancy Kroeger, Manager
James Shea, Supervisor
EMP: 54 Privately Held
WEB: www.ororapackagingsolutions.com
SIC: 5113 2653 Paper & products, wrap-
ping or coarse; boxes, corrugated: made
from purchased materials
HQ: Orora Packaging Solutions
6600 Valley View St
Buena Park CA 90620
714 562-6000

(G-11194)
**ORTHODONTIC TECHNOLOGIES
INC**
3315 W 12th St (77008-6121)
P.O. Box 4871 (77210-4871)
PHONE................................800 522-4636
Diane Johnson, President
EMP: 30
SQ FT: 3,500
SALES (est): 4MM Privately Held
WEB: www.specialtyappliances.com
SIC: 3843 8072 Orthodontic appliances;
dental laboratories

(G-11195)
ORTIZ INC
Also Called: Gold Star Construction
5380 W 34th St (77092-6626)
PHONE................................713 688-0374
Octavio Ortiz, President
EMP: 30
SALES (est): 3.9MM Privately Held
SIC: 3531 Plows: construction, excavating
& grading

(G-11196)
**OSAKA GAS USA
CORPORATION (HQ)**
1330 Post Oak Blvd Fl 19 (77056-3063)
PHONE................................713 354-9100
Hisaichi Yoneyama, President
Hisashi Fujii, Vice Pres
Masahiko Nakamura, Vice Pres
SEI Tamada, Vice Pres
Peters Joe, Opers Staff
EMP: 10 EST: 2007
SALES (est): 268MM Privately Held
WEB: www.osakagasusa.com
SIC: 2911 Gases & liquefied petroleum
gases

(G-11197)
OSIES INC (PA)
12734 Tanner Rd (77041-6511)
P.O. Box 842152 (77284-2152)
PHONE................................713 849-5131
Jose Rodriquez, President
Victor H Rodriguez, Vice Pres
Hugo Rodriguez, Manager
Antonio Alvarez, Assistant
EMP: 40
SQ FT: 90,000
SALES (est): 7.6MM Privately Held
WEB: www.osies.com
SIC: 3533 Oil & gas field machinery

(G-11198)
OSISOFT LLC
14701 Saint Marys Ln # 600 (77079-2921)
PHONE................................281 920-6170
Terese Juntz, Vice Pres
John Baier, Engineer
Kim Penamora, Engineer
Dan Lopez, Senior Engr
Richard Zbranak, Accounts Mgr
EMP: 10
SALES (corp-wide): 184MM Privately
Held
WEB: www.osisoft.com
SIC: 7373 7372 7371 Computer inte-
grated systems design; application com-
puter software; custom computer
programming services
PA: Osisoft, Llc
1600 Alvarado St
San Leandro CA 94577
510 297-5800

(G-11199)
OTCR INC
Also Called: Tri-C Resources
909 Wirt Rd (77024-3405)
PHONE................................713 685-3600
Michael M Cone, President
John Christopher Cone, COO
Robert T Herrin III, Vice Pres
P Mark Holmes, Vice Pres
Chris Cone, Safety Mgr
EMP: 18
SQ FT: 16,000
SALES (est): 8MM Privately Held
WEB: www.tricresources.com
SIC: 1382 Oil & gas exploration services

(G-11200)
OTECO INC (PA)
2828 Trout St (77093-5546)
PHONE................................713 695-3693
William E Pielop III, President
David Seifert, Superintendent
Carl Moener, Corp Secy
James P Lester, Vice Pres
Stuart Pielop, Vice Pres
▲ EMP: 140 EST: 1938
SQ FT: 400,000
SALES (est): 31MM Privately Held
WEB: www.oteco.com
SIC: 3561 3462 3599 Industrial pumps &
parts; iron & steel forgings; machine
shop, jobbing & repair

(G-11201)
OTECO INC
2811 Trout St (77093-5545)
PHONE................................713 695-3693
EMP: 75
SALES (corp-wide): 31MM Privately
Held
WEB: www.oteco.com
SIC: 3561 3462 Pumps, oil well & field;
iron & steel forgings
PA: Oteco, Inc.
2828 Trout St
Houston TX 77093
713 695-3693

(G-11202)
**OUTDOOR FURN REFINISHING
INC**
Also Called: Allied Powder Coating
6030 England St (77021-2714)
P.O. Box 321106 (77221-1106)
PHONE................................713 741-9779
Larry Dean, President
Mike Blackburn, President
Brian Kelly, Plant Mgr
Megan Zhu, Sales Staff
EMP: 100
SQ FT: 70,000
SALES (est): 11MM Privately Held
WEB: www.alliedpowder.com
SIC: 3471 Plating & polishing

(G-11203)
**OUTDOOR FURNITURE
REFINISHING**
6010 Saint Augustine St (77021-2616)
PHONE................................713 741-9779
Larry Dean, President
EMP: 12
SQ FT: 2,000
SALES (est): 1.2MM Privately Held
WEB: www.alliedpowder.com
SIC: 3471 Plating & polishing

(G-11204)
**OUTDOOR LIGHTING SERVICES
LP**
Also Called: Design Electric
5115 Steadmont Dr (77040-6525)
PHONE................................713 690-6301
Joe Heiman, Manager
EMP: 172
SALES (corp-wide): 787.7MM Privately
Held
WEB: www.americanlighting.com
SIC: 1731 3993 1611 General electrical
contractor; signs & advertising specialties;
highway & street construction
HQ: Outdoor Lighting Services Lp
4401 West Gate Blvd # 310
Austin TX 78745
512 440-7985

(G-11205)
OUTFRONT MEDIA LLC
Also Called: Outdoor Systems Advertising
1600 Studemont St (77007-3825)
PHONE................................713 868-2284
EMP: 82
SALES (corp-wide): 1.7B Publicly Held
WEB: www.outfrontmedia.com
SIC: 7312 3993 Outdoor advertising serv-
ices; signs & advertising specialties
HQ: Outfront Media Llc
405 Lexington Ave Fl 14
New York NY 10174
212 297-6400

(G-11206)
**OVERLAY PRODUCT SYSTEMS
INC**
Also Called: Alloy Products Group
3657 Briarpark Dr (77042-5264)
PHONE................................281 552-3500
▲ EMP: 73
SQ FT: 14,000
SALES (est): 9.8MM
SALES (corp-wide): 57.1MM Privately
Held
WEB: www.triten.com
SIC: 3312 3356 Pipes, iron & steel; non-
ferrous rolling & drawing

PA: Triten Corporation
10300 Town Park Dr Se4
Houston TX 77072
832 214-5000

(G-11207)
OVERTON ENERGY LLC
4265 San Felipe St # 1040 (77027-2929)
PHONE..................................713 580-7250
R Carter Overton, *CEO*
EMP: 13
SALES (est): 773.9K **Privately Held**
SIC: 1389 Building oil & gas well foundations on site

(G-11208)
OWENS CORNING SALES LLC
8360 Market St (77029-2418)
PHONE..................................713 672-8338
William Moore, *Branch Mgr*
Jimmy Morin, *Government*
EMP: 100 **Publicly Held**
WEB: www.owenscorning.com
SIC: 2952 2951 Roofing materials; asphalt paving mixtures & blocks
HQ: Owens Corning Sales, Llc
1 Owens Corning Pkwy
Toledo OH 43659
419 248-8000

(G-11209)
OXY INC (HQ)
5 Greenway Plz Ste 2400 (77046-0532)
P.O. Box 27570 (77227-7570)
PHONE..................................713 215-7000
Vicki A Hollub, *President*
Donald L Moore, *President*
Shayne Buchanan, *Vice Pres*
James Clarken, *Vice Pres*
Z Melissa Hunt, *Vice Pres*
▲ EMP: 225
SALES (est): 2.5B
SALES (corp-wide): 21.2B **Publicly Held**
WEB: www.oxy.com
SIC: 1311 1382 Crude petroleum production; natural gas production; oil & gas exploration services
PA: Occidental Petroleum Corporation
5 Greenway Plz Ste 110
Houston TX 77046
713 215-7000

(G-11210)
OXY USA INC
5 Greenway Plz Ste 110 (77046-0521)
P.O. Box 2289 (77252-2289)
PHONE..................................713 215-7000
John W Morgan, *President*
EMP: 125
SALES (corp-wide): 21.2B **Publicly Held**
WEB: www.oxy.com
SIC: 1311 Crude petroleum production; natural gas production
HQ: Oxy Usa Inc.
1001 S County Rd W
Odessa TX 79763
432 335-0995

(G-11211)
OXY USA WTP LP
Karen Sinard Fl 20 Flr 20 (77046)
P.O. Box 4294 (77210-4294)
PHONE..................................713 366-5303
Thomas Menges, *General Ptnr*
EMP: 99
SALES (est): 4.6MM
SALES (corp-wide): 21.2B **Publicly Held**
WEB: www.oxy.com
SIC: 1382 Oil & gas exploration services
PA: Occidental Petroleum Corporation
5 Greenway Plz Ste 110
Houston TX 77046
713 215-7000

(G-11212)
P & M BLASTING & COATING INC
7826 Harms Rd (77041-2125)
P.O. Box 840552 (77284-0552)
PHONE..................................713 896-4691
Mike S Wallace, *President*
EMP: 15
SALES (est): 1.7MM **Privately Held**
SIC: 3471 3479 Sand blasting of metal parts; painting of metal products

(G-11213)
P & N MACHINE COMPANY INC
12450 Windfern Rd (77064-3199)
PHONE..................................281 469-9140
EMP: 74
SQ FT: 23,000
SALES (est): 11.6MM **Privately Held**
WEB: www.pandnmachine.com
SIC: 3599 Machine shop, jobbing & repair

(G-11214)
P W PLATFORMS INC
4010 Broad St (77087-2132)
PHONE..................................713 731-7155
Bobby Pyler Jr, *President*
EMP: 11
SALES (est): 1.6MM **Privately Held**
WEB: www.pwplatforms.com
SIC: 3499 3537 Ladders, portable: metal; platforms, stands, tables, pallets & similar equipment

(G-11215)
P2 ENERGY SOLUTIONS INC
Also Called: Excalibur Computer Systems
1221 Lamar St Ste 1400 (77010-3073)
PHONE..................................713 787-6300
Faisal Kidwai, *Vice Pres*
Chris Wilke, *Vice Pres*
Leslie Simmons, *Accountant*
Thomas Burdette, *Sales Staff*
Gary Prezak, *Branch Mgr*
EMP: 70 **Privately Held**
WEB: www.p2energysolutions.com
SIC: 7372 Business oriented computer software
PA: P2 Energy Solutions, Inc.
1670 Broadway Ste 2800
Denver CO 80202

(G-11216)
P2ES HOLDINGS LLC
1221 Lamar St Ste 1300 (77010-3073)
PHONE..................................713 481-2000
David Muse, *Manager*
EMP: 100 **Privately Held**
WEB: www.p2energysolutions.com
SIC: 7372 5045 Business oriented computer software; computers
HQ: P2es Holdings, Llc
1670 Broadway Ste 2800
Denver CO 80202
303 292-0990

(G-11217)
PACIFIC DRILLING SERVICES INC
800 Town And Country Blvd # 5 (77024-4552)
PHONE..................................713 334-6662
Paul Reese, *CEO*
Tony Seeliger, *Senior VP*
Michael Acuff, *Vice Pres*
Lisa Buchanan, *Vice Pres*
Corey Thompson, *Vice Pres*
◆ EMP: 100
SALES (est): 47.4MM
SALES (corp-wide): 105.4MM **Privately Held**
WEB: www.pacificdrilling.com
SIC: 1381 Drilling oil & gas wells
HQ: Pacific Drilling, Llc
800 Town And Country Blvd # 500
Houston TX 77024
713 334-6662

(G-11218)
PACIFIC MWD INC
8250 W Little York Rd (77040-5314)
P.O. Box 40755 (77240-0755)
PHONE..................................713 466-1616
Kirk Slawson, *Sales Mgr*
Kimy Hoang, *Sales Staff*
Son Le, *Manager*
EMP: 23
SALES (est): 4.6MM **Privately Held**
WEB: www.pacificmwd.com
SIC: 1389 Oil field services

(G-11219)
PACIFIC REFINING COMPANY (PA)
9 Greenway Plz (77046-0905)
PHONE..................................713 877-6929
Coastal Energy Corporation, *General Ptnr*

Ron Matthews, *Treasurer*
EMP: 38
SALES (est): 2.9MM **Privately Held**
SIC: 2911 5172 Asphalt or asphaltic materials, made in refineries; petroleum products

(G-11220)
PACKAGING ONE INC
Also Called: Gaylord Boxes USA
6016 Knute St (77028-4915)
PHONE..................................713 674-0302
Baltazar Sanchez, *Vice Pres*
Michael Saint, *Marketing Staff*
EMP: 12
SALES (est): 1.7MM **Privately Held**
WEB: www.usagaylordboxes.com
SIC: 2611 2631 Pulp mills, mechanical & recycling processing; container, packaging & boxboard

(G-11221)
PAGE/NTRNTNAL CMMNICATIONS LLC
2748 Bingle Rd (77055-1135)
PHONE..................................713 341-6619
EMP: 108 EST: 2011
SALES (est): 14.8MM **Privately Held**
WEB: www.page-intl.com
SIC: 2759 Commercial printing

(G-11222)
PALACIOS & SONS LLC
9101 Jameel Rd Ste 110 (77040-6015)
PHONE..................................713 463-5851
Joost Van Welij, *Sales Mgr*
EMP: 9
SALES (corp-wide): 5.8MM **Privately Held**
SIC: 2032 Mexican foods: packaged in cans, jars, etc.
PA: Palacios & Sons, L.L.C.
1431 Greenway Dr Ste 800
Irving TX 75038
469 449-2060

(G-11223)
PALETERIA EL PIBE
636 E Crosstimbers St (77022-3724)
PHONE..................................281 541-8777
Christian Bustamante, *President*
EMP: 16
SALES (est): 2.8MM **Privately Held**
WEB: www.paleteriaelpibe.com
SIC: 2024 Ice cream, packaged: molded, on sticks, etc.; ice cream & ice milk

(G-11224)
PALLET OPS LLC
4847 Blaffer St (77026-3104)
PHONE..................................713 554-6972
John Maclay, *CEO*
EMP: 40
SQ FT: 2,000
SALES (est): 5.2MM **Privately Held**
WEB: www.pallet-ops.com
SIC: 2448 Pallets, wood

(G-11225)
PALOMA PARTNERS III LLC
1021 Main St Ste 2450 (77002-6530)
PHONE..................................713 650-8500
Christopher N O'Sullivan, *President*
John O Hastings, *Exec VP*
Mark J Gabrisch, *Senior VP*
RE Poirrier Jr, *CFO*
EMP: 19
SALES (est): 267.8K
SALES (corp-wide): 1.3B **Privately Held**
WEB: www.palomaresources.com
SIC: 1382 Geological exploration, oil & gas field
PA: Gulfport Energy Corporation
3001 Quail Springs Pkwy
Oklahoma City OK 73134
405 252-4600

(G-11226)
PAMCO LTD
4550 Post Oak Place Dr (77027-3165)
PHONE..................................713 621-0002
Merry Beth Truitt, *General Ptnr*
Anne P Lindsey, *General Ptnr*
EMP: 35
SALES (est): 2.5MM **Privately Held**
SIC: 3069 Molded rubber products

(G-11227)
PAN ASIAN CHEMICALS INC
5444 Westheimr Rd # 1570 (77056-5395)
PHONE..................................713 621-1888
James Wrubel, *CEO*
◆ EMP: 11
SQ FT: 3,000
SALES (est): 8MM **Privately Held**
WEB: www.panasianchem.com
SIC: 2899 Chemical supplies for foundries

(G-11228)
PAN INC
24 Greenway Plz Ste 965 (77046-2454)
PHONE..................................713 589-6850
Jo Ruth Kaplan, *President*
David Warshawsky, *VP Mktg*
Robert Kaplan, *Shareholder*
Kathy Kaplan Berkman, *Admin Sec*
EMP: 50
SALES (est): 3.4MM **Privately Held**
SIC: 2531 Seats, automobile

(G-11229)
PANASONIC AVIONICS CORPORATION
3340 Greens Rd Ste D700 (77032-2368)
PHONE..................................346 242-1599
Gregory Perkins, *Principal*
EMP: 16 **Privately Held**
WEB: www.panasonic.aero
SIC: 3728 Aircraft parts & equipment
HQ: Panasonic Avionics Corporation
26200 Enterprise Way
Lake Forest CA 92630

(G-11230)
PANEL-TECH INCORPORATED (PA)
7800 Breen Dr (77064-8400)
PHONE..................................713 896-6900
Ron Grant, *President*
Cary Grant, *Superintendent*
Jerrold Grant, *Vice Pres*
EMP: 40
SQ FT: 15,000
SALES (est): 7.8MM **Privately Held**
WEB: www.ptimillwork.com
SIC: 2431 Millwork

(G-11231)
PANELMATIC TEXAS INC
9826 Windmill Park Ln (77064-3301)
P.O. Box 41021 (77241-1021)
PHONE..................................281 890-1678
Richard P Leach, *President*
Al Pekkanen, *Project Mgr*
David D Adamson, *CFO*
David Mock, *Info Tech Mgr*
▼ EMP: 27
SQ FT: 22,000
SALES (est): 8.2MM
SALES (corp-wide): 42.4MM **Privately Held**
WEB: www.panelmatic.com
SIC: 3613 8711 Control panels, electric; designing: ship, boat, machine & product
PA: Panelmatic, Inc.
258 Donald Dr
Fairfield OH 45014
513 829-3666

(G-11232)
PANGEA ENTERPRISES INC
5333 Westheimr Rd # 1050 (77056-5407)
PHONE..................................956 542-9494
Marco Pesquera, *President*
EMP: 25 EST: 1998
SALES (est): 4.5MM **Privately Held**
WEB: www.pangeasite.com
SIC: 3443 8711 8742 3731 Industrial vessels, tanks & containers; industrial engineers; industrial & labor consulting services; commercial cargo ships, building & repairing; commercial passenger ships, building & repairing

(G-11233)
PANHANDLE EASTRN PIPE LINE LP
1221 Mckinney St Ste 2252 (77010-2007)
PHONE..................................713 627-5400
Paul M Anderson, *President*
EMP: 16 **Publicly Held**

WEB:
www.peplmessenger.energytransfer.com
SIC: 4922 1321 Pipelines, natural gas; natural gas liquids
HQ: Panhandle Eastern Pipe Line Company, Lp
8111 Westchester Dr # 600
Dallas TX 75225
214 981-0700

(G-11234)
PAR HAWAII REFINING LLC (HQ)
825 Town And Country Ln # 150 (77024-2232)
PHONE....................281 899-4800
Joseph Israel, *President*
Chet Greene, *Vice Pres*
John Kaiser, *Vice Pres*
Eric Lee, *Vice Pres*
Andrew Nomura, *Vice Pres*
▲ **EMP:** 225
SQ FT: 15,000
SALES (est): 197.2MM
SALES (corp-wide): 5.4B **Publicly Held**
WEB: www.parhawaii.com
SIC: 5541 2911 Gasoline service stations; petroleum refining
PA: Par Pacific Holdings, Inc.
825 Town And Country Ln # 1500
Houston TX 77024
281 899-4800

(G-11235)
PAR PACIFIC HOLDINGS INC (PA)
825 Town And Country Ln # 1500 (77024-2235)
PHONE....................281 899-4800
Robert S Silberman, *Ch of Bd*
William C Pate, *President*
Mike Miyashiro, *General Mgr*
Richard Green, *Superintendent*
Joseph Israel, *Senior VP*
EMP: 80
SALES: 5.4B **Publicly Held**
WEB: www.parpacific.com
SIC: 1311 2911 4923 5172 Crude petroleum production; crude petroleum & natural gas production; petroleum refining; gas transmission & distribution; petroleum products

(G-11236)
PAR PETROLEUM LLC (HQ)
825 Town And Country Ln # 1500 (77024-2235)
PHONE....................281 899-4800
Hung Tran, *Manager*
Lance Tanaka, *Director*
John Young Jr,
EMP: 9
SALES (est): 125.6MM
SALES (corp-wide): 5.4B **Publicly Held**
WEB: www.parpacific.com
SIC: 1311 Crude petroleum & natural gas production
PA: Par Pacific Holdings, Inc.
825 Town And Country Ln # 1500
Houston TX 77024
281 899-4800

(G-11237)
PARABELLUM ENERGY LLC
1302 Waugh Dr Ste 161 (77019-3908)
PHONE....................832 460-6521
Michael Barham, *Managing Prtnr*
Shannon McAdams, *Partner*
EMP: 15
SALES (est): 610.2K **Privately Held**
WEB: www.parabellumenergy.com
SIC: 1382 Oil & gas exploration services

(G-11238)
PARADIGM SES LLC
1001 West Loop S Ste 700k (77027-9084)
PHONE....................713 402-6140
Prince Thomas, *President*
EMP: 10
SALES (est): 779.1K **Privately Held**
WEB: www.paradigmses.com
SIC: 7371 7372 Computer software development; computer software systems analysis & design, custom; prepackaged software; application computer software; business oriented computer software

(G-11239)
PARADIGM SRP LLC
Also Called: Drivetanks.com
11811 Brantly Ave (77034-5599)
PHONE....................877 677-9899
John Lindsey, *Vice Pres*
Joseph Degidio, *Mng Member*
▲ **EMP:** 15
SQ FT: 2,000
SALES (est): 1.4MM **Privately Held**
WEB: www.paradigmsrp.com
SIC: 3812 Defense systems & equipment

(G-11240)
PARAGON OFFSHORE PLC (DH)
3151 Briarpark Dr Ste 700 (77042-3809)
PHONE....................832 783-4000
Dean E Taylor, *CEO*
J Robinson West, *Ch of Bd*
James Swent, *President*
George Sandison, *Chairman*
Anirudha Pangarkar, *COO*
EMP: 11 **EST:** 2014
SALES (est): 636.1MM **Publicly Held**
WEB: www.paragonoffshore.com
SIC: 1382 Oil & gas exploration services
HQ: Borr Drilling Management As
Fridtjof Nansens Plass 4
Oslo 0160
224 830-00

(G-11241)
PARKER DRILLING COMPANY (PA)
5 Greenway Plz Ste 100 (77046-0506)
PHONE....................281 406-2000
Sandy Esslemon, *CEO*
Hazel Fraser, *Regional Mgr*
Nick Henley, *Business Mgr*
Kelly Thorman, *Counsel*
Jennifer F Simons, *Senior VP*
◆ **EMP:** 179
SALES (est): 571MM **Publicly Held**
WEB: www.parkerdrilling.com
SIC: 1381 7353 Drilling oil & gas wells; oil equipment rental services; oil field equipment, rental or leasing; oil well drilling equipment, rental or leasing

(G-11242)
PARKER DRILLING MGT SVCS LTD
5 Greenway Plz Ste 100 (77046-0506)
PHONE....................281 406-2000
◆ **EMP:** 150 **EST:** 1999
SALES (est): 15MM
SALES (corp-wide): 571MM **Publicly Held**
WEB: www.parkerdrilling.com
SIC: 1381 Drilling oil & gas wells
PA: Parker Drilling Company
5 Greenway Plz Ste 100
Houston TX 77046
281 406-2000

(G-11243)
PARKER DRILLING OFFSHR CO LLC
5 Greenway Plz Ste 100 (77046-0506)
PHONE....................281 406-2000
Bruce J Korver, *Vice Pres*
Tommy Jones, *Manager*
Joshua Lambert, *Manager*
Dana Rasco, *Manager*
John E Menger, *Manager*
EMP: 15
SALES (est): 2.8MM
SALES (corp-wide): 571MM **Publicly Held**
WEB: www.parkerdrilling.com
SIC: 1381 Drilling oil & gas wells
PA: Parker Drilling Company
5 Greenway Plz Ste 100
Houston TX 77046
281 406-2000

(G-11244)
PARKER SCHOOL UNIFORMS LLC
12524 Memorial Dr (77024-6000)
PHONE....................713 465-1635
EMP: 25
SALES (corp-wide): 81.8MM **Privately Held**
SIC: 2389 Mfg Apparel/Accessories

PA: Parker School Uniforms, Llc
6300 W By Northwest Blvd # 100
Houston TX 77040
713 957-1511

(G-11245)
PARKER SYSTEMS INC
6601 Harrisburg Blvd (77011-4429)
PHONE....................800 262-4891
Connie Parker, *Ch of Bd*
Michael Parker, *President*
EMP: 10 **EST:** 1954
SQ FT: 12,500 **Privately Held**
SIC: 2298 3496 Slings, rope; woven wire products

(G-11246)
PARKER-HANNIFIN CORPORATION
Also Called: Texas Thermowell
16101 Vallen Dr (77041-4030)
PHONE....................409 924-0300
Miguel Gonzalez, *Electrical Engi*
Brandon Tucker, *Manager*
Nicholas Holton, *Manager*
Shawn Landry, *Manager*
Victor Rasanow, *Manager*
EMP: 25
SALES (corp-wide): 13.7B **Publicly Held**
WEB: www.phtruck.com
SIC: 3823 Industrial instrmnts msrmnt display/control process variable
PA: Parker-Hannifin Corporation
6035 Parkland Blvd
Cleveland OH 44124
216 896-3000

(G-11247)
PARMAN CAPITAL GROUP LLC
1000 La St Ste 5900 (77002)
PHONE....................713 751-2700
Hushang Ansary, *Ch of Bd*
EMP: 2301
SALES (est): 20.4MM **Privately Held**
SIC: 1389 7353 Testing, measuring, surveying & analysis services; oil equipment rental services

(G-11248)
PARTEN OPERATING INC (PA)
211 Hghland Crotx Dr Ste (77073)
PHONE....................281 874-2101
John R Parten, *President*
Virginia Cortinas, *Vice Pres*
EMP: 10
SQ FT: 10,000
SALES (est): 12.2MM **Privately Held**
SIC: 1311 Crude petroleum production

(G-11249)
PARTICLE DRILLING TECH INC
11050 W Little York Rd Q (77041-5056)
PHONE....................713 223-3031
John D Schiller Jr, *CEO*
Gordon Tibbitts, *Vice Pres*
J Chris Boswell, *CFO*
David Elifs, *CFO*
Alan Carlson, *Manager*
EMP: 19
SQ FT: 48,750
SALES (est): 5.3MM **Privately Held**
WEB: www.particledrilling.com
SIC: 1381 Directional drilling oil & gas wells

(G-11250)
PARTNERS METALFAB LP
Also Called: Metal Craft
1309 Akron St (77029-2517)
PHONE....................713 672-6888
Larry Freeman, *Owner*
Edward Gonzalez, *General Mgr*
Jose Gonzalez, *Project Mgr*
EMP: 30 **EST:** 1981
SQ FT: 14,000
SALES (est): 6.1MM **Privately Held**
WEB: www.partnersmetalfab.com
SIC: 3441 Fabricated structural metal

(G-11251)
PARTNERS SPECIALTIES INC
12405 Fuqua St (77034-4557)
P.O. Box 34547 (77234-4547)
PHONE....................281 922-9102
Walt Warren, *Vice Pres*
EMP: 50

SALES (est): 20K **Privately Held**
WEB: www.psi-psi.com
SIC: 5541 1389 1623 Gasoline service stations; building oil & gas well foundations on site; oil & gas pipeline construction

(G-11252)
PARTRAC GEOMARINE INC
16225 Park Ten Pl Ste 500 (77084-5152)
PHONE....................713 338-3495
Sam Athey, *President*
EMP: 15
SQ FT: 400
SALES (est): 409.4K **Privately Held**
WEB: www.partrac-geomarine.com
SIC: 8748 8999 1389 8711 Environmental consultant; geological consultant; geophysical consultant; oil consultants; consulting engineer; environmental research
PA: Partrac Limited
Suite 440, Baltic Chambers
Glasgow G2 6H

(G-11253)
PARTY PROPS INC
4025 Willowbend Blvd # 30 (77025-5726)
PHONE....................713 868-5433
Greg Miller, *President*
Russell S Grones, *Principal*
Andrea R Mendez, *Corp Secy*
Rusty Grones, *Sales Staff*
EMP: 21
SQ FT: 40,000
SALES (est): 3.1MM **Privately Held**
WEB: www.partypropsinc.com
SIC: 7359 3648 2391 Party supplies rental services; lighting equipment; curtains & draperies

(G-11254)
PAS GROUP LLC (PA)
Also Called: P A S
13100 Space Center Blvd (77059-3653)
PHONE....................281 286-6565
Eddie Habibi, *President*
Tamara Anderson, *Vice Pres*
Krystal White, *Opers Staff*
David Covert, *Engineer*
Ajinkya Nikam, *Engineer*
EMP: 96
SQ FT: 2,000
SALES (est): 26MM **Privately Held**
WEB: www.pas.com
SIC: 7372 Prepackaged software

(G-11255)
PASADENA REFINING SYSTEM INC (DH)
10350 Richmond Ave # 1400 (77042-4002)
PHONE....................713 920-1874
Fernando Oliveira, *CEO*
Fernando Feitosa De Oliveira, *CEO*
Francisco Neto, *President*
Bradley Durtschi, *Manager*
◆ **EMP:** 139
SALES (est): 88.6MM
SALES (corp-wide): 146.5B **Publicly Held**
WEB: www.petrobras.com
SIC: 2911 Petroleum refining
HQ: Chevron U.S.A. Inc.
6001 Bollinger Canyon Rd D1248
San Ramon CA 94583
925 842-1000

(G-11256)
PASON SYSTEMS USA CORP (HQ)
7701 W Little York Rd # 800 (77040-5493)
PHONE....................713 693-8700
Zaid Rankine, *President*
Bryce McLean, *Vice Pres*
Keith Leroy, *Opers Staff*
Scott Schmidt, *Opers Staff*
Damon Dickson, *Accounts Mgr*
EMP: 89
SQ FT: 10,000

▲ = Import ▼ = Export
◆ = Import/Export

SALES (est): 64.3MM
SALES (corp-wide): 222MM **Privately Held**
WEB: www.energytoolbase.com
SIC: 1389 8999 7371 3577 Well plugging & abandoning, oil & gas; testing, measuring, surveying & analysis services; geological consultant; computer software systems analysis & design, custom; computer peripheral equipment
PA: Pason Systems Inc
    6130 3 St Se
    Calgary AB T2H 1
    403 301-3400

(G-11257)
PATARA STONE INC
6550 Long Point Rd Ste A (77055-2627)
PHONE................................713 681-2301
Tahsin Gurpinar, *President*
Evren Gurpinar, *Vice Pres*
EMP: 22 EST: 2013
SQ FT: 40,000
SALES (est): 5.5MM **Privately Held**
WEB: www.patarastone.com
SIC: 5198 1422 5032 3253 Wallcoverings; limestones, ground; marble building stone; floor tile, ceramic

(G-11258)
PATCO MACHINE & FAB INC
2002 Humble Westfield Rd (77073-2510)
PHONE................................281 443-2837
EMP: 24
SQ FT: 15,400
SALES (est): 11.8MM **Privately Held**
WEB: www.patcomachandfab.com
SIC: 5084 3599 Industrial machinery & equipment; machine shop, jobbing & repair

(G-11259)
PATINA METALS INC
9303 Clay Rd (77080-1598)
PHONE................................713 462-6117
Jeff Emmott, *President*
Walter Emmott, *Vice Pres*
Walter E Emmott, *Admin Sec*
EMP: 32 EST: 1965
SQ FT: 3,000
SALES (est): 5.3MM **Privately Held**
WEB: www.patinametals.com
SIC: 3446 Ornamental metalwork

(G-11260)
PATIO ONE FURNITURE LP (PA)
10520 Harwin Dr (77036-1506)
PHONE................................713 789-8080
Hamid Mehrinfar, *Partner*
Catherine Mehrinfar, *Partner*
▲ EMP: 10 EST: 1979
SQ FT: 16,000
SALES (est): 2.5MM **Privately Held**
WEB: www.patio1.com
SIC: 5712 2511 5719 2519 Outdoor & garden furniture; wood lawn & garden furniture; wicker, rattan or reed home furnishings; wicker & rattan furniture; furniture

(G-11261)
PATTERSON-UTI DRLG INTL INC
10713 W Sam Houston Pkwy (77064-3583)
P.O. Box 1416, Snyder (79550-1416)
PHONE................................214 765-5530
William A Hendricks Jr, *CEO*
Justin Brown, *Superintendent*
Rodrigo Orta, *Superintendent*
Charles Pfluger, *Superintendent*
Erin Nix, *Counsel*
EMP: 100
SALES (est): 30.8MM
SALES (corp-wide): 1.1B **Publicly Held**
WEB: www.patenergy.com
SIC: 1381 Drilling oil & gas wells
PA: Patterson-Uti Energy, Inc.
    10713 W Sam Houston Pkwy
    Houston TX 77064
    281 765-7100

(G-11262)
PATTERSON-UTI ENERGY INC (PA)
10713 W Sam Houston Pkwy (77064-3583)
PHONE................................281 765-7100
Mark S Siegel, *Ch of Bd*
William Andrew Hendricks Jr, *President*
James M Holcomb, *President*
Seth D Wexler, *Senior VP*
Mike Drickamer, *Vice Pres*
EMP: 60
SALES: 1.1B **Publicly Held**
WEB: www.patenergy.com
SIC: 1381 1389 1311 Directional drilling oil & gas wells; oil & gas wells: building, repairing & dismantling; cementing oil & gas well casings; crude petroleum & natural gas; crude petroleum production; natural gas production

(G-11263)
PATY INVESTMENTS INC (PA)
4540 S Pinemont Dr # 110 (77041-9300)
PHONE................................713 688-7686
EMP: 20 EST: 1972
SQ FT: 10,000
SALES (est): 11.2MM **Privately Held**
WEB: www.patyinc.com
SIC: 2369 2361 Girls' & children's outerwear; girls' & children's dresses, blouses & shirts

(G-11264)
PD SUPPLY INC
10803 Vinecrest Dr Ste 1 (77086-1792)
PHONE................................713 435-6100
EMP: 28
SALES (est): 5.2MM
SALES (corp-wide): 1.1B **Privately Held**
WEB: www.precisiondrilling.com
SIC: 3533 Oil & gas drilling rigs & equipment
HQ: Precision Drilling Company, Lp
    10350 Richmond Ave # 700
    Houston TX 77042

(G-11265)
PDQ MACHINE SHOP INC
15151 Henry Rd (77060-5311)
PHONE................................832 327-4455
Richard G Westfall, *President*
Nancy Westfall, *Office Mgr*
EMP: 24
SQ FT: 15,000
SALES (est): 4.5MM **Privately Held**
WEB: www.pdqmachine.com
SIC: 3599 Machine shop, jobbing & repair

(G-11266)
PDVSA SERVICES INC
Also Called: Bariven
1293 Eldridge Pkwy (77077-1670)
P.O. Box 4403 (77210-4403)
PHONE................................281 531-0004
Iyanu De Cajias, *CEO*
Tim Marshman, *Principal*
Jesus Guaraco, *Chairman*
Tanya Bonilla, *Treasurer*
Maria Gimenez, *Finance Mgr*
◆ EMP: 60
SQ FT: 25,000
SALES (est): 15.5MM **Privately Held**
WEB: www.psi.pdv.com
SIC: 2911 6221 Fractionation products of crude petroleum, hydrocarbons; commodity brokers, contracts
HQ: Bariven Sa
    Centro Empresarial Eurobuilding, Piso 10
    Caracas D.F.

(G-11267)
PEARSON EDUCATION INC
11999 Katy Fwy (77079-1611)
PHONE................................281 496-0657
EMP: 27
SALES (corp-wide): 7.7B **Privately Held**
SIC: 2731 Books-Publishing/Printing
HQ: Pearson Education, Inc.
    1 Lake St
    Upper Saddle River NJ 07030
    201 236-7000

(G-11268)
PECK & COMPANY
98 Dennis St (77006-1556)
PHONE................................713 526-2590
Bill I Peck, *President*
Bill Peck, *Vice Pres*
EMP: 24
SQ FT: 12,000
SALES (est): 2.5MM **Privately Held**
WEB: www.peckandcompany.com
SIC: 2514 2522 Metal household furniture; office furniture, except wood

(G-11269)
PEDRAZA HVAC INC
11318 Timber Crest Dr (77065-2945)
PHONE................................281 970-4834
Job D Pedraza, *President*
Marco Pedraza, *Mayor*
EMP: 15
SALES (est): 1MM **Privately Held**
WEB: www.pedrazagroup.com
SIC: 3585 Heating & air conditioning combination units

(G-11270)
PEEK TRAFFIC CORPORATION
5401 N Sam Houston Pkwy W (77086-1436)
PHONE................................281 453-0200
Alejandro Brunell, *CEO*
Rolando Garcia, *COO*
Alejandro Fuentes, *CFO*
EMP: 130
SQ FT: 70,000
SALES (est): 27.5MM
SALES (corp-wide): 57.1MM **Privately Held**
WEB: www.peektraffic.com
SIC: 3669 5063 7372 Traffic signals, electric; signaling equipment, electrical; business oriented computer software
PA: Signal Group, Inc.
    5401 N Sam Houston Pkwy W
    Houston TX 77086
    281 453-0200

(G-11271)
PELICAN ENERGY PARTNERS LP (PA)
2050 W Sam Houston Pkwy S # 1550 (77042-3666)
PHONE................................713 559-7110
Mike Scott, *Partner*
Joseph Winkler, *Partner*
Chris Koranek, *Vice Pres*
Iann Poole, *Vice Pres*
Nicole Meier, *Accountant*
EMP: 63 EST: 2012
SALES (est): 17.1MM **Privately Held**
WEB: www.pelicanenergypartners.com
SIC: 6726 3533 Investment offices; oil field machinery & equipment

(G-11272)
PELICAN INDUSTRIAL INC
8550 Westland West Blvd (77041-1214)
PHONE................................832 678-4808
Xiadyan Miad, *Principal*
Walter Maldonado, *Marketing Staff*
▲ EMP: 24
SALES (est): 4.7MM **Privately Held**
WEB: www.pelicancnc.com
SIC: 3523 Farm machinery & equipment

(G-11273)
PELICAN REFINING COMPANY LLC (PA)
Also Called: Pelican Asphalt Refining
4400 Post Oak Pkwy Ste 26 (77027-3433)
P.O. Box 56109 (77256-6109)
PHONE................................713 877-7777
Oscar Wyatt Jr, *Mng Member*
Byron A Hamilton,
▲ EMP: 9
SALES (est): 3.1MM **Privately Held**
WEB: www.pelicanrefining.com
SIC: 2911 Asphalt or asphaltic materials, made in refineries

(G-11274)
PELICAN TANK PARTS INC
Also Called: Pelican Worldwide
14710 Hathrow Forest Pkwy (77032-5402)
PHONE................................713 862-5557

Garth Belue, *Principal*
EMP: 17
SALES (est): 2.5MM **Privately Held**
WEB: www.pelicanworldwide.com
SIC: 3053 Gaskets, packing & sealing devices

(G-11275)
PELICAN WORLDWIDE INCORPORATED
14710 Hathrow Forest Pkwy (77032-5402)
PHONE................................713 862-5557
Thomas Chapman, *President*
◆ EMP: 35
SQ FT: 12,000
SALES (est): 5.8MM **Privately Held**
WEB: www.pelicanww.us
SIC: 3053 Gaskets, packing & sealing devices

(G-11276)
PELLETIZER KNIVES INC (PA)
9703 Telge Rd (77095-5005)
PHONE................................281 859-4492
Greg Messina, *President*
Evelyn Tofte, *Principal*
Bill Tofte, *Vice Pres*
Michael Tofte, *Treasurer*
Anna Gaudet, *Controller*
EMP: 17 EST: 1971
SQ FT: 22,000
SALES (est): 2.7MM **Privately Held**
WEB: www.pelletizerknivesinc.com
SIC: 3423 Knives, agricultural or industrial

(G-11277)
PENN VIRGINIA CORPORATION (PA)
16285 Park Ten Pl Ste 500 (77084-7213)
PHONE................................713 722-6500
David Geenberg, *Ch of Bd*
Darin G Holderness, *Ch of Bd*
Darrin J Henke, *President*
Nancy M Snyder, *Exec VP*
Julia Gwaltney, *Senior VP*
EMP: 20 EST: 1882
SALES: 440.8MM **Publicly Held**
WEB: www.pennvirginia.com
SIC: 1382 Oil & gas exploration services

(G-11278)
PENN VIRGINIA MC CORPORATION
14701 Saint Marys Ln # 275 (77079-2933)
PHONE................................713 722-6500
Clay Sullivan, *President*
Jodi Hasley, *Manager*
▲ EMP: 65
SALES (est): 5MM
SALES (corp-wide): 440.8MM **Publicly Held**
WEB: www.pennvirginia.com
SIC: 1311 Crude petroleum production; natural gas production
PA: Penn Virginia Corporation
    16285 Park Ten Pl Ste 500
    Houston TX 77084
    713 722-6500

(G-11279)
PENN VIRGINIA MC ENERGY LLC
14701 Saint Marys Ln # 275 (77079-2921)
PHONE................................713 722-6500
Clay Sullivan,
EMP: 38
SALES (est): 2.2MM
SALES (corp-wide): 440.8MM **Publicly Held**
WEB: www.pennvirginia.com
SIC: 1382 Oil & gas exploration services
PA: Penn Virginia Corporation
    16285 Park Ten Pl Ste 500
    Houston TX 77084
    713 722-6500

(G-11280)
PENN VIRGINIA OIL & GAS LP (HQ)
16285 Park Ten Pl Ste 500 (77084-7213)
PHONE................................713 722-6500
H Baird Whitehead, *CEO*
John Brooks, *Vice Pres*
Tammy Hinkle, *Vice Pres*
Milton Holub, *Purchasing*

Steven A Hartman, *CFO*
EMP: 14
SALES (est): 30MM
SALES (corp-wide): 440.8MM **Publicly Held**
WEB: www.pennvirginia.com
SIC: 1382 Oil & gas exploration services
PA: Penn Virginia Corporation
　　16285 Park Ten Pl Ste 500
　　Houston TX 77084
　　713 722-6500

(G-11281)
PENN VIRGINIA OIL & GAS CORP (HQ)
14701 Saint Marys Ln # 275 (77079-2921)
PHONE..................................610 687-8900
H Baird Whitehead, *President*
John Brooks, *Vice Pres*
Steven A Hartman, *Vice Pres*
Ann Horton, *Vice Pres*
Keith Horton, *Vice Pres*
EMP: 18
SQ FT: 6,000
SALES (est): 47.8MM
SALES (corp-wide): 440.8MM **Publicly Held**
WEB: www.pennvirginia.com
SIC: 1382 Oil & gas exploration services
PA: Penn Virginia Corporation
　　16285 Park Ten Pl Ste 500
　　Houston TX 77084
　　713 722-6500

(G-11282)
PENN VIRGINIA OIL & GAS GP LLC
14701 Saint Marys Ln # 275 (77079-2921)
PHONE..................................713 722-6500
John A Brooks, *COO*
Steven A Hartman, *Senior VP*
Nancy M Snyder,
EMP: 40
SALES (est): 3.4MM
SALES (corp-wide): 440.8MM **Publicly Held**
WEB: www.pennvirginia.com
SIC: 1382 Oil & gas exploration services
PA: Penn Virginia Corporation
　　16285 Park Ten Pl Ste 500
　　Houston TX 77084
　　713 722-6500

(G-11283)
PENNTEX MIDSTREAM PARTNERS LLC
11931 Wickchester Ln (77043-4574)
PHONE..................................214 981-0700
Kenneth Hertel, *Vice Pres*
Thomas F Karam,
Robert O Bond,
Steven R Jones,
EMP: 65
SALES (est): 4.1MM **Publicly Held**
SIC: 1382 Oil & gas exploration services
HQ: Etp Legacy Lp
　　8111 Westchester Dr # 600
　　Dallas TX 75225
　　214 981-0700

(G-11284)
PENNZOIL-QUAKER STATE COMPANY (DH)
Also Called: Sopus Products
150 N Dairy Ashford Rd (77079-1115)
P.O. Box 2967 (77252-2967)
PHONE..................................800 237-8645
◆ **EMP:** 840
SQ FT: 700,000
SALES (est): 702.4MM
SALES (corp-wide): 344.8B **Privately Held**
WEB: www.pennzoil.com
SIC: 2992 Oils & greases, blending & compounding
HQ: Shell Oil Company
　　150 N Dairy Ashford Rd A
　　Houston TX 77079
　　713 241-6161

(G-11285)
PENTAGON ENERGY LLC
7441 E Orem Dr (77075-5329)
PHONE..................................203 451-8382
Ryan Comerford, *Mng Member*

Luis Eduardo Guiterrez, *Manager*
Alvaro Campins,
Alberto Chiesara,
Luis Gutierrez,
EMP: 30
SALES (est): 1.7MM **Privately Held**
WEB: www.pentagon-energy.com
SIC: 1382 Oil & gas exploration services

(G-11286)
PENTAIR VALVES & CONTROLS LLC (HQ)
Also Called: Tyco Valves & Controls
10707 Clay Rd Ste 200 (77041-6190)
PHONE..................................713 986-4665
David N Farr, *CEO*
Edward L Monser, *President*
Ed Purvis, *COO*
Sara Yang Bosco, *Exec VP*
Steven J Pelch, *Exec VP*
▲ **EMP:** 409
SALES (est): 290.9MM
SALES (corp-wide): 16.7B **Publicly Held**
SIC: 3491 Pressure valves & regulators, industrial; process control regulator valves
PA: Emerson Electric Co.
　　8000 West Florissant Ave
　　Saint Louis MO 63136
　　314 553-2000

(G-11287)
PEPPERIDGE FARM INCORPORATED
1303 Rosemeadow (77094)
PHONE..................................713 385-2010
Jacob Field, *Sales Staff*
Russ Spillers, *Sales Staff*
EMP: 25
SALES (corp-wide): 8.6B **Publicly Held**
WEB: www.pepperidgefarm.com
SIC: 5461 2052 2099 2053 Bakeries; cookies; bread crumbs, not made in bakeries; frozen bakery products, except bread
HQ: Pepperidge Farm, Incorporated
　　595 Westport Ave
　　Norwalk CT 06851
　　203 846-7000

(G-11288)
PEPSI-COLA METRO BTLG CO INC
Also Called: Pepsico
9300 La Porte Fwy (77017-1930)
PHONE..................................713 645-4111
Chris Van Horn, *General Mgr*
Mike Frank, *Safety Dir*
Monica Miller, *Human Res Mgr*
Amber Morrow, *Sales Staff*
Chris Telotte, *Sales Staff*
EMP: 200
SALES (corp-wide): 67.1B **Publicly Held**
WEB: www.pepsico.com
SIC: 2086 Carbonated soft drinks, bottled & canned
HQ: Pepsi-Cola Metropolitan Bottling Company, Inc.
　　1111 Westchester Ave
　　White Plains NY 10604
　　914 767-6000

(G-11289)
PEREGRINE PETROLEUM LLC
Also Called: Peregrine Petroleum Group
2929 Allen Pkwy Ste 1520 (77019-2132)
PHONE..................................713 630-8965
Jeremy T Greene, *Branch Mgr*
Candace Hays, *Manager*
Bill Nelson, *Bd of Directors*
Shanna Wentzel, *Technician*
EMP: 20 **Privately Held**
WEB: www.peregrinegp.com
SIC: 1382 Oil & gas exploration services
PA: Peregrine Petroleum, Llc
　　2101 Cedar Springs Rd
　　Dallas TX 75201

(G-11290)
PERFECTFITMEALS LLC (PA)
10370 Richmond Ave Ste 13 (77042-4141)
PHONE..................................713 868-5300
Bradley Wilson, *CEO*
Wendy Snead, *Controller*
Jack E McGehee,
EMP: 10

SQ FT: 9,302
SALES (est): 39.9MM **Privately Held**
WEB: www.perfectfitmeals.com
SIC: 2099 Food preparations

(G-11291)
PERKUP COFFEES LLC
11600 Big John St (77038-3334)
PHONE..................................281 445-6744
Tom Duffy, *Sales Mgr*
Dari Nasari, *Mng Member*
EMP: 30
SALES (est): 2.2MM **Privately Held**
SIC: 5149 5499 2095 Coffee & tea; coffee; roasted coffee

(G-11292)
PERMIAN BASIN JOINT VENTR LLC
2000 Post Oak Blvd B (77056-4499)
PHONE..................................713 296-6000
Steven Farris,
John Chung,
EMP: 20
SQ FT: 224,000
SALES (est): 533.8K
SALES (corp-wide): 6.4B **Publicly Held**
SIC: 1382 Oil & gas exploration services
PA: Apache Corporation
　　2000 Post Oak Blvd Ste 10
　　Houston TX 77056
　　713 296-6000

(G-11293)
PERMIAN NDT INC
14950 Heathrow Forest Pkw (77032-3855)
PHONE..................................432 563-3638
Mike Cooper, *CEO*
Cindy Murphy, *President*
EMP: 40
SALES (est): 5MM **Privately Held**
SIC: 1389 Oil field services

(G-11294)
PERRY SLINGSBY SYSTEMS INC
10642 W Little York Rd (77041-4014)
PHONE..................................561 743-7000
Rory Satterfeild, *Vice Pres*
◆ **EMP:** 60
SALES (est): 8.9MM
SALES (corp-wide): 1.3MM **Privately Held**
SIC: 3731 Submarines, building & repairing
PA: Triton Group Holdings Ltd
　　Walton Road Thorp Arch
　　Wetherby LS23
　　193 784-2424

(G-11295)
PETER PAUL PETROLEUM COMPANY
9805 Katy Fwy Ste 500 (77024-1271)
PHONE..................................713 209-1100
Peter D Huddleston, *President*
Flora M Huddleston, *Corp Secy*
William P Huddleston, *Vice Pres*
John P Krawtz, *Vice Pres*
Greg Mitschke, *VP Finance*
EMP: 36
SALES (est): 2.8MM **Privately Held**
WEB: www.huddlestonco.com
SIC: 1311 1382 Crude petroleum production; natural gas production; oil & gas exploration services

(G-11296)
PETERSON BECKNER INDS INC
1310 Spears Rd (77067-1522)
PHONE..................................281 872-1806
Conrad Hernandez, *Vice Pres*
Charlie Smith, *CFO*
Jason Shry, *CTO*
EMP: 10 **Privately Held**
WEB: www.petersonbeckner.com
SIC: 3441 Fabricated structural metal
HQ: Peterson Beckner Industries, Inc.
　　10700 North Fwy Ste 950
　　Houston TX 77037

(G-11297)
PETNAIR VALVES & CONTROLS
10707 Clay Rd Ste 200 (77041-6190)
P.O. Box 802428 (77280-2428)
PHONE..................................713 986-8468
EMP: 32
SALES (est): 5.4MM **Privately Held**
SIC: 3491 Industrial valves

(G-11298)
PETNET HOUSTON LLC
1028 Dreyfus St (77030-5016)
PHONE..................................713 791-1734
Gene McGrevin, *Principal*
EMP: 10
SALES (est): 1.5MM
SALES (corp-wide): 67.4B **Privately Held**
WEB: www.petscaninfo.com
SIC: 2835 Radioactive diagnostic substances
HQ: Petnet Solutions, Inc.
　　810 Innovation Dr
　　Knoxville TN 37932
　　865 218-2000

(G-11299)
PETRASOFT COUNSULTING
738 Highway 6 S (77079-4015)
PHONE..................................832 448-5600
Rameshkumar Sivaraman, *Principal*
Taimoor Rab, *Software Engr*
EMP: 10
SALES (est): 934.3K **Privately Held**
WEB: www.petrasoft.com
SIC: 7371 7372 Computer software development; business oriented computer software

(G-11300)
PETRO CHEM INDUSTRIES INC
5629 Cheswood St (77087-4038)
P.O. Box 266718 (77207-6718)
PHONE..................................713 645-5024
Clifton Wolf, *President*
Jane Goerz, *Corp Secy*
Jackie Land, *Purch Agent*
Melba Wolf, *Treasurer*
EMP: 33 **EST:** 1974
SQ FT: 28,000
SALES (est): 13.3MM **Privately Held**
WEB: www.cpc-pchem.com
SIC: 5084 7699 3563 Packaging machinery & equipment; compressor repair; air & gas compressors

(G-11301)
PETRO-TECH ENVIRONMENTAL LLC
8502 Cypress St Bldg 3 (77012-1735)
PHONE..................................713 926-9986
Jose Lopez, *Mng Member*
Robert Burington,
Ricardo Saucede,
EMP: 9 **EST:** 2007
SQ FT: 152,460
SALES (est): 800K **Privately Held**
WEB: www.petrotechenvironmental.com
SIC: 4953 1389 ; oil field services

(G-11302)
PETROHAB LLC (PA)
4930 Dacoma St Ste G (77092-7715)
PHONE..................................281 407-3800
Samer Al-Azem, *President*
▲ **EMP:** 20
SQ FT: 6,500
SALES (est): 1.5MM **Privately Held**
WEB: www.petrohab.com
SIC: 3548 3842 Resistance welders, electric; clothing, fire resistant & protective

(G-11303)
PETROHAWK ENERGY CORPORATION (DH)
1360 Post Oak Blvd Ste 15 (77056-3030)
PHONE..................................713 961-8500
Timothy Cutt, *President*
David Powell, *Vice Pres*
Jeffrey Lee Sahlberg, *Vice Pres*
John Allen Simmons, *Vice Pres*
Rodney Mark Skaufel, *Vice Pres*
EMP: 9
SQ FT: 6,400

▲ = Import ▼=Export
◆ =Import/Export

SALES (est): 843.5MM
SALES (corp-wide): 278.4B **Privately Held**
SIC: 1311 Crude petroleum production
HQ: Bp America Production Company
501 Westlake Park Blvd
Houston TX 77079
281 366-2000

(G-11304)
PETROLEUM ANALYZER COMPANY LP (PA)
Also Called: Pac
8824 Fallbrook Dr (77064-4855)
PHONE..............................281 940-1803
Eric Schellenberger, *President*
Olu Lawson, *Controller*
Jacques Lapeyre, *Sales Staff*
Henry Montoya, *Sales Staff*
Shannon Wade, *Sales Staff*
◆ EMP: 100
SALES (est): 40.5MM **Privately Held**
WEB: www.paclp.com
SIC: 3826 Petroleum product analyzing apparatus

(G-11305)
PETROLEUM ELASTOMERS INC
757 Kenrick Dr Ste 124 (77060-3639)
PHONE..............................281 591-1500
Michael Ward, *President*
Michael Viator, *Corp Secy*
◆ EMP: 40
SQ FT: 10,000
SALES (est): 2.6MM **Privately Held**
SIC: 1389 Oil field services

(G-11306)
PETROLEUM ENGINEERS INTL (HQ)
1030 Regional Park Dr (77060-1117)
PHONE..............................337 984-2603
Don E Claxton, *President*
C F Kimball III, *Vice Pres*
Alvin Bellaire Jr, *Treasurer*
Edgar Giles, *Controller*
Steve Hennigan, *Exec Dir*
EMP: 23
SALES (est): 1.9MM
SALES (corp-wide): 2.3MM **Privately Held**
SIC: 8711 1381 Petroleum engineering; drilling oil & gas wells
PA: The Cymri Corporation
11011 Richmond Ave # 525
Houston TX 77042
713 479-7070

(G-11307)
PETROLEUM GEO-SERVICES INC (HQ)
Also Called: Pgs Americas
15375 Memorial Dr Ste 100 (77079-4138)
PHONE..............................281 509-8000
Jon Erik Reinhardsen, *President*
Rune Eng, *President*
Guillaume Cambois, *Exec VP*
Per Arild Reksnes, *Exec VP*
Aker Kva Rner, *Exec VP*
▲ EMP: 200
SALES (est): 823MM
SALES (corp-wide): 896MM **Privately Held**
SIC: 3827 8713 1382 Optical instruments & lenses; surveying services; oil & gas exploration services; geophysical exploration, oil & gas field
PA: Pgs Asa
Lilleakerveien 4c
Oslo 0283
675 264-00

(G-11308)
PETROLEUM INDUSTRY INSPECTORS
1817 Tidwell Ln (77093-6631)
PHONE..............................713 377-2637
Phillip Zaragoza, *President*
Hector Cervantes, *Vice Pres*
Laura Zaragoza, *Treasurer*
EMP: 20
SQ FT: 3,500 **Privately Held**
SIC: 1389 Pipe testing, oil field service

(G-11309)
PETROLUEM MACHINERY INC
Also Called: Petroleum Machinery
6005 N Shepherd Dr Ste H2 (77091-4253)
PHONE..............................713 697-4999
Miguel Saldana, *President*
Roman Martinez, *Vice Pres*
▲ EMP: 9
SQ FT: 8,000
SALES (est): 1.2MM **Privately Held**
SIC: 3599 Machine shop, jobbing & repair

(G-11310)
PETRON INDUSTRIES INC (HQ)
Also Called: Pason Offshore
7701 W Little York Rd (77040-5398)
PHONE..............................713 693-8700
Marcel Kessler, *CEO*
Donald Disheroon, *President*
Douglas Ladendorf, *President*
Enrico Ladendorf, *President*
David Elliott, *Vice Pres*
▲ EMP: 75
SQ FT: 34,000
SALES (est): 19.3MM
SALES (corp-wide): 222MM **Privately Held**
WEB: www.pason.com
SIC: 3679 3823 3533 Electronic circuits; industrial instrmnts msrmnt display/control process variable; oil & gas field machinery
PA: Pason Systems Inc
6130 3 St Se
Calgary AB T2H 1
403 301-3400

(G-11311)
PETROSANTANDER INC (PA)
Also Called: Petrosantander Colombia
6363 Woodway Dr Ste 350 (77057-1798)
PHONE..............................713 784-8700
Christopher Whyte, *CEO*
Ian Gollop, *Exec VP*
Troy Finney, *Vice Pres*
Jeremy Mathalone, *Vice Pres*
Victor Low, *Admin Sec*
▲ EMP: 15
SQ FT: 9,533
SALES (est): 57.3MM **Privately Held**
SIC: 1311 Crude petroleum production

(G-11312)
PETRUSTECH OIL & GAS LLC (PA)
5500 N Sam Houston Pkwy W (77086-1571)
P.O. Box 394, Lockport LA (70374-0394)
PHONE..............................281 781-0020
Daniel Schmidt, *President*
Alice Ribeiro,
EMP: 18
SALES (est): 3.2MM **Privately Held**
WEB: www.petrustech.com
SIC: 1389 Oil field services; gas field services

(G-11313)
PEYTON SALAS & MENDOZA LLC
Also Called: PSM
10101 Southwest Fwy # 400 (77074-1126)
PHONE..............................512 784-5875
Roberto D Salas, *President*
EMP: 27
SALES (est): 3.1MM **Privately Held**
SIC: 3317 7389 3599 3353 Welded pipe & tubes; ; machine & other job shop work; tubes, welded, aluminum; coils, pipe: fabricated from purchased pipe; boiler & boiler shop work

(G-11314)
PFI MOLDING INC
Also Called: Osborne Bearing Technologies
8777 Tallyho Rd Ste 200 (77061-3434)
PHONE..............................713 946-3300
Phillip Aguilar, *President*
EMP: 10
SQ FT: 25,000
SALES (est): 2.1MM **Privately Held**
WEB: www.pfimolding.com
SIC: 3089 3544 Injection molding of plastics; dies, plastics forming

(G-11315)
PFM LLC (PA)
3200 Southwest Fwy # 3300 (77027-7528)
PHONE..............................713 664-7767
Bob Portman, *President*
EMP: 18
SQ FT: 600
SALES (est): 5MM **Privately Held**
WEB: www.pfm.com
SIC: 1389 Oil field services

(G-11316)
PGI INTERNATIONAL LTD
Also Called: Parker Pgi
16101 Vallen Dr (77041-4030)
PHONE..............................713 466-0056
Spence Nimberger, *Partner*
Anne Smalling, *General Ptnr*
Mark Simpson, *Manager*
◆ EMP: 385
SQ FT: 185,000
SALES (est): 91.5MM
SALES (corp-wide): 13.7B **Publicly Held**
SIC: 3494 5084 3541 3451 Valves & pipe fittings; industrial machinery & equipment; machine tools, metal cutting type; screw machine products
PA: Parker-Hannifin Corporation
6035 Parkland Blvd
Cleveland OH 44124
216 896-3000

(G-11317)
PGS AMERICAS INC (DH)
Also Called: Petroleum Geo-Services
15375 Memorial Dr Ste 100 (77079-4138)
PHONE..............................281 509-8000
Jon Erik Reinhardsen, *President*
Sven O Havig, *President*
Jerry Courtney, *Vice Pres*
James Brasher, *Admin Sec*
▲ EMP: 61
SALES (est): 119.5MM
SALES (corp-wide): 896MM **Privately Held**
SIC: 1382 Oil & gas exploration services
HQ: Petroleum Geo-Services, Inc.
15375 Memorial Dr Ste 100
Houston TX 77079
281 509-8000

(G-11318)
PGS FINANCE INC
15150 Memorial Dr (77079-4304)
PHONE..............................281 509-8000
EMP: 614
SALES (est): 28.4MM
SALES (corp-wide): 896MM **Privately Held**
SIC: 3827 Optical instruments & lenses
HQ: Petroleum Geo-Services, Inc.
15375 Memorial Dr Ste 100
Houston TX 77079
281 509-8000

(G-11319)
PGS IMAGING INC
15375 Memorial Dr Ste 100 (77079-4138)
PHONE..............................281 509-8000
Christopher Usher, *President*
John Gillooly, *Vice Pres*
Richard M Zoll, *Vice Pres*
EMP: 300
SALES (est): 59.7MM **Privately Held**
SIC: 1382 8731 Geophysical exploration, oil & gas field; commercial physical research

(G-11320)
PHARMSCRIPT LLC
1718 Fry Rd Ste 125 (77084-5845)
PHONE..............................281 492-7220
Sarah Hinojosa, *Manager*
John Norcross, *Director*
EMP: 40
SALES (corp-wide): 703.5K **Privately Held**
WEB: www.pharmscript.com
SIC: 2834 Druggists' preparations (pharmaceuticals)
HQ: Pharmscript L.L.C.
150 Pierce St
Somerset NJ 08873

(G-11321)
PHAROS MARINE AUTMTC PWR INC (HQ)
10810 W Little York Rd (77041-4050)
P.O. Box 801057 (77280-1057)
PHONE..............................713 228-5208
Scott Dickinson, *CEO*
Kenneth Meador, *President*
Jeff Rosner, *Business Mgr*
Jennifer Colunga, *Vice Pres*
Sam Trenchard, *Vice Pres*
◆ EMP: 45 EST: 1946
SQ FT: 30,000
SALES (est): 17.4MM
SALES (corp-wide): 18.9MM **Privately Held**
WEB: www.automaticpower.com
SIC: 3812 5063 Navigational systems & instruments; batteries
PA: Pronav, Inc.
4305 Hwy 35 S
Rockport TX 78382
361 727-3300

(G-11322)
PHILLIP E MOSLEY & ASSOCIATES
Also Called: P E Moseley & Assoc
12121 Wickchester Ln # 300 (77079-1206)
PHONE..............................281 496-1249
Philip E Mosley, *President*
Marie Moseley, *CFO*
EMP: 10
SQ FT: 2,000
SALES (est): 828K **Privately Held**
WEB: www.pmoseley.com
SIC: 7379 1389 Computer related consulting services; oil consultants

(G-11323)
PHILLIP TOWNSEND ASSOC INC (PA)
509 N Sam Houston Pkwy E # 600 (77060-4130)
P.O. Box 90327 (77290-0327)
PHONE..............................281 873-8733
Dave Wombach, *CEO*
Peter Callais, *Vice Pres*
Barjor Dastur, *Vice Pres*
Clifford Lee, *Vice Pres*
Ramesh Patel, *Accounting Mgr*
EMP: 23
SALES (est): 7.2MM **Privately Held**
WEB: www.ptai.com
SIC: 2819 Industrial inorganic chemicals

(G-11324)
PHILLIPS 66 (PA)
2331 Citywest Blvd (77042-2862)
P.O. Box 421959 (77242-1959)
PHONE..............................281 293-6600
Greg C Garland, *Ch of Bd*
Earl Burns, *General Mgr*
Gregory Finn, *General Mgr*
Rusty Ratliff, *Superintendent*
Anna McClain, *Chief*
◆ EMP: 188
SALES (est): 109.5B **Publicly Held**
WEB: www.phillips66.com
SIC: 1311 2911 2869 Crude petroleum & natural gas; petroleum refining; olefins

(G-11325)
PHILLIPS 66 CARRIER LLC
3010 Briarpark Dr (77042-3706)
P.O. Box 421959 (77242-1959)
PHONE..............................855 283-9237
Greg C Garland, *Mng Member*
EMP: 147 EST: 2013
SALES: 461.8MM
SALES (corp-wide): 109.5B **Publicly Held**
WEB: www.phillips66partners.com
SIC: 4613 4612 2911 Refined petroleum pipelines; crude petroleum pipelines; petroleum refining
HQ: Phillips 66 Partners Lp
2331 Citywest Blvd
Houston TX 77042
855 283-9237

(G-11326)
PHILLIPS 66 PARTNERS LP (DH)
2331 Citywest Blvd (77042-2862)
P.O. Box 421959 (77242-1959)
PHONE....................................855 283-9237
Greg C Garland, *Ch of Bd*
Phillips 66 Project Developmen, *General Ptnr*
J T Liberti, *COO*
David Knowles, *Maint Spvr*
Bo Miller, *Maint Spvr*
EMP: 12 **EST:** 2013
SALES (est): 1.4B
SALES (corp-wide): 109.5B **Publicly Held**
WEB: www.phillips66partners.com
SIC: 1311 5541 Crude petroleum & natural gas; gasoline service stations
HQ: Phillips 66 Project Development Inc.
2331 Citywest Blvd
Houston TX 77042
855 283-9237

(G-11327)
PHILLIPS IRON WORKS INC
2903 Gano St (77009-6927)
PHONE....................................337 364-2337
Coral Eichenour, *President*
EMP: 20
SQ FT: 5,000
SALES (est): 1.8MM **Privately Held**
WEB: www.phillipsiw.com
SIC: 7699 3714 3312 Engine repair & replacement, non-automotive; motor vehicle parts & accessories; blast furnaces & steel mills

(G-11328)
PHOEBEN INC
Also Called: Emily Armenta Designs
10601 S Sam Huston Pkwy W (77071-3140)
PHONE....................................832 486-9500
Emily Armenta, *President*
EMP: 11
SQ FT: 2,500
SALES (est): 2.8MM **Privately Held**
WEB: www.armentacollection.com
SIC: 3911 Jewelry, precious metal

(G-11329)
PHOENIX SERVICES LLC (PA)
10260 Westheimer Rd # 460 (77042-3108)
PHONE....................................713 952-5533
Mark Fisher, *CEO*
EMP: 15 **EST:** 1996
SALES (est): 6.2MM **Privately Held**
WEB: www.phoenixoilfieldservices.com
SIC: 2869 Fuels

(G-11330)
PHOENIX TECHNOLOGY SVCS USA (HQ)
1805 Brittmoore Rd (77043-2213)
PHONE....................................713 337-0600
Edward Chiaramonte, *President*
Trey Garmon, *General Mgr*
Michael Buker, *Vice Pres*
Ian Stevenson, *Engineer*
Blake Elms, *Sales Staff*
EMP: 10
SQ FT: 66,666
SALES (est): 114MM
SALES (corp-wide): 134.5MM **Privately Held**
SIC: 1381 Directional drilling oil & gas wells
PA: Phoenix Technology Services Inc
250 2 St Sw Suite 1400
Calgary AB T2P 0
403 543-4466

(G-11331)
PIERCE PACKAGING CO
9020 Jackrabbit Rd (77095-3397)
PHONE....................................815 636-5656
Brandon Dunn, *Branch Mgr*
EMP: 32
SALES (corp-wide): 58.7MM **Privately Held**
WEB: www.piercedistribution.com
SIC: 4783 2441 Containerization of goods for shipping; boxes, wood

PA: Pierce Packaging Co.
2028 E Riverside Blvd
Loves Park IL 61111
815 636-5650

(G-11332)
PIN OAK CAREGIVERS LLC
4811 Mcdermed Dr (77035-3401)
PHONE....................................713 301-3481
Jane Seger, *Principal*
EMP: 11
SALES (est): 950.9K **Privately Held**
SIC: 3452 Pins

(G-11333)
PINEFOREST JEWELRY INC
Also Called: Pfj
1141 Uvalde Rd (77015-3743)
PHONE....................................713 451-1321
James K Mills, *President*
Linda Mills, *Treasurer*
Lisa Rodriguez, *Bookkeeper*
EMP: 12 **EST:** 1986
SQ FT: 7,200
SALES (est): 1.6MM **Privately Held**
WEB: www.pineforestjewelry.com
SIC: 5944 7631 3423 5094 Jewelry, precious stones & precious metals; watch, clock & jewelry repair; jewelers' hand tools; jewelry

(G-11334)
PIONEER EXPLORATION COMPANY (PA)
1900 Saint James Pl # 800 (77056-4133)
PHONE....................................281 893-9400
Younas Chaudhary, *President*
John Gilbert, *Partner*
EMP: 20
SALES (est): 48.3MM **Privately Held**
WEB: www.pecogas.com
SIC: 1311 1321 Crude petroleum production; natural gas liquids

(G-11335)
PIPELINE INSPECTION COMPANY
1919 Antoine Dr (77055-1898)
P.O. Box 55648 (77255-5648)
PHONE....................................713 681-5837
James Campbell, *General Mgr*
Greg N Miller, *Managing Dir*
Beverly Wren, *Chairman*
Al Simon, *Vice Pres*
Sergei Chernyshov, *Engineer*
EMP: 25
SQ FT: 9,000
SALES (est): 4.5MM **Privately Held**
WEB: www.spyinspect.com
SIC: 7359 3812 3825 Equipment rental & leasing; search & navigation equipment; test equipment for electronic & electrical circuits

(G-11336)
PIPELINE SEAL & INSULATOR INC
Also Called: PSI
6455 Clara Rd Ste 300 (77041-5389)
PHONE....................................713 747-6948
▲ **EMP:** 80
SALES (est): 15MM **Privately Held**
WEB: www.gptindustries.com
SIC: 3498 3086 3053 Fabricated pipe & fittings; plastics foam products; gaskets, packing & sealing devices

(G-11337)
PIPING TECHNOLOGY & PDTS INC
3770 South Loop E (77021-6141)
PHONE....................................713 731-0030
Durga Agrawal, *Branch Mgr*
▲ **EMP:** 10
SALES (corp-wide): 137.4MM **Privately Held**
WEB: www.pipingtech.com
SIC: 3494 Expansion joints pipe
PA: Piping Technology & Products, Inc.
3701 Holmes Rd
Houston TX 77051
800 787-5914

(G-11338)
PIPING TECHNOLOGY & PDTS INC (PA)
3701 Holmes Rd (77051-1545)
P.O. Box 34506 (77234-4506)
PHONE....................................800 787-5914
Durga D Agrawal, *President*
Jerry Fisher, *Managing Prtnr*
Lauren Decatur, *Business Mgr*
Justin Long, *Business Mgr*
Aarati Agrawal, *Vice Pres*
◆ **EMP:** 740
SQ FT: 500,000
SALES (est): 137.4MM **Privately Held**
WEB: www.pipingtech.com
SIC: 3494 8711 3441 Expansion joints pipe; engineering services; fabricated structural metal

(G-11339)
PITA PAL INDUSTRIES INC
3100 Canal St (77003-1602)
PHONE....................................713 777-7482
Joseph Navon, *President*
Melissa Navon, *Vice Pres*
Bill Amstead, *Sales Staff*
Jim Hawkins, *Sales Staff*
Laura Clark, *Office Mgr*
◆ **EMP:** 90
SQ FT: 35,000
SALES (est): 17.6MM **Privately Held**
WEB: www.pitapal.com
SIC: 2099 5499 Food preparations; health foods

(G-11340)
PIW VENTURES LTD (PA)
Also Called: Houston Walls & Decor
9311 Katy Fwy Ste H (77024-1518)
PHONE....................................713 932-9311
Tom McMan, *Manager*
EMP: 12
SQ FT: 5,300
SALES (est): 1.5MM **Privately Held**
WEB: www.wallpaperstogo.com
SIC: 5231 5949 5719 2591 Wallpaper; fabric, remnants; window furnishings; mini blinds

(G-11341)
PJ PIPING INC
651 N Shepherd Dr Ste 440 (77007-1332)
PHONE....................................713 730-3457
Daniel Munro, *President*
Daniel Composto, *Vice Pres*
Jasmin Lye, *Opers Mgr*
James Short, *Opers Staff*
Kenrick Hutson, *Manager*
EMP: 12
SALES (est): 501.6K **Privately Held**
WEB: www.pjpiping.com
SIC: 3494 Pipe fittings

(G-11342)
PLAINS EXPLORATION & PROD CO (PA)
700 Milam St Ste 3100 (77002-2764)
PHONE....................................713 579-6000
John Traub, *President*
EMP: 14
SALES (est): 3.7MM **Privately Held**
WEB: www.fcx.com
SIC: 1382 Oil & gas exploration services

(G-11343)
PLAINS GP HOLDINGS LP (PA)
333 Clay St Ste 1600 (77002-4101)
PHONE....................................713 646-4100
Willie Chiang, *Ch of Bd*
Harry N Pefanis, *President*
Stephen Falgoust, *Managing Dir*
Darren Alexander, *General Ptnr*
Eric Leblanc, *General Ptnr*
EMP: 28
SALES: 33.6B **Publicly Held**
WEB: www.plainsallamerican.com
SIC: 4612 1321 Crude petroleum pipelines; natural gas liquids; fractionating natural gas liquids

(G-11344)
PLAINS RESOURCES INC (PA)
700 Milam St Ste 3100 (77002-2764)
PHONE....................................713 579-5000
John T Raymond, *President*

John F Wombwell, *Exec VP*
Stephen A Thorington, *CFO*
EMP: 9 **EST:** 1976
SQ FT: 6,780
SALES (est): 955.3K **Privately Held**
WEB: www.plainsallamerican.com
SIC: 1311 5171 Crude petroleum production; petroleum terminals

(G-11345)
PLASTECO INC
8535 Market St (77029-2421)
P.O. Box 24158 (77229-4158)
PHONE....................................713 673-7710
Kiyoshi Sandow, *President*
Bryan Sandow, *Vice Pres*
Pamela Murray, *Manager*
Heath Pocock, *Manager*
EMP: 22 **EST:** 1944
SQ FT: 38,000
SALES (est): 4.1MM **Privately Held**
WEB: www.plasteco.com
SIC: 3444 Sheet metalwork

(G-11346)
PLASTIX PLUS LLC
10818 Barely Ln Ste A (77070-5964)
PHONE....................................281 469-3451
Michael K Snow, *Mng Member*
Justin Branam, *Supervisor*
William Haskins,
EMP: 25
SQ FT: 500
SALES (est): 3.6MM **Privately Held**
WEB: www.pptexas.com
SIC: 3089 Injection molding of plastics

(G-11347)
PLATE CUT INC
2190 North Loop W Ste 106 (77018-8007)
P.O. Box 701188 (77270-1188)
PHONE....................................713 802-1291
Joe Rice, *President*
Tracy Allen, *Director*
EMP: 13
SALES (est): 3.3MM **Privately Held**
WEB: www.platecuttx.com
SIC: 3441 Fabricated structural metal

(G-11348)
PLATINUM ENERGY RESOURCES INC
Galleria Tower 1 270 (77056)
PHONE....................................713 364-7822
Barry Kostiner, *CEO*
John Ghermezian, *President*
Ralph W Schofield, *COO*
Ruben Colchado, *Vice Pres*
James Dorman, *Vice Pres*
EMP: 100
SALES (est): 12.1MM **Privately Held**
WEB: www.t5energy.com
SIC: 1382 Oil & gas exploration services

(G-11349)
PLS INC
Also Called: Petroleum Listing Service
10850 Richmond Ave # 300 (77042-4793)
PHONE....................................713 650-1212
Ronald W Wise, *President*
Dan Coy, *Production*
David Cohen, *Manager*
Felipe Saldana, *Technology*
Jeff Wiles, *Software Dev*
EMP: 25
SALES (est): 4.1MM **Privately Held**
WEB: www.plsx.com
SIC: 8742 2759 Business consultant; directories (except telephone); printing

(G-11350)
PLUMBLINE INC
Also Called: Plumbline Architecture Wdwrk
11422 Craighead Dr Ste B (77025-5859)
PHONE....................................713 462-9500
Robert L Hunt, *President*
Bonita Hunt, *Admin Sec*
EMP: 14
SQ FT: 15,000
SALES (est): 1.8MM **Privately Held**
SIC: 2431 Doors, wood

(G-11351)
PLUNKETT RESEARCH LTD
4102 Bellaire Blvd (77025-1004)
P.O. Box 541737 (77254-1737)
PHONE..................................713 932-0000
Jack W Plunkett, *General Ptnr*
EMP: 25
SALES (est): 2MM **Privately Held**
WEB: www.plunkettresearch.com
SIC: 1382 Oil & gas exploration services

(G-11352)
PLUSPETROL INTERNATIONAL INC
5599 San Felipe St # 100 (77056-2724)
PHONE..................................713 961-1095
Ricardo Rey, *President*
Amy Rodriguez, *Principal*
Maria Ximena Storni, *Principal*
Lety Gilde, *Buyer*
Steve McGuire, *Senior Engr*
◆ **EMP:** 10
SQ FT: 7,200
SALES (est): 1.1MM
SALES (corp-wide): 1.2B **Privately Held**
WEB: www.pluspetrol.com
SIC: 1382 Oil & gas exploration services
HQ: Pluspetrol Energy S.A.
    Lima 339
    Ciudad De Buenos Aires C1073

(G-11353)
PMQ ALTERNATIVES INC
6120 W By Northwest Blvd # 190
(77040-4906)
PHONE..................................713 690-7672
Pat Mayer, *President*
EMP: 9
SALES (est): 1.1MM **Privately Held**
WEB: www.pmqa.net
SIC: 3999 Manufacturing industries

(G-11354)
POLARIS LED INC
7787 Pinemont Dr Ste B (77040-6216)
PHONE..................................832 582-6263
Sean Nankami, *President*
Rocky Nankani, *COO*
Marites Nankani, *Vice Pres*
EMP: 12
SQ FT: 10,000
SALES (est): 0 **Privately Held**
WEB: www.polarisledus.com
SIC: 3674 Light emitting diodes

(G-11355)
POLLY KNAPP PIG INC
1209 Hardy St (77020-2011)
PHONE..................................713 222-0146
Kenneth M Knapp, *President*
Mitzi Walker, *President*
EMP: 40
SQ FT: 23,000
SALES (est): 6.3MM **Privately Held**
WEB: www.pollypig.com
SIC: 3086 Insulation or cushioning material, foamed plastic

(G-11356)
POLY SAC INC
7920 Westpark Dr (77063-6418)
PHONE..................................713 978-7888
John Ying, *President*
▲ **EMP:** 30
SQ FT: 85,000
SALES (est): 9.5MM **Privately Held**
WEB: www.polysac.net
SIC: 3089 2673 Holders: paper towel, grocery bag, etc.: plastic; bags: plastic, laminated & coated

(G-11357)
POLYMED THERAPEUTICS INC
6200 Savoy Dr Ste 1200 (77036-3324)
PHONE..................................713 777-7088
William WEI Zuo, *President*
Zhenguo Luo, *Vice Pres*
David Matson, *Vice Pres*
Lu Yiu, *Vice Pres*
Xiaojing LI, *CFO*
▲ **EMP:** 10 **EST:** 1999
SQ FT: 25,000

SALES (est): 1.6MM
SALES (corp-wide): 101.2MM **Publicly Held**
WEB: www.polymedt.com
SIC: 2834 Pharmaceutical preparations
PA: Athenex, Inc.
    1001 Main St Ste 600
    Buffalo NY 14203
    716 427-2950

(G-11358)
POLYMER DYNAMICS INC
Also Called: TX 7 Engine Treatment
11211 Neeshaw Dr (77065-4735)
PHONE..................................281 894-6382
Carl F Benton III, *President*
Rose Benton, *Vice Pres*
▲ **EMP:** 17
SQ FT: 16,000
SALES (est): 1.8MM **Privately Held**
WEB: www.polydyntx7.com
SIC: 3479 2911 Coating of metals & formed products; oils, lubricating

(G-11359)
POLYMERS SALES & LOGISTICS LLC
450 Gears Rd Ste 240 (77067-4513)
PHONE..................................281 874-8072
EMP: 11
SQ FT: 5,846
SALES (est): 333.5K **Privately Held**
SIC: 5084 3085 Chemical process equipment; plastics bottles

(G-11360)
POLYNT COMPOSITES USA INC
Also Called: C C P
2434 Holmes Rd (77051-1016)
PHONE..................................713 799-1800
Marquez Mike, *QC Mgr*
Bob Finden, *Branch Mgr*
David Maurin, *Manager*
Rebecca Bierschwal, *Info Tech Dir*
Lyjeana Swope, *Technician*
EMP: 43
SALES (corp-wide): 2.2B **Privately Held**
WEB: www.polynt.com
SIC: 2821 2851 Plastics materials & resins; marine paints
HQ: Polynt Composites Usa Inc.
    99 E Cottage Ave
    Carpentersville IL 60110

(G-11361)
POLYSPEC (TX) LLC
1255 Cutten Rd (77066)
PHONE..................................281 397-0033
Adrian Hunt, *Principal*
EMP: 10
SALES (est): 1.7MM **Privately Held**
WEB: www.polyspec.com
SIC: 2822 Ethylene-propylene rubbers, EPDM polymers

(G-11362)
POLYTEX FIBERS CORP
Also Called: Ultrapak
9341 Baythorne Dr (77041-7785)
PHONE..................................713 690-9055
Isaac Bazbaz, *President*
Hector Vides, *Superintendent*
Alex Huis In T Veld, *COO*
Joseph Erickson, *Safety Mgr*
Maricela Salazar, *Purch Agent*
◆ **EMP:** 113 **EST:** 1982
SQ FT: 228,000
SALES (est): 35.9MM **Privately Held**
WEB: www.polytex.com
SIC: 2393 3081 2221 Textile bags; polypropylene film & sheet; polypropylene broadwoven fabrics

(G-11363)
POLYTEX FIBERS INTERNATIONAL
9333 Baythorne Dr (77041-7737)
PHONE..................................713 690-9055
Isaac Bazbaz, *President*
Octavio Chavez, *Maintence Staff*
EMP: 300
SALES (est): 32.9MM **Privately Held**
WEB: www.polytex.com
SIC: 3082 Unsupported plastics profile shapes

(G-11364)
POLYWELD USA INC
1620 E Richey Rd (77073-3511)
PHONE..................................281 821-4156
Wakeel Ahmad, *President*
Basi Esso, *Principal*
▲ **EMP:** 13 **EST:** 1994
SALES (est): 2.9MM **Privately Held**
WEB: www.polyweldusa.com
SIC: 3089 Injection molding of plastics

(G-11365)
PORT CITY INC
Also Called: Port City Cabinet Works
2075 N Wayside Dr (77020-5610)
P.O. Box 15194 (77220-5194)
PHONE..................................713 673-7272
Richard Morris, *President*
Moe Trevino, *General Mgr*
Janice Davison, *Accounting Mgr*
EMP: 25 **EST:** 1927
SQ FT: 21,000
SALES (est): 5.3MM **Privately Held**
WEB: www.portcitycabinetworks.com
SIC: 3083 3086 1731 Plastic finished products, laminated; plastics foam products; electronic controls installation

(G-11366)
PORTABLE PIPE HANGERS INC
Also Called: Php Systems & Design
5534 Harvey Wilson Dr (77020-8017)
PHONE..................................713 672-5088
Arthur J Valentz, *President*
Alejandro Ramirez, *Engineer*
Lynn Valentz, *Treasurer*
Valerie Amaro, *Personnel*
John Engel, *Sales Mgr*
EMP: 25
SQ FT: 40,000
SALES (est): 9MM **Privately Held**
WEB: www.phpsd.com
SIC: 3499 7389 Strapping, metal; metal ladders; design services

(G-11367)
PORTER READY-MIX INC
Also Called: Porter Ready Mix Spring Plant
1601 Westfield Loop Rd (77073-2703)
P.O. Box 981, Porter (77365-0981)
PHONE..................................281 443-6363
Nathan Perkinson, *Branch Mgr*
EMP: 18
SALES (corp-wide): 9.7MM **Privately Held**
WEB: www.porterreadymix.com
SIC: 3273 Ready-mixed concrete
PA: Porter Ready-Mix, Inc.
    25152 Loop 494
    Porter TX 77365
    281 354-5181

(G-11368)
PORTSMOUTH TRADING CO INC
Also Called: Robin Guitars
3526 E T C Jester Blvd (77018-6023)
PHONE..................................713 957-0470
Dave Wintz, *President*
Wittrock John, *Vice Pres*
EMP: 9
SQ FT: 5,000
SALES (est): 911.7K **Privately Held**
SIC: 3931 5736 Musical instruments; musical instrument stores

(G-11369)
POST OAK ENERGY CAPITAL LP (PA)
34 S Wynden Dr Ste 300 (77056-2531)
PHONE..................................713 571-9393
Frost W Cochran, *Partner*
Ryan Mathews, *Counsel*
Rainey Janke, *Vice Pres*
April Thomson, *Office Mgr*
Frost Cochran, *Director*
EMP: 13
SALES (est): 124.1MM **Privately Held**
WEB: www.postoakenergy.com
SIC: 1382 Oil & gas exploration services

(G-11370)
POST OAK GRAPHICS INC
Also Called: Post Oak Graphics
16010 Barkers Point Ln # 150
(77079-9001)
PHONE..................................713 850-3563

Charles T Wells, *President*
A W Lester, *Vice Pres*
EMP: 10 **EST:** 1982
SALES (est): 480.8K **Privately Held**
WEB: www.postoakgraphics.com
SIC: 2752 Color lithography

(G-11371)
POWELL ELECTRICAL SYSTEMS INC
4201 Southwest Fwy (77027-7201)
PHONE..................................713 599-0324
Clayton Greg, *Mfg Spvr*
Bruce Mullins, *Branch Mgr*
EMP: 50
SALES (corp-wide): 518.5MM **Publicly Held**
WEB: www.powellind.com
SIC: 5063 3699 Electrical supplies; electrical equipment & supplies
HQ: Powell Electrical Systems, Inc.
    8550 Mosley Rd
    Houston TX 77075
    713 944-6900

(G-11372)
POWELL ELECTRICAL SYSTEMS INC (HQ)
Also Called: Pemco
8550 Mosley Rd (77075-1180)
PHONE..................................713 944-6900
Thomas W Powell, *Ch of Bd*
Brett Cope, *President*
Stephen Manke, *Business Mgr*
Ricky Deiss, *Production*
Homero Gonzaga, *Engineer*
◆ **EMP:** 638 **EST:** 1947
SQ FT: 735,300
SALES (est): 504.5MM
SALES (corp-wide): 518.5MM **Publicly Held**
WEB: www.powellind.com
SIC: 3625 Control equipment, electric
PA: Powell Industries, Inc.
    8550 Mosley Rd
    Houston TX 77075
    713 944-6900

(G-11373)
POWELL ELECTRICAL SYSTEMS INC
Also Called: Powell Industries
7232 Airport Blvd (77061-3931)
P.O. Box 1218 (77217)
PHONE..................................713 790-1700
Eder Cavazos, *Project Mgr*
Steven Stazo, *Research*
David Truong, *Research*
Nazar Hira, *Engineer*
Preston Kent, *Engineer*
EMP: 600
SALES (corp-wide): 518.5MM **Publicly Held**
WEB: www.powellind.com
SIC: 3625 8621 Relays & industrial controls; professional membership organizations
HQ: Powell Electrical Systems, Inc.
    8550 Mosley Rd
    Houston TX 77075
    713 944-6900

(G-11374)
POWELL ELECTRICAL SYSTEMS INC
Also Called: Powell Offshore
16535 Jacintoport Blvd (77015-6540)
PHONE..................................281 452-4885
Lisa Davis, *Principal*
Emil Leutwyler, *Principal*
Ellie Roberts, *Principal*
Dale Schulz, *Principal*
Jorge Thomas, *Opers-Prdtn-Mfg*
EMP: 50
SQ FT: 51,120
SALES (corp-wide): 518.5MM **Publicly Held**
WEB: www.powellind.com
SIC: 5063 8711 3448 Electrical supplies; engineering services; prefabricated metal buildings
HQ: Powell Electrical Systems, Inc.
    8550 Mosley Rd
    Houston TX 77075
    713 944-6900

(G-11375)
POWELL ELECTRICAL SYSTEMS INC
Also Called: Powell Apparatus Service Div
7232 Airport Blvd (77061-3931)
PHONE....................................713 944-6900
Luke Cowan, *Engineer*
Soham Datta, *Engineer*
Dwayne Dubose, *Controller*
Dennis Thonsgard, *Manager*
Delena Dally, *Manager*
EMP: 600
SALES (corp-wide): 518.5MM **Publicly Held**
WEB: www.powellind.com
SIC: 3625 Relays & industrial controls
HQ: Powell Electrical Systems, Inc.
　　8550 Mosley Rd
　　Houston TX 77075
　　713 944-6900

(G-11376)
POWELL INDUSTRIES INC (PA)
8550 Mosley Rd (77075-1180)
P.O. Box 12818 (77217-2818)
PHONE....................................713 944-6900
Brett A Cope, *Ch of Bd*
Mark Curry, *Business Mgr*
Don R Madison, *Exec VP*
Milburn E Honeycutt, *Vice Pres*
Dennis Thonsgard, *Vice Pres*
▼ **EMP:** 300
SQ FT: 428,515
SALES: 518.5MM **Publicly Held**
WEB: www.powellind.com
SIC: 3612 3613 3625 3643 Power & dis-
tribution transformers; switchgear &
switchgear accessories; motor controls &
accessories; bus bars (electrical conduc-
tors); industrial process control instru-
ments

(G-11377)
POWER PLASTIC INC
5879 W 34th St (77092-6401)
PHONE....................................713 957-3695
Lien Bui, *President*
Tin Dinh, *Vice Pres*
Lehman William L, *Vice Pres*
EMP: 10
SQ FT: 12,000
SALES (est): 800K **Privately Held**
SIC: 3841 Surgical & medical instruments

(G-11378)
POWER PROCESS DEVELOPMENTS INC
Also Called: Quesco Turbo Machinery Svcs
100 Hutcheson St (77003-2510)
PHONE....................................713 926-5840
Antonio Quintanilla, *President*
◆ **EMP:** 15
SQ FT: 28,000
SALES (est): 2MM **Privately Held**
WEB: www.quescoturbo.com
SIC: 3511 Turbines & turbine generator
sets

(G-11379)
POWER TEMP SYSTEMS INC
1428 N Sam Houston Pkwy E # 170
(77032-2942)
PHONE....................................281 617-7889
EMP: 12
SALES (est): 2MM **Privately Held**
WEB: www.powertemp.com
SIC: 3699 Electrical equipment & supplies

(G-11380)
PPC USA INC
Also Called: Ppc Insulators
363 N Sam Houston Pkwy E # 700
(77060-2408)
PHONE....................................281 257-8222
Cleber Angelo, *Managing Dir*
◆ **EMP:** 20
SQ FT: 8,000
SALES: 17.7MM
SALES (corp-wide): 177.9K **Privately
Held**
WEB: www.ppcinsulators.com
SIC: 3264 Insulators, electrical: porcelain
PA: Saddle Luxco Holding S.a R.L.
　　Rue Edward Steichen 2
　　Luxembourg

(G-11381)
PPG INDUSTRIES INC
Also Called: PPG 8325
3423 N Sam Houston Pkwy W # 301
(77086-1488)
PHONE....................................713 683-8025
Debbie Ellis, *Branch Mgr*
EMP: 24
SALES (corp-wide): 15.3B **Publicly Held**
WEB: www.ppg.com
SIC: 2851 Paints & allied products
PA: Ppg Industries, Inc.
　　1 Ppg Pl
　　Pittsburgh PA 15272
　　412 434-3131

(G-11382)
PPG INDUSTRIES INC
3530 Lang Rd (77092-6105)
PHONE....................................713 576-8418
James Roan, *Branch Mgr*
EMP: 24
SALES (corp-wide): 15.3B **Publicly Held**
WEB: www.ppg.com
SIC: 2851 Paints & allied products
PA: Ppg Industries, Inc.
　　1 Ppg Pl
　　Pittsburgh PA 15272
　　412 434-3131

(G-11383)
PPG INDUSTRIES INC
Also Called: PPG 8323
13306 Fm 1960 Rd W (77065-4002)
PHONE....................................281 890-4481
Marcos Sanchez, *Manager*
EMP: 24
SALES (corp-wide): 15.3B **Publicly Held**
WEB: www.ppg.com
SIC: 2851 Paints & allied products
PA: Ppg Industries, Inc.
　　1 Ppg Pl
　　Pittsburgh PA 15272
　　412 434-3131

(G-11384)
PRAXAIR SURFACE TECH INC
7615 Fairview St (77041-2111)
PHONE....................................713 849-9474
EMP: 27 **Privately Held**
WEB: www.praxair.com
SIC: 3479 3548 Coating of metals &
formed products; coating, rust preventive;
hot dip coating of metals or formed products; electric welding equipment
HQ: Praxair Surface Technologies, Inc.
　　1500 Polco St
　　Indianapolis IN 46222
　　317 240-2500

(G-11385)
PRECISE STEEL INC
1335 Boyles St Ste 110 (77020-7562)
P.O. Box 920755 (77292-0755)
PHONE....................................713 673-6300
▲ **EMP:** 32 EST: 2002
SQ FT: 17,000
SALES (est): 7.5MM **Privately Held**
WEB: www.precisesteelinc.com
SIC: 3441 Fabricated structural metal

(G-11386)
PRECISION ADDITIVES INC
1441 Park Ten Blvd (77084-5028)
PHONE....................................713 896-0606
Jeff Steinkirchner, *President*
Matt Reno, *Regional Mgr*
Steven Bonaventura, *Vice Pres*
Chris Bowhay, *Vice Pres*
John Wilkerson, *Vice Pres*
▲ **EMP:** 25
SQ FT: 8,000
SALES (est): 1.2MM **Privately Held**
WEB: www.precisionadditives.com
SIC: 2819 5169 2891 Industrial inorganic
chemicals; chemical additives; adhesives

(G-11387)
PRECISION COMPONENTS
7311 Old Galveston Rd # 110
(77034-1434)
PHONE....................................888 554-4999
▲ **EMP:** 19
SALES (est): 3.8MM **Privately Held**
WEB: www.pc-houston.com
SIC: 3441 Fabricated structural metal

(G-11388)
PRECISION CUSTOM MACHINING INC
Also Called: Newman Company
14237 Aston St (77040-5409)
PHONE....................................713 462-8622
Henry C Newman, *President*
Pamela Newman, *Vice Pres*
Frank Juhasz, *Manager*
EMP: 10
SQ FT: 3,000
SALES (est): 500K **Privately Held**
WEB: www.atprecision.com
SIC: 3599 Custom machinery; machine
shop, jobbing & repair

(G-11389)
PRECISION DIRECTIONAL SVCS INC
10350 Richmond Ave # 700 (77042-4485)
PHONE....................................713 975-1209
EMP: 17
SALES (est): 1.8MM **Privately Held**
WEB: www.precisiondrilling.com
SIC: 1381 Directional drilling oil & gas
wells

(G-11390)
PRECISION DRILLING COMPANY LP (DH)
Also Called: Precision Drilling US
10350 Richmond Ave # 700 (77042-4485)
PHONE....................................713 435-6100
Thomas P Richards, *Partner*
Forrest Conley, *Partner*
Donald Guedry Jr, *Partner*
Gary D Lee, *Partner*
David Wehlmann, *Partner*
▲ **EMP:** 55
SQ FT: 250,000
SALES (est): 1.3B
SALES (corp-wide): 1.1B **Privately Held**
WEB: www.precisiondrilling.com
SIC: 1381 Drilling oil & gas wells
HQ: Precision Drilling Corporation
　　10370 Richmond Ave # 600
　　Houston TX 77042
　　713 435-6100

(G-11391)
PRECISION DRILLING CORPORATION (HQ)
10370 Richmond Ave # 600 (77042-4136)
PHONE....................................713 435-6100
Kevin Neveu, *CEO*
Thomas P Richards, *Ch of Bd*
William R Ziegler, *Vice Ch Bd*
Gary D Lee, *Partner*
David J Crowley, *COO*
◆ **EMP:** 2800
SQ FT: 28,617
SALES (est): 5.2B
SALES (corp-wide): 1.1B **Privately Held**
WEB: www.precisiondrilling.com
SIC: 1381 Directional drilling oil & gas
wells
PA: Precision Drilling Corporation
　　525 8 Ave Sw Suite 800
　　Calgary AB T2P 1
　　403 716-4500

(G-11392)
PRECISION ENERGY SERVICES INC
2442 Greens Rd (77032-1332)
PHONE....................................281 892-0600
EMP: 56 **Privately Held**
SIC: 3533 Oil field machinery & equipment
HQ: Precision Energy Services, Inc.
　　2000 Saint James Pl
　　Houston TX 77056

(G-11393)
PRECISION ENERGY SERVICES INC (DH)
2000 Saint James Pl (77056-4123)
PHONE....................................713 693-4000
Duroc Danner, *President*
◆ **EMP:** 110
SQ FT: 81,900
SALES (est): 201.8MM **Privately Held**
SIC: 3533 1389 Oil field machinery &
equipment; oil field services

HQ: Weatherford International, Llc
　　2000 Saint James Pl
　　Houston TX 77056
　　713 693-4000

(G-11394)
PRECISION POLYMER ENGRG LTD
4702 N Sam Houston Pkwy W
(77086-1499)
PHONE....................................713 482-0123
John Guite, *Vice Pres*
Mike Petzolt, *Regl Sales Mgr*
EMP: 10
SALES (corp-wide): 2.4B **Publicly Held**
WEB: www.prepol.com
SIC: 2891 Sealing compounds, synthetic
rubber or plastic
HQ: Precision Polymer Engineering Limited
　　Greenbank Road
　　Blackburn LANCS

(G-11395)
PRECISION TECH
Also Called: Precision Drilling
14041 Vickery Dr (77032-2667)
PHONE....................................281 227-5750
Duane Cuku, *Bd of Directors*
◆ **EMP:** 60
SALES (est): 3.5MM **Privately Held**
WEB: www.precisiondrilling.com
SIC: 1381 Drilling oil & gas wells

(G-11396)
PRECISION WELL LOGGING INC
924 Wakefield Dr (77018-6204)
P.O. Box 10163 (77206-0163)
PHONE....................................713 681-3435
Carl T Greer, *CEO*
Dan Greer, *President*
Billie S Greer, *Corp Secy*
Jim Henry, *Sales Mgr*
Marshall Byrd, *Sales Staff*
EMP: 47
SQ FT: 24,000
SALES: 6.6MM **Privately Held**
WEB: www.pwl-inc.com
SIC: 1389 Oil field services

(G-11397)
PRECO TURBINE COMPRSR SVCS INC
Also Called: A-C Compressor
17619 Aldine Westfield Rd (77073-5005)
PHONE....................................281 821-9620
Ernest H Gault, *CEO*
John Rice, *President*
Mark E Buchanan, *Vice Pres*
Barbara A Cameron, *Vice Pres*
James O Nelson, *Vice Pres*
◆ **EMP:** 130
SQ FT: 130,000
SALES (est): 17.5MM
SALES (corp-wide): 95.2B **Publicly Held**
WEB: www.bakerhughes.com
SIC: 7699 3511 1389 Industrial machinery
& equipment repair; pumps & pumping
equipment repair; compressor repair; tur-
bines & turbine generator sets; cementing
oil & gas well casings
PA: General Electric Company
　　5 Necco St
　　Boston MA 02210
　　617 443-3000

(G-11398)
PREDOMINANT PUMPS & AUTOMATION
910 Pinafore Ln (77039-1416)
PHONE....................................281 987-0204
Seth Douglas, *COO*
EMP: 15
SALES (corp-wide): 1.9MM **Privately
Held**
WEB: www.predominantpumps.com
SIC: 3561 3586 Pumps & pumping equip-
ment; oil pumps, measuring or dispensing
PA: Predominant Pumps & Automation So-
lutions Llc
　　5704 Dolores St
　　Houston TX 77057
　　713 775-3033

(G-11399)
PREMIER CONCRETE PRODUCTS INC
Also Called: Csg Industries
5102 Galveston Rd (77017-5463)
PHONE..................................713 641-2727
Frank Guerre, *Manager*
EMP: 15 Privately Held
WEB: www.premier-concrete.com
SIC: 3272 Concrete products
PA: Premier Concrete Products, Inc.
510 Oneal Lane Ext
Baton Rouge LA 70819

(G-11400)
PREMIER DIRECTIONAL DRLG LP
363 N Sam Houston Pkwy E # 300 (77060-2405)
PHONE..................................281 673-4000
Michael Kennedy, *Partner*
EMP: 140 EST: 2012
SALES (est): 27.2MM Privately Held
WEB: www.premierdirectionaldrilling.com
SIC: 1381 1781 Directional drilling oil & gas wells; water well drilling

(G-11401)
PREMIER MACHINING SERVICES
16230 Westpark Dr (77082-3700)
PHONE..................................281 558-3242
Jose Ramirez, *President*
Jesse Padilla, *Executive*
EMP: 16
SQ FT: 10,000
SALES (est): 2.3MM Privately Held
SIC: 3599 Machine shop, jobbing & repair

(G-11402)
PREMIER OILFIELD GROUP LLC (PA)
11335 Clay Rd Ste 180 (77041-1117)
PHONE..................................713 492-2057
Steve Cobb, *CEO*
Ray Parchejo, *Technology*
EMP: 13 EST: 2015
SQ FT: 24,000
SALES (est): 17.4MM Privately Held
WEB: www.pofg.com
SIC: 1389 Testing, measuring, surveying & analysis services

(G-11403)
PREMIER PIPE LLC (DH)
15600 John F Kennedy Blvd (77032-2349)
PHONE..................................832 300-8100
Scott Durole, *President*
Debra Leonard-Garza, *Partner*
Karen Anderson, *General Mgr*
Joe Schumacher, *General Mgr*
Cortland Marrow, *Business Mgr*
▼ EMP: 22
SQ FT: 1,300
SALES (est): 85.9MM Privately Held
WEB: www.prempipe.com
SIC: 1389 Oil field services
HQ: Sumitomo Corporation Of Americas
300 Madison Ave
New York NY 10017
212 207-0700

(G-11404)
PREMIER PRINTING & LTR SVC INC
Also Called: Premier Company, The
815 Live Oak St (77003-3220)
P.O. Box 7699 (77270-7699)
PHONE..................................713 868-6300
William D Justice, *Ch of Bd*
Martha Justice, *President*
▲ EMP: 40 EST: 1925
SQ FT: 80,000
SALES (est): 5.2MM Privately Held
WEB: www.premiercompany.com
SIC: 2752 7331 7377 5199 Commercial printing, offset; mailing service; computer rental & leasing; advertising specialties; bookbinding & related work; commercial printing

(G-11405)
PREMIUM OILFIELD TECH LLC (HQ)
5727 Brittmoore Rd (77041-5614)
PHONE..................................281 670-5200
Abhishek Shah, *Engineer*
Anthony Delgado, *Sales Mgr*
Kim Hewell, *Mng Member*
Danny Casino,
▲ EMP: 55 EST: 2013
SQ FT: 40,000
SALES (est): 42.5MM
SALES (corp-wide): 17.6MM Privately Held
WEB: www.premiumoilfield.com
SIC: 1389 Oil field services
PA: Gec Camco Llc
5727 Brittmoore Rd
Houston TX 77041
218 679-6500

(G-11406)
PREMIUM VALVE SERVICES LLC (HQ)
260 N Sam Houston Pkwy E (77060-2018)
PHONE..................................281 457-2565
W James Griswold, *CEO*
▲ EMP: 12
SQ FT: 12,000
SALES (est): 3.6MM Privately Held
SIC: 7699 3533 Valve repair, industrial; oil & gas field machinery

(G-11407)
PREMIUM WELDING INC
4122 Creekmont Dr (77091-5326)
PHONE..................................713 957-2724
Jessee Ramirez, *President*
Alex Flores, *President*
▲ EMP: 18
SQ FT: 16,000
SALES (est): 2.4MM Privately Held
WEB: www.premiumwelding.com
SIC: 7692 Welding repair

(G-11408)
PREMIUM WELDING & MFG INC
4122 Creekmont Dr (77091-5326)
PHONE..................................713 957-2724
Alberto Uribe, *President*
EMP: 60 EST: 2007
SALES (est): 3.7MM Privately Held
WEB: www.premiumwelding.com
SIC: 7692 Welding repair

(G-11409)
PRESS MASTERS INC (PA)
3814 Bissonnet St (77005-1141)
PHONE..................................713 661-9100
EMP: 12
SALES (est): 1.4MM Privately Held
SIC: 2741 Miscellaneous publishing

(G-11410)
PRESSURE POINT SERVICE
Also Called: P N I Accuflow
6430 Springer St (77087-3446)
PHONE..................................713 641-2325
Alfred Gaudin, *President*
EMP: 18
SQ FT: 16,000
SALES (est): 2.9MM Privately Held
SIC: 3498 Pipe fittings, fabricated from purchased pipe

(G-11411)
PRESTIGE EMBOSSING COMPANY INC
9777 W Gulf Bank Rd # 900 (77040-3198)
P.O. Box 41690 (77241-1690)
PHONE..................................713 864-0578
Johnny Calzada, *President*
Kim Calzada, *President*
Robert Graham, *Vice Pres*
Joshua Benoit, *Opers Staff*
Kim Calveza, *Officer*
EMP: 38
SALES (est): 4.8MM Privately Held
WEB: www.prestigeembossing.com
SIC: 2759 Embossing on paper

(G-11412)
PRIMARY SOURCING CORP (HQ)
2930 Rogerdale Rd (77042-4119)
PHONE..................................713 952-5405
Georgios Varsmis, *President*
▲ EMP: 68
SQ FT: 50,000
SALES (est): 25.7MM Publicly Held
WEB: www.primarys.com
SIC: 3672 Printed circuit boards

(G-11413)
PRIME DOWNHOLE MFG LLC (PA)
800 Northpark Central Dr (77073-6388)
PHONE..................................832 957-3200
Leif Syversen, *Ch of Bd*
John Wade, *President*
Ray Pena, *Vice Pres*
Shawn Housley, *CFO*
Debbie Williamson, *Human Resources*
EMP: 36
SALES (est): 5.2MM Privately Held
WEB: www.primedownhole.com
SIC: 7692 5082 Automotive welding; oil field equipment

(G-11414)
PRIME NATURAL RESOURCES INC
1201 La St Ste 2700 (77002)
PHONE..................................832 531-8555
Monica Garza, *Executive Asst*
EMP: 18
SALES (est): 189.2K Privately Held
WEB: www.flexsteelpipe.com
SIC: 1382 Oil & gas exploration services
PA: Prime Natural Resources, Llc
1201 La St Ste 2700
Houston TX 77002

(G-11415)
PRIME NATURAL RESOURCES LLC (PA)
1201 La St Ste 2700 (77002)
PHONE..................................713 953-3200
Maria Sclarandi, *Opers Staff*
Daniel Simonds, *Accounts Exec*
Jan Veldwijk, *Mng Member*
Jerrod Ervin, *Director*
EMP: 11
SALES (est): 48.1MM Privately Held
WEB: www.primenri.com
SIC: 1311 Crude petroleum & natural gas

(G-11416)
PRIME OPERATING COMPANY (HQ)
9821 Katy Fwy Ste 1050 (77024-1218)
PHONE..................................713 735-0000
Charles E Drimal Jr, *CEO*
Beverly A Cummings, *CFO*
Virginia Forese, *Human Res Dir*
James F Gilbert, *Admin Sec*
Lynne Pizor, *Asst Sec*
EMP: 21
SQ FT: 10,083
SALES (est): 7.2MM
SALES (corp-wide): 104.8MM Publicly Held
SIC: 6519 1389 1382 Real property lessors; construction, repair & dismantling services; oil & gas exploration services
PA: Primeenergy Corporation
9821 Katy Fwy Ste 1050
Houston TX 77024
713 735-0000

(G-11417)
PRIMEENERGY CORPORATION (PA)
9821 Katy Fwy Ste 1050 (77024-1218)
PHONE..................................713 735-0000
EMP: 45 EST: 1973
SALES: 104.8MM Publicly Held
WEB: www.primeenergy.com
SIC: 1311 Crude petroleum & natural gas production

(G-11418)
PRINCE ENERGY LLC (DH)
Also Called: TS Grinding
15311 Vantage Pkwy W # 3 (77032-1954)
PHONE..................................713 955-5398
Ronald A Rose Sr, *CEO*
Harvey Oyler, *President*
Bryan Conlin, *Opers Staff*
Cecilia Cervantes, *Purchasing*
Lauren Bergeron, *Human Res Dir*
◆ EMP: 32
SQ FT: 124,000
SALES (est): 122MM
SALES (corp-wide): 369K Privately Held
SIC: 2819 Industrial inorganic chemicals
HQ: Prince Minerals Llc
15311 Vantage Pkwy W # 3
Houston TX 77032
646 747-4222

(G-11419)
PRINCE MINERALS LLC (DH)
15311 Vantage Pkwy W # 3 (77032-1954)
PHONE..................................646 747-4222
John Ropp, *President*
Kim Craig, *Vice Pres*
Kristin Schenck, *Vice Pres*
Roderik J F Alewijnse, *CFO*
Matthew Groth, *Manager*
◆ EMP: 54
SQ FT: 22,946
SALES (est): 203.7MM
SALES (corp-wide): 369K Privately Held
WEB: www.princecorp.com
SIC: 3356 3295 Zirconium; silicon, ultra high purity: treated
HQ: Prince International Corporation
15311 Vantage Pkwy W # 35
Houston TX 77032
646 747-4222

(G-11420)
PRINCE SIGNS LLC
6432 Cunningham Rd (77041-4714)
PHONE..................................281 345-4488
Asghar Zainuddin, *Engineer*
Taher Evvi, *Mng Member*
Taher Ali,
EMP: 13
SQ FT: 15,000
SALES (est): 1.9MM Privately Held
WEB: www.princesigns.com
SIC: 3993 Neon signs

(G-11421)
PRINT SYSTEMS INC (PA)
4537 Brittmoore Rd (77041-8005)
PHONE..................................713 812-8126
William H Turo, *President*
Mikel Turo, *Opers Staff*
EMP: 11
SQ FT: 22,000
SALES (est): 3.4MM Privately Held
WEB: www.labels2.com
SIC: 2752 Commercial printing, lithographic

(G-11422)
PRINTMAILERS INC
Also Called: PMI
707 West Rd (77038-2505)
PHONE..................................832 201-2000
Stephen G Johns, *President*
▲ EMP: 90
SQ FT: 48,000
SALES (est): 12.3MM Privately Held
WEB: www.pminet.com
SIC: 2752 7331 Commercial printing, offset; mailing service

(G-11423)
PRISM RESOURCES INC
Also Called: Precision Components
7301 Galveston Rd (77034-1406)
PHONE..................................713 947-2800
Brent E Kindle, *President*
Michele R Milner, *Vice Pres*
Mike Milner, *Manager*
Rebecca Mireles, *Administration*
▲ EMP: 50
SQ FT: 20,000
SALES (est): 17.3MM Privately Held
WEB: www.pc-houston.com
SIC: 3441 Building components, structural steel

(G-11424)
PRO DIGI EMBROIDERY
5755 Bonhomme Rd Ste 410 (77036-2013)
PHONE..................................713 339-4373
Arvid Forstein, *Owner*
EMP: 12
SALES (est): 765.5K Privately Held
WEB: www.pdemb.com
SIC: 2395 Embroidery products, except schiffli machine

GEOGRAPHIC

(G-11425)
PRO MACHINE LP
6119 Brittmoore Rd (77041-5610)
PHONE...................................713 466-3210
Alan Knust, *Partner*
Allan Brunson, *Foreman/Supr*
Dane Haveman, *Purchasing*
Greg Walker, *QC Mgr*
Hans Namink, *Manager*
EMP: 52
SQ FT: 16,000
SALES (est): 9.3MM **Privately Held**
SIC: 3599 Machine shop, jobbing & repair

(G-11426)
PRO-GRIND INC
5637 Hogue St (77087-4011)
PHONE..................................713 645-2966
Carl Stringer, *President*
Robin Stringer, *Vice Pres*
EMP: 35
SQ FT: 25,000
SALES (est): 4.7MM **Privately Held**
WEB: www.pro-grind.com
SIC: 3599 Machine shop, jobbing & repair

(G-11427)
PRO-KLEEN INC
Also Called: Pro-Kleen Industries
4800 Fidelity St (77029-3563)
PHONE..................................713 855-2760
Kevin Turpin, *Branch Mgr*
EMP: 22
SALES (corp-wide): 15.2MM **Privately Held**
WEB: www.prokleenutah.com
SIC: 1799 3479 1721 Sandblasting of building exteriors; painting of metal products; industrial painting
PA: Pro-Kleen, Inc.
5351 Sw 100th St
Augusta KS 67010
316 775-6898

(G-11428)
PRO-PLASTICS INC
9530 Baythorne Dr (77041-7712)
PHONE..................................713 690-9000
Ramy Law, *President*
EMP: 89
SALES (corp-wide): 12.4MM **Privately Held**
WEB: www.proplastics.com
SIC: 2673 Plastic bags: made from purchased materials
PA: Pro-Plastics, Inc.
9530 Baythorne Dr
Houston TX 77041
713 690-9000

(G-11429)
PRO-PLASTICS INC (PA)
9530 Baythorne Dr (77041-7712)
PHONE..................................713 690-9000
Ramy Law, *President*
Emily Rogacion, *Vice Pres*
Tony Yeung, *Vice Pres*
Jenny Wu, *Credit Staff*
Elizabeth Rogacion, *VP Sales*
▲ **EMP:** 41
SQ FT: 65,000
SALES (est): 12.4MM **Privately Held**
WEB: www.proplastics.com
SIC: 2673 Plastic bags: made from purchased materials

(G-11430)
PROCEGAS LLC
111 Berry Rd (77022-3126)
PHONE..................................832 652-2129
Carlos Balza, *CEO*
Fernando Garcia, *Opers Mgr*
Darrell Gordon, *CFO*
Jennifer Ratto, *Office Mgr*
Marlon Rivas, *Manager*
EMP: 50
SQ FT: 100,000
SALES (est): 13.3MM **Privately Held**
WEB: www.procegas.com
SIC: 3533 Oil & gas field machinery
PA: Procegas Ca
Calle Guaicapuro
Puerto La Cruz

(G-11431)
PROCESS MANUFACTURING CORP
415a N Wayside Dr Ste A (77020-7516)
PHONE..................................713 426-1403
Robert Reider, *President*
EMP: 74 **EST:** 1999
SQ FT: 65,000
SALES (est): 24.3MM **Privately Held**
WEB: www.processmfgcorp.com
SIC: 3441 Building components, structural steel

(G-11432)
PROCESS RECOVERY SYSTEMS INC
5930 Par Four Dr (77088-6634)
PHONE..................................281 448-8180
John Tyson, *President*
Elanore Tyson, *Admin Sec*
EMP: 12
SQ FT: 15,000
SALES (est): 903.5K **Privately Held**
WEB: www.brinereduction.com
SIC: 1321 5078 Liquefied petroleum gases (natural) production; refrigeration equipment & supplies

(G-11433)
PROCRAFT CABINETRY INC
4647 Pine Timbers St (77041-9323)
PHONE..................................832 203-5736
Tao Zheng, *Branch Mgr*
EMP: 10
SALES (corp-wide): 11.3MM **Privately Held**
WEB: www.procraftcabinetry.com
SIC: 2434 Wood kitchen cabinets
PA: Procraft Cabinetry, Inc.
429 Mcnally Dr
Nashville TN 37211
615 528-0399

(G-11434)
PROCUREMENT SERVICES DEL INC
Also Called: Petrosaudi Oil Services
363 N Sam Houston Pkwy E (77060-2404)
PHONE..................................832 243-6330
Nigel Burton, *CEO*
Perry Paul, *Opers Staff*
Scott McClendon, *Controller*
Virginia Fulton, *Finance Mgr*
Roland Caffet, *Manager*
◆ **EMP:** 22
SQ FT: 5,000
SALES (est): 25.9MM **Privately Held**
WEB: www.petrosaudi.com
SIC: 1382 Oil & gas exploration services

(G-11435)
PROCYRION INC
3900 Essex Ln Ste 850 (77027-5195)
PHONE..................................713 579-9224
Benjamin Hertzog, *CEO*
Eric S Fain, *President*
AV Edidin, *Senior VP*
James Toll, *Opers Mgr*
William Clifton, *Research*
EMP: 10
SALES (est): 817.3K **Privately Held**
WEB: www.procyrion.com
SIC: 3841 Diagnostic apparatus, medical

(G-11436)
PRODEKTIVE SPECIALTY SVCS LLC
1110 Nasa Pkwy Ste 450 (77058-3346)
PHONE..................................713 425-3075
Arvin Varghese, *President*
EMP: 50
SQ FT: 1,000
SALES (est): 1.2MM **Privately Held**
SIC: 7372 1799 Application computer software; rigging & scaffolding

(G-11437)
PRODUCTION TECH & SVCS INC
Also Called: P T S
1463 Highway 6 S Ths (77077-2134)
PHONE..................................281 498-7399
Dr Robert Hoff Sr, *President*
Carolina Noel, *Accountant*
Abeer Alsouliman, *Technology*
Carter Garrett, *Shareholder*

Hazel Hoff, *Shareholder*
◆ **EMP:** 20
SALES (est): 1.8MM **Privately Held**
WEB: www.pts-technology.com
SIC: 1389 7353 Testing, measuring, surveying & analysis services; oil field equipment, rental or leasing

(G-11438)
PROFESSIONAL MACHINE WORKS
7583 Morley St (77061-2828)
PHONE..................................713 645-7562
Juan Anuan Antonio T Macias, *President*
EMP: 15
SQ FT: 19,000
SALES (est): 2MM **Privately Held**
WEB: www.professional-machine.com
SIC: 3599 7692 Machine shop, jobbing & repair; welding repair

(G-11439)
PROFESSIONAL RENTAL TOOLS LLC (PA)
Also Called: Prt Offshore
1111 North Loop W Ste 140 (77008-1700)
P.O. Box 80189, Lafayette LA (70598-0189)
PHONE..................................713 808-9756
Andrew Robertson, *Mng Member*
EMP: 39
SQ FT: 20,000
SALES: 34.1K **Privately Held**
WEB: www.prtoffshore.com
SIC: 7353 1389 Oil field equipment, rental or leasing; oil field services

(G-11440)
PROFESSIONALIZED PDTS & SVCS
Also Called: Ppsi
10905 Brooklet Dr (77099-3503)
PHONE..................................281 933-9427
William G Huang, *President*
Jerry Huang, *Vice Pres*
Benjamin Huynh, *Materials Mgr*
Hanh Pham, *Purch Mgr*
May Huang, *Treasurer*
EMP: 34
SQ FT: 16,000
SALES (est): 6.3MM **Privately Held**
WEB: www.ppsimanufacturing.com
SIC: 3823 7371 7629 8711 Temperature measurement instruments, industrial; industrial flow & liquid measuring instruments; industrial process measurement equipment; on-stream gas/liquid analysis instruments, industrial; computer software development; electronic equipment repair; professional engineer

(G-11441)
PROFITABLE DECISIONS INC
7814 Nairn St (77074-5321)
PHONE..................................281 972-3030
Ronald Lee Russell Jr, *CEO*
EMP: 10
SALES (est): 790K **Privately Held**
WEB: www.profitabledecisions.com
SIC: 7372 Prepackaged software

(G-11442)
PROGRESSIVE COML AQUATICS INC (PA)
2510 Farrell Rd (77073-4000)
PHONE..................................281 982-0212
Russell Leto, *President*
John C Davis, *President*
Payton Davis, *Asst Supt*
Steven E Davis, *Vice Pres*
Tim Phelps, *Vice Pres*
EMP: 54
SQ FT: 17,259
SALES (est): 5.4MM **Privately Held**
WEB: www.proaquatic.com
SIC: 3949 5169 Swimming pools, plastic; industrial chemicals

(G-11443)
PROGRESSIVE MACHINE WORKS LTD
19515 Oil Center Blvd (77073-3356)
PHONE..................................281 209-9990
Alan Carmichael, *President*
EMP: 25 **Privately Held**

SIC: 3599 Machine shop, jobbing & repair

(G-11444)
PROMAN USA INC (DH)
600 Travis St Ste 3680 (77002-2995)
PHONE..................................713 943-2200
Timothy Vail, *CEO*
Heather Hale, *CEO*
Jarrod Hodson, *President*
Brent Gwaltney, *COO*
Danny Wilson, *Exec VP*
EMP: 15
SALES (est): 5.6MM
SALES (corp-wide): 533.7K **Privately Held**
WEB: www.g2xenergy.com
SIC: 2869 Fuels
HQ: Proman Ag
Samstagernstrasse 41
Wollerau SZ 8832
438 882-999

(G-11445)
PROMAN USA (PAMPA) LLC (DH)
600 Travis St Ste 3600 (77002-2928)
PHONE..................................713 943-2200
Brent Hendrickson, *Controller*
Susan Hinton,
Jim Bob Mitchell,
EMP: 11
SALES (est): 2.2MM
SALES (corp-wide): 533.7K **Privately Held**
WEB: www.g2xenergy.com
SIC: 2869 Fuels
HQ: Proman Usa, Inc.
600 Travis St Ste 3680
Houston TX 77002
713 943-2200

(G-11446)
PROMAXIMA MANUFACTURING LTD (PA)
5310 Ashbrook Dr (77081-4102)
PHONE..................................800 231-6652
Bob Leppke, *President*
Lisa A Stringfellow, *CFO*
Jane Manhard, *Accountant*
Cindy Steele, *Regl Sales Mgr*
Scott Rayner, *Accounts Exec*
▲ **EMP:** 68
SQ FT: 82,000
SALES (est): 30.7MM **Privately Held**
WEB: www.promaxima.com
SIC: 5941 3949 Exercise equipment; exercise equipment

(G-11447)
PROMAXIMA MFG LLP PROM
5310 Ashbrook Dr (77081-4102)
PHONE..................................713 667-9606
Bob Leppke, *Principal*
Sean Flores, *Purch Agent*
EMP: 10
SQ FT: 3,000
SALES (est): 1.4MM **Privately Held**
WEB: www.promaxima.com
SIC: 3999 Manufacturing industries

(G-11448)
PROMETHEUS ENERGY GROUP INC (DH)
10305 Richmond Ave # 825 (77042-4103)
PHONE..................................832 456-6500
Jim Aivalis, *President*
Michiel Boersma, *Chairman*
Len York, *CFO*
Lisa Parker, *Manager*
EMP: 44
SQ FT: 7,000
SALES (est): 13.2MM
SALES (corp-wide): 47MM **Publicly Held**
WEB: www.stabilisenergy.com
SIC: 1321 Natural gas liquids production
HQ: Stabilis Energy, Inc.
10375 Richmond Ave # 700
Houston TX 77042
409 833-1115

(G-11449)
PROPEL ENERGY LLC (PA)
1923 Woodhead St (77019-6123)
PHONE..................................713 463-6500
William Scarff, *President*
W Scott Dole, *Principal*
Gregory S Floyd, *Principal*

Alan S Pennington, *Principal*
Rich Smiley, *Principal*
EMP: 9
SALES (est): 4MM **Privately Held**
WEB: www.propelenergy.com
SIC: 1382 Oil & gas exploration services

(G-11450)
PROPORTIONAL TECHNOLOGIES INC
Also Called: P T I
12233 Robin Blvd (77045-4826)
PHONE................................713 747-7324
Jeffrey L Lacy, *President*
Myrna Edrada Lacy, *Vice Pres*
Myrna Lacy, *Vice Pres*
Athanasios Athanasiades, *Engineer*
Rebecca Warfield, *Accountant*
EMP: 31
SQ FT: 28,000
SALES (est): 7.3MM **Privately Held**
WEB: www.proportionaltech.com
SIC: 3674 8731 Nuclear detectors, solid state; commercial physical research; medical research, commercial

(G-11451)
PROROCK GRANITE & CABINETS INC
8620 Windswept Ln (77063-5724)
PHONE................................832 486-9414
Ricardo D Mendoza, *CEO*
▲ EMP: 17 EST: 2008
SQ FT: 2,000
SALES (est): 1.7MM **Privately Held**
SIC: 2434 Wood kitchen cabinets

(G-11452)
PROS INC
3200 Kirby Dr (77098-3230)
PHONE................................713 335-5151
Andres D Reiner, *President*
Blair Crump, *COO*
Stefon Schultz, *CFO*
Ron Woestemeyer, *Bd of Directors*
EMP: 1000
SALES (est): 83.5MM **Publicly Held**
WEB: www.pros.com
SIC: 7372 Prepackaged software
PA: Pros Holdings, Inc.
  3200 Kirby Dr Ste 600
  Houston TX 77098

(G-11453)
PROS HOLDINGS INC (PA)
3200 Kirby Dr Ste 600 (77098-1039)
PHONE................................713 335-5151
William Russell, *Ch of Bd*
Andres D Reiner, *President*
Benson Yuen, *President*
Jimmy Leal, *Managing Dir*
Les Rechan, *COO*
EMP: 107
SALES (est): 250.3MM **Publicly Held**
WEB: www.pros.com
SIC: 7371 7372 Computer software development; prepackaged software

(G-11454)
PROSEP TECHNOLOGIES INC
5512 Clara Rd (77041-7204)
PHONE................................281 504-2040
Neil Poxon, *CEO*
Jay Keener, *General Mgr*
John Sabey, *Principal*
Matthew Call, *Vice Pres*
Ian Robertson, *Vice Pres*
▲ EMP: 20
SALES (est): 1.3MM **Privately Held**
WEB: www.prosep.com
SIC: 1311 Crude petroleum & natural gas

(G-11455)
PROSERV CRANE & EQUIPMENT INC (PA)
Also Called: Proserv Anchor Crane Group
455 Aldine Bender Rd (77060-4403)
P.O. Box 670965 (77267-0965)
PHONE................................281 405-9048
Gary Stein, *Ch of Bd*
Neal Wilson, *President*
Hal Carruth, *Sales Staff*
Matthew Everitt, *Branch Mgr*
▼ EMP: 55
SQ FT: 58,500

SALES (est): 57MM **Privately Held**
WEB: www.proservcrane.com
SIC: 3536 7389 Cranes, overhead traveling; crane & aerial lift service

(G-11456)
PROSERV OPERATIONS INC
15151 Sommermeyer St (77041-5332)
PHONE................................337 984-8054
Vernon Parker, *Engineer*
Nicola Powditch, *Manager*
EMP: 493 **Privately Held**
WEB: www.proserv.com
SIC: 1389 Fire fighting, oil & gas field
PA: Proserv Operations, Inc.
  13105 Nw Fwy Ste 250
  Houston TX 77040

(G-11457)
PROSERV OPERATIONS INC
15151 Sommermeyer St (77041-5332)
PHONE................................832 467-3110
Alex Lansdowne, *Project Mgr*
Lauren Calautti, *Sales Staff*
Nicola Powditch, *Manager*
Stephan Mason, *Manager*
EMP: 411 **Privately Held**
SIC: 3492 Control valves, fluid power: hydraulic & pneumatic
PA: Proserv Operations, Inc.
  13105 Nw Fwy Ste 250
  Houston TX 77040

(G-11458)
PROSERV OPERATIONS INC
1231 Lumpkin Rd (77043-4101)
PHONE................................713 468-8778
Brett Robinson, *Technical Mgr*
Keathya Hill, *Controller*
Dwayne Sawyer, *Sales Staff*
Nicola Powditch, *Manager*
EMP: 411 **Privately Held**
WEB: www.proserv.com
SIC: 3491 Process control regulator valves
PA: Proserv Operations, Inc.
  13105 Nw Fwy Ste 250
  Houston TX 77040

(G-11459)
PROSERV OPERATIONS INC
Also Called: Subsea Technology
15151 Sommermeyer St (77041-5332)
PHONE................................713 983-7222
Nicola Powditch, *Manager*
EMP: 18 **Privately Held**
WEB: www.proserv.com
SIC: 1389 Oil & gas wells: building, repairing & dismantling
PA: Proserv Operations, Inc.
  13105 Nw Fwy Ste 250
  Houston TX 77040

(G-11460)
PROSERV OPERATIONS INC
2437 Peyton Rd (77032-2019)
PHONE................................281 807-2100
Nicola Powditch, *Manager*
EMP: 276 **Privately Held**
WEB: www.proserv.com
SIC: 1389 Fire fighting, oil & gas field
PA: Proserv Operations, Inc.
  13105 Nw Fwy Ste 250
  Houston TX 77040

(G-11461)
PROSKE PLASTIC PRODUCTS INC
6701 Supply Row (77011-4517)
P.O. Box 231008 (77223-1008)
PHONE................................713 926-9941
Chester T Walker, *President*
Harold Glen Haddox, *Vice Pres*
Sid Early, *Production*
Mimi Walker, *Treasurer*
Mariann Gomez, *Office Admin*
EMP: 30 EST: 1953
SQ FT: 12,000
SALES (est): 4.3MM **Privately Held**
WEB: www.proskeplastics.com
SIC: 3083 3443 3088 Plastic finished products, laminated; fabricated plate work (boiler shop); plastics plumbing fixtures

(G-11462)
PROTECHNICS (PA)
Also Called: Core Lab
6510 W Sam Houston Pkwy N (77041-5105)
PHONE................................713 328-2320
Mike Flecker, *Vice Pres*
Peter W Boks, *Vice Pres*
Alastair J Crombie, *Vice Pres*
Kevin G Daniels, *Vice Pres*
Donald Dumas, *Vice Pres*
EMP: 17
SALES (est): 1.9MM **Privately Held**
WEB: www.corelab.com
SIC: 1389 Oil field services

(G-11463)
PROTEGE ENERGY III LLC (PA)
55 Waugh Dr Ste 400 (77007-5839)
PHONE................................918 728-3092
Martin Thalken, *Ch of Bd*
David Boncaldo, *President*
Tarah Angelidis, *Vice Pres*
Morris Hall, *Vice Pres*
Jason Pugh, *Opers Staff*
EMP: 15
SALES (est): 500K **Privately Held**
WEB: www.protege-energy.com
SIC: 1382 Oil & gas exploration services

(G-11464)
PROTEK SPECIALTY COMPANY
10315 Brighton Ln (77031-2815)
P.O. Box 965, Stafford (77497-0965)
PHONE................................713 667-6691
Don E Moore, *President*
Divina Moore, *Vice Pres*
EMP: 12 EST: 1946
SALES (est): 2.9MM **Privately Held**
WEB: www.protekspecialty.com
SIC: 3561 3533 Pumps, domestic: water or sump; oil & gas field machinery

(G-11465)
PROTOLINE INC
10650 Stancliff Rd (77099-4331)
PHONE................................281 561-0802
Paresh Jasani, *President*
Gautam Jasani, *Vice Pres*
Suresh Jasani, *Treasurer*
Ramesh Jasani, *Admin Sec*
Dhruv Patel, *Analyst*
EMP: 15
SQ FT: 18,000
SALES (est): 2.2MM **Privately Held**
WEB: www.protoline.com
SIC: 3672 Circuit boards, television & radio printed

(G-11466)
PROVIBTECH INC (PA)
Also Called: Predictech
7636 Harwin Dr Ste 112 (77036-1951)
PHONE................................713 830-7601
Donald Ll, *President*
◆ EMP: 28
SQ FT: 5,000
SALES (est): 16.4MM **Privately Held**
WEB: www.vibravista.com
SIC: 3829 Vibration meters, analyzers & calibrators

(G-11467)
PROWORX INC
Also Called: Proworx Architectural Signage
12309 Hodges St (77085-1103)
PHONE................................713 666-3131
Manuel Vasquez, *President*
William Clarke, *Vice Pres*
Mario Olvera, *Project Mgr*
EMP: 20
SQ FT: 10,000
SALES (est): 1.9MM **Privately Held**
WEB: www.proworxinc.com
SIC: 7389 3993 Sign painting & lettering shop; electric signs

(G-11468)
PRYSMIAN CBLES SYSTEMS USA LLC
Also Called: Draka USA Distributions
1610 Greens Rd (77032-1195)
PHONE................................281 209-1070
Sterrett Lloyd, *COO*
Bill Foe, *Branch Mgr*
Gary Savage, *Technical Staff*

EMP: 15 **Privately Held**
WEB: www.strongman.com
SIC: 3357 Communication wire
HQ: Prysmian Cables And Systems Usa, Llc
  4 Tesseneer Dr
  Highland Heights KY 41076
  859 572-8000

(G-11469)
PSI MIDSTREAM PARTNERS LP
114 Fawnlake Dr (77079-7309)
PHONE................................713 554-2880
Robert L Powell III, *President*
Eric Pitcher, *Partner*
EMP: 20
SQ FT: 4,800
SALES (est): 4.7MM **Privately Held**
WEB: www.psimidstream.com
SIC: 1382 Oil & gas exploration services

(G-11470)
PT TRUCKS INC
6509 Romona Blvd (77086-3314)
PHONE................................713 338-1375
Joseph Pham, *CEO*
Loi Nguyen, *President*
◆ EMP: 20
SALES (est): 1MM **Privately Held**
SIC: 3715 Truck trailers

(G-11471)
PTS - POWER TEMP SYSTEMS INC
1646 Rankin Rd Ste 300 (77073-4907)
PHONE................................337 806-9779
Richard Ryder, *Technology*
EMP: 10 **Privately Held**
WEB: www.powertemp.com
SIC: 3699 Electrical equipment & supplies
PA: Pts - Power Temp Systems, Inc.
  1428 N Sam Hston Pkwy E S
  Lafayette LA 70501

(G-11472)
PUMP ARTS INC
10034 Easthaven Blvd (77075-3299)
P.O. Box 750725 (77275-0725)
PHONE................................713 946-0500
James Stevens, *President*
EMP: 22 EST: 1962
SQ FT: 60,500
SALES (est): 3MM **Privately Held**
WEB: www.pumparts.com
SIC: 3599 3463 3594 3561 Machine shop, jobbing & repair; pump & compressor forgings, nonferrous; fluid power pumps & motors; pumps & pumping equipment

(G-11473)
PURE BIOFUELS CORP
3811 Shadow Trace Cir (77082-5637)
PHONE................................281 540-9317
Chris Tewell, *Ch of Bd*
Luis Goyzueta, *President*
EMP: 28
SALES (est): 2MM **Privately Held**
WEB: www.purebiofuels.com
SIC: 2869 Fuels

(G-11474)
PUROLATOR EFP LLC (DH)
Also Called: Niagara Screen Products
8733 Daffodil St (77063-5610)
P.O. Box 630145 (77263-0145)
PHONE................................713 977-0610
Bruce A Klein, *CFO*
Norm Johnson, *Mng Member*
▲ EMP: 85
SALES (est): 20.2MM
SALES (corp-wide): 13.7B **Publicly Held**
WEB: www.purolator-efp.com
SIC: 3569 Filters
HQ: Clarcor Inc.
  840 Crescent Centre Dr # 600
  Franklin TN 37067
  615 771-3100

(G-11475)
PURSUIT OIL & GAS LLC
840 Gessner Rd Ste 850 (77024-4487)
PHONE................................832 706-2299
Kirk Stilman, *CEO*
Shubhanan Dakshindas, *Vice Pres*
Spencer Finch, *Vice Pres*

Ryan Fitzpatrick, *Vice Pres*
Scott Szalkowski, *Vice Pres*
EMP: 15 **EST:** 2014
SQ FT: 10,304
SALES (est): 633.8K **Privately Held**
WEB: www.pursuitog.com
SIC: 1382 Oil & gas exploration services

(G-11476)
PV AMERICAN INC
1907 Upland Dr Ofc (77043-3030)
PHONE..................................713 270-7772
Chris Ausobsky, *President*
Peter Tran, *Corp Secy*
Son Van Luu, *Vice Pres*
Hugh Ausobsky, *Opers Mgr*
Alex Tran, *Purch Mgr*
EMP: 10 **EST:** 2000
SALES (est): 920.7K **Privately Held**
WEB: www.pvamerican.com
SIC: 3599 Machine shop, jobbing & repair

(G-11477)
PXP GULF COAST INC (DH)
700 Milam St Ste 3100 (77002-2764)
PHONE..................................713 579-6000
James C Flores, *President*
Doss R Bourgeois, *Exec VP*
Winston M Talbert, *Exec VP*
John F Wombwell, *Exec VP*
EMP: 147
SALES (est): 61.9MM
SALES (corp-wide): 14.4B **Publicly Held**
WEB: www.pxpfinancial.com
SIC: 1311 Crude petroleum & natural gas
HQ: Freeport-Mcmoran Oil & Gas Llc
　700 Milam St Ste 3100
　Houston TX 77002
　713 579-6000

(G-11478)
PXP OFFSHORE LLC
700 Milam St Ste 3100 (77002-2764)
PHONE..................................713 579-6000
EMP: 12
SALES (est): 692.6K
SALES (corp-wide): 16.4B **Publicly Held**
SIC: 1382 Oil/Gas Exploration Services
HQ: Freeport-Mcmoran Oil & Gas Llc
　700 Milam St Ste 3100
　Houston TX 77002
　713 579-6000

(G-11479)
PYRAMID GOM INC
1800 West Loop S Ste 1950 (77027-3212)
PHONE..................................281 822-0801
EMP: 22
SALES (est): 1.7MM **Privately Held**
SIC: 1382 Oil/Gas Exploration Services

(G-11480)
PYRANHA INC
Also Called: Pyranha Insecticides
6602 Cunningham Rd (77041-4726)
PHONE..................................832 467-3840
Garry Cunningham, *President*
David Cunningham, *Vice Pres*
Mary Anna Naumann, *Admin Sec*
EMP: 10
SQ FT: 15,000
SALES (est): 3.4MM **Privately Held**
WEB: www.pyranhainc.com
SIC: 3523 7342 Sprayers & spraying machines, agricultural; pest control services

(G-11481)
Q M COMPANY INC
4846 W O S T Dr (77013-3035)
PHONE..................................713 673-1917
David Martin, *President*
Martin Mike, *Director*
EMP: 12 **EST:** 1975
SQ FT: 4,800
SALES (est): 2.3MM **Privately Held**
WEB: www.qmcompany.com
SIC: 3599 Machine shop, jobbing & repair

(G-11482)
QAE INC
16945 Northchase Dr # 2200 (77060-2152)
PHONE..................................281 436-5500
Michael Bankes, *QC Mgr*
Robert G Davis, *Exec Dir*
EMP: 80

SALES (est): 2.5MM **Privately Held**
WEB: www.qaeworld.com
SIC: 1382 Oil & gas exploration services

(G-11483)
QMAX AMERICA INC
Also Called: Q'Max America Envmtl Solutions
11700 Katy Fwy Enrgy Twr (77079)
PHONE..................................817 732-2423
Reginald Northcott, *President*
Kevin King, *General Mgr*
▼ **EMP:** 49
SQ FT: 6,000
SALES (est): 2.1MM
SALES (corp-wide): 245.6MM **Privately Held**
WEB: www.qmax.com
SIC: 1389 Mud service, oil field drilling
PA: Q'max Solutions Inc
　585 8 Ave Sw Suite 1210
　Calgary AB T2P 1
　403 269-2242

(G-11484)
QMAX SOLUTIONS INC
1315 W Sam Houston Pkwy N S (77043-4020)
PHONE..................................832 672-4459
Linda Hickmanteeters, *Human Res Mgr*
Gilberto Ochoa, *Manager*
EMP: 14
SALES (est): 5.6MM **Privately Held**
WEB: www.qmaxcolombia.com
SIC: 1389 Oil field services

(G-11485)
QO INC (PA)
10402 Valley Forge Dr (77042-1911)
PHONE..................................713 224-7823
Gerard J Coogan, *President*
EMP: 11 **EST:** 1997
SALES (est): 2MM **Privately Held**
WEB: www.qoinc.com
SIC: 1389 Oil consultants

(G-11486)
QPOWER INCORPORATED
Also Called: Maxpower of Texas
5610 Savoy Dr (77036-2224)
PHONE..................................713 266-5295
Matthew E Bund, *President*
▲ **EMP:** 50
SQ FT: 36,000
SALES (est): 7.2MM **Privately Held**
WEB: www.qpowerinc.com
SIC: 3651 Speaker systems

(G-11487)
QRI INTERNATIONAL LLC (HQ)
909 Fannin St Ste 2200 (77010-1043)
PHONE..................................713 485-8800
Simon K Hodson, *Chairman*
Donald Tang, *Chairman*
Debbora Church, *Exec Sec*
▲ **EMP:** 13 **EST:** 2007
SALES (est): 33.4MM
SALES (corp-wide): 33.6MM **Privately Held**
WEB: www.qrigroup.com
SIC: 1389 1381 2911 Oil field services; drilling oil & gas wells; fractionation products of crude petroleum, hydrocarbons
PA: Quantum Reservoir Impact, Llc
　909 Fannin St Ste 2200
　Houston TX 77010
　713 485-8800

(G-11488)
QSD MANUFACTURING INC
5700 Mitchelldale St (77092-7030)
PHONE..................................713 957-0599
Walter Joo, *President*
EMP: 14
SQ FT: 4,800
SALES (est): 2.7MM **Privately Held**
WEB: www.qsdmfg.com
SIC: 3599 Machine shop, jobbing & repair

(G-11489)
QTS LLC
5084 Steadmont Dr (77040-6524)
PHONE..................................713 462-7072
Enrique Rojas, *Mng Member*
▲ **EMP:** 37
SQ FT: 12,400

SALES (est): 5.3MM **Privately Held**
WEB: www.masonrycare.com
SIC: 3281 Bathroom fixtures, cut stone

(G-11490)
QUAIL TOOLS LP
15401 Vantage Pkwy W # 100 (77032-1968)
PHONE..................................281 445-1777
Tip Cain, *Manager*
EMP: 62
SALES (corp-wide): 571MM **Publicly Held**
WEB: www.quailtools.com
SIC: 1389 Oil field services
HQ: Quail Tools, L.P.
　3713 Highway 14
　New Iberia LA 70560
　337 365-8154

(G-11491)
QUAKER STATE INVESTMENT CORP
700 Milam St (77002-2806)
PHONE..................................713 546-4000
EMP: 10
SALES (est): 19.2K
SALES (corp-wide): 305.1B **Privately Held**
SIC: 2911 Petroleum Refiner
HQ: Shell Petroleum Inc.
　910 Louisiana St Ste 420
　Houston TX 77002
　713 241-6161

(G-11492)
QUALITY BAKERY PRODUCTS INC
14330 Interdrive W (77032-3316)
PHONE..................................281 449-4977
Martin Shafer, *President*
Mike Tills, *Vice Pres*
Ron Rupertus, *Production*
Henry P Wellborn, *Admin Sec*
▲ **EMP:** 65
SQ FT: 50,000
SALES (est): 15.8MM **Privately Held**
WEB: www.qualitybakeryproducts.net
SIC: 2053 2099 Cakes, bakery: frozen; dessert mixes & fillings

(G-11493)
QUALITY COPPER & ALLOYS LLC
515 Garden Oaks Blvd (77018-5505)
PHONE..................................346 223-1032
Bobby Freiertag, *Mng Member*
ARI Kogut,
Dan Schatzman,
EMP: 13
SALES (est): 2.3MM **Privately Held**
WEB: www.qcalloys.com
SIC: 3351 Copper & copper alloy sheet, strip, plate & products

(G-11494)
QUALITY HAND BINDERY INC
8520 Sweetwater Ln E42 (77037-2826)
PHONE..................................281 445-8682
Georgia Weisinger, *President*
Charlene Belmont, *Vice Pres*
EMP: 10
SQ FT: 10,000
SALES (est): 350K **Privately Held**
SIC: 2789 Bookbinding & related work

(G-11495)
QUALITY LNINGS FABRICATION INC (PA)
3601 W 12th St (77008-6007)
P.O. Box 924392 (77292-4392)
PHONE..................................713 863-7013
Larry P Shepherd, *President*
Hugh White Jr, *Treasurer*
EMP: 50
SQ FT: 45,935
SALES (est): 13MM **Privately Held**
WEB: www.qlfinc.com
SIC: 3312 3613 5051 3446 Structural shapes & pilings, steel; control panels, electric; steel decking; architectural metalwork; fabricated structural metal

(G-11496)
QUALITY MAT COMPANY
14214 East Fwy (77015-5910)
PHONE..................................713 455-3990
Amy Woolls, *Principal*
Joe Penland Jr, *Vice Pres*
Kim Davenport, *Sales Staff*
EMP: 18
SALES (corp-wide): 49.3MM **Privately Held**
WEB: www.qmat.com
SIC: 2426 Furniture stock & parts, hardwood
PA: Quality Mat Company
　6550 Tram Rd
　Beaumont TX 77713
　409 898-1170

(G-11497)
QUALITY MATTRESS COMPANY INC
Also Called: Quality Bedding Company
5331 Prudence Dr Ste A (77045-5173)
PHONE..................................713 433-9155
Dana Schnitzer, *President*
Russell Schnitzer, *Vice Pres*
EMP: 18 **EST:** 1972
SQ FT: 18,500
SALES (est): 2.5MM **Privately Held**
WEB: www.qualitymattress.net
SIC: 2515 3842 Mattresses, innerspring or box spring; box springs, assembled; surgical appliances & supplies

(G-11498)
QUALITY PRECISION COATINGS LLC
9105 Ley Rd (77078-4409)
PHONE..................................713 631-8141
Brian Kantrell Jordan, *Principal*
Brian Jordan, *Principal*
EMP: 9
SALES (est): 375K **Privately Held**
WEB: www.qpcoatings.com
SIC: 2851 Paints & allied products

(G-11499)
QUALITY PRODUCT FINISHING INC
9610 Frbanks N Houston Rd (77064-6215)
P.O. Box 690787 (77269-0787)
PHONE..................................281 469-6970
▲ **EMP:** 45
SQ FT: 2,400
SALES (est): 6.3MM **Privately Held**
WEB: www.qpfinishing.com
SIC: 3479 Coating of metals & formed products

(G-11500)
QUALITY SIGNS INC
10205 Market St (77029-2344)
PHONE..................................713 671-9222
EMP: 30
SQ FT: 10,000
SALES (est): 3MM **Privately Held**
WEB: www.qualitysignshouston.com
SIC: 3993 7359 Electric signs; sign rental

(G-11501)
QUALITY STORE EQUIPMENT INC
7800 Harwin Dr Ste C (77036-1811)
PHONE..................................713 278-8634
EMP: 12
SALES (est): 938.2K **Privately Held**
SIC: 2542 Mfg Partitions/Fixtures-Nonwood
HQ: Shanghai Prima Gift Co., Ltd.
　No.8, Jinxuan Rd., Nanqiao Town,
　Fengxian Dist.
　Shanghai
　213 365-8888

(G-11502)
QUALITY TRBCHRGER CMPNENTS LLC
6902 Signat Dr (77041-2719)
PHONE..................................713 849-4200
Gary Monina, *Natl Sales Mgr*
Eric Baldaccini,
Steven L Beal,
▲ **EMP:** 20
SQ FT: 6,000

SALES (est): 3.9MM **Privately Held**
WEB: www.qualityturbochargercomponents.com
SIC: 7539 3743 7699 3519 Automotive turbocharger & blower repair; railroad locomotives & parts, electric or nonelectric; marine engine repair; parts & accessories, internal combustion engines

(G-11503)
QUALITY TUBING INC (HQ)
10303 Sheldon Rd (77049-1254)
P.O. Box 9819 (77213-0819)
PHONE............................281 456-0751
John J Macwilliams, *Chairman*
Greg Jorgenson, *Vice Pres*
Dale R Klink, *Vice Pres*
John R Martin, *Vice Pres*
Hope Anderson, *Materials Mgr*
◆ EMP: 135
SQ FT: 84,000
SALES (est): 50.6MM
SALES (corp-wide): 8.4B **Publicly Held**
WEB: www.nov.com
SIC: 3599 Tubing, flexible metallic
PA: National Oilwell Varco, Inc.
   7909 Parkwood Circle Dr
   Houston TX 77036
   713 346-7500

(G-11504)
QUANEX BUILDING PRODUCTS CORP (PA)
1800 West Loop S Ste 1500 (77027-3246)
PHONE............................731 961-4600
William C Griffiths, *Ch of Bd*
John Sleva, *President*
Kim Moore, *Managing Dir*
George L Wilson, *COO*
Kevin P Delaney, *Senior VP*
EMP: 23
SALES: 851.5MM **Publicly Held**
WEB: www.quanex.com
SIC: 3272 3353 Building materials, except block or brick; concrete; aluminum sheet & strip

(G-11505)
QUANEX SCREENS LLC (HQ)
Also Called: Quanex Homeshield, LLC
1800 West Loop S Ste 1500 (77027-3246)
PHONE............................713 961-4600
Brent Korb,
Kevin Delany,
EMP: 74
SALES (est): 20.1MM **Publicly Held**
WEB: www.quanex.com
SIC: 3272 Concrete products

(G-11506)
QUANTUM INK COMPANY
16802 Barker Springs Rd # 900 (77084-5077)
PHONE............................713 688-2288
Robert Bodner, *Sales Mgr*
Amanda Rapp, *Sales Staff*
Glen Davidson, *Manager*
Miranda Clark, *Executive Asst*
EMP: 11 **Privately Held**
WEB: www.quantumink.com
SIC: 2899 Ink or writing fluids
PA: Quantum Ink Company
   4651 Melton Ave
   Louisville KY 40213

(G-11507)
QUANTUM INVESTMENT GROUP INC (PA)
16600 Park Row (77084-5019)
PHONE............................281 994-5400
Orville Duane Gaither Sr, *CEO*
Douglas W Gaither, *President*
Louis Doublet, *Vice Pres*
James Hammelman, *Vice Pres*
Ken Shuebach, *CFO*
EMP: 32
SQ FT: 11,000
SALES (est): 11.2MM **Privately Held**
SIC: 1311 1382 Crude petroleum production; natural gas production; oil & gas exploration services

(G-11508)
QUANTUM RESERVOIR IMPACT LLC (PA)
909 Fannin St Ste 2200 (77010-1043)
PHONE............................713 485-8800
Nansen G Saleri, *CEO*
EMP: 23
SALES (est): 33.6MM **Privately Held**
WEB: www.qrigroup.com
SIC: 2911 1389 Fractionation products of crude petroleum, hydrocarbons; oil field services

(G-11509)
QUARRIES DIRECT INTL LLC
Also Called: Qdi Stone
5800 Centralcrest St (77092-7006)
PHONE............................713 808-9849
Ibrahim Arif Surmen, *Principal*
Greg Richter, *Opers Mgr*
Jaira Keys, *Marketing Staff*
▲ EMP: 20
SALES (est): 3.3MM **Privately Held**
WEB: www.qdisurfaces.com
SIC: 3281 Cut stone & stone products

(G-11510)
QUEST-TEC SOLUTIONS INC (DH)
Also Called: Daniel Level Gages
13960 S Wayside Dr (77048-5219)
PHONE............................281 240-0440
Rhett V Baker, *President*
Michele White, *Vice Pres*
Ray Rucksdashel, *CFO*
Ben Coutee, *Sales Staff*
◆ EMP: 35
SQ FT: 44,000
SALES (est): 5.5MM
SALES (corp-wide): 3.2B **Publicly Held**
WEB: www.questtecsolutions.com
SIC: 3829 Measuring & controlling devices
HQ: Baro Controls, Inc.
   4655 Wright Rd Ste 200
   Stafford TX 77477
   281 561-0900

(G-11511)
QUICK TICK INTERNATIONAL INC
10541 Fm 1960 Rd W # 501 (77070-6337)
PHONE............................832 249-6400
EMP: 35
SQ FT: 9,000
SALES (est): 4.4MM **Privately Held**
WEB: www.quicktick.com
SIC: 2752 Tickets, lithographed

(G-11512)
QUIETAIRE COOLING INC
505 N Hutcheson St (77003-1343)
PHONE............................713 228-9421
Don Dolson, *President*
EMP: 20
SALES (est): 3.8MM
SALES (corp-wide): 3.5MM **Privately Held**
SIC: 3564 Ventilating fans: industrial or commercial
PA: Quietaire Corporation
   505 N Hutcheson St
   Houston TX 77003
   713 228-9421

(G-11513)
QUIETAIRE CORPORATION (PA)
505 N Hutcheson St (77003-1399)
PHONE............................713 228-9421
Donald D Dolson, *CEO*
Lenore Dolson, *Corp Secy*
Darrell Dolson, *Vice Pres*
▲ EMP: 17 EST: 1937
SQ FT: 65,000
SALES (est): 3.5MM **Privately Held**
WEB: www.quietaire.com
SIC: 3564 3441 Ventilating fans: industrial or commercial; fabricated structural metal

(G-11514)
QUIETFLEX MANUFACTURING CO LP
4518 Brittmoore Rd (77041-8006)
PHONE............................877 694-3669
Ardee Toppe, *Partner*
◆ EMP: 400

SQ FT: 3,000
SALES (est): 228.8MM **Privately Held**
WEB: www.quietflex.com
SIC: 3444 1799 3599 Ducts, sheet metal; fiberglass work; tubing, flexible metallic
HQ: Goodman Manufacturing Company, Lp
   19001 Kermier Rd
   Waller TX 77484
   713 861-2500

(G-11515)
QUINTANA ENERGY SERVICES INC
1415 La St Ste 2900 (77002)
PHONE............................832 518-4094
Corbin J Robertson Jr, *Ch of Bd*
Christopher J Baker, *President*
Keefer M Lehner, *CFO*
Max L Bouthillette, *Ch Credit Ofcr*
EMP: 1500
SALES: 484.2MM **Privately Held**
WEB: www.quintanaenergyservices.com
SIC: 1311 1389 Crude petroleum & natural gas; mud service, oil field drilling

(G-11516)
QUINTANA ENERGY SERVICES LP (PA)
1415 La St Ste 2900 (77002)
PHONE............................832 518-4094
Corbin J Robertson Jr, *Partner*
EMP: 13 EST: 2014
SALES (est): 1B **Privately Held**
WEB: www.quintanaenergyservices.com
SIC: 1389 1381 Acidizing wells; oil field services; cementing oil & gas well casings; well logging; directional drilling oil & gas wells

(G-11517)
QUINTANA MINERALS BRAZIL LLC (HQ)
1415 La St Ste 2400 (77002)
PHONE............................713 751-7500
EMP: 13
SQ FT: 10,000
SALES (est): 5.4MM
SALES (corp-wide): 263.9MM **Publicly Held**
WEB: www.quintana-id.com
SIC: 1311 1382 Crude petroleum & natural gas production; crude petroleum production; natural gas production; oil & gas exploration services
PA: Natural Resource Partners L.P.
   1201 La St Ste 3400
   Houston TX 77002
   713 751-7507

(G-11518)
QUINTANA MINERALS CORPORATION
1415 La St Ste 2400 (77002)
PHONE............................713 751-7500
Corbin J Robertson, *President*
Oliver Rodz, *Managing Dir*
Warren Hawkins, *Vice Pres*
Paul Cornell, *CFO*
Shelley Manley, *Controller*
EMP: 50
SALES (est): 6.9MM **Privately Held**
WEB: www.qeplp.com
SIC: 1382 Oil & gas exploration services

(G-11519)
R & D ADVANTAGE INC
2000 Saint James Pl (77056-4123)
PHONE............................713 836-4000
Mike Larronde, *President*
James M Hudgins, *Vice Pres*
Joseph C Henry, *Admin Sec*
EMP: 100
SQ FT: 15,000
SALES (est): 80.3K **Privately Held**
SIC: 3533 Oil field machinery & equipment
HQ: Precision Energy Services, Inc.
   2000 Saint James Pl
   Houston TX 77056

(G-11520)
R & R HEAT EXCHANGERS INC
1414 E Richey Rd Bldg C (77073-3563)
PHONE............................281 951-0003
Marvin Forrest, *President*
▲ EMP: 9

SALES (est): 1MM **Privately Held**
WEB: www.rrheatexchanger.com
SIC: 3443 Heat exchangers, condensers & components; finned tubes, for heat transfer; heat exchangers, plate type; heat exchangers: coolers (after, inter), condensers, etc.

(G-11521)
R & S STEEL FABRICATING CO
9900 Beaumont Hwy (77078-4904)
PHONE............................713 675-9007
Blas Ramirez, *President*
Pablo Saivas, *Vice Pres*
EMP: 10
SQ FT: 22,564
SALES (est): 1.9MM **Privately Held**
WEB: www.rs-steelfab.com
SIC: 3441 Fabricated structural metal

(G-11522)
R C SCHMIDT & SON INC
1215 Akron St (77029-2101)
PHONE............................713 673-5911
Mike D Schmidt, *President*
R D Schmidt, *Vice Pres*
Schmidt J T, *Vice Pres*
EMP: 10 EST: 1964
SQ FT: 32,000
SALES (est): 1.7MM **Privately Held**
SIC: 3599 Machine shop, jobbing & repair

(G-11523)
R M S INC
Also Called: Bowtex Company
1624 Oak Tree Dr (77080-7238)
P.O. Box 800125 (77280-0125)
PHONE............................713 467-2043
Steven R Montgomery, *President*
EMP: 9
SQ FT: 14,000
SALES (est): 1.7MM **Privately Held**
WEB: www.rhinosleeve.com
SIC: 2499 5049 Surveyors' stakes, wood; surveyors' instruments

(G-11524)
R R DONNELLEY & SONS COMPANY
Also Called: Houston Fullfillment Center
6600 Long Point Rd # 103 (77055-2649)
PHONE............................713 957-8910
Ann Allen, *Branch Mgr*
EMP: 46
SALES (corp-wide): 6.2B **Publicly Held**
WEB: www.rrd.com
SIC: 2754 Commercial printing, gravure
PA: R. R. Donnelley & Sons Company
   35 W Wacker Dr
   Chicago IL 60601
   312 326-8000

(G-11525)
R R DONNELLEY & SONS COMPANY
Also Called: R R Donnelley
2001 Kirby Dr Ste 400 (77019-6083)
PHONE............................713 630-1000
Darrell Whitley, *Branch Mgr*
EMP: 35
SQ FT: 41,111
SALES (corp-wide): 6.2B **Publicly Held**
WEB: www.rrd.com
SIC: 2759 Commercial printing
PA: R. R. Donnelley & Sons Company
   35 W Wacker Dr
   Chicago IL 60601
   312 326-8000

(G-11526)
R R DONNELLEY & SONS COMPANY
Also Called: Wetmore & Company
1645 W Sam Houston Pkwy N (77043-3114)
P.O. Box 40668 (77240-0668)
PHONE............................713 468-7175
Bob Stoltman, *Branch Mgr*
EMP: 407
SALES (corp-wide): 6.2B **Publicly Held**
WEB: www.rrd.com
SIC: 2752 Commercial printing, lithographic

PA: R. R. Donnelley & Sons Company
35 W Wacker Dr
Chicago IL 60601
312 326-8000

(G-11527)
R R DONNELLEY & SONS COMPANY
Also Called: RR Donnelley Global
6315 W By Northwest Blvd (77040-4973)
PHONE...................................713 354-1300
EMP: 109
SALES (corp-wide): 6.2B **Publicly Held**
WEB: www.rrd.com
SIC: 2754 Commercial printing, gravure
PA: R. R. Donnelley & Sons Company
35 W Wacker Dr
Chicago IL 60601
312 326-8000

(G-11528)
R SLATER ENTERPRISES LLC
Also Called: Slater Gate and Fence
14119 Fm 529 Rd (77041-2506)
PHONE...................................832 456-4900
Jason Hartzog, *Sales Staff*
Chaille Slater, *Mng Member*
Rick Slater,
EMP: 10
SQ FT: 10,000
SALES (est): 1.9MM **Privately Held**
WEB: www.slaterenterprises.com
SIC: 3089 3448 Fences, gates & accessories: plastic; carports: prefabricated metal

(G-11529)
R W MACHINE INC
1414 E Richey Rd (77073-3563)
P.O. Box 670348 (77267-0348)
PHONE...................................281 784-1600
Richard Wyman, *President*
Linda Wyman, *Corp Secy*
Bob Dominguez, *Technical Mgr*
Jesse Lampkin, *Supervisor*
EMP: 22
SQ FT: 22,000
SALES (est): 3.8MM **Privately Held**
WEB: www.rwmachineinc.com
SIC: 3599 Machine shop, jobbing & repair

(G-11530)
RADIA ENTERPRISES INC (PA)
Also Called: Career Uniforms
3800 Juniper St (77087-4406)
PHONE...................................713 645-3600
Rupendra Radia, *President*
Andy Ramroop, *General Mgr*
Anil Ramroop, *General Mgr*
Sridhar Subramaniam, *Engineer*
Michael Domosiaris, *Natl Sales Mgr*
▲ **EMP:** 22
SQ FT: 20,000
SALES (est): 3.4MM **Privately Held**
WEB: www.spectrumuniforms.com
SIC: 2326 Medical & hospital uniforms, men's

(G-11531)
RADIANT INDUS SOLUTIONS INC
Also Called: Radiant Uv
2121 Brittmoore Rd # 3900 (77043-2200)
PHONE...................................713 972-0196
Troy Smith, *CEO*
Maria E Smith, *Vice Pres*
Dan Smith, *Sales Mgr*
Jenna Baker, *Sales Staff*
▲ **EMP:** 13
SALES (est): 3.3MM **Privately Held**
WEB: www.radiantuv.com
SIC: 3564 Air purification equipment

(G-11532)
RADIX US LLC
Also Called: Radix Engineering and Software
820 Gessner Ster 875 (77024)
PHONE...................................832 377-9601
Flavio Guimaraes, *CEO*
EMP: 20
SQ FT: 200

SALES (est): 1.2MM **Privately Held**
WEB: www.radixeng.com
SIC: 7371 3569 7373 8711 Computer software systems analysis & design, custom; liquid automation machinery & equipment; computer integrated systems design; computer systems analysis & design; computer-aided design (CAD) systems service; office computer automation systems integration; mechanical engineering; chemical engineering
PA: Radix Engenharia E Desenvolvimento De Software S/A
Rua Do Passeio 00038
Rio De Janeiro RJ 20021

(G-11533)
RAE ENERGY SOLUTIONS INC
10757 Cutten Rd Bldg 1 (77066-5026)
PHONE...................................281 440-3434
Ben Mackay, *CEO*
Douglas McIntyre, *President*
Richard Olphert, *President*
Scott Black, *Vice Pres*
Ryan Fokens, *Vice Pres*
EMP: 9 **EST:** 2013
SQ FT: 17,000
SALES (est): 177.1K **Privately Held**
WEB: www.rae.com
SIC: 3533 3567 Oil field machinery & equipment; induction heating equipment

(G-11534)
RAI OF SUNSHINE LLC
11314 White Gate Ln (77067-3356)
PHONE...................................832 271-0144
EMP: 60 **EST:** 2015
SALES (est): 2.1MM **Privately Held**
SIC: 2339 Mfg Women's/Misses' Outerwear

(G-11535)
RAM INDSTRIES ACQUISITIONS LLC
5615 W Fuqua St Bldg C (77085-4079)
PHONE...................................281 495-9056
Tim Payton, *CEO*
John Deveau, *Vice Pres*
Chris Shore, *Vice Pres*
Joe Benetz, *CFO*
Trina Polaniec, *Sales Staff*
EMP: 80
SALES (est): 11.6MM **Privately Held**
WEB: www.ramwindows.com
SIC: 3442 Window & door frames; casements, aluminum; louver windows, metal; screens, window, metal

(G-11536)
RAM WINCH AND HOIST LTD
14603 Chrisman Rd (77039-1116)
PHONE...................................281 999-8665
John Greer, *Controller*
Sky Cheney, *Sales Mgr*
Kathy Ames, *Sales Staff*
Cindy Morgan, *Sales Staff*
Roger McCorkle, *Manager*
▲ **EMP:** 46
SALES (est): 16.5MM **Privately Held**
WEB: www.ramwinch.com
SIC: 5084 3531 Hoists; winches

(G-11537)
RAMPAK GROUP INC
1356 Kress St (77020-7421)
PHONE...................................713 678-8898
Patrick A Totsch, *President*
Judy Chin, *Vice Pres*
◆ **EMP:** 14
SQ FT: 87,000
SALES (est): 3.2MM **Privately Held**
WEB: www.rampakgroup.com
SIC: 3841 3822 3823 3829 Blood pressure apparatus; pressure controllers, airconditioning system type; pressure measurement instruments, industrial; fuel system instruments, aircraft

(G-11538)
RAN TECHNOLOGIES INC
10627 Kinghurst Dr (77099-3507)
PHONE...................................281 530-3248
Ann E Niemer, *President*
Roman M Niemer, *Vice Pres*
Alex Niemer, *Project Mgr*
Irina Niemer, *Admin Sec*

EMP: 44
SQ FT: 20,000
SALES (est): 4.9MM **Privately Held**
WEB: www.rantechnologies.com
SIC: 3613 Control panels, electric

(G-11539)
RANCHO LPG HOLDINGS LLC
333 Clay St Ste 1600 (77002-4101)
PHONE...................................713 993-5331
Jason Balasch, *Mng Member*
EMP: 20
SALES (est): 122.1K **Publicly Held**
SIC: 2911 Petroleum refining
HQ: Plains All American Pipeline L.P.
333 Clay St Ste 1600
Houston TX 77002
713 646-4100

(G-11540)
RANCO INDUSTRIES INC
3421 Rusk St (77003-3318)
PHONE...................................713 228-5543
Randy Allen, *President*
Austin Allen, *CFO*
Anne Snelgrove, *Accounting Mgr*
Linda Peck, *Credit Mgr*
David Blomquist, *Sales Mgr*
▲ **EMP:** 25 **EST:** 1979
SQ FT: 52,000
SALES (est): 5MM **Privately Held**
WEB: www.rhinomats.com
SIC: 3069 Floor coverings, rubber

(G-11541)
RANCO RHINO MATS & MATTING
3421 Rusk St (77003-3318)
PHONE...................................713 228-5543
Randy Allen, *Owner*
Annie Snelgrove, *Accounting Mgr*
EMP: 12
SALES (est): 756.3K **Privately Held**
WEB: www.rhinomats.com
SIC: 3069 Fabricated rubber products

(G-11542)
RANDALL & DEWEY JEFFERIS
3 Allen Ctr 333 Clay 10 (77002)
PHONE...................................281 774-2000
David Rockecharlie, *President*
Jack P Randall, *Principal*
Ralph Eads, *Chairman*
Kyle Guidry, *Vice Pres*
Traci Sims, *Marketing Staff*
EMP: 75
SQ FT: 11,000
SALES (est): 3.3MM **Privately Held**
WEB: www.jefferies.com
SIC: 1389 Oil consultants

(G-11543)
RANDY WRECKER SERVICE INC
Also Called: Texas National Fleet Pnt & Bdy
10127 Sussex Ln (77041-6119)
PHONE...................................713 690-4000
Bobby Dougherty, *President*
Roberts Dougherty, *Vice Pres*
EMP: 15 **EST:** 1978
SQ FT: 4,000
SALES (est): 2MM **Privately Held**
SIC: 2499 7532 Spools, reels & pulleys: wood; body shop, automotive; paint shop, automotive

(G-11544)
RANGER CONVEYING & SUPPLY CO (PA)
4701 Clinton Dr (77020-7803)
PHONE...................................713 671-0004
Brent Singer, *President*
Jordan Singer, *Vice Pres*
Murray Hinz, *Sales Staff*
Jerry Liebmann, *Sales Staff*
EMP: 58
SQ FT: 30,000
SALES (est): 13.4MM **Privately Held**
WEB: www.rangerconveying.com
SIC: 3535 5084 Conveyors & conveying equipment; materials handling machinery

(G-11545)
RANGER ENERGY SERVICES INC (PA)
10350 Richmond Ave # 550 (77042-4469)
PHONE...................................713 935-8900
Merrill A Miller, *Ch of Bd*
Darron M Anderson, *President*
Matt Hooker, *COO*
Lance Perryman, *Exec VP*
J Matt Hooker, *Senior VP*
EMP: 90 **EST:** 2014
SQ FT: 29,000
SALES (est): 336.9MM **Publicly Held**
WEB: www.rangerenergy.com
SIC: 1389 Oil field services

(G-11546)
RANGER ENERGY SERVICES LLC
10350 Richmond Ave # 550 (77042-4129)
PHONE...................................713 461-9000
Jason Podraza, *CFO*
EMP: 500
SALES (corp-wide): 336.9MM **Publicly Held**
WEB: www.rangerenergy.com
SIC: 1389 Well plugging & abandoning, oil & gas
HQ: Ranger Energy Services, Llc
10350 Richmond Ave # 550
Houston TX 77042
832 391-5600

(G-11547)
RANGER STEEL SUPPLY LP (PA)
1225 North Loop W Ste 650 (77008-1871)
PHONE...................................713 633-1306
Roy Whitley, *Founder*
Jeff McPherson, *Vice Pres*
David Orme, *Vice Pres*
Cathy Ledford, *Asst Controller*
Nick Edel, *Sales Staff*
◆ **EMP:** 22 **EST:** 1958
SQ FT: 7,000
SALES (est): 10.4MM **Privately Held**
WEB: www.rangersteel.com
SIC: 5051 3315 Structural shapes, iron or steel; steel wire & related products

(G-11548)
RAPID HOSE
10207 Oakpoint Dr (77043-4221)
PHONE...................................713 468-4673
Tiago Portela Da Silva, *Principal*
EMP: 14 **EST:** 2013
SALES (est): 2.2MM **Privately Held**
WEB: www.rapidhose.com
SIC: 3599 Industrial machinery

(G-11549)
RAPID TURN LASER & MACHINE LTD (PA)
757 Kenrick Dr Ste 100 (77060-3639)
PHONE...................................281 447-5000
Michael Viator, *Managing Prtnr*
Gary Gonzalez, *General Ptnr*
Michael Ward, *General Ptnr*
EMP: 15
SQ FT: 5,000
SALES (est): 2.5MM **Privately Held**
WEB: www.rapidturnlaser.com
SIC: 3443 Fabricated plate work (boiler shop)

(G-11550)
RASCH GRAPHIC SERVICES CORP
8648 Glenmont Dr Ste 100 (77036-1932)
PHONE...................................713 785-5750
Arnan R Rasch, *President*
Brandon Rasch, *Vice Pres*
Shane Rasch, *Production*
Gloria Miller,
▲ **EMP:** 40
SQ FT: 25,000
SALES (est): 5.7MM **Privately Held**
WEB: www.raschgraphics.com
SIC: 2789 Binding only: books, pamphlets, magazines, etc.

G
E
O
G
R
A
P
H
I
C

(G-11551)
RASHIDAH LLC
13214 Walnut Lake Rd (77065-3225)
PHONE.................................281 469-5277
Abid Ali, *Principal*
EMP: 9
SALES (est): 788.4K **Privately Held**
SIC: 2448 Pallets, wood

(G-11552)
RATIONAL SYSTEMS LLC
8 Greenway Plz Ste 702 (77046-0892)
PHONE.................................832 476-8468
Viren Kapadia, *President*
EMP: 22
SALES (est): 1.3MM **Privately Held**
WEB: www.rationalenergi.com
SIC: 8748 7371 7373 7372 Business
consulting; custom computer program-
ming services; turnkey vendors, computer
systems; utility computer software

(G-11553)
RAVAGO MFG AMERICAS LLC
Also Called: RMA
1031 Goodnight Trl (77060-1105)
PHONE.................................281 443-6220
Rodney Garrett, *Principal*
John King, *Accounts Mgr*
EMP: 19
SALES (est): 3.5MM **Privately Held**
SIC: 3089 3999 Air mattresses, plastic;
plastic containers, except foam; atomiz-
ers, toiletry

(G-11554)
RAYS FLOW CONTROL LLC
Also Called: Rays Valve
9700 Richmond Ave Ste 104 (77042-4625)
PHONE.................................832 827-3427
Michael Chen, *Mng Member*
Alex Lin,
Shane Lin,
EMP: 18
SALES (est): 954K **Privately Held**
WEB: www.raysvalve.com
SIC: 3491 5085 Industrial valves; pistons
& valves

(G-11555)
RAYSON COMPANY
7914 Breen Dr (77064-8421)
PHONE.................................713 680-0540
EMP: 50
SALES (est): 305.5K **Privately Held**
WEB: www.raysoncompany.com
SIC: 5085 3599 Fasteners, industrial:
nuts, bolts, screws, etc.

(G-11556)
RB PROCESSING LLC (PA)
740 Bradfield Rd (77060-3109)
PHONE.................................281 992-3500
Raymond B Rice Jr,
EMP: 9 EST: 2008
SQ FT: 87,120
SALES (est): 4MM **Privately Held**
WEB: www.rbproductsinc.com
SIC: 2819 Industrial inorganic chemicals

(G-11557)
RBF PORT NECHES LLC (HQ)
2229 San Felipe St # 950 (77019-5670)
PHONE.................................713 386-2600
Paul P Soanes, *CEO*
Tracy Doyle, *General Mgr*
▲ EMP: 20
SQ FT: 3,000
SALES (est): 24.9MM **Privately Held**
WEB: www.rbfuels.com
SIC: 2869 Fuels

(G-11558)
RE CAMPBELL COMPANY LTD
3502 Pinemont Dr (77018-1332)
PHONE.................................713 957-8721
Gail Benningfield, *Partner*
Joyce Campbell, *Partner*
R E Campbell, *Partner*
Lanette Currie, *Partner*
Gene Campbell, *General Ptnr*
EMP: 34 EST: 1979

SALES: 4.3MM **Privately Held**
WEB: www.recampbell.com
SIC: 3443 3441 3446 3444 Fabricated
plate work (boiler shop); fabricated structural metal; scaffolds, mobile or stationary: metal; sheet metalwork; welding
repair

(G-11559)
RE PIPE INC
Also Called: Ipr South Central
7600 S Santa Fe Dr Ste E (77061-4500)
PHONE.................................713 634-0439
Fax: 713 634-0489
EMP: 75 EST: 2005
SALES (est): 7.4MM
SALES (corp-wide): 880K **Privately Held**
SIC: 3498 Mfg Fabricated Pipe/Fittings
HQ: Inland Pipe Rehabilitation, Llc
2002 Timberloch Pl # 550
The Woodlands TX 30094
281 362-1131

(G-11560)
READY CABLE OF HOUSTON INC
11315 W Little York Rd # 2 (77041-4933)
PHONE.................................713 856-5132
Robert Limke, *President*
◆ EMP: 75
SALES (est): 3.9MM **Privately Held**
SIC: 3272 Concrete products

(G-11561)
REAGENT CHEMICAL & RES INC
1300 Post Oak Blvd (77056-3043)
PHONE.................................713 626-1843
David Sullivant, *Sales Mgr*
Cindy Beaumont, *Sales Staff*
Myra Midkiff, *Branch Mgr*
Gail Molek, *Director*
EMP: 13
SALES (corp-wide): 376.8MM **Privately Held**
WEB: www.prosysfill.com
SIC: 2819 3949 Sulfur, recovered or re-
fined, incl. from sour natural gas; targets,
archery & rifle shooting
PA: Reagent Chemical & Research, Inc.
115 Rte 202
Ringoes NJ 08551
908 284-2800

(G-11562)
REAGENT CHEMICAL & RES INC
2710 Appelt Dr (77015-6558)
P.O. Box 179, Channelview (77530-0179)
PHONE.................................281 862-9464
Francois Jones, *Regional Mgr*
Michael Bumbgarner, *Manager*
Rejhi Dyson, *Analyst*
EMP: 25
SALES (corp-wide): 376.8MM **Privately Held**
WEB: www.prosysfill.com
SIC: 2819 3949 Sulfur, recovered or re-
fined, incl. from sour natural gas; targets,
archery & rifle shooting
PA: Reagent Chemical & Research, Inc.
115 Rte 202
Ringoes NJ 08551
908 284-2800

(G-11563)
REAL ENERGY SOLUTIONS INC (PA)
438 Heights Blvd (77007-2520)
PHONE.................................713 864-9076
Michael White, *President*
Francisco Yanez, *Regional Mgr*
Janette Gallegos, *Asst Controller*
Louie Nguyen, *Sales Staff*
Aurora Diaz, *Office Mgr*
EMP: 17
SALES (est): 7.9MM **Privately Held**
WEB: www.resyes.com
SIC: 3799 Recreational vehicles

(G-11564)
REBAR SUPPLY COMPANY LTD
7834 Fairview St (77041-2116)
PHONE.................................713 937-8999
Teresa A Whorton, *President*
▲ EMP: 35
SQ FT: 2,300

SALES (est): 8.7MM **Privately Held**
WEB: www.rebarsupplyco.com
SIC: 3441 Fabricated structural metal

(G-11565)
RECTORSEAL LLC (HQ)
2601 Spenwick Dr (77055-1035)
PHONE.................................713 263-8001
◆ EMP: 60 EST: 1991
SALES (est): 25.1MM
SALES (corp-wide): 385.8MM **Publicly Held**
WEB: www.rectorseal.com
SIC: 2992 2891 Oils & greases, blending
& compounding; sealing compounds for
pipe threads or joints
PA: Csw Industrials, Inc.
5420 Lyndon B Johnson Fwy
Dallas TX 75240
214 884-3777

(G-11566)
RED ARROW ENERGY LLC
4265 San Felipe St # 1040 (77027-2920)
PHONE.................................713 580-7250
Robert Carter Overton,
Brock Hudson,
Allen McGee,
EMP: 15
SALES (est): 813.3K **Privately Held**
WEB: www.redarrowenergy.com
SIC: 1382 Oil & gas exploration services

(G-11567)
RED NEWS INC
2537 S Gessner Rd Ste 126 (77063-2090)
PHONE.................................281 888-1448
Ginger Wheless, *President*
EMP: 10
SQ FT: 2,000
SALES (est): 790K **Privately Held**
WEB: www.rednews.com
SIC: 2721 Periodicals

(G-11568)
RED RIVER COMPRESSION LLC (PA)
Also Called: Red River Manufacturing
8300 Cypress Creek Pkwy # 450
(77070-5699)
P.O. Box 690365 (77269-0365)
PHONE.................................832 831-0532
Ruben Kendrick, *CEO*
Dan Crocker, *CEO*
Mark Glaze, *COO*
Hege Risberg, *CFO*
Howard Edens, *Controller*
EMP: 15
SQ FT: 25,000
SALES (est): 5.8MM **Privately Held**
WEB: www.aes-rr.com
SIC: 3563 Air & gas compressors

(G-11569)
RED RIVER COMPRESSION SVCS LLC (PA)
Also Called: Advantage Energy Solutions
8300 Cypress Creek Pkwy # 450
(77070-5699)
P.O. Box 690365 (77269-0365)
PHONE.................................832 831-0532
James Gayle, *CEO*
EMP: 21
SALES (est): 6.7MM **Privately Held**
WEB: www.redrivercomp.com
SIC: 3699 Heat emission operating appa-
ratus

(G-11570)
RED TECHNOLOGY ALLIANCE LLC
2101 Cy W Blvd Bldg Fl 2 (77042)
PHONE.................................713 839-4689
Jim Buckingham, *President*
EMP: 20
SALES (est): 885.1K **Privately Held**
SIC: 1382 Oil & gas exploration services

(G-11571)
RED WILLOW OFFSHORE LLC
1415 La St Ste 3650 (77002)
PHONE.................................281 822-7500
Steven Brittian, *Superintendent*
Jason Hooten, *Exec VP*
Brent Wilson, *Project Engr*

Deva Fowler, *Asst Controller*
Krista Vandiver, *Finance Mgr*
EMP: 90
SALES (est): 6.9MM **Privately Held**
WEB: www.rwpc.us
SIC: 8748 1382 Business consulting; oil &
gas exploration services

(G-11572)
REDCLIFF MIDSTREAM LLC
1331 Lamar St Ste 1675 (77010-3133)
PHONE.................................713 655-9500
Michael Walsh,
EMP: 30 EST: 2017
SALES (est): 3MM **Privately Held**
WEB: www.canyonmidstream.com
SIC: 1382 Oil & gas exploration services

(G-11573)
REDCO DISTRIBUTION LLC (PA)
2155 Silber Rd Ste 100 (77055-2624)
PHONE.................................832 320-4950
JD Denning, *General Mgr*
Mel Ransom, *General Mgr*
Alicial Powell, *Controller*
Keith Moore, *Sales Mgr*
Ron Ferguson, *Sales Staff*
▲ EMP: 32
SALES (est): 4.1MM **Privately Held**
WEB: www.redcodistribution.com
SIC: 3996 Hard surface floor coverings

(G-11574)
REDDY ICE CORPORATION
6004 N Shepherd Dr Ste B (77091-4261)
PHONE.................................713 691-2773
Mike Eddleman, *General Mgr*
Juan Betancourt, *Plant Engr*
Doris Bell,
EMP: 50 **Privately Held**
WEB: www.reddyice.com
SIC: 2097 Manufactured ice
HQ: Reddy Ice Corporation
5710 Lbj Fwy Ste 300
Dallas TX 75240
214 526-6740

(G-11575)
REDMAN ENERGY CORPORATION
10375 Richmond Ave # 920 (77042-4143)
PHONE.................................713 782-2870
J Jeff Voncannon, *President*
EMP: 9
SALES (est): 739.4K **Privately Held**
WEB: www.redmanmc.com
SIC: 1382 Oil & gas exploration services

(G-11576)
REED-HYCALOG
6806 Willow Brook Park (77066-3014)
PHONE.................................832 422-4070
EMP: 100
SALES (est): 2.3MM **Privately Held**
SIC: 1389 Oil/Gas Field Services

(G-11577)
REEF INDUSTRIES INC (PA)
9209 Almeda Genoa Rd (77075-2339)
PHONE.................................713 507-4200
Troy Taylor, *President*
David Michalek, *Plant Mgr*
Natalie Irwin, *CFO*
Tracey McArthur, *Human Res Mgr*
Tracey Nissen, *Human Res Mgr*
▼ EMP: 30 EST: 1957
SQ FT: 24,000
SALES (est): 21.6MM **Privately Held**
WEB: www.reefindustries.com
SIC: 3083 3081 3089 3086 Plastic fin-
ished products, laminated; plastic film &
sheet; plastic hardware & building prod-
ucts; insulation or cushioning material,
foamed plastic; plastics materials & resins

(G-11578)
REEF INDUSTRIES INC
10020 Mykawa Rd (77048-1394)
P.O. Box 750250 (77275-0250)
PHONE.................................713 507-4329
Troy Taylor, *President*
Patrick Bowens, *Manager*
EMP: 55

SALES (corp-wide): 21.6MM **Privately Held**
WEB: www.reefindustries.com
SIC: 3083 3081 3089 3086 Plastic finished products, laminated; unsupported plastics film & sheet; plastic containers, except foam; insulation or cushioning material, foamed plastic
PA: Reef Industries, Inc.
9209 Almeda Genoa Rd
Houston TX 77075
713 507-4200

(G-11579)
REEF SERVICES LLC (DH)
1515 W Sam Houston Pkwy N
(77043-3112)
PHONE.............................432 560-5600
Larry Odonnell, *CEO*
Wayne A Clayton, *CFO*
Clay Baten,
Art Donnelly,
EMP: 35
SALES (est): 61.6MM
SALES (corp-wide): 1.2B **Publicly Held**
WEB: www.reefcorp.com
SIC: 3533 Oil & gas drilling rigs & equipment

(G-11580)
REEL POWER OIL & GAS INC
Also Called: Tulsa Power
8780 West Rd (77064-1440)
PHONE.............................713 937-4494
Tom Frey, *CEO*
Matt Rohwer, *CFO*
EMP: 50
SQ FT: 100,000
SALES (est): 16.6MM
SALES (corp-wide): 41.8MM **Privately Held**
WEB: www.reelpowerog.com
SIC: 3533 Gas field machinery & equipment; oil field machinery & equipment
PA: Reel Power International Corp.
5101 S Council Rd Ste 100
Oklahoma City OK 73179
405 609-3326

(G-11581)
REEL-LOGIX LLC
Also Called: REEL-LOGIX SOLUTIONS
227 Hambrick Rd (77060-5729)
P.O. Box 273041 (77277-3041)
PHONE.............................713 369-3139
Anthony Saragusa, *President*
EMP: 35
SALES (est): 1MM **Privately Held**
SIC: 3499 2499 Reels, cable: metal; spools, reels & pulleys: wood; reels, plywood

(G-11582)
REFRIGRATION GASKETS TEXAS INC (PA)
729 W 22nd St (77008-1727)
P.O. Box 924703 (77292-4703)
PHONE.............................713 880-8066
Stanley Piasczyk, *President*
Myra Piazczyk, *Vice Pres*
EMP: 12
SQ FT: 3,200
SALES (est): 2.4MM **Privately Held**
WEB: www.refrigerationgaskets.com
SIC: 3053 7623 5078 Gaskets & sealing devices; refrigeration repair service; refrigeration equipment & supplies

(G-11583)
REGAL INTERESTS INC
Also Called: Regal Chef
3515 Eastex Frwy (77026-3507)
P.O. Box 21172 (77226-1172)
PHONE.............................713 222-8231
Jim Hoffman, *CEO*
Donald Dean, *President*
Joseph Pizzitola Jr, *Exec VP*
Harold Clemmons, *Admin Sec*
EMP: 13
SALES (est): 95K **Privately Held**
SIC: 2099 5963 Food preparations; direct selling establishments

(G-11584)
REGENCY DESOTO-HESCO SVCS LLC
1415 La St Ste 2700 (77002)
PHONE.............................281 408-1200
Michael J Bradley, *Mng Member*
EMP: 32
SALES (est): 1MM **Publicly Held**
SIC: 1311 Crude petroleum & natural gas
HQ: Regency Energy Partners Lp
8111 Westchester Dr # 600
Dallas TX 75225
214 750-1771

(G-11585)
REGENCY PURCHASING INC
Also Called: Designers Furniture Mfg
8419 Bascom Ln (77080-3601)
PHONE.............................713 973-0315
David F Longwood, *President*
EMP: 35
SALES (est): 3.7MM **Privately Held**
SIC: 2519 Household furniture, except wood or metal: upholstered

(G-11586)
REGISTER TAPES UNLIMITED LP
1445 Langham Creek Dr (77084-5012)
PHONE.............................281 206-2500
Edward D Endsley, *President*
Ashley Mate, *COO*
Gordon Miller, *Vice Pres*
Kenneth Griffith, *CFO*
Joe Geanetta, *Marketing Staff*
EMP: 150 **EST:** 2003
SALES (est): 55.3K
SALES (corp-wide): 54.7MM **Privately Held**
WEB: www.rtui.com
SIC: 7319 2752 Distribution of advertising material or sample services; promotional printing, lithographic
PA: Indoormedia, Inc.
1445 Langham Creek Dr
Houston TX 77084
800 247-4793

(G-11587)
REICHHOLD INDUSTRIES INC
1503 Haden Rd (77015-6455)
P.O. Box 96128 (77213-6128)
PHONE.............................713 453-5431
David Jacobson, *Opers Mgr*
Mike Fields, *Manager*
Vidal Benavides, *Manager*
Benavides Vidal, *Manager*
EMP: 14 **Privately Held**
WEB: www.reichhold.com
SIC: 2821 2851 Polyesters; paints & allied products
PA: Reichhold Industries, Inc.
100 E Cottage Ave
Carpentersville IL 60110

(G-11588)
RELIABLE BUS RESOURCES LLC
Also Called: Rbr Machine
6327 N Sam Houston Pkwy W
(77086-2040)
PHONE.............................281 469-6400
Rodger Brogdon, *CEO*
Andrew Kattula, *President*
Lee Brubaker, *Vice Pres*
Christopher Howell, *Vice Pres*
Cheryl Brogdon, *CFO*
EMP: 22 **EST:** 2014
SALES (est): 1.1MM **Privately Held**
WEB: www.rbrmachine.com
SIC: 3541 Machine tools, metal cutting type

(G-11589)
RELIABLE EDM LTD (PA)
6940 Fulton St (77022-4835)
PHONE.............................713 692-5454
Carl Sommer, *President*
Jared Holloway, *General Mgr*
Philip Sommer, *Vice Pres*
Steve Sommer, *Vice Pres*
Damon Banks, *Production*
▲ **EMP:** 18
SQ FT: 18,000

SALES (est): 3.6MM **Privately Held**
WEB: www.reliableedm.com
SIC: 3599 Machine shop, jobbing & repair

(G-11590)
RELIABLE HOSE SOLUTIONS LLC (PA)
Also Called: Hose-Tex
5097 Ashley Ct (77041-6912)
PHONE.............................713 983-9090
EMP: 13 **EST:** 2013
SALES (est): 3.5MM **Privately Held**
WEB: www.reliablehose.com
SIC: 5085 5261 3052 Hose, belting & packing; hydroponic equipment & supplies; air line or air brake hose, rubber or rubberized fabric

(G-11591)
RELIABLE PUMP CONSULTANTS INC
12951 South Fwy (77047-1923)
PHONE.............................713 640-2718
Glen E Reed, *President*
Cottrell Marshall, *Opers Mgr*
Anthony Johnson, *Inv Control Mgr*
Darrell Collins, *Purch Agent*
Leroy Thomas, *Purch Agent*
▲ **EMP:** 46
SALES (est): 15MM **Privately Held**
WEB: www.reliablepumps.com
SIC: 3569 3561 Blast cleaning equipment, dustless; pumps, oil well & field

(G-11592)
RELIABLE WIRELINE LLC
2656 S Loop W Ste 395 (77054-5603)
PHONE.............................713 280-7995
Kevin Dartez, *CFO*
Heather Ross, *CFO*
Fred Pounds,
Brandon Bailey,
Kevin Bailey,
EMP: 50
SQ FT: 20,000
SALES (est): 20.4MM **Privately Held**
WEB: www.reliablewireline.com
SIC: 1389 Well plugging & abandoning, oil & gas; cementing oil & gas well casings; perforating well casings; well logging

(G-11593)
RELIANCE PRCISION MFG PARTNERS
10541 Cypress Creek Pkwy # 402
(77070-6337)
PHONE.............................281 894-0044
William Fielder Jr, *Exec Dir*
EMP: 15
SALES (est): 1.8MM **Privately Held**
WEB: www.reliance-mfg.com
SIC: 3999 Dock equipment & supplies, industrial

(G-11594)
REMINGTON OIL AND GAS CORP
400 N Sam Houston Pkwy E # 601
(77060-3500)
PHONE.............................281 618-0400
Owen Kratz, *CEO*
EMP: 10
SALES (est): 634.9K
SALES (corp-wide): 751.9MM **Publicly Held**
SIC: 1382 Oil & gas exploration services
PA: Helix Energy Solutions Group, Inc.
3505 W Sam Houston Pkwy N S
Houston TX 77043
281 618-0400

(G-11595)
REMLAP MANUFACTURING INC
5757 Teague Rd (77041-7598)
PHONE.............................713 462-3199
Gary M Palmer, *President*
Brenda Palmer, *General Mgr*
Brenda Webb, *General Mgr*
Carolyn Palmer, *Admin Sec*
EMP: 15
SQ FT: 6,600
SALES (est): 2.9MM **Privately Held**
WEB: www.remlapmfg.com
SIC: 3533 Drilling tools for gas, oil or water wells

(G-11596)
REMORA ENERGY MANAGEMENT LLC
5709 Val Verde St 100 (77057-5717)
PHONE.............................832 325-2300
Fax: 832 325-2301
EMP: 16
SALES (est): 1.1MM **Privately Held**
SIC: 1382 Oil/Gas Exploration Services
PA: Remora Energy International Lp
C/O: Appleby
Hamilton

(G-11597)
RENAISSANCE CMPT GROUP NOT INC
2747 Briargrove Dr # 940 (77057-5207)
P.O. Box 37148 (77237-7148)
PHONE.............................713 256-6067
Barry Simmons, *Ch of Bd*
Romi Simmons, *President*
William Levine, *CFO*
Heather Shampoe, *Admin Sec*
EMP: 15
SALES (est): 490K **Privately Held**
SIC: 7371 7372 7374 Custom computer programming services; educational computer software; computer graphics service

(G-11598)
RENAISSANCE OFFSHORE LLC
920 Mmrial Cy Way Ste 800 (77024)
PHONE.............................832 333-7700
Jeffrey Soine, *CEO*
Mike Koenig, *Vice Pres*
Larry Tolleson, *Vice Pres*
Brian Romere, *CFO*
Bit Fingerhut, *Controller*
EMP: 25
SQ FT: 22,644
SALES (est): 83.8MM **Privately Held**
WEB: www.renaissanceoffshore.com
SIC: 1389 1311 Oil field services; natural gas production

(G-11599)
RENEWABLE BIOFUELS INC (PA)
Also Called: Rbf
2229 San Felipe St # 950 (77019-5670)
PHONE.............................713 386-2600
Paul Soanes, *President*
Jonathan L Phillips, *COO*
Roger Fowler, *Senior VP*
John Cusick, *Vice Pres*
Aurko Dutta, *Vice Pres*
EMP: 20
SALES (est): 24.9MM **Privately Held**
WEB: www.rbfuels.com
SIC: 2869 Fuels

(G-11600)
RENFROW METALSMITHS LLC
37 Lyerly St (77022-3007)
PHONE.............................832 724-8517
Daniel S Sugulas II,
EMP: 9
SALES (est): 1.2MM **Privately Held**
WEB: www.renfrowco.com
SIC: 3441 3449 Fabricated structural metal; miscellaneous metalwork

(G-11601)
REPUBLIC HEAT TREAT INC
8902 N Main St (77022-3512)
P.O. Box 10203 (77206-0203)
PHONE.............................713 692-3308
Fax: 713 692-3910
EMP: 13
SQ FT: 6,000
SALES (est): 1.8MM **Privately Held**
SIC: 3398 Metal Heat Treating

(G-11602)
REPUBLIC MFG GROUP INC
Also Called: Republic Bag
8419 Tewantin Dr (77061-4615)
PHONE.............................713 847-7542
Stephen N Schroeder, *President*
Gary Wingfeld, *General Mgr*
Alfred B Teo, *Chairman*
John Reier, *Treasurer*
Kevin Foster, *Maintence Staff*
▲ **EMP:** 77
SQ FT: 3,000

▲ = Import ▼=Export
◆ =Import/Export

SALES (est): 17.9MM **Privately Held**
WEB: www.republicbag.com
SIC: 2673 Plastic bags: made from purchased materials

(G-11603)
REPUBLIC TUBE LLC
11200 Mesa Dr (77078-1206)
PHONE..................................832 672-6000
John J Hubbard, *Mng Member*
EMP: 150
SALES (est): 19.6MM
SALES (corp-wide): 137.6MM **Privately Held**
WEB: www.republictube.com
SIC: 3052 3069 Plastic hose; tubing, rubber
PA: Atlas Tubular, Llc
1710 S Highway 77
Robstown TX 78380
361 387-7505

(G-11604)
RESA POWER LLC (PA)
Also Called: Resa Service
8300 Cypress Pkwy Ste 225 (77070)
PHONE..................................832 900-8340
Monte Roach, *CEO*
Mark Angus, *COO*
David McAnelly, *COO*
Chis Weaver, *CFO*
Debra Arekat, *Controller*
EMP: 12
SALES (est): 77.2MM **Privately Held**
WEB: www.resapower.com
SIC: 3612 3699 Power & distribution transformers; electrical equipment & supplies

(G-11605)
RESERVE COMPRESSION CORP
Also Called: Reserve Equipment
13310 Hempstead Rd (77040-5811)
PHONE..................................713 783-8851
Keith Paul, *CEO*
James P Meredith, *President*
Jeffrey R Paul, *Vice Pres*
Nancy P Boyd, *Treasurer*
EMP: 32 EST: 2010
SALES (est): 610.4K **Privately Held**
WEB: www.reserveequipment.com
SIC: 1389 7353 Gas compressing (natural gas) at the fields; oil equipment rental services

(G-11606)
RESERVE EQUIPMENT INC
13310 Hempstead Rd (77040-5811)
PHONE..................................713 939-8988
Keith Paul, *President*
James P Meredith, *Vice Pres*
Jeffrey R Paul, *Vice Pres*
Nancy Boyd, *Treasurer*
William Hills, *Supervisor*
EMP: 20 EST: 1960
SQ FT: 1,400
SALES (est): 3MM **Privately Held**
WEB: www.reserveequipment.com
SIC: 1389 7353 Gas compressing (natural gas) at the fields; oil equipment rental services

(G-11607)
RESMETRICS LLC
6801 Portwest Dr Ste 190 (77024-8080)
PHONE..................................832 592-1900
Brandon Hamilton, *VP Opers*
Lyoid Fussell, *Sales Mgr*
EMP: 25
SQ FT: 13,000
SALES (est): 1MM **Privately Held**
WEB: www.resmetrics.com
SIC: 1382 Oil & gas exploration services

(G-11608)
RESOURCE ENERGY SERVICE CORP
Also Called: Rensco
11200 Westheimer Rd # 525 (77042-3219)
PHONE..................................713 953-5300
Stanley J Buffington, *President*
EMP: 70
SALES (est): 7.1MM **Privately Held**
WEB: www.resources2energy.com
SIC: 1381 Directional drilling oil & gas wells

(G-11609)
RESOURCE METALS COMPANY
14311 Reeveston Rd (77039-1516)
PHONE..................................281 442-8600
Mitchell Trotter, *President*
Michael Noble, *President*
Joe Spradling, *Sales Staff*
◆ EMP: 20
SQ FT: 30,000
SALES (est): 6.5MM **Privately Held**
WEB: www.resourcemetals.com
SIC: 5051 3599 Forgings, ferrous; machine shop, jobbing & repair

(G-11610)
RESOURCE OILFIELD PDTS CO INC
Also Called: Resource Metals Company
14311 Reeveston Rd (77039-1516)
PHONE..................................281 442-8600
Michael Noble, *President*
Mitchell Trotter, *Treasurer*
Mitch Trotter, *Info Tech Mgr*
EMP: 12
SALES (est): 1.8MM **Privately Held**
WEB: www.resourcemetals.com
SIC: 3364 Nonferrous die-castings except aluminum

(G-11611)
RESPIRATORY TECHNOLOGY CORP (PA)
Also Called: Restech
11011 Brooklet Dr Ste 300 (77099-3573)
PHONE..................................858 673-3700
Leo Roucher, *Ch of Bd*
Debra Krahel, *President*
Bree Fisk, *Manager*
Jeff Schipper, *Director*
EMP: 12
SALES (est): 2.9MM **Privately Held**
WEB: www.restech.com
SIC: 3845 Electromedical equipment

(G-11612)
RESPONSIBLE PRTG & SIGNS LLC
1403 Brittmoore Rd (77043-4005)
PHONE..................................713 722-0100
Ahmad Ashami, *President*
Adam Ahmad, *Chief*
Ahmad Afhami, *Director*
EMP: 10
SQ FT: 7,228
SALES (est): 1.5MM **Privately Held**
WEB: www.asheghaneh.com
SIC: 2752 Commercial printing, offset

(G-11613)
RESTLINE BEDDING PRODUCTS INC
5401 Gulf Fwy (77023-4641)
P.O. Box 12806 (77217-2806)
PHONE..................................713 921-1900
Tami E Aanderson, *President*
Cody Siebert, *Treasurer*
EMP: 11 EST: 1958
SQ FT: 52,500
SALES (est): 1MM **Privately Held**
SIC: 2515 Mattresses, containing felt, foam rubber, urethane, etc.; box springs, assembled

(G-11614)
RESULT ENTERPRISES INC (PA)
Also Called: High Tech Finishing
6201 Royalton St (77081-2926)
PHONE..................................713 666-0550
Carl A Bartuch, *CEO*
Lee H Whitley, *President*
Donald Ralston, *Principal*
Naomi Lockhart, *Regional Mgr*
Richard C Niefield, *Vice Pres*
EMP: 58
SQ FT: 26,000
SALES (est): 10.2MM **Privately Held**
WEB: www.htf.net
SIC: 3471 Chromium plating of metals or formed products; gold plating; polishing, metals or formed products

(G-11615)
RHR ACQUISITION CO LLC (PA)
Also Called: SEI Heat Treat
6910 Fulton St (77022-4860)
PHONE..................................713 699-3892
Leo Martinez, *Opers Staff*
Louis Flores, *Executive*
Richard Rau, *Executive*
Larry Gutierrez, *Maintence Staff*
EMP: 15
SALES (est): 2.3MM **Privately Held**
WEB: www.seiheat.com
SIC: 3398 Metal heat treating

(G-11616)
RIAZUL IMPORTS LLC
16402 Falcons Cove Dr (77095-5435)
PHONE..................................713 894-9177
Inaki Orozco,
EMP: 10
SALES (est): 537.1K **Privately Held**
WEB: www.riazul.com
SIC: 2085 Distilled & blended liquors

(G-11617)
RIBA FOODS INC (PA)
3701 Arc St (77063-5235)
P.O. Box 630461 (77263-0461)
PHONE..................................713 975-7001
Miguel A Barrios Jr, *President*
Miguel A Barrios Sr, *Vice Pres*
Cherron Kee, *Accounting Mgr*
Janie Salas, *Sales Staff*
Carl Nguyen, *Maintence Staff*
▲ EMP: 65
SQ FT: 50,000
SALES (est): 13.5MM **Privately Held**
WEB: www.ribafoods.com
SIC: 2099 Food preparations

(G-11618)
RICE METAL FABRICATORS INC
13824 Hempstead Rd (77040-5414)
PHONE..................................713 462-1978
Gary D Rice, *President*
Glenna Rice, *Corp Secy*
Kevin Rice, *Vice Pres*
EMP: 10 EST: 1968
SQ FT: 20,000
SALES (est): 2MM **Privately Held**
SIC: 3441 Fabricated structural metal

(G-11619)
RICHMOND PRINTING LLC
5825 Schumacher Ln (77057-7108)
PHONE..................................713 952-0800
Samad Gire, *VP Bus Dvlpt*
Javeed Gire, *Accounts Exec*
Mohamed A Gire, *Mng Member*
Imaddudin Gire,
Zahoor Ahmed Gire,
EMP: 63
SQ FT: 40,000
SALES (est): 11.4MM **Privately Held**
WEB: www.richmondprinting.com
SIC: 2752 Commercial printing, offset

(G-11620)
RIDGEWOOD ENERGY CORPORATION
1254 Enclave Pkwy Ste 600 (77077-2574)
PHONE..................................281 293-8488
Maria Haggerty, *President*
Niloy Shah, *Exec VP*
Greg Tabor, *Exec VP*
Gang Duan, *Engineer*
Kathleen McSherry, *CFO*
EMP: 23
SALES (corp-wide): 13.2MM **Privately Held**
WEB: www.ridgewoodenergy.com
SIC: 1382 Oil & gas exploration services
PA: Ridgewood Energy Corporation
14 Philips Pkwy
Montvale NJ 07645
201 307-0470

(G-11621)
RIGID GLOBAL BUILDINGS LLC (PA)
18933 Aldine Westfield Rd (77073-3817)
PHONE..................................281 443-9065
Alireza Ghodsi, *President*
Duke Santillan, *General Mgr*
Larry Black, *District Mgr*
Brien Collins, *District Mgr*
Matt Horrom, *District Mgr*
▼ EMP: 270
SALES (est): 55MM **Privately Held**
WEB: www.rigidbuilding.com
SIC: 3448 Prefabricated metal buildings

(G-11622)
RIGNET INC (PA)
15115 Park Row Ste 300 (77084-5075)
P.O. Box 941629 (77094-8629)
PHONE..................................281 674-0100
James H Browning, *Ch of Bd*
Steven E Pickett, *President*
James Barnett Jr, *Senior VP*
Brad Eastman, *Senior VP*
Jay Hilbert, *Senior VP*
▼ EMP: 148
SQ FT: 28,808
SALES: 242.9MM **Publicly Held**
WEB: www.rig.net
SIC: 7379 4899 4813 7372 Computer related maintenance services; data communication services; ; business oriented computer software

(G-11623)
RIL USA INC
2000 W Sam Houston Pkwy S # 700 (77042-3621)
PHONE..................................713 430-8700
John Fitzereld, *CEO*
◆ EMP: 15
SQ FT: 10,000
SALES (est): 2B **Privately Held**
SIC: 1382 Oil & gas exploration services
PA: Reliance Industries Limited
3rd Floor, Maker Chamber Iv,
Mumbai MH 40002

(G-11624)
RILCO MANUFACTURING CO INC (PA)
12700 Tanner Rd (77041-6511)
PHONE..................................713 466-4777
Anthony J Zagorski, *Ch of Bd*
Kenneth L Zagorski, *President*
Brett A Zagorski, *Vice Pres*
Alma Vazquez, *Project Mgr*
Claudia Huato, *Manager*
◆ EMP: 109
SQ FT: 50,000
SALES (est): 43MM **Privately Held**
WEB: www.rilco.com
SIC: 3086 Plastics foam products

(G-11625)
RINGERS TECHNOLOGY GROUP INC (PA)
Also Called: Ringers Gloves
3443 N Sam Houston Pkwy W (77086-1482)
PHONE..................................281 953-5300
Mushahid Khan, *CEO*
Jim Bailey, *President*
Christina Beahm, *Vice Pres*
Scott Jones, *Vice Pres*
Kevin Weatherford, *Vice Pres*
▲ EMP: 10
SALES (est): 28.8MM **Privately Held**
WEB: www.ringersgloves.com
SIC: 3151 Gloves, leather: work

(G-11626)
RITTAL CORP
13810 Hollister Dr # 170 (77086-1210)
PHONE..................................937 399-0500
Jim Barth, *Sales Staff*
Marcus Brooks, *Branch Mgr*
Ray Snyder, *Director*
EMP: 15
SALES (corp-wide): 1.4B **Privately Held**
WEB: www.rittal.us
SIC: 3469 Electronic enclosures, stamped or pressed metal
HQ: Rittal North-America Llc
425 N Martingale Rd # 1540
Schaumburg IL 60173
847 240-4600

(G-11627)
RIVA SERVICES LLC
12231 1/2 Fm 529 Rd (77041-2805)
P.O. Box 745 (77001-0745)
PHONE..................................713 675-2525
James E Petersen,

EMP: 75
SQ FT: 500,000
SALES (est): 5MM **Privately Held**
SIC: 6531 3511 Real estate agents & managers; turbines & turbine generator sets & parts

(G-11628)
RIVIANA FOODS INC
1702 Taylor St (77007-3949)
PHONE..................................713 529-3251
Steve Isaacson, *Manager*
EMP: 300
SQ FT: 68,001 **Privately Held**
WEB: www.riviana.com
SIC: 2044 2099 2041 Rice milling; food preparations; flour & other grain mill products
HQ: Riviana Foods Inc.
　　2777 Allen Pkwy Fl 15
　　Houston TX 77019
　　713 529-3251

(G-11629)
RIVIANA FOODS INC (HQ)
2777 Allen Pkwy Fl 15 (77019-2133)
P.O. Box 2636 (77252-2636)
PHONE..................................713 529-3251
Joseph A Hafner Jr, *Ch of Bd*
Charles R Godchaux, *Vice Ch Bd*
Bastiaan G De Zeeuw, *President*
Mark Denman, *COO*
Joseph Nevenglosky, *Senior VP*
◆ **EMP:** 190
SQ FT: 57,500
SALES (est): 708.5MM **Privately Held**
WEB: www.riviana.com
SIC: 2052 2033 5141 2044 Cookies; saltine crackers; fruit juices: packaged in cans, jars, etc.; tomato products: packaged in cans, jars, etc.; groceries, general line; milled rice

(G-11630)
RIVIANA INTERNATIONAL INC (DH)
Also Called: Riviana Foods
2777 Allen Pkwy Fl 15 (77019-2133)
P.O. Box 2636 (77252-2636)
PHONE..................................713 529-3251
Bastiaan Dezeeuw, *President*
Enrique Zaragoza, *Vice Pres*
Mikel Lopez, *Engineer*
D Troy Derouem, *CFO*
Mary Gullett, *Admin Sec*
▲ **EMP:** 250
SQ FT: 30,000
SALES (est): 90.2MM **Privately Held**
WEB: www.riviana.com
SIC: 2041 2044 Flour & other grain mill products; milled rice
HQ: Riviana Foods Inc.
　　2777 Allen Pkwy Fl 15
　　Houston TX 77019
　　713 529-3251

(G-11631)
RIVIERA OPERATING LLC (HQ)
600 Travis St Ste 5100 (77002-3031)
PHONE..................................713 227-1868
Michael Linn, *President*
Mark Ellis, *COO*
Lisa Anderson, *Senior VP*
Roland Keddie, *Senior VP*
Charlene Ripley, *Senior VP*
EMP: 66
SALES (est): 371.1MM
SALES (corp-wide): 479.7MM **Publicly Held**
WEB: www.rivieraresourcesinc.com
SIC: 1382 Oil & gas exploration services
PA: Riviera Resources, Inc.
　　717 Texas St Ste 2000
　　Houston TX 77002
　　281 840-4000

(G-11632)
RIVIERA RESOURCES INC (PA)
717 Texas St Ste 2000 (77002-2854)
PHONE..................................281 840-4000
David B Rottino, *President*
Daniel Furbee, *COO*
Holly Anderson, *Exec VP*
Jim Frew, *Exec VP*
Darren Schluter, *Exec VP*
EMP: 15

SALES: 479.7MM **Publicly Held**
WEB: www.linnenergy.com
SIC: 1382 Oil & gas exploration services

(G-11633)
RJ GLOBAL WIKA LP
Also Called: Wika USA
10910 W Sam Houston Pkwy (77064-6327)
PHONE..................................281 897-9222
◆ **EMP:** 43
SQ FT: 23,000
SALES (est): 9.2MM
SALES (corp-wide): 545.6MM **Privately Held**
WEB: www.rjglobalwikallc.com
SIC: 3441 Fabricated structural metal
HQ: Wika Instrument, Lp
　　1000 Wiegand Blvd
　　Lawrenceville GA 30043

(G-11634)
RKI INC (PA)
2301 Central Pkwy (77092-7720)
P.O. Box 924677 (77292-4677)
PHONE..................................713 688-4414
Thomas C Rawson, *President*
Leslie T Horvath, *Vice Pres*
Richard F Koenig, *Vice Pres*
Richard Koenig, *Vice Pres*
Ronnie D Moser, *Vice Pres*
▲ **EMP:** 270 **EST:** 1911
SQ FT: 200,000
SALES (est): 59.1MM **Privately Held**
WEB: www.rki-us.com
SIC: 3713 3531 Truck bodies & parts; winches; cranes

(G-11635)
RMC PLASTICS INC
629 Aldine Mail Rd (77037)
PHONE..................................713 722-9322
EMP: 15
SQ FT: 12,000
SALES (est): 5MM **Privately Held**
WEB: www.rmcplastics.com
SIC: 3089 Injection molding of plastics

(G-11636)
RMC RELIABLE MACHINISTS CORP
7102 Belgold St (77066-1004)
PHONE..................................281 444-2181
Chung Van Nguyen, *President*
Linh Nguyen, *General Mgr*
Tam Nguyen, *Foreman/Supr*
Vinh Nguyen, *Engineer*
Marilyn Nguyen, *Human Res Mgr*
▲ **EMP:** 40
SALES (est): 6.7MM **Privately Held**
WEB: www.rmcreliablemachinists.com
SIC: 3599 Machine shop, jobbing & repair

(G-11637)
RMC USA INC (DH)
920 Memorial City Way (77024-2649)
PHONE..................................713 650-6200
Gilberto Perez, *President*
Hendrik Van Brenk, *Vice Pres*
Stephanie Grant Ade, *Controller*
▲ **EMP:** 19
SALES (est): 270.3MM **Privately Held**
SIC: 3273 3272 3271 5031 Ready-mixed concrete; concrete products, precast; pipe, concrete or lined with concrete; concrete block & brick; building materials, exterior; building materials, interior
HQ: Cemex, Inc.
　　10100 Katy Fwy Ste 300
　　Houston TX 77043
　　713 650-6200

(G-11638)
RMF MANUFACTURING LLC
7922 Hansen Rd (77061-3429)
PHONE..................................713 910-9777
Eric Wagner, *Principal*
R C Robertson, *Principal*
EMP: 60 **EST:** 1962
SQ FT: 14,400
SALES (est): 14.2MM **Privately Held**
SIC: 3444 3443 Sheet metalwork; plate work for the metalworking trade

(G-11639)
RMI TITANIUM COMPANY LLC
7600 S Santa Fe Dr Ste C (77061-4500)
PHONE..................................713 466-8222
Terry Payne, *Branch Mgr*
EMP: 15
SALES (corp-wide): 14.1B **Publicly Held**
WEB: www.arconic.com
SIC: 3356 Titanium
HQ: Rmi Titanium Company, Llc
　　1000 Warren Ave
　　Niles OH 44446
　　330 652-9952

(G-11640)
ROAD RUNNER SERVICE POINT
4926 N Mccarty St (77013-3012)
PHONE..................................713 675-5110
Jose Lopez, *Owner*
EMP: 27
SALES (est): 1.2MM **Privately Held**
SIC: 7692 Welding repair

(G-11641)
ROADRUNNER RUBBER CORP
4824 Downs Ln (77093-5912)
P.O. Box 130566 (77219-0566)
PHONE..................................713 697-0633
▲ **EMP:** 15 **EST:** 1964
SQ FT: 36,000
SALES (est): 3.1MM **Privately Held**
WEB: www.roadrunnertires.com
SIC: 3011 Tires & inner tubes

(G-11642)
ROBERT K DEAN
Also Called: Apple Contractors
5707 Garden Ln Ste B (77092)
PHONE..................................713 681-2218
Robert K Dean, *Owner*
EMP: 12
SQ FT: 15,000
SALES (est): 1.3MM **Privately Held**
WEB: www.applecontractors.net
SIC: 2431 Millwork

(G-11643)
ROBERT L ROWAN & ASSOCIATES
Also Called: Rowan, Robt L & Assoc
3816 Dacoma St (77092-8718)
P.O. Box 920760 (77292-0760)
PHONE..................................713 681-5811
Robert L Rowan Jr, *CEO*
Charlie Rowan, *President*
Lillian Rowan, *Corp Secy*
Robert Rowan, *Director*
EMP: 10
SQ FT: 6,000
SALES (est): 5.5MM **Privately Held**
WEB: www.rlrowan.com
SIC: 5051 5084 3452 Concrete reinforcing bars; pollution control equipment, air (environmental); bolts, metal

(G-11644)
ROBERTSON-CECO II CORPORATION (HQ)
10943 N Sam Huston Pkwy W (77064-5758)
PHONE..................................281 897-7788
Norman C Chambers, *President*
Michelle Barreda, *President*
Steve Conner, *Maint Spvr*
Mark E Johnson, *Treasurer*
Dorinda Irby, *HR Admin*
▼ **EMP:** 241
SALES (est): 253.1MM
SALES (corp-wide): 4.8B **Publicly Held**
WEB: www.robertson-cecoii.mfgpages.com
SIC: 3448 Buildings, portable: prefabricated metal
PA: Cornerstone Building Brands, Inc.
　　5020 Weston Pkwy Ste 400
　　Cary NC 27513
　　866 419-0042

(G-11645)
ROBINSON PIPE & SUPPLY INC
Also Called: Robinson Pipe & Sign
915 N Mccarty St (77029-2423)
P.O. Box 2073, Bellaire (77402-2073)
PHONE..................................713 672-4152
Cary Robinson, *President*
Ross Robinson, *Owner*

Kim Hogan, *Accountant*
EMP: 25
SALES (est): 6.6MM **Privately Held**
WEB: www.robinsonpipe.net
SIC: 3911 Jewelry, precious metal

(G-11646)
ROBOGISTICS LLC (PA)
363 N Sam Houston Pkwy E # 1100 (77060-2404)
PHONE..................................409 234-1033
Salahuddin Wyatt-Khan, *President*
EMP: 12
SQ FT: 2,000
SALES (est): 5.8MM **Privately Held**
WEB: www.txrobogistics.com
SIC: 3569 Robots, assembly line: industrial & commercial

(G-11647)
ROC INDUSTRIES INC
Also Called: ROC Carbon Company
1605 Brittmoore Rd (77043-3107)
PHONE..................................713 468-7743
Myrtle L Ricks-Somerford, *Ch of Bd*
Curtis Sager, *President*
Cuong Tu, *Opers Mgr*
Bonnie Puckett, *Sales Staff*
Mike Thacker, *Sales Staff*
EMP: 22
SQ FT: 30,000
SALES (est): 4.2MM **Privately Held**
WEB: www.roccarbon.com
SIC: 3624 5085 5084 3568 Carbon & graphite products; gaskets & seals; processing & packaging equipment; power transmission equipment; steel foundries

(G-11648)
ROCA USA INC
7100 Business Park Dr (77041-4021)
PHONE..................................713 983-8008
Alejandro Garcia, *Manager*
EMP: 18
SALES (corp-wide): 50.5MM **Privately Held**
WEB: www.rocatileusa.com
SIC: 5032 3253 Ceramic wall & floor tile; ceramic wall & floor tile
HQ: Roca Usa Inc.
　　11190 Nw 25th St
　　Doral FL 33172
　　305 357-6569

(G-11649)
ROCK FIN COUNTERTOPS INC
Also Called: Rock Fin Minerals
5830 Gessner Rd Ste A (77041-6004)
PHONE..................................713 460-4441
Raja S Settipalli, *CEO*
▲ **EMP:** 25
SQ FT: 20,000
SALES (est): 8.3MM **Privately Held**
WEB: www.granitecountershouston.com
SIC: 2899 5211 Drilling mud; counter tops

(G-11650)
ROCKCLIFF ENERGY MGT LLC
717 Texas St (77002-2761)
PHONE..................................713 351-0525
Alan Smith, *CEO*
Jesse Heath, *CFO*
Gregory McCain, *Ch Credit Ofcr*
EMP: 25
SALES (est): 807K **Privately Held**
WEB: www.rockcliffenergy.com
SIC: 1311 Crude petroleum & natural gas production

(G-11651)
ROCKPOINT APPAREL COMPANY
Also Called: Rockpoint Marketplace
9925 Aldine Westfield Rd (77093-5405)
PHONE..................................713 699-9896
Olivia Olivo, *Vice Pres*
Richard Olivo, *Vice Pres*
Samuel Olivo Jr, *Vice Pres*
Carrie Olivo, *Manager*
Pete Alvarado, *Webmaster*
EMP: 15
SALES (est): 708.8K **Privately Held**
WEB: www.rockpointmarketplace.com
SIC: 2321 2353 2299 Hats & caps; men's & boys' sports & polo shirts

▲ = Import ▼ =Export
◆ =Import/Export

(G-11652)
ROCKWELL AUTOMATION INC
4325 W S Houston Pky N100 (77043)
PHONE.................................713 353-2400
Barry Elliott, *Vice Pres*
Hasan Syed, *Project Mgr*
Stephen Gill, *Engineer*
Leonard Kincer, *Engineer*
Allen Rentcome, *Engineer*
EMP: 15 **Publicly Held**
WEB: www.rockwellautomation.com
SIC: 3625 Relays & industrial controls
PA: Rockwell Automation, Inc.
  1201 S 2nd St
  Milwaukee WI 53204

(G-11653)
ROCKWELL PRECISION INC
8926 Solon Rd (77064-1231)
PHONE.................................281 890-9331
Herman Cotrino, *President*
Vera Cotrino, *Vice Pres*
Dan Cotrino, *Treasurer*
Lauren Harward, *Executive*
EMP: 19
SQ FT: 5,000
SALES (est): 8.2MM **Privately Held**
WEB: www.rpitex.com
SIC: 3533 Oil field machinery & equipment

(G-11654)
RODA DEACO VALVE INC
8824 Fallbrook Dr (77064-4855)
PHONE.................................780 465-4429
Russ Haddadin, *President*
EMP: 22
SALES (est): 638.6K **Privately Held**
WEB: www.rodadeaco.com
SIC: 3491 Industrial valves

(G-11655)
RODBOUBAN CORPORATION
5211 Kleinbrook Dr (77066-4387)
PHONE.................................972 841-8989
Rodney Banks, *CEO*
EMP: 50
SALES (est): 1MM **Privately Held**
SIC: 3999 Manufacturing industries

(G-11656)
ROGII INC
11750 Katy Fwy Ste 1010 (77079-1257)
PHONE.................................346 714-8694
Igor Uvarov, *Director*
Igor Kuvaev, *Director*
EMP: 20 **EST:** 2013
SALES (est): 141.8K **Privately Held**
WEB: www.rogii.com
SIC: 7371 7372 Computer software development; application computer software

(G-11657)
ROHART COMPANY
Also Called: Sterling Manufacturing
150 Bennington St (77022-4863)
PHONE.................................713 695-5333
Thomas Hicks, *President*
Mike Dushinske, *Managing Dir*
Anita Maloney, *Human Resources*
EMP: 45
SQ FT: 100,000
SALES (est): 16.5MM **Privately Held**
WEB: www.sterlinghouston.com
SIC: 3086 Packaging & shipping materials, foamed plastic

(G-11658)
ROK PROTECTIVE SYSTEMS INC
2313 W Sam Houston Pkwy S (77042)
PHONE.................................713 467-6999
EMP: 9
SQ FT: 7,000
SALES: 3MM **Privately Held**
SIC: 7382 2851 Security Systems Services Mfg Paints/Allied Products

(G-11659)
ROMA STEAM BATH INC
10555 W Little York Rd (77041-4043)
PHONE.................................281 578-9945
Jay Robins, *President*
Nelson Burruss, *Vice Pres*
Dennis Tottenham, *Shareholder*
EMP: 13

SQ FT: 9,000 **Privately Held**
WEB: www.romasteambath.com
SIC: 3511 Steam turbine generator set units, complete

(G-11660)
ROMAR/MEC LLC
218 Richey Rd (77090-5804)
P.O. Box 1172, Spring (77383-1172)
PHONE.................................281 440-1725
Willard D Harris,
Gerald L Dasbach,
▲ **EMP:** 18
SALES (est): 6.5MM **Privately Held**
WEB: www.fitupgear.com
SIC: 3494 Steam fittings & specialties

(G-11661)
RONCO MACHINE AND MFG INC
10833 W Hardy Rd (77076-2836)
PHONE.................................713 697-8717
Ron Laderer, *President*
EMP: 11
SQ FT: 15,000
SALES (est): 1.8MM **Privately Held**
WEB: www.roncomachineinc.com
SIC: 3599 Machine shop, jobbing & repair

(G-11662)
ROSE ELECTRONICS
10707 Stancliff Rd (77099-4344)
P.O. Box 742571 (77274-2571)
PHONE.................................281 933-7673
Pete Macourek, *Partner*
David Rahvar, *Partner*
Alan Howard, *General Mgr*
Sheila Pearson, *Vice Pres*
Craig Adams, *Materials Mgr*
▲ **EMP:** 135
SQ FT: 44,163
SALES (est): 31.7MM **Privately Held**
WEB: www.rose.com
SIC: 3577 3575 Computer peripheral equipment; computer terminals

(G-11663)
ROSE MACHINE & FAB INC (PA)
9031 Ley Rd (77078-4407)
PHONE.................................713 670-9007
Richard Rose, *President*
▲ **EMP:** 14
SQ FT: 60,000
SALES (est): 5.2MM **Privately Held**
WEB: www.ellwoodrm.com
SIC: 3441 Fabricated structural metal

(G-11664)
ROSEMOUNT INC
10241 W Little York Rd (77040-3228)
PHONE.................................713 396-8700
Gary Lawwernce, *Branch Mgr*
Glen Bradford, *Director*
EMP: 28
SALES (corp-wide): 16.7B **Publicly Held**
WEB: www.rosemount.com
SIC: 3823 Manometers, industrial process type
HQ: Rosemount Inc.
  8200 Market Blvd
  Chanhassen MN 55317
  952 906-8888

(G-11665)
ROSEMUNT TANK GGING N AMER INC
Also Called: Emerson Process Management
6005 Rogerdale Rd Sc200.2 (77072-1656)
P.O. Box 730018, Dallas (75373-0017)
PHONE.................................281 988-4000
Berry Lance, *President*
Desmond Bailey, *Vice Pres*
Glenn Klimchuk, *Vice Pres*
Tom Stovall, *Vice Pres*
Shivani Shah, *Project Mgr*
▲ **EMP:** 20
SQ FT: 5,000
SALES (est): 9.1MM
SALES (corp-wide): 16.7B **Publicly Held**
WEB: www.emerson.com
SIC: 3823 Industrial instrmnts msrmnt display/control process variable
PA: Emerson Electric Co.
  8000 West Florissant Ave
  Saint Louis MO 63136
  314 553-2000

(G-11666)
ROSETTA RESOURCES OFFSHORE LLC
1111 Bagby St Ste 1600 (77002-2547)
PHONE.................................713 335-2400
Michael J Rosinski,
Bill Berilgen,
EMP: 110
SQ FT: 54,816
SALES (est): 159.4MM
SALES (corp-wide): 146.5B **Publicly Held**
SIC: 1382 Oil & gas exploration services
HQ: Nbl Texas, Llc
  1001 Noble Energy Way
  Houston TX 77070
  281 872-3100

(G-11667)
ROSETTA RESOURCES OPERATING LP
1001 Noble Energy Way (77070-1435)
PHONE.................................281 872-3100
Charles J Rimer, *President*
John A Huser, *Vice Pres*
Robert B Marlatt, *Vice Pres*
Kevin E Haggard, *Treasurer*
Bernard P Castro, *Asst Treas*
EMP: 200
SQ FT: 54,000
SALES (est): 32.9MM
SALES (corp-wide): 146.5B **Publicly Held**
SIC: 1382 Oil & gas exploration services
HQ: Nbl Texas, Llc
  1001 Noble Energy Way
  Houston TX 77070
  281 872-3100

(G-11668)
ROTARY COMPONENTS INTL INC
Also Called: Rci
814 Logandale Ln (77032-1519)
P.O. Box 60429 (77205-0429)
PHONE.................................281 590-6484
David C Edgar, *CEO*
Ron L Edgar, *President*
Jason Edgar, *Vice Pres*
Derek C Schulz, *Sales Staff*
EMP: 10
SALES (est): 2.3MM **Privately Held**
WEB: www.rciusa.net
SIC: 1389 1381 3533 Lease tanks, oil field: erecting, cleaning & repairing; redrilling oil & gas wells; oil & gas drilling rigs & equipment

(G-11669)
ROTARY DRILLING TOOLS USA LLC (DH)
Also Called: Rdt-USA
1201 Louisiana St Fl 28 (77002-5607)
PHONE.................................979 387-3223
Sealy Morris, *CEO*
William S Morris, *President*
Tim Novosad, *COO*
Jorge Bejar, *Vice Pres*
Vincent Washburn, *Controller*
◆ **EMP:** 23
SQ FT: 45,000
SALES (est): 60.8MM
SALES (corp-wide): 29.6MM **Privately Held**
WEB: www.rdt-usa.co
SIC: 3498 3533 Fabricated pipe & fittings; oil & gas drilling rigs & equipment

(G-11670)
ROTHE JOINT VENTURE LP
2101 Nasa Pkwy Bldg 9 (77058-3607)
PHONE.................................281 483-3852
Jerry Klowalchik, *Manager*
EMP: 100
SALES (corp-wide): 5.7MM **Privately Held**
WEB: www.rxjv-alliant.com
SIC: 3812 3769 Aircraft/aerospace flight instruments & guidance systems; guided missile & space vehicle parts & auxiliary equipment
PA: Rothe Joint Venture, L.P
  4614 Sinclair Rd
  San Antonio TX 78222
  210 648-3131

(G-11671)
ROTO-VERSAL COMPRESSION SVCS
13223 Fm 529 Rd (77041-2532)
P.O. Box 841035 (77284-1035)
PHONE.................................713 538-2800
Charlie Kirchhoff, *Mng Member*
Dirk Dailey,
Ken Plocek,
EMP: 21
SALES (est): 4.8MM **Privately Held**
WEB: www.roto-versal.com
SIC: 1389 Gas field services

(G-11672)
ROTOR-TECH INC
10613 Stebbins Cir (77043-3232)
PHONE.................................713 984-8900
Gardner Baldwin, *Ch of Bd*
Dave Echols, *President*
Mario Pena, *Purchasing*
Joe Vara, *Engineer*
Robert Foster, *Sales Staff*
▲ **EMP:** 11
SQ FT: 9,000
SALES (est): 3MM **Privately Held**
WEB: www.rotor-tech.com
SIC: 3561 Pumps & pumping equipment

(G-11673)
ROTORK CONTROLS INC
1811 Brittmoore Rd # 100 (77043-2299)
PHONE.................................713 353-7887
Jeff Kelley, *Manager*
EMP: 17
SALES (corp-wide): 864.5MM **Privately Held**
WEB: www.rotork.com
SIC: 3491 Industrial valves
HQ: Rotork Controls Inc.
  675 Mile Crossing Blvd
  Rochester NY 14624
  585 247-2304

(G-11674)
ROTORK CONTROLS INC
9777 W Gulf Bank Rd # 15 (77040-3137)
PHONE.................................713 983-7381
Tom Matthews, *General Mgr*
Chris Dicicco, *Director*
Tim Cobbold, *Bd of Directors*
EMP: 12
SALES (corp-wide): 864.5MM **Privately Held**
WEB: www.rotork.com
SIC: 3625 Actuators, industrial
HQ: Rotork Controls Inc.
  675 Mile Crossing Blvd
  Rochester NY 14624
  585 247-2304

(G-11675)
ROVOP INC
13719 Fm 529 Rd (77041-2522)
PHONE.................................281 231-2626
EMP: 11 **EST:** 2014
SALES (est): 1.2MM **Privately Held**
WEB: www.rovop.com
SIC: 1389 Oil field services

(G-11676)
ROWAN COMPANIES LLC (HQ)
5847 San Felipe St # 330 (77057-3000)
PHONE.................................713 621-7800
Thomas P Burke, *President*
W Matt Ralls, *Chairman*
Jodi Landry, *Regional Mgr*
Vicki Taylor, *COO*
Stephen Butz, *Exec VP*
◆ **EMP:** 120 **EST:** 1947
SALES (est): 1.4B
SALES (corp-wide): 67.2MM **Privately Held**
WEB: www.enscorowan.com
SIC: 1381 3531 3533 Drilling oil & gas wells; loaders, shovel: self-propelled; drill rigs

(G-11677)
ROWAN DRILLING COMPANY INC (HQ)
2800 Post Oak Blvd # 5450 (77056-6100)
PHONE.................................713 621-7800
Thomas P Burke, *CEO*
Mathew Ralls, *Principal*

W Matt Ralls, *Chairman*
John L Buvens, *Exec VP*
Mark A Keller, *Exec VP*
▲ **EMP:** 10
SQ FT: 52,000
SALES (est): 154MM
SALES (corp-wide): 67.2MM **Privately Held**
WEB: www.enscorowan.com
SIC: 1381 Directional drilling oil & gas wells

(G-11678)
ROWAN MARINE DRILLING INC
2800 Post Oak Blvd # 5450 (77056-6100)
PHONE....................................713 621-7800
C R Palmer, *Chairman*
EMP: 120
SALES (est): 3.8MM
SALES (corp-wide): 67.2MM **Privately Held**
WEB: www.enscorowan.com
SIC: 1381 Drilling oil & gas wells
PA: Rowan Companies Limited
　　78 Cannon Street Cannon Place
　　London　EC4N

(G-11679)
ROWAN PETROLEUM INC
2800 Post Oak Blvd Fl 54 (77056-6168)
PHONE....................................713 621-7800
Danny McNease, *President*
C R Palmer, *Chairman*
R G Croyle, *Vice Chairman*
Jerry Allamon, *Exec VP*
Mark H Hay, *Treasurer*
EMP: 120
SQ FT: 52,000
SALES (est): 10MM
SALES (corp-wide): 67.2MM **Privately Held**
WEB: www.enscorowan.com
SIC: 1381 Drilling oil & gas wells; oil royalty traders
PA: Rowan Companies Limited
　　78 Cannon Street Cannon Place
　　London　EC4N

(G-11680)
ROXAR　INC
Also Called: Roxar Flow Measurement
6005 Rogerdale Rd (77072-1656)
PHONE....................................281 879-2600
Fax: 713 482-6401
▲ **EMP:** 30
SALES (est): 4.8MM
SALES (corp-wide): 22.3B **Publicly Held**
SIC: 3824 7371 3613 Mfg Fluid Meters/Devices Computer Programming Svc Mfg Switchgear/Boards
PA: Emerson Electric Co.
　　8000 W Florissant Ave
　　Saint Louis MO 63136
　　314 553-2000

(G-11681)
ROY B WHEELER COMPANY INC
911 Martin St (77018-2123)
P.O. Box 10995 (77206-0995)
PHONE....................................713 692-9729
James B Wheeler, *President*
Tony Haney, *Vice Pres*
Susan Haney, *Admin Sec*
EMP: 20 **EST:** 1969
SQ FT: 4,800
SALES (est): 3MM **Privately Held**
SIC: 3599 Machine shop, jobbing & repair

(G-11682)
ROYAL BATHS MANUFACTURING CO (PA)
Also Called: Royal Manufacturing
14635 Chrisman Rd (77039-1116)
PHONE....................................281 442-3400
Caesar Hage, *Exec VP*
Sonya Pratt, *Credit Staff*
Hether Alford, *Human Resources*
Bryce Boyd, *Mktg Dir*
Russell Dickson, *Mng Member*
EMP: 300
SQ FT: 52,000

SALES (est): 170.5MM **Privately Held**
WEB: www.royal-mfg.com
SIC: 3842 3949 3432 3281 Whirlpool baths, hydrotherapy equipment; sporting & athletic goods; plumbing fixture fittings & trim; cut stone & stone products

(G-11683)
ROYAL PUBLISHING　INC
Also Called: Prestige Printers
3560 Lang Rd (77092-6105)
PHONE....................................713 895-9727
Kum Soon Chae, *President*
JW Halderman, *Site Mgr*
EMP: 23
SQ FT: 14,000
SALES (est): 3.1MM **Privately Held**
WEB: www.prestigeprinters.com
SIC: 2752 Commercial printing, offset

(G-11684)
ROYAL TECHNOCRATS INC
Also Called: Rti
7447 Harwin Dr Ste 270 (77036-2081)
PHONE....................................713 776-8300
Shahana Anjum, *President*
Mohammed Ali, *Vice Pres*
Ali Mohammed, *Opers Mgr*
Mark Anthony, *Info Tech Mgr*
Kamraan Ali, *Admin Sec*
EMP: 20
SALES (est): 2.3MM **Privately Held**
WEB: www.royaltechnocrats.com
SIC: 7371 7373 8243 7372 Computer software systems analysis & design, custom; office computer automation systems integration; software training, computer; business oriented computer software; computer related consulting services

(G-11685)
ROYAL WHITE CEMENT INC (HQ)
8316 East Fwy (77029-1612)
PHONE....................................713 676-0000
Marcel El Fadi, *President*
Michael Arustamov, *Regl Sales Mgr*
Bill Goglas, *Sales Staff*
Ahmed Aldabbagh, *Manager*
Jacques Fady, *Admin Sec*
◆ **EMP:** 35
SQ FT: 100,000
SALES (est): 14.7MM
SALES (corp-wide): 4.7MM **Privately Held**
WEB: www.royalwhitecement.com
SIC: 2891 Cement, except linoleum & tile
PA: Royal White Holdings Inc.
　　8316 East Fwy
　　Houston TX 77029
　　713 676-0000

(G-11686)
ROYALTY METAL FINISHING　INC
10050 W Gulf Bank Rd # 200 (77040-3159)
P.O. Box 41654 (77241-1654)
PHONE....................................281 208-4455
Mark Dupree, *President*
Sylvia Dupree, *Vice Pres*
EMP: 21
SQ FT: 44,000
SALES (est): 2.5MM **Privately Held**
WEB: www.royaltymetalfinishing.com
SIC: 3479 Coating of metals & formed products

(G-11687)
ROYCO INDUSTRIES INC
802 Riley Rd (77047-6123)
PHONE....................................713 413-9191
Chris Roy, *President*
EMP: 9
SQ FT: 200
SALES (est): 1.3MM **Privately Held**
SIC: 3498 Fabricated pipe & fittings

(G-11688)
RP MACHINE SHOP
8628 Rannie Rd (77080-3526)
PHONE....................................713 939-7522
Arpad Soos, *Owner*
EMP: 11
SQ FT: 2,500
SALES (est): 100K **Privately Held**
SIC: 3599 Machine shop, jobbing & repair

(G-11689)
RPR PRODUCTS　INC (PA)
407 Delz St (77018-1617)
PHONE....................................713 697-7003
Robert J Chovanec, *President*
Daniel Callaway, *Corp Secy*
Doyle G Adair, *Treasurer*
▲ **EMP:** 63
SQ FT: 80,000
SALES (est): 31.5MM **Privately Held**
WEB: www.rprhouston.com
SIC: 3444 Sheet metalwork

(G-11690)
RSC ACQUISITIONS (HQ)
Also Called: Rex Supply Company
14751 Kirby Dr (77047-2568)
P.O. Box 670587, Detroit MI (48267-0587)
PHONE....................................713 222-2251
Joseph J Madden, *President*
Joe Madden, *President*
Lawrence A Wolfe, *Owner*
Tom Wright, *Vice Pres*
Craig Fishel, *CFO*
▼ **EMP:** 77
SALES (est): 26.1MM
SALES (corp-wide): 183.1MM **Privately Held**
WEB: www.pts-tools.com
SIC: 5085 3545 5084 Mill supplies; machine tool accessories; machine tools & accessories
PA: Berkshire Production Supply Llc
　　40333 W 14 Mile Rd
　　Novi MI 48377
　　586 755-2200

(G-11691)
RSD SUPPLY　INC
Also Called: R S D Supply
13225 Fm 529 Rd Ste N (77041-2598)
PHONE....................................713 983-6363
Greg Sharpe, *President*
Larry Samek, *General Mgr*
David Marrs, *Vice Pres*
EMP: 21
SQ FT: 20,000 **Privately Held**
WEB: www.rsdsupply.com
SIC: 5082 5085 3317 Oil field equipment; valves, pistons & fittings; valves & fittings; seamless pipes & tubes

(G-11692)
RTI EXTRUSIONS　INC
Also Called: Rti Fabrication
7600 S Santa Fe Dr Ste C (77061-4500)
PHONE....................................713 641-6010
Larry Wright, *Manager*
▲ **EMP:** 117 **EST:** 1994
SQ FT: 142,000
SALES (est): 36.6MM
SALES (corp-wide): 14.1B **Publicly Held**
WEB: www.rtiintl.com
SIC: 3356 Titanium & titanium alloy bars, sheets, strip, etc.
PA: Howmet Aerospace Inc.
　　201 Isabella St Ste 200
　　Pittsburgh PA 15212
　　412 553-1940

(G-11693)
RUBICON OLFLD INTL HLDINGS LLC (PA)
10613 W Sam Hston Pkwy600 (77064-4663)
PHONE....................................832 386-2500
Mike Reeves, *CEO*
Scott Watson, *COO*
Benoit Deschamps, *Vice Pres*
Mike Porter, *Store Mgr*
John Griggs, *CFO*
EMP: 14 **EST:** 2015
SALES (est): 108.5MM **Privately Held**
WEB: www.rubicon-oilfield.com
SIC: 1389 Oil field services

(G-11694)
RUDINGER ENTERPRISES　INC
10018 Talley Ln (77041-6128)
PHONE....................................713 939-1234
John Rudinger, *Branch Mgr*
EMP: 15
SALES (corp-wide): 6.1MM **Privately Held**
WEB: www.swtruckrigging.com
SIC: 3713 Truck & bus bodies

PA: Rudinger Enterprises, Inc.
　　10010 Talley Ln
　　Houston TX 77041
　　281 356-6219

(G-11695)
RUDINGER ENTERPRISES　INC (PA)
Also Called: Southwest Truck Rigging & Eqp
10010 Talley Ln (77041-6128)
PHONE....................................281 356-6219
John W Rudinger, *President*
Brent A Blake, *Vice Pres*
Rick Hays, *Vice Pres*
Patrick Hays, *Project Mgr*
Chester Howard, *Foreman/Supr*
EMP: 35
SQ FT: 15,000
SALES (est): 6.1MM **Privately Held**
WEB: www.swtruckrigging.com
SIC: 3713 Truck beds; truck bodies (motor vehicles)

(G-11696)
RUIZ DISTRIBUTING CO
7515 Long Point Rd Ste 3 (77055-3703)
PHONE....................................713 682-7008
Jorge Ruiz, *President*
Delia Ruiz, *Vice Pres*
EMP: 10
SQ FT: 10,046
SALES (est): 1MM **Privately Held**
WEB: www.ruizdistributing.com
SIC: 2086 Bottled & canned soft drinks

(G-11697)
RULON ELC ILLUMINATIONS CO INC
Also Called: Illuminations Lighting Design
607 Durham Dr (77007-5316)
PHONE....................................713 863-1133
Thomas E Kretzschmar, *President*
Tom Kretzschmar, *Principal*
Rick Luberger, *Vice Pres*
Mike Martinez, *Warehouse Mgr*
Kimberly Forrest, *Controller*
EMP: 47
SQ FT: 10,000
SALES (est): 7.7MM **Privately Held**
WEB: www.illuminationslighting.com
SIC: 3648 1731 3646 3645 Lighting equipment; lighting contractor; commercial indusl & institutional electric lighting fixtures; residential lighting fixtures

(G-11698)
RUSSELL INDUSTRIES　INC (PA)
6125 Nordling Rd (77076-4037)
PHONE....................................713 692-7225
Donald J Russell, *Principal*
Donald Russell, *Principal*
Angela Russell, *Vice Pres*
▲ **EMP:** 10
SQ FT: 18,000
SALES (est): 5.7MM **Privately Held**
WEB: www.palletracksystems.com
SIC: 5084 3496 Materials handling machinery; power plant machinery; miscellaneous fabricated wire products

(G-11699)
RUSSELL MFG & FABG INC
14518 Reeveston Rd (77039-1125)
PHONE....................................281 590-8185
Scott Russell, *President*
Stanley Russell, *Vice Pres*
Anna Russell, *Admin Sec*
EMP: 20
SQ FT: 36,000
SALES (est): 5MM **Privately Held**
WEB: www.russell-mfg.com
SIC: 3312 Blast furnaces & steel mills

(G-11700)
RUSSIAN-AMERICAN QUALITY
Also Called: Raqcs
2441 Del Monte Dr (77019-3409)
PHONE....................................713 522-0453
Vel Berzin, *General Ptnr*
EMP: 32
SQ FT: 6,500
SALES (est): 1.2MM **Privately Held**
SIC: 1389 Oil & gas wells: building, repairing & dismantling

▲ = Import ▼=Export
◆ =Import/Export

(G-11701)
RUTHERFORD OIL CORPORATION (PA)
8 Greenway Plz Ste 1400 (77046-0800)
PHONE.................................713 622-5555
▲ EMP: 15
SALES (est): 11.4MM Privately Held
WEB: www.rutherfordoil.com
SIC: 1382 1311 Oil & gas exploration services; crude petroleum production; natural gas production

(G-11702)
RUTHERFORD-MORAN EXPLORATION
8 Greenway Plz Ste 1400 (77046-0800)
PHONE.................................859 254-4775
Michael Rutherford, President
Sidney Fjones Jr, Vice Pres
EMP: 20
SALES (est): 1.1MM Privately Held
SIC: 1382 1381 Oil & gas exploration services; drilling oil & gas wells

(G-11703)
RVO MANUFACTURING LLC
15040 Northgreen Blvd (77032-3000)
PHONE.................................832 229-5114
Ronak Patel, President
EMP: 10
SALES (est): 349.4K Privately Held
SIC: 2295 Metallizing of fabrics

(G-11704)
RWG (REPAIR OVERHAULS USA INC (HQ)
6223 W Sam Houston Pkwy N
(77041-5145)
PHONE.................................713 538-9700
Keith Brady, President
Mick Conway, Business Mgr
Russell Grant, Business Mgr
Mark Paterson, Exec VP
Kelly Wilson, Vice Pres
◆ EMP: 60
SQ FT: 43,000
SALES (est): 14.1MM
SALES (corp-wide): 213.7MM Privately Held
WEB: www.rwgroup.com
SIC: 3511 Turbines & turbine generator sets
PA: Rwg (Repair & Overhauls) Limited
Kirkhill Drive Kirkhill Industrial Estate
Aberdeen AB21
122 479-7000

(G-11705)
S & G PLASTICS INC
8399 Kempwood Dr (77055-1031)
PHONE.................................713 467-8766
David Linzel, President
Brenda Linzel, Corp Secy
EMP: 25
SQ FT: 13,000
SALES (est): 5.7MM Privately Held
WEB: www.sgplastics.net
SIC: 2673 Plastic bags: made from purchased materials

(G-11706)
S & H SHTMTL & FABG CO INC
Also Called: S & H Manufacturing Co
7218 Canal St Houston (77011)
P.O. Box 99080 (77261-0080)
PHONE.................................713 926-8805
Chrystel Smith, President
Margan Nixon, Treasurer
EMP: 25
SQ FT: 12,000
SALES (est): 3.4MM Privately Held
WEB: www.sandhmanufacturing.com
SIC: 3444 3644 Sheet metalwork; pole line hardware

(G-11707)
S & N PUMP COMPANY
Also Called: Clyde Union
8002 Breen Dr (77064-8416)
P.O. Box 3013, Cypress (77410-3013)
PHONE.................................281 445-2243
Jeremy Smeltser, President
Kevin Lilly, Vice Pres
Richard Draper, Manager
◆ EMP: 38

SQ FT: 21,000
SALES (est): 11.1MM
SALES (corp-wide): 1.5B Publicly Held
WEB: www.snpump.com
SIC: 5084 7699 3561 Pumps & pumping equipment; pumps & pumping equipment repair; pumps & pumping equipment
PA: Spx Flow, Inc.
13320 Balntyn Corp Pl
Charlotte NC 28277
704 752-4400

(G-11708)
S & S X-RAY PRODUCTS INC (PA)
Also Called: Talon
10625 Telge Rd (77095-5023)
PHONE.................................281 815-1300
Norman Shoenfeld MD, President
Diane Shoenfeld, Principal
Sandra Pavlas, COO
Jim Beegle, Manager
Kay Guidry, HR Admin
▲ EMP: 70
SALES (est): 8.3MM Privately Held
WEB: www.ssxray.com
SIC: 3844 Radiographic X-ray apparatus & tubes

(G-11709)
S + S INDUSTRIES INC (PA)
Also Called: Sns Plating
5614 Nunn St (77087-4134)
PHONE.................................713 643-8888
George Andrews, President
Greg Andrews, Vice Pres
Alberto Gomez, Plant Mgr
Bianca Bertrand-Lira, Purchasing
Bianca Lira, Supervisor
▲ EMP: 69
SQ FT: 110,000
SALES (est): 17.5MM Privately Held
WEB: www.ssind.com
SIC: 3471 Electroplating of metals or formed products

(G-11710)
S K INDUSTRIES INC
11934 Hempstead Rd (77092-6099)
PHONE.................................713 462-6997
Robert G Sydow, President
Lucille Sydow, Vice Pres
Seung Hong, Manager
EMP: 9
SQ FT: 15,000
SALES (est): 1.3MM Privately Held
WEB: www.skind1.com
SIC: 3599 Machine shop, jobbing & repair

(G-11711)
S K RESOURCES INC
7700 San Felipe St # 500 (77063-1615)
PHONE.................................713 782-1075
Paul Sigmund, President
Greg Kane, Vice Pres
EMP: 16
SALES (est): 883.8K Privately Held
SIC: 1382 Oil & gas exploration services

(G-11712)
S P (TEXAS) INC
Also Called: S P TX General Comm Printer
7121 Chimney Rock Rd (77081-6606)
PHONE.................................713 666-5166
Joseph Chung, President
EMP: 9
SQ FT: 5,000
SALES (est): 1.7MM Privately Held
SIC: 5084 2752 2791 2789 Printing trades machinery, equipment & supplies; commercial printing, lithographic; typesetting; bookbinding & related work

(G-11713)
S R HILL AND ASSOC INTL INC
4265 San Felipe St # 1100 (77027-2920)
P.O. Box 22091 (77227-2091)
PHONE.................................713 960-6617
Steven R Hill, Owner
EMP: 11
SQ FT: 80,000
SALES (est): 1.2MM Privately Held
WEB: www.shillassociatesinc.com
SIC: 1389 Oil consultants

(G-11714)
S/T HEALTH GROUP CONSULTING
3033 Chimney Rock Rd # 550
(77056-6249)
PHONE.................................281 491-5555
Richard Tulio, President
Guy Shivitz, Partner
Steve Pitzer, Vice Pres
David Wertz, Opers Staff
EMP: 11
SALES (est): 1MM Privately Held
WEB: www.sthealthgroup.com
SIC: 2834 8742 Pharmaceutical preparations; industry specialist consultants

(G-11715)
SABINE HUB SERVICES LLC
2811 Hayes Rd (77082-2642)
PHONE.................................214 721-9474
EMP: 35 EST: 2017
SALES (est): 119.9K
SALES (corp-wide): 6B Publicly Held
WEB: www.henryhub.enlink.com
SIC: 1321 Natural gas liquids
HQ: Enlink Midstream Partners, Lp
1722 Routh St Ste 1300
Dallas TX 75201

(G-11716)
SABINE INVESTOR HOLDINGS LLC
1415 La St Ste 1600 (77002)
PHONE.................................832 242-9600
David J Sambrooks, Ch of Bd
EMP: 289
SALES (est): 6.4MM Privately Held
WEB: www.sabineoil.com
SIC: 1311 Crude petroleum production

(G-11717)
SABINE OIL & GAS CORPORATION (DH)
1415 Louisiana St # 1600 (77002-7490)
PHONE.................................832 242-9600
David J Sambrooks, Ch of Bd
Thomas N Chewning, Principal
Jonathan F Foster, Principal
Alex T Krueger, Principal
Patrick R McDonald, Principal
EMP: 10
SALES (est): 267.6MM Privately Held
WEB: www.sabineoil.com
SIC: 1311 Crude petroleum production
HQ: Osaka Gas Usa Corporation
1330 Post Oak Blvd Fl 19
Houston TX 77056
713 354-9100

(G-11718)
SABINE OIL & GAS LLC
1415 La St Ste 1600 (77002)
PHONE.................................832 242-9600
David Sambrooks, CEO
Helen Tate, CEO
Duane C Radtke, Ch of Bd
Todd Levesque, COO
Paul Babcock, Vice Pres
EMP: 15
SALES (est): 10.2MM Privately Held
WEB: www.sabineoil.com
SIC: 1311 Crude petroleum production

(G-11719)
SABLE PERMIAN RESOURCES LLC (PA)
700 Milam St Ste 3100 (77002-2764)
PHONE.................................713 579-8000
Kenneth Cunningham, Principal
Robin Veariel, Principal
Doss R Bourgeois, COO
Lee Alcock, Counsel
John F Wombwell, Exec VP
EMP: 23
SALES (est): 221.8MM Privately Held
WEB: www.sableres.com
SIC: 1382 Oil & gas exploration services

(G-11720)
SABLE PRMIAN RESOURCES FIN LLC (HQ)
700 Milam St Ste 3100 (77002-2764)
P.O. Box 14670, Oklahoma City OK
(73113-0670)
PHONE.................................713 579-8000
Jeffrey Mobley, CEO
Jerrald J Straton, COO
John F Wombwell, Exec VP
Ryan Turner, CFO
Laura Manwell, Treasurer
EMP: 11 EST: 2014
SALES (est): 30.3MM
SALES (corp-wide): 1.2MM Privately Held
WEB: www.sableres.com
SIC: 8742 1382 Management consulting services; oil & gas exploration services

(G-11721)
SABRE ALLOYS LP
6039 Thomas Rd Ste B (77041-4934)
P.O. Box 841846 (77284-1846)
PHONE.................................281 405-8580
Matt Keith, Partner
Mike Sassin, Sales Staff
Ernie Valdez, Sales Staff
EMP: 18 EST: 2011
SALES (est): 7.1MM Privately Held
WEB: www.sabrealloys.com
SIC: 3312 Stainless steel

(G-11722)
SAE TOWERS LTD (DH)
16945 Northchase Dr # 1910 (77060-2135)
PHONE.................................281 763-2282
Gustavo Cedeno, CEO
Chip Breitweiser, Vice Pres
Yasaswy Kothari, CFO
Pat Schultz, Finance
Gustavo Valbuena, Director
EMP: 10
SQ FT: 4,000
SALES (est): 1.3MM Privately Held
WEB: www.saetowers.com
SIC: 3312 Structural shapes & pilings, steel

(G-11723)
SAEXPLORATION HOLDINGS INC (PA)
1160 Dairy Ashford Rd # 160 (77079-3097)
PHONE.................................281 258-4400
Michael Faust, Ch of Bd
Janus Rosborough, General Mgr
Richard Trupp, General Mgr
Michael Briggs, Business Mgr
D Edgecombe, Vice Pres
EMP: 15
SALES: 255.2MM Privately Held
WEB: www.saexploration.com
SIC: 1382 7374 Oil & gas exploration services; data processing service

(G-11724)
SAFEPLEX SYSTEMS INC
10801 Hammerly Blvd # 242 (77043-1922)
PHONE.................................832 582-7029
Lawrence Beckman, President
Larry Lengyel, Vice Pres
Shirley Becker, Office Mgr
EMP: 15
SQ FT: 9,300
SALES (est): 3MM Privately Held
WEB: www.safeplexsystems.com
SIC: 3829 Measuring & controlling devices

(G-11725)
SAFESPACE CONCEPTS INC
1424 N Post Oak Rd (77055-5401)
PHONE.................................713 956-0820
Barbara B Carlson, President
Naess Katrin J, Vice Pres
Jean Mande, CFO
Gerald S Johnson, Mktg Dir
Ivan Hernandez, Marketing Staff
EMP: 12
SQ FT: 6,500
SALES (est): 1.4MM Privately Held
WEB: www.safespaceconcepts.com
SIC: 3949 2531 Playground equipment; school furniture

(G-11726)
SAFETY N95 LLC
5300 N Braeswood Blvd (77096-3307)
PHONE..........................281 624-1812
Veronica Jonier Thomas, *CEO*
James Kenneth Thomas, *Mng Member*
EMP: 10
SALES (est): 377.1K **Privately Held**
SIC: 3842 Personal safety equipment

(G-11727)
SAFETY WEAR LTD
11050 W Little York Rd B2 (77041-5056)
PHONE..........................832 243-0100
Elaine Meyers, *VP Opers*
Angie Williams, *Sales Mgr*
Louis Robichaux, *Manager*
EMP: 12
SALES (corp-wide): 2.7MM **Privately Held**
WEB: www.safetywearltd.net
SIC: 3842 Clothing, fire resistant & protective
PA: Safety Wear Ltd
519 I 10 Fwy E
Orange TX 77630
409 883-8000

(G-11728)
SAFOCO INC
9901 Regal Row (77040-3244)
PHONE..........................713 956-5936
Dave Lymberopoulos, *President*
Mike Pry, *Mfg Mgr*
John Collins, *Purchasing*
Andrew Kadavy, *Engineer*
Julian Shepherd, *Engineer*
▲ EMP: 26
SALES (est): 13.9MM **Privately Held**
WEB: www.safoco.com
SIC: 3533 Oil & gas field machinery

(G-11729)
SAGL ENTERPRISES INC
Also Called: Travisoft
24 Greenway Plz Ste 800 (77046-2407)
PHONE..........................281 496-3737
Lauren W Fischer, *CEO*
Lauren William Fischer, *CEO*
Lauren Fischer, *Managing Dir*
Jerry Walker, *QA Dir*
Michael Matthews, *Engineer*
EMP: 26
SQ FT: 9,500
SALES (est): 2.3MM
SALES (corp-wide): 3.4B **Privately Held**
WEB: www.travisoft.com
SIC: 7372 7371 Business oriented computer software; custom computer programming services
HQ: Volaris Group Inc
5060 Spectrum Way Suite 100
Mississauga ON L4W 5
647 951-9345

(G-11730)
SAIFEE CORPORATION
Also Called: AAA Pallet
1220 Shotwell St (77020-7349)
PHONE..........................713 674-2000
EMP: 20
SALES (est): 3.9MM **Privately Held**
WEB: www.houstonpallets.com
SIC: 2448 Pallets, wood

(G-11731)
SAINT ARNOLD BREWING COMPANY
2000 Lyons Ave (77020-2028)
PHONE..........................713 686-9494
Brock Wagner, *President*
Justin Earnest, *Plant Engr*
Donny Kilbourn, *CFO*
Kelsey Lamb, *Regl Sales Mgr*
Ashlyn Alaniz, *Sales Staff*
▲ EMP: 9
SQ FT: 18,000
SALES (est): 2.3MM **Privately Held**
WEB: www.saintarnold.com
SIC: 2082 5149 Beer (alcoholic beverage); groceries & related products

(G-11732)
SAIPEM AMERICA INC (HQ)
1311 Broadfield Blvd Fl 6 (77084-5186)
PHONE..........................281 552-5600

Massimo Ferraris, *Ch of Bd*
Fabio Bini, *Principal*
Roberto Noce, *Business Mgr*
Vincenvo Auciello, *Corp Secy*
Jaideep Chowdhary, *Project Dir*
◆ EMP: 192
SALES (est): 199.3MM
SALES (corp-wide): 3B **Privately Held**
SIC: 8711 1389 Marine engineering; oil field services
PA: Saipem Spa
Via Martiri Di Cefalonia 67
San Donato Milanese MI 20097
024 423-1

(G-11733)
SALCO PRODUCTS INC
11747 Windfern Rd Ste 500 (77064-4883)
PHONE..........................630 783-2570
Mike Ott, *Vice Pres*
EMP: 30
SALES (corp-wide): 49.3MM **Privately Held**
WEB: www.salcoproducts.com
SIC: 3743 5013 Railroad equipment; motor vehicle supplies & new parts
PA: Salco Products Inc.
1385 101st St Ste A
Lemont IL 60439
630 783-2570

(G-11734)
SALT CREEK MIDSTREAM LLC
20329 State Highway 249 4thf (77070-2655)
PHONE..........................281 655-3200
Garrett Mecke, *Mng Member*
Dave Cooke, *Administration*
EMP: 14
SALES (est): 566.2K
SALES (corp-wide): 933.5K **Privately Held**
SIC: 1389 Building oil & gas well foundations on site
HQ: Scm Intermediate Holdco, Llc
20329 State Highway 249 # 4
Houston TX 77070
281 655-3200

(G-11735)
SALZGTTER MNNSMANN STNLESS TBE
12050 W Little York Rd (77041-4503)
PHONE..........................713 466-7278
Michael Bellinghausen, *CEO*
Anthony Thurman, *President*
Jean-Christop Chassaigne, *Managing Dir*
Gro Ansicht Gian, *Managing Dir*
Aaron Hemund, *Managing Dir*
◆ EMP: 95
SQ FT: 140,000
SALES (est): 62MM
SALES (corp-wide): 9.4B **Privately Held**
WEB: www.mannesmann-stainless-tubes.com
SIC: 5051 3356 3317 Pipe & tubing, steel; lead & zinc; tubes, seamless steel
HQ: Mannesmann Stainless Tubes Gmbh
Wiesenstr. 36
Mulheim An Der Ruhr 45473

(G-11736)
SAM AND SAB INC
Also Called: Total Innvtive Cntrls Solution
6919 Maynard Rd (77041)
PHONE..........................713 983-7500
Meherun N Ahmed, *President*
Al Ahmed, *Treasurer*
EMP: 22 EST: 2008
SQ FT: 5,000
SALES (est): 2.5MM **Privately Held**
SIC: 3694 8711 Engine electrical equipment; engineering services

(G-11737)
SAMCO ENTERPRISES INC (PA)
16115 Aldine Westfield Rd (77032-1305)
P.O. Box 60829 (77205-0829)
PHONE..........................281 443-6505
Frances E Frisby, *President*
Joel Frisby III, *Vice Pres*
Denise Lavoi, *Vice Pres*
Vicki Levering, *Vice Pres*
Robert Chapman, *Sales Associate*
EMP: 20
SQ FT: 400,000 **Privately Held**

WEB: www.samcoenterprises.com
SIC: 7699 3491 5084 5085 Valve repair, industrial; pressure valves & regulators, industrial; compressors, except air conditioning; industrial supplies

(G-11738)
SAMCO SALES INC
7444 Calhoun Rd (77033-3409)
PHONE..........................713 733-5700
Ray Cortez, *President*
Monica Cortez, *Sales Executive*
Randy Cortez, *Marketing Mgr*
▲ EMP: 10
SQ FT: 13,000
SALES (est): 5.4MM **Privately Held**
WEB: www.samcosales.com
SIC: 3462 Iron & steel forgings

(G-11739)
SAMEDAN OIL CORPORATION (PA)
Also Called: Noble Energy
1001 Noble Energy Way (77070-1435)
P.O. Box 909, Ardmore OK (73402-0909)
PHONE..........................580 223-4110
Charles D Davidson, *CEO*
Chris Michel, *Vice Pres*
Kathy Estep, *Accountant*
Reba Reid, *Senior Mgr*
EMP: 13
SALES (est): 134.7MM **Privately Held**
WEB: www.nblenergy.com
SIC: 1311 Crude petroleum production; natural gas production

(G-11740)
SAMUEL SON & CO (USA) INC
5022 Ashley Ct (77041-6911)
PHONE..........................713 462-5000
Delfi Boone, *Sales Staff*
Jim Conn, *Manager*
EMP: 60
SALES (corp-wide): 1.8B **Privately Held**
WEB: www.samuel.com
SIC: 5051 3291 Steel; abrasive metal & steel products
HQ: Samuel, Son & Co. (Usa) Inc.
1401 Davey Rd Ste 300
Woodridge IL 60517
630 783-8900

(G-11741)
SANARE ENERGY PARTNERS LLC
777 N Eldridge Pkwy # 300 (77079-4524)
PHONE..........................713 626-9696
Robert Bob Gerdes, *President*
Avery Alcorn, *CFO*
Wade Smith, *Marketing Staff*
EMP: 15 EST: 2017
SALES (est): 40MM **Privately Held**
WEB: www.sanarepartners.com
SIC: 1382 Oil & gas exploration services
PA: Orinoco Natural Resources, Llc
192 Summerfield Ct # 203
Roanoke VA 24019
713 626-9696

(G-11742)
SANCHEZ OIL & GAS CORPORATION (PA)
1360 Post Oak Blvd # 2400 (77056-3052)
PHONE..........................713 783-8000
Antonio R Sanchez Jr, *Ch of Bd*
Patricio D Sanchez, *President*
Gerry Willinger, *Managing Prtnr*
Patricio Sanchez, *COO*
Cameron W George, *Exec VP*
EMP: 150
SALES (est): 396.4MM **Privately Held**
WEB: www.sanchezog.com
SIC: 1382 Oil & gas exploration services

(G-11743)
SANCHEZ OIL & GAS CORPORATION
1111 Bagy 1600 (77002)
PHONE..........................713 783-8000
Bill Mortellaro, *Superintendent*
Richard Taylor, *Superintendent*
Patricio Sanchez, *Exec VP*
Scott Dunlap, *VP Opers*
Jordan Robison, *Production*
EMP: 33

SALES (corp-wide): 396.4MM **Privately Held**
WEB: www.sanchezog.com
SIC: 1382 Oil & gas exploration services
PA: Sanchez Oil & Gas Corporation
1360 Post Oak Blvd # 2400
Houston TX 77056
713 783-8000

(G-11744)
SANCUS ENERGY AND POWER LLC (PA)
11767 Katy Fwy Ste 700 (77079-1715)
PHONE..........................832 460-1000
EMP: 32 EST: 2011
SALES (est): 14MM **Privately Held**
WEB: www.sancusenergy.com
SIC: 8731 1389 1623 Natural resource research; haulage, oil field; natural gas compressor station construction

(G-11745)
SANDALWOOD EXPLORATION LP
1220 Augusta Dr Ste 400 (77057-2262)
PHONE..........................713 759-6095
John F Ligon, *Partner*
EMP: 12
SQ FT: 10,000
SALES (est): 1.4MM **Privately Held**
WEB: www.soginc.net
SIC: 1382 Oil & gas exploration services

(G-11746)
SANDALWOOD OIL & GAS INC (PA)
1220 Augusta Dr Ste 400 (77057-2262)
PHONE..........................713 759-6095
Phil Fleming, *Vice Pres*
Donald Lindberg, *CFO*
John F Ligon, *Mng Member*
James A Cisarik, *Vice Pres*
Donald J Lindberg, *Vice Pres*
EMP: 12
SQ FT: 10,000
SALES (est): 2.3MM **Privately Held**
WEB: www.soginc.net
SIC: 1382 1311 Oil & gas exploration services; crude petroleum & natural gas production; crude petroleum production; natural gas production

(G-11747)
SANI-WELD INC
1614 Isom St (77039-5310)
PHONE..........................281 442-0667
Douglas Manchester, *President*
Barbara Manchester, *Vice Pres*
Neil Manchester, *Executive*
Cecilia Montgomery, *Executive*
EMP: 25
SQ FT: 10,000
SALES (est): 5MM **Privately Held**
WEB: www.sani-weld.com
SIC: 3443 3556 Fabricated plate work (boiler shop); food products machinery

(G-11748)
SANITIZENOW INC
10502 Fallstone Rd (77099-4302)
PHONE..........................602 699-3150
Mary Bolouri, *President*
EMP: 37
SALES (est): 2.4MM **Privately Held**
WEB: www.sanitizenow.co
SIC: 2842 Sanitation preparations

(G-11749)
SANTOS CMI INC (USA)
400 N Sam Houston Pkwy E # 590 (77060-3568)
P.O. Box 580127 (77258-0127)
PHONE..........................713 273-4140
Fernando Rivera, *Director*
EMP: 10
SALES (est): 520.9K **Privately Held**
WEB: www.santoscmi.com
SIC: 3674 1389 Thermoelectric devices, solid state; building oil & gas well foundations on site

▲ = Import ▼=Export
◆ =Import/Export

(G-11750)
SARACEN ENERGY ADVISORS LP
3033 W Alabama St (77098-2001)
PHONE................................713 285-2900
Neil Kelley, *Partner*
Michael Kusch, *Partner*
EMP: 13
SALES (est): 2.3MM **Privately Held**
WEB: www.saracenenergy.com
SIC: 1311 Crude petroleum & natural gas

(G-11751)
SARATOGA RESOURCES INC (PA)
9225 Katy Fwy Ste 100 (77024-1521)
P.O. Box 79962 (77279-8962)
PHONE................................713 458-1560
Thomas F Cooke, *Ch of Bd*
Randal B McDonald Jr, *VP Finance*
EMP: 10
SALES (est): 54.3MM **Publicly Held**
WEB: www.saratogaresources.com
SIC: 1311 1382 Crude petroleum production; oil & gas exploration services

(G-11752)
SARBALI ALLOYS LLC
8860 Scranton St (77075-1009)
PHONE................................281 384-3500
Irfan Patel, *Mng Member*
▲ **EMP:** 23
SALES (est): 9.7MM **Privately Held**
SIC: 3341 Aluminum smelting & refining (secondary)

(G-11753)
SASOL (USA) CORPORATION (HQ)
12120 Wickchester Ln (77079-1211)
PHONE................................281 588-3000
Mike Thomas, *President*
Jon Harris, *Exec VP*
Vuyo Kahla, *Exec VP*
Charles Staggs, *Project Mgr*
Mark Borel, *Opers Staff*
EMP: 14
SALES (est): 300.5MM
SALES (corp-wide): 10.7MM **Privately Held**
WEB: www.sasolnorthamerica.com
SIC: 1382 Oil & gas exploration services
PA: Sasol Ltd
Sasol Place
Gauteng GP 2146
103 445-000

(G-11754)
SASOL CHEMICALS (USA) LLC
11821 East Fwy Ste 600 (77029-1960)
PHONE................................713 428-5652
EMP: 186
SALES (corp-wide): 10.7MM **Privately Held**
WEB: www.sasolnorthamerica.com
SIC: 2869 5169 Alcohols, industrial: denatured (non-beverage); detergents & soaps, except specialty cleaning
HQ: Sasol Chemicals (Usa) Llc
12120 Wickchester Ln
Houston TX 77079
281 588-3000

(G-11755)
SASOL CHEMICALS (USA) LLC
1914 Haden Rd (77015-6408)
PHONE................................713 428-5400
EMP: 140
SALES (corp-wide): 10.7MM **Privately Held**
WEB: www.sasolnorthamerica.com
SIC: 2869 2819 Industrial organic chemicals; industrial inorganic chemicals
HQ: Sasol Chemicals (Usa) Llc
12120 Wickchester Ln
Houston TX 77079
281 588-3000

(G-11756)
SASOL CHEMICALS (USA) LLC (HQ)
Also Called: Ceralox Division
12120 Wickchester Ln (77079-1211)
P.O. Box 19029 (77224-9029)
PHONE................................281 588-3000

Michael S Thomas, *President*
Eric Roper, *General Mgr*
Alan Cameron, *Managing Dir*
Herbert Peters, *Managing Dir*
Susan N Vanderwalt, *Principal*
◆ **EMP:** 249
SQ FT: 120,000
SALES (est): 350MM
SALES (corp-wide): 10.7MM **Privately Held**
WEB: www.sasolnorthamerica.com
SIC: 2869 5169 Alcohols, industrial: denatured (non-beverage); detergents & soaps, except specialty cleaning
PA: Sasol Ltd
Sasol Place
Gauteng GP 2146
103 445-000

(G-11757)
SASOL CHEMICALS NORTH AMER LLC
12120 Wickchester Ln (77079-1211)
PHONE................................281 588-3000
David Constable, *CEO*
Tim Bennett, *President*
Michael Sthomas, *President*
Pat Quinlan, *Principal*
Ted Lelek, *Vice Pres*
◆ **EMP:** 16
SALES (est): 12.7MM
SALES (corp-wide): 10.7MM **Privately Held**
WEB: www.sasolnorthamerica.com
SIC: 2869 Industrial organic chemicals
HQ: Sasol (Usa) Corporation
12120 Wickchester Ln
Houston TX 77079
281 588-3000

(G-11758)
SAUDI BASIC INDUSTRIES CORP
19706 Gulfwind Dr (77094-2932)
PHONE................................713 532-4999
EMP: 10
SALES (est): 1MM **Privately Held**
SIC: 3241 Mfg Hydraulic Cement

(G-11759)
SAVANT ALASKA LLC (HQ)
4601 Washington Ave # 220 (77007-5471)
P.O. Box 112212, Anchorage AK (99511-2212)
PHONE................................907 868-1258
Mary Rush, *Manager*
Carl F Giesler Jr,
EMP: 46
SALES (est): 224.9K
SALES (corp-wide): 70.5MM **Privately Held**
SIC: 8621 1311 Professional membership organizations; crude petroleum & natural gas production
PA: Glacier Oil & Gas Corp.
188 W Nthrn Lghts Blvd St
Anchorage AK 99503
832 658-2200

(G-11760)
SAXET PETROLEUM INC
510 Bering Dr Ste 600 (77057-1472)
PHONE................................713 783-4883
Robert E O'Brien, *President*
Brian E O'Brien, *Chairman*
John T Brim, *Exec VP*
Sia Wells, *Vice Pres*
Walker R Colt, *Engineer*
EMP: 12
SALES (est): 1MM **Privately Held**
WEB: www.riplpsaxet.com
SIC: 1382 Oil & gas exploration services

(G-11761)
SAXON ENGINEERING INC
Also Called: Saxon Technologies
6946 Signat Dr (77041-2719)
PHONE................................713 466-7500
Steven Parker-Smith, *President*
Charles Southern, *Plant Mgr*
Caroline Smith, *Bookkeeper*
EMP: 40
SQ FT: 12,000
SALES (est): 6.7MM **Privately Held**
WEB: www.saxontechnologies.com
SIC: 3599 Machine shop, jobbing & repair

(G-11762)
SBM OFFSHORE USA INC (HQ)
Also Called: Imodco Services
1255 Enclave Pkwy (77077-1846)
PHONE................................281 848-6000
Bruno Chabas, *CEO*
Stein Rasmussen, *President*
Miguel Hernandez, *Business Mgr*
Alexander Baume, *Vice Pres*
Steve Leverette, *Vice Pres*
◆ **EMP:** 300
SQ FT: 80,000
SALES (est): 57.6MM
SALES (corp-wide): 3.3B **Privately Held**
WEB: www.sbmoffshore.com
SIC: 1382 Oil & gas exploration services
PA: Sbm Offshore N.V.
Evert Van De Beekstraat 1
Luchthaven Schiphol
202 363-000

(G-11763)
SBU GROUP LP
Also Called: Apollo Distributors
10852 Kinghurst Dr (77099-3415)
PHONE................................281 564-6464
Sushma Verma, *President*
▲ **EMP:** 19
SQ FT: 19,000
SALES (est): 5.4MM **Privately Held**
WEB: www.apollobeauty.com
SIC: 2653 Corrugated boxes, partitions, display items, sheets & pad

(G-11764)
SCALE FREE COMPANY INC
16420 W Hardy Rd Ste 100 (77060-6227)
PHONE................................281 873-5555
Belinda Denman, *President*
Leonard Olavessen, *Manager*
EMP: 16
SALES (est): 362.5K **Privately Held**
SIC: 2899 Chemical preparations

(G-11765)
SCHENCK PROCESS LLC
Also Called: Mac Flotronics
13813 Fm 529 Rd (77041-2520)
PHONE................................816 891-9300
Colin Mattox, *Manager*
EMP: 70
SQ FT: 67,855
SALES (corp-wide): 177.9K **Privately Held**
WEB: www.schenckprocess.com
SIC: 3535 3823 3625 Pneumatic tube conveyor systems; industrial instrmnts msrmnt display/control process variable; relays & industrial controls
HQ: Schenck Process Llc
7901 Nw 107th Ter
Kansas City MO 64153
816 891-9300

(G-11766)
SCHLUMBERGER INTERNATIONAL (DH)
Also Called: Reed Tool
7030 Ardmore St (77054-2302)
PHONE................................713 747-4000
Gilbert H Tausch, *Ch of Bd*
Robert J Caldwell, *President*
Rene Huck, *President*
Ron Macinnes, *President*
Merle C Muckleroy, *President*
EMP: 600 **EST:** 1942
SQ FT: 536,000
SALES (est): 911.2MM **Publicly Held**
SIC: 1389 3561 3492 3533 Oil field services; pumps, oil well & field; fluid power valves & hose fittings; oil & gas field machinery
HQ: Schlumberger Technology Corp
300 Schlumberger Dr
Sugar Land TX 77478
281 285-8500

(G-11767)
SCHLUMBERGER LIMITED (HQ)
5599 San Felipe St Fl 17 (77056-2790)
PHONE................................713 513-2000
Olivier Le Peuch, *CEO*
Paal Kibsgaard, *Ch of Bd*
Ashok Belani, *President*
Donald Ross, *President*
Rajeev Sonthalia, *President*

EMP: 40
SALES: 23.6B **Publicly Held**
WEB: www.slb.com
SIC: 1381 1389 1382 3825 Directional drilling oil & gas wells; well logging; geophysical exploration, oil & gas field; geological exploration, oil & gas field; measuring instruments & meters, electric; meters: electric, pocket, portable, panelboard, etc.; controls, revolution & timing instruments; counters, revolution & timing instruments; counters, revolution; data loggers, industrial process type

(G-11768)
SCHLUMBERGER LIMITED
1430 Enclave Pkwy (77077-2499)
PHONE................................713 513-2000
Casey Henry, *Manager*
EMP: 19 **Publicly Held**
WEB: www.smith.com
SIC: 1381 1389 1382 Directional drilling oil & gas wells; well logging; geophysical exploration, oil & gas field; geological exploration, oil & gas field
HQ: Schlumberger Limited
5599 San Felipe St Fl 17
Houston TX 77056
713 513-2000

(G-11769)
SCHLUMBERGER NORGE AS
Also Called: Reslink
1121 Buschong St (77039-1102)
PHONE................................281 227-9854
Terje Gunneroed, *Branch Mgr*
EMP: 15
SQ FT: 17,952 **Publicly Held**
WEB: www.slb.ru
SIC: 3533 Oil field machinery & equipment; gas field machinery & equipment
HQ: Schlumberger Norge As
Risabergvegen 3
Tananger 4056
519 460-00

(G-11770)
SCHLUMBERGER OMNES INC (DH)
5599 San Felipe St Fl 17 (77056-2790)
PHONE................................713 375-3400
Paal Kibsgaard, *CEO*
Xavier Flinois, *President*
Andrew Gould, *Chairman*
Tiffany Chestnut, *Warehouse Mgr*
Vincent Gerstner, *Engineer*
EMP: 298
SQ FT: 22,500
SALES (est): 24.8B **Publicly Held**
SIC: 1382 1389 Oil & gas exploration services; construction, repair & dismantling services
HQ: Schlumberger Limited
5599 San Felipe St Fl 17
Houston TX 77056
713 513-2000

(G-11771)
SCHLUMBERGER RIG TECH INC (DH)
Also Called: I D M Controls
6650 Bingle Rd (77092-1105)
PHONE................................713 849-1700
EMP: 97 **EST:** 1973
SALES (est): 16.9MM **Publicly Held**
WEB: www.omron.com
SIC: 7629 5063 3625 Electronic equipment repair; motor controls, starters & relays: electric; motor controls, electric
HQ: Schlumberger Limited
5599 San Felipe St Fl 17
Houston TX 77056
713 513-2000

(G-11772)
SCHLUMBERGER TECHNOLOGY CORP
1200 Enclave Pkwy (77077-1764)
PHONE................................832 310-2155
EMP: 148 **Publicly Held**
SIC: 1382 Oil/Gas Exploration Services
HQ: Schlumberger Technology Corp
100 Gillingham Ln
Sugar Land TX 77478
281 285-8500

(G-11773)
SCHLUMBERGER TECHNOLOGY CORP
6350 W Sam Houston Pkwy N # 200
(77041-5172)
PHONE.....................713 482-0700
Ed Siebirps, *Branch Mgr*
EMP: 200 **Publicly Held**
SIC: 1389 Oil field services
HQ: Schlumberger Technology Corp
300 Schlumberger Dr
Sugar Land TX 77478
281 285-8500

(G-11774)
SCHLUMBERGER TECHNOLOGY CORP
Also Called: Geoquest
5599 San Felipe St # 100 (77056-2724)
PHONE.....................713 513-2000
Ihab Toma, *Manager*
Reggie Montemayor, *Manager*
EMP: 350 **Publicly Held**
SIC: 1389 Oil field services
HQ: Schlumberger Technology Corp
300 Schlumberger Dr
Sugar Land TX 77478
281 285-8500

(G-11775)
SCHLUMBERGER TECHNOLOGY CORP
5599 San Felipe St Fl 16 (77056-2790)
PHONE.....................713 513-2000
Nick Causton, *Branch Mgr*
EMP: 31 **Publicly Held**
SIC: 1389 Oil field services
HQ: Schlumberger Technology Corp
300 Schlumberger Dr
Sugar Land TX 77478
281 285-8500

(G-11776)
SCHLUMBERGER TECHNOLOGY CORP
Also Called: Schlumberger, Well Completions
7275 Grand Blvd (77054-3409)
PHONE.....................713 747-1040
EMP: 35 **Privately Held**
SIC: 3533 Mfg Oil Field Equipment
HQ: Schlumberger Technology Corp
100 Gillingham Ln
Sugar Land TX 77478
281 285-8500

(G-11777)
SCHLUMBERGER TECHNOLOGY CORP
Also Called: Schlumberger, Well Completions
7030 Ardmore St (77054-2302)
PHONE.....................713 747-4000
Bobby Reagan, *Production*
Peter Goode, *Branch Mgr*
EMP: 40 **Publicly Held**
SIC: 1389 Oil field services
HQ: Schlumberger Technology Corp
300 Schlumberger Dr
Sugar Land TX 77478
281 285-8500

(G-11778)
SCHLUMBERGER TECHNOLOGY CORP
Schlumberger Oilfield Services
4646 W Sam Houston Pkwy N
(77041-8214)
PHONE.....................281 285-1300
Gary Kolstad, *Vice Pres*
EMP: 100 **Publicly Held**
SIC: 1389 Oil field services
HQ: Schlumberger Technology Corp
300 Schlumberger Dr
Sugar Land TX 77478
281 285-8500

(G-11779)
SCHLUMBERGER TECHNOLOGY CORP
4501 S Pinemont Dr # 106 (77041-9328)
PHONE.....................281 285-3501
EMP: 139 **Privately Held**
SIC: 1382 Oil/Gas Exploration Svcs

HQ: Schlumberger Technology Corp
100 Gillingham Ln
Sugar Land TX 77478
281 285-8500

(G-11780)
SCHLUMBERGER TECHNOLOGY CORP
3600 Briarpark Dr (77042-5206)
PHONE.....................281 285-8500
Melodie Hebert, *Branch Mgr*
Carlos Sanchez, *Manager*
EMP: 139 **Publicly Held**
SIC: 1382 1389 3533 3586 Geophysical exploration, oil & gas field; geological exploration, oil & gas field; well logging; cementing oil & gas well casings; pumping of oil & gas wells; oil field services; oil & gas field machinery; measuring & dispensing pumps
HQ: Schlumberger Technology Corp
300 Schlumberger Dr
Sugar Land TX 77478
281 285-8500

(G-11781)
SCHNEIDER ELC SYSTEMS USA INC (HQ)
Also Called: Invensys Process Systems
10900 Equity Dr (77041-8226)
PHONE.....................713 329-1600
Michael J Caliel, *President*
Jay S Ehle, *Vice Pres*
Gary Frebjeger, *Vice Pres*
Victoria Jule, *Vice Pres*
Peter Kent, *Vice Pres*
▲ EMP: 60
SQ FT: 5,500
SALES (est): 904.4MM
SALES (corp-wide): 177.9K **Privately Held**
WEB: www.se.com
SIC: 3822 Temperature controls, automatic; refrigeration controls (pressure); refrigeration/air-conditioning defrost controls; humidity controls, air-conditioning types
PA: Schneider Electric Se
35 Rue Joseph Monier
Rueil Malmaison
146 046-982

(G-11782)
SCHNEIDER ELECTRIC IT USA INC
Also Called: Gutor North America
12121 Wickchester Ln # 40 (77079-1230)
PHONE.....................888 994-8867
EMP: 20
SALES (corp-wide): 177.9K **Privately Held**
WEB: www.apc.ru
SIC: 3679 Mfg Electronic Components
HQ: Schneider Electric It Usa, Inc.
70 Mechanic St
Foxboro MA 02035

(G-11783)
SCHUMACHER COMPANY INC
5610 Polk St (77023-2191)
PHONE.....................713 923-5548
Andrew Schumacher, *President*
Brittany Leigh, *Vice Pres*
Lorna Sullivan, *Human Res Mgr*
Victor Gonzalez, *Manager*
Jerry Heavin, *Info Tech Mgr*
▲ EMP: 85
SALES (est): 12.7MM
SALES (corp-wide): 15.6MM **Privately Held**
WEB: www.schumachercoinc.com
SIC: 3471 Electroplating of metals or formed products
PA: Schumacher International, Inc.
5610 Polk St
Houston TX 77023
713 923-5548

(G-11784)
SCHUMACHER INTERNATIONAL INC (PA)
5610 Polk St (77023-2106)
PHONE.....................713 923-5548
Andrew Schumacher, *President*
Hazel Smith, *President*

Mindy Birnbaum, *Purch Agent*
James Hollingsworth, *Director*
Donna J Parks, *Admin Sec*
EMP: 16 EST: 1941
SALES (est): 15.6MM **Privately Held**
WEB: www.schumachercoinc.com
SIC: 3471 3479 Electroplating & plating; painting, coating & hot dipping

(G-11785)
SCHWEITZER ENGRG LABS INC
10110 W Sam Houston Pkwy (77064-7508)
PHONE.....................509 334-8154
Richard Kirby, *Engineer*
Pratik Patel, *Engineer*
Dharmendra Prajapati, *Engineer*
Sasikala Sreerama, *Engineer*
EMP: 22
SALES (corp-wide): 986.7MM **Privately Held**
WEB: www.selinc.com
SIC: 3825 Instruments to measure electricity
PA: Schweitzer Engineering Laboratories Inc.
2350 Ne Hopkins Ct
Pullman WA 99163
509 332-1890

(G-11786)
SCIENTIFIC DRILLING INTL INC (PA)
16071 Grnspint Pk Dr Ste (77060)
P.O. Box 301036, Dallas (75303-1036)
PHONE.....................281 443-3300
Pamela S Pierce, *President*
Dana Armstrong, *Senior VP*
Daniel R Carter, *Senior VP*
Dr Gerald Heisig, *Senior VP*
Douglas McGregor, *Senior VP*
◆ EMP: 120
SQ FT: 25,000
SALES (est): 20.8MM **Privately Held**
WEB: www.scientificdrilling.com
SIC: 1381 1389 Directional drilling oil & gas wells; surveying wells

(G-11787)
SCIENTIFIC DRILLING INTL INC
Also Called: Houston Technology Center
1100 Rankin Rd (77073-4716)
PHONE.....................281 214-7600
Gerald Heisig, *Branch Mgr*
EMP: 38
SALES (corp-wide): 20.8MM **Privately Held**
WEB: www.scientificdrilling.com
SIC: 1381 Drilling oil & gas wells
PA: Scientific Drilling International, Inc.
16071 Grnspint Pk Dr Ste
Houston TX 77060
281 443-3300

(G-11788)
SCOMI EQUIPMENT INC (HQ)
6607 Theall Rd (77066-1213)
PHONE.....................281 260-6016
Shah Hakim Zain, *CEO*
Michael Kent Walker, *President*
Stephen Fredrick Bracker, *Vice Pres*
David Gergen, *Technical Mgr*
Perry Lyman, *Engineer*
◆ EMP: 20
SQ FT: 5,000
SALES (est): 89.4MM **Privately Held**
WEB: www.scomiequipment.com
SIC: 1389 Oil field services

(G-11789)
SCORPION OILTOOLS INC
13913 Faber St (77037-1921)
PHONE.....................281 999-2222
Jacob Baryam, *CEO*
Ben Engelhart, *General Mgr*
▲ EMP: 20
SALES (est): 6.7MM **Privately Held**
WEB: www.scorpion.com
SIC: 3533 Oil & gas field machinery

(G-11790)
SCOTIA GROUP INC (PA)
411 N Sam Houston Pkwy E # 130
(77060-3545)
PHONE.....................281 448-6188
▲ EMP: 12 EST: 1981
SQ FT: 7,897

SALES (est): 13.1MM **Privately Held**
SIC: 1389 Oil consultants

(G-11791)
SCOTT FETZER COMPANY
4300 Windfern Rd (77041-8942)
PHONE.....................713 996-7331
Tim Wiggins, *Branch Mgr*
EMP: 176
SALES (corp-wide): 254.6B **Publicly Held**
WEB: www.scottfetzer.com
SIC: 3635 Household vacuum cleaners
HQ: The Scott Fetzer Company
28800 Clemens Rd
Westlake OH 44145
440 892-3000

(G-11792)
SCOTTS MIRACLE-GRO COMPANY
16518 Aldine Westfield Rd (77032-1363)
PHONE.....................281 821-1022
William McCain, *Manager*
EMP: 39
SALES (corp-wide): 4.1B **Publicly Held**
WEB: www.scottsmiraclegro.com
SIC: 2873 Nitrogenous fertilizers
PA: The Scotts Miracle-Gro Company
14111 Scottslawn Rd
Marysville OH 43040
937 644-0011

(G-11793)
SCRUPLES PROF SALON PDTS INC
20411 Imperial Valley Dr (77073-5504)
PHONE.....................952 469-4646
Frank Liguori, *CEO*
Jack Storey, *Ch of Bd*
Tracy Ligouri Lubeley, *Co-President*
Mia Ligouri McHugh, *Co-President*
Michael Riley, *COO*
▲ EMP: 40
SALES (est): 9.8MM **Privately Held**
WEB: www.scrupleshaircare.com
SIC: 2844 Shampoos, rinses, conditioners: hair

(G-11794)
SDRG CONTROLS INC
8234 Braniff St (77061-5204)
P.O. Box 750681 (77275-0681)
PHONE.....................713 242-0822
Paul Doland, *President*
Alex Obrazstov, *Vice Pres*
Jeff Bihl, *Engineer*
Meredithe Moore, *Admin Sec*
EMP: 10
SQ FT: 6,000
SALES (est): 1.6MM **Privately Held**
WEB: www.sdrg.com
SIC: 3613 8711 Control panels, electric; electrical or electronic engineering

(G-11795)
SEA EAGLE FORD LLC
1155 Dairy Ashford Rd # 2 (77079-3021)
PHONE.....................720 390-6244
Eric McCrady, *President*
Grace Ford, *COO*
Cathy Anderson, *CFO*
Alexander Hunter III, *Admin Sec*
EMP: 39
SQ FT: 1,200
SALES (est): 914.5K
SALES (corp-wide): 203.5MM **Publicly Held**
WEB: www.sundanceenergy.net
SIC: 1382 1311 Oil & gas exploration services; crude petroleum & natural gas
PA: Sundance Energy, Inc.
1050 17th St Ste 700
Denver CO 80265
303 543-5700

(G-11796)
SEABED GEOSOLUTIONS (US) INC (PA)
10350 Richmond Ave # 800 (77042-4129)
PHONE.....................713 904-2244
Gabriel Pommier, *Chief*
Martin Hartland, *Exec VP*
Laurie Wigle, *Exec VP*
Kjetil Ramsoy, *CFO*

Jeremie Le Moal, *CFO*
EMP: 30
SQ FT: 23,000
SALES (est): 19.3MM **Privately Held**
WEB: www.seabed-geo.com
SIC: 1382 Geophysical exploration, oil & gas field

(G-11797)
SEABOARD HOLDINGS INC (DH)
Also Called: Weir Seaboard
13822 Furman Rd (77047-4626)
P.O. Box 450989 (77245-0989)
PHONE..................................713 644-3535
J Kelly Joy, *President*
Joe McNeill, *Manager*
▲ **EMP:** 45
SALES (est): 43.5MM
SALES (corp-wide): 3.4B **Privately Held**
WEB: www.global.weir
SIC: 3533 Oil field machinery & equipment

(G-11798)
SEABOARD INTERNATIONAL INC (DH)
Also Called: Weir Seaboard International
13815 South Fwy (77047-1941)
P.O. Box 450989 (77245-0989)
PHONE..................................713 644-3535
Kelly Joy, *CEO*
Nick Martin, *President*
Steve Noon, *President*
Marcus Poyer, *District Mgr*
Stephen Christie, *Vice Pres*
◆ **EMP:** 55
SQ FT: 2,500
SALES (est): 34.3MM
SALES (corp-wide): 3.4B **Privately Held**
WEB: www.global.weir
SIC: 3533 3491 Oil field machinery & equipment; industrial valves
HQ: Seaboard Holdings, Inc.
13822 Furman Rd
Houston TX 77047
713 644-3535

(G-11799)
SEADRILL AMERICAS INC (DH)
11025 Equity Dr Ste 150 (77041-8247)
PHONE..................................713 407-8900
Ian Hope, *CEO*
Ben Bollinger, *Vice Pres*
Chris Edwards, *Vice Pres*
Jose Firmo, *Vice Pres*
William Traylor, *Vice Pres*
◆ **EMP:** 75
SQ FT: 24,500
SALES (est): 214.5MM **Privately Held**
WEB: www.seadrill.com
SIC: 1381 Drilling oil & gas wells
HQ: Seadrill Offshore As
Finnestadveien 28
Stavanger 4029
513 099-00

(G-11800)
SEAFLEX INC
14325 W Hardy Rd (77060-4616)
PHONE..................................281 448-8821
Lora Zimmer, *Office Mgr*
Andrew Townend, *Incorporator*
▲ **EMP:** 70
SQ FT: 26,000
SALES (est): 5.3MM **Privately Held**
SIC: 3842 Personal safety equipment

(G-11801)
SEAH STEEL CALIFORNIA LLC
14550 Torrey Chase Blvd # 345 (77014-1038)
PHONE..................................281 873-7800
Gene Lee, *Vice Pres*
EMP: 10 **Privately Held**
WEB: www.seahusa.com
SIC: 1389 Cementing oil & gas well casings
HQ: Seah Steel California, Llc
2100 Main St Ste 100
Irvine CA 92614
949 655-8000

(G-11802)
SEAH STEEL USA LLC (DH)
16952 Leonard Rd (77049-1800)
PHONE..................................832 734-0044

Kim Kiyong, *Controller*
Gene Lee,
◆ **EMP:** 70 **EST:** 2016
SQ FT: 1,089,000
SALES (est): 49.5MM **Privately Held**
WEB: www.seahsteelusa.com
SIC: 3547 Pipe & tube mills
HQ: Seah Steel California, Llc
2100 Main St Ste 100
Irvine CA 92614
949 655-8000

(G-11803)
SEAHAWK DRILLING INC (PA)
5 Greenway Plz Ste 2700 (77046-0512)
P.O. Box 1564, West Chester OH (45071-1564)
PHONE..................................713 369-7300
▲ **EMP:** 14 **EST:** 1994
SALES (est): 46.5MM **Privately Held**
SIC: 1381 Drilling oil & gas wells

(G-11804)
SEAL-JET OF TEXAS INC
Also Called: Metric Standards & Odds
4702 Steffani Ln (77041-7814)
P.O. Box 5407, Katy (77491-5407)
PHONE..................................713 983-7233
Talal Choukeir, *President*
▲ **EMP:** 25
SQ FT: 10,000
SALES (est): 4.2MM **Privately Held**
WEB: www.msoindustries.com
SIC: 3053 3492 Gaskets & sealing devices; fluid power valves & hose fittings

(G-11805)
SEALING TECHNOLOGY INC
11152 Westheimer Rd # 762 (77042-3208)
PHONE..................................281 330-6363
Steve Allen, *President*
EMP: 25
SQ FT: 5,000
SALES (est): 2.5MM **Privately Held**
WEB: www.sealingtechnologyinc.com
SIC: 3053 Gaskets, all materials

(G-11806)
SEATRAX INC (HQ)
13223 Fm 529 Rd (77041-2532)
P.O. Box 840687 (77284-0687)
PHONE..................................713 896-6500
William D Morrow, *President*
Tom McKinney, *Corp Secy*
John Hale, *Vice Pres*
John Pfister, *Vice Pres*
Larry Kerner, *Project Mgr*
◆ **EMP:** 325
SQ FT: 50,000
SALES (est): 123MM **Privately Held**
WEB: www.seatrax.com
SIC: 3531 3536 Cranes, ship; hoists, cranes & monorails

(G-11807)
SEATRAX INC
13218 Weiman Rd (77041-2538)
PHONE..................................713 896-6500
EMP: 11 **Privately Held**
WEB: www.seatrax.com
SIC: 3531 3536 Cranes, ship; hoists, cranes & monorails
HQ: Seatrax, Inc.
13223 Fm 529 Rd
Houston TX 77041

(G-11808)
SEAWALL SPECIALTY COMPANY INC
Also Called: Key Maps of Houston
5922 Richmond Ave Ste C (77057-6343)
PHONE..................................713 522-9064
EMP: 18
SQ FT: 3,000
SALES (est): 1.7MM **Privately Held**
SIC: 5199 5999 2741 Whol Nondurable Goods Ret Misc Merchandise Misc Publishing

(G-11809)
SEAWOLF RSWD RESOURCES LP
811 Main St Fl 18 (77002-6119)
PHONE..................................713 518-1763
Greg Heinlein, *CFO*
EMP: 12

SALES (est): 226.9K **Privately Held**
SIC: 1389 Gas field services

(G-11810)
SEAWOLF TRANSPORT LP
811 Main St Fl 18 (77002-6119)
PHONE..................................713 518-1763
Greg Heinlein, *CFO*
EMP: 12
SALES (est): 226.9K **Privately Held**
SIC: 1389 Pumping of oil & gas wells

(G-11811)
SEC ENERGY PRODUCTS & SVCS LP (DH)
9523 Frbanks N Houston Rd (77064-6212)
PHONE..................................281 890-9977
Kurt Loustalot, *President*
Ralph Gates, *Partner*
Robert Pierce, *Partner*
E Randall West, *Partner*
Randall West, *Partner*
▲ **EMP:** 32
SQ FT: 120,000
SALES (est): 97MM **Publicly Held**
WEB: www.sec-ep.com
SIC: 3563 Air & gas compressors
HQ: Etp Legacy Lp
8111 Westchester Dr # 600
Dallas TX 75225
214 981-0700

(G-11812)
SEEBRIDGE MEDIA LLC
707 West Rd (77038-2505)
PHONE..................................832 201-2000
Steve Evans, *Business Mgr*
Mark Coark, *Mng Member*
EMP: 125
SALES (est): 27MM **Privately Held**
WEB: www.thomasprintworks.com
SIC: 2752 Commercial printing, offset

(G-11813)
SEFTON STEEL LP
1830 Aldine Mail Rte (77039-5324)
P.O. Box 670407 (77267-0407)
PHONE..................................281 449-8677
Patrick Collier, *Managing Prtnr*
James Maples, *Vice Pres*
Sefton Steel Services,
EMP: 75
SQ FT: 50,000
SALES (est): 27.5MM **Privately Held**
WEB: www.seftonsteel.com
SIC: 3441 Fabricated structural metal

(G-11814)
SEIDLS BINDERY INC
8035 Blankenship Dr (77055-1075)
P.O. Box 550229 (77255-0229)
PHONE..................................713 681-3815
Bill Seidl Jr, *President*
Jean Seidl, *Vice Pres*
Debbie Redditt, *CFO*
Steven Anton, *Executive*
▲ **EMP:** 45 **EST:** 1975
SQ FT: 43,000
SALES (est): 10.9MM **Privately Held**
WEB: www.seidlsbindery.com
SIC: 2789 Trade binding services

(G-11815)
SEISMIC EQP SOLUTIONS INC
3402 Bacor Rd (77084-7206)
PHONE..................................832 288-4427
Glen Huscroft, *President*
Paul Mitcham, *Vice Pres*
Rick Luke, *CFO*
◆ **EMP:** 30
SQ FT: 10,000
SALES (est): 8MM **Privately Held**
WEB: www.globalses.com
SIC: 1382 Seismograph surveys

(G-11816)
SEISMIC EXCHANGE INC (PA)
4805 Westway Park Blvd (77041-2003)
PHONE..................................832 590-5100
P C Havens, *President*
Jeff Lester, *Vice Pres*
Shirley Ross, *Vice Pres*
Hong Messina, *Project Mgr*
Eric Schuster, *Project Mgr*
◆ **EMP:** 30
SQ FT: 12,000

SALES (est): 27.4MM **Privately Held**
WEB: www.seismicexchange.com
SIC: 1382 Seismograph surveys

(G-11817)
SEITEL
10811 Westview Dr Bldg C (77043-5047)
PHONE..................................832 295-8300
Randy Sides, *President*
Donna Anderson, *Controller*
EMP: 90
SALES (est): 3.3MM **Privately Held**
WEB: www.seitel.com
SIC: 1382 Oil & gas exploration services
HQ: Seitel Inc
10811 S Westview Circle D
Houston TX 77043
713 881-8900

(G-11818)
SEITEL INC (HQ)
10811 S Westview Circle D (77043-2748)
PHONE..................................713 881-8900
Gregory P Spivy, *Ch of Bd*
Robert D Monson, *President*
Kevin P Callaghan, *COO*
Joann Lippman, *Senior VP*
Marcia H Kendrick, *CFO*
▲ **EMP:** 22
SQ FT: 80,125
SALES (est): 90.2MM **Privately Held**
WEB: www.seitel.com
SIC: 1382 Seismograph surveys; geophysical exploration, oil & gas field

(G-11819)
SEITEL MANAGEMENT INC
10811 S Westview Cir (77043-2747)
PHONE..................................713 881-8900
Randy Stilley, *President*
Marcia Kendrick, *Principal*
EMP: 100
SALES (est): 3.7MM **Privately Held**
WEB: www.seitel.com
SIC: 1382 Oil & gas exploration services
HQ: Seitel Inc
10811 S Westview Circle D
Houston TX 77043
713 881-8900

(G-11820)
SELDON ENERGY PARTNERS LLC
6610 Malibu Dr (77092-4010)
PHONE..................................503 807-4300
Mark B Smith, *CEO*
Barry Barksdale, *Principal*
Tol Harris, *Principal*
Richard Marlin, *Principal*
Chris Portmann, *Principal*
EMP: 10 **EST:** 2011
SALES (est): 1.6MM **Privately Held**
WEB: www.seldonenergy.com
SIC: 3621 4911 Power generators; distribution, electric power

(G-11821)
SELECT ENERGY SERVICES INC (PA)
1233 West Loop S Ste 1400 (77027-9122)
P.O. Box 1715, Gainesville (76241-1715)
PHONE..................................713 235-9500
John D Schmitz, *Ch of Bd*
Eric Mattson, *Exec VP*
David Nightingale, *Exec VP*
Cody Ortowski, *Exec VP*
Paul Pistono, *Exec VP*
EMP: 81
SALES: 1.2B **Publicly Held**
WEB: www.selectenergyservices.com
SIC: 1389 Oil field services

(G-11822)
SELECT ENERGY SERVICES LLC
1233 West Loop S Ste 1400 (77027-9122)
PHONE..................................713 296-1000
Paul Pistono, *Exec VP*
Mitchell Shauf, *Senior VP*
Nate Banda, *Vice Pres*
Nathanael Banda, *Vice Pres*
Justin Briscoe, *Vice Pres*
EMP: 15

SALES (corp-wide): 1.2B **Publicly Held**
WEB: www.selectenergyservices.com
SIC: 1389 Oil field services
HQ: Select Energy Services, Llc
    1820 N I 35
    Gainesville TX 76240
    940 668-1818

(G-11823)
SELECT SANDS AMERICA CORP (PA)
363 N Sm Hstn Pkwy E 1050 (77060)
PHONE..............................501 276-5928
Zigurds Vitols, *President*
EMP: 10
SALES (est): 5.3MM **Privately Held**
WEB: www.selectsands.com
SIC: 3297 Cement refractories

(G-11824)
SELF INDUSTRIES
Also Called: Thornton Drum Ring
6900 Cavalcade St (77028-5802)
PHONE..............................713 672-2559
J Mike McDowell, *President*
Gary Waylander, *Vice Pres*
Evan Epple, *Plant Mgr*
▲ **EMP:** 22
SQ FT: 40,000
SALES (est): 4.3MM
SALES (corp-wide): 133.4MM **Privately Held**
WEB: www.selfplex.com
SIC: 3466 3412 Closures, stamped metal; metal barrels, drums & pails
HQ: The F C Thornton Company
    3491 Mary Taylor Rd
    Birmingham AL 35235
    205 655-3284

(G-11825)
SEMASYS INC (HQ)
4480 Blalock Rd (77041-9119)
PHONE..............................713 869-8331
Gary M Watts, *President*
Michael Duckworth, *Business Mgr*
Robert Watts III, *Senior VP*
Jeanna Bent, *Vice Pres*
Richard H Darnell, *Vice Pres*
▲ **EMP:** 120
SQ FT: 100,000
SALES (est): 36.8MM
SALES (corp-wide): 37.1MM **Privately Held**
WEB: www.semasys.com
SIC: 3089 3993 2759 2396 Extruded finished plastic products; displays & cutouts, window & lobby; screen printing; printing & embossing on plastics fabric articles; mail order house; partitions & fixtures, except wood
PA: Uni-Sun Inc
    4480 Blalock Rd
    Houston TX 77041
    713 869-8331

(G-11826)
SEMMT INC
3900 Essex Ln Ste 250 (77027-5181)
PHONE..............................713 966-5829
Martin Lindenberg, *President*
EMP: 9
SALES (est): 540.8K **Privately Held**
SIC: 3841 Surgical & medical instruments

(G-11827)
SENCHA INC
2950 North Loop W Ste 700 (77092-8806)
PHONE..............................713 523-4433
Randy Jacops, *CEO*
Scott Mullarkey, *Partner*
EMP: 80
SALES (est): 3.7MM
SALES (corp-wide): 137.5MM **Privately Held**
WEB: www.sencha.com
SIC: 7372 Application computer software
PA: Idera, Inc.
    2950 North Loop W Ste 700
    Houston TX 77092
    713 523-4433

(G-11828)
SENDERO INDUSTRIES LLC
6814 Thornwall St (77092-4607)
PHONE..............................713 868-6960

Anthony Cortez, *Project Mgr*
Grant R Gilbert,
EMP: 24
SALES (est): 9.3MM **Privately Held**
WEB: www.txsendero.com
SIC: 3554 Paper industries machinery

(G-11829)
SENECA RESOURCES COMPANY LLC (HQ)
1201 La St Ste 2600 (77002)
PHONE..............................713 654-2600
John P McGinnis, *President*
Steven J Conley, *Senior VP*
Justin I Loweth, *Senior VP*
Brad Elliott, *Vice Pres*
Kelly Erisman, *Purch Mgr*
EMP: 50 **EST:** 1913
SQ FT: 25,000
SALES (est): 615MM
SALES (corp-wide): 1.5B **Publicly Held**
WEB: www.natfuel.com
SIC: 1382 Oil & gas exploration services
PA: National Fuel Gas Company
    6363 Main St Ste 1
    Williamsville NY 14221
    716 857-7000

(G-11830)
SENECA RESOURCES CORPORATION
1201 Louisiana St Ste 400 (77002-5613)
PHONE..............................713 374-6300
EMP: 56
SALES (corp-wide): 1.6B **Publicly Held**
SIC: 1382 Oil/Gas Exploration Services
HQ: Seneca Resources Corporation
    1201 Louisiana St Ste 400
    Houston TX 77002
    713 654-2600

(G-11831)
SENSIA LLC (HQ)
200 Westlake Park Blvd # 1400 (77079-2682)
PHONE..............................866 773-6742
Allan Rentcome, *Mng Member*
EMP: 20
SALES (est): 57.4MM **Publicly Held**
WEB: www.sensiaglobal.com
SIC: 3533 Oil & gas field machinery

(G-11832)
SEPTH GROUP LLC
Also Called: A G Welding
8125 Mcgee Ln (77071-2260)
PHONE..............................713 988-4200
Guy Felton, *President*
Puddin Green, *Office Mgr*
EMP: 20
SQ FT: 7,000
SALES (est): 2.2MM **Privately Held**
WEB: www.agwelding.com
SIC: 7692 1791 3441 3446 Welding repair; structural steel erection; fabricated structural metal; architectural metalwork

(G-11833)
SERAMPORE INDS PRIVATE LTD INC (HQ)
Also Called: Sip Industries
8876 Gulf Fwy Ste 500 (77017-6592)
PHONE..............................713 923-6111
Tilak Agarwal, *President*
Chuck Carrigan, *Regional Mgr*
Gloria Garcia, *Sales Staff*
Blake Ortega, *Sales Staff*
Shauna Shaw, *Sales Staff*
◆ **EMP:** 40
SQ FT: 40,000
SALES (est): 10.8MM **Privately Held**
WEB: www.sipindustries.com
SIC: 3599 3494 Grinding castings for the trade; pipe fittings

(G-11834)
SERCEL INC (DH)
17200 Park Row (77084-4925)
PHONE..............................281 492-6688
◆ **EMP:** 500 **EST:** 1972
SALES (est): 127.7MM
SALES (corp-wide): 29.2MM **Privately Held**
SIC: 3829 Geophysical & meteorological testing equipment

(G-11835)
SEREMEDI INC
2450 Holcombe Blvd Ste J (77021-2041)
PHONE..............................832 671-8622
Kim Evans, *CEO*
Cody Menard, *Chief Engr*
EMP: 9
SALES (est): 503.1K **Privately Held**
WEB: www.seremedi.com
SIC: 7372 Business oriented computer software

(G-11836)
SERIMAX NORTH AMERICA LLC
Also Called: Umax Pipeline Contractors
11315 W Little York Rd # 4 (77041-4933)
PHONE..............................832 230-2700
Frederick Castrec, *President*
Sean Lynch, *Vice Pres*
Michael Bru, *Project Mgr*
Christian Loeffler, *Project Mgr*
Ted Combs, *Controller*
▲ **EMP:** 75
SQ FT: 9,000
SALES (est): 20MM
SALES (corp-wide): 5.9MM **Privately Held**
SIC: 3533 Oil & gas field machinery
HQ: Serimax Holdings
    Serimer Zone Industrielle Paris Nord 2
    Roissy En France 95700
    156 489-050

(G-11837)
SERIOUS CIGARS LLC
6608 Fm 1960 Rd W Ste D (77069-3910)
PHONE..............................281 397-9800
Ron Lesseraux, *Owner*
EMP: 9
SALES (est): 840.3K **Privately Held**
WEB: www.seriouscigars.com
SIC: 5993 2441 3911 Cigar store; cigar boxes, wood & part wood; cigar & cigarette accessories

(G-11838)
SERMATECH DYNAMIC
7615 Fairview St (77041-2111)
PHONE..............................713 849-9474
EMP: 12 **EST:** 2012
SALES (est): 1.4MM **Privately Held**
SIC: 3812 Mfg Search/Navigation Equipment

(G-11839)
SERVICE METAL PRODUCTS COMPANY
3500 E Crosstimbers St (77093-8818)
PHONE..............................281 499-3020
EMP: 32
SALES (corp-wide): 9.6MM **Privately Held**
WEB: www.servicemetal.net
SIC: 3325 Steel foundries
PA: Service Metal Products Company
    4300 Planned Indus Dr
    Saint Louis MO 63120
    314 421-1441

(G-11840)
SERVICE PHOTO COPY INC
Also Called: Service, Visual Communication
815 Walker St Ste 101 (77002-5748)
PHONE..............................713 225-1988
Judy Jo Baiamonte, *CEO*
Gene Baiamonte, *Vice Pres*
Jerry S Baiamonte, *Vice Pres*
EMP: 19
SQ FT: 4,500
SALES (est): 2MM **Privately Held**
WEB: www.downtown-houston-printing.com
SIC: 7334 2752 Photocopying & duplicating services; commercial printing, offset

(G-11841)
SEVERE SERVICE VALVE INC
2800 Post Oak Blvd (77056-6100)
PHONE..............................832 390-2380
David Watts, *Vice Pres*
Peter Jacson, *Engineer*
Xiaoyan Chen, *Manager*
▲ **EMP:** 58
SQ FT: 8,000

SALES (est): 6.5MM **Privately Held**
WEB: www.ssvvalve.com
SIC: 3491 Industrial valves

(G-11842)
SFI-GRAY STEEL LLC
Also Called: Sfi Gray Steel
3511 W 12th St (77008-6005)
PHONE..............................713 864-6450
Edward J Lehner, *CEO*
Micheal Arnold, *Principal*
Terence Rogers, *CFO*
▲ **EMP:** 3000
SQ FT: 72,000
SALES (est): 23.6MM **Publicly Held**
WEB: www.sfigray.com
SIC: 3325 5051 Steel foundries; metals service centers & offices
HQ: Joseph T. Ryerson & Son, Inc.
    227 W Monroe St Fl 27
    Chicago IL 60606
    312 292-5000

(G-11843)
SG INTERESTS I LTD (PA)
100 Waugh Dr Ste 400 (77007-5962)
PHONE..............................713 951-0100
Russell Gordy, *Principal*
Shaun Gordy, *Vice Pres*
Robert Guinn, *Vice Pres*
Sharin Scott, *Treasurer*
Julianna Adams, *Accountant*
EMP: 17
SALES (est): 23.6MM **Privately Held**
SIC: 1311 1321 Crude petroleum & natural gas; natural gas liquids

(G-11844)
SHADE SHOP INC
4122 Richmond Ave (77027-6820)
PHONE..............................713 623-0750
Claude L Sams, *President*
Elizabeth Sams, *Vice Pres*
Mitch Jarmin, *Manager*
EMP: 9
SQ FT: 6,000
SALES (est): 1.4MM **Privately Held**
WEB: www.theshadeshop.net
SIC: 5719 5023 2431 Venetian blinds; window shades; venetian blinds; window shades; vertical blinds; window covering parts & accessories; windows & window parts & trim, wood

(G-11845)
SHAREWELL LP
Also Called: Sharewell Energy Services
1111 North Loop W Ste 705 (77008-4714)
PHONE..............................281 288-2560
Thomas Wilson, *Partner*
Todd Caspary, *General Ptnr*
William Mc Crea, *Controller*
◆ **EMP:** 20
SQ FT: 4,500
SALES (est): 7.4MM **Privately Held**
WEB: www.sharewellhdd.com
SIC: 3829 3533 5082 Surveying instruments & accessories; oil field machinery & equipment; oil field equipment

(G-11846)
SHAREWELL HDD LLC
Also Called: Sharewell Hdd Services
21315 W Hardy Rd (77073-2219)
PHONE..............................281 288-2560
Todd Caspary, *CEO*
Matthew Patterson, *Controller*
Rob Coyle, *Sales Mgr*
Jess Briscoe, *Sales Staff*
William F McCrea,
EMP: 21 **EST:** 2012
SALES (est): 4.5MM **Privately Held**
WEB: www.sharewellhdd.com
SIC: 3546 Drills & drilling tools

(G-11847)
SHASTA BEVERAGES INC
Also Called: National Beverage
7333 Major St (77061-5098)
PHONE..............................713 634-0094
Randi Phelps, *Opers-Prdtn-Mfg*
EMP: 30
SQ FT: 108,900

SALES (corp-wide): 1B Publicly Held
WEB: www.shastapop.com
SIC: 2086 Soft drinks: packaged in cans, bottles, etc.
HQ: Shasta Beverages, Inc.
26901 Indl Blvd
Hayward CA 94545
954 581-0922

(G-11848)
SHAUN K BOYER
Also Called: National Buildings
11730 Aldine Westfield Rd (77093-1842)
PHONE.................................281 442-3800
Steven Reynolds, President
Shaun Boyer, Owner
Liliana Loya, Principal
Kyle Boyer, Vice Pres
EMP: 10
SQ FT: 1,000
SALES (est): 3.7MM Privately Held
WEB: www.nationalbuildings.com
SIC: 1791 5039 3448 1522 Exterior wall system installation; metal buildings; pre-fabricated metal buildings; hotel/motel & multi-family home construction

(G-11849)
SHAW ACQUISITION HOLDINGS LLC
Also Called: Shaw Group, The
19450 Sh 249 N Ste 450 (77070)
PHONE.................................337 562-3471
Michael Hibbbing, CFO
Micheal Childers, Mng Member
EMP: 750
SALES (est): 80MM Privately Held
SIC: 3498 Fabricated pipe & fittings

(G-11850)
SHAW FABRICATORS INC
7705 Hall Rd (77075-4614)
PHONE.................................713 991-5313
James Scott, General Mgr
James Bernhard Jr, Chairman
George R Shepherd, Exec VP
Robert Belk, CFO
EMP: 66
SALES (est): 934.8K
SALES (corp-wide): 8.4B Privately Held
WEB: www.cbi.com
SIC: 3498 3312 Pipe sections fabricated from purchased pipe; piping systems for pulp paper & chemical industries; blast furnaces & steel mills
HQ: Cb&I Group Inc.
757 N Eldridge Pkwy
Houston TX

(G-11851)
SHAWCOR PIPE PROTECTION LLC
Also Called: Shaw Pipeline Services
5175 World Houston Pkwy # 100 (77032-2624)
PHONE.................................281 940-0700
Les Hutchison, Branch Mgr
Dale Rampersad, Manager
EMP: 30
SALES (corp-wide): 1.1B Privately Held
WEB: www.shawcor.com
SIC: 3479 Coating or wrapping steel pipe
HQ: Shawcor Pipe Protection Llc
5875 N Sam Houston Pkwy W # 200
Houston TX 77086

(G-11852)
SHAWCOR PIPE PROTECTION LLC (DH)
5875 N Sam Houston Pkwy W # 200 (77086-1578)
PHONE.................................281 886-2350
Henri Tausch, President
Keith Crook, Vice Pres
Carlos Escobar, Vice Pres
Timothy L Hutzul, Vice Pres
Farhan Imam, Vice Pres
◆ EMP: 55
SQ FT: 10,000
SALES (est): 73.3MM
SALES (corp-wide): 1.1B Privately Held
WEB: www.shawcor.com
SIC: 3479 Coating or wrapping steel pipe

HQ: Shawcor Inc.
5875 N Sam Houston Pkwy W # 200
Houston TX 77086
281 886-2350

(G-11853)
SHAWDASHIAN GROUP LLC
7322 Suthwest Fwy Ste 710 (77074)
PHONE.................................832 649-3800
Maria Soughall-Shaw, CEO
EMP: 25
SALES (est): 1.2MM Privately Held
WEB: www.shawdashiangroup.com
SIC: 8742 2721 Marketing consulting services; magazines: publishing & printing

(G-11854)
SHD OIL & GAS LLC
1415 La St Ste 3410 (77002)
PHONE.................................713 595-4274
Demarco Bell, CEO
EMP: 19
SALES (est): 411.6K Privately Held
SIC: 1382 Oil & gas exploration services

(G-11855)
SHEARWATER GEOSERVICES INC
Also Called: Dolphin Geophysical
945 Bunker Hill Rd # 650 (77024-1364)
PHONE.................................281 921-8000
Roy Bampton, Vice Pres
Andreas Aubert, Treasurer
Stuart Denny, Sales Staff
Huy MAI, Director
EMP: 13
SALES (est): 2.5MM Privately Held
WEB: www.shearwatergeo.com
SIC: 1382 8999 Geophysical exploration, oil & gas field; geophysical consultant
PA: Dolphin Geophysical As
Damsgardsveien 131
Laksevag

(G-11856)
SHELDON INDUSTRIES INC
Also Called: Sheldon Containers
6016 Knute St (77028-4915)
P.O. Box 23066 (77228-3066)
PHONE.................................713 398-2427
Lupe Sanchez, President
Baltazar Sanchez, Vice Pres
EMP: 14 EST: 1988
SQ FT: 60,000
SALES (est): 3.2MM Privately Held
WEB: www.sheldoncontainer.com
SIC: 2631 Container board

(G-11857)
SHELL CATALYSTS & TECH LP (HQ)
910 Louisiana St Ste 2900 (77002-4911)
PHONE.................................713 241-3000
Richard H Stade, General Ptnr
Patrick Gripka, Marketing Staff
◆ EMP: 85
SALES (est): 163.7MM
SALES (corp-wide): 344.8B Privately Held
WEB: www.criterioncatalysts.com
SIC: 2819 2869 Catalysts, chemical; industrial organic chemicals
PA: Royal Dutch Shell Plc
Shell Centre
London SE1 7
207 934-1234

(G-11858)
SHELL CHEMICAL LP (DH)
Also Called: Shell Chemicals
910 Louisiana St (77002-4916)
P.O. Box 2463 (77252-2463)
PHONE.................................855 697-4355
◆ EMP: 20 EST: 1929
SQ FT: 5,000
SALES (est): 525.8MM
SALES (corp-wide): 344.8B Privately Held
WEB: www.shell.us
SIC: 2869 Industrial organic chemicals
HQ: Shell Oil Company
150 N Dairy Ashford Rd A
Houston TX 77079
713 241-6161

(G-11859)
SHELL GULF OF MEXICO INC
777 Walker St (77002-5316)
PHONE.................................713 241-6161
M V Gaffigan, Principal
EMP: 10
SALES (est): 509.4K
SALES (corp-wide): 344.8B Privately Held
WEB: www.shell.us
SIC: 1382 Oil & gas exploration services
HQ: Shell Petroleum Inc.
910 Louisiana St Ste 420
Houston TX 77002
713 241-6161

(G-11860)
SHELL OIL COMPANY (DH)
150 N Dairy Ashford Rd A (77079-1116)
P.O. Box 2463 (77252-2463)
PHONE.................................713 241-6161
Marvin Odum, President
Nasser Beydoun, Partner
Joyce Neumann, General Mgr
Richard Strouse, General Mgr
Gilbert Arevalo, Principal
◆ EMP: 1000 EST: 1922
SALES (est): 3.1B
SALES (corp-wide): 344.8B Privately Held
WEB: www.shell.com
SIC: 5541 4612 1311 2821 Filling stations, gasoline; crude petroleum pipelines; crude petroleum production; natural gas production; epoxy resins; polypropylene resins; olefins; alcohols, non-beverage; petroleum refining; gasoline; jet fuels; kerosene
HQ: Shell Petroleum Inc.
910 Louisiana St Ste 420
Houston TX 77002
713 241-6161

(G-11861)
SHELL OIL COMPANY
7510 Ardmore St (77054-4204)
PHONE.................................713 241-6471
EMP: 15
SALES (corp-wide): 344.8B Privately Held
WEB: www.shell.com
SIC: 1382 Geological exploration, oil & gas field
HQ: Shell Oil Company
150 N Dairy Ashford Rd A
Houston TX 77079
713 241-6161

(G-11862)
SHELL OIL COMPANY
9255 Riddlewood Ln (77025-4228)
PHONE.................................713 332-7606
EMP: 165
SALES (corp-wide): 344.8B Privately Held
WEB: www.shell.com
SIC: 2911 Petroleum Refiner
HQ: Shell Oil Company
150 N Dairy Ashford Rd A
Houston TX 77079
713 241-6161

(G-11863)
SHELL OIL COMPANY
700 Milam St Ste 125 (77002-2815)
P.O. Box 2967 (77252-2967)
PHONE.................................713 546-4000
EMP: 15
SALES (corp-wide): 305.1B Privately Held
SIC: 2911 Petroleum Refining
HQ: Shell Oil Company
150 N Dairy Ashford Rd A
Houston TX 77079
713 241-6161

(G-11864)
SHELL OIL COMPANY
5521 Gasmer Dr (77035-4501)
P.O. Box 481 (77001-0481)
PHONE.................................713 721-6282
EMP: 25
SALES (corp-wide): 344.8B Privately Held
WEB: www.shell.com
SIC: 2911 Petroleum Refiner

HQ: Shell Oil Company
150 N Dairy Ashford Rd A
Houston TX 77079
713 241-6161

(G-11865)
SHEPERD MAURY
Also Called: Film Technology
2221 Canada Dry St (77023-4503)
P.O. Box 230228 (77223-0228)
PHONE.................................713 921-3456
Maury Shepherd, Owner
Tina Bayllr, Principal
EMP: 40
SALES (est): 4.3MM Privately Held
WEB: www.filmtechnology.net
SIC: 2821 Plastics materials & resins

(G-11866)
SHERIDAN PROD PARTNERS I-A LP (PA)
1360 Post Oak Blvd Ste 25 (77056-3030)
PHONE.................................713 548-1000
Lisa Stewart, Partner
Matthew Assiff, CFO
EMP: 13
SALES (est): 53MM Privately Held
WEB: www.sheridanproduction.com
SIC: 1382 Oil & gas exploration services

(G-11867)
SHERIDAN PRODUCTION CO LLC (PA)
1360 Post Oak Blvd # 2500 (77056-3049)
PHONE.................................713 548-1000
Lisa A Stewart, President
Thomas Voytovich, General Mgr
Randy Ferrell, District Mgr
James K Bass, Exec VP
Eric L Harry, Exec VP
EMP: 130
SALES (est): 830MM Privately Held
WEB: www.sheridanproduction.com
SIC: 1382 Oil & gas exploration services

(G-11868)
SHIMADZU SCIENTIFIC INSTRS INC
9940 W Sam Houston Pkwy S (77099-5305)
PHONE.................................713 467-1151
Benjamin Figard, Principal
Kelly Hines, Administration
EMP: 11 Privately Held
WEB: www.ssi.shimadzu.com
SIC: 3826 Analytical instruments
HQ: Shimadzu Scientific Instruments Incorporated
7102 Riverwood Dr
Columbia MD 21046
800 477-1227

(G-11869)
SHINTECH INCORPORATED (HQ)
3 Greenway Plz Ste 1150 (77046-0325)
P.O. Box 301059, Dallas (75303-1059)
PHONE.................................713 965-0713
Chihiro Kanagawa, Ch of Bd
Y Saitoh, Vice Pres
Ervin E Schroeder, VP Mfg
Gary Davis, Purch Agent
Marcy Irwin, Sales Staff
◆ EMP: 14
SQ FT: 8,500
SALES (est): 233.2MM Privately Held
WEB: www.shintech.com
SIC: 2821 Polyvinyl chloride resins (PVC)

(G-11870)
SHIPCOM WIRELESS INC (PA)
11200 Richmond Ave # 552 (77082-2639)
PHONE.................................281 558-5252
Abeezar Tyebji, CEO
Reddy Cherukupally, Exec VP
Mustafa Tyebbhoy, Exec VP
Philip Matkovsky, Vice Pres
Rajvinder Grewal, QC Mgr
EMP: 78
SALES (est): 50MM Privately Held
WEB: www.shipcomwireless.com
SIC: 7374 7373 7372 Data entry service; systems integration services; prepackaged software

(G-11871)
SHIPLEY DO-NUT FLOUR SUP INC
Also Called: Shipley Donut Shops
1128 West Rd (77038-2140)
PHONE.............................281 575-1766
Maria Sevilla, *Owner*
EMP: 9
SALES (corp-wide): 57.2MM **Privately Held**
WEB: www.shipleydonuts.com
SIC: 5461 2051 Doughnuts; doughnuts, except frozen
PA: Shipley Do-Nut Flour And Supply Co Llc
5200 N Main St
Houston TX 77009
713 869-4636

(G-11872)
SHIPLEY DO-NUT FLOUR SUP INC
10517 S Post Oak Rd (77035-3305)
PHONE.............................713 728-9366
Chang Lee, *General Mgr*
EMP: 9
SALES (corp-wide): 57.2MM **Privately Held**
WEB: www.shipleydonuts.com
SIC: 5461 2051 Doughnuts; doughnuts, except frozen
PA: Shipley Do-Nut Flour And Supply Co Llc
5200 N Main St
Houston TX 77009
713 869-4636

(G-11873)
SHIPLEY DO-NUT FLOUR SUP INC
Also Called: Shipley Donut Shops
5847 W Airport Blvd (77035-4227)
PHONE.............................713 729-2381
ME Chan, *Owner*
EMP: 10
SALES (corp-wide): 57.2MM **Privately Held**
WEB: www.shipleydonuts.com
SIC: 5461 2051 Doughnuts; doughnuts, except frozen
PA: Shipley Do-Nut Flour And Supply Co Llc
5200 N Main St
Houston TX 77009
713 869-4636

(G-11874)
SHORTHORN RESOURCES INC
2636 S Loop W 50 (77054-2680)
PHONE.............................713 668-0550
Wayne Huff, *President*
Steven Scott, *Vice Pres*
Will Smith, *Agent*
Thomas M Scott,
EMP: 12
SALES (est): 826.7K **Privately Held**
WEB: www.shorthornres.com
SIC: 1382 Oil & gas exploration services

(G-11875)
SHOWCASE WINDOWS & DOORS INC
Also Called: Showcase Cstm Vnyl Wndows Door
1702 Cullen Blvd (77023-3506)
PHONE.............................713 926-8500
Gerald Bodzy, *President*
EMP: 35
SALES (est): 3MM **Privately Held**
WEB: www.showcasewindows.com
SIC: 2431 Windows, wood

(G-11876)
SIANA OIL & GAS CO LLC
Also Called: Siana Operating
400 N Sam Houston Pkwy E # 601 (77060-3500)
PHONE.............................713 568-1082
Tom M Ragsdale,
EMP: 10
SQ FT: 1,100
SALES (est): 1.8MM **Privately Held**
SIC: 1311 1382 Crude petroleum & natural gas; oil & gas exploration services

(G-11877)
SIDEWINDER DRILLING INC (HQ)
20475 State Highway 249 # 300 (77070-2755)
PHONE.............................832 320-7600
Jon C Cole, *CEO*
J Anthony Gallegos, *President*
Michael Hill, *Superintendent*
Bruce Humphries, *COO*
F Bruce Humphries, *COO*
EMP: 60
SALES (est): 203.6MM **Publicly Held**
WEB: www.sidewinderdrilling.com
SIC: 1381 Drilling oil & gas wells
PA: Independence Contract Drilling, Inc.
20475 State Highway 249 # 300
Houston TX 77070
281 598-1230

(G-11878)
SIEMENS ENERGY INC
16530 Peninsula St Bldg 3 (77015-6504)
PHONE.............................281 328-3777
Mark Pringle, *Manager*
David Branton, *Info Tech Mgr*
EMP: 209
SALES (corp-wide): 4B **Privately Held**
WEB: www.new.siemens.com
SIC: 3511 Turbines & turbine generator sets
PA: Siemens Energy, Inc.
4400 N Alafaya Trl
Orlando FL 32826
407 736-2000

(G-11879)
SIEMENS INDUSTRY INC
Also Called: Siemens Water Technology
7222 Clinton Dr (77020-7548)
PHONE.............................713 671-9510
EMP: 15
SALES (corp-wide): 89.6B **Privately Held**
SIC: 3569 Mfg General Industrial Machinery
HQ: Siemens Industry, Inc.
1000 Deerfield Pkwy
Buffalo Grove IL 60089
847 215-1000

(G-11880)
SIENKO PRECISION INC
10102 Sussex Ln (77041-6120)
P.O. Box 40932 (77240-0932)
PHONE.............................713 462-7482
EMP: 20
SQ FT: 10,000
SALES (est): 3.3MM **Privately Held**
WEB: www.sienkoprecision.com
SIC: 3599 Machine shop, jobbing & repair

(G-11881)
SIERRA RESOURCES LLC
333 Clay St Ste 3600 (77002-4109)
P.O. Box 130546 (77219-0546)
PHONE.............................713 365-6100
Robert Fabris, *Vice Pres*
John Eads, *Mng Member*
Bronita Black,
Dennis Black,
Timothy S Brown,
EMP: 12
SQ FT: 4,500
SALES (est): 0 **Privately Held**
WEB: www.sierraresources.energy
SIC: 1382 Oil & gas exploration services

(G-11882)
SIFCO APPLIED SRFC CNCEPTS LLC
7620 Bluff Point Dr (77086-1764)
PHONE.............................281 444-6500
Chris Bzdusek, *Manager*
EMP: 10
SALES (corp-wide): 7.1MM **Privately Held**
WEB: www.sifcoasc.com
SIC: 3471 Plating of metals or formed products
PA: Sifco Applied Surface Concepts, Llc
5708 E Schaaf Rd
Cleveland OH 44131
216 524-0099

(G-11883)
SIGMA CORPORATION
5000 Askins Ln (77093-3006)
PHONE.............................281 987-1200
Sandra Salins, *Accountant*
Marti Benson, *Sales Mgr*
David Brugger, *Sales Staff*
Greg McAdams, *Sales Staff*
Kwame Williams, *Sales Staff*
EMP: 35
SALES (corp-wide): 133.6MM **Privately Held**
WEB: www.sigmaco.com
SIC: 2299 Upholstery filling, textile
PA: Sigma Corporation
700 Goldman Dr
Cream Ridge NJ 08514
609 758-0800

(G-11884)
SIGMA ELECTRONICS INC (PA)
10830 Kinghurst Dr (77099-3415)
PHONE.............................800 874-7121
Tomas Palm, *President*
Dan Japhet Jr, *President*
Irma Azuara, *Corp Secy*
Thomas Hill, *Vice Pres*
Gretchen Japhet, *Director*
EMP: 38
SQ FT: 28,750
SALES (est): 5.5MM **Privately Held**
WEB: www.sigmaxfmr.com
SIC: 3825 3677 3612 Transformers, portable: instrument; power measuring equipment, electrical; electronic coils, transformers & other inductors; transformers, except electric

(G-11885)
SIGMA FASTENERS INC
16723 Aldine Westfield Rd (77032-1349)
PHONE.............................281 214-8800
Cristine Baker, *President*
Jon Sellers, *General Mgr*
Anthony Denyer, *Business Mgr*
Joe Salinas, *Mfg Staff*
Hieu Dang, *Engineer*
▲ **EMP:** 72
SQ FT: 38,000
SALES (est): 26.2MM **Privately Held**
WEB: www.sigmafasteners.com
SIC: 5085 3399 Fasteners, industrial: nuts, bolts, screws, etc.; metal fasteners

(G-11886)
SIGMA MBL GRANITE-HOUSTON INC
5930 Centralcrest St (77092-7008)
PHONE.............................713 290-8530
Simon Kanaan, *President*
Curtis Roane, *Superintendent*
Jeff Armstrong, *Vice Pres*
Ramzi L Kanaan, *Vice Pres*
Chris Landrum, *Project Mgr*
▲ **EMP:** 50
SQ FT: 9,000
SALES (est): 6.7MM **Privately Held**
WEB: www.sigmamarble.com
SIC: 3281 Marble, building: cut & shaped

(G-11887)
SIGMA TUBE & BAR LLC (PA)
363 N Sam Houston Pkwy E (77060-2404)
PHONE.............................281 369-5525
Christopher Friend, *President*
Tommy Ausbern, *Vice Pres*
Murray Kammerer, *Vice Pres*
Clark Woodward, *Plant Mgr*
Patricia Bryan, *Purch Agent*
▲ **EMP:** 17
SQ FT: 5,000
SALES (est): 16.5MM **Privately Held**
WEB: www.sigmatb.com
SIC: 5051 3312 Steel; pipes & tubes

(G-11888)
SIGMUND KANE & HATCH INC
Also Called: Skh Management
7700 San Felipe St # 500 (77063-1615)
PHONE.............................713 782-1075
Paul J Sigmund, *President*
Keith Hatch, *Vice Pres*
Greg Kane, *Vice Pres*
EMP: 16
SALES (est): 897.9K **Privately Held**
SIC: 1382 Oil & gas exploration services

(G-11889)
SIGN FACTORY INC
5101 Ashley Ct (77041-6914)
PHONE.............................713 849-4575
Rita A Roberts, *CEO*
Alvis D Roberts, *President*
EMP: 22
SQ FT: 27,000
SALES (est): 2.3MM **Privately Held**
WEB: www.thesignfactory.net
SIC: 3993 Signs & advertising specialties

(G-11890)
SIGNAD INC
Also Called: Sign-Ad
1010 North Loop (77009-1133)
P.O. Box 8626 (77249-8626)
PHONE.............................713 861-6013
Wesley Gilbreath Jr, *President*
Stacy Dronet, *Opers Mgr*
Stephanie Akhtar, *Human Res Dir*
Stacy Abel, *Accounts Exec*
Holly McBrayer, *Accounts Exec*
EMP: 15
SQ FT: 20,000
SALES (est): 2.4MM **Privately Held**
WEB: www.signad.com
SIC: 3993 Signs & advertising specialties

(G-11891)
SIGNAL GROUP INC (PA)
5401 N Sam Houston Pkwy W (77086-1436)
PHONE.............................281 453-0200
Alejandro Fuentes, *CFO*
Elizabeth Northrup, *Corp Comm Staff*
John Procter, *Corp Comm Staff*
Charles Cooper, *Director*
EMP: 18
SALES (est): 57.1MM **Privately Held**
WEB: www.signalgp.com
SIC: 7389 3669 Flagging service (traffic control); traffic signals, electric

(G-11892)
SIGNAL PEAK SILICA LLC
4605 Post Oak Place Dr (77027-9729)
PHONE.............................281 822-4568
Vic Serri, *CEO*
Jackson Wise, *COO*
Garrett Thompson, *CFO*
Chris Samanns, *Ch Credit Ofcr*
EMP: 200
SALES (est): 549.6K **Privately Held**
WEB: www.spsilica.com
SIC: 1442 1382 1446 Sand mining; oil & gas exploration services; silica sand mining

(G-11893)
SIGNATURE ARCH & BLIND
Also Called: Signature Window Coverings
10720 Jones Rd (77065-4216)
PHONE.............................281 469-2500
EMP: 30
SALES (est): 2.9MM **Privately Held**
WEB: www.signaturearch.com
SIC: 2431 5023 Window frames, wood; window covering parts & accessories

(G-11894)
SIGNATURE PRESS INC
3300 Kingswood St (77092-7400)
PHONE.............................713 956-8555
Carl Dixon, *President*
Jimmy Seiford, *Vice Pres*
Lisa Turner, *Vice Pres*
Brian Carr, *Manager*
▲ **EMP:** 45
SQ FT: 24,000
SALES (est): 3.9MM **Privately Held**
WEB: www.aspenimg.com
SIC: 2752 Commercial printing, offset

(G-11895)
SILCO INC (PA)
1215 Gessner Rd (77055-6013)
PHONE.............................713 785-6272
John Boland, *President*
David Grebenc, *Vice Pres*
◆ **EMP:** 9
SQ FT: 8,000
SALES (est): 3.3MM **Privately Held**
WEB: www.silco-inc.com
SIC: 2891 Adhesives & sealants

(G-11896)
SILGAN PLASTICS OF TEXAS (PA)
6814 Kirbyville St (77033-1108)
PHONE.................................713 242-0923
Phil Mezger, *General Mgr*
▲ **EMP:** 15
SQ FT: 308,000
SALES (est): 4MM **Privately Held**
WEB: www.silganplastics.com
SIC: 3089 Plastic containers, except foam

(G-11897)
SILVA TECHNOLOGIES INC
Also Called: B and L Machine
3228 Maxroy St (77008-6223)
PHONE.................................713 869-3631
Peter Silva, *President*
Hector Silva, *Vice Pres*
▲ **EMP:** 22
SALES (est): 4.4MM **Privately Held**
WEB: www.blmachine.com
SIC: 3599 Machine shop, jobbing & repair

(G-11898)
SILVER STAR I PWR PARTNERS LLC
700 Louisiana St (77002-2700)
PHONE.................................713 354-2168
EMP: 50
SALES (est): 3.4MM
SALES (corp-wide): 240.2B **Privately Held**
SIC: 2869 Alternative Fuels - Wind Energy
HQ: Bp Alternative Energy North America Inc.
700 Louisiana St Ste 3300
Houston TX 77002

(G-11899)
SILVERBOW RESOURCES INC (PA)
575 N Dairy Ashford Rd (77079-1117)
PHONE.................................281 874-2700
Sean C Woolverton, *CEO*
Marcus C Rowland, *Ch of Bd*
Steven W Adam, *COO*
Christopher M Abundis, *CFO*
W Eric Schultz, *Controller*
EMP: 86
SQ FT: 34,275
SALES (est): 288.6MM **Publicly Held**
WEB: www.sbow.com
SIC: 1311 Crude petroleum & natural gas production

(G-11900)
SILVERWELL TECHNOLOGY INC
6824 N Sam Houston Pkwy W (77064-3528)
PHONE.................................281 389-3020
◆ **EMP:** 15
SQ FT: 14,000
SALES (est): 2.6MM **Privately Held**
SIC: 3491 Industrial valves
HQ: Silverwell Energy Limited
Unit 6
Cambridge CAMBS CB22

(G-11901)
SIMDESK TECHNOLOGIES INC
3900 Essex Ln Fl 5 (77027-5133)
PHONE.................................713 244-0850
Gray Hall, *Ch of Bd*
Stephen R Lesem, *President*
Walt Girior, *Vice Pres*
EMP: 20
SALES (est): 2.5MM **Privately Held**
SIC: 3695 Computer software tape & disks: blank, rigid & floppy

(G-11902)
SIMON PRINTING COMPANY
10810 Craighead Dr (77025-5804)
PHONE.................................713 666-1296
B L Simon, *President*
Bernard L Simon, *President*
H B Simon, *President*
Richard L Simon, *Corp Secy*
S K Simon, *Corp Secy*
EMP: 48 **EST:** 1938
SQ FT: 16,500

SALES (est): 12.9MM **Privately Held**
WEB: www.simonprinting.com
SIC: 2752 2789 Commercial printing, offset; bookbinding & related work

(G-11903)
SIMPLELEGAL INC
1360 Post Oak Blvd # 2200 (77056-3030)
PHONE.................................415 763-5366
Nathan Wenzel, *CEO*
Tina Fan, *Vice Pres*
Jasmine Tinkess, *Finance*
Craig Raeburn, *VP Sales*
Karen Moor, *Sales Dir*
EMP: 11
SALES (est): 385.1K **Privately Held**
WEB: www.simplelegal.com
SIC: 7372 Business oriented computer software

(G-11904)
SIMPLY DONUTS
11711 Jones Rd (77070-5311)
PHONE.................................281 955-6374
Chan Thol, *Principal*
EMP: 11
SALES (est): 241.1K **Privately Held**
SIC: 5812 5461 2051 Eating places; doughnuts; doughnuts, except frozen

(G-11905)
SINOCHEM AMERICAN HOLDINGS (HQ)
1330 Post Oak Blvd # 2500 (77056-3031)
PHONE.................................713 263-8880
Yu Chen, *President*
Guotu Mao, *CFO*
David Garrett, *Manager*
▲ **EMP:** 25
SALES (est): 52.5MM **Privately Held**
WEB: www.sinochem-american.com
SIC: 5'69 5172 5191 5162 Organic chemicals, synthetic; chemicals, industrial & heavy; petroleum products; crude oil; fertilizer & fertilizer materials; plastics materials; fertilizers, mixing only

(G-11906)
SINOCHEM PETROLEUM USA LP
1330 Post Oak Blvd # 600 (77056-3166)
PHONE.................................832 742-8670
EMP: 15 **EST:** 2014
SALES (est): 959.5K **Privately Held**
SIC: 1382 Geological exploration, oil & gas field
PA: Sinochem Group Co., Ltd.
Middle Block, Kaichen World Trade Center, 28 Fuxingmennei Street Beijing

(G-11907)
SIRI GRANITE INC
4849 Cranswick Rd (77041-7721)
PHONE.................................832 203-8322
EMP: 16 **EST:** 2015
SALES (est): 110.6K **Privately Held**
WEB: www.sirigranite.com
SIC: 1799 1743 3281 5211 Counter top installation; marble installation, interior; granite, cut & shaped; counter tops

(G-11908)
SISTER2SSTER DSTINY TRNSPT LLC
11510 Homestead Rd # 299 (77016-1237)
PHONE.................................346 337-6637
Rolanda Bell, *Principal*
EMP: 10
SALES (est): 374.7K **Privately Held**
SIC: 3711 4011 4121 4789 Motor vehicles & car bodies; railroads, line-haul operating; taxicabs; transportation services; regulation, administration of transportation

(G-11909)
SITEWORKS INCORPORATED
363 W Canino Rd (77037-3713)
PHONE.................................281 931-1000
Alex Newton, *President*
Troy Mc Cune, *Vice Pres*
EMP: 49
SQ FT: 30,000

SALES (est): 6.4MM **Privately Held**
WEB: www.siteworkscaststone.com
SIC: 3281 3272 Cut stone & stone products; concrete products

(G-11910)
SIVCO INC
5713 Cunningham Rd (77041-4719)
P.O. Box 40471 (77240-0471)
PHONE.................................713 466-1100
Nancy Sivyer, *Corp Secy*
Alan F Phillips, *Exec VP*
Alan Phillips, *Exec VP*
James C Caesar, *Foreman/Supr*
◆ **EMP:** 20 **EST:** 1964
SQ FT: 36,000
SALES (est): 5.4MM **Privately Held**
SIC: 3317 3494 Steel pipe & tubes; pipe fittings

(G-11911)
SK GC AMERICAS INC (HQ)
Also Called: Sk Energy Houston
11700 Katy Fwy Ste 900 (77079-1222)
PHONE.................................713 341-5820
Jeong Joon Yu, *President*
Mike Brown, *Technical Mgr*
Jae Hoon Seol, *Admin Sec*
◆ **EMP:** 14
SALES (est): 8.4MM **Privately Held**
SIC: 1382 Oil & gas exploration services

(G-11912)
SK GLOBAL SOFTWARE LLC
940 Gemini St Ste 200 (77058-2790)
P.O. Box 733054, Dallas (75373-3054)
PHONE.................................301 963-7300
Scott Caudle, *CEO*
Debbie Monninger, *Bookkeeper*
Kevin Casselman, *Manager*
Tim Kahne, *CTO*
Richard Sandler, *Security Dir*
EMP: 15
SALES (est): 4MM **Privately Held**
WEB: www.sksoft.com
SIC: 7372 Prepackaged software

(G-11913)
SKF USA INC
Also Called: SKF Machine Tool Services
3443 N Sam Houston Pkwy W (77086-1482)
PHONE.................................281 506-3250
Andre Dubryn, *Sales Staff*
James Vest, *Branch Mgr*
Mark McQueen, *Manager*
EMP: 58
SALES (corp-wide): 8.9B **Privately Held**
WEB: www.chicago-rawhide.com
SIC: 3053 Gaskets & sealing devices
HQ: Skf Usa Inc.
890 Forty Foot Rd
Lansdale PA 19446
267 436-6000

(G-11914)
SKH MANAGEMENT LP
Also Called: Skh Resources
7600 San Felipe St 200 (77063-1703)
PHONE.................................713 782-1075
Paul J Sigmund, *Partner*
EMP: 15
SALES (est): 1.3MM **Privately Held**
SIC: 1382 Oil & gas exploration services

(G-11915)
SM ENERGY COMPANY
580 Westlake Park Blvd (77079-2662)
PHONE.................................281 677-2800
G Leyendecker, *Vice Pres*
Zeke Hinojosa, *Foreman/Supr*
Fran Zwick, *Executive Asst*
EMP: 26
SALES (corp-wide): 1.5B **Publicly Held**
WEB: www.sm-energy.com
SIC: 1382 Oil & gas exploration services
PA: Sm Energy Company
1775 N Sherman St # 1200
Denver CO 80203
303 861-8140

(G-11916)
SM ENERGY COMPANY
Also Called: L L O G Exploration Co
777 N Eldridge Pkwy # 1100 (77079-4425)
PHONE.................................281 677-2800

Robin P Diedrich, *Vice Pres*
Greg Lyendecker, *Manager*
Dave Thompson, *Manager*
Erin Esquivel, *Analyst*
Dinah Schlecht, *Analyst*
EMP: 19
SALES (corp-wide): 1.5B **Publicly Held**
WEB: www.sm-energy.com
SIC: 1311 1382 Crude petroleum production; oil & gas exploration services
PA: Sm Energy Company
1775 N Sherman St # 1200
Denver CO 80203
303 861-8140

(G-11917)
SMA DISTRIBUTORS
6519 Mohawk St (77016-2211)
PHONE.................................281 442-0890
Stacey Ayers, *Owner*
EMP: 15
SALES (est): 633K **Privately Held**
SIC: 2395 Pleating & stitching

(G-11918)
SMART IMAGING TECHNOLOGIES CO
1770 Saint James Pl # 414 (77056-3471)
PHONE.................................713 589-3500
Vitali Khvatkov, *President*
Ira Bleiweiss, *Vice Pres*
Vladimir Nesh, *Vice Pres*
EMP: 40
SQ FT: 2,500
SALES (est): 4.2MM **Privately Held**
WEB: www.smartimtech.com
SIC: 3695 7371 7372 Computer software tape & disks: blank, rigid & floppy; custom computer programming services; prepackaged software

(G-11919)
SMART PIPE COMPANY INC
6955 High Life Dr (77066-3715)
PHONE.................................281 945-5700
Gary Littlestar, *CEO*
Justin Reed, *Opers Spvr*
Aron Ekelund, *Opers Staff*
Brian House, *Production*
Ted Mortenson, *CFO*
EMP: 18
SALES (est): 3.1MM **Privately Held**
WEB: www.smart-pipe.com
SIC: 3089 1623 Plastic processing; plastic hardware & building products; pipeline wrapping

(G-11920)
SMC INDUSTRIES INC
2260 Appelt Dr (77015-6593)
PHONE.................................281 860-9950
Jacob Pena, *Plant Mgr*
Christine Diegel, *Controller*
George Bauer, *Manager*
Anita Hicks, *Manager*
EMP: 9
SALES (corp-wide): 6.1MM **Privately Held**
WEB: www.smcindustries.com
SIC: 3296 5033 Insulation: rock wool, slag & silica minerals; insulation materials
PA: Smc Industries, Inc.
3239 Phnxville Pike Bldg 1
Malvern PA 19355
610 647-5687

(G-11921)
SMI MANUFACTURING INC (HQ)
13312 E Hardy Rd (77039-2822)
PHONE.................................281 449-0345
Marion Eagles, *President*
Michael E Humphrey, *Vice Pres*
Sam Grovner, *Vice Pres*
Jim Nelson, *Vice Pres*
Nathan Post, *Vice Pres*
▲ **EMP:** 75 **EST:** 1969
SQ FT: 50,000
SALES (est): 12.1MM
SALES (corp-wide): 252.3MM **Privately Held**
WEB: www.afglobalcorp.com
SIC: 3441 3533 Fabricated structural metal; oil field machinery & equipment

PA: Ameriforge Group Inc.
945 Bunker Hill Rd # 500
Houston TX 77024
713 393-4200

(G-11922)
SMITH ENERGY COMPANY
Also Called: Smith Lester Management
1001 Sannin St Ste 3850　(77002)
P.O. Box 52890　(77052-2890)
PHONE..............................713 651-9102
Lester H Smith, *President*
Joyce Knecht, *Treasurer*
Bonnie Samford, *Admin Sec*
▲ **EMP:** 12
SQ FT: 3,000
SALES (est): 1.7MM **Privately Held**
WEB: www.smithenergyservices.com
SIC: 1311 1382 Crude petroleum produc-
tion; oil & gas exploration services

(G-11923)
SMITH INTERNATIONAL INC
(DH)
Also Called: Schlumberger
1310 Rankin Rd　(77073-4802)
PHONE..............................281 443-3370
Andrew Gould, *CEO*
Paal Kibsgaard, *President*
Barry W Panzer, *Managing Dir*
Ashok Belani, *Exec VP*
Joshua Gatell, *Project Mgr*
◆ **EMP:** 550
SQ FT: 246,000
SALES (est): 5.4B **Publicly Held**
WEB: www.smithcodevelopment.com
SIC: 3532 3533 Drills, bits & similar equip-
ment; oil & gas field machinery
HQ: Schlumberger Limited
5599 San Felipe St Fl 17
Houston TX 77056
713 513-2000

(G-11924)
SMITH PRODUCTION INC (PA)
14425 Torrey Chase Blvd # 190
(77014-1637)
PHONE..............................281 583-0196
Glenn Smith, *President*
Judy Smith, *Admin Sec*
▲ **EMP:** 25
SQ FT: 3,500
SALES (est): 5.1MM **Privately Held**
SIC: 1382 Oil & gas exploration services

(G-11925)
SMOLECULE INC
1003 Ruthven St　(77019-5238)
PHONE..............................512 262-9938
Rui Sun, *President*
EMP: 10
SALES (est): 409.5K **Privately Held**
SIC: 2819 Chemicals, reagent grade: re-
fined from technical grade

(G-11926)
SMURFIT KAPPA NORTH AMER
LLC
Also Called: Smurfit Kappa Houston
7800 Washington Ave　(77007-7801)
PHONE..............................713 869-5900
EMP: 22 **Privately Held**
WEB: www.smurfitkappa.com
SIC: 2679 3993 2653 Paperboard prod-
ucts, converted; signs & advertising spe-
cialties; corrugated & solid fiber boxes
HQ: Smurfit Kappa North America Llc
125 E John Carpenter Fwy # 925
Irving TX 75062
800 306-8326

(G-11927)
SN & DB HOLDINGS INC
Also Called: Economy Metal Works
8400 Villa Dr　(77061-4602)
PHONE..............................713 645-3370
Daryl Berger, *President*
Steve Nierman, *Vice Pres*
EMP: 30
SQ FT: 20,000
SALES (est): 8.6MM **Privately Held**
SIC: 3444 Sheet metalwork

(G-11928)
SN MIDSTREAM LLC
700 Milam St Ste 600　(77002-2862)
PHONE..............................713 783-8000
Antonio R Sanchez III, *CEO*
EMP: 26
SALES (est): 2.5MM
SALES (corp-wide): 1B **Privately Held**
WEB: www.sanchezenergycorp.com
SIC: 1382 Oil & gas exploration services
PA: Mesquite Energy, Inc.
700 Milam St Ste 600
Houston TX 77002
713 756-2700

(G-11929)
SN OPERATING LLC
700 Milam St Ste 600　(77002-2862)
P.O. Box 61859　(77208-1859)
PHONE..............................713 951-0233
EMP: 35 EST: 2015
SALES (est): 193.2K
SALES (corp-wide): 1B **Privately Held**
WEB: www.sanchezenergycorp.com
SIC: 1311 Crude petroleum & natural gas
PA: Mesquite Energy, Inc.
700 Milam St Ste 600
Houston TX 77002
713 756-2700

(G-11930)
SNELSON OILFIELD LTG CO INC
Also Called: Indatech
14655 Chmpn Frest Dr Apt　(77069)
PHONE..............................713 937-3600
Wes Mohr, *President*
EMP: 9
SALES (corp-wide): 3.2MM **Privately**
Held
WEB: www.snelsonlights.com
SIC: 1389 Oil field services
PA: Snelson Oilfield Lighting Company, Inc.
3619 Alice St
Fort Worth TX 76110
817 926-0571

(G-11931)
SOFEC INC (DH)
Also Called: Modec Sofec
15011 Katy Fwy Ste 500　(77094-0010)
PHONE..............................713 510-6600
Rick Hall, *President*
Brent Salyer, *Business Mgr*
Terry Boatman, *Vice Pres*
James Hodges, *Vice Pres*
Jeremy Baty, *Project Mgr*
◆ **EMP:** 91
SQ FT: 170,000
SALES (est): 39.4MM **Privately Held**
WEB: www.sofec.com
SIC: 3533 8742 Oil & gas drilling rigs &
equipment; construction project manage-
ment consultant
HQ: Modec International, Inc.
15011 Katy Fwy Ste 500
Houston TX 77094
281 529-8100

(G-11932)
SOHO
2528 Amherst St　(77005-3238)
PHONE..............................713 526-3755
EMP: 15
SALES (est): 622.8K **Privately Held**
SIC: 5541 3999 Gasoline Service Station
Mfg Misc Products

(G-11933)
SOJITZ ENERGY VENTURE INC
2000 Houston Ave　(77007-2944)
PHONE..............................713 963-9101
Hiroshi Kawahara, *President*
Shinji Harada, *President*
Daisuke Yasada, *Senior VP*
Laura Gould, *Vice Pres*
Alan Rimel, *Vice Pres*
EMP: 10
SALES (est): 3.2MM **Privately Held**
SIC: 1311 Crude petroleum production
PA: Sojitz Corporation
2-1-1, Uchisaiwaicho
Chiyoda-Ku TKY 100-0

(G-11934)
SOLANO FURNITURE
INCORPORATED
8211 Fairbanks White Oak　(77040-4216)
P.O. Box 920911　(77292-0911)
PHONE..............................713 849-4855
David Solano, *President*
EMP: 15
SQ FT: 19,906
SALES (est): 1.6MM **Privately Held**
SIC: 2599 2521 2512 2511 Factory furni-
ture & fixtures; wood office furniture; up-
holstered household furniture; wood
household furniture

(G-11935)
SOLAR TURBINES
INCORPORATED
10203 Sam Houston Park Dr # 300
(77064-4671)
PHONE..............................713 895-2300
Edgar Guevara, *Managing Dir*
Eun Kim, *Project Mgr*
Gilbert Oliveros, *Project Mgr*
Marcelino Rodriguez, *Project Mgr*
Jeremy Hartings, *Opers Mgr*
EMP: 280
SALES (corp-wide): 53.8B **Publicly Held**
WEB: www.solarturbines.com
SIC: 3511 Gas turbine generator set units,
complete
HQ: Solar Turbines Incorporated
2200 Pacific Hwy
San Diego CA 92101
619 544-5000

(G-11936)
SOLARIS OILFIELD TECH LLC
9811 Katy Fwy Ste 900　(77024-1283)
PHONE..............................281 501-3070
Gregory A Lanham, *CEO*
Jonathan Scheiner, *Vice Pres*
Tawnya McNack, *Accountant*
John Janousek, *Human Resources*
EMP: 263
SALES (est): 16.1MM
SALES (corp-wide): 241.6MM **Publicly**
Held
WEB: www.solarisoilfield.com
SIC: 1389 Oil field services
PA: Solaris Oilfield Infrastructure, Inc.
9811 Katy Fwy Ste 700
Houston TX 77024
281 501-3070

(G-11937)
SOLARIS OLFLD
INFRSTRCTURE INC (PA)
9811 Katy Fwy Ste 700　(77024-1281)
PHONE..............................281 501-3070
William A Zartler, *Ch of Bd*
Kyle S Ramachandran, *President*
Kelly L Price, *COO*
Yvonne Fletcher, *Vice Pres*
Edwin Lau, *Vice Pres*
EMP: 17 EST: 2014
SALES (est): 241.6MM **Publicly Held**
WEB: www.solarisoilfield.com
SIC: 1389 Oil field services

(G-11938)
SOLENIS LLC
6121 Almeda Genoa Rd　(77048-4538)
PHONE..............................713 991-3722
EMP: 10
SALES (corp-wide): 901.3MM **Privately**
Held
WEB: www.solenis.com
SIC: 2899 Water treating compounds
HQ: Solenis Llc
2475 Pinnacle Dr
Wilmington DE 19803
866 337-1533

(G-11939)
SOLENIS LLC
Also Called: Ashland Water Technologies
6060 South Loop E Ste 212　(77033-1042)
PHONE..............................713 738-6815
EMP: 14
SALES (corp-wide): 901.3MM **Privately**
Held
WEB: www.solenis.com
SIC: 2899 Water treating compounds

HQ: Solenis Llc
2475 Pinnacle Dr
Wilmington DE 19803
866 337-1533

(G-11940)
SOLID ROCK READY MIX INC
5515 Breen Dr　(77086-4042)
PHONE..............................281 931-3003
Gloria Zermeno, *President*
EMP: 17
SQ FT: 2,600
SALES (est): 1.5MM **Privately Held**
WEB: www.solidrockreadymix.com
SIC: 3273 Ready-mixed concrete

(G-11941)
SOLMAX GEOSYNTHETICS LLC
19103 Gundle Rd　(77073-3515)
PHONE..............................281 443-8564
Charles A Sorrentino, *President*
Peter McCourt, *President*
Mark Whitney, *President*
Mike Kirksey, *Exec VP*
Jeffery Nigh, *Exec VP*
◆ **EMP:** 300
SQ FT: 110,400
SALES (est): 124.2MM
SALES (corp-wide): 2.1MM **Privately**
Held
WEB: www.gseworld.com
SIC: 3081 Polyethylene film
HQ: Gse Holding, Inc.
19103 Gundle Rd
Houston TX 77073
281 443-8564

(G-11942)
SOLOFILL LLC (PA)
3515 Avignon Ct　(77082-2722)
P.O. Box 840595　(77284-0595)
PHONE..............................832 675-9862
Robert Vu, *Mng Member*
Jackie Vu, *Manager*
▲ **EMP:** 11
SALES (est): 3.5MM **Privately Held**
WEB: www.solofill.com
SIC: 3589 Coffee brewing equipment

(G-11943)
SOLUGEN INC (PA)
14549 Minetta St　(77035-6523)
PHONE..............................713 380-2134
Gaurab Chakrabarti, *CEO*
Jason Roberts, *President*
Sean Hunt, *COO*
Thomas Swanson, *Vice Pres*
Alan Pike, *Controller*
EMP: 70
SQ FT: 1,000
SALES: 7.6MM **Privately Held**
WEB: www.solugentech.com
SIC: 2879 Agricultural disinfectants

(G-11944)
SOLVAY AMERICA INC (HQ)
Also Called: Solvay North America
3737 Buffalo Speedway # 800
(77098-3099)
P.O. Box 27328　(77227-7328)
PHONE..............................713 525-4000
Rene Degreve, *President*
David G Birney, *Principal*
Noel Boulos, *Business Mgr*
Bill Bachman, *Vice Pres*
E J Buckingham, *Vice Pres*
◆ **EMP:** 50
SALES (est): 1.4B
SALES (corp-wide): 13.8MM **Privately**
Held
WEB: www.solvay.com
SIC: 2819 Industrial inorganic chemicals
PA: Solvay
Rue De Ransbeek 310
Bruxelles　1120
226 421-11

(G-11945)
SOLVAY CHEMICALS INC (DH)
Also Called: Solvay America
3737 Buffalo Speedway　(77098-3099)
P.O. Box 27328　(77227-7328)
PHONE..............................713 525-6800
Richard Hogan, *CEO*
Michael Lacey, *President*
Ron Hughes, *Exec VP*

Vance Erickson, *Senior VP*
Paul Hogan, *Senior VP*
◆ **EMP:** 150
SQ FT: 100,000
SALES (est): 909.6MM
SALES (corp-wide): 13.8MM **Privately Held**
WEB: www.solvay.us
SIC: 1474 2819 Soda ash (natural) mining; peroxides, hydrogen peroxide
HQ: Solvay America, Inc.
3737 Buffalo Speedway # 800
Houston TX 77098
713 525-4000

(G-11946)
SOLVAY FLUORIDES LLC
3737 Buffalo Spdwy Ste 80 (77098-3099)
PHONE...............................713 525-6700
Mark Looney,
◆ **EMP:** 63 **EST:** 1995
SALES (est): 26.1MM
SALES (corp-wide): 13.8MM **Privately Held**
WEB: www.solvay.us
SIC: 2819 2869 2812 Fluorine, elemental; industrial organic chemicals; alkalies & chlorine
HQ: Solvay Chemicals, Inc.
3737 Buffalo Speedway
Houston TX 77098
713 525-6800

(G-11947)
SOLVAY INFO SVCS NAFTA LLC
3737 Buffalo Spdwy Ste 80 (77098-3099)
P.O. Box 27328 (77227-7328)
PHONE...............................713 525-6000
E J Buckingham, *Vice Pres*
Carolyn S Egbert, *Vice Pres*
Bennett H Gilbert, *Vice Pres*
Philip M Uhrhan,
Carlos R Escobar, *Admin Sec*
EMP: 54
SALES (est): 6.6MM
SALES (corp-wide): 13.8MM **Privately Held**
WEB: www.solvay.com
SIC: 2819 Industrial inorganic chemicals
HQ: Solvay America, Inc.
3737 Buffalo Speedway # 800
Houston TX 77098
713 525-4000

(G-11948)
SOLVAY NORTH AMERICA LLC
3737 Buffalo Spdwy Ste 80 (77098-3099)
P.O. Box 27328 (77227-7328)
PHONE...............................713 525-6000
Carolyn Egbert,
E J Buckingham,
Edgar H Case,
EMP: 300
SALES (est): 28.8MM
SALES (corp-wide): 13.8MM **Privately Held**
WEB: www.solvay.us
SIC: 2819 Industrial inorganic chemicals
HQ: Solvay America, Inc.
3737 Buffalo Speedway # 800
Houston TX 77098
713 525-4000

(G-11949)
SOMERSET HOUSE PUBLISHING INC
Also Called: Bargainartusa.com
10688 Haddington Dr (77043-3229)
P.O. Box 869, Fulshear (77441-0869)
PHONE...............................713 932-6847
Larry Smith, *President*
Stephanie H Allen, *General Mgr*
EMP: 30
SQ FT: 38,000
SALES (est): 2.5MM **Privately Held**
WEB: www.somersetfineart.com
SIC: 2741 Art copy & poster publishing

(G-11950)
SONARDYNE INC
8280 Willow Place Dr N # 130 (77070-5778)
PHONE...............................281 890-2120
Kim Swords, *General Mgr*
John Ramsden, *Managing Dir*
Shaun Dunn, *Business Mgr*

Simon Reeves, *Vice Pres*
Barry Cairns, *Vice Pres*
▲ **EMP:** 18
SQ FT: 11,520
SALES (est): 28MM
SALES (corp-wide): 49.6MM **Privately Held**
WEB: www.sonardyne.com
SIC: 3829 Surveying instruments & accessories
HQ: Sonardyne Limited
Ocean House
Yateley HANTS GU46
125 287-2288

(G-11951)
SOND INDUSTRIES LLC
6403 Brittmoore Rd (77041-5118)
PHONE...............................281 372-8220
Sukhbir Sond, *Mng Member*
EMP: 17
SALES (est): 640.8K **Privately Held**
WEB: www.sondindustries.com
SIC: 3599 Machine shop, jobbing & repair

(G-11952)
SONGA OFFSHORE
Also Called: Songa Drilling
2925 Briarpark Dr Ste 100 (77042-3735)
P.O. Box 421533 (77242-1533)
PHONE...............................713 781-0670
Asbjorn Vivik, *President*
Cenk Yavas, *Vice Pres*
Jorge Garcia-Duran, *Project Mgr*
Michael Liga, *Project Mgr*
Anthony Morrow, *Project Mgr*
▼ **EMP:** 50
SALES (est): 2MM **Privately Held**
WEB: www.lan-inc.com
SIC: 1381 Drilling oil & gas wells

(G-11953)
SOR INC
Setex Products
5175 Ashley Ct (77041-6914)
PHONE...............................409 842-3334
Kevin Sourdellia, *Branch Mgr*
EMP: 13
SALES (corp-wide): 28.2MM **Privately Held**
WEB: www.sorinc.com
SIC: 3829 Thermometers & temperature sensors
PA: Sor, Inc.
14685 W 105th St
Lenexa KS 66215
913 888-2630

(G-11954)
SOR INC
Smart Sensors
5175 Ashley Ct (77041-6914)
PHONE...............................281 272-5333
Charisse Konrady, *Treasurer*
William Pearson, *Credit Mgr*
Greg Pryor, *Cust Mgr*
Srinivasan Seetharaman, *Manager*
EMP: 25
SALES (corp-wide): 28.2MM **Privately Held**
WEB: www.sorinc.com
SIC: 3823 Industrial instrmnts msrmnt display/control process variable
PA: Sor, Inc.
14685 W 105th St
Lenexa KS 66215
913 888-2630

(G-11955)
SORB ALL COMPANY
2300 Nance St (77020-5733)
P.O. Box 21148 (77226-1148)
PHONE...............................713 223-4575
Danny Thomason, *Owner*
EMP: 13 **EST:** 2011
SALES (est): 2.8MM **Privately Held**
WEB: www.sorballco.com
SIC: 2841 Soap & other detergents

(G-11956)
SOS CUETARA USA INC
10700 North Frwy Ste 800 (77037-1158)
PHONE...............................281 272-8800
Jesus Salazar-Bello, *President*
Lee Adams, *Vice Pres*
Raul Jaime Salazar-Bello, *Vice Pres*

Bronson Schultz, *Vice Pres*
▲ **EMP:** 250
SALES (est): 470MM
SALES (corp-wide): 177.9K **Privately Held**
SIC: 2044 Rice milling
HQ: Deoleo Sa
Calle Autovia Madrid-Cadiz, Km 388
Cordoba 14610
915 589-505

(G-11957)
SOURCE OPERATIONS GROUP LLC
11807 Westheimer Rd # 550 (77077-6790)
PHONE...............................888 557-7079
John Werner, *Mng Member*
Sean Andrews, *Director*
EMP: 30
SALES (est): 12.6MM **Privately Held**
SIC: 4911 4924 6221 3679 ; ; commodity brokers, contracts; power supplies, all types: static

(G-11958)
SOURCE VITAL LLC
1291 N Post Oak Rd # 125 (77055-7268)
PHONE...............................713 622-2190
Robert P Colgin, *CEO*
Helen K Pope, *President*
Samantha Cubillos, *Vice Pres*
Madeleine Pope, *Vice Pres*
EMP: 10
SQ FT: 6,450
SALES (est): 409.5K **Privately Held**
WEB: www.sourcevital.com
SIC: 2844 5999 Toilet preparations; toiletries, cosmetics & perfumes

(G-11959)
SOUTH BAY RESOURCES LLC (PA)
952 Echo Ln Ste 375 (77024-2814)
P.O. Box 924373 (77292-4373)
PHONE...............................713 785-8700
Steve Slack, *Mng Member*
Scott Rubsamen,
Steve Tobias,
EMP: 10
SQ FT: 5,000
SALES (est): 1.7MM **Privately Held**
WEB: www.sbres.com
SIC: 1382 Oil & gas exploration services

(G-11960)
SOUTH BELT PRESS INC
Also Called: South Belt Ellington Leader
11555 Beamer Rd Ste 200 (77089-2357)
PHONE...............................281 484-4337
David Flickinger, *President*
Marie Flickinger, *Vice Pres*
Micheline Hutson, *Treasurer*
EMP: 15 **EST:** 1975
SQ FT: 8,400
SALES (est): 66.4K **Privately Held**
WEB: www.southbeltleader.com
SIC: 2711 Job printing & newspaper publishing combined

(G-11961)
SOUTH COAST GRINDING CO LLC
5730 Ledbetter St (77087-4022)
PHONE...............................713 649-0001
Bill French, *President*
Marc Granger, *Vice Pres*
EMP: 13
SQ FT: 12,500
SALES (est): 2MM **Privately Held**
WEB: www.southcoastgrinding.com
SIC: 3599 Grinding castings for the trade; machine shop, jobbing & repair

(G-11962)
SOUTH COAST PRODUCTS LP
Also Called: South Coast Products & PDT Dev
20 Southbelt Indus Dr (77047-7010)
P.O. Box 450109 (77245-0109)
PHONE...............................713 434-2141
John Cantu, *Partner*
Ken Williams, *Opers Mgr*
Dennis James, *Sales Staff*
Markie Oldham, *Sales Staff*
Jimmy Trees, *Sales Staff*

◆ **EMP:** 32 **EST:** 1967
SQ FT: 180,000
SALES (est): 10.4MM **Privately Held**
WEB: www.socousa.com
SIC: 2891 2992 Sealing compounds for pipe threads or joints; lubricating oils & greases

(G-11963)
SOUTH COAST TERMINALS LP (PA)
Also Called: S C Terminals
7402 Wallisville Rd (77020-3595)
PHONE...............................713 672-2401
Artie Mc Ferrin, *Partner*
Sammie Yarbrough, *Sales Executive*
Cesar Martinez, *Manager*
◆ **EMP:** 90 **EST:** 1964
SQ FT: 3,600
SALES (est): 19.2MM **Privately Held**
WEB: www.scterm.com
SIC: 2992 1389 5169 2899 Oils & greases, blending & compounding; lease tanks, oil field: erecting, cleaning & repairing; chemicals & allied products; chemical bulk station & terminal; chemical preparations

(G-11964)
SOUTH EAST PALLET INC
6519 Rupley Cir (77087-3441)
P.O. Box 262393 (77207-2393)
PHONE...............................713 645-6131
Ramon Nava, *Owner*
EMP: 9
SALES (est): 784.1K **Privately Held**
SIC: 2448 Pallets, wood

(G-11965)
SOUTH HOUSTON CONCRETE PIPE CO
828 Old Gnoa Red Bluff Rd (77034-4011)
P.O. Box 101, South Houston (77587-0101)
PHONE...............................713 946-2831
Dale G Stone, *Vice Pres*
Melvin Hopkins, *Vice Pres*
EMP: 24
SQ FT: 1,000
SALES (est): 5.9MM **Privately Held**
WEB: www.shcponline.com
SIC: 3272 Concrete products used to facilitate drainage

(G-11966)
SOUTH TEXAS BOLT & FITTING INC
Also Called: Stb
4845 Homestead Rd Ste 500 (77028-5835)
PHONE...............................713 673-5376
Lance Byrnes, *President*
▲ **EMP:** 45
SQ FT: 30,000
SALES (est): 6.3MM
SALES (corp-wide): 182.5MM **Privately Held**
SIC: 3452 5085 3965 Bolts, metal; fasteners, industrial: nuts, bolts, screws, etc.; fasteners
HQ: Lamons Gasket Company
7300 Airport Blvd
Houston TX 77061
713 222-0284

(G-11967)
SOUTH TEXAS PRECISION INC
6989 W Little York Rd K (77040-4847)
PHONE...............................713 939-0101
Walter Shouten, *President*
EMP: 13
SQ FT: 5,000
SALES (est): 1.9MM **Privately Held**
WEB: www.southtexasprecision.com
SIC: 3599 Machine shop, jobbing & repair

(G-11968)
SOUTH TEXAS STEEL SVC CO LLC
226 E Tidwell Rd (77022-1622)
PHONE...............................713 699-2500
EMP: 10 **Privately Held**
WEB: www.stssc.com
SIC: 3441 Fabricated structural metal

GEOGRAPHIC

PA: South Texas Steel Service Company
Llc
201 E Crestwood Dr
Victoria TX 77901

(G-11969)
SOUTHAST VCATIONAL ALIANCE INC (PA)
Also Called: Sva Logistics
6018 Nunn St (77087-5123)
P.O. Box 23276 (77228-3276)
PHONE..................713 847-0697
Nathaniel Rido, *President*
EMP: 65
SALES (est): 3MM **Privately Held**
WEB: www.svabiz.com
SIC: 2393 4731 Textile bags; freight transportation arrangement

(G-11970)
SOUTHCROSS ENRGY PRTNERS GP LL
2103 Citywest Blvd (77042-2833)
PHONE..................214 979-3792
John E Bonn, *President*
Michael B Howe,
EMP: 291
SALES (est): 2.5MM
SALES (corp-wide): 42.4MM **Privately Held**
WEB: www.southcrossenergy.com
SIC: 1321 Natural gas liquids
PA: Southcross Holdings Lp
1717 Main St Ste 5200
Dallas TX 75201
214 979-3700

(G-11971)
SOUTHDOWN INC
1200 Smith St Ste 2400 (77002-4315)
PHONE..................713 650-6200
Clarence Comer, *President*
Edgar J Marston III, *Exec VP*
J Bruce Thompkins, *Exec VP*
James L Persky, *Senior VP*
Karen A Twitchell, *Treasurer*
EMP: 400
SQ FT: 9,600
SALES (est): 20MM **Privately Held**
SIC: 3241 3273 Cement, hydraulic; ready-mixed concrete
HQ: Cemex Cement, Inc.
10100 Katy Fwy Ste 300
Houston TX 77043
713 650-6200

(G-11972)
SOUTHERN ARCHTCTRAL SYSTEMS IN
Also Called: Sasi
10038 Talley Ln (77041-6128)
P.O. Box 40223 (77240-0223)
PHONE..................713 462-6379
David Labernz, *President*
Ron Di Bisalo, *Controller*
EMP: 22
SQ FT: 20,000
SALES (est): 2.5MM **Privately Held**
SIC: 3446 Architectural metalwork

(G-11973)
SOUTHERN CHNESE NWSPAPERS PUBG
Also Called: Southern Chinese Daily News
11122 Bellaire Blvd (77072-2608)
PHONE..................281 498-4310
Wea H Lee, *President*
▲ **EMP:** 14
SQ FT: 10,000
SALES (est): 1.1MM **Privately Held**
WEB: www.today-america.com
SIC: 2711 Newspapers, publishing & printing

(G-11974)
SOUTHERN HEAT EXCHANGER CORP
4206 Fidelity St (77029-3550)
PHONE..................281 668-4619
Brian Tucker, *Vice Pres*
Taylor Johnson, *Engineer*
Brandon Harbin, *CFO*
Phil Smith, *Sales Mgr*
Steve Boes, *Sales Staff*
EMP: 35 **Privately Held**

WEB: www.sheco.com
SIC: 3443 Heat exchangers: coolers (after, inter), condensers, etc.; condensers, steam
HQ: Southern Heat Exchanger Corporation
6100 Old Montgomery Hwy
Tuscaloosa AL 35405
205 345-5335

(G-11975)
SOUTHERN JWLY MFG HOUSTON CO
Also Called: S J Manufacturing
9830 Clay Rd (77080-1102)
PHONE..................713 460-5533
A D Stokes, *President*
EMP: 21
SQ FT: 6,500
SALES (est): 2.6MM **Privately Held**
SIC: 3911 Jewelry, precious metal

(G-11976)
SOUTHERN NOODLE COMPANY
6518 Wilcrest Dr (77072-2037)
PHONE..................281 988-7778
Xu Qing Hou, *President*
EMP: 10
SQ FT: 22,000
SALES (est): 874.4K **Privately Held**
SIC: 2098 2032 2041 2052 Noodles (e.g. egg, plain & water), dry; chow mein: packaged in cans, jars, etc.; flour mixes; cookies; grocery stores, chain; canned goods: fruit, vegetables, seafood, meats, etc.

(G-11977)
SOUTHERN SPRING MANUFACTURING
915 Pinemont Dr (77018-1401)
P.O. Box 926166 (77292-6166)
PHONE..................713 692-7191
Howard Payne, *President*
Rick King, *Vice Pres*
EMP: 15 **EST:** 1970
SQ FT: 8,000
SALES (est): 2.4MM **Privately Held**
WEB: www.southernspring.net
SIC: 3496 Miscellaneous fabricated wire products

(G-11978)
SOUTHERN TRANSFORMERS
15200 North Fwy (77090-6306)
PHONE..................713 923-1191
John Janik, *Principal*
EMP: 12 **EST:** 2007
SALES (est): 1.9MM **Privately Held**
WEB: www.electronicpowerdesign.com
SIC: 3625 3825 Control equipment, electric; instruments to measure electricity

(G-11979)
SOUTHERN TUBE LLC
13500 Industrial Rd (77015-6817)
PHONE..................713 231-2929
Eddy Chen, *Project Mgr*
Michael Lewis, *Prdtn Mgr*
Anthony Derosso, *QC Mgr*
Teruo Ishii, *CFO*
Ralston Simon, *Manager*
▲ **EMP:** 46
SALES (est): 14.8MM **Privately Held**
WEB: www.southern-tube.com
SIC: 3533 3317 Drilling tools for gas, oil or water wells; steel pipe & tubes

(G-11980)
SOUTHWEST GALVANIZING INC (PA)
737 Aleen St (77029-1601)
P.O. Box 24188 (77229-4188)
PHONE..................800 799-8413
Wanda Wright, *President*
Tim Piatt, *General Mgr*
Dennis Driskell, *Vice Pres*
Steve Mauterstock, *Vice Pres*
David Shannon, *Vice Pres*
▼ **EMP:** 131
SQ FT: 6,000
SALES (est): 20.7MM **Privately Held**
WEB: www.swgalvanizing.com
SIC: 3479 Galvanizing of iron, steel or end-formed products

(G-11981)
SOUTHWEST MACHINE WORKS INC
60 Southbelt Indus Dr (77047-7010)
P.O. Box 450665 (77245-0665)
PHONE..................713 433-6824
Marie Novak, *CEO*
Kenneth Novak, *President*
Anton Novak, *Vice Pres*
James Novak, *Treasurer*
EMP: 18
SQ FT: 2,500
SALES (est): 4.4MM **Privately Held**
WEB: www.swmw.co
SIC: 3599 Machine shop, jobbing & repair

(G-11982)
SOUTHWEST OCEAN SERVICES INC
Also Called: Swos
5721 Harvey Wilson Dr (77020-8025)
PHONE..................713 671-9101
Jacob Poroo, *CEO*
J Tracy Carrico, *Vice Pres*
Nick Talevich, *Purch Mgr*
Brandon Bundens, *Engineer*
Grant Gaspard, *Sales Staff*
◆ **EMP:** 35
SQ FT: 56,000
SALES (est): 13.2MM **Privately Held**
WEB: www.swos.net
SIC: 2298 Ropes & fiber cables; rope, except asbestos & wire

(G-11983)
SOUTHWEST PRECISION PRTRS LP
1055 Conrad Sauer Dr (77043-5201)
PHONE..................713 777-3333
Tim A Tully, *Partner*
Jim Walker, *General Mgr*
Karl Kluetz, *Vice Pres*
G Tod Tully, *Vice Pres*
Tom Bigham, *Opers Staff*
EMP: 95
SALES (est): 35.8MM **Privately Held**
WEB: www.swpp.com
SIC: 2752 2791 Commercial printing, offset; typesetting

(G-11984)
SOUTHWEST SPICE COMPANY LLC
Also Called: Gulf Pacific Ingredients LLC
12010 Taylor Rd (77041-1239)
PHONE..................713 860-5300
Christian Benckmann, *President*
Patrick J Casserly, *CFO*
EMP: 9
SALES (est): 738.1K **Privately Held**
WEB: www.gulfpac.com
SIC: 2099 Seasonings & spices

(G-11985)
SOUTHWESTERN PAINT PANELS LLC
2019 Sandydale Ln (77039-4301)
P.O. Box 891983, Oklahoma City OK (73189-1983)
PHONE..................281 442-0000
Michael Wilkes, *CEO*
Mary Zamiatowski, *Opers Staff*
EMP: 13 **EST:** 2008
SALES (est): 1.3MM **Privately Held**
WEB: www.swpaintpanels.com
SIC: 3599 Chemical milling job shop

(G-11986)
SOUTHWESTERN PLATING COMPANY
1312 Halpern St (77009-6497)
P.O. Box 8837 (77249-8837)
PHONE..................713 223-1331
Shirley Ferguson, *President*
Leonard Ferguson, *Corp Secy*
H Glynn Ferguson, *Vice Pres*
Charles Ferguson, *Chief Mktg Ofcr*
Matt Ferguson, *Corp Comm Staff*
EMP: 100 **EST:** 1947
SQ FT: 60,000
SALES (est): 11.1MM **Privately Held**
WEB: www.swplating.com
SIC: 3471 Electroplating of metals or formed products

(G-11987)
SPACE AGE LMNATING BINDERY INC
3400 White Oak Dr (77007-2646)
PHONE..................713 868-1471
Shelly Nesloney, *President*
Clinton P Nesloney, *Vice Pres*
David Tyson, *Technical Mgr*
Tina Tyson, *Treasurer*
Terri Kaley, *Admin Sec*
EMP: 18 **EST:** 1955
SQ FT: 10,000
SALES (est): 2.2MM **Privately Held**
WEB: www.spaceagebindery.com
SIC: 2782 Looseleaf binders & devices

(G-11988)
SPACE CITY MACHINE & TOOL CO
8101 Leghorn St (77040-5850)
PHONE..................713 939-0011
Jeffery Shane Elliott, *President*
Chad Kelley, *President*
Pam Dahl, *Corp Secy*
EMP: 17
SQ FT: 10,000
SALES (est): 2.4MM **Privately Held**
SIC: 3599 Machine shop, jobbing & repair

(G-11989)
SPACE CITY PUBLISHING
17045 El Camino Real # 103 (77058-2623)
P.O. Box 590764 (77259-0764)
PHONE..................281 480-3600
Kim Carlisle, *Principal*
EMP: 9 **EST:** 2007
SALES (est): 800.1K **Privately Held**
WEB: www.spacecitypublishing.com
SIC: 2741 Miscellaneous publishing

(G-11990)
SPACE EXPLORATION TECH CORP
13100 Space Center Blvd (77059-3653)
PHONE..................310 363-6000
Braden Fischer, *Opers Staff*
Krishna Pribadi, *Engineer*
Kyle Bolton, *Business Anlyst*
Paul Dovi, *Manager*
Richard Franzl, *Software Engr*
EMP: 875
SALES (corp-wide): 2B **Privately Held**
WEB: www.spacex.com
SIC: 3761 Rockets, space & military, complete
PA: Space Exploration Technologies Corp.
1 Rocket Rd
Hawthorne CA 90250
310 363-6000

(G-11991)
SPACEMAN HOME & OFFICE INC
3556 W T C Jester Blvd (77018-5047)
PHONE..................713 688-8808
David Linda, *President*
Daniel Herman, *Marketing Staff*
Michelle Levine, *Office Mgr*
EMP: 10
SQ FT: 4,000
SALES (est): 1.5MM **Privately Held**
WEB: www.spacemanager.com
SIC: 2522 Cabinets, office: except wood

(G-11992)
SPARKLE LIGHTING SERVICES
7938 Wright Rd (77041-2432)
PHONE..................713 856-8500
Syed Sarwar, *President*
Javad Minavi, *Vice Pres*
Charles Spooner, *Buyer*
Anthony Eoff, *Sales Staff*
Stephen Griffin, *Manager*
EMP: 22
SQ FT: 25,000
SALES (est): 3.8MM **Privately Held**
WEB: www.signcoamerica.com
SIC: 5046 1799 3993 Signs, electrical; sign installation & maintenance; signs & advertising specialties

(G-11993)
SPARROWS OFFSHORE LLC (HQ)
Also Called: Sparrows Group
6758 Northwinds Dr (77041-3013)
PHONE................................832 467-7300
Steve Bertone, *Vice Pres*
Patrick Yoes, *Project Mgr*
Scot Sprencel, *Mfg Spvr*
Steve Swanson, *Opers Staff*
Matt Barcelona, *Engineer*
◆ EMP: 50
SALES (est): 62.3MM
SALES (corp-wide): 62.6MM **Privately Held**
WEB: www.sparrowsgroup.com
SIC: 3531 Cranes
PA: Sparrows Offshore International Group Ltd.
Seton House
Aberdeen AB23
122 470-4868

(G-11994)
SPARTAN REINFORCING LLC (PA)
Also Called: Cancom Services
15840 Fm 529 Rd Ste 303 (77095-2569)
PHONE................................832 271-1721
Adrian Cano, *President*
EMP: 20
SQ FT: 12,000
SALES (est): 15MM **Privately Held**
WEB: www.spartanreinforcing.com
SIC: 3449 5051 Bars, concrete reinforcing: fabricated steel; forms, concrete construction (steel)

(G-11995)
SPEAKERMAX INC
Also Called: Speakermax.com
17203 Bamwood Dr (77090-2431)
PHONE................................281 880-9922
Brent Green, *President*
Michael Moore, *Marketing Staff*
▲ EMP: 15
SQ FT: 20,500
SALES (est): 1.5MM **Privately Held**
WEB: www.famousstages.com
SIC: 3651 7359 Speaker systems; equipment rental & leasing

(G-11996)
SPEC AMERICAS LLC
340 N Sam Houston Pkwy E # 110 (77060-3312)
PHONE................................281 812-7732
Chad Swim,
EMP: 20 EST: 2013
SALES (est): 5.5MM **Privately Held**
WEB: www.spec-pro.com
SIC: 3569 Testing chambers for altitude, temperature, ordnance, power

(G-11997)
SPECIALIZED MANUFACTURING LTD
1209 W 17th St (77008-3439)
PHONE................................713 864-2551
Kevin Kolb, *President*
EMP: 25
SQ FT: 50,000
SALES (est): 5MM **Privately Held**
WEB: www.specialized-mfg.com
SIC: 3549 Metalworking machinery

(G-11998)
SPECIALTY BINDERY SERVICE INC
Also Called: Specialty Bindery and Printing
2211 Norfolk St Ste 805 (77098-4056)
PHONE................................713 869-0594
Patricia B Fidler, *President*
Carmen Vigil, *Manager*
EMP: 10 EST: 1970
SALES (est): 1.5MM **Privately Held**
WEB: www.sbpmail.com
SIC: 2789 Binding only: books, pamphlets, magazines, etc.

(G-11999)
SPECIALTY HEAT TREAT INC
11307 W Little York Rd (77041-4916)
P.O. Box 79326 (77279-9326)
PHONE................................713 937-3101

Tom Moore, *President*
Mary Moore, *Corp Secy*
Sam Moore, *Vice Pres*
Fritz Huss, *Engineer*
Doug Chamberlain, *Sales Mgr*
EMP: 46
SQ FT: 18,500
SALES (est): 8.7MM **Privately Held**
WEB: www.specialtyheattreat.com
SIC: 3398 Metal heat treating

(G-12000)
SPECIALTY METAL FINISHING INC
1915 W Dallas St (77019-4412)
PHONE................................713 528-5428
Clifton O Love, *President*
Clifton Love, *President*
Love Charlene E, *Vice Pres*
EMP: 10
SQ FT: 4,500
SALES (est): 750K **Privately Held**
WEB: www.specialtymetalfinishing.com
SIC: 3471 Plating of metals or formed products; polishing, metals or formed products

(G-12001)
SPECIALTY SAND COMPANY INC (PA)
16601 Garrett Rd (77044-5957)
PHONE................................281 456-9553
William A Keckley, *President*
Warren Michael, *COO*
Wayne Rowe, *Opers Mgr*
Shelly Sammis, *CFO*
Teryon Doucet, *Sales Staff*
▲ EMP: 21
SQ FT: 2,500
SALES (est): 8.2MM **Privately Held**
WEB: www.specialtysand.com
SIC: 1446 Blast sand mining; foundry sand mining

(G-12002)
SPECIALTY TOWER LIGHTING LTD
1630 Elmview Dr (77080-7223)
PHONE................................713 722-8123
George A Jackson, *President*
Meredith Nichols, *Vice Pres*
Alberto Resnedez, *Sales Staff*
◆ EMP: 10
SALES (est): 1.5MM **Privately Held**
WEB: www.specialtytowerlighting.com
SIC: 3648 Airport lighting fixtures: runway approach, taxi or ramp

(G-12003)
SPECIALTY VALVE GROUP LLC
3550 W T C Jester Blvd (77018-5047)
PHONE................................281 385-8200
Marco Nicolayevsky, *Mng Member*
◆ EMP: 22
SQ FT: 3,000
SALES (est): 1.5MM **Privately Held**
WEB: www.specialityvalvegroup.com
SIC: 3491 Industrial valves

(G-12004)
SPECKTRUM
301 Wilcrest Dr (77042-1047)
PHONE................................832 892-0863
Jeremiah Tuck, *CEO*
Jeremiah C Tuck,
EMP: 15
SALES (est): 123.7K **Privately Held**
SIC: 2023 8322 2086 7299 Dietary supplements, dairy & non-dairy based; general counseling services; water, pasteurized: packaged in cans, bottles, etc.; personal document & information services; personal financial services; financial management for business; financial consultant

(G-12005)
SPECS FAMILY PARTNERS LTD
Also Called: Specs Liquor Stores
2314 W Holcombe Blvd (77030-2010)
PHONE................................713 669-1722
David Best, *Manager*
Mike Boaz, *Manager*
EMP: 13

SALES (corp-wide): 155.2MM **Privately Held**
WEB: www.specsonline.com
SIC: 2084 5921 Wines, brandy & brandy spirits; hard liquor
PA: Spec's Family Partners, Ltd.
2410 Smith St
Houston TX 77006
713 526-8787

(G-12006)
SPECTRASEIS INC
10815 Woodedge Dr (77070-5341)
PHONE................................303 658-9171
Ross Newman, *CEO*
Corey Sisler, *CFO*
Kent Johnson, *VP Sales*
EMP: 40
SALES (est): 6.2MM **Privately Held**
WEB: www.esgsolutions.com
SIC: 1382 Geophysical exploration, oil & gas field

(G-12007)
SPECTRASENSORS INC (HQ)
4333 W Sam Houston Pkwy N (77043-1221)
PHONE................................713 466-3172
George Balogh, *CEO*
Alfred Feitisch, *Vice Pres*
Bryce Ford, *Vice Pres*
Jorge Jones, *Vice Pres*
EMP: 25
SALES (est): 16.6MM
SALES (corp-wide): 291.8MM **Privately Held**
WEB: www.spectrasensors.com
SIC: 3826 Analytical instruments
PA: Endress+Hauser Ag
Kagenstrasse 2
Reinach BL 4153
617 157-700

(G-12008)
SPECTRUM CORPORATION (PA)
Also Called: Spectrum Message Centers
10048 Easthaven Blvd (77075-3298)
P.O. Box 750456 (77275-0456)
PHONE................................713 944-6200
J B Bishop, *President*
Bernard Correa, *Corp Secy*
Randy Rawlings, *Exec VP*
Jeff Bishop, *Vice Pres*
Jeff J Bishop, *Vice Pres*
▲ EMP: 100
SQ FT: 44,000
SALES (est): 24.2MM **Privately Held**
WEB: www.specorp.com
SIC: 3993 Scoreboards, electric

(G-12009)
SPECTRUM QUALITY STANDARDS
17360 Groschke Rd (77084-4626)
P.O. Box 2346, Sugar Land (77487-2346)
PHONE................................281 578-7575
Carmen Gentes, *Finance*
Gary Lew, *Mng Member*
Michael Bieluwka, *Technician*
Mike Bieluwka, *Technician*
EMP: 13
SALES (est): 3.1MM **Privately Held**
WEB: www.spectrumstandards.com
SIC: 2869 Fluorinated hydrocarbon gases

(G-12010)
SPEEDCAST AMERICAS INC (HQ)
4400 S Sam Houston Pkwy E (77048-5902)
PHONE................................281 340-2057
Michael Healy, *Principal*
Jay Goldberg, *Counsel*
Greg Howes, *Vice Pres*
Toni Rudnicki, *Vice Pres*
Frances Jackson, *Office Mgr*
EMP: 14
SALES (est): 140.3MM **Privately Held**
WEB: www.speedcast.com
SIC: 3663 Satellites, communications

(G-12011)
SPEEDWAY LLC
2454 Delwin St (77034-2116)
PHONE................................713 943-9002
EMP: 66 **Publicly Held**

WEB: www.speedway.com
SIC: 1311 Crude petroleum production
HQ: Speedway Llc
500 Speedway Dr
Enon OH 45323
937 864-3000

(G-12012)
SPEEDWAY LLC
1201 Louisiana St Ste 700 (77002-5603)
P.O. Box 2040 (77252-2040)
PHONE................................877 609-4255
Bryce C Thueson, *Admin Mgr*
EMP: 310 **Publicly Held**
WEB: www.speedway.com
SIC: 1382 Oil & gas exploration services
HQ: Speedway Llc
500 Speedway Dr
Enon OH 45323
937 864-3000

(G-12013)
SPEEDWAY LLC
1501 Mckinney St (77010-4010)
PHONE................................713 496-4000
John Hess, *Branch Mgr*
EMP: 10 **Publicly Held**
WEB: www.speedway.com
SIC: 1311 Crude petroleum & natural gas
HQ: Speedway Llc
500 Speedway Dr
Enon OH 45323
937 864-3000

(G-12014)
SPF CORPORATION OF AMERICA
6529 Cunningham Rd # 2105 (77041-4746)
PHONE................................713 983-9373
Yasuhiro Senda, *President*
▲ EMP: 15
SQ FT: 3,000
SALES (est): 2.3MM **Privately Held**
WEB: www.spfusa.com
SIC: 3441 3356 Fabricated structural metal; titanium
HQ: Spf Co.,Ltd.
5-1, Horitatori, Mizuho-Ku
Nagoya AIC 467-0

(G-12015)
SPIKE ELECTRIC AND CONTRLS LLC
Also Called: Spike Electrical Supply
5914 E Sam Houston Pkwy S (77034-5561)
PHONE................................832 243-5372
Allen C Attaway, *President*
Terry Macaulay, *CFO*
EMP: 15
SALES (est): 3.6MM **Privately Held**
WEB: www.spikeelectric.com
SIC: 5099 3699 Firearms & ammunition, except sporting; high-energy particle physics equipment

(G-12016)
SPIRE MARKETING INC (DH)
3773 Richmond Ave Ste 300 (77046-1139)
PHONE................................346 308-7549
George Godat, *Vice Pres*
EMP: 20
SALES (est): 9.1MM
SALES (corp-wide): 1.8B **Publicly Held**
WEB: www.lacledeenergy.com
SIC: 1382 Oil & gas exploration services
HQ: Spire Resources Llc
700 Market St
Saint Louis MO 63101
314 342-0500

(G-12017)
SPITZER INDUSTRIES INC
13863 Industrial Rd (77015-6822)
PHONE................................713 230-4200
Cullen Spitzer, *Branch Mgr*
John Wagner, *Manager*
EMP: 27
SALES (corp-wide): 185MM **Privately Held**
WEB: www.spitzerind.com
SIC: 3441 Fabricated structural metal

PA: Spitzer Industries, Inc.
12141 Wickc Ln Ste 750
Houston TX 77079
832 783-7000

(G-12019)
SPITZER INDUSTRIES INC
10543 Fisher Rd (77041-4083)
PHONE..................713 466-1518
Ted Johnson, *Manager*
EMP: 39
SALES (corp-wide): 185MM **Privately
Held**
WEB: www.spitzerind.com
SIC: 3441 Fabricated structural metal
PA: Spitzer Industries, Inc.
12141 Wickc Ln Ste 750
Houston TX 77079
832 783-7000

(G-12019)
SPITZER INDUSTRIES INC (PA)
12141 Wickc Ln Ste 750 (77079)
PHONE..................832 783-7000
Cullen R Spitzer, *President*
Ansari Hosein, *Superintendent*
Milo Thibeadeau, *COO*
Charlie O'Hara, *Senior VP*
Charles Ohara, *Vice Pres*
▲ **EMP:** 320
SQ FT: 9,000
SALES (est): 185MM **Privately Held**
WEB: www.spitzerind.com
SIC: 3441 Fabricated structural metal

(G-12020)
SPITZER INDUSTRIES INC
11433 Brittmoore Park Dr (77041-6919)
PHONE..................713 856-9208
Fax: 713 466-1950
EMP: 23
SALES (corp-wide): 185MM **Privately
Held**
SIC: 3441 Structural Metal Fabrication
PA: Spitzer Industries, Inc.
12141 Wickc Ln Ste 750
Houston TX 77079
832 783-7000

(G-12021)
SPM FLOW CONTROL INC
8300 Cypress Creek Pkwy # 450
(77070-5654)
PHONE..................281 820-7807
Kevin Delaat, *Manager*
EMP: 138
SALES (corp-wide): 3.4B **Privately Held**
WEB: www.global.weir
SIC: 3533 Oil & gas field machinery
HQ: S.P.M. Flow Control, Inc.
7601 Wyatt Dr
Fort Worth TX 76108
817 246-2461

(G-12022)
SPOOLTECH LLC
9325 Highway 6 N (77095-2403)
PHONE..................281 861-6800
Clinton Derrick, *President*
Charles Richards, *Maintence Staff*
EMP: 50
SQ FT: 7,000
SALES (est): 5.5MM **Privately Held**
WEB: www.spooltech.com
SIC: 2499 Spools, wood

(G-12023)
SPRAYMETAL INC
5610 Polk St (77023-2106)
PHONE..................713 923-2000
Paul Coselli, *President*
Andrew Schumacher, *President*
Donna Parks, *Admin Sec*
EMP: 15
SALES (est): 1.7MM
SALES (corp-wide): 15.6MM **Privately
Held**
WEB: www.schumachercoinc.com
SIC: 3479 Coating of metals & formed
products
PA: Schumacher International, Inc.
5610 Polk St
Houston TX 77023
713 923-5548

(G-12024)
SPRECHER & SCHUH INC (DH)
Also Called: Sprecher Schuh
15910 Intl Plz Dr (77032-2439)
P.O. Box 602288, Charlotte NC (28260-2288)
PHONE..................281 442-9000
Theodore D Crandall, *Ch of Bd*
Michael J Dudas, *President*
Micheal Flanagan, *Principal*
Steven W Etzel, *Treasurer*
Samantha Smith, *Manager*
EMP: 25
SALES (est): 3.6MM **Publicly Held**
WEB: www.sprecherschuh.com
SIC: 3625 Motor controls, electric
HQ: Rockwell Automation Switzerland
Gmbh
Industriestrasse 20
Aarau AG 5000
628 372-121

(G-12025)
**SPRING BOLT AND NUT MFG
LTD**
3280 Wheat St (77086-2226)
PHONE..................281 448-4440
Tim Mallone, *President*
Baron Yarborough, *General Mgr*
Richard Sivley, *Vice Pres*
Bob Sivley, *Manager*
Juan Veloz, *Manager*
EMP: 15
SALES (est): 3.1MM **Privately Held**
WEB: www.springboltandnut.com
SIC: 3452 Bolts, nuts, rivets & washers

(G-12026)
**SPRING BRANCH SHTMTL CO
INC**
Also Called: Curbco
7960 Fallbrook Dr (77064-3418)
P.O. Box 690806 (77269-0806)
PHONE..................281 469-8855
Marie Hudspeth, *President*
Scott Maske, *Superintendent*
John L Hudspeth, *Vice Pres*
John Hudspeth, *Vice Pres*
Curtis McNeill, *VP Sales*
EMP: 15
SQ FT: 4,000
SALES (est): 3.2MM **Privately Held**
WEB: www.curbco.com
SIC: 3444 Sheet metalwork

(G-12027)
**SPRING ENGINEERS HOUSTON
LTD (PA)**
9740 Tanner Rd (77041-7621)
PHONE..................713 690-9488
Ken Penske, *Division Pres*
Kelly Strickland, *Manager*
EMP: 23
SALES (est): 5.3MM **Privately Held**
WEB: www.springhouston.com
SIC: 3495 3469 Wire springs; metal
stampings

(G-12028)
**SPX FLOW TECHNOLOGY USA
INC**
8800 Westplain Dr (77041-1400)
PHONE..................281 897-2964
Bob Wert, *Manager*
EMP: 23
SALES (corp-wide): 1.5B **Publicly Held**
WEB: www.spx.com
SIC: 3556 3559 Dairy & milk machinery;
pharmaceutical machinery
HQ: Spx Flow Technology Usa, Inc.
13320 Balntyn Corp Pl
Charlotte NC 28277
704 808-3848

(G-12029)
SQUARE MILE ENERGY LLC
Also Called: Kiwienergy
5847 San Felipe St # 2949 (77057-3010)
PHONE..................713 266-3685
Kerry G Bonner, *President*
Mark E Gregg, *President*
Gary W Loveless, *Chairman*
Alfred B Bettis, *Vice Pres*
Mollie J Allen, *Vice Pres*
EMP: 25

SALES (est): 7.5MM **Privately Held**
WEB: www.sqmenergy.com
SIC: 1382 Oil & gas exploration services

(G-12030)
SRG VENTURES LLC
Also Called: Srg Solutions
565 W 38th St (77018-6401)
P.O. Box 10806 (77206-0806)
PHONE..................281 214-8560
Soheil Saheb,
Kevin M Rollins,
EMP: 42
SALES (est): 9.1MM **Privately Held**
WEB: www.srgstairs.com
SIC: 3446 2396 2499 2521 Stairs, stair-
cases, stair treads: prefabricated metal;
furniture trimmings, fabric; furniture inlays
(veneers); wood office furniture; bar furni-
ture; hotel furniture; furniture refinishing;
furniture repair & maintenance

(G-12031)
SSAB TEXAS INC
13609 Industrial Rd # 114 (77015-6835)
PHONE..................713 341-7700
David Britten, *President*
Michele Klebuc-Simes, *Vice Pres*
Phillip Marusarz, *CFO*
Gregory Burnett, *Treasurer*
Preston Shatto, *Regl Sales Mgr*
◆ **EMP:** 125
SALES (est): 23.1MM
SALES (corp-wide): 7.9B **Privately Held**
SIC: 3312 Blast furnaces & steel mills
HQ: Ssab Enterprises, Llc
11 N Water St Ste 17000
Mobile AL 36602

(G-12032)
SSI INTERESTS LP
3770 Gramercy St (77025-1216)
PHONE..................713 221-3488
Jack McClure, *Partner*
Sean A Moore, *General Ptnr*
▲ **EMP:** 9 **EST:** 1997
SQ FT: 35,000
SALES (est): 1.2MM **Privately Held**
SIC: 3431 Plumbing fixtures: enameled
iron cast iron or pressed metal

(G-12033)
ST JUDE CANDLE COMPANY LP
4851 Homestead Rd Ste 102 (77028-5837)
PHONE..................281 768-7800
John Tillotson, *Managing Prtnr*
Tanya Schneider, *Vice Pres*
Larry Fridel, *Production*
William Grimsley, *CFO*
David Wingard, *CFO*
▲ **EMP:** 51
SQ FT: 65,000
SALES (est): 7.1MM **Privately Held**
WEB: www.stjudecc.com
SIC: 3999 Candles

(G-12034)
STABIL DRILL SPECIALTIES LLC
608 Richey Rd (77090-5710)
PHONE..................281 583-0127
Freddy Gebhardt, *Vice Pres*
Danny Young, *Vice Pres*
Ron Richardson, *Manager*
Chris Baker, *Manager*
James Boyd, *Representative*
EMP: 25 **Publicly Held**
WEB: www.stabildrill.com
SIC: 1389 7359 Gas field services; oil field
services; equipment rental & leasing
HQ: Stabil Drill Specialties, L.L.C.
110 Candlewood Dr
Lafayette LA 70508
337 837-3001

(G-12035)
STABILIS ENERGY INC (PA)
10375 Richmond Ave # 700 (77042-4165)
PHONE..................832 456-6500
Jim Reddinger, *President*
Donald Norris, *Engineer*
Andrew Puhala, *CFO*
Darlene Calfee, *Manager*
Charles Dauber, *Director*
EMP: 56 **EST:** 1996

SALES: 47MM **Publicly Held**
WEB: www.stabilisenergy.com
SIC: 1321 Natural gas liquids; natural gas
liquids production

(G-12036)
STABILIS ENERGY LLC (HQ)
Also Called: Stabilis Energy Services
10375 Richmond Ave # 700 (77042-4165)
PHONE..................409 833-1115
Casey Crenshaw, *CEO*
Koby Knight, *Vice Pres*
Stephen Coombes, *Plant Mgr*
Jim Reddinger, *CFO*
Trey Brandimarte, *Finance*
EMP: 49
SALES (est): 29.5MM
SALES (corp-wide): 47MM **Publicly Held**
WEB: www.stabilisenergy.com
SIC: 1321 Liquefied petroleum gases (nat-
ural) production
PA: Stabilis Energy, Inc.
10375 Richmond Ave # 700
Houston TX 77042
832 456-6500

(G-12037)
STAGE 3 SEPARATION LLC
2000 Silber Rd (77055-2623)
PHONE..................713 868-4040
Frederick Lausen Jr, *CEO*
Tom Atkinson, *General Mgr*
Marco Hoyos, *Area Mgr*
Jake Talasek, *Area Mgr*
Matt Carlson, *Vice Pres*
EMP: 100
SALES (est): 49.6MM **Privately Held**
WEB: www.s3s.com
SIC: 1389 Mud service, oil field drilling

(G-12038)
**STAINLESS STL CSTM
FBRCTORS IN**
2116 Almeda Genoa Rd (77047-4410)
P.O. Box 450132 (77245-0132)
PHONE..................713 433-0495
Henry Gonzales, *President*
Mary Gonzales, *Corp Secy*
Lawrence Gonzales, *Vice Pres*
David Harrison, *Engineer*
EMP: 20
SQ FT: 12,000
SALES (est): 3.8MM **Privately Held**
WEB: www.sscustomfabinc.com
SIC: 3469 3441 Kitchen fixtures & equip-
ment: metal, except cast aluminum; fabri-
cated structural metal

(G-12039)
STAIRWAYS INC
4166 Pinemont Dr (77018-1106)
PHONE..................713 680-3110
John M Anderson, *President*
Caroline Anderson, *Corp Secy*
Kerry Anderson, *Vice Pres*
Mark Anderson, *Vice Pres*
Bob Osier, *Technology*
▼ **EMP:** 50
SQ FT: 22,500
SALES (est): 10.4MM **Privately Held**
WEB: www.stairwaysinc.com
SIC: 3446 2431 Stairs, staircases, stair
treads: prefabricated metal; staircases &
stairs, wood

(G-12040)
**STALLION OILFIELD CNSTR LLC
(PA)**
950 Corbindale Rd Ste 400 (77024-2849)
PHONE..................713 528-5544
Craig M Johnson,
EMP: 20
SALES (est): 11.2MM **Privately Held**
WEB: www.stallionoilfield.com
SIC: 1389 Oil field services

(G-12041)
**STALLION OILFIELD HOLDINGS
LTD (PA)**
950 Corbindale Rd Ste 400 (77024-2849)
PHONE..................713 528-5544
David C Mannon, *CEO*
Hill Dishman, *Exec VP*
David Schorlemer, *Exec VP*
Stephen Thorness, *Vice Pres*

EMP: 27
SALES (est): 1.4B Privately Held
WEB: www.stallionoilfield.com
SIC: 1389 Oil field services

(G-12042)
STALLION OILFIELD SERVICES LTD (HQ)
950 Corbindale Rd Ste 400 (77024-2849)
P.O. Box 1486 (77251-1486)
PHONE......................................713 528-5544
Craig Johnson, CEO
Chad Entwistle, Superintendent
Matt Gutierrez, Superintendent
Hill Dishman, COO
Mike Moore, Vice Pres
EMP: 90
SALES (est): 1.3B Privately Held
WEB: www.stallionoilfield.com
SIC: 1389 Oil field services

(G-12043)
STANDARD RENEWABLE ENERGY LP (DH)
Also Called: Newpoint Energy Solutions
4460 W 12th St (77055-7204)
PHONE......................................281 763-2020
Steven Cory, Principal
EMP: 58
SQ FT: 12,000
SALES (est): 16.4MM
SALES (corp-wide): 35.7MM Privately Held
WEB: www.sre3.com
SIC: 5074 3822 Heating equipment & panels, solar; energy cutoff controls, residential or commercial types
HQ: Gridpoint, Inc.
1911 Freedom Dr Ste 850
Reston VA 20190
703 667-7000

(G-12044)
STAR ENGRAVING COMPANY INC
500 Century Plaza Dr # 145 (77073-6385)
P.O. Box 5407, Kingwood (77325-5407)
PHONE......................................281 951-5808
Margaret Stephens, President
John M Stephens, President
Debbie Cannaliato, Vice Pres
EMP: 9
SQ FT: 10,000
SALES (est): 1.1MM Privately Held
WEB: www.starengraving.com
SIC: 2759 Stationery: printing

(G-12045)
STAR PIPE LLC (PA)
Also Called: Star Pipe Products
4018 Westhollow Pkwy (77082-4604)
PHONE......................................281 558-3000
Doug Allen, Division Mgr
John Marney, Sales Staff
Pete Lisowski, Manager
Sanjeev Jashwant, Senior Mgr
Ramesh Bhutada,
◆ EMP: 100
SQ FT: 187,000
SALES (est): 57.3MM Privately Held
WEB: www.starpipeproducts.com
SIC: 3498 Pipe fittings, fabricated from purchased pipe

(G-12046)
STAR PIPE PRODUCTS LTD (PA)
4018 Westhollow Pkwy (77082-4604)
PHONE......................................281 558-3000
Ramesh Bhutada, Partner
Dan McCutcheon, Partner
Jon Larsen, Regional Mgr
Rishi Bhutada, Vice Pres
Jason Onan, Vice Pres
◆ EMP: 150
SQ FT: 187,000
SALES (est): 166.2MM Privately Held
WEB: www.starpipeproducts.com
SIC: 3498 Pipe fittings, fabricated from purchased pipe

(G-12047)
STAR PIPE USA LLC (HQ)
Also Called: Sp Foundry
4018 Westhollow Pkwy (77082-4604)
P.O. Box 1509, Coffeyville KS (67337-7809)
PHONE......................................620 251-5700
Navin Bhargava, Purchasing
Ramesh Bhutada, Mng Member
Navin K Bharagava,
Daniel McCutcheon,
EMP: 67 EST: 2016
SALES (est): 30.3MM Privately Held
WEB: www.spfoundry.com
SIC: 3498 3325 3321 Fabricated pipe & fittings; alloy steel castings, except investment; gray & ductile iron foundries

(G-12048)
STARJB
10419 Gold Point Dr (77064-7122)
PHONE......................................713 408-8327
Zarema Dubinsky, Business Mgr
EMP: 10
SALES (est): 1.1MM Privately Held
WEB: www.starjb.com
SIC: 3533 Drilling tools for gas, oil or water wells

(G-12049)
STARPAK PLASTICS INC
9690 W Wingfoot Rd (77041-9037)
PHONE......................................713 329-9183
Jacob Bazbaz, President
EMP: 99
SALES (est): 11.9MM Privately Held
WEB: www.starpakltd.com
SIC: 2673 Garment bags (plastic film): made from purchased materials

(G-12050)
STARTEX LINEN CO
7011 Lozier St (77021-4618)
PHONE......................................713 782-4419
Yoaz Schroit, President
Theresa Szymkowski, Vice Pres
Teresa Szymkowski, VP Sales
EMP: 15
SQ FT: 3,000
SALES (est): 1.4MM Privately Held
WEB: www.startexlinen.com
SIC: 2299 5699 Linen fabrics; uniforms & work clothing

(G-12051)
STATE SIGN CORPORATION
7630 Hansen Rd (77061-3410)
P.O. Box 750429 (77275-0429)
PHONE......................................713 943-1831
Daniel P Zoch, President
Ismael Herrera, General Mgr
Becky A Zoch, Vice Pres
Thomas Ericah, Project Mgr
David Lampkin, Project Mgr
EMP: 52 EST: 1957
SQ FT: 18,000
SALES (est): 5.8MM Privately Held
WEB: www.statesign.com
SIC: 1799 3993 Sign installation & maintenance; signs & advertising specialties

(G-12052)
STATEWIDE TRAFFIC SIGNAL CO
1509 W 34th St (77018-6213)
PHONE......................................713 680-2875
Billy D Ralls, President
Charles Bobo, Exec VP
Joseph G Spanos, Vice Pres
Maria Ochoa, Executive
EMP: 40
SQ FT: 1,200
SALES (est): 8.3MM Privately Held
WEB: www.statewidetrafficsignals.com
SIC: 3669 Traffic signals, electric

(G-12053)
STEEL DESIGNS INC (PA)
13303 Emmett Rd (77041-2590)
PHONE......................................713 937-3006
Howard F Bermel, President
Michael Large, Senior VP
Richard Bridgers, Vice Pres
Joan C Bermel, Admin Sec
EMP: 22
SQ FT: 14,000

SALES (est): 4.3MM Privately Held
SIC: 3446 3444 3441 Stairs, staircases, stair treads: prefabricated metal; railings, bannisters, guards, etc.: made from metal pipe; ladders, for permanent installation: metal; sheet metalwork; fabricated structural metal

(G-12054)
STEEL EFFECTS LLC
12300 Zavalla St (77085-1122)
P.O. Box 35707 (77235-5707)
PHONE......................................713 729-1100
Kami Eisemann, Mng Member
EMP: 10
SQ FT: 6,000
SALES (est): 955.9K Privately Held
WEB: www.steel-effects.com
SIC: 3441 Fabricated structural metal

(G-12055)
STEEPLECHASE DIAGNOSTIC CENTER
10694 Jones Rd Ste 150 (77065-4260)
PHONE......................................281 955-0440
Bill Richie, Director
Frank Battaglia, Admin Sec
EMP: 22
SALES (est): 3.3MM Privately Held
WEB: www.diagnosticinjury.com
SIC: 2835 In vitro & in vivo diagnostic substances

(G-12056)
STEFFANI METALS INC
6811 Satsuma Dr (77041-2709)
P.O. Box 41337 (77241-1337)
PHONE......................................713 896-9160
Larry Krueger, President
Traci Warner, Corp Secy
EMP: 15 EST: 1981
SQ FT: 20,000
SALES (est): 6MM Privately Held
WEB: www.steffanimetals.com
SIC: 3441 Fabricated structural metal

(G-12057)
STEM CELL INNOVATIONS INC (PA)
11222 Richmond Ave # 180 (77082-6662)
PHONE......................................281 679-7000
EMP: 38
SQ FT: 44,000
SALES: 86.8K Privately Held
SIC: 2834 8731 Study Manufacture And Sale Of Pharmaceutical Products

(G-12058)
STEPHENS A-1 LBR & PALLET INC
Also Called: A-1 Lumber & Pallet Co
16701 Mathis Church Rd (77090-3705)
PHONE......................................281 440-6444
EMP: 30
SQ FT: 25,000
SALES (est): 4MM Privately Held
WEB: www.a1lumberpallet.com
SIC: 2448 Pallets, wood

(G-12059)
STERLING DRLG FUND 1983-1 LP
Also Called: Prime Energy Management
9821 Katy Fwy Ste 1050 (77024-1218)
PHONE......................................203 358-5700
Julie Portnoy, Manager
EMP: 108
SALES (est): 6.5MM Privately Held
SIC: 1381 Directional drilling oil & gas wells

(G-12060)
STERLING GROUP LP (PA)
Also Called: Clayton, Dubilier & Rice
9 Greenway Plz Ste 2400 (77046-0897)
PHONE......................................713 877-8257
Frank J Hevrdejs, Partner
Gregory L Elliott, Partner
C Kevin Garland, Partner
John D Hawkins, Partner
Chryl Hoz, Partner
EMP: 40

SALES (est): 365.5MM Privately Held
WEB: www.sterling-group.com
SIC: 6799 3441 3648 3641 Investors; fabricated structural metal; lighting equipment; electric lamps; sheet metalwork

(G-12061)
STEVE GIBSON
12826 Fm 529 Rd (77041-2631)
PHONE......................................713 937-8838
Steve Gibson, Owner
EMP: 15
SALES (est): 1MM Privately Held
SIC: 2431 Millwork

(G-12062)
STEWART & STEVENSON LLC (HQ)
55 Waugh Dr Ste 1000 (77007-5834)
PHONE......................................713 751-2700
John Merrifield, President
Jared Shannon, General Mgr
John B Simmons, Vice Chairman
Kamron Massumi, Counsel
Richard Banas, Vice Pres
◆ EMP: 100
SALES (est): 4.2B
SALES (corp-wide): 2.8B Publicly Held
WEB: www.stewartandstevenson.com
SIC: 5084 5082 3533 7353 Industrial machinery & equipment; oil field equipment; oil & gas field machinery; oil & gas drilling rigs & equipment; oil equipment rental services
PA: Kirby Corporation
55 Waugh Dr Ste 1000
Houston TX 77007
713 435-1000

(G-12063)
STEWART STEVENSON CAPITL CORP
601 W 38th St (77018-6403)
P.O. Box 2968 (77252-2968)
PHONE......................................713 868-7700
Michael L Grimes, President
Pat Mc Phee, Manager
▼ EMP: 100
SALES (est): 1.2B
SALES (corp-wide): 2.8B Publicly Held
WEB: www.stewartandstevenson.com
SIC: 5084 5013 5078 5082 Engines & transportation equipment; engines & parts, diesel; engines, gasoline; materials handling machinery; automotive supplies & parts; refrigeration units, motor vehicles; general construction machinery & equipment; road construction equipment; forestry equipment; military motor vehicle assembly; truck trailers, used in plants, docks, terminals, etc.
HQ: Stewart & Stevenson Llc
55 Waugh Dr Ste 1000
Houston TX 77007

(G-12064)
STEWART STEVENSON PWR PDTS LLC
55 Waugh Dr Ste 1000 (77007-5834)
P.O. Box 1776, Harvey LA (70059-1776)
PHONE......................................504 347-4326
Rickey Boudreaux, General Mgr
Charles Chituet, Vice Pres
Chris Staszak, Opers Mgr
Jim Embry, VP Sales
EMP: 120
SALES (corp-wide): 2.8B Publicly Held
WEB: www.stewartandstevenson.com
SIC: 5084 7538 3519 Engines & parts, diesel; engine repair; internal combustion engines
HQ: Stewart & Stevenson Power Products, Llc
55 Waugh Dr Ste 800
Houston TX 77007

(G-12065)
STEWART STEVENSON PWR PDTS LLC (DH)
55 Waugh Dr Ste 800 (77007-5824)
PHONE......................................713 751-2600
Bob Hargrave, President
Aven Sharp, General Mgr
Frank Tuch, General Mgr
Mark Sudia, Engineer

Sylvia Jimerson, *Payroll Mgr*
◆ **EMP:** 169
SALES (est): 2.6B
SALES (corp-wide): 2.8B **Publicly Held**
WEB: www.stewartandstevenson.com
SIC: 1389 5084 5082 3533 Construction, repair & dismantling services; bailing, cleaning, swabbing & treating of wells; gas field services; oil field services; industrial machinery & equipment; oil field equipment; oil & gas field machinery; oil & gas drilling rigs & equipment; oil equipment rental services

(G-12066)
STEWART TUBULAR PRODUCTS LLC
5951 N Houston Rosslyn Rd (77091-3403)
PHONE.................................713 682-1486
Brandon Bethea, *Principal*
Daniel V Phan, *Principal*
Andrew Davis, *Technician*
▼ **EMP:** 16
SALES (est): 2.4MM **Privately Held**
WEB: www.stewarttubular.com
SIC: 2241 Hose fabric, tubular

(G-12067)
STINGER CHEMICAL LLC
Also Called: Stinger Auto Appearance Pdts
1100 Pleasantville Dr (77029-3232)
PHONE.................................713 227-1340
Warren Davis, *CEO*
Stuart Durham, *COO*
Fritz Seewald III, *Vice Pres*
Chris Barboza, *Sales Mgr*
Greg Rothrock, *Sales Staff*
◆ **EMP:** 54
SQ FT: 93,500
SALES (est): 20MM **Privately Held**
WEB: www.stingerchemicals.com
SIC: 2992 2842 7542 2841 Lubricating oils & greases; automobile polish; washing & polishing, automotive; soap & other detergents

(G-12068)
STOLLER GROUP INC (PA)
9090 Katy Fwy Ste 400 (77024-1696)
PHONE.................................713 461-1493
Russell Thomas, *General Mgr*
Jerry Stoller, *Principal*
Larry Lintner, *Regional Mgr*
EMP: 11
SALES (est): 124.1MM **Privately Held**
WEB: www.stollerusa.com
SIC: 3999 Plants, artificial & preserved

(G-12069)
STOLLER INTERNATIONAL INC (HQ)
9090 Katy Fwy Ste 400 (77024-1696)
PHONE.................................713 461-1493
Jerry Stoller, *Ch of Bd*
Larry Lintner, *Regional Mgr*
Albert N Liptay, *Vice Pres*
Joe Rice, *Vice Pres*
Robert Shortell, *Vice Pres*
◆ **EMP:** 23
SQ FT: 10,000
SALES (est): 124.1MM **Privately Held**
WEB: www.stollerusa.com
SIC: 5191 2879 Fertilizer & fertilizer materials; agricultural chemicals
PA: Stoller Group, Inc.
9090 Katy Fwy Ste 400
Houston TX 77024
713 461-1493

(G-12070)
STONE BOND TECHNOLOGIES
1021 Main St Ste 1550 (77002-6522)
PHONE.................................713 622-8798
Antonio M Szabo, *Owner*
Pamela Szab, *Senior VP*
Michael Gronewaller, *Vice Pres*
Scott Shadrach, *Vice Pres*
Irma Barrientos, *Marketing Staff*
EMP: 15
SQ FT: 6,287
SALES (est): 2.1MM **Privately Held**
WEB: www.stonebond.com
SIC: 7372 Application computer software

(G-12071)
STONE CAST INC
2300 Karbach St Bldg B (77092-8004)
P.O. Box 131517 (77219-1517)
PHONE.................................713 683-6780
Carl Radcliffe, *President*
Sheena Khan, *Admin Sec*
EMP: 12
SQ FT: 5,000
SALES (est): 1.5MM **Privately Held**
WEB: www.stonecastinc.com
SIC: 3272 Stone, cast concrete

(G-12072)
STORAGE & PROCESSORS INC
8500 Clinton Dr (77029-3616)
P.O. Box 15526 (77220-5526)
PHONE.................................832 360-2800
Joe Trapolino, *President*
EMP: 73
SALES (est): 7.8MM
SALES (corp-wide): 5.5MM **Privately Held**
WEB: www.storageandprocessors.com
SIC: 4214 4225 3498 Local trucking with storage; general warehousing & storage; coils, pipe: fabricated from purchased pipe
HQ: Steel And Pipe Supply Company, Inc.
555 Poyntz Ave Ste 122
Manhattan KS 66502
785 587-5100

(G-12073)
STORK TECHNICAL SVCS USA INC (DH)
3350 Rogerdale Rd Ste G (77042-4161)
PHONE.................................832 781-5700
Nestor Sanabria, *Principal*
Jorge Estrada, *Principal*
Richard Tang, *Opers Staff*
EMP: 100
SQ FT: 15,000 **Privately Held**
WEB: www.stork.com
SIC: 1389 Oil field services
HQ: Stork Technical Services (Rbg) Limited
Norfolk House
Aberdeen AB21
122 472-2888

(G-12074)
STRAND ENERGY LC
440 Louisiana St Ste 2600 (77002-1059)
PHONE.................................713 658-8096
Kent Brock, *President*
Scott M Airey, *Vice Pres*
Rick Hemmen, *Opers Mgr*
Todd Messer, *CFO*
EMP: 14
SQ FT: 5,000
SALES (est): 3.1MM **Privately Held**
WEB: www.strandenergy.com
SIC: 1311 1382 Crude petroleum production; oil & gas exploration services

(G-12075)
STRATAS FOODS LLC
1302 Harris St (77020-7663)
PHONE.................................713 671-0057
EMP: 9 **Privately Held**
WEB: www.stratasfoods.com
SIC: 2079 Edible fats & oils
PA: Stratas Foods Llc
7970 Stage Hills Blvd
Bartlett TN 38133

(G-12076)
STREAM-FLO USA LLC (DH)
8726 Fallbrook Dr (77064-3317)
PHONE.................................903 912-1022
Mark McNeill, *Ch of Bd*
Duncan McNeill, *Ch of Bd*
Fran Bobb, *President*
Michelle Kinnes, *General Mgr*
Tarik Radwan, *District Mgr*
▲ **EMP:** 63
SALES (est): 77.2MM
SALES (corp-wide): 38.3MM **Privately Held**
WEB: www.streamflo.com
SIC: 3533 Oil field machinery & equipment
HQ: Stream-Flo Industries Ltd
4505 74 Ave Nw
Edmonton AB
780 468-6789

(G-12077)
STREAMLINE POLYMERS LLC
16950 Wallisville Rd (77049-5014)
PHONE.................................832 376-4500
Chris Goldstraw, *CEO*
Beth Gibson, *Principal*
Martin Tomerlin, *Principal*
EMP: 27
SALES (est): 108.9K **Privately Held**
WEB: www.streamlinepolymers.com
SIC: 2834 Pharmaceutical preparations

(G-12078)
STREAMLINE SUPPLY INC
10711 Valley Forge Dr (77042-1423)
PHONE.................................713 914-0330
EMP: 10
SALES (est): 1.1MM **Privately Held**
SIC: 3533 Mfg Oil/Gas Field Machinery

(G-12079)
STRESS ENGINEERING SVCS INC
Also Called: Mohr Research & Engrg Div
13062 Westwind E Blvd (77041)
PHONE.................................713 466-1527
Nancy Gerow, *Branch Mgr*
EMP: 40
SALES (corp-wide): 99.7MM **Privately Held**
WEB: www.stress.com
SIC: 8711 8734 3829 Consulting engineer; testing laboratories; geophysical & meteorological testing equipment
PA: Stress Engineering Services, Inc.
13800 Westfair East Dr
Houston TX 77041
281 955-2900

(G-12080)
STRONG CONCRETE SERVICES INC (PA)
13617 Ralph Culver Rd (77086-1513)
PHONE.................................281 847-9304
Brooks Strong, *President*
EMP: 27
SQ FT: 12,000
SALES (est): 4.4MM **Privately Held**
SIC: 3714 Third axle attachments or six wheel units for motor vehicles

(G-12081)
STRONG INDUSTRIES INC
13617 Ralph Culver Rd (77086-1513)
PHONE.................................281 448-9315
Brooks Lee Strong, *President*
Randy Dorsey, *Vice Pres*
Lorri Strong, *Vice Pres*
Michael Page, *Engineer*
Josh Fisher, *Manager*
EMP: 25
SQ FT: 12,000
SALES (est): 8.6MM **Privately Held**
WEB: www.superdumps.com
SIC: 3714 3532 3531 Third axle attachments or six wheel units for motor vehicles; mining machinery; construction machinery
PA: Strong Concrete Services, Inc
13617 Ralph Culver Rd
Houston TX 77086

(G-12082)
STRONGFAB SOLUTIONS INC
9209 Windfern Rd (77064-7719)
P.O. Box 41266 (77241-1266)
PHONE.................................713 856-6511
Roberto L Tulio, *President*
Luis Morales, *COO*
EMP: 40
SQ FT: 25,000
SALES (est): 9.6MM **Privately Held**
WEB: www.strongfab.com
SIC: 3533 Gas field machinery & equipment

(G-12083)
STUCKEY TERRY & ASSOCIATES
Also Called: Stuckey's Specialty Tool
2511 Lauder Rd (77039-3117)
P.O. Box 670287 (77267-0287)
PHONE.................................281 590-8628
Terry Stuckey, *President*
Sarah E Stuckey, *Vice Pres*

▲ **EMP:** 21
SQ FT: 15,000
SALES (est): 4.7MM **Privately Held**
WEB: www.stuckeyspecialtytools.com
SIC: 3533 8711 Oil field machinery & equipment; consulting engineer

(G-12084)
STX SERVICE AMERICAS LLC
11995 Fm 529 Rd (77041-3011)
PHONE.................................713 637-4030
Michele Laughlin, *President*
▲ **EMP:** 11 **EST:** 2012
SQ FT: 20,000
SALES (est): 2.4MM **Privately Held**
WEB: www.stxserviceamericas.com
SIC: 3731 7538 Shipbuilding & repairing; diesel engine repair: automotive
HQ: Stx Marine Service Co., Ltd.
102 Jungang-Daero, Jung-Gu
Busan 48938

(G-12085)
STYLE PUBLICATIONS
Also Called: Style Magazine
2646 S Loop W Ste 270 (77054-5608)
P.O. Box 14035 (77221-4035)
PHONE.................................713 748-6300
Francis Page Jr, *Owner*
EMP: 12
SALES (est): 581.3K **Privately Held**
WEB: www.stylemagazine.com
SIC: 2721 7374 Magazines: publishing & printing; computer graphics service

(G-12086)
SUBSEA 7 (US) LLC (HQ)
17220 Katy Fwy Ste 100 (77094-1485)
PHONE.................................713 430-1100
Jean Cahuzac, *CEO*
Ian Cobban, *President*
Lorri Brown, *Principal*
Brian Schacht, *Business Mgr*
John Evans, *COO*
◆ **EMP:** 147
SALES (est): 84.1MM **Privately Held**
WEB: www.subsea7.com
SIC: 1629 3731 Marine construction; offshore supply boats, building & repairing

(G-12087)
SUBSEA COMPANY
4527 Brittmoore Rd (77041-8005)
PHONE.................................281 324-0558
Andy Cates, *President*
Thomas A Cates, *President*
Ricahard Davidson, *Vice Pres*
Barry McMiles, *Vice Pres*
Tim Nelson, *Opers Mgr*
▲ **EMP:** 21
SQ FT: 14,000
SALES (est): 2.9MM **Privately Held**
WEB: www.thesubsea.com
SIC: 1389 Oil field services

(G-12088)
SUBSEA HYDRAULIC LEADS LLC
Also Called: Shl
6401 Cunningham Rd (77041-4713)
PHONE.................................832 327-4853
Edward Flores, *Project Mgr*
James Drapela, *Mng Member*
EMP: 9
SALES: 7MM **Privately Held**
WEB: www.subsealeads.com
SIC: 3492 Hose & tube couplings, hydraulic/pneumatic

(G-12089)
SUBSEA TECHNOLOGY INC
Also Called: S S T
6911 Signat Dr (77041-2718)
PHONE.................................281 498-7399
Robert Hoff, *CEO*
David Hosie, *President*
Rick Griffey, *Co-Owner*
Glenn Grimes, *Co-Owner*
Jeremiah Carstensen, *Plant Mgr*
▼ **EMP:** 70
SQ FT: 2,000
SALES (est): 3.6MM **Privately Held**
WEB: www.pts-technology.com
SIC: 1389 Oil field services

(G-12090)
SUDAGLASS FIBER TECHNOLOGY
14714 Perthshire Rd A (77079-7615)
P.O. Box 440481 (77244-0481)
PHONE...................................281 496-5427
▲ EMP: 61
SQ FT: 4,000
SALES (est): 5.2MM **Privately Held**
SIC: 3296 Mfg Mineral Wool

(G-12091)
SUHM SPRING WORKS INC (PA)
14650 Hathrow Forest Pkwy (77032-5404)
PHONE...................................713 224-9293
Mark E Scarborough, *President*
Richard Vargas, *Vice Pres*
Williams Brenda, *QC Mgr*
Vanessa Beas, *Sales Staff*
Belinda Deleon, *Sales Staff*
EMP: 130 EST: 1885
SQ FT: 8,000
SALES: 32.6MM **Privately Held**
WEB: www.suhm.net
SIC: 3495 3493 Wire springs; coiled flat springs

(G-12092)
SULZER USA INC
1255 Enclave Pkwy Ste 300 (77077-2767)
PHONE...................................832 886-2300
Kelli Edell, *President*
EMP: 23 EST: 2017
SALES (est): 5.3MM **Privately Held**
WEB: www.sulzer.com
SIC: 3561 Pumps & pumping equipment

(G-12093)
SUMEHR INC
Also Called: Kissaluvs
12302 Sienna Rosa Ln (77041-6077)
PHONE...................................713 849-5528
Tashi Nibber, *President*
Randip Singh, *Vice Pres*
EMP: 11
SQ FT: 3,000
SALES (est): 1.1MM **Privately Held**
SIC: 2399 5137 Diapers, except disposable: made from purchased materials; diapers

(G-12094)
SUMMIT MIDSTREAM PARTNERS LP (PA)
910 Louisiana St Ste 4200 (77002-4950)
PHONE...................................832 413-4770
Leonard W Mallett, *President*
Matthew Delaney, *General Ptnr*
Peter Labbat, *General Ptnr*
Scott Rogan, *General Ptnr*
Jeff Spinner, *General Ptnr*
▲ EMP: 47
SALES: 443.5MM **Publicly Held**
WEB: www.summitmidstream.com
SIC: 1311 4922 Crude petroleum & natural gas; natural gas transmission

(G-12095)
SUMMIT STEEL FABRICATORS INC
Also Called: Summit Steel Services
2004 Federal Rd (77015-6716)
PHONE...................................713 451-6960
Roland Rodriguez, *President*
John Kim, *Vice Pres*
Erasmo Rodriguez, *Vice Pres*
Herman Ortiz, *Project Mgr*
David Calanchi, *Foreman/Supr*
EMP: 65
SQ FT: 21,000
SALES (est): 25.3MM **Privately Held**
WEB: www.summitsteelfab.com
SIC: 3446 3441 Stairs, fire escapes, balconies, railings & ladders; fabricated structural metal

(G-12096)
SUMNER MANUFACTURING CO LLC
Also Called: Sumner Manufacturing Co Inc
7514 Alabonson Rd (77088-4036)
PHONE...................................281 999-6900
Robert H Collins Jr, *President*
Lawrence R Velez, *Vice Pres*
Tomie Esparza, *Export Mgr*
Guillermo Santiago, *Production*
Emil Griffin, *Purchasing*
▲ EMP: 160 EST: 1966
SQ FT: 80,000
SALES (est): 35.9MM
SALES (corp-wide): 2B **Privately Held**
WEB: www.sumner.com
SIC: 3423 3537 Hand & edge tools; trucks, tractors, loaders, carriers & similar equipment
PA: Southwire Company, Llc
1 Southwire Dr
Carrollton GA 30119
770 832-4242

(G-12097)
SUN COAST RESOURCES INC (PA)
6405 Cavalcade St Bldg 1 (77026-4315)
PHONE...................................713 844-9600
Kathy E Lehne, *President*
Lisa L Smith, *Corp Secy*
Yadira Benitez, *Representative*
EMP: 153
SQ FT: 9,500
SALES (est): 1B **Privately Held**
WEB: www.suncoastresources.com
SIC: 5172 2992 5084 1389 Petroleum brokers; lubricating oils & greases; oil well machinery, equipment & supplies; oil field services

(G-12098)
SUNBELT HOT TUBS LLC
Also Called: Sunbelt Spas
3924 Dunvale Rd (77063-5818)
PHONE...................................281 575-9814
Robert Markiton, *President*
EMP: 102 EST: 1979
SQ FT: 40,000
SALES (est): 21.5MM **Privately Held**
WEB: www.sunbeltspas.com
SIC: 3088 Hot tubs, plastic or fiberglass

(G-12099)
SUNBELT STUD WELDING INC
6381 Windfern Rd (77040-4964)
PHONE...................................713 939-8903
Eric A Ford, *President*
Katie Kuehnert, *Sales Associate*
Jeff Ford, *Marketing Staff*
Melissa Ford, *Admin Sec*
▲ EMP: 13
SQ FT: 19,000
SALES (est): 3.5MM **Privately Held**
WEB: www.sunbeltstudwelding.com
SIC: 3399 Metal fasteners

(G-12100)
SUNCOAST POST-TENSION LTD (DH)
509 N Sam Houston Pkwy E # 300 (77060-4130)
PHONE...................................281 445-8886
◆ EMP: 200 EST: 2007
SALES: 279.3MM
SALES (corp-wide): 2.9B **Privately Held**
WEB: www.suncoast-pt.com
SIC: 3315 3316 3496 3449 Cable, steel: insulated or armored; cold finishing of steel shapes; miscellaneous fabricated wire products; miscellaneous metalwork
HQ: Keller North America, Inc.
7550 Teague Rd Ste 300
Hanover MD 21076
410 551-8200

(G-12101)
SUNCOAST POST-TENSION LTD
15422 Lillja Rd (77060-5220)
PHONE...................................281 445-8886
Pete Scoppa, *Manager*
SRI Srinivasan, *Info Tech Dir*
EMP: 200
SALES (corp-wide): 2.9B **Privately Held**
WEB: www.suncoast-pt.com
SIC: 3315 3316 Cable, steel: insulated or armored; cold finishing of steel shapes
HQ: Suncoast Post-Tension, Ltd.
509 N Sam Houston Pkwy E # 300
Houston TX 77060
281 445-8886

(G-12102)
SUNNY SKY PRODUCTS LLC (PA)
11747 Windfern Rd Ste 100 (77064-4880)
PHONE...................................713 683-9399
▲ EMP: 60 EST: 1998
SQ FT: 30,000
SALES (est): 22.2MM **Privately Held**
WEB: www.sunnyskyproducts.com
SIC: 2086 Carbonated beverages, nonalcoholic: bottled & canned

(G-12103)
SUNSHINE MACHINE INC
13515 Ann Louise Rd (77086-1501)
PHONE...................................281 445-0326
Nen V Nguyen, *President*
Khoi Doan, *Vice Pres*
EMP: 11
SQ FT: 14,000
SALES (est): 2.1MM **Privately Held**
WEB: www.sunshinemachineinc.com
SIC: 3714 7539 Motor vehicle parts & accessories; machine shop, automotive

(G-12104)
SUNTRONIC INC
Also Called: Suntronic Electronic Assembly
10501 Kipp Way Dr Ste 350 (77099-2761)
PHONE...................................281 879-9562
John Ly, *President*
Mary Chao, *Vice Pres*
EMP: 45
SQ FT: 15,000
SALES (est): 6.5MM **Privately Held**
WEB: www.suntronicinc.com
SIC: 3671 Picture tube reprocessing

(G-12105)
SUPER HEATERS LLC
10260 Westheimer Rd # 460 (77042-3110)
P.O. Box 421328 (77242-1328)
PHONE...................................713 952-5533
Mark Fisher, *CEO*
EMP: 40
SALES (est): 6.4MM **Privately Held**
SIC: 3561 1389 Pumps, oil well & field; oil field services

(G-12106)
SUPER IMPRINT SOLUTIONS LLC
Also Called: Express Custom USB
1980 Post Oak Blvd Ste 15 (77056-3899)
PHONE...................................877 570-5573
Amit Momin, *Accounts Mgr*
Rainish Sunesara,
EMP: 9
SALES (est): 500K **Privately Held**
WEB: www.expresscustomusb.com
SIC: 2759 Promotional printing

(G-12107)
SUPER LOPEZ TORTILLAS LLC
7314 Harrisburg Blvd (77011-4739)
PHONE...................................713 921-1237
Javier Lopez, *President*
EMP: 75
SALES (est): 2.2MM **Privately Held**
WEB: www.super-lopez.com
SIC: 2099 Tortillas, fresh or refrigerated

(G-12108)
SUPERBAG USA CORP (PA)
9291 Baythorne Dr (77041-7742)
P.O. Box 437000 (77243-7000)
PHONE...................................713 462-1173
Simon Bazbaz, *President*
Carl Hisle, *Vice Pres*
Santiago Martinez, *Project Mgr*
Hugo Balcazar, *Opers Mgr*
Anna Hernandez, *Opers Mgr*
▲ EMP: 275
SQ FT: 190,000
SALES (est): 155MM **Privately Held**
WEB: www.superbag.com
SIC: 2673 5411 Plastic bags: made from purchased materials; grocery stores

(G-12109)
SUPERBAG USA CORP
9201 Baythorne Dr (77041-7735)
PHONE...................................713 462-1173
Simon Bazbaz, *President*
EMP: 154 **Privately Held**
WEB: www.superbag.com
SIC: 2673 Plastic bags: made from purchased materials
PA: Superbag U.S.A. Corp.
9291 Baythorne Dr
Houston TX 77041

(G-12110)
SUPERIOR CLADDING PRODUCTS LLC
11505 Todd St (77055-1305)
PHONE...................................281 405-9400
Jesse Trubia, *Mng Member*
EMP: 23 EST: 2014
SALES (est): 2.9MM **Privately Held**
WEB: www.scphou.com
SIC: 3272 Concrete products

(G-12111)
SUPERIOR ENERGY SERVICES INC
16610 Aldine Westfield Rd (77032-1352)
PHONE...................................281 784-5717
Brandon Osborn, *Opers Staff*
Bryce Traweek, *Manager*
Ann Cegielski, *Director*
EMP: 23 **Publicly Held**
WEB: www.superiorenergy.com
SIC: 1389 Oil field services
PA: Superior Energy Services, Inc.
1001 La St Ste 2900
Houston TX 77002

(G-12112)
SUPERIOR ENERGY SERVICES INC (PA)
Also Called: Ips Optimization
1001 La St Ste 2900 (77002)
PHONE...................................713 654-2200
Terence E Hall, *Ch of Bd*
David D Dunlap, *President*
Albert Montanez, *District Mgr*
Blaine Edwards, *Counsel*
Jennifer Phan, *Counsel*
EMP: 84
SALES (est): 1.4B **Publicly Held**
WEB: www.superiorenergy.com
SIC: 1389 3533 7353 Servicing oil & gas wells; well plugging & abandoning, oil & gas; oil & gas field machinery; oil field equipment, rental or leasing

(G-12113)
SUPERIOR ENERGY SERVICES LLC
Also Called: Sales Office
11000 Equity Dr Ste 150 (77041-8240)
PHONE...................................281 999-0047
Julia Meade, *Business Mgr*
Saju Pappan, *Vice Pres*
Jeremy McConnell, *Opers Mgr*
Kirk Eicher, *Manager*
Lynn Hebert, *Manager*
EMP: 20 **Publicly Held**
WEB: www.superiorenergy.com
SIC: 7353 1389 Oil field equipment, rental or leasing; servicing oil & gas wells; well plugging & abandoning, oil & gas
HQ: Superior Energy Services, L.L.C.
203 Commission Blvd
Lafayette LA 70508
337 714-4545

(G-12114)
SUPERIOR ENERGY SERVICES LLC
Also Called: Superior Completion Services
16610 Aldine Westfield Rd (77032-1352)
PHONE...................................281 784-5700
Ed Smith, *Branch Mgr*
EMP: 53 **Publicly Held**
WEB: www.superiorenergy.com
SIC: 1389 7353 Well plugging & abandoning, oil & gas; oil field equipment, rental or leasing
HQ: Superior Energy Services, L.L.C.
203 Commission Blvd
Lafayette LA 70508
337 714-4545

(G-12115)
SUPERIOR GRATING INC
3006 April Ln (77092-7216)
PHONE...................................713 686-9475
Leo Gonze, *President*

Jason Gonze, *Vice Pres*
EMP: 17
SQ FT: 17,000
SALES (est): 3.6MM **Privately Held**
WEB: www.metelmex.com
SIC: 3446 3441 Gratings, tread: fabricated metal; fabricated structural metal

(G-12116)
SUPERIOR INFORMATION SYSTEMS
Also Called: Superior Is
7100 Regency Square Blvd # 125 (77036-3202)
PHONE..................713 524-8998
J E Ivison, *Principal*
Joe Ivison, *Manager*
EMP: 15
SALES (corp-wide): 2.1MM **Privately Held**
SIC: 8748 7372 8741 Systems analysis & engineering consulting services; prepackaged software; management services
PA: Superior Information Systems
435 Murphy Rd Ste 168
Stafford TX 77477
713 524-8998

(G-12117)
SUPERIOR IT SOLUTIONS LLC
Also Called: Elevated Techology
16350 Park Ten Pl (77084-5146)
PHONE..................713 501-1260
Jason Rorie, *Owner*
EMP: 12 **EST:** 2006
SALES (est): 1.6MM **Privately Held**
WEB: www.jaxsupport.com
SIC: 7372 Business oriented computer software

(G-12118)
SUPERIOR PROCESSING SERVICE
1100 Louisiana St Ste 350 (77002-5258)
PHONE..................713 759-6900
John W Croft Jr, *President*
Peterj Pavluk, *General Mgr*
Markc Snapp, *Vice Pres*
J C Walter III, *Vice Pres*
Emily Herrmann, *Treasurer*
EMP: 21
SALES (est): 1.1MM
SALES (corp-wide): 11.3MM **Privately Held**
SIC: 1311 Natural gas production
PA: Superior Natural Gas Corp
1100 Louisiana St Ste 350
Houston TX 77002
713 759-6900

(G-12119)
SUPERIOR SHOT PEENING INC (PA)
Also Called: Ndustri.com
13930 Luthe Rd (77039-1810)
PHONE..................281 449-6559
Albert Johnson, *President*
Gayle Blasingame, *Corp Secy*
Van Blasingame, *Vice Pres*
Thomas Sheldon, *CFO*
Tom Sheldon, *CFO*
▲ **EMP:** 83
SQ FT: 22,500
SALES (est): 17MM **Privately Held**
WEB: www.superiorshotpeening.com
SIC: 1081 3479 Metal mining services; painting, coating & hot dipping

(G-12120)
SUPERIOR THREADED PRODUCTS LP
9045 E Sam Houston Pkwy N (77044-1851)
PHONE..................281 459-3131
Bill Bean, *Partner*
Ann Rodrigues, *Purchasing*
Frank Harris, *QC Mgr*
Doug Cook, *Sales Mgr*
Daniel May, *Sales Staff*
EMP: 50
SALES (est): 14.2MM **Privately Held**
WEB: www.stphou.com
SIC: 3541 Pipe cutting & threading machines

(G-12121)
SUPERIOR TRAILER SALES CO
4624 N Mccarty St (77013-3636)
PHONE..................713 674-2676
EMP: 30
SALES (corp-wide): 98MM **Privately Held**
SIC: 3792 Mfg Travel Trailers/Campers
PA: Superior Trailer Sales Co.
501 Us Highway 80 E
Mesquite TX 75182
972 226-3893

(G-12122)
SUPREME ELECTRICAL SVCS INC
Also Called: Lime Instrument
1187 Brittmoore Rd (77043-5003)
PHONE..................713 676-2588
C Jim Stewart, *President*
Matthew Bennett, *Vice Pres*
Dane Ray, *CFO*
Laura Hamby, *Asst Controller*
E'Lisa Kackley, *Receptionist*
EMP: 75
SQ FT: 14,000
SALES (est): 53.4MM **Privately Held**
WEB: www.supreme-electrical.com
SIC: 4911 3823 Electric services; industrial process control instruments

(G-12123)
SUPREME MANUFACTURING COMPANY
Also Called: Supreme Rubber Products
7102 Chippewa Blvd (77086-3227)
PHONE..................281 447-3153
Walter T Burke, *President*
Tom Burke, *Corp Secy*
Michael Kight, *Exec VP*
Roy Scavez, *Vice Pres*
EMP: 14
SQ FT: 24,000
SALES (est): 2.6MM **Privately Held**
WEB: www.patriotpiston.com
SIC: 3069 Hard rubber & molded rubber products

(G-12124)
SURFACE TECHNIQUES INC
1545 Blalock Rd (77080-7318)
P.O. Box 19462 (77224-9462)
PHONE..................713 932-8050
EMP: 18 **EST:** 1976
SQ FT: 12,000
SALES (est): 2.5MM **Privately Held**
WEB: www.surfacetechnique.com
SIC: 3471 Anodizing (plating) of metals or formed products

(G-12125)
SURGE OPERATING LLC (PA)
7850 N Sam Houston Pkwy W S (77064-3319)
PHONE..................832 333-2300
Dexter Burleigh, *CEO*
Phil Webb, *COO*
Pete Bowser, *Vice Pres*
Jessica Conway, *Vice Pres*
Joe Fleming, *Vice Pres*
EMP: 34
SALES (est): 146MM **Privately Held**
WEB: www.surgeenergya.com
SIC: 1381 Drilling oil & gas wells

(G-12126)
SURGITECH INC
13225 Fm 529 Rd Ste E (77041-2598)
PHONE..................800 975-6850
Glenn R McColpin, *President*
EMP: 23
SALES (est): 131.9K **Privately Held**
WEB: www.marginal-wells.com
SIC: 1382 Oil & gas exploration services

(G-12127)
SURVEYS & ANALYSIS INC
800 Town And Country Blvd # 500 (77024-4563)
PHONE..................508 842-4011
Roland A Coutu III, *President*
Neil Dulmaine, *Vice Pres*
EMP: 50 **EST:** 1966

SALES (est): 5.2MM **Privately Held**
WEB: www.surveysandanalysis.com
SIC: 7389 3533 Inspection & testing services; pipeline & power line inspection service; gas field machinery & equipment

(G-12128)
SW HEALTH CARE SOLUTIONS LLC
6418 Star Shadow Ln (77066-3265)
PHONE..................832 578-6694
Asim Saber, *Mng Member*
EMP: 14
SALES (est): 600K **Privately Held**
SIC: 7372 Application computer software

(G-12129)
SWD ENTERPRISES LLC
1148 Arlington St (77008-7050)
PHONE..................281 846-6851
David Dunnavant,
EMP: 36
SALES (est): 201.3K
SALES (corp-wide): 5.3MM **Privately Held**
SIC: 1389 Gas field services; oil field services
HQ: Four Wood Energy Partners Llc
33 Plymouth St Ste 302
Montclair NJ 07042
212 701-4500

(G-12130)
SWECO FAB INC
Also Called: Piping Technology & Products
3701 Holmes Rd (77051-1545)
P.O. Box 34546 (77234-4546)
PHONE..................713 731-0030
Durga Agrawal, *President*
Garline Howard, *Principal*
Rakesh Agrawal, *Vice Pres*
Sushila Agrawal, *Vice Pres*
Randy J Bailey, *Vice Pres*
▼ **EMP:** 390 **EST:** 1957
SQ FT: 450,000
SALES (est): 42MM
SALES (corp-wide): 137.4MM **Privately Held**
WEB: www.swecofab.com
SIC: 3494 3444 3443 3441 Pipe fittings; sheet metalwork; fabricated plate work (boiler shop); fabricated structural metal
PA: Piping Technology & Products, Inc.
3701 Holmes Rd
Houston TX 77051
800 787-5914

(G-12131)
SWEET
801 Town And Country Blvd A120 (77024-4578)
PHONE..................713 647-9338
Sandy Tran, *Principal*
▲ **EMP:** 13
SALES (est): 1.6MM **Privately Held**
WEB: www.ilovesweet.com
SIC: 2053 Cakes, bakery: frozen

(G-12132)
SWHT LLC
Also Called: Southwest Heat Treat
1733 Lauder Rd (77039-3027)
PHONE..................281 442-6694
Chris Johnson, *General Mgr*
Jay Carroll, *Sales Mgr*
Megan Gillett, *Office Mgr*
Bobby Lawrence,
EMP: 25
SALES (est): 5.5MM **Privately Held**
WEB: www.swheattreat.com
SIC: 3398 Metal heat treating

(G-12133)
SWN PRODUCTION COMPANY LLC (HQ)
2350 N Sam Houston Pkwy E S (77032-3100)
PHONE..................281 618-4700
Steven L Mueller, *President*
Kevin Cotton, *Superintendent*
Jeffrey B Sherrick, *Senior VP*
Josh Anders, *Vice Pres*
Randall Barron, *Vice Pres*
EMP: 50

SALES (est): 397.8MM
SALES (corp-wide): 3B **Publicly Held**
WEB: www.swn.com
SIC: 1382 1311 Oil & gas exploration services; crude petroleum production; natural gas production
PA: Southwestern Energy Company Inc
10000 Energy Dr
Spring TX 77389
832 796-1000

(G-12134)
SYLVAN ENERGY LLC
920 Mmrial Cy Way Ste 200 (77024)
PHONE..................412 222-9600
Neil M Sullivan, *CEO*
Many Emamzadeh, *Exec VP*
EMP: 52 **EST:** 1999
SALES (est): 4.8MM **Privately Held**
SIC: 1382 Oil & gas exploration services

(G-12135)
SYNERGY OIL & GAS LP
9821 Katy Fwy Ste 805 (77024-1295)
PHONE..................713 827-9988
Duane H King, *Partner*
EMP: 15
SALES (est): 1.7MM **Privately Held**
WEB: www.synergyog.com
SIC: 1311 1381 1382 Crude petroleum production; drilling oil & gas wells; oil & gas exploration services

(G-12136)
SYNTECH CHEMICALS INC
14822 Hooper Rd (77047-7315)
PHONE..................713 433-5818
Christiaan Stevens, *President*
James Gordon, *Vice Pres*
Gordon James, *Vice Pres*
Lynette Ash, *Admin Sec*
▲ **EMP:** 35
SQ FT: 210,000
SALES (est): 7.2MM **Privately Held**
WEB: www.syntech.com
SIC: 2819 2869 2899 Industrial inorganic chemicals; industrial organic chemicals; chemical preparations

(G-12137)
SYNTEX SUPER MATERIALS INC
2020 Rankin Rd (77073-5100)
PHONE..................281 821-9495
Mary Ann Kuo, *President*
▲ **EMP:** 35
SALES (est): 7MM **Privately Held**
WEB: www.syntexinc.com
SIC: 3291 Tungsten carbide abrasive

(G-12138)
SYNTHESIS ENERGY SYSTEMS INC (PA)
Also Called: U-Gas
3 Riverway Ste 300 (77056-2071)
PHONE..................713 579-0600
Robert Rigdon, *CEO*
Lorenzo Lamadrid, *Ch of Bd*
Johnathan Winter, *Vice Pres*
Wade Taber, *VP Engrg*
WEI Sun, *Engineer*
EMP: 11
SQ FT: 7,300
SALES (est): 7,300 **Privately Held**
WEB: www.synthesisenergy.com
SIC: 1311 Coal gasification

(G-12139)
SYSTEM DEVELOPMENT INC
Also Called: Sdi
3603 Westcenter Dr # 100 (77042-5222)
PHONE..................713 266-5667
Paul Boutan, *President*
Ester Boutan, *Exec Officer*
Peter Ferrer, *Vice Pres*
Paul Weber, *Vice Pres*
Aldo Ovalle, *Project Engr*
▲ **EMP:** 25
SQ FT: 6,500
SALES (est): 3.1MM **Privately Held**
WEB: www.sdicgm.com
SIC: 7371 5734 7372 Computer software systems analysis & design, custom; computer software writers, freelance; software, business & non-game; business oriented computer software

▲ = Import ▼ =Export
◆ =Import/Export

(G-12140)
SYTEK ELECTRIC CORPORAITON
1233 W 34th St (77018-6207)
PHONE................................713 862-8813
Michael Williamson, *President*
Samantha Williams, *General Mgr*
Dawn Palmer, *Sales Mgr*
Darren Broussard, *Sales Staff*
Kc Cashman, *Manager*
EMP: 34
SALES (est): 6.2MM **Privately Held**
WEB: www.sytekelectric.com
SIC: 7694 1731 Electric motor repair; switchgear & related devices installation

(G-12141)
SYZYGY PLASMONICS INC
9000 Kirby Dr (77054-2504)
PHONE................................806 470-5779
Trevor Best, *CEO*
Suman Khatiwada, *Co-Owner*
EMP: 12
SALES (est): 128.5K **Privately Held**
WEB: www.plasmonics.tech
SIC: 2819 Catalysts, chemical

(G-12142)
T L PRECISION WELDING INC
10533 Fisher Rd (77041-4083)
PHONE................................713 896-4500
EMP: 12 **EST:** 1997
SQ FT: 20,000
SALES (est): 2MM **Privately Held**
WEB: www.tlprecision.com
SIC: 7692 Welding repair

(G-12143)
T-3 ENERGY SERVICES INC (DH)
140 Cypress Station Dr # 225
(77090-1686)
PHONE................................713 944-5950
Linn S Harson, *Admin Sec*
▲ **EMP:** 14
SQ FT: 189,000
SALES (est): 85.1MM
SALES (corp-wide): 8.4B **Publicly Held**
SIC: 5211 3491 7699 Energy conservation products; pressure valves & regulators, industrial; industrial equipment services
HQ: Robbins & Myers, Inc.
10586 Highway 75 N
Willis TX 77378
936 890-1064

(G-12144)
T-TEX EQUIPMENT LP
8302 Almeda Genoa Rd (77075-2560)
P.O. Box 751267 (77275-1267)
PHONE................................713 991-7070
Clarence Todd, *Partner*
EMP: 16
SQ FT: 13,920
SALES (est): 1.6MM **Privately Held**
WEB: www.ttexequipment.com
SIC: 5231 3589 5084 Paint & painting supplies; paint brushes, rollers, sprayers & other supplies; sandblasting equipment; safety equipment

(G-12145)
TA CHEN INTERNATIONAL INC
9525 Wallisville Rd (77013-4605)
PHONE................................713 672-0177
Tammy Kuo, *Manager*
Wilma Terry, *Relg Ldr*
EMP: 50
SQ FT: 122,008 **Privately Held**
WEB: www.tachen.com
SIC: 5051 3494 Steel; valves & pipe fittings
HQ: Ta Chen International, Inc.
5855 Obispo Ave
Long Beach CA 90805
562 808-8000

(G-12146)
TACO & TORTILLA FACTORY INC
Also Called: Taco Tote
6154 Westheimer Rd (77057-4557)
PHONE................................713 706-3233
EMP: 15

SQ FT: 600
SALES (est): 990K **Privately Held**
SIC: 2099 Mfg Food Preparations

(G-12147)
TAF INCORPORATED (PA)
Also Called: Commercial Chemical Products
5427 Gessner Rd (77041-7497)
PHONE................................713 896-4040
Diane Chruchwell, *President*
Tom Churchwell, *Vice Pres*
EMP: 20
SQ FT: 25,000
SALES (est): 4.6MM **Privately Held**
SIC: 2842 Specialty cleaning, polishes & sanitation goods

(G-12148)
TAIT RADIO COMMUNICATIONS
15340 Park Row (77084-2887)
PHONE................................281 944-3539
Garry Diack, *CEO*
Frank Owen, *President*
Peter Drake, *Partner*
Zach Nanney, *Partner*
John Gorrell, *Vice Pres*
EMP: 43
SALES (est): 7.2MM **Privately Held**
WEB: www.taitradio.com
SIC: 3663 Radio broadcasting & communications equipment

(G-12149)
TALLY ENERGY SERVICES (PA)
5611 Baird Ct (77041-2035)
PHONE................................832 530-4880
Chris Dorrs, *CEO*
Mayra Black, *Office Mgr*
EMP: 13
SALES (est): 49.1MM **Privately Held**
WEB: www.tallyenergy.com
SIC: 1381 Directional drilling oil & gas wells

(G-12150)
TALOS ENERGY INC (PA)
333 Clay St Ste 3300 (77002-4104)
PHONE................................713 328-3000
Neal P Goldman, *Ch of Bd*
Timothy S Duncan, *President*
Stephen E Heitzman, *COO*
Stephen Heitzman, *COO*
William S Moss III, *Exec VP*
EMP: 109
SALES: 927.6MM **Publicly Held**
WEB: www.talosenergy.com
SIC: 1382 1311 Oil & gas exploration services; crude petroleum production

(G-12151)
TALOS ENERGY LLC (DH)
500 Dallas St Ste 2000 (77002-4727)
PHONE................................713 328-3000
Timothy S Duncan, *President*
Deborah Huston, *Counsel*
John L Harrison, *Exec VP*
Stephen E Heitzman, *Exec VP*
John A Parker, *Exec VP*
EMP: 32 **EST:** 2012
SALES (est): 148.8MM
SALES (corp-wide): 927.6MM **Publicly Held**
WEB: www.talosenergyllc.com
SIC: 1382 Oil & gas exploration services
HQ: Talos Production Llc
500 Dallas St Ste 2000
Houston TX 77002
713 328-3000

(G-12152)
TALOS ERT LLC (DH)
Also Called: E R T
500 Dallas St Ste 2000 (77002-4727)
PHONE................................281 618-0590
Timothy S Duncan, *President*
Stephen E Heitzman, *Exec VP*
John A Parker, *Exec VP*
Shannon E Young III, *Senior VP*
Owen Kratz, *Director*
EMP: 17
SQ FT: 900

SALES (est): 165.2MM
SALES (corp-wide): 927.6MM **Publicly Held**
WEB: www.talosenergyllc.com
SIC: 1311 1389 Crude petroleum production; processing service, gas
HQ: Talos Production Llc
500 Dallas St Ste 2000
Houston TX 77002
713 328-3000

(G-12153)
TALOS PETROLEUM LLC
16800 Greenspt Pk Dr 225s (77060-2304)
PHONE................................281 872-1999
Brett Heath, *Manager*
EMP: 15
SALES (corp-wide): 927.6MM **Publicly Held**
WEB: www.stoneenergy.com
SIC: 1382 Oil & gas exploration services
HQ: Talos Petroleum Llc
625 E Kaliste Saloom Rd
Lafayette LA 70508

(G-12154)
TALOS PRODUCTION LLC (HQ)
500 Dallas St Ste 2000 (77002-4727)
PHONE................................713 328-3000
Timothy S Duncan, *President*
John L Harrison, *Exec VP*
Stephen E Heitzman, *Exec VP*
William S Moss III, *Exec VP*
John A Parker, *Exec VP*
EMP: 9
SALES (est): 314.1MM
SALES (corp-wide): 927.6MM **Publicly Held**
WEB: www.talosenergyllc.com
SIC: 1382 1311 1389 Geophysical exploration, oil & gas field; crude petroleum production; processing service, gas
PA: Talos Energy Inc.
333 Clay St Ste 3300
Houston TX 77002
713 328-3000

(G-12155)
TAM INTERNATIONAL INC (PA)
4620 Southerland Rd (77092-3020)
PHONE................................713 462-7617
Bentley Sanford, *Ch of Bd*
Michael Machowski, *President*
Jody Echols, *Production*
Christopher Haugh, *Engineer*
Robert Castillo, *Design Engr*
◆ **EMP:** 200
SQ FT: 60,000
SALES (est): 117.9MM **Privately Held**
WEB: www.tamintl.com
SIC: 3533 Oil & gas field machinery

(G-12156)
TAM INTERNATIONAL INC
6935 Pinemont Dr (77092-2403)
PHONE................................713 462-7617
Bently Sanford, *President*
EMP: 11
SALES (corp-wide): 117.9MM **Privately Held**
WEB: www.tamintl.com
SIC: 3533 Oil & gas field machinery
PA: Tam International, Inc.
4620 Southerland Rd
Houston TX 77092
713 462-7617

(G-12157)
TAOS RESOURCES OPER CO LLC
10700 North Fwy Ste 930 (77037-1142)
PHONE................................713 993-0774
Logan Magruder, *CEO*
Keith Fite, *Exec VP*
Larry Macicek, *Vice Pres*
Carrie Calahan, *Prdtn Mgr*
Ray Dorothy, *Production*
▲ **EMP:** 10
SALES (est): 2.6MM **Privately Held**
WEB: www.futureacq.com
SIC: 1382 Oil & gas exploration services

(G-12158)
TAPER-LOK CORPORATION (HQ)
945 Bunker Hill Rd # 500 (77024-1358)
PHONE................................713 467-3333
Jeffrey Lunsford, *President*
Charles Armbrust, *CFO*
Norma Martinez, *Sales Staff*
Tim John, *Business Dir*
◆ **EMP:** 17
SALES (est): 1.9MM
SALES (corp-wide): 252.3MM **Privately Held**
WEB: www.afglobalcorp.com
SIC: 3462 Aircraft forgings, ferrous
PA: Ameriforge Group Inc.
945 Bunker Hill Rd # 500
Houston TX 77024
713 393-4200

(G-12159)
TARGA GAS MARKETING LLC
1000 La St Ste 4300 (77002)
PHONE................................713 584-1000
James W Whalen, *CEO*
Joe Bob Perkins, *CEO*
Michael A Heim, *President*
Jeffrey J McParland, *President*
Stacy E Duke, *Vice Pres*
EMP: 15
SALES (est): 811K **Publicly Held**
WEB: www.targaresources.com
SIC: 1311 Crude petroleum & natural gas
HQ: Targa Resources Holdings Lp
1000 La St Ste 4700
Houston TX 77002

(G-12160)
TARGA RESOURCES GP LLC
811 Louisiana St Ste 2100 (77002-1412)
PHONE................................713 873-1000
Jeffrey J McParland, *President*
Matthew J Meloy, *CFO*
James W Whalen,
Rene R Joyce,
EMP: 48
SALES (est): 2.3MM **Publicly Held**
WEB: www.targaresources.com
SIC: 1389 Servicing oil & gas wells
HQ: Targa Resources Partners Lp
811 Louisiana St Ste 2100
Houston TX 77002

(G-12161)
TARGET STONE LLC
11514 Hempstead Rd (77092-7106)
PHONE................................832 827-8663
Yingfeng MA,
Xiaozhou Xie,
EMP: 20
SALES (est): 818.5K **Privately Held**
WEB: www.targetstoneusa.com
SIC: 1799 1743 1771 1411 Counter top installation; marble installation, interior; flooring contractor; granite dimension stone; bathroom fixtures, cut stone; marbleboard (stone face hard board)

(G-12162)
TARKETT INC
1705 Oliver St (77007-3821)
P.O. Box 3145 (77253-3145)
PHONE................................800 366-2689
Scott Caldwell, *Branch Mgr*
Liz Marcello, *Senior Mgr*
EMP: 10
SALES (corp-wide): 589.6K **Privately Held**
WEB: www.tarkettna.com
SIC: 3996 Asphalted-felt-base floor coverings: linoleum, carpet
HQ: Tarkett, Inc.
30000 Aurora Rd
Solon OH 44139
800 899-8916

(G-12163)
TASCON INC
Also Called: Tascon Industries
7607 Fairview (77041-2111)
P.O. Box 40970 (77240-0970)
PHONE................................713 937-0900
James Adamoli, *President*
Mark Adamoli, *Vice Pres*
EMP: 39 **EST:** 1976
SQ FT: 4,000

SALES (est): 4MM **Privately Held**
WEB: www.tasconindustries.com
SIC: 2823 5065 Cellulosic manmade fibers; electronic parts & equipment

(G-12164)
TAUBER EXPLORATION & PROD CO
55 Waugh Dr Ste 600 (77007-5837)
PHONE....................................713 869-5656
Richard E Tauber, *President*
Patricia Bell, *Vice Pres*
Bell Patricia Ann Tauber, *Vice Pres*
David W Tauber, *Vice Pres*
Jerry Tauber Jr, *Vice Pres*
EMP: 10 **EST:** 1968
SALES (est): 1.9MM **Privately Held**
WEB: www.tauberoil.com
SIC: 1311 6792 Crude petroleum production; oil leases, buying & selling on own account

(G-12165)
TAXA INC
Also Called: Cricket Trailer
1830 W 15th St (77008-3422)
PHONE....................................713 861-2540
Garrett Finney, *CEO*
Amitav Misra, *President*
J Antonio Gonzalez, *COO*
▲ **EMP:** 19
SALES (est): 9.1MM **Privately Held**
WEB: www.taxaoutdoors.com
SIC: 5084 3799 Trailers, industrial; trailers & trailer equipment

(G-12166)
TAYLOR COMMUNICATIONS INC
13105 Nw Fwy Ste 1110 (77040-6320)
PHONE....................................713 456-4089
David Fisher, *Branch Mgr*
Scott Osborn, *Manager*
EMP: 46
SALES (corp-wide): 2.5B **Privately Held**
WEB: www.taylorcorp.com
SIC: 2759 Commercial printing
HQ: Taylor Communications, Inc.
1725 Roe Crest Dr
North Mankato MN 56003
866 541-0937

(G-12167)
TAYLOR PUBLISHING COMPANY
Also Called: Campus Impressions
2211 Norfolk St Ste 603 (77098-4055)
PHONE....................................713 782-0700
Lisa Schwartz, *Manager*
EMP: 12 **Privately Held**
WEB: www.balfour.com
SIC: 2759 Commercial printing
HQ: Taylor Publishing Company
1550 W Mockingbird Ln
Dallas TX 75235
214 637-2800

(G-12168)
TAYLORS OILFIELD MFG INC
14401 Interdrive E (77032-3333)
PHONE....................................281 442-4084
John Gordon, *QC Mgr*
Randy Reuss, *QC Mgr*
Lennard Taylor, *Sales Staff*
Kenneth Istre, *Manager*
Kim Marquette, *Administration*
EMP: 47
SQ FT: 19,200 **Privately Held**
WEB: www.tayloroilfield.com
SIC: 3533 3546 Oil field machinery & equipment; power-driven handtools
PA: Taylor's Oilfield Manufacturing, Inc.
225 Burgess Dr
Broussard LA 70518

(G-12169)
TC SANITIZER CO LLC
16711 Hollister St Ste I (77066-1429)
PHONE....................................832 296-4561
Chris Whitmeyer,
EMP: 80
SALES (est): 2.6MM **Privately Held**
SIC: 2842 Sanitation preparations, disinfectants & deodorants

(G-12170)
TEAM ALLOYS LLC
7350 Roundhouse Ln (77078-4527)
PHONE....................................713 360-1060
William Bootz, *President*
Brenda Hall, *QC Mgr*
▲ **EMP:** 22
SALES (est): 14.9MM **Privately Held**
WEB: www.teamalloys.com
SIC: 3317 Steel pipe & tubes

(G-12171)
TEAM COOPERHEAT-MQS INC (HQ)
5858 Westheimer Rd # 625 (77057-5650)
PHONE....................................713 673-3660
EMP: 21
SALES (est): 136.8MM
SALES (corp-wide): 1.1B **Publicly Held**
SIC: 8734 3398 3567 3255 Testing laboratories; metal heat treating; heating units & devices, industrial: electric; clay refractories
PA: Team, Inc.
13131 Dar Ashford Ste 600
Sugar Land TX 77478
281 331-6154

(G-12172)
TEAM OIL TOOLS LLC
4310 N Sam Houston Pkwy E (77032-3807)
PHONE....................................918 461-8104
Donald Tinker,
Mike Sommers,
▼ **EMP:** 30
SALES (est): 5.8MM **Privately Held**
SIC: 3533 Oil field machinery & equipment

(G-12173)
TEAM PVF LLC
7350 Roundhouse Ln (77078-4527)
P.O. Box 204043, Dallas (75320-4043)
PHONE....................................281 714-1582
Kenneth Albano, *CFO*
William Bootz, *Mng Member*
EMP: 45
SALES (est): 5MM **Privately Held**
WEB: www.teamalloys.com
SIC: 2299 Pipe & boiler covering, felt

(G-12174)
TECHNIEK LLC
2215 Harbor St (77020-7505)
PHONE....................................832 618-7085
John Garcia, *President*
Ezequiel Bosma, *Opers Staff*
EMP: 23
SQ FT: 30,000
SALES (est): 3.1MM **Privately Held**
WEB: www.tnktx.com
SIC: 3443 Process vessels, industrial: metal plate

(G-12175)
TECHNIP S&W INTERNATIONAL INC
11740 Katy Fwy Ste 100 (77079-1254)
PHONE....................................281 870-1111
Ta Barfield Jr, *President*
Chuck Sekinger, *Vice Pres*
Milissa Stagg, *Treasurer*
Karen Hahn, *Manager*
Krishna Merchant, *Manager*
◆ **EMP:** 35
SALES (est): 4.8MM
SALES (corp-wide): 13.4B **Privately Held**
WEB: www.technip.com
SIC: 3498 8748 8711 Fabricated pipe & fittings; environmental consultant; mechanical engineering; consulting engineer
HQ: Technip Usa, Inc.
11740 Katy Fwy Ste 100
Houston TX 77079

(G-12176)
TECHNOLOGIES ALLIANCE INC (HQ)
Also Called: Oilpatch Technologies
6401 N Eldridge Pkwy (77041-3505)
PHONE....................................281 442-8825
Paul C Berner Jr, *President*
Edward M Galle Jr, *Vice Pres*
Kevin Gendron, *Treasurer*
Daniel Klatt, *Manager*
▲ **EMP:** 32
SQ FT: 20,000
SALES (est): 9.2MM
SALES (corp-wide): 414.8MM **Publicly Held**
WEB: www.oilpatchtech.com
SIC: 1389 Oil field services
PA: Dril-Quip, Inc.
6401 N Eldridge Pkwy
Houston TX 77041
713 939-7711

(G-12177)
TECHNOLOGY FLEET PRODUCTS INC
2331 Watts St (77030-1139)
PHONE....................................713 907-8394
Charles Barrett Shepherd, *Branch Mgr*
EMP: 13
SALES (corp-wide): 1MM **Privately Held**
WEB: www.technologyfleetproducts.com
SIC: 2899 Patching plaster, household
PA: Technology Fleet Products, Inc.
13810 Ambrose St
Houston TX 77045
281 569-4350

(G-12178)
TECMAG INC
10161 Harwin Dr Ste 150 (77036-1684)
PHONE....................................713 667-8747
John Delayre, *President*
Lauren Langford, *Admin Sec*
EMP: 11
SQ FT: 8,000
SALES (est): 2.7MM
SALES (corp-wide): 141.3MM **Privately Held**
WEB: www.tecmag.com
SIC: 3826 Analytical instruments
PA: Avingtrans Plc
Chatteris Business Park
Chatteris CAMBS PE16

(G-12179)
TECNON SUPPLY LLC
1185 Brittmoore Rd (77043-5003)
P.O. Box 79769 (77279-9769)
PHONE....................................281 888-9045
Oliver E Nava,
EMP: 10
SALES (est): 1.7MM **Privately Held**
WEB: www.tecnonsupply.com
SIC: 3531 Construction machinery

(G-12180)
TECNOTRAT METAL PROCESSING LLC
9429 Frbanks N Houston Rd (77064-6210)
PHONE....................................281 894-9189
Gerardo Reyna, *General Mgr*
Fidel Garza,
EMP: 14
SQ FT: 4,500
SALES (est): 955.1K **Privately Held**
WEB: www.tecnotratmetalprocessing.com
SIC: 3451 Screw machine products

(G-12181)
TECPETROL CORPORATION
2200 West Loop S Ste 400 (77027-3531)
PHONE....................................713 974-3322
Horacio Marin, *CEO*
Daniel Valencio, *General Mgr*
Lucas Murphy, *Business Mgr*
Carlos Mamani, *COO*
Carlos Ormachea, *Exec VP*
EMP: 42
SALES (est): 13.5MM **Privately Held**
WEB: www.tecpetrol.com
SIC: 1382 Oil & gas exploration services

(G-12182)
TEEBAUD CO LLC
Also Called: Constance & Company
8732 Clay Rd Ste 109 (77080-8105)
PHONE....................................713 682-5161
Alain Holderer, *Mng Member*
Constance R Holderer,
▼ **EMP:** 10
SQ FT: 3,500
SALES (est): 1.6MM **Privately Held**
WEB: www.teebaud.com
SIC: 3089 Synthetic resin finished products

(G-12183)
TEFCO II LC
19407 Park Row Ste 120 (77084-4878)
P.O. Box 5831, Katy (77491-5831)
PHONE....................................281 398-9684
Dee Anne Robinson, *President*
▲ **EMP:** 10
SQ FT: 2,600
SALES (est): 1.5MM **Privately Held**
WEB: www.tefcoindustries.com
SIC: 2821 Plastics materials & resins

(G-12184)
TEFKAB FOOTWEAR LLC
9330 W Arprt Blvd Ste 190 (77031)
PHONE....................................281 988-0977
Dennis Comeau, *President*
▲ **EMP:** 10
SQ FT: 10,000 **Privately Held**
SIC: 3144 Sandals, women's

(G-12185)
TEIKOKU USA INC
Chempump Division Teikoku USA
5880 Bingle Rd (77092-2113)
PHONE....................................713 983-9901
Christian Halupa, *Electrical Engi*
Tim Erwin, *Branch Mgr*
James McDaniel, *Executive*
Kathy Comeaux, *Admin Asst*
EMP: 21
SQ FT: 83,120 **Privately Held**
WEB: www.chempump.com
SIC: 3561 3594 Pumps & pumping equipment; fluid power pumps & motors
HQ: Teikoku Usa Inc.
959 Mearns Rd
Warminster PA 18974

(G-12186)
TEJAS BOILER SERVICES INC
7206 Elbert St (77028-3114)
P.O. Box 23895 (77228-3895)
PHONE....................................713 631-8200
Lonnie D Fryer, *President*
Jay Files, *Vice Pres*
Tom Stansbury, *Vice Pres*
EMP: 40
SQ FT: 6,000 **Privately Held**
SIC: 3443 7699 Boiler & boiler shop work; boiler repair shop

(G-12187)
TEJAS CASING LTD
Also Called: Tejas Tubular Products
8740 Miller Road 2 (77049-1947)
PHONE....................................281 215-1500
Maximo A Tejeda, *President*
Jesus Vargas, *Manager*
EMP: 85
SQ FT: 35,000
SALES (est): 35.1MM **Privately Held**
WEB: www.tejastubular.com
SIC: 3317 Steel pipe & tubes
PA: Tejas Tubular Products, Inc.
8799 North Loop E Ste 300
Houston TX 77029

(G-12188)
TEJAS TUBULAR PRODUCTS INC (PA)
8799 North Loop E Ste 300 (77029-1242)
PHONE....................................281 822-3400
Maximo A Tejeda, *President*
Darrell Ballinger, *Vice Pres*
Max Tejeda Jr, *Vice Pres*
Aditya Khandavelli, *Plant Mgr*
Pablo Albarican, *Project Mgr*
◆ **EMP:** 267
SQ FT: 7,000
SALES (est): 200.7MM **Privately Held**
WEB: www.tejastubular.com
SIC: 3317 3498 Steel pipe & tubes; tube fabricating (contract bending & shaping); couplings, pipe: fabricated from purchased pipe

(G-12189)
TEKTRONIX INC
4500 S Wayside Dr (77087-1117)
PHONE....................................713 691-3658
EMP: 19
SALES (corp-wide): 6.4B **Publicly Held**
WEB: www.tek.com
SIC: 3825 Instruments to measure electricity

HQ: Tektronix, Inc.
14150 Sw Karl Braun Dr
Beaverton OR 97005
800 833-9200

(G-12190)
TELCO INTERCONTINENTAL CORP
9812 Whithorn Dr (77095-5001)
PHONE..................................281 500-8270
Frank C Liang, *President*
MEI-Yun Liang, *Vice Pres*
Helen Wang, *Director*
MEI Liang, *Executive*
▲ EMP: 24
SQ FT: 25,000
SALES (est): 13.6MM **Privately Held**
WEB: www.telcointercon.com
SIC: 5063 5065 3575 Electronic wire & cable; telephone equipment; cathode ray tube (CRT), computer terminal

(G-12191)
TELEDYNE INSTRUMENTS INC
Also Called: Teledyne Bolt
5825 Chimney Rock Rd (77081-2714)
PHONE..................................713 666-2561
John Payne, *Managing Prtnr*
Phil Manrique, *Opers Staff*
Leonardo Carballo, *Marketing Staff*
Daniel Ellinwood, *Manager*
Terry Bell, *Technical Staff*
EMP: 201
SALES (corp-wide): 3.1B **Publicly Held**
WEB: www.teledyne.com
SIC: 3678 3694 3829 Electronic connectors; engine electrical equipment; seismographs
HQ: Teledyne Instruments, Inc.
16830 Chestnut St
City Of Industry CA 91748
626 934-1500

(G-12192)
TELKIN SHEETMETAL INC
Also Called: Telkin Piping System
7313 Domino Ln (77076-1403)
P.O. Box 16219 (77222-6219)
PHONE..................................713 691-3707
Ben Botello, *President*
Danny Ferguson, *General Mgr*
Michael Botello, *Vice Pres*
Jessica Hale, *Manager*
EMP: 40 EST: 1996
SQ FT: 50,000
SALES (est): 4.5MM **Privately Held**
WEB: www.telkinsheetmetal.net
SIC: 3444 Sheet metalwork

(G-12193)
TELLURIAN INC (PA)
1201 La St Ste 3100 (77002)
PHONE..................................832 962-4000
Charif Souki, *Ch of Bd*
Octavio Simoes, *President*
Martin Houston, *Vice Chairman*
R Keith Teague, *COO*
AMI Arief, *Senior VP*
EMP: 32
SALES: 28.7MM **Publicly Held**
WEB: www.tellurianinc.com
SIC: 1382 Oil & gas exploration services

(G-12194)
TELLURIAN INVESTMENTS INC (HQ)
1201 Louisiana St # 3100 (77002-5631)
PHONE..................................832 962-4000
Keith Teague, *COO*
Mac Broderick, *Vice Pres*
Andy Krueger, *Vice Pres*
Antoine Lafargue, *CFO*
Jonathan Seeley, *Financial Analy*
EMP: 13
SALES (est): 6.8MM
SALES (corp-wide): 28.7MM **Publicly Held**
WEB: www.tellurianinc.com
SIC: 1321 Butane (natural) production
PA: Tellurian Inc.
1201 La St Ste 3100
Houston TX 77002
832 962-4000

(G-12195)
TELXON CORPORATION
9000 Hempstead Rd Ste 220 (77008-6039)
PHONE..................................713 868-5511
Joseph Patterson, *Branch Mgr*
EMP: 250
SQ FT: 41,000
SALES (corp-wide): 4.4B **Publicly Held**
SIC: 3577 Data conversion equipment, media-to-media: computer
HQ: Telxon Corporation
1 Zebra Plz
Holtsville NY 11742
631 738-2400

(G-12196)
TEMA OIL AND GAS COMPANY (HQ)
16200 Park Row Ste 300 (77084-7348)
PHONE..................................281 829-3206
Alan Townsend, *President*
Henry A Rosenberg Jr, *Chairman*
Brian Ayers, *Vice Pres*
EMP: 35 EST: 1999
SALES (est): 302.3MM
SALES (corp-wide): 501.8MM **Privately Held**
WEB: www.rosehillresources.com
SIC: 1382 Oil & gas exploration services
PA: Rosemore, Inc.
100 Light St Fl 2500
Baltimore MD 21202
410 347-7080

(G-12197)
TENARIS COILED TUBES LLC
8700 Clay Rd (77080-8110)
PHONE..................................713 460-1500
Joel Smith, *Principal*
EMP: 12 EST: 2009
SALES (est): 2.7MM **Privately Held**
WEB: www.tenaris.com
SIC: 3494 Pipe fittings

(G-12198)
TENARIS COILED TUBES LLC
8615 E Sam Houston Pkwy N (77044-1843)
PHONE..................................281 458-2883
Paolo Rocca, *CEO*
Edgardo Carlos, *CFO*
Raul Estrada, *Technician*
Dennis Dunlap,
Scott Stephens,
◆ EMP: 123
SQ FT: 80,000
SALES (est): 37.5MM
SALES (corp-wide): 183.7K **Privately Held**
WEB: www.tenaris.com
SIC: 3317 Tubes, seamless steel
HQ: Maverick Tube Corporation
2200 West Loop S Ste 800
Houston TX 77027
713 767-4400

(G-12199)
TENARIS GLOBAL SVCS USA CORP
302 Mccarty St (77029-1140)
PHONE..................................936 525-3101
Lee Pereira, *Engineer*
Kathy Worchesik, *Credit Staff*
David Kennedy, *Branch Mgr*
Juan Martinez, *Manager*
EMP: 16
SALES (corp-wide): 183.7K **Privately Held**
WEB: www.tenaris.com
SIC: 3317 Steel pipe & tubes
HQ: Tenaris Global Services (Usa) Corporation
2200 West Loop S Ste 800
Houston TX 77027
713 767-4400

(G-12200)
TENARIS GLOBAL SVCS USA CORP (DH)
2200 West Loop S Ste 800 (77027-3532)
PHONE..................................713 767-4400
Brad Lowe, *President*
Hernan Desimone, *District Mgr*
David Reed, *District Mgr*
Barbara Crosby, *COO*

Delene Rice, *Vice Pres*
◆ EMP: 52
SALES (est): 1B
SALES (corp-wide): 183.7K **Privately Held**
WEB: www.tenaris.com
SIC: 3317 Seamless pipes & tubes
HQ: Tenaris S.A.
Boulevard Royal 26
Luxembourg 2449
264 789-78

(G-12201)
TENARIS RODS (USA) INC
2200 West Loop S Ste 800 (77027-3532)
PHONE..................................713 767-4400
Miguel A Cabanillas, *CEO*
EMP: 50 EST: 2013
SALES (est): 8.6MM
SALES (corp-wide): 183.7K **Privately Held**
WEB: www.tenaris.com
SIC: 3312 Rods, iron & steel: made in steel mills
HQ: Tenaris S.A.
Boulevard Royal 26
Luxembourg 2449
264 789-78

(G-12202)
TENDEKA INC
6650 W Sam Houston Pkwy N # 420 (77041-5153)
PHONE..................................832 827-4211
Gary Smart, *CEO*
Scott Watters, *COO*
Gillian King, *Vice Pres*
Derek Taylor, *Vice Pres*
Michael Konopczynski, *Engineer*
◆ EMP: 100
SALES (est): 8.2MM **Privately Held**
WEB: www.tendeka.com
SIC: 1389 Oil field services

(G-12203)
TENDENCI INC (PA)
611 Dairy Ashford Rd # 4 (77079-3900)
PHONE..................................281 497-6567
Edward Schipul, *CEO*
Ed Schipul, *CEO*
Rachel Schipul, *Vice Pres*
Broden Schipul, *Prgrmr*
Linda Link, *Exec Dir*
EMP: 27
SQ FT: 1,000
SALES (est): 4.8MM **Privately Held**
WEB: www.tendenci.com
SIC: 5099 7371 7373 3699 Robots, service or novelty; computer software systems analysis & design, custom; software programming applications; computer systems analysis & design; security devices; assembly machines, including robotic

(G-12204)
TENT COMPANY LLC
2333 Wirtcrest Ln Ste F (77055-1345)
PHONE..................................832 623-8958
Walberto Vasquez, *CEO*
EMP: 10
SALES (est): 363K **Privately Held**
WEB: www.tentcohouston.com
SIC: 2394 7359 Canopies, fabric: made from purchased materials; tent & tarpaulin rental

(G-12205)
TENTS OF SOUTHWEST INC
5920 Killough St (77086-3915)
PHONE..................................713 692-8565
Randy Moore, *President*
▲ EMP: 20
SQ FT: 19,500
SALES (est): 2.1MM **Privately Held**
WEB: www.tentsofthesouthwest.com
SIC: 2394 7359 5999 Tents: made from purchased materials; tent & tarpaulin rental; tents

(G-12206)
TEPEE PETROLEUM COMPANY INC
3700 Buffalo Speedway # 1010 (77098-3700)
PHONE..................................713 659-8300
Townes G Pressler Jr, *President*

Cynthia Schaeffer, *Executive Asst*
EMP: 9
SQ FT: 2,500
SALES (est): 1MM **Privately Held**
WEB: www.tepeepetroleum.com
SIC: 1382 1311 Oil & gas exploration services; crude petroleum production

(G-12207)
TERCEL OILFIELD PDTS USA LLC (HQ)
Also Called: Encore Bits
10613 W Sam Houston Pkwy (77064-4663)
PHONE..................................832 386-2500
Mike Reeves, *CEO*
John Griggs, *CFO*
▲ EMP: 30
SQ FT: 60,000
SALES (est): 20.1MM
SALES (corp-wide): 108.5MM **Privately Held**
WEB: www.rubicon-oilfield.com
SIC: 1389 Oil field services
PA: Rubicon Oilfield International Holdings, Llc
10613 W Sam Hston Pkwy600
Houston TX 77064
832 386-2500

(G-12208)
TERNIUM USA INC (DH)
2200 West Loop S Ste 945 (77027-3578)
PHONE..................................318 698-7500
Hector Obeso, *President*
Hugo Solis, *President*
Fernando Landa, *Principal*
Marcelo Ramos, *Director*
Ezequiel A Camerini, *Admin Sec*
▲ EMP: 105
SQ FT: 7,500
SALES (est): 30.5MM
SALES (corp-wide): 183.7K **Privately Held**
WEB: www.us.ternium.com
SIC: 3479 Coating of metals & formed products

(G-12209)
TERRA ENERGY PARTNERS LLC (PA)
3050 Post Oak Blvd # 1500 (77056-6569)
PHONE..................................281 936-0355
Paul Benacquista, *Vice Pres*
Bruce Chrisman, *Vice Pres*
Tiffany Pollock, *Vice Pres*
Alice Stubblefield, *Opers Staff*
Scott Dembowski, *Production*
EMP: 34
SALES (est): 394.4MM **Privately Held**
WEB: www.terraep.com
SIC: 1311 1382 Crude petroleum & natural gas; oil & gas exploration services

(G-12210)
TERVITA LLC (DH)
Also Called: Mobley Oilfield Services
10613 W Sam Houston Pkwy (77064-4657)
PHONE..................................832 399-4500
John Gibson Jr, *President*
Gary Edwards, *General Mgr*
David Werklund, *Principal*
Rob Dawson, *Exec VP*
Steve Foster, *Exec VP*
EMP: 70
SALES (est): 198.1MM
SALES (corp-wide): 10.3B **Publicly Held**
WEB: www.tervita.com
SIC: 1389 Oil field services

(G-12211)
TESCO CORPORATION (DH)
515 W Greens Rd Ste 1200 (77067-4536)
PHONE..................................713 359-7000
Fernando R Assing, *President*
Brian Bakken, *General Mgr*
Chris Atkinson, *Principal*
C Farthing, *Principal*
Veronica Matthews, *Principal*
▲ EMP: 113
SALES (est): 148.2MM **Privately Held**
WEB: www.nabors.com
SIC: 3533 Oil & gas drilling rigs & equipment; oil field machinery & equipment

HQ: Nabors Industries, Inc.
515 W Greens Rd Ste 1200
Houston TX 77067
281 874-0035

(G-12212)
TESCO CORPORATION (US)
(DH)
Also Called: Tesco Drilling Tech U S A
515 W Greens Rd Ste 1200 (77067-4536)
PHONE..................................713 359-7000
Fernando R Assing, *President*
Steve Allan, *Project Mgr*
Christopher L Boone, *CFO*
◆ **EMP:** 100
SALES (est): 134.7MM **Privately Held**
WEB: www.nabors.com
SIC: 1381 1389 3511 5082 Drilling oil &
gas wells; oil field services; turbines & tur-
bine generator sets & parts; oil field
equipment; derricks, oil or gas field
HQ: Tesco Corporation
515 W Greens Rd Ste 1200
Houston TX 77067
713 359-7000

(G-12213)
TEST INCORPORATED
Also Called: Test Automation & Controls
6213 W Sam Houston Pkwy N
(77041-5145)
PHONE..................................713 983-2800
EMP: 19
SALES (est): 3.6MM **Privately Held**
SIC: 3826 Mfg Analytical Instruments

(G-12214)
TESTMASTERS INC
5711 Cunningham Rd (77041-4719)
P.O. Box 19249 (77224-9249)
PHONE..................................713 896-1885
Mark Outten, *President*
Charles Kaminsky, *Opers Mgr*
Greg Schick, *QC Mgr*
Kathy P Outten, *Admin Sec*
EMP: 22
SALES (est): 2MM **Privately Held**
WEB: www.testmasters.net
SIC: 1389 Pipe testing, oil field service

(G-12215)
TETON BUILDINGS LLC
2701 Magnet St (77054-4509)
PHONE..................................307 473-7543
Fabio Fronda, *Mng Member*
▼ **EMP:** 32
SQ FT: 150,000
SALES (est): 5.6MM **Privately Held**
WEB: www.tetonbuildings.com
SIC: 2451 Mobile homes, personal or pri-
vate use; mobile homes, industrial or
commercial use

(G-12216)
TEX-LAM MANUFACTURING INC
Also Called: Tex-Lam Toilet Partition Mfg
7219 Stuebner Airline Rd (77091-2409)
PHONE..................................713 695-5975
Wayne Gautreaux, *President*
Diane Gautreaux, *Corp Secy*
Ben Barker, *Project Mgr*
Tod Wood, *Sales Staff*
Randall Snyder, *Sales Executive*
▲ **EMP:** 30
SQ FT: 44,200
SALES (est): 6.3MM **Privately Held**
WEB: www.texlam.com
SIC: 3088 Toilet fixtures, plastic

(G-12217)
TEX-TUBE COMPANY
1503 N Post Oak Rd (77055-5409)
P.O. Box 55710 (77255-5710)
PHONE..................................713 686-4351
Isidro Cantu, *President*
Julio C Villarrel, *President*
Billy Watson, *Opers Staff*
Kenyotta Mayberry, *Production*
Frank Sorell, *Supervisor*
◆ **EMP:** 150
SQ FT: 280,000
SALES (est): 51.5MM **Privately Held**
WEB: www.tex-tube.com
SIC: 3317 3999 Tubes, seamless steel; at-
omizers, toiletry

(G-12218)
TEXACO EXPLORATION & PROD
INC (DH)
1500 Louisiana St (77002-7308)
P.O. Box 1404 (77251-1404)
PHONE..................................800 962-1223
Clarence P Cazalot Jr, *President*
▲ **EMP:** 360
SQ FT: 30,000
SALES (est): 1.1B
SALES (corp-wide): 146.5B **Publicly**
Held
WEB: www.chevronwithtechron.com
SIC: 5541 5511 1321 Filling stations,
gasoline; automobiles, new & used; natu-
ral gas liquids
HQ: Texaco Inc.
6001 Bollinger Canyon Rd
San Ramon CA 94583
925 842-1000

(G-12219)
TEXAN ELECTRIC CO INC
7011 Dixie Dr (77087-5217)
P.O. Box 266388 (77207-6388)
PHONE..................................713 645-6560
Kenneth Hodges, *President*
Larry Coleman, *Vice Pres*
Tim Earhart, *Manager*
EMP: 70
SQ FT: 18,000
SALES (est): 14.6MM **Privately Held**
WEB: www.texanelectric.com
SIC: 3625 1731 Industrial controls: push
button, selector switches, pilot; electronic
controls installation

(G-12220)
TEXAS ALUMINUM INDUSTRIES
INC
2900 Patio Dr (77017-7309)
PHONE..................................713 941-7186
Thomas Thompson, *President*
Ted V Thomas, *Controller*
EMP: 260 **EST:** 1954
SQ FT: 375,000
SALES (est): 35.2MM
SALES (corp-wide): 10.9B **Publicly Held**
WEB: www.kristiwill-2014showcase.com
SIC: 3448 3443 3354 3444 Screen en-
closures; fabricated plate work (boiler
shop); aluminum extruded products;
awnings, sheet metal
HQ: Metals Usa, Inc.
4901 Nw 17th Way Ste 405
Fort Lauderdale FL 33309
954 202-4000

(G-12221)
TEXAS AUTO TRIM
6025 Bissonnet St (77081-6903)
PHONE..................................713 661-5557
Danny Patel, *Owner*
Curtis Boehm, *Sales Staff*
▲ **EMP:** 36
SALES (est): 1MM **Privately Held**
WEB: www.texasautotrim.com
SIC: 2399 Seat covers, automobile

(G-12222)
TEXAS BOLT & NUT COMPANY
LTD
6300 W By Northwest Blvd # 600
(77040-4968)
PHONE..................................713 869-7111
Brian Rawson, *CEO*
Robert Sloan, *Treasurer*
Gloria Hernandez, *Sales Staff*
EMP: 25
SQ FT: 13,974
SALES (est): 12MM **Privately Held**
WEB: www.fluidsealingproducts.com
SIC: 3452 Bolts, metal; nuts, metal

(G-12223)
TEXAS BRINE COMPANY LLC
(HQ)
4800 San Felipe St (77056-3908)
PHONE..................................713 877-2700
Mark Cartwright, *Vice Pres*
Patrick Conklin, *Vice Pres*

MAI Huynh, *Vice Pres*
Fred Wolgel, *Vice Pres*
Bruce Martin, *VP Opers*
EMP: 36 **EST:** 1946
SQ FT: 10,000
SALES (est): 45.8MM
SALES (corp-wide): 247.1MM **Privately**
Held
WEB: www.texasbrine.com
SIC: 4619 2899 Slurry pipeline operation;
salt
PA: Texas United Corporation
4800 San Felipe St
Houston TX 77056
713 877-1793

(G-12224)
TEXAS CATHOLIC HERALD INC
Also Called: Texas Catholic Herald The
1700 San Jacinto St (77002-8216)
PHONE..................................713 659-5461
Daniel Dinardo, *Principal*
Erik Noriega, *Principal*
Cindi Garcia, *Business Mgr*
Joe Ravon, *Treasurer*
Christopher Cronin, *Accountant*
EMP: 11 **EST:** 1964
SALES (est): 616.2K **Privately Held**
WEB: www.archgh.org
SIC: 2711 Newspapers: publishing only,
not printed on site

(G-12225)
TEXAS CEMENT PRODUCTS
INC (PA)
Also Called: Tex-Rite
4000 Pinemont Dr (77018-1104)
PHONE..................................713 682-8411
Hector Abella Yunes, *President*
Martin Martinez Riano, *President*
Claudia Ortega, *Purch Agent*
Jorge Valdez, *Research*
Liz Doty, *Sales Staff*
▲ **EMP:** 30 **EST:** 1964
SQ FT: 10,000
SALES (est): 5MM **Privately Held**
WEB: www.texrite.com
SIC: 3272 Concrete products

(G-12226)
TEXAS CONCRETE
ENTERPRISE LLC
3506 Cherry St (77026-3502)
PHONE..................................713 227-1122
Raj Desai-Radeh, *Mng Member*
Somaiah Kurre,
EMP: 19
SALES (est): 9.2MM **Privately Held**
WEB: www.thetexasconcrete.com
SIC: 3273 Ready-mixed concrete

(G-12227)
TEXAS CONCRETE ENTP
RDYMX INC
6001 Homestead Rd (77028-5022)
PHONE..................................713 227-1122
Hemendra Patel, *President*
Vipul Patel, *Manager*
EMP: 38
SQ FT: 3,000
SALES (est): 15MM **Privately Held**
WEB: www.texasconcretereadymix.com
SIC: 3273 Ready-mixed concrete

(G-12228)
TEXAS CRUDE ENERGY INC
2803 Buffalo Spdwy # 105 (77098-1011)
P.O. Box 56586 (77256-6586)
PHONE..................................713 599-9900
Peter Fluor, *Chairman*
Helen Crowder, *Treasurer*
Douglas E Brien, *Treasurer*
Charles Weiner, *Shareholder*
Kathryn G Remkes, *Admin Sec*
EMP: 15
SQ FT: 12,000
SALES (est): 1.5MM **Privately Held**
SIC: 1311 Crude petroleum production

(G-12229)
TEXAS CRUDE ENERGY LLC
2803 Buffalo Speedway # 105
(77098-1011)
PHONE..................................713 599-9900
EMP: 35 **EST:** 2011

SQ FT: 8,000
SALES (est): 13.9MM **Privately Held**
SIC: 1311 Crude petroleum production

(G-12230)
TEXAS FISH GAME PUBG CO L
L C
247 Airtex Dr (77090-6627)
PHONE..................................281 227-3001
Roy Neves, *Mng Member*
▲ **EMP:** 14
SQ FT: 3,000
SALES (est): 1.2MM **Privately Held**
WEB: www.fishgame.com
SIC: 5941 2721 Sporting goods & bicycle
shops; magazines: publishing only, not
printed on site

(G-12231)
TEXAS FURNACE LLC
Also Called: Meridian
7037 Brittmoore Rd (77041-3210)
P.O. Box 40696 (77240-0696)
PHONE..................................713 466-1504
Cody Martin, *VP Mfg*
Lawanna S Martin, *Mng Member*
Roger D Martin, *Mng Member*
EMP: 10 **EST:** 2000
SQ FT: 90,000
SALES (est): 2MM **Privately Held**
WEB: www.texasfurnace.com
SIC: 3585 Furnaces, warm air: electric
PA: Allstyle Coil Company, L.P.
7037 Brittmoore Rd
Houston TX 77041

(G-12232)
TEXAS GASKET AND PACKING
CO
1255 Lathrop St (77020-7540)
P.O. Box 15698 (77220-5698)
PHONE..................................713 674-7531
Fax: 713 674-0005
▲ **EMP:** 16
SQ FT: 12,000
SALES (est): 2.6MM **Privately Held**
SIC: 5085 3053 Mfg
Gaskets/Packing/Sealing Devices Whol
Industrial Supplies

(G-12233)
TEXAS GLOBAL SYSTEMS INC
(PA)
8700 Commerce Park Dr # 201
(77036-7497)
PHONE..................................832 403-4238
Thomas K Adetomiwa, *President*
Seyi Bolu, *Director*
EMP: 10
SQ FT: 750
SALES (est): 1.5MM **Privately Held**
WEB: www.texasglobalsystems.com
SIC: 8711 1389 Engineering services;
servicing oil & gas wells

(G-12234)
TEXAS HONING INC
Also Called: Standard Machine Works
5602 Arapahoe St (77020-7320)
PHONE..................................713 673-1111
EMP: 61
SALES (corp-wide): 254.6B **Publicly**
Held
WEB: www.pccenergy.com
SIC: 3599 Machine shop, jobbing & repair
HQ: Texas Honing, Inc.
1710 Mykawa Rd
Pearland TX 77581
281 485-8339

(G-12235)
TEXAS HONING INC
2000 Aldine Western Rd (77038-1208)
PHONE..................................281 953-5900
Jeff Coleman, *Manager*
EMP: 40
SALES (corp-wide): 254.6B **Publicly**
Held
WEB: www.pccenergy.com
SIC: 3599 Grinding castings for the trade
HQ: Texas Honing, Inc.
1710 Mykawa Rd
Pearland TX 77581
281 485-8339

PA: Grupo Villacero, S.A. De C.V.
Ocampo No. 250 Pte.
Monterrey N.L. 64000

(G-12236)
TEXAS INE INC (PA)
Also Called: TTI Oil
6438 Long Dr (77087-3408)
PHONE....................281 601-4884
Octavio Arrambide, *President*
Daniel Villarreal, *Vice Pres*
Eli Gutierrez, *Prdtn Mgr*
Erica Pena, *Purchasing*
EMP: 80
SALES (est): 10MM **Privately Held**
WEB: www.ttioil.com
SIC: 3822 1389 Controls, combination oil
& hydronic; oil field services

(G-12237)
TEXAS INJECTION MOLDING
LLC
8820 Frey Rd (77034-3502)
PHONE....................281 489-4292
Jeff Applegate, *Mng Member*
Nubia Cabrera, *Manager*
EMP: 80
SALES (est): 7MM **Privately Held**
WEB: www.texasinjectionmolding.com
SIC: 3089 Injection molding of plastics

(G-12238)
TEXAS LINER SERVICE LLC
6618 Spindle Dr (77086-3832)
PHONE....................281 445-5050
Paul Ehmer, *Mng Member*
▲ **EMP:** 11
SALES (est): 1.2MM **Privately Held**
SIC: 3795 Tanks & tank components

(G-12239)
TEXAS MEDICAL TECHNOLOGY
LLC
6115 Skyline Dr Ste C (77057-7030)
PHONE....................832 512-7727
Dimitri Menin, *Principal*
Omri Shafran, *Mng Member*
Marc Harvey, *Director*
EMP: 10
SALES (est): 1MM **Privately Held**
SIC: 3841 Surgical & medical instruments

(G-12240)
TEXAS MEDPLAST LLC
Also Called: Savvy
6630 Roxburgh Dr Ste 171 (77041-5217)
PHONE....................832 288-2106
Luis Pabon, *COO*
Diego Olmos, *Mng Member*
EMP: 12
SALES (est): 1MM **Privately Held**
SIC: 3069 3821 Floor coverings, rubber;
incubators, laboratory

(G-12241)
TEXAS METAL EQUIPMENT CO
LTD (PA)
Also Called: M T E
6707 Mayard Rd (77041-2696)
PHONE....................713 466-8722
Andrew Harman, *President*
Don W Harman, *General Ptnr*
Lester Harman, *Vice Pres*
Tracy Meester, *Vice Pres*
Tracy Meester-Carter, *Vice Pres*
EMP: 38 **EST:** 1944
SQ FT: 24,000
SALES (est): 16.5MM **Privately Held**
WEB: www.tmeco.com
SIC: 3821 2599 Laboratory apparatus &
furniture; restaurant furniture, wood or
metal

(G-12242)
TEXAS OILTECH
LABORATORIES INC
10630 Fallstone Rd (77099-4304)
P.O. Box 741905 (77274-1905)
PHONE....................281 495-2400
Dr Phil Sorurbakhsh, *CEO*
Faye Fatehi, *President*
Philip Sorurbakhsh, *Opers Staff*
Fatemeh Fatehi, *Mktg Coord*
Imraan Nabi, *Program Mgr*
EMP: 21
SQ FT: 13,000

SALES (est): 8.8MM **Privately Held**
WEB: www.tol-lp.com
SIC: 1389 8731 Oil field services; environ-
mental research

(G-12243)
TEXAS PETROCHEMICALS LP
(DH)
500 Dallas St Ste 2000 (77002-4727)
PHONE....................713 477-9211
Charles W Shaver, *President*
Peggy Macatangay, *Vice Pres*
Joshua Nehlig, *Plant Mgr*
Todd Smith, *Project Mgr*
Esteban Compean, *Warehouse Mgr*
◆ **EMP:** 20
SALES (est): 115.1MM **Privately Held**
WEB: www.tpcgrp.com
SIC: 2869 Butadiene (industrial organic
chemical)
HQ: Tpc Group Llc
1 Allen Ctr 500 Dllas S 1 Allen Center
Houston TX 77002
713 477-9211

(G-12244)
TEXAS PETROCHEMICALS LP
3 Riverway Ste 1500 (77056-1935)
PHONE....................713 627-7474
Charlie Shaver, *CEO*
Brown Tiffany, *Manager*
EMP: 89 **Privately Held**
WEB: www.tpcgrp.com
SIC: 2869 Industrial organic chemicals
HQ: Texas Petrochemicals Lp
500 Dallas St Ste 2000
Houston TX 77002
713 477-9211

(G-12245)
TEXAS PMW INC
Also Called: Penn Machine of Texas
315 N Wayside Dr (77020-7514)
PHONE....................713 679-7900
Ronald Lafferty, *President*
Charles J Lafferty Jr, *Chairman*
EMP: 65
SALES (est): 10.6MM
SALES (corp-wide): 42.7MM **Privately**
Held
WEB: www.pennusa.com
SIC: 3498 5085 Pipe fittings, fabricated
from purchased pipe; industrial supplies
PA: Pennsylvania Machine Works, Llc
201 Bethel Ave
Upper Chichester PA 19014
610 497-3300

(G-12246)
TEXAS POWDER COATING INC
10010 Chickasaw Ln (77041-6150)
PHONE....................713 690-6226
Warren D Hawkins, *President*
EMP: 9
SALES (est): 1MM **Privately Held**
WEB: www.houstonpowdercoaters.com
SIC: 3479 Painting of metal products

(G-12247)
TEXAS REPUBLIC SIGNS LLC
2211 Pech Rd (77055-1117)
PHONE....................832 727-5415
Matthew Haltom, *Mng Member*
Brad Everett, *Manager*
Bernie Narvaez, *Manager*
Jon Marshall,
EMP: 42 **EST:** 2014
SQ FT: 10,000
SALES (est): 767.4K **Privately Held**
WEB: www.texasrepublicsigns.com
SIC: 3993 Signs & advertising specialties

(G-12248)
TEXAS SEWING INC
Also Called: Texas Uniform Manufacture
9210 Clarewood Dr (77036-3520)
PHONE....................713 271-5466
Yun Hui Hu, *President*
Tony Tran, *Supervisor*
EMP: 9
SQ FT: 7,544
SALES (est): 1.8MM **Privately Held**
SIC: 5137 2326 Women's & children's
clothing; medical & hospital uniforms,
men's; industrial garments, men's & boys'

(G-12249)
TEXAS SHAPES INC
6470 Rupley Cir (77087-3440)
PHONE....................713 641-1000
Ray H Kaufhold II, *President*
Donnie Hill, *Vice Pres*
▲ **EMP:** 40
SQ FT: 18,000
SALES (est): 7.2MM **Privately Held**
SIC: 3599 Machine shop, jobbing & repair

(G-12250)
TEXAS SOURCE GROUP INC
Also Called: Ascendant Tsg
207 Stratford St (77006-3219)
PHONE....................713 464-9702
Julie Maranto, *President*
Bill C Pugh, *Chairman*
Nancy M Maranto, *Exec VP*
EMP: 11
SQ FT: 5,500
SALES (est): 436.5K **Privately Held**
WEB: www.ascendanttsg.com
SIC: 8243 7372 Software training, com-
puter; application computer software
PA: Edoorways Corporation, Inc.
507 Pressler St Apt 4128
Austin TX 78703

(G-12251)
TEXAS STAIRS AND RAILS INC
11365 Eastex Fwy (77093-2136)
PHONE....................281 987-2115
▲ **EMP:** 25
SQ FT: 15,000
SALES (est): 7.1MM **Privately Held**
WEB: www.tsarinc.com
SIC: 3446 Stairs, staircases, stair treads:
prefabricated metal; railings, bannisters,
guards, etc.: made from metal pipe

(G-12252)
TEXAS STEEL CONVERSION
INC (PA)
3101 Holmes Rd (77051-1199)
PHONE....................713 733-6013
Charles D McPhail, *Ch of Bd*
Brian Binau, *President*
Heather Ransom, *Business Mgr*
Alfred Cox, *Vice Pres*
Frank Serna, *Vice Pres*
◆ **EMP:** 200
SQ FT: 500,000
SALES (est): 168.2MM **Privately Held**
WEB: www.texassteelconversion.com
SIC: 3398 Metal heat treating

(G-12253)
TEXAS STEEL CONVERSION
INC
110 Cypress Station Dr # 160
(77090-1630)
PHONE....................832 230-8228
Byron Kocian, *Accounts Mgr*
EMP: 163
SALES (corp-wide): 168.2MM **Privately**
Held
WEB: www.texassteelconversion.com
SIC: 3498 Fabricated pipe & fittings
PA: Texas Steel Conversion, Inc.
3101 Holmes Rd
Houston TX 77051
713 733-6013

(G-12254)
TEXAS STEEL CONVERSION
INC
Also Called: TSC Superior Hdd
7203 Miller Road 2 (77049-4821)
PHONE....................281 452-2260
EMP: 35
SALES (corp-wide): 168.2MM **Privately**
Held
WEB: www.texassteelconversion.com
SIC: 3498 Fabricated pipe & fittings
PA: Texas Steel Conversion, Inc.
3101 Holmes Rd
Houston TX 77051
713 733-6013

(G-12255)
TEXAS STEEL CONVERSION
INC
7401 C E King Pkwy (77044-2810)
PHONE....................281 459-2905

Brian Binau, *President*
EMP: 125
SQ FT: 120,577
SALES (corp-wide): 168.2MM **Privately**
Held
WEB: www.texassteelconversion.com
SIC: 3498 1791 Fabricated pipe & fittings;
structural steel erection
PA: Texas Steel Conversion, Inc.
3101 Holmes Rd
Houston TX 77051
713 733-6013

(G-12256)
TEXAS TEMPERED GLASS INC
1901 Little York Rd (77093-3231)
PHONE....................713 697-2828
Quang Nguyen, *President*
▲ **EMP:** 35
SQ FT: 95,000
SALES (est): 6.1MM **Privately Held**
WEB: www.ttgwebsite.com
SIC: 3423 Cutters, glass

(G-12257)
TEXAS TISSUE CONVERTING
LLC
1521 Greens Rd Ste 300 (77032-1232)
PHONE....................281 821-0429
Joseph Suarez, *CFO*
Patty Cassell, *Human Res Mgr*
Luis F Gomez, *Mng Member*
◆ **EMP:** 70
SALES (est): 1MM **Privately Held**
WEB: www.texastissue.com
SIC: 2621 5113 2676 Paper mills; indus-
trial & personal service paper; sanitary
paper products

(G-12258)
TEXAS UNITED CORPORATION
(PA)
4800 San Felipe St (77056-3908)
PHONE....................713 877-1793
Wayne Sneed, *CEO*
Iris P Webre, *Ch of Bd*
R W Sneed, *President*
Cathy Gillis, *Senior VP*
Scott Whitelaw, *Vice Pres*
EMP: 50
SQ FT: 75,000
SALES (est): 247.1MM **Privately Held**
WEB: www.unitedsalt.com
SIC: 1479 2819 4619 2899 Amblygonite
mining; sodium & potassium compounds,
exc. bleaches, alkalies, alum.; brine;
slurry pipeline operation; salt; ceramic
fiber; heavy construction equipment rental

(G-12259)
TEXCO TRIM INC
1407 W Patton St (77009-4516)
P.O. Box 8616 (77249-8616)
PHONE....................713 861-1892
Bryan Snoek, *President*
Dale Winter, *Vice Pres*
Chuck Jones, *Safety Mgr*
EMP: 60
SQ FT: 25,000
SALES (est): 4.4MM
SALES (corp-wide): 12.3MM **Privately**
Held
WEB: www.texcotrim.com
SIC: 3561 7699 Pumps, oil well & field;
valve repair, industrial
PA: Texco Holding Company
1407 W Patton St
Houston TX 77009
713 861-1100

(G-12260)
TEXLA ENERGY MANAGEMENT
INC
1100 La St Ste 4700 (77002)
PHONE....................713 655-9900
Lacy H Williams II, *President*
Danette Marrs, *Vice Pres*
Randy Miller, *CFO*
David Musgrove, *Marketing Staff*
George Fritz, *Administration*
EMP: 19
SQ FT: 6,000
SALES: 1.4B **Privately Held**
WEB: www.texlaenergy.com
SIC: 1382 Oil & gas exploration services

(G-12261)
TEXPAC FOODS LLC
Also Called: La Tang Cuisine
3824 Artdale St (77063-5246)
PHONE..................................713 780-4876
Fax: 713 780-4296
EMP: 14
SQ FT: 10,000
SALES: 600K **Privately Held**
SIC: 2038 Mfg Frozen Specialties

(G-12262)
TEXPERT MACHINE CO INC
6018 Gardendale Dr (77092-7022)
P.O. Box 925159 (77292-5159)
PHONE..................................713 263-7000
Lawrence Fritsch, *President*
David Surbrook, *Vice Pres*
EMP: 13
SQ FT: 13,000
SALES (est): 1.4MM **Privately Held**
SIC: 3599 Machine shop, jobbing & repair

(G-12263)
TEXSEIS INC
2618 Hollow Hook Rd (77080-3814)
PHONE..................................713 465-3181
J M Graul, *President*
C D Williams, *Principal*
Graul John M, *Vice Pres*
EMP: 9
SALES (est): 973.5K **Privately Held**
WEB: www.texseis.com
SIC: 1382 Seismograph surveys

(G-12264)
TEXTOOL COMPANY
1124 Hackney St (77023-3312)
P.O. Box 15621 (77220-5621)
PHONE..................................713 923-5595
Louie E Wiess, *President*
David Prescott, *Vice Pres*
Lometa Prescott, *Treasurer*
EMP: 29 EST: 1945
SQ FT: 28,000
SALES (est): 5.1MM **Privately Held**
WEB: www.textoolcompany.com
SIC: 3728 3599 Aircraft parts & equipment; machine shop, jobbing & repair

(G-12265)
TEXTRAY & STRUT LTD
1209 W 17th St (77008-3439)
PHONE..................................713 864-2551
Max West, *CEO*
Cliff Aturm, *President*
EMP: 40 EST: 1997
SALES (est): 3.6MM **Privately Held**
WEB: www.channel-track.com
SIC: 3315 Cable, steel: insulated or armored

(G-12266)
TF HUDGINS HOLDINGS INC (PA)
4405 Directors Row (77092-8605)
PHONE..................................713 682-3651
Katherine L Kohlmeyer, *Director*
George B Kelly, *Director*
EMP: 118
SALES (est): 70MM **Privately Held**
WEB: www.tfhudgins.com
SIC: 3569 5013 5085 3823 Lubrication equipment, industrial; filters, air & oil; industrial supplies; industrial process control instruments

(G-12267)
TFP CORPORATION
10183 Windfern Rd (77064-5813)
PHONE..................................281 598-2330
Troy Meredith, *General Mgr*
EMP: 35
SALES (corp-wide): 39.4MM **Privately Held**
WEB: www.tfpcorp.com
SIC: 3965 Fasteners
PA: Tfp Corporation
460 Lake Rd
Medina OH 44256
330 725-7741

(G-12268)
TGS-NOPEC GEOPHYSICAL COMPANY (DH)
10451 Clay Rd (77041-8753)
PHONE..................................713 860-2100
Hnery H Hamilton, *CEO*
David W Worthington, *Ch of Bd*
Pierre Benichou, *President*
J Kimberly Abdallah, *Vice Pres*
Wayne Millice, *Vice Pres*
◆ EMP: 63
SQ FT: 22,888
SALES (est): 421.2MM **Privately Held**
WEB: www.tgs.com
SIC: 1382 Oil & gas exploration services

(G-12269)
THERMAL DESIGNS INC (PA)
5352 Prudence Dr (77045-5194)
PHONE..................................713 433-6003
Gardner Baldwin, *CEO*
Tom Dearing, *President*
Hamid Saemi, *Research*
Brad Ward, *Sales Mgr*
Brian Evans, *Sales Staff*
▲ EMP: 21 EST: 1979
SQ FT: 20,000
SALES (est): 2.1MM **Privately Held**
WEB: www.tdius.com
SIC: 3479 Coating of metals & formed products

(G-12270)
THERMO ELCTRON PROCESS SYSTEMS
9303 W Sam Houston Pkwy S (77099-5226)
PHONE..................................713 272-0404
William J Zolner, *President*
EMP: 100
SALES (est): 14MM
SALES (corp-wide): 25.5B **Publicly Held**
SIC: 3825 Recorders, oscillographic
PA: Thermo Fisher Scientific Inc.
168 3rd Ave
Waltham MA 02451
781 622-1000

(G-12271)
THERMO-MOLD INC
5801 Berry Brook Dr (77017-6755)
PHONE..................................713 944-6336
Barry J Johnson, *President*
EMP: 13
SQ FT: 18,500
SALES (est): 2.2MM **Privately Held**
WEB: www.thermo-mold.com
SIC: 3089 Molding primary plastic; injection molding of plastics

(G-12272)
THERMOCONTROL INC
5700 Hartsdale Dr (77036-2112)
P.O. Box 1102, Mount Pleasant (75456-1102)
PHONE..................................713 780-8600
Anabel L Daily, *President*
EMP: 50
SQ FT: 32,000
SALES (est): 7.9MM
SALES (corp-wide): 25.3MM **Privately Held**
WEB: www.thermocontrol-inc.sbcontract.com
SIC: 3829 Measuring & controlling devices
PA: Daily Instruments Corporation
5700 Hartsdale Dr
Houston TX 77036
713 780-8600

(G-12273)
THOMAS BUS GULF COAST GP INC
8806 Mississippi St (77029-4402)
PHONE..................................713 580-8600
Thomas Bus, *General Mgr*
Gary Fenn, *General Mgr*
Gregg Peterson, *General Mgr*
Rick Stewart, *Co-CEO*
Robert F Garwood, *Co-CEO*
EMP: 37 EST: 1999

SALES (est): 6.2MM
SALES (corp-wide): 244.6MM **Privately Held**
SIC: 3711 5012 5013 7538 Buses, all types, assembly of; commercial vehicles; truck tractors; trucks, commercial; motor vehicle supplies & new parts; truck engine repair, except industrial
PA: Selectransportation Resources Llc
9550 North Loop E
Houston TX 77029
713 672-4115

(G-12274)
THOMAS PRINTWORKS
707 West Rd (77038-2505)
PHONE..................................832 201-2000
Todd Rohani, *Branch Mgr*
EMP: 10
SALES (est): 1.5MM **Privately Held**
WEB: www.thomasprintworks.com
SIC: 2752 Commercial printing, lithographic

(G-12275)
THOMAS REPROGRAPHICS INC
Also Called: A & E - The Graphics Complex
3232 Chimney Rock Rd (77056-6203)
PHONE..................................713 977-6363
Glen Donnelly, *Branch Mgr*
EMP: 12
SALES (corp-wide): 62.7MM **Privately Held**
WEB: www.thomasprintworks.com
SIC: 7334 2759 Blueprinting service; commercial printing
PA: Thomas Reprographics, Inc.
600 N Central Expy
Richardson TX 75080
972 231-7227

(G-12276)
THOMAS REPROGRAPHICS INC
361 Greens Rd (77060-1903)
PHONE..................................281 875-2500
Carol Nelson, *Manager*
EMP: 12
SALES (corp-wide): 62.7MM **Privately Held**
WEB: www.thomasprintworks.com
SIC: 2759 1382 Commercial printing; oil & gas exploration services
PA: Thomas Reprographics, Inc.
600 N Central Expy
Richardson TX 75080
972 231-7227

(G-12277)
THOMASON FAMILY CORPORATION
2300 Nance St (77020-5733)
P.O. Box 21148 (77226-1148)
PHONE..................................713 223-4575
Jack H Thomason, *President*
Jack Daniel Thomason, *Corp Secy*
Wilma Thomason, *Vice Pres*
EMP: 10 EST: 1968
SQ FT: 18,000
SALES (est): 1.4MM **Privately Held**
SIC: 2841 2842 Soap & other detergents; specialty cleaning preparations

(G-12278)
THOMPSON PAPER PDTS TEXAS INC
3800 Tanglewilde St # 407 (77063-5168)
P.O. Box 2886 (77252-2886)
PHONE..................................713 869-6636
Jim Myers, *President*
Dinah Myers, *Corp Secy*
EMP: 45 EST: 1963
SQ FT: 42,000
SALES (est): 8.3MM **Privately Held**
SIC: 2675 2631 Folders, filing, die-cut; made from purchased materials; paperboard mills

(G-12279)
THOMPSON SCALE COMPANY
9000 Jameel Rd Ste 190 (77040-5061)
PHONE..................................713 932-9071
EMP: 20
SQ FT: 9,000

SALES (est): 3MM **Privately Held**
WEB: www.thompsonscale.com
SIC: 3545 3625 Scales, measuring (machinists' precision tools); control circuit relays, industrial

(G-12280)
THORNTREE LP (PA)
Also Called: Thorntree Slate & Marble
10105 W Gulf Bank Rd (77040-3121)
PHONE..................................713 690-8200
Stuart Rae, *President*
◆ EMP: 20 EST: 1979
SQ FT: 12,800
SALES (est): 4.4MM **Privately Held**
WEB: www.thorntreeslate.com
SIC: 3281 5023 Slate products; floor coverings

(G-12281)
THORPE PLANT SERVICES INC (HQ)
6833 Kirbyville St (77033-1107)
P.O. Box 330407 (77233-0407)
PHONE..................................713 644-1247
Jeff Duncombe, *Principal*
Nick Noto, *Vice Pres*
EMP: 43
SALES (est): 12.4MM
SALES (corp-wide): 61.8MM **Privately Held**
WEB: www.thorpeplantmaintenance-andengineering.com
SIC: 3441 Building components, structural steel
PA: Thorpe Specialty Services Corporation
6833 Kirbyville St
Houston TX 77033
713 644-1247

(G-12282)
THREADING & PRECISION MFG LLC
Also Called: Ofs International
7735 Miller Road 3 (77049-1737)
PHONE..................................281 452-3036
Konstantin Semerikov, *President*
EMP: 150
SALES (est): 11.5MM **Privately Held**
WEB: www.ofsint.com
SIC: 1389 Oil field services

(G-12283)
THREE BROTHERS BAKERY INC (PA)
4036 S Braeswood Blvd (77025-3304)
PHONE..................................713 666-2253
Robert Jucker, *President*
Chuck Krauthamer, *General Mgr*
Sigmund Jucker, *Vice Pres*
Julie Calderon, *Sales Mgr*
Jason Tidwell, *Manager*
EMP: 18
SQ FT: 5,000
SALES (est): 2.7MM **Privately Held**
WEB: www.3brothersbakery.com
SIC: 5461 2051 Bread; bakery: wholesale or wholesale/retail combined

(G-12284)
THRUSTMASTER OF TEXAS INC
6900 Thrustmaster Dr (77041-2682)
P.O. Box 840189 (77284-0189)
PHONE..................................713 937-6295
Joe Bekker, *President*
Jon Holvik, *Exec VP*
Xiaohong Dou, *Vice Pres*
Rigo Ramirez, *Manager*
Rick Martin, *IT/INT Sup*
◆ EMP: 275
SQ FT: 240,000
SALES (est): 89.9MM **Privately Held**
WEB: www.thrustmaster.net
SIC: 3531 Marine related equipment

(G-12285)
THUG CITY RECORDS
204 E 30th St (77018-8402)
PHONE..................................832 264-4892
EMP: 15
SALES (est): 407.4K **Privately Held**
SIC: 5735 7389 3652 Records; recording studio, noncommercial records; master records or tapes, preparation of

(G-12286)
THUNDERCO INC
909 Fisher St (77018-5305)
P.O. Box 920795 (77292-0795)
PHONE..................................713 681-4686
Ricky Edrington, *CEO*
Walter O Edrington, *CEO*
Rick Edrington, *President*
EMP: 9
SQ FT: 12,000
SALES (est): 1.6MM **Privately Held**
WEB: www.thunderco.com
SIC: 3625 Control equipment, electric

(G-12287)
TIBCO SOFTWARE INC
1600 Smith St Ste 3890 (77002-7374)
PHONE..................................713 344-2045
Richard Hash, *Engineer*
Kenneth Johansson, *Engineer*
Marcelo Gallardo, *Sales Executive*
Brian Pierce, *Manager*
Bradley Moore, *Executive*
EMP: 25
SALES (corp-wide): 885.6MM **Privately Held**
WEB: www.tibco.com
SIC: 7372 Prepackaged software
HQ: Tibco Software Inc.
3307 Hillview Ave
Palo Alto CA 94304

(G-12288)
TIDAL ENERGY MARKETING US LLC
1100 La St Ste 3600 (77002)
PHONE..................................713 650-8900
Leigh S Cruess, *President*
Steve Myers, *Exec VP*
Jim Parmer, *Exec VP*
Chris Kaitson, *Vice Pres*
Brian Simmons, *Vice Pres*
EMP: 200
SALES (est): 7.7MM
SALES (corp-wide): 3.7B **Privately Held**
SIC: 1311 4923 Crude petroleum & natural gas; gas transmission & distribution
HQ: Enbridge (U.S.) Inc.
1100 Louisiana St # 3300
Houston TX 77002

(G-12289)
TIDELAND SIGNAL CORPORATION (HQ)
7100 Bus Pk Dr Ste B (77041)
PHONE..................................713 681-6101
Matt B Scheuing, *President*
Clive W Quickenden, *Vice Pres*
Dale R Williams, *Vice Pres*
Dale Williams, *Vice Pres*
Leland Denson, *Production*
◆ **EMP:** 68 **EST:** 1954
SQ FT: 60,000
SALES (est): 20.6MM **Publicly Held**
WEB: www.tidelandsignal.com
SIC: 3812 Navigational systems & instruments

(G-12290)
TIGER INDUSTRIES INC
11955 Fm 529 Rd (77041-3017)
P.O. Box 41304 (77241-1304)
PHONE..................................713 896-9300
Carl L Guillot, *President*
Mary Guillot, *Treasurer*
Elizabeth O Guillot, *Shareholder*
EMP: 20
SQ FT: 16,000
SALES (est): 4.4MM **Privately Held**
WEB: www.tigerindustriesinc.com
SIC: 3443 5082 Heat exchangers, condensers & components; oil field equipment

(G-12291)
TIGER VALVE HOUSTON CO LLC
15862 Diplomatic Plaza Dr (77032-2669)
PHONE..................................281 227-9911
▲ **EMP:** 15
SALES (est): 3.6MM **Privately Held**
WEB: www.tigervalve.com
SIC: 5085 3592 Valves & fittings; valves

(G-12292)
TIMKEN GEARS & SERVICES INC
Also Called: Philadelphia Gear
10830 Train Ct (77041-7041)
PHONE..................................713 224-4900
Boyd Swearingen, *Manager*
Greg Dillon,
EMP: 45
SALES (corp-wide): 3.7B **Publicly Held**
WEB: www.philagear.com
SIC: 3462 Gear & chain forgings; gears, forged steel; anchors, forged
HQ: Timken Gears & Services Inc.
935 1st Ave Ste 200
King Of Prussia PA 19406

(G-12293)
TIMKENSTEEL MATERIAL SVCS LLC
14730 Yarberry St (77039-1031)
P.O. Box 90246 (77290-0246)
PHONE..................................281 449-0319
Shawn Seanor, *President*
Tim Timken, *Principal*
Charles Elder, *Vice Pres*
Dmitry Skornetskiy, *Sales Engr*
Barbara Moore,
▼ **EMP:** 120
SQ FT: 150,000
SALES (est): 26.1MM
SALES (corp-wide): 1.2B **Publicly Held**
WEB: www.timkensteel.com
SIC: 3599 Machine shop, jobbing & repair
PA: Timkensteel Corporation
1835 Dueber Ave Sw
Canton OH 44706
330 471-7000

(G-12294)
TIP TOP SHEET METAL INC
2309 W Mount Houston Rd (77038-3613)
PHONE..................................281 931-7823
Paula Felton, *President*
Robin Felton, *Vice Pres*
EMP: 25
SQ FT: 5,000
SALES (est): 4.3MM **Privately Held**
SIC: 5033 3444 Roofing, asphalt & sheet metal; roof deck, sheet metal

(G-12295)
TITAN BOP RUBBER PRODUCTS INC
9447 Bamboo Rd (77041-7703)
PHONE..................................713 895-9230
Ryan Kindel, *Opers Staff*
Ferial Saleh, *Director*
Salim Saleh, *Director*
▲ **EMP:** 50
SALES (est): 163.4K **Privately Held**
WEB: www.titanbopinc.com
SIC: 3069 Medical & laboratory rubber sundries & related products

(G-12296)
TITAN CHEMICAL CORPORATION
6710 Cadillac St (77021-2412)
P.O. Box 14569 (77221-4569)
PHONE..................................713 747-3134
Scott Haber, *President*
Thomas Haber, *Vice Pres*
Doris Haber, *Admin Sec*
EMP: 13
SQ FT: 27,000
SALES (est): 3.4MM **Privately Held**
WEB: www.titanchemical.us
SIC: 2842 5169 Cleaning or polishing preparations; chemicals & allied products

(G-12297)
TITAN ENVIRONMENTAL USA LLC
15847 Kimberlee St (77049-2011)
PHONE..................................713 849-1311
Brett Burkard, *CEO*
Kelly Sitarz, *President*
Derek Bishop, *CFO*
Juice Lambert, *VP Sales*
EMP: 20

SALES (est): 6.3MM
SALES (corp-wide): 27.6MM **Privately Held**
WEB: www.titanenvirousa.com
SIC: 2833 Vitamins, natural or synthetic: bulk, uncompounded
PA: Titan Environmental Containment Ltd
777 Quest Blvd
Ile Des Chenes MB R0A 0
204 878-3955

(G-12298)
TITAN SOLUTIONS
825 Town And Country Ln # 1200 (77024-2246)
PHONE..................................281 973-9653
Richard Leffingwell, *Partner*
EMP: 15
SALES (est): 643.6K **Privately Held**
WEB: www.titan-solutions.net
SIC: 8748 2431 Business consulting; millwork

(G-12299)
TITAN TOOL & DIE COMPANY
10050 W Gulf Bank Rd # 200 (77040-3159)
PHONE..................................713 849-4300
EMP: 15
SQ FT: 14,000
SALES (est): 1.6MM **Privately Held**
SIC: 3544 Mfg Tools Dies & Molds

(G-12300)
TITANIUM FABRICATION CORP
Also Called: Phx Grp - Txas Div Ttanium Fab
5121 Hiltonview Rd (77086-1310)
PHONE..................................832 375-1800
R G Kuykendall, *Manager*
Michael Finke, *Manager*
EMP: 10
SALES (corp-wide): 729MM **Privately Held**
WEB: www.tifab.com
SIC: 3498 3444 3443 Fabricated pipe & fittings; sheet metalwork; heat exchangers: coolers (after, inter), condensers, etc.
HQ: Titanium Fabrication Corp
110 Lehigh Dr
Fairfield NJ 07004
973 227-5300

(G-12301)
TITANIUM WELDING SERVICES LLC
5871 Belneath St (77033-2229)
PHONE..................................281 380-7043
Elizabeth Martinez,
EMP: 17
SALES (est): 982K **Privately Held**
SIC: 7692 Welding repair

(G-12302)
TITEX INC
Also Called: T I Tex
4800 Clinton Dr (77020-7902)
PHONE..................................713 678-8890
Jason Wang, *President*
Steve Weidenheft, *Vice Pres*
Sherry Wang, *Treasurer*
Diana Wang, *Admin Sec*
EMP: 20
SQ FT: 92,000
SALES (est): 2.7MM **Privately Held**
SIC: 2673 Plastic bags: made from purchased materials

(G-12303)
TIW CORPORATION (HQ)
6401 N Eldridge Pkwy (77041-3505)
P.O. Box 35729 (77235-5729)
PHONE..................................713 939-7711
Stephen R Pearce, *President*
Nathaniel Adkins, *District Mgr*
Britt O Braddick, *Exec VP*
Ed Royer, *Vice Pres*
Carl C Washington, *CFO*
◆ **EMP:** 200 **EST:** 1917
SQ FT: 86,000
SALES (est): 87.6MM
SALES (corp-wide): 414.8MM **Publicly Held**
WEB: www.tiwoiltools.com
SIC: 3533 Oil field machinery & equipment; gas field machinery & equipment

PA: Dril-Quip, Inc.
6401 N Eldridge Pkwy
Houston TX 77041
713 939-7711

(G-12304)
TIW INTERNATIONAL INC (DH)
6401 N Eldridge Pkwy (77041-3505)
P.O. Box 35729 (77235-5729)
PHONE..................................713 729-2110
Steve Pearce, *President*
Britt Braddick, *Exec VP*
Carl Washington, *CFO*
EMP: 10
SALES: 5.1MM
SALES (corp-wide): 414.8MM **Publicly Held**
WEB: www.tiwoiltools.com
SIC: 3533 Oil field machinery & equipment
HQ: Tiw Corporation
6401 N Eldridge Pkwy
Houston TX 77041
713 939-7711

(G-12305)
TKO SPORTS GROUP USA LIMITED
4660 Pine Timbers St # 198 (77041-9351)
PHONE..................................713 895-9270
Gary W Kurtz, *President*
Steve Yang, *Senior VP*
Andrew Henderson, *Vice Pres*
◆ **EMP:** 20
SALES (est): 3.8MM **Privately Held**
WEB: www.tkostrength.com
SIC: 5091 3949 Fitness equipment & supplies; gymnasium equipment
PA: Tko Sports Group Usa Ltd.
4660 Pine Timbers St # 198
Houston TX 77041

(G-12306)
TLC TONERLAND LP
3990 North Fwy (77022)
PHONE..................................713 692-6650
Wayne Harryman, *Principal*
EMP: 13
SALES (est): 1.8MM **Privately Held**
SIC: 2044 Rice milling

(G-12307)
TM LUCKETT ENTERPRISES LLC
Also Called: Temptation Publishing
5444 Westheimr Rd # 1080 (77056-5357)
PHONE..................................866 216-7278
Tempestt Luckett, *CEO*
Tempestt Marie Luckett, *Mng Member*
EMP: 10
SALES (est): 44.3MM **Privately Held**
WEB: www.classycreditrepair.com
SIC: 2731 7299 7389 8741 Books: publishing only; information services, consumer; styling of fashions, apparel, furniture, textiles, etc.; business management

(G-12308)
TMCO INC
Also Called: Measurement Company, The
4100 N Sam Houston Pkwy W (77086-1465)
P.O. Box 40, Simonton (77476-0040)
PHONE..................................713 465-3255
H Wayne Carroll, *President*
Donna Wallace, *Corp Secy*
Scott Orr, *CFO*
▲ **EMP:** 73
SALES (est): 10.7MM **Privately Held**
WEB: www.tmcousa.com
SIC: 3494 Valves & pipe fittings

(G-12309)
TMK NORTH AMERICA INC
10120 Houston Oaks Dr (77064-3514)
PHONE..................................281 949-1023
Chuck King, *President*
Mike Christopher, *Vice Pres*
◆ **EMP:** 17
SALES (est): 6.3MM
SALES (corp-wide): 18.6MM **Privately Held**
WEB: www.tmk-group.com
SIC: 3317 Steel pipe & tubes

HQ: Tmk Global Sa
Boulevard Du Theatre 2
GenCve GE 1204
228 186-466

(G-12310)
TNN MACHINING COMPANY LLC
8330 W Little York Rd (77040-4341)
PHONE....................................713 849-0062
Tien V Nguyen, *Mng Member*
Tien Nguyen, *Mng Member*
EMP: 28
SALES (est): 4.4MM **Privately Held**
WEB: www.tnnmfg.com
SIC: 3599 Machine shop, jobbing & repair

(G-12311)
TNN MANUFACTURING COMPANY INC
8330 W Little York Rd (77040-4341)
PHONE....................................713 849-0062
Sam Nguyen, *President*
Tien Nguyen, *Vice Pres*
John Roman, *Manager*
Trang Tran, *Office Admin*
Lan Vu, *Admin Sec*
▲ EMP: 55
SQ FT: 10,000
SALES (est): 12.9MM **Privately Held**
WEB: www.tnnmfg.com
SIC: 3452 3599 Nuts, metal; machine shop, jobbing & repair

(G-12312)
TNN NEW WORLD
6834 Flintlock Rd (77040-4476)
PHONE....................................281 598-6680
Jiem Nguyen, *Principal*
EMP: 55
SALES (est): 2.7MM **Privately Held**
WEB: www.tnnmanufacturing.com
SIC: 3599 Machine shop, jobbing & repair

(G-12313)
TNS INDUSTRIES INC
Also Called: Texas National Solutions
6818 Satsuma Dr (77041-2710)
PHONE....................................713 690-4000
Robert W Daugherty, *President*
EMP: 25
SALES (est): 6.8MM **Privately Held**
SIC: 3441 Fabricated structural metal

(G-12314)
TNT MACHINE
1105 Upland Dr Ste B2 (77043-4708)
PHONE....................................713 722-0622
Tom Turner, *President*
EMP: 12
SALES (est): 1.7MM **Privately Held**
SIC: 3599 Machine shop, jobbing & repair

(G-12315)
TNT PRINTING
Also Called: T N T Printing
2111 Hartwick Rd (77093-1101)
PHONE....................................281 449-9090
Tom Neal, *Owner*
EMP: 9 EST: 1978
SQ FT: 8,600
SALES (est): 750.1K **Privately Held**
WEB: www.tnconsultinginc.com
SIC: 2789 2752 2791 2759 Bookbinding & related work; commercial printing, offset; typesetting; commercial printing; automotive & apparel trimmings

(G-12316)
TOOL AND DIE BY H&H INC
1216 Illinios St S (77002)
PHONE....................................713 943-0545
Hector Villarreal, *CEO*
Jose Carreon, *Business Mgr*
EMP: 21
SALES (est): 3.9MM **Privately Held**
WEB: www.handhcorp.com
SIC: 3544 Special dies & tools

(G-12317)
TOOL-FLO MANUFACTURING INC
14745 Kirby Dr (77047-2568)
PHONE....................................713 941-1080
Dennis P Flolo, *President*

Sandra J Flolo, *Corp Secy*
Katheryn Holland, *Vice Pres*
K D Quinby, *Vice Pres*
James Mendez, *Plant Mgr*
▲ EMP: 145
SQ FT: 88,000
SALES (est): 36MM **Privately Held**
WEB: www.toolflo.com
SIC: 3541 5085 3545 Machine tool replacement & repair parts, metal cutting types; machine tools, metal cutting: exotic (explosive, etc.); industrial supplies; machine tool accessories

(G-12318)
TOOLCO PRECISION MACHINE INC
14701 Park Almeda Dr (77047-7003)
P.O. Box 450186 (77245-0186)
PHONE....................................713 433-3700
Abiel Gonzalez, *President*
Belinda Gonzalez, *Admin Sec*
EMP: 12
SQ FT: 10,000
SALES (est): 753.7K **Privately Held**
WEB: www.toolcopm.com
SIC: 3469 Metal stampings

(G-12319)
TOOLEX INC
7570 Morley St (77061-2827)
PHONE....................................713 644-8071
Marcel Carrascosa, *President*
Howard Nelson, *Vice Pres*
Darnell Carrascosa, *Treasurer*
Martin Carrascosa, *Sales Staff*
Bill Smith, *Sales Executive*
EMP: 22
SQ FT: 14,000
SALES (est): 3.7MM **Privately Held**
WEB: www.toolexinc.com
SIC: 3599 Machine shop, jobbing & repair

(G-12320)
TOOLING TECHNOLOGIES MFG LLC
11680 Brittmoore Park Dr (77041-6917)
PHONE....................................713 722-8501
Timothy M Levrier,
Bill Maurer,
EMP: 16
SALES (est): 1.5MM **Privately Held**
WEB: www.toolingtechmfg.com
SIC: 3999 5085 5084 Coin-operated amusement machines; industrial supplies; industrial tools; industrial machine parts

(G-12321)
TOP-CO CEMENTING PRODUCTS INC
10613 W Sam Houston Pkwy (77064-4663)
PHONE....................................832 300-3660
Mike Reeves, *CEO*
Kenneth Lowther, *Managing Dir*
Scott Watson, *COO*
Gerald Bushong, *Vice Pres*
John Griggs, *CFO*
▼ EMP: 125 EST: 2006
SALES (est): 30.5MM
SALES (corp-wide): 108.5MM **Privately Held**
WEB: www.rubicon-oilfield.com
SIC: 3769 3533 1389 Casings, missiles & missile components: storage; oil field machinery & equipment; cementing oil & gas well casings
PA: Rubicon Oilfield International Holdings, Llc
10613 W Sam Hston Pkwy600
Houston TX 77064
832 386-2500

(G-12322)
TOPWAY GLOBAL INC
8738 Westpark Dr (77063-5814)
PHONE....................................713 784-1808
George Yen, *Principal*
EMP: 50
SALES (est): 4.6MM **Privately Held**
SIC: 2834 Chlorination tablets & kits (water purification)

(G-12323)
TORCSILL FOUNDATIONS LLC (PA)
12000 Aerospace Ave # 115 (77034-5576)
P.O. Box 69, Weatherford OK (73096-0069)
PHONE....................................281 825-5200
Tim Swift, *CEO*
Lyle Love, *Ch of Bd*
John Mitchell, *District Mgr*
Chris Haltom, *Business Mgr*
Tyler Lundy, *Business Mgr*
EMP: 53
SALES (est): 233.2MM **Privately Held**
WEB: www.torcsill.com
SIC: 1389 1542 Gas field services; non-residential construction

(G-12324)
TORRES BROTHERS
4247 Fuqua St (77048-5007)
PHONE....................................713 732-4237
Eriberto Torres, *Principal*
EMP: 13 EST: 2014
SALES (est): 3.9MM **Privately Held**
WEB: www.torresbrothersinc.com
SIC: 3273 Ready-mixed concrete

(G-12325)
TORTUGA OPERATING CO (PA)
7412 Shadyvilla Ln (77055-5116)
PHONE....................................713 680-3600
EMP: 9 EST: 1976
SQ FT: 7,000
SALES (est): 1.6MM **Privately Held**
SIC: 1311 Crude petroleum production; natural gas production

(G-12326)
TOSHIBA INTERNATIONAL CORP
10510 Okanella St (77041-5347)
PHONE....................................713 466-0277
Bill Nutini, *Vice Pres*
Danny Luu, *Production*
Wakako Minami, *Buyer*
Frank McClung, *Sales Staff*
Wayne Liem, *Director*
EMP: 9 **Privately Held**
WEB: www.tabs.toshiba.com
SIC: 3621 Motors & generators
HQ: Toshiba International Corporation
13131 W Little York Rd
Houston TX 77041
800 231-1412

(G-12327)
TOSHIBA INTERNATIONAL CORP (DH)
13131 W Little York Rd (77041-5807)
PHONE....................................800 231-1412
Koichi Yanabe, *CEO*
Kelly Rodriguez, *President*
Larry Bennett, *Business Mgr*
Enrique Anaya, *Production*
Oscar Custodio Castre, *Production*
◆ EMP: 850 EST: 1967
SQ FT: 615,000
SALES (est): 513MM **Privately Held**
WEB: www.tabs.toshiba.com
SIC: 3621 5084 5063 3613 Motors & generators; engines & transportation equipment; generators; switchgear & switchboard apparatus; fluid power pumps & motors; computer storage devices
HQ: Toshiba America Inc
1251 Ave Of Amrcas Ste 41
New York NY 10020
212 596-0600

(G-12328)
TOSHIBA INTERNATIONAL CORP
Led Lighting Division
10435 Okanella St (77041-5359)
PHONE....................................713 466-0277
Shinichiro Akiba, *CEO*
EMP: 9 **Privately Held**
WEB: www.tabs.toshiba.com
SIC: 3621 Motors & generators
HQ: Toshiba International Corporation
13131 W Little York Rd
Houston TX 77041
800 231-1412

(G-12329)
TOTAL E&P RES & TECH USA LLC
1201 La St Ste 1800 (77002)
PHONE....................................713 647-3000
Herve Coutrix,
EMP: 34 EST: 2016
SALES (est): 2.4MM **Privately Held**
WEB: www.totalpetrochemicalsrefiningusa.com
SIC: 2821 Plastics materials & resins

(G-12330)
TOTAL E&P USA INC
1201 La St Ste 1800 (77002)
P.O. Box 4397 (77210-4397)
PHONE....................................713 647-3000
Jean-Michel Lavergne, *President*
Ken Porche, *General Mgr*
Mark Redeker, *Principal*
David N Rosenthal, *Principal*
Isaac Sultan, *Principal*
◆ EMP: 139 EST: 1989
SALES (est): 52.9MM
SALES (corp-wide): 7B **Publicly Held**
WEB: www.totalpetrochemicalsrefiningusa.com
SIC: 1311 1382 1381 Crude petroleum & natural gas; oil & gas exploration services; drilling oil & gas wells
HQ: Total Holdings Usa, Inc.
1201 La St Ste 1800
Houston TX 77002
713 483-5000

(G-12331)
TOTAL HOLDINGS USA INC (HQ)
1201 La St Ste 1800 (77002)
P.O. Box 674411 (77267-4411)
PHONE....................................713 483-5000
Agnes D'Oliveira, *CEO*
Kevin Clark, *Counsel*
Edouard Bense, *Project Mgr*
Jeff Saint, *Production*
Eduardo Andresik, *VP Bus Dvlpt*
◆ EMP: 50
SALES (est): 12.8B
SALES (corp-wide): 7B **Publicly Held**
WEB: www.totalpetrochemicalsusa.com
SIC: 1382 1311 Oil & gas exploration services; crude petroleum & natural gas

(G-12332)
TOTAL PTRCHEMICALS REF USA INC (DH)
1201 La St Ste 1800 (77002)
P.O. Box 674411 (77267-4411)
PHONE....................................713 483-5000
Geoffroy Petit, *CEO*
Christophe Geronbeau, *Chairman*
Isabelle Kieffer, *Vice Pres*
Alan Sweny, *Opers Staff*
Festus Nwagwu, *Production*
◆ EMP: 362
SALES (est): 819.8MM
SALES (corp-wide): 7B **Publicly Held**
WEB: www.totalpetrochemicalsrefiningusa.com
SIC: 2899 2869 2911 Chemical preparations; fuels; gasoline
HQ: Total Holdings Usa, Inc.
1201 La St Ste 1800
Houston TX 77002
713 483-5000

(G-12333)
TOTAL PTRCHEMICALS SEC USA INC
1201 La St Ste 1800 (77002)
PHONE....................................713 483-5000
Aubrey Byerly, *Vice Pres*
EMP: 47
SALES (est): 1.9MM
SALES (corp-wide): 7B **Publicly Held**
WEB: www.totalpetrochemicalsrefiningusa.com
SIC: 2821 Plastics materials & resins
HQ: Total Petrochemicals & Refining Usa, Inc.
1201 La St Ste 1800
Houston TX 77002
713 483-5000

(G-12334)
TOTAL SPECIALTIES USA INC (DH)
1201 La St Ste 1800 (77002)
P.O. Box 1063, Linden NJ (07036-1063)
PHONE..................................713 969-4651
Mart Newstead, *CEO*
Ernst Wanten, *President*
Anthony Soriano, *President*
Franck Bagouet, *Senior VP*
Robert Devenney, *Vice Pres*
◆ EMP: 28
SALES (est): 38.1MM
SALES (corp-wide): 7B **Publicly Held**
WEB: www.totalspecialties.com
SIC: 2992 Oils & greases, blending & compounding
HQ: Elf Aquitaine, Inc.
2000 Market St
Philadelphia PA
215 419-7000

(G-12335)
TOUCHSHARE INC (PA)
815 Briarpark Dr (77042-1555)
PHONE..................................626 639-5460
Robert Pette, *CEO*
Ann Widay, *Sales Staff*
Steve Rasmussen, *Office Mgr*
EMP: 12
SQ FT: 3,000
SALES (est): 2MM **Privately Held**
SIC: 7372 Prepackaged software

(G-12336)
TOWN & COUNTRY PRINTING INC
Also Called: Minuteman Press
1171 Brittmoore Rd (77043-5003)
PHONE..................................713 973-6666
Albert Goldrich, *CEO*
Derek Mercer, *President*
Louise Mercer, *Admin Sec*
EMP: 13
SQ FT: 1,600
SALES (est): 1.8MM **Privately Held**
WEB: www.mmptcpp.com
SIC: 2752 Commercial printing, lithographic

(G-12337)
TPG SOFTWARE INC
5858 Westheimer Rd # 620 (77057-5643)
PHONE..................................713 974-1375
Ursula H Felmet, *CEO*
Slavek R Rotkiewicz, *President*
Ian Martin, *Vice Pres*
Rick Shnitger, *Vice Pres*
Chris Dahlman, *Opers Staff*
EMP: 24
SQ FT: 5,101
SALES (est): 4.6MM **Privately Held**
WEB: www.tpgsoftware.com
SIC: 7372 7371 Business oriented computer software; computer software development & applications

(G-12338)
TRACEY TECHNOLOGIES CORP
16720 Hedgecroft Dr # 208 (77060-3643)
PHONE..................................281 445-1666
Joe S Wakil, *CEO*
Ray Sievert, *VP Sales*
Gerard Doyle, *Manager*
Lamar F Laster, *Shareholder*
R G Martin MD, *Shareholder*
▲ EMP: 9
SQ FT: 4,500
SALES (est): 222.6K **Privately Held**
WEB: www.traceytechnologies.com
SIC: 3841 Ophthalmic instruments & apparatus

(G-12339)
TRADCO INC
9400 Bamboo Rd (77041-7704)
PHONE..................................713 333-9300
Federico Gonzalez, *President*
Guillermo Gonzalez Jr, *Vice Pres*
Mark Pearce, *Sales Staff*
Juan Artiga, *Manager*
▲ EMP: 18
SQ FT: 20,000

SALES (est): 12.1MM **Privately Held**
WEB: www.tradco.com
SIC: 5051 3441 Steel; fabricated structural metal

(G-12340)
TRADEMARKS PROMOTIONAL PDTS LP
11333 Todd St (77055-1300)
PHONE..................................713 255-6506
Audrey N Devenport, *General Ptnr*
R Michael Devenport, *General Ptnr*
Todd Longenecker, *Prdtn Mgr*
Melissa Shaffer, *Accounts Mgr*
Elaine Simmons, *Accounts Mgr*
▼ EMP: 65
SQ FT: 36,000
SALES (est): 14.7MM **Privately Held**
WEB: www.tmarks.com
SIC: 5199 2329 Advertising specialties; men's & boys' sportswear & athletic clothing

(G-12341)
TRADEWINDS PETROTRADE LLC
8955 Katy Fwy Ste 220 (77024-1675)
PHONE..................................713 465-7590
James E Scott III, *Administration*
EMP: 10
SALES (est): 109K **Privately Held**
WEB: www.tradewindspetrotrade.com
SIC: 1382 Oil & gas exploration services

(G-12342)
TRANE US INC
16335 Central Green Blvd (77032-5146)
PHONE..................................832 747-2000
EMP: 62 **Privately Held**
WEB: www.huntondistribution.com
SIC: 3585 Refrigeration & heating equipment
HQ: Trane U.S. Inc.
3600 Pammel Creek Rd
La Crosse WI 54601
608 787-2000

(G-12343)
TRANE US INC
10555 Westpark Dr (77042-5232)
PHONE..................................713 266-3900
Greg McMeans, *Vice Pres*
Dick Hunton, *Branch Mgr*
EMP: 100 **Privately Held**
WEB: www.trane.com
SIC: 3585 Refrigeration & heating equipment
HQ: Trane U.S. Inc.
3600 Pammel Creek Rd
La Crosse WI 54601
608 787-2000

(G-12344)
TRANS-PECOS PIPELINE LLC
1300 Main St (77002-6803)
PHONE..................................713 989-2606
Kelcy L Warren, *Mng Member*
EMP: 47
SALES (est): 176.6K **Publicly Held**
SIC: 1321 Natural gas liquids
HQ: Etp Legacy Lp
8111 Westchester Dr # 600
Dallas TX 75225
214 981-0700

(G-12345)
TRANS-TEC MACHINE LTD
6320 Ridgemont St (77087-3310)
PHONE..................................713 643-9114
EMP: 45
SQ FT: 35,000
SALES (est): 7.5MM **Privately Held**
WEB: www.transtecmachine.com
SIC: 3599 3443 Machine shop, jobbing & repair; fabricated plate work (boiler shop)

(G-12346)
TRANSAMERICAN NATURAL GAS CORP
1300 N Sam Houston Pkwy E (77032-2949)
PHONE..................................281 372-5304
John R Stanley, *Chairman*
EMP: 220 EST: 1969

SALES (est): 8.2MM **Privately Held**
SIC: 1382 1311 4922 Oil & gas exploration services; natural gas production; natural gas transmission

(G-12347)
TRANSCANADA TURBINES INC
11221 Cutten Rd Bldg 4 (77066-3719)
PHONE..................................281 880-2900
◆ EMP: 34 EST: 2000
SQ FT: 4,128
SALES (est): 5.8MM
SALES (corp-wide): 34.6MM **Privately Held**
SIC: 3511 Turbines & turbine generator set units, complete
PA: Transcanada Turbines Ltd
998 Hamilton Blvd Ne
Airdrie AB T4A 0
403 420-4200

(G-12348)
TRANSCANADA USA SERVICES INC
700 Louisiana St Ste 700 # 700 (77002-2873)
PHONE..................................832 320-5000
Andrew Park, *Opers Staff*
Derek Barlow, *Electrical Engi*
Tim Gunter, *Manager*
Lee Hanson, *Manager*
Ryan Stewart, *Consultant*
EMP: 33
SALES (est): 4.1MM
SALES (corp-wide): 9.9B **Privately Held**
WEB: www.tcenergy.com
SIC: 1382 Pipelines, natural gas
PA: Tc Energy Corporation
450 1 St Sw
Calgary AB T2P 5
403 920-2000

(G-12349)
TRANSCEAN OFFSHORE DPWTER DRLG (DH)
Also Called: Transocean Sedco Forex
1414 Enclave Pkwy (77077-2023)
P.O. Box 4255 (77210-4255)
PHONE..................................713 232-7500
Steven L Newman, *CEO*
Terry Bonno, *Vice Pres*
Ihab Toma, *Vice Pres*
David A Tonnel, *Vice Pres*
Cynthia Chapman, *Safety Mgr*
◆ EMP: 9
SQ FT: 59,352
SALES (est): 31.9MM
SALES (corp-wide): 4.1B **Privately Held**
WEB: www.deepwater.com
SIC: 1381 Drilling oil & gas wells
HQ: Transocean Inc.
4 Greenway Plz Ste 700
Houston TX 77046
713 232-7500

(G-12350)
TRANSCEND SOLUTIONS LLC
14432 John F Kennedy Blvd (77032-5300)
PHONE..................................936 689-5618
Roy McDoniel, *Engineer*
Mathews Thundyil, *Mng Member*
EMP: 10
SALES (est): 984.4K **Privately Held**
WEB: www.trnscnd.com
SIC: 3677 Filtration devices, electronic

(G-12351)
TRANSCONTINENTAL ENERGY CORP
Also Called: Calco Equipment and Supply
9000 Emmott Rd Ste E (77040-3547)
P.O. Box 692408 (77269-2408)
PHONE..................................713 856-6755
EMP: 9
SQ FT: 5,000
SALES (est): 648.2K **Privately Held**
SIC: 1389 Oil Field Srvcs Of Drilling Equipment

(G-12352)
TRANSOCEAN INC (HQ)
4 Greenway Plz Ste 700 (77046-0406)
P.O. Box 2765 (77252-2765)
PHONE..................................713 232-7500
Steven Newman, *President*

Darrell Pelley, *President*
Danny Reeves, *Superintendent*
John Stephens, *Superintendent*
John Stobart, *COO*
◆ EMP: 150 EST: 1953
SQ FT: 59,352
SALES (est): 11B
SALES (corp-wide): 4.1B **Privately Held**
WEB: www.deepwater.com
SIC: 1381 Drilling oil & gas wells
PA: Transocean Ltd.
Turmstrasse 30
Steinhausen ZG
417 490-500

(G-12353)
TRANSOCEAN OFFSHORE USA INC
4 Greenway Plz Ste 700 (77046-0406)
P.O. Box 2765 (77252-2765)
PHONE..................................713 232-7500
Michael Talbert, *President*
Steven L Newman, *Principal*
Robert L Herrin, *Vice Pres*
Ihab Toma, *Vice Pres*
◆ EMP: 53
SALES (est): 7.9MM **Privately Held**
WEB: www.deepwater.com
SIC: 1381 Drilling oil & gas wells

(G-12354)
TRANSTAR OILFIELD SERVICES LLC
10402 Vrana Dr (77049-1202)
P.O. Box 3378, Crosby (77532-2378)
PHONE..................................281 456-7822
Dalton Dean,
EMP: 20
SQ FT: 6,032
SALES (est): 2.2MM **Privately Held**
WEB: www.transtaroilfield.com
SIC: 1389 Oil field services

(G-12355)
TRANSWORLD WORLDWIDE INC
4 Greenway Plz (77046-0400)
P.O. Box 2765 (77252-2765)
PHONE..................................713 232-7500
Robert L Long, *President*
EMP: 500
SALES (est): 38.9MM
SALES (corp-wide): 4.1B **Privately Held**
SIC: 1381 1311 Drilling oil & gas wells; crude petroleum & natural gas production
HQ: Transocean Inc.
4 Greenway Plz Ste 700
Houston TX 77046
713 232-7500

(G-12356)
TRAVIS BODY AND TRAILER INC
Also Called: Travis Trailers
13955 Fm 529 Rd (77041-2502)
PHONE..................................713 466-5888
Steven Retzloff, *Ch of Bd*
Charles Hughes, *President*
Jason R Backs, *Vice Pres*
Jeff Grant, *Purchasing*
Douglas Gwin, *CFO*
EMP: 100
SQ FT: 85,000
SALES (est): 1.5MM
SALES (corp-wide): 1.2B **Publicly Held**
WEB: www.travistrailers.com
SIC: 3715 Trailer bodies
HQ: Truck Bodies & Equipment International, Inc.
1 Independence Plz # 820
Birmingham AL 35209

(G-12357)
TRAVIS PEAK RESOURCES LLC
1100 La St Ste 5100 (77002)
PHONE..................................512 814-0345
James Addison, *CEO*
George Grunau, *Vice Pres*
Jerry Ilseng, *Vice Pres*
Ben Ellis, *CFO*
Mike Lewis, *Controller*
EMP: 15
SALES (est): 320.3K **Privately Held**
WEB: www.travispkr.com
SIC: 1382 Oil & gas exploration services

(G-12358)
TRAVIS SOFTWARE INC
24 Greenway Plz Ste 800 (77046-2407)
PHONE................................281 496-3737
Lauren Fischer, *Principal*
EMP: 18
SALES (est): 1.4MM **Privately Held**
WEB: www.travisoft.com
SIC: 7372 Business oriented computer
software

(G-12359)
TRAXSALES LLC
6830 N Eldridge Pkwy # 3 (77041-2625)
PHONE................................713 466-7177
Dave Mink, *Owner*
Scott Dawe,
EMP: 26 EST: 2010
SALES (est): 415.1K **Privately Held**
WEB: www.traxsales.com
SIC: 7372 Prepackaged software

(G-12360)
**TRELLEBORG OFFSHORE US
INC**
10375 Richmond Ave # 1725 (77042-4475)
PHONE................................281 774-2600
Mark Engus, *President*
Bob Kelly, *Vice Pres*
Marc Myers, *Opers Mgr*
Greg Olive, *Engineer*
Kevin McNelis, *VP Finance*
◆ EMP: 400
SALES (est): 101.8MM
SALES (corp-wide): 3.8B **Privately Held**
WEB: www.trelleborg.com
SIC: 3533 Oil field machinery & equipment
HQ: Trelleborg Corporation
200 Veterans Blvd Ste 3
South Haven MI 49090
269 639-9891

(G-12361)
TRI RESOURCES INC
1000 La St Ste 4300 (77002)
PHONE................................713 584-1000
EMP: 10
SALES (corp-wide): 5.8B **Publicly Held**
SIC: 1389 Oil/Gas Field Services
HQ: Tri Resources, Inc.
1000 Louisiana St # 4300
Houston TX 77002
713 584-1000

(G-12362)
TRI RESOURCES INC (HQ)
Also Called: Targa Resources
811 Louisiana St Ste 2100 (77002-1412)
PHONE................................713 584-1000
Rene R Joyce, *CEO*
Joe Bob Perkins, *President*
James W Whalen, *President*
Paul W Chung, *Exec VP*
Jeffrey J McParland, *CFO*
◆ EMP: 26
SALES (est): 146.9MM **Publicly Held**
WEB: www.triresources.com
SIC: 1381 1382 1321 Drilling oil & gas
wells; oil & gas exploration services; liq-
uefied petroleum gases (natural) produc-
tion

(G-12363)
TRI-MAX CORPORATION
Also Called: Drillbit Industries
6324 Cunningham Rd (77041-4712)
PHONE................................713 937-8808
Adel A Sheshtawy, *CEO*
Flavia Caldera, *Admin Sec*
▲ EMP: 30 EST: 1974
SQ FT: 20,000
SALES (est): 2MM **Privately Held**
SIC: 3533 Oil field machinery & equipment

(G-12364)
**TRI-STAR PETROLEUM
COMPANY**
9 Greenway Plz Ste 3100 (77046-0994)
PHONE................................713 222-0011
James Butler Jr, *Vice Pres*
James H Butler, *Vice Pres*
EMP: 9
SQ FT: 1,679

SALES (est): 1.5MM **Privately Held**
WEB: www.tri-stargroup.com
SIC: 1382 Oil & gas exploration services

(G-12365)
**TRIANGLE REPRODUCTIONS
INC (PA)**
8168 Westpark Dr Ste A (77063-6325)
P.O. Box 630969 (77263-0969)
PHONE................................713 780-0236
Robert C Christy, *President*
Toby Dagenhart, *Vice Pres*
Chrysanthie Pappas, *Accounts Exec*
Chuck Winfree, *Accounts Exec*
Kim Gill, *Sales Staff*
EMP: 25
SALES (est): 8.9MM **Privately Held**
WEB: www.triangletexas.com
SIC: 5999 2759 Drafting equipment & sup-
plies; commercial printing

(G-12366)
TRIARCH INDUSTRIES INC (PA)
9550 W Wingfoot Rd # 140 (77041-9124)
PHONE................................713 690-9977
Bruce Wingate, *President*
▲ EMP: 49
SALES (est): 3MM **Privately Held**
SIC: 2851 Coating, air curing

(G-12367)
TRIBUTE ENERGY INC
2100 West Loop S Ste 1500 (77027-3519)
PHONE................................281 768-5300
Jaihoon Rew, *President*
Cesar Purgato, *CFO*
Terry Kim, *Admin Sec*
◆ EMP: 18
SQ FT: 5,000
SALES: 119.3MM **Privately Held**
WEB: www.tributeenergy.com
SIC: 5169 3295 2821 Chemicals & allied
products; clay for petroleum refining,
chemically processed; elastomers, non-
vulcanizable (plastics)

(G-12368)
TRICAN WELL SERVICE LP
5825 N Sam Houston Pkwy W # 600
(77086-1551)
PHONE................................281 716-9152
Dale M Dusterhoft, *CEO*
Donald R Luft, *President*
Murray L Cobbe, *Chairman*
Michael A Baldwin, *Senior VP*
James S McKeem, *Senior VP*
▼ EMP: 501
SQ FT: 3,900
SALES (est): 3.4MM **Privately Held**
SIC: 2911 1481 1389 Mineral oils, natu-
ral; pumping or draining, nonmetallic min-
eral mines; oil field services

(G-12369)
TRICON ENERGY INC (PA)
777 Post Oak Blvd Ste 550 (77056-3315)
PHONE................................713 963-0066
Ignacio Torras, *President*
Bryan Elwood, *Vice Pres*
Brian Morris, *CFO*
Tanvir Ali, *Treasurer*
Sanjay Moolji, *Director*
◆ EMP: 56
SALES (est): 256.2MM **Privately Held**
WEB: www.triconenergy.com
SIC: 2899 2812 2821 2869 Chemical
preparations; alkalies; polymethyl
methacrylate resins (plexiglass); fuels

(G-12370)
TRICON ENERGY LTD
777 Post Oak Blvd Ste 550 (77056-3315)
PHONE................................713 963-0066
Ignacio Torras, *CEO*
EMP: 100
SALES (est): 4.4MM **Privately Held**
WEB: www.triconenergy.com
SIC: 2899 Chemical preparations
HQ: Tricon International, Ltd.
777 Post Oak Blvd Ste 550
Houston TX 77056
713 963-0066

(G-12371)
**TRICON INTERNATIONAL LTD
(HQ)**
Also Called: Tricon Energy
777 Post Oak Blvd Ste 550 (77056-3315)
PHONE................................713 963-0066
Ignacio Torras, *President*
Brian Morris, *CFO*
EMP: 50 EST: 1997
SQ FT: 11,000
SALES (est): 200.2MM **Privately Held**
WEB: www.triconenergy.com
SIC: 7373 3643 5063 Systems software
development services; connectors & ter-
minals for electrical devices; electric
alarms & signaling equipment; alarm sys-
tems

(G-12372)
**TRIDENT CRATING & SERVICES
INC**
14320 Interdrive E (77032-3330)
PHONE................................281 227-3999
Robert Allmaras, *President*
Brandi Moak, *Export Mgr*
James Bryant, *Sales Staff*
◆ EMP: 35
SQ FT: 12,000
SALES (est): 5.3MM **Privately Held**
WEB: www.tridentcrating.com
SIC: 2441 Cases, wood

(G-12373)
TRILLIANT SURGICAL LLC
727 N Shepherd Dr Ste 100 (77007-1320)
PHONE................................800 495-2919
Brandon Beckendorf, *Vice Pres*
David George, *Vice Pres*
Meagan Hubbard, *Opers Staff*
Meagan Olson, *Opers Staff*
Gina Adibi, *Engineer*
EMP: 9
SALES (est): 2MM **Privately Held**
WEB: www.trilliantsurgical.com
SIC: 3841 3842 Surgical & medical instru-
ments; implants, surgical

(G-12374)
TRIMIRA LLC
952 Echo Ln Ste 333 (77024-2832)
PHONE................................713 984-8994
Michael J Smith, *CFO*
H Kirby Atwood,
David A Burns,
Hugh L Hyde,
EMP: 14
SALES (est): 907.9K **Privately Held**
SIC: 3841 Surgical & medical instruments

(G-12375)
**TRINITY RIVER ENERGY LLC
(DH)**
15021 Katy Fwy Ste 200 (77094-1914)
PHONE................................817 872-7898
EMP: 17
SALES (est): 14.8MM **Publicly Held**
SIC: 1381 Largest Operator In The Barnett
Shale
HQ: Kkr Natural Resources Fund I-A L.P.
9 W 57th St Ste 4200
New York NY 10019
212 750-8300

(G-12376)
**TRINITY RIVER ENERGY OPER
LLC (DH)**
15021 Katy Fwy Ste 200 (77094-1914)
PHONE................................817 872-7800
EMP: 9
SALES (est): 1.5MM **Privately Held**
SIC: 1382 Oil/Gas Exploration Services
HQ: Trinity River Energy, Llc
15021 Katy Fwy Ste 200
Houston TX 77094
817 872-7898

(G-12377)
TRIOFAB INC
6515 Carson Rd (77048-3821)
PHONE................................713 417-1205
Maria Duron Hernandez, *President*
Gerardo Hernandez Jr, *Admin Sec*
EMP: 13
SQ FT: 10,500

SALES (est): 2MM **Privately Held**
WEB: www.triofabinc.com
SIC: 3441 Fabricated structural metal

(G-12378)
**TRISTAR GLOBL ENRGY
SLTONS INC**
12600 N Featherwood Dr # 330
(77034-4443)
PHONE................................713 463-9200
Thomas McQueary, *Principal*
Jackie Nunn, *Vice Pres*
Maria Flores, *Hum Res Coord*
Meghan Kidwell, *Marketing Mgr*
Chris Huk, *Manager*
EMP: 17
SALES (est): 2.5MM **Privately Held**
WEB: www.tristarpetroserv.com
SIC: 1389 Lease tanks, oil field: erecting,
cleaning & repairing

(G-12379)
TRISTAR WEB GRAPHICS INC
4010 Airline Dr (77022-4114)
PHONE................................713 691-0001
Masaud Baaba, *CEO*
Martin S Blick, *President*
Omar Megerisi, *Chairman*
Duane Elkevizth, *Warehouse Mgr*
Theresa Chen, *CFO*
EMP: 105 EST: 1953
SQ FT: 55,000
SALES (est): 16.9MM
SALES (corp-wide): 17.1MM **Privately
Held**
WEB: www.new.tristarwebgraphics.com
SIC: 2752 2711 Circulars, lithographed;
newspapers, publishing & printing
PA: Tristar Holdings Inc
4010 Airline Dr
Houston TX 77022
713 691-0001

(G-12380)
TRISTREAM ENERGY LLC (PA)
10370 Richmond Ave # 400 (77042-4141)
PHONE................................281 240-8444
Kendall Purgason, *CEO*
Reid Smith, *CEO*
Tony Catalano, *COO*
Mike Urban, *Exec VP*
Cesar Espino, *Senior VP*
EMP: 25
SALES (est): 24.4MM **Privately Held**
WEB: www.tristreamenergy.com
SIC: 1389 Gas field services

(G-12381)
TRITON DATA SERVICES INC
17171 Park Row Ste 320 (77084-4927)
PHONE................................281 578-9700
Donald Craig, *President*
David Kingma, *Corp Secy*
Rick Colson, *Vice Pres*
Ashley Villa, *Marketing Staff*
Brad Currie, *Manager*
EMP: 12
SQ FT: 3,000
SALES (est): 1.3MM **Privately Held**
WEB: www.tritondataservices.com
SIC: 1382 Seismograph surveys

(G-12382)
TROSBY OF GEORGIA INC
4029 Ella Lee Ln (77027-3910)
PHONE................................713 526-7332
Eugene O'Donnell, *CEO*
▲ EMP: 9
SALES (est): 759.2K **Privately Held**
WEB: www.trosbyfurniture.com
SIC: 2511 Wood household furniture

(G-12383)
TROTTI SERVICE COMPANY INC
9210 Meadow Vista Blvd (77064-2012)
PHONE................................281 894-5095
Reba Trotti, *President*
David Trotti, *Vice Pres*
Ryan Trotti, *Vice Pres*
EMP: 14 EST: 1981
SQ FT: 5,000
SALES (est): 3MM **Privately Held**
WEB:
SIC: 1711 7623 3444 Warm air heating &
air conditioning contractor; air condition-
ing repair; sheet metalwork

(G-12384)
TRULITE INC
Also Called: (A DEVELOPMENT STAGE COMPANY)
3731 Linkview Dr (77025-3511)
PHONE..............................713 432-7238
John Sifonis, *President*
EMP: 12
SALES (est): 1.3MM **Privately Held**
WEB: www.trulite.com
SIC: 3621 Generator sets: gasoline, diesel or dual-fuel

(G-12385)
TRULITE GL ALUM SOLUTIONS LLC
3333 Holly Hall St (77021-5547)
PHONE..............................800 395-4224
Patrick May, *General Mgr*
Cristella Hurt, *Sales Staff*
Troy Johns, *Manager*
Dulce Sandoval, *Manager*
Jim Shepherd, *Manager*
EMP: 128 **Privately Held**
WEB: www.trulite.com
SIC: 5231 3211 Glass; construction glass
PA: Trulite Glass & Aluminum Solutions, Llc
403 Westpark Ct Ste 201
Peachtree City GA 30269

(G-12386)
TRUPPLY LLC
2956 Farrell Rd (77073-4009)
PHONE..............................281 516-8100
Mukhtar Kadri,
EMP: 14
SQ FT: 8,000
SALES (est): 2.4MM **Privately Held**
WEB: www.trupply.com
SIC: 5085 3441 Valves & fittings; fabricated structural metal

(G-12387)
TRUSSWAY LLC CENTRAL
9411 Alcorn St (77093-6753)
PHONE..............................713 691-6900
Jim Thomas, *CEO*
EMP: 14
SALES (est): 314.4K **Privately Held**
WEB: www.trussway.com
SIC: 2439 Trusses, except roof: laminated lumber
HQ: Trussway Manufacturing, Inc.
9411 Alcorn St
Houston TX 77093

(G-12388)
TRUSSWAY LLC EAST
9411 Alcorn St (77093-6753)
PHONE..............................713 691-6900
Jim Thomas, *CEO*
EMP: 15
SALES (est): 4.4MM **Privately Held**
WEB: www.trussway.com
SIC: 2439 Trusses, except roof: laminated lumber
HQ: Trussway Manufacturing, Inc.
9411 Alcorn St
Houston TX 77093

(G-12389)
TRUSSWAY HOLDINGS INC (PA)
9411 Alcorn St (77093-6753)
PHONE..............................713 691-6900
Bill Adams, *President*
Jim Hall, *Sales Staff*
EMP: 15
SQ FT: 850,000
SALES (est): 307.3MM **Privately Held**
WEB: www.trussway.com
SIC: 2439 Trusses, except roof: laminated lumber

(G-12390)
TRUSSWAY MANUFACTURING INC (DH)
9411 Alcorn St (77093-6753)
PHONE..............................719 322-9662
Jim Thomas, *CEO*
Steve Stewart, *President*
Tony Harris, *Vice Pres*
David Pogue, *Vice Pres*
Erik Brooks, *Maint Spvr*
EMP: 200
SQ FT: 85,000

SALES (est): 262.6MM **Privately Held**
WEB: www.trussway.com
SIC: 2439 5031 Trusses, wooden roof; structural assemblies, prefabricated: wood

(G-12391)
TRUSSWAY TRANSPORTATION INC
9411 Alcorn St (77093-6753)
PHONE..............................713 691-6900
Jim Thomas, *CEO*
EMP: 501
SALES (est): 25.6MM **Privately Held**
WEB: www.trussway.com
SIC: 2439 Trusses, except roof: laminated lumber
HQ: Trussway Construction, Inc.
9411 Alcorn St
Houston TX 77093

(G-12392)
TRYLENE INC
10650 Stancliff Rd (77099-4331)
PHONE..............................281 980-0400
Paresh Jasani, *President*
Michelle Duffy, *Marketing Staff*
EMP: 22 EST: 2011
SALES (est): 3.7MM **Privately Held**
WEB: www.trylene.com
SIC: 3672 3679 Printed circuit boards; electronic circuits; harness assemblies for electronic use: wire or cable

(G-12393)
TRYTON TOOLS USA INC (PA)
20329 State Highway 249 # 125 (77070-2655)
P.O. Box 722833, Norman OK (73070-9145)
PHONE..............................832 717-7125
Garnet Amundson, *CEO*
Jeff Newman, *Vice Pres*
EMP: 32 EST: 2013
SQ FT: 3,000
SALES (est): 1.7MM **Privately Held**
WEB: www.trytontoolservices.com
SIC: 1389 Construction, repair & dismantling services

(G-12394)
TS DISTRIBUTORS INC (PA)
4404 Windfern Rd (77041-8918)
P.O. Box 431133 (77243-1133)
PHONE..............................832 467-5400
Bradley A Stein, *President*
Bruce Peele, *Prdtn Mgr*
Michael England, *Prdtn Mgr*
Brian Buck, *Purch Mgr*
Valerie Fulmer, *Purch Agent*
▲ EMP: 70
SALES (est): 11.5MM **Privately Held**
WEB: www.tsdistributors.com
SIC: 3446 Architectural metalwork

(G-12395)
TSC MANUFACTURING AND SUP LLC (HQ)
13788 West Rd Ste 100 (77041-1139)
PHONE..............................832 456-3900
Larry Li, *Controller*
Mengzhen Zhang, *Mng Member*
Binghua Jiang, *Mng Member*
Carrie Yin, *Manager*
Judy Zhu, *Manager*
◆ EMP: 40
SQ FT: 100,000
SALES (est): 17.5MM **Privately Held**
WEB: www.tscms.com
SIC: 3561 Pumps & pumping equipment

(G-12396)
TSC OFFSHORE CORPORATION (PA)
7611 Railhead Ln (77086-3255)
PHONE..............................832 456-3900
Robert A Sliva, *CEO*
Robert S Shinfield, *President*
Robert J Ream, *Senior VP*
Scott Fullerton, *Vice Pres*
William R Lewis, *Vice Pres*
▲ EMP: 1300 EST: 1990
SQ FT: 100,000

SALES (est): 193.1MM **Privately Held**
WEB: www.tscoffshore.com
SIC: 3533 Oil & gas drilling rigs & equipment

(G-12397)
TSC OFFSHORE CORPORATION
13788 West Rd Ste 100 (77041-1139)
PHONE..............................832 456-3900
Anthony Concetcion, *Manager*
EMP: 10
SALES (corp-wide): 193.1MM **Privately Held**
WEB: www.tscoffshore.com
SIC: 3533 7353 Oil & gas drilling rigs & equipment; oil well drilling equipment, rental or leasing
PA: Tsc Offshore Corporation
7611 Railhead Ln
Houston TX 77086
832 456-3900

(G-12398)
TSRC SPECIALTY MATERIALS LLC (HQ)
Also Called: Dexco Polymers L.P.
12012 Wickchester Ln # 28 (77079-1229)
PHONE..............................281 754-5800
Christopher Mudd, *Managing Prtnr*
Richard Guerrant, *Vice Pres*
Craig Leopard, *Plant Mgr*
Mark Berard, *Research*
Charles Monzo, *Sales Staff*
◆ EMP: 9
SALES (est): 19.9MM **Privately Held**
WEB: www.tsrc.com
SIC: 2821 Plastics materials & resins

(G-12399)
TTC TRAMMELL CO INC
109 Engel St (77011-2233)
P.O. Box 230493 (77223-0493)
PHONE..............................713 921-7121
Bruce E Trammell, *President*
EMP: 20
SQ FT: 18,000
SALES (est): 2.1MM **Privately Held**
WEB: www.ttctrammell.com
SIC: 2759 2262 3479 Screen printing; decals: printing; tags: printing; tickets: printing; screen printing: manmade fiber & silk broadwoven fabrics; name plates: engraved, etched, etc.

(G-12400)
TTWF LP
2801 Post Oak Blvd (77056-6136)
PHONE..............................713 960-9111
Albert Chao, *Partner*
M Steven Bender, *Partner*
James Chao, *Partner*
Andrew Kenner, *Partner*
George J Mangieri, *Partner*
◆ EMP: 17405
SALES (est): 203.9MM **Privately Held**
WEB: www.westlake.com
SIC: 2821 2869 2865 Polyethylene resins; olefins; styrene

(G-12401)
TUBOSCOPE (HOLDING US) LLC (PA)
2919 Holmes Rd (77051-1025)
PHONE..............................713 799-5100
Isaac Joseph, *President*
Clay C Williams, *Vice Pres*
▲ EMP: 16
SALES (est): 104.5MM **Privately Held**
WEB: www.nov.com
SIC: 1381 Drilling oil & gas wells

(G-12402)
TUBULAR INSTRUMENTAT
Also Called: Total Instrumentation Contrls
15151 Sommermeyer St (77041-5332)
PHONE..............................832 467-3110
Mark Provine, *CEO*
Steven Madden, *Partner*
Glendina Robertson, *Partner*
Leslie Robertson, *Partner*
▲ EMP: 248
SQ FT: 15,000
SALES (est): 46.1MM **Privately Held**
SIC: 3492 Control valves, fluid power: hydraulic & pneumatic

(G-12403)
TUBULAR REPAIR LLC (DH)
1201 Louisiana St Fl 28 (77002-5607)
PHONE..............................979 387-3223
Sealy Morris, *President*
William Morris, *President*
EMP: 21
SALES (est): 10.9MM
SALES (corp-wide): 29.6MM **Privately Held**
WEB: www.tubularrepair.com
SIC: 3533 Drilling tools for gas, oil or water wells

(G-12404)
TUBULAR SERVICES LLC (HQ)
1010 Mccarty St (77029-2493)
PHONE..............................713 675-6212
Rick Hickman, *Principal*
Todd Richardson, *Vice Pres*
Robert Sherrill, *Vice Pres*
Michael Caldwell, *Opers Mgr*
Cordee Novak, *Purch Mgr*
EMP: 50
SQ FT: 140,700
SALES (est): 193.8MM **Privately Held**
WEB: www.tubularservices.com
SIC: 1389 Running, cutting & pulling casings, tubes & rods; oil field services

(G-12405)
TUBULAR SERVICES LLC
2030 Jacintoport Blvd (77015-6518)
PHONE..............................281 452-4353
Russell Rhodes, *President*
EMP: 180
SQ FT: 35,704 **Privately Held**
WEB: www.tubularservices.com
SIC: 1389 Running, cutting & pulling casings, tubes & rods
HQ: Tubular Services, Llc
1010 Mccarty St
Houston TX 77029

(G-12406)
TUBULAR SOLUTIONS INC
1401 Brittmoore Rd (77043-4005)
PHONE..............................713 391-8005
EMP: 11 EST: 2015
SALES (est): 1.6MM **Privately Held**
WEB: www.tubularsolutionsinc.com
SIC: 3498 Tube fabricating (contract bending & shaping)

(G-12407)
TURBECO INC (HQ)
Also Called: Petrovalve
8846 N Sam Houston Pkwy W # 150 (77064-2305)
PHONE..............................713 849-9911
John W Chisholm, *President*
Steven A Reeves, *COO*
Jesse E Neyman, *CFO*
H Richard Walton, *CFO*
Robert Cutsinger, *Sales Staff*
▲ EMP: 10
SALES (est): 51.5MM
SALES (corp-wide): 119.3MM **Publicly Held**
WEB: www.flotekind.com
SIC: 1389 5082 Oil field services; oil field equipment
PA: Flotek Industries, Inc.
8846 N Sam Houston Pkwy W # 150
Houston TX 77064
713 849-9911

(G-12408)
TURBINE AIR SYSTEMS LTD
Also Called: T A S
6110 Cullen Blvd (77021-3316)
PHONE..............................713 877-8700
Joseph Grumski, *CEO*
Mike Brady, *President*
Doug Backlund, *Vice Pres*
Jim Yoon, *Vice Pres*
Gerald Clark, *Opers Staff*
◆ EMP: 120
SQ FT: 85,000
SALES (est): 100MM **Privately Held**
WEB: www.tas.com
SIC: 3585 Refrigeration equipment, complete

(G-12409)
TURBINE COMPONENT REPAIR INC
Also Called: T C R
3608 Pinemont Dr (77018-1334)
PHONE................................713 895-9551
Dean Hendricks, *President*
James Davidson, *General Mgr*
Kent Williams, *Treasurer*
Steve Osborne, *Supervisor*
EMP: 10
SQ FT: 20,190
SALES (est): 1.7MM **Privately Held**
WEB: www.tcrhouston.com
SIC: 3599 Machine shop, jobbing & repair

(G-12410)
TURBO MACHINE TECHNOLOGY INC
16038 Waverly Dr (77032-1218)
P.O. Box 14074, Humble (77347-9774)
PHONE................................281 443-4646
Lidia Martinuc Jr, *President*
Radu Popescu, *Opers Mgr*
EMP: 10
SQ FT: 6,250
SALES (est): 1MM **Privately Held**
WEB: www.turbomt.net
SIC: 3599 Machine shop, jobbing & repair

(G-12411)
TURBOWELD
6951 W Little York Rd (77040-4809)
PHONE................................713 896-6467
EMP: 75
SALES (est): 4.8MM **Privately Held**
SIC: 3441 Structural Metal Fabrication

(G-12412)
TURNER CAPITAL INC
Also Called: Bay Area Printing
17305 El Camino Real (77058-2718)
PHONE................................281 488-4900
Mary E Turner, *President*
Jeff R Turner, *Vice Pres*
EMP: 10
SQ FT: 5,000
SALES (est): 1.6MM **Privately Held**
WEB: www.store.bayareaprinting.com
SIC: 2752 7336 7334 5999 Commercial printing, offset; graphic arts & related design; photocopying & duplicating services; packaging materials: boxes, padding, etc.

(G-12413)
TURRUBIARTES BENEDICTO
Also Called: B&C Metal Works
7600 S Santa Fe Dr Bldg 1 (77061-4508)
PHONE................................832 675-1569
Benedicto Turrubiartes, *Owner*
EMP: 9 EST: 2012
SALES (est): 223.6K **Privately Held**
WEB: www.bcmetalworks.net
SIC: 3449 1761 Miscellaneous metalwork; sheet metalwork

(G-12414)
TWIN EAGLE SAND LOGISTICS LLC (HQ)
8847 W Sam Houston Pkwy N (77040-5668)
PHONE................................713 341-7300
Chris Black, *COO*
Jeremy Davis, *Exec VP*
Tom Godbold, *Exec VP*
Jimmy Thomas, *Exec VP*
Kevin Beasley, *Vice Pres*
EMP: 26
SALES (est): 22.1MM **Privately Held**
WEB: www.twineagle.com
SIC: 1321 4924 3999 Natural gas liquids; natural gas distribution; atomizers, toiletry

(G-12415)
TWIN HILL ACQUISITION CO INC
5630 Renwick Dr (77081-1504)
PHONE................................888 206-0699
Scott Silverstein, *President*
Matthew Gordon, *Business Mgr*
Laura Ann Smith, *Vice Pres*
Brian T Vaclavik, *Vice Pres*
Stuart Vogt, *Vice Pres*
▲ EMP: 35
SQ FT: 5,000

SALES (est): 4.6MM
SALES (corp-wide): 16MM **Privately Held**
WEB: www.twinhill.com
SIC: 2326 Work uniforms
PA: Th Holdco Inc.
6380 Rogerdale Rd
Houston TX 77072
888 206-0699

(G-12416)
TWR LIGHTING INC
10810 W Little York Rd # 13 (77041-4050)
PHONE................................713 973-6905
Kenneth Meador, *President*
Edwin A Wahlen Jr, *Chairman*
Jeff Huehlefeld, *Vice Pres*
Raymond Kraemer, *Vice Pres*
Jessica Gonzales, *Manager*
◆ EMP: 52
SQ FT: 44,000
SALES (est): 11.3MM **Privately Held**
WEB: www.twrlighting.com
SIC: 3648 Lighting equipment

(G-12417)
TXG INDUSTRIES INC
10893 Shadow Wood Dr (77043-2863)
PHONE................................713 222-0220
Conover Able, *President*
Gary Able, *Vice Pres*
Jeff Mason, *Sales Staff*
▲ EMP: 27 EST: 2010
SQ FT: 20,000
SALES (est): 6.1MM **Privately Held**
WEB: www.txgind.com
SIC: 3053 Gaskets, all materials

(G-12418)
TYCO ENGINEERED PDTS & SVCS (DH)
9600 W Gulf Bank Rd (77040-3112)
PHONE................................609 720-4200
Robert Mead, *President*
John J Guarnieri, *Vice Pres*
Barbara Miller, *Treasurer*
Pilar Giraldo, *Finance Mgr*
▲ EMP: 100 EST: 1947
SQ FT: 41,000
SALES (est): 313.9MM **Privately Held**
SIC: 3625 3621 3491 Actuators, industrial; motors & generators; automatic regulating & control valves
HQ: Tyco International Management Company, Llc
9 Roszel Rd Ste 2
Princeton NJ 08540
609 720-4200

(G-12419)
TYCO INTERNATIONAL MGT CO LLC
8323 N Aldrich Pkwy (77041)
PHONE................................713 644-8872
EMP: 14 **Privately Held**
WEB: www.tyco.com
SIC: 3999 1711 1731 3669 Fire extinguishers, portable; fire sprinkler system installation; safety & security specialization; fire detection systems, electric; industrial valves
HQ: Tyco International Management Company, Llc
9 Roszel Rd Ste 2
Princeton NJ 08540
609 720-4200

(G-12420)
TYCO SIMPLEXGRINNELL
Anvil Products Division
6618 Navigation Blvd (77011-1342)
P.O. Box 2789, Longview (75606-2789)
PHONE................................903 759-4417
Brenda Windham, *Accountant*
John Perry, *Branch Mgr*
Cindy Wade, *Manager*
EMP: 256 **Privately Held**
WEB: www.tycosimplexgrinnell.com
SIC: 3498 Fabricated pipe & fittings
HQ: Grinnell Llc
1501 Nw 51st St
Boca Raton FL 33431
561 988-3658

(G-12421)
TYSON FOODS INC
300 Portwall St (77029-1336)
PHONE................................713 678-1893
Ryan Bosse, *Principal*
Robert Bergquist, *Opers Mgr*
Robin Wiggins, *Controller*
David Guerrero, *Manager*
EMP: 276
SALES (corp-wide): 43.1B **Publicly Held**
WEB: www.tysonfoods.com
SIC: 2015 2032 2096 2048 Chicken slaughtering & processing; ethnic foods: canned, jarred, etc.; tortillas: packaged in cans, jars etc.; potato chips & similar snacks; tortilla chips; feeds from meat & from meat & vegetable meals; beef products from beef slaughtered on site
PA: Tyson Foods, Inc.
2200 W Don Tyson Pkwy
Springdale AR 72762
479 290-4000

(G-12422)
U S WEATHERFORD L P
4420 W Greens Rd (77066-4858)
PHONE................................281 674-6500
Curtis Brown, *Office Mgr*
EMP: 18 **Privately Held**
WEB: www.weatherford.com
SIC: 1389 Oil field services
HQ: U S Weatherford L P
179 Weatherford Dr
Schriever LA 70395
985 493-6100

(G-12423)
U S WEATHERFORD L P
18155 Chisholm Trl (77060-1101)
PHONE................................281 443-5627
EMP: 18 **Privately Held**
WEB: www.weatherford.com
SIC: 3533 Oil & gas field machinery
HQ: U S Weatherford L P
179 Weatherford Dr
Schriever LA 70395
985 493-6100

(G-12424)
U S WEATHERFORD L P
11909 Spencer Rd Fm529 (77041-3000)
PHONE................................713 983-5000
EMP: 25
SQ FT: 99,561 **Privately Held**
WEB: www.weatherford.com
SIC: 1389 Oil field services
HQ: U S Weatherford L P
179 Weatherford Dr
Schriever LA 70395
985 493-6100

(G-12425)
U S WEATHERFORD L P
Also Called: Well Completion Technologies
9600 W Gulf Bank Rd (77040-3112)
PHONE................................832 590-4130
EMP: 9 **Privately Held**
WEB: www.weatherford.com
SIC: 1389 Oil field services
HQ: U S Weatherford L P
179 Weatherford Dr
Schriever LA 70395
985 493-6100

(G-12426)
U S WEATHERFORD L P
918 Hodgkins St (77032-2812)
PHONE................................281 449-1383
Randy Hall, *District Mgr*
Leslie Deason, *Manager*
Ahmed El Bardissy, *Manager*
Ferdy Handojo, *Manager*
Scott Polglase, *Manager*
EMP: 15 **Privately Held**
WEB: www.weatherford.com
SIC: 1389 Oil field services
HQ: U S Weatherford L P
179 Weatherford Dr
Schriever LA 70395
985 493-6100

(G-12427)
U S WEATHERFORD L P
10655 Bammel N Houston Rd (77086-2761)
PHONE................................281 847-0121

EMP: 250 **Privately Held**
WEB: www.weatherford.com
SIC: 1389 Oil field services
HQ: U S Weatherford L P
179 Weatherford Dr
Schriever LA 70395
985 493-6100

(G-12428)
ULTIMATE COMFORT MANUFACTURING
8510 South Loop E (77017-1934)
PHONE................................713 641-0100
Reyes Ortiz, *Owner*
EMP: 10
SALES (est): 905.2K **Privately Held**
SIC: 2515 Mattresses, innerspring or box spring

(G-12429)
ULTRA CHEM LTD
Also Called: Sharp Chemical Co
6700 Dixie Dr (77087-5110)
PHONE................................713 641-1444
Dan Yarberry, *Manager*
EMP: 10 EST: 1970
SALES (est): 1.2MM **Privately Held**
WEB: www.alloutboardmarine.com
SIC: 2869 Industrial organic chemicals

(G-12430)
ULTRAFLOTE LLC (PA)
3640 W 12th St (77008-6050)
PHONE................................713 461-2100
Stephen Hall, *President*
Nicholas Wargetz, *President*
Ronald Kern, *Vice Pres*
Gary Marshall, *Vice Pres*
Keith Van Note, *Vice Pres*
▼ EMP: 40 EST: 1972
SQ FT: 12,000
SALES (est): 9.6MM **Privately Held**
WEB: www.ultraflote.com
SIC: 3355 Aluminum rolling & drawing

(G-12431)
UNCONVNTONAL GAS SOLUTIONS LLC
10002 Windfern Rd (77064-5817)
PHONE................................346 353-1048
George Paul, *CEO*
EMP: 10
SALES (est): 99K **Privately Held**
WEB: www.ugs.solutions
SIC: 3559 3563 3569 Refinery, chemical processing & similar machinery; air & gas compressors; gas producers, generators & other gas related equipment

(G-12432)
UNDERWRITERS INDEMNITY
2925 Richmond Ave # 1600 (77098-3130)
PHONE................................713 961-1300
Joseph E Dondanville, *CFO*
EMP: 21
SQ FT: 11,000
SALES (est): 1MM
SALES (corp-wide): 1B **Publicly Held**
SIC: 1389 6331 Construction, repair & dismantling services; automobile insurance
PA: Rli Corp.
9025 N Lindbergh Dr
Peoria IL 61615
309 692-1000

(G-12433)
UNI-FORM COMPONENTS CO (DH)
10703 Sheldon Rd (77044-6003)
PHONE................................281 456-9724
Stephen B Songer, *President*
Robert W Webb, *Admin Sec*
▲ EMP: 54
SALES (est): 26.1MM
SALES (corp-wide): 254.6B **Publicly Held**
WEB: www.uniformcomponents.com
SIC: 3443 Fabricated plate work (boiler shop)
HQ: Marmon Group Llc
181 W Madison St Ste 2600
Chicago IL 60602
312 372-9500

▲ = Import ▼=Export
◆ =Import/Export

(G-12434)
UNION CARBIDE CORPORATION (DH)
Also Called: DOW CHEMICAL
1254 Enclave Pkwy (77077-2564)
P.O. Box 186, Port Lavaca (77979-0186)
PHONE..............................281 966-2727
Richard A Wells, *President*
Ignacio Molina, *CFO*
EMP: 277 **EST:** 1917
SALES: 3.7B
SALES (corp-wide): 38.5B **Publicly Held**
WEB: www.unioncarbide.com
SIC: 2821 2869 Thermosetting materials; thermoplastic materials; ethylene oxide
HQ: The Dow Chemical Company
2211 H H Dow Way
Midland MI 48642
989 636-1000

(G-12435)
UNION CARBIDE CORPORATION
10235 W Little York Rd # 230
(77040-3229)
PHONE..............................713 849-7000
Patrick E Gottschalk, *Principal*
EMP: 55
SALES (corp-wide): 38.5B **Publicly Held**
WEB: www.unioncarbide.com
SIC: 2869 Ethylene oxide
HQ: Union Carbide Corporation
1254 Enclave Pkwy
Houston TX 77077
281 966-2727

(G-12436)
UNION PRINTERS INC
Also Called: Kwik Kopy Printing
4001 San Jacinto St (77004-4021)
PHONE..............................713 526-6364
Shabbir A Dadabhoy, *President*
Dorothy Brooks, *COO*
Javed Rashid, *Vice Pres*
EMP: 12
SQ FT: 11,000
SALES (est): 1.6MM **Privately Held**
SIC: 2752 7331 Commercial printing, offset; mailing service

(G-12437)
UNION TANK CAR COMPANY
10515 Sheldon Rd (77044-6001)
PHONE..............................281 456-9381
Guadaupe Salinas, *Manager*
EMP: 300
SALES (corp-wide): 254.6B **Publicly Held**
WEB: www.utlx.com
SIC: 3743 Train cars & equipment, freight or passenger
HQ: Union Tank Car Company
175 W Jackson Blvd # 2100
Chicago IL 60604
312 431-3111

(G-12438)
UNION TANK CAR COMPANY
16923 Beaumont Hwy (77049-1050)
PHONE..............................281 847-8200
Steve Songer, *General Mgr*
EMP: 136
SALES (corp-wide): 254.6B **Publicly Held**
WEB: www.utlx.com
SIC: 3743 Train cars & equipment, freight or passenger
HQ: Union Tank Car Company
175 W Jackson Blvd # 2100
Chicago IL 60604
312 431-3111

(G-12439)
UNION TECH CO LLC
11727 Veterans Mem Dr (77067-2607)
PHONE..............................281 583-7601
Scott Hsia, *President*
Judy Hsia, *Vice Pres*
Robert Hsia, *Vice Pres*
Robert Herbert, *Sales Staff*
Rick Lombardi, *VP Mktg*
◆ **EMP:** 27
SQ FT: 25,000

SALES (est): 43MM **Privately Held**
WEB: www.uniontechmfg.com
SIC: 3599 3546 3545 Machine shop, jobbing & repair; power-driven handtools; machine tool accessories

(G-12440)
UNIQUE SYSTEM LLC
5355 W Sam Houston Pkwy N # 320 (77041-5235)
PHONE..............................713 937-6193
EMP: 11
SALES (est): 1.3MM
SALES (corp-wide): 4MM **Privately Held**
SIC: 7372 Prepackaged Software
PA: Unique System, L.L.C.
6534 Petropark Dr
Houston TX 77041
337 365-5650

(G-12441)
UNIQUE WOOD PRODUCTS INC
9915 Tanner Rd (77041-7549)
PHONE..............................713 462-5045
Harold Miller, *President*
EMP: 15
SQ FT: 30,000
SALES (est): 2.4MM **Privately Held**
WEB: www.uniquewoodproducts.com
SIC: 2426 Hardwood dimension & flooring mills

(G-12442)
UNISTAR PLASTICS LLC
6415 Allegheny St (77021-2208)
PHONE..............................713 242-8377
Mike Herman, *Branch Mgr*
Herman Bensurto, *Manager*
EMP: 60 **Privately Held**
WEB: www.unistarplastics.com
SIC: 2673 Bags: plastic, laminated & coated
PA: Unistar Plastics Llc
5821 Citrus Blvd Ste B
New Orleans LA 70123

(G-12443)
UNIT DRILLING COMPANY
Also Called: Unit Petroleum
110 Cypress Station Dr # 11 (77090-1630)
PHONE..............................713 960-8870
Jim Kahlden, *Branch Mgr*
EMP: 25
SALES (corp-wide): 674.6MM **Privately Held**
WEB: www.unitcorp.com
SIC: 1381 Redrilling oil & gas wells
HQ: Unit Drilling Company
8200 S U Dr
Tulsa OK 74132

(G-12444)
UNIT PETROLEUM COMPANY
110 Cypress Station Dr # 113 (77090-1626)
PHONE..............................713 960-8870
James K Kahlden, *Branch Mgr*
Michael Mazzella, *Exploration*
EMP: 14
SALES (corp-wide): 674.6MM **Privately Held**
WEB: www.unitpetroleum.com
SIC: 1382 Oil & gas exploration services
HQ: Unit Petroleum Company
8200 S U Dr
Tulsa OK 74132
918 493-7700

(G-12445)
UNITED CASING INCORPORATED
10901 Sheldon Rd (77044-6007)
PHONE..............................281 456-0212
Susie Mayfield, *Human Resources*
Steve Loomis, *Sales Staff*
Mandi Bates, *Office Mgr*
Jennifer Townsend, *Office Mgr*
Gary Patterson, *Manager*
EMP: 10
SALES (corp-wide): 30.3MM **Privately Held**
WEB: www.unitedcasing.com
SIC: 5084 1389 Oil well machinery, equipment & supplies; oil field services

PA: United Casing Incorporated
8505 Tech Frest Pl Ste 40
The Woodlands TX 77381
281 586-0195

(G-12446)
UNITED CASING TUBULAR SERVICES
10901 Sheldon Rd (77044-6007)
PHONE..............................281 456-0212
Tor Zaphne, *Owner*
EMP: 25
SALES (est): 551.2K **Privately Held**
WEB: www.unitedcasing.com
SIC: 1389 Oil field services

(G-12447)
UNITED FILM SOLUTIONS INC
15864 W Hardy Rd Ste 760 (77060-3177)
PHONE..............................713 715-4197
Claudia Sucar, *President*
EMP: 16
SALES (est): 941.2K **Privately Held**
WEB: www.unitedfilmsolutions.com
SIC: 2821 Plastics materials & resins

(G-12448)
UNITED GALVANIZING INC
6123 Cunningham Rd (77041-4707)
P.O. Box 40207 (77240-0207)
PHONE..............................713 466-4161
Julia A Kahla, *President*
▲ **EMP:** 150 **EST:** 1970
SALES (est): 21MM
SALES (corp-wide): 2.7B **Publicly Held**
WEB: www.valmontcoatings.com
SIC: 3479 Coating of metals & formed products
PA: Valmont Industries, Inc.
1 Valmont Plz Ste 500
Omaha NE 68154
402 963-1000

(G-12449)
UNITED MINERALS AND PRPTS INC
Also Called: Cimbar Performance Mineral
14047 Industrial Rd (77015-6826)
PHONE..............................713 881-9466
Tab Kellough, *Principal*
EMP: 30
SALES (corp-wide): 32.4MM **Privately Held**
WEB: www.cimbar.com
SIC: 3295 Nonresidential building operators
PA: United Minerals And Properties, Inc.
49 Jackson Lake Rd Ste O
Chatsworth GA 30705
770 387-0319

(G-12450)
UNITED OILFIELD SUPPLY LLC
Also Called: United Industrial Products
630 Brittmoore Rd (77079-6119)
P.O. Box 922, Galveston (77553-0922)
PHONE..............................713 489-2000
EMP: 10 **EST:** 2011
SALES (est): 860K **Privately Held**
SIC: 3494 Mfg Valves/Pipe Fittings

(G-12451)
UNITED PLASTICS GROUP INC
7865 Northcourt Rd (77040-5615)
PHONE..............................713 466-5563
Maurice Murphy, *CEO*
Sandy Cook, *Opers Mgr*
Alejandro Diaz, *Engineer*
Neil Parsons, *Manager*
EMP: 29
SALES (est): 9.4MM **Privately Held**
WEB: www.upgintl.com
SIC: 3089 Injection molded finished plastic products

(G-12452)
UNITED PLASTICS INC
2005 Canal St (77003-1005)
PHONE..............................713 222-2186
Patrick Yu, *President*
KY Ho, *Vice Pres*
▲ **EMP:** 22
SALES (est): 3.9MM **Privately Held**
SIC: 2673 Pliofilm bags: made from purchased materials; plastic bags: made from purchased materials

(G-12453)
UNITED SALT BAYTOWN LLC (HQ)
Also Called: U S C
4800 San Felipe St # 100 (77056-3908)
PHONE..............................713 877-2600
James O Donnell, *President*
Dennis Bradley, *President*
Wayne Sneed, *Senior VP*
Larry Erickson, *Vice Pres*
Theresa Feldman, *Vice Pres*
◆ **EMP:** 25 **EST:** 1929
SQ FT: 6,500
SALES (est): 24.3MM
SALES (corp-wide): 247.1MM **Privately Held**
WEB: www.unitedsalt.com
SIC: 2899 Salt
PA: Texas United Corporation
4800 San Felipe St
Houston TX 77056
713 877-1793

(G-12454)
UNITED SALT CARLSBAD LLC
Also Called: Usc
4800 San Felipe St # 100 (77056-3908)
PHONE..............................713 877-2600
Emmanuel J Daniel, *President*
Stacey Owens, *Treasurer*
Cathy Gillies, *Admin Sec*
EMP: 66
SALES (est): 26MM
SALES (corp-wide): 24.1MM **Privately Held**
WEB: www.unitedsalt.com
SIC: 2899 1479 Salt; salt (common) mining
PA: Usc Holdings Corporation
4800 San Felipe St # 100
Houston TX 77056
713 877-2600

(G-12455)
UNITED SALT CORPORATION
4800 San Felipe St (77056-3908)
PHONE..............................713 877-2600
Jim O'Donnell, *President*
Kyle Rash, *Vice Pres*
Mark Williams, *Vice Pres*
Dennis Bradley, *Plant Mgr*
Jason Laws, *Plant Mgr*
EMP: 12
SALES (est): 1.6MM **Privately Held**
WEB: www.unitedsalt.com
SIC: 2899 Salt

(G-12456)
UNITED SALT SALTVILLE LLC
4800 San Felipe St # 100 (77056-3908)
PHONE..............................713 877-2600
Ernest C Sands II, *President*
Stacey Owens, *Treasurer*
Cathy Gillies, *Admin Sec*
EMP: 23
SALES (est): 5.2MM
SALES (corp-wide): 24.1MM **Privately Held**
WEB: www.unitedsalt.com
SIC: 2899 5499 Salt; health & dietetic food stores
PA: Usc Holdings Corporation
4800 San Felipe St # 100
Houston TX 77056
713 877-2600

(G-12457)
UNITED STATES MINERAL PDTS CO
3340 Bingle Rd (77055-1037)
PHONE..............................713 462-1709
Jim Osbourn, *Manager*
Ken Brown, *Manager*
EMP: 70
SQ FT: 26,585
SALES (corp-wide): 46.6MM **Privately Held**
WEB: www.isolatek.com
SIC: 3296 Mineral wool insulation products
PA: United States Mineral Products Company Inc
41 Furnace St
Stanhope NJ 07874
973 347-1200

(G-12458)
UNITED STRUCTURES AMERICA INC (PA)
Also Called: U S A
1912 Buschong St (77039-1213)
P.O. Box 9237, Spring (77387-9237)
PHONE.....................281 442-8247
Dain Drake, *President*
Stephen Dees, *District Mgr*
Steve Koonce, *District Mgr*
Kyle Parrish, *Exec VP*
Damon Drake, *Vice Pres*
◆ **EMP:** 330
SQ FT: 200,000
SALES (est): 98.1MM **Privately Held**
WEB: www.usabldg.com
SIC: 3448 Buildings, portable: prefabricated metal

(G-12459)
UNITED STRUCTURES AMERICA INC
3717 Sunset Blvd (77005-2029)
P.O. Box 9237, Spring (77387-9237)
PHONE.....................281 442-8247
Kent Smith, *District Mgr*
Damon Drake, *Vice Pres*
David Drake, *Vice Pres*
Tim Jones, *Manager*
EMP: 180
SALES (corp-wide): 98.1MM **Privately Held**
WEB: www.usabldg.com
SIC: 3448 Buildings, portable: prefabricated metal
PA: United Structures Of America, Inc.
1912 Buschong St
Houston TX 77039
281 442-8247

(G-12460)
UNIVATION TECHNOLOGIES LLC (DH)
5555 San Felipe St # 1950 (77056-2746)
PHONE.....................713 892-3650
Eddie Brown, *Accountant*
Steve Stanley,
S P Koch, *Admin Sec*
▼ **EMP:** 195
SALES (est): 56.3MM
SALES (corp-wide): 38.5B **Publicly Held**
WEB: www.univation.com
SIC: 2819 8731 Catalysts, chemical; commercial physical research
HQ: The Dow Chemical Company
2211 H H Dow Way
Midland MI 48642
989 636-1000

(G-12461)
UNIVERSAL ENSCO INC (DH)
Also Called: Universalpegasus International
4848 Loop Central Dr # 137 (77081-2355)
PHONE.....................713 425-6000
Philip Luna, *CEO*
Wendy Donahue, *Vice Pres*
Pano Zhonga, *Vice Pres*
Daniel H Rebman, *Project Engr*
Valerie Cloke, *VP Human Res*
EMP: 31
SALES (est): 114.8MM **Publicly Held**
WEB: www.universalpegasus.com
SIC: 1389 Gas field services
HQ: Universalpegasus International, Inc.
4848 Loop Central Dr # 137
Houston TX 77081
713 425-6000

(G-12462)
UNIVERSAL ORNAMENTS INC
2305 Bennington St (77093-8913)
PHONE.....................713 699-1500
Gerardo Lopez, *President*
Fatima Lopez, *Corp Secy*
Carlos Guerrero, *Vice Pres*
▲ **EMP:** 60
SQ FT: 98,572
SALES (est): 2.8MM **Privately Held**
WEB: www.universalornaments.com
SIC: 3441 Fabricated structural metal

(G-12463)
UNIVERSAL PRESSURE PUMPING INC (HQ)
10713 W Sam Huston Pkwy N (77064-3584)
PHONE.....................432 221-7000
William A Hendricks Jr, *CEO*
John Carnett, *Senior VP*
Lee Kilpatrick, *Opers Staff*
Shane Bush, *Engineer*
John E Vollmer III, *CFO*
EMP: 100
SALES (est): 227.7MM
SALES (corp-wide): 1.1B **Publicly Held**
WEB: www.patenergy.com
SIC: 1381 Drilling oil & gas wells
PA: Patterson-Uti Energy, Inc.
10713 W Sam Houston Pkwy
Houston TX 77064
281 765-7100

(G-12464)
UNIVERSAL SOLAR TECHNOLOGY INC
10685 Hazelhurst Dr # 21698 (77043-3299)
PHONE.....................832 764-8260
Paul D Landrew, *CEO*
Darrell Calloway, *President*
EMP: 19
SQ FT: 8,200
SALES (est): 14.8MM **Privately Held**
WEB: www.ustnevada.com
SIC: 3433 Heating equipment, except electric

(G-12465)
UNIVERSAL WIRE WORKS INC
15 Drennan St (77003-1911)
PHONE.....................713 649-3828
P Bruce Belk, *President*
Jarrod Belk, *Opers Staff*
EMP: 10
SQ FT: 12,700
SALES (est): 1MM **Privately Held**
WEB: www.uniwire.net
SIC: 3315 Wire & fabricated wire products

(G-12466)
UNIVERSE TCHNCAL TRNSLTION INC
9225 Katy Fwy Ste 400 (77024-1531)
PHONE.....................713 827-8800
Marion Rifkind, *President*
Mark Krasnov, *Vice Pres*
▲ **EMP:** 40
SQ FT: 4,500
SALES (est): 4.3MM **Privately Held**
WEB: www.universetranslation.com
SIC: 7389 2791 Translation services; typesetting

(G-12467)
UNIVERSITY HOUSTON - SYSTEM
Also Called: Hilton
4450 University Dr (77204-3028)
PHONE.....................713 741-2447
Fernando Cuellar, *General Mgr*
EMP: 150
SALES (corp-wide): 951.2MM **Privately Held**
WEB: www.uh.edu
SIC: 7011 5812 3578 Hotels & motels; family restaurants; banking machines
PA: University Of Houston - System
4302 University Dr
Houston TX 77204
832 842-3100

(G-12468)
UNIVERSITY OF HOUSTON SYSTEM
Also Called: U of H Newspaper
1 Main St (77002-1014)
PHONE.....................713 221-8192
Sandra Brown, *Librarian*
Jennifer Huenemeier, *Sr Project Mgr*
Dena Aiyenuwa, *Manager*
Eddie Arias, *Manager*
Joel Martinez, *Manager*
EMP: 15

SALES (corp-wide): 951.2MM **Privately Held**
WEB: www.uh.edu
SIC: 2711 8221 Newspapers; university
PA: University Of Houston - System
4302 University Dr
Houston TX 77204
832 842-3100

(G-12469)
UNIVERSITY OF HOUSTON SYSTEM
Arte Publico Press
4880 Calhoun Rd Ste 2 (77204-2610)
PHONE.....................713 743-2841
Nicolas Kanellos, *Principal*
EMP: 30
SALES (corp-wide): 951.2MM **Privately Held**
WEB: www.uh.edu
SIC: 2731 8221 Book publishing; university
PA: University Of Houston - System
4302 University Dr
Houston TX 77204
832 842-3100

(G-12470)
UNLIMITED CUSTOM EMBROIDERY
10507 Fallstone Rd (77099-4301)
PHONE.....................713 773-0111
Quyen Tran, *President*
Jasmine Tran, *Executive*
▲ **EMP:** 18
SQ FT: 8,000 **Privately Held**
WEB: www.uce-tx.com
SIC: 2395 Embroidery products, except schiffli machine

(G-12471)
UNO NETWORK LLC
9999 Bellaire Blvd # 1122 (77036-3579)
PHONE.....................844 885-5000
Tiffany Ovo, *Manager*
Bao Ngo,
▲ **EMP:** 20
SQ FT: 2,000
SALES (est): 589.2K **Privately Held**
WEB: www.unoipbox.com
SIC: 2741

(G-12472)
UOP LLC
Also Called: Honeywell UOP
2101 Citywest Blvd Bldg 1 (77042-2849)
PHONE.....................832 551-9638
Brad Elrich, *Systems Staff*
Vic Rice, *Director*
EMP: 45
SALES (corp-wide): 36.7B **Publicly Held**
WEB: www.uop.honeywell.com
SIC: 2819 2911 Catalysts, chemical; petroleum refining
HQ: Uop Llc
25 E Algonquin Rd
Des Plaines IL 60016
847 391-2000

(G-12473)
UP & OUT COMMUNICATIONS (PA)
Also Called: Outsmart Magazine
3406 Audubon Pl (77006-4412)
PHONE.....................713 520-7237
Greg Alan Jeu, *Owner*
Megan E Smith, *Editor*
Megan Smith, *Editor*
John Wright, *Assistant*
EMP: 10
SQ FT: 2,000
SALES (est): 1.2MM **Privately Held**
WEB: www.outsmartmagazine.com
SIC: 2731 2721 Book publishing; magazines: publishing only, not printed on site

(G-12474)
UPG COMPANY LLC (HQ)
7865 Northcourt Rd # 100 (77040-5616)
PHONE.....................713 466-5563
Yan Jiang, *General Mgr*
Neil Parsons, *Business Mgr*
Sandy Cook, *Plant Mgr*
Gareth Huggins, *Project Mgr*
Freddy Venegas, *Engineer*

EMP: 200
SALES (est): 60MM **Privately Held**
WEB: www.upgintl.com
SIC: 3089 Molding primary plastic
PA: Turnspire Capital Partners Llc
1290 Ave Of The Amrcas St
New York NY 10104
212 372-9583

(G-12475)
UPS INC
1605 Nagle St (77003-4525)
PHONE.....................713 222-7300
Chad O Cossey, *President*
Steve Daugherty, *Vice Pres*
Pamela Cossey, *Admin Sec*
EMP: 50
SALES (est): 6.2MM **Privately Held**
WEB: www.locations.ups.com
SIC: 3677 Filtration devices, electronic

(G-12476)
UPSTART ACQUISITIONS CORP
Also Called: Bet-Lar Services
10225 Woodedge Dr (77070-6001)
PHONE.....................281 469-0815
Daniel S Schrader, *President*
Luigi Massa, *Principal*
Felipe Morales, *Principal*
Richelle L Schrader, *Principal*
EMP: 12
SQ FT: 6,000
SALES (est): 2.1MM **Privately Held**
WEB: www.betlarservices.com
SIC: 3599 Machine shop, jobbing & repair

(G-12477)
URBAN PUBLISHERS INC (PA)
Also Called: Papercity Magazine
3411 Richmond Ave Ste 600 (77046-3420)
PHONE.....................713 524-0606
James Kastleman, *President*
Moni Bickers, *Publisher*
Catherine Anspon, *Editor*
Jenny Antill, *Editor*
Laurann Claridge, *Editor*
EMP: 28
SQ FT: 9,000
SALES (est): 4.8MM **Privately Held**
WEB: www.papercitymag.com
SIC: 2721 Magazines: publishing only, not printed on site

(G-12478)
URBAN SHEET METAL INC (PA)
4512 Montrose Blvd (77006-5828)
PHONE.....................713 522-6441
Sherry E Davis, *President*
Frank Robertson, *Vice Pres*
EMP: 50
SALES (est): 5.5MM **Privately Held**
WEB: www.urbanlofts.com
SIC: 3444 Sheet metalwork

(G-12479)
URIBE STEEL
7213 Miller Road 2 (77049-4821)
PHONE.....................281 452-5696
EMP: 13
SQ FT: 10,800
SALES (est): 2MM **Privately Held**
SIC: 3441 Fabricated structural metal

(G-12480)
URSA RESOURCES GROUP II LLC (PA)
602 Sawyer St Ste 710 (77007-7510)
PHONE.....................713 456-3000
Matthew B Steele, *President*
Tyler Crabtree, *CFO*
EMP: 17
SALES (est): 30.5MM **Privately Held**
WEB: www.ursaresources.com
SIC: 1382 Oil & gas exploration services

(G-12481)
US BELLOWS INC
3701 Holmes Rd (77051-1545)
P.O. Box 34506 (77234-4506)
PHONE.....................713 731-0030
Durga D Agrawal, *President*
Scott Stelmar, *General Mgr*
James Sweeney, *General Mgr*
Rakesh Agrawal, *Vice Pres*
Rk Agrawal, *Vice Pres*
EMP: 350 **EST:** 1997

▲ = Import ▼=Export
◆ =Import/Export

SQ FT: 450,000
SALES (est): 28.7MM **Privately Held**
WEB: www.usbellows.com
SIC: **3449** 3568 3498 3494 Joists, fabricated bar; power transmission equipment; fabricated pipe & fittings; valves & pipe fittings; fabricated structural metal

(G-12482)
US BOLT MANUFACTURING INC
12895 Main St (77035-5601)
P.O. Box 35535 (77235-5535)
PHONE................................713 726-1000
Thomas Johnson, *President*
Sandra Fletcher, *Vice Pres*
Romeo Rodriguez, *Prdtn Mgr*
Kevin Wilson, *Mfg Staff*
Lori Woodruff, *Controller*
EMP: 60
SQ FT: 25,000
SALES (est): 30.3MM **Privately Held**
WEB: www.usbolt.com
SIC: **5085** 3452 Fasteners, industrial: nuts, bolts, screws, etc.; nuts, metal

(G-12483)
US HOSE CORP
Also Called: Willcox-U S Hose Div
2020 Greens Rd Ste 400 (77032-1527)
PHONE................................281 458-0400
Kevin Manning, *Sales Mgr*
Joe Marentette, *Manager*
EMP: 17
SALES (corp-wide): 79.6MM **Privately Held**
WEB: www.unitedflexible.com
SIC: **3494** Valves & pipe fittings
HQ: U.S. Hose Corp
815 Forestwood Dr
Romeoville IL 60446
815 886-1140

(G-12484)
US JOINER LLC
Also Called: Infinity Marine Offshore, LLC
12775 Nimitz St Bldg A (77015-5603)
P.O. Box 96147 (77213-6147)
PHONE................................713 330-1700
David F Madigan, *President*
Terry McDonald, *Project Mgr*
Beau Burris, *Opers Mgr*
Lloyd Burris,
▲ EMP: 50
SALES (est): 2.9MM
SALES (corp-wide): 128.4MM **Privately Held**
SIC: **1389** Construction, repair & dismantling services
HQ: Us Joiner Llc
5690 Three Notch D Rd # 200
Crozet VA 22932
434 220-8500

(G-12485)
US LBM HOLDINGS LLC
929 Gessner Rd Ste 1900 (77024-2317)
PHONE................................713 650-6200
L T Gibson, *Mng Member*
EMP: 175
SALES (corp-wide): 1.9B **Privately Held**
WEB: www.uslbm.com
SIC: **2951** 5032 3281 1629 Asphalt & asphaltic paving mixtures (not from refineries); asphalt mixture; limestone, cut & shaped; dredging contractor; construction sand & gravel
HQ: Us Lbm Holdings, Llc
1000 Corporate Grove Dr
Buffalo Grove IL 60089

(G-12486)
US LED LTD
Also Called: US Led
6807 Portwest Dr (77024-8008)
PHONE................................713 972-9191
Ron Farmer, *Managing Prtnr*
Margarita Farmer, *Partner*
Darko Dimitric, *General Mgr*
Paul Jeziorowski, *VP Bus Dvlpt*
Brittany Dimitric, *Accounts Mgr*
▲ EMP: 43
SQ FT: 34,000
SALES (est): 20MM **Privately Held**
WEB: www.usled.com
SIC: **3646** Commercial indusl & institutional electric lighting fixtures

(G-12487)
US PETROCHEMICALS INC
5075 Westheimer Rd # 675 (77056-5643)
P.O. Box 460412 (77056-8412)
PHONE................................713 871-1951
Laique A Rehman, *President*
◆ EMP: 11
SQ FT: 2,000
SALES: 102.9MM **Privately Held**
WEB: www.uspetrochemicals.com
SIC: **5169** 2865 5052 5172 Synthetic resins, rubber & plastic materials; organic chemicals, synthetic; chemicals, industrial & heavy; benzene; xylene; sulfur; gases, liquefied petroleum (propane); naphtha

(G-12488)
US SAND LLC
5177 Richmond Ave # 1220 (77056-6727)
PHONE................................713 333-3001
EMP: 10
SALES (est): 718K **Privately Held**
SIC: **1311** Crude Petroleum/Natural Gas Production

(G-12489)
US SIGNS INC (PA)
6807 Portwest Dr (77024-8008)
PHONE................................713 977-7900
Ronald Farmer, *President*
Rick Cox, *Project Mgr*
Kristy Crep, *Project Mgr*
Eddie Garcia, *Cust Mgr*
EMP: 14
SALES (est): 2.2MM **Privately Held**
WEB: www.vixxo.com
SIC: **3993** Signs & advertising specialties

(G-12490)
US SILICA HOLDINGS INC
12012 Wickchester Ln # 300 (77079-1229)
PHONE................................281 258-2170
Bryan A Shinn, *Branch Mgr*
EMP: 14
SALES (corp-wide): 1.4B **Publicly Held**
WEB: www.ussilica.com
SIC: **3296** 1446 2819 Insulation: rock wool, slag & silica minerals; silica sand mining; silica compounds
PA: U.S. Silica Holdings, Inc.
24275 Katy Fwy Ste 600
Katy TX 77494
281 258-2170

(G-12491)
US VT
Also Called: US VT Severe Service Valves
6828 Flintlock Rd (77040-4323)
PHONE................................713 856-9171
Trang Tran, *President*
Thomas Phan, *Opers Staff*
EMP: 35
SALES (est): 2.2MM **Privately Held**
WEB: www.us-vt.com
SIC: **3491** Industrial valves

(G-12492)
US WELL SERVICES INC (PA)
1360 Post Oak Blvd # 1800 (77056-3023)
PHONE................................832 562-3730
David L Treadwell, *Ch of Bd*
Joel Broussard, *President*
Nathan Houston, *COO*
Dean Fullerton, *Vice Pres*
Mark D Wolf, *Vice Pres*
EMP: 15 EST: 2012
SALES: 514.7MM **Publicly Held**
WEB: www.uswellservices.com
SIC: **1389** Hydraulic fracturing wells

(G-12493)
US ZINC CORPORATION (PA)
2727 Allen Pkwy Ste 800 (77019-2152)
PHONE................................713 926-1705
Tracy Baugh, *President*
Francisco Moreira, *Exec VP*
Joe Kight, *Vice Pres*
Richard M Rosenber, *Vice Pres*
Kenneth Writhe, *Controller*
◆ EMP: 30
SQ FT: 10,000
SALES (est): 182.2MM **Privately Held**
WEB: www.uszinc.com
SIC: **3341** Secondary nonferrous metals

(G-12494)
US ZINC NORTH AMERICA INC
Also Called: U.S. Zinc-Houston Dust Plant
6020 Esperson St (77011-2330)
PHONE................................713 926-1705
EMP: 171 **Privately Held**
WEB: www.uszinc.com
SIC: **3356** Zinc & zinc alloy bars, plates, sheets, etc.
PA: U.S. Zinc North America, Inc.
2727 Allen Pkwy Ste 800
Houston TX 77019

(G-12495)
US ZINC NORTH AMERICA INC
Also Called: U.S. Zinc-Houston Metal Plant
6020 Navigation Blvd (77011-1132)
PHONE................................713 926-1705
EMP: 86 **Privately Held**
WEB: www.uszinc.com
SIC: **3356** Zinc & zinc alloy bars, plates, sheets, etc.
PA: U.S. Zinc North America, Inc.
2727 Allen Pkwy Ste 800
Houston TX 77019

(G-12496)
US ZINC NORTH AMERICA INC (PA)
Also Called: Votorantim Metais N Amer Inc
2727 Allen Pkwy Ste 800 (77019-2152)
PHONE................................713 926-1705
Rodrigo Daud, *President*
Joao Bosco Silva, *Director*
Manfred Stanek, *Director*
◆ EMP: 25
SALES (est): 42.3MM **Privately Held**
WEB: www.uszinc.com
SIC: **3356** Zinc & zinc alloy bars, plates, sheets, etc.

(G-12497)
USA PETROLEUM EQUIPMENT SUP CO
40 Fm 1960 Rd W 181 (77090-3530)
PHONE................................281 893-2471
Tom Luong, *President*
▼ EMP: 11
SALES (est): 2.1MM **Privately Held**
WEB: www.usapetroequips.com
SIC: **3533** Oil & gas field machinery

(G-12498)
USA PETROVALVE INC
Also Called: Flotek Pump Services
10603 W Sam Houston Pkwy (77064-4660)
PHONE................................713 466-9881
Terry Lowrey, *Principal*
Zlata Grenoble, *Research*
Roberto Basurto, *Administration*
EMP: 13 EST: 2008
SALES (est): 1.6MM **Privately Held**
WEB: www.flotekind.com
SIC: **2899** Chemical preparations

(G-12499)
USA PRECISION LLC
Also Called: USA Precision Machining Co
8028 Van Hut Ln (77044-2432)
PHONE................................281 458-7304
Chester Montgomery, *Managing Prtnr*
Jennifer Guillory, *Materials Mgr*
Eric Bell, *Foreman/Supr*
Bob Boyles, *Sales Mgr*
Chester R Montgomery Sr, *Mng Member*
EMP: 20
SQ FT: 10,000
SALES (est): 3.9MM **Privately Held**
WEB: www.usaprecision.com
SIC: **3599** Machine shop, jobbing & repair

(G-12500)
USA PRINTING CORPORATION (PA)
11122 Bellaire Blvd (77072-2608)
PHONE................................281 498-4310
Wea Lee, *President*
Wea H Lee, *President*
Cathy Lee, *Vice Pres*
EMP: 12
SQ FT: 30,000

SALES (est): 2.8MM **Privately Held**
WEB: www.chineseseattlenews.com
SIC: **2711** 2741 2796 2752 Newspapers, publishing & printing; shopping news: publishing & printing; platemaking services; commercial printing, lithographic

(G-12501)
USA PROMLITE TECHNOLOGY INC
7001 Corporate Dr Ste 213 (77036-5115)
PHONE................................832 868-8866
EMP: 10 EST: 2009
SQ FT: 1,500
SALES: 561.8K **Privately Held**
SIC: **3646** Mfg Commercial Lighting Fixtures

(G-12502)
USA SPORTS INC
Also Called: Troy Barbell and Fitness
10600 Shadow Wood Dr # 301 (77043-2848)
PHONE................................713 957-2882
Louis Lien, *President*
David Allen, *Project Dir*
Robert Chen, *Senior Buyer*
Jessica Lien, *Treasurer*
Valerie Yang, *Human Resources*
◆ EMP: 70
SQ FT: 150,000
SALES (est): 20.5MM **Privately Held**
WEB: www.troyfitness.com
SIC: **3949** Exercise equipment

(G-12503)
USM INC
12303 Fuqua St (77034-4555)
PHONE................................281 619-0144
Chris Johnson, *CEO*
Paul Johnson, *President*
John Constantine, *CFO*
Theresa Walmsley, *Office Mgr*
Stephanie Gilbert, *Manager*
▲ EMP: 75
SQ FT: 37,500
SALES (est): 8.8MM **Privately Held**
WEB: www.usminc.com
SIC: **3999** Models, general, except toy

(G-12504)
USON LP (PA)
8640 N Eldridge Pkwy (77041-1233)
PHONE................................281 671-2000
Michael Ophielz, *Partner*
Alan Eschbach, *Partner*
Christine Frith-Brown, *Partner*
Mark Robison, *Partner*
Gustavo Rivas, *Vice Pres*
▲ EMP: 50 EST: 1995
SQ FT: 35,000
SALES (est): 21MM **Privately Held**
WEB: www.uson.com
SIC: **3823** 3829 3825 Industrial flow & liquid measuring instruments; measuring & controlling devices; instruments to measure electricity

(G-12505)
UTEX INDUSTRIES INC (DH)
10810 Katy Fwy Ste 100 (77043-5013)
P.O. Box 79227 (77279-9200)
PHONE................................713 467-1000
Michael P Balas, *CEO*
Charlie Pitts, *Business Mgr*
Mike Blake, *Vice Pres*
Chuck Rankin, *Vice Pres*
Dave Lindinger, *Plant Mgr*
▲ EMP: 75 EST: 1940
SQ FT: 50,000
SALES (est): 164.4MM **Privately Held**
WEB: www.utexind.com
SIC: **3053** 3061 Packing, rubber; gaskets, all materials; oil seals, rubber; oil & gas field machinery rubber goods (mechanical)

(G-12506)
UTEX INDUSTRIES INC
Accuseal
4330 Brittmoore Rd (77041-8002)
PHONE................................832 358-0350
Jack Stoner, *Branch Mgr*
EMP: 103

SALES (corp-wide): 164.4MM **Privately Held**
WEB: www.utexind.com
SIC: 3053 Gaskets, packing & sealing devices
HQ: Utex Industries, Inc.
10810 Katy Fwy Ste 100
Houston TX 77043
713 467-1000

(G-12507)
UTLX MANUFACTURING LLC
16923 Old Beaumont 90 (77049)
PHONE................................281 847-8200
Jeremy De La Cerda, *President*
Randall J McDougal Sr,
Randall S McDougall,
EMP: 550
SALES (est): 136.5MM
SALES (corp-wide): 254.6B **Publicly Held**
WEB: www.utlx.com
SIC: 3795 Tank recovery vehicles
HQ: Union Tank Car Company
175 W Jackson Blvd # 2100
Chicago IL 60604
312 431-3111

(G-12508)
UV LOGISTICS LLC
Also Called: United Vision Logistics
15005 Crosby Fwy (77049-1835)
PHONE................................281 436-2310
EMP: 9 **Privately Held**
WEB: www.uvlogistics.com
SIC: 4213 1389 Contract haulers; haulage, oil field
HQ: Uv Logistics, Llc
4021 Ambssdor Cffery Pkwy
Lafayette LA 70503
337 291-6700

(G-12509)
V & V INDUSTRIES INC
Also Called: Hudson Machine Works
1419 Hays St (77009-6417)
P.O. Box 16101 (77222-6101)
PHONE................................713 224-1751
Kim Bui, *President*
Anthony Vo, *Manager*
EMP: 18
SALES (est): 3.6MM **Privately Held**
SIC: 3533 Oil field machinery & equipment

(G-12510)
V GAS LLC
12221 Fm 529 Rd (77041-2805)
PHONE................................713 896-8531
David Weaver, *Project Mgr*
Sandeep Ramachandran, *Marketing Staff*
Norman Villarina, *Mng Member*
Ashley Bowles, *Manager*
Chase Robertson,
EMP: 17
SQ FT: 126,500
SALES (est): 7.8MM **Privately Held**
WEB: www.vgasllc.com
SIC: 3559 Petroleum refinery equipment

(G-12511)
V RESPECT
4351 Richmeadow Dr (77048-5589)
PHONE................................281 780-6267
Trishina J Morant, *Owner*
EMP: 9
SALES (est): 289.9K **Privately Held**
SIC: 2211 Apparel & outerwear fabrics, cotton

(G-12512)
V-KOOL INC
8515 Jackrabbit Rd Ste B (77095-3191)
PHONE................................713 856-8333
Martin O Watts, *President*
EMP: 9 EST: 1998
SALES (est): 878.4K **Privately Held**
WEB: www.v-kool-usa.com
SIC: 3081 1799 Unsupported plastics film & sheet; glass tinting, architectural or automotive

(G-12513)
V-TEQ MANUFACTURING INC
5218 Brittmoore Rd (77041-7108)
PHONE................................713 466-0660
Van N Ho, *President*

Becky T Ho, *Vice Pres*
EMP: 15
SALES (est): 2.1MM **Privately Held**
WEB: www.vteqinc.com
SIC: 3599 Machine shop, jobbing & repair

(G-12514)
VAALCO ENERGY INC (PA)
9800 Richmond Ave Ste 700 (77042-4685)
PHONE................................713 623-0801
Cary Bounds, *CEO*
Andrew L Fawthrop, *Ch of Bd*
William R Thomas, *President*
David Desautels, *Exec VP*
Thor Pruckl, *Exec VP*
EMP: 35
SALES: 84.5MM **Publicly Held**
WEB: www.vaalco.com
SIC: 1311 Crude petroleum production

(G-12515)
VAALCO GABON (ETAME) INC
9800 Richmond Ave Ste 700 (77042-4685)
PHONE................................713 623-0801
Steven P Guidry, *CEO*
W Russell Schneirman, *President*
Robert L Gerry III, *Chairman*
Cary Bounds, *COO*
Eric J Christ, *Vice Pres*
◆ EMP: 21
SALES (est): 4.1MM **Publicly Held**
WEB: www.vaalco.com
SIC: 1381 1382 Drilling oil & gas wells; oil & gas exploration services
PA: Vaalco Energy, Inc.
9800 Richmond Ave Ste 700
Houston TX 77042

(G-12516)
VACATION PUBLICATIONS INC (PA)
Also Called: Where To Retire Magazine
5851 San Felipe St # 500 (77057-3076)
PHONE................................713 974-6903
R Alan Fox, *CEO*
Robert Carney, *Ch of Bd*
Alan Fox, *Publisher*
Elizabeth Armstrong, *Editor*
Dave Hart, *Prdtn Dir*
EMP: 450
SQ FT: 12,000
SALES (est): 78.2MM **Privately Held**
WEB: www.vacationsmagazine.com
SIC: 4724 2721 2731 Tourist agency arranging transport, lodging & car rental; magazines: publishing only, not printed on site; book publishing

(G-12517)
VALCO INSTRUMENTS COMPANY (PA)
7811 Westview Dr (77055-5030)
P.O. Box 55603 (77255-5603)
PHONE................................713 688-9345
Stanley Stearns, *President*
Max Loy, *Prdtn Mgr*
John Beard, *Production*
Christy Brisbin, *Production*
Curston Grover, *Production*
▲ EMP: 271
SQ FT: 25,000
SALES (est): 62.1MM **Privately Held**
WEB: www.vici.com
SIC: 3823 3826 3494 On-stream gas/liquid analysis instruments, industrial; analytical instruments; valves & pipe fittings

(G-12518)
VALCO INSTRUMENTS COMPANY
8300 Waterbury Dr Ste 400 (77055-3469)
PHONE................................713 688-9345
Bruce Schulman, *CEO*
David Lazarine, *Accountant*
Randy Sanderlin, *Supervisor*
EMP: 14
SALES (corp-wide): 62.1MM **Privately Held**
WEB: www.vici.com
SIC: 3823 Industrial instrmnts msrmnt display/control process variable
PA: Valco Instruments Company, Inc
7811 Westview Dr
Houston TX 77055
713 688-9345

(G-12519)
VALERO REFINING-TEXAS LP
9701 Manchester St (77012-2408)
P.O. Box 5038 (77262-5038)
PHONE................................713 923-6641
Jeff McKay, *Warehouse Mgr*
Allen Dusek, *Engineer*
Rob Moore, *Engineer*
John Wallace, *Engineer*
Edgard Mena, *Design Engr*
EMP: 500
SALES (corp-wide): 108.3B **Publicly Held**
WEB: www.valero.com
SIC: 2911 Petroleum refining
HQ: Valero Refining-Texas, L.P.
1 Valero Way
San Antonio TX 78249
210 345-2000

(G-12520)
VALERUS FELD SLTONS HLDNGS LLC (DH)
919 Milam St Ste 1000 (77002-5386)
PHONE................................713 744-6100
Christian I Brown, *President*
Robyn Underwood, *Counsel*
Barry White, *Counsel*
Tush Doshi, *Vice Pres*
James Gill, *Vice Pres*
◆ EMP: 37
SALES (est): 216.6MM
SALES (corp-wide): 7.1B **Privately Held**
WEB: www.snclavalin.com
SIC: 1382 6719 Oil & gas exploration services; investment holding companies, except banks

(G-12521)
VALERUS FIELD SOLUTIONS LP (DH)
919 Milam St Ste 1000 (77002-5386)
PHONE................................877 983-7500
Steve R Gill, *CEO*
James R Gill, *COO*
Tom Birney, *Vice Pres*
Shelton McMath, *Vice Pres*
Kevin Moroney, *CFO*
▼ EMP: 24
SALES (est): 36.1MM
SALES (corp-wide): 7.1B **Privately Held**
WEB: www.snclavalin.com
SIC: 1382 Oil & gas exploration services

(G-12522)
VALLOUREC DRLG PDTS USA INC
Also Called: Vallourec Drilling Pdts USA
6300-6230 Navigation Blvd (77011)
P.O. Box 230589 (77223-0589)
PHONE................................713 844-3700
Doug Fields, *President*
Bryce Thueson, *Corp Secy*
◆ EMP: 251
SALES (est): 93.5MM
SALES (corp-wide): 5.9MM **Privately Held**
SIC: 3317 Pipes, wrought: welded, lock joint or heavy riveted
HQ: Vallourec Holdings, Inc.
2106 City W Blvd Ste 1300
Houston TX 77042
713 479-3200

(G-12523)
VALLOUREC TUBE-ALLOY LLC (HQ)
1050 E Richey Rd (77073-6422)
PHONE................................713 462-7613
Grady Harrison, *President*
Coignac Nicolas, *Vice Pres*
Elliott Smith, *Vice Pres*
Dan Dexter, *Engineer*
Curt Double, *Engineer*
▲ EMP: 140
SALES (est): 64.1MM
SALES (corp-wide): 5.9MM **Privately Held**
WEB: www.vallourec.com
SIC: 3533 3317 Oil & gas field machinery; steel pipe & tubes
PA: Vallourec
27 Avenue Du General Leclerc
Boulogne Billancourt 92100
149 093-500

(G-12524)
VALLOUREC USA CORPORATION (DH)
2107 Citywest Blvd # 130 (77042-2827)
PHONE................................713 479-3200
David R Hamrick, *President*
Bertrand Frischmann, *President*
Philippe Carlier, *Vice Pres*
Didier Hornet, *Vice Pres*
Alexandre Lyra, *Vice Pres*
◆ EMP: 31
SALES (est): 11.7MM
SALES (corp-wide): 5.9MM **Privately Held**
WEB: www.vallourec.com
SIC: 3317 Steel pipe & tubes
HQ: Vallourec Holdings, Inc.
2106 City W Blvd Ste 1300
Houston TX 77042
713 479-3200

(G-12525)
VAM USA LLC (DH)
Also Called: Pts Vam Co
4424 W Sam Houston Pkwy N S (77041-8243)
PHONE................................281 821-5510
Eric Shuster, *President*
Kenneth Holloman, *Partner*
Cedric Lucquin, *General Mgr*
Didier Hornet, *Chairman*
Matthew Parr, *Business Mgr*
◆ EMP: 137
SQ FT: 201,000
SALES (est): 120MM
SALES (corp-wide): 5.9MM **Privately Held**
WEB: www.vam-usa.com
SIC: 3498 Tube fabricating (contract bending & shaping)
HQ: Vallourec Industries Inc
4424 W Sam Houston Pkwy N # 150
Houston TX 77041
281 821-5510

(G-12526)
VAN LONDON COMPANY (HQ)
Also Called: Van London-Phoenix Company
10540 Rockley Rd (77099-3545)
PHONE................................713 772-6641
Drew Hall, *CEO*
Ellen Van, *VP Sales*
Jared Melaas, *Sales Staff*
Van Phoenix, *Marketing Mgr*
Van D Chu, *Manager*
▲ EMP: 35
SQ FT: 10,000
SALES (est): 16.3MM
SALES (corp-wide): 28.3MM **Privately Held**
WEB: www.vl-pc.com
SIC: 3826 Thermal analysis instruments, laboratory type
PA: Alpha Measurement Solutions, Llc
10540 Rockley Rd
Houston TX 77099
832 456-4100

(G-12527)
VAN LONDON COMPANY INC
Also Called: Vatco
10540 Rockley Rd Ste 100 (77099-3530)
PHONE................................713 772-6641
Wilma Van London, *Ch of Bd*
Kurt Van London, *President*
Tom Williams, *Vice Pres*
EMP: 15 EST: 1961
SQ FT: 8,000
SALES (est): 2.7MM **Privately Held**
SIC: 3825 Instruments to measure electricity

(G-12528)
VANGUARD MACHINERY INTL LLC
3609 Clinton Dr (77020-6227)
PHONE................................713 462-5800
Jean Harris, *Mng Member*
▲ EMP: 12
SALES (est): 4.3MM **Privately Held**
WEB: www.vanguardmachinery.com
SIC: 3545 Machine tool accessories

(G-12529)
VANGUARD METAL TECHNOLOGIES
5737 Heffernan St (77087-4113)
PHONE....................................713 641-1859
Carl V Alexander, *President*
EMP: 30
SQ FT: 16,000
SALES (est): 3MM **Privately Held**
WEB: www.ssind.com
SIC: 3471 Electroplating of metals or formed products

(G-12530)
VANTACORE PARTNERS LLC (HQ)
1201 La St Ste 3400 (77002)
PHONE....................................215 751-1403
Colin Oerton, *CEO*
Perry Donahoo, *Partner*
EMP: 14
SALES (est): 21.5MM
SALES (corp-wide): 4.4MM **Privately Held**
WEB: www.nrplp.com
SIC: 1422 2951 1611 Crushed & broken limestone; asphalt & asphaltic paving mixtures (not from refineries); concrete construction: roads, highways, sidewalks, etc.
PA: Vantacore Intermediate Holding, Llc
1201 La St Ste 3400
Houston TX 77002
215 751-1403

(G-12531)
VANTAGE DRILLER I CO
777 Post Oak Blvd Ste 800 (77056-3215)
PHONE....................................281 404-4700
Christopher G Declaire, *Principal*
EMP: 50
SALES (est): 109K **Privately Held**
WEB: www.vantagedrilling.com
SIC: 1381 Drilling oil & gas wells

(G-12532)
VANTAGE DRILLING INTL INC (PA)
Also Called: VANTAGE DEEPWATER DRILLING
777 Post Oak Blvd Ste 800 (77056-3215)
PHONE....................................281 404-4700
Ihab Toma, *CEO*
Douglas W Halkett, *COO*
Christopher G Declaire, *Vice Pres*
Nicolas J Evanoff, *Vice Pres*
Linda Ibrahim, *Vice Pres*
◆ **EMP:** 23
SALES: 760.8MM **Privately Held**
WEB: www.vantagedrilling.com
SIC: 1381 Service well drilling

(G-12533)
VANTAGE ENERGY SERVICES INC
Also Called: Vantage Industries
777 Post Oak Blvd Ste 800 (77056-3215)
PHONE....................................281 404-4700
Paul A Bragg, *President*
Alessandro Marco, *CIO*
Marcelo D Guiscardo, *Director*
Jorge E Estrada M, *Director*
John C G O'Leary, *Director*
EMP: 30
SQ FT: 4,300
SALES (est): 5.5MM **Privately Held**
WEB: www.vantagedrilling.com
SIC: 1381 1382 Drilling oil & gas wells; oil & gas exploration services
PA: Vantage Drilling Company
C/O: Kpmg (Liquidator)
George Town GR CAYMAN

(G-12534)
VARCO LP (HQ)
Also Called: Tuboscope
2835 Holmes Rd (77051-1023)
P.O. Box 808 (77001-0808)
PHONE....................................713 799-5272
John F Lauletta, *Partner*
J F Maroney, *Partner*
Joseph C Winkler, *Partner*
Ronald Irvin, *Purch Mgr*
◆ **EMP:** 200
SQ FT: 460,000

SALES (est): 190.9MM
SALES (corp-wide): 8.4B **Publicly Held**
WEB: www.nov.com
SIC: 1389 3479 Testing, measuring, surveying & analysis services; pipe testing, oil field service; coating or wrapping steel pipe
PA: National Oilwell Varco, Inc.
7909 Parkwood Circle Dr
Houston TX 77036
713 346-7500

(G-12535)
VARCO SHAFFER INC
875 Lockwood Dr (77020-7917)
PHONE....................................713 672-1711
EMP: 40
SALES (corp-wide): 21.4B **Publicly Held**
SIC: 3599 3542 7692 Mfg Industrial Machinery Mfg Machine Tools-Forming Welding Repair
HQ: Varco Shaffer, Inc.
12950 W Little York Rd
Houston TX 77041
713 937-5000

(G-12536)
VARCO SHAFFER INC
12950 W Little York Rd (77041-4212)
PHONE....................................713 937-5000
Mark Merit, *President*
Lowell Stouder, *Vice Pres*
Daniel Molinaro, *Treasurer*
◆ **EMP:** 630
SQ FT: 400,000
SALES (est): 83.2MM
SALES (corp-wide): 8.4B **Publicly Held**
SIC: 3533 Oil field machinery & equipment
PA: National Oilwell Varco, Inc.
7909 Parkwood Circle Dr
Houston TX 77036
713 346-7500

(G-12537)
VAREL ENERGY SOLUTIONS (HQ)
Also Called: Varel Intl Enrgy Svcs Inc
4730 Consulate Plaza Dr # 190 (77032-2679)
PHONE....................................972 242-1160
Guillermo Aponte, *President*
Patrick Boivin, *VP Mfg*
Ernesto Guevara, *Prdtn Mgr*
Daniel Lozano, *Production*
Tony Beavers, *Engineer*
▲ **EMP:** 10
SALES (est): 710.3MM
SALES (corp-wide): 10.7B **Privately Held**
WEB: www.varelmining.com
SIC: 3545 1381 Drill bits, metalworking; drilling oil & gas wells
PA: Sandvik Ab
Hogbovagen 45
Sandviken 811 3
262 600-00

(G-12538)
VAREL INTERNATIONAL IND LLC (DH)
Also Called: Varel Energy Solutions
4730 Consulate Plaza Dr # 190 (77032-2679)
PHONE....................................281 272-6000
Thomas Seeney, *Regional Mgr*
Brad Takenaka, *Regional Mgr*
Suliman Makkawi, *District Mgr*
Chris Nicolson, *Area Mgr*
Pat A Neal, *Vice Pres*
◆ **EMP:** 89
SALES (est): 699MM
SALES (corp-wide): 10.7B **Privately Held**
WEB: www.varelintl.com
SIC: 1381 3545 Drilling water intake wells; drill bits, metalworking

(G-12539)
VASTAR RESOURCES INC
15375 Memorial Dr (77079-4138)
P.O. Box 3092 (77253-3092)
PHONE....................................281 584-6000
Chuck Davidson, *CEO*
EMP: 700
SALES (corp-wide): 278.4B **Privately Held**
SIC: 1311 Natural gas production

HQ: Vastar Resources, Inc.
501 Westlake Park Blvd
Houston TX

(G-12540)
VAX-IMMUNE LLC
3718 Sunset Blvd Ste 301 (77005-2030)
PHONE....................................832 423-0055
Leonard E Weisman, *Partner*
Joaquin Altenberg, *CFO*
EMP: 15
SALES (est): 182.9K **Privately Held**
WEB: www.vaximmune.com
SIC: 2836 5047 3841 2835 Biological products, except diagnostic; diagnostic equipment, medical; diagnostic apparatus, medical; microbiology & virology diagnostic products; veterinary diagnostic substances

(G-12541)
VCM INDUSTRIES INC
6202 Lumberdale Rd (77092-1316)
PHONE....................................713 462-7444
Alexander Maass, *President*
Robert Burkhardt, *Treasurer*
EMP: 55
SQ FT: 4,500
SALES (est): 5.7MM **Privately Held**
SIC: 3599 3494 Machine shop, jobbing & repair; valves & pipe fittings

(G-12542)
VECTOR GROUP INC
Also Called: Freudenberg Oil & Gas Tech
4301 S Pinemont Dr # 104 (77041-9377)
PHONE....................................713 979-4444
Malcolm Gore, *President*
EMP: 15
SALES (est): 2.5MM
SALES (corp-wide): 10.5B **Privately Held**
WEB: www.fogt.com
SIC: 8711 3494 Engineering services; valves & pipe fittings
HQ: Freudenberg Oil & Gas, Llc
10035 Brookriver Dr # 400
Houston TX 77040
281 233-1400

(G-12543)
VECTOR SEISMIC DATA PROCESSING (PA)
10001 Richmond Ave (77042-4205)
P.O. Box 351088, Westminster CO (80035-1088)
PHONE....................................303 571-1515
Mark Ziegler, *President*
Janice J Ziegler, *Corp Secy*
Jennifer McPhearson, *Manager*
Bryan Hineser, *Info Tech Mgr*
EMP: 17
SQ FT: 3,000
SALES (est): 2.4MM **Privately Held**
WEB: www.vector-seismic.com
SIC: 1382 Seismograph surveys

(G-12544)
VEEDER-ROOT FUELQUEST LLC
8 Greenway Plz Ste 300 (77046-1001)
PHONE....................................713 222-5700
EMP: 12
SALES (est): 1.4MM
SALES (corp-wide): 6.4B **Publicly Held**
WEB: www.fuelquest.com
SIC: 7372 7379 3714 Prepackaged software; computer related consulting services; fuel systems & parts, motor vehicle
HQ: Gilbarco Inc.
7300 W Friendly Ave
Greensboro NC 27410
336 547-5000

(G-12545)
VELOCITY PROMOTIONS LLC
Also Called: Rapid Wristbands
1100 Hercules Ave Ste 320 (77058-2760)
PHONE....................................800 523-8078
Christopher Schoen,
EMP: 9
SALES (est): 173.7K **Privately Held**
WEB: www.rapidwristbands.com
SIC: 2759 Screen printing

(G-12546)
VENETIAN BLIND FLR CVG SP LTD
Also Called: Carpet One
2504 Bissonnet St (77005-1424)
PHONE....................................713 528-2404
William Gaul, *CEO*
Tom Connell, *President*
John Carloss, *Vice Pres*
Matt Cavanaugh, *Sales Staff*
Martin Deleon, *Sales Staff*
EMP: 24 **EST:** 1952
SQ FT: 11,000
SALES (est): 5MM **Privately Held**
WEB: www.vbaf.com
SIC: 5719 1771 2426 5023 Venetian blinds; window shades; concrete work; hardwood dimension & flooring mills; home furnishings

(G-12547)
VENTIL USA INC
906 Gemini St (77058-2704)
PHONE....................................281 280-0141
Robert A Jaspers, *President*
Arthur G Baars, *Vice Pres*
Jeramy Dickson, *Opers Staff*
EMP: 12
SALES (est): 270.4K **Privately Held**
WEB: www.ventil-usa.com
SIC: 3823 Industrial instrmnts msrmnt display/control process variable

(G-12548)
VENTILATION SERVICE INC
Also Called: VSI
14723 Silver Sands St (77095-2822)
PHONE....................................713 683-1003
Fax: 713 683-1716
EMP: 17
SALES (est): 3.4MM **Privately Held**
SIC: 3444 Mfg Sheet Metalwork

(G-12549)
VERA BRADLEY INC
303 Memorial City Ste 303 # 303 (77024-2679)
PHONE....................................713 647-0323
EMP: 54
SALES (corp-wide): 495.2MM **Publicly Held**
WEB: www.verabradley.com
SIC: 3171 Women's handbags & purses
PA: Vera Bradley, Inc.
12420 Stonebridge Rd
Roanoke IN 46783
260 482-4673

(G-12550)
VERDUN OIL COMPANY LLC
55 Waugh Dr Ste 400 (77007-5839)
PHONE....................................713 554-4577
Tim Nein, *President*
Jason Lagrega, *COO*
Martin Perez, *Vice Pres*
Will Rider, *Vice Pres*
Zach Fellows, *Production*
EMP: 50
SALES (est): 314.5K **Privately Held**
WEB: www.verdunoilco.com
SIC: 1382 Oil & gas exploration services
PA: Encap Investments L.P.
1100 La St Ste 4900
Houston TX 77002

(G-12551)
VERE TECHNOLOGY LLC (PA)
4541 Brittmoore Rd (77041-8005)
PHONE....................................832 532-6745
Greg Hottle, *CEO*
▲ **EMP:** 30 **EST:** 2014
SALES (est): 5MM **Privately Held**
SIC: 3561 Pumps & pumping equipment

(G-12552)
VERIPOS (US) INC
15990 N Barkers (77079)
PHONE....................................281 966-7600
Rami Tadros, *General Mgr*
Stephen Browne, *Director*
Laura Butler, *Director*
Ian George Cobban, *Director*
Steven Williams, *Director*
EMP: 11
SQ FT: 6,000

SALES (est): 1.7MM **Privately Held**
WEB: www.veripos.com
SIC: 3663 Radio & TV communications equipment

(G-12553)
VEROPE USA INC
1101 Pleasantville Dr B (77029-3248)
PHONE..........................832 831-0132
Pierre Verreet, *President*
Chase Richter, *Sales Staff*
John Chappell, *Manager*
▲ **EMP:** 10
SALES (est): 5MM **Privately Held**
WEB: www.verope.com
SIC: 3496 Miscellaneous fabricated wire products

(G-12554)
VERSABAR INC (PA)
11349 Fm 529 Rd (77041-3207)
PHONE..........................713 937-3100
Jon Khachaturian, *President*
Dick H Piner Jr, *Corp Secy*
Martin Dworak, *Vice Pres*
Ian Todd, *Project Dir*
Connie Leblanc, *Project Mgr*
◆ **EMP:** 180
SALES (est): 61.6MM **Privately Held**
WEB: www.vbar.com
SIC: 7353 1389 Cranes & aerial lift equipment, rental or leasing; testing, measuring, surveying & analysis services

(G-12555)
VERTEC POLYMERS INC
6880 Wynnwood Ln (77008-5024)
PHONE..........................866 283-7832
Shawn Smith, *President*
Timothy Witt, *Opers Mgr*
▲ **EMP:** 14
SQ FT: 12,000
SALES (est): 3.1MM **Privately Held**
WEB: www.vertecpolymers.com
SIC: 2821 2822 Polymethyl methacrylate resins (plexiglass); ethylene-propylene rubbers, EPDM polymers

(G-12556)
VERTEX ENERGY INC (PA)
1331 Gemini St Ste 250 (77058-2764)
PHONE..........................866 660-8156
Benjamin P Cowart, *Ch of Bd*
John Strickland, *COO*
Alvaro Ruiz, *Vice Pres*
Greg Butler, *Project Mgr*
Chris Carlson, *CFO*
EMP: 30
SQ FT: 5,893
SALES: 163.3MM **Publicly Held**
WEB: www.vertexenergy.com
SIC: 2911 Petroleum refining

(G-12557)
VETCO GRAY LLC
Also Called: GE Oil & Gas
12221 N Huston Rosslyn Rd (77086-3216)
P.O. Box 2291 (77252-2291)
PHONE..........................281 445-8968
Donnie Willmann, *Branch Mgr*
EMP: 700
SQ FT: 149,850
SALES (corp-wide): 23.8B **Publicly Held**
WEB: www.ge.com
SIC: 3533 Oil field machinery & equipment
HQ: Vetco Gray, Llc
　　12221 N Huston Rosslyn Rd
　　Houston TX 77086
　　281 448-4410

(G-12558)
VETCO GRAY LLC (DH)
Also Called: GE Oil & Gas
12221 N Huston Rosslyn Rd (77086-3216)
P.O. Box 2291 (77252-2291)
PHONE..........................281 448-4410
Claudi Santiago, *President*
Sam Aquillano, *Vice Pres*
Johnny Hernandez, *Info Tech Dir*
◆ **EMP:** 30
SQ FT: 293,000
SALES (est): 827.5MM
SALES (corp-wide): 23.8B **Publicly Held**
WEB: www.ge.com
SIC: 3533 Oil field machinery & equipment

HQ: Nuovo Pignone International Srl
　　Via Felice Matteucci 2
　　Firenze FI 50127
　　055 423-211

(G-12559)
VEXA PAK LLC
6902 Palestine St A (77020-7528)
PHONE..........................713 671-1100
Antonio Gonzales, *Mng Member*
◆ **EMP:** 12
SQ FT: 25,000
SALES (est): 3.1MM **Privately Held**
WEB: www.vexapak.com
SIC: 2992 Lubricating oils & greases

(G-12560)
VFL ENERGY TECHNOLOGIES INC
12431 Taylor Rd (77041-1229)
PHONE..........................713 466-9883
Louis P Vickio Jr, *CEO*
Antonio Caruso, *General Mgr*
Mary B Vickio, *Vice Pres*
Eddie Vickio, *Electrical Engi*
Russell Reed, *Marketing Staff*
EMP: 11 **EST:** 1998
SQ FT: 2,200
SALES (est): 3.2MM **Privately Held**
WEB: www.vflet.com
SIC: 1389 Oil field services; measurement of well flow rates, oil & gas

(G-12561)
VFUELS LLC
12221 Fm 529 Rd (77041-2805)
PHONE..........................713 456-3443
Matt Miller, *Project Mgr*
Souheil Abboud,
EMP: 10 **EST:** 2013
SQ FT: 45,000
SALES (est): 2.3MM **Privately Held**
WEB: www.vfuels.com
SIC: 3533 Oil & gas field machinery

(G-12562)
VGCM LLC
Also Called: Houston Yard
14047 Industrial Rd (77015-6826)
PHONE..........................713 455-1465
David Louis, *Manager*
EMP: 12 **Publicly Held**
WEB:
　　www.houstonlawnmowingservice.com
SIC: 1411 Dimension stone
HQ: Vgcm, Llc
　　1200 Urban Center Dr
　　Vestavia AL 35242

(G-12563)
VIBRATION MANAGEMENT CORP
5930 Thomas Rd (77041-4905)
PHONE..........................713 983-8462
Ashish Tripathi, *President*
Vijay K Tripathi, *President*
Lycongthuan Lee, *Accountant*
Meena Tripathi, *Shareholder*
▲ **EMP:** 25
SQ FT: 2,500
SALES (est): 29.9MM **Privately Held**
WEB: www.vimco.biz
SIC: 3625 Noise control equipment

(G-12564)
VICKERY STREET FABRICATORS INC
Also Called: Troubleshooters, The
4525 Saunders Rd (77093-5030)
P.O. Box 421485 (77242-1485)
PHONE..........................713 695-9195
Scott Cote, *Principal*
EMP: 32
SQ FT: 40,000
SALES (est): 10.8MM **Privately Held**
WEB: www.tshooters.net
SIC: 3441 1799 Fabricated structural metal; ornamental metal work

(G-12565)
VICTAULIC-BERMAD LLC
9424 W Little York Rd (77040-3316)
PHONE..........................713 856-1700
Nadav Yakir, *CEO*
Tiffannie Daniels, *Opers Staff*

Rami Levkovich, *Engineer*
Nancy Xie, *Finance*
Leah Marossie, *Sales Staff*
▲ **EMP:** 20 **EST:** 2015
SALES (est): 1.7MM
SALES (corp-wide): 69MM **Privately Held**
WEB: www.vbtech.com
SIC: 3491 Industrial valves
PA: Bermad Cs Ltd.
　　Kibbutz
　　Evron 22808
　　498 553-11

(G-12566)
VICTOR NICOLLE INC
Also Called: Real Estate Invstmnts/Vni Prpt
15255 Vntage Prsrve Pkwy (77070-2199)
PHONE..........................713 896-4911
Victor Martinez, *President*
EMP: 11
SALES (est): 675.7K **Privately Held**
SIC: 7389 3533 6531 8742 Inspection & testing services; oil & gas field machinery; real estate agent, commercial; real estate consultant

(G-12567)
VICTORIOUS MUSIC CO
11811i 10th St Ste 330 (77044-6255)
PHONE..........................713 450-3306
Rod Jackson, *Owner*
EMP: 14 **EST:** 2001
SALES (est): 424.5K **Privately Held**
WEB: www.sanjacintomusic.com
SIC: 8299 3931 Musical instrument lessons; musical instruments

(G-12568)
VILLPAC INC
Also Called: Triangel Food
1101 Mercury Dr (77029-2005)
P.O. Box 210, League City (77574-0210)
PHONE..........................713 672-1255
John Merchant, *President*
Lu Anne Merchant, *Senior VP*
EMP: 11
SQ FT: 4,000
SALES (est): 1.2MM **Privately Held**
WEB: www.villpac.com
SIC: 2499 Food handling & processing products, wood

(G-12569)
VINH HO MACHINE SHOP INC
Also Called: Spinning Wheel Shop
4941 Gessner Rd (77041-7807)
PHONE..........................713 896-7828
Vinh Ho, *President*
EMP: 10
SQ FT: 10,500
SALES (est): 1.4MM **Privately Held**
SIC: 3599 Machine shop, jobbing & repair

(G-12570)
VIPER DRILLING INTERNATIONAL
8524 Highway 6 N Ste 478 (77095-2103)
P.O. Box 460068, San Antonio (78246-0068)
PHONE..........................832 917-5804
Mark Harbert,
Howard Gaddis,
Robert Grove,
Rhonda Mills,
EMP: 99 **EST:** 2013
SALES (est): 3.1MM **Privately Held**
SIC: 1389 Oil field services

(G-12571)
VISIONMONITOR SOFTWARE LLC (PA)
11451 Katy Fwy Ste 510 (77079-2021)
PHONE..........................713 935-0500
Suma Chackola, *Project Mgr*
Bryan Guilliams, *Software Dev*
T Mantor,
Alan Smith,
EMP: 12
SQ FT: 3,200
SALES (est): 2MM **Privately Held**
WEB: www.visionmonitor.com
SIC: 7372 Prepackaged software

(G-12572)
VISON TECH PRODUCTS LLC
6464 Cunningham Rd (77041-4714)
PHONE..........................832 850-6085
Son Le, *President*
Lisa Nunn, *Purchasing*
EMP: 12
SALES (est): 1.8MM **Privately Held**
WEB: www.visontechproducts.com
SIC: 3272 Dry mixture concrete

(G-12573)
VISTA CNTRS & CLOSURES LLC
4003 Leeland St (77023-3011)
PHONE..........................713 609-9250
Cathy Teng, *Treasurer*
Peter Bennett, *Mng Member*
Patrick Gwen, *Director*
◆ **EMP:** 13
SALES (est): 2.8MM **Privately Held**
WEB: www.vistacontainers.net
SIC: 3089 Caps, plastic

(G-12574)
VISUAL COMFORT OF AMERICA LLC
Also Called: Visual Comfort & Co.
22400 Nw Lake Dr (77095-5204)
PHONE..........................713 686-5999
Andy Singer, *President*
Meredith Welsh, *President*
Charles Neal, *Vice Pres*
Ronnie Moseley, *Warehouse Mgr*
Mehdi Benhayoun, *Production*
◆ **EMP:** 95
SQ FT: 26,000
SALES (est): 37.6MM **Privately Held**
WEB: www.visualcomfort.com
SIC: 3645 Desk lamps; floor lamps; table lamps; wall lamps

(G-12575)
VITA INTERNATIONAL INC
12050 Proctor St (77038-2706)
PHONE..........................281 591-1300
Khaled Shaaban, *President*
Zachary Shaaban, *President*
Lisa A Shaaban, *Corp Secy*
Ashraf Benshaaban, *Vice Pres*
McClanahan Wally, *Vice Pres*
EMP: 27
SQ FT: 16,000
SALES (est): 9.2MM **Privately Held**
WEB: www.vitainternational.com
SIC: 3533 Oil field machinery & equipment

(G-12576)
VITOL AMERICAS CORP (DH)
2925 Richmond Ave Ste 11 (77098-3138)
PHONE..........................713 230-1000
William James Randall, *CEO*
Robert Di Padova, *Human Resources*
◆ **EMP:** 83
SQ FT: 10,000
SALES (est): 1.5B
SALES (corp-wide): 7.4MM **Privately Held**
WEB: www.barnesandnoble.com
SIC: 1311 Crude petroleum & natural gas production; natural gas production
HQ: Vitol Us Holding Co.
　　2925 Richmond Ave Ste 11
　　Houston TX 77098
　　713 230-1000

(G-12577)
VITZROCELLUSA INC
10804 Fallstone Rd # 200 (77099-3469)
PHONE..........................832 850-7095
Seung Kook Jang, *President*
Andrew Kim, *Vice Pres*
Ji Park, *Opers Mgr*
Joey Kim, *Sales Mgr*
Kevin Yoon, *Sales Mgr*
EMP: 10
SALES (est): 389.6K **Privately Held**
WEB: www.vitzrocellusa.com
SIC: 3691 Alkaline cell storage batteries

(G-12578)
VIXXO CORPORATION
4801 Woodway Dr Ste 160w (77056-1641)
PHONE..........................713 977-7900
EMP: 218

▲ = Import ▼ = Export
◆ = Import/Export

SALES (corp-wide): 127.3MM **Privately Held**
WEB: www.vixxo.com
SIC: 3993 Signs & advertising specialties
PA: Vixxo Corporation
7000 E Shea Blvd Ste 1970
Scottsdale AZ 85254
480 614-4559

(G-12579)
VMG WELDING
5035 Jefferson St (77023-1914)
PHONE.................................832 605-3933
Victor M Guerrero, *Partner*
EMP: 10
SALES (est): 208.8K **Privately Held**
SIC: 7692 Welding repair

(G-12580)
VOICE MEDIA GROUP INC
Also Called: Houston Press
2603 La Branch St (77004-1136)
PHONE.................................713 280-2400
Danielle McCormick, *Opers Staff*
Jessica Risley, *Opers Staff*
Margaret Downing, *Branch Mgr*
Joshua Brettschneider, *Manager*
Amber Martinez, *Technology*
EMP: 85
SALES (corp-wide): 241.4MM **Privately Held**
WEB: www.voicemediagroup.com
SIC: 2711 7922 Newspapers: publishing only, not printed on site; theatrical producers & services
PA: Voice Media Group, Inc.
969 N Broadway
Denver CO 80203
303 296-7744

(G-12581)
VOLTA LLC
1616 Gears Rd (77067-4106)
PHONE.................................832 369-2420
James Pixley, *Mfg Mgr*
Bradley Davis, *Mng Member*
Brad Davis, *Mng Member*
Julio Parpacen,
▲ EMP: 105
SQ FT: 40,500
SALES: 70.9MM **Privately Held**
WEB: www.volta-us.com
SIC: 3613 Time switches, electrical switchgear apparatus

(G-12582)
VULCAN INDUSTRIAL HOLDINGS LLC (PA)
1990 Post Oak Blvd # 2400 (77056-3818)
PHONE.................................715 294-3200
Mike Krump,
EMP: 12
SALES (est): 5.1MM **Privately Held**
WEB: www.vulcanindustrial.com
SIC: 3532 Mining machinery

(G-12583)
VULCAN MATERIALS COMPANY
6505 Homestead Rd (77028-5043)
PHONE.................................713 631-7200
David Corso, *Sales Staff*
Anthony Flores, *Branch Mgr*
EMP: 17 **Publicly Held**
WEB: www.vulcanmaterials.com
SIC: 3273 Ready-mixed concrete
PA: Vulcan Materials Company
1200 Urban Center Dr
Vestavia AL 35242

(G-12584)
W B MASON CO INC
8518 W Little York Rd (77040-4124)
PHONE.................................888 926-2766
EMP: 40
SALES (corp-wide): 1B **Privately Held**
WEB: www.wbmason.com
SIC: 5943 5712 2752 Office forms & supplies; office furniture; commercial printing, lithographic
PA: W. B. Mason Co., Inc.
59 Ctr St
Brockton MA 02301
508 586-3434

(G-12585)
W M GREENS CONSTRUCTION SVCS
611 Cravens St (77076-5115)
PHONE.................................713 692-2291
Michael D Green, *President*
Tim Green, *Manager*
EMP: 30
SALES (est): 5MM **Privately Held**
SIC: 1389 Construction, repair & dismantling services

(G-12586)
W R GRACE & CO-CONN
Also Called: W R Grace Construction Pdts
4323 Crites St (77003-1311)
PHONE.................................713 223-8353
Stephen Day, *Branch Mgr*
EMP: 20
SALES (corp-wide): 1.9B **Publicly Held**
WEB: www.grace.com
SIC: 3531 Bituminous, cement & concrete related products & equipment
HQ: W. R. Grace & Co.-Conn.
7500 Grace Dr
Columbia MD 21044

(G-12587)
W R GRACE & CO-CONN
Also Called: W R Grace Davison Chemical Div
4750 Blaffer St (77026-3103)
PHONE.................................713 675-6445
Rodrik Emaneul, *Manager*
EMP: 14
SALES (corp-wide): 1.9B **Publicly Held**
WEB: www.grace.com
SIC: 2891 Adhesives & sealants
HQ: W. R. Grace & Co.-Conn.
7500 Grace Dr
Columbia MD 21044

(G-12588)
W&T OFFSHORE INC (PA)
5718 Westheimer Rd # 700 (77057-5785)
PHONE.................................713 626-8525
Tracy W Krohn, *Ch of Bd*
Jay Hachen, *General Mgr*
Sharon Rodgers, *Counsel*
David M Bump, *Exec VP*
David Bump, *Exec VP*
EMP: 123
SALES (est): 534.9MM **Publicly Held**
WEB: www.wtoffshore.com
SIC: 1311 1321 Crude petroleum & natural gas; crude petroleum & natural gas production; crude petroleum production; natural gas production; natural gas liquids

(G-12589)
W-INDUSTRIES OF LOUISIANA
6602 Petropark Dr (77041-4922)
PHONE.................................281 921-3067
EMP: 12
SALES (corp-wide): 23.7MM **Privately Held**
WEB: www.w-industries.com
SIC: 3823 Controllers for process variables, all types
PA: W-Industries Of Louisiana
11500 Charles Rd
Jersey Village TX 77041
713 466-9463

(G-12590)
WABTEC CORPORATION
Also Called: Wabtec Global Services
7402 Eastex Fwy (77093-8826)
PHONE.................................713 222-0792
Chad Taylor, *Branch Mgr*
EMP: 60 **Publicly Held**
WEB: www.wabtec.com
SIC: 3743 Railroad equipment
HQ: Wabtec Corporation
30 Isabella St
Pittsburgh PA 15212

(G-12591)
WACHS SUBSEA LLC
15331 Vantage Pkwy E (77032-1939)
PHONE.................................713 983-0784
Tim Sheehan, *Vice Pres*
David Lai, *Director*
▼ EMP: 20 EST: 2007

SALES (est): 3.8MM **Privately Held**
WEB: www.ehwachs.com
SIC: 3498 Tube fabricating (contract bending & shaping)

(G-12592)
WADDINGTON N AMER - HOUSTON
14345 Nw Fwy (77040-4927)
PHONE.................................713 686-6700
Sajjad Ebrahim, *President*
Mike Evans, *Principal*
Dominic Didomizio, *Vice Pres*
Ali Ebrahim, *Vice Pres*
Peter Tedesco, *Vice Pres*
▲ EMP: 65
SQ FT: 60,000
SALES (est): 12.5MM
SALES (corp-wide): 3.3B **Publicly Held**
WEB: www.thewaddingtongroup.com
SIC: 3089 Injection molding of plastics
HQ: Waddington North America, Inc.
50 E Rver Ctr Blvd Ste 65
Covington KY 41011

(G-12593)
WAGNER PLATE WORKS LLC (PA)
6250 N Rosslyn Rd (77091)
P.O. Box 9756, Tulsa OK (74157-0756)
PHONE.................................713 462-1946
Eric Wagner,
John Peters,
EMP: 35
SALES (est): 7.6MM **Privately Held**
WEB: www.wagnerplateworks.com
SIC: 3443 3444 Plate work for the metalworking trade; sheet metalwork

(G-12594)
WALKER INDUSTRIAL MACHINING
4949 W Orem Dr Ofc (77045-4163)
PHONE.................................713 434-5000
Robert A Walker Sr, *President*
Marie Walker, *Admin Sec*
EMP: 10
SQ FT: 10,000
SALES (est): 801.3K **Privately Held**
WEB: www.walkerindustrial.com
SIC: 3599 Machine shop, jobbing & repair

(G-12595)
WALKUP COMPANY
5945 Armour Dr (77020-8193)
PHONE.................................713 675-6383
William E Walkup Jr, *President*
Oliver S Walkup, *Corp Secy*
Laura Roberts, *Vice Pres*
Raymond B Walkup, *Vice Pres*
Raymond Walkup, *Vice Pres*
EMP: 55 EST: 1944
SQ FT: 55,000
SALES (est): 12.2MM **Privately Held**
WEB: www.walkupco.com
SIC: 3443 3441 Fabricated plate work (boiler shop); fabricated structural metal

(G-12596)
WALMING INC
9530 Baythorne Dr (77041-7712)
PHONE.................................713 690-9000
Ramy Law, *President*
Binh Ly, *Vice Pres*
EMP: 30
SQ FT: 18,000
SALES (est): 3.6MM **Privately Held**
SIC: 2673 Plastic bags: made from purchased materials

(G-12597)
WALTER OIL & GAS CORPORATION
Also Called: Walter Oil & Gas Weather Data
1100 Louisiana St Ste 200 (77002-5299)
PHONE.................................713 659-1221
J C Walter III, *Ch of Bd*
Wayne Holmes, *Superintendent*
Lulu G Galmiche, *Vice Pres*
C James Looke, *Vice Pres*
Walter A Sparks, *Vice Pres*
▼ EMP: 50
SQ FT: 23,000

SALES (est): 57.6MM **Privately Held**
WEB: www.walteroil.com
SIC: 1382 1311 Oil & gas exploration services; crude petroleum production; natural gas production

(G-12598)
WAPITI OPERATING LLC (PA)
Also Called: Wapiti Energy
800 Gessner Rd Ste 700 (77024-4284)
PHONE.................................713 365-8500
Richard Agee, *CEO*
Richard E Agee, *Ch of Bd*
Bart Agee, *President*
Garret Holt, *COO*
John H Karnes, *CFO*
EMP: 82
SALES (est): 11.4MM **Privately Held**
WEB: www.wapitienergy.com
SIC: 1382 1311 Oil & gas exploration services; crude petroleum & natural gas

(G-12599)
WAREING ATHON & CO
2229 San Felipe St (77019-5644)
PHONE.................................713 222-8804
Peter S Wareing, *Partner*
Merrell Athon, *Partner*
EMP: 400
SQ FT: 2,500
SALES (est): 30.9MM **Privately Held**
SIC: 3272 4513 4225 Concrete stuctural support & building material; air courier services; general warehousing

(G-12600)
WARTSILA NORTH AMERICA INC (HQ)
11710 N Gessner Rd Ste A (77064-1325)
PHONE.................................281 233-6200
Stefan Wiik, *Ch of Bd*
Aaron Bresnahan, *President*
Shelledy Dan, *Business Mgr*
Mark Kennedy, *Business Mgr*
Ryan Kennedy, *Business Mgr*
◆ EMP: 151
SQ FT: 89,000
SALES (est): 279.5MM
SALES (corp-wide): 5.7B **Privately Held**
WEB: www.wartsila.com
SIC: 1629 5084 1382 4789 Power plant construction; engines & parts, diesel; aerial geophysical exploration oil & gas; cargo loading & unloading services; offshore supply boats, building & repairing
PA: Wartsila Öyj Abp
Hiililaiturinkuja 2
Helsinki 00180
107 090-000

(G-12601)
WATER ENERGY TECHNOLOGIES
Also Called: Wet
9741 Tappenbeck Dr (77055-4101)
PHONE.................................713 464-7117
James R Beddingfield, *President*
▼ EMP: 12
SALES (est): 4.5MM **Privately Held**
WEB: www.waterenergy.com
SIC: 3589 Water treatment equipment, industrial

(G-12602)
WATER STANDARD MGT US INC (HQ)
4265 San Felipe St # 620 (77027-2941)
PHONE.................................713 400-4777
Amanda Brock, *CEO*
Paul Choules, *Senior VP*
Lisa Henthorne, *Senior VP*
Jim Wodehouse, *Senior VP*
Andrea Hayden, *Vice Pres*
EMP: 35
SQ FT: 12,000
SALES (est): 9.3MM **Privately Held**
WEB: www.waterstandard.com
SIC: 3589 Water treatment equipment, industrial

(G-12603)
WATER STD SPRATION SYSTEMS LLC
Also Called: Monarch Separators
5410 Trafalgar Dr (77045-6034)
PHONE....................................713 433-7441
Kirk Wagner, *President*
EMP: 12
SALES (est): 510.6K **Privately Held**
WEB: www.waterstandard.com
SIC: 3589 Water treatment equipment, industrial
HQ: Water Standard Management (Us), Inc.
4265 San Felipe St # 620
Houston TX 77027

(G-12604)
WATERFORD OPERATING LLC
3555 Timmons Ln Ste 1115 (77027-6449)
PHONE....................................713 255-6200
EMP: 12
SQ FT: 13,000
SALES (est): 535.2K **Privately Held**
SIC: 1382 Oil/Gas Exploration Services

(G-12605)
WATSON GRINDING AND MFG CO
4525 Gessner Rd (77041-8837)
P.O. Box 800426 (77280-0426)
PHONE....................................713 466-3053
John M Watson, *President*
Robert White, *COO*
Kelly L Watson, *Vice Pres*
Jason White, *Vice Pres*
Robert L White, *Vice Pres*
▲ EMP: 100
SQ FT: 28,000
SALES (est): 58.6MM **Privately Held**
WEB: www.watsongrinding.com
SIC: 3533 3599 Oil & gas field machinery; machine shop, jobbing & repair

(G-12606)
WATTS WATER TECHNOLOGIES INC
Also Called: Watts Industries Houston
8550 Hansen Rd (77075-1006)
PHONE....................................713 943-0688
Bill Toomey, *Vice Pres*
Betty Garland, *Finance Mgr*
Mike York, *Manager*
Wayne Adcock, *Technical Staff*
Paul Bothner, *Director*
EMP: 100
SALES (corp-wide): 1.6B **Publicly Held**
WEB: www.watts.com
SIC: 3491 3625 3494 Valves, automatic control; relays & industrial controls; valves & pipe fittings
PA: Watts Water Technologies, Inc.
815 Chestnut St
North Andover MA 01845
978 688-1811

(G-12607)
WAUKESHA-PEARCE INDUSTRIES LLC (HQ)
Also Called: Waukesha-Pearce Industries Inc
12320 Main St (77035-6206)
P.O. Box 35068 (77235-5068)
PHONE....................................713 723-1050
Al H Bentley, *CEO*
Laurie Leshin, *President*
Louis M Pearce III, *President*
James Berumen, *District Mgr*
Alex Maldonado, *District Mgr*
◆ EMP: 300 EST: 1925
SQ FT: 200,000
SALES (est): 312.3MM
SALES (corp-wide): 396MM **Privately Held**
WEB: www.wpi.com
SIC: 5084 5082 3621 Engines, gasoline; general construction machinery & equipment; generators & sets, electric
PA: Pearce Industries, Inc.
12320 Main St
Houston TX 77035
713 723-1050

(G-12608)
WAYNE WILK
8807 W Sam Houston Pkwy N S (77040-5346)
PHONE....................................570 326-1164
Charles E Jones, *Principal*
Marcia Krause, *Sales Staff*
Tyra Larson, *Sales Staff*
Will Wissman, *Sales Staff*
Robert Holifield, *Manager*
▼ EMP: 50
SALES (est): 57.1K **Publicly Held**
WEB: www.f-e-t.com
SIC: 3533 Oil field machinery & equipment
PA: Forum Energy Technologies, Inc.
10344 Sam Houston Park Dr # 300
Houston TX 77064

(G-12609)
WEARABLES ETC INC
Also Called: Wearable Etc
8130 Westglen Dr Ste 100 (77063-6330)
PHONE....................................713 339-1373
Arnvid Froystein, *President*
EMP: 12
SQ FT: 3,500
SALES (est): 1.2MM **Privately Held**
WEB: www.diecastairplanes.com
SIC: 2395 Embroidery products, except schiffli machine

(G-12610)
WEARALLOY INC
Also Called: Blue Creek Foundry
1313 Lombardy St (77023-3534)
PHONE....................................979 543-1133
Mark Hanson, *President*
Ruth Hanson, *Vice Pres*
Thomas Stavena, *Facilities Mgr*
EMP: 20
SALES (est): 3MM **Privately Held**
WEB: www.bluecreekfoundry.com
SIC: 3366 Copper foundries

(G-12611)
WEATHERFORD ARTIFICIA (DH)
2000 Saint James Pl (77056-4123)
P.O. Box 27608 (77227-7608)
PHONE....................................713 836-4000
Rex Wilson, *Mng Member*
Joseph C Henry,
Keith R Morley,
◆ EMP: 120
SALES (est): 269MM **Privately Held**
WEB: www.weatherford.com
SIC: 3561 5084 Pumps, oil well & field; pumps & pumping equipment
HQ: Weatherford International, Llc
2000 Saint James Pl
Houston TX 77056
713 693-4000

(G-12612)
WEATHERFORD INTERNATIONAL LLC
Weatherford Products
12227 Fm 529 Rd Ste A (77041-2811)
PHONE....................................281 652-1300
Elina Kozlova, *Human Res Mgr*
Jake Mallet, *Branch Mgr*
Bobby Jarrett, *Technical Staff*
EMP: 27
SQ FT: 30,000 **Privately Held**
WEB: www.weatherford.com
SIC: 1389 Oil field services
HQ: Weatherford International, Llc
2000 Saint James Pl
Houston TX 77056
713 693-4000

(G-12613)
WEATHERFORD INTERNATIONAL LLC (HQ)
2000 Saint James Pl (77056-4123)
P.O. Box 27608 (77227-7608)
PHONE....................................713 693-4000
Lance R Marklinger, *President*
Alex Garcia, *District Mgr*
Josh Pitts, *District Mgr*
Bart Roberts, *District Mgr*
Jim Hollingsworth, *Business Mgr*
◆ EMP: 800 EST: 1980
SALES (est): 8.3B **Privately Held**
WEB: www.weatherford.com
SIC: 1389 Oil field services

(G-12614)
WEATHERFORD INTERNATIONAL LLC
738 Highway 6 S (77079-4015)
PHONE....................................281 759-5100
EMP: 23 **Privately Held**
WEB: www.weatherford.com
SIC: 1389 Construction, repair & dismantling services
HQ: Weatherford International, Llc
2000 Saint James Pl
Houston TX 77056
713 693-4000

(G-12615)
WEATHERFORD INTERNATIONAL LLC
12227 Spencer Rd (77041-2800)
PHONE....................................832 955-0000
EMP: 44 **Privately Held**
WEB: www.weatherford.com
SIC: 1389 Oil field services
HQ: Weatherford International, Llc
2000 Saint James Pl
Houston TX 77056
713 693-4000

(G-12616)
WEATHERFORD INTERNATIONAL LLC
Also Called: Weatherford Completion
9600 W Gulf Bank Rd (77040-3112)
PHONE....................................832 590-4000
Anthony Machala, *Engineer*
George Duncan, *Branch Mgr*
John Sellers, *Manager*
EMP: 26 **Privately Held**
WEB: www.weatherford.com
SIC: 1389 Oil field services
HQ: Weatherford International, Llc
2000 Saint James Pl
Houston TX 77056
713 693-4000

(G-12617)
WEATHERFORD INTERNATIONAL LLC
16134 W Hardy Rd (77060-1663)
PHONE....................................281 260-5700
Russ Beall, *Branch Mgr*
EMP: 20 **Privately Held**
WEB: www.weatherford.com
SIC: 1389 Oil field services
HQ: Weatherford International, Llc
2000 Saint James Pl
Houston TX 77056
713 693-4000

(G-12618)
WEATHERFORD INTERNATIONAL LLC
2442 Greens Rd (77032-1332)
PHONE....................................281 460-7863
◆ EMP: 9 **Privately Held**
WEB: www.weatherford.com
SIC: 1389 Oil field services
HQ: Weatherford International, Llc
2000 Saint James Pl
Houston TX 77056
713 693-4000

(G-12619)
WEATHERFORD INTERNATIONAL LLC
16210 W Hardy Rd (77060-1664)
PHONE....................................281 260-2707
Greg Hardy, *Project Mgr*
James Ellinwood, *Mfg Staff*
John Clegg, *Research*
Chris Yarbrough, *Engineer*
Brian Aspelin, *Technician*
EMP: 125 **Privately Held**
WEB: www.weatherford.com
SIC: 1389 Oil field services
HQ: Weatherford International, Llc
2000 Saint James Pl
Houston TX 77056
713 693-4000

(G-12620)
WEATHERFORD INTERNATIONAL INC (PA)
2000 Saint James Pl (77056-4123)
PHONE....................................713 836-4000
EMP: 9
SALES (est): 8.4MM **Privately Held**
SIC: 1381 Oil/Gas Well Drilling

(G-12621)
WEATHERFORD INTERNATIONAL LTD
Also Called: WEATHERFORD ARTIFICIAL LIFT SY
2000 Saint James Pl (77056-4123)
PHONE....................................713 836-4000
Bernard Durorc-Dannard, *CEO*
Marc Clark, *District Mgr*
Mitchell Elliott, *District Mgr*
Anthony McGuirk, *District Mgr*
Thomas Reed, *District Mgr*
EMP: 45
SALES (est): 1.3MM **Privately Held**
WEB: www.weatherford.com
SIC: 1381 Service well drilling

(G-12622)
WEATHERFORD WELL SCREEN TECHNO
11939 Aldine Westfield Rd (77093-1001)
PHONE....................................281 670-0005
EMP: 10
SALES (est): 102.9K **Privately Held**
SIC: 3999 Atomizers, toiletry

(G-12623)
WEATHRFORD ARTFL LIFT SYSTEMS
5611 Baird Ct (77041-2035)
PHONE....................................281 630-5919
EMP: 11 **Privately Held**
WEB: www.weatherford.com
SIC: 3842 Limbs, artificial
HQ: Weatherford Artificial Lift Systems, Llc
2000 Saint James Pl
Houston TX 77056
713 836-4000

(G-12624)
WEDGE MEASUREMENT & CONTROL LP
1415 La St Ste 1500 (77002)
PHONE....................................713 490-9555
EMP: 196
SALES (est): 2.8MM
SALES (corp-wide): 1.1B **Privately Held**
SIC: 1389 Oil And Gas Field Services, Nec, Nsk
PA: Wedge Group Incorporated
1415 La St Ste 3000
Houston TX 77002
713 739-6500

(G-12625)
WEDGE MEASUREMENT SYSTEMS LLC (HQ)
Also Called: Wedge M & C Services
1415 La St Ste 1500 (77002)
PHONE....................................713 490-9444
Thomas D Cathey, *President*
Gregory J Armstrong, *Vice Pres*
Nishith H Patel, *Vice Pres*
Richard J Reese, *Admin Sec*
EMP: 150
SALES (est): 108.6MM
SALES (corp-wide): 1.1B **Privately Held**
WEB: www.wedgegroup.com
SIC: 1389 Measurement of well flow rates, oil & gas
PA: Wedge Group Incorporated
1415 La St Ste 3000
Houston TX 77002
713 739-6500

(G-12626)
WEI-CHUAN USA INC
7439 Langtry St (77040-6635)
PHONE....................................713 690-3677
Stephen Chen, *Branch Mgr*
EMP: 15
SQ FT: 32,346
SALES (corp-wide): 116.9MM **Privately Held**
WEB: www.weichuanusa.com
SIC: 2038 5142 Frozen specialties; packaged frozen goods
PA: Wei-Chuan U.S.A., Inc.
13031 Temple Ave
City Of Industry CA 91746
626 225-7168

▲ = Import ▼ =Export
◆ =Import/Export

(G-12627)
WELBOR TECHNOLOGY INC
15045 Woodham Dr (77073-6024)
PHONE..................................713 980-2345
John Birckhead, *President*
Chris Mayeu, *Vice Pres*
Andrew Kragas, *Engineer*
EMP: 13
SQ FT: 16,000
SALES (est): 5.3MM **Privately Held**
WEB: www.welbor.com
SIC: 5113 5063 3824 8711 Shipping supplies; electrical apparatus & equipment; mechanical & electromechanical counters & devices; engineering services; design services

(G-12628)
WELDFIT CORPORATION
Also Called: Gulf Coast Welding
4133 Southerland Rd (77092-4416)
PHONE..................................713 460-3700
Steven Maddan, *CEO*
Willie Kubeczka, *President*
Mary Ann Kubeczka, *Principal*
Matt Rahimi, *Business Mgr*
Corey Reynolds, *Foreman/Supr*
▲ **EMP:** 180
SQ FT: 30,000
SALES (est): 28.4MM **Privately Held**
WEB: www.weldfit.com
SIC: 3599 7692 3444 Machine shop, jobbing & repair; welding repair; sheet metalwork

(G-12629)
WELDING MATERIAL SALES INC
8811 Wallisville Rd Ste C (77029-1338)
PHONE..................................713 672-4166
Kelly Gaspard, *Manager*
EMP: 11
SALES (corp-wide): 17MM **Privately Held**
WEB: www.weldingmaterialsales.com
SIC: 7692 Welding repair
PA: Welding Material Sales, Inc.
1340 Reed Rd
Geneva IL 60134
630 232-6421

(G-12630)
WELDING OUTLETS INC
Also Called: W O I
1341 Hill Rd (77039-5118)
PHONE..................................281 590-0190
EMP: 82
SALES (est): 9.6MM **Privately Held**
WEB: www.woihouston.com
SIC: 3317 3678 3498 Welded pipe & tubes; electronic connectors; fabricated pipe & fittings

(G-12631)
WELLDYNAMICS INC (HQ)
3000 N Sam Houston Pkwy E (77032-3219)
PHONE..................................281 297-1211
Jeffrey Allen Miller, *President*
Erick Morrell, *Production*
Bob Gissler, *Engineer*
Paul James, *Engineer*
Colton Puckett, *Project Engr*
◆ **EMP:** 32
SALES (est): 4.6MM
SALES (corp-wide): 1.9MM **Privately Held**
WEB: www.halliburton.com
SIC: 1389 Oil field services

(G-12632)
WELLS MANUFACTURING LLC
Also Called: Wells Mfg
14425 Wagg Way Houston (77041)
PHONE..................................713 690-4204
Patsy A Wells, *CEO*
James T Wells, *COO*
John A Wells, *Vice Pres*
John Wells, *Engineer*
EMP: 24
SQ FT: 25,000
SALES (est): 4.7MM **Privately Held**
WEB: www.wells-mfg.net
SIC: 3541 3599 Machine tools, metal cutting type; machine & other job shop work; machine shop, jobbing & repair

(G-12633)
WELLSTREAM INC (PA)
Also Called: Prime Flexible Products
11202 Equity Dr Ste 350 (77041-8220)
PHONE..................................281 249-0900
Gordon Chapman, *President*
▲ **EMP:** 9
SALES (est): 1.5MM **Privately Held**
SIC: 3569 Filters & strainers, pipeline

(G-12634)
WERTHER INTERNATIONAL INC
Also Called: Silentaire Technology
8614 Veterans Memorial Dr (77088-5048)
PHONE..................................800 655-4781
Kurt Leiber, *President*
Roumen Atanason, *General Mgr*
Max Lieber, *Vice Pres*
Sandra Cruz, *Administration*
Sandra Martinez, *Administration*
▲ **EMP:** 13
SQ FT: 12,000
SALES (est): 5.8MM **Privately Held**
WEB: www.werther.com
SIC: 5013 5084 3563 Automobile service station equipment; compressors; air conditioning; air & gas compressors

(G-12635)
WEST COAST GROUP INC
Also Called: Galaxy Stones
9134 North Fwy (77037-2006)
PHONE..................................281 447-2020
Ray Quartomy, *President*
EMP: 10
SALES (est): 1.3MM **Privately Held**
SIC: 3281 Cut stone & stone products

(G-12636)
WEST U MARBLE LLC
Also Called: Almeda Cultured Marble
14715 Park Almeda Dr (77047-7003)
PHONE..................................713 433-4424
Bill Munoz, *Mng Member*
EMP: 17
SQ FT: 6,000
SALES (est): 1.8MM **Privately Held**
WEB: www.westumarble.com
SIC: 3281 1743 Marble, building: cut & shaped; terrazzo, tile, marble, mosaic work

(G-12637)
WEST-COM NRSE CALL SYSTEMS INC
6060 South Loop E Ste 216 (77033-1042)
PHONE..................................713 731-2500
Sam Hayden, *Manager*
EMP: 12 **Privately Held**
WEB: www.westcomncs.com
SIC: 3663 Radio broadcasting & communications equipment
PA: West-Com Nurse Call Systems, Inc.
2200 Cordelia Rd
Fairfield CA 94534

(G-12638)
WESTAR GRAPHICS INC
2500 Central Pkwy Ste D (77092-7713)
PHONE..................................713 957-4575
John Terrell, *President*
Bobbie Thurman, *Office Mgr*
EMP: 10
SQ FT: 6,000
SALES (est): 1.4MM **Privately Held**
WEB: www.westargraphics.com
SIC: 2752 Commercial printing, offset

(G-12639)
WESTBROOK SALES & DISTRG CORP
11 Lockwood Ave (77020)
P.O. Box 15614 (77220-5614)
PHONE..................................713 675-6438
Charles Westbrook, *President*
EMP: 168
SALES (corp-wide): 119.8MM **Privately Held**
WEB: www.westbrookmfg.com
SIC: 3494 Pipe fittings
PA: Westbrook Sales And Distributing Corporation
1111 Lockwood Dr
Houston TX 77020
713 675-6438

(G-12640)
WESTERLY EXPLORATION INC (PA)
3701 Kirby Dr Ste 514 (77098-3926)
P.O. Box 27590 (77227-7590)
PHONE..................................713 524-7755
EMP: 16
SALES (est): 11MM **Privately Held**
SIC: 1311 Crude petroleum production

(G-12641)
WESTERN ATLAS INTL INC (PA)
Also Called: Western Geophysical
3900 Essex Ln (77027-5133)
P.O. Box 1407 (77251-1407)
PHONE..................................713 972-4000
John R Russell, *President*
Michael E Keane, *Vice Pres*
Norman L Roberts, *Vice Pres*
Virginia S Young, *Vice Pres*
EMP: 450
SQ FT: 224,000
SALES (est): 162.1MM **Privately Held**
SIC: 1382 1389 7372 Seismograph surveys; well logging; prepackaged software

(G-12642)
WESTERN CONTAINER CORPORATION
3801 Distribution Blvd (77018-6605)
PHONE..................................713 691-0730
Robert Harris, *Manager*
EMP: 120
SQ FT: 233,253
SALES (corp-wide): 37.2B **Publicly Held**
WEB: www.westerncontainercoke.com
SIC: 3085 Plastics bottles
HQ: Western Container Corporation
2277 Plaza Dr Ste 270
Sugar Land TX 77479
346 309-3238

(G-12643)
WESTERN FALCON LLC (PA)
1304 Langham Creek Dr # 122 (77084-5041)
PHONE..................................832 391-9461
Wayne L Caldwell, *Ch of Bd*
Louis A Russo, *President*
Rob Davis, *Vice Pres*
Jim Hickman, *Sales Mgr*
▼ **EMP:** 29
SALES (est): 6.2MM **Privately Held**
WEB: www.westernfalcon.com
SIC: 3069 Liner strips, rubber

(G-12644)
WESTERNGECO LLC (DH)
10001 Richmond Ave (77042-4205)
P.O. Box 2469 (77252-2469)
PHONE..................................713 789-9600
Thomas Scoulios, *President*
Simon Ayat, *Exec VP*
Kevin Deal, *Vice Pres*
David McGarthland, *Treasurer*
Patricia Evans, *Sales Staff*
◆ **EMP:** 1200
SQ FT: 555,400
SALES (est): 4.4B **Publicly Held**
SIC: 1382 Seismograph surveys
HQ: Schlumberger Technology Corp
300 Schlumberger Dr
Sugar Land TX 77478
281 285-8500

(G-12645)
WESTGATE GRAPHICS
Also Called: Westside Graphics
2500 Central Pkwy Ste D (77092-7713)
PHONE..................................713 688-1292
Charlene Terrell, *Owner*
Kevin Kilgore, *Prdtn Mgr*
Adre Kilgore, *Manager*
EMP: 10
SQ FT: 41,341
SALES (est): 1.1MM **Privately Held**
WEB: www.westsidegraphicsinc.com
SIC: 2782 2759 Looseleaf binders & devices; commercial printing

(G-12646)
WESTLAKE CHEMICAL CORPORATION (PA)
2801 Post Oak Blvd Ste 60 (77056-6136)
PHONE..................................713 960-9111
James Chao, *Ch of Bd*
Albert Chao, *President*
Greg Slemons, *Superintendent*
Nina Montalbano, *COO*
Joel Iglesias, *Counsel*
EMP: 370
SALES: 8.1B **Publicly Held**
WEB: www.westlake.com
SIC: 2821 Polyethylene resins

(G-12647)
WESTLAKE CHEMICAL OPCO LP (DH)
2801 Post Oak Blvd (77056-6136)
PHONE..................................713 960-9111
Albert Chao, *Partner*
EMP: 22
SALES (est): 5.5MM **Publicly Held**
WEB: www.westlake.com
SIC: 2821 Plastics materials & resins
HQ: Westlake Chemical Partners Lp
2801 Post Oak Blvd Ste 60
Houston TX 77056
713 585-2900

(G-12648)
WESTLAKE CHEMICAL PARTNERS LP (HQ)
2801 Post Oak Blvd Ste 60 (77056-6136)
PHONE..................................713 585-2900
Albert Chao, *President*
Westlake C LLC, *General Ptnr*
M Steven Bender, *CFO*
EMP: 12
SALES: 1B **Publicly Held**
WEB: www.wlkpartners.com
SIC: 2869 Ethylene; propylene, butylene; carbon disulfide

(G-12649)
WESTLAKE LONGVIEW CORPORATION
Also Called: Westlake Chemical
2801 Post Oak Blvd # 650 (77056-6140)
PHONE..................................713 960-9111
Albert Chao, *President*
James Chao, *Chairman*
M Steven Bender, *CFO*
◆ **EMP:** 102
SALES (est): 65.1MM **Publicly Held**
WEB: www.westlake.com
SIC: 2821 Plastics materials & resins
PA: Westlake Chemical Corporation
2801 Post Oak Blvd Ste 60
Houston TX 77056

(G-12650)
WESTLAKE MONOMERS CORP
2801 Post Oak Blvd (77056-6136)
PHONE..................................270 395-4151
Albert Chao, *President*
EMP: 12
SALES (est): 3.7MM **Privately Held**
WEB: www.westlake.com
SIC: 2821 Plastics materials & resins

(G-12651)
WESTLAKE OLEFINS CORPORATION (HQ)
2801 Post Oak Blvd Fl 6 (77056-6136)
PHONE..................................713 960-9111
Albert Chao, *President*
David Chao, *Bd of Directors*
◆ **EMP:** 50
SQ FT: 90,000
SALES (est): 2B **Publicly Held**
WEB: www.westlake.com
SIC: 2869 2822 Ethylene; polyethylene, chlorosulfonated (hypalon)

(G-12652)
WESTLAKE POLYMERS LLC (DH)
2801 Post Oak Blvd # 650 (77056-6140)
PHONE..................................713 960-9111
Albert Chao, *CEO*
James Chao, *Ch of Bd*
M Steven Bender, *CFO*
◆ **EMP:** 250
SQ FT: 90,000
SALES (est): 1.9B **Publicly Held**
WEB: www.westlake.com
SIC: 2673 2869 Bags: plastic, laminated & coated; ethylene

(G-12653)
WESTLAKE PVC CORPORATION (HQ)
2801 Post Oak Blvd (77056-6136)
PHONE.....................................713 960-9111
Albert Chao, *President*
Bob Businger, *Senior VP*
Steve Bender, *CFO*
▲ EMP: 125
SQ FT: 90,000
SALES (est): 91MM **Publicly Held**
WEB: www.westlake.com
SIC: 2295 3084 Resin or plastic coated fabrics; plastics pipe

(G-12654)
WESTLAKE VINYLS INC
Also Called: Westlake CA&o
2801 Post Oak Blvd # 600 (77056-6136)
PHONE.....................................800 321-8550
Carlos Pitre, *Engineer*
EMP: 17 **Publicly Held**
WEB: www.westlake.com
SIC: 2821 Plastics materials & resins
HQ: Westlake Vinyls, Inc.
　　2468 Industrial Pkwy
　　Calvert City KY 42029

(G-12655)
WESTLAKE VINYLS COMPANY LP (HQ)
2801 Post Oak Blvd Ste 60 (77056-6136)
PHONE.....................................713 960-9111
Albert Chao, *CEO*
James Chao, *Chairman*
M Steven Bender, *Senior VP*
Robert Buesinger, *Senior VP*
Wayne Morse, *Senior VP*
◆ EMP: 200
SQ FT: 90,000
SALES (est): 281MM **Publicly Held**
WEB: www.westlake.com
SIC: 2812 2869 2821 Alkalies & chlorine; olefins; plastics materials & resins

(G-12656)
WESTRADE USA INC
6363 Woodway Dr Ste 150 (77057-1758)
PHONE.....................................713 785-0053
Raimundo Riojas, *President*
Raimundo A Riojas Jr, *Vice Pres*
Miriam Berger, *Admin Sec*
▲ EMP: 12
SQ FT: 2,000
SALES (est): 2.6MM **Privately Held**
SIC: 5169 2879 Industrial chemicals; agricultural chemicals

(G-12657)
WESTROCK CP LLC
8440 Tewantin Dr (77061-4616)
PHONE.....................................281 830-0131
Tom Laumyer, *Manager*
EMP: 100
SALES (corp-wide): 17.5B **Publicly Held**
WEB: www.westrock.com
SIC: 2653 3412 Boxes, corrugated: made from purchased materials; metal barrels, drums & pails
HQ: Westrock Cp, Llc
　　1000 Abernathy Rd Ste 125
　　Atlanta GA 30328

(G-12658)
WESTROCK CP LLC
Smurfit-Stone Container
1180 West Loop N (77055-7241)
PHONE.....................................281 893-8918
Bob Clark, *Manager*
EMP: 28
SALES (corp-wide): 17.5B **Publicly Held**
WEB: www.westrock.com
SIC: 2653 Boxes, corrugated: made from purchased materials
HQ: Westrock Cp, Llc
　　1000 Abernathy Rd Ste 125
　　Atlanta GA 30328

(G-12659)
WESTWAY FEED PRODUCTS LLC
Also Called: Westway Terminal
9325 E Avenue S (77012-2321)
PHONE.....................................713 514-1000
James Culver, *Principal*

EMP: 40
SALES (corp-wide): 7.7B **Privately Held**
WEB: www.contanda.com
SIC: 2048 Prepared feeds
HQ: Westway Feed Products Llc
　　365 Canal St Ste 2929
　　New Orleans LA 70130
　　504 934-1850

(G-12660)
WHIRLWIND HOLDING COMPANY INC (PA)
Also Called: Whirlwind Building Components
8234 Hansen Rd (77075-1002)
P.O. Box 75280 (77234-5280)
PHONE.....................................713 946-7140
Jack Sturdivant, *CEO*
Ty Sturdivant, *President*
Julie Friedrich, *Corp Secy*
Bob Carlson, *Manager*
Corey Oevermann, *Maintence Staff*
EMP: 339
SQ FT: 295,000
SALES (est): 134.4MM **Privately Held**
WEB: www.whirlwindsteel.com
SIC: 3448 Buildings, portable: prefabricated metal

(G-12661)
WHIRLWIND STEEL BUILDINGS INC (HQ)
Also Called: Whirlwind Building Systems
8234 Hansen Rd (77075-1002)
P.O. Box 75280 (77234-5280)
PHONE.....................................713 946-7140
Jack Sturdivant, *President*
Tyson Sturdivant, *Principal*
Jeff Feaster, *Vice Pres*
Dave Fulton, *Vice Pres*
Lynn Widrick, *Vice Pres*
◆ EMP: 359 EST: 1991
SALES (est): 134.4MM **Privately Held**
WEB: www.whirlwindsteel.com
SIC: 3448 Buildings, portable: prefabricated metal; prefabricated metal components

(G-12662)
WHITE OAK OPERATING CO LLC
Also Called: White Oak Energy
16945 Northchase Dr # 17 (77060-2135)
PHONE.....................................281 876-2025
Tom Isler, *President*
Scott Nonhof, *President*
Lloyd White, *Area Mgr*
Joe Lauer, *COO*
Mike Rayburn Jr, *COO*
EMP: 19
SQ FT: 4,600
SALES (est): 11.9MM **Privately Held**
WEB: www.whiteoakenergy.com
SIC: 1382 Oil & gas exploration services

(G-12663)
WHITE STAR STEEL INC
2200 Harbor St (77020-7506)
P.O. Box 15518 (77220-5518)
PHONE.....................................713 675-6501
Okey Johnson III, *President*
Jack Harris, *Vice Pres*
Greg Johnson, *VP Opers*
Marcella Cox, *Purch Mgr*
Okey B Johnson Jr, *Treasurer*
▲ EMP: 56
SQ FT: 43,000
SALES (est): 24.9MM
SALES (corp-wide): 41MM **Privately Held**
WEB: www.whitestarsteel.com
SIC: 5051 3312 3316 Steel; blast furnaces & steel mills; cold finishing of steel shapes
PA: Nashville Steel Corporation
　　7211 Centennial Blvd
　　Nashville TN 37209
　　615 350-7933

(G-12664)
WHITEFIELD PLASTICS CORP
2300 Ww Thorne Blvd (77073-3316)
PHONE.....................................281 214-8510
Bill Whitefield, *President*
William H Whitefield, *President*
Donald D Whitefield, *Vice Pres*
Mike Bice, *Sales Staff*

Michael Fisher, *Marketing Staff*
▲ EMP: 20
SQ FT: 13,000
SALES (est): 4.4MM **Privately Held**
WEB: www.whitefieldplastics.com
SIC: 2822 Synthetic rubber

(G-12665)
WHITNEY OIL & GAS LLC
920 Mmrial Cy Way Ste 200 (77024)
PHONE.....................................504 218-2929
EMP: 10
SALES (est): 159K **Privately Held**
WEB: www.hancockwhitney.com
SIC: 1389 Well plugging & abandoning, oil & gas

(G-12666)
WILDHORSE RESOURCES LLC
920 Mmrial Cy Way Ste 700 (77024)
P.O. Box 18496, Oklahoma City OK (73154-0496)
PHONE.....................................713 568-4910
Amir Radfar, *Vice Pres*
John Hermes, *Foreman/Supr*
Micah Nelson, *Foreman/Supr*
John Nabors, *Opers Staff*
Kyle Allen, *Production*
EMP: 40
SALES (est): 19.7MM **Publicly Held**
WEB: www.chk.com
SIC: 1382 Oil & gas exploration services
HQ: Brazos Valley Longhorn, L.L.C.
　　6100 N Western Ave
　　Oklahoma City OK 73118
　　713 568-4910

(G-12667)
WILLIAM PRICE DISTLG CO LLC
970 Wakefield Dr (77018-6204)
PHONE.....................................713 364-9225
Bryan Clary, *President*
EMP: 9
SALES (est): 1MM **Privately Held**
WEB: www.williampricedistilling.com
SIC: 2085 Distilled & blended liquors

(G-12668)
WILLIAMS ALLOY & WELDING
11425 W Little York Rd (77041-4918)
PHONE.....................................713 896-9096
EMP: 9
SALES (est): 733.1K **Privately Held**
SIC: 7692 Welding Repair

(G-12669)
WILLIAMS COMPANIES INC
4233 W Richey Rd (77066-3395)
PHONE.....................................281 444-6441
John Seldenrust, *Vice Pres*
Sam Wooley, *Project Mgr*
Marc Edwards, *Opers Mgr*
Clayton Bowerman, *Foreman/Supr*
David Fennell, *Opers Spvr*
EMP: 13
SALES (corp-wide): 8.2B **Publicly Held**
WEB: www.williams.com
SIC: 4922 1389 Pipelines, natural gas; gas compressing (natural gas) at the fields
PA: The Williams Companies Inc
　　1 Williams Ctr
　　Tulsa OK 74172
　　918 573-2000

(G-12670)
WILLIAMS GAS PIPELINE-TRANSCO (HQ)
Also Called: Williams Field Services-Gulf C
2800 Post Oak Blvd # 300 (77056-6100)
P.O. Box 1396 (77251-1396)
PHONE.....................................713 215-2000
▲ EMP: 206
SALES (est): 813.8MM
SALES (corp-wide): 8.2B **Publicly Held**
WEB: www.williams.com
SIC: 1321 1221 1222 Natural gas liquids; surface mining, bituminous; bituminous coal-underground mining
PA: The Williams Companies Inc
　　1 Williams Ctr
　　Tulsa OK 74172
　　918 573-2000

(G-12671)
WILLINGHAM SYSTEMS LLC
Also Called: Web Devices
9201 Winkler Dr (77017-5913)
PHONE.....................................713 928-3936
Mark Willingham, *Mng Member*
Mary Pomykal,
Scott Rousseau,
▲ EMP: 62
SALES (est): 8.8MM **Privately Held**
WEB: www.webdevices-usa.com
SIC: 2399 Aprons, breast (harness)

(G-12672)
WILSON ENVIRONMENTAL MGT INC
9613 Maribelle Way (77055-4312)
P.O. Box 431761 (77243-1761)
PHONE.....................................713 984-0800
Jay Swindle, *President*
Reeba McCullum, *Vice Pres*
EMP: 14
SQ FT: 1,750
SALES (est): 900K **Privately Held**
WEB: www.wilsonemi.com
SIC: 3589 Water treatment equipment, industrial

(G-12673)
WILSON INTERNATIONAL INC
7402 N Eldridge Pkwy (77041-1902)
PHONE.....................................281 823-4700
John J Kennedy, *President*
EMP: 21
SALES (est): 15.5MM
SALES (corp-wide): 2.9B **Publicly Held**
SIC: 5084 7353 3533 Oil well machinery, equipment & supplies; oil field equipment, rental or leasing; drilling tools for gas, oil or water wells
PA: Now Inc.
　　7402 N Eldridge Pkwy
　　Houston TX 77041
　　281 823-4700

(G-12674)
WILSON PRECISION MCH WORKS LP
16321 Loch Katrine Ln E1 (77084-2971)
PHONE.....................................832 721-9918
Gary McCann, *Partner*
David Hsu, *Partner*
Nelson Hsu, *Partner*
Eddie Inman, *Partner*
EMP: 10
SQ FT: 5,000
SALES (est): 1.5MM **Privately Held**
SIC: 3599 Machine shop, jobbing & repair

(G-12675)
WILSON SUPPLY CORPORATE OFFICE
7402 N Eldridge Pkwy (77041-1902)
PHONE.....................................713 237-3309
EMP: 16
SALES (est): 1.5MM **Privately Held**
SIC: 1799 3463 3541 Trade Contractor Mfg Nonferrous Forgings Mfg Machine Tools-Cutting

(G-12676)
WILSONART LLC
552 Garden Oaks Blvd (77018-5506)
PHONE.....................................713 576-5500
Kevin Kaulfus, *Manager*
EMP: 18
SALES (corp-wide): 4.9B **Privately Held**
WEB: www.wilsonart.com
SIC: 2821 2541 Plastics materials & resins; table or counter tops, plastic laminated
HQ: Wilsonart Llc
　　2501 Wilsonart Dr
　　Temple TX 76504
　　254 207-7000

(G-12677)
WINDLASS METALWORKS LLC
Also Called: Bulk Material Equipment
7042 Satsuma Dr (77041-1810)
PHONE.....................................713 849-9292
Melissa Joyce, *Opers Mgr*
Ranit Windlass, *Mng Member*
EMP: 11
SQ FT: 20,000

SALES (est): 2.3MM **Privately Held**
WEB: www.windlassmetalworks.com
SIC: 3537 3444 .3443 Stacking machines, automatic; sheet metalwork; metal housings, enclosures, casings & other containers; fabricated plate work (boiler shop)

(G-12678)
WINDY COVE ENERGY LLC
11757 Katy Fwy Ste 300 (77079-1718)
PHONE...................................281 402-1880
EMP: 10
SALES (est): 411.2K **Privately Held**
SIC: 3533 Mfg Oil/Gas Field Machinery

(G-12679)
WINTERS INSTRUMENTS INC
Also Called: Winters Instruments
5400 W Sam Houston Pkwy N (77041-5134)
PHONE...................................281 880-8607
Anna Alaniz, *Business Mgr*
Cory Russell, *Business Mgr*
Tracy Ulloa, *Finance Mgr*
Stephen Bradley, *Regl Sales Mgr*
Angie Pinney, *Sales Staff*
EMP: 15
SALES (corp-wide): 10.2MM **Privately Held**
WEB: www.winters.com
SIC: 3823 Industrial instrmnts msrmnt display/control process variable
HQ: Winter's Instruments Inc
455 Cayuga Rd Ste 650
Buffalo NY 14225

(G-12680)
WOLAR INDUSTRIAL INC (PA)
1313 Lombardy St (77023-3534)
PHONE...................................713 926-2440
Jaime Lara, *CEO*
Celina M Lara, *Director*
Cristina M Lara, *Director*
Jorge G Lara, *Director*
Maria C Lara, *Director*
◆ EMP: 61
SQ FT: 30,000
SALES (est): 14MM **Privately Held**
WEB: www.wolar.com
SIC: 3053 3325 Gaskets, all materials; steel foundries

(G-12681)
WOMBLE COMPANY INC
12821 Industrial Rd (77015-6802)
PHONE...................................713 636-8700
Alice F Womble, *President*
Larry McKinney, *VP Opers*
Mary Elgohary, *Controller*
Jenee Womble-Stepanakis, *Admin Sec*
EMP: 480
SQ FT: 7,000
SALES (est): 166.8MM **Privately Held**
WEB: www.wombleco.com
SIC: 3479 Coating of metals & formed products; painting, coating & hot dipping

(G-12682)
WONTON FOOD CORPORATION
2902 Caroline St (77004-2726)
PHONE...................................832 366-1280
Ho Sing Lee, *President*
Xiaoling Huang, *Assistant*
▲ EMP: 41 EST: 1976
SQ FT: 60,000
SALES (est): 8.6MM **Privately Held**
WEB: www.wontonfood.com
SIC: 2099 Food preparations
PA: Wonton Food Inc.
220 Moore St 222
Brooklyn NY 11206

(G-12683)
WOO KEE FOODS INC
11243 S Gessner Rd Ste A (77071-1919)
PHONE...................................832 818-6988
Kevin K K Tang, *President*
▲ EMP: 10
SALES (est): 808K **Privately Held**
SIC: 2099 Noodles, uncooked: packaged with other ingredients

(G-12684)
WOOD COUNTY ENERGY LLC
16600 Park Row (77084-5019)
PHONE...................................281 994-5400

O Duane Gaither II, *Mng Member*
EMP: 30 EST: 2012
SALES (est): 823.8K **Privately Held**
SIC: 1389 Oil & gas field services

(G-12685)
WOOD GROUP MANAGEMENT SVCS INC (HQ)
17325 Park Row (77084-4932)
PHONE...................................281 828-3500
Allister G Langlands, *CEO*
Alan Semple, *President*
Jesus Olivas, *Superintendent*
Roslyn Hicks, *Chairman*
Dave Gerg, *Area Mgr*
◆ EMP: 44
SQ FT: 13,000
SALES (est): 2.6B
SALES (corp-wide): 12.7B **Privately Held**
WEB: www.woodplc.com
SIC: 1389 Oil consultants
PA: John Wood Group Plc
15 Justice Mill Lane
Aberdeen AB11
122 485-1000

(G-12686)
WOOD GROUP POWER GP LLC (DH)
17420 Katy Fwy Ste 300 (77094-1324)
PHONE...................................281 828-3500
Bob Keiller, *Mng Member*
George Gaudette, *Mng Member*
Allister G Langlands, *Mng Member*
Alan G Semple, *Mng Member*
▲ EMP: 25
SALES (est): 7.2MM
SALES (corp-wide): 12.7B **Privately Held**
SIC: 4581 7699 3724 Aircraft servicing & repairing; industrial equipment services; turbines, aircraft type

(G-12687)
WOOD GROUP USA INC (HQ)
17325 Park Row (77084-4932)
PHONE...................................832 809-8000
Andrew Stewart, *CEO*
Don Leinweber, *President*
Keith Wakefield, *Area Mgr*
Gretchen Gardener, *Business Mgr*
Jennifer Bullock, *Vice Pres*
◆ EMP: 985
SQ FT: 200,000
SALES (est): 1.2B
SALES (corp-wide): 12.7B **Privately Held**
WEB: www.woodplc.com
SIC: 8742 8711 1389 7389 Construction project management consultant; consulting engineer; construction, repair & dismantling services; purchasing service
PA: John Wood Group Plc
15 Justice Mill Lane
Aberdeen AB11
122 485-1000

(G-12688)
WOOD GROUP USA INC
17420 Katy Fwy Ste 300 (77094-1324)
PHONE...................................281 647-8300
Allister G Langlands, *Ch of Bd*
EMP: 16
SALES (corp-wide): 12.7B **Privately Held**
WEB: www.woodplc.com
SIC: 1389 Oil field services
HQ: Wood Group Usa, Inc.
17325 Park Row
Houston TX 77084
832 809-8000

(G-12689)
WOODFIELD PHARMACEUTICAL LLC
10863 Rockley Rd (77099-3405)
PHONE...................................281 530-3077
Adam Runsdorf, *President*
Jay Patel, *QC Mgr*
Amanda Kirkpatrick, *Director*
Kalpen Patel, *Director*
Matt Kennington, *Maintence Staff*
▲ EMP: 58
SQ FT: 36,124
SALES (est): 10MM **Privately Held**
WEB: www.wdprx.com
SIC: 2834 Pharmaceutical preparations

(G-12690)
WOODSIDE ENERGY (USA) INC
5151 San Felipe St # 1200 (77056-3609)
PHONE...................................713 963-8490
Don Voelte, *CEO*
Jeff Soine, *President*
Thomas Murphy, *Vice Pres*
Troy Hayden, *CFO*
▲ EMP: 101
SALES (est): 12.7MM **Privately Held**
WEB: www.woodside.com.au
SIC: 1382 Oil & gas exploration services
PA: Woodside Petroleum Ltd.
11 Mount St
Perth WA 6000

(G-12691)
WORKOVER SOLUTIONS INC
10011 Windfern Rd (77064-5812)
PHONE...................................361 947-8695
EMP: 38 **Privately Held**
WEB: www.workoversolutions.com
SIC: 1389 Oil field services
PA: Workover Solutions, Inc.
156 S Campus Dr
Imperial PA 15126

(G-12692)
WORLD JOURNAL LA LLC
Also Called: World Journel of Texas
10415 Westpark Dr Apt A (77042-5314)
PHONE...................................713 771-4363
Linda Lin, *Manager*
EMP: 10 **Privately Held**
WEB: www.worldjournal.com
SIC: 2711 Newspapers: publishing only, not printed on site
HQ: World Journal La, Llc
1588 Corporate Center Dr
Monterey Park CA 91754
323 268-4982

(G-12693)
WORLDWIDE MANUFACTURING INC
3721 Lapas Dr (77023-6435)
PHONE...................................713 645-6552
EMP: 47
SALES (est): 2.8MM **Privately Held**
SIC: 3452 Mfg Bolts/Screws/Rivets

(G-12694)
WORLDWIDE OILFIELD MACHINE INC (PA)
Also Called: W O M
11809 Canemont St (77035-6505)
PHONE...................................713 729-9200
Sudhir S Puranik, *President*
Amol Pawar, *Mfg Mgr*
Juan Martinez, *Foreman/Supr*
Cinthia Ruiz, *Purch Agent*
Ashish T Eit, *Engineer*
◆ EMP: 130
SQ FT: 44,000
SALES (est): 54.9MM **Privately Held**
WEB: www.womgroup.com
SIC: 3533 Oil field machinery & equipment

(G-12695)
WORLDWIDE OILFIELD MACHINE INC
Also Called: Wom
11625 Fairmont St (77035-6509)
PHONE...................................713 721-5200
Prasanna Pardeshi, *Vice Pres*
Edward Darce, *Accounts Mgr*
EMP: 28
SALES (corp-wide): 54.9MM **Privately Held**
WEB: www.womgroup.com
SIC: 3533 Oil field machinery & equipment
PA: Worldwide Oilfield Machine, Inc.
11809 Canemont St
Houston TX 77035
713 729-9200

(G-12696)
WORLDWIDE OILFIELD MACHINE INC
Blowout Preventor Division
5800 Cunningham Rd (77041-4702)
PHONE...................................713 937-0795
Rajan Sundararajan, *Manager*
EMP: 30
SQ FT: 27,100

SALES (corp-wide): 54.9MM **Privately Held**
WEB: www.womgroup.com
SIC: 3533 Oil field machinery & equipment
PA: Worldwide Oilfield Machine, Inc.
11809 Canemont St
Houston TX 77035
713 729-9200

(G-12697)
WORTH BEAUTY LLC
3101 Richmond Ave Ste 200 (77098-3013)
PHONE...................................713 660-0025
Steve Machiorlette, *President*
EMP: 12
SALES (est): 669.3K **Privately Held**
WEB: www.blendsmart.com
SIC: 2844 Toilet preparations

(G-12698)
WPT LLC (HQ)
2801 Postoakblvd Ste 600 (77056)
PHONE...................................713 960-9111
Albert Chao, *Partner*
Wayne Morse, *Partner*
▲ EMP: 23
SQ FT: 900
SALES (est): 3MM **Publicly Held**
SIC: 2869 Ethylene

(G-12699)
WRB REFINING LP (PA)
2331 Citywest Blvd (77042-2862)
PHONE...................................281 293-6600
Larry M Ziemba, *Managing Prtnr*
▼ EMP: 14
SALES (est): 17.8MM **Privately Held**
SIC: 2911 Petroleum refining

(G-12700)
WSH LAND INC (PA)
Also Called: Webb, Shannon & Haas Assoc
2727 Allen Pkwy Ste 1815 (77019-2195)
PHONE...................................713 622-4823
David C Shannon Jr, *President*
Ben Webb, *Principal*
EMP: 16
SALES (est): 1.4MM **Privately Held**
WEB: www.wshland.com
SIC: 1382 Oil & gas exploration services

(G-12701)
WWT INTERNATIONAL INC
Also Called: Western Well Tool
9817 Whithorn Dr (77095-5027)
PHONE...................................281 345-8019
Bruce Moore, *Branch Mgr*
EMP: 12
SALES (corp-wide): 9MM **Privately Held**
WEB: www.wwtco.com
SIC: 1389 Oil field services
PA: Wwt International, Inc.
9758 Whithorn Dr
Houston TX 77095
281 345-8019

(G-12702)
WWT INTERNATIONAL INC (PA)
Also Called: Western Well Tool
9758 Whithorn Dr (77095-5025)
PHONE...................................281 345-8019
Rudolph Ernst Krueger, *President*
Thomas Bragaw, *Vice Pres*
James C Hilbert, *Vice Pres*
Lisa Ryan, *CFO*
Peggy Markowski, *Executive Asst*
▲ EMP: 10
SQ FT: 5,361
SALES (est): 9MM **Privately Held**
WEB: www.wwtco.com
SIC: 1389 Oil field services

(G-12703)
WWWHOUSTONSIGNMAKERCO M
4208 Washington Ave (77007-5638)
PHONE...................................281 990-7446
Thao Huynh, *Owner*
EMP: 10
SALES (est): 709.2K **Privately Held**
WEB: www.houstonsignmaker.com
SIC: 3993 Neon signs

(G-12704)
XACT TECHNOLOGIES USA CORP
9851 Fllbrook Pnes Dr Ste (77064)
PHONE..........................403 862-3383
Eric Amos, *CEO*
EMP: 10
SALES (est): 311.4K **Privately Held**
WEB: www.xacttechnologies.com
SIC: 3357 Manufacturing industries

(G-12705)
XCL RESOURCES LLC
600 N Shepherd Dr Ste 390 (77007-4580)
PHONE..........................346 335-1081
Grayson Lisenby, *CEO*
Blake McKenna, *Exec VP*
Eric Matus, *CTO*
EMP: 30
SALES (est): 3MM **Privately Held**
WEB: www.xclresources.com
SIC: 1381 Directional drilling oil & gas wells

(G-12706)
XEDIA PROCESS SOLUTIONS LLC
5773 Woodway Dr 181 (77057-1501)
PHONE..........................832 356-8347
Scott Buckwald, *CEO*
Jonathan Fabri, *CTO*
EMP: 20
SALES (est): 233K
SALES (corp-wide): 1.7MM **Privately Held**
WEB: www.xediaprocess.com
SIC: 3589 Water treatment equipment, industrial
PA: Blackbuck Resources Llc
3200 Southwest Fwy # 3400
Houston TX 77027
832 356-8347

(G-12707)
XENTAUR CORPORATION
4140 World Hstn Pkwy # 180 (77032-2490)
PHONE..........................631 345-3434
Christopher Mueller, *CEO*
Craig Allshouse, *President*
Brian Flanagan, *Engineer*
Betty Kenyon, *Controller*
David Hailey, *Manager*
EMP: 23
SALES (est): 4.8MM **Privately Held**
WEB: www.cosaxentaur.com
SIC: 3823 Industrial instrmnts msrmnt display/control process variable

(G-12708)
XTO ENERGY INC
1 Riverway Ste 700 (77056-1988)
PHONE..........................817 870-2800
Jeremy Greene, *Manager*
Brian Aylor, *Technician*
Dustin Simpson, *Advisor*
Suzanne Spahr, *Associate*
EMP: 44
SALES (corp-wide): 264.9B **Publicly Held**
WEB: www.xtoenergy.com
SIC: 1311 Crude petroleum production
HQ: Xto Energy Inc.
22777 Sprngwoods Vlg Pkwy
Spring TX 77389

(G-12709)
XTRALIGHT MANUFACTURING LTD
8812 Frey Rd (77034-3502)
PHONE..........................713 943-9927
Jerry Caroom, *CEO*
Richard Shirley, *COO*
Kim Ward, *COO*
Ken Stelly, *Plant Mgr*
Benjamin Bertens, *Buyer*
▲ EMP: 80
SQ FT: 95,000
SALES (est): 48MM **Privately Held**
WEB: www.xtralight.com
SIC: 3648 3646 Outdoor lighting equipment; commercial indusl & institutional electric lighting fixtures; fluorescent lighting fixtures, commercial

(G-12710)
XTREME FORCE INC
Also Called: Xtreme Force Wheel
1234 N Post Oak Rd (77055-7262)
PHONE..........................281 397-0073
Antonio Simaj, *Director*
EMP: 10
SALES (est): 374.7K **Privately Held**
WEB: www.xtremeforcewheels.com
SIC: 3714 Wheels, motor vehicle

(G-12711)
XTREME HIGH PRFMCE CATINGS INC
7410 Miller Road 2 (77049-4818)
PHONE..........................281 695-8880
Thomas Balke, *CEO*
EMP: 23
SQ FT: 22,000
SALES (est): 5.3MM **Privately Held**
WEB: www.xtremesandblastingandpaint.com
SIC: 3599 Custom machinery

(G-12712)
XXTREME PIPE STORAGE LLC
Also Called: Inspection Oilfield Services
7814 Miller Road 3 (77049-1734)
P.O. Box 19569 (77224-9569)
PHONE..........................281 452-9015
Steve Turner, *President*
Robert Messer, *CFO*
EMP: 45
SALES (est): 1MM
SALES (corp-wide): 31.6MM **Privately Held**
WEB: www.steeltradingcorp.com
SIC: 1389 Pipe testing, oil field service
HQ: Xxtreme Group, L.L.C.
14825 Saint Marys Ln # 125
Houston TX 77079

(G-12713)
YAMHILL VALLEY VINEYARDS INC
7786 Blankenship Dr # 700 (77055-1002)
PHONE..........................281 822-9463
EMP: 12
SALES (corp-wide): 1.6MM **Privately Held**
WEB: www.yamhill.com
SIC: 2084 Advertising specialties
PA: Yamhill Valley Vineyards Inc
16250 Sw Oldsville Rd
Mcminnville OR 97128
503 843-3100

(G-12714)
YCI METHANOL ONE LLC
10777 Westheimer Rd # 800 (77042-3455)
P.O. Box 510, Vacherie LA (70090-0510)
PHONE..........................832 924-1998
Chaoliang Yao, *President*
Jinshu Wang, *Chairman*
James Diaz, *Vice Pres*
Wendy Zeng, *Financial Analy*
Xing Guan, *Finance*
EMP: 80
SALES (est): 5.9MM **Privately Held**
WEB: www.yci-us.com
SIC: 2899 Chemical preparations
PA: Koch Methanol Investments, Llc
1209 N Orange St
Wilmington DE 19801
302 658-7581

(G-12715)
YELLOW ROSE STL FBRICATORS INC
Also Called: MEYER SMITH
14239 Sommermeyer St (77041-6202)
PHONE..........................713 862-7339
Jay Esmay, *President*
EMP: 22
SALES (est): 4.7MM **Privately Held**
WEB: www.meyersmithinc.com
SIC: 3446 Stairs, fire escapes, balconies, railings & ladders

(G-12716)
YELLOWJACKET OILFIELD SVCS LLC
5151 Katy Fwy Ste 206 (77007-2260)
PHONE..........................432 381-0104
Dustin Morgan, *CEO*
EMP: 15
SALES (corp-wide): 25.4MM **Privately Held**
WEB: www.yjosllc.com
SIC: 1389 Oil field services
PA: Yellowjacket Oilfield Services, L.L.C.
200 N Loraine St Ste 1150
Midland TX 79701
432 242-7570

(G-12717)
YELLOWSTONE BRANDS LTD (PA)
777 Post Oak Blvd Ste 250 (77056-3236)
PHONE..........................713 650-0065
John Keren, *Vice Pres*
Vreij A Kolandjian, *Mng Member*
Charlie Kujawa,
EMP: 9
SALES (est): 1.7MM **Privately Held**
WEB: www.yellowstonecapital.com
SIC: 2038 Ethnic foods, frozen; dinners, frozen & packaged

(G-12718)
YOKOGAWA LEISURE ANALYSIS DIV
Also Called: Yokogawa Corporation America
910 Gemini St (77058-2704)
PHONE..........................281 488-0409
EMP: 15
SQ FT: 12,000
SALES (est): 1.9MM **Privately Held**
SIC: 3826 5049 Analytical Instruments, Nsk

(G-12719)
YP LLC
2525 North Loop W Ste 600 (77008-1094)
PHONE..........................713 867-6500
Dennis Payne, *Branch Mgr*
Vance Collins, *Executive*
EMP: 250
SALES (est): 1.4B **Publicly Held**
WEB: www.corporate.thryv.com
SIC: 2741 Miscellaneous publishing
HQ: Yp Llc
2247 Northlake Pkwy Fl 4
Tucker GA 30084
866 570-8863

(G-12720)
ZACKSON RESOURCES INC
7600 San Felipe St 200 (77063-1703)
PHONE..........................713 782-1075
Paul Sigmund, *President*
Gregory J Kane, *Admin Sec*
EMP: 15
SALES (est): 739.8K **Privately Held**
SIC: 1311 Crude petroleum production

(G-12721)
ZARVONA ENERGY LLC
1001 Mckinney St Ste 1800 (77002-6421)
PHONE..........................713 600-0600
Kathryn S Macaskie, *CEO*
Deborah Linder, *Business Mgr*
Matthew Jurgens, *COO*
Rob Macaskie, *Vice Pres*
Carl Abshire, *Foreman/Supr*
EMP: 10 EST: 2015
SALES (est): 175.6K **Privately Held**
WEB: www.zarvonaenergy.com
SIC: 1382 1389 Oil & gas exploration services; cementing oil & gas well casings

(G-12722)
ZAZA ENERGY LLC (HQ)
1301 Mckinney St Ste 2800 (77010-3079)
PHONE..........................713 595-1900
Todd A Brooks, *CEO*
Thomas Bowman, *Exec VP*
William A Dressel, *Exec VP*
Beth A Cornwell, *Vice Pres*
Paul F Jansen, *CFO*
EMP: 10
SALES (est): 10.5MM
SALES (corp-wide): 16MM **Privately Held**
WEB: www.zazaenergy.com
SIC: 1382 Oil & gas exploration services
PA: Zaza Energy Corporation
1301 Mckinney St Ste 2850
Houston TX 77010
713 595-1900

(G-12723)
ZAZA ENERGY CORPORATION (PA)
1301 Mckinney St Ste 2850 (77010-3117)
PHONE..........................713 595-1900
Herbert C Williamson III, *Ch of Bd*
Todd Alan Brooks, *President*
Patrick A Dunn, *Counsel*
Paul F Jansen, *CFO*
Sam Callaway, *Manager*
EMP: 12
SALES (est): 16MM **Privately Held**
WEB: www.zazaenergy.com
SIC: 1382 Oil & gas exploration services

(G-12724)
ZEDI US INC
Also Called: Southern Flow
5875 N Sam Houston Pkwy W (77086-1561)
P.O. Box 924449 (77292-4449)
PHONE..........................713 527-9591
John Utter, *Manager*
EMP: 9
SALES (corp-wide): 16.7B **Publicly Held**
WEB: www.zedisolutions.com
SIC: 1389 Oil field services
HQ: Zedi Us Inc.
101 Ibex Ln
Broussard LA 70518
337 233-2066

(G-12725)
ZEPHYR GAS SERVICES LLC
20405 State Highway 249 # 2 (77070-2618)
PHONE..........................281 376-2980
Glen Wind, *Partner*
Lance Perryman, *Vice Pres*
Cody Smith, *Controller*
EMP: 31
SQ FT: 2,200
SALES (est): 2MM **Publicly Held**
SIC: 1389 Chemically treating wells
HQ: Regency Gas Services Lp
2001 Bryan St Ste 3700
Dallas TX 75201
214 750-1771

(G-12726)
ZERO PRODUCTS INC
Also Called: Zero Fasteners
219 Baywood St (77011-2301)
P.O. Box 24146 (77229-4146)
PHONE..........................713 675-0123
Tom Mullen III, *President*
Katie Lee, *Vice Pres*
EMP: 35
SQ FT: 30,000
SALES (est): 9.5MM **Privately Held**
WEB: www.zerofast.com
SIC: 5085 3452 Fasteners, industrial: nuts, bolts, screws, etc.; bolts, nuts, rivets & washers

(G-12727)
ZETA ENERGY LLC
5300 N Braeswood Blvd (77096-3307)
PHONE..........................732 581-0838
Charles Maslin, *CEO*
Tom Pilette, *Vice Pres*
Michael Zemble, *CFO*
EMP: 12
SALES (est): 514.4K **Privately Held**
SIC: 3691 Batteries, rechargeable

(G-12728)
ZEUS DEVELOPMENT CORP
16 Courtlandt Pl (77006-4013)
PHONE..........................713 952-9500
Robert Nimocks, *President*
EMP: 12
SQ FT: 5,000
SALES (est): 1MM **Privately Held**
WEB: www.stratasadvisors.com
SIC: 2741 8742 Miscellaneous publishing; management consulting services

(G-12729)
ZILKHA BIOMASS FUELS I LLC
1001 Mckinney St Ste 1925 (77002-6431)
PHONE..........................713 979-9961
Jack Holmes, *CEO*
Larry Weick, *Senior VP*
Doris Horton, *Accountant*
EMP: 30

SALES (est): 8.4MM **Privately Held**
WEB: www.zilkhabiomass.com
SIC: 2493 Reconstituted wood products

(G-12730)
ZIMMERMANN & JANSEN INC
Also Called: IMI Z & J
4525 Kennedy Commerce Dr
(77032-3425)
P.O. Box 3365, Humble (77347-3365)
PHONE.....................................281 446-8000
▲ EMP: 58
SQ FT: 50,000
SALES (est): 18.6MM
SALES (corp-wide): 3.2B **Privately Held**
SIC: 3494 3492 Valves & pipe fittings;
control valves, fluid power: hydraulic &
pneumatic
HQ: Zimmermann & Jansen Gmbh
Klingholzstr. 7
Wiesbaden 65189

(G-12731)
ZOCHEM LLC
109 N Post Oak Ln Ste 415 (77024-7847)
PHONE.....................................615 446-8791
Jimmy Kight, *Plant Mgr*
EMP: 30
SALES (corp-wide): 132K **Privately Held**
WEB: www.zochem.com
SIC: 2816 Zinc pigments: zinc oxide, zinc
sulfide
PA: Zochem Llc
600 Printwood Dr
Dickson TN 37055
615 446-8791

(G-12732)
ZOR N TERPRIZE
5955 Ridgeway Dr (77033-2135)
PHONE.....................................832 304-0504
Roslyn Shorter, *Owner*
Jozelle Patterson Burwell, *Principal*
EMP: 14
SQ FT: 1,610
SALES (est): 1.2MM **Privately Held**
SIC: 2741

(G-12733)
ZSPACE LLC
Also Called: Houston Sign Company
5801 Chimney Rock Rd (77081-2714)
PHONE.....................................713 662-3123
Eduardo Colunga, *Prdtn Mgr*
Debbie Jerolymack, *Sales Mgr*
Nathan Olinger, *Accounts Mgr*
Alan Olinger,
Maria Heath, *Graphic Designe*
EMP: 15
SQ FT: 10,000
SALES (est): 2.6MM **Privately Held**
WEB: www.houstonsign.com
SIC: 2499 2262 3993 Signboards, wood;
printing: manmade fiber & silk broadwo-
ven fabrics; signs, not made in custom
sign painting shops

Howe
Grayson County

(G-12734)
J DS MACHINE SHOP
805 Mardell Ln (75459-4458)
PHONE.....................................903 532-6240
Toll Free:.............................877   -
Judy Finney, *Owner*
EMP: 11
SQ FT: 7,000
SALES (est): 1.1MM **Privately Held**
SIC: 3366 Bushings & bearings

(G-12735)
MAGNI- POWER COMPANY
1800 1900 N Collins Fwy (75459)
P.O. Box 578 (75459-0578)
PHONE.....................................903 532-5533
Jim Bearden, *Manager*
EMP: 130
SQ FT: 1,441
SALES (corp-wide): 28.8MM **Privately
Held**
WEB: www.magnipower.com
SIC: 3444 Sheet metalwork

PA: Magni- Power Company
5511 E Lincoln Way
Wooster OH 44691
330 264-3637

(G-12736)
**MAGNI-FAB SOUTHWEST CO
(HQ)**
811 N Collins Fwy (75459-3647)
P.O. Box 578 (75459-0578)
PHONE.....................................903 532-5533
Bala Venkataraman, *President*
Tom Signer, *Safety Mgr*
D Flickinger, *Treasurer*
J W Taggart, *Admin Sec*
EMP: 50 EST: 1971
SQ FT: 168,000
SALES (est): 14.2MM
SALES (corp-wide): 28.8MM **Privately
Held**
WEB: www.magnipower.com
SIC: 3441 Fabricated structural metal
PA: Magni- Power Company
5511 E Lincoln Way
Wooster OH 44691
330 264-3637

Hubbard
Hill County

(G-12737)
RADKE MACHINE & TOOL INC
603 Ne 4th St (76648-2516)
PHONE.....................................254 576-2513
Donald Radke, *President*
David Holman, *Corp Secy*
Jason Radke, *Plant Mgr*
EMP: 22
SQ FT: 8,200
SALES (est): 4.1MM **Privately Held**
WEB: www.radkemachine.com
SIC: 3599 7692 3544 Machine shop, job-
bing & repair; welding repair; special dies,
tools, jigs & fixtures

Hughes Springs
Cass County

(G-12738)
AMERIPACK FOODS LLC
601 Fm 161 S (75656-6989)
PHONE.....................................903 639-4007
Gregory McMillon,
Dwayne Lejeune,
EMP: 23
SALES (est): 4.1MM **Privately Held**
WEB: www.ameripackfoods.com
SIC: 2099 Food preparations

(G-12739)
EAST TEXAS PIPE SERVICE INC
Fm Rd 161 S (75656)
P.O. Box 99 (75656-0099)
PHONE.....................................903 639-2541
Orville Cameron, *President*
Cameron Randy L, *Vice Pres*
EMP: 14 EST: 1977
SALES (est): 950K **Privately Held**
SIC: 1389 Oil field services; pipe testing,
oil field service

(G-12740)
**FARM CTCH CTFISH
PRCESSORS INC**
1221 601 Hwy 161 S (75656)
PHONE.....................................903 639-2394
Gregory McMillon, *Principal*
Dwayne T Le Jeune, *Director*
EMP: 80
SALES (est): 9MM **Privately Held**
SIC: 2092 Fresh or frozen packaged fish

Hull
Liberty County

(G-12741)
HARDS MARINE SERVICE LTD
Also Called: Hards Marine Service
266 County Road 2075 (77564-6837)
P.O. Box 2259, Dayton (77535-0038)
PHONE.....................................281 452-0848
Charles Hard, *President*
Jim McClain Jr, *Manager*
EMP: 66
SALES (est): 11.8MM **Privately Held**
WEB: www.hardsmarine.com
SIC: 3732 Boat building & repairing

Humble
Harris County

(G-12742)
ABASCO LLC
8561 E North Belt (77396-2915)
PHONE.....................................281 446-1500
Chuck La Bounty, *General Mgr*
Sue Tschoepe, *General Mgr*
Chuck Labounty, *Vice Pres*
Jeremy Cooper, *Opers Mgr*
Clint Labounty, *Sales Staff*
◆ EMP: 20
SQ FT: 30,000
SALES (est): 7.5MM **Privately Held**
WEB: www.abasco.com
SIC: 1389 3537 Construction, repair & dis-
mantling services; platforms, stands, ta-
bles, pallets & similar equipment

(G-12743)
ACE CONTROLS LLC
327 Derrick Dr (77338-4993)
PHONE.....................................713 589-5494
Sergio Gonzalez, *Regl Sales Mgr*
Agmed Aguirre, *Mng Member*
Albert Ortiz,
EMP: 12
SALES (est): 1.4MM **Privately Held**
WEB: www.acecontrolsllc.com
SIC: 3625 Control equipment, electric

(G-12744)
**AIRLINE MORTUARY
ASSOCIATES**
Also Called: A M A
1331 S Houston Ave (77338-4826)
P.O. Box 5953, Kingwood (77325-5953)
PHONE.....................................281 540-4141
Jon Bumbaugh, *President*
EMP: 9
SALES (est): 1.2MM **Privately Held**
WEB: www.airtrayman.com
SIC: 3499 Boxes for packing & shipping,
metal

(G-12745)
AMERICAN FRICTION INC
2401 Wilson Rd (77396-1533)
P.O. Box 729 (77347-0729)
PHONE.....................................713 818-5919
Jimmie D Jackson, *Partner*
Dan Jackson, *Partner*
Steve Jackson, *Partner*
▲ EMP: 10
SQ FT: 3,000
SALES (est): 1.4MM **Privately Held**
WEB: www.americanfriction.com
SIC: 3714 Motor vehicle parts & acces-
sories

(G-12746)
AMERICANA CABINETS LLC
5839 Bender Rd (77396-2006)
PHONE.....................................281 973-8255
William Jaegli,
EMP: 9
SALES (est): 119.3K **Privately Held**
SIC: 2434 Wood kitchen cabinets

(G-12747)
ASHER ENTERPRISES INC
Also Called: Asher Plumbing Company
19703 Highway 59 N (77338-3527)
PHONE.....................................281 446-8131

EMP: 20
SALES (est): 2.7MM **Privately Held**
SIC: 3569 Mfg General Industrial Machin-
ery

(G-12748)
ASPEN MANUFACTURING LLC
373 Atascocita Rd (77396-3606)
PHONE.....................................281 441-6500
David Piccione, *President*
Jason Ludeke, *COO*
Chris Mullin, *Opers Staff*
Randy Kellum, *Sales Mgr*
Donald Greif, *Sales Staff*
▲ EMP: 188 EST: 2011
SQ FT: 136,000
SALES (est): 62MM **Privately Held**
WEB: www.aspenmfg.com
SIC: 3585 Air conditioning equipment,
complete

(G-12749)
BRYNE SHEET METAL INC
848 S Houston Ave (77338-4831)
PHONE.....................................281 354-1100
James E Byrne, *President*
Mary Ann Byrne, *Corp Secy*
James Byrne, *Sr Consultant*
EMP: 60
SQ FT: 4,000
SALES (est): 3.2MM **Privately Held**
WEB: www.byrnemetals.com
SIC: 1761 3444 Sheet metalwork; forming
machine work, sheet metal

(G-12750)
BYRNE METALS CORP
848 S Houston Ave (77338-4831)
PHONE.....................................281 354-1100
James E Byrne, *President*
Steve Black, *Vice Pres*
Kevin Beard, *Project Mgr*
Trent Lewis, *Project Mgr*
Mary Ann Byrne, *Treasurer*
EMP: 20
SQ FT: 4,000
SALES (est): 4.7MM **Privately Held**
WEB: www.byrnemetals.com
SIC: 3444 Sheet metalwork

(G-12751)
CAM-TECH PRODUCTS INC
1811 Humble Place Dr (77338-5278)
P.O. Box 1177 (77347-1177)
PHONE.....................................281 548-0188
Frank Campisi, *President*
Diana Campisi, *Vice Pres*
Kevin Cqampisi, *Vice Pres*
Wendy Langston, *Vice Pres*
Tom Novaria, *QC Mgr*
EMP: 15
SQ FT: 5,000
SALES (est): 4MM **Privately Held**
WEB: www.cam-tech.com
SIC: 3533 5082 Bits, oil & gas field tools:
rock; oil field equipment

(G-12752)
**CAPROCK PERMIAN
PROCESSING LLC**
5810 Wilson Rd Ste 100 (77396-2943)
PHONE.....................................832 914-1679
EMP: 14 EST: 2016
SALES (est): 3.6MM **Privately Held**
SIC: 1311 Crude petroleum & natural gas

(G-12753)
CDI ENERGY PRODUCTS INC
Also Called: Fenner Advanced Sealing Tech
8103 Rankin Rd (77396-1484)
PHONE.....................................281 446-6662
Leonard Casey, *President*
Furman Kelley, *President*
Victor Jackson, *General Mgr*
Edwin Chavez, *Vice Pres*
Tito Chavez, *Plant Mgr*
▲ EMP: 370
SQ FT: 200,000
SALES (est): 107.9MM
SALES (corp-wide): 1.1B **Privately Held**
WEB: www.cdiproducts.com
SIC: 3053 Oil seals, rubber
HQ: Fenner Advanced Sealing Technolo-
gies, Inc.
975 Market St Ste 201a
Fort Mill SC 29708

(G-12754)
CENTURY ARCONDITIONING SUP L P
Also Called: Johnson Contrls Authorized Dlr
1919 Humble Place Dr (77338-5280)
PHONE.................................281 446-7820
EMP: 11 Privately Held
WEB: www.centuryac.com
SIC: 5075 3585 Air conditioning equipment, except room units; air conditioning equipment, complete
PA: Century Aircondicioning Supply, L. P.
10510 W Sam Huston Pkwy S
Houston TX 77099
281 933-3991

(G-12755)
CERADYNE INC
2838 N Strathford Ln (77345-5413)
PHONE.................................281 773-4135
EMP: 11
SALES (corp-wide): 32.1B Publicly Held
WEB: www.ceradyne.com
SIC: 3299 Non-metallic mineral statuary & other decorative products
HQ: Ceradyne, Inc.
1922 Barranca Pkwy
Irvine CA 92606
949 862-9600

(G-12756)
CHALLENGE MCH & FABRICATION
6460 Aldine Bender Rd (77396-3360)
PHONE.................................281 441-3115
David Brewer, President
Christopher Burris, Technology
EMP: 15 EST: 1970
SQ FT: 10,000
SALES (est): 2.2MM Privately Held
WEB: www.challengemachinefab.com
SIC: 3599 Machine shop, jobbing & repair

(G-12757)
CHEVRON PHILLIPS CHEM CO LP
1862 Kingwood Dr (77339-3048)
PHONE.................................281 359-6500
Mary J Hagenson, Partner
EMP: 101
SQ FT: 63,293
SALES (corp-wide): 3.5B Privately Held
WEB: www.cpchem.com
SIC: 2821 Plastics materials & resins
HQ: Chevron Phillips Chemical Company Lp
10001 Six Pines Dr
The Woodlands TX 77380
832 813-4100

(G-12758)
CLUTCHCO INTERNATIONAL INC (PA)
319 Derrick Dr (77338-4993)
P.O. Box 1089 (77347-1089)
PHONE.................................281 446-1297
Mike Killion, President
Trevor Shibley, VP Sales
Mark Marshall, Sales Staff
Larry McMasters, Branch Mgr
EMP: 40
SQ FT: 10,000
SALES (est): 10.4MM Privately Held
WEB: www.clutchcointl.com
SIC: 3568 Clutches, except vehicular

(G-12759)
CLUTCHCO USA
319 Derrick Dr (77338-4993)
P.O. Box 1089 (77347-1089)
PHONE.................................936 588-3501
Mike Killian, President
David Willis, Opers Mgr
Mark Bell, Sales Staff
Mario Martinez, Sales Staff
Joanna Tinsley, Branch Mgr
EMP: 10
SALES (est): 1MM Privately Held
WEB: www.clutchcointl.com
SIC: 3568 Clutches, except vehicular

(G-12760)
CNS TECH WLDG & FABRICATION LC
1881 Treble Dr (77338-5270)
PHONE.................................281 239-2555
Charles Lewis, President
Fran Sterling, Vice Pres
Frank Sterling, Mng Member
EMP: 43
SALES (est): 5MM Privately Held
WEB: www.trcw.com
SIC: 7692 Welding repair

(G-12761)
COMBINED RFRGN RESOURCES INC
Also Called: Smart Family Cooling Products
1118 1st St E (77338-4922)
PHONE.................................281 540-7552
Timothy Baker, President
Ryan Baker, Vice Pres
Christine Baker, Admin Sec
Amber Gregory, Receptionist
▲ EMP: 25
SQ FT: 50,000
SALES (est): 13.2MM Privately Held
WEB: www.smartcoolingproducts.com
SIC: 5075 5078 7623 3585 Air conditioning equipment, except room units; refrigeration equipment & supplies; refrigeration service & repair; refrigeration equipment, complete

(G-12762)
CUSTOM KITCHEN EQP CO INC
2601 Wilson Rd (77396-3709)
P.O. Box 1209 (77347-1209)
PHONE.................................281 446-8187
Jerald E Redmon, President
Peggy Redmon, Corp Secy
Glenn Redmon, Vice Pres
EMP: 27
SQ FT: 40,000
SALES (est): 5.8MM Privately Held
SIC: 3469 Kitchen fixtures & equipment: metal, except cast aluminum

(G-12763)
DIRECT TRAILER LP
Also Called: Direct Trailer & Equipment Co
20550 Townsen Blvd # 1001 (77338-4445)
PHONE.................................281 713-8925
Derrick Dilts, President
Walter Creech, COO
John L Quaid, CFO
Robert Horton, CTO
◆ EMP: 40
SALES (est): 7.5MM Privately Held
WEB: www.directtrailer.com
SIC: 3792 Camping trailers & chassis

(G-12764)
E G C CORPORATION
Also Called: Egc Corp Careers
8103 Lancoln Rd (77396)
P.O. Box 16080, Houston (77222-6080)
PHONE.................................281 774-6100
Jean-Michel Tiard, President
L A Ruggiero, Vice Pres
Donald L Hibbetts, Admin Sec
EMP: 300 EST: 1959
SQ FT: 89,000
SALES (est): 87.8K
SALES (corp-wide): 8.8MM Privately Held
WEB: www.cdiproducts.com
SIC: 3053 3089 Gaskets & sealing devices; injection molding of plastics
HQ: Compagnie Plastic Omnium Se
19 Avenue Jules Carteret
Lyon 69007
472 767-778

(G-12765)
ELECTRONIC TECHNICAL SVCS CORP
Also Called: Etsco
2616 Wilson Rd (77396-3705)
P.O. Box 1785, Porter (77365-1785)
PHONE.................................281 446-4414
David De Leon, President
Stacie Martin, Purch Mgr
EMP: 42
SQ FT: 16,000
SALES (est): 12.6MM Privately Held
WEB: www.etsco.net
SIC: 3625 5065 8711 5047 Industrial controls: push button, selector switches, pilot; electronic parts; engineering services; medical equipment & supplies; electrical repair shops

(G-12766)
FAITH MANUFACTURING CO INC
Also Called: M & J Manufacturing
406 Atascocita Rd (77396-3607)
PHONE.................................281 441-9595
Norman Webster, President
Larry Gustine, Vice Pres
Ken Griswold, Mfg Staff
Yajaira Garcia, Purchasing
Mila Walker, Accountant
EMP: 112
SQ FT: 30,000
SALES (est): 28MM Privately Held
WEB: www.faithmfg.com
SIC: 3533 Oil field machinery & equipment

(G-12767)
FORGED COMPONENTS INC (PA)
14527 Smith Rd (77396-2748)
PHONE.................................281 441-4088
Karl Lyons, President
Lee White, VP Opers
Brian Kellogg, Project Mgr
Edward Murphy, Opers Mgr
Russell Walling, Mfg Staff
◆ EMP: 120
SQ FT: 10,000
SALES (est): 56.1MM Privately Held
WEB: www.forgedcomponents.com
SIC: 3462 3498 5051 5085 Iron & steel forgings; pipe fittings, fabricated from purchased pipe; iron & steel (ferrous) products; forgings, ferrous; valves & fittings; valves & pipe fittings; fabricated plate work (boiler shop)

(G-12768)
FRANKLIN MACHINE & GEAR CORP
5903 Frost St (77396-3214)
PHONE.................................281 441-3177
EMP: 17
SQ FT: 16,000
SALES (est): 3.1MM Privately Held
WEB: www.franklingear.com
SIC: 3599 3462 Machine shop, jobbing & repair; chains, forged steel

(G-12769)
GENERAL ELECTRIC COMPANY
18710 Atscocita Forest Dr (77346-5104)
PHONE.................................281 812-0634
Todd Willis, Sales Staff
Mel Ward, Branch Mgr
EMP: 458
SALES (corp-wide): 95.2B Publicly Held
WEB: www.ge.com
SIC: 3511 Turbines & turbine generator sets
PA: General Electric Company
5 Necco St
Boston MA 02210
617 443-3000

(G-12770)
GILL ASSOC PRPRTY MGT SYSTEMS
Also Called: Gapms
1212 1st St E Ste C (77338-5917)
PHONE.................................832 644-9751
Vertina Gill, CEO
Darrell Gill, COO
EMP: 9 EST: 2016
SALES (est): 730.8K Privately Held
SIC: 1541 1795 7389 1721 Renovation, remodeling & repairs: industrial buildings; demolition, buildings & other structures; ; exterior residential painting contractor; residential lighting fixtures; construction site cleanup

(G-12771)
GRAYWOLF INDUSTRIAL INC (DH)
14500 Smith Rd (77396-2747)
PHONE.................................281 441-5400
Michael Lampert, CEO
Fortune Atigogo, Principal
Micheal Horn, Principal
Kelly Duncan, CFO
Mark Taylor, Finance
EMP: 30
SALES (est): 82.9MM Publicly Held
WEB: www.graywolf.com
SIC: 1791 1541 3449 3441 Structural steel erection; steel building construction; miscellaneous metalwork; expansion joints (structural shapes), iron or steel
HQ: Dbm Global Inc.
3020 E Camelback Rd # 100
Phoenix AZ 85016
602 252-7787

(G-12772)
GULF COAST ALLOY WELDING INC
4403 Theiss Rd (77338-1050)
P.O. Box 1327 (77347-1327)
PHONE.................................281 821-0543
Joel Deschamps, President
◆ EMP: 25
SQ FT: 30,000
SALES (est): 10.3MM Privately Held
WEB: www.gcaw.com
SIC: 3441 Fabricated structural metal

(G-12773)
GULF MANUFACTURING INC (PA)
Also Called: G M I
1221 Indiana St (77396-1524)
P.O. Box 2872 (77347-2872)
PHONE.................................281 446-0093
Steve R Maness, President
John Berzas, General Mgr
EMP: 40
SALES (est): 7.1MM Privately Held
WEB: www.gmigroup.com
SIC: 3462 Flange, valve & pipe fitting forgings, ferrous

(G-12774)
HALF PRICE BKS REC MGZINES INC
9743 Fm 1960 Bypass Rd W (77338-4067)
PHONE.................................281 540-3950
Julie Blankenship, General Mgr
Julie Blankenship, Manager
EMP: 17
SALES (corp-wide): 211.7MM Privately Held
WEB: www.becomegreen.info
SIC: 2721 5735 5932 Magazines: publishing & printing; records; book stores, secondhand
PA: Half Price Books, Records, Magazines, Incorporated
5803 E Northwest Hwy
Dallas TX 75231
214 360-0833

(G-12775)
HENDERSON DRILLING PDTS INC
6750 Bender Rd (77396-2107)
PHONE.................................281 661-3627
Dan Henderson, CEO
James Lank, President
Peter Knight, Exec VP
Rachel Bonnette, Marketing Staff
Pt Honeycutt, Director
EMP: 15
SQ FT: 9,000
SALES (est): 3.9MM
SALES (corp-wide): 16.2MM Privately Held
WEB: www.hendersonrigs.com
SIC: 3546 Drills & drilling tools
PA: Henderson Oilfield Products, Llc
6202 Storey Dr
Humble TX 77396
281 661-3627

(G-12776)
HGHT INC
14446 Smith Rd (77396-2745)
PHONE.................................281 446-1155
Craig Deemer, President
Derek Hjorth, Vice Pres
▲ EMP: 9 EST: 2011

SALES (est): 2.8MM **Privately Held**
SIC: 7539 3433 Radiator repair shop, automotive; radiators, except electric

(G-12777)
HOUSTON GLOBAL HEAT TRANSF LLC
14446 Smith Rd (77396-2745)
PHONE..................................281 446-1155
Randy Vanberg, *President*
Kevin Visscher, *General Mgr*
Derek Hjorth, *Senior VP*
Brian Barney, *Vice Pres*
John Gaska, *Vice Pres*
EMP: 75
SALES (est): 81MM **Publicly Held**
SIC: 3433 Radiators, except electric
PA: Forum Energy Technologies, Inc.
10344 Sam Houston Park Dr # 300
Houston TX 77064

(G-12778)
HUMBLE INDUSTRIES INC
2707 Wilson Rd (77396-3714)
P.O. Box 2592 (77347-2592)
PHONE..................................281 987-9175
David Pierce, *President*
Kristopher Pierce, *Principal*
Stacy Pierce, *Marketing Mgr*
Stacy Warren, *Director*
▲ EMP: 10 EST: 1981
SQ FT: 5,200
SALES (est): 1.5MM **Privately Held**
WEB: www.humbleindustries.com
SIC: 3053 Gaskets, all materials

(G-12779)
HUMBLE TEXAS SIGNS LLC
20702 Townsen Blvd (77338-4490)
PHONE..................................281 812-2100
Collin Cantrell, *Sales Mgr*
Steve Partin, *Sales Staff*
Donald Ritter, *Sales Staff*
Bart Peterschick, *Mng Member*
EMP: 45
SALES (est): 5.6MM **Privately Held**
WEB: www.humblesignco.com
SIC: 3993 Signs & advertising specialties

(G-12780)
J-KRAFT INC (PA)
4643 E Richey Rd (77338-3469)
P.O. Box 60089, Houston (77205-0089)
PHONE..................................281 876-2535
Jeremy L McCutchen, *President*
Charles W Lucas, *Director*
Tammy McCutchey, *Director*
▼ EMP: 45
SQ FT: 60,000
SALES (est): 8.6MM **Privately Held**
WEB: www.jkraftinc.com
SIC: 1751 2434 Cabinet & finish carpentry; wood kitchen cabinets

(G-12781)
JASMINE LEWIS
Also Called: Jazzy's Southern Creations
18551 Timber Forest Dr (77346-2539)
PHONE..................................325 200-5769
Jasmine Lewis, *Owner*
EMP: 12
SALES (est): 430K **Privately Held**
SIC: 3944 Craft & hobby kits & sets

(G-12782)
KEVIN GOSS
Also Called: Venture Precision
1881 Treble Dr (77338-5270)
PHONE..................................281 812-1600
Kevin Goss, *Owner*
EMP: 25 EST: 2008
SALES (est): 8MM **Privately Held**
WEB: www.ventureprecision.com
SIC: 3599 Amusement park equipment

(G-12783)
LAWLER FOODS LTD (HQ)
Also Called: Lawler's Dessert
2200 S Houston Ave (77396-1513)
P.O. Box 2558 (77347-2558)
PHONE..................................281 446-0059
Agustina Arellano, *Safety Dir*
Jesse Leal, *Production*
Robert Presta, *Production*
Robert Nemanich, *Purch Mgr*
Matthew Clifford, *Financial Analy*

▲ EMP: 200
SQ FT: 60,000
SALES (est): 80MM
SALES (corp-wide): 130MM **Privately Held**
WEB: www.lawlers.com
SIC: 2051 2053 Cakes, pies & pastries; cakes, bakery: except frozen; frozen bakery products, except bread
PA: Desserts Llc
30 7th St E
Saint Paul MN 55101
612 356-5200

(G-12784)
LAWLER FOODS LTD
Also Called: Lawler Foods Construction
1219 Carpenter Rd (77396-1535)
P.O. Box 2558 (77347-2558)
PHONE..................................281 540-3321
Bill Lawler, *Branch Mgr*
EMP: 160
SQ FT: 72,293
SALES (corp-wide): 130MM **Privately Held**
WEB: www.lawlers.com
SIC: 2051 Bakery: wholesale or wholesale/retail combined
HQ: Lawler Foods, Ltd.
2200 S Houston Ave
Humble TX 77396
281 446-0059

(G-12785)
LOTTCO INC
19747 Highway 59 N # 410 (77338-3576)
P.O. Box 2408 (77347-2408)
PHONE..................................832 773-4345
Larry Lott, *CEO*
Allen Lott, *Vice Pres*
Keith Bradley, *VP Sales*
EMP: 20
SQ FT: 1,600
SALES (est): 150.8K **Privately Held**
WEB: www.lottcoinc.com
SIC: 1381 1781 Service well drilling; water well drilling

(G-12786)
MACRO TEX MACHINE WORKS LLC
2632 Wilson Rd (77396-3705)
PHONE..................................281 540-2141
Juan A Mendoza, *President*
Julio Mendez, *Purchasing*
EMP: 10
SQ FT: 6,000
SALES (est): 1.5MM **Privately Held**
WEB: www.macrotexmachinework.com
SIC: 3452 3451 3599 Bolts, nuts, rivets & washers; screw machine products; machine & other job shop work

(G-12787)
MARINE RUBBER INC (PA)
Also Called: Marine Urethane
2000 Wilson Rd (77396-1537)
P.O. Box 2438 (77347-2438)
PHONE..................................281 446-4132
EMP: 14 EST: 1973
SQ FT: 16,000
SALES (est): 4.4MM **Privately Held**
WEB: www.marineurethane.com
SIC: 2821 5088 Polyurethane resins; marine supplies

(G-12788)
MCGASKETS & PTFE SPC INC
6010 Dwyer Dr (77396-3264)
P.O. Box 473, Galena Park (77547-0473)
PHONE..................................713 847-6700
Walter C McCormick, *President*
Kurt W McCormick, *Vice Pres*
EMP: 15
SQ FT: 15,000
SALES (est): 3MM **Privately Held**
WEB: www.mcgaskets.com
SIC: 3053 Gaskets, all materials

(G-12789)
METAL ZINC LLC (PA)
19408 Kenswick Dr (77338-8147)
P.O. Box 62628, Houston (77205-2628)
PHONE..................................832 252-9116
Don Knight, *Principal*
Peter F Walsh, *Mng Member*

EMP: 9 EST: 2015
SALES (est): 3.5MM **Privately Held**
WEB: www.metalzincmfg.com
SIC: 3444 Sheet metalwork

(G-12790)
NORKOL INC
Also Called: Norkol Industrial Film
1731 Treble Dr (77338-5254)
PHONE..................................832 644-1481
Jeff Davis, *Branch Mgr*
EMP: 20
SALES (corp-wide): 247.3MM **Privately Held**
WEB: www.norkol.com
SIC: 2671 Plastic film, coated or laminated for packaging
PA: Norkol, Inc.
11650 W Grand Ave
Northlake IL 60164
708 531-1000

(G-12791)
ONE SOURCE SEC & SOUND INC (PA)
2925 Fm 1960 Rd E (77338-5329)
PHONE..................................713 934-7400
Steve G Smith, *CEO*
Jason Smith, *Ch of Bd*
Josh Wilder, *COO*
Marcos Rivas, *Vice Pres*
Steve Smith, *Vice Pres*
EMP: 20
SALES (est): 15MM **Privately Held**
WEB: www.os2s.com
SIC: 7382 3578 1731 1771 Security systems services; automatic teller machines (ATM); lighting contractor; foundation & footing contractor

(G-12792)
PETROCHEM FIELD SERVICES INC
2429 Wilson Rd (77396-1533)
P.O. Box 60047, Houston (77205-0047)
PHONE..................................281 441-2550
Sergio Sanchez, *President*
Tina Hallmark, *Manager*
Howard Smith, *Admin Sec*
◆ EMP: 60
SALES (est): 52.6MM **Privately Held**
WEB: www.pfs-us.com
SIC: 1389 Oil field services

(G-12793)
PETROTRIM SERVICES LLC
1881 Treble Dr (77338-5270)
PHONE..................................281 821-2111
Kevin Goss,
Jason Beck,
▲ EMP: 45
SQ FT: 40,000
SALES (est): 3MM **Privately Held**
WEB: www.petrotrim.com
SIC: 3533 8711 Oil field machinery & equipment; engineering services

(G-12794)
PIPELINE TECHNIQUE LLC
6605 Rankin Rd (77396-1321)
PHONE..................................281 570-1363
Patrick Boerner, *CEO*
Alan Morrison, *General Mgr*
Robbert Reddering, *Project Mgr*
Ramandeep Panesar, *Project Engr*
Thelma Zuniga, *Manager*
▲ EMP: 200
SQ FT: 8,000
SALES (est): 13.3MM
SALES (corp-wide): 2.1MM **Privately Held**
WEB: www.pipelinewelders.com
SIC: 1389 Oil & gas wells: building, repairing & dismantling
HQ: Pipeline Technique Ltd.
Deveronside Works
Huntly
146 679-5888

(G-12795)
RB MACHINE WORKS INC
2407 Wilson Rd (77396-1533)
P.O. Box 218 (77347-0218)
PHONE..................................281 446-1414
Roger H Bethune, *President*
EMP: 45

SQ FT: 28,000
SALES (est): 7.6MM **Privately Held**
WEB: www.rbmachineworks.com
SIC: 3599 Machine shop, jobbing & repair

(G-12796)
REACTIVE DOWNHOLE TLS USA INC
19945 Aldine Westfield Rd (77338-3303)
PHONE..................................281 821-6566
Mike Allen, *CEO*
Nicholas Atkins, *Director*
Jill Webster, *Director*
▲ EMP: 34
SALES (est): 7.9MM
SALES (corp-wide): 5.6MM **Privately Held**
WEB: www.reactivetools.com
SIC: 3533 Oil & gas field machinery
PA: Reactive Downhole Tools Limited
Balgownie Lodge
Aberdeen AB22
122 482-7224

(G-12797)
RUSSELL OILFIELD EQUIPMENT CO
1910 Humble Place Dr (77338-5279)
PHONE..................................281 540-8982
David D Russell, *President*
Karen S Russell, *Corp Secy*
Seth Brady, *Vice Pres*
William Russell, *Vice Pres*
Blake Jackson, *Sales Staff*
▲ EMP: 14
SQ FT: 10,000
SALES (est): 7.4MM **Privately Held**
WEB: www.russelloilfield.com
SIC: 5084 3533 5082 Oil well machinery, equipment & supplies; oil & gas drilling rigs & equipment; oil field equipment

(G-12798)
SOUTHWEST IMPREGLON R INC
15014 Lee Rd (77396-3221)
PHONE..................................281 441-2000
Gregory S Butler, *President*
Tim Edwards, *Opers Mgr*
Jesus Navarro, *Opers Staff*
Beverly Aldana, *Purchasing*
Terry Bourdon, *QC Mgr*
EMP: 25 EST: 1974
SQ FT: 25,000
SALES (est): 4.2MM **Privately Held**
WEB: www.swimpreglon.com
SIC: 3479 2911 Coating of metals & formed products; oils, lubricating; greases, lubricating

(G-12799)
SPECIALTY PROCESS EQP CORP
1931 Humble Place Dr # 207 (77338-5257)
PHONE..................................281 812-7732
Zafar Sheikh, *President*
Tasnim Sheikh, *Corp Secy*
Zafar Shiekh, *Plant Mgr*
◆ EMP: 75
SQ FT: 25,000
SALES (est): 16.1MM **Privately Held**
WEB: www.spec-pro.com
SIC: 3823 Industrial instrmnts msrmnt display/control process variable

(G-12800)
TACKI MAC GRIPS
Also Called: Avon Golf Grips
22000 Northpark Dr (77339-3803)
PHONE..................................281 358-6738
Dave Kelley, *President*
▲ EMP: 9
SALES (est): 1.2MM **Privately Held**
WEB: www.tackimac.com
SIC: 3069 Grips or handles, rubber

(G-12801)
TECALEMIT INC
Also Called: PCL Air Technology
6324 Greens Rd (77396-2027)
PHONE..................................281 446-7300
Torsten Kutschnski, *President*
Steve Thompson, *Vice Pres*
▲ EMP: 100
SQ FT: 500

SALES (est): 17.1MM
SALES (corp-wide): 1.9B **Privately Held**
WEB: www.pcltireinflationusa.com
SIC: 3823 3586 Fluidic devices, circuits & systems for process control; gasoline pumps, measuring or dispensing
HQ: Horngroup Holding Gmbh & Co. Kg
　　　Munketoft 42
　　　Flensburg　24937
　　　461 869-60

(G-12802)
TEJAS UTILITY CONSTRUCTION INC
8503 Pines Place Dr (77346-2222)
PHONE...............................281 299-5097
John Holloway, *CEO*
EMP: 10
SALES (est): 390.7K **Privately Held**
SIC: 1389 Hot shot service; mud service, oil field drilling

(G-12803)
TGS-NOPEC GEOPHYSICAL COMPANY
2345 Atascocita Rd (77396-3504)
PHONE...............................281 319-4944
Rod Starr, *Vice Pres*
John Adamick, *Vice Pres*
Candice Grimm, *Manager*
EMP: 41 **Privately Held**
WEB: www.tgs.com
SIC: 1382 Oil & gas exploration services
HQ: Tgs-Nopec Geophysical Company
　　　10451 Clay Rd
　　　Houston TX 77041

(G-12804)
THERMTECH INC
14723 Ashland Pines Ln (77396-4121)
P.O. Box 5318, Kingwood (77325-5318)
PHONE...............................281 359-7555
William H Hedges, *CEO*
Margery O Hedges, *Vice Pres*
EMP: 27
SQ FT: 14,000
SALES (est): 5.7MM **Privately Held**
WEB: www.proact-usa.com
SIC: 3564 Air purification equipment

(G-12805)
TRAY-TEC INC
2598 Wilson Rd (77396-3703)
P.O. Box 35 (77347-0035)
PHONE...............................281 441-7314
Leonardo Botello, *President*
Gary Thomas, *Superintendent*
Darell Fowler, *Vice Pres*
Chuck Flores, *Project Mgr*
Angel Botello, *Treasurer*
EMP: 20
SQ FT: 6,000
SALES (est): 4.5MM **Privately Held**
WEB: www.traytec.com
SIC: 8748 3443 Business consulting; towers (bubble, cooling, fractionating, etc.): metal plate

(G-12806)
TRISTAR PACKAGING INC
1731 Treble Dr (77338-5254)
P.O. Box 1015 (77347-1015)
PHONE...............................281 540-2613
Mohammed Karani, *President*
Naresh Pandit, *Sales Dir*
◆ **EMP:** 10
SQ FT: 22,000
SALES (est): 2.4MM **Privately Held**
WEB: www.tristarpackaginginc.com
SIC: 2674 2673 5199 Paper bags: made from purchased materials; plastic & pliofilm bags; packaging materials

(G-12807)
WORLDFAB INC
2626 Wilson Rd (77396-3705)
P.O. Box 14508 (77347-4508)
PHONE...............................281 446-9777
Jeff Huckaby, *President*
Christy REA, *Vice Pres*
Casey Cranford, *Administration*
EMP: 15 **EST:** 2011
SALES (est): 2.7MM **Privately Held**
WEB: www.worldfabinc.com
SIC: 3449 Bars, concrete reinforcing: fabricated steel

Huntington
Angelina County

(G-12808)
ADAM NERREN LTD
2612 Fm Rd 328 (75949)
P.O. Box 1240 (75949-1240)
PHONE...............................936 422-4800
Adam Nerren, *Principal*
EMP: 9
SALES (est): 1.1MM **Privately Held**
SIC: 2421 Custom sawmill

(G-12809)
D & L TIMBER INC
403 Martin Cochran Rd (75949-3837)
PHONE...............................936 422-3153
Darwin Blake, *President*
Lisa Blake, *Admin Sec*
EMP: 35 **EST:** 1994
SALES (est): 3MM **Privately Held**
SIC: 2411 Logging camps & contractors

(G-12810)
KEITH CARRELL LOGGING INC
1775 Pahal Rd (75949-4257)
P.O. Box 43 (75949-0043)
PHONE...............................936 422-3375
Keith Carrell, *President*
Judy Carrell, *Admin Sec*
EMP: 25
SALES (est): 3.4MM **Privately Held**
SIC: 2411 5031 Logging camps & contractors; lumber: rough, dressed & finished

Huntsville
Walker County

(G-12811)
FALCON WOOD PRODUCTS 2 LTD
Also Called: Quality Wood Products
7031 State Highway 75 S (77340-7281)
PHONE...............................936 295-9381
Kenneth Cox, *General Ptnr*
EMP: 20
SQ FT: 14,000
SALES (est): 2MM **Privately Held**
SIC: 2541 Cabinets, except refrigerated: show, display, etc.: wood

(G-12812)
GARDNER GLASS PRODUCTS INC
7553 Highway 75 S (77340-2485)
PHONE...............................936 291-7271
Martin Deal, *Manager*
EMP: 100
SALES (corp-wide): 85.2MM **Privately Held**
WEB: www.gardnerglass.com
SIC: 3231 Mirrored glass
PA: Gardner Glass Products, Inc.
　　　301 Elkin Hwy
　　　North Wilkesboro NC 28659
　　　336 651-9300

(G-12813)
HENKE ENTERPRISES INC
1792 Highway 30 E (77320-9227)
PHONE...............................936 291-2026
Keith Henke, *President*
Matt Henke, *General Mgr*
Melissa Henke, *Admin Sec*
EMP: 12
SALES (est): 1.3MM **Privately Held**
WEB: www.henkeenterprises.com
SIC: 3669 Traffic signals, electric

(G-12814)
HYPONEX CORPORATION
1284 State Highway 75 N (77320-1086)
PHONE...............................936 291-6386
Jeff Flowers, *Branch Mgr*
EMP: 46
SALES (corp-wide): 4.1B **Publicly Held**
WEB: www.scotts.com
SIC: 2873 Fertilizers: natural (organic), except compost

HQ: Hyponex Corporation
　　　14111 Scottslawn Rd
　　　Marysville OH 43040
　　　937 644-0011

(G-12815)
JOHNSON CNSTR CLEARING LLC
11 Deerfield Rd (77340-9702)
P.O. Box 9589 (77340-0027)
PHONE...............................281 659-1428
Rex Johnson, *Foreman/Supr*
Michael Johnson, *Mng Member*
Michael Olan Johnson, *Mng Member*
Tresha Johnson,
EMP: 49
SALES (est): 20MM **Privately Held**
WEB: www.johnsonconstructionclearing.com
SIC: 1389 Excavating slush pits & cellars

(G-12816)
LIQUID MINERALS GROUP LTD
37 Fm 2793 Rd (77340-2729)
P.O. Box 1700, New Waverly (77358-1700)
PHONE...............................936 291-2424
Mark Hughes, *CEO*
Dan Smith, *President*
Andrew Holland, *Manager*
Bonnie McGilvrey, *Manager*
Nathaniel J Smoter, *Manager*
◆ **EMP:** 25
SALES (est): 8.4MM
SALES (corp-wide): 130.6MM **Privately Held**
WEB: www.liquidminerals.com
SIC: 2819 Industrial inorganic chemicals
PA: Pilot Chemical Company Of Ohio
　　　2744 E Kemper Rd
　　　Cincinnati OH 45241
　　　513 326-0600

(G-12817)
M & M DESIGNS INC
1981 Quality Blvd (77320-8761)
P.O. Box 1228 (77342-1228)
PHONE...............................936 295-2682
▲ **EMP:** 32
SQ FT: 10,000
SALES (est): 4.4MM **Privately Held**
WEB: www.m-mdesigns.com
SIC: 2759 2396 2752 Screen printing; automotive & apparel trimmings; commercial printing, lithographic

(G-12818)
MATERIA INC
7629 Highway 75 S (77340-2487)
PHONE...............................936 295-4040
Chuck Woodson, *Branch Mgr*
Wesleyne Greer, *Senior Mgr*
EMP: 12
SALES (corp-wide): 21.9MM **Privately Held**
WEB: www.materia-inc.com
SIC: 3699 Electrical equipment & supplies
PA: Materia, Inc.
　　　60 N San Gabriel Blvd
　　　Pasadena CA 91107
　　　626 584-8400

(G-12819)
MICRO ENGINEERING INC
Also Called: Micro Star Technologies
511 Fm 3179 Rd (77340-2286)
PHONE...............................936 291-6891
Michelle Oates, *President*
Scott Oates, *Vice Pres*
Scott Goodman, *IT/INT Sup*
Cathy Ryan, *Admin Sec*
EMP: 12
SQ FT: 4,880
SALES (est): 500K **Privately Held**
SIC: 3841 Knives, surgical

(G-12820)
NEWSPAPER HOLDING INC
Also Called: Huntsville Item
1409 10th St (77320-3805)
P.O. Box 539 (77342-0539)
PHONE...............................936 295-5407
Rita Haldwin, *Manager*
EMP: 50

SALES (corp-wide): 23.7B **Privately Held**
WEB: www.oskaloosa.com
SIC: 2711 Newspapers, publishing & printing
HQ: Newspaper Holding, Inc.
　　　425 Locust St
　　　Johnstown PA 15901
　　　814 532-5102

(G-12821)
OLIVER BROTHERS SAWMILL
Also Called: Oliver Brothers Lumber Co
1537 Us Highway 190 (77340-7385)
PHONE...............................936 295-0931
Fax: 936 295-0941
EMP: 9
SQ FT: 1,000
SALES (est): 520K **Privately Held**
SIC: 2421 Sawmill

(G-12822)
PILOT CHEMICAL COMPANY OHIO
Also Called: Liquid Minerals
37 Fm 2793 Rd (77340-2729)
PHONE...............................936 291-2424
EMP: 25
SALES (corp-wide): 130.6MM **Privately Held**
WEB: www.pilotchemical.com
SIC: 2819 Industrial inorganic chemicals
PA: Pilot Chemical Company Of Ohio
　　　2744 E Kemper Rd
　　　Cincinnati OH 45241
　　　513 326-0600

(G-12823)
PRAXAIR INC
1223 Financial Plz (77340-3505)
PHONE...............................936 295-3912
EMP: 20
SALES (corp-wide): 11.4B **Publicly Held**
SIC: 2813 Mfg Industrial Gases
PA: Praxair, Inc.
　　　10 Riverview Dr
　　　Danbury CT 06810
　　　203 837-2000

(G-12824)
STEELY LUMBER CO INC
1405 Southwood Dr (77340-2479)
PHONE...............................936 295-5898
Kelvin Steely, *Owner*
Deann Steely, *Corp Secy*
EMP: 55 **EST:** 1964
SQ FT: 2,000
SALES (est): 9.3MM **Privately Held**
WEB: www.steelylumber.com
SIC: 2421 Lumber: rough, sawed or planed

(G-12825)
TEXAS DEPT CRIMINAL JUSTICE
Also Called: TCI Garment Division
Wine Unit (77349-0001)
PHONE...............................936 295-6371
Charles Bill, *Principal*
EMP: 900
SALES (corp-wide): 128.4B **Privately Held**
WEB: www.tdcj.texas.gov
SIC: 9223 2515 Prison, government; mattresses & foundations
HQ: Texas Department Of Criminal Justice
　　　861b Interstate 45 N # 22
　　　Huntsville TX 77320
　　　936 295-6371

(G-12826)
TXI OPERATIONS LP
51 Champion Woodyard Rd (77340-2711)
PHONE...............................936 295-7672
Michael Nicholas, *Manager*
EMP: 141 **Publicly Held**
WEB: www.martinmarietta.com
SIC: 3273 Ready-mixed concrete
HQ: Txi Operations Lp
　　　1341 W Mockingbird Ln 700w
　　　Dallas TX 75247

(G-12827)
U S WEATHERFORD L P
Also Called: Weatherford CPS
7587 State Highway 75 S (77340-2485)
PHONE...............................936 435-8118
Kelly Ammons, *Manager*

▲ = Import ▼=Export
◆ =Import/Export

EMP: 9 **Privately Held**
WEB: www.weatherford.com
SIC: 1389 Oil field services
HQ: U S Weatherford L P
179 Weatherford Dr
Schriever LA 70395
985 493-6100

(G-12828)
U S WEATHERFORD L P
Weatherford Well Construction
7587 Highway 75 S (77340-2485)
PHONE.....................936 295-0080
Johnny Debaugh, *Branch Mgr*
EMP: 27
SQ FT: 60,000 **Privately Held**
WEB: www.weatherford.com
SIC: 1389 Oil field services
HQ: U S Weatherford L P
179 Weatherford Dr
Schriever LA 70395
985 493-6100

(G-12829)
**WEATHERFORD
INTERNATIONAL LLC**
7587 State Highway 75 S (77340-2485)
PHONE.....................985 493-6100
Eric Huseth, *General Mgr*
Tracey Reyes, *General Mgr*
Scott Antonsen, *District Mgr*
Wade Pitre, *District Mgr*
Christopher Schmidt, *District Mgr*
EMP: 400 **Privately Held**
WEB: www.weatherford.com
SIC: 1389 Oil field services
HQ: Weatherford International, Llc
2000 Saint James Pl
Houston TX 77056
713 693-4000

(G-12830)
**WEATHERFORD
INTERNATIONAL LLC**
Also Called: Weatherford Completion
7587 Hwy 785 S (77340)
P.O. Box 389 (77342-0389)
PHONE.....................713 693-4000
Mike Baker, *Manager*
EMP: 23 **Privately Held**
WEB: www.weatherford.com
SIC: 1389 Oil field services
HQ: Weatherford International, Llc
2000 Saint James Pl
Houston TX 77056
713 693-4000

Hurst
Tarrant County

(G-12831)
**ADVANCED AERO COATINGS
LLC (PA)**
9004 Trinity Blvd (76053-7620)
PHONE.....................817 280-0467
Rodney Pittman, *Principal*
Floyd Pittman, *Mng Member*
David Bullard, *Mng Member*
EMP: 18
SALES (est): 4.8MM **Privately Held**
WEB: www.advancedaerocoatings.com
SIC: 3399 Laminating steel

(G-12832)
AHLERS AEROSPACE INC (PA)
3621 Raider Dr (76053-7907)
PHONE.....................817 553-2155
Peter Kayfus, *President*
Larry Ahlers, *Corp Secy*
Robert Chambers, *Engineer*
Josie New, *Finance*
Stephanie Cusimano, *Office Mgr*
EMP: 20 EST: 1996
SQ FT: 18,000
SALES: 2.7MM **Privately Held**
WEB: www.ahlers-aerospace.com
SIC: 7699 3812 Aircraft & heavy equipment repair services; search & navigation equipment

(G-12833)
**ANADITE CAL RESTORATION TR
(PA)**
711 W Hurst Blvd (76053-7698)
PHONE.....................817 282-9171
William W Curtis, *Trustee*
Ann Weldon, *Administration*
EMP: 19
SALES (est): 4.2MM **Privately Held**
SIC: 3471 3365 3364 Anodizing (plating) of metals or formed products; plating of metals or formed products; finishing, metals or formed products; aluminum & aluminum-based alloy castings; magnesium & magnesium-base alloy die-castings

(G-12834)
ARLINGTON CAST STONE INC
721 W Hurst Blvd (76053-7605)
PHONE.....................817 284-5933
Nick Easen, *President*
EMP: 15
SQ FT: 7,200
SALES (est): 2.4MM **Privately Held**
WEB: www.arlingtoncaststone.com
SIC: 5032 5211 3272 Granite building stone; lumber & other building materials; stone, cast concrete

(G-12835)
**AZZ - TEXAS WELDED WIRE
LLC**
Also Called: Texas Welded Wire LLC
637 W Hurst Blvd Ste B (76053-7621)
P.O. Box 1485 (76053-1485)
PHONE.....................817 282-4560
Gordon Briggs, *Mng Member*
▼ EMP: 20
SQ FT: 20,000
SALES (est): 3.4MM
SALES (corp-wide): 1B **Publicly Held**
SIC: 3496 Miscellaneous fabricated wire products
PA: Azz Inc.
3100 W 7th St Ste 500
Fort Worth TX 76107
817 810-0095

(G-12836)
AZZ INCORPORATED
Also Called: North American Galvanizing
625 W Hurst Blvd (76053-7603)
PHONE.....................817 268-2414
Gordon Briggs, *Plant Mgr*
Sherry Miller, *Office Mgr*
Karen Bryant, *Executive*
EMP: 65
SQ FT: 28,208
SALES (corp-wide): 1B **Publicly Held**
WEB: www.azz.com
SIC: 3479 Hot dip coating of metals or formed products; galvanizing of iron, steel or end-formed products
PA: Azz Inc.
3100 W 7th St Ste 500
Fort Worth TX 76107
817 810-0095

(G-12837)
BELL TEXTRON INC
3405 Lake Knoll Ct (76053-7862)
PHONE.....................817 280-1587
Kip Campbell, *Principal*
Erik Barnes, *Engineer*
Matt Houters, *Engineer*
Brandon Thomas, *Engineer*
Sonja Clark, *Manager*
EMP: 10
SALES (corp-wide): 13.6B **Publicly Held**
WEB: www.bellflight.com
SIC: 3728 3721 Research & dev by manuf., aircraft parts & auxiliary equip; motorized aircraft
HQ: Bell Textron Inc.
3255 Bell Flight Blvd
Fort Worth TX 76118
817 280-2011

(G-12838)
BELL TEXTRON INC
Also Called: Bell Helicopter Plant 2
3000 S Norwood Dr (76053-7851)
P.O. Box 482, Fort Worth (76101-0482)
PHONE.....................817 280-2011
David Livingston, *Engineer*

Karl Sipple, *Engineer*
George Hawkins, *Branch Mgr*
Emmanuel Correa, *Supervisor*
Lorie Casas, *Analyst*
EMP: 50
SALES (corp-wide): 13.6B **Publicly Held**
WEB: www.bellflight.com
SIC: 3728 Aircraft parts & equipment
HQ: Bell Textron Inc.
3255 Bell Flight Blvd
Fort Worth TX 76118
817 280-2011

(G-12839)
BELL TEXTRON INC
Also Called: Bell Publications
600 E Hurst Blvd (76053-8030)
P.O. Box 482, Fort Worth (76101-0482)
PHONE.....................817 280-2011
Sean Holly, *Vice Pres*
Cazandra Farrar, *Opers Staff*
Mark Lemke, *Purchasing*
Spencer Coker, *Engineer*
Jesse Tamez, *Plant Engr*
EMP: 68
SALES (corp-wide): 13.6B **Publicly Held**
WEB: www.bellflight.com
SIC: 3728 Aircraft parts & equipment
HQ: Bell Textron Inc.
3255 Bell Flight Blvd
Fort Worth TX 76118
817 280-2011

(G-12840)
BMC WEST LLC
Also Called: BMC West Door Plant
104 E Hurst Blvd (76053-7802)
PHONE.....................817 952-3124
Duane Sanders, *Chairman*
EMP: 50
SALES (corp-wide): 7.2B **Publicly Held**
WEB: www.buildwithbmc.com
SIC: 5211 2431 Lumber & other building materials; door frames, wood
HQ: Bmc West, Llc
4800 Falls Of Neuse Rd # 400
Raleigh NC 27609
919 431-1000

(G-12841)
**CAPLINGERS CRANE & EQP
SVC INC**
Also Called: C C E
10741 Tube Dr (76053-7909)
PHONE.....................817 685-0710
Jimmy C Caplinger, *President*
Judy M Caplinger, *President*
Roland Dominguez, *Project Mgr*
Les Jones, *Engineer*
Lori Smith, *Financial Exec*
▲ EMP: 20
SQ FT: 12,000
SALES (est): 8.3MM **Privately Held**
WEB: www.craneandhoist.com
SIC: 5084 7699 3536 Cranes, industrial; industrial machinery & equipment repair; hoists, cranes & monorails

(G-12842)
**CHEMICAL LIME-SOUTHWEST
LLC**
Hurst Terminal Us72
3110 S Precinct Line Rd (76053-7615)
P.O. Box 35 (76053-0035)
PHONE.....................817 268-1188
Terry Morrs, *General Mgr*
EMP: 20
SALES (corp-wide): 2.6MM **Privately Held**
WEB: www.lhoist.com
SIC: 3274 Lime
HQ: Chemical Lime-Southwest, Llc
3700 Hulen St
Fort Worth TX 76107
817 732-8164

(G-12843)
CHOIERS COMPANY
2716 Fox Glenn Ct (76054-2778)
PHONE.....................817 312-1364
▲ EMP: 126
SALES (est): 6.9MM **Privately Held**
SIC: 2038 Mfg Frozen Specialties

(G-12844)
DELTA RIGGING & TOOLS INC
Also Called: Tuffy Products
1149 W Hurst Blvd (76053-7403)
PHONE.....................877 889-8833
George Suarez, *Branch Mgr*
James Morton, *Manager*
EMP: 75
SALES (corp-wide): 3.1B **Privately Held**
WEB: www.deltarigging.com
SIC: 2298 3429 3496 Cordage & twine; manufactured hardware (general); miscellaneous fabricated wire products
HQ: Delta Rigging & Tools, Inc.
125 Mccarty St
Houston TX 77029

(G-12845)
HWM HURST INC
645 W Hurst Blvd (76053-7603)
P.O. Box 1485 (76053-1485)
PHONE.....................817 268-6111
Greg Haskin, *CEO*
Russell Wallace, *President*
James B Mason, *Corp Secy*
EMP: 35
SQ FT: 21,000
SALES (est): 3.2MM **Privately Held**
SIC: 3479 3471 Galvanizing of iron, steel or end-formed products; plating & polishing

(G-12846)
INDEX SKATEBOARDING
3312 S Riley Ct (76054-1913)
PHONE.....................817 887-9779
Dameon Rowe, *Owner*
EMP: 10
SALES (est): 191K **Privately Held**
SIC: 3949 Skateboards

(G-12847)
**KELLY-MOORE PAINT COMPANY
INC**
Also Called: Kelly-Moore Paints
303 W Hurst Blvd (76053-7705)
PHONE.....................817 268-1511
Justin Green, *Manager*
Ronald Kayser, *Executive*
EMP: 10
SALES (corp-wide): 564.3MM **Privately
Held**
WEB: www.kellymoore.com
SIC: 5198 5231 2851 Paints; paint & painting supplies; paints & allied products
PA: Kelly-Moore Paint Company Inc
987 Commercial St
San Carlos CA 94070
650 592-8337

(G-12848)
**KELLY-MOORE PAINT COMPANY
INC**
Also Called: Kelly-Moore Paints
305 Hurst (76053)
PHONE.....................800 772-7408
Ramon Bell, *Principal*
EMP: 12
SALES (corp-wide): 564.3MM **Privately
Held**
WEB: www.kellymoore.com
SIC: 2851 Paints: oil or alkyd vehicle or water thinned
PA: Kelly-Moore Paint Company Inc
987 Commercial St
San Carlos CA 94070
650 592-8337

(G-12849)
**LHOIST NORTH AMERICA ALA
LLC**
Also Called: Hurst Terminal Us72
3110 S Precinct Line Rd (76053-7615)
P.O. Box 35, Fort Worth (76244-0035)
PHONE.....................817 268-1187
Chris Boring, *Plant Mgr*
EMP: 30
SALES (corp-wide): 2.6MM **Privately
Held**
SIC: 3274 5032 Lime; limestone
HQ: Lhoist North America Of Alabama, Llc
5600 Clearfork Main St # 300
Fort Worth TX 76109
817 732-8164

(G-12850)
LHOIST NORTH AMERICA TEXAS LTD
Also Called: Hurst Terminal Us72
3110 S Precinct Line Rd (76053-7615)
P.O. Box 35 (76053-0035)
PHONE....................817 732-8164
Chris Boring, *Plant Mgr*
Tollie Smith, *Sales Staff*
Craig Dunlap, *Manager*
EMP: 23
SALES (corp-wide): 2.6MM **Privately Held**
WEB: www.lhoist.com
SIC: 3274 Dolomitic lime, dead-burned dolomite
HQ: Lhoist North America Of Texas, Ltd.
5600 Clearfork Main St
Fort Worth TX 76109
817 732-8164

(G-12851)
MANUFCTRING OPRATIONS MGT INTL
3417 Raider Dr Ste 10 (76053-7900)
PHONE....................682 521-5800
Monique Nguyen, *President*
Peter Nguyen, *Vice Pres*
EMP: 11
SQ FT: 5,000
SALES (est): 1MM **Privately Held**
SIC: 3469 8748 Machine parts, stamped or pressed metal; business consulting

(G-12852)
MMW FAB LTD
Also Called: Mmw Industries
1155 W Hurst Blvd (76053-7403)
P.O. Box 217 (76053-0217)
PHONE....................817 589-0881
Miller Bros, *General Ptnr*
Miller N Bros, *General Ptnr*
Scott Senter, *Project Mgr*
Terry Miller, *Opers Staff*
Stacy Shingler, *Accounting Mgr*
EMP: 80
SQ FT: 33,664
SALES (est): 41.7MM **Privately Held**
WEB: www.mmwfabrication.com
SIC: 3441 Fabricated structural metal for bridges

(G-12853)
MODERN FORGE TEXAS LLC
733 W Hurst Blvd (76053-7607)
PHONE....................817 268-0781
Gregory Heim, *CEO*
Richard Heim, *COO*
Patrick Thompson, *COO*
EMP: 51
SALES (est): 740.8K
SALES (corp-wide): 8.8MM **Privately Held**
WEB: www.modernforge.com
SIC: 3462 Iron & steel forgings
PA: Modern Drop Forge Company, Llc
8757 Colorado St
Merrillville IN 46410
708 489-4208

(G-12854)
OPTIMUM PATH SYSTEMS INC
8301 Bowspirit Ln (76053-7427)
PHONE....................813 990-8204
Junwen Yuan, *President*
Steve Webel, *COO*
EMP: 10
SALES (est): 600K **Privately Held**
WEB: www.optimumpathinc.com
SIC: 7372 7371 Business oriented computer software; computer software development

(G-12855)
PROCESS AUTOMATION DESIGN INC (PA)
3508 Raider Dr (76053-7906)
P.O. Box 457 (76053-0457)
PHONE....................817 283-1500
Scott Carlson, *President*
Stephanie Duelm, *Corp Secy*
Mark Carlson, *Vice Pres*
EMP: 28
SQ FT: 22,000
SALES (est): 5.4MM **Privately Held**
WEB: www.processauto.net
SIC: 3625 Control equipment, electric

(G-12856)
SAFETY SEAL PISTON RING CO
10736 S Pipeline Rd (76053-7811)
PHONE....................817 283-1574
Don Bynum, *Manager*
EMP: 20
SQ FT: 13,200
SALES (corp-wide): 15.7MM **Privately Held**
WEB: www.sswesco.com
SIC: 3592 Pistons & piston rings
PA: Safety Seal Piston Ring Company
4000 S Airport Rd
Marshall TX 75672
903 938-9241

(G-12857)
SATURN MANUFACTURING CORP
3608 Raider Dr (76053-7908)
PHONE....................817 267-3961
Otis Larry McGee, *President*
EMP: 20
SQ FT: 8,000
SALES (est): 2.6MM **Privately Held**
SIC: 3599 Machine shop, jobbing & repair

(G-12858)
SCREEN PLAY PROMOTIONS INC
Also Called: Crown Trophy
420 Greatvine Hwy Ste 118 (76054)
PHONE....................817 788-8608
Brian Thompson, *President*
EMP: 9
SALES (est): 820.4K **Privately Held**
WEB: www.spscreenprint.com
SIC: 5999 3466 2399 2499 Trophies & plaques; crowns & closures; banners, pennants & flags; trophy bases, wood

(G-12859)
SONS DESIGN & MFG INC
Also Called: Sdmi
1541 Central Park Dr (76053-7401)
PHONE....................817 595-9800
Clif Gibson, *President*
Heather Addicks, *Opers Mgr*
Kalene Hills, *Director*
EMP: 9
SQ FT: 12,000
SALES (est): 1.2MM **Privately Held**
WEB: www.sonsdmi.com
SIC: 3549 Wiredrawing & fabricating machinery & equipment, ex. die

(G-12860)
TALBOT GROUP INC
Also Called: Idpro
421 W Harwood Rd Ste 110 (76054-2948)
PHONE....................866 866-5020
John Robinson, *CEO*
Howard Vancleave, *President*
Damon Menendez, *Vice Pres*
EMP: 10
SQ FT: 4,000
SALES (est): 400K **Privately Held**
WEB: www.talbots.com
SIC: 3089 Identification cards, plastic

Hutchins
Dallas County

(G-12861)
ADOLPHS LITHO SERVICES INC
1600 S Intrstate 45 Svc R (75141)
PHONE....................972 225-5303
Adolph Novy, *President*
Rosemary Novy, *Corp Secy*
Brian Novy, *Vice Pres*
David Novy, *Vice Pres*
Steven Novy, *Vice Pres*
▲ **EMP:** 11
SALES (est): 1.6MM **Privately Held**
SIC: 7699 2752 Printing trades machinery & equipment repair; commercial printing, lithographic

(G-12862)
AS AMERICA INC
801 E Wintergreen Rd (75141-4257)
PHONE....................214 530-9831
EMP: 19 **Privately Held**
WEB: www.americanstandard-us.com
SIC: 3261 3432 Vitreous plumbing fixtures; plumbing fixture fittings & trim
HQ: As America, Inc.
1 Centennial Ave Ste 101
Piscataway NJ 08854

(G-12863)
BRIM LAUNDRY MACHINERY CO INC
302 Nichols Dr (75141-4066)
PHONE....................214 630-4517
Mark P Brim, *President*
Cory Marchand, *Parts Mgr*
Barbara Brim, *CFO*
Ron Banks, *Sales Staff*
Steven Horwitz, *Manager*
EMP: 40
SQ FT: 10,000
SALES (est): 13MM **Privately Held**
WEB: www.brimldry.com
SIC: 5087 7699 3582 Laundry equipment & supplies; industrial equipment services; commercial laundry equipment

(G-12864)
CLASSIC PICTURE COMPANY INC
Also Called: Classic Galleries
1601 S Main St (75141-3530)
P.O. Box 679 (75141-0679)
PHONE....................972 225-7590
EMP: 14
SQ FT: 40,000
SALES (est): 1.6MM **Privately Held**
SIC: 2499 3499 Mfg Picture Frames

(G-12865)
CONSOLIDATED CASTING LLC
Also Called: Signicast Hutchins
1501 S I 45 Svc Rd (75141-9425)
PHONE....................972 225-7305
Marc Riquelme, *President*
Patricia Miguel, *General Mgr*
Ted Kraus, *Plant Mgr*
Scott Shambaugh, *Opers Staff*
Perry Skinner, *Purchasing*
▲ **EMP:** 160
SQ FT: 80,000
SALES (est): 91MM
SALES (corp-wide): 1.5B **Privately Held**
WEB: www.signicast.com
SIC: 3324 3369 Commercial investment castings, ferrous; nonferrous foundries
HQ: Signicast Llc
1800 Innovation Way
Hartford WI 53027
262 673-2700

(G-12866)
GORDONS SPECIALTIES INC
Also Called: Gsi Highway Products
720 W Wintergreen Rd (75141-3706)
PHONE....................972 225-1660
John Williams, *President*
David Harkless, *Supervisor*
Carolyn Sharp, *Assistant*
EMP: 40
SQ FT: 40,000
SALES (est): 36MM **Privately Held**
WEB: www.gsihighway.com
SIC: 5051 3312 3441 Iron & steel (ferrous) products; rails & accessories; rails, steel or iron; building components, structural steel

(G-12867)
HUTCHINS OIL AND LUBE
202 Myron Goff St (75141-0439)
PHONE....................972 225-0846
Dean Kadour, *General Mgr*
EMP: 20
SALES (est): 909.8K **Privately Held**
SIC: 1389 2542 Oil field services; partitions & fixtures, except wood

(G-12868)
MCNEILUS TRUCK AND MFG INC
1101 Hwy 45 S (75141)
P.O. Box 458 (75141-0458)
PHONE....................972 225-2313
Chris O'Neal, *Chancellor*
EMP: 50
SQ FT: 11,600
SALES (corp-wide): 6.8B **Publicly Held**
WEB: www.mcneilus.com
SIC: 3713 5082 5064 3531 Cement mixer bodies; concrete processing equipment; garbage disposals; construction machinery
HQ: Mcneilus Truck And Manufacturing, Inc.
524 E Highway St
Dodge Center MN 55927
507 374-6321

(G-12869)
MK SPECIALTY METAL FABRICATORS
Also Called: M K Spcialty Metal Fabricators
725 W Wintergreen Rd (75141-3707)
PHONE....................972 225-6562
James Aldridge, *President*
Tommy Thompkins, *Vice Pres*
EMP: 35
SQ FT: 20,000
SALES (est): 7.2MM **Privately Held**
WEB: www.mkspecialty.com
SIC: 3441 Fabricated structural metal

(G-12870)
PALLET REPAIR SERVICES INC
1012 W Wintergreen Rd (75141-3715)
PHONE....................972 913-1110
Rick Story, *President*
Eddie Lacost, *Vice Pres*
Joseph R Story Jr, *Vice Pres*
Vicky Guy, *Office Admin*
EMP: 70
SQ FT: 7,000
SALES (est): 14MM **Privately Held**
WEB: www.palletrepairservices.com
SIC: 2448 Pallets, wood

(G-12871)
TEXAS AUTOMATION PRODUCTS INC
Also Called: Burns Tool Co
300 Nichols Dr (75141-4066)
PHONE....................972 289-0300
Joe McSpadden, *President*
EMP: 17
SQ FT: 12,500
SALES (est): 2.8MM **Privately Held**
WEB: www.texasautomationproducts.com
SIC: 3599 Machine shop, jobbing & repair

(G-12872)
TEXAS HYDRAULIC & EQP CO INC
810 Skyline Dr (75141-4151)
P.O. Box 570009, Dallas (75357-0009)
PHONE....................214 748-7551
Marden D Leonard, *President*
EMP: 10
SQ FT: 13,843
SALES (est): 1.3MM **Privately Held**
WEB: www.texhyd.com
SIC: 3537 5084 Lift trucks, industrial: fork, platform, straddle, etc.; industrial machinery & equipment; lift trucks & parts

(G-12873)
WILLIAMS & DAVIS BOILERS INC
Also Called: W & D
2044 Interstate 45 S (75141)
PHONE....................972 225-2356
Jay E Davis, *President*
Jennifer Caradine, *Vice Pres*
Jim Caradine, *Executive*
EMP: 30 **EST:** 1921
SQ FT: 30,000
SALES (est): 7.5MM **Privately Held**
WEB: www.w-dboilers.com
SIC: 3443 7699 Boiler & boiler shop work; boiler repair shop

Hutto
Williamson County

(G-12874)
A R MACHINING INC
632 W Front St (78634-4078)
P.O. Box 817 (78634-0817)
PHONE..................................512 846-1789
Anthony Dobias, *President*
Don Wright, *Director*
EMP: 45
SQ FT: 20,000
SALES (est): 12MM **Privately Held**
WEB: www.armachining.com
SIC: 3533 3761 Oil & gas drilling rigs & equipment; guided missiles & space vehicles

(G-12875)
ALPHA READY MIX LLC
212 Investment Loop (78634-4010)
PHONE..................................512 846-2221
Tatiana Leadbetter, *Mng Member*
Sergio L Sanchez,
EMP: 12
SQ FT: 4,000
SALES (est): 2.3MM **Privately Held**
WEB: www.alphareadymixaustin.com
SIC: 3273 Ready-mixed concrete

(G-12876)
B FINISHING CO INC
208 Tradesmen Dr (78634-4017)
PHONE..................................512 759-2100
Keith Jorden, *President*
EMP: 10 EST: 1995
SQ FT: 4,000
SALES (est): 1MM **Privately Held**
SIC: 3471 Electroplating of metals or formed products

(G-12877)
CHARLES BARTON
Also Called: Cast Limestone Products Texas
105 Green Pasture (78634-4003)
PHONE..................................512 759-1231
Charles Barton, *Owner*
Michele Barton, *Principal*
EMP: 20
SQ FT: 18,000
SALES (est): 2MM **Privately Held**
WEB: www.castoneusa.com
SIC: 5211 5032 5999 3272 Concrete & cinder block; limestone; concrete & cinder block; architectural supplies; stone, cast concrete

(G-12878)
ENHANCED PRODUCTION TECH INC
Also Called: E P T
402 Tradesmens Park Dr (78634-4022)
PHONE..................................512 759-2009
Terry Bell, *President*
Dawn Dicken, *Office Admin*
▲ EMP: 9
SQ FT: 19,000
SALES (est): 2.2MM **Privately Held**
WEB: www.eptek.com
SIC: 7389 3672 8711 Hand tool designers; printed circuit boards; mechanical engineering

(G-12879)
HUTTO HOLDING GROUP INC
902 Tradesmens Park Loop (78634-4047)
PHONE..................................512 832-8746
Arthur Serrano, *President*
John Wilkerson, *Vice Pres*
Sam Cardozo, *VP Opers*
Sherryl L Serrano,
Ron C McManus,
EMP: 52
SQ FT: 37,000
SALES (est): 5MM **Privately Held**
SIC: 1521 3446 1522 Single-family housing construction; stairs, staircases, stair treads: prefabricated metal; apartment building construction

(G-12880)
IOWA TECHNIQUES INC
524 Tradesmens Park Dr (78634-4027)
PHONE..................................512 846-2403
Matt Kool, *President*
Lori Ordon, *Accountant*
Michael Thornton, *Technology*
EMP: 10
SQ FT: 15,600
SALES (est): 1.7MM **Privately Held**
WEB: www.iowatechniques.com
SIC: 5087 3582 5999 Janitors' supplies; drycleaning equipment & machinery, commercial; cleaning equipment & supplies

(G-12881)
JRS COMPANY INC
200 County Road 199 (78634-4270)
P.O. Box 2035, Covina CA (91722-8035)
PHONE..................................626 967-2432
Frank Hecox, *President*
Ronald De Long, *Vice Pres*
Paula Smith, *Shareholder*
Richard Smith, *Shareholder*
EMP: 100
SQ FT: 30,000
SALES (est): 15.7MM **Privately Held**
WEB: www.jrscoinc.com
SIC: 3089 3479 3353 Engraving of plastic; name plates: engraved, etched, etc.; aluminum sheet, plate & foil

(G-12882)
KEY SCIENTIFIC PRODUCTS
1113 E Reynolds St (78634)
PHONE..................................512 846-1440
Carol Zentner, *President*
Kat Baitz, *Owner*
Karol Zentner, *Vice Pres*
Becky Scotton, *VP Opers*
EMP: 27
SALES (est): 1.2MM **Privately Held**
WEB: www.keyscientific.com
SIC: 5049 3826 Laboratory equipment, except medical or dental; laser scientific & engineering instruments

(G-12883)
PI-CO PRCISION FABRICATION INC
223 Tradesmen Dr (78634-4017)
PHONE..................................512 759-1026
Jerry Jordan, *President*
Glen Pierce, *Vice Pres*
Patricia Edmondson, *Purchasing*
Russ Kinyon, *Prgrmr*
Kathy Jordan, *Executive*
▲ EMP: 40
SQ FT: 35,000
SALES (est): 8.1MM **Privately Held**
WEB: www.picofab.com
SIC: 3444 Sheet metal specialties, not stamped

(G-12884)
PLAYGRUND SHADE STRUCTURES INC
505 Trdesmen Pk Dr Ste A (78634-4153)
PHONE..................................512 642-6124
William G Wolfe, *President*
▼ EMP: 9
SQ FT: 1,200
SALES (est): 883.7K **Privately Held**
WEB: www.kidstruction.com
SIC: 3949 1799 Playground equipment; playground construction & equipment installation

(G-12885)
STARMARK SOLUTIONS LLC
200 County Road 197 (78634-5141)
PHONE..................................877 823-7847
Keith Benson, *Mng Member*
Emily Benson, *Mng Member*
EMP: 50
SALES (est): 3.2MM **Privately Held**
WEB: www.starmarkacademy.com
SIC: 3999 Pet supplies

(G-12886)
TEXAS FIXTURES AND INTERIORS
3874 Limmer Loop (78634-4523)
PHONE..................................512 846-1998
William Russ, *President*
Ann Castle, *Vice Pres*
Bobby Castle, *Vice Pres*
Dawn Mays, *Purch Mgr*
Keli J Russ, *Admin Sec*

▲ EMP: 55
SALES (est): 9.8MM **Privately Held**
WEB: www.texasfixtures.com
SIC: 2541 2431 Cabinets, except refrigerated: show, display, etc.: wood; store fixtures, wood; millwork

(G-12887)
UTILITY COMPOSITES INC
Also Called: Raptor
888 County Road 108 (78634-3406)
PHONE..................................512 846-4027
Pamela Tucker, *CEO*
Randall Morris, *President*
Don Bankston, *Executive*
▲ EMP: 10
SALES (est): 1.9MM **Privately Held**
WEB: www.raptornails.com
SIC: 3965 Fasteners, buttons, needles & pins

(G-12888)
WEST PHALIA MARKET INC
409 W Front St (78634-4204)
PHONE..................................512 846-1155
Pat Rabroker, *Principal*
EMP: 10
SALES (corp-wide): 1.1MM **Privately Held**
WEB: www.westphaliamarket.com
SIC: 2099 2011 Food preparations; meat packing plants
PA: West Phalia Market Inc
734 State Highway 320
Lott TX 76656
254 584-4060

Idalou
Lubbock County

(G-12889)
HOLLAND AND ASSOCIATES LLC
812 Mimosa Ave (79329-9031)
P.O. Box 1326 (79329-1326)
PHONE..................................806 892-3504
Cliff Holland, *Owner*
Clifford B Holland,
EMP: 16
SALES (est): 1.6MM **Privately Held**
SIC: 3541 Milling machines

(G-12890)
ROBBCO PUMPS INC
12610 N Fm 400 (79329-6099)
PHONE..................................806 892-2290
Don Robb, *President*
Berle Robb, *Vice Pres*
EMP: 11
SQ FT: 21,000
SALES (est): 3.7MM
SALES (corp-wide): 164.8MM **Privately Held**
WEB: www.robbcopumps.com
SIC: 5084 3561 Pumps & pumping equipment; pumps & pumping equipment
HQ: Wolf Pump, Inc
18014 N Interstate Hwy 27
Abernathy TX
806 298-2514

Ingleside
San Patricio County

(G-12891)
3 DIAMOND SERVICES LLC
Also Called: Diamond Specialty Services
1296 6th St (78362-6137)
PHONE..................................361 442-6949
Veronica Cortez, *Human Resources*
Michael Rowland,
EMP: 12
SALES (est): 634.8K **Privately Held**
WEB:
www.diamondspecialtyservicesllc.com
SIC: 2911 Petroleum refining

(G-12892)
CITY TORTILLA FACTORY INC
2715 Main St (78362-5910)
P.O. Box 366 (78362-0366)
PHONE..................................361 776-3578
Omega Rodriguez, *President*
EMP: 14
SQ FT: 5,000
SALES (est): 1.3MM **Privately Held**
SIC: 2099 Tortillas, fresh or refrigerated

(G-12893)
D J YOUNG PUBLISHING
Also Called: Wingspan
2181 Capeheart St (78362-6222)
PHONE..................................361 238-4188
David Young, *Owner*
EMP: 10
SALES (est): 263.9K **Privately Held**
SIC: 2711 Newspapers: publishing only, not printed on site

(G-12894)
DYNAMIC INDUSTRIES INC
1074 Fm 2725 (78362-4744)
PHONE..................................361 775-1500
Noe Gonzales, *General Mgr*
EMP: 15
SALES (corp-wide): 266.6MM **Privately Held**
WEB: www.dynamicind.com
SIC: 3441 Fabricated structural metal
PA: Dynamic Industries, Inc.
400 Poydras St Ste 1800
New Orleans LA 70130
504 684-1305

(G-12895)
E I DU PONT DE NEMOURS & CO
Also Called: Dupont
4127 Hwy 361 (78362)
PHONE..................................361 776-1872
James Ellis, *Branch Mgr*
Lonnie Watkins, *Administration*
EMP: 50
SALES (corp-wide): 14.2B **Publicly Held**
WEB: www.dupont.com
SIC: 2869 3585 2813 Industrial organic chemicals; refrigeration & heating equipment; industrial gases
HQ: E. I. Du Pont De Nemours And Company
974 Centre Rd Bldg 735
Wilmington DE 19805
302 485-3000

(G-12896)
LIVE OAK MATERIALS INC
Garrett Rd And Fm 2725 (78362)
P.O. Box 1269, Aransas Pass (78335-1269)
PHONE..................................361 775-0065
Anderson R Garrett, *President*
Tonya Garrett, *Treasurer*
EMP: 43
SQ FT: 7,500
SALES (est): 9.3MM **Privately Held**
WEB: www.liveoakmaterials.com
SIC: 3273 5032 1422 Ready-mixed concrete; brick, stone & related material; crushed & broken limestone

(G-12897)
NORTH SHORE BOAT WORKS INC
1645 Main St (78362-4625)
P.O. Box 907 (78362-0907)
PHONE..................................361 776-2525
William L Fuller, *President*
Debra Smith, *Corp Secy*
EMP: 9
SQ FT: 5,000
SALES (est): 1.3MM **Privately Held**
WEB: www.northshoreboatworks.com
SIC: 3732 Boat building & repairing

(G-12898)
OCEANEERING INTERNATIONAL INC
2552 4th St (78362-5911)
PHONE..................................361 776-7251
Tj Hurlburt, *Engineer*
Justin Bullard, *Project Engr*
Sheena Ang, *Controller*
Richmond Ataiwhere, *Finance Mgr*

Kiran Babu, *Hum Res Coord*
EMP: 10
SALES (corp-wide): 2B **Publicly Held**
WEB: www.oceaneering.com
SIC: 1389 Testing, measuring, surveying & analysis services
PA: Oceaneering International Inc
11911 Fm 529 Rd
Houston TX 77041
713 329-4500

(G-12899)
OXYMAR INC
Hwy 361 (78362)
PHONE..................................361 776-6321
◆ **EMP:** 180
SQ FT: 5,000
SALES (est): 24.8MM **Privately Held**
SIC: 2821 Mfg Plastic Materials/Resins

Iola
Grimes County

(G-12900)
SCOTT FENNELL INC
7322 County Road 118 (77861-5285)
PHONE..................................817 822-1283
Scott Fennell, *CEO*
Mandy Fennell, *Vice Pres*
EMP: 26
SALES (est): 252K **Privately Held**
WEB: www.fennellinc.com
SIC: 3357 1731 7389 Fiber optic cable (insulated); fiber optic cable installation;

(G-12901)
WILLDA BEAST LLC
15823 Fm 244 (77861-4332)
P.O. Box 12250, College Station (77842-2250)
PHONE..................................979 268-6760
Michelle Baca, *Sales Staff*
William Wren,
EMP: 14
SALES (est): 3.2MM **Privately Held**
WEB: www.willda-beast.com
SIC: 1389 Haulage, oil field

Iowa Park
Wichita County

(G-12902)
AFFILIATED ENERGY PRODUCTS INC
900 Nw 287 Access Rd (76367)
PHONE..................................940 592-4169
David Kulbeth, *Ch of Bd*
Julia Ward, *Corp Secy*
Charles Donnell, *Vice Pres*
Stoney Rice, *Treasurer*
Ben Chapman, *Sales Staff*
EMP: 31 **EST:** 2007
SALES (est): 3.6MM **Privately Held**
WEB: www.aepmachine.com
SIC: 3599 Machine shop, jobbing & repair

(G-12903)
BILL GILMORE WELDING INC
1150 Us 287 E (76367)
P.O. Box 896 (76367-0896)
PHONE..................................940 592-4945
Billy Joe Gilmore, *President*
B J Gilmore, *President*
Kathy Smith, *Corp Secy*
Billy Clark Gilmore, *Vice Pres*
EMP: 22
SQ FT: 14,200
SALES (est): 1.9MM **Privately Held**
SIC: 7538 7539 7692 General truck repair; trailer repair; welding repair

(G-12904)
ENTEX FABRICATION INC
1010 Texowa Rd (76367-2747)
P.O. Box 609 (76367-0609)
PHONE..................................940 592-2173
Michael Reed, *President*
Michael N Avey, *Corp Secy*
John Thomas Kaiser Jr, *Vice Pres*
David Reed, *Vice Pres*
EMP: 35

SQ FT: 16,000 **Privately Held**
WEB: www.entexfab.com
SIC: 3443 3444 3441 Stills, pressure: metal plate; sheet metalwork; fabricated structural metal

(G-12905)
EXPRESS ENERGY SVCS OPER LP
426 Rifle Range Rd (76367-7002)
PHONE..................................940 592-4391
EMP: 15
SALES (corp-wide): 825.2MM **Privately Held**
SIC: 1389 Oil/Gas Field Services
PA: Express Energy Services Operating, Lp
9800 Richmond Ave Ste 500
Houston TX 77042
713 625-7400

(G-12906)
FULFER VANEK WELL SERVICING CO
5941 Pace Rd (76367-7611)
PHONE..................................940 438-2276
Ricky Vanek, *President*
Elizabeth Fulfer Vanek, *Vice Pres*
EMP: 20 **EST:** 1950
SALES (est): 700K **Privately Held**
SIC: 1389 Oil field services

(G-12907)
OIL WELL CHEMICAL CO INC
Also Called: Park Tank Trucks Service
W Expressway At Cy Limits (76367)
P.O. Box 637 (76367-0637)
PHONE..................................940 592-2012
G R Rusk, *President*
EMP: 13
SQ FT: 3,000
SALES (est): 741K **Privately Held**
SIC: 1389 5169 Haulage, oil field; chemicals & allied products

(G-12908)
QUALITY MANUFACTURING INC
5873 Fm 369 N (76367-6030)
P.O. Box 2564, Wichita Falls (76307-2564)
PHONE..................................940 592-5790
Dean Fournier, *President*
Mary Ann Fournier, *Vice Pres*
EMP: 10
SQ FT: 6,816
SALES (est): 3.1MM **Privately Held**
SIC: 3533 3599 Oil field machinery & equipment; gas field machinery & equipment; custom machinery

(G-12909)
S 5 MANUFACTURING LLC
500 W Highway St (76367-2802)
PHONE..................................940 592-2100
▲ **EMP:** 9
SALES (est): 819.5K **Privately Held**
WEB: www.s-5.com
SIC: 3999 Manufacturing industries

(G-12910)
SEALED AIR CORPORATION
1301 W Magnolia Ave (76367-1410)
PHONE..................................940 592-2111
EMP: 75
SALES (corp-wide): 4.7B **Publicly Held**
WEB: www.sealedair.com
SIC: 2673 3086 Bags: plastic, laminated & coated; garment & wardrobe bags, (plastic film); food storage & trash bags (plastic); plastic & pliofilm bags; packaging & shipping materials, foamed plastic
PA: Sealed Air Corporation
2415 Cascade Pointe Blvd
Charlotte NC 28208
980 221-3235

(G-12911)
SPRUIELL DRILLING CO (PA)
307 N Wall St (76367-1645)
P.O. Box 946 (76367-0946)
PHONE..................................940 592-5471
Russel Spruiell, *President*
Janet Clapp, *Corp Secy*
Wendell House, *Vice Pres*
House Wendal, *Vice Pres*
EMP: 14
SQ FT: 2,000

SALES (est): 2.6MM **Privately Held**
WEB: www.spruielldrilling.com
SIC: 1381 1311 Directional drilling oil & gas wells; crude petroleum production

Ira
Scurry County

(G-12912)
ABRAXAS PETROLEUM CORPORATION
11141 Cr 2138 (79527)
P.O. Box 158 (79527-0158)
PHONE..................................325 573-6010
EMP: 9
SQ FT: 3,000
SALES (corp-wide): 86.2MM **Publicly Held**
SIC: 1311 Crude Petroleum/Natural Gas Production
PA: Abraxas Petroleum Corporation
18803 Meisner Dr
San Antonio TX 78258
210 490-4788

(G-12913)
OCCIDENTAL PETROLEUM CORP
14005 Fm 1610 (79527-2149)
PHONE..................................325 574-8567
EMP: 9
SALES (corp-wide): 21.2B **Publicly Held**
WEB: www.oxy.com
SIC: 1311 1382 2819 2869 Crude petroleum production; natural gas production; oil & gas exploration services; potassium compounds or salts, except hydroxide or carbonate; sodium compounds or salts, inorg., ex. refined sod. chloride; sodium silicate, water glass; ethylene; propylene, butylene; ethylene glycols; chlorine, compressed or liquefied; caustic soda, sodium hydroxide
PA: Occidental Petroleum Corporation
5 Greenway Plz Ste 110
Houston TX 77046
713 215-7000

(G-12914)
SHARIDGE INC
Hwy 350 (79527)
P.O. Box 47 (79527-0047)
PHONE..................................325 573-4242
Barry C Cribbs, *President*
Jody Cribbs, *General Mgr*
EMP: 21
SQ FT: 50,000
SALES (est): 3MM **Privately Held**
SIC: 1389 Oil field services

(G-12915)
SOUTHWEST ROYALTIES INC
County Rd 3138 (79527)
PHONE..................................325 573-4977
H H Wommack III, *CEO*
EMP: 23
SALES (corp-wide): 146.5B **Publicly Held**
SIC: 1311 Crude petroleum production
HQ: Southwest Royalties, Inc.
6 Desta Dr Ste 2100
Midland TX 79705
432 688-3008

Iraan
Pecos County

(G-12916)
BARRERA CONTRACTORS INC
104 S Underwood St (79744)
PHONE..................................432 639-2516
Ricardo Barrera, *President*
Briza Barrera, *Corp Secy*
EMP: 18
SQ FT: 1,800
SALES (est): 5.4MM **Privately Held**
SIC: 1389 4212 1382 Construction, repair & dismantling services; local trucking, without storage; oil & gas exploration services

(G-12917)
CIMAREX ENERGY CO
S Interstate 10 Unit Pump (79744)
P.O. Box 548 (79744-0548)
PHONE..................................432 634-1674
EMP: 76
SALES (corp-wide): 2.3B **Publicly Held**
WEB: www.cimarex.com
SIC: 1382 Oil & gas exploration services
PA: Cimarex Energy Co.
1700 N Lincoln St # 3700
Denver CO 80203
303 295-3995

(G-12918)
GARRISON CONTRACTORS INC (PA)
205 W 6th St (79744)
P.O. Box 968 (79744-0968)
PHONE..................................432 639-2811
Todd Bauseh, *President*
Randolph Kelly, *Exec VP*
Mikie L Kelly, *Vice Pres*
EMP: 20 **EST:** 1946
SQ FT: 1,500
SALES (est): 2MM **Privately Held**
WEB: www.garrisoncontractorsinc.com
SIC: 1389 Oil field services; gas field services

(G-12919)
KEY ENERGY DRILLING INC
220 S Drake St (79744)
P.O. Box 595 (79744-0595)
PHONE..................................432 639-2534
Mario C Rivero, *Branch Mgr*
EMP: 30
SALES (corp-wide): 413.8MM **Publicly Held**
WEB: www.keyenergy.com
SIC: 1381 1382 Drilling oil & gas wells; oil & gas exploration services
HQ: Key Energy Drilling, Inc.
1301 Mckinney St Ste 1800
Houston TX 77010

(G-12920)
NABORS WELL SERVICES LTD
Hwy 349 S (79744)
P.O. Box 576 (79744-0576)
PHONE..................................432 836-4332
Ernest Sparks, *Branch Mgr*
EMP: 25 **Privately Held**
WEB: www.nabors.com
SIC: 1389 1382 Servicing oil & gas wells; oil & gas exploration services
HQ: Nabors Well Services Ltd.
515 W Greens Rd Ste 1200
Houston TX 77067
281 874-0035

Iredell
Bosque County

(G-12921)
FARM & RANCH CONSTRUCTION LLC
14641 Highway 6 (76649-4763)
P.O. Box 69 (76649-0069)
PHONE..................................254 364-2226
Chris Chick, *CEO*
EMP: 38
SALES (est): 6MM **Privately Held**
WEB: www.frctex.com
SIC: 1389 4971 1623 1611 Building oil & gas well foundations on site; grading oil & gas well foundations; impounding reservoir, irrigation; electric power line construction; gravel or dirt road construction

Irving
Dallas County

(G-12922)
ACCUTEK INC
8051 Jetstar Dr Ste 175 (75063-2802)
PHONE..................................972 915-6888
EMP: 50 **EST:** 2014
SALES (est): 3.9MM **Privately Held**
WEB: www.accutekpackaging.com
SIC: 3565 Packaging machinery

▲ = Import ▼=Export
◆ =Import/Export

(G-12923)
ADVANCED ARM DYNAMICS
Also Called: Southwest Center of Excellence
3501 N Macarthur Blvd (75062-3651)
PHONE..............................214 260-3197
Rob Dodson, *Manager*
EMP: 9
SALES (corp-wide): 10.9MM **Privately Held**
WEB: www.armdynamics.com
SIC: 3842 Prosthetic appliances
PA: Advanced Arm Dynamics
123 W Torrance Blvd # 203
Redondo Beach CA 90277
310 372-3050

(G-12924)
ADVANCED ELEC & MTR CONTRLS
Also Called: Aeamc
1801 Hurd Dr (75038-4311)
PHONE..............................972 253-7783
Randy Roumillat, *President*
David Muir, *General Mgr*
Ana Gonzalez, *Accounting Mgr*
Tim Brewer, *Sales Staff*
Ashley Ledbetter, *Sales Staff*
EMP: 30
SQ FT: 50,000
SALES (est): 3.2MM **Privately Held**
WEB: www.aeamc.com
SIC: 3613 3625 Panel & distribution boards & other related apparatus; switchboards & parts, power; motor control centers

(G-12925)
AEROSTAR GLOBAL LOGISTICS LLC
9500 N Royal Ln Ste 170 (75063-2426)
P.O. Box 224318, Dallas (75222-4318)
PHONE..............................630 458-8844
Anthony V Fiacchino, *CEO*
Anthony D Fiacchino, *President*
Serge Bernard, *Vice Pres*
Terrence Brown, *Vice Pres*
Mike Podjasek, *Controller*
◆ EMP: 27
SALES (est): 16.8MM **Privately Held**
WEB: www.aerostarglobal.com
SIC: 4731 4225 3482 Freight forwarding; general warehousing & storage; shotgun ammunition: empty, blank or loaded

(G-12926)
AIRMEC INC
2102 Vanco Dr (75061-8896)
PHONE..............................972 438-4015
C Richard Bacon, *President*
John Bacon, *Vice Pres*
Lou Bacon, *Treasurer*
EMP: 20
SQ FT: 14,000
SALES (est): 2.7MM **Privately Held**
SIC: 3069 Molded rubber products

(G-12927)
ALERIS OHIO MANAGEMENT INC
5525 N Macarthur Blvd (75038-2615)
PHONE..............................972 815-0800
EMP: 12 **Privately Held**
WEB: www.aleris.com
SIC: 3331 Primary copper
HQ: Aleris Ohio Management, Inc.
25825 Science Park Dr # 400
Cleveland OH 44122

(G-12928)
AMERICAN BOTTLING COMPANY
Also Called: Dr Pepper
2304 Century Center Blvd (75062-4906)
PHONE..............................972 579-1024
Shiloh Marston, *Human Resources*
Craig Staser, *Sales Staff*
Michael Grant, *Branch Mgr*
Aaron Roark, *Manager*
Jason Smith, *Director*
EMP: 100 **Publicly Held**
WEB: www.keurigdrpepper.com
SIC: 2086 5149 Soft drinks: packaged in cans, bottles, etc.; groceries & related products

HQ: The American Bottling Company
5301 Legacy Dr
Plano TX 75024

(G-12929)
AMERICAN BOTTLING COMPANY
Also Called: Southwest Fountain Supply
2304 Century Center Blvd (75062-4906)
P.O. Box 655024, Dallas (75265-5024)
PHONE..............................972 721-8197
Glenn Glasco, *Branch Mgr*
EMP: 175 **Publicly Held**
WEB: www.keurigdrpepper.com
SIC: 2086 Soft drinks: packaged in cans, bottles, etc.
HQ: The American Bottling Company
5301 Legacy Dr
Plano TX 75024

(G-12930)
AMERICAN HONDA MOTOR CO INC
4525 W Royal Ln (75063-2556)
PHONE..............................972 929-5444
EMP: 150 **Privately Held**
WEB: www.hondacertified.com
SIC: 5511 3711 Automobiles, new & used; motor vehicles & car bodies
HQ: American Honda Motor Co., Inc.
1919 Torrance Blvd
Torrance CA 90501
310 783-2000

(G-12931)
ANVIL INTERNATIONAL LLC
1401 Valley View Ln # 150 (75061-3603)
PHONE..............................800 451-4414
Brandon Gunnell, *Branch Mgr*
EMP: 21
SALES (corp-wide): 425.3MM **Privately Held**
WEB: www.anvilintl.com
SIC: 3498 Fabricated pipe & fittings
PA: Anvil International, Llc
160 Frenchtown Rd
North Kingstown RI 02852
401 558-2578

(G-12932)
ARGOS USA LLC
Also Called: Southern Star Concrete
8500 Freport Pkwy Ste 200 (75063)
PHONE..............................972 621-0999
EMP: 17
SQ FT: 3,300 **Privately Held**
WEB: www.argos-us.com
SIC: 3273 Ready-mixed concrete
HQ: Argos Usa Llc
3015 Windward Plz Ste 300
Alpharetta GA 30005
678 368-4300

(G-12933)
ARGOS USA LLC
5150 Valley View Ln (75038-2701)
PHONE..............................972 256-6571
Bobby Skelton, *Manager*
EMP: 70
SQ FT: 768 **Privately Held**
WEB: www.argos-us.com
SIC: 3273 Ready-mixed concrete
HQ: Argos Usa Llc
3015 Windward Plz Ste 300
Alpharetta GA 30005
678 368-4300

(G-12934)
ASTURA MEDICAL
Also Called: Hyghte Holdings
4949 W Royal Ln (75063-2514)
PHONE..............................760 814-8047
Joel Gandrall, *President*
Megan Henley, *Principal*
EMP: 10
SQ FT: 4,500
SALES (est): 759.7K **Privately Held**
WEB: www.asturamedical.com
SIC: 3841 Surgical & medical instruments

(G-12935)
AUTO AIR EXPORT INC (PA)
Also Called: Omega Environmental Tech
1401 Valley View Ln # 100 (75061-3603)
PHONE..............................972 812-7000
Peter Butterfield, *CEO*

Pedro Garza, *Production*
Sally Crow, *Human Resources*
Grissel Delaespriella, *Sales Staff*
Tommy France, *Mktg Dir*
◆ EMP: 83
SQ FT: 165,000
SALES (est): 90.7MM **Privately Held**
WEB: www.omega-usa.com
SIC: 5075 3585 5531 Air conditioning equipment, except room units; air conditioning, motor vehicle; automobile air conditioning equipment, sale, installation

(G-12936)
AUTOSTAR SOLUTIONS INC
7301 State Highway 161 # 400 (75039-2802)
PHONE..............................817 377-2995
Allen Dobbins, *President*
Russ Asbury, *CFO*
Antonio Rajan, *Officer*
EMP: 50
SQ FT: 7,000
SALES (est): 5.9MM
SALES (corp-wide): 70.1MM **Privately Held**
WEB: www.autostarsolutions.com
SIC: 7372 Business oriented computer software
PA: Dealersocket, Inc.
100 Avenida La Pata
San Clemente CA 92673
949 900-0300

(G-12937)
AVID MEDIA VENTURE INC
Also Called: Avid Gofer Magazine
1825 W Walnut Hill Ln # 10 (75038-3218)
PHONE..............................972 550-9000
EMP: 22
SALES (est): 2.2MM **Privately Held**
WEB: www.myavidgolfer.com
SIC: 2721 Magazines: publishing only, not printed on site

(G-12938)
AVID MEDIA VENTURES INC
Also Called: Avid Golfer Magazine
1825 W Walnut Hill Ln # 10 (75038-3218)
PHONE..............................972 550-9000
Craig Rosengarden, *President*
Eli Jordan, *Editor*
Laura Webster, *Marketing Mgr*
EMP: 19
SALES (est): 1.9MM **Privately Held**
WEB: www.myavidgolfer.com
SIC: 2721 Magazines: publishing only, not printed on site

(G-12939)
AVK CONSTRUCTION GROUP INC
2311 Texas Dr Ste 105 (75062-7071)
PHONE..............................972 255-9464
Ajay Kothari, *President*
Ruth Martinez, *Office Mgr*
EMP: 12
SQ FT: 5,000
SALES (est): 837.6K **Privately Held**
SIC: 1389 Construction, repair & dismantling services

(G-12940)
AZTECA MILLING LP (DH)
5601 Executive Dr Ste 650 (75038-2508)
P.O. Box 237, Edinburg (78540-0237)
PHONE..............................956 383-4911
Isidro Moreno, *General Mgr*
Derek Akers, *Opers Staff*
Omar Balandran, *Sales Mgr*
Alberto Cadamuro, *Sales Mgr*
Jose J Lopez, *Sales Mgr*
▲ EMP: 180 EST: 1980
SQ FT: 4,000
SALES (est): 136.4MM **Privately Held**
WEB: www.aztecamilling.com
SIC: 2041 Flour & other grain mill products
HQ: Gruma Corporation
5601 Executive Dr Ste 800
Irving TX 75038
972 232-5000

(G-12941)
AZTECA MILLING LP
1159 Cottonwood Ln # 130 (75038-6106)
PHONE..............................972 232-5363

Mike Foss, *Prdtn Mgr*
EMP: 10 **Privately Held**
WEB: www.aztecamilling.com
SIC: 2041 Flour & other grain mill products
HQ: Azteca Milling, L.P.
5601 Executive Dr Ste 650
Irving TX 75038
956 383-4911

(G-12942)
BAKER HUGHES A GE COMPANY LLC
1333 Cooper Dr Ste 350 (75061-5525)
PHONE..............................972 550-3933
Jason Price, *Principal*
EMP: 40
SALES (corp-wide): 23.8B **Publicly Held**
WEB: www.bakerhughes.com
SIC: 1389 Oil field services
HQ: Baker Hughes Holdings Llc
17021 Aldine Westfield Rd
Houston TX 77073
713 439-8600

(G-12943)
BARCANA INC (PA)
2301 Crown Ct (75038-4305)
PHONE..............................800 638-4533
▲ EMP: 15
SQ FT: 38,000
SALES (est): 2.7MM **Privately Held**
WEB: www.barcana.com
SIC: 3999 Christmas trees, artificial; wreaths, artificial

(G-12944)
BARK TO BASICS LLC (PA)
600 Las Colinas Blvd E (75039-5616)
PHONE..............................913 825-1760
Terry Garberg,
Dennis Garberg,
EMP: 16
SQ FT: 35,000
SALES (est): 1.6MM **Privately Held**
SIC: 2047 5149 Dog food; dog food

(G-12945)
BELL AND HOWELL LLC
8080 Tristar Dr Ste 106 (75063-2823)
PHONE..............................972 753-0711
David Livingston, *District Mgr*
Tammy McCall, *Finance Mgr*
Thomas Krieger, *Accounts Exec*
Timika Brown, *Marketing Staff*
Keith Harshman, *Manager*
EMP: 140 **Privately Held**
WEB: www.bellhowell.net
SIC: 7372 Publishers' computer software
PA: Bell And Howell, Llc
3791 S Alston Ave
Durham NC 27713

(G-12946)
BELL SPORTS CORP (DH)
6333 N State Highway 161 # 300 (75038-2218)
PHONE..............................469 417-6600
Dan Arment, *President*
▲ EMP: 45
SQ FT: 27,197
SALES (est): 273.4MM **Privately Held**
WEB: www.bwpcpa.com
SIC: 3949 3751 5091 Helmets, athletic; bicycles & related parts; bicycle parts & accessories
HQ: Brg Sports, Inc.
1700 E Higgins Rd Ste 500
Des Plaines IL 60018
224 585-5200

(G-12947)
BESTOLIFE CORPORATION (DH)
2126 Vanco Dr (75061-8816)
PHONE..............................972 865-8961
Gary Stufflebeme, *President*
Misty Romines, *Principal*
Sharon White, *Vice Pres*
Joe Dugger, *CFO*
Bob Greenwood, *Sales Mgr*
◆ EMP: 30
SALES (est): 13.6MM
SALES (corp-wide): 276.4MM **Privately Held**
WEB: www.bestolife.com
SIC: 2891 5172 Sealing compounds for pipe threads or joints; petroleum products

---

HQ: Rsr Corporation
2777 N Stemmons Fwy # 2000
Dallas TX 75207
214 631-6070

(G-12948)
BIO WORLD MERCHANDISING INC (PA)
Also Called: Bioworld
1159 Cottonwood Ln (75038-6106)
PHONE......................972 488-0655
Rajeen Malik, *President*
Omar Cantu, *Exec VP*
Nathan Grant, *Vice Pres*
Jerry Koske, *Vice Pres*
Jennifer Staley, *Vice Pres*
◆ **EMP:** 133
SALES (est): 137.2MM **Privately Held**
WEB: www.bioworldmerch.com
SIC: 2353 3161 2253 5199 Hats & caps; clothing & apparel carrying cases; hats & headwear, knit; leather goods, except footwear, gloves, luggage, belting; rubber & plastics footwear

(G-12949)
BLUE RIDGE MTN RESOURCES INC (HQ)
122 W John Carpenter Fwy # 300 (75039-2013)
P.O. Box 12359, Spring (77391-2359)
PHONE......................469 444-1647
John K Reinhart, *President*
Keith Yankowsky, *COO*
R Glenn Dawson, *Exec VP*
Jim Denny, *Exec VP*
H C Ferguson III, *Exec VP*
EMP: 41
SQ FT: 20,700
SALES (est): 323.7MM
SALES (corp-wide): 3B **Publicly Held**
WEB: www.magnumhunterresources.com
SIC: 1382 Oil & gas exploration services
PA: Southwestern Energy Company Inc
10000 Energy Dr
Spring TX 77389
832 796-1000

(G-12950)
BOY SCOUTS OF AMERICA (PA)
1325 W Walnut Hill Ln (75038-3096)
P.O. Box 152079 (75015-2079)
PHONE......................972 580-2000
Robert Mazzuca, *CEO*
Robert M Gates, *President*
Rex W Tillerson, *President*
Bryan Wursten, *Editor*
Terrence Dunn, *Vice Pres*
▲ **EMP:** 520
SQ FT: 157,000
SALES (est): 335.9MM **Privately Held**
WEB: www.scouting.org
SIC: 8641 5136 5091 2721 Boy Scout organization; uniforms, men's & boys'; camping equipment & supplies; magazines: publishing only, not printed on site

(G-12951)
BP AERO ENGINE SERVICES LLC
5260 Valley View Ln (75038-2724)
PHONE......................972 252-2800
Dennis Walsh, *CEO*
EMP: 27
SALES (est): 5MM **Privately Held**
WEB: www.bpaero.com
SIC: 3724 Aircraft engines & engine parts

(G-12952)
BP AEROSPACE LLC
4965 Hanson Dr (75038-3302)
PHONE......................972 252-2800
Dennis M Walsh, *CEO*
James Demick, *Opers Mgr*
Clay Patterson, *Purch Mgr*
Steven Proctor, *Purchasing*
Fred Reiff, *Engineer*
◆ **EMP:** 100
SQ FT: 18,000
SALES (est): 10MM **Privately Held**
WEB: www.bpaero.com
SIC: 3728 Aircraft parts & equipment

(G-12953)
BUILDERS FIRSTSOURCE INC
8701 Sterling St Ste 180 (75063-2574)
PHONE......................972 621-2233
Cozart Chris, *Mfg Staff*
Tony Huckeba, *Purchasing*
Scott Wallace, *Sales Staff*
Scott Lee, *Branch Mgr*
Reagan Saldana, *Manager*
EMP: 70
SALES (corp-wide): 7.2B **Publicly Held**
WEB: www.bldr.com
SIC: 5031 2439 Lumber: rough, dressed & finished; structural wood members
PA: Builders Firstsource, Inc.
2001 Bryan St Ste 1600
Dallas TX 75201
214 880-3500

(G-12954)
BURNCO TEXAS LLC
Also Called: Gateway Concrete
8505 Freport Pkwy Ste 150 (75063)
PHONE......................940 242-3100
Scott Burns, *Principal*
Chris Saurenmann, *Project Mgr*
Stewart Owings, *QC Mgr*
Mark Bulger, *Sales Staff*
Robert Herman, *Sales Staff*
EMP: 30 EST: 2013
SALES (est): 13.4MM
SALES (corp-wide): 204.5MM **Privately Held**
WEB: www.burnco.com
SIC: 3273 Ready-mixed concrete
PA: Burnco Rock Products Ltd
155 Glendeer Cir Se Suite 200
Calgary AB T2H 2
403 255-2600

(G-12955)
C & G PLASTICS INC
1716 Parkside Ave (75061-6940)
PHONE......................972 254-2541
Charles Seargeant, *President*
Glenda Seargeant, *Vice Pres*
EMP: 17
SQ FT: 15,000
SALES (est): 1.2MM **Privately Held**
SIC: 3089 Injection molding of plastics

(G-12956)
C P E INC
Also Called: A-1 Servomotor Repair
3330 Stovall St (75061-4036)
PHONE......................972 313-1133
Jimmie M Stanfield, *President*
Bobbie T Stanfield, *Corp Secy*
David Stanfield, *Vice Pres*
Tim Taylor, *Purchasing*
Donna Stanfield, *Admin Sec*
▲ **EMP:** 11
SQ FT: 12,000
SALES (est): 2.3MM **Privately Held**
WEB: www.servorepair.com
SIC: 7694 Electric motor repair

(G-12957)
C T & S METAL FABRICATORS INC
Also Called: C.T. and S. Metalworks, Inc.
1513 Maryland Dr (75061-5725)
PHONE......................972 554-9629
Janet Witter, *President*
Bruce Witter, *COO*
EMP: 25
SALES (est): 591.7K **Privately Held**
WEB: www.ctands.com
SIC: 3441 Fabricated structural metal

(G-12958)
C&C SOFTWARE (PA)
703 N Irving Heights Dr (75061-7936)
P.O. Box 560008, Dallas (75356-0008)
PHONE......................714 635-3603
Mike Murray, *President*
William Buntain, *Vice Pres*
EMP: 43
SALES (est): 3.9MM **Privately Held**
WEB: www.candcsoftware.com
SIC: 7372 Prepackaged software

(G-12959)
CAPT NEMOS STEAK SUBMARINES
1426 N Irving Heights Dr (75061-5447)
PHONE......................972 438-7777
William Miller Jr, *Owner*
EMP: 10
SALES (est): 628.9K **Privately Held**
WEB: www.nemosubs.com
SIC: 2051 Bread, cake & related products

(G-12960)
CARBO CERAMICS INC (PA)
6565 N Macarthur Blvd # 1050 (75039-2490)
PHONE......................281 921-6400
◆ **EMP:** 9 EST: 1987
SALES (est): 870K **Privately Held**
SIC: 3299 Mfg Nonmetallic Mineral Products

(G-12961)
CARBO CERAMICS INC
6565 N Macarthur Blvd # 1 (75039-2490)
PHONE......................972 401-0090
Albert Malmberg, *Regional Mgr*
Jacki Etheredge, *Office Mgr*
Gary Kolstad, *Branch Mgr*
Katie Tucker, *Manager*
Jason Goodwin, *Director*
EMP: 12
SALES (corp-wide): 161.7MM **Privately Held**
WEB: www.carboceramics.com
SIC: 3299 Mica products
PA: Carbo Ceramics Inc.
575 N Dairy Ashford Rd # 300
Houston TX 77079
281 921-6400

(G-12962)
CASH PROCESSING SOLUTIONS INC
Also Called: De La Rue Cash Systems
6401 Commerce Dr (75063-2628)
PHONE......................972 582-1100
Martin Sutherland, *CEO*
Philip Rogerson, *Chairman*
Rupert Middleton, *COO*
Jitesh Sodha, *CFO*
▲ **EMP:** 268
SQ FT: 30,000
SALES (est): 82.2MM
SALES (corp-wide): 603.2MM **Privately Held**
WEB: www.delarue.com
SIC: 3559 Screening equipment, electric
PA: De La Rue Plc
De Le Rue House
Basingstoke HANTS RG22
125 660-5000

(G-12963)
CELANESE AMERICAS LLC (HQ)
Also Called: Kep Americas
222 Colinas Blvd W # 900 (75039-5421)
PHONE......................972 443-4000
Christopher W Jensen, *President*
Ronnie D Berry, *Vice Pres*
Vanessa Dupuis, *Vice Pres*
John W Howard, *Vice Pres*
Chuck B Kyrish, *Vice Pres*
◆ **EMP:** 12
SALES (est): 7.1B
SALES (corp-wide): 5.6B **Publicly Held**
WEB: www.celanese.com
SIC: 2821 2819 2824 5169 Plastics materials & resins; industrial inorganic chemicals; organic fibers, noncellulosic; chemicals & allied products
PA: Celanese Corporation
222 Las Colinas Blvd W
Irving TX 75039
972 443-4000

(G-12964)
CELANESE CORPORATION (PA)
222 Las Colinas Blvd W (75039-5421)
PHONE......................972 443-4000
Lori J Ryerkerk, *Ch of Bd*
Dheeraj Kumar, *Principal*
Jacqueline Hall, *Counsel*
A Lynne Puckett, *Senior VP*
Wade Nelson, *Vice Pres*
◆ **EMP:** 500

SALES: 5.6B **Publicly Held**
WEB: www.celanese.com
SIC: 2819 2821 2869 Industrial inorganic chemicals; polyethylene resins; acetates: amyl, butyl & ethyl; acetic & chloroacetic acid & metallic salts

(G-12965)
CELANESE EVA PERFORMANCE
222 Las Colinas Blvd W (75039-5421)
P.O. Box 169003 (75016-9003)
PHONE......................972 443-4000
Mark Rohr, *CEO*
Mark Murray, *President*
Scott Sutton, *Exec VP*
Lori Johnston, *Senior VP*
Gjon N Nivica Jr, *Senior VP*
◆ **EMP:** 10
SALES (est): 8.1MM
SALES (corp-wide): 5.6B **Publicly Held**
WEB: www.celanese.com
SIC: 2819 Industrial inorganic chemicals
PA: Celanese Corporation
222 Las Colinas Blvd W
Irving TX 75039
972 443-4000

(G-12966)
CELANESE INTERNATIONAL CORP
222 Las Colinas Blvd W (75039-5421)
PHONE......................972 443-4000
Mark C Rohr, *CEO*
Todd Elliott, *Senior VP*
Christopher W Jensen, *Senior VP*
Scott Richardson, *Senior VP*
Jay Townsend, *Senior VP*
◆ **EMP:** 880
SALES (est): 718.3MM
SALES (corp-wide): 5.6B **Publicly Held**
WEB: www.celanese.com
SIC: 2819 2869 Industrial inorganic chemicals; acetates: amyl, butyl & ethyl
PA: Celanese Corporation
222 Las Colinas Blvd W
Irving TX 75039
972 443-4000

(G-12967)
CENTENNIAL MOISTURE CTRL INC (PA)
1780 Hurd Dr (75038-4324)
PHONE......................214 350-7689
Joseph C Tamer, *President*
James R Ford, *Vice Pres*
Gail Monroe, *Manager*
Teresanne D Tamer, *Admin Sec*
EMP: 76
SQ FT: 35,000
SALES (est): 18.9MM **Privately Held**
WEB: www.centennialmc.com
SIC: 1799 1541 2891 Waterproofing; renovation, remodeling & repairs: industrial buildings; caulking compounds

(G-12968)
CHAMPION PALLET & PACKAGING
1126 Hidden Rdg Apt 2145 (75038-7976)
P.O. Box 1356, Terrell (75160-0024)
PHONE......................972 551-2474
Hun Choung, *President*
EMP: 30 EST: 1994
SQ FT: 15,000
SALES (est): 6.3MM **Privately Held**
SIC: 2448 3086 Pallets, wood; packaging & shipping materials, foamed plastic
PA: Choung Group, Inc.
5764 Gleneagles Dr
Plano TX

(G-12969)
CHEM-AQUA INC (HQ)
Also Called: Anco
2727 Chemsearch Blvd (75062-6454)
P.O. Box 152170 (75015-2170)
PHONE......................972 438-0232
Irvin Levy, *President*
John Mayfield, *Regional Mgr*
Kim Wooten, *Regional Mgr*
Kevin Gajewski, *District Mgr*
Philip Heath, *District Mgr*
▼ **EMP:** 20

SALES (est): 24.5MM
SALES (corp-wide): 1B **Privately Held**
WEB: www.chemaqua.com
SIC: **3589** Water treatment equipment, industrial
PA: Nch Corporation
2727 Chemsearch Blvd
Irving TX 75062
972 438-0211

(G-12970)
CHRISTMAS BY KREBS CORPORATION (PA)
8324 Sterling St (75063-2525)
PHONE..................972 929-2880
Walter Krebs, *CEO*
Eberhard Krebs, *Ch of Bd*
Thomas Krebs, *President*
Jacob Thomas, *Accountant*
Bill Wolf, *Sales Mgr*
◆ EMP: 10
SQ FT: 12,000
SALES (est): 7MM **Privately Held**
WEB:
www.wholesale.christmasbykrebs.com
SIC: **3231** Products of purchased glass

(G-12971)
CISCO SYSTEMS INC
7301 State Highway 161 # 200
(75039-2818)
PHONE..................469 420-4700
Keith Harmon, *Business Mgr*
Roddie Hasan, *Engineer*
Neil Martin, *Engineer*
Roman McDonald, *Engineer*
Johnny McKeever, *Engineer*
EMP: 60
SALES (corp-wide): 49.3B **Publicly Held**
WEB: www.cisco.com
SIC: **3577** Data conversion equipment, media-to-media: computer
PA: Cisco Systems, Inc.
170 W Tasman Dr
San Jose CA 95134
408 526-4000

(G-12972)
CITY OF IRVING
Also Called: Traffic & Transportation
825 W Irving Blvd (75060-2860)
P.O. Box 152288 (75015-2288)
PHONE..................972 721-2646
Jordan Wright, *Manager*
James Cline, *Director*
Arturo Gonzalez, *Officer*
EMP: 44
SALES (corp-wide): 342.2MM **Privately Held**
WEB: www.cityofirving.org
SIC: **3669** 9111 Transportation signaling devices; mayors' offices
PA: City Of Irving
825 W Irving Blvd
Irving TX 75060
972 721-2600

(G-12973)
CLOROX SALES COMPANY
8500 Freport Pkwy Ste 275 (75063)
PHONE..................972 915-0430
Rick Rexing, *Manager*
EMP: 12
SALES (corp-wide): 6.7B **Publicly Held**
WEB: www.thecloroxcompany.com
SIC: **2861** Charcoal, except activated
HQ: The Clorox Sales Company
1221 Broadway Fl 13
Oakland CA 94612

(G-12974)
CLOUD LOGIX LLC
8432 Sterling St Ste 200 (75063-2585)
P.O. Box 3829, Grapevine (76099-3829)
PHONE..................682 310-0665
Brenda Stanfield, *President*
Thomas K Cagney, *Principal*
Stephen Salazar, *Administration*
Ryne Smith, *Administration*
EMP: 24
SALES (est): 1.2MM **Privately Held**
WEB: www.supplychainlogix.com
SIC: **7372** 7373 5734 Prepackaged software; computer integrated systems design; software, business & non-game

(G-12975)
CMC STEEL US LLC (HQ)
6565 N Macarthur Blvd # 8 (75039-2490)
PHONE..................214 689-4300
Danna Cary, *CEO*
Jackie Porter, *Human Res Dir*
Rick Fulton, *Manager*
EMP: 12
SALES (est): 39.5MM
SALES (corp-wide): 5.4B **Publicly Held**
WEB: www.cmc.com
SIC: **3399** 3441 3312 Staples, nonferrous metal or wire; fabricated structural metal; blast furnaces & steel mills; bars & bar shapes, steel, hot-rolled; structural shapes & pilings, steel
PA: Commercial Metals Company
6565 N Macarthur Blvd # 800
Irving TX 75039
214 689-4300

(G-12976)
CNA HOLDINGS LLC (DH)
222 Las Colinas Blvd W (75039-5421)
PHONE..................972 443-4000
Edward Collins, *President*
◆ EMP: 45 EST: 1918
SALES (est): 6.9B
SALES (corp-wide): 5.6B **Publicly Held**
SIC: **2823** 2821 2819 5169 Acetate fibers, triacetate fibers; rayon fibers, straw, strips & yarn; plastics materials & resins; polyesters; vinyl resins; nylon resins; industrial inorganic chemicals; manmade fibers; commercial physical research
HQ: Celanese Americas Llc
222 Colinas Blvd W # 900
Irving TX 75039
972 443-4000

(G-12977)
COMMERCIAL METALS COMPANY (PA)
Also Called: CMC
6565 N Macarthur Blvd # 800
(75039-6283)
P.O. Box 1046, Dallas (75221-1046)
PHONE..................214 689-4300
Barbara R Smith, *Ch of Bd*
Thien Nguyen, *Managing Dir*
Tracy L Porter, *COO*
Jody K Absher, *Vice Pres*
Adam R Hickey, *Vice Pres*
EMP: 366 EST: 1915
SQ FT: 105,916
SALES: 5.4B **Publicly Held**
WEB: www.cmc.com
SIC: **3312** 3441 Blast furnaces & steel mills; bars & bar shapes, steel, hot-rolled; fabricated structural metal

(G-12978)
CONTEL FEDERAL SYSTEMS INC
600 Hidden Rdg (75038-3809)
PHONE..................972 718-5600
William M Edwards III, *President*
EMP: 1500
SQ FT: 800,000
SALES (est): 1B
SALES (corp-wide): 131.8B **Publicly Held**
SIC: **3661** 4813 Telephone & telegraph apparatus; telephone communication, except radio
PA: Verizon Communications Inc.
1095 Ave Of The Americas
New York NY 10036
212 395-1000

(G-12979)
CONVOY SERVICING CO
101 Decker Ct Ste 100 (75062-2792)
P.O. Box 561667, Dallas (75356-1667)
PHONE..................214 638-3050
Lester Bell, *Principal*
Donny Valentine, *Associate*
EMP: 12
SALES (est): 1.9MM **Privately Held**
WEB: www.convoyservicing.com
SIC: **1389** Roustabout service

(G-12980)
COOPER LIGHTING LLC
9500 N Royal Ln Ste 140 (75063-2469)
PHONE..................972 929-9400
Joe Quattrochi, *EMP: 100*
SALES (corp-wide): 6.9B **Privately Held**
WEB: www.cooperlighting.com
SIC: **3645** 3646 Residential lighting fixtures; commercial indusl & institutional electric lighting fixtures
HQ: Cooper Lighting, Llc
1121 Highway 74 S
Peachtree City GA 30269
770 486-4800

(G-12981)
COSMETIC LABORATORIES INC
3131 Premier Dr (75063-2636)
PHONE..................972 986-9098
Douglas M Johnson, *President*
Brett Johnson, *Vice Pres*
▲ EMP: 30
SQ FT: 25,000
SALES (est): 8.1MM **Privately Held**
WEB: www.cosmeticlaboratories.com
SIC: **2844** Cosmetic preparations

(G-12982)
COVEY SOFTWARE SYSTEMS INC
1825 W Walnut Hill Ln # 12 (75038-3218)
PHONE..................972 353-8716
Sukumar Arumugam, *President*
EMP: 11 EST: 1997
SQ FT: 300
SALES (est): 1.1MM **Privately Held**
WEB: www.coveysoft.com
SIC: **7372** 7379 Prepackaged software; computer related consulting services

(G-12983)
CROSSFIRE INC
Also Called: Crossfire Car Audio
3247 Story Rd W (75038-3532)
PHONE..................972 570-0800
James Song, *Principal*
Amy Hong, *CFO*
Christo Patiasina, *Shareholder*
▲ EMP: 20
SQ FT: 24,000
SALES (est): 3.3MM **Privately Held**
WEB: www.crossfirecaraudio.com
SIC: **3651** 5731 Speaker systems; amplifiers: radio, public address or musical instrument; sound equipment, automotive

(G-12984)
CRYSTAL DISTRIBUTION INC
6701 N Belt Line Rd (75063-6003)
PHONE..................763 391-7790
EMP: 49 **Privately Held**
WEB: www.cdicurbs.com
SIC: **3444** Sheet metalwork
PA: Crystal Distribution Inc.
17560 Tyler St Nw
Elk River MN 55330

(G-12985)
CRYSTAL IMAGES INC
1915 Peters Rd Ste 313 (75061-3246)
PHONE..................972 438-2337
Prince Maliyil, *President*
George Maliyil, *Vice Pres*
EMP: 10
SALES (est): 832.6K **Privately Held**
WEB: www.crystalimagesinc.com
SIC: **7389** 3229 Engraving service; glassware, art or decorative

(G-12986)
CT & S INC
Also Called: CT & S Meta Works
1513 Maryland Dr (75061-5725)
PHONE..................972 438-9796
Janet Witter, *CEO*
Bruce Witter, *COO*
Wendy Decker, *Accountant*
Brad Berland, *Sales Staff*
EMP: 30
SALES (est): 6.6MM **Privately Held**
WEB: www.ctands.com
SIC: **3441** Fabricated structural metal

(G-12987)
CUSTOM BILT HOLDINGS LLC (PA)
Also Called: Custom Bilt Metals
3001 Skyway Cir N Ste 160 (75038-3546)
PHONE..................214 699-4876
Michael Kowal, *President*
Gilbert Codrington, *Vice Pres*
Bruce Van Alstine, *Opers Staff*
Susan Merrill, *CFO*
Debbie Eanes, *Controller*
EMP: 14 EST: 2009
SQ FT: 5,000
SALES (est): 40MM **Privately Held**
WEB: www.custombiltmetals.com
SIC: **5033** 3444 Roofing, asphalt & sheet metal; metal roofing & roof drainage equipment; roof deck, sheet metal

(G-12988)
DAEGIS INC (HQ)
600 Las Colinas Blvd E # 1500
(75039-5651)
PHONE..................214 584-6400
Timothy P Bacci, *President*
Deborah Jillson, *President*
Susan K Conner, *COO*
Gambhir Nagaraju, *Engineer*
John Doolittle, *Treasurer*
EMP: 32
SQ FT: 14,878
SALES: 25.1MM
SALES (corp-wide): 3.1B **Privately Held**
WEB: www.opentext.com
SIC: **7372** 7375 Prepackaged software; information retrieval services
PA: Open Text Corporation
275 Frank Tompa Dr
Waterloo ON N2L 0
519 888-7111

(G-12989)
DALLAS COFFEE EXCHANGE
3201 N Britain Rd (75062-4563)
PHONE..................214 507-5903
Phil Acquaviva, *Partner*
EMP: 10
SALES (est): 543.5K **Privately Held**
SIC: **3999** Manufacturing industries

(G-12990)
DALLAS ROSTI INC
2109 Vanco Dr (75061-8815)
PHONE..................972 554-1597
Jerre Ross, *General Mgr*
Jonas Ewing, *Managing Dir*
Jacek Lubowicki, *Manager*
EMP: 10
SALES (est): 1.2MM **Privately Held**
WEB: www.rosti.com
SIC: **3089** Injection molding of plastics

(G-12991)
DAR INTERNATIONAL INC
2200 Creekside Cir S (75063-3351)
PHONE..................972 402-0493
Alberto Iannariello, *President*
Diana Iannariello, *Vice Pres*
EMP: 10
SALES (est): 190.5K **Privately Held**
WEB: www.darinter.com
SIC: **5088** 3492 5599 Aircraft equipment & supplies; valves, hydraulic, aircraft; aircraft dealers

(G-12992)
DARLING INGREDIENTS INC (PA)
5601 N Macarthur Blvd (75038-2616)
P.O. Box 141481 (75014-1481)
PHONE..................972 717-0300
Randall C Stuewe, *Ch of Bd*
Brad Frost, *General Mgr*
Phillip Harmon, *General Mgr*
Warren Rob, *General Mgr*
Rick Speaks, *District Mgr*
▼ EMP: 200
SALES: 3.3B **Publicly Held**
WEB: www.darlingii.com
SIC: **2077** Animal & marine fats & oils; grease rendering, inedible; tallow rendering, inedible; bone meal, except as animal feed

(G-12993)
DARLING INGREDIENTS INC
251 O Connor Ridge Blvd (75038-6532)
P.O. Box 3185, Melvindale MI (48122-0185)
PHONE..................................313 928-7400
Curtis Crawford, General Mgr
Jerome Levy, General Mgr
Mike Hudlow, Exec VP
Michael Carr, Vice Pres
Luthi Debbie, Vice Pres
EMP: 79
SALES (corp-wide): 3.3B Publicly Held
WEB: www.darlingii.com
SIC: 2077 2076 2048 2833 Grease rendering, inedible; tallow rendering, inedible; bone meal, except as animal feed; meat meal & tankage, except as animal feed; vegetable oil mills; prepared feeds; animal oils, medicinal grade: refined or concentrated
PA: Darling Ingredients Inc.
5601 N Macarthur Blvd
Irving TX 75038
972 717-0300

(G-12994)
DARLING INGREDIENTS INC
Also Called: Darling Global Holdings Inc.
5601 N Macarthur Blvd (75038-2616)
PHONE..................................972 717-0300
Randall C Stuewe, CEO
EMP: 220
SALES (est): 77.4K
SALES (corp-wide): 3.3B Publicly Held
WEB: www.darlingii.com
SIC: 2077 Animal & marine fats & oils
PA: Darling Ingredients Inc.
5601 N Macarthur Blvd
Irving TX 75038
972 717-0300

(G-12995)
DELIGENT LLC
1231 Greenway Dr Ste 270 (75038-2721)
PHONE..................................972 550-6111
Lina Joshi, Technology
Aruna Nagandla,
Kasar Prabhath,
EMP: 50
SQ FT: 2,200
SALES (est): 3.4MM Privately Held
WEB: www.deligentllc.com
SIC: 7372 Prepackaged software

(G-12996)
DESSERT DREAMS INC
409 N Briery Rd (75061-6331)
PHONE..................................972 313-2138
Shari Carlson, President
Matthew Melcher, Vice Pres
Adela Carlson, Admin Sec
EMP: 20
SQ FT: 9,000
SALES (est): 750K Privately Held
WEB: www.dessertdreams.net
SIC: 2051 Bakery: wholesale or wholesale/retail combined

(G-12997)
DEWIND CO (DH)
2201 W Royal Ln Ste 200 (75063-3205)
PHONE..................................469 420-9886
Young Jae Choi, CEO
Danny Shin, COO
▲ EMP: 25
SALES (est): 18.9MM Privately Held
SIC: 3511 Turbines & turbine generator sets

(G-12998)
DFW A-1 PALLET INC
Also Called: A1 Pallet
3000 E Grauwyler Rd (75061-3421)
P.O. Box 540215, Dallas (75354-0215)
PHONE..................................972 401-3502
Steve Free, President
Jill Free, President
Wilber Villalta, Vice Pres
EMP: 60
SQ FT: 20,000
SALES (est): 11.2MM Privately Held
WEB: www.dfwa1.com
SIC: 5211 2448 Lumber & other building materials; wood pallets & skids

(G-12999)
DFW OILFIELD SERVICES INC
8432 Sterling St Ste 101 (75063-2567)
PHONE..................................972 893-8025
Rick Caruthers, President
EMP: 12 EST: 2007
SQ FT: 3,000
SALES (est): 432.4K Privately Held
SIC: 1389 Oil field services

(G-13000)
DK CONTROLS LLC
3680 W Royal Ln Ste 175 (75063-2903)
PHONE..................................972 580-9300
Kevin I Moon, President
Jennifer Lowry, Opers Staff
Lance Walters, Production
Robert Browning, QC Mgr
Rob Wetsel, Engineer
EMP: 20
SQ FT: 2,800
SALES (est): 5.8MM Privately Held
WEB: www.dkcontrols.net
SIC: 3625 Relays & industrial controls

(G-13001)
DOMTAR INDUSTRIES LLC
Enterprise Group
8800 Sterling St (75063-2535)
PHONE..................................972 929-3565
Alan Pederson, Engineer
Jim Hudson, Manager
Dave Crippin, Technical Staff
EMP: 111
SALES (corp-wide): 5.2B Privately Held
WEB: www.domtar.com
SIC: 2621 Paper mills
HQ: Domtar Industries Llc
100 Kingsley Park Dr
Fort Mill SC 29715
803 802-7500

(G-13002)
DOMTAR PAPER COMPANY LLC
8800 Sterling St (75063-2535)
PHONE..................................972 929-8581
Kim Evetts, Branch Mgr
EMP: 225
SALES (corp-wide): 5.2B Privately Held
WEB: www.domtar.com
SIC: 2621 Paper mills
HQ: Domtar Paper Company, Llc
234 Kingsley Park Dr
Fort Mill SC 29715

(G-13003)
DRAEGER SAFETY DIAGNOSTICS INC (DH)
4040 W Royal Ln Ste 136 (75063-2845)
PHONE..................................972 929-1100
Michael Reinhart, President
Clint Toomey, Regional Mgr
Rita Lin, Business Mgr
Todd Gavin, Vice Pres
Lloyd Stern, Vice Pres
EMP: 30 EST: 1998
SALES (est): 16.9MM
SALES (corp-wide): 3B Privately Held
WEB: www.draegerinterlock.com
SIC: 3829 7359 Measuring & controlling devices; equipment rental & leasing
HQ: Draeger, Inc.
3135 Quarry Rd
Telford PA 18969
215 721-5400

(G-13004)
DW ENERGY GROUP
104 Decker Ct Ste 300 (75062-2757)
PHONE..................................214 758-0880
Martin White, President
Rick Boneau, COO
Josh Espinosa, Exec VP
Kevin Ozee, Exec VP
Fred Hernandez, Vice Pres
EMP: 25
SALES (est): 6.3MM Privately Held
WEB: www.dwenergygroup.com
SIC: 3533 Gas field machinery & equipment; oil field machinery & equipment

(G-13005)
EATON CORPORATION
4545 Fuller Dr (75038-6530)
P.O. Box 970041, Dallas (75397-0041)
PHONE..................................972 541-0461
EMP: 260 Privately Held
WEB: www.eatonelectrical.com
SIC: 3714 Motor vehicle engines & parts
HQ: Eaton Corporation
1000 Eaton Blvd
Cleveland OH 44122
440 523-5000

(G-13006)
ECLIPSE RESOURCES HOLDINGS LP
122 W John Carpenter Fwy # 300 (75039-2013)
P.O. Box 12359, Spring (77391-2359)
PHONE..................................814 308-9754
Benjamin W Hulburt, Principal
EMP: 227 EST: 2014
SALES (est): 4MM Privately Held
WEB: www.eclipseresources.com
SIC: 1311 Crude petroleum & natural gas

(G-13007)
ECLIPSE RESOURCES I LP (HQ)
122 W John Carpenter Fwy # 300 (75039-2013)
P.O. Box 12359, Spring (77391-2359)
PHONE..................................814 308-9754
Bryan Moody, President
Benjamin W Hulburt, Partner
Matthew R Denezza, Partner
Melissa Hamsher, Partner
Christopher K Hulburt, Partner
EMP: 19
SALES (est): 110.8MM
SALES (corp-wide): 3B Publicly Held
WEB: www.eclipseresources.com
SIC: 1311 1382 Crude petroleum production; oil & gas exploration services
PA: Southwestern Energy Company Inc
10000 Energy Dr
Spring TX 77389
832 796-1000

(G-13008)
ECLIPSE RESOURCES-PA LP
122 W John Carpenter Fwy # 300 (75039-2013)
P.O. Box 12359, Spring (77391-2359)
PHONE..................................814 409-7006
Christopher Hulburt, Exec VP
EMP: 15
SALES (est): 10MM
SALES (corp-wide): 3B Publicly Held
WEB: www.montageresources.com
SIC: 1382 Oil & gas exploration services
PA: Southwestern Energy Company Inc
10000 Energy Dr
Spring TX 77389
832 796-1000

(G-13009)
EDGE FABRICATION INC
1800 Hurd Dr (75038-4310)
PHONE..................................972 714-3893
Andrew Cohen, President
Karen Cohen, Vice Pres
Paul Riggs, Prdtn Mgr
Tommy Edmonds, Supervisor
EMP: 50
SALES (est): 9.2MM Privately Held
WEB: www.edgefabinc.com
SIC: 3444 Sheet metalwork

(G-13010)
EF JOHNSON COMPANY (DH)
1440 Corporate Dr (75038-2401)
PHONE..................................972 819-0700
John Suzuki, CEO
Michael Jalbert, COO
Duane Anderson, CFO
Bruce Stephan, Train & Dev Mgr
Brittany Dixon, Marketing Staff
EMP: 131
SQ FT: 40,000
SALES (est): 32.1MM Privately Held
WEB: www.efjohnson.com
SIC: 3663 Transmitter-receivers, radio; airborne radio communications equipment

(G-13011)
EF JOHNSON TECHNOLOGIES INC (HQ)
1440 Corporate Dr (75038-2401)
PHONE..................................972 819-0700
Duane Anderson, President
Jim Green, COO
John R Cagle, Senior VP
Timi Jackson, Vice Pres
Gabriel Zamfir, Program Mgr
EMP: 33
SALES (est): 47.5MM Privately Held
WEB: www.efjohnson.com
SIC: 4812 3663 Radio telephone communication; radio broadcasting & communications equipment

(G-13012)
EGS PRODUCTION MACHINING INC
2332 E Grauwyler Rd (75061-3314)
PHONE..................................972 438-2251
Tom Sellers, President
Bruce Goocher, Vice Pres
Matt Sellers, Accounts Exec
EMP: 25 EST: 1980
SALES (est): 3.4MM Privately Held
WEB: www.egsprod.com
SIC: 3599 Machine shop, jobbing & repair

(G-13013)
ELDER RUBBER INCORPORATED
Also Called: Porter Seal Company
2102 Vanco Dr (75061-8816)
PHONE..................................214 426-2890
Dupont Zhou, President
Joan Weyser, General Mgr
Walter Berry, COO
▲ EMP: 22
SQ FT: 15,000
SALES (est): 3MM Privately Held
WEB: www.elderrubber.com
SIC: 3069 Reclaimed rubber (reworked by manufacturing processes)

(G-13014)
ELECTRONIC DRILLING CONTROL
Also Called: Edc
3110 Story Rd W (75038-3513)
P.O. Box 166499 (75016-6499)
PHONE..................................972 257-0322
Wm H Brantley III, President
William H Brantley III, President
Brain Cook, Prdtn Mgr
Terri Lehrer, Credit Mgr
Betty Wood, Accountant
EMP: 60 EST: 1975
SQ FT: 32,000
SALES (est): 14.5MM Privately Held
SIC: 5065 7629 3559 3699 Electronic parts & equipment; electrical repair shops; ozone machines; electrical equipment & supplies

(G-13015)
ENVIRNMNTAL SGNAGE SLTIONS INC
Also Called: Asi Signage Innovations
8181 Jetstar Dr Ste 110 (75063-2857)
PHONE..................................972 915-3800
James Wolfe, CEO
Fred Wilson, President
Todd Carey, General Mgr
Erin Carey, Business Mgr
Dan Salamone, Business Mgr
▲ EMP: 41
SQ FT: 20,000
SALES (est): 6.2MM Privately Held
WEB: www.asisignage.com
SIC: 3446 Architectural metalwork
PA: Asi Sign Systems, Inc.
8181 Jetstar Dr Ste 110
Irving TX 75063

(G-13016)
ENVIROTAINER INC (DH)
222 Las Colinas Blvd W (75039-5421)
PHONE..................................972 831-3800
Simon Angeldorff, CEO
Tommy Wikstrm, Ch of Bd
Pascal Leuenberger, Partner
Steve Maietta, Principal
Mattias Almgren, Chairman
EMP: 12
SALES (est): 2.6MM Privately Held
WEB: www.envirotainer.com
SIC: 2631 Container, packaging & boxboard

HQ: Envirotainer International Ab
Staffans Vag 2a
Sollentuna
101 882-952

(G-13017)
EXELA TECHNOLOGIES INC (PA)
2701 E Grauwyler Rd (75061-3414)
PHONE..........................844 935-2832
Ronald Cogburn, *CEO*
Par Chadha, *Ch of Bd*
Mark Fairchild, *President*
Srini Murali, *President*
Vitalie Robu, *President*
EMP: 53
SALES: 1.5B **Publicly Held**
WEB: www.exelatech.com
SIC: 7372 Business oriented computer software

(G-13018)
EXIDE TECHNOLOGIES LLC
Also Called: GNB Industrial Power
9500 N Royal Ln Ste 150 (75063-2469)
PHONE..........................972 633-6900
Daniel Staab, *Manager*
EMP: 15
SALES (corp-wide): 2.1B **Privately Held**
WEB: www.exide.com
SIC: 3691 3629 Storage batteries; battery chargers, rectifying or nonrotating
PA: Exide Technologies, Llc
13000 Drfeld Pkwy Bldg 20
Milton GA 30004
678 566-9000

(G-13019)
EXIDE TECHNOLOGIES LLC
8181 Jetstar Dr Ste 120 (75063-2857)
PHONE..........................972 870-0337
Earl Whitley, *Manager*
EMP: 13
SALES (corp-wide): 2.1B **Privately Held**
WEB: www.exide.com
SIC: 5013 3629 Automotive batteries; battery chargers, rectifying or nonrotating
PA: Exide Technologies, Llc
13000 Drfeld Pkwy Bldg 20
Milton GA 30004
678 566-9000

(G-13020)
EXPAL USA INC (DH)
433 Las Colinas Blvd E # 900 (75039-5513)
PHONE..........................903 472-4970
Steven Dart, *President*
David Lueking, *QC Mgr*
Ladonna Woods, *Admin Sec*
EMP: 20
SALES (est): 4.2MM
SALES (corp-wide): 48MM **Privately Held**
WEB: www.maxamcorp.com
SIC: 3483 2892 3559 Ammunition, except for small arms; primary explosives, fuses & detonators; detonators, high explosives; secondary high explosives; emulsions (explosive); ammunition & explosives, loading machinery
HQ: Expal Systems Sa
Avenida Partenon (Campo De La Naciones), 16 - Plt 5
Madrid 28042
917 220-100

(G-13021)
EXXON MOBIL CORPORATION (PA)
Also Called: Exxonmobil
5959 Las Colinas Blvd (75039-2298)
PHONE..........................972 940-6000
Darren W Woods, *Ch of Bd*
Alex Jaikovsky, *Regional Mgr*
Larry Lane, *Regional Mgr*
Tom Kim, *Area Mgr*
Abin Thomas, *Business Mgr*
▼ **EMP:** 400 **EST:** 1882
SALES (est): 264.9B **Publicly Held**
WEB: www.exxonmobilchemical.com
SIC: 2911 4612 5541 5171 Petroleum refining; crude petroleum pipelines; gasoline service stations; petroleum bulk stations & terminals; generation, electric power

(G-13022)
FALCON EVENTS LLC ☉
3001 Gateway Dr Ste 130 (75063-2668)
PHONE..........................800 895-6934
Joshua Butler, *Mng Member*
EMP: 80 **EST:** 2020
SALES: 2.1MM **Privately Held**
SIC: 2741 7389 3663 ; music & broadcasting services; studio equipment, radio & television broadcasting

(G-13023)
FDL OPERATING LLC
5221 N O Connor Blvd # 1100 (75039-3714)
PHONE..........................469 453-7346
Porter Trimble,
Jim Mayfield,
Jake Plunk,
EMP: 25 **EST:** 2014
SALES (est): 5.4MM **Privately Held**
WEB: www.fdlenergy.com
SIC: 1389 Oil & gas wells: building, repairing & dismantling

(G-13024)
FEDEX OFFICE & PRINT SVCS INC
3201 W Arprt Fwy Ste 100 (75062)
PHONE..........................972 570-5110
EMP: 12
SALES (corp-wide): 69.2B **Publicly Held**
WEB: www.fedex.com
SIC: 7334 2759 Photocopying & duplicating services; commercial printing
HQ: Fedex Office And Print Services, Inc.
7900 Legacy Dr
Plano TX 75024
800 463-3339

(G-13025)
FELLOWSHIP TECHNOLOGIES LP
6363 N State Highway 161 (75038-2269)
PHONE..........................469 442-0100
Jeffery Hook, *Partner*
Kingsley Allen, *Partner*
Allen Horak, *Partner*
Jeff Pelletier, *Partner*
Tammy Polk, *Partner*
EMP: 66
SQ FT: 27,300
SALES (est): 6.2MM **Privately Held**
WEB: www.fellowshipone.com
SIC: 7372 Prepackaged software

(G-13026)
FIGUEROA BROTHERS INC
Also Called: FB
1740 Hurd Dr (75038-4324)
PHONE..........................214 351-9060
Greg P Figueroa, *CEO*
Kevin Anderson, *Vice Pres*
David O Figueroa Jr, *Vice Pres*
David O Figueroa Sr, *CFO*
▲ **EMP:** 20
SQ FT: 50,000
SALES (est): 5.9MM **Privately Held**
WEB: www.figbros.com
SIC: 2099 Seasonings: dry mixes; spices, including grinding

(G-13027)
FLOWSERVE CORPORATION (PA)
5215 N Ocnnor Blvd Ste 23 Connor (75039)
PHONE..........................972 443-6500
Roger L Fix, *Ch of Bd*
R Scott Rowe, *President*
Sanjay Chowbey, *President*
Kirk Wilson, *President*
Michael Carr, *Division Mgr*
EMP: 277 **EST:** 1912
SQ FT: 125,000
SALES (est): 3.9B **Publicly Held**
WEB: www.flowserve.com
SIC: 3561 3491 3621 3494 Pumps & pumping equipment; industrial valves; pressure valves & regulators, industrial; regulators (steam fittings); valves, nuclear; motors & generators; valves & pipe fittings; pump & compressor forgings, nonferrous; cast iron pipe & fittings

(G-13028)
FLOWSERVE CORPORATION
4343 W Royal Ln Ste 106 (75063-2299)
PHONE..........................800 446-0401
Lara Chalmers, *Vice Pres*
Jordan Janes, *Sales Staff*
Johnny Van Der Linden, *Manager*
EMP: 14
SALES (corp-wide): 3.9B **Publicly Held**
WEB: www.flowserve.com
SIC: 3561 3491 3621 3494 Industrial pumps & parts; industrial valves; motors & generators; valves & pipe fittings; pump & compressor forgings, nonferrous; cast iron pipe & fittings
PA: Flowserve Corporation
5215 N Ocnnor Blvd Ste 23 Connor
Irving TX 75039
972 443-6500

(G-13029)
FLOWSERVE INTERNATIONAL INC (HQ)
5215 N O Connor Blvd # 2300 (75039-5418)
PHONE..........................972 443-6500
Mark A Blinn, *CEO*
Mark D Dailey, *Senior VP*
Tina Jackson, *Facilities Mgr*
Tina Corley, *Executive Asst*
EMP: 11
SALES (est): 42.1MM
SALES (corp-wide): 3.9B **Publicly Held**
WEB: www.flowserve.com
SIC: 3561 Pumps & pumping equipment
PA: Flowserve Corporation
5215 N Ocnnor Blvd Ste 23 Connor
Irving TX 75039
972 443-6500

(G-13030)
FLOWSERVE US INC (HQ)
Also Called: FCD Division
5215 N Oconnor Blvd Ste Connor (75039)
PHONE..........................972 443-6500
R Scott Rowe, *President*
Michael S Staff, *President*
Thomas L Pajonas, *Exec VP*
Mark D Dailey, *Senior VP*
Keith E Gillespie, *Senior VP*
▲ **EMP:** 100
SALES (est): 773.1MM
SALES (corp-wide): 3.9B **Publicly Held**
WEB: www.flowserve.com
SIC: 3561 3491 Industrial pumps & parts; valves, automatic control
PA: Flowserve Corporation
5215 N Ocnnor Blvd Ste 23 Connor
Irving TX 75039
972 443-6500

(G-13031)
FORPROJECT TECHNOLOGY INC
4020 N Macarthur Blvd # 1 (75038-6419)
PHONE..........................214 550-8156
Glenn Gallop, *President*
Stuart Trahan, *CTO*
Ken Inglis, *Software Dev*
John Krahula, *Sr Consultant*
EMP: 15 **Privately Held**
WEB: www.forproject.com
SIC: 7372 Prepackaged software

(G-13032)
FORTERRA INC (HQ)
511 E John Carpenter Fwy # 6 (75062-3911)
PHONE..........................469 458-7973
Karl H Watson Jr, *CEO*
Chris Meyer, *Ch of Bd*
Rich Hunter, *COO*
Vik Bhatia, *Exec VP*
Lori M Browne, *Exec VP*
EMP: 4729
SALES: 1.5B **Publicly Held**
WEB: www.forterrabp.com
SIC: 3272 3569 Concrete products used to facilitate drainage; cylinder pipe, prestressed or pretensioned concrete; filters & strainers, pipeline
PA: Forterra Us Holdings, Llc
511 E John Carpenter Fwy
Irving TX 75062
469 284-8678

(G-13033)
FORTERRA PIPE & PRECAST LLC (DH)
511 E John Carpenter Fwy (75062-3911)
P.O. Box 660025, Dallas (75266-0025)
PHONE..........................469 458-7973
Jerry Swanson, *Sales Staff*
Chris Meyer,
Scott Szwejbka,
Charlie Carder, *Representative*
◆ **EMP:** 70
SQ FT: 47,696
SALES (est): 1.3B
SALES (corp-wide): 1.5B **Publicly Held**
WEB: www.forterrabp.com
SIC: 3272 1771 Precast terrazo or concrete products; concrete work
HQ: Forterra, Inc.
511 E John Carpenter Fwy # 6
Irving TX 75062
469 458-7973

(G-13034)
FORTERRA US HOLDINGS LLC (PA)
511 E John Carpenter Fwy (75062-3911)
PHONE..........................469 284-8678
Samuel D Loughlin, *Ch of Bd*
Lori M Browne, *Senior VP*
Ed Sexe, *Senior VP*
Matthew Wayman, *Vice Pres*
William Matthew Brown, *CFO*
EMP: 28 **EST:** 2016
SALES (est): 1.5B **Publicly Held**
WEB: www.forterrabp.com
SIC: 3272 Concrete products used to facilitate drainage

(G-13035)
FREEFLIGHT ACQUISITION CORP (PA)
Also Called: Freeflight Systems
8080 Tristar Dr Ste 100 (75063-2823)
PHONE..........................254 662-0000
Timothy S Taylor, *CEO*
John Ojeda, *Prdtn Mgr*
James Barnes, *Production*
Gerry Goldstein, *Buyer*
Brad Brunson, *Technical Mgr*
EMP: 15
SQ FT: 8,000
SALES (est): 15MM **Privately Held**
WEB: www.freeflightsystems.com
SIC: 3812 Antennas, radar or communications; defense systems & equipment

(G-13036)
FRITO-LAY NORTH AMERICA INC
701 N Wildwood Dr (75061-8831)
PHONE..........................972 579-2543
Jim Smith, *General Mgr*
Umberto Valtierra, *Maint Spvr*
Montreal Dukes, *Electrical Engi*
Fritz Wise, *Manager*
Fred Davis, *Technical Staff*
EMP: 800
SALES (corp-wide): 67.1B **Publicly Held**
WEB: www.fritolay.com
SIC: 2096 2099 Potato chips & similar snacks; food preparations
HQ: Frito-Lay North America, Inc.
7701 Legacy Dr
Plano TX 75024

(G-13037)
GENERAL ELECTRIC COMPANY
6051 N State Highway 161 (75038-2227)
PHONE..........................972 444-2000
Bill Hoyt, *Manager*
EMP: 14
SALES (corp-wide): 95.2B **Publicly Held**
WEB: www.ge.com
SIC: 3641 Electric lamps
PA: General Electric Company
5 Necco St
Boston MA 02210
617 443-3000

(G-13038)
GKN AEROSPACE INC (DH)
6031 Connection Dr # 600 (75039-2613)
PHONE..........................972 432-1900
Kevin Cummings, *President*
Frank Jon Evans, *Vice Pres*

Abby Lilly, *Vice Pres*
John M O'Donnell, *Vice Pres*
Jonathon Levine, *Director*
EMP: 12
SALES (est): 3.5MM
SALES (corp-wide): 14.1B **Privately Held**
SIC: 3812 Aircraft/aerospace flight instruments & guidance systems; acceleration indicators & systems components, aerospace
HQ: Gkn Aerospace Services Limited
2nd Floor, One Central Boulevard,
Blythe Valley Park
Solihull W MIDLANDS B90 8
121 210-9800

(G-13039)
GLOBAL PWR TECHNICAL SVCS INC
400 Las Colinas Blvd E (75039-5579)
PHONE..................214 574-2700
EMP: 41
SALES (est): 5.2MM
SALES (corp-wide): 245.7MM **Publicly Held**
WEB: www.globalpower.com
SIC: 3568 Power transmission equipment
PA: Williams Industrial Services Group Inc.
100 Crscent Ctr Pkwy Ste
Tucker GA 30084
770 879-4400

(G-13040)
GOOD SPORTSMAN MARKETING LLC (PA)
Also Called: GSM Outdoors
5250 Frye Rd (75061-6028)
P.O. Box 535189, Grand Prairie (75053-5189)
PHONE..................877 269-8490
Eddie Castro, *Principal*
◆ **EMP:** 32
SALES (est): 33.4MM **Privately Held**
WEB: www.gsmoutdoors.com
SIC: 5199 3663 7382 3648 Variety store merchandise; amplifiers, RF power & IF; protective devices, security; lighting equipment

(G-13041)
GOODIER COSMETICS LLC
5930 Campus Circle Dr W (75063-2605)
PHONE..................214 630-1803
Maria Carell, *CEO*
Tatiana Kelly, *Chairman*
Robert Muller, *COO*
Nirmal Shah, *Research*
▲ **EMP:** 170
SALES (est): 16.3MM **Privately Held**
WEB: www.goodiercosmetics.com
SIC: 2844 5087 Cosmetic preparations; beauty salon & barber shop equipment & supplies

(G-13042)
GPEG LLC
400 Las Colinas Blvd E (75039-5579)
PHONE..................214 574-2700
Lee Nguyen, *Vice Pres*
Kindra Herrera, *Engineer*
EMP: 48
SALES (est): 2.1MM
SALES (corp-wide): 245.7MM **Publicly Held**
SIC: 3568 Power transmission equipment
PA: Williams Industrial Services Group Inc.
100 Crscent Ctr Pkwy Ste
Tucker GA 30084
770 879-4400

(G-13043)
GRUMA CORPORATION
Also Called: Mission Foods
5601 Executive Dr (75038-2508)
PHONE..................972 232-5000
Juan Delarosa, *Site Mgr*
Jorge Trevino, *Engineer*
Maria Hughes, *Enginr/R&D Asst*
Robert Worley, *Branch Mgr*
James Kuykendall, *Manager*
EMP: 175 **Privately Held**
WEB: www.missionfoods.com

SIC: 2075 2099 2096 5149 Soybean oil, cake or meal; tortillas, fresh or refrigerated; spices, including grinding; sauces: dry mixes; tortilla chips; specialty food items; frozen specialties; pickles, sauces & salad dressings
HQ: Gruma Corporation
5601 Executive Dr Ste 800
Irving TX 75038
972 232-5000

(G-13044)
GRUMA CORPORATION (HQ)
Also Called: Mission Foods
5601 Executive Dr Ste 800 (75038-2508)
PHONE..................972 232-5000
Javier Velez Bautista, *President*
Juan A Gonzalez Moreno, *Chairman*
Bill Yarger, *Business Mgr*
Ward Delaney, *Vice Pres*
Felipe Rubio Lamas, *Vice Pres*
▲ **EMP:** 240
SALES: 2.2B **Privately Held**
WEB: www.missionfoods.com
SIC: 0723 2096 2099 Flour milling custom services; tortilla chips; food preparations

(G-13045)
GTC TECHNOLOGY LLC
8505 Freport Pkwy Ste 210 (75063)
PHONE..................817 685-9125
Brad Fleming, *General Mgr*
Crystal Bell, *Human Res Mgr*
EMP: 34 **Privately Held**
WEB: www.gtctech.com
SIC: 3312 3316 Rods, iron & steel: made in steel mills; sheet, steel, cold-rolled: from purchased hot-rolled
PA: Gtc Technology Llc
1001 S Dairy Ashford Rd # 500
Houston TX 77077

(G-13046)
GUJARAT FLRCHMCALS AMRICAS LLC
Also Called: Gfl Americas, LLC
1212 Corporate Dr Ste 540 (75038-2502)
PHONE..................512 446-7700
Brian Barkes, *General Mgr*
David Kaufmann, *General Mgr*
Laura Shekleton, *Business Mgr*
Randy Morgan, *Mng Member*
James Downing, *Mng Member*
▲ **EMP:** 17
SALES (est): 4MM **Privately Held**
WEB: www.gflamericas.com
SIC: 3585 Refrigeration equipment, complete
HQ: Gfl Limited
Inox Towers,
Noida UP

(G-13047)
GWM PRODUCTS LLC
Also Called: Keneric Healthcare
8925 Sterling St Ste 100 (75063-1993)
PHONE..................855 872-2013
EMP: 25
SALES (est): 2.9MM **Privately Held**
SIC: 3842 Mfg Surgical Appliances/Supplies

(G-13048)
HANNON HYDRAULICS INC (PA)
Also Called: Hannon Offshore Drilling Eqp
625 N Loop 12 (75061-8796)
PHONE..................972 438-2870
H Wade Reed, *CEO*
Aaron Reed, *President*
Mark Klatt, *Vice Pres*
Don Mullins, *Vice Pres*
Brandon McGuinness, *Purchasing*
▲ **EMP:** 65 **EST:** 1975
SQ FT: 44,000
SALES (est): 25.5MM **Privately Held**
WEB: www.hannonoffshore.com
SIC: 7699 3593 3594 Hydraulic equipment repair; fluid power cylinders, hydraulic or pneumatic; motors: hydraulic, fluid power or air

(G-13049)
HANSON AGGREGATES LLC (DH)
Also Called: Southern Star Concrete
8505 Freport Pkwy Ste 500 (75063)
PHONE..................469 417-1200
Daniel Harrington, *CEO*
Michael Hyer, *Vice Pres*
Seyda Pirinccioglu, *CFO*
Donna Ashabranner, *Human Res Dir*
Karen Holbrooks, *Office Mgr*
EMP: 250 **EST:** 1968
SALES (est): 471.1MM
SALES (corp-wide): 20.8B **Privately Held**
WEB: www.heidelbergcement.com
SIC: 3273 2951 5032 Ready-mixed concrete; asphalt paving mixtures & blocks; gravel; sand, construction

(G-13050)
HANSON AGGREGATES LLC
5150 Valley View Ln (75038-7014)
PHONE..................972 256-6571
Carter Pajtterton, *Branch Mgr*
EMP: 24
SALES (corp-wide): 20.8B **Privately Held**
WEB: www.heidelbergcement.com
SIC: 3273 Ready-mixed concrete
HQ: Hanson Aggregates Llc
8505 Freport Pkwy Ste 500
Irving TX 75063
469 417-1200

(G-13051)
HANSON AGGREGATES NEW YORK LLC (DH)
8505 Freport Pkwy Ste 500 (75063)
PHONE..................972 621-0345
George Piazza,
▲ **EMP:** 48
SALES (est): 21.7MM
SALES (corp-wide): 20.8B **Privately Held**
SIC: 3273 Ready-mixed concrete

(G-13052)
HANSON LEHIGH INC (HQ)
300 E John Carpenter Fwy (75062-2727)
P.O. Box 660225, Dallas (75266-0225)
PHONE..................972 653-5500
Jon Morrish, *CEO*
Robert Pischke, *President*
Kurt Milliman, *General Mgr*
Josh McJunkin, *Regional Mgr*
Joshua Kornely, *Counsel*
◆ **EMP:** 500
SALES (est): 7B
SALES (corp-wide): 20.8B **Privately Held**
WEB: www.lehighhanson.com
SIC: 1442 1422 1423 3297 Sand mining; gravel & pebble mining; crushed & broken limestone; crushed & broken granite; cement refractories; ready-mixed concrete; concrete products used to facilitate drainage
PA: Heidelbergcement Ag
Berliner Str. 6
Heidelberg 69120
622 148-10

(G-13053)
HARTSFIELD & PIERCE CABINET CO
Also Called: Hartsfield Cabinet
200 Sewell Ct (75038-6281)
PHONE..................972 288-5487
David R Hartsfield, *President*
Janelle Hartsfield, *Vice Pres*
EMP: 11 **EST:** 1971
SQ FT: 11,900
SALES (est): 1.2MM **Privately Held**
WEB: www.hartsfieldcabinets.com
SIC: 2434 Wood kitchen cabinets

(G-13054)
HAYAKAWA ELECTRONICS AMER INC
1425 Greenway Dr Ste 140 (75038-2416)
PHONE..................972 457-0064
Yoshihiro Murakawa, *CEO*
Allison Bailey, *CFO*
Masahiro Hayakawa, *Admin Sec*
◆ **EMP:** 21

SALES (est): 3.4MM **Privately Held**
WEB: www.hayakawaus.com
SIC: 3679 Harness assemblies for electronic use: wire or cable
PA: Hayakawa Densen Kogyo Co.,Ltd.
422, Nishinobusue
Himeji HYO 670-0

(G-13055)
HEALTH MANAGEMENT SYSTEMS INC (HQ)
Also Called: HMS Business Services
5615 High Point Dr # 100 (75038-2434)
P.O. Box 166409 (75016-6409)
PHONE..................214 453-3000
EMP: 250
SQ FT: 146,000
SALES (est): 273.4MM
SALES (corp-wide): 626.4MM **Publicly Held**
WEB: www.hms.com
SIC: 7374 7372 Data processing & preparation; application computer software
PA: Hms Holdings Corp.
5615 High Point Dr # 100
Irving TX 75038
214 453-3000

(G-13056)
HIGH POINT DESIGN LLC
2010 Century Center Blvd (75062-4905)
PHONE..................972 753-2622
Steve Dillier, *Senior Engr*
Dan Sheldon, *Mng Member*
Charlotte Sheldon, *Bd of Directors*
Lulie Kay Sheldon, *Bd of Directors*
Peggylinn Sheldon, *Bd of Directors*
EMP: 10
SALES (est): 1.5MM **Privately Held**
WEB: www.hptdesign.com
SIC: 3679 7372 Electronic circuits; prepackaged software

(G-13057)
HILLSHIRE BRANDS COMPANY
Also Called: Bil Mar Foods
9901 Valley Ranch Pkwy E (75063-4730)
PHONE..................972 556-0392
EMP: 322
SALES (corp-wide): 43.1B **Publicly Held**
WEB: www.sterlingbay.com
SIC: 2013 Sausages & other prepared meats
HQ: The Hillshire Brands Company
400 S Jefferson St Ste 1n
Chicago IL 60607
312 614-6000

(G-13058)
HOLLMAN INC (PA)
Also Called: Hollman Court Systems
1825 W Walnut Hill Ln # 110 (75038-4453)
PHONE..................972 815-4000
Travis Hollman, *President*
Pierce Audry, *CFO*
▲ **EMP:** 150
SQ FT: 150,000
SALES (est): 53.3MM **Privately Held**
WEB: www.hollman.com
SIC: 1629 2541 2435 2411 Athletic & recreation facilities construction; lockers, except refrigerated: wood; hardwood veneer & plywood; logging

(G-13059)
HOV SERVICES INC (HQ)
2701 E Grauwyler Rd (75061-3414)
PHONE..................248 837-7100
Suresh Yannamani, *President*
Raymond Wise, *Vice Pres*
Ivan Trejos, *Manager*
Brenda Miotke, *Administration*
EMP: 25
SQ FT: 47,000
SALES (est): 105.1MM
SALES (corp-wide): 1.5B **Publicly Held**
WEB: www.exelatech.com
SIC: 7374 7334 7389 2752 Data processing & preparation; photocopying & duplicating services; microfilm recording & developing service; decals, lithographed; mailing service; data processing consultant

▲ = Import ▼ =Export
◆ =Import/Export

PA: Exela Technologies, Inc.
2701 E Grauwyler Rd
Irving TX 75061
844 935-2832

(G-13060)
HUMAN RESOURCE MICRO SYSTEMS
7301 State Highway 161 (75039-2816)
PHONE.....................415 362-8400
Tom Lucas, *President*
EMP: 14
SQ FT: 5,100
SALES (est): 704K
SALES (corp-wide): 28.1MM **Privately Held**
SIC: 7371 7372 8742 Computer software development; prepackaged software; personnel management consultant
HQ: Bpo Management Services, Inc.
8175 E Kaiser Blvd 100
Anaheim CA 92808
714 974-2670

(G-13061)
HW HOLDCO LLC
Also Called: Hanley Wood Exhibition Div
6191 N State Highway 161 (75038-2246)
PHONE.....................972 536-6300
Nathan Huber, *Marketing Mgr*
James Boddorf,
Sheila Harris, *Administration*
EMP: 45
SALES (corp-wide): 153.4MM **Privately Held**
WEB: www.hwresidentialnetwork.com
SIC: 2499 7389 Decorative wood & woodwork; promoters of shows & exhibitions
PA: Hw Holdco, Llc
1 Thomas Cir Nw Ste 600
Washington DC 20005
202 452-0800

(G-13062)
I NET SOFTWARE TECHNOLOGIES
9901 Valley Ranch Pkwy E (75063-4730)
PHONE.....................972 401-0100
Rohitha Kodali, *President*
Bill Garry, *Recruiter*
EMP: 25
SALES: 1.6MM **Privately Held**
WEB: www.inetsoftinc.com
SIC: 7372 Prepackaged software

(G-13063)
IBM GLOBAL SYSTEMS INC
Also Called: Jolt Technologies
1303 W Walnut Hill Ln # 13 (75038-3030)
PHONE.....................972 468-1944
Kranthi Javvaji, *President*
Rama RAO, *Recruiter*
EMP: 10
SQ FT: 1,200
SALES (est): 3.5MM **Privately Held**
WEB: www.ibmglobal.us
SIC: 7372 Application computer software

(G-13064)
INSTITUTE FLGHT OPRTONS DSPTCH
Also Called: Ifod
2300 Valley View Ln # 250 (75062-1721)
PHONE.....................817 967-4424
Cassie Blake, *Manager*
Ana M Moreno, *Manager*
EMP: 9
SALES (est): 729.7K **Privately Held**
WEB: www.airlinedispatcher.com
SIC: 3728 Aircraft training equipment

(G-13065)
IPR TRANSOIL CORPORATION (PA)
Also Called: Ipr Energy Group
909 Lake Carolyn Pkwy # 8 (75039-3908)
PHONE.....................972 257-1900
Mahmoud K Dabbous, *President*
Sam Dabbous, *COO*
Marcie A Goss, *Senior VP*
Darius Shahsavari, *Senior VP*
Joann Deborde, *Buyer*
EMP: 15

SALES (est): 7.9MM **Privately Held**
WEB: www.iprgoc.com
SIC: 1382 Oil & gas exploration services

(G-13066)
IRVING COUNTER INC
101 N Irving Heights Dr (75061-7924)
P.O. Box 153105 (75015-3105)
PHONE.....................972 438-4343
Marvin Randle, *President*
John Randle, *Vice Pres*
EMP: 42
SQ FT: 70,000
SALES (est): 10.9MM **Privately Held**
WEB: www.irvingcountertop.net
SIC: 5032 5031 3281 2541 Marble building stone; building materials, interior; cut stone & stone products; wood partitions & fixtures
PA: Irving Counter Top Inc.
101 N Irving Heights Dr
Irving TX 75061

(G-13067)
ITW PLYMERS SALANTS N AMER INC (DH)
420 Decker Dr Ste 160 (75062-4314)
PHONE.....................972 438-9111
Juan Valls, *President*
Bob Seiple, *General Mgr*
Danielle Pack, *Regional Mgr*
Mark J Croll, *Vice Pres*
Mark W Croll, *Vice Pres*
◆ EMP: 110
SALES (est): 32MM
SALES (corp-wide): 1.5B **Publicly Held**
WEB: www.itwsealants.com
SIC: 2891 Sealants
HQ: Omg, Inc.
153 Bowles Rd
Agawam MA 01001
413 789-0252

(G-13068)
JDC ENTERPRISES INC
Also Called: Vendor Guide, The
2900 Gateway Dr Ste 625 (75063-2667)
P.O. Box 1701, Euless (76039-1701)
PHONE.....................972 550-1880
Deborah Newman, *President*
Amy Rumpler, *COO*
John Simmons, *Vice Pres*
Morgan Novey, *Production*
James Simmons, *Director*
EMP: 20
SQ FT: 6,979
SALES (est): 2.3MM **Privately Held**
WEB: www.vgvisuals.com
SIC: 2741 2721 3993 7311 Directories: publishing only, not printed on site; periodicals; signs & advertising specialties; advertising agencies; advertising, promotional & trade show services

(G-13069)
JP ENERGY PARTNERS LP (DH)
600 Las Colinas Blvd E # 2000 (75039-5607)
PHONE.....................972 444-0300
J Patrick Barley, *President*
Shiming Chen, *Senior VP*
Michael Croney, *Vice Pres*
Patrick J Welch, *CFO*
EMP: 50
SALES: 493.9MM
SALES (corp-wide): 805.3MM **Privately Held**
WEB: www.jpenergypartners.com
SIC: 1321 5171 Propane (natural) production; petroleum bulk stations & terminals

(G-13070)
JPT GRAPHICS INC
212 W Irving Blvd (75060-2919)
PHONE.....................972 785-1013
Shirley Lewenstein, *President*
Shirly Lewenstein, *President*
Francisco Lewenstein, *Principal*
Debbie Shea, *Production*
Pancho Lewenstein, *Sales Staff*
EMP: 9
SQ FT: 2,700
SALES (est): 1.5MM **Privately Held**
WEB: www.jptgraphics.com
SIC: 2752 Commercial printing, offset

(G-13071)
JVB ELECTRONICS INC
Also Called: Multilayer Technology
3835 Conflans Rd (75061-3914)
PHONE.....................972 877-8085
Viny Mulani, *President*
Tim Martin, *Principal*
Alan Cochrane, *COO*
Naren Tarpara, *Exec VP*
Bharat Chodavadia, *Vice Pres*
EMP: 35
SQ FT: 30,000
SALES (est): 8.4MM **Privately Held**
WEB: www.multilayer.com
SIC: 3672 Printed circuit boards

(G-13072)
KAINEXUS INC (PA)
4225 Wingren Dr Ste 115 (75062-2762)
PHONE.....................512 522-3940
Gregory Jacobson, *CEO*
Matt Paliulis, *COO*
Ryan Confer, *Vice Pres*
Mark Graban, *Vice Pres*
Jeff Roussel, *Vice Pres*
EMP: 10
SQ FT: 1,000
SALES (est): 1.5MM **Privately Held**
WEB: www.kainexus.com
SIC: 7372 7371 Prepackaged software; software programming applications

(G-13073)
KAWNEER COMPANY INC
3216 Royalty Row (75062-4942)
PHONE.....................972 438-1212
Steve Kesterson, *Sales Staff*
David Brown, *Manager*
EMP: 20
SALES (corp-wide): 7.2B **Publicly Held**
WEB: www.alcoa.com
SIC: 3446 3442 Architectural metalwork; metal doors
HQ: Kawneer Company, Inc.
555 Guthridge Ct
Norcross GA 30092
770 449-5555

(G-13074)
KEYLESSCO LLC
1825 W Walnut Hill Ln # 10 (75038-3218)
PHONE.....................972 331-2773
Estera Kuhlmann, *President*
Joseph Hollman, *Principal*
EMP: 15
SALES (est): 10.6MM **Privately Held**
WEB: www.keyless.co
SIC: 3669 Emergency alarms

(G-13075)
KIMBERLY-CLARK CORPORATION (PA)
351 Phelps Dr (75038-6540)
P.O. Box 619100, Dallas (75261-9100)
PHONE.....................972 281-1200
Michael D Hsu, *President*
Gonzalo Uribe, *President*
Beverly Garcia, *Regional Mgr*
William D Dunn, *Business Mgr*
Fran Walsh, *Business Mgr*
◆ EMP: 277 EST: 1872
SALES: 19.1B **Publicly Held**
WEB: www.kimberly-clark.com
SIC: 2676 2621 Sanitary paper products; towels, napkins & tissue paper products; feminine hygiene paper products; infant & baby paper products; facial tissue stock

(G-13076)
KIMBERLY-CLARK WORLDWIDE INC (HQ)
351 Phelps Dr (75038-6540)
PHONE.....................972 281-1200
Thomas J Falk, *CEO*
David L Bernard, *Vice Pres*
Jolene L Varney, *Treasurer*
Timothy C Everett, *Admin Sec*
EMP: 15
SALES (est): 17.5MM
SALES (corp-wide): 19.1B **Publicly Held**
SIC: 2676 3842 Sanitary paper products; surgical appliances & supplies

PA: Kimberly-Clark Corporation
351 Phelps Dr
Irving TX 75038
972 281-1200

(G-13077)
KINGDOM COAL LLC (PA)
8650 Freeport Pkwy # 100 (75063-1916)
PHONE.....................817 840-6646
Mark Wilson, *CEO*
Doug Warriner, *President*
Tom Duszyski, *CFO*
EMP: 19
SQ FT: 9,000
SALES (est): 50MM **Privately Held**
WEB: www.kingdomenergygroup.com
SIC: 1241 Coal mining services

(G-13078)
KNICKERBOCKER PARTITION CORP
Also Called: Toilet Partitions Washroom ACC
3230 Royalty Row (75062-4942)
PHONE.....................972 438-5330
Will Ross, *Sales/Mktg Mgr*
EMP: 10
SALES (corp-wide): 6.6MM **Privately Held**
WEB: www.knickerbockerpartition.com
SIC: 2542 3089 5999 5719 Partitions for floor attachment, prefabricated: except wood; panels, building: plastic; technical aids for the handicapped; bath accessories; partitions
PA: Knickerbocker Partition Corp.
260 Spagnoli Rd
Melville NY 11747
516 546-0550

(G-13079)
KRAFT HEINZ FOODS COMPANY
Also Called: Kraft Foods
8150 Springwood Dr # 200 (75063-5810)
P.O. Box 168528 (75016-8528)
PHONE.....................847 646-2000
Bob Heitzman, *Manager*
EMP: 30
SALES (corp-wide): 24.9B **Publicly Held**
WEB: www.kraftheinzcompany.com
SIC: 2033 Canned fruits & specialties
HQ: Kraft Heinz Foods Company
1 Ppg Pl Ste 3400
Pittsburgh PA 15222
412 456-5700

(G-13080)
L3HARRIS TECHNOLOGIES INC
8105 N Belt Line Rd Ste 1 (75063-6262)
PHONE.....................972 550-2300
Dave Moss, *Manager*
EMP: 53
SALES (corp-wide): 11.3B **Publicly Held**
WEB: www.harris.com
SIC: 3812 Search & navigation equipment
PA: L3harris Technologies, Inc.
1025 W Nasa Blvd
Melbourne FL 32919
321 727-9100

(G-13081)
LA CREME INC
Also Called: La Creme Coffee & Tea
3225 Premier Dr Ste 100 (75063-2676)
PHONE.....................214 352-8090
Judy Tuley, *President*
B B Tuley, *Chairman*
R E Galer, *Admin Sec*
EMP: 19
SQ FT: 6,000
SALES (est): 2.4MM **Privately Held**
WEB: www.lacremecoffeeandtea.com
SIC: 2095 5046 Coffee roasting (except by wholesale grocers); coffee brewing equipment & supplies

(G-13082)
LAIRD PLASTICS INC (HQ)
Also Called: North American Plastics
5800 Campus Circle Dr E # 150 (75063-2701)
PHONE.....................469 299-7000
Jason Askew, *CEO*
Bing J Carbone, *President*
Douglas T McNair, *Chairman*
Patrick Lagerborg, *CFO*
Nicole Burns, *Controller*

◆ **EMP:** 277 **EST:** 1981
SQ FT: 3,528
SALES (est): 266.4MM **Privately Held**
WEB: www.lairdplastics.com
SIC: 3089 5162 Windows, plastic; plastics materials

(G-13083)
LAUREN ENGINEERS & CONSTRS INC
1212 Corporate Dr Ste 100 (75038-2505)
P.O. Box 1761, Abilene (79604-1761)
PHONE..................................469 417-7600
Brian Gray, *Branch Mgr*
EMP: 33
SALES (corp-wide): 254.5MM **Privately Held**
WEB: www.laurenec.com
SIC: 1541 3441 Industrial buildings & warehouses; fabricated structural metal
HQ: Lauren Engineers & Constructors, Inc.
901 S 1st St
Abilene TX 79602
325 670-9660

(G-13084)
LAY COOLEY RE HOLDINGS 1 LLC
Also Called: Clay Cooley Chrysler
1000 E Airport Fwy (75062-4813)
PHONE..................................972 721-4500
Clay E Cooley, *President*
EMP: 23
SALES (est): 8.8MM **Privately Held**
WEB: www.claycooleycjd.com
SIC: 5511 3714 7539 Automobiles, new & used; motor vehicle parts & accessories; automotive repair shops

(G-13085)
LEHIGH CEMENT COMPANY LLC (DH)
300 E John Carpenter Fwy (75062-2727)
PHONE..................................877 534-4442
Helmut S Erhard, *Ch of Bd*
Robert Breyer, *President*
Dave Buchanan, *General Mgr*
Keith Korthuis, *General Mgr*
Randy Perrotta, *General Mgr*
▲ **EMP:** 250 **EST:** 2008
SQ FT: 114,000
SALES (est): 675.6MM
SALES (corp-wide): 20.8B **Privately Held**
WEB: www.lehighhanson.com
SIC: 3241 3273 5032 Portland cement; ready-mixed concrete; aggregate

(G-13086)
LEXMARK INTERNATIONAL INC
5215 N O Connor Blvd # 480 (75039-3795)
PHONE..................................214 257-0001
Lee Kaplan, *Branch Mgr*
EMP: 20 **Privately Held**
WEB: www.lexmark.com
SIC: 3577 Printers, computer
HQ: Lexmark International Inc.
740 W New Circle Rd
Lexington KY 40511

(G-13087)
LIVING STREAM
Also Called: Living Stream Ministry
3600 Esters Rd (75062-2833)
P.O. Box 165521 (75016-5521)
PHONE..................................972 257-1166
Tim House, *Manager*
EMP: 9
SALES (corp-wide): 17.7MM **Privately Held**
WEB: www.lsm.org
SIC: 2731 Pamphlets: publishing only, not printed on site
PA: Living Stream
2431 W La Palma Ave
Anaheim CA 92801
714 991-4681

(G-13088)
LONE STAR CONTAINER SALES CORP (PA)
Also Called: Dixie Reel & Box Co
700 N Wildwood Dr (75061-8832)
P.O. Box 177357 (75017-7357)
PHONE..................................972 579-1551
John Mc Leod, *CEO*

Lorene Cash, *Corp Secy*
John W McLeod Jr, *Vice Pres*
Richard Ward, *Vice Pres*
Monty Willoughby, *Plant Supt*
◆ **EMP:** 14
SQ FT: 240,000
SALES: 8.6MM **Privately Held**
WEB: www.lonestarbox.com
SIC: 2653 Boxes, corrugated: made from purchased materials

(G-13089)
LONE STAR CORRUGATED CONT CORP
700 N Wildwood Dr (75061-8832)
P.O. Box 177357 (75017-7357)
PHONE..................................972 579-1551
John W Mc Leod Jr, *President*
Richard Ward, *Vice Pres*
Monte Willoughby, *Plant Mgr*
John McLeod, *CFO*
Troy Jenkins, *Controller*
▲ **EMP:** 135
SQ FT: 250,000
SALES (est): 24.3MM **Privately Held**
WEB: www.lonestarbox.com
SIC: 2653 3993 2759 Boxes, corrugated: made from purchased materials; signs & advertising specialties; commercial printing

(G-13090)
LSG SKY CHEFS N AMER SLTONS IN
6191 N State Highway 161 (75038-2246)
PHONE..................................972 793-9517
Yvonne De Santiago, *Analyst*
▲ **EMP:** 300
SALES (est): 30MM **Privately Held**
SIC: 3469 Kitchen fixtures & equipment: metal, except cast aluminum

(G-13091)
LSP PRODUCTS GROUP INC (HQ)
Also Called: Tech Specialty
2727 Chemsearch Blvd (75062-6454)
PHONE..................................775 884-4242
Rick Mejia, *President*
David Bacon, *President*
Rich Robinson, *Vice Pres*
Glen Scivally, *Vice Pres*
Vincent Borrello, *Senior Buyer*
▲ **EMP:** 71
SQ FT: 85,000
SALES (est): 15.8MM
SALES (corp-wide): 1B **Privately Held**
WEB: www.lspproducts.com
SIC: 3089 Plastic hardware & building products
PA: Nch Corporation
2727 Chemsearch Blvd
Irving TX 75062
972 438-0211

(G-13092)
LUMINANT GENERATION CO LLC (HQ)
6555 Sierra Dr (75039-2479)
PHONE..................................214 812-4600
Mac McFarland, *President*
Richard R Federwisch, *Senior VP*
Joseph C Ho, *Senior VP*
Stpehen G Horn, *Senior VP*
Robert Frenzel, *CFO*
▲ **EMP:** 86
SALES (est): 2.2B
SALES (corp-wide): 11.8B **Publicly Held**
WEB: www.luminant.com
SIC: 4911 3621 Generation, electric power; power generators
PA: Vistra Corp.
6555 Sierra Dr
Irving TX 75039
214 812-4600

(G-13093)
LWO ACQUISITIONS COMPANY LLC
Also Called: Circuitronics
1920 Hurd Dr (75038-4312)
PHONE..................................972 573-1140
Renee Rump, *President*
Mike Dugue, *Purch Agent*
Antonio Kirby, *Buyer*

Mary Sommer, *Controller*
Katherine Bradford, *VP Sales*
▲ **EMP:** 95
SQ FT: 80,000
SALES (est): 25MM **Privately Held**
WEB: www.circuitronics.com
SIC: 3672 3678 3679 Printed circuit boards; electronic connectors; electronic circuits; electronic crystals; electronic loads & power supplies; electronic switches

(G-13094)
MAPLE INDUSTRIES LLC
Also Called: Sanijet
2100 Century Cir (75062-4953)
PHONE..................................972 745-2283
Chris Jones, *President*
Russ Walker, *Vice Pres*
Phillip Klement, *VP Sales*
▲ **EMP:** 15
SALES (est): 2.4MM **Privately Held**
WEB: www.purewaterbaths.com
SIC: 3842 Whirlpool baths, hydrotherapy equipment

(G-13095)
MARLO SALES INC
Also Called: Marketing Plus
2511 Texas Dr Ste 100 (75062-7023)
PHONE..................................972 721-9755
G P Boyer, *CEO*
Mike Kelly, *President*
Kevin Ritch, *CFO*
EMP: 18
SQ FT: 5,800
SALES (est): 2MM **Privately Held**
WEB: www.marketingplus.cc
SIC: 2311 Military uniforms, men's & youths': purchased materials

(G-13096)
MATHESON TRI-GAS INC
909 Lake Carolyn Pkwy # 1300 (75039-4821)
PHONE..................................972 560-5700
Tyler Luce, *Plant Mgr*
Christopher Scully, *Engineer*
Scott Kallman, *Branch Mgr*
Jeremiah Berlinger, *Manager*
Sharhonda Bishop, *Manager*
EMP: 140 **Privately Held**
WEB: www.mathesongas.com
SIC: 2813 5084 5169 Industrial gases; welding machinery & equipment; industrial gases
HQ: Matheson Tri-Gas, Inc.
3 Mountainview Rd Ste 3 # 3
Warren NJ 07059
908 991-9200

(G-13097)
MAXAM NORTH AMERICA INC (DH)
433 Las Colinas Blvd E # 900 (75039-5513)
PHONE..................................801 233-6000
German Morales, *CEO*
Stanton Johnso, *President*
Fernando Beitia, *Vice Pres*
Carl Lubbe, *Vice Pres*
John Watson, *Vice Pres*
◆ **EMP:** 17
SQ FT: 3,000
SALES: 62.5MM
SALES (corp-wide): 48MM **Privately Held**
WEB: www.maxamcorp.com
SIC: 2892 5169 Explosives; explosives
HQ: Maxam Europe Sa
Avenida Partenon (Campo De Las Naciones), 16 - Quinta Plt
Madrid 28042
917 220-100

(G-13098)
MAXIM INTEGRATED PRODUCTS INC
6431 Longhorn Dr (75063-2738)
PHONE..................................214 458-0357
David Muise, *Manager*
EMP: 528
SALES (corp-wide): 2.1B **Publicly Held**
WEB: www.maximintegrated.com
SIC: 3674 Microcircuits, integrated (semiconductor)

PA: Maxim Integrated Products, Inc.
160 Rio Robles
San Jose CA 95134
408 601-1000

(G-13099)
MAXIMUM INDUSTRIES INC
1408 W Walnut Hill Ln (75038-3009)
PHONE..................................214 614-6936
Rodie Woodard, *President*
EMP: 40
SQ FT: 44,000
SALES (est): 5.9MM **Privately Held**
WEB: www.maximumind.com
SIC: 7389 1481 Metal cutting services; scrap steel cutting; nonmetallic mineral services

(G-13100)
MCCORMICK & COMPANY INC
3300 Century Cir (75062-4901)
PHONE..................................972 721-9318
Betsy Byrd, *Plant Mgr*
Becky Bird, *Manager*
Blanca Ferrer, *Clerk*
EMP: 95
SQ FT: 50,184
SALES (corp-wide): 5.6B **Publicly Held**
WEB: www.mccormick.com
SIC: 2099 Spices, including grinding
PA: Mccormick & Company Incorporated
24 Schilling Rd Ste 1
Hunt Valley MD 21031
410 771-7301

(G-13101)
MCCORMICK & COMPANY INC
200 Union Bower Ct # 214 (75061-5836)
PHONE..................................214 329-7044
EMP: 104
SALES (corp-wide): 5.6B **Publicly Held**
WEB: www.mccormick.com
SIC: 2099 Spices, including grinding
PA: Mccormick & Company Incorporated
24 Schilling Rd Ste 1
Hunt Valley MD 21031
410 771-7301

(G-13102)
MCKESSON CORPORATION (PA)
6555 State Highway 161 (75039-2402)
PHONE..................................972 446-4800
Brian S Tyler, *CEO*
Rebecca McKillican, *CEO*
Eyad Farah, *President*
Nimesh Jhaveri, *President*
Jeremy Massett, *Principal*
◆ **EMP:** 755
SALES: 231B **Publicly Held**
WEB: www.mckesson.com
SIC: 5122 5047 5199 7372 Pharmaceuticals; proprietary (patent) medicines; druggists' sundries; medical equipment & supplies; first aid supplies; general merchandise, non-durable; prepackaged software

(G-13103)
MEDALLION DELAWARE BASIN LLC
222 Las Colinas Blvd W (75039-5421)
PHONE..................................972 746-4401
Randy N Lentz, *President*
Randy Lentz, *President*
Paul C Doll, *Vice Pres*
EMP: 153
SALES (est): 4.8MM **Privately Held**
WEB: www.medallionmidstream.com
SIC: 1382 Oil & gas exploration services
PA: Medallion Midstream, Llc
909 Lake Carolyn Pkwy # 1
Irving TX 75039

(G-13104)
MEDALLION MIDSTREAM LLC (PA)
909 Lake Carolyn Pkwy # 1 (75039-3908)
PHONE..................................972 746-4401
Randy N Lentz, *President*
Dana B Amaya, *Vice Pres*
Ralph C Lewis, *Vice Pres*
Blaine Meyer, *Opers Mgr*
Paul Doll, *CFO*
EMP: 41

▲ = Import ▼=Export
◆ =Import/Export

SALES (est): 273.5MM **Privately Held**
WEB: www.medallionmidstream.com
SIC: 1382 Oil & gas exploration services

(G-13105)
MENTOR TEXAS LP
3041 Skyway Cir N (75038-3540)
PHONE..................................972 252-6060
Andy Tymkiw, *President*
David Derrick, *Engineer*
Sandra Mena, *Technical Staff*
▲ EMP: 350
SQ FT: 108,000
SALES (est): 67.8MM
SALES (corp-wide): 82B **Publicly Held**
WEB: www.its.jnj.com
SIC: 3842 Implants, surgical
HQ: Mentor Worldwide Llc
31 Technology Dr Ste 200
Irvine CA 92618
800 636-8678

(G-13106)
MERCRON INC
610 Hanover Ln (75062-8918)
PHONE..................................972 690-6565
Ken Zeiler, *President*
Martha A Zeiler, *Vice Pres*
EMP: 10
SQ FT: 3,400
SALES (est): 930K **Privately Held**
WEB: www.mercron.com
SIC: 3648 5063 Arc lighting fixtures; lighting fixtures

(G-13107)
MERCURY OPERATING LLC
6321 Campus Circle Dr E (75063-2712)
P.O. Box 166531 (75016-6531)
PHONE..................................214 935-1698
Ted Etheredge, *COO*
Pablo Cortez, *Opers Staff*
Josh Brenner, *Production*
Barry Meffert, *Production*
Lonnie Kysiak, *Engineer*
EMP: 10
SALES (est): 2.9MM **Privately Held**
WEB: www.mercuryoperating.com
SIC: 1382 Oil & gas exploration services

(G-13108)
MICHAELS COMPANIES INC (PA)
8000 Bent Branch Dr (75063-6023)
PHONE..................................972 409-1300
James A Quella, *Ch of Bd*
Ashley Buchanan, *President*
J Robert Koch, *Exec VP*
Lisa De Perio, *Vice Pres*
Robert Patterson, *Opers Mgr*
EMP: 88
SQ FT: 296,000
SALES: 5B **Publicly Held**
WEB: www.investors.michaels.com
SIC: 5945 3999 2273 Arts & crafts supplies; framed artwork; mats & matting; door mats: paper, grass, reed, coir, sisal, jute, rags, etc.

(G-13109)
MICROSOFT CORPORATION
7000 State Hwy (75039)
PHONE..................................469 775-0000
Nelson Riera, *Senior Partner*
Robert Bill, *Engineer*
Alyson Gerlach, *Accounts Exec*
Joanna Smith, *Accounts Exec*
Scott Kildebeck, *Sales Staff*
EMP: 200
SQ FT: 196,800
SALES (corp-wide): 143B **Publicly Held**
WEB: www.microsoft.com
SIC: 7372 Application computer software
PA: Microsoft Corporation
1 Microsoft Way
Redmond WA 98052
425 882-8080

(G-13110)
MICROSOFT CORPORATION
7100 State Highway 161 (75039-2428)
PHONE..................................469 775-0000
Tim Ryan, *President*
Cristiane Pajaro, *Manager*
Sanjay Veera, *Technical Staff*
EMP: 100

SALES (corp-wide): 143B **Publicly Held**
WEB: www.microsoft.com
SIC: 7372 Application computer software
PA: Microsoft Corporation
1 Microsoft Way
Redmond WA 98052
425 882-8080

(G-13111)
MICROSOFT CORPORATION
7000 State Highway 161 (75039-2418)
P.O. Box 85038, Dallas (75284-0001)
PHONE..................................972 345-3610
Charlie McCoy, *Partner*
Lori Glass, *Human Resources*
Lulu Chalmers, *Sales Staff*
Lacey Bathala, *Program Mgr*
Nicholas Debnam, *Program Mgr*
EMP: 35
SALES (corp-wide): 143B **Publicly Held**
WEB: www.microsoft.com
SIC: 7372 Application computer software
PA: Microsoft Corporation
1 Microsoft Way
Redmond WA 98052
425 882-8080

(G-13112)
NATIONAL STONE INC
1419 Chamberlain St (75060-6266)
PHONE..................................214 651-7667
Steve Broussard, *President*
Scott Broussard, *Treasurer*
EMP: 15
SQ FT: 130,000
SALES (est): 1.5MM **Privately Held**
WEB: www.nationalstone.com
SIC: 3281 Household articles, except furniture: cut stone

(G-13113)
NBR WHEELS AND TIRES LLC
Also Called: Fury Offroad Tires
9010 N Royal Ln Ste 100 (75063-2423)
PHONE..................................855 575-3879
Yu Yang, *Mng Member*
Hong WEI,
EMP: 21 EST: 2015
SQ FT: 24,000
SALES (est): 3MM **Privately Held**
WEB: www.furytires.com
SIC: 3011 Automobile tires, pneumatic

(G-13114)
NCH CORPORATION (PA)
Also Called: Chemsearch Division
2727 Chemsearch Blvd (75062-6454)
P.O. Box 152126 (75015-2126)
PHONE..................................972 438-0211
Irvin Levy, *President*
Levy John, *Exec VP*
Lester A Levy, *Exec VP*
Robert M Levy, *Exec VP*
Joe O'Sullivan, *Exec VP*
◆ EMP: 605 EST: 1965
SQ FT: 319,000
SALES: 1B **Privately Held**
WEB: www.nch.com
SIC: 2842 2899 3432 3548 Specialty cleaning preparations; water treating compounds; plumbing fixture fittings & trim; welding & cutting apparatus & accessories; metal fasteners

(G-13115)
NCH CORPORATION
Also Called: Partsmaster
1400 E Northgate Dr (75062-4716)
PHONE..................................972 438-0381
James Marshall, *Vice Pres*
Raymond Clay, *Branch Mgr*
EMP: 2500
SALES (corp-wide): 1B **Privately Held**
WEB: www.heatingrepairsgrandprairie.com
SIC: 3429 2842 2899 3432 Metal fasteners; specialty cleaning preparations; water treating compounds; plumbing fixture fittings & trim
PA: Nch Corporation
2727 Chemsearch Blvd
Irving TX 75062
972 438-0211

(G-13116)
NCH CORPORATION
Also Called: Mohawk Laboratories Division
2730 Carl Rd (75062-6405)
P.O. Box 152170 (75015-2170)
PHONE..................................972 438-0551
Lonnie McMillan, *Division Mgr*
Irena Kildisas, *General Mgr*
Dan Mason, *Vice Pres*
John Surdo, *Vice Pres*
Paul Mc Callen, *Plant Mgr*
EMP: 160
SALES (corp-wide): 1B **Privately Held**
WEB: www.heatingrepairsgrandprairie.com
SIC: 2819 7349 2842 Industrial inorganic chemicals; chemical cleaning services; specialty cleaning, polishes & sanitation goods
PA: Nch Corporation
2727 Chemsearch Blvd
Irving TX 75062
972 438-0211

(G-13117)
NCH CORPORATION
2500 Carl Rd (75062-6403)
PHONE..................................972 438-0024
Chris Johnson, *Plant Mgr*
Chris Bonilla, *Manager*
Nick Molina, *Maintence Staff*
EMP: 22
SALES (corp-wide): 1B **Privately Held**
WEB: www.heatingrepairsgrandprairie.com
SIC: 2842 Specialty cleaning preparations
PA: Nch Corporation
2727 Chemsearch Blvd
Irving TX 75062
972 438-0211

(G-13118)
NCH CORPORATION
Also Called: Mega Metal Systems
1570 E Northgate Dr (75062-4789)
P.O. Box 971342, Dallas (75397-1342)
PHONE..................................800 336-0450
Milton Levy Sr, *Principal*
Matt Oldroyd, *Exec Dir*
EMP: 9
SALES (est): 631.8K **Privately Held**
WEB: www.nch.com
SIC: 2842 Specialty cleaning, polishes & sanitation goods

(G-13119)
NCH CORPORATION
Also Called: Certified Laboratories
2727 Chemsearch Blvd (75062-6454)
P.O. Box 152170 (75015-2170)
PHONE..................................972 438-0211
Russell Raines, *Project Mgr*
Bobby Bouchard, *Sales Staff*
Sean Danna, *Sales Staff*
Melissa Garver, *Sales Staff*
Phillip Hendrick, *Sales Staff*
EMP: 18
SALES (corp-wide): 1B **Privately Held**
WEB: www.heatingrepairsgrandprairie.com
SIC: 2842 Specialty cleaning preparations
PA: Nch Corporation
2727 Chemsearch Blvd
Irving TX 75062
972 438-0211

(G-13120)
NCH CORPORATION
Also Called: Chemsearch Fe
2727 Chemsearch Blvd (75062-6454)
PHONE..................................972 438-0211
Matthew Branch, *Division Mgr*
Joe O Sullivan, *Principal*
Lisa Jeske, *Sales Mgr*
Janie Clemens, *Accounts Mgr*
Tamara Conley, *Sales Staff*
EMP: 18
SALES (corp-wide): 1B **Privately Held**
WEB: www.heatingrepairsgrandprairie.com
SIC: 2842 Specialty cleaning preparations
PA: Nch Corporation
2727 Chemsearch Blvd
Irving TX 75062
972 438-0211

(G-13121)
NCI GROUP INC
Also Called: Mesco Metal Buildings
5244 Bear Creek Ct (75061-6011)
PHONE..................................817 488-8511
Steve Heil, *President*
Michael Hogan, *District Mgr*
George W Jeffries, *Vice Pres*
Richard Dahlgren, *Sales Mgr*
Jeffrey Koehoorn, *Sales Mgr*
EMP: 75
SALES (corp-wide): 4.8B **Publicly Held**
WEB: www.cornerstonebuildingbrands.com
SIC: 3448 Prefabricated metal buildings
HQ: Nci Group, Inc.
10943 N Sam Huston Pkwy W
Houston TX 77064
281 897-7788

(G-13122)
NETVIA GROUP LLC
Also Called: W-Tek
230 Irby Ln (75061-7046)
PHONE..................................972 573-1400
Jeff Forbus, *President*
Richard McKeel, *General Mgr*
Dean Butler, *Business Mgr*
Brady Hurst, *Exec VP*
Joe Baggett,
▲ EMP: 35
SQ FT: 18,000
SALES (est): 6.3MM **Privately Held**
WEB: www.netviagroup.com
SIC: 3672 Printed circuit boards

(G-13123)
NEW YORK AIR BRAKE LLC
5201 Regent Blvd Ste 130 (75063-2428)
PHONE..................................972 893-2400
William Sturtz, *General Mgr*
Taylor Boggs, *Engineer*
Dana Gregory, *Engineer*
Powers Scott, *Engineer*
Arun Shashidhara, *Engineer*
EMP: 14
SALES (corp-wide): 711.6K **Privately Held**
WEB: www.nyab.com
SIC: 3743 Railroad equipment
HQ: New York Air Brake Llc
748 Starbuck Ave
Watertown NY 13601

(G-13124)
NEXTGENAUTO LLC
Also Called: Nextgenbill
1431 Greenlane Rd Ste 775 (75038)
PHONE..................................888 481-9756
Kartikeya Kakarala, *Mng Member*
EMP: 15
SALES (corp-wide): 5MM **Privately Held**
WEB: www.rumbleon.com
SIC: 7372 Business oriented computer software
PA: Nextgenauto Llc
10400 Lttle Patuxent Pkwy
Columbia MD 21044
972 953-9262

(G-13125)
NOKIA INC
6363 N State Highway 161 # 800 (75038-2262)
PHONE..................................214 496-0329
Fax: 972 894-5050
EMP: 179
SALES (est): 100MM
SALES (corp-wide): 15.8B **Privately Held**
SIC: 3663 Mfg Radio/Tv Communication Equipment
PA: Nokia Oyj
Karaportti 3
Espoo 02610
104 488-000

(G-13126)
NORTHROP GRUMMAN CORPORATION
Also Called: Northrop Grumman Intl Trdg
8710 Freport Pkwy Ste 200 (75063)
PHONE..................................214 524-0102
Vicki Burchfield, *Engineer*
Donna Moore, *Accountant*
Melanie Mackey, *Office Mgr*
Pablo Gonzalez, *Program Mgr*
Kieja Adolphus, *Manager*

GEOGRAPHIC

EMP: 55 Publicly Held
WEB: www.northropgrumman.com
SIC: 3812 Aircraft/aerospace flight instruments & guidance systems
PA: Northrop Grumman Corporation
2980 Fairview Park Dr
Falls Church VA 22042

(G-13127)
NORTHROP GRUMMAN SYSTEMS CORP
Also Called: Northrop Grumman Information
8710 Freport Pkwy Ste 180 (75063)
PHONE..................469 524-0109
Bowie Tanya, *Payroll Mgr*
Mark Chiu, *Software Engr*
EMP: 40 Publicly Held
WEB: www.northropgrumman.com
SIC: 3812 Search & navigation equipment
HQ: Northrop Grumman Systems Corporation
2980 Fairview Park Dr
Falls Church VA 22042
703 280-2900

(G-13128)
NORTHRUP GRMMAN TECHNICAL SVCS
8710 Freport Pkwy Ste 200 (75063)
PHONE..................405 736-8207
Marcel Post, *Business Anlyst*
Robert Damiano, *Manager*
Mike Head, *Technology*
EMP: 14
SALES (est): 2.6MM **Privately Held**
WEB: www.northropgrumman.com
SIC: 3812 Search & navigation equipment

(G-13129)
NUEVO LEON TORTILLA FACTORY
820 E Irving Blvd (75060-3148)
PHONE..................972 721-1984
Tim Hulsey, *Owner*
EMP: 20
SALES (est): 1.2MM **Privately Held**
SIC: 2099 Tortillas, fresh or refrigerated

(G-13130)
OBRIEN HOGMAN ASSOCIATES LLC
9001 Sterling St (75063-2515)
PHONE..................972 823-1900
Lance Obrien, *Maint Spvr*
Peter O Brien, *Mng Member*
Gary Hogman,
EMP: 10
SQ FT: 10,000
SALES (est): 4MM **Privately Held**
SIC: 2434 Wood kitchen cabinets

(G-13131)
OMEGA PRINTING LP
2906 Story Rd W (75038-3511)
PHONE..................972 256-1234
Kiran Dhir, *CEO*
Vijay Dhir, *President*
EMP: 9
SQ FT: 6,000
SALES (est): 1MM **Privately Held**
WEB: www.omegaprint.com
SIC: 2752 Commercial printing, offset

(G-13132)
ORACLE AMERICA INC
Also Called: Sun Microsystems
1431 Greenway Dr Ste 145 (75038-2493)
PHONE..................972 580-0629
Scott Henderson, *Branch Mgr*
EMP: 9
SALES (corp-wide): 39B **Publicly Held**
WEB: www.ea.com
SIC: 7372 Prepackaged software
HQ: Oracle America, Inc.
500 Oracle Pkwy
Redwood City CA 94065
650 506-7000

(G-13133)
ORBITAL SYSTEMS LLC
3807 Carbon Rd (75038-3415)
PHONE..................972 915-3669
Carl Schoeneberger,
Allan Bundens,
Richard Fogle,

◆ **EMP: 25**
SQ FT: 19,000
SALES (est): 6MM **Privately Held**
WEB: www.orbitalsystems.com
SIC: 3829 3679 Meteorologic tracking systems; antennas, receiving
HQ: Communications & Power Industries Llc
811 Hansen Way
Palo Alto CA 94304

(G-13134)
OSG USA INC (HQ)
1945 W Walnut Hill Ln (75038-4408)
PHONE..................800 837-2223
Jiro Osawa, *CEO*
Michael Grantham, *President*
Bob Kress, *District Mgr*
Jeffry Tennant, *Exec VP*
Sherri Tiani, *Controller*
▲ **EMP: 50 EST: 1968**
SQ FT: 37,000
SALES (est): 58.1MM **Privately Held**
WEB: www.osgtool.com
SIC: 5084 3541 Machine tools & metalworking machinery; machine tools, metal cutting type

(G-13135)
OSO PERFORATING LLC
3225 Premier Dr Ste 150 (75063-2679)
PHONE..................972 754-7773
David Knecht, *CFO*
Joseph Hunt,
EMP: 14
SALES (est): 3.3MM **Privately Held**
WEB: www.osoperf.com
SIC: 3533 Drilling tools for gas, oil or water wells

(G-13136)
OTA COMPRESSION LLC (PA)
102 Decker Ct Ste 204 (75062-2740)
P.O. Box 141747 (75014-1747)
PHONE..................972 831-1300
Grant Swartzwelder, *President*
Cory Fletcher, *Accounts Mgr*
EMP: 38
SALES (est): 31.1MM **Privately Held**
WEB: www.otacompression.com
SIC: 3585 Evaporative condensers, heat transfer equipment

(G-13137)
OUTSTNDING GRPHIC SLUTIONS INC
Also Called: Fastsigns
4070 N Belt Line Rd (75038-5028)
PHONE..................972 255-2022
Jeffrey B Youngblood, *President*
Cory Merchant, *Vice Pres*
EMP: 9
SALES (est): 1.4MM **Privately Held**
WEB: www.fastsigns.com
SIC: 3993 Signs & advertising specialties

(G-13138)
OWENS CORNING SALES LLC
201 N Nursery Rd (75061-7727)
PHONE..................972 438-1050
Jose Campos, *Sales Staff*
Steve Cowan, *Branch Mgr*
EMP: 160
SQ FT: 2,376 **Publicly Held**
WEB: www.owenscorning.com
SIC: 2951 5033 1761 2952 Asphalt paving mixtures & blocks; roofing, asphalt & sheet metal; roofing contractor; asphalt felts & coatings
HQ: Owens Corning Sales, Llc
1 Owens Corning Pkwy
Toledo OH 43659
419 248-8000

(G-13139)
PANINI AMERICA INC (DH)
5325 F A A Blvd Ste 100 (75061-3608)
PHONE..................817 662-5300
Mark Warsop, *CEO*
Chris Wilkins, *Editor*
Brian Bayne, *Business Mgr*
John P Harris, *Corp Secy*
Michael J Anderson, *Vice Pres*
▲ **EMP: 75**
SQ FT: 50,000

SALES (est): 30.7MM **Privately Held**
WEB: www.paniniamerica.net
SIC: 2752 2782 Cards, lithographed; albums
HQ: Panini Spa
Viale Emilio Po 380
Modena MO 41126
059 382-111

(G-13140)
PEARSON EDUCATION INC
Also Called: Prentice Hall
6025 Commerce Dr Ste 550 (75063-2666)
PHONE..................972 870-1048
Brenda Cole, *Manager*
EMP: 10
SALES (corp-wide): 5B **Privately Held**
SIC: 2731 Books: publishing only
HQ: Pearson Education, Inc.
221 River St
Hoboken NJ 07030
201 236-7000

(G-13141)
PERITUS INC
222 Las Colinas Blvd W # 745 (75039-5511)
PHONE..................817 726-4626
Ramprasad Mavuleti, *President*
EMP: 120
SQ FT: 1,600
SALES (est): 11.2MM **Privately Held**
WEB: www.peritusinc.com
SIC: 7371 7374 7373 7372 Computer software development; data entry service; systems software development services; computer systems analysis & design; turnkey vendors, computer systems; application computer software

(G-13142)
PETROBAL OMEGA 1 LLC
6191 N State Highway 161 (75038-2246)
PHONE..................972 284-5120
Owen Windham, *Mng Member*
EMP: 40
SQ FT: 4,500
SALES (est): 14.2MM **Privately Held**
WEB: www.petrobalusa.com
SIC: 1382 Oil & gas exploration services

(G-13143)
PHYSICIANS WELLNESS GROUP INC
Also Called: Pwg
1431 Greenway Dr Ste 800 (75038-2574)
PHONE..................817 703-2102
Michael Jareou, *CEO*
EMP: 20
SALES (est): 175MM **Privately Held**
SIC: 2834 Proprietary drug products

(G-13144)
PIONEER NATURAL RESOURCES CO (PA)
777 Hidden Rdg (75038-3802)
PHONE..................972 444-9001
J Kenneth Thompson, *Ch of Bd*
Scott D Sheffield, *President*
Beth Davis, *Partner*
Travis Soechting, *Superintendent*
Mark S Berg, *Exec VP*
EMP: 401
SALES: 9.3B **Publicly Held**
WEB: www.pxd.com
SIC: 1311 Crude petroleum production

(G-13145)
PIONEER NTRAL RSRCES PMPG SVCS
777 Hidden Rdg (75038-3802)
PHONE..................972 444-9001
Kyle Zemlak, *Mng Member*
Richard Dealy,
EMP: 100
SALES (est): 400.5MM
SALES (corp-wide): 9.3B **Publicly Held**
SIC: 1389 Pumping of oil & gas wells
PA: Pioneer Natural Resources Company
777 Hidden Rdg
Irving TX 75038
972 444-9001

(G-13146)
PIONEER SANDS LLC (HQ)
Also Called: Premier Silica
777 Hidden Rdg (75038-3802)
PHONE..................972 444-9001
Denny Bullard, *President*
Michael Siragusa, *Vice Pres*
Rich Dealy, *CFO*
Mark Berg,
Aidan Connolly,
EMP: 76
SALES (est): 585.7MM
SALES (corp-wide): 9.3B **Publicly Held**
WEB: www.pwgillibrand.com
SIC: 1446 Silica sand mining
PA: Pioneer Natural Resources Company
777 Hidden Rdg
Irving TX 75038
972 444-9001

(G-13147)
PIONEER WATER MANAGEMENT LLC
Also Called: Pioneer Natural Resources Co
777 Hidden Rdg (75038-3802)
PHONE..................800 242-2607
Timothy L Dove, *President*
Scott D Sheffield, *Chairman*
Chris J Cheatwood, *Vice Pres*
Richard P Dealy, *Vice Pres*
Danny L Kellum, *Vice Pres*
EMP: 15
SALES (est): 47.4MM
SALES (corp-wide): 9.3B **Publicly Held**
SIC: 1311 Crude petroleum production
PA: Pioneer Natural Resources Company
777 Hidden Rdg
Irving TX 75038
972 444-9001

(G-13148)
PIONER NTRL RSRC WLL SRVCS LLC
5205 N O Connor Blvd # 200 (75039-3712)
PHONE..................972 969-3670
James Cunningham,
Richard Dealy,
Keith Pickett,
EMP: 50
SQ FT: 2,000
SALES (est): 200.2MM
SALES (corp-wide): 9.3B **Publicly Held**
SIC: 1389 Servicing oil & gas wells
PA: Pioneer Natural Resources Company
777 Hidden Rdg
Irving TX 75038
972 444-9001

(G-13149)
PLASTIFORM INC (PA)
3418 International Pl (75062-4920)
PHONE..................972 241-2593
Jeff Jones, *President*
Elwyn Jones, *Vice Pres*
Rosa Santana, *Admin Asst*
EMP: 16
SQ FT: 11,500
SALES (est): 3.9MM **Privately Held**
WEB: www.plastiform-dallas.com
SIC: 3089 Injection molding of plastics

(G-13150)
PLASTIFORM INC
3245 Royalty Row (75062-4943)
PHONE..................972 579-8803
Donna Lee, *Opers Mgr*
Jeff Jones, *Manager*
EMP: 14
SALES (corp-wide): 3.9MM **Privately Held**
WEB: www.plastiform-dallas.com
SIC: 3081 Unsupported plastics film & sheet
PA: Plastiform, Inc.
3418 International Pl
Irving TX 75062
972 241-2593

(G-13151)
PLASTRONICS CO
3251 Story Rd W (75038-3532)
PHONE..................972 986-0474
Dennis Dean, *President*
EMP: 20
SQ FT: 7,500

▲ = Import ▼=Export
◆ =Import/Export

SALES (est): 4.1MM **Privately Held**
WEB: www.plastronics.com
SIC: **3559** 3643 Semiconductor manufacturing machinery; current-carrying wiring devices

(G-13152)
PLASTRONICS INTERCONNECTIONS (PA)
2601 Texas Dr (75062-7092)
PHONE..............................972 258-2580
Wayne Pfaff, *CEO*
David Pfaff, *President*
▲ EMP: 10
SQ FT: 10,000
SALES (est): 5.2MM **Privately Held**
WEB: www.h-pins.com
SIC: **3089** 3825 3643 Plastic processing; instruments to measure electricity; current-carrying wiring devices

(G-13153)
PLASTRONICS INTERCONNECTIONS
Also Called: Plas II
2920 Story Rd W (75038-3511)
PHONE..............................972 255-1964
Kurt Shehee, *Engineer*
Rick Ellis, *Branch Mgr*
EMP: 40
SALES (corp-wide): 5.2MM **Privately Held**
WEB: www.plastronics.com
SIC: **3089** Injection molding of plastics
PA: Plastronics Interconnections Inc
2601 Texas Dr
Irving TX 75062
972 258-2580

(G-13154)
PRECISION FORMED PLASTICS INC
3245 Royalty Row (75062-4943)
PHONE..............................972 579-8803
Jeffrey L Jones, *President*
Brad Elledge, *Business Mgr*
Elwyn Jones, *Vice Pres*
Jenny Olascoaga, *Executive*
EMP: 27
SQ FT: 23,000
SALES (est): 4.5MM **Privately Held**
WEB: www.plastiform-dallas.com
SIC: **3089** Injection molding of plastics

(G-13155)
PREMARK HEALTH SCIENCE INC
Also Called: Con-Trac Packaging
3200 Story Rd W (75038-3531)
PHONE..............................972 894-0020
William David Palmer, *President*
Doug Fagan, *Purchasing*
Anna Palmer, *Purchasing*
Laura Paul, *Office Mgr*
Anna Lynne Palmer, *Manager*
EMP: 32 EST: 2007
SQ FT: 25,000
SALES (est): 7.2MM **Privately Held**
WEB: www.premarkhs.com
SIC: **2023** 2844 2834 Dry, condensed, evaporated dairy products; toilet preparations; vitamin preparations

(G-13156)
PREMIER PLASTICS DALLAS INC (PA)
Also Called: Premier Technical Plastics
2109 Vanco Dr (75061-8815)
PHONE..............................972 554-1597
Colleen H McCalmont, *CEO*
Jim McCalmont, *President*
Joe Garza, *Managing Dir*
Jerre Ross, *Vice Pres*
Frank Rodriguez, *Materials Mgr*
▲ EMP: 60
SQ FT: 70,000
SALES (est): 18.5MM **Privately Held**
WEB: www.premiertechnicalplastics.com
SIC: **3089** Injection molding of plastics

(G-13157)
PROGRESSIVE LABORATORIES INC
Also Called: Kordial Ntrnts Prof Spplements
3131 Story Rd W (75038-3514)
PHONE..............................972 518-9660
Joseph C O'Neal, *CEO*
Larry Thompson, *President*
Carol Thompson, *Vice Pres*
Ernesto Montoya, *Warehouse Mgr*
Howard Johns, *Purch Mgr*
▲ EMP: 78
SQ FT: 42,000
SALES (est): 198MM **Privately Held**
WEB: www.progressivelabs.com
SIC: **2834** Vitamin, nutrient & hematinic preparations for human use

(G-13158)
PROGRESSIVE STEEL & WIRE LLC (DH)
1321 Greenway Dr (75038-2504)
PHONE..............................972 999-8778
Ken Fishbein, *Co-CEO*
Mona Zinman, *Co-CEO*
EMP: 15
SQ FT: 30,000
SALES (est): 11.7MM **Privately Held**
WEB: www.grip-rite.com
SIC: **3315** Nails, steel: wire or cut
HQ: Primesource Building Products, Inc.
1321 Greenway Dr
Irving TX 75038
972 999-8500

(G-13159)
PROJECT SERVICES GROUP INC
2040 Century Center Blvd # 10 (75062-4922)
PHONE..............................972 812-7370
Mark Boswell, *President*
Larry Jordan, *Vice Pres*
Steve Lair, *Vice Pres*
Daniel Boswell, *Project Mgr*
Tom Galloway, *Project Mgr*
▲ EMP: 65
SQ FT: 68,000
SALES (est): 18.2MM **Privately Held**
WEB: www.psg-dallas.com
SIC: **3589** 3556 Commercial cooking & foodwarming equipment; food products machinery

(G-13160)
PROMOTIONAL PRODUCTS ASSN INTL
3125 Skyway Cir N (75038-3539)
PHONE..............................972 252-0404
Todd Pottebaum, *Ch of Bd*
Paul Bellantone, *President*
Tina Berres, *Editor*
James Khattak, *Editor*
Dana Geiger, *Regional Mgr*
EMP: 79
SQ FT: 25,000
SALES: 20.1MM **Privately Held**
WEB: www.ppai.org
SIC: **8611** 2741 2721 7389 Trade associations; miscellaneous publishing; periodicals; advertising, promotional & trade show services

(G-13161)
PROSERV CRANE & EQUIPMENT INC
Also Called: Proserv Anchor Crane Group
2020 E Grauwyler Rd (75061-3235)
PHONE..............................972 438-5100
Fran Witt, *Manager*
EMP: 60
SALES (corp-wide): 57MM **Privately Held**
WEB: www.proservcrane.com
SIC: **3536** 7699 5084 3531 Cranes, overhead traveling; construction equipment repair; hoists; backhoes, tractors, cranes, plows & similar equipment
PA: Proserv Crane & Equipment Inc
455 Aldine Bender Rd
Houston TX 77060
281 405-9048

(G-13162)
RAMBLER NEWSPAPERS INC
627 S Rogers Rd (75060-3753)
P.O. Box 177731 (75017-7731)
PHONE..............................972 870-1992
John Starkey, *Principal*
EMP: 9
SALES (est): 479.6K **Privately Held**
WEB: www.ramblernewspapers.com
SIC: **2711** Newspapers, publishing & printing

(G-13163)
RCL TECHNOLOGIES INC
103 E Pioneer Dr (75061-7645)
PHONE..............................214 870-3703
Danny Boyer, *President*
EMP: 9
SALES (est): 950K **Privately Held**
WEB: www.rcl.com
SIC: **3663** Satellites, communications

(G-13164)
RELOCATION SYSTEMS INC
8904 N Royal Ln (75063-2545)
PHONE..............................972 241-2300
Jerome H Haas, *President*
Margaret L Parks, *Chairman*
Margaret Parks, *Chairman*
Tammy R Stanford, *Vice Pres*
Neil Plunkett, *CFO*
▲ EMP: 34
SQ FT: 56,000
SALES (est): 4.5MM **Privately Held**
SIC: **7389** 2449 4783 Packaging & labeling services; rectangular boxes & crates, wood; packing goods for shipping

(G-13165)
REVISION LLC
Also Called: Revisions Skin Care
5930 Campus Circle Dr W (75063-2605)
PHONE..............................972 756-1026
Chris Greene, *Opers Staff*
John Hinds, *CFO*
Veronica Gevik, *Accounts Exec*
Diana Villarmarzo, *Accounts Exec*
Aaron Strinko, *Director*
◆ EMP: 35
SQ FT: 60,000
SALES (est): 10.7MM **Privately Held**
WEB: www.revisionskincare.com
SIC: **2844** 7231 5122 Face creams or lotions; beauty shops; cosmetics

(G-13166)
ROCK ISLAND DONUT SHOP
2336 Rock Island Rd (75060-2409)
PHONE..............................972 254-5069
Cheng Seo, *Owner*
Kyu Han, *Owner*
EMP: 15
SALES (est): 1.3MM **Privately Held**
SIC: **2051** 5149 5461 Doughnuts, except frozen; crackers, cookies & bakery products; doughnuts

(G-13167)
S & S MACHINE INC
Also Called: S & S Machine Shop
450 Gates Dr (75061-7695)
PHONE..............................972 438-6282
Jimmy W Guest, *President*
Don Wright, *Corp Secy*
Mike Guess, *Vice Pres*
EMP: 65 EST: 1975
SQ FT: 21,000
SALES (est): 11.9MM **Privately Held**
WEB: www.ss-machine.com
SIC: **3728** Aircraft body assemblies & parts

(G-13168)
S&S INDUSTRIES INC
2204 Century Center Blvd (75062-4900)
PHONE..............................972 438-7150
Samuel Savariego, *Ch of Bd*
Velinda Savariego, *Vice Pres*
EMP: 190
SQ FT: 140,000
SALES (est): 18.9MM **Privately Held**
SIC: **3542** Sheet metalworking machines

(G-13169)
SAFRAN USA INC
2201 W Royal Ln Ste 150 (75063-3206)
PHONE..............................469 941-8150
Peter Lengyel, *President*
George Richard, *Manager*
Goyal Nupur, *Director*
Christopher Merritt, *General Counsel*
EMP: 50
SALES (corp-wide): 799.9MM **Privately Held**
WEB: www.safran-usa.com
SIC: **3643** Connectors & terminals for electrical devices
HQ: Safran Usa, Inc.
700 S Washington St # 320
Alexandria VA 22314
703 351-9898

(G-13170)
SAFRAN USA INC
2201 W Royal Ln Ste 150 (75063-3206)
PHONE..............................469 941-8150
Iain Lawn, *Director*
EMP: 73
SALES (corp-wide): 799.9MM **Privately Held**
WEB: www.safran-usa.com
SIC: **3724** Research & development on aircraft engines & parts
HQ: Safran Usa, Inc.
700 S Washington St # 320
Alexandria VA 22314
703 351-9898

(G-13171)
SAMUEL SON & CO (USA) INC
2303 Century Center Blvd (75062-4971)
P.O. Box 676507, Dallas (75267-6507)
PHONE..............................972 438-3949
Thomas Toth, *Vice Pres*
Tom Toth, *Manager*
Tom McKevitt, *Manager*
EMP: 60
SALES (corp-wide): 1.8B **Privately Held**
WEB: www.samuel.com
SIC: **5051** 3365 5084 Steel; aluminum foundries; metalworking tools (such as drills, taps, dies, files)
HQ: Samuel, Son & Co. (Usa) Inc.
1401 Davey Rd Ste 300
Woodridge IL 60517
630 783-8900

(G-13172)
SANTECH INDUSTRIES LLC
1401 Valley View Ln # 100 (75061-3603)
PHONE..............................817 589-1212
Chris Sims, *President*
Valerie Rowe, *Sales Staff*
Jimmy Simpson, *Info Tech Dir*
Michael D Brookshire, *Admin Sec*
▲ EMP: 22 EST: 2012
SALES (est): 13MM **Privately Held**
WEB: www.santech.com
SIC: **5085** 3714 8742 Gaskets; motor vehicle parts & accessories; management consulting services
PA: Auto Air Export, Inc.
1401 Valley View Ln # 100
Irving TX 75061

(G-13173)
SCREENFAB LLC (PA)
610 N Wildwood Dr (75061-8830)
P.O. Box 560484, Dallas (75356-0484)
PHONE..............................972 438-2860
Donald Rauschuber, *President*
Suzy Vega, *Sales Staff*
Jennifer Patterson, *Office Mgr*
▲ EMP: 30
SQ FT: 14,000
SALES (est): 3.9MM **Privately Held**
WEB: www.screenfab.net
SIC: **2431** Window screens, wood frame

(G-13174)
SECURETECH SYSTEMS INC
Also Called: Securetech, Ssi
4500 Fuller Dr Ste 135 (75038-6505)
PHONE..............................817 869-0569
Juliana Goldenberg, *President*
Kathy Engroff, *General Mgr*
Kurt Steven Kirby, *Vice Pres*
Kurt Kirby, *Vice Pres*
Brian Goldenberg, *Bookkeeper*
EMP: 10
SQ FT: 4,200

SALES: 1.8MM **Privately Held**
WEB: www.securetechwave.com
SIC: **7382** 3669 Protective devices, security; emergency alarms

(G-13175)
SELECT MILLWORK INC
300 Union Bower Ct # 310 (75061-5800)
PHONE...................................972 445-8287
Paul A Gause, *President*
Billy A Harrington, *Vice Pres*
EMP: 14
SQ FT: 10,000
SALES (est): 1.2MM **Privately Held**
SIC: **2431** Millwork

(G-13176)
SHADOWSOFT INC
7750 N Macarthur Blvd # 1 (75063-7514)
PHONE...................................972 841-2469
Bruce Stringfellow, *President*
Cara Hill, *Marketing Staff*
EMP: 24
SALES (est): 2.2MM **Privately Held**
WEB: www.shadowsoft.com
SIC: **7372** Prepackaged software

(G-13177)
SIEMENS ENERGY INC
8600 N Royal Ln Unit 100 (75063-2500)
PHONE...................................972 929-5044
Paul Benson, *Design Engr*
Chuck Misenheimer, *Accounts Mgr*
Chuck Hartong, *Manager*
Kristin Hall, *Technical Staff*
Monica Maheshwari, *Sr Software Eng*
EMP: 10
SALES (corp-wide): 4B **Privately Held**
WEB: www.new.siemens.com
SIC: **3511** Turbines & turbine generator sets
PA: Siemens Energy, Inc.
    4400 N Alafaya Trl
    Orlando FL 32826
    407 736-2000

(G-13178)
SIEMENS INDUSTRY INC
8600 N Royal Ln Unit 100 (75063-2500)
PHONE...................................972 550-8488
Margaret Mulvihill, *General Mgr*
Hemang Shah, *General Mgr*
Darryl Stickler, *General Mgr*
Paul Tierney, *General Mgr*
Scott Cammarata, *Regional Mgr*
EMP: 200
SALES (corp-wide): 67.4B **Privately Held**
WEB: www.new.siemens.com
SIC: **3822** Air conditioning & refrigeration controls
HQ: Siemens Industry, Inc.
    1000 Deerfield Pkwy
    Buffalo Grove IL 60089
    847 215-1000

(G-13179)
SIGNAL METAL INDUSTRIES INC (PA)
850 E Pioneer Dr (75061-7796)
P.O. Box 171178 (75017-1178)
PHONE...................................972 438-1022
Ryan K Robinson, *President*
Robert K Robinson II, *Co-President*
James Fortier, *Senior VP*
Edward Dee, *Vice Pres*
Charlie Kirkman, *Vice Pres*
▲ EMP: 175
SQ FT: 150,000
SALES (est): 28.7MM **Privately Held**
WEB: www.signalmetal.com
SIC: **3441** 8711 Fabricated structural metal; engineering services

(G-13180)
SILVER CREEK OIL & GAS LLC
Also Called: Silver Creek Resources
5525 N Macarthur Blvd # 7 (75038-2615)
PHONE...................................972 573-1630
John Sanchez, *President*
Ryan Hennigan, *Engineer*
Brian Dutton, *VP Finance*
Amber Syphrett, *Accountant*
Bryant Kimberlin, *IT/INT Sup*
EMP: 60

SALES (est): 49.5MM **Privately Held**
WEB: www.silvercreekog.com
SIC: **1382** 4925 Oil & gas exploration services; gas production and/or distribution

(G-13181)
SIPLAST INC (DH)
1000 Rochelle Blvd (75062-3940)
PHONE...................................469 995-2200
Jim Mollenhoff, *President*
Gregory Washington, *Engineer*
Jakob Harder, *Treasurer*
Niels O Johannesson, *Director*
Jan J Kuhl, *Director*
◆ EMP: 35
SQ FT: 22,000
SALES (est): 34.5MM
SALES (corp-wide): 689.8K **Privately Held**
WEB: www.siplast.com
SIC: **2952** Roof cement: asphalt, fibrous or plastic
HQ: Icopal Danmark Aps
    Lyskar 5
    Herlev 2730
    448 855-00

(G-13182)
SMURFIT KAPPA NORTH AMER LLC (HQ)
Also Called: Coi Graphics
125 E John Carpenter Fwy # 925
(75062-2624)
PHONE...................................800 306-8326
Greg Hall, *President*
David Hanf, *Regional Mgr*
Marty Rusk, *Vice Pres*
Christine Maple, *Project Mgr*
Ruben Mireles, *Technical Mgr*
▲ EMP: 300
SALES (est): 876.5MM **Privately Held**
WEB: www.smurfitkappa.com
SIC: **2653** 2671 2657 Boxes, corrugated: made from purchased materials; packaging paper & plastics film, coated & laminated; folding paperboard boxes

(G-13183)
SOLOVIS INC (DH)
5030 Riverside Dr Ste 200 (75039-4655)
PHONE...................................678 234-4583
Joshua Smith, *CEO*
James Burke, *Senior VP*
Bob Myers, *Vice Pres*
Caleb Doise, *CTO*
Emmitte Griggs, *Officer*
EMP: 11
SALES (est): 3.8MM
SALES (corp-wide): 4.2B **Publicly Held**
WEB: www.solovis.com
SIC: **8741** 7372 Business management; prepackaged software
HQ: Evestment, Inc.
    100 Glenridge Point Pkwy # 100
    Atlanta GA 30342
    678 569-2388

(G-13184)
SONOCO PRODUCTS COMPANY
Also Called: Sonoco Industrial Products
5111 Frye Rd (75061-6012)
PHONE...................................817 461-5616
David Anderson, *Manager*
Aaron Powers, *Maintence Staff*
EMP: 40
SALES (corp-wide): 5.3B **Publicly Held**
WEB: www.sonoco.com
SIC: **2655** 5113 Tubes, fiber or paper: made from purchased material; paper tubes & cores
PA: Sonoco Products Company
    1 N 2nd St
    Hartsville SC 29550
    843 383-7000

(G-13185)
SOUTHERN STUD WELD INC
Also Called: Barton Resources
3645 Conflans Rd (75061-6362)
PHONE...................................972 790-3339
Don Pelham, *Sales Staff*
Lynn Haynes, *Manager*
Bill Miranda, *Technical Staff*
EMP: 10

SALES (corp-wide): 2.6MM **Privately Held**
WEB: www.taggingsystem.com
SIC: **3356** Welding rods
PA: Southern Stud Weld, Inc
    16552 Air Center Blvd
    Houston TX 77032
    713 691-0897

(G-13186)
SOUTHWEST MACHINE & MFG CO INC
108 N Rogers Rd (75061-7229)
P.O. Box 171207 (75017-1207)
PHONE...................................972 254-2014
Linda Pound, *President*
▼ EMP: 20
SQ FT: 15,000
SALES (est): 3.4MM **Privately Held**
WEB: www.southwestmach.com
SIC: **3599** Machine shop, jobbing & repair

(G-13187)
SPAETH MACHINE SHOP INC
Also Called: Spaeth Pump & Equipment Co
2120 E Grauwyler Rd (75061-3210)
P.O. Box 560564, Dallas (75356-0564)
PHONE...................................972 438-3804
William P Spaeth, *President*
Jo Spaeth, *Corp Secy*
Mark R Spaeth, *Vice Pres*
EMP: 20 EST: 1898
SQ FT: 9,000
SALES (est): 5.3MM **Privately Held**
WEB: www.spaethmachine.com
SIC: **3599** Machine shop, jobbing & repair

(G-13188)
SPECTRUM LIFESCIENCES LLC
Also Called: or Disposables
3400 Royalty Row (75062-4946)
PHONE...................................214 492-0506
Michelle Fleming, *Branch Mgr*
EMP: 21
SALES (corp-wide): 270.2MM **Publicly Held**
WEB: www.repligen.com
SIC: **3841** 3821 3842 Surgical & medical instruments; laboratory apparatus & furniture; surgical appliances & supplies; drapes, surgical (cotton); sterilizers, hospital & surgical
HQ: Spectrum Lifesciences, Llc
    18617 S Broadwick St
    Rancho Dominguez CA 90220
    310 885-4600

(G-13189)
STUART-DEAN CO INC
460 S Belt Line Rd # 430 (75060-2194)
PHONE...................................972 513-9781
Colin Turcotte, *COO*
Ervin Buba, *Manager*
EMP: 18
SALES (corp-wide): 65.4MM **Privately Held**
WEB: www.stuartdean.com
SIC: **3471** Plating & polishing
PA: Stuart-Dean Co. Inc.
    450 Fashion Ave Ste 3800
    New York NY 10123
    212 273-6900

(G-13190)
SUNCOAST POST-TENSION LTD
2215 E Pioneer Dr D (75061-8805)
PHONE...................................972 287-0307
Eric Dyes, *Manager*
EMP: 107
SALES (corp-wide): 2.9B **Privately Held**
WEB: www.suncoast-pt.com
SIC: **3315** 3316 Steel wire & related products; cold finishing of steel shapes
HQ: Suncoast Post-Tension, Ltd.
    509 N Sam Houston Pkwy E # 300
    Houston TX 77060
    281 445-8886

(G-13191)
TAYLOR - DEAL AVIATION LLC
Also Called: T D A
911 Maryland Dr (75061-5748)
PHONE...................................972 220-0943
EMP: 60
SQ FT: 11,809

SALES (est): 26.3MM **Privately Held**
SIC: **3721** Mfg Aircraft

(G-13192)
TEXAS METAL EQUIPMENT CO LTD
8704 N Royal Ln (75063-2539)
PHONE...................................214 446-7200
Penny Jo Palmer, *Project Mgr*
Bill Carter, *VP Bus Dvlpt*
Ryan Williamson, *Sales Staff*
Don W Harman, *Branch Mgr*
EMP: 34
SALES (corp-wide): 16.5MM **Privately Held**
WEB: www.tmeco.com
SIC: **3821** Laboratory apparatus & furniture
PA: Texas Metal Equipment Company, Ltd.
    6707 Mayard Rd
    Houston TX 77041
    713 466-8722

(G-13193)
THERMAL EDGE INC
1800 Hurd Dr (75038-4310)
PHONE...................................972 580-0200
Andrew Cohen, *President*
Karen Cohen, *Owner*
Ryan Fruend, *Sales Staff*
▲ EMP: 42
SQ FT: 13,000
SALES (est): 11MM **Privately Held**
WEB: www.thermal-edge.com
SIC: **3585** Air conditioning equipment, complete

(G-13194)
THRU INC
909 Lake Carolyn Pkwy # 750
(75039-3908)
PHONE...................................214 496-0100
Lee Harrison, *CEO*
EMP: 61
SQ FT: 14,000
SALES (est): 4MM **Privately Held**
WEB: www.thruinc.com
SIC: **7372** Prepackaged software

(G-13195)
THRU HOLDING COMPANY LLC (PA)
909 Lake Carolyn Pkwy # 7 (75039-3908)
PHONE...................................214 496-0100
Al Carvalho, *Vice Pres*
Lee Harrsion, *Manager*
Don Davis,
Mike McCoy,
Scot McKay,
EMP: 19
SQ FT: 10,000
SALES (est): 4.6MM **Privately Held**
WEB: www.thruinc.com
SIC: **7372** Prepackaged software

(G-13196)
TOUCHPAY HOLDINGS LP
Also Called: PAYMENT SYSTEMS
7801 Mesquite Bend Dr # 101
(75063-6043)
P.O. Box 3182, Coppell (75019-3101)
PHONE...................................972 215-0133
Ronny Park, *Partner*
Daniel Burgess, *Partner*
Andrew McAfee, *QC Mgr*
Keith Benton, *Sales Staff*
EMP: 39
SQ FT: 3,000
SALES: 8.5MM **Privately Held**
WEB: www.touchpayonline.com
SIC: **3578** 7374 Automatic teller machines (ATM); data processing & preparation

(G-13197)
TRANSTEX LLC (DH)
1111 Louisiana Ste 4520 (75038)
PHONE...................................832 369-6986
Zach Grichor, *Business Mgr*
Robert Shimek, *Vice Pres*
J Greg Sargan,
EMP: 10
SALES (est): 3.2MM
SALES (corp-wide): 3B **Publicly Held**
WEB: www.transtexhunter.com
SIC: **1382** Oil & gas exploration services

(G-13198)
TRAVELHOST PRINTING INC
433 Las Colinas Blvd E (75039-5581)
P.O. Box 140395 (75014-0395)
PHONE....................972 556-0541
James E Buerger, *President*
EMP: 45
SALES (est): 4.9MM **Privately Held**
SIC: 2721 Magazines: publishing & printing

(G-13199)
TREND MICRO INCORPORATED (HQ)
225 E John Carpenter Fwy # 1500
(75062-2282)
PHONE....................408 257-1500
Eva Chen, *CEO*
Lane Bess, *President*
Ian Browde, *President*
Mike Gable, *President*
Mahendra Negi, *COO*
▲ EMP: 153
SQ FT: 75,000
SALES (est): 6.4MM **Privately Held**
WEB: www.store.trendmicro.com
SIC: 5045 7382 7372 Computer software; security systems services; prepackaged software

(G-13200)
TWO ELK INVESTMENTS LLC
Also Called: Billor Machine Tool Service
6025 Commerce Dr Ste 510 (75063-2666)
PHONE....................972 465-3608
Luke Shagets, *Owner*
EMP: 15
SALES (est): 2.3MM **Privately Held**
WEB: www.billor.com
SIC: 3541 Machine tools, metal cutting type

(G-13201)
U S PLATING LLP
2215 Century Cir (75062-4903)
PHONE....................972 871-2800
James Gale, *Managing Prtnr*
Diana Gale, *Partner*
Eric Gale, *Vice Pres*
Vince Gale, *Vice Pres*
EMP: 15
SQ FT: 45,000
SALES (est): 2.2MM **Privately Held**
WEB: www.usplatingtx.com
SIC: 3471 Electroplating of metals or formed products; finishing, metals or formed products

(G-13202)
ULTIMATE KRONOS GROUP
600 Las Colinas Blvd E (75039-5616)
PHONE....................469 221-1823
Ryan Reagan, *Branch Mgr*
Sandy Martin, *Executive*
EMP: 16
SALES (corp-wide): 471.5MM **Privately Held**
WEB: www.kronos.com
SIC: 7372 Business oriented computer software
HQ: Ultimate Kronos Group
900 Chelmsford St
Lowell MA 01851
978 250-9800

(G-13203)
ULTIMATE KRONOS GROUP
Also Called: Kronos South Central
600 E John Carpenter Fwy (75062-3990)
PHONE....................469 221-1800
Sheree Bowen, *Project Mgr*
Harriet Bond, *Manager*
Joseph Gieder, *Consultant*
Ghufran Mohammad, *Technical Staff*
EMP: 35
SALES (corp-wide): 471.5MM **Privately Held**
WEB: www.kronos.com
SIC: 7372 Business oriented computer software
HQ: Ultimate Kronos Group
900 Chelmsford St
Lowell MA 01851
978 250-9800

(G-13204)
US HOME SYSTEMS INC (HQ)
2951 Kinwest Pkwy (75063-3134)
PHONE....................214 488-6300
Murray H Gross, *President*
Richard B Goodner, *Vice Pres*
Robert A Defronzo, *CFO*
Steven L Gross, *Chief Mktg Ofcr*
EMP: 38
SALES (est): 79.5MM
SALES (corp-wide): 110.2B **Publicly Held**
WEB: www.ushomesystems.com
SIC: 3429 5031 1751 Manufactured hardware (general); kitchen cabinets; cabinet & finish carpentry
PA: The Home Depot Inc
2455 Paces Ferry Rd Se
Atlanta GA 30339
770 433-8211

(G-13205)
W B MASON CO INC
5425 Faa Blvd (75061-3611)
PHONE....................888 926-2766
EMP: 43
SALES (corp-wide): 1B **Privately Held**
WEB: www.wbmason.com
SIC: 5943 5712 2752 Office forms & supplies; office furniture; commercial printing, lithographic
PA: W. B. Mason Co., Inc.
59 Ctr St
Brockton MA 02301
508 586-3434

(G-13206)
WESTERN SHEET METAL INC
2406 Hinton Dr (75061-5710)
PHONE....................804 732-0230
Billy W Junell, *President*
Mike Junell, *Vice Pres*
Wesley S Junell, *Admin Sec*
EMP: 24
SQ FT: 22,000
SALES (est): 3.8MM **Privately Held**
WEB: www.westernsheetmetal.com
SIC: 3444 Sheet metalwork

(G-13207)
WEYERHAEUSER COMPANY
8800 Sterling St (75063-2535)
PHONE....................972 929-8581
Kim Evetts, *Manager*
EMP: 76
SALES (corp-wide): 6.5B **Publicly Held**
WEB: www.weyerhaeuser.com
SIC: 2761 2759 Manifold business forms; commercial printing
PA: Weyerhaeuser Company
220 Occidental Ave S
Seattle WA 98104
206 539-3000

(G-13208)
WORKIVA INC
600 Las Colinas Blvd E # 900
(75039-5633)
PHONE....................817 308-1153
Matthew M Rizai, *Ch of Bd*
Martin J Vanderploeg, *President*
J Stuart Miller, *Exec VP*
Jeffrey D Trom, *Exec VP*
Zeina ADI, *Manager*
EMP: 500
SALES (corp-wide): 297.8MM **Publicly Held**
WEB: www.workiva.com
SIC: 7372 Application computer software
PA: Workiva Inc.
2900 University Blvd
Ames IA 50010
888 275-3125

(G-13209)
WRIGHTS AMMUNITIONS LLC
2300 Valley View Ln # 213 (75062-1721)
PHONE....................972 257-1111
Leonard Wright,
Lamar Wright,
EMP: 75 **EST:** 2013
SQ FT: 2,000
SALES (est): 5MM **Privately Held**
SIC: 3482 5099 Small arms ammunition; firearms & ammunition, except sporting

(G-13210)
X PRESS BAGS INC
707 Robbie Dr Ste 150 (75061-6297)
PHONE....................972 513-9899
Kim Johnston, *Principal*
EMP: 11
SALES (est): 838.6K **Privately Held**
SIC: 2741 Miscellaneous publishing

(G-13211)
XOCHITL INC
Also Called: Salsa Xochitl
6020 Colwell Blvd (75039-3113)
PHONE....................214 800-3551
Carlos Salinas, *President*
Jeanne Tallmadge, *Vice Pres*
Lee Gravette, *Controller*
Diana Goode, *Credit Staff*
▲ EMP: 30
SALES (est): 7MM **Privately Held**
WEB: www.salsaxochitl.com
SIC: 2099 2096 Sauces: gravy, dressing & dip mixes; potato chips & similar snacks

(G-13212)
ZOETIS INC
5430 Faa Blvd Ste 140 (75061-6019)
PHONE....................817 293-8887
EMP: 14
SALES (corp-wide): 6.2B **Publicly Held**
WEB: www.zoetis.com
SIC: 2834 Pharmaceutical preparations
PA: Zoetis Inc.
10 Sylvan Way Ste 105
Parsippany NJ 07054
973 822-7000

Italy
Ellis County

(G-13213)
GREEN INDUSTRIES INC
Also Called: Ammonia Services
1874 S Hwy 77 (76651)
P.O. Box 219, Waxahachie (75168-0219)
PHONE....................972 483-6408
George Scruggs III, *President*
Valinda Scruggs, *Admin Sec*
EMP: 9
SQ FT: 7,000
SALES (est): 1.7MM **Privately Held**
SIC: 2873 Nitrogenous fertilizers

(G-13214)
MONOLITHIC CONSTRUCTORS INC
Also Called: Monolithic Dome Institute
177 Dome Park Pl (76651-3710)
PHONE....................972 483-7423
David B South Sr, *President*
James L Byrne, *Vice Pres*
Gary L Clark, *Vice Pres*
Michael South, *Vice Pres*
Kelly Lewis, *Export Mgr*
▲ EMP: 47
SQ FT: 2,513
SALES (est): 11.1MM **Privately Held**
WEB: www.monolithicdome.com
SIC: 1541 1542 1521 3443 Industrial buildings & warehouses; commercial & office building, new construction; new construction, single-family houses; fabricated plate work (boiler shop)

Itasca
Hill County

(G-13215)
JCB INC
Also Called: Conveying Pwr Transm Solutions
1199 E Main St (76055-3406)
P.O. Box 146 (76055-0146)
PHONE....................254 687-2200
Oscar G Castillo Jr, *President*
Vicki Cockerham, *General Mgr*
Amanda Marbut, *General Mgr*
Monty Chutz, *Vice Pres*
Brent Marbut, *Vice Pres*
EMP: 15

SALES (est): 2.3MM **Privately Held**
WEB: www.c-pts.com
SIC: 3612 Transformers, except electric

(G-13216)
LEACH TRAILERS LLP
701 S Hill St (76055-2917)
PHONE....................254 687-2616
Doug Leach, *Partner*
Davonia Leach, *Partner*
EMP: 25
SQ FT: 30,000
SALES (est): 2.4MM **Privately Held**
WEB: www.leachtrailers.com
SIC: 3713 Truck bodies & parts

Jacksboro
Jack County

(G-13217)
BUCK PRODUCTION
3691 Mountain Home Rd (76458-3529)
PHONE....................940 567-3005
Billy Sanders, *Owner*
EMP: 12
SALES (est): 804.4K **Privately Held**
SIC: 1311 Crude petroleum production

(G-13218)
DOUBLE K DRILLING LLC
518 Us Highway 281 N (76458-3506)
P.O. Box 1031 (76458-7031)
PHONE....................940 567-2855
Kasey R Swan,
Kori C Lewis,
EMP: 15
SALES (est): 615.4K **Privately Held**
WEB: www.doublekenergyservices.com
SIC: 1381 Drilling oil & gas wells

(G-13219)
DOUBLE K WELL SERVICE LP
518 Us Highway 281 N (76458-3506)
P.O. Box 1031 (76458-7031)
PHONE....................940 567-2855
Kasey Swan, *Managing Prtnr*
EMP: 12
SALES (est): 2.6MM **Privately Held**
WEB: www.doublekenergyservices.com
SIC: 1381 Directional drilling oil & gas wells

(G-13220)
EOG RESOURCES INC
954 S Main St (76458-2711)
PHONE....................940 567-9777
EMP: 42
SALES (corp-wide): 7.6B **Publicly Held**
SIC: 1382 Oil/Gas Exploration Services
PA: Eog Resources, Inc.
1111 Bagby Sky Lbby 2
Houston TX 77002
713 651-7000

(G-13221)
HURD OIL FIELD SERVICE INC
500 S Main St (76458-2704)
P.O. Box 728 (76458-0728)
PHONE....................940 567-3131
Henry R Hurd, *President*
Brent Hurd, *Vice Pres*
EMP: 30
SALES (est): 4.6MM **Privately Held**
WEB: www.hurdcrane.com
SIC: 1389 Oil field services

(G-13222)
MERCER WELL SERVICE INC
902 S Main St (76458-2711)
PHONE....................940 567-5991
EMP: 75
SALES (corp-wide): 4.1MM **Privately Held**
SIC: 1389 Servicing oil & gas wells
PA: Mercer Well Service Inc
616 W Main St
Whitesboro TX 76273
903 564-3730

(G-13223)
SWANS PRODUCTION INC
518 Us Highway 281 N (76458-3506)
PHONE....................940 567-3147
Ken Swan, *President*

EMP: 11 **EST:** 1982
SQ FT: 3,800
SALES (est): 2.5MM **Privately Held**
SIC: 1381 Drilling oil & gas wells

(G-13224)
XSTAR RESOURCES LLC
4237 Salt Creek Rd (76458-3845)
PHONE..................................817 495-9306
Mark D McBryde, *Mng Member*
EMP: 10
SALES (est): 519.6K **Privately Held**
SIC: 1382 Oil & gas exploration services

Jacksonville
Cherokee County

(G-13225)
ALLIED TRUSS LLC
387 County Road 3216 (75766)
P.O. Box 158, Bullard (75757-0158)
PHONE..................................903 586-1982
Brandon Tannery, *Vice Pres*
Jonathan Kindle, *Sales Staff*
Rick Kindle, *Mng Member*
Ashtyn Brown, *Manager*
EMP: 35
SALES (est): 5.5MM **Privately Held**
WEB: www.alliedtruss.com
SIC: 2421 2439 5031 5033 Building &
structural materials, wood; trusses,
wooden roof; building materials, exterior;
building materials, interior; roofing & sid-
ing materials; floor coverings; roofing ma-
terial; flooring, wood

(G-13226)
ARRINGTON LBR & PALLET CO INC
445 Country Rd 1538 (75766)
P.O. Box 1900 (75766-1900)
PHONE..................................903 586-4070
Ernest C Arrington, *President*
Eddie R Arrington, *Vice Pres*
Garrett Bryant, *Safety Dir*
Kent Kirkpatrick, *Plant Mgr*
Frank Telles, *Safety Mgr*
EMP: 170
SQ FT: 1,200
SALES (est): 33MM **Privately Held**
WEB: www.arringtonlumber.com
SIC: 2448 Pallets, wood

(G-13227)
ARRINGTON SAWMILL INC
Also Called: Arrington Lumber
Hwy 69 S (75766)
P.O. Box 1898 (75766-1898)
PHONE..................................903 586-4070
Ernest C Arrington, *President*
Margaret G Arrington, *Corp Secy*
EMP: 200
SALES (est): 21.2MM **Privately Held**
WEB: www.arringtonlumber.com
SIC: 2448 Pallets, wood

(G-13228)
BAXTER HEALTHCARE CORPORATION
Baxter Convertors
200 Mcknight St (75766-3635)
P.O. Box 2046 (75766-2046)
PHONE..................................903 586-6502
Francis Poinsette, *Purch Agent*
Bob Horrick, *Engineer*
Grebb Sanforb, *Manager*
EMP: 550
SQ FT: 120,000
SALES (corp-wide): 11.6B **Publicly Held**
WEB: www.baxter.com
SIC: 3841 Surgical & medical instruments
HQ: Baxter Healthcare Corporation
1 Baxter Pkwy
Deerfield IL 60015
224 948-2000

(G-13229)
BERRYS TIN SHOP INC
Also Called: Berry's Air Conditioning
300 E Tena St (75766-3044)
P.O. Box 1508 (75766-1508)
PHONE..................................903 586-3552
Barber K Berry, *President*

Betty Ruth Berry, *Corp Secy*
Steven J Berry, *Vice Pres*
EMP: 10 **EST:** 1936
SQ FT: 27,000
SALES (est): 1.6MM **Privately Held**
WEB: www.berrystinshop.net
SIC: 3448 1711 1761 Prefabricated metal
buildings; warm air heating & air condi-
tioning contractor; sheet metalwork

(G-13230)
BUILDERS BEST INC (PA)
201 Broiles St (75766-3634)
PHONE..................................903 586-8283
Charles Anderson, *Ch of Bd*
John Anderson, *President*
Radu Flore, *Safety Mgr*
Jerrie Frazier, *Sales Staff*
Mel Peters, *Sales Staff*
▲ **EMP:** 100
SQ FT: 50,000
SALES (est): 18.8MM **Privately Held**
WEB: www.buildersbest.com
SIC: 3498 3444 Fabricated pipe & fittings;
ventilators, sheet metal

(G-13231)
C & R MACHINE INC
Also Called: Magnetrode
2907 Fm 1910 W (75766-7014)
PHONE..................................903 795-3378
Charlotte Melton, *President*
Raymond G Melton Sr, *Vice Pres*
Shelly Lipe, *Office Mgr*
EMP: 11
SQ FT: 3,000
SALES (est): 500K **Privately Held**
SIC: 3599 Machine shop, jobbing & repair

(G-13232)
CARDINAL HEALTH 200 LLC
200 Mcknight St (75766-3635)
P.O. Box 2046 (75766-2046)
PHONE..................................903 586-6502
Brad Sanford, *Plant Mgr*
Ryan Eckles, *Engineer*
Tim Taylor, *Engineer*
Joshua Kupke, *Manager*
Dane Clark, *Info Tech Mgr*
EMP: 200
SALES (corp-wide): 152.9B **Publicly Held**
WEB: www.cardinalhealth.com
SIC: 5122 3842 Pharmaceuticals; surgical
appliances & supplies
HQ: Cardinal Health 200, Llc
3651 Birchwood Dr
Waukegan IL 60085

(G-13233)
CENTURY INDUS COATINGS INC
37094 Us Highway 69 N (75766-1529)
P.O. Box 830 (75766-0830)
PHONE..................................903 586-9197
Dean Harvey, *President*
Omarie Harvey, *Corp Secy*
Clayton D Harvey, *Vice Pres*
Dusty Harvey, *VP Opers*
Brian N Martin, *VP Sls/Mktg*
▲ **EMP:** 35
SQ FT: 60,000
SALES (est): 13MM
SALES (corp-wide): 4.4B **Publicly Held**
WEB: www.centurypaint.com
SIC: 2851 Paints & paint additives; enam-
els; lacquer: bases, dopes, thinner;
stains: varnish, oil or wax
HQ: Axalta Coating Systems, Llc
2001 Market St Ste 3600
Philadelphia PA 19103
855 547-1461

(G-13234)
D & L TOOLING AND PLASTICS INC
950 Se Loop 456 (75766-6172)
PHONE..................................903 586-9894
EMP: 50 **EST:** 1972
SQ FT: 55,000
SALES (est): 10.3MM **Privately Held**
WEB: www.dlplastics.com
SIC: 3089 Injection molded finished plastic
products; injection molding of plastics

(G-13235)
DACON INDUSTRIES CO
119 Progress St (75766-9372)
PHONE..................................903 589-7456
Ryan Bay, *Manager*
EMP: 50 **Privately Held**
WEB: www.daconindustries.com
SIC: 3069 Rubber automotive products
PA: Dacon Industries Co.
10661 N Lombard St
Portland OR 97203

(G-13236)
DEMENT PLASTICS LLC
1065 County Road 1407 (75766-7767)
PHONE..................................903 586-9894
Darrell Dement, *Owner*
EMP: 40
SALES (est): 2.6MM **Privately Held**
WEB: www.dlplastics.com
SIC: 3089 Injection molding of plastics

(G-13237)
ENERGY TRANSFER FUEL LP
1044 N Jackson St (75766-3804)
PHONE..................................903 931-1922
Kenneth Carter, *Plant Supt*
George Hodges, *Engineer*
Jason Murley, *Engineer*
Andrea Pineda, *Accountant*
Sallie Newberry, *Manager*
EMP: 16 **Publicly Held**
WEB: www.energytransfer.com
SIC: 2869 Fuels
HQ: Energy Transfer Fuel, Lp
8111 Westchester Dr # 600
Dallas TX 75225
214 981-0700

(G-13238)
FEDERAL HEATH SIGN COMPANY LLC
1500 N Bolton St (75766-4036)
PHONE..................................903 589-2100
Chris Tuohy, *Opers Mgr*
Cindy Spurgeon, *Purch Mgr*
Carl Bradshaw, *Engineer*
Kevin Eason, *Engineer*
George Albanese, *Design Engr*
EMP: 41
SALES (corp-wide): 3.2B **Privately Held**
WEB: www.federalheath.com
SIC: 3993 Neon signs
HQ: Federal Heath Sign Company, Llc
2300 St Hwy 121
Euless TX 76039

(G-13239)
FUELAND INC
1623 S Jackson St (75766-3027)
PHONE..................................972 899-3727
Stephen W Alexander, *President*
Jeff Beardsley, *Software Engr*
Tad Marko, *Software Dev*
EMP: 9
SALES (est): 1.1MM **Privately Held**
WEB: www.rollbackrewards.com
SIC: 2869 Fuels

(G-13240)
GME INC
515 Se Loop 456 (75766-9479)
P.O. Box 2017 (75766-2017)
PHONE..................................903 586-7581
Glen T Hamilton, *President*
Edith Hamilton, *Corp Secy*
Ben Hamilton, *Vice Pres*
Glen Hamilton, *Controller*
Chance Hamilton, *Human Res Mgr*
EMP: 25
SQ FT: 25,000
SALES (est): 3.4MM **Privately Held**
WEB: www.gme-inc.com
SIC: 3544 3599 Special dies & tools; ma-
chine shop, jobbing & repair

(G-13241)
GOURMET GRDNS SPCLTY FOODS INC
300 E Tena St (75766-3044)
PHONE..................................903 284-6215
Kara Hancock, *CEO*
Fred Montgomery, *Vice Pres*
EMP: 31
SQ FT: 30,000

SALES (est): 10.4MM **Privately Held**
WEB: www.gourmetgardens.com
SIC: 2035 2033 Relishes, fruit & veg-
etable; canned fruits & specialties

(G-13242)
H D INDUSTRIES INC
Highway 79 S (75766)
P.O. Box 8250 (75766-8250)
PHONE..................................903 586-6126
Harold Dillingham, *President*
Melinda Dillingham, *IT/INT Sup*
EMP: 32
SQ FT: 7,500
SALES (est): 8.8MM **Privately Held**
WEB: www.pro-patch.com
SIC: 3531 Construction machinery

(G-13243)
HALBERT MILL COMPANY TEXAS INC (PA)
3939 Fm 347 N (75766-7020)
P.O. Box 927 (75766-0927)
PHONE..................................903 683-2788
Holly Varga, *President*
Martha Hughes, *Vice Pres*
David Stone, *Treasurer*
EMP: 16
SQ FT: 34,500
SALES: 7MM **Privately Held**
WEB: www.halbertmill.com
SIC: 5031 2621 2679 Veneer; offset
paper; paper products, converted

(G-13244)
JACKSONVILLE CANDY CO INC
Also Called: Holcomb Candy Co
218 E Woodrow St 18 (75766-4846)
P.O. Box 1067 (75766-1067)
PHONE..................................903 586-8334
Lewis Holcomb, *President*
Lisa Holcomb, *Vice Pres*
EMP: 20 **EST:** 1924
SQ FT: 15,000
SALES (est): 2.2MM **Privately Held**
WEB: www.jacksonvilletxedc.com
SIC: 2064 5145 Candy & other confec-
tionery products; candy

(G-13245)
JACKSONVILLE TOOL & DIE INC
1044 E Loop 456 (75766-9717)
P.O. Box 2077 (75766-2077)
PHONE..................................903 586-6030
Pete Betts, *President*
Jeanie Betts, *Vice Pres*
EMP: 10
SQ FT: 6,500
SALES (est): 1.4MM **Privately Held**
WEB: www.jvilletool.com
SIC: 3089 3544 Injection molding of plas-
tics; special dies, tools, jigs & fixtures

(G-13246)
JESTA MACHINE
4373 Fm 1910 W (75766-6446)
PHONE..................................903 721-9168
Jessie Hack, *Principal*
EMP: 10
SALES (est): 1.4MM **Privately Held**
WEB: www.jestamachine.com
SIC: 3599 Machine shop, jobbing & repair

(G-13247)
KLEIN PRODUCTS OF TEXAS INC
16576 Us Highway 79 E (75766-9387)
P.O. Box 2066 (75766-2066)
PHONE..................................903 589-4546
Barry K McManus, *President*
Mary Walley, *Executive*
▼ **EMP:** 45
SQ FT: 70,000
SALES (est): 23.8MM **Privately Held**
WEB: www.kleinproducts.com
SIC: 3531 3443 Construction machinery;
tanks, lined: metal plate

(G-13248)
M & H CRATES INC
4022 Farm Rd 347 (75766)
PHONE..................................903 683-5351
Andy McCown, *President*
Randy McCown, *President*
Davy Sanders, *Vice Pres*
EMP: 95 **EST:** 1976

SQ FT: 30,000
SALES (est): 8MM Privately Held
WEB: www.login.microsoftonline.com
SIC: 2448 2436 Pallets, wood; veneer stock, softwood

(G-13249)
MAGNETRODE CORPORATION
Also Called: C & R Machine
2907 Fm 1910 W (75766-7014)
PHONE...................................903 795-3378
Charlotte Melton, *President*
Raymond G Melton Sr, *Vice Pres*
EMP: 20 EST: 1947
SQ FT: 3,500
SALES (est): 2MM Privately Held
SIC: 3548 Electric welding equipment

(G-13250)
METALLOID CORPORATION
1720 N Quevado St (75766-4065)
PHONE...................................800 686-3201
EMP: 10
SALES (corp-wide): 15MM Privately Held
WEB: www.metalloidcorp.com
SIC: 2899 Metal treating compounds
PA: Metalloid Corporation
1160 White St
Sturgis MI 49091
800 686-3201

(G-13251)
MODINE JACKSONVILLE INC
Also Called: Modine Manufacturing
224 Talley Nichols Dr (75766-3605)
P.O. Box 1798 (75766-1798)
PHONE...................................903 589-0009
David Myers, *Branch Mgr*
EMP: 25
SALES (corp-wide): 1.9B Publicly Held
WEB: www.modinecoatings.com
SIC: 3479 Coating of metals & formed products
HQ: Modine Jacksonville, Inc.
1423 W Ormsby Ave
Louisville KY 40210
502 634-9458

(G-13252)
MYCO PLASTICS INC
902 Cherokee Trl (75766-3758)
P.O. Box 1613 (75766-1613)
PHONE...................................903 586-0551
Ed Sneider, *President*
Joshua Hanna, *Vice Pres*
Johnny Propes, *Maint Spvr*
Dee Crosby, *Human Res Mgr*
EMP: 40
SQ FT: 27,000
SALES (est): 7.1MM Privately Held
WEB: www.mycoplastics.com
SIC: 3089 Injection molding of plastics

(G-13253)
NEWSPAPER HOLDING INC
Also Called: Jacksonville Daily Progress
525 E Commerce St (75766-4909)
P.O. Box 711 (75766)
PHONE...................................903 586-2236
Amy Miller, *Manager*
EMP: 16
SQ FT: 10,000
SALES (corp-wide): 23.7B Privately Held
WEB: www.oskaloosa.com
SIC: 2711 Newspapers: publishing only, not printed on site
HQ: Newspaper Holding, Inc.
425 Locust St
Johnstown PA 15901
814 532-5102

(G-13254)
OPTI-BLAST INC
4032 N Jackson St (75766-5140)
PHONE...................................903 589-0452
Jason Floyd, *President*
Karen Perry, *General Mgr*
Chris Howard, *Vice Pres*
Troy Boggs, *Products*
◆ EMP: 10
SQ FT: 30,000
SALES (est): 2.5MM Privately Held
WEB: www.optiblast.com
SIC: 3291 Synthetic abrasives

(G-13255)
PANEL PROCESSING TEXAS INC
1010 S Bolton St (75766-3310)
PHONE...................................903 586-2423
Eric Smith, *President*
Brent Belcher, *Opers Mgr*
Rhonda Swinney, *Treasurer*
Johnny Gardner, *Maintence Staff*
EMP: 40
SQ FT: 80,000
SALES (est): 8.5MM
SALES (corp-wide): 95.4MM Privately Held
WEB: www.panel.com
SIC: 2541 Store fixtures, wood; display fixtures, wood
PA: Panel Processing, Inc.
120 N Industrial Hwy
Alpena MI 49707
800 433-7142

(G-13256)
PEACOCK PLASTICS COMPANY
Also Called: Speedy Products
225 Cash St (75766-8868)
PHONE...................................903 586-2531
Joe L Peacock, *President*
Richard S Peacock-Vice Preside, *Corp Secy*
James Hoke Peacock II, *Vice Pres*
Peacock R S, *Vice Pres*
Claudia Vestal, *Director*
EMP: 12
SQ FT: 10,000
SALES (est): 600K Privately Held
SIC: 3089 Injection molded finished plastic products

(G-13257)
PI HOLDINGS INC
Also Called: Plastics Holdings, Inc.
1613 N Bolton St (75766-5103)
P.O. Box 1674 (75766-1674)
PHONE...................................903 586-2408
John Parker, *President*
EMP: 51 EST: 2010
SALES (est): 9.9MM Privately Held
WEB: www.plasticsholdings.com
SIC: 3089 Injection molded finished plastic products

(G-13258)
SNOKE SPECIAL PRODUCTS CO INC (PA)
2050 N Jackson St (75766-3806)
P.O. Box 1897 (75766-1897)
PHONE...................................903 586-3618
W V Snoke, *Ch of Bd*
Freda Bittner, *Corp Secy*
Jerry Morris, *Vice Pres*
John Wilson, *Vice Pres*
▲ EMP: 15
SQ FT: 45,000
SALES (est): 7.8MM Privately Held
SIC: 3585 Parts for heating, cooling & refrigerating equipment

(G-13259)
STEN CORPORATION
4555 N Jackson St (75766-9692)
PHONE...................................903 586-0914
Joe Helen-Barton, *Manager*
EMP: 13
SALES (corp-wide): 5MM Privately Held
WEB: www.stencorporation.com
SIC: 3842 Surgical appliances & supplies
PA: Sten Corporation
10501 Wayzata Blvd # 102
Hopkins MN 55305
952 545-2776

(G-13260)
SUPERIOR DIE CAST LLC
1020 S Bolton St (75766-3310)
P.O. Box 2154 (75766-7154)
PHONE...................................903 586-0637
Allen Werner, *President*
EMP: 25
SQ FT: 31,000

SALES (est): 4.6MM Privately Held
WEB: www.superiordiecastllc.net
SIC: 3364 3363 3369 3365 Zinc & zinc-base alloy die-castings; aluminum die-castings; nonferrous foundries; aluminum foundries

(G-13261)
TALLYHO PLASTICS INC (PA)
1020 S Bolton St (75766-3348)
PHONE...................................903 586-2263
Jack Martinsen, *President*
EMP: 88
SQ FT: 104,000
SALES (est): 4.9MM Privately Held
WEB: www.tallyhoplastics.com
SIC: 3089 Injection molding of plastics; molding primary plastic; plastic containers, except foam

(G-13262)
TEKNOR COLOR COMPANY
4545 N Jackson St (75766-9692)
P.O. Box 280 (75766-0280)
PHONE...................................903 586-0583
Dennis Baker, *Branch Mgr*
Brenda Johnson, *Executive*
EMP: 80
SALES (corp-wide): 1B Privately Held
WEB: www.teknorapex.com
SIC: 2821 2851 2816 Thermoplastic materials; paints & allied products; inorganic pigments
HQ: Teknor Color Company
505 Central Ave
Pawtucket RI 02861

(G-13263)
TELEPHONE DIRECTORY OF TEXAS
404 Wynn Dr (75766-4976)
PHONE...................................903 586-2987
Jim Vining, *President*
Lois S Vining, *Treasurer*
Tony Vining, *Master*
EMP: 27
SQ FT: 5,600
SALES (est): 2.1MM Privately Held
WEB: www.tdtyellowpages.com
SIC: 2741 Directories, telephone: publishing & printing

(G-13264)
TEXAS VESSELS FABRICATION LLC
1991 Us Highway 175 W (75766-7799)
PHONE...................................903 541-4883
Hung Nguyen, *Mng Member*
Roger Hedges, *Mng Member*
Robert Lafon, *Mng Member*
EMP: 45
SALES (est): 8MM Privately Held
SIC: 3443 3441 Vessels, process or storage (from boiler shops); metal plate; fabricated structural metal

(G-13265)
TEXWELD & FABRICATION INC
200 N Gillespie Ave (75766-4600)
P.O. Box 2373 (75766-0086)
PHONE...................................903 586-1775
Jim Hamblet, *President*
Bonnie Hamblet, *Corp Secy*
EMP: 9
SQ FT: 13,250
SALES (est): 825K Privately Held
WEB: www.texweld.com
SIC: 3441 7692 Fabricated structural metal; welding repair

(G-13266)
WESTERN PULP PRODUCTS CO
1577 N Bolton St (75766-4035)
P.O. Box 1838 (75766-1838)
PHONE...................................903 586-3608
Kyle Curt, *Branch Mgr*
EMP: 40
SQ FT: 33,000

SALES (corp-wide): 11.3MM Privately Held
WEB: www.westernpulp.com
SIC: 4953 2679 2671 2631 Recycling, waste materials; papier mache articles, except statuary & art goods; packaging paper & plastics film, coated & laminated; paperboard mills; fiber cans, drums & similar products
PA: Western Pulp Products Co.
5025 Sw Hout St
Corvallis OR 97333
541 757-1151

(G-13267)
WFC COMPANY INC
Also Called: Warminster Fiberglass
1428 Elberta St (75766-3839)
PHONE...................................903 586-0476
Larry Brannan, *Plant Mgr*
James A Phlieger, *Opers-Prdtn-Mfg*
Bob Cepil, *Sales Engr*
EMP: 21
SQ FT: 2,000
SALES (est): 13MM Privately Held
WEB: www.warminsterfiberglass.com
SIC: 3089 Plastic hardware & building products
PA: W.F.C. Company, Inc.
725 County Line Rd
Southampton PA 18966
215 953-1260

Jarrell
Williamson County

(G-13268)
A J BRAUER STONE
251 County Road 235 (76537-1100)
P.O. Box 39' (76537-0039)
PHONE...................................512 746-5792
A J Brauer III, *Owner*
▲ EMP: 52
SALES (est): 4.7MM Privately Held
WEB: www.bstoneandtile.com
SIC: 3281 Cut stone & stone products

(G-13269)
AL3 INCORPORATED
13685 N I 35 (76537)
P.O. Box 6 (76537-0006)
PHONE...................................512 746-4200
Ernesto Cruz, *Branch Mgr*
EMP: 25
SALES (corp-wide): 3.9MM Privately Held
WEB: www.al3inc.com
SIC: 3441 Fabricated structural metal
PA: Al3 Incorporated
1417 Hamilton St
Racine WI 53404
262 637-2595

(G-13270)
HILLSTONE COMPANY
1946 County Rd 239 (76537)
P.O. Box 524 (76537-0524)
PHONE...................................512 746-5544
Miguel Olalde, *CEO*
EMP: 20
SALES (est): 3.4MM Privately Held
SIC: 1429 5032 Trap rock, crushed & broken-quarrying; stone, crushed or broken

(G-13271)
J & J STONE COMPANY
4400 W Fm 487 (76537-1258)
P.O. Box 172 (76537-0172)
PHONE...................................512 869-3527
Jose Espinoza, *President*
EMP: 35
SALES (est): 4.6MM Privately Held
WEB: www.jjstone.com
SIC: 3281 Stone, quarrying & processing of own stone products

(G-13272)
SIMPSON STONE COMPANY
3410 W Fm 487 (76537-1769)
PHONE...................................512 746-2204
Brenda Wilbur, *Managing Prtnr*
Mark McCray, *CFO*
EMP: 25

SQ FT: 2,400
SALES (est): 3.9MM **Privately Held**
WEB: www.simpsonstone.com
SIC: 1411 Dimension stone

(G-13273)
SUPERIOR STONE INC
455 County Road 344 (76537-1189)
PHONE....................512 746-2608
David Abud, *Manager*
EMP: 19
SALES (corp-wide): 1.1MM **Privately Held**
WEB: www.superiorstoneinc.com
SIC: 5032 1422 Limestone; crushed & broken limestone
PA: Superior Stone Inc
7011 Fm 2244 Rd
Austin TX 78746
512 327-4509

(G-13274)
TAYLOR PRESS PRODUCTS COMPANY
13675 N Interstate 35 (76537-1281)
P.O. Box 737 (76537-0737)
PHONE....................512 746-5556
James E Taylor, *President*
Tom Fuller, *Principal*
Edward Taylor, *Vice Pres*
Hugh Taylor, *Vice Pres*
Bridget Nastasi, *Human Resources*
EMP: 28 **EST:** 1945
SQ FT: 30,000
SALES (est): 10MM **Privately Held**
WEB: www.taylor-products.com
SIC: 3469 Metal stampings

Jasper
Jasper County

(G-13275)
FLURRY AND SON LOGGING CONTR
706 Maol Rd (75951)
PHONE....................409 384-5441
EMP: 12
SALES (est): 1.4MM **Privately Held**
SIC: 2411 Logging

(G-13276)
FORESTRY SUPPLY SERVICE INC (PA)
Also Called: Ftr Equipment
104 N Manuel St (75951-3846)
PHONE....................409 384-3213
Mike D Whiteworth, *President*
Gay Whitworth, *Corp Secy*
Benis Whitworth, *Vice Pres*
Glenn Kelley, *Sales Staff*
EMP: 11
SQ FT: 3,760
SALES (est): 2.1MM **Privately Held**
WEB: www.forestrysupply.net
SIC: 5999 5082 3531 Farm equipment & supplies; logging & forestry machinery & equipment; forestry related equipment

(G-13277)
HEARST CORPORATION
Also Called: Jasper Newsboy
702 S Wheeler St (75951-4544)
PHONE....................409 384-3441
Willis Webb, *Dir Ops-Prd-Mfg*
Andrea Whitney, *Manager*
EMP: 11
SALES (corp-wide): 7.9B **Privately Held**
WEB: www.hearst.com
SIC: 2711 7313 Newspapers: publishing only, not printed on site; newspaper advertising representative
PA: The Hearst Corporation
300 W 57th St Fl 42
New York NY 10019
212 649-2000

(G-13278)
LINCOLN LUMBER LLC
2500 Us Highway 96 S (75951-6034)
PHONE....................409 384-2587
Blake Barrington, *Manager*
EMP: 33 **Privately Held**
WEB: www.lincolnusa.com

SIC: 2421 Building & structural materials, wood
PA: Lincoln Lumber, Llc
1390 Fm 1314
Conroe TX 77301

(G-13279)
LOUISIANA-PACIFIC CORPORATION
Hgwy 190 E (75951)
PHONE....................409 383-0767
David Padgett, *Branch Mgr*
EMP: 89
SALES (corp-wide): 2.8B **Publicly Held**
WEB: www.lpcorp.com
SIC: 2493 Reconstituted wood products
PA: Louisiana-Pacific Corporation
414 Union St Ste 2000
Nashville TN 37219
615 986-5600

(G-13280)
TERRA BIOCHEM LLC
610 Mcqueen St (75951-2324)
PHONE....................409 489-1700
EMP: 13 **EST:** 2011
SALES (est): 2.9MM **Privately Held**
WEB: www.terrabiochem.net
SIC: 2819 Industrial inorganic chemicals

(G-13281)
TEXAS ELECTRIC COOPS INC
Texas Electric Treating Div
2240 Bevil Loop (75951-5655)
PHONE....................409 384-4633
Kay Collier, *Office Mgr*
Charles R Faulds, *Manager*
Billy Caldwell, *Manager*
William Alvord, *Supervisor*
Justin Dennis, *Supervisor*
EMP: 75
SALES (corp-wide): 200MM **Privately Held**
WEB: www.texas-ec.org
SIC: 2499 5169 2491 Poles, wood; coal tar products, primary & intermediate; wood preserving
PA: Texas Electric Cooperatives, Inc.
1122 Colorado St Ste 2400
Austin TX 78701
512 454-0311

(G-13282)
TRAEGER WOOD PELLETS
606 Mcqueen St (75951-2324)
PHONE....................409 384-5331
Jason Miller, *Branch Mgr*
EMP: 9 **EST:** 2015
SALES (est): 963.3K **Privately Held**
WEB: www.traegergrills.com
SIC: 2448 Pallets, wood

Jefferson
Marion County

(G-13283)
CITY OF JEFFERSON
Also Called: Waste Water Treatment Plant
1401 N Line St (75657-2702)
PHONE....................903 665-2832
EMP: 11
SALES (corp-wide): 1.9MM **Privately Held**
WEB: www.jeffersontxrentals.com
SIC: 9199 3589 General government administration; sewage & water treatment equipment
PA: City Of Jefferson
102 N Polk St
Jefferson TX 75657
903 665-3922

(G-13284)
HAWK INSTALLATION & CNSTR INC
555 Fm 728 (75657-6686)
P.O. Box 1047 (75657-6047)
PHONE....................903 665-8080
Lance Derrick, *Project Mgr*
George Horsly, *Branch Mgr*
EMP: 10

SALES (corp-wide): 24.4MM **Privately Held**
WEB: www.hawkinstallation.com
SIC: 3541 Vertical turning & boring machines (metalworking)
PA: Hawk Installation And Construction, Inc.
315 N Main St
Bogata TX 75417
903 632-4464

(G-13285)
NORBORD TEXAS LP
Also Called: Norbord Texas Limited
500 Nexfor Blvd (75657-1055)
P.O. Box 632750, Nacogdoches (75963-2750)
PHONE....................936 568-8009
Peter C Wijnbergen, *CEO*
Norbord Georgia, *General Ptnr*
Marlene Hall, *Opers Staff*
Caleb Walls, *Accounting Mgr*
Erica Woody, *Accountant*
◆ **EMP:** 1000 **EST:** 2002
SALES (est): 152.7MM
SALES (corp-wide): 1.7B **Privately Held**
WEB: www.norbord.com
SIC: 2493 Reconstituted wood products
PA: Norbord Inc
1 Toronto St Suite 600
Toronto ON M5C 2
416 365-0705

(G-13286)
PORE TECHNOLOGY INC
498 Fm 881 (75657-7711)
P.O. Box 854 (75657-0854)
PHONE....................903 601-4466
John G Sims, *President*
Barbara Dischino, *Vice Pres*
Gregory Sims, *Vice Pres*
Paul Sims, *Vice Pres*
EMP: 20
SQ FT: 12,000
SALES (est): 3.8MM **Privately Held**
WEB: www.poretech.com
SIC: 2821 5162 Plastics materials & resins; plastics materials

(G-13287)
REDDY ICE GROUP INC
6 19th St W (75657)
PHONE....................254 753-7378
David Tenberg, *Opers-Prdtn-Mfg*
Earl Mason, *Supervisor*
EMP: 9
SQ FT: 14,114 **Privately Held**
WEB: www.reddyice.com
SIC: 2097 5199 Manufactured ice; ice, manufactured or natural
HQ: Reddy Ice Group, Inc.
5720 Lbj Fwy Ste 200
Dallas TX 75240

(G-13288)
SONOCO PRODUCTS COMPANY
Hwy 59 S (75657)
P.O. Box 689 (75657-0689)
PHONE....................903 665-3966
Henry Henderson, *Branch Mgr*
EMP: 65
SALES (corp-wide): 5.3B **Publicly Held**
WEB: www.sonoco.com
SIC: 2631 2655 Paperboard mills; fiber cans, drums & similar products
PA: Sonoco Products Company
1 N 2nd St
Hartsville SC 29550
843 383-7000

(G-13289)
TJ BLACKBURN SYRUP WORKS INC
22382 Hwy 49 W (75657)
P.O. Box 928 (75657-0928)
PHONE....................903 665-2541
Jeffrey Fuquay, *President*
Ronnie Bullard Jr, *Corp Secy*
EMP: 65 **EST:** 1986
SQ FT: 2,300

SALES (est): 18.1MM **Privately Held**
SIC: 2099 2033 2087 Syrups; molasses, mixed or blended: from purchased ingredients; peanut butter; jams, jellies & preserves: packaged in cans, jars, etc.; jams, including imitation: packaged in cans, jars, etc.; jellies, edible, including imitation: in cans, jars, etc.; preserves, including imitation: in cans, jars, etc.; flavoring extracts & syrups

Jermyn
Jack County

(G-13290)
T & S MANUFACTURING INC
8044 State Highway 114 (76459-6000)
P.O. Box 336 (76459-0336)
PHONE....................940 342-2005
Price A Taylor, *President*
Jim Taylor, *Vice Pres*
James Taylor, *Sales Staff*
EMP: 18 **EST:** 1979
SQ FT: 6,000
SALES (est): 3.1MM **Privately Held**
WEB: www.tsfeeders.com
SIC: 3523 Cattle feeding, handling & watering equipment

Jersey Village
Harris County

(G-13291)
ARGOS USA LLC
16060 Dillard Dr (77040-2082)
PHONE....................713 664-4527
Curtis Sutton, *Sales Staff*
Joe Lucas, *Manager*
Troy Reed, *Director*
EMP: 70 **Privately Held**
WEB: www.argos-us.com
SIC: 3273 Ready-mixed concrete
HQ: Argos Usa Llc
3015 Windward Plz Ste 300
Alpharetta GA 30005
678 368-4300

(G-13292)
ARSHAM METAL INDUSTRIES INC
Also Called: Arsham Aluminum Alloys
11280 Charles Rd (77041-2400)
PHONE....................713 896-8585
Sheldon Arsham, *President*
EMP: 35
SQ FT: 30,000
SALES (est): 10.8MM **Privately Held**
WEB: www.arshamet.com
SIC: 3365 5051 5093 Aluminum & aluminum-based alloy castings; metals service centers & offices; metal scrap & waste materials

(G-13293)
BETTIS CORPORATION
19200 Northwest Fwy (77065-4715)
PHONE....................281 879-2300
Todd Lowe, *Principal*
Carl Witchet, *Senior Mgr*
▲ **EMP:** 172
SQ FT: 145,698
SALES (est): 2.2MM **Privately Held**
WEB: www.emerson.com
SIC: 3823 Industrial instrmnts msrmnt display/control process variable

(G-13294)
BRUSH MECHANICAL INC
11811 Charles Rd (77041-2411)
P.O. Box 79412, Houston (77279-9412)
PHONE....................713 937-9027
Dwayne Brush, *CEO*
EMP: 10
SQ FT: 11,000
SALES (est): 2.4MM **Privately Held**
WEB: www.brushmechanical.com
SIC: 1796 3441 Installing building equipment; fabricated structural metal

(G-13295)
CEMEX INC
16100 Dillard Dr (77040-2077)
PHONE...................................713 332-4070
EMP: 12 Privately Held
WEB: www.cemex.com
SIC: 3273 Ready-mixed concrete
HQ: Cemex, Inc.
10100 Katy Fwy Ste 300
Houston TX 77043
713 650-6200

(G-13296)
COASTAL FLANGE INC
11906 Fm 529 Rd (77041-3012)
P.O. Box 40443, Houston (77240-0443)
PHONE...................................713 937-3333
Myron G Haley, CEO
Gary Haley, President
Mark Mekeel, Vice Pres
Johnathan Ocampo, Prdtn Mgr
Colleen Rogers, Human Res Mgr
◆ EMP: 40
SQ FT: 22,000
SALES (est): 7.8MM Privately Held
WEB: www.coastalflange.com
SIC: 3463 3494 Flange, valve or pipe fitting forgings, nonferrous; valves & pipe fittings

(G-13297)
CSE W-INDUSTRIES INC (HQ)
Also Called: Inc Cse W-Industries
11500 Charles Rd (77041-2406)
PHONE...................................713 466-9463
Greg Hanson, CEO
Salil Gopinath, COO
Ken Castlebury, Vice Pres
Jim Abshire, Manager
Keith Browne, Supervisor
▼ EMP: 200
SQ FT: 58,000
SALES (est): 98.8MM Privately Held
WEB: www.w-industries.com
SIC: 3625 3613 3594 3494 Relays & industrial controls; control panels, electric; fluid power pumps & motors; valves & pipe fittings

(G-13298)
DETSCO INC
Also Called: General Cntr For Ptro UST/AST
7230 Senate Ave (77040-3057)
P.O. Box 40545, Houston (77240-0545)
PHONE...................................713 999-5260
Dale Temple, President
Chris Anderson, Office Admin
EMP: 15 EST: 1977
SQ FT: 2,400
SALES (est): 4.2MM Privately Held
WEB: www.detsco.us.com
SIC: 1799 1389 1795 1771 Industrial buildings, new construction; demolition, buildings & other structures; concrete work; service station equipment installation, maintenance & repair; shoring & underpinning work; petroleum storage tank installation, underground

(G-13299)
EMERSON PROCESS MANAGEMENT
19200 Northwest Fwy (77065-4715)
P.O. Box 508, Houston (77001-0508)
PHONE...................................281 477-4100
EMP: 150
SALES (corp-wide): 16.7B Publicly Held
WEB: www.emerson.com
SIC: 3594 3593 Fluid power pumps & motors; fluid power actuators, hydraulic or pneumatic
HQ: Emerson Process Management Valve Automation, Inc.
8100 West Florissant Ave
Saint Louis MO 63136
314 553-2000

(G-13300)
INDUSTRIAL MACHINE REPAIR INC
11407 Charles Rd (77041-2436)
PHONE...................................713 937-7995
Tom Piasecki, President
Leon Plasecki, Vice Pres
EMP: 12

SQ FT: 5,000
SALES (est): 1.9MM Privately Held
WEB: www.industrialmachineinc.com
SIC: 3599 Industrial machinery & equipment repair

(G-13301)
JOISTS OF TEXAS INC
16118 Singapore Ln (77040-2040)
PHONE...................................713 466-1212
J R West, President
Jack L Donaho, Vice Pres
EMP: 38
SQ FT: 40,000
SALES (est): 4.8MM Privately Held
SIC: 3449 Joists, fabricated bar

(G-13302)
NORTHWEST DRIVE TRAIN INC
Also Called: Northwest Drive Train Service
11432 Fm 529 Rd (77041-3002)
PHONE...................................713 937-8499
Tony Bugai, President
Kim Bugai, Corp Secy
Sue Krueger, Shareholder
▲ EMP: 18
SQ FT: 5,000
SALES (est): 4.4MM Privately Held
WEB: www.nwdrivetrain.com
SIC: 5531 3714 5013 7539 Truck equipment & parts; axles, motor vehicle; automotive hardware; powertrain components repair services

(G-13303)
OCEANEERING INTERNATIONAL INC
Also Called: Oceaneering Multiflex USA
11800 Charles Rd (77041-2412)
PHONE...................................713 856-9375
Rick Van Almelo, Project Mgr
William Trainor, Engineer
Chad Barber, Project Engr
Scott Pierce, Manager
Luciana Abib, Technical Staff
EMP: 29
SALES (corp-wide): 2B Publicly Held
WEB: www.oceaneering.com
SIC: 1389 Oil field services
PA: Oceaneering International Inc
11911 Fm 529 Rd
Houston TX 77041
713 329-4500

(G-13304)
PALL CORPORATION
17489 Village Green Dr (77040-1004)
PHONE...................................713 896-9995
Ali Arshad, Principal
Mike Quattrini, Regional Mgr
EMP: 750
SALES (corp-wide): 17.9B Publicly Held
WEB: www.pall.com
SIC: 3842 Surgical appliances & supplies
HQ: Pall Corporation
25 Harbor Park Dr
Port Washington NY 11050
516 484-5400

(G-13305)
SUN MACHINE LTD
Also Called: Sun Manufacturing Company
11220 Charles Rd (77041-2400)
PHONE...................................832 448-1201
Richard A Billeck, President
Becky Schumann, Purchasing
Kent Wiechart, Engineer
Kristin Percle, Manager
EMP: 43
SQ FT: 9,000
SALES (est): 10MM Privately Held
WEB: www.sun-mfg.com
SIC: 3599 Machine shop, jobbing & repair

(G-13306)
W-INDUSTRIES OF LOUISIANA (PA)
Also Called: Control Concepts and Tech
11500 Charles Rd (77041-2406)
P.O. Box 820, Maurice LA (70555-0820)
PHONE...................................713 466-9463
Donnie Smith, CEO
R Lynn, President
John Campbell, Exec VP
Brad Bailey, Vice Pres
Michael Bain, Vice Pres

EMP: 108
SQ FT: 3,600
SALES (est): 23.7MM Privately Held
WEB: www.w-industries.com
SIC: 3823 Controllers for process variables, all types

Jewett
Leon County

(G-13307)
MESSER LLC
Also Called: Boc Gases
7149 Fm 39 N (75846)
P.O. Box 159 (75846-0159)
PHONE...................................903 626-4877
Ray Commander, Branch Mgr
EMP: 20
SALES (corp-wide): 1.2B Privately Held
WEB: www.praxair.com
SIC: 5084 2813 Welding machinery & equipment; industrial gases
HQ: Messer Llc
200 Somerset Corp Blvd # 7000
Bridgewater NJ 08807
908 464-8100

(G-13308)
NUCOR CORPORATION
Nucor Steel Cafeteria
8812 Hwy 79 W (75846)
P.O. Box 126 (75846-0126)
PHONE...................................903 626-4461
EMP: 400
SALES (corp-wide): 22.5B Publicly Held
WEB: www.nucor.com
SIC: 3312 Blast furnaces & steel mills
PA: Nucor Corporation
1915 Rexford Rd Ste 400
Charlotte NC 28211
704 366-7000

(G-13309)
TEXAS WESTMORELAND COAL CO
4336 Farm Rd 39 (75846)
P.O. Box 915 (75846-0915)
PHONE...................................903 626-5485
Robert P King, CEO
J Denny Kincsley, President
Russell H Werner, Treasurer
Kenneth J Uva, Director
Jennifer S Grafton, Admin Sec
▲ EMP: 54
SALES (est): 31.2MM
SALES (corp-wide): 1.2B Privately Held
WEB: www.westmoreland.com
SIC: 1241 Coal mining services
HQ: Old Westmoreland Mining Llc
490 N 31st St Ste 308
Billings MT
719 442-2600

Joaquin
Shelby County

(G-13310)
G & G LOGGING LLC
209 County Road 3274 (75954-5009)
PHONE...................................936 269-9086
Jason Griffin, President
Jerry Griffin, Vice Pres
EMP: 50
SALES (est): 518.6K Privately Held
SIC: 2411 7389 Logging camps & contractors;

(G-13311)
HLH TIMBER COMPANY LLC
380 County Road 3790 (75954-3860)
PHONE...................................936 269-4199
Heith L Harper, Mng Member
Heith Harper, Mng Member
EMP: 24
SALES (est): 3MM Privately Held
SIC: 2411 Logging

Johnson City
Blanco County

(G-13312)
HARVEST HOUSE FARMS
506 N Nugent Ave (78636)
P.O. Box 1870 (78636-1870)
PHONE...................................830 868-7253
Kip Thompson, Owner
EMP: 14
SALES (est): 1.2MM Privately Held
SIC: 2011 Meat packing plants

(G-13313)
TEXAS HILLS VINEYARD INC
878 Ranch Rd 2766 (78636)
P.O. Box 1480 (78636-1480)
PHONE...................................830 868-2321
Gary L Gilstrap, President
Logan Lombard, Principal
Cathy Gilstrap, Vice Pres
EMP: 13
SALES (est): 652.9K Privately Held
WEB: www.texashillsvineyard.com
SIC: 2084 Wines

Jonestown
Travis County

(G-13314)
5 STAR FABRICATIONS INC
18794 Fm 1431 (78645-9666)
PHONE...................................512 267-0470
Gary Fiveash, President
Melina Fiveash, Admin Sec
EMP: 15
SQ FT: 8,000
SALES (est): 2MM Privately Held
WEB: www.5starfabrications.com
SIC: 3441 Fabricated structural metal

(G-13315)
IONDESIGN INC
18700 White Rim Trl (78645-2944)
PHONE...................................512 260-5778
Darren Larson, President
Rick Prekup, Vice Pres
Hector Arredondo, Design Engr
Richard Prekup, VP Bus Dvlpt
Jennifer Larson, Treasurer
EMP: 15
SALES (est): 4MM Privately Held
WEB: www.iondsn.com
SIC: 3672 8711 Circuit boards, television & radio printed; electrical or electronic engineering

Joshua
Johnson County

(G-13316)
AMERICAN CARPORTS INC
457 N Brdwy St (76058)
PHONE...................................866 730-9865
Milton Castillo, President
EMP: 20
SALES (corp-wide): 3.3MM Privately Held
WEB: www.americancarportsinc.com
SIC: 3448 Garages, portable: prefabricated metal
PA: American Carports, Inc.
1415 Clay St
Colusa CA 95932
866 730-9865

(G-13317)
AMERICAN STEEL CARPORTS INC (PA)
457 N Broadway St (76058-3413)
P.O. Box 38 (76058-0038)
PHONE...................................866 471-8761
Venancio Torres, President
Primo Castillo, Vice Pres
Melton Castillo, Treasurer
Joseph Brown, Sales Staff
Vivian Ramos, Marketing Mgr
EMP: 45

SALES (est): 16.5MM **Privately Held**
WEB: www.americansteelinc.com
SIC: 3448 Carports: prefabricated metal

(G-13318)
ATLAS MACHINE AND WLDG SVC INC
860 S Broadway St (76058-3153)
PHONE................................817 558-7778
Wylie J Jones, *President*
Jeana Jones, *Vice Pres*
Alan Knight, *Sales Staff*
EMP: 32
SQ FT: 25,000
SALES (est): 4.8MM **Privately Held**
WEB: www.atlasmachineandwelding.com
SIC: 3599 Machine shop, jobbing & repair

(G-13319)
BRADY MACHINE INC
6125 Sky Rd (76058-4048)
PHONE................................817 309-3302
Edward J Brady, *President*
Barbara Brady, *Admin Sec*
EMP: 9 **EST:** 1995
SALES (est): 1.1MM **Privately Held**
SIC: 3599 Machine shop, jobbing & repair

(G-13320)
FIXTURE EXCHANGE CORPORATION
1720 Summit Dr (76058-5222)
PHONE................................817 429-2496
Sthephen Sturman, *President*
Daniel Sturman, *Corp Secy*
David Sturman, *Vice Pres*
Stephen Sturman, *Vice Pres*
Rick Jobe, *Sales Executive*
EMP: 30 **EST:** 1961
SALES (est): 6.2MM **Privately Held**
WEB: www.fixturex.com
SIC: 2541 2434 Table or counter tops, plastic laminated; vanities, bathroom: wood

(G-13321)
M & T NATURAL STONE
5605 Thousand Oaks Dr (76058-6005)
PHONE................................817 556-2107
EMP: 14
SALES (est): 830K **Privately Held**
SIC: 1429 Crushed/Broken Stone

(G-13322)
MALLORYS WESTERN & LEATHER SUP
Also Called: Sheynne Bag & Accessories
328 N Broadway St Ste B (76058-3089)
P.O. Box 35 (76058-0035)
PHONE................................817 558-0804
Allan Jay Mallory, *Ch of Bd*
Arnold L Mallory, *President*
Helen L Mallory, *Corp Secy*
Ethan Mallory, *Executive*
EMP: 15
SQ FT: 10,500
SALES (est): 1.3MM **Privately Held**
WEB: www.malloryprint.com
SIC: 2387 3559 5137 5136 Apparel belts; boot making & repairing machinery; purses; gloves, women's & children's; gloves, men's & boys'

(G-13323)
MB RANCH KING BLINDS LLC
4629 County Road 805 (76058-5622)
PHONE................................817 558-7320
Mark Bogart, *President*
EMP: 28
SALES (est): 4MM **Privately Held**
WEB: www.ranchkingblinds.com
SIC: 3949 Hunting equipment

(G-13324)
R-TEX SERVICES LLC
8124 Fm 1902 (76058-5838)
P.O. Box 1055 (76058-1055)
PHONE................................817 774-3333
Kevin Tuman, *Superintendent*
Justin McIntosh, *Vice Pres*
Dallas Williams, *Project Mgr*
Cody Williams, *CFO*
Jerry Richardson,
EMP: 65

SALES (est): 23.2MM **Privately Held**
WEB: www.rtexservices.com
SIC: 1531 1731 3315 1794 Operative builders; electrical work; wire & fabricated wire products; excavation work; servicing oil & gas wells

(G-13325)
SB SOUTHERN WELDING LLC
3941 Windmill Rd (76058-5435)
P.O. Box 958, Waxahachie (75168-0958)
PHONE................................469 517-0410
Gregory Shane Boston, *Owner*
Dwayne Dean, *Opers Mgr*
EMP: 40
SALES (est): 6.7MM **Privately Held**
WEB: www.trailersbysouthern.com
SIC: 7692 Automotive welding

(G-13326)
SC MANUFACTURING TEXAS LLC
6401 County Road 912 (76058-4407)
PHONE................................817 556-3689
Chris Miller, *Mng Member*
EMP: 28 **EST:** 2014
SQ FT: 25,000
SALES (est): 4MM **Privately Held**
WEB: www.scm-texas.com
SIC: 3545 Cutting tools for machine tools

(G-13327)
TRAILERS BY SOUTHERN LLC
3941 Windmill Rd (76058-5435)
PHONE................................469 517-0410
Tyler Boston, *Mng Member*
Shane Boston, *Mng Member*
Dwayne Dean, *Mng Member*
Alexa Fincher, *Mng Member*
Jake Hinds, *Mng Member*
EMP: 40
SALES (est): 2.7MM **Privately Held**
WEB: www.trailersbysouthern.com
SIC: 3715 3441 Truck trailers; fabricated structural metal

(G-13328)
UMC ENERGY SOLUTIONS INC (PA)
461 N Broadway St (76058-3413)
P.O. Box 1610 (76058-1610)
PHONE................................432 524-2456
Thomas Gentry, *President*
Greg Hodder, *CFO*
▲ **EMP:** 42
SALES (est): 18.8MM **Privately Held**
WEB: www.umcenergy.com
SIC: 3823 Computer interface equipment for industrial process control

---

Jourdanton
Atascosa County

(G-13329)
CAPITAL WELL SERVICE LLC
1437 E St (78026-1625)
P.O. Box 91137, San Antonio (78209-9096)
PHONE................................830 767-2036
EMP: 185
SQ FT: 2,000
SALES (est): 22.7MM **Privately Held**
SIC: 1381 Oil/Gas Well Drilling

(G-13330)
ENERGES OILFIELD SOLUTIONS LLC
1438 E St (78026-1624)
PHONE................................830 769-1484
Ryan Daly, *Opers Mgr*
Jared Alexander, *Opers Staff*
Jeremy Ginn, *Manager*
EMP: 11
SALES (corp-wide): 41MM **Privately Held**
WEB: www.enercorpsandsolutions.com
SIC: 1389 Oil field services
HQ: Enercorp Engineered Solutions, Llc
　　25700 I 45 N Ste 110
　　The Woodlands TX 77386
　　832 791-1276

(G-13331)
GREEN & HANSEN LLC
Also Called: Legacy Energy Services
3276 County Road 303 (78026-4928)
PHONE................................210 289-2482
Peter Green, *Mng Member*
EMP: 65
SALES (est): 2.1MM **Privately Held**
WEB: www.legacyenerserv.com
SIC: 1389 1799 1794 Oil field services; construction site cleanup; excavation & grading, building construction

(G-13332)
HUSS SERVICES INC
Also Called: Crossroads Tanks
3550 County Road 303 (78026-4961)
PHONE................................817 819-4138
Amanda Wrigley, *Vice President*
Ellaine Huss, *President*
John Huss, *Principal*
EMP: 12 **EST:** 2010
SALES (est): 10MM **Privately Held**
WEB: www.crossroadstanks.com
SIC: 2899 Fuel tank or engine cleaning chemicals

(G-13333)
JUGGERNAUT MACHINERY LLC
7475 W Fm 140 (78026-4930)
PHONE................................210 399-3374
David Stainthorpe, *President*
EMP: 17 **EST:** 2014
SALES (est): 22MM **Privately Held**
SIC: 3599 Machine & other job shop work

(G-13334)
ST READY MIX LLC
2585 S State Highway 16 (78026-5468)
PHONE................................830 480-0933
Shelton Posey,
EMP: 20
SALES (est): 100.4K
SALES (corp-wide): 115.5K **Privately Held**
SIC: 3273 Ready-mixed concrete
PA: South Texas Ready Mix, Llc
　　2585 S State Highway 16
　　Jourdanton TX 78026
　　830 569-2414

(G-13335)
TRIPLE S READY MIX LLC
2585 S State Highway 16 (78026-5468)
PHONE................................830 769-2629
EMP: 30
SQ FT: 5,000
SALES (est): 1.2MM **Privately Held**
SIC: 3273 Ready-mixed concrete

(G-13336)
WILEY LEASE CO LTD
Also Called: Wiley Lease Service
903 W State Highway 97 (78026-4216)
P.O. Box 610 (78026-0610)
PHONE................................830 277-0112
Kathryn Wiley, *Partner*
Belo Wiley, *Partner*
William Wiley, *Partner*
EMP: 12 **EST:** 1967
SALES (est): 3.6MM **Privately Held**
SIC: 1389 Oil field services

Junction
Kimble County

(G-13337)
CEDAR FIBER COMPANY INC
Fm 2169 (76849)
P.O. Box 127 (76849-0127)
PHONE................................325 446-2571
William Mc Millan, *President*
Tommy Holmes, *Owner*
Bill McMillan, *Manager*
EMP: 30
SALES (corp-wide): 5.9MM **Privately Held**
WEB: www.cedarfiber.com
SIC: 2861 2899 Wood distillation products; drilling mud
PA: Cedar Fiber Company Inc
　　2900 Weslayan St Ste 410
　　Houston TX 77027
　　713 621-5666

(G-13338)
CEDAR FIBER COMPANY INC
644 Industrial Dr (76849)
P.O. Box 56306, Houston (77256-6306)
PHONE................................325 446-2571
Bill McMillan, *Branch Mgr*
Craig Brooks, *Manager*
EMP: 56
SALES (corp-wide): 5.9MM **Privately Held**
WEB: www.cedarfiber.com
SIC: 2493 Reconstituted wood products
PA: Cedar Fiber Company Inc
　　2900 Weslayan St Ste 410
　　Houston TX 77027
　　713 621-5666

(G-13339)
GRAYDEN CEDARWORKS INC
8782 Ranch Rd 2169 Jct (76849)
P.O. Box 325 (76849-0325)
PHONE................................325 446-3366
Claude S Bruell, *President*
▲ **EMP:** 30
SALES (est): 4MM **Privately Held**
WEB: www.graydencedarworks.com
SIC: 2899 5169 Essential oils; essential oils

(G-13340)
VITALPURE LABS LLC
100 Industrial Dr (76849-6450)
PHONE................................573 469-1302
Owen Kenney, *Principal*
David Dennis, *Principal*
Kent Hoggan, *Principal*
EMP: 25
SALES (est): 1.1MM **Privately Held**
SIC: 2899 Chemical preparations

Justin
Denton County

(G-13341)
DNB STAINLESS CONCEPTS LLC
9535 Swafford Rd Ste 100 (76247-2213)
P.O. Box 612, Ponder (76259-0612)
PHONE................................940 479-0079
Becky Glasscock, *CFO*
David Glasscock,
EMP: 15
SQ FT: 25,000
SALES (est): 1.4MM **Privately Held**
SIC: 3469 Kitchen fixtures & equipment: metal, except cast aluminum

(G-13342)
E X P FABRICATION LLC
9435 Swafford Rd (76247-2205)
PHONE................................940 453-3382
Les Porter, *President*
John Hart, *Vice Pres*
Trey Jenkins, *Treasurer*
EMP: 23
SALES (est): 3.5MM **Privately Held**
WEB: www.expfabrication.com
SIC: 7692 Welding repair

(G-13343)
ENTERPRISE SEC SLTONS TXAS INC
Also Called: Esst
316 E 5th St (76247-4630)
P.O. Box 339 (76247-0339)
PHONE................................940 320-3778
David Jones, *CEO*
David R Jones, *CEO*
Jeffrey Goodrich, *Vice Pres*
Michael Savoie, *Vice Pres*
Amber Prince, *Finance*
EMP: 22
SQ FT: 1,300
SALES (est): 1.5MM **Privately Held**
WEB: www.esstexas.com
SIC: 7382 1731 3699 Burglar alarm maintenance & monitoring; safety & security specialization; security control equipment & systems

---

▲ = Import ▼=Export
◆ =Import/Export

(G-13344)
IRWIN STEEL LLC
15740 Highway 114 (76247-8511)
PHONE..............................817 636-2508
James C Irwin, *President*
Bryan Irwin, *Vice Pres*
Lee Irwin, *Vice Pres*
EMP: 120
SALES (est): 26.7MM **Privately Held**
WEB: www.irwinsteel.net
SIC: 3441 Fabricated structural metal

(G-13345)
JOSEPH MCSWEENY ENTPS LLC
Also Called: Texas Ice Cream
14920 Fm 156 S (76247-7836)
P.O. Box 92211, Southlake (76092-0102)
PHONE..............................214 334-8181
Joseph McSweeny, *CEO*
EMP: 9
SALES (est): 820.5K **Privately Held**
WEB: www.texasicecream.com
SIC: 2024 Ice cream & frozen desserts

Karnes City
Karnes County

(G-13346)
PERALES GROUP VENTURES INC (PA)
Also Called: PMI Oil Tools
506 W 3rd St (78118-3506)
P.O. Box 40 (78118-0040)
PHONE..............................830 780-3336
Simon Perales, *President*
Kathryn Perales, *General Counsel*
Remigio Perales, *Admin Sec*
EMP: 10
SQ FT: 30,000
SALES (est): 500K **Privately Held**
SIC: 3533 Drilling tools for gas, oil or water wells

Katy
Fort Bend County

(G-13347)
ACE ENERGY SOLUTIONS INC
24275 Katy Fwy Ste 325 (77494-7266)
PHONE..............................281 394-9989
Cody Schluens, *CEO*
Quinton Rogers, *Exec VP*
Dennis Brown, *Vice Pres*
Paul Oliphant, *CFO*
Cameron Schluens, *CFO*
EMP: 15
SQ FT: 6,000
SALES (est): 4.4MM **Privately Held**
WEB: www.aceenergysolutions.com
SIC: 1389 Oil field services

(G-13348)
AD DISPLAY SIGN SYSTEMS INC
27255 Katy Fwy (77494-1073)
P.O. Box 888 (77492-0888)
PHONE..............................281 392-8325
Greg Zwick, *CEO*
Chris Brast, *Vice Pres*
Paul Coats, *Vice Pres*
Eric Zwick, *Project Mgr*
Hernandez Rene, *Foreman/Supr*
EMP: 35
SQ FT: 16,000
SALES (est): 4.9MM **Privately Held**
WEB: www.addisplaysigns.com
SIC: 3993 7336 Electric signs; graphic arts & related design

(G-13349)
ALTIUM PACKAGING
27807 Highway Blvd (77494-1030)
PHONE..............................281 391-4244
Gaco Rangel, *Manager*
EMP: 10
SALES (corp-wide): 12.5B **Publicly Held**
WEB: www.altiumpkg.com
SIC: 3089 Plastic containers, except foam

HQ: Altium Packaging Llc
2500 Windy Ridge Pkwy Se # 1400
Atlanta GA 30339
678 742-4600

(G-13350)
ARGOS USA LLC
28601 Highway Blvd (77494-1079)
PHONE..............................281 391-4554
EMP: 14 **Privately Held**
WEB: www.argos-us.com
SIC: 3273 Ready-mixed concrete
HQ: Argos Usa Llc
3015 Windward Plz Ste 300
Alpharetta GA 30005
678 368-4300

(G-13351)
BAKER STEEL COMPANY INC (PA)
7600 Cherokee St (77494-1050)
P.O. Box 7925, Houston (77270-7925)
PHONE..............................713 479-9399
Darrin R Baker, *President*
Chris Baker, *Vice Pres*
Clifton D Baker, *Vice Pres*
David R Baker, *Vice Pres*
Mark Baker, *Vice Pres*
EMP: 26 **EST:** 1940
SQ FT: 14,000
SALES (est): 7.2MM **Privately Held**
WEB: www.bakersteel.com
SIC: 3441 Building components, structural steel

(G-13352)
BLACK DIAMOND ENERGY INC (PA)
26022 Sebey Ridge Ln (77494-2624)
PHONE..............................307 684-2910
Eric Koval, *President*
Joseph Breznai, *Vice Pres*
EMP: 25 **EST:** 2000
SALES (est): 4MM **Privately Held**
WEB: www.blackdiamondenergy.com
SIC: 1381 Drilling oil & gas wells

(G-13353)
BROOKSIDE EQUIPMENT SALES INC
Also Called: John Deere Authorized Dealer
28715 Katy Brookshire Rd (77494-8200)
PHONE..............................281 391-2165
Antonio Velasquez, *Manager*
EMP: 10
SALES (corp-wide): 22.2MM **Privately Held**
WEB: www.brooksideusa.com
SIC: 3523 5082 Farm machinery & equipment; construction & mining machinery
PA: Brookside Equipment Sales Inc
3715 S Sam Houston Pkwy E
Houston TX 77047
713 943-7100

(G-13354)
CADRE MATERIAL PRODUCTS LLC
24275 Katy Fwy Ste 100 (77494-7253)
PHONE..............................301 682-0600
Bryan Shinn, *CEO*
Donald Merril, *CFO*
Michael Thompson, *Treasurer*
Christine Marshall, *Admin Sec*
Sean Klein, *Asst Sec*
EMP: 94
SALES (est): 4MM **Privately Held**
WEB: www.ussilica.com
SIC: 2819 Industrial inorganic chemicals

(G-13355)
CAMERON INTERNATIONAL CORP
Also Called: Drilling & Production Systems
29501 Katy Fwy (77494-7801)
PHONE..............................281 391-4600
Glenda Cope, *Buyer*
Mike Callahan, *Branch Mgr*
EMP: 49 **Publicly Held**
WEB: www.products.slb.com
SIC: 1389 Oil field services
HQ: Cameron International Corporation
4646 W Sam Houston Pkwy N
Houston TX 77041

(G-13356)
CAMERON INTERNATIONAL CORP
Cameron Elastomer Technology
29501 Katy Fwy (77494-7801)
PHONE..............................281 391-4600
Mike Callahan, *General Mgr*
EMP: 60 **Publicly Held**
WEB: www.products.slb.com
SIC: 8731 2821 Commercial physical research; plastics materials & resins
HQ: Cameron International Corporation
4646 W Sam Houston Pkwy N
Houston TX 77041

(G-13357)
CEMEX CONSTRUCTION MTLS S LLC
Also Called: Katy Rm
27734 Katy Brookshire Rd (77494-1033)
PHONE..............................281 391-2655
Ron Bingham, *Manager*
EMP: 10 **Privately Held**
WEB: www.cemexusa.com
SIC: 3273 Ready-mixed concrete
HQ: Cemex Construction Materials South, Llc
2088 E 20th St
Yuma AZ 85365
928 343-4100

(G-13358)
CONSTNTIN PRECISION INSTRS INC
7633 Cherokee St (77494-1050)
P.O. Box 1260 (77492-1260)
PHONE..............................713 461-9090
Carl Moore, *Owner*
Brenda Moore, *Corp Secy*
John Bailey, *Foreman/Supr*
Ron Cox, *Purchasing*
Cole Young, *Sales Staff*
▲ **EMP:** 37
SQ FT: 27,000
SALES (est): 8MM **Privately Held**
WEB: www.cpiprecision.com
SIC: 3599 Machine shop, jobbing & repair

(G-13359)
DEEPWATER SUBSEA LLC
410 W Grand Pkwy S # 100 (77494-8361)
PHONE..............................832 356-6781
Michael Fry, *CEO*
Steven Knotts, *Opers Staff*
Lesley Dinu,
EMP: 26
SALES (est): 1MM **Privately Held**
WEB: www.deepwatersubsea.com
SIC: 1389 8742 Oil consultants; training & development consultant

(G-13360)
DS SERVICES OF AMERICA INC
Also Called: Sparkletts
27815 Highway Blvd (77494-1030)
PHONE..............................281 391-3770
Ron Jones, *Manager*
Eileen Dunn,
EMP: 20
SALES (corp-wide): 41.7MM **Privately Held**
WEB: www.water.com
SIC: 2086 5963 Pasteurized & mineral waters, bottled & canned; bottled water delivery
HQ: Ds Services Of America, Inc.
2300 Windy Ridge Pkwy Se
Atlanta GA 30339
770 933-1400

(G-13361)
EXPRESS INC
5000 Katy Mills Cir # 736 (77494-4410)
PHONE..............................281 712-7187
Tuan Dang, *Principal*
EMP: 2535 **Publicly Held**
WEB: www.express.com
SIC: 2741 Miscellaneous publishing
PA: Express, Inc.
1 Express Dr
Columbus OH 43230

(G-13362)
GGC USS HOLDINGS LLC
24275 Katy Fwy Ste 100 (77494-7253)
PHONE..............................800 345-6170
EMP: 701
SALES (est): 10MM **Privately Held**
SIC: 1446 Silica mining; silica sand mining

(G-13363)
HEINES CUSTOM DRAPERIES INC
27223 Highway Blvd (77494-1040)
PHONE..............................281 391-3103
Tony Rochelcau, *Ch of Bd*
Carole Rochelcau, *President*
EMP: 58
SQ FT: 16,000
SALES (est): 5MM **Privately Held**
WEB: www.heinescustomdraperies.com
SIC: 2391 Draperies, plastic & textile: from purchased materials

(G-13364)
IGLOO PRODUCTS CORP
30603 Katy Brookshire Rd (77494-8206)
PHONE..............................713 461-5955
Reggie Yannuzzi, *Branch Mgr*
Elizabeth Landers, *Manager*
EMP: 500 **Privately Held**
WEB: www.igloocoolers.com
SIC: 3086 Plastics foam products
HQ: Igloo Products Corp.
777 Igloo Rd
Katy TX 77494
281 394-6800

(G-13365)
IGLOO PRODUCTS CORP (HQ)
777 Igloo Rd (77494-2972)
PHONE..............................281 394-6800
David Allen, *President*
Josh Militello, *Senior VP*
Brad Connor, *Vice Pres*
Todd Ensor, *Vice Pres*
Angela A Sizemore, *Vice Pres*
◆ **EMP:** 1000
SQ FT: 1,800,000
SALES (est): 512.4MM **Privately Held**
WEB: www.igloocoolers.com
SIC: 3086 Ice chests or coolers (portable), foamed plastic

(G-13366)
JAGUAR EXPLORATION INC
440 Cobia Dr Ste 1204 (77494-7224)
PHONE..............................281 920-2668
Julio M Jimeno, *CEO*
▲ **EMP:** 13
SALES (est): 2.5MM **Privately Held**
WEB: www.jaguarexp.com
SIC: 1311 Oil & gas exploration services

(G-13367)
KATY PRINTERS INC
5807 Highway Blvd (77494-1206)
P.O. Box 808 (77492-0808)
PHONE..............................281 391-7072
Mark Dittert, *President*
Matthew Dittert, *Corp Secy*
Kathryn Dittert, *Vice Pres*
EMP: 9
SQ FT: 3,000
SALES (est): 870K **Privately Held**
WEB: www.printingshopkatytx.com
SIC: 5112 2759 Office supplies; commercial printing

(G-13368)
KATY STEEL CO INCORPORATED (PA)
28011 Highway Blvd 90 (77494-1019)
P.O. Box 735 (77492-0735)
PHONE..............................281 391-7047
Denver W Rupard, *CEO*
Scott Rupard, *President*
Janet Adamick, *Bookkeeper*
Robert Sanchez, *Representative*
EMP: 44
SQ FT: 2,808
SALES (est): 8.8MM **Privately Held**
WEB: www.katysteel.com
SIC: 3449 3441 Miscellaneous metalwork; fabricated structural metal

(G-13369)
KIRK CONSTRUCTION INC
26823 Willow Ln (77494-5421)
PHONE...................................281 392-4063
Joe G Kirk, *President*
Joe Kirk, *Principal*
EMP: 15
SQ FT: 2,000
SALES (est): 2.4MM **Privately Held**
WEB: www.kirkconstruction.com
SIC: 3531 Concrete plants

(G-13370)
L B PIPE & COUPLING PDTS LLC
549 Stonegate Dr (77494-5652)
P.O. Box 1364, Magnolia (77353-1364)
PHONE...................................832 934-1850
Chad Jordan, *CEO*
James Legg, *General Mgr*
Anthony Greco, *Sales Staff*
EMP: 35
SALES (est): 6.7MM **Privately Held**
WEB: www.lbpipeandcouplingproducts.com
SIC: 3498 Couplings, pipe: fabricated from purchased pipe

(G-13371)
MEDLINE INDUSTRIES INC
501 Commerce Pkwy (77494-4128)
PHONE...................................281 574-6200
Lara Simmons, *Principal*
Jim Fabac, *Sales Staff*
Jim Long, *Sales Staff*
EMP: 148
SALES (corp-wide): 11.3B **Privately Held**
WEB: www.medline.com
SIC: 3842 3841 2326 2392 Surgical appliances & supplies; surgical & medical instruments; men's & boys' work clothing; household furnishings; broadwoven fabric mills, cotton; medical & hospital equipment
PA: Medline Industries, Inc.
3 Lakes Dr
Northfield IL 60093
847 949-5500

(G-13372)
MOORE CONTROL SYSTEMS INC
1435 Katy Flewellen Rd (77494-6350)
P.O. Box 677 (77492-0677)
PHONE...................................281 392-7747
Jae K Moore, *President*
Blaine Joseph, *General Mgr*
Rolando Garcia, *Superintendent*
Michael Garcia, *Project Mgr*
Ramie Rushing, *Project Mgr*
EMP: 80
SQ FT: 10,000
SALES (est): 23.8MM **Privately Held**
WEB: www.moore-control.com
SIC: 8711 3625 3823 Electrical or electronic engineering; designing: ship, boat, machine & product; relays & industrial controls; industrial instrmnts msrmnt display/control process variable

(G-13373)
NUTREX AMERICA INC
24044 Cnco Vlg Ctr Blvd S (77494-8432)
PHONE...................................714 943-9119
Danny Kim, *Exec Dir*
EMP: 30
SALES (est): 100K **Privately Held**
SIC: 2834 Vitamin, nutrient & hematinic preparations for human use

(G-13374)
OIL & GAS CONSULTANTS INTL INC
Also Called: Petroskills
25403 Kingsland Blvd (77494-2001)
PHONE...................................832 426-1200
J Ford Brett, *CEO*
EMP: 16

SALES (corp-wide): 6.2MM **Privately Held**
WEB: www.fordbrett.com
SIC: 7371 7375 8299 1389 Computer software development; information retrieval services; educational service, non-degree granting: continuing educ.; detection & analysis service, gas; oil & gas exploration services
PA: Oil & Gas Consultants International, Inc.
2930 S Yale Ave
Tulsa OK 74114
918 828-2500

(G-13375)
ONYX VENTURE GROUP LLC
Also Called: Quizno's Subs
2719 Falcon Knoll Ln (77494-2421)
PHONE...................................281 395-4791
Eric B Webb, *President*
Laurice Webb, *Vice Pres*
EMP: 15
SQ FT: 1,625
SALES (est): 339.7K **Privately Held**
WEB: www.quiznos.com
SIC: 5812 3572 5112 7376 Sandwiches & submarines shop; computer storage devices; stationery & office supplies; computer facilities management; computer related maintenance services

(G-13376)
PAVESTONE LLC
830 Brookline (77494-1702)
PHONE...................................281 769-5098
Fred Byers, *General Mgr*
Fred Byers, *General Mgr*
Brad Hayes, *Plant Mgr*
Craig Mattson, *Plant Mgr*
Jeff Ressel, *Plant Mgr*
EMP: 50 **Privately Held**
WEB: www.pavestone.com
SIC: 3272 5032 3531 Concrete products; paving materials; construction machinery
HQ: Pavestone, Llc
5 Concourse Pkwy Ste 1900
Atlanta GA 30328
404 926-3167

(G-13377)
ROBERT LESHEA INC
24319 Bay Hill Blvd (77494-1836)
PHONE...................................803 407-9284
Steve Torchia, *CEO*
EMP: 16
SALES (est): 1.4MM **Privately Held**
SIC: 3993 Signs & advertising specialties

(G-13378)
S&M INTERNATIONAL CO INC
22422 Crescent Cove Ct (77494-2221)
PHONE...................................281 749-8289
G Liu, *President*
H Liu, *Senior VP*
K Hua, *CFO*
◆ EMP: 28
SQ FT: 5,900
SALES (est): 8MM **Privately Held**
SIC: 8741 5172 5169 3826 Management services; petroleum products; chemicals & allied products; analytical instruments

(G-13379)
SAME DAY DUMPSTER RENTAL LLC
6725 S Fry Rd Ste 700-310 (77494-8102)
PHONE...................................866 223-6227
Edin Hasanovic, *Mng Member*
EMP: 10
SALES (est): 375.5K **Privately Held**
SIC: 3443 Dumpsters, garbage

(G-13380)
TREVWAY INC
6725 S Fry Rd Ste 700538 (77494-8102)
PHONE...................................832 687-6269
Fabian Trevino, *Owner*
EMP: 16
SALES (corp-wide): 3MM **Privately Held**
WEB: www.trevinctx.com
SIC: 3271 1799 Blocks, concrete: landscape or retaining wall; shoring & underpinning work

PA: Trevway, Inc.
5705 4th St
Katy TX 77493
855 487-3892

(G-13381)
U S SILICA COMPANY (HQ)
24275 Katy Fwy Ste 100 (77494-7253)
PHONE...................................301 682-0600
Bryan Shinn, *President*
Amber Hamilton, *Division Mgr*
John Blanchard, *Vice Pres*
Bradford Casper, *Vice Pres*
Bradford B Casper, *Vice Pres*
◆ EMP: 25
SALES (est): 442.5MM
SALES (corp-wide): 1.4B **Publicly Held**
WEB: www.ussilica.com
SIC: 1446 1455 1459 Silica sand mining; kaolin mining; aplite mining
PA: U.S. Silica Holdings, Inc.
24275 Katy Fwy Ste 600
Katy TX 77494
281 258-2170

(G-13382)
US SILICA HOLDINGS INC (PA)
Also Called: US SILICA
24275 Katy Fwy Ste 600 (77494-7271)
PHONE...................................281 258-2170
Charles Shaver, *Ch of Bd*
Bryan A Shinn, *President*
Bradford B Casper, *President*
Don Weinheimer, *President*
Michael L Winkler, *COO*
EMP: 26 EST: 1902
SALES (est): 1.4B **Publicly Held**
WEB: www.ussilica.com
SIC: 1446 Silica mining; silica sand mining

(G-13383)
USS HOLDINGS INC
24275 Katy Fwy Ste 100 (77494-7253)
PHONE...................................301 682-0600
Bryan Shinn, *CEO*
Michael Thompson, *Treasurer*
Christine Marshall, *Admin Sec*
Sean Klein, *Asst Sec*
◆ EMP: 10
SALES (est): 581K
SALES (corp-wide): 1.4B **Publicly Held**
WEB: www.ussilica.com
SIC: 2819 Industrial inorganic chemicals
HQ: Hourglass Holdings, Llc
8490 Progress Dr Ste 300
Frederick MD 21701

(G-13384)
VERIOVOX CORPORATION
608 Pederson Rd (77494-1704)
PHONE...................................713 409-7216
Kent E Brownell, *President*
Don Brownell, *Vice Pres*
Christina Corona, *Vice Pres*
Jessie Flores Jr, *Vice Pres*
EMP: 20
SQ FT: 17,500
SALES (est): 2.8MM **Privately Held**
SIC: 3441 Fabricated structural metal

(G-13385)
YORK GROUP INC
24406 Bay Hill Blvd (77494-6175)
PHONE...................................412 995-1600
Eldon Nuss, *Branch Mgr*
EMP: 10
SALES (corp-wide): 1.5B **Publicly Held**
WEB: www.matthewscremation.com
SIC: 3995 Burial caskets
HQ: The York Group Inc
2 N Shore Ctr
Pittsburgh PA 15212
412 995-1600

Katy
Harris County

(G-13386)
3-D HONING INC
1103 Glenwood Dr (77493-2130)
P.O. Box 1050 (77492-1050)
PHONE...................................281 391-8989
George Duchesne, *President*
Shirley Duchesne, *President*

Shawn Duchesne, *Treasurer*
EMP: 9
SQ FT: 7,200
SALES (est): 996.3K **Privately Held**
WEB: www.honinghouston.com
SIC: 7699 3471 Aircraft & heavy equipment repair services; cleaning, polishing & finishing

(G-13387)
3CORE SOFTWARE CORPORATION (PA)
1840 Snake River Rd Ste E (77449-7755)
PHONE...................................281 440-3000
Tony Fera, *President*
Frank Fang, *Software Dev*
EMP: 14
SQ FT: 4,100
SALES (est): 1.7MM **Privately Held**
WEB: www.3coresoftware.com
SIC: 7372 Prepackaged software

(G-13388)
ADVANCED RUPTURE DISK TECH INC
Also Called: Advanced Rpture Disk Advnced R
1010 Avenue A (77493-2462)
P.O. Box 670248, Houston (77267-0248)
PHONE...................................281 591-6700
David Denning, *President*
Shannon Birchum, *Vice Pres*
Mark Van Soestberg, *Marketing Staff*
Josh Huff, *Technical Staff*
EMP: 9
SALES (est): 1.5MM **Privately Held**
WEB: www.rupturedisk.com
SIC: 2899 Chemical supplies for foundries

(G-13389)
BAW ATHLETIC WEAR LP
Also Called: Baw Enterprises
5040 Franz Rd (77493-3652)
PHONE...................................281 391-3335
Steve Brammer, *Partner*
Mike Chong, *Partner*
▲ EMP: 14
SALES (est): 2MM **Privately Held**
WEB: www.bawonline.com
SIC: 2329 Men's & boys' sportswear & athletic clothing

(G-13390)
BRAMMERS ATHLETIC WEARHOUSE LP
Also Called: Baw
5017 E 5th St (77493-2115)
PHONE...................................281 391-1441
Nancy Brammer, *Partner*
Steve Brammer, *Partner*
EMP: 13
SQ FT: 3,200
SALES (est): 1.3MM **Privately Held**
WEB: www.brammers.net
SIC: 5699 5611 2396 7389 Uniforms; clothing, sportswear, men's & boys'; screen printing on fabric articles; sewing contractor

(G-13391)
CAMPBELL CONCRETE & MTLS LP
24610 Franz Rd (77493-5800)
PHONE...................................281 391-4700
Boy Gybson, *Manager*
EMP: 14
SQ FT: 13,290
SALES (corp-wide): 20.8B **Privately Held**
WEB: www.michaeljames.com
SIC: 3273 Ready-mixed concrete
HQ: Campbell Concrete & Materials, L.P.
16155 Park Row Ste 120
Houston TX 77084
281 592-5201

(G-13392)
CLEARPATH ENGINEERING INC
20456 Wstfeld Commerce Dr (77449)
PHONE...................................832 856-9040
Fasih Hussain Agha, *President*
Aftab Ahmed, *Director*
Junaid S Khan, *Director*
EMP: 25
SALES (est): 1.2MM **Privately Held**
SIC: 3648 Lighting equipment

(G-13393)
CUSTOM SOLUTIONS GROUP LLC (PA)
1419 Avenue A (77493-1948)
PHONE.....................281 507-9569
Kerry B Kreiling, *President*
Brenda Kreiling, *Vice Pres*
EMP: 12
SALES (est): 400K **Privately Held**
WEB: www.customsolutionsgroup.org
SIC: 3821 Laboratory apparatus & furniture

(G-13394)
DELTA REFRACTORIES INC
21557 Provincial Blvd A (77450-7558)
P.O. Box 6 (77492-0146)
PHONE.....................281 944-9644
▲ **EMP:** 10 **EST:** 1971
SQ FT: 1,700
SALES (est): 3.2MM **Privately Held**
WEB: www.deltarefractories.com
SIC: 3297 Nonclay refractories

(G-13395)
DISCOVERY ACQUISITION SVCS LLC
4141 Katy Hockley Rd (77493-4893)
PHONE.....................281 371-2700
Terry A Gordon, *President*
John Odette, *President*
John Volke, *President*
Jim White, *President*
Jimmy Walker, *Opers Mgr*
EMP: 28
SALES (est): 6.6MM **Privately Held**
WEB: www.discoveryacquisition.com
SIC: 1382 Oil & gas exploration services

(G-13396)
DNV GL NOBLE DENTON USA LLC
1400 Ravello Rd (77449-5164)
PHONE.....................281 396-1000
Richard Barnes, *President*
Charles Gibune, *Engineer*
Steven Slauter, *Treasurer*
Brenda Ashburn, *Controller*
Andy Law, *Consultant*
EMP: 400
SALES (est): 50.2MM
SALES (corp-wide): 2.3B **Privately Held**
WEB: www.dnvgl.com
SIC: 8711 8734 7371 8742 Marine engineering; calibration & certification; computer software development & applications; quality assurance consultant; gas field services
HQ: Dnv Gl Group As
Veritasveien 1
Hovik 1363
675 799-00

(G-13397)
DRONE LABS LLC
Also Called: Drone Detector
2507 Blue Reef Dr (77449-4794)
PHONE.....................214 538-1467
Zain Naboulsi, *President*
EMP: 10
SALES (est): 1MM **Privately Held**
SIC: 3812 1731 Search & detection systems & instruments; electronic detection systems (aeronautical); fire detection & burglar alarm systems specialization

(G-13398)
DYNA DRILL TECHNOLOGIES LLC (DH)
Also Called: Dyna-Drill
23400 Colonial Pkwy (77493-3598)
PHONE.....................281 227-1250
Leif R Syversen, *President*
Chris G Janda, *Vice Pres*
Michael L Papasan, *Vice Pres*
Jeffrey L Tepera, *Vice Pres*
Jaclynn J Gardiner, *Treasurer*
◆ **EMP:** 160 **EST:** 2009
SALES (est): 51.7MM **Publicly Held**
WEB: www.dyna-drill.com
SIC: 3533 3546 Oil & gas drilling rigs & equipment; power-driven handtools
HQ: Schlumberger Limited
5599 San Felipe St Fl 17
Houston TX 77056
713 513-2000

(G-13399)
ECOSTIM INC
Also Called: Eco-Stim Energy Solutions
1773 Westborough Dr 110 (77449-3295)
PHONE.....................281 531-7200
Alexander Nikolatos, *President*
Bobby Chapman, *COO*
EMP: 80 **EST:** 2012
SALES (est): 8.3MM **Publicly Held**
WEB: www.ecostim-es.com
SIC: 1311 Crude petroleum & natural gas
PA: Eco-Stim Energy Solutions, Inc.
1773 Wstbrough Dr Ste 110
Katy TX 77449

(G-13400)
ENVIROCLEANSE LLC
22762 Westheimer Pkwy (77450-8825)
PHONE.....................713 840-0404
Matthew D Anderson, *COO*
Andrew K Chaglasian, *CFO*
C Bobby Waid, *Mng Member*
EMP: 20 **EST:** 2017
SALES (est): 581.8K
SALES (corp-wide): 254.6B **Publicly Held**
WEB: www.eco-enviro.com
SIC: 2842 Sanitation preparations, disinfectants & deodorants
HQ: Charter Brokerage Llc
383 Main Ave Ste 21
Norwalk CT 06851
203 840-7500

(G-13401)
ESCONDIDO RESOURCES II MGT LLC (PA)
2002 W Grand Pkwy N # 205 (77449-1963)
PHONE.....................713 662-0332
William E Deupree, *President*
Chris Crowson, *Vice Pres*
Andy Ellis, *Vice Pres*
Mark E Semmelbeck, *Vice Pres*
Kurt Von Plonski, *Vice Pres*
EMP: 12
SALES (est): 15MM **Privately Held**
WEB: www.eroc.com
SIC: 1382 Oil & gas exploration services

(G-13402)
EXER-TECH INC
1227 Price Plz (77449-6422)
PHONE.....................281 493-2220
William D Berry, *President*
Andrea Berry, *Treasurer*
EMP: 15
SQ FT: 6,000
SALES (est): 2.9MM **Privately Held**
WEB: www.exer-tech.net
SIC: 3829 Physical property testing equipment

(G-13403)
FEDEX OFFICE & PRINT SVCS INC
430 S Mason Rd Ste 108 (77450-2448)
PHONE.....................281 395-0077
EMP: 16
SALES (corp-wide): 69.2B **Publicly Held**
WEB: www.fedex.com
SIC: 7334 2752 Photocopying & duplicating services; commercial printing, lithographic
HQ: Fedex Office And Print Services, Inc.
7900 Legacy Dr
Plano TX 75024
800 463-3339

(G-13404)
FOX MARKETING CORPORATION (PA)
Also Called: Foxmark
21601 Park Row Dr (77449-2453)
PHONE.....................713 686-8300
Richard M Fox, *President*
Bob Barr, *President*
Jamie Garza, *Sales Staff*
Chris Chance, *Executive*
EMP: 15
SQ FT: 45,000
SALES (est): 4MM **Privately Held**
WEB: www.foxmarkcorp.com
SIC: 2752 Commercial printing, offset

(G-13405)
FRAMEWORK OFFSHORE LLC
Also Called: Foot Prints
20127 Chateau Bend Dr (77450-5057)
PHONE.....................281 610-1078
▲ **EMP:** 30
SALES (est): 1MM **Privately Held**
SIC: 1389 Oilfield Service

(G-13406)
FRONTLINE GEOSERVICES LTD
4141 Katy Hockley Rd (77493-4893)
PHONE.....................281 371-2800
Patty Calaway, *President*
Jeff Linder, *Vice Pres*
Scott Lyons, *Director*
EMP: 20 **EST:** 2000
SALES (est): 1.1MM **Privately Held**
WEB: www.discoveryacquisition.com
SIC: 1382 Oil & gas exploration services

(G-13407)
HUBBELL INDUSTRIAL CONTRLS INC
Also Called: Powerohm Resistors
5713 13th St (77493-1638)
PHONE.....................281 391-6800
Timothy H Powers, *Ch of Bd*
EMP: 65
SALES (corp-wide): 4.1B **Publicly Held**
WEB: www.hubbell.com
SIC: 3625 Motor controls, electric
HQ: Hubbell Industrial Controls, Inc.
4301 Cheyenne Dr
Archdale NC 27263
336 434-2800

(G-13408)
IMAGE DISPLAY SYSTEMS INC
Also Called: Signmaxx
1403 Vanderwilt Ln (77449-1799)
PHONE.....................281 395-9100
Guy E Allcorn, *President*
EMP: 10
SQ FT: 11,000
SALES (est): 1.3MM **Privately Held**
WEB: www.signmaxx.com
SIC: 3993 Signs & advertising specialties

(G-13409)
INDUSTRIAL PRO FAB LLC
23735 Ayscough Ln (77493-3419)
PHONE.....................713 205-7245
Casey Wayne Ponton,
EMP: 9
SALES (est): 831.6K **Privately Held**
WEB: www.industrialprofab.com
SIC: 3441 7692 Fabricated structural metal; welding repair

(G-13410)
INVISION AUTOMATED SYSTEMS INC
20434 Knolls Spring Trl (77450-6667)
PHONE.....................713 461-6642
Donald Zapata, *Principal*
▲ **EMP:** 13
SALES (est): 2MM **Privately Held**
WEB: www.insorters.com
SIC: 3556 Food products machinery

(G-13411)
ITS ENGINEERED SYSTEMS INC
Also Called: Its Water Technology
6818 Fm 2855 Rd (77493-7503)
PHONE.....................281 371-8026
Chet Erwin, *President*
Robert Welch, *President*
Larry Hanncock, *Vice Pres*
▼ **EMP:** 80
SQ FT: 82,000
SALES (est): 26.6MM **Privately Held**
WEB: www.itses.com
SIC: 3589 Water treatment equipment, industrial

(G-13412)
K-T BOLT MFG CO
1150 Katy Fort Bend Rd (77493-2136)
P.O. Box 683 (77492-0683)
PHONE.....................281 391-2196
Randy Peck, *President*
Charles O Peck Jr, *Principal*
EMP: 46
SQ FT: 22,000

SALES (est): 10.7MM **Privately Held**
WEB: www.k-tbolt.com
SIC: 3452 Bolts, metal

(G-13413)
K-T GALVANIZING CO INC (PA)
5105 3rd St (77493-2111)
P.O. Box 560 (77492-0560)
PHONE.....................281 391-9201
Alfred Peck, *President*
Mike Manning, *Plant Mgr*
Chris Logan, *VP Sales*
Jennifer Logan, *Accounts Mgr*
EMP: 25
SQ FT: 9,000
SALES (est): 5.8MM **Privately Held**
WEB: www.ktgalvanizing.com
SIC: 3479 Coating of metals & formed products

(G-13414)
KATY IND PUBLICATIONS & PRTG
5364 Franz Rd (77493-1747)
PHONE.....................281 396-6250
Matt Herring, *Manager*
EMP: 15 **EST:** 1992
SALES (est): 587.3K **Privately Held**
WEB: www.katychristianmagazine.com
SIC: 2741 Miscellaneous publishing

(G-13415)
KATY MAGAZINE LLC
605 Park Grove Dr Ste A (77450-5585)
PHONE.....................281 579-9840
Matt Katsarelis, *Publisher*
Katrina Katsarelis, *Chief*
Katrina E Katsarelis,
EMP: 15
SQ FT: 2,380
SALES (est): 1.9MM **Privately Held**
WEB: www.katymagazine.com
SIC: 2721 Magazines: publishing & printing

(G-13416)
KATY SPRING & MFG INC
3535 Schlipf Rd (77493-7530)
PHONE.....................281 391-1888
James West, *CEO*
Scott Pitney, *President*
Jason West, *General Mgr*
Ryan Thorpe, *Opers Mgr*
Cindy Fredrich, *Purchasing*
EMP: 50
SQ FT: 30,000
SALES (est): 12.4MM **Privately Held**
WEB: www.katyspring.com
SIC: 3495 Wire springs

(G-13417)
KATY STONE & GRAVEL INC
4383 Katy Hockley Rd (77493-4830)
P.O. Box 6474 (77491-6474)
PHONE.....................281 371-3003
Veronica Escobedo, *President*
Ruben Espinoza, *Vice Pres*
EMP: 10
SALES (est): 1.4MM **Privately Held**
WEB: www.katystoneandgravel.com
SIC: 1442 Construction sand & gravel

(G-13418)
KNUST-GODWIN LLC (DH)
5686 Stone Ln (77449)
PHONE.....................713 785-1060
Colleen Rejcek, *Partner*
Adrian Berlanga, *Prdtn Mgr*
John Clark, *Materials Mgr*
John Stenger, *Buyer*
Troy Jeansonne, *QC Mgr*
◆ **EMP:** 89 **EST:** 2009
SQ FT: 116,000
SALES (est): 35.8MM
SALES (corp-wide): 2.6MM **Privately Held**
WEB: www.kgsbo.com
SIC: 3599 Machine shop, jobbing & repair
HQ: Schoeller-Bleckmann Oilfield Equipment Aktiengesellschaft
HauptstraBe 2
Ternitz 2630
263 031-50

(G-13419)
**KOBELCO CONSTRUCTION
MCHY USA (DH)**
22350 Merchants Way (77449-7811)
PHONE.............................281 684-8761
Katsuhiko Morita, *President*
Ronald Hargrave, *Vice Pres*
Randy Hall, *VP Opers*
Eric Hoffman, *Manager*
◆ **EMP:** 25
SQ FT: 86,000
SALES (est): 17.9MM **Privately Held**
WEB: www.kobelco-usa.com
SIC: 5082 3531 General construction machinery & equipment; excavators: cable, clamshell, crane, derrick, dragline, etc.; tractors, crawler

(G-13420)
**KOBELCO CRANES NORTH
AMER INC**
22350 Merchants Way (77449-7811)
PHONE.............................713 856-5755
Tatsuo Maruo, *CEO*
Shinsuke Izumi, *President*
Izuru Niwa, *Corp Secy*
Jack Fendrick, *Vice Pres*
▲ **EMP:** 14
SALES (est): 4.7MM **Privately Held**
SIC: 3536 Hoists, cranes & monorails

(G-13421)
KOY CONCRETE LTD
5013 3rd St (77493-2109)
PHONE.............................281 391-2178
Lonny Schneider, *Manager*
EMP: 30
SQ FT: 10,310
SALES (corp-wide): 14.9MM **Privately
Held**
WEB: www.koyconcrete.com
SIC: 3273 1771 Ready-mixed concrete; concrete work
PA: Koy Concrete, Ltd.
　　770 Highway 90 E
　　Sealy TX 77474
　　979 885-3551

(G-13422)
LASERWELD INC
Also Called: Laserlight
1350 Schlipf Rd (77493-5006)
PHONE.............................713 333-0804
Mark E Lewis, *President*
Jose Yamada, *Manager*
▲ **EMP:** 25
SQ FT: 150,000
SALES (est): 6.7MM **Privately Held**
WEB: www.laserweldinc.com
SIC: 7692 3535 3496 1799 Automotive welding; unit handling conveying systems; wire cloth & woven wire products; athletic & recreation facilities construction; welding on site

(G-13423)
LIFETIME FILTER INC
1005 Katyland Dr (77493-2531)
PHONE.............................281 391-8060
David Pemberton, *General Mgr*
Jimmy Cagle, *Principal*
Maresca Anthony R, *Vice Pres*
EMP: 420
SQ FT: 20,000
SALES (est): 44.7MM
SALES (corp-wide): 4.7B **Publicly Held**
SIC: 3564 Filters, air: furnaces, air conditioning equipment, etc.
HQ: Baker Distributing Company Llc
　　14610 Breakers Dr Ste 100
　　Jacksonville FL 32258
　　904 407-4500

(G-13424)
MASTER VALVE USA INC
23555 Clay Rd (77493-3036)
PHONE.............................832 838-4999
Frank Feng, *President*
Ping Hu, *Vice Pres*
EMP: 12
SALES (est): 2MM **Privately Held**
WEB: www.mastervalveusa.com
SIC: 3491 Industrial valves

(G-13425)
MIDSTAR ENERGY LP
1840 Snake River Rd Ste E (77449-7755)
PHONE.............................281 940-3022
Will Moritz, *Partner*
EMP: 20
SALES (est): 14MM **Privately Held**
WEB: www.midstarenergy.com
SIC: 1381 Directional drilling oil & gas wells

(G-13426)
**NATURAL ENERGY RESOURCES
INC**
20042 Cresent Creek Dr (77449-7494)
PHONE.............................832 631-5013
Frederick Franklin, *CEO*
James Williams Jr, *President*
EMP: 53
SALES (est): 8.6MM **Privately Held**
SIC: 1499 5999 4931 4953 Gem stones (natural) mining; gems & precious stones; ; recycling, waste materials

(G-13427)
**NEUMAN & ESSER
INVESTMENTS INC (HQ)**
1502 E Summitry Cir (77449-5350)
PHONE.............................281 497-5113
Scott De Baldo, *Managing Dir*
Henning Von Haefen, *CFO*
EMP: 29
SALES: 59.2MM
SALES (corp-wide): 277.8MM **Privately
Held**
WEB: www.neuman-esser.de
SIC: 3563 Air & gas compressors
PA: Neuman & Esser Verwaltungs- Und
　　Beteiligungsges. Mbh
　　Werkstr.
　　Ubach-Palenberg 52531
　　245 148-101

(G-13428)
**NEUMAN & ESSER USA INC
(DH)**
1502 E Summitry Cir (77449-5350)
PHONE.............................281 497-5113
Scott Debaldo, *President*
Manuel Morales, *Exec VP*
Fred Trackwell, *Vice Pres*
Henning Von Haefen, *Vice Pres*
Sergio Echevarria, *Engineer*
◆ **EMP:** 43
SQ FT: 100,000
SALES (est): 36.8MM
SALES (corp-wide): 277.8MM **Privately
Held**
WEB: www.neuman-esser.de
SIC: 7699 3563 Industrial machinery & equipment repair; air & gas compressors
HQ: Neuman & Esser Gmbh & Co. Kg
　　Werkstr.
　　Ubach-Palenberg 52531
　　245 148-101

(G-13429)
NOREMAC GAS LLC
22136 Westheimer Pkwy # 425
(77450-8296)
PHONE.............................281 248-6423
Cameron W Brown, *Mng Member*
EMP: 13
SALES (est): 1.6MM **Privately Held**
WEB: www.noremacgas.com
SIC: 4924 3593 Natural gas distribution; fluid power cylinders & actuators

(G-13430)
NOVOMET USA INC (PA)
23567 Clay Rd (77493-3036)
PHONE.............................832 437-5998
Richard Savoie, *President*
◆ **EMP:** 15
SQ FT: 25,000
SALES (est): 5.1MM **Privately Held**
WEB: www.novometgroup.com
SIC: 1389 Pipe testing, oil field service

(G-13431)
**OPTIBLEND INDUSTRIES INC
(DH)**
29738 Goynes Rd (77493-6569)
PHONE.............................281 584-0047
Asoke Deysarkar, *Principal*

Terry Cooper, *Facilities Mgr*
Brian Decaires, *Engineer*
Suresh Pala, *CFO*
Suresh D Pala, *Treasurer*
EMP: 43
SALES (est): 27.2MM
SALES (corp-wide): 72.1MM **Privately
Held**
WEB: www.pfpindustries.com
SIC: 5169 3532 Organic chemicals, synthetic; trucks (dollies), mining

(G-13432)
**POINTSMITH PNT-F-PRCHASE
MGT S**
21202 Park Row Dr (77449-5384)
PHONE.............................281 599-5900
Mitch Bryant, *Corp Secy*
Jared Bryant, *COO*
Bridgett Janota, *Prdtn Mgr*
Felipe Resendez, *Maint Spvr*
Jason Oehrlein, *Engineer*
▲ **EMP:** 167
SQ FT: 184,750
SALES (est): 46.2MM **Privately Held**
WEB: www.pointsmith.com
SIC: 2759 7389 7336 Commercial printing; inventory stocking service; creative services to advertisers, except writers

(G-13433)
PRO PAVERS HOUSTON LLC
22603 Beckendorff Rd (77449-6708)
PHONE.............................281 665-4718
Daniel Porter, *Principal*
EMP: 27
SALES (est): 7MM **Privately Held**
WEB: www.propavershouston.com
SIC: 2951 Asphalt paving mixtures & blocks

(G-13434)
RAE ENERGY INC
1621 Prime West Pkwy (77449)
PHONE.............................281 578-6523
Anthony Ponpefract, *President*
Jairo Perez, *Treasurer*
◆ **EMP:** 150
SQ FT: 30,000
SALES (est): 16.1MM **Privately Held**
WEB: www.ojs.com
SIC: 1389 Oil field services

(G-13435)
RECS SIGNS LLC
1523 Vanderwilt Ln (77449-1897)
PHONE.............................832 226-8000
Robert Ermatinger, *Mng Member*
EMP: 12
SALES (est): 62.9K **Privately Held**
SIC: 3993 Signs & advertising specialties

(G-13436)
REVOLUTION SCREENING INC
Also Called: Revolution Screening In Texas
21821 Katy Fwy Ste 102a (77450-1804)
PHONE.............................916 712-4458
Mike G Forsyth, *Branch Mgr*
EMP: 20
SALES (corp-wide): 2.5MM **Privately
Held**
WEB: www.revolutionscreening.com
SIC: 2396 Screen printing on fabric articles
PA: Revolution Screening Inc
　　2523 Evergreen Ave
　　West Sacramento CA 95691
　　916 604-6865

(G-13437)
**RILCO MANUFACTURING CO
INC**
5446 1st St (77493-2509)
PHONE.............................713 466-4777
Katharine Homsi, *General Mgr*
Kenneth L Zagorski, *Branch Mgr*
Celso Hernandez, *Manager*
EMP: 83
SALES (corp-wide): 43MM **Privately
Held**
WEB: www.rilco.com
SIC: 3441 Fabricated structural metal
PA: Rilco Manufacturing Company, Inc.
　　12700 Tanner Rd
　　Houston TX 77041
　　713 466-4777

(G-13438)
SALTER PRECISION MACHINING
1115 Glenwood Dr (77493-2130)
P.O. Box 1005 (77492-1005)
PHONE.............................281 391-4118
John D Salter, *President*
EMP: 15
SQ FT: 5,600
SALES (est): 1.1MM **Privately Held**
WEB: www.saltermachine.com
SIC: 3599 Machine shop, jobbing & repair

(G-13439)
SAXON DRILLING LP (HQ)
23400 Clnl Pkwy Bldg H222 (77493)
PHONE.............................281 712-4529
Dale Tremblay, *Partner*
▼ **EMP:** 48
SALES (est): 13.9MM
SALES (corp-wide): 928.1MM **Privately
Held**
SIC: 1381 Drilling oil & gas wells
PA: Saxon Energy Services Inc
　　700 4 Ave Sw Unit 500
　　Calgary AB
　　403 716-4150

(G-13440)
**SEPSA PRECAST SOLUTIONS
CORP**
5503 Fry Rd (77449-5845)
PHONE.............................832 291-8930
EMP: 18
SALES (corp-wide): 1.5MM **Privately
Held**
WEB: www.sepsausa.com
SIC: 3272 Precast terrazo or concrete products
PA: Sepsa Precast Solutions Corp
　　15031 Woodham Dr Ste 370
　　Houston TX 77073
　　281 821-4400

(G-13441)
SFP HYDRAULICS INC (PA)
22240 Merchants Way # 100 (77449-7827)
PHONE.............................281 347-8080
Kevin Rafefske, *President*
RAO Choday, *Vice Pres*
Neil Maxwell, *Vice Pres*
Aleksa Samardzija, *Production*
▲ **EMP:** 9
SQ FT: 20,000
SALES (est): 3.2MM **Privately Held**
WEB: www.sfphyd.com
SIC: 3593 Fluid power actuators, hydraulic or pneumatic

(G-13442)
SIGMA DRILLING TECH LLC
1004 Avenue A (77493-2462)
PHONE.............................281 656-9298
Justin Manley, *Mng Member*
EMP: 15
SALES (est): 202K **Privately Held**
WEB: www.sigmadrillingtech.com
SIC: 3561 7389 Industrial pumps & parts; business services

(G-13443)
SLPC INC
Also Called: Sunline Products
1454 E Summitry Cir (77449-5326)
PHONE.............................281 398-6655
Jack Elliott, *President*
Elissa Elliott, *Sales Staff*
EMP: 21
SQ FT: 4,000
SALES (est): 2.1MM **Privately Held**
WEB: www.sunlineproducts.com
SIC: 2759 5199 Screen printing; advertising specialties

(G-13444)
SONIAS ACCESSORIES
21714 Denali Range Ct (77449-4527)
PHONE.............................832 443-7586
Sonia B Bloise,
EMP: 9
SALES (est): 498.5K **Privately Held**
WEB: www.sonia-sa.com
SIC: 3911 Jewelry, precious metal

(G-13445)
STRATGIC LTIGATION PARTNERS LP
21324 Provincial Blvd (77450-7580)
PHONE...........................713 995-8225
Jose Torres, *Partner*
Donna Miller, *Partner*
EMP: 120
SQ FT: 6,000
SALES (est): 5MM **Privately Held**
WEB: www.slplegal.com
SIC: 2834 8111 Pharmaceutical preparations; legal services

(G-13446)
SUBSEA SERVICES INTL INC
Also Called: Rae Energy
1621 Prime West Pkwy (77449)
PHONE...........................281 578-6523
Douglas McIntyre, *CEO*
Dan Cooney, *Vice Pres*
Gareth Forbes, *CFO*
Jiaro Perez, *CFO*
Viktoriya Moity, *Office Mgr*
EMP: 100
SALES (est): 21.5MM
SALES (corp-wide): 4.4MM **Privately Held**
SIC: 3533 Oil field machinery & equipment
HQ: Rae Energy Uk Limited
23 Berkeley Square
London W1J 6

(G-13447)
SUNLINE PRODUCT
1454 E Summitry Cir (77449-5326)
PHONE...........................281 398-6655
Jack Elliott, *President*
Scott Carr, *Vice Pres*
Sandi Yoakum, *Controller*
Marc Elliott, *Sales Staff*
Ezra Horsley, *Sales Staff*
EMP: 14
SALES (est): 2.2MM **Privately Held**
WEB: www.sunlineproducts.com
SIC: 2759 Screen printing

(G-13448)
TELEDRILL INC
18303 W Little York Rd (77449-5761)
PHONE...........................281 550-0434
Bob Macdonald, *Principal*
Ford Creighton, *Opers Spvr*
Gabor Vecseri, *Senior Engr*
EMP: 10
SALES (est): 1.7MM **Privately Held**
WEB: www.teledrill.com
SIC: 3541 Drilling machine tools (metal cutting)

(G-13449)
TEXAS FOOD SOLUTIONS LLC
25002 Clay Rd (77493-2942)
PHONE...........................713 579-5634
Wendy Snead, *Branch Mgr*
EMP: 58
SALES (corp-wide): 39.9MM **Privately Held**
WEB: www.texasfoodsolutions.com
SIC: 2099 Food preparations
HQ: Texas Food Solutions Llc
10370 Richmond Ave # 130
Houston TX 77042
713 868-5300

(G-13450)
THIINK BIIG TAX SERVICE INC
21919 Clay Rd Apt 4211 (77449-2929)
PHONE...........................832 606-3380
Erica Tirado, *CEO*
Shalona Hubert, *COO*
Briah Davis, *CFO*
EMP: 10 EST: 2017
SALES (est): 198K **Privately Held**
WEB: www.thiinkbiiginc.com
SIC: 4581 3953 7349 7389 Aircraft cleaning & janitorial service; seal presses, notary & hand; janitorial service, contract basis; notary publics; caterers

(G-13451)
TORANS PRECISION FABRICATING
5230 E 5th St (77493-2118)
P.O. Box 596 (77492-0596)
PHONE...........................281 371-2352
Elton Torans, *President*
Kathy Torans, *Vice Pres*
EMP: 9
SQ FT: 12,000
SALES (est): 1.2MM **Privately Held**
WEB: www.torans.net
SIC: 3444 Sheet metalwork

(G-13452)
TROPISCAPES INC
Also Called: Paver Connection
25810 Clay Rd (77493-9716)
PHONE...........................281 371-2955
Randell Carpenter, *President*
EMP: 40
SQ FT: 4,000
SALES (est): 2.5MM **Privately Held**
WEB: www.paverconnection.com
SIC: 0782 0721 1611 5082 Landscape contractors; irrigation system operation, not providing water; surfacing & paving; pavers; pavers

(G-13453)
U S WEATHERFORD L P
1040 Schlipf Rd (77493-6571)
PHONE...........................832 424-0000
Dave Christensen, *Vice Pres*
Agustin Esquivel, *Foreman/Supr*
Fernando Mundo, *Engineer*
Stephen Bosch, *Manager*
Colby Burns, *Manager*
EMP: 200 **Privately Held**
WEB: www.weatherford.com
SIC: 1389 Oil field services
HQ: U S Weatherford L P
179 Weatherford Dr
Schriever LA 70395
985 493-6100

(G-13454)
VETERANS MFG LLC
5446 1st St Ste A (77493-2509)
P.O. Box 699 (77492-0699)
PHONE...........................713 854-9261
Michael Hlozek, *Mng Member*
Stephen Jahn, *Mng Member*
EMP: 9
SALES (est): 154.5K **Privately Held**
WEB: www.vetsmfg.com
SIC: 3842 5999 9229 Personal safety equipment; clothing, fire resistant & protective; alarm & safety equipment stores; public safety statistics center, government

(G-13455)
WELLTEC INC (DH)
22440 Merchants Way (77449-7813)
PHONE...........................281 371-1200
Jorgen Hallundbaek, *President*
Antonius Aji, *General Mgr*
Youcef Abdesselam, *Business Mgr*
Vsevolod Bugrov, *Business Mgr*
Steve French, *Exec VP*
▲ EMP: 35 EST: 2000
SQ FT: 30,000
SALES (est): 84MM
SALES (corp-wide): 249MM **Privately Held**
WEB: www.welltec.com
SIC: 1389 Oil field services
HQ: Welltec A/S
Gydevang 25
AllerOd 3450
481 435-14

Kaufman
Kaufman County

(G-13456)
ADVANCE TABCO INC
Also Called: Pantex Manufacturing
2000 S Houston St (75142-3602)
P.O. Box 885 (75142-0885)
PHONE...........................972 932-4148
Milton Schwartz, *Ch of Bd*
Alice Schwartz, *President*
Daniel Schwartz, *Vice Pres*
Penny Schwartz-Hutner, *Vice Pres*
Dennis Vinson, *Manager*
▼ EMP: 12
SQ FT: 25,000
SALES (est): 3.7MM
SALES (corp-wide): 73.2MM **Privately Held**
SIC: 3589 Cooking equipment, commercial
WEB: www.advancetabco.com
PA: Kinplex Corp.
325 Wireless Blvd Ste 1
Hauppauge NY 11788
631 242-4800

(G-13457)
AMERICAN LIBERTY OIL CO LP (PA)
3725 W Us Highway 175 (75142-5237)
P.O. Box 1077 (75142-5400)
PHONE...........................972 932-2266
James Y Wynne,
W B Wynne,
Wreno S Wynne,
EMP: 10 EST: 1931
SQ FT: 6,000
SALES (est): 1.7MM **Privately Held**
WEB: www.americanlibertyoil.com
SIC: 2911 Gasoline

(G-13458)
CLEAR FILM PRINTING INC
3000 E Us Highway 175 (75142-8845)
P.O. Box 728 (75142-0728)
PHONE...........................972 962-4422
Norman Olivarez, *President*
Daryl Olivarez, *General Mgr*
Angela Olivarez, *Vice Pres*
EMP: 16
SQ FT: 10,000 **Privately Held**
WEB: www.clearfilmprinting.com
SIC: 2759 Flexographic printing

(G-13459)
KAUFMAN INDEPENDENT SCHOOL DST
Also Called: Kaufman Isd Print Shop
1001 S Houston St (75142-2213)
PHONE...........................972 932-6940
Todd Williams, *Owner*
EMP: 35
SQ FT: 1,192
SALES (corp-wide): 52.5MM **Privately Held**
WEB: www.kaufmanisd.net
SIC: 3955 Print cartridges for laser & other computer printers
PA: Kaufman Independent School District
1000 S Houston St
Kaufman TX 75142
972 932-2622

(G-13460)
MICA STEELWORKS INC
1200 Rand Rd (75142-2613)
PHONE...........................972 287-5410
Larry Minor, *Branch Mgr*
EMP: 149
SALES (corp-wide): 93.4MM **Privately Held**
WEB: www.micacorporation.com
SIC: 3312 Blast furnaces & steel mills
PA: Mica Steelworks, Inc.
5750 N Riverside Dr
Fort Worth TX 76137
817 529-5000

(G-13461)
MUELLER SUPPLY COMPANY INC
3550 E Us Highway 175 (75142-7634)
PHONE...........................972 932-3208
Tyler Jones, *Branch Mgr*
EMP: 35
SALES (corp-wide): 180.3MM **Privately Held**
WEB: www.muellerinc.com
SIC: 3448 Prefabricated metal components
PA: Mueller Supply Company, Inc.
1913 Hutchins Ave
Ballinger TX 76821
325 365-3555

(G-13462)
NEW ALTRNATIVE GREEN ENRGY INC
Also Called: New Age
9973 County Road 115 (75142-8332)
PHONE...........................972 523-9970
Dan Verakis, *President*
Mike Wilson, *Chairman*
John Caidwell, *COO*
Jeffrey James, *CFO*
EMP: 14
SALES (est): 629K **Privately Held**
WEB: www.newageincusa.com
SIC: 2813 Hydrogen

(G-13463)
NUMO MANUFACTURING INC
1072 E Us Highway 175 (75142-3560)
PHONE...........................800 253-0434
Charlie Meyer, *President*
Martin Jim, *Vice Pres*
Rebecca Williams, *Purchasing*
Ashli Bryant, *Accounts Mgr*
Theresa Osburn, *Accounts Mgr*
▼ EMP: 150
SQ FT: 200,000
SALES (est): 21.6MM
SALES (corp-wide): 88MM **Privately Held**
WEB: www.numomfg.com
SIC: 3089 Plastic containers, except foam
PA: Kolder, Inc.
1601 N Closner Blvd
Edinburg TX 78541
956 381-9851

(G-13464)
TABLES MANUFACTURING INC
Also Called: Advance Tabco
2000 S Houston St (75142-3602)
P.O. Box 885 (75142-0885)
PHONE...........................972 932-4148
Milton Schwartz, *Ch of Bd*
Alice Schwartz, *President*
Daniel Schwartz, *Vice Pres*
Penny Schwartz-Hutner, *Vice Pres*
Dennis Vinson, *Opers Mgr*
▼ EMP: 353
SQ FT: 70,000
SALES (est): 33.8MM
SALES (corp-wide): 73.2MM **Privately Held**
WEB: www.advancetabco.com
SIC: 2599 3556 2511 Restaurant furniture, wood or metal; food products machinery; wood household furniture
PA: Kinplex Corp.
325 Wireless Blvd Ste 1
Hauppauge NY 11788
631 242-4800

Keene
Johnson County

(G-13465)
TEXAS POCKET SPRINGS TECH INC
460 County Rd 318 (76059)
P.O. Box 2469, Cleburne (76033-2469)
PHONE...........................817 645-7666
Martin Harold Wolfson, *President*
Tessa Wolfson, *Treasurer*
▲ EMP: 58
SQ FT: 55,000
SALES (est): 8.3MM **Privately Held**
WEB: www.texaspocketsprings.com
SIC: 2515 Mattresses, innerspring or box spring

Keller
Tarrant County

(G-13466)
A FAB INDUSTRIES LLC
Also Called: A Fab & Construction
8330 B Old Denton Rd (76244)
P.O. Box 932 (76244-0932)
PHONE...........................817 337-4776
Scott Anderson, *President*
Brian Anderson, *Mng Member*
EMP: 22

SQ FT: 1,500
SALES (est): 7.5MM **Privately Held**
WEB: www.afabindustries.com
SIC: 3441 Fabricated structural metal

(G-13467)
FOAM FABRICATORS INC
900 Keller Pkwy Ste 101 (76248-3638)
P.O. Box 547 (76244-0547)
PHONE................................817 379-6520
Kent Sibley, *Branch Mgr*
Nancy Roser, *Manager*
EMP: 19 **Publicly Held**
WEB: www.foamfabricatorsinc.com
SIC: 5199 3086 Foam rubber; plastics
foam products
HQ: Foam Fabricators, Inc.
8722 E San Alberto # 200
Scottsdale AZ 85258

(G-13468)
**LOCKHEED MARTIN
CORPORATION**
810 Clearwater Ln (76248-2853)
P.O. Box 748, Fort Worth (76101-7450)
PHONE................................817 763-4246
Vance Coffman, *President*
Keith Breeding, *Engineer*
Russ Countryman, *Engineer*
EMP: 253 **Publicly Held**
WEB: www.lockheedmartin.com
SIC: 3812 Search & navigation equipment
PA: Lockheed Martin Corporation
6801 Rockledge Dr
Bethesda MD 20817

(G-13469)
ORACLE CORPORATION
144 Mount Gilead Rd (76248-3915)
PHONE................................817 422-5231
Randy Moore, *Principal*
EMP: 302
SALES (corp-wide): 39B **Publicly Held**
WEB: www.oracle.com
SIC: 7372 Business oriented computer
software
PA: Oracle Corporation
2300 Oracle Way
Austin TX 78741
737 867-1000

(G-13470)
TEX-ART STONE INC
8900 Davis Blvd (76248-0304)
PHONE................................817 481-9602
Josh Shatley, *President*
Betsy B Shatley, *Corp Secy*
Jack Shatley, *Vice Pres*
Betsey Shatley, *Safety Mgr*
EMP: 15
SQ FT: 12,000
SALES (est): 2.7MM **Privately Held**
WEB: www.tex-art.com
SIC: 3281 3271 3272 Curbing, paving &
walkway stone; blocks, concrete or cin-
der: standard; concrete products, precast;
fountains, concrete

Kemah
Galveston County

(G-13471)
**COASTAL RESOURCES GROUP
LLC**
2105 Anders Ln Ste D (77565-3248)
PHONE................................281 549-4132
Cindy Henson, *Director*
Dan Kendrick,
Chad Henson,
EMP: 15
SALES (est): 2.7MM **Privately Held**
WEB: www.coastalrgp.com
SIC: 7372 Educational computer software

(G-13472)
COMPUTER COMFORTS INC
367 Columbia Mem Pkwy (77565-3187)
P.O. Box 2186, Houston (77252-2186)
PHONE................................281 535-2288
Frank Kolavo, *President*
Luci Minchew, *COO*
Samantha Kolavo, *Marketing Staff*
EMP: 11

SQ FT: 2,000
SALES (est): 4.9MM **Privately Held**
WEB: www.computercomforts.com
SIC: 2522 Office furniture, except wood

(G-13473)
ES CUSTOM BOATS LLC
2332 Anders Ln (77565-3145)
PHONE................................832 864-2331
John Eric Simmons, *Mng Member*
EMP: 16
SALES (est): 767.3K **Privately Held**
WEB: www.escustomboats.com
SIC: 3732 Boat building & repairing

(G-13474)
FORGE TECH INC
900 Anders Ln Ste 15 (77565-2689)
P.O. Box 1179 (77565-1179)
PHONE................................888 854-8414
Mathew Rybicki, *President*
Ken Vejr, *Chairman*
Larry Povse, *Vice Pres*
Don Buchan, *VP Sales*
Robert Buckley, *Manager*
EMP: 9
SALES (est): 600K **Privately Held**
WEB: www.forgetechinc.com
SIC: 7692 7389 1796 Welding repair; ; in-
stalling building equipment

(G-13475)
GILKES INC
471 Columbia Mem Pkwy (77565-8114)
PHONE................................832 932-5282
Nick Pike, *President*
Andy Poole, *Exec VP*
David Priestley, *Vice Pres*
Alan Robinson, *Design Engr*
Angela Williams, *Office Mgr*
◆ **EMP:** 38 **EST:** 1978
SALES (est): 8.8MM
SALES (corp-wide): 36.7MM **Privately
Held**
WEB: www.gilkes.com
SIC: 3561 Pumps & pumping equipment
HQ: Gilbert Gilkes & Gordon Limited
Canal Iron Works
Kendal LA9 7
153 972-0028

(G-13476)
JOHN C MAUDLIN INC
Also Called: North Canvas & Upholstery
1207 Marina Bay Dr (77565-2563)
P.O. Box 1205 (77565-1205)
PHONE................................281 334-7224
John C Maudlin, *President*
EMP: 14
SQ FT: 6,000
SALES (est): 1.1MM **Privately Held**
SIC: 2394 Canvas & related products

(G-13477)
**MAUDLIN ASSETS
MANAGEMENT INC**
1929 Highway 146 (77565-2002)
P.O. Box 699 (77565-0699)
PHONE................................281 334-7566
Earl T Maudlin, *CEO*
Kirk Tindall, *President*
Reed Leistad, *Vice Pres*
Cliff Lenert, *Vice Pres*
Terrilee Maudlin, *Admin Sec*
▲ **EMP:** 45 **EST:** 1938
SQ FT: 45,000
SALES (est): 11MM **Privately Held**
WEB: www.maudlinproducts.com
SIC: 3469 Stamping metal for the trade

(G-13478)
ONWARD LLC
66 Harbor Ln (77565-2648)
PHONE................................281 535-2739
Autrey McVicker II, *CEO*
Lynn Cisneros, *CFO*
EMP: 15
SQ FT: 1,100
SALES (est): 1.7MM **Privately Held**
WEB: www.crewonward.com
SIC: 1389 Oil consultants

(G-13479)
SEABROOK SEAFOOD INC
1419 Lawrence Rd (77565-2642)
P.O. Box 776 (77565-0776)
PHONE................................281 334-2546
EMP: 50
SQ FT: 30,000
SALES (est): 9.4MM **Privately Held**
WEB: www.seabrookseafood.com
SIC: 2092 5812 Fresh or frozen packaged
fish; eating places

(G-13480)
TRISEAL INC
Also Called: Texas Transmitter
900 Anders Ln Ste 9 (77565-2689)
P.O. Box 38 (77565-0038)
PHONE................................713 589-5380
Will Garvin, *President*
EMP: 10
SALES (est): 1.2MM **Privately Held**
WEB: www.texastransmitter.com
SIC: 3823 Industrial instrmnts msrmnt dis-
play/control process variable

(G-13481)
**VECTOR INDUSTRIAL GROUP
LLC**
803 Marina Bay Dr (77565-2539)
PHONE................................281 967-1093
Sandy Cunningham,
EMP: 10
SALES (est): 283.1K **Privately Held**
SIC: 3999 Manufacturing industries

(G-13482)
**WATERFRONT PUBLISHING INC
(PA)**
Also Called: Telltales Magazines
228 Marina Bay Dr Ste B (77565-3243)
P.O. Box 1044, Seabrook (77586-1044)
PHONE................................281 334-2202
Sharon Kay Dubois, *President*
EMP: 13
SQ FT: 3,199
SALES (est): 1.1MM **Privately Held**
SIC: 2791 2721 Typesetting; periodicals

Kemp
Kaufman County

(G-13483)
CHIMERA LAB LTD
9461 E Highway 175 (75143-3357)
PHONE................................214 428-3901
Dennis Boyle, *Partner*
EMP: 10
SALES (est): 100K **Privately Held**
SIC: 3651 Speaker monitors

(G-13484)
ENVIRO CAMS LLC
201 N Elm St (75143-7728)
PHONE................................430 255-7006
Jennifer Spears,
EMP: 11
SQ FT: 30,000
SALES (est): 453.7K **Privately Held**
WEB: www.selfstoragecams.com
SIC: 3699 Security control equipment &
systems

(G-13485)
**LACY CONSTRUCTION
SERVICES LLC**
Also Called: Lcs
6012 Ashley Rd (75143-3394)
PHONE................................903 498-0683
John Lacy, *Mng Member*
EMP: 13
SALES (est): 2.1MM **Privately Held**
SIC: 3441 3446 1791 Fabricated struc-
tural metal; building components, struc-
tural steel; stairs, fire escapes, balconies,
railings & ladders; exterior wall system in-
stallation

Kempner
Lampasas County

(G-13486)
**MEZGER ENTERPRISES LTD
(PA)**
Fm Rd 2808 (76539)
PHONE................................254 547-8174
William Mezger, *President*
Ben Goodwin, *Corp Secy*
Ronny Shroyer, *Regl Sales Mgr*
EMP: 60 **EST:** 1978
SQ FT: 11,500
SALES (est): 6.9MM **Privately Held**
WEB: www.mezgerstone.com
SIC: 1422 Crushed & broken limestone

(G-13487)
PERMIAN LIMESTONE
Fm 2808 (76539)
P.O. Box 1553, Lampasas (76550-0013)
PHONE................................254 547-8207
Bill Mezger, *President*
EMP: 40
SALES (est): 3.8MM **Privately Held**
SIC: 5039 3281 Construction materials;
cut stone & stone products

Kenedy
Karnes County

(G-13488)
J & X TRUCKING LLC (PA)
1052 County Road 160 (78119-5316)
PHONE................................830 583-0611
Kevin Parikh, *President*
Rodolfo Cantu, *Vice Pres*
EMP: 25 **EST:** 2011
SQ FT: 505,296
SALES (est): 2.1MM **Privately Held**
WEB: www.jandxenergy.com
SIC: 4212 1382 1389 Local trucking, with-
out storage; geophysical exploration, oil &
gas field; building oil & gas well founda-
tions on site; grading oil & gas well foun-
dations; oil & gas wells: building, repairing
& dismantling; impounding & storing salt
water, oil & gas field

(G-13489)
MO-VAC SERVICE COMPANY
Hwy 181 (78119)
P.O. Box 725 (78119-0725)
PHONE................................830 583-3622
Roland Oliveraz, *Manager*
Eloy Munez, *Manager*
EMP: 13
SALES (corp-wide): 156.8MM **Privately
Held**
WEB: www.mo-vac.com
SIC: 1389 Mud service, oil field drilling
PA: Mo-Vac Service Company
3721 S Mccoll Rd
Edinburg TX 78539
956 682-6381

(G-13490)
**NEXGEN WTR SOLUTIONS LTD
LBLTY (PA)**
951 County Road 160 (78119-5315)
PHONE................................830 583-9915
James Thomas Burns, *Mng Member*
EMP: 25 **EST:** 2017
SQ FT: 5,000
SALES (est): 4MM **Privately Held**
SIC: 1389 Oil field services

(G-13491)
**STALLION OILFIELD SERVICES
LTD**
204 Private Road 1125 1 (78119-4287)
PHONE................................830 583-6927
Jarod Davis, *Manager*
R Ramos, *Director*
EMP: 48 **Privately Held**
WEB: www.stallionoilfield.com
SIC: 1389 Oil field services
HQ: Stallion Oilfield Services Ltd.
950 Corbindale Rd Ste 400
Houston TX 77024
713 528-5544

(G-13492)
TIERRA LEASE SERVICE LLC
311 S Sunset Strip St (78119-3061)
P.O. Box 366 (78119-0366)
PHONE..............................830 583-3717
Joseph Newberry, *CEO*
Tommy Tise, *President*
Juan Chapa, *COO*
Frank Stabler, *CFO*
John Chapa,
EMP: 300
SALES (est): 57.6MM Privately Held
WEB: www.tierraleaseservice.com
SIC: 1389 Oil field services

(G-13493)
VOYAGER ENERGY SERVICES LLC
1 Airport Rd (78119)
PHONE..............................830 583-9590
EMP: 19
SALES (est): 6.8MM Privately Held
WEB: www.voyagertx.com
SIC: 3533 5211 Oil field machinery & equipment; insulation & energy conservation products

Kennard
Houston County

(G-13494)
BASA RESOURCES INC
6729 Fm 2781 (75847-6813)
PHONE..............................936 655-2477
Ronny Odell, *Principal*
EMP: 15 Privately Held
WEB: www.basaresources.com
SIC: 1311 Crude petroleum production
PA: Basa Resources, Inc.
   14875 Landmark Blvd # 400
   Dallas TX 75254

Kennedale
Tarrant County

(G-13495)
AA TRUCK SLEEPER LLC
705 W Kennedale Pkwy B (76060-3268)
P.O. Box 1067 (76060-1067)
PHONE..............................817 834-4781
Wally Bearden, *Sales Staff*
Wayne Baylor,
EMP: 11
SQ FT: 5,000
SALES (est): 2.2MM
SALES (corp-wide): 4.1MM Privately Held
WEB: www.aatrucksleeper.com
SIC: 3713 Truck & bus bodies
PA: Mocap Partners, L.P.
   5535 Airport Fwy
   Haltom City TX 76117
   817 920-7599

(G-13496)
ACE RUBBER PRODUCTS INC
832 Valley Ln (76060-4424)
P.O. Box 129 (76060-0129)
PHONE..............................817 572-1011
James R Ott, *President*
Arthur O Briant, *President*
Arthur O'Briant, *Vice Pres*
▲ EMP: 15
SQ FT: 15,000
SALES (est): 2.1MM Privately Held
WEB: www.acerubberproducts.com
SIC: 3053 3069 3061 Gaskets & sealing devices; molded rubber products; mechanical rubber goods

(G-13497)
HARRISON JET GUNS II LP
6915 Hudson Village Crk (76060-7419)
PHONE..............................817 478-9216
Theodore Harrison, *Partner*
EMP: 64
SQ FT: 46,756
SALES (corp-wide): 9.4MM Privately Held
WEB: www.harrisonjetguns.com
SIC: 2892 Explosives

PA: Harrison Jet Guns Ii Lp
   8582 Katy Fwy Ste 162
   Houston TX 77024
   713 467-8282

(G-13498)
HEXPOL COMPOUNDING LLC
Also Called: Chase Elastomers
635 Tower Dr (76060-3013)
PHONE..............................817 483-9797
Walt Williams, *Manager*
EMP: 73
SQ FT: 57,600
SALES (corp-wide): 1.6B Privately Held
WEB: www.hexpolcompounding.com
SIC: 3087 2891 2821 2822 Custom compound purchased resins; adhesives & sealants; plastics materials & resins; synthetic rubber
HQ: Hexpol Compounding Llc
   14330 Kinsman Rd
   Burton OH 44021
   440 834-4644

(G-13499)
MIKE CONKLES CUSTOM CABINETS
318 W Mansfield Hwy (76060-2420)
P.O. Box 468 (76060-0468)
PHONE..............................817 483-9658
Michael Conkle, *President*
Cara Conkle, *Vice Pres*
EMP: 40
SQ FT: 25,000
SALES (est): 4.8MM Privately Held
WEB: www.mikeconkle.com
SIC: 1751 2434 Cabinet building & installation; wood kitchen cabinets

(G-13500)
MONTGOMERY MFG CO LLC
Also Called: MMC
118 Industrial Ct (76060-4800)
PHONE..............................817 478-3221
Peter Zehr, *President*
EMP: 14
SQ FT: 11,000
SALES (est): 4.6MM Privately Held
WEB: www.montgomerymfg.com
SIC: 2841 Detergents, synthetic organic or inorganic alkaline

(G-13501)
RE WATSON & ASSOCIATES INC
620 Tower Dr (76060-3012)
P.O. Box 691 (76060-0691)
PHONE..............................817 478-4401
Mark A Watson, *President*
Cindy Watson, *Vice Pres*
▲ EMP: 35
SQ FT: 10,000
SALES: 2.7MM Privately Held
WEB: www.re-watson.com
SIC: 3231 2499 Doors, glass: made from purchased glass; picture & mirror frames, wood

(G-13502)
REDI-MIX LP
4040 S Eden Rd (76060-7412)
PHONE..............................817 561-9785
Mark Weir, *Manager*
EMP: 33
SQ FT: 4,224
SALES (corp-wide): 1.4B Publicly Held
SIC: 3273 Ready-mixed concrete
HQ: Redi-Mix Lp
   1445 Mac Arthur Dr # 136
   Carrollton TX 75007
   972 242-4550

(G-13503)
SPEED-FAB-CRETE CORP INTL
1150 E Kennedale Pkwy (76060-3008)
P.O. Box 15580, Fort Worth (76119-0580)
PHONE..............................817 572-0351
David Bloxom, *President*
Jeff Harwell, *Division Mgr*
Roger Hamm, *Superintendent*
Jeff Spedding, *Vice Pres*
Janis Petry, *Project Mgr*
▲ EMP: 125
SQ FT: 8,900

SALES (est): 46.5MM Privately Held
WEB: www.speedfab-crete.com
SIC: 1542 3272 Commercial & office building, new construction; concrete products

(G-13504)
SUBURBAN SHEET METAL LTD
528 Eden Rd (76060-3000)
P.O. Box 739 (76060-0739)
PHONE..............................817 478-0801
Steve A Simmons, *President*
Cheryl Simmons, *Vice Pres*
Caleb Green, *Warehouse Mgr*
EMP: 22
SQ FT: 23,000
SALES (est): 3.8MM Privately Held
WEB: www.suburbansheetmetal.com
SIC: 3444 Gutters, sheet metal; ducts, sheet metal

(G-13505)
TMF GRAPHICS INC
Also Called: Foxy Propaganda
408 W Kennedale Pkwy (76060-4616)
PHONE..............................817 483-0237
Tom M Fowler, *President*
Brian Hamilton, *Vice Pres*
Paige Hodges, *Prdtn Mgr*
EMP: 15
SQ FT: 4,000
SALES (est): 2.5MM Privately Held
WEB: www.foxypropaganda.com
SIC: 2752 Commercial printing, offset

(G-13506)
UM ABRASIVES INC
831 Trent St (76060-4411)
PHONE..............................817 572-1344
Nicholas K Ferrara, *President*
Mike Ferrara, *Vice Pres*
Mary Ferrara, *Treasurer*
Alex Ferrara, *Admin Sec*
EMP: 10
SQ FT: 21,000
SALES (est): 1.3MM Privately Held
WEB: www.umabrasives.com
SIC: 3291 Abrasive products
PA: Ultramatic Equipment Co.
   8603 E Royal Palm Rd # 260
   Scottsdale AZ 85258
   480 951-6000

(G-13507)
US GALVANIZING LP
1530 Gilman Rd (76060)
P.O. Box 1485, Hurst (76053-1485)
PHONE..............................817 572-2280
Russell Wallace, *Partner*
Greg Haskin, *Partner*
Jim Mason, *Partner*
EMP: 45
SALES (est): 4.3MM Privately Held
SIC: 3479 Galvanizing of iron, steel or end-formed products

Kermit
Winkler County

(G-13508)
BASIC ENERGY SERVICES INC
312 E Hwy 302 (79745)
P.O. Box 53710, Midland (79710-3710)
PHONE..............................432 586-2586
EMP: 130
SALES (corp-wide): 567.2MM Publicly Held
WEB: www.basices.com
SIC: 1389 Oil field services
PA: Basic Energy Services, Inc.
   801 Cherry St Unit 2
   Fort Worth TX 76102
   817 334-4100

(G-13509)
BASS ENTERPRISES PRODUCTION CO
7 Mile Rd Ne (79745)
PHONE..............................432 586-2563
EMP: 26
SALES (corp-wide): 255.7MM Privately Held
WEB: www.texaco.com
SIC: 1311 Crude petroleum & natural gas

PA: Bass Enterprises Production Co
   201 Main St Ste 2700
   Fort Worth TX 76102
   817 698-0200

(G-13510)
BUSTERS WELL SERVICE INC (PA)
1600 Monahans Hwy (79745)
P.O. Box 1119 (79745-1119)
PHONE..............................432 586-2533
Jessie Shelton, *President*
Mike Sims, *Vice Pres*
Angie Sims, *Treasurer*
EMP: 72
SQ FT: 3,000
SALES (est): 11.2MM Privately Held
SIC: 1381 1781 Reworking oil & gas wells; water well drilling

(G-13511)
ELD OPERATIONS LLC
4529 E State Rt 302 (79745)
PHONE..............................630 338-5425
EMP: 73
SALES (est): 1.8MM Privately Held
SIC: 2411 Logging

(G-13512)
EOG RESOURCES INC
107 E Winkler St (79745-4200)
PHONE..............................432 586-9141
Mark Papa, *Branch Mgr*
Christine Fallon, *Legal Staff*
EMP: 14
SALES (corp-wide): 17.3B Publicly Held
WEB: www.eogresources.com
SIC: 1382 Oil & gas exploration services
PA: Eog Resources, Inc.
   1111 Bagby Sky Lbby 2
   Houston TX 77002
   713 651-7000

(G-13513)
PB MATERIALS HOLDINGS INC
Also Called: Kermit Concrete
602 N East Ave (79745-3505)
PHONE..............................432 208-2761
Dave L Vickers, *CEO*
Audrey Daniel,
Steven Underwood,
EMP: 80
SALES (corp-wide): 26.1MM Privately Held
WEB: www.pb-materials.com
SIC: 3273 Ready-mixed concrete
PA: Pb Materials Holdings, Inc.
   4001 E 42nd St Ste 100
   Odessa TX 79762
   432 563-8036

(G-13514)
POWER LINE INFRSTRCTURE SVCS I
Also Called: Tessco
422 W Austin St (79745-2402)
P.O. Box 771 (79745-0771)
PHONE..............................432 586-2518
Lindale Witner, *Manager*
EMP: 40
SALES (corp-wide): 579MM Privately Held
WEB: www.tesscoenergy.com
SIC: 1389 Oil field services
HQ: Power Line Infrastructure Services, Inc.
   1031 Andrews Hwy
   Midland TX 79701
   432 682-1991

(G-13515)
WEATHRFORD ARTFL LIFT SYSTEMS
159 W Hwy 302 (79745)
PHONE..............................432 586-3883
EMP: 32 Privately Held
WEB: www.weatherford.com
SIC: 1389 Oil field services
HQ: Weatherford Artificial Lift Systems, Llc
   2000 Saint James Pl
   Houston TX 77056
   713 836-4000

Kerrville
Kerr County

(G-13516)
ADVANCED WEAPONS AND ARMOR INC
2220 Medina Hwy (78028-8041)
P.O. Box 291571 (78029-1571)
PHONE.................................830 459-5263
Chris L Griffin, *President*
EMP: 30
SALES (est): 5MM **Privately Held**
SIC: 3484 5091 Small arms; firearms, sporting

(G-13517)
ALL PLASTIC LLC
200 Holdsworth Dr (78028-3372)
PHONE.................................830 896-6464
EMP: 55
SALES (est): 15.7MM **Privately Held**
WEB: www.all-plastics.com
SIC: 3089 Injection molding of plastics

(G-13518)
ANDERSON SOFTWARE LLC
1645 Harper Rd (78028-2994)
P.O. Box 294867 (78029-4867)
PHONE.................................936 569-0447
Stephanie Anderson, *General Mgr*
Chelsea Shipman, *Vice Pres*
Kevin Anderson,
EMP: 10
SALES (est): 285K **Privately Held**
WEB: www.andersoft.com
SIC: 7372 7371 Application computer software; computer software development

(G-13519)
FOX TANK COMPANY (PA)
117 Airport Commerce Pkwy (78028-7013)
P.O. Box 295309 (78029-5309)
PHONE.................................830 792-0770
Richard Fox, *President*
Nathan Fox, *Vice Pres*
Josh McCasland, *Accounts Exec*
Scott Coco, *Sales Staff*
EMP: 16
SALES (est): 16.6MM **Privately Held**
WEB: www.foxtankcompany.com
SIC: 5084 3443 Tanks, storage; industrial vessels, tanks & containers

(G-13520)
HERRING PRINTING CO
615 Water St (78028-5394)
PHONE.................................830 257-7242
Joe R Herring Sr, *President*
Joe R Herring Jr, *Manager*
EMP: 10 EST: 1965
SQ FT: 4,200
SALES (est): 600K **Privately Held**
WEB: www.herringprinting.com
SIC: 2752 Commercial printing, offset

(G-13521)
INGRAM READYMIX INC
2022 Sidney Baker St C (78028-2530)
PHONE.................................830 896-4525
Andy Simon, *Manager*
EMP: 17
SALES (corp-wide): 125.6MM **Privately Held**
WEB: www.ingramreadymixinc.com
SIC: 3273 Ready-mixed concrete
PA: Ingram Readymix, Inc.
3580 Farm Market 482
New Braunfels TX 78132
830 625-9156

(G-13522)
LASMER INDUSTRIES INC
555 Mill Run (78028-9457)
PHONE.................................830 895-4400
Charles Hickey Jr, *President*
Larry Howard, *General Mgr*
Doris Evelyn Hickey, *Vice Pres*
EMP: 14
SQ FT: 20,000
SALES (est): 2MM **Privately Held**
WEB: www.lasmer.com
SIC: 3711 Military motor vehicle assembly

(G-13523)
MILTON BERNHARD MEAT PROC
2590 Junction Hwy Ste D (78028-9467)
P.O. Box 58, Ingram (78025-0058)
PHONE.................................830 367-2995
Mark Lampson, *President*
EMP: 12
SALES (est): 650K **Privately Held**
WEB: www.bernhardmeat.com
SIC: 2013 5421 Sausages & other prepared meats; meat markets, including freezer provisioners

(G-13524)
MOONEY AEROSPACE GROUP LTD (PA)
165 Al Mooney Rd (78028-8388)
PHONE.................................830 896-6000
Sol Mayer, *President*
Barry Hodkin, *Vice Pres*
EMP: 37
SQ FT: 353,634
SALES (est): 13.4MM **Privately Held**
WEB: www.mooney.com
SIC: 3721 3728 7699 Aircraft; aircraft parts & equipment; aircraft flight instrument repair

(G-13525)
MOONEY AIRPLANE COMPANY INC
165 Al Mooney Rd (78028-8388)
PHONE.................................830 896-6000
Dennis E Ferguson, *CEO*
Solomon Mayer, *President*
Jon Greenwood, *CFO*
EMP: 400
SQ FT: 210,000
SALES (est): 58.1MM **Privately Held**
WEB: www.mooney.com
SIC: 3721 3724 Aircraft; aircraft engines & engine parts

(G-13526)
SOUTHERN NEWSPAPERS INC
Also Called: Kerrville Daily Times
429 Jefferson St (78028-4412)
P.O. Box 1428 (78029)
PHONE.................................830 896-7000
Greg Shrader, *Publisher*
Bill Begley, *Editor*
Christina McDonald, *Business Mgr*
Lissa Vahldiek, *COO*
Maynard Webb, *COO*
EMP: 21
SALES (corp-wide): 140.3MM **Privately Held**
WEB: www.sninews.com
SIC: 2711 Job printing & newspaper publishing combined
PA: Southern Newspapers, Inc.
5701 Woodway Dr Ste 131
Houston TX 77057
713 266-5481

(G-13527)
SYRGIS HOLDINGS INC (PA)
1607 Junction Hwy (78028-9300)
PHONE.................................361 438-1139
Todd Gaddie, *Vice Pres*
EMP: 9
SALES (est): 804.5K **Privately Held**
SIC: 3533 Oil & gas field machinery

(G-13528)
VIANT MEDICAL INC
200 Holdsworth Dr (78028-3372)
PHONE.................................830 792-1156
EMP: 15
SALES (corp-wide): 458.7MM **Privately Held**
WEB: www.viantmedical.com
SIC: 3841 Surgical & medical instruments
HQ: Viant Medical, Inc.
6 Century Ln
South Plainfield NJ 07080
908 561-0717

Kilgore
Gregg County

(G-13529)
A & M TUBULAR MAINTENANCE INC
1004 N Longview St (75662-5420)
PHONE.................................903 983-1007
Fax: 903 983-3187
EMP: 50
SQ FT: 5,000
SALES (est): 1.9MM **Privately Held**
SIC: 1389 Oil Field Service
HQ: Tesco Corporation (Us)
515 W Greens Rd Ste 1200
Houston TX 77067

(G-13530)
A & R ENTERPRISES INC (PA)
Also Called: Service Electric
4302 State Highway 42 (75662-8641)
P.O. Box 1578 (75663-1578)
PHONE.................................903 984-9057
Grady McBryde III, *President*
Jimmy Wolford, *Vice Pres*
EMP: 19
SQ FT: 2,000
SALES (est): 3.3MM **Privately Held**
WEB: www.serviceelectricco.com
SIC: 1731 7694 General electrical contractor; electric motor repair

(G-13531)
ALINET OILFIELD SERVICES CORP
2019 S Henderson Blvd A (75662-3567)
P.O. Box 2468 (75663-2468)
PHONE.................................903 984-2307
Thomas F Patton III, *President*
EMP: 30
SALES (est): 5MM **Privately Held**
SIC: 1389 Oil & gas field services

(G-13532)
ARPCO VALVES & CONTROLS LLC
120 Marvin A Smith Rd (75662-5373)
P.O. Box 68, Overton (75684-0068)
PHONE.................................903 834-7007
Gary Turner, *President*
EMP: 11 EST: 2010
SALES (est): 1.5MM **Privately Held**
WEB: www.arpcovalves.com
SIC: 1389 Servicing oil & gas wells; oil field services

(G-13533)
BAKER PETROLITE
Also Called: Baker Hughes
1100 Stone Rd Ste 107 (75662-5494)
P.O. Box 2019 (75663-2019)
PHONE.................................903 984-0251
Kevin Cline, *Accounts Mgr*
Larry White, *Manager*
EMP: 20
SALES (corp-wide): 23.8B **Publicly Held**
WEB: www.bakerhughes.com
SIC: 1389 Oil field services
HQ: Baker Petrolite
2121 W Mary St
Garden City KS 67846

(G-13534)
C&S LEASE SERVICE LC (PA)
1873 Fm 1252 E (75662-4916)
P.O. Box 1049 (75663-1049)
PHONE.................................903 988-8642
Shawn Bates, *President*
Jeffrey Gayler, *Vice Pres*
Robert Wood, *Vice Pres*
Chris Hightree, *Project Mgr*
Jesse Killian, *Project Mgr*
EMP: 50
SQ FT: 2,200
SALES (est): 11.9MM **Privately Held**
WEB: www.cslease.com
SIC: 1389 1623 6531 7389 Oil field services; pipeline construction; real estate agents & managers; financial services; insurance agents, brokers & service; barber & beauty shop equipment

(G-13535)
CANON SAFETY SERVICES LTD (PA)
Also Called: Canon Safety/ Rhi Group
1800 Cox Dr (75662-8576)
P.O. Box 5504, Longview (75608-5504)
PHONE.................................903 984-5928
Rodney Hammer, *President*
Matt Croom, *General Mgr*
Rod Hammer, *Principal*
Tony Barto, *Vice Pres*
Robyn Ashmore, *Purch Mgr*
EMP: 14
SALES (est): 7.6MM **Privately Held**
WEB: www.csrhigroup.com
SIC: 1389 Oil field services; gas field services

(G-13536)
COMMAND PACKAGING LLC
Also Called: Pak-Sher
2500 N Longview St (75662-6840)
PHONE.................................903 984-8596
EMP: 10 **Privately Held**
WEB: www.commandpackaging.com
SIC: 2673 Bags: plastic, laminated & coated
HQ: Command Packaging, Llc
3840 E 26th St
Vernon CA 90058
323 980-0918

(G-13537)
COMPLETE PIPE SERVICES LLC
5678 Fm 1249 E (75662-8127)
P.O. Box 1753 (75663-1753)
PHONE.................................903 988-1124
Mike White,
EMP: 45
SALES (est): 4.4MM **Privately Held**
WEB: www.completepipeservices.com
SIC: 1389 Pipeline & power line inspection service

(G-13538)
CORE LABORATORIES LP
Also Called: Protechnics
2505 State Hwy (75662)
PHONE.................................903 984-4223
Todd Sachse, *Manager*
EMP: 54
SALES (corp-wide): 668.2MM **Privately Held**
WEB: www.corelab.com
SIC: 1389 Oil field services
HQ: Core Laboratories Lp
6316 Windfern Rd
Houston TX 77040

(G-13539)
CPI SATCOM & ANTENNA TECH INC
Also Called: Large Antennas Division
2600 N Longview St (75662-6842)
PHONE.................................903 984-0555
Earl Davis, *General Mgr*
Betty Pruitt, *Vice Pres*
Daniel Atkins, *Engineer*
Alan Pollard, *Branch Mgr*
Dan Roessner, *Info Tech Dir*
EMP: 395 **Privately Held**
WEB: www.gdmissionsystems.com
SIC: 3663 Antennas, transmitting & communications
HQ: Cpi Satcom & Antenna Technologies Inc.
1700 Cable Dr Ne
Conover NC 28613
704 462-7330

(G-13540)
CPI SATCOM & ANTENNA TECH INC
Also Called: Gd Satcom-Cpg
2600 N Longview St (75662-6842)
PHONE.................................903 984-0555
Brian Mc Cormick, *Manager*
Jeremy Maggart, *Instructor*
EMP: 70 **Privately Held**
WEB: www.gdmissionsystems.com
SIC: 3663 Antennas, transmitting & communications

HQ: Cpi Satcom & Antenna Technologies Inc.
1700 Cable Dr Ne
Conover NC 28613
704 462-7330

(G-13541)
CREATIVE COATINGS INC (PA)
Also Called: East Texas Paint & Coating
428 N Longview St (75662-5810)
PHONE..................................903 984-8454
Lisa Turner, *President*
E Dale Turner, *Vice Pres*
Diane Malone, *Manager*
EMP: 10 **EST:** 1970
SQ FT: 17,280
SALES (est): 2.2MM **Privately Held**
WEB: www.ccipaints.com
SIC: 2851 5198 Paints & paint additives; lacquers, varnishes, enamels & other coatings; paint brushes, rollers, sprayers

(G-13542)
CUDD PRESSURE CONTROL INC
Also Called: Cudd Pumping Services
2600 N Hwy 135 (75662)
P.O. Box 1447 (75663-1447)
PHONE..................................903 988-2161
Marty Yohn, *Manager*
EMP: 150
SALES (corp-wide): 1.7B **Publicly Held**
WEB: www.cuddenergyservices.com
SIC: 1389 1382 Oil field services; oil & gas exploration services
HQ: Cudd Pressure Control, Inc.
2828 Tech Forest Blvd
The Woodlands TX 77381
832 295-5555

(G-13543)
CW FORD RENTALS LP (PA)
1603 N Longview St (75662-5447)
P.O. Box 3156 (75663-3156)
PHONE..................................903 935-7608
Danny Modisette, *Mng Member*
EMP: 26
SQ FT: 10,000
SALES (est): 15MM **Privately Held**
SIC: 1389 Gas field services

(G-13544)
DIALOG WIRELINE SERVICES L L C (PA)
3100 Maverick Dr (75662-9032)
PHONE..................................903 988-2311
Chris Chitwood, *President*
James Bubba, *Vice Pres*
Derek Garland, *Vice Pres*
Tim Marsh, *Vice Pres*
Mark Blanks, *CFO*
EMP: 49
SQ FT: 20,000
SALES (est): 20.4MM **Privately Held**
WEB: www.dialogwireline.com
SIC: 1389 Oil field services

(G-13545)
DOUBLE R CONSTRUCTION INC
6202 State Highway 42 N (75662-5398)
P.O. Box 2919 (75663-2919)
PHONE..................................903 452-7890
Ricky Leslie, *President*
Ronnie Hallonquist, *Vice Pres*
EMP: 22
SQ FT: 800
SALES (est): 3.7MM **Privately Held**
SIC: 1389 Construction, repair & dismantling services

(G-13546)
DRAG N FLY TRUCKING
434 Copperhead Trl (75662-2182)
PHONE..................................903 987-0027
Raymond Allen, *Owner*
EMP: 15
SALES (est): 750K **Privately Held**
SIC: 1389 Haulage, oil field

(G-13547)
DRILLTOOLS
4001 Enterprise St (75662-7791)
P.O. Box 3366 (75663-3366)
PHONE..................................903 986-3745
Chris S Thompson, *Principal*
Dallyce Morris,

EMP: 14 **EST:** 2010
SALES (est): 2.3MM **Privately Held**
WEB: www.drilltoolsinc.com
SIC: 1389 Oil field services

(G-13548)
DROVER ENERGY SERVICES LLC
2505 N Longview St (75662-6839)
PHONE..................................903 986-8911
Jeff Bolding, *CEO*
Kathleen Kee, *COO*
▲ **EMP:** 20
SALES (est): 1.9MM **Privately Held**
WEB: www.droverenergy.com
SIC: 1389 Oil field services

(G-13549)
EDWARDS SPTIC GREASE TRCK SVCS
2821 State Highway 42 N (75662-5380)
PHONE..................................903 643-7585
EMP: 12
SALES (est): 1.1MM **Privately Held**
WEB: www.edwardsseptic.net
SIC: 5039 3089 Septic tanks; septic tanks, plastic

(G-13550)
ENCORE WELLHEAD SYSTEMS LLC
2850 State Highway 42 (75662-8896)
PHONE..................................903 983-4481
EMP: 29
SALES (corp-wide): 37.9MM **Privately Held**
WEB: www.encorewellhead.com
SIC: 1389 Bailing, cleaning, swabbing & treating of wells
PA: Encore Wellhead Systems, Llc
3403 Marquart St
Houston TX 77027
832 742-1350

(G-13551)
ESCO GROUP LLC
2103 State Highway 31 E (75662-6809)
PHONE..................................903 984-3726
EMP: 50
SALES (corp-wide): 3.4B **Privately Held**
WEB: www.escocorp.com
SIC: 3535 Conveyors & conveying equipment
HQ: Esco Group Llc
2141 Nw 25th Ave
Portland OR 97210
503 228-2141

(G-13552)
ESTIS COMPRESSION LLC
2019 State Highway 135 N (75662-6211)
P.O. Box 3247 (75663-3247)
PHONE..................................318 397-5557
Dennis W Estis,
EMP: 41
SALES (est): 5.7MM **Privately Held**
WEB: www.estiscompression.com
SIC: 1389 Oil field services

(G-13553)
FESCO LTD
206 Beall St (75662-5002)
PHONE..................................903 984-4814
Cody Daniels, *Production*
Cheryl Antonini, *Office Mgr*
John Lockman, *Branch Mgr*
Ruby Soza, *Supervisor*
EMP: 26
SQ FT: 3,000
SALES (corp-wide): 201MM **Privately Held**
WEB: www.fescoinc.com
SIC: 1389 Oil field services
PA: Fesco, Ltd.
1000 Fesco Dr
Alice TX 78332
361 664-3479

(G-13554)
FMC TECHNOLOGIES INC
640 Four S Indus Blvd (75662-5292)
PHONE..................................281 591-4000
EMP: 12

SALES (corp-wide): 13.4B **Privately Held**
WEB: www.technipfmc.com
SIC: 3533 Oil field machinery & equipment
HQ: Fmc Technologies, Inc.
11740 Katy Fwy Enrgy Twr
Houston TX 77079
281 591-4000

(G-13555)
FREEDOM COMMUNICATION TECH INC
2002 Synergy Blvd Ste 200 (75662-7799)
PHONE..................................844 903-7333
Ricardo Viloria, *President*
EMP: 25
SALES (est): 6.7MM
SALES (corp-wide): 772.7MM **Publicly Held**
WEB: www.freedomcte.com
SIC: 3829 Measuring & controlling devices
PA: Astronics Corporation
130 Commerce Way
East Aurora NY 14052
716 805-1599

(G-13556)
GEONIX OPERATING LP (PA)
2008 N Longview St (75662-6830)
P.O. Box 2169 (75663-2169)
PHONE..................................903 983-3249
Brad George, *General Mgr*
Terry George, *General Ptnr*
Diane Gilberg, *Receptionist*
EMP: 20
SQ FT: 25,000
SALES (est): 1MM **Privately Held**
WEB: www.geonixlp.com
SIC: 1389 Oil field services

(G-13557)
HEAVY EQUIPMENT MAINTENANCE CO (PA)
Also Called: Hemco
418 Hwy 42 West Access Rd (75662)
P.O. Box 3333 (75663-3333)
PHONE..................................903 984-9076
Jewel Beasley, *President*
Bonnie Beasley, *Corp Secy*
Robert Little, *Systems Dir*
EMP: 29
SQ FT: 8,000
SALES (est): 3.6MM **Privately Held**
WEB: www.hemcokilgoretx.com
SIC: 7699 5084 3599 Industrial machinery & equipment repair; engines, gasoline; machine shop, jobbing & repair

(G-13558)
HERRIN WELDING SERVICE INC
Also Called: Herrin Haulers
11763 County Road 281 N (75662-9020)
PHONE..................................903 984-7139
Larry Herrin, *President*
Karen Hartnett, *Treasurer*
Judy Moore, *Shareholder*
Donna Whitkey, *Shareholder*
Jean Clinkscales, *Admin Sec*
EMP: 14
SQ FT: 38,000
SALES: 492.5K **Privately Held**
WEB: www.herrinhauler.com
SIC: 7692 Welding repair

(G-13559)
HYDESSCO LLC
2505 N Longview St (75662-6839)
PHONE..................................903 983-2021
Lloyd Vanderwater, *General Mgr*
Greg Todd,
EMP: 15
SQ FT: 28,000
SALES (est): 2.9MM **Privately Held**
WEB: www.hydessco.com
SIC: 1389 Oil field services

(G-13560)
KEY ENERGY DRILLING INC
111 State Highway 31 E (75662-6213)
P.O. Box 671 (75663-0671)
PHONE..................................713 651-4300
Brett Dupree, *Manager*
EMP: 9

SALES (corp-wide): 413.8MM **Publicly Held**
WEB: www.keyenergy.com
SIC: 1381 1389 Drilling oil & gas wells; oil field services
HQ: Key Energy Drilling, Inc.
1301 Mckinney St Ste 1800
Houston TX 77010

(G-13561)
KIL-TEX OILFIELD SERVICES LLC
524 Gladewater St (75662-2408)
PHONE..................................903 736-5051
Aurelio A Amaro, *President*
Evelyn Amaro, *Admin Sec*
EMP: 9
SALES (est): 1.5MM **Privately Held**
WEB: www.kiltexllc.com
SIC: 1389 Oil field services

(G-13562)
KOMATSU MINING CORP
Also Called: Joy Global
2320 State Highway 42 N (75662-5556)
PHONE..................................903 983-7744
Dave Jones, *President*
Connie Abernathy, *Assistant*
EMP: 48 **Privately Held**
WEB: www.mining.komatsu
SIC: 3532 Mining machinery
HQ: Komatsu Mining Corp.
100 E Wscnsin Ave Ste 278
Milwaukee WI 53202
414 319-8500

(G-13563)
LONE STAR CAST MCH PARTNERS LP
3102 Maverick Dr (75662-9032)
PHONE..................................903 986-8300
James Lane Vanderslice, *Partner*
Sherry Vanderslice, *Partner*
EMP: 12
SALES (est): 700K **Privately Held**
WEB: www.lonestarcasting.com
SIC: 3569 3324 3325 Centrifuges, industrial; aerospace investment castings, ferrous; alloy steel castings, except investment; bushings, cast steel: except investment

(G-13564)
LONG TRUSTS
118 S Kilgore St (75662-2516)
P.O. Box 3096 (75663-3096)
PHONE..................................903 984-5017
Virginia Long, *Trustee*
Sammy Adamson, *Trustee*
Larry T Long, *Trustee*
Lary Long, *Trustee*
Laura Cox, *Bookkeeper*
EMP: 15 **EST:** 1971
SQ FT: 2,000
SALES (est): 1.7MM **Privately Held**
SIC: 1311 Crude petroleum production; natural gas production

(G-13565)
LUFKIN INDUSTRIES LLC
1120 Marvin A Smith Rd (75662-5294)
PHONE..................................903 986-9080
EMP: 24
SALES (corp-wide): 148.5B **Publicly Held**
SIC: 1389 Oil/Gas Field Services
HQ: Lufkin Industries, Llc
601 S Raguet St
Lufkin TX 75904
936 634-2211

(G-13566)
LUFKIN INDUSTRIES LLC
Also Called: Lufkin Automation
7155 Hwy 42 N (75662)
P.O. Box 3095 (75663-3095)
PHONE..................................903 984-3875
Jass Stephens, *Branch Mgr*
EMP: 27
SALES (corp-wide): 1B **Privately Held**
WEB: www.bhge.com
SIC: 1389 Oil field services
PA: Lufkin Gears Llc
409 Ellis Ave
Lufkin TX 75904
936 634-2211

(G-13567)
MA-TEX WIRE ROPE CO INC (DH)
Also Called: Matex Co
1975 Frm To Mkt Rd 1252 E (75662)
PHONE..............................903 984-9691
Clarence Michael Matthews, *President*
Ken Norris, *Accounts Mgr*
Steve Drew, *Sales Staff*
▲ **EMP:** 20 **EST:** 1983
SQ FT: 11,080
SALES (est): 13.2MM
SALES (corp-wide): 3.1B **Privately Held**
WEB: www.matex.us
SIC: 5051 2298 7699 Rope, wire (not in-
sulated); slings, rope; miscellaneous au-
tomotive repair services
HQ: Bishop Lifting Products, Inc.
125 Mccarty St
Houston TX
713 674-2266

(G-13568)
MARTIN MIDSTREAM GP LLC
4200 Stone Rd (75662-6935)
P.O. Box 191 (75663-0191)
PHONE..............................903 983-6200
Ruben S Martin, *President*
Randall L Tauscher, *COO*
Scot A Shoup, *Senior VP*
Robert D Bondurant, *CFO*
Chris H Booth, *EMP:* 735
SALES (est): 18.1MM
SALES (corp-wide): 1.6B **Privately Held**
WEB: www.martinmidstream.com
SIC: 5171 1321 4226 Petroleum bulk sta-
tions; natural gas liquids production; pe-
troleum & chemical bulk stations &
terminals for hire
PA: Martin Resource Management Corpo-
ration
4200 Stone Rd
Kilgore TX 75662
903 983-6200

(G-13569)
MARTIN MIDSTREAM PARTNERS LP (PA)
4200 Stone Rd (75662-6935)
P.O. Box 191 (75663-0191)
PHONE..............................903 983-6200
Ruben S Martin, *Partner*
Martin Midstream GP LLC, *General Ptnr*
Randall L Tauscher, *COO*
Scot A Shoup, *Senior VP*
Jeff Ballew, *Vice Pres*
EMP: 74
SALES: 847.1MM **Publicly Held**
WEB: www.martinmidstream.com
SIC: 5171 1321 4226 Petroleum bulk sta-
tions; natural gas liquids production; pe-
troleum & chemical bulk stations &
terminals for hire

(G-13570)
MARTIN RESOURCE MGT CORP (PA)
4200 Stone Rd (75662-6935)
P.O. Box 191 (75663-0191)
PHONE..............................903 983-6200
Ruben S Martin III, *President*
Scot A Shoup, *Senior VP*
Mike Lawrence, *Vice Pres*
Johnnie Murry, *Vice Pres*
Douglas Towns, *Vice Pres*
◆ **EMP:** 140
SQ FT: 55,000
SALES: 1.6B **Privately Held**
WEB: www.themartincompanies.com
SIC: 2911 4924 5984 5172 Gases & liq-
uefied petroleum gases; natural gas distri-
bution; liquefied petroleum gas, delivered
to customers' premises; fuel oil; crude oil;
gases, liquefied petroleum (propane)

(G-13571)
MARTIN UNDERGROUND STORAGE
Also Called: Martin Gas Sales Kilgore Texas
4200 Stone Rd (75662-6935)
P.O. Box 191 (75663-0191)
PHONE..............................903 983-1551
Ruben S Martin III, *President*
Don Liles, *Credit Mgr*

George Moon, *Sales Staff*
Wesley Skelton, *Admin Sec*
EMP: 100
SALES (est): 609K
SALES (corp-wide): 1.6B **Privately Held**
WEB: www.martinmidstream.com
SIC: 1389 Oil field services
HQ: Martin Product Sales Llc
4200 Stone Rd
Kilgore TX 75662
903 983-6200

(G-13572)
MAVERICK WELL SERVICE LLC
Also Called: Kbr Well Service
300 Fm 1252 E (75662-5385)
P.O. Box 1842 (75663-1842)
PHONE..............................903 983-6050
James Abell, *President*
James Idell, *Vice Pres*
William R Maxwell, *Vice Pres*
Rodney L Williams, *Treasurer*
Stacy Green Wood, *Human Resources*
EMP: 15 **EST:** 2006
SALES (est): 3.5MM **Privately Held**
WEB: www.maverickwellservice.com
SIC: 1389 Oil field services

(G-13573)
MEGA OIL CORPORATION
Also Called: Omega Oilfield Services
226 Hwy 42 W Access Rd (75662-0001)
P.O. Box 1793 (75663-1793)
PHONE..............................903 984-7050
John Newman, *President*
EMP: 30
SALES (est): 6.4MM **Privately Held**
WEB: www.omegaoilfield.com
SIC: 1389 Oil field services

(G-13574)
MERRITT PRFRRED COMPONENTS INC (PA)
703 Old Highway 135 S (75662-7673)
P.O. Box 1209 (75663-1209)
PHONE..............................903 983-1592
AP Merritt Jr, *President*
Jeffrey D Frisby, *Chairman*
Thomas C Merritt, *Corp Secy*
Bryan Johnston, *Vice Pres*
M David Kornblatt, *Vice Pres*
EMP: 55 **EST:** 1928
SQ FT: 75,000
SALES (est): 18.6MM **Privately Held**
WEB: www.merrittpreferred.com
SIC: 3599 3533 3728 7692 Machine
shop, jobbing & repair; oil field machinery
& equipment; aircraft parts & equipment;
wing assemblies & parts, aircraft; gears,
aircraft power transmission; aircraft land-
ing assemblies & brakes; welding repair;
guided missile & space vehicle parts &
auxiliary equipment

(G-13575)
MODISETTE WELDING & SUPPLY
3616 River Rd (75662-4989)
P.O. Box 2977 (75663-2977)
PHONE..............................903 984-2502
Christopher Modisette, *President*
Lori Davis,
EMP: 30
SQ FT: 12,000
SALES (est): 4.5MM **Privately Held**
WEB: www.modisette-oilfield.com
SIC: 7692 Welding repair

(G-13576)
MUSTANG GAS COMPRESSION LLC (PA)
2500 Woodbine Dr (75662-1269)
P.O. Box 866, Bellville (77418-0866)
PHONE..............................903 218-4459
John Mark Story, *President*
R Phipps, *Vice Pres*
Nic Rogers, *Vice Pres*
M S Chapline, *Treasurer*
EMP: 55 **EST:** 2007
SALES (est): 65.5MM **Privately Held**
WEB: www.mustangcompression.com
SIC: 1389 Oil field services

(G-13577)
NATIONAL OILWELL VARCO INC
Also Called: National Oilwell Bowen Tls Div
3108 Maverick Dr (75662-9032)
P.O. Box 1888 (75663-1888)
PHONE..............................903 984-2553
Roderick Taylor, *Technical Mgr*
Don Colley, *Manager*
EMP: 19
SALES (corp-wide): 8.4B **Publicly Held**
WEB: www.nov.com
SIC: 3533 5082 Oil field machinery &
equipment; oil field equipment
PA: National Oilwell Varco, Inc.
7909 Parkwood Circle Dr
Houston TX 77036
713 346-7500

(G-13578)
NOAHS SERVICE & SUPPLY LLC
1092 Marvin A Smith Rd (75662-5391)
P.O. Box 996 (75663-0996)
PHONE..............................903 218-6888
EMP: 9 **EST:** 2013
SQ FT: 800
SALES (est): 12MM **Privately Held**
WEB: www.performancebaseballtx.com
SIC: 1389 Oil field services

(G-13579)
NORTH AMERCN TUBULAR SVCS LLC
991 Marvin A Smith Rd (75662-5366)
P.O. Box 2070 (75663-2070)
PHONE..............................903 984-0625
Shawn R Grubbs, *Principal*
EMP: 13
SQ FT: 4,500
SALES (est): 1.9MM **Privately Held**
SIC: 1389 Pipe testing, oil field service;
servicing oil & gas wells

(G-13580)
OIL STATES ENERGY SERVICES LLC
3201 Goforth Rd (75662-8921)
PHONE..............................903 986-3791
Murray Dallas, *President*
EMP: 16
SALES (corp-wide): 1B **Publicly Held**
WEB: www.oses.com
SIC: 3533 5082 Oil field machinery &
equipment; oil field equipment
HQ: Oil States Energy Services, L.L.C.
333 Clay St Ste 2100
Houston TX 77002
713 425-2400

(G-13581)
PERMIAN TANK & MFG INC
3405 S Henderson Blvd (75662-4351)
P.O. Box 428 (75663-0428)
PHONE..............................903 984-2516
Dennis Pusser, *Branch Mgr*
Robert Ratzlaff, *Asst Mgr*
EMP: 95
SALES (corp-wide): 99.4MM **Privately Held**
WEB: www.permiantank.com
SIC: 3443 5082 Tanks, standard or cus-
tom fabricated: metal plate; oil field equip-
ment
PA: Permian Tank & Manufacturing, Inc.
2701 W Interstate 20
Odessa TX 79766
432 580-1050

(G-13582)
PIPE PROS LLC
3000 State Highway 42 (75662-8790)
PHONE..............................903 981-7801
Glenn Burkhart, *Branch Mgr*
EMP: 62
SALES (corp-wide): 100.6MM **Privately Held**
WEB: www.pipe-pros.com
SIC: 3494 Pipe fittings
PA: Pipe Pros, Llc
1729 N Clarkwood Rd # 10
Corpus Christi TX 78409
361 289-9090

(G-13583)
PREMIER PRESSURE PUMPING LLC
2310 Industrial Blvd (75662-9322)
P.O. Box 3567, Longview (75606-3567)
PHONE..............................903 981-0081
Lewis Brooks, *President*
Billy Williams, *Opers Mgr*
Ryan Dowling, *Engineer*
Nick Foster, *Accounts Mgr*
Thomas Bufkin, *Officer*
EMP: 15
SQ FT: 5,500
SALES (est): 12MM **Privately Held**
WEB: www.p3tx.com
SIC: 2911 Fractionation products of crude
petroleum, hydrocarbons

(G-13584)
PRO-TEST INC (PA)
454 Fm 1252 E (75662-0003)
PHONE..............................903 986-8404
Steve Stidham, *President*
Jeania Stidham, *Treasurer*
EMP: 31 **EST:** 2000
SALES (est): 4.5MM **Privately Held**
WEB: www.protestinc.net
SIC: 1382 Oil & gas exploration services

(G-13585)
PUMPS PLUS PUMP & VALVE REPAIR
508 S Commerce St (75662-2439)
PHONE..............................903 987-9232
Lance Silvertooth, *Owner*
EMP: 11 **EST:** 2013
SALES (est): 2.4MM **Privately Held**
WEB: www.pumpsplustx.com
SIC: 3561 Pumps & pumping equipment

(G-13586)
REVOLUTION PLASTICS LLC
Also Called: Paksher
2500 N Longview St (75662-6840)
PHONE..............................903 984-8596
Paul Haddad, *Sales Staff*
John Conway, *Manager*
Steve Jackson, *Manager*
EMP: 160
SALES (corp-wide): 18.7MM **Privately Held**
WEB: www.revolutionplastics.com
SIC: 3081 Polyethylene film
PA: Revolution Plastics, Llc
8801 Frazier Pike
Little Rock AR 72206
844 490-7873

(G-13587)
RIDDLES DEHI & CHEM SVC CO LLC
Also Called: E&P Services Group
1873 Fm 1252 E (75662-4916)
P.O. Box 1050 (75663-1050)
PHONE..............................903 986-3904
Bud Allred, *Sales Staff*
Jimmy Burgess, *Sales Staff*
Brian P Hancock,
Shawn M Bates,
EMP: 10
SQ FT: 200
SALES (est): 753.4K **Privately Held**
WEB: www.epservicesgroup.com
SIC: 1389 Oil field services

(G-13588)
RUSK COUNTY WELL SERVICE INC
118 S Kilgore St (75662-2516)
P.O. Box 1336 (75663-1336)
PHONE..............................903 984-5017
Larry T Long, *President*
Bettye V Long, *Corp Secy*
Paul E Bolt, *Vice Pres*
EMP: 20 **EST:** 1962
SQ FT: 1,200
SALES (est): 1.2MM **Privately Held**
WEB: www.ruskcountyoem.org
SIC: 1389 Servicing oil & gas wells

(G-13589)
SHALE FLOW SPECIALTIES LLC (PA)
300 Marvin A Smith Rd (75662-5382)
P.O. Box 6174, Longview (75608-6174)
PHONE.....................................903 218-6120
Jay Dean, *President*
Scott Harrell, *Human Res Mgr*
EMP: 22
SALES (est): 3.1MM **Privately Held**
WEB: www.givemshale.com
SIC: 1389 Oil field services

(G-13590)
SKEETER PRODUCTS INC (DH)
Also Called: Skeeter Boats
1 Skeeter Rd (75662-6157)
PHONE.....................................903 984-0541
Ben Spectals, *President*
Jeff Stone, *Senior VP*
Shannon Crawford, *Buyer*
Kim Ruiz, *Treasurer*
▼ EMP: 296 EST: 1948
SQ FT: 190,000
SALES (est): 100MM **Privately Held**
WEB: www.skeeterboats.com
SIC: 3732 Boats, fiberglass: building & re-pairing
HQ: Yamaha Motor Corporation Usa
6555 Katella Ave
Cypress CA 90630
714 761-7300

(G-13591)
SOUTHERN PLASTICS INC
Also Called: Csi
1010 Energy Dr (75662-5534)
PHONE.....................................903 984-6229
Thomas Degnan, *President*
Malcolm P Bundey, *President*
Marshall K White, *Principal*
Charles Cox, *Vice Pres*
Robet Smith, *Vice Pres*
▲ EMP: 159
SALES (est): 35.6MM **Privately Held**
SIC: 3089 Molding primary plastic
PA: Closure Systems International Hold-ings, Inc.
7820 Innovation Blvd # 10
Indianapolis IN 46278

(G-13592)
SPM FLOW CONTROL INC
1102 State Highway 31 W (75662-6746)
PHONE.....................................903 984-8153
William Free, *Branch Mgr*
EMP: 138
SALES (corp-wide): 3.4B **Privately Held**
WEB: www.global.weir
SIC: 3533 Oil & gas field machinery
HQ: S.P.M. Flow Control, Inc.
7601 Wyatt Dr
Fort Worth TX 76108
817 246-2461

(G-13593)
SSI MAXIM COMPANY INC
312 Higginbotham Rd (75662-2918)
P.O. Box 1954 (75663-1954)
PHONE.....................................903 984-5600
Pete Godfrey, *President*
Chris Steeley, *Vice Pres*
J Ty Sharp, *CFO*
Jeff Easley, *Sales Staff*
Paul Escobar, *Sales Staff*
EMP: 9
SQ FT: 2,400
SALES (est): 2.1MM **Privately Held**
WEB: www.ssimaxim.com
SIC: 2869 2879 Industrial organic chemi-cals; insecticides & pesticides

(G-13594)
STEELMAN INDUSTRIES INC
2800 State Highway 135 N (75662-8948)
P.O. Box 1461 (75663-1461)
PHONE.....................................903 984-3061
Richard Fraser, *CEO*
Danny L Bell, *President*
Adrian Spraglin, *Materials Mgr*
Roger Maxwell, *Engineer*
Margaret Tyler, *Controller*
◆ EMP: 41
SQ FT: 42,000

SALES (est): 12.3MM **Privately Held**
WEB: www.steelman.com
SIC: 3567 3675 Heating units & devices, industrial: electric; electronic capacitors

(G-13595)
STREAM-FLO USA LLC
3000 Synergy Blvd (75662-7758)
P.O. Box 700 (75663-0700)
PHONE.....................................903 983-2992
Mark McNeill, *Ch of Bd*
EMP: 16
SALES (corp-wide): 38.3MM **Privately Held**
WEB: www.streamflo.com
SIC: 3533 Oil field machinery & equipment
HQ: Stream-Flo Usa Llc
8726 Fallbrook Dr
Houston TX 77064
903 912-1022

(G-13596)
TESCO SERVICES INC
104 Longview St (75662)
PHONE.....................................903 983-1007
EMP: 51 **Privately Held**
SIC: 1389 Oil Well Services
HQ: Tesco Services Inc.
11330 Brittmoore Park Dr
Houston TX 77041
337 354-0966

(G-13597)
TSI FLOW PRODUCTS INC
322 S Longview St (75662-2430)
PHONE.....................................903 984-2870
Chad Yoder, *Branch Mgr*
EMP: 10
SALES (corp-wide): 27MM **Privately Held**
WEB: www.tsiflowproducts.com
SIC: 5085 3715 3548 Valves & fittings; truck trailers; electric welding equipment
PA: Tsi Flow Products, Inc.
5656 Wheatley St
Houston TX 77091
713 691-0668

(G-13598)
U S WEATHERFORD L P
2013 State Highway 135 N (75662-6211)
PHONE.....................................903 729-2106
Roger Chick, *Branch Mgr*
EMP: 10 **Privately Held**
WEB: www.weatherford.com
SIC: 1389 Oil field services
HQ: U S Weatherford L P
179 Weatherford Dr
Schriever LA 70395
985 493-6100

(G-13599)
U S WEATHERFORD L P
2013 Hwy 135 N (75662)
PHONE.....................................903 984-5541
Walter McOwen, *Manager*
EMP: 20
SQ FT: 21,300 **Privately Held**
WEB: www.weatherford.com
SIC: 1389 7353 Fishing for tools, oil & gas field; oil field equipment, rental or leasing
HQ: U S Weatherford L P
179 Weatherford Dr
Schriever LA 70395
985 493-6100

(G-13600)
UNIVERSAL OUTLETS INC
200 Smackover St (75662-3166)
P.O. Box 2609 (75663-2609)
PHONE.....................................903 983-3261
Nikki Haskins, *President*
EMP: 13
SQ FT: 7,500
SALES (est): 2.5MM **Privately Held**
WEB: www.univoutlets.com
SIC: 3498 3494 Pipe fittings, fabricated from purchased pipe; pipe fittings

(G-13601)
WARRIOR ENERGY SERVICES CORP
3306 Goforth Rd (75662-8924)
PHONE.....................................903 984-9093
EMP: 15 **Publicly Held**
SIC: 1389 Oil/Gas Field Services

HQ: Warrior Energy Services Corporation
100 Rosecrest Dr
Columbus MS 70518
662 329-1047

(G-13602)
WESTBROOK HOT SHOT SERVICE INC
579 Cargill Rd (75662-8402)
P.O. Box 2219 (75663-2219)
PHONE.....................................903 987-1400
Lenita Westbrook, *Exec Dir*
EMP: 9
SALES (est): 911.7K **Privately Held**
SIC: 1389 Hot shot service

(G-13603)
WOOLLEY FISHING TOOL INC
3000 Laird Hill Rd (75662)
PHONE.....................................903 984-3553
J Woolley, *President*
EMP: 28
SQ FT: 30,000
SALES (est): 4.6MM **Privately Held**
WEB: www.woolleytool.com
SIC: 7359 1389 3599 5051 Tool rental; pipe testing, oil field service; machine shop, jobbing & repair; pipe & tubing, steel
PA: Woolley Tool Inc
3000 Laird Hill Rd
Kilgore TX 75662
903 984-3553

(G-13604)
WOOLLEY TOOL INC (PA)
3000 Laird Hill Rd (75662)
P.O. Box 1249 (75663-1249)
PHONE.....................................903 984-3553
Dan Woolley, *President*
EMP: 10
SQ FT: 30,000
SALES (est): 4.6MM **Privately Held**
WEB: www.woolleytool.com
SIC: 7359 1389 3599 5051 Tool rental; pipe testing, oil field service; machine shop, jobbing & repair; pipe & tubing, steel

(G-13605)
XTO ENERGY INC
700 State Highway 31 E (75662-6226)
PHONE.....................................903 983-8800
Ricky Holcomb, *Manager*
EMP: 9
SALES (corp-wide): 264.9B **Publicly Held**
WEB: www.xtoenergy.com
SIC: 1311 Crude petroleum production
HQ: Xto Energy Inc.
22777 Sprngwoods Vlg Pkwy
Spring TX 77389

Killeen
Bell County

(G-13606)
BLACK STAR STYLES LLC
308 Estate Dr (76549-5665)
PHONE.....................................832 207-4563
George Afful,
EMP: 180
SQ FT: 60,000
SALES (est): 95MM **Privately Held**
SIC: 8741 2844 Management services; perfumes & colognes

(G-13607)
FRANK MAYBORN ENTERPRISES INC
Also Called: Killeen Daily Herald
1809 Florence Rd (76541-8977)
P.O. Box 1300 (76540-1300)
PHONE.....................................254 501-7499
Terry Gandy, *General Mgr*
Ray Reed, *General Mgr*
Jasmine Barnes, *Accounts Exec*
Marissa Reyna, *Accounts Exec*
Terry Schaub, *Adv Dir*
EMP: 116

SALES (corp-wide): 34MM **Privately Held**
WEB: www.tdtnews.com
SIC: 2711 Newspapers: publishing only, not printed on site
PA: Frank Mayborn Enterprises Inc
10 S 3rd St
Temple TX 76501
254 774-5200

(G-13608)
FRANK MAYBORN ENTERPRISES INC
Also Called: Fort Hood Herald
1809 Florence Rd (76541-8977)
P.O. Box 27 (76540-0027)
PHONE.....................................254 634-6666
Daniel Cernero, *Editor*
Terry Gandy, *Manager*
Judy Shumate, *Manager*
EMP: 155
SALES (corp-wide): 34MM **Privately Held**
WEB: www.tdtnews.com
SIC: 2711 Newspapers, publishing & print-ing
PA: Frank Mayborn Enterprises Inc
10 S 3rd St
Temple TX 76501
254 774-5200

(G-13609)
K & J BUSINESSES INC
Also Called: Spectrum Printing
401 Cheyenne Dr (76542-1396)
PHONE.....................................254 628-9208
Terri Keese, *CEO*
Scott Keese, *President*
EMP: 11 EST: 2003
SQ FT: 5,000 **Privately Held**
WEB: www.spk3.com
SIC: 2752 Commercial printing, offset

(G-13610)
KILLEEN BLUEPRINT CO
102 College St (76541-6106)
P.O. Box 1088 (76540-1088)
PHONE.....................................254 634-2779
Robert Mitchell, *President*
Gale E Mitchell, *President*
EMP: 30
SALES (est): 1.7MM **Privately Held**
WEB: www.kdhnews.com
SIC: 7334 2759 Blueprinting service; com-mercial printing

(G-13611)
KILLEEN CRUSHED STONE
4101 Trimmier Rd (76542-3606)
P.O. Box 10759 (76547-0759)
PHONE.....................................254 526-2526
Gary McLean, *Partner*
Jimmy McLean, *Partner*
EMP: 20
SALES (est): 1.6MM **Privately Held**
WEB: www.killeenreadymix.com
SIC: 1429 Boulder, crushed & broken-quarrying

(G-13612)
KILLEEN MARBLE
450 N Roy Reynolds Dr F (76543-4208)
PHONE.....................................254 699-3408
Benny Fajkus, *Owner*
EMP: 20
SALES (est): 2MM **Privately Held**
WEB: www.marblekilleen.com
SIC: 1741 3281 3088 2434 Marble ma-sonry, exterior construction; cut stone & stone products; plastics plumbing fixtures; wood kitchen cabinets

(G-13613)
KILLEEN READY MIX LTD
4101 Trimmier Rd (76542-3606)
P.O. Box 10759 (76547-0759)
PHONE.....................................254 634-4514
Gary McLean, *President*
Jimmy McLean, *Vice Pres*
EMP: 20
SALES (est): 3.2MM **Privately Held**
WEB: www.killeenreadymix.com
SIC: 3273 Ready-mixed concrete

(G-13614)
KNOT HOLE LLC
Also Called: Knot Hole , The
2802 Atkinson Ave (76543-4017)
PHONE..................................254 634-0773
Gerald Corn, *President*
Liz Corn, *Vice Pres*
EMP: 35
SQ FT: 16,200
SALES (est): 3.3MM **Privately Held**
WEB: www.theknotholetx.com
SIC: 2434 2517 Wood kitchen cabinets;
home entertainment unit cabinets, wood

(G-13615)
**LOCKHEED MARTIN
CORPORATION**
4601 Jacobs Ln (76543-4255)
PHONE..................................334 347-4472
Billy Gilliam, *Maint Spvr*
Mike Rakes, *Branch Mgr*
Greg Anderson, *Analyst*
EMP: 435 **Publicly Held**
WEB: www.lockheedmartin.com
SIC: 3812 Search & navigation equipment
PA: Lockheed Martin Corporation
6801 Rockledge Dr
Bethesda MD 20817

(G-13616)
PEPSI-COLA BOTTLING GROUP
Also Called: Pepsico
612 N Twin Creek Dr (76543-4233)
PHONE..................................254 953-7433
Steve Hildinger, *General Mgr*
Tracy Bearmann, *Manager*
EMP: 40
SALES (corp-wide): 67.1B **Publicly Held**
WEB: www.pepsico.com
SIC: 2086 Carbonated soft drinks, bottled
& canned
HQ: Pepsi-Cola Bottling Group
1111 Westchester Ave
White Plains NY 10604

(G-13617)
TERESA A MCVICKER PC
Also Called: Medical Staffing Solutions
1008 N 4th St (76541-3409)
PHONE..................................254 526-2823
EMP: 9
SALES: 150K **Privately Held**
SIC: 3841 8099 Mfg Surgical/Medical In-
struments Health/Allied Services

(G-13618)
**WRIGHT LANDSCAPING & CNST
LLC**
4100 S Clear Creek Rd (76549)
PHONE..................................254 213-3912
EMP: 20
SALES (est): 477.9K **Privately Held**
SIC: 1799 8742 3531 8741 Special
Trade Contractor Mgmt Consulting Svcs
Mfg Construction Mach Management
Services Engineering Services

(G-13619)
Z-MODULAR KILLEEN LLC
710 Swanner Loop (76543-4200)
PHONE..................................254 833-6645
Wendy McIlvride,
Michael McNamara,
Hayes Warren,
EMP: 80
SALES (est): 2.8MM **Privately Held**
WEB: www.zekelman.com
SIC: 3317 Pipes, seamless steel
PA: Zekelman Industries, Inc.
227 W Monroe St Ste 2600
Chicago IL 60606

Kingsbury
Guadalupe County

(G-13620)
**MERIDIAN CONSTRUCTION
SERVICES**
1075 York Crossing Rd (78638-1631)
PHONE..................................830 305-5700
Jesse Tapia, *President*
EMP: 10

SALES (est): 150K **Privately Held**
WEB: www.meridian-construction-services-
corporation.business.site
SIC: 3449 Bars, concrete reinforcing: fabricated steel

Kingsland
Llano County

(G-13621)
CHAPMAN DOCK INC
Also Called: Chapman's
2247 W Ranch Road 1431 (78639-5997)
PHONE..................................325 388-6545
Mark Chapman, *President*
Stacie Chapman, *Vice Pres*
EMP: 35
SALES (est): 2.7MM **Privately Held**
WEB: www.chapmandocks.com
SIC: 7692 Welding repair

(G-13622)
RNB CONTROLS INC
4623 W Ranch Road 1431 (78639-3254)
P.O. Box 1162, Marble Falls (78654-1162)
PHONE..................................325 388-6023
Lee Reimenschneider, *President*
James H Brewer, *Corp Secy*
Fred Former Jr, *Vice Pres*
EMP: 23 EST: 2010
SALES (est): 4.4MM **Privately Held**
WEB: www.rnbcontrols.com
SIC: 3613 Control panels, electric; panel &
distribution boards & other related appa-
ratus

Kingsville
Kleberg County

(G-13623)
**ALAMO CONCRETE PRODUCTS
L**
801 N 6th St (78363-4507)
P.O. Box 778 (78364-0778)
PHONE..................................361 592-5114
Jesse Galden, *Principal*
EMP: 11
SALES (est): 612.5K **Privately Held**
SIC: 3273 Ready-mixed concrete

(G-13624)
**CORTWEAR SPORTS AP & EQP
LLC**
1015 S 6th St (78363-6245)
PHONE..................................361 728-1868
Roel Cortinas,
EMP: 11
SQ FT: 2,500
SALES (est): 308.9K **Privately Held**
WEB: www.cortwear.com
SIC: 2323 3949 Men's & boys' neckwear;
sporting & athletic goods

(G-13625)
COWBOY PUMPS
129 W Huisache Ave (78363-5426)
PHONE..................................361 221-9786
Occo Ewers, *President*
Micheal Ewers, *Vice Pres*
Stacie Ewers, *Manager*
EMP: 35
SALES (est): 4.5MM **Privately Held**
WEB: www.cowboypumps.com
SIC: 3586 Oil pumps, measuring or dis-
pensing

(G-13626)
DON BROCK DISTRIBUTOR INC
400 General Cavazos Blvd (78363-7205)
P.O. Box 1203 (78364-1203)
PHONE..................................361 592-5126
Donald M Brock Jr, *President*
Brock Deloris S, *Vice Pres*
Will Hawkins, *VP Opers*
EMP: 70
SALES (est): 7.8MM **Privately Held**
SIC: 1389 Oil field services

(G-13627)
**FRANKLIN WELDING SERVICE
INC**
1710 Young Dr (78363)
P.O. Box 511 (78364-0511)
PHONE..................................361 592-1322
EMP: 102
SQ FT: 15,000
SALES (est): 14.4MM **Privately Held**
WEB: www.franklinweldingservice.com
SIC: 7692 Welding repair

(G-13628)
**INFRARED THERMAL IMAGING
INC**
703 W Richard Ave (78363-4269)
PHONE..................................361 779-1197
Ray Asbury, *President*
Rick Haese, *Vice Pres*
EMP: 11 EST: 2004
SALES (est): 761.5K **Privately Held**
WEB: www.itimaging.com
SIC: 3624 7389 Electrodes, thermal &
electrolytic uses: carbon, graphite; in-
spection & testing services

(G-13629)
INGRAM READYMIX INC
Also Called: Ingram Ready Mix
2601 E Corral Ave (78363-4107)
PHONE..................................361 516-1756
Bruce Ingram, *Manager*
EMP: 21
SALES (corp-wide): 125.6MM **Privately
Held**
WEB: www.ingramreadymixinc.com
SIC: 3273 Ready-mixed concrete
PA: Ingram Readymix, Inc.
3580 Farm Market 482
New Braunfels TX 78132
830 625-9156

(G-13630)
**INTEGRITY DELAWARE LLC
(DH)**
Also Called: Integrity Delaware Holdco
2710 E Corral Ave (78363-4109)
P.O. Box 5342 (78364-5342)
PHONE..................................361 595-5561
William Duncan, *President*
▲ EMP: 23
SQ FT: 5,000
SALES (est): 44.3MM
SALES (corp-wide): 254.6B **Publicly
Held**
WEB: www.integrityindustries.com
SIC: 2899 Chemical preparations

(G-13631)
**KINGSVILLE PUBLISHING
COMPANY**
Also Called: Kingsville Record
1831 W Santa Gertrudis St (78363-3447)
P.O. Box B (78364-1604)
PHONE..................................361 592-4304
Christopher Maher, *General Mgr*
EMP: 10 EST: 1906
SQ FT: 26,000
SALES (est): 888K
SALES (corp-wide): 189.3MM **Privately
Held**
WEB: www.kingsvillerecord.com
SIC: 2711 Commercial printing & newspa-
per publishing combined; newspapers:
publishing only, not printed on site
PA: King Ranch, Inc.
3 Riverway Ste 1600
Houston TX 77056
832 681-5700

(G-13632)
L3 TECHNOLOGIES INC
614 Mccain St (78363-5038)
PHONE..................................361 516-8396
Aurelio Trevino, *Branch Mgr*
EMP: 181
SALES (corp-wide): 11.3B **Publicly Held**
WEB: www.l3t.com
SIC: 3699 Flight simulators (training aids),
electronic
HQ: L3 Technologies, Inc.
600 3rd Ave Fl 34
New York NY 10016
212 805-5234

(G-13633)
LA FAMOSA TORTILLA
Also Called: La Famosa Tortilla Factory
620 E Alice Ave (78363-4637)
PHONE..................................361 592-5596
Eliseo Torres, *President*
Rosa Torres, *Owner*
EMP: 10
SQ FT: 3,200
SALES (est): 666.4K **Privately Held**
SIC: 2099 Tortillas, fresh or refrigerated

(G-13634)
PROCO INC
129 W Huisache Ave (78363-5426)
PHONE..................................361 516-1112
Tim Noyes, *Vice Pres*
Otto Ewers, *Director*
Michael Ewers, *Director*
EMP: 45 EST: 1977
SQ FT: 15,000
SALES (est): 8.3MM **Privately Held**
WEB: www.procofab.com
SIC: 3443 3537 3444 Tanks for tank
trucks, metal plate; industrial trucks &
tractors; sheet metalwork

(G-13635)
**TEXAS CEMENTING SERVICES
INC**
2620 E Corral Ave (78363-4102)
PHONE..................................361 516-1127
Sarah A Shaw, *Principal*
EMP: 11
SALES (est): 936.2K **Privately Held**
WEB: www.texascementing.com
SIC: 1389 Oil field services

(G-13636)
TEXAS PERFORATORS INC
2005 N 14th St (78363-3311)
P.O. Box 5781 (78364-5781)
PHONE..................................361 516-0541
Roger Polley, *President*
Greg Larsen, *Principal*
Amy Polley, *Corp Secy*
Mary Larsen, *Admin Sec*
EMP: 20
SQ FT: 6,500
SALES (est): 2.4MM **Privately Held**
SIC: 1389 Well logging

Kingwood
Harris County

(G-13637)
ALLESTEC CORPORATION
810 Russell Palmer Rd B (77339-2756)
P.O. Box 6092 (77325-6092)
PHONE..................................281 359-1519
Leslie Larson, *President*
Bob Illig, *Technician*
EMP: 11
SQ FT: 6,700
SALES (est): 1.1MM **Privately Held**
WEB: www.allestec.com
SIC: 3669 3829 1731 Fire detection sys-
tems, electric; temperature sensors, ex-
cept industrial process & aircraft; fire
detection & burglar alarm systems spe-
cialization

(G-13638)
BAKKEN EXPRESS LLC
12 Shorelake Dr (77339-3601)
PHONE..................................281 359-8382
EMP: 10
SALES (est): 650K **Privately Held**
SIC: 1389 Oil/Gas Field Services

(G-13639)
BARKLEY HOLDINGS LLC
5011 Walnut Hills Dr (77345-2411)
PHONE..................................832 413-4400
Henry Salem, *Mng Member*
EMP: 11
SALES (est): 414.6K **Privately Held**
SIC: 3491 Industrial valves

(G-13640)
BASIN WATER INC
700 Rockmead Dr Ste 105 (77339-2111)
PHONE..................................877 312-8950

▲ = Import ▼=Export
◆ =Import/Export

EMP: 12 **Privately Held**
SIC: 2819 Sodium & potassium compounds, exc. bleaches, alkalies, alum.
PA: Basin Water, Inc.
550 W C St Fl 19
San Diego CA

(G-13641)
EPRODUCTION SOLUTIONS LLC
Also Called: Weatherford Artificial Lift
22001 Northpark Dr (77339-3804)
PHONE....................................281 348-1000
Haldun Unalmis, *Engineer*
Dharmesh Mehta, *Mng Member*
Douglas Lukey,
Danielle Nicholas,
Dianne Ralston,
◆ EMP: 276 EST: 2000
SALES (est): 135.1MM **Privately Held**
WEB: www.weatherford.com
SIC: 3491 5084 1389 Automatic regulating & control valves; safety equipment; oil field services
HQ: Weatherford International, Llc
2000 Saint James Pl
Houston TX 77056
713 693-4000

(G-13642)
ES GROUP OF TEXAS INC
Also Called: Es Windpower
3903 Shady Terrace Dr (77345-1184)
PHONE....................................281 796-6214
Kerry Kisslinger, *President*
Kerry D Kisslinger, *Director*
▲ EMP: 12 EST: 2013
SALES (est): 792.4K **Privately Held**
WEB: www.ibigrouptexas.com
SIC: 3999 Manufacturing industries

(G-13643)
FLANGES INC
3306 Spring Manor Dr (77345-2457)
PHONE....................................713 673-4117
Glemn Latham, *President*
James Latham, *President*
Debra Latham, *Treasurer*
Glen Latham, *Treasurer*
EMP: 10
SALES (est): 1.2MM **Privately Held**
WEB: www.federalflange.com
SIC: 3462 Iron & steel forgings

(G-13644)
G & G MACHINE & MAINTENANCE (PA)
5110 Timber Shade Dr (77345-1734)
PHONE....................................713 673-4235
Rita Grantham, *President*
EMP: 25
SQ FT: 20,000
SALES (est): 3.3MM **Privately Held**
WEB: www.ggmachine.com
SIC: 3599 7699 Machine shop, jobbing & repair; industrial equipment services

(G-13645)
INEOS CALABRIAN CORPORATION (DH)
1521 Green Oak Pl Ste 200 (77339-2013)
PHONE....................................281 348-2303
◆ EMP: 10 EST: 1987
SQ FT: 4,600
SALES (est): 17.5MM
SALES (corp-wide): 1.9MM **Privately Held**
WEB: www.ineoscalabrian.com
SIC: 2819 5162 5169 Industrial inorganic chemicals; plastics materials; chemicals & allied products
HQ: Ineos Enterprises Holdings Limited
Unit 14
Runcorn WA7 1
192 851-6948

(G-13646)
JACKIE TODARO
Also Called: America Screen Graphics
1701 Northpark Dr Ste 15 (77339-1642)
P.O. Box 6988 (77325-6988)
PHONE....................................281 354-2581
Jackie Todaro, *Owner*
EMP: 12
SQ FT: 6,000

SALES (est): 1.5MM **Privately Held**
WEB: www.americanscreengraphics.com
SIC: 2396 3993 7389 Screen printing on fabric articles; signs & advertising specialties; embroidering of advertising on shirts, etc.

(G-13647)
LENDFLOW INC
1525 Lakeville Dr Ste 121 (77339-2069)
PHONE....................................512 265-1261
Jon Fry, *CEO*
EMP: 10
SALES (est): 221.8K **Privately Held**
SIC: 7372 Business oriented computer software

(G-13648)
M3 PARTNERS LLC (PA)
Also Called: UPS Stores, The
6010 Royal Point Ct (77345-3316)
PHONE....................................602 561-6464
Kevin Foley, *Vice Pres*
Don Higginson, *Vice Pres*
Jim Hillquist, *Vice Pres*
David Lee, *Vice Pres*
Eric Maida, *Vice Pres*
EMP: 21
SQ FT: 1,000
SALES (est): 3MM **Privately Held**
WEB: www.theupsstore.com
SIC: 7389 7336 2759 Mailbox rental & related service; commercial art & graphic design; commercial printing

(G-13649)
MATUTECH LTD LIABILITY COMPANY
5402 Creek Shadows Dr (77339-1217)
PHONE....................................832 989-3208
Joshua Matute,
EMP: 10
SALES (est): 100K **Privately Held**
SIC: 2741

(G-13650)
NK ENERGY LLC
26897 Kings Pk Hollow Dr (77339-1437)
PHONE....................................832 857-8228
Kevin Langley, *Mng Member*
EMP: 10
SALES (est): 157.2K **Privately Held**
WEB: www.nknrg.com
SIC: 5047 3533 Medical & hospital equipment; gas field machinery & equipment; oil field machinery & equipment

(G-13651)
ORION ENGINEERED CARBONS LLC (HQ)
Also Called: Oec LLC USA
4501 Magnolia Cove Dr (77345-2252)
PHONE....................................832 445-3300
Jack Clem, *CEO*
Jorg Kruger, *Senior VP*
Mark Leigh, *Senior VP*
Jeff Malenky, *Senior VP*
Lixing Min, *Senior VP*
◆ EMP: 100
SALES (est): 307.5MM
SALES (corp-wide): 889.5K **Privately Held**
WEB: www.orioncarbons.com
SIC: 2895 Carbon black
PA: Orion Engineered Carbons S.A.
Route De Treves 6
Niederanven 2633
270 480-60

(G-13652)
RAIN CII CARBON LLC (HQ)
2627 Chestnut Ridge Dr # 200 (77339-1777)
PHONE....................................281 318-2400
Gerry Sweeney, *President*
Mike Tillman, *COO*
Bob Tonti, *Senior VP*
Jodi Canadas, *QC Mgr*
Paul Francese, *CFO*
◆ EMP: 34
SQ FT: 10,000

SALES (est): 44.1MM **Privately Held**
WEB: www.raincii.com
SIC: 2999 8741 8748 Coke, calcined petroleum: made from purchased materials; financial management for business; environmental consultant

(G-13653)
RT PRECISION MACHINERY LP
3227 Glade Springs Dr (77339-1949)
PHONE....................................281 354-0910
Ted McLean, *President*
Gladys Echegaray, *Manager*
EMP: 30
SQ FT: 12,000
SALES (est): 5.8MM **Privately Held**
SIC: 3533 Oil & gas field machinery

(G-13654)
THRYV INC
1521 Green Oak Pl Ste 210 (77339-2278)
PHONE....................................281 312-3258
Patricia Williams, *Manager*
EMP: 10
SALES (corp-wide): 1.4B **Publicly Held**
WEB: www.thryv.com
SIC: 2741 Directories, telephone: publishing only, not printed on site
HQ: Thryv, Inc.
2200 W Airfield Dr
Dfw Airport TX 75261
972 453-7000

(G-13655)
U S WEATHERFORD L P
22001 Northpark Dr 100a (77339-3804)
PHONE....................................281 348-1000
EMP: 18 **Privately Held**
WEB: www.weatherford.com
SIC: 1389 Oil field services
HQ: U S Weatherford L P
179 Weatherford Dr
Schriever LA 70395
985 493-6100

(G-13656)
U S WEATHERFORD L P
22001 Northpark Dr (77339-3804)
PHONE....................................281 348-1090
Bird Greg, *District Mgr*
Roy Massey, *Mfg Staff*
Mazhar Hussain, *Engineer*
David Dyer, *Human Resources*
Robyn Gamage, *Cust Mgr*
EMP: 200 **Privately Held**
WEB: www.weatherford.com
SIC: 3498 3533 Fabricated pipe & fittings; oil & gas field machinery
HQ: U S Weatherford L P
179 Weatherford Dr
Schriever LA 70395
985 493-6100

(G-13657)
UNIVERSAL KIDS LLC
21369 Kings Guild Ln (77339-2595)
PHONE....................................832 374-1082
Tyeisha M Boothe, *Mng Member*
EMP: 21 EST: 2016
SALES (est): 640.9K **Privately Held**
SIC: 2361 Girls' & children's dresses, blouses & shirts

(G-13658)
VALENCE MIDSTREAM LTD
Also Called: Dalence Operating Company
600 Rockmead Dr Ste 200 (77339-2105)
PHONE....................................281 359-3659
Walter Scherr III, *CEO*
Jon Averhoff, *President*
EMP: 25
SALES (est): 1.6MM **Privately Held**
WEB: www.valenceoperating.com
SIC: 1382 Oil & gas exploration services

(G-13659)
VALENCE OPERATING COMPANY (PA)
600 Rockmead Dr Ste 200 (77339-2105)
PHONE....................................281 359-3659
Walter J Scherr III, *CEO*
Stephen Manning, *COO*
Jean Hacker, *Vice Pres*
Ken Shell, *Opers Mgr*
Doug Scherr, *CFO*
EMP: 35

SQ FT: 10,000
SALES (est): 22.9MM **Privately Held**
WEB: www.valenceoperating.com
SIC: 1311 Crude petroleum production; natural gas production

(G-13660)
WEATHERFORD ARTIFICIA
22001 Northpark Dr (77339-3804)
PHONE....................................918 224-7428
Joe Early, *Branch Mgr*
EMP: 15 **Privately Held**
WEB: www.weatherford.com
SIC: 3471 Plating & polishing
HQ: Weatherford Artificial Lift Systems, Llc
2000 Saint James Pl
Houston TX 77056
713 836-4000

Knippa
Uvalde County

(G-13661)
LEGACY VULCAN LLC
Also Called: Knippa Quarry
10503 E Us Highway 90 (78870)
P.O. Box 9 (78870-0009)
PHONE....................................830 934-2625
Ronald Robles, *Branch Mgr*
EMP: 12 **Publicly Held**
WEB: www.vulcanmaterials.com
SIC: 3273 Ready-mixed concrete
HQ: Legacy Vulcan, Llc
1200 Urban Center Dr
Vestavia AL 35242
205 298-3000

Knox City
Knox County

(G-13662)
BAKER PETROLITE LLC
3009 State Highway 222 E (79529-2815)
PHONE....................................940 658-3574
Carl Waalin, *Manager*
EMP: 9 **Privately Held**
WEB:
www.bakerhughesdirect.lookchem.com
SIC: 1389 Oil field services
HQ: Baker Petrolite Llc
12645 W Airport Blvd
Sugar Land TX 77478
281 276-5400

(G-13663)
BASIC ESA INC
100 Birch St (79529)
P.O. Box 567 (79529-0567)
PHONE....................................817 334-4100
Steven Pepper, *President*
Kay Pepper, *Corp Secy*
David Counts, *Vice Pres*
EMP: 75 EST: 1981
SQ FT: 1,000
SALES (est): 10.3MM
SALES (corp-wide): 567.2MM **Publicly Held**
SIC: 1389 Servicing oil & gas wells
PA: Basic Energy Services, Inc.
801 Cherry St Unit 2
Fort Worth TX 76102
817 334-4100

(G-13664)
LYNN ELECTRIC MOTOR CO INC
1011 E Main St (79529)
P.O. Box 477 (79529-0477)
PHONE....................................940 657-3511
Scott Lynn, *President*
Jimmy R Lynn, *President*
Laura Hines, *Director*
EMP: 15
SQ FT: 6,000 **Privately Held**
SIC: 5999 7694 3621 Electronic parts & equipment; electric motor repair; motors & generators

(G-13665)
SHORTES INC
Hwy 222 E (79529)
P.O. Box 189 (79529-0189)
PHONE....................................940 658-3576

Bennett Shortes, *President*
EMP: 27
SQ FT: 25,000
SALES (est): 3.4MM **Privately Held**
WEB: www.shortesinc.com
SIC: 1629 1389 4922 4613 Oil refinery construction; oil field services; natural gas transmission; refined petroleum pipelines; crude petroleum pipelines; water, sewer & utility lines

Kosse
Limestone County

(G-13666)
FROST CRUSHED STONE CO INC
Fm 1771 & County Rd 248 (76653)
P.O. Box 272, Mexia (76667-0272)
PHONE..........................254 587-2472
Marcus Frost, *President*
EMP: 114
SQ FT: 2,000
SALES (est): 23.4MM **Privately Held**
SIC: 1422 Crushed & broken limestone

(G-13667)
U S SILICA COMPANY
Farm To Market Road 2749 R 27 (76653)
P.O. Box 98 (76653-0098)
PHONE..........................254 375-2225
Mack Jones, *Division Mgr*
Danny Screws, *Facilities Mgr*
Stephanie Broadus, *Opers Staff*
David Decareaux, *Regl Sales Mgr*
Matt Haile, *Regl Sales Mgr*
EMP: 24
SALES (corp-wide): 1.4B **Publicly Held**
WEB: www.ussilica.com
SIC: 3295 1446 Kaolin, ground or otherwise treated; industrial sand
HQ: U. S. Silica Company
24275 Katy Fwy Ste 100
Katy TX 77494
301 682-0600

Kountze
Hardin County

(G-13668)
AMERICAN THERMOWELL INC
4861 Paula Rd (77625-6687)
P.O. Box 8607, Lumberton (77657-0607)
PHONE..........................409 246-1111
Chester M Sangwin, *President*
H M Bickerton, *Chairman*
Loretta Hood, *Vice Pres*
EMP: 13 EST: 1999
SALES (est): 2.5MM **Privately Held**
WEB: www.americanthermowell.com
SIC: 2821 Thermosetting materials

(G-13669)
CADRE TIMBER PRODUCTS INC
Also Called: Tanner Timber Products
4527 Highway 327 (77625-6943)
P.O. Box 190 (77625-0190)
PHONE..........................409 246-3573
Brian Tanner, *President*
EMP: 21
SALES (est): 1.9MM **Privately Held**
WEB: www.tannerservices.net
SIC: 2421 Sawmills & planing mills, general

(G-13670)
FORGED COMPONENTS INC
Also Called: Western Texas Forge Flange Co
1299 Highway 69 S (77625-6953)
PHONE..........................409 246-2427
Carl Wilson, *Manager*
EMP: 46
SALES (corp-wide): 56.1MM **Privately Held**
WEB: www.forgedcomponents.com
SIC: 3462 Iron & steel forgings
PA: Forged Components, Inc.
14527 Smith Rd
Humble TX 77396
281 441-4088

(G-13671)
GRIFFITH OIL FIELD SERVICES
Also Called: C & S Cnstr Backhoe Svcs
3747 Fm 1293 Rd (77625-7924)
P.O. Box 944 (77625-0944)
PHONE..........................409 246-8530
Sammie Griffith, *President*
Sandra Griffith, *Vice Pres*
EMP: 9
SALES (est): 701.2K **Privately Held**
WEB: www.dsmechanical.net
SIC: 1389 Oil field services

(G-13672)
RIVERSIDE MACHINE SHOP INC
4002 Highway 327 (77656)
P.O. Box 1146, Silsbee (77656-1146)
PHONE..........................409 246-1600
Jamie Bennett, *President*
Cathy Bennett, *Vice Pres*
EMP: 12
SQ FT: 16,000
SALES (est): 1.4MM **Privately Held**
SIC: 3599 Machine shop, jobbing & repair

(G-13673)
STREAMLINE PROD SYSTEMS INC (HQ)
1447 Highway 69 S (77625-6957)
P.O. Box 20418, Beaumont (77720-0418)
PHONE..........................800 780-4011
Mike Renick, *President*
William Bainbridge, *Executive*
Becky Leblanc, *Administration*
EMP: 100
SALES (est): 60.8MM **Privately Held**
WEB: www.streamlinetexas.com
SIC: 1389 5084 Oil field services; industrial machinery & equipment

Krum
Denton County

(G-13674)
MCKAY EQUIPMENT CO
3099 S Branch Rd (76249-8022)
P.O. Box 69040, Odessa (79769-0040)
PHONE..........................432 381-5510
Jerry R Mc Kay, *President*
Kelly McKay, *Vice Pres*
Joyce A Mc Kay, *Treasurer*
EMP: 17 EST: 1978
SQ FT: 5,000
SALES (est): 3.6MM **Privately Held**
SIC: 3533 5084 Oil field machinery & equipment; oil well machinery, equipment & supplies

(G-13675)
MIKE STRAND
Also Called: Denton Custom Window
820 E Mccart St (76249-5634)
P.O. Box 729 (76249-0729)
PHONE..........................940 482-3426
Mike Strand, *Owner*
EMP: 10
SQ FT: 6,000
SALES (est): 1.2MM **Privately Held**
WEB: www.customexteriorstx.com
SIC: 1521 3089 General remodeling, single-family houses; window frames & sash, plastic

(G-13676)
SKLEDAR-GREENE LLC
Also Called: Wolf-Solutions
4243 Fm 1173 (76249-6833)
PHONE..........................817 454-4214
Lena Saucillo, *Principal*
Dustin Greene, *Mng Member*
EMP: 11
SALES (est): 2.5MM **Privately Held**
WEB: www.wolf-solution.com
SIC: 3714 3613 1731 Motor vehicle engines & parts; control panels, electric; electronic controls installation

Kyle
Hays County

(G-13677)
ASSOCIATED TELEPHONE
151 Kirkham Cir Unit B (78640-9703)
PHONE..........................512 288-6215
John Bills, *President*
EMP: 12
SALES (est): 1.7MM **Privately Held**
SIC: 2741 7372 Directories: publishing & printing; application computer software

(G-13678)
AUSTIN ELEVATOR COMPANY LLC
336 Millennium Dr (78640-5142)
P.O. Box 2202 (78640-1807)
PHONE..........................512 376-2107
Sara Fairchild, *Administration*
EMP: 13
SQ FT: 4,000
SALES: 1.3MM **Privately Held**
WEB: www.austinelevator.com
SIC: 7699 3534 Elevators: inspection, service & repair; elevators & moving stairways

(G-13679)
BARTON PUBLICATIONS INC
1717 N Burleson St (78640-5323)
P.O. Box 2530 (78640-1815)
PHONE..........................512 262-1110
Wynette Barton, *President*
Winnette Barton, *President*
EMP: 20
SALES (est): 643.3K **Privately Held**
SIC: 2711 Commercial printing & newspaper publishing combined

(G-13680)
COWGIRL BRANDS LLC
23703 Int State Hwy35 Ste (78640)
P.O. Box 1747 (78640-1747)
PHONE..........................512 466-3816
Karen Lee, *Mng Member*
EMP: 10
SQ FT: 5,000
SALES (est): 750K **Privately Held**
SIC: 3565 Bottle washing & sterilizing machines

(G-13681)
CRYOGENIC PLASTICS INC
Also Called: CPI - Marine
1098 Windy Hill Rd (78640-6127)
P.O. Box 2040 (78640-1803)
PHONE..........................512 295-2683
Oliver Ring, *President*
Dena David, *General Mgr*
Dale Polley, *General Mgr*
Bill Clark, *Research*
Matt Darst, *Sales Staff*
▲ **EMP:** 34
SQ FT: 5,400
SALES: 3.9MM **Privately Held**
WEB: www.cpitx.com
SIC: 2821 Plastics materials & resins

(G-13682)
FIRST TIME RIGHT
1000 Desert Rose Cv (78640-4305)
PHONE..........................832 264-5057
Amanda Giessen, *President*
EMP: 45
SALES (est): 1.9MM **Privately Held**
SIC: 3823 Programmers, process type

(G-13683)
K & J WOODWORKS LLC
86 S Old Spanish Trl (78640-9331)
PHONE..........................512 668-4237
Brandi Blair, *Bookkeeper*
Trish Wells, *Manager*
Jim Kickertz,
EMP: 85
SQ FT: 18,000
SALES (est): 14.7MM **Privately Held**
WEB: www.kjwoodworks.com
SIC: 2541 2521 Store & office display cases & fixtures; store fixtures, wood; wood office furniture

(G-13684)
LAWE INDUSTRIES LLC
6170 Fm 2770 (78640-8944)
PHONE..........................512 262-1933
Dan Lee, *Owner*
EMP: 18
SALES (corp-wide): 8.5MM **Privately Held**
SIC: 2741 Miscellaneous publishing
PA: Lawe Industries, Llc
24165 W Interstate 10
San Antonio TX 78257
210 833-9497

(G-13685)
MISCELLANEOUS STEEL INDS INC
400 Bunton Creek Rd (78640-4432)
PHONE..........................512 268-2831
Ronnie V Fann, *President*
Juan Garcia, *Vice Pres*
Tommy Stanley, *Vice Pres*
Matthew Edevold, *Project Mgr*
Rob Mann, *Project Mgr*
EMP: 32
SQ FT: 50,000
SALES (est): 10.8MM **Privately Held**
SIC: 3446 Stairs, staircases, stair treads: prefabricated metal

(G-13686)
RSI INC (PA)
Also Called: Computer Rggdztion Integration
1670 Kohlers Xing (78640-6052)
PHONE..........................512 268-7500
Harish K Malkani, *President*
Fran Hanlin, *Purchasing*
▲ **EMP:** 35
SQ FT: 40,000
SALES (est): 18.8MM **Privately Held**
WEB: www.rsi-cri.com
SIC: 5051 5063 3571 3053 Cable, wire; wire & cable; electronic computers; gaskets & sealing devices; current-carrying wiring devices

(G-13687)
TRANSMEDIA DYNAMICS INC
7212 Goforth Rd Ste 109 (78640-4269)
PHONE..........................512 971-2313
Tony Taylor, *CEO*
Mustafa Mohammed, *Project Engr*
EMP: 35
SALES (est): 626.1K
SALES (corp-wide): 164.6K **Privately Held**
WEB: www.tmd.tv
SIC: 7372 8748 Application computer software; business oriented computer software; systems engineering consultant, ex. computer or professional
HQ: Transmedia Dynamics Limited
Tower House
Aylesbury BUCKS HP20
129 674-5080

(G-13688)
WHITEHORSE MANUFACTURING CO
Also Called: Insul-Pipe Systems
15000 Camino Real (78640-3992)
P.O. Box 1527, Buda (78610-1527)
PHONE..........................512 376-2112
Steve Tarrilion, *CEO*
Brad Tarrilion, *Vice Pres*
EMP: 13
SQ FT: 6,000
SALES (est): 3MM **Privately Held**
WEB: www.insul-pipe.net
SIC: 3086 Insulation or cushioning material, foamed plastic

(G-13689)
YARRINGTON ROAD MATERIALS
1401 Yarrington Rd (78640-6648)
P.O. Box 967 (78640-0967)
PHONE..........................512 754-3573
Edward Coleman, *Owner*
Henrietta Coleman, *Co-Owner*
EMP: 60

SALES (est): 6.9MM **Privately Held**
WEB: www.yrmaterials.com
SIC: **1429** 1442 Igneous rock, crushed & broken-quarrying; construction sand & gravel

La Coste
Medina County

(G-13690)
R J MANGOLD GRAIN CO INC
16112 S Front St (78039)
P.O. Box 69 (78039-0069)
PHONE..............................830 985-3323
Sylvan J Mangold, *President*
David Mangold, *Corp Secy*
EMP: 13 EST: 1934
SQ FT: 4,000
SALES (est): 2.2MM **Privately Held**
WEB: www.mangoldgrain.com
SIC: **2048** 5191 Prepared feeds; seeds: field, garden & flower

La Feria
Cameron County

(G-13691)
INNOVATIVE BLOCK S TEXAS LTD (PA)
240 E 1st St (78559-5014)
P.O. Box 30 (78559-0030)
PHONE..............................956 797-4200
Charles Mueller, *President*
▲ EMP: 9
SQ FT: 60,000
SALES (est): 6MM **Privately Held**
WEB: www.innovativeblock.com
SIC: **3271** Concrete block & brick

(G-13692)
SIEMENS INDUSTRY INC
2805 W Expy 83 Ste A (78559-6288)
PHONE..............................956 797-5075
Daniel Alvarez, *Manager*
EMP: 87
SALES (corp-wide): 67.4B **Privately Held**
WEB: www.new.siemens.com
SIC: **3822** Air conditioning & refrigeration controls
HQ: Siemens Industry, Inc.
1000 Deerfield Pkwy
Buffalo Grove IL 60089
847 215-1000

La Grange
Fayette County

(G-13693)
CARLTON INDUSTRIES LP
4225 W State Highway 71 (78945-5150)
P.O. Box 280 (78945-0280)
PHONE..............................979 242-5055
Kay M Carlton, *Managing Prtnr*
Richard Carlton, *Partner*
EMP: 45
SQ FT: 20,000
SALES (est): 7.6MM **Privately Held**
WEB: www.carltonusa.com
SIC: **2759** 2679 3993 Decals: printing; labels, paper: made from purchased material; signs, not made in custom sign painting shops

(G-13694)
ENCORE CABINETS LTD
1000 E Eblin St (78945-2916)
P.O. Box 458 (78945-0458)
PHONE..............................979 968-9482
D S Rodgers II, *CEO*
Pat Walker, *Manager*
EMP: 30
SALES (est): 3MM **Privately Held**
WEB: www.encore-cabinets.business.site
SIC: **5031** 2434 Kitchen cabinets; wood kitchen cabinets

(G-13695)
FAYETTE COUNTY RECORD INC
127 S Washington St (78945-2628)
P.O. Box 400 (78945-0400)
PHONE..............................979 968-3155
Kyle Barton, *President*
Eileen Rloehr, *Manager*
EMP: 9
SQ FT: 4,050
SALES (est): 682.6K **Privately Held**
WEB: www.fayettecountyrecord.com
SIC: **2711** 2791 Commercial printing & newspaper publishing combined; typesetting

(G-13696)
GRAPHTEX INC
Also Called: Hengst Printing & Supplies
155 W Travis St (78945-2620)
PHONE..............................979 968-6333
Sandra Hengst, *President*
Don Hengst, *Corp Secy*
EMP: 12
SQ FT: 7,500
SALES (est): 1.5MM **Privately Held**
WEB: www.hengstprinting.com
SIC: **2752** 5021 5044 Commercial printing, lithographic; office furniture; office equipment

(G-13697)
KATYSWEET CONFECTIONERS INC
4321 W State Highway 71 (78945-5150)
P.O. Box 1237 (78945-8237)
PHONE..............................979 242-5172
Kay Carlton, *President*
Garland Hart, *General Mgr*
Katie Bellue, *Sales Staff*
EMP: 25
SALES (est): 3.3MM **Privately Held**
WEB: www.katysweet.com
SIC: **2064** 5947 Candy & other confectionery products; gift, novelty & souvenir shop

(G-13698)
MCGUIRE INDUSTRIES INC
4429 W State Highway 71 (78945-5150)
PHONE..............................979 968-5131
Wiley Adams, *Manager*
EMP: 10
SALES (corp-wide): 8.4MM **Privately Held**
WEB: www.mcguireindustries.com
SIC: **1389** Oil field services
PA: Mcguire Industries, Inc.
2416 W 42nd St
Odessa TX 79764
432 550-4141

(G-13699)
MULTISOURCES LTD
Also Called: Stemco
9305 Feydler Rd (78945)
PHONE..............................979 247-4305
Nelson Dallmeyer, *Manager*
Gene Bleke, *Director*
EMP: 12
SALES (corp-wide): 13.9MM **Privately Held**
SIC: **1442** Gravel mining
PA: Multisources, Ltd
126 E Turbo Dr
San Antonio TX 78216
210 349-2491

(G-13700)
PRAUSE MARKET LLC
Also Called: Prause's Market
2036 W Guenther Ln (78945-6071)
PHONE..............................979 968-3259
Glenn Prause, *Principal*
James A Prause, *Principal*
Garry Prause, *Mng Member*
Kathy Anders, *Mng Member*
Brian Prause, *Mng Member*
EMP: 10
SALES (est): 747.7K **Privately Held**
SIC: **2013** 5421 5812 Sausages & other prepared meats; meat markets, including freezer provisioners; American restaurant

(G-13701)
SUPAKS INC
Also Called: Emax
907 E State Highway 71 (78945-4421)
PHONE..............................979 968-5654
Robert E Supak, *President*
Delores J Supak, *Treasurer*
Delores Supak, *Admin Sec*
EMP: 9
SQ FT: 30,000
SALES (est): 1.5MM **Privately Held**
WEB: www.supaksbuildingsupply.com
SIC: **3448** 1761 5719 Prefabricated metal buildings; roofing, siding & sheet metal work; metalware

(G-13702)
TEXOIL SERVICES
4449 W State Highway 71 (78945-5150)
P.O. Box 146, Plum (78952-0146)
PHONE..............................979 242-5571
Lynn Gibson, *Partner*
Curtis Carden, *Partner*
EMP: 10
SQ FT: 4,000
SALES (est): 1.3MM **Privately Held**
WEB: www.texoilservices.com
SIC: **1389** 5084 Oil field services; roustabout service; oil well machinery, equipment & supplies

(G-13703)
TIETJEN INC
Also Called: Tiet Jens Lone Star Truck Eqp
6035 State Highway 159 (78945-4517)
PHONE..............................979 249-3888
EMP: 20 EST: 1915
SQ FT: 7,000
SALES (est): 1.7MM **Privately Held**
WEB: www.lonestartruckequ.com
SIC: **7692** 3714 3713 3446 Welding repair; bumpers & bumperettes, motor vehicle; truck & bus bodies; architectural metalwork; sheet metalwork

La Marque
Galveston County

(G-13704)
A&A MACHINE & FABRICATION LLC (PA)
3101 Texas Ave (77568-3206)
PHONE..............................409 938-4274
Charles Hutchins, *Managing Prtnr*
Andy Kallinger, *Superintendent*
David Vasichko, *Vice Pres*
Theresa White, *Buyer*
Taylor Nyquist, *Engineer*
▲ EMP: 83
SALES (est): 20MM **Privately Held**
WEB: www.aagroup.com
SIC: **3599** 3443 Machine shop, jobbing & repair; process vessels, industrial: metal plate

(G-13705)
ALEXS AIR CONDITIONING INC (PA)
706 Bayou Rd (77568-4153)
P.O. Box 405 (77568-0405)
PHONE..............................409 935-2496
Troy Alexander, *President*
EMP: 25
SQ FT: 7,500
SALES (est): 3.7MM **Privately Held**
WEB: www.alexsair.com
SIC: **1711** 3441 Warm air heating & air conditioning contractor; fabricated structural metal

(G-13706)
BAKER PETROLITE LLC
209 Fm 1765 Rd (77568-3312)
PHONE..............................409 935-2248
EMP: 17
SALES (corp-wide): 9.8B **Publicly Held**
SIC: **1389** Oil/Gas Field Services
HQ: Baker Petrolite Llc
12645 W Airport Blvd
Sugar Land TX 77478
281 276-5400

(G-13707)
BEBCO ENVMTL CONTRLS CORP
4725 Lawndale St (77568-3008)
P.O. Box 128, Hitchcock (77563-0128)
PHONE..............................844 397-4822
Michael Baucom, *CEO*
Beth Moody, *CFO*
EMP: 30 EST: 2012
SQ FT: 6,000
SALES (est): 7.9MM **Privately Held**
WEB: www.okbebco.com
SIC: **3585** Heating & air conditioning combination units

(G-13708)
INDUSTRIAL CMMSSNING CONS INTL
Also Called: Icci
714 Highway 3 (77568-5938)
PHONE..............................833 873-4224
Stephen Quinn, *CEO*
Mark Elliott, *COO*
Joshua Phelps, *VP Opers*
William Bogar, *CFO*
EMP: 18
SALES (est): 27.6K **Privately Held**
SIC: **8711** 7349 1629 3559 Engineering services; chemical cleaning services; power plant construction; refinery, chemical processing & similar machinery; derricks, oil or gas field

(G-13709)
KIN-TEK ANALYTICAL INC
504 Laurel St (77568-4202)
PHONE..............................409 938-3627
William W Botts, *CEO*
EMP: 9
SALES (est): 1.2MM **Privately Held**
WEB: www.kin-tek.com
SIC: **3826** Analytical instruments

(G-13710)
KIN-TEK LABORATORIES INC
504 Laurel St (77568-4202)
PHONE..............................409 938-3627
James Mc Kinley Jr, *President*
James J Mc Kinley Jr, *President*
Danet Vrazel, *Project Engr*
Spencer Hallaway, *Supervisor*
EMP: 12
SQ FT: 7,000
SALES (est): 2.4MM **Privately Held**
WEB: www.kin-tek.com
SIC: **3826** Analytical instruments

(G-13711)
LAND & SEA SERVICES 1 INC
Also Called: John Deere Authorized Dealer
1900 Oak St (77568-6021)
PHONE..............................409 935-9466
Larry Alexander, *President*
Chris Cotter, *Vice Pres*
EMP: 9
SQ FT: 3,594
SALES (est): 2.5MM **Privately Held**
WEB: www.landandseaservices.com
SIC: **3732** 7538 5082 Boats, fiberglass: building & repairing; recreational vehicle repairs; construction & mining machinery

(G-13712)
PARAGON FABRICATORS INC
500 Main St (77568-5617)
PHONE..............................409 935-6602
Harrom M Nipp, *CEO*
James M Saulsberry, *President*
Devin Myers, *Vice Pres*
EMP: 25 EST: 1975
SQ FT: 40,000
SALES (est): 6.9MM **Privately Held**
WEB: www.paragontexas.com
SIC: **3443** Industrial vessels, tanks & containers

(G-13713)
PARKLINE INC
Also Called: Bebco Industries
4725 Lawndale St (77568-3008)
PHONE..............................409 935-1037
Tj Wallace, *Production*
Don Antley, *Enginr/R&D Mgr*
Stacy Powell, *Sales Dir*
EMP: 53

SALES (corp-wide): 41.9MM **Privately Held**
WEB: www.parkline.com
SIC: 3448 3613 3444 3441 Prefabricated metal buildings; control panels, electric; sheet metalwork; fabricated structural metal
PA: Parkline, Inc.
　　328 Eleanor Indus Pk Dr
　　Eleanor WV 25070
　　800 786-4855

(G-13714)
PARTNER METALFAB LP
Also Called: Robbins Metal Fabricators
319 Volney St (77568-3129)
P.O. Box 1129 (77568-1129)
PHONE................................409 933-0026
Larry Freeman, *President*
Edward Gonzalez, *General Mgr*
Rose Mary Freeman, *Vice Pres*
EMP: 12
SQ FT: 10,000
SALES (est): 859K **Privately Held**
WEB: www.partnersmetalfab.com
SIC: 3441 Fabricated structural metal

La Porte
Harris County

(G-13715)
AAA PIPE CLEANING CORPORATION
Also Called: AAA Flexible Pipe
3900 Underwood Rd (77571-3930)
PHONE................................281 476-5200
Michael A Fisco, *President*
Dennis Fisco, *Exec VP*
EMP: 30
SQ FT: 7,604
SALES (corp-wide): 9.3MM **Privately Held**
WEB: www.advancedplumber.com
SIC: 3999 7699 1711 1623 Pipe cleaners; sewer cleaning & rodding; plumbing contractors; sewer line construction
PA: Aaa Pipe Cleaning Corporation
　　7277 Bessemer Ave
　　Cleveland OH 44127
　　216 341-2900

(G-13716)
ACUREN INSPECTION INC
101 Old Underwood Rd (77571-9480)
PHONE................................281 228-0000
Kyle Conaway, *Division Mgr*
Bruce Sirotiak, *Division Mgr*
Todd Harley, *Regional Mgr*
Matthew Chase, *Engineer*
Bob Milne, *Engineer*
EMP: 1000
SALES (corp-wide): 1.5B **Privately Held**
WEB: www.acuren.com
SIC: 1389 8071 7389 Testing, measuring, surveying & analysis services; testing laboratories; inspection & testing services
HQ: Acuren Inspection, Inc.
　　30 Main St Ste 402
　　Danbury CT 06810
　　203 702-8740

(G-13717)
AIR LIQUIDE AMERICA LP
11450 W Fairmont Pkwy (77571-6000)
PHONE................................281 474-8490
EMP: 15
SALES (corp-wide): 129.8MM **Privately Held**
WEB: www.industry.airliquide.us
SIC: 2813 Industrial gases
HQ: Air Liquide America L.P.
　　9811 Katy Fwy Ste 100
　　Houston TX 77024
　　713 624-8000

(G-13718)
AIR LIQUIDE AMERICA LP
11440 W Fairmont Pkwy (77571-6000)
PHONE................................281 291-5360
Ace Ririe, *Manager*
EMP: 100

SALES (corp-wide): 129.8MM **Privately Held**
WEB: www.industry.airliquide.us
SIC: 2813 Industrial gases
HQ: Air Liquide America L.P.
　　9811 Katy Fwy Ste 100
　　Houston TX 77024
　　713 624-8000

(G-13719)
AIRGAS USA LLC
11426 W Fairmont Pkwy (77571-6000)
P.O. Box 200269, Houston (77216-0001)
PHONE................................281 474-8400
Phillipe Andreanie, *Manager*
EMP: 34
SALES (corp-wide): 129.8MM **Privately Held**
WEB: www.airgas.com
SIC: 2813 Oxygen, compressed or liquefied; hydrogen; nitrogen
HQ: Airgas Usa, Llc
　　259 N Radnor Chester Rd
　　Radnor PA 19087
　　216 642-6600

(G-13720)
ALTIVIA SPECIALTY CHEM LLC
1901 W H St (77571-4500)
PHONE................................713 658-9000
Derick R Meadows, *Plant Mgr*
Frank J Hayes, *CFO*
Glenn E Gosnell, *Technical Staff*
EMP: 115
SALES (corp-wide): 34MM **Privately Held**
WEB: www.altivia.com
SIC: 2869 Industrial organic chemicals
HQ: Altivia Specialty Chemicals Llc
　　1100 La St Ste 4800
　　Houston TX 77002
　　713 658-9000

(G-13721)
AMERICAN RAILCAR INDS INC
222 N 16th St (77571-3165)
PHONE................................281 471-1930
Dwaine Davidson, *Principal*
EMP: 10
SALES (corp-wide): 476.8MM **Privately Held**
WEB: www.americanrailcar.com
SIC: 3743 Railroad equipment, except locomotives
HQ: American Railcar Industries, Inc.
　　100 Clark St
　　Saint Charles MO 63301

(G-13722)
AMERITEK HEAT TREATING AND F
420 S 16th St (77571-4613)
PHONE................................281 480-5637
Dennis Beasley, *President*
Apolla Beasley, *Corp Secy*
EMP: 122
SQ FT: 8,000
SALES (est): 25.6MM **Privately Held**
WEB: www.htsameritek.com
SIC: 3398 Metal heat treating

(G-13723)
AMPAC FINE CHEMICALS TEXAS LLC
914 S 16th St (77571)
P.O. Box 2049 (77572-2049)
PHONE................................281 842-1459
Aslam Malik, *President*
Joe Warchol, *CFO*
Deanna Riccardi, *Admin Sec*
EMP: 30
SQ FT: 5,000
SALES (est): 2.5MM **Privately Held**
WEB: www.ampacfinechemicals.com
SIC: 2834 Pharmaceutical preparations

(G-13724)
ANALYTIC STRESS RELIEVING INC
Also Called: Western Stress
125 N 17th St (77571-3191)
PHONE................................281 471-9600
Rusty Martin, *Project Mgr*
John McGee, *Manager*
David Johns, *Manager*

Johnny White, *Manager*
John Lindsay, *Director*
EMP: 80
SALES (corp-wide): 224.8MM **Privately Held**
WEB: www.analyticstress.com
SIC: 3398 1389 Metal heat treating; oil field services
PA: Analytic Stress Relieving, Inc.
　　3118 W Pinhook Rd Ste 202
　　Lafayette LA 70508
　　337 237-8790

(G-13725)
BAY AREA INDUSTRIAL CONTRS LP
Also Called: Forest Health Bariatric Center
1606 Sens Rd (77571-9304)
PHONE................................281 471-0400
EMP: 150
SQ FT: 3,000
SALES (est): 4.4MM **Privately Held**
SIC: 7692 1795 4959 Welding Repair Wrecking/Demolition Contractor Sanitary Services

(G-13726)
CENTRIFUGE REPAIR & ENGRG LP
Also Called: Cre
302 N 16th St (77571-3167)
P.O. Box 868 (77572-0868)
PHONE................................281 471-3767
Ronald P Holt, *Partner*
Margaret Latimer, *Partner*
Doug Latimer, *General Ptnr*
Bart Latimer, *CFO*
Michelle Daniel, *Accounts Mgr*
▲ **EMP:** 14
SQ FT: 20,000
SALES (est): 3.3MM
SALES (corp-wide): 6.7MM **Privately Held**
WEB: www.centrifugelp.com
SIC: 3556 Food products machinery
PA: Mechanical Repair & Engineering Lp
　　202 N 18th St
　　La Porte TX 77571
　　281 471-7811

(G-13727)
CHEMICAL LIME-SOUTHWEST LLC
Also Called: Laporte Plant Us70
801 N 16th St (77571-3189)
PHONE................................281 471-4500
Joel Digulio, *Terminal Mgr*
EMP: 37
SQ FT: 1,000
SALES (corp-wide): 2.6MM **Privately Held**
WEB: www.lhoist.com
SIC: 3274 Lime
HQ: Chemical Lime-Southwest, Llc
　　3700 Hulen St
　　Fort Worth TX 76107
　　817 732-8164

(G-13728)
CHEMOURS COMPANY FC LLC
12501 Strang Rd (77571-8704)
PHONE................................281 471-2771
EMP: 14
SALES (corp-wide): 6.6B **Publicly Held**
WEB: www.chemours.com
SIC: 2879 Agricultural chemicals
HQ: The Chemours Company Fc Llc
　　1007 Market St
　　Wilmington DE 19898
　　302 773-1000

(G-13729)
COLT SERVICES LP (PA)
626 N 16th St (77571-3173)
P.O. Box 1078 (77572-1078)
PHONE................................281 471-9099
John W Clark, *Partner*
Carole C Clark, *Partner*
Jeff Martin, *Division Mgr*
Jerry Robb, *General Mgr*
David Gonzalez, *Engineer*
▼ **EMP:** 46
SQ FT: 30,000

SALES (est): 11.5MM **Privately Held**
WEB: www.coltonline.com
SIC: 7699 1389 Boiler & heating repair services; construction, repair & dismantling services

(G-13730)
CONCEPT CONTROLS INC
1318 Underwood Rd Ste 110 (77571-9471)
PHONE................................281 476-4400
EMP: 19 **EST:** 2016
SALES (est): 3.5MM **Privately Held**
WEB: www.conceptcontrols.com
SIC: 3823 Industrial instrmnts msrmnt display/control process variable

(G-13731)
DOOSAN TURBOMACHINERY SVCS INC
12000 N P St (77571-9385)
PHONE................................713 364-7500
Billy Coleman, *President*
Desare Emigh, *Purch Mgr*
Glenn Turner, *VP Engrg*
Brianna Riley, *CFO*
◆ **EMP:** 80
SALES (est): 18.8MM **Privately Held**
WEB: www.doosanturbomachineryservices.com
SIC: 3541 8711 Machine tools, metal cutting: exotic (explosive, etc.); machine tool design
PA: Doosan Heavy Industries & Construction Co., Ltd.
　　22 Doosanvolvo-Ro, Seongsan-Gu
　　Changwon 51711

(G-13732)
DOW CHEMICAL COMPANY
13300 Bay Area Blvd (77571)
P.O. Box 1330 (77572-1330)
PHONE................................281 474-4495
Shiela Donnelly, *Branch Mgr*
Kevin Sokora, *Director*
EMP: 100
SALES (corp-wide): 38.5B **Publicly Held**
WEB: www.dow.com
SIC: 2819 2821 Industrial inorganic chemicals; plastics materials & resins
HQ: The Dow Chemical Company
　　2211 H H Dow Way
　　Midland MI 48642
　　989 636-1000

(G-13733)
DOW CHEMICAL COMPANY
550 Independence Pkwy S (77571-9768)
P.O. Box 685 (77572-0685)
PHONE................................713 246-0369
John Harrison, *Branch Mgr*
Tom Argue, *Manager*
Kevin Romero, *Technology*
EMP: 38
SALES (corp-wide): 38.5B **Publicly Held**
WEB: www.dow.com
SIC: 2819 2851 Industrial inorganic chemicals; polyurethane coatings
HQ: The Dow Chemical Company
　　2211 H H Dow Way
　　Midland MI 48642
　　989 636-1000

(G-13734)
E I DU PONT DE NEMOURS & CO
Also Called: Dupont
11621 Strang Rd (77571-9749)
PHONE................................281 470-2371
Robert Vigil, *Engineer*
Randy Bailey, *Manager*
EMP: 49
SALES (corp-wide): 14.2B **Publicly Held**
WEB: www.dupont.com
SIC: 2819 Industrial inorganic chemicals
HQ: E. I. Du Pont De Nemours And Company
　　974 Centre Rd Bldg 735
　　Wilmington DE 19805
　　302 485-3000

(G-13735)
ENDRESS + HAUSER INC
10057 Porter Rd (77571-7593)
PHONE................................281 867-3400
David Hager, *Branch Mgr*
EMP: 108

SALES (corp-wide): 291.8MM **Privately Held**
WEB: www.us.endress.com
SIC: 3823 Industrial instrmnts msrmnt display/control process variable
HQ: Endress + Hauser Inc
2350 Endress Pl
Greenwood IN 46143
317 535-7138

(G-13736)
EQUISTAR CHEMICALS LP
1515 Miller Cut Off Rd (77571-9810)
PHONE.....................................713 209-7000
Christopher Cain, *Branch Mgr*
Dave Bang, *Technology*
EMP: 1100
SALES (corp-wide): 34.9B **Privately Held**
WEB: www.lyondellbasell.com
SIC: 2821 Alcohols, non-beverage
HQ: Equistar Chemicals, Lp
1221 Mckinney St Ste 300
Houston TX 77010

(G-13737)
FOREMARK PERFORMANCE CHEM INC
12511 Strang Rd (77571-8704)
PHONE.....................................281 867-1330
Randy Owens, *CEO*
Brian Wilson, *Vice Pres*
EMP: 25
SALES (corp-wide): 66MM **Privately Held**
WEB: www.foremarkperformance.com
SIC: 2869 Formaldehyde (formalin)
PA: Foremark Performance Chemicals, Inc.
2450 S Shore Blvd Ste 402
League City TX 77573
281 867-1330

(G-13738)
FRYOUX TANKERMAN SVC OF TEXAS
915 S 8th St (77571-4994)
PHONE.....................................281 842-9400
Jimmy Fryoux, *President*
Fryoux J Raymond, *Vice Pres*
EMP: 40
SALES (est): 2.6MM **Privately Held**
WEB: www.fryoux.com
SIC: 3743 Tank freight cars & car equipment

(G-13739)
GLT FABRICATORS INC
2902 E 13th St Ste 200 (77571-9647)
PHONE.....................................713 670-9700
Leslie Montemayor, *Sales Staff*
Timothy Scott, *Director*
EMP: 25
SALES (corp-wide): 5MM **Privately Held**
WEB: www.gltfabricators.com
SIC: 3644 3498 3296 Insulators & insulation materials, electrical; tube fabricating (contract bending & shaping); mineral wool
PA: Glt Fabricators, Inc.
6810 Cochran Rd
Solon OH 44139
440 914-1122

(G-13740)
GREIF INC
10700 Strang Rd (77571-9731)
PHONE.....................................281 470-4469
Frank Gianocaro, *Plant Supt*
Tim Seymore, *Plant Mgr*
EMP: 48
SALES (corp-wide): 4.5B **Publicly Held**
WEB: www.deltacogroup.com
SIC: 2655 Fiber cans, drums & similar products
PA: Greif, Inc.
425 Winter Rd
Delaware OH 43015
740 549-6000

(G-13741)
GREIF INC
10850 Strang Rd (77571-9733)
PHONE.....................................281 470-4400
EMP: 16

SALES (corp-wide): 4.5B **Publicly Held**
WEB: www.deltacogroup.com
SIC: 2655 Fiber cans, drums & similar products
PA: Greif, Inc.
425 Winter Rd
Delaware OH 43015
740 549-6000

(G-13742)
GULF STATES MATERIALS INC
555 Sens Rd (77571-9762)
P.O. Box 1425 (77572-1425)
PHONE.....................................281 470-8645
Dale M Junghans, *President*
EMP: 30
SQ FT: 600
SALES (est): 8.3MM **Privately Held**
WEB: www.gulfstatesmaterials.com
SIC: 2951 Road materials, bituminous (not from refineries)

(G-13743)
HEXA CONTAINMENT LLC
709 S 16th St (77571-4618)
PHONE.....................................281 884-8026
Jordan Blunbell, *Mng Member*
EMP: 50
SALES (est): 2.3MM **Privately Held**
WEB: www.hexacontainment.com
SIC: 3272 Liquid catch basins, tanks & covers: concrete

(G-13744)
HICKHAM INDUSTRIES
11518 Old La Porte Rd (77571-9516)
PHONE.....................................713 567-2700
Darayus Pardivala, *President*
EMP: 10
SALES (est): 1MM **Privately Held**
SIC: 3999 Manufacturing industries

(G-13745)
HOERBIGER SERVICE INC
Also Called: Revak Turbo Machinery
12206 W Fairmont Pkwy (77571-6004)
PHONE.....................................281 474-4458
Lindel Keene, *Branch Mgr*
EMP: 98
SALES (corp-wide): 114.7MM **Privately Held**
WEB: www.keeneturbomachineryservices.com
SIC: 3531 Construction machinery
HQ: Hoerbiger Service Inc.
1191 E Nwport Ctr Dr Ste
Deerfield Beach FL 33442
281 955-5888

(G-13746)
HOUSTON JVIC OPERATIONS
2217 Sens Rd (77571-9209)
PHONE.....................................281 476-5775
EMP: 9
SALES (est): 523K **Privately Held**
WEB: www.jvic.com
SIC: 3599 Machine shop, jobbing & repair

(G-13747)
ICL SPECIALTY PRODUCTS INC
902 Sens Rd (77571-9766)
PHONE.....................................281 471-4700
John Mazzola, *Manager*
EMP: 25
SALES (corp-wide): 737.3MM **Privately Held**
WEB: www.iclfood.com
SIC: 2819 Phosphorus, elemental
HQ: Icl Specialty Products Inc.
622 Emerson Rd Ste 500
Saint Louis MO 63141
314 983-7500

(G-13748)
ILLINOIS TOOL WORKS INC
Also Called: CMOS X-RAY DBA ENVISION CMOSXRAY
3200 Awesome Ln (77571-8406)
PHONE.....................................713 944-3200
Lawrence Swift, *Branch Mgr*
EMP: 18
SALES (corp-wide): 14.1B **Publicly Held**
WEB: www.qsa-global.com
SIC: 3861 Film, sensitized motion picture; X-ray, still camera, etc.

PA: Illinois Tool Works Inc.
155 Harlem Ave
Glenview IL 60025
847 724-7500

(G-13749)
IMERYS PERLITE USA INC
Also Called: Harborlite
201 N 18th St (77571-3154)
P.O. Box 1014 (77572-1014)
PHONE.....................................281 471-3122
Shawn Velasquez, *Finance Mgr*
Cassandra Rucky, *Supervisor*
EMP: 14
SQ FT: 7,500
SALES (corp-wide): 3.1MM **Privately Held**
WEB: www.imerys.com
SIC: 2819 Industrial inorganic chemicals
HQ: Imerys Perlite Usa, Inc.
1732 N 1st St Ste 450
San Jose CA 95112

(G-13750)
INDUSTRIAL INSPTN INNOVATION
10700 Deaf Smith St (77571-9547)
PHONE.....................................281 636-7215
Eugene Nichols, *Owner*
EMP: 10
SALES (est): 796.6K **Privately Held**
SIC: 3312 Tool & die steel

(G-13751)
INEOS AMERICAS LLC
1230 Independence Pkwy S (77571-9811)
PHONE.....................................713 307-3000
Kathryn Shuler, *Business Mgr*
Paul Adams, *Vice Pres*
Ray Supak, *Safety Mgr*
Tom Tinker, *Maint Spvr*
Michael Davis, *Opers Staff*
EMP: 40
SALES (corp-wide): 1.9MM **Privately Held**
WEB: www.ineos.com
SIC: 2821 Plastics materials & resins
HQ: Ineos Americas Llc
2600 S Shore Blvd Ste 500
League City TX 77573
251 535-6600

(G-13752)
INEOS AMERICAS LLC
Also Called: Ineos Oligomers
1514 Miller Cut Off Rd (77571-9809)
PHONE.....................................713 767-5714
Sally Stephens, *Purch Mgr*
Timothy Camp, *Business Anlyst*
Jed Bowdy, *Branch Mgr*
EMP: 34
SALES (corp-wide): 1.9MM **Privately Held**
WEB: www.ineos.com
SIC: 2821 Plastics materials & resins
HQ: Ineos Americas Llc
2600 S Shore Blvd Ste 500
League City TX 77573
251 535-6600

(G-13753)
INTEGRATED POWER SERVICES LLC
1500 E Main St (77571-5738)
PHONE.....................................281 471-4611
Donald Pace, *Production*
Blake Tucker, *Branch Mgr*
EMP: 50
SALES (corp-wide): 843.2MM **Privately Held**
WEB: www.ips.us
SIC: 7694 Electric motor repair
HQ: Integrated Power Services Llc
250 Executive Center Dr # 100
Greenville SC 29615

(G-13754)
INTERGULF CORPORATION (PA)
Also Called: Circon Environmental
428 Highway 146 S (77571-4830)
P.O. Box 1590 (77572-1590)
PHONE.....................................281 474-4210
Steve R Rhyne, *President*
Rick Crump, *Vice Pres*
Nikki Harrell, *Personnel Exec*
Roberto Gomez, *Manager*

Harry Thomas, *Manager*
◆ EMP: 75
SQ FT: 4,800
SALES (est): 25.2MM **Privately Held**
WEB: www.circonenviro.com
SIC: 2911 2992 5172 4449 Petroleum refining; lubricating oils & greases; petroleum brokers; canal & intracoastal freight transportation; canal barge operations; petroleum haulage, local; liquid petroleum transport, non-local

(G-13755)
INTERNATIONAL PLANT SVCS LLC
1602 Old Underwood Rd (77571-9649)
PHONE.....................................281 867-8400
Karim Ayed, *CEO*
Homer Gray, *General Mgr*
Aileen Galang, *Accounting Mgr*
Craig Crawford,
Joe Ghantous,
EMP: 376
SQ FT: 10,000
SALES (corp-wide): 32.9MM **Publicly Held**
WEB: www.intlplantservices.com
SIC: 8711 7692 1629 Engineering services; welding repair; oil refinery construction
PA: Texas Gulf Energy, Inc.
1602 Old Underwood Rd
La Porte TX 77571

(G-13756)
INTREPID INDUSTRIES INC
2305 S Battleground Rd (77571-9475)
PHONE.....................................281 479-8301
Erich Bredl, *President*
Rick Shepley, *Senior VP*
Chase Kurtin, *Prdtn Mgr*
Paxton Guidroz, *Sales Mgr*
Addrenna Fontenett, *Sales Staff*
▲ EMP: 9
SQ FT: 7,500
SALES (est): 2.2MM **Privately Held**
WEB: www.intrepidindustries.com
SIC: 3089 Molding primary plastic

(G-13757)
INVISTA CAPITAL MANAGEMENT LLC
12455 Strang Rd (77571-9806)
PHONE.....................................281 470-3434
Ken Stevens, *Branch Mgr*
EMP: 44
SALES (corp-wide): 36.8B **Privately Held**
WEB: www.invista.com
SIC: 2821 Plastics materials & resins
HQ: Invista Capital Management, Llc
2801 Centerville Rd
Wilmington DE 19808
302 683-3000

(G-13758)
JAKE HARRIS & SONS INC
632 S 16th St (77571-4617)
P.O. Box 1117 (77572-1117)
PHONE.....................................281 471-0214
EMP: 12
SQ FT: 20,000
SALES (est): 2.8MM **Privately Held**
SIC: 3498 Tube fabricating (contract bending & shaping)

(G-13759)
JV INDUSTRIAL COMPANIES LTD
2221 Sens Rd (77571-9209)
PHONE.....................................281 417-7019
EMP: 10 **Privately Held**
SIC: 7692 Welding Repair
HQ: J.V. Industrial Companies, Ltd.
3741 Red Bluff Rd Ste 200
Pasadena TX 78221
713 568-2600

(G-13760)
K2 INDUSTRIAL SERVICES INC (DH)
1900 Old Underwood Rd (77571-9674)
PHONE.....................................850 477-6437
Ted L Mansfield, *CEO*
Rick Napier, *COO*
Bruce Moon, *Project Mgr*
Brian Sanders, *Project Mgr*

Jose Padilla, *Opers Mgr*
EMP: 10
SALES (est): 321.1MM
SALES (corp-wide): 2.8B **Privately Held**
WEB: www.k2industrial.com
SIC: 2842 1799 Specialty cleaning preparations; coating, caulking & weather, water & fireproofing
HQ: Asrc Industrial Services, Llc
　　1501 W Ftnhead Pkwy # 550
　　Tempe AZ 85282
　　707 644-7455

(G-13761)
KAP PROJECT SERVICES LTD
1200 Highway 146 S # 260 (77571-6131)
PHONE.................................877 527-7762
Scott Kammerer, *President*
Red Bird Group, *General Ptnr*
Sid Dickerson, *Opers Mgr*
Ricky Palacios, *Site Mgr*
Roger George, *Accounts Mgr*
EMP: 95
SQ FT: 5,000
SALES (est): 3.8MM **Privately Held**
WEB: www.kapproservices.com
SIC: 1382 Oil & gas exploration services

(G-13762)
KATOEN NTIE SPECIALTY CHEM INC
102 Old Underwood Rd (77571-9472)
PHONE.................................281 941-1001
EMP: 45
SALES (corp-wide): 9.1MM **Privately Held**
SIC: 2899 Chemical preparations
PA: Katoen Natie Specialty Chemicals, Inc.
　　10925 Sh 225 Bldg 5
　　La Porte TX 77571
　　281 470-5423

(G-13763)
KATOEN NTIE SPECIALTY CHEM INC (PA)
10925 Sh 225 Bldg 5 (77571)
P.O. Box 1479 (77572-1479)
PHONE.................................281 470-5423
Katleen Bracquene, *President*
EMP: 15 EST: 2012
SALES (est): 9.1MM **Privately Held**
SIC: 2899 Chemical preparations

(G-13764)
KOBELCO COMPRESSORS AMER INC
11817 W Fairmont Pkwy (77571-6003)
PHONE.................................713 470-1290
Pakaaki Hayapa, *President*
Tomoko Uchiyama, *Marketing Staff*
EMP: 250 **Privately Held**
WEB: www.kobelcocompressors.com
SIC: 3563 Air & gas compressors
HQ: Kobelco Compressors America, Inc.
　　1450 W Rincon St
　　Corona CA 92878

(G-13765)
KURARAY AMERICA INC
12501 Strang Rd (77571-8704)
PHONE.................................281 471-2771
William O Walker, *Manager*
EMP: 22 **Privately Held**
WEB: www.kuraray.us.com
SIC: 2819 2879 2869 2865 Industrial inorganic chemicals; agricultural chemicals; industrial organic chemicals; cyclic crudes & intermediates
HQ: Kuraray America, Inc.
　　2625 Bay Area Blvd Ste 60
　　Houston TX 77058

(G-13766)
LEADER GASKET TECHNOLOGIES INC (DH)
Also Called: International Gasket & Supply
850 Sens Rd (77571-9765)
PHONE.................................281 542-0600
Michael Winters, *CEO*
Tim Howell, *CFO*
Damien Turknett, *Manager*
John Durham, *Shareholder*
◆ **EMP:** 69

SALES (est): 35MM **Privately Held**
WEB: www.leadergt.com
SIC: 3053 5072 5085 Gaskets & sealing devices; bolts, nuts & screws; gaskets & seals
HQ: Eriks N.V.
　　Mariaplaats 21
　　Utrecht 3511
　　303 690-100

(G-13767)
LECHI FOODS
10625 W Fairmont Pkwy (77571-6006)
PHONE.................................281 470-6200
CHI Nguyen, *Director*
▲ **EMP:** 25
SALES (est): 2MM **Privately Held**
WEB: www.lechifoods.com
SIC: 2032 Chinese foods: packaged in cans, jars, etc.

(G-13768)
LINDE GAS NORTH AMERICA LLC (PA)
11603 Strang Rd (77571-9749)
PHONE.................................713 767-4100
Aldo Belloni, *Ch of Bd*
Patrick F Murphy, *President*
Robert Wowk, *Principal*
Christian Bruch, *Exec VP*
Eduardo Menezes, *Exec VP*
EMP: 58
SALES (est): 15.6MM **Privately Held**
WEB: www.linde.com
SIC: 2899 2813 Chemical preparations; industrial gases

(G-13769)
LINDE INC
Praxair
100 Strang Rd (77571-7524)
P.O. Box 1927 (77572-1927)
PHONE.................................281 471-4585
T R Lee, *Branch Mgr*
EMP: 30 **Privately Held**
WEB: www.praxair.com
SIC: 2813 Industrial gases
HQ: Linde Inc.
　　10 Riverview Dr
　　Danbury CT 06810
　　203 837-2000

(G-13770)
LYCRA COMPANY LLC
12455 Strang Rd (77571-9806)
PHONE.................................218 842-4613
David Trerotola, *CEO*
EMP: 10
SALES (corp-wide): 36.8B **Privately Held**
WEB: www.lycra.com
SIC: 2221 Textile mills, broadwoven: silk & manmade, also glass
HQ: The Lycra Company Llc
　　2711 Centerville Rd # 300
　　Wilmington DE 19808
　　316 226-9361

(G-13771)
LYONDELLBASELL INDUSTRIES INC
1515 Miller Cut Off Rd (77571-9810)
P.O. Box 2009 (77572-2009)
PHONE.................................713 209-1248
Ryan Franger, *Supervisor*
Shane Rowlan, *Technician*
EMP: 14
SALES (corp-wide): 34.9B **Privately Held**
WEB: www.lyondellbasell.com
SIC: 2821 5169 Plastics materials & resins; chemicals & allied products
HQ: Lyondellbasell Industries, Inc.
　　1221 Mckinney St Ste 300
　　Houston TX 77010

(G-13772)
LYONDLLBSELL ADVNCED PLYMERS I
1300 Mccabe Rd (77571-6137)
PHONE.................................281 867-3000
EMP: 125
SALES (corp-wide): 34.9B **Privately Held**
WEB: www.lyondellbasell.com
SIC: 2821 Plasticizer/additive based plastic materials; molding compounds, plastics

HQ: Lyondellbasell Advanced Polymers Inc.
　　1221 Mckinney St Ste 300
　　Houston TX 77010
　　713 309-7200

(G-13773)
MAINLINERS WELDING ACADEMY
10001 Porter Rd (77571-7597)
PHONE.................................409 229-1632
Merced Arroyo, *Mng Member*
EMP: 15
SALES (est): 30.3K **Privately Held**
WEB: www.mainlinersweldingacademy.com
SIC: 7692 Welding repair

(G-13774)
MARTIN MIDSTREAM PARTNERS LP
2904 N 23rd St (77571-3182)
PHONE.................................281 471-2211
Ed Grimm, *Branch Mgr*
EMP: 16
SQ FT: 7,350
SALES (corp-wide): 847.1MM **Publicly Held**
WEB: www.martinmidstream.com
SIC: 4924 1321 4226 2819 Natural gas distribution; natural gas liquids; petroleum & chemical bulk stations & terminals for hire; sulfur, recovered or refined, incl. from sour natural gas; coastwide transportation, freight; gases, liquefied petroleum (propane)
PA: Martin Midstream Partners L.P.
　　4200 Stone Rd
　　Kilgore TX 75662
　　903 983-6200

(G-13775)
MECHANICAL REPAIR & ENGRG LP (PA)
202 N 18th St (77571-3153)
P.O. Box 1542 (77572-1542)
PHONE.................................281 471-7811
Doug Latimer, *Managing Prtnr*
Doug F Latimer Jr, *Partner*
Margaret Latimer, *Partner*
Lynn Johnson, *Vice Pres*
Allen Exnicious, *Manager*
EMP: 31
SQ FT: 30,000
SALES (est): 6.7MM **Privately Held**
WEB: www.centrifugelp.com
SIC: 3599 Machine shop, jobbing & repair

(G-13776)
MESSER LLC
11603 Strang Rd (77571-9749)
PHONE.................................713 767-4155
Jacob Simon, *Plant Mgr*
Jerrod Hughes, *Site Mgr*
Jared Piette, *Project Engr*
Rustam Sethna, *Info Tech Mgr*
Marcella Viera, *Admin Asst*
EMP: 10
SALES (corp-wide): 1.2B **Privately Held**
WEB: www.praxair.com
SIC: 2813 Industrial gases
HQ: Messer Llc
　　200 Somerset Corp Blvd # 7000
　　Bridgewater NJ 08807
　　908 464-8100

(G-13777)
METTON AMERICA INC
2727 Miller Cut Off Rd (77571-9760)
PHONE.................................281 479-8078
Yuji Takada, *CEO*
Garland Lee, *Senior VP*
Katsuhiro Kuroda, *Treasurer*
Kazutaka Nishikawa, *Director*
Teruyasu Yoneda, *Director*
◆ **EMP:** 23
SQ FT: 2,000
SALES (est): 10.4MM **Privately Held**
WEB: www.metton.com
SIC: 2821 Plastics materials & resins
PA: Sojitz Corporation
　　2-1-1, Uchisaiwaicho
　　Chiyoda-Ku TKY 100-0

(G-13778)
MODERN AG PRODUCTS LLC
Also Called: Dragon Industries & Products
816 W Barbours Cut Blvd (77571-3236)
PHONE.................................281 470-1903
EMP: 50 **Privately Held**
WEB: www.dragonproductsltd.com
SIC: 3441 3442 3412 Fabricated structural metal; metal doors, sash & trim; metal barrels, drums & pails
HQ: Modern Ag Products, Llc
　　1655 Louisiana St
　　Beaumont TX 77701
　　409 833-2665

(G-13779)
NOLTEX LLC
12220 Strang Rd (77571-9740)
PHONE.................................281 842-5000
Katsumi Nishii, *President*
K Asano, *Principal*
R Boeding, *Principal*
Jimmy Thompson, *Opers Mgr*
Tim Le, *Engineer*
◆ **EMP:** 100
SALES (est): 4MM **Privately Held**
WEB: www.noltexllc.com
SIC: 2821 3999 Plastics materials & resins; atomizers; toiletry
HQ: Nippon Gohsei (U.S.A.) Co., Ltd.
　　12220 Strang Rd
　　La Porte TX 77571

(G-13780)
OHMSTEDE LTD
12415 Highway 225 (77571-9592)
PHONE.................................281 471-4140
Brett Bettison, *General Mgr*
Shawn Pettersen, *Purch Mgr*
Paul Pike, *Purchasing*
Lavern Williams, *Office Mgr*
Hershall Lain, *Branch Mgr*
EMP: 106
SALES (corp-wide): 9.1B **Publicly Held**
WEB: www.ohmstede.com
SIC: 3443 3494 3541 Heat exchangers: coolers (after, inter); condensers, etc.; valves & pipe fittings; cutoff machines (metalworking machinery)
HQ: Ohmstede Ltd.
　　895 N Main St
　　Beaumont TX 77701
　　409 833-6375

(G-13781)
OXY VINYLS LP
2800 Park Rd 1836 (77571)
P.O. Box 500, Deer Park (77536-5000)
PHONE.................................281 476-2927
EMP: 40
SALES (corp-wide): 21.2B **Publicly Held**
WEB: www.oxy.com
SIC: 2821 Vinyl resins
HQ: Oxy Vinyls, Lp
　　14555 Dallas Pkwy Ste 400
　　Dallas TX 75254
　　877 699-8465

(G-13782)
OXY VINYLS LP
2400 Miller Cut Off Rd (77571-9759)
PHONE.................................281 476-8000
Rob Peterson, *Branch Mgr*
EMP: 19
SALES (corp-wide): 21.2B **Publicly Held**
WEB: www.oxy.com
SIC: 2899 Chemical preparations
HQ: Oxy Vinyls, Lp
　　14555 Dallas Pkwy Ste 400
　　Dallas TX 75254
　　877 699-8465

(G-13783)
PONDEROSA PRECISION PLAS INC
Also Called: Oilfield Protectors Supply
106 N 15th St (77571-4856)
PHONE.................................281 471-3221
Jim Cartwright, *President*
D Slaman, *Vice Pres*
Dan Slaman, *Vice Pres*
Shirley Cartwright, *Treasurer*
James R Cartwright, *Director*
EMP: 15
SQ FT: 5,000

SALES (est): 2.6MM **Privately Held**
WEB: www.ponderosaplastics.com
SIC: 3089 Molding primary plastic

(G-13784)
PPG INDUSTRIES INC
11505 Highway 225 (77571-4513)
PHONE....................281 842-9518
Steve Dickey, *Branch Mgr*
EMP: 24
SALES (corp-wide): 15.3B **Publicly Held**
WEB: www.ppg.com
SIC: 2851 Paints & allied products
PA: Ppg Industries, Inc.
   1 Ppg Pl
   Pittsburgh PA 15272
   412 434-3131

(G-13785)
PUFFER-SWEIVEN HOLDINGS INC
Also Called: Process Products
903 Highway 146 S (77571-4839)
PHONE....................281 470-2000
Andy Bauml, *Accounts Mgr*
Ryan Baker, *Sales Staff*
Fred Burban, *Sales Staff*
Ray Demmon, *Sales Staff*
Gil Hernandez, *Sales Staff*
EMP: 45
SQ FT: 21,392
SALES (corp-wide): 300.7MM **Privately Held**
WEB: www.puffer.com
SIC: 5084 3612 3494 Controlling instruments & accessories; transformers, except electric; valves & pipe fittings
PA: Puffer-Sweiven Holdings, Inc.
   4230 Greenbriar Dr
   Stafford TX 77477
   281 240-2000

(G-13786)
QA SUPPORT LP
11005 W Fairmont Pkwy (77571-6001)
P.O. Box 1339 (77572-1339)
PHONE....................281 307-1000
Deborah Brown, *Partner*
Gaylon Brown, *Partner*
Betty Wortham, *Partner*
David Wortham, *General Ptnr*
Ray Fain, *Vice Pres*
EMP: 35
SQ FT: 10,000
SALES: 5.5MM **Privately Held**
WEB: www.qasupport.com
SIC: 8711 3822 Consulting engineer; hardware for environmental regulators

(G-13787)
REVAK KEENE TURBOMACHINERY LP (PA)
12204 W Fairmont Pkwy (77571-6004)
P.O. Box 1119 (77572-1119)
PHONE....................281 427-8800
Lynn A Revak, *Partner*
Lendell Keene, *Partner*
Linda Keene, *Partner*
EMP: 75
SQ FT: 522,720
SALES (est): 10MM **Privately Held**
WEB: www.keeneturbomachineryservices.com
SIC: 3511 7699 Gas turbine generator set units, complete; industrial machinery & equipment repair

(G-13788)
RFV ENTERPRISES INC
Also Called: Vesco Business Products
425 N 10th St (77571-3104)
P.O. Box 1852 (77572-1852)
PHONE....................281 842-1877
Robin Vest, *President*
EMP: 10
SQ FT: 1,200
SALES (est): 4.5MM **Privately Held**
WEB: www.vescolp.com
SIC: 5943 5712 2752 Office forms & supplies; office furniture; commercial printing, lithographic

(G-13789)
SOLVAY CHEMICALS INC
1130 Independence Pkwy S (77571-9814)
PHONE....................713 307-3800

David Birney, *Manager*
Elizabeth A Adams, *Technical Staff*
EMP: 75
SALES (corp-wide): 13.8MM **Privately Held**
WEB: www.solvay.us
SIC: 1474 2812 Soda ash (natural) mining; soda ash, sodium carbonate (anhydrous)
HQ: Solvay Chemicals, Inc.
   3737 Buffalo Speedway
   Houston TX 77098
   713 525-6800

(G-13790)
SOUTH COAST TERMINALS LP
10900 Strang Rd (77571-9735)
PHONE....................281 842-1286
Delisa Lopez, *Office Mgr*
Robin Martin, *Manager*
EMP: 20
SALES (corp-wide): 19.2MM **Privately Held**
WEB: www.scterm.com
SIC: 2992 Oils & greases, blending & compounding
PA: South Coast Terminals, Lp
   7402 Wallisville Rd
   Houston TX 77020
   713 672-2401

(G-13791)
SPECIALTY TANK SERVICES LTD
Also Called: S T S
2225 Sens Rd (77571-9209)
PHONE....................281 470-4880
Joe Durham, *General Ptnr*
▲ EMP: 12
SALES (est): 999.7K
SALES (corp-wide): 12.1B **Publicly Held**
WEB: www.strongholdinspection.com
SIC: 3795 Tanks & tank components
HQ: Stronghold, Ltd.
   1140 Sens Rd
   La Porte TX 77571

(G-13792)
SULZER TURBO SVCS HOUSTON INC
11518 Old La Porte Rd (77571-9516)
PHONE....................713 567-2700
Darayus Pardivala, *President*
Michael Curran, *Vice Pres*
Scott Fahey, *Vice Pres*
Doug Sewell, *Vice Pres*
Javier Spilere, *Engineer*
◆ EMP: 330
SQ FT: 210,000
SALES (est): 114.1MM
SALES (corp-wide): 3.7B **Privately Held**
WEB: www.sulzerts.com
SIC: 3569 Centrifuges, industrial
HQ: Sulzer Us Holding Inc.
   1255 Enclave Pkwy Ste 300
   Houston TX 77077
   346 207-9660

(G-13793)
TAURUS INDUSTRIAL GROUP LLC
3810 Underwood Rd (77571-3928)
PHONE....................713 554-0157
Greg Reintjes, *President*
EMP: 35
SALES (corp-wide): 50MM **Privately Held**
WEB: www.hi-techindustrial.com
SIC: 7692 1742 Welding repair; plastering, drywall & insulation
PA: Hi-Tech Industrial Services, Llc
   14720 W 99th St Ste B
   Lenexa KS 66215
   913 276-3300

(G-13794)
TEXAS ELECTRIC EQP CO LTD
9401 Highway 225 (77571-8702)
P.O. Box 1378 (77572-1378)
PHONE....................281 479-6086
Edward Hoerner, *President*
John Neal, *Electrical Engi*
EMP: 33 EST: 1972
SQ FT: 30,000

SALES (est): 5MM **Privately Held**
WEB: www.teeco.net
SIC: 7694 5063 Electric motor repair; motors, electric; generators

(G-13795)
TEXAS STRESS INC (PA)
1304 Underwood Rd (77571-9468)
P.O. Box 1089, Deer Park (77536-1089)
PHONE....................281 930-0897
Joni Hager, *CEO*
Gary Hager, *President*
Brenda Phillips, *Corp Secy*
Tony Pipes, *Opers Mgr*
Kimberly Webb, *Safety Mgr*
EMP: 45
SQ FT: 15,000
SALES (est): 8MM **Privately Held**
WEB: www.texasstress.com
SIC: 3398 Metal heat treating

(G-13796)
TIGER TOWER SERVICES LLC
1605 S Battleground Rd (77571-9491)
PHONE....................281 951-2500
Kieth Hurst, *President*
William Dobbins, *Division Mgr*
Don Harvey, *Vice Pres*
Blake Arbour, *Marketing Staff*
Chad Cassell, *Admin Mgr*
EMP: 46
SALES (est): 10.6MM **Privately Held**
WEB: www.altairstrickland.com
SIC: 3559 Refinery, chemical processing & similar machinery

(G-13797)
TOTAL PTRCHEMICALS REF USA INC
Also Called: Research & Technology
1902 Independence Pkwy S (77571-9828)
P.O. Box 1200, Deer Park (77536-1200)
PHONE....................281 542-9542
Jim Waguespack, *Branch Mgr*
Kenneth Blackmon, *Manager*
EMP: 151
SALES (corp-wide): 7B **Publicly Held**
WEB: www.totalpetrochemicalsrefiningusa.com
SIC: 2899 2821 Chemical preparations; styrene resins
HQ: Total Petrochemicals & Refining Usa, Inc.
   1201 La St Ste 1800
   Houston TX 77002
   713 483-5000

(G-13798)
TOTAL PTRCHMCALS USA FUNDATION
1818 Independence Pkwy S (77571-9803)
P.O. Box 674411, Houston (77267-4411)
PHONE....................713 483-5000
Graeme Burnett, *President*
Robert Kilpatrick, *Vice Pres*
Jim Parks, *Treasurer*
Karen Isom, *Executive*
Tim Coffy, *Admin Sec*
EMP: 11
SALES (est): 1.7MM **Privately Held**
WEB: www.totalpetrochemicalsrefiningusa.com
SIC: 2821 Plastics materials & resins

(G-13799)
VALERO REFINING-TEXAS LP
1200 N Broadway St (77571-3031)
P.O. Box 1129 (77572-1129)
PHONE....................281 470-4900
Dave Johnson, *Branch Mgr*
EMP: 118
SALES (corp-wide): 108.3B **Publicly Held**
WEB: www.valero.com
SIC: 2911 2899 Fuel additives; chemical preparations
HQ: Valero Refining-Texas, L.P.
   1 Valero Way
   San Antonio TX 78249
   210 345-2000

La Vernia
Wilson County

(G-13800)
AIRE PLASTICS INC
132 Industrial Dr (78121-5830)
P.O. Box 782 (78121-0782)
PHONE....................830 779-2289
Terry Post, *President*
Sean Post, *Vice Pres*
Darin Sjogren, *Plant Mgr*
Judy Post, *Treasurer*
Jason Post, *Director*
▲ EMP: 14
SQ FT: 12,600
SALES (est): 2.2MM **Privately Held**
WEB: www.aireplastics.com
SIC: 3089 Injection molding of plastics

(G-13801)
FLOWCO PROD SOLUTIONS LLC
109 S Parkway Dr (78121-4883)
PHONE....................830 779-2163
J Spencer, *Manager*
EMP: 49
SALES (corp-wide): 49.5MM **Privately Held**
WEB: www.flowcosolutions.com
SIC: 3533 Oil & gas field machinery
PA: Flowco Production Solutions L.L.C
   20405 State Highway 249 # 600
   Houston TX 77070
   281 528-6298

(G-13802)
KAYCO SPRAY BOOTHS INC
135 Industrial Dr (78121-5830)
PHONE....................830 779-2051
William Fowler Jr, *President*
Sharon K Fowler, *Vice Pres*
EMP: 10
SQ FT: 12,000
SALES (est): 2.1MM **Privately Held**
WEB: www.kaycospraybooths.com
SIC: 3444 Booths, spray: prefabricated sheet metal

(G-13803)
TOMLINSON OILFIELD SERVICE
14414 Us Highway 87 W 3c (78121-5922)
P.O. Box 332 (78121-0332)
PHONE....................956 802-0030
Tommy J Tomlinson, *President*
EMP: 18
SALES (est): 2MM **Privately Held**
SIC: 1389 Oil field services

Lago Vista
Travis County

(G-13804)
CB SOLUTIONS LP
21508 Lake Park Dr (78645-6106)
PHONE....................512 267-9596
Cary Brown, *Principal*
EMP: 13
SALES (est): 2.6MM **Privately Held**
WEB: www.cbsolutionslp.com
SIC: 3495 Precision springs

(G-13805)
CRYER LIMITED PARTNERSHIP (PA)
Also Called: Specialty Machine
20202 Alfalfa Dr (78645-4805)
P.O. Box 4606 (78645-0013)
PHONE....................512 267-4944
EMP: 50
SQ FT: 32,000
SALES (est): 7.9MM **Privately Held**
WEB: www.specialtymachinelp.com
SIC: 3599 Machine shop, jobbing & repair

(G-13806)
LIGHT EMTTING DDS-NLIMITED LLC
Also Called: Leds Unlimited
3300 Parliament Cv (78645-6574)
PHONE....................512 267-7315
Ken Kaup, *VP Bus Dvlpt*

Tracy Nelson, *Sales Staff*
Manny Lopez,
Lance Nelson,
Lyle Nelson,
▼ **EMP:** 15
SALES (est): 1.2MM **Privately Held**
SIC: 3641 7389 Electric light bulbs, complete;

(G-13807)
MESA DRILLING INC
1805 Kingfisher Ridge Cv (78645-8044)
PHONE....................................713 993-7082
Don Bockhorn, *President*
EMP: 9
SALES (est): 789.3K **Privately Held**
SIC: 1389 Oil field services

(G-13808)
SEMICONDUCTOR TECHNOLOGY INC
Also Called: S T I
1924 American Dr (78645-7801)
PHONE....................................512 468-8687
Lloyd Rodenbeck, *President*
EMP: 10
SQ FT: 3,500
SALES (est): 3MM **Privately Held**
WEB: www.semi-tech-inc.com
SIC: 3674 Transistors

(G-13809)
TRAVISTIN INC
5609 Lakeshore Dr (78645)
PHONE....................................512 275-4812
EMP: 11
SALES (est): 1MM **Privately Held**
SIC: 7372 Prepackaged Software Services

Lake Dallas
Denton County

(G-13810)
COMMUNICATIONS CONVEYOR CO INC
Also Called: Comco Systems
306 W Overly Dr (75065-2538)
PHONE....................................940 498-1850
Melissa Carder, *Ch of Bd*
James Gary Paul, *President*
Diane Mages, *Admin Sec*
▲ **EMP:** 40
SQ FT: 23,000
SALES (est): 12.1MM **Privately Held**
WEB: www.comcosystems.com
SIC: 3535 3669 Pneumatic tube conveyor systems; intercommunication systems, electric

(G-13811)
SUN NEWSPAPERS
Also Called: Lake Cities Sun
275 Market St (75065-3610)
P.O. Box 860248, Plano (75086-0248)
PHONE....................................940 497-4141
Mark Henry, *Owner*
EMP: 10 **EST:** 1985
SALES (est): 376.3K **Privately Held**
WEB: www.lakecitiesprinting.com
SIC: 2711 Newspapers: publishing only, not printed on site

Lake Worth
Tarrant County

(G-13812)
BLAZE EQUIPMENT LLC
4200 White St (76135-2208)
PHONE....................................817 439-0453
▲ **EMP:** 17 **EST:** 2012
SALES (est): 5.8MM **Privately Held**
WEB: www.blaze-equip.com
SIC: 5046 1799 5084 3537 Commercial equipment; rigging & scaffolding; drilling equipment, excluding bits; forklift trucks

Lakeside
Tarrant County

(G-13813)
WHECO ELECTRIC INC
Also Called: Wheco Controls
8501 Jacksboro Hwy (76135-4332)
PHONE....................................817 244-6660
Kent Meyerhoeffer, *President*
Cynthia Wyatt, *Personnel*
Michael Hinton, *Prgrmr*
Melissa Miller, *Administration*
▲ **EMP:** 22
SQ FT: 8,500
SALES: 3.3MM **Privately Held**
WEB: www.whecocontrols.com
SIC: 1731 3589 General electrical contractor; sewage treatment equipment

Lakeway
Travis County

(G-13814)
AUSTIN BOATS & MOTORS INC
Also Called: Austin Boats and Motors
1208 Ranch Road 620 S (78734-6312)
PHONE....................................512 263-1266
Jeff Parker, *President*
Martin Boyer, *Vice Pres*
EMP: 12
SQ FT: 22,000
SALES (est): 3.6MM **Privately Held**
WEB: www.austinboats.com
SIC: 5551 7699 3732 Motor boat dealers; marine supplies; boat repair; boat building & repairing

(G-13815)
B2B COPIES LLC
1310 Ranch Road 620 S A5 (78734-6343)
PHONE....................................512 402-9775
Paul Meyertons,
EMP: 9
SALES (est): 960.2K **Privately Held**
WEB: www.b2bcopies.com
SIC: 2754 7334 7336 Color printing, gravure; photocopying & duplicating services; graphic arts & related design

(G-13816)
HILL COUNTRY SITE SUPPLY LLC
1202 Lakeway Dr (78734-4473)
P.O. Box 342468, Austin (78734-0042)
PHONE....................................512 608-0069
EMP: 9
SALES (est): 18.7MM **Privately Held**
SIC: 5039 3272 Whol Construction Materials Mfg Concrete Products

(G-13817)
LAKE SERVICES INC
109 Ranch Road 620 N (78734-3902)
PHONE....................................512 261-3625
Walter Judkins, *President*
EMP: 12
SALES (est): 372.1K **Privately Held**
WEB: www.lakeservicesinc.com
SIC: 7692 Welding repair

(G-13818)
ONE WATER SOURCE LLC (PA)
Also Called: Water Source One
211 Rr 620 N Ste 140 (78734-3904)
P.O. Box 163535, Austin (78716-3535)
PHONE....................................512 347-9280
Dave Evans, *President*
Steve Brazier, *Vice Pres*
Sid Maxwell, *Vice Pres*
Ben Mottesheard, *Vice Pres*
Stephen Brazier, *CFO*
▲ **EMP:** 11
SQ FT: 3,000
SALES (est): 1.4MM **Privately Held**
WEB: www.watersourceone.com
SIC: 2086 Mineral water, carbonated: packaged in cans, bottles, etc.

(G-13819)
SIENERGY LP
3 Lakeway Centre Ct # 110 (78734-2692)
P.O. Box 660141, Dallas (75266-0141)
PHONE....................................281 778-6250
June Dively, *CEO*
Joe King, *Area Mgr*
Paul Kennedy, *Vice Pres*
Julie Myhre, *Vice Pres*
John Mitchell, *Opers Staff*
EMP: 18
SALES (est): 2.7MM **Privately Held**
WEB: www.sienergy.com
SIC: 1311 Crude petroleum & natural gas

(G-13820)
STITCH GALLERY INC
1200 Lakeway Dr Ste 2 (78734-4467)
PHONE....................................512 550-6172
EMP: 18
SQ FT: 2,600
SALES (est): 1MM **Privately Held**
WEB: www.stitchgalleryaustin.com
SIC: 3552 2395 Embroidery machines; embroidery & art needlework

(G-13821)
STOKES SIGN COMPANY INC (PA)
Also Called: Signs 2 Go Lakeway
1909 Ranch Road 620 S C (78734-6205)
PHONE....................................512 263-7446
Nancy Hearn, *President*
Stephen H Vic, *President*
Stephen Hearn, *Vice Pres*
Karen Hoeker, *Manager*
EMP: 10
SALES (est): 1.1MM **Privately Held**
WEB: www.stokessigncompany.com
SIC: 3993 Signs & advertising specialties

Lamesa
Dawson County

(G-13822)
B & B ROUSTABOUT INC
211 S Lynn Ave (79331-6337)
P.O. Box 421 (79331-0421)
PHONE....................................806 872-7276
Brandon Boss, *CEO*
EMP: 63
SALES (est): 2.2MM **Privately Held**
SIC: 1389 Roustabout service

(G-13823)
B-P SUPPLY INC
1317 S Lynn Ave (79331-7431)
PHONE....................................806 872-9169
Bill Parnell, *Branch Mgr*
EMP: 26
SALES (corp-wide): 19.3MM **Privately Held**
WEB: www.bpsupplyinc.com
SIC: 1389 Oil field services
PA: B-P Supply, Inc.
1400 W Broadway St
Andrews TX 79714
432 523-7820

(G-13824)
BRITT DIRT CONTRACTING INC (PA)
Also Called: Britt Construction Company
1900 Seminole Rd (79331-4215)
PHONE....................................806 872-5194
Tommy D Churchwill, *President*
Billy Smith, *Vice Pres*
Edward Evans, *Treasurer*
EMP: 14
SALES (est): 2.8MM **Privately Held**
SIC: 1389 5082 Construction, repair & dismantling services; contractors' materials

(G-13825)
JADE SERVICES INC
701 N 1st St (79331-5409)
PHONE....................................806 870-3883
Alvin Jarrett, *President*
EMP: 30 **EST:** 2010
SALES (est): 2.8MM **Privately Held**
SIC: 1389 Gas field services

(G-13826)
KEY ENERGY SERVICES INC
2015 S Highway 87 (79331-5929)
P.O. Box 130, Welch (79377-0130)
PHONE....................................806 872-6688
EMP: 23
SALES (corp-wide): 436.1MM **Publicly Held**
SIC: 1389 Oil & Gas Well Service
PA: Key Energy Services, Inc.
1301 Mckinney St Ste 1800
Houston TX 77010
713 651-4300

(G-13827)
KEY ENERGY SERVICES INC
319 Big Spring Hwy 87 (79331)
PHONE....................................806 872-8331
Charlie Dyer, *Branch Mgr*
EMP: 57
SALES (corp-wide): 413.8MM **Publicly Held**
WEB: www.keyenergy.com
SIC: 1389 1381 Servicing oil & gas wells; drilling oil & gas wells
PA: Key Energy Services, Inc.
1301 Mckinney St Ste 1800
Houston TX 77010
713 651-4300

(G-13828)
LAMESA REPORTER INC
Also Called: Lamesa Press Reporter
523 N 1st St (79331-5405)
P.O. Box 710 (79331-0710)
PHONE....................................806 872-2177
Walter Buckel, *President*
Russel Skiles, *Principal*
Regina Crutcher, *Editor*
Dwight Heins, *Editor*
Cummuns Eugene, *Director*
EMP: 9
SQ FT: 7,560
SALES (est): 350K **Privately Held**
WEB: www.pressreporter.com
SIC: 2711 Newspapers: publishing only, not printed on site

(G-13829)
SAM STEVENS INC
2101 Lubbock Hwy (79331-2629)
PHONE....................................806 872-8365
Sam E Stevens, *President*
Latane Stevens, *Corp Secy*
Randy McKnight, *Vice Pres*
Ricky McKnight, *Vice Pres*
EMP: 25 **EST:** 1939
SQ FT: 20,000
SALES (est): 6.1MM **Privately Held**
WEB: www.samstevensinc.com
SIC: 3523 5251 Farm machinery & equipment; hardware

(G-13830)
SMITH FANS INC
501 S Dallas Ave (79331-7127)
PHONE....................................806 872-8465
Dudley Smith, *President*
Smith Roy Dudley, *Vice Pres*
Max Smith, *Vice Pres*
EMP: 10
SQ FT: 12,000
SALES (est): 1.8MM **Privately Held**
WEB: www.smithfans.com
SIC: 3564 Blowers & fans

(G-13831)
U S SILICA COMPANY
300 County Road 11 (79331-1606)
PHONE....................................806 470-2035
EMP: 11
SALES (corp-wide): 1.4B **Publicly Held**
WEB: www.ussilica.com
SIC: 2819 Industrial inorganic chemicals
HQ: U. S. Silica Company
24275 Katy Fwy Ste 100
Katy TX 77494
301 682-0600

Lampasas
Lampasas County

(G-13832)
CANALES SHEETMETAL & WELDING
1306 E Ave (76550)
PHONE..................................512 556-8613
Tony Canales, *President*
EMP: 11
SQ FT: 3,750
SALES (est): 2.2MM **Privately Held**
WEB: www.networknsc.com
SIC: 3585 1799 1761 Refrigeration & heating equipment; welding on site; sheet metalwork

(G-13833)
CLAUSSEN INC
Also Called: Lampasas Building Components
1303 Mclean St (76550-1233)
P.O. Box 668 (76550-0005)
PHONE..................................512 556-2180
Wilson Neely, *President*
Daniel Claussen, *Vice Pres*
EMP: 15
SQ FT: 12,000
SALES (est): 3.1MM **Privately Held**
WEB: www.lbctruss.com
SIC: 2439 Trusses, wooden roof

(G-13834)
HILL COUNTRY PUBLISHING CO (PA)
Also Called: Print Shop, The
416 S Live Oak St (76550-2940)
P.O. Box 631 (76550-0005)
PHONE..................................512 556-6262
Fred Lowe, *President*
Jim Lowe, *Vice Pres*
EMP: 22 EST: 1905
SQ FT: 4,500
SALES (est): 1.2MM **Privately Held**
WEB: www.lampasasdispatchrecord.com
SIC: 2711 2752 5112 5044 Newspapers, publishing & printing; commercial printing, lithographic; office supplies; copying equipment

(G-13835)
OIL STATES INDUSTRIES INC
1720 Central Texas Expy (76550-3421)
PHONE..................................512 556-5471
Robert Reed, *Branch Mgr*
EMP: 26
SALES (corp-wide): 1B **Publicly Held**
WEB: www.oilstates.com
SIC: 3069 Hard rubber & molded rubber products
HQ: Oil States Industries, Inc.
7701 S Cooper St
Arlington TX 76001

Lancaster
Dallas County

(G-13836)
ADVANCED MACHINING & TOOL INC
1616 N Interstate 35 E (75134-2606)
PHONE..................................972 228-1987
Elsie Walker, *President*
Bill Walker, *Vice Pres*
John Walker, *Vice Pres*
Russell Boatman, *Foreman/Supr*
Bret Tarber, *Treasurer*
EMP: 54
SQ FT: 15,500
SALES (est): 9.7MM **Privately Held**
SIC: 3441 7699 Fabricated structural metal; welding equipment repair

(G-13837)
ANKO PRODUCTS COMPANY OF TEXAS
Also Called: Break-Thru Products
146 Industrial St (75134-3456)
PHONE..................................972 227-4466
Mike Tharp, *President*
Ginger Tharp, *Vice Pres*
EMP: 8

SQ FT: 13,000
SALES (est): 1.8MM **Privately Held**
WEB: www.ankosales.com
SIC: 2841 5999 5169 Detergents, synthetic organic or inorganic alkaline; scouring compounds; cleaning equipment & supplies; detergents

(G-13838)
AQUATIC CO
Lasco Bathware
151 Industrial St (75134-3401)
PHONE..................................972 227-6692
Craig Nyenhuis, *Opers-Prdtn-Mfg*
Paul Van Slyke, *Accounting Mgr*
EMP: 120
SALES (corp-wide): 463.9MM **Privately Held**
WEB: www.aquaticbath.com
SIC: 3088 Shower stalls, fiberglass & plastic
HQ: Aquatic Co.
665 Industrial Rd
Savannah TN 38372

(G-13839)
BENTWOOD COMPANIES INC (PA)
Also Called: Bentwood Kitchens
2007 N Lncster Htchins Rd (75134-3417)
P.O. Box 308 (75146-0308)
PHONE..................................972 227-6855
Steven Randall Pittard, *President*
Kevin Bryant, *Vice Pres*
Wyman O Stewart, *Vice Pres*
EMP: 60
SQ FT: 40,000
SALES (est): 7.8MM **Privately Held**
WEB: www.bentwoodkitchens.com
SIC: 2434 2541 1751 Wood kitchen cabinets; cabinets, except refrigerated: show, display, etc.: wood; cabinet & finish carpentry

(G-13840)
BIG SHOT LLC
Also Called: Alvin Emile Maxwell
202 W Park Place Dr # 202 (75134-3250)
P.O. Box 762 (75146-0762)
PHONE..................................504 877-2335
Maxwell Alvin Emile, *Administration*
EMP: 30
SALES (est): 34.5K **Privately Held**
SIC: 7699 1389 3711 3799 Cleaning services; construction, repair & dismantling services; truck tractors for highway use, assembly of; carriages, horse drawn; transport vessels, troop: building & repairing

(G-13841)
BRASSCRAFT MANUFACTURING CO
Also Called: Brass Craft Thomasville
555 S Lncster Hutchins Rd (75146-3816)
PHONE..................................248 305-6000
Clay Heard, *Human Res Dir*
Hugh Sarber, *Branch Mgr*
EMP: 71
SALES (corp-wide): 7.1B **Publicly Held**
WEB: www.brasscraft.com
SIC: 3432 Plumbing fixture fittings & trim
HQ: Brasscraft Manufacturing Company
39600 Orchard Hill Pl
Novi MI 48375
248 305-6000

(G-13842)
CENTRAL RENOVATION SOLUTIONS
3146 Springfield Ave (75134-1212)
PHONE..................................469 567-2400
Jeff Calvery, *Owner*
EMP: 15
SALES (est): 1.3MM **Privately Held**
WEB: www.crscabinets.com
SIC: 2434 Wood kitchen cabinets

(G-13843)
INVERTER DESIGNS INC
Also Called: Tech Lite
2111 N Lncster Htchins Rd (75134-3419)
PHONE..................................972 227-9085
Ricky Lynch, *President*
William Cutchall, *Treasurer*

▲ EMP: 10
SQ FT: 2,500
SALES (est): 1.2MM **Privately Held**
WEB: www.aldor.net
SIC: 3621 Inverters, rotating: electrical

(G-13844)
LETCO GROUP LLC
Also Called: Living Earth Technology
3150 S I 35 E (75146-4500)
PHONE..................................972 274-2835
Jeffrey Yarborough, *Manager*
EMP: 14
SQ FT: 560
SALES (corp-wide): 78.3MM **Privately Held**
WEB: www.livingearth.net
SIC: 2499 2875 Mulch, wood & bark; potting soil, mixed
PA: The Letco Group Llc
1901 Cal Crossing Rd
Dallas TX 75220
972 506-8575

(G-13845)
LGS TECHNOLOGIES LP
2950 W Wintergreen Rd (75134-1840)
P.O. Box 763039, Dallas (75376-3039)
PHONE..................................972 224-9201
Terry Buckley, *President*
Ford Ferguson III, *Partner*
Sandra Larson, *Partner*
Greg Wickliffe, *Maint Spvr*
Jason Henderson, *Human Res Mgr*
▲ EMP: 66
SQ FT: 153,000
SALES (est): 10.8MM
SALES (corp-wide): 11.1MM **Privately Held**
WEB: www.lgstechnologies.com
SIC: 3053 Gaskets, packing & sealing devices
PA: Loma Alta Corporation
6210 N Central Expy
Lancaster TX
214 368-5264

(G-13846)
M P N INC
101 Industrial St (75134-3401)
PHONE..................................972 227-1210
EMP: 17 **Privately Held**
WEB: www.activeradiator.com
SIC: 3714 Radiators & radiator shells & cores, motor vehicle
PA: M. P. N., Inc.
3675 Amber St
Philadelphia PA 19134

(G-13847)
MASTER BUILDERS LLC
2355 W Longhorn Dr (75134-2113)
PHONE..................................972 228-7400
Ed Orr, *Branch Mgr*
EMP: 101
SALES (corp-wide): 20.3MM **Privately Held**
WEB: www.basf.com
SIC: 2869 Industrial organic chemicals
HQ: Master Builders, Llc
23700 Chagrin Blvd
Beachwood OH 44122
800 228-3318

(G-13848)
SPEP ACQUISITION CORP
Also Called: Sierra Pacific Engrg & Pdts
2986 S Longhorn Dr (75134-2122)
PHONE..................................310 608-0693
Larry Mirick, *Branch Mgr*
EMP: 10
SALES (corp-wide): 20.6MM **Privately Held**
WEB: www.spep.com
SIC: 3429 5072 8711 Manufactured hardware (general); hardware; engineering services
PA: S.P.E.P. Acquisition Corp.
4041 Via Oro Ave
Long Beach CA 90810
310 608-0693

(G-13849)
TEXAS NAMEPLATE COMPANY INC
Also Called: Tnc
2200 W Longhorn Dr (75134-2117)
P.O. Box 150499, Dallas (75315-0499)
PHONE..................................214 428-8341
R Dale Crownover, *CEO*
Preston Smith, *Opers Staff*
Tiffany Hairston, *Finance Mgr*
Ryan Crownover, *Manager*
Susie Chatt, *Executive*
▲ EMP: 63
SQ FT: 30,000
SALES (est): 8.9MM **Privately Held**
WEB: www.nameplate.com
SIC: 3479 3083 3993 Name plates: engraved, etched, etc.; laminated plastics plate & sheet; signs & advertising specialties

(G-13850)
WNA CUPS ILLUSTRATED INC
Also Called: Wna Lancaster
2155 W Longhorn Dr (75134-2105)
PHONE..................................972 224-8407
Michael G Evans, *President*
Ray Chan, *Treasurer*
Paul Gipson, *Finance Spvr*
Michael J Christopher, *Admin Sec*
▲ EMP: 120
SQ FT: 98,000
SALES (est): 35.3MM
SALES (corp-wide): 3.3B **Publicly Held**
WEB: www.wna.biz
SIC: 3089 3086 Molding primary plastic; cups & plates, foamed plastic
HQ: Waddington North America, Inc.
50 E Rver Ctr Blvd Ste 65
Covington KY 41011

Lane City
Wharton County

(G-13851)
PERMA POM PARTNERSHIP LTD
Also Called: Pepco Promotional Products
9611 S State Hwy 60 (77453)
P.O. Box 950, Wharton (77488-0950)
PHONE..................................979 532-3106
Robert F Sliva, *President*
Robbie Norra, *Engineer*
Jeff Sliva, *Manager*
Bill Genzer, *Info Tech Mgr*
Reagan Wrench, *Art Dir*
EMP: 100
SQ FT: 120,000
SALES (est): 19.8MM **Privately Held**
WEB: www.pepcopoms.com
SIC: 3949 Sporting & athletic goods

Laredo
Webb County

(G-13852)
A E SANTOS & CO
Also Called: Santos, A E De Mexico
1518 Sherman St (78040-1257)
P.O. Box 1517 (78042-1517)
PHONE..................................956 723-8359
Alfonso E Santos, *Owner*
▲ EMP: 35
SQ FT: 2,000
SALES (est): 5MM **Privately Held**
WEB: www.vivapanchocharcoal.com
SIC: 2819 Charcoal (carbon), activated

(G-13853)
AB-TEX BEVERAGE LTD
4700 Santa Maria Ave (78041-5616)
PHONE..................................956 722-9934
Carlos Rodriguez, *Branch Mgr*
EMP: 50
SALES (corp-wide): 67.1B **Publicly Held**
WEB: www.pepsico.com
SIC: 2086 Soft drinks: packaged in cans, bottles, etc.; water, pasteurized: packaged in cans, bottles, etc.

GEOGRAPHIC

HQ: Ab-Tex Beverage, Ltd.
650 Colonial Dr
Abilene TX 79603
325 673-7171

(G-13855)
ACE CARTON & TAPE OF LAREDO
919 Santa Maria Ave (78040-4963)
PHONE.................................956 727-1600
Fax: 956 723-3586
EMP: 15
SALES (est): 1MM **Privately Held**
SIC: 3069 5113 Mfg Fabricated Rubber Products Whol Industrial/Service Paper

(G-13855)
ACE MACHINE & FABRICATION INC
7226 Hwy 359 (78043-5105)
PHONE.................................956 727-4223
Bill A Busbice Jr, *Branch Mgr*
EMP: 9
SALES (corp-wide): 7.4MM **Privately Held**
SIC: 3599 Machine shop, jobbing & repair
PA: Ace Machine & Fabrication Inc
2706 W Admiral Doyle Dr
New Iberia LA 70560
337 369-6100

(G-13856)
AKWEL CADILLAC USA INC
110 Consolidation Pt (78045-1881)
PHONE.................................956 718-8387
EMP: 12 **Privately Held**
WEB: www.akwel-automotive.com
SIC: 3061 Mechanical rubber goods
HQ: Akwel Cadillac Usa, Inc
603 7th St
Cadillac MI 49601
231 775-6571

(G-13857)
AKWEL CADILLAC USA INC
8511 Milo Rd (78045-1893)
PHONE.................................956 717-4147
Jose Villegaf, *Branch Mgr*
EMP: 12 **Privately Held**
WEB: www.akwel-automotive.com
SIC: 3061 Mechanical rubber goods
HQ: Akwel Cadillac Usa, Inc
603 7th St
Cadillac MI 49601
231 775-6571

(G-13858)
ANIMAL PAINTBALL LLC
Also Called: Animal Customs
5460 Springfield Ave # 106 (78041-3878)
PHONE.................................956 753-8272
▲ **EMP:** 9
SALES (est): 830K **Privately Held**
SIC: 3949 5941 Mfg Sporting/Athletic Goods Ret Sporting Goods/Bicycles

(G-13859)
APTIV SERVICES US LLC
301 Vallecillo Rd (78045-4401)
PHONE.................................915 783-4201
Mario Hernandez, *Branch Mgr*
EMP: 180
SALES (corp-wide): 14.4B **Privately Held**
WEB: www.delphi.com
SIC: 3714 Warehousing, self-storage
HQ: Aptiv Services Us, Llc
5725 Innovation Dr
Troy MI 48098

(G-13860)
APTIV SERVICES US LLC
Also Called: Park of Penske Logistics
13701 Fm 1472 (78045-7847)
PHONE.................................956 693-3300
Carlos Torres, *Branch Mgr*
EMP: 209
SALES (corp-wide): 14.4B **Privately Held**
WEB: www.delphi.com
SIC: 3714 Motor vehicle parts & accessories
HQ: Aptiv Services Us, Llc
5725 Innovation Dr
Troy MI 48098

(G-13861)
APTIV SERVICES US LLC
Also Called: Delphi Thermal Systems
8410 W Bob Bullock Loop (78045-1876)
PHONE.................................956 237-9066
EMP: 15
SALES (corp-wide): 14.4B **Privately Held**
WEB: www.delphi.com
SIC: 3714 Motor vehicle parts & accessories
HQ: Aptiv Services Us, Llc
5725 Innovation Dr
Troy MI 48098

(G-13862)
AQUANEERS CORP
1211 San Dario Ave # 464 (78040-4505)
PHONE.................................956 727-1250
Guillermo G Cano, *President*
Bruno Garcia, *General Mgr*
EMP: 25
SALES (est): 2.4MM **Privately Held**
WEB: www.aquaneers.com
SIC: 3589 Water treatment equipment, industrial
PA: Inova, S.A. De C.V.
Prol. Las Torres No. 125
San Pedro Garza Garcia N.L. 66367

(G-13863)
ARANDA IRONWORKS INC
6201 Mcpherson Rd Unit 2 (78041-6214)
PHONE.................................956 722-5084
Jose Aranda, *President*
Theresa Aranda, *Corp Secy*
EMP: 14 **EST:** 1962
SQ FT: 19,000
SALES (est): 1.7MM **Privately Held**
WEB: www.arandaironworksinctx.com
SIC: 7692 Welding repair

(G-13864)
AZAR SERVICES LLC
201 W Hillside Rd Ste 23 (78041-3197)
PHONE.................................956 717-0023
Baltazar Ramos, *Mng Member*
Ricardo Ramos,
EMP: 14 **EST:** 2010
SALES (est): 2MM **Privately Held**
SIC: 1389 Oil field services

(G-13865)
BACKER EHP INC
13209 S Unitec Dr (78045-9443)
PHONE.................................615 556-7501
Rick Ruiz, *Manager*
EMP: 15
SALES (corp-wide): 2.6B **Privately Held**
WEB: www.backerehp.com
SIC: 3634 Heating units, for electric appliances
HQ: Backer Ehp Inc.
4700 John Bragg Hwy
Murfreesboro TN 37127

(G-13866)
BAKER HUGHES A GE COMPANY LLC
402 Boomtown St (78043-4728)
PHONE.................................956 791-0466
Curt Parsons, *Manager*
EMP: 31
SALES (corp-wide): 23.8B **Publicly Held**
WEB: www.bhge.com
SIC: 1389 Oil field services
HQ: Baker Hughes Holdings Llc
17021 Aldine Westfield Rd
Houston TX 77073
713 439-8600

(G-13867)
BAKER HUGHES HOLDINGS LLC
5718 San Bernardo Ave (78041-3010)
PHONE.................................956 285-2002
EMP: 87
SALES (corp-wide): 23.8B **Publicly Held**
WEB: www.bakerhughes.com
SIC: 1389 Oil field services
HQ: Baker Hughes Holdings Llc
17021 Aldine Westfield Rd
Houston TX 77073
713 439-8600

(G-13868)
BORDER LEASE SERVICES INC
3905 Rotary Dr (78043-4738)
P.O. Box 1660 (78044-1660)
PHONE.................................956 728-1959
Ramiro Alarcon, *President*
Elsa Alarcon, *Vice Pres*
EMP: 80
SALES (est): 9.9MM **Privately Held**
WEB: www.borderleaseservices.com
SIC: 1389 Oil field services

(G-13869)
BORDER WELL SERVICES INC
7195 State Highway 359 (78043-5107)
P.O. Box 1925 (78044-1925)
PHONE.................................956 753-7540
Jesus Alarcon, *President*
Veronica Cantu, *Human Res Dir*
Mel Garcia, *Supervisor*
Rolando Ramirez, *Supervisor*
EMP: 70 **EST:** 2000
SALES (est): 9.3MM **Privately Held**
WEB: www.bws-tx.com
SIC: 1389 Oil field services

(G-13870)
BORGWARNER PDS ANDERSON LLC
417 Union Pacific Blvd (78045-9428)
PHONE.................................765 778-6499
Rudolph Miles, *Manager*
EMP: 100
SALES (corp-wide): 10.1B **Publicly Held**
WEB: www.borgwarner.com
SIC: 3714 3694 Motor vehicle parts & accessories; engine electrical equipment
HQ: Borgwarner Pds (Anderson), L.L.C.
13975 Borgwarner Dr
Noblesville IN 46060

(G-13871)
BRANSON ULTRASONICS CORP
12013 Sara Rd (78045-1804)
PHONE.................................956 729-1550
Leandro Garza, *Manager*
EMP: 41
SALES (corp-wide): 16.7B **Publicly Held**
WEB: www.bransonic.com
SIC: 3699 Cleaning equipment, ultrasonic, except medical & dental
HQ: Branson Ultrasonics Corporation
41 Eagle Rd Ste 1
Danbury CT 06810
203 796-0400

(G-13872)
CADENA SERVICES LLC
405 Martens Rd (78041)
PHONE.................................956 727-9391
EMP: 17
SQ FT: 2,500
SALES (est): 1.6MM **Privately Held**
SIC: 1389 Oil/Gas Field Services

(G-13873)
CENTRAL PALLETS NO 2
7910 Mines Rd (78045-8549)
P.O. Box 2623 (78044-2623)
PHONE.................................956 726-4023
Raul Maldonado, *Owner*
EMP: 14
SALES (est): 875.7K **Privately Held**
SIC: 2448 Pallets, wood

(G-13874)
CITY READY MIX INC
1810 Main Ave (78040-6731)
P.O. Box 2631 (78044-2631)
PHONE.................................956 722-6315
Benito Hurtado Sr, *President*
Benito Hurtado Jr, *Treasurer*
Claudia Hurtado, *Admin Sec*
EMP: 36
SQ FT: 16,000
SALES (est): 11.9MM **Privately Held**
WEB: www.cityreadymix.com
SIC: 3273 Ready-mixed concrete

(G-13875)
CONTINENTAL AUTO SYSTEMS INC
Also Called: Continental Guadalajara
11302c Eastpoint Dr (78045-6619)
PHONE.................................847 862-0366
Natalia Horbach, *Branch Mgr*
EMP: 323
SALES (corp-wide): 49.2B **Privately Held**
WEB: www.continental-automotive.com
SIC: 3714 Motor vehicle parts & accessories
HQ: Continental Automotive Systems, Inc.
1 Continental Dr
Auburn Hills MI 48326
248 393-5300

(G-13876)
COOPER-STANDARD AUTOMOTIVE INC
1001 Carriers Dr (78045-9471)
PHONE.................................956 717-3835
Danny Ramos, *General Mgr*
Griselda Rodriguez, *Opers Mgr*
Manuel Aguilar, *Manager*
Raul Hernandez, *Executive*
EMP: 14
SALES (corp-wide): 3.1B **Publicly Held**
WEB: www.cooperstandard.com
SIC: 3714 Motor vehicle parts & accessories
HQ: Cooper-Standard Automotive Inc.
40300 Traditions Dr
Northville MI 48168
248 596-5900

(G-13877)
DCAF INC
Also Called: G & F Oil Field Services
401 Mayfair Dr (78045-8171)
P.O. Box 451182 (78045-0029)
PHONE.................................956 286-9177
Filiberto Lopez, *President*
Guadalupe Vasquez, *General Mgr*
EMP: 32
SQ FT: 320
SALES (est): 6MM **Privately Held**
WEB: www.4xindustrial.com
SIC: 1389 Oil field services

(G-13878)
DENNIS ENERGY SERVICES INC
E Hwy 359 (78044)
P.O. Box 1914 (78044-1914)
PHONE.................................956 712-1114
Daniel B Dennis, *President*
Mary Mynard, *Controller*
EMP: 11
SQ FT: 4,000
SALES (est): 1.9MM **Privately Held**
WEB: www.dennisenergy.com
SIC: 1389 Oil field services

(G-13879)
DFA DAIRY BRANDS FLUID LLC
Also Called: Hygeia Dairy
8119 San Dario Ave (78045-7276)
PHONE.................................956 722-1718
Tano Trevino, *Branch Mgr*
EMP: 14
SALES (corp-wide): 15.8B **Privately Held**
SIC: 2026 Fluid milk
HQ: Dfa Dairy Brands Fluid, Llc
1405 N 98th St
Kansas City KS 66111
816 801-6455

(G-13880)
DIAMANTE CONSTRUCTION & DESIGN
909 Queens Ct (78045-2080)
PHONE.................................361 449-7072
Norman Spacek, *Owner*
EMP: 10
SALES (est): 59.5K **Privately Held**
SIC: 7389 1389 Design services; construction, repair & dismantling services

(G-13881)
DLHBOWLES INC
12114 J E F Dr Ste A (78045-1834)
PHONE.................................410 800-6548
Jaime Garza, *Manager*
EMP: 12
SALES (corp-wide): 252.6MM **Privately Held**
WEB: www.dlhbowles.com
SIC: 3714 Motor vehicle parts & accessories

PA: Dlhbowles, Inc.
2422 Leo Ave Sw
Canton OH 44706
330 478-2503

(G-13882)
EL MANANA INC
6010 Mcpherson Rd Ste 300 (78041-6209)
PHONE....................................956 712-1122
Juan Edwardo Guerra, *General Mgr*
Juan Eduardo Guera, *General Mgr*
EMP: 14
SALES (est): 703.5K **Privately Held**
SIC: 2711 Newspapers: publishing only, not printed on site

(G-13883)
FELIPE ARREAZOLA
Also Called: Felipe & Felipe Imports
3218 Diaz St (78043-4921)
PHONE....................................956 334-3136
Felipe Arreazola, *Owner*
EMP: 18 EST: 1995
SALES (est): 1.7MM **Privately Held**
WEB: www.austinmoore.net
SIC: 2514 5099 Metal lawn & garden furniture; durable goods

(G-13884)
FESCO LTD
4801 Fesco (78043-9801)
PHONE....................................956 724-7501
Davy Ward, *Manager*
EMP: 50
SALES (corp-wide): 201MM **Privately Held**
WEB: www.fescoinc.com
SIC: 1389 8734 Testing, measuring, surveying & analysis services; testing laboratories
PA: Fesco, Ltd.
1000 Fesco Dr
Alice TX 78332
361 664-3479

(G-13885)
FLEXTRONICS AMERICA LLC
8311 Killam Indus Blvd (78045-1894)
PHONE....................................408 576-7000
EMP: 265 **Privately Held**
WEB: www.flex.com
SIC: 3672 Printed circuit boards
HQ: Flextronics America, Llc
6201 America Center Dr
San Jose CA 95002
408 576-7000

(G-13886)
FLEXTRONICS AMERICA LLC
5802 Bob Bullock Loop (78041-8807)
PHONE....................................408 576-7990
EMP: 265 **Privately Held**
WEB: www.flex.com
SIC: 3672 Printed circuit boards
HQ: Flextronics America, Llc
6201 America Center Dr
San Jose CA 95002
408 576-7000

(G-13887)
FORKLIFTS USA INC
8116 San Gabriel Dr (78045-7017)
PHONE....................................956 568-9797
Juan Pasquel, *President*
EMP: 10
SQ FT: 2,000
SALES (est): 229.6K **Privately Held**
WEB: www.forkliftsalesusa.com
SIC: 7699 3537 Industrial machinery & equipment repair; forklift trucks

(G-13888)
GALL ART NOVELTIES LLC
2019 Jefferson St (78040-1732)
PHONE....................................956 290-3124
Humberto Gallegos, *Mng Member*
EMP: 10
SALES (est): 160K **Privately Held**
SIC: 2253 Hats & headwear, knit

(G-13889)
GATEWAY METAL RECYCLING INC
13491 S Unitec Dr (78045-9415)
PHONE....................................956 723-0409
EMP: 18

SQ FT: 20,000
SALES (est): 144K **Privately Held**
SIC: 3341 5093 Secondary Nonferrous Metal Producer Whol Scrap/Waste Material

(G-13890)
HEARST CORPORATION
Also Called: Laredo Morning Times
111 Esperanza Dr (78041-2607)
P.O. Box 2129 (78044-2129)
PHONE....................................956 728-2500
Adriana Devally, *General Mgr*
William Green, *Superintendent*
Bill Green, *Principal*
Pann Tony, *Accounts Exec*
Malena Charur, *Administration*
EMP: 110
SALES (corp-wide): 7.9B **Privately Held**
WEB: www.hearst.com
SIC: 2711 Newspapers, publishing & printing
PA: The Hearst Corporation
300 W 57th St Fl 42
New York NY 10019
212 649-2000

(G-13891)
HENNIGES AUTO MEXICO SA DE CV
13209 S Unitec Dr (78045-9443)
PHONE....................................956 794-3606
Thomas Wolanzyk, *Branch Mgr*
EMP: 45 **Privately Held**
WEB: www.hennigesautomotive.com
SIC: 3061 Automotive rubber goods (mechanical)
HQ: Henniges Automotive Mexico, S.A. De C.V.
Blvd. Gomez Palacio No. 265
Gomez Palacio DGO. 35070

(G-13892)
HOME MART INC
6419 Mcpherson Rd (78041-6215)
PHONE....................................956 724-4521
Juan Ramirez, *President*
Juan Antonio Alvarado, *Controller*
▼ EMP: 16
SQ FT: 20,000
SALES (est): 1.9MM **Privately Held**
SIC: 2434 5712 5713 5231 Wood kitchen cabinets; cabinet work, custom; floor covering stores; paint, glass & wallpaper; household appliance stores

(G-13893)
HOMEART DESIGNS INC
6419 Mcpherson Rd (78041-6215)
PHONE....................................956 724-4412
Juan Ramirez, *Principal*
Juan Alvarado, *Accounting Mgr*
◆ EMP: 10
SALES (est): 1MM **Privately Held**
WEB: www.homearte.com
SIC: 2434 7389 Wood kitchen cabinets;

(G-13894)
HOWRED CORPORATION
5823 Northgate Ln # 2037 (78041-2662)
PHONE....................................956 712-1003
Howard Watson, *Branch Mgr*
EMP: 197
SALES (corp-wide): 27.3MM **Privately Held**
WEB: www.howred.com
SIC: 2621 Paper mills
PA: Howred Corporation
7887 San Felipe St # 122
Houston TX 77063
713 781-3980

(G-13895)
INDUSTRIAL ACCESSORIES INC
1113 Park St Apt 1 (78040-3136)
PHONE....................................956 728-7524
EMP: 10
SALES (est): 770K **Privately Held**
SIC: 3625 Mfg Relays/Industrial Controls

(G-13896)
INGRAM READYMIX INC
8719 San Dario Ave (78045-7252)
PHONE....................................956 722-8736
Serapio Gomez, *Manager*
EMP: 19

SALES (corp-wide): 125.6MM **Privately Held**
WEB: www.ingramreadymixinc.com
SIC: 3273 Ready-mixed concrete
PA: Ingram Readymix, Inc.
3580 Farm Market 482
New Braunfels TX 78132
830 625-9156

(G-13897)
INTERNATIONAL BEVERAGE INC
1901 Aduanales Ln (78041-5603)
P.O. Box 2769 (78044-2769)
PHONE....................................956 727-2995
Joel I Munis, *President*
Diana Garcia, *Treasurer*
▼ EMP: 18
SQ FT: 20,000
SALES (est): 1.5MM **Privately Held**
SIC: 2086 Carbonated beverages, nonalcoholic: bottled & canned

(G-13898)
JABIL INC
130 Flecha Ln (78045-7027)
PHONE....................................727 577-9749
Kenny Wilson, *Branch Mgr*
EMP: 317
SALES (corp-wide): 27.2B **Publicly Held**
WEB: www.jabil.com
SIC: 3672 Printed circuit boards
PA: Jabil Inc.
10560 Dr Mrtn Lther King
Saint Petersburg FL 33716
727 577-9749

(G-13899)
JK MANUFACTURING INC
Also Called: American Sales
1910 San Bernardo Ave (78040-4840)
P.O. Box 677 (78042-0677)
PHONE....................................956 723-6893
Joe W Kirkpatrick, *President*
Rigler Michael G, *Vice Pres*
Maria Cristina Kirkpatrick, *Treasurer*
EMP: 18 EST: 1967
SQ FT: 10,000
SALES (est): 3MM **Privately Held**
WEB: www.kirkpatrickleather.com
SIC: 3199 5941 Holsters, leather; leather belting & strapping; firearms; hunting equipment

(G-13900)
JUAN GARZA
Also Called: Print X Press
4820 Mcpherson Rd Ste 1 (78041-7330)
PHONE....................................956 723-6687
Juan Garza, *Owner*
Diana Garza, *Co-Owner*
David Garza, *Vice Pres*
EMP: 9
SQ FT: 2,100
SALES (est): 800.2K **Privately Held**
WEB: www.printxpressinc.com
SIC: 2752 7334 Commercial printing, offset; photocopying & duplicating services

(G-13901)
KASPER PRO VAC SERVICE INC
4440 E Del Mar Blvd (78041-6560)
P.O. Box 452328 (78045-0057)
PHONE....................................956 796-0765
Lazaro Garza-Gongora Jr, *President*
Mary Rodrigueez, *Bookkeeper*
EMP: 40
SALES (est): 3.1MM **Privately Held**
WEB: www.kasperprovac.com
SIC: 1389 4212 Oil field services; local trucking, without storage

(G-13902)
KILLAM OIL CO LTD (PA)
4320 University Blvd (78041-1934)
P.O. Box 499 (78042-0499)
PHONE....................................956 724-7141
David Killam, *Managing Prtnr*
Cliffe Killam, *Partner*
Ted Allen, *Engineer*
Brittany Black, *Engineer*
Tano Carranza, *Property Mgr*
EMP: 35
SQ FT: 14,651

SALES (est): 41.7K **Privately Held**
WEB: www.killamoil.com
SIC: 1382 1311 Oil & gas exploration services; crude petroleum & natural gas production

(G-13903)
LA INDIA PACKING CO
Also Called: Tasting Room Cafe
1520 Marcella Ave (78040-7900)
PHONE....................................956 723-3772
Elsa R Arguindegui, *President*
EMP: 22 EST: 1923
SQ FT: 5,000
SALES (est): 4.5MM **Privately Held**
WEB: www.laindiaherbsandspices.com
SIC: 5149 2099 2066 2091 Condiments; spices & seasonings; seasonings: dry mixes; chocolate; shrimp, preserved & cured

(G-13904)
LABELMAX INC
5601 Cerrito Prieto Ct (78041-3317)
PHONE....................................956 718-3961
Jorge Martinez, *CEO*
Edgar V Martinez, *President*
Alain Martinez, *Shareholder*
▲ EMP: 80
SALES (est): 10.3MM **Privately Held**
WEB: www.labelmaxinc.com
SIC: 2679 Tags & labels, paper

(G-13905)
LAREDO COCA-COLA BOTTLING CO (HQ)
1402 Industrial Blvd (78041-2508)
PHONE....................................956 726-2671
Justintino Villarreal, *Manager*
Sean Whitehead, *Manager*
EMP: 200 EST: 1930
SALES (est): 25.8MM
SALES (corp-wide): 309.5MM **Privately Held**
SIC: 2086 Bottled & canned soft drinks
PA: Austin Coca-Cola Bottling Company
1 Coca Cola Pl
San Antonio TX 78219
210 225-2601

(G-13906)
LAREDO READY MIX LTD
18015 Mines Rd (78045-8187)
P.O. Box 116 (78042-0116)
PHONE....................................956 723-7429
Rodolfo Garcia, *Partner*
Lauro Arce, *Opers Mgr*
EMP: 70
SALES (est): 13.6MM **Privately Held**
WEB: www.laredoreadymix.com
SIC: 3273 Ready-mixed concrete

(G-13907)
LIBCON INC (PA)
Also Called: Libra Leasing
8016 Killam Indus Blvd (78045-1837)
P.O. Box 1759 (78044-1759)
PHONE....................................956 724-6459
Douglas Howland, *President*
Richard Leyendecker, *Vice Pres*
EMP: 72
SQ FT: 900
SALES (est): 7.3MM **Privately Held**
WEB: www.libcon.com
SIC: 1771 2951 Foundation & footing contractor; asphalt paving mixtures & blocks

(G-13908)
MAHLE BEHR MFG MGT INC
13701 Mines Rd (78045-7847)
PHONE....................................248 735-3623
Wilm Uhlenbecker, *Bd of Directors*
EMP: 10
SALES (est): 374.7K **Privately Held**
SIC: 3714 Motor vehicle parts & accessories

(G-13909)
MAHLE SYSTEMA DE FILTRACION D
13493 Port Dr (78045-9401)
PHONE....................................956 753-9100
Alfredo Lopez, *President*
Eloy Gonzalez, *Vice Pres*
▲ EMP: 9

GEOGRAPHIC

SALES (est): 660K **Privately Held**
SIC: 3465 Body parts, automobile: stamped metal

(G-13910)
MATTEL INC
8702 Killam Indus Blvd (78045-1825)
PHONE....................310 252-2000
Raphael Vanegas, *Branch Mgr*
EMP: 10
SALES (corp-wide): 4.5B **Publicly Held**
WEB: www.mattel.com
SIC: 3944 Games, toys & children's vehicles
PA: Mattel, Inc.
333 Continental Blvd
El Segundo CA 90245
310 252-2000

(G-13911)
MENDES PRINTING CO INC
1020 Sanchez St (78040-4820)
PHONE....................956 722-2222
Hector Mendes, *President*
EMP: 10 **EST:** 1960
SALES (est): 750K **Privately Held**
WEB: www.mendesprintingii.com
SIC: 2752 Commercial printing, offset

(G-13912)
MERIT ENERGY COMPANY LLC
5919 State Highway 359 (78043-5098)
PHONE....................956 728-6206
EMP: 31 **Privately Held**
WEB: www.meritenergy.com
SIC: 1311 Crude petroleum production
PA: Merit Energy Company, Llc
13737 Noel Rd Ste 1200
Dallas TX 75240

(G-13913)
MODERN MACHINE SHOP INC
2000 Blaine St (78043-5203)
P.O. Box 1969 (78044-1969)
PHONE....................956 722-4656
Danny Garcia, *President*
Ricardo Garcia, *Exec VP*
EMP: 55 **EST:** 1941
SQ FT: 100,000
SALES (est): 13.9MM **Privately Held**
WEB: www.modern-machine.com
SIC: 3599 3449 Machine shop, jobbing & repair; bars, concrete reinforcing: fabricated steel

(G-13914)
MONTECITO OILFIELD SVCS LLC
1505 Clle Dl Nrte 460 (78041)
PHONE....................956 337-6082
Santiago G Garza, *Principal*
EMP: 15
SQ FT: 43,560
SALES (est): 1.2MM **Privately Held**
SIC: 1389 Oil field services

(G-13915)
MORALES MACHINE SP & TRNSP LLC
5795 State Highway 359 (78043-4869)
P.O. Box 2762 (78044-2762)
PHONE....................956 722-4485
Alfredo Morales, *Owner*
Cynthia Flores, *Office Mgr*
EMP: 10
SQ FT: 4,500
SALES (est): 2.6MM **Privately Held**
WEB: www.moralesmachineshop.com
SIC: 3569 Lubrication machinery, automatic

(G-13916)
MOTOR CRIER SFETY SLUTIONS INC
5717 Springfield Ave (78041-3282)
P.O. Box 451309 (78045-0032)
PHONE....................956 726-3377
Alvin Scribner, *President*
Gerardo X Lopez, *Principal*
Ignacio Rodriguez, *Principal*
EMP: 15
SALES (est): 990K **Privately Held**
WEB: www.mcssinc.com
SIC: 8742 7372 Public utilities consultant; application computer software

(G-13917)
OWENS-BROCKWAY GLASS CONT INC
13711 Regional Dr (78045-9404)
PHONE....................956 717-4200
EMP: 39
SALES (corp-wide): 6.6B **Publicly Held**
WEB: www.o-i.com
SIC: 3221 Glass containers
HQ: Owens-Brockway Glass Container Inc.
1 Michael Owens Way
Perrysburg OH 43551

(G-13918)
OXY INC
6213 State Highway 359 (78043-4774)
PHONE....................956 728-6200
Gary Lee, *Manager*
EMP: 30
SALES (corp-wide): 21.2B **Publicly Held**
WEB: www.oxy.com
SIC: 1311 Crude petroleum production
HQ: Oxy Inc.
5 Greenway Plz Ste 2400
Houston TX 77046
713 215-7000

(G-13919)
PENINSULA STEEL INC
Also Called: Peninsula Steel Elm Tree
4119 Free Trade St Ste A (78045-7952)
PHONE....................956 795-1966
Alejandra Machorro, *Branch Mgr*
EMP: 20
SALES (corp-wide): 12MM **Privately Held**
WEB: www.peninsulasteel.com
SIC: 3315 Steel wire & related products
PA: Peninsula Steel, Inc.
4504 Sydney Rd
Plant City FL 33566
956 795-1966

(G-13920)
PEPSI COLA BOTTLING CO LAREDO
Also Called: Pepsi-Cola
4700 Santa Maria Ave (78041-5728)
PHONE....................956 722-9934
Carlos Rodriguez, *Manager*
EMP: 38 **EST:** 1940
SQ FT: 24,000
SALES (est): 3.7MM **Privately Held**
WEB: www.pepsioflaredo.com
SIC: 2086 Carbonated soft drinks, bottled & canned

(G-13921)
PHOTONIC INC
1907 Aduanales Ln (78041-5603)
P.O. Box 188 (78042-0188)
PHONE....................956 722-3326
Alonso Diaz, *Principal*
Mary C Diaz, *Corp Secy*
Porfirio H Melendez, *Exec VP*
EMP: 20
SQ FT: 55,000
SALES (est): 1MM **Privately Held**
WEB: www.photonic-corp.com
SIC: 5045 7372 3577 3575 Computer peripheral equipment; computer software; prepackaged software; computer peripheral equipment; computer terminals, monitors & components; radio telephone communication

(G-13922)
PPG INDUSTRIES INC
Also Called: PPG 9657
719 Gale St (78041-6153)
PHONE....................956 791-1191
Sal Hernandez, *Manager*
EMP: 24
SALES (corp-wide): 15.3B **Publicly Held**
WEB: www.ppg.com
SIC: 2851 Paints & allied products
PA: Ppg Industries, Inc.
1 Ppg Pl
Pittsburgh PA 15272
412 434-3131

(G-13923)
REDDY ICE CORPORATION
4301 Jaime Zapata Memoria (78043-4727)
PHONE....................956 723-3838

Celso Urive, *Manager*
EMP: 12 **Privately Held**
WEB: www.reddyice.com
SIC: 2097 Manufactured ice
HQ: Reddy Ice Corporation
5710 Lbj Fwy Ste 300
Dallas TX 75240
214 526-6740

(G-13924)
ROBERT BOSCH AUTO STEERING LLC
11302 Eastpoint Dr Ste C (78045-6622)
PHONE....................956 857-4436
Tim Edwards, *Branch Mgr*
EMP: 27
SALES (corp-wide): 295.5MM **Privately Held**
WEB: www.bosch.com
SIC: 3714 Motor vehicle parts & accessories
HQ: Robert Bosch Automotive Steering Llc
15 Spiral Dr
Florence KY 41042

(G-13925)
ROBERT BOSCH LLC
11302 Eastpoint Dr Ste C (78045-6622)
PHONE....................956 753-6082
Tim Edwards, *Branch Mgr*
EMP: 19
SALES (corp-wide): 295.5MM **Privately Held**
WEB: www.bosch.us
SIC: 3714 Motor vehicle parts & accessories
HQ: Robert Bosch Llc
38000 Hills Tech Dr
Farmington Hills MI 48331
248 876-1000

(G-13926)
ROBERTSHAW CONTROLS COMPANY
13602 N Unitec Dr (78045-9409)
P.O. Box 421757, Indianapolis IN (46242-1757)
PHONE....................956 724-4400
Marcela Martinez, *Manager*
EMP: 11 **Privately Held**
WEB: www.robertshaw.com
SIC: 3612 Distribution transformers, electric
HQ: Robertshaw Controls Company
1222 Hamilton Pkwy
Itasca IL 60143

(G-13927)
SANMINA CORPORATION
Also Called: Shared Services
417 Union Pacific Blvd (78045-9428)
PHONE....................408 964-3500
Matt Baragona, *General Mgr*
Weida Hendrix, *Senior Buyer*
Ricky Schriner, *Clerk*
EMP: 31 **Publicly Held**
WEB: www.sanmina.com
SIC: 3672 Printed circuit boards
PA: Sanmina Corporation
2700 N 1st St
San Jose CA 95134

(G-13928)
SANMINA CORPORATION
11901 Gavin Rd (78045-1831)
PHONE....................408 964-3500
Valerie Bowar, *Purchasing*
Jennifer Xu, *Engineer*
Mike Reynolds, *Sales Staff*
Randi Suttles, *Regional*
EMP: 214 **Publicly Held**
WEB: www.sanmina.com
SIC: 3672 Printed circuit boards
PA: Sanmina Corporation
2700 N 1st St
San Jose CA 95134

(G-13929)
SANMINA CORPORATION
Also Called: Sanmina-Sci Shared Services
11921 Hayter Rd (78045-1878)
PHONE....................956 523-6800
EMP: 54 **Publicly Held**
WEB: www.sanmina.com
SIC: 3672 Printed circuit boards

PA: Sanmina Corporation
2700 N 1st St
San Jose CA 95134

(G-13930)
SCHNEDER ELC BLDNGS AMRCAS INC
5914 San Bernardo Ave (78041-2506)
PHONE....................859 243-8254
EMP: 108
SALES (corp-wide): 177.9K **Privately Held**
WEB: www.se.com
SIC: 3699 Electrical equipment & supplies
HQ: Schneider Electric Buildings Americas, Inc.
1650 W Crosby Rd
Carrollton TX 75006
972 323-1111

(G-13931)
SCHNEIDER ELECTRIC USA INC
1215 San Dario Ave (78040-4505)
PHONE....................877 248-3781
Mirriam Garcia, *Branch Mgr*
EMP: 277
SALES (corp-wide): 177.9K **Privately Held**
WEB: www.ccagp.com
SIC: 3613 Bus bar structures
HQ: Schneider Electric Usa, Inc.
1 Boston Pl Ste 2700
Boston MA 02108
978 975-9600

(G-13932)
SELECT ENERGY SERVICES LLC
Also Called: Alice Southern Equipment
321 Wildcat (78043-4733)
PHONE....................956 286-7100
Barry Gilpin, *Marketing Mgr*
Henry Gutierrez, *Branch Mgr*
EMP: 150
SALES (corp-wide): 1.2B **Publicly Held**
WEB: www.selectenergyservices.com
SIC: 1389 Oil field services
HQ: Select Energy Services, Llc
1820 N I 35
Gainesville TX 76240
940 668-1818

(G-13933)
SELECT ENERGY SERVICES LLC
Also Called: Stx - Office
6010 Mcpherson Rd Ste 100 (78041-6207)
PHONE....................956 723-4900
EMP: 59
SALES (corp-wide): 1.2B **Publicly Held**
WEB: www.selectenergyservices.com
SIC: 1389 Oil field services
HQ: Select Energy Services, Llc
1820 N I 35
Gainesville TX 76240
940 668-1818

(G-13934)
SONY ELECTRONICS INC
Sony Wrld Repr Part Ctr Amrcas
11302 Eastpoint Dr (78045-6622)
PHONE....................858 942-2400
Oscar Riveron, *Opers Dir*
Mabel Gonzalez, *Branch Mgr*
EMP: 110
SQ FT: 180,000 **Privately Held**
WEB: www.sony.com
SIC: 3695 5065 Magnetic tape; radio parts & accessories
HQ: Sony Electronics Inc.
16535 Via Esprillo Bldg 1
San Diego CA 92127
858 942-2400

(G-13935)
SOUTH TEXAS NEON SIGNS CO
317 Masterson Rd (78046-8476)
P.O. Box 1751 (78044-1751)
PHONE....................956 723-4665
Maria Antonieta Molina, *President*
Juan Antonio Molina, *Vice Pres*
EMP: 9
SQ FT: 7,500

SALES (est): 1.2MM **Privately Held**
WEB: www.southtexasneonsigns.net
SIC: 3993 Neon signs; signs, not made in custom sign painting shops

(G-13936)
SUMMMA INTERNATIONAL LLC (HQ)
710 Union Pacific Blvd (78045-9432)
PHONE..........................630 519-3632
Arturo M Gonzalez, *President*
Seth Kaufman, *Sales Mgr*
Robin Kulton, *Manager*
EMP: 10
SQ FT: 50,000
SALES (est): 1.3MM **Privately Held**
SIC: 2047 Dog & cat food

(G-13937)
TESTCO WELL SERVICES LLC
6016 E Hwy 44 (78043)
P.O. Box 2209, Alice (78333-2209)
PHONE..........................361 396-0626
Giancarlo Nisimblat,
John E Crisp,
John Daniel Crisp,
Charles C Forbes Jr,
EMP: 57
SQ FT: 2,000
SALES (est): 2.7MM **Privately Held**
SIC: 1389 Pipe testing, oil field service

(G-13938)
TORTILLAS SANTOS LLC
606 Amistad Dr (78041-6872)
PHONE..........................956 712-3800
Ricardo Santos,
EMP: 9
SALES (est): 785.7K **Privately Held**
WEB: www.prosano.mx
SIC: 2096 Tortilla chips

(G-13939)
TRINITYS COVENANT LLC
1603 Sweden Ln (78045-8381)
PHONE..........................210 620-3694
Adib Name, *CEO*
EMP: 11
SALES (est): 226K **Privately Held**
SIC: 5812 1521 1389 1541 Fast food restaurants & stands; snack shop; repairing fire damage, single-family houses; construction, repair & dismantling services; renovation, remodeling & repairs: industrial buildings

(G-13940)
WW WIRELINE CO INC (PA)
1719 Guadalupe St (78043-3449)
P.O. Box 450450 (78045-0010)
PHONE..........................956 712-9473
Paul H Ward, *President*
Edwin G Ward, *Vice Pres*
Mario Caballero, *Safety Mgr*
Margaret Ward, *Admin Sec*
EMP: 28
SALES (est): 12.1MM **Privately Held**
WEB: www.wwwireline.com
SIC: 1389 Oil field services

Latexo
Houston County

(G-13941)
ALLOY POLYMERS TEXAS LP
Hwy 287 & Fm2160 # 2160 (75849)
PHONE..........................936 544-4043
Gene Segman, *Mng Member*
EMP: 33
SALES (est): 3MM **Privately Held**
WEB: www.rtpcompany.com
SIC: 2821 Plastics materials & resins

(G-13942)
AQUAPHARM PCHEM LLC (PA)
Also Called: Clearwater Engineer Chemistry
3985 Us Hwy 287 N (75849)
PHONE..........................346 237-4300
Mark Stanley,
Reed Killion,
Dharmesh Mangwani,
◆ **EMP:** 17
SQ FT: 1,742,400

SALES (est): 7.6MM **Privately Held**
WEB: www.apchem.com
SIC: 3589 5082 Water treatment equipment, industrial; oil field equipment

Lavon
Collin County

(G-13943)
GRACY CABINETS
10963 State Highway 205 (75166-1832)
PHONE..........................972 843-3123
Roger Gracy, *Owner*
EMP: 10
SALES (est): 605.5K **Privately Held**
WEB: www.gracycabinets.com
SIC: 2434 Wood kitchen cabinets

League City
Galveston County

(G-13944)
ADVANCED WELDING SOLUTIONS LLC
2600 S Shore Blvd Ste 300 (77573-2944)
PHONE..........................713 473-0099
Dale Johnston, *President*
David Brown, *Treasurer*
EMP: 50 **EST:** 2013
SALES (est): 5.1MM
SALES (corp-wide): 429.8MM **Privately Held**
WEB: www.advancedweldingsolutions.com
SIC: 7692 Welding repair
PA: Park Corporation
6200 Riverside Dr
Cleveland OH 44135
216 267-4870

(G-13945)
AMERICAN FINCL MKTG GROUP INC
Also Called: Afmg Industrial Services
2600 S Shore Blvd Ste 300 (77573-2944)
P.O. Box 631, Kemah (77565-0631)
PHONE..........................866 679-9241
Kevin Reeves, *CEO*
EMP: 12
SALES (est): 358.7K **Privately Held**
WEB: www.amfingroup.com
SIC: 3731 3575 1629 6411 Commercial cargo ships, building & repairing; lighthouse tenders, building & repairing; submarine tenders, building & repairing; keyboards, computer, office machine; dams, waterways, docks & other marine construction; life insurance agents; fire loss appraisal

(G-13946)
AMERICAN HOMESTAR CORPORATION (PA)
2450 S Shore Blvd Ste 300 (77573-2997)
PHONE..........................281 334-9700
Finis F Teeter, *President*
Charlie Boyer, *COO*
Charles N Carney Jr, *COO*
Craig A Reynolds, *CFO*
Diane Wilganowski, *Accounting Mgr*
EMP: 50
SALES: 139.9MM **Privately Held**
WEB: www.americanhomestarmortgage.com
SIC: 2451 4213 5271 6351 Mobile homes, personal or private use; mobile homes transport; mobile homes; credit & other financial responsibility insurance; warranty insurance, home; mobile home site operators

(G-13947)
AMERICAN HOMESTAR LANCASTER LP (HQ)
2450 S Shore Blvd Ste 300 (77573-2997)
PHONE..........................281 334-9700
Craig Reynolds, *CFO*
EMP: 50
SQ FT: 90,000

SALES (est): 20.4MM
SALES (corp-wide): 139.9MM **Privately Held**
WEB: www.americanhomestar.com
SIC: 2451 Mobile homes
PA: American Homestar Corporation
2450 S Shore Blvd Ste 300
League City TX 77573
281 334-9700

(G-13948)
BAYSIDE INDUSTRIAL INC
614 Clear Creek Ave (77573-3800)
PHONE..........................832 632-2815
Lester Knupple, *President*
Jeremy Saulsberry, *Vice Pres*
EMP: 20
SALES (est): 1.2MM **Privately Held**
WEB: www.baysideindustrial-tx.com
SIC: 3443 3441 1629 Industrial vessels, tanks & containers; tanks, standard or custom fabricated: metal plate; fabricated structural metal; land preparation construction; industrial plant construction

(G-13949)
BEHEMOTH CORPORATION
Also Called: PC Connexion
202 Reynolds Ave (77573-4159)
PHONE..........................281 332-4798
Luanne Edelman, *President*
Marc Edelman, *Vice Pres*
Jose Moctezuma, *Sales Staff*
EMP: 35
SQ FT: 13,500
SALES (est): 10.7MM **Privately Held**
WEB: www.pc-cable.com
SIC: 3575 5734 1731 5063 Computer terminals; software, business & non-game; computer installation; lighting fixtures; lighting fixtures

(G-13950)
BLAST ENVMTL & INDUS SVCS
416 Highway 3 S (77573-3809)
PHONE..........................281 557-1000
Sam Gonzales, *President*
EMP: 40
SALES (est): 1.1MM **Privately Held**
WEB: www.blasteandisupport.com
SIC: 7349 4959 3629 7699 Chemical cleaning services; environmental cleanup services; blasting machines, electrical; septic tank cleaning service; labor resource services

(G-13951)
CAASCO SIGNS INC
Also Called: C A A S C O Mfg & Installation
1340 Highway 3 S Ste Ab (77573-5416)
P.O. Box 58502, Houston (77258-8502)
PHONE..........................281 332-1502
EMP: 9
SQ FT: 11,500
SALES (est): 647K **Privately Held**
WEB: www.creativesigntc.com
SIC: 3993 Signs, not made in custom sign painting shops

(G-13952)
CEDA INTERNATIONAL INC (DH)
2600 S Shore Blvd Ste 300 (77573-2944)
PHONE..........................281 478-2600
Joe Kinder, *President*
Roger Hearn, *Senior VP*
EMP: 12
SQ FT: 4,000
SALES (est): 63.7MM
SALES (corp-wide): 5.3B **Privately Held**
WEB: www.davenport-co.com
SIC: 1389 Oil field services
HQ: Ceda International Corporation
11012 Macleod Trail Se Suite 625
Calgary AB
403 253-3233

(G-13953)
CLS INDSTRIAL PURIFICATION LLC (PA)
2551 S Shore Blvd Ste C (77573-2979)
PHONE..........................281 538-4669
George Mendakis, *President*
Anthony Weetman, *Opers Staff*
Marco Rios, *Mfg Staff*
Christian Ahrens, *Sales Staff*
◆ **EMP:** 31

SALES (est): 2MM **Privately Held**
WEB: www.clsind.com
SIC: 2819 Industrial inorganic chemicals

(G-13954)
D AND C STORM SOLUTIONS
1401 W Leag Cy Pkwy Ste 1 (77573)
PHONE..........................281 557-3450
Cary Brooks, *Principal*
EMP: 10
SALES (est): 955.8K **Privately Held**
WEB: www.dandcstormsolutions.com
SIC: 3829 Weather tracking equipment

(G-13955)
EMPIRE WIRELINE LLC
400 Hobbs Rd Ste 201 (77573-3880)
P.O. Box 967, Manvel (77578-0967)
PHONE..........................985 264-7746
Sean McCool, *COO*
EMP: 12 **EST:** 2016
SALES (est): 274.6K **Privately Held**
WEB: www.empirewireline.com
SIC: 1389 Oil field services

(G-13956)
F & L COATINGS AND CON LLC
1902 E Independence Ave (77573-7305)
P.O. Box 1113 (77574-1113)
PHONE..........................281 316-2203
Eric Lewis, *President*
Monique Ferrie,
EMP: 11
SALES (est): 1.4MM **Privately Held**
WEB: www.flcoatings.com
SIC: 2851 1721 Epoxy coatings; industrial painting

(G-13957)
FOREMARK PERFORMANCE CHEM INC (PA)
2450 S Shore Blvd Ste 402 (77573-4865)
PHONE..........................281 867-1330
Randy Owens, *CEO*
Brian Wilson, *Vice Pres*
Kevin Oliver, *CFO*
Dana Eagar, *VP Mktg*
EMP: 29
SALES (est): 66MM **Privately Held**
WEB: www.foremarkperformance.com
SIC: 2869 Formaldehyde (formalin)

(G-13958)
HEADCOVERS UNLIMITED INC
Also Called: Headcovers.com
214 S Iowa Ave (77573-4016)
PHONE..........................281 334-4287
Danielle Yates, *Director*
▲ **EMP:** 10
SALES (est): 1.3MM **Privately Held**
WEB: www.headcovers.com
SIC: 2369 5699 2253 5999 Headwear: girls', children's & infants'; costumes & wigs; hats & headwear, knit; toiletries, cosmetics & perfumes; men's & boys' hats, scarves & gloves

(G-13959)
INDIES PRODUCTIONS LLC
Also Called: Indies Coffee Bar & Speakeasy
2406 Lake Front Ct (77573-2811)
PHONE..........................281 508-3920
Brandon Jones, *Principal*
EMP: 9
SALES (est): 445.1K **Privately Held**
SIC: 2095 Roasted coffee

(G-13960)
INEOS AMERICAS LLC (DH)
Also Called: Ineos Nitriles
2600 S Shore Blvd Ste 500 (77573-2944)
PHONE..........................251 535-6600
Ron Deakins, *President*
Robert Delozier, *Superintendent*
Christopher Harding, *Business Mgr*
Surya Kavuri, *Business Mgr*
Jackson Ray, *Business Mgr*
◆ **EMP:** 130
SALES (est): 438.9MM
SALES (corp-wide): 1.9MM **Privately Held**
WEB: www.ineos.com
SIC: 2869 2865 Acetone, synthetic; phenol, alkylated & cumene

HQ: Ineos Holdings Limited
Global Business Centre
Lyndhurst HANTS SO43
238 028-7043

(G-13961)
INEOS NEW PLANET BIOENERGY LLC
2600 S Shore Blvd Ste 500 (77573-2944)
PHONE..............................630 857-7143
Tex Carter, *Vice Pres*
Adam Chabot, *Director*
Mark Niederschulte,
Dan Cummings,
David King,
EMP: 75
SALES (est): 10MM **Privately Held**
WEB: www.ineos.com
SIC: 2821 Plastics materials & resins

(G-13962)
INEOS NITRILES USA LLC (DH)
2600 S Shore Blvd Ste 250 (77573-3091)
PHONE..............................281 535-6600
Dan Williamson, *Engineer*
Jim Ratcliffe,
▲ **EMP:** 41
SALES (est): 437MM
SALES (corp-wide): 1.9MM **Privately Held**
WEB: www.ineos.com
SIC: 2821 Plastics materials & resins
HQ: Ineos Americas Llc
2600 S Shore Blvd Ste 500
League City TX 77573
251 535-6600

(G-13963)
INEOS OLGMERS CHCLAT BAYOU LLC (DH)
2600 S Shore Blvd Ste 250 (77573-3091)
PHONE..............................281 535-6738
Joseph Walton, *President*
Robert Joe Sokol, *Director*
EMP: 16
SALES (est): 1.9MM
SALES (corp-wide): 1.9MM **Privately Held**
SIC: 2873 Nitrogenous fertilizers
HQ: Ineos Americas Llc
2600 S Shore Blvd Ste 500
League City TX 77573
251 535-6600

(G-13964)
INEOS STYROLUTION AMERICA LLC
2600 S Shore Blvd Ste 300 (77573-2944)
PHONE..............................281 474-1009
David Indahl, *Sales Mgr*
EMP: 30
SALES (corp-wide): 1.9MM **Privately Held**
WEB: www.styrolution.com
SIC: 2821 Plastics materials & resins
HQ: Ineos Styrolution America Llc
4245 Meridian Pkwy # 151
Aurora IL 60504

(G-13965)
INEOS USA LLC (DH)
2600 S Shore Blvd Ste 500 (77573-2944)
PHONE..............................281 535-6600
Robert Learman, *CEO*
Charles Obst, *Managing Dir*
Jim Ratcliffe, *Chairman*
Fatima Ho, *Chairman*
Alex Hogan, *Business Mgr*
◆ **EMP:** 243
SQ FT: 150,000
SALES (est): 909.4MM
SALES (corp-wide): 1.9MM **Privately Held**
WEB: www.ineos.com
SIC: 2821 3999 Plastics materials & resins; atomizers, toiletry
HQ: Ineos Group Ag
Avenue Des Uttins 3
Rolle VD
216 277-040

(G-13966)
INEOS USA LLC
Ineos Nitriles
2600 S Shore Blvd Ste 250 (77573-3091)
PHONE..............................281 535-6600
Rob Nevin, *Branch Mgr*
EMP: 27
SALES (corp-wide): 1.9MM **Privately Held**
WEB: www.ineos.com
SIC: 2821 Plastics materials & resins
HQ: Ineos Usa Llc
2600 S Shore Blvd Ste 500
League City TX 77573

(G-13967)
JCS MARINE OILFIELD SVC INC
501 E Walker St (77573-4043)
PHONE..............................281 338-7835
John Costanza, *President*
Nelda K Constanza, *Corp Secy*
JP Costanza, *Vice Pres*
EMP: 20
SQ FT: 6,400
SALES (est): 2.1MM **Privately Held**
WEB: www.jcs-marine.com
SIC: 1389 Oil field services

(G-13968)
LEGACY OFFSHORE LLC
Also Called: Legacy Offshore International
2951 Marina Bay Dr (77573-2735)
PHONE..............................281 334-2266
EMP: 15 **EST:** 2007
SQ FT: 7,000
SALES (est): 11.9MM **Privately Held**
SIC: 1382 Oil/Gas Exploration Services

(G-13969)
NORDIC TANKERS
2551 S Shore Blvd Ste A (77573-2979)
PHONE..............................281 538-3250
Dean Kelly, *General Mgr*
Terje Askvig, *Principal*
Andreas Christensen, *Opers Mgr*
Charity Hughes, *Opers Staff*
Michael Murphy, *Manager*
EMP: 10
SALES (est): 1MM **Privately Held**
WEB: www.nordictankers.com
SIC: 3795 Tanks & tank components

(G-13970)
OFFICE FURN CMPANIES TEXAS LLC
Also Called: Greater Houston Office Pdts
1309 W League City Pkwy (77573-6313)
P.O. Box 899 (77574-0899)
PHONE..............................281 724-1533
Russell E Tidwell, *Principal*
Stephani Brown, *Vice Pres*
EMP: 10
SALES (est): 808.6K **Privately Held**
SIC: 5712 5044 5112 2521 Furniture stores; office equipment; calculating machines; stationery & office supplies; wood office furniture; office furniture, except wood

(G-13971)
OHMSTEDE INDUSTRIAL SVCS INC
2450 S Shore Blvd Ste 120 (77573-3092)
PHONE..............................409 840-6644
Douglas R Harrington Jr, *CEO*
Robert Greeson, *Principal*
Bill Reid, *Chairman*
William P Reid, *Vice Pres*
Daniel Eaton, *CFO*
▲ **EMP:** 850
SALES (est): 118.3MM
SALES (corp-wide): 9.1B **Publicly Held**
WEB: www.ohmstede.com
SIC: 3443 Fabricated plate work (boiler shop)
HQ: Ohmstede Ltd.
895 N Main St
Beaumont TX 77701
409 833-6375

(G-13972)
OHMSTEDE LTD
2450 S Shore Blvd (77573-2994)
PHONE..............................409 840-6644
EMP: 14

SALES (corp-wide): 9.1B **Publicly Held**
WEB: www.ohmstede.com
SIC: 3443 Fabricated plate work (boiler shop)
HQ: Ohmstede Ltd.
895 N Main St
Beaumont TX 77701
409 833-6375

(G-13973)
OIL & GAS TECHNOLOGY FUND INC
2600 S Shore Blvd Ste 300 (77573-2944)
PHONE..............................281 671-7142
EMP: 12 **EST:** 1998
SQ FT: 2,380
SALES (est): 685.4K **Privately Held**
WEB: www.ogtf.com
SIC: 1382 Oil & gas exploration services

(G-13974)
PC CABLE CONNEXION INC
202 Reynolds Ave (77573-4159)
PHONE..............................281 338-5400
Luanne Edelman, *President*
Marc Edelman, *Vice Pres*
Jeannie Segovia, *Accounts Mgr*
EMP: 15
SALES (est): 2.8MM **Privately Held**
WEB: www.pc-cable.com
SIC: 5063 7378 3571 Wire & cable; power wire & cable; computer maintenance & repair; electronic computers

(G-13975)
PLANT PROCESS EQUIPMENT INC (PA)
280 Reynolds Ave (77573-4159)
P.O. Box 389 (77574-0389)
PHONE..............................281 332-2589
Stephen Kennedy, *President*
Joe Borg, *President*
Joe Brog, *Senior VP*
Ken Reynaud, *Senior VP*
Josh Burnett, *Vice Pres*
EMP: 30
SQ FT: 17,500
SALES (est): 17.8MM **Privately Held**
WEB: www.plant-process.com
SIC: 3443 Fabricated plate work (boiler shop)

(G-13976)
PRO-TEM INC
Also Called: Pti Systems
2525 S Shore Blvd Ste 401 (77573-2990)
PHONE..............................281 334-5547
Peter T Clemmons, *President*
Charles E Clemmons, *Chairman*
Aaron Clemmons, *CFO*
Barbara Clemmons, *Admin Sec*
EMP: 12
SQ FT: 6,000
SALES (est): 3.1MM **Privately Held**
WEB: www.pti-sys.com
SIC: 7372 Operating systems computer software

(G-13977)
PROCESS LEVEL TECHNOLOGY LTD
888 Clear Creek Ave (77573-5402)
P.O. Box 705 (77574-0705)
PHONE..............................281 332-6241
Wade L Donehue, *President*
▲ **EMP:** 10
SQ FT: 10,000
SALES (est): 1.9MM **Privately Held**
WEB: www.mag-gage.com
SIC: 3823 Level & bulk measuring instruments, industrial process; liquid level instruments, industrial process type

(G-13978)
REFINED INDUSTRIAL SUPPLY INC
Also Called: Refined Industrial Services
3312 Delesandri Ln (77573)
PHONE..............................409 789-1794
Amanda O'Balle, *President*
EMP: 30
SQ FT: 7,700

SALES (est): 3MM **Privately Held**
SIC: 3498 3443 8621 Fabricated pipe & fittings; industrial vessels, tanks & containers; professional membership organizations

(G-13979)
STI VIBRATION MONITORING INC
1010 E Main St (77573-2450)
PHONE..............................281 334-0766
Franklin V Howard Jr, *Principal*
Torsten Bark, *Business Mgr*
Natalie Henderson, *Accounts Mgr*
Terri Weber, *Manager*
EMP: 10
SALES (est): 2.1MM **Privately Held**
WEB: www.stiweb.com
SIC: 3829 Vibration meters, analyzers & calibrators

(G-13980)
SUMMIT SPORTSWEAR INC
406 Dunes Ridge Way (77573-0710)
PHONE..............................281 335-5370
Timothy K Snedecor, *President*
EMP: 9
SALES (est): 676.4K **Privately Held**
WEB: www.summitsportsweartx.com
SIC: 2395 2261 3993 Embroidery products, except schiffli machine; screen printing of cotton broadwoven fabrics; signs & advertising specialties

(G-13981)
TEXAS SOLAR RESOURCES INC
2310 Lees Ct (77573-3410)
PHONE..............................281 846-4968
Jeremy Sampson, *CEO*
Suzanne Sampson, *President*
EMP: 14
SQ FT: 12,000
SALES (est): 1.6MM **Privately Held**
WEB: www.x-tremeled.com
SIC: 3646 5074 Commercial indusl & institutional electric lighting fixtures; heating equipment & panels, solar

(G-13982)
WILLIAMS OPTOMETRIST
Also Called: Lake City Opitical & Vision
910 W Main St (77573-2024)
PHONE..............................281 332-6021
Jack Williams, *Owner*
EMP: 10
SALES (est): 453.7K **Privately Held**
WEB: www.jfwilliamsod.com
SIC: 3851 Frames & parts, eyeglass & spectacle

Leakey
Real County

(G-13983)
TEXAROME INC
1585 E Ranch Rd (78873)
P.O. Box 159 (78873-0159)
PHONE..............................830 232-6079
Gueric Boucard, *President*
Rick Boucard, *Engineer*
Leslie Rodriguez, *Finance Mgr*
▲ **EMP:** 21
SQ FT: 1,000
SALES (est): 2.3MM **Privately Held**
WEB: www.texarome.com
SIC: 2861 Hardwood distillates

Leander
Williamson County

(G-13984)
ABSOLUTE MACHINE & TOOLING LLC
16001 Rnald W Reagan Blvd (78641-2594)
PHONE..............................512 259-7676
Debbie Witbeck, *CEO*
John Van Witbeck, *Owner*
EMP: 11

▲ = Import ▼=Export
◆ =Import/Export

SALES (est): 2.8MM **Privately Held**
SIC: 3544 3541 3599 Special dies, tools, jigs & fixtures; vertical turning & boring machines (metalworking); machine shop, jobbing & repair

(G-13985)
CROCKER CRANE RENTALS LP
8600 Fm 2243 (78641-1623)
P.O. Box 1469 (78646-1469)
PHONE..................512 258-1323
Sandy Green, *Managing Prtnr*
Joyce Crocker, *Managing Prtnr*
Mike Green, *Managing Prtnr*
Tracey Miller, *Office Mgr*
Ron Miller, *Director*
EMP: 20
SALES (est): 4.6MM **Privately Held**
WEB: www.crockercrane.com
SIC: 7353 3531 1799 Cranes & aerial lift equipment, rental or leasing; backhoes, tractors, cranes, plows & similar equipment; rigging & scaffolding

(G-13986)
CYPRESS TECHNOLOGIES LP (PA)
Also Called: C T C
17301 Fm 1431 (78641-9461)
PHONE..................512 267-9973
Jgreg Child, *President*
Jacqueline L Child, *President*
Susan Child, *General Mgr*
David A Child, *Vice Pres*
Ariel Santos, *Production*
EMP: 45
SQ FT: 18,000
SALES (est): 10.9MM **Privately Held**
WEB: www.cypressmfg.com
SIC: 3577 5045 7378 Computer peripheral equipment; computer peripheral equipment; computer peripheral equipment repair & maintenance

(G-13987)
DENNIS STEEL INC
1105 Leander Dr (78641-2022)
P.O. Box 1529 (78646-1529)
PHONE..................512 259-4001
David R Dennis, *President*
Justin Dyke, *Foreman/Supr*
EMP: 100
SQ FT: 1,800
SALES: 8.8MM **Privately Held**
WEB: www.dennissteel.com
SIC: 3312 3441 1791 Plate, sheet & strip, except coated products; fabricated structural metal; structural steel erection

(G-13988)
ELECTRONICS & METALS INDS INC
Also Called: E M I
17414 Fm 1431 (78641-9460)
P.O. Box 669, Cedar Park (78630-0669)
PHONE..................512 267-0113
Patrick Reese Davis, *CEO*
Michael Davis, *President*
EMP: 23
SQ FT: 26,000
SALES: 872.7K **Privately Held**
WEB: www.pcbpop.com
SIC: 3672 3643 Printed circuit boards; power line cable

(G-13989)
EW & WG LP
Also Called: Precise Machining Co
995 N Bagdad Rd (78641-4552)
P.O. Box 1682 (78646-1682)
PHONE..................512 528-8771
Elaine Williams, *Managing Prtnr*
EMP: 16
SALES (est): 1.7MM **Privately Held**
WEB: www.precisemachiningco.com
SIC: 3599 Machine shop, jobbing & repair

(G-13990)
FALLBROOK TECHNOLOGIES INC (PA)
1501 Leander Dr (78641-2020)
PHONE..................512 714-1964
David Hancock, *President*
Al Kammerer, *President*
Sharon O'Leary, *President*

William G Klehm III, *Chairman*
Alain Charlois, *Exec VP*
▲ EMP: 35
SALES (est): 17.3MM **Privately Held**
WEB: www.fallbrooktech.com
SIC: 3751 Bicycles & related parts

(G-13991)
HARDWOOD PRODUCTS & DOORS INC
9430 Eastranch Rd 2243 (78641)
P.O. Box 645 (78646-0645)
PHONE..................512 259-3094
Joann Luersen, *President*
Kenneth Ray Kelly, *Principal*
Wallace Luersen, *Shareholder*
EMP: 10
SQ FT: 15,000
SALES (est): 1.4MM **Privately Held**
WEB: www.hardwoodproduct.airweb.ne
SIC: 2431 Doors, wood; door trim, wood

(G-13992)
INNOWAVE RF LLC
190 N Bagdad Rd Ste A (78641-3997)
PHONE..................737 200-7090
Priya Ravisekar, *CEO*
EMP: 20 EST: 2011
SALES (est): 5MM **Privately Held**
WEB: www.innowaverf.com
SIC: 3679 Microwave components

(G-13993)
INTEGRATED METAL PRODUCTS INC
302 N Bagdad Rd (78641-7807)
P.O. Box 585 (78646-0585)
PHONE..................512 259-4143
Robert T Mills Jr, *President*
Elizabeth Mills, *Corp Secy*
David Tidwell, *Purch Mgr*
Orjan Blomqvist, *QC Mgr*
Paula Ischy, *Receptionist*
EMP: 30
SQ FT: 20,000
SALES (est): 6.3MM **Privately Held**
WEB: www.impinc.net
SIC: 3444 Sheet metal specialties, not stamped

(G-13994)
LONE STAR READY-MIX LP (PA)
9210 Fm 2243 (78641-1624)
P.O. Box 579, Del Valle (78617-0579)
PHONE..................512 260-0300
Ana Rodriguez, *General Ptnr*
EMP: 17
SQ FT: 37,000
SALES (est): 3MM **Privately Held**
SIC: 3273 Ready-mixed concrete

(G-13995)
MAPOSA TINASHE
Also Called: Maposa Services
307 Greener Dr Leander (78641)
PHONE..................512 704-4601
Tinashe Maposa, *Owner*
EMP: 10
SALES (est): 1MM **Privately Held**
SIC: 5511 7363 4424 4212 Trucks, tractors & trailers: new & used; truck driver services; intercoastal transportation, freight; lumber & timber trucking; semi-trailers for missile transportation

(G-13996)
ONE SOURCE MFG TECH LLC
1106 Leander Dr (78641-2000)
PHONE..................512 259-3272
Kevin Shipley, *Mng Member*
Eugene Muto,
EMP: 53
SQ FT: 16,000
SALES (est): 13MM **Privately Held**
WEB: www.osmtech.com
SIC: 2821 3599 7692 3544 Plastics materials & resins; machine shop, jobbing & repair; welding repair; special dies, tools, jigs & fixtures

(G-13997)
SULLIVAN WELDING INC
9250 Fm 2243 (78641-1624)
PHONE..................512 259-3440
Steve Sullivan, *President*
Harold Chapman, *Vice Pres*

EMP: 16
SALES (est): 681.1K **Privately Held**
SIC: 7692 1799 Welding repair; welding on site

(G-13998)
SUNCOAST POST-TENSION LTD
1500 Leander Dr (78641-2021)
PHONE..................512 259-7908
Russell Price, *General Mgr*
David Rodriguez, *Safety Dir*
Daniel Latham, *Plant Mgr*
Fahim Qasimi, *Project Mgr*
Lam Nguyen, *Project Engr*
EMP: 45
SALES (corp-wide): 2.9B **Privately Held**
WEB: www.suncoast-pt.com
SIC: 3272 3441 5211 Concrete products; fabricated structural metal; masonry materials & supplies
HQ: Suncoast Post-Tension, Ltd.
509 N Sam Houston Pkwy E # 300
Houston TX 77060
281 445-8886

Leesburg
Camp County

(G-13999)
EASTEX CRUDE COMPANY (PA)
10907 State Highway 11 W (75451-2524)
PHONE..................903 856-2401
Tom Hanks, *Partner*
Marianne Russell, *Accountant*
Callie Hanks, *Marketing Staff*
Callie Johnson, *Marketing Staff*
Karen Cheshier, *Manager*
EMP: 40
SQ FT: 4,500
SALES (est): 49.8MM **Privately Held**
WEB: www.eastexcrude.com
SIC: 1382 Oil & gas exploration services

(G-14000)
EASTEX CRUDE TRUCKING LLC
10851 State Highway 11 W (75451-2523)
PHONE..................800 443-8580
Thomas O Hanks, *Director*
EMP: 291
SALES (est): 28.5MM **Privately Held**
WEB: www.eastexcrude.com
SIC: 1382 Oil & gas exploration services

Leonard
Fannin County

(G-14001)
BROTHERS WHOLESALE LLC
601 S Cedar St (75452-2827)
P.O. Box 1189 (75452-1189)
PHONE..................903 587-2900
Jj Lyday,
EMP: 9
SALES (est): 1.2MM **Privately Held**
SIC: 3442 Metal doors, sash & trim

(G-14002)
ROCK SOLID CRUSHED STONE INC
110 W Cottonwood St (75452-2108)
P.O. Box 1080 (75452-1080)
PHONE..................903 587-3448
Bobby Pannkuk Jr, *President*
Libby Schroeder, *Vice Pres*
EMP: 10
SALES (est): 958.5K **Privately Held**
SIC: 1422 7389 Cement rock, crushed & broken-quarrying;

Levelland
Hockley County

(G-14003)
ALLIED OIL FIELD MCH PUMP LLC
202 Hulon Moreland Rd (79336-1300)
P.O. Box 879 (79336-0879)
PHONE..................806 894-7263

Randy Samsel, *Vice Pres*
Ricky Gaona, *Foreman/Supr*
Steve Corgill, *Mfg Staff*
David Owens, *Human Res Mgr*
Butch Bawcom, *Natl Sales Mgr*
EMP: 95
SQ FT: 4,000
SALES (est): 13.2MM **Privately Held**
WEB: www.alliedoilfield.com
SIC: 1389 Oil field services

(G-14004)
BUTCHS RAT HOLE ANCHR SVC INC (PA)
700 Austin St (79336-4502)
P.O. Box 1323 (79336-1323)
PHONE..................806 894-6294
Scott Bryant, *President*
Judy Bryant, *Principal*
L D Bryant, *Principal*
Lance James, *District Mgr*
Norman Allen, *CFO*
EMP: 20
SQ FT: 2,500
SALES (est): 26.6MM **Privately Held**
WEB: www.brhas.com
SIC: 1389 Oil field services; testing, measuring, surveying & analysis services; construction, repair & dismantling services

(G-14005)
CEMEX CONSTRUCTION MTLS S LLC
Also Called: Cem - Lubbock Terminal
117 Commerce St (79336-2005)
PHONE..................501 350-2696
EMP: 36 **Privately Held**
WEB: www.cemexusa.com
SIC: 3273 Ready-mixed concrete
HQ: Cemex Construction Materials South, Llc
2088 E 20th St
Yuma AZ 85365
928 343-4100

(G-14006)
DIAMOND ETHANOL LLC (HQ)
103 S Fm 2646 (79336-9502)
PHONE..................806 897-0911
Cecil O'Brate, *Mng Member*
Jonathan Canalizo, *Analyst*
Nick Hatcher,
Thomas Willis,
EMP: 17
SALES (est): 4.3MM **Privately Held**
WEB: www.conestogaenergy.com
SIC: 3915 Diamond cutting & polishing
PA: Palmer Energy Company, Inc.
5577 Airport Hwy Ste 101
Toledo OH 43615
419 539-9180

(G-14007)
GRAVITY OILFIELD SERVICES LLC
Also Called: Paul Musslewhite Trucking Co
1700 10th St (79336-4218)
PHONE..................806 894-3151
Richard Ellis, *Branch Mgr*
EMP: 35
SALES (corp-wide): 422.8MM **Privately Held**
WEB: www.gravityoilfieldservices.com
SIC: 1389 Oil field services
HQ: Gravity Oilfield Services Llc
3300 N A St Bldg 4-100
Midland TX 79705

(G-14008)
GRAY ENERGY SERVICES LLC
1912 West Ave (79336)
PHONE..................806 894-6008
Larry Robbins,
EMP: 540
SALES (est): 7.3MM **Privately Held**
SIC: 1389 Well logging

(G-14009)
HOCKLEY COUNTY PUBLISHING CO
Also Called: Levelland Hockley News Press
711 Austin St (79336-4523)
P.O. Box 1628 (79336-1628)
PHONE..................806 894-3121
Stephen A Henry, *President*

Pat Henry, *Vice Pres*
EMP: 12
SQ FT: 7,000
SALES (est): 608.7K **Privately Held**
WEB: www.levellandnews.net
SIC: 2711 5994 Newspapers: publishing
only, not printed on site; news dealers &
newsstands
PA: Stephen & Pat Enterprises Inc
711 Austin St
Levelland TX 79336

(G-14010)
M & Q OILFIELD SERVICE INC
1107 W Fm 300 (79336-6229)
P.O. Box 1451 (79336-1451)
PHONE..................................806 894-4025
John A Quilantan, *President*
Maria Betancourt, *Vice Pres*
EMP: 15
SQ FT: 4,000
SALES (est): 1MM **Privately Held**
WEB: www.mqoilfieldservice.net
SIC: 1389 Roustabout service

(G-14011)
NORTH BASIN COATING INC
(PA)
2041 W State Road 300 (79336-7640)
P.O. Box 730 (79336-0730)
PHONE..................................806 894-1531
Richard Mc Cormick, *CEO*
Linda Mc Cormick, *President*
Ken Harding, *CFO*
EMP: 36
SQ FT: 25,000
SALES (est): 16.2MM **Privately Held**
WEB: www.northbasincoating.com
SIC: 1389 Oil field services

(G-14012)
PAUL MUSSLEWHITE TRCKG
CO LLC
1700 10th St (79336-4218)
P.O. Box 848 (79336-0848)
PHONE..................................806 894-3151
Richard Ellis,
EMP: 600 **EST:** 2011
SALES (est): 8.1MM **Privately Held**
WEB: www.sacramentofencecompany.net
SIC: 1389 Haulage, oil field

(G-14013)
ROSS CO SERVICES COMPANY
INC
2341 E Ellis St (79336-2726)
P.O. Box 669 (79336-0669)
PHONE..................................806 894-1511
Bradley McInroe, *President*
A B McInroe, *Vice Pres*
Patricia McInroe, *Admin Sec*
EMP: 19
SQ FT: 2,400
SALES (est): 1.2MM **Privately Held**
SIC: 1389 Oil field services

(G-14014)
RWLS LLC (PA)
Also Called: Renegade Wireline Services
14 Crockett Cir (79336-8004)
P.O. Box 852 (79336-0852)
PHONE..................................806 897-0231
Matthew Gray,
Randy Cassady,
EMP: 23 **EST:** 2009
SALES (est): 25.9MM **Privately Held**
WEB: www.renegadewls.com
SIC: 1389 Oil field services

(G-14015)
S & G DISPOSAL
1001 8th St (79336-4407)
PHONE..................................806 894-6044
S Kirby Rogers, *Partner*
Guy Rush, *Partner*
EMP: 12
SQ FT: 800
SALES (est): 544.9K **Privately Held**
SIC: 1389 5082 Impounding & storing salt
water, oil & gas field; oil field equipment

(G-14016)
SEVEN CONSTRUCTION INC
102 Duval Dr (79336-8006)
P.O. Box 1304 (79336-1304)
PHONE..................................806 894-5685
Sherry Moore, *President*
EMP: 9
SALES (est): 517K **Privately Held**
SIC: 1389 Gas field services; oil field serv-
ices

(G-14017)
SWABCO INC
2341 E Ellis St (79336-2726)
P.O. Box 669 (79336-0669)
PHONE..................................806 894-1511
Bradley McInroe, *President*
EMP: 13
SALES (est): 1.4MM **Privately Held**
SIC: 1389 Oil field services

(G-14018)
YELLOWJACKET OILFIELD
SVCS LLC
102 Avenue Q (79336-4912)
PHONE..................................432 242-7615
Juan Rodriguez, *Manager*
EMP: 17
SALES (corp-wide): 25.4MM **Privately
Held**
WEB: www.yjosllc.com
SIC: 1389 Oil field services
PA: Yellowjacket Oilfield Services, L.L.C.
200 N Loraine St Ste 1150
Midland TX 79701
432 242-7570

Lewisville
Denton County

(G-14019)
1ST SOURCE RESTAURANT
SVCS INC
665 E Jones St (75057-2617)
PHONE..................................214 551-5338
Travis Fogle, *President*
Crystal Fogle, *Vice Pres*
EMP: 13 **EST:** 2008
SALES (est): 2.5MM **Privately Held**
WEB: www.arcstx.com
SIC: 3441 3585 Fabricated structural
metal; refrigeration & heating equipment;
air conditioning equipment, complete

(G-14020)
ALL-STATE INDUSTRIES INC
Also Called: All State Belting
1400 Lakeway Dr (75057-6000)
PHONE..................................972 434-4222
Doug Street, *Manager*
EMP: 34
SALES (corp-wide): 86.7MM **Privately
Held**
WEB: www.all-stateind.com
SIC: 3053 3052 Gaskets, packing & seal-
ing devices; rubber & plastics hose & belt-
ings
HQ: All-State Industries, Inc.
500 S 18th St
West Des Moines IA 50265
515 223-5843

(G-14021)
ANNEX MANUFACTURING LLC
1801 Waters Ridge Dr (75057-6027)
PHONE..................................817 293-8762
Tony Rhinehart, *Purch Mgr*
Jose Ibarra, *Controller*
Stephen Stull,
▲ **EMP:** 30
SALES (est): 5.1MM **Privately Held**
WEB: www.annexac.com
SIC: 3585 Parts for heating, cooling & re-
frigerating equipment

(G-14022)
APPAREL GROUP LTD (DH)
883 Trinity Dr (75056-5297)
PHONE..................................214 469-3300
Chris Nakatani, *CEO*
Thomas J Dietrich, *President*
Lisa Mullman, *President*
Shaun Duncan, *General Mgr*

Ken Bloomberg, *Business Mgr*
◆ **EMP:** 150 **EST:** 1934
SQ FT: 181,000
SALES (est): 109.3MM **Privately Held**
WEB: www.theapparelgroup.com
SIC: 2339 2321 Sportswear, women's;
men's & boys' dress shirts; sport shirts,
men's & boys': from purchased materials

(G-14023)
ARGOS USA LLC
1225 S Railroad St (75057-4818)
PHONE..................................972 436-3026
Billy Collinsworth, *Branch Mgr*
EMP: 14 **Privately Held**
WEB: www.argos-us.com
SIC: 3273 Ready-mixed concrete
HQ: Argos Usa Llc
3015 Windward Plz Ste 300
Alpharetta GA 30005
678 368-4300

(G-14024)
ARNOLD STONE INC (PA)
Also Called: Tri Star Diversified
405 State Highway 121 Byp A250
(75067-4183)
P.O. Box 898, Prosper (75078-0898)
PHONE..................................972 248-1953
Michael D Arnold, *President*
EMP: 18
SALES (est): 33.5MM **Privately Held**
WEB: www.arnoldstone.com
SIC: 1629 3281 Mine loading & discharg-
ing station construction; stone, quarrying
& processing of own stone products

(G-14025)
BAKERY EXPRESS CENTL
TEXAS LP
1301a Ridgeview Ste 400 (75057-6019)
P.O. Box 293328 (75029-3328)
PHONE..................................972 221-8394
Charles Burman, *Partner*
Michael Remsberg, *Partner*
Jim Sutter, *Partner*
Rick Wolfe, *Partner*
EMP: 75
SQ FT: 47,000
SALES (est): 19.4MM **Privately Held**
SIC: 2051 Sponge goods, bakery: except
frozen

(G-14026)
BARTUSH-SCHNITZIUS FOODS
CO
1137 N Kealy Ave (75057-3188)
P.O. Box 396 (75067-0396)
PHONE..................................972 219-1270
John AA Rubi, *President*
Rex Arnold, *Vice Pres*
Joseph M Bartush, *Vice Pres*
Stephen Holloway, *Vice Pres*
John K Sheets, *Vice Pres*
▲ **EMP:** 50
SQ FT: 52,000
SALES (est): 12.1MM **Privately Held**
WEB: www.bartushfoods.com
SIC: 2035 2033 2087 2099 Dressings,
salad: raw & cooked (except dry mixes);
tomato products: packaged in cans, jars,
etc.; beverage bases; vinegar

(G-14027)
BENDT DISTILLING LLC
225 S Charles St (75057-3903)
PHONE..................................214 814-0545
EMP: 24 **EST:** 2012
SALES (est): 3.5MM **Privately Held**
WEB: www.bendtdistillingco.com
SIC: 2085 Distilled & blended liquors

(G-14028)
BLACKSTONE MEDICAL INC
(PA)
Also Called: Orthofix Spinal Implants
3451 Plano Pkwy (75056-9453)
PHONE..................................214 937-2000
Robert S Vaters, *CEO*
Chris Salvatore, *President*
Ronald Stevenson, *General Mgr*
Emily Buxton, *CFO*
EMP: 63 **EST:** 1996
SQ FT: 19,000

SALES (est): 41.4MM **Privately Held**
WEB: www.orthofix.com
SIC: 3841 3842 Surgical & medical instru-
ments; orthopedic appliances

(G-14029)
BRAND COMMERCIAL
SERVICES INC
414 E Church St (75057-4008)
PHONE..................................844 232-7263
Michael Sales, *CEO*
Donald Sales, *President*
EMP: 40
SQ FT: 10,000
SALES (est): 2MM **Privately Held**
WEB: www.brandservicestx.com
SIC: 7623 3631 3632 Refrigeration serv-
ice & repair; barbecues, grills & braziers
(outdoor cooking); household refrigerators
& freezers

(G-14030)
BRIGHT INDUSTRIES LLC (PA)
4400 State Highway 121 # 90
(75056-4561)
PHONE..................................972 410-6500
Christopher R Bright, *Partner*
W Jack Carlile, *Partner*
David R Clink, *Partner*
Clay Vn Bright, *General Ptnr*
Gary Grossman, *Vice Pres*
EMP: 43
SALES (est): 9.5MM **Privately Held**
WEB: www.brightcomarketing.com
SIC: 1311 Crude petroleum production;
natural gas production

(G-14031)
BULLOCH FABRICATING INC
450 E Purnell Rd (75057-4116)
PHONE..................................972 221-6277
Scott Bulloch, *President*
Nancy Bulloch, *Corp Secy*
Jim Pierson, *Prdtn Mgr*
Jacob Pierson, *Design Engr*
Steve Valdez, *Design Engr*
EMP: 65
SQ FT: 100,000
SALES (est): 12.7MM **Privately Held**
WEB: www.bullochfab.com
SIC: 3441 Fabricated structural metal

(G-14032)
CAMPBELL GRINDING &
MACHINE
582 Benjamins Way (75057-2674)
PHONE..................................972 221-2211
Kevin Latham, *President*
Brenda Latham, *Vice Pres*
EMP: 19
SQ FT: 8,500
SALES (est): 2.8MM **Privately Held**
WEB: www.campbellgrinding.com
SIC: 3599 3545 3544 Grinding castings
for the trade; machine shop, jobbing & re-
pair; machine tool accessories; special
dies, tools, jigs & fixtures

(G-14033)
CARL ZEISS VISION INC
440 E Vista Ridge Mall Dr (75067-3704)
PHONE..................................972 906-9663
Carl Zeiss, *Owner*
EMP: 15 **Privately Held**
WEB: www.vision.zeiss.com
SIC: 3827 Optical instruments & lenses
HQ: Carl Zeiss Vision Inc.
12121 Scripps Summit Dr
San Diego CA 92131

(G-14034)
CEDARCIDE INDUSTRIES INC
1025 N Mill St Ste D (75057-3040)
P.O. Box 549, Spring (77383-0549)
PHONE..................................281 367-5075
David Glassel, *President*
Dave Glassel, *Principal*
Danae Bateman, *Corp Secy*
Whitney Teague, *Mktg Dir*
EMP: 10
SALES (est): 1.7MM **Privately Held**
WEB: www.cedarcide.com
SIC: 2879 Pesticides, agricultural or
household

(G-14035)
CF INDUSTRIES INC
Also Called: Axxea Systems
1620 E State Highway 121 A100
(75056-4819)
PHONE.................................214 460-2804
Mathew Merklein, *President*
Kelly Merklein, *Vice Pres*
EMP: 40
SQ FT: 27,000
SALES (est): 6.2MM **Privately Held**
WEB: www.cfindustries.com
SIC: 3699 3669 Electrical equipment &
supplies; emergency alarms

(G-14036)
CHIPPENHOOK CORPORATION (HQ)
Also Called: Chippenhook Services
1955 Lakeway Dr Ste 210 (75056-6435)
PHONE.................................800 527-5866
Barry Rutherford, *President*
Paul Dietz, *President*
Richard Cathcart, *Vice Pres*
Kevin Odonnell, *Vice Pres*
Keith Ford, *Treasurer*
◆ **EMP:** 44 **EST:** 1992
SALES (est): 12.5MM **Privately Held**
WEB: www.chippenhook.com
SIC: 2599 8711 Factory furniture & fix-
tures; construction & civil engineering;
structural engineering

(G-14037)
CITY OF COLONY THE
Also Called: Pump Station
4180 Main St (75056-2806)
PHONE.................................972 625-4471
Tod Marina, *Superintendent*
EMP: 14
SALES (corp-wide): 60MM **Privately Held**
WEB: www.thecolonytx.gov
SIC: 3589 Sewage & water treatment
equipment
PA: The Colony City Of Inc
6800 Main St
The Colony TX 75056
972 625-1756

(G-14038)
CLEMENTS NUT CO INC
614 E Main St (75057-4052)
P.O. Box 14538, Oklahoma City OK
(73113-0538)
PHONE.................................972 436-4596
Richard H Clements, *President*
Edward B Clements, *Vice Pres*
Robert H Clements, *Vice Pres*
Robert Clements, *Vice Pres*
EMP: 25
SQ FT: 30,000
SALES (est): 5.9MM
SALES (corp-wide): 75MM **Privately Held**
WEB: www.clementsfoodscompany.com
SIC: 2099 5159 2068 Peanut butter; nuts
& nut by-products; salted & roasted nuts
& seeds
PA: Clements Foods Co.
6601 N Harvey Pl
Oklahoma City OK 73116
405 842-3308

(G-14039)
CUNNINGHAM AUTOMOTIVE INC
1079 W Round Grove Rd (75067-7905)
PHONE.................................972 900-0405
Antonio Pierce, *CEO*
EMP: 12
SALES (est): 19MM **Privately Held**
SIC: 5511 3711 Automobiles, new & used;
automobile assembly, including specialty
automobiles

(G-14040)
DALLAS TOWING AND AUTONET INC (PA)
1605 Lakeway Dr (75057-6007)
PHONE.................................972 219-8484
Wayne Robinson, *President*
Shirley Robinson, *Corp Secy*
◆ **EMP:** 21
SQ FT: 88,000

SALES (est): 62.8MM **Privately Held**
SIC: 5013 3714 3713 Automotive supplies & parts; motor vehicle parts & accessories; truck & bus bodies

(G-14041)
DBSPECTRA INC
1590 E Business Hwy 121 (75056)
PHONE.................................469 322-0080
EMP: 23
SALES (est): 3.5MM **Privately Held**
SIC: 3663 Mfg Radio/Tv Communication
Equipment

(G-14042)
DBSPECTRA INC
1590 E Hwy 121 Bus Bldg A (75056)
PHONE.................................469 322-0080
Charles A York, *CEO*
Jim Bankston, *Vice Pres*
Mike Washington, *Project Mgr*
Mike Serafin, *Purchasing*
Paul Cartin, *Engineer*
▼ **EMP:** 70
SQ FT: 60,000
SALES (est): 13.9MM **Privately Held**
WEB: www.dbspectra.com
SIC: 3663 Radio & TV communications
equipment

(G-14043)
DC CONTROLS INC
335 Mcdonnell St (75057-4807)
P.O. Box 895 (75067-0895)
PHONE.................................361 906-0123
David Edelbrock, *President*
Mary White, *President*
Jerry Garsa, *Manager*
EMP: 10
SALES (est): 994.4K **Privately Held**
WEB: www.dc-controls.net
SIC: 5084 7389 3429 Instruments & con-
trol equipment; design, commercial & in-
dustrial; door opening & closing devices,
except electrical

(G-14044)
DJO GLOBAL INC (HQ)
2900 Lake Vista Dr (75067-3889)
PHONE.................................800 321-9549
Brady Shirley, *President*
Steven Ingel, *Exec VP*
Jeanine Kestler, *Exec VP*
Bradley J Tandy, *Exec VP*
Tony Allen, *Vice Pres*
◆ **EMP:** 550
SQ FT: 70,000
SALES (est): 1.2B
SALES (corp-wide): 3.3B **Publicly Held**
WEB: www.djoglobal.com
SIC: 3842 Surgical appliances & supplies;
implants, surgical
PA: Colfax Corporation
420 Natl Bus Pkwy Ste 500
Annapolis Junction MD 20701
301 323-9000

(G-14045)
DUSOLD DESIGNS INC
1491 N Kealy Ave Ste 29 (75057-2680)
PHONE.................................972 221-1455
Mike Dusold, *President*
Aaron Sockwell, *Managing Prtnr*
Pam Dusold, *Vice Pres*
Pamela Dusold, *Vice Pres*
Mike McLeroy, *Technician*
EMP: 14
SALES (est): 1.3MM **Privately Held**
WEB: www.dusolddesigns.com
SIC: 7532 3444 Paint shop, automotive;
booths, spray: prefabricated sheet metal

(G-14046)
E A SWEEN COMPANY
Also Called: C D C
1301 Ridgeview Ste 100 (75057-6018)
PHONE.................................972 219-0566
Mark Gray, *General Mgr*
Ronald Myshka, *Vice Pres*
Bryan Virgin, *Vice Pres*
Kirstin Beager, *Research*
Douglas Wolff, *Finance Mgr*
EMP: 78

SALES (corp-wide): 262.5MM **Privately Held**
WEB: www.deliexpress.com
SIC: 2099 Syrups
PA: E. A. Sween Company
16101 W 78th St
Eden Prairie MN 55344
952 937-9440

(G-14047)
ECLIPSE MEDCORP LLC
5916 Stone Creek Dr Ste 1 (75056-2645)
PHONE.................................800 759-6876
Paul O Brien, *Partner*
Tom O Brien, *Mng Member*
EMP: 61
SQ FT: 23,478
SALES (est): 16.1MM **Privately Held**
WEB: www.eclipsemed.com
SIC: 3841 3845 Surgical & medical instru-
ments; electromedical equipment

(G-14048)
ELMER CHRISTY
Also Called: Triple C Hauling
4000 Ace Ln Trlr 432 (75067-8042)
PHONE.................................972 436-0273
Fax: 972 222-0179
EMP: 9
SALES (est): 630K **Privately Held**
SIC: 3532 Mfg Mining Machinery

(G-14049)
ERICSSON SMART FACTORY INC
2601 S Valley Pkwy (75067)
PHONE.................................469 266-3776
Erick Simonsson, *CEO*
EMP: 78
SALES (est): 3.1MM
SALES (corp-wide): 23.5B **Privately Held**
SIC: 3661 Telephone dialing devices, auto-
matic
HQ: Ericsson Inc.
6300 Legacy Dr
Plano TX 75024
972 583-0000

(G-14050)
FOAM SUPPLIES INC
590 Benjamins Way (75057-2674)
PHONE.................................972 436-7008
Scott Keske, *Sales Mgr*
John Hall, *Branch Mgr*
EMP: 20
SALES (corp-wide): 28.5MM **Privately Held**
WEB: www.foamsupplies.com
SIC: 2821 3586 3565 3086 Plastics ma-
terials & resins; measuring & dispensing
pumps; packaging machinery; plastics
foam products
PA: Foam Supplies, Inc.
13389 Lakefront Dr
Earth City MO 63045
314 344-3330

(G-14051)
GENESIS BIOSYSTEMS INC
1500 Eagle Ct (75057-2330)
PHONE.................................972 315-7888
▲ **EMP:** 30
SQ FT: 12,400
SALES (est): 5.9MM **Privately Held**
WEB: www.genesisbiosystems.com
SIC: 3841 Diagnostic apparatus, medical

(G-14052)
HILL PLASTICS INC
1415 Crescent Ave (75057-2644)
PHONE.................................972 436-9717
Bradley Hill, *President*
Cody Hill, *Vice Pres*
EMP: 13
SQ FT: 20,000
SALES (est): 1.3MM **Privately Held**
WEB: www.hillplastics.com
SIC: 3089 Injection molding of plastics;
plastic processing

(G-14053)
HOYA LENS OF AMERICA INC (DH)
651 E Corporate Dr (75057-6403)
PHONE.................................972 221-4141
Paul B Dougher, *President*

Michael Ness, *Principal*
Yuji Eshii, *CFO*
Brian Fitzsimmons, *Sales Staff*
Koji Shinohara, *Admin Sec*
▲ **EMP:** 96 **EST:** 1999
SQ FT: 62,000
SALES (est): 21.4MM **Privately Held**
WEB: www.hoyavision.com
SIC: 5048 3851 Ophthalmic goods; lens
grinding, except prescription: ophthalmic

(G-14054)
HOYA OPTICAL LABS AMERICA INC
397 State Highway 121 Byp (75067-4051)
PHONE.................................972 221-4141
EMP: 99
SALES (est): 2.6MM **Privately Held**
SIC: 3851 Ophthalmic Goods, Nsk

(G-14055)
HUFFMAN & HUFFMAN INC
243 Ridgeway Cir (75067-4532)
PHONE.................................972 434-3640
Gary Huffman, *President*
Sherry Huffman, *Corp Secy*
Rod Huffman, *Vice Pres*
EMP: 9 **EST:** 1951
SALES (est): 2.9MM **Privately Held**
SIC: 3589 7389 Sewage & water treat-
ment equipment; swimming pool filter &
water conditioning systems;

(G-14056)
INNOVATIVE IDM LLC (PA)
Also Called: Automation Controls Direct
301 W Vsta Rdge Mall Dr S (75067)
PHONE.................................214 574-9500
Eugene Gray, *President*
Elliot Austin, *Business Mgr*
Timothy Mueller II, *Vice Pres*
Todd Mueller, *Opers Staff*
Tamara Gray, *Controller*
EMP: 35
SQ FT: 20,000
SALES (est): 89.7MM **Privately Held**
WEB: www.innovativeidm.com
SIC: 5063 7622 3699 Electrical apparatus
& equipment; antenna repair & installa-
tion; electrical equipment & supplies

(G-14057)
ISO COVERS LLC
711 E Jones St Ste A (75057-2667)
PHONE.................................972 221-4410
Vin Spano, *Mng Member*
Dan Sherill,
EMP: 10 **EST:** 2007
SALES (est): 700K **Privately Held**
SIC: 2231 Felts, blanketing & upholstery
fabrics: wool

(G-14058)
JAMEX INC
2871 Lake Vista Dr # 200 (75067-8411)
PHONE.................................214 265-7141
Douglas W Quebe, *President*
Bob Bkonecny, *Vice Pres*
Kelsey Jones, *Asst Controller*
Donna Moore, *Executive*
Priscilla O'Malley, *Admin Sec*
◆ **EMP:** 18
SQ FT: 6,700
SALES (est): 6.3MM **Privately Held**
WEB: www.jamexinc.com
SIC: 1381 1311 Drilling oil & gas wells;
crude petroleum & natural gas production

(G-14059)
JANUS SIGNS
Also Called: Fastsigns
1306 W Main St (75067-3326)
PHONE.................................972 420-8770
Valerie Jackson, *Manager*
EMP: 10
SALES (corp-wide): 1.2MM **Privately Held**
WEB: www.fastsigns.com
SIC: 3993 Signs & advertising specialties
PA: Janus Signs, Inc.
9742 Skillman St
Dallas TX 75243
214 503-1333

(G-14060)
LEATHERWOOD PLASTICS
1426 Crescent Ave (75057-2645)
PHONE................................972 221-7656
Dwight Leatherwood, *President*
Karen Leatherwood, *Vice Pres*
EMP: 15
SQ FT: 19,000
SALES (est): 2.7MM **Privately Held**
WEB: www.leatherwood.com
SIC: 3089 Injection molding of plastics

(G-14061)
LEVEL UP TRANSPORTATION LLC
405 State Highway 121 Byp (75067-8214)
PHONE................................214 210-0701
Latasha Jackson,
EMP: 10
SALES (est): 150K **Privately Held**
SIC: 3537 Trucks: freight, baggage, etc.:
industrial, except mining

(G-14062)
LIGHTS FANTASTIC PRO
2525 E State Highway 121 (75056-5006)
PHONE................................469 568-1111
Ben Parra, *Office Mgr*
EMP: 9
SALES (est): 939K **Privately Held**
WEB: www.lightsfantasticpro.com
SIC: 3646 Ceiling systems, luminous

(G-14063)
MEDICAL EXTRUSION TECH INC
1400 Waters Ridge Dr (75057-6005)
PHONE................................951 698-4346
Rikki Bauer, *Manager*
EMP: 22 **Privately Held**
WEB: www.medicalextrusion.com
SIC: 3082 Unsupported plastics profile
shapes
PA: Medical Extrusion Technologies Inc.
26608 Pierce Cir Ste A
Murrieta CA 92562

(G-14064)
MENASHA PACKAGING COMPANY LLC
2710 Edmonds Ln Lane42 (75067-6731)
PHONE................................330 419-3505
Josh Mc Duffee, *Branch Mgr*
EMP: 24
SALES (corp-wide): 1.6B **Privately Held**
WEB: www.menasha.com
SIC: 2653 Corrugated & solid fiber boxes
HQ: Menasha Packaging Company, Llc
1645 Bergstrom Rd
Neenah WI 54956
920 751-1000

(G-14065)
METL-SPAN LLC
1720 Lakepointe Dr # 101 (75057-6425)
PHONE................................972 221-6656
Karl F Hielscher, *President*
Chris Kramer, *General Mgr*
David Garcia, *Superintendent*
Joseph Calsada, *Business Mgr*
Kevin Franz, *Business Mgr*
◆ EMP: 370
SQ FT: 110,000
SALES (est): 74.7K
SALES (corp-wide): 4.8B **Publicly Held**
WEB: www.metlspan.com
SIC: 3448 Panels for prefabricated metal
buildings
PA: Cornerstone Building Brands, Inc.
5020 Weston Pkwy Ste 400
Cary NC 27513
866 419-0042

(G-14066)
METRO CUTTING AND SEALING INC
1740 N Stemmons Fwy (75067-2203)
P.O. Box 337 (75067-0337)
PHONE................................972 434-8722
Bill Hunt, *President*
Linda Hunt, *Treasurer*
Sherrie Calley, *Sales Staff*
Debbie Gatten, *Manager*
EMP: 30 EST: 1998
SQ FT: 5,000

SALES (est): 4.4MM **Privately Held**
WEB: www.metrocuttingandsealing.com
SIC: 1771 3271 Concrete work; concrete
block & brick

(G-14067)
MICHAEL R ATTEBERRY
Also Called: R&M Retro Services
784 N Kealy Ave (75057-3134)
PHONE................................214 222-3064
Michael R Atteberry, *Owner*
Mike Atterberry, *Owner*
EMP: 11
SALES (est): 1.4MM **Privately Held**
SIC: 3646 Commercial indusl & institu-
tional electric lighting fixtures

(G-14068)
MINDPOWER INTERNATIONAL INC (PA)
3832 Red Oak Trl (75056-4622)
PHONE................................469 287-2735
David Sellers, *CEO*
Sean Harte, *President*
EMP: 10
SQ FT: 1,500
SALES (est): 607K **Privately Held**
SIC: 7379 7372 Computer related consult-
ing services; prepackaged software

(G-14069)
MLC SIGNS LP
Also Called: Fastsigns
1306 W Main St (75067-3326)
PHONE................................972 420-8770
Catherine Monson, *CEO*
Andrea Levine, *Principal*
EMP: 18
SALES (est): 2.1MM **Privately Held**
WEB: www.fastsigns.com
SIC: 3993 Signs & advertising specialties

(G-14070)
MORROW CABINETS INC
136 E College St (75057-3981)
PHONE................................972 221-7551
Randy Morrow, *President*
EMP: 18
SQ FT: 16,000
SALES (est): 300K **Privately Held**
WEB: www.morrowcabinets.com
SIC: 2434 Wood kitchen cabinets

(G-14071)
NATIONAL SWTCHGEAR SYSTEMS INC (PA)
Also Called: Nat'l Switchgear
649 Franklin (75057-2301)
PHONE................................972 420-0149
Douglas F Powell, *President*
Kim Koehler, *General Mgr*
Adam Tappe, *General Mgr*
Robert Koren, *Vice Pres*
Ross Smelley, *Vice Pres*
EMP: 31
SQ FT: 7,000
SALES (est): 8MM **Privately Held**
WEB: www.nationalswitchgear.com
SIC: 5063 3699 3613 1731 Circuit break-
ers; switchgear; electrical equipment &
supplies; switchgear & switchboard appa-
ratus; electrical work

(G-14072)
NCI GROUP INC
Metl-Span A Division Nci Group
1720 Lakepointe Dr # 101 (75057-6458)
PHONE................................972 221-6656
Karl F Hielscher, *President*
Alyson Huntington-Jone, *Vice Pres*
Stephen Parnes, *Plant Mgr*
Hunter Whorton, *Engineer*
William Pittman, *Sales Mgr*
EMP: 85
SALES (corp-wide): 4.8B **Publicly Held**
WEB: www.cornerstonebuildingbrands.com
SIC: 3448 Panels for prefabricated metal
buildings
HQ: Nci Group, Inc.
10943 N Sam Huston Pkwy W
Houston TX 77064
281 897-7788

(G-14073)
NELSON BROS READY MIX LTD
721 E Main St (75057-4123)
PHONE................................972 436-6558
Randy Owens, *President*
EMP: 52
SALES (est): 22.7MM **Privately Held**
SIC: 3273 Ready-mixed concrete

(G-14074)
NORTH AMERICAN RESEARCH CORP
Also Called: Narco
519 Huffines Blvd (75056-9552)
P.O. Box 1318 (75067-1318)
PHONE................................972 492-1800
Robert F Clarke, *CEO*
Patrick Shaughnessy, *President*
Pat R Shaughnessy, *General Mgr*
▲ EMP: 14 EST: 1969
SQ FT: 30,000
SALES (est): 3.4MM **Privately Held**
WEB: www.narcochem.com
SIC: 2841 Soap & other detergents

(G-14075)
ORACLE SYSTEMS CORPORATION
6624 Sunrise Dr (75056-3780)
PHONE................................713 658-6925
EMP: 252
SALES (corp-wide): 39B **Publicly Held**
SIC: 7372 Prepackaged software
HQ: Oracle Systems Corporation
500 Oracle Pkwy
Redwood City CA 94065

(G-14076)
ORTHOFIX INC
Orthofix Spinal Implants
3451 Plano Pkwy (75056-9453)
PHONE................................214 937-2000
EMP: 200 **Privately Held**
WEB: www.orthofix.com
SIC: 3841 3842 Surgical & medical instru-
ments; orthopedic appliances
PA: Orthofix Inc.
3451 Plano Pkwy
Lewisville TX 75056

(G-14077)
ORTHOFIX INC
3451 Plano Pkwy (75056-9453)
P.O. Box 849806, Dallas (75284-9806)
PHONE................................214 937-2000
Robert Vater, *COO*
N Dodoi, *Vice Pres*
Steve Martin, *Vice Pres*
Brigitta Pop, *Buyer*
Brad Mason, *Director*
EMP: 200
SQ FT: 69,924 **Privately Held**
WEB: www.orthofix.com
SIC: 3841 3845 Surgical & medical instru-
ments; electromedical equipment
PA: Orthofix Inc.
3451 Plano Pkwy
Lewisville TX 75056

(G-14078)
ORTHOFIX INC (PA)
3451 Plano Pkwy (75056-9453)
PHONE................................214 937-2000
Theresa Church, *President*
Matt Fordyce, *President*
Paul Gonsalves, *President*
John Lovell, *President*
Jon Serbousek, *President*
▲ EMP: 233
SALES (est): 93.3MM **Privately Held**
WEB: www.orthofix.com
SIC: 3841 Medical instruments & equip-
ment, blood & bone work

(G-14079)
ORTHOFIX MEDICAL INC (PA)
3451 Plano Pkwy (75056-9453)
PHONE................................214 937-2000
Ronald A Matricaria, *Ch of Bd*
Jon Serbousek, *President*
Davide Bianchi, *President*
Paul Gonsalves, *President*
Kevin Kenny, *President*
EMP: 10 EST: 1987

SALES: 459.9MM **Privately Held**
WEB: www.orthofix.com
SIC: 3841 Surgical & medical instruments

(G-14080)
OVERHEAD DOOR CORPORATION (DH)
2501 S State Hwy 121 Ste (75067)
PHONE................................469 549-7100
Dennis Stone, *President*
Mike Kridel, *President*
Steve Burgess, *General Mgr*
Brett Schiebner, *General Mgr*
Sandra Brown, *Principal*
◆ EMP: 140
SQ FT: 64,000
SALES (est): 705.4MM **Privately Held**
WEB: www.overheaddoor.com
SIC: 3442 2431 3699 3537 Garage
doors, overhead: metal; doors, wood;
door opening & closing devices, electrical;
industrial trucks & tractors; vacuum clean-
ers & sweepers, electric: industrial

(G-14081)
OWENS MACHINE AND TOOL COMPANY
561 N Cowan Ave Ste 201 (75057-3099)
PHONE................................972 219-2354
Danita Grill, *President*
Roger Grill, *Treasurer*
Candace Chatman, *Manager*
Rebecca Garcia, *Manager*
EMP: 40
SQ FT: 20,000
SALES (est): 7.1MM **Privately Held**
WEB: www.owensmachine.com
SIC: 3599 Machine shop, jobbing & repair

(G-14082)
POWDER METALLURGY COMPANY INC
201 E College St (75057-4081)
PHONE................................972 436-3502
Lawrence L Bobo, *Ch of Bd*
Mike Kuehler, *President*
Vickie Reid, *Manager*
EMP: 47
SQ FT: 20,000
SALES (est): 4.3MM **Privately Held**
WEB: www.powdermetallurgyco.com
SIC: 3399 Powder, metal

(G-14083)
PRESIDIO NTWRKED SLTONS GROUP
1955 Lakeway Dr Ste 220 (75057-6448)
PHONE................................469 549-3800
Robert Cagnazzi, *CEO*
Andy Cadwell, *President*
Dave Hart, *COO*
Eric Schondorf, *Vice Pres*
Paul Fletcher, *CFO*
▲ EMP: 470
SQ FT: 34,656
SALES (est): 119.7MM
SALES (corp-wide): 3B **Privately Held**
WEB: www.presidio.com
SIC: 5045 7372 7373 Computers, periph-
erals & software; prepackaged software;
computer integrated systems design
HQ: Presidio Networked Solutions Llc
8161 Maple Lawn Blvd # 1
Fulton MD 20759
212 652-5700

(G-14084)
R R DONNELLEY & SONS COMPANY
1550 Lakeway Dr Ste 500 (75057-6015)
PHONE................................972 459-1493
Cindy Auken, *Manager*
EMP: 12
SALES (corp-wide): 6.2B **Publicly Held**
WEB: www.rrd.com
SIC: 2759 Commercial printing
PA: R. R. Donnelley & Sons Company
35 W Wacker Dr
Chicago IL 60601
312 326-8000

▲ = Import ▼=Export
◆ =Import/Export

(G-14085)
R R DONNELLEY & SONS COMPANY
Also Called: R R Donnelley
1550 Lakeway Dr Ste 200 (75057-6025)
PHONE..................................(972) 459-1400
Clark Smilie Jr, *Branch Mgr*
EMP: 50
SALES (corp-wide): 6.2B **Publicly Held**
WEB: www.rrd.com
SIC: 2759 Commercial printing
PA: R. R. Donnelley & Sons Company
35 W Wacker Dr
Chicago IL 60601
312 326-8000

(G-14086)
R R DONNELLEY & SONS COMPANY
Also Called: R R Donnelley
1550 Lakeway Dr Ste 100 (75057-6051)
PHONE..................................972 353-6130
John Siebert, *Manager*
EMP: 100
SALES (corp-wide): 6.2B **Publicly Held**
WEB: www.rrd.com
SIC: 2752 2761 2677 Commercial printing, lithographic; manifold business forms; envelopes
PA: R. R. Donnelley & Sons Company
35 W Wacker Dr
Chicago IL 60601
312 326-8000

(G-14087)
RANGER AIR AVIATION LLC
2670 Edmonds Ln Ste 200 (75067-6732)
PHONE..................................972 245-6699
Mark T Perlioni, *Partner*
Robert W Hill, *Partner*
EMP: 13
SQ FT: 28,500
SALES (est): 10MM
SALES (corp-wide): 298.5MM **Privately Held**
WEB: www.rangeraav.com
SIC: 5088 3724 Aircraft & parts; aircraft engines & engine parts
PA: Aviation Technical Services, Inc.
3121 109th St Sw
Everett WA 98204
425 347-3030

(G-14088)
RICOS MANUFACTURING CO INC
600 Tittle Dr (75056)
PHONE..................................210 226-4168
EMP: 40
SALES (est): 2.4MM
SALES (corp-wide): 86.9MM **Privately Held**
SIC: 2096 2064 Mfg Potato Chips/Snacks Mfg Candy/Confectionery
PA: Liberto Specialty Company Inc
830 S Presa St
San Antonio TX 78210
210 222-1415

(G-14089)
ROCKET DISTRIBUTION LLC
344 Mcdonnell St (75057-4808)
PHONE..................................817 688-9454
EMP: 15
SQ FT: 25,000
SALES: 2MM **Privately Held**
SIC: 3949 Mfg Sporting/Athletic Goods

(G-14090)
ROCKWELL AUTOMATION INC
6601 Cascades Ct Ste 130 (75056-4587)
PHONE..................................972 417-5400
James Morris, *Area Mgr*
Barnett James, *Engineer*
Jeff Andre, *Manager*
EMP: 62 **Publicly Held**
WEB: www.rockwellautomation.com
SIC: 3625 Electric controls & control accessories, industrial
PA: Rockwell Automation, Inc.
1201 S 2nd St
Milwaukee WI 53204

(G-14091)
SOUTHWEST SOLUTIONS GROUP INC (PA)
2535 E State Highway 121 110b (75056-5025)
P.O. Box 671784, Dallas, (75267-1784)
PHONE..................................972 250-1970
Raymond L Streight, *President*
Randy Brant, *Vice Pres*
Craig Crock, *Vice Pres*
O Richard Riemer, *Vice Pres*
Timothy Bronars, *Accounts Mgr*
EMP: 25
SALES (est): 32.3MM **Privately Held**
WEB: www.southwestsolutions.com
SIC: 5021 2542 2541 Filing units; partitions & fixtures, except wood; wood partitions & fixtures

(G-14092)
SSC SIGNS & LIGHTING LLC
2090 Mcgee Ln (75077-1703)
PHONE..................................972 219-2495
Craig Waldrum, *Vice Pres*
Kaitlynn Kiddy, *Project Mgr*
Brandon Butcher, *Sr Project Mgr*
Jason Kinkaid,
EMP: 35
SALES (est): 2.2MM **Privately Held**
WEB: www.sscsigns.com
SIC: 3993 Electric signs

(G-14093)
STANDARD MOTOR PRODUCTS INC
Four Seasons Hayden Division
1801 Waters Ridge Dr (75057-6027)
PHONE..................................972 316-8100
Dala Burks, *Principal*
Ray Nicholas, *Vice Pres*
Brian Lee, *Purch Mgr*
Kevin Phillips, *QC Mgr*
Archie Pinto, *Engineer*
EMP: 10
SALES (corp-wide): 1.1B **Publicly Held**
WEB: www.haydenauto.com
SIC: 3694 Automotive electrical equipment
PA: Standard Motor Products, Inc.
3718 Northern Blvd # 600
Long Island City NY 11101
718 392-0200

(G-14094)
STANDARD MOTOR PRODUCTS INC
Four Seasons - Corporate Offs
1801 Waters Ridge Dr (75057-6027)
P.O. Box 299009 (75029-9009)
PHONE..................................972 316-8100
Michael Carney, *General Mgr*
Ray Nicholas, *Vice Pres*
Rey Nicholas, *Vice Pres*
Jeff Kaler, *Purch Mgr*
Todd Keller, *Engineer*
EMP: 160
SQ FT: 430,000
SALES (corp-wide): 1.1B **Publicly Held**
WEB: www.smpcorp.com
SIC: 3714 3423 5013 7537 Motor vehicle parts & accessories; hand & edge tools; motor vehicle supplies & new parts; automotive transmission repair shops; power transmission equipment
PA: Standard Motor Products, Inc.
3718 Northern Blvd # 600
Long Island City NY 11101
718 392-0200

(G-14095)
STANDARD MOTOR PRODUCTS INC
Catalog / Tchncal Temp Contrls
1801 Waters Ridge Dr (75057-6027)
PHONE..................................972 316-8100
Chuck Watters, *Engineer*
Dale Burks, *Branch Mgr*
EMP: 150
SALES (corp-wide): 1.1B **Publicly Held**
WEB: www.smpcorp.com
SIC: 3714 7539 Motor vehicle parts & accessories; automotive air conditioning repair

PA: Standard Motor Products, Inc.
3718 Northern Blvd # 600
Long Island City NY 11101
718 392-0200

(G-14096)
T R W MODERNFOLD COMPANY INC
Also Called: Modernfold Door Specialties
1501 Fairway Dr 100 (75057-2329)
PHONE..................................214 357-2572
Glynn Trahan, *President*
EMP: 10
SALES (corp-wide): 5.9MM **Privately Held**
WEB: www.trwfamily.com
SIC: 1541 5211 2531 Industrial buildings, new construction; door & window products; blackboards, wood
PA: T R W Modernfold Company, Inc.
6754 Bourgeois Rd
Houston TX 77066
281 919-1668

(G-14097)
TC SIGNS INC
1620 E State Highway 121 (75056-4800)
PHONE..................................972 492-2801
Charla Hensel, *President*
David Wager, *Vice Pres*
Don Hensel, *Manager*
EMP: 10
SQ FT: 12,000
SALES (est): 620K **Privately Held**
WEB: www.tcsigns.net
SIC: 3993 Signs & advertising specialties

(G-14098)
TORAY COMPOSITE MTLS AMER INC
700 Parker Sq Ste 275 (75028-7449)
PHONE..................................972 899-2930
Buster Tipton, *Branch Mgr*
Kosuke Suzuki, *Manager*
EMP: 10 **Privately Held**
WEB: www.toraycma.com
SIC: 3624 Fibers, carbon & graphite
HQ: Toray Composite Materials America, Inc.
19002 50th Ave E
Tacoma WA 98446

(G-14099)
TRIATHLON BTRY SOLUTIONS INC
2025 Midway Rd Ste 200 (75056-9540)
PHONE..................................469 301-2128
Taylor G Frederickson, *President*
EMP: 23
SQ FT: 19,000
SALES (est): 189.4K
SALES (corp-wide): 17.5MM **Privately Held**
WEB: www.triathlon-batteries.com
SIC: 3691 Storage batteries
HQ: Triathlon Holding Gmbh
Am Brand 11-13
Pyrbaum 90602
911 780-9600

(G-14100)
UNIVERSAL DISPLAY & FIXS CO
Also Called: Ful-Vue Display Systems
726 E Hwy 121 (75057-4159)
PHONE..................................972 221-5157
John Phillips, *CEO*
EMP: 350
SALES (corp-wide): 110.7MM **Privately Held**
WEB: www.udfc.com
SIC: 2542 3993 3496 Fixtures: display, office or store: except wood; signs & advertising specialties; miscellaneous fabricated wire products
PA: Universal Display And Fixture Company
726 E Hwy 121
Lewisville TX 75057
972 434-8067

(G-14101)
UNIVERSAL DISPLAY AND FIX CO (PA)
Also Called: Udfc
726 E Hwy 121 (75057-4159)
PHONE..................................972 434-8067
F De Jesus, *President*
Mauricio Maldonado, *General Mgr*
Joseph Battaglia, *Exec VP*
Joe Battaglia, *Vice Pres*
Jim Kelly, *Vice Pres*
◆ EMP: 150
SALES (est): 110.7MM **Privately Held**
WEB: www.udfc.com
SIC: 2542 3993 Racks, merchandise display or storage: except wood; signs & advertising specialties

(G-14102)
URANIUM RESOURCES INC
650 S Edmonds Ln Ste 108 (75067-3554)
PHONE..................................972 219-3330
EMP: 12
SALES: 1MM
SALES (corp-wide): 15.8MM **Publicly Held**
SIC: 7389 3295 Business Services Mfg Minerals-Ground/Treated
PA: Westwater Resources, Inc.
6950 S Potomac St Ste 300
Centennial CO 80112
303 531-0516

(G-14103)
US REMODELERS INC
Also Called: Century 21 Cabinet Refacing
405 State Highway 121 Byp A250 (75067-4183)
PHONE..................................214 488-6300
Murray H Gross, *CEO*
Richard B Goodner, *Vice Pres*
David Gross, *Vice Pres*
Steven L Gross, *Vice Pres*
Robert A Defronzo, *CFO*
EMP: 20
SQ FT: 70,000
SALES (est): 59.2MM
SALES (corp-wide): 110.2B **Publicly Held**
SIC: 1799 2434 2431 Kitchen cabinet installation; wood kitchen cabinets; millwork
HQ: U.S. Home Systems, Inc.
2951 Kinwest Pkwy
Irving TX 75063
214 488-6300

(G-14104)
VARIEON INC
Also Called: Easy Comm & Alarm
565 E Church St (75057-4009)
PHONE..................................469 916-1099
Young W Yi, *CEO*
Alex Park, *CFO*
EMP: 16
SALES (est): 2.1MM **Privately Held**
WEB: www.ecasecurity.com
SIC: 3861 Cameras & related equipment

(G-14105)
VENUS SPA
4770 State Highway 121 (75056-2913)
PHONE..................................214 469-1615
EMP: 40
SALES (est): 154.2K **Privately Held**
WEB: www.venussalonsandspa.com
SIC: 7231 2844 7299 Unisex hair salons; manicure preparations; massage parlor

(G-14106)
VINSON PROCESS CONTROLS CO LP (PA)
2747 Highpoint Oaks Dr (75067-8190)
PHONE..................................972 459-8200
John C Huskinson, *President*
Monte Pearson, *Area Mgr*
Brian Rice, *Business Mgr*
Glenn Broome, *COO*
Edward Mitchell, *Project Mgr*
▲ EMP: 85
SQ FT: 60,000

SALES (est): 39.9MM **Privately Held**
WEB: www.vinsonprocess.com
SIC: 5084 3533 3498 Controlling instruments & accessories; oil well machinery, equipment & supplies; oil & gas field machinery; fabricated pipe & fittings; tube fabricating (contract bending & shaping)

(G-14107)
VIRA INSIGHT LLC (PA)
2701 S Valley Pkwy (75067-2076)
PHONE....................................800 366-2345
Jeff Jones, *CEO*
Nick Farinola, *President*
Peter Rozes, *Exec VP*
Kimberly Ferrante-Pitluk, *Vice Pres*
Sam Grow, *Vice Pres*
◆ **EMP:** 141
SALES (est): 64.3MM **Privately Held**
WEB: www.virainsight.com
SIC: 2542 Office & store showcases & display fixtures

(G-14108)
VIRA INSIGHT LLC
2701 S Valley Pkwy (75067-2076)
PHONE....................................800 366-2345
Jeff Jones, *CEO*
EMP: 55
SQ FT: 330,000
SALES (corp-wide): 64.3MM **Privately Held**
WEB: www.virainsight.com
SIC: 2542 Office & store showcases & display fixtures
PA: Vira Insight, Llc
　　2701 S Valley Pkwy
　　Lewisville TX 75067
　　800 366-2345

(G-14109)
VOGT ICE LLC
Also Called: Turbo Refrigerating
522 S Edmonds Ln Ste 102 (75067-3622)
P.O. Box 396, Denton (76202-0396)
PHONE....................................940 387-4301
Elmer L Beard, *Managing Prtnr*
Mark Smith, *Technical Staff*
EMP: 37
SALES (est): 5.4MM **Privately Held**
WEB: www.vogtice.com
SIC: 3585 Refrigeration & heating equipment

(G-14110)
WARABEYA TEXAS INC
Also Called: Prime Deli
1301a Ridgeview Ste 200 (75057-6016)
PHONE....................................972 219-7110
Craig Weidner, *President*
Harry Nakamura, *President*
EMP: 71
SQ FT: 32,000
SALES (est): 17.4MM **Privately Held**
SIC: 2099 Ready-to-eat meals, salads & sandwiches
PA: Prima Meat Packers, Ltd.
　　4-12-2, Higashishinagawa
　　Shinagawa-Ku TKY 140-0

(G-14111)
WEBVENT INC
2540 King Arthur Blvd 209h (75056-5833)
PHONE....................................617 418-4126
Richard Borry, *President*
Frank Spenk, *Division Mgr*
Matt Taylor, *Division Mgr*
Nicolas Kuppers, *Principal*
Sean Soth, *Vice Pres*
EMP: 10
SALES (est): 742.9K **Privately Held**
WEB: www.webvent.tv
SIC: 7372 Application computer software

(G-14112)
WELCH HVAC INCORPORATED
118 Lynn Ave Ste 602 (75057-3706)
PHONE....................................214 222-8600
Timothy Welch, *CEO*
Nicholas Laughner, *President*
Brandi Stefanski, *Treasurer*
EMP: 15
SQ FT: 1,100

SALES: 16.9MM **Privately Held**
SIC: 1711 3433 3585 Heating & air conditioning contractors; gas infrared heating units; refrigeration & heating equipment

(G-14113)
ZYNEX INC
421 S Mill St Pmb 167 (75057-3947)
PHONE....................................972 221-5050
Jeane Dobbs, *CEO*
Russell Moore, *President*
Raelynn Maloney, *Vice Pres*
Madison Willers, *Supervisor*
EMP: 9
SQ FT: 20,000
SALES (est): 500K **Privately Held**
WEB: www.zynex.com
SIC: 3565 Labeling machines, industrial

Liberty
Liberty County

(G-14114)
BAKER HUGHES A GE COMPANY LLC
Hwy 146 N Liberty (77575)
PHONE....................................936 336-7218
Steve Webb, *Manager*
EMP: 28
SALES (corp-wide): 23.8B **Publicly Held**
WEB: www.bakerhughes.com
SIC: 1389 Oil field services
HQ: Baker Hughes Holdings Llc
　　17021 Aldine Westfield Rd
　　Houston TX 77073
　　713 439-8600

(G-14115)
BLACKGOLD SERVICES INC
3608 E Highway 90 (77575-9663)
P.O. Box 1526 (77575-1526)
PHONE....................................936 336-9600
William H Howse, *Principal*
EMP: 23
SALES (est): 5.2MM **Privately Held**
WEB: www.blackgoldservicesinc.com
SIC: 1389 Oil field services

(G-14116)
BOOMERANG TUBE LLC
1100 Fm 3361 Rd (77575-8810)
PHONE....................................713 289-5555
Kennethia Ingram, *Regional Mgr*
Jon Dickson, *Manager*
Michael Lewis, *Manager*
Tim Clark, *Director*
Gregg Eisenberg,
EMP: 265
SALES (corp-wide): 277.8MM **Privately Held**
WEB: www.boomerangtube.com
SIC: 3317 Steel pipe & tubes
PA: Boomerang Tube, Llc
　　14567 North Outer 40 Rd # 50
　　Chesterfield MO 63017
　　636 534-5555

(G-14117)
DRUM EQUIPMENT INC
311 River Bend Rd (77575-3967)
PHONE....................................936 336-9256
Delton Drum, *Principal*
EMP: 9
SALES (est): 994.3K **Privately Held**
SIC: 1389 Oil field services

(G-14118)
G S PETROLEUM INC
4408 N Main St (77575-3586)
P.O. Box 767 (77575-0767)
PHONE....................................936 336-4114
Curtis Hudnall, *President*
EMP: 25
SALES (est): 1.7MM **Privately Held**
SIC: 1311 Crude petroleum production

(G-14119)
HARTMAN NEWSPAPERS LP
Also Called: Vindicator, The
1939 Trinity St Ste A (77575-4851)
P.O. Box 9189 (77575-2889)
PHONE....................................936 336-3611
Carol Skewes, *Manager*
EMP: 10

SALES (corp-wide): 32.2MM **Privately Held**
WEB: www.portlavacawave.com
SIC: 2711 Newspapers: publishing only, not printed on site
PA: Hartman Newspapers L.P.
　　1914 4th St
　　Rosenberg TX 77471
　　281 342-8691

(G-14120)
KDR SUPPLY INC (PA)
3112 Beaumont Ave (77575)
PHONE....................................936 334-1353
Rocky Day Fisher, *Owner*
Kenny Simmons, *General Mgr*
Kenneth Fisher, *Purch Mgr*
Bruce Finley, *Sales Mgr*
Kristopher Albert, *Sales Staff*
EMP: 17
SQ FT: 27,000
SALES (est): 12.2MM **Privately Held**
WEB: www.kdrsupply.com
SIC: 3317 3312 5013 5085 Steel pipe & tubes; pipes & tubes; pipes, iron & steel; pumps, oil & gas; industrial fittings; oil refining machinery, equipment & supplies; oil well machinery, equipment & supplies

(G-14121)
LIBERTY FORGE INC
1507 Fort Worth St (77575-4763)
P.O. Box 1210 (77575-1210)
PHONE....................................936 336-5785
▲ **EMP:** 60 EST: 1974
SQ FT: 55,000
SALES (est): 11.9MM **Privately Held**
WEB: www.libertyforgeinc.com
SIC: 3462 Armor plate, forged iron or steel

(G-14122)
LIBERTY PLANT MAINTENANCE INC
1939 Trinity St (77575-4829)
PHONE....................................281 923-5307
Scott Krzyzanowski, *President*
EMP: 14
SALES (est): 1.7MM **Privately Held**
WEB: www.libertydaytonchamber.com
SIC: 3545 Measuring tools & machines, machinists' metalworking type

(G-14123)
LYNCO WELL SERVICE INC
1590 Wallisville Rd (77575)
P.O. Box 10190 (77575-7690)
PHONE....................................936 336-7332
EMP: 45
SQ FT: 1,600
SALES (est): 3.4MM **Privately Held**
SIC: 1381 Oil/Gas Well Drilling

(G-14124)
NUTRITION SUPPLY CORP
Also Called: Nutritional Scientific
317 Industrial Cir (77575-3447)
PHONE....................................936 334-0514
Frank Jordan, *President*
Mark Campbell, *Vice Pres*
Connie Jordan, *Treasurer*
EMP: 11
SQ FT: 4,000
SALES (est): 1.2MM **Privately Held**
WEB: www.healthinspirationministry.com
SIC: 5499 2833 Vitamin food stores; vitamins, natural or synthetic: bulk, uncompounded

(G-14125)
SATURN POLYMERS INC
3718 E Highway 90 (77575-8626)
PHONE....................................936 334-0675
Neil Mitchell, *President*
EMP: 9
SQ FT: 5,000
SALES (est): 1.5MM **Privately Held**
SIC: 2865 Chemical indicators

(G-14126)
VALES WELDING SERVICE
301 Industrial Pl (77575-3424)
P.O. Box 1123 (77575-1123)
PHONE....................................936 336-5148
James Vales, *Owner*
EMP: 10
SQ FT: 7,904

SALES (est): 491.5K **Privately Held**
SIC: 7692 Welding repair

(G-14127)
WARD MC CARTY INC
4408 N Main St (77575-3586)
P.O. Box 788 (77575-0788)
PHONE....................................936 336-3132
Curtis Hudnall, *President*
John Hudnall, *Vice Pres*
EMP: 30
SQ FT: 3,000
SALES (est): 1.2MM **Privately Held**
SIC: 1389 Oil field services

Liberty Hill
Williamson County

(G-14128)
NZONE GUIDANCE LLC (PA)
140 Falon Ln (78642-4318)
PHONE....................................512 778-5353
Amy Hagen, *Accounting Mgr*
EMP: 10 EST: 2014
SALES (est): 10MM **Privately Held**
WEB: www.nzoneguidance.com
SIC: 1381 Drilling oil & gas wells

(G-14129)
SPECTRA DYNAMICS CORPORATION
315 Craigen Rd (78642-6215)
PHONE....................................512 255-2233
Jeannie Slack, *CEO*
Mark Slack, *President*
EMP: 11
SQ FT: 15,000
SALES (est): 2.5MM **Privately Held**
WEB: www.spectra-dynamics.com
SIC: 3826 Chromatographic equipment, laboratory type

(G-14130)
USA FRAMETEK LLC
Also Called: U S A Frametek
1300 County Road 257 (78642-4704)
PHONE....................................512 515-6500
William P Rhodes, *CEO*
EMP: 30
SQ FT: 50,000
SALES (est): 4MM **Privately Held**
WEB: www.usaframetek.com
SIC: 3441 3448 Fabricated structural metal; prefabricated metal buildings

(G-14131)
VISUALML OPERATIONS LLC
301 Spring Creek Dr (78642-9426)
PHONE....................................855 847-8256
EMP: 9 EST: 2012
SALES (est): 450K **Privately Held**
SIC: 7372 7389 Prepackaged Software Services

Lindale
Smith County

(G-14132)
849 RED BARON SUPPLY CO LLC (PA)
2561 S Main St Bldg B (75771-7722)
PHONE....................................903 882-1700
Jerry Alexander, *Principal*
EMP: 24
SALES (est): 3.5MM **Privately Held**
WEB: www.redbaroncompanies.com
SIC: 3273 Ready-mixed concrete

(G-14133)
BENCHMARK MANUFACTURING INC
Also Called: Imageair
211 S Industrial St (75771)
P.O. Box 2170 (75771-2170)
PHONE....................................903 882-4311
Cindy Snow, *President*
Steven W Hallock, *Vice Pres*
EMP: 50
SQ FT: 25,000

SALES (est): 5MM **Privately Held**
SIC: 3621 3677 3498 Coils, for electric motors or generators; electronic coils, transformers & other inductors; fabricated pipe & fittings

(G-14134)
D & H QUALITY CABINETS
18558 Us Highway 69 N (75771-6006)
P.O. Box 1895 (75771-1895)
PHONE.................................903 882-0274
Rick D Thrasher, *Owner*
Amy Price, *Manager*
EMP: 12
SQ FT: 7,000
SALES (est): 1MM **Privately Held**
WEB: www.dandhcabinets.com
SIC: 2434 5712 Wood kitchen cabinets; cabinet work, custom

(G-14135)
M G ENGINEERING LLC (PA)
19678 County Road 4125 (75771-6488)
PHONE.................................626 913-1562
Dick Kreps,
EMP: 10 **EST:** 1965
SQ FT: 10,000
SALES (est): 705.1K **Privately Held**
SIC: 3599 Machine shop, jobbing & repair

(G-14136)
THERMO MFG SYSTEMS LLC
Also Called: Thermo Materials
301 Walnut Springs Rd (75771-6813)
P.O. Box 218 (75771-0218)
PHONE.................................903 881-8771
Mark Pavic, *President*
Van Owens, *Vice Pres*
Jane Bentley, *Finance Dir*
Collin Qualls, *Sales Staff*
Fred Kunz, *Mktg Dir*
EMP: 12
SALES (est): 1MM **Privately Held**
WEB: www.thermomaterials.com
SIC: 2952 Roofing felts, cements or coatings

Linden
Cass County

(G-14137)
WELLS FAMILY HOLDING CO LLC
Also Called: Reliant NDT
3551 Texas Highway 11 (75563-3824)
P.O. Box 539 (75563-0539)
PHONE.................................903 756-5656
Larry Wells, *President*
Linda Wells, *Corp Secy*
Tanya Bond, *Administration*
EMP: 30
SALES (est): 3.5MM **Privately Held**
WEB: www.reliantndt.com
SIC: 1389 7389 Oil consultants; inspection & testing services; industrial & commercial equipment inspection service

Little Elm
Denton County

(G-14138)
1-STOP ENTERPRISES LLC
2640 Deer Hollow Dr (75068-6811)
PHONE.................................678 485-9873
Raymond Lockhart Jr, *President*
EMP: 31
SQ FT: 3,100
SALES (est): 2.6MM **Privately Held**
WEB: www.1stopent.com
SIC: 3825 7371 Electrical energy measuring equipment; computer software systems analysis & design, custom

(G-14139)
FIRST CLASS FREIGHTAGE LLC
1408 Villa Paloma Blvd (75068-4922)
PHONE.................................469 486-4695
Shambrielle Speights, *CEO*
EMP: 10

SALES (est): 105.1K **Privately Held**
SIC: 3537 Trucks, tractors, loaders, carriers & similar equipment

(G-14140)
NCR SOLUTIONS LLC
3947 Spinnaker Run Pt (75068-3113)
PHONE.................................405 413-8278
Nassif Chbani, *CEO*
Ravindran Alagarsamy, *President*
EMP: 13
SALES (est): 2.8MM **Privately Held**
WEB: www.ncrsolutions.com
SIC: 3575 3578 7379 7374 Computer terminals; point-of-sale devices; computer related maintenance services; data processing & preparation; custom computer programming services; software programming applications

(G-14141)
RETRACTABLE TECHNOLOGIES INC
511 Lobo Ln (75068-5331)
P.O. Box 9 (75068-0009)
PHONE.................................972 294-1010
Thomas J Shaw, *Ch of Bd*
Larry Salerne, *COO*
Shayne Blythe, *Vice Pres*
Russell B Kuhlman, *Vice Pres*
Michele M Larios, *Vice Pres*
◆ **EMP:** 140
SALES (est): 41.8MM **Privately Held**
WEB: www.retractable.com
SIC: 3841 Holders, surgical needle

(G-14142)
SOUTHEAST LAND SERVICES LLC
1200 Lake Haven Dr (75068-5321)
PHONE.................................724 256-9259
Erick Jenevein, *Mng Member*
EMP: 15
SALES (est): 674.9K **Privately Held**
WEB: www.southeastland.com
SIC: 1311 Oil shale mining

Little River Academy
Bell County

(G-14143)
TEXAS INDUSTRIAL REMCOR INC
1807 N Highway 95 (76554-2721)
P.O. Box 872 (76554-0872)
PHONE.................................254 982-4236
EMP: 10 **EST:** 1972
SQ FT: 14,000
SALES (est): 2.2MM **Privately Held**
WEB: www.sprayervalves.com
SIC: 3523 Farm machinery & equipment

Littlefield
Lamb County

(G-14144)
DENIMATRIX LLC
Also Called: American Denimatrix
1926 Fm 54 (79339)
P.O. Box 2827, Lubbock (79408-2827)
PHONE.................................806 385-6401
EMP: 13
SALES (est): 1.8MM **Privately Held**
SIC: 2211 Cotton Broadwoven Fabric Mill

(G-14145)
ICT HOLDINGS LLC (PA)
1861 Fm 54 (79339-6166)
PHONE.................................713 652-6600
Scott Seaman,
EMP: 25
SALES (est): 1.3MM **Privately Held**
SIC: 2869 Industrial organic chemicals

(G-14146)
IMPACT COMPOSITE TECH LTD
312 Phelps Ave (79339-3430)
PHONE.................................806 385-1015
Cherie Casas, *Manager*
EMP: 20

SALES (corp-wide): 2.3MM **Privately Held**
WEB: www.impactcomposite.com
SIC: 2655 3089 2861 Cores, fiber: made from purchased material; plastic processing; gum & wood chemicals
PA: Impact Composite Technology, Ltd.
1221 Mckinney St
Houston TX
713 652-6602

(G-14147)
NOLTEX TRUSS LITTLEFIELD LP (PA)
Also Called: North Texas Truss Co
1012 E Wylon Jnnings Blvd (79339-4160)
P.O. Box 1190 (79339-1190)
PHONE.................................806 385-5533
Skokie Schlehuber, *Partner*
Josh Crosby, *Sales Staff*
Kelley Kevin, *Sales Staff*
Deann McCullough, *Office Mgr*
Chris Sparks, *Contractor*
EMP: 12
SALES (est): 6.2MM **Privately Held**
WEB: www.noltextruss.com
SIC: 2439 Trusses, wooden roof

(G-14148)
NORTH TEXAS TRUSS
1012 E Wylon Jnnings Blvd (79339-4160)
P.O. Box 1190 (79339-1190)
PHONE.................................806 385-5533
Travis Nolte, *Partner*
Jason Nolte, *Partner*
Joseph Nolte, *Partner*
Richard Nolte, *Partner*
EMP: 40
SQ FT: 30,000
SALES (est): 6MM **Privately Held**
WEB: www.noltextruss.com
SIC: 2439 Trusses, wooden roof

(G-14149)
SELECT BUTTER & PACKAGING LLC
1926 Fm 54 (79339-6142)
PHONE.................................214 568-9000
Rance Miles,
EMP: 12
SALES (est): 482.7K **Privately Held**
SIC: 2099 Butter, renovated & processed
PA: Select Milk Producers, Inc.
5151 Belt Line Rd Ste 455
Dallas TX 75254

Livingston
Polk County

(G-14150)
B & B STAKE CO
1907 S Houston Ave (77351-4414)
P.O. Box 604 (77351-0011)
PHONE.................................936 327-2161
Roy Sanders, *Partner*
Tony Glynn Sanders, *Partner*
EMP: 9 **EST:** 1950
SQ FT: 18,200
SALES (est): 1.3MM **Privately Held**
WEB: www.bandbstakeco.com
SIC: 2499 3553 Surveyors' stakes, wood; lathes, wood turning: including accessories

(G-14151)
COLVIN TIMBER COMPANY LC
1714 Nettles Cemetery Rd (77351-8152)
PHONE.................................936 563-4404
Anthony Colvin,
Beverly Colvin,
EMP: 12
SALES (est): 1.3MM **Privately Held**
SIC: 2411 Logging camps & contractors

(G-14152)
DCF INVESTMENTS LLC
Also Called: Fosters Work & Play
3601 Us Highway 190 W (77351-8728)
PHONE.................................281 744-7445
David Foster,
EMP: 18

SALES (est): 3.5MM **Privately Held**
WEB: www.fostersworknplay.com
SIC: 3537 Industrial trucks & tractors

(G-14153)
FOOD GROUP VENTURES LLC
Also Called: Subway
202 N Washington Ave # 100 (77351-3212)
PHONE.................................936 327-4443
EMP: 9 **Privately Held**
WEB: www.foodgroupventures.com
SIC: 5812 2052 2035 Sandwiches & submarines shop; cookies; dressings, salad: raw & cooked (except dry mixes)
PA: Food Group Ventures, L.L.C.
1862 Greenfield Plz
Bryan TX 77802

(G-14154)
FORD CONTRACT SERVICES INC
335 Old Highway 35 N (77351-2785)
P.O. Box 70665, Houston (77270-0665)
PHONE.................................713 862-2960
Jim Ford, *CEO*
Robin Ford, *President*
EMP: 25
SQ FT: 35,000
SALES (est): 3.5MM **Privately Held**
WEB: www.fordcontract.com
SIC: 3479 Coating of metals & formed products

(G-14155)
FOREST OGLETREE PRODUCTS INC
Also Called: Mill Ridge Golf Center
1410 Noblitt St (77351-3046)
P.O. Box 1196 (77351-0021)
PHONE.................................936 327-2424
Kelton L Ogletree, *President*
Ben R Ogletree III, *Vice Pres*
Gregory Ogletree, *Vice Pres*
EMP: 33
SQ FT: 2,500
SALES (est): 2.9MM **Privately Held**
WEB: www.millridgegolf.com
SIC: 2421 7992 Custom sawmill; public golf courses

(G-14156)
FOUNTAIN VALLEY FOODS INC
304 W Mill St (77351-3227)
P.O. Box 9882, Colorado Springs CO (80932-0882)
PHONE.................................281 592-0610
James R Loyacono, *President*
Virginia Steinecke, *Admin Sec*
EMP: 10
SALES (est): 1.6MM **Privately Held**
WEB: www.fountainvalleyfoods.com
SIC: 5141 2022 Food brokers; dips, cheese-based

(G-14157)
INVENTORY SERVICES NETWORK
175 Musket (77351)
PHONE.................................972 660-7365
EMP: 45
SALES (est): 1.4MM **Privately Held**
SIC: 7372 Prepackaged Software Services

(G-14158)
KING ROY JR LOGGING INC
Rr 3 Box 399 (77351)
PHONE.................................936 563-4899
Roy A King Jr, *President*
Joyce Ann King, *Admin Sec*
EMP: 15
SALES (est): 1.2MM **Privately Held**
SIC: 2411 Logging

(G-14159)
MONTANA NELSON READY MIX LLC
709 Us 59 Loop S (77351)
PHONE.................................936 328-5688
Montana Nelson,
EMP: 9
SALES (corp-wide): 500K **Privately Held**
SIC: 3273 Ready-mixed concrete

PA: Montana Nelson Ready Mix, L.L.C.
911 E Church St
Livingston TX
936 327-8450

(G-14160)
POLK COUNTY PUBLISHING CO (PA)
Also Called: Enterprise
100 E Calhoun St (77351-2908)
P.O. Box 1276 (77351-0023)
PHONE..................................936 327-4357
Alvin Holley, *President*
EMP: 30
SQ FT: 17,000
SALES (est): 6MM **Privately Held**
WEB: www.easttexasnews.com
SIC: 2711 2752 Newspapers, publishing & printing; commercial printing, lithographic

(G-14161)
SELECT POWER SPORT INC
4400 Us Highway 190 W (77351-8713)
PHONE..................................936 967-2332
Alexander Whatley, *President*
EMP: 10
SALES (est): 1.8MM **Privately Held**
WEB: www.selectpowersport.com
SIC: 3799 5091 5012 All terrain vehicles (ATV); watersports equipment & supplies; automobiles & other motor vehicles

(G-14162)
STANMAR MANUFACTURING INC
5800 Us Highway 190 W (77351-8757)
PHONE..................................936 967-3040
Stanley G Crow, *President*
Margaret Crow, *Treasurer*
Mark Crow, *Treasurer*
Greg Crow, *Admin Sec*
Delana Fogleman, *Admin Sec*
◆ **EMP:** 10
SQ FT: 34,000
SALES (est): 1.7MM **Privately Held**
WEB: www.stanmar.com
SIC: 3559 Chemical machinery & equipment

(G-14163)
VF INDUSTRIAL PARK INC
440 Highway 59 Loop S (77351-9096)
PHONE..................................936 327-7881
Ray Puente, *Manager*
EMP: 26
SALES (corp-wide): 10.4B **Publicly Held**
SIC: 2326 Men's & boys' work clothing
HQ: Vf Industrial Park, Inc.
801 Hill Ave Ofc
Reading PA 19610
610 378-0408

(G-14164)
WIPCO ACQUISITION LLC
Also Called: Worldwide Instrument
3373 Us Highway 59 S (77351)
P.O. Box 87 (77351-0002)
PHONE..................................936 327-8250
Ernie Oelze, *Mng Member*
Debbie Ward, *Executive*
Scott Mactier,
EMP: 17
SQ FT: 12,000
SALES (est): 2.7MM **Privately Held**
WEB: www.wipcompany.com
SIC: 3469 3533 Machine parts, stamped or pressed metal; oil & gas field machinery

Lockhart
Caldwell County

(G-14165)
CALDWELL MANUFACTURING INC
1309 Industrial Blvd (78644)
P.O. Box 866 (78644-0866)
PHONE..................................512 398-4549
Mark Allen George, *President*
Elspeth George, *Vice Pres*
Jennifer Bolen, *Production*
EMP: 18
SQ FT: 14,000

SALES (est): 3.3MM **Privately Held**
WEB: www.caldwellmfg.com
SIC: 3599 Machine shop, jobbing & repair

(G-14166)
DGG GROUP LLC
Also Called: Lockhart Fine Foods
1403 E Mlk Jr Indus Blvd (78644-3701)
PHONE..................................512 398-4523
George Ghilarducci,
Deborah Nease,
Glenn Nease,
EMP: 17
SQ FT: 39,000
SALES (est): 2.2MM **Privately Held**
WEB: www.lockhartfoods.com
SIC: 2052 5149 Cookies & crackers; groceries & related products

(G-14167)
DORMAE PRODUCTS INC
Also Called: Serta Mattress Company
1300 Blackjack St (78644-4695)
PHONE..................................512 398-2650
Milton Smith, *President*
Michael Karotkin, *President*
Brian Karotkin, *Vice Pres*
Paul Gardner, *Director*
Lonnie Karotkin, *Admin Sec*
EMP: 300 EST: 1954
SQ FT: 125,000
SALES (est): 47.1MM **Privately Held**
WEB: www.serta.com
SIC: 2515 Mattresses, containing felt, foam rubber, urethane, etc.; box springs, assembled

(G-14168)
GARNEA LLC
Also Called: Wella Organics
1403 Mlk Jr Indus Blvd E (78644-3701)
PHONE..................................512 398-4523
Deborah Nease, *Mng Member*
Bernardo Garza,
EMP: 22
SALES (est): 8MM **Privately Held**
SIC: 2068 Nuts: dried, dehydrated, salted or roasted

(G-14169)
HAZELETT DRILLING AND SUP CORP
915 Old Mcmahan Rd (78644-4008)
PHONE..................................512 398-6682
George Hazelett, *President*
Bonnie Hazelett, *Vice Pres*
Jackie Clifton, *Bookkeeper*
EMP: 45
SALES (est): 8.3MM **Privately Held**
WEB: www.hazelettdrilling.com
SIC: 1381 1781 Drilling oil & gas wells; water well drilling

(G-14170)
LIVENGOOD FEEDS INC (PA)
300 N Colorado St (78644-2162)
P.O. Box 1080 (78644-1080)
PHONE..................................512 398-2351
Burt R Livengood, *President*
Gail Livengood, *Vice Pres*
Peter Langton, *Foreman/Supr*
Rodney Kennemer, *Manager*
Christine Smith, *Info Tech Dir*
EMP: 35
SQ FT: 10,000
SALES (est): 35MM **Privately Held**
WEB: www.livengoodfeeds.com
SIC: 5191 5621 2048 Feed; fertilizer & fertilizer materials; insecticides; seeds: field, garden & flower; ready-to-wear apparel, women's; prepared feeds

(G-14171)
LOCKHART TRUSS CO INC
1505 Blackjack St (78644-4849)
PHONE..................................512 398-5300
Felix Guerra III, *President*
Johnny Martinez, *Office Mgr*
EMP: 19
SALES (est): 2.6MM **Privately Held**
WEB: www.lockharttruss.com
SIC: 2439 Trusses, wooden roof

(G-14172)
REED PROTOTYPE AND MODEL INC
Also Called: R P M
303 W San Antonio St (78644-2655)
PHONE..................................512 457-0560
Philip Reed, *President*
Jacqui Frohman, *Business Mgr*
EMP: 13
SQ FT: 13,600
SALES (est): 3MM **Privately Held**
SIC: 3089 Injection molded finished plastic products

Lolita
Jackson County

(G-14173)
AMTOPP CORPORATION (HQ)
101 Interplast Blvd (77971-4115)
P.O. Box 405 (77971-0405)
PHONE..................................361 874-3000
Y C Wang, *Ch of Bd*
John Young, *President*
Homer Hsieh, *President*
Brian Wang, *Plant Mgr*
Jame Wong, *Plant Mgr*
◆ **EMP:** 272
SQ FT: 800,000
SALES (est): 184.7MM **Privately Held**
WEB: www.inteplast.com
SIC: 3081 Unsupported plastics film & sheet

(G-14174)
CHALLENGER SERVICES INC
2169 County Road 429 (77971-4102)
PHONE..................................361 874-4433
Mary Catherine Ledwik, *President*
Brad Ledwik, *General Mgr*
Janet Saunders, *Controller*
EMP: 15
SALES (est): 5.8MM **Privately Held**
WEB: www.challengertx.com
SIC: 1442 Construction sand mining

(G-14175)
INTEGRTED BAGGING SYSTEMS CORP (HQ)
Also Called: Ibs
101 Interplast Blvd (77971-4115)
P.O. Box 405 (77971-0405)
PHONE..................................361 874-3000
Dr John Young, *President*
Joe Chen, *President*
▲ **EMP:** 15
SQ FT: 700,000
SALES (est): 96.7MM **Privately Held**
WEB: www.inteplast.com
SIC: 3081 Packing materials, plastic sheet

(G-14176)
INTEPLAST GROUP CORPORATION
Also Called: Interplast Group
101 Interplast Blvd (77971-4115)
P.O. Box 405 (77971-0405)
PHONE..................................361 874-3000
Hongping Zhang, *Technical Mgr*
EMP: 58 **Privately Held**
WEB: www.inteplast.com
SIC: 3081 Polypropylene film & sheet; polyethylene film; polyvinyl film & sheet; packing materials, plastic sheet
PA: Inteplast Group Corporation
9 Peach Tree Hill Rd
Livingston NJ 07039

(G-14177)
STONE WELL SERVICE INC
Fm 1593 3 Mi N Fm 15 St (77971)
P.O. Box 217 (77971-0217)
PHONE..................................361 874-4211
Jery Stone, *President*
June Stone, *Treasurer*
EMP: 26
SQ FT: 7,500
SALES (est): 2MM **Privately Held**
SIC: 1389 Oil field services

Lometa
Lampasas County

(G-14178)
TEXAS BEST PANELS INC
15614 N Highway 183 (76853-3435)
P.O. Box 149 (76853-0149)
PHONE..................................512 752-3777
Marvin Dubose, *President*
EMP: 20
SQ FT: 26,000
SALES (est): 4.5MM **Privately Held**
WEB: www.portablepanels.com
SIC: 3446 Fences or posts, ornamental iron or steel

Lone Oak
Hunt County

(G-14179)
CANNON CNON INDUS MCHINING INC
203 Norton St (75453-1701)
PHONE..................................972 293-6278
Kevin J Cannon Sr, *Director*
Andrea Cannon Sr, *Director*
EMP: 9
SALES (est): 1.4MM **Privately Held**
WEB: www.cannonmachining.com
SIC: 3469 7699 Machine parts, stamped or pressed metal; industrial machinery & equipment repair

Lone Star
Morris County

(G-14180)
A & E MACHINE SHOP INC (PA)
Also Called: A & E Mill & Welding Supply
920 E Industrial Blvd (75668-2803)
P.O. Box 190 (75668-0190)
PHONE..................................903 656-3485
Earl C Alexander, *President*
Angie Allison, *Store Mgr*
Cindi Caraway, *Controller*
Rusty Russell, *Sales Staff*
Vincent Walker, *Sales Staff*
▲ **EMP:** 27 EST: 1965
SQ FT: 5,000
SALES (est): 5.1MM **Privately Held**
WEB: www.aemach.com
SIC: 3599 5085 Machine shop, jobbing & repair; welding supplies

(G-14181)
A&A COATING INC
3679 Fm 250 (75668)
P.O. Box 476 (75668-0476)
PHONE..................................903 656-2581
Charles Coleman, *Ch of Bd*
Charles Colemin, *Ch of Bd*
James Dodson, *President*
Doyle Campbell, *Opers Mgr*
Jim Sanger, *Shareholder*
EMP: 45
SQ FT: 160,000
SALES (est): 12.6MM **Privately Held**
WEB: www.aacoating.net
SIC: 3479 Coating or wrapping steel pipe

(G-14182)
FRIEDMAN INDUSTRIES INC
Texas Tubular Products Div
3681 Fm 250 Rd 250th (75668)
P.O. Box 388 (75668-0388)
PHONE..................................903 639-2511
Howard Henderson, *Manager*
EMP: 65
SALES (corp-wide): 142.1MM **Publicly Held**
WEB: www.friedmanindustries.com
SIC: 3312 5051 3498 Plate, steel; pipe & tubing, steel; fabricated pipe & fittings
PA: Friedman Industries, Incorporated
1121 Judson Rd Ste 124
Longview TX 75601
903 639-3431

(G-14183)
INDELECT CORPORATION
Also Called: Industrial Electric Motor Co
102 E Industrial Blvd (75668-2801)
P.O. Box 220 (75668-0220)
PHONE..................................903 656-2518
Krystal Bunt, *President*
Robert Rodden, *General Mgr*
EMP: 23 EST: 1975
SQ FT: 16,000
SALES (est): 3.6MM **Privately Held**
WEB: www.indelectcorp.com
SIC: 7694 3621 Electric motor repair; coil
winding service; motors & generators

(G-14184)
SCOT HONE CORPORATION
Also Called: Scot Industries
Hwy 250 E (75668)
PHONE..................................903 639-2551
Steven Wilmeth, *President*
H D Wilmeth, *Vice Pres*
Ray Folyer, *Plant Mgr*
Thomas S Wilmeth, *Treasurer*
Jason Morgan, *Sales Executive*
▲ EMP: 100
SQ FT: 8,000
SALES (est): 22.9MM **Privately Held**
WEB: www.scotindustries.com
SIC: 5085 3291 Abrasives; hones

(G-14185)
UNITED STATES STEEL CORP
6866 Us Highway 259 S (75668-3102)
P.O. Box 1000 (75668-1000)
PHONE..................................903 656-6521
Randy Hodges, *Engineer*
Todd Grisham, *Train & Dev Mgr*
John Shivers, *Branch Mgr*
Ed Konrady, *Department Mgr*
Steve Daniel, *Manager*
EMP: 100
SALES (corp-wide): 12.9B **Publicly Held**
WEB: www.ussteel.com
SIC: 3325 3312 5051 5014 Steel
foundries; sheet or strip, steel, hot-rolled;
steel; truck tires & tubes; motor vehicle
parts & accessories
PA: United States Steel Corp
600 Grant St
Pittsburgh PA 15219
412 433-1121

Longview
Gregg County

(G-14186)
4-A OILFIELD ENTERPRISES
11178 Fm 968 W (75602-7284)
PHONE..................................903 668-3815
William Ainsworth, *Owner*
EMP: 15
SALES (est): 1.2MM **Privately Held**
SIC: 1389 Construction, repair & disman-
tling services

(G-14187)
**ABB ENTERPRISE SOFTWARE
INC**
Also Called: A B B Small Pwr Trnsfrmers Lqu
300 W Cotton St (75601-6222)
PHONE..................................903 237-1030
Jerry Dixon, *General Mgr*
EMP: 30
SALES (corp-wide): 27.9B **Privately Held**
WEB: www.new.abb.com
SIC: 3612 3613 Transformers, except
electric; switchgear & switchboard appa-
ratus
HQ: Abb Inc.
305 Gregson Dr
Cary NC 27511

(G-14188)
AIR LIQUIDE AMERICA LP
5361 W Loop 281 S (75603-8410)
PHONE..................................903 237-1740
Carolyn Sims, *Plant Mgr*
Rudi Strickland, *Branch Mgr*
EMP: 14

SALES (corp-wide): 129.8MM **Privately
Held**
WEB: www.industry.airliquide.us
SIC: 2813 Industrial gases
HQ: Air Liquide America L.P.
9811 Katy Fwy Ste 100
Houston TX 77024
713 624-8000

(G-14189)
AIR LIQUIDE LARGE INDS US LP
5361 W Loop 281 S (75603-8410)
PHONE..................................903 237-1739
Clyde Hank Jeffcoats, *Manager*
EMP: 34
SALES (corp-wide): 129.8MM **Privately
Held**
WEB: www.airliquide.com
SIC: 2813 Industrial gases
HQ: Air Liquide Large Industries U.S. Lp
9811 Katy Fwy Ste 100
Houston TX 77024
713 624-8000

(G-14190)
**AIR POWER SALES & SERVICE
LLC**
823 W Marshall Ave (75601-6237)
PHONE..................................903 236-0500
Retha Weidner, *Sales Staff*
Lynda Peterson,
EMP: 22
SALES (est): 118.1K **Privately Held**
WEB: www.airpowersales.com
SIC: 3563 7359 Air & gas compressors;
rental store, general

(G-14191)
**AJAX TOCCO MAGNETHERMIC
CORP**
5807 W Marshall Ave (75604-6013)
P.O. Box 150220 (75615-0220)
PHONE..................................903 297-2526
Tracy A Dula, *Principal*
Gary Ayers, *Marketing Staff*
EMP: 11
SALES (corp-wide): 1.6B **Publicly Held**
WEB: www.ajaxtocco.com
SIC: 3567 3612 7699 Metal melting fur-
naces, industrial: electric; electric furnace
transformers; industrial machinery &
equipment repair
HQ: Ajax Tocco Magnethermic Corporation
1745 Overland Ave Ne
Warren OH 44483
330 372-8511

(G-14192)
**ALPHA OMEGA RECYCLING
INC**
315 Whatley Rd (75604-6036)
PHONE..................................903 297-7272
Myron W Wilson, *President*
Mark Wayne, *Vice Pres*
Bobby Pointer, *Plant Mgr.*
Bethany Ross, *Officer*
EMP: 18
SQ FT: 16,000
SALES (est): 10.6MM **Privately Held**
WEB: www.alphaomegarecycling.com
SIC: 3341 4953 Secondary nonferrous
metals; recycling, waste materials
PA: Amlon Resources Group (Arg), Llc
10 E 40th St Rm 3610
New York NY 10016
212 685-4456

(G-14193)
ALPHA SATCOM INC
1221 Judson Rd Ste 300 (75601-3922)
PHONE..................................903 238-8888
Bill Anton, *President*
Kay Evans, *Sales Dir*
EMP: 10
SQ FT: 1,100
SALES (est): 5MM **Privately Held**
WEB: www.alpha-satcom.com
SIC: 3663 1799 Antennas, transmitting &
communications; antenna installation

(G-14194)
AMERICAN RAILCAR INDS INC
Also Called: Shippers Carline Div
300 Stevens St (75604-4730)
PHONE..................................903 759-4406

Leslie Stinntt, *Branch Mgr*
Les Stinnett, *Executive*
EMP: 60
SALES (corp-wide): 476.8MM **Privately
Held**
WEB: www.americanrailcar.com
SIC: 3743 Railroad equipment
HQ: American Railcar Industries, Inc.
100 Clark St
Saint Charles MO 63301

(G-14195)
AMERICAN RAILCAR INDS INC
600 Foundry Dr (75604-5222)
PHONE..................................903 759-3946
Harry Phillips, *Branch Mgr*
EMP: 230
SALES (corp-wide): 476.8MM **Privately
Held**
WEB: www.americanrailcar.com
SIC: 3312 3369 3325 Blast furnaces &
steel mills; nonferrous foundries; steel
foundries
HQ: American Railcar Industries, Inc.
100 Clark St
Saint Charles MO 63301

(G-14196)
**APPLIED CONSULTANTS INC
(PA)**
2100 N Eastman Rd (75601-3355)
P.O. Box 8021 (75607-8021)
PHONE..................................903 643-0956
Glenn Davis, *President*
Matt Cheney, *Vice Pres*
Chad Cook, *Vice Pres*
Rip Morris, *Vice Pres*
Fred Walker, *Vice Pres*
EMP: 30
SALES (est): 8MM **Privately Held**
WEB: www.appliedconsultants.com
SIC: 7389 3053 Inspection & testing serv-
ices; packing: steam engines, pipe joints,
air compressors, etc.

(G-14197)
ASP WESTWARD LP
320 E Methvin St (75601-7323)
PHONE..................................903 237-7700
Billy Holder, *Vice Pres*
EMP: 11
SALES (corp-wide): 91.3MM **Privately
Held**
WEB: www.chron.com
SIC: 2711 Newspapers, publishing & print-
ing
PA: Asp Westward, L.P.
523 N Sam Houston Pkwy E
Houston TX 77060
713 256-0953

(G-14198)
AXIS ENERGY SERVICES LLC
199 Corporate Rd (75603-7054)
PHONE..................................903 643-3700
EMP: 10
SALES (est): 2.1MM **Privately Held**
WEB: www.axisofs.com
SIC: 1381 Drilling water intake wells

(G-14199)
AXIS WELL SERVICES LLC (PA)
851 W Harrison Rd (75604-5208)
PHONE..................................903 759-0082
Stephen D Shore, *President*
Grace Shore, *Corp Secy*
David Etchelecu, *Human Resources*
Bobby Amen, *Supervisor*
Jerry Surratt, *Officer*
EMP: 52 EST: 2011
SQ FT: 3,000
SALES (est): 116.4MM **Privately Held**
WEB: www.xraybill.com
SIC: 1389 Servicing oil & gas wells

(G-14200)
BAR H WELDING LLC
Also Called: Bar H Welding Consult
1381 E I 20 Access Rd (75603-4335)
P.O. Box 2766, Kilgore (75663-2766)
PHONE..................................903 806-3110
Michael Haggard, *CEO*
EMP: 9
SQ FT: 10,560

SALES (est): 700K **Privately Held**
WEB: www.barhwelding.com
SIC: 3548 3441 Electrodes, electric weld-
ing; fabricated structural metal

(G-14201)
BASIC ENERGY SERVICES INC
5209 Estes Pkwy (75603-9449)
PHONE..................................903 295-0817
Comelita Williams, *Human Resources*
Roger Massey, *Manager*
David Godair, *Maintence Staff*
EMP: 20
SALES (corp-wide): 567.2MM **Publicly
Held**
WEB: www.basices.com
SIC: 1389 Servicing oil & gas wells; oil field
services
PA: Basic Energy Services, Inc.
801 Cherry St Unit 2
Fort Worth TX 76102
817 334-4100

(G-14202)
BIO-DERM LABORATORIES INC
1600 Redmon Rd (75602-4829)
P.O. Box 8070 (75607-8070)
PHONE..................................903 753-6744
Frank Pohl, *President*
Michael Pohl, *Vice Pres*
Sherry Evans, *Export Mgr*
▼ EMP: 25
SQ FT: 30,000
SALES (est): 3.3MM **Privately Held**
WEB: www.biogroom.com
SIC: 3999 Pet supplies

(G-14203)
**BOIS DARC INTERNATIONAL
TRADE**
205 E Timpson St (75602-1239)
P.O. Box 2147 (75606-2147)
PHONE..................................903 758-2647
Amos Snow III, *President*
EMP: 27
SQ FT: 35,000
SALES (est): 3.9MM **Privately Held**
WEB: www.boisdarccoils.com
SIC: 3585 5075 Parts for heating, cooling
& refrigerating equipment; air conditioning
equipment, except room units

(G-14204)
BUFFCO PRODUCTION INC
Also Called: Bpi Equipment and Service
5006 State Highway 31 N (75603)
P.O. Box 2243 (75606-2243)
PHONE..................................903 988-8199
Frank M Bufkin III, *President*
Shane McConnell, *Vice Pres*
Jason T Moore, *Vice Pres*
Jason Moore, *Vice Pres*
Jerry Qualls, *Accountant*
EMP: 17
SQ FT: 3,000
SALES (est): 8.7MM **Privately Held**
WEB: www.buffcoproduction.com
SIC: 1311 1382 Crude petroleum produc-
tion; oil & gas exploration services

(G-14205)
BURROWS R & H MACHINE LLC
2694 S Access Rd (75602-6114)
P.O. Box 8606 (75607-8606)
PHONE..................................903 753-1550
Brian Traywick, *General Mgr*
Brittany Kelley, *Purchasing*
Rae Burrows, *Mng Member*
EMP: 43
SQ FT: 26,800
SALES (est): 8.1MM **Privately Held**
WEB: www.rhmachinellc.com
SIC: 3599 Machine shop, jobbing & repair

(G-14206)
C & C WESTERN WEAR INC
Also Called: Mike's Custom Hatters
1700 N Eastman Rd Ste 101 (75601-3398)
PHONE..................................903 753-8991
Eugene C Helms, *President*
Carolyn Helms, *Corp Secy*
Helms Mary C, *Vice Pres*
Michael C Helms, *Vice Pres*
EMP: 10 EST: 1977
SQ FT: 10,000

SALES (est): 1.1MM **Privately Held**
WEB: www.mikescustomhatters.com
SIC: 5661 5699 2353 5611 Men's boots;
western apparel; hats & caps; hats, men's
& boys'

(G-14207)
CAPACITY OF TEXAS INC
Also Called: Trailer Jockey
401 Capacity Dr (75604-5341)
PHONE....................903 759-0610
Scott Lord, *President*
Joseph Belle, *Vice Pres*
Jerry Looney, *Vice Pres*
Donald Collins Jr, *Treasurer*
Nick Miles, *VP Mngmt*
◆ **EMP:** 125 **EST:** 1975
SQ FT: 122,000
SALES (est): 76.5MM **Publicly Held**
WEB: www.capacitytrucks.com
SIC: 3537 Tractors, used in plants, docks,
terminals, etc.: industrial
HQ: Collins Industries, Inc.
15 Compound Dr
Hutchinson KS 67502
620 663-5551

(G-14208)
CARRUTH NURSERY IRRIGATION
137 Gilmer Rd (75604-4616)
PHONE....................903 236-7555
Lloyd Carruth, *President*
EMP: 10
SALES (est): 664.8K **Privately Held**
WEB: www.carruthirrigationandlandscap-
ing.com
SIC: 0181 1711 0781 5083 Nursery
stock, growing of; irrigation sprinkler system installation; landscape services; lawn
& garden machinery & equipment; hair-
cloth: wool, mohair or similar fibers; sod-
ding contractor

(G-14209)
CATHODIC RECTIFIERS INC
802 Fisher Rd (75604-5224)
P.O. Box 150618 (75615-0618)
PHONE....................903 759-6813
EMP: 11 **EST:** 1973
SQ FT: 2,400
SALES (est): 1.1MM **Privately Held**
WEB: www.cathodicrectifiers.com
SIC: 3679 Rectifiers, electronic

(G-14210)
COLLINS SURVEYING AND MAPPING
910a Judson Rd (75601-5113)
PHONE....................903 234-8051
David Collins, *President*
Russ Collins, *Project Mgr*
Patti Sutton, *Administration*
EMP: 28
SQ FT: 4,200
SALES (est): 1.9MM **Privately Held**
WEB: www.collinssurveying.com
SIC: 8713 1389 Surveying services; sur-
veying wells

(G-14211)
COLONY CABINETS INC
Also Called: CCI Group
900 Estes Dr (75602-6103)
PHONE....................903 753-2488
Ted Stevens, *President*
Pat Stevens, *Corp Secy*
Jesse Hawkins, *Project Mgr*
Kersten Hill, *Sales Staff*
Vicky Nowels, *Info Tech Mgr*
EMP: 30
SQ FT: 30,000
SALES (est): 4.9MM **Privately Held**
WEB: www.ccigroup.com
SIC: 2434 Wood kitchen cabinets

(G-14212)
COMPRSSION CONTRLS RENTALS LLC
5797 Fm 2011 (75603-4337)
PHONE....................903 643-7970
Randy Broussard, *President*
Jerry Cubine, *Vice Pres*
EMP: 11

SALES (est): 1.1MM **Privately Held**
SIC: 1389 Oil field services

(G-14213)
CONTRACTORS SUPPLIES INC
417 Calvin Blvd (75602-1005)
PHONE....................903 753-5766
Pau Sellers, *Opers-Prdtn-Mfg*
EMP: 20
SALES (corp-wide): 30.6MM **Privately
Held**
WEB: www.csiconcrete.com
SIC: 3273 5031 Ready-mixed concrete;
lumber, plywood & millwork
PA: Contractor's Supplies, Inc.
304 Webber St
Lufkin TX 75904
936 634-3341

(G-14214)
COOPER OPTICAL CO INC (PA)
306 W Whaley St (75601-6321)
P.O. Box 1502 (75606-1502)
PHONE....................903 753-7606
Linda Gayle Cooper, *President*
Betty Joe Cooper, *Vice Pres*
EMP: 10
SQ FT: 2,200
SALES (est): 1MM **Privately Held**
SIC: 5995 3851 Eyeglasses, prescription;
ophthalmic goods

(G-14215)
COX TEXAS NEWSPAPERS LP
Add Graphix
320 E Methvin St (75601-7323)
P.O. Box 1792 (75606-1792)
PHONE....................903 237-7777
Gary Boarders, *Branch Mgr*
EMP: 180
SQ FT: 68,440 **Privately Held**
WEB: www.statesman.com
SIC: 2711 Commercial printing & newspa-
per publishing combined
HQ: Cox Texas Newspapers, Lp
305 S Congress Ave
Austin TX 78704
512 445-3500

(G-14216)
CROSBY GROUP LLC
2414 Crosby Way (75602-4701)
PHONE....................918 834-4611
Chris Burbick, *Mng Member*
EMP: 300
SALES (corp-wide): 284.1MM **Privately
Held**
WEB: www.thecrosbygroup.com
SIC: 3462 3713 3533 Machinery forgings,
ferrous; truck & bus bodies; oil & gas field
machinery
PA: The Crosby Group Llc
2857 Dawson Rd
Tulsa OK 74110
918 834-4611

(G-14217)
CUBIX SOFTWARE LTD INC
306 Bridgers Hill Rd (75604-9630)
PHONE....................903 297-7771
Fax: 903 297-7775
EMP: 12
SQ FT: 5,000
SALES (est): 930K **Privately Held**
SIC: 7372 Automation Software & Services

(G-14218)
CW RESOURCES INC
811 Gilmer Rd (75604-3621)
PHONE....................903 759-8822
Carl Westerman, *President*
James Osborn, *Executive*
EMP: 10
SQ FT: 1,000
SALES (est): 2.7MM **Privately Held**
WEB: www.cwresources.com
SIC: 1382 1311 Oil & gas exploration serv-
ices; crude petroleum production; natural
gas production

(G-14219)
CYPRESS RIVER LOGGING CORP
4015 Valley Ranch Rd (75602-6678)
PHONE....................903 236-7696
Gary Van Deusen, *President*

Jackie Vandusen, *Vice Pres*
EMP: 15
SALES (est): 1.4MM **Privately Held**
SIC: 2411 Logging camps & contractors

(G-14220)
DAILY ELECTRIC INC
Also Called: Daily Electric Motor
700 S Eastman Rd (75602-2302)
PHONE....................903 753-2732
Alan Porter, *President*
Ava Porter, *Corp Secy*
EMP: 9
SQ FT: 6,900
SALES (est): 1.3MM **Privately Held**
WEB: www.dailyelectricmotor.com
SIC: 7694 Rewinding services; electric
motor repair

(G-14221)
DALLAS PLASTICS LLC
900 Jordan Valley Rd (75604-5225)
PHONE....................903 291-0960
Miguel Sanchez, *Branch Mgr*
EMP: 10 **Privately Held**
WEB: www.dallasplastics.com
SIC: 2821 Plastics materials & resins
PA: Dallas Plastics Llc
924 Dalworth Dr
Mesquite TX 75149

(G-14222)
DAN BLOCKER PETROLEUM CONS
2704 E Marshall Ave (75601-5925)
P.O. Box 4492 (75606-4492)
PHONE....................903 234-2093
Dan Blocker, *President*
EMP: 60
SQ FT: 300
SALES (est): 5.4MM **Privately Held**
WEB: www.blockerconsulting.com
SIC: 1389 Oil consultants

(G-14223)
DEALERS TRUCK EQUIPMENT CO INC
1231 W Marshall Ave (75604-5121)
P.O. Box 631 (75606-0631)
PHONE....................903 758-4451
Jimmy Huff, *Mfg Staff*
Larry Painter, *Enginr/R&D Mgr*
EMP: 13
SALES (corp-wide): 25.5MM **Privately
Held**
WEB: www.dealerstruck.com
SIC: 3714 5013 5531 5014 Motor vehicle
parts & accessories; motor vehicle sup-
plies & new parts; truck equipment &
parts; truck tires & tubes
PA: Dealers Truck Equipment Company,
Inc.
2460 Midway St
Shreveport LA 71108
318 635-7567

(G-14224)
DFA DAIRY BRANDS FLUID LLC
405 Ambassador Row (75604-5941)
P.O. Box 509 (75606-0509)
PHONE....................903 758-8211
Chance Alexander, *Branch Mgr*
EMP: 9
SALES (corp-wide): 15.8B **Privately Held**
SIC: 2026 Fluid milk
HQ: Dfa Dairy Brands Fluid, Llc
1405 N 98th St
Kansas City KS 66111
816 801-6455

(G-14225)
E & A VENTURES LLC
Also Called: Unlimited Cabinets and Doors
114 Stevens St (75604-4723)
PHONE....................903 297-0829
Ander Fuertes, *CEO*
Nick Fuertes,
EMP: 30
SQ FT: 15,000
SALES (est): 3.2MM **Privately Held**
WEB: www.unlimitedcabinetsanddoors.com
SIC: 2434 Wood kitchen cabinets

(G-14226)
EAST TEXAS ACOUSTICAL INC
7793 Us Highway 259 (75605-7390)
P.O. Box 540, Judson (75660-0540)
PHONE....................903 663-3820
Keith Childress, *President*
M Sue Childress, *Corp Secy*
Bobby J Helpinstill, *Vice Pres*
EMP: 15
SQ FT: 15,000
SALES (est): 2.4MM **Privately Held**
SIC: 5169 2273 5713 Sealants; floor cov-
erings, textile fiber; floor tile; carpets

(G-14227)
EAST TEXAS MACHINE WORKS INC
2808 W Marshall Ave (75604-5023)
PHONE....................903 759-9796
Neil D Swisher, *President*
Kathleen Swisher, *Corp Secy*
Randall Swisher, *Vice Pres*
Joey Pipkin, *Plant Mgr*
Sallie Nichols, *Foreman/Supr*
EMP: 67
SQ FT: 36,000
SALES (est): 12.9MM **Privately Held**
WEB: www.etmworks.com
SIC: 3599 7692 Machine shop, jobbing &
repair; welding repair

(G-14228)
EAST TEXAS RADIATOR INC (PA)
703 W Cotton St (75604-5505)
PHONE....................903 753-7286
EMP: 25
SQ FT: 15,000
SALES (est): 5.4MM **Privately Held**
WEB: www.etxrad.com
SIC: 3585 3443 Evaporative condensers,
heat transfer equipment; heat exchang-
ers: coolers (after, inter), condensers, etc.

(G-14229)
EAST TEXAS RADIATOR INC
100 Coolant Ln (75604-4733)
PHONE....................903 759-3877
Leroy Linseisen, *Branch Mgr*
EMP: 16
SALES (corp-wide): 5.4MM **Privately
Held**
WEB: www.etxrad.com
SIC: 3585 Evaporative condensers, heat
transfer equipment
PA: East Texas Radiator, Inc.
703 W Cotton St
Longview TX 75604
903 753-7286

(G-14230)
EASTMAN CHEMICAL COMPANY
300 Kodak Blvd (75602-6113)
P.O. Box 7444 (75607-7444)
PHONE....................423 229-2000
Leonard Bradley, *Superintendent*
James Ray, *Principal*
Jamie Moseley, *Business Mgr*
Tom Brown, *Purch Mgr*
Steve Hunt, *Engineer*
EMP: 50 **Publicly Held**
WEB: www.eastman.com
SIC: 2869 2865 2823 2821 Industrial or-
ganic chemicals; cyclic crudes & interme-
diates; cellulosic manmade fibers;
polyethylene resins
PA: Eastman Chemical Company
200 S Wilcox Dr
Kingsport TN 37660

(G-14231)
EASTMAN CHEMICAL COMPANY
2290 Callahan Rd (75602-7623)
PHONE....................903 237-6755
Mark Bogo, *Branch Mgr*
EMP: 50 **Publicly Held**
WEB: www.eastman.com
SIC: 2821 Plastics materials & resins
PA: Eastman Chemical Company
200 S Wilcox Dr
Kingsport TN 37660

(G-14232)
EVERLITE INC (PA)
607 Fisher Rd (75604-5202)
P.O. Box 2228, Columbus OH (43216-2228)
PHONE....................................903 297-3444
Gary Baas, *President*
EMP: 37
SQ FT: 36,040
SALES (est): 2.9MM **Privately Held**
WEB: www.everlite.us
SIC: 3715 1799 3713 3354 Trailer bodies; welding on site; truck & bus bodies; aluminum extruded products

(G-14233)
EXPRO AMERICAS LLC
Also Called: Power Well Services
5396 Se Loop 281 (75602-7188)
PHONE....................................903 753-2003
Keith Palmer, *CEO*
Robert Lance, *Supervisor*
EMP: 30 **Privately Held**
WEB: www.exprogroup.com
SIC: 1389 Oil field services
HQ: Expro Americas, Llc
1311 Brdfeld Blvd Ste 400
Houston TX 77084

(G-14234)
FLANDERS ELECTRIC LTD
901 W Harrison Rd (75604-5606)
P.O. Box 97, White Oak (75693-0097)
PHONE....................................903 759-9439
David R Patterson, *President*
Roy Patterson, *Chairman*
Roy A Patterson, *Chairman*
Allen Patterson, *COO*
Zach Hudson, *Opers Mgr*
▲ EMP: 70
SQ FT: 37,100
SALES: 28.6MM
SALES (corp-wide): 137.9MM **Privately Held**
WEB: www.flandersinc.com
SIC: 7694 5063 Electric motor repair; motors, electric
PA: Flanders Electric Motor Service, Inc.
8101 Baumgart Rd
Evansville IN 47725
812 867-7421

(G-14235)
FLINT HILLS RESOURCES LP
118 Huntsman Way (75602-6105)
PHONE....................................903 239-5200
Carolyn Seale, *Safety Mgr*
Pierre Donaldson, *Engrg Mgr*
Bill Bodiford, *Engineer*
Ronnie Parkhurst, *Engineer*
Bill Shelton, *Manager*
EMP: 52
SALES (corp-wide): 36.8B **Privately Held**
WEB: www.fhr.com
SIC: 2869 Industrial organic chemicals
HQ: Flint Hills Resources, Lp
4111 E 37th St N
Wichita KS 67220
800 292-3133

(G-14236)
FLOWERS BAKING CO TYLER LLC
403 Ambassador Row (75604-5941)
PHONE....................................903 758-2369
Larry McMillon, *Principal*
EMP: 16
SQ FT: 9,000
SALES (corp-wide): 4.1B **Publicly Held**
WEB: www.flowersfoods.com
SIC: 2051 Bread, cake & related products
HQ: Flowers Baking Company Of Tyler, Llc
1200 W Erwin St
Tyler TX 75702
903 595-2421

(G-14237)
FRIEDMAN INDUSTRIES INC (PA)
1121 Judson Rd Ste 124 (75601-5119)
PHONE....................................903 758-3431
Mike Taylor, *Ch of Bd*
Robert Sparkman, *President*
Howard Henderson, *VP Opers*
Alex Larue, *CFO*

Connie Hughes, *VP Sales*
EMP: 89 EST: 1965
SALES: 142.1MM **Publicly Held**
WEB: www.friedmanindustries.com
SIC: 3316 3317 Sheet, steel, cold-rolled: from purchased hot-rolled; steel pipe & tubes

(G-14238)
G B COIL INC
5902 Old Highway 80 (75604-6010)
PHONE....................................903 212-2645
Gary Bechtold, *Ch of Bd*
Jack Greer, *President*
Wanda Greer, *Corp Secy*
EMP: 30
SQ FT: 14,000
SALES (est): 480.6K **Privately Held**
WEB: www.gbcoil.com
SIC: 3621 Coils, for electric motors or generators

(G-14239)
GEA ASSOCIATES INC
Also Called: Econo-Print
705 Plum Creek Rd (75605-7546)
P.O. Box 711, Judson (75660-0711)
PHONE....................................903 295-2727
Glenn Erwin, *President*
EMP: 9
SALES (est): 305.7K **Privately Held**
WEB: www.gea.com
SIC: 2752 5943 Commercial printing, offset; office forms & supplies

(G-14240)
GENE POWELL INVESTMENTS INC
1523 Colony Cir (75604-4455)
P.O. Box 5513 (75608-5513)
PHONE....................................903 234-1155
N Eugene Powell, *President*
Jane Powell, *Treasurer*
EMP: 12 EST: 1963
SQ FT: 2,850
SALES (est): 1.7MM **Privately Held**
SIC: 1311 Crude petroleum production

(G-14241)
GENPAK LLC
1101 W Harrison Rd (75604-5610)
PHONE....................................903 297-4445
Elizabeth Holmes, *Principal*
Chuck Lapley, *Plant Mgr*
Liz Holmes, *Purch Mgr*
Chasitiy Johns, *Purchasing*
Deb Meyers, *VP Finance*
EMP: 150
SQ FT: 1,652 **Privately Held**
WEB: www.genpak.com
SIC: 3089 2821 Pallets, plastic; plastics materials & resins
HQ: Genpak Llc
10601 Westlake Dr
Charlotte NC 28273
800 626-6695

(G-14242)
GILLESPIE COATINGS OPER LLC
211 Gum Springs Rd (75602-1799)
PHONE....................................903 753-0393
Paula Cargill Kaplan, *Ch of Bd*
Charles A Kaplan, *President*
Jeff Martin, *Vice Pres*
Amanda Severson, *Assistant*
EMP: 25
SQ FT: 14,000
SALES (est): 4.6MM **Privately Held**
WEB: www.gillespiecoatings.com
SIC: 2851 Paints & allied products

(G-14243)
GREGG INDUS INSULATORS INC (DH)
201 Estes Dr (75602-6100)
P.O. Box 4347 (75606-4347)
PHONE....................................903 757-5754
CHI N Swallo, *President*
Thomac C Merritt, *Principal*
David Brooks, *Vice Pres*
Ames R Billingsley, *Treasurer*
Mike Merritt, *Treasurer*
EMP: 441
SQ FT: 85,000

SALES (est): 38.2MM
SALES (corp-wide): 1.6B **Privately Held**
WEB: www.greggindustrialinsulators.com
SIC: 1799 2493 Insulation of pipes & boilers; insulating board, hard pressed

(G-14244)
H L HAILEY ENTERPRISES INC
Also Called: Industrial Machinery Service
3020 W Loop 281 (75604-2594)
PHONE....................................903 759-1881
David Hailey, *President*
EMP: 18
SALES (est): 5.5MM **Privately Held**
SIC: 5082 7694 General construction machinery & equipment; armature rewinding shops

(G-14245)
H LORIMER CORPORATION
2401 Highway 322 (75603)
P.O. Box 12321 (75607-2321)
PHONE....................................903 643-3239
Harold Letourneau, *President*
Mary Letourneau, *Admin Sec*
EMP: 26
SQ FT: 10,000
SALES (est): 10.4MM **Privately Held**
WEB: www.lorimercorp.com
SIC: 3561 3592 3613 3599 Industrial pumps & parts; valves, engine; control panels, electric; custom machinery; valves & pipe fittings

(G-14246)
HALLIBURTON COMPANY
212 Industrial Dr (75602-4718)
PHONE....................................903 981-7032
Daren Hicks, *General Mgr*
EMP: 21 **Publicly Held**
WEB: www.halliburton.com
SIC: 1389 Oil field services
PA: Halliburton Company
3000 N Sam Houston Pkwy E
Houston TX 77032

(G-14247)
HART ENGINEERING COMPANY
Also Called: Longview Photocopying
109 W Hoyt Dr (75601-3614)
PHONE....................................903 758-0166
David Gillespie, *President*
Martha A Newman, *Corp Secy*
Laney Newman, *Vice Pres*
Lee W Newman, *Vice Pres*
Dwain C Kelm Pe, *Project Mgr*
EMP: 22 EST: 1934
SQ FT: 5,400
SALES (est): 1.1MM **Privately Held**
SIC: 8713 8711 2752 7334 Surveying services; civil engineering; commercial printing, lithographic; photocopying & duplicating services

(G-14248)
HUDSON GRAPHICS INC
Also Called: Hudson Prtg & Graphic Design
611 S Mobberly Ave (75602-2033)
P.O. Box 7010 (75607-7010)
PHONE....................................903 758-1773
Steven R Cartwright, *President*
John Harton, *Vice Pres*
Robert Mitchell, *Officer*
EMP: 35 EST: 1959
SQ FT: 16,000
SALES (est): 5.5MM **Privately Held**
WEB: www.hudsonprint.com
SIC: 2752 7311 7336 2791 Commercial printing, offset; advertising agencies; graphic arts & related design; typesetting

(G-14249)
IMEX VETERINARY INC
1001 Mckesson Dr (75604-5673)
PHONE....................................903 295-2196
Hall Griffin, *President*
Matt Hearn, *VP Opers*
T Griffin, *Treasurer*
Betsy Griffin, *Sales Dir*
Billy Emmons, *Prgrmr*
EMP: 12
SQ FT: 10,000
SALES (est): 1.6MM **Privately Held**
WEB: www.imexvet.com
SIC: 3841 0742 Surgical instruments & apparatus; veterinary services, specialties

(G-14250)
INDEVCO PLAS - LONGVIEW LLC
800 Jordan Valley Rd (75604-5221)
PHONE....................................903 291-1115
▲ EMP: 18
SALES (est): 4MM **Privately Held**
WEB: www.indevcoplastics.com
SIC: 2822 Polyethylene, chlorosulfonated (hypalon)

(G-14251)
INDUSTRIAL CHEM TEX INC
117 Edgewood St (75604-4804)
P.O. Box 6964 (75608-6964)
PHONE....................................903 759-2642
Harvey Frank Fudge, *President*
Jerry P Fudge, *Vice Pres*
EMP: 9
SQ FT: 10,000
SALES (est): 1.2MM **Privately Held**
WEB: www.chemtex.net
SIC: 2842 Cleaning or polishing preparations

(G-14252)
INSTRUMENT & VALVE SERVICES CO
1300 E Whaley St Ste B (75601-6835)
PHONE....................................903 753-9922
Russell Shepard, *Manager*
EMP: 12
SALES (corp-wide): 16.7B **Publicly Held**
SIC: 3823 Industrial instrmnts msrmnt display/control process variable
HQ: Instrument & Valve Services Company
205 S Center St
Marshalltown IA 50158

(G-14253)
INZER ADVANCE DESIGNS INC
124 W Tyler St (75601-6317)
P.O. Box 2981 (75606-2981)
PHONE....................................903 236-4012
John Inzer, *President*
Brandon Henson, *Accounting Dir*
▲ EMP: 40
SQ FT: 5,000
SALES (est): 3.6MM **Privately Held**
WEB: www.inzernet.com
SIC: 2329 2322 Athletic (warmup, sweat & jogging) suits: men's & boys'; underwear, men's & boys': made from purchased materials

(G-14254)
J&A FABRICATION
510 N Edith St (75601-5213)
PHONE....................................903 981-0136
Billy Chery, *Owner*
Billy Brutchin, *General Mgr*
EMP: 10 EST: 2017
SALES (est): 1MM **Privately Held**
WEB: www.j-a-fabricationllc.business.site
SIC: 3441 1799 Fabricated structural metal; welding on site

(G-14255)
J-W GATHERING COMPANY (DH)
122 Dovel Rd (75603-7063)
P.O. Box 8488 (75607-8488)
PHONE....................................903 643-3413
Howard Westerman, *CEO*
Laura J Westerman, *Corp Secy*
R T Clement, *Exec VP*
L H Leners, *Vice Pres*
Ernie Herterich, *Engineer*
EMP: 17
SALES (est): 11.3MM **Privately Held**
WEB: www.jwpower.com
SIC: 1382 Oil & gas exploration services
HQ: J-W Operating Company
15505 Wright Brothers Dr
Addison TX 75001
972 233-8191

(G-14256)
JASON JONES
Also Called: E T Associates
903 Memphis St (75604-5415)
PHONE....................................903 753-6045
▲ EMP: 10
SQ FT: 6,250
SALES (est): 770K **Privately Held**
SIC: 2431 Mfg Millwork

(G-14257)
JOY GLBAL LNGVIEW OPRTIONS LLC (DH)
2400 S Macarthur Dr (75602)
P.O. Box 2307 (75606-2307)
PHONE.................................903 237-7000
Edward L Dokeny II, *President*
Brad C Rogers, *Senior VP*
N Pharr Smith, *Senior VP*
James M Sullivan, *Vice Pres*
Kenneth J Stark, *Treasurer*
◆ EMP: 1000
SQ FT: 215,000
SALES (est): 415.9MM **Privately Held**
SIC: 3533 3532 3531 3312 Well logging equipment; drill rigs; trucks (dollies); mining; loading machines, underground: mobile; construction machinery; plate, steel; plate, sheet & strip, except coated products
HQ: Komatsu Mining Corp.
100 E Wscnsin Ave Ste 278
Milwaukee WI 53202
414 319-8500

(G-14258)
JOY GLBAL LNGVIEW OPRTIONS LLC
Letourneau Tech Stl Pdts
2400 Macarthur St (75602-5300)
P.O. Box 2307 (75606-2307)
PHONE.................................903 237-7000
Robert Chesnik, *President*
Josh Emerson, *Engineer*
Dave Brown, *Supervisor*
Clayton Pierce, *Supervisor*
EMP: 800
SQ FT: 4,000
WEB: www.news-journal.com
SIC: 1382 Oil & gas exploration services
HQ: Joy Global Longview Operations Llc
2400 S Macarthur Dr
Longview TX 75602
903 237-7000

(G-14259)
KEANE GROUP HOLDINGS LLC
4836 W Loop 281 S (75603-8405)
PHONE.................................903 247-1053
Bo Arledge, *Manager*
EMP: 64
SALES (corp-wide): 1.8B **Publicly Held**
WEB: www.nextierofs.com
SIC: 1389 Oil field services
HQ: Keane Group Holdings, Llc
3990 Rogerdale Rd
Houston TX 77042
713 960-0381

(G-14260)
KEEPRITE REFRIGERATION INC
Also Called: Superior Coils
1998 Fm 2011 (75603-4204)
PHONE.................................903 643-2261
Keith N Leonard, *President*
▲ EMP: 84
SALES (est): 32.5MM
SALES (corp-wide): 77MM **Privately Held**
WEB: www.k-rp.com
SIC: 3585 Air conditioning equipment, complete
PA: National Refrigeration & Air Conditioning Products, Inc.
539 Dunksferry Rd
Bensalem PA 19020
215 244-1400

(G-14261)
KOMATSU MINING CORP
2400 Macarthur St (75602-5300)
P.O. Box 2307 (75606-2307)
PHONE.................................903 237-7000
Daniel Eckermann, *Branch Mgr*
EMP: 48 **Privately Held**
WEB: www.mining.komatsu
SIC: 3532 Mining machinery
HQ: Komatsu Mining Corp.
100 E Wscnsin Ave Ste 278
Milwaukee WI 53202
414 319-8500

(G-14262)
LACY OPERATIONS LTD (PA)
222 E Tyler St (75601-7220)
P.O. Box 2146 (75606-2146)
PHONE.................................903 758-8276
Neal A Hawthorn, *Vice Pres*
Ann Lacy Crain II, *Vice Pres*
Bluford Walter Crain III, *Vice Pres*
Rogers Lacy Crain, *Vice Pres*
Susan Mincey, *Vice Pres*
EMP: 23 EST: 1947
SQ FT: 26,000
SALES (est): 6.3MM **Privately Held**
WEB: www.rlacy.com
SIC: 1382 Oil & gas exploration services

(G-14263)
LEBUS INTERNATIONAL INC (PA)
215 Industrial Dr (75602-4719)
P.O. Box 2352 (75606-2352)
PHONE.................................903 758-5521
Charles F Lebus, *CEO*
Frank L Lebus III, *President*
Terry Bailey, *Foreman/Supr*
James Barton, *Purch Mgr*
Jim Barton, *Purch Agent*
▲ EMP: 100
SQ FT: 95,000
SALES (est): 24.3MM **Privately Held**
WEB: www.lebus-intl.com
SIC: 3429 3443 3496 7699 Pulleys metal; drums, knockout (reflux, etc.): metal plate; wire winding; aircraft & heavy equipment repair services

(G-14264)
LETOURNEAU TECH AMER INC
2400 Macarthur St (75602-5300)
P.O. Box 2307 (75606-2307)
PHONE.................................903 237-7000
Thomas P Burke, *CEO*
Dan Eckermann, *CEO*
Robert Chesnik, *President*
Anniken Hoelsaeter, *Vice Pres*
Jack McElroy, *Vice Pres*
◆ EMP: 53
SALES (est): 19MM **Privately Held**
SIC: 5082 5084 3531 General construction machinery & equipment; industrial machinery & equipment; construction machinery
HQ: Joy Global Longview Operations Llc
2400 S Macarthur Dr
Longview TX 75602
903 237-7000

(G-14265)
LOCK DOCK INC
Also Called: AAA Lock & Safe
3506 W Loop 281 101 (75604-2668)
P.O. Box 9865 (75608-9865)
PHONE.................................903 759-1288
Ralph Warren, *CEO*
Tommy Warren, *President*
EMP: 16
SALES (est): 467.9K **Privately Held**
WEB: www.locksmithlongview.com
SIC: 7699 5031 5999 3429 Locksmith shop; windows; doors; millwork; vaults & safes; door locks, bolts & checks

(G-14266)
LONGVIEW ASPHALT INC (HQ)
20 Robert Wilson Rd (75602-4886)
P.O. Box 3661 (75606-3661)
PHONE.................................903 758-0065
James D Madden, *President*
Rodney Price, *General Mgr*
Eddy Updike, *General Mgr*
Douglas Madden, *Vice Pres*
Rachel Pairsh, *CFO*
EMP: 12
SQ FT: 2,800
SALES (est): 21.9MM
SALES (corp-wide): 95MM **Privately Held**
WEB: www.longviewasphalt.com
SIC: 2951 Asphalt & asphaltic paving mixtures (not from refineries)
PA: Madden Contracting Company, Llc
11288 Hwy 371
Minden LA 71055
318 377-0927

(G-14267)
LONGVIEW ASPHALT INC
1301 Ray St (75602-4927)
P.O. Box 3661 (75606-3661)
PHONE.................................903 758-4428
Rodney Price, *Manager*
EMP: 9
SALES (corp-wide): 95MM **Privately Held**
WEB: www.longviewasphalt.com
SIC: 2951 5032 1771 Asphalt & asphaltic paving mixtures (not from refineries); paving materials; blacktop (asphalt) work
HQ: Longview Asphalt, Inc.
20 Robert Wilson Rd
Longview TX 75602
903 758-0065

(G-14268)
LONGVIEW BRASS & ALUMINUM CO
4217 Estes Pkwy (75603-0907)
P.O. Box 7098 (75607-7098)
PHONE.................................903 758-8171
Alton L Coley, *President*
Alton Coley, *Vice Pres*
Clint Coley, *Info Tech Mgr*
EMP: 15 EST: 1948
SQ FT: 16,400
SALES (est): 1MM **Privately Held**
WEB: www.lbafoundry.com
SIC: 3365 3366 Aluminum & aluminum-based alloy castings; castings (except die): brass

(G-14269)
LONGVIEW FAB & MACHINE INC
57 Frj Dr (75602-4703)
PHONE.................................903 238-8300
R Bradley Stovall, *President*
▲ EMP: 34
SALES (est): 5.8MM **Privately Held**
WEB: www.longviewfab.com
SIC: 1796 1799 3441 3599 Millwright; welding on site; fabricated structural metal; machine shop, jobbing & repair

(G-14270)
LONGVIEW MECHANICAL CONTRS INC (PA)
Also Called: LMC FABRICATION SERVICES
827 Fisher Rd (75604-5206)
PHONE.................................903 759-1331
David Funderburk, *President*
Randy Funderburk, *Exec VP*
Clay Funderburk, *Vice Pres*
Clint Funderburk, *Vice Pres*
▼ EMP: 35
SQ FT: 75,000
SALES (est): 13.4MM **Privately Held**
WEB: www.lmcurbs.com
SIC: 3441 3531 3444 Fabricated structural metal; roofing equipment; sheet metalwork

(G-14271)
LONGVIEW NEWS JOURNAL
320 E Methvin St (75601-7323)
P.O. Box 1792 (75606-1792)
PHONE.................................903 237-7711
Stephen McHaney,
EMP: 10
SALES (est): 662.5K **Privately Held**
WEB: www.news-journal.com
SIC: 2711 Newspapers, publishing & printing

(G-14272)
LST HEAT TREATING LLC
8 Gum Valley Cir (75602-9500)
P.O. Box 2569 (75606-2569)
PHONE.................................903 757-2115
Richard Lane, *General Mgr*
Eva Touchstone, *Treasurer*
Scott Touchstone,
EMP: 9
SQ FT: 6,700 **Privately Held**
WEB: www.lstheattreating.com
SIC: 3398 Brazing (hardening) of metal; tempering of metal

(G-14273)
M-C PRODUCTION AND DRLG CO INC
Fm 1844 (75604)
PHONE.................................903 297-2251
David Michael Chandler, *President*
EMP: 20
SQ FT: 2,800
SALES (est): 4.6MM **Privately Held**
SIC: 1311 Crude petroleum production; natural gas production

(G-14274)
MARBLE GALLERY INC
1229 Market St (75604-5665)
PHONE.................................903 759-4726
Janeth Laypon, *CEO*
Steve Layton, *Vice Pres*
Darrell Walter, *Treasurer*
Kathy Walter, *Admin Sec*
EMP: 15 EST: 2001
SALES (est): 1.1MM **Privately Held**
SIC: 3281 Marble, building: cut & shaped

(G-14275)
MCDONALD LIGHTING & MAINT SUP
Also Called: McDonald Sales & Service
1200 Regal Oak Dr (75604-2143)
P.O. Box 9416 (75608-9416)
PHONE.................................903 297-8181
David McDonald, *President*
Linda McDonald, *Corp Secy*
EMP: 9
SQ FT: 6,000
SALES (est): 1.7MM **Privately Held**
WEB: www.mcdonald-lighting-maintenance-supply-in-longview-tx.cityfos.com
SIC: 2842 5063 Cleaning or polishing preparations; lighting fixtures

(G-14276)
MICRO METL CORPORATION
201 Kodak Blvd (75602-6106)
PHONE.................................903 248-4800
Jim Lindgren, *Branch Mgr*
EMP: 68 **Privately Held**
WEB: www.micrometl.com
SIC: 3444 Sheet metalwork
PA: Micro Metl Corporation
3035 N Shadeland Ave # 300
Indianapolis IN 46226

(G-14277)
MISSIONARY TECH TEAM
Also Called: M.T.T.
25 Frj Dr (75602-4703)
PHONE.................................903 757-4530
Randy Harris, *President*
Pete Ellison, *Chairman*
Birne D Wiley, *Founder*
Arnold Von Hagen, *Vice Chairman*
EMP: 18
SQ FT: 9,600
SALES: 833.2K **Privately Held**
WEB: www.techteam.org
SIC: 8661 7374 3861 Non-church religious organizations; computer graphics service; graphic arts plates, sensitized

(G-14278)
MOBILE PRODUCTS INC
Also Called: Laymor
401 Capacity Dr (75604-5341)
PHONE.................................800 323-0135
Scott Lord, *CEO*
▼ EMP: 40
SALES (est): 7.7MM **Publicly Held**
WEB: www.laymor.com
SIC: 3991 Street sweeping brooms, hand or machine
PA: Rev Group, Inc.
245 S Executive Dr # 100
Brookfield WI 53005

(G-14279)
MOBLEY OILFIELD SERVICES LP
Fm Rd 2087 (75603)
PHONE.................................903 234-2179
Donald Barkman, *Partner*
Steven Mobley, *Partner*
EMP: 46 EST: 1997
SQ FT: 2,500

SALES (est): 1.6MM **Privately Held**
SIC: **1389** Oil field services

(G-14280)
MOMENTUM PRESSURE CONTROL LLC (HQ)
199 Corporate Rd (75603-7054)
P.O. Box 8427 (75607-8427)
PHONE.................................903 643-3700
▲ EMP: 27 EST: 2012
SQ FT: 5,500
SALES (est): 17MM **Privately Held**
WEB: www.axisofs.com
SIC: **1389** Oil field services
PA: Momentum Pressure Control Group, Llc
199 Corporate Rd
Longview TX 75603
903 643-3700

(G-14281)
MOMENTUM PRSSURE CTRL RNTL LLC
3820 Creekwood Cir (75602-4533)
PHONE.................................903 643-3700
Dirk Lee,
Robert Hope,
EMP: 73
SALES (est): 2.3MM
SALES (corp-wide): 17MM **Privately Held**
WEB: www.axisofs.com
SIC: **3822** Hydronic pressure or temperature controls
HQ: Momentum Pressure Control L.L.C.
199 Corporate Rd
Longview TX 75603
903 643-3700

(G-14282)
MORSCO SUPPLY LLC
Also Called: Johnson Contrls Authorized Dlr
930 N Fredonia St (75601-5315)
PHONE.................................903 234-2183
John Towery, *Purchasing*
David Bailey, *Sales Mgr*
Ronni Rise, *Manager*
EMP: 14 **Privately Held**
WEB: www.morsco.com
SIC: **5074** 5999 5085 5051 Plumbing fittings & supplies; plumbing & heating supplies; valves & fittings; pipe & tubing, steel; pipe fittings, fabricated from purchased pipe; flange, valve & pipe fitting forgings, ferrous
HQ: Morsco Supply, Llc
15850 Dallas Pkwy Fl 2
Dallas TX 75248
877 709-2227

(G-14283)
NATURAL GAS PIPELINE AMER LLC
19935 Fm 449 (75605-6840)
PHONE.................................903 758-0154
Doug Schroer, *Branch Mgr*
EMP: 13 **Publicly Held**
WEB: www.kindermorgan.com
SIC: **4922** 1311 Pipelines, natural gas; crude petroleum & natural gas
HQ: Natural Gas Pipeline Company Of America Llc
1001 Louisiana St
Houston TX 77002
713 369-9000

(G-14284)
NEWPARK DRILLING FLUIDS LLC
211 Cherokee St (75604-4932)
PHONE.................................903 297-2210
Gary McDonald, *Manager*
EMP: 50
SALES (corp-wide): 747.7MM **Publicly Held**
WEB: www.newpark.com
SIC: **1389** Oil field services
HQ: Newpark Drilling Fluids Llc
21920 Merchants Way
Katy TX 77449

(G-14285)
NORRIS CYLINDER COMPANY (HQ)
4818 W Loop 281 S (75603-8405)
PHONE.................................903 757-7633
Jerry Van Auken, *President*
Brian McGuire, *President*
Chuck Manz, *Vice Pres*
A Mark Zeffiro, *Vice Pres*
Robert J Zalupski, *Treasurer*
◆ EMP: 228
SQ FT: 263,000
SALES (est): 49.1MM
SALES (corp-wide): 877.1MM **Publicly Held**
WEB: www.norriscylinder.com
SIC: **3443** Cylinders, pressure: metal plate
PA: Trimas Corporation
38505 Woodward Ave # 200
Bloomfield Hills MI 48304
248 631-5450

(G-14286)
NUCOR STEEL LONGVIEW LLC (HQ)
5400 W Loop 281 Bldg 52 (75603)
P.O. Box 7697 (75607-7697)
PHONE.................................800 256-5757
Phil Bischof, *Sales Mgr*
Dan McCullen, *Mng Member*
▼ EMP: 60
SALES (est): 36.4MM
SALES (corp-wide): 22.5B **Publicly Held**
SIC: **3312** Plate, steel
PA: Nucor Corporation
1915 Rexford Rd Ste 400
Charlotte NC 28211
704 366-7000

(G-14287)
ON-SITE BENNETT SERVICES LLC
Also Called: Boss Crane & Rigging
4836 W Loop 281 S (75603-8405)
PHONE.................................855 239-2505
David Cowley, *President*
Jerry Loe, *Vice Pres*
Dean Rowland, *Opers Mgr*
Jeff McGuire, *Opers Staff*
Michele Creed, *Human Res Mgr*
EMP: 75
SALES (est): 4.6MM **Privately Held**
WEB: www.bosscrane.com
SIC: **3537** Cranes, industrial truck
PA: Bennett International Group, L.L.C.
1001 Industrial Pkwy
Mcdonough GA 30253

(G-14288)
PATTERSON MANUFACTURING INC
3794 Bell Meadows Dr (75605-6479)
PHONE.................................903 757-0523
Jerry Patterson, *President*
James Patterson, *Vice Pres*
▲ EMP: 16
SQ FT: 15,000
SALES (est): 1.9MM **Privately Held**
WEB: www.pattersonmanufacturingco.com
SIC: **2434** 2431 Wood kitchen cabinets; millwork; moldings, wood: unfinished & prefinished; door frames, wood

(G-14289)
PETROSTAR SERVICES LLC
Also Called: Tri State Pressure Control
1740 Callahan Rd (75602-7212)
PHONE.................................903 247-6390
EMP: 12
SALES (est): 800K **Privately Held**
WEB: www.tspc.us
SIC: **1389** 5541 Oil field services; gasoline service stations

(G-14290)
PRIMERA ENERGY LLC
446 Forest Sq (75605-4401)
PHONE.................................210 490-8200
Brian Alfaro,
EMP: 13
SALES (est): 5.3MM **Privately Held**
WEB: www.primeraenergyllc.com
SIC: **1381** Drilling oil & gas wells

(G-14291)
QES PRESSURE CONTROL LLC
Also Called: Great White Pressure Control
5104 Estes Pkwy (75603-9477)
PHONE.................................903 643-0700
Billy Sciber, *Branch Mgr*
EMP: 15
SALES (corp-wide): 1B **Privately Held**
WEB: www.quintanaenergyservices.com
SIC: **1381** Drilling oil & gas wells
HQ: Qes Pressure Control Llc
4500 Se 59th St
Oklahoma City OK 73135

(G-14292)
QES WIRELINE LLC
291 Johnny Clark Rd (75603-4315)
PHONE.................................903 720-8805
Larry Cabana, *Principal*
EMP: 17
SALES (corp-wide): 1B **Privately Held**
WEB: www.quintanaenergyservices.com
SIC: **1389** Oil field services
HQ: Qes Wireline Llc
801 Cherry St Ste 800
Fort Worth TX 76102
817 546-4970

(G-14293)
R LACY INC
222 E Tyler St (75601-7220)
P.O. Box 2146 (75606-2146)
PHONE.................................903 758-8276
EMP: 14
SALES (est): 1.5MM **Privately Held**
WEB: www.rlacy.com
SIC: **1382** Oil & gas exploration services

(G-14294)
R LACY SERVICES LTD (PA)
222 E Tyler St (75601-7220)
P.O. Box 2146 (75606-2146)
PHONE.................................903 758-8276
Darren Groce, *President*
Darren Grace, *President*
Richard Kilby, *Business Mgr*
Brent Haas, *Vice Pres*
Walter Tehan, *VP Opers*
EMP: 26
SALES (est): 15.6MM **Privately Held**
WEB: www.rlacy.com
SIC: **1382** Oil & gas exploration services

(G-14295)
REMTEX INC
Also Called: Remtex Precision Machining
23 Frj Dr (75602-4703)
P.O. Box 3241 (75606-3241)
PHONE.................................903 758-0461
Robert D Embrey, *President*
Billie Embrey, *Vice Pres*
Gary Embrey, *CFO*
EMP: 14
SQ FT: 12,000
SALES (est): 2.2MM **Privately Held**
WEB: www.remtexmachining.com
SIC: **3545** Precision tools, machinists'

(G-14296)
RG-5 COMPANY LP
Also Called: Rg3 Meter Company
2912 S Access Rd (75602-6112)
PHONE.................................903 753-3456
Katrina Gregory, *General Ptnr*
Thomas Sands, *Warehouse Mgr*
Christy King, *Accountant*
▲ EMP: 10
SQ FT: 20,000
SALES (est): 2MM **Privately Held**
WEB: www.rg3meter.com
SIC: **3824** Positive displacement meters; totalizing meters; consumption registering; turbine meters; water meters

(G-14297)
RHE HATCO INC
Also Called: Rough Hats
302 Huntsman Way (75602-6107)
PHONE.................................903 753-2631
Frank Greco, *Manager*
Santiago Gesualdo, *Manager*
Dennis Henson, *Director*
EMP: 150

SALES (corp-wide): 96MM **Privately Held**
WEB: www.resistol.com
SIC: **2353** Hats & caps
PA: Rhe Hatco, Inc.
601 Marion Dr
Garland TX 75042
972 494-0511

(G-14298)
RICHS MACHINERY COMPANY INC
1207 Fm 1845 S (75603-8414)
P.O. Box 7456 (75607-7456)
PHONE.................................903 758-0531
Terre Richardson, *President*
Bobbie S Evans, *Corp Secy*
Diane R Richardson, *Vice Pres*
EMP: 25
SQ FT: 20,000
SALES (est): 4.3MM **Privately Held**
WEB: www.richsmachinery.com
SIC: **3599** Machine shop, jobbing & repair

(G-14299)
RKT OPERATING LLC
2706 E Marshall Ave (75601-5925)
P.O. Box 781, Harleton (75651-0781)
PHONE.................................903 686-0284
Richard Keith Tidwell, *Mng Member*
EMP: 30
SALES (est): 18MM **Privately Held**
SIC: **1389** Oil field services

(G-14300)
S L P BACKHOE SERVICE
12961 State Highway 149 (75603-6847)
P.O. Box 7847 (75607-7847)
PHONE.................................903 643-8258
Francisco Olvera, *Owner*
EMP: 14
SALES (est): 570.3K **Privately Held**
WEB: www.slpconstruction.net
SIC: **1389** Oil field services

(G-14301)
SAC MANUFACTURING INC
Also Called: Southern Associates
10730 State Highway 149 (75603-6916)
PHONE.................................903 643-9100
David Gillespie, *President*
EMP: 13
SQ FT: 5,936
SALES (est): 2.1MM **Privately Held**
WEB: www.sacmfg.us
SIC: **3441** Fabricated structural metal

(G-14302)
SAS GLOBAL CORPORATION
Vessell Technology
9486 Fm 2011 (75603-7308)
P.O. Box 6570 (75608-6570)
PHONE.................................903 643-9111
Tony Leslie, *General Mgr*
Milton Evans, *Purchasing*
EMP: 65
SALES (corp-wide): 44.4MM **Privately Held**
WEB: www.sasglobalcorp.com
SIC: **3443** Fabricated plate work (boiler shop)
PA: Sas Global Corporation
21601 Mullin Ave
Warren MI 48089
248 414-4470

(G-14303)
SATTERWHITE COMPANIES INC (PA)
Also Called: Satterwhite Log Homes
8405 Us Highway 259 (75605-7384)
PHONE.................................903 663-1729
Sam Satterwhite, *President*
Travonda Satterwhite, *Vice Pres*
Tim Cooper, *Opers Staff*
Kim Zapata, *Accountant*
Lisa Adkinson, *Sales Staff*
EMP: 55 EST: 1974
SQ FT: 6,500
SALES (est): 13.5MM **Privately Held**
WEB: www.slh.net
SIC: **2452** 1521 1794 Log cabins, prefabricated, wood; new construction, single-family houses; excavation work

(G-14304)
SCHLUMBERGER
TECHNOLOGY CORP
Also Called: Schlumberger Oilfield Services
301 Capacity Dr (75604-5339)
PHONE..............................903 297-0222
Kevin Armstrong, *Branch Mgr*
EMP: 35 **Publicly Held**
SIC: 1389 Oil field services
HQ: Schlumberger Technology Corp
　　300 Schlumberger Dr
　　Sugar Land TX 77478
　　281 285-8500

(G-14305)
SCHLUMBERGER
TECHNOLOGY CORP
Also Called: Dowell Schlumberger
301 Capacity Dr (75604-5339)
PHONE..............................903 297-0222
Jeff Sorocak, *Manager*
EMP: 200
SQ FT: 6,000 **Publicly Held**
SIC: 1389 Oil field services
HQ: Schlumberger Technology Corp
　　300 Schlumberger Dr
　　Sugar Land TX 77478
　　281 285-8500

(G-14306)
SCOTT ENVIRONMENTAL SVCS
INC
Also Called: Sesi
4804 Judson Rd Ste B (75605-1075)
P.O. Box 6215 (75608-6215)
PHONE..............................903 663-4635
Jonathan B Scott, *President*
Jim A Scott, *Vice Pres*
Norvell E Wisdom Jr, *Vice Pres*
Jeanne M Scott, *Treasurer*
EMP: 25
SQ FT: 3,000
SALES (est): 2.1MM **Privately Held**
WEB: www.scottenergy.com
SIC: 1389 Oil field services

(G-14307)
SCOTT NEWLAND OFFICE
Also Called: North Crete Services
3920 Fm 2879 (75605-6586)
PHONE..............................903 758-1500
Scott Newland, *Owner*
EMP: 12
SALES (est): 6.3MM **Privately Held**
WEB: www.longviewhomebuilder.com
SIC: 3531 Concrete plants

(G-14308)
SHOCO PRODUCTION LP
1518 Colony Cir (75604-4454)
PHONE..............................903 759-0082
Ron Shore, *Partner*
Carrie Gatons, *Controller*
David Etchelcu, *Manager*
EMP: 14
SALES (est): 1.4MM **Privately Held**
WEB: www.shoco.com
SIC: 1389 Servicing oil & gas wells

(G-14309)
SMURFIT KAPPA BATES LLC
2811 Robert Cargill Dr (75602-4871)
P.O. Box 2949 (75606-2949)
PHONE..............................903 234-1100
Barry Hamblett,
EMP: 14 **Privately Held**
WEB: www.batescontainer.com
SIC: 2653 Boxes, corrugated: made from
　　purchased materials
HQ: Smurfit Kappa Bates, Llc
　　6433 Davis Blvd
　　North Richland Hills TX 76182
　　817 498-3200

(G-14310)
SPECIALTY COILS LLC
5902 Old Highway 80 (75604-6010)
P.O. Box 2642 (75606-2642)
PHONE..............................903 212-2645
Chad Collins, *General Mgr*
Michael Collins, *Engineer*
Chase Citelli, *Accounts Exec*
Chris Terrell, *Accounts Exec*
Steve Wilson, *Accounts Exec*
EMP: 40

SALES (est): 6.5MM **Privately Held**
WEB: www.specialtycoils.com
SIC: 3677 Coil windings, electronic

(G-14311)
SPRINGHILL PALLETS LLC
164 Sven Pines Cut Off Rd (75605)
P.O. Box 6663 (75608-6663)
PHONE..............................903 297-6090
Larry Jones, *Partner*
EMP: 12 **Privately Held**
WEB: www.springhillpallet.com
SIC: 2448 5084 Pallets, wood; materials
　　handling machinery

(G-14312)
STEMCO PRODUCTS INC (HQ)
Also Called: Stemco Motor Wheel
300 Industrial Dr (75602-4720)
P.O. Box 1989 (75606-1989)
PHONE..............................903 758-9981
W Ed Meador, *CEO*
Chris Surdo, *General Mgr*
Art Tibbs, *General Mgr*
Richard Salazar, *Principal*
Matthew Stempniak, *Principal*
▼ **EMP:** 10
SALES (est): 99MM
SALES (corp-wide): 1.2B **Publicly Held**
WEB: www.stemco.com
SIC: 3714 3465 Brake drums, motor vehi-
　　cle; hub caps, automobile: stamped metal
PA: Enpro Industries, Inc.
　　5605 Carnegie Blvd # 500
　　Charlotte NC 28209
　　704 731-1500

(G-14313)
STREAM-FLO USA LLC
701 Glencrest Ln (75601-5145)
P.O. Box 700, Kilgore (75663-0700)
PHONE..............................903 753-6785
Jeremy Moore, *Principal*
Evie Jevicky, *Manager*
EMP: 30
SALES (corp-wide): 38.3MM **Privately
Held**
WEB: www.streamflo.com
SIC: 3533 Oil field machinery & equipment
HQ: Stream-Flo Usa Llc
　　8726 Fallbrook Dr
　　Houston TX 77064
　　903 912-1022

(G-14314)
TEGRON HOLDING LLC (DH)
Also Called: Glenmount Global Solutions
5912 Old Highway 80 Ste B (75604-6046)
PHONE..............................903 759-1088
Steve Voelzke, *CEO*
Crystal Williamson, *Buyer*
Stewart Brinnkoeter, *Purchasing*
Todd Dye, *Engineer*
Thomas Gibson, *Technology*
EMP: 30
SQ FT: 7,500
SALES (est): 14MM
SALES (corp-wide): 7.2MM **Privately
Held**
WEB: www.glenmountglobal.com
SIC: 3823 5084 Controllers for process
　　variables, all types; conveyor systems
HQ: Glenmount Global Solutions, Llc
　　5530 Union Centre Dr
　　West Chester OH 45069
　　219 762-0700

(G-14315)
TEXAS COMMUNITY MEDIA LLC
Also Called: Longview News Journal
320 E Methvin St (75601-7323)
PHONE..............................903 757-3311
Belinda McLaughlin, *Editor*
Denise Lytle, *CFO*
Jeffrey Martin, *Sales Executive*
Phil Latham, *Office Mgr*
Stephen McHaney, *Mng Member*
EMP: 140
SQ FT: 120,000
SALES (est): 9.9MM **Privately Held**
WEB: www.news-journal.com
SIC: 2711 Newspapers, publishing & print-
　　ing

(G-14316)
TEXAS INDUSTRIES INC
Also Called: T X I
433 E College St (75601-7551)
PHONE..............................903 758-7351
David East, *Manager*
EMP: 18
SQ FT: 2,800 **Publicly Held**
WEB: www.martinmarietta.com
SIC: 3273 3271 Ready-mixed concrete;
　　blocks, concrete or cinder: standard
HQ: Texas Industries, Inc.
　　1503 Lyndon B Johnson Fwy
　　Dallas TX 75234
　　972 647-6700

(G-14317)
TEXAS IRON & STEEL LLC
Also Called: Texas Iron & Steel Hauling
288 Pr 2317 (75603)
P.O. Box 7317 (75607-7317)
PHONE..............................903 758-9498
Matt Wright, *CFO*
David Wright, *Mng Member*
Karen Wright,
EMP: 14
SQ FT: 30,000
SALES (est): 11MM **Privately Held**
WEB: www.texasironandsteel.com
SIC: 5051 3312 3446 Steel; stainless
　　steel; purlins, light gauge steel

(G-14318)
TEXAS PIPE WORKS INC (PA)
2810 Bill Owens Pkwy # 400 (75605-2139)
P.O. Box 2937 (75606-2937)
PHONE..............................936 825-6571
Mark Blanks Jr, *President*
Eric Blanks, *Purchasing*
Jessica Valadez, *Purchasing*
Fred Mayfield, *Finance*
▲ **EMP:** 9
SQ FT: 5,000
SALES (est): 28.4MM **Privately Held**
WEB: www.texaspipeworks.com
SIC: 3498 Couplings, pipe: fabricated from
　　purchased pipe

(G-14319)
THOMAS OILFIELD SERVICES
LLC (PA)
4250 Se Loop 281 (75602-7184)
P.O. Box 6617 (75608-6617)
PHONE..............................855 778-5940
Greg R Peeler, *President*
Casey Barrier, *Superintendent*
Mary Peeler, *Vice Pres*
Rene Gudino, *Opers Mgr*
Robert Hill, *Opers Mgr*
EMP: 55 **EST:** 2009
SALES (est): 42.5MM **Privately Held**
WEB: www.thomasoilfieldservices.com
SIC: 1389 Oil field services

(G-14320)
TRANS-GULF DRILLING SVCS
INC
1201 W Loop 281 Ste 200 (75604-2957)
PHONE..............................903 759-0010
C Kyle Smith, *President*
Kyle Smith, *President*
EMP: 9
SALES (est): 660K **Privately Held**
SIC: 1381 Drilling oil & gas wells

(G-14321)
TRINITY INDUSTRIES 068
708 Jordan Valley Rd (75604-5232)
PHONE..............................903 295-0356
Bill Wright, *Principal*
Nancy Tooke, *Human Res Mgr*
EMP: 11
SALES (est): 3.2MM **Privately Held**
SIC: 3999 Manufacturing industries

(G-14322)
TRINITY INDUSTRIES PLANT 181
140 Shady Brook Ln (75602-9576)
PHONE..............................214 631-4420
Michael Holland, *Foreman/Supr*
Daniel Hesser, *Purchasing*
Nanci Escobedo, *Accountant*
Frank Meyer, *Human Resources*
Rick Simmons, *Manager*
EMP: 14 **EST:** 2011

SALES (est): 3.7MM **Privately Held**
WEB: www.trin.net
SIC: 3999 Manufacturing industries

(G-14323)
TRUPOINT WELL SERVICES
LLC
851 W Harrison Rd (75604-5208)
PHONE..............................940 683-2871
EMP: 28 **EST:** 2014
SALES (est): 207.3K
SALES (corp-wide): 116.4MM **Privately
Held**
SIC: 1389 Servicing oil & gas wells
PA: Axis Well Services, Llc
　　851 W Harrison Rd
　　Longview TX 75604
　　903 759-0082

(G-14324)
TUFF SHED INC
2719 E Marshall Ave (75601-5926)
PHONE..............................903 236-9126
Brandon Weems, *Sr Corp Ofcr*
Steve Coleman, *Manager*
EMP: 24
SALES (corp-wide): 292.4MM **Privately
Held**
WEB: www.tuffshedpro.com
SIC: 2452 Prefabricated wood buildings
PA: Tuff Shed, Inc.
　　1777 S Harrison St # 600
　　Denver CO 80210
　　303 753-8833

(G-14325)
TURN-TEX MACHINE & TOOL
INC
5910b Old Highway 80 (75604-6010)
P.O. Box 68, White Oak (75693-0068)
PHONE..............................903 759-0989
Dale Grider, *President*
EMP: 12 **EST:** 1979
SQ FT: 7,000
SALES (est): 2.1MM **Privately Held**
WEB: www.turntextool.com
SIC: 3533 Oil & gas field machinery

(G-14326)
TYLER TECHNOLOGIES INC
911 E Loop 281 (75605-5012)
PHONE..............................903 753-4292
Randy Bruce, *Project Mgr*
Jill Crockett, *Project Mgr*
Ginger Hain, *Project Mgr*
Michael Honiker, *Project Mgr*
Teresa Perry, *Project Mgr*
EMP: 45
SALES (corp-wide): 1B **Publicly Held**
WEB: www.tylertech.com
SIC: 7372 5734 Operating systems com-
　　puter software; business oriented com-
　　puter software; computer peripheral
　　equipment
PA: Tyler Technologies, Inc.
　　5101 Tennyson Pkwy
　　Plano TX 75024
　　972 713-3700

(G-14327)
U S FOAM INC (PA)
Also Called: USF
800 E Cotton St (75602-1318)
PHONE..............................903 753-3901
Angela C Ozment, *CEO*
Alden E Ozment, *President*
EMP: 14 **EST:** 1993
SQ FT: 9,700
SALES (est): 2.6MM **Privately Held**
WEB: www.usfoam.com
SIC: 2899 Foam charge mixtures

(G-14328)
UNLIMITED STONE LLC
114 Stevens St (75604-4723)
PHONE..............................903 297-0829
Miguel Fuertes, *Mng Member*
Ander Fuertes, *Mng Member*
EMP: 10
SALES (est): 1MM **Privately Held**
WEB: www.unlimitedcabinetsanddoors.com
SIC: 3281 3499 Granite, cut & shaped;
　　doors, safe & vault: metal

(G-14329)
VESSEL TECHNOLOGY
9486 Fm 2011 (75603-7308)
PHONE....................................903 643-9111
Sandy Tippit, *Vice Pres*
John Arden, *Production*
Ron Mitchell, *Purch Mgr*
Robert Lee, *Design Engr*
Tim Sisney, *Design Engr*
EMP: 14
SALES (est): 2.2MM **Privately Held**
WEB: www.vesseltechnology.com
SIC: 3441 Fabricated structural metal

(G-14330)
W P C SERVICES L L C
5810 W Marshall Ave (75604-6014)
PHONE....................................903 686-0597
Richard Williams, *Mng Member*
EMP: 10 EST: 2009
SALES (est): 1.7MM **Privately Held**
WEB: www.wpcservices.com
SIC: 3599 Machine shop, jobbing & repair

(G-14331)
WARFAB OILFIELD SERVICES INC
607 Fisher Rd (75604-5202)
PHONE....................................903 295-1011
Malcoln Clebenstine, *President*
EMP: 30
SALES (est): 11.1MM **Privately Held**
WEB: www.warfabinc.com
SIC: 3533 Oil & gas field machinery

(G-14332)
WD NORTON INC
Also Called: Overhead Door Co Longview, TX
1000 W Cotton St (75604-5528)
PHONE....................................903 758-0301
Charles Gladden, *Manager*
EMP: 15
SQ FT: 8,600
SALES (corp-wide): 5.9MM **Privately Held**
WEB: www.overheadtyler.com
SIC: 1751 7699 5211 3699 Window & door (prefabricated) installation; door & window repair; garage doors, sale & installation; door opening & closing devices, electrical; fence construction
PA: W.D. Norton, Inc.
2000 Anthony Dr
Tyler TX 75701
903 561-3483

(G-14333)
WEATHERFORD INTERNATIONAL LLC
219 Industrial Dr (75602-4719)
PHONE....................................903 353-9700
Edward Gaston, *District Mgr*
Donnie Bohmfalk, *Sales Staff*
Scott Clark, *Manager*
Dale Stanley, *Supervisor*
Dedra Brannon, *Admin Asst*
EMP: 26 **Privately Held**
WEB: www.weatherford.com
SIC: 1389 Oil field services
HQ: Weatherford International, Lic
2000 Saint James Pl
Houston TX 77056
713 693-4000

(G-14334)
WEATHRFORD ARTFL LIFT SYSTEMS
Fm 2751 (75601)
P.O. Box 129, Judson (75660-0129)
PHONE....................................903 663-1966
Jack Garmond, *Branch Mgr*
EMP: 40
SQ FT: 33,850 **Privately Held**
WEB: www.weatherford.com
SIC: 1389 Oil field services
HQ: Weatherford Artificial Lift Systems, Llc
2000 Saint James Pl
Houston TX 77056
713 836-4000

(G-14335)
WEST MACHINE & TOOL INC
211 Industrial Dr (75602-4719)
P.O. Box 3503 (75606-3503)
PHONE....................................903 758-5401
Wayne West, *President*
EMP: 18
SQ FT: 8,000
SALES (est): 3.3MM **Privately Held**
WEB: www.westmachineinc.com
SIC: 3599 7692 Machine shop, jobbing & repair; welding repair

(G-14336)
WESTLAKE CHEMICAL CORPORATION
2290 Callahan Rd (75602-7623)
P.O. Box 8388 (75607-8388)
PHONE....................................903 242-7513
Ray Laplante, *Principal*
Laura Stafford, *Production*
Kelly Chad, *Senior Buyer*
Trisha Herron, *Purchasing*
Dorene Smith, *Manager*
EMP: 300 **Publicly Held**
WEB: www.westlake.com
SIC: 2821 Polyethylene resins
PA: Westlake Chemical Corporation
2801 Post Oak Blvd Ste 60
Houston TX 77056

(G-14337)
WESTLAKE LONGVIEW CORPORA
2290 Callahan Rd (75602-7623)
PHONE....................................903 242-7500
Jason Ousley, *President*
EMP: 14
SALES (est): 2.5MM **Privately Held**
WEB: www.westlake.com
SIC: 2821 Plastics materials & resins

(G-14338)
WIRELINE INCORPORATED
710 Skinner Ln (75605-7352)
P.O. Box 5638 (75608-5638)
PHONE....................................903 663-1963
Brent Heichelheim, *President*
Alan Howell, *Vice Pres*
Sonya G Heichelheim, *Admin Sec*
EMP: 20
SALES (est): 2.1MM **Privately Held**
SIC: 1389 Servicing oil & gas wells; oil field services

(G-14339)
XTO ENERGY INC
5652 Fm 2208 S (75605-6554)
P.O. Box 4396 (75606-4396)
PHONE....................................903 553-3800
Bob Penny, *Manager*
Bobby Stark, *Manager*
EMP: 60
SALES (corp-wide): 264.9B **Publicly Held**
WEB: www.xtoenergy.com
SIC: 1311 Crude petroleum production; natural gas production
HQ: Xto Energy Inc.
22777 Sprngwoods Vlg Pkwy
Spring TX 77389

Loop
Gaines County

(G-14340)
OXY USA INC
1056 Fm 1066 E (79342-2203)
P.O. Box 1272, Denver City (79323-1272)
PHONE....................................806 637-5965
John Dorrow, *Branch Mgr*
EMP: 113
SALES (corp-wide): 21.2B **Publicly Held**
SIC: 1311 Crude petroleum production; natural gas production
HQ: Oxy Usa Inc.
1001 S County Rd W
Odessa TX 79763
432 335-0995

Lorena
Mclennan County

(G-14341)
IMPACT FIRE SERVICES LLC
214 Mid Tex Rd (76655-3611)
PHONE....................................254 857-4990
Mauro Barrera, *Sales Staff*
Mario Bustos, *Sales Staff*
Benjamin Fowler, *Branch Mgr*
Randal Mills, *Director*
EMP: 35
SALES (corp-wide): 39.8MM **Privately Held**
WEB: www.impactfireservices.com
SIC: 3669 Fire alarm apparatus, electric
HQ: Impact Fire Services, Llc
103 12th St Ste 200
Pflugerville TX 78660

(G-14342)
K-LINE MACHINE LTD
Also Called: Lorena Machine
2919 Rosenthal Pkwy (76655-3838)
PHONE....................................254 857-4848
Jerry Kline, *Partner*
Carolyn Kline, *Partner*
Ladonna Kline, *Partner*
Steve Kline, *Partner*
EMP: 9
SQ FT: 6,500
SALES (est): 800K **Privately Held**
WEB: www.k-linemachine.com
SIC: 3599 Machine shop, jobbing & repair

(G-14343)
NSEC LLC
Also Called: National Stage Equipment Co.
3854 Old Lorena Rd (76655-3277)
P.O. Box 429 (76655-0429)
PHONE....................................254 756-0651
Linda K Jander, *Mng Member*
Tim R Jander,
EMP: 12 EST: 1946
SQ FT: 4,000
SALES (est): 1.5MM **Privately Held**
WEB: www.nationalstageequipment.com
SIC: 2391 1799 Curtains & draperies; drapery track installation

Lorenzo
Crosby County

(G-14344)
LORENZO TEXTILE MILLS INC
417 Fillmore St (79343)
P.O. Box 69 (79343-0069)
PHONE....................................806 634-5506
Stuart Beckett, *President*
A W Lott, *Corp Secy*
Kenneth Lott, *Vice Pres*
Larry Work, *Shareholder*
EMP: 21
SQ FT: 40,800
SALES (est): 805.2K **Privately Held**
SIC: 2281 Polyester yarn, spun: made from purchased staple

(G-14345)
SHERIDAN PRODUCTION CO LLC
2131 County Road 109 (79343-3629)
PHONE....................................806 842-3521
Tony Guerra,
EMP: 56 **Privately Held**
WEB: www.sheridanproduction.com
SIC: 1382 Oil & gas exploration services
PA: Sheridan Production Company Llc
1360 Post Oak Blvd # 2500
Houston TX 77056

Los Fresnos
Cameron County

(G-14346)
ECOLOGICAL SERVICES INTL INC
41786 Fm 510 (78566-4846)
PHONE....................................956 233-4609
F Paul Seales, *CEO*
Rusty Justice, *COO*
Blas Breceda, *Treasurer*
EMP: 70
SQ FT: 245,000
SALES (est): 5MM **Privately Held**
WEB: www.ecologicalservicesintl.com
SIC: 3949 3449 Sporting & athletic goods; miscellaneous metalwork

(G-14347)
LFN LLC
Also Called: La Feria News
203 N Arroyo Blvd (78566-3236)
P.O. Box 990 (78566-0990)
PHONE....................................956 330-6838
Donald Right,
Mary Elizabeth Right,
EMP: 12
SQ FT: 1,000
SALES (est): 500K **Privately Held**
SIC: 2711 Newspapers, publishing & printing

(G-14348)
SHALLOW SPORT OF TEXAS INC
Also Called: Shallow Sport Boats
41146 Schafer Rd (78566-4790)
P.O. Box 934, Port Isabel (78578-0934)
PHONE....................................956 233-9489
Kyra Hudson, *President*
Weslee Hudson, *Vice Pres*
Natalie Rankin, *Office Mgr*
Brittany Sorrell, *Assistant*
EMP: 18 EST: 1997
SALES (est): 3.9MM **Privately Held**
WEB: www.shallowsportboats.com
SIC: 3732 Boat building & repairing

Los Indios
Cameron County

(G-14349)
APTIV SERVICES US LLC
Also Called: Delphi
601 Joaquin Cavazos Rd (78567-9601)
PHONE....................................956 366-4600
Danny Savoie, *Principal*
Richard Delarosa, *Supervisor*
EMP: 300
SALES (corp-wide): 14.4B **Privately Held**
WEB: www.delphi.com
SIC: 3714 Motor vehicle parts & accessories
HQ: Aptiv Services Us, Llc
5725 Innovation Dr
Troy MI 48098

(G-14350)
TOYODA GSEI BRWNSVLLE TXAS LLC
Also Called: Tgbtx
107 Joaquin Cavazos Rd (78567)
PHONE....................................956 290-8802
Ritoshi Hizutari, *President*
Toru Koyama, *Chairman*
Jorge Vela, *Accountant*
Masakzu Hashimoto, *Director*
◆ EMP: 18 EST: 2012
SALES (est): 180MM **Privately Held**
SIC: 3711 Automobile bodies, passenger car, not including engine, etc.
HQ: Toyoda Gosei North America Corporation
1400 Stephenson Hwy
Troy MI 48083
248 280-2100

Louise
Wharton County

(G-14351)
CIC CONSTRUCTION INC
38337 Us Hwy 59 (77455)
P.O. Box 425 (77455-0425)
PHONE....................................979 648-2968
Clyde Townsend, *President*
Ivan Townsend, *Vice Pres*
Olvin Laureano, *Director*
EMP: 70

SQ FT: 750
SALES (est): 10MM **Privately Held**
SIC: 1389 Construction, repair & dismantling services

(G-14352)
K-C LEASE SERVICE INC
Also Called: Matagorda Construction & Mtls
128 S Fm 441 Rd (77455-4058)
P.O. Box 428 (77455-0428)
PHONE....................................979 323-9911
Alton Krauskopf, *CEO*
Bruce Krauskopf, *President*
Delores Krauskopf, *Corp Secy*
Danielle Montegue, *Vice Pres*
EMP: 40
SALES (est): 6.2MM **Privately Held**
SIC: 1389 7389 Lease tanks, oil field: erecting, cleaning & repairing; oil field services;

(G-14353)
MUSTANG EXPLORATION CO INC
106 N Orange (77455)
P.O. Box 467 (77455-0467)
PHONE....................................979 648-2641
John H Roades, *President*
Jackie Roades, *Corp Secy*
Herbert H Roades, *Shareholder*
EMP: 15 **EST:** 1967
SALES (est): 1.8MM **Privately Held**
SIC: 1311 0112 Crude petroleum production; natural gas production; rice

(G-14354)
WENGLAR SERVICES INC
700 North St (77455)
P.O. Box 40 (77455-0040)
PHONE....................................979 648-2225
Doug Wengler, *President*
Catherine Wengler, *Vice Pres*
EMP: 14 **Privately Held**
WEB: www.wenglarservices.com
SIC: 2044 Enriched rice (vitamin & mineral fortified)

Lovelady
Houston County

(G-14355)
UNIVERSAL OILFIELD SERVICES
160 E Houston St (75851-2323)
P.O. Box 310 (75851-0310)
PHONE....................................936 636-2324
James McCarty, *President*
EMP: 24
SALES (est): 2.4MM **Privately Held**
SIC: 1389 Servicing oil & gas wells

Lubbock
Lubbock County

(G-14356)
ABS PRINTING SERVICES
Also Called: Alternative Business Services
524 E 40th St Unit A (79404-2807)
PHONE....................................806 747-3702
Ralph Gronenfeld, *President*
EMP: 12
SALES (est): 870.6K **Privately Held**
SIC: 2741 Business service newsletters: publishing & printing

(G-14357)
ABSOLUTE FUELS LLC
2517 74th St (79423-1405)
PHONE....................................806 712-0330
EMP: 32
SQ FT: 2,800
SALES (est): 344.7K **Privately Held**
SIC: 2911 Petroleum Refiner

(G-14358)
ADAMS MANUFACTURING CO (PA)
Also Called: Adams Paint Company
1416 N University Ave (79415-1114)
P.O. Box 5276 (79408-5276)
PHONE....................................806 744-0839

James M Adams, *President*
Ron Adams, *President*
James T Adams, *Vice Pres*
EMP: 14 **EST:** 1955
SQ FT: 11,400
SALES (est): 3.2MM **Privately Held**
WEB: www.adamspaintcompany.com
SIC: 2851 5231 Paints & paint additives; paint, glass & wallpaper

(G-14359)
ALPHA LABS INC
101 Sherman Ave (79415-3607)
PHONE....................................806 744-1960
Arthur Green, *Principal*
Sandi Holdridge, *Clerk*
EMP: 13
SALES (est): 1.7MM **Privately Held**
WEB: www.alphalabs.us
SIC: 2899 Water treating compounds

(G-14360)
ALUMINUM METAL PRODUCTS INC
Also Called: Bartos Irrigation Equipment
6802 Martin L King Blvd (79404-6015)
PHONE....................................806 745-6026
Jim Bartos, *President*
Bartos Bedrick, *Vice Pres*
Edith Canale, *Treasurer*
▼ **EMP:** 14 **EST:** 1956
SQ FT: 7,600
SALES (est): 2MM **Privately Held**
WEB: www.bartosirrigation.com
SIC: 3498 3523 Fabricated pipe & fittings; farm machinery & equipment

(G-14361)
AMERICAN PETROLEUM WELDING INC
Also Called: Profab
4002 N Fm 2528 (79416-2451)
P.O. Box 98116 (79499-8116)
PHONE....................................806 747-7272
Randall J Wright, *President*
William Darrell Young, *Vice Pres*
Tyler Wright, *Purchasing*
Heather Alison, *Sales Mgr*
Heather Ellison, *Sales Staff*
EMP: 35
SQ FT: 30,000
SALES (est): 7.2MM **Privately Held**
WEB: www.profab.net
SIC: 3561 3444 Pumps & pumping equipment; pipe, sheet metal

(G-14362)
APACHE CORPORATION
2811 N State Road 168 (79407-8808)
P.O. Box 193, Smyer (79367-0193)
PHONE....................................806 234-2058
Gery Franklin, *Manager*
EMP: 10
SALES (corp-wide): 6.4B **Publicly Held**
WEB: www.apachecorp.com
SIC: 1311 Crude petroleum production
PA: Apache Corporation
2000 Post Oak Blvd Ste 10
Houston TX 77056
713 296-6000

(G-14363)
ARCHER-DANIELS-MIDLAND COMPANY
ADM
2300 E 50th St (79404-4128)
PHONE....................................806 723-5117
Joe Mendoza, *Production*
John Chisum, *Manager*
EMP: 100
SALES (corp-wide): 64.6B **Publicly Held**
WEB: www.adm.com
SIC: 2041 2076 5131 2079 Flour & other grain mill products; vegetable oil mills; cotton goods; edible fats & oils; prepared feeds
PA: Archer-Daniels-Midland Company
77 W Wacker Dr Ste 4600
Chicago IL 60601
312 634-8100

(G-14364)
ASSOCIATED GROUP INVESTMENT CO
Also Called: A-Rock Materials
12 Mile W Slide Rd (79404)
P.O. Box 64023 (79464-4023)
PHONE....................................806 794-9507
Evelyn Graves, *President*
Jerry Graves, *Corp Secy*
Graves Ty C, *Vice Pres*
EMP: 18 **EST:** 1970
SQ FT: 500
SALES (est): 1.9MM **Privately Held**
SIC: 1442 Gravel mining

(G-14365)
BASILEIA INVESTMENTS INC
Also Called: Ohair Shutters
2001 N Avenue P (79403-2105)
P.O. Box 2764 (79408-2764)
PHONE....................................806 765-5791
Brant O'Hair, *President*
George Tucker, *Vice Pres*
Greg Riggan, *Engineer*
Ricky Welch, *Office Mgr*
▲ **EMP:** 146
SQ FT: 270,000
SALES (est): 15.7MM **Privately Held**
WEB: www.ohair.com
SIC: 2431 Window shutters, wood; door shutters, wood

(G-14366)
BATTERY SOLUTIONS INC
2301 Avenue B (79404-1000)
PHONE....................................806 771-3777
Margaret Gafford, *President*
Dan Gafford, *Sales Mgr*
EMP: 11
SQ FT: 9,000
SALES (est): 2.3MM **Privately Held**
WEB: www.batterysolutionsinc.com
SIC: 5531 3691 Batteries, automotive & truck; storage batteries

(G-14367)
BAYER CROPSCIENCE LP
3410 N Elm Ave (79403-1610)
PHONE....................................806 741-2010
EMP: 62
SALES (corp-wide): 65.6B **Privately Held**
WEB: www.backedbybayer.com
SIC: 2879 Agricultural chemicals
HQ: Bayer Cropscience Lp
2 Tw Alexander Dr
Durham NC 27709
919 549-2000

(G-14368)
BAYER CROPSCIENCE LP
Also Called: Aventis Cropscience
103 Erskine St (79403-3303)
PHONE....................................806 765-8846
Mike Gilbert, *Manager*
Austin Burrow, *Manager*
EMP: 21
SALES (corp-wide): 65.6B **Privately Held**
WEB: www.backedbybayer.com
SIC: 2879 Agricultural chemicals
HQ: Bayer Cropscience Lp
2 Tw Alexander Dr
Durham NC 27709
919 549-2000

(G-14369)
BECK STEEL INC
401 N Loop 289 (79403-2703)
PHONE....................................806 762-3255
▲ **EMP:** 144 **EST:** 1972
SQ FT: 110,000
SALES (est): 51.8MM **Privately Held**
WEB: www.becksteel.com
SIC: 1791 3441 Structural steel erection; fabricated structural metal

(G-14370)
BENTON OIL CO
3102 Clovis Rd (79415-1611)
PHONE....................................806 763-5302
Tod Forbes, *General Mgr*
EMP: 10
SALES (est): 1MM **Privately Held**
SIC: 1382 8742 Oil & gas exploration services; marketing consulting services

(G-14371)
BERGSTEIN ENTERPRISES LTD
2310 Fordham St (79415-2002)
P.O. Box 191 (79408-0191)
PHONE....................................806 741-1080
Peter Bergstein, *President*
Terry Payton, *Controller*
EMP: 15
SALES (est): 1.3MM **Privately Held**
WEB: www.bergsteinenterprises.com
SIC: 1382 Oil & gas exploration services

(G-14372)
BERGSTEIN WELL SERVICING LLC
2416 Erskine St (79415-2006)
P.O. Box 226 (79408-0226)
PHONE....................................806 741-1095
Peter Bergstein, *Mng Member*
EMP: 45
SALES (est): 3MM **Privately Held**
SIC: 1389 Oil field services

(G-14373)
BIGHAM BROTHERS INC
705 E Slaton Rd (79404-5833)
P.O. Box 3338 (79452-3338)
PHONE....................................806 745-0384
Von D Kimball, *President*
John M Tye III, *Vice Pres*
Benjamin Parker, *Mfg Mgr*
Tonya Baker, *Purchasing*
▲ **EMP:** 55
SQ FT: 72,000
SALES (est): 11MM **Privately Held**
WEB: www.bighambrothers.com
SIC: 3523 Soil preparation machinery, except turf & grounds
PA: Andrew W. Byrd & Co. Llc
3100 West End Ave Ste 500
Nashville TN 37203

(G-14374)
BIOREMEDIATION CONTRS CONS INC
Also Called: Bcc
3302 122nd St (79423-5586)
P.O. Box 53427 (79453-3427)
PHONE....................................806 771-8033
Randy Andrews, *President*
Paul Porter, *Vice Pres*
Leslie Andrews, *Admin Sec*
EMP: 17
SQ FT: 7,500
SALES (est): 3MM **Privately Held**
WEB: www.bcccorp.com
SIC: 8744 1389 ; oil field services

(G-14375)
BLUE BELL CREAMERIES LP
401 E Lehigh St (79403-2803)
PHONE....................................806 749-9005
Ty Koontz, *Branch Mgr*
EMP: 17
SQ FT: 1,225
SALES (corp-wide): 929.3MM **Privately Held**
WEB: www.bluebell.com
SIC: 2024 5143 Ice cream, packaged: molded, on sticks, etc.; ice cream & ices
PA: Blue Bell Creameries, L.P.
1101 S Blue Bell Rd
Brenham TX 77833
979 836-7977

(G-14376)
BMC WEST LLC
801 E 40th St (79404-3007)
PHONE....................................806 747-1580
Steve Robertson, *Branch Mgr*
EMP: 30
SALES (corp-wide): 7.2B **Publicly Held**
WEB: www.buildwithbmc.com
SIC: 2431 Millwork
HQ: Bmc West, Llc
4800 Falls Of Neuse Rd # 400
Raleigh NC 27609
919 431-1000

(G-14377)
BOF SERVICES INC (PA)
2416 Erskine St (79415-2006)
P.O. Box 2724 (79408-2724)
PHONE....................................806 741-1080
Peter Bergstein, *President*

EMP: 35 EST: 1994
SALES (est): 16.2MM Privately Held
SIC: 1389 1382 Oil field services; oil & gas exploration services

(G-14378)
BOOKBINDING & LAMINATING SPC
6522 8th St (79416-3778)
PHONE....................806 785-1126
John Kirk, *Principal*
EMP: 15
SALES (est): 740K Privately Held
SIC: 2789 Bookbinding & related work

(G-14379)
BORDER STATES INDUSTRIES INC
Nunn Elc Sup A Div Brder Sttes
520 E 50th St (79404-3726)
PHONE....................806 765-5741
Mitch Robison, *Branch Mgr*
EMP: 18
SALES (corp-wide): 2.4B Privately Held
WEB: www.borderstates.com
SIC: 5063 5065 5074 1711 Electrical supplies; electronic parts & equipment; plumbing & hydronic heating supplies; plumbing, heating, air-conditioning contractors; plastics plumbing fixtures; vitreous plumbing fixtures
PA: Border States Industries, Inc.
2400 38th St S
Fargo ND 58104
701 293-5834

(G-14380)
BRANDON & CLARK INC (PA)
Also Called: American Wire and Insul Sups
3623 Interstate 27 (79404-2349)
PHONE....................806 771-5600
Walt Clark, *President*
Gary Clark, *Vice Pres*
Roger Clark, *Vice Pres*
Ellis Kight, *CFO*
Ryan Thompson, *Sales Staff*
EMP: 101
SQ FT: 45,220
SALES (est): 49.3MM Privately Held
WEB: www.brandonclark.com
SIC: 7694 5063 Electric motor repair; power transmission equipment, electric

(G-14381)
BRANDON & CLARK INC
Also Called: Transformer Division
4605 Locust Ave (79404-3839)
PHONE....................806 771-5646
Scott Clark, *Branch Mgr*
Josh Clark, *Manager*
Sammy Wilson, *Manager*
EMP: 45
SALES (corp-wide): 49.3MM Privately Held
WEB: www.brandonclark.com
SIC: 7694 5063 Electric motor repair; power transmission equipment, electric
PA: Brandon & Clark, Inc.
3623 Interstate 27
Lubbock TX 79404
806 771-5600

(G-14382)
BREEDLOVE FOODS INC
1818 N Mlk Blvd (79403-9760)
PHONE....................806 741-0404
Bill Miller, *CEO*
Manuel Black, *Plant Mgr*
Cyd Seideman, *CFO*
▼ EMP: 42
SQ FT: 89,000
SALES: 5.1MM Privately Held
WEB: www.breedlove.org
SIC: 2099 8699 Food preparations; charitable organization

(G-14383)
BROADBAND TECHNOLOGY CORP (PA)
Also Called: Energy Manufacturing Gov Contg
4414 82nd St Unit 212 (79424-3369)
PHONE....................806 698-0396
Gary Harber, *President*
EMP: 24

SQ FT: 3,000
SALES (est): 1.4MM Privately Held
WEB: www.asfo.org
SIC: 8742 7379 8231 8748 Management consulting services; computer related consulting services; libraries; energy conservation consultant; environmental consultant; electrotherapeutic apparatus; medical & hospital equipment

(G-14384)
BROWN AND ANTHONY INC
Also Called: Bingo Express
3601 N Loop 289 Unit 1 (79415-1508)
PHONE....................806 762-1975
Rodney Brown, *President*
Olan Anthony, *Vice Pres*
Olion Anthony D, *Vice Pres*
Retha Anthony, *Treasurer*
Vondra Brown, *Admin Sec*
EMP: 15
SQ FT: 20,000
SALES (est): 925.8K Privately Held
WEB: www.bingoexpress.net
SIC: 1389 7999 Lease tanks, oil field: erecting, cleaning & repairing; bingo hall

(G-14385)
BUNGE MILLING SOUTHWEST INC
4401 82nd St Unit 1150 (79424-3396)
P.O. Box 484, Muleshoe (79347-0484)
PHONE....................806 799-3755
Victor Lira, *Prdtn Mgr*
Hasley Michael, *Human Resources*
Jesus Aylua, *Branch Mgr*
Javier Gutierrez, *Maintence Staff*
Alex Torres,
EMP: 10 Privately Held
WEB: www.minsa.com
SIC: 2041 5153 Corn meal; grain elevators
HQ: Bunge Milling (Southwest), Inc.
1972 County Road 1068
Muleshoe TX 79347

(G-14386)
BUSINESS FOR AMERICAN MINORITY
5808 78th St (79424-1722)
PHONE....................806 786-5052
Patricia Brand, *President*
EMP: 15
SALES (est): 250K Privately Held
SIC: 2759 Commercial printing

(G-14387)
CAMPUS DESIGN INCORPORATED
Also Called: Advance Graphix
520 23rd St (79404-1002)
PHONE....................806 744-9998
Stephen L Massengale, *President*
Matt White, *Opers Mgr*
Tammy Cox, *Prdtn Mgr*
Meagan Rieder, *Sales Dir*
Amanda Godlove, *Sales Staff*
EMP: 18
SQ FT: 15,000
SALES (est): 2.6MM Privately Held
WEB: www.advancedgraphix.net
SIC: 2396 5699 2759 Screen printing on fabric articles; fabric printing & stamping; T-shirts, custom printed; sports apparel; screen printing

(G-14388)
CAP ROCK WINERY INC
408 E Woodrow Rd (79423-7809)
PHONE....................806 863-2704
Phillip Anderson, *CEO*
Kyra Simmons, *Office Mgr*
Jana English, *Director*
Mike Kostelich, *Instructor*
Tim Abascal, *Master*
▲ EMP: 12
SQ FT: 26,252
SALES (est): 1.9MM Privately Held
WEB: www.caprockwinery.orderport.net
SIC: 2084 Wines

(G-14389)
CAPROCK MANUFACTURING INC
616 E Slaton Rd (79404-5820)
PHONE....................806 745-6454
Ryan Provenzano, *President*
▲ EMP: 50
SQ FT: 520,000
SALES (est): 13.4MM
SALES (corp-wide): 847.4MM Publicly Held
WEB: www.caprock-mfg.com
SIC: 3089 Injection molding of plastics
PA: Nn, Inc.
6210 Ardrey Kell Rd # 600
Charlotte NC 28277
980 264-4300

(G-14390)
CAPROCK MATERIALS LLC
1924 Marshall St Bldg 200 (79415-1938)
PHONE....................806 778-0343
Teddy Hickman, *Principal*
EMP: 11
SALES (est): 961.7K Privately Held
SIC: 2951 1429 1422 Concrete, asphaltic (not from refineries); trap rock, crushed & broken-quarrying; cement rock, crushed & broken-quarrying

(G-14391)
CEV MULTIMEDIA LTD
1020 Se Loop 289 (79404-6007)
PHONE....................806 745-8820
Dusty Moore, *President*
Linda White, *President*
Mark Johnson, *Partner*
Gordon W Davis, *General Ptnr*
Clayton Franklin, *Vice Pres*
EMP: 50
SQ FT: 12,300
SALES (est): 3.6MM Privately Held
WEB: www.icevonline.com
SIC: 2741 7812 7372 8299 Miscellaneous publishing; educational motion picture production; educational computer software; educational services

(G-14392)
CHEP (USA) INC
Also Called: Palex Systems
7507 Spur 331 (79404-8401)
PHONE....................806 577-4447
Dusty Palmer, *General Mgr*
Johnny Palmer, *Manager*
EMP: 30 Privately Held
WEB: www.chep.com
SIC: 2448 5085 Pallets, wood; industrial supplies
HQ: Chep (U.S.A.) Inc.
5897 Windward Pkwy
Alpharetta GA 30005
770 668-8100

(G-14393)
CISCO SYSTEMS INC
1208 14th St Bsmt (79401-3918)
PHONE....................800 553-6387
Barbara Walker, *Branch Mgr*
EMP: 691
SALES (corp-wide): 49.3B Publicly Held
WEB: www.cisco.com
SIC: 3577 Computer peripheral equipment
PA: Cisco Systems, Inc.
170 W Tasman Dr
San Jose CA 95134
408 526-4000

(G-14394)
CLEARFORK PETROLEUM INC
519 Main St (79401-3524)
P.O. Box 5117 (79408-5117)
PHONE....................806 763-5625
Kaye Medlock, *President*
EMP: 22
SQ FT: 5,450
SALES (est): 1.6MM Privately Held
SIC: 1382 Oil & gas exploration services

(G-14395)
COCA-COLA REFRESHMENTS USA INC
6101 Avenue A (79404-5151)
PHONE....................806 472-3200
James Long, *Branch Mgr*

EMP: 25
SQ FT: 55,366
SALES (corp-wide): 37.2B Publicly Held
WEB: www.coca-colacompany.com
SIC: 2086 2087 5145 5149 Bottled & canned soft drinks; concentrates, drink; syrups, fountain; groceries & related products; carbon dioxide
HQ: Coca-Cola Refreshments Usa, Inc.
2500 Windy Ridge Pkwy Se
Atlanta GA 30339
770 989-3000

(G-14396)
CONSOLIDATED COTTON GIN CO
8606 Highway 87 (79423-3537)
P.O. Box 2547 (79408-2547)
PHONE....................806 745-1191
Jerry Stanford, *President*
Russell Sutton, *Vice Pres*
▲ EMP: 55
SQ FT: 9,300
SALES (est): 5.1MM Privately Held
SIC: 3559 5084 3523 Cotton ginning machinery; industrial machinery & equipment; farm machinery & equipment

(G-14397)
CRAFTSMAN PRINTERS INC
535 32nd St (79404-2117)
PHONE....................806 744-8429
Ronald Peters, *President*
Connie Cole, *Vice Pres*
Lance Peters, *Vice Pres*
Mike Peters, *Vice Pres*
Thelda Peters, *Vice Pres*
EMP: 30
SQ FT: 18,000
SALES (est): 7MM Privately Held
WEB: www.craftsmanprinters.com
SIC: 2752 3993 Commercial printing, offset; signs & advertising specialties

(G-14398)
CSJB HOLDINGS INC
Also Called: J & B Industrial Services
521 Ne Loop 289 (79403-2806)
PHONE....................806 749-4300
Johnathan Birk, *President*
Edward Garbowski, *Vice Pres*
▲ EMP: 87
SQ FT: 48,000
SALES (est): 24MM Privately Held
WEB: www.jandbindustrial.com
SIC: 3599 Machine & other job shop work

(G-14399)
CUSTOM IRON WORKS
12701 Highway 87 (79423-7435)
PHONE....................806 745-2757
Joe Stroud, *Owner*
EMP: 9
SQ FT: 6,000
SALES (est): 806.9K Privately Held
WEB: www.customironworkslubbock.com
SIC: 3272 3446 Steps, prefabricated concrete; stairs, staircases, stair treads: prefabricated metal

(G-14400)
D & S DRILLING LTD
8008 Slide Rd Ste 29 (79424-2828)
PHONE....................806 794-8866
EMP: 10
SALES (est): 451.9K Privately Held
SIC: 1381 Oil/Gas Well Drilling

(G-14401)
DENNY KINCER INC
Also Called: Kincer, L T Company
4101 87th St (79423-2921)
PHONE....................806 762-1069
Denny Kincer, *President*
Norma L Kincer, *Corp Secy*
▼ EMP: 20
SQ FT: 30,000 Privately Held
WEB: www.ltkincer.com
SIC: 5083 5084 3556 3523 Agricultural machinery; farm equipment parts & supplies; agricultural machinery & equipment; industrial machinery & equipment; food products machinery; farm machinery & equipment

(G-14402)
DERAN INC (PA)
9405 N County Road 2000 (79415-9632)
PHONE...............................806 746-6926
Doug Randolph, *President*
Troy D Randolph, *Vice Pres*
▲ EMP: 23
SQ FT: 53,900
SALES (est): 4.1MM **Privately Held**
WEB: www.derangear.com
SIC: 3561 3599 3566 Pumps, domestic:
water or sump; machine shop, jobbing &
repair; speed changers, drives & gears

(G-14403)
DERAN GEAR INC
9405 N County Road 2000 (79415-9632)
P.O. Box 5666 (79408-5666)
PHONE...............................806 746-6926
Douglas E Randolph, *President*
Sharon E Lindsay, *Corp Secy*
Troy Randolph Jr, *Vice Pres*
Doug Randolph, *CTO*
▲ EMP: 58 EST: 1980
SQ FT: 43,000
SALES (est): 9.2MM **Privately Held**
WEB: www.derangear.com
SIC: 3566 Gears, power transmission, ex-
cept automotive

(G-14404)
DFA DAIRY BRANDS FLUID LLC
201 University Ave (79415-3426)
PHONE...............................806 765-8833
Cindy Smith, *Info Tech Mgr*
EMP: 81
SALES (corp-wide): 15.8B **Privately Held**
WEB: www.deanfoods.com
SIC: 2026 5143 Milk processing (pasteur-
izing, homogenizing, bottling); cheese; ice
cream & ices; yogurt
HQ: Dfa Dairy Brands Fluid, Llc
1405 N 98th St
Kansas City KS 66111
816 801-6455

(G-14405)
DIAMOND PLASTICS CORPORATION
2323 Marshall St (79415-1227)
PHONE...............................806 763-8021
John Pitman, *Finance Mgr*
Brian Green, *Info Tech Dir*
Larry Schmidt, *Technical Staff*
EMP: 100
SALES (corp-wide): 125.8MM **Privately Held**
WEB: www.dpcpipe.com
SIC: 3084 3354 3089 Plastics pipe; tube,
extruded or drawn, aluminum; plastic pro-
cessing
PA: Diamond Plastics Corporation
1212 Johnstown Rd
Grand Island NE 68803
765 287-9234

(G-14406)
ECONOMY MILLS LTD
5828 Fm 41 (79424-6806)
PHONE...............................806 765-5547
Clyde Tatum III, *Partner*
Claude Tatum II, *General Ptnr*
EMP: 14
SQ FT: 7,200
SALES (est): 205K **Privately Held**
WEB: www.economymills.com
SIC: 2048 Feed concentrates

(G-14407)
ESSENCE BOTTLING CO TEXAS INC
2401 Ne Loop 289 (79403-2902)
P.O. Box 3667 (79452-3667)
PHONE...............................806 993-1391
Shaun Hurley, *President*
Angie McMeans, *Vice Pres*
EMP: 15
SQ FT: 307,000
SALES (est): 8MM **Privately Held**
WEB: www.essencebottling.com
SIC: 2086 Water, pasteurized: packaged in
cans, bottles, etc.

(G-14408)
ESTILL INC
4704 88th St (79424-4110)
PHONE...............................806 789-1548
W Estill, *Principal*
EMP: 9
SALES (est): 819.5K **Privately Held**
SIC: 1381 Service well drilling

(G-14409)
FEEDERS SUPPLY
15902 County Road 2170 (79423-4697)
PHONE...............................806 889-3391
David Mason, *President*
Steve Mason, *Vice Pres*
EMP: 12 EST: 1972
SQ FT: 1,500
SALES (est): 1.1MM **Privately Held**
SIC: 2048 Livestock feeds

(G-14410)
FITHEN PROPERTIES
1703 E 50th St (79404-4038)
P.O. Box 3604 (79452-3604)
PHONE...............................806 762-1121
Lawrence Fithen, *President*
Stan Fithen, *Vice Pres*
EMP: 15
SALES (est): 1.3MM **Privately Held**
SIC: 2899 Fire extinguisher charges

(G-14411)
FORD GIN SERVICE INC
904 Private Road 7150 (79423-7158)
PHONE...............................806 745-3433
Danny Ford, *President*
EMP: 12
SALES (est): 3.4MM **Privately Held**
SIC: 5084 3559 Industrial machinery &
equipment; cotton ginning machinery

(G-14412)
FORTERRA PIPE & PRECAST LLC
1624 Marshall St (79403-2522)
P.O. Box 5667 (79408-5667)
PHONE...............................806 765-6721
David Ockerman, *Branch Mgr*
EMP: 40
SQ FT: 1,710
SALES (corp-wide): 1.5B **Publicly Held**
WEB: www.forterrabp.com
SIC: 3272 Pressure pipe, reinforced con-
crete
HQ: Forterra Pipe & Precast, Llc
511 E John Carpenter Fwy
Irving TX 75062
469 458-7973

(G-14413)
FRANKS MACHINE SHOP LLP
4302 Adrian St (79415-2712)
PHONE...............................806 747-4854
Frank Kiss, *Partner*
EMP: 9
SQ FT: 16,000
SALES (est): 950K **Privately Held**
SIC: 3561 Pumps, domestic: water or
sump

(G-14414)
GALYEAN INVESTMENTS LLC
Also Called: Galyean Insulating
1101 E Slaton Rd (79404-6005)
P.O. Box 3787 (79452-3787)
PHONE...............................806 368-5430
Nick Elliff, *Manager*
Thomas Galyean,
Kelly Galyean,
EMP: 17
SQ FT: 10,000
SALES (est): 7MM **Privately Held**
WEB: www.galyeaninsulating.com
SIC: 3644 Insulators & insulation materials,
electrical

(G-14415)
GARRISON BROS SIGNS INC
2523 E 50th St (79404-4131)
PHONE...............................806 744-1161
Timothy Garrison, *President*
Raymond L Garrison, *Vice Pres*
Beverly Garrison, *Treasurer*
Paula Garrison, *Admin Sec*
EMP: 15

SQ FT: 3,000
SALES (est): 2.1MM **Privately Held**
WEB: www.garrisonsigns.com
SIC: 3993 Signs, not made in custom sign
painting shops; electric signs; neon signs

(G-14416)
GLASS MAGIC INC (PA)
4302 W Loop 289 Unit B (79407-3769)
P.O. Box 64893 (79464-4893)
PHONE...............................806 535-4724
Glen Hartman, *CEO*
EMP: 18
SQ FT: 10,861
SALES (est): 1.9MM **Privately Held**
WEB: www.glassmagic.com
SIC: 7536 3429 Automotive glass replace-
ment shops; motor vehicle hardware

(G-14417)
GOLF GREENS TEXASCOM
5107 150th St (79424-6631)
PHONE...............................806 559-7048
Bill Hillstrom, *Principal*
EMP: 10
SALES (est): 783.4K **Privately Held**
WEB: www.golfgreenstexas.com
SIC: 3999 Plants, artificial & preserved

(G-14418)
GOODART CANDY INC
335 E 40th St (79404-2811)
P.O. Box 901 (79408-0901)
PHONE...............................806 747-2600
Robert L Borden Jr, *President*
Ron Harbuck, *Vice Pres*
Elsie Shirley, *Admin Sec*
EMP: 15 EST: 1949
SQ FT: 12,500
SALES (est): 620K **Privately Held**
SIC: 2064 Candy & other confectionery
products

(G-14419)
HT ENERGY LLC
Also Called: Raw Services
1415 Buddy Holly Ave (79401-4007)
PHONE...............................806 771-7769
Joe D Hardin, *President*
Gary Ryan Aycock, *Vice Pres*
EMP: 30 EST: 2016
SALES (est): 4.6MM **Privately Held**
WEB: www.rawoilgas.com
SIC: 1381 Drilling oil & gas wells

(G-14420)
HUMDINGER EQUIPMENT LTD
3202 Clovis Rd (79415-1145)
PHONE...............................806 771-9944
Chad Phares, *Partner*
EMP: 40
SALES (est): 21MM **Privately Held**
WEB: www.humdingerequipment.com
SIC: 5082 3531 General construction ma-
chinery & equipment; construction ma-
chinery

(G-14421)
HUNTER MILLWORKS INC
902 Ne Loop 289 (79403-3000)
P.O. Box 2513 (79408-2513)
PHONE...............................806 792-4864
Rebecca Poole, *President*
Patricia McCarthy, *Vice Pres*
Sue Slutz, *Project Mgr*
Ronald Keaton, *Prdtn Mgr*
Jennifer Kieth, *Treasurer*
EMP: 21
SQ FT: 48,000
SALES (est): 2.7MM **Privately Held**
WEB: www.huntermillworks.com
SIC: 2431 Moldings, wood: unfinished &
prefinished

(G-14422)
HURLEY PACKAGING TEXAS INC
2902 E Municipal Dr (79403-2900)
P.O. Box 3667 (79452-3667)
PHONE...............................806 687-6179
Thomas Hurley, *President*
Karen L Hurley, *Corp Secy*
◆ EMP: 44
SQ FT: 55,000

SALES (est): 14.5MM **Privately Held**
SIC: 2653 5199 7389 Boxes, corrugated:
made from purchased materials; packaging materials; packaging & labeling services

(G-14423)
HYDRITE CHEMICAL CO
2701 E 66th St (79404-5508)
PHONE...............................806 368-5660
John A Honkamp, *CEO*
EMP: 31
SALES (corp-wide): 686.3MM **Privately Held**
WEB: www.hydrite.com
SIC: 2899 Chemical preparations
PA: Hydrite Chemical Co.
300 N Patrick Blvd Fl 2
Brookfield WI 53045
262 792-1450

(G-14424)
IMAGE FURNISHINGS INC
Also Called: Image Millworks
3208 Oberlin St (79415-1404)
P.O. Box 53323 (79453-3323)
PHONE...............................806 747-6500
EMP: 10
SQ FT: 11,250
SALES (est): 1.1MM **Privately Held**
SIC: 2599 2499 1751 Mfg Furniture/Fix-
tures Wood Products Carpentry Con-
tractor

(G-14425)
IMPERIAL PUMPS CO
Also Called: Gardner Pumps
4716 79th St (79424-3206)
PHONE...............................806 791-5242
Charles Choate, *Owner*
EMP: 10
SALES (est): 683.5K **Privately Held**
SIC: 3563 5084 Air & gas compressors;
pumps & pumping equipment

(G-14426)
INDUSTRIAL MOLDING CORPORATION (HQ)
Also Called: IMC
616 E Slaton Rd (79404-5897)
PHONE...............................806 474-1047
◆ EMP: 95
SQ FT: 100,000
SALES (est): 25.5MM
SALES (corp-wide): 847.4MM **Publicly Held**
WEB: www.nninc.com
SIC: 3089 Injection molded finished plastic
products; injection molding of plastics
PA: Nn, Inc.
6210 Ardrey Kell Rd # 600
Charlotte NC 28277
980 264-4300

(G-14427)
J KEITHS JEWELRY INC
8001 Quaker Ave Ste H (79424-3368)
PHONE...............................806 791-0092
James Keith Smith, *President*
EMP: 10
SQ FT: 980
SALES (est): 1.1MM **Privately Held**
WEB: www.jkeithjewelry.com
SIC: 5944 3915 Jewelry, precious stones
& precious metals; jewelers' materials &
lapidary work

(G-14428)
J PS FUND WEAR
5120 69th St (79424-1602)
PHONE...............................806 794-5777
Janice Pamperin, *Owner*
EMP: 11
SQ FT: 9,200
SALES (est): 1.1MM **Privately Held**
WEB: www.fundwear.com
SIC: 2759 Screen printing

(G-14429)
JDH PACIFIC INC
521 Ne Loop 289 (79403-2806)
PHONE...............................562 926-8088
EMP: 43 **Privately Held**
WEB: www.jdhpacific.com
SIC: 3321 Gray iron castings

▲ = Import ▼=Export
◆ =Import/Export

PA: Jdh Pacific, Inc.
14821 Artesia Blvd
La Mirada CA 90638

(G-14430)
JGB OILFIELD SERVICES LLC
5420 86th St (79424-3506)
PHONE..................................806 789-2796
Jerry Brown, *President*
EMP: 12
SQ FT: 1,200
SALES (est): 1.4MM **Privately Held**
SIC: 1389 Oil field services

(G-14431)
JOHNSON GEAR INC
1110 N Avenue T (79415-1902)
PHONE..................................806 749-6400
Doug Randolph, *President*
▼ **EMP:** 14
SALES (est): 2.2MM **Privately Held**
SIC: 3566 Gears, power transmission, except automotive

(G-14432)
K W BROCK DIRECTORIES INC
7310 Slide Rd (79424-2512)
PHONE..................................806 687-6270
David Taylor, *Branch Mgr*
EMP: 13
SALES (corp-wide): 28MM **Privately Held**
WEB: www.namesandnumbers.com
SIC: 2759 Advertising literature: printing
PA: K W Brock Directories Inc
1225 E Centennial Dr
Pittsburg KS 66762
620 231-4000

(G-14433)
KIMBELL GIN MACHINERY COMPANY
Also Called: Kimbell-Bishard
226 Ne Loop 289 232 (79403-2810)
P.O. Box 1356 (79408-1356)
PHONE..................................806 763-6645
Richard W Kimbell Jr, *President*
Donnie Wren, *General Mgr*
Rita C Kimbell, *Corp Secy*
EMP: 80
SQ FT: 23,250
SALES (est): 1.1MM **Privately Held**
WEB: www.kgmfans.com
SIC: 7699 3559 3552 3541 Agricultural equipment repair services; cotton ginning machinery; textile machinery; machine tools, metal cutting type

(G-14434)
LA BELLA VIDA INC
Also Called: La Diosa Cellars
901 17th St (79401-5101)
PHONE..................................806 744-3600
Sylvia McPherson, *President*
EMP: 12
SALES (est): 1MM **Privately Held**
WEB: www.ladiosacellars.com
SIC: 2084 Wines

(G-14435)
LEEAGRA INC
117 E 70th St (79404-5834)
PHONE..................................800 825-3446
Lynn Lee, *President*
Rick Radon, *Sales Staff*
Terrence Brown, *Marketing Mgr*
▲ **EMP:** 23
SQ FT: 5,500
SALES (est): 5MM **Privately Held**
WEB: www.leeagra.com
SIC: 3523 Sprayers & spraying machines, agricultural; cattle feeding, handling & watering equipment; cabs, tractors & agricultural machinery; trailers & wagons, farm

(G-14436)
LENNOX INDUSTRIES INC
2435 S Loop 289 Ste 900 (79423-1519)
PHONE..................................806 412-4160
Charlie Beaty, *Branch Mgr*
EMP: 148
SALES (corp-wide): 3.8B **Publicly Held**
WEB: www.lennoxcommercial.com
SIC: 3585 Furnaces, warm air: electric

HQ: Lennox Industries Inc.
2100 Lake Park Blvd
Richardson TX 75080
972 497-5000

(G-14437)
LISCO LLP
2101 E 50th St (79404-4123)
P.O. Box 11466 (79408-7466)
PHONE..................................806 762-5126
Steve Lanham, *Partner*
John Lanham, *General Ptnr*
Bernice Yedersberger, *CFO*
Linda Stallone, *VP Sales*
EMP: 14
SQ FT: 17,000
SALES (est): 1.3MM **Privately Held**
WEB: www.liscosports.com
SIC: 3949 2394 Team sports equipment; tarpaulins, fabric: made from purchased materials

(G-14438)
LISCOSPORTS LLC
Also Called: Lisco Tents
2101 E 50th St (79404-4123)
PHONE..................................806 762-5126
Steve Lanham, *Mng Member*
Jennifer Lanham, *Admin Sec*
EMP: 15
SALES (est): 1MM **Privately Held**
WEB: www.liscosports.com
SIC: 3949 Sporting & athletic goods

(G-14439)
LLANO ESTACADO WINERY INC (PA)
3426 E Fm 1585 (79452)
P.O. Box 3487 (79452-3487)
PHONE..................................806 745-2258
Mark Hymann, *President*
Mark Hayman, *President*
Mary L Fuchs, *VP Admin*
Mary L McGill, *Vice Pres*
Andre Meyer, *Vice Pres*
▲ **EMP:** 24 **EST:** 1975
SQ FT: 15,000
SALES (est): 3.7MM **Privately Held**
WEB: www.llanowine.com
SIC: 2084 Wines

(G-14440)
LUBBOCK ARTFL LIMB & BRACE LTD
Also Called: Lubbock Artfl Limb & Brace Ltd
4421 19th St (79407-2408)
PHONE..................................806 799-1518
Sheila Phillips, *President*
EMP: 15
SQ FT: 1,800
SALES (est): 1.5MM **Privately Held**
WEB:
www.lubbockartificiallimbandbrace.com
SIC: 3842 Prosthetic appliances; limbs, artificial

(G-14441)
LUBBOCK GAS & BUILDING INC
8205 Avenue F (79404-6339)
PHONE..................................806 745-9695
William R Tipton, *President*
EMP: 10
SQ FT: 2,400
SALES (est): 1.8MM **Privately Held**
SIC: 5984 3448 Propane gas, bottled; buildings, portable: prefabricated metal

(G-14442)
LUBBOCK SKYLIGHT MANUFACTURING
701 N Interstate 27 (79403-2629)
PHONE..................................806 744-2300
Russell Shaw, *Owner*
Sylvia Moore, *Sales Mgr*
EMP: 14
SQ FT: 14,000
SALES (est): 1.3MM **Privately Held**
WEB: www.lubbockskylight.com
SIC: 3444 Sheet metalwork

(G-14443)
LUMMUS CORPORATION
501 E Hunter St (79403-9728)
PHONE..................................806 745-1191
EMP: 9 **Privately Held**

WEB: www.lummus.com
SIC: 5083 3559 Farm & garden machinery; cotton ginning machinery
PA: Lummus Corporation
225 Bourne Blvd
Savannah GA 31408

(G-14444)
MB NUTRITIONAL SCIENCES LLC
6508 E Fm 40 (79403-7624)
PHONE..................................806 778-2697
Matthew Ballou, *Partner*
Michael Ballou, *Partner*
EMP: 9
SQ FT: 30,000
SALES (est): 300K **Privately Held**
WEB: www.mbfeeds.com
SIC: 2048 Livestock feeds

(G-14445)
MCPHERSON CELLARS INC
1615 Texas Ave (79401-5140)
PHONE..................................806 687-9463
Kim A McPherson, *President*
Emily Simpson, *Opers Staff*
EMP: 12
SALES (est): 156.9K **Privately Held**
WEB: www.mcphersoncellars.com
SIC: 2084 Wines

(G-14446)
MESQUITE SERVICES LLC
6839 82nd St Ste 101 (79424-5082)
PHONE..................................806 368-7726
Greg Pipkin, *CFO*
EMP: 30
SALES (corp-wide): 20.9MM **Privately Held**
WEB: www.mesquiteservices.com
SIC: 1389 Oil field services
PA: Mesquite Services, Llc
2313 E Greene St
Carlsbad NM 88220
575 887-4847

(G-14447)
MIDTOWN PRTG & GRAPHICS INC
7720 University Ave (79423-2144)
PHONE..................................806 744-3382
Patti Frullo, *President*
John Frullo, *Vice Pres*
Casey Harmon, *Marketing Staff*
Dwanya Pierce, *Supervisor*
Martha Coldiron,
EMP: 20
SQ FT: 10,000
SALES (est): 4.1MM **Privately Held**
WEB: www.midtownprint.com
SIC: 2752 5199 Commercial printing, offset; advertising specialties

(G-14448)
MODULE TRUCK SYSTEMS INC (PA)
Also Called: M T S
2010 E 50th St (79404-4044)
P.O. Box 3910 (79452-3910)
PHONE..................................806 783-0777
Janet Betts, *President*
Janet Kristinek Betts, *General Mgr*
Curtis Griffith, *Chairman*
Roy James Mc Carley, *Vice Pres*
John Tyson, *Vice Pres*
EMP: 42
SQ FT: 63,000
SALES (est): 11.5MM **Privately Held**
WEB: www.moduletruck.com
SIC: 3523 7699 5531 3713 Farm machinery & equipment; farm machinery repair; truck equipment & parts; truck & bus bodies

(G-14449)
NATIONAL OIL & LUBE NEWS INC
2345 50th St (79412-2565)
PHONE..................................806 762-4464
Steve Hurt, *President*
Eli Torres, *Vice Pres*
EMP: 12

SALES (est): 570K **Privately Held**
WEB: www.noln.net
SIC: 2711 Job printing & newspaper publishing combined

(G-14450)
NCI BUILDING SYSTEMS LP
Also Called: NBC
5711 E Fm 40 (79403-7193)
P.O. Box 10133 (79408-3133)
PHONE..................................806 747-4291
EMP: 54
SALES (est): 16.3K **Privately Held**
SIC: 3441 Building components, structural steel

(G-14451)
NCI GROUP INC
Also Called: Metal Building Components Mbci
5711 E Fm 40 (79403-7193)
P.O. Box 10133 (79408-3133)
PHONE..................................806 747-4291
Jeff Berryman, *Branch Mgr*
EMP: 50
SQ FT: 3,120
SALES (corp-wide): 4.8B **Publicly Held**
WEB: www.metal-prep.com
SIC: 3448 3444 Buildings, portable: prefabricated metal; sheet metalwork
HQ: Nci Group, Inc.
10943 N Sam Huston Pkwy W
Houston TX 77064
281 897-7788

(G-14452)
OPEN ROAD MOBILITY LLC (PA)
7411 82nd St (79424-4935)
PHONE..................................806 866-0275
Tina Gibson, *General Mgr*
Stanley Beam, *Manager*
Jaime Jimenez, *Manager*
Jerry Beck,
Mack Lum,
EMP: 15
SQ FT: 3,321
SALES (est): 2.4MM **Privately Held**
WEB: www.openroadmobility.com
SIC: 5047 3999 Medical equipment & supplies; wheelchair lifts

(G-14453)
ORBIT INDUSTRIES INC
Also Called: Orbit Powder Coating
4106 N Fm 2528 (79416-2452)
PHONE..................................806 744-8300
Mario Perea, *President*
Lucy Perea, *Corp Secy*
EMP: 15
SQ FT: 2,500
SALES (est): 1.8MM **Privately Held**
WEB: www.orbittx.com
SIC: 3479 Coating of metals & formed products

(G-14454)
ORTEGA BATH ENVIRONMENTS INC
Also Called: Venetian Marble Kitchen & Bath
2834 Clovis Rd (79415-1604)
PHONE..................................806 763-5777
Tommy Lowrie, *President*
Linda Brown, *Vice Pres*
EMP: 26
SQ FT: 25,000
SALES (est): 4.4MM
SALES (corp-wide): 3.4MM **Privately Held**
SIC: 5032 3281 Granite building stone; granite, cut & shaped
PA: Venetian Marble Co Of Lubbock, Inc.
2834 Clovis Rd
Lubbock TX 79415
806 763-5777

(G-14455)
OSTEOGENICS BIOMEDICAL INC
4620 71st St Spc 78 (79424-2261)
PHONE..................................806 796-1923
Chad Bartee, *CEO*
Kendra Bernstein, *Sales Staff*
Brenna Wilson, *Manager*
Dustyn Webb, *Director*
EMP: 16
SQ FT: 5,000

SALES (est): 900K **Privately Held**
WEB: www.osteogenics.com
SIC: 3841 8748 7389 Surgical & medical instruments; test development & evaluation service; design services

(G-14456)
PANHANDLE PACKING & GASKET INC
Also Called: Lubbock Gasket & Supply
402 19th St (79401-5329)
P.O. Box 2154 (79408-2154)
PHONE..................................806 763-2801
Clay Bryan Goldston, *Vice Pres*
Larry Williams, *Purchasing*
Jason Culp, *Manager*
Brad Goldston, *Officer*
Amber Goldston, *Officer*
EMP: 48
SQ FT: 28,000
SALES (est): 18.3MM **Privately Held**
WEB: www.lubbockgasket.com
SIC: 5085 3053 3599 Bearings; gaskets, all materials; machine shop, jobbing & repair

(G-14457)
PARKS PRINTING CO
1715 19th St (79401-4808)
PHONE..................................806 747-2881
Don R Parks, *President*
Linda Franklin, *Manager*
EMP: 10
SQ FT: 18,800
SALES (est): 1.6MM **Privately Held**
WEB: www.parkscolor.com
SIC: 2752 Commercial printing, offset

(G-14458)
PATE TRUCKING CO LLC
4025 112th St (79423-6749)
PHONE..................................575 392-4441
Tom Bullard, *Branch Mgr*
EMP: 20
SALES (corp-wide): 23.1MM **Privately Held**
WEB: www.patetrucking.com
SIC: 4212 1389 Liquid transfer services; oil field services
PA: Pate Trucking Co., Llc
2763 Highway 214
Denver City TX 79323
806 592-2772

(G-14459)
PB MATERIALS HOLDINGS INC
Also Called: Arm Trucking
2803 114th St (79423-8202)
PHONE..................................806 745-5332
Dasili Bostan, *Branch Mgr*
EMP: 25
SALES (corp-wide): 26.1MM **Privately Held**
WEB: www.pb-materials.com
SIC: 3273 Ready-mixed concrete
PA: Pb Materials Holdings, Inc.
4001 E 42nd St Ste 100
Odessa TX 79762
432 563-8036

(G-14460)
PEPSI-COLA METRO BTLG CO INC
131 Se Loop 289 (79404-5809)
PHONE..................................806 745-7711
Emsley Baker Jr, *General Mgr*
Matthew Igoe, *Sales Staff*
EMP: 40
SQ FT: 40,000
SALES (corp-wide): 67.1B **Publicly Held**
WEB: www.pepsico.com
SIC: 2086 Carbonated soft drinks, bottled & canned
HQ: Pepsi-Cola Metropolitan Bottling Company, Inc.
1111 Westchester Ave
White Plains NY 10604
914 767-6000

(G-14461)
PERFORMANCE LABEL COMPANY
311 E 40th St (79404-2811)
PHONE..................................806 763-1663
Larry Sides, *President*

Ross Sides, *Vice Pres*
◆ **EMP:** 14
SQ FT: 30,000
SALES (est): 2.5MM **Privately Held**
WEB: www.plctx.com
SIC: 2672 5113 Labels (unprinted), gummed: made from purchased materials; industrial & personal service paper

(G-14462)
PLAINS MEAT CO LTD
812 Avenue G (79401-2730)
P.O. Box 922 (79408-0922)
PHONE..................................806 765-5595
John Q Adams, *President*
Howard Griffin, *Vice Pres*
EMP: 25
SQ FT: 7,500
SALES (est): 7MM **Privately Held**
WEB: www.plainsmeatcompany.com
SIC: 5147 2013 2011 Meats, cured or smoked; meats, fresh; sausages & other prepared meats; meat packing plants

(G-14463)
PMG DIGITAL INC
6011 43rd St (79407-3712)
PHONE..................................806 747-7446
Michelle M Terry, *President*
Tim Cook, *Sales Associate*
Calvin Terry, *Admin Sec*
EMP: 16
SQ FT: 30,000
SALES (est): 1.7MM **Privately Held**
WEB: www.pmgdigital.com
SIC: 3823 Digital displays of process variables

(G-14464)
PPG INDUSTRIES INC
Also Called: PPG 8318
5920 66th St Unit 1 (79424-5927)
PHONE..................................806 794-0180
Danny Cypret, *Branch Mgr*
EMP: 24
SALES (corp-wide): 15.3B **Publicly Held**
WEB: www.ppg.com
SIC: 2851 Paints & allied products
PA: Ppg Industries, Inc.
1 Ppg Pl
Pittsburgh PA 15272
412 434-3131

(G-14465)
PROFESSNAL RBILD OPTMAL SVC LL (PA)
Also Called: Pros Company
2523 86th St (79423-3387)
PHONE..................................806 749-7761
Rhett Newberry, *CEO*
Grant Swartzwelder, *Principal*
Ben Seymore, *Engineer*
John Henry, *Sales Engr*
EMP: 22
SALES (est): 5.1MM **Privately Held**
WEB: www.theprosco.com
SIC: 3599 Machine shop, jobbing & repair

(G-14466)
PURINA ANIMAL NUTRITION LLC
212 E Harvard St (79403-2800)
PHONE..................................806 761-7200
Armin Johnson, *Manager*
EMP: 35
SALES (corp-wide): 6.1B **Privately Held**
WEB: www.purinamills.com
SIC: 2048 Prepared feeds
HQ: Purina Animal Nutrition Llc
100 Danforth Dr
Gray Summit MO 63039

(G-14467)
PYCO INDUSTRIES INC (PA)
2901 Avenue A (79404-2231)
P.O. Box 841 (79408-0841)
PHONE..................................806 747-3434
Robert Lacy, *President*
Tommy Horsford, *Chairman*
Ronnie Gilbert, *Senior VP*
Rodney Kuss, *Vice Pres*
Tony Morton, *Vice Pres*
EMP: 148 **EST:** 1936
SQ FT: 28,358
SALES (est): 222.1MM **Privately Held**
WEB: www.pycoindustries.com
SIC: 2074 Cottonseed oil, cake or meal

(G-14468)
QUEST AND SONS INC
Also Called: A E Quest & Sons
222 E 34th St (79404-2212)
PHONE..................................806 744-2351
Mike Mc Casland, *President*
Tom Ed Reynolds, *Treasurer*
EMP: 21 **EST:** 1938
SQ FT: 37,920
SALES (est): 2.1MM **Privately Held**
WEB: www.questcanvas.com
SIC: 3949 2221 2394 Sporting & athletic goods; broadwoven fabric mills, manmade; tarpaulins, fabric: made from purchased materials

(G-14469)
R J C ENTERPRISES INC
Also Called: Comet Cleaners and Laundry
5404 4th St (79416-4355)
PHONE..................................806 793-8238
Ron Caffey, *President*
Caffey Steve, *Vice Pres*
EMP: 20 **EST:** 1982
SQ FT: 1,500
SALES (est): 501.5K **Privately Held**
WEB: www.cometcleaners.com
SIC: 7216 2842 Cleaning & dyeing, except rugs; laundry cleaning preparations

(G-14470)
RAIDER MANUFACTURING LTD
Also Called: Bc Supply
2008 E 50th St (79404-4044)
PHONE..................................806 762-3227
Breck Colquett, *President*
Karla Colquett, *Human Res Dir*
Jerry Soucy, *Manager*
◆ **EMP:** 60
SQ FT: 170,000
SALES (est): 26.8MM **Privately Held**
WEB: www.bcsupply.com
SIC: 5085 3559 3449 3523 Industrial supplies; cotton ginning machinery; miscellaneous metalwork; farm machinery & equipment; sheet metalwork

(G-14471)
RED RIVER COMMODITIES INC
212 Ne Loop 289 (79403-2810)
PHONE..................................806 763-9747
Chuck Woodbury, *Warehouse Mgr*
Mike Williams, *Manager*
Travis Chaney, *Manager*
Travis Wegner, *Manager*
Carroll Williams, *Manager*
EMP: 30
SALES (corp-wide): 836.8MM **Privately Held**
WEB: www.redriv.com
SIC: 5153 2048 5145 2064 Grains; prepared feeds; nuts, salted or roasted; candy & other confectionery products
HQ: Red River Commodities, Inc.
501 N 42nd St N
Fargo ND 58102
701 282-2600

(G-14472)
RILEY-BUILT INC
7802 Genoa Ave (79424-1713)
PHONE..................................806 798-9684
William S Riley, *President*
Rosa M Riley, *Admin Sec*
▲ **EMP:** 9 **EST:** 2001
SALES (est): 1.3MM **Privately Held**
WEB: www.rileybuilt.com
SIC: 3523 Cattle feeding, handling & watering equipment

(G-14473)
RISE N SHINE DONUTS
7803 University Ave (79423-2129)
PHONE..................................806 745-5282
Lane Sokleng, *Owner*
EMP: 10
SALES (est): 627.9K **Privately Held**
SIC: 2051 Doughnuts, except frozen

(G-14474)
RUSSELL E WOMACK INC
1300 E 42nd St (79404-3516)
P.O. Box 3967 (79452-3967)
PHONE..................................806 747-2581
EMP: 35 **EST:** 1927
SQ FT: 27,400

SALES (est): 6.6MM **Privately Held**
WEB: www.casserolebean.com
SIC: 2099 Food preparations

(G-14475)
SAMUEL JACKSON INCORPORATED
3900 Upland Ave (79407-5109)
P.O. Box 16587 (79490-6587)
PHONE..................................806 795-5218
S Chris Jackson, *President*
Martin Mehner, *President*
Amy Jackson Recht, *Principal*
Emily Jackson-Thatcher, *Vice Pres*
Neil Turner, *Vice Pres*
EMP: 20
SQ FT: 43,000
SALES (est): 4.6MM **Privately Held**
WEB: www.samjackson.com
SIC: 3559 Cotton ginning machinery

(G-14476)
SAMUEL JACKSON MFG CO
3900 Upland Ave (79407-5109)
PHONE..................................806 795-5218
Samuel G Jackson, *Owner*
Mark Davis, *Production*
Gerry Jackson, *Office Mgr*
EMP: 15 **EST:** 1954
SQ FT: 20,700
SALES (est): 1.3MM **Privately Held**
WEB: www.samjackson.com
SIC: 3559 3444 Cotton ginning machinery; forming machine work, sheet metal

(G-14477)
SANCO METAL FABRICATORS LLC
9102 Highway 87 (79423-9506)
P.O. Box 53816 (79453-3816)
PHONE..................................806 745-9674
Danny Sanders,
Sheryl Sanders,
EMP: 14
SQ FT: 17,500
SALES (est): 1MM **Privately Held**
WEB: www.sancometalfab.com
SIC: 3441 3443 Fabricated structural metal; tanks, standard or custom fabricated: metal plate

(G-14478)
SHEPHERD SHUTTER COMPANY INC
Also Called: Shepherd Shutters
4411 Brownfield Dr (79410)
PHONE..................................806 799-3458
Doyle Shepherd, *Ch of Bd*
Keith D Shepherd, *President*
EMP: 9 **EST:** 1951
SQ FT: 10,000
SALES (est): 640K **Privately Held**
SIC: 2431 Blinds (shutters), wood

(G-14479)
SIDES PRINTING COMPANY INC
Also Called: Performance Label Company
313 E 40th St (79404-2811)
PHONE..................................806 765-8168
Larry D Sides, *President*
EMP: 12
SQ FT: 7,800
SALES (est): 1.3MM **Privately Held**
WEB: www.plctx.com
SIC: 2752 2759 Commercial printing, offset; flexographic printing

(G-14480)
SIGNS ON GO
304 County Road 7200 (79404-7951)
PHONE..................................806 722-7446
Kaci Tucker, *Owner*
Gary Tucker, *Owner*
Keith Highsmith, *Manager*
EMP: 11
SALES (est): 375K **Privately Held**
WEB: www.signsonthego.com
SIC: 3993 Signs & advertising specialties

(G-14481)
SITEPRO LLC
9502 Highway 87 (79423-7496)
PHONE..................................806 687-5326
Johnathan Cox, *COO*
Brendan Bean, *Vice Pres*

Michael Chavez, *Vice Pres*
Britt Wuensche, *Vice Pres*
Jordan Broome, *Electrical Engi*
EMP: 70
SALES (est): 19.3MM **Privately Held**
WEB: www.sitepro.com
SIC: 1389 Oil field services

(G-14482)
SKW MANUFACTURING LLC
4224 Adrian St (79415-2712)
PHONE.................................806 763-8118
Bill Wall, *President*
Greg Seales, *Vice Pres*
Steve Kemp, *Admin Sec*
EMP: 20 **EST:** 2012
SALES (est): 1.7MM **Privately Held**
SIC: 3599 Machine shop, jobbing & repair

(G-14483)
SOCORRO EXPLORATION INC
8008 Slide Rd Ste 37b (79424-2828)
P.O. Box 64658 (79464-4658)
PHONE.................................806 798-2790
G Barney Adams, *President*
Kandis Adams, *Vice Pres*
EMP: 9
SQ FT: 2,000
SALES (est): 877.4K **Privately Held**
WEB: www.cloroxteam.com
SIC: 1311 Crude petroleum production

(G-14484)
SOUTHWEST CANVAS MFG CO (PA)
1325 E 37th St (79404-2533)
PHONE.................................806 747-0201
Jerry D Bullard, *President*
Treva Jenkins, *Corp Secy*
Gregory Lynn Bullard, *Vice Pres*
EMP: 12
SQ FT: 8,940
SALES (est): 700K **Privately Held**
WEB: www.canvasandsignworks.com
SIC: 7699 2394 Awning repair shop; awnings, fabric: made from purchased materials

(G-14485)
SOUTHWEST TEXTILES INC (PA)
Also Called: Chartwell Global Sourcing
4606 91st St (79424-5036)
P.O. Box 710, Abernathy (79311-0710)
PHONE.................................806 687-4001
Charles Thompson, *President*
Lee Jackson, *General Mgr*
Tom Surrency, *Vice Pres*
Richelle Redman, *CFO*
Harold Thompson, *Admin Sec*
▲ **EMP:** 75
SQ FT: 110,000
SALES (est): 4.8MM **Privately Held**
SIC: 2281 Cotton yarn, spun

(G-14486)
STAINLESS MFG & SEALS SVC
Also Called: Airtight Mobile Gasket & Seals
1431 N Gary Ave (79415-1401)
PHONE.................................806 795-8932
Rod Nitcher, *Owner*
EMP: 9
SQ FT: 15,000
SALES (est): 954.8K **Privately Held**
WEB: www.airtightstainless.com
SIC: 3444 5085 Sheet metalwork; gaskets

(G-14487)
STANDARD E&S LLC (PA)
2310 Fordham St (79415-2002)
P.O. Box 2724 (79408-2724)
PHONE.................................806 741-1080
Pieter Bergstein, *CEO*
Robbye Hendricks, *Human Res Mgr*
EMP: 30
SALES (est): 76.9MM **Privately Held**
WEB: www.thestandardenergy.com
SIC: 1389 Oil field services

(G-14488)
SUN-STAR ELECTRIC INC
7722 34th St (79407-4999)
PHONE.................................806 793-2812
Jim Rice, *CEO*
Al Pouria, *Managing Dir*
Randy Gage, *COO*
Bill King, *Opers Mgr*

Linda Ross, *Purch Mgr*
◆ **EMP:** 65
SQ FT: 60,000
SALES (est): 31MM **Privately Held**
WEB: www.sunstarusa.com
SIC: 3621 7694 7379 Motors, electric; motor repair services;

(G-14489)
SUNGOLD FOODS INC
901 E 66th St (79404-5505)
PHONE.................................806 748-2500
Scott Trapp, *Branch Mgr*
EMP: 14
SALES (corp-wide): 836.8MM **Privately Held**
SIC: 2068 Salted & roasted nuts & seeds
HQ: Sungold Foods, Inc.
11505 38th St S
Horace ND 58047
701 282-2600

(G-14490)
TABCO MACHINES INC
1114 N Avenue T (79415-1902)
PHONE.................................806 749-5649
Todd Benson, *President*
Rachel Benson, *Treasurer*
EMP: 30
SQ FT: 30,000
SALES (est): 3.6MM **Privately Held**
WEB: www.ceollano.net
SIC: 3599 Machine shop, jobbing & repair

(G-14491)
TCI COATINGS INC
4501 Bradley St (79415-2755)
PHONE.................................806 762-0871
John Choat, *Sales Staff*
Rebecca Granados, *Office Mgr*
Charles Horton, *Manager*
EMP: 13
SQ FT: 17,040
SALES (corp-wide): 3.3MM **Privately Held**
WEB: www.tci-coatings.com
SIC: 5231 2851 Paint; paints & allied products
PA: Tci Coatings, Inc.
8000 Anderson Sq Ste 111
Austin TX 78757
512 444-2824

(G-14492)
TEXAS PRECISION MFG INC
610 28th St (79404-1508)
P.O. Box 3640 (79452-3640)
PHONE.................................806 741-1166
Erika Hoeve, *President*
Travis Plasek, *Prdtn Mgr*
Gregory J Hoeve, *Admin Sec*
EMP: 38
SQ FT: 25,000
SALES (est): 3.8MM **Privately Held**
WEB: www.texasprecisionmfg-tx.com
SIC: 3568 3751 3599 3594 Couplings, shaft: rigid, flexible, universal joint, etc.; motorcycles & related parts; machine shop, jobbing & repair; fluid power pumps & motors

(G-14493)
TEXAS SHEET METAL WORKS
1102 E 50th St (79404-3830)
P.O. Box 10226 (79408-3226)
PHONE.................................806 765-8404
Arthur Rampy, *Owner*
Diane Spier, *General Mgr*
EMP: 9 **EST:** 1931
SQ FT: 13,000
SALES (est): 600K **Privately Held**
WEB: www.stroudstexassheetmetalllc.com
SIC: 3444 Sheet metalwork

(G-14494)
TEXCRAFT INC
3917 Clovis Rd (79415-1303)
PHONE.................................806 744-6651
P K Hufstedler, *President*
Pamela K Hufstedler, *President*
Dwayne Bandy, *Opers Mgr*
Tony Arnold, *Mfg Staff*
EMP: 14
SQ FT: 26,750

SALES (est): 2.6MM **Privately Held**
WEB: www.texcraft.biz
SIC: 3441 Fabricated structural metal

(G-14495)
TEXLAND PETROLEUM LP
6812 Wayne Ave Ste F (79424-1633)
P.O. Box 1177, Levelland (79336-1177)
PHONE.................................806 894-4657
Tom Fox, *Manager*
EMP: 40
SALES (corp-wide): 35.2MM **Privately Held**
WEB: www.texpetro.com
SIC: 1389 Oil field services
PA: Texland Petroleum, L.P.
777 Main St Ste 3200
Fort Worth TX 76102
817 336-2751

(G-14496)
TOFS LLC
Also Called: Total Oilfield Services
5802 E Highway 62 (79403-7247)
PHONE.................................806 543-9833
Zachary H Edwards, *CEO*
EMP: 19
SALES (est): 626.1K **Privately Held**
WEB: www.totalpumpservice.com
SIC: 1389 Testing, measuring, surveying & analysis services; oil field services

(G-14497)
TRANSITIONS INDUSTRIES LLC
4415 66th St Ste 101 (79414-4811)
PHONE.................................806 698-6200
Bobby G Brown, *Ch of Bd*
Gregory Burkholder, *COO*
EMP: 12 **EST:** 2004
SALES (est): 3.4MM **Privately Held**
WEB: www.tlcunit.com
SIC: 2599 Hospital beds

(G-14498)
TREW INVESTMENTS INC
Also Called: Hurricane Office Supply & Prtg
1407 E Fm 1585 (79423-7639)
PHONE.................................806 749-3200
Dean Trew, *Principal*
Andy Kavanaugh, *Principal*
Daylon Smith, *Principal*
Tyler Smith, *Principal*
Carter Trew, *Principal*
EMP: 13
SQ FT: 34,000
SALES (est): 2.3MM **Privately Held**
WEB: www.hurricaneprinting.net
SIC: 5943 2752 Office forms & supplies; commercial printing, lithographic

(G-14499)
TRIPLE C CONCRETE LUBBOCK LTD
2008 E 50th St (79404-4044)
PHONE.................................806 762-3227
Karla Colquett, *Partner*
Breck Colquett, *Partner*
EMP: 20
SQ FT: 4,000
SALES (est): 2.7MM **Privately Held**
WEB: www.triplecconcreteoflubbock.com
SIC: 3273 Ready-mixed concrete

(G-14500)
TURBINE SUPPLY COMPANY
2222 N Interstate 27 (79403-2222)
PHONE.................................806 763-5901
Tony Nicholas, *Owner*
Dave Lacombe, *General Mgr*
EMP: 15
SQ FT: 15,395
SALES (est): 1.5MM **Privately Held**
WEB: www.turbinesupplyco.com
SIC: 3599 Machine shop, jobbing & repair

(G-14501)
TURNBOW OIL FIELD SERVICES LLC
3510 Woodrow Rd (79423-4612)
PHONE.................................817 880-3833
Chad Turnbow, *Mng Member*
Stefanie R Turnbow, *Manager*
EMP: 10
SALES (est): 883.6K **Privately Held**
SIC: 1389 Roustabout service

(G-14502)
TYCO FIRE PRODUCTS LP
8902 N Interstate 27 (79403-6713)
PHONE.................................806 472-2400
Len Schiavone, *President*
Pat Ortiz, *Buyer*
▲ **EMP:** 567
SALES (est): 147.1MM **Privately Held**
SIC: 3569 Filters
HQ: Tyco International Management Company, Llc
9 Roszel Rd Ste 2
Princeton NJ 08540
609 720-4200

(G-14503)
TYCO FIRE PRODUCTS LP
Also Called: Tyco Fire Protection Products
8902 N Interstate 27 (79403-6713)
PHONE.................................806 472-2400
Steve Shields, *Engineer*
Len Schiazone, *Manager*
EMP: 600 **Privately Held**
WEB: www.tyco-fire.com
SIC: 3569 Building components, structural steel
HQ: Tyco Fire Products Lp
1400 Pennbrook Pkwy
Lansdale PA 19446
215 362-0700

(G-14504)
TYLER TECHNOLOGIES INC
Also Called: Tyler Public Safety
5519 53rd St (79414-1677)
PHONE.................................806 797-0761
Janet Joiner, *Vice Pres*
Patrick Morales, *Project Mgr*
Loreley Torres, *Project Mgr*
Jon Phillips, *Regl Sales Mgr*
Kirk Cunningham, *Sales Staff*
EMP: 250
SALES (corp-wide): 1B **Publicly Held**
WEB: www.tylertech.com
SIC: 7372 Prepackaged software
PA: Tyler Technologies, Inc.
5101 Tennyson Pkwy
Plano TX 75024
972 713-3700

(G-14505)
USM MANUFACTURING LLC
Also Called: Praters
2206 114th St (79423-7235)
PHONE.................................806 791-0220
Benny Cousatte, *Principal*
John Bottoni, *Opers Staff*
Justin Sullivan, *Mfg Staff*
Larry Keneda, *Purchasing*
Martin Calzada, *Manager*
EMP: 30
SQ FT: 70,000
SALES (est): 6.2MM **Privately Held**
WEB: www.praters.com
SIC: 2099 5421 5147 2038 Ready-to-eat meals, salads & sandwiches; meat & fish markets; meats, cured or smoked; frozen specialties; frozen fruits & vegetables; sausages & other prepared meats

(G-14506)
VENETIAN MARBLE CO LUBBOCK INC (PA)
Also Called: Venetian of Lubbock
2834 Clovis Rd (79415-1604)
P.O. Box 5177 (79408-5177)
PHONE.................................806 763-5777
Royce G Newsom, *President*
Tommy Lowrie, *Vice Pres*
Brad Marshall, *Vice Pres*
EMP: 26 **EST:** 1966
SQ FT: 21,865
SALES (est): 3.4MM **Privately Held**
WEB: www.alliedstoneinc.com
SIC: 3088 3281 Bathroom fixtures, plastic; sinks, plastic; cut stone & stone products

(G-14507)
VERTICAL TRBINE SPCIALISTS INC
Also Called: Vts Pumps
1802 E 50th St Unit 106 (79404-4006)
PHONE.................................806 743-5555
EMP: 58 **EST:** 1955
SQ FT: 130,000

SALES (est): 11.5MM **Privately Held**
WEB: www.vtsfabs.com
SIC: 3561 Pumps & pumping equipment

(G-14508)
W&W-AFCO STEEL LLC
Also Called: W & W Steel Co
2221 Erskine St (79415-2003)
P.O. Box 2219 (79408-2219)
PHONE..................................806 765-5781
Jay Meador, *Sales Mgr*
EMP: 130
SQ FT: 95,000
SALES (corp-wide): 9B **Publicly Held**
WEB: www.wwafcosteel.com
SIC: 3441 4225 7389 Building compo-
nents, structural steel; general warehous-
ing; brokers, business: buying & selling
business enterprises
HQ: W&W-Afco Steel Llc
1730 W Reno Ave
Oklahoma City OK 73106
405 235-3621

(G-14509)
WES-TEX MANUFACTURING INC
6201 Martin L King Blvd (79404-5503)
P.O. Box 3313 (79452-3313)
PHONE..................................806 749-3795
EMP: 16
SQ FT: 12,500
SALES (est): 3.8MM **Privately Held**
SIC: 3715 Truck trailers

(G-14510)
WEST TEXAS LEE CO INC
117 E 70th St (79404-5834)
PHONE..................................800 825-3346
EMP: 29 **EST:** 1949
SQ FT: 10,000
SALES (est): 4.4MM **Privately Held**
WEB: www.leeagra.com
SIC: 3523 Tractors, farm

(G-14511)
WESTX PACKAGING COMPANY
508 Lubbock Bus Pk Blvd (79403-1829)
P.O. Box 5158, Aloha OR (97006-0158)
PHONE..................................806 686-4447
Paul Lin, *President*
Rey Ingusnza, *Supervisor*
Melling Lin, *Admin Sec*
EMP: 12 **EST:** 2006
SQ FT: 60,000
SALES (est): 4.1MM **Privately Held**
WEB: www.westxpackaging.com
SIC: 2674 Bags: uncoated paper & multi-
wall

(G-14512)
WHOLESALE ENVELOPE INC
2410 Rice St (79415-1220)
P.O. Box 53292 (79453-3292)
PHONE..................................806 762-2255
Dale Somers, *President*
Joyce Somers, *Corp Secy*
Gay McAfee,
EMP: 24
SQ FT: 12,000
SALES (est): 3.1MM **Privately Held**
WEB: www.wholesaleenvelope.com
SIC: 2759 Commercial printing

(G-14513)
WILBERT FUNERAL SERVICES INC
W.t.X. Wilbert Vault Co.
2301 Auburn St (79415-3025)
PHONE..................................806 762-1162
Sylvester Jackson, *Opers-Prdtn-Mfg*
Dell Hilburn, *Administration*
EMP: 12
SQ FT: 3,000
SALES (corp-wide): 9B **Publicly Held**
WEB: www.greensborowilbert.com
SIC: 3272 Burial vaults, concrete or pre-
cast terrazzo
HQ: Wilbert Funeral Services, Inc.
10965 Granada Ln Ste 300
Overland Park KS 66211
913 345-2120

(G-14514)
WORLD OF JEANS & TOPS
Also Called: Phillys
6002 Slide Rd (79414-4310)
PHONE..................................806 788-1233
EMP: 14 **Publicly Held**
WEB: www.tillys.com
SIC: 5611 2339 2389 Men's & boys' cloth-
ing stores; women's & misses' acces-
sories; men's miscellaneous accessories
HQ: World Of Jeans & Tops
10 Whatney
Irvine CA 92618
949 609-5599

(G-14515)
X-FAB TEXAS INC (DH)
2301 N University Ave (79415-1717)
PHONE..................................806 747-4400
Rudi De Winters, *CEO*
Lloyd Whetzel, *President*
Carlos Stahr, *Business Mgr*
Manfred Riemer, *COO*
Thomas Hartung, *Vice Pres*
▲ **EMP:** 390
SQ FT: 725,000
SALES (est): 84.4MM **Privately Held**
WEB: www.xfabtexas.com
SIC: 3674 Integrated circuits, semiconduc-
tor networks, etc.; wafers (semiconductor
devices)
HQ: X-Fab Semiconductor Foundries
Gmbh
Haarbergstr. 67
Erfurt 99097
361 427-6000

(G-14516)
YATES CARPET INCORPORATED
Also Called: Yates Flooring Center
1901 W Loop 289 Ste 11 (79407-1725)
PHONE..................................806 795-9942
Joel Jaime, *Manager*
EMP: 40
SALES (corp-wide): 7.5MM **Privately
Held**
WEB: www.yatesflooring.com
SIC: 5231 1752 2591 5713 Paint, glass
& wallpaper; carpet laying; mini blinds;
floor covering stores
PA: Yates Carpet Incorporated
1901 W Loop 289
Lubbock TX 79407
806 795-0070

Lueders
Jones County

(G-14517)
CONTINENTAL QUARRIES
Also Called: Continental Capstone
2699 Fm 142 (79533-2247)
PHONE..................................325 228-4180
Lynn Caldwell, *General Mgr*
EMP: 18 **EST:** 1999
SALES (est): 1.3MM **Privately Held**
SIC: 1411 1499 Limestone, dimension-
quarrying; bituminous limestone quarrying

(G-14518)
MEZGER ENTERPRISES LTD
1011 County Road 164 (79533-2248)
P.O. Box 1553, Lampasas (76550-0013)
PHONE..................................254 547-8207
John Malone, *General Mgr*
Ben Goodwin, *Manager*
Tony Brotherwood, *Data Proc Staff*
EMP: 60
SALES (corp-wide): 6.9MM **Privately
Held**
WEB: www.mezgerstone.com
SIC: 3281 Cut stone & stone products
PA: Mezger Enterprises, Ltd.
Fm Rd 2808
Kempner TX 76539
254 547-8174

Lufkin
Angelina County

(G-14519)
2011 ANGELINA MFG LLC
Also Called: Angelina Tank & Manufacturing
1916 Old Mill Rd (75904-1824)
P.O. Box 155110 (75915-5110)
PHONE..................................936 632-8330
EMP: 100 **EST:** 2011
SQ FT: 8,000
SALES (est): 13.5MM **Privately Held**
WEB: www.angelinatank.com
SIC: 3443 Fuel tanks (oil, gas, etc.): metal
plate

(G-14520)
ANGELINA STEEL INC
1702 N Raguet St (75904-2144)
P.O. Box 3636 (75903-3636)
PHONE..................................936 634-6649
James Huggins, *President*
Susan Biscamp, *Office Mgr*
EMP: 10
SQ FT: 13,000
SALES (est): 1.7MM **Privately Held**
WEB: www.angelinasteel.com
SIC: 3441 Fabricated structural metal

(G-14521)
CACTUS EXPRESS LP
3860 E State Highway 103 (75901-1079)
P.O. Box 40 (75902-0040)
PHONE..................................936 632-3031
Brent Bostost, *General Ptnr*
EMP: 80
SALES (est): 8.8MM **Privately Held**
SIC: 2741 Miscellaneous publishing

(G-14522)
CHEROKEE INDUS FABRICATORS LTD
5499 E State Highway 103 (75901-1292)
P.O. Box 1137 (75902-1137)
PHONE..................................936 634-2108
Tutt T Oliver, *Partner*
Rebecca Oliver, *Partner*
EMP: 16
SQ FT: 16,250
SALES (est): 2.7MM **Privately Held**
WEB: www.cherokeeindfab.net
SIC: 3444 3443 Sheet metalwork; fabri-
cated plate work (boiler shop)

(G-14523)
CONTRACTORS SUPPLIES INC (PA)
304 Webber St (75904-2652)
P.O. Box 150140 (75915-0140)
PHONE..................................936 634-3341
EMP: 30
SQ FT: 10,000
SALES (est): 30.6MM **Privately Held**
WEB: www.csiconcrete.com
SIC: 3273 5082 Ready-mixed concrete;
contractors' materials

(G-14524)
DOUBLE R BRND PRMIUM FD PDTS L
800 Ellen Trout Dr (75904-1224)
PHONE..................................713 868-0030
Rodney Roth, *President*
EMP: 100
SALES (est): 7.8MM **Privately Held**
SIC: 2099 Food preparations

(G-14525)
DREAMWRKS ANSTHESIA ASSOC PLLC
Also Called: Specialty Billings
505 S John Redditt Dr (75904-3120)
PHONE..................................936 639-3036
Gail Nichols, *Partner*
George Nichols, *Partner*
EMP: 10
SALES (est): 892.9K **Privately Held**
SIC: 3841 Anesthesia apparatus

(G-14526)
ELKCORP
Also Called: Cyber Shield
308 Ellen Trout Dr (75904-1356)
PHONE..................................936 633-6387
Ben McKnight, *Branch Mgr*
EMP: 20
SALES (corp-wide): 2.5B **Privately Held**
WEB: www.gaf.com
SIC: 3471 Electroplating of metals or
formed products
HQ: Elkcorp
14911 Quorum Dr Ste 600
Dallas TX 75254
972 851-0500

(G-14527)
FESCO LTD
3702 Ellen Trout Dr (75904-1115)
PHONE..................................936 632-7036
Dillon Coleman, *Manager*
EMP: 55
SALES (corp-wide): 201MM **Privately
Held**
WEB: www.fescoinc.com
SIC: 1389 Oil field services
PA: Fesco, Ltd.
1000 Fesco Dr
Alice TX 78332
361 664-3479

(G-14528)
FORESTRY SUPPLY SERVICE INC
Also Called: Ftr Equipment
3853 S Us Highway 69 (75901-2129)
PHONE..................................936 632-3394
Denton Metts, *Branch Mgr*
Glenda Roach,
EMP: 10 **Privately Held**
WEB: www.forestrysupply.net
SIC: 5999 5082 3531 Farm equipment &
supplies; logging & forestry machinery &
equipment; forestry related equipment
PA: Forestry Supply Service, Inc.
104 N Manuel St
Jasper TX 75951

(G-14529)
GEORGIA-PACIFIC LLC
1429 E Lufkin Ave (75901-4997)
P.O. Box 938 (75902-0938)
PHONE..................................936 634-3308
EMP: 65
SALES (corp-wide): 36.8B **Privately Held**
WEB: www.gp.com
SIC: 2821 Plastics materials & resins
HQ: Georgia-Pacific Llc
133 Peachtree St Nw
Atlanta GA 30303
404 652-4000

(G-14530)
HIGH ROLLER SAND OPERATING LLC
203 S 1st St (75901-3825)
PHONE..................................936 632-6033
Shandi Porterfield, *Manager*
EMP: 12
SALES (est): 1.1MM **Privately Held**
WEB: www.highrollersand.com
SIC: 3531 Construction machinery

(G-14531)
JEWELL HUDGENS INC
1107 N Raguet St (75904-2133)
P.O. Box 3626 (75903-3626)
PHONE..................................936 634-3731
Tom Billingsley, *President*
Ernest M Hudgens, *Vice Pres*
Manse Draper, *Sales Staff*
Tony Durant, *Sales Staff*
Cay Billingsley, *Manager*
EMP: 29 **EST:** 1947
SQ FT: 45,000
SALES (est): 5.8MM **Privately Held**
WEB: www.jewellhudgens.com
SIC: 3599 Machine shop, jobbing & repair
PA: B & H Roller Company Inc
1107 N Raguet St
Lufkin TX 75904
936 632-6691

(G-14532)
LOCKHEED MARTIN CORPORATION
1008 N John Redditt Dr (75904-2628)
P.O. Box 150340 (75915-0340)
PHONE..............................936 633-4800
Glenn David Woods, *Principal*
Samantha Helleck, *Opers Mgr*
William Lambert, *QC Mgr*
David Bennett, *Engineer*
Mark Yoder, *Engineer*
EMP: 99 Publicly Held
WEB: www.lockheedmartin.com
SIC: 3812 Search & navigation equipment
PA: Lockheed Martin Corporation
   6801 Rockledge Dr
   Bethesda MD 20817

(G-14533)
LONGHORN MULCHING INC
7003 E State Highway 103 (75901-1231)
PHONE..............................936 699-1160
James E Pyle, *President*
Leigh Ann Pyle, *Office Mgr*
EMP: 28
SQ FT: 14,000
SALES (est): 5MM Privately Held
WEB: www.longhornmulching.com
SIC: 1629 1794 0711 3531 Land clearing
   contractor

(G-14534)
LOVELADY DIRECTIONAL DRILLING
2946 Ted Trout Dr (75904-3552)
P.O. Box 150707 (75915-0707)
PHONE..............................936 675-4598
Henry Lovelady, *Owner*
EMP: 11
SQ FT: 8,400
SALES (est): 1.5MM Privately Held
SIC: 1381 Directional drilling oil & gas
   wells

(G-14535)
LUFKIN ARMATURE WORKS INC
Also Called: Lufkin Armture Works Whsng Div
2300 N Timberland Dr (75901-1328)
P.O. Box 455 (75902-0455)
PHONE..............................936 632-6607
EMP: 14
SALES (est): 3.2MM Privately Held
WEB: www.lufkinarmature.com
SIC: 5063 7694 Transformers, electric;
   switches, except electronic; motors, elec-
   tric; motor controls, starters & relays:
   electric; rewinding stators

(G-14536)
LUFKIN COCA COLA BOTTLING CO
Also Called: Coca-Cola
704 Webber St (75904-2612)
P.O. Box 878 (75902-0878)
PHONE..............................936 639-2355
Lynne D Haney, *President*
Jim Watkins, *Corp Secy*
James A Watkins, *Vice Pres*
Jana Mooney, *Finance*
Julie Rhodes, *Human Res Mgr*
EMP: 80
SALES (est): 16.9MM Privately Held
WEB: www.lufkincocacola.com
SIC: 2086 Bottled & canned soft drinks

(G-14537)
LUFKIN CREOSOTING CO INC
5865 S Us Highway 69 (75901-2170)
P.O. Box 1207 (75902-1207)
PHONE..............................936 634-2211
David F Vines, *President*
Christopher L Boone, *Vice Pres*
Marion V Brown, *Vice Pres*
Marion Brown, *Vice Pres*
Alejandro Cestero, *Vice Pres*
▲ **EMP: 81 EST: 1902**
SQ FT: 2,800
SALES (est): 14.5MM
SALES (corp-wide): 1.6B Privately Held
WEB: www.lufkintexas.org
SIC: 2491 2421 Preserving (creosoting) of
   wood; sawmills & planing mills, general

HQ: Mcfarland Cascade Holdings, Inc.
   1640 E Marc St
   Tacoma WA 98421
   253 572-3033

(G-14538)
LUFKIN ELECTRIC CO
2300 N Timberland Dr (75901-1328)
P.O. Box 1227 (75902-1227)
PHONE..............................936 639-2377
Vaughn Turner, *President*
Cecil Turner, *Treasurer*
John Worley, *Director*
EMP: 13
SALES (est): 2.4MM Privately Held
WEB: www.weisingerelectricinc.com
SIC: 7694 Electric motor repair

(G-14539)
LUFKIN GEARS LLC (PA)
Also Called: Baker Hughes
409 Ellis Ave (75904-3818)
PHONE..............................936 634-2211
John F Glick, *President*
Brian J Gifford, *Vice Pres*
C D Hay, *Vice Pres*
Scott Semlinger, *Vice Pres*
Christopher L Boone, *CFO*
◆ **EMP: 277 EST: 1902**
SQ FT: 33,000
SALES (est): 1B Privately Held
WEB: www.bhge.com
SIC: 3561 3321 3462 Pumps & pumping
   equipment; pumps, oil well & field; gray
   iron castings; ductile iron castings; iron &
   steel forgings; pump, compressor & tur-
   bine forgings

(G-14540)
LUFKIN GEARS LLC
300 Winston (75904)
PHONE..............................936 634-2211
Steve Reynolds, *Manager*
EMP: 200
SALES (corp-wide): 1B Privately Held
WEB: www.bhge.com
SIC: 1389 Truck trailers
PA: Lufkin Gears Llc
   409 Ellis Ave
   Lufkin TX 75904
   936 634-2211

(G-14541)
LUFKIN INDUSTRIES LLC
Lufkin Trailer Division
Hwy 69 S (75901)
PHONE..............................936 634-2211
Scott Semlnger, *Opers-Prdtn-Mfg*
EMP: 345
SALES (corp-wide): 1B Privately Held
WEB: www.bhge.com
SIC: 3715 3713 3711 Truck trailers; truck
   & bus bodies; motor vehicles & car bodies
PA: Lufkin Gears Llc
   409 Ellis Ave
   Lufkin TX 75904
   936 634-2211

(G-14542)
LUFKIN INDUSTRIES LLC
Also Called: Lufkin-Oilfield
3935 Fm 326 (75901-1720)
PHONE..............................936 634-2211
John F Glick, *President*
EMP: 24
SALES (corp-wide): 1B Privately Held
WEB: www.bhge.com
SIC: 1389 Oil field services
PA: Lufkin Gears Llc
   409 Ellis Ave
   Lufkin TX 75904
   936 634-2211

(G-14543)
LUFKINS SIX B CONSTRUCTION
Also Called: Six B Construction,
5168 Ted Trout Dr (75904-7401)
P.O. Box 154335 (75915-4335)
PHONE..............................936 632-3470
Danny M Vines, *President*
EMP: 15
SALES (est): 1.9MM Privately Held
SIC: 3629 Electronic generation equipment

(G-14544)
PID GROUP INC
400 Southpark Dr (75904-5708)
PHONE..............................936 699-4743
Scott Slusher, *Principal*
Daniel Alexander, *Marketing Staff*
EMP: 55
SQ FT: 6,000
SALES (est): 11MM Privately Held
WEB: www.pidservices.com
SIC: 3449 Miscellaneous metalwork

(G-14545)
PILGRIMS PRIDE CORPORATION
1800 W Frank Ave (75904-3100)
P.O. Box 547 (75902-0547)
PHONE..............................936 639-1174
Chad Martin, *Superintendent*
Arturo Fernandez, *Human Res Mgr*
EMP: 1500 Publicly Held
WEB: www.pilgrims.com
SIC: 2015 Chicken, slaughtered & dressed
HQ: Pilgrim's Pride Corporation
   1770 Promontory Cir
   Greeley CO 80634
   970 506-8000

(G-14546)
PUMPWORKS CASTINGS LLC
1001 E Park Ave (75901-1503)
PHONE..............................936 634-4206
James Maxwell,
Micheal Madison,
Kevin J Randle,
EMP: 18
SQ FT: 33,000
SALES (est): 2MM Privately Held
SIC: 3325 Alloy steel castings, except in-
   vestment

(G-14547)
QG PRINTING CORP
3001 Atkinson Dr (75901-1525)
PHONE..............................936 634-3357
Shane Norman, *Branch Mgr*
Brady Ivy, *Technician*
EMP: 11
SALES (corp-wide): 3.9B Publicly Held
WEB: www.quad.com
SIC: 2752 Commercial printing, offset
HQ: Qg Printing Corp.
   N61w23044 Harrys Way
   Sussex WI 53089

(G-14548)
REDZONE COIL TUBING LLC (DH)
203 S 1st St (75901-3825)
PHONE..............................936 632-2645
Benjamin Dee Winston, *President*
John Bull, *Regional Mgr*
Blaine Ducksworth, *Safety Mgr*
Quay Struckmeyer, *Opers Spvr*
Jason Skufca, *Engineer*
EMP: 63
SALES (est): 125MM
SALES (corp-wide): 832.9MM Publicly Held
WEB: www.redzonecoil.com
SIC: 1389 Oil field services
HQ: Beckman Production Services, Inc.
   3786 Beebe Rd
   Kalkaska MI 49646
   231 258-9524

(G-14549)
REDZONE HOLDCO LLC
203 S 1st St (75901-3825)
PHONE..............................936 632-2645
EMP: 14
SALES (est): 78.8K
SALES (corp-wide): 832.9MM Publicly Held
SIC: 1389 Oil field services
PA: Nine Energy Service, Inc.
   2001 Kirby Dr Ste 200
   Houston TX 77019
   281 730-5100

(G-14550)
RENFRO LOGGING I LTD
1404 E Denman Ave (75901-5860)
PHONE..............................936 208-6177
John Renfro, *Partner*

Karen Renfro, *Partner*
EMP: 20 EST: 1989
SALES (est): 1.8MM Privately Held
SIC: 2411 Logging camps & contractors

(G-14551)
SHIELDCOAT TECHNOLOGIES INC
Also Called: Cybershield of Texas
308 Ellen Trout Dr (75904-1356)
PHONE..............................936 633-6387
Bobby Marshall, *CEO*
James T Skelly, *President*
▲ **EMP: 45**
SQ FT: 130,000
SALES (est): 8.6MM Privately Held
WEB: www.cybershieldinc.com
SIC: 3089 Plates, plastic

(G-14552)
SOUTHERN NEWSPAPERS INC
Also Called: Lufkin Daily News
300 Ellis Ave (75904-3817)
P.O. Box 1089 (75902-1089)
PHONE..............................936 632-6631
Billy Ricks, *Production*
Debra Hughs, *Accounts Exec*
Jamie Derrow, *Mktg Dir*
Tammy Kedrowicz, *Adv Dir*
Macy Del, *Manager*
EMP: 52
SALES (corp-wide): 140.3MM Privately Held
WEB: www.sninews.com
SIC: 2711 Commercial printing & newspa-
   per publishing combined
PA: Southern Newspapers, Inc.
   5701 Woodway Dr Ste 131
   Houston TX 77057
   713 266-5481

(G-14553)
T & B CONSTRUCTION SVCS LLC
Also Called: Pipe Welding Specialist
4188 Fm 326 (75901-1893)
P.O. Box 166, Huntington (75949-0166)
PHONE..............................936 824-3914
Joe Johnson, *General Mgr*
Tim Johnson, *Mng Member*
Greg Burkett, *Manager*
EMP: 55
SQ FT: 36,000
SALES (est): 6.6MM Privately Held
WEB: www.tbcon.net
SIC: 3441 Building components, structural
   steel

(G-14554)
TEER LOGGING INC
Also Called: Teer, Wilbern
9793 E State Highway 103 (75901-1263)
PHONE..............................936 632-6862
Marjorie Teer, *President*
Wilbern Teer, *Vice Pres*
EMP: 14
SALES (est): 1.4MM Privately Held
SIC: 2411 Logging camps & contractors

(G-14555)
TEXAS METAL CASTING CO (PA)
5400 Lotus Ln (75904-1780)
P.O. Box 3259 (75903-3259)
PHONE..............................936 639-1131
Don E Smith, *President*
Mark Pope, *Vice Pres*
Truett Watts, *Purch Agent*
Rosemary Smith, *Treasurer*
EMP: 46 EST: 1968
SQ FT: 15,000
SALES (est): 6.3MM Privately Held
WEB: www.texasmetalcasting.com
SIC: 3366 Copper foundries

(G-14556)
WILLIAMS LOGGING
Also Called: Royce Williams Logging
401 E Denman Ave (75901-4001)
PHONE..............................936 632-6891
Royce Williams, *Owner*
Jessica McElroy, *Corp Secy*
EMP: 10
SQ FT: 800
SALES (est): 690K Privately Held
SIC: 2411 Logging camps & contractors

(G-14557)
WINSTON LAND & CATTLE CO INC
Also Called: General Ptnr Wnstn Lnd & Cattl
4501 Us Highway 59 N (75901-8513)
P.O. Box 2359 (75902-2359)
PHONE..................................936 634-6321
Benjamin D Winston, *President*
Simon W Winston, *Vice Pres*
EMP: 10 **EST:** 1970
SQ FT: 3,500
SALES (est): 1MM **Privately Held**
WEB: www.winston.propertyware.com
SIC: 6519 1311 1611 Real property lessors; crude petroleum production; general contractor, highway & street construction

Luling
Caldwell County

(G-14558)
ALEXANDER TANK CO
2400 E Pierce St (78648-4849)
P.O. Box 589 (78648-0589)
PHONE..................................830 875-2759
W B Alexander, *President*
Seth Powell, *General Mgr*
Ben F Alexander, *Vice Pres*
Ruby J Alexander, *Admin Sec*
Azemy Wells, *Administration*
EMP: 12
SALES (est): 2.2MM **Privately Held**
WEB: www.alexandertank.com
SIC: 3599 Machine shop, jobbing & repair

(G-14559)
APEX/FCC LLC
2200 E Pierce St (78648-4856)
P.O. Box 1135 (78648-1135)
PHONE..................................830 875-2429
Barry Dickens, *General Mgr*
EMP: 18
SALES (corp-wide): 5.8MM **Privately Held**
WEB: www.apexfcc.com
SIC: 1382 Oil & gas exploration services
PA: Apex/Fcc, L.L.C.
　　4137 S Sherwood Forest Bl
　　Baton Rouge LA 70816
　　225 766-0445

(G-14560)
EDF TRADING NORTH AMERICA LLC
930 E Pierce St (78648-2710)
P.O. Box 1110 (78648-1110)
PHONE..................................830 351-5075
James Schnieder, *Opers Mgr*
EMP: 10
SALES (corp-wide): 4.2MM **Privately Held**
WEB: www.edftrading.com
SIC: 1381 Drilling oil & gas wells
HQ: Edf Trading North America, Llc
　　601 Travis St Ste 1700
　　Houston TX 77002
　　281 781-0333

(G-14561)
ELGI RUBBER COMPANY LLC
600 N Magnolia Ave (78648-1951)
P.O. Box 1025 (78648-1025)
PHONE..................................830 875-5539
Bill Mohler, *General Mgr*
John Joseph,
Robert W Mohler,
▲ **EMP:** 38
SALES (est): 8.6MM **Privately Held**
WEB: www.elgirubber.com
SIC: 3069 Hard rubber & molded rubber products
PA: Elgi Rubber Company Limited
　　2000, Trichy Road,
　　Coimbatore TN 64100

(G-14562)
LULING WELL SERVICE
1251 Hoover St (78648-2025)
PHONE..................................830 875-9181
Francisco Obregon, *Partner*
Amiliano Obregon, *Partner*
EMP: 12

SALES (est): 581.3K **Privately Held**
SIC: 1389 Servicing oil & gas wells

(G-14563)
PROGRESS DRILLING INC
1575 N Magnolia Ave (78648)
PHONE..................................830 875-3442
James Montgomery, *President*
EMP: 45
SQ FT: 4,000
SALES (est): 6.5MM **Privately Held**
WEB: www.progressdrilling.com
SIC: 1381 Directional drilling oil & gas wells

(G-14564)
R & F INDUSTRIES INC
402 W Davis St (78648-2254)
P.O. Box 590 (78648-0590)
PHONE..................................830 875-6927
Raymond McGolthlin, *President*
Stanley McGlothlin, *Vice Pres*
Rose McGolthlin, *Director*
EMP: 10
SALES (est): 2.2MM **Privately Held**
WEB: www.randfindustries.com
SIC: 2899 Chemical preparations

(G-14565)
TEXSTAR ENERGY CORPORATION
402 W Davis St (78648-2254)
PHONE..................................830 875-5919
EMP: 9
SALES (est): 925.4K **Privately Held**
SIC: 1381 Oil/Gas Well Drilling

Lumberton
Hardin County

(G-14566)
BEAUMONT MACHINE WORKS INC
11357 Beasley Dr (77657)
P.O. Box 22639, Beaumont (77720-2639)
PHONE..................................409 838-0261
James R Travrsi, *President*
Frank Travrsi Jr, *Admin Sec*
EMP: 56
SALES (est): 8.6MM **Privately Held**
WEB: www.beaumontmachineworks.com
SIC: 3599 3443 Machine shop, jobbing & repair; fabricated plate work (boiler shop)

(G-14567)
DELTA STUDWELD INC
618 S Village Creek Pkwy (77657-7752)
PHONE..................................409 755-0720
Mike Neal, *Manager*
EMP: 13
SALES (corp-wide): 3.7MM **Privately Held**
WEB: www.deltastudweld.com
SIC: 3444 Studs & joists, sheet metal
PA: Delta Studweld Inc
　　21557 Provincial Blvd
　　Katy TX 77450
　　281 391-7410

(G-14568)
MERRILLS SOUTHERN MAID
Also Called: Southern Maid Donut
690 S Main St (77657-7571)
PHONE..................................409 755-2400
Dennis Merrill, *Owner*
EMP: 9
SALES (est): 275.4K **Privately Held**
WEB: www.southernmaiddonuts.com
SIC: 5461 2051 5311 5812 Doughnuts; doughnuts, except frozen; department stores; eating places

(G-14569)
RATLIFF INDUSTRIES INC
9514 Ratliff St (77657-6005)
P.O. Box 8359 (77657-0359)
PHONE..................................409 755-1830
Mike Ratliff, *President*
Van Ratliff, *Admin Sec*
EMP: 24
SQ FT: 14,000

SALES (est): 7.5MM **Privately Held**
WEB: www.ratliffinc.com
SIC: 3441 Fabricated structural metal

(G-14570)
SINGLETON ML INC
Also Called: Boutte's Boudin
568 N Lhs Dr (77657-8623)
P.O. Box 8030 (77657-0030)
PHONE..................................409 755-0893
Marion L Singleton, *President*
Loretta Singleton, *Vice Pres*
EMP: 12
SALES (est): 250K **Privately Held**
WEB: www.bouttesboudin.com
SIC: 2013 5421 5812 Sausages from purchased meat; meat markets, including freezer provisioners; Cajun restaurant

Lyford
Willacy County

(G-14571)
CITATION OIL & GAS CORP
Also Called: Willamar Plant
7766 Citation Cnty Rd (78569-2103)
P.O. Box 2 (78569-0002)
PHONE..................................956 248-5741
Mike Malone, *Manager*
EMP: 9
SALES (corp-wide): 283.5MM **Privately Held**
WEB: www.cogc.com
SIC: 1311 Crude petroleum production; natural gas production
PA: Citation Oil & Gas Corp.
　　14077 Cutten Rd
　　Houston TX 77069
　　281 891-1000

Lytle
Atascosa County

(G-14572)
ANDERSONS INC
Also Called: Andersons Lytle Grain, The
20615 Interstate 35 S (78052-3403)
PHONE..................................913 748-4401
Adam Weedman, *Branch Mgr*
EMP: 15
SALES (corp-wide): 8.1B **Publicly Held**
WEB: www.andersonsinc.com
SIC: 2041 Flour & other grain mill products
PA: The Andersons Inc
　　1947 Briarfield Blvd
　　Maumee OH 43537
　　419 893-5050

(G-14573)
CABINET CREATION INC
14421 Main St (78052-9721)
P.O. Box 722 (78052-0722)
PHONE..................................830 709-4116
Nolan Oakley, *President*
Fred Mosely, *Vice Pres*
EMP: 27
SQ FT: 10,500
SALES (est): 3.8MM **Privately Held**
WEB: www.ccicountertops.com
SIC: 2541 2521 2434 Counter & sink tops; wood office furniture; wood kitchen cabinets

(G-14574)
TRIPLE S WELDING CO
18303 Wisdom Rd (78052-9720)
PHONE..................................210 464-2878
Salvador Solis, *Co-Owner*
Amanda Grace Solis, *Co-Owner*
EMP: 15
SQ FT: 1,280
SALES (est): 1MM **Privately Held**
WEB: www.tripleswelding.com
SIC: 7692 Welding repair

Mabank
Kaufman County

(G-14575)
DELAFIELD CORPORATION
1103 N 3rd St (75147-8105)
PHONE..................................903 887-2860
Vivian Votava, *Manager*
Russell Lenz, *Manager*
EMP: 12
SALES (corp-wide): 40.4MM **Privately Held**
WEB: www.dftcorp.com
SIC: 3492 Fluid power valves & hose fittings
PA: Delafield Corporation
　　1520 Flower Ave
　　Duarte CA 91010
　　626 303-0740

(G-14576)
EAGLE METAL PRODUCTS LLC (PA)
802 N 3rd St (75147-2357)
P.O. Box 1267 (75147-1267)
PHONE..................................903 887-3581
Thomas F Whatley, *President*
Gene Coats, *Vice Pres*
Wayne McDonald, *Vice Pres*
Matt Vinson, *Engineer*
Gary Sapp, *Treasurer*
EMP: 23
SQ FT: 15,000
SALES (est): 5.9MM **Privately Held**
WEB: www.eaglemetal.com
SIC: 3469 3452 3446 3443 Stamping metal for the trade; bolts, nuts, rivets & washers; architectural metalwork; fabricated plate work (boiler shop); fabricated structural metal

(G-14577)
JIT MANUFACTURING INC
1420 S 3rd St (75147-7580)
P.O. Box 1329 (75147-1329)
PHONE..................................903 887-0226
David L Dealva Sr, *CEO*
Victoria Bishop, *General Mgr*
Kevin Bishop, *Vice Pres*
Lynda Chiles, *Controller*
▲ **EMP:** 50
SQ FT: 15,000
SALES: 7MM **Privately Held**
WEB: www.jitmfginc.com
SIC: 3993 Advertising artwork

(G-14578)
LSMW LONE STAR MACHINE WORKS
2048 S 3rd St (75147-7346)
PHONE..................................844 837-4200
Mikel Craig Payne, *President*
Jack Atkinson, *General Mgr*
Karlissa P Phillips, *Office Mgr*
EMP: 44
SQ FT: 40,000
SALES (est): 12MM **Privately Held**
WEB: www.lonestarmachineworks.com
SIC: 3599 Machine shop, jobbing & repair

(G-14579)
MITCHELL MACHINE & FABRICATING
16490 Fm 90 (75147-3051)
P.O. Box 852138, Mesquite (75185-2138)
PHONE..................................903 880-0249
Norma Mitchell, *President*
Harold R Mitchell, *Vice Pres*
Robert Mitchell, *Manager*
EMP: 10
SQ FT: 5,000
SALES (est): 840K **Privately Held**
SIC: 3545 3544 3089 3444 Precision tools, machinists'; forms (molds), for foundry & plastics working machinery; industrial molds; injection molding of plastics; sheet metalwork; test equipment for electronic & electrical circuits

(G-14580)
MONITOR
Also Called: Media One
1316 S 3rd St Ste 108 (75147-7680)
P.O. Box 48 (75147-0048)
PHONE.................................903 887-4511
John Buzzetta, *President*
EMP: 20
SALES (est): 500K **Privately Held**
WEB: www.themonitor.net
SIC: 2711 Commercial printing & newspaper publishing combined; newspapers, publishing & printing

(G-14581)
SIMPLFIED STRL THRMFORMING INC
Also Called: S.S.T. Enterprises
14062 State Highway 198 (75147-5444)
P.O. Box 428 (75147-0428)
PHONE.................................903 887-8546
Sam Orsak, *President*
Barbara Orsak, *Vice Pres*
J Stephen Orsak, *Vice Pres*
EMP: 9
SQ FT: 6,500
SALES (est): 375K **Privately Held**
SIC: 3089 Extruded finished plastic products

(G-14582)
SOLAR TURBINES INCORPORATED
904 Fm 90 (75147-8126)
PHONE.................................903 880-1461
Brad Turner, *Project Mgr*
Brandon Bannister, *Mfg Staff*
Aaron Soucy, *Design Engr*
Paul Kieffer, *Branch Mgr*
EMP: 285
SALES (corp-wide): 53.8B **Publicly Held**
WEB: www.solarturbines.com
SIC: 3511 Turbines & turbine generator sets & parts
HQ: Solar Turbines Incorporated
2200 Pacific Hwy
San Diego CA 92101
619 544-5000

(G-14583)
SOLAR TURBINES INCORPORATED
904 Solar Turbine Way # 90 (75147-8116)
P.O. Box 1486 (75147-1486)
PHONE.................................903 880-1200
Steve Baskin, *Mfg Staff*
Alice Munis, *Buyer*
Ed Schmidt, *Manager*
EMP: 10
SALES (corp-wide): 53.8B **Publicly Held**
WEB: www.solarturbines.com
SIC: 3511 Gas turbine generator set units, complete
HQ: Solar Turbines Incorporated
2200 Pacific Hwy
San Diego CA 92101
619 544-5000

Madisonville
Madison County

(G-14584)
B & J MACHINE WORKS INC
402 Industrial Park Ln (77864-4499)
P.O. Box 568 (77864-0568)
PHONE.................................936 348-6371
T J Savell, *President*
Howard B Savell, *Vice Pres*
Jane Savell, *Manager*
Billy Savell, *Consultant*
EMP: 12
SQ FT: 6,250
SALES (est): 1.7MM **Privately Held**
WEB: www.bjmachineworks.com
SIC: 3599 Machine shop, jobbing & repair

(G-14585)
C P BAILEY CNSTR CO INC
Also Called: Centex Supply
1618 Highway 75 N (77864-4375)
P.O. Box 218 (77864-0218)
PHONE.................................936 348-3627
Don Bodenhamer, *President*

Jt Vincent, *Purchasing*
Pam Bodenhamer, *Treasurer*
EMP: 9
SALES (est): 1.8MM **Privately Held**
WEB: www.centexsupply.net
SIC: 1389 4925 Gas field services; gas production and/or distribution

(G-14586)
DASILVEIRA SOUTHWEST INC
712 Industrial Blvd (77864)
PHONE.................................936 349-1900
Elieer Guzman, *President*
Peter Cuellar, *Corp Secy*
Jose Alcantar, *Vice Pres*
▲ EMP: 21
SQ FT: 50,000
SALES: 2.7MM **Privately Held**
WEB: www.dasilveira.com
SIC: 3523 Barn stanchions & standards

(G-14587)
JAC ENTERPRISES INC
Also Called: Midway Trailer & Equipment
1809 Interstate 45 N (77864-4886)
PHONE.................................936 348-3997
Wilma A Lane, *President*
John Lane, *Manager*
EMP: 12 EST: 2007
SALES (est): 1.1MM **Privately Held**
WEB: www.bigtextrailerworld.com
SIC: 3715 5012 Truck trailers; automobiles & other motor vehicles

(G-14588)
JAC ENTERPRISES INC
Also Called: Midway Tire
301 Crossroads (77864-3419)
P.O. Box 1404 (77864-1404)
PHONE.................................936 348-3934
Wilma A Lane, *President*
Wilma A Layne, *President*
EMP: 12
SALES (est): 2MM **Privately Held**
WEB: www.bigtextrailerworld.com
SIC: 3713 7692 Truck & bus bodies; welding repair

(G-14589)
MADISONVILLE SERVICE CONTR LP
3989 Interstate 45 N (77864-4468)
P.O. Box 201 (77864-0201)
PHONE.................................936 348-5506
Dennis Williams, *Partner*
EMP: 10
SALES (est): 790K **Privately Held**
SIC: 1389 Oil field services

(G-14590)
TEXAS INTRNAL PIPE COATING LLC
8463 Highway 75 S (77864-2323)
P.O. Box 1749 (77864-6749)
PHONE.................................936 348-2508
James T Davis, *President*
Gary Rost, *General Mgr*
Robert Torres, *Vice Pres*
Robert Allen, *Maint Spvr*
Steve Shaffer, *Sales Mgr*
EMP: 49
SQ FT: 50,000
SALES (est): 8MM **Privately Held**
WEB: www.texasinternalpipecoating.com
SIC: 3479 Coating of metals & formed products
HQ: Hilong Holding Limited
Rm 3206 Times Sq Twr One
Causeway Bay HK

Magnolia
Montgomery County

(G-14591)
BINCO CONTRACTING SERVICES
17619 Winding Creek Ln (77355-3264)
PHONE.................................281 356-3144
Doug Binford, *Owner*
Delores Binford, *Partner*
EMP: 13

SALES (est): 732K **Privately Held**
SIC: 3444 5051 Roof deck, sheet metal; steel decking

(G-14592)
BISON PROFAB INC
12519 Wanda Ln (77354-2060)
P.O. Box 1359, Tomball (77377-1359)
PHONE.................................281 356-0026
David M Sigurdson, *President*
Jake Kelly, *Vice Pres*
Michael J Stock, *Vice Pres*
Lisa Fowler, *Traffic Mgr*
Thomas Polcyn, *Opers Staff*
EMP: 35
SQ FT: 36,650
SALES (est): 8.6MM **Privately Held**
WEB: www.bisonprofab.com
SIC: 3444 Sheet metal specialties, not stamped

(G-14593)
CAMPBELL CONCRETE & MTLS LP
19503 Fm 1488 Rd (77355)
PHONE.................................281 356-5444
EMP: 11
SQ FT: 2,380
SALES (corp-wide): 20.8B **Privately Held**
WEB: www.michaeljames.com
SIC: 3273 Ready-mixed concrete
HQ: Campbell Concrete & Materials, L.P.
16155 Park Row Ste 120
Houston TX 77084
281 592-5201

(G-14594)
CFG INDUSTRIES LLC
22535 Magnolia Hills Dr (77354-8895)
PHONE.................................281 259-7244
EMP: 9 EST: 2016
SALES (est): 166.9K **Privately Held**
SIC: 3491 Industrial valves

(G-14595)
CHAMPION SALES & MANUFACTURING
32510 Decker Prairie Rd (77355-3875)
P.O. Box 1279, Pinehurst (77362-1279)
PHONE.................................281 356-6162
Carolyn K Franey, *President*
Jeri Lynn Litterer, *Treasurer*
EMP: 22
SQ FT: 7,000
SALES (est): 4.5MM **Privately Held**
WEB: www.championgaskets.com
SIC: 3053 Gaskets, all materials

(G-14596)
CHIEF FIRE SYSTEMS INC
32628 Decker Prairie Rd (77355-4277)
P.O. Box 419, Pinehurst (77362-0419)
PHONE.................................281 252-5800
Brett Camden, *President*
Robert Camden, *Vice Pres*
Eli Milsas, *Vice Pres*
EMP: 60
SALES (corp-wide): 2.4B **Privately Held**
WEB: www.chieffiresystems.net
SIC: 3569 Sprinkler systems, fire: automatic
HQ: Century Fire Protection, Llc
2450 Satellite Blvd
Duluth GA 30096

(G-14597)
COMPLETE MFG SVCS INC
33525 Dobbin Huffsmith Rd (77354-2071)
P.O. Box 1612 (77353-1612)
PHONE.................................281 252-3111
Ronald Smith, *President*
EMP: 24
SQ FT: 17,500
SALES (est): 4.9MM **Privately Held**
WEB: www.completemanufacturing.net
SIC: 3441 Fabricated structural metal

(G-14598)
COYOTE READY MIX LLC ✪
25277 Fm 1488 Rd (77355-2071)
PHONE.................................832 432-2025
Krystopher Moore, *Mng Member*
Chevella Moore, *Administration*
Glen Bonds,
Jewana Smith, *Assistant*

EMP: 13 EST: 2020
SALES (est): 541.3K **Privately Held**
SIC: 3273 Ready-mixed concrete

(G-14599)
CROWN TO GROUND SUPPLY INC
6315b Fm 1488 Rd Ste 148 (77354-2526)
PHONE.................................936 588-7457
Terra Crissman, *Exec Dir*
▲ EMP: 15
SALES (est): 2.3MM **Privately Held**
WEB: www.crowntogroundsupply.com
SIC: 3498 5085 3699 Fabricated pipe & fittings; industrial fittings; electrical equipment & supplies

(G-14600)
DIAMOND LIVING LLC
33031 Tamina Rd (77354-2273)
PHONE.................................281 766-1600
James A Caldwell,
Joseph Duncan,
▲ EMP: 10 EST: 2010
SQ FT: 8,000
SALES (est): 6.9MM **Privately Held**
WEB: www.dlfloors.com
SIC: 3253 2426 Ceramic wall & floor tile; flooring, hardwood

(G-14601)
DIRECTIONAL PRJ SUPPORT INC
33311 Lois Ln (77354-3257)
PHONE.................................281 259-7819
Douglas R Stern Jr, *Principal*
Daniel Calhoun, *Chief*
Tina Kelley, *Agent*
Amanda Kelley, *Administration*
EMP: 9
SALES (est): 2.4MM **Privately Held**
WEB: www.dpshdd.com
SIC: 1381 Directional drilling oil & gas wells

(G-14602)
DRW PRECISION INC
13113 Noack Rd (77355-7942)
PHONE.................................281 356-4900
Devin Williams, *President*
Karrie Williams, *Vice Pres*
EMP: 10
SALES (est): 1.7MM **Privately Held**
WEB: www.drwprecision.com
SIC: 3599 Machine shop, jobbing & repair

(G-14603)
ELITE ENTRANCES LLC
30225 Tudor Way Ste B (77355-4299)
P.O. Box 1017 (77353-1017)
PHONE.................................832 922-7444
Jason Martens, *President*
EMP: 25
SALES (est): 609.7K **Privately Held**
WEB: www.eliteentrances.com
SIC: 3699 1751 Door opening & closing devices, electrical; window & door (prefabricated) installation

(G-14604)
EMERALD MASONRY & STUCCO
28075 Fm 2978 Rd Ste A (77354-5367)
PHONE.................................281 356-9400
Michael R Brock, *Principal*
EMP: 9
SALES (est): 1.3MM **Privately Held**
WEB: www.woodlandsonline.com
SIC: 3299 Stucco

(G-14605)
ENVIROFLEX DESIGN & MFG
Also Called: EDM
29639 Fm 2978 Rd (77354-5123)
P.O. Box 260, Tomball (77377-0260)
PHONE.................................281 356-6700
Michael D Wiseman, *President*
▲ EMP: 10
SQ FT: 7,000
SALES (est): 2.3MM **Privately Held**
WEB: www.enviroflexmfg.com
SIC: 3589 3537 Sewage treatment equipment; dollies (hand or power trucks), industrial except mining

(G-14606)
FILTER-ALL INC
6907 Fm 1488 Rd (77354-1436)
P.O. Box 1250 (77353-1250)
PHONE..................................281 356-1257
Tom Bivens, *President*
Shirley Bivens, *Corp Secy*
EMP: 20
SQ FT: 10,000
SALES (est): 3.6MM **Privately Held**
WEB: www.filterallinc.com
SIC: 3564 Filters, air: furnaces, air conditioning equipment, etc.

(G-14607)
FIVE - JAB INC
16202 Butera Rd (77355-3793)
P.O. Box 1063, Tomball (77377-1063)
PHONE..................................281 356-7767
James Bohannon, *President*
Janet Bohannon, *President*
Brandy Jatzlau, *Production*
Melissa Pampell, *Production*
King Tomlinson, *Engineer*
EMP: 60
SALES (est): 21MM **Privately Held**
WEB: www.fivejab.com
SIC: 1311 Crude petroleum & natural gas

(G-14608)
HYVAIR CORPORATION (PA)
Also Called: Hydraulic and Pneumatic Eqp
31341 Friendship Dr (77355-2603)
PHONE..................................281 259-7768
Kenneth Vairin, *President*
Betty Vairin, *Vice Pres*
Mike Bellamy, *Sales Staff*
Scott Vairin, *Manager*
▲ **EMP:** 18 **EST:** 1977
SQ FT: 15,000
SALES (est): 5.3MM **Privately Held**
WEB: www.hyvair.com
SIC: 3594 5084 Fluid power pumps & motors; hydraulic systems equipment & supplies

(G-14609)
IBE SMT EQUIPMENT INC
318 Corporate Wood Dr (77354-2381)
PHONE..................................281 259-9660
Stephen Hakes, *President*
Pamela Hakes, *Vice Pres*
Alex Dalgleish, *Director*
Jared Garver, *Director*
▲ **EMP:** 11
SQ FT: 30,000
SALES (est): 2.2MM **Privately Held**
WEB: www.ibesmt.com
SIC: 3672 5065 Printed circuit boards; electronic parts & equipment

(G-14610)
INSIGNIA MARKETING INC
Also Called: Visicare
32731 Egypt Ln Ste 301 (77354-3662)
PHONE..................................281 465-0040
Christine McAtee, *President*
Shanon Hall, *Supervisor*
▲ **EMP:** 15
SQ FT: 5,000
SALES (est): 1.7MM **Privately Held**
WEB: www.insignia24hr.com
SIC: 5199 3999 3993 7336 Advertising specialties; advertising display products; signs & advertising specialties; commercial art & graphic design; medical & hospital equipment

(G-14611)
J 2 FABRICATIONS LLC
Also Called: J2 Fabrications
327 Magnolia Bus Pk Dr (77354-8913)
PHONE..................................281 989-2984
EMP: 10 **EST:** 2018
SALES (est): 819.8K **Privately Held**
WEB: www.j2fab.com
SIC: 3441 Fabricated structural metal

(G-14612)
KDR OUTDOOR & LEISURE PDTS INC
Also Called: Kistler Rods
30603 Beyette Rd (77355-2632)
PHONE..................................281 259-8033
Trey Kistler, *President*
Cindy Pyle, *Sales Mgr*

▲ **EMP:** 10
SALES (est): 200K **Privately Held**
WEB: www.kistlerrods.com
SIC: 5941 3949 Bait & tackle; rods & rod parts, fishing

(G-14613)
L B FOSTER COMPANY
21270 Fm 1488 Rd (77355-1615)
PHONE..................................832 934-3107
Rick Schaefer, *Manager*
EMP: 50
SQ FT: 30,000
SALES (corp-wide): 655MM **Publicly Held**
WEB: www.lbfoster.com
SIC: 4225 5051 3441 3321 General warehousing & storage; metals service centers & offices; fabricated structural metal; gray & ductile iron foundries; blast furnaces & steel mills; plastics foam products
PA: L. B. Foster Company
　　415 Holiday Dr 1
　　Pittsburgh PA 15220
　　412 928-3400

(G-14614)
LEGACY TUBULAR LLC
39013 Fm 1774 Rd (77355-2642)
P.O. Box 1347 (77353-1347)
PHONE..................................281 363-1900
Jennifer Stringer, *Mng Member*
Preston Benditz,
EMP: 11 **EST:** 2012
SALES (est): 1.7MM **Privately Held**
WEB: www.legacytubular.com
SIC: 3317 Steel pipe & tubes

(G-14615)
LINCOLN MANUFACTURING INC (PA)
31209 Fm 2978 Rd (77354-2388)
PHONE..................................281 252-9494
Eric Ward, *President*
Rick Cook, *General Mgr*
Chris Ritter, *General Mgr*
Jacob Sponseller, *General Mgr*
John Burns, *Vice Pres*
◆ **EMP:** 350
SQ FT: 65,000
SALES (est): 118.7MM **Privately Held**
WEB: www.lincolnmanufacturing.com
SIC: 3533 5082 Oil field machinery & equipment; oil field equipment

(G-14616)
LINCOLN MANUFACTURING INC
31209 2978 Rd (77354)
PHONE..................................281 357-1541
Erik Ward, *President*
EMP: 60
SALES (corp-wide): 118.7MM **Privately Held**
WEB: www.lincolnmanufacturing.com
SIC: 5511 5082 3498 Automobiles, new & used; oil field equipment; fabricated pipe & fittings
PA: Lincoln Manufacturing, Inc.
　　31209 Fm 2978 Rd
　　Magnolia TX 77354
　　281 252-9494

(G-14617)
M&M MACHINE SHOP LLC
101 Morris Rd (77354-3900)
PHONE..................................832 934-1542
Marina Andras, *Principal*
EMP: 21 **EST:** 2008
SALES (est): 3.2MM **Privately Held**
WEB: www.mm-machine.com
SIC: 3599 Machine shop, jobbing & repair

(G-14618)
MERLA LLC
Also Called: Merla Wellhead Solutions
706 Honea Egypt Rd (77354-2394)
PHONE..................................281 931-6900
Carlos Marques, *Mng Member*
Samit Suheil,
▲ **EMP:** 25
SALES (est): 5.6MM **Privately Held**
WEB: www.merla.com
SIC: 3823 3321 Industrial instrmnts msrmnt display/control process variable; water pipe, cast iron

(G-14619)
NABORS DRILLING TECH USA INC
Also Called: Canrig Drilling Technology
14703 Fm 1488 Rd (77354-8820)
PHONE..................................281 259-8887
Gregory Kostiuk, *Vice Pres*
Bobby Coleman, *Safety Mgr*
Richard Pratt, *Senior Buyer*
Pamela Swearingen, *Buyer*
Steven Forrest, *Technical Mgr*
EMP: 400 **Privately Held**
WEB: www.nabors.com
SIC: 1389 Oil field services
HQ: Nabors Drilling Technologies Usa, Inc.
　　515 W Greens Rd Ste 1200
　　Houston TX 77067
　　281 874-0035

(G-14620)
PILEWORKS LLC
Also Called: Ape Piling Products, LLC
24430 Fm 1488 Rd Ste A (77355-2043)
PHONE..................................936 372-9760
Lawrence Hughes, *CEO*
EMP: 25
SALES (est): 1.9MM **Privately Held**
WEB: www.pileworks.com
SIC: 3532 Drills, bits & similar equipment
PA: American Piledriving Equipment, Inc.
　　7032 S 196th St
　　Kent WA 98032

(G-14621)
PRODUCTION FACILITIES EQP INC
28010 Fm 2978 Rd (77354-5110)
PHONE..................................281 356-1107
Paul H Carr, *President*
Lance H Carr, *Vice Pres*
Jacob Carr, *Sales Staff*
EMP: 30
SQ FT: 3,000
SALES (est): 6.7MM **Privately Held**
WEB: www.pfecinc.com
SIC: 1389 Oil field services

(G-14622)
PROFESSIONAL FABRICATION INC
Also Called: Pro Fab
714c Honea Egypt Rd Ste C (77354-2394)
PHONE..................................936 321-7070
Jennifer Walker, *President*
Henry Walker, *Vice Pres*
EMP: 25
SQ FT: 24,000
SALES (est): 2.7MM **Privately Held**
WEB: www.profabincorporated.com
SIC: 1799 3589 Food service equipment installation; commercial cooking & food-warming equipment

(G-14623)
RAMIN CORPORATION
39019 Fm 149 Rd (77354-1801)
PHONE..................................281 356-5178
James A Ramin, *CEO*
Stacy Collins, *President*
Sue A Ramin, *Principal*
Sue Ramin, *Exec VP*
Brad Webb, *VP Opers*
EMP: 12
SQ FT: 7,500
SALES (est): 1MM **Privately Held**
WEB: www.ramincorporation.com
SIC: 3229 8711 Scientific glassware; consulting engineer

(G-14624)
RICKETT RICKY SAND & GRAVEL
41922 N Mill Dr (77354-1850)
P.O. Box 1242 (77353-1242)
PHONE..................................281 356-3103
Ricky Rickett, *Owner*
EMP: 10
SALES (est): 922K **Privately Held**
SIC: 1442 Gravel mining

(G-14625)
RUSH APPAREL LLC
1810 Cattle Dr (77354-5072)
PHONE..................................713 208-5194
Paul Ivanovsky, *Mng Member*

EMP: 10
SALES (est): 15MM **Privately Held**
WEB: www.shop.emmalousboutique.com
SIC: 5611 5137 5621 7372 Men's & boys' clothing stores; clothing, men's & boys': everyday, except suits & sportswear; women's & children's clothing; women's clothing stores; application computer software

(G-14626)
SCAN-PAC MFG INC
Also Called: Texas Friction Materials
31502 Sugar Bend Dr (77355-6401)
P.O. Box 980 (77353-0980)
PHONE..................................281 356-1640
Shivaglal Cheruvalath, *President*
Richard Barr, *Vice Pres*
Andrew Huntington, *Engineer*
David Hunt, *Accounts Mgr*
Janice Gerard, *Cust Mgr*
EMP: 20
SALES (corp-wide): 13MM **Privately Held**
WEB: www.scanpac.com
SIC: 3568 5082 3536 3429 Bearings, bushings & blocks; oil field equipment; hoists, cranes & monorails; manufactured hardware (general); ceramic fiber
PA: Scan-Pac Mfg., Inc.
　　N84w13480 Leon Rd Ste A
　　Menomonee Falls WI 53051
　　262 250-0429

(G-14627)
SELECT MAT LLC
30355 Old Hockley Rd (77355-6073)
PHONE..................................833 205-1515
Joshua King, *CEO*
Cecil Bell Jr,
Kerri Prentice,
EMP: 14
SALES (est): 136.9K **Privately Held**
WEB: www.selectmat.com
SIC: 5199 2448 2491 Wood carvings; skids, wood; poles, posts & pilings: treated wood

(G-14628)
TEXAS GAS UTILITIES LLC
9750 Fm 1488 Rd (77354-1619)
PHONE..................................281 252-6700
Robert Barnwell, *Mng Member*
EMP: 10
SALES (est): 1.6MM **Privately Held**
WEB: www.txgas.net
SIC: 2813 Industrial gases

(G-14629)
THIRD COAST SERVICES LLC
36530 Coleman Rd (77355-1502)
PHONE..................................832 934-0240
James Giles, *President*
Josh Jakubik, *Vice Pres*
Joshua D Jakubik,
EMP: 100
SALES (est): 13.2MM **Privately Held**
WEB: www.thirdcoastservices.com
SIC: 3669 1799 1731 Traffic signals, electric; sign installation & maintenance; lighting contractor

(G-14630)
TIM YOCKEY
Also Called: Turnkey Anticorrosion
32550 Decker Prairie Rd (77355-3875)
PHONE..................................281 252-6175
Tim Yockey, *Owner*
EMP: 10
SQ FT: 15,000
SALES (est): 721.8K **Privately Held**
WEB: www.anticorrosiontech.com
SIC: 5084 3479 8748 Hydraulic systems equipment & supplies; coating or wrapping steel pipe; business consulting

(G-14631)
TOMBALL SHEET METAL LP
24620 Hardin Store Rd (77354-3913)
PHONE..................................281 356-1200
Tim Collins, *Partner*
Linda Black, *Office Mgr*
EMP: 30 **EST:** 1978
SQ FT: 5,000

SALES (est): 6.5MM **Privately Held**
WEB: www.tomballsheetmetal.com
SIC: 3444 Sheet metalwork

(G-14632)
TPWS INC
Also Called: Teale Pipewell Solutions
21602 Timber Ridge Dr (77355-4981)
PHONE..................................713 291-5518
Robert Teale, *President*
EMP: 12 EST: 2010
SALES (est): 1MM **Privately Held**
WEB: www.tealepipeweldsolutions.com
SIC: 3548 Gas welding equipment

(G-14633)
TUBAL CAIN INDUSTRIES INC
Also Called: Tubal Cain Hydraulic Solutions
706 Honea Egypt Rd (77354-2394)
P.O. Box 2393, Beaumont (77704-2393)
PHONE..................................281 789-7087
Alexon David, *Branch Mgr*
EMP: 15
SALES (corp-wide): 13.6MM **Privately Held**
WEB: www.tubal-cain.com
SIC: 3315 Welded steel wire fabric
PA: Tubal Cain Industries, Inc.
5665 N Main St
Vidor TX 77662
409 786-1783

Malakoff
Henderson County

(G-14634)
BAIKOWSKI MALAKOFF INC
1631 W Royall Blvd (75148-6202)
P.O. Box 487 (75148-0487)
PHONE..................................903 489-1910
Tom Carbone, *President*
Tom Lassanske, *Technology*
◆ EMP: 15
SQ FT: 50,000
SALES (est): 3.6MM
SALES (corp-wide): 37.4MM **Privately Held**
WEB: www.baikowskimalakoff.com
SIC: 2819 3399 Industrial inorganic chemicals; aluminum atomized powder
HQ: Baikowski International Corp
6601 Northpark Blvd Ste H
Charlotte NC 28216
704 587-7100

(G-14635)
IRONHORSE UNLIMITED INC
Also Called: Malakoff Trading
11101 State Highway 31 W (75148-7158)
P.O. Box 578 (75148-0578)
PHONE..................................903 489-2075
Phillip Surls, *President*
Keith Butler, *General Mgr*
Kim Surls, *Vice Pres*
Lindsay Dixon, *Admin Sec*
EMP: 175
SALES (est): 3.9MM **Privately Held**
WEB: www.ironhorseunlimited.com
SIC: 1389 Cementing oil & gas well casings

(G-14636)
OLIVER MACHINERY INC
Also Called: OLIVER MACHINERY INC DBA OLIVER MFG
10847 State Highway 31 W (75148-7156)
P.O. Box 788 (75148-0788)
PHONE..................................903 489-2250
Brenda Oliver, *President*
EMP: 10 EST: 2013
SALES (est): 1.2MM **Privately Held**
WEB: www.oliverlonghorns.com
SIC: 3541 Machine tools, metal cutting type

(G-14637)
TEMPERTURE MEASUREMENT SYSTEMS
1502 E Royall Blvd (75148-9247)
PHONE..................................800 967-6498
Dale Stout, *President*
Kelly Diane Grace, *Vice Pres*
EMP: 20 EST: 1980
SQ FT: 13,000

SALES (est): 4.5MM **Privately Held**
WEB: www.tms80.com
SIC: 3823 3829 Temperature measurement instruments, industrial; measuring & controlling devices

Malone
Hill County

(G-14638)
HUSE PROCESSING INC
Also Called: Huse Country Meats
3697 State Highway 171 (76660-3053)
PHONE..................................254 533-2205
EMP: 9
SQ FT: 15,000
SALES (est): 1.4MM **Privately Held**
WEB: www.husescountrymeats.com
SIC: 2011 2013 Meat packing plants; sausages & other prepared meats

Manchaca
Travis County

(G-14639)
JELLISON INC
Also Called: Jelco
11405 Conroy Ln (78652-3904)
P.O. Box 151085, Austin (78715-1085)
PHONE..................................512 282-5256
Jared Jelllison, *President*
Jordon Jellison, *Vice Pres*
EMP: 20
SALES (est): 3.9MM **Privately Held**
WEB: www.jellisoncompany.com
SIC: 2426 Flooring, hardwood

(G-14640)
PROPERTY WORKS CENTRAL TEXAS
Also Called: Manchaca Metals
12928 Lowden Ln Unit G (78652-3634)
PHONE..................................512 940-9353
Kyle Lane Albrecht, *President*
Kyle Albrecht, *Mng Member*
EMP: 13
SALES (est): 967.3K **Privately Held**
WEB: www.propertyworksofcentraltexas.com
SIC: 1629 3441 Land clearing contractor; fabricated structural metal

(G-14641)
PROTOTYPE MACHINE CO
Randolph Austin Co, Div
2119 W Fm 1626 (78652-4501)
P.O. Box 988 (78652-0589)
PHONE..................................512 282-1590
EMP: 40
SQ FT: 70,660
SALES (corp-wide): 10.3MM **Privately Held**
WEB: www.randolphaustin.com
SIC: 3599 3089 3561 3498 Machine shop, jobbing & repair; extruded finished plastic products; pumps & pumping equipment; fabricated pipe & fittings; laminated plastics plate & sheet
PA: Prototype Machine Co.
818 Prototype Rd
Flatonia TX 78941
361 865-3230

Manor
Travis County

(G-14642)
AIR LIQUIDE AMERICA CORP
12700 Beltex Rd (78653-4556)
PHONE..................................512 748-5943
Benoit Potier, *CEO*
Pascal Vinet, *Vice Pres*
Steve Popst, *Executive*
EMP: 12
SALES (est): 1.8MM **Privately Held**
SIC: 2813 Carbon dioxide

(G-14643)
ASSOCIATED SUPPLY COMPANY INC
12805 Us Highway 290 E (78653-4507)
PHONE..................................512 272-8922
Kirby Carpenter, *Branch Mgr*
Lorena Benavides, *Manager*
EMP: 33
SALES (corp-wide): 127.4MM **Privately Held**
WEB: www.ascojcb.com
SIC: 5211 7359 5082 3531 Lumber & other building materials; stores & yards equipment rental; contractors' materials; backhoes, tractors, cranes, plows & similar equipment
PA: Associated Supply Company, Inc.
2102 E Slaton Rd
Lubbock TX 79404
806 745-2000

(G-14644)
AUSTIN TEXAS PRINT INC
12917 Snow Ln (78653-5191)
PHONE..................................512 507-2684
James Graham, *CEO*
EMP: 9
SALES (est): 974.8K **Privately Held**
WEB: www.austintexasprint.com
SIC: 2752 Commercial printing, offset

(G-14645)
AUSTINUTS WHOLESALE INC
12911 Beltex Rd (78653-4510)
PHONE..................................512 272-8007
Doron Ilai, *President*
Ramiro Sanchez, *Vice Pres*
◆ EMP: 40
SQ FT: 10,500
SALES (est): 7.1MM **Privately Held**
WEB: www.austinuts.com
SIC: 2068 Salted & roasted nuts & seeds

(G-14646)
BRISTLECONE VENTURES 2 LLC
Also Called: Falcon Structures
7717 Gilbert Rd (78653-5468)
P.O. Box 142714, Austin (78714-2714)
PHONE..................................512 231-9603
Stephen Shang, *CEO*
EMP: 20
SALES (est): 3MM **Privately Held**
WEB: www.falconstructures.com
SIC: 2451 Mobile buildings: for commercial use

(G-14647)
C H INDUSTRIES INC
12918 Beltex Rd (78653-4510)
PHONE..................................512 278-1100
Jim Benbrook, *General Mgr*
Anthony Crockett, *Vice Pres*
Jack Wehrle, *Branch Mgr*
Brandon Abernathy, *Senior Mgr*
EMP: 9
SALES (corp-wide): 71.6MM **Privately Held**
WEB: www.delawaredynamicsmi.com
SIC: 3444 Sheet metalwork
HQ: C H Industries, Inc
1700 Columbian Club Dr
Carrollton TX 75006
972 416-1304

(G-14648)
PGS AMERICAS INC
12555 Harris Branch Pkwy (78653-4794)
PHONE..................................512 670-8700
Anders Jacobson, *Vice Pres*
EMP: 55
SALES (corp-wide): 896MM **Privately Held**
SIC: 1382 Oil & gas exploration services
HQ: Pgs Americas, Inc.
15375 Memorial Dr Ste 100
Houston TX 77079

(G-14649)
SOUTHERN SHUTTERS INC
Also Called: Southern Shutters & Blinds
12804 Beltex Rd (78653-4510)
PHONE..................................512 272-9711
Mark Edmondson, *President*
Johnny Roman, *Manager*

EMP: 11
SQ FT: 6,000
SALES (est): 1.5MM **Privately Held**
WEB: www.southernshuttersusa.com
SIC: 3442 5719 1799 Shutters, door or window: metal; window shades; glass tinting, architectural or automotive

(G-14650)
TEXAS INDUSTRIES INC
18601 Fm 969 (78653-5102)
PHONE..................................512 276-7990
Joe Parks, *Branch Mgr*
EMP: 32 **Publicly Held**
WEB: www.martinmarietta.com
SIC: 3273 Ready-mixed concrete
HQ: Texas Industries, Inc.
1503 Lyndon B Johnson Fwy
Dallas TX 75234
972 647-6700

(G-14651)
WINCOR NIXDORF INC
12521 Harris Branch Pkwy (78653-5076)
PHONE..................................512 252-5622
Scott Leyendecker, *Opers Mgr*
Thierry Gonnot, *Sales Staff*
Eckard Heidloff, *Branch Mgr*
Matthew Fresquez, *Software Engr*
Steve Ainsworth, *Director*
EMP: 9
SALES (corp-wide): 4.4B **Publicly Held**
WEB: www.dieboldnixdorf.com
SIC: 3578 4225 Automatic teller machines (ATM); general warehousing & storage
HQ: Wincor Nixdorf Inc.
12345 N Lamar Blvd # 200
Austin TX 78753
512 676-5000

Mansfield
Tarrant County

(G-14652)
AEROWINDTECH INC
2411 Fm 917 Ste 200 (76063-7422)
PHONE..................................817 438-4777
Jennifer Whitney, *CEO*
Michael Landon, *COO*
EMP: 15
SQ FT: 6,000
SALES (est): 1MM **Privately Held**
WEB: www.aerowindtech.com
SIC: 3081 Plastic film & sheet

(G-14653)
AFT INDUSTRIES INC
Aft Fasteners
204 S 6th Ave (76063-2304)
PHONE..................................469 865-2800
Johnny Rose, *President*
Brad Chandler, *Purchasing*
Don Owens, *Sales Staff*
Ed Robbins, *Sales Staff*
EMP: 37
SALES (corp-wide): 7.4MM **Privately Held**
WEB: www.aft-corp.com
SIC: 3471 Electroplating of metals or formed products
PA: Aft Industries, Inc
204 S 6th Ave
Mansfield TX 76063
972 988-1999

(G-14654)
AFT INDUSTRIES INC (PA)
Also Called: Metal Finishing
204 S 6th Ave (76063-2304)
PHONE..................................972 988-1999
Johnny M Rose, *President*
Pete Lopez, *Sales Staff*
Jeff Chandler, *Sales Executive*
Wendy Counts,
Annette Yager,
EMP: 49
SALES (est): 7.4MM **Privately Held**
WEB: www.aft-corp.com
SIC: 5085 3471 Industrial supplies; fasteners, industrial: nuts, bolts, screws, etc.; electroplating of metals or formed products

GEOGRAPHIC

(G-14655)
AMERICAN CARTON COMPANY INC
607 S Wisteria St (76063-2432)
PHONE...............................817 473-2992
Jana M Harris, *CEO*
Alayna Oliver, *COO*
Joe G Harris, *Exec VP*
Jenise Cox, *CFO*
Jenise R Cox, *Treasurer*
EMP: 40
SQ FT: 55,000
SALES (est): 9.3MM
SALES (corp-wide): 34.6MM **Privately Held**
WEB: www.americancarton.com
SIC: 2653 Boxes, corrugated: made from purchased materials
PA: Harris Packaging Corporation
    1600 Carson St
    Haltom City TX 76117
    817 429-6262

(G-14656)
ARDEX ENGINEERED CEMENTS INC
201 Airport Dr (76063-2211)
PHONE...............................817 435-5020
Marshall Seavers, *Plant Mgr*
▼ EMP: 60
SALES (est): 6.1MM **Privately Held**
SIC: 3241 Cement, hydraulic

(G-14657)
BASELL USA INC
100 S Mitchell Rd (76063-5604)
PHONE...............................682 518-0687
Fred Young, *Principal*
Stephanie Castillo, *Accountant*
Bruce Dahm, *Technology*
Stratford Caughman, *Analyst*
▼ EMP: 12
SALES (est): 1.4MM **Privately Held**
WEB: www.lyondellbasell.com
SIC: 2821 Plastics materials & resins

(G-14658)
BULK LIQUID STORAGE SYSTEMS LP
950 S 6th Ave (76063-2725)
PHONE...............................817 473-0083
Keith Baugh, *Partner*
EMP: 20
SALES (est): 2.4MM **Privately Held**
SIC: 3061 Mechanical rubber goods

(G-14659)
CENTERLINE TRAILERS INC
1301 E Dallas St (76063-2537)
PHONE...............................817 477-5533
Rick Benton, *President*
EMP: 19
SALES (est): 3.6MM **Privately Held**
WEB: www.center-linetrailers.com
SIC: 3715 Truck trailers

(G-14660)
CENTRAL DYNAMIC MFG INC
300 Industrial Blvd (76063-3616)
P.O. Box 679 (76063-0679)
PHONE...............................817 473-3899
Sheryl D Mc Coy, *President*
Tim Sims, *Exec VP*
EMP: 40
SQ FT: 25,000
SALES (est): 7.2MM **Privately Held**
SIC: 3599 Machine shop, jobbing & repair

(G-14661)
CHALK MOUNTAIN SVCS TEXAS LLC (PA)
990 N Walnut Creek Dr # 1001 (76063-1572)
P.O. Box 675 (76063-0675)
PHONE...............................817 473-1931
Andy Cox, *Vice Pres*
David Woods, *Manager*
Rebecca Rice, *Supervisor*
Gerald Curry,
Truitt J Kimbrough,
EMP: 25
SQ FT: 6,225

SALES (est): 296.3MM **Privately Held**
WEB: www.cmstx.com
SIC: 1389 Oil field services; gas field services

(G-14662)
CHEMGUARD INC (DH)
204 S 6th Ave (76063-2304)
PHONE...............................817 473-9964
George R Oliver, *President*
Steve Grisko, *General Mgr*
Twana Connors, *Opers Staff*
Glenn McClanahan, *Engineer*
Adrian Palacios, *Technology*
◆ EMP: 12
SQ FT: 45,000
SALES (est): 15.9MM **Privately Held**
WEB: www.chemguard.com
SIC: 2843 3569 Surface active agents; firefighting apparatus & related equipment
HQ: Tyco Fire Products Lp
    1400 Pennbrook Pkwy
    Lansdale PA 19446
    215 362-0700

(G-14663)
CITE CORPORATION (PA)
710 S 5th Ave (76063-1973)
PHONE...............................817 477-1549
Loy A Waddell, *President*
Virginia Waddell, *Treasurer*
EMP: 11
SQ FT: 5,900
SALES (est): 1.7MM **Privately Held**
SIC: 3589 Water treatment equipment, industrial

(G-14664)
CROWN BUILDING PRODUCTS LLC
2155 Fm 1187 (76063)
PHONE...............................214 636-5163
Juan Prestamo, *Principal*
▲ EMP: 28 EST: 2011
SALES (est): 6.7MM **Privately Held**
WEB: www.crownrooftiles.com
SIC: 3272 Roofing tile & slabs, concrete

(G-14665)
DK DRILL I LP (HQ)
Also Called: Drill King International
820 S 6th Ave (76063-2734)
PHONE...............................817 539-2500
Amber Broseh, *Partner*
Larry Broseh, *General Ptnr*
Latisha Shipman, *Sales Staff*
Roy Cline, *Manager*
▲ EMP: 50
SQ FT: 60,000
SALES (est): 6MM **Privately Held**
SIC: 5084 3931 3423 Drilling equipment, excluding bits; percussion instruments & parts; hammers (hand tools)

(G-14666)
DK DRILL I MANAGEMENT CO LLC (PA)
820 S 6th Ave (76063-2734)
PHONE...............................817 539-2500
Mack Broseh, *Transptn Dir*
Larry Spurrell, *Opers Staff*
Ashley Finder, *Human Resources*
Leo Goranov, *Marketing Mgr*
Amber Broseh, *Officer*
◆ EMP: 48
SQ FT: 60,000
SALES (est): 17.1MM **Privately Held**
SIC: 3728 3532 Aircraft assemblies, sub-assemblies & parts; research & dev by manuf., aircraft parts & auxiliary equip; wing assemblies & parts, aircraft; empennage (tail) assemblies & parts, aircraft; drills, bits & similar equipment

(G-14667)
DRYCO SKYLIGHTS INC
11800 E Farm Rd 917 (76063)
P.O. Box 343 (76063-0343)
PHONE...............................817 477-3441
Wade Presley, *President*
Debbie Presley, *Vice Pres*
EMP: 9
SQ FT: 15,000 **Privately Held**
WEB: www.drycoskylights.com
SIC: 3211 Skylight glass

(G-14668)
DURA-TECH PROCESSES INC
1204 Antler Dr (76063-2711)
P.O. Box 833 (76063-0833)
PHONE...............................817 473-7888
Frederick N Hubbell Jr, *Ch of Bd*
Rick Hubbell, *President*
Paul Hubbell, *Vice Pres*
Adam Hubbell, *Treasurer*
Jason Hubbell, *Admin Sec*
EMP: 15 EST: 1977
SQ FT: 28,500
SALES (est): 2.4MM **Privately Held**
WEB: www.dura-tech.net
SIC: 3471 Plating of metals or formed products

(G-14669)
ENERGY TRANSFER LP
2001 Stephens Ave (76063-8328)
PHONE...............................682 518-7583
EMP: 12 **Publicly Held**
WEB: www.energytransfer.com
SIC: 2869 Fuels
PA: Energy Transfer Lp
    8111 Westchester Dr # 600
    Dallas TX 75225

(G-14670)
EVANS COMPOSITES INC
300 S Wisteria St (76063-2454)
PHONE...............................817 477-9014
Mark Walton, *CEO*
Settha Sophabmixay, *Opers Dir*
Randy Sickels, *Purchasing*
Kimba Downey, *Manager*
▲ EMP: 27
SQ FT: 40,000
SALES (est): 4.2MM **Privately Held**
WEB: www.evanscomposites.com
SIC: 7699 3721 Aircraft & heavy equipment repair services; aircraft

(G-14671)
EVO IDT LLC
Also Called: Evo Integrated Drilling Tech
820 S 6th Ave (76063-2734)
PHONE...............................817 637-0149
Justin S Deerman, *Mng Member*
EMP: 40
SQ FT: 60,000
SALES (est): 2.9MM **Privately Held**
SIC: 3545 7389 Machine tool accessories; brokers' services

(G-14672)
EXCELL MACHINE CO INC
602 S 4th Ave (76063-1928)
P.O. Box 2220 (76063-0040)
PHONE...............................817 473-6121
William F Blair, *President*
Jim Blair, *Vice Pres*
Judy Blair, *Admin Sec*
EMP: 25 EST: 1978
SQ FT: 18,000
SALES (est): 5.2MM **Privately Held**
WEB: www.excellmachine.com
SIC: 3599 Machine shop, jobbing & repair

(G-14673)
FIVEPAYNE LLC
7400 Rendon Bloodworth Rd (76063-4915)
PHONE...............................817 310-0907
Robert Payne, *Mng Member*
EMP: 10
SALES (corp-wide): 14MM **Privately Held**
WEB: www.greentreepackaging.com
SIC: 2421 Lumber: rough, sawed or planed
PA: Fivepayne, Llc
    818 S Main St Ste 200
    Grapevine TX 76051
    817 310-0147

(G-14674)
FRONTIER BOLT COMPANY TEXAS (PA)
555 Airport Dr (76063-2715)
PHONE...............................817 477-5319
Ricky Ford, *President*
Will Berger, *Sales Staff*
Kevin Ford, *Sales Staff*
Dave Hall, *Sales Staff*
Cheris Knight, *Manager*
EMP: 17
SQ FT: 30,000

SALES (est): 8.8MM **Privately Held**
WEB: www.frontierbolt.com
SIC: 5072 3452 Bolts; screws; bolts, metal; screws, metal

(G-14675)
GAMMA AEROSPACE LLC (PA)
601 Airport Dr (76063-2718)
PHONE...............................817 477-2193
Steve Sigfusson, *President*
Thomas Raif, *Contract Mgr*
Julio Tovar, *Manager*
EMP: 115
SALES (est): 23.9MM **Privately Held**
WEB: www.gammaaero.com
SIC: 3365 Aerospace castings, aluminum

(G-14676)
GAMMA ENGINEERING INC
601 Airport Dr (76063-2718)
PHONE...............................817 477-2193
Sandra Bontke, *President*
Nathan Bontke, *Vice Pres*
Richard J Bontke, *Vice Pres*
Kelli Savering, *Vice Pres*
EMP: 110
SQ FT: 50,000
SALES (est): 29.1MM **Privately Held**
WEB: www.gammaeng.com
SIC: 3444 3469 3398 Forming machine work, sheet metal; stamping metal for the trade; metal heat treating

(G-14677)
GRANITE SECURITY PRODUCTS INC
Also Called: Winchester Safes
99 Regency Pkwy Ste 207 (76063-7819)
PHONE...............................817 483-0910
Kyle Walters, *President*
Chris Walters, *Prdtn Mgr*
◆ EMP: 50
SQ FT: 15,000
SALES (est): 16MM **Privately Held**
WEB: www.winchestersafes.com
SIC: 3949 3315 Cases, gun & rod (sporting equipment); fence gates posts & fittings: steel

(G-14678)
GTECH PRECISION INDS USA LTD
900 N Walnut Creek Dr # 1001 (76063-8046)
PHONE...............................817 539-8014
Joseph W Brown, *Partner*
▲ EMP: 10
SALES (est): 13.3K **Privately Held**
WEB: www.gtechprecision.com
SIC: 3571 3612 3661 3444 Electronic computers; transformers, except electric; telephones & telephone apparatus; metal housings, enclosures, casings & other containers; computer terminals, monitors & components

(G-14679)
HARLOW AROSTRUCTURES TEXAS LLC
800 S 6th Ave (76063-2734)
PHONE...............................817 583-8820
Jim Barnes, *Mng Member*
EMP: 55
SALES (est): 2MM **Privately Held**
SIC: 3365 Aerospace castings, aluminum

(G-14680)
HARRIS MANUFACTURING COMPANY
Also Called: Harris Manufacturing Esop Co
625 S Wisteria St Ste 101 (76063-2529)
PHONE...............................972 262-3524
Steve Robertson, *President*
Mark Robertson, *Admin Sec*
◆ EMP: 20
SQ FT: 29,000
SALES (est): 4.1MM **Privately Held**
WEB: www.harrismfg.net
SIC: 3443 3479 Metal parts; etching, photochemical

▲ = Import ▼=Export
◆ =Import/Export

(G-14681)
HAYES FARM
7580 Bennett Lawson Rd (76063-4604)
P.O. Box 40530, Fort Worth (76140-0530)
PHONE......................................817 477-1661
George Luebtke, *Owner*
Trisha Luebtke, *Co-Owner*
EMP: 30
SALES (est): 3MM **Privately Held**
SIC: 2011 Meat packing plants

(G-14682)
HONEYWELL INTERNATIONAL INC
100 Highway 287 N (76063-3471)
PHONE......................................817 215-9800
EMP: 673
SALES (corp-wide): 36.7B **Publicly Held**
WEB: www.honeywell.com
SIC: 3724 Aircraft engines & engine parts
PA: Honeywell International Inc.
300 S Tryon St
Charlotte NC 28202
704 627-6200

(G-14683)
ISCO INDUSTRIES INC
Also Called: Fraser Mining & Industrial Sup
2441 Mathis Rd (76063-5719)
PHONE......................................817 477-2900
Hal Smith, *Regl Sales Mgr*
Tom Fraser, *Branch Mgr*
EMP: 25
SALES (corp-wide): 202.8MM **Privately Held**
WEB: www.isco-pipe.com
SIC: 5085 1241 5162 3498 Valves & fittings; mine preparation services; plastics materials & basic shapes; fabricated pipe & fittings
PA: Isco Industries, Inc.
100 Witherspoon St
Louisville KY 40202
800 345-4726

(G-14684)
JOHNSON COUNTY FOAM INC
565 Airport Dr (76063-2715)
PHONE......................................817 477-5061
Sarah Lewis, *President*
Bill Lewis, *Vice Pres*
EMP: 21
SQ FT: 22,500
SALES (est): 5.4MM **Privately Held**
WEB: www.johnsoncountyfoam.com
SIC: 3086 Plastics foam products

(G-14685)
LOK-MOR INC
661 Airport Dr (76063-2718)
P.O. Box 151224, Arlington (76015-7224)
PHONE......................................817 477-0232
Jerry Dunsmore, *President*
Jack Kerr, *Corp Secy*
Tom Shelton, *Vice Pres*
Kevin Kerr, *Sales Staff*
▲ **EMP:** 35
SQ FT: 50,000
SALES (est): 9.2MM **Privately Held**
WEB: www.lok-mor.com
SIC: 3452 Nuts, metal

(G-14686)
LONE STAR AVIATION CORPORATION
604 S Wisteria St (76063-2423)
PHONE......................................682 518-8882
Jim Mantos, *President*
Valerie Mantos, *Treasurer*
▲ **EMP:** 12
SALES (est): 2.3MM **Privately Held**
WEB: www.lonestaraviation.com
SIC: 3728 Aircraft parts & equipment

(G-14687)
MARK HOUSE OF HOT RODS INC
2301 Highway 1187 Ste 101 (76063-6133)
PHONE......................................817 466-9942
Mark Idding, *President*
EMP: 20
SALES (est): 3.2MM **Privately Held**
WEB: www.txhouseofhotrods.com
SIC: 3355 Rods, rolled, aluminum

(G-14688)
MARSHALL-GRUBER COMPANY LLC
220 Airport Dr (76063-2212)
PHONE......................................682 518-7400
John Hoskinson, *President*
Steve Miller, *Branch Mgr*
EMP: 17
SQ FT: 50,000
SALES (corp-wide): 19.8MM **Privately Held**
WEB: www.rjmarshall.com
SIC: 3544 4225 3531 Industrial molds; general warehousing & storage; construction machinery
HQ: Marshall-Gruber Company, Llc
26776 W 12 Mile Rd Ste 20
Southfield MI 48034
248 353-4100

(G-14689)
MARTIN SPROCKET & GEAR INC
Also Called: Conveyor Division
811 S 4th Ave (76063-2207)
PHONE......................................817 473-1520
Belinda Rojas, *Mfg Mgr*
Ed Turner, *Personnel*
Ed Cmakal, *Supervisor*
EMP: 80
SALES (corp-wide): 539MM **Privately Held**
WEB: www.martinsprocket.com
SIC: 3566 3535 Gears, power transmission, except automotive; conveyors & conveying equipment
PA: Martin Sprocket & Gear, Inc.
3100 Sprocket Dr
Arlington TX 76015
817 258-3000

(G-14690)
MASSEY HOLDING & CONSULTANTS
Also Called: M H & C Cabling
4150 Britton Rd (76063-8719)
PHONE......................................817 477-3176
Dan Massey, *President*
EMP: 40
SALES (est): 950K
SALES (corp-wide): 4.7MM **Privately Held**
SIC: 3643 Current-carrying wiring devices
PA: Rhimco Industries, Inc.
4150 Britton Rd
Mansfield TX 76063
817 477-3176

(G-14691)
MASTER METER INC
101 Regency Pkwy (76063-5093)
PHONE......................................817 842-8000
Jerry Potter, *President*
Ronnie Veach, *Exec VP*
Charles Arnold, *Vice Pres*
Tim Hanes, *Vice Pres*
Megan Toparlak, *Vice Pres*
◆ **EMP:** 146
SQ FT: 51,000
SALES (est): 50.1MM **Privately Held**
WEB: www.mastermeter.com
SIC: 3824 Water meters
PA: Arad Ltd.
Kibbutz
Dalia 19239

(G-14692)
MAUSER PACKAGING SOLUTIONS
1501 E Dallas St (76063-2405)
PHONE......................................817 473-0259
Kenneth M Roessler, *Principal*
James Bradberry, *Engineer*
EMP: 11
SALES (corp-wide): 1.1B **Privately Held**
WEB: www.mauserpackaging.com
SIC: 3411 Metal cans
HQ: Bway Corporation
375 Northridge Rd Ste 600
Atlanta GA 30350

(G-14693)
MBS CONSTRUCTION I LTD
1315 Fm 1187 Ste 115 (76063)
P.O. Box 333 (76063-0333)
PHONE......................................817 473-0328
Robert Sherrill, *President*
EMP: 40
SQ FT: 1,600
SALES (est): 4.7MM **Privately Held**
SIC: 2599 Factory furniture & fixtures

(G-14694)
MEDHAB LLC
3216 Essex Dr (76063-7624)
PHONE......................................817 233-5271
Johnny Ross,
Jim Bagan,
Roger Beasley,
James R Brooks,
James Buchanan,
EMP: 25
SALES (est): 2.4MM **Privately Held**
WEB: www.medhab.com
SIC: 3842 Surgical appliances & supplies

(G-14695)
METRO FIRE APPRTUS SPECIALISTS
1501 Heritage Pkwy # 103 (76063-8345)
PHONE......................................817 467-0911
Craig N Russell, *President*
James Cook, *Purch Agent*
Randy Lee, *Manager*
EMP: 9
SALES (corp-wide): 14.5MM **Privately Held**
WEB: www.mfas.com
SIC: 3669 7549 Smoke detectors; automotive maintenance services
PA: Metro Fire Apparatus Specialists, Inc.
17350 Sh 249 Ste 250
Houston TX 77064
713 692-0911

(G-14696)
MILLWORK SOLUTIONS LTD
Also Called: Smith Millworks Solutions
1008 Magnolia St (76063-1745)
PHONE......................................817 473-3934
Robin Smith, *President*
Donna Cantrell, *Project Mgr*
EMP: 20
SQ FT: 9,400
SALES (est): 1.7MM **Privately Held**
WEB: www.millwork.solutions
SIC: 2431 Millwork

(G-14697)
NEW TECH SYSTEMS INC (PA)
603 S Wisteria St (76063-2432)
P.O. Box 639 (76063-0639)
PHONE......................................817 779-6262
Patrick Hanlon, *President*
Warren Averitt, *Vice Pres*
Tom Kibler, *Vice Pres*
David Barron, *Buyer*
Corbin Glenn, *Engineer*
▼ **EMP:** 50
SQ FT: 52,000
SALES (est): 14.2MM **Privately Held**
WEB: www.newtechsystems.com
SIC: 3533 Oil field machinery & equipment

(G-14698)
OLDCASTLE INFRASTRUCTURE INC
1100 Heritage Pkwy (76063-2759)
P.O. Box 2277 (76063-0047)
PHONE......................................817 477-2914
Daryl Mitchell, *VP Business*
Glenn Stinson, *Branch Mgr*
EMP: 55
SALES (corp-wide): 30.6B **Privately Held**
WEB: www.oldcastleinfrastructure.com
SIC: 3272 Concrete products, precast
HQ: Oldcastle Infrastructure, Inc.
7000 Central Pkwy Ste 800
Atlanta GA 30328
470 602-2000

(G-14699)
OMNIMAX INTERNATIONAL INC
Amerimax Building Products
700 S 2nd Ave (76063-1919)
PHONE......................................817 473-1541
Mitchell B Lewis, *CEO*
EMP: 30 **Privately Held**
WEB: www.omnimax.com
SIC: 5211 3354 Home centers; aluminum extruded products
HQ: Omnimax International, Inc.
30 Technology Pkwy S # 400
Peachtree Corners GA 30092

(G-14700)
PARADIGM CONCEPT LLC
1613 Monte Carlo Dr (76063-6292)
PHONE......................................817 896-7729
Winnie Aduayi, *Managing Dir*
Abiye Alamina, *Director*
Efe Efemini, *Director*
Kola Oyeyemi, *Director*
EMP: 10 **EST:** 2016
SALES (est): 321.4K **Privately Held**
SIC: 2731 Book publishing

(G-14701)
PARAGON PACKAGING INC (PA)
1500 E Broad St (76063-1807)
PHONE......................................817 477-5211
Mike Polarek, *President*
Rito Quiroz, *Store Mgr*
Mike Crayne, *Engineer*
Julia Vasquez, *Human Res Mgr*
Dean Martin, *Sales Mgr*
EMP: 50
SQ FT: 85,000
SALES (est): 10.9MM **Privately Held**
WEB: www.plasticind.com
SIC: 2759 3089 3085 Screen printing; blow molded finished plastic products; plastics bottles

(G-14702)
PCX AEROSTRUCTURES TX LP
800 S 6th Ave (76063-2734)
PHONE......................................817 583-8820
Jeff Frisby, *President*
▲ **EMP:** 50
SALES (est): 14.4MM
SALES (corp-wide): 100MM **Privately Held**
WEB: www.pcxaero.com
SIC: 3728 Aircraft parts & equipment
PA: Pcx Aerostructures, Llc
300 Fenn Rd
Newington CT 06111
860 666-2471

(G-14703)
PLASTIC INDUSTRIES INC
Also Called: Plastic Industries Mansfield
1500 E Broad St (76063-1807)
PHONE......................................817 477-5211
Rob Pearson, *CFO*
EMP: 60 **Privately Held**
WEB: www.plasticind.com
SIC: 3085 Plastics bottles
HQ: Plastic Industries, Inc.
1 Tara Blvd
Nashua NH 03062
603 888-1315

(G-14704)
PRINTERS SERVICE FLORIDA INC
Also Called: American Blanket
6740 Exchange Dr (76063-3000)
PHONE......................................817 477-1291
James Hunter, *Manager*
EMP: 15
SALES (corp-wide): 3.8MM **Privately Held**
WEB: www.prisco.com
SIC: 2752 Commercial printing, offset
PA: Printers Service Of Florida, Inc.
26 Blanchard St
Newark NJ 07105
973 589-7800

(G-14705)
QEP CO INC
300 S 6th Ave (76063-2306)
PHONE......................................817 477-1183
Dave Nichols, *Manager*
EMP: 20
SALES (corp-wide): 240.4MM **Privately Held**
WEB: www.qepcorporate.com
SIC: 2891 Adhesives

GEOGRAPHIC

PA: Q.E.P. Co., Inc.
1001 Broken Sound Pkwy Nw A
Boca Raton FL 33487
561 994-5550

(G-14706)
QUALITY FIBERGLASS INC
105 Industrial Blvd (76063-3611)
P.O. Box 694, Crowley (76036-0694)
PHONE.................................817 473-3563
Lenny Warren, *President*
Linton G Warren, *Chairman*
EMP: 10
SQ FT: 11,000
SALES (est): 1.5MM **Privately Held**
SIC: 2821 Plastics materials & resins

(G-14707)
RAMTECH BUILDING SYSTEMS INC
1400 Highway 287 S (76063-5799)
PHONE.................................817 473-9376
Michael Slataper, *President*
Roland Brown, *Vice Pres*
Lincoln Moss, *Vice Pres*
Gary White, *Vice Pres*
Stewart Richardson, *Project Mgr*
EMP: 35
SQ FT: 76,800
SALES (est): 9.9MM **Privately Held**
WEB: www.ramtechmodular.com
SIC: 1542 3448 2452 Commercial & office building, new construction; prefabricated metal buildings; prefabricated wood buildings

(G-14708)
RDS METAL LP
911 S 5th Ave (76063-2728)
P.O. Box 327 (76063-0327)
PHONE.................................817 539-7400
Chris Culver, *General Ptnr*
▲ **EMP:** 17
SQ FT: 42,000
SALES (est): 8.9MM **Privately Held**
SIC: 5051 3353 3399 Sheets, metal; coils, sheet aluminum; metal fasteners

(G-14709)
REDCASTLE MANUFACTURING LLC
1501 Heritage Pkwy # 103 (76063-8345)
PHONE.................................817 350-6300
Darrell Mitchell, *Mng Member*
◆ **EMP:** 17
SQ FT: 11,000
SALES (est): 5.7MM **Privately Held**
WEB: www.redcastlemfg.com
SIC: 3535 Unit handling conveying systems

(G-14710)
RELIANCE COATED FABRICS INC
950 S 6th Ave (76063-2725)
PHONE.................................817 453-8829
Frank Bonilla Linero, *President*
EMP: 18
SALES (est): 1.1MM **Privately Held**
WEB: www.reliance-coated-fabrics-inc.sb-contract.com
SIC: 3812 Search & navigation equipment

(G-14711)
RHIMCO INDUSTRIES INC (PA)
4150 Britton Rd (76063-8796)
PHONE.................................817 477-3176
EMP: 33 **EST:** 1969
SQ FT: 54,000
SALES (est): 4.7MM **Privately Held**
WEB: www.rhimco.com
SIC: 3643 Electric connectors

(G-14712)
RMD MANUFACTURING LTD
1402 Highway 287 S (76063-5702)
PHONE.................................817 477-5321
Michael Slataper, *Managing Prtnr*
Tommy McCool, *Purch Agent*
EMP: 50
SQ FT: 65,000
SALES (est): 8.6MM **Privately Held**
SIC: 2452 Modular homes, prefabricated, wood

(G-14713)
RODCO-BRANDT MANUFACTURING
600 S 2nd Ave (76063-1917)
P.O. Box 270 (76063-0270)
PHONE.................................817 477-4118
Lee Rodriguez, *Managing Prtnr*
Eddie Brandt, *Partner*
▼ **EMP:** 25
SQ FT: 80,000
SALES (est): 5.6MM **Privately Held**
WEB: www.rodco-brandt.com
SIC: 2531 7641 2511 2426 Public building & related furniture; furniture repair & maintenance; wood household furniture; hardwood dimension & flooring mills

(G-14714)
ROPAK SOUTHWEST INC
1501 E Dallas St (76063-2405)
PHONE.................................817 473-0259
David Williams, *CEO*
Greg Toft, *President*
EMP: 117
SQ FT: 5,000
SALES (est): 17.9MM
SALES (corp-wide): 1.1B **Privately Held**
WEB: www.mauserpackaging.com
SIC: 3089 Pallets, plastic
HQ: Ropak Corporation
10540 Talbert Ave 200w
Fountain Valley CA 92708
714 845-2845

(G-14715)
SANDVIK MINING & CNSTR USA LLC
Also Called: Drill-Master International
1300 Heritage Pkwy (76063-2796)
PHONE.................................817 453-2800
Fax: 817 453-2389
EMP: 100
SALES (corp-wide): 8.8B **Privately Held**
SIC: 3532 Mfg Mining Machinery
HQ: Sandvik Mining & Construction Usa Llc
13500 Nw County Road 235
Alachua FL 32615
386 462-4100

(G-14716)
SCTRAY COMPANY
949 S 6th Ave (76063-2726)
PHONE.................................817 473-0233
Robert Nicol, *Branch Mgr*
EMP: 100
SALES (corp-wide): 62.2MM **Privately Held**
WEB: www.sctray.com
SIC: 2631 2657 Cardboard; folding paperboard boxes
PA: Sctray Company
220 Compress St
Chattanooga TN 37405
423 756-5121

(G-14717)
SELLMARK CORPORATION
2201 Heritage Pkwy (76063-5628)
PHONE.................................817 225-0310
James Sellers, *CEO*
Dianna Sellers, *CEO*
Trey Weidner, *Vice Pres*
Corbin Hubbard, *Production*
Margie Saenz, *Opers-Prdtn-Mfg*
◆ **EMP:** 85 **EST:** 2000
SQ FT: 2,500
SALES (est): 57.7MM **Privately Held**
WEB: www.sellmark.net
SIC: 3949 5091 Camping equipment & supplies; hunting equipment & supplies; camping equipment & supplies

(G-14718)
SENTRIMAX CENTRIFUGES USA INC
108 Sentry Dr (76063-3608)
PHONE.................................817 453-8112
Thomas J Maxwell, *President*
Jeff Johannson, *General Mgr*
Matt Penny, *CFO*
EMP: 10
SALES (est): 2.3MM **Privately Held**
WEB: www.sentrimax.com
SIC: 3569 Centrifuges, industrial

(G-14719)
SOUTHERN CHAMPION TRAY LP
949 S 6th Ave (76063-2726)
PHONE.................................817 477-3485
EMP: 18 **Privately Held**
WEB: www.sctray.com
SIC: 2675 Die-cut paper & board
PA: Southern Champion Tray, L.P.
220 Compress St
Chattanooga TN 37405

(G-14720)
STANDARD PAINTS INC
940 S 6th Ave (76063-2725)
PHONE.................................817 477-5060
Mel P Turner, *President*
Jim Hughes, *Vice Pres*
EMP: 18 **EST:** 1952
SQ FT: 30,000
SALES (est): 5.1MM **Privately Held**
WEB: www.standardpaints.com
SIC: 2851 Paints & paint additives

(G-14721)
TAMRA GROUP INC
1052 S 2nd Ave Ste 200 (76063-2705)
PHONE.................................817 453-3370
Carl Skelley, *President*
EMP: 20
SQ FT: 30,000
SALES (est): 4.7MM **Privately Held**
WEB: www.engageindustrial.com
SIC: 3549 5084 Metalworking machinery; conveyor systems

(G-14722)
TEXAS REFINERY CORP
Also Called: Warehouse
500 Airport Dr (76063-2216)
P.O. Box 776 (76063-0776)
PHONE.................................682 518-1405
Chris Pate, *Principal*
EMP: 10
SALES (corp-wide): 25.5MM **Privately Held**
WEB: www.texasrefinery.com
SIC: 5211 5172 3479 2992 Roofing material; petroleum products; painting, coating & hot dipping; brake fluid (hydraulic): made from purchased materials
PA: Texas Refinery Corp.
840 N Main St
Fort Worth TX 76164
817 332-1161

(G-14723)
TRINITY FORGE INC
947 Trinity Dr (76063-2730)
PHONE.................................817 473-1515
Richard Johnston, *President*
John Fairbanks, *Vice Pres*
Harry Kelly, *Vice Pres*
Mike Lobsiger, *Vice Pres*
James Parsley, *Vice Pres*
EMP: 200 **EST:** 1955
SQ FT: 100,000
SALES (est): 67.4MM **Privately Held**
WEB: www.trinityforge.com
SIC: 3462 Iron & steel forgings
PA: Lone Star Investment Advisors Llc
4455 Lyndon B Johnson Fwy # 300
Dallas TX 75244

(G-14724)
TWISTED S SERVICES INC
7864 Retta Mansfield Rd (76063-4329)
P.O. Box 2228 (76063-0040)
PHONE.................................817 473-6959
Joshua Smith, *President*
Stan William, *Business Mgr*
Scott Meek, *Vice Pres*
EMP: 50
SALES (est): 5.1MM **Privately Held**
WEB: www.mojolimo.com
SIC: 1389 Oil field services

(G-14725)
UTILITY AGENCY & IMPORT INC
2417 Fm 917 (76063-7401)
PHONE.................................817 477-9888
Christina H Morrison, *CEO*
Richard J Morrison, *President*
Raymond Morrison, *Vice Pres*
▲ **EMP:** 10 **EST:** 2012

SALES (est): 3.9MM **Privately Held**
WEB: www.uaireps.com
SIC: 5063 3613 3612 Insulators, electrical; power circuit breakers; power & distribution transformers

(G-14726)
VALLEY ROLLER COMPANY INC
101 Sentry Dr (76063-3601)
PHONE.................................817 453-8950
Mike Chase, *Owner*
Bob Durden, *Safety Dir*
Eric Herd, *Maint Spvr*
Pat Johnson, *Representative*
EMP: 18
SALES (corp-wide): 3.3B **Privately Held**
WEB: www.maxcessintl.com
SIC: 3069 Roll coverings, rubber
HQ: Valley Roller Company, Inc.
N257 Stoney Brook Rd
Appleton WI 54915
920 733-1991

(G-14727)
VAN NU TECHNOLOGY INC
2155 Highway 1187 (76063-5956)
P.O. Box 759 (76063-0759)
PHONE.................................817 276-3300
Fred Ufolla, *CEO*
EMP: 88
SQ FT: 118,000
SALES (est): 11.6MM **Privately Held**
WEB: www.nuvan.com
SIC: 3715 5511 Semitrailers for truck tractors; trucks, tractors & trailers: new & used

(G-14728)
WALTON PROCESS TECH INC
Also Called: W P T
300 S Wisteria St (76063-2454)
PHONE.................................682 518-9002
Mark Walton, *President*
Gerardo Gonzalez, *Engineer*
Greg Chrzanowski, *Info Tech Mgr*
Judith Hayward, *Info Tech Mgr*
Jeff French, *Technology*
EMP: 20
SQ FT: 10,000
SALES (est): 6MM **Privately Held**
WEB: www.autoclaves.com
SIC: 3823 Thermal conductivity instruments, industrial process type

(G-14729)
WESCO REFRACTORIES INC
301 S 6th Ave (76063-2305)
PHONE.................................682 518-5035
Richard D Showmaker, *President*
Christopher Todd Showmaker, *Business Mgr*
Shirley R Showmaker, *Corp Secy*
Chris Showmaker, *Sales Staff*
EMP: 19
SQ FT: 45,000
SALES (est): 3.4MM **Privately Held**
WEB: www.wescorefractories.com
SIC: 3297 3255 Nonclay refractories; fire clay blocks, bricks, tile or special shapes

(G-14730)
WORTH EQP PARTS & SVC CO INC
812 S 2nd Ave (76063)
P.O. Box 597 (76063-0597)
PHONE.................................817 473-7266
Scarlett Prater, *Corp Secy*
Stephen J Prater, *Director*
EMP: 21
SQ FT: 16,000
SALES (est): 3.7MM **Privately Held**
WEB: www.worthequipment.com
SIC: 3559 Automotive related machinery

Manvel
Brazoria County

(G-14731)
AMTEX PRCISION FABRICATION INC
3920 Bahler Ave (77578-2823)
PHONE.................................281 489-7042
Walter E Melton, *President*

Constance Melton, *Corp Secy*
Jacob Melton, *Vice Pres*
Adrian Melton, *Sales Staff*
▲ **EMP:** 18
SQ FT: 23,000
SALES (est): 4.4MM **Privately Held**
WEB: www.amtexprecision.com
SIC: 3444 Sheet metal specialties, not stamped

(G-14732)
BAYLAND INC
7900 Bissell Rd (77578-4866)
P.O. Box 467 (77578-0467)
PHONE.................................281 489-1930
Jim Moses, *President*
Betty Cessna, *Director*
EMP: 11 **EST:** 1978
SQ FT: 45,000
SALES (est): 1MM **Privately Held**
WEB: www.bayland.com
SIC: 3089 Plastic containers, except foam

(G-14733)
E-Z LINE PIPE SUPPORT CO LLC
21340 Highway 6 (77578-3832)
P.O. Box 767 (77578-0767)
PHONE.................................713 675-6693
Howard C Palmer, *President*
Trey Palmer, *Vice Pres*
Jeremy Hutson, *Manager*
Chris Bock,
Olivia Garcia,
EMP: 50
SQ FT: 30,000
SALES (est): 16.3MM **Privately Held**
WEB: www.ezline.com
SIC: 3441 Building components, structural steel

(G-14734)
GULF COAST CON & SHELL INC
4401 County Road 58 (77578-2956)
PHONE.................................281 238-8883
Dean Koy, *President*
EMP: 60
SALES (est): 16.1MM **Privately Held**
WEB: www.gcconcrete.com
SIC: 3273 Ready-mixed concrete

(G-14735)
NATIONAL CRANE CMPLNCE INSPCTO
17512 Highway 6 Ste F15 (77578-3752)
P.O. Box 567, Rosharon (77583-0567)
PHONE.................................888 720-6224
Bono Salas, *President*
Joe Johnson, *Vice Pres*
Terry Stuckey, *CFO*
EMP: 22
SQ FT: 1,500
SALES (est): 3.5MM **Privately Held**
WEB: www.nccillc.com
SIC: 7699 3429 Industrial machinery & equipment repair; manufactured hardware (general)

(G-14736)
NATIONAL MACHINE & WORKHOLDING
Also Called: National Machine & Work Holdg
7102 Bissell Rd (77578-4689)
P.O. Box 517 (77578-0517)
PHONE.................................281 489-0490
David Gates, *President*
Sandra Gates, *Vice Pres*
EMP: 15
SQ FT: 18,000
SALES (est): 1.1MM **Privately Held**
WEB: www.gatesmachine.com
SIC: 3599 Machine shop, jobbing & repair

(G-14737)
RONALD NOLES
Also Called: Selon Plating
7042 Bissell Rd (77578-4606)
PHONE.................................281 489-7727
Fax: 281 489-7711
EMP: 10
SQ FT: 1,400
SALES: 360K **Privately Held**
SIC: 3471 Plating/Polishing Service

(G-14738)
SOUTHWEST QUALITY MOLDING LP
7900 Bissell Rd (77578-4866)
P.O. Box 439 (77578-0439)
PHONE.................................281 643-4500
Perry Estes, *President*
Regina Estes, *Corp Secy*
Darryl Estes, *Vice Pres*
▲ **EMP:** 20 **EST:** 1980
SQ FT: 31,500
SALES (est): 3.8MM **Privately Held**
WEB: www.sqminc.net
SIC: 3089 Injection molding of plastics

Marble Falls
Burnet County

(G-14739)
BOB HUGHES DISPLAYS LLC
6617 Singleton Bend Rd (78654-3320)
PHONE.................................713 468-7726
Robert Hughes Jr, *Mng Member*
◆ **EMP:** 11 **EST:** 1956
SALES (est): 1.3MM **Privately Held**
WEB: www.flags2020.com
SIC: 3993 5199 Advertising novelties; advertising specialties

(G-14740)
CACTUS CYN QUARRIES OF TEXAS
7232 County Road 120 (78654-7848)
PHONE.................................830 693-4331
Andrew Carson, *President*
Mary Jo Carson, *Corp Secy*
Jack Carson, *Vice Pres*
EMP: 11
SQ FT: 2,000
SALES (est): 1.3MM **Privately Held**
SIC: 1423 1429 Crushed & broken granite; marble, crushed & broken-quarrying; quartzite, crushed & broken-quarrying

(G-14741)
CAPITOL AGGREGATES INC
719 County Rd 121 (78654)
P.O. Box 99 (78654-0099)
PHONE.................................830 693-3533
Doyle Lindsey, *Manager*
EMP: 19 **Privately Held**
WEB: www.capitolaggregates.com
SIC: 1442 Construction sand mining
HQ: Capitol Aggregates, Inc.
2330 N Loop 1604 W
San Antonio TX 78248
210 871-6100

(G-14742)
DELRAY MACHINE LLC
Also Called: Delray Machine Works
2407 Commerce St (78654-3916)
P.O. Box 1115 (78654-1115)
PHONE.................................830 693-5110
Gerald Hugonin, *Principal*
EMP: 11
SQ FT: 6,000
SALES (est): 1.1MM **Privately Held**
WEB: www.delraymachine.com
SIC: 3599 7692 Machine shop, jobbing & repair; welding repair

(G-14743)
GIBRALTAR GLOBAL LLC
4303 W Innovation Loop (78654-3883)
PHONE.................................512 715-9650
Bill Neusch, *Partner*
Jessie Hackworth, *Executive Asst*
▲ **EMP:** 10
SALES (est): 2MM **Privately Held**
WEB: www.gibraltarus.com
SIC: 3499 Barricades, metal

(G-14744)
HORNSBYS CUSTOM CABINETS
2701 Commerce St (78654-3911)
PHONE.................................830 693-2420
Jim Hornsby, *Principal*
Daniel Hornsby,
Rebecca Sveda,
EMP: 11
SQ FT: 4,500

SALES (est): 806.3K **Privately Held**
WEB: www.hornsbycabinets.com
SIC: 2434 Wood kitchen cabinets

(G-14745)
INGRAM READYMIX INC
2701 N Us Highway 281 (78654-3809)
PHONE.................................830 693-4396
Craig Seward, *Branch Mgr*
EMP: 20
SALES (corp-wide): 125.6MM **Privately Held**
WEB: www.ingramreadymixinc.com
SIC: 3273 Ready-mixed concrete
PA: Ingram Readymix, Inc.
3580 Farm Market 482
New Braunfels TX 78132
830 625-9156

(G-14746)
JM HUBER CORPORATION
Engineer Minerals Division
90 Avenue N (78654-6125)
P.O. Box 1060 (78654-1060)
PHONE.................................830 693-3575
Frank Byrd, *Director*
EMP: 55
SALES (corp-wide): 889.5MM **Privately Held**
WEB: www.huber.com
SIC: 2819 Industrial inorganic chemicals
PA: J.M. Huber Corporation
499 Thornall St Ste 8
Edison NJ 08837
732 549-8600

(G-14747)
LEGACY VULCAN LLC
Also Called: Spicewood Quarry & Asphalt
5525 E State Highway 71 (78654)
PHONE.................................830 693-2756
Craig Perkins, *Manager*
EMP: 12 **Publicly Held**
WEB: www.vulcanmaterials.com
SIC: 3273 Ready-mixed concrete
HQ: Legacy Vulcan, Llc
1200 Urban Center Dr
Vestavia AL 35242
205 298-3000

(G-14748)
NATIONAL OILWELL VARCO INC
1 N Ridge Loop (78654)
PHONE.................................830 693-5312
Tracy Lee, *Plant Mgr*
EMP: 23
SALES (corp-wide): 8.4B **Publicly Held**
WEB: www.nov.com
SIC: 3533 3324 Oil field machinery & equipment; steel investment foundries
PA: National Oilwell Varco, Inc.
7909 Parkwood Circle Dr
Houston TX 77036
713 346-7500

(G-14749)
PEC MANUFACTURING
4401 W Innovation Loop (78654-3884)
P.O. Box 940 (78654-0940)
PHONE.................................830 693-7879
Greg Mills, *Partner*
Kelsey Mills, *Opers Mgr*
◆ **EMP:** 10
SQ FT: 24,000
SALES (est): 1.5MM **Privately Held**
WEB: www.pec-clutches.com
SIC: 3714 Motor vehicle parts & accessories

(G-14750)
R J MACHINE COMPANY INC
130 Northridge Rd (78654-3803)
P.O. Box 1449 (78654-7449)
PHONE.................................830 693-7493
Gary H Martin, *President*
Trent Stout, *Partner*
Jake Costin, *Controller*
Chandler Schuessler, *Sales Staff*
Jody Browning, *Administration*
◆ **EMP:** 18 **EST:** 1980
SQ FT: 15,000
SALES (est): 4.4MM **Privately Held**
WEB: www.rjmachineonline.com
SIC: 3599 Machine shop, jobbing & repair

(G-14751)
V&G DYNAMIC MACHINE LLC
701 Industrial Blvd (78654-4741)
PHONE.................................830 693-4743
Adam Mansuri, *President*
EMP: 17
SALES (est): 704.9K **Privately Held**
WEB: www.vgdynamic.com
SIC: 3599 Industrial machinery

(G-14752)
WORD CONSTRUCTORS LLC
Hwy 281 (78654)
P.O. Box 364 (78654-0364)
PHONE.................................830 693-2933
Kenneth Roy, *Manager*
EMP: 18
SALES (corp-wide): 111.8MM **Privately Held**
WEB: www.deanword.com
SIC: 2951 1442 1422 Paving mixtures; gravel mining; crushed & broken limestone
PA: Word Constructors, L.L.C.
1245 River Rd
New Braunfels TX 78130
830 625-2365

Marfa
Presidio County

(G-14753)
LOCKHEED MARTIN CORPORATION
21 Miles W Of Mrfa Hwy 90 (79843)
P.O. Box 845 (79843-0845)
PHONE.................................432 358-4474
Roland Johnson Jr, *Manager*
EMP: 26 **Publicly Held**
WEB: www.lockheedmartin.com
SIC: 3812 Search & navigation equipment
PA: Lockheed Martin Corporation
6801 Rockledge Dr
Bethesda MD 20817

(G-14754)
RIO GRANDE MINING COMPANY
Also Called: Shafter Mine
97243 Us Hwy 67 (79843)
PHONE.................................432 229-4737
EMP: 80 **EST:** 2001
SQ FT: 100,000
SALES (est): 11.3MM **Privately Held**
WEB: www.marfapublicradio.org
SIC: 1044 Underground silver mining

Marion
Guadalupe County

(G-14755)
AW TEXAS INC
565 Bolton Rd (78124-6046)
PHONE.................................210 381-0117
Satoru Kasuya, *President*
EMP: 200
SALES (est): 8.5MM **Privately Held**
SIC: 3714 Transmissions, motor vehicle

(G-14756)
FORCE PRESSURE CONTROL LLC
11895 W Interstate 10 (78124-6510)
PHONE.................................361 210-9650
Jack Robertson, *Business Mgr*
Harrison Daniel, *Vice Pres*
Wesley Mangan, *Vice Pres*
Melissa Startz, *Treasurer*
Jacob Startz, *Mng Member*
EMP: 111
SALES (est): 5.1MM **Privately Held**
SIC: 3533 Oil field machinery & equipment

(G-14757)
JAGUAR ENERGY SERVICES LLC
11890 W Ih 10 (78124-6591)
P.O. Box 1444, Crowley LA (70527-1444)
PHONE.................................337 250-4030
Jason Monk, *Branch Mgr*
EMP: 16

G E O G R A P H I C

SALES (corp-wide): 61.2MM **Privately Held**
WEB: www.jaguar-energy.com
SIC: 1389 Oil field services
PA: Jaguar Energy Services, Llc
301 N Parkerson Ave
Crowley LA 70526
800 734-5803

(G-14758)
TAPRITE-FASSCO MFG INC
105 S Center St (78124)
P.O. Box 336 (78124-0336)
PHONE..................................830 914-2539
Clayton Bauer, *Manager*
EMP: 16
SALES (corp-wide): 3.1B **Privately Held**
WEB: www.taprite.com
SIC: 3585 Soda fountain & beverage dispensing equipment & parts
HQ: Taprite, Inc.
3248 Northwestern
San Antonio TX 78238
210 523-0800

Marlin
Falls County

(G-14759)
KEITH PROPERTIES INC
Also Called: Ace Hardware
122 Live Oak St (76661-2852)
PHONE..................................254 883-2531
Kenneth Becker, *Branch Mgr*
EMP: 13
SALES (corp-wide): 31.9MM **Privately Held**
WEB: www.keithacehardware.com
SIC: 3546 5251 Saws & sawing equipment; hardware
PA: Keith Properties, Inc.
1390 N Houston St
Lorena TX 76655
254 857-8667

Marshall
Harrison County

(G-14760)
AMERICAN TIETEK LLC
429 S Memory Ln (75670-8405)
PHONE..................................903 503-5538
Dale Ramthun, *Vice Pres*
Liguang Dong, *Manager*
EMP: 41 EST: 2010
SALES (est): 6.8MM **Privately Held**
WEB: www.tietek.net
SIC: 3089 Planters, plastic

(G-14761)
AMERICAN WOOD FIBERS INC
6203 Fm 1998 (75672-3021)
PHONE..................................903 923-8700
Jody Jones, *Natl Sales Mgr*
Jim Schuman, *Regl Sales Mgr*
Ginger Walker, *Office Mgr*
Thomas Green, *Manager*
EMP: 40 **Privately Held**
WEB: www.awf.com
SIC: 2499 2421 Wood flour; mulch or sawdust products, wood; sawdust, shavings & wood chips
PA: American Wood Fibers, Inc.
9740 Patuxent Woods Dr # 500
Columbia MD 21046

(G-14762)
ARK LA TEX SURVEYING CO INC
305 W Rusk St Ste B (75670-3246)
P.O. Box 1345 (75671-1345)
PHONE..................................903 938-9939
Mark Patheal, *President*
Patheal Chrys, *Vice Pres*
Chrys Patheal, *Vice Pres*
Jinni Uselton, *Bookkeeper*
EMP: 18
SQ FT: 2,500
SALES (est): 1.7MM **Privately Held**
WEB: www.arklatexsurveying.com
SIC: 8713 1389 Surveying services; surveying wells

(G-14763)
BEAR CREEK SMOKEHOUSE LLC
10857 State Highway 154 (75670-8105)
PHONE..................................903 935-5217
Charles R Shoults Jr, *Vice Pres*
Mike Whyte, *Sales Staff*
▲ **EMP:** 40 EST: 1943
SQ FT: 45,193
SALES (est): 8.6MM **Privately Held**
WEB: www.bearcreeksmokehouse.com
SIC: 2013 5421 5149 5499 Sausages & other prepared meats; meat markets, including freezer provisioners; soups, except frozen; health foods

(G-14764)
BLACK HORSE TEST SERVICES
11441 State Highway 43 S (75670-7537)
P.O. Box 384, Nome (77629-0384)
PHONE..................................903 938-8554
EMP: 10 EST: 2010
SALES (est): 370K **Privately Held**
SIC: 1389 Oil/Gas Field Services

(G-14765)
CABOT NORIT AMERICAS INC (DH)
3200 University Ave (75670-4842)
P.O. Box 790 (75671-0790)
PHONE..................................903 938-9211
Maarten Knuttel, *CEO*
Ronald D Thompson, *CEO*
Friedrich Von Gottberg, *President*
Paul Ganzeboom, *Exec VP*
Robert Davies, *Vice Pres*
◆ **EMP:** 155 EST: 1918
SALES (est): 54.2MM
SALES (corp-wide): 2.6B **Publicly Held**
SIC: 2819 Charcoal (carbon), activated
HQ: Norit International B.V.
Astronaut 34
Amersfoort 3824
334 648-911

(G-14766)
CABOT NORIT AMERICAS INC
Also Called: Darco Activated Carbon
3200 University Ave (75670-4842)
P.O. Box 790 (75671-0790)
PHONE..................................800 641-9245
Travis Mileur, *Branch Mgr*
EMP: 239
SQ FT: 30,000
SALES (corp-wide): 2.6B **Publicly Held**
SIC: 2819 Charcoal (carbon), activated
HQ: Cabot Norit Americas, Inc.
3200 University Ave
Marshall TX 75670
903 938-9211

(G-14767)
CADDO CREEK RESOURCES CO LLC
3900 Fm 1186 (75672-2116)
PHONE..................................903 927-1130
W Gene Beener, *President*
Carroll L Dewing, *Vice Pres*
J Patrick Sullivan Jr, *Vice Pres*
Eric A Dale, *Treasurer*
John D Neumann, *Admin Sec*
EMP: 9
SALES (est): 1.6MM
SALES (corp-wide): 140.9MM **Publicly Held**
SIC: 1221 Strip mining, lignite
HQ: The North American Coal Corporation
5340 Legacy Dr Ste 300
Plano TX 75024
972 448-5400

(G-14768)
CADDO PACKING CO INC
609 S Washington Ave (75670-5327)
P.O. Box 327 (75671-0327)
PHONE..................................903 935-2211
Pat W Parrish, *President*
Judy Parrish, *Corp Secy*
EMP: 9 EST: 1935
SQ FT: 10,000
SALES (est): 1.5MM **Privately Held**
SIC: 2011 5147 Meat packing plants; meats & meat products

(G-14769)
CAMTERRA RSOURCES PARTNERS LTD (PA)
2615 E End Blvd S (75672-7425)
P.O. Box 2069 (75671-2069)
PHONE..................................903 938-9949
Paul Marchand, *President*
Steve B Carlile, *Partner*
Allen C Staggers, *Partner*
Jennifer Bourdon, *Accountant*
Sherrill Munds, *Accountant*
EMP: 20
SQ FT: 2,000
SALES (est): 8.3MM **Privately Held**
WEB: www.camterra.com
SIC: 1382 Oil & gas exploration services

(G-14770)
CASEY PRODUCTS LLC
Also Called: La Tee Da
1070 Pumpkin Center Rd (75672-3330)
P.O. Box 740, Scottsville (75688-0740)
PHONE..................................903 927-3500
Steve Carlile, *General Ptnr*
David McMinn,
EMP: 35
SALES (est): 2MM **Privately Held**
WEB: www.ltdfundraising.com
SIC: 5963 2844 5961 6794 Party-plan merchandising; perfumes & colognes; catalog & mail-order houses; franchises, selling or licensing

(G-14771)
CITY OF MARSHALL
1600 Starr St (75670-5632)
PHONE..................................903 935-4500
Frank Johnson, *Manager*
EMP: 13
SALES (corp-wide): 22.6MM **Privately Held**
WEB: www.marshalltexas.net
SIC: 9621 7694 Transportation department: government, non-operating; hermetics repair
PA: Marshall, City Of (Inc)
401 S Alamo Blvd
Marshall TX 75670
903 935-4416

(G-14772)
DAVIS CHEMICAL SERVICES LLC
281 Gateway Park Dr (75672)
P.O. Box 1369 (75671-1369)
PHONE..................................903 938-3800
Randall Root, *CFO*
Jim Davis, *Mng Member*
EMP: 162
SALES (est): 16.5MM **Privately Held**
WEB: www.davischemicalservices.com
SIC: 1382 Oil & gas exploration services

(G-14773)
DAVIS COILED TUBING SVCS LLC (PA)
6310 Elysian Fields Rd (75671)
P.O. Box 310 (75671-0310)
PHONE..................................903 927-5555
Jim Davis,
EMP: 95
SQ FT: 8,000
SALES (est): 4.7MM **Privately Held**
SIC: 1382 Oil & gas exploration services

(G-14774)
DAVIS ENERGY SERVICES LLC
6310 Elysian Fields Rd (75671)
P.O. Box 460 (75671-0460)
PHONE..................................903 935-9269
Jim L Davis, *President*
EMP: 200
SALES (est): 3.6MM
SALES (corp-wide): 413.8MM **Publicly Held**
SIC: 1389 Oil & gas wells: building, repairing & dismantling
PA: Key Energy Services, Inc.
1301 Mckinney St Ste 1800
Houston TX 77010
713 651-4300

(G-14775)
EAST TEXAS PLATING INC
1707 Commerce St (75672-9233)
PHONE..................................903 935-7000
Fred Laughlin, *President*
Cheri H Dorbritz, *Admin Sec*
EMP: 10
SQ FT: 1,500
SALES (est): 975.1K **Privately Held**
SIC: 3471 Electroplating of metals or formed products

(G-14776)
ELECTROTECHNICS CORPORATION
Also Called: Eltec
1310 Commerce St (75672-9267)
PHONE..................................903 938-1901
William Marshall, *CEO*
April Spears, *President*
Kevin Marlton, *Vice Pres*
EMP: 21
SQ FT: 20,000
SALES (est): 2.5MM **Privately Held**
WEB: www.elteccorp.com
SIC: 3679 3643 3613 Electronic switches; current-carrying wiring devices; switchgear & switchboard apparatus

(G-14777)
FLUID DISPOSAL SPECIALTIES INC
8000 Us Highway 59 S (75672-4170)
P.O. Box 417, Homer LA (71040-0417)
PHONE..................................903 927-2050
Corey Bird, *Manager*
EMP: 16
SALES (corp-wide): 24.8MM **Privately Held**
WEB: www.fluiddisposalspecialtiesinc.com
SIC: 1389 Oil field services
PA: Fluid Disposal Specialties, Inc.
209 Sam Baird Rd
Homer LA 71040
318 927-6178

(G-14778)
FRONTIER TUBULAR SOLUTIONS LLC
Also Called: Turner Bros Crane & Rigging
11441 State Highway 43 S (75670-7537)
PHONE..................................903 236-2100
David Crowley, *Manager*
EMP: 42 **Privately Held**
WEB: www.frontiertubular.com
SIC: 3531 Crane carriers
PA: Frontier Tubular Solutions Llc
1300 S Meridian Ave # 501
Oklahoma City OK 73108

(G-14779)
GARRISON METAL PRODUCTS INC (PA)
2902 W Pinecrest Dr (75670-7060)
P.O. Box 1761 (75671-1761)
PHONE..................................903 938-1319
Ronald A Garrison, *President*
EMP: 20 EST: 1954
SQ FT: 63,000
SALES (est): 2.8MM **Privately Held**
WEB: www.garrisonmetalproducts.com
SIC: 3444 Sheet metalwork

(G-14780)
GENERAL CABLE CORPORATION
9975 Us Highway 80 W (75670-8523)
P.O. Box 430, Scottsville (75688-0430)
PHONE..................................903 938-8151
Jeff Buck, *Branch Mgr*
Patrick Prevost, *Bd of Directors*
Justin Wiggins, *Maintence Staff*
EMP: 42 **Privately Held**
WEB: www.generalcable.com
SIC: 3355 3357 Cable, aluminum: made in rolling mills; nonferrous wiredrawing & insulating
HQ: General Cable Corporation
4 Tesseneer Dr
Highland Heights KY 41076

(G-14781)
HARRIS POTTERIES LP
333 Marshall St (75670-2975)
PHONE..................................903 938-8884
Ed Arntson, *Manager*
EMP: 80
SALES (corp-wide): 19.3MM **Privately Held**
WEB: www.harrispotteries.com
SIC: 3269 Cookware: stoneware, coarse earthenware & pottery
PA: Harris Potteries, L.P.
    707 Skokie Blvd Ste 220
    Northbrook IL 60062
    847 564-5544

(G-14782)
HOWELL OIL & GAS INC
3700 E End Blvd S (75672-7426)
P.O. Box 1228 (75671-1228)
PHONE..................................903 935-0999
Steve Howell, *President*
EMP: 11
SQ FT: 5,100
SALES (est): 1.8MM **Privately Held**
SIC: 1382 1311 Oil & gas exploration services; crude petroleum production; natural gas production

(G-14783)
HUB CITY INDUSTRIES
11441 State Highway 43 S (75670-7537)
PHONE..................................903 938-8554
EMP: 30 **EST:** 2008
SALES (est): 969.2K **Privately Held**
SIC: 1389 Oil/Gas Field Services

(G-14784)
JRO LLC
6000 E End Blvd S (75672-8305)
PHONE..................................903 472-0924
Jeff Kester, *Manager*
EMP: 15
SALES (est): 781.9K **Privately Held**
SIC: 3799 All terrain vehicles (ATV)

(G-14785)
LA TEE DA LLC
Also Called: La-Te-Da Frgrnce For HM L L C
1070 Pumpkin Center Rd (75672-3330)
P.O. Box 740, Scottsville (75688-0740)
PHONE..................................903 927-3500
◆ **EMP:** 30
SQ FT: 64,000
SALES: 7.2MM **Privately Held**
SIC: 5947 2844 Ret Gifts/Novelties Mfg Toilet Preparations
PA: Home & Garden Party, Ltd.
    1070 Pumpkin Center Rd
    Marshall TX 75672

(G-14786)
LASER PROS INTERNATIONAL CORP
1402 Commerce St (75672-9275)
PHONE..................................715 369-5995
Billy Horton, *Manager*
Jill Demcak, *Supervisor*
EMP: 38 **Privately Held**
WEB: www.laserpros.com
SIC: 5045 7629 3577 Printers, computer; business machine repair, electric; computer peripheral equipment
PA: Laser Pros International Corp.
    1 International Ln
    Rhinelander WI 54501

(G-14787)
LEWIS ENGINEERING COMPANY
1608 E Houston St (75670-4442)
P.O. Box Y (75671-0590)
PHONE..................................903 938-6754
Steven D Lewis, *President*
Marjorie H Lewis, *Corp Secy*
Deven Nicks, *Manager*
Jeff Thomas, *Manager*
Diane Lewis, *Shareholder*
EMP: 42 **EST:** 1961
SQ FT: 14,000
SALES: 4.3MM **Privately Held**
WEB: www.lewisengineeringco.com
SIC: 3499 3451 3489 Machine bases, metal; screw machine products; ordnance & accessories

(G-14788)
MAGNUM MACHINE AND MFG CO
5029 Us Highway 59 N (75670-2303)
PHONE..................................903 935-5300
Kenneth M Fitzgerald, *President*
James M Fitzgerald, *Vice Pres*
Georgeanna Fitzgerald, *Admin Sec*
EMP: 12
SQ FT: 15,000
SALES (est): 2.1MM **Privately Held**
WEB: www.magnummm.com
SIC: 3599 Machine shop, jobbing & repair; machine & other job shop work

(G-14789)
MARSHALL MINERALS INC
707 Evans St (75670-1817)
P.O. Box 1626 (75671-1626)
PHONE..................................903 938-8301
EMP: 20
SQ FT: 10,200
SALES (corp-wide): 4.8MM **Privately Held**
WEB: www.seminerals.com
SIC: 2048 Prepared feeds
PA: Marshall Minerals, Inc.
    1100 Dothan Rd
    Bainbridge GA 39817
    229 246-3396

(G-14790)
MARSHALL NEWS MESSENGER INC
Also Called: Cox North Carolina Publication
309 E Austin St (75670-3475)
P.O. Box 730 (75671-0730)
PHONE..................................903 935-7914
Jerry Pye, *Publisher*
Caleb Brabham, *Editor*
Nathan Hague, *Editor*
Phill Latham, *Manager*
Brenna Barnett, *Executive*
EMP: 25
SQ FT: 16,316
SALES (est): 889K **Privately Held**
WEB: www.marshallnewsmessenger.com
SIC: 2711 Newspapers, publishing & printing

(G-14791)
MARSHALL POTTERY INC (DH)
Also Called: Deroma USA
4901 Elysian Fields Rd (75670-5330)
P.O. Box 1839 (75671-1839)
PHONE..................................903 938-9201
Stefano Celletti, *President*
◆ **EMP:** 125
SALES (est): 23.7MM
SALES (corp-wide): 177.9K **Privately Held**
WEB: www.marshallpottery.com
SIC: 3269 5719 5947 Pottery household articles, except kitchen articles; pottery; gift shop

(G-14792)
MARTEX WELL SERVICES LLP (PA)
Also Called: Darby Equipment Company
805 Cox Rd (75671)
P.O. Box 2048 (75671-2048)
PHONE..................................903 938-3574
Richard Roark, *Partner*
Kenneth Q Carlile, *Partner*
Quinton B Carlile, *Partner*
Steve B Carlile, *Partner*
EMP: 61
SALES (est): 16.8MM **Privately Held**
WEB: www.martexco.com
SIC: 1389 Oil field services

(G-14793)
MASTER WOODCRAFT CABINETRY LLC (HQ)
232 N Marshall Indus Blvd (75670-2442)
PHONE..................................903 935-0500
Gene Ponder, *CEO*
Alan Ponder, *Vice Pres*
Neil Little, *Project Mgr*
Patsy Ponder, *CFO*
Billy Palmer, *Sales Mgr*
▲ **EMP:** 97
SQ FT: 600,000

SALES (est): 73.2MM
SALES (corp-wide): 1.7B **Privately Held**
WEB: www.mwccabinetry.com
SIC: 2434 Wood kitchen cabinets
PA: Acproducts, Inc.
    4600 Arrowhead Dr
    Ann Arbor MI 48105
    214 469-3000

(G-14794)
MASTERCRAFT WOOD PRODUCTS LP
232 N Marshall Indus Ave (75670-2442)
PHONE..................................903 935-0500
Gene Ponder, *General Ptnr*
Rozenna Lewane, *Vice Pres*
Joe Harpold, *Plant Supt*
Larry Walls, *Plant Mgr*
Stewart Stearman, *Sales Staff*
EMP: 350
SALES (est): 35.9MM **Privately Held**
WEB: www.mastercraft.com
SIC: 2434 Wood kitchen cabinets

(G-14795)
NORM PIPE INC
907 Cox Rd (75672-8385)
PHONE..................................903 702-8966
David Batalla, *President*
EMP: 60
SALES (est): 1MM **Privately Held**
SIC: 1389 Construction, repair & dismantling services

(G-14796)
NORTH AMERICAN TECH GROUP INC (PA)
429 S Memory Ln (75670-8405)
PHONE..................................972 996-5750
D Patrick Long, *Ch of Bd*
Joe B Dorman, *General Counsel*
EMP: 15
SQ FT: 189,000 **Privately Held**
SIC: 2491 Railroad cross-ties, treated wood

(G-14797)
PERGAN
710 Bussey Rd (75670-2676)
PHONE..................................903 938-5141
Donna Chochos, *Branch Mgr*
EMP: 68
SALES (corp-wide): 128MM **Privately Held**
WEB: www.pergan.com
SIC: 2819 2869 Elements; industrial organic chemicals
HQ: Pergan Hilfsstoffe Fur Industrielle Prozesse Gmbh
    Schlavenhorst 71
    Bocholt 46395
    287 199-020

(G-14798)
POLYNT COMPOSITES USA INC
Also Called: Cook Composites
5851 Fm 1998 (75672-3324)
PHONE..................................903 938-9571
Bill Tiller, *Manager*
EMP: 14
SQ FT: 2,400
SALES (corp-wide): 2.2B **Privately Held**
WEB: www.polynt.com
SIC: 2821 Plastics materials & resins
HQ: Polynt Composites Usa Inc.
    99 E Cottage Ave
    Carpentersville IL 60110

(G-14799)
PRINT SHOP
214 S Bolivar St (75670-4106)
PHONE..................................903 295-2727
EMP: 23 **EST:** 1982
SQ FT: 6,000
SALES (est): 2MM **Privately Held**
WEB: www.theprintshop.us
SIC: 2752 Commercial printing, offset

(G-14800)
REPUBLIC NAT INDS TEXAS LP (HQ)
Also Called: Republic Industries
1400 Warren Dr (75672-5893)
PHONE..................................903 935-3680
Gary Edwards, *Partner*

Trent Garner, *Vice Pres*
Aj Wesseler, *Vice Pres*
Perry Ryals, *Plant Mgr*
Brett Thompson, *Accounts Mgr*
▲ **EMP:** 103
SQ FT: 400,000
SALES (est): 135.2MM
SALES (corp-wide): 139.3MM **Privately Held**
WEB: www.republicind.com
SIC: 5211 2541 2434 Cabinets, kitchen; wood partitions & fixtures; vanities, bathroom: wood
PA: Republic National Cabinet Corporation
    1400 Warren Dr
    Marshall TX 75672
    903 935-3680

(G-14801)
REPUBLIC NATIONAL CABINET CORP (PA)
Also Called: Rncc
1400 Warren Dr (75672-5893)
PHONE..................................903 935-3680
Paul F Patek, *President*
Jeffrey Kroyer, *Vice Pres*
Chris Thomas, *Vice Pres*
Doug Mzyk, *CFO*
Marsha Durham, *Treasurer*
EMP: 12
SALES (est): 139.3MM **Privately Held**
WEB: www.republicind.com
SIC: 2434 5031 Wood kitchen cabinets; kitchen cabinets

(G-14802)
SAFETY SEAL PISTON RING CO (PA)
4000 S Airport Rd (75672-5505)
P.O. Box J (75671-0140)
PHONE..................................903 938-9241
W Stanley Baker Jr, *President*
Don Bynum, *Manager*
Louise Baker, *Shareholder*
EMP: 27 **EST:** 1951
SQ FT: 48,000
SALES (est): 15.7MM **Privately Held**
WEB: www.sswesco.com
SIC: 3592 Pistons & piston rings; valves, engine

(G-14803)
SNIDER INDUSTRIES LLP
3311 Sue Belle Lake Rd (75670-2622)
P.O. Box 668 (75671-0668)
PHONE..................................903 938-9221
Julianna Parr, *President*
Jill Brewer, *General Ptnr*
Ronald L Snider, *Vice Pres*
John Minter, *Safety Mgr*
Suzanne Turner, *Marketing Staff*
▲ **EMP:** 100 **EST:** 1942
SQ FT: 6,000
SALES (est): 13.3MM **Privately Held**
WEB: www.sniderindustries.com
SIC: 2421 Lumber: rough, sawed or planed

(G-14804)
SUN GRO HORTICULTURE DIST INC
1010 Commerce St (75672-8827)
PHONE..................................903 938-7348
EMP: 27
SALES (corp-wide): 105.8MM **Privately Held**
SIC: 1499 2875 Nonmetallic Mineral Mining Manufacturing Of Fertilizers-Mix Only
PA: Sun Gro Horticulture Distribution Inc.
    770 Silver St
    Agawam MA 01001
    413 786-4343

(G-14805)
TIETEK GLOBAL LLC
429 S Memory Ln (75670-8405)
PHONE..................................281 444-3494
EMP: 25
SALES (est): 888.8K **Privately Held**
SIC: 3089 Mfg Plastic Products

(G-14806)
WALTER SOLOMON
Also Called: Wonderduck Decoys
505 Price St (75670-2067)
PHONE..................................903 938-2096

(PA)=Parent Co (HQ)=Headquarters (DH)=Div Headquarters
✿ = New Business established in last 2 years

Walter Solomon, *Owner*
Walter Soloman, *Owner*
▲ **EMP:** 10
SQ FT: 200
SALES (est): 1.2MM **Privately Held**
WEB: www.wonderduck.com
SIC: 3949 Hunting equipment

(G-14807)
WEATHERFORD ARTIFICIA
5605 Medco Dr (75672-8826)
PHONE.....................903 935-2416
EMP: 32 **Privately Held**
SIC: 3561 Heavy Construction Equipment Rental
HQ: Weatherford Artificial Lift Systems, Llc
2000 Saint James Pl
Houston TX 77056
713 836-4000

(G-14808)
WESCO VALVE & MANUFACTURING CO (HQ)
4000 S Airport Rd (75672-5505)
P.O. Box J (75671-0140)
PHONE.....................903 938-9241
Stanley Baker, *President*
Joe McNamara, *Corp Secy*
Sarah Harper, *Human Resources*
H L Spears, *Sales Mgr*
Tanner Spears, *Sales Mgr*
EMP: 50 **EST:** 1961
SALES (est): 11.6MM
SALES (corp-wide): 15.7MM **Privately Held**
WEB: www.sswesco.com
SIC: 3592 Valves, engine
PA: Safety Seal Piston Ring Company
4000 S Airport Rd
Marshall TX 75672
903 938-9241

(G-14809)
WOODLAWN MANUFACTURING LTD
275 N Marshall Indus Ave (75670-2444)
PHONE.....................903 938-1882
Gary Boone, *CEO*
Cory Mayo, *President*
Lanita Burchfield, *Purchasing*
Carla Ponder, *CFO*
EMP: 140
SQ FT: 45,000
SALES (est): 16.7MM **Privately Held**
WEB: www.woodlawnmanufacturing.com
SIC: 3599 Machine shop, jobbing & repair

Martindale
Caldwell County

(G-14810)
LONESTAR BADGE & SIGN INC
301 Quail Run Rd (78655-3950)
P.O. Box 387 (78655-0387)
PHONE.....................512 357-2261
Harold Hanusch, *President*
Lindsay Sherow, *COO*
Alicia Caddell, *Opers Mgr*
Levi Hanusch, *Opers Mgr*
Mary Pate, *Sales Mgr*
▲ **EMP:** 14
SQ FT: 10,000
SALES (est): 2.5MM **Privately Held**
WEB: www.lonestarbadge.com
SIC: 3089 3999 Identification cards, plastic; identification badges & insignia; identification tags, except paper

Maryneal
Nolan County

(G-14811)
RIVER CEMENT SALES COMPANY
202 County Road 306 (79535-1118)
PHONE.....................325 288-4224
EMP: 17
SALES (corp-wide): 395.5MM **Privately Held**
WEB: www.buzziunicemusa.com
SIC: 3241 Portland cement

HQ: Buzzi Unicem Usa Inc
100 Brodhead Rd Ste 230
Bethlehem PA 18017
610 882-5000

Mason
Mason County

(G-14812)
CLEANFUEL HOLDINGS INC
Also Called: Cleanfuel USA
824 Wheeler St (76856-3002)
P.O. Box 183, Art (76820-0183)
PHONE.....................512 864-0300
Curtis Donaldson, *Principal*
Oliver G Rick Richard III, *Chairman*
JD Wright, *Controller*
W Henry Harmon, *Director*
EMP: 37
SALES (est): 6.9MM **Privately Held**
SIC: 3714 Fuel systems & parts, motor vehicle

(G-14813)
ERNA FRAC SAND LC
224 Evans Ln (76856-5504)
P.O. Box 1249 (76856-1249)
PHONE.....................325 265-4400
Brett Nix, *Managing Prtnr*
Trey Curtis, *Manager*
Chris Hicks, *Manager*
EMP: 45
SALES (est): 9.5MM **Privately Held**
WEB: www.ernafracsand.com
SIC: 1442 Construction sand & gravel

(G-14814)
FLOTEK INDUSTRIES INC
Also Called: Trinity Tool
1402 Ft Mckavitt (76856)
P.O. Box 899 (76856-0899)
PHONE.....................325 347-0005
Rock Dicke, *Manager*
EMP: 13
SALES (corp-wide): 119.3MM **Publicly Held**
WEB: www.flotekind.com
SIC: 3533 Oil & gas field machinery
PA: Flotek Industries, Inc.
8846 N Sam Houston Pkwy W # 150
Houston TX 77064
713 849-9911

(G-14815)
MASON BOTTLING COMPANY (PA)
Also Called: Dr Pepper
210 N Avenue A (76856-2618)
P.O. Box 369 (76856-0369)
PHONE.....................325 347-5150
William W Koock, *President*
A F Holloway, *Vice Pres*
Joyce Holloway, *Admin Sec*
EMP: 18 **EST:** 1929
SQ FT: 1,600
SALES: 5.9MM **Privately Held**
WEB: www.masontxcoc.com
SIC: 2086 Bottled & canned soft drinks; soft drinks: packaged in cans, bottles, etc.

Matador
Motley County

(G-14816)
KOCH INDUSTRIES INC
Also Called: Matador Ranch
072 S State Hwy 70 (79244)
P.O. Box 839 (79244-0839)
PHONE.....................806 347-2645
Jane Campbell, *Branch Mgr*
EMP: 12
SALES (corp-wide): 36.8B **Privately Held**
WEB: www.kochindusinc.com
SIC: 2911 5172 5169 4922 Petroleum refining; petroleum products; chemicals & allied products; natural gas transmission; crude petroleum production; natural gas production; refinery, chemical processing & similar machinery

PA: Koch Industries, Inc.
4111 E 37th St N
Wichita KS 67220
316 828-5500

Mathis
San Patricio County

(G-14817)
HARRIS FABRICATION LLC
525 N State Highway 359 (78368-2026)
PHONE.....................361 547-6910
Gary Cunningham, *Mng Member*
Glennis Cunningham,
EMP: 13
SQ FT: 6,000 **Privately Held**
SIC: 1799 3523 Welding on site; barn, silo, poultry, dairy & livestock machinery; planting, haying, harvesting & processing machinery; soil preparation machinery, except turf & grounds

Maxwell
Caldwell County

(G-14818)
MAXWELL MANUFACTURING INC
55 2nd St Ste 1 (78656-9709)
P.O. Box 280 (78656-0280)
PHONE.....................512 357-2772
Randy Russell, *President*
Ken Kasee, *Vice Pres*
Glenn Smith, *Vice Pres*
Wendie Bryan, *Treasurer*
EMP: 40
SQ FT: 80,000
SALES (est): 8.9MM **Privately Held**
SIC: 3089 Injection molding of plastics

Mc Camey
Upton County

(G-14819)
MCCAMEY WELL SERVICE INC
1368 E 24th St (79752)
P.O. Box 1396 (79752-1396)
PHONE.....................432 208-2769
Martha Venegas, *President*
EMP: 11
SALES (est): 1.4MM **Privately Held**
SIC: 1389 Oil field services

Mc Gregor
Mclennan County

(G-14820)
DESIGN PACKAGING GROUP LTD
103 N Garfield St (76657-1334)
PHONE.....................254 840-2500
Bob Sirwaitis, *President*
Don Franklin, *Acting Pres*
EMP: 16
SQ FT: 20,000
SALES (est): 1.8MM **Privately Held**
WEB: www.designpackaginggroup.com
SIC: 2782 Looseleaf binders & devices

(G-14821)
PLASTIC MOLDED PRODUCTS INC
110 Ne 1st St (76657-1214)
PHONE.....................254 840-3721
Kris Bohne, *President*
William D Bohne, *Vice Pres*
EMP: 20
SQ FT: 25,000
SALES (est): 2MM **Privately Held**
WEB: www.injectionmoldingplus.net
SIC: 3089 Boxes, plastic; injection molded finished plastic products

(G-14822)
PURINA ANIMAL NUTRITION LLC
1135 E Mcgregor Dr (76657-1304)
PHONE.....................254 840-3276
Chad Miller, *Manager*
EMP: 35
SALES (corp-wide): 6.1B **Privately Held**
WEB: www.purinamills.com
SIC: 2048 Prepared feeds
HQ: Purina Animal Nutrition Llc
100 Danforth Dr
Gray Summit MO 63039

(G-14823)
SPACE EXPLORATION TECH CORP
8550 Case Rd (76657-3651)
PHONE.....................310 363-6000
Kristopher Kroc, *Manager*
EMP: 250
SALES (corp-wide): 2B **Privately Held**
WEB: www.spacex.com
SIC: 3761 Rockets, space & military, complete
PA: Space Exploration Technologies Corp.
1 Rocket Rd
Hawthorne CA 90250
310 363-6000

(G-14824)
SPACEX ROCKET DEV TEST FCILTY
1 Rocket Rd (76657-3991)
PHONE.....................254 840-5771
EMP: 15
SALES (est): 2.8MM **Privately Held**
WEB: www.spacex.com
SIC: 3761 Guided missiles & space vehicles

(G-14825)
TRANE US INC
182 Cotton Belt Pkwy (76657-3411)
PHONE.....................254 299-6300
Greg Groves, *Branch Mgr*
EMP: 150 **Privately Held**
WEB: www.trane.com
SIC: 3585 Heating & air conditioning combination units
HQ: Trane U.S. Inc.
3600 Pammel Creek Rd
La Crosse WI 54601
608 787-2000

(G-14826)
TURNER MANUFACTURING CO INC
1288 N Lone Star Pkwy (76657-1056)
PHONE.....................254 840-2891
Charles B Turner, *President*
EMP: 16 **EST:** 1981
SQ FT: 7,600
SALES (est): 1.2MM **Privately Held**
SIC: 3493 Torsion bar springs

Mc Kinney
Collin County

(G-14827)
CITY OF MCKINNEY
Also Called: McKinney Central Fire Dept
301 N Mcdonald St (75069)
PHONE.....................972 547-7657
Danny Kisner, *Chief*
EMP: 100
SALES (corp-wide): 221.2MM **Privately Held**
WEB: www.mckinneytexas.org
SIC: 3711 9224 Fire department vehicles (motor vehicles), assembly of;
PA: City Of Mckinney
222 N Tennessee St
Mckinney TX 75069
972 542-2675

▲ = Import ▼=Export
◆ =Import/Export

Mc Queeney
Guadalupe County

(G-14828)
GEORGIA-PACIFIC BLDG PDTS LLC
Fm 78 Cypress Ridge Rd (78123)
PHONE...................................830 557-5802
Gordon Labus, *Branch Mgr*
EMP: 14
SALES (corp-wide): 36.8B **Privately Held**
WEB: www.buildgp.com
SIC: 3275 Wallboard, gypsum
HQ: Georgia-Pacific Building Products Llc
133 Peachtree St Ne
Atlanta GA 30303

(G-14829)
JH BIOTECH INC
360 Koepsel Rd (78123-2100)
PHONE...................................830 557-4220
EMP: 24
SALES (corp-wide): 15.4MM **Privately Held**
WEB: www.jhbiotech.com
SIC: 2875 Fertilizers, mixing only
PA: Jh Biotech, Inc.
4951 Olivas Park Dr
Ventura CA 93003
805 650-8933

(G-14830)
REPUBLIC PLASTICS LTD (PA)
355 Schumann Rd (78123-3260)
PHONE...................................830 557-5574
Doug Ross, *President*
Gino Inman, *General Ptnr*
Dan Brooks, *Production*
Jason Schroeder, *CFO*
▲ EMP: 50
SQ FT: 240,000
SALES (est): 56.5MM **Privately Held**
WEB: www.republicplastics.com
SIC: 3086 3081 5113 Plastics foam products; unsupported plastics film & sheet; disposable plates, cups, napkins & eating utensils

McAllen
Hidalgo County

(G-14831)
ACJ PRODUCE & SPICES LLC
4324 W Military Hwy (78503-8830)
PHONE...................................956 627-4246
Rey Gonzalez Jr, *Principal*
EMP: 20
SALES (est): 671.8K **Privately Held**
SIC: 2099 Seasonings & spices

(G-14832)
AEF PLATING LLC
4000 W Ursula Ave (78503-9004)
PHONE...................................956 994-1991
Boyd P Cockrill, *President*
EMP: 24
SQ FT: 32,000
SALES (est): 2.5MM **Privately Held**
WEB: www.aefplating.com
SIC: 3471 Electroplating of metals or formed products

(G-14833)
AIM MEDIA TEXAS OPERATING LLC (PA)
Also Called: Monitor, The
1400 E Nolana Ave (78504-6111)
P.O. Box 3267 (78502-3267)
PHONE...................................956 683-4000
Jeremy L Halbreich, *CEO*
William R Starks, *President*
Debbie Grant, *Controller*
▲ EMP: 311
SALES (est): 98.1MM **Privately Held**
WEB: www.digitalaimmedia.com
SIC: 2711 4899 Newspapers, publishing & printing; data communication services

(G-14834)
ALOE QUEEN INC
2601 Zinnia Ave (78504-4802)
P.O. Box 720057 (78504-0057)
PHONE...................................956 631-8869
Raul Lopez, *President*
Anna Lopez, *Manager*
EMP: 30
SALES (est): 4.5MM **Privately Held**
WEB: www.aloequeen.com
SIC: 2844 Toilet preparations

Mcallen
Hidalgo County

(G-14835)
ALPS ELECTRIC NORTH AMER INC
7100 Intl Pkwy Ste 100 (78503)
PHONE...................................956 217-6500
Juan Ontiveros, *Engineer*
Don Kurth, *Branch Mgr*
Abraham Alvarez, *Manager*
EMP: 69 **Privately Held**
WEB: www.alps.com
SIC: 5013 4731 3714 Motor vehicle supplies & new parts; freight transportation arrangement; motor vehicle parts & accessories
HQ: Alps Alpine North America, Inc.
3151 Jay St Ste 101
Santa Clara CA 95054

McAllen
Hidalgo County

(G-14836)
AM-MEX PRODUCTS INC (PA)
3801 W Military Hwy (78503-8810)
P.O. Box 5006 (78502-5006)
PHONE...................................956 631-7916
Donald P King, *President*
Frank King, *Vice Pres*
Mike Bowen, *VP Opers*
Gloria Blanco, *Finance*
Claudia Reyna, *Manager*
▲ EMP: 30
SQ FT: 250,000
SALES (est): 245.1MM **Privately Held**
WEB: www.ammexproducts.com
SIC: 3714 7361 3672 Motor vehicle electrical equipment; labor contractors (employment agency); printed circuit boards

(G-14837)
AMERICA EMPACK INC (PA)
6401 S 36th St Bldg H28 (78503-8924)
PHONE...................................956 618-3922
Sung Kyun Kim, *President*
▲ EMP: 21
SALES: 14.7MM **Privately Held**
WEB: www.americaempack.com
SIC: 2653 Corrugated boxes, partitions, display items, sheets & pad

(G-14838)
AMERICA SAMKWANG INC (PA)
6801 S 33rd St Ste M (78503-8968)
PHONE...................................956 686-0221
Myoungki Kim, *CEO*
Samme Yunes, *Manager*
▲ EMP: 27
SQ FT: 144,000
SALES: 10MM **Privately Held**
WEB: www.samkwangmx.com
SIC: 3089 Injection molding of plastics

(G-14839)
ATLAS COPCO COMPRESSORS LLC
Also Called: Systems Product Co Houston N
224 N Mccoll Rd (78501-9371)
PHONE...................................281 453-6800
Mark Steven, *General Mgr*
Keith Herbster, *General Mgr*
John Vitt, *General Mgr*
Stephanie Moore, *Credit Mgr*
Jim May, *Regl Sales Mgr*
EMP: 300

SALES (corp-wide): 10.7B **Privately Held**
WEB: www.atlascopco.us
SIC: 5084 3563 Processing & packaging equipment; air & gas compressors
HQ: Atlas Copco Compressors Llc
300 Technology Center Way # 5
Rock Hill SC 29730
866 472-1015

(G-14840)
AXIOMAGNETS LLC
817 Chicago Ave (78501-2771)
PHONE...................................956 283-5920
Jose Hinojosa,
Alejandro Hinojosa,
EMP: 15
SALES (est): 2.6MM **Privately Held**
WEB: www.moldshield.com
SIC: 5162 2821 Plastics resins; molding compounds, plastics

(G-14841)
BERSAL ENERGY LLC
Also Called: Wholesaler Oilfield Equipment
4900 W Expressway 83 (78501-3050)
PHONE...................................956 270-1155
Julio Berman, *CEO*
EMP: 10
SALES (est): 993.2K **Privately Held**
WEB: www.bersal-energy-llc.business.site
SIC: 5172 3532 3533 3731 Petroleum products; drills & drilling equipment, mining (except oil & gas); drill rigs; drilling & production platforms, floating (oil & gas)

(G-14842)
BETTCHER MANUFACTURING LLC (PA)
Also Called: Bettcher Mfg & Met Stampg
6801 S 33rd St Ste 9 (78503-8834)
PHONE...................................956 618-5805
Forrest D Hayes, *Mng Member*
Kent J Frisby,
Geoffrey A Lezan,
Jeremiah Lynch,
Patrick Lyons,
▲ EMP: 100 EST: 1998
SQ FT: 70,000
SALES (est): 52.7MM **Privately Held**
WEB: www.bettcherllc.us
SIC: 3469 Metal stampings

(G-14843)
BETTCHER MANUFACTURING LLC
5801 George Mcvay Dr (78503-9022)
PHONE...................................956 519-0468
Anthony Matti, *General Mgr*
Edward Telegdy, *Opers Mgr*
Baldo Sepulbeda, *Manager*
EMP: 51
SALES (corp-wide): 52.7MM **Privately Held**
WEB: www.bettcherllc.us
SIC: 3469 Metal stampings
PA: Bettcher Manufacturing, Llc
6801 S 33rd St Ste 9
Mcallen TX 78503
956 618-5805

(G-14844)
BEYOND CREATIONS LLC
909 W Dove Ave (78504-3502)
PHONE...................................956 972-1903
Gary Johnson, *CFO*
Claudia D Alba,
Gary L Johnson,
EMP: 10
SALES (est): 1.1MM **Privately Held**
WEB: www.beyondcreations.com
SIC: 3499 Novelties & giftware, including trophies

Mcallen
Hidalgo County

(G-14845)
BISSELL INC
Also Called: Bissell Mc Allen
5700 S Intl Pkwy Ste B (78503)
PHONE...................................956 631-5077
Sheri Leffert, *Sales Staff*
Jerry Combs, *Manager*

EMP: 50
SALES (corp-wide): 1B **Privately Held**
WEB: www.bissell.com
SIC: 3635 5064 Household vacuum cleaners; vacuum cleaners
HQ: Bissell Inc.
2345 Walker Ave Nw
Grand Rapids MI 49544
616 453-4451

McAllen
Hidalgo County

(G-14846)
CARE PRODUCTS INC
6 N 12th St (78501-4669)
PHONE...................................956 383-6049
Charles L Graham, *President*
EMP: 35
SALES (est): 5MM **Privately Held**
WEB: www.careproductsinc.com
SIC: 2511 Wood household furniture

(G-14847)
CINCH CONNECTORS INC
6900 S Bentsen Rd (78503-8706)
PHONE...................................956 686-1151
Bill Winderweedle, *Principal*
Soraya Hernandez, *Production*
Timothy Andre Jones, *Engineer*
EMP: 350
SALES (corp-wide): 492.4MM **Publicly Held**
WEB: www.belfuse.com
SIC: 3643 5088 3678 3761 Connectors & terminals for electrical devices; aircraft equipment & supplies; electronic connectors; guided missiles & space vehicles
HQ: Cinch Connectors Inc.
1700 S Finley Rd
Lombard IL 60148
630 705-6001

(G-14848)
CLEMENTSON INC (HQ)
3721 N Mccoll Rd (78501-9163)
P.O. Box 2587 (78502-2587)
PHONE...................................956 631-9121
Arnold Perez, *President*
EMP: 30
SALES (est): 10.9MM
SALES (corp-wide): 156.8MM **Privately Held**
SIC: 8711 1382 Petroleum engineering; oil & gas exploration services
PA: Mo-Vac Service Company
3721 S Mccoll Rd
Edinburg TX 78539
956 682-6381

(G-14849)
COCA COLA BTLG OF SHREVEPORT
Also Called: Coca-Cola
2400 W Expressway 83 (78501-7768)
PHONE...................................956 632-3773
Canuto Martinez, *Manager*
EMP: 80
SALES (corp-wide): 37.2B **Publicly Held**
WEB: www.na.ko.com
SIC: 2086 Bottled & canned soft drinks
HQ: Coca Cola Bottling Co Of Shreveport, Inc
14185 Dallas Pkwy # 1400
Dallas TX 75254
214 902-2600

(G-14850)
COMPOSITE ACCESS PRODUCTS LP
5216 N 26th St (78504-4803)
PHONE...................................956 765-2907
William Nunnery, *Principal*
EMP: 12
SALES (est): 2MM **Privately Held**
WEB: www.justcapthat.com
SIC: 3272 Manhole covers or frames, concrete

(G-14851)
COPY PLUS LLC
4500 N 10th St Ste 240 (78504-2963)
PHONE...................................956 668-7587

Ray Rosales, *Marketing Staff*
Vivian Alvarado, *Manager*
Leonel Cantu,
Alonzo Cantu,
Agustin Martinez,
EMP: 18
SQ FT: 8,000
SALES (est): 4MM **Privately Held**
WEB: www.copyplusonline.net
SIC: 2752 5112 Commercial printing, off-set; office supplies

(G-14852)
D&G ENERGY CORPORATION (PA)
10225 N Bentsen Rd (78504-6089)
P.O. Box 4675 (78502-4675)
PHONE...................956 686-6040
M Garcia, *President*
Leandro Garcia, *Vice Pres*
EMP: 15 EST: 2007
SQ FT: 200
SALES (est): 2.8MM **Privately Held**
WEB: www.dgenergycorp.com
SIC: 5063 3669 1731 Signaling equipment, electrical; traffic signals, electric; electrical work

(G-14853)
DFA DAIRY BRANDS FLUID LLC
525 Beaumont Ave (78501-2737)
PHONE...................956 686-0511
Howard Hotcaveg, *Branch Mgr*
EMP: 71
SALES (corp-wide): 15.8B **Privately Held**
SIC: 2026 Milk & cream, except fermented, cultured & flavored
HQ: Dfa Dairy Brands Fluid, Llc
   1405 N 98th St
   Kansas City KS 66111
   816 801-6455

(G-14854)
EATON CORPORATION
5800 S 42nd St Ste G (78503-7791)
P.O. Box 4828 (78502-4828)
PHONE...................956 283-1468
EMP: 14 **Privately Held**
WEB: www.eatonelectrical.com
SIC: 3511 Hydraulic turbine generator set units, complete
HQ: Eaton Corporation
   1000 Eaton Blvd
   Cleveland OH 44122
   440 523-5000

(G-14855)
EDI WEYERHAEUSER MCALLEN
200 N 26th St (78501-7506)
PHONE...................956 682-9406
Cesar Elizondo, *Principal*
EMP: 9
SALES (est): 1MM **Privately Held**
SIC: 2653 Corrugated & solid fiber boxes

(G-14856)
EL PERIODICO U S A INC
801 E Fir Ave (78501-9320)
PHONE...................956 631-5628
Miguel Letelier, *President*
Sally Serda, *Administration*
EMP: 15
SALES (est): 844.8K **Privately Held**
WEB: www.elperiodicousa.com
SIC: 2711 Newspapers, publishing & printing

(G-14857)
EMERSON ELECTRIC CO
6100 S International Pkwy (78503-8993)
PHONE...................956 994-1427
Roy Rodriguez, *Branch Mgr*
Fernando Padilla, *Manager*
EMP: 23
SALES (corp-wide): 16.7B **Publicly Held**
WEB: www.emerson.com
SIC: 3823 Industrial instrmnts msrmnt display/control process variable
PA: Emerson Electric Co.
   8000 West Florissant Ave
   Saint Louis MO 63136
   314 553-2000

(G-14858)
EMERSON ELECTRIC CO
5109 Tanya Ave Ste 300 (78503-2802)
PHONE...................956 683-0694
Earnest Sanchez, *General Mgr*
EMP: 18
SALES (corp-wide): 16.7B **Publicly Held**
WEB: www.emerson.com
SIC: 3823 Industrial instrmnts msrmnt display/control process variable
PA: Emerson Electric Co.
   8000 West Florissant Ave
   Saint Louis MO 63136
   314 553-2000

(G-14859)
EMU PLASTICS TEX LIMITED INC
6100 S 35th St (78503-8820)
PHONE...................956 618-5200
Charmaine Chin King, *President*
Lisa King, *Vice Pres*
Clifton Mahathey, *Opers Staff*
EMP: 30
SQ FT: 40,000
SALES (est): 10.9MM **Privately Held**
WEB: www.emuplasticstx.com
SIC: 3089 Injection molding of plastics

(G-14860)
FEDEX OFFICE & PRINT SVCS INC
2812 N 10th St (78501-1915)
PHONE...................956 682-4040
EMP: 20
SALES (corp-wide): 69.2B **Publicly Held**
WEB: www.fedex.com
SIC: 7334 2759 Photocopying & duplicating services; commercial printing
HQ: Fedex Office And Print Services, Inc.
   7900 Legacy Dr
   Plano TX 75024
   800 463-3339

(G-14861)
FIBERIO TECHNOLOGY CORPORATION
4409 Wanda Ave Ste B (78503-8866)
PHONE...................956 207-5448
Ellery Buchanan, *President*
Stephen Kay, *Vice Pres*
Brian Gilliam, *CFO*
Karen Lozano, *CTO*
EMP: 30
SALES (est): 4.9MM **Privately Held**
WEB: www.fiberiotech.com
SIC: 8731 2824 Commercial physical research; polyester fibers

(G-14862)
FIRE SYSTEMS OF TEXAS LLC
11500 N 10th St (78504-9580)
P.O. Box 997, Edinburg (78540-0997)
PHONE...................956 391-1191
Carol J Wychopen, *Mng Member*
EMP: 30
SALES (est): 6.6MM **Privately Held**
SIC: 3569 Sprinkler systems, fire: automatic

(G-14863)
GALVOTEC ALLOYS INC (PA)
6712 S 36th St (78503-8896)
PHONE...................956 630-3500
Rogelio E Garza, *President*
Scott Shook, *General Mgr*
Frank Lorenzo, *Business Mgr*
Myrna A Garza, *Vice Pres*
Jorge Martinez, *QC Mgr*
◆ **EMP:** 125
SQ FT: 35,000
SALES (est): 30.2MM **Privately Held**
WEB: www.galvotec.com
SIC: 3365 3341 3369 Aluminum foundries; magnesium smelting & refining (secondary); zinc & zinc-base alloy castings, except die-castings

(G-14864)
GE ENGINE SVCS - MCALLEN L P
Also Called: McAllen P&Rs Service Center
6200 S 42nd St (78503-8856)
PHONE...................956 971-5200
Daniel Campos, *General Mgr*

▲ **EMP:** 575
SQ FT: 110,000
SALES (est): 111.2MM
SALES (corp-wide): 95.2B **Publicly Held**
WEB: www.mcallenmedicalcenter.com
SIC: 3724 Aircraft engines & engine parts
HQ: Ge Aviation Systems Llc
   1 Neumann Way
   Cincinnati OH 45215
   937 898-9600

(G-14865)
GEM SERVICES LLP
1201 S 1st St (78501-1110)
PHONE...................210 863-2020
Garrett Mann, *Partner*
EMP: 20
SALES (est): 1.8MM **Privately Held**
WEB: www.gemservicesllp.com
SIC: 1389 7359 Oil field services; equipment rental & leasing

(G-14866)
GENCO ENERGY SERVICES INC (PA)
1701 W State Highway 107 (78504-9550)
PHONE...................956 380-3710
Murray Meggison, *President*
Paul Albrecht, *General Mgr*
Brad Meggison, *Opers Staff*
Tony Freitas, *CFO*
Jenna Cao, *Treasurer*
EMP: 31
SALES (est): 221.9MM **Privately Held**
WEB: www.genco.us
SIC: 1389 Oil field services

(G-14867)
GRANCHELLI CONSTRUCTION LLC
2001 Industrial Dr (78504-4009)
PHONE...................956 928-1122
Veronica De Leon, *Office Mgr*
James J Granchelli,
EMP: 11
SALES (est): 1MM **Privately Held**
WEB: www.granchelliconstruction.com
SIC: 1531 1542 3273 1541 ; commercial & office building contractors; commercial & office buildings, renovation & repair; institutional building construction; ready-mixed concrete; industrial buildings, new construction

(G-14868)
HUMANETICS II LTD
7021 S Bentsen Rd (78503-8842)
PHONE...................956 994-9200
Servando Munguia, *Sales Executive*
Louise Beldon, *Branch Mgr*
EMP: 100
SALES (corp-wide): 71.6MM **Privately Held**
WEB: www.humanetics.com
SIC: 3444 3599 Sheet metalwork; machine shop, jobbing & repair
HQ: Humanetics Ii, Ltd.
   1700 Columbian Club Dr
   Carrollton TX 75006
   972 416-1304

(G-14869)
HUNTINGTON SKY PRODUCTION LTD (PA)
Also Called: Fastsigns
4117 N 10th St (78504-3004)
PHONE...................956 618-1800
Rod Snell, *Partner*
Rose Snell, *Partner*
EMP: 15 EST: 2006
SALES (est): 1MM **Privately Held**
WEB: www.fastsigns.com
SIC: 3993 Signs & advertising specialties

(G-14870)
I O U ENTERPRISES INC
Also Called: Rgv Optical Lab
423 W Nolana Ave (78504-3012)
PHONE...................956 631-3366
Bill Bieker, *President*
Brian Bieker, *Manager*
EMP: 10
SALES (est): 250K **Privately Held**
SIC: 5048 3827 Lenses, ophthalmic; optical instruments & lenses

(G-14871)
INDUSTRIAL COILS LLC
809 E Fir Ave (78501-9320)
PHONE...................956 664-9496
Jim Bush,
EMP: 12
SALES (est): 1.8MM **Privately Held**
WEB: www.indcoils.com
SIC: 3549 Coiling machinery

(G-14872)
INLAND PRODUCTS INC
Also Called: Inland Transport
3505 Xenops Ave (78504-5002)
PHONE...................956 627-5700
William R Muse, *President*
Edward Huxel, *Vice Pres*
EMP: 46
SQ FT: 40,000
SALES (est): 3.3MM **Privately Held**
WEB: www.inlandproducts.com
SIC: 2079 2077 Vegetable refined oils (except corn oil); cottonseed oil, refined: not made in cottonseed oil mills; animal fats, oils & meals

(G-14873)
INNOVATIVE BLOCK S TEXAS LTD
1400 N Mccoll Rd Ste 201 (78501-9613)
PHONE...................956 682-3181
David Riegert, *Branch Mgr*
EMP: 11
SALES (corp-wide): 6MM **Privately Held**
WEB: www.innovativeblock.com
SIC: 3271 Concrete block & brick
PA: Innovative Block Of South Texas, Ltd.
   240 E 1st St
   La Feria TX 78559
   956 797-4200

(G-14874)
INTERNATIONAL PAPER COMPANY
200 N 26th St (78501-7506)
PHONE...................956 682-9406
EMP: 160
SALES (corp-wide): 22.3B **Publicly Held**
WEB: www.internationalpaper.com
SIC: 2631 2653 5113 Paperboard mills; boxes, corrugated: made from purchased materials; corrugated & solid fiber boxes
PA: International Paper Company
   6400 Poplar Ave
   Memphis TN 38197
   901 419-9000

(G-14875)
ISAVELA ENTERPRISES INC
721 N Col Rowe Blvd (78501-2516)
PHONE...................800 918-8242
Jaime Muriel, *President*
Sandra Muriel, *Director*
EMP: 55
SQ FT: 5,000
SALES (est): 2MM **Privately Held**
WEB: www.isavela.com
SIC: 3842 Surgical appliances & supplies

(G-14876)
JALEM WELDING SERVICE LLC
414 Cottonwood Ave (78501-2722)
P.O. Box 3356 (78502-3356)
PHONE...................956 467-2355
EMP: 10 EST: 2014
SALES (est): 46.5K **Privately Held**
SIC: 7692 1771 Welding repair; stucco, gunite & grouting contractors

(G-14877)
JBS USA FOOD COMPANY
6800 S Ware Rd Ste 109 (78503-8814)
PHONE...................956 632-3800
Ramon Flores, *Executive*
EMP: 272 **Publicly Held**
WEB: www.jbssa.com
SIC: 2011 Meat packing plants
HQ: Jbs Usa Food Company
   1770 Promontory Cir
   Greeley CO 80634
   970 506-8000

(G-14878)
JCI ROOFING LLC
2916 N 1st Ln (78501-9422)
PHONE..................956 227-1745
Juan Antonio Hernandez,
EMP: 12
SALES (est) 753.5K **Privately Held**
SIC: 2493 Insulation & roofing material, reconstituted wood

(G-14879)
JIM MELHART PIANO AND ORGAN CO
Also Called: Melhart Music Center
3325 N 10th St (78501-1927)
PHONE..................956 682-6147
Jimmie Melhart, *President*
EMP: 22
SQ FT: 12,000
SALES (est): 5.1MM **Privately Held**
WEB: www.melhart.com
SIC: 3651 5736 Amplifiers: radio, public address or musical instrument; pianos

(G-14880)
JOHNSON CONTROLS BE OPERATION
5201 George Mcvay Dr (78503-8876)
PHONE..................956 782-3000
Jose Luis Salinas, *Manager*
EMP: 900 **Privately Held**
WEB: www.johnsoncontrols.com
SIC: 3822 Air conditioning & refrigeration controls
PA: Johnson Controls Be Operations Mexico, S. De R.L. De C.V.
David Alfaro Siqueiros No. 104
San Pedro Garza Garcia N.L. 66278

Mcallen
Hidalgo County

(G-14881)
JOHNSON CONTROLS INC
5201 Gorge Mcvay Dr Ste I (78503)
P.O. Box 591, Milwaukee WI (53201-0591)
PHONE..................956 782-3000
Benjamin Jones, *Engineer*
EMP: 153 **Privately Held**
WEB: www.johnsoncontrols.com
SIC: 3714 4225 Motor vehicle parts & accessories; general warehousing
HQ: Johnson Controls, Inc.
5757 N Green Bay Ave
Glendale WI 53209
800 382-2804

McAllen
Hidalgo County

(G-14882)
KENNETH FOX SUPPLY COMPANY (PA)
Also Called: San Antonio Bag & Burlap
2200 Fox Dr (78504-4150)
P.O. Box 2288 (78502-2288)
PHONE..................956 682-6176
Kenneth Fox, *President*
Craig Fox, *Exec VP*
Keith Fox, *Vice Pres*
Lucas Fox, *Production*
Cynthia Rodriguez, *Purchasing*
◆ **EMP:** 107 **EST:** 1965
SQ FT: 130,000
SALES (est): 21.8MM **Privately Held**
WEB: www.foxbag.com
SIC: 2393 5113 Bags & containers, except sleeping bags: textile; shipping supplies

(G-14883)
KINGS ECO PLASTICS LLC
4001 W Military Hwy (78503-8812)
PHONE..................956 631-1115
Owen Stewart, *President*
Rodolfo Carrizales, *Engineer*
Sue Tseng,
▲ **EMP:** 62
SQ FT: 40,000

SALES (est): 15.6MM **Privately Held**
WEB: www.kingsprosperity.com
SIC: 3089 Injection molding of plastics; injection molded finished plastic products

(G-14884)
LAREDO COCA-COLA BOTTLING CO
2400 W Expressway 83 (78501-7768)
PHONE..................956 686-8827
Carlos Ramos, *Branch Mgr*
EMP: 250
SALES (corp-wide): 309.5MM **Privately Held**
SIC: 2086 Bottled & canned soft drinks
HQ: The Laredo Coca-Cola Bottling Company
1402 Industrial Blvd
Laredo TX 78041
956 726-2671

(G-14885)
LITTLE GREEN APPLES INC (PA)
2201 W Dove Ave Ste 1 (78504-4081)
PHONE..................956 668-0028
Alfredo Marroquin, *CEO*
EMP: 12
SQ FT: 8,084
SALES (est): 946.6K **Privately Held**
SIC: 2531 2511 Public building & related furniture; wood household furniture

(G-14886)
M A E W INC
Also Called: Eeac
422 S 11th St (78501-4918)
P.O. Box 5454 (78502-5454)
PHONE..................956 627-3554
Elias Woloski, *President*
Gary Lenz, *CFO*
▲ **EMP:** 12
SQ FT: 1,000
SALES (est): 1MM **Privately Held**
WEB: www.eeacusa.com
SIC: 3911 Jewelry, precious metal

(G-14887)
MCALLEN BAG & SUPPLY COMPANY
1608 Pecan Blvd (78501-4260)
P.O. Box 1208 (78505-1208)
PHONE..................956 686-6571
Lonnie Gegenheimer Jr, *President*
Betty Gegenheimer, *Vice Pres*
EMP: 11
SQ FT: 60,000
SALES (est): 2.5MM **Privately Held**
WEB: www.mcallen.org
SIC: 5085 2393 2448 Industrial supplies; bags & containers, except sleeping bags: textile; pallets, wood

(G-14888)
MCALLEN METAL STAMPING INC
3500 W Military Hwy (78503-8819)
PHONE..................956 682-3438
William Pendergrass, *President*
Bill Pendergrass, *President*
Ralph Garcia, *Vice Pres*
EMP: 15
SQ FT: 20,000
SALES (est): 3.4MM **Privately Held**
WEB: www.mcallenmetalstamping.com
SIC: 3469 Stamping metal for the trade

(G-14889)
MCALLEN SPORTS INC (PA)
108 S 16th St (78501-5129)
PHONE..................956 687-5500
Jorge Salcines, *President*
Joe Escamilla, *General Mgr*
EMP: 45
SQ FT: 11,000
SALES (est): 4.8MM **Privately Held**
WEB: www.mcallensports.com
SIC: 5941 5091 5999 5699 Bicycle & bicycle parts; sporting & recreation goods; trophies & plaques; sports apparel; screen printing; embroidery products, except schiffli machine

(G-14890)
MCCOY CORPORATION
Also Called: Mc Coy Building Supply 451
3209 W Business 83 (78501-8248)
PHONE..................956 618-3104
Ram Pequeno, *Branch Mgr*
EMP: 35
SALES (corp-wide): 881.1MM **Privately Held**
WEB: www.mccoys.com
SIC: 2431 Window frames, wood
PA: Mccoy Corporation
1350 N Ih 35
San Marcos TX 78666
512 353-5400

(G-14891)
MOHAWK INDUSTRIES INC
1201 N Jackson Rd (78501-5760)
PHONE..................956 630-4709
EMP: 156 **Publicly Held**
WEB: www.mohawkind.com
SIC: 2273 Finishers of tufted carpets & rugs
PA: Mohawk Industries, Inc.
160 S Industrial Blvd
Calhoun GA 30701

(G-14892)
MONTANO INVESTMENTS INC
Also Called: Digital Office Systems
4800 W Expressway 83 (78501-3015)
PHONE..................956 630-1877
Eristeo Montano, *President*
Daniel Montano, *Vice Pres*
Danny Montano, *Executive*
EMP: 25
SQ FT: 2,600
SALES (est): 3.6MM **Privately Held**
WEB: www.digitalrgv.com
SIC: 5044 7389 5065 3577 Copying equipment; printers' services: folding, collating; facsimile equipment; printers & plotters

(G-14893)
MVP PLASTICS SA LLC
4001 W Military Hwy (78503-8812)
PHONE..................440 834-1790
Darrell McNair, *CEO*
Darrell L McNair, *CEO*
EMP: 15
SALES (est): 808.1K **Privately Held**
WEB: www.mvpplastics.com
SIC: 3089 Injection molding of plastics

(G-14894)
NIBCO INC
Nibco De Reynosa
6410 S 33rd St (78503-8855)
P.O. Box 2348 (78502-2348)
PHONE..................574 295-3000
Charles Garrett, *Manager*
EMP: 50
SALES (corp-wide): 704.3MM **Privately Held**
WEB: www.nibco.com
SIC: 3494 5074 Valves & pipe fittings; plumbing fittings & supplies
PA: Nibco Inc.
1516 Middlebury St
Elkhart IN 46516
574 295-3000

(G-14895)
NUCO TOOL INC (PA)
1408 E Upas Ave (78501-5632)
PHONE..................956 383-6620
Gerardo Nunez, *President*
EMP: 20
SALES (est): 2.2MM **Privately Held**
SIC: 3465 Automotive stampings

(G-14896)
OCONN LLC
Also Called: ASAP Printing Solutions
2104 Highland Ave (78501-6171)
PHONE..................956 630-6116
Shawn O'Conner,
Sean O'Connor,
EMP: 10
SALES (est): 1.1MM **Privately Held**
WEB: www.asapprintingsolutions.com
SIC: 3993 Signs & advertising specialties

(G-14897)
OXY USA INC
401 Dallas Ave (78501-2777)
PHONE..................956 429-0600
Curtis Price, *Branch Mgr*
EMP: 125
SALES (corp-wide): 21.2B **Publicly Held**
SIC: 1311 Crude petroleum production; natural gas production
HQ: Oxy Usa Inc.
1001 S County Rd W
Odessa TX 79763
432 335-0995

(G-14898)
PALMER STEEL SUPPLIES INC
4300 Acapulco Ave (78503-8823)
P.O. Box 10 (78505-0010)
PHONE..................956 686-6575
James G Thompson, *President*
Palmer A Thompson, *Corp Secy*
Keyes Ramee, *Vice Pres*
Jose Cano, *Prgrmr*
EMP: 150 **EST:** 1954
SQ FT: 150,000
SALES (est): 57.1MM **Privately Held**
WEB: www.palmersteel.com
SIC: 3441 1791 Building components, structural steel; structural steel erection

Mcallen
Hidalgo County

(G-14899)
PANASONIC CORP NORTH AMERICA
Panasonic Industrial Devices
4900 Gorge Mcvay Dr Ste C (78503)
PHONE..................956 984-3432
Ronald J Green, *President*
Kellie Setsuda, *Credit Staff*
Michael Marcario, *Manager*
EMP: 2800 **Privately Held**
WEB: www.na.panasonic.com
SIC: 3651 3675 3471 Audio electronic systems; electronic capacitors; plating & polishing
HQ: Panasonic Corporation Of North America
2 Riverfront Plz Ste 200
Newark NJ 07102
201 348-7000

McAllen
Hidalgo County

(G-14900)
REGAL BELOIT AMERICA INC
6901 S International Pkwy (78503-0017)
PHONE..................956 213-0503
Emilio Lopez, *Project Mgr*
EMP: 12
SALES (corp-wide): 3.2B **Publicly Held**
WEB: www.regalbeloit.com
SIC: 3644 Electric conduits & fittings
HQ: Regal Beloit America, Inc.
200 State St
Beloit WI 53511
608 364-8800

(G-14901)
RIO GRANDE IMAGING CENTER INC
101 E Ridge Rd (78503-1847)
PHONE..................956 668-6900
Joe Martinez, *Director*
Nancy Reeder, *Director*
Janet West, *Administration*
EMP: 15
SALES (est): 1.6MM **Privately Held**
WEB: www.riohealth.com
SIC: 3845 8071 Magnetic resonance imaging device, nuclear; X-ray laboratory, including dental

(G-14902)
RIO TRUSS LP
100 N Bentsen Rd (78501-8157)
P.O. Box 2163 (78505-2163)
PHONE..................956 682-9822
Brent Thornton, *Managing Prtnr*

Marshall K Doherty, *Partner*
EMP: 13
SQ FT: 12,000
SALES (est): 2.2MM **Privately Held**
WEB: www.riotruss.com
SIC: 2439 Trusses, wooden roof

(G-14903)
RVG PRODIRECT LLC
1913 W Houston Ave (78501-7228)
PHONE..................................956 627-6161
Patrick J Hettler,
EMP: 10
SALES (est): 331.8K **Privately Held**
SIC: 2311 Men's & boys' uniforms

Mcallen
Hidalgo County

(G-14904)
SAINT-GOBAIN ABRASIVES INC
6100 Intl Pkwy Ste 300 (78503)
PHONE..................................956 519-5047
Patrick Millot, *CEO*
EMP: 10
SALES (corp-wide): 328.4MM **Privately Held**
WEB: www.saint-gobain.com
SIC: 3291 Abrasive products
HQ: Saint-Gobain Abrasives, Inc.
　1 New Bond St
　Worcester MA 01606
　508 795-5000

McAllen
Hidalgo County

(G-14905)
SCHNEIDER ELECTRIC
5801 George Mcvay Dr C (78503-9022)
PHONE..................................956 205-7533
Hector Vela, *Principal*
EMP: 12
SALES (est): 2.3MM **Privately Held**
SIC: 3699 Electrical equipment & supplies

(G-14906)
SITESELECT INC
Also Called: Siteselect Medical Tech
1100 E Jasmine Ave # 105 (78501-4393)
PHONE..................................956 207-5587
Bob Pourgol, *CEO*
EMP: 29
SALES (est): 300K **Privately Held**
WEB: www.lexciimedical.com
SIC: 3841 Surgical & medical instruments

(G-14907)
SMEAD MANUFACTURING COMPANY
3801 W Military Hwy (78503-8810)
PHONE..................................956 631-1418
Kevin Collman, *Manager*
EMP: 12
SALES (corp-wide): 227.5MM **Privately Held**
WEB: www.smead.com
SIC: 2675 Folders, filing, die-cut: made from purchased materials
PA: Smead Manufacturing Company Inc
　600 Smead Blvd
　Hastings MN 55033
　651 437-4111

(G-14908)
SNAP OILFIELD SERVICES LLC
3605 N 42nd Ln (78501-0220)
PHONE..................................956 322-1210
Juan Aristeo Cantu, *Mng Member*
Margarita Cantu, *Mng Member*
EMP: 23
SALES (est): 1MM **Privately Held**
SIC: 1389 Oil field services

(G-14909)
SWEET DREAMS INC
1300 E Upas Ave (78501-5619)
PHONE..................................956 687-2737
F Denise Sansing, *President*
Scott Beard, *Vice Pres*
▲ **EMP:** 90

SQ FT: 15,000
SALES (est): 9.9MM **Privately Held**
WEB: www.sweet-dreams.com
SIC: 2392 Pillows, bed: made from purchased materials; comforters & quilts: made from purchased materials; tablecloths: made from purchased materials

(G-14910)
TEKNA IMPACT
5800 S 42nd St Ste E (78503-7791)
PHONE..................................956 213-8285
Emilio Fuentes, *General Mgr*
Michael Nixon, *Mng Member*
EMP: 19
SALES (est): 3.1MM **Privately Held**
WEB: www.tekna-impact.com
SIC: 2759 Labels & seals: printing

(G-14911)
TEXAS LOGIC INC
Also Called: Hamer Enterprises
4200 N Bicentennial Dr A (78504-4160)
PHONE..................................956 682-3466
William C Hamer, *CEO*
Jodi Hamer, *COO*
Rey Banda, *Consultant*
EMP: 14
SQ FT: 7,500
SALES (est): 5.1MM **Privately Held**
WEB: www.hamerenterprises.com
SIC: 5045 7372 Computers; application computer software

(G-14912)
TI GROUP AUTO SYSTEMS LLC
3900 W Ursula Ave (78503-9006)
PHONE..................................956 686-5400
Richard Kolpasky, *Principal*
Steve Taylor, *Exec Dir*
EMP: 30
SQ FT: 29,000
SALES (corp-wide): 3.7B **Privately Held**
WEB: www.tifluidsystems.com
SIC: 3714 Motor vehicle parts & accessories
HQ: Ti Group Automotive Systems, Llc
　2020 Taylor Rd
　Auburn Hills MI 48326
　248 296-8000

(G-14913)
VALLEY DIE CASTINGS INC
5216 N 26th St (78504-4803)
PHONE..................................956 630-0268
Charles Brown, *President*
Irma Gonzalez, *Office Mgr*
Monico Castro, *Sr Project Mgr*
EMP: 19
SQ FT: 16,100
SALES (est): 5.7MM **Privately Held**
WEB: www.valleydiecast.com
SIC: 3364 Zinc & zinc-base alloy die-castings

(G-14914)
VALLEY HERBAL PRODUCTS INC
Also Called: Vhp Foods Company
2601 Zinnia Ave (78504-4802)
PHONE..................................956 631-8869
Raul Lopez, *President*
Adrian Alonzo, *Vice Pres*
Veronica Moreno, *Treasurer*
Anna Lopez, *Admin Sec*
EMP: 12
SALES: 721.9K **Privately Held**
WEB: www.valleyherbalproducts.com
SIC: 2023 Dietary supplements, dairy & non-dairy based

(G-14915)
VALLEY ORTHPD & PROSTHETICS (PA)
2216 N 10th St (78501-4002)
P.O. Box 331580, Corpus Christi (78463-1580)
PHONE..................................956 686-0032
Norma Zuniga, *Principal*
James Dorman, *Vice Pres*
Dorman Leone, *Vice Pres*
EMP: 9
SQ FT: 2,000
SALES (est): 1MM **Privately Held**
SIC: 3842 Orthopedic appliances

(G-14916)
VAUGHAN INVESTMENTS INC
Also Called: Burton
108 E Us Highway 83 (78501-8933)
PHONE..................................956 686-3725
Eliberto Fernandez, *Manager*
EMP: 10
SALES (corp-wide): 34MM **Privately Held**
WEB: www.burtoncompanies.com
SIC: 5013 5531 5085 5084 Automotive supplies & parts; automobile & truck equipment & parts; bearings; pumps & pumping equipment; hose & tube fittings & assemblies, hydraulic/pneumatic
PA: Vaughan Investments, Inc.
　529 E Hwy 83
　Weslaco TX 78596
　956 968-3121

(G-14917)
VERTIV CORPORATION
5109 Tanya Ave Bldg B (78503-2801)
PHONE..................................956 683-2948
EMP: 268
SALES (corp-wide): 4.4B **Publicly Held**
WEB: www.vertiv.com
SIC: 3613 Regulators, power
HQ: Vertiv Corporation
　1050 Dearborn Dr
　Columbus OH 43085
　614 888-0246

(G-14918)
WELLS VEHICLE ELECTRONICS LP
Also Called: Wells Manufacturing
4312 W Military Hwy (78503-8830)
PHONE..................................956 630-4310
Jared Robinson, *Engineer*
Raul Setien, *Manager*
Carlos Ortega, *Technician*
EMP: 240 **Privately Held**
WEB: www.wellsve.com
SIC: 3714 Motor vehicle electrical equipment
HQ: Wells Vehicle Electronics, L.P.
　385 W Rolling Meadows Dr
　Fond Du Lac WI 54937
　920 922-5900

(G-14919)
WES-TEX PURE MINERALS INC
4900 W Expy 83 Ste 231 (78501-3053)
PHONE..................................432 250-7010
Carlos Aguirre, *President*
Juan D Hinojosa, *Shareholder*
EMP: 15
SALES (est): 277.3K **Privately Held**
SIC: 4731 1499 Freight forwarding; mineral abrasives mining

(G-14920)
ZEBRA TECHNOLOGIES CORPORATION
2705 Ebony Ave (78501-7557)
PHONE..................................956 630-0315
Douglas Fox, *Vice Pres*
Aracely Corona, *Plant Mgr*
Kari McClelland, *Accounts Mgr*
EMP: 383
SALES (corp-wide): 4.4B **Publicly Held**
WEB: www.zebra.com
SIC: 3577 Bar code (magnetic ink) printers
PA: Zebra Technologies Corporation
　3 Overlook Pt
　Lincolnshire IL 60069
　847 634-6700

(G-14921)
ZEBRA TECHNOLOGIES CORPORATION
5400 George Mcvay Dr (78503-8882)
PHONE..................................956 571-3770
James Reid, *Sales Staff*
Ron Harter, *Manager*
EMP: 383
SALES (corp-wide): 4.4B **Publicly Held**
WEB: www.zebra.com
SIC: 3577 Bar code (magnetic ink) printers
PA: Zebra Technologies Corporation
　3 Overlook Pt
　Lincolnshire IL 60069
　847 634-6700

McKinney
Collin County

(G-14922)
ACCURATE DIE CUTTING INC (PA)
Also Called: Print Art
413 Interchange St (75071-1830)
PHONE..................................972 562-7921
Chris Alguire, *President*
William J Alguire, *Principal*
Laura Jenkins, *Accounting Mgr*
Greg Walters, *Accounts Exec*
EMP: 38
SQ FT: 66,000
SALES (est): 7.6MM **Privately Held**
WEB: www.printart-adc.com
SIC: 2653 2752 2675 Sheets, solid fiber: made from purchased materials; pads, corrugated: made from purchased materials; sheets, corrugated: made from purchased materials; commercial printing, lithographic; die-cut paper & board

(G-14923)
ANCHOR GRAPHICS INC
Also Called: Anchor Graphics Marketing
3943 E University Dr (75069-1300)
P.O. Box 1558, Pilot Point (76258-1558)
PHONE..................................972 422-4300
Dorothy Laird, *CEO*
Leslie Black, *President*
Leslie Goolsby, *President*
EMP: 20
SQ FT: 12,000
SALES (est): 5MM **Privately Held**
WEB: www.anchorgraphics.com
SIC: 2752 2754 2269 Tags, lithographed; labels: gravure printing; labels, cotton: printed

McKinney
Collin County

(G-14924)
B&B ROADWAY SEC SOLUTIONS LLC (PA)
5900 S Lk Frest Dr Ste 23 (75070)
PHONE..................................972 385-7899
Paul Matthews, *President*
Daniel Landreneau, *Business Mgr*
Matthew D Peeples, *CFO*
Tristian Hoermann, *Sales Staff*
Omar Rascon, *Sales Staff*
EMP: 15
SQ FT: 7,000
SALES (est): 11.5MM **Privately Held**
WEB: www.bbrss.net
SIC: 3462 3648 3499 Armor plate, forged iron or steel; lighting equipment; marine horns, compressed air or steam

McKinney
Collin County

(G-14925)
BBC BIOCHEMICAL CORPORATION
2090 Commerce Dr (75069-8203)
P.O. Box 1320, Mount Vernon WA (98273-1320)
PHONE..................................360 542-8400
Adrian Biesecker, *President*
Laura Biesecker, *CFO*
Ashley Stuart, *Mktg Coord*
Greg Robertson, *Manager*
▲ **EMP:** 108
SALES (est): 45.6MM
SALES (corp-wide): 63.5MM **Privately Held**
WEB: www.bbcus.com
SIC: 5169 2869 2819 Industrial chemicals; laboratory chemicals, organic; chemicals, reagent grade: refined from technical grade
PA: Slmp, Llc
　2090 Commerce Dr
　Mckinney TX 75069
　972 436-1010

(G-14926)
BIO-SIGNAL TECHNOLOGIES LLC
5201 Collin Mckinney Pkwy (75070-5180)
PHONE....................214 405-0524
Erik Alfonso Nilsen,
EMP: 9
SALES (est): 474.1K **Privately Held**
WEB: www.bio-signal.com
SIC: 3845 8731 Electromedical equipment; commercial physical research

(G-14927)
BLUESTONE INDUSTRIES LLC
Also Called: Factory Outlet Tooling
3001 S Hardin Blvd # 110 (75070-7736)
PHONE....................469 916-8090
Christopher Springer, *Mng Member*
EMP: 20 EST: 2018
SALES (est): 43.6K **Privately Held**
WEB: www.fotcnc.com
SIC: 3999 Barber & beauty shop equipment

(G-14928)
BOCHELLE INC
Also Called: McKinney/Frisco Overhead Door
855 E Cottage Hill Pkwy (75071-7333)
P.O. Box 824 (75070-8144)
PHONE....................972 837-1080
Misty Bogard, *President*
Jack Bogard, *Vice Pres*
EMP: 12 EST: 2014
SALES (est): 2.6MM **Privately Held**
WEB:
www.mckinneyfriscooverheaddoor.com
SIC: 3442 2431 Garage doors, overhead: metal; garage doors, overhead: wood

(G-14929)
BRANDON INDUSTRIES INC
1601 Wilmeth Rd (75069-8250)
PHONE....................972 542-3000
Brandon Hall, *President*
Elizabeth Barrett, *Vice Pres*
Janet C Hall, *Vice Pres*
William Gann, *Sales Staff*
Whitney Turner, *Director*
◆ **EMP:** 30
SQ FT: 40,000
SALES (est): 5.9MM **Privately Held**
WEB: www.brandonindustries.com
SIC: 3645 3646 3444 3354 Residential lighting fixtures; commercial indusl & institutional electric lighting fixtures; mail (post office) collection or storage boxes, sheet metal; aluminum extruded products

(G-14930)
BROACH BILT MANUFACTURING INC
Also Called: B B M
2140 Redbud Blvd Ste A (75069-8226)
PHONE....................972 529-9100
Sara Lee Broach, *President*
Jared Broach, *Manager*
Sherri Johnson, *Executive*
▲ **EMP:** 35
SQ FT: 15,000
SALES (est): 11.3MM **Privately Held**
WEB: www.bbm-inc.net
SIC: 3672 Printed circuit boards

(G-14931)
CAMOZZI PNEUMATICS INC
2160 Redbud Blvd Ste 101 (75069-8229)
PHONE....................972 548-8885
Attilio Camozzi, *President*
David Kitzmiller, *Managing Dir*
Kevin Perry, *Business Mgr*
Vico Camozzi, *Corp Secy*
Troy Baker, *Natl Sales Mgr*
▲ **EMP:** 25
SQ FT: 40,000
SALES (est): 9.4MM
SALES (corp-wide): 177.9K **Privately Held**
WEB: www.camozzi-usa.com
SIC: 5084 3593 3494 3492 Pneumatic tools & equipment; fluid power cylinders & actuators; valves & pipe fittings; fluid power valves & hose fittings
HQ: Camozzi Automation Spa
Via Eritrea 20/I
Brescia BS 25126
030 375-8097

(G-14932)
COOKIES-N-MILK INC
181 Industrial Blvd (75069-7220)
PHONE....................214 491-6370
Michael Blasko, *President*
EMP: 10
SALES (est): 1.7MM **Privately Held**
WEB: www.cookiesnmilkinc.com
SIC: 2099 Frosting mixes, dry: for cakes, cookies, etc.

(G-14933)
CROSSLINK MCKNNEY PWDR CTING L
2787 County Road 407 # 1 (75071-4111)
PHONE....................972 542-5441
Robert D Weinkauf, *Mng Member*
Ryan M Weinkauf,
EMP: 10
SQ FT: 7,200
SALES (est): 400K **Privately Held**
WEB: www.crosslinkmckinney.com
SIC: 3479 Coating of metals & formed products

(G-14934)
DATA VOICE INTERNATIONAL INC
Also Called: Datavoice International
2200 Bush Dr (75070-7547)
PHONE....................972 390-8808
Roy Rooker, *President*
Ron Bentley, *COO*
Michael Keilhofer, *Vice Pres*
Archie Milby, *Vice Pres*
Ron Aiken, *Sales Staff*
EMP: 10
SQ FT: 1,800
SALES (est): 1.2MM **Privately Held**
WEB: www.datavoiceint.com
SIC: 7372 Prepackaged software

(G-14935)
DAVID MCNEFF INC
Also Called: Arabella's
114 E Louisiana St Frnt (75069-4463)
PHONE....................972 562-0607
Linda McNeff, *President*
EMP: 10
SQ FT: 10,000
SALES (est): 801.7K **Privately Held**
SIC: 2331 2335 2339 5621 Women's & misses' blouses & shirts; women's, juniors' & misses' dresses; women's & misses' outerwear; ready-to-wear apparel, women's; furniture stores; florists

(G-14936)
DFA DAIRY BRANDS FLUID LLC
1220 N Tennessee St (75069-2116)
PHONE....................972 542-9391
EMP: 14
SALES (corp-wide): 15.8B **Privately Held**
SIC: 2026 Fluid milk
HQ: Dfa Dairy Brands Fluid, Llc
1405 N 98th St
Kansas City KS 66111
816 801-6455

(G-14937)
DOMINION VOTING SYSTEMS INC
2010 Redbud Blvd Ste 110 (75069-8258)
PHONE....................214 907-3010
John Poulos, *President*
Susan Martin, *Director*
EMP: 13 EST: 2010
SALES (est): 2.2MM **Privately Held**
WEB: www.dominionvoting.com
SIC: 3579 Voting machines

(G-14938)
EASTMAN KODAK COMPANY
87 Stone Hinge Dr (75069-1941)
PHONE....................214 585-4955
Wm M Bartolucci, *Principal*
EMP: 65
SALES (corp-wide): 1.2B **Publicly Held**
WEB: www.kodak.com
SIC: 3861 Film, sensitized motion picture, X-ray, still camera, etc.
PA: Eastman Kodak Company
343 State St
Rochester NY 14650
585 724-4000

(G-14939)
EMERSON PRCESS MGT RGLTOR TECH (HQ)
3200 Emerson Way (75069-7918)
P.O. Box 8004 (75070-8004)
PHONE....................972 548-3585
Randy R Page, *President*
Ed Herron, *Plant Mgr*
Teresa A Burnett, *Treasurer*
Katie Pitlik, *Human Resources*
Curtis Bagby, *Sales Staff*
▲ **EMP:** 25
SQ FT: 5,400
SALES (est): 83.4MM
SALES (corp-wide): 16.7B **Publicly Held**
WEB: www.fisherregulators.com
SIC: 3823 Industrial instrmnts msrmnt display/control process variable
PA: Emerson Electric Co.
8000 West Florissant Ave
Saint Louis MO 63136
314 553-2000

(G-14940)
ENCORE WIRE CORPORATION (PA)
1329 Millwood Rd (75069-7157)
PHONE....................972 562-9473
Daniel L Jones, *Ch of Bd*
Joe Gibson, *Assistant VP*
Wt Bigbee, *Vice Pres*
Todd Clayton, *Vice Pres*
Lea Jones, *Vice Pres*
EMP: 275
SQ FT: 2,100,000
SALES: 1.2B **Publicly Held**
WEB: www.encorewire.com
SIC: 3357 Building wire & cable, nonferrous

(G-14941)
ENCORE WIRE CORPORATION
1410 Millwood Rd (75069-7158)
PHONE....................972 562-9473
Matt Ford, *Controller*
Kevin Kieffer, *VP Mktg*
Steve Griffin, *Branch Mgr*
EMP: 143
SALES (corp-wide): 1.2B **Publicly Held**
WEB: www.encorewire.com
SIC: 3357 Building wire & cable, nonferrous
PA: Encore Wire Corporation
1329 Millwood Rd
Mckinney TX 75069
972 562-9473

(G-14942)
FIGTREE TECHNOLOGIES INC
430 S Hwy 5 (75069-9414)
P.O. Box 3249 (75070-8185)
PHONE....................469 361-6643
Mike D Grayson, *President*
Pamela Grayson, *Corp Secy*
EMP: 9
SQ FT: 2,000
SALES (est): 919.1K **Privately Held**
SIC: 7372 Application computer software

(G-14943)
FISHER CONTROLS INTL LLC
Fisher Regulators
310 E University Dr (75069-1872)
P.O. Box 8004 (75070-8004)
PHONE....................972 542-5512
Larry Flatt, *President*
James Race, *Opers Mgr*
EMP: 400
SQ FT: 175,111
SALES (corp-wide): 16.7B **Publicly Held**
WEB: www.emersonprocess.com
SIC: 3491 3625 3612 3432 Valves, automatic control; relays & industrial controls; transformers, except electric; plumbing fixture fittings & trim; nonferrous die-castings except aluminum
HQ: Fisher Controls International Llc
205 S Center St
Marshalltown IA 50158
641 754-3011

(G-14944)
FOOD SOURCE INC (HQ)
Also Called: Blount Fine Foods
2200 Redbud Blvd (75069-8217)
PHONE....................972 548-9001
Gaetano Riccardi, *CEO*
Richard Riccardi, *President*
Catherine Fotre, *Engineer*
▲ **EMP:** 70
SQ FT: 30,000
SALES (est): 20.8MM
SALES (corp-wide): 80.7MM **Privately Held**
WEB: www.blountfinefoods.com
SIC: 2038 2098 2035 Ethnic foods, frozen; macaroni & spaghetti; pickles, sauces & salad dressings
PA: Blount Fine Foods Corp.
630 Currant Rd
Fall River MA 02720
774 888-1300

(G-14945)
G2 RESTORATION LLC
2241 Redbud Blvd (75069-3397)
PHONE....................469 296-4275
James Rice,
EMP: 20
SALES (est): 891K **Privately Held**
WEB: www.g2waterrestoration.com
SIC: 3823 Water quality monitoring & control systems

(G-14946)
HEADINGTON ENERGY PARTNERS LLC
1700 Redbud Blvd Ste 400 (75069-3295)
PHONE....................214 307-5400
Aaron Smith, *Vice Pres*
Sandra Reed, *Accounting Mgr*
Gary McKay, *Manager*
Pat Smith,
Wendy Schwertner, *Technician*
EMP: 26 EST: 2014
SALES (est): 11.5MM **Privately Held**
WEB: www.headingtonenergy.com
SIC: 1382 Oil & gas exploration services

(G-14947)
J B R ENTERPRISES INC
Also Called: McKinney Pipe & Steel
196 Industrial Blvd (75069-7221)
PHONE....................972 542-3939
Jan Bogart Richardson, *President*
Robert Richardson, *Vice Pres*
EMP: 9 EST: 1998
SQ FT: 10,000
SALES (est): 1.5MM **Privately Held**
SIC: 3448 7692 Prefabricated metal components; welding repair

(G-14948)
KVP INTERNATIONAL INC
1501 Corporate (75069-8204)
PHONE....................626 633-0077
Ken Bowman, *CEO*
Roberto Godoy, *Opers Staff*
Alan McCool, *Purch Mgr*
Mary Ann Gehring, *CFO*
Gabe Martinez, *Mktg Dir*
◆ **EMP:** 41
SALES (est): 9.8MM **Privately Held**
WEB: www.kvpvet.com
SIC: 3842 5047 Abdominal supporters, braces & trusses; veterinarians' equipment & supplies

(G-14949)
KWIVIK INC
5100 Eldorado Pkwy # 102 (75070-6510)
PHONE....................469 424-3144
Renee Ahlgren, *Principal*
EMP: 12
SALES (est): 529.1K **Privately Held**
SIC: 3829 Measuring & controlling devices

Mckinney
Collin County

(G-14950)
LACORE LABS INC
901 Wilmeth Rd (75069)
PHONE..............................469 995-7791
Terry Lacore, *President*
Dan Krist, *Director*
Jenifer Grace, *Admin Sec*
EMP: 16
SQ FT: 20,000
SALES (est): 2.9MM **Privately Held**
WEB: www.lacorelabs.com
SIC: 3999 8733 Barber & beauty shop
equipment; scientific research agency

McKinney
Collin County

(G-14951)
LATTIMORE MATERIALS CORP
1000 E University Dr (75069-2428)
PHONE..............................972 569-4622
Delinn James, *Manager*
EMP: 100
SALES (corp-wide): 1.7B **Privately Held**
WEB: www.lafargeholcim.us
SIC: 3273 3272 Ready-mixed concrete;
concrete products
HQ: Lattimore Materials Corp.
15900 Dooley Rd
Addison TX 75001
972 221-4646

(G-14952)
LEIGHTNER ELECTRONICS INC
1501 S Tennessee St (75069-7126)
PHONE..............................972 542-0176
Daniel Leightner, *President*
Timothy Leightner, *Vice Pres*
Paige Lanier, *Opers Mgr*
Brian Jenkins, *Prdtn Mgr*
Gary Sohn, *Purch Mgr*
EMP: 17
SQ FT: 10,000
SALES (est): 2.8MM **Privately Held**
WEB: www.leightner.com
SIC: 3677 Transformers power supply,
electronic type

(G-14953)
LEONS FINE FOODS INC (PA)
Also Called: Leon's Texas Cuisine
2100 Redbud Blvd (75069-8215)
P.O. Box 1850 (75070-8160)
PHONE..............................972 529-5050
Bob L Clements, *President*
▲ **EMP:** 200 **EST:** 1945
SQ FT: 49,116
SALES (est): 33.3MM **Privately Held**
WEB: www.texascuisine.com
SIC: 2099 2013 Food preparations;
sausages & other prepared meats

(G-14954)
LHOIST NORTH AMERICA INC
205 S Mcdonald St (75069-5658)
PHONE..............................214 544-1717
Bobby Crabb, *Branch Mgr*
EMP: 23
SALES (corp-wide): 2.6MM **Privately Held**
WEB: www.lhoist.com
SIC: 3274 Quicklime
HQ: Lhoist North America, Inc.
5600 Clearfork Main St # 300
Fort Worth TX 76109
817 732-8164

(G-14955)
MAGNETIC TECHNOLOGY INC
1627 Bray Central Dr (75069-8206)
PHONE..............................214 544-2700
Sheila Burrow, *President*
Roger Bolin, *President*
Marcus Burrow, *President*
▼ **EMP:** 22
SQ FT: 27,000
SALES (est): 1.5MM **Privately Held**
WEB: www.magnetictechnology.com
SIC: 3677 3621 3612 3564 Electronic
transformers; motors & generators; trans-
formers, except electric; blowers & fans

(G-14956)
MANNER POLYMERS INC
500 Interchange St (75071-1885)
PHONE..............................972 542-6789
Raj Bhargava, *President*
Charles Reid, *Vice Pres*
Joe Farr, *Project Mgr*
Brian Reynolds, *Prdtn Mgr*
Tracy Paul, *Materials Mgr*
▲ **EMP:** 40
SQ FT: 50,000
SALES (est): 17.5MM **Privately Held**
WEB: www.mannerpolymers.com
SIC: 2821 Plastics materials & resins

(G-14957)
MARION ENERGY INC
901 N Mcdonald St (75069-2164)
PHONE..............................435 789-6959
Jeffrey Clarke, *President*
Karel Louman, *Admin Sec*
EMP: 15
SQ FT: 3,500
SALES (est): 3.6MM **Privately Held**
WEB: www.marionenergy.com
SIC: 1382 Oil & gas exploration services

(G-14958)
NOBIX INC
7916 Wichita Falls Blvd (75071-5668)
PHONE..............................925 659-3500
David J Warda, *President*
David A Block, *COO*
EMP: 26
SALES (est): 1.7MM **Privately Held**
WEB: www.nobix.com
SIC: 7372 Operating systems computer
software

(G-14959)
OEM OUTSOURCING LLC
7809 Trixie Trail Dr (75070-4816)
PHONE..............................972 742-7950
James Sutherland,
▲ **EMP:** 25
SALES (est): 1.7MM **Privately Held**
WEB: www.oemoutsourcing.com
SIC: 3999 Manufacturing industries

(G-14960)
ORIGINCLEAR INC (PA)
2535 E University Dr (75069-0904)
PHONE..............................323 939-6645
T Riggs Eckelberry, *Ch of Bd*
Tom Marchesello, *COO*
Daniel Early, *Chief Engr*
Jean-Louis Kindler, *Ch Credit Ofcr*
EMP: 18 **EST:** 2007
SALES (est): 3.5MM **Publicly Held**
WEB: www.originclear.com
SIC: 3589 2869 Water treatment equip-
ment, industrial; fuels

(G-14961)
P & A GRAPHICS LLC
Also Called: M Press
2100 Couch Dr (75069-7315)
PHONE..............................972 632-2100
Ashley J Abbott, *CEO*
Steve McGuyer, *Purch Agent*
Paul Preston, *Mng Member*
EMP: 17
SQ FT: 34,000
SALES (est): 5.5MM **Privately Held**
WEB: www.thepackageiseverything.com
SIC: 2657 Folding paperboard boxes

(G-14962)
PACIFIC RESOURCES INTL LLC
Also Called: PRI
211 E Louisiana St (75069-4344)
PHONE..............................214 504-3853
Dwight Nordstrom, *President*
Douglas Sorensen, *General Mgr*
Pat Lawerence, *CFO*
EMP: 400

SALES (est): 1.5MM **Privately Held**
WEB: www.magnetictechnology.com
SIC: 8711 5084 8742 3999 Consulting
engineer; industrial machinery & equipment; manufacturing management consultant; barber & beauty shop equipment

(G-14963)
PESTROUTES OPCO LLC
4500 Eldorado Pkwy Ste 3 (75070-5757)
PHONE..............................404 800-7378
Patrick McKittrick, *CEO*
Kevin Hanks, *CFO*
Asim Bhatti, *Manager*
Mark Stewart, *Manager*
Joel Reynolds, *Technical Staff*
EMP: 60
SALES (est): 6.8MM **Privately Held**
WEB: www.pestroutes.com
SIC: 7372 Business oriented computer
software

(G-14964)
PHASEWARE INC
1700 Redbud Blvd Ste 120 (75069-3282)
PHONE..............................214 432-9043
Randall Nelson, *CEO*
Hoyt Mann, *President*
Keith Wellman, *Regl Sales Mgr*
Jack Sumrall, *Sales Staff*
EMP: 10 **EST:** 2004
SALES (est): 1.1MM **Privately Held**
WEB: www.phaseware.com
SIC: 7372 Business oriented computer
software

(G-14965)
PPG INDUSTRIES INC
Also Called: PPG 8351
921 Redbud Blvd Ste 100 (75069-3377)
PHONE..............................214 544-0700
Rob Garwood, *Manager*
EMP: 24
SALES (corp-wide): 15.3B **Publicly Held**
WEB: www.ppg.com
SIC: 2851 Paints & allied products
PA: Ppg Industries, Inc.
1 Ppg Pl
Pittsburgh PA 15272
412 434-3131

(G-14966)
PRC-DESOTO INTERNATIONAL INC
Also Called: PPG Arspace Eldorado Solutions
200 Industrial Blvd (75069-7303)
PHONE..............................972 540-0360
David P Morris, *Vice Pres*
▲ **EMP:** 99
SALES (est): 9.4MM
SALES (corp-wide): 15.3B **Publicly Held**
SIC: 2891 Sealing compounds, synthetic
rubber or plastic
PA: Ppg Industries, Inc.
1 Ppg Pl
Pittsburgh PA 15272
412 434-3131

(G-14967)
PRIMO MICROPHONES INC (HQ)
1805 Couch Dr (75069-7393)
P.O. Box 1570 (75070-8155)
PHONE..............................972 548-9807
▲ **EMP:** 58 **EST:** 1969
SQ FT: 40,000
SALES (est): 7.5MM **Privately Held**
WEB: www.primomic.com
SIC: 3651 3661 Microphones; telephones
& telephone apparatus

(G-14968)
RAYTHEON COMPANY
2501 W University Dr (75071-1300)
P.O. Box 801 (75070-8010)
PHONE..............................972 952-2007
EMP: 200
SALES (corp-wide): 56.5B **Publicly Held**
WEB: www.rtx.com
SIC: 3812 Defense systems & equipment
HQ: Raytheon Company
870 Winter St
Waltham MA 02451
781 522-3000

(G-14969)
RAYTHEON COMPANY
2501 W University Dr (75071-1300)
PHONE..............................972 952-2007
Billy Cook, *Branch Mgr*
EMP: 99
SALES (corp-wide): 56.5B **Publicly Held**
WEB: www.rtx.com
SIC: 3812 Sonar systems & equipment
HQ: Raytheon Company
870 Winter St
Waltham MA 02451
781 522-3000

(G-14970)
RAYTHEON COMPANY
2501 W University Dr (75071-1300)
PHONE..............................972 952-4067
Dawn Marrocco, *Principal*
Christopher Solecki, *Engineer*
EMP: 132
SALES (corp-wide): 56.5B **Publicly Held**
WEB: www.rtx.com
SIC: 3812 Search & navigation equipment
HQ: Raytheon Company
870 Winter St
Waltham MA 02451
781 522-3000

(G-14971)
RICHMONDS AMERICAN SVC CTR INC
8600 Verona Dr (75071-5007)
PHONE..............................972 681-2222
Curt Richmond, *President*
EMP: 19
SALES (est): 2.1MM **Privately Held**
SIC: 5211 2394 3699 Garage doors, sale
& installation; canvas awnings &
canopies; door opening & closing de-
vices, electrical

(G-14972)
RITEKS INC
415 Interchange St (75071-1830)
PHONE..............................972 529-1118
Edward E Boss, *President*
Gayla Boss, *Vice Pres*
Todd Enderle, *Technical Mgr*
Ryan Horne, *Manager*
Keith Fisher, *Technical Staff*
EMP: 20 **Privately Held**
WEB: www.riteks.com
SIC: 2899 5085 Chemical preparations;
packing, industrial
PA: Riteks, Inc.
11917 Cutten Rd
Houston TX 77066

(G-14973)
SABRE SENTINEL INTL LLC (PA)
Also Called: Strategic SEC Intelligence Co
321 N Central Expy # 204 (75070-3544)
PHONE..............................972 529-6570
Gregory Maxwell, *Persnl Mgr*
Peter J Costas,
Brian Connors,
M Evan Jensen,
Greg Vernon,
EMP: 27
SQ FT: 2,600
SALES (est): 683.2K **Privately Held**
WEB: www.sabresentinel.com
SIC: 7382 7381 3812 3721 Security sys-
tems services; detective & armored car
services; search & navigation equipment;
aircraft

(G-14974)
SIMCO LONGHORN LEATHER
Also Called: Longhorn Leather Co
1425 N Tennessee St (75069-1833)
P.O. Box 8008 (75070-8008)
PHONE..............................972 542-8700
A J Hughes Sr, *President*
James S Chambers, *Corp Secy*
Donald Motsenbocker, *Vice Pres*
Melinda Corn, *Purch Mgr*
Ken Davy, *Incorporator*
▼ **EMP:** 75
SQ FT: 125,000
SALES (est): 8.4MM **Privately Held**
WEB: www.actioncompany.com
SIC: 3199 3172 Saddles or parts; per-
sonal leather goods

▲ = Import ▼=Export
◆ =Import/Export

(G-14975)
SIMPSON STRONG-TIE COMPANY INC
2221 Country Ln (75069-1241)
PHONE..................................972 542-0326
Keith Cullum, *Engineer*
Brian Foster, *Sales Staff*
Sheila Johnson, *Sales Staff*
Phil Bert, *Manager*
Brandt McCoy, *Manager*
EMP: 175
SALES (corp-wide): 1.1B **Publicly Held**
WEB: www.strongtie.com
SIC: 3444 3678 Studs & joists, sheet metal; electronic connectors
HQ: Simpson Strong-Tie Company Inc.
5956 W Las Positas Blvd
Pleasanton CA 94588
925 560-9000

(G-14976)
SLEEP DISORDER CENTERS LLC
7900 Henneman Way Ste 220
(75070-3125)
PHONE..................................972 390-2014
EMP: 14
SALES (corp-wide): 987.5K **Privately Held**
SIC: 3821 Laboratory apparatus, except heating & measuring
PA: Sleep Disorder Centers Llc
14000 N Portland Ave # 200
Oklahoma City OK 73134
405 606-2727

(G-14977)
SPECTRUM SEMICONDUCTOR TECH LC
404 Mckinney Pkwy Ste C (75071-1877)
P.O. Box 777 (75070-8143)
PHONE..................................972 562-2552
Robert C Hobbs, *President*
Stacy Hobbs, *Principal*
EMP: 10
SQ FT: 4,500
SALES (est): 980K **Privately Held**
WEB: www.spectrumsemi.com
SIC: 3559 2851 Semiconductor manufacturing machinery; paints & allied products

(G-14978)
SPORT SOURCE INC
400 W Virginia St Ste 200 (75069-4558)
PHONE..................................972 509-5707
Charlie Kadupski, *President*
EMP: 10
SQ FT: 6,000
SALES (est): 59K **Privately Held**
WEB: www.thesportsource.com
SIC: 2721 Periodicals: publishing only

(G-14979)
STEELFAB TEXAS INC (HQ)
301 S Mcdonald St (75069-5669)
PHONE..................................972 562-7720
Thomas J Reeves, *Ch of Bd*
David Garrett, *President*
Mitchell Reeves, *President*
David Merrifield, *Vice Pres*
Gary Whisenhunt, *Vice Pres*
EMP: 30 **EST:** 1978
SQ FT: 5,500
SALES (est): 16.7MM
SALES (corp-wide): 445MM **Privately Held**
WEB: www.steelfab-inc.com
SIC: 3441 Fabricated structural metal
PA: Steelfab, Inc.
3025 Westport Rd
Charlotte NC 28208
704 394-5376

(G-14980)
SUNBELT MIXES INC
2100 Redbud Blvd (75069-8215)
P.O. Box 660 (75070-8141)
PHONE..................................972 529-5155
Bob Clements, *Ch of Bd*
EMP: 15
SALES (est): 2.4MM **Privately Held**
WEB: www.sunbeltmixes.com
SIC: 2041 Flour & other grain mill products

(G-14981)
SYNAPTIC CLOUD LLC (PA)
5900 S Lake Forest Dr # 120 (75070-2198)
PHONE..................................972 591-0151
Yasser Elgebaly, *President*
Ayman Omar,
EMP: 20 **EST:** 2014
SALES (est): 4.2MM **Privately Held**
SIC: 3572 Computer storage devices

(G-14982)
TIMBER BLINDS MFG LTD (PA)
Also Called: Timberblindmetroshade
800 Elm St (75069-6757)
PHONE..................................972 569-9100
Mike Hayes, *Partner*
Pete Boleneus, *Partner*
Jamie Ward, *Vice Pres*
Heather Bardin, *Purchasing*
Todd Brown, *Regl Sales Mgr*
◆ **EMP:** 280
SALES (est): 65.9MM **Privately Held**
WEB: www.timberblinds.com
SIC: 2591 Window blinds

(G-14983)
TMC FOUNDATION INC (PA)
190 Industrial Blvd (75069-7225)
PHONE..................................214 212-4645
Guy C Saussus, *President*
Pierre Herpain, *Shareholder*
Stephanie Herpain, *Shareholder*
EMP: 10
SQ FT: 30,000 **Privately Held**
SIC: 1771 3532 3533 Foundation & footing contractor; drills, bits & similar equipment; drilling tools for gas, oil or water wells

(G-14984)
TYG PRODUCTS LP
1800 N Mcdonald St (75071-0365)
PHONE..................................972 542-1828
Jeff Chen, *General Ptnr*
Scott Lasalle, *Human Res Dir*
Joseph Tao, *Sales Staff*
Tony Davis, *Manager*
Steven C Lin, *Technology*
◆ **EMP:** 100
SALES (est): 27.7MM **Privately Held**
SIC: 3465 3714 3089 Body parts, automobile: stamped metal; motor vehicle parts & accessories; automotive parts, plastic
PA: Tong Yang Co.
13, Shuijing Lane
Shetou Hsiang CHA 511

(G-14985)
VECTOR SYSTEMS INC
411 Mckinney Pkwy (75071-1825)
PHONE..................................214 544-9500
James B Ovens, *President*
Denise B Ovens, *Corp Secy*
Kenneth R Smith, *Vice Pres*
Mark Corson, *Project Mgr*
John Osburn, *Project Engr*
EMP: 56
SQ FT: 36,000
SALES (est): 15MM **Privately Held**
WEB: www.vectorsystems-usa.com
SIC: 3625 3613 3823 3559 Industrial electrical relays & switches; control circuit relays, industrial; control equipment, electric; electric controls & control accessories, industrial; control panels, electric; panelboards & distribution boards, electric; power connectors, electric; power switching equipment; industrial process measurement equipment; refinery, chemical processing & similar machinery

(G-14986)
VERTRAUEN CHEMIE SOLUTIONS INC (PA)
Also Called: Quadrant Chemical
200 Industrial Blvd (75069-7303)
PHONE..................................469 283-0789
John Jamieson, *CEO*
Genna Jackson, *Purch Agent*
John Benefield, *Director*
Michael Prentiss, *Director*
EMP: 40 **EST:** 2016
SQ FT: 25,000

SALES (est): 45MM **Privately Held**
WEB: www.vertrauen-us.com
SIC: 2891 Adhesives & sealants

(G-14987)
VSI SOLUTIONS INC
Also Called: Bankpoint
5900 S Lake Forest Dr # 300 (75070-2193)
PHONE..................................855 712-7677
Thomas Heruska, *CEO*
Sandy Teel, *Sr Consultant*
EMP: 14
SALES (est): 1.6MM **Privately Held**
WEB: www.getbankpoint.com
SIC: 7372 Business oriented computer software

(G-14988)
WATSON & CHALIN HOLDING CORP (PA)
725 E University Dr (75069-2325)
PHONE..................................972 547-6020
Gary E Gerstenslager, *President*
Donald R Watson, *President*
Matthew J Joy, *Vice Pres*
Warren J Kellener, *Treasurer*
Randy Reid, *Controller*
▼ **EMP:** 32
SQ FT: 215,000
SALES (est): 53.1MM **Privately Held**
WEB: www.watsonsuspensions.com
SIC: 3714 Motor vehicle parts & accessories

(G-14989)
WATSON & CHALIN MFG INC (HQ)
725 E University Dr (75069-2325)
PHONE..................................972 547-6020
Donald R Watson, *President*
William Raine Adams Jr, *Corp Secy*
Thomas N Chalin, *Vice Pres*
Wayne H Goble III, *Vice Pres*
Matthew J Joy, *Vice Pres*
▲ **EMP:** 89
SQ FT: 215,000
SALES (est): 53.1MM **Privately Held**
WEB: www.watsonsuspensions.com
SIC: 3714 Motor vehicle parts & accessories

(G-14990)
WELLS/MCCOY STEEL SERVICES INC
423 Metro Park Dr (75071-1828)
PHONE..................................469 742-0888
Brad McCoy, *President*
Danny Wells, *Corp Secy*
Tom Zopp, *Project Mgr*
Tyler Wells, *Production*
Kaylee Dhane, *Purch Agent*
EMP: 30
SQ FT: 32,000
SALES (est): 7MM **Privately Held**
WEB: www.wellsmccoysteel.com
SIC: 3441 Fabricated structural metal

(G-14991)
XARMR CORPORATION (PA)
5900 S Lake Forest Dr (75070-2193)
PHONE..................................972 385-7899
Paul Matthews, *President*
EMP: 9 **EST:** 1948
SALES (est): 1.4MM **Privately Held**
WEB: www.bb-armr.com
SIC: 3669 Transportation signaling devices; highway signals, electric; signaling apparatus, electric; traffic signals, electric

(G-14992)
YANKON LIGHTING INC
Also Called: Megaever Lighting
1581 Corporate Dr Ste 100 (75069-8211)
PHONE..................................469 248-0749
Leo LI, *CEO*
EMP: 16
SALES (est): 2MM **Privately Held**
WEB: www.yankon-lighting.com
SIC: 3645 Lamp & light shades
PA: Yankon.Co., Ltd.
No.568, Renmin Avenue West Section, Caoe Sub-District, Shangyu D
Shaoxing 31230

McKinney
Hunt County

(G-14993)
UPTIME SOLUTIONS INC
2809 Sunset Rdg (75072-4205)
PHONE..................................214 497-9635
Greg Thomas, *President*
EMP: 13 **EST:** 1999
SALES (est): 1.3MM **Privately Held**
WEB: www.gitlab-01.roovpn.com
SIC: 3699 Security control equipment & systems

Megargel
Archer County

(G-14994)
TEAM PRIDE EXTRUSIONS INC
Also Called: T P E
10472 Fm 210 (76370)
P.O. Box 70 (76370-0070)
PHONE..................................940 562-2205
Darryl Anderson, *President*
Anna-Lynn Anderson, *Corp Secy*
Todd Lewallen, *Vice Pres*
Maria Killy, *Accounts Mgr*
▲ **EMP:** 32
SQ FT: 3,700
SALES (est): 5.5MM **Privately Held**
WEB: www.teamprideextrusions.com
SIC: 3353 5051 Aluminum sheet & strip; aluminum bars, rods, ingots, sheets, pipes, plates, etc.

Melissa
Collin County

(G-14995)
COMMERCIAL METALS COMPANY
Also Called: C M C Construction Services
2202 Mckinney St (75454-9734)
PHONE..................................972 838-9050
Ronnie Poulk, *Branch Mgr*
EMP: 20
SALES (corp-wide): 5.4B **Publicly Held**
WEB: www.cmc.com
SIC: 3312 Blast furnaces & steel mills
PA: Commercial Metals Company
6565 N Macarthur Blvd # 800
Irving TX 75039
214 689-4300

(G-14996)
DAYCOR ENTERPRISES INC
2702 Mckinney St (75454-9738)
P.O. Box 95 (75454-0095)
PHONE..................................972 838-2700
Phillip Day, *President*
EMP: 15
SQ FT: 6,000
SALES (est): 1.1MM **Privately Held**
WEB: www.daycorenterprises.com
SIC: 1751 2434 Cabinet building & installation; wood kitchen cabinets

(G-14997)
FARRIS CONCRETE COMPANY
2425 Throckmorton Rd (75454-2406)
PHONE..................................972 838-2217
Mike Farris, *President*
EMP: 100
SQ FT: 6,000
SALES (est): 7.1MM **Privately Held**
SIC: 3273 Ready-mixed concrete

(G-14998)
MELISSA RENEWABLES LLC
3820 Sam Rayburn Hwy (75454-2602)
P.O. Box 61447, Midland (79711-1447)
PHONE..................................432 563-0447
Paul Morrow,
Luke N Morrow,
EMP: 21 **EST:** 2016

SALES (est): 628.2K
SALES (corp-wide): 11.9MM **Privately Held**
WEB: www.morrowrenewables.com
SIC: 1382 Oil & gas exploration services
PA: Morrow Renewables, Llc
3300 N A St Ste 120
Midland TX 79705
432 563-0447

Memphis
Hall County

(G-14999)
TOTAL ALLOY FOUNDRY INC
2100 Greenwood St (79245)
P.O. Box 429 (79245-0429)
PHONE..........................806 259-2255
William Elliott, *President*
Mark Little, *General Mgr*
Megan Holman, *Manager*
EMP: 19
SALES (est): 2.6MM **Privately Held**
WEB: www.totalalloyus.com
SIC: 3339 Primary nonferrous metals

Menard
Menard County

(G-15000)
RANCH HOUSE MEAT COMPANY LLC
303 W San Saba Ave (76859-2905)
P.O. Box 977 (76859-0977)
PHONE..........................325 396-4536
Max L Stabel,
EMP: 18 **EST:** 1978
SQ FT: 6,400
SALES (est): 1.9MM **Privately Held**
WEB: www.brisket.net
SIC: 5421 2011 Meat markets, including freezer provisioners; meat packing plants

Mercedes
Hidalgo County

(G-15001)
ALOECORP INC
701 Vogel Dr (78570-4332)
PHONE..........................956 223-6931
Mick Anderson, *President*
Ramiro Gallegos, *QC Mgr*
EMP: 29 **Privately Held**
WEB: www.aloecorp.com
SIC: 0191 2844 General farms, primarily crop; toilet preparations
HQ: Aloecorp Inc
2121 S State St
Tacoma WA 98405
360 486-7400

(G-15002)
ANDERSON BEAN BOOT CO INC
1750 E Expy 83 (78570-9403)
P.O. Box 36 (78570-0036)
PHONE..........................956 565-2618
Ryan Vaughn, *Manager*
EMP: 25
SQ FT: 8,000
SALES (corp-wide): 15.6MM **Privately Held**
WEB: www.andersonbean.com
SIC: 3143 5139 Men's footwear, except athletic; boots
HQ: Anderson Bean Boot Co., Inc.
105 S Vermont Ave
Mercedes TX 78570

(G-15003)
ANDERSON BEAN BOOT CO INC (HQ)
105 S Vermont Ave (78570-2518)
P.O. Box 36 (78570-0036)
PHONE..........................956 565-2618
John T Evans, *CEO*
John P Moody, *President*
Aurora Flores, *Corp Secy*
Robert McAllen, *Vice Pres*

EMP: 10
SALES (est): 2.8MM
SALES (corp-wide): 15.6MM **Privately Held**
WEB: www.andersonbean.com
SIC: 3143 3144 Boots, dress or casual: men's; boots, canvas or leather: women's
PA: Western Leather Goods, Inc.
1740 E Expressway 83
Mercedes TX 78570
800 717-1853

(G-15004)
BUILDERS FIRSTSOURCE INC
302 N Mile 2 1/2 East Rd (78570-4019)
PHONE..........................956 755-0301
David Valle, *Sales Mgr*
Jerard Garcia, *Branch Mgr*
EMP: 45
SALES (corp-wide): 7.2B **Publicly Held**
WEB: www.bldr.com
SIC: 5211 2431 2421 Lumber products; millwork; building & structural materials, wood
PA: Builders Firstsource, Inc.
2001 Bryan St Ste 1600
Dallas TX 75201
214 880-3500

(G-15005)
HEXION INC
Borden
303 Industrial Park (78570)
PHONE..........................956 565-6301
Jim Guffey, *Manager*
EMP: 18
SALES (corp-wide): 1.5B **Privately Held**
WEB: www.hexion.com
SIC: 2869 Industrial organic chemicals
HQ: Hexion Inc.
180 E Broad St Fl 26
Columbus OH 43215
614 225-4000

(G-15006)
HURLEY INTERNATIONAL LLC
5001 E Expressway 83 (78570-4571)
PHONE..........................956 514-1700
EMP: 105
SALES (corp-wide): 25.3B **Publicly Held**
SIC: 2329 Mfg Men's/Boy's Clothing
HQ: Hurley International Llc
1945 Placentia Ave Ste G
Costa Mesa CA 92627
949 548-9375

(G-15007)
KENNETH COLE PRODUCTIONS INC
5001 E Expy 83 (78570-4571)
PHONE..........................956 825-7116
EMP: 102
SALES (corp-wide): 816.9MM **Privately Held**
SIC: 3143 Footwear
HQ: Kenneth Cole Productions, Inc.
400 Plaza Dr Ste 300
Secaucus NJ 10019
212 265-1500

(G-15008)
NIKE INC
5001 E Expressway 83 (78570-4571)
PHONE..........................956 565-2446
Ernesto Canto, *Principal*
EMP: 38
SALES (corp-wide): 37.4B **Publicly Held**
WEB: www.nike.com
SIC: 3021 Rubber & plastics footwear
PA: Nike, Inc.
1 Sw Bowerman Dr
Beaverton OR 97005
503 671-6453

(G-15009)
O D C L INC
Also Called: Lily of The Desert
324 Industrial Park (78570-4300)
PHONE..........................956 565-3131
Donald Lovelace, *Manager*
Rosa Del Castillo, *Admin Asst*
EMP: 40 **Privately Held**
WEB: www.lilyofthedesert.com

SIC: 2087 2834 2844 5149 Beverage bases, concentrates, syrups, powders & mixes; ointments; suntan lotions & oils; organic & diet foods
PA: O D C L Inc
1887 Geesling Rd
Denton TX 76208

(G-15010)
SOUTHERN FIELDS ALOE INC
Mile 2 E & Mile 6 N St Mi (78570)
P.O. Box 1330 (78570-1330)
PHONE..........................956 565-5102
John Sigrist, *President*
Orquidea Mata, *Vice Pres*
EMP: 15
SQ FT: 4,500
SALES (est): 829.6K **Privately Held**
WEB: www.aloeking.com
SIC: 0181 2844 5149 Plants, potted: growing of; cosmetic preparations; organic & diet foods

(G-15011)
WESTERN LEATHER GOODS INC (PA)
Also Called: Anderson Bean Boot Company
1740 E Expressway 83 (78570-9403)
P.O. Box 895 (78570-0895)
PHONE..........................800 717-1853
John T Evans, *Ch of Bd*
John P Moody, *President*
Aurora Flores, *Corp Secy*
Robert A McAllen, *Vice Pres*
EMP: 60
SQ FT: 33,500
SALES (est): 15.6MM **Privately Held**
WEB: www.andersonbean.com
SIC: 3143 Boots, dress or casual: men's

(G-15012)
WESTERN LEATHER GOODS INC
1750 E Expy 83 (78570-9403)
P.O. Box 36 (78570-0036)
PHONE..........................956 565-2618
John Moody, *Manager*
EMP: 50
SALES (corp-wide): 15.6MM **Privately Held**
WEB: www.andersonbean.com
SIC: 3143 Boots, dress or casual: men's
PA: Western Leather Goods, Inc.
1740 E Expressway 83
Mercedes TX 78570
800 717-1853

Meridian
Bosque County

(G-15013)
DOUBLE B FOODS INC
109 E Morgan (76665-4820)
P.O. Box 615 (76665-0615)
PHONE..........................254 435-6187
Patrick O'Ray, *CEO*
Donald Wall, *CFO*
Rene Valdez, *Manager*
EMP: 120
SALES (corp-wide): 17.6MM **Privately Held**
WEB: www.doubleb.com
SIC: 2013 2011 Sausages & related products, from purchased meat; meat packing plants
PA: Double B Foods, Inc.
800 W Arbrook Blvd
Arlington TX 76015
469 567-6000

Merkel
Taylor County

(G-15014)
DOSSEY OILFIELD SERVICES LLC
2450 Fm 1235 (79536-7550)
PHONE..........................325 928-0001
Robin R Dosser, *Principal*
Dwayne Dosser,
EMP: 10 **EST:** 2011

SALES (est): 1.6MM **Privately Held**
WEB: www.dosseroilfieldservice-sandgarage.com
SIC: 1389 Oil field services

(G-15015)
DUNAGIN TRANSPORT COMPANY (PA)
10179 S Access Rd I 20 20 I (79536)
P.O. Box 208 (79536-0208)
PHONE..........................325 928-5253
Bradley Dunasin, *President*
Bradley Dunagin, *President*
Randall Dunagin, *Vice Pres*
Danna Dunagin, *Treasurer*
Marsha Crow, *Accountant*
EMP: 31
SALES (est): 17MM **Privately Held**
WEB: www.dunagintransport.com
SIC: 1389 Oil field services

(G-15016)
R A BEAIRD OIL CO (PA)
410 Oak (79536-5118)
PHONE..........................325 928-5220
Roger Beaird, *Owner*
EMP: 10
SALES (est): 565.6K **Privately Held**
SIC: 1311 1389 Crude petroleum production; natural gas production; gas field services

(G-15017)
R E JANES GRAVEL CO
Fm 126 (79536)
PHONE..........................325 736-5008
R E Janes, *Owner*
EMP: 30
SALES (corp-wide): 91.4MM **Privately Held**
SIC: 5032 1442 Brick, stone & related material; construction sand & gravel
PA: R. E. Janes Gravel Co.
4021 84th St
Lubbock TX
512 442-7871

(G-15018)
TRANSITION SUPERIOR SYSTEMS LC
Also Called: Superior Systems & Tech
274 County Road 287 (79536-7522)
PHONE..........................325 690-0248
Sammy Peacock,
EMP: 11
SALES (est): 2.2MM **Privately Held**
SIC: 3443 7389 Industrial vessels, tanks & containers;

Mertzon
Irion County

(G-15019)
APACHE CORPORATION
301 Ranch Rd 2469 (76941)
P.O. Box 440 (76941-0440)
PHONE..........................325 835-2323
EMP: 46
SALES (corp-wide): 6.4B **Publicly Held**
WEB: www.apachecorp.com
SIC: 1311 Crude petroleum production
PA: Apache Corporation
2000 Post Oak Blvd Ste 10
Houston TX 77056
713 296-6000

(G-15020)
CONOCOPHILLIPS COMPANY
Also Called: Conoco Natural Gas & Gas Lqds
7 Miles S W Of Mertzon (76941)
P.O. Box 740 (76941-0740)
PHONE..........................325 835-4451
Charles Surmons, *Manager*
EMP: 50
SALES (corp-wide): 36.6B **Publicly Held**
WEB: www.conocophillips.com
SIC: 5541 2911 Filling stations, gasoline; gases & liquefied petroleum gases
HQ: Conocophillips Company
925 N Eldridge Pkwy
Houston TX 77079
281 293-1000

(G-15021)
TALAJAK INC
809 N 5th St (76941)
P.O. Box 924 (76941-0924)
PHONE....................325 632-5341
Lizette Mase, *President*
Tom Mase, *Vice Pres*
EMP: 10
SALES (est): 2.2MM **Privately Held**
WEB: www.talajak.com
SIC: 1389 Oil field services

Mesquite
Dallas County

(G-15022)
A-ERO TEC GRAPHICS INC
12709 Eastgate Dr (75181-2001)
PHONE....................972 289-9854
M W Prestridge, *President*
Sandra Prestridge, *Corp Secy*
EMP: 30
SQ FT: 10,000
SALES (est): 2.4MM **Privately Held**
WEB: www.cometsigns.com
SIC: 7389 3993 Sign painting & lettering
shop; electric signs; neon signs

(G-15023)
ACCURA SYSTEMS INC
326 Clay Rd (75182-9711)
PHONE....................972 226-0195
Frank Finan, *President*
Mike Rubner, *COO*
Brian Prestemon, *VP Mfg*
Dwayne Ogburn, *Plant Mgr*
Diane Stone, *Purch Agent*
▲ EMP: 126
SQ FT: 87,000
SALES (est): 48MM **Privately Held**
WEB: www.accurasystems.com
SIC: 3443 3441 3442 Fabricated plate
work (boiler shop); fabricated structural
metal; metal doors, sash & trim

(G-15024)
ADELL CORPORATION
200 Adell Blvd (75182-9340)
PHONE....................972 226-4600
Marvin Adell, *Principal*
Jennifer Adell, *CFO*
EMP: 40
SQ FT: 162,500
SALES (est): 7.3MM **Privately Held**
WEB: www.adellcorporation.com
SIC: 3429 3714 Manufactured hardware
(general); motor vehicle parts & acces-
sories

(G-15025)
ALLOY CASTING CO INC
3900 S Peachtree Rd (75180-2724)
P.O. Box 800008 (75180-0008)
PHONE....................800 527-1318
Jon Mc Graw, *President*
Sue Buckley, *Office Mgr*
▼ EMP: 30 EST: 1944
SQ FT: 14,000
SALES (est): 5.7MM **Privately Held**
WEB: www.alloynet.com
SIC: 3365 5072 Aluminum & aluminum-
based alloy castings; hardware

(G-15026)
ANCHOR TEXACONE LLC
4111 Forney Rd (75149-2722)
PHONE....................972 288-4404
Wallace Wheeler, *Vice Pres*
Jordan Frye, *VP Bus Dvlpt*
Gina Valdez, *Sales Staff*
Tony Valdez, *Sales Staff*
Gina Little, *Office Mgr*
EMP: 26
SQ FT: 20,000
SALES (est): 6.2MM **Privately Held**
WEB: www.texacone.com
SIC: 3053 3061 Gaskets & sealing de-
vices; mechanical rubber goods

(G-15027)
ARGOS USA LLC
1719 W Scyene Rd (75149-3637)
PHONE....................972 285-8823
Stuart Owings, *General Mgr*

EMP: 10 **Privately Held**
WEB: www.argos-us.com
SIC: 3273 Ready-mixed concrete
HQ: Argos Usa Llc
3015 Windward Plz Ste 300
Alpharetta GA 30005
678 368-4300

(G-15028)
ASSOCIATED TRUSS COMPANY
Also Called: Associated Truss & Lumber
388 S Larkin Rd (75182-9222)
P.O. Box 851629 (75185-1629)
PHONE....................972 226-1973
David Gerhauser, *President*
Ben Gerhauser, *Vice Pres*
Cortney Johnson, *Project Mgr*
Jason Key, *Opers Mgr*
Corey Nelsen, *Opers Staff*
▼ EMP: 95
SQ FT: 100,000
SALES (est): 39.2MM **Privately Held**
WEB: www.associatedtruss.com
SIC: 5211 2439 Lumber & other building
materials; trusses, wooden roof

(G-15029)
BAGS ELITE INC
Also Called: B E I
3030 E Meadows Blvd (75150-6639)
P.O. Box 270227, Dallas (75227-0227)
PHONE....................972 279-7798
Tom Jones, *Ch of Bd*
Jim Shaw, *President*
Kathy D Shaw, *Vice Pres*
George Shelton, *Vice Pres*
Doneen Shaw, *CFO*
▲ EMP: 25
SQ FT: 10,500
SALES (est): 4MM **Privately Held**
WEB: www.bagselite.com
SIC: 3086 3429 2393 Ice chests or cool-
ers (portable), foamed plastic; ice chests
or coolers, portable, except foam plastic;
textile bags

(G-15030)
BEACH SHEET METAL COMPANY INC
353 Long Creek Rd (75182-9273)
PHONE....................972 226-4440
Douglas A Beaty, *President*
Brian Rock, *Vice Pres*
John Douglas Beaty, *Treasurer*
John Beaty, *Treasurer*
Debbie Trosclair, *Marketing Staff*
EMP: 27
SQ FT: 8,000
SALES (est): 4.4MM **Privately Held**
WEB: www.beachsheetmetal.com
SIC: 1761 5039 3444 Sheet metalwork;
eaves troughing, parts & supplies; sheet
metalwork

(G-15031)
BENJAMIN MOORE & CO
700 W Kearney St (75149-3290)
PHONE....................972 285-6346
Wayne McElyea, *Manager*
EMP: 60
SALES (corp-wide): 254.6B **Publicly Held**
WEB: www.benjaminmoore.com
SIC: 2851 5231 5198 Paints & allied
products; paint; paints
HQ: Benjamin Moore & Co.
101 Paragon Dr
Montvale NJ 07645
201 573-9600

(G-15032)
BENTLEY CONSULTANTS CO INC
12717 Eastgate Dr Ste 4 (75181-2026)
PHONE....................972 289-2750
Guy Bentley, *President*
James Douglas, *Vice Pres*
EMP: 10 EST: 1967
SQ FT: 7,000
SALES (est): 1.3MM **Privately Held**
WEB: www.bentleyco.com
SIC: 3089 8748 Injection molding of plas-
tics; business consulting

(G-15033)
BRADY CORPORATION
1801 Big Town Blvd # 100 (75149-1011)
PHONE....................214 275-9595
Nena Benologa, *Branch Mgr*
EMP: 9
SALES (corp-wide): 1B **Publicly Held**
WEB: www.bradyid.com
SIC: 3577 Computer peripheral equipment
PA: Brady Corporation
6555 W Good Hope Rd
Milwaukee WI 53223
414 358-6600

(G-15034)
CLOWN CO INC
706 E Kearney St (75149-2612)
PHONE....................972 288-6954
Mike McWorther, *President*
EMP: 11
SQ FT: 2,000
SALES (est): 1.6MM **Privately Held**
WEB: www.clownco.com
SIC: 2759 Screen printing

(G-15035)
COUNTRY GLASS & MIRROR INC
1250 Us Highway 80 E (75149-1444)
PHONE....................972 216-9100
Karen Risinger, *President*
Charles Risinger Jr, *Vice Pres*
Joe Lambertson, *Manager*
David Hartley, *Admin Sec*
EMP: 22
SQ FT: 15,000
SALES (est): 4.6MM **Privately Held**
WEB: www.cgm-us.com
SIC: 1793 3446 3442 Glass & glazing
work; architectural metalwork; metal
doors, sash & trim

(G-15036)
COX INDUSTRIES INC
Also Called: Cox Fence Fittings
11324 Russell St (75180-1053)
PHONE....................972 288-7555
Charles Haley, *CEO*
William T Cox, *Shareholder*
EMP: 45
SQ FT: 58,000
SALES (est): 9MM **Privately Held**
SIC: 3315 3479 Fence gates posts & fit-
tings: steel; galvanizing of iron, steel or
end-formed products

(G-15037)
DALLAS PLASTICS LLC (PA)
924 Dalworth Dr (75149-4148)
PHONE....................972 289-5500
Kevin Pierce, *CEO*
Mike Cooper, *Plant Mgr*
James Krause, *Prdtn Mgr*
Chris Pierce, *Purch Mgr*
Sam Stinchcomb, *Controller*
EMP: 50
SQ FT: 25,000
SALES (est): 17.6MM **Privately Held**
WEB: www.dallasplastics.com
SIC: 2821 Plastics materials & resins

(G-15038)
DANIEL STEEL INDUSTRIES INC
Also Called: Martin's Mill Store
4640 N Belt Line Rd (75182-2201)
PHONE....................214 235-4509
Jerry D Daniel, *President*
Rhonda McCune, *General Mgr*
Gerald W Koller, *Corp Secy*
Franklin Malone, *Vice Pres*
Dominic Digiammatteo, *Sales Staff*
EMP: 35 EST: 1971
SQ FT: 1,500
SALES (est): 10.4MM **Privately Held**
WEB: www.danielsteelind.com
SIC: 3441 3449 Fabricated structural
metal; miscellaneous metalwork

(G-15039)
DISPLAY SURCE DESIGN FCTRY LTD (PA)
1371 S Town East Blvd (75149-6700)
PHONE....................972 288-7471
Henry Leaverton, *CEO*
Tom Leaverton, *COO*

Tom Norman, *Vice Pres*
John Matejcik, *Engineer*
Javier Espinosa, *Chief Mktg Ofcr*
EMP: 130 EST: 1976
SQ FT: 52,000
SALES (est): 39.2MM **Privately Held**
WEB: www.dsadisplay.com
SIC: 3496 3993 Miscellaneous fabricated
wire products; signs & advertising special-
ties

(G-15040)
DIVERSITY PETROLEUM LP
3819 Towne Crossing Blvd (75150-2799)
P.O. Box 2109, Rockwall (75087-5009)
PHONE....................972 772-6025
Charles D Perez, *Partner*
EMP: 10
SQ FT: 4,100
SALES (est): 1.1MM **Privately Held**
WEB: www.mdregroup.com
SIC: 1382 Oil & gas exploration services

(G-15041)
EUROPA SPORTS PRODUCTS INC
1851 Big Town Blvd # 500 (75149-1035)
PHONE....................214 388-7444
Cory Dahl, *Sales Staff*
Conrad Domalski, *Sales Staff*
Denise Nester, *Sales Staff*
Lauren Pearlman, *Sales Staff*
James Ruffini, *Manager*
EMP: 19 **Privately Held**
WEB: www.europasports.com
SIC: 2023 5941 Dietary supplements,
dairy & non-dairy based; sporting goods &
bicycle shops
PA: Europa Sports Products, Inc.
11401 Granite St Ste H
Charlotte NC 28273

(G-15042)
FRITZ INDUSTRIES INC (PA)
500 N Sam Houston Rd (75149-2733)
P.O. Box 170040, Dallas (75217-0040)
PHONE....................972 285-5471
Dan Montgomery, *President*
Steve Laramay, *President*
Eric Ulfsparre, *VP Opers*
Marco Mauricio, *Opers Mgr*
Chad Smith, *Facilities Mgr*
◆ EMP: 320 EST: 1956
SQ FT: 628,673
SALES (est): 103.4MM **Privately Held**
WEB: www.fritzind.com
SIC: 2899 Chemical preparations

(G-15043)
FRITZ INDUSTRIES INC
2950 Executive Blvd (75149-2802)
PHONE....................972 288-5425
EMP: 35
SALES (corp-wide): 131.8MM **Privately Held**
SIC: 2899 Mfg Chemical Preparations
PA: Fritz Industries, Inc.
500 N Sam Houston Rd
Mesquite TX 75149
972 285-5471

(G-15044)
FRITZ-PAK CORPORATION
4821 Eastover Cir (75149-1049)
PHONE....................214 221-9494
Gabriel Ojeda, *President*
Jane Ojeda, *Treasurer*
◆ EMP: 16
SQ FT: 25,000
SALES (est): 3.5MM **Privately Held**
WEB: www.fritzpak.com
SIC: 3273 Ready-mixed concrete

(G-15045)
GOURMET CUISINE INC
214 S Town East Blvd (75149-2810)
PHONE....................972 289-7441
Rick Roberts, *Vice Pres*
Ebony Johnson, *Manager*
Ren Thomas, *Director*
EMP: 32
SALES (est): 9.1MM **Privately Held**
WEB: www.gourmet-cuisine.com
SIC: 2038 Frozen specialties

GEOGRAPHIC

(G-15046)
GRACON CONSTRUCTION INC
4343 Lasater Rd (75181-3222)
P.O. Box 360039, Dallas (75336-0039)
PHONE..........................972 222-8533
Kenneth A Graves, *President*
Tim Beck, *Superintendent*
Joel G Graves, *Vice Pres*
Michael A Graves, *Vice Pres*
Cory Graves, *Project Mgr*
EMP: 75
SQ FT: 5,000
SALES (est): 24.3MM **Privately Held**
WEB: www.gracon.biz
SIC: 1629 3589 Waste water & sewage treatment plant construction; water treatment equipment, industrial

(G-15047)
H & K INTERNATIONAL INC (DH)
2200 Skyline Dr (75149-1957)
P.O. Box 180729, Dallas (75218-0729)
PHONE..........................214 818-3500
David Bobbett, *CEO*
Mike Azhadi, *President*
Keith Cassidy, *Managing Dir*
Patrick Maccann, *Managing Dir*
Brian Ranilow, *Chairman*
◆ EMP: 200
SQ FT: 210,000
SALES (est): 55.4MM **Privately Held**
WEB: www.hki.com
SIC: 3556 5087 3589 Food products machinery; restaurant supplies; cooking equipment, commercial

(G-15048)
HANSON CONCRETE BALCH SPRINGS
13950 Lake June Rd (75180-4854)
PHONE..........................972 289-0601
Bisrat Shidashi, *Principal*
EMP: 13
SALES (est): 696.1K **Privately Held**
SIC: 3273 Ready-mixed concrete

(G-15049)
HAYES COMPANY LLC
Also Called: Hayes Retail Services
1201 Chase Rd (75149-2764)
PHONE..........................972 288-9755
Pablo Rodarte, *Manager*
EMP: 200
SALES (corp-wide): 24.8MM **Privately Held**
WEB: www.hayesco.com
SIC: 3446 Ornamental metalwork
PA: Hayes Company Llc
559 W Douglas Ave
Wichita KS 67213
316 838-8000

(G-15050)
HB FULLER COMPANY
Global Coatings Div
3500 Executive Blvd (75149-2700)
PHONE..........................972 728-0707
Jack Haynes, *Opers-Prdtn-Mfg*
EMP: 40
SQ FT: 25,000
SALES (corp-wide): 2.7B **Publicly Held**
WEB: www.hbfuller.com
SIC: 2891 Glue
PA: H.B. Fuller Company
1200 Willow Lake Blvd
Saint Paul MN 55110
651 236-5900

(G-15051)
HIGHLITE INC
4320 Action Dr (75150-6683)
PHONE..........................214 741-4116
Steve Vastine, *President*
EMP: 10
SQ FT: 10,000
SALES (est): 1.3MM **Privately Held**
WEB: www.thearchguys.com
SIC: 3442 1799 Metal doors, sash & trim; window treatment installation

(G-15052)
HOWARD KEITH MELTON
Also Called: A A A Backhoe
2408 Liles Ln (75181-4705)
PHONE..........................972 222-1900
Keith Melton, *Owner*

Keith Nelton, *Owner*
EMP: 19
SQ FT: 500
SALES (est): 1MM **Privately Held**
SIC: 3531 Backhoes

(G-15053)
IRIS USA INC
3401 Innovative Way (75149-2755)
PHONE..........................972 329-0400
Adam Lue, *Production*
Masaki Mizutani, *Sales Mgr*
Craig Lucker, *Sales Staff*
Masao Watanabe, *Manager*
Dennis Carmichael, *Manager*
EMP: 21 **Privately Held**
WEB: www.irisusainc.com
SIC: 3089 Plastic containers, except foam
HQ: Iris Usa, Inc.
13423 W Cactus Rd
Surprise AZ 85379

(G-15054)
J-N FENCE CO INC
305 Us Highway 80 E (75150-5825)
P.O. Box 851268 (75185-1268)
PHONE..........................972 226-7205
James Novey, *President*
James Novy, *Vice Pres*
Sid Agent, *CFO*
JC Cook, *VP Sales*
Scott McGee, *Sales Staff*
EMP: 23
SQ FT: 18,000
SALES (est): 2.9MM **Privately Held**
WEB: www.jnfence.com
SIC: 1799 3446 Fence construction; architectural metalwork

(G-15055)
JOHNS DOVETAIL SHOP
2123 Bridger Dr (75149-8649)
PHONE..........................972 557-0775
John Chapman, *Owner*
EMP: 10
SQ FT: 6,500
SALES (est): 716.5K **Privately Held**
SIC: 2541 Store & office display cases & fixtures

(G-15056)
KEITH & COMPANY INC
Also Called: Keith & Company Machining
1813 S Town East Blvd (75149-1128)
PHONE..........................972 285-3588
Mark Keith, *President*
Julie Keith, *Vice Pres*
EMP: 15
SQ FT: 4,800
SALES (est): 1.2MM **Privately Held**
SIC: 3599 Machine shop, jobbing & repair

(G-15057)
KNIGHTS LANDSCAPING LLC
2000 Spring Mills Rd (75181-2102)
PHONE..........................972 971-4213
Jeremy Knight,
EMP: 12
SALES (est): 442.2K **Privately Held**
SIC: 0781 1521 1542 0782 Landscape planning services; single-family housing construction; commercial & office building, new construction; landscape contractors; construction management; construction sand & gravel

(G-15058)
LEGAL DIRECTORIES PUBG CO
1313 Oates Dr (75150-6803)
P.O. Box 495069, Garland (75049-5069)
PHONE..........................214 321-3238
William E Brown, *Ch of Bd*
Diane Chapman, *President*
Dianne Marshall, *Editor*
Jimmy Lynn, *Treasurer*
Bert Gravley, *Marketing Staff*
EMP: 60
SQ FT: 40,000
SALES (est): 5MM **Privately Held**
WEB: www.legaldirectories.com
SIC: 2741 Directories: publishing & printing

(G-15059)
M2W INC
Also Called: Marketing 2 Wynne
2318 N Belt Line Rd # 716 (75150-5898)
P.O. Box 1896, Allen (75013-0033)
PHONE..........................972 407-1332
Clare Wynne, *President*
Wendee Pennington, *Finance Dir*
Raul Landino, *Marketing Mgr*
Eric Garrett, *Manager*
Lindsay Gottshall, *Manager*
EMP: 75 EST: 1998
SALES (est): 715K **Privately Held**
WEB: www.m2winc.com
SIC: 8742 7389 3993 7319 Marketing consulting services; ; advertising artwork; advertising novelties; transit advertising services; distribution of advertising material or sample services

(G-15060)
MAGEE MACHINE AND MFG INC
Also Called: Magee Machine & Mfg.
3535 Executive Blvd (75149-2709)
PHONE..........................972 285-2554
Michael E Magee, *President*
Travis Magee, *COO*
EMP: 12
SQ FT: 30,000
SALES (est): 296.8K **Privately Held**
WEB: www.mageemachine.com
SIC: 3599 7692 5051 Machine shop, jobbing & repair; welding repair; metals service centers & offices

(G-15061)
MASONITE INTERNATIONAL
2300 Skyline Dr (75149-1974)
PHONE..........................972 686-5500
Reyna Trejo, *Principal*
Larry Yu, *Purch Agent*
Vicky Russell, *Regl Sales Mgr*
▲ EMP: 9
SALES (est): 972.8K **Privately Held**
WEB: www.masonite.com
SIC: 2431 Doors, wood

(G-15062)
MCELROY METAL MILL INC
460 Clay Rd (75182-9700)
PHONE..........................972 226-7075
Carl McKinney, *Manager*
Barry Johnston, *Executive*
EMP: 15
SALES (corp-wide): 362MM **Privately Held**
WEB: www.mcelroymetal.com
SIC: 3448 Prefabricated metal buildings
PA: Mcelroy Metal Mill, Inc.
1500 Hamilton Rd
Bossier City LA 71111
318 747-8000

(G-15063)
MORRISON PRODUCTS INC
3400 Us Highway 80 E (75149-1102)
PHONE..........................972 279-4000
David Reeves, *Production*
Rob McPhil, *Branch Mgr*
EMP: 100
SALES (corp-wide): 206.8MM **Privately Held**
WEB: www.morrisonproducts.com
SIC: 3564 3585 3444 3441 Blowers & fans; refrigeration & heating equipment; sheet metalwork; fabricated structural metal
PA: Morrison Products, Inc.
16900 S Waterloo Rd
Cleveland OH 44110
216 486-4000

(G-15064)
NEW SAW INC
3248 Executive Blvd (75149-2704)
PHONE..........................972 288-2117
Steve Williams, *President*
EMP: 25
SALES (est): 1.9MM **Privately Held**
SIC: 1751 2434 Cabinet building & installation; wood kitchen cabinets

(G-15065)
ORORA VISUAL TX LLC
Also Called: Horticultural Printers
3210 Innovative Way (75149-2756)
PHONE..........................972 289-0705
Larry King, *CEO*
Joann Lombardo, *Production*
EMP: 100 **Privately Held**
WEB: www.ororavisual.com
SIC: 2752 5023 Commercial printing, offset; floor cushion & padding
HQ: Orora Visual Tx Llc
3210 Innovative Way
Mesquite TX 75149
972 289-0705

(G-15066)
ORORA VISUAL TX LLC
3638 Executive Blvd (75149-2712)
PHONE..........................972 289-0705
Kevin Camp, *CFO*
Penny Valencia, *Client Mgr*
EMP: 10 **Privately Held**
WEB: www.ororavisual.com
SIC: 2752 2754 Commercial printing, offset; commercial printing, gravure
HQ: Orora Visual Tx Llc
3210 Innovative Way
Mesquite TX 75149
972 289-0705

(G-15067)
PARAGON INDUSTRIES LP
2011 S Town East Blvd (75149-1122)
PHONE..........................972 288-7557
John R Hohenshelt, *Partner*
Gwen Rinkenberger, *Controller*
Robye Shaffer, *Comptroller*
◆ EMP: 83
SQ FT: 53,000
SALES (est): 11.5MM **Privately Held**
WEB: www.paragonweb.com
SIC: 3567 Ceramic kilns & furnaces; electrical furnaces, ovens & heating devices, exc. induction

(G-15068)
PARAGON INDUSTRIES INC
2011 S Town East Blvd (75149-1122)
PHONE..........................972 288-7557
Joseph Landis, *President*
Maria Garcia, *Plant Mgr*
David Vives, *Opers Mgr*
Patti Kelly, *Traffic Mgr*
Robye Shaffer, *Accounting Mgr*
▲ EMP: 99
SALES (est): 18.8MM **Privately Held**
WEB: www.paragonweb.com
SIC: 3567 Industrial furnaces & ovens

(G-15069)
PEPSI BOTTLING GROUP
Also Called: Pepsico
4532 Interstate 30 (75150-2028)
PHONE..........................214 324-8500
Chris McCool, *Vice Pres*
Joe Foist, *Prdtn Mgr*
Kristof Van Thielen, *Engineer*
Tiffany Nix, *Director*
▲ EMP: 88
SALES (est): 28.7MM **Privately Held**
WEB: www.pepsico.com
SIC: 2086 Carbonated soft drinks, bottled & canned

(G-15070)
PEPSI-COLA METRO BTLG CO INC
4532 Us Highway 67 (75150-2097)
PHONE..........................214 324-8500
Bruce Grass, *General Mgr*
EMP: 325
SQ FT: 100,000
SALES (corp-wide): 67.1B **Publicly Held**
WEB: www.pepsico.com
SIC: 2086 Soft drinks: packaged in cans, bottles, etc.
HQ: Pepsi-Cola Metropolitan Bottling Company, Inc.
1111 Westchester Ave
White Plains NY 10604
914 767-6000

(G-15071)
PICKLE JUICE COMPANY
Also Called: Pickle Juice Sport
206 S Town East Blvd (75149-2810)
PHONE..........................972 755-0289
Steve Gardner, *President*
Steve Collet, *Vice Pres*
Filip Keuppens, *Vice Pres*
EMP: 15
SQ FT: 20,000
SALES (est): 10MM Privately Held
WEB: www.picklepower.com
SIC: 2086 Bottled & canned soft drinks

(G-15072)
PROFORM GROUP INC
2400 Skyline Dr (75149-1989)
PHONE..........................214 206-4100
Victoria Carson, *Branch Mgr*
EMP: 38
SALES (corp-wide): 53.8MM Privately Held
WEB: www.proformgroupinc.com
SIC: 3713 Truck bodies (motor vehicles)
PA: Proform Group, Inc.
4400 Don Cayo Dr
Muskogee OK 74403
918 682-8666

(G-15073)
PWR TECHNOLOGIES LLC
18601 Lbj Fwy Ste 700 (75150-6441)
PHONE..........................469 609-3537
Robert Wolfe, *Co-Owner*
Darrick Pratt, *Co-Owner*
Rueben Reese, *Co-Owner*
EMP: 10
SALES (est): 261.2K Privately Held
WEB: www.pwrtechnologies.com
SIC: 7379 4813 8748 7372 Computer related consulting services; ; telecommunications consultant; application computer software; software programming applications

(G-15074)
QUALITY BUSINESS SOLUTIONS
2830 Anchor Dr (75150-3602)
PHONE..........................972 285-2000
Sue Mc Cormick, *Owner*
EMP: 20
SQ FT: 10,000
SALES (est): 1.1MM Privately Held
SIC: 3861 7389 Toners, prepared photographic (not made in chemical plants); printers' services: folding, collating

(G-15075)
RODEO PLASTIC BAG & FILM LLC
3328 Executive Blvd (75149-2706)
PHONE..........................972 216-3331
Vicki Lacy, *Accountant*
Sean Whiteley,
EMP: 100
SQ FT: 150,000
SALES (est): 4.2MM Privately Held
SIC: 3089 3081 Plastic containers, except foam; polyethylene film
PA: Delta Plastics Of The South, Llc
8801 Frazier Pike
Little Rock AR 72206

(G-15076)
SAW CUSTOM MILLWORK INC
3248 Executive Blvd (75149-2704)
PHONE..........................972 288-2118
Steve Williams, *President*
EMP: 28
SQ FT: 20,000
SALES (est): 1.7MM Privately Held
SIC: 1751 5211 2521 2431 Cabinet building & installation; millwork & lumber; wood office furniture; millwork

(G-15077)
TAIGA COOLERS LLC
2200 Big Town Blvd # 130 (75149-1004)
PHONE..........................214 762-3648
John S Hohenshelt, *President*
EMP: 9
SALES (est): 985K Privately Held
WEB: www.taigacoolers.com
SIC: 3949 Sporting & athletic goods

(G-15078)
TAYLOR COMMUNICATIONS INC
4808 Eastover Cir Ste 101 (75149-1006)
PHONE..........................214 275-3200
Dianne Villarreal, *Branch Mgr*
Kelly Smirl, *Consultant*
EMP: 24
SALES (corp-wide): 2.5B Privately Held
WEB: www.taylorcorp.com
SIC: 2759 Commercial printing
HQ: Taylor Communications, Inc.
1725 Roe Crest Dr
North Mankato MN 56003
866 541-0937

(G-15079)
TECHNICAL SERVICES INTL
Also Called: My Jack Products
1522 Mclead Dr (75149-4502)
PHONE..........................972 285-7400
Rod B Shockley, *Principal*
Rick Cingrana, *Manager*
▲ EMP: 20
SALES (est): 3.3MM Privately Held
WEB: www.tsi-mj.com
SIC: 3531 Construction machinery

(G-15080)
TEXAS METAL INDUSTRIES INC
1331 Us Highway 80 E # 15 (75150-5711)
PHONE..........................972 288-2333
Cary Carter, *President*
◆ EMP: 50
SALES (est): 7.6MM Privately Held
WEB: www.txmetal.com
SIC: 3471 1799 Finishing, metals or formed products; ornamental metal work

(G-15081)
TRIDENT LABORATORIES INC
200 Adell Blvd (75182-9340)
PHONE..........................972 226-4986
Loren Adell, *President*
Michael Adell, *Vice Pres*
EMP: 50
SALES (est): 5MM Privately Held
SIC: 3069 3442 Injection molded finished plastic products; metal doors, sash & trim

(G-15082)
TRUMED TECHNOLOGIES INC
1801 Big Town Blvd # 100 (75149-1011)
PHONE..........................952 882-0611
Kathryn Trudeau, *President*
Kevin Stanek, *COO*
▲ EMP: 30
SQ FT: 13,500
SALES (est): 3.2MM
SALES (corp-wide): 1B Publicly Held
SIC: 2675 5047 Paper die-cutting; medical equipment & supplies
PA: Brady Corporation
6555 W Good Hope Rd
Milwaukee WI 53223
414 358-6600

(G-15083)
US CORRUGATED MESQUITE LLC
Also Called: Kapstone
700 N Sam Houston Rd (75149-2736)
PHONE..........................801 798-7331
Bill Elam, *Principal*
David Doherty, *Vice Pres*
EMP: 10
SALES (est): 2.2MM Privately Held
WEB: www.kapstonepaper.com
SIC: 2653 Boxes, corrugated: made from purchased materials

(G-15084)
US MACHINERY PARTS SALES INC
2144 N Belt Line Rd Ste H (75150-5860)
PHONE..........................972 551-3551
Jimmy Sweeney, *President*
Jackie Sweeney, *Vice Pres*
EMP: 30
SALES (est): 1MM Privately Held
SIC: 3069 5085 Molded rubber products; rubber goods, mechanical

(G-15085)
WESTROCK CONTAINER LLC
700 N Sam Houston Rd (75149-2736)
PHONE..........................972 285-8865
EMP: 100
SALES (corp-wide): 17.5B Publicly Held
WEB: www.westrock.com
SIC: 2653 Boxes, corrugated: made from purchased materials
HQ: Westrock Container, Llc
1601 Blairs Ferry Rd Ne
Cedar Rapids IA 52402
319 393-3610

Mexia
Limestone County

(G-15086)
ACCURATE PMPG CONTRACTINGS INC
1824 Highway 84 W (76667-2376)
P.O. Box 670 (76667-0670)
PHONE..........................254 562-9747
Olan O Foley Jr, *President*
Patricia Foley, *Vice Pres*
EMP: 13
SALES (est): 2.3MM Privately Held
SIC: 1389 Servicing oil & gas wells

(G-15087)
BROWN OIL & GAS CO INC
901 S Belknap St (76667-3522)
P.O. Box 688 (76667-0688)
PHONE..........................254 562-2818
Fred S Brown, *President*
EMP: 15 EST: 1934
SQ FT: 1,200
SALES (est): 2.4MM Privately Held
SIC: 1311 Crude petroleum production; natural gas production

(G-15088)
BWS CONSTRUCTION LLC
1310 E Milam St (76667-2533)
P.O. Box 1022, Groesbeck (76642-1022)
PHONE..........................254 562-6820
EMP: 15
SQ FT: 1,600
SALES (est): 600K Privately Held
SIC: 1389 Oil/Gas Field Services

(G-15089)
CENTRAL TEXAS OILFIELD SUP CO
Also Called: Central Texas Oilfield Svcs
Rr 4 Box 406 (76667)
P.O. Box 688 (76667-0688)
PHONE..........................254 562-5522
Joan Teel, *President*
Fred Brown III, *President*
Sharlett Vanwinkle, *Corp Secy*
Hitt Sue, *Vice Pres*
▲ EMP: 9
SALES (est): 622.1K Privately Held
SIC: 1389 5084 Servicing oil & gas wells; oil well machinery, equipment & supplies

(G-15090)
LONE STAR BODY SYSTEMS LLC
1618 W Highway 84 (76667-4556)
PHONE..........................254 472-0852
Richard Bailey, *Mng Member*
EMP: 33
SALES (est): 7.8MM Privately Held
WEB: www.lsbody.com
SIC: 3713 Truck & bus bodies

(G-15091)
SUN-TIMES MEDIA GROUP INC
Also Called: Mexia Daily News
214 N Railroad St (76667-2850)
P.O. Box 431 (76667-0431)
PHONE..........................254 562-2868
Elsie Randecker, *Office Mgr*
EMP: 13
SALES (corp-wide): 5.2MM Privately Held
WEB: www.chicago.suntimes.com
SIC: 2711 Commercial printing & newspaper publishing combined

HQ: Sun-Times Media Group, Inc.
30 N Racine Ave Ste 300
Chicago IL 60607
312 321-3000

(G-15092)
SWARCO-REFLEX LLC (HQ)
900 N Denton St (76667-2101)
P.O. Box 1558 (76667-1558)
PHONE..........................254 562-9879
Jon Sproul, *President*
Frances Stockbridge, *Corp Secy*
▲ EMP: 22
SALES (est): 9.9MM
SALES (corp-wide): 85.2MM Privately Held
WEB: www.swarco.com
SIC: 3231 5084 Reflector glass beads, for highway signs or reflectors; industrial machinery & equipment
PA: Swarco America, Inc.
270 Rutherford Ln
Columbia TN 38401
931 388-5900

(G-15093)
SWARCO-REFLEX LLC
Hwy 84 (76667)
P.O. Box 1558 (76667-1558)
PHONE..........................254 562-9879
Carl McCollum, *Branch Mgr*
EMP: 30
SALES (corp-wide): 85.2MM Privately Held
WEB: www.swarco.com
SIC: 3231 Reflector glass beads, for highway signs or reflectors
HQ: Swarco-Reflex, Llc
900 N Denton St
Mexia TX 76667

Mico
Medina County

(G-15094)
SENTRY OIL & GAS LLC
Also Called: Sentry Oil and Gas
170 Pr 1731 Ste 100 (78056-5457)
PHONE..........................212 753-6367
Jack Pryor, *Ch of Bd*
Thomas Marshall,
Thomas Belton,
Mark Magarity,
EMP: 30
SALES (est): 924.8K Privately Held
WEB: www.sentryoilandgas.com
SIC: 1311 1321 1381 1382 Crude petroleum production; natural gas liquids; drilling oil & gas wells; oil & gas exploration services; oil field services

Midkiff
Upton County

(G-15095)
DCP MIDSTREAM LLC
1788 Pegasus Fld (79755)
PHONE..........................432 693-2204
EMP: 21
SALES (corp-wide): 2.2B Privately Held
SIC: 5172 1321 Whol Petroleum Products Natural Gas Liquids Production
PA: Dcp Midstream Llc
370 17th St Ste 2500
Denver CO 80202
303 633-2900

(G-15096)
PIONEER NATURAL RESOURCES CO
24500 E Farm Market 309 (79755)
PHONE..........................432 535-2444
Larry Hambek, *Manager*
EMP: 70
SALES (corp-wide): 9.3B Publicly Held
WEB: www.pxd.com
SIC: 1321 1311 Natural gas liquids; crude petroleum production
PA: Pioneer Natural Resources Company
777 Hidden Rdg
Irving TX 75038
972 444-9001

(G-15097)
TARGA PPLINE MID-CONTINENT LLC
17400 E Fm 2401 (79755)
PHONE..................432 535-2484
Denny Latham, *Branch Mgr*
EMP: 57 **Publicly Held**
SIC: 1389 Processing service, gas
HQ: Targa Pipeline Mid-Continent Llc
110 W 7th St Ste 2300
Tulsa OK 74119
918 574-3500

(G-15098)
WESTERN GAS RESOURCES INC
Also Called: Benedum Gas Plant
Hc 34 Box 20 (79755)
P.O. Box 190 (79755-0190)
PHONE..................432 693-2302
Rick Ferguson, *Manager*
EMP: 15
SALES (corp-wide): 21.2B **Publicly Held**
WEB: www.oxy.com
SIC: 4923 1321 Gas transmission & distribution; natural gas liquids
HQ: Western Gas Resources, Inc.
1099 18th St
Denver CO 80202

Midland
Midland County

(G-15099)
3 AMOREZ LLC
7000 S County Road 1165 (79706-2227)
P.O. Box 3395 (79702-3395)
PHONE..................432 269-4199
Cynthia Marquez, *Mng Member*
EMP: 10 EST: 2018
SALES (est): 600K **Privately Held**
SIC: 1389 Oil field services

(G-15100)
A 1 DISTRIBUTORS SIGN SUPPLY
Also Called: A-1 Distributors
1100 Garden City Hwy (79701-8352)
P.O. Box 2641 (79702-2641)
PHONE..................432 682-0083
Dave Tomlin, *President*
EMP: 100
SALES (est): 9.8MM **Privately Held**
WEB: www.a1graphicsolutions.com
SIC: 5085 3993 3446 2396 Signmaker equipment & supplies; signs & advertising specialties; architectural metalwork; automotive & apparel trimmings

(G-15101)
A P MANUFACTURING INCORPORATED
Also Called: Wireline Supply
1 E Industrial Loop (79701-8514)
P.O. Box 7922, Odessa (79760-7922)
PHONE..................432 638-4708
Andy Pearce, *President*
EMP: 20
SALES (est): 1.2MM **Privately Held**
WEB: www.wirelinesupply.com
SIC: 3315 Wire & fabricated wire products

(G-15102)
A-1 SIIGN ENGRAVERS INC
1200 Garden City Hwy (79701-8353)
P.O. Box 2641 (79702-2641)
PHONE..................432 682-3492
David Tomlin, *President*
Blocker Dalynn M, *Vice Pres*
Penny Sullivan, *Accounting Mgr*
Jay Nichols, *Regl Sales Mgr*
Saide Moya, *Supervisor*
EMP: 25
SQ FT: 10,000
SALES (est): 3.2MM **Privately Held**
WEB: www.a1graphicsolutions.com
SIC: 3993 Signs, not made in custom sign painting shops

(G-15103)
ABSOLUTE ROUSTABOUT SVC LLC
6218 N C R 1150 (79705)
P.O. Box 5377 (79704-5377)
PHONE..................432 488-8788
Brandon Audas, *Mng Member*
Frankie Barela,
EMP: 100
SALES (est): 11MM **Privately Held**
WEB: www.absoluteroustabout.com
SIC: 1389 Roustabout service

(G-15104)
ACME ENERGY SERVICES INC
Also Called: Big Dog Drilling
110 N Marienfeld St # 200 (79701-4412)
PHONE..................432 561-5271
Autry Stephens, *President*
Luke Wardell, *Project Mgr*
Damon Button, *CFO*
Chris Hayes, *Manager*
EMP: 700
SALES (est): 52.6MM **Privately Held**
WEB: www.bigdogdrilling.net
SIC: 1381 1389 Drilling oil & gas wells; haulage, oil field

(G-15105)
ADROIT FABRICATION INC
3504 Princeton Ave (79703-5011)
PHONE..................432 288-0656
Kelly Vaughan, *President*
EMP: 11
SQ FT: 12,000
SALES (est): 635.8K **Privately Held**
SIC: 3533 Oil & gas field machinery

(G-15106)
ADVANCED STIMULATION TECH INC (PA)
2903 E Interstate 20 (79706-4201)
P.O. Box 2948 (79702-2948)
PHONE..................432 617-3250
Autry C Stephens, *Ch of Bd*
Robert Booth, *President*
Bobby Tubbs, *General Mgr*
Lewis Niewoehner, *Principal*
EMP: 60
SQ FT: 11,766
SALES (est): 12.4MM **Privately Held**
WEB: www.advstimtech.com
SIC: 1389 Acidizing wells; hydraulic fracturing wells

(G-15107)
ADVENTURE EXPLRTION PRTNERS LL
500 W Texas Ave Ste 600 (79701-4237)
P.O. Box 11354 (79702-8354)
PHONE..................432 684-8006
Peter R Shcherer, *CEO*
Paul L Lucas, *President*
Scot Northern, *CFO*
Keaton Waters, *Executive*
EMP: 10
SALES (est): 1.4MM **Privately Held**
WEB: www.adventurexpl.com
SIC: 1382 Oil & gas exploration services

(G-15108)
AGGIETECH ENERGY SERVICES LLC (PA)
Also Called: Big Bear-Aggietech
5101 W Interstate 20 (79706)
P.O. Box 7742 (79708-7742)
PHONE..................432 682-3131
Mark Bales, *President*
Toben Scott, *President*
Paul Gonzales, *Vice Pres*
KY Smith, *Vice Pres*
Sergio Leyva, *Opers Staff*
EMP: 130
SALES (est): 29.3MM **Privately Held**
WEB: www.aggietechoil.com
SIC: 3561 7699 Pumps & pumping equipment; pumps & pumping equipment repair

(G-15109)
AGGIETECH OIL LTD
Also Called: Bbat
5101 W Interstate 20 (79708)
P.O. Box 7742 (79708-7742)
PHONE..................432 682-3131
Mark Bales, *CEO*

Toben Scott, *President*
Aggietech Investments, *General Ptnr*
KY Smith, *Business Mgr*
Terry Stahl, *Senior VP*
EMP: 16
SALES (est): 3.7MM **Privately Held**
WEB: www.aggietechoil.com
SIC: 1382 Oil & gas exploration services

(G-15110)
AIM DIRECTIONAL SERVICES LLC
7606 W Highway 80 (79706-2882)
PHONE..................432 934-0628
Thomas Rinald, *President*
EMP: 20 **Privately Held**
WEB: www.aimdir.com
SIC: 1381 Directional drilling oil & gas wells
PA: Aim Directional Services, Llc
500 N Water St Ste 400
Corpus Christi TX 78401

(G-15111)
ALAMO PRESSURE PUMPING LLC (PA)
11000 W County Rd (79707)
P.O. Box 4597 (79704-4597)
PHONE..................432 695-6210
Tim Ondrak, *Vice Pres*
Candice Harris, *Controller*
Rj Sikes, *Mng Member*
Jeff Hansen,
EMP: 290
SALES (est): 189.6MM **Privately Held**
WEB: www.fracing.com
SIC: 1389 Hydraulic fracturing wells

(G-15112)
ALLEN ORTHOTICS & PROSTHETICS (PA)
2502 W Ohio Ave (79701-5848)
PHONE..................432 683-3788
Michael J Allen, *President*
Allen Laverne, *Vice Pres*
EMP: 16 EST: 1954
SQ FT: 5,800
SALES (est): 2.5MM **Privately Held**
WEB: www.allenoandp.com
SIC: 3842 Limbs, artificial; prosthetic appliances

(G-15113)
ALLIANCE FIELD SERVICES LLC
12801 W County Road 91 (79707-5805)
P.O. Box 2588, Odessa (79760-2588)
PHONE..................432 332-4308
John Adams,
Larry Jones,
Harvey J Page,
EMP: 100
SQ FT: 8,000
SALES (est): 10.7MM
SALES (corp-wide): 226.9MM **Privately Held**
WEB: www.alliancefieldservices.com
SIC: 1389 Oil field services
PA: Ref-Chem L.P.
1128 S Grandview Ave
Odessa TX 79761
432 332-8531

(G-15114)
AMERUS OILFIELD SOLUTIONS LLC
2306 N Fm 1788 (79707-1565)
P.O. Box 60636 (79711-0636)
PHONE..................432 559-0843
Charles R Caulsbury Jr,
EMP: 11
SALES (est): 1.9MM **Privately Held**
WEB: www.amerusoilfieldsolutions.com
SIC: 3533 Oil & gas field machinery

(G-15115)
ANADARKO PETROLEUM CORPORATION
10 Desta Dr Ste 650e (79705-4533)
P.O. Box 50458 (79710-0458)
PHONE..................432 684-2800
John Applegath, *Manager*
Dale Barnes, *Analyst*
EMP: 24

SALES (corp-wide): 21.2B **Publicly Held**
WEB: www.oxy.com
SIC: 1311 Crude petroleum production
HQ: Anadarko Petroleum Corporation
1201 Lake Robbins Dr
The Woodlands TX 77380
832 636-1000

(G-15116)
APACHE CORPORATION
303 Veterans Airpark Ln # 3000 (79705-4561)
PHONE..................713 296-6000
Guinn Burks, *Foreman/Supr*
David Cabrera, *Foreman/Supr*
Joey Rumfield, *Opers Staff*
Samuel Hakes, *Engineer*
Kris Hasselbach, *Engineer*
EMP: 15
SALES (corp-wide): 6.4B **Publicly Held**
WEB: www.apachecorp.com
SIC: 1311 Crude petroleum production
PA: Apache Corporation
2000 Post Oak Blvd Ste 10
Houston TX 77056
713 296-6000

(G-15117)
APPLIED US ENERGY INC
Also Called: Reliance Industrial
2904 S County Road 1250 (79706-2639)
PHONE..................432 689-0102
EMP: 19
SALES (corp-wide): 3.2B **Publicly Held**
WEB: www.relianceindustrial.com
SIC: 1389 Pipe testing, oil field service
HQ: Applied Us Energy, Inc.
1 Applied Plz
Cleveland OH 44115
325 227-8915

(G-15118)
ARCHROCK INC
9704 W Interstate 20 (79706-2620)
PHONE..................432 567-1050
Randy Rohalff, *President*
EMP: 11 **Publicly Held**
WEB: www.archrock.com
SIC: 1389 7699 Gas compressing (natural gas) at the fields; industrial machinery & equipment repair
PA: Archrock, Inc.
9807 Katy Fwy Ste 100
Houston TX 77024

(G-15119)
ARRINGTON OIL & GAS OPER LLC
500 W Wall St Ste 300 (79701-5093)
PHONE..................432 682-6685
David H Arrington, *President*
Kathy Krell, *Accountant*
Jim Stein, *Manager*
EMP: 60
SALES (est): 3.4MM **Privately Held**
WEB: www.arringtonoil.com
SIC: 1382 Oil & gas exploration services

(G-15120)
ARROWHEAD OPERATING INC
400 E Loop 250 N Ste 107 (79705-4449)
PHONE..................432 683-9700
Jack Chambers, *President*
Beau Chambers, *Vice Pres*
EMP: 13
SALES (est): 7.5MM **Privately Held**
SIC: 1382 Oil & gas exploration services

(G-15121)
ASSOCIATED PUBLISHING COMPANY
Also Called: Area-Wide Phone Book
4519 N Garfield St (79705-3415)
PHONE..................432 687-1756
Andrew Satropous, *Manager*
EMP: 20
SALES (corp-wide): 7.9B **Privately Held**
SIC: 2741 7331 2731 Telephone & other directory publishing; direct mail advertising services; book publishing
HQ: Associated Publishing Company, Inc
61 John Muir Dr
Buffalo NY 14228

▲ = Import ▼=Export
◆ =Import/Export

(G-15122)
ATLANTIC OPERATING INC
300 N Marienfeld St # 400 (79701-4345)
P.O. Box 3759 (79702-3759)
PHONE.................................432 683-3272
Richard A Jennings, *President*
Lee Thomas, *COO*
EMP: 10
SQ FT: 5,000
SALES (est): 2.3MM **Privately Held**
WEB: www.victerra.com
SIC: 1382 Oil & gas exploration services

(G-15123)
ATLAS WELL SERVICE LLC
2709 N Big Spring St (79705-6627)
P.O. Box 52337 (79710-2337)
PHONE.................................432 683-3835
J J Eascerwood, *Manager*
Steve M Coulon,
EMP: 20
SALES (est): 2.2MM **Privately Held**
WEB: www.atlaswellservice.com
SIC: 1381 Drilling oil & gas wells

(G-15124)
AUS-MEX COMPANY INC (PA)
Also Called: La Bodega Restaurant
7820 W Highway 80 (79706-2850)
PHONE.................................432 561-8866
Brian Johnson, *President*
Alois Munzer, *President*
EMP: 96
SQ FT: 17,674
SALES (est): 8MM **Privately Held**
WEB: www.ausmexcompany.com
SIC: 2099 2096 Tortillas, fresh or refrigerated; tortilla chips

(G-15125)
AUTO DRIL INC
915 E County Road 125 (79706-6459)
PHONE.................................432 561-8455
James Ray, *President*
Chris Junker, *Manager*
EMP: 12
SQ FT: 4,000
SALES (est): 2.5MM **Privately Held**
SIC: 1389 Oil field services

(G-15126)
B & J WELDING SUPPLY LTD
8102 W I 20 (79706)
PHONE.................................432 563-1277
Jason Jones, *President*
EMP: 18
SALES (corp-wide): 10.6MM **Privately Held**
WEB: www.bjweldingsupply.com
SIC: 7692 Welding repair
PA: B & J Welding Supply, Ltd.
1512 E 50th St
Lubbock TX 79404
806 747-1542

(G-15127)
B J ELECTRIC MOTOR SERVICE
2900 W Francis Ave (79701-8500)
PHONE.................................432 570-4100
Charles M White, *President*
Joy White, *Controller*
EMP: 10
SQ FT: 7,500
SALES (est): 1.4MM **Privately Held**
WEB: www.bjelectricmotors.net
SIC: 7694 5063 3621 Rewinding services; motors, electric; motors & generators

(G-15128)
BAKER HGHES OLFLD OPRTIONS LLC
6 Desta Dr Ste 5300 (79705-5518)
PHONE.................................432 685-8900
Chad Nichols, *Accounts Mgr*
Mike Gerstner, *Branch Mgr*
EMP: 21 **Privately Held**
WEB: www.bakerhughes.com
SIC: 1389 Oil field services
PA: Baker Hughes Oilfield Operations Llc
2001 Rankin Rd
Houston TX 77073

(G-15129)
BAKER HGHES OLFLD OPRTIONS LLC
Also Called: Baker Atlas
2001 Commerce Dr (79703-7502)
P.O. Box 4337 (79704-4337)
PHONE.................................432 694-7761
John Sebian, *Superintendent*
EMP: 20 **Privately Held**
WEB: www.bakerhughes.com
SIC: 1389 1382 Oil field services; seismograph surveys
PA: Baker Hughes Oilfield Operations Llc
2001 Rankin Rd
Houston TX 77073

(G-15130)
BAKER HGHES OLFLD OPRTIONS LLC
2105 Market St (79703-7510)
PHONE.................................432 694-9517
Ron Collins, *Manager*
EMP: 35 **Privately Held**
WEB: www.bakerhughes.com
SIC: 1389 1382 Oil field services; oil & gas exploration services
PA: Baker Hughes Oilfield Operations Llc
2001 Rankin Rd
Houston TX 77073

(G-15131)
BAKER HUGHES A GE COMPANY LLC
6 Desta Dr Ste 5300 (79705-5518)
PHONE.................................432 685-8900
Ricky Harper, *Branch Mgr*
EMP: 27
SALES (corp-wide): 23.8B **Publicly Held**
WEB: www.bakerhughes.com
SIC: 1389 Oil field services
HQ: Baker Hughes Holdings Llc
17021 Aldine Westfield Rd
Houston TX 77073
713 439-8600

(G-15132)
BAKER HUGHES A GE COMPANY LLC
Also Called: Hughes Christensen
2105 Market St (79703-7510)
PHONE.................................432 681-8300
Joel Hobds, *Manager*
EMP: 30
SALES (corp-wide): 23.8B **Publicly Held**
WEB: www.bakerhughes.com
SIC: 1389 Oil field services
HQ: Baker Hughes Holdings Llc
17021 Aldine Westfield Rd
Houston TX 77073
713 439-8600

(G-15133)
BASELINE ENERGY SERVICES LP
5001 W Wadley Ave (79707-2520)
PHONE.................................432 248-9112
EMP: 10
SALES (corp-wide): 10.1MM **Privately Held**
WEB: www.baseline-enserv.com
SIC: 3621 Power generators
PA: Baseline Energy Services, L.P.
201 N Foch St
Fort Worth TX 76107
817 889-0056

(G-15134)
BASIC ENERGY SERVICES INC
5805 E Highway 80 (79706-4562)
PHONE.................................432 620-5500
Charlie Swift, *Vice Pres*
Steve Newman, *Vice Pres*
Brad Shelton, *Opers Staff*
David Jones, *Engineer*
Kyle Courtright, *Sales Staff*
EMP: 35
SALES (corp-wide): 567.2MM **Publicly Held**
WEB: www.basices.com
SIC: 1389 Oil field services
PA: Basic Energy Services, Inc.
801 Cherry St Unit 2
Fort Worth TX 76102
817 334-4100

(G-15135)
BASIC ENERGY SERVICES INC
Also Called: Rebel Testers
3503 S County Road 1210 (79706-6204)
PHONE.................................432 620-0880
Cavin Horne, *Branch Mgr*
EMP: 11
SALES (corp-wide): 567.2MM **Publicly Held**
WEB: www.basices.com
SIC: 1389 Oil field services
PA: Basic Energy Services, Inc.
801 Cherry St Unit 2
Fort Worth TX 76102
817 334-4100

(G-15136)
BC OPERATING INC
4000 N Big Spring St # 310 (79705-4628)
P.O. Box 50820 (79710-0820)
PHONE.................................432 684-9696
Michael E Black, *President*
William Crump, *Vice Pres*
Carlos Mata, *Vice Pres*
Kristin Schmidt, *Engineer*
Melissa Archer, *Office Mgr*
EMP: 35
SALES (est): 20.9MM **Privately Held**
WEB: www.bcoperating.com
SIC: 1382 Oil & gas exploration services

(G-15137)
BELVAN PARTNERS LP (DH)
211 N Colorado St (79701-4607)
PHONE.................................432 682-4349
James L Davis, *President*
David Davis, *Vice Pres*
Richard Hatchett, *CFO*
Nancy Chandler, *Treasurer*
Donald Bland, *Marketing Staff*
EMP: 11
SALES (est): 2.1MM
SALES (corp-wide): 96.1MM **Privately Held**
SIC: 4925 4924 5172 1311 Gas production and/or distribution; natural gas distribution; petroleum products; crude petroleum & natural gas; petroleum refining

(G-15138)
BENCHMARK RESEARCH & TECH INC
4113 W Industrial Ave (79703-7704)
PHONE.................................432 697-8171
Wayne Kinsey, *President*
David N Harry, *Vice Pres*
Mark Kinsey, *Vice Pres*
EMP: 150
SQ FT: 4,100
SALES (est): 13.1MM
SALES (corp-wide): 1.2B **Publicly Held**
SIC: 8731 2899 5169 Commercial physical research; chemical preparations; industrial chemicals
HQ: Benchmark Performance Group, Inc.
2801 Post Oak Blvd
Houston TX 77056
713 986-2500

(G-15139)
BIG D EQUIPMENT COMPANY LTD
Also Called: Big D Companies
4501 E Highway 80 (79706-4410)
P.O. Box 7808 (79708-7808)
PHONE.................................432 682-1664
Don Tomlin, *President*
Nick Tomlin, *Vice Pres*
EMP: 85 **EST:** 1977
SQ FT: 11,500
SALES (est): 15.1MM **Privately Held**
WEB: www.bigdco.com
SIC: 7359 1389 Equipment rental & leasing; construction, repair & dismantling services

(G-15140)
BIG LAKE SERVICES COMPANY LLC
3709 S State Highway 349 (79706-6412)
P.O. Box 10494 (79702-7494)
PHONE.................................432 686-0475
Casey Davidson,
EMP: 184

SALES (est): 5.1MM
SALES (corp-wide): 832.9MM **Publicly Held**
WEB: www.biglakeservices.com
SIC: 1389 Oil field services
HQ: Beckman Production Services, Inc.
3786 Beebe Rd
Kalkaska MI 49646
231 258-9524

(G-15141)
BIG ROCK ENERGY SERVICES INC
602 N Baird St Ste 204 (79701-4767)
P.O. Box 3700 (79702-3700)
PHONE.................................432 235-8509
Rod Macdonald, *President*
EMP: 22
SALES (est): 4MM **Privately Held**
SIC: 1381 Service well drilling

(G-15142)
BIG STAR OIL & GAS LLC
5102 N County Road 1150 (79705-9502)
P.O. Box 51470 (79710-1470)
PHONE.................................432 687-4900
Stella M Swanson,
Bradley C Cross,
Kathy Myers,
EMP: 30
SQ FT: 4,600
SALES (est): 10.5MM **Privately Held**
WEB: www.bigstaroil.com
SIC: 1382 Oil & gas exploration services

(G-15143)
BLUE QUAIL ENERGY SERVICES LLC (PA)
2261 Wolfcamp Cir (79706-4329)
P.O. Box 80122 (79708-0122)
PHONE.................................432 684-0999
Mark Machen, *CEO*
EMP: 29 **EST:** 2011
SALES (est): 30.4MM **Privately Held**
WEB: www.blue-quail.com
SIC: 1389 1781 Oil field services; water well drilling

(G-15144)
BOAZ ENERGY II LLC
201 W Wall St (79701-4529)
P.O. Box 50595 (79710-0595)
PHONE.................................432 253-7074
Lauren Merriman, *Manager*
EMP: 12
SALES (est): 1.4MM **Privately Held**
WEB: www.boazenergy.com
SIC: 1382 Oil & gas exploration services

(G-15145)
BOBCAT CONTRACTING LLC
3612 S County Road 1198 (79706-6318)
P.O. Box 663, Hillsboro (76645-0663)
PHONE.................................432 332-1141
Glen Carter, *General Mgr*
EMP: 50 **Privately Held**
WEB: www.bobcatcontracting.com
SIC: 3829 Instrumentation for reactor controls, auxiliary
PA: Bobcat Contracting, L.L.C.
1721 Hcr 3106
Hillsboro TX 76645

(G-15146)
BOLD ENERGY II LLC
600 N Marienfeld St # 1000 (79701-4491)
PHONE.................................432 686-1100
David Cox, *Exec VP*
Shannon Klier, *Prdtn Mgr*
Joseph Castillo,
EMP: 10
SALES (est): 1.6MM **Privately Held**
SIC: 1382 Oil & gas exploration services

(G-15147)
BORDER STATES INDUSTRIES INC
Nunn Elc Sup A Div Brder Sttes
3303 W Illinois Ave Ste A (79703-6232)
PHONE.................................432 520-0230
Byron Rowe, *Mktg Dir*
Patricia Marquez, *Branch Mgr*
EMP: 13

SALES (corp-wide): 2.4B **Privately Held**
WEB: www.borderstates.com
SIC: 5063 5065 5074 1711 Electrical supplies; electronic parts & equipment; plumbing & hydronic heating supplies; plumbing, heating, air-conditioning contractors; plastics plumbing fixtures; vitreous plumbing fixtures
PA: Border States Industries, Inc.
2400 38th St S
Fargo ND 58104
701 293-5834

(G-15148)
BORETS US INC
2222 Commerce Dr (79703-7506)
PHONE............................432 697-1900
Basem Alghazal, *Business Mgr*
Damir Khaliulin, *Prdtn Mgr*
Hamam Abdelmagid, *Engineer*
Stephen Pettit, *Engineer*
William Faubel, *VP Bus Dvlpt*
EMP: 36 **Privately Held**
WEB: www.borets.com
SIC: 1389 Oil field services
HQ: Borets U.S., Inc.
1600 N Garnett Rd
Tulsa OK 74116

(G-15149)
BRAZCO DEVELOPMENT INC (PA)
414 W Texas Ave Ste 304 (79701-4415)
P.O. Box 174 (79702-0174)
PHONE............................432 684-8031
Dan P Black Sr, *President*
Black Pat, *Vice Pres*
EMP: 11
SQ FT: 1,900
SALES (est): 1.4MM **Privately Held**
SIC: 6552 1311 Subdividers & developers; crude petroleum production

(G-15150)
BRINKERHOFF INSPECTION INC (PA)
Also Called: Smob
707 Tradewinds Blvd Ste A (79706-2702)
PHONE............................432 924-2915
Steven Sheffield, *President*
EMP: 11
SALES (est): 10.7MM **Privately Held**
SIC: 1389 Oil field services

(G-15151)
BRINKERHOFF INSPECTION INC
Also Called: Smob
2509 N County Road 1287 (79707-2160)
PHONE............................432 770-4626
Bront Bird, *Owner*
EMP: 30
SALES (corp-wide): 10.7MM **Privately Held**
WEB: www.smobservices.com
SIC: 1389 Oil field services
PA: Brinkerhoff Inspection Inc
707 Tradewinds Blvd Ste A
Midland TX 79706
432 924-2915

(G-15152)
BRUCE A WILBANKS COMPANY INC
Also Called: Wilbanks, Bruce A Company
505 N Big Spring St # 500 (79701-4301)
P.O. Box 2579 (79702-2579)
PHONE............................432 682-7582
Joe Wilbanks, *President*
Steve Wilbanks, *Vice Pres*
Hazel Wilbanks, *Treasurer*
EMP: 10
SQ FT: 1,000
SALES (est): 1.6MM **Privately Held**
SIC: 1311 Crude petroleum production; natural gas production

(G-15153)
BURNS WELDING WORKS INC
804 Collins Ave (79701-7938)
P.O. Box 3121 (79702-3121)
PHONE............................432 682-0495
Sherril Lee Burns Jr, *President*
Kimberly Burns, *Corp Secy*
Larry H Burns, *Vice Pres*
·**EMP:** 14 **EST:** 1957

SQ FT: 1,500
SALES (est): 758.8K **Privately Held**
SIC: 1799 1389 7692 Welding on site; building oil & gas well foundations on site; welding repair

(G-15154)
CABALLO LOCO MIDSTREAM LLC
Also Called: Caballo Loco Marketing
400 E Loop 250 N Ste 113 (79705-4449)
PHONE............................432 262-1011
EMP: 15 **EST:** 2013
SQ FT: 1,050
SALES (est): 1MM **Privately Held**
WEB: www.caballolocomidstream.com
SIC: 1382 7389 Oil & gas exploration services;

(G-15155)
CALLON PETROLEUM COMPANY
6 Desta Dr Ste 4000 (79705-5581)
PHONE............................432 218-2800
Jimmy Baggett, *Branch Mgr*
EMP: 50
SALES (corp-wide): 671.5MM **Publicly Held**
WEB: www.callon.com
SIC: 5172 1382 Petroleum products; oil & gas exploration services
PA: Callon Petroleum Company
2000 W Sam Houston Pkwy S # 2000
Houston TX 77042
281 589-5200

(G-15156)
CAMBRIAN MANAGEMENT LTD (PA)
415 W Wall St Ste 900 (79701-4537)
P.O. Box 272 (79702-0272)
PHONE............................432 620-9181
Alan D Means, *President*
Karen Lowder, *Partner*
Sal Pagano, *Principal*
Jim Nicholson, *Engineer*
Andy Rickard, *Engineer*
EMP: 17
SQ FT: 2,300
SALES (est): 5.3MM **Privately Held**
WEB: www.cambrianmgmt.com
SIC: 8742 8711 3541 Construction project management consultant; engineering services; machine tools, metal cutting type

(G-15157)
CENTURY GRAPHICS & SIGN INC
501 W Indl Ave (79701)
P.O. Box 8309 (79708-8309)
PHONE............................432 686-8244
Marshall Fox, *President*
Brannon Tomlin, *Business Mgr*
Jana Floyd, *Purch Mgr*
Lupe Bonilla, *Sales Mgr*
Trey Thompson, *Sales Staff*
EMP: 38
SQ FT: 1,071
SALES (est): 8.6MM **Privately Held**
WEB: www.centurygs.com
SIC: 2752 7336 3993 2395 Decals, lithographed; silk screen design; signs & advertising specialties; pleating & stitching

(G-15158)
CHARGER SERVICES LLC
23 W Industrial Loop (79701-8521)
P.O. Box 53070 (79710-3070)
PHONE............................432 218-7674
Kyle Davis, *President*
Jake Davis, *Principal*
EMP: 24 **EST:** 2012
SALES (est): 14.9MM **Privately Held**
WEB: www.chargerservices.com
SIC: 1381 1781 3533 1623 Drilling oil & gas wells; water well drilling; drill rigs; oil & gas pipeline construction

(G-15159)
CHARTS LTD
2031 Trade Dr (79706-2838)
P.O. Box 2983 (79702-2983)
PHONE............................432 697-7801
Dirk Dieterich, *Partner*

David Miller, *Partner*
EMP: 25
SQ FT: 5,000
SALES (est): 3.4MM **Privately Held**
WEB: www.charts-ltd.com
SIC: 1389 4932 Measurement of well flow rates, oil & gas; gas & other services combined

(G-15160)
CHEM ROCK TECHNOLOGIES LLC
2404 E County Road 123 (79706-6483)
PHONE............................432 940-2299
Larry Elkin, *Branch Mgr*
EMP: 16
SALES (corp-wide): 6.5MM **Privately Held**
SIC: 1382 Oil & gas exploration services
PA: Chem Rock Technologies, Llc
1111 Ritter Dr
Cedar Park TX 78613
512 865-4186

(G-15161)
CHEVRON MIDCONTINENT LP (HQ)
500 W Illinois Ave # 100 (79701-4234)
PHONE............................432 498-8600
Jack D Hightower, *Ch of Bd*
A J Best, *President*
George G Staley, *Exec VP*
Susan D Rowland, *Vice Pres*
Gary M Dupriest, *VP Opers*
EMP: 148
SQ FT: 119,000
SALES (est): 79.2MM
SALES (corp-wide): 146.5B **Publicly Held**
WEB: www.cottonbledsoe.com
SIC: 1382 Oil & gas exploration services
PA: Chevron Corporation
6001 Bollinger Canyon Rd
San Ramon CA 94583
925 842-1000

(G-15162)
CHEVRON USA INC
6301 Deauville (79706-2964)
PHONE............................432 687-7100
Phil Ardoin, *Project Mgr*
Jigar Adhvaryu, *Opers Staff*
Raymond Hosford, *Engineer*
L S May, *Finance Other*
Bryan Gelotti, *Credit Staff*
EMP: 230
SALES (corp-wide): 146.5B **Publicly Held**
WEB: www.chevron.com
SIC: 5541 1382 Filling stations, gasoline; oil & gas exploration services
HQ: Chevron U.S.A. Inc.
6001 Bollinger Canyon Rd D1248
San Ramon CA 94583
925 842-1000

(G-15163)
CHI ENERGY INC
Also Called: Bergman, William R
212 N Main St Ste 200 (79701-5231)
P.O. Box 1799 (79702-1799)
PHONE............................432 685-5001
William R Bergman, *President*
EMP: 9
SQ FT: 8,100
SALES (est): 2.7MM **Privately Held**
SIC: 1311 Crude petroleum production; natural gas production

(G-15164)
CHIEF OILFIELD TECH LLC
2309 Garden City Hwy (79701-1549)
P.O. Box 80293 (79708-0293)
PHONE............................432 614-4481
Thomas Jason Rich, *CEO*
EMP: 10
SQ FT: 3,000
SALES (est): 1.9MM **Privately Held**
WEB: www.chiefofs.com
SIC: 3533 1389 Oil & gas field machinery; servicing oil & gas wells

(G-15165)
CHOATE CO INC
Also Called: Wade Choate Office
4902 N Midkiff Rd (79705-2515)
P.O. Box 80190 (79708-0190)
PHONE............................432 687-5977
EMP: 25
SQ FT: 4,000
SALES (est): 2.6MM **Privately Held**
SIC: 1382 Oil/Gas Exploration Services

(G-15166)
CIMAREX ENERGY CO
600 N Marienfeld St # 600 (79701-4405)
PHONE............................432 571-7800
Jason Trent, *Foreman/Supr*
Scott Gengler, *Production*
Nick Koch, *Production*
Steve Heitzman, *Engineer*
Mary Ketter, *Engineer*
EMP: 40
SALES (corp-wide): 2.3B **Publicly Held**
WEB: www.cimarex.com
SIC: 1382 Oil & gas exploration services
PA: Cimarex Energy Co.
1700 N Lincoln St # 3700
Denver CO 80203
303 295-3995

(G-15167)
CITATION OIL & GAS CORP
2609 S County Road 1242 (79706-2705)
PHONE............................432 262-7600
Pharris Ivy, *Superintendent*
Jim Evans, *Branch Mgr*
EMP: 10
SALES (corp-wide): 283.5MM **Privately Held**
WEB: www.cogc.com
SIC: 1311 Crude petroleum production
PA: Citation Oil & Gas Corp.
14077 Cutten Rd
Houston TX 77069
281 891-1000

(G-15168)
CLAJON HOLDING CORP
Also Called: Clayton Williams Energy
6 Desta Dr Ste 3000 (79705-5537)
PHONE............................432 682-6324
Clayton W Williams Jr, *President*
Shirley Faught, *Superintendent*
Paul Latham, *Vice Pres*
Robert Lyon, *Vice Pres*
Brock Thompson, *Vice Pres*
EMP: 170
SQ FT: 10,000
SALES (est): 8.4MM **Privately Held**
WEB: www.nblenergy.com
SIC: 1311 6512 Crude petroleum production; natural gas production; commercial & industrial building operation

(G-15169)
COG OPERATING LLC (HQ)
600 W Illinois Ave (79701-4882)
PHONE............................432 685-0727
Timothy A Leach, *CEO*
Ricky Tolbert, *Superintendent*
Darin G Holderness, *CFO*
Willson Beebe, *Financial Analy*
Sherri Rotan, *Payroll Mgr*
EMP: 141
SQ FT: 27,087
SALES (est): 912.8MM **Privately Held**
WEB: www.concho.com
SIC: 1382 Oil & gas exploration services

(G-15170)
COIL TUBING PARTNERS LLC
8411 W I 20 Frontage Rd (79706)
PHONE............................432 201-4111
Barry Boudreaux, *Branch Mgr*
EMP: 21
SALES (corp-wide): 21.9MM **Privately Held**
WEB: www.coiltubingpartners.com
SIC: 1389 Oil field services
PA: Coil Tubing Partners, L.L.C.
2014 W Pinhook Rd Ste 200
Lafayette LA 70508
337 806-2100

▲ = Import ▼=Export
◆ =Import/Export

(G-15171)
COLGATE ENERGY LLC
300 N Marienfeld St # 1000 (79701-4334)
PHONE...............................432 695-4222
Robert R Shannon, *Principal*
Jordan Cox, *Vice Pres*
EMP: 35
SALES (est): 99.1K **Privately Held**
WEB: www.colgateenergy.com
SIC: 1382 Oil & gas exploration services

(G-15172)
COLGATE ENERGY PARTNERS LLC
300 N Marienfeld St # 1000 (79701-4334)
PHONE...............................432 695-4222
Jordan Cox, *Vice Pres*
Kristin Whittenberg, *Asst Controller*
Michael Poynter, *Finance*
William Hickey, *Mng Member*
Stewart Coleman, *Mng Member*
EMP: 11
SALES (est): 242.1K **Privately Held**
WEB: www.colgateenergy.com
SIC: 1382 4911 Oil & gas exploration services; electric services

(G-15173)
COMPASS WELL SERVICES LLC
10013 W County Road 157 (79706-8051)
PHONE...............................432 561-5970
Colin F Raymond,
EMP: 30
SALES (corp-wide): 80MM **Privately Held**
WEB: www.compasswellservices.com
SIC: 1389 1382 Cementing oil & gas well casings; oil & gas exploration services
PA: Compass Well Services, Llc
4100 Intl Plz Ste 500
Fort Worth TX 76109
817 244-2555

(G-15174)
COMPOSITE LINING SYSTEMS LP
7812 W Highway 80 (79706-2850)
P.O. Box 50423 (79710-0423)
PHONE...............................432 617-0242
Joe Schwalbch, *Partner*
Kenneth Ross, *Partner*
Rick Keena, *Controller*
Billy Browning, *Supervisor*
Doug Thomasson, *Supervisor*
EMP: 103
SALES (est): 18MM **Privately Held**
WEB: www.glassbore.com
SIC: 1799 3083 Epoxy application; laminated plastics plate & sheet

(G-15175)
CONCHO OIL & GAS LLC
600 W Ill Ave Midland (79701)
PHONE...............................432 683-7443
Gerald Tomlinson, *Superintendent*
EMP: 111
SALES (est): 5.5MM **Privately Held**
WEB: www.concho.com
SIC: 1311 5983 Crude petroleum & natural gas; fuel oil dealers
PA: Concho Resources Inc.
600 W Illinois Ave
Midland TX 79701

(G-15176)
CONCHO RESOURCES INC
550 W Texas Ave Ste 945 (79701-4233)
PHONE...............................432 221-0400
Joseph Wright, *Exec VP*
Larry Gates, *Vice Pres*
Dave Giffin, *Vice Pres*
Steve Guthrie, *Vice Pres*
Kyle Rose, *Vice Pres*
EMP: 16 **Privately Held**
WEB: www.concho.com
SIC: 1311 Crude petroleum production
PA: Concho Resources Inc.
600 W Illinois Ave
Midland TX 79701

(G-15177)
CONCHO RESOURCES INC (PA)
600 W Illinois Ave (79701-4882)
PHONE...............................432 683-7443

Timothy A Leach, *Ch of Bd*
Jack F Harper, *President*
C William Giraud, *COO*
David Schwan, *Counsel*
Joe Wright, *Exec VP*
EMP: 332
SALES: 4.5B **Privately Held**
WEB: www.concho.com
SIC: 1311 Crude petroleum & natural gas; crude petroleum & natural gas production; crude petroleum production

(G-15178)
CORE LABORATORIES LP
Also Called: Pro Techniques
705 W Wadley Ave Ste 250 (79705-5300)
PHONE...............................432 687-5797
Matthew Perry, *Principal*
Stephen Loving, *Vice Pres*
EMP: 54
SALES (corp-wide): 668.2MM **Privately Held**
WEB: www.corelab.com
SIC: 1389 Oil field services
HQ: Core Laboratories Lp
6316 Windfern Rd
Houston TX 77040

(G-15179)
CORONADO MIDSTREAM LLC (HQ)
300 N Mrnfield St Ste 120 (79701)
PHONE...............................432 684-3870
Andrew A Deck, *CEO*
EMP: 50
SALES (est): 16.7MM
SALES (corp-wide): 6B **Publicly Held**
SIC: 1321 Natural gas liquids production
PA: Enlink Midstream, Llc
1722 Routh St Ste 1300
Dallas TX 75201
214 953-9500

(G-15180)
CORPRO INC
2003 Commerce Dr (79703-7502)
PHONE...............................432 563-0775
Trebor Wheren, *Office Mgr*
EMP: 20
SALES (corp-wide): 12.5MM **Privately Held**
WEB: www.tenaris.com
SIC: 3545 Drill bits, metalworking
HQ: Corpro, Inc.
12950 S Kirkwood Rd # 16
Stafford TX 77477

(G-15181)
COWBOYS RESOURCES CORP (PA)
415 W Wall St Ste 1800 (79701-4434)
P.O. Box 2594 (79702-2594)
PHONE...............................432 686-7797
Steve Castle, *President*
EMP: 9
SALES (est): 1MM **Privately Held**
SIC: 1382 Oil & gas exploration services

(G-15182)
CROWN OIL PARTNERS LP
303 Veterans Airpark Ln # 6101 (79705-4550)
PHONE...............................432 683-2950
Crown Ventures LLC, *Partner*
Michael Black, *Principal*
Michael E Black, *Principal*
EMP: 11
SALES (est): 1.3MM **Privately Held**
SIC: 1382 Oil & gas exploration services

(G-15183)
CROWNQUEST OPERATING LLC
18 Desta Dr (79705-4507)
P.O. Box 53310 (79710-3310)
PHONE...............................432 818-0300
Luke Dunn, *Vice Pres*
Bayler Boydston, *Engineer*
Will Lane, *Engineer*
Stephen McDonald, *Engineer*
Sarah Yocham, *HR Admin*
EMP: 60
SQ FT: 21,000
SALES (est): 42.8MM **Privately Held**
WEB: www.crownquest.com
SIC: 1382 Oil & gas exploration services

(G-15184)
CROWNROCK LP
Also Called: Crownquest
500 W Texas Ave Ste 500 # 500 (79701-4211)
PHONE...............................432 818-0300
Tim Dunn, *Partner*
Ken Beattie, *COO*
M Craig Clark, *Vice Pres*
W Michael Scott, *Vice Pres*
Lee Dunn, *VP Bus Dvlpt*
EMP: 140
SQ FT: 30,000
SALES (est): 288MM **Privately Held**
WEB: www.crownquest.com
SIC: 1382 Oil & gas exploration services

(G-15185)
CSI COMPRESSCO SUB INC
3809 S Fm 1788 (79706-2662)
PHONE...............................432 563-1170
EMP: 518
SALES (corp-wide): 1B **Publicly Held**
WEB: www.csicompressco.com
SIC: 7359 7699 3563 Propane equipment rental; industrial equipment services; air & gas compressors
HQ: Csi Compressco Sub Inc.
24955 I 45 N
The Woodlands TX 77380
832 482-1399

(G-15186)
DANOS LLC
1501 W Francis Ave (79701-8702)
PHONE...............................985 219-3313
EMP: 195
SALES (corp-wide): 747.5MM **Privately Held**
WEB: www.danos.com
SIC: 1389 Oil field services
PA: Danos, L.L.C.
3878 W Main St
Gray LA 70359
985 693-3313

(G-15187)
DAWSON GEOPHYSICAL COMPANY (PA)
508 W Wall St Ste 800 (79701-5034)
PHONE...............................432 684-3000
Stephen C Jumper, *Ch of Bd*
C Ray Tobias, *COO*
James W Thomas, *Exec VP*
James Thomas, *Exec VP*
K Forsdick, *Vice Pres*
EMP: 111
SQ FT: 34,570
SALES: 145.7MM **Publicly Held**
WEB: www.dawson3d.com
SIC: 1382 8713 Geophysical exploration, oil & gas field; surveying services

(G-15188)
DEEP WELL TUBULAR SERVICE INC
6604 W Highway 80 (79706-2802)
PHONE...............................432 699-6675
Tim L Gilliam, *President*
Shelly Gilliam, *Admin Sec*
EMP: 12
SQ FT: 2,000
SALES (est): 1.1MM **Privately Held**
WEB: www.dwservices.com
SIC: 1389 Oil field services

(G-15189)
DELAWARE RIVER SWD LLC
400 N Marienfeld St Ste 2 (79701-4300)
PHONE...............................432 683-7443
Frank Agar Jr,
EMP: 51
SALES (est): 683.5K **Privately Held**
SIC: 1311 Crude petroleum & natural gas production
PA: Concho Resources Inc.
600 W Illinois Ave
Midland TX 79701

(G-15190)
DELEK US HOLDINGS INC
306 W Wall St (79701-5100)
PHONE...............................432 684-4210
EMP: 52

SALES (corp-wide): 9.3B **Publicly Held**
WEB: www.delekus.com
SIC: 2911 Petroleum refining
PA: Delek Us Holdings, Inc.
7102 Commerce Way
Brentwood TN 37027
615 771-6701

(G-15191)
DEVON PERMIAN CORPORATION
Also Called: Cog Operating
600 W Illinois Ave (79701-4882)
PHONE...............................432 685-0727
Timothy Leach, *CEO*
David Chroback, *Vice Pres*
Curt F Kamradt, *CFO*
EMP: 115
SALES (est): 4.3MM **Privately Held**
WEB: www.concho.com
SIC: 1311 Crude petroleum production

(G-15192)
DIAMONDBACK E&P LLC (HQ)
500 W Texas Ave Ste 1200 (79701-4203)
PHONE...............................866 531-3667
Travis Stice, *CEO*
Aron Nunez, *Foreman/Supr*
Ashley Bechner, *Engineer*
Jennifer Bussell, *Engineer*
Teresa Dick, *CFO*
EMP: 54
SQ FT: 7,000
SALES (est): 66.5MM
SALES (corp-wide): 3.9B **Publicly Held**
WEB: www.diamondbackenergy.com
SIC: 1382 Oil & gas exploration services
PA: Diamondback Energy, Inc.
500 W Texas Ave Ste 1200
Midland TX 79701
432 221-7400

(G-15193)
DIAMONDBACK ENERGY INC (PA)
500 W Texas Ave Ste 1200 (79701-4203)
PHONE...............................432 221-7400
Travis D Stice, *CEO*
Steven E West, *Ch of Bd*
Tracy Dick, *Exec VP*
Matt Zmigrosky, *Exec VP*
Daniel Wesson, *Senior VP*
EMP: 26
SALES: 3.9B **Publicly Held**
WEB: www.diamondbackenergy.com
SIC: 1311 Oil & gas exploration services

(G-15194)
DON-NAN PUMP AND SUPPLY CO INC (PA)
Also Called: Don-Nan Machine & Mfg
3427 E Garden Cy Hwy 158 (79706)
P.O. Box 11367 (79702-8367)
PHONE...............................432 682-7742
Don V Carruth, *President*
Jesse Rogers, *Safety Dir*
Jeff Beal, *Store Mgr*
Jonathan Granados, *Store Mgr*
Keith Brown, *Warehouse Mgr*
◆ EMP: 140
SQ FT: 36,000
SALES (est): 179.6MM **Privately Held**
WEB: www.don-nan.com
SIC: 1389 3599 3561 Oil field services; custom machinery; pumps & pumping equipment

(G-15195)
DOUBLE T OILFIELD SERVICE LLC
4707 E County Road 133 (79706-0202)
P.O. Box 62650, San Angelo (76906-2650)
PHONE...............................325 315-2370
Tim Acosta,
EMP: 15
SQ FT: 2,000
SALES (est): 3.6MM **Privately Held**
WEB: www.doubletoil.com
SIC: 1389 Oil field services

(G-15196)
DOYLE HARTMAN OIL PRODUCER
Also Called: Domar Leasing
500 N Main St (79701-4712)
P.O. Box 10426 (79702-7426)
PHONE................................432 684-4011
EMP: 16 EST: 1975
SQ FT: 7,000
SALES (est): 1.7MM Privately Held
SIC: 1311 Crude petroleum production;
   natural gas production

(G-15197)
DRILFORMANCE LLC
5400 N Big Spring St (79705-2001)
PHONE................................832 704-2025
Rusty Petree, CEO
EMP: 10
SALES (corp-wide): 7.1MM Privately
Held
WEB: www.drilformance.com
SIC: 3532 Drills, bits & similar equipment
PA: Drilformance Llc
   15815 Waverly Dr
   Houston TX 77032
   832 772-7808

(G-15198)
DURHAM INC
505 N Big Spring St # 403 (79701-4301)
PHONE................................432 684-5557
Lynn D Durham Sr, President
Kevin Durham, Vice Pres
Lynn D Durham Jr, Vice Pres
James F Garrett, Treasurer
Sam Janet Durham, Director
EMP: 10 EST: 1945
SQ FT: 6,000
SALES (est): 978.6K Privately Held
WEB: www.durhamstaffing.com
SIC: 1311 Crude petroleum production

(G-15199)
DYNAMIC FISHING & RENTALS LLC
3400 N County Road 1148 (79705-4026)
P.O. Box 150 (79702-0150)
PHONE................................432 684-3898
Gus Munoz, Mng Member
EMP: 12
SALES (est): 1MM Privately Held
WEB: www.dynamicfr.com
SIC: 1389 Oil field services

(G-15200)
DYNASTY WIRELINE SERVICES LLC
6800 W Highway 80 (79706-3185)
P.O. Box 52076 (79710-2076)
PHONE................................432 363-3100
S Clay Bomer, President
William Poli, Vice Pres
EMP: 33
SALES (est): 830.5K Privately Held
WEB: www.dynastywireline.com
SIC: 1389 Construction, repair & disman-
   tling services

(G-15201)
E Z ROUSTABOUT
1400 S Fairgrounds Rd (79701-1404)
P.O. Box 10816 (79702-7816)
PHONE................................432 556-8419
Emilio Zbia, Owner
EMP: 10
SALES (est): 585.7K Privately Held
SIC: 1389 7389 Haulage, oil field;

(G-15202)
EAGLE PCO LLC
3109 W County Rd 1108 (79706)
PHONE................................432 400-2771
Jenniger Black, Branch Mgr
EMP: 10 Privately Held
WEB: www.trendservicesinc.com
SIC: 3533 1389 Oil field machinery &
   equipment; oil field services
PA: Eagle Pco Llc
   5808 Fm 3455 Rd
   Navasota TX 77868

(G-15203)
EAGLE ROCK MANUFACTURING LLC
1113 Dayton Rd (79706-3806)
PHONE................................432 682-3030
EMP: 10
SALES (est): 1.4MM Privately Held
SIC: 3533 Mfg Oil/Gas Field Machinery

(G-15204)
EAGLECLAW MIDSTREAM SVCS LLC
414 W Texas Ave Ste 315 (79701-4415)
P.O. Box 5889 (79704-5889)
PHONE................................432 789-1333
Robert Milam, President
Blake Bixler, Vice Pres
Kenneth Clark, Vice Pres
Robert Cotton, Engineer
Alexandra Marner, Human Resources
EMP: 20
SALES (est): 687.7K Privately Held
WEB: www.eagleclawmidstream.com
SIC: 1382 Oil & gas exploration services

(G-15205)
EASTLAND OIL CO (PA)
Also Called: Eastland Resources
415 W Wall St Ste 1415 (79701-4437)
P.O. Box 3488 (79702-3488)
PHONE................................432 683-6293
Robert R Donnelly, President
Margaret A Lester, Corp Secy
Garrett Donnelly, Officer
EMP: 12 EST: 1922
SQ FT: 2,500
SALES (est): 1.7MM Privately Held
WEB: www.eastlandoil.com
SIC: 1311 Crude petroleum production;
   natural gas production

(G-15206)
EDMAR COMPANY LLC
3000 N Grfield St Ste 108 (79705)
PHONE................................432 686-8888
Marilyn M Judson, Manager
Donald Judson,
EMP: 10
SALES (est): 1.1MM Privately Held
SIC: 1311 Crude petroleum & natural gas
   production

(G-15207)
EGL RESOURCES INC
223 W Wall St Ste 900 (79701-4567)
P.O. Box 10886 (79702-7886)
PHONE................................432 687-6560
W Wesley Perry, CEO
John A Starck, President
John A Langhoff, Corp Secy
Robert Snyder, Exec VP
Michael D Newman, Vice Pres
EMP: 12
SQ FT: 10,000
SALES (est): 2.4MM Privately Held
WEB: www.eglresources.com
SIC: 1381 Drilling oil & gas wells

(G-15208)
ELEVATION RESOURCES LLC
200 N Loraine St Ste 1010 (79701-4755)
PHONE................................432 686-7500
Steven H Pruett, President
Gary Dupriest, COO
EMP: 9
SQ FT: 11,800
SALES (est): 5.6MM Privately Held
WEB: www.elevationres.com
SIC: 1311 Crude petroleum & natural gas
   production

(G-15209)
ELLIS MANUFACTURING CO INC (PA)
Also Called: Ellis Pumps and Tools
8101 W Industrial Ave (79706-2897)
P.O. Box 5152 (79704-5152)
PHONE................................432 561-8819
Matthew Ellis, President
Marlene Byrd, Corp Secy
Rob Cann, Manager
EMP: 39 EST: 1999
SQ FT: 30,000
SALES (est): 7MM Privately Held
WEB: www.ellispumps.com
SIC: 3561 Pumps & pumping equipment

(G-15210)
ENDEAVOR ENERGY RESOURCES LP (PA)
110 N Marienfeld St # 200 (79701-4400)
PHONE................................432 687-1575
Autry C Stephens, Partner
Patrick Martinez, General Mgr
Jerry Waltrip, General Mgr
Brady Lee, Superintendent
Chuck Speer, Superintendent
▲ EMP: 30
SQ FT: 4,000
SALES (est): 543.9MM Privately Held
WEB: www.endeavorenergylp.com
SIC: 1311 8748 Crude petroleum produc-
   tion; business consulting

(G-15211)
ENDEAVOR ENERGY RESOURCES LP
Also Called: ACS Pump & Supply
110 N Mrianefield Ste 200 (79706)
PHONE................................432 221-9300
Jeff Duncan, General Mgr
EMP: 59
SALES (corp-wide): 543.9MM Privately
Held
WEB: www.acs-pumpandsupply.com
SIC: 1311 Crude petroleum production
PA: Endeavor Energy Resources, L.P.
   110 N Marienfeld St # 200
   Midland TX 79701
   432 687-1575

(G-15212)
ENDEAVOR ENERGY RESOURCES LP
Also Called: Pumping Unit Technologies
3000 Fm 715 (79706-4256)
PHONE................................432 683-4292
Austin Booker, Supervisor
William Krueger, General Counsel
Billy Rice, Analyst
EMP: 47
SALES (corp-wide): 543.9MM Privately
Held
WEB: www.acs-pumpandsupply.com
SIC: 1389 Oil field services
PA: Endeavor Energy Resources, L.P.
   110 N Marienfeld St # 200
   Midland TX 79701
   432 687-1575

(G-15213)
ENDEAVOR ENERGY RESOURCES LP
414 W Texas Ave Ste 316 (79701-4419)
PHONE................................432 687-1575
EMP: 12
SALES (corp-wide): 543.9MM Privately
Held
WEB: www.acs-pumpandsupply.com
SIC: 1311 Crude petroleum production
PA: Endeavor Energy Resources, L.P.
   110 N Marienfeld St # 200
   Midland TX 79701
   432 687-1575

(G-15214)
ENDEAVOR ENERGY RESOURCES LP
Also Called: Electrical Maintenance & Cnstr
6501 S Fm 1788 (79706-6012)
P.O. Box 60446 (79711-0446)
PHONE................................432 563-5000
Simon Barr, General Mgr
Lance Robertson, COO
Mike Short, VP Legal
Robert Booth, Vice Pres
Shad Frazier, Vice Pres
EMP: 40
SALES (corp-wide): 543.9MM Privately
Held
WEB: www.acs-pumpandsupply.com
SIC: 1389 Construction, repair & disman-
   tling services; oil field services
PA: Endeavor Energy Resources, L.P.
   110 N Marienfeld St # 200
   Midland TX 79701
   432 687-1575

(G-15215)
ENDURANCE ROUSTABOUT
2618 Franklin Ave (79701-6310)
P.O. Box 11006 (79702-8006)
PHONE................................432 697-1300
EMP: 10
SALES (est): 922.9K Privately Held
WEB: www.endurance-roustabout.com
SIC: 1389 Oil field services

(G-15216)
ENERGEN CORPORATION (HQ)
500 W Texas Ave Ste 500 # 500
(79701-4211)
PHONE................................205 326-2700
James T McManus II, President
Dave Bolton, Vice Pres
JD McCombs, Foreman/Supr
Charles W Porter Jr, CFO
John Molen, Admin Sec
EMP: 16
SALES: 961MM
SALES (corp-wide): 3.9B Publicly Held
SIC: 1311 4924 4922 1321 Crude petro-
   leum production; natural gas distribution;
   natural gas transmission; natural gas liq-
   uids
PA: Diamondback Energy, Inc.
   500 W Texas Ave Ste 1200
   Midland TX 79701
   432 221-7400

(G-15217)
ENERGEN RESOURCES CORPORATION
3300 N A St Ste 10 (79705-5421)
PHONE................................432 687-1155
Mliss Evans, Engineer
Joe Niederhofer, Branch Mgr
Karl Swelling, Technology
Stephen Bartlett, Analyst
EMP: 11
SALES (corp-wide): 3.9B Publicly Held
WEB: www.energen.com
SIC: 1311 4922 Crude petroleum produc-
   tion; natural gas transmission
HQ: Energen Resources Corporation
   605 Rchard Arrngton Jr Bl
   Birmingham AL 35203
   205 326-2710

(G-15218)
ENERGEN RESOURCES CORPORATION
500 W Texas Ave Ste 500 # 500
(79701-4211)
PHONE................................205 326-2700
Holly Lagrone, Vice Pres
EMP: 75
SALES (corp-wide): 3.9B Publicly Held
WEB: www.energen.com
SIC: 1382 Oil & gas exploration services
HQ: Energen Resources Corporation
   605 Rchard Arrngton Jr Bl
   Birmingham AL 35203
   205 326-2710

(G-15219)
ENERQUEST RESOURCES LLC
18 Desta Dr (79705-4507)
PHONE................................432 685-3116
EMP: 40 EST: 1999
SALES (est): 1.2MM Privately Held
SIC: 1241 Exploration, anthracite mining

(G-15220)
ENLINK N TEXAS GATHERING LP
5023 Princeton Ave Ste 2 (79703-4540)
PHONE................................432 221-9757
Barry E Davis, CEO
Joe A Davis, Exec VP
William W Davis, Exec VP
Michael J Garberding, Exec VP
Stan Golemon, Senior VP
EMP: 35
SALES (est): 7.2MM
SALES (corp-wide): 6B Publicly Held
SIC: 1311 Natural gas production
PA: Enlink Midstream, Llc
   1722 Routh St Ste 1300
   Dallas TX 75201
   214 953-9500

(G-15221)
ENTERPRISE PRODUCTS COMPANY
4500 E Highway 80 (79706-4435)
PHONE..................................432 221-7700
EMP: 50
SALES (corp-wide): 32.7B Publicly Held
WEB: www.enterpriseproducts.com
SIC: 1321 4925 Natural gas liquids; gas production and/or distribution
HQ: Enterprise Products Company
1100 Louisiana St
Houston TX 77002
713 381-6500

(G-15222)
ENTERPRISE PRODUCTS COMPANY
1031 Andrews Hwy (79701-3805)
PHONE..................................432 686-5421
Courtney Ragfbale, Branch Mgr
EMP: 25
SALES (corp-wide): 32.7B Publicly Held
WEB: www.enterpriseproducts.com
SIC: 1321 Natural gas liquids
HQ: Enterprise Products Company
1100 Louisiana St
Houston TX 77002
713 381-6500

(G-15223)
EOG RESOURCES INC
5509 Champions Dr (79706-2843)
P.O. Box 183 (79702-0183)
PHONE..................................432 686-3600
Ezra Yacob, Vice Pres
Mark King, Foreman/Supr
Alan Covington, Engineer
Alexis Guba, Engineer
Graham Taylor, Engineer
EMP: 66
SALES (corp-wide): 17.3B Publicly Held
WEB: www.eogresources.com
SIC: 1382 1311 Oil & gas exploration services; crude petroleum & natural gas production
PA: Eog Resources, Inc.
1111 Bagby Sky Lbby 2
Houston TX 77002
713 651-7000

(G-15224)
EVCO FABRICATION INC
10925 W County Rd 125 (79711)
P.O. Box 60694 (79711-0694)
PHONE..................................432 561-8561
Andy Stanco, President
Anne C Dickson, Vice Pres
EMP: 45
SQ FT: 12,800
SALES (est): 5.6MM Privately Held
SIC: 3443 Fabricated plate work (boiler shop)

(G-15225)
EXL PETROLEUM LP
6 Desta Dr Ste 2800 (79705-5554)
PHONE..................................432 686-8080
Doug Robison, Partner
Victoria Burgess, Payroll Mgr
EMP: 12
SALES (est): 2.4MM Privately Held
WEB: www.exlpetroleum.com
SIC: 1382 Oil & gas exploration services

(G-15226)
EXL PETROLEUM MANAGEMENT LLC (PA)
6 Desta Dr Ste 2800 (79705-5554)
PHONE..................................432 686-8080
Douglas Robison, CEO
Scott Dinger, COO
Kregg Conder, CFO
EMP: 20
SQ FT: 15,000
SALES (est): 20MM Privately Held
WEB: www.exlpetroleum.com
SIC: 1382 Oil & gas exploration services

(G-15227)
EXL PETROLEUM OPERATING INC
6 Desta Dr Ste 2800 (79705-5554)
PHONE..................................432 686-8080
Douglas Robison, President

Scott Dinger, COO
Kregg Conder, CFO
EMP: 19
SQ FT: 15,000
SALES (est): 20MM Privately Held
WEB: www.exlpetroleum.com
SIC: 1382 Oil & gas exploration services
PA: Exl Petroleum Management, Llc
6 Desta Dr Ste 2800
Midland TX 79705
432 686-8080

(G-15228)
FALCON BAY ENERGY L L C
200 N Loraine St Ste 1550 (79701-4765)
PHONE..................................432 682-7424
John McGoldrick, Ch of Bd
William Ford, President
Richard Albro, Vice Pres
Anthony Sam, Vice Pres
EMP: 12
SALES (est): 3.5MM Privately Held
SIC: 1382 Oil & gas exploration services

(G-15229)
FAYETTEVILLE-FLOYD GAS COMPANY (PA)
500 W Wall St Ste 300 (79701-5093)
P.O. Box 2071 (79702-2071)
PHONE..................................432 682-6685
David H Arrington, President
Keith Bucy, General Mgr
Amy Dodson, Accounting Mgr
Gay N McGuire, Manager
EMP: 60
SALES (est): 72.9MM Privately Held
SIC: 1311 Crude petroleum production; natural gas production

(G-15230)
FIVESTONES ENERGY LLC
5211 Preston Dr (79707-5104)
P.O. Box 51082 (79710-1082)
PHONE..................................432 618-9929
Alan D Peters, Managing Dir
EMP: 11
SALES (est): 1.3MM Privately Held
WEB: www.fivese.com
SIC: 1382 Oil & gas exploration services

(G-15231)
FLEAUX SERVICES LOUISIANA LLC
2161 Commerce Dr (79703-7504)
PHONE..................................432 694-0004
EMP: 17
SALES (corp-wide): 25MM Privately Held
WEB: www.fleaux.com
SIC: 1389 Construction, repair & dismantling services
PA: Fleaux Services Of Louisiana Llc
230 Lynbrook Blvd
Shreveport LA 71106
318 603-0024

(G-15232)
FLOCAP INJECTION SERVICES LLC
11002 W County Road 77 (79707-1688)
P.O. Box 62113 (79711-2113)
PHONE..................................432 614-1609
James W Shrauner,
Dusty Floyd,
Jackie D Redman,
Jeffrey D Smith,
EMP: 19
SALES (est): 2.5MM Privately Held
SIC: 1381 Drilling oil & gas wells

(G-15233)
FULLER PRODUCTION INC
1010 W Wall St (79701-6638)
PHONE..................................432 683-5661
Lloyd R French, President
Marcia D Braus, Treasurer
EMP: 12
SALES (est): 826.1K Privately Held
WEB: www.debergeracdesign.com
SIC: 1311 Crude petroleum production

(G-15234)
GALLEON MINING TOOLS INC
Also Called: Galleon Turbeco
11316 County Rd 128 W (79711)
P.O. Box 60595 (79711-0595)
PHONE..................................432 563-1867
Gary Tatum, President
▲ EMP: 17
SALES (est): 2.2MM Privately Held
WEB: www.galleonmti.com
SIC: 3532 Drills & drilling equipment, mining (except oil & gas)

(G-15235)
GE OIL & GAS PRESSURE CTRL LP
306 W Wall St Ste 1414 (79701-5100)
PHONE..................................432 686-0720
Scott Bender, Branch Mgr
EMP: 100
SALES (corp-wide): 95.2B Publicly Held
WEB: www.woodplc.com
SIC: 1389 Oil field services
HQ: Ge Oil & Gas Pressure Control Lp
4424 W Sam Houston Pkwy N S
Houston TX 77041
281 398-8901

(G-15236)
GEL TECHNOLOGIES CORP
24 Smith Rd Ste 200 (79705-4410)
P.O. Box 51438 (79710-1438)
PHONE..................................432 683-1881
EMP: 16
SQ FT: 2,500
SALES: 3.5MM Privately Held
SIC: 1389 Oil Field Services

(G-15237)
GM OILFIELD & TRCKG SVCS LLC
Also Called: GM Trucking
4514 E Cnty Rd 133 Midland (79706)
PHONE..................................432 934-6525
George Magallanes Jr, Mng Member
EMP: 40
SQ FT: 10,000
SALES (est): 12.3MM Privately Held
WEB: www.gmtruckingmidland.com
SIC: 1389 Haulage, oil field

(G-15238)
GP II ENERGY INC
303 Veterans Airpark Ln # 4113 (79705-4547)
P.O. Box 50682 (79710-0682)
PHONE..................................432 684-4748
George P Mitchell II, President
EMP: 12
SQ FT: 2,500
SALES (est): 1.7MM Privately Held
SIC: 1311 Crude petroleum production

(G-15239)
GRAVITY OILFIELD SERVICES INC (PA)
3300 N A St Bldg 4-100 (79705-5431)
PHONE..................................432 218-7888
Rob Rice, President
Troy Botts, Co-CEO
Philip Wright, Exec VP
Jason Taylor, Vice Pres
Keith Muncy, CFO
EMP: 21 EST: 2017
SALES: 422.8MM Privately Held
WEB: www.gravityoilfieldservices.com
SIC: 1389 Oil field services

(G-15240)
GRAVITY OILFIELD SERVICES LLC (HQ)
3300 N A St Bldg 4-100 (79705-5431)
PHONE..................................432 218-7889
Rob Rice, CEO
Jose Feliciano, Ch of Bd
Troy Botts Jr, COO
Keith Muncy, CFO
Randal T Klein, Director
▼ EMP: 143
SQ FT: 30,000

SALES (est): 419.6MM
SALES (corp-wide): 422.8MM Privately Held
WEB: www.gravityoilfieldservices.com
SIC: 1389 7353 Oil & gas wells: building, repairing & dismantling; oil equipment rental services
PA: Gravity Oilfield Services Inc.
3300 N A St Bldg 4-100
Midland TX 79705
432 218-7888

(G-15241)
GUARDIAN INSPTN TBULAR MGT LLC
2712 E Interstate 20 (79706-4225)
PHONE..................................403 233-7561
James Teppan, Vice Pres
William P Buckley, Director
John D Tikkanen, Director
Timothy D Hutzul, Admin Sec
EMP: 11
SALES (est): 1.3MM Privately Held
SIC: 4619 5063 2241 Coal pipeline operation; wire & cable; hose fabric, tubular

(G-15242)
GYRODATA INCORPORATED
10504 W County Road 72 (79707-4405)
PHONE..................................432 561-8458
Frank Pawlik, Manager
EMP: 10
SALES (corp-wide): 394.1MM Privately Held
WEB: www.gyrodata.com
SIC: 1389 Oil field services
PA: Gyrodata Incorporated
23000 Nw Lake Dr
Houston TX 77095
713 461-3146

(G-15243)
H L BROWN JR
300 W La Ave Ste 100 (79701)
P.O. Box 2237 (79702-2237)
PHONE..................................432 683-5216
Hubert L Brown Jr,
EMP: 17
SQ FT: 5,000
SALES (est): 1.2MM Privately Held
WEB: www.hlbrownoperating.com
SIC: 1382 1311 Oil & gas exploration services; crude petroleum production

(G-15244)
HEARST CORPORATION
Also Called: Dollar Saver
201 E Illinois Ave (79701-4852)
P.O. Box 1650 (79702-1650)
PHONE..................................432 682-5311
David Wedel, Publisher
Tim Fischer, Editor
Jeff Habram, Manager
EMP: 110
SALES (corp-wide): 7.9B Privately Held
WEB: www.hearst.com
SIC: 2711 2791 Newspapers: publishing only, not printed on site; typesetting
PA: The Hearst Corporation
300 W 57th St Fl 42
New York NY 10019
212 649-2000

(G-15245)
HENRY RESOURCES LLC
3525 Andrews Hwy (79703-5056)
PHONE..................................432 694-3000
Terry R Creech, CEO
Richard Danny Campbell, President
David Bledsoe, Vice Pres
Brenda Gray-Whatley, CFO
J Loy Helm, Treasurer
EMP: 50
SQ FT: 40,000
SALES (est): 9MM Privately Held
WEB: www.henrymidland.org
SIC: 1382 Oil & gas exploration services

(G-15246)
HIGHLAND CONCRETE CO
10716 State Highway 191 # 7 (79707-1550)
P.O. Box 14168, Odessa (79768-4168)
PHONE..................................432 561-5858
Dan Arnold, President
Shawna Arnold, Corp Secy

Larry Bates, *Corp Secy*
Ryan Hoerauf, *Vice Pres*
EMP: 20
SALES (est): 62K
SALES (corp-wide): 37.4MM **Privately
Held**
SIC: 3273 Ready-mixed concrete
PA: Permian Basin Materials, Llc
4001 E 42nd St Ste 100
Odessa TX 79762
432 614-6201

(G-15247)
HILLIARD ENERGY INC (PA)
125 W Missouri Ave (79701-2561)
PHONE....................................432 683-9100
Brent D Hilliard, *President*
Louann Johnson, *Exec VP*
Larry Amador, *Vice Pres*
Vicki Glover, *Broker*
Sterling Hilliard, *Manager*
EMP: 40 EST: 1996
SQ FT: 10,000
SALES (est): 8.7MM **Privately Held**
WEB: www.hilliardenergy.com
SIC: 1389 Oil consultants

(G-15248)
HOLMES AUTO SUPPLY INC
3301 Bankhead Hwy (79701-6704)
P.O. Box 2483 (79702-2483)
PHONE....................................432 689-8008
Jimmy Holmes, *Principal*
Joyce Holmes, *Principal*
Shirley Holmes, *Principal*
Larry Holmes, *Vice Pres*
Michael Holmes, *Administration*
EMP: 12
SQ FT: 2,100
SALES (est): 925K **Privately Held**
WEB: www.holmes.parts
SIC: 5015 3423 Automotive parts & sup-
plies, used; screw drivers, pliers, chisels,
etc. (hand tools)

(G-15249)
HORSESHOE OPERATING INC
110 W La Ave Ste 200 (79701)
P.O. Box 51790 (79710-1790)
PHONE....................................432 683-1448
J Cecil Rhodes, *President*
EMP: 11
SQ FT: 3,500
SALES (est): 989.4K **Privately Held**
SIC: 1311 Crude petroleum production;
natural gas production

(G-15250)
ICT ENERGY SOLUTIONS LLC
Also Called: Ignite Combustion Technologies
2211 N County Road 1120 (79706-4517)
P.O. Box 52572 (79710-2572)
PHONE....................................432 203-0576
John D Bridges, *Mng Member*
John E Nava,
EMP: 97 EST: 2016
SALES (est): 3.9MM **Privately Held**
SIC: 3533 Oil & gas field machinery

(G-15251)
**IGNITION SYSTEMS & CONTRLS
INC (HQ)**
6300 W Highway 80 (79706-2848)
P.O. Box 60372 (79711-0372)
PHONE....................................432 697-6472
Dwayne Armstrong, *President*
Richard Folger, *Principal*
Ryan Sudderth, *Sales Staff*
Tommy Giddens, *Manager*
Mark Tittel, *Technical Staff*
EMP: 28
SQ FT: 10,000
SALES (est): 3.6MM
SALES (corp-wide): 731.7MM **Privately
Held**
WEB: www.ignition-systems.com
SIC: 3694 7699 Ignition systems, high fre-
quency; industrial machinery & equipment
repair
PA: Warren Equipment Company
10325 Younger Rd
Midland TX 79706
432 571-8462

(G-15252)
**INDEPENDENCE RESOURCES
MGT LLC**
6914 N County Road 1294 (79707-9025)
PHONE....................................832 916-2300
Mike Van Horn, *Executive*
EMP: 28
SALES (corp-wide): 191.2MM **Publicly
Held**
WEB: www.independenceresources.com
SIC: 1382 Oil & gas exploration services
HQ: Independence Resources Manage-
ment, Llc
11450 Cmpaq Ctr Dr W Bldg
Houston TX 77070
832 916-2300

(G-15253)
INTEGRITY SERVICES LLC
9701 Farm To Market 307 Et 3 (79706)
P.O. Box 5989 (79704-5989)
PHONE....................................432 682-0703
Schyler Click, *Mng Member*
Jay M Click, *Mng Member*
Michael Gallaher, *Mng Member*
EMP: 60
SALES (est): 13.8MM **Privately Held**
WEB: www.integritywellservices.com
SIC: 1381 Drilling oil & gas wells

(G-15254)
**INTREPID DRCTNAL DRLG
SPCLSTS (PA)**
Also Called: Intrepid Drctnal Drlg Spclists
10314 State Highway 191 (79707-1496)
PHONE....................................432 617-0593
Clint Leazer, *President*
James Metcalf, *Vice Pres*
Matthew Babb, *VP Finance*
EMP: 50
SQ FT: 25,000
SALES (est): 17.2MM **Privately Held**
WEB: www.intrepid-dds.com
SIC: 1381 Drilling oil & gas wells

(G-15255)
IOS INSPECTION
2600 E I 20 (79706)
PHONE....................................432 684-6440
Paco McLaughlin, *COO*
Jimmy Clark, *Vice Pres*
Justin Jarski, *Vice Pres*
Jody Arceneaux, *CFO*
EMP: 20
SALES (est): 2MM **Privately Held**
WEB: www.iosinspection.com
SIC: 3532 3443 8711 Drills, core; boiler
casing, metal plate; engineering services

(G-15256)
IRION COUNTY PLANT (PA)
211 N Colorado St (79701-4607)
P.O. Box 16, Barnhart (76930-0016)
PHONE....................................432 682-6311
EMP: 9
SQ FT: 400
SALES (est): 585.1K **Privately Held**
WEB: www.irioncotxgenweb.com
SIC: 1321 Casing-head butane & propane
production; ethane (natural) production;
natural gas liquids production; propane
(natural) production

(G-15257)
**J & W SERVICES & EQUIPMENT
CO (PA)**
Also Called: J&W Wellhead
3510 E State Highway 158 (79706-4228)
P.O. Box 11021 (79702-8021)
PHONE....................................432 689-3947
Brent Beck, *President*
Ron Hebert, *Division Mgr*
Cade Walton, *COO*
Al Moreno, *Plant Mgr*
Scott Blakely, *Opers Mgr*
▲ **EMP:** 67
SQ FT: 10,000
SALES (est): 64.6MM **Privately Held**
WEB: www.jandwservices.com
SIC: 1389 Oil field services

(G-15258)
JAMES LEE DAVIS (PA)
Also Called: Davis, J L Company
211 N Colorado St (79701-4607)
PHONE....................................432 682-6311
James Lee Davis, *Owner*
Brendon Cole, *Vice Pres*
Nancy Chandler, *Manager*
EMP: 100
SQ FT: 21,000
SALES (est): 350MM **Privately Held**
WEB: www.westtexasgas.com
SIC: 5172 4923 1311 Petroleum products;
gas transmission & distribution; crude pe-
troleum production; natural gas produc-
tion

(G-15259)
JM COX RESOURCES LP (PA)
400 W Wall St (79701-4404)
P.O. Box 2217 (79702-2217)
PHONE....................................432 682-9435
Kelly Cox, *General Mgr*
EMP: 12 EST: 2003
SQ FT: 20,000
SALES (est): 50.4MM **Privately Held**
WEB: www.keystoneconsultants-llc.com
SIC: 1311 Crude petroleum production

(G-15260)
JMR INDUSTRIES LTD (PA)
3606 E State Highway 158 (79706-4229)
P.O. Box 80610 (79708-0610)
PHONE....................................432 557-9721
James E Roark, *President*
James K Shelton, *Vice Pres*
EMP: 10
SQ FT: 5,000
SALES (est): 920.7K **Privately Held**
WEB: www.jmrservices.com
SIC: 1389 Fire fighting, oil & gas field

(G-15261)
**JOHN H HENDRIX
CORPORATION (PA)**
6 Desta Dr Ste 2100 (79705-5556)
P.O. Box 3040 (79702-3040)
PHONE....................................432 684-6631
EMP: 9 EST: 1976
SALES (est): 1.2MM **Privately Held**
SIC: 1311 0212 Crude petroleum produc-
tion; natural gas production; beef cattle
except feedlots

(G-15262)
JTA SERVICE
1107 Maple Ave (79705-6806)
P.O. Box 52131 (79710-2131)
PHONE....................................432 556-0091
Jaime Bujanda, *Principal*
EMP: 10
SALES (est): 919.3K **Privately Held**
SIC: 1389 Servicing oil & gas wells

(G-15263)
**JWB CONSULTING SERVICE
INC**
2116 S County Road 1122 (79706-4991)
P.O. Box 8, Tuscola (79562-0008)
PHONE....................................817 675-6419
Jacky Brown, *President*
Candice Brown, *Vice Pres*
EMP: 12
SALES (est): 593K **Privately Held**
SIC: 1389 8748 7389 Oil consultants;
business consulting;

(G-15264)
K D M HOT OIL SERVICE INC
2400 Fm 715 (79706-4208)
P.O. Box 3044 (79702-3044)
PHONE....................................432 683-0831
Kenneth Machacek, *President*
A A Machacek, *Vice Pres*
EMP: 9
SQ FT: 4,800
SALES (est): 900K **Privately Held**
SIC: 1389 Oil field services

(G-15265)
K&F EQUIPMENT LLC
2310 College Ave (79701-6834)
P.O. Box 4551 (79704-4551)
PHONE....................................432 664-0758
EMP: 13

SALES (est): 1.1MM **Privately Held**
SIC: 1389 Cementing oil & gas well casings

(G-15266)
KEL-TECH INC (DH)
3408 E State Highway 158 (79706-4240)
P.O. Box 11383 (79702-8383)
PHONE....................................432 684-4700
Kenneth Golder, *President*
Jennifer Morningstar, *Treasurer*
Daryl Rogers, *Accounting Mgr*
Chris Barnard, *Admin Sec*
EMP: 42 EST: 1983
SALES (est): 95MM
SALES (corp-wide): 4.4B **Privately Held**
WEB: www.keltechinc.com
SIC: 1389 8731 Oil field services; chemi-
cal laboratory, except testing
HQ: Clariant Corporation
4000 Monroe Rd
Charlotte NC 28205
704 331-7000

(G-15267)
KEPLER AEROSPACE LTD
2908 Enterprise Ln (79706-3637)
PHONE....................................855 553-7537
Brent Nelson, *Principal*
EMP: 20
SALES (est): 153.8K **Privately Held**
WEB: www.kepleraerospace.com
SIC: 3728 Aircraft parts & equipment

(G-15268)
KEPLER SPACECORE INC
2908 Enterprise Ln (79706-3637)
PHONE....................................855 553-7537
EMP: 20
SALES (est): 869.9K **Privately Held**
WEB: www.kepleraerospace.com
SIC: 3728 Mfg Aircraft Parts/Equipment

(G-15269)
KEY ENERGY SERVICES INC
6 Desta Dr Ste 4300 (79705-5565)
PHONE....................................432 620-0300
Katherine Hargis, *Vice Pres*
John Davisson, *Opers Staff*
Bruce Jarvis, *Purch Agent*
Troy Wacha, *Sales Staff*
Ron Laidley, *Manager*
EMP: 15
SALES (corp-wide): 413.8MM **Publicly
Held**
WEB: www.keyenergy.com
SIC: 1389 4212 7353 Servicing oil & gas
wells; local trucking, without storage; oil
field equipment, rental or leasing
PA: Key Energy Services, Inc.
1301 Mckinney St Ste 1800
Houston TX 77010
713 651-4300

(G-15270)
KEY ENERGY SERVICES INC
1811 Garden City Hwy (79701-8364)
PHONE....................................432 570-7440
EMP: 18
SALES (corp-wide): 713MM **Publicly
Held**
SIC: 1381 Oil/Gas Well Drilling
PA: Key Energy Services, Inc.
1301 Mckinney St Ste 1800
Houston TX 77010
713 651-4300

(G-15271)
**KGH INTERMEDIATE HOLDCO II
LLC**
6913 N Fm 1788 (79707-5074)
PHONE....................................432 563-1708
Josh Comstock, *CEO*
Michael Paredez, *Opers Staff*
Abraham Ayala, *Supervisor*
EMP: 12
SALES (corp-wide): 1.8B **Publicly Held**
SIC: 1382 Oil & gas exploration services
HQ: Kgh Intermediate Holdco Ii, Llc
2121 Sage Rd
Houston TX 77056
713 960-0381

(G-15272)
LAREDO PETROLEUM INC
508 W Wall St Ste 600 (79701-5073)
PHONE................................432 684-9955
Randy A Foutch, *CEO*
Patrick J Curth, *Vice Pres*
Cory Belz, *Manager*
EMP: 50
SALES (est): 5.3MM **Privately Held**
WEB: www.laredopetro.com
SIC: 1382 Oil & gas exploration services

(G-15273)
LEESON ENERGY SERVICES LLC
2130 S Loop 250 W Ste 3 (79703-7401)
P.O. Box 10396 (79702-7396)
PHONE................................432 689-7000
David Bostic, *General Mgr*
EMP: 10
SALES (est): 732.5K **Privately Held**
WEB: www.leesonenergyservices.com
SIC: 1389 Oil field services

(G-15274)
LEGACY RESERVES INC (PA)
303 W Wall St Ste 1800 (79701-5106)
PHONE................................432 689-5200
James Daniel Westcott, *CEO*
Kyle M Hammond, *President*
Robert L Norris, *CFO*
Cory J Elliott, *CIO*
Micah C Foster, *
EMP: 10
SALES (est): 480MM **Privately Held**
WEB: www.legacyreserves.com
SIC: 1311 Crude petroleum & natural gas

(G-15275)
LEGACY RESERVES LP
1200 W County Road 114 (79706-3800)
P.O. Box 10848 (79702-7848)
PHONE................................432 967-3490
Reserves Legacy, *Branch Mgr*
EMP: 20
SALES (corp-wide): 480MM **Privately Held**
WEB: www.legacylp.com
SIC: 1382 Oil & gas exploration services
HQ: Legacy Reserves Lp
15 Smith Rd Ste 3000
Midland TX 79705

(G-15276)
LEGACY RESERVES LP (HQ)
15 Smith Rd Ste 3000 (79705-5423)
PHONE................................432 689-5200
James Daniel Westcott, *CEO*
Paul T Horne, *Ch of Bd*
Kyle M Hammond, *President*
Ronald Ragland, *Superintendent*
John Russell, *Superintendent*
EMP: 67
SALES (est): 479.9MM
SALES (corp-wide): 480MM **Privately Held**
WEB: www.legacylp.com
SIC: 1311 Crude petroleum & natural gas;
crude petroleum & natural gas production;
crude petroleum production
PA: Legacy Reserves Inc.
303 W Wall St Ste 1800
Midland TX 79701
432 689-5200

(G-15277)
LEGACY RESERVES OPER GP LLC
Also Called: Legacy Resources
303 W Wall St Ste 1400 (79701-5126)
P.O. Box 10848 (79702-7848)
PHONE................................432 689-5200
Kyle M Hamm, *President*
Dan G Leroy, *President*
Kyle A McGraw, *President*
James Daniel Westcott, *President*
David Hinson, *Prdtn Mgr*
EMP: 221 EST: 2006
SALES (est): 1.5MM
SALES (corp-wide): 480MM **Privately Held**
WEB: www.legacylp.com
SIC: 1382 Oil & gas exploration services

HQ: Legacy Reserves Lp
15 Smith Rd Ste 3000
Midland TX 79705

(G-15278)
LENOIR WATER TRANSFER INC
400 E Loop 250 N Ste 107 (79705-4449)
P.O. Box 52468 (79710-2468)
PHONE................................432 686-8200
Jack Chambers, *President*
Scott Lenoir, *Vice Pres*
Beau Chambers, *Admin Sec*
EMP: 55
SALES (est): 4.7MM **Privately Held**
WEB: www.lenoir-water-transfer-inc.business.site
SIC: 1389 Oil field services

(G-15279)
LENORAH OPERATORS LLC
5003 E State Highway 158 (79706-7205)
PHONE................................432 684-9822
Jerry Greer, *Mng Member*
Linda Turner, *
EMP: 25 EST: 2007
SQ FT: 1,440
SALES (est): 4.9MM **Privately Held**
WEB: www.lenorahoperators.com
SIC: 1389 Oil field services

(G-15280)
LIBERTY MASK LLC
8501 W State Highway 158 (79707-1312)
PHONE................................214 915-2133
Tashfeen Qayyum, *Mng Member*
Jeff Leary, *
EMP: 30
SALES (est): 873.4K **Privately Held**
SIC: 2281 Yarn spinning mills

(G-15281)
LIGHTNING OILFIELD SVCS INC
9309 W I 20 (79706)
PHONE................................817 439-5558
EMP: 97
SALES (corp-wide): 25.7MM **Privately Held**
WEB: www.lightningos.com
SIC: 1389 Oil field services
PA: Lightning Oilfield Services, Inc.
11830 N Saginaw Blvd
Saginaw TX 76179
817 439-5558

(G-15282)
LIMESTONE EXPLORATION II LLC
901 W Missouri Ave (79701-6629)
P.O. Box 5036 (79704-5036)
PHONE................................432 695-6970
Kevin Herrmann, *CEO*
Bruce Burdett, *Partner*
Terrell Downing, *Partner*
William Q Rogers, *Partner*
Jason Delorenzo, *
EMP: 12
SALES (est): 1.5MM **Privately Held**
WEB: www.limestone2.com
SIC: 1382 Oil & gas exploration services

(G-15283)
LINE QUEST LLC
7607 W Industrial Ave (79706-2803)
P.O. Box 51810 (79710-1810)
PHONE................................432 218-4980
Shawn Hailey, *Mng Member*
EMP: 50
SQ FT: 6,000
SALES (est): 3MM **Privately Held**
WEB: www.linequestllc.com
SIC: 1389 Oil field services

(G-15284)
LONE STAR OIL & GAS INC
1003 N Big Spring St (79701-3339)
P.O. Box 2696 (79702-2696)
PHONE................................432 686-9390
Jim Kauthen, *President*
EMP: 23
SQ FT: 500
SALES (est): 2.6MM **Privately Held**
SIC: 1311 Crude petroleum & natural gas

(G-15285)
LONE STAR SIGNS OF WEST TEXAS
1008 E Florida Ave (79701-8252)
P.O. Box 3793 (79702-3793)
PHONE................................432 683-0016
Dwain Tomlin, *President*
Karen Tomlin, *Vice Pres*
Efrain Vasquez, *Sales Staff*
Mondo Bonilla, *Director*
EMP: 25
SQ FT: 10,000
SALES (est): 3.4MM **Privately Held**
WEB: www.lssigns.com
SIC: 3993 Electric signs

(G-15286)
LOSS OIL FIELD SERVICES LLC
307 E Texas Ave (79701-2568)
P.O. Box 2876 (79702-2876)
PHONE................................432 695-6914
Carlos E Lujan, *Principal*
Carlos Lujan, *Principal*
EMP: 35 EST: 2014
SALES (est): 3MM **Privately Held**
SIC: 1389 Oil field services

(G-15287)
LPC CRUDE OIL INC
303 W Wall St Ste 102 (79701-5114)
P.O. Box 3821 (79702-3821)
PHONE................................432 682-8555
Steve Mills, *President*
Janet St Hilaire, *Admin Asst*
EMP: 100
SALES (est): 9.6MM
SALES (corp-wide): 6B **Publicly Held**
WEB: www.lpccrude.com
SIC: 1382 Oil & gas exploration services
PA: Enlink Midstream, Llc
1722 Routh St Ste 1300
Dallas TX 75201
214 953-9500

(G-15288)
LUBRI TECH PRODUCTS
1400 N County Road 1110 (79706-4558)
PHONE................................214 870-4070
Sid Ivy, *Owner*
EMP: 21
SQ FT: 10,000
SALES (est): 3MM **Privately Held**
WEB: www.lubritechusa.com
SIC: 3533 Oil & gas field machinery

(G-15289)
M3P DIRECTIONAL SERVICES LTD
7600 W County Road 116 (79706-2819)
P.O. Box 2552 (79702-2552)
PHONE................................432 561-8801
Michael H Mayer, *
EMP: 10 EST: 2003
SALES (est): 1MM **Privately Held**
WEB: www.m3pdirectional.com
SIC: 1381 Directional drilling oil & gas wells

(G-15290)
M3P WATER SERVICES LLC
Also Called: Water Cleaning Service
415 W Wall St Ste 835 (79701-4592)
P.O. Box 10983 (79702-7983)
PHONE................................432 570-7500
Michael Mayer, *Mng Member*
EMP: 9
SALES (est): 1.4MM **Privately Held**
WEB: www.watercleaningservices.com
SIC: 3589 Water treatment equipment, industrial

(G-15291)
MAJESTIC PETROLEUM SVCS LLC
3505 N County Road 1148 (79705-4072)
PHONE................................432 686-2023
Santiago Zubia, *Mng Member*
Maria Zubia, *Director*
Maria Aguirre, *
Caleb Zubia, *
EMP: 60
SALES (est): 4.8MM **Privately Held**
WEB: www.majesticps.com
SIC: 1389 Servicing oil & gas wells

(G-15292)
MALLARD COMPLETIONS LLC
7100 I 20 (79706)
PHONE................................432 381-8508
Darron M Anderson, *President*
Matthew Hooker, *COO*
Lance Perryman, *Vice Pres*
J Brandon Blossman, *CFO*
EMP: 51
SALES (est): 4.4MM
SALES (corp-wide): 336.9MM **Publicly Held**
WEB: www.mallardcompletions.com
SIC: 1382 Oil & gas exploration services
PA: Ranger Energy Services, Inc.
10350 Richmond Ave # 550
Houston TX 77042
713 935-8900

(G-15293)
MARSHALL & WINSTON INC (PA)
6 Desta Dr Ste 3100 (79705-5538)
P.O. Box 50880 (79710-0880)
PHONE................................432 684-6373
EMP: 14
SQ FT: 8,500
SALES (est): 3.3MM **Privately Held**
WEB: www.mar-win.com
SIC: 1311 Crude petroleum production

(G-15294)
MAVERICK FIELD SERVICES LLC
3601 N County Road 1148 (79705-4070)
PHONE................................432 685-5021
EMP: 12
SALES (corp-wide): 14.7MM **Privately Held**
WEB: www.maverickfieldservices.com
SIC: 1311 Crude petroleum & natural gas
PA: Field Maverick Services Llc
4447 W State Highway 71
La Grange TX 78945
979 242-3000

(G-15295)
MAVERICK WELL PLUGGERS LLC
3007 N Cr 110 (79706)
P.O. Box 2439 (79702-2439)
PHONE................................432 458-3780
Wayne Pinkerton, *Principal*
Brody Pinkerton, *Vice Pres*
Lee Robbins, *CFO*
EMP: 42
SALES (est): 3.5MM **Privately Held**
WEB: www.maverickwellpluggers.net
SIC: 1389 Geophysical exploration, oil & gas field

(G-15296)
MCCLINTON ENERGY GROUP L L C
12620 State Highway 191 (79707-1580)
PHONE................................432 563-5500
Beau McClinton, *Branch Mgr*
EMP: 105
SALES (corp-wide): 67.3MM **Privately Held**
WEB: www.mcclintonenergy.com
SIC: 1381 3351 Drilling oil & gas wells; tubing, copper & copper alloy
PA: Mcclinton Energy Group, L. L. C.
11200 W Interstate 20
Odessa TX 79765
432 563-5500

(G-15297)
MCMILLAN WELDING
Also Called: Endeavor Energy Resources
110 N Mrenseld Ste 200 (79701)
PHONE................................432 687-4625
Audrey Stephens, *Owner*
EMP: 60
SALES (est): 3.2MM **Privately Held**
WEB: www.mcmillanwelding.com
SIC: 1389 Oil field services

(G-15298)
MEWBOURNE OIL COMPANY
500 W Texas Ave Ste 1020 (79701-4279)
PHONE................................432 682-3715
Larry Cunningham, *Manager*
EMP: 13

SALES (corp-wide): 458.1MM **Privately Held**
WEB: www.mewbourne.net
SIC: 1382 Oil & gas exploration services
HQ: Mewbourne Oil Company
　　3620 Old Bullard Rd
　　Tyler TX 75701
　　903 561-2900

(G-15299)
MEYER ENERGY SERVICES LLC (PA)
4311 E County Road 45　(79705-2473)
PHONE..............................830 377-1099
Rob Miller, *Vice Pres*
Jonathan Meyer,
EMP: 15
SALES (est): 42.2MM **Privately Held**
WEB: www.meyerenergyservices.com
SIC: 1382 Oil & gas exploration services

(G-15300)
MEYER ENERGY SERVICES LLC
3001 W Loop 250 N Ste C10　(79705-3252)
PHONE..............................830 377-1099
Jonathan Meyer,
EMP: 58
SALES (corp-wide): 42.2MM **Privately Held**
WEB: www.meyerenergyservices.com
SIC: 1382 Oil & gas exploration services
PA: Meyer Energy Services, Llc
　　4311 E County Road 45
　　Midland TX 79705
　　830 377-1099

(G-15301)
MIDLAND ENERGY INC
110 N Marienfeld St # 101　(79701-4400)
P.O. Box 10911　(79702-7911)
PHONE..............................432 683-6686
Syed Javaid Anwar, *President*
EMP: 27
SQ FT: 3,000
SALES (est): 675.3K **Privately Held**
WEB: www.midlandenergylibrary.net
SIC: 1311 Crude petroleum production

(G-15302)
MIDLAND ROUSTABOUT SERVICE INC
5800 E I 20　(79706)
P.O. Box 7906　(79708-7906)
PHONE..............................432 682-5017
Carles W Gibson, *President*
Dana Copeland, *Corp Secy*
David Brown, *Vice Pres*
Barbara Gibson, *Director*
Patricia Brown, *Admin Sec*
EMP: 75
SQ FT: 2,500
SALES (est): 10.2MM **Privately Held**
WEB: www.midlandroustabout.com
SIC: 1389 Roustabout service; oil field services

(G-15303)
MIDLAND WELLHEAD INC
Also Called: B & M Tool Co
40 E Industrial Loop　(79701-8510)
P.O. Box 1554　(79702-1554)
PHONE..............................432 682-0856
Alan Morgan, *President*
Keith Morgan, *President*
▲ **EMP:** 36
SQ FT: 3,200
SALES (est): 4.7MM **Privately Held**
WEB: www.b-mtool.com
SIC: 3599 3532 3545 3533 Machine shop, jobbing & repair; drills & drilling equipment, mining (except oil & gas); machine tool accessories; oil & gas field machinery

(G-15304)
MILLENNIUM RESOURCES LP
414 W Texas Ave Ste 411　(79701-4415)
P.O. Box 80393　(79708-0393)
PHONE..............................432 687-4074
Steve James, *Partner*
Michelle James, *Partner*
EMP: 26
SALES (est): 2.8MM **Privately Held**
SIC: 1389 Oil field services

(G-15305)
MINERAL TECHNOLOGIES INC
2052 Commerce Dr　(79703-7502)
P.O. Box 5823　(79704-5823)
PHONE..............................432 685-3520
Carter D Copeland, *President*
EMP: 12
SQ FT: 3,000
SALES (est): 3.1MM **Privately Held**
WEB: www.mtienergy.com
SIC: 1311 Crude petroleum & natural gas

(G-15306)
MIRANDA ENERGY CORPORATION
24 Smith Rd Ste 601　(79705-4412)
PHONE..............................432 685-1953
Troy G Martin, *President*
Troy Martin Jr, *Vice Pres*
Martin Diane T, *Vice Pres*
Dan Kerr, *Treasurer*
EMP: 10
SALES (est): 1.4MM **Privately Held**
WEB: www.adtlmaa.com
SIC: 1311 Crude petroleum production

(G-15307)
MRC GLOBAL (US) INC
Also Called: M R C
511 W Missouri Ave　(79701-5016)
PHONE..............................432 620-0059
Ronnie Crossland, *Branch Mgr*
EMP: 23 **Publicly Held**
WEB: www.mrcglobal.com
SIC: 1311 5051 5085 Crude petroleum & natural gas; pipe & tubing, steel; industrial supplies; valves & fittings
HQ: Mrc Global (Us) Inc.
　　1301 Mckinney St Ste 2300
　　Houston TX 77010
　　877 294-7574

(G-15308)
MUDSMITH LTD
1309 W County Road 114　(79706-3818)
P.O. Box 50723　(79710-0723)
PHONE..............................432 687-6837
Kenneth Goldsmith, *Partner*
EMP: 10
SQ FT: 449,626
SALES (est): 5.3MM **Privately Held**
WEB: www.mudsmith.com
SIC: 1382 5169 1381 Oil & gas exploration services; chemical additives; drilling oil & gas wells

(G-15309)
NABORS WELL SERVICES LTD
Also Called: Administrative Office
3300 N A St Bldg 2-200　(79705-5408)
P.O. Box 51670　(79710-1670)
PHONE..............................432 683-5000
Johnny Slauther, *Branch Mgr*
EMP: 20 **Privately Held**
WEB: www.nabors.com
SIC: 1389 Oil field services
HQ: Nabors Well Services Ltd.
　　515 W Greens Rd Ste 1200
　　Houston TX 77067
　　281 874-0035

(G-15310)
NATIONAL OILWELL VARCO INC
2206 W New Jersey Ave　(79701-7761)
PHONE..............................432 683-6696
EMP: 23
SALES (corp-wide): 8.4B **Publicly Held**
WEB: www.nov.com
SIC: 3533 Oil & gas field machinery
PA: National Oilwell Varco, Inc.
　　7909 Parkwood Circle Dr
　　Houston TX 77036
　　713 346-7500

(G-15311)
NATURAL GAS SERVICES GROUP INC (PA)
Also Called: Ngsg
508 W Wall St Ste 550　(79701-5079)
PHONE..............................432 262-2700
EMP: 171
SQ FT: 13,135

SALES: 78.4MM **Publicly Held**
WEB: www.ngsgi.com
SIC: 1389 7353 3563 Gas field services; oil field equipment, rental or leasing; air & gas compressors

(G-15312)
NBL PERMIAN LLC
Also Called: Clayton W Williams Jr
6 Desta Dr Ste 1100　(79705-5510)
PHONE..............................979 542-5571
Fax: 830 535-7750
EMP: 28
SALES (corp-wide): 3.4B **Publicly Held**
SIC: 1311 Crude Petroleum/Natural Gas Production
HQ: Nbl Permian Llc
　　1001 Noble Energy Way
　　Houston TX 77070
　　281 872-3100

(G-15313)
NBL PERMIAN LLC
6 Desta Dr Ste 1100　(79705-5510)
PHONE..............................432 688-3430
Mel G Riggs, *Manager*
EMP: 16
SALES (corp-wide): 146.5B **Publicly Held**
WEB: www.nblenergy.com
SIC: 1382 Oil & gas exploration services
HQ: Nbl Permian Llc
　　1001 Noble Energy Way
　　Houston TX 77070
　　281 872-3100

(G-15314)
NCS PEARSON INC
3300 N A St Bldg 4-228　(79705-5407)
PHONE..............................432 685-0033
B J Compton, *Manager*
EMP: 99
SALES (corp-wide): 5B **Privately Held**
WEB: www.pearsonassessments.com
SIC: 3577 Optical scanning devices
HQ: Ncs Pearson Inc
　　5601 Green Valley Dr # 220
　　Bloomington MN 55437
　　952 681-3000

(G-15315)
NEARBURG PRODUCING COMPANY
3300 N A St Bldg 2-120　(79705-5444)
PHONE..............................432 686-8235
Linda Hicks, *Branch Mgr*
EMP: 12
SALES (corp-wide): 19.9MM **Privately Held**
SIC: 1311 Crude petroleum production; natural gas production
PA: Nearburg Producing Company Inc
　　5447 Glen Lakes Dr
　　Dallas TX 75231
　　214 739-1778

(G-15316)
NEW TERACO INC (DH)
Also Called: Teraco, Inc.
2080 Commerce Dr　(79703-7502)
PHONE..............................800 687-3999
Harrison A Bubrosky, *CEO*
Diana White, *President*
Pravin Kamble, *Exec VP*
Pam Mercer, *Purchasing*
Martin Agati, *Regl Sales Mgr*
EMP: 30
SALES (est): 16.3MM **Privately Held**
WEB: www.archway.com
SIC: 3089 3993 Identification cards, plastic; advertising novelties

(G-15317)
NEWPARK ENVIRONMENTAL SVCS LLC
3001 N Big Spring St　(79705-5375)
PHONE..............................432 682-5411
Gary Frazier, *Opers Mgr*
EMP: 24
SALES (corp-wide): 747.7MM **Publicly Held**
WEB: www.newpark.com
SIC: 1389 Oil field services

HQ: Newpark Environmental Services Llc
　　207 Towncenter Pkwy Fl 2
　　Lafayette LA 70506
　　337 984-4445

(G-15318)
NEXGEN WTR SOLUTIONS LTD LBLTY
4407 S County Road 1265　(79706-5537)
PHONE..............................432 234-8404
Kelvin Doggett, *Manager*
EMP: 15
SALES (corp-wide): 4MM **Privately Held**
SIC: 1389 Oil field services
PA: Nexgen Water Solutions Limited Liability Company
　　951 County Road 160
　　Kenedy TX 78119
　　830 583-9915

(G-15319)
NITRO WELL SERVICE LLC
13020 State Highway 191 G　(79707-1668)
P.O. Box 1511, Odessa　(79760-1511)
PHONE..............................432 617-1128
F R Mitchell,
EMP: 23
SALES (est): 5.1MM **Privately Held**
WEB: www.yjosllc.com
SIC: 1389 Oil field services

(G-15320)
NITROGEN SERVICES LLC
Also Called: N2
921 N Fairgrounds Rd　(79706-4366)
PHONE..............................925 336-1560
Ronald E Booth, *President*
Cary Brown, *Manager*
EMP: 115
SALES (est): 2.7MM
SALES (corp-wide): 51MM **Privately Held**
WEB: www.portablenitro.com
SIC: 2813 1381 1799 Nitrogen; directional drilling oil & gas wells; dewatering
PA: Cross Country Infrastructure Services Inc.
　　2251 Rifle St
　　Aurora CO 80011
　　303 361-6797

(G-15321)
NOLTEX TRUSS LITTLEFIELD LP
3101 Garden City Hwy　(79701-1562)
PHONE..............................432 687-1241
EMP: 21 **Privately Held**
WEB: www.noltextruss.com
SIC: 2439 Trusses, wooden roof
PA: Noltex Truss Littlefield, L.P.
　　1012 E Wylon Jnnings Blvd
　　Littlefield TX 79339

(G-15322)
O-TEX PUMPING LLC (PA)
306 W Wall St Ste 700　(79701-5170)
PHONE..............................432 685-9901
Brent Barbour, *President*
Dale Jackson, *Office Mgr*
Chad Welch, *Supervisor*
EMP: 88
SALES (est): 146MM **Privately Held**
WEB: www.otexpumping.com
SIC: 1382 Oil & gas exploration services

(G-15323)
OCCIDENTAL OIL AND GAS CORP
Also Called: OXY
6001 Deauville　(79706-2671)
P.O. Box 50250　(79710-0250)
PHONE..............................432 685-5600
EMP: 400
SALES (corp-wide): 21.2B **Publicly Held**
WEB: www.oxy.com
SIC: 1311 Crude petroleum production
HQ: Occidental Oil And Gas Corporation
　　5 Greenway Plz Ste 110
　　Houston TX 77046

(G-15324)
OCTANE ENERGY CONSULTING LLC
310 W Wall St Ste 810 (79701-5124)
P.O. Box 1592 (79702-1592)
PHONE...............................432 685-7736
Jared Blong, *CEO*
Joe Cervantes, *COO*
Kyle Charles, *Consultant*
Tommy Monsey, *Consultant*
Joshua Stephens, *Consultant*
EMP: 14 **EST:** 2013
SQ FT: 1,676
SALES (est): 809.1K **Privately Held**
WEB: www.octane-energy.com
SIC: 1381 8741 1389 8711 Drilling oil & gas wells; management services; oil consultants; petroleum engineering

(G-15325)
OCTG MATERIAL HDLG SYSTEMS INC
2614 Flynt (79701-8524)
PHONE...............................432 687-5420
Richard A Sparks, *President*
EMP: 18
SALES (est): 4.4MM **Privately Held**
WEB: www.octg.business.site
SIC: 3533 Oil field machinery & equipment

(G-15326)
OIL STATES ENERGY SERVICES LLC
2601 S County Road 1257 (79706-2845)
PHONE...............................432 563-1304
Charles Helms, *Mng Member*
EMP: 20
SALES (corp-wide): 1B **Publicly Held**
WEB: www.oses.com
SIC: 3533 5082 5084 7353 Oil field machinery & equipment; oil field equipment; safety equipment; oil field equipment, rental or leasing; equipment rental & leasing
HQ: Oil States Energy Services, L.L.C.
333 Clay St Ste 2100
Houston TX 77002
713 425-2400

(G-15327)
OMNI AIR & NITROGEN LTD
8809 E Highway 80 (79706-4770)
PHONE...............................432 288-9087
Kathy Rodriguez, *Partner*
John Burkholder, *Regl Sales Mgr*
Lowell Millican, *Sales Staff*
Marco Barreno, *Manager*
EMP: 17
SALES (est): 446.1K **Privately Held**
WEB: www.omniairnitrogen.com
SIC: 1389 Servicing oil & gas wells

(G-15328)
ONYX CONTRACTORS OPERATIONS LP
1010 S Fm 1788 (79706-2629)
P.O. Box 60547 (79711-0547)
PHONE...............................432 561-8900
Maurizio Iaqueniello, *President*
Paul Iaquaniello, *Vice Pres*
Robert Helms, *Controller*
Zach Reynolds, *Manager*
EMP: 59
SQ FT: 12,050
SALES (est): 18.8MM **Privately Held**
WEB: www.onyxcontractors.com
SIC: 4941 1542 1389 Water supply; commercial & office building contractors; oil field services

(G-15329)
ORIGIN BIO SOLUTIONS LLC
1308 S Midkiff Rd Ste 229 (79701-8586)
P.O. Box 80327 (79708-0327)
PHONE...............................432 570-4081
EMP: 12
SALES (est): 510K **Privately Held**
SIC: 1389 8731 Oil/Gas Field Services Commercial Physical Research

(G-15330)
ORYX MIDSTREAM SERVICES LLC
4000 N Big Spring St # 400 (79705-4629)
PHONE...............................432 684-4272
Bret Wiggs, *CEO*
Karl Pflugerl, *President*
Martin McHale, *COO*
Josh Ham, *Exec VP*
Michael Rose, *Exec VP*
EMP: 25
SALES (est): 4.6MM **Privately Held**
WEB: www.oryxmidstream.com
SIC: 1382 Oil & gas exploration services

(G-15331)
ORYX STHERN DEL OIL GTHRING TR
Also Called: ORYX TRANS PERMIAN
4000 N Big Spring St # 300 (79705-4629)
PHONE...............................432 684-4272
Brett Wiggs, *Mng Member*
Melissa Archer, *Manager*
EMP: 18 **EST:** 2015
SALES (est): 179.6MM **Privately Held**
WEB: www.oryxmidstream.com
SIC: 1382 Oil & gas exploration services
PA: Oryx Southern Delaware Holdings Llc
4000 N Big Spring St # 300
Midland TX 79705
432 684-4272

(G-15332)
OTIS INSTRUMENTS INC
3308 Norden Dr (79706-6021)
PHONE...............................432 563-0007
EMP: 30
SALES (corp-wide): 7.5MM **Privately Held**
SIC: 3829 Mfg Measuring/Controlling Devices
PA: Otis Instruments, Inc.
301 S Texas Ave
Bryan TX 77803
979 776-7700

(G-15333)
OUTLAWS OILFIELD SERVICE LLC
415 W Wall St Ste 612 (79701-4449)
PHONE...............................432 445-0005
Alan Arreola, *Mng Member*
Gary Arreola,
EMP: 35
SALES (est): 2.5MM **Privately Held**
SIC: 4212 1389 Liquid haulage, local; gas field services

(G-15334)
OXY INC
6001 Deauville (79706-2671)
P.O. Box 50250 (79710-0250)
PHONE...............................432 685-5600
Matt Hyde, *Opers-Prdtn-Mfg*
EMP: 12
SALES (corp-wide): 21.2B **Publicly Held**
WEB: www.oxy.com
SIC: 1311 Crude petroleum production
HQ: Oxy Inc.
5 Greenway Plz Ste 2400
Houston TX 77046
713 215-7000

(G-15335)
PANDEMX LLC
10008 W County Road 150 (79706-3027)
PHONE...............................432 638-3055
Jared Davis,
EMP: 20
SALES (est): 913.5K **Privately Held**
WEB: www.pandemx.solutions
SIC: 2869 Alcohols, non-beverage

(G-15336)
PARALLEL PETROLEUM LLC (PA)
1004 N Big Spring St (79701-3354)
P.O. Box 10587 (79702-7587)
PHONE...............................432 684-3727
Michael Aduijo, *President*
Joseph Shryack, *Opers Mgr*
Blake Edwards, *Production*
Jongnam Lim, *CFO*
Juanita Perez, *Administration*
EMP: 34

SQ FT: 30,000
SALES (est): 50MM **Privately Held**
WEB: www.parallel-petro.com
SIC: 1311 1382 Crude petroleum production; oil & gas exploration services

(G-15337)
PARSLEY ENERGY LLC (DH)
1703 E County Road 120 (79706-4060)
P.O. Box 11090 (79702-8090)
PHONE...............................432 818-2100
Darrell Thompson, *Opers Staff*
Floyd Bates, *Engineer*
Ryan Dalton, *CFO*
James Neblett, *Finance Mgr*
Alexia Donohue, *Accounting Mgr*
EMP: 20 **EST:** 2013
SALES (est): 82MM
SALES (corp-wide): 9.3B **Publicly Held**
WEB: www.parsleyenergy.com
SIC: 1311 Crude petroleum production
HQ: Parsley Energy, Inc.
303 Colorado St Ste 3000
Austin TX 78701
737 704-2300

(G-15338)
PARSLEY ENERGY OPERATIONS LLC
1703 E County Road 120 (79706-4060)
P.O. Box 11090 (79702-8090)
PHONE...............................432 818-2100
Paul Treadwell, *Vice Pres*
Ryan Dalton, *CFO*
Bryan Sheffield, *Mng Member*
Landon Hamer, *Analyst*
EMP: 65
SALES (est): 20.9MM
SALES (corp-wide): 9.3B **Publicly Held**
WEB: www.parsleyenergy.com
SIC: 1382 Oil & gas exploration services
HQ: Parsley Energy, Llc
1703 E County Road 120
Midland TX 79706
432 818-2100

(G-15339)
PATRIOT PREMIUM THREADING SERV
8300 W Highway 80 (79706-2604)
P.O. Box 13660, Odessa (79768-3660)
PHONE...............................432 250-6001
Scott Seal, *Prdtn Mgr*
Jesse Ruiz, *Facilities Mgr*
Lisa Luedecke, *Finance Mgr*
Scott Powell, *Sales Staff*
Steve Tucker, *Sales Staff*
EMP: 67
SALES (est): 24.5MM **Privately Held**
WEB: www.patriotthreading.com
SIC: 3671 Gas or vapor tubes

(G-15340)
PATRIOT RESOURCES INC
110 W La Ave Ste 500 (79701)
PHONE...............................432 686-9801
Ben A Strickling III, *President*
Joe D Strickling, *Vice Pres*
Joe Strickling, *Vice Pres*
Herbert E Ware III, *Vice Pres*
Karen Allen, *Accounting Mgr*
EMP: 15
SALES (est): 10.9MM **Privately Held**
WEB: www.patriot-resources.com
SIC: 1311 Crude petroleum production

(G-15341)
PATTERSON-UTI ACQUISITION LLC
Also Called: Tmbr/Sharp Drilling
9915 W Industrial Ave (79706-2800)
PHONE...............................432 561-9382
Cloyce Talbott, *CEO*
Mark S Siegel, *Ch of Bd*
Glenn Patterson, *President*
John Vollmer, *Senior VP*
Jonathon D Nelson, *CFO*
▲ **EMP:** 340
SQ FT: 15,000
SALES (est): 104MM
SALES (corp-wide): 1.1B **Publicly Held**
WEB: www.patenergy.com
SIC: 1381 Drilling oil & gas wells

PA: Patterson-Uti Energy, Inc.
10713 W Sam Houston Pkwy
Houston TX 77064
281 765-7100

(G-15342)
PATTERSON-UTI ENERGY INC
9915 W Industrial Ave (79706-2800)
PHONE...............................432 561-9382
Shirriel Nos, *Sales Executive*
Marisela Baeza, *Administration*
EMP: 57
SALES (corp-wide): 1.1B **Publicly Held**
WEB: www.patenergy.com
SIC: 1381 Directional drilling oil & gas wells
PA: Patterson-Uti Energy, Inc.
10713 W Sam Houston Pkwy
Houston TX 77064
281 765-7100

(G-15343)
PATTERSON-UTI ENERGY INC
410 N Loraine St (79701-4716)
PHONE...............................432 682-9401
Steve McCoy, *Vice Pres*
Doyce Haney, *Vice Pres*
EMP: 10
SALES (corp-wide): 1.1B **Publicly Held**
WEB: www.patenergy.com
SIC: 1381 1311 Directional drilling oil & gas wells; crude petroleum production
PA: Patterson-Uti Energy, Inc.
10713 W Sam Houston Pkwy
Houston TX 77064
281 765-7100

(G-15344)
PEAK PRESSURE CONTROL LLC
12914 W County Road 91 (79707-5814)
PHONE...............................432 563-5800
Ann G Fox, *President*
David Crombie, *President*
EMP: 50 **EST:** 2011
SALES (est): 2.2MM
SALES (corp-wide): 832.9MM **Publicly Held**
WEB: www.nineenergyservice.com
SIC: 1389 Oil field services
PA: Nine Energy Service, Inc.
2001 Kirby Dr Ste 200
Houston TX 77019
281 730-5100

(G-15345)
PERMIAN PETROLEUM SERVICES INC
4601 S State Highway 349 (79706-7009)
P.O. Box 3663 (79702-3663)
PHONE...............................432 682-0434
Sandra Greer, *President*
Evelyn J Green, *Principal*
Edward O Greer, *Principal*
EMP: 30 **EST:** 1974
SQ FT: 5,600
SALES (est): 3.9MM **Privately Held**
WEB: www.permianpetroleumservices.com
SIC: 1389 1382 Oil field services; haulage, oil field; oil & gas exploration services

(G-15346)
PERMIAN SIGN CO INC
4111 S County Road 1276 (79706-3042)
P.O. Box 60685 (79711-0685)
PHONE...............................432 563-3072
Derek Dunton, *President*
Darrel Dunton, *Vice Pres*
Paula Bass, *Treasurer*
Laura Hernandez, *Bookkeeper*
Clifford Ray, *Sales Staff*
EMP: 15
SQ FT: 16,000
SALES (est): 1MM **Privately Held**
WEB: www.permiansign.com
SIC: 3993 Electric signs; neon signs

(G-15347)
PETROLIMA LLC
203 W Wall St Ste 1100 (79701-4520)
P.O. Box 1113 (79702-1113)
PHONE...............................432 695-9989
JD Smith, *CEO*
Susie Neale, *Principal*
Josh Lorenz, *COO*

Chad Sherley, *CFO*
EMP: 17 **EST:** 2015
SALES (est): 1.2MM **Privately Held**
WEB: www.encorepermian.com
SIC: 1382 Oil & gas exploration services

(G-15348)
PETROPLEX ACIDIZING INC (PA)
Also Called: Pai
3716 S Canny Rd S 1305 1305 S (79705)
P.O. Box 60365 (79711-0365)
PHONE..............................432 563-1299
Tony Cunningham, *President*
Erin Underwood, *Vice Pres*
Kyle Cunningham, *Opers Staff*
Jamie Terry, *CFO*
Dustin Anderson, *Sales Staff*
EMP: 41 **EST:** 1981
SQ FT: 6,700
SALES (est): 18MM **Privately Held**
WEB: www.petroplex.com
SIC: 1389 Servicing oil & gas wells

(G-15349)
PETROPLEX ENERGY INC
3011 Garden City Hwy (79701-1560)
PHONE..............................432 687-2222
Darrell Blakeney, *Opers Mgr*
EMP: 14
SALES (corp-wide): 7.7MM **Privately Held**
WEB: www.midlandenergylibrary.net
SIC: 1381 Drilling oil & gas wells
PA: Petroplex Energy, Inc.
110 N Marienfeld St # 101
Midland TX 79701
432 570-7030

(G-15350)
PETROPLEX PIPE & CNSTR INC (PA)
2802 W County Road 111 (79706-3840)
P.O. Box 5412 (79704-5412)
PHONE..............................432 697-4540
Thomas R Bridges Jr, *President*
Joann Bridges, *Vice Pres*
EMP: 91
SQ FT: 7,500
SALES (est): 27.3MM **Privately Held**
WEB: www.petroplexpipe.com
SIC: 1389 1623 Roustabout service; oil & gas pipeline construction

(G-15351)
PIEDRA OPERATING LLC (PA)
400 W Illinois Ave # 1070 (79701-4399)
P.O. Box 10485 (79702-7485)
PHONE..............................432 685-9005
Katharine Brown, *COO*
Ruth Culley, *Controller*
Julie Edgerton, *Controller*
Chip Smith, *Mng Member*
Armand Smith Jr,
EMP: 12
SALES (est): 2.1MM **Privately Held**
WEB: www.piedrallc.com
SIC: 1381 Drilling oil & gas wells

(G-15352)
PILOT THOMAS LOGISTICS LLC
Also Called: Cactus Fuel
7316 S County Road 1270 (79706-6124)
PHONE..............................432 741-1514
Ashton Craddick, *Branch Mgr*
EMP: 30
SALES (corp-wide): 5B **Privately Held**
WEB: www.pilotthomas.com
SIC: 2869 Fuels
HQ: Pilot Thomas Logistics Llc
201 N Rupert St Ste 101
Fort Worth TX 76107
817 877-8300

(G-15353)
PIONEER DRILLING SERVICES LTD
Also Called: Pioneer West Texas Division
4401 E Highway 80 (79706-4489)
PHONE..............................432 684-7360
EMP: 10
SALES (corp-wide): 575.7MM **Privately Held**
WEB: www.pioneeres.com
SIC: 1381 Drilling oil & gas wells

HQ: Pioneer Drilling Services, Ltd.
1250 Ne Loop 410 Ste 1000
San Antonio TX 78209
210 828-7689

(G-15354)
PIONEER NATURAL RESOURCES CO
3617 N Big Spring St (79705-4569)
P.O. Box 3178 (79702-3178)
PHONE..............................432 683-4768
Scott Sheffield, *CEO*
Jake Balderrama, *Foreman/Supr*
Jay Snider, *Foreman/Supr*
Blake Brazelton, *Manager*
Randy Golson, *Manager*
EMP: 32
SALES (corp-wide): 9.3B **Publicly Held**
WEB: www.pxd.com
SIC: 5735 1382 Records; aerial geophysical exploration oil & gas
PA: Pioneer Natural Resources Company
777 Hidden Rdg
Irving TX 75038
972 444-9001

(G-15355)
PIONEER NATURAL RESOURCES CO
4815 E Highway 80 (79706-4475)
PHONE..............................432 571-2800
Roger Minner, *Accountant*
Larry Hambek, *Branch Mgr*
Armando Pillado, *IT/INT Sup*
EMP: 130
SQ FT: 7,798
SALES (corp-wide): 9.3B **Publicly Held**
WEB: www.pxd.com
SIC: 1311 1382 Crude petroleum production; oil & gas exploration services
PA: Pioneer Natural Resources Company
777 Hidden Rdg
Irving TX 75038
972 444-9001

(G-15356)
PIONEER NTRAL RSOURCES USA INC
3617 N Big Spring St (79705-4569)
P.O. Box 3178 (79702-3178)
PHONE..............................432 683-4768
Cary Brown, *CEO*
Greg Galler, *Manager*
EMP: 86
SALES (corp-wide): 9.3B **Publicly Held**
WEB: www.pxd.com
SIC: 1311 Crude petroleum production; natural gas production
HQ: Pioneer Natural Resources Usa, Inc.
5205 N Oconnor Blvd Ste Connor
Irving TX 75039
972 444-9001

(G-15357)
PIONEER NTRAL RSOURCES USA INC
Also Called: Parker & Par
3617 N Big Spring St (79705-4569)
P.O. Box 3178 (79702-3178)
PHONE..............................432 684-0023
Terry Pender, *Manager*
EMP: 74
SALES (corp-wide): 9.3B **Publicly Held**
WEB: www.pxd.com
SIC: 1382 Business planning & organizing services
HQ: Pioneer Natural Resources Usa, Inc.
5205 N Oconnor Blvd Ste Connor
Irving TX 75039
972 444-9001

(G-15358)
PIPE PROS LLC
2716 S County Road 1207 (79706-3825)
PHONE..............................432 699-4245
Pedro Rios, *Branch Mgr*
EMP: 31
SALES (corp-wide): 100.6MM **Privately Held**
WEB: www.pipe-pros.com
SIC: 3494 Pipe fittings
PA: Pipe Pros, Llc
1729 N Clarkwood Rd # 10
Corpus Christi TX 78409
361 289-9090

(G-15359)
PIRANHA SCIENTIFIC LLC
11910 State Highway 191 (79707-1571)
PHONE..............................855 585-5200
Ryan Larsen, *Mng Member*
EMP: 10
SALES (est): 95.9K **Privately Held**
SIC: 1382 Oil & gas exploration services

(G-15360)
PIRATE OILFIELD SERVICES INC
3303 E County Road 44 (79705)
P.O. Box 52840 (79710-2840)
PHONE..............................432 260-9040
Mark Torres, *President*
Chisum Moore, *Vice Pres*
EMP: 35
SALES (est): 6.5MM
SALES (corp-wide): 22.3MM **Privately Held**
SIC: 1389 Oil & gas wells: building, repairing & dismantling
PA: Elite Group Inc
1175 Place Du Frere-Andre
Montreal QC H3B 3
514 383-4720

(G-15361)
POLYFLOW LLC
2309 E Interstate 20 (79701-2060)
PHONE..............................432 686-2001
Paul Almanza, *QC Mgr*
Jim Moore, *Mng Member*
Jeremy Jones, *Manager*
EMP: 50
SALES (est): 17.4MM **Privately Held**
WEB: www.thermoflexpipe.com
SIC: 3084 Plastics pipe

(G-15362)
PRECISION FRAC LLC
10008 W County Road 150 (79706-3027)
PHONE..............................855 967-1023
Trinity D Crawford,
Mason Askins,
Chad Carson,
Jared Davis,
Chris Martin,
EMP: 15
SALES (est): 1.3MM **Privately Held**
WEB: www.precisionfrac.com
SIC: 7999 4499 2385 Diving instruction, underwater; boathouses, commercial; waterproof outerwear

(G-15363)
PROBITY ENERGY PARTNERS LLC
3407 Caldera Blvd (79707-2825)
P.O. Box 7307 (79708-7307)
PHONE..............................432 570-1122
Charles R Saulsbury Jr,
Steve Jeter,
EMP: 20
SALES (est): 816.8K **Privately Held**
WEB: www.probityswd.com
SIC: 1382 Oil & gas exploration services

(G-15364)
PRODUCTION LIFT SYSTEMS INC
Also Called: Plsi
14 E Industrial Loop (79701-8510)
P.O. Box 9423 (79708-9423)
PHONE..............................432 699-1200
Michael Swihart, *President*
Herman Garza, *General Mgr*
Michael Evans, *Opers Mgr*
EMP: 50
SQ FT: 20,000
SALES (est): 10MM **Privately Held**
WEB: www.productionlift.com
SIC: 1389 Oil field services

(G-15365)
PROFESSNAL DRCTIONAL ENTPS INC
Also Called: Pro Directional
3001 S County Road 1260 (79706-2625)
PHONE..............................432 695-6152
EMP: 39

SALES (corp-wide): 289.6MM **Privately Held**
WEB: www.prodirectional.com
SIC: 1389 Oil field services
PA: Professional Directional Enterprises, Inc.
850 Conroe Park West Dr
Conroe TX 77303
936 441-7266

(G-15366)
PROPETRO HOLDING CORP (PA)
1706 S Midkiff Rd Ste B (79701-8844)
PHONE..............................432 688-0012
Phillip A Gobe, *Ch of Bd*
David Sledge, *COO*
Adam Munoz, *Senior VP*
David Schorlemer, *CFO*
Mark Berg, *Director*
EMP: 12 **EST:** 2005
SALES (est): 2B **Publicly Held**
WEB: www.propetroservices.com
SIC: 1382 Oil & gas exploration services

(G-15367)
PROPETRO SERVICES INC
4 S Industrial Loop (79701-8561)
PHONE..............................432 685-0059
EMP: 10
SALES (corp-wide): 2B **Publicly Held**
WEB: www.propetroservices.com
SIC: 1381 Service well drilling
HQ: Propetro Services, Inc.
1706 S Midkiff Rd Ste B
Midland TX 79701
432 688-0012

(G-15368)
PROPETRO SERVICES INC (HQ)
1706 S Midkiff Rd Ste B (79701-8844)
P.O. Box 873 (79702-0873)
PHONE..............................432 688-0012
Beau Tenney, *Division Mgr*
Matt Pro, *Opers Mgr*
Juan Bravo, *Engineer*
John Lavoi, *Treasurer*
Sam Sledge, *Investment Ofcr*
▲ **EMP:** 89
SQ FT: 4,000
SALES (est): 742MM
SALES (corp-wide): 2B **Publicly Held**
WEB: www.propetroservices.com
SIC: 1382 Oil & gas exploration services
PA: Propetro Holding Corp.
1706 S Midkiff Rd Ste B
Midland TX 79701
432 688-0012

(G-15369)
PROTORQUE ENERGY INC (PA)
2606 E Interstate 20 (79706-4250)
PHONE..............................432 208-1404
EMP: 50 **EST:** 2017
SALES (est): 4.2MM **Privately Held**
WEB: www.protorquetech.com
SIC: 1389 Oil And Gas Field Services, Nec, Nsk

(G-15370)
PRUCKA-LANEY INC (PA)
Also Called: Frac Tank Supply Company
3204 Sunburst Dr (79707-5273)
PHONE..............................432 687-0799
Larry Prucka, *President*
Gerald Laney, *Vice Pres*
▲ **EMP:** 10 **EST:** 1999
SQ FT: 4,000
SALES (est): 1.1MM **Privately Held**
WEB: www.fractanksupply.com
SIC: 3533 Drilling tools for gas, oil or water wells

(G-15371)
PURITY OILFIELD SERVICES LLC
11109 W County Road 46 (79707-2135)
PHONE..............................844 221-1500
Richard Mathis, *Opers Mgr*
Isaac Estes, *Manager*
EMP: 57
SALES (corp-wide): 4.1B **Privately Held**
WEB: www.purityoilfieldservices.com
SIC: 1389 Oil field services

HQ: Purity Oilfield Services, Llc
2101 Cedar Springs Rd # 650
Dallas TX 75201
214 880-8400

(G-15372)
Q2 ARTIFICIAL LIFT SVCS LLC
3611 E State Highway 158 (79706-4229)
PHONE..................................903 983-1432
Jim Irvin, *Opers Spvr*
Reece Donovan, *Branch Mgr*
Boyd Pryznyk, *Branch Mgr*
Ryan Thibault, *Branch Mgr*
Jimmy Poindexter, *Manager*
EMP: 55
SALES (est): 2.8MM
SALES (corp-wide): 121.9MM **Privately
Held**
WEB: www.q2als.com
SIC: 1389 Servicing oil & gas wells
PA: Q2 Artificial Lift Services Ulc
7883 Edgar Industrial Way
Red Deer AB T4P 3
403 343-8802

(G-15373)
QUALITY LOGGING INC
1800 Dayton Rd (79706-3844)
P.O. Box 2463 (79702-2463)
PHONE..................................432 682-7168
Paul Simmons, *President*
David Watts, *Vice Pres*
Richard Martin, *Opers Mgr*
John Peace, *Opers Staff*
Bill Simmons, *Treasurer*
EMP: 70
SQ FT: 2,400
SALES (est): 7.3MM **Privately Held**
WEB: www.qualitylogging.com
SIC: 1389 Well logging

(G-15374)
QUIKRETE COMPANIES LLC
3517 W Industrial Ave (79703-7737)
PHONE..................................432 694-5432
EMP: 46 **Privately Held**
WEB: www.quikrete.com
SIC: 3272 Concrete products
HQ: The Quikrete Companies Llc
5 Concourse Pkwy Ste 1900
Atlanta GA 30328
404 634-9100

(G-15375)
**R A D ROUSTABOUT SERVICE
LLC**
1508 S Jefferson St (79701-8260)
PHONE..................................432 664-2430
Anita Yharte, *Mng Member*
EMP: 9 EST: 2011
SALES (est): 170K **Privately Held**
SIC: 1389 Roustabout service

(G-15376)
R T M INTERESTS LLC
550 W Texas Ave Ste 945 (79701-4233)
PHONE..................................432 683-7700
Richard McMillan, *President*
EMP: 12
SALES (est): 189.4K **Privately Held**
SIC: 5812 1321 Eating places; liquefied
petroleum gases (natural) production

(G-15377)
RANDCO INDUSTRIES INC
Also Called: R Young Fabrications
2702 W County Road 130 (79706-6225)
P.O. Box 9908 (79708-9908)
PHONE..................................432 520-0820
Randy Young, *President*
Becky Young, *Corp Secy*
Scott Young, *Vice Pres*
Sebastian Pinal, *QC Mgr*
Sobeida Benavides, *Assistant*
EMP: 25
SQ FT: 4,200
SALES (est): 10MM **Privately Held**
WEB: www.randcoindustries.com
SIC: 3441 7692 Fabricated structural
metal; welding repair

(G-15378)
REATTA ENERGY INC
306 W Wall St Ste 1100 (79701-5173)
P.O. Box 10727 (79702-7727)
PHONE..................................432 682-7495

J Rube Purvis, *President*
EMP: 10
SALES (est): 1.6MM **Privately Held**
SIC: 2911 3433 Gases & liquefied petro-
leum gases; gas-oil burners, combination

(G-15379)
**REEF CHEMICAL
CORPORATION INC**
7906 W Highway 80 (79706-2825)
P.O. Box 11347 (79702-8347)
PHONE..................................432 560-5600
Kevin C Moore, *CEO*
Ella Sue Luft, *Corp Secy*
Bobby Hunt, *Vice Pres*
Mike Pressnall, *Vice Pres*
EMP: 146 EST: 1976
SALES (est): 13.8MM **Privately Held**
WEB: www.reefcorp.com
SIC: 1389 Servicing oil & gas wells

(G-15380)
RELIANCE ENERGY INC (PA)
300 N Marienfeld St # 1100 (79701-4384)
PHONE..................................432 683-4816
Gary McKinny, *Ch of Bd*
B Jack Reed, *CFO*
EMP: 25
SQ FT: 4,000
SALES (est): 24.3MM **Privately Held**
WEB: www.reimid.com
SIC: 1311 Crude petroleum production;
natural gas production

(G-15381)
REMNANT OIL COMPANY LLC
6 Desta Dr Ste 5100 (79705-5574)
P.O. Box 5375 (79704-5375)
PHONE..................................432 695-6997
E Gray, *Exec VP*
Vicki Kay, *Vice Pres*
Britt Hirth, *Engineer*
Michael McGraw, *Engineer*
David A Richards, *Controller*
EMP: 15
SALES (est): 705.2K **Privately Held**
WEB: www.remnantoil.com
SIC: 1311 Crude petroleum & natural gas

(G-15382)
**RESOLUTE NATURAL
RESOURCES LLC**
4000 N Big Spring St # 500 (79705-4630)
PHONE..................................432 684-7475
Doug Dietrich, *Manager*
EMP: 25
SALES (corp-wide): 2.3B **Publicly Held**
SIC: 1382 Oil & gas exploration services
HQ: Resolute Natural Resources Company,
Llc
1700 N Lincoln St # 3950
Denver CO 80203
303 534-4600

(G-15383)
REYNOLDS BROTHERS LTD (PA)
315 N Colorado St (79701-4603)
PHONE..................................432 682-7393
Gene C Reynolds Jr, *President*
EMP: 22
SQ FT: 10,000
SALES (est): 3.3MM **Privately Held**
WEB: www.reynoldsbros.com
SIC: 7334 2752 5021 5112 Blueprinting
service; commercial printing, offset; office
furniture; office supplies; typesetting;
bookbinding & related work

(G-15384)
RG EXPLORATION LLC
10 Desta Dr Ste 260e (79705-4508)
P.O. Box 50203 (79710-0203)
PHONE..................................405 650-1207
Patrick Drennon,
Monte Stovall,
EMP: 9
SALES (est): 797.3K **Privately Held**
SIC: 1381 Drilling oil & gas wells

(G-15385)
RING ENERGY INC (PA)
901 W Wall St Fl 3 (79701-6673)
P.O. Box 11350 (79702-8350)
PHONE..................................432 682-7464
Kelly Hoffman, *CEO*
Lloyd T Rochford, *Ch of Bd*

William R Broaddrick, *CFO*
Jeanette Serna, *Technician*
EMP: 29
SQ FT: 15,000
SALES (est): 120MM **Publicly Held**
WEB: www.ringenergy.com
SIC: 1311 Crude petroleum production

(G-15386)
RING ENERGY INC
200 N Loraine St Ste 1245 (79701-4756)
P.O. Box 11350 (79702-8350)
PHONE..................................432 682-7464
EMP: 11
SALES (corp-wide): 120MM **Publicly
Held**
WEB: www.ringenergy.com
SIC: 1311 Crude petroleum & natural gas
PA: Ring Energy Inc.
901 W Wall St Fl 3
Midland TX 79701
432 682-7464

(G-15387)
RK PETROLEUM CORP
406 N Main St (79701-4710)
P.O. Box 8528 (79708-8528)
PHONE..................................432 683-4319
Rudolph W Kuzmich, *Ch of Bd*
Clinton J Kuzmich, *President*
Stephen W Kuzmich, *President*
Stephen Kuzmich, *Vice Pres*
Glenn Prescott, *Vice Pres*
EMP: 18 EST: 1956
SQ FT: 10,000
SALES: 16.8MM **Privately Held**
WEB: www.rkpetroleum.com
SIC: 1311 1382 Crude petroleum produc-
tion; oil & gas exploration services

(G-15388)
ROLLTEX INC
Also Called: Rolltex Bearing
901 W Florida Ave (79701-7905)
P.O. Box 2615 (79702-2615)
PHONE..................................432 570-7576
EMP: 9 EST: 1974
SQ FT: 10,000
SALES (est): 2.9MM **Privately Held**
WEB: www.rolltexinc.com
SIC: 5085 3594 Bearings; pumps, hy-
draulic power transfer

(G-15389)
**ROXWELL PERFORMANCE
DRLG LLC**
Also Called: R D T
7613 W Industrial Ave (79706-2803)
PHONE..................................432 617-0419
Roger Muniz,
Keith Martin,
EMP: 14
SALES (est): 1.9MM **Privately Held**
SIC: 1381 Drilling oil & gas wells

(G-15390)
RSP PERMIAN INC (HQ)
600 W Illinois Ave (79701-4882)
PHONE..................................432 683-7443
Steven Gray, *CEO*
Zane Arrott, *COO*
James Mutrie, *Vice Pres*
Michael Healey, *Opers Staff*
Scott McNeill, *CFO*
EMP: 25
SALES: 803.7MM **Privately Held**
WEB: www.rsppermian.com
SIC: 1311 Crude petroleum production

(G-15391)
RSP PERMIAN LLC
200 N Loraine St Ste 800 (79701-4754)
PHONE..................................432 818-1300
Zane Arrott, *Branch Mgr*
Barry Tigh, *Analyst*
Richard Ramsey, *Legal Staff*
EMP: 14 **Privately Held**
WEB: www.rsppermian.com
SIC: 1382 Oil & gas exploration services
HQ: Rsp Permian, L.L.C.
3141 Hood St Ste 700
Dallas TX 75219

(G-15392)
**SAGA PETRO LTD LBLTY CO
COLO**
200 N Loraine St Ste 1300 (79701-4779)
PHONE..................................432 687-6200
J Charles Farmer, *President*
EMP: 18
SALES (est): 2.4MM **Privately Held**
SIC: 1311 Crude petroleum & natural gas

(G-15393)
SAHARA OPERATING COMPANY
306 W Wall St Ste 1025 (79701-5105)
P.O. Box 4130 (79704-4130)
PHONE..................................432 697-0967
Rob McAlpine, *President*
George McAlpine, *Vice Pres*
Elizabeth McAlpine, *Treasurer*
EMP: 15
SQ FT: 1,875
SALES (est): 1.7MM **Privately Held**
WEB: www.saharaoper.com
SIC: 1311 Crude petroleum production;
natural gas production

(G-15394)
**SALAZAR SERVICE AND TRCKG
CORP (PA)**
5511 Starboard Dr (79706-2184)
PHONE..................................432 523-9658
Porfirio Salazar, *President*
Jennifer Martinez, *Manager*
Claudia Guaderrama, *Technology*
Maria Salazar, *Admin Sec*
EMP: 35 EST: 2002
SALES (est): 18.7MM **Privately Held**
WEB: www.salazarservice.com
SIC: 1389 Servicing oil & gas wells; oil field
services

(G-15395)
SALTEL-INDUSTRIES INC
6213 W County Road 112 (79706-3725)
PHONE..................................432 238-1076
Saltel Louis, *Principal*
EMP: 10
SALES (est): 820.8K **Privately Held**
SIC: 1389 Construction, repair & disman-
tling services

(G-15396)
**SCHLUMBERGER
TECHNOLOGY CORP**
Also Called: Schlumberger Oilfield Services
4704 W Hwy 80 (79703)
PHONE..................................432 694-0000
EMP: 21 **Publicly Held**
SIC: 1389 1382 Oil/Gas Field Services
Oil/Gas Exploration Services
HQ: Schlumberger Technology Corp
100 Gillingham Ln
Sugar Land TX 77478
281 285-8500

(G-15397)
**SCHLUMBERGER
TECHNOLOGY CORP**
Also Called: Schlumberger Well Services
7104 W County Road 116 (79706-2960)
PHONE..................................432 683-0047
John Reinhart, *Opers-Prdtn-Mfg*
EMP: 125 **Publicly Held**
SIC: 1389 Oil field services
HQ: Schlumberger Technology Corp
300 Schlumberger Dr
Sugar Land TX 77478
281 285-8500

(G-15398)
**SCHLUMBERGER
TECHNOLOGY CORP**
Also Called: Dowell Schlumberger
1204 W Scharbauer Dr (79705-8733)
PHONE..................................432 571-4600
Oscar Marshall, *Manager*
EMP: 60 **Publicly Held**
SIC: 1389 Oil field services
HQ: Schlumberger Technology Corp
300 Schlumberger Dr
Sugar Land TX 77478
281 285-8500

GEOGRAPHIC

(G-15399)
SCIENTIFIC DRILLING INTL INC
Also Called: Directional Drilling
2034 Trade Dr (79706-2838)
P.O. Box 9699 (79708-9699)
PHONE................................432 563-1339
Fax: 432 697-0324
EMP: 41
SALES (corp-wide): 20.8MM **Privately Held**
SIC: 1381 Oil/Gas Well Drilling
PA: Scientific Drilling International, Inc.
　16071 Greenspoint Park
　Houston TX 77060
　281 443-3300

(G-15400)
SCORPION FLOWBACK LLC
2318 E County Road 123 (79706-6648)
PHONE................................432 302-1628
John R Lawson, *Mng Member*
EMP: 15
SALES (est): 347.4K **Privately Held**
WEB: www.enercorpsandsolutions.com
SIC: 1382 Oil & gas exploration services

(G-15401)
SEABOARD OIL CO
Also Called: Seaboard Operating
3100 N A St Ste B-200 (79705-5384)
P.O. Box 50180 (79710-0180)
PHONE................................432 684-7005
E E Runyan, *Ch of Bd*
Gary B Gilliam, *Officer*
EMP: 16
SQ FT: 17,500
SALES (est): 3.5MM **Privately Held**
SIC: 1311 Crude petroleum production
PA: Seaboard Acquisition Partners Inc
　3100 N A St Ste B-201
　Midland TX

(G-15402)
SEABOARD OPERATING INC
3100 N A St Bldg B (79705-5358)
PHONE................................432 684-7005
Edward Runyan, *President*
EMP: 20 EST: 2010
SALES (est): 715.6K **Privately Held**
SIC: 1389 Oil field services

(G-15403)
SELMAN & ASSOCIATES LTD
10114 Liberator Ln (79706-2626)
P.O. Box 61150 (79711-1150)
PHONE................................432 563-0084
Tom H Selman, *President*
Juanita Selman, *Partner*
Ana Gomez, *Comp Tech*
EMP: 120
SALES (est): 16.6MM **Privately Held**
WEB: www.selmanlog.com
SIC: 1389 1382 Mud service, oil field
　drilling; oil & gas exploration services

(G-15404)
SES OPERATING INC
223 W Wall St Fl 9 (79701-4531)
PHONE................................432 687-6560
Wesley Perry, *CEO*
EMP: 20
SALES (est): 1MM **Privately Held**
SIC: 1381 Drilling oil & gas wells

(G-15405)
SHARP ROUSTABOUT & CNSTR LLC
4304 E County Road 130 (79706-6718)
P.O. Box 50296 (79710-0296)
PHONE................................432 528-6360
Rosemary Rubio, *Mng Member*
EMP: 26
SALES (est): 3MM **Privately Held**
WEB: www.sharproustabtllc.com
SIC: 1389 Oil field services

(G-15406)
SHENANDOAH PETROLEUM CORP
24 Smith Rd Ste 601 (79705-4412)
PHONE................................432 685-1964
Troy Martin Jr, *President*
Ryan Bartholomee, *CFO*
Diane Martin, *Treasurer*
Carolyn Cagle, *Admin Sec*

EMP: 18
SQ FT: 2,000
SALES (est): 4.7MM **Privately Held**
WEB: www.thebarmranch.com
SIC: 1311 Crude petroleum production;
　natural gas production

(G-15407)
SHERIDAN PROD PARTNERS I-A LP
200 N Loraine St Ste 530 (79701-4747)
PHONE................................432 683-5271
Michael McCool, *VP Opers*
Gary Lochary, *Production*
Michelle Caruso, *Accountant*
Lisa Stewart, *Branch Mgr*
EMP: 247 **Privately Held**
WEB: www.sheridanproduction.com
SIC: 1382 Oil & gas exploration services
PA: Sheridan Production Partners I-A, L.P.
　1360 Post Oak Blvd Ste 25
　Houston TX 77056

(G-15408)
SHERMAN BRANSON CONSTRUCTION
Also Called: Wtb
10400 W County Road 77 (79707-1682)
PHONE................................432 684-4740
Branson Sherman, *President*
EMP: 80 EST: 2013
SALES (est): 2MM **Privately Held**
WEB: www.wtb-spray.com
SIC: 7353 1389 Oil field equipment, rental
　or leasing; gas field services

(G-15409)
SILVERTIP COMPLETION SVCS LLC
9816 W County Road 146 (79706-2260)
P.O. Box 53487 (79710-3487)
PHONE................................432 701-9020
William Wood, *
EMP: 45
SALES (est): 55.2MM **Privately Held**
WEB: www.silvertipcompletions.com
SIC: 1389 Processing service, gas

(G-15410)
SLAUGHTER & STANLEY CNSTR INC
Also Called: S & S Construction
921 N Fairgrounds Rd (79706-4366)
P.O. Box 1741, Big Spring (79721-1741)
PHONE................................432 264-0031
A J Stanley, *President*
Jess Slaughter, *Vice Pres*
Sherrie Stanley, *Treasurer*
Jana Slaughter, *Admin Sec*
EMP: 10 EST: 1999
SALES (est): 287.7K
SALES (corp-wide): 453.4K **Privately Held**
SIC: 1389 Oil field services
PA: Linestar Services, Inc.
　4203 Montrose Blvd
　Houston TX 77006
　832 830-8531

(G-15411)
SM ENERGY COMPANY
6301 Holiday Hill Rd # 1 (79707-2112)
P.O. Box 46518, Denver CO (80201-6518)
PHONE................................432 688-1700
Newt Newton, *Senior VP*
Tom Morrow, *Prdtn Mgr*
Mark Bondy, *Production*
David Carrillo, *Manager*
Marvin Moore, *Director*
EMP: 100
SALES (corp-wide): 1.5B **Publicly Held**
WEB: www.sm-energy.com
SIC: 1311 1382 Crude petroleum produc-
　tion; natural gas production; oil & gas ex-
　ploration services
PA: Sm Energy Company
　1775 N Sherman St # 1200
　Denver CO 80203
　303 861-8140

(G-15412)
SMITH INDUSTRIES INC
3601 E State Highway 158 (79706-4229)
P.O. Box 870 (79702-0870)
PHONE................................432 683-9722

Rick B Smith, *CEO*
Ty Hartley, *Vice Pres*
EMP: 40
SALES (est): 27.7MM **Privately Held**
WEB: www.smithindustriestx.com
SIC: 1389 Oil field services

(G-15413)
SOC INDUSTRIES LLC
2324 Fm 715 (79706-4234)
PHONE................................432 620-0040
Russ Hale, *Sales Staff*
EMP: 30 EST: 2007
SALES (est): 3.5MM **Privately Held**
WEB: www.socind.net
SIC: 1389 Pipe testing, oil field service; oil
　field services; servicing oil & gas wells

(G-15414)
SOLAR TURBINES INCORPORATED
2912 S County Road 1255 (79706-2681)
PHONE................................800 851-6594
Kyle Walker, *Branch Mgr*
Javier Marquez, *Supervisor*
EMP: 89
SALES (corp-wide): 53.8B **Publicly Held**
WEB: www.solarturbines.com
SIC: 3511 Gas turbine generator set units,
　complete
HQ: Solar Turbines Incorporated
　2200 Pacific Hwy
　San Diego CA 92101
　619 544-5000

(G-15415)
SOLNEXUS CHEMICAL LLC
6001 W Industrial Ave (79706-2841)
PHONE................................432 689-6180
Steve Goree, *Manager*
EMP: 13
SALES (est): 3.7MM **Privately Held**
WEB: www.solnexuschemical.com
SIC: 2899 Chemical preparations

(G-15416)
SRH TOOLS LLC
1104 N County Road 1090 (79706-4629)
PHONE................................432 686-1058
Samuel Roman, *Mng Member*
Griselda Roman, *
EMP: 30
SQ FT: 1,100
SALES (est): 430K **Privately Held**
WEB: www.srhtools.com
SIC: 1389 Cementing oil & gas well cas-
　ings

(G-15417)
SSI LIFT USA LTD
Also Called: Ssi Artificial Lift USA
9702 E County Rd 97 (79706)
PHONE................................432 488-6427
Dave Kennedy, *President*
EMP: 23
SALES (est): 1MM **Privately Held**
SIC: 3561 3537 Pumps, oil well & field; lift
　trucks, industrial: fork, platform, straddle,
　etc.

(G-15418)
STADIUM CHAIR CO LLC
206 N Midkiff Rd Ste 2b (79701-6289)
P.O. Box 1356, Shirley MA (01464-1356)
PHONE................................432 682-4682
Arlene Gardner, *Mktg Coord*
Carl Wilhite, *
▲ EMP: 10
SALES (est): 570K **Privately Held**
WEB: www.stadiumchair.com
SIC: 2531 5021 Chairs, portable folding;
　chairs

(G-15419)
STEADY FLOW TESTERS LLC
1518 E County Road 140 (79706-7296)
PHONE................................432 258-1184
Sergio Robles, *Mng Member*
EMP: 12
SALES (est): 900K **Privately Held**
SIC: 1389 Testing, measuring, surveying &
　analysis services

(G-15420)
STEWARD ENTERPRISES INC
Also Called: Steward Cable
1921 Alta Vista Dr (79706-3855)
P.O. Box 11270 (79702-8270)
PHONE................................432 687-2553
Bill Steward Jr, *President*
Billy Steward Jr, *President*
Rhonda Elliott, *Corp Secy*
Linda Steward, *Director*
▲ EMP: 195
SQ FT: 55,000
SALES (est): 42.9MM
SALES (corp-wide): 8.6B **Publicly Held**
SIC: 3357 1382 Nonferrous wiredrawing &
　insulating; seismograph surveys
PA: Amphenol Corporation
　358 Hall Ave
　Wallingford CT 06492
　203 265-8900

(G-15421)
STURGEON SERVICES TEXAS INC
1100 E County Road 140 (79706-7140)
PHONE................................661 322-4408
Paul H Sturgeon, *President*
EMP: 15
SALES (est): 748.6K **Privately Held**
WEB: www.sturgeonservices.com
SIC: 3531 Road construction & mainte-
　nance machinery

(G-15422)
SUBMERSIBLE OIL SERVICES INC
2707 S County Road 1208 (79706-3826)
P.O. Box 80130 (79708-0130)
PHONE................................432 699-1506
Tom Vineyard, *President*
▲ EMP: 106
SALES (est): 12MM
SALES (corp-wide): 95.2B **Publicly Held**
SIC: 5084 1389 Pumps & pumping equip-
　ment; oil field services
HQ: Ge Oil & Gas Esp, Inc.
　5500 Se 59th St
　Oklahoma City OK 73135
　405 670-1431

(G-15423)
SUMMIT PETROLEUM LLC
550 W Texas Ave Ste 700 (79701-4250)
PHONE................................432 682-9800
Mat R Johnson, *Exec VP*
Jim Behrmann, *Vice Pres*
Gary Caraveo, *Foreman/Supr*
Gayland King, *Foreman/Supr*
Ryan Hamilton, *Production*
EMP: 23
SALES (est): 5.6MM **Privately Held**
WEB: www.summitpetroleumllc.com
SIC: 1382 Oil & gas exploration services

(G-15424)
SUN ENERGY SERVICES LLC
Also Called: Deep Well Services
10303 W County Road 148 (79706-2276)
PHONE................................432 701-9000
EMP: 15 **Privately Held**
WEB: www.deepwellservices.com
SIC: 1382 Oil & gas exploration services
PA: Sun Energy Services Llc
　307 W New Castle St
　Zelienople PA 16063

(G-15425)
SUN WEST MUD COMPANY INC (PA)
Also Called: SW Fluids
3002 W Front St (79701-7145)
P.O. Box 80593 (79708-0593)
PHONE................................432 689-0777
Malcolm N Outlaw, *President*
Debbie J Outlaw, *Vice Pres*
David Bleeker, *Warehouse Mgr*
Raymond Gonzales, *Warehouse Mgr*
Tiffany Outlaw, *Purchasing*
EMP: 11
SQ FT: 15,000
SALES (est): 19.1MM **Privately Held**
WEB: www.sunwestfluids.com
SIC: 1389 Oil field services

▲ = Import ▼=Export
◆ =Import/Export

(G-15426)
SUSIES SOUTH FORTY
CONFECTIONS (PA)
401 S Marienfeld St (79701-5002)
P.O. Box 4040 (79704-4040)
PHONE................................432 570-4040
Susie Hitchcock-Hall, *Owner*
Mike Hall, *Vice Pres*
▲ EMP: 68
SQ FT: 20,000
SALES (est): 9MM **Privately Held**
WEB: www.susiessouthforty.com
SIC: 2064 5947 2066 5441 Candy &
other confectionery products; gift, novelty
& souvenir shop; chocolate & cocoa prod-
ucts; candy, nut & confectionery stores

(G-15427)
SWIFTWATER ENERGY
SERVICES LLC
2401 N County Road 1287 (79707-2133)
PHONE................................405 203-5419
Brandon Fields, *Superintendent*
Hunter Morris, *Principal*
Nick Rives, *Sales Mgr*
EMP: 9 EST: 2015
SALES (est): 2.4MM
SALES (corp-wide): 1B **Publicly Held**
WEB: www.tetratec.com
SIC: 7353 1389 Oil field equipment, rental
or leasing; impounding & storing salt
water, oil & gas field
PA: Tetra Technologies, Inc.
24955 Interstate 45
The Woodlands TX 77380
281 367-1983

(G-15428)
T & T TESTERS INC
1302 Dayton Rd (79706-3807)
P.O. Box 2364 (79702-2364)
PHONE................................432 682-5456
Carolyn Watts, *President*
Tommy Watts, *Vice Pres*
EMP: 15
SQ FT: 1,000
SALES (est): 1.5MM **Privately Held**
SIC: 1389 Oil field services

(G-15429)
T-REY PROPERTIES INC
3700 E Hwy 158 (79706)
P.O. Box 2476 (79702-2476)
PHONE................................432 570-6822
Brian Watson, *President*
Kevin Smith, *Division Mgr*
Cliff Ward, *Opers Mgr*
EMP: 25 EST: 1999
SALES (est): 998.6K **Privately Held**
WEB: www.t-reyproperties.com
SIC: 1389 Oil field services

(G-15430)
TALL CITY WELL SERVICE CO
LP
Also Called: V S T
303 Veterans Airpark Ln # 4105
(79705-4554)
PHONE................................432 618-9937
Joel Solis, *Partner*
EMP: 11
SALES (est): 1.3MM **Privately Held**
SIC: 1389 Oil field services

(G-15431)
TAUREX DRILL BITS LLC
Also Called: PDC Logic
9 E Industrial Loop (79701-8514)
PHONE................................432 684-4711
Tom Waitman, *Branch Mgr*
EMP: 32
SALES (corp-wide): 20.1MM **Privately
Held**
WEB: www.taurexbits.com
SIC: 3547 Billet mills
PA: Taurex Drill Bits, Llc
2601 Venture Dr
Norman OK 73069
405 321-8850

(G-15432)
TAURUS OIL INC
2052 Commerce Dr (79703-7502)
PHONE................................432 685-3520
Carter Copeland, *President*

Faught Jesse A Jr, *Vice Pres*
EMP: 11
SQ FT: 2,000
SALES (est): 1.5MM **Privately Held**
SIC: 1382 Oil & gas exploration services

(G-15433)
TCO FIELD SERVICE INC
3601 Garden City Hwy (79706)
P.O. Box 11225 (79702-8225)
PHONE................................432 682-5355
Terry Johnson, *President*
Brad Neatherlin, *Superintendent*
Shawn Miller, *Opers Mgr*
EMP: 40
SALES (est): 5.9MM **Privately Held**
WEB: www.tcofldsvc.com
SIC: 1389 Oil field services

(G-15434)
TDR SERVICES INC (PA)
4 Golden Gate Ste 3 (79707)
P.O. Box 51988 (79710-1988)
PHONE................................422 606-6084
Robert Roland, *President*
Trey Roland, *COO*
EMP: 55
SQ FT: 8,000
SALES (est): 8.5MM **Privately Held**
SIC: 1389 Servicing oil & gas wells

(G-15435)
TEGRAEXCEL ENERGY
SERVICES LLC
2807 Douglas Dr (79701-3831)
PHONE................................412 508-0690
Benjamin Kail, *Mng Member*
Mark Amador, *Mng Member*
EMP: 10
SALES (est): 2.5MM **Privately Held**
WEB: www.tegraexcel.com
SIC: 4011 1389 Railroads, line-haul oper-
ating; haulage, oil field; hydraulic fractur-
ing wells

(G-15436)
TEXAS INCINERATOR CO INC
2401 Neill Ave (79701-8809)
P.O. Box 9128 (79708-9128)
PHONE................................432 687-5045
Mike Brady, *President*
W H Brady, *Vice Pres*
George Hancock, *Vice Pres*
Ron Brady, *Shareholder*
EMP: 10
SQ FT: 6,000
SALES (est): 6.9MM **Privately Held**
WEB: www.texasincinerator.com
SIC: 3567 3523 Incinerators, metal: do-
mestic or commercial; soil preparation
machinery, except turf & grounds

(G-15437)
THREE SPAN OIL & GAS INC
400 W Illinois Ave # 1250 (79701-4399)
P.O. Box 51538 (79710-1538)
PHONE................................432 684-6511
Earl Baldridge, *President*
EMP: 10 EST: 1992
SQ FT: 3,000
SALES (est): 4.1MM **Privately Held**
WEB: www.threespan.com
SIC: 1382 Oil & gas exploration services

(G-15438)
TMP TRUCK & TRAILER LP
2700 Rankin Hwy (79706-4000)
P.O. Box 10366 (79702-7366)
PHONE................................432 686-2500
William C Pennington, *President*
EMP: 20 EST: 2000
SQ FT: 15,000
SALES (est): 2MM **Privately Held**
WEB: www.gotmp.com
SIC: 5599 5531 5012 5013 Utility trailers;
automobile & truck equipment & parts;
trailers for trucks, new & used; trailers for
passenger vehicles; trailer parts & acces-
sories; truck parts & accessories; sheet
metalwork

(G-15439)
TOMCAT GLOBAL
CORPORATION (PA)
2160 Commerce Dr (79703-7504)
P.O. Box 550 (79702-0550)
PHONE................................432 694-7070
Mike Garl, *President*
Adam Gross, *Prdtn Mgr*
EMP: 65
SALES (est): 8.2MM **Privately Held**
WEB: www.tomcatglobal.com
SIC: 3648 Stage lighting equipment

(G-15440)
TOTAL OPERATIONS PROD
SVCS LLC
12614 W County Road 91 (79707-5811)
PHONE................................432 332-9777
Brian D Green, *President*
George Treadaway, *Maint Spvr*
EMP: 17
SALES (est): 3.6MM **Privately Held**
WEB: www.total-operations.com
SIC: 1381 Drilling oil & gas wells

(G-15441)
TOTAL ROD CONCEPTS INC
2800 S County Road 1207 (79706-3756)
PHONE................................432 689-0300
Douglas A Branch, *Principal*
EMP: 12
SALES (est): 3.7MM **Privately Held**
WEB: www.trcsuckerrods.com
SIC: 3355 Rods, rolled, aluminum

(G-15442)
TRANS-TEX CEMENTING SVCS
LLC
5019 Basin St (79703-7505)
P.O. Box 50455 (79710-0455)
PHONE................................432 699-4400
Doug Givhan, *Partner*
▲ EMP: 70
SALES (est): 7.6MM **Privately Held**
WEB: www.transtexservices.com
SIC: 1389 Cementing oil & gas well cas-
ings

(G-15443)
TRANSCEND DRILLING
COMPANY INC
1118 S Fm 1788 (79706-2635)
PHONE................................432 618-1100
Scott Bryant, *CEO*
Mark Franklin, *COO*
Kevin Kelley, *Manager*
EMP: 76
SALES (est): 3.5MM
SALES (corp-wide): 26.6MM **Privately
Held**
SIC: 1381 Drilling oil & gas wells
PA: Butch's Rat Hole & Anchor Service, Inc.
700 Austin St
Levelland TX 79336
806 894-6294

(G-15444)
TREY RESOURCES INC
601 N Marienfeld St # 400 (79701-4365)
P.O. Box 50272 (79710-0272)
PHONE................................432 570-6898
David M Thomas III, *President*
Leah T Rudnicki, *Vice Pres*
Mitzi B Thomas, *Treasurer*
EMP: 25
SALES (est): 18.3MM **Privately Held**
WEB: www.treyresources.net
SIC: 1381 Drilling oil & gas wells

(G-15445)
TRI RESOURCES INC
Also Called: Dynegy
6 Desta Dr Ste 3300 (79705-5524)
PHONE................................432 688-0555
Clark White, *Exec VP*
EMP: 12 **Publicly Held**
WEB: www.triresources.com
SIC: 1321 Natural gas liquids
HQ: Tri Resources Inc.
811 Louisiana St Ste 2100
Houston TX 77002
713 584-1000

(G-15446)
TRIPLE N SERVICES INC
1110 W County Road 114 (79706-3817)
P.O. Box 7807 (79708-7807)
PHONE................................432 687-1994
James F Newman, *President*
Steven Newman, *Vice Pres*
Holly Newman, *Treasurer*
EMP: 49
SQ FT: 23,600
SALES (est): 19.9MM **Privately Held**
WEB: www.triplenservices.com
SIC: 1382 Oil & gas exploration services

(G-15447)
TROY VINES INCORPORATED
Also Called: Vines Ready Mix
2817 S State Highway 349 (79706-4003)
P.O. Box 1351 (79702-1351)
PHONE................................432 682-7031
Imogene Vines, *President*
Johnnie Vines, *Vice Pres*
EMP: 17
SALES (est): 4.8MM
SALES (corp-wide): 2.2B **Publicly Held**
WEB: www.troyvinesconcrete.com
SIC: 3273 Ready-mixed concrete
HQ: Summit Materials, Llc
1550 Wynkoop St Ste 300
Denver CO 80202
303 893-0012

(G-15448)
TRUCOASTAL OIL AND GAS
SVCS
5002 Basin St (79703-7525)
P.O. Box 7312 (79708-7312)
PHONE................................432 413-9950
Orlando Rule, *Principal*
Isaac Esparza, *Principal*
Eric Pardo, *Principal*
EMP: 17
SALES (est): 799.9K **Privately Held**
WEB: www.trucoastaltransports.com
SIC: 1389 Oil & gas field services

(G-15449)
TURN RIGHT TOOLS LLC (PA)
2408 S County Road 1245 (79706-2926)
P.O. Box 80631 (79708-0631)
PHONE................................432 704-5490
Amanda Windle, *Controller*
Don B Cobb, *
Daniel J Moore, *
EMP: 26
SQ FT: 1,600
SALES (est): 6MM **Privately Held**
WEB: www.turnrighttools.com
SIC: 1381 Drilling oil & gas wells

(G-15450)
TWISTED R OILFIELD SVCS LLC
1008 Clemente Ct (79706-2920)
PHONE................................432 312-3110
Brad Richard, *Mng Member*
EMP: 12
SALES (est): 411.9K **Privately Held**
SIC: 1389 Oil & gas field services

(G-15451)
TZC SERVICES LLC
200 W Illinois Ave # 260 (79701-4682)
P.O. Box 161585, Austin (78716-1585)
PHONE................................432 517-1212
Steven Johnson, *CEO*
EMP: 10
SALES (est): 314.3K **Privately Held**
WEB: www.tzcservices.com
SIC: 1382 Oil & gas exploration services

(G-15452)
U S WEATHERFORD L P
10000 Pilot Ave (79706-2615)
P.O. Box 60787 (79711-0787)
PHONE................................432 561-8892
Guadalupe Iglesias, *Treasurer*
Russell Pullin, *Branch Mgr*
EMP: 25 **Privately Held**
WEB: www.weatherford.com
SIC: 3533 Oil & gas field machinery
HQ: U S Weatherford L P
179 Weatherford Dr
Schriever LA 70395
985 493-6100

(G-15453)
U S WEATHERFORD L P
10 Desta Dr Ste 350e (79705-4530)
PHONE..................................432 682-7321
Kerry James, *Area Mgr*
Mike Johnson, *Manager*
EMP: 10 **Privately Held**
WEB: www.weatherford.com
SIC: 1389 Oil field services
HQ: U S Weatherford L P
179 Weatherford Dr
Schriever LA 70395
985 493-6100

(G-15454)
UNION DRILLING INC
9105 W County Road 127 (79706)
P.O. Box 62280 (79711-2280)
PHONE..................................432 682-6111
EMP: 132
SALES (corp-wide): 55MM **Privately Held**
SIC: 1381 Oil And Gas Extraction
HQ: Union Drilling, Inc.
952 Echo Ln Ste 460
Houston TX 77024
817 735-8793

(G-15455)
UNITED CASING INCORPORATED
Also Called: United Casing Tubular Services
3610 E State Highway 158 (79706-4229)
PHONE..................................432 682-0110
Joe Ramon, *Supervisor*
EMP: 35
SALES (corp-wide): 30.3MM **Privately Held**
WEB: www.unitedcasing.com
SIC: 8999 3312 Actuarial consultant; pipes & tubes
PA: United Casing Incorporated
8505 Tech Frest Pl Ste 40
The Woodlands TX 77381
281 516-0195

(G-15456)
UNITEX OIL & GAS LLC
508 W Wall St Ste 1000 (79701-5003)
PHONE..................................432 685-0014
David C Wilson,
Jared Schroeder,
EMP: 11
SALES (est): 1.6MM **Privately Held**
WEB: www.unitexoilandgas.com
SIC: 1382 Oil & gas exploration services

(G-15457)
UNIVERSAL PRESSURE PUMPING INC
4517 W Industrial Ave (79703-7603)
P.O. Box 52190 (79710-2190)
PHONE..................................432 699-3205
Caleb Roberts, *District Mgr*
Adam Lord, *Technician*
EMP: 11
SALES (corp-wide): 1.1B **Publicly Held**
WEB: www.patenergy.com
SIC: 1381 Drilling oil & gas wells
HQ: Universal Pressure Pumping, Inc.
10713 W Sam Huston Pkwy N
Houston TX 77064

(G-15458)
UNIVERSAL VALVE COMPANY INC
Also Called: Universal Vlve Crane Spcalists
3501 W Industrial Ave (79703-7737)
PHONE..................................432 689-6341
Kevin Leary, *President*
Jorge Morrison, *Purchasing*
EMP: 28
SQ FT: 4,000
SALES (est): 5MM **Privately Held**
WEB: www.universalvalveco.com
SIC: 1389 1382 Oil field services; oil & gas exploration services

(G-15459)
V-F PETROLEUM INC
500 W Texas Ave Ste 350 (79701-4210)
P.O. Box 1889 (79702-1889)
PHONE..................................432 683-3344
Thomas Beall, *CEO*
Jerry M Gahr, *President*

Sandra K Lawlis, *Vice Pres*
EMP: 10
SQ FT: 3,000
SALES (est): 3.1MM **Privately Held**
WEB: www.vfpetroleum.com
SIC: 1311 Crude petroleum production; natural gas production

(G-15460)
VALIANT ARTFL LIFT SLTIONS LLC
2806 N County Road 1148 (79705-4116)
PHONE..................................432 253-2233
Juan Korszyk, *Vice Pres*
Frank Claborn, *Branch Mgr*
EMP: 12
SALES (corp-wide): 17.5MM **Privately Held**
WEB: www.valiant-als.com
SIC: 3533 7353 Oil field machinery & equipment; oil field equipment, rental or leasing
PA: Valiant Artificial Lift Solutions, Llc
1 Leadership Sq N
Oklahoma City OK 73102
405 605-4567

(G-15461)
VALOR CONTAINMENTS LLC
1207 S Midland Dr (79703-7602)
PHONE..................................432 202-4220
Mario Corona,
EMP: 12 EST: 2017
SALES (est): 329.6K **Privately Held**
SIC: 3999 Manufacturing industries

(G-15462)
VIPER ENERGY PARTNERS LP
Also Called: DIAMONDBACK
500 W Texas Ave Ste 1200 (79701-4203)
PHONE..................................432 221-7400
Travis D Stice, *CEO*
Viper E LLC, *General Ptnr*
Russell Pantermuehl, *Exec VP*
Teresa L Dick, *CFO*
Joanna Hord, *Consultant*
EMP: 141
SALES: 298.2MM
SALES (corp-wide): 3.9B **Publicly Held**
WEB: www.viperenergy.com
SIC: 1311 Crude petroleum production
PA: Diamondback Energy, Inc.
500 W Texas Ave Ste 1200
Midland TX 79701
432 221-7400

(G-15463)
WAGNER & BROWN LTD (PA)
200 N Loraine St Ste 950 (79701-4799)
P.O. Box 1714 (79702-1714)
PHONE..................................432 682-7936
A J Brune, *CEO*
Arthur Brune, *CFO*
Lawrence Rhodes, *Asst Controller*
James Barton, *Accounting Mgr*
Bobleta Cleere, *Human Res Mgr*
EMP: 60
SALES (est): 12MM **Privately Held**
WEB: www.wbltd.com
SIC: 1311 Crude petroleum production; natural gas production

(G-15464)
WALSH PETROLEUM INC
301 N Colorado St Ste 359 (79701-4603)
P.O. Box 3528 (79702-3528)
PHONE..................................432 684-5937
Linda Hill, *Vice Pres*
Craig Holly, *Vice Pres*
Justin St Clair, *Foreman/Supr*
Fred G Walsh, *Director*
EMP: 10
SQ FT: 2,000
SALES (est): 2.3MM **Privately Held**
SIC: 8711 1311 Petroleum engineering; crude petroleum production; natural gas production

(G-15465)
WARRIOR TECHNOLOGIES LLC
400 W Illinois Ave # 1120 (79701-4310)
PHONE..................................432 818-0498
EMP: 9
SALES (est): 2.3MM **Privately Held**
WEB: www.warriortechnologies.net
SIC: 1389 Oil field services

(G-15466)
WEATHERFORD ARTIFICIA
10000 Pilot Ave (79706-2615)
PHONE..................................432 561-5505
EMP: 32 **Privately Held**
WEB: www.weatherford.com
SIC: 3561 Pumps, oil well & field
HQ: Weatherford Artificial Lift Systems, Llc
2000 Saint James Pl
Houston TX 77056
713 836-4000

(G-15467)
WELLBORE FISHING RENTL TLS LLC
12100 Jordy Rd (79707-2191)
PHONE..................................432 563-1478
EMP: 10
SALES (corp-wide): 32.2MM **Privately Held**
WEB: www.wfrtools.com
SIC: 1389 Oil field services
PA: Wellbore Fishing & Rental Tools, Llc
9868 E Main St
Houma LA 70363
985 879-4705

(G-15468)
WELLSITE AUTOMATION
1513 W Montgomery Ave (79701-8059)
PHONE..................................432 218-9361
Pete Lowe, *Owner*
Brian Olds, *Technician*
EMP: 12
SALES (est): 780K **Privately Held**
WEB: www.pocsupply.com
SIC: 3823 Controllers for process variables, all types

(G-15469)
WESCO INTERNATIONAL INC
3303 W Illinois Ave (79703-6213)
PHONE..................................432 699-2680
Johnny C Woollums, *Project Mgr*
Hugo Zelaya, *Sales Staff*
EMP: 13 **Publicly Held**
WEB: www.wesco.com
SIC: 5063 3699 Electrical supplies; electrical equipment & supplies
PA: Wesco International, Inc.
225 W Station Square Dr # 700
Pittsburgh PA 15219

(G-15470)
WILSON SYSTEMS INC
3100 N A St Bldg A (79705-5361)
PHONE..................................432 684-5567
Word B Wilson, *President*
John Wilson II, *Vice Pres*
Mickey Long, *Vice Pres*
Nikki Haley Wilson, *Admin Sec*
EMP: 17
SQ FT: 8,100
SALES (est): 3.8MM **Privately Held**
WEB: www.wilson-systems.com
SIC: 7353 2819 Oil well drilling equipment, rental or leasing; brine

(G-15471)
WTG GAS PROCESSING LP (PA)
211 N Colorado St (79701-4607)
PHONE..................................432 682-4349
Ealmoor GP, *General Ptnr*
James L Davis, *General Ptnr*
Bobby Roach, *Safety Dir*
Kendall McCasland, *Safety Mgr*
Dave Freeman, *VP Bus Dvlpt*
EMP: 20
SALES (est): 30.2MM **Privately Held**
WEB: www.wtggasprocessing.com
SIC: 1321 Natural gasoline production

(G-15472)
WTG SUTH PERMIAN MIDSTREAM LLC
211 N Colorado St (79701-4607)
PHONE..................................432 682-4349
Michael Davis, *President*
Richard Hatchett, *Vice Pres*
Barbara Geffken, *Controller*
EMP: 10
SALES (est): 487.1K **Privately Held**
WEB: www.westtexasgas.com
SIC: 1389 Processing service, gas

(G-15473)
XOG OPERATING LLC
1801 W Texas Ave (79701-6561)
P.O. Box 352 (79702-0352)
PHONE..................................432 683-3171
Danny Soulier, *Vice Pres*
Randall Capps, *Project Mgr*
Jennifer Bowman, *Accounting Mgr*
Linda Phelps, *Office Mgr*
Logan Capps, *Manager*
EMP: 31
SALES (est): 8.8MM **Privately Held**
WEB: www.xogoperating.com
SIC: 1382 Oil & gas exploration services

(G-15474)
XTO ENERGY INC
6401 Holiday Hill Rd # 5 (79707-2157)
PHONE..................................432 682-8873
Earl Richardson, *Superintendent*
Dudley McMinn, *Safety Mgr*
Kim Grey, *Office Mgr*
Melba Daniels, *Director*
EMP: 125
SALES (corp-wide): 264.9B **Publicly Held**
WEB: www.xtoenergy.com
SIC: 1311 Crude petroleum production
HQ: Xto Energy Inc.
22777 Sprngwoods Vlg Pkwy
Spring TX 77389

Midlothian
Ellis County

(G-15475)
BUCKLEY OIL COMPANY (PA)
2900 Kemp Ranch Xing (76065-1670)
PHONE..................................214 421-4147
Robert E Dodson, *President*
Randy Smith, *General Mgr*
David Moore, *Exec VP*
Sylvia Dodson, *Vice Pres*
Linda Henry, *Vice Pres*
EMP: 34
SQ FT: 2,400
SALES (est): 19.2MM **Privately Held**
WEB: www.buckleyoil.com
SIC: 2911 5171 Solvents; petroleum bulk stations

(G-15476)
CHEMTRADE SOLUTIONS LLC
Also Called: General Chemical
500 N 9th St (76065-2723)
P.O. Box 921 (76065-0921)
PHONE..................................972 775-2307
Rick Hopping, *Branch Mgr*
EMP: 40
SQ FT: 4,700
SALES (corp-wide): 1.1B **Privately Held**
WEB: www.chemtradelogistics.com
SIC: 2819 Sodium & potassium compounds, exc. bleaches, alkalies, alum.
HQ: Chemtrade Solutions Llc
90 E Halsey Rd Ste 301
Parsippany NJ 07054

(G-15477)
CW DAVIS ENTERPRISES INC (PA)
Also Called: Dtac
5130 Edgefield Ln (76065-4401)
PHONE..................................972 723-1247
Janie Davis, *CEO*
Bob Watts, *President*
Marc Davis, *Vice Pres*
Justin Shaw, *Production*
Kris Clopton, *Sales Staff*
▼ **EMP:** 28 EST: 1968
SQ FT: 18,000
SALES (est): 7.5MM **Privately Held**
WEB: www.dtac.com
SIC: 5075 3585 Automotive air conditioners; compressors for refrigeration & air conditioning equipment

▲ = Import ▼ =Export
◆ =Import/Export

(G-15478)
DALLAS MARBLE COMPANY INC
Also Called: Dallas Marble Installation
1014 Lake Grove Loop (76065-5640)
P.O. Box 766, Cedar Hill (75106-0766)
PHONE....................972 291-9145
Joe Haught, *President*
EMP: 65
SALES (est): 3MM **Privately Held**
WEB: www.domainnamesdallas.com
SIC: 3281 1741 Marble, building: cut & shaped; marble masonry, exterior construction

(G-15479)
DOUBLE C CANVAS & REPAIRS INC
4551 Old Highway 67 N (76065-4368)
P.O. Box 478 (76065-0478)
PHONE....................972 723-8000
Roy Childres, *President*
Mary Childres, *Vice Pres*
EMP: 9
SQ FT: 7,500
SALES (est): 1.2MM **Privately Held**
WEB: www.doubleccanvas.com
SIC: 2394 Canvas awnings & canopies; canvas covers & drop cloths; tarpaulins, fabric: made from purchased materials

(G-15480)
ENNIS INC (PA)
2441 Presidential Pkwy (76065-3723)
PHONE....................972 775-9801
Keith S Walters, *Ch of Bd*
Michael D Magill, *Exec VP*
Ronald M Graham, *Vice Pres*
Richard L Travis Jr, *CFO*
Wayne Leaks, *IT/INT Sup*
EMP: 502
SQ FT: 28,000
SALES: 438.4MM **Publicly Held**
WEB: www.ennis.com
SIC: 2761 2759 2331 2329 Manifold business forms; business forms: printing; T-shirts & tops, women's: made from purchased materials; men's & boys' sportswear & athletic clothing

(G-15481)
GERDAU AMERISTEEL CORP
Also Called: Gerdau Midlothian
300 Ward Rd (76065-9646)
PHONE....................972 779-7010
John Whitehead, *Engineer*
Roel Silva, *Marketing Staff*
EMP: 9 **Privately Held**
WEB: www.jobs.gerdau.com
SIC: 3312 Blast furnaces & steel mills
HQ: Gerdau Ameristeel Corp.
4221 W Boy Scout Blvd # 600
Tampa FL 33607

(G-15482)
GERDAU AMERISTEEL US INC
300 Ward Rd (76065-9646)
PHONE....................972 775-8241
Mario Longhi, *CEO*
Robert E Lewis, *Vice Pres*
Barbara Smith, *CFO*
Chris Bullard, *Manager*
Dale Harman, *Manager*
◆ EMP: 1450
SQ FT: 815,000
SALES (est): 228.8MM **Privately Held**
WEB: www.gerdau.com
SIC: 3312 Blast furnaces & steel mills
HQ: Gerdau Ameristeel Us Inc.
4221 W Boy Scout Blvd # 600
Tampa FL 33607
813 286-8383

(G-15483)
GERDAU AMERISTEEL US INC
Gerdau Ameristeel Midlothian
300 Ward Rd (76065-9646)
PHONE....................972 775-8241
Roel Silva, *Marketing Staff*
David Maedgen, *Branch Mgr*
EMP: 900 **Privately Held**
WEB:
SIC: 3312 Blast furnaces & steel mills

HQ: Gerdau Ameristeel Us Inc.
4221 W Boy Scout Blvd # 600
Tampa FL 33607
813 286-8383

(G-15484)
MARTIN MARIETTA MATERIALS INC
245 Ward Rd (76065-9645)
PHONE....................972 647-4985
Randy Walser, *President*
Leann Kirkpatrick, *Supervisor*
Karen McDonald, *Admin Mgr*
EMP: 11 **Publicly Held**
WEB: www.martinmarietta.com
SIC: 3273 Ready-mixed concrete
PA: Martin Marietta Materials Inc
2710 Wycliff Rd
Raleigh NC 27607

(G-15485)
METRO SPROCKET & GEAR INC
1258 Eastgate Rd (76065-6231)
P.O. Box 766 (76065-0766)
PHONE....................972 723-3240
Gilbert L Tenery, *President*
Vicki Tenery, *Vice Pres*
EMP: 10
SQ FT: 7,600
SALES (est): 1.6MM **Privately Held**
WEB: www.metrosprocket.com
SIC: 3568 3566 Sprockets (power transmission equipment); gears, power transmission, except automotive

(G-15486)
MIDLOTHIAN LNG LLC
5091 Brookhollow Dr (76065-5314)
PHONE....................818 450-3668
Cem Hacioglu, *President*
Frank Martelli, *Vice Pres*
Edward McKenna Jr, *CFO*
Jennifer Stockett, *Marketing Mgr*
EMP: 15
SQ FT: 8,000
SALES (est): 27MM **Privately Held**
WEB: www.midlothian-tx.org
SIC: 1321 Natural gas liquids

(G-15487)
NARSTCO INC (DH)
300 Ward Rd (76065-9646)
PHONE....................972 775-5560
Anthony Musa, *President*
Scott Amox, *Safety Mgr*
Heather Wilson, *Engineer*
Melanie Aden, *Human Res Mgr*
Tom Daly, *Sales Staff*
▲ EMP: 90
SALES (est): 31.1MM
SALES (corp-wide): 988.6MM **Privately Held**
WEB: www.narstco.com
SIC: 3312 Rails, steel or iron
HQ: Railworks Corporation
5 Penn Plz Fl 15
New York NY 10001
212 502-7900

(G-15488)
NCI GROUP INC
Powerfoam Insulation
550 Murray St 287 (76065-5112)
PHONE....................972 299-5556
Mike Power, *Branch Mgr*
EMP: 20
SQ FT: 6,250
SALES (corp-wide): 4.8B **Publicly Held**
WEB: www.cornerstonebuildingbrands.com
SIC: 3448 Prefabricated metal buildings
HQ: Nci Group, Inc.
10943 N Sam Huston Pkwy W
Houston TX 77064
281 897-7788

(G-15489)
OMNI CONTRACTING
Also Called: Grant, Thomas Jr.
505 Chelsea Dr (76065-8735)
P.O. Box 170006, Irving (75017-0006)
PHONE....................972 890-4536
Thomas Grant, *Partner*
Jason Black, *Partner*
EMP: 10 EST: 2012

SALES (est): 334.3K **Privately Held**
WEB: www.omnicontracting.com
SIC: 7692 7699 Welding repair; industrial machinery & equipment repair

(G-15490)
PALLET KING ENTERPRISES INC
Also Called: A & M Fence Sup & Installation
107 N 5th St (76065-2915)
P.O. Box 590 (76065-0590)
PHONE....................972 723-3249
Michael A Rodgers, *President*
EMP: 10 EST: 1996
SALES (est): 1MM **Privately Held**
WEB: www.amfencesupply.com
SIC: 2448 Pallets, wood

(G-15491)
PROGRESSIVE COMPONENTS INC
1010 Eastgate Rd (76065-6230)
P.O. Box 1535 (76065-1535)
PHONE....................972 775-6932
Wayne Jones, *President*
Francis Wilson, *General Mgr*
EMP: 10
SQ FT: 15,000
SALES (est): 2.5MM **Privately Held**
WEB: www.progressive-components.business.site
SIC: 2431 5169 Woodwork, interior & ornamental; adhesives & sealants

(G-15492)
QUALICO STEEL COMPANY INC
2800 Miller Rd (76065-5343)
PHONE....................972 775-1400
Jim Blakeney, *Branch Mgr*
EMP: 51
SALES (corp-wide): 58.3MM **Privately Held**
WEB: www.qualicosteel.com
SIC: 3325 3441 Steel foundries; fabricated structural metal
PA: Qualico Steel Company, Inc.
7797 E State Highway 52
Webb AL 36376
334 793-1290

(G-15493)
RA-LOCK SECURITY SOLUTIONS INC
3570 N Highway 67 Ste B (76065-4349)
P.O. Box 549, Cedar Hill (75106-0549)
PHONE....................972 775-6301
Jay J Gage, *CEO*
David Price, *President*
Sean Woodward, *Principal*
Pat Gage, *Treasurer*
EMP: 30
SALES (est): 5MM **Privately Held**
WEB: www.ralock.com
SIC: 3499 3429 Fire- or burglary-resistive products; manufactured hardware (general)

(G-15494)
RAYS WELDING SHOP INC
530 Curtis Ray Rd (76065-5960)
PHONE....................972 775-2822
Richard C Ray, *President*
Jean Volini, *Corp Secy*
EMP: 10
SQ FT: 29,050
SALES (est): 1.9MM **Privately Held**
SIC: 3441 Fabricated structural metal

(G-15495)
TEXAS INDUSTRIES INC
Tximidlothian
245 Ward Rd (76065-9629)
PHONE....................972 775-3449
Randy Walser, *General Mgr*
EMP: 28 **Publicly Held**
WEB: www.martinmarietta.com
SIC: 3273 3271 3241 Ready-mixed concrete; blocks, concrete or cinder: standard; cement, hydraulic
HQ: Texas Industries, Inc.
1503 Lyndon B Johnson Fwy
Dallas TX 75234
972 647-6700

(G-15496)
WORLDWIDE LOCKING SYSTEMS INC
3570 N Highway 67 Ste A (76065-4349)
P.O. Box 549, Cedar Hill (75106-0549)
PHONE....................972 775-6320
Jj Gage, *CEO*
David J Price, *President*
Rhonda Hagan, *Administration*
EMP: 11
SALES (est): 990.6K **Privately Held**
SIC: 3429 5099 Locks or lock sets; locks & lock sets

(G-15497)
ZEMER INTERNATIONAL LLC
1800 Dove Ln (76065-4435)
PHONE....................214 227-2320
Eduardo Martinez, *Mng Member*
Enrique Zepeda Navarro,
▲ EMP: 20
SALES (est): 5.3MM **Privately Held**
SIC: 1411 Limestone, dimension-quarrying

(G-15498)
ZEMER INTERNATIONAL MO INC
1800 Dove Ln (76065-4435)
PHONE....................214 227-2320
Eduardo Martinez, *President*
Hector Alba, *Controller*
EMP: 25
SALES (est): 1.9MM **Privately Held**
SIC: 1459 Shale (common) quarrying

Midway
Madison County

(G-15499)
MIDWAY OILFIELD CONSTRS INC (PA)
Also Called: Midway Energy Services
12627 State Highway 21 E (75852-2833)
PHONE....................936 348-3721
EMP: 350 EST: 1981
SQ FT: 2,000
SALES (est): 385.5MM **Privately Held**
WEB: www.midwayoilfield.com
SIC: 1389 1623 Oil field services; oil & gas pipeline construction

Milford
Ellis County

(G-15500)
HUNTING TITAN INC
143 Hcr 4361 (76670)
PHONE....................972 493-2580
Sheila Fletcher, *Branch Mgr*
Patrick Valentino, *Manager*
EMP: 100
SALES (corp-wide): 960MM **Privately Held**
WEB: www.hunting-intl.com
SIC: 3533 Oil field machinery & equipment
HQ: Hunting Titan, Inc.
11785 Highway 152
Pampa TX 79065
806 665-3781

Millsap
Parker County

(G-15501)
COLDSTREAM ENERGY HOLDINGS LLC
464 Cool Jct (76066-2141)
PHONE....................940 682-4772
J W Varner, *Branch Mgr*
EMP: 30 **Privately Held**
WEB: www.coldstreamenergy.com
SIC: 3441 Fabricated structural metal
PA: Coldstream Energy Holdings, Llc
8150 N Cntrl Expy # 1550
Dallas TX 75206

(G-15502)
GEODYNAMICS INC (HQ)
10400 W Interstate 20 (76066-3185)
PHONE 817 341-5300
David Wesson, *President*
Nathan Clark, *COO*
John Berner, *Vice Pres*
Chris Chalker, *Vice Pres*
Efrain Munoz, *Vice Pres*
◆ **EMP:** 220
SQ FT: 16,000
SALES (est): 62.1MM
SALES (corp-wide): 1B **Publicly Held**
WEB: www.perf.com
SIC: 2892 3533 Explosives; oil & gas field machinery; oil field machinery & equipment
PA: Oil States International, Inc.
   333 Clay St Ste 4620
   Houston TX 77002
   713 652-0582

(G-15503)
INNOVATIVE BUILDING PRODUCTS
2350 Bennett Rd (76066-3023)
PHONE 940 387-0408
John S Justin, *Ch of Bd*
Edward L Stout, *President*
Richard J Savitz, *Treasurer*
Dennis Knautz, *VP Finance*
EMP: 25
SALES (est): 2.7MM
SALES (corp-wide): 254.6B **Publicly Held**
WEB: www.ibpglassblock.com
SIC: 3229 3354 Blocks & bricks, glass; aluminum extruded products
HQ: Acme Brick Company
   3024 Acme Brick Plz
   Fort Worth TX 76109

(G-15504)
LEGACY VULCAN LLC
Southwest Division
1111 Gilbert Pit Rd (76066-3611)
PHONE 817 594-4524
Lynne Tatum, *Plant Mgr*
Lamm Piton, *Manager*
David Brabson, *Manager*
Trevor Phipps, *Manager*
EMP: 50 **Publicly Held**
WEB: www.vulcanmaterials.com
SIC: 3273 Ready-mixed concrete
HQ: Legacy Vulcan, Llc
   1200 Urban Center Dr
   Vestavia AL 35242
   205 298-3000

(G-15505)
RODENS ALL STAR MCH & MFG INC
3998 Fairview Rd (76066-2926)
PHONE 817 927-2825
Thomas Earl Roden, *President*
Tom Roden, *Vice Pres*
Tony Roden, *Vice Pres*
Angie Hill, *Treasurer*
▲ **EMP:** 38
SALES (est): 11.6MM **Privately Held**
WEB: www.rodensallstar.com
SIC: 3399 Brads: aluminum, brass or other nonferrous metal or wire

Mineola
Wood County

(G-15506)
DONOVAN WHITE CABINETS INC
1348 Bromberg St (75773-2854)
PHONE 903 569-5611
Hank Neill, *President*
Annette Horn, *Corp Secy*
White Donovan F Jr, *Director*
EMP: 10
SQ FT: 5,250
SALES (est): 1MM **Privately Held**
SIC: 2434 Vanities, bathroom: wood

(G-15507)
EAST TXAS ARCHTCTRAL SHTMTAL L
1450 Bromberg St (75773-2820)
P.O. Box 180 (75773-0180)
PHONE 903 569-6909
Brian Steck, *Mng Member*
Tony Macevicius, *Director*
Wendy Steck,
EMP: 13
SALES (est): 4.3MM **Privately Held**
WEB: www.etas-inc.com
SIC: 3446 Architectural metalwork

(G-15508)
EZ-ROUTER INC
140 County Road 2840 (75773-5918)
PHONE 903 569-3190
Edwin D Berry, *President*
David J Sullivan, *Corp Secy*
John Johnson, *Vice Pres*
EMP: 21
SALES (est): 3.1MM **Privately Held**
WEB: www.ez-router.com
SIC: 3599 Machine shop, jobbing & repair

(G-15509)
KEMP-MEEK MANUFACTURING INC
101 Park Central Rd (75773-9378)
P.O. Box 670 (75773-0670)
PHONE 903 569-9700
J L Meek, *President*
Norma Meek, *Treasurer*
EMP: 14
SQ FT: 6,000
SALES (est): 2.1MM **Privately Held**
WEB: www.kempmeek.com
SIC: 3824 3678 Water meters; electronic connectors

(G-15510)
MINEOLA PACKING COMPANY
906 E Broad St (75773-2608)
P.O. Box 928 (75773-0928)
PHONE 903 569-5355
Johnie C Henderson, *President*
Susan Lee, *Corp Secy*
Pam Henderson, *Vice Pres*
Yvonne Henderson, *Vice Pres*
EMP: 50 **EST:** 1961
SQ FT: 25,000
SALES (est): 12.4MM **Privately Held**
WEB: www.mineolapacking.com
SIC: 5147 2011 Meats, fresh; meat packing plants

(G-15511)
SAFE-T-PET INC
Also Called: Spirit Pin
224 County Road 2455 (75773-6930)
P.O. Box 905 (75773-0905)
PHONE 903 569-0590
Newt Watson, *President*
Shelley Watson, *Vice Pres*
EMP: 12
SQ FT: 8,000
SALES (est): 1.5MM **Privately Held**
WEB: www.safe-t-pet.com
SIC: 3469 2759 3442 3944 Automobile license tags, stamped metal; laser printing; window & door frames; board games, children's & adults'

(G-15512)
SOUTHEAST WOOD TREATING INC
Also Called: Southeast Wood Georgia Pacific
701 Freeman St (75773-2549)
P.O. Box 893 (75773-0893)
PHONE 903 569-9441
Linda Smith, *Manager*
EMP: 17
SALES (corp-wide): 127.5MM **Privately Held**
WEB: www.sewood.net
SIC: 5031 2491 Lumber: rough, dressed & finished; wood preserving
PA: Southeast Wood Treating, Inc.
   3077 Carter Hill Rd
   Montgomery AL 36111
   321 631-1003

(G-15513)
SOUTHWEST METAL SYSTEMS LLC
Also Called: Southwest Mtal Systems Sthwest
485 E Loop 564 (75773)
P.O. Box 300 (75773-0300)
PHONE 903 569-8811
Adam Steck, *Mng Member*
Melissa Randell,
EMP: 20
SALES (est): 3.6MM **Privately Held**
WEB: www.southwest-metal.com
SIC: 5039 3448 Metal buildings; prefabricated metal buildings; prefabricated metal components

(G-15514)
TRINIDAD BENHAM HOLDING CO
322 Freeman St (75773-2442)
P.O. Box 29 (75773-0029)
PHONE 903 569-2283
Bill Dearmond, *CFO*
Donna Conley, *Marketing Staff*
EMP: 80.
SALES (corp-wide): 421.9MM **Privately Held**
WEB: www.trinidadbenham.com
SIC: 2099 Food preparations
PA: Trinidad Benham Holding Company
   3650 S Yosemite St # 300
   Denver CO 80237
   303 220-1400

(G-15515)
WOOD SHED TRUSS
1345 N Us Highway 69 (75773-3726)
P.O. Box 794 (75773-0794)
PHONE 903 569-2147
Ed Teel, *Owner*
Jeffery B Keith, *Principal*
Jeffery Keith, *Exec VP*
EMP: 15
SALES (est): 1.9MM **Privately Held**
WEB: www.woodshedtruss.com
SIC: 2439 Trusses, wooden roof

(G-15516)
WOOD SHED TRUSSE
Hwy 69 (75773)
P.O. Box 794 (75773-0794)
PHONE 903 569-2147
Ed Teel, *President*
EMP: 13
SALES (est): 1MM **Privately Held**
WEB: www.woodshedtruss.com
SIC: 2439 Trusses, wooden roof

Mineral Wells
Palo Pinto County

(G-15517)
ACCURACY PRODUCTS INC
3800 N Highway 281 (76067-2422)
P.O. Box 1325 (76068-1325)
PHONE 940 325-0714
Joseph Hawkins, *President*
▲ **EMP:** 12
SQ FT: 16,000
SALES (est): 1.7MM **Privately Held**
WEB: www.accuracyproductsinc.com
SIC: 3599 Machine shop, jobbing & repair

(G-15518)
ANTENNA PRODUCTS CORPORATION
101 Se 25th Ave (76067-5715)
P.O. Box 520 (76068-0520)
PHONE 940 325-3301
Robert Fitzgerald, *CEO*
Clark D Wraight, *President*
Jim Walker, *Business Mgr*
Richard Gilley, *Exec VP*
Chris Stevens, *Purch Mgr*
▲ **EMP:** 66
SQ FT: 65,000
SALES (est): 15.3MM
SALES (corp-wide): 15.5MM **Privately Held**
WEB: www.antennaproducts.com
SIC: 3663 Antennas, transmitting & communications

PA: Qar Industries, Inc.
   101 Se 25th Ave
   Mineral Wells TX 76067
   940 325-3301

(G-15519)
BOONE INDUSTRIES
155 Henderson Rd (76067-1501)
PHONE 940 325-6215
Billy Boone, *Owner*
EMP: 15
SQ FT: 3,000 **Privately Held**
SIC: 2339 Jeans: women's, misses' & juniors'

(G-15520)
CANTEX INC
2407 Martin L King Blvd (76067)
PHONE 817 215-7000
EMP: 13 **Privately Held**
WEB: www.cantexinc.com
SIC: 3084 Plastics pipe
HQ: Cantex Inc.
   301 Commerce St Ste 2700
   Fort Worth TX 76102

(G-15521)
CANTEX INC
2101 Se 1st St (76067-5601)
PHONE 940 325-3344
John Morgan, *Engineer*
Cheryl McAllister, *Human Res Mgr*
Mark Selep, *Branch Mgr*
Jerry Chandler, *Manager*
David Hutto, *Manager*
EMP: 300 **Privately Held**
WEB: www.cantexinc.com
SIC: 3084 Plastics pipe
HQ: Cantex Inc.
   301 Commerce St Ste 2700
   Fort Worth TX 76102

(G-15522)
CENTRON INTERNATIONAL INC
Also Called: Nov Fiberglass Systems
600 Fm 1195 (76067-9014)
P.O. Box 878, Burkburnett (76354-0878)
PHONE 940 328-1032
James S Marlen, *Ch of Bd*
Conway Beasley, *President*
Javier Solis, *Vice Pres*
Gary Wagner, *Treasurer*
◆ **EMP:** 122
SQ FT: 71,677
SALES (est): 13.4MM
SALES (corp-wide): 8.4B **Publicly Held**
SIC: 3084 3089 Plastics pipe; fittings for pipe, plastic
HQ: Ameron International Corporation
   7909 Parkwood Circle Dr
   Houston TX 77036
   713 375-3700

(G-15523)
CLIFF DUNTA BROS INC
Also Called: Comet Cleaners
2301 Sw 4th Ave (76067-8671)
PHONE 940 325-4855
Gary Rhodes, *President*
EMP: 13
SALES (est): 375K **Privately Held**
WEB: www.cometcleaners.com
SIC: 2842 Drycleaning preparations

(G-15524)
DALLAS PRODUCTION INC
300 Travis St (76067-8840)
PHONE 940 328-1241
Bert Thomas, *Production*
Sharon Maitlen, *Accountant*
Brian Benge, *Branch Mgr*
EMP: 25
SALES (corp-wide): 48MM **Privately Held**
SIC: 1311 Crude petroleum production; natural gas production
PA: Dallas Production, Inc.
   4600 Greenville Ave # 300
   Dallas TX 75206
   214 369-9266

(G-15525)
ELECTROMEDICAL PDTS INTL INC (PA)
Also Called: Epii
2201 Garrett Morris Pkwy (76067-9034)
PHONE..................................940 328-0788
Daniel Kirsch, *Ch of Bd*
Tracey Kirsch, *President*
Tracey B Kirsch, *President*
Andrew J Miclot, *President*
Jeffrey A Marksberry, *Vice Pres*
▲ EMP: 26
SQ FT: 8,000
SALES (est): 3.1MM Privately Held
WEB: www.alpha-stim.com
SIC: 3845 5047 Electrotherapeutic apparatus; electro-medical equipment

(G-15526)
GENESYS AEROSYSTEMS GROUP INC (HQ)
1 S Tec Way (76067-9236)
PHONE..................................800 872-7832
Roger Smith, *President*
Tricia Crawford, *Vice Pres*
Gordon Pratt, *Vice Pres*
Ricardo Price, *Vice Pres*
Dean Boston, *Engineer*
EMP: 130
SALES (est): 41.9MM
SALES (corp-wide): 2.8B Publicly Held
WEB: www.genesys-aerosystems.com
SIC: 3812 3728 Aircraft/aerospace flight instruments & guidance systems; aircraft parts & equipment
PA: Moog Inc.
400 Jamison Rd
Elma NY 14059
716 652-2000

(G-15527)
H M W FABRICATIONS INC
539 Taylor Rd (76067-9257)
PHONE..................................940 325-0300
Hank Moss, *Director*
EMP: 18
SALES (est): 850K Privately Held
WEB: www.hmwfabricationsinc.com
SIC: 7692 Welding repair

(G-15528)
HANSON LEHIGH INC
7510 Highway 180 E (76067-9504)
PHONE..................................972 653-3735
Lalit Bhatnagar, *Principal*
EMP: 270
SALES (corp-wide): 20.8B Privately Held
WEB: www.lehighhanson.com
SIC: 1442 Sand mining
HQ: Hanson Lehigh Inc
300 E John Carpenter Fwy
Irving TX 75062

(G-15529)
HYDROSCIENCE TECHNOLOGIES INC
6100 Columbia Rd (76067-9240)
P.O. Box 121459, Fort Worth (76121-1459)
PHONE..................................940 325-8221
Fred Woodland, *President*
Eric Boyer, *Vice Pres*
Bill Behrens, *Plant Mgr*
Chuck Holt, *Project Mgr*
Kelli Buschow, *Purch Agent*
▲ EMP: 30
SQ FT: 70,000
SALES (est): 6.2MM Privately Held
WEB: www.seamap.com
SIC: 3812 Warfare counter-measure equipment

(G-15530)
KERR OILFIELD COMPANY
7104 Highway 180 E (76067-9588)
P.O. Box 1209 (76068-1209)
PHONE..................................940 327-0447
Kevin Ward, *President*
Kevin E Ward, *Principal*
Randy Cheek, *Shareholder*
EMP: 30
SQ FT: 2,000
SALES (est): 5.1MM Privately Held
SIC: 1389 Oil field services

(G-15531)
KMI FABRICATORS INC
410 Boyd Rd (76067-9246)
PHONE..................................940 325-7841
John Neff, *President*
Sally Neff, *President*
Carol Dickey, *Manager*
EMP: 20
SQ FT: 10,000
SALES (est): 5.5MM Privately Held
WEB: www.kmifab.com
SIC: 3443 Tanks, standard or custom fabricated: metal plate

(G-15532)
MERIDIAN BRICK LLC
500 Ne 14th Ave (76067-4037)
PHONE..................................940 325-9466
Curtis Adams, *Opers-Prdtn-Mfg*
EMP: 60
SALES (corp-wide): 441MM Privately Held
WEB: www.meridianbrick.com
SIC: 3271 3251 Concrete block & brick; brick & structural clay tile
PA: Meridian Brick Llc
6455 Shiloh Rd D
Alpharetta GA 30005
770 645-4500

(G-15533)
MURPHY & MURPHY INC (PA)
315 Ne 9th Ave (76067-4549)
P.O. Box 788 (76068-0788)
PHONE..................................940 325-2666
Terry L Murphy, *President*
Jeannette Murphy, *Corp Secy*
Murphy E J, *Vice Pres*
EMP: 11 EST: 1941
SQ FT: 1,000
SALES (est): 1.5MM Privately Held
SIC: 3273 1771 1442 Ready-mixed concrete; concrete work; construction sand & gravel

(G-15534)
NORTH TXAS PRSSURE VESSELS INC (PA)
301 Travis St Walters Ind K S Indusrial Pr (76067)
P.O. Box 1096 (76068-1096)
PHONE..................................940 327-0800
Keith Boyd, *President*
Keith Boyb, *President*
Scotty Whrtsept, *Vice Pres*
Karen Uptmore, *Office Mgr*
Brande Sims, *Admin Asst*
▲ EMP: 32
SQ FT: 10,000
SALES (est): 5.1MM Privately Held
WEB: www.ntpvinc.com
SIC: 3443 Fuel tanks (oil, gas, etc.): metal plate

(G-15535)
OHM PHARMA INC
2940 Fm 3028 (76067-9258)
P.O. Box 757 (76068-0757)
PHONE..................................940 325-4797
Dr Robert Melo, *President*
Tomasz Mazur, *Prdtn Mgr*
▲ EMP: 30
SQ FT: 30,000
SALES (est): 500K Privately Held
WEB: www.ohmpharma.com
SIC: 2834 Medicines, capsuled or ampuled

(G-15536)
PECOFACET (US) INC (DH)
Also Called: Pecofacet US
118 Washington Ave (76067-9502)
P.O. Box 640 (76068-0640)
PHONE..................................940 325-2575
M Dunman Perry Jr, *Ch of Bd*
Scott Thompson, *President*
Joann Shepard-Ristau, *General Mgr*
Brian Czajkowski, *VP Admin*
David Burns, *Vice Pres*
◆ EMP: 280 EST: 1936
SQ FT: 200,000
SALES (est): 223.1MM
SALES (corp-wide): 13.7B Publicly Held
WEB: www.promo.parker.com
SIC: 5082 3823 Oil field equipment; flow instruments, industrial process type

HQ: Clarcor Inc.
840 Crescent Centre Dr # 600
Franklin TN 37067
615 771-3100

(G-15537)
PEDLEY NETS INC
4711 S Highway 281 (76067-1157)
P.O. Box 7 (76068-0007)
PHONE..................................940 328-0448
Philip Pedley, *Ch of Bd*
Douglas Pedley, *President*
Irwin Weller, *General Mgr*
Dixie Pedley, *Corp Secy*
EMP: 10
SQ FT: 10,000
SALES (est): 998.3K Privately Held
WEB: www.pedleynets.com
SIC: 2298 Nets, rope

(G-15538)
QAR INDUSTRIES INC (PA)
101 Se 25th Ave (76067-5715)
PHONE..................................940 325-3301
Becky Dumis, *General Mgr*
Pam Tatum, *Buyer*
Rob Farquharson, *Consultant*
Robert E Fitzgerald, *Exec Dir*
EMP: 10
SALES (est): 15.5MM Privately Held
WEB: www.antennaproducts.com
SIC: 3663 Antennas, transmitting & communications

(G-15539)
RICHARDS SIGNS & CRANES INC
1215 Sw 1st St (76067-5189)
P.O. Box 66 (76068-0066)
PHONE..................................940 325-6585
Robert Russell Richards, *President*
Robert L Richards, *Vice Pres*
Kim Richards, *Treasurer*
EMP: 11
SALES (est): 995.3K Privately Held
SIC: 3993 7353 Signs & advertising specialties; cranes & aerial lift equipment, rental or leasing

(G-15540)
ROGERS MANUFACTURING INC
109 Sw Mrtn Lther King Jr (76067-5865)
P.O. Box 518 (76068-0518)
PHONE..................................940 325-7806
Leah Gillespie, *President*
Bruce Gillespie, *Vice Pres*
Tammy Leitgeb, *Treasurer*
EMP: 9
SQ FT: 32,000
SALES (est): 1MM Privately Held
WEB: www.rogers-mfg-inc.com
SIC: 3541 3542 Machine tools, metal cutting type; machine tools, metal forming type

(G-15541)
S-TEC CORPORATION
Also Called: Genesys Aerosystems
1 S Tec Way (76067-9236)
PHONE..................................800 872-7832
Roger Smith, *President*
Gordon Pratt, *Vice Pres*
Ricardo Price, *Vice Pres*
Casey Dankers, *Opers Staff*
Tammy Crawford, *CFO*
◆ EMP: 149
SQ FT: 56,000
SALES: 41.7MM
SALES (corp-wide): 2.8B Publicly Held
WEB: www.genesys-aerosystems.com
SIC: 3812 3728 Aircraft/aerospace flight instruments & guidance systems; aircraft control systems, electronic; aircraft parts & equipment
HQ: Genesys Aerosystems Group, Inc.
1 S Tec Way
Mineral Wells TX 76067
800 872-7832

(G-15542)
SOUTHWIRE COMPANY LLC
3800 Se Industrial Pkwy (76067-9132)
PHONE..................................940 328-1047
Charlie Murrah, *Exec VP*
Brian Parsons, *Manager*
Richard Temblador, *Director*

EMP: 18
SALES (corp-wide): 2B Privately Held
WEB: www.southwireea.com
SIC: 3351 3355 3357 3599 Wire, copper & copper alloy; cable, aluminum: made in rolling mills; wire, aluminum: made in rolling mills; building wire & cable, nonferrous; machine shop, jobbing & repair
PA: Southwire Company, Llc
1 Southwire Dr
Carrollton GA 30119
770 832-4242

(G-15543)
TRU-TEST INC
528 Grant Rd (76067-9212)
PHONE..................................940 327-8020
Cliff Cobb, *President*
Troy Huseman, *Vice Pres*
Dieter Steiner, *Prdtn Mgr*
Nathan Mitchell, *Purch Mgr*
Jason Williams, *Sales Staff*
▲ EMP: 35
SALES (est): 14MM Privately Held
WEB: www.livestock.tru-test.com
SIC: 5083 3612 3596 Agricultural machinery & equipment; transformers, except electric; scales & balances, except laboratory
PA: Carbine Aginvest Corporation Limited
38 The Boulevard
Hamilton 3200

(G-15544)
UPHAM OIL & GAS COMPANY LP (PA)
999 Energy Ave (76067-9106)
P.O. Box 940 (76068-0940)
PHONE..................................940 325-4491
Chester R Upham Jr, *Partner*
Johnny Benavides, *Technology*
Mary M Mayes, *Director*
EMP: 48 EST: 1956
SQ FT: 5,500
SALES (est): 8.4MM Privately Held
WEB: www.upham.us
SIC: 1382 1311 2911 Oil & gas exploration services; crude petroleum production; natural gas production; petroleum refining

(G-15545)
VENTAMATIC LTD (PA)
Also Called: Cool Attic
100 Washington Ave (76067-9502)
P.O. Box 728 (76068-0728)
PHONE..................................940 325-7887
Terry Siegel, *Partner*
Jim Laughlin, *Vice Pres*
Kirk Bolton, *Engineer*
Steve Tarpley, *Engineer*
Henry Cox, *Train & Dev Mgr*
◆ EMP: 140 EST: 1948
SQ FT: 110,000
SALES (est): 33.4MM Privately Held
WEB: www.bvc.com
SIC: 3564 Ventilating fans: industrial or commercial

(G-15546)
WATKINS METAL FABRICATION INC
544 Grant Rd (76067-9212)
P.O. Box 1268 (76068-1268)
PHONE..................................940 325-6008
Jon R Watkins, *President*
Stephen M Brown, *Vice Pres*
EMP: 36 EST: 2000
SALES (est): 15MM Privately Held
WEB: www.watkins-industries.com
SIC: 3441 Fabricated structural metal

Mission
Hidalgo County

(G-15547)
A&E OILFIELD SERVICES LLC
3701 E Lincoln Ave (78573-4507)
PHONE..................................956 380-5098
Mario Alberto Rodriguez, *Mng Member*
EMP: 80
SALES (est): 4.3MM Privately Held
SIC: 1389 Oil field services

(G-15548)
ACERO FAB INC
12225 N Bryan Rd (78573-6717)
PHONE............................956 584-1166
Gladys Hernandez, *Manager*
John Martinez Jr, *Director*
EMP: 12 **EST:** 2006
SQ FT: 8,000
SALES (est): 3.6MM **Privately Held**
WEB: www.acerofab.trustab.org
SIC: 3499 Bank chests, metal

(G-15549)
CCMM INC
107 Rio Grande Dr (78572-7418)
P.O. Box 31, Mount Vernon MO (65712-0031)
PHONE............................936 827-7930
Robert McCullah, *President*
EMP: 10
SALES (est): 414.8K **Privately Held**
SIC: 3845 5047 Electromedical equipment; medical & hospital equipment

(G-15550)
COLAIR INC (PA)
1221 E Interstate 2 A (78572-6078)
PHONE............................956 631-9889
Ruben Sanchez, *President*
Adolfo R Sanchez, *President*
Anna Sanchez, *Corp Secy*
Patty Sanchez, *Controller*
Humberto Santos, *Manager*
EMP: 15
SQ FT: 7,000
SALES (est): 2.8MM **Privately Held**
WEB: www.colairinc.com
SIC: 1711 3585 Refrigeration contractor; warm air heating & air conditioning contractor; plumbing contractors; heating & air conditioning combination units

(G-15551)
COMMSCOPE TECHNOLOGIES LLC
Also Called: Andrew Solutions
4101 E Military Hwy Ste A (78572-1668)
PHONE............................956 205-6000
Mike Melcher, *Branch Mgr*
EMP: 40 **Publicly Held**
SIC: 3663 Radio & TV communications equipment
HQ: Commscope Technologies Llc
　4 Westbrook Corporate Ctr
　Westchester IL 60154
　708 236-6600

(G-15552)
EXPRESS ENERGY SVCS OPER LP
8520 N Moorefield Rd (78574-4497)
PHONE............................713 625-7403
Jim Nelson, *Branch Mgr*
EMP: 30
SALES (corp-wide): 770.4MM **Privately Held**
WEB: www.eeslp.com
SIC: 1389 Oil field services
PA: Express Energy Services Operating, Lp
　9800 Richmond Ave Ste 500
　Houston TX 77042
　713 625-7400

(G-15553)
F AND B HOLDINGS LLC
Also Called: Lone Star Citrus Growers
9625 N Moorefield Rd (78574-4598)
PHONE............................956 424-7775
Manuel Torrech, *Plant Mgr*
Jud Flower, *Mng Member*
Trent Bishop,
Tj Flowers,
William J Flowers,
EMP: 25 **EST:** 2006
SQ FT: 25,000
SALES (est): 25MM **Privately Held**
WEB: www.lonestarcitrus.com
SIC: 2033 0174 Fruits: packaged in cans, jars, etc.; citrus fruits

(G-15554)
FLINT ENERGY SERVICES INC
11916 W Mile 7 Rd (78573-1503)
PHONE............................956 585-9779
Hector Saenz, *Branch Mgr*
EMP: 25
SALES (corp-wide): 13.2B **Publicly Held**
WEB: www.aecom.com
SIC: 1389 Oil field services
HQ: Flint Energy Services Inc.
　6200 S Quebec St Ste 1
　Greenwood Village CO 80111
　918 294-3030

(G-15555)
GENERAL GARAGE DOOR SERVICE
7216 W Interstate 2 (78572-9526)
PHONE............................956 782-7373
Ascencion Torres, *Manager*
EMP: 15 **Privately Held**
WEB: www.thegeneralusa.com
SIC: 3446 Gates, ornamental metal
PA: General Garage Door Service, Inc
　1801 Mozelle St
　Pharr TX 78577

(G-15556)
J & R VALLEY OILFIELD SVCS INC
Also Called: Valley Swabbing & Flowback Svc
8100 N Moorefield Rd (78574)
P.O. Box 310 (78573-0006)
PHONE............................956 581-7235
Jose M Flores, *President*
Diana I Flores, *Vice Pres*
EMP: 60
SQ FT: 5,000
SALES (est): 8.3MM **Privately Held**
SIC: 1389 Oil field services

(G-15557)
JT SWABBING SERVICES INC
6803 Western Rd (78574-6465)
P.O. Box 1327 (78573-0023)
PHONE............................956 580-8954
Jose Trevino, *President*
Leticia Trevino, *Vice Pres*
Milva Ysaguiwgre, *Admin Sec*
EMP: 10
SALES (est): 2.4MM **Privately Held**
SIC: 1389 Bailing, cleaning, swabbing & treating of wells; oil field services

(G-15558)
L & R PRE-CAST CON WORKS INC
3807 N Bentsen Palm Dr (78574-8200)
PHONE............................956 583-6293
Rufino Garza, *President*
Lisa Carlos, *Vice Pres*
EMP: 30 **EST:** 1998
SALES (est): 6.3MM **Privately Held**
WEB: www.lrprecast.com
SIC: 3272 Concrete products, precast

(G-15559)
LG ELECTRONICS ALABAMA INC
Also Called: L G Electronics
3805 Plantation Grv (78572-6211)
PHONE............................956 784-6500
Raul De Leon, *QC Mgr*
Kevin Kim, *Branch Mgr*
EMP: 540 **Privately Held**
WEB: www.lg.com
SIC: 3651 Television receiving sets
HQ: Lg Electronics Alabama, Inc.
　201 James Record Rd Sw
　Huntsville AL 35824
　256 772-8860

(G-15560)
METAL PROCESSING INTL LP
Also Called: Texas Metal Processing Intl
1108 Business Park Dr (78572-6083)
PHONE............................956 205-0083
Mona Adkisson, *Partner*
Sam L Adkisson, *Partner*
John Randolph, *General Ptnr*
Roy Foster, *Plant Mgr*
Rafael Ramirez, *Prdtn Mgr*
EMP: 40
SALES (est): 5.1MM **Privately Held**
WEB: www.ecoat.us
SIC: 3479 Coating of metals & formed products

PA: Oklahoma Custom Coating, Limited Liability Company
　1801 Boren Blvd
　Seminole OK 74868

(G-15561)
P & C OIL FIELD SERVICE LLC
1213 Blake St (78572-3513)
PHONE............................956 581-1725
Jaime Villareal, *General Mgr*
Pedro Cantu Jr, *Opers Staff*
EMP: 30
SALES (est): 555.8K **Privately Held**
WEB: www.triplejoilfieldservices.com
SIC: 1389 Oil field services

(G-15562)
RAMON GUARDIOLA
Also Called: Northern Dental Supplies
2545 E Griffin Pkwy U146 (78572-3320)
PHONE............................956 330-8026
Ramon Guardiola, *CEO*
▲ **EMP:** 10
SQ FT: 1,000
SALES (est): 665.4K **Privately Held**
SIC: 3843 5047 Dental equipment & supplies; dental equipment & supplies

(G-15563)
ROYAL TECHNOLOGIES CORPORATION
Also Called: Hi-Tech Plastics
1200 Trinity St (78572-1633)
PHONE............................956 424-9388
James Vanderkolk, *President*
Trung Nguyen, *Plant Mgr*
Steve Vandusen, *Opers Staff*
Brian Burkett, *Production*
Rafael Vargas, *QC Mgr*
EMP: 132
SALES (corp-wide): 204MM **Privately Held**
WEB: www.royaltechnologies.com
SIC: 3089 Injection molding of plastics
PA: Royal Technologies Corporation
　3765 Quincy St
　Hudsonville MI 49426
　616 669-3393

(G-15564)
STARION USA INC
3805 Plntn Grv Blvd (78572-6211)
PHONE............................956 283-1289
Yong Sung Lee, *President*
Dong Shik Son, *General Mgr*
Jong K Moon, *Admin Sec*
▲ **EMP:** 30
SALES (est): 5.2MM **Privately Held**
SIC: 3634 Electric housewares & fans
PA: Starion Co.,Ltd
　Banyeo-Dong
　Busan 48039

(G-15565)
T S MOORE PRINTING CO INC
Also Called: Moore, T S Print-It
2311 Amethyst Ave (78574-2240)
PHONE............................956 687-6868
Thomas S Moore, *President*
Carol Moore, *Corp Secy*
EMP: 9
SALES (est): 750K **Privately Held**
SIC: 2752 Commercial printing, offset

(G-15566)
TECNOVAL LLC
3805 Plntn Grv Blvd # 43 (78572-6223)
PHONE............................956 782-1111
Agustin Cuesta,
▲ **EMP:** 10 **EST:** 2010
SALES (est): 1.3MM **Privately Held**
SIC: 3592 Valves

(G-15567)
TEXAS CITRUS EXCHANGE
702 E Interstate 2 (78572-5701)
PHONE............................956 585-8321
Judy Rodriguez, *President*
Dodson Galloway, *Vice Pres*
Ninfa Sepulveda, *Controller*
Boyd Beasley, *Director*
James Hoffman, *Admin Sec*
◆ **EMP:** 140
SQ FT: 180,000

SALES (est): 39.9MM **Privately Held**
WEB: www.tcxjuice.com
SIC: 2033 5148 Fruit juices: fresh; fruits, fresh

(G-15568)
TRANSIT READY MIX LLC
7205 N La Homa Rd (78574-0815)
P.O. Box 3154 (78573-0054)
PHONE............................956 584-0039
Jesus Roberto Carlos, *Mng Member*
Juan A Almaguer Jr,
Melba D Almaguer,
Nancy Leal,
Antonio E Mercado,
EMP: 15 **EST:** 2014
SQ FT: 1,800
SALES (est): 1.7MM **Privately Held**
SIC: 3272 Concrete products

(G-15569)
TREVINO JR GUSTAVO
Also Called: Party Ice Co
4200 W Mile 3 Rd (78574-1303)
PHONE............................956 585-2522
Gustavo Trevino Jr, *Owner*
EMP: 9
SQ FT: 5,000
SALES (est): 420K **Privately Held**
SIC: 2097 Ice cubes

(G-15570)
TRIPLE J OILFIELD SERVICES INC
300 Trinity St (78572-1649)
P.O. Box 1665 (78573-0029)
PHONE............................956 585-1949
Jimmy Jones, *President*
Paulette Jones, *Admin Sec*
EMP: 73
SALES (est): 9.6MM **Privately Held**
WEB: www.triplejoilfieldservices.com
SIC: 1389 Oil field services

(G-15571)
VALLEY CALICHE PRODUCTS INC
3656 Iowa Rd (78574-0100)
P.O. Box 1086 (78573-0017)
PHONE............................956 581-2751
R H Thompson, *President*
Cory Thompson, *Principal*
Mark Motheral, *Corp Secy*
EMP: 65 **EST:** 1965
SQ FT: 2,500
SALES (est): 12.8MM **Privately Held**
SIC: 2951 5032 Asphalt & asphaltic paving mixtures (not from refineries); sand, construction

(G-15572)
VALLY PARK USA CORP
Also Called: Valet Parking By Vally Park
3504 Santa Inez Cir (78572-7592)
PHONE............................956 994-0000
Paul Petit, *President*
EMP: 12
SALES (est): 580K **Privately Held**
WEB: www.vallypark.com
SIC: 7521 3559 Automobile parking; parking facility equipment & supplies

(G-15573)
VIARDEN LAB LLC
2005 E Griffin Pkwy (78572-0027)
PHONE............................956 294-0260
Mariana Correa,
EMP: 10
SALES (est): 100K **Privately Held**
SIC: 2842 Sanitation preparations, disinfectants & deodorants

(G-15574)
WONDERFUL CITRUS PACKING LLC
4000 E Goodwin Rd (78574-9525)
PHONE............................956 205-7300
EMP: 14
SALES (corp-wide): 1.5B **Privately Held**
SIC: 0723 0174 2033 Crop Marketing Prep Citrus Fruit Grove Mfg Canned Fruits/Vegtbl

▲ = Import ▼=Export
◆ =Import/Export

HQ: Wonderful Citrus Packing Llc
1901 S Lexington St
Delano CA 93215
661 720-2400

Missouri City
Fort Bend County

(G-15575)
ALTECH CONTROLS CORPORATION
13203 Stafford Rd Ste 500 (77489-2258)
PHONE...................................281 207-2775
EMP: 10
SQ FT: 7,000
SALES (est): 2.1MM **Privately Held**
SIC: 3822 Mfg Environmental Controls

(G-15576)
C D & N MANUFACTURING INC
Also Called: Cnc Manufacturing
1011 Buffalo Run (77489-1463)
PHONE...................................281 438-2499
James Crosby, *President*
Derek Bence, *Plant Mgr*
Michael York, *Mfg Staff*
Rollie Martinez, *QC Mgr*
Michelle Marcinko, *Sales Staff*
EMP: 64 EST: 1988
SQ FT: 37,500
SALES (est): 13.8MM **Privately Held**
WEB: www.cnc-mfg.net
SIC: 3599 Machine shop, jobbing & repair

(G-15577)
CARE LABORATORIES INC
12706 Settemont Rd (77489-8012)
P.O. Box 637 (77459-0637)
PHONE...................................281 835-9600
Paul Kehrer, *President*
Kelly Kehrer, *Vice Pres*
Virginia Krueger, *Manager*
EMP: 15
SQ FT: 7,000
SALES (est): 3.4MM **Privately Held**
WEB: www.carelabs.com
SIC: 5169 2842 Industrial chemicals; specialty cleaning preparations

(G-15578)
CLEARVLUE COMBUSTN SYSTEMS INC
4402 Ringrose Dr (77459-2963)
PHONE...................................281 261-9543
Richard Haase, *President*
EMP: 15
SALES (est): 1.7MM **Privately Held**
WEB: www.clearvalue.com
SIC: 3519 Internal combustion engines

(G-15579)
DAVID L JENNINGS
Also Called: Pti Pvment Repr Pdts Aka Pvptc
9603 Pennington Ln (77459-6233)
PHONE...................................281 778-3223
David L Jennings, *Owner*
▼ EMP: 60
SALES (est): 700K **Privately Held**
WEB: www.pavepatch.com
SIC: 1611 2951 1771 3272 Concrete construction: roads, highways, sidewalks, etc.; asphalt & asphaltic paving mixtures (not from refineries); blacktop (asphalt) work; building materials, except block or brick; concrete

(G-15580)
E I DU PONT DE NEMOURS & CO
4107 Lake Ct (77459-2305)
PHONE...................................281 471-2771
Wilson S TSE, *Principal*
EMP: 339
SALES (corp-wide): 14.2B **Publicly Held**
WEB: www.dupont.com
SIC: 2879 Agricultural chemicals
HQ: E. I. Du Pont De Nemours And Company
974 Centre Rd Bldg 735
Wilmington DE 19805
302 485-3000

(G-15581)
LONGER PROTECTIVE LLC
13215 Stafford Rd Ste 300 (77489-2190)
PHONE...................................832 987-1790
Michael Zhong,
EMP: 10
SALES (est): 450.6K **Privately Held**
SIC: 2672 Masking tape: made from purchased materials

(G-15582)
LUCERE LLC
Also Called: Innovative Electronics/Sfe
3803 Garden Way (77459-6483)
P.O. Box 1367, Stafford (77497-1367)
PHONE...................................281 240-7355
Richard Stone,
Nannette Stone,
EMP: 21
SQ FT: 2,000
SALES (est): 3.5MM **Privately Held**
WEB: www.matherneis.com
SIC: 3679 1389 Electronic circuits; oil field services

(G-15583)
LUFKIN INDUSTRIES LLC
Also Called: Lufkin Automation
811 Willow Oak Dr 800 (77489-2468)
PHONE...................................281 495-1100
EMP: 10
SALES (corp-wide): 1B **Privately Held**
WEB: www.bhge.com
SIC: 3321 3462 3561 Gray iron castings; iron & steel forgings; pumps, oil well & field
PA: Lufkin Gears Llc
409 Ellis Ave
Lufkin TX 75904
936 634-2211

(G-15584)
MADMACKENZIE SOLUTIONS LLC
9119 Highway 6 Ste 230 (77459-4879)
PHONE...................................281 615-8102
EMP: 50 EST: 2017
SALES (est): 5MM **Privately Held**
WEB: www.madmackenzie.com
SIC: 2911 Fractionation products of crude petroleum, hydrocarbons

(G-15585)
NORTH BLUE OAK INC
Also Called: Balbia
1306 Fm 1092 Rd Ste 508 (77459-1535)
PHONE...................................844 778-2336
Allessandro Falcone, *CEO*
EMP: 10
SQ FT: 1,200
SALES (est): 750K **Privately Held**
WEB: www.northblueoak.com
SIC: 2064 5141 Candy & other confectionery products; groceries, general line

(G-15586)
NSM INC
Also Called: Cornerstone Valve
1535 Industrial Dr (77489-1008)
PHONE...................................281 880-8188
Vini Gupta, *CEO*
EMP: 12
SALES (est): 618.5K **Privately Held**
SIC: 3491 Industrial valves

(G-15587)
RELIANCE INDUSTRIES INC (PA)
Also Called: Reliance Mixers
1900 Fm 1092 Rd Ste A (77459-1733)
P.O. Box 1146, Stafford (77497-1146)
PHONE...................................281 499-9926
Devandra Desai, *President*
Navin Chanchlani, *General Mgr*
Vineet Pandey, *General Mgr*
Jonathan Kain, *Principal*
Ronald Leasure, *Principal*
◆ EMP: 20
SQ FT: 22,000
SALES: 3.4MM **Privately Held**
WEB: www.reliancemixers.com
SIC: 3531 3599 Construction machinery; machine shop, jobbing & repair

(G-15588)
RESERVE ANALYSTS ASSOC INC
2130 Glenn Lakes Ln (77459-4435)
PHONE...................................281 438-3000
Allen C Barron, *President*
Allen Kelley, *Vice Pres*
EMP: 12
SQ FT: 25,000
SALES (est): 1.2MM **Privately Held**
WEB: www.reserve-analysts.com
SIC: 1389 Oil consultants
PA: Opportune Llp
711 Louisiana St Ste 3100
Houston TX 77002

(G-15589)
REYNOLDS LIFT TECHNOLOGIES LLC
14043 S Gessner Rd (77489-1000)
PHONE...................................866 629-6298
Edward Curt, *President*
Carl Braganza, *Manager*
EMP: 11
SALES (est): 578K **Privately Held**
WEB: www.reynoldslift.com
SIC: 3533 Oil & gas field machinery

(G-15590)
RICH PRODUCTS CORPORATION
14847 Fairway Pines Dr (77489-3398)
PHONE...................................281 835-7100
EMP: 14
SALES (corp-wide): 6.7B **Privately Held**
WEB: www.richs.com
SIC: 2053 Frozen bakery products, except bread
PA: Rich Products Corporation
1 Robert Rich Way
Buffalo NY 14213
716 878-8000

(G-15591)
RICH PRODUCTS CORPORATION
Also Called: Twinstar Bakery
13221 S Gessner Rd (77489-1014)
PHONE...................................281 410-6600
John Oakley, *Superintendent*
Aaron Spiwak, *Opers Mgr*
Claus Weingaertner, *Director*
EMP: 200
SALES (corp-wide): 6.7B **Privately Held**
WEB: www.richs.com
SIC: 2053 Frozen bakery products, except bread
PA: Rich Products Corporation
1 Robert Rich Way
Buffalo NY 14213
716 878-8000

(G-15592)
SHADOWGRAPH INC
1545 Industrial Dr (77489-1008)
PHONE...................................281 208-1280
Derek Hayford, *President*
EMP: 13
SQ FT: 8,000
SALES (est): 1.6MM **Privately Held**
WEB: www.shadowgraph-inc.com
SIC: 2759 Screen printing

(G-15593)
SHIPLEY DO - NUTS
Also Called: Shipley Do-Nuts
1701 Texas Pkwy (77489-2171)
PHONE...................................281 499-5234
EMP: 15
SALES (est): 450K **Privately Held**
SIC: 5812 2051 Eating Place Mfg Bread/Related Products

(G-15594)
SMITH INTERNATIONAL INC
468 Kenny Rd 143 (77459)
PHONE...................................254 697-4488
Doug Cocks, *Branch Mgr*
EMP: 14 **Publicly Held**
WEB: www.smithdevelopment.com
SIC: 1389 Oil field services
HQ: Smith International, Inc.
1310 Rankin Rd
Houston TX 77073
281 443-3370

(G-15595)
SOUTHWEST ELCTRONIC ENRGY CORP
823 Buffalo Run (77489-1628)
P.O. Box 31340, Houston (77231-1340)
PHONE...................................281 240-4000
C Len Benckenstein, *CEO*
Daniel Kleinburg, *Engineer*
Jim Woodward, *Engineer*
Beth Rayhill, *Controller*
David O'Banion, *Sales Staff*
▲ EMP: 75
SQ FT: 30,000
SALES (est): 15.3MM **Publicly Held**
WEB: www.swe.com
SIC: 3691 3692 Storage batteries; primary batteries, dry & wet
PA: Ultralife Corporation
2000 Technology Pkwy
Newark NY 14513

(G-15596)
TRI LEAF INDUSTRIES LLC
6140 Highway 6 Ste 178 (77459-3802)
PHONE...................................830 742-3700
Kurt Schlogl, *Mng Member*
Casey Brown, *Mng Member*
David Obrian, *Mng Member*
Woody Williams, *Mng Member*
EMP: 60
SALES (est): 3.4MM **Privately Held**
SIC: 1389 Oil field services

(G-15597)
UNIFIRST CORPORATION
13513 S Gessner Rd (77489-1018)
PHONE...................................281 261-9632
EMP: 44
SALES (corp-wide): 1.8B **Publicly Held**
WEB: www.unifirst.com
SIC: 7218 2326 Industrial uniform supply; work clothing supply; men's & boys' work clothing
PA: Unifirst Corporation
68 Jonspin Rd
Wilmington MA 01887
978 658-8888

(G-15598)
VALVE INDEX INTERNATIONAL INC
14039 S Gessner Rd (77489-1000)
P.O. Box 16476, Sugar Land (77496-6476)
PHONE...................................281 712-8246
Jian Ji, *President*
Miao LI, *Vice Pres*
EMP: 9
SALES (est): 1.2MM **Privately Held**
WEB: www.valveindex.com
SIC: 3491 Industrial valves

Monahans
Ward County

(G-15599)
AZTECA FABRICATION
201 N Industrial Rd (79756)
PHONE...................................432 943-8888
Tommy Moore, *Owner*
Craig Moore, *Partner*
EMP: 21
SALES (est): 8.7MM **Privately Held**
WEB: www.aztecafabrication.com
SIC: 3444 Sheet metalwork

(G-15600)
BEST MADE DESIGNS LLC
309 S Betty Ave Unit C (79756-4212)
P.O. Box 475 (79756-0475)
PHONE...................................432 943-9995
Wes Davis, *COO*
Angel Hernandez, *Manager*
Steve Walker, *Info Tech Mgr*
Jeff Wemmer,
Bryan Heflin,
EMP: 50 EST: 1997
SQ FT: 32,000
SALES (est): 5.5MM **Privately Held**
WEB: www.specopsbrand.com
SIC: 2389 2221 Men's miscellaneous accessories; broadwoven fabric mills, manmade

(G-15601)
BRIGGS NEWS ALLIANCE LLC
Also Called: Monahans News, The
107 W 2nd St (79756-4235)
P.O. Box 767 (79756-0767)
PHONE..............................432 943-4313
Smokey Briggs,
EMP: 9
SALES (est): 674.3K Privately Held
WEB: www.themonahansnews.com
SIC: 2711 2721 Newspapers: publishing
　only, not printed on site; periodicals: pub-
　lishing only

(G-15602)
**COMPRESSOR ELEMENTS
SERVICE**
2306 S Stockton Ave (79756-7610)
P.O. Box 809 (79756-0809)
PHONE..............................432 943-6701
Steve Swarb, President
Jess Warden, Opers Dir
Travis Combs, Foreman/Supr
Randy Crabtree, Foreman/Supr
Joseph Ozuna, Foreman/Supr
EMP: 14
SQ FT: 30,000
SALES (est): 2.8MM Privately Held
WEB: www.compressorelements.com
SIC: 3563 Air & gas compressors

(G-15603)
**CRAFT WIRELINE SERVICES
INC**
4400 S Loop 464 Rd (79756-9000)
P.O. Box 410 (79756-0410)
PHONE..............................432 943-5150
Melvin Robert Craft, President
Ella Craft, Vice Pres
Adrian Porres, Officer
EMP: 12
SQ FT: 69,600
SALES (est): 1.4MM Privately Held
SIC: 3699 1389 Lead-in wires, electric
　lamp; electrical welding equipment; elec-
　trostatic particle accelerators; generators,
　ultrasonic; construction, repair & disman-
　tling services

(G-15604)
**GRACO FISHING & RENTAL TLS
INC**
Also Called: Graco Oilfield Services
3601 S I 20 Service Rd (79756)
P.O. Box 391 (79756-0391)
PHONE..............................432 943-5019
Bobby Gibson, Manager
EMP: 19
SALES (corp-wide): 25.6MM Privately
Held
WEB: www.gracooilfieldservices.com
SIC: 1389 Oil field services
PA: Graco Fishing & Rental Tools, Inc.
　5300 Town And Cntry Blvd
　Frisco TX 75034
　214 618-3930

(G-15605)
HULK OILFIELD SERVICES INC
4911 S Arizona St (79756-9256)
P.O. Box 806 (79756-0806)
PHONE..............................432 803-7060
Troy E Benson, CEO
EMP: 15
SALES (est): 390.8K Privately Held
SIC: 1389 Oil & gas field services

(G-15606)
**J & M ENERGY SERVICES LP
(PA)**
1705 S Stockton Ave (79756-6527)
P.O. Box 50257, Bowling Green KY
(42102-2857)
PHONE..............................432 943-7770
Javier Marquez, Partner
EMP: 36
SALES (est): 6.1MM Privately Held
SIC: 1389 Oil field services

(G-15607)
JORN WELL SERVICE
412 W Sealy Ave (79756-3816)
P.O. Box 1154 (79756-1154)
PHONE..............................432 943-5699
Nina Arroyo, Partner

Cruz Arroyo, Partner
EMP: 15 EST: 1996
SALES (est): 922.3K Privately Held
SIC: 1389 Oil field services

(G-15608)
LOBO TUBING TESTER INC
1203 S Dwight Ave (79756-5714)
P.O. Box 1066 (79756-1066)
PHONE..............................432 943-5441
Allen Cunningham, President
Lynn Cunningham, Corp Secy
EMP: 9 EST: 1970
SALES (est): 759.3K Privately Held
SIC: 1389 Testing, measuring, surveying &
　analysis services

(G-15609)
MONAHANS ELECTRIC INC
3000 S Stockton Ave (79756-7810)
P.O. Box 1539 (79756-1539)
PHONE..............................432 943-3246
Jeff Johnson, CEO
Chuck Lowrey, CFO
EMP: 25 EST: 1961
SQ FT: 30,000
SALES (est): 3.5MM
SALES (corp-wide): 142.7MM Privately
Held
WEB: www.monahans.org
SIC: 7694 Electric motor repair
PA: Expanse Electrical Company, Llc
　6413 N State Hwy 349 Bldg
　Midland TX 79705
　432 580-7095

(G-15610)
NABORS WELL SERVICES LTD
110 Industrail (79756-2118)
PHONE..............................432 943-2227
Mike Fuentez, Branch Mgr
Mark Andrews, Admin Secy
EMP: 62 Privately Held
WEB: www.nabors.com
SIC: 1389 Oil field services
HQ: Nabors Well Services Ltd.
　515 W Greens Rd Ste 1200
　Houston TX 77067
　281 874-0035

(G-15611)
**OIL STATES ENERGY SERVICES
LLC**
3104 S Stockton Ave (79756-7812)
PHONE..............................432 943-2556
Celia Page, Manager
EMP: 10
SALES (corp-wide): 1B Publicly Held
WEB: www.oses.com
SIC: 1389 Gas field services; oil field serv-
　ices
HQ: Oil States Energy Services, L.L.C.
　333 Clay St Ste 2100
　Houston TX 77002
　713 425-2400

(G-15612)
**QUELL PETROLEUM SERVICES
INC**
Also Called: Monahans Nipple-Up Service
700 N Loop 464 (79756)
P.O. Box 1552 (79756-1552)
PHONE..............................432 943-8400
Henry Cutbirth, President
David Cutbirth, Corp Secy
▲ EMP: 40
SQ FT: 3,000
SALES (est): 6.6MM Privately Held
WEB: www.monahansnippleup.com
SIC: 1389 0711 3599 Oil field services;
　soil chemical treatment services; soil test-
　ing services; machine shop, jobbing & re-
　pair

(G-15613)
RED ENERGY SERVICES LP
1005 W 31st St (79756-7701)
P.O. Box 143 (79756-0143)
PHONE..............................432 943-2746
Eduardo Marquez, Partner
Daniel Marquez, Partner
EMP: 10
SALES (est): 1.1MM Privately Held
SIC: 1389 Oil & gas wells: building, repair-
　ing & dismantling

(G-15614)
REDDY ICE CORPORATION
1310 E Sealy Ave (79756-4052)
P.O. Box 1567 (79756-1567)
PHONE..............................432 943-4541
Brandon Stevens, Manager
EMP: 10 Privately Held
WEB: www.reddyice.com
SIC: 2097 Manufactured ice
HQ: Reddy Ice Corporation
　5710 Lbj Fwy Ste 300
　Dallas TX 75240
　214 526-6740

(G-15615)
WTE SERVICES LLC
7662 Fm 1219 S (79756)
P.O. Box 394 (79756-0394)
PHONE..............................432 547-2300
James Morrison,
EMP: 36
SALES (est): 499K Privately Held
SIC: 1389 Oil field services

Mont Belvieu
Chambers County

(G-15616)
CAINS WELDING SERVICE INC
9533 N Highway 146 (77523-9600)
P.O. Box 907 (77580-0907)
PHONE..............................281 303-9517
Artis Standley, President
Mark Hopson, Vice Pres
Leslie Larrison, Treasurer
Jeannie Follis, Admin Sec
EMP: 30
SQ FT: 1,000
SALES (est): 3.2MM Privately Held
SIC: 7692 1541 3444 Welding repair; in-
　dustrial buildings & warehouses; sheet
　metalwork

(G-15617)
**ENTERPRISE PRODUCTS OPER
LLC**
Also Called: Belvieu Enviromental Fuel
10207 Fm Rd 1942 (77580)
P.O. Box 573 (77580-0573)
PHONE..............................281 385-4200
EMP: 81
SALES (corp-wide): 32.7B Publicly Held
WEB: www.enterpriseproducts.com
SIC: 2911 Petroleum refining
HQ: Enterprise Products Operating Llc
　1100 La St Ste Ste 1000
　Houston TX 77002

(G-15618)
**ENTERPRISE PRODUCTS OPER
LLC**
10910 Evil Dr (77580)
P.O. Box 573 (77580-0573)
PHONE..............................832 501-4000
Bob Moss, Vice Pres
Kelly Tinsley, Opers Staff
Andrew May, Purch Mgr
Courtney Allen, Accountant
Grayson Hall, Accountant
EMP: 64
SALES (corp-wide): 32.7B Publicly Held
WEB: www.enterpriseproducts.com
SIC: 2911 Petroleum refining
HQ: Enterprise Products Operating Llc
　1100 La St Ste Ste 1000
　Houston TX 77002

(G-15619)
TEXAS BRINE COMPANY LLC
Also Called: Texas Brine Baytown Company
401 W Winfree Rd (77580)
PHONE..............................281 385-6048
Jack Jameyson, Manager
EMP: 10
SALES (corp-wide): 247.1MM Privately
Held
WEB: www.texasbrine.com
SIC: 2819 Industrial inorganic chemicals
HQ: Texas Brine Company, Llc
　4800 San Felipe St
　Houston TX 77056
　713 877-2700

Mont Belvieu
Harris County

(G-15620)
POLY-AMERICA LP
Also Called: Pol-Tex International
13830 Hatcherville Rd (77521-7528)
P.O. Box 1440 (77580-1440)
PHONE..............................281 385-3700
Kathleen Miller, Accountant
Doug Dawson, Branch Mgr
Joe Brown, Manager
EMP: 75
SALES (corp-wide): 561.6MM Privately
Held
WEB: www.poly-americarecycling.com
SIC: 2821 Plastics materials & resins
PA: Poly-America, L.P.
　2000 W Marshall Dr
　Grand Prairie TX 75051
　972 337-7100

(G-15621)
TALKE USA INC
13822 Hatcherville Rd (77521-7528)
PHONE..............................832 260-8325
Alexander Boehm, Manager
EMP: 20
SQ FT: 2,570,040
SALES (corp-wide): 226MM Privately
Held
WEB: www.talke.com
SIC: 4783 2899 Packing & crating; chemi-
　cal preparations
HQ: Talke Usa, Inc.
　13330 Hatcherville Rd
　Mont Belvieu TX 77521
　832 307-7269

Mont Belvieu
Liberty County

(G-15622)
**LYONDELL CHEMICAL
COMPANY**
11815 Highway 146 (77535-6618)
PHONE..............................281 385-7010
Penny Massey, Manager
EMP: 18
SALES (corp-wide): 34.9B Privately Held
WEB: www.lyondellbasell.com
SIC: 2869 Industrial organic chemicals
HQ: Lyondell Chemical Company
　1221 Mckinney St Ste 300
　Houston TX 77010
　713 309-7200

(G-15623)
TRI RESOURCES INC
Also Called: Dynegy
10119 Highway 146 (77535-5859)
PHONE..............................281 385-3200
Bob Boyd, Branch Mgr
EMP: 120 Publicly Held
WEB: www.triresources.com
SIC: 1321 Natural gas liquids
HQ: Tri Resources Inc.
　811 Louisiana St Ste 2100
　Houston TX 77002
　713 584-1000

Montgomery
Montgomery County

(G-15624)
ABM INTERNATIONAL INC
18473 Kinkaid Rd E (77316-4109)
P.O. Box 1820 (77356-1856)
PHONE..............................936 441-4401
Neal Schwarzberger, CEO
Neal A Schwarzberger, President
Heidi Farmer, Executive
▲ EMP: 65 EST: 1947
SQ FT: 90,000
SALES (est): 14.7MM Privately Held
WEB: www.abminternational.com
SIC: 3552 3842 Textile machinery; per-
　sonal safety equipment; clothing, fire re-
　sistant & protective

▲ = Import ▼=Export
◆ =Import/Export

(G-15625)
ALLAMON TOOL COMPANY INC
18935 Freeport Dr (77356-4446)
PHONE....................................936 449-5433
Shirley Allamon, *President*
Jessica Taylor, *VP Admin*
Jerry P Allamon, *Vice Pres*
Tim Harrison, *Manager*
David Armstrong, *Representative*
EMP: 30
SQ FT: 15,000
SALES (est): 6.9MM **Privately Held**
WEB: www.allamontool.com
SIC: **1389** 8711 Oil field services; engineering services

(G-15626)
ALLOY CNC LLC
18473 Kinkaid Rd E (77316-4109)
PHONE....................................936 449-4001
EMP: 10 EST: 2016
SALES (est): 174.1K **Privately Held**
WEB: www.alloycnc.com
SIC: **3444** 3599 Sheet metalwork; machine shop, jobbing & repair

(G-15627)
CAJUN READY MIX LTD
204 Kings Ln (77356-4414)
PHONE....................................936 597-8455
Debbie Patin, *Partner*
Deborah Patin, *Partner*
Troy Patin, *Mng Member*
EMP: 25
SALES (est): 8.5MM **Privately Held**
WEB: www.ingramreadymixinc.com
SIC: **3273** Ready-mixed concrete

(G-15628)
COMPLIANCE GROUP INC
14884 Highway 105 W # 100 (77356-5248)
PHONE....................................936 447-6100
Kent Pritchett, *President*
Stacy Munsinger, *Manager*
Shelli Myers, *Manager*
Kristyn Christie, *Consultant*
EMP: 10
SALES (est): 624.1K
SALES (corp-wide): 51.3MM **Privately Held**
WEB: www.thecompliancegroup.com
SIC: **1389** Oil consultants
PA: Linestar Integrity Services Llc
4203 Montrose Blvd
Houston TX 77006
832 830-8531

(G-15629)
COMPUTERIZED TRAFFIC INC
2220 Fm 1486 Rd (77316-2200)
PHONE....................................281 252-0505
Dean Benignus, *President*
Michael Benignus, *Vice Pres*
EMP: 9
SALES (est): 1.5MM **Privately Held**
WEB: www.computerizedtraffic.com
SIC: **3669** Traffic signals, electric

(G-15630)
CRETIC ENERGY CORP
11633 Grandview Dr (77356-4276)
PHONE....................................713 922-3784
Joseph Michetti, *President*
EMP: 16
SALES (est): 1.3MM **Privately Held**
WEB: www.cretic.net
SIC: **1389** Oil field services

(G-15631)
DELTA MARINE TECHNOLOGIES
Also Called: Delta Subsea
550 Club Dr Ste 345 (77316-3095)
PHONE....................................936 582-7237
Scott Dingman, *President*
Jim Wagner, *Vice Pres*
EMP: 20
SALES (est): 680K **Privately Held**
WEB: www.deltasubsea-rov.com
SIC: **1389** Oil consultants

(G-15632)
DSTJ CORPORATION
13948 Parrish Trl (77316-2027)
PHONE....................................936 447-1174
Jo Ann-Harlan, *President*
Jo Ann Harlan, *President*

David A Harlan, *Principal*
Donald P Harlan, *Vice Pres*
Sharon H Haas, *Treasurer*
EMP: 10
SQ FT: 4,000
SALES (est): 964.8K **Privately Held**
SIC: **1311** 2911 Crude petroleum production; natural gas production; gases & liquefied petroleum gases

(G-15633)
F3 FOAM LLC
3450 Spring Branch Rd (77316-2559)
PHONE....................................936 661-3172
Earnest Paul Stroade, *Mng Member*
Paul Chad Kirby, *Mng Member*
EMP: 9
SALES (est): 1.5MM **Privately Held**
WEB: www.f3foam.com
SIC: **3086** 2952 Insulation or cushioning material, foamed plastic; roof cement: asphalt, fibrous or plastic

(G-15634)
HOUSTON NORTH REMODEL
13151 Walden Rd Apt 158 (77356-8584)
PHONE....................................936 314-4654
Steven Rich, *Owner*
EMP: 14
SALES (est): 278.8K **Privately Held**
SIC: **1389** Construction, repair & dismantling services

(G-15635)
KODIAK GAS SERVICES LLC (HQ)
15320 Highway 105 W # 210 (77356-2602)
PHONE....................................936 539-3300
EMP: 300 EST: 2011
SQ FT: 1,300
SALES (est): 35.2MM
SALES (corp-wide): 32MM **Privately Held**
WEB: www.kodiakgas.com
SIC: **1389** Pumping of oil & gas wells
PA: Eqt Infrastructure Iii
1114 Ave Of The Americas
New York NY 10036
917 281-0850

(G-15636)
MCC HOLDINGS INC
Also Called: Crane Valve North America
9860 Johnson Rd (77316-9494)
PHONE....................................936 588-5301
Nuwan Dantanarayana, *Branch Mgr*
Chris Reichert, *Manager*
EMP: 65
SALES (corp-wide): 3.2B **Publicly Held**
WEB: www.craneenergy.com
SIC: **3491** Industrial valves
HQ: Mcc Holdings, Inc.
4526 Res Frest Dr Ste 400
The Woodlands TX 77381
936 271-6500

(G-15637)
NORTH AMERICAN TRADE CORP
Also Called: Noramco
18948 Freeport Dr (77356-4445)
PHONE....................................936 588-1010
Jorge Guiloff, *President*
Jacqueline Guiloff, *Vice Pres*
George Hoepner, *Vice Pres*
Mike Connery, *Info Tech Mgr*
◆ EMP: 16 EST: 1984
SQ FT: 22,000
SALES (est): 21.1MM **Privately Held**
WEB: www.noramcousa.com
SIC: **5082** 3949 5085 Oil field equipment; treadmills; industrial supplies

(G-15638)
PEGASUS OPTMZTION MANAGERS LLC
15320 Highway 105 W # 210 (77356-2602)
PHONE....................................979 213-4101
Richard Childress, *Vice Pres*
Marshall Taylor, *Engineer*
Carlos Rodriguez, *CFO*
Susan Shwarts, *Administration*
EMP: 200

SALES (est): 5.7MM **Privately Held**
WEB: www.pegasus15.com
SIC: **1389** Oil & gas field services

(G-15639)
PRECISION TACKLE INC
13100 Fm 149 Rd Ste 109 (77316-9311)
P.O. Box 709 (77356-0709)
PHONE....................................936 597-6145
Rose Marie Hall, *President*
William Hall, *Vice Pres*
EMP: 18
SQ FT: 700
SALES (est): 1.3MM **Privately Held**
WEB: www.thecajunthunder.com
SIC: **3949** Fishing tackle, general

(G-15640)
PREMIER WORLDWIDE INC
3819 Honea Egypt Rd (77316-9475)
PHONE....................................281 752-0014
Robbie Brundrett, *President*
Deepak Bhatti, *Director*
EMP: 15
SQ FT: 15,000
SALES (est): 1.5MM **Privately Held**
WEB: www.premierwwi.com
SIC: **7389** 1389 Petroleum refinery inspection service; oil & gas wells: building, repairing & dismantling

(G-15641)
SPIRIT INDUSTRIES INC
21973 Eva St (77356-2011)
P.O. Box 329 (77356-0329)
PHONE....................................936 597-5144
Geral Fauss, *President*
Deryl Fauss, *Vice Pres*
Susan Fauss, *Vice Pres*
Gerald Fauss, *Controller*
EMP: 35
SQ FT: 37,000
SALES (est): 6.4MM **Privately Held**
WEB: www.spiritindustries.com
SIC: **3069** 3089 Balloons, advertising & toy: rubber; novelties, plastic

(G-15642)
STRATUM ENERGY ROMANIA LLC
445 Edgewood Dr (77356-8428)
PHONE....................................832 813-8947
EMP: 14 EST: 2008
SALES (est): 836.7K **Privately Held**
SIC: **1382** Oil/Gas Exploration Services

(G-15643)
SURF SUBSEA INC
5010 Honea Egypt Rd (77316-2323)
PHONE....................................281 305-4411
Jim Chiles, *CEO*
Wade Abadie, *President*
Jim McClaugherty, *Vice Pres*
▲ EMP: 29
SALES (est): 8.6MM **Privately Held**
WEB: www.surfsubsea.com
SIC: **3533** Oil & gas field machinery

(G-15644)
TXTB TECH LLC
17350 Sunset Ranch Dr (77316-2331)
PHONE....................................832 928-5740
Sherri Ward, *Vice Pres*
Jeff Gallatin,
EMP: 12
SQ FT: 4,200
SALES (est): 292.6K **Privately Held**
SIC: **7692** Welding repair

Mount Enterprise
Rusk County

(G-15645)
SPIVEY STAKE & SUPPLY INC (PA)
Also Called: Enterprise Pipe & Steel
16384 Us Highway 259 S (75681-3234)
P.O. Box 349 (75681-0349)
PHONE....................................903 822-3888
EMP: 30 EST: 1970
SQ FT: 19,000

SALES (est): 3.5MM **Privately Held**
SIC: **2499** 2421 5211 Surveyors' stakes, wood; sawmills & planing mills, general; lumber & other building materials

Mount Pleasant
Titus County

(G-15646)
BEST FENDER PRODUCTS INC (PA)
2364 Texas Highway 49 (75455-5201)
P.O. Box 1258 (75456-1258)
PHONE....................................903 577-0510
John R McCollum, *Principal*
O C Ross, *Vice Pres*
Oc Ross, *VP Opers*
Chuck Pearson, *Opers Mgr*
Shan Wilkins, *Opers Mgr*
EMP: 55
SQ FT: 1,500
SALES (est): 25.3MM **Privately Held**
WEB: www.bestfender.com
SIC: **3444** Sheet metalwork

(G-15647)
BOGGS ENTERPRISES INC
Also Called: Country Cottage Florist
1232 Dove Ave (75455-2502)
PHONE....................................903 572-8722
Donald Boggs, *President*
Annaleisa Boggs, *President*
EMP: 10
SQ FT: 2,500
SALES (est): 450K **Privately Held**
WEB: www.mountpleasantbeef.com
SIC: **0751** 5147 2011 5992 Slaughtering: custom livestock services; meats, fresh; meat packing plants; florists

(G-15648)
CALDWELL MACHINE AND GEAR INC
2370 Farm Road 127 (75455-9105)
P.O. Box 1869 (75456-1869)
PHONE....................................903 572-1660
Charles S Caldwell, *President*
Maria B Caldwell, *Vice Pres*
Isabel Caldwell, *Officer*
Thomas Caldwell, *Officer*
EMP: 10
SQ FT: 7,400
SALES (est): 1.5MM **Privately Held**
WEB: www.caldwellmachineandgear.com
SIC: **3541** 5084 5083 Gear cutting & finishing machines; dairy products manufacturing machinery; food product manufacturing machinery; milk products manufacturing machinery & equipment; pulp (wood) manufacturing machinery; agricultural machinery & equipment

(G-15649)
CYPRESS LUMBER COMPANY INC
4191 S Us Highway 271 (75455-8554)
P.O. Box 1216 (75456-1216)
PHONE....................................903 572-6561
John Roach, *President*
Celest Roach, *Corp Secy*
EMP: 12 EST: 1961
SQ FT: 4,800
SALES (est): 1.5MM **Privately Held**
SIC: **2421** Sawmills & planing mills, general

(G-15650)
DEKORON WIRE AND CABLE LLC
1300 Industrial Rd (75455-2614)
PHONE....................................903 572-0657
Gregory J Smith, *President*
James Blevins, *Vice Pres*
Mathew J Nadakal, *Vice Pres*
Mitchell Walker, *Vice Pres*
Steve Bonnell, *Mng Member*
▲ EMP: 80
SALES (est): 19MM
SALES (corp-wide): 254.6B **Publicly Held**
WEB: www.dekoroncable.com
SIC: **3496** Miscellaneous fabricated wire products

HQ: Marmon Group Llc
181 W Madison St Ste 2600
Chicago IL 60602
312 372-9500

(G-15651)
IMFAB INC
3047 Farm Road 2348 N (75455-8983)
PHONE..................................903 577-0510
John R McCollum, *Director*
EMP: 40 EST: 2018
SALES (est): 5.9MM **Privately Held**
WEB: www.imfabinc.com
SIC: 3444 3699 3542 Sheet metalwork;
electrical welding equipment; presses:
forming, stamping, punching, sizing (ma-
chine tools)
PA: Best Fender Products, Inc.
2364 Texas Highway 49
Mount Pleasant TX 75455

(G-15652)
INTERNATIONAL SULPHUR INC
1386 N Frontage Rd (75455-6499)
PHONE..................................903 577-5500
Jerry J Jennett, *CEO*
Jesse L Maranville, *Vice Pres*
Pam Hawkins, *Engineer*
Lanny R Luttrell, *Director*
Marci Henderson, *Executive*
EMP: 28 EST: 1950
SQ FT: 30,000
SALES (est): 8.3MM
SALES (corp-wide): 18.7MM **Privately
Held**
WEB: www.internationalsulphur.com
SIC: 2819 Sulfur, recovered or refined, incl.
from sour natural gas
PA: Georgia Gulf Sulfur Corporation
1729 Dow St
Valdosta GA 31601
229 244-0000

(G-15653)
LMP READYMIX LLC
775 E 16th St (75455-2247)
P.O. Box 1599 (75456-1599)
PHONE..................................903 572-2500
Ashley Hightower,
EMP: 10
SALES (est): 2.4MM **Privately Held**
WEB: www.lmpconcrete.com
SIC: 3273 Ready-mixed concrete

(G-15654)
MEDIA PALMER INC
Also Called: Mount Pleasant Daily Tribune
210 S Van Buren Ave (75455-4440)
P.O. Box 1177 (75456-1177)
PHONE..................................903 572-1705
Robert L Palmer, *President*
Barbara Caldwell, *Vice Pres*
Frances Lobpries, *Vice Pres*
EMP: 32
SALES (est): 2.2MM **Privately Held**
WEB: www.tribnow.com
SIC: 2711 Newspapers, publishing & print-
ing

(G-15655)
MID-AMERICA PET FOOD LLC
2024 N Frontage Rd (75455-6474)
P.O. Box 532 (75456-0532)
PHONE..................................903 572-5900
Juan Duenez, *Prdtn Mgr*
Brian Bragg, *Technology*
Ken Colbey, *Officer*
Scott Glover,
Mari Farrell, *Assistant*
▼ EMP: 50
SQ FT: 3,200
SALES (est): 20MM **Privately Held**
WEB: www.victorpetfood.com
SIC: 5999 2048 Pet food; livestock feeds

(G-15656)
NEWLY WEDS FOODS INC
4125 Farm Road 3417 (75455-0717)
PHONE..................................903 577-3200
Tyler Windom, *Sales Staff*
George Winchester, *Branch Mgr*
EMP: 41
SALES (corp-wide): 128.2MM **Privately
Held**
WEB: www.newlywedsfoods.com
SIC: 2099 Food preparations

PA: Newly Weds Foods, Inc.
4140 W Fullerton Ave
Chicago IL 60639
773 489-7000

(G-15657)
PILGRIMS PRIDE CORPORATION
1107 Monticello Rd (75455-5529)
P.O. Box 1268 (75456-1268)
PHONE..................................903 575-3540
Rick Cogdill, *Manager*
Shirlon Jones, *Supervisor*
EMP: 99 **Publicly Held**
WEB: www.pilgrims.com
SIC: 2015 Chicken, slaughtered &
dressed; chicken, processed: fresh
HQ: Pilgrim's Pride Corporation
1770 Promontory Cir
Greeley CO 80634
970 506-8000

(G-15658)
PILGRIMS PRIDE CORPORATION
Also Called: Pilgrim's Pride Rendering/By-P
1030 Pilgrim St (75455-5927)
P.O. Box 1268 (75456-1268)
PHONE..................................903 575-3403
Joni Worrell, *Human Res Mgr*
Chris Horn, *Sales Mgr*
Brad Cameron, *Sales Staff*
Tommy Brown, *Manager*
EMP: 287 **Publicly Held**
WEB: www.pilgrims.com
SIC: 2015 Poultry slaughtering & process-
ing
HQ: Pilgrim's Pride Corporation
1770 Promontory Cir
Greeley CO 80634
970 506-8000

(G-15659)
PILGRIMS PRIDE CORPORATION
1210 Pilgrim St (75455-5926)
PHONE..................................903 575-3748
Dontrell Lawson, *Branch Mgr*
EMP: 293 **Publicly Held**
WEB: www.pilgrims.com
SIC: 2015 Poultry slaughtering & process-
ing
HQ: Pilgrim's Pride Corporation
1770 Promontory Cir
Greeley CO 80634
970 506-8000

(G-15660)
PRIEFERT MFG CO INC
Also Called: Priefert Complex Designs
2630 S Jefferson Ave (75455-5961)
P.O. Box 1540 (75456-1540)
PHONE..................................903 572-1741
Eddie Priefert, *President*
William Priefert, *Chairman*
Nathan Priefert, *Vice Pres*
Virginia Priefert, *Vice Pres*
Heather Parkerson, *Purch Agent*
◆ EMP: 800
SQ FT: 700,000
SALES (est): 228.8MM **Privately Held**
WEB: www.priefert.com
SIC: 3523 3446 3444 3317 Cattle feed-
ing, handling & watering equipment; hay-
ing machines: mowers, rakes, stackers,
etc.; poultry brooders, feeders & waterers;
turf & grounds equipment; architectural
metalwork; sheet metalwork; welded pipe
& tubes; custom roll formed products

(G-15661)
QUALITY TRAILER PRODUCTS LP
Also Called: Rockwell American
609 E 16th St (75455-2245)
PHONE..................................903 572-7932
Staci Carney, *Safety Mgr*
Larry Blake, *Manager*
EMP: 22
SALES (corp-wide): 2.6B **Privately Held**
WEB: www.rockwellamerican.com
SIC: 3799 Trailers & trailer equipment

HQ: Quality Trailer Products, Lp
604 W Main St
Azle TX 76020
817 444-4518

(G-15662)
ROADCLIPPER ENTERPRISES INC (PA)
Also Called: Diamond C Trailer Mfg
4006 Farm Road 3417 (75455-8784)
PHONE..................................903 572-2834
James Mike Crabb, *CEO*
Jeffery Crabb, *President*
Mike Crabb, *General Mgr*
Jacob Crabb, *Sales Staff*
Randall Prewitt, *Sales Staff*
▼ EMP: 75
SQ FT: 54,000
SALES (est): 18.7MM **Privately Held**
WEB: www.diamondc.com
SIC: 3523 Tractors, farm

(G-15663)
SAINT-GOBAIN PRFMCE PLAS CORP
Also Called: Dekron Wiring Cable
1300 Industrial Rd (75455-2614)
PHONE..................................903 572-3475
Rick Loveless, *Manager*
EMP: 75
SALES (corp-wide): 328.4MM **Privately
Held**
WEB: www.plastics.saint-gobain.com
SIC: 2821 Plastics materials & resins
HQ: Saint-Gobain Performance Plastics
Corporation
31500 Solon Rd
Solon OH 44139
440 836-6900

(G-15664)
TRANS-TEXAS TIRE LLC (PA)
Also Called: Trans-Texas Tire Mt Pleasant
1106 Industrial Rd (75455-2610)
PHONE..................................903 572-0267
Tom Walker, *President*
Amanda Walker, *Vice Pres*
Richard Walker, *Vice Pres*
Linda Walker, *Treasurer*
Bianca Peoples, *Office Mgr*
▲ EMP: 26
SALES (est): 1.1MM **Privately Held**
SIC: 3714 3011 Wheel rims, motor vehi-
cle; industrial tires, pneumatic

(G-15665)
WHW PROPERTIES INC
Also Called: Chief Fabrication
100 S Edwards Ave (75455-4300)
P.O. Box 109 (75456-0109)
PHONE..................................903 572-4161
William Whitaker, *President*
Darren Cox, *Principal*
EMP: 20
SALES (est): 410K **Privately Held**
SIC: 5812 3441 Fast-food restaurant, in-
dependent; fabricated structural metal

Mount Vernon
Franklin County

(G-15666)
CARLTON MFG INC
Also Called: Carlton Mfg Associates
I-30 S Service Rd (75457)
P.O. Box 539 (75457-0539)
PHONE..................................903 537-4591
Rob Behymer, *General Mgr*
Robert Behymer, *General Mgr*
Duane Root, *Branch Mgr*
Dale Sellers, *Director*
EMP: 75
SALES (corp-wide): 9.4MM **Privately
Held**
SIC: 2512 2511 Living room furniture: up-
holstered on wood frames; wood house-
hold furniture
PA: Carlton Mfg., Inc.
20093 E Penn Ave Ste 3
Dunnellon FL 34432
352 465-2153

Mt Pleasant
Titus County

(G-15667)
PILGRIMS PRIDE CORPORATION
Pilgrim's Pride Protein Conver
1000 S Otyson St (75455-5530)
P.O. Box 1268, Mount Pleasant (75456-
1268)
PHONE..................................903 575-1000
Billy Clark, *Area Mgr*
Curt Beadle, *Branch Mgr*
EMP: 2500 **Publicly Held**
WEB: www.pilgrims.com
SIC: 2015 Poultry, processed
HQ: Pilgrim's Pride Corporation
1770 Promontory Cir
Greeley CO 80634
970 506-8000

Muenster
Cooke County

(G-15668)
COOKE COUNTY CRUSHED STONE
8416 W Highway 82 (76252)
P.O. Box 775, Gainesville (76241-0775)
PHONE..................................940 759-4104
Donald Denton, *President*
Cheryl Denton, *Vice Pres*
EMP: 11 EST: 2011
SALES (est): 880.6K **Privately Held**
SIC: 1422 Crushed & broken limestone

(G-15669)
HACKER BROTHERS WELL SERVICE
Hwy 373 (76252)
P.O. Box 39 (76252-0039)
PHONE..................................940 759-4196
Kenneth Hacker, *President*
James Hacker, *Admin Sec*
Freddie Hacker, *Asst Sec*
EMP: 9
SALES (est): 649.5K **Privately Held**
SIC: 1389 Servicing oil & gas wells

(G-15670)
HESS JERRY OPERATING COMPANY
310 N Magnolia St (76252-1510)
P.O. Box 557 (76252-0557)
PHONE..................................940 759-4791
Gerald Hess, *Owner*
EMP: 11 EST: 1981
SQ FT: 850
SALES (est): 1.4MM **Privately Held**
SIC: 1381 Drilling oil & gas wells

(G-15671)
MUENSTER DRILLING COMPANY
415 County Road 350 (76252-4720)
P.O. Box 53 (76252-0053)
PHONE..................................940 759-4949
Chris A Hess, *President*
Doyle Hess, *Vice Pres*
Frank Hess, *Vice Pres*
Angelo B Nasche, *Vice Pres*
La Verna Nasche, *Admin Sec*
EMP: 16 EST: 1980
SQ FT: 5,000
SALES (est): 1.2MM **Privately Held**
WEB: www.muenstermilling.com
SIC: 1381 Directional drilling oil & gas
wells

(G-15672)
R-INTERESTS LLC
Also Called: Rumber Materials
621 W Division St (76252-2627)
PHONE..................................940 759-4181
Brian Adams, *CEO*
William Adams, *Principal*
EMP: 19

SALES (est): 4.2MM **Privately Held**
WEB: www.rumber.com
SIC: **3069** 7389 Reclaimed rubber (re-worked by manufacturing processes); business services

(G-15673)
RUMBER MATERIALS INCORPORATED
621 W Division St (76252-2627)
PHONE..........................940 759-4181
J'Lynn Hare, *Principal*
Brenda Rojas, *Ch Credit Ofcr*
Chip Chrisman, *Sales Staff*
EMP: 9 EST: 2015
SALES (est): 282.9K **Privately Held**
WEB: www.rumber.com
SIC: **3069** 8611 Reclaimed rubber (re-worked by manufacturing processes); business associations

(G-15674)
SUPERIOR MCHNING FBRCATION INC
15551 W Hwy 82 (76252)
P.O. Box 66 (76252-0066)
PHONE..........................940 759-5066
Giles Waltershcheid, *President*
Giles Walterscheid, *President*
Ricky Cook, *Opers Mgr*
Jeff Walterscheid, *Opers Mgr*
Wesley Sicking, *Production*
EMP: 135
SQ FT: 100,000
SALES (est): 18.3MM **Privately Held**
WEB: www.superior-machining.net
SIC: **3599** Machine shop, jobbing & repair

(G-15675)
UNIVERSAL MACHINING INDS INC
810 E Division St (76252-2769)
PHONE..........................940 759-2430
Steven Trubenbach, *President*
Melinda Klement, *Purchasing*
EMP: 90
SQ FT: 60,000
SALES (est): 16.2MM **Privately Held**
WEB: www.universalmachiningind.com
SIC: **3599** Machine shop, jobbing & repair

Muleshoe
Bailey County

(G-15676)
BUNGE MILLING SOUTHWEST INC (DH)
Also Called: Minsa Corporation
1972 County Road 1068 (79347-9225)
P.O. Box 484 (79347-0484)
PHONE..........................800 852-8291
Andres Martin, *President*
Aaron L Elliott, *Treasurer*
Ivan Ahumada, *Sales Staff*
Gilberto Ramirez, *Supervisor*
Gregory A Billhartz, *Admin Sec*
▲ EMP: 75
SALES (est): 23.9MM **Privately Held**
WEB: www.minsa.com
SIC: **2041** 5149 Corn meal; groceries & related products
HQ: Bunge North America, Inc.
1391 Tmberlake Manor Pkwy
Chesterfield MO 63017
314 292-2000

(G-15677)
KINDER MORGAN (DELAWARE) INC
Rr 2 (79347-9802)
PHONE..........................806 272-3309
Richard D Kinder, *Ch of Bd*
Paul Steinway, *President*
Gary Kohen, *Business Mgr*
Mike Tilton, *Business Mgr*
Van Williams, *Counsel*
EMP: 200
SALES (est): 198.7MM **Publicly Held**
WEB: www.kindermorgan.com
SIC: **4923** 4922 1311 1382 Gas transmission & distribution; natural gas transmission; crude petroleum & natural gas; oil & gas exploration services

PA: Kinder Morgan Inc
1001 La St Ste 1000
Houston TX 77002

(G-15678)
L & L PALLET SUPPLY INC (PA)
1230 Us Highway 84 (79347-6693)
P.O. Box 1130, Farwell (79325-1130)
PHONE..........................806 272-5041
Thomas Landry, *President*
Frank Landry, *Vice Pres*
Kathy Landry, *Admin Sec*
EMP: 15 EST: 1997
SQ FT: 15,500
SALES (est): 2MM **Privately Held**
WEB: www.llpallet.com
SIC: **2448** Pallets, wood

(G-15679)
TRIPLE NICKEL INC
Also Called: C K Nickels
413 E American Blvd (79347-4017)
PHONE..........................806 272-5589
Chad Nickels, *President*
Kayla Nickels, *Vice Pres*
EMP: 15
SQ FT: 1,100
SALES (est): 3.5MM **Privately Held**
WEB: www.cknickels.com
SIC: **2032** Beans & bean sprouts, canned, jarred, etc.

Murchison
Henderson County

(G-15680)
NINE ENERGY SERVICE INC
679 Callender Lake Dr (75778-5101)
PHONE..........................903 469-3922
Ann Fox, *Branch Mgr*
EMP: 18
SALES (corp-wide): 832.9MM **Publicly Held**
WEB: www.nineenergyservice.com
SIC: **1389** Oil field services
PA: Nine Energy Service, Inc.
2001 Kirby Dr Ste 200
Houston TX 77019
281 730-5100

(G-15681)
PULL RITE TRAILERS LLC (HQ)
9350 State Highway 31 E (75778-3456)
PHONE..........................903 502-5000
Clyde Wayne Scott, *Mng Member*
EMP: 15
SALES (est): 600K
SALES (corp-wide): 4MM **Privately Held**
WEB: www.pullritetrailers.com
SIC: **3715** 5084 Truck trailers; trailers, industrial
PA: Rising S Company Llc
9350 State Highway 31 E
Murchison TX 75778
214 455-0560

(G-15682)
RISING S COMPANY LLC (PA)
Also Called: Rising S Bunkers
9350 State Highway 31 E (75778-3456)
PHONE..........................214 455-0560
Clyde Wayne Scott, *CEO*
Gary Lynch, *CFO*
EMP: 40 EST: 2013
SALES (est): 4MM **Privately Held**
WEB: www.risingsbunkers.com
SIC: **3441** 3499 3715 8322 Building components, structural steel; money chests, steel; truck trailers; emergency shelters; ornamental metal work

Murphy
Collin County

(G-15683)
BRAIDED GREEN BROKERAGE LLC
709 Paint Creek Rd (75094-4360)
PHONE..........................480 729-5506
William M Hogan,
EMP: 15

SALES (est): 1.2MM **Privately Held**
SIC: **3564** 5999 Air purification equipment; air purification equipment

Nacogdoches
Nacogdoches County

(G-15684)
ALLSPORT DYNAMICS INC
2724 Se Stallings Dr (75961-7442)
P.O. Box 632237 (75963-2237)
PHONE..........................936 569-1003
Jeff Brewer, *President*
Brad Jacobson, *Vice Pres*
Joey Michelle, *Vice Pres*
Gary White, *Vice Pres*
EMP: 16
SQ FT: 11,000
SALES (est): 500K **Privately Held**
WEB: www.allsportdynamics.com
SIC: **3842** 5999 Supports: abdominal, ankle, arch, kneecap, etc.; orthopedic & prosthesis applications

(G-15685)
ANIMAL SCIENCE PRODUCTS INC
3418 Rayburn Dr (75961-7723)
P.O. Box 631408 (75963-1408)
PHONE..........................936 560-0003
Bailey Reynolds, *President*
Bridget R Arrant, *Corp Secy*
Corey Bland, *Production*
Michael Kunk, *CFO*
Bill Weaver, *CFO*
◆ EMP: 40
SQ FT: 41,000
SALES (est): 17MM **Privately Held**
WEB: www.asp-inc.com
SIC: **5199** 2048 Pet supplies; feed supplements

(G-15686)
BRIGHT COOP INC (PA)
803 W Seale St (75964-5226)
P.O. Box 635001 (75963-5001)
PHONE..........................936 564-8378
Clem Russell, *President*
John Swearingen, *General Mgr*
Wanda J Russell, *Corp Secy*
Mark Horner, *Vice Pres*
◆ EMP: 175 EST: 1951
SALES (est): 48.5MM **Privately Held**
WEB: www.brightcoop.com
SIC: **3496** 3715 Cages, wire; truck trailer chassis

(G-15687)
CAB INCORPORATED
Also Called: Cab Flange Manufacturing
2306 Rayburn Dr (75961-6832)
PHONE..........................936 569-9430
Mike Vanderbosch, *President*
Parth Sharma, *Managing Dir*
Sanjeev Jaganoor, *Engineer*
Karan Kumar, *Engineer*
Yogesh Vashisth, *Engineer*
EMP: 40 **Privately Held**
WEB: www.cabinc.com
SIC: **3317** 3462 Steel pipe & tubes; flange, valve & pipe fitting forgings, ferrous
HQ: Cab Incorporated
5411 Cole Rd
Buford GA 30518
678 745-2100

(G-15688)
CAL-TEX LUMBER COMPANY INC
2912 Rayburn Dr (75961-7468)
P.O. Box 631010 (75963-1010)
PHONE..........................936 564-6426
Suzanne Patterson, *President*
Dave Cooper, *Corp Secy*
George A Schmidbauer, *Vice Pres*
Ronnie Clark, *Director*
EMP: 156
SQ FT: 200,000
SALES (est): 24.8MM **Privately Held**
WEB: www.caltexlbr.com
SIC: **2421** Lumber: rough, sawed or planed

(G-15689)
CANEY CREEK MOULDING INC
12072 Fm 343 (75964-4749)
PHONE..........................936 560-1331
David Mills, *President*
Gary Brandon, *Vice Pres*
EMP: 24
SQ FT: 10,000
SALES (est): 3.1MM **Privately Held**
SIC: **2426** Hardwood dimension & flooring mills

(G-15690)
CARRIZO WOOD PRODUCTS INC
8807 Fm 2259 (75961)
P.O. Box 136, Woden (75978-9002)
PHONE..........................936 569-0582
Joe Biggerstaff, *President*
Phil Carrell, *Corp Secy*
Phillip Cadman, *Vice Pres*
EMP: 37
SQ FT: 8,840
SALES (est): 3.5MM **Privately Held**
WEB: www.carrizowood.com
SIC: **2448** 2421 Wood pallets & skids; sawmills & planing mills, general

(G-15691)
CHEMICAL TRACERS INC
2097 County Road 256 (75965-0418)
PHONE..........................936 564-1866
Charlie Carlis, *President*
EMP: 15
SALES (est): 611.5K **Privately Held**
WEB: www.chemtracers.com
SIC: **1389** Oil & gas field services

(G-15692)
COOPER POWER SYSTEMS LLC
Eaton
2315 Se Stallings Dr (75961-6808)
PHONE..........................936 569-9422
Brian Schazler, *General Mgr*
Derick Rodrigues, *Supervisor*
EMP: 230 **Privately Held**
WEB: www.cooperindustries.com
SIC: **3677** 3612 Electronic coils, transformers & other inductors; transformers, except electric
HQ: Cooper Power Systems, Llc
2300 Badger Dr
Waukesha WI 53188
262 896-2400

(G-15693)
CS PLATINUM SPORTS LLC
916 Ruby St (75961-4114)
P.O. Box 632486 (75963-2486)
PHONE..........................936 559-1883
Lynn Broomfield, *Manager*
John Frederick, *Software Dev*
EMP: 12
SALES (est): 150K **Privately Held**
WEB: www.port-a-field.com
SIC: **3949** Sporting & athletic goods

(G-15694)
DAILY SENTINEL
4920 Colonial Dr (75965-3021)
P.O. Box 630068 (75963-0068)
PHONE..........................936 631-2607
Rick Craig, *Publisher*
Rosie Pool, *Business Mgr*
EMP: 9
SALES (est): 426.9K
SALES (corp-wide): 140.3MM **Privately Held**
WEB: www.dailysentinel.com
SIC: **2711** Newspapers: publishing only, not printed on site
PA: Southern Newspapers, Inc.
5701 Woodway Dr Ste 131
Houston TX 77057
713 266-5481

(G-15695)
E-COATING INC
Also Called: Lee Container
1413 S University Dr (75961-6488)
P.O. Box 153323, Lufkin (75915-3323)
PHONE..........................936 715-0700
Wayne Harbuck, *President*
Jim Thoma, *Vice Pres*

Steve Bradford, *Plant Supt*
Medford Knowles, *Treasurer*
EMP: 15
SQ FT: 100,000
SALES (est): 920K **Privately Held**
WEB: www.leecontainer.com
SIC: 3479 Coating electrodes

(G-15696)
FEW READY MIX CORP
1423 Bennett Clark Rd (75961-6407)
PHONE.................................936 560-5675
Danny Kipps, *President*
Danny Walker, *Owner*
Kevin Kipp, *General Mgr*
EMP: 90 **EST:** 1954
SALES (est): 6MM
SALES (corp-wide): 7.8MM **Privately Held**
WEB: www.fewreadymix.com
SIC: 3273 5082 Ready-mixed concrete; concrete processing equipment
PA: Few Ready Mix Concrete Co.
700 E Milam St
Jasper TX
409 384-5469

(G-15697)
FMC CORPORATION
3226 N University Dr # 100 (75965-2684)
PHONE.................................936 559-0031
Edwin Emborgo, *Branch Mgr*
EMP: 10
SALES (corp-wide): 4.6B **Publicly Held**
WEB: www.fmc.com
SIC: 2812 Soda ash, sodium carbonate (anhydrous)
PA: Fmc Corporation
2929 Walnut St
Philadelphia PA 19104
215 299-6000

(G-15698)
FORETRAVEL INC (PA)
Also Called: Foretravel Motorcoach
1221 Nw Stallings Dr (75964-3059)
PHONE.................................936 564-8367
Lyle Reed, *Ch of Bd*
Gregory Amys, *President*
Tyle Fore, *Marketing Staff*
Jody White, *Representative*
▲ **EMP:** 350
SQ FT: 200,000
SALES (est): 67MM **Privately Held**
WEB: www.foretravel.com
SIC: 3711 3716 Motor homes, self-contained, assembly of; motor homes

(G-15699)
G & S LUMBER CO INC
291 S Us Highway 59 (75964-8441)
P.O. Box 635110 (75963-5110)
PHONE.................................936 564-7676
Kenneth W Sutton, *President*
Kurt Sutton, *Treasurer*
Claudette Sutton, *Admin Sec*
EMP: 38
SALES (est): 5MM **Privately Held**
WEB: www.gslumber.com
SIC: 2426 2421 Dimension, hardwood; sawmills & planing mills, general

(G-15700)
KAMPUS BOOKS
305 E College St (75965-3569)
PHONE.................................936 560-0033
Jay Naroozian, *Owner*
EMP: 11
SQ FT: 4,000
SALES (est): 692K **Privately Held**
WEB: www.kampusbookssfa.com
SIC: 5942 2261 College book stores; screen printing of cotton broadwoven fabrics

(G-15701)
LAKESIDE TRAILER SALES
Also Called: Lakeside Trailer Park
7225 North St (75965-1147)
PHONE.................................936 564-6252
Forest A Dillon, *Owner*
Kevin Dillon, *General Mgr*
EMP: 12 **EST:** 1968
SQ FT: 600

SALES (est): 1MM **Privately Held**
SIC: 5271 6515 5039 3448 Mobile homes; mobile home site operators; mobile homes; septic tanks; buildings, portable: prefabricated metal; waste water & sewage treatment plant construction

(G-15702)
LANGLEY MANUFACTURING INC
252 County Road 822 (75964-4458)
P.O. Box 632732 (75963-2732)
PHONE.................................936 569-8824
Ed Langley, *President*
Beverly Langley, *Vice Pres*
EMP: 10
SQ FT: 10,000
SALES (est): 2MM **Privately Held**
WEB: www.langleymfg.net
SIC: 3469 Stamping metal for the trade

(G-15703)
MAST MOTORSPORTS LLC
330 Nw Stallings Dr (75964-3838)
PHONE.................................936 560-2218
Chris Durrett, *General Mgr*
Jason Sanders, *CFO*
Russell Lehart, *Sales Mgr*
Horace Mast, *Mng Member*
EMP: 20
SALES (est): 4.7MM **Privately Held**
WEB: www.mastmotorsports.com
SIC: 3714 Motor vehicle engines & parts

(G-15704)
NACOGDOCHES COCA COLA BTLG CO
Also Called: Coca-Cola
3321 Nw Stallings Dr (75964-1403)
PHONE.................................936 564-0268
B F Ashcroft, *President*
EMP: 100 **EST:** 1925
SALES (est): 15.6MM **Privately Held**
SIC: 2086 5962 2097 Bottled & canned soft drinks; candy & snack food vending machines; manufactured ice; block ice

(G-15705)
NACOGDOCHES OIL AND GAS INC
816 North St (75961-4480)
P.O. Box 632418 (75963-2418)
PHONE.................................936 560-4747
Michael L Finley, *President*
EMP: 13
SALES (est): 3MM **Privately Held**
SIC: 1382 Oil & gas exploration services

(G-15706)
NIBCO INC
Nacogdoches Division
723 S Fredonia St (75961-5555)
PHONE.................................936 564-8321
Ed Sharon, *Branch Mgr*
EMP: 400
SALES (corp-wide): 704.3MM **Privately Held**
WEB: www.nibco.com
SIC: 3491 5085 3494 3432 Industrial valves; valves & fittings; valves & pipe fittings; plumbing fixture fittings & trim
PA: Nibco Inc.
1516 Middlebury St
Elkhart IN 46516
574 295-3000

(G-15707)
NORBORD TEXAS NACOGDOCHES INC
2301 Se Stallings Dr (75961-6873)
P.O. Box 632750 (75963-2750)
PHONE.................................936 568-8000
Peter C Wijnbergen, *President*
Jim E Ward, *General Mgr*
Jim Ward, *Manager*
Jim Black, *Director*
Jeff Johnson, *Director*
EMP: 121
SALES (est): 24.4MM
SALES (corp-wide): 1.7B **Privately Held**
SIC: 2493 Reconstituted wood products
PA: Norbord Inc
1 Toronto St Suite 600
Toronto ON M5C 2
416 365-0705

(G-15708)
PARKER-HANNIFIN CORPORATION
Also Called: Engineered Polymer Systems Div
403 Industrial Dr (75964-1297)
PHONE.................................936 560-8900
Terry Rice, *Buyer*
Tom Smith, *Engineer*
Amy Nichols, *Human Res Mgr*
Dale Burnett, *Branch Mgr*
Thomas Tatum, *Manager*
EMP: 250
SALES (corp-wide): 13.7B **Publicly Held**
WEB: www.phtruck.com
SIC: 2891 3069 3061 Sealants; rubber automotive products; rubber rolls & roll coverings; molded rubber products; mechanical rubber goods
PA: Parker-Hannifin Corporation
6035 Parkland Blvd
Cleveland OH 44124
216 896-3000

(G-15709)
PILGRIMS PRIDE CORPORATION
Also Called: Pilgrims Pride Prpred Fods Div
928 Martin Luther King Jr (75961-6000)
PHONE.................................936 564-3306
Ronnie Eddy, *Manager*
Larry Acuna, *Manager*
EMP: 199 **Publicly Held**
WEB: www.pilgrims.com
SIC: 2015 0254 2011 Turkey, processed: fresh; chicken hatchery; meat packing plants
HQ: Pilgrim's Pride Corporation
1770 Promontory Cir
Greeley CO 80634
970 506-8000

(G-15710)
PILGRIMS PRIDE CORPORATION
Also Called: Nacogdoches Feed Mill
Fm 1275 S (75963)
P.O. Box 630910 (75963-0910)
PHONE.................................936 560-3901
Ralph Simons, *Manager*
EMP: 28 **Publicly Held**
WEB: www.pilgrimspride.com
SIC: 2015 Poultry slaughtering & processing
HQ: Pilgrim's Pride Corporation
1770 Promontory Cir
Greeley CO 80634
970 506-8000

(G-15711)
R R DONNELLEY & SONS COMPANY
Also Called: Moore Business Forms
5903 North St (75965-1323)
P.O. Box 631441 (75963-1441)
PHONE.................................936 564-4683
Greg Kolff, *Controller*
Brenda Raeardon, *Manager*
EMP: 250
SALES (corp-wide): 6.2B **Publicly Held**
WEB: www.rrd.com
SIC: 2759 2761 Business forms: printing; manifold business forms
PA: R. R. Donnelley & Sons Company
35 W Wacker Dr
Chicago IL 60601
312 326-8000

(G-15712)
RHONDA GRIFFIN
Also Called: Griffin Logging Co
5093 County Road 411 (75961-0127)
P.O. Box 129, Woden (75978-9002)
PHONE.................................936 715-0735
EMP: 12
SALES (est): 707K **Privately Held**
SIC: 2411 Logging camps & contractors

(G-15713)
SOLARO ENERGY INC
1704 S Fredonia St (75964-5813)
PHONE.................................575 838-3813
Dennis A Grubb, *President*
Emilia Dikunova, *Vice Pres*
Michelle Ray, *Manager*

EMP: 13 **EST:** 2011
SALES (est): 4.9MM **Privately Held**
WEB: www.solaroenergy.com
SIC: 4911 5063 3674 ; light bulbs & related supplies; light sensitive devices; light sensitive devices, solid state

(G-15714)
SOUTHWEST CANNERS TEXAS INC
617 Industrial Dr (75964-1291)
PHONE.................................936 569-9737
Steven A Cahillane, *President*
Ben C Garren Jr, *Vice Pres*
William D Hawkins III, *Vice Pres*
Christopher P Nolan, *Vice Pres*
Thomas Doane Still, *Vice Pres*
EMP: 65
SALES (est): 9.1MM
SALES (corp-wide): 10.9MM **Privately Held**
WEB: www.swcanners.com
SIC: 2086 Soft drinks: packaged in cans, bottles, etc.
PA: Southwest Canners, Inc.
2301 W 18th St
Portales NM 88130
575 356-6623

(G-15715)
TEXAS FARM PRODUCTS COMPANY (PA)
Also Called: Lone Star Farm & Home Center
915 S Fredonia St (75964-5913)
P.O. Box 630009 (75963-0009)
PHONE.................................936 564-3711
M S Bud Wright III, *Principal*
Michael Compton, *Vice Pres*
Keith Sharbono, *Warehouse Mgr*
Travis Cotten, *CFO*
Raymond Batten, *VP Sales*
◆ **EMP:** 155 **EST:** 1930
SQ FT: 150,000
SALES (est): 59.6MM **Privately Held**
WEB: www.tfpnutrition.com
SIC: 2047 Dog & cat food

(G-15716)
TEXAS INDUSTRIES INC
1211 Bennett Clark Rd (75961-6403)
PHONE.................................936 564-8301
Hans Robertson, *Manager*
EMP: 24 **Publicly Held**
WEB: www.martinmarietta.com
SIC: 3241 Cement, hydraulic
HQ: Texas Industries, Inc.
1503 Lyndon B Johnson Fwy
Dallas TX 75234
972 647-6700

(G-15717)
TYSON FOODS INC
2208 Se Stallings Dr (75961-6870)
PHONE.................................936 569-7967
Jerry Robinson, *Opers-Prdtn-Mfg*
Morris Hill, *Manager*
EMP: 100
SALES (corp-wide): 43.1B **Publicly Held**
WEB: www.tysonfoods.com
SIC: 2015 Poultry slaughtering & processing
PA: Tyson Foods, Inc.
2200 W Don Tyson Pkwy
Springdale AR 72762
479 290-4000

(G-15718)
WINGATE ARCHTECTURAL MILLWORKS
7516 Us Highway 59 N (75964-1471)
P.O. Box 632535 (75963-2535)
PHONE.................................936 560-1040
Dale Lambright, *President*
Alan Romans, *Corp Secy*
David Billiott, *Project Mgr*
Al Romans, *Treasurer*
Brandy McShan, *Assistant*
EMP: 40
SQ FT: 75,000
SALES: 3.6MM **Privately Held**
WEB: www.wingatemillwork.com
SIC: 2431 Doors, wood

Naples
Morris County

(G-15719)
MAPA MANUFACTURING LLC
Also Called: M A P A
103 W Cj Wise Pkwy (75568)
P.O. Box 129 (75568-0129)
PHONE..............................903 897-2371
▲ EMP: 9 EST: 1998
SQ FT: 10,000
SALES (est): 1.6MM Privately Held
WEB: www.mapaproducts.com
SIC: 3317 Steel pipe & tubes

(G-15720)
RANDY MYERS ENTERPRISES INC
Also Called: Stagecoach Trailers
511 County Road 4311 (75568-6324)
PHONE..............................903 897-0681
Randy Myers, CEO
EMP: 25
SQ FT: 2,000
SALES (est): 5.1MM Privately Held
SIC: 3715 Truck trailer chassis

Nash
Bowie County

(G-15721)
DETROIT FORMING INC
Also Called: D F I Form-Fit
697 N Pecan St (75569-2109)
PHONE..............................903 832-4653
Mike Turner, Plant Mgr
Rodney James M, Director
EMP: 32
SALES (corp-wide): 78.4MM Privately Held
WEB: www.detroitforming.net
SIC: 3089 5199 Plastic containers, except foam; packaging materials
PA: Detroit Forming, Inc.
19100 W 8 Mile Rd
Southfield MI 48075
248 352-8108

(G-15722)
JCM INDUSTRIES INC
200 Old Boston Rd (75569-2626)
P.O. Box 1220 (75569-1220)
PHONE..............................903 832-2581
Gladys J Morriss, Ch of Bd
Ronald R Collins, President
Julie Collins, Corp Secy
Cynthia Bryan Goerke, Exec VP
Jason Minter, Project Mgr
EMP: 135
SQ FT: 60,000
SALES (est): 40.2MM Privately Held
WEB: www.jcmindustries.us
SIC: 3494 3498 3429 Pipe fittings; fabricated pipe & fittings; manufactured hardware (general)

(G-15723)
RK RANCO INDUSTRIES LLC
294 Cantrell St (75569-3006)
P.O. Box 640 (75569-0640)
PHONE..............................903 831-5992
Randy Kimble, Mng Member
Keith Richardson,
EMP: 11
SQ FT: 20,000
SALES (est): 2.1MM Privately Held
WEB: www.rancoind.com
SIC: 3549 Metalworking machinery

(G-15724)
TEXARKAN FENCE
359 Dodd St (75569-2725)
PHONE..............................870 779-0660
Michael Keith Pace, Principal
EMP: 12
SALES (est): 735.3K Privately Held
WEB: www.texarkanafence.com
SIC: 5211 3446 Fencing; fences, gates, posts & flagpoles

Navasota
Grimes County

(G-15725)
BD HILDEBRANDT ENTPS INC
Also Called: Hilco Metal Roofing Supply
12503 Highway 6 (77868-7210)
PHONE..............................936 825-0500
Brad D Hildebrandt, Principal
Stephanie Perez, Sales Staff
EMP: 17 EST: 2009
SALES (est): 2.8MM Privately Held
WEB: www.hilcosupply.com
SIC: 3444 1761 3448 Eaves, sheet metal; roof deck, sheet metal; architectural sheet metal work; panels for prefabricated metal buildings

(G-15726)
BLADE RUNNER TURBOMACHINERY SE
3552 County Road 325 (77868-7193)
PHONE..............................713 669-1155
Kenneth Shaw,
Margo Shaw,
EMP: 40
SALES (est): 1.8MM Privately Held
WEB: www.bladerunnerturbo.com
SIC: 7623 7692 7694 Air conditioning repair; welding repair; armature rewinding shops

(G-15727)
C&M MACHINING LP
5898 Fm 3455 Rd (77868-6816)
PHONE..............................936 825-8139
C R Pasket, President
Scott Pasket, Partner
M J Pasket, Corp Secy
Travis Pasket, Buyer
EMP: 25
SQ FT: 15,758
SALES (est): 4MM Privately Held
WEB: www.candmmachining.com
SIC: 3599 Machine shop, jobbing & repair

(G-15728)
D & R SPECIALTIES INC
7400 Fm 1774 Rd (77868-6200)
PHONE..............................936 873-2947
Raymond A Pasket, President
Russell Pasket, Corp Secy
Gary Pasket, Vice Pres
Dorothy Pasket, Treasurer
EMP: 40
SQ FT: 31,500
SALES (est): 5.7MM Privately Held
WEB: www.dandrspecialties.com
SIC: 7692 3599 3444 Welding repair; machine shop, jobbing & repair; sheet metalwork

(G-15729)
DYNALLOY INDUSTRIES INC (PA)
25880 State Highway 6 S (77868-8226)
P.O. Box 10357, College Station (77842-0357)
PHONE..............................936 825-2532
Rueben L Tamez Sr, Ch of Bd
R L Tamez Jr, President
Taylor Tamez, COO
Helen Watson, Vice Pres
Tracey Landolt, Cust Mgr
EMP: 37
SQ FT: 25,000
SALES (est): 6.3MM Privately Held
WEB: www.dynalloyinc.com
SIC: 3291 2819 Tungsten carbide abrasive; industrial inorganic chemicals

(G-15730)
DYNALLOY INDUSTRIES INC
25 880 Hwy 6 S (77868)
P.O. Box 10357, College Station (77842-0357)
PHONE..............................936 825-2532
Rubin Tamez Jr, Manager
EMP: 20

SALES (corp-wide): 6.3MM Privately Held
WEB: www.dynalloyinc.com
SIC: 3291 2819 Tungsten carbide abrasive; industrial inorganic chemicals
PA: Dynalloy Industries, Inc.
25880 State Highway 6 S
Navasota TX 77868
936 825-2532

(G-15731)
EAGLE PCO LLC (PA)
Also Called: Eagle Pressure Control
5808 Fm 3455 Rd (77868-6816)
PHONE..............................817 678-8998
Jennifer Black, CFO
Mike Clerk,
Heather Scruggf, Assistant
EMP: 80
SALES (est): 23MM Privately Held
WEB: www.trendservicesinc.com
SIC: 3533 1389 Oil field machinery & equipment; oil field services

(G-15732)
ELLWOOD ADVNCED COMPONENTS LLC
Also Called: E A C
10908 County Road 419 (77868-2379)
PHONE..............................336 969-4000
Richard Allendar, President
Robert Richter, Controller
▲ EMP: 145
SQ FT: 200,000
SALES (est): 16.1MM
SALES (corp-wide): 586MM Privately Held
SIC: 3462 Pump, compressor & turbine forgings
PA: Ellwood Group, Inc.
600 Commercial Ave
Ellwood City PA 16117
724 752-3680

(G-15733)
ELLWOOD TXAS FRGE NAVASOTA LLC
10908 County Road 419 (77868-2379)
P.O. Box 1030 (77868-1030)
PHONE..............................936 825-7531
Thaly Palanisamy, Opers Mgr
Matt Wood, Engineer
Laurie Glameyer, Human Res Mgr
Richard Allender, Mng Member
Benjamin Rodriguez, Technology
◆ EMP: 340
SALES (est): 165.1MM
SALES (corp-wide): 586MM Privately Held
SIC: 3462 Iron & steel forgings
PA: Ellwood Group, Inc.
600 Commercial Ave
Ellwood City PA 16117
724 752-3680

(G-15734)
EXPER-TECH PRODUCTS COMPANY
Also Called: Spring Products International
124 N La Salle St (77868-3018)
P.O. Box 1550 (77868-1550)
PHONE..............................936 825-3573
Norman Neeley, President
David Neeley, Sales Mgr
Jerrod Lane, Marketing Staff
Loti Neeley, Office Mgr
EMP: 16
SQ FT: 20,000
SALES (est): 2.3MM Privately Held
WEB: www.spring-products.com
SIC: 3495 3496 3469 Wire springs; miscellaneous fabricated wire products; metal stampings

(G-15735)
FORGED COMPONENTS INC
9533 Fm 379 (77868-7234)
P.O. Box 728 (77868-0728)
PHONE..............................936 825-7518
Pat Craddeock, Branch Mgr
Jennifer Henk, Office Admin
Pat Craddock, Executive
EMP: 60

SALES (corp-wide): 56.1MM Privately Held
WEB: www.forgedcomponents.com
SIC: 3462 Iron & steel forgings
PA: Forged Components, Inc.
14527 Smith Rd
Humble TX 77396
281 441-4088

(G-15736)
GLOBAL VACUUM SYSTEMS INC
Also Called: Gvs
15431 Highway 6 (77868-7238)
P.O. Box 1610 (77868-1610)
PHONE..............................800 843-0866
Leland C Sutton Jr, President
Leslie Sechelski, Purch Agent
Karen O Sutton, Treasurer
Ryan Goodman, Sales Staff
EMP: 18
SALES (est): 5.5MM Privately Held
WEB: www.globalvacuumsystems.com
SIC: 3829 Pressure & vacuum indicators, aircraft engine

(G-15737)
GRANT PRIDECO INC
9475 Fm 1227 Rd (77868-5227)
P.O. Box 1310 (77868-1310)
PHONE..............................936 825-7070
Billy Chunn, President
Michael Gray, Supervisor
◆ EMP: 26
SALES (est): 5.8MM Privately Held
SIC: 3312 Blast furnaces & steel mills

(G-15738)
K & C MEAT PROCESSING
124 Durden St (77868-7241)
P.O. Box 1057 (77868-1057)
PHONE..............................936 825-6944
Kent Fisher, Owner
EMP: 10
SALES (est): 702.4K Privately Held
SIC: 2011 Meat packing plants

(G-15739)
NATIONAL OILWELL VARCO INC
9475 Fm 1227 Indus Park 1227 Industrial (77868)
P.O. Box 1310 (77868-1310)
PHONE..............................936 825-7070
Gregorio Gonzalez, Plant Supt
Octabio Ramirez, Foreman/Supr
Billy Chunn, Opers-Prdtn-Mfg
Donna Abke, Purch Agent
James Wampler, Buyer
EMP: 157
SALES (corp-wide): 8.4B Publicly Held
WEB: www.nov.com
SIC: 3498 3568 3462 3398 Pipe sections fabricated from purchased pipe; power transmission equipment; iron & steel forgings; metal heat treating
PA: National Oilwell Varco, Inc.
7909 Parkwood Circle Dr
Houston TX 77036
713 346-7500

(G-15740)
NATIONAL OILWELL VARCO LP
Also Called: N O V Wilson Tx19
9542 Interstate Dr (77868-7284)
PHONE..............................936 825-2211
EMP: 90
SALES (corp-wide): 7.3B Publicly Held
SIC: 3533 Mfg Oil/Gas Field Machinery
HQ: National Oilwell Varco, L.P.
7909 Parkwood Circle Dr
Houston TX 77036
713 960-5100

(G-15741)
NAVASOTA CONCRETE INC
5970 Fm 3455 Rd (77868-6818)
PHONE..............................936 825-8106
Travis M Nelson, President
David R Nelson, Corp Secy
Bradley Nelson, Opers Staff
EMP: 17
SQ FT: 200,000
SALES (est): 3.8MM Privately Held
WEB: www.navasotaconcrete.com
SIC: 3273 Ready-mixed concrete

(G-15742)
PRECISION PRINTING & OFF SUP
Also Called: Precision Print & Office Sup
206 E Washington Ave (77868-3028)
PHONE..............................936 825-2488
David Roshner, *Owner*
EMP: 15 EST: 1977
SALES (est): 1.4MM Privately Held
WEB: www.shoprecision.com
SIC: 5943 2752 Office forms & supplies;
commercial printing, offset

(G-15743)
TEXAS CUSTOM COATERS INC
9468 Interstate Dr (77868-5019)
PHONE..............................936 825-7211
David Keelan, *President*
James Davis, *Vice Pres*
EMP: 11
SQ FT: 33,000
SALES (est): 1.6MM Privately Held
WEB: www.texascustomcoaters.com
SIC: 3479 Coating of metals & formed
products

(G-15744)
TEXAS PIPE WORKS INC
9444 Industrial Dr (77868-9512)
P.O. Box 1225 (77868-1225)
PHONE..............................936 825-0652
Joey Halverson, *Business Mgr*
Kevin Richbourg, *Engineer*
Ricky Setters, *Finance Mgr*
Rayann Daniel, *Human Res Mgr*
Duane Capps, *Manager*
EMP: 115
SALES (corp-wide): 28.4MM Privately
Held
WEB: www.texaspipeworks.com
SIC: 3312 Pipes & tubes
PA: Texas Pipe Works, Inc.
2810 Bill Owens Pkwy # 400
Longview TX 75605
936 825-6571

(G-15745)
TUBOSCOPE PIPELINE SVCS INC
9574 Fm 1227 Rd (77868-4546)
PHONE..............................936 870-3680
Lloyd Coker, *Branch Mgr*
EMP: 19
SALES (corp-wide): 8.4B Publicly Held
WEB: www.nov.com
SIC: 1389 Oil field services
HQ: Tuboscope Pipeline Services Inc.
2835 Holmes Rd
Houston TX 77051

Nederland
Jefferson County

(G-15746)
BG ABSOLUTE
2920 N Twin City Hwy (77627-3462)
P.O. Box 308 (77627-0308)
PHONE..............................409 724-0300
Trayce Aoudoin, *Owner*
Ross Guidrey, *Owner*
EMP: 10 EST: 2012
SALES (est): 1MM Privately Held
WEB: www.bgconstructiontx.com
SIC: 3089 Gutters (glass fiber reinforced),
fiberglass or plastic

(G-15747)
BROCK ENTERPRISES LLC
Also Called: Custom Blast Services
4835 Bourque Rd (77627)
P.O. Box 488 (77627-0488)
PHONE..............................409 729-6353
Blaine Boudreaux, *Manager*
EMP: 20 Privately Held
WEB: www.brockgroup.com
SIC: 1629 3471 1721 Blasting contractor,
except building demolition; plating & pol-
ishing; painting & paper hanging
HQ: Brock Enterprises Llc
10343 Sam Houston Park Dr # 200
Houston TX 77064
281 807-8200

(G-15748)
CHEMTREAT INC
4200 N Twin City Hwy (77627-3151)
PHONE..............................409 724-1111
James Thomas, *Area Mgr*
Jim Brickey, *Manager*
Phil Clark, *Manager*
Esteban Lopez, *Manager*
John Rolph, *Manager*
EMP: 22
SQ FT: 23,025
SALES (corp-wide): 17.9B Publicly Held
WEB: www.chemtreat.com
SIC: 2899 Water treating compounds
HQ: Chemtreat, Inc.
5640 Cox Rd Ste 300
Glen Allen VA 23060
804 935-2000

(G-15749)
COASTAL READY MIX INC
6363 N Twin Cy Hwy Unit 1 (77627)
P.O. Box 20, Sour Lake (77659-0020)
PHONE..............................409 287-3307
Gary W Whitman, *President*
Debbie L Whitman, *Vice Pres*
EMP: 30
SQ FT: 2,000
SALES (est): 9MM Privately Held
SIC: 3273 Ready-mixed concrete

(G-15750)
COKERS DOORS & MOULDINGS INC
4116 N Twin City Hwy (77627-3147)
PHONE..............................409 727-4600
Travis Coker, *President*
Tonya Moore, *Accounting Mgr*
Benny Arpin, *Sales Staff*
Landon Wright, *Sales Associate*
EMP: 17
SQ FT: 12,300
SALES (est): 3.2MM Privately Held
WEB: www.cokersdoors.com
SIC: 2431 5211 Doors, wood; lumber &
other building materials

(G-15751)
DENBURY ONSHORE LLC
4512 Hodgson Rd (77627-8892)
PHONE..............................409 729-0211
Robbie Hudson, *Counsel*
Ron Greene, *Branch Mgr*
EMP: 26
SALES (corp-wide): 1.2B Publicly Held
WEB: www.denbury.com
SIC: 1382 Oil & gas exploration services
HQ: Denbury Onshore, Llc
5320 Legacy Dr
Plano TX 75024
972 673-2000

(G-15752)
EASTEX RUBBER & GASKET CO
2633 Highway 69 N (77627-8839)
P.O. Box 1240 (77627-1240)
PHONE..............................409 727-6800
Mark Johnston, *President*
Vesta Halay Johnston, *Vice Pres*
Bryan Vincent, *Vice Pres*
Susan Halay Vincent, *Treasurer*
Kathryn Halay Heinen, *Admin Sec*
EMP: 11
SQ FT: 13,000
SALES (est): 3MM Privately Held
WEB: www.eastexrubber.com
SIC: 3052 3053 Rubber belting; gaskets,
all materials

(G-15753)
GREG CORKRAN ENTERPRISES INC
2274 Highway 69 N (77627-8872)
PHONE..............................409 720-9199
Greg Corkran, *President*
EMP: 25 EST: 1996
SQ FT: 9,600
SALES (est): 1MM Privately Held
SIC: 4225 3713 3711 Miniwarehouse,
warehousing; truck bodies & parts; motor
vehicles & car bodies

(G-15754)
HEXA CONTAINMENT LLC
6900 Patillo Rd (77627)
P.O. Box 337, Hamshire (77622-0337)
PHONE..............................713 360-9221
Jordan N Blundell, *Mng Member*
◆ EMP: 26
SQ FT: 25,000
SALES (est): 292.8K Privately Held
WEB: www.hexacontainment.com
SIC: 3443 Reactor containment vessels,
metal plate

(G-15755)
LUCITE INTERNATIONAL INC
6350 N Twin City Hwy (77627-3157)
PHONE..............................409 729-1300
Marney Gillmore, *General Mgr*
Kevin Davis, *QC Mgr*
Saleem Khan, *Sales Mgr*
Alan Gallagher, *Sales Staff*
Alex Plummer, *Manager*
EMP: 139 Privately Held
WEB: www.lucitediy.com
SIC: 3089 2821 Extruded finished plastic
products; acrylic resins
HQ: Lucite International, Inc.
6070 Poplar Ave Ste 600
Memphis TN 38119
901 381-2474

(G-15756)
OCI BEAUMONT LLC
5470 N Twin City Hwy (77627-3168)
PHONE..............................409 723-1900
Ahmed El-Hoshy, *CEO*
Danny Mearse, *Engineer*
Beshoy Guirguis, *CFO*
Bryon Chase, *Info Tech Dir*
Jason Everett, *Administration*
▲ EMP: 120 EST: 2010
SQ FT: 10,500
SALES (est): 112.5MM
SALES (corp-wide): 3B Privately Held
WEB: www.oci.nl
SIC: 5169 2869 Ammonia; methyl alcohol,
synthetic methanol
HQ: Oci Partners Lp
5470 N Twin City Hwy
Nederland TX 77627
409 723-1900

(G-15757)
OCI PARTNERS LP (HQ)
5470 N Twin City Hwy (77627-3168)
P.O. Box 1647 (77627-1647)
PHONE..............................409 723-1900
Ahmed K El-Hoshy, *President*
Robert Cleversy, *Plant Mgr*
Joey Hagmann, *Plant Mgr*
Dennis Steggink, *Project Mgr*
Ray Renfrow, *Opers Staff*
EMP: 13
SALES: 438.3MM
SALES (corp-wide): 3B Privately Held
WEB: www.ocipartnerslp.com
SIC: 2861 2873 Methanol, natural (wood
alcohol); ammonium nitrate, ammonium
sulfate; anhydrous ammonia
PA: Oci N.V.
Honthorststraat 19
Amsterdam
207 234-500

(G-15758)
PEAK INDUSTRIAL SERVICES INC
3525 Tanner Ln (77627-8011)
P.O. Box 12040, Beaumont (77726-2040)
PHONE..............................409 729-0345
Ben B Parks, *President*
▲ EMP: 12
SQ FT: 1,500
SALES (est): 1.4MM Privately Held
SIC: 1389 Lease tanks, oil field: erecting,
cleaning & repairing

(G-15759)
PETROFUELS QUALITY MKTG LP
Also Called: Enviro Solutions
2300 Highway 365 Ste 400 (77627-6281)
P.O. Box 888, Bridge City (77611-0888)
PHONE..............................409 722-6880
Tracey Webb, *President*

Karl Romero, *Partner*
Ricky Harrington, *General Mgr*
EMP: 14 EST: 1999
SQ FT: 1,500
SALES (est): 6MM Privately Held
WEB: www.industriallogistics.com
SIC: 1389 Processing service, gas

(G-15760)
RT TECHNICAL SOLUTIONS LLC
4484 Hodgson Rd (77627-8820)
PHONE..............................409 721-9100
Tina Burks, *Controller*
Chad Simmons, *Manager*
Kasey Taylor, *Officer*
EMP: 25
SQ FT: 7,000
SALES (est): 3.9MM Privately Held
WEB: www.rttechnical.com
SIC: 1389 Testing, measuring, surveying &
analysis services

(G-15761)
V&L INDUSTRAIL SERVICES INC
511 S 3rd St (77627-2308)
PHONE..............................409 724-3336
Emilio Velasco, *President*
EMP: 10
SALES (est): 645.9K Privately Held
SIC: 3563 Vacuum (air extraction) sys-
tems, industrial

Needville
Fort Bend County

(G-15762)
AMERICAN WHOLESALE LBR & MFG
9100 Kneitz Rd (77461-7157)
PHONE..............................281 342-7020
Richard M Janczak, *President*
EMP: 50
SQ FT: 2,500
SALES (est): 6.5MM Privately Held
SIC: 5031 2421 Lumber: rough, dressed &
finished; resawing lumber into smaller di-
mensions

(G-15763)
REX MECHANICAL INC
8806 Main St (77461-8139)
P.O. Box 582 (77461-0582)
PHONE..............................979 793-3340
Rex Jones, *President*
Melvin Jones, *Vice Pres*
Andy Dalmolin, *Project Mgr*
EMP: 26
SALES (est): 7MM Privately Held
WEB: www.rexmechanical.com
SIC: 7623 3585 Air conditioning repair; air
conditioning equipment, complete

(G-15764)
SUNDOWN CNC INC
3210 Horak St (77461-8317)
P.O. Box 800 (77461-0800)
PHONE..............................281 342-8314
Leroy G Zellars, *President*
Micheal Zellars, *President*
Michele Janicek, *Corp Secy*
Donna Zellars, *Treasurer*
EMP: 9
SQ FT: 8,000
SALES (est): 700K Privately Held
SIC: 3599 Machine shop, jobbing & repair

Nevada
Collin County

(G-15765)
JOHNSON MACHINE & TOOL INC
6930 Highway 78 S (75173-6278)
PHONE..............................972 843-5065
Russell Johnson, *President*
Laurel Johnson, *Vice Pres*
EMP: 9
SQ FT: 6,500
SALES (est): 250K Privately Held
SIC: 3599 Machine shop, jobbing & repair

2021 Harris Texas
Manufacturers Directory

▲ = Import ▼=Export
◆ =Import/Export

(G-15766)
RUSHIN TRUSS LTD
15590 County Road 543 (75173-8131)
PHONE.................................972 442-3544
Kevin St John, *Managing Prtnr*
Brandon Tally, *Office Mgr*
EMP: 15
SQ FT: 21,000
SALES (est): 2.1MM **Privately Held**
SIC: 2439 Trusses, wooden roof

New Boston
Bowie County

(G-15767)
NEW BOSTON CONCRETE INC (PA)
100 S Mccoy Blvd (75570-3624)
P.O. Box 326 (75570-0326)
PHONE.................................903 628-3556
Tim Graham, *President*
Todd Graham, *Corp Secy*
Terry Graham, *Vice Pres*
Dawn Williams, *Info Tech Mgr*
EMP: 19
SQ FT: 9,000
SALES (est): 4.5MM **Privately Held**
WEB: www.newbostonconcrete.com
SIC: 3273 Ready-mixed concrete

(G-15768)
PALLETONE OF TEXAS LP
1020 W Us Highway 82 (75570-2416)
P.O. Box 97 (75570-0097)
PHONE.................................903 628-5695
K C Fletcher, *CFO*
Jacob Garrett, *Sales Mgr*
Russell Miller,
▲ **EMP:** 120
SQ FT: 60,000
SALES (est): 15.4MM
SALES (corp-wide): 476.2MM **Privately Held**
WEB: www.palletone.com
SIC: 2448 Pallets, wood
PA: Palletone, Inc
6001 Foxtrot Ave
Bartow FL 33830
800 771-1147

(G-15769)
VSE CORPORATION
154 Service (75570-6746)
PHONE.................................903 831-0192
Joseph Brown, *Branch Mgr*
EMP: 99
SALES (corp-wide): 752.6MM **Publicly Held**
WEB: www.vsecorp.com
SIC: 3728 Military aircraft equipment & armament
PA: Vse Corporation
6348 Walker Ln
Alexandria VA 22310
703 960-4600

(G-15770)
WEST FRASER INC
Hwy 82 E (75570)
P.O. Box 578 (75570-0578)
PHONE.................................903 628-2506
Kenda Kendagarrettwes, *Controller*
Roger Chitwood, *Manager*
Phillip House, *Technical Staff*
EMP: 125
SALES (corp-wide): 3.6B **Privately Held**
WEB: www.westfraser.com
SIC: 2421 5031 2426 Lumber: rough, sawed or planed; lumber: rough, dressed & finished; hardwood dimension & flooring mills
HQ: West Fraser, Inc.
1900 Exeter Rd Ste 105
Germantown TN 38138
901 620-4200

New Braunfels
Comal County

(G-15771)
ABC FIRE SYSTEMS LLC
166 Trade Center Dr (78130-2306)
PHONE.................................830 625-3473
Lee S Lane, *President*
Chelsey Wiatrek, *Office Mgr*
EMP: 9 **EST:** 2009
SQ FT: 4,000
SALES (est): 1.4MM **Privately Held**
WEB: www.abcfiresys.com
SIC: 7389 3569 7382 1731 Fire extinguisher servicing; sprinkler systems, fire: automatic; fire alarm maintenance & monitoring; safety & security specialization; fire detection & burglar alarm systems specialization; sprinkler contractors; fire sprinkler system installation

(G-15772)
ADM MILLING CO
398 E San Antonio St (78130-4538)
PHONE.................................830 625-2301
Adam Oliver, *Manager*
EMP: 35
SALES (corp-wide): 64.6B **Publicly Held**
SIC: 2041 Grain mills (except rice)
HQ: Adm Milling Co.
8000 W 110th St Ste 300
Overland Park KS 66210
913 491-9400

(G-15773)
AMERICAN PRINTING INDUSTRIES (PA)
1788 S Business Ih 35 (78130-6468)
P.O. Box 310182 (78131-0182)
PHONE.................................830 624-9000
Romelia Moya, *President*
Richard R Moya, *Vice Pres*
EMP: 9
SQ FT: 2,500
SALES (est): 654K **Privately Held**
SIC: 2752 Commercial printing, offset

(G-15774)
APOLO COMMERCIAL LLC
899 S Castell Ave Ste 205 (78130-7625)
PHONE.................................956 688-8207
Juan Carlos M Iglesias, *General Mgr*
Sylvia Santos, *Administration*
EMP: 10
SQ FT: 500
SALES (est): 579.3K **Privately Held**
SIC: 2035 Pickled fruits & vegetables

(G-15775)
BCAD ZION CORPORATION
Also Called: Quality Welding & Fabrication
9425 Schoenthal Rd (78132-4503)
PHONE.................................210 657-9090
Rebecca Hendrix, *CEO*
Don Hendrix, *Admin Sec*
EMP: 15
SALES (est): 3.9MM **Privately Held**
WEB: www.qwftexas.com
SIC: 7692 1799 3499 Welding repair; welding on site; aerosol valves, metal

(G-15776)
BROWNS WELDING & MANUFACTURING
6701 Fm 1101 (78130-7111)
PHONE.................................830 625-8712
Roger Dale Brown, *President*
Neva Frassmann, *Admin Sec*
EMP: 13
SQ FT: 9,000
SALES (est): 1.5MM **Privately Held**
WEB: www.browns-truckaccessories.com
SIC: 3711 7692 Truck & tractor truck assembly; welding repair

(G-15777)
CARBON AND CLAY COMPANY
Also Called: My Magic Mud
1965 Post Rd Ste 600 (78130-5987)
PHONE.................................844 624-4263
Jessica Arman, *CEO*
Justin Arman, *President*
Chad Thomas, *COO*

Ian Evins, *Manager*
EMP: 25
SQ FT: 18,000
SALES (est): 8.6MM **Privately Held**
WEB: www.mymagicmud.com
SIC: 2844 Toothpastes or powders, dentifrices

(G-15778)
CEMEX INC
Also Called: Cemex USA
2580 Wald Rd (78132-4983)
PHONE.................................830 625-7338
Ken Kerr, *Manager*
Gary Pinault, *Maintence Staff*
EMP: 100 **Privately Held**
WEB: www.cemex.com
SIC: 3273 3241 Ready-mixed concrete; cement, hydraulic
HQ: Cemex, Inc.
10100 Katy Fwy Ste 300
Houston TX 77043
713 650-6200

(G-15779)
CEMEX CONSTRUCTION MTLS S LLC
Also Called: New Braunfels Quarry
2682 Wald Rd (78132-4900)
PHONE.................................830 608-3556
Alwyn Thorpe, *Manager*
Bryan Martin, *Maintence Staff*
EMP: 85 **Privately Held**
WEB: www.cemexusa.com
SIC: 1422 8711 Crushed & broken limestone; construction & civil engineering
HQ: Cemex Construction Materials South, Llc
2088 E 20th St
Yuma AZ 85365
928 343-4100

(G-15780)
CEMEX CONSTRUCTION MTLS S LLC
Also Called: Cem - Balcones Plant
2580 Wald Rd (78132-4983)
PHONE.................................210 250-4100
Gilberto Perez, *Branch Mgr*
EMP: 36 **Privately Held**
WEB: www.cemexusa.com
SIC: 3273 Ready-mixed concrete
HQ: Cemex Construction Materials South, Llc
2088 E 20th St
Yuma AZ 85365
928 343-4100

(G-15781)
CENTEX MECHATRONICS LLC
1484 Churchill Dr (78130-3615)
P.O. Box 1556, Seguin (78156-8556)
PHONE.................................830 387-4131
Judi Hargrove, *Vice Pres*
Ryan Stollewerk, *Vice Pres*
Patrick Salazar, *Project Mgr*
Tony Hargrove, *Mng Member*
Robin Hargrove, *Products*
EMP: 10 **EST:** 2013
SQ FT: 4,000
SALES (est): 1.8MM **Privately Held**
WEB: www.ctxmech.com
SIC: 3569 5084 General industrial machinery; industrial machinery & equipment

(G-15782)
CGT US LIMITED
695 Holcan Dr (78130-0010)
PHONE.................................830 627-4800
Craig Richardson, *CEO*
Jim Powell, *Opers Staff*
Joshua Robbins, *Engineer*
Leslie Johnson, *Human Resources*
Steve Stephenson, *Technician*
EMP: 120
SQ FT: 300,000
SALES (est): 81K
SALES (corp-wide): 202.9MM **Privately Held**
WEB: www.cgtower.com
SIC: 3711 Motor vehicles & car bodies
PA: Canadian General-Tower Limited
52 Middleton St
Cambridge ON N1R 5
519 623-1633

(G-15783)
CHECKS IN MAIL INC
2435 Goodwin Ln (78135-0002)
P.O. Box 311886 (78131-1886)
PHONE.................................830 609-5500
Charles T Dawson, *CEO*
Don Dolan, *Senior VP*
Steve Johnson, *Vice Pres*
Peter A Fera Jr, *CFO*
▲ **EMP:** 425
SQ FT: 100,000
SALES (est): 52.5MM **Publicly Held**
WEB: www.secure.checksinthemail.com
SIC: 2782 2752 Checkbooks; commercial printing, lithographic
HQ: Vericast Corp.
15955 La Cantera Pkwy
San Antonio TX 78256
210 697-8888

(G-15784)
COLORADO MATERIALS LTD (PA)
4501 Hunter Rd (78132)
P.O. Box 2109, San Marcos (78667-2109)
PHONE.................................512 353-7757
Steve Riordan, *Manager*
EMP: 12
SALES (est): 8.1MM **Privately Held**
WEB: www.coloradomaterialsltd.com
SIC: 2951 Asphalt paving mixtures & blocks

(G-15785)
COLORADO MATERIALS LTD
5080 Fm 2439 (78132)
PHONE.................................512 396-1555
Brandon Casanova, *Sales Staff*
EMP: 99
SALES (est): 2.6MM
SALES (corp-wide): 150MM **Privately Held**
WEB: www.coloradomaterialsltd.com
SIC: 1429 Sandstone, crushed & broken-quarrying
PA: Hunter Industries, Ltd.
4501 Hunter Rd
San Marcos TX 78666
512 353-7757

(G-15786)
COMAL CONCRETE PRODUCTS INC
4222 Fm 482 (78132-5005)
PHONE.................................830 606-4732
Jerry Dean Watkins, *President*
Joanne Easter, *Vice Pres*
James Watkins, *Vice Pres*
Sharon Watkins, *Admin Sec*
EMP: 12
SALES (est): 2.6MM **Privately Held**
WEB: www.comalconcrete.com
SIC: 3272 Septic tanks, concrete; grease traps, concrete

(G-15787)
DETEX CORPORATION (PA)
302 Detex Dr (78130-3099)
PHONE.................................800 729-3839
Philip N Haselton, *CEO*
John Blodgett, *President*
Odelia Caballero, *General Mgr*
Ken Kuehler, *General Mgr*
David Alexander, *Plant Mgr*
▲ **EMP:** 88 **EST:** 1923
SQ FT: 52,000
SALES (est): 16.1MM **Privately Held**
WEB: www.detex.com
SIC: 3699 Security devices

(G-15788)
DYNA GROUP INTERNATIONAL INC (PA)
1661 S Seguin Ave (78130-3856)
PHONE.................................830 620-4400
Roger R Tuttle, *Ch of Bd*
Jeff Smith, *Vice Pres*
Jeffrey Smith, *Vice Pres*
Cody Homewood, *Purchasing*
Sandra K Tristan, *Treasurer*
EMP: 95
SQ FT: 70,000

SALES (est): 13.4MM **Publicly Held**
WEB: www.gap1.com
SIC: 3993 3499 5199 3961 Signs & advertising specialties; picture frames, metal; gifts & novelties; keychains, except precious metal

(G-15789)
EGGEMEYER LAND CLEARING LLC
333 N Solms Rd (78132-5033)
P.O. Box 312289 (78131-2289)
PHONE..............................210 366-4100
Steve Eggemeyer, *Owner*
Elizabeth Melendez, *Office Mgr*
Trina Eggemeyer,
EMP: 32
SALES (est): 6.2MM **Privately Held**
WEB: www.eggemeyerlandclearing.com
SIC: 1629 2499 Land clearing contractor; mulch or sawdust products, wood

(G-15790)
ENERSOL GROUP INC
Also Called: Bandit Energy Services
1015 W San Antonio St (78130-5507)
P.O. Box 5650, Granbury (76049-0650)
PHONE..............................830 387-4011
Mark Price, *President*
Guy Price, *Corp Secy*
EMP: 25
SALES (est): 8.2MM **Privately Held**
WEB: www.enersol-group.com
SIC: 1382 Oil & gas exploration services

(G-15791)
ESPINOZA STONE INC
8200 N Interstate 35 (78130-7166)
PHONE..............................830 629-2530
Jose Espinoza, *Branch Mgr*
EMP: 90
SALES (corp-wide): 36.1MM **Privately Held**
WEB: www.espinozastone.com
SIC: 5211 5032 1411 Masonry materials & supplies; building stone; dimension stone
PA: Espinoza Stone, Inc.
　　1465 County Road 234
　　Georgetown TX 78633
　　512 930-1398

(G-15792)
FISCHBECK WELDING INC
537 Kohlenberg Rd (78130-2632)
PHONE..............................830 625-3249
Keith A Wersterfer, *President*
Steve Morgan, *Vice Pres*
EMP: 18
SQ FT: 12,000
SALES (est): 4.4MM **Privately Held**
WEB: www.fischbeckwelding.com
SIC: 3441 Fabricated structural metal

(G-15793)
FOLAS INC
Also Called: Salof Companies
1150 Schwab Rd (78132-4987)
PHONE..............................830 625-1613
George A Salof, *President*
Robert Luhrs, *Treasurer*
Donna Salof, *Admin Sec*
◆ **EMP:** 45
SQ FT: 20,000
SALES (est): 10.5MM **Privately Held**
SIC: 3585 Refrigeration equipment, complete

(G-15794)
GEM SIGN SERVICE INC
1631 Whispering Woods Trl (78132-3016)
PHONE..............................830 609-1052
Gaye L Meyers, *President*
Gene R Meyers, *Vice Pres*
EMP: 13
SQ FT: 13,500
SALES (est): 1.2MM **Privately Held**
SIC: 3993 1799 Signs, not made in custom sign painting shops; electric signs; sign installation & maintenance

(G-15795)
GIVCO INC
22133 Old Nacogdoches Rd (78132-4850)
PHONE..............................830 624-8598
Doris Givens, *President*

Wayne Givens, *General Mgr*
Phyllis Friefenhahn, *Treasurer*
Kristina Perez, *Sales Associate*
EMP: 9 EST: 1997
SQ FT: 16,000
SALES (est): 1.5MM **Privately Held**
WEB: www.givco.net
SIC: 3444 Booths, spray: prefabricated sheet metal

(G-15796)
GLAXOSMITHKLINE LLC
2239 S Abbey Loop (78130-8965)
PHONE..............................830 481-8939
EMP: 26
SALES (corp-wide): 43.6B **Privately Held**
WEB: www.us.gsk.com
SIC: 2834 Pharmaceutical preparations
HQ: Glaxosmithkline Llc
　　5 Crescent Dr
　　Philadelphia PA 19112
　　215 751-4000

(G-15797)
GREAT AMERICAN PRODUCTS LTD
Also Called: Sports Cave
1661 S Seguin Ave (78130-3856)
PHONE..............................830 620-4400
Roger R Tuttle, *President*
Jeffrey L Smith, *Vice Pres*
Stephanie Zapata, *Project Mgr*
Raquel Rosales, *Human Resources*
David Berger, *Sales Mgr*
◆ **EMP:** 115
SQ FT: 70,000
SALES (est): 11.8MM
SALES (corp-wide): 13.4MM **Publicly Held**
WEB: www.greatamericanproducts.com
SIC: 3499 Novelties & specialties, metal
PA: Dyna Group International, Inc
　　1661 S Seguin Ave
　　New Braunfels TX 78130
　　830 620-4400

(G-15798)
GUADALUPE BREWING COMPANY LLC
1586 Wald Rd (78132-5018)
PHONE..............................512 878-9214
Keith Kilker, *Vice Pres*
Anna Kilker, *Mng Member*
EMP: 9 EST: 2010
SALES (est): 400K **Privately Held**
WEB: www.guadalupebrew.com
SIC: 2082 5921 Beer (alcoholic beverage); beer (packaged)

(G-15799)
GUADALUPE VALLEY VENTURES LP
36101 Fm 3159 (78132-5903)
PHONE..............................830 885-4411
Robert Hunt, *Exec VP*
Ken D Brannies, *Manager*
EMP: 20
SALES (est): 1.3MM
SALES (corp-wide): 74.6MM **Privately Held**
SIC: 3229 Fiber optics strands
PA: Guadalupe Valley Telephone Cooperative, Inc.
　　36101 Fm 3159
　　New Braunfels TX 78132
　　830 885-4411

(G-15800)
HALL PLATING CO (PA)
915 Gruene River Dr (78132-3269)
PHONE..............................830 620-7825
James W Hall, *Owner*
Verna Hall, *Co-Owner*
EMP: 12 EST: 1977
SQ FT: 23,500
SALES (est): 1.4MM **Privately Held**
SIC: 3471 Electroplating of metals or formed products

(G-15801)
HANSON AGGREGATES LLC
21303 Fm 2252 (78132)
PHONE..............................210 658-7461
John Faust, *Manager*
EMP: 75

SALES (corp-wide): 20.8B **Privately Held**
WEB: www.heidelbergcement.com
SIC: 2951 1422 Asphalt paving mixtures & blocks; crushed & broken limestone
HQ: Hanson Aggregates Llc
　　8505 Freport Pkwy Ste 500
　　Irving TX 75063
　　469 417-1200

(G-15802)
HANSON AGGREGATES LLC
Corner Of Fm 2252 (78132)
PHONE..............................210 658-3533
John Faust, *Branch Mgr*
EMP: 11
SALES (corp-wide): 20.8B **Privately Held**
WEB: www.heidelbergcement.com
SIC: 3241 5032 1422 Cement, hydraulic; stone, crushed or broken; crushed & broken limestone
HQ: Hanson Aggregates Llc
　　8505 Freport Pkwy Ste 500
　　Irving TX 75063
　　469 417-1200

(G-15803)
HORIZON STRUCTURAL SYSTEMS INC
3950 W State Highway 46 (78132-3750)
PHONE..............................830 629-8000
Tim Kensing, *President*
John Bordano, *Vice Pres*
Kevin Schmidt, *Engineer*
Sue Clark, *Controller*
Jeff Hayes, *Sales Mgr*
EMP: 9
SQ FT: 1,000
SALES (est): 2.2MM **Privately Held**
WEB: www.horizonstructural.com
SIC: 3448 5039 Prefabricated metal buildings; metal buildings

(G-15804)
HVM TECHNOLOGY INC
360 Mckenna Ave (78130-7822)
PHONE..............................830 626-5552
Michael R Saldana, *CEO*
Brandon Potempa, *Engineer*
Greg Janecek, *Manager*
EMP: 20
SQ FT: 7,000
SALES (est): 3.8MM **Privately Held**
WEB: www.hvmtech.com
SIC: 3679 Power supplies, all types: static; electronic circuits

(G-15805)
INGRAM READYMIX INC
3580 Fm 482 (78132-5012)
PHONE..............................830 606-9619
Joe Gonzales, *Manager*
EMP: 21
SALES (corp-wide): 125.6MM **Privately Held**
WEB: www.ingramreadymixinc.com
SIC: 3273 Ready-mixed concrete
PA: Ingram Readymix, Inc.
　　3580 Farm Market 482
　　New Braunfels TX 78132
　　830 625-9156

(G-15806)
JOHN B SMITH
Also Called: Mr Bird
1320 Industrial Dr (78130-3655)
PHONE..............................830 620-9090
John B Smith, *Owner*
Birch Smith, *Principal*
EMP: 135
SALES (est): 15.1MM **Privately Held**
WEB: www.mrbird.com
SIC: 2048 Bird food, prepared

(G-15807)
KENERGY OILFIELD SOLUTIONS LLC (PA)
1619 E Common St Ste 401 (78130-3456)
PHONE..............................979 574-6356
Scott Kenley, *Mng Member*
EMP: 11 EST: 2014
SALES (est): 1.9MM **Privately Held**
WEB: www.kenergyoilfieldsolutions.com
SIC: 3561 Pumps & pumping equipment

(G-15808)
KENSING IRON WORKS INC
3950 W State Highway 46 (78132-3750)
PHONE..............................830 625-2815
Mark Kensing, *President*
EMP: 10 EST: 1995
SQ FT: 35,000
SALES (est): 1.8MM **Privately Held**
WEB: www.cceo.org
SIC: 3441 Fabricated structural metal

(G-15809)
LHOIST NORTH AMERICA INC
Also Called: New Braunfesl Plant Us62
350 Apg Ln (78132-5035)
PHONE..............................830 625-2327
Robert Kerr, *Opers Mgr*
Joseph Cook, *Plant Engr*
Jason Stanley, *Sales Staff*
Jay Bhopathy, *Business Anlyst*
John Ruble, *Sr Project Mgr*
EMP: 100
SALES (corp-wide): 2.6MM **Privately Held**
WEB: www.lhoist.com
SIC: 3274 Lime
HQ: Lhoist North America, Inc.
　　5600 Clearfork Main St # 300
　　Fort Worth TX 76109
　　817 732-8164

(G-15810)
LHOIST NORTH AMERICA TEXAS LTD
Also Called: New Braunfels Plant Us62
350 Apg Ln (78132-5035)
PHONE..............................830 625-2327
Robert Kerr, *Plant Mgr*
Sam Wells, *Plant Mgr*
EMP: 23
SALES (corp-wide): 2.6MM **Privately Held**
WEB: www.lhoist.com
SIC: 3274 Lime
HQ: Lhoist North America Of Texas, Ltd.
　　5600 Clearfork Main St
　　Fort Worth TX 76109
　　817 732-8164

(G-15811)
MARBLE MASTERS OF TEXAS INC
1334 Fieldcrest (78130-3516)
PHONE..............................830 303-7744
John Haake, *President*
Judy Adams, *Treasurer*
EMP: 47 EST: 1975
SQ FT: 32,000
SALES (est): 5.3MM **Privately Held**
WEB: www.marblemastersx.com
SIC: 3281 3087 Bathroom fixtures, cut stone; custom compound purchased resins

(G-15812)
MARK PRESTIGIOUS
850 Nor Tex Dr (78132-4856)
PHONE..............................210 820-0093
Amy Swaney, *Owner*
EMP: 12
SALES (corp-wide): 2.7MM **Privately Held**
WEB: www.tpmpromo.com
SIC: 2499 Trophy bases, wood
PA: The Mark Prestigious Inc
　　8611 N New Braunfels Ave
　　San Antonio TX 78217
　　210 820-0093

(G-15813)
MINAE PRODUCTS INC
Also Called: Future Mart
863 N Interstate 35 J (78130-3780)
P.O. Box 310491 (78131-0491)
PHONE..............................830 620-1303
Nancy Peevyhouse, *Manager*
EMP: 12
SALES (est): 2MM **Privately Held**
SIC: 2834 Vitamin, nutrient & hematinic preparations for human use

(G-15814)
MR BIRD
1197 Eikel St (78130-5527)
PHONE..............................830 620-9090

Birch Smith, *Owner*
Jim Cantrell, *Manager*
EMP: 10
SQ FT: 10,000
SALES (est): 86.4K **Privately Held**
WEB: www.mrbird.com
SIC: 2048 Bird food, prepared

(G-15815)
NATIONWIDE TANK & PIPE LLC
3567 Ih 35 S (78132-5268)
PHONE..............................830 387-4027
Sherri Fowler, *Vice Pres*
David Pain, *Mng Member*
EMP: 50 **EST:** 2012
SALES (est): 655.7K **Privately Held**
WEB: www.nationwidetankandpipe.com
SIC: 3089 Plastic & fiberglass tanks

(G-15816)
NEOPOD SYSTEMS LLC
7850 Old Bastrop Rd (78130-7264)
PHONE..............................954 603-3100
Kay Benavidez, *Project Mgr*
Ankur Makkar, *Project Mgr*
Michael Miller, *Opers Mgr*
Melanie Deleon, *Purchasing*
EMP: 10 **Privately Held**
WEB: www.neopodsystems.com
SIC: 2452 Prefabricated wood buildings
PA: Neopod Systems Llc
   1329 Shotgun Rd
   Sunrise FL 33326

(G-15817)
NEW BRAUNFELS MACHINE INC
311 Fm 306 Bldg 3 (78130-2586)
PHONE..............................830 226-7179
Bryan Murphy, *President*
EMP: 22
SQ FT: 6,000
SALES (est): 700K **Privately Held**
WEB: www.nbmachineinc.com
SIC: 3599 Machine & other job shop work

(G-15818)
PATRICK S MOLAK CORP
Also Called: Grape Vine, The
1612 Hunter Rd (78130-3006)
PHONE..............................830 606-0093
Vance Miller, *General Mgr*
EMP: 12
SALES (corp-wide): 3.7MM **Privately Held**
WEB: www.gristmillrestaurant.com
SIC: 2084 5813 Wines; bar (drinking places)
PA: Patrick S Molak, Corp.
   1287 Gruene Rd
   New Braunfels TX 78130
   830 606-1281

(G-15819)
PLY-TECH INC
1630 W State Highway 46 (78132-4737)
PHONE..............................830 625-3913
Ron Krueger, *President*
Ronald Krueger, *Vice Pres*
Don Kiesling, *Accountant*
▲ **EMP:** 11
SQ FT: 18,000
SALES (est): 1.2MM **Privately Held**
WEB: www.plytechinc.com
SIC: 2221 Broadwoven fabric mills, man-made

(G-15820)
RIO RESOURCES LLC
1171 Gruene Rd Ste 105 (78130-3028)
PHONE..............................830 438-4841
Dale Yates,
EMP: 20
SALES (est): 946K **Privately Held**
WEB: www.rioresourcesllc.com
SIC: 3589 Water treatment equipment, industrial

(G-15821)
SENIOR OPERATIONS LLC
Senior Flexonics Pathway
2400 Longhorn Indus Dr (78130-2530)
PHONE..............................830 629-8080
Dorian Shillingford, *CEO*
David Partridge, *General Mgr*
Terry O'Connell, *Vice Pres*

James Shank, *Prdtn Mgr*
Paul Elrod, *Opers Staff*
EMP: 250
SQ FT: 125,000
SALES (corp-wide): 1.4B **Privately Held**
WEB: www.seniorflexonics.com
SIC: 3494 3599 Expansion joints pipe; hose, flexible metallic; tubing, flexible metallic
HQ: Senior Operations Llc
   300 E Devon Ave
   Bartlett IL 60103
   630 372-3500

(G-15822)
SENIOR OPERATIONS LLC
Also Called: Senior Flextronics Pathway
2311 Lifehaus Indus Dr (78130-3048)
PHONE..............................830 629-8080
EMP: 200
SALES (corp-wide): 1.4B **Privately Held**
WEB: www.seniorflexonics.com
SIC: 3494 Expansion joints pipe
HQ: Senior Operations Llc
   300 E Devon Ave
   Bartlett IL 60103
   630 372-3500

(G-15823)
SIMPSON HELMETS INC
328 Fm 306 (78130-2556)
PHONE..............................830 625-1774
E J Simpson, *Ch of Bd*
Mark Johnson, *President*
Scott Mosteller, *COO*
William Sullivan, *CFO*
EMP: 112
SALES (est): 8MM **Privately Held**
WEB: www.simpsonraceproducts.com
SIC: 3949 Sporting & athletic goods
PA: Carousel Capital Company, L.L.C.
   201 N Tryon St Ste 2450
   Charlotte NC 28202

(G-15824)
SOUTHERN NEWSPAPERS INC
1342 Industrial Dr (78130-3655)
PHONE..............................830 625-5232
Henry Coelleo, *Branch Mgr*
EMP: 15
SALES (corp-wide): 140.3MM **Privately Held**
WEB: www.sninews.com
SIC: 2711 Newspapers, publishing & printing
PA: Southern Newspapers, Inc.
   5701 Woodway Dr Ste 131
   Houston TX 77057
   713 266-5481

(G-15825)
SOUTHERN NEWSPAPERS INC
Also Called: Herald Zeitung
549 Landa St (78130-6109)
P.O. Box 311328 (78131-1328)
PHONE..............................830 625-9144
Neice Bell, *Publisher*
Mikala Compton, *Editor*
Lauren Corbell, *Editor*
Jennifer Leal, *Business Mgr*
Henry Coello, *Prdtn Dir*
EMP: 43
SQ FT: 12,000
SALES (corp-wide): 140.3MM **Privately Held**
WEB: www.sninews.com
SIC: 2711 Commercial printing & newspaper publishing combined
PA: Southern Newspapers, Inc.
   5701 Woodway Dr Ste 131
   Houston TX 77057
   713 266-5481

(G-15826)
STAY-TUFF FENCE MFG INC
1067 Fm 306 Ste 102 (78130-4684)
PHONE..............................830 608-9302
William Dougherty, *Owner*
Howard Athas, *Sales Staff*
Howard Athus, *Sales Staff*
Harold Shipman, *Sales Staff*
Randy Lenz, *Manager*
▲ **EMP:** 33 **EST:** 2000
SQ FT: 10,000

SALES (est): 5.2MM **Privately Held**
WEB: www.staytuff.com
SIC: 3446 5039 Fences, gates, posts & flagpoles; wire fence, gates & accessories

(G-15827)
TEXAS INDUSTRIES INC
7781 Fm 1102 (78132-3418)
PHONE..............................512 396-4244
Clifton Stapleton, *Manager*
EMP: 140 **Publicly Held**
WEB: www.martinmarietta.com
SIC: 3251 3241 Brick clay: common face, glazed, vitrified or hollow; cement, hydraulic
HQ: Texas Industries, Inc.
   1503 Lyndon B Johnson Fwy
   Dallas TX 75234
   972 647-6700

(G-15828)
TEXAS TITOS INC
1411 Fm 1101 Ste A (78130-2622)
PHONE..............................830 626-1123
Darrell Sollberger, *President*
Chris Snider, *COO*
EMP: 10 **EST:** 1994
SQ FT: 30,000
SALES (est): 1.7MM **Privately Held**
WEB: www.texastitos.com
SIC: 2032 Canned specialties

(G-15829)
TRACKER ENERGY SERVICES INC
1312 Havenwood Blvd (78132-4158)
PHONE..............................830 837-0806
Jeff Rogers, *President*
Billy Raihl, *Superintendent*
Jeremy Blevins, *Vice Pres*
EMP: 40
SALES (est): 2.5MM **Privately Held**
WEB: www.trackerenergy.com
SIC: 1389 Construction, repair & dismantling services

(G-15830)
VANT MARKETING INC
193 1/2 W San Antonio St # 306
(78130-5196)
PHONE..............................830 217-2523
Jillian Sturdivant, *CEO*
Donald Dingee, *CFO*
EMP: 10
SALES (est): 1.2MM **Privately Held**
WEB: www.vantmarketing.com
SIC: 2741

(G-15831)
VULCAN MATERIALS COMPANY
19347 N Interstate 35 (78132-4843)
PHONE..............................830 624-4944
EMP: 22 **Publicly Held**
WEB: www.vulcanmaterials.com
SIC: 1422 Crushed & broken limestone
PA: Vulcan Materials Company
   1200 Urban Center Dr
   Vestavia AL 35242

(G-15832)
WICKED VOODOO ESPRESSO LLC
1975 Lou Ann Dr (78130-1213)
PHONE..............................360 631-1447
Wicked Espresso, *President*
EMP: 25
SALES (est): 264.2K **Privately Held**
WEB: www.wickedvoodooespresso.com
SIC: 5812 5149 5046 2095 Coffee shop; coffee & tea; coffee brewing equipment & supplies; roasted coffee; coffee

(G-15833)
WP RESOURCES LLC
Also Called: Wp Resources Consulting
340 Rancho Rd (78130-1810)
PHONE..............................512 913-7234
William Wesley Carnes,
EMP: 15
SALES (est): 1.1MM **Privately Held**
SIC: 1389 Gas field services

New Caney
Montgomery County

(G-15834)
ALPHA FABRICATORS INC
18900 E Industrial Pkwy (77357-3507)
PHONE..............................713 694-1392
EMP: 28
SQ FT: 40,000
SALES (est): 4.2MM **Privately Held**
SIC: 3441 Structural Metal Fabrication

(G-15835)
BIG STATE FABRICATION INC
19891 W Industrial Park (77357)
PHONE..............................281 572-1375
David Paul Turner, *President*
Kathleen Turner, *Manager*
John Harris, *Shareholder*
EMP: 27
SQ FT: 15,000
SALES (est): 5MM **Privately Held**
WEB: www.bigstatefab.com
SIC: 3441 Fabricated structural metal

(G-15836)
COMMAND TUBULAR PRODUCTS LLC
18911 W Industrial Pkwy (77357-3504)
PHONE..............................281 572-3900
Charles Garvey, *Mng Member*
▲ **EMP:** 300
SALES (est): 5.3MM **Privately Held**
WEB: www.commandtubular.com
SIC: 3532 Drills & drilling equipment, mining (except oil & gas)

(G-15837)
COMMUNITY MOTORS INC
22159 Kent Dr (77357-8417)
PHONE..............................281 354-8087
Thomas Nesloney, *President*
Wanda Nesloney, *Treasurer*
EMP: 11
SQ FT: 14,000
SALES (est): 2.2MM **Privately Held**
WEB: www.communitymotorsinc.net
SIC: 7694 5999 7699 5084 Electric motor repair; motors, electric; compressor repair; processing & packaging equipment; generators

(G-15838)
ELECTRICAL CONTRLS HOUSTON INC
Also Called: Exp Controls
21061 Gene Campbell Blvd (77357-3843)
P.O. Box 55408, Houston (77255-5408)
PHONE..............................281 501-0729
Roberto Stanchi, *President*
EMP: 15
SALES (est): 3.2MM **Privately Held**
WEB: www.expcontrols.com
SIC: 3613 Panel & distribution boards & other related apparatus; control panels, electric

(G-15839)
FASTORQ BOLTING SYSTEMS INC
18914 E Industrial Pkwy (77357-3507)
PHONE..............................281 449-6466
William Washington, *President*
Harry Maynes, *Vice Pres*
◆ **EMP:** 12 **EST:** 1981
SQ FT: 24,000
SALES (est): 2.5MM
SALES (corp-wide): 3.5B **Publicly Held**
WEB: www.fastorq.com
SIC: 3546 5072 7359 7699 Power-driven handtools; power tools & accessories; equipment rental & leasing; power tool repair
PA: Snap-On Incorporated
   2801 80th St
   Kenosha WI 53143
   262 656-5200

(G-15840)
GEORGE A STURDEVANT INC
Also Called: Fastorq
18914 E Industrial Pkwy (77357-3507)
PHONE..............................281 449-6466

GEOGRAPHIC

Mark Murphy, *President*
Bill Washington, *CFO*
▲ **EMP:** 14
SALES (est): 2.6MM **Privately Held**
WEB: www.fastorq.com
SIC: 3542 Mechanical (pneumatic or hydraulic) metal forming machines

(G-15841)
GREAT SOUTHERN READY MIX LLC
20333 Us Highway 59　(77357-8267)
PHONE....................................281 689-9339
Kyle Dinapoli, *President*
EMP: 23
SALES (est): 3MM
SALES (corp-wide): 8.3MM **Privately Held**
WEB: www.greatsouthernreadymix.com
SIC: 3273 Ready-mixed concrete
PA: Great Southern Stabilized, Llc
　　1 Hallett Dr
　　Porter TX 77365
　　281 812-3900

(G-15842)
JAYCO STEEL SERVICES INC
22788 Antique Ln　(77357-4800)
P.O. Box 1139　(77357-1139)
PHONE....................................281 399-0189
Regina Lee Goodrum, *President*
EMP: 30
SQ FT: 1,500
SALES (est): 5MM **Privately Held**
SIC: 3315 3444 5051 3441 Steel wire & related products; concrete forms, sheet metal; metals service centers & offices; fabricated structural metal; installing building equipment

(G-15843)
L R G SERVICES INC
21830 Pinebrook Dr　(77357-3912)
P.O. Box 1413　(77357-1413)
PHONE....................................713 504-4470
Larry Garza, *President*
EMP: 16
SALES (est): 2.3MM **Privately Held**
SIC: 1389 Construction, repair & dismantling services

(G-15844)
LONE STAR LIVESTOCK EQP CO INC
20115 Ada Ln　(77357-6803)
P.O. Box 442　(77357-0442)
PHONE....................................281 399-3550
Warren Bodenhamer, *CEO*
Brandon Bodenhamer, *President*
EMP: 10
SQ FT: 10,000
SALES (est): 1.5MM **Privately Held**
SIC: 3523 Farm machinery & equipment

(G-15845)
PATHWAY CONTROL PRODUCTS INC
22262 Cuttler Rd　(77357-4838)
PHONE....................................281 354-3699
Wade Brehm, *Vice Pres*
H Patrick Jones, *Vice Pres*
Mike Jones, *Sales Staff*
Stephany Everett, *Admin Sec*
EMP: 13 EST: 2004
SALES (est): 2.6MM **Privately Held**
WEB: www.pathwaycontrol.com
SIC: 3491 Industrial valves

(G-15846)
PIQ MACHINE LLC
22800 Gabriel　(77357-4968)
P.O. Box 514　(77357-0514)
PHONE....................................281 354-9873
Vicki S Dodson, *Principal*
EMP: 10 EST: 2012
SALES (est): 215.4K **Privately Held**
WEB: www.piqmachine.com
SIC: 3599 Machine shop, jobbing & repair

(G-15847)
PRESIDENTIAL BILLIARDS LP
20221 Caroline Way　(77357-3506)
PHONE....................................281 572-4733
Elaine Gerber, *Managing Prtnr*
Elisabeth Tweedy, *Cust Mgr*

EMP: 11
SALES (est): 1.4MM **Privately Held**
WEB: www.presidentialbilliards.com
SIC: 3949 Billiard & pool equipment & supplies, general

(G-15848)
PROTECTIVE INDUSTRIES INC
Tri-Star
19233 Fm 1485 Rd　(77357-3745)
PHONE....................................281 399-2600
Crey Rosethenbegger, *Manager*
EMP: 9
SALES (corp-wide): 3.3B **Privately Held**
WEB: www.caplugs.com
SIC: 2891 Sealing compounds for pipe threads or joints
HQ: Protective Industries, Inc.
　　2150 Elmwood Ave
　　Buffalo NY 14207
　　716 876-9951

New London
Rusk County

(G-15849)
C & C LOGGING
Also Called: C & C Oil Field
4105 Rusk County Rd　(75682)
PHONE....................................903 895-4738
Danny A Cook, *Owner*
EMP: 10
SALES (est): 460.4K **Privately Held**
SIC: 4789 1389 Log loading & unloading; oil field services

(G-15850)
ETOS INC
Also Called: East Texas Oilfield Services
595 N Main Hwy　(75682)
P.O. Box 288　(75682-0288)
PHONE....................................903 895-2220
Terry McFarland, *President*
EMP: 72
SQ FT: 2,300
SALES (est): 10.8MM **Privately Held**
SIC: 1389 Oil field services

(G-15851)
RECLAMATION CONTRACTORS TEXAS
Also Called: R.C.T. & Company
10503 Hwy 323　(75682)
P.O. Box 16　(75682-0016)
PHONE....................................903 895-4584
Dale K Farrow, *Owner*
EMP: 45
SQ FT: 2,500
SALES (est): 8.1MM **Privately Held**
SIC: 1629 1389 Land preparation construction; land reclamation; earthmoving contractor; oil field services

New Waverly
Walker County

(G-15852)
AMERICOM
555 State Rt 150　(77358)
PHONE....................................936 344-9052
Dewayne Pennington, *Principal*
EMP: 28
SALES (est): 4MM **Privately Held**
WEB: www.americomsitedevelopment.com
SIC: 2759 Commercial printing

(G-15853)
AUTUMNWOOD MILLWORKS LLC
6462 Fm 1374 Rd　(77358-3934)
PHONE....................................936 344-9784
Martha M Rucker,
EMP: 11
SALES (est): 1.6MM **Privately Held**
WEB: www.autumnwoodmillworks.com
SIC: 2431 Millwork

(G-15854)
B & R PRODUCTIONS INC
5909 Fm 1374 Rd　(77358-3925)
P.O. Box 398　(77358-0398)
PHONE....................................936 291-7827
Bryon Gardner, *President*
Regina Gardner, *Vice Pres*
EMP: 30 EST: 1994
SQ FT: 18,000
SALES (est): 4.5MM **Privately Held**
SIC: 3599 Machine shop, jobbing & repair

(G-15855)
BASELINE MFG PARTNERS LP
1070 Tafelski Rd　(77358-4500)
P.O. Box 1776　(77358-1776)
PHONE....................................936 344-2858
Nolan Ray Buckner, *Partner*
Debra Piatkowski, *Principal*
EMP: 12
SALES (est): 950K **Privately Held**
SIC: 3449 Miscellaneous metalwork

(G-15856)
CHEMEX MODULAR LLC
2722 Interstate Hwy 45 S　(77358)
PHONE....................................801 565-8099
Richard Cooper Cleveland, *COO*
Stewart Brandt, *Project Mgr*
Jake Tillery, *Project Engr*
Muhammad Uzair Ali, *Treasurer*
David Kehoe,
▼ **EMP:** 100
SALES (est): 17.1MM **Privately Held**
WEB: www.chemexmodular.com
SIC: 1629 2911 5084 1389 Oil refinery construction; petroleum refining; oil refining machinery, equipment & supplies; gas field services

(G-15857)
CHERYL L MCDANIEL
Also Called: Accent Ribbons
76 Ranch Rd　(77358-3999)
PHONE....................................281 814-0533
Cheryl L McDaniel,
EMP: 12 EST: 2001
SALES (est): 500K **Privately Held**
SIC: 2241 Ribbons

(G-15858)
CRAIG GODWIN INC (PA)
Also Called: United Machine Works
9353 State Highway 75 S　(77358-4225)
PHONE....................................936 344-6548
Joseph E Adams, *President*
Kevin Tomczak, *COO*
Michael P Maraist, *Treasurer*
EMP: 38
SALES (est): 17.3MM **Privately Held**
SIC: 3599 Machine shop, jobbing & repair

(G-15859)
CRAIG GODWIN INC
Also Called: United Machine Works
220a Longstreet Rd　(77358-3420)
P.O. Box 525　(77358-0525)
PHONE....................................936 344-6548
Daisy Flores, *Sales Staff*
Simons, *Manager*
EMP: 24
SQ FT: 5,000
SALES (corp-wide): 17.3MM **Privately Held**
SIC: 3533 Oil & gas field machinery
PA: Godwin Craig Inc
　　9353 State Highway 75 S
　　New Waverly TX 77358
　　936 344-6548

(G-15860)
DOWNHOLE DRILLING DYNAMICS LLC (PA)
220 Longstreet Rd　(77358-3420)
P.O. Box 1417　(77358-1417)
PHONE....................................936 344-9329
Kathrin Von Gynz-Rekowski, *Manager*
Joseph Adams,
Greg Godvin,
Kevin Tomczek,
EMP: 10
SALES (est): 665.5K **Privately Held**
WEB: www.rivaldt.com
SIC: 3541 Drilling machine tools (metal cutting)

(G-15861)
UFP NEW WAVERLY LLC
146b Fm 2793　(77358)
PHONE....................................936 295-3411
Allen T Peters, *President*
Michael R Cole, *Treasurer*
Scott Worthington, *Mng Member*
David A Tutas, *Admin Sec*
▼ **EMP:** 100
SALES (est): 11.8MM
SALES (corp-wide): 4.4B **Publicly Held**
WEB: www.ufpi.com
SIC: 2491 2439 2426 2499 Wood preserving; structural wood members; trusses, wooden roof; dimension, hardwood; fencing, docks & other outdoor wood structural products; fencing, wood
PA: Ufp Industries, Inc.
　　2801 E Beltline Ave Ne
　　Grand Rapids MI 49525
　　616 364-6161

Newark
Wise County

(G-15862)
ELITE METAL FABRICATORS INC
907 Georgetta Ln　(76071)
PHONE....................................817 489-2599
Jay Darter, *President*
Robert Darter, *Vice Pres*
EMP: 15
SQ FT: 6,000
SALES (est): 3.2MM **Privately Held**
WEB: www.elitemetalfabinc.com
SIC: 3441 Fabricated structural metal

Newcastle
Young County

(G-15863)
THREE P OPERATING COMPANY
620 Broadway St　(76372)
P.O. Box 490　(76372-0490)
PHONE....................................940 846-3326
Josh Phillips, *Partner*
EMP: 10
SQ FT: 2,000
SALES (est): 817K **Privately Held**
SIC: 1311 Crude petroleum production

Newton
Newton County

(G-15864)
MOBILE SPECIALTY VEHICLES INC
811 County Road 2076　(75966-6802)
PHONE....................................409 383-0521
Daniel S Ayres, *President*
Darrell Luce, *Vice Pres*
Jim Smith, *Vice Pres*
◆ **EMP:** 15
SALES (est): 3.2MM **Privately Held**
WEB: www.mobilespecialtyvehicles.com
SIC: 3713 Specialty motor vehicle bodies

(G-15865)
NEWTON POLE CO INC
Hwy 877 08cr1001　(75966)
PHONE....................................409 379-2715
Terry L Mc Leod, *President*
Heilda Mc Leod, *Vice Pres*
EMP: 11
SALES (est): 1.5MM **Privately Held**
WEB: www.newtonisd.net
SIC: 2491 Poles & pole crossarms, treated wood

▲ = Import ▼=Export
◆ =Import/Export

Nixon

Gonzales County

(G-15866)
HOLMES FOODS INC (PA)
101 S Liberty Ave (78140-2401)
PHONE..................................830 582-1551
Phillip A Morris, *CEO*
Phillip Morris, *President*
Tommy Lester, *Corp Secy*
Philip Hartung, *Senior VP*
Fred Barlow, *Vice Pres*
EMP: 250 **EST:** 1962
SALES (est): 64.9MM **Privately Held**
WEB: www.holmesfoods.com
SIC: 2015 Poultry, processed; poultry, slaughtered & dressed

(G-15867)
KENERGY OILFIELD SOLUTIONS LLC
806 Fm 1681 (78140-4109)
PHONE..................................830 263-9951
EMP: 69
SALES (corp-wide): 1.9MM **Privately Held**
WEB: www.kenergyoilfieldsolutions.com
SIC: 1389 Oil field services
PA: Kenergy Oilfield Solutions Llc
1619 E Common St Ste 401
New Braunfels TX 78130
979 574-6356

Nocona

Montague County

(G-15868)
DESIGN FLEX LLC
1108 E Highway 82 (76255-3000)
P.O. Box 593 (76255-0593)
PHONE..................................940 825-6629
Michael Waldrip, *Owner*
EMP: 18
SQ FT: 7,000
SALES (est): 990K **Privately Held**
WEB: www.worldmagnetics.com
SIC: 3829 Printing equipment, photographic

(G-15869)
ONEAL OIL COMPANY
200 Oaklawn Ave (76255-3109)
P.O. Box 538 (76255-0538)
PHONE..................................940 825-3716
Verna O'Neal, *Principal*
EMP: 11
SQ FT: 2,600
SALES (est): 5.5MM **Privately Held**
SIC: 1389 Oil field services; gas field services

(G-15870)
PEBA OIL & GAS CO
Also Called: Not Previous User
313 Clay St (76255-2105)
PHONE..................................940 825-4825
Ellis R Horton Jr, *Owner*
Joe Perron, *Manager*
EMP: 15
SQ FT: 1,000
SALES (est): 3.5MM **Privately Held**
WEB: www.pebaoilandgas.com
SIC: 1382 Oil & gas exploration services

Nolanville

Bell County

(G-15871)
LHOIST NORTH AMERICA TEXAS LTD
Also Called: Nolanville Plant Usf7
11714 Highway Fm 439 (76559)
P.O. Box 1189, Belton (76513-5189)
PHONE..................................254 698-6610
Aaron Jones, *Plant Mgr*
EMP: 34

SALES (corp-wide): 2.6MM **Privately Held**
WEB: www.lhoist.com
SIC: 1422 5032 Crushed & broken limestone; brick, except refractory
HQ: Lhoist North America Of Texas, Ltd.
5600 Clearfork Main St
Fort Worth TX 76109
817 732-8164

Nordheim

Dewitt County

(G-15872)
NITRO FLUIDS LLC (PA)
117 Broadway (78141-3111)
P.O. Box 585, Yorktown (78164-0585)
PHONE..................................361 938-5300
Jackie R Simpson Jr,
EMP: 23
SALES (est): 4.3MM **Privately Held**
SIC: 1389 Oil field services

North Richland Hills

Tarrant County

(G-15873)
AIRTECH SUPPLY INC
6625 Iron Horse Blvd (76180-6027)
PHONE..................................501 525-7707
Del Keith, *President*
Adam Friedl, *Engineer*
Kalim Holoch, *Engineer*
Sara Keith, *Treasurer*
Matt Prince, *Info Tech Dir*
EMP: 45 **EST:** 1996
SALES (est): 4.9MM **Privately Held**
WEB: www.airtechsupply.com
SIC: 3728 Aircraft parts & equipment

(G-15874)
B & W REMODELING INC
Also Called: B & W Cabinets & Millwork
8200 Precinct Line Rd (76182-8608)
PHONE..................................817 485-0444
Kevin Deaton, *President*
Michael Deaton, *Vice Pres*
Jim Burch, *Manager*
Linda Stodghill, *Admin Sec*
EMP: 45
SQ FT: 1,000
SALES (est): 6.5MM **Privately Held**
WEB: www.bwcabinets.com
SIC: 2434 1521 Wood kitchen cabinets; general remodeling, single-family houses

(G-15875)
CW AEROTECH SERVICES (PA)
8825 Bud Jenson Dr (76180-5412)
PHONE..................................817 595-1949
Tom Purvin, *President*
Robert Wehr, *Principal*
Ron Childs, *General Ptnr*
EMP: 14
SQ FT: 900
SALES (est): 3.5MM **Privately Held**
WEB: www.west.exch090.serverdata.net
SIC: 8742 3728 Industry specialist consultants; aircraft body assemblies & parts

(G-15876)
DFW COMFORT EXPERTS INC
Also Called: Stark Heating & Air
5750 Rufe Snow Dr Ste 120 (76180-6140)
PHONE..................................817 633-2665
Ben Stark, *President*
EMP: 14
SALES (est): 221.9K **Privately Held**
WEB: www.stark-services.com
SIC: 3585 Heating & air conditioning combination units

(G-15877)
ESNA LLC (HQ)
Also Called: Fitz Aerospace, LLC
6625 Iron Horse Blvd (76180-6027)
PHONE..................................817 281-8816
Steve Huey, *COO*
Keith Engstrom, *Prdtn Mgr*
William Shannon, *Mfg Staff*
Sharon Baughman, *Purch Dir*
Tim Cosby, *Engineer*

EMP: 253
SQ FT: 15,500
SALES (est): 59.5MM
SALES (corp-wide): 166.5MM **Privately Held**
WEB: www.fitzaero.com
SIC: 3728 5088 3429 3366 Aircraft parts & equipment; aircraft & parts; manufactured hardware (general); bushings & bearings
PA: Novaria Group, L.L.C.
6300 Ridglea Pl Ste 800
Fort Worth TX 76116
817 381-3810

(G-15878)
FASTENER SPECIALTY INC
6625 Iron Horse Blvd (76180-6027)
PHONE..................................972 988-0064
Beth Jones, *President*
George R Jones, *Chairman*
Justin Tucker, *Exec Dir*
▲ **EMP:** 12
SQ FT: 10,400
SALES (est): 2MM **Privately Held**
WEB: www.fastenerspecialty.com
SIC: 3678 Electronic connectors

(G-15879)
PRESTIGE AMERITECH LTD
7201 Iron Horse Blvd (76180-6153)
PHONE..................................817 427-2700
Mike Bowen, *Partner*
Dan Reese, *General Ptnr*
Jeff McCarty, *Engineer*
Glen Casey, *Sales Staff*
Richard Bennett, *Manager*
▲ **EMP:** 300
SQ FT: 220,000
SALES (est): 53.6MM **Privately Held**
WEB: www.prestigeameritech.com
SIC: 3069 Medical & laboratory rubber sundries & related products

(G-15880)
SEY TEC INC
8825 Bud Jenson Dr (76180-5412)
PHONE..................................817 595-1949
David Seybert, *President*
Tammy Seybert, *Vice Pres*
Donna Kilgore, *Purch Mgr*
Earnest Johnson, *QC Mgr*
Ronnie Childs, *VP Sales*
EMP: 37
SALES (est): 15.9MM **Privately Held**
WEB: www.seytec.com
SIC: 3429 Keys, locks & related hardware; pulleys metal; locks or lock sets

(G-15881)
SMURFIT KAPPA BATES LLC (DH)
6433 Davis Blvd (76182-4717)
P.O. Box 822028, Fort Worth (76182-2028)
PHONE..................................817 498-3200
Bob Brown, *COO*
Ron Welch, *Vice Pres*
Sean Jones, *Safety Mgr*
Tony Campbell, *Facilities Mgr*
Doug Cuppett, *Opers Staff*
▲ **EMP:** 180 **EST:** 1963
SQ FT: 180,000
SALES (est): 115.7MM **Privately Held**
WEB: www.batescontainer.com
SIC: 2653 5113 Boxes, corrugated: made from purchased materials; bags, paper & disposable plastic

(G-15882)
TEXFORCE RESTORATION SVCS LLC
5424 Rufe Snow Dr Ste 410 (76180-6635)
PHONE..................................817 775-3556
Robert Raymond, *CEO*
EMP: 12 **EST:** 2015
SALES (est): 434.3K **Privately Held**
WEB: www.texforce-restoration.com
SIC: 1741 1389 Tuckpointing or restoration; construction, repair & dismantling services

(G-15883)
TYSON FOODS INC
6350 Browning Ct (76180-6013)
PHONE..................................817 485-8912
Terry Patton, *President*

Lori McFarland, *Financial Exec*
Rebecca Hogan, *Human Resources*
Jason Kempenski, *Regl Sales Mgr*
Marte Amrine, *Manager*
EMP: 1020
SALES (est): 43.1B **Publicly Held**
WEB: www.tysonfoods.com
SIC: 2015 Poultry slaughtering & processing
PA: Tyson Foods, Inc.
2200 W Don Tyson Pkwy
Springdale AR 72762
479 290-4000

North Zulch

Madison County

(G-15884)
BULLDOG WIRELINE INC
18462 Highway 21 W (77872-7050)
PHONE..................................936 399-3999
Daniel Tidwell, *Vice Pres*
Adolphus Y Jennings, *Branch Mgr*
EMP: 17
SALES (corp-wide): 1.8MM **Privately Held**
WEB: www.bulldogwireline.com
SIC: 1389 Oil field services
PA: Bulldog Wireline Inc
13757 S Dowling Rd
College Station TX 77845
979 260-9034

Northlake

Denton County

(G-15885)
FARMER BROS CO (PA)
Also Called: Farmer Brothers
1912 Farmer Brothers Dr (76262-1857)
PHONE..................................682 549-6767
Randy E Clark, *Ch of Bd*
Christopher Mottern, *Ch of Bd*
Deverl Maserang, *President*
Ellen D Iobst, *COO*
Jennifer Brown, *Counsel*
EMP: 135 **EST:** 1912
SQ FT: 538,000
SALES (est): 501.3MM **Publicly Held**
WEB: www.farmerbros.com
SIC: 2095 5149 Coffee roasting (except by wholesale grocers); coffee & tea; coffee, green or roasted; spices & seasonings; sugar, refined

(G-15886)
FARMER BROS CO
Also Called: Farmers Brothers Coffee
1912 Farmer Brothers Dr (76262-1857)
PHONE..................................682 549-6600
Jonathan Nix, *Production*
Jason Barrett, *Sales Staff*
Tim Bradford, *Sales Staff*
Jason Nachtigal, *Sales Staff*
Anita Thompson, *Marketing Staff*
EMP: 17
SALES (corp-wide): 501.3MM **Publicly Held**
WEB: www.farmerbros.com
SIC: 2095 5499 5963 5149 Coffee roasting (except by wholesale grocers); coffee; direct selling establishments; coffee, green or roasted
PA: Farmer Bros. Co.
1912 Farmer Brothers Dr
Northlake TX 76262
682 549-6767

(G-15887)
HYDRO CONDUIT OF TEXAS LP
8363 E Sam Lee Ln (76262-6400)
PHONE..................................817 491-4321
EMP: 21 **Privately Held**
WEB: www.rinkerpipe.com
SIC: 3272 Concrete products
HQ: Hydro Conduit Of Texas, Lp
6560 Langfield Rd 3-H
Houston TX 77092

O Brien
Haskell County

(G-15888)
FIVE STAR ROUSTABOUTS LLC
Also Called: Five Star Construction
1925 County Road 196 (79539-2500)
PHONE..................................940 657-4778
Michael Ray Sheedy,
Ray Coker,
Janet Kay,
Mike Sheedy,
EMP: 24 **EST:** 2010
SALES (est): 2.3MM **Privately Held**
SIC: 1389 Oil field services

Oak Ridge North
Montgomery County

(G-15889)
IBAC INTERESTS LP
610 Todd St (77385-7333)
PHONE..................................281 681-0122
Richard Abbott, *Partner*
EMP: 15
SALES (est): 713.5K **Privately Held**
WEB: www.goibac.com
SIC: 3565 Packaging machinery

(G-15890)
SARDISCO ENTERPRISES INC
Also Called: Asi Standards
27635 Commerce Oaks Dr (77385-4405)
PHONE..................................281 419-9229
John B Sardisco, *President*
Jeff Graham, *Manager*
EMP: 10
SALES (est): 557.4K **Privately Held**
WEB: www.asistandards.com
SIC: 1389 Gas field services

Oakhurst
San Jacinto County

(G-15891)
ELM MACHINE INC
50 Elm St (77359)
P.O. Box 1819, Trinity (75862-1819)
PHONE..................................936 377-5001
William Knight, *President*
EMP: 12
SQ FT: 6,000
SALES (est): 1MM **Privately Held**
SIC: 3599 Machine shop, jobbing & repair

Oakwood
Leon County

(G-15892)
BARRILLEAUX INC
1412 W Broad St (75855-4563)
P.O. Box 128 (75855-0128)
PHONE..................................903 545-2280
Glen Barrilleaux, *Principal*
Jesus Tellez, *Purch Agent*
EMP: 100
SALES (est): 4.3MM **Privately Held**
WEB: www.barrilleauxinc.com
SIC: 1389 Oil field services

(G-15893)
OAKWOOD STEEL FABRICATION INC
491 W Us Highway 79 (75855-4564)
PHONE..................................903 545-2266
Regie Hargrabe, *President*
Benny Stevens, *Vice Pres*
EMP: 14
SQ FT: 10,800
SALES (est): 2.2MM **Privately Held**
WEB: www.oakwoodsteel.com
SIC: 3441 Fabricated structural metal

Odem
San Patricio County

(G-15894)
CHEMTRADE CHEMICALS US LLC
5302 County Road 2047 (78370-4412)
PHONE..................................361 368-2200
Carl Codney, *Branch Mgr*
EMP: 12
SALES (corp-wide): 1.1B **Privately Held**
WEB: www.generalchem.com
SIC: 2819 Industrial inorganic chemicals
HQ: Chemtrade Chemicals Us Llc
90 E Halsey Rd
Parsippany NJ 07054

(G-15895)
EPIC ENERGY SERVICES LLC
6397 Highway 77 (78370-4313)
PHONE..................................361 222-1226
Rebecca Bosworth,
Chester Bosworth III,
EMP: 125 **EST:** 2016
SALES (est): 579.9K **Privately Held**
WEB: www.epicenergyservices.us
SIC: 1389 1611 1799 Building oil & gas
well foundations on site; highway & street
maintenance; erection & dismantling of
forms for poured concrete

(G-15896)
FLOZONE MEASUREMENT LTD
6091 Highway 77 (78370-4283)
PHONE..................................432 488-2799
John Beningo, *Branch Mgr*
EMP: 28
SALES (corp-wide): 15.2MM **Privately Held**
WEB: www.flozonemeasurement.com
SIC: 3823 Industrial process measurement equipment
PA: Flozone Measurement, Ltd.
3981 S County Road 1297
Odessa TX 79765
432 488-2799

Odessa
Ector County

(G-15897)
A-1 GASKET & INDUSTRIAL SUPPLY (PA)
2022 W 2nd St (79763-4410)
P.O. Box 4998 (79760-4998)
PHONE..................................432 332-1444
Rick Delgeo, *Manager*
▲ **EMP:** 12
SQ FT: 3,000
SALES (est): 1.6MM **Privately Held**
SIC: 3053 Gaskets, all materials

(G-15898)
ACCELERATED PROD SVCS INC
1460 Windway (79763-4912)
PHONE..................................432 334-8580
Bill Simmons, *Manager*
EMP: 33
SALES (corp-wide): 87.7MM **Privately Held**
WEB: www.apergyals.com
SIC: 3561 Pumps & pumping equipment
PA: Accelerated Production Services, Inc.
3771 Eureka Way
Erie CO 80516
281 403-5793

(G-15899)
ACCELERATED PUMP
1460 W Interstate 20 (79763-4908)
PHONE..................................432 582-2335
Scooter Murray, *President*
EMP: 11 **EST:** 2012
SALES (est): 2.4MM **Privately Held**
SIC: 3561 Pumps & pumping equipment

(G-15900)
ACE CMPLTION ENHNCMENT SVCS LP
Also Called: Chemical Blending Facility
1301 W 1st St (79763-2826)
PHONE..................................432 653-0732
Thomas Parker, *Vice Pres*
EMP: 153
SALES (corp-wide): 33.6MM **Privately Held**
WEB: www.acecompletions.com
SIC: 2869 5169 Laboratory chemicals, organic; industrial chemicals
PA: Ace Completion Enhancement Services, Lp
620 N Grant Ave
Odessa TX 79761
888 256-5325

(G-15901)
ACE CMPLTION ENHNCMENT SVCS LP
250 Solo Rd Ste B (79762-8534)
PHONE..................................432 703-7169
EMP: 34
SALES (corp-wide): 33.6MM **Privately Held**
WEB: www.acecompletions.com
SIC: 2869 Laboratory chemicals, organic
PA: Ace Completion Enhancement Services, Lp
620 N Grant Ave
Odessa TX 79761
888 256-5325

(G-15902)
ADOBE OILFIELD LTD
Also Called: Adobe Oilfield Services
705 W Hillmont Rd (79764-1931)
P.O. Box 12490 (79768-2490)
PHONE..................................432 337-3731
Raymond Bohannen, *President*
EMP: 9
SALES (est): 1.2MM **Privately Held**
SIC: 1389 Oil field services

(G-15903)
ADVANCE FABRICATION SVCS LLC (PA)
Also Called: Afs
4315 S County Road 1290 (79765-9506)
PHONE..................................432 561-8776
John Holley, *Mng Member*
Micheal Black, *Mng Member*
Craig S Atchison,
W Sterling Warren,
EMP: 20
SALES (est): 3MM **Privately Held**
SIC: 3533 Gas field machinery & equipment

(G-15904)
AGUILAR OILFIELD SERVICES
Also Called: Fermin Aguilar Welding Svcs
4250 N Stockton Ave (79764-9350)
P.O. Box 69263 (79769-0263)
PHONE..................................432 230-2548
Fermin Aguilar, *President*
EMP: 20
SALES (est): 1MM **Privately Held**
WEB: www.arguijooilfieldservices.com
SIC: 1389 Oil field services

(G-15905)
AIM MEDIA TEXAS LLC
Also Called: Odessa American
700 N Grant Ave Ste 800 (79761-4556)
PHONE..................................432 337-4661
Richard E Mirman, *Partner*
Francis Irvine, *Business Mgr*
EMP: 135
SALES (est): 8.7MM **Privately Held**
WEB: www.oaoa.com
SIC: 2711 Newspapers, publishing & printing

(G-15906)
AIRDRAULICS
3351 Nw Loop 338 (79764-3114)
PHONE..................................432 381-7867
Larry Webb, *Owner*
EMP: 9
SQ FT: 7,200

SALES (est): 1.6MM **Privately Held**
WEB: www.thehoseconnectioninc.com
SIC: 3594 7699 Fluid power pumps & motors; hydraulic equipment repair

(G-15907)
AIRGEN EQUIPMENT LLC
3600 Kermit Hwy (79764-6431)
P.O. Box 13978 (79768-3978)
PHONE..................................432 332-1870
Glen Aaron McGuire,
Craig Coppedge,
EMP: 15
SQ FT: 8,000
SALES (est): 4MM **Privately Held**
WEB: www.airgeninc.com
SIC: 5084 7694 Machine tools & metalworking machinery; rebuilding motors, except automotive

(G-15908)
ALL CITY WELL SERVICE
1410 W Interstate 20 (79763-4908)
PHONE..................................432 332-8863
Randall Capps, *Principal*
EMP: 15
SALES (est): 950K **Privately Held**
WEB: www.tcws.com
SIC: 1389 Servicing oil & gas wells

(G-15909)
ALLBRIGHT & ASSOCIATES INC
8011 Andrews Hwy (79765-2822)
PHONE..................................432 366-8897
Beverly Allbright, *President*
James W Allbright, *President*
Michael Allbright, *Vice Pres*
EMP: 14 **EST:** 1976
SQ FT: 32,000
SALES (est): 1.5MM **Privately Held**
WEB: www.allbrightandassociates.com
SIC: 3599 7692 3494 Machine shop, jobbing & repair; welding repair; valves & pipe fittings

(G-15910)
ALLEYS INDUSTRIAL SERVICE INC
6826 N County Rd W (79764-2634)
P.O. Box 611 (79760-0611)
PHONE..................................432 362-0200
Belinda Alley, *President*
EMP: 11
SQ FT: 22,000
SALES (est): 1.9MM **Privately Held**
SIC: 3599 Machine shop, jobbing & repair

(G-15911)
ALLIANCE MACHINE & SPC INC
8711 Andrews Hwy (79765-2836)
P.O. Box 13531 (79768-3531)
PHONE..................................432 367-9113
Rick Blethroade, *President*
Donald Woodward, *Vice Pres*
Rhonda Blethroade, *Treasurer*
EMP: 11
SALES (est): 2.8MM **Privately Held**
SIC: 7694 Armature rewinding shops

(G-15912)
ALLIED EQUIPMENT INC
8000 Golder Ave (79764-2330)
P.O. Box 14188 (79768-4188)
PHONE..................................432 367-6000
Ron Worley, *President*
Griffin Smith, *Business Mgr*
Justin Orr, *Manager*
Dorin Scheianu, *Director*
EMP: 60
SQ FT: 13,000
SALES (est): 25.9MM **Privately Held**
WEB: www.alliedeq.com
SIC: 3533 5084 Oil & gas field machinery; industrial machinery & equipment

(G-15913)
AMERICAN INDUSTRIAL MACHINE
3401 N County Rd W (79764-6404)
PHONE..................................432 366-3516
John Hudson, *Partner*
EMP: 17 **EST:** 2011
SALES (est): 2.8MM **Privately Held**
WEB: www.aimodessa.com
SIC: 3599 Machine shop, jobbing & repair

(G-15914)
AMERICAN SAFETY SERVICES INC (PA)
8715 Andrews Hwy (79765-2836)
P.O. Box 12874 (79768-2874)
PHONE...................................432 552-7625
Michael Kevin Hokett, *President*
Tiffany Hokett, *Vice Pres*
Wendell Faulkner, *CFO*
Chester Miller, *Sales Staff*
Shawn Todd, *Sales Staff*
EMP: 200
SQ FT: 4,000
SALES (est): 24.9MM **Privately Held**
WEB: www.americansafety.net
SIC: 7389 5999 4959 8744 Safety inspection service; safety supplies & equipment; environmental cleanup services; ; servicing oil & gas wells

(G-15915)
ANGUS MEASUREMENT SERVICES LP (PA)
3800 Nw Loop 338 (79764-3123)
P.O. Box 14440 (79768-4440)
PHONE...................................432 332-7200
EMP: 10
SQ FT: 3,000
SALES (est): 5.1MM **Privately Held**
WEB: www.angusmeasurement.com
SIC: 3829 Measuring & controlling devices

(G-15916)
ANZURES WELDING ROUSTABOUT A
5742 W Turner St (79763-8892)
PHONE...................................432 385-4122
Luis Anzures, *Owner*
EMP: 9
SALES (est): 387.9K **Privately Held**
SIC: 1389 Construction, repair & dismantling services

(G-15917)
APOLLO PERFORATORS INC
12801 W I 20 (79765)
P.O. Box 12940 (79768-2940)
PHONE...................................432 563-0891
Jerry D Lee, *President*
Peggy G Lee, *Corp Secy*
EMP: 32 EST: 1981
SALES (est): 5.9MM **Privately Held**
WEB: www.apolloperforators.com
SIC: 1389 Oil field services

(G-15918)
ARGUIJO OILFIELD SERVICES INC
2800 W 42nd St (79764-6317)
P.O. Box 14861 (79768-4861)
PHONE...................................432 550-5650
Lisa Hibler, *Principal*
Barbara Arguijo, *Corp Secy*
James W Hibler, *Vice Pres*
EMP: 50
SQ FT: 1,000
SALES (est): 9.6MM **Privately Held**
WEB: www.arguijooilfieldservices.com
SIC: 1389 4212 Oil field services; local trucking, without storage

(G-15919)
ARROW PRINTING INC
109 N Hancock Ave (79761-5411)
PHONE...................................432 335-3407
Jim Golden, *President*
EMP: 47
SQ FT: 20,000
SALES (est): 4.3MM **Privately Held**
WEB: www.apodessa.com
SIC: 2752 Commercial printing, offset

(G-15920)
ATK OILFIELD TRNSP USA INC
7701 E Highway 191 # 932 (79762-5350)
P.O. Box 50070, Midland (79710-0070)
PHONE...................................432 452-3550
Artie T Kos, *President*
Les Ovelson, *COO*
Brent Wilkie, *Vice Pres*
Darcy Campbell, *CFO*
Clyde Bonnell, *Director*
EMP: 70 EST: 2013

SALES (est): 6.1MM
SALES (corp-wide): 210.1K **Privately Held**
SIC: 1389 Oil field services
PA: Atk Oilfield Transportation Inc
   520 5 Ave Sw Suite 800
   Calgary AB

(G-15921)
AXIS WELL SERVICES LLC
1390 W Interstate 20 (79763-4909)
PHONE...................................432 333-1111
Dee Johns, *Branch Mgr*
EMP: 54
SALES (corp-wide): 116.4MM **Privately Held**
WEB: www.xraybill.com
SIC: 1389 Servicing oil & gas wells; oil field services
PA: Axis Well Services, Llc
   851 W Harrison Rd
   Longview TX 75604
   903 759-0082

(G-15922)
BAKER HGHES OLFLD OPRTIONS LLC
Also Called: Baker Oil Tools
10912 W Highway 80 E (79765-9412)
PHONE...................................432 563-1900
Rickie Harper, *Manager*
EMP: 30 **Privately Held**
WEB: www.bakerhughes.com
SIC: 1389 Oil field services
PA: Baker Hughes Oilfield Operations Llc
   2001 Rankin Rd
   Houston TX 77073

(G-15923)
BAKER HUGHES A GE COMPANY LLC
6165 W Murphy St (79763-7511)
PHONE...................................432 248-3000
Scott Smith, *Opers Mgr*
Ali Aljizeeri, *Engineer*
Mike Wiggins, *Branch Mgr*
EMP: 400
SALES (corp-wide): 23.8B **Publicly Held**
WEB: www.bakerhughes.com
SIC: 1389 Oil field services
HQ: Baker Hughes Holdings Llc
   17021 Aldine Westfield Rd
   Houston TX 77073
   713 439-8600

(G-15924)
BAKER OPERATING INC
700 W 65th St (79764-2765)
PHONE...................................432 367-5808
Stephen P Baker, *President*
Vicky Baker, *Corp Secy*
EMP: 9
SQ FT: 1,200
SALES (est): 1.8MM **Privately Held**
SIC: 1311 Crude petroleum production

(G-15925)
BAKER PETROLITE
10520 W Interstate 20 (79765-9407)
PHONE...................................432 498-9191
Roy Young, *Manager*
EMP: 25
SALES (corp-wide): 23.8B **Publicly Held**
WEB: www.bakerhughes.com
SIC: 1389 Oil field services
HQ: Baker Petrolite
   2121 W Mary St
   Garden City KS 67846

(G-15926)
BALDERAS WELDING SERVICES LLC
1403 N Washington Ave (79761-3723)
PHONE...................................432 661-3164
Juan Balderas, *Principal*
EMP: 15 EST: 2015
SALES (est): 956.3K **Privately Held**
SIC: 1389 Oil field services

(G-15927)
BASIC ENERGY SERVICES INC
G & L Tool
2900 E Interstate 20 (79766-8837)
PHONE...................................432 580-8821
David Bostic, *Manager*

EMP: 15
SQ FT: 1,250
SALES (corp-wide): 567.2MM **Publicly Held**
WEB: www.basices.com
SIC: 1389 Oil field services
PA: Basic Energy Services, Inc.
   801 Cherry St Unit 2
   Fort Worth TX 76102
   817 334-4100

(G-15928)
BASIC ENERGY SERVICES LP
3301 N Fm 1936 (79764-8609)
P.O. Box 69526 (79769-0526)
PHONE...................................432 530-0907
Mike Blue, *Branch Mgr*
EMP: 100
SALES (corp-wide): 567.2MM **Publicly Held**
WEB: www.basices.com
SIC: 1389 1382 Oil & gas wells: building, repairing & dismantling; oil & gas exploration services
HQ: Basic Energy Services, L.P.
   801 Cherry St Unit 2
   Fort Worth TX 76102

(G-15929)
BB CHEMICALS INC
16107 W University Blvd (79764-9140)
P.O. Box 69337 (79769-0337)
PHONE...................................432 381-2595
Bruce Babb, *President*
EMP: 20
SALES (est): 4.3MM
SALES (corp-wide): 59.6MM **Privately Held**
SIC: 3731 5085 1389 2899 Drilling & production platforms, floating (oil & gas); pipeline wrappings, anti-corrosive; testing, measuring, surveying & analysis services; drilling mud
PA: Greenwell Energy Solutions, Llc
   2000 Edwards St Unit B
   Houston TX 77007
   713 993-7772

(G-15930)
BCM & ASSOCIATES INC
2638 S Fulton Ave (79766-8819)
P.O. Box 13077 (79768-3077)
PHONE...................................432 580-7161
Ben Montgomery, *President*
EMP: 12
SQ FT: 2,000
SALES (est): 1.2MM **Privately Held**
WEB: www.bcmandassociates.com
SIC: 1389 Oil field services

(G-15931)
BCM & ASSOCIATES INC
2674 W County Rd S (79766)
P.O. Box 13077 (79768-3077)
PHONE...................................432 580-7161
Ben Montogmery, *President*
EMP: 28
SALES (est): 1MM **Privately Held**
WEB: www.bcmandassociates.com
SIC: 1389 1382 Haulage, oil field; oil & gas exploration services

(G-15932)
BELARCO INDUS CLG ODESSA LLC
3511 W Arcadia St (79764-1347)
P.O. Box 4678 (79760-4678)
PHONE...................................432 381-0999
Alfred Alvarado, *President*
John Hernandez, *Opers Mgr*
EMP: 25
SQ FT: 1,600
SALES (est): 3.5MM **Privately Held**
WEB: www.belarcoindustrialcleaning.com
SIC: 1389 Cleaning wells

(G-15933)
BIG BEE DRILLING INC
1509 W 2nd St (79763-4320)
P.O. Box 4598 (79760-4598)
PHONE...................................432 333-2932
Omer L Bishop, *President*
Taylor Bobby L, *Vice Pres*
Gary Bishop, *Treasurer*
Yakov Nakhimovich, *Software Dev*
EMP: 70

SQ FT: 30,000
SALES (est): 7.7MM **Privately Held**
WEB: www.blinefilter.com
SIC: 3533 Drill rigs

(G-15934)
BIG E SERVICES LLC
6106 Cargo Rd (79762-8533)
P.O. Box 62047, Midland (79711-2047)
PHONE...................................432 550-2443
Ethan Uranga, *Plant Mgr*
Manny Muro, *Opers Mgr*
Mark Gonzales, *Opers Staff*
Sonny Hernandez, *Sales Staff*
Johnny Howell, *Sales Staff*
EMP: 14
SALES (est): 1.9MM **Privately Held**
WEB: www.bigeservicesllc.com
SIC: 1389 Cement making machinery

(G-15935)
BISON DRLG & FIELD SVCS LLC
12201 W County Road 122 (79765-8825)
P.O. Box 61727, Midland (79711-1727)
PHONE...................................405 463-6912
Kaes Banthos, *CEO*
Peggy Geer,
EMP: 200 EST: 2010
SALES (est): 48.7MM **Privately Held**
WEB: www.mammothenergy.com
SIC: 1381 Drilling oil & gas wells

(G-15936)
BLACK STAR ENERGY SERVICES LLC (PA)
Also Called: Blackstar Energy Services
12502 W County Rd 100 (79765)
P.O. Box 62027, Midland (79711-2027)
PHONE...................................432 272-3395
Kevin Blackwood, *President*
John Powell, *Opers Mgr*
Joey Poe, *Opers Staff*
Kayla Roach, *CFO*
EMP: 39
SALES (est): 45.4MM **Privately Held**
WEB: www.blackstarenergyservices.com
SIC: 5063 3731 1623 Generators; radar towers, floating; transmitting tower (telecommunication) construction

(G-15937)
BLAKELY CONSTRUCTION CO INC
Also Called: Blakely Oilfield Maint & Cnstr
2830 W I 20 (79763)
P.O. Box 712 (79760-0712)
PHONE...................................432 363-6650
Randy Blakely, *President*
Carol Blakely, *Corp Secy*
Carrie Blakely, *Vice Pres*
Aldo Lotito, *Vice Pres*
Rick Swinney, *Consultant*
EMP: 200 EST: 1963
SQ FT: 7,000
SALES (est): 32.6MM **Privately Held**
WEB: www.blakelycc.com
SIC: 1389 Construction, repair & dismantling services

(G-15938)
BLAXTONE ENERGY LLC
904 W 69th St (79764-2729)
PHONE...................................432 250-9039
Kenneth Wilkerson,
EMP: 10
SALES (est): 2.9MM **Privately Held**
WEB: www.blaxtone.us
SIC: 1389 Oil field services

(G-15939)
BLP SETTLEMENT COMPANY
Also Called: Bishop Lifting
3346 Kermit Hwy (79764-6425)
PHONE...................................432 332-0381
Guy Langford, *Manager*
EMP: 22
SALES (corp-wide): 3.1B **Privately Held**
WEB: www.lifting.com
SIC: 3496 Miscellaneous fabricated wire products
HQ: Blp Settlement Company
   125 Mccarty St
   Houston TX 77029
   713 674-2266

(G-15940)
BORDER STATES INDUSTRIES INC
Also Called: Zimco Elc Sup A Div Brder Stte
850 W University Blvd (79764-7100)
PHONE....................432 332-0591
Harry Halsell, *Branch Mgr*
EMP: 22
SALES (corp-wide): 2.4B **Privately Held**
WEB: www.borderstates.com
SIC: **5063** 5065 5074 1711 Electrical supplies; electronic parts & equipment; plumbing & hydronic heating supplies; plumbing, heating, air-conditioning contractors; plastics plumbing fixtures; vitreous plumbing fixtures
PA: Border States Industries, Inc.
2400 38th St S
Fargo ND 58104
701 293-5834

(G-15941)
BRANDON & CLARK INC
930 S County Rd W (79763-4803)
PHONE....................432 332-0163
Walt Clark, *President*
Mikky Navarrete, *Manager*
EMP: 9
SQ FT: 2,000
SALES (corp-wide): 49.3MM **Privately Held**
WEB: www.brandonclark.com
SIC: **7694** 5063 Electric motor repair; motors, electric
PA: Brandon & Clark, Inc.
3623 Interstate 27
Lubbock TX 79404
806 771-5600

(G-15942)
BRANDON & CLARK INC
Also Called: Odessa Division
930 S Country Rd W (79763)
PHONE....................432 332-0163
Mikky Navarrete, *Branch Mgr*
EMP: 14
SALES (corp-wide): 49.3MM **Privately Held**
WEB: www.brandonclark.com
SIC: **7694** 5063 Electric motor repair; power transmission equipment, electric
PA: Brandon & Clark, Inc.
3623 Interstate 27
Lubbock TX 79404
806 771-5600

(G-15943)
BRIDGES EQUIPMENT LTD (PA)
2122 Maurice Rd (79763-4813)
P.O. Box 11335 (79760-8335)
PHONE....................432 333-9741
Mike Bridges, *Owner*
Jimmy Bridges, *Owner*
Jody Halford, *Opers Mgr*
Jeff Tucker, *Opers Mgr*
Vince Carlisle, *Foreman/Supr*
◆ EMP: 45
SALES (est): 9.6MM **Privately Held**
WEB: www.bridgesequipment.com
SIC: **1389** Oil field services

(G-15944)
BRIDGESTONE HOSEPOWER LLC
3511 Mankins Ave (79764-6530)
PHONE....................432 367-4673
Ken Jones, *Vice Pres*
EMP: 23 **Privately Held**
WEB: www.hosepower.com
SIC: **5085** 3542 Pistons & valves; crimping machinery, metal
HQ: Bridgestone Hosepower, Llc
50 Industrial Loop N
Orange Park FL 32073

(G-15945)
BRONCS INC
4200 N Sierra Ave (79764-2540)
P.O. Box 12370 (79768-2370)
PHONE....................432 614-8305
Brian Shoemaker, *President*
Robert Maxwell, *Director*
William A Maxwell, *Director*
EMP: 15 **EST:** 2013

SALES (est): 1.9MM **Privately Held**
SIC: **1389** Construction, repair & dismantling services

(G-15946)
BURNSCO BLOWT PRVNTR RPR & SRV
3401 N County Rd W (79764-6404)
PHONE....................432 367-5329
Kenneth Burns II, *President*
EMP: 15
SQ FT: 2,000
SALES (est): 500K **Privately Held**
SIC: **1389** Oil field services

(G-15947)
BUSINESS INVESTMENT & DEV CORP
312 E 2nd St (79761-5408)
P.O. Box 7238 (79760-7238)
PHONE....................432 335-3410
Jimmy D Golden, *President*
Julie Thompson Preston, *Vice Pres*
John L Holderness, *Treasurer*
EMP: 47
SQ FT: 2,500
SALES (est): 3.7MM **Privately Held**
SIC: **6794** 2759 Franchises, selling or licensing; commercial printing

(G-15948)
BYRD OILFIELD SERVICES LLC
4320 Johnson Rd (79764-3862)
PHONE....................432 385-7635
EMP: 33 **Privately Held**
WEB: www.byrdoilfield.com
SIC: **1389** Oil field services
PA: Byrd Oilfield Services, Llc
4725 Loop 322
Abilene TX 79602

(G-15949)
C H I ALPHA WHITESTONE INC
Also Called: Center Line Machine
600 E Yukon Rd (79762-2968)
P.O. Box 12068 (79768-2068)
PHONE....................432 367-0006
Michael Strickland, *President*
Jane Brigger, *Vice Pres*
Martin A P, *Vice Pres*
EMP: 13
SQ FT: 5,000
SALES (est): 1.6MM **Privately Held**
WEB: www.ersbiofilter.com
SIC: **3599** Machine shop, jobbing & repair

(G-15950)
C HINTON ENTERPRISES INC
Also Called: C Hinton Entps Fshing Rentl Tl
7111 Andrews Hwy (79765-2804)
P.O. Box 14187 (79768-4187)
PHONE....................432 339-0411
Clyde Hinton, *President*
▲ EMP: 20
SQ FT: 40,000
SALES (est): 24MM **Privately Held**
SIC: **1389** 7353 Fishing for tools, oil & gas field; oil equipment rental services

(G-15951)
C S AGUIRRE SONS INC
6829 W 16th St (79763-6411)
P.O. Box 70037 (79769-1037)
PHONE....................432 381-5221
Carlos S Aguirre, *President*
Conrad L Aguirre, *Vice Pres*
EMP: 10
SQ FT: 7,500
SALES (est): 2.2MM **Privately Held**
WEB: www.csaguirre.com
SIC: **3441** Fabricated structural metal

(G-15952)
CAGLE FISHING & RENTAL TLS INC (PA)
5221 W 42nd St (79764-1152)
P.O. Box 7769 (79760-7769)
PHONE....................432 381-3061
Tom Passmore Jr, *President*
Ileana Cagle, *Corp Secy*
Kim Passmore, *Vice Pres*
Vikki Thiebaud, *Controller*
Randy McVey, *Sales Executive*
EMP: 15
SQ FT: 4,800

SALES (est): 7.4MM **Privately Held**
WEB: www.caglefishing.com
SIC: **7353** 1389 Oil field equipment, rental or leasing; fishing for tools, oil & gas field

(G-15953)
CAMERON INTERNATIONAL CORP
Also Called: Cooper Compression
8927 Andrews Hwy (79765-1308)
PHONE....................432 362-2511
Chuck Potes, *Manager*
EMP: 60 **Publicly Held**
WEB: www.products.slb.com
SIC: **3533** Oil & gas field machinery
HQ: Cameron International Corporation
4646 W Sam Houston Pkwy N
Houston TX 77041

(G-15954)
CANARY LLC
2401 S Market St (79766-9701)
PHONE....................432 563-1970
Martin Tomlin, *Opers Staff*
Steve Young, *Branch Mgr*
EMP: 106 **Privately Held**
WEB: www.canaryusa.com
SIC: **1389** Oil field services
PA: Canary, Llc
17207 N Perimeter Dr # 120
Scottsdale AZ 85255

(G-15955)
CARBERY FABRICATORS COMPANY
9214 Cromwell Ter (79764-1216)
PHONE....................432 337-5015
EMP: 15
SQ FT: 26,800
SALES: 2.1MM **Privately Held**
SIC: **3443** 3498 3444 3441 Mfg Fabricated Plate Wrk Mfg Fabrctd Pipe/Fitting Mfg Sheet Metalwork Structural Metal Fabrctn

(G-15956)
CEMENTOS READY MIX
11041 W 42nd St (79764-9264)
P.O. Box 69367 (79769-0367)
PHONE....................432 385-7477
Elias Rodriguez Jr, *Administration*
EMP: 9
SALES (est): 1.5MM **Privately Held**
SIC: **3273** Ready-mixed concrete

(G-15957)
CEMEX CEMENT INC
104 W Interstate 20 (79761-6836)
P.O. Box 1547 (79760-1547)
PHONE....................432 385-2800
Robert Standback, *Branch Mgr*
EMP: 85 **Privately Held**
WEB: www.cemexusa.com
SIC: **3273** Ready-mixed concrete
HQ: Cemex Cement, Inc.
10100 Katy Fwy Ste 300
Houston TX 77043
713 650-6200

(G-15958)
CEMEX USA INC
16501 W Murphy St (79763-7880)
P.O. Box 1547 (79760-1547)
PHONE....................432 385-2892
EMP: 120
SALES (corp-wide): 15.4B **Privately Held**
SIC: **3273** Mfg Ready Mixed Concrete & Concrete Products
HQ: Cemex U.S.A., Inc.
929 Gessner Rd Ste 1900
Houston TX 77024
713 650-6200

(G-15959)
CHAMPIONX LLC
Also Called: Nalco Champion
115 Proctor Ave (79762-8503)
PHONE....................432 363-9105
Jeff Brown, *Branch Mgr*
EMP: 80
SALES (corp-wide): 1.1B **Publicly Held**
WEB: www.ecolab.com
SIC: **2819** Chemicals & allied products

HQ: Championx Llc
11177 S Stadium Dr
Sugar Land TX 77478
281 632-6500

(G-15960)
CHOAT ENTERPRISES INC
3300 Sherbrook Rd (79762-5036)
PHONE....................432 367-8459
Joe Duncan, *President*
Valerie Duncan, *Corp Secy*
James Choat, *Vice Pres*
EMP: 25
SQ FT: 150,000
SALES (est): 781.8K **Privately Held**
SIC: **1389** 0782 Pipe testing, oil field service; lawn care services

(G-15961)
CIMARRON ENERGY HOLDING CO LLC
Also Called: Diverse Energy Systems
2600 W 81st St (79764-1702)
PHONE....................432 563-9700
EMP: 25
SALES (corp-wide): 48.8MM **Privately Held**
SIC: **3585** 1711 Fabrication And Repair Of Heating Equipment
HQ: Cimarron Energy Holding Company, Llc
1012 24th Ave Nw Ste 100
Norman OK 73072
405 928-7373

(G-15962)
CIRCLE 8 CRANE SERVICES LLC
Also Called: Circle 8 Fluid Services
2989 S County Rd W (79766-2523)
PHONE....................432 332-6900
EMP: 77
SALES (corp-wide): 277.2MM **Privately Held**
WEB: www.circle8services.com
SIC: **1389** Oil field services
PA: Circle 8 Crane Services Llc
3174 County Road 48
Robstown TX 78380
361 933-0696

(G-15963)
COBRA COATING
2300 E Murphy St (79761-5809)
P.O. Box 13982 (79768-3982)
PHONE....................432 332-0272
Isaiah Andarrete, *President*
EMP: 18
SQ FT: 15,000
SALES (est): 2.2MM **Privately Held**
SIC: **3479** Coating of metals with plastic or resins

(G-15964)
COM-PAC SYSTEMS INC
2412 S Market St (79766-9701)
PHONE....................432 332-4515
Jack Don Motley, *President*
Donna Jean Motley, *Vice Pres*
Donna Motley, *Vice Pres*
Brock Duke, *Engineer*
Rick Mobley, *Sales Executive*
EMP: 19
SALES (est): 5.8MM **Privately Held**
WEB: www.compressorpackaging.com
SIC: **3563** Air & gas compressors

(G-15965)
COMPRESSOR DESIGNS INC
12201 W County Road 128 (79765-9442)
P.O. Box 60007, Midland (79711-0007)
PHONE....................432 425-0044
Terry Rice, *President*
Jim Brown, *Sales Mgr*
EMP: 17
SALES (est): 1.6MM **Privately Held**
WEB: www.compressordesigns.com
SIC: **3563** 3564 Air & gas compressors; dust or fume collecting equipment, industrial

(G-15966)
COOK COMPRESSION
2605 W 42nd St (79764-6314)
PHONE....................432 367-7786
Brandi Cegielski, *Senior Buyer*

Niklaus Pedersen, *Sales Staff*
Craig Reeves, *Branch Mgr*
Deniece Daly, *Manager*
Ricky Redding, *Technician*
EMP: 18
SALES (corp-wide): 7.1B **Publicly Held**
WEB: www.cookcompression.com
SIC: 3563 Air & gas compressors
HQ: Cook Compression
11951 Spectrum Blvd
Houston TX 77047

(G-15967)
COORSTEK INC
Also Called: Coorstek Odessa
3565 W 16th St (79763-2615)
PHONE.............................432 381-0052
Tracy Curtan, *Branch Mgr*
EMP: 11
SALES (corp-wide): 346.3MM **Privately Held**
WEB: www.coorstek.com
SIC: 3264 Porcelain electrical supplies
HQ: Coorstek, Inc.
14143 Denver West Pkwy # 400
Lakewood CO 80401
303 271-7000

(G-15968)
CORCHEM MANUFACTURING INC
1227 S Murphy St (79766-8811)
PHONE.............................432 332-1335
Jonathon Wood, *CEO*
Daryl Bibens, *Vice Pres*
Anet S Woods, *Vice Pres*
Janet Wood, *Director*
EMP: 15
SALES (est): 4.2MM **Privately Held**
WEB: www.corchem.com
SIC: 2851 2843 Shellac (protective coating); surface active agents

(G-15969)
CORROSION LTD
4321 S County Road 1290 (79765-9506)
PHONE.............................432 561-8504
Brian Langford, *President*
Tommy Farrell, *President*
Lynn Farrell, *Vice Pres*
EMP: 30
SQ FT: 4,000
SALES (est): 2.9MM **Privately Held**
WEB: www.corrosionltd.com
SIC: 1389 Chemically treating wells

(G-15970)
COTTONS INSPECTION SERVICE INC
102 E Yukon Rd (79765)
P.O. Box 14368 (79768-4368)
PHONE.............................432 366-2631
EMP: 25 **EST:** 1973
SQ FT: 2,400
SALES (est): 2.6MM **Privately Held**
SIC: 1389 Testing, measuring, surveying & analysis services

(G-15971)
CUDD PRESSURE CONTROL INC
Also Called: Cudd Pumping Services
1300 S John Ben Sheppard (79766-0002)
PHONE.............................432 580-3544
Jerry Harley, *Manager*
Jason Marcon, *Manager*
Bill Taylor, *Manager*
Beau Deloge, *Supervisor*
Nathan Price, *Supervisor*
EMP: 100
SALES (corp-wide): 1.7B **Publicly Held**
WEB: www.cuddenergyservices.com
SIC: 1389 Pumping of oil & gas wells; oil field services
HQ: Cudd Pressure Control, Inc.
2828 Tech Forest Blvd
The Woodlands TX 77381
832 295-5555

(G-15972)
CUDD PUMPING SERVICES INC
Also Called: Cudd Energy Services
1300 S John Ben Sheppard (79766-0002)
PHONE.............................432 580-3544
Jerry Harley, *District Mgr*

EMP: 350
SALES (corp-wide): 1.7B **Publicly Held**
WEB: www.cuddenergyservices.com
SIC: 1382 7694 Geological exploration, oil & gas field; coil winding service
HQ: Cudd Pumping Services, Inc.
2828 Tech Forest Blvd
The Woodlands TX 77381

(G-15973)
CUMMINS SOUTHERN PLAINS LLC
Also Called: Southern Plains Power
1210 S Grandview Ave (79761-7139)
P.O. Box 633 (79760-0633)
PHONE.............................432 332-9121
Mike Foster, *Sales/Mktg Mgr*
EMP: 18
SQ FT: 28,190
SALES (corp-wide): 19.8B **Publicly Held**
WEB: www.cummins.com
SIC: 5084 3519 Engines & parts, air-cooled; internal combustion engines
HQ: Cummins Southern Plains Llc
600 N Watson Rd
Arlington TX 76011
817 640-6801

(G-15974)
DARVILLE CO
Also Called: Honeywell Authorized Dealer
311 W 42nd St (79764-4003)
PHONE.............................432 580-9675
Mark Darville, *President*
Ryan Chelette, *Technician*
Jan Futrell, *Technician*
Cory Partin, *Technician*
EMP: 15
SQ FT: 4,000
SALES (est): 1.7MM **Privately Held**
WEB: www.darvilleco.com
SIC: 1711 1521 5075 3444 Warm air heating & air conditioning contractor; general remodeling, single-family houses; air conditioning equipment, except room units; sheet metalwork

(G-15975)
DEVONIAN DIRT WORKS LLC
11611 W County Road 122 (79765-9708)
P.O. Box 60530, Midland (79711-0530)
PHONE.............................432 253-7777
EMP: 9
SALES (est): 1.2MM **Privately Held**
WEB: www.devonian.services
SIC: 1389 Roustabout service

(G-15976)
DIAMOND TANK RENTAL INC
Also Called: DTR
2655 S County Rd W (79766-8807)
P.O. Box 4751 (79760-4751)
PHONE.............................432 337-0011
Roger M Turner, *President*
Rob Ingle, *Senior VP*
Robert C Turner, *Vice Pres*
Gary Cooper, *Opers Staff*
Cary Thornton, *Executive*
EMP: 35 **EST:** 1965
SQ FT: 6,000
SALES (est): 9.7MM **Privately Held**
WEB: www.diamondtankrental.com
SIC: 7359 1389 Equipment rental & leasing; haulage, oil field

(G-15977)
DIGITAL FORGE MEDIA LLC
11339 W University Blvd (79764-9100)
PHONE.............................432 559-6068
EMP: 15
SALES (est): 1.4MM **Privately Held**
SIC: 2836 Mfg Biological Products

(G-15978)
DON-NAN PUMP AND SUPPLY CO INC
8350 W 42nd St (79764-8854)
PHONE.............................432 530-1925
Paul Turmatliss, *Manager*
EMP: 12
SALES (corp-wide): 179.6MM **Privately Held**
WEB: www.don-nan.com
SIC: 1389 Oil field services

PA: Don-Nan Pump And Supply Co., Inc.
3427 E Garden Cy Hwy 158
Midland TX 79706
432 682-7742

(G-15979)
DOUBLE D TONGS INC
7507 Andrews Hwy (79765-2812)
P.O. Box 69863 (79769-0863)
PHONE.............................432 381-0602
Robert D Duncan, *President*
EMP: 24
SALES (est): 3.8MM **Privately Held**
WEB: www.doubledtong.com
SIC: 1389 Construction, repair & dismantling services

(G-15980)
DRILLFORM DRILLING EQP INC
12120 W County Road 100 (79765-2245)
PHONE.............................281 948-9122
Todd H McCorriston, *Director*
EMP: 21
SALES (est): 1.2MM **Privately Held**
WEB: www.drillform.com
SIC: 3533 7353 Oil & gas drilling rigs & equipment; oil well drilling equipment, rental or leasing

(G-15981)
E L FARMER & COMPANY (PA)
Also Called: E L F
3800 E 42nd St Ste 417 (79762-5928)
P.O. Box 3512 (79760-3512)
PHONE.............................432 366-2010
Jimmie B Todd, *President*
Carroll Brents, *Vice Pres*
David Musgraves, *Vice Pres*
Richard Scott, *Opers Staff*
Kathy Kasper, *Accounting Mgr*
EMP: 42 **EST:** 1910
SQ FT: 2,000
SALES (est): 87MM **Privately Held**
WEB: www.elfarmer.com
SIC: 1389 Haulage, oil field

(G-15982)
EAGLE COMPLETION USA LTD
13600 W I 20 E (79765)
PHONE.............................432 561-7000
Lindsay Rhoades, *Principal*
EMP: 30
SALES (est): 823.8K **Privately Held**
SIC: 1389 Oil field services

(G-15983)
EAGLE MANUFACTURING & SVC LTD
13600 W Interstate 20 (79765-9691)
P.O. Box 60850, Midland (79711-0850)
PHONE.............................432 561-7000
Darrell Dillard, *President*
Mike Black, *Shareholder*
EMP: 50
SQ FT: 18,000
SALES (est): 9.3MM **Privately Held**
WEB: www.eaglerigusa.com
SIC: 3533 Oil & gas drilling rigs & equipment

(G-15984)
ECKEL HEAT TREATING CO
Also Called: Eckel Manufacturing Company
8035 N County Rd W (79764-1963)
P.O. Box 1375 (79760-1375)
PHONE.............................432 362-4336
Terry L Eckel, *President*
EMP: 60 **EST:** 1978
SALES (est): 4.7MM
SALES (corp-wide): 24.8MM **Privately Held**
SIC: 3398 Metal heat treating
PA: Eckel Manufacturing Company, Inc.
8035 N County Rd W
Odessa TX 79764
432 362-4336

(G-15985)
ECKEL MANUFACTURING CO INC (PA)
Also Called: Eckel International
8035 N County Rd W (79764-1963)
P.O. Box 1375 (79760-1375)
PHONE.............................432 362-4336
Terry Eckel, *President*
Terry L Eckel, *President*

Randy Stuart, *Vice Pres*
Randy Stewart, *Engineer*
Marilyn Ventrcek, *Human Res Mgr*
◆ **EMP:** 70 **EST:** 1958
SQ FT: 141,000
SALES (est): 24.8MM **Privately Held**
WEB: www.eckel.com
SIC: 3533 3398 Oil field machinery & equipment; metal heat treating

(G-15986)
EJR CONSULTING SERVICES INC
Also Called: Oil & Gas Drilling Production
5601 Ponderosa Dr (79762-9430)
P.O. Box 13810 (79768-3810)
PHONE.............................432 634-2905
Elvis Rogers, *President*
EMP: 15 **EST:** 2007
SALES (est): 126.9K **Privately Held**
SIC: 8748 1382 Business consulting; oil & gas exploration services

(G-15987)
ELECTRONIC DATA DEVICES CO (PA)
840 Oxford Dr (79764-1238)
P.O. Box 12128 (79768-2128)
PHONE.............................432 366-8699
Robert Williams, *President*
Mike Jolly, *Production*
Stephenie Williams, *Treasurer*
EMP: 24
SQ FT: 8,000
SALES (est): 3.6MM **Privately Held**
WEB: www.eddevices.com
SIC: 3533 3824 3823 Oil field machinery & equipment; gas meters, domestic & large capacity: industrial; turbine flow meters, industrial process type

(G-15988)
EMPIRE TUBING TONGS INC
Also Called: Western Repair Service
4801 N County Rd W (79764-3954)
P.O. Box 69078 (79769-0078)
PHONE.............................432 366-7702
Glen L Clark, *President*
Shelley Philips, *Corp Secy*
EMP: 10
SQ FT: 13,416
SALES (est): 1.1MM **Privately Held**
SIC: 1389 Oil field services

(G-15989)
ENERGES SERVICES LLC
Also Called: Energes Odessa
2161 W Interstate 20 Svcr (79766-9708)
PHONE.............................432 307-0650
Terry Peltes, *CEO*
EMP: 112
SALES (corp-wide): 62.2MM **Privately Held**
WEB: www.energesservicesllc.com
SIC: 1389 Oil field services
PA: Energes Services, Llc
140 S Dearborn St Ste 420
Chicago IL 60603
970 353-5133

(G-15990)
ENERGY FABRICATION INC
3750 Kermit Hwy (79764-6433)
PHONE.............................432 362-0591
Thomas D Southall, *President*
Danny Woodard, *Opers Mgr*
Juan Madrid, *Parts Mgr*
Natalie Pounder, *Office Mgr*
Edward Davila, *Manager*
EMP: 30
SQ FT: 15,000
SALES (est): 7.8MM **Privately Held**
WEB: www.energyfabrication.com
SIC: 3713 7692 3715 Truck & bus bodies; welding repair; truck trailers

(G-15991)
ENERTECH INDUSTRIES INC
321 Georgia St (79764-2808)
P.O. Box 71 (79760-0071)
PHONE.............................432 550-0543
Taylor Grimes, *President*
Michael Ashton, *Chairman*
Charlie Bredemeyer, *Sales Associate*
EMP: 27
SQ FT: 20,000

SALES (est): 1.8MM **Privately Held**
WEB: www.enertechindustries.com
SIC: 1389 Oil field services

(G-15992)
ENTREC CORPORATION
4003 Scr 1294 (79765)
PHONE..................432 301-2794
Travis Black, *Safety Mgr*
Tommy Patterson, *Manager*
EMP: 80
SALES (corp-wide): 135.3MM **Privately Held**
WEB: www.entrec.com
SIC: 1389 Oil field services
PA: Entrec Corporation
28712 114 Ave
Acheson AB T7X 6
780 962-1600

(G-15993)
ETECH ENVMTL SAFETY SOLUTIONS (PA)
13000 W County Road 100 (79765-2234)
P.O. Box 8469, Midland (79708-8469)
PHONE..................432 563-2200
Shonna Estep, *President*
Jim Hitchcock, *District Mgr*
Shane Estep, *Vice Pres*
Tamika Joiner, *Project Mgr*
Ronny Matte, *Project Mgr*
EMP: 31
SQ FT: 4,000
SALES (est): 15MM **Privately Held**
WEB: www.etechenv.com
SIC: 8748 8641 8744 4959 Energy conservation consultant; environmental consultant; environmental protection organization; ; environmental cleanup services; construction site cleanup; construction, repair & dismantling services

(G-15994)
EVERETT LLC
Also Called: Rio Services
2970 N Eastview Ave (79764-8568)
P.O. Box 69139 (79769-0139)
PHONE..................432 381-5700
Claude Everett Jr, *Mng Member*
Herman D Everett,
EMP: 14 **EST:** 2008
SALES (est): 2.3MM **Privately Held**
SIC: 1389 Oil field services

(G-15995)
EXPRESS ENERGY SVCS OPER LP
2258 N Mercury Ave (79763-1954)
PHONE..................432 530-1111
Jack Raegan, *Manager*
EMP: 200
SALES (corp-wide): 770.4MM **Privately Held**
WEB: www.eeslp.com
SIC: 1389 Oil field services
PA: Express Energy Services Operating, Lp
9800 Richmond Ave Ste 500
Houston TX 77042
713 625-7400

(G-15996)
EZ PIPE PADDLER PADDING MCH
Also Called: EZ Pipeline
3276 N County Rd W (79766)
P.O. Box 11456 (79760-8456)
PHONE..................432 333-9587
Thomas Cronk Jr, *President*
EMP: 20
SQ FT: 3,000
SALES (est): 3.1MM **Privately Held**
WEB: www.ezpadders.com
SIC: 3533 1623 Oil & gas field machinery; pipeline wrapping

(G-15997)
F & W INDUSTRIES INC
6698 Andrews Hwy (79762-2850)
P.O. Box 12271 (79768-2271)
PHONE..................432 563-8895
Russell Worthen, *Principal*
Andrea Spradley, *Admin Asst*
EMP: 13

SALES (est): 1.8MM **Privately Held**
WEB: www.fwcoatings.com
SIC: 3471 3479 Sand blasting of metal parts; coating, rust preventive

(G-15998)
FAB TEX OILFIELD SERVICES INC
2228 Steven Rd (79764-1825)
P.O. Box 13862 (79768-3862)
PHONE..................432 339-1011
Shannon Coan, *President*
Ashton Williams, *Principal*
Teresa Moore, *Manager*
EMP: 80
SALES (est): 1.7MM **Privately Held**
WEB: www.fabtexoilfieldservices.com
SIC: 3441 7692 Fabricated structural metal; welding repair

(G-15999)
FABCO INDUSTRIES INC
8406 Sprague Rd (79764-1747)
P.O. Box 1551 (79760-1551)
PHONE..................432 367-4988
Danny Barlau, *President*
Bess Barlau, *Vice Pres*
Ronnie Buckner, *Manager*
Fred Hubbard, *Manager*
Jamie Hubbard, *Admin Sec*
EMP: 10 **EST:** 1979
SQ FT: 14,800
SALES (est): 1.5MM **Privately Held**
WEB: www.fabcoindustries.net
SIC: 3713 5013 3711 Truck beds; truck parts & accessories; motor vehicles & car bodies

(G-16000)
FESCO LTD
2600 S Einstein Ave (79766-8941)
P.O. Box 60232, Midland (79711-0232)
PHONE..................432 332-3211
Doug McNeely, *Manager*
Doug Mc Neely, *Manager*
EMP: 27
SALES (corp-wide): 201MM **Privately Held**
WEB: www.fescoinc.com
SIC: 1389 Construction, repair & dismantling services; oil field services
PA: Fesco, Ltd.
1000 Fesco Dr
Alice TX 78332
361 664-3479

(G-16001)
FISHER CONSTRUCTION
2463 W Catlin St (79766-8816)
P.O. Box 1328 (79760-1328)
PHONE..................432 332-7532
Mike Fisher, *Owner*
EMP: 50
SQ FT: 5,000
SALES (est): 3.1MM **Privately Held**
SIC: 1389 1541 1623 Oil field services; industrial buildings, new construction; water, sewer & utility lines

(G-16002)
FISHING TOOL/CRYSTIN INC
Also Called: Fishing Tool Repair and Mfg
8001 Golder Ave (79764-2532)
P.O. Box 14314 (79768-4314)
PHONE..................432 366-6504
Larry Hackleman, *President*
Justin Hackleman, *Principal*
Jonnie Hackleman, *Director*
EMP: 35
SQ FT: 12,000
SALES (est): 3.5MM **Privately Held**
WEB: www.crystin.com
SIC: 3533 7699 3494 Oil field machinery & equipment; drilling tools for gas, oil or water wells; industrial machinery & equipment repair; valves & pipe fittings

(G-16003)
FITZ TORQUE CONVERTORS INC
Also Called: Fitz Torque Converter
2616 Cessna Ave (79764-6528)
P.O. Box 3907 (79760-3907)
PHONE..................432 362-3261
Michael Fitzgerald, *President*
Scott Fitzgerald, *Vice Pres*

Jerry Harrold, *Parts Mgr*
Tori Yardley, *Office Mgr*
EMP: 29 **EST:** 1960
SQ FT: 16,000
SALES (est): 13.1MM **Privately Held**
WEB: www.fitzequipment.net
SIC: 5084 3566 7699 Compressors, except air conditioning; torque converters, except automotive; industrial machinery & equipment repair; compressor repair

(G-16004)
FLINT HILLS RESOURCES LP
2495 S Grandview Ave (79766-9108)
PHONE..................432 640-8933
Mike Wilkes, *Branch Mgr*
EMP: 400
SALES (corp-wide): 36.8B **Privately Held**
WEB: www.fhr.com
SIC: 2911 Petroleum refining
HQ: Flint Hills Resources, Lp
4111 E 37th St N
Wichita KS 67220
800 292-3133

(G-16005)
FLOZONE MEASUREMENT LTD (PA)
3981 S County Road 1297 (79765-9510)
P.O. Box 13887 (79768-3887)
PHONE..................432 488-2799
Chris Holcomb, *General Ptnr*
Bo Hutson, *Business Dir*
EMP: 30 **EST:** 2002
SALES (est): 15.2MM **Privately Held**
WEB: www.flozonemeasurement.com
SIC: 3823 Industrial process measurement equipment

(G-16006)
FMC TECHNOLOGIES INC
12620 W County Road 133 (79765-8001)
PHONE..................432 561-8063
James Benson, *Branch Mgr*
EMP: 15
SALES (corp-wide): 13.4B **Privately Held**
WEB: www.technipfmc.com
SIC: 3533 Oil field machinery & equipment
HQ: Fmc Technologies, Inc.
11740 Katy Fwy Enrgy Twr
Houston TX 77079
281 591-4000

(G-16007)
FMC TECHNOLOGIES INC
3500 N County Rd W (79764-6407)
PHONE..................432 563-0335
Hunter Henderson, *Sales/Mktg Mgr*
EMP: 10
SALES (corp-wide): 13.4B **Privately Held**
WEB: www.technipfmc.com
SIC: 3533 Oil field machinery & equipment
HQ: Fmc Technologies, Inc.
11740 Katy Fwy Enrgy Twr
Houston TX 77079
281 591-4000

(G-16008)
FORUM ENERGY TECHNOLOGIES INC
Also Called: Forum Oilfield Technologies
2495 S Grandview Ave (79766-9108)
PHONE..................432 550-9000
EMP: 82 **Publicly Held**
WEB: www.f-e-t.com
SIC: 1389 Oil field services
PA: Forum Energy Technologies, Inc.
10344 Sam Houston Park Dr # 300
Houston TX 77064

(G-16009)
FULLCO MACHINE WORKS
Also Called: Fullco General Machine Works
12915 W County Road 122 (79765-8808)
P.O. Box 60529, Midland (79711-0529)
PHONE..................432 563-3443
Gary Fullen Sr, *President*
Karen Fullen, *Vice Pres*
EMP: 15
SQ FT: 22,000
SALES (est): 1.8MM **Privately Held**
SIC: 3533 Oil field machinery & equipment

(G-16010)
GARDNER DENVER INC
8620 E Highway 191 (79765-8757)
P.O. Box 12987 (79768-2987)
PHONE..................432 366-5433
Terrance Sova, *Sales Staff*
EMP: 350
SALES (corp-wide): 2.4B **Publicly Held**
WEB: www.gardnerdenver.com
SIC: 3564 3563 Blowers & fans; air & gas compressors including vacuum pumps
HQ: Gardner Denver, Inc.
800 Beaty St
Davidson NC 28036

(G-16011)
GASKET SERVICE INC
2120 Kermit Hwy (79761-1102)
P.O. Box 2373 (79760-2373)
PHONE..................432 332-0853
C Saul Deras, *President*
Alice Deras, *Corp Secy*
EMP: 18
SQ FT: 20,000
SALES (est): 3.3MM **Privately Held**
WEB: www.gasketservice.com
SIC: 3053 5085 Gaskets, all materials; packing materials; gaskets; packing, industrial

(G-16012)
GCC PERMIAN LLC
16501 W Murphy St (79763-7880)
P.O. Box 1547 (79760-1547)
PHONE..................432 385-2800
Ron Henley, *President*
EMP: 100
SALES (est): 415.9K **Privately Held**
WEB: www.gccusa.com
SIC: 3531 Batching plants, for aggregate concrete & bulk cement
HQ: Gcc Of America, Inc.
600 S Cherry St 10th
Denver CO 80246

(G-16013)
GEMSTAR INC
6501 Trunk St (79762-8530)
P.O. Box 12376 (79768-2376)
PHONE..................432 362-2315
Kevin Gray, *President*
Gregory E Gray, *Vice Pres*
Teresa L Trotter, *Vice Pres*
Russell Perry, *Foreman/Supr*
Janice Foutz, *Human Res Mgr*
EMP: 40 **EST:** 1957
SQ FT: 55,000
SALES (est): 12.9MM **Privately Held**
WEB: www.gemstarfab.com
SIC: 3533 3398 7699 Oil & gas field machinery; metal heat treating; industrial machinery & equipment repair

(G-16014)
GEORGE BROS FABRICATION CO INC
4023 S County Road 1282 (79765-9697)
P.O. Box 60245, Midland (79711-0245)
PHONE..................432 563-3390
Craig Cummins, *President*
EMP: 10
SQ FT: 25,600
SALES (est): 930K **Privately Held**
WEB: www.geobrofab.com
SIC: 3443 1629 Industrial vessels, tanks & containers; industrial plant construction

(G-16015)
GLOBE CHEMICAL LLC
Also Called: Tech Management
13316 W County Road 100 (79765-2217)
P.O. Box 51168, Midland (79710-1168)
PHONE..................432 684-4939
Troy Botts Jr, *President*
Troy Burton, *Senior VP*
Phillip Wright, *Senior VP*
Guerman Aliev, *Director*
Richard N Ellis, *Director*
EMP: 13
SALES (est): 1.6MM **Privately Held**
SIC: 2899 Chemical preparations

(G-16016)
GONCO OILFIELD SERVICES LLC
2817 John Ben Shpperd Pkw (79762-8111)
PHONE..................................432 208-2389
Julio Gonzales, *President*
EMP: 9 **EST:** 2013
SALES (est): 552.3K **Privately Held**
SIC: 1389 Oil field services

(G-16017)
GRAND ISLE SHIPYARD INC
325 Solo Rd (79762-8505)
PHONE..................................432 362-0019
Nate Rothstein, *Project Mgr*
Manny Salazer, *Manager*
EMP: 89
SALES (corp-wide): 257.1MM **Privately Held**
WEB: www.gisy.com
SIC: 1389 Oil field services
PA: Grand Isle Shipyard, Llc
18838 Highway 3235
Galliano LA 70354
985 475-5238

(G-16018)
GREAT BASIN PETROLEUM SVCS LP
4909 S County Road 1303 (79765-9641)
PHONE..................................432 561-9702
John M Molina, *General Ptnr*
Jose F Molina, *General Ptnr*
EMP: 80
SQ FT: 8,400
SALES (est): 12MM **Privately Held**
SIC: 1389 1382 Oil field services; geological exploration, oil & gas field

(G-16019)
GREENWELL ENERGY SOLUTIONS LLC
16107 W University Blvd (79764-9140)
PHONE..................................432 381-2595
Bruce Babb, *Owner*
EMP: 11
SALES (corp-wide): 59.6MM **Privately Held**
WEB: www.greenwellsolutions.com
SIC: 1389 Oil field services
PA: Greenwell Energy Solutions, Llc
2000 Edwards St Unit B
Houston TX 77007
713 993-7772

(G-16020)
GUARDIAN WELLHEAD PROTECTION
6907 E Commerce St (79762-9732)
P.O. Box 13188 (79768-3188)
PHONE..................................432 368-5449
EMP: 100
SALES (est): 127.9K **Privately Held**
WEB: www.greenesenergy.com
SIC: 1389 Oil field services

(G-16021)
H & S VALVE (PA)
6704 N County Rd W (79764-2696)
PHONE..................................432 362-0486
Les Littlejohn, *President*
Byron Harrison, *COO*
Jack Thompson, *Vice Pres*
Gary Weaver, *CFO*
Greg Gardenhire, *Sales Mgr*
EMP: 25
SQ FT: 6,000
SALES (est): 8.5MM **Privately Held**
WEB: www.hsvalveinc.com
SIC: 7699 3491 Compressor repair; pressure valves & regulators, industrial

(G-16022)
H & T AUGER COMPANY (PA)
4519 Brazos Ave (79764-3975)
P.O. Box 69140 (79769-0140)
PHONE..................................432 362-4471
Thomas L Taylor Sr, *President*
Frankie Taylor, *Treasurer*
EMP: 20 **EST:** 1968
SQ FT: 45,000
SALES (est): 7.4MM **Privately Held**
SIC: 3532 3545 7699 3536 Auger mining equipment; drill bits, metalworking; industrial machinery & equipment repair; hoists, cranes & monorails; oil & gas field machinery; hand & edge tools

(G-16023)
H C HOWELL COMPANY
Also Called: H C L
901 W 59th St (79764-3505)
PHONE..................................432 368-0835
Betty J Howell, *President*
Terry Ruddock, *Vice Pres*
Mary Rhodes, *Treasurer*
Laura Ruddock, *Admin Sec*
EMP: 10 **EST:** 1978
SQ FT: 3,500
SALES (est): 1.6MM **Privately Held**
WEB: www.hchowell.com
SIC: 3533 7699 5084 Oil field machinery & equipment; industrial machinery & equipment repair; petroleum industry machinery

(G-16024)
HALLIBURTON COMPANY
6155 W Murphy St (79763-7511)
PHONE..................................432 571-8600
Lynn Palmore, *Branch Mgr*
EMP: 20 **Publicly Held**
WEB: www.halliburton.com
SIC: 1389 1629 Oil field services; cementing oil & gas well casings; fire fighting, oil & gas field; perforating well casings; power plant construction; chemical plant & refinery construction; oil refinery construction; marine construction
PA: Halliburton Company
3000 N Sam Houston Pkwy E
Houston TX 77032

(G-16025)
HAMILTON MACHINE & MFG INC
2120 W 44th St (79764-3909)
P.O. Box 70239 (79769-1239)
PHONE..................................432 362-8030
Philip Hamilton, *President*
Shane Hamilton, *Vice Pres*
Robert Neal, *Production*
Victor Hiller, *Engineer*
Rachel Minor, *Human Res Dir*
▲ **EMP:** 50
SQ FT: 70,000
SALES (est): 6.1MM **Privately Held**
WEB: www.hamiltonmachine.net
SIC: 3599 Machine shop, jobbing & repair

(G-16026)
HARBISON-FISCHER INC
Also Called: Harbison-Fischer Sales Co
1311 E Pool Rd (79765-8803)
P.O. Box 7557 (79760-7557)
PHONE..................................432 580-3592
Jordan Davidson, *Sales Staff*
Scott Altenbern, *Manager*
EMP: 13
SQ FT: 1,512
SALES (corp-wide): 1.1B **Publicly Held**
WEB: www.apergyals.com
SIC: 3533 Oil field machinery & equipment
HQ: Harbison-Fischer, Inc.
901 N Crowley Rd
Crowley TX 76036
817 297-2211

(G-16027)
HARD BAND INDUSTRIES INC
12200 W County Road 129 (79765-9418)
P.O. Box 61528, Midland (79711-1528)
PHONE..................................432 563-3752
Merle Spence, *President*
EMP: 15
SQ FT: 3,500
SALES (est): 2.3MM **Privately Held**
WEB: www.hardbandindustries.com
SIC: 1389 Oil field services

(G-16028)
HUFFMAN COMPANY LTD
2373 W Interstate 20 (79766)
PHONE..................................432 332-5723
Dan C Huffman, *Partner*
Ernest Thomas, *Purch Agent*
Kevin Carlton, *Engineer*
Kurt Coombs, *Engineer*
EMP: 16
SQ FT: 35,000
SALES (est): 4.1MM **Privately Held**
WEB: www.huffmanco.com
SIC: 7699 3443 Industrial machinery & equipment repair; heat exchangers, plate type

(G-16029)
IMMUNOTEK BIO CENTERS LLC
1363 W University Blvd (79764-7121)
PHONE..................................432 307-6774
Angela Hawk, *Manager*
EMP: 27
SALES (corp-wide): 27MM **Privately Held**
WEB: www.immunotek.com
SIC: 2836 Blood derivatives
PA: Immunotek Bio Centers, L.L.C.
3900 N Causeway Blvd # 1200
Metairie LA 70002
337 500-1175

(G-16030)
INDUSTRIAL INSUL & SHTMTL INC
3339 Kermit Hwy (79764-6424)
P.O. Box 13450 (79768-3450)
PHONE..................................432 332-8203
Coy Edge, *President*
Patricia Edge, *Vice Pres*
EMP: 40 **EST:** 1964
SQ FT: 20,000
SALES (est): 7.7MM **Privately Held**
WEB: www.iismi.com
SIC: 3444 1742 3296 3086 Sheet metalwork; insulation, buildings; mineral wool; plastics foam products

(G-16031)
INTERNATIONAL CHEMICAL TECHNOL
2710 W Hillmont Rd (79764-1740)
PHONE..................................432 339-9361
Joe Marquez, *President*
EMP: 14
SALES (est): 1.2MM **Privately Held**
SIC: 3533 Oil field machinery & equipment

(G-16032)
INTERSTATE GAS TREATING INC
7141 Club Dr (79762-5451)
PHONE..................................432 362-9291
Ronald Rains, *President*
EMP: 40
SALES (est): 5.9MM **Privately Held**
WEB: www.ramafab.com
SIC: 3533 Oil & gas field machinery

(G-16033)
INTERSTATE TREATING INC
Also Called: Rama Fabrication
2310 Prospect (79762-5463)
PHONE..................................432 362-9291
Ronald D Rains, *Branch Mgr*
EMP: 29 **Privately Held**
WEB: www.intertreat.com
SIC: 3533 Oil & gas field machinery
PA: Interstate Treating, Inc.
7141 Club Dr
Odessa TX 79762

(G-16034)
INTERSTATE TREATING INC (PA)
7141 Club Dr (79762-5451)
P.O. Box 1386 (79760-1386)
PHONE..................................432 362-9291
Ronald D Rains, *President*
Chad Denney, *Project Mgr*
Barry Donner, *Project Mgr*
Bill Hix, *Project Mgr*
David Thomason, *Project Mgr*
▼ **EMP:** 68
SQ FT: 3,049,200
SALES (est): 18.2MM **Privately Held**
WEB: www.intertreat.com
SIC: 7353 1629 1389 5084 Oil equipment rental services; industrial plant construction; processing service, gas; petroleum industry machinery; sheet metalwork; fabricated structural metal

(G-16035)
J PATRICK SERVICES LLC
7230 Manford Ln (79765-5002)
P.O. Box 764 (79760-0764)
PHONE..................................432 214-5443
John Patrick Morales, *Mng Member*
EMP: 18 **EST:** 2015
SALES (est): 2MM **Privately Held**
SIC: 1389 4213 Oil field services; heavy machinery transport

(G-16036)
J-HOBBS MACHINE CORPORATION
3807 S C R 1297 (79765)
P.O. Box 13868 (79768-3868)
PHONE..................................432 563-1526
Jim Hobbs, *President*
Ronald Self, *Vice Pres*
Sheila Roberts, *Executive*
▲ **EMP:** 22 **EST:** 1980
SQ FT: 7,200
SALES (est): 4.7MM **Privately Held**
WEB: www.jhobbsmachine.com
SIC: 3533 7389 Oil & gas field machinery; metal cutting services

(G-16037)
J-W OPERATING COMPANY
250 Solo Rd (79762-8506)
PHONE..................................432 332-0111
Bill Hurlbut, *Branch Mgr*
EMP: 23 **Privately Held**
WEB: www.jwpower.net
SIC: 1389 Oil field services
HQ: J-W Operating Company
15505 Wright Brothers Dr
Addison TX 75001
972 233-8191

(G-16038)
JAB RENTALS INC
Also Called: Jab Services
2627 Faudree Rd Ste B (79765-8740)
P.O. Box 14738 (79768-4738)
PHONE..................................432 296-6464
Bobby Hill, *President*
Andrew Aramsay, *Vice Pres*
Jeremy Hill, *Vice Pres*
EMP: 20
SALES (est): 800K **Privately Held**
SIC: 1389 Oil field services

(G-16039)
JIMMY SMART (PA)
Also Called: Cougar Cleaning Equipment
3841 Nw Loop 338 (79764-3124)
P.O. Box 13985 (79768-3985)
PHONE..................................432 381-5450
Lydia Smart, *Owner*
Thomas Cooper, *General Mgr*
EMP: 29
SQ FT: 6,400
SALES (est): 3.1MM **Privately Held**
WEB: www.cougarcleaning.com
SIC: 7699 5999 2842 7549 Industrial equipment cleaning; cleaning equipment & supplies; specialty cleaning preparations; glass tinting, automotive; cleaning equipment, high pressure, sand or steam

(G-16040)
JMD OILFIELD & RIG SERVICE LLC
7035 Andrews Hwy (79765-2803)
P.O. Box 12070 (79768-2070)
PHONE..................................469 261-2415
Leonardo Saenz,
EMP: 28 **EST:** 2010
SQ FT: 5,000
SALES (est): 7MM **Privately Held**
WEB: www.jmdoil.com
SIC: 1389 7699 Gas field services; industrial machinery & equipment repair

(G-16041)
JMD OILFIELD AND RIG SVC LLC
7035 Andrews Hwy (79765-2803)
P.O. Box 12070 (79768-2070)
PHONE..................................432 208-9941
Leonard M Saenz, *Manager*
EMP: 25

SALES (est): 626.3K **Privately Held**
WEB: www.jmdoil.com
SIC: 1389 Servicing oil & gas wells

(G-16042)
JORDAN SPOOLING SERVICE INC
Also Called: Jordan Wire Rope
2400 W 56th St (79764-3719)
PHONE...............................432 366-6040
Ronny E Jordan, *President*
Jana Jordan, *Vice Pres*
Jennifer Jordan, *Bookkeeper*
EMP: 22
SALES (est): 10.3MM **Privately Held**
WEB: www.jordanwirerope.com
SIC: 5051 1389 Rope, wire (not insulated); oil field services

(G-16043)
JW WILLIAMS INC
901 S County Rd W (79763-2583)
P.O. Box 60410, Midland (79711-0410)
PHONE...............................307 237-8345
Matthew Elrod, *Branch Mgr*
EMP: 10
SALES (corp-wide): 13.2B **Publicly Held**
SIC: 3533 Gas field machinery & equipment
HQ: J.W. Williams, Inc.
2180 W Renauna Ave
Casper WY 82601
307 237-8345

(G-16044)
KEANE GROUP HOLDINGS LLC
8200 E Ih 20 (79766-2104)
PHONE...............................432 488-3800
Jacob Hughes, *Engineer*
Kevin Owens, *Branch Mgr*
Jose Puente, *Manager*
Kevin Sutton, *Manager*
Robert Bagley, *Supervisor*
EMP: 250
SALES (corp-wide): 1.8B **Publicly Held**
WEB: www.nextierofs.com
SIC: 1389 Oil field services
HQ: Keane Group Holdings, Llc
3990 Rogerdale Rd
Houston TX 77042
713 960-0381

(G-16045)
KELLEYS CONTROLS INCORPORATED (PA)
Also Called: Kci
210 E 57th St (79762-3609)
P.O. Box 13807 (79768-3807)
PHONE...............................432 362-7998
RC Quinton Kelley Jr, *President*
Quinton Kelley, *President*
Patricia Kelley, *Vice Pres*
Kim Odonnell, *Sales Associate*
EMP: 15
SQ FT: 15,000
SALES (est): 3MM **Privately Held**
WEB: www.kelleyscontrols.com
SIC: 5065 3613 7373 3625 Electronic parts; panel & distribution boards & other related apparatus; systems integration services; relays & industrial controls

(G-16046)
KENNER CO INC
Also Called: Kennerprinting
1103 N Texas Ave (79761-3815)
PHONE...............................432 333-1921
Jack W Kenner, *Ch of Bd*
Jacque Kenner, *Treasurer*
EMP: 12
SQ FT: 6,200
SALES (est): 1.2MM **Privately Held**
SIC: 2752 2789 2759 Commercial printing, offset; bookbinding & related work; commercial printing

(G-16047)
KEY ENERGY SERVICES INC
Also Called: Yale E Key
5347 W 42nd St (79764-1326)
P.O. Box 69609 (79769-0609)
PHONE...............................432 381-1301
Jerry Ridling, *Manager*
EMP: 46

SALES (corp-wide): 413.8MM **Publicly Held**
WEB: www.keyenergy.com
SIC: 1389 Oil field services
PA: Key Energy Services, Inc.
1301 Mckinney St Ste 1800
Houston TX 77010
713 651-4300

(G-16048)
KEY ENERGY SERVICES INC
10202 W 42nd St (79764-8934)
PHONE...............................432 586-2591
EMP: 55
SALES (corp-wide): 436.1MM **Publicly Held**
SIC: 1389 1381 Oil/Gas Field Services Oil/Gas Field Well Drilling
PA: Key Energy Services, Inc.
1301 Mckinney St Ste 1800
Houston TX 77010
713 651-4300

(G-16049)
KEY ENERGY SERVICES INC
12320 W Interstate 20 E (79765-9658)
PHONE...............................432 561-5682
Jeff Moore, *Manager*
EMP: 42
SALES (corp-wide): 413.8MM **Publicly Held**
WEB: www.keyenergy.com
SIC: 1389 1381 Servicing oil & gas wells; drilling oil & gas wells
PA: Key Energy Services, Inc.
1301 Mckinney St Ste 1800
Houston TX 77010
713 651-4300

(G-16050)
KEY ENERGY SERVICES INC
12400 W Interstate 20 (79765-9620)
PHONE...............................432 488-2800
Kenneth Brown, *Branch Mgr*
EMP: 46
SALES (corp-wide): 413.8MM **Publicly Held**
WEB: www.keyenergy.com
SIC: 1389 Oil field services
PA: Key Energy Services, Inc.
1301 Mckinney St Ste 1800
Houston TX 77010
713 651-4300

(G-16051)
KEYSCAN INC
6408 Richwood Rd (79762-5141)
PHONE...............................201 918-2396
Dov Aharonson, *President*
Ophira Rosolio, *Treasurer*
Felix Placer, *Sales Mgr*
▲ **EMP:** 15
SALES (est): 471.5K **Privately Held**
WEB: www.keyscan.com
SIC: 3575 3572 5045 3577 Keyboards, computer, office machine; computer storage devices; computer auxiliary storage units; computers, peripherals & software; computers & accessories, personal & home entertainment; computer peripheral equipment; optical scanning devices

(G-16052)
KIKERS MACHINE WORKS INC
4001 N Fm 1936 (79764-8621)
P.O. Box 69590 (79769-0590)
PHONE...............................432 381-8142
Danny Kiker, *President*
EMP: 12
SQ FT: 4,000
SALES (est): 1.1MM **Privately Held**
WEB: www.kikermachine.com
SIC: 3599 3446 3444 3441 Machine shop, jobbing & repair; architectural metalwork; sheet metalwork; fabricated structural metal; millwork

(G-16053)
KIRKS MACHINE WORKS
210 W 57th St (79764-3557)
PHONE...............................432 368-5333
Jack Kirks, *Owner*
Jackie Kirks, *Partner*
Jimmy Kirks, *Partner*
EMP: 9
SQ FT: 5,600

SALES (est): 1.1MM **Privately Held**
SIC: 3533 Oil & gas field machinery

(G-16054)
KNIGHT OIL TOOLS LLC
3700 N Fm 1936 (79764-8644)
PHONE...............................432 530-1010
Mark McCauley, *Branch Mgr*
EMP: 20
SALES (corp-wide): 66.3MM **Privately Held**
WEB: www.knightoiltools.com
SIC: 1389 Oil field services
HQ: Knight Oil Tools, Llc
2727 Se Evangeline Trwy
Lafayette LA 70508
337 233-0464

(G-16055)
KNIGHTEN MACHINE AND SVC INC (PA)
Also Called: Knighten Industries
3800 E 42nd St Ste 333 (79762-5927)
P.O. Box 12587 (79768-2587)
PHONE...............................877 457-7204
William L Knighten, *President*
Derrick Katzer, *Regional Mgr*
Bill Smith, *Area Mgr*
Brian Knighten, *Vice Pres*
Brad Eberle, *Opers Mgr*
EMP: 40
SQ FT: 14,500
SALES (est): 24.2MM **Privately Held**
WEB: www.knightenindustries.com
SIC: 3599 7692 Machine shop, jobbing & repair; welding repair

(G-16056)
KUYKENDALL BTM HOLE PRESSURE
4917 S County Road 1305 (79765-9645)
P.O. Box 52670, Midland (79710-2670)
PHONE...............................432 563-5231
Fax: 432 563-5246
EMP: 26
SALES (est): 2.4MM **Privately Held**
SIC: 1389 Oil/Gas Field Services

(G-16057)
L & C SAFETY INC
Also Called: Standard Safety & Supply
2469 E 11th St (79761-4232)
P.O. Box 14987 (79768-4987)
PHONE...............................432 653-0393
Tyler Barcena, *President*
EMP: 100
SALES (est): 25.7MM **Privately Held**
WEB: www.standardtx.com
SIC: 1389 Fire fighting, oil & gas field

(G-16058)
L G PUMP INC
8400 Andrews Hwy (79765-2829)
PHONE...............................432 550-3445
Larry Slaughter, *President*
Judy Slaughter, *Bookkeeper*
EMP: 20
SQ FT: 5,000
SALES (est): 5MM **Privately Held**
SIC: 4212 1389 Petroleum haulage, local; oil field services

(G-16059)
L L T INC (PA)
2462 W Interstate 20 (79763-5022)
P.O. Box 658, Comfort (78013-0658)
PHONE...............................830 914-3800
Clinton Wood, *President*
John Kothmann, *Vice Pres*
EMP: 10
SALES (est): 776K **Privately Held**
WEB: www.largelifttruck.com
SIC: 3537 Forklift trucks

(G-16060)
LAPAZ TORTILLA FACTORY
1112 S Crane Ave (79763-4661)
PHONE...............................432 337-7735
Alfonso Leal, *Owner*
EMP: 9
SQ FT: 11,105
SALES (est): 586.8K **Privately Held**
SIC: 2099 Tortillas, fresh or refrigerated

(G-16061)
LEWIS CASING CREWS INC (PA)
8931 Andrews Hwy (79765-1308)
P.O. Box 13747 (79768-3747)
PHONE...............................432 366-8077
Patrick Lewis, *President*
La Donna Lewis Weaver, *Vice Pres*
EMP: 19
SQ FT: 12,000
SALES (est): 2MM **Privately Held**
WEB: www.lewiscasingcrews.com
SIC: 1389 7359 Cementing oil & gas well casings; oil field services; tool rental

(G-16062)
LIBERTY FISHING RENTL TLS INC
Also Called: Liberty Rverse Units Rentl Tls
313 E 96th St (79765-1466)
P.O. Box 13590 (79768-3590)
PHONE...............................432 381-0551
Monnie Sparkman, *President*
Robert E Sparkman, *President*
John Sparkman, *Vice Pres*
EMP: 32 **EST:** 1956
SQ FT: 8,000
SALES (est): 1.2MM **Privately Held**
SIC: 1389 Oil field services

(G-16063)
LIDE INDUSTRIES LLC (HQ)
2701 W Interstate 20 (79766-9102)
PHONE...............................254 562-0233
Jennifer Dykes, *Purchasing*
Howard Seely, *CFO*
Laurie Capps, *Sales Staff*
Brian Cronan, *Mng Member*
Billy Lide,
▲ **EMP:** 102 **EST:** 2000
SQ FT: 100,000
SALES (est): 27.3MM
SALES (corp-wide): 99.4MM **Privately Held**
WEB: www.lideindustries.com
SIC: 3795 3443 Tanks & tank components; fabricated plate work (boiler shop)
PA: Permian Tank & Manufacturing, Inc.
2701 W Interstate 20
Odessa TX 79766
432 580-1050

(G-16064)
LONE STAR GASKET AND SUP INC
5012 Andrews Hwy (79762-4241)
P.O. Box 2615 (79760-2615)
PHONE...............................432 333-1615
Ken Wallace, *President*
EMP: 16
SALES (est): 3.2MM **Privately Held**
WEB: www.lonestargasket.net
SIC: 3053 Gaskets, all materials

(G-16065)
LONE STAR INSTRMNTTION ELC COR (PA)
2222 W 42nd St (79764-6305)
PHONE...............................432 368-7827
Ronnie Hobbs, *President*
Rickey Richters, *Superintendent*
Shanon Davis, *Vice Pres*
Bob Dawson, *Vice Pres*
Israel Ramirez, *Vice Pres*
EMP: 65 **EST:** 2009
SALES (est): 26.6MM **Privately Held**
WEB: www.lonestarcorporation.com
SIC: 3699 Electrical equipment & supplies

(G-16066)
LWF SERVICES LLC
11231 W County Road 127 (79765-9413)
P.O. Box 14993 (79768-4993)
PHONE...............................432 425-9795
Jeffrey Lawson, *Mng Member*
EMP: 10 **EST:** 2013
SALES (est): 1.1MM **Privately Held**
WEB: www.lwfservices.com
SIC: 7692 Welding repair

(G-16067)
M TRIPPLE OIL TOOL INC
8317 Andrews Hwy (79765-2828)
P.O. Box 13090 (79768-3090)
PHONE...............................432 337-1452

Michael D Olliff, *President*
Joshua Olliff, *Vice Pres*
Kevin Skalenda, *QC Mgr*
Richard Regester, *Sales Staff*
Anita Kelly, *Admin Sec*
EMP: 26
SQ FT: 17,000
SALES (est): 5.1MM **Privately Held**
WEB: www.tripplem.com
SIC: 3069 7699 Hard rubber & molded rubber products; industrial equipment services

(G-16068)
MACHINE TECH SERVICES INC
Also Called: Production Pump
3831 Nw Loop 338 (79764-3124)
PHONE.................................432 385-0891
David Barrow, *Branch Mgr*
EMP: 9 **Privately Held**
WEB: www.westechmachine.com
SIC: 3599 Machine shop, jobbing & repair
PA: Machine Tech Services Inc
2708 25th St
Snyder TX 79549

(G-16069)
MADDEN SYSTEMS INC
1801 E Pearl St (79761-5647)
PHONE.................................432 332-0255
Fax: 432 332-6541
EMP: 16
SQ FT: 12,000
SALES (est): 1.2MM **Privately Held**
SIC: 1389 3829 Oil Well Logging Service Mfg Geophysical Measuring Equipment

(G-16070)
MARKCO MACHINE WORKS INC (PA)
6501 Golder Ave (79764-2831)
P.O. Box 12165 (79768-2165)
PHONE.................................432 362-8921
Marquis Taliaferro, *CEO*
Mark E Taliaserro III, *President*
Kenneth L M Taliaserro, *Corp Secy*
Michael Taliaferro, *Vice Pres*
EMP: 22
SQ FT: 22,000
SALES (est): 3.8MM **Privately Held**
WEB: www.markcomachine.com
SIC: 3533 7699 Oil field machinery & equipment; industrial machinery & equipment repair

(G-16071)
MARTELS MACHINE SHOP
330 S Grandview Ave (79761-5622)
PHONE.................................432 333-4556
Maxie Hodges, *Owner*
EMP: 9
SQ FT: 8,000
SALES (est): 1MM **Privately Held**
WEB: www.martelsmachine.com
SIC: 3599 7692 Machine shop, jobbing & repair; welding repair

(G-16072)
MARTIN RESOURCE MGT CORP
7589 W Murphy St (79763)
P.O. Box 3704 (79760-3704)
PHONE.................................432 381-0271
Dale Langston, *Manager*
EMP: 18
SALES (corp-wide): 1.6B **Privately Held**
WEB: www.themartincompanies.com
SIC: 2819 2874 Nonmetallic compounds; phosphatic fertilizers
PA: Martin Resource Management Corporation
4200 Stone Rd
Kilgore TX 75662
903 983-6200

(G-16073)
MASON FENCING AND CNSTR LLC
Also Called: New Horizons Landscape MGT
400 S Grandview Ave (79761-5736)
PHONE.................................432 272-8347
Dalton Mason, *CEO*
EMP: 22

SALES (est): 607.2K **Privately Held**
SIC: 0781 0782 3271 1799 Landscape services; landscape contractors; blocks, concrete: landscape or retaining wall; fence construction; concrete construction: roads, highways, sidewalks, etc.

(G-16074)
MAXIE HODGES
Also Called: Martel's Machine Shop
330 S Grandview Ave (79761-5622)
PHONE.................................432 333-4556
Maxie Hodges, *Owner*
Kenny Hodges, *General Mgr*
EMP: 9
SALES (est): 1MM **Privately Held**
SIC: 3599 7692 Machine shop, jobbing & repair; welding repair

(G-16075)
MAYFIELD PAPER COMPANY INC
2321 E 2nd St (79761-4911)
PHONE.................................432 580-4118
Steve Lawlis, *Manager*
EMP: 17
SQ FT: 28,520
SALES (corp-wide): 76.8MM **Privately Held**
WEB: www.mayfieldpaper.com
SIC: 2679 Paper products, converted
PA: Mayfield Paper Company, Inc.
1115 S Hill St
San Angelo TX 76903
325 653-1444

(G-16076)
MC CRELESS COMPANY (PA)
1318 N Grant Ave (79761-3897)
PHONE.................................432 332-1213
John Patton, *Principal*
Anita Price, *Office Mgr*
EMP: 10 **EST:** 1946
SQ FT: 3,500
SALES (est): 1.4MM **Privately Held**
WEB: www.mccrelessco.com
SIC: 2759 7389 5199 2396 Screen printing; laminating service; engraving service; advertising specialties; automotive & apparel trimmings

(G-16077)
MCCLINTON ENERGY GROUP L L C (PA)
11200 W Interstate 20 (79765-2501)
P.O. Box 15110 (79768-5110)
PHONE.................................432 563-5500
Tony McClinton, *Mng Member*
EMP: 20 **EST:** 2011
SALES (est): 67.3MM **Privately Held**
WEB: www.mcclintonenergy.com
SIC: 1381 3351 Drilling oil & gas wells; tubing, copper & copper alloy

(G-16078)
MEISTER INDUSTRIES INC (PA)
Also Called: Longhorn Custom Coating
2301 W 42nd St (79764-6308)
P.O. Box 4693 (79760-4693)
PHONE.................................432 366-2875
Charlene Meister, *President*
EMP: 20
SQ FT: 20,000
SALES (est): 4.3MM **Privately Held**
WEB: www.longhorncustomcoating.com
SIC: 3479 3353 Coating of metals with plastic or resins; aluminum sheet, plate & foil

(G-16079)
MEISTER INDUSTRIES INC
Also Called: Longhorn Custom Coating
4021 Rasco Ave (79764-6541)
P.O. Box 4693 (79760-4693)
PHONE.................................432 425-0293
Joe Brainco, *Manager*
EMP: 30
SQ FT: 17,480
SALES (corp-wide): 4.3MM **Privately Held**
WEB: www.longhorncustomcoating.com
SIC: 3479 Coating of metals & formed products

PA: Meister Industries, Inc.
2301 W 42nd St
Odessa TX 79764
432 366-2875

(G-16080)
MELCO BLOWOUT PREVENTER SPC (PA)
4001 W County Rd (79764)
PHONE.................................432 362-0491
Kenneth L Burns II, *President*
EMP: 9
SQ FT: 10,000
SALES (est): 714.2K **Privately Held**
SIC: 3533 Oil field machinery & equipment

(G-16081)
METAL SPECIALTIES INC (PA)
3345 Kermit Hwy (79764-6424)
P.O. Box 69072 (79769-0072)
PHONE.................................432 332-8762
Bill Roberson, *President*
Danny Walker, *Vice Pres*
Tommy Woodall, *Vice Pres*
Betsy Rhodes, *Treasurer*
EMP: 27
SQ FT: 22,000
SALES (est): 5.1MM **Privately Held**
WEB: www.metalspecialtiesinc.com
SIC: 3444 Sheet metalwork

(G-16082)
MIDCO MACHINE
11228 W County Road 127 (79765-9413)
P.O. Box 61243, Midland (79711-1243)
PHONE.................................432 563-2010
Steve Holcomb, *Owner*
Judy Holcomb, *Manager*
EMP: 12
SQ FT: 9,000
SALES (est): 1.7MM **Privately Held**
WEB: www.midcomachine.com
SIC: 3599 Machine shop, jobbing & repair

(G-16083)
MORGAN KINDER TREATING LP
Also Called: Southtex Treaters
13405 E Highway 191 (79765-8512)
P.O. Box 60480, Midland (79711-0480)
PHONE.................................432 563-2766
Alan Hill, *Mfg Staff*
Nader Khaki, *Purchasing*
EMP: 10 **Publicly Held**
WEB: www.kindermorgantreating.com
SIC: 1311 1321 4922 Crude petroleum & natural gas production; natural gas production; fractionating natural gas liquids; pipelines, natural gas
HQ: Morgan Kinder Treating Lp
407 Holt Rd
Victoria TX 77905
361 578-1312

(G-16084)
MSA INDUSTRIES INC
2742 W Interstate 20 (79763-5105)
P.O. Box 2786 (79760-2786)
PHONE.................................432 337-6062
Michael S Ashton, *President*
Ashton Dana, *Vice Pres*
EMP: 16
SQ FT: 2,000
SALES (est): 1.5MM **Privately Held**
SIC: 1389 3471 Oil field services; plating & polishing

(G-16085)
NABORS DRILLING TECH USA INC
2500 Oregon St (79764-1711)
PHONE.................................281 874-0035
Richard Zartler, *Branch Mgr*
EMP: 111 **Privately Held**
WEB: www.nabors.com
SIC: 1389 Oil field services
HQ: Nabors Drilling Technologies Usa, Inc.
515 W Greens Rd Ste 1200
Houston TX 77067
281 874-0035

(G-16086)
NALCO CHAMPION WELLCHEM
6601 Trunk St (79762-8531)
PHONE.................................432 366-0971
EMP: 10

SALES (est): 439.6K **Privately Held**
SIC: 1389 Oil field services

(G-16087)
NATIONAL OILWELL VARCO INC
1901 W 2nd St (79763-4407)
P.O. Box 69940 (79769-0940)
PHONE.................................432 333-4196
Randy Raglin, *Manager*
EMP: 15
SQ FT: 19,140
SALES (corp-wide): 8.4B **Publicly Held**
WEB: www.nov.com
SIC: 1389 Oil field services
PA: National Oilwell Varco, Inc.
7909 Parkwood Circle Dr
Houston TX 77036
713 346-7500

(G-16088)
NATIONAL OILWELL VARCO INC
2040 Oregon St (79764-1819)
PHONE.................................432 528-4354
Chris Price, *Manager*
EMP: 30
SALES (corp-wide): 8.4B **Publicly Held**
WEB: www.nov.com
SIC: 1389 Oil field services
PA: National Oilwell Varco, Inc.
7909 Parkwood Circle Dr
Houston TX 77036
713 346-7500

(G-16089)
NATIONAL OILWELL VARCO INC
7636 Hwy 80 (79765)
PHONE.................................432 563-2150
Art Lowry, *Vice Pres*
EMP: 12
SALES (corp-wide): 8.4B **Publicly Held**
WEB: www.nov.com
SIC: 1389 Oil field services
PA: National Oilwell Varco, Inc.
7909 Parkwood Circle Dr
Houston TX 77036
713 346-7500

(G-16090)
NATIONAL OILWELL VARCO INC
10720 W Interstate 20 (79765-9415)
P.O. Box 69208 (79769-0208)
PHONE.................................432 381-4111
Mark Bennett, *Manager*
Cory Frasier, *Info Tech Mgr*
EMP: 13
SALES (corp-wide): 8.4B **Publicly Held**
WEB: www.nov.com
SIC: 5084 3533 Petroleum industry machinery; oil & gas field machinery
PA: National Oilwell Varco, Inc.
7909 Parkwood Circle Dr
Houston TX 77036
713 346-7500

(G-16091)
NATIONAL OILWELL VARCO INC
83 Groening St (79765)
PHONE.................................432 563-1173
Daniel Cole, *Opers Mgr*
Darla Rippe, *Office Mgr*
EMP: 32
SALES (corp-wide): 8.4B **Publicly Held**
WEB: www.nov.com
SIC: 3533 Oil & gas field machinery
PA: National Oilwell Varco, Inc.
7909 Parkwood Circle Dr
Houston TX 77036
713 346-7500

(G-16092)
NAVARRETE INDUSTRIES LLC
2300 E Murphy St (79761-5809)
P.O. Box 13982 (79768-3982)
PHONE.................................432 332-0272
Isaiah Navarrete,
EMP: 17 **EST:** 2008
SALES (est): 950K **Privately Held**
SIC: 3999 Manufacturing industries

(G-16093)
NIPCO INC (PA)
2104 W 42nd St (79764-6303)
P.O. Box 69240 (79769-0240)
PHONE..432 362-1936
Dean Fields, *President*
Brent Fields, *Vice Pres*
EMP: 15
SQ FT: 6,000
SALES (est): 3.3MM **Privately Held**
SIC: 3479 7389 Coating of metals with
plastic or resins; personal service agents,
brokers & bureaus

(G-16094)
O F M PUMP INC
2243 N Fm 1936 (79763-5976)
P.O. Box 12192 (79768-2192)
PHONE..432 381-7390
Larry Gorrell, *President*
Larry Rackley, *Admin Sec*
▲ EMP: 20
SQ FT: 15,000
SALES (est): 3.7MM **Privately Held**
WEB: www.ofmpump.net
SIC: 3561 7699 Pumps, oil well & field;
pumps & pumping equipment repair

(G-16095)
ODESSA BABBITT BEARING
COMPANY
6112 N County Rd W (79764-3497)
P.O. Box 7178 (79760-7178)
PHONE..432 366-2836
Ray Holdridge, *CEO*
Greg Masters, *General Mgr*
EMP: 39
SALES (corp-wide): 15.3MM **Privately**
Held
WEB: www.obbco.com
SIC: 3568 5085 Bearings, plain; industrial
supplies
HQ: Odessa Babbitt Bearing Company
3205 Kermit Hwy
Odessa TX 79764
432 337-5341

(G-16096)
ODESSA JPK INVESTMENTS
LTD
Also Called: Penatek
6830 E Business 20 (79762-5405)
P.O. Box 15037 (79768-5037)
PHONE..432 368-0888
Seth Langford, *Mng Member*
Greta Rigney, *Admin Asst*
EMP: 50
SQ FT: 1,575
SALES (est): 1MM
SALES (corp-wide): 7.4MM **Privately**
Held
WEB: www.penatek.com
SIC: 3366 Copper foundries
PA: H & T Auger Company
4519 Brazos Ave
Odessa TX 79764
432 362-4471

(G-16097)
ODESSA SEPARATOR INC (PA)
1001 E Pearl St (79761-5667)
PHONE..432 580-7111
Bert Frost, *Ch of Bd*
Mark Lowe, *President*
Dan Culbertson, *Vice Pres*
William Davidson, *Manager*
Cavin Frost, *Director*
EMP: 40
SQ FT: 25,000
SALES (est): 18.2MM **Privately Held**
WEB: www.odessaseparator.com
SIC: 5082 3533 Oil field equipment; oil &
gas field machinery

(G-16098)
ODESSA TORTILLA & TAMALE
FCTRY
Also Called: Manuels Tortilla Tamale Fctry
1915 E 2nd St (79761-5311)
PHONE..432 332-6676
Manuel Gonsalez III, *President*
Evelyn Gonzalez, *Vice Pres*
EMP: 20
SQ FT: 6,000

SALES (est): 3MM **Privately Held**
WEB: www.manuelstamales.com
SIC: 2099 2032 2096 Tortillas, fresh or refrigerated; tamales: packaged in cans,
jars, etc.; tortilla chips

(G-16099)
OIL COUNTRY
MANUFACTURING INC
13400 W Highway 80 E (79765-5000)
PHONE..432 563-8014
Bernard Duroc-Danner, *President*
Klusmeyer J C, *Vice Pres*
Scott Caruthers, *Manager*
EMP: 30
SQ FT: 10,000
SALES (est): 4.3MM **Privately Held**
SIC: 5084 7699 3533 Oil well machinery,
equipment & supplies; industrial machin-
ery & equipment repair; oil field machin-
ery & equipment
PA: Weatherford International Public Lim-
ited Company
70 Sir John Rogerson's Quay
Dublin

(G-16100)
OILFIELD SERVICES & TECH
LLC
Also Called: Ofs International
3333 Brazos Ave (79764-6553)
PHONE..432 614-0076
Doug Dunford, *Branch Mgr*
EMP: 30
SALES (corp-wide): 14.8MM **Privately**
Held
WEB: www.ofsint.com
SIC: 3533 2813 Oil & gas drilling rigs &
equipment; industrial gases
PA: Oilfield Services & Technologies, Llc
7735 Miller Road 3
Houston TX 77049
281 452-3036

(G-16101)
OILWELL HYDRAULICS INC (PA)
1460 Windway (79763-4912)
PHONE..432 334-8580
Melvin E Kelly, *Co-President*
Terry Kelly, *Co-President*
Doug Herrom, *Vice Pres*
▲ EMP: 11
SQ FT: 16,000
SALES (est): 3.8MM **Privately Held**
SIC: 3561 5084 Pumps, oil well & field; in-
dustrial machinery & equipment

(G-16102)
OPERATIONS ROD PERMIAN L C
9009 N County Rd W (79764-1214)
P.O. Box 12907 (79768-2907)
PHONE..432 367-4149
Fred N Huston, *President*
David Omachel, *Sales Staff*
EMP: 22
SALES (est): 1.9MM **Privately Held**
WEB: www.permianrod.com
SIC: 1389 Oil field services

(G-16103)
ORION PACIFIC INC (HQ)
2525 E Pearl St (79761-5912)
P.O. Box 4148 (79760-4148)
PHONE..432 332-0058
Nicholas J Fowler, *President*
J Allen Chaffee, *Corp Secy*
Michael M Fowler, *Vice Pres*
Dan Carpenter, *CFO*
▼ EMP: 60
SQ FT: 101,000
SALES (est): 13.2MM
SALES (corp-wide): 13.9MM **Privately**
Held
SIC: 2671 Plastic film, coated or laminated
for packaging
PA: Madison Minerals Corporation
712 Main St Ste 1700
Houston TX
713 223-5730

(G-16104)
ORREX PLASTICS COMPANY
LLC (PA)
Also Called: Orion Orrex
2800 S Orrex Ave (79766-9106)
P.O. Box 4269 (79760-4269)
PHONE..432 332-1229
Blake Batte, *CEO*
Michael M Fowler, *President*
Nicholas J Fowler, *Vice Pres*
Ralph Santana, *Plant Mgr*
Eric Ilang-Ilang, *Opers Mgr*
▲ EMP: 24 EST: 1997
SALES (est): 8.2MM **Privately Held**
WEB: www.orrex.com
SIC: 2671 3087 2891 Plastic film, coated
or laminated for packaging; custom com-
pound purchased resins; adhesives &
sealants

(G-16105)
OVERLAND TANK INC
2700 E Interstate 20 (79766-8850)
P.O. Box 2080, Abilene (79604-2080)
PHONE..325 673-7132
Jerry Rush, *President*
Jana Rush, *Vice Pres*
Kyle Davis, *Parts Mgr*
Betty Atkins, *CFO*
David Foster, *Manager*
EMP: 50
SQ FT: 45,000
SALES (est): 9.2MM **Privately Held**
WEB: www.rushoverland.com
SIC: 3537 Industrial trucks & tractors

(G-16106)
PB MATERIALS HOLDINGS INC
(PA)
4001 E 42nd St Ste 100 (79762-5931)
PHONE..432 563-8036
Dave L Vickers, *CEO*
Mike Gilchrist, *Principal*
Jeremy House, *Principal*
Casey Harrington, *Sales Staff*
Taylor Warren, *Manager*
EMP: 37 EST: 2013
SALES (est): 26.1MM **Privately Held**
WEB: www.pb-materials.com
SIC: 3272 1442 1411 Concrete products;
construction sand & gravel; limestone &
marble dimension stone

(G-16107)
PBP FABRICATION INC
1117 S Tripp Ave (79763-8604)
PHONE..432 381-5542
Joe URT, *President*
James R Hurt, *Corp Secy*
David Perry, *Engineer*
Tanya McGehee, *Accounting Mgr*
Sherry Hurt, *Admin Sec*
EMP: 26
SQ FT: 32,000
SALES (est): 7.9MM **Privately Held**
WEB: www.pbpfab.com
SIC: 3533 Oil field machinery & equipment

(G-16108)
PCS FERGUSON INC
Also Called: Apergy
1460 W Interstate 20 (79763-4908)
PHONE..432 334-8580
Rudy Rodriguez, *Manager*
EMP: 20
SALES (corp-wide): 1.1B **Publicly Held**
WEB: www.apergyals.com
SIC: 3561 Industrial pumps & parts
HQ: Pcs Ferguson, Inc.
3771 Eureka Way
Frederick CO 80516
720 407-3550

(G-16109)
PENATEK LLC
6830 Cargo Rd (79762)
P.O. Box 15037 (79768-5037)
PHONE..432 368-0888
EMP: 28
SALES (est): 1.4MM **Privately Held**
SIC: 3559 Mfg Misc Industry Machinery

(G-16110)
PENATEK FOUNDRY &
MACHINING
6830 E Business 20 (79762-5405)
P.O. Box 15037 (79768-5037)
PHONE..432 368-0888
Jim Reese, *Principal*
Guy Hodges, *Vice Pres*
Oscar Velasco, *Vice Pres*
Greta Rigney, *CFO*
EMP: 30
SQ FT: 20,000
SALES (est): 500K **Privately Held**
WEB: www.penatek.com
SIC: 3325 Steel foundries

(G-16111)
PERMIAN ANCHORS INC
4915 S County Road 1303 (79765-9641)
P.O. Box 12238 (79768-2238)
PHONE..432 563-0205
Steven Herriage, *Owner*
Sylvia Herriage, *Vice Pres*
EMP: 21
SQ FT: 4,000
SALES (est): 1.8MM **Privately Held**
WEB: www.permiananchors.com
SIC: 1389 Oil field services

(G-16112)
PERMIAN BASIN DERRICK SVCS
LP
1532 S Redondo Ave (79763-8726)
P.O. Box 69172 (79769-0172)
PHONE..432 332-2315
Santos Quintels, *President*
EMP: 9
SQ FT: 12,000
SALES (est): 3MM **Privately Held**
WEB: www.permianservices.com
SIC: 1389 Construction, repair & disman-
tling services

(G-16113)
PERMIAN BASIN EQP & SUP
LLC
4 Casa Loma (79765-8954)
PHONE..432 563-1044
Calvin J Poindexter Jr, *Mng Member*
EMP: 22 EST: 2008
SALES (est): 5.5MM **Privately Held**
SIC: 2111 3999 Cigarettes; cigarette &
cigar products & accessories

(G-16114)
PERMIAN BASIN MATERIALS
LLC (PA)
Also Called: Crockett County Mining
4001 E 42nd St Ste 100 (79762-5931)
P.O. Box 14168 (79768-4168)
PHONE..432 614-6201
Jeremy House, *President*
EMP: 43
SALES (est): 37.4MM **Privately Held**
SIC: 1442 Construction sand & gravel

(G-16115)
PERMIAN BSIN HMES LAND
MAG LLC
865 Power Dr (79761)
P.O. Box 14395, Mill Creek WA (98082-
2395)
PHONE..737 256-0799
Johnathan Venable, *Partner*
Sean M McKinley,
EMP: 12
SALES (est): 250K **Privately Held**
WEB: www.store.printmaniac.com
SIC: 2721 Magazines: publishing & printing

(G-16116)
PERMIAN ENTERPRISES LTD
2121 W Murphy St (79763-4810)
PHONE..432 332-0903
Jack Wood, *Partner*
Don Wood, *General Ptnr*
Tammy Crawford, *CFO*
Chris Holcomb, *Sales Staff*
Raymond Marrero, *Director*
EMP: 45
SQ FT: 12,000
SALES (est): 18.6MM **Privately Held**
WEB: www.permianenterprises.com
SIC: 3317 Steel pipe & tubes

(G-16117)
PERMIAN H2O SOLUTIONS LLC (PA)
875 Central Dr Ste 7a (79761-4242)
P.O. Box 13235 (79768-3235)
PHONE................................432 214-4520
Wesley Hudnall, *Mng Member*
EMP: 13
SALES (est): 2MM **Privately Held**
SIC: 7699 1381 Pumps & pumping equipment repair; service well drilling

(G-16118)
PERMIAN TANK & MFG INC
8800 Nw Loop 338 (79764-3005)
PHONE................................432 550-7317
Glen Womack, *Branch Mgr*
EMP: 52
SALES (corp-wide): 99.4MM **Privately Held**
WEB: www.permiantank.com
SIC: 3443 Tanks, standard or custom fabricated: metal plate; vessels, process or storage (from boiler shops): metal plate
PA: Permian Tank & Manufacturing, Inc.
2701 W Interstate 20
Odessa TX 79766
432 580-1050

(G-16119)
PERMIAN TANK & MFG INC (PA)
2701 W Interstate 20 (79766-9102)
P.O. Box 4456 (79760-4456)
PHONE................................432 580-1050
Jon Cohen, *Principal*
Arturo Luna, *Prdtn Mgr*
David Allen, *Sales Staff*
Alice Womack, *Shareholder*
Joe Lucas, *Administration*
EMP: 60
SQ FT: 200,000
SALES (est): 99.4MM **Privately Held**
WEB: www.permiantank.com
SIC: 3443 Tanks, standard or custom fabricated: metal plate; vessels, process or storage (from boiler shops): metal plate

(G-16120)
PETRO MECHANICAL SERVICES LLC
Also Called: Petro Mechanical Supply
2451 N Fm 1936 (79763-5930)
P.O. Box 9083, Longview (75608-9083)
PHONE................................800 727-1398
Danny Watkins, *President*
Mark Fischer, *Treasurer*
Katherine Weir, *Administration*
EMP: 75
SALES (est): 2MM **Privately Held**
WEB: www.petroms.com
SIC: 1389 Servicing oil & gas wells

(G-16121)
PETROPLEX CABINETS INC
2710 Henderson Ave (79764-7440)
P.O. Box 12848 (79768-2848)
PHONE................................432 333-2025
Larry K Crawford, *President*
Larry Crawford, *President*
EMP: 9
SQ FT: 7,500
SALES (est): 584.1K **Privately Held**
SIC: 2434 2521 5712 2431 Wood kitchen cabinets; wood office furniture; furniture stores; millwork

(G-16122)
PHEASANT RUBBER COMPANY INC
2426 W 40th St (79764-6506)
PHONE................................432 367-5137
Edward Davis, *CEO*
Bonnie Eason, *Corp Secy*
Harold Ed Davis, *Director*
EMP: 12
SQ FT: 8,000
SALES (est): 1.7MM **Privately Held**
WEB: www.pheasantrubber.com
SIC: 3069 3544 Molded rubber products; special dies, tools, jigs & fixtures

(G-16123)
PLANK COATINGS INC
4103 N Tripp Ave (79764-8890)
P.O. Box 889 (79760-0889)
PHONE................................432 530-1234
David Plank, *President*
Agustin Ulate, *Vice Pres*
Agustine Ulate, *Vice Pres*
Augustine Ulate, *Vice Pres*
Justino Ulate, *Vice Pres*
EMP: 12 **EST:** 1964
SALES (est): 1MM **Privately Held**
SIC: 1389 Oil field services

(G-16124)
PRECISION COATINGS
9019 N County Rd W (79764-1214)
PHONE................................432 362-7696
Tony Branco, *President*
EMP: 11
SALES (est): 1.6MM **Privately Held**
WEB: www.precision-coatingss.com
SIC: 3479 Coating of metals & formed products

(G-16125)
PRECISION FLOW INC
1609 W 2nd St (79763-4322)
P.O. Box 7137 (79760-7137)
PHONE................................432 332-0266
David Baussoudt, *Manager*
EMP: 16
SQ FT: 20,051
SALES (corp-wide): 6.5MM **Privately Held**
WEB: www.precisionflowinc.com
SIC: 3823 On-stream gas/liquid analysis instruments, industrial
PA: Precision Flow, Inc.
725 N Avenue E
Odessa TX 79763
432 381-5131

(G-16126)
PRO INSPECTION INC
6975 E Commerce St (79762-9732)
P.O. Box 12908 (79768-2908)
PHONE................................432 362-2247
Fred O Wilson III, *President*
Loretta Burge, *Corp Secy*
Mike Wilson, *Vice Pres*
EMP: 10
SQ FT: 7,200
SALES (est): 1.4MM **Privately Held**
WEB: www.proiss.com
SIC: 1389 Oil field services; pipe testing, oil field service

(G-16127)
PROGRESSIVE SALES INC (PA)
1201 S County Rd W (79763-5015)
PHONE................................432 333-6631
Craig Winborn, *President*
Donna Winborn, *Vice Pres*
▲ **EMP:** 27
SQ FT: 4,000
SALES (est): 10.6MM **Privately Held**
WEB: www.progressive-salesinc.com
SIC: 5085 5561 3792 3537 Valves & fittings; recreational vehicle dealers; travel trailers & campers; industrial trucks & tractors; miscellaneous fabricated wire products; valves & pipe fittings

(G-16128)
QUALI-TEX BALL & SEAT CO
3300 N Fm 1936 (79764-8609)
P.O. Box 70410 (79769-1410)
PHONE................................432 332-3755
Jerry Anderson, *President*
Lynette Anderson, *Corp Secy*
JD Anderson, *Vice Pres*
▼ **EMP:** 20 **EST:** 2010
SALES (est): 4.4MM **Privately Held**
WEB: www.qualitexballandseat.com
SIC: 3533 Oil field machinery & equipment

(G-16129)
R B TESTERS INC (PA)
8705 N County Rd W (79764-1953)
P.O. Box 3005 (79760-3005)
PHONE................................432 582-2500
Roy Bobbitt, *President*
EMP: 18
SQ FT: 3,000

SALES (est): 2.5MM **Privately Held**
WEB: www.rbtesters.com
SIC: 1389 Pipe testing, oil field service

(G-16130)
R3 ENERGY SERVICES LLC
Also Called: R3 Edge
5075 E 52nd St Apt A204 (79762-5180)
PHONE................................432 335-7800
EMP: 10
SALES: 3MM **Privately Held**
SIC: 3533 Mfg Oil/Gas Field Machinery

(G-16131)
RACK INDUSTRIES LLC
701 W Murphy St (79763-4639)
P.O. Box 53051, Midland (79710-3051)
PHONE................................432 687-1868
Karla Tucker, *President*
George Kiker, *COO*
Kahla Kiker, *CFO*
EMP: 55
SALES (est): 22.8MM **Privately Held**
WEB: www.rackindustriestx.com
SIC: 3443 Fabricated plate work (boiler shop)

(G-16132)
RAMA FABRICATION INC (PA)
2310 Prospect (79762-5463)
P.O. Box 7346 (79760-7346)
PHONE................................432 362-9291
Ronald D Rains, *CEO*
Sonny Walters, *President*
John Haug, *Engineer*
Bill Bowden, *Admin Sec*
EMP: 20
SQ FT: 35,000
SALES (est): 3.1MM **Privately Held**
WEB: www.intertreat.com
SIC: 3533 7699 Oil field machinery & equipment; industrial equipment services

(G-16133)
RAPID SERVICE INC (PA)
Also Called: Campbell Testing Company
2724 W 40th St (79764-6552)
P.O. Box 4356 (79760-4356)
PHONE................................432 367-7283
Tom C Campbell, *President*
Paul Campbell, *Vice Pres*
EMP: 10
SQ FT: 5,000
SALES (est): 1.6MM **Privately Held**
SIC: 1389 Pipe testing, oil field service

(G-16134)
REDI SERVICES
8001 E Interstate 20 (79765-9450)
PHONE................................432 272-1583
Joel Wiedrich, *General Mgr*
EMP: 30
SALES (est): 811.4K **Privately Held**
WEB: www.rediservicesllc.com
SIC: 1389 Oil field services

(G-16135)
REED FIBERGLASS INC
102 Reed Ave (79761-5917)
PHONE................................432 332-8265
Rhonda L Reed, *President*
Guy Reed, *Corp Secy*
Matt Reed, *Vice Pres*
EMP: 10
SQ FT: 33,000
SALES (est): 800K **Privately Held**
WEB: www.reedfiberglass.com
SIC: 5999 3089 Fiberglass materials, except insulation; fiber, vulcanized

(G-16136)
RELENTLESS OILFIELD SVCS LLC
12165 W Drvers Hall Of Fa (79763-8304)
PHONE................................432 242-1160
Juan Rodriguez, *CEO*
EMP: 12
SALES (est): 600K **Privately Held**
WEB: www.relentlessoilfieldservices.com
SIC: 1389 Haulage, oil field

(G-16137)
REXTAC LLC (PA)
2501 S Grandview Ave (79766-9169)
P.O. Box 4148 (79760-4148)
PHONE................................432 332-0058

Greg Davis, *Plant Mgr*
Elizabeth Aldrich, *Export Mgr*
Karina O Hernandez, *Purch Mgr*
Rogelio Mota, *Purchasing*
Chris Gerstner, *Engineer*
◆ **EMP:** 117
SALES (est): 65MM **Privately Held**
WEB: www.rextac.com
SIC: 2671 Plastic film, coated or laminated for packaging

(G-16138)
RFC DRILLING LLC
6001 W Murphy St (79763-7557)
PHONE................................432 276-3505
Gary Holley, *President*
Eric Dowden, *Manager*
EMP: 115
SQ FT: 3,300
SALES (est): 243.4K
SALES (corp-wide): 298.1MM **Privately Held**
WEB: www.rfcdrilling.com
SIC: 1381 Drilling oil & gas wells
PA: Republic Financial Corporation
5251 Dtc Pkwy Ste 300
Greenwood Village CO 80111
303 751-3501

(G-16139)
RIG TECHNOLOGY INC
4422 Johnson Rd (79764-3883)
P.O. Box 446, Brownwood (76804-0446)
PHONE................................432 362-2789
Michael D Hamilton, *President*
Michael Hamilton, *President*
Karen Hamilton, *Corp Secy*
EMP: 50
SALES (est): 8.8MM **Privately Held**
SIC: 1389 Oil field services

(G-16140)
RIG WORKS INC
2310 Steven Rd (79764-1827)
PHONE................................432 366-4501
John W Brake, *President*
Jennifer Brake, *Corp Secy*
▼ **EMP:** 12
SALES (est): 476.3K **Privately Held**
WEB: www.rig-works.com
SIC: 3533 Drilling tools for gas, oil or water wells

(G-16141)
RILEY INDUSTRIAL SERVICES INC
1251 Oibc Dr (79766)
PHONE................................432 332-9630
Keith Jones, *Manager*
EMP: 25
SALES (corp-wide): 28.6MM **Privately Held**
WEB: www.rileyindustrial.com
SIC: 1629 1721 3471 Blasting contractor, except building demolition; exterior commercial painting contractor; sand blasting of metal parts
PA: Riley Industrial Services, Inc.
2615 San Juan Blvd
Farmington NM 87401
505 327-4947

(G-16142)
RITCHIE-VINCENT INC (PA)
Also Called: Images Ink
301 S Lincoln Ave (79761-6220)
P.O. Box 7545 (79760-7545)
PHONE................................432 337-5133
Phillip Vincent, *President*
EMP: 10
SQ FT: 1,200
SALES (est): 13.7MM **Privately Held**
SIC: 2261 2396 Screen printing of cotton broadwoven fabrics; automotive & apparel trimmings

(G-16143)
ROUNDHOUSE ELC & EQP CO INC
2224 S Grandview Ave (79766-9100)
P.O. Box 1232 (79760-1232)
PHONE................................432 333-3923
Gene Abbott, *President*
Armando Gonzales, *VP Sales*
EMP: 13

SALES (est): 2MM **Privately Held**
WEB: www.roundhouseelectric.com
SIC: 7629 7694 5063 Generator repair;
electric motor repair; motors, electric

(G-16144)
ROYWELL LLC
2425 E Interstate 20 (79766-8828)
PHONE....................................432 332-0703
Greg Badgett, *Branch Mgr*
EMP: 20
SALES (corp-wide): 7.8MM **Privately
Held**
WEB: www.roywell.com
SIC: 1389 Oil field services
HQ: Roywell Llc
1600 Highway 6 Ste 220
Sugar Land TX 77478
713 661-4747

(G-16145)
RUSH SALES COMPANY
Also Called: Rush Overland Manufacturing
2700 E I 20 Service Rd (79766)
P.O. Box 2488 (79760-2488)
PHONE....................................432 337-2397
Jim Poer, *CEO*
Chad Spooner, *President*
Herman Adams, *COO*
Jana Rush, *Vice Pres*
Russell Battenfield, *Foreman/Supr*
◆ EMP: 220
SQ FT: 46,000
SALES (est): 67.3MM **Privately Held**
WEB: www.rushoverland.com
SIC: 3533 5511 Oil field machinery &
equipment; new & used car dealers

(G-16146)
RWLS LLC
Also Called: Renegade Wireline Services
2811 E Pearl St (79761-5902)
PHONE....................................432 664-0020
Tony Ibarra, *Branch Mgr*
EMP: 49
SALES (corp-wide): 25.9MM **Privately
Held**
WEB: www.renegadewls.com
SIC: 1389 Oil field services
PA: Rwls, Llc
14 Crockett Cir
Levelland TX 79336
806 897-0231

(G-16147)
S O A PUMP & SUPPLY INC
3361 Nw Loop 338 (79764-3114)
P.O. Box 69806 (79769-0806)
PHONE....................................432 381-2380
Freddy G Arocha, *President*
Marcus Sailler, *Principal*
Terry Osteen, *Vice Pres*
EMP: 10
SQ FT: 22,800
SALES (est): 2.6MM **Privately Held**
WEB: www.don-nan.com
SIC: 1389 Oil field services

(G-16148)
S Q I INC
Also Called: Southwestern Machine Products
820 W 83rd St (79764-1916)
P.O. Box 12262 (79768-2262)
PHONE....................................432 366-9264
Bill Nyborg, *President*
Tracey Nyborg, *Treasurer*
Mike Trogden, *Sales Staff*
EMP: 15
SQ FT: 16,000
SALES (est): 6MM **Privately Held**
WEB: www.stabilizer.com
SIC: 3533 3545 Bits, oil & gas field tools:
rock; machine tool accessories

(G-16149)
SANBAR BALLS & SEATS INC
3300 N Fm 1936 (79764-8609)
P.O. Box 70410 (79769-1410)
PHONE....................................432 332-3755
Jerry Anderson, *President*
Cypert Dennie, *Vice Pres*
Bennie Haiduk, *Vice Pres*
EMP: 12
SQ FT: 7,500

SALES (est): 990K **Privately Held**
WEB: www.qualitexballandseat.com
SIC: 2531 3561 Seats, miscellaneous
public conveyances; pumps & pumping
equipment

(G-16150)
SAVANNA DRILLING LLC
1500 Windway (79763-4906)
PHONE....................................432 614-1055
William Kosich, *General Mgr*
Elaine Torrie, *Controller*
Daniel Halyk,
Kyle Swingle,
Dan Uresk,
▼ EMP: 13
SALES (est): 628.7K
SALES (corp-wide): 568.8MM **Privately
Held**
WEB: www.savannaenergy.com
SIC: 1381 1389 Drilling oil & gas wells; di-
rectional drilling oil & gas wells; bailing,
cleaning, swabbing & treating of wells
HQ: Savanna Energy Services (U.S.A.)
Corp.
2445 Tech Frest B Ste 200
The Woodlands TX 77381
281 907-4800

(G-16151)
**SENTRY WELLHEAD SYSTEMS
LLC**
11016 E Interstate 20 (79765)
PHONE....................................432 661-5810
David Holder, *Branch Mgr*
EMP: 10
SALES (corp-wide): 13.5MM **Privately
Held**
WEB: www.sentrywellhead.com
SIC: 1389 Oil & gas wells: building, repair-
ing & dismantling
PA: Sentry Wellhead Systems, Llc
1780 Hughes Landing Blvd # 675
Spring TX 77380
281 210-0070

(G-16152)
SHANEDA MACHINE INC
2500 E Pearl St (79761-5911)
PHONE....................................432 333-7083
EMP: 50 EST: 1979
SQ FT: 10,000
SALES (est): 6.3MM **Privately Held**
WEB: www.shaneda.com
SIC: 7699 3599 3339 Pumps & pumping
equipment repair; machine shop, jobbing
& repair; babbitt metal (primary)

(G-16153)
SIVALLS INC (PA)
2200 E 2nd St (79761-4910)
P.O. Box 2792 (79760-2792)
PHONE....................................432 337-3571
S S Latimer, *CEO*
C R Sivalls, *President*
Stephanie S Latimer, *Vice Pres*
William J Lewallen, *Vice Pres*
Roland Tignor, *Project Mgr*
◆ EMP: 100 EST: 1947
SQ FT: 85,000
SALES: 90MM **Privately Held**
WEB: www.sivalls.com
SIC: 3443 5085 Fuel tanks (oil, gas, etc.):
metal plate; valves & fittings

(G-16154)
SLOAN ENERGY SERVICES LLC
4803 Plaza Blvd Ste 802 (79762-4920)
PHONE....................................432 653-0205
Lacie Ann Walters, *Mng Member*
Christopher Walters, *Mng Member*
EMP: 23
SQ FT: 1,000
SALES (est): 5MM **Privately Held**
WEB: www.sloanenergyservices.com
SIC: 1389 Oil field services

(G-16155)
SMCO L & M LP
6600 N County Rd W (79764-2632)
PHONE....................................432 550-7116
Marlin Scott, *Partner*
EMP: 30
SQ FT: 2,400

SALES (est): 2.1MM **Privately Held**
WEB: www.smcotx.com
SIC: 1389 Servicing oil & gas wells

(G-16156)
SMITH INTERNATIONAL INC
Also Called: Smith Bits Division
2120 Maurice Rd (79763-4813)
PHONE....................................432 337-5541
Vance Ford, *Manager*
EMP: 30
SQ FT: 2,544 **Publicly Held**
WEB: www.smithcodevelopment.com
SIC: 1389 Oil field services
HQ: Smith International, Inc.
1310 Rankin Rd
Houston TX 77073
281 443-3370

(G-16157)
SMITH INTERNATIONAL INC
8700 Nw Loop 338 (79764-3004)
P.O. Box 12365 (79768-2365)
PHONE....................................432 550-6909
Danny Renfro, *Branch Mgr*
EMP: 32 **Publicly Held**
WEB: www.smithcodevelopment.com
SIC: 1389 Oil field services
HQ: Smith International, Inc.
1310 Rankin Rd
Houston TX 77073
281 443-3370

(G-16158)
SOUTHTEX TREATERS INC (PA)
13405 E Highway 191 (79765-8512)
P.O. Box 60480, Midland (79711-0480)
PHONE....................................432 563-2766
David C Morrow, *President*
Jerry Holloway, *General Mgr*
Luke Morrow, *Principal*
Paul Morrow, *Principal*
Nader Khaki, *Project Mgr*
EMP: 51
SQ FT: 6,000
SALES (est): 13.7MM **Privately Held**
WEB: www.kindermorgantreating.com
SIC: 2911 Gases & liquefied petroleum
gases

(G-16159)
SPARTAN PUMPS INC
2435 W 42nd St (79764-6310)
PHONE....................................713 858-9887
Kevin Liu, *President*
EMP: 9 EST: 2017
SALES (est): 1.4MM **Privately Held**
WEB: www.spartanpumps.com
SIC: 3561 Industrial pumps & parts

(G-16160)
SPECTRA ENGINEERING INC
825 W 68th St (79764-2714)
PHONE....................................432 367-8413
EMP: 21
SQ FT: 12,000
SALES (est): 2.4MM
SALES (corp-wide): 4MM **Privately Held**
SIC: 3533 Mfg Oil Field Equipment
PA: Allen & Bennett, Inc.
825 W 68th St
Odessa TX
432 367-4920

(G-16161)
**SPIRIT GLOBL ENRGY SLTIONS
INC**
1460 Windway (79763-4912)
PHONE....................................432 522-2288
Ali Raza, *President*
Charlie Fowler, *Vice Pres*
Floyd Hightower, *Mfg Spvr*
Kerry Varnell, *Mfg Spvr*
Issa Sabbah, *Accountant*
EMP: 50
SALES (est): 8.7MM
SALES (corp-wide): 1.1B **Publicly Held**
WEB: www.apergyals.com
SIC: 1389 Oil field services
HQ: Apergy Artificial Lift International, Llc
2445 Tech Frest Blvd Ste
Spring TX 77381
281 403-5742

(G-16162)
SPM FLOW CONTROL INC
2424 E Ih 20 (79766-8829)
PHONE....................................432 580-3887
Dewayne Horton, *Principal*
EMP: 138
SALES (corp-wide): 3.4B **Privately Held**
WEB: www.global.weir
SIC: 3533 Oil & gas field machinery
HQ: S.P.M. Flow Control, Inc.
7601 Wyatt Dr
Fort Worth TX 76108
817 246-2461

(G-16163)
SQS NDT LP (PA)
2600 W I 20 (79763)
P.O. Box 13977 (79768-3977)
PHONE....................................432 614-9920
Doug Frey, *Partner*
Elic Brymer, *Partner*
Michael Lewis, *Partner*
Amber Lewis, *Manager*
EMP: 18
SQ FT: 10,000
SALES (est): 3.5MM **Privately Held**
WEB: www.sqsndtlp.com
SIC: 1389 Testing, measuring, surveying &
analysis services

(G-16164)
**STANDARD STRUCTURES INC
(PA)**
Also Called: S S I
1500 W Interstate 20 (79763-4904)
P.O. Box 1912 (79760-1912)
PHONE....................................432 580-5353
John P Evans, *President*
Letha Reynolds, *Treasurer*
Nick Evans, *Sales Staff*
Chris Jacquez, *Sales Staff*
Debbie Evans, *Executive*
EMP: 75
SQ FT: 52,000
SALES (est): 15.9MM **Privately Held**
WEB: www.standardstructuresinc.com
SIC: 3448 Buildings, portable: prefabri-
cated metal

(G-16165)
**STEALTH OILWELL SERVICES
LLC**
7668 W 42nd St (79764-8879)
P.O. Box 69063 (79769-0063)
PHONE....................................432 333-3600
Cody Gill, *Managing Prtnr*
Stacey Gill, *Sales Staff*
Leslie Gill,
EMP: 53 EST: 2011
SALES (est): 5.8MM **Privately Held**
WEB: www.stealthoilwell.com
SIC: 1389 Oil field services

(G-16166)
STEALTH PUMP & SUPPLY LLC
7680 W 42nd St (79764-8879)
P.O. Box 70040 (79769-1040)
PHONE....................................432 385-7770
Blake Lisenbe, *COO*
Brianna Arnold, *CFO*
Leslie Gill, *Mng Member*
EMP: 30 EST: 2016
SQ FT: 12,500
SALES (est): 11MM **Privately Held**
SIC: 3561 5084 Pumps & pumping equip-
ment; pumps & pumping equipment

(G-16167)
STRIKE LLC
5101 W County Rd S (79766)
PHONE....................................888 353-1444
Ronnie Walters, *Principal*
EMP: 25
SALES (corp-wide): 1.4B **Privately Held**
WEB: www.strikeusa.com
SIC: 1389 Servicing oil & gas wells
PA: Strike, Llc
1800 Hughes Landing Blvd # 500
The Woodlands TX 77380
713 389-2400

▲ = Import ▼=Export
◆ =Import/Export

(G-16168)
SULZER PUMP SERVICES (US) INC
Also Called: Odessa Service Center
340 S Meadow Ave (79761-5659)
P.O. Box 4418 (79760-4418)
PHONE....................432 614-2574
Joel Walker, *Branch Mgr*
EMP: 26
SALES (corp-wide): 3.7B Privately Held
WEB: www.sulzer.com
SIC: 7692 Welding repair
HQ: Sulzer Pump Services (Us) Inc.
101 Old Underwood Rd G
La Porte TX 77571
281 417-7110

(G-16169)
SUNSET WELL SERVICE INC
4318 S County Road 1290 (79765-9506)
P.O. Box 7139, Midland (79708-7139)
PHONE....................432 561-8600
Mary Anne Bagly, *President*
EMP: 40
SALES (est): 9.2MM Privately Held
SIC: 1381 Drilling oil & gas wells

(G-16170)
SUPERIOR CONTROLS INC
2103 W Murphy St (79763-4834)
PHONE....................432 332-4051
Kirk Leslie, *President*
Sherrie Keating, *Corp Secy*
Eddie Bedrick, *Vice Pres*
Mark Laroche, *Engineer*
David L Leslie,
EMP: 9 EST: 1959
SQ FT: 4,000
SALES (est): 2MM Privately Held
WEB: www.superiorcontrolsinc.com
SIC: 3625 Electric controls & control accessories, industrial

(G-16171)
SUPERIOR ENERGY SERVICES LLC
Also Called: Completion Services
2723 W Hillmont Rd (79764-1760)
PHONE....................432 385-3000
EMP: 44 Publicly Held
WEB: www.superiorenergy.com
SIC: 1389 Well plugging & abandoning, oil & gas; oil field services
HQ: Superior Energy Services, L.L.C.
203 Commission Blvd
Lafayette LA 70508
337 714-4545

(G-16172)
TAYLOR MADE BIT CO LLC
4519 Brazos Ave (79764-3975)
PHONE....................432 362-4471
Thomas Taylor Jr,
EMP: 15
SALES (est): 436.7K Privately Held
SIC: 3999 Manufacturing industries

(G-16173)
TCM INVESTMENTS INC
2121 W 44th St (79764-3908)
P.O. Box 12987 (79768-2987)
PHONE....................432 366-5433
Bert Vicars, *Principal*
▲ EMP: 27
SQ FT: 19,500
SALES (est): 683.1K
SALES (corp-wide): 2.4B Publicly Held
SIC: 7699 3594 3561 3533 Industrial equipment services; fluid power pumps & motors; pumps & pumping equipment; oil & gas field machinery
HQ: Gardner Denver, Inc.
800 Beaty St
Davidson NC 28036

(G-16174)
TERRA METRICS LTD
Also Called: Whitlock Instruments
1300 N Texas Ave (79761-3850)
PHONE....................432 337-3412
Race Ritchie, *President*
Larry Lee Ritchie, *President*
Julia Ritchie, *Corp Secy*
Judy Ritchie, *Vice Pres*
Jason Tidwell, *Manager*

EMP: 13
SQ FT: 4,000
SALES (est): 4.5MM Privately Held
WEB: www.noflo.com
SIC: 3699 7629 Electrical equipment & supplies; electrical repair shops

(G-16175)
TEXAS KENWORTH CO
Mhc Kenworth- Odessa
5251 W Interstate 20 (79763-5518)
PHONE....................432 381-3300
Paul Rukat, *Manager*
EMP: 54
SALES (corp-wide): 1B Privately Held
WEB: www.texastrucksales.com
SIC: 4231 3537 Trucking terminal facilities; trucks, tractors, loaders, carriers & similar equipment
HQ: Texas Kenworth Co.
4040 Irving Blvd
Dallas TX 75247
214 920-7300

(G-16176)
THOMAS OILFIELD SERVICES LLC
5327 W 42nd St (79764-1326)
PHONE....................903 806-0582
EMP: 52
SALES (corp-wide): 42.5MM Privately Held
WEB: www.thomasoilfieldservices.com
SIC: 1389 Oil field services
PA: Thomas Oilfield Services, Llc
4250 Se Loop 281
Longview TX 75602
855 778-5940

(G-16177)
THOMPSON & THOMPSON
Also Called: Thompson J Cleo Oil Producers
117 W Yukon Rd (79764-2817)
P.O. Box 12577 (79768-2577)
PHONE....................214 953-1177
Christy Thompson, *Vice Pres*
Jeff Birkelbach, *Manager*
EMP: 12
SQ FT: 2,686
SALES (corp-wide): 25.5MM Privately Held
SIC: 1311 Crude petroleum production; natural gas production
PA: Thompson & Thompson
325 N Saint Paul St # 4300
Dallas TX 75201
214 953-1177

(G-16178)
THOMPSON WELDING
Also Called: Thompson Hard Metal Service
3602 W 11th St (79763-3288)
P.O. Box 4451 (79760-4451)
PHONE....................432 381-1531
Marcus Thompson, *President*
EMP: 9
SQ FT: 4,820
SALES (est): 763.4K Privately Held
WEB: www.thompsonswelding.com
SIC: 7692 Welding repair

(G-16179)
TILLERY & PARKS COMPANY LP
8836 Andrews Hwy (79765-1305)
P.O. Box 2846 (79760-2846)
PHONE....................432 366-2700
Johnny Howton, *Ltd Ptnr*
EMP: 10
SQ FT: 9,600
SALES (est): 1.4MM Privately Held
WEB: www.tillery-parks.com
SIC: 1389 Oil field services

(G-16180)
TOMMY CHAPPELL LLC
8 Santa Fe Pl (79765-8520)
PHONE....................432 967-2469
Tommy Chappell, *President*
EMP: 12
SALES (est): 844.8K Privately Held
SIC: 3561 3533 7699 Pumps & pumping equipment; oil & gas field machinery; pumps & pumping equipment repair

(G-16181)
TOWNSEND INTERNATIONAL INC (PA)
5381 W 42nd St (79764-1327)
P.O. Box 13568 (79768-3568)
PHONE....................432 381-8750
▲ EMP: 11 EST: 1975
SQ FT: 17,800
SALES (est): 3MM Privately Held
SIC: 3533 3494 Oil field machinery & equipment; valves & pipe fittings

(G-16182)
TRIPP CONSTRUCTION INC
1073 N Fm 1936 (79763-7502)
P.O. Box 1711 (79760-1711)
PHONE....................432 381-2440
Joseph C Young, *President*
Katy Young, *Treasurer*
EMP: 30 EST: 1958
SQ FT: 1,800
SALES (est): 4.4MM Privately Held
SIC: 1389 Oil field services

(G-16183)
TRUE SHOT LLC
10901 W County Road 125 (79765-9673)
PHONE....................972 505-0433
Richard D Cross, *President*
EMP: 14
SALES (est): 558.7K Privately Held
SIC: 3829 Surveying & drafting equipment

(G-16184)
TUBOSCOPE PIPELINE SVCS INC
2269 S Fulton Ave (79766-8818)
PHONE....................432 337-1570
Mike Podrazik, *Manager*
EMP: 11
SALES (corp-wide): 8.4B Publicly Held
WEB: www.nov.com
SIC: 1389 Oil field services
HQ: Tuboscope Pipeline Services Inc.
2835 Holmes Rd
Houston TX 77051

(G-16185)
U S WEATHERFORD L P
Also Called: Weatherford Enterra
710 S Faudree Rd (79766-8863)
PHONE....................432 550-9297
Michael Owen, *Manager*
Julio De Young, *Manager*
Lawrence Johnson, *Manager*
EMP: 60 Privately Held
WEB: www.weatherford.com
SIC: 1389 Oil field services
HQ: U S Weatherford L P
179 Weatherford Dr
Schriever LA 70395
985 493-6100

(G-16186)
U S WEATHERFORD L P
8870 Nw Loop 338 (79764-3005)
PHONE....................432 530-4900
Junior Dominguez, *Manager*
EMP: 23 Privately Held
WEB: www.weatherford.com
SIC: 1389 Oil field services
HQ: U S Weatherford L P
179 Weatherford Dr
Schriever LA 70395
985 493-6100

(G-16187)
U S WEATHERFORD L P
2263 W Bell St (79766-8947)
PHONE....................432 332-4798
David Wallender, *Branch Mgr*
EMP: 20 Privately Held
WEB: www.weatherford.com
SIC: 2899 Oil treating compounds
HQ: U S Weatherford L P
179 Weatherford Dr
Schriever LA 70395
985 493-6100

(G-16188)
UNIT CORPORATION
6005 Eastridge Rd Ste 160 (79762-5027)
PHONE....................432 362-0901
EMP: 91

SALES (corp-wide): 674.6MM Privately Held
WEB: www.unitcorp.com
SIC: 1382 Oil & gas exploration services
PA: Unit Corporation
8200 S Unit Dr
Tulsa OK 74132
918 493-7700

(G-16189)
UNITED INDUSTRIES INC (PA)
3926 N County Rd W (79764-6415)
P.O. Box 4575 (79760-4575)
PHONE....................432 362-2361
William A Kennedy, *President*
Glen Kennedy, *Vice Pres*
EMP: 50
SQ FT: 60,000
SALES (est): 6.9MM Privately Held
WEB: www.unitedwellsinc.com
SIC: 3563 3568 Air & gas compressors including vacuum pumps; bearings, bushings & blocks

(G-16190)
UNIVERSAL WELL SERVICE LLC
1101 E Pool Rd (79766-8834)
PHONE....................432 272-6686
EMP: 25 Privately Held
WEB: www.universaltravel.biz
SIC: 3553 Box making machines, for wooden boxes
PA: Universal Well Service Llc
1717 Saint James Pl # 310
Houston TX 77056

(G-16191)
UNLIMITED FRAC SAND LLC
4210 Cnty Rd 1286 Ste 401 (79765)
PHONE....................800 560-1246
EMP: 20
SALES (est): 327.3K Privately Held
SIC: 1389 1446 Oil/Gas Field Services Industrial Sand Mining

(G-16192)
UTEX INDUSTRIES INC
1104 Market Ave (79761-5824)
P.O. Box 4358 (79760-4358)
PHONE....................432 333-4151
Linda Bretting, *Human Resources*
Deborah Adams, *Office Mgr*
Mike Teegarden, *Branch Mgr*
EMP: 40
SALES (corp-wide): 164.4MM Privately Held
WEB: www.utexind.com
SIC: 3053 Gaskets & sealing devices
HQ: Utex Industries, Inc.
10810 Katy Fwy Ste 100
Houston TX 77043
713 467-1000

(G-16193)
VALLEY PROTEINS INC
2441 Catalina Dr (79763-2403)
PHONE....................432 334-0449
Candy Armstrong, *Purch Agent*
Bobby Hane, *Manager*
Jeff Zemlicka, *Manager*
EMP: 70
SALES (corp-wide): 473.5MM Privately Held
WEB: www.valleyproteins.com
SIC: 2077 Rendering
PA: Valley Proteins (De), Inc.
151 Valpro Dr
Winchester VA 22603
540 877-2533

(G-16194)
VALTEK INDUSTRIES INC
2120 W 44th St (79764-3909)
P.O. Box 70239 (79769-1239)
PHONE....................432 339-8481
Shane Hamilton, *Principal*
Krislyn Perkins, *Accountant*
Daniel Rodriguez, *Sales Staff*
Mike Broadstreet, *Manager*
EMP: 13
SALES (est): 1.5MM Privately Held
WEB: www.valtekind.com
SIC: 3999 Barber & beauty shop equipment

(G-16195)
VANGUARD PERMIAN LLC
4001 Penbrook St Ste 201 (79762-5977)
PHONE..................................432 362-2209
EMP: 11 EST: 2016
SALES (est): 1.2MM **Privately Held**
SIC: 1382 Oil & gas exploration services

(G-16196)
VARCO LP
4710 Andrews Hwy (79762-5543)
PHONE..................................432 550-6802
Robert Kidder, *Branch Mgr*
EMP: 25
SQ FT: 8,136
SALES (corp-wide): 8.4B **Publicly Held**
WEB: www.nov.com
SIC: 1389 Testing, measuring, surveying & analysis services
HQ: Varco, L.P.
2835 Holmes Rd
Houston TX 77051
713 799-5272

(G-16197)
VARCO LP
Also Called: Administration Office
2400 Steven Rd (79764-7101)
P.O. Box 60340, Midland (79711-0340)
PHONE..................................432 362-0581
Tiffany Davis, *Sales Staff*
Joe Yates, *Branch Mgr*
EMP: 46
SALES (corp-wide): 8.4B **Publicly Held**
WEB: www.nov.com
SIC: 1389 Oil field services
HQ: Varco, L.P.
2835 Holmes Rd
Houston TX 77051
713 799-5272

(G-16198)
VARCO LP
100 E 61st St (79762-3613)
PHONE..................................432 367-9726
Calvin Taylor, *Manager*
EMP: 25
SQ FT: 9,600
SALES (corp-wide): 8.4B **Publicly Held**
WEB: www.nov.com
SIC: 3479 Coating or wrapping steel pipe
HQ: Varco, L.P.
2835 Holmes Rd
Houston TX 77051
713 799-5272

(G-16199)
VARCO LP
2269 S Fulton Ave (79766-8818)
PHONE..................................432 337-1570
Gary Lancaster, *Opers Staff*
Jean Drugan, *Sales Staff*
Mike Podrazik, *Manager*
EMP: 50
SALES (corp-wide): 8.4B **Publicly Held**
WEB: www.nov.com
SIC: 3479 Coating or wrapping steel pipe
HQ: Varco, L.P.
2835 Holmes Rd
Houston TX 77051
713 799-5272

(G-16200)
VAREL INTERNATIONAL IND LLC
2415 W 44th St (79764-3959)
PHONE..................................432 550-4816
Marty Malone, *Branch Mgr*
EMP: 14
SALES (corp-wide): 10.7B **Privately Held**
WEB: www.varelintl.com
SIC: 3545 Drill bits, metalworking
HQ: Varel International Ind., Llc
4730 Consulate Plaza Dr # 190
Houston TX 77032
281 272-6000

(G-16201)
VIKING COIL TUBING LLC
335 S County Rd W (79763-4801)
PHONE..................................432 580-7555
Noah M Mitchell, *Mng Member*
EMP: 53
SQ FT: 25,000

SALES (est): 31.9MM
SALES (corp-wide): 203MM **Privately Held**
WEB: www.viking-ct.com
SIC: 1389 Oil field services
PA: Conquest Completion Services, Llc
742 N Ashley Ridge Loop
Shreveport LA 71106
318 747-5544

(G-16202)
VIPER BLASTING & COATING INC
2700 E Interstate 20 (79766-8850)
P.O. Box 2488 (79760-2488)
PHONE..................................432 337-9711
Jerry Rush, *President*
Russell Battenfield, *Treasurer*
Jerry Grant, *Admin Sec*
EMP: 13
SALES (est): 916.7K **Privately Held**
SIC: 1389 Oil field services

(G-16203)
VIVA WELL SERVICING COMPANY LP
3747 W 8th St (79763-3936)
P.O. Box 4437 (79760-4437)
PHONE..................................432 552-0800
David A Kimbell Jr, *CEO*
Michael Giroir, *VP Accounting*
Jessica Grado, *Human Res Dir*
Rosa Gonzales, *Human Res Mgr*
Tom Connolly, *Sales Staff*
EMP: 30
SQ FT: 700
SALES (est): 7.4MM **Privately Held**
WEB: www.vivawsc.com
SIC: 1389 Oil field services

(G-16204)
WCI CONSTRUCTION INC
3408 S County Rd W (79766-8915)
P.O. Box 769379, San Antonio (78245-9342)
PHONE..................................432 530-4009
Javier Cruz, *CEO*
Rebecca Cruz, *Vice Pres*
EMP: 12
SQ FT: 2,800
SALES (est): 3.2MM **Privately Held**
SIC: 1389 7513 Lease tanks, oil field: erecting, cleaning & repairing; truck rental & leasing, no drivers

(G-16205)
WEATHERFORD ARTIFICIA
2818 W 42nd St (79764-6317)
PHONE..................................432 550-6118
Steve Huffman, *Manager*
Kathleen Huffman, *Manager*
EMP: 13 Privately Held
WEB: www.weatherford.com
SIC: 1389 Oil field services
HQ: Weatherford Artificial Lift Systems, Llc
2000 Saint James Pl
Houston TX 77056
713 836-4000

(G-16206)
WEATHERFORD ARTIFICIA
Also Called: Leamco Bearing and Supply
8866 Nw Loop 338 (79764-3005)
P.O. Box 60050, Midland (79711-0050)
PHONE..................................432 368-3865
James Williams, *Regional Mgr*
EMP: 25 Privately Held
WEB: www.weatherford.com
SIC: 1389 Oil field services
HQ: Weatherford Artificial Lift Systems, Llc
2000 Saint James Pl
Houston TX 77056
713 836-4000

(G-16207)
WEATHERFORD INTERNATIONAL LLC
2263 W Bell St (79766-8947)
PHONE..................................432 332-1318
Russell Sailler, *Branch Mgr*
EMP: 68 Privately Held
WEB: www.weatherford.com
SIC: 1389 Oil field services

HQ: Weatherford International, Llc
2000 Saint James Pl
Houston TX 77056
713 693-4000

(G-16208)
WEATHERFORD INTERNATIONAL LLC
8860 Nw Loop 338 (79764-3005)
PHONE..................................432 563-0598
Cody Combs, *Branch Mgr*
EMP: 68 Privately Held
WEB: www.weatherford.com
SIC: 1389 Oil field services
HQ: Weatherford International, Llc
2000 Saint James Pl
Houston TX 77056
713 693-4000

(G-16209)
WEATHRFORD ARTFL LIFT SYSTEMS
905 S Grandview Ave (79761-7134)
PHONE..................................432 334-4500
Sam Burns, *Manager*
Kenneth Kok, *Manager*
EMP: 75
SQ FT: 10,900 **Privately Held**
WEB: www.weatherford.com
SIC: 1389 Oil field services
HQ: Weatherford Artificial Lift Systems, Llc
2000 Saint James Pl
Houston TX 77056
713 836-4000

(G-16210)
WELL-FOAM INC
4215 N Sierra Ave (79764-9329)
P.O. Box 14910 (79768-4910)
PHONE..................................432 276-3290
William Maxwell, *President*
Robert Maxwell, *President*
Payton Kemp, *Sales Staff*
Mark Benham, *Admin Sec*
EMP: 156
SALES (est): 39MM **Privately Held**
WEB: www.wellfoaminc.com
SIC: 1389 7389 Oil field services; business services

(G-16211)
WESTECH SEAL INC
Also Called: Westech Bearing
7200 Sprague Rd (79764-2446)
P.O. Box 14610 (79768-4610)
PHONE..................................432 367-1188
Mark Merritt, *CEO*
EMP: 16
SQ FT: 25,000
SALES (est): 3.5MM **Privately Held**
WEB: www.westechseal.com
SIC: 2891 3561 3562 Sealants; industrial pumps & parts; ball bearings & parts

(G-16212)
WILDCAT OIL TOOLS LLC
1400 Windway (79763-4912)
PHONE..................................432 332-4241
EMP: 20
SALES (corp-wide): 831.5K **Privately Held**
WEB: www.wildcatoiltools.com
SIC: 1389 Oil field services
PA: Wildcat Oil Tools, Llc
706 N Colorado St
Midland TX 79701
432 687-5221

(G-16213)
WNCO VALVE INTERNATIONAL INC
5114 Golder Ave (79764-4059)
P.O. Box 13776 (79768-3776)
PHONE..................................432 362-2136
Tommy Ward, *President*
Don Nuckols, *Vice Pres*
EMP: 15
SQ FT: 2,176
SALES (est): 2.5MM **Privately Held**
WEB: www.wncovalve.com
SIC: 3491 7699 Industrial valves; valve repair, industrial

(G-16214)
WTB LLC
Also Called: West Texas Boring
1201 Oicd Dr (79766-8711)
P.O. Box 69396 (79769-0396)
PHONE..................................432 366-1026
Craig Morse, *President*
Lonnie Lucas, *Superintendent*
Mark Jones, *COO*
Hailey Stevens, *Manager*
EMP: 25 EST: 1975
SQ FT: 5,800
SALES (est): 2MM **Privately Held**
WEB: www.westtexasboring.com
SIC: 3541 Drilling & boring machines

(G-16215)
WWL INDUSTRIES INC
Also Called: B D W Company
2412 W 42nd St (79764-6309)
P.O. Box 3466 (79760-3466)
PHONE..................................432 362-0326
Billy D White, *President*
Susan White Leathers, *Vice Pres*
Marcy Weatherby, *Treasurer*
Wesley Buck Jones, *Sales Mgr*
EMP: 42
SQ FT: 27,000
SALES (est): 15.3MM **Privately Held**
WEB: www.wwlindustries.com
SIC: 5084 3533 7692 7629 Drilling equipment, excluding bits; oil field machinery & equipment; welding repair; electrical repair shops

---

Oglesby
Coryell County

(G-16216)
UNIQUE MACHINE SHOP INC
101 Baird St (76561-2003)
P.O. Box 7 (76561-0007)
PHONE..................................254 456-2972
Perry E Head, *President*
Roger Berryhill, *Vice Pres*
EMP: 25 EST: 1978
SQ FT: 40,000
SALES (est): 3.9MM **Privately Held**
SIC: 3599 Machine shop, jobbing & repair

Old Ocean
Brazoria County

(G-16217)
HONEYWELL INTERNATIONAL INC
Gate 34 Hwgy 35 (77463)
P.O. Box 618 (77463-0618)
PHONE..................................979 491-2802
Oles Simonson, *Principal*
Gary Henson, *Telecom Exec*
EMP: 44
SALES (corp-wide): 36.7B **Publicly Held**
WEB: www.honeywell.com
SIC: 3724 Aircraft engines & engine parts
PA: Honeywell International Inc.
300 S Tryon St
Charlotte NC 28202
704 627-6200

Old River Winfree
Liberty County

(G-16218)
LAND INDUSTRIAL TRIAL SEVICES
16940 County Line (77535-9920)
PHONE..................................281 385-2504
Terry Michael Land, *President*
Paula Land, *Vice Pres*
EMP: 12
SALES (est): 1.9MM **Privately Held**
SIC: 3479 Coating electrodes

Olden
Eastland County

(G-16219)
CREATIVE MENUS&FOLDERS LLC
Also Called: Texas Covers
409 Old Hwy 80 (76466)
P.O. Box 12 (76466-0012)
PHONE..............................254 653-2775
Anand Maruwada, *Mng Member*
Andy Sherman, *Manager*
EMP: 19
SALES (est): 962K **Privately Held**
WEB: www.texascovers.com
SIC: 2731 2675 3089 2392 Pamphlets: publishing & printing; photographic mats, mounts & folders; laminating of plastic; placemats, plastic or textile; business service newsletters: publishing & printing

Olney
Young County

(G-16220)
CONSTRUCTION EQP MFG CO INC
Also Called: Cemco
782 Highway 251 S (76374-2384)
P.O. Box 14 (76374-0014)
PHONE..............................940 257-6215
Carla Perry, *President*
Larry D Cobb, *Vice Pres*
EMP: 26
SQ FT: 30,000
SALES (est): 6MM **Privately Held**
WEB: www.cemcoinc.com
SIC: 3531 Concrete plants

(G-16221)
HYPERTEC INC
301 E Main St (76374-1925)
P.O. Box 248 (76374-0248)
PHONE..............................940 564-5600
Phillip P Janca, *President*
Stephanie Janca Davis, *Vice Pres*
EMP: 17
SQ FT: 8,700
SALES (est): 1.7MM **Privately Held**
WEB: www.hypertec.com
SIC: 3841 Surgical & medical instruments

(G-16222)
OLNEY DOOR & SCREEN CO
1019 W Main St (76374-1621)
PHONE..............................940 564-3543
Greg Miller, *President*
EMP: 45
SQ FT: 35,000
SALES (est): 6.2MM **Privately Held**
WEB: www.olneysales.com
SIC: 3442 Metal doors; screen doors, metal; screens, window, metal

(G-16223)
OLNEY SALES INC
1019 W Main St (76374-1621)
P.O. Box 176 (76374-0176)
PHONE..............................940 564-3592
Melvin Greenhaw, *President*
EMP: 26
SQ FT: 1,800
SALES (est): 1.7MM **Privately Held**
WEB: www.olneysales.com
SIC: 3442 Screen & storm doors & windows

(G-16224)
PSI INDUSTRIES INC
Also Called: P S I Extrusions
1436 W Main St (76374-1653)
PHONE..............................940 564-3563
Matt Thomas, *Branch Mgr*
EMP: 31 **Privately Held**
WEB: www.psiextrusions.com
SIC: 3354 Aluminum extruded products
PA: Psi Industries, Inc.
1860 Hurd Dr
Irving TX 75038

(G-16225)
TOWER EXTRUSIONS LTD (PA)
1003 State Highway 79 S (76374-2257)
P.O. Box 218 (76374-0218)
PHONE..............................940 564-5681
William McClelland, *President*
Mark L McClelland, *General Ptnr*
Joe Rollans, *Prdtn Mgr*
Harrison Wellman, *Opers Staff*
Colson Ballard, *Production*
▲ **EMP:** 207
SQ FT: 300,000
SALES (est): 123.3MM **Privately Held**
WEB: www.towerext.com
SIC: 3354 Aluminum extruded products

Olton
Lamb County

(G-16226)
HALLS LUMBER INC
108 Ave E (79064)
P.O. Box 240, Quanah (79252-0240)
PHONE..............................806 285-2393
Joe Hall, *President*
Betty Hall, *Corp Secy*
Ronald Digby, *Vice Pres*
EMP: 11
SQ FT: 4,000
SALES (est): 1.6MM **Privately Held**
SIC: 3273 1794 5211 Ready-mixed concrete; excavation work; millwork & lumber

(G-16227)
OLTON WELDING & MACHINE INC
Also Called: Elmer Lewis Enterprises
1115 1st St (79064)
P.O. Box 529 (79064-0529)
PHONE..............................806 285-3006
Elmer L Lewis, *President*
EMP: 10
SQ FT: 1,300
SALES (est): 1.2MM **Privately Held**
WEB: www.oltonwelding.com
SIC: 7699 3523 5932 Farm machinery repair; farm machinery & equipment; used merchandise stores

Onalaska
Polk County

(G-16228)
CUTTING EDGE ONSITE MCHNING LL
359 N Fm 356 (77360-7539)
PHONE..............................832 663-6120
EMP: 11
SALES (est): 1.8MM **Privately Held**
WEB: www.ceomachining.com
SIC: 3599 Machine shop, jobbing & repair

Orange
Orange County

(G-16229)
AKROTEX FILMS INC
Fm 1006 (77631)
P.O. Box 1508 (77631-1508)
PHONE..............................409 886-0632
Eva Smith, *Manager*
EMP: 30
SALES (corp-wide): 35.4MM **Privately Held**
SIC: 3081 2611 Unsupported plastics film & sheet; pulp manufactured from waste or recycled paper
PA: Akrotex Films, Inc.
1301 S Childers Rd
Orange TX 77630
409 886-0111

(G-16230)
AKROTEX FILMS INC (PA)
1301 S Childers Rd (77630-7011)
P.O. Box 1508 (77631-1508)
PHONE..............................409 886-0111
Ross Smith, *CEO*
Rick Keszeg, *Vice Pres*

Larry Webb, *CFO*
Jana Clark, *Human Resources*
Eva Smith, *Admin Sec*
▼ **EMP:** 40
SQ FT: 500,000
SALES (est): 35.4MM **Privately Held**
SIC: 3081 5162 4213 4214 Unsupported plastics film & sheet; plastics materials & basic shapes; trucking, except local; local trucking with storage

(G-16231)
AMERICAN AIRBOAT CORPORATION
108 Lutcher Dr (77632-2702)
PHONE..............................409 883-7725
Stan Floyd, *President*
Faron Floyd, *Vice Pres*
Sandra Navarro, *Office Mgr*
EMP: 20
SQ FT: 9,000
SALES (est): 1.5MM **Privately Held**
WEB: www.americanairboats.com
SIC: 4489 3732 5551 Airboats; motorboats, inboard or outboard: building & repairing; boat dealers

(G-16232)
ARLANXEO USA LLC
Rubber Division
4647 Fm 1006 (77630-8016)
PHONE..............................409 883-9990
Richard Worsham, *Opers Mgr*
Gary Myers, *Engineer*
John Schmidt, *Manager*
Kevin Brasher, *IT/INT Sup*
EMP: 400 **Privately Held**
WEB: www.arlanxeo.com
SIC: 2822 Synthetic rubber
HQ: Arlanxeo Usa Llc
111 Ridc Park West Dr
Pittsburgh PA 15275
412 809-1000

(G-16233)
CANDLE COTTAGE
3644 W Roundbunch Rd (77630-9018)
PHONE..............................409 720-7087
Shanna Ferro, *Owner*
EMP: 6
SQ FT: 2,800
SALES (est): 854K **Privately Held**
WEB: www.candlecottage.com
SIC: 5999 3999 Candle shops; candles

(G-16234)
CHEVRON PHILLIPS CHEM CO LP
5309 Fm 1006 (77630-8030)
P.O. Box 7400 (77631-7400)
PHONE..............................409 882-6000
Don Sitton, *Opers-Prdtn-Mfg*
Tammy Locks, *Engineer*
Gene Mires, *Engineer*
Rodney Pacetti, *Technology*
E Glenn Duncan, *Admin Sec*
EMP: 200
SALES (corp-wide): 3.5B **Privately Held**
WEB: www.cpchem.com
SIC: 2821 Polyethylene resins
HQ: Chevron Phillips Chemical Company Lp
10001 Six Pines Dr
The Woodlands TX 77380
832 813-4100

(G-16235)
CHEVRON PHILLIPS CHEM CO LP
5309 Farm Mkt Rd Ste 106 (77631)
P.O. Box 7400 (77631-7400)
PHONE..............................409 882-6262
Charleen Dixon, *Branch Mgr*
EMP: 134
SALES (corp-wide): 3.5B **Privately Held**
WEB: www.cpchem.com
SIC: 2821 Plastics materials & resins
HQ: Chevron Phillips Chemical Company Lp
10001 Six Pines Dr
The Woodlands TX 77380
832 813-4100

(G-16236)
CONRAD ORANGE SHIPYARD INC
710 Market St (77630-6620)
P.O. Box 1670 (77631-1670)
PHONE..............................409 670-4900
◆ **EMP:** 150
SQ FT: 140,000
SALES (est): 31MM
SALES (corp-wide): 263.8MM **Publicly Held**
WEB: www.conradindustries.com
SIC: 3731 Tugboats, building & repairing
HQ: Conrad Shipyard, L.L.C.
1501 Front St
Morgan City LA 70380
985 384-3060

(G-16237)
CRUMPLERS SHIPBUILDING CO INC
1799 S Childers Rd (77630-7071)
P.O. Box 2067 (77631-2067)
PHONE..............................409 886-7934
EMP: 20
SQ FT: 30,000
SALES (est): 1.9MM **Privately Held**
SIC: 3731 3732 Shipbuilding & repairing; boat building & repairing

(G-16238)
DUPHIL INC (PA)
6608 Interstate 10 W (77632-8350)
PHONE..............................409 883-8550
Jennie Scalfano, *President*
April Knapp, *Business Mgr*
Ron Redkey, *Vice Pres*
Tommy Breaux, *Project Mgr*
Pam Flanigan, *Accountant*
EMP: 30 **EST:** 1968
SALES (est): 51.4MM **Privately Held**
WEB: www.duphil.com
SIC: 1389 Oil field services

(G-16239)
E I DU PONT DE NEMOURS & CO
Also Called: Dupont Packg & Indus Polymers
2739 Fm 1006 (77630-8007)
P.O. Box 1089 (77631-1089)
PHONE..............................409 883-8411
J V Woodrick, *Branch Mgr*
EMP: 124
SALES (corp-wide): 14.2B **Publicly Held**
WEB: www.dupont.com
SIC: 2821 2865 Thermoplastic materials; dyes & pigments
HQ: E. I. Du Pont De Nemours And Company
974 Centre Rd Bldg 735
Wilmington DE 19805
302 485-3000

(G-16240)
E I DU PONT DE NEMOURS & CO
Also Called: Sabine River Works
3055 Fm 1006 (77630-8045)
PHONE..............................409 886-6442
EMP: 900
SALES (corp-wide): 14.2B **Publicly Held**
WEB: www.dupont.com
SIC: 2879 2824 Agricultural chemicals; nylon fibers
HQ: E. I. Du Pont De Nemours And Company
974 Centre Rd Bldg 735
Wilmington DE 19805
302 485-3000

(G-16241)
E I DU PONT DE NEMOURS & CO
Also Called: Dupont
2739 Fm 1006 (77630-8007)
P.O. Box 1089 (77631-1089)
PHONE..............................409 883-8411
Jan Lerou, *Principal*
Martha Foley, *Production*
Elena Labrador, *Engineer*
Shannon Meerscheidt, *Engineer*
Matt Peterson, *Engineer*
EMP: 410
SALES (corp-wide): 14.2B **Publicly Held**
WEB: www.dupont.com
SIC: 2819 Industrial inorganic chemicals

HQ: E. I. Du Pont De Nemours And Company
974 Centre Rd Bldg 735
Wilmington DE 19805
302 485-3000

(G-16242)
FIRESTONE POLYMERS LLC
5713 Farm Rd 1006 (77630)
PHONE.................................409 924-4500
Gary Defrates, *Branch Mgr*
Nelson Bernard, *Manager*
EMP: 200
SALES (corp-wide): 147.6MM **Privately Held**
WEB: www.firestonepolymers.com
SIC: 3069 Latex, foamed
PA: Firestone Polymers, Llc
381 W Wilbeth Rd
Akron OH 44301
330 379-7000

(G-16243)
FLOYD TATE A
Also Called: Better Built Metal Buildings
10383 Highway 12 Ste 116 (77632-7416)
PHONE.................................409 745-3256
Tate Floyd, *Owner*
EMP: 10
SALES (est): 350K **Privately Held**
WEB: www.betterbuilt-metalbuildings.com
SIC: 1791 3448 Building front installation metal; buildings, portable: prefabricated metal

(G-16244)
GARY L NOBLE INC
Also Called: Noble Machine Works
17439 Highway 62 S (77630-8726)
P.O. Box 354, Bridge City (77611-0354)
PHONE.................................409 886-0552
Gary L Noble, *President*
EMP: 9
SQ FT: 6,000
SALES (est): 861.9K **Privately Held**
SIC: 3599 Machine shop, jobbing & repair

(G-16245)
GRAYSON SULZER INC
Also Called: Grayson Armature
3904 Tulane Rd (77630-5469)
P.O. Box 2905 (77631-2905)
PHONE.................................409 882-9112
Fax: 409 882-9287
EMP: 20
SALES (est): 3.9MM **Privately Held**
SIC: 7694 Armature Rewinding
HQ: Sulzer Us Holding Inc.
2277 Plaza Dr Ste 600
Sugar Land TX 77077
832 886-2299

(G-16246)
HONEYWELL INTERNATIONAL INC
3927 Farm Rd 1006 (77630)
P.O. Box 640 (77631-0640)
PHONE.................................409 886-7445
Craig Robnik, *Branch Mgr*
EMP: 87
SALES (corp-wide): 36.7B **Publicly Held**
WEB: www.honeywell.com
SIC: 2899 3812 Chemical preparations; aircraft/aerospace flight instruments & guidance systems
PA: Honeywell International Inc.
300 S Tryon St
Charlotte NC 28202
704 627-6200

(G-16247)
INDUSTRIAL THERMAL SVCS LLC
2711 Highway 87 S (77630-9094)
P.O. Box 2258, Nederland (77627-8258)
PHONE.................................409 886-9700
Nev Aras, *Vice Pres*
Jason Dyson, *Opers Mgr*
Ryan Crowell, *Sales Staff*
Ryan Aras, *Mng Member*
EMP: 30
SALES (est): 9.1MM **Privately Held**
WEB: www.its-thermal.com
SIC: 3398 Metal heat treating

(G-16248)
INLAND BOAT WORKS INC
2842 E Roundbunch Rd (77630-6892)
P.O. Box 397, Bridge City (77611-0397)
PHONE.................................409 988-0005
Randy Lee, *President*
Ricky Lee, *General Mgr*
EMP: 10
SALES (est): 1.8MM **Privately Held**
WEB: www.inlandboats.com
SIC: 3732 Boat building & repairing

(G-16249)
INVISTA CAPITAL MANAGEMENT LLC
Farm Market Road 1006 (77631)
PHONE.................................409 886-6982
Steve McCracken, *Branch Mgr*
EMP: 44
SALES (corp-wide): 36.8B **Privately Held**
WEB: www.invista.com
SIC: 2821 Plastics materials & resins
HQ: Invista Capital Management, Llc
2801 Centerville Rd
Wilmington DE 19808
302 683-3000

(G-16250)
INVISTA CAPITAL MANAGEMENT LLC
3055 Fm 1006 (77630-8045)
PHONE.................................409 886-9373
Raul Trochez, *Manager*
EMP: 517
SALES (corp-wide): 36.8B **Privately Held**
WEB: www.invista.com
SIC: 2821 Polyethylene resins
HQ: Invista Capital Management, Llc
2801 Centerville Rd
Wilmington DE 19808
302 683-3000

(G-16251)
KARLTEX MACHINE INC
10201 Fm 1130 (77632-1084)
PHONE.................................409 883-5889
Thelma Fragstein, *President*
Gunther Fragstein, *Vice Pres*
Karl Fragstein, *Vice Pres*
Seigfried Fragstein, *Controller*
Donnie Cobb, *Manager*
EMP: 15
SQ FT: 12,000
SALES (est): 1.8MM **Privately Held**
SIC: 3599 Machine shop, jobbing & repair

(G-16252)
LION ELASTOMERS ORANGE LLC
5713 Farm To Mkt Rd 1006 (77630)
PHONE.................................409 924-4500
Jesse Zeringue, *President*
Jeff Jordan, *Vice Pres*
Bobby Rakhoff, *Vice Pres*
Neil Jurkovic, *CFO*
Keith Gordon, *Director*
EMP: 164
SALES (est): 7.9MM **Privately Held**
WEB: www.lionelastomers.com
SIC: 2822 Butadiene rubbers, polybutadiene; styrene-butadiene rubbers, (over 50% butadiene), SBR, GRS
PA: Lion Copolymer Holdings, Llc
36191 Highway 30
Geismar LA 70734

(G-16253)
M & P SEALING CO (PA)
11125 Interstate 10 E (77630-7813)
P.O. Box 19039, Houston (77224-9039)
PHONE.................................409 745-2002
Tim Mattingly, *CEO*
Dan Coleman, *President*
▲ **EMP:** 14
SQ FT: 18,000
SALES (est): 2.8MM **Privately Held**
WEB: www.mp-sealing.com
SIC: 3053 Gaskets, all materials

(G-16254)
MUELLER SUPPLY COMPANY INC
6311 Ih 10 E (77630-1057)
PHONE.................................409 886-2233
Melvin Franklin, *Manager*

EMP: 9
SALES (corp-wide): 180.3MM **Privately Held**
WEB: www.muellerinc.com
SIC: 3448 Prefabricated metal buildings
PA: Mueller Supply Company, Inc.
1913 Hutchins Ave
Ballinger TX 76821
325 365-3555

(G-16255)
ORANGE COUNTY INDUSTRIAL INC
4568 Farming Market 408 (77630)
P.O. Box 448, Orangefield (77639-0448)
PHONE.................................409 697-3559
Ryan Guote, *President*
Wayne Marso, *Sales Mgr*
EMP: 9 EST: 2000
SALES (est): 1.3MM **Privately Held**
SIC: 3086 Insulation or cushioning material, foamed plastic

(G-16256)
ORION ENGINEERED CARBONS LLC
Also Called: Advanced Fillers & Pigments
1513 Echo Ave (77632-2059)
PHONE.................................409 883-9966
Russell Webb, *Manager*
EMP: 52
SALES (corp-wide): 889.5K **Privately Held**
WEB: www.orioncarbons.com
SIC: 2895 Carbon black
HQ: Orion Engineered Carbons Llc
4501 Magnolia Cove Dr
Kingwood TX 77345
832 445-3300

(G-16257)
PRINTPACK INC
Also Called: Flexible Packing Group
4715 Fm 1006 (77630-4360)
P.O. Box 1389 (77631-1389)
PHONE.................................409 883-9325
Steve Aguillard, *Plant Mgr*
Kim Cordova, *Materials Mgr*
Billy Dyer, *Engineer*
Alan Reynolds, *Engineer*
Craig Adrio, *Sales Staff*
EMP: 250
SALES (corp-wide): 1.3B **Privately Held**
WEB: www.printpack.com
SIC: 2673 3081 Bags: plastic, laminated & coated; plastic film & sheet
HQ: Printpack, Inc.
2800 Overlook Pkwy Ne
Atlanta GA 30339
404 460-7000

(G-16258)
ROGERS LUMBER CO INC
8330 Old Highway 90 (77630-8089)
PHONE.................................409 745-1953
Vincent Rogers, *President*
Mary Jane Rogers, *Corp Secy*
Jerry Rogers, *Vice Pres*
EMP: 20
SQ FT: 2,000
SALES (est): 3.2MM **Privately Held**
WEB: www.rogerslumbercompany.com
SIC: 2421 Lumber: rough, sawed or planed

(G-16259)
S & T INTERNATIONAL INC
7376 Cohenour Rd (77632-5953)
P.O. Box 570, Mauriceville (77626-0570)
PHONE.................................409 745-4990
Linda Ballard, *CEO*
Scott Ballard, *President*
▼ **EMP:** 25
SQ FT: 34,600
SALES (est): 7.9MM **Privately Held**
WEB: www.st-intl.com
SIC: 3317 Steel pipe & tubes

(G-16260)
SABINE RIVER & NORTHERN RR CO
5830 Old Highway 87 (77632-0482)
PHONE.................................409 746-2453
David Kleinknecht, *President*
EMP: 22
SQ FT: 2,000

SALES (est): 30.2K **Privately Held**
SIC: 2499 Fencing, docks & other outdoor wood structural products

(G-16261)
SABINE RIVER AUTHORITY TEXAS (PA)
Also Called: S R A
12777 Highway 87 N (77632-7482)
P.O. Box 579 (77631-0579)
PHONE.................................409 746-2192
Earl Williams, *President*
David Williams, *Division Mgr*
Jerry Clark, *General Mgr*
David Montagne, *Exec VP*
Jamie East, *Technical Mgr*
EMP: 25
SQ FT: 15,000
SALES: 42.2MM **Privately Held**
WEB: www.sratx.org
SIC: 4941 3822 Water supply; hydronic controls

(G-16262)
SHARP-BILT LLC
6902 Interstate 10 W (77632-8029)
P.O. Box 964, Vidor (77670-0964)
PHONE.................................409 886-0066
Marshall Sharp, *Partner*
Janet Dougharty, *Partner*
EMP: 13
SQ FT: 8,000
SALES (est): 880K **Privately Held**
WEB: www.sharpbilt.com
SIC: 3441 3599 Fabricated structural metal; machine shop, jobbing & repair

(G-16263)
SIGNODE INDUSTRIAL GROUP LLC
Muller
19440 Fm 1130 (77632-7636)
PHONE.................................409 745-2600
Rob Jacob, *General Mgr*
EMP: 24
SALES (corp-wide): 11.6B **Publicly Held**
WEB: www.signode.com
SIC: 3565 2671 Packing & wrapping machinery; packaging paper & plastics film, coated & laminated
HQ: Signode Industrial Group Llc
3650 W Lake Ave
Glenview IL 60026
847 724-7500

(G-16264)
SULZER ELECTRO-MECHANICAL SERV
Also Called: Sulzer Grayson
3904 Tulane Rd (77630-5469)
PHONE.................................409 882-9112
Rj Reynolds, *Manager*
EMP: 20
SALES (corp-wide): 3.7B **Privately Held**
SIC: 7694 Electric motor repair
HQ: Sulzer Electro-Mechanical Services (Us) Inc.
1910 Jasmine Dr
Pasadena TX 77503
713 473-3231

(G-16265)
TOP DECK INC
10861 Highway 62 N (77632-7027)
P.O. Box 459, Mauriceville (77626-0459)
PHONE.................................409 745-3955
Jeffrey W Dalton, *President*
Robert Williams, *Superintendent*
Dennis Malone, *Vice Pres*
Chris Hantz, *Project Mgr*
Jamey Macfarlane, *Treasurer*
EMP: 50
SQ FT: 25,880
SALES: 15.8MM **Privately Held**
WEB: www.topdeckinc.net
SIC: 1799 1721 7699 7692 Coating of metal structures at construction site; industrial painting; mechanical instrument repair; welding repair

(G-16266)
TRAMPOLINE USA INC
9010 Interstate 10 W (77632-8042)
PHONE.................................800 872-6765
John Murdock Jr, *Branch Mgr*

EMP: 11
SALES (corp-wide): 1.5MM **Privately Held**
WEB: www.trampolineusa.com
SIC: **3949** Sporting & athletic goods
HQ: Trampolines Usa, Inc.
8672 Interstate 10 W
Orange TX 77632
409 745-3139

(G-16267)
TRAMPOLINES USA INC (HQ)
8672 Interstate 10 W (77632-8412)
PHONE.................................409 745-3139
John Murdock, *President*
Connie Williams, *Sales Staff*
Johnny Murdock III, *Marketing Staff*
▲ EMP: 13
SQ FT: 20,000
SALES (est): 1.5MM **Privately Held**
WEB: www.1800trampoline.com
SIC: **5941 3631** Trampolines & equipment;
playground equipment; barbecues, grills
& braziers (outdoor cooking)
PA: Family Store Network, Llc
8672 Interstate 10 W
Orange TX 77632
409 745-3139

Orange Grove
Jim Wells County

(G-16268)
MARTINEZ OIL & GAS LLC (PA)
223 Mdow Trl Orange Grv Orange Grove
(78372)
PHONE.................................361 384-9500
EMP: 40
SQ FT: 2,000
SALES (est): 3MM **Privately Held**
SIC: **1381** Service well drilling

(G-16269)
**OIL STATES ENERGY SERVICES
LLC**
405 E Orange Ave (78372-3699)
P.O. Box 1320 (78372-1320)
PHONE.................................361 384-0041
Stacey Herschap, *Manager*
EMP: 15
SALES (corp-wide): 1B **Publicly Held**
WEB: www.oses.com
SIC: **3533 5082** Oil field machinery &
equipment; oil field equipment
HQ: Oil States Energy Services, L.L.C.
333 Clay St Ste 2100
Houston TX 77002
713 425-2400

(G-16270)
**TORNADO PRODUCTION SVCS
LLC**
1587 W Fm 624 (78372)
P.O. Box 1707 (78372-1707)
PHONE.................................361 384-9020
Darren Scott Kirchhoff,
Luis Charow,
Roger Floyd,
EMP: 64
SQ FT: 8,500
SALES (est): 18.3MM **Privately Held**
WEB: www.tornadoproductionservices.com
SIC: **1389** Chemically treating wells

Orangefield
Orange County

(G-16271)
LYNX WELL SERVICE INC
Also Called: Orange Oilfield Supply
5443 Fm 408 (77639)
P.O. Box 309 (77639-0309)
PHONE.................................409 735-2604
Robert P Cormier, *President*
EMP: 10
SALES (est): 1.3MM **Privately Held**
WEB: www.orangeoilfield.com
SIC: **1389** Oil field services

Orchard
Fort Bend County

(G-16272)
EFI PANEL SYSTEMS LLC
Also Called: Efi Panels
9631 Hwy 36 W (77464)
PHONE.................................281 533-9100
Robert Navon, *Mng Member*
EMP: 65
SALES (est): 2MM **Privately Held**
WEB: www.efipanels.com
SIC: **3444** Sheet metalwork

(G-16273)
EFI PANELS LLC
9631 Hwy 36 (77464)
PHONE.................................615 301-0745
David Ware, *President*
EMP: 10 EST: 2009
SALES (est): 1.6MM **Privately Held**
WEB: www.efipanels.com
SIC: **3441** Fabricated structural metal

Ore City
Upshur County

(G-16274)
LA FAMA FOODS INC
Also Called: La Fama Tortilla Factory
7566 Us Highway 259 N (75683-5639)
PHONE.................................903 968-4500
Raul Roel, *President*
Sandra Roel, *Corp Secy*
Reggie Roel, *Vice Pres*
R Tomas Roel, *Plant Mgr*
EMP: 90
SQ FT: 20,000
SALES (est): 46.9MM **Privately Held**
WEB: www.lafamafoods.com
SIC: **5148 5963 2099** Vegetables, fresh;
food services, direct sales; tortillas, fresh
or refrigerated

Overton
Rusk County

(G-16275)
BASIC ENERGY SERVICES INC
1995 State Highway 42 N (75684-7371)
P.O. Box 550 (75684-0550)
PHONE.................................903 895-4448
EMP: 45
SALES (corp-wide): 805.6MM **Publicly
Held**
SIC: **1389** Oil Field Service Contractor
PA: Basic Energy Services, Inc.
801 Cherry St Unit 2
Fort Worth TX 76102
817 334-4100

(G-16276)
BIG TOM CONSTRUCTION INC
17636 Fm 2089 (75684-4461)
PHONE.................................903 752-1008
Tom Hall Jr, *Principal*
EMP: 9
SALES (est): 760K **Privately Held**
SIC: **1389** Oil field services

(G-16277)
**WLDG WILKERSON &
FABRICATION**
10702 County Road 173 N (75684-3212)
PHONE.................................817 528-1032
EMP: 15
SALES: 130K **Privately Held**
SIC: **7692 3441** Welding & Fabrication

Ozona
Crockett County

(G-16278)
APPROACH RESOURCES INC
638 State Hwy 163 N (76943)
PHONE.................................325 392-8900
Justin Griggs, *Supervisor*

EMP: 10
SALES (corp-wide): 114MM **Privately
Held**
WEB: www.approachresources.com
SIC: **1311 1382** Crude petroleum & natu-
ral gas; oil & gas exploration services
PA: Approach Resources Inc.
6500 West Fwy Ste 900
Fort Worth TX 76116
817 989-9000

(G-16279)
D M GLOVER INCORPORATED
Also Called: Glover Company, The
2973 Inter State 10 E (76943)
P.O. Box 948 (76943-0948)·
PHONE.................................325 392-2561
Mike Glover, *President*
EMP: 19
SQ FT: 6,800
SALES (est): 4MM **Privately Held**
WEB: www.theglovercompany.com
SIC: **1389** Oil field services

(G-16280)
DCP MIDSTREAM LLC
594 S State Hwy 163 (76943)
PHONE.................................325 392-1000
Brad Powell, *Manager*
EMP: 11
SALES (corp-wide): 1.9B **Privately Held**
WEB: www.dcpmidstream.com
SIC: **2813** Industrial gases
PA: Dcp Midstream, Llc
370 17th St Ste 2500
Denver CO 80202
303 633-2900

(G-16281)
DJH SERVICES LLC
Hwy 163 N (76943)
P.O. Box 1473 (76943-1473)
PHONE.................................325 392-3671
Don Rockwell, *Manager*
EMP: 12
SALES (corp-wide): 9.8MM **Privately
Held**
SIC: **1311** Crude petroleum production
PA: Djh Services Llc
712 Main St Ste 1900
Houston TX 77002
713 228-5911

(G-16282)
EOG RESOURCES INC
Hwy 163 S (76943)
PHONE.................................325 392-3782
Albert Billman, *Engineer*
Tuyen Nguyen, *Accountant*
Mike Huntington, *Manager*
EMP: 15
SALES (corp-wide): 17.3B **Publicly Held**
WEB: www.eogresources.com
SIC: **1382** Oil & gas exploration services
PA: Eog Resources, Inc.
1111 Bagby Sky Lbby 2
Houston TX 77002
713 651-7000

(G-16283)
FESCO LTD
105 Medical Dr (76943)
P.O. Box 1568 (76943-1568)
PHONE.................................325 392-3773
Tom Anderson, *Sales/Mktg Mgr*
EMP: 16
SALES (corp-wide): 201MM **Privately
Held**
WEB: www.fescoinc.com
SIC: **7389 1389** Inspection & testing serv-
ices; oil field services
PA: Fesco, Ltd.
1000 Fesco Dr
Alice TX 78332
361 664-3479

(G-16284)
GLOVER INC
Also Called: Glover Company
2973 Hwy 10 E (76943)
PHONE.................................325 392-2561
Mike Glover, *President*
Tai Araujo, *Office Admin*
Sandy Glover, *Admin Sec*
EMP: 14

SALES (est): 1MM **Privately Held**
WEB: www.theglovercompany.com
SIC: **1389** Oil field services

(G-16285)
LILLY CONSTRUCTION INC
603 Ave H (76943)
P.O. Box 1567 (76943-1567)
PHONE.................................325 392-2669
Jana Wilson, *President*
Suzy N Harrison, *Principal*
Dave Wilson, *Vice Pres*
EMP: 43 EST: 1955
SQ FT: 9,000
SALES (est): 5.5MM **Privately Held**
WEB: www.lillyconstructioninc.com
SIC: **1389 3273** Construction, repair & dis-
mantling services; ready-mixed concrete

(G-16286)
NABORS WELL SERVICES LTD
Hwy 163 N (76943)
PHONE.................................325 392-2313
Jamey Bauerlein, *Branch Mgr*
EMP: 18 **Privately Held**
WEB: www.nabors.com
SIC: **1389** Oil field services
HQ: Nabors Well Services Ltd.
515 W Greens Rd Ste 1200
Houston TX 77067
281 874-0035

(G-16287)
THOMPSON & THOMPSON
Also Called: Double T Ranch
117 Ave H (76943)
P.O. Box 2099 (76943-2099)
PHONE.................................325 392-3721
James Dolby, *Manager*
EMP: 15
SALES (corp-wide): 25.5MM **Privately
Held**
SIC: **1311 0212 1389** Crude petroleum
production; beef cattle except feedlots; oil
field services
PA: Thompson & Thompson
325 N Saint Paul St # 4300
Dallas TX 75201
214 953-1177

(G-16288)
TOM THORP TRANSPORTS
102 Bob White Dr (76943)
PHONE.................................325 392-8323
Tom Thorp, *Owner*
EMP: 70
SALES (est): 1.6MM **Privately Held**
SIC: **1389 4213** Oil field services; trucking,
except local

(G-16289)
**TRIPLE C HARDWARE &
LUMBER INC**
Also Called: Do It Best
1116 Ave E (76943)
P.O. Box 934 (76943-0934)
PHONE.................................325 392-4123
Cole W Crenwelge, *President*
Tommy Connor, *Vice Pres*
Russell D Crenwelge, *Admin Sec*
EMP: 21
SQ FT: 5,000
SALES (est): 10MM **Privately Held**
WEB: www.triplechardware.com
SIC: **5211 5251 3429 5072** Planing mill
products & lumber; fencing; builders'
hardware; builders' hardware; hardware

(G-16290)
U S WEATHERFORD L P
211 Crockett Ln (76943)
P.O. Box 4129 (76943-4129)
PHONE.................................325 392-3715
Johnny Smith, *Manager*
EMP: 16 **Privately Held**
WEB: www.weatherford.com
SIC: **1389** Oil field services
HQ: U S Weatherford L P
179 Weatherford Dr
Schriever LA 70395
985 493-6100

Paint Rock
Concho County

(G-16291)
INGRIDS CUSTOM HAND WOVEN
Hwy 83 (76866)
P.O. Box 115 (76866-0115)
PHONE....................................325 732-4370
Reinhard Schoffthaler, *President*
Ingrid Haas, *Vice Pres*
EMP: 15
SQ FT: 5,000
SALES (est): 280K **Privately Held**
WEB: www.texashandwoven.com
SIC: 2273 2231 2392 Rugs, machine woven; blankets & blanketings: wool or similar fibers; household furnishings

Palacios
Matagorda County

(G-16292)
TRANSPORT BOATS
1729 1st St (77465-3407)
PHONE....................................361 972-6629
Donny L Tran, *Principal*
John Frankson, *Principal*
EMP: 11
SALES (est): 950K **Privately Held**
WEB: www.transportboats.com
SIC: 3732 Boat building & repairing

(G-16293)
TRES PALACIOS MARINE LP
111 Friery Rd (77465-6838)
P.O. Box 1285 (77465-1285)
PHONE....................................361 972-3097
Harry J Fiegel Jr, *Partner*
EMP: 35
SALES (est): 5.8MM **Privately Held**
WEB: www.palaciosmarineindustrial.com
SIC: 3441 Boat & barge sections, prefabricated metal

Palestine
Anderson County

(G-16294)
ACID AND CEMENTING SVCS INC
3212 W Oak St (75801-5407)
P.O. Box 1258 (75802-1258)
PHONE....................................903 729-2500
Charles D Walker, *President*
EMP: 40
SALES (est): 6MM **Privately Held**
WEB: www.acid-cement.com
SIC: 1389 Oil field services; cementing oil & gas well casings

(G-16295)
AEROSPACE FASTENERS INC
255 N Us Highway 287 (75803-2022)
PHONE....................................903 723-0693
Jason Elfarr, *President*
Carole Elfarr, *Vice Pres*
Jose Roman, *Sales Staff*
Aundria Baker, *Receptionist*
EMP: 30
SALES (est): 8.5MM **Privately Held**
WEB: www.aerospacefasteners.com
SIC: 3728 Aircraft parts & equipment

(G-16296)
BAZE CHEMICAL INC
2187 E Fm 323 (75801-8867)
PHONE....................................903 723-3146
Greg Skusca, *Principal*
EMP: 20 **Privately Held**
WEB: www.bazechemical.com
SIC: 2869 Industrial organic chemicals
PA: Baze Chemical, Inc.
3801 Mankins Ave
Odessa TX 79764

(G-16297)
CALVARY VALVE INC
Also Called: CVI
220 Threll St (75803-6650)
PHONE....................................903 729-0485
Jimmy W Ray, *President*
Glen W Morgan, *Vice Pres*
Gerald J Nelson, *Vice Pres*
Brian Alston, *Sales Staff*
▲ **EMP:** 13
SALES (est): 3.3MM **Privately Held**
WEB: www.calvaryvalve.com
SIC: 3491 7699 Industrial valves; valve repair, industrial

(G-16298)
D & D SWABBING LLC
3471 E Us Highway 84 (75801-1432)
P.O. Box 737 (75802-0737)
PHONE....................................903 729-7922
Douglas Smith,
EMP: 19
SQ FT: 1,000
SALES (est): 1.5MM **Privately Held**
SIC: 1389 Oil field services

(G-16299)
HEADWATERS CNSTR MTLS LLC (DH)
Also Called: Palestine Concrete Tile Co
2500 W Reagan St (75801-2201)
PHONE....................................903 729-2217
Bobby L Whishant, *President*
Harlan M Hatfield, *Vice Pres*
Donald P Newman, *CFO*
Scott Jackson, *Treasurer*
Mike Mildenhall, *Admin Sec*
EMP: 50
SQ FT: 15,000
SALES (est): 10.8MM **Privately Held**
WEB: www.headwaterscm.com
SIC: 3271 Blocks, concrete or cinder: standard

(G-16300)
KENNER WELL SVC OF PALESTINE
4329 S State Highway 19 (75801-7924)
P.O. Box 557 (75802-0557)
PHONE....................................903 729-3196
Chris Kenner, *President*
Mary Corman, *Executive*
Mary Kay Corman, *Admin Sec*
EMP: 22
SALES (est): 2.5MM **Privately Held**
WEB: www.kennerwellservice.com
SIC: 1389 1381 Oil field services; drilling oil & gas wells

(G-16301)
KEY ENERGY SERVICES INC
8801 S Us Highway 79 (75801-7236)
PHONE....................................903 538-2280
Keith Holliman, *Manager*
EMP: 83
SALES (corp-wide): 413.8MM **Publicly Held**
WEB: www.keyenergy.com
SIC: 1389 1381 Haulage, oil field; drilling oil & gas wells
PA: Key Energy Services, Inc.
1301 Mckinney St Ste 1800
Houston TX 77010
713 651-4300

(G-16302)
MARY OF PUDDIN HILL INC
512 N John St (75801-2725)
PHONE....................................903 455-2651
Ken Bain, *President*
EMP: 16
SQ FT: 50,000
SALES (est): 1.6MM **Privately Held**
WEB: www.puddinhill.com
SIC: 2051 2064 Bakery: wholesale or wholesale/retail combined; candy & other confectionery products

(G-16303)
MCCURDY SERVICES INC
2223 W Point Tap Rd (75803-2150)
PHONE....................................903 729-5681
David Douglas, *Branch Mgr*
EMP: 25

SALES (corp-wide): 32.2MM **Privately Held**
SIC: 1389 Oil field services
PA: Mccurdy Services, Inc.
6229 Fourwinds Dr
Bryan TX
979 778-2961

(G-16304)
MOUNTAIN PURE TX LLC
777 Willow Creek Pkwy (75801-4339)
PHONE....................................903 723-1362
John Stacks,
▲ **EMP:** 25 **EST:** 2007
SALES (est): 4.4MM **Privately Held**
WEB: www.mountainpurebeverage.com
SIC: 2086 2899 Fruit drinks (less than 100% juice): packaged in cans, etc.; distilled water

(G-16305)
NEWSPAPER HOLDING INC
Also Called: Palestine Herald-Press
519 N Elm St (75801-2927)
P.O. Box 379 (75802-0379)
PHONE....................................903 729-0281
Larry Mayo, *Manager*
EMP: 60
SALES (corp-wide): 23.7B **Privately Held**
WEB: www.oskaloosa.com
SIC: 2711 Newspapers, publishing & printing
HQ: Newspaper Holding, Inc.
425 Locust St
Johnstown PA 15901
814 532-5102

(G-16306)
OILFIELD ANCHOR COMPANY INC
Also Called: P & L Rentals
600 N John St (75801-2727)
P.O. Box 3929 (75801)
PHONE....................................903 723-2833
Shawnda Stone, *President*
EMP: 75
SQ FT: 4,000
SALES (est): 13.5MM **Privately Held**
SIC: 1389 2911 Oil field services; oils, fuel

(G-16307)
OWENS CORNING SALES LLC
10658 W State Highway 294 (75801-6501)
PHONE....................................903 538-2271
Mike Crosby, *Branch Mgr*
EMP: 55 **Publicly Held**
WEB: www.owenscorning.com
SIC: 3296 Fiberglass insulation
HQ: Owens Corning Sales, Llc
1 Owens Corning Pkwy
Toledo OH 43659
419 248-8000

(G-16308)
SANDERSON FARMS INC
Also Called: Sanderson Farms Proc Plant
400 Sanderson Farms Pkwy (75803-5418)
PHONE....................................903 723-2112
Joe Sanderson, *CEO*
Timothy Rigney, *Admin Sec*
EMP: 99
SALES (est): 1.5MM **Privately Held**
SIC: 2015 Variety meats (fresh edible organs), poultry

(G-16309)
WEISSKER MFG LTD LBLTY CO
10658 W State Highway 294 (75801-6501)
PHONE....................................903 538-2271
Tony R Wade,
Tony Wade,
William G Wade,
▲ **EMP:** 16
SALES (est): 2.1MM **Privately Held**
WEB: www.weissker.com
SIC: 3231 Reflector glass beads, for highway signs or reflectors

Palmview
Hidalgo County

(G-16310)
FORDYCE LTD
3601 N Abram Rd (78572-1800)
P.O. Box 790, Penitas (78576-0790)
PHONE....................................956 581-0672
Rudy Flores, *Manager*
John Wells, *Manager*
EMP: 32
SALES (corp-wide): 278.6MM **Privately Held**
SIC: 3531 1442 Asphalt plant, including gravel-mix type; construction sand & gravel
PA: Fordyce, Ltd.
120 S Main St
Victoria TX 77901
361 573-4309

(G-16311)
MAGIC VALLEY CONCRETE LLC (PA)
3609 W Palma Vista Dr (78572-1861)
PHONE....................................956 432-0600
Rufino Garza,
Ramiro Flores,
Joe Larry Hinojosa, *Clerk*
EMP: 30
SQ FT: 1,600
SALES (est): 15MM **Privately Held**
WEB: www.capatexas.com
SIC: 3273 Ready-mixed concrete

(G-16312)
RIO VALLEY PIPE LLC (PA)
Also Called: Capa
3609 W Palma Vista Dr (78572-1861)
PHONE....................................956 580-3466
Ramiro J Flores, *Partner*
Lori Garza, *Human Res Mgr*
Monica Pena, *Human Resources*
Dorian Madrigal, *Sales Mgr*
Rufino Garza, *Mng Member*
EMP: 39 **EST:** 2007
SALES (est): 16MM **Privately Held**
WEB: www.capatexas.com
SIC: 3272 Pipe, concrete or lined with concrete

(G-16313)
VALLEY WELDING SERVICE
Also Called: Valley Welding & Crane Service
1313 N Moorefield Rd (78572-7014)
PHONE....................................956 585-1043
EMP: 50
SQ FT: 15,000
SALES (est): 7.2MM **Privately Held**
WEB: www.thebluebook.com
SIC: 3441 7353 Fabricated structural metal; cranes & aerial lift equipment, rental or leasing

Pampa
Gray County

(G-16314)
ARCHROCK INC
305 S Price Rd (79065-6908)
PHONE....................................806 669-8900
David McFatter, *Area Mgr*
Trent Watson, *Manager*
EMP: 51 **Publicly Held**
WEB: www.archrock.com
SIC: 1389 7699 Gas compressing (natural gas) at the fields; industrial machinery & equipment repair
PA: Archrock, Inc.
9807 Katy Fwy Ste 100
Houston TX 77024

(G-16315)
BAKER HGHES OLFLD OPRTIONS INC
Also Called: Baker Oil Tools
1043 N Price Rd (79065-5905)
P.O. Box 2377 (79066-2377)
PHONE....................................806 665-5786
Fax: 806 665-0016
EMP: 10

SALES (corp-wide): 9.8B **Publicly Held**
SIC: 1389 Sales Gas Sales And Services
HQ: Baker Hughes Oilfield Operations Llc
17021 Aldine Westfield Rd
Houston TX 77073
713 879-1000

(G-16316)
BRADLEY OPERATING COMPANY
11805 W Mccullough St (79065-1778)
PHONE.....................806 665-7130
James Bradley, *President*
EMP: 13
SQ FT: 2,200
SALES (est): 2.1MM **Privately Held**
SIC: 1311 Crude petroleum production; natural gas production

(G-16317)
CABOT CORPORATION
3 Miles W On Hwy 60 (79065)
P.O. Box 5001 (79066-5001)
PHONE.....................806 661-3100
Jay Doubman, *Vice Pres*
Dale Plart, *Opers-Prdtn-Mfg*
Barbara Tolbert, *Human Res Mgr*
EMP: 140
SALES (corp-wide): 2.6B **Publicly Held**
WEB: www.cabot-corp.com
SIC: 2895 3624 Carbon black; carbon & graphite products
PA: Cabot Corporation
2 Seaport Ln Ste 1300
Boston MA 02210
617 345-0100

(G-16318)
CAMERON INTERNATIONAL CORP
Cooper Nickels
423 S Gray St (79065-7203)
PHONE.....................806 665-1647
David Stidham, *Manager*
EMP: 23 **Publicly Held**
WEB: www.products.slb.com
SIC: 7699 7538 3714 3563 Industrial machinery & equipment repair; engine rebuilding: automotive; motor vehicle parts & accessories; air & gas compressors
HQ: Cameron International Corporation
4646 W Sam Houston Pkwy N
Houston TX 77041

(G-16319)
COPAN CORPORATION
Also Called: Romines & Warner
101 Doyle St (79065-6903)
P.O. Box 2077 (79066-2077)
PHONE.....................806 665-1267
James L Romines, *President*
Kevin Romines, *Vice Pres*
Romines Freddie, *Director*
Shirlene Topper, *Admin Sec*
EMP: 9
SQ FT: 3,000
SALES (est): 1MM **Privately Held**
WEB: www.pampatx.com
SIC: 1381 1389 Directional drilling oil & gas wells; servicing oil & gas wells

(G-16320)
CRALL PRODUCTS INC
Also Called: Zw
2930 Hwy 152 W (79065)
P.O. Box 2399 (79066-2399)
PHONE.....................806 665-8446
Curtis Heard, *President*
Debbie McMinn, *Admin Sec*
▲ EMP: 38 EST: 1946
SQ FT: 30,000
SALES (est): 8.5MM **Privately Held**
WEB: www.crallproducts.com
SIC: 3443 3569 Vessels, process or storage (from boiler shops): metal plate; filters, general line: industrial

(G-16321)
CTW BRAKE RIMS INC
Pampa Industrial Park E (79065)
P.O. Box 2142 (79066-2142)
PHONE.....................806 665-0289
Bill Willis, *President*
Leona Willis, *Corp Secy*
Lindon Willis, *Vice Pres*
EMP: 12

SQ FT: 30,000
SALES (est): 1.9MM **Privately Held**
WEB: www.willismfg.com
SIC: 3533 Oil field machinery & equipment

(G-16322)
EXCEL PRODUCTION CO
1050 N Price Rd (79065-5911)
P.O. Box 1800 (79066-1800)
PHONE.....................806 665-0366
Jack T Curtis Jr, *Partner*
Joe E Curtis, *Partner*
David Cory, *CFO*
EMP: 10 EST: 1982
SQ FT: 8,000
SALES (est): 2.9MM **Privately Held**
WEB: www.excelproduction.com
SIC: 1311 Crude petroleum production; natural gas production

(G-16323)
FRED BROWN METHANOL INC
101 Naida St (79065-6901)
P.O. Box 1916 (79066-1916)
PHONE.....................806 665-0034
C Wilber Walls, *President*
Walls Judy, *Vice Pres*
EMP: 15
SALES (est): 2.7MM **Privately Held**
SIC: 5984 1311 Liquefied petroleum gas dealers; crude petroleum & natural gas production

(G-16324)
GRYPHON PRODUCTION CO LLC
216 S Price Rd (79065-6916)
P.O. Box 509, Amarillo (79105-0509)
PHONE.....................806 688-9697
Brad Fischer,
EMP: 20
SALES (est): 1.2MM **Privately Held**
SIC: 1382 Oil & gas exploration services

(G-16325)
HOLMAN WELL SERVICE LLC
11401 Highway 152 (79065-1405)
P.O. Box 960 (79066-0960)
PHONE.....................806 665-3355
Dennis Holman, *Mng Member*
Denise Holman, *Mng Member*
Scott White,
EMP: 70
SQ FT: 6,100
SALES (est): 4.4MM **Privately Held**
SIC: 1389 Oil field services

(G-16326)
LARRY & MATT INC (PA)
Also Called: B & G Electric
241 Western St (79065)
PHONE.....................806 665-4418
Matt Hinton, *President*
Larry Beck, *Corp Secy*
EMP: 97
SQ FT: 3,500
SALES (est): 18.9MM **Privately Held**
WEB: www.bgepdiesel.com
SIC: 1389 5085 1731 4971 Oil field services; industrial supplies; electric power systems contractors; irrigation systems; irrigation equipment

(G-16327)
LINEAGE LLC
11784 Highway 152 (79065-1408)
P.O. Box 2359 (79066-2359)
PHONE.....................806 688-7384
Kevin Carlson, *President*
Kathi Bagley, *Vice Pres*
Bonnie Carlson, *Treasurer*
James L Bagley, *Admin Sec*
EMP: 25
SALES (est): 6.1MM **Privately Held**
WEB: www.lineagellc.com
SIC: 3423 Plumbers' hand tools

(G-16328)
MELVIN HAMMON
Also Called: Hammon's Janitorial
622 E Foster Ave (79065-6608)
PHONE.....................806 665-2667
Melvin L Hammon, *Owner*
EMP: 13

SALES (est): 358.6K **Privately Held**
SIC: 7349 6514 7217 1311 Janitorial service, contract basis; dwelling operators, except apartments; carpet & furniture cleaning on location; crude petroleum production

(G-16329)
MIDCOAST ENERGY LLC
Also Called: Enbridge Pipelines
1313 N Hobart St (79065-4121)
PHONE.....................806 663-7700
Lenard Norrid, *Manager*
EMP: 15
SALES (corp-wide): 1.2B **Privately Held**
WEB: www.midcoastenergy.com
SIC: 1382 Oil & gas exploration services
HQ: Midcoast Energy, Llc
1501 Mckinney St Ste 600
Houston TX 77010
713 821-2000

(G-16330)
O-TEX PUMPING LLC
1865 Mccullough St (79065-1632)
PHONE.....................806 665-0552
Larry Kirchner, *President*
EMP: 50
SALES (corp-wide): 146MM **Privately Held**
WEB: www.otexpumping.com
SIC: 1389 Oil field services
PA: O-Tex Pumping, L.L.C.
306 W Wall St Ste 700
Midland TX 79701
432 685-9901

(G-16331)
PAMPA CONCRETE CO INC
220 W Tyng Ave (79065-7312)
P.O. Box 1700 (79066-1700)
PHONE.....................806 669-3111
Bill J Williamson, *President*
EMP: 15
SQ FT: 1,200
SALES (est): 2.1MM **Privately Held**
WEB: www.pampatx.com
SIC: 3273 Ready-mixed concrete

(G-16332)
PAMPA MACHINE & SUPPLY INC
112 Western St (79065-1133)
P.O. Box 2558 (79066-2558)
PHONE.....................806 665-0013
Tony Richardson, *President*
Loren Coucs, *Admin Sec*
EMP: 15
SQ FT: 8,750
SALES (est): 3.4MM **Privately Held**
SIC: 5084 3599 7692 Oil well machinery, equipment & supplies; machine shop, jobbing & repair; welding repair

(G-16333)
PARSLEYS SHTMTL & ROOFG CO
214 E Tyng Ave (79065-7452)
P.O. Box 221 (79066-0221)
PHONE.....................806 669-6461
Randy Parsley, *President*
Maudie Alexander, *Manager*
Kerry Parsley, *Shareholder*
EMP: 45
SQ FT: 3,000
SALES (est): 2.7MM **Privately Held**
WEB: www.parsleysroofing.com
SIC: 5033 1761 3444 Roofing, asphalt & sheet metal; roofing contractor; sheet metalwork; sheet metalwork

(G-16334)
PETCO PETROLEUM CORPORATION
Se Of City (79065)
P.O. Box 2456 (79066-2456)
PHONE.....................806 669-3947
Dennis Laycock, *Branch Mgr*
EMP: 76 **Privately Held**
WEB: www.petcopetroleum.com
SIC: 1311 Crude petroleum production
PA: Petco Petroleum Corporation
108 E Ogden Ave Ste 100
Hinsdale IL 60521

(G-16335)
PREMIERE WELL SERVICE
2101 Mccullough St (79065)
P.O. Box 1096 (79066-1096)
PHONE.....................806 669-3227
Allan Snapp, *President*
EMP: 28
SQ FT: 30,000
SALES (est): 2.7MM **Privately Held**
SIC: 1389 Oil field services

(G-16336)
PTS INC
Also Called: Pampa News
403 W Atchison Ave (79065-6303)
P.O. Box 2198 (79066-2198)
PHONE.....................806 669-2525
Reigdon Woods, *Branch Mgr*
EMP: 15 **Privately Held**
WEB: www.thepampanews.com
SIC: 2711 Newspapers, publishing & printing
PA: Pts, Inc.
221 35th St Ne Ste A
Fort Payne AL

(G-16337)
REGENCY CRUDE MARKETING LLC
8442 County Road 3 (79065-1409)
PHONE.....................806 665-3491
Jaime Valdez, *Branch Mgr*
EMP: 90 **Publicly Held**
SIC: 1311 Crude petroleum & natural gas
HQ: Regency Crude Marketing Llc
1415 La St Ste 2700
Houston TX 77252

(G-16338)
REGENCY ENERGY PARTNERS LP
Also Called: Regency Field Services
220 N Ballard St (79065-6540)
PHONE.....................806 665-2551
Gene Kemph, *Manager*
EMP: 13 **Publicly Held**
WEB: www.energytransfer.com
SIC: 1321 Natural gas liquids
HQ: Regency Energy Partners Lp
8111 Westchester Dr # 600
Dallas TX 75225
214 750-1771

(G-16339)
SULPHUR RIVER GATHERING LP
1313 N Hobart St (79065-4121)
PHONE.....................806 663-7700
Terri Larson, *Branch Mgr*
EMP: 12
SALES (corp-wide): 11.4MM **Privately Held**
SIC: 3569 Gas producers, generators & other gas related equipment
PA: Sulphur River Gathering, Lp
4851 Lyndon B Johnson Fwy # 550
Dallas TX 75244
214 373-1091

(G-16340)
SWM INTERNATIONAL INC
Also Called: Specialty Welding and Machine
2225 Alcock St (79065-5711)
P.O. Box 1794 (79066-1794)
PHONE.....................806 665-8747
Dawna Mauldin, *President*
Chris Arnzen, *Foreman/Supr*
▲ EMP: 100
SQ FT: 120,000
SALES (est): 61MM **Privately Held**
WEB: www.swmtx.com
SIC: 3533 Oil & gas drilling rigs & equipment; drilling tools for gas, oil or water wells

(G-16341)
THURMOND-MCGLOTHLIN LLC (PA)
1428 N Banks St (79065-4108)
P.O. Box 2358 (79066-2358)
PHONE.....................806 665-5700
Olen Douglass, *Opers Mgr*
Jack W Chisum,
Ken Hudgeons,
EMP: 9

SQ FT: 2,000
SALES (est): 34.6MM **Privately Held**
WEB: www.tm-ems.com
SIC: **1389** 5084 8734 Oil consultants;
testing, measuring, surveying & analysis
services; meters, consumption registering; testing laboratories

(G-16342)
TOP O TEXAS OILFIELD
SERVICES (PA)
408 S Price Rd (79065)
P.O. Box 2354 (79066-2354)
PHONE..................................806 665-2501
Jerrod Imeo, *President*
Jerrod Imel, *Executive*
EMP: 23
SALES (est): 4.9MM **Privately Held**
WEB: www.topotexas.net
SIC: **1389** Oil field services

(G-16343)
TRIANGLE WELL SERVICING CO
129 S Price Rd (79065-6914)
P.O. Box 1159 (79066-1159)
PHONE..................................806 665-8459
Deborah Hoover, *President*
Vickie Lynn Hoover, *Corp Secy*
Debbie Hartman, *Vice Pres*
EMP: 15 EST: 1948
SQ FT: 5,000
SALES (est): 2.9MM **Privately Held**
WEB: www.trianglewellservice.com
SIC: **1389** Oil field services

(G-16344)
W & W FIBERGLASS TANK
COMPANY
Also Called: W&W
100 N Price Rd (79065-6900)
PHONE..................................806 669-1128
Wayne Wilson, *CEO*
Judd Wilson, *President*
Jona Little, *Corp Secy*
▲ EMP: 58 EST: 1978
SQ FT: 12,000
SALES (est): 23.9MM **Privately Held**
WEB: www.wwtank.com
SIC: **3089** 7699 3088 Plastic & fiberglass
tanks; tank repair; plastics plumbing fix-
tures

(G-16345)
WILLIAM L ARRINGTON
Also Called: Arrington Companies
408 W Kingsmill Ave 171a (79065-6343)
P.O. Box 31 (79066-0031)
PHONE..................................806 669-3324
William L Arrington, *Owner*
EMP: 9 EST: 1961
SQ FT: 800
SALES (est): 3.5MM **Privately Held**
WEB:
www.arringtonparishcouncil.btck.co.uk
SIC: **1311** 1382 0212 0111 Crude petro-
leum production; natural gas production;
oil & gas exploration services; beef cattle
except feedlots; wheat; milo farm

(G-16346)
WO ENERGY OF NEVADA INC
(HQ)
Also Called: Wo Operating
11705 Highway 152 (79065-1414)
PHONE..................................806 665-8298
Jeff Johnson, *Ch of Bd*
James R Latimer III, *President*
Miles O'Loughlin, *President*
Scott White, *Vice Pres*
EMP: 9
SQ FT: 3,500
SALES (est): 4.9MM **Privately Held**
SIC: **1311** Crude petroleum production

Panhandle
Carson County

(G-16347)
CORNERSTONE SYNERGY LLC
Also Called: Cornerstone Energy Services
1150 Us Hwy 60 Panhandle (79068)
P.O. Box 1473 (79068-1473)
PHONE..................................806 679-9178

Luke Durst,
Tori Durst,
Chad Young,
EMP: 15
SQ FT: 6,000
SALES (est): 1MM **Privately Held**
SIC: **1389** Gas field services

(G-16348)
VIBRA-WHIRL SPORTS LTD
94 Main St (79068-3011)
P.O. Box 966 (79068-0966)
PHONE..................................806 537-3526
Marvin Sparks, *Partner*
Glen Swafford, *Partner*
▲ EMP: 25 EST: 1953
SQ FT: 16,000
SALES (est): 3.2MM **Privately Held**
WEB: www.vibrawhirl.com
SIC: **1799** 1629 3949 Court construction,
indoor athletic; athletic field construction;
tennis court construction; sporting & ath-
letic goods

Panola
Panola County

(G-16349)
PANOLA EQUIPMENT INC
County Rte 335 (75685)
P.O. Box 244 (75685-0244)
PHONE..................................903 633-2545
Bob Fonville, *President*
EMP: 15
SQ FT: 2,000
SALES (est): 1.3MM **Privately Held**
SIC: **5261** 1389 Lawnmowers & tractors;
oil field services

Pantego
Tarrant County

(G-16350)
ARCTIC STAR RFRGN MFG CO
Also Called: Arctic Star of Texas
3540 W Pioneer Pkwy (76013-4625)
PHONE..................................817 274-1396
James R Dunnagan, *President*
Joseph Jean, *Plant Mgr*
▲ EMP: 26
SALES (est): 4.9MM **Privately Held**
WEB: www.arcticstar.com
SIC: **3585** Cabinets, show & display, refrig-
erated; counters & counter display cases,
refrigerated

(G-16351)
PRODIGY PAINTING
2309 Superior Dr (76013-6014)
P.O. Box 122139, Arlington (76012-8139)
PHONE..................................817 277-2468
Tariq Cobety, *Owner*
EMP: 30
SQ FT: 1,500
SALES (est): 1.2MM **Privately Held**
WEB: www.kobty.org
SIC: **3479** Painting, coating & hot dipping

(G-16352)
SOUTHWEST CABINET
CORPORATION
Also Called: Anton Cabinetry
2002 W Pioneer Pkwy (76013-6006)
PHONE..................................817 460-8681
▲ EMP: 91 EST: 1974
SQ FT: 50,000
SALES: 14.1MM **Privately Held**
WEB: www.antoncabinetry.com
SIC: **2521** 7389 Cabinets, office: wood;
furniture finishing

(G-16353)
TEXAS PNEUMATIC SYSTEMS
INC (PA)
2404 Superior Dr (76013-6015)
PHONE..................................817 794-0068
Bernard E Rookey, *President*
Staley George, *Director*
EMP: 70
SQ FT: 10,000

SALES (est): 15.9MM **Privately Held**
WEB: www.txps.com
SIC: **3494** 7699 4581 Valves & pipe fittings; aircraft & heavy equipment repair
services; aircraft servicing & repairing

Paradise
Wise County

(G-16354)
TEXAS INDUSTRIES INC
Also Called: T X I
2939 W Highway 114 (76073-2614)
P.O. Box 37 (76073-0037)
PHONE..................................940 969-6021
Gary Williams, *Manager*
EMP: 22 **Publicly Held**
WEB: www.martinmarietta.com
SIC: **1442** Sand mining
HQ: Texas Industries, Inc.
1503 Lyndon B Johnson Fwy
Dallas TX 75234
972 647-6700

(G-16355)
TLR ENERGY SERVICES INC
(PA)
122 County Road 3341 (76073-2404)
PHONE..................................940 969-2400
Kendall Williams, *President*
Larry Williams, *Vice Pres*
Kim Reynolds, *Admin Sec*
EMP: 10
SQ FT: 3,200
SALES (est): 900K **Privately Held**
WEB: www.tlrwelding.com
SIC: **3441** 1799 Fabricated structural
metal; welding on site

(G-16356)
TLR WELDING & FABRICATING
INC
122 County Road 3341 (76073-2404)
PHONE..................................940 969-2400
Kendall Williams, *President*
Kendall J Williams, *Principal*
EMP: 19 EST: 2010
SALES (est): 2.4MM **Privately Held**
WEB: www.tlrwelding.com
SIC: **7692** Welding repair

Paris
Lamar County

(G-16357)
AEQUS OIL AND GAS LLC
2220 W Park St (75460-1636)
PHONE..................................832 616-3110
Aravind Melligeri, *Principal*
EMP: 18
SALES (est): 2.6MM **Privately Held**
WEB: www.aequs.com
SIC: **3999** Atomizers, toiletry

(G-16358)
BIMBO BAKERIES USA INC
2020 19th St Nw (75460-1708)
PHONE..................................903 785-6401
Ben Hickman, *General Mgr*
Julie Foley, *Vice Pres*
Craig Walth, *VP Sales*
Mark Castle, *Sales Mgr*
Jim Mc Cormick, *Marketing Staff*
EMP: 700 **Privately Held**
WEB: www.arnoldbread.com
SIC: **2051** Bread, all types (white, wheat,
rye, etc): fresh or frozen; cakes, bakery:
except frozen
HQ: Bimbo Bakeries Usa, Inc
255 Business Center Dr # 200
Horsham PA 19044
215 347-5500

(G-16359)
CAMPBELL SOUP COMPANY
500 Nw Loop 286 (75460-1820)
PHONE..................................903 784-3341
Roberto Leopardi, *Vice Pres*
David Parcher, *Plant Mgr*
Johnny Wooten, *Administration*
EMP: 169

SALES (corp-wide): 8.6B **Publicly Held**
WEB: www.campbellsoupcompany.com
SIC: **5461** 2038 2033 2052 Bakeries;
frozen specialties; canned fruits & specialties; cookies & crackers; bread, cake
& related products; potato chips & similar
snacks
PA: Campbell Soup Company
1 Campbell Pl
Camden NJ 08103
856 342-4800

(G-16360)
CHISUM SITE & STEEL INC
121 County Road 11400 (75462-8918)
P.O. Box 876 (75461-0876)
PHONE..................................903 783-0058
Susan Harper, *President*
Ww Harper, *Vice Pres*
EMP: 25
SQ FT: 13,000
SALES (est): 4.3MM **Privately Held**
SIC: **3441** Fabricated structural metal

(G-16361)
ELITE CABINETS & CLOSETS
133 Pine Bluff St (75460-4227)
PHONE..................................903 737-0848
Gary Weatherred, *Owner*
EMP: 10
SALES (est): 883.7K **Privately Held**
WEB: www.paristxcabinetry.com
SIC: **2434** Wood kitchen cabinets

(G-16362)
JAMES SKINNER CO
2020 19th St Nw (75460-1708)
PHONE..................................903 784-7174
Stacy Osborne, *Supervisor*
EMP: 10 EST: 2013
SALES (est): 841.6K **Privately Held**
SIC: **2051** Bakery products, partially
cooked (except frozen)

(G-16363)
JEMASCO INC
11808 Farm Road 906 E (75462-1016)
PHONE..................................903 784-3014
Buddy Michael, *President*
Virginia Michael, *Corp Secy*
Ronny E Michael, *Vice Pres*
Tim Michael, *Vice Pres*
EMP: 45
SQ FT: 20,000
SALES (est): 7.8MM **Privately Held**
WEB: www.jemasco.com
SIC: **2499** Mulch, wood & bark

(G-16364)
KIMBERLY-CLARK
CORPORATION
2466 Farm Road 137 (75460-1204)
PHONE..................................903 737-5100
Alan Deupree, *Fire Chief*
Jeff Frankland, *Opers Mgr*
Barbara Jeans, *Opers Staff*
Stephanie Darst, *Engineer*
Trent Lancaster, *Engineer*
EMP: 530
SALES (corp-wide): 19.1B **Publicly Held**
WEB: www.huggies.com
SIC: **2621** 2676 Sanitary tissue paper; in-
fant & baby paper products
PA: Kimberly-Clark Corporation
351 Phelps Dr
Irving TX 75038
972 281-1200

(G-16365)
METRO GATE & MFG CO INC
(PA)
Also Called: Quicksilver Arena
Hwy 82 W (75460)
P.O. Box 1609 (75461-1609)
PHONE..................................903 785-8911
Richard Sharrock, *President*
EMP: 25
SALES (est): 3.4MM **Privately Held**
WEB: www.quicksilverarenas.com
SIC: **2435** 3089 3315 Panels, hardwood
plywood; fences, gates & accessories:
plastic; steel wire & related products

(G-16366)
POTTERS INDUSTRIES LLC
1601 19th St Nw (75460-2307)
PHONE..................................903 785-1633
Steven Kennedy, *Buyer*
Owen Fox, *Manager*
EMP: 75
SALES (corp-wide): 167.9MM **Privately Held**
WEB: www.pqcorp.com
SIC: 3231 5039 Reflector glass beads, for highway signs or reflectors; glass construction materials
PA: Potters Industries, Llc
300 Lindenwood Dr
Malvern PA 19355
610 651-4700

(G-16367)
RODGERS-WADE MFG CO INC
Also Called: Rogers Wade
1401 3rd St Sw (75460-7002)
PHONE..................................903 739-2500
Ww Harper, *CEO*
John Hamer, *President*
Enrique Loza, *Project Mgr*
Tommy Hitchcock, *VP Bus Dvlpt*
Brandon Hoog, *CIO*
◆ **EMP:** 45
SALES (est): 8MM
SALES (corp-wide): 28MM **Privately Held**
WEB: www.rodgerswade.com
SIC: 2541 Wood partitions & fixtures
PA: Harrison, Walker And Harper, Lp
2510 S Church St
Paris TX 75460
903 517-5161

(G-16368)
ROGER HOOPER
Also Called: Red River Publishing
101 Lamar Ave (75460-4218)
P.O. Box 1194 (75461-1194)
PHONE..................................903 784-3328
Roger Hooper, *Owner*
Louann Hodge, *Sales Executive*
EMP: 10
SQ FT: 3,500
SALES (est): 420K **Privately Held**
WEB: www.redrivercoc.com
SIC: 2741 Shopping news: publishing only, not printed on site

(G-16369)
RW COX INC
1690 19th St Sw (75460-6824)
PHONE..................................903 739-8088
Ronnie Cox, *President*
Alicia Cox, *Vice Pres*
EMP: 45
SQ FT: 10,000
SALES (est): 9.9MM **Privately Held**
WEB: www.rwcoxinc.com
SIC: 1711 3548 Mechanical contractor; electrodes, electric welding

(G-16370)
SOUTHERN NEWSPAPERS INC
Also Called: Paris News
5050 Se Loop 286 (75460-6576)
P.O. Box 1078 (75461-1078)
PHONE..................................903 785-6900
Mike Graxiola, *Manager*
EMP: 50
SALES (corp-wide): 140.3MM **Privately Held**
WEB: www.sninews.com
SIC: 2759 2711 Newspapers: printing; newspapers
PA: Southern Newspapers, Inc.
5701 Woodway Dr Ste 131
Houston TX 77057
713 266-5481

(G-16371)
TECHSYS CHASSIS INC
524 S Church St (75460-7157)
PHONE..................................903 395-4155
M Pike Burkhart Sr, *President*
Kay Burkhart, *Corp Secy*
M Pike Burkhart Jr, *Vice Pres*
EMP: 45
SQ FT: 34,000

SALES (est): 8.7MM **Privately Held**
WEB: www.techsyschassis.com
SIC: 3715 3714 3523 Truck trailer chassis; axles, motor vehicle; tractors, farm

(G-16372)
TURNER INDUSTRIES GROUP LLC
1200 19th St Sw (75460)
PHONE..................................903 782-9379
Randal Dupuy, *Superintendent*
Chris Bailey, *Vice Pres*
Todd Westerman, *Opers Spvr*
Jason Allen, *Inv Control Mgr*
Tom Glasbock, *Manager*
EMP: 919
SALES (corp-wide): 1B **Privately Held**
WEB: www.turner-industries.com
SIC: 3498 Fabricated pipe & fittings
PA: Turner Industries Group Llc
8687 United Plaza Blvd # 103
Baton Rouge LA 70809
225 922-5050

(G-16373)
VALLEY FEED MILL INC PARIS (PA)
315 W Center St (75460-1899)
PHONE..................................903 785-3501
David Edzards, *President*
Jack Edzards, *Vice Pres*
EMP: 30
SQ FT: 32,000
SALES (est): 5.4MM **Privately Held**
WEB: www.paristexas.com
SIC: 2048 5153 Prepared feeds; grains

(G-16374)
WELASCO INC
1950 19th St Sw (75460-6865)
P.O. Box 1175 (75461-1175)
PHONE..................................903 784-5562
Cliff Leach, *President*
Bill Leach, *Vice Pres*
Sheri Sheffield, *Admin Sec*
EMP: 10
SQ FT: 11,000
SALES (est): 780K **Privately Held**
WEB: www.welasco.net
SIC: 3599 7692 Machine shop, jobbing & repair; welding repair

Pasadena
Harris County

(G-16375)
3S TEAM LLC
5330 Vista Rd (77505-2260)
P.O. Box 5594 (77508-5594)
PHONE..................................918 396-4155
Robert Fudge, *President*
Joe Fudge, *Principal*
Philip Levin, *CFO*
George Pyszynski, *Office Mgr*
EMP: 99
SALES (est): 9.2MM **Privately Held**
WEB: www.3s-team.com
SIC: 1389 Oil & gas field services

(G-16376)
ACCURATE CARGO TREATMENT
3139 Federal Rd Ste D (77504-1986)
PHONE..................................281 685-8573
Robert Sax, *Owner*
EMP: 12
SALES (est): 2MM **Privately Held**
WEB: www.cargotreatment.com
SIC: 2899 Fuel treating compounds

(G-16377)
ADRIAN SCOTT INDUSTRIES INC
Also Called: A S I
306 1/2 Pampa St (77504-1448)
P.O. Box 250 (77501-0250)
PHONE..................................713 941-3300
Adrian Scott, *President*
Susan Scott, *Treasurer*
EMP: 10
SQ FT: 8,000

SALES (est): 1.1MM **Privately Held**
WEB: www.adrianscottindustries.com
SIC: 2261 2262 Fire resistance finishing of cotton broadwoven fabrics; fire resistance finishing: manmade & silk broadwoven

(G-16378)
ADS CUSTOM SIGNS INC
4402 Glen Avon Dr (77505-4231)
PHONE..................................713 943-0895
Daniel Hickey, *Owner*
EMP: 9 **EST:** 2000
SALES (est): 877.4K **Privately Held**
WEB: www.adssigns.net
SIC: 3993 Signs, not made in custom sign painting shops

(G-16379)
AGRIFOS LLC
Also Called: Rentech Nitrogen
2001 Jackson Rd (77506)
PHONE..................................713 920-5300
Farouk Chaouni,
▼ **EMP:** 110 **EST:** 1998
SALES (est): 4.6MM **Publicly Held**
WEB: www.agrifos.com
SIC: 1479 Fertilizer mineral mining
HQ: Cvr Nitrogen, Lp
10877 Wilshire Blvd Fl 10
Los Angeles CA 90024
310 571-9800

(G-16380)
AIR LIQUIDE AMERICA LP
9810 Bay Area Blvd (77507-1864)
P.O. Box 200411, Houston (77216-0001)
PHONE..................................281 474-5800
Jason Miller, *Opers Mgr*
EMP: 16
SALES (corp-wide): 129.8MM **Privately Held**
WEB: www.industry.airliquide.us
SIC: 2813 Industrial gases
HQ: Air Liquide America L.P.
9811 Katy Fwy Ste 100
Houston TX 77024
713 624-8000

(G-16381)
AIR LIQUIDE AMERICA LP
Air Liquide Industrial US
3011 Pasadena Fwy Ste 190 (77503-1004)
P.O. Box 3047, Houston (77253-3047)
PHONE..................................713 438-6000
Mark Bivens, *Principal*
Vicki Elliott, *Branch Mgr*
Travis Cummings, *Manager*
Grady Miller, *Manager*
Pete Tucker, *Director*
EMP: 400
SALES (corp-wide): 129.8MM **Privately Held**
WEB: www.industry.airliquide.us
SIC: 2813 5169 Industrial gases; industrial gases
HQ: Air Liquide America L.P.
9811 Katy Fwy Ste 100
Houston TX 77024
713 624-8000

(G-16382)
AIRGAS USA LLC
11400 Bay Area Blvd (77507-1712)
PHONE..................................281 474-8300
Colin Kennedy, *Vice Pres*
James Stonecipher, *Plant Mgr*
Al Cusson, *Prdtn Mgr*
Ken Clark, *Manager*
Ruben Delgado, *Technical Staff*
EMP: 26
SALES (corp-wide): 129.8MM **Privately Held**
WEB: www.airgas.com
SIC: 5084 5169 2813 Welding machinery & equipment; industrial gases; industrial gases
HQ: Airgas Usa, Llc
259 N Radnor Chester Rd
Radnor PA 19087
216 642-6600

(G-16383)
ALBEMARLE CATALYSTS COMPANY LP
13000 Baypark Rd (77507-1104)
PHONE..................................281 474-2864

Luther C Luke Kissam, *CEO*
Mark Rohr, *Managing Prtnr*
◆ **EMP:** 265
SALES (est): 77.7MM **Publicly Held**
WEB: www.albemarle.com
SIC: 2821 Plastics materials & resins
PA: Albemarle Corporation
4250 Congress St Ste 900
Charlotte NC 28209

(G-16384)
ALBEMARLE CORPORATION
2500 N South St (77503-2570)
P.O. Box 2500 (77501-2500)
PHONE..................................713 740-1866
Douglas Auger, *Project Engr*
Mark Vanderic, *Manager*
Kenny Davis, *Manager*
Kevin Lejeune, *Technology*
EMP: 11 **Publicly Held**
WEB: www.albemarle.com
SIC: 2819 Industrial inorganic chemicals
PA: Albemarle Corporation
4250 Congress St Ste 900
Charlotte NC 28209

(G-16385)
ALBEMARLE CORPORATION
13000 Baypark Rd (77507-1104)
PHONE..................................281 474-2864
Michael Brown, *Division VP*
Michael Eckerd, *Opers Mgr*
Joel Conway, *Purch Mgr*
Charlie Vadovic, *Research*
Tom Szuch, *Engineer*
EMP: 300 **Publicly Held**
WEB: www.albemarle.com
SIC: 2819 2899 Industrial inorganic chemicals; chemical preparations
PA: Albemarle Corporation
4250 Congress St Ste 900
Charlotte NC 28209

(G-16386)
ALBEMARLE CORPORATION
Also Called: Albemarle
2500 N South St (77503-2570)
PHONE..................................713 740-1000
Bob Weber, *Engineer*
Mark Vranbrick, *Manager*
Parks Ravenscraft, *Manager*
EMP: 700 **Publicly Held**
WEB: www.albemarle.com
SIC: 2821 2819 2813 2869 Plastics materials & resins; industrial inorganic chemicals; industrial gases; industrial organic chemicals
PA: Albemarle Corporation
4250 Congress St Ste 900
Charlotte NC 28209

(G-16387)
AMERICAN ACRYL LP
4631 Old Highway 146 B (77507-1877)
PHONE..................................281 909-2600
Masayuki Ito, *General Mgr*
John Buhman, *Treasurer*
Susan Wyatt, *Controller*
John Steinbach, *Sales Staff*
Paul Petitt, *Supervisor*
▲ **EMP:** 69 **EST:** 1997
SALES: 151MM **Privately Held**
WEB: www.americanacryl.com
SIC: 2869 Industrial organic chemicals
PA: Nippon Shokubai Co., Ltd.
4-1-1, Koraibashi, Chuo-Ku
Osaka OSK 541-0

(G-16388)
AMERICAN ACRYL NA LLC
4631 Old Highway 146 B (77507-1877)
PHONE..................................281 909-2600
Masayuki Ito, *Mng Member*
EMP: 68
SALES: 151MM **Privately Held**
WEB: www.americanacryl.com
SIC: 2869 Amines, acids, salts, esters

(G-16389)
ARKEMA INC
Also Called: Clear Lake Plant
9502b Bayport Blvd (77507-1402)
PHONE..................................713 751-7340
Dillard Meadows, *Plant Mgr*
Daniel Overstreet, *Director*
EMP: 123

SALES (corp-wide): 120.6MM **Privately Held**
WEB: www.arkema-americas.com
SIC: **2819** Industrial inorganic chemicals
HQ: Arkema Inc.
900 First Ave
King Of Prussia PA 19406
610 205-7000

(G-16390)
ARMOR PLATE INC
Also Called: Wilcor and Armor Plate
2823 Randolph Rd (77503-4245)
P.O. Box 5625 (77508-5625)
PHONE..................................281 487-2023
Tony Wilson, *President*
Cynthia Wilson, *Vice Pres*
Malinda Juel, *Accounting Mgr*
Tommy Precht, *Sales Mgr*
Arturo Gomez, *Sales Staff*
EMP: 20 EST: 1980
SALES (est): 3.4MM **Privately Held**
WEB: www.armorplateinc.com
SIC: **2891** Adhesives & sealants

(G-16391)
ATHLON SOLUTIONS LLC (DH)
11200 Bay Area Blvd (77507-1714)
PHONE..................................713 457-2400
Chris Garrison, *Research*
Samir Shah, *Manager*
Buzz Vaccaro, *Manager*
Eric Axcell, *Director*
◆ EMP: 18
SALES (est): 3.8MM **Publicly Held**
WEB: www.athlonsolutions.com
SIC: **2819** Industrial inorganic chemicals

(G-16392)
BAKER PETROLITE LLC
13200 Baypark Rd (77507-1108)
PHONE..................................281 474-5166
Gerald Martin, *Branch Mgr*
EMP: 100 **Privately Held**
WEB:
www.bakerhughesdirect.lookchem.com
SIC: **2819 2899** Industrial inorganic chemicals; chemical preparations
HQ: Baker Petrolite Llc
12645 W Airport Blvd
Sugar Land TX 77478
281 276-5400

(G-16393)
BASF CORPORATION
4403 La Porte Rd (77501)
P.O. Box 600 (77501-0600)
PHONE..................................281 884-4400
Wayne Curtis, *Opers Staff*
Bik Bhandari, *Plt & Fclts Mgr*
Patrick Harmon, *Manager*
EMP: 26
SALES (corp-wide): 65.6B **Privately Held**
WEB: www.basf.com
SIC: **2869** Industrial organic chemicals
HQ: Basf Corporation
100 Park Ave
Florham Park NJ 07932
973 245-6000

(G-16394)
BAUER VISUAL GRAPHICS INC (PA)
1600 Strawberry Rd (77502-2606)
P.O. Box 3442 (77501-3442)
PHONE..................................713 473-5241
EMP: 15
SQ FT: 5,500
SALES (est): 3.2MM **Privately Held**
WEB: www.bvginc.com
SIC: **5099 3993 2759 5084** Signs, except electric; signs, not made in custom sign painting shops; tags: printing; labels & seals: printing; industrial machinery & equipment; bar code (magnetic ink) printers

(G-16395)
BAY DEER PROCESSING INC
Also Called: Bay Area Deer Processing
2243 Pasadena Blvd (77502-3177)
PHONE..................................713 472-6000
Robert Yates, *President*
Peggy Yates, *Vice Pres*
EMP: 11
SQ FT: 7,140

SALES (est): 1.4MM **Privately Held**
WEB: www.bayareadeerprocessing.com
SIC: **2011** Meat packing plants

(G-16396)
BAYOU CITY PUMP WORKS LP (PA)
109 N Richey St Ste A (77506-1071)
PHONE..................................713 472-7722
W D Emmons, *President*
Ann Emmons, *Vice Pres*
EMP: 12
SQ FT: 5,600
SALES (est): 3.9MM **Privately Held**
SIC: **5084 3594 7699 3561** Pumps & pumping equipment; fluid power pumps & motors; pumps & pumping equipment repair; pumps & pumping equipment

(G-16397)
BEE JAY MOLDING INC
1511 Genoa Red Bluff Rd (77504-4033)
PHONE..................................281 487-0377
Lee Evett, *Manager*
EMP: 30
SALES (corp-wide): 3.1MM **Privately Held**
WEB: www.beejaymolding.com
SIC: **3089 3544** Molding primary plastic; special dies, tools, jigs & fixtures
PA: Bee Jay Molding Inc
39500 Interstate 10 W
Boerne TX 78006
830 249-2425

(G-16398)
BENDCO INC
Also Called: Bendco/Bending & Coiling Co
801 Houston Ave (77502-2213)
P.O. Box 3384 (77501-3384)
PHONE..................................713 473-1557
James A Friery, *CEO*
Ricky Ford Friery, *President*
▲ EMP: 42
SQ FT: 60,000
SALES (est): 12.2MM **Privately Held**
WEB: www.bendco.com
SIC: **3317 3443 3714** Steel pipe & tubes; industrial vessels, tanks & containers; motor vehicle parts & accessories

(G-16399)
BRENNTAG PACIFIC INC
5100 Underwood Rd (77507-1079)
PHONE..................................281 474-5400
EMP: 15
SALES (corp-wide): 11.1B **Privately Held**
SIC: **2819 2873** Mfg Sodium Ammonium Thiosulfate & Potassium Products
HQ: Brenntag Pacific, Inc.
10747 Patterson Pl
Santa Fe Springs CA 90670
562 903-9626

(G-16400)
CARBIDE TECHNOLOGIES INC
Also Called: Www.carbidetech
524 Vermillion Dr (77506-1733)
P.O. Box 1852 (77501-1852)
PHONE..................................713 475-0444
Joe Contreras, *President*
Ruth Contreras, *Vice Pres*
David Villareal, *Vice Pres*
EMP: 12
SQ FT: 6,000
SALES (est): 2MM **Privately Held**
WEB: www.carbidetech.com
SIC: **3599** Machine shop, jobbing & repair

(G-16401)
CARPENTER CHEMICAL CO INC
11002 Choate Rd (77507-1598)
PHONE..................................281 474-5111
Myron H Reinhart, *President*
▲ EMP: 45
SALES (est): 9.3MM
SALES (corp-wide): 1.8B **Privately Held**
SIC: **2899** Chemical preparations
PA: Carpenter Co.
5016 Monument Ave
Richmond VA 23230
804 359-0800

(G-16402)
CELANESE LTD
1423 Hwy 225 (77506)
PHONE..................................713 456-1525
Todd Selarno, *Branch Mgr*
EMP: 45
SALES (corp-wide): 5.6B **Publicly Held**
WEB: www.celanese.com
SIC: **2821** Plastics materials & resins
HQ: Celanese Ltd.
225 E John Carpenter Fwy
Irving TX 75062

(G-16403)
CELANESE LTD
9502 Bayport Blvd (77507-1498)
P.O. Box 580375, Houston (77258-0375)
PHONE..................................281 474-0554
Glenn Ward, *Vice Pres*
Robert Guenther, *Purch Agent*
Ed Clark, *Engineer*
Boyd Hanna, *Project Engr*
Andrew Shuff, *Business Anlyst*
EMP: 35
SALES (corp-wide): 5.6B **Publicly Held**
WEB: www.celanese.com
SIC: **2821 2824 2865 2869** Plastics materials & resins; organic fibers, noncellulosic; cyclic crudes & intermediates; industrial organic chemicals
HQ: Celanese Ltd.
225 E John Carpenter Fwy
Irving TX 75062

(G-16404)
CENTAURI TECHNOLOGIES LP
5200 Underwood Rd (77507-1058)
PHONE..................................281 474-4675
Kyle Killebrew, *Partner*
Don Vanderslice, *Opers Mgr*
Lugene Orr, *Office Mgr*
Sam Lane, *Business Dir*
▲ EMP: 27
SALES (est): 10.9MM **Privately Held**
WEB: www.centauriusa.com
SIC: **2869** Industrial organic chemicals

(G-16405)
CHANNEL SHEET METAL INC
1908 Magnolia Dr (77503-2905)
P.O. Box 5545 (77508-5545)
PHONE..................................713 473-2878
Rebecca Love, *President*
Eric Wewer, *Accountant*
Dennis Meador, *Manager*
EMP: 10
SQ FT: 10,500
SALES (est): 1.4MM **Privately Held**
WEB: www.channelsheetmetal.net
SIC: **3441** Fabricated structural metal

(G-16406)
CHCA BAYSHORE LP
Also Called: HCA Hston Healthcare Southeast
4000 Spencer Hwy (77504-1202)
PHONE..................................713 359-2000
Jeanna Bamburg, *CEO*
Gerhard Wittick, *Ch Radiology*
Sue Garcia, *Corp Comm Staff*
Clifford Ferguson, *MIS Dir*
Clifford Serguson, *MIS Mgr*
EMP: 9 EST: 2014
SALES (est): 2.7MM **Publicly Held**
WEB: www.hcahoustonhealthcare.com
SIC: **3829** Medical diagnostic systems, nuclear
PA: Hca Healthcare, Inc.
1 Park Plz
Nashville TN 37203

(G-16407)
CHEMQUEST CHEMICALS LLC
9730 Bay Area Blvd (77507-1866)
PHONE..................................281 291-9966
Sherry Thompson, *VP Opers*
John Fries, *Sales Mgr*
John Berschied, *Director*
Stephen Raper, *Director*
Nick Higham,
◆ EMP: 23
SQ FT: 15,000

SALES (est): 11.7MM **Privately Held**
WEB: www.chemquestchemicals.com
SIC: **2899 2819** Chemical preparations; chemicals, high purity: refined from technical grade

(G-16408)
CHEVRON PHILLIPS CHEM CO LP
Plastics Division
1400 Jefferson (77506-2001)
P.O. Box 792 (77501-0792)
PHONE..................................713 475-3666
Van Long, *Plant Mgr*
Willie Isom, *Opers Staff*
Ray Sewell, *Engineer*
Mitch Krutliek, *Manager*
Robert Dixon, *Manager*
EMP: 200
SALES (corp-wide): 3.5B **Privately Held**
WEB: www.cpchem.com
SIC: **2821** Plastics materials & resins
HQ: Chevron Phillips Chemical Company Lp
10001 Six Pines Dr
The Woodlands TX 77380
832 813-4100

(G-16409)
CITY OF PASADENA
Also Called: Sanitation Department
120 N Pasadena Blvd (77506-1344)
PHONE..................................713 475-7884
Isidoro Rodriguez, *Administration*
EMP: 47
SQ FT: 7,140
SALES (corp-wide): 178.9MM **Privately Held**
WEB: www.pasadenaedc.com
SIC: **2842** Sanitation preparations
PA: City Of Pasadena
1149 Ellsworth Dr Ste 400
Pasadena TX 77506
713 475-5545

(G-16410)
CLARIANT CORPORATION
9502 Bayport Blvd (77507-1402)
P.O. Box 58190, Houston (77258-8190)
PHONE..................................832 753-3042
L J Packett, *Manager*
EMP: 350
SALES (corp-wide): 4.4B **Privately Held**
WEB: www.clariant.com
SIC: **2819** Industrial inorganic chemicals
HQ: Clariant Corporation
4000 Monroe Rd
Charlotte NC 28205
704 331-7000

(G-16411)
COASTAL GULF & INTL INC
1604 Shaver St (77502-2026)
PHONE..................................713 740-9800
Michael Caravella, *Principal*
Jack Iskandar, *Safety Mgr*
Sagar Irrinki, *Manager*
Daryl Guilliams, *Technology*
Trish Leger, *Admin Asst*
EMP: 66
SALES (corp-wide): 17.8MM **Privately Held**
WEB: www.portal.coastalgulf.com
SIC: **1081** Metal mining services
PA: Coastal Gulf & International, Inc.
13615 River Rd
Luling LA 70070
985 785-0765

(G-16412)
CONSCI LTD
Also Called: Consolidated Sciences
1416 Southmore Ave (77502-1305)
PHONE..................................713 920-1696
Carol J Meyer, *Partner*
Cynthia Rodriguez, *General Mgr*
William M Geiger, *General Ptnr*
EMP: 11
SQ FT: 25,000
SALES (est): 2MM **Privately Held**
WEB: www.consci.com
SIC: **8734 3821** Testing laboratories; laboratory apparatus & furniture

(G-16413)
CONTROL SOLUTIONS INC (DH)
Also Called: Solutions Pest Pet and Pools
5903 Genoa Red Bluff Rd (77507-1041)
PHONE................................281 892-2500
Mark A Boyd, *President*
Richard Anderson, *Partner*
Jake Wylie, *Area Mgr*
Curtis Clark, *Exec VP*
Allan Fulcher, *Vice Pres*
◆ **EMP:** 40
SQ FT: 106,000
SALES (est): 48.2MM **Privately Held**
WEB: www.controlsolutionsinc.com
SIC: 2879 5191 5999 Agricultural chemicals; pesticides; insecticides; pet supplies; swimming pool chemicals, equipment & supplies
HQ: Adama Agricultural Solutions Ltd
Golan
Airport City 70199
732 321-000

(G-16414)
COOPER VALVES LLC (HQ)
818 E Sam Houston Pkwy S (77503-2304)
P.O. Box 7589 (77508-7589)
PHONE................................832 409-6050
Greg Gilbert, *VP Engrg*
Shreyas Parameshwaran, *Design Engr*
Bob King, *Sales Staff*
Jesse Quinones, *Sales Staff*
Tianzhi Cai, *Mng Member*
▲ **EMP:** 49 EST: 1930
SQ FT: 56,000
SALES (est): 7.9MM **Publicly Held**
WEB: www.coopervalves.com
SIC: 3491 Automatic regulating & control valves; process control regulator valves; valves, automatic control; gas valves & parts, industrial

(G-16415)
DELTA VALVES AND CONTROLS LLC
2843 Westside Dr Ste 17 (77502-4843)
PHONE................................713 205-1904
Clintone Rawls, *Manager*
EMP: 12
SALES (est): 795.6K **Privately Held**
WEB: www.deltavalvesandcontrols.com
SIC: 3592 Valves

(G-16416)
DIANAL AMERICA INC
9675 Bayport Blvd (77507-1403)
P.O. Box 206948, Dallas (75320-6948)
PHONE................................713 758-8100
Hakaru Inaoka, *President*
Andrea Pace, *COO*
Philip Bernard, *Production*
Jason Bell, *Research*
Anri Shaw, *Accountant*
◆ **EMP:** 47
SQ FT: 50,000
SALES (est): 16.2MM **Privately Held**
WEB: www.dianal.com
SIC: 2821 Acrylic resins; polyethylene resins
HQ: Mitsubishi Chemical Holdings America, Inc.
655 3rd Ave Fl 15
New York NY 10017

(G-16417)
DITTA MEAT COMPANY
Also Called: Ditta Meat Foodservice Co
4924 Oak Ave (77503-3717)
P.O. Box 5623 (77508-5623)
PHONE................................281 487-2010
Sammy P Ditta, *President*
Helen Ditta, *Corp Secy*
Vincent Ditta, *Vice Pres*
Ray Hewston, *Facilities Mgr*
Doyle Sloan, *Engineer*
EMP: 67
SQ FT: 12,500
SALES (est): 31.9MM **Privately Held**
WEB: www.dittameat.com
SIC: 5147 5142 2013 2011 Meats, fresh; packaged frozen goods; sausages & other prepared meats; meat packing plants

(G-16418)
DIXIE CHEMICAL COMPANY INC (PA)
10601 Bay Area Blvd (77507-1719)
PHONE................................281 474-3271
William Doherty, *CEO*
Alexander Grous, *Business Mgr*
William Snyder, *Senior VP*
Michael Gromacki, *Vice Pres*
Eric Massengill, *Opers Mgr*
◆ **EMP:** 46
SQ FT: 22,000
SALES (est): 54.8MM **Privately Held**
WEB: www.dixiechemical.com
SIC: 2869 2819 5169 Industrial organic chemicals; industrial inorganic chemicals; drilling mud

(G-16419)
DORSETT BROS CONCRETE SUP INC (PA)
3210 Lilac St (77505-2212)
P.O. Box 5766 (77508-5766)
PHONE................................281 487-0264
Bill Dorsett, *President*
David Dorsett, *Vice Pres*
Don Dorsett, *Vice Pres*
James Dorsett, *Vice Pres*
Ralph Dorsett, *Vice Pres*
EMP: 25 EST: 1977
SQ FT: 2,000
SALES (est): 13.9MM **Privately Held**
SIC: 3273 Ready-mixed concrete

(G-16420)
DOW CHEMICAL COMPANY
9502b Bayport Blvd (77507-1402)
PHONE................................713 751-7285
Sharon Anderwald, *Branch Mgr*
EMP: 75
SALES (corp-wide): 38.5B **Publicly Held**
WEB: www.dow.com
SIC: 2819 Industrial inorganic chemicals
HQ: The Dow Chemical Company
2211 H H Dow Way
Midland MI 48642
989 636-1000

(G-16421)
DUPONT SPECIALTY PDTS USA LLC
Also Called: Dupont High Performance Mtl
9701 Bayport Blvd (77507-1493)
PHONE................................281 474-8614
J E Roosa, *Branch Mgr*
EMP: 50
SALES (corp-wide): 21.5B **Publicly Held**
WEB: www.dupont.com
SIC: 2819 Industrial inorganic chemicals
HQ: Dupont Specialty Products Usa, Llc
974 Centre Rd
Wilmington DE 19805
302 774-3034

(G-16422)
E R CARPENTER LP
Also Called: Carpenter Co.
11002 Choate Rd (77507-1500)
PHONE................................281 474-7257
Christopher Ruchte, *Manager*
EMP: 145
SALES (corp-wide): 54.6MM **Privately Held**
WEB: www.carpenter.com
SIC: 3086 3087 2822 Carpet & rug cushions, foamed plastic; custom compound purchased resins; synthetic rubber
PA: E. R. Carpenter, L.P.
2611 N General Bruce Dr
Temple TX 76501
804 359-0800

(G-16423)
ELITE SPECIALTY WELDING LLC
Also Called: Elite Industrial Services
1411 Preston Ave (77503-2513)
PHONE................................832 649-4251
Bart Maple, *President*
Bradley Calcote, *Vice Pres*
Mike Keller, *CFO*
EMP: 60 EST: 2009
SQ FT: 9,000

SALES (est): 12.9MM **Privately Held**
SIC: 1541 7692 Industrial buildings, new construction; welding repair

(G-16424)
EMERSON ATMTN SLTONS FNAL CTRL
4607 New West Rd (77507-1887)
PHONE................................832 261-2400
Paul Austin, *Branch Mgr*
EMP: 65
SALES (corp-wide): 16.7B **Publicly Held**
WEB: www.pentair.com
SIC: 3491 Industrial valves
HQ: Emerson Automation Solutions Final Control Us Lp
10707 Clay Rd
Houston TX 77041

(G-16425)
EMERSON AUTOMATION SOLUTIONS
4607 New West Rd (77507-1887)
PHONE................................832 261-2400
Paul Austin, *Branch Mgr*
EMP: 75
SALES (corp-wide): 16.7B **Publicly Held**
WEB: www.pentair.com
SIC: 3491 Industrial valves
HQ: Emerson Automation Solutions Final Control Us Lp
10707 Clay Rd
Houston TX 77041

(G-16426)
EMERSON PRCESS MGT VLVE ATMTN
Also Called: Emerson Automation Solutions
4607 New West Rd (77507-1887)
PHONE................................832 261-2400
Paul Austin, *Principal*
EMP: 70
SALES (corp-wide): 16.7B **Publicly Held**
WEB: www.emerson.com
SIC: 3823 Industrial instrmnts msrmnt display/control process variable
HQ: Emerson Process Management Valve Automation, Inc.
8100 West Florissant Ave
Saint Louis MO 63136
314 553-2000

(G-16427)
EMS USA INC (HQ)
5391 Bay Oaks Dr (77505-1405)
PHONE................................713 595-7600
Alexander J Buehler, *CEO*
James S Schroder, *President*
Mark S Campbell, *Senior VP*
Steve List, *CFO*
Jessica Fasquelle, *Manager*
EMP: 122 EST: 2000
SQ FT: 3,000
SALES (est): 179.8MM
SALES (corp-wide): 1.1B **Privately Held**
SIC: 1389 Construction, repair & dismantling services
PA: Energy Maintenance Services Group I, Inc.
5391 Bay Oaks Dr
Pasadena TX 77505
713 595-7600

(G-16428)
ENGINEERED PUMP SERVICES INC
Also Called: E P S
109 N Richey St Ste A (77506-1071)
PHONE................................713 472-7722
Sean Tracey, *Vice Pres*
EMP: 17
SQ FT: 12,000
SALES (est): 2.5MM **Privately Held**
SIC: 7699 3561 Pumps & pumping equipment repair; industrial machinery & equipment repair; industrial pumps & parts; hydrojet marine engine units

(G-16429)
ENRUD RESOURCES INC (PA)
1006 Vista Rd (77504-1616)
PHONE................................713 943-1600
Roy Massengale, *President*
Wayne Boudreaux, *Vice Pres*
EMP: 12

SALES (est): 3.3MM **Privately Held**
WEB: www.enrud.com
SIC: 7389 8711 2499 Air pollution measuring service; heating & ventilation engineering; cooling towers, wood or wood & sheet metal combination

(G-16430)
EQUISTAR CHEMICALS LP
5761 Underwood Rd (77507-1031)
PHONE................................281 474-4040
Mike Vandersick, *Manager*
EMP: 23
SALES (corp-wide): 34.9B **Privately Held**
WEB: www.lyondellbasell.com
SIC: 2869 2899 Ethylene; chemical preparations
HQ: Equistar Chemicals, Lp
1221 Mckinney St Ste 300
Houston TX 77010

(G-16431)
ETHYL CORPORATION
1000 N South St (77503-2516)
P.O. Box 472 (77501-0472)
PHONE................................713 740-8300
Johnnie Sandles, *Opers Staff*
Azfar Chodhury, *Branch Mgr*
EMP: 91
SALES (corp-wide): 2.1B **Publicly Held**
WEB: www.ethyl.com
SIC: 2869 2899 2992 Amyl alcohol; alcohols, industrial: denatured (non-beverage); chemical preparations; lubricating oils & greases
HQ: Ethyl Corporation
330 S 4th St
Richmond VA 23219
804 788-5000

(G-16432)
EUGENE B SMITH & CO INC
Also Called: Moody Compress & Warehouse Co
404 N Witter St (77506-1330)
P.O. Box 3578, Galveston (77552-0578)
PHONE................................409 763-6401
Frank Culligan, *Manager*
EMP: 28
SALES (est): 12.5MM **Privately Held**
WEB: www.ebsmithco.com
SIC: 4221 4731 3842 Cotton compresses & warehouses; freight transportation arrangement; cotton & cotton applicators
PA: Eugene B Smith & Co Inc
4514 Cole Ave Ste 706
Dallas TX 75205
214 528-9800

(G-16433)
EURECAT U S INCORPORATED
13100 Baypark Rd (77507-1194)
PHONE................................281 842-6700
Frederic Jardin, *Vice Pres*
Hosea Cheung, *Research*
Steve Mayo, *VP Business*
Tim Campbell, *Regl Sales Mgr*
Alfredo Romero, *Sales Staff*
EMP: 18
SALES (corp-wide): 2MM **Privately Held**
WEB: www.eurecat.com
SIC: 2819 Catalysts, chemical
HQ: Eurecat U. S. Incorporated
1331 Gemini St Ste 310
Houston TX 77058
281 218-0669

(G-16434)
EVONIK CORPORATION
Also Called: Air Products
1423 Pasadena Fwy (77506-1526)
P.O. Box 3326 (77501-3326)
PHONE................................713 477-6841
Russell Chandler, *Manager*
EMP: 230
SALES (corp-wide): 1.7B **Privately Held**
WEB: www.sorry.evonik.com
SIC: 2899 2869 2865 2821 Chemical preparations; industrial organic chemicals; cyclic crudes & intermediates; plastics materials & resins
HQ: Evonik Corporation
299 Jefferson Rd
Parsippany NJ 07054
973 929-8000

(G-16435)
EXCEL LABEL LLC (PA)
Also Called: Houston Label Company
909 Shaver St (77506-4411)
PHONE.............................713 477-6995
Richard Ryholt, *Mng Member*
Nina Grande, *Manager*
Hans Ryholt,
Eulalia Ryholt,
EMP: 53
SQ FT: 1,100
SALES (est): 8.8MM **Privately Held**
WEB: www.houstonlabel.com
SIC: 2759 Labels & seals: printing

(G-16436)
FAIRMONT DIAGNSTC CNTR &
OPEN
3692 E Sam Houston Pkwy S
(77505-3137)
PHONE.............................713 946-1500
Jack L Baker, *President*
EMP: 25
SALES (est): 3.4MM **Privately Held**
WEB: www.gulfcoastmri.com
SIC: 3841 8071 Diagnostic apparatus,
medical; medical laboratories

(G-16437)
FLANGE PROTECTION &
GASKETS
2535 Preston Ave (77503-3764)
PHONE.............................281 991-4550
Arthur W Boehm, *President*
Richard C Boehm, *Vice Pres*
Daniel A Boehm, *CFO*
Tom Boehm, *Sales Staff*
EMP: 10
SQ FT: 10,000
SALES (est): 1.5MM **Privately Held**
WEB: www.flangeprotection.com
SIC: 3462 3053 Flange, valve & pipe fit-
ting forgings, ferrous; gaskets, all materi-
als

(G-16438)
FLOWSERVE CORPORATION
4001 Flowserve Way (77503-2651)
PHONE.............................713 374-7100
Michael Mancuso, *Vice Pres*
David Marshall, *Branch Mgr*
Misty Aluna, *Manager*
EMP: 64
SALES (corp-wide): 3.9B **Publicly Held**
WEB: www.flowserve.com
SIC: 3491 Process control regulator valves
PA: Flowserve Corporation
5215 N Ocnnor Blvd Ste 23 Connor
Irving TX 75039
972 443-6500

(G-16439)
FLOWSERVE CORPORATION
4001 Emerald Field Dr (77503-1448)
PHONE.............................412 787-8803
Barry Hart, *Sales Executive*
Tim Baker, *Branch Mgr*
EMP: 10
SALES (corp-wide): 3.9B **Publicly Held**
WEB: www.flowserve.com
SIC: 3561 Pumps & pumping equipment
PA: Flowserve Corporation
5215 N Ocnnor Blvd Ste 23 Connor
Irving TX 75039
972 443-6500

(G-16440)
FLOWSERVE CORPORATION
4015 Lowserve Way (77503)
PHONE.............................281 241-3500
Westly Maida, *General Mgr*
John Jay, *Vice Pres*
Adrian Garcia, *Mfg Staff*
Tori Holmes, *Engineer*
Jessica Garcia, *Sales Associate*
EMP: 20
SALES (corp-wide): 3.9B **Publicly Held**
WEB: www.flowserve.com
SIC: 3561 Pumps & pumping equipment
PA: Flowserve Corporation
5215 N Ocnnor Blvd Ste 23 Connor
Irving TX 75039
972 443-6500

(G-16441)
FLOWSERVE US INC
4001 Flowserve Way 100 (77503-2651)
PHONE.............................979 549-0029
Tyler Harden, *Branch Mgr*
EMP: 13
SALES (corp-wide): 3.9B **Publicly Held**
WEB: www.flowserve.com
SIC: 3561 Pumps & pumping equipment
HQ: Flowserve Us Inc.
5215 N Oconnor Blvd Ste Connor
Irving TX 75039
972 443-6500

(G-16442)
FLOWSERVE US INC
4001 Flowserve Way 300 (77503-2651)
PHONE.............................502 267-2205
Mike Smith, *General Mgr*
EMP: 9
SALES (corp-wide): 3.9B **Publicly Held**
WEB: www.flowserve.com
SIC: 3561 Pumps & pumping equipment
HQ: Flowserve Us Inc.
5215 N Oconnor Blvd Ste Connor
Irving TX 75039
972 443-6500

(G-16443)
FORMERS INTERNATIONAL INC
(PA)
3333 Watters Rd (77504-2012)
PHONE.............................281 833-3310
John Dominguez Jr, *CEO*
Frances Dominguez, *Vice Pres*
Joel Castro, *Prdtn Mgr*
Ken Dushane, *Engineer*
John Dominguez III, *CFO*
EMP: 38 EST: 1975
SQ FT: 9,000
SALES (est): 13.4MM **Privately Held**
WEB: www.formers.com
SIC: 3565 Packing & wrapping machinery

(G-16444)
FORMERS INTERNATIONAL INC
3533 Preston Ave (77505-2008)
PHONE.............................281 998-9570
Alex Morillo, *Sales Staff*
EMP: 38
SALES (corp-wide): 13.4MM **Privately**
Held
WEB: www.formers.com
SIC: 3565 Packing & wrapping machinery
PA: Formers International, Inc.
3333 Watters Rd
Pasadena TX 77504
281 833-3310

(G-16445)
GAGEMAKER LP
Also Called: E S Tooling Co
712 Southmore Ave (77502-1110)
P.O. Box 87709, Houston (77287-7709)
PHONE.............................713 472-7360
Nita T Frank, *Partner*
Jimmy I Frank, *Partner*
John R Wolff III, *General Ptnr*
▲ EMP: 50
SQ FT: 10,000
SALES (est): 24.6MM **Privately Held**
WEB: www.gagemaker.com
SIC: 5084 3823 3829 Industrial machin-
ery & equipment; industrial instrmnts
msrmnt display/control process variable;
meteorological instruments

(G-16446)
GARDNER DENVER INC
Gardner Dnver Engnred Pckg Ctr
407 Eagle Ave (77506-2204)
PHONE.............................832 421-5469
Tom Bull, *Manager*
EMP: 56
SALES (corp-wide): 2.4B **Publicly Held**
WEB: www.gardnerdenver.com
SIC: 3563 3569 3559 3589 Air & gas
compressors; gas producers, generators
& other gas related equipment; refinery,
chemical processing & similar machinery;
sewage & water treatment equipment; oil
& gas field machinery
HQ: Gardner Denver, Inc.
800 Beaty St
Davidson NC 28036

(G-16447)
GAYESCO-WIKA USA LP (PA)
Also Called: Gay Engineering & Sales Co.
229 Beltway Green Blvd (77503-1300)
PHONE.............................713 941-8540
Dale Dutcher, *President*
Blake Costanzi, *COO*
Shari Eickelman, *Vice Pres*
Michael Strebel, *Vice Pres*
Debbie Wright, *Vice Pres*
◆ EMP: 138
SQ FT: 14,000
SALES (est): 19MM **Privately Held**
WEB: www.wika.us
SIC: 3823 Temperature measurement in-
struments, industrial

(G-16448)
GGCTR INC
Also Called: Gulf Coast Tool & Rental
5213 Spencer Hwy (77505-1511)
P.O. Box 7529 (77508-7529)
PHONE.............................832 456-4585
Darren White, *CEO*
Kevin Gary, *President*
Patrick Kahanek, *COO*
Steve Mendoza, *Branch Mgr*
EMP: 21
SALES (est): 6.3MM **Privately Held**
WEB: www.gctr.com
SIC: 1541 3599 3561 3541 Renovation,
remodeling & repairs: industrial buildings;
custom machinery; industrial pumps &
parts; machine tool replacement & repair
parts, metal cutting types

(G-16449)
GOLDLINE INTERNATIONAL INC
110 N Shaver St (77506-1131)
PHONE.............................713 475-0631
Debbie Baggett, *President*
George W Lobb, *Admin Sec*
EMP: 35
SQ FT: 200,000
SALES (est): 8.8MM **Privately Held**
WEB: www.goldlinesafewalk.com
SIC: 3537 Trucks, tractors, loaders, carri-
ers & similar equipment

(G-16450)
GRAYSON ARMATURE WORKS
INC
315 Curtis Ave (77502-2005)
PHONE.............................713 473-4404
R L Grayson, *Ch of Bd*
Arthur Trevino, *Vice Pres*
Roxanne Trevino, *Admin Sec*
▲ EMP: 12 EST: 1972
SQ FT: 3,200
SALES (est): 3.7MM **Privately Held**
WEB: www.graysonarminc.com
SIC: 7694 5063 Electric motor repair; mo-
tors, electric

(G-16451)
GVCC INC
Also Called: Gulf Coast Control Valves
3923 Mickey Gilley Blvd B (77505-3019)
PHONE.............................281 416-4772
Robert Dalton, *President*
Lawerence Walker, *Vice Pres*
Blake Barnes, *CFO*
Karen McMillian, *Admin Sec*
EMP: 9
SQ FT: 8,000
SALES (est): 2.1MM **Privately Held**
SIC: 3592 Valves

(G-16452)
HALDOR TOPSOE INC
10010 Bayport Blvd (77507-1494)
PHONE.............................281 228-5000
Martin Piwetz, *Vice Pres*
Klaus Larsen, *Site Mgr*
James Yarzy, *Purchasing*
Troy Waters, *Train & Dev Mgr*
Mark Kuchenmeister, *Accounts Mgr*
EMP: 130
SALES (corp-wide): 878MM **Publicly**
Held
WEB: www.topsoe.com
SIC: 2819 Catalysts, chemical
HQ: Haldor Topsoe, Inc.
17629 El Cmino Real Ste 3
Houston TX 77058
281 228-5000

(G-16453)
HANDWHEELS INC
6933 Olson Ln (77505-3403)
PHONE.............................281 998-0560
EMP: 50
SQ FT: 3,750
SALES (est): 7MM **Privately Held**
WEB: www.handwheelsinc.com
SIC: 3545 Machine tool accessories

(G-16454)
HMJ PLASTERING LLC
Also Called: Hj Plastering
716 Cavalier Ln (77502-4524)
PHONE.............................713 941-2807
Jose Gonzalez, *President*
Maria Gonzalez, *Vice Pres*
EMP: 15
SQ FT: 90,000
SALES (est): 1MM **Privately Held**
SIC: 1771 3299 1741 Exterior concrete
stucco contractor; blocks & brick, sand
lime; concrete block masonry laying

(G-16455)
HORIBA INSTRUMENTS INC
Also Called: Horiba Scientific
5390 Bay Oaks Dr (77505-3964)
PHONE.............................949 250-4811
Scott Morris, *Branch Mgr*
EMP: 60 **Privately Held**
WEB: www.horiba.com
SIC: 3826 Analytical instruments
HQ: Horiba Instruments Incorporated
9755 Research Dr
Irvine CA 92618
949 250-4811

(G-16456)
HUNTER INC
Also Called: Hunter Slings & Cables
802 Pasadena Fwy (77506-1415)
P.O. Box 6097 (77506-0097)
PHONE.............................713 473-9333
Thomas L Newlin Sr, *President*
Tim Newlin, *General Mgr*
Kathy Newlin, *Treasurer*
EMP: 20
SQ FT: 11,000
SALES (est): 3.3MM **Privately Held**
WEB: www.hunterinc.business.site
SIC: 3496 Miscellaneous fabricated wire
products

(G-16457)
INEOS AMERICAS LLC
Pasadena Division
3503 Pasadena Fwy (77503-1136)
P.O. Box 1959 (77501-1959)
PHONE.............................713 920-4300
Paul Carrico, *CEO*
Amy Narvaez, *Plant Mgr*
Steve Christiansen, *Manager*
EMP: 75
SALES (corp-wide): 1.9MM **Privately**
Held
WEB: www.ineos.com
SIC: 2821 Plastics materials & resins
HQ: Ineos Americas Llc
2600 S Shore Blvd Ste 500
League City TX 77573
251 535-6600

(G-16458)
INEOS STYROLUTION AMERICA
LLC
12222 Port Rd (77507-1800)
PHONE.............................281 474-1000
Greg Musler, *Project Dir*
Michael Garvey, *Transportation*
Margaret Martin, *Purchasing*
Chrissy Ulrich, *Purchasing*
Robert Hooker, *Manager*
EMP: 13
SALES (corp-wide): 1.9MM **Privately**
Held
WEB: www.styrolution.com
SIC: 2821 Plastics materials & resins
HQ: Ineos Styrolution America Llc
4245 Meridian Pkwy # 151
Aurora IL 60504

(G-16459)
INNOVA SUPPLY INC (PA)
Also Called: Solutions Pest & Lawn
2739 Pasadena Blvd (77502-3267)
PHONE..............................713 473-3345
Zachary Colander, *CEO*
Robert Howell, *General Mgr*
Keith McCoy, *VP Sales*
Tony Gracia, *Sales Staff*
Adam Ramirez, *Sales Staff*
▼ **EMP:** 20
SALES (est): 10.9MM **Privately Held**
WEB: www.solutionsstores.com
SIC: 2879 2211 5191 1541 Fungicides, herbicides; mosquito netting; pesticides; pharmaceutical manufacturing plant construction

(G-16460)
INNOVTIVE TRNROUND CONTRLS LTD
3512 Fairmont Pkwy (77504-3006)
P.O. Box 5835 (77508-5835)
PHONE..............................281 998-9547
Troy Cassels, *Partner*
William Berry, *Vice Pres*
Sonny Best, *Vice Pres*
Dale E Martin, *Vice Pres*
EMP: 250
SQ FT: 6,614
SALES (est): 28.6MM **Privately Held**
WEB: www.itc.jobs
SIC: 1382 Oil & gas exploration services

(G-16461)
INSPECTORATE AMERICA CORP
Also Called: (LAB DIV)
141 N Pasadena Blvd (77506-1309)
PHONE..............................281 291-9000
EMP: 25
SALES (corp-wide): 271.7MM **Privately Held**
SIC: 7389 1389 Business Services Oil/Gas Field Services
HQ: Inspectorate America Corp
1300 Hercules Ave Ste 105
Houston TX 77058
713 944-2000

(G-16462)
INSTRUMENT & VALVE SERVICES CO
Emerson Process Management
5404 Spencer Hwy (77505-1516)
PHONE..............................281 998-6600
Brett Arnett, *Plant Mgr*
Brian Young, *Branch Mgr*
EMP: 100
SQ FT: 3,000
SALES (corp-wide): 16.7B **Publicly Held**
SIC: 3823 Industrial instrmnts msrmnt display/control process variable
HQ: Instrument & Valve Services Company
205 S Center St
Marshalltown IA 50158

(G-16463)
INSTRUMENT & VALVE SERVICES CO
1465 E Sam Houston Pkwy S
(77503-2342)
PHONE..............................281 884-8639
EMP: 50
SALES (corp-wide): 16.7B **Publicly Held**
SIC: 3823 Industrial instrmnts msrmnt display/control process variable
HQ: Instrument & Valve Services Company
205 S Center St
Marshalltown IA 50158

(G-16464)
JOHN CRANE INC
Also Called: John'crane
4001 Fair Dr (77507-1732)
P.O. Box 58450, Webster (77598-8450)
PHONE..............................281 474-1700
Toll Free:..............................877 -
Colin Ure, *General Mgr*
Mark Edmonson, *Opers Spvr*
Carlos Mejia, *Sales Engr*
Dale Fadner, *Branch Mgr*
Mark Pitts, *Manager*
EMP: 90
SQ FT: 40,500

SALES (corp-wide): 3.1B **Privately Held**
WEB: www.johncrane.com
SIC: 3053 5085 Gaskets & sealing devices; packing materials; gaskets
HQ: John Crane Inc.
227 W Monroe St Ste 1800
Chicago IL 60606
312 605-7800

(G-16465)
JOHNSON MATTHEY INC
Also Called: Tracerco
4106 New West Rd (77507-1882)
PHONE..............................281 291-7769
Norman Lanier, *Principal*
David Bucior, *Business Mgr*
Andrew Booton, *Vice Pres*
Gary Gildert, *Marketing Mgr*
Margaret Bletsch, *Marketing Staff*
EMP: 71
SALES (corp-wide): 18.8B **Privately Held**
WEB: www.jmmedical.com
SIC: 1389 Gas field services
HQ: Johnson Matthey Inc.
435 Devon Park Dr Ste 600
Wayne PA 19087
610 971-3000

(G-16466)
JUNIPER SPECIALTY PRODUCTS LLC (PA)
120 N Munger St (77506-1326)
PHONE..............................346 310-6241
Don O'Shea, *Senior VP*
Chris Peters, *Mng Member*
John William Hemmings, *CTO*
EMP: 12
SALES (est): 8.4MM **Privately Held**
SIC: 2999 2842 Waxes, petroleum: not produced in petroleum refineries; beeswax, processing of

(G-16467)
JX NIPPON CHEMICAL TEXAS INC
Also Called: Ncti
10500 Bay Area Blvd (77507-1722)
PHONE..............................713 754-1000
Hajime Kado, *CEO*
Haruo Nakano, *Ch of Bd*
Barbara Pugh, *General Mgr*
Cliff Thompson, *General Mgr*
Kevin Asada, *Vice Pres*
◆ **EMP:** 94
SQ FT: 4,000
SALES (est): 53.9MM **Privately Held**
WEB: www.jxncti.co
SIC: 2899 2911 Chemical preparations; solvents
HQ: Eneos Corporation
1-1-2, Otemachi
Chiyoda-Ku TKY 100-0

(G-16468)
KANEKA NORTH AMERICA LLC (DH)
6161 Underwood Rd (77507-1096)
P.O. Box 72478969, Philadelphia PA
(19170-0001)
PHONE..............................281 474-7084
Kazuhiko Fujii, *President*
Brian Wilson, *Superintendent*
Shinkai Mizuho, *Corp Secy*
Steven Skarke, *Exec VP*
Bill Phenicie, *Senior VP*
◆ **EMP:** 227
SALES (est): 96.8MM **Privately Held**
WEB: www.kaneka.com
SIC: 2821 3081 2023 Plastics materials & resins; unsupported plastics film & sheet; dry, condensed, evaporated dairy products
HQ: Kaneka Americas Holding, Inc.
6250 Underwood Rd
Pasadena TX 77507
281 474-7084

(G-16469)
KIOR INC (PA)
13001 Baypark Rd (77507-1103)
PHONE..............................281 694-8700
Fred Cannon, *CEO*
Christopher A Artzer, *President*
Samir Kaul, *Principal*
D Mark Leland, *Principal*
David J Paterson, *Principal*

EMP: 31
SQ FT: 20,000
SALES: 1.8MM **Privately Held**
WEB: www.kior.com
SIC: 2869 Ethyl alcohol, ethanol

(G-16470)
LAGAN INTERESTS INC
Also Called: Inkspot Printing
2301 Shaver St (77502-4643)
PHONE..............................713 472-1100
Anthony R Lagan, *President*
Pam Lagan, *Vice Pres*
EMP: 10
SQ FT: 1,700
SALES (est): 1.1MM **Privately Held**
WEB: www.inkspotprinting.com
SIC: 2752 Commercial printing, offset

(G-16471)
LEE LINCO PLASTICS INC
Also Called: Techstar Molding
1511 Genoa Red Bluff Rd (77504-4033)
PHONE..............................281 487-0377
Lee Evett, *President*
Jeff Anderson, *Opers Staff*
Tammie Wilson, *Finance*
Jeffrey Anderson, *Director*
Linda Evett, *Admin Sec*
▲ **EMP:** 45
SQ FT: 17,475
SALES (est): 6.9MM **Privately Held**
WEB: www.techstarmolding.com
SIC: 3089 Molding primary plastic; injection molding of plastics

(G-16472)
LEELINCO PLASTICS INC
1511 Genoa Red Bluff Rd (77504-4033)
PHONE..............................281 487-0377
Evett Lee, *President*
Linda Evett, *Admin Sec*
EMP: 11 EST: 1997
SALES (est): 1.3MM **Privately Held**
WEB: www.techstarmolding.com
SIC: 3089 Injection molding of plastics

(G-16473)
LIGHTNING BOLT & SUPPLY INC
211 W Harris Ave (77506-3411)
PHONE..............................713 920-2525
Wendell Wallace, *President*
EMP: 11
SALES (est): 2MM **Privately Held**
WEB: www.lightningboltsupply.com
SIC: 3643 Lightning protection equipment

(G-16474)
LISLE VIOLIN SHOP (PA)
4510 Burke Rd Ste A (77504-4037)
PHONE..............................281 487-7303
Richard Mark Lisle, *Owner*
Ian Schexnider, *Analyst*
EMP: 11
SQ FT: 4,200
SALES (est): 2.3MM **Privately Held**
WEB: www.violins.com
SIC: 3931 5736 7699 7359 Violins & parts; musical instrument stores; musical instrument repair services; musical instrument rental services

(G-16475)
LONZA INC
9700 Bayport Blvd (77507-1495)
PHONE..............................281 291-2300
Ryan Holder, *Mfg Mgr*
Stephan Kutzer, *Manager*
Majid Rafiq, *Manager*
EMP: 80
SALES (corp-wide): 777MM **Privately Held**
WEB: www.lonza.com
SIC: 2819 2865 2851 2821 Inorganic metal compounds or salts; cyclic crudes & intermediates; paints & allied products; plastics materials & resins; inorganic pigments
HQ: Lonza Llc
412 Mount Kemble Ave # 200
Morristown NJ 07960
201 316-9200

(G-16476)
LUBRIZOL CORPORATION
Also Called: Lubrizol Production Plant
12801 Bay Area Blvd (77507-1397)
P.O. Box 158, Deer Park (77536-0158)
PHONE..............................281 479-2851
Tony Shick, *Plant Mgr*
Ruben Garibay, *Project Engr*
Larry Norwood, *Branch Mgr*
Anthony Shick, *Manager*
Diane Englert, *Supervisor*
EMP: 20
SALES (corp-wide): 254.6B **Publicly Held**
WEB: www.lubrizol.com
SIC: 2899 Chemical preparations
HQ: The Lubrizol Corporation
29400 Lakeland Blvd
Wickliffe OH 44092
440 943-4200

(G-16477)
LYONDELL CHEMICAL COMPANY
10801 Choate Rd (77507-1503)
PHONE..............................281 474-4191
Steve Kennedy, *Plant Mgr*
Jack Fletcher, *Project Mgr*
Rob Phillips, *Project Mgr*
Jeffrey Sonnier, *Terminal Mgr*
Annette Harrison, *Opers Staff*
EMP: 78
SALES (corp-wide): 34.9B **Privately Held**
WEB: www.lyondellbasell.com
SIC: 2869 Industrial organic chemicals
HQ: Lyondell Chemical Company
1221 Mckinney St Ste 300
Houston TX 77010
713 309-7200

(G-16478)
MACDERMID CANNING LTD (DH)
223 Brockman St (77506-1101)
PHONE..............................713 472-5081
Mark Hollinger, *President*
Donald Ogilvie, *Exec VP*
Patricia Janssen, *Vice Pres*
Phyllis Chronister, *CFO*
◆ **EMP:** 25
SQ FT: 40,000
SALES (est): 10.4MM
SALES (corp-wide): 1.8B **Publicly Held**
SIC: 2992 2911 5087 5169 Oils & greases, blending & compounding; fuel additives; cleaning & maintenance equipment & supplies; chemicals, industrial & heavy; chemical preparations
HQ: Macdermid, Incorporated
245 Freight St
Waterbury CT 06702
203 575-5700

(G-16479)
MANNINGS USA INC
Also Called: Bolttech Mannings
290 Beltway Green Blvd (77503-1372)
PHONE..............................281 443-7474
Charlie Gregory, *Manager*
EMP: 25 **Privately Held**
WEB: www.manningsusa.com
SIC: 3398 Metal heat treating
PA: Mannings, U.S.A., Inc.
200 Richards Ave
Dover NJ 07801

(G-16480)
MAR-CON SERVICES LLC
1410 Preston Ave Ste H (77503-2554)
P.O. Box 837, Deer Park (77536-0837)
PHONE..............................713 473-1800
Ada L Villarreal,
Rafael M Ramos,
Robert Ramos Jr,
EMP: 55
SQ FT: 1,400
SALES (est): 9.4MM **Privately Held**
SIC: 1623 1622 3271 Underground utilities contractor; bridge construction; paving blocks, concrete

(G-16481)
MATHESON TRI-GAS INC
13440 Bay Area Blvd (77507-1317)
PHONE..............................281 474-1291
Ray Roberts, *Branch Mgr*
EMP: 9 **Privately Held**

WEB: www.mathesongas.com
SIC: 2813 5084 Industrial gases; welding machinery & equipment
HQ: Matheson Tri-Gas, Inc.
3 Mountainview Rd Ste 3 # 3
Warren NJ 07059
908 991-9200

(G-16482)
MERIDIAN ENERGY GROUP INC
9590 New Decade Dr (77507-1076)
PHONE.............................281 291-0510
Dan Borgen, *CEO*
EMP: 30
SALES (corp-wide): 3.7MM **Privately Held**
WEB: www.meridianenergygroupinc.com
SIC: 1382 Seismograph surveys
PA: Meridian Energy Group, Inc.
2070 Bus Ctr Dr Ste 160
Irvine CA 92612
949 207-3815

(G-16483)
MFG CHEMICAL LLC
9700 Bayport Blvd (77507-1406)
PHONE.............................281 291-2300
Abe Zahand, *Plant Mgr*
John Wilson, *Opers Mgr*
Darin Gyomory, *CFO*
EMP: 45
SALES (corp-wide): 27.4MM **Privately Held**
WEB: www.mfgchemical.com
SIC: 2819 Chemicals, reagent grade: refined from technical grade
PA: Mfg Chemical, Llc
1804 Kimberly Park Dr
Dalton GA 30720
706 226-4114

(G-16484)
MID-WEST HOSE & SPECIALTY
2500 Pasadena Fwy (77506-1616)
PHONE.............................713 472-2900
EMP: 12
SALES (corp-wide): 223.9MM **Privately Held**
WEB: www.midwesthose.com
SIC: 5085 3492 Hose, belting & packing; hose & tube fittings & assemblies, hydraulic/pneumatic
PA: Mid-West Hose & Specialty, Inc.
3312 S I 35 Service Rd
Oklahoma City OK 73129
405 670-6718

(G-16485)
MOLECULAR BIOLOGICALS LLC
5413 Crenshaw Rd Ste 200 (77505-3165)
P.O. Box 460329, San Antonio (78246-0329)
PHONE.............................281 998-1227
Arturo Martinez MD,
EMP: 24
SQ FT: 2,500
SALES (est): 1MM **Privately Held**
WEB: www.molecularbiologicals.com
SIC: 2834 Dermatologicals

(G-16486)
MONUMENT CHEMICAL LLC
10200 Bay Area Blvd (77507-1852)
PHONE.............................281 474-5550
Abe Zahand, *Branch Mgr*
EMP: 40 **Privately Held**
WEB: www.monumentchemical.com
SIC: 2822 2843 2869 Synthetic rubber; surface active agents; alcohols, non-beverage
PA: Monument Chemical, Llc
6510 Telecom Dr Ste 425
Indianapolis IN 46278

(G-16487)
NATIONAL HOSE AQUISITION CORP (DH)
Also Called: National Hose & Accessory
1831 Richey St (77502-1710)
P.O. Box 4887 (77502-0887)
PHONE.............................713 920-2030
Don Fritzinger, *CEO*
◆ **EMP:** 66 **EST:** 1985

SALES (est): 22.5MM
SALES (corp-wide): 3.1B **Privately Held**
WEB: www.nationalhose.com
SIC: 3069 3541 3449 Reclaimed rubber (reworked by manufacturing processes); machine tools, metal cutting: exotic (explosive, etc.); miscellaneous metalwork

(G-16488)
NEWINN INC
Also Called: Flame Retardant Clothes
2300 Pasadena Fwy Ste 101 (77506-1600)
PHONE.............................713 473-8188
Helen Do Nguyen, *President*
Tom H Nguyen, *Vice Pres*
Thau T Nguyen, *Director*
Hau Thi Do, *Director*
EMP: 18
SQ FT: 9,000
SALES (est): 2.9MM **Privately Held**
WEB: www.fireprotectionoutfitters.com
SIC: 2326 5099 5085 Work uniforms; safety equipment & supplies; industrial supplies

(G-16489)
NISSAN CHEMICAL HOUSTON CORP
12330 Bay Area Blvd (77507-1301)
PHONE.............................281 291-0200
Robert Griffith, *President*
Masayuki Harada, *Treasurer*
▲ **EMP:** 18
SALES (est): 4.2MM **Privately Held**
WEB: www.nissanchem-usa.com
SIC: 2869 5169 Industrial organic chemicals; chemicals & allied products
HQ: Nissan Chemical America Corporation
10333 Richmond Ave # 1100
Houston TX 77042

(G-16490)
NOREL ANIMAL NUTRITION USA INC
5365 Bay Oaks Dr (77505-1405)
PHONE.............................281 741-8211
Francisco Moral, *CEO*
Enriqueta Martinez, *Controller*
▲ **EMP:** 10
SALES (est): 249.4K **Privately Held**
WEB: www.norel.net
SIC: 2048 Feed supplements

(G-16491)
NOVA CHEMICALS INC
12222 Port Rd (77507-1800)
PHONE.............................281 474-1000
Jeffrey Lipton, *Principal*
EMP: 53 **Privately Held**
WEB: www.novachem.com
SIC: 2821 Polystyrene resins
HQ: Nova Chemicals Inc.
1555 Coraopolis Hts Rd
Moon Township PA 15108
412 490-4000

(G-16492)
OXY VINYLS LP
4403 Pasadena Fwy (77503-1111)
P.O. Box 849 (77501-0849)
PHONE.............................281 884-4000
John Oxley, *Director*
EMP: 15
SALES (corp-wide): 21.2B **Publicly Held**
WEB: www.oxy.com
SIC: 2821 Vinyl resins
HQ: Oxy Vinyls, Lp
14555 Dallas Pkwy Ste 400
Dallas TX 75254
877 699-8465

(G-16493)
PCI NITROGEN LLC
2001 Jackson Rd (77506)
PHONE.............................713 920-5300
Dave Gutacker, *CEO*
Robert Kovacich, *COO*
▼ **EMP:** 100
SALES (est): 48.2MM **Privately Held**
WEB: www.ioccorp.com
SIC: 2874 Ammonium phosphate

(G-16494)
PCS TELECOM INC (PA)
1726 Richey St (77502-1709)
PHONE.............................281 469-3367

Michelle Lopez, *President*
Mark Lopez, *Vice Pres*
EMP: 40
SALES: 2.1MM **Privately Held**
WEB: www.pcstelecominc.com
SIC: 7389 3699 5099 4899 Telephone services; security control equipment & systems; video & audio equipment; communication signal enhancement network system; fiber optic cable installation

(G-16495)
PEROXYCHEM LLC
12000 Bay Area Blvd (77507-1310)
PHONE.............................281 474-4171
Janice Hendrickson, *Prdtn Mgr*
Jamie Pond, *Prdtn Mgr*
Gistar Williams, *Production*
Shahid Azam, *Engineer*
Michael Bin, *Engineer*
EMP: 75
SALES (corp-wide): 1.7B **Privately Held**
WEB: www.peroxychem.com
SIC: 2833 2819 Organic medicinal chemicals: bulk, uncompounded; industrial inorganic chemicals
HQ: Peroxychem Llc
1 Cmmrce Sq 2005 Mkt St
Philadelphia PA 19103
267 422-2400

(G-16496)
PHYTO-SOURCE LP
12502 Bay Area Blvd (77507-1308)
PHONE.............................281 474-7500
Bill Sonnier, *CEO*
Dan Corredor, *CFO*
▲ **EMP:** 40
SQ FT: 20,000
SALES (est): 6.1MM **Privately Held**
WEB: www.trecchem.com
SIC: 2869 Perfumes, flavorings & food additives

(G-16497)
PPG INDUSTRIES INC
Also Called: PPG 8302
5334 Spencer Hwy (77505-1514)
PHONE.............................281 487-6416
Terri Garman, *Manager*
EMP: 24
SALES (corp-wide): 15.3B **Publicly Held**
WEB: www.ppg.com
SIC: 2851 Paints & allied products
PA: Ppg Industries, Inc.
1 Ppg Pl
Pittsburgh PA 15272
412 434-3131

(G-16498)
PRODUCT QUALITY MANAGEMENT LLC
Also Called: Testing Laboratory
1710 Preston Ave Ste 160 (77503-2901)
PHONE.............................713 538-3028
Samuel Caban, *President*
Samuel I Caban,
EMP: 10
SALES (est): 344.7K **Privately Held**
WEB: www.prodqual.com
SIC: 1389 8734 Testing, measuring, surveying & analysis services; testing laboratories

(G-16499)
PROSTAR MANUFACTURING INC (PA)
5519 Bay Oaks Dr (77505-3960)
P.O. Box 75166, Houston (77234-5166)
PHONE.............................281 910-0110
Kevin Kiran, *President*
EMP: 14
SALES (est): 10.4MM **Privately Held**
WEB: www.prostarmfg.us
SIC: 3441 3443 3498 Fabricated structural metal; fabricated plate work (boiler shop); fabricated pipe & fittings

(G-16500)
PROSTAR MANUFACTURING INC
5519 Bay Oaks Dr (77505-3960)
P.O. Box 75166, Houston (77234-5166)
PHONE.............................936 585-0737
EMP: 13

SALES (corp-wide): 10.4MM **Privately Held**
WEB: www.prostarmfg.us
SIC: 3999 Barber & beauty shop equipment
PA: Prostar Manufacturing Inc
5519 Bay Oaks Dr
Pasadena TX 77505
281 910-0110

(G-16501)
REAGENS USA INC
9640 Bayport Blvd (77507-1404)
P.O. Box 2117, La Porte (77572-2117)
PHONE.............................281 291-8484
Enrico Crocetti, *President*
Harnish Shah, *General Mgr*
Robert Wells, *Vice Pres*
Madhvi Shah, *QC Dir*
Bob Wells, *Sales Mgr*
◆ **EMP:** 25
SQ FT: 16,000
SALES (est): 12.3MM
SALES (corp-wide): 117.7MM **Privately Held**
WEB: www.reagens-group.com
SIC: 2899 Chemical preparations
PA: Reagens Spa
Via Codronchi 4
San Giorgio Di Piano BO 40016
051 663-9111

(G-16502)
SAFETY RX SERVICES & SUP CORP (PA)
2835 E Sam Houston Pkwy S (77503-4015)
PHONE.............................281 487-0505
Martin Meza, *General Mgr*
John Thomas, *Principal*
Roberto Estrada, *Representative*
EMP: 20 **EST:** 1989
SALES (est): 2.5MM **Privately Held**
WEB: www.srxo.com
SIC: 3851 Protective eyeware

(G-16503)
SCHUTZ CONTAINER SYSTEMS INC
5000 Underwood Rd (77507-1001)
PHONE.............................281 474-5200
Dylan Hogue, *Plant Mgr*
Steven Vittorio, *Manager*
EMP: 120
SALES (corp-wide): 2B **Privately Held**
WEB: www.schuetz.net
SIC: 2655 Fiber cans, drums & similar products
HQ: Schutz Container Systems, Inc.
200 Aspen Hill Rd
Branchburg NJ 08876

(G-16504)
SEKISUI SPCIALTY CHEM AMER LLC
1423 Pasadena Fwy (77506-1526)
PHONE.............................713 456-1525
Drew Olson, *Branch Mgr*
EMP: 10 **Privately Held**
WEB: www.sekisui-sc.com
SIC: 2899 Chemical preparations
HQ: Sekisui Specialty Chemicals America, Llc
1501 Lyndon B Johnson Fwy
Dallas TX 75234

(G-16505)
SFC GLOBAL SUPPLY CHAIN INC
Also Called: Schwan's Food Manufacturing
1251 Scarborough Ln (77506-4103)
PHONE.............................713 740-7200
Greg Miller, *General Mgr*
Rich Wingfield, *Site Mgr*
Sara Wight, *Research*
Kari Peterson, *Marketing Mgr*
Arnie Strebe, *Branch Mgr*
EMP: 251 **Privately Held**
WEB: www.schwanscompany.com
SIC: 2038 2045 2099 Pizza, frozen; pizza doughs, prepared: from purchased flour; food preparations

▲ = Import ▼=Export
◆ =Import/Export

HQ: Sfc Global Supply Chain, Inc.
115 W College Dr
Marshall MN 56258
507 532-3274

(G-16506)
SHF INC
Also Called: Specialty Hose Fittings
8103 Red Bluff Rd (77507-1064)
PHONE..................................832 456-2000
Michael Chapman, *President*
EMP: 241
SALES (est): 116.7K
SALES (corp-wide): 1.2B **Privately Held**
WEB: www.shfinc.com
SIC: 3494 3592 3492 Well adapters;
valves; fluid power valves & hose fittings;
hose & tube fittings & assemblies, hy-
draulic/pneumatic
PA: Harbour Group Ltd.
7733 Forsyth Blvd Fl 23
Saint Louis MO 63105
314 727-5550

(G-16507)
SOLID CRATE LLC
409 Pasadena Fwy (77506-1410)
PHONE..................................713 475-9926
Jamie Garcia,
Heather Garcia,
EMP: 10
SALES (est): 1.4MM **Privately Held**
WEB: www.solidcrate.com
SIC: 2449 Rectangular boxes & crates,
wood

(G-16508)
SOLVAY USA INC
5761 Underwood Rd Ste B (77507-1031)
PHONE..................................281 984-3030
Carl Stewart, *Manager*
EMP: 26
SALES (corp-wide): 13.8MM **Privately
Held**
WEB: www.solvay.us
SIC: 2819 Industrial inorganic chemicals
HQ: Solvay Usa Inc.
504 Carnegie Ctr
Princeton NJ 08540
609 860-4000

(G-16509)
**SOUTHERN IONICS
INCORPORATED**
Also Called: Chemical Plant
12901 Baypark Rd (77507-1198)
PHONE..................................281 474-4826
Gretchen Van Beers, *Sales Mgr*
Shane Cornelall, *Branch Mgr*
EMP: 50
SALES (corp-wide): 88.8MM **Privately
Held**
WEB: www.southernionics.com
SIC: 2819 Industrial inorganic chemicals
PA: Southern Ionics Incorporated
579 Commerce St
West Point MS 39773
662 494-3055

(G-16510)
SPEEDORANGE INC
2406 Pasadena Fwy (77506-1602)
PHONE..................................281 448-5900
Roger Dischert, *CEO*
Corinne B Dischert, *Vice Pres*
EMP: 10
SALES (est): 1MM **Privately Held**
SIC: 3533 Oil field machinery & equipment

(G-16511)
**STAN THOMPSON
INVESTMENTS**
2106 Hickory Ln (77502-4028)
PHONE..................................713 910-2320
Stanley R Thompson, *President*
EMP: 25
SQ FT: 10,000
SALES (est): 2.8MM **Privately Held**
SIC: 3446 Architectural metalwork

(G-16512)
**STANDARD MACHINE WORKS
INC**
Also Called: Smw
2823 Strawberry Rd (77502-5202)
PHONE..................................713 673-1111
Robert S Steele, *President*
Edlar B Blanton III, *President*
Edlar B Blanton IV, *Vice Pres*
EMP: 15 EST: 1944
SQ FT: 11,000
SALES (est): 3.3MM **Privately Held**
WEB: www.standardmachine.com
SIC: 3533 Oil field machinery & equipment

(G-16513)
**SULZER ELECTRO-
MECHANICAL SERV (DH)**
Also Called: Sulzer Grayson
1910 Jasmine Dr (77503-3224)
PHONE..................................713 473-3231
Jim Mugford, *President*
Richard Grayson, *Vice Pres*
▲ EMP: 54
SALES (est): 25.4MM
SALES (corp-wide): 3.7B **Privately Held**
SIC: 7694 5063 Electric motor repair; mo-
tors, electric
HQ: Sulzer Us Holding Inc.
1255 Enclave Pkwy Ste 300
Houston TX 77077
346 207-9660

(G-16514)
SUMMA GROUP LLC (PA)
1485 E Sam Houston Pkwy S
(77503-2348)
PHONE..................................713 524-2768
Joseph V Summa, *Mng Member*
EMP: 9
SALES (est): 61.5MM **Privately Held**
WEB: www.techcorr.com
SIC: 1389 Oil consultants

(G-16515)
SUN PRODUCTS CORPORATION
12400 Bay Area Blvd (77507-1331)
PHONE..................................281 474-9855
Fax: 281 474-7546
EMP: 30
SALES (corp-wide): 1.3B **Privately Held**
SIC: 2841 Mgr Detergent
PA: The Sun Products Corporation
60 Danbury Rd
Wilton CT 06902
203 254-6700

(G-16516)
SUNRISE CHEMICAL LLC
10500 Bay Area Blvd (77507-1722)
PHONE..................................713 754-1000
Joe Charney, *General Mgr*
Jim Kado, *Principal*
Takeharu Tonozaki, *Principal*
Jo Charney, *Accounts Mgr*
▼ EMP: 87
SQ FT: 20,000
SALES (est): 20MM **Privately Held**
SIC: 2869 Industrial organic chemicals
PA: Nihon Oil Y.K.
1-7, Dokichokita
Marugame KGA 763-0

(G-16517)
TDW SERVICES INC
Also Called: Pasadena Service Center
9409 New Century Dr (77507-1834)
PHONE..................................281 291-8156
Jimmy Roter, *Branch Mgr*
EMP: 15
SALES (corp-wide): 221.1MM **Privately
Held**
WEB: www.tdwilliamson.com
SIC: 1389 Oil field services
HQ: Tdw Services, Inc.
6801 S 65th West Ave
Tulsa OK 74131
918 447-5000

(G-16518)
TECHEMET LP
6025 Genoa Red Bluff Rd (77507-1049)
PHONE..................................281 991-8300
Bryce Ward, *Senior Partner*
Sandra Ward, *Partner*

Stewart Prentice, *Partner*
Mark Ward, *Partner*
Shawn Dougherty, *Engineer*
◆ EMP: 85
SQ FT: 40,000
SALES (est): 40.3MM **Privately Held**
WEB: www.techemet.com
SIC: 3341 Platinum group metals, smelting
& refining (secondary)

(G-16519)
TRECORA CHEMICAL INC
12500 Bay Area Blvd (77507-1308)
PHONE..................................281 474-7500
Peter Loggenbert, *President*
Larry Birdsell, *General Mgr*
Arthur Steier, *Chairman*
Stephen Johnson, *Vice Pres*
Jeb Jonas, *Plant Mgr*
◆ EMP: 67
SQ FT: 5,000
SALES (est): 30MM
SALES (corp-wide): 258.9MM **Publicly
Held**
WEB: www.trecchem.com
SIC: 2869 2999 2899 2842 Industrial or-
ganic chemicals; waxes, petroleum: not
produced in petroleum refineries; chemi-
cal preparations; specialty cleaning, pol-
ishes & sanitation goods
PA: Trecora Resources
1650 Highway 6 Ste 190
Sugar Land TX 77478
281 980-5522

(G-16520)
TRPG INC
909 Shaver St (77506-4411)
PHONE..................................713 477-6995
Eulalia Ryholt, *President*
EMP: 10
SALES (est): 700.4K **Privately Held**
SIC: 2672 Coated & laminated paper

(G-16521)
UNIPAL INTL LTD CO TEXAS
5202 Red Bluff Rd (77503-4409)
PHONE..................................850 232-5586
Brad Upfield, *General Mgr*
Norwyn Newby, *CFO*
H Larry Leasure, *Mng Member*
EMP: 12
SQ FT: 50,000
SALES (est): 1.7MM **Privately Held**
SIC: 2653 Pallets, corrugated: made from
purchased materials

(G-16522)
**UNITED SHTDOWN SFETY
TEXAS INC (HQ)**
6104 Red Bluff Rd (77505-3604)
PHONE..................................877 805-5155
Lee Whitaker, *President*
Daryl Helmer, *CFO*
EMP: 15
SQ FT: 20,000
SALES (est): 8.3MM
SALES (corp-wide): 100.9MM **Privately
Held**
WEB: www.unitedsafety.net
SIC: 1382 Oil & gas exploration services
PA: United Safety Ltd
104 East Lake Rd Ne
Airdrie AB T4A 2
403 912-3690

(G-16523)
VEE INTERESTS LLC
1911 Jasmine Dr (77503-3223)
PHONE..................................832 864-2001
Joe Vaughn, *Principal*
EMP: 11
SALES (est): 1.2MM **Privately Held**
SIC: 3999 Atomizers, toiletry

(G-16524)
VICEROY INC (HQ)
3225 Pasadena Blvd (77503-3101)
PHONE..................................713 475-4518
Rl Rives, *President*
Mark Buchanan, *Vice Pres*
Bruce Bever, *Treasurer*
Richard Locklear, *Admin Sec*
EMP: 41
SQ FT: 7,500

SALES (est): 228.5MM
SALES (corp-wide): 95.2B **Publicly Held**
WEB: www.viceroyhotelsandresorts.com
SIC: 1629 3443 1796 8742 Power plant
construction; pipe, standpipe & culverts;
power generating equipment installation;
management consulting services; business consulting; engineering help service
PA: General Electric Company
5 Necco St
Boston MA 02210
617 443-3000

(G-16525)
**WELLHEAD CONTROL
PRODUCTS INC**
501 N Richey St (77506-1062)
P.O. Box 1283, Bellaire (77402-1283)
PHONE..................................713 475-2283
Ray Hunt Jr, *President*
Kevin Hunt, *Vice Pres*
EMP: 20
SQ FT: 12,000
SALES (est): 2.6MM **Privately Held**
WEB: www.wellheadcontrol.com
SIC: 1389 Oil field services

(G-16526)
WIL-COR INC
2823 Randolph Rd (77503-4245)
P.O. Box 5646 (77508-5646)
PHONE..................................281 487-6547
Cynthia A Wilson, *President*
EMP: 18
SQ FT: 18,000
SALES (est): 2.4MM **Privately Held**
WEB: www.wilcorinc.com
SIC: 2891 1799 Epoxy adhesives; fiber-
glass work

(G-16527)
WILKINS & ASSOCIATES INC
Also Called: Artwin Graphics
1128 Pasadena Blvd (77506-4724)
PHONE..................................713 472-6585
Marilyn Wilkins, *President*
EMP: 11
SQ FT: 500
SALES (est): 1.8MM **Privately Held**
WEB: www.artwingraphics.com
SIC: 2752 7334 Commercial printing, off-
set; photocopying & duplicating services

(G-16528)
XTERRA INDUSTRIES LLC
Also Called: Xterra Trench Shields
5385 Bay Oaks Dr (77505-1405)
PHONE..................................281 998-0442
EMP: 50
SALES (est): 10.1MM
SALES (corp-wide): 12.4MM **Privately
Held**
SIC: 3355 Aluminum Rolling/Drawing
PA: Pacific Shoring Products, Llc
265 Roberts Ave
Santa Rosa CA 95407
707 575-9014

(G-16529)
ZEON CHEMICALS LP
11235 Choate Rd (77507-1798)
PHONE..................................281 474-9693
Robert Grahek, *Branch Mgr*
EMP: 38 **Privately Held**
WEB: www.zeonchemicals.com
SIC: 3061 Automotive rubber goods (me-
chanical); oil & gas field machinery rubber
goods (mechanical)
HQ: Zeon Chemicals L.P.
4111 Bells Ln
Louisville KY 40211

(G-16530)
**ZEON CHEMICALS TEXAS INC
(HQ)**
11235 Choate Rd (77507-1798)
PHONE..................................502 775-2000
William Niederst, *President*
Martin Brennan, *Vice Pres*
▼ EMP: 43
SQ FT: 3,000
SALES (est): 15.3K **Privately Held**
WEB: www.zeonchemicals.com
SIC: 3061 Automotive rubber goods (me-
chanical); oil & gas field machinery rubber
goods (mechanical)

Pattison
Waller County

(G-16531)
**CRUDECHEM TECHNOLOGY
LLC (PA)**
1998 Fm 362 Rd (77423-9412)
PHONE..................................832 206-0790
Miles Grendel, *Mng Member*
EMP: 13
SQ FT: 435,600
SALES: 12.3MM **Privately Held**
SIC: 1389 Chemically treating wells

(G-16532)
H D H INSTRUMENTS CORP
3166 Hwy 359 N (77466)
P.O. Box 709 (77466-0709)
PHONE..................................281 375-6835
John Hovas, *President*
Greg Hovas, *Owner*
EMP: 130
SQ FT: 27,000
SALES (est): 27MM **Privately Held**
WEB: www.hdhinstruments.com
SIC: 3533 Drilling tools for gas, oil or water
wells

Pawnee
Bee County

(G-16533)
**LARIAT CONSTRUCTION
SERVICES (PA)**
12596 Fm 673 (78145)
P.O. Box 617 (78145-0617)
PHONE..................................361 318-9104
Steve Small, *President*
EMP: 9 **EST:** 1997
SALES (est): 2.3MM **Privately Held**
WEB: www.lariat.us
SIC: 1389 Construction, repair & disman-
tling services

(G-16534)
**PIONEER NTRAL RSOURCES
USA INC**
Also Called: Pawnee Gas Plant
2 Mi S On Hwy 673 (78145)
PHONE..................................361 456-7201
Joe Gray, *Manager*
EMP: 19
SALES (corp-wide): 9.3B **Publicly Held**
WEB: www.pawneeisd.net
SIC: 1311 Crude petroleum production
HQ: Pioneer Natural Resources Usa, Inc.
5205 N Oconnor Blvd Ste Connor
Irving TX 75039
972 444-9001

Pearland
Brazoria County

(G-16535)
A E & SONS LLC
2211 Lost Bridge Ln (77584-1875)
P.O. Box 451674, Houston (77245-1674)
PHONE..................................281 898-4021
Alton Sells, *Mng Member*
Sunshine Hamilton,
EMP: 15
SALES (est): 266.3K **Privately Held**
SIC: 1389 7389 Servicing oil & gas wells;

(G-16536)
**ABG CONTRACTING GROUP
LLC**
10223 Broadway St P351 (77584-7880)
PHONE..................................281 431-7223
Alejandro Gonzalez, *President*
Robert Escovedo, *Principal*
EMP: 30 **EST:** 2007
SALES (est): 3.8MM **Privately Held**
SIC: 5082 1799 2952 3444 General con-
struction machinery & equipment; coating,
caulking & weather, water & fireproofing;
tar paper, roofing; metal roofing & roof
drainage equipment

(G-16537)
AIM OILFIELD SERVICES
2640 Broadway St Ste 106 (77581-4907)
PHONE..................................281 814-9787
Steve Robinson, *President*
EMP: 14 **EST:** 2016
SALES (est): 1.2MM **Privately Held**
WEB: www.aimoilfieldservices.com
SIC: 1389 Fuel oil dealers

(G-16538)
AIM SOLAR SCREENS INC
2641 Roy Rd (77581-7641)
PHONE..................................281 997-1543
Nancy Hernandez, *President*
EMP: 10
SQ FT: 5,000
SALES (est): 160K **Privately Held**
SIC: 2431 Door screens, wood frame

(G-16539)
ARMADILLO BLAST COAT INC
1537 Stone Rd (77581-8075)
PHONE..................................281 485-2743
Martin Griffin, *Exec Dir*
EMP: 45
SALES (est): 65.3K **Privately Held**
WEB: www.armadilloblastcoat.com
SIC: 5199 3479 Decals; coating of metals
& formed products

(G-16540)
**ASSOCIATED WELDING SUPPLY
INC**
3002 S Main St (77581-4712)
PHONE..................................281 485-2755
Paul Delisi, *President*
Jesse Vasquez, *Vice Pres*
Richard Stryk, *Purchasing*
◆ **EMP:** 17 **EST:** 1975
SQ FT: 10,000
SALES (est): 4.2MM **Privately Held**
WEB: www.associatedweldingsupply.com
SIC: 7692 Welding repair

(G-16541)
BAWCO INC
3910 Fm 1128 Rd (77584-7520)
PHONE..................................281 485-3337
Wayne E Blackburn, *President*
Bill Holley, *Corp Secy*
EMP: 13
SQ FT: 20,000
SALES (est): 1.8MM **Privately Held**
WEB: www.bawcoindustries.com
SIC: 3441 Fabricated structural metal

(G-16542)
CAPROCK OIL TOOLS INC
3446 S Main St (77581-4733)
PHONE..................................281 485-4777
Thomas G Gault, *President*
Rebecca Gault, *Vice Pres*
Maria Davis, *Production*
Levi Lunt, *Engineer*
Amanda OHM, *Senior Engr*
EMP: 22
SALES (est): 5.7MM **Privately Held**
WEB: www.caprockoiltools.com
SIC: 3532 Drills, bits & similar equipment

(G-16543)
CHAPMAN SHAMEKA
Also Called: Basic Babes
2017 Mountain Creek St (77584-8748)
PHONE..................................281 507-8790
Shameka Chapman, *Owner*
EMP: 10
SALES (est): 310K **Privately Held**
SIC: 2331 Women's & misses' blouses &
shirts

(G-16544)
CK &B MACHINE SHOP
2413 Roy Rd (77581-8601)
PHONE..................................281 485-5760
Carlos Bazquaz, *Owner*
EMP: 9
SQ FT: 4,000
SALES (est): 556.9K **Privately Held**
WEB: www.ckbmachining.com
SIC: 3449 Miscellaneous metalwork

(G-16545)
CKB MACHINING LLC
6953 Brookside Rd (77581-2133)
PHONE..................................281 485-5760
Carlos Vasquez, *Mng Member*
EMP: 13
SALES (est): 517.4K **Privately Held**
WEB: www.ckbmachining.com
SIC: 3542 3541 Machine tools, metal
forming type; machine tools, metal cutting
type

(G-16546)
**COASTAL WIRELINE SERVICES
INC**
Also Called: Gulf Coast Well Analysis
3909 Halik St (77581-2903)
PHONE..................................281 485-6548
Glen S Johnson, *President*
Marco Chavez, *Vice Pres*
Robert Coker, *Vice Pres*
Ginnetta Coker, *Treasurer*
Annie Chavez, *Admin Sec*
EMP: 11
SQ FT: 6,000
SALES (est): 1.9MM **Privately Held**
WEB: www.thirdcoastanalyticaltechnolo-
gies.com
SIC: 1389 Well logging; perforating well
casings; testing, measuring, surveying &
analysis services

(G-16547)
COLUMNS INC
Also Called: Southern Product Finishing
1011 N Main St (77581-2207)
P.O. Box 895 (77588-0895)
PHONE..................................281 485-3254
Bobby R Henson, *President*
Kevin Henson, *Vice Pres*
Bobby Henson, *Purch Agent*
Noah Heckathorne, *Purchasing*
Bruce Sparks, *Sales Staff*
EMP: 15
SQ FT: 47,250
SALES (est): 3.2MM **Privately Held**
WEB: www.spfinishing.com
SIC: 3446 Architectural metalwork

(G-16548)
**COMPOSITECH PRODUCTS MFG
INC**
4531 S Main St (77581-6607)
P.O. Box 2673 (77588-2673)
PHONE..................................281 648-3557
Jeffery P Knauss, *President*
Melissa Baker, *Comptroller*
Craig Williams, *Sales Mgr*
Sara Pybus, *Mktg Dir*
Jimmy Walker, *Technology*
▲ **EMP:** 25
SQ FT: 18,000
SALES (est): 9.4MM **Privately Held**
WEB: www.compositech-filters.com
SIC: 3563 5084 5085 Vacuum pumps, ex-
cept laboratory; industrial machinery &
equipment; filters, industrial

(G-16549)
**CONCRETE PRODUCERS
SOLUTIONS**
11807 Sea Shadow Bnd (77584-6807)
PHONE..................................281 398-6244
Ed G Jackson, *CEO*
Ron J Paget, *President*
◆ **EMP:** 10
SQ FT: 25,000 **Privately Held**
SIC: 2899 Concrete curing & hardening
compounds

(G-16550)
**CPI WIRECLOTH & SCREENS
INC (PA)**
2425 Roy Rd (77581-8601)
P.O. Box 1710 (77588-1710)
PHONE..................................281 485-2300
Glenn Lilie, *President*
Judith Lillie, *Corp Secy*
Michelle Lillie, *Exec VP*
Lory Johnson, *Vice Pres*
Michelle Lilie, *Vice Pres*
◆ **EMP:** 52 **EST:** 1968
SQ FT: 40,000

SALES (est): 7.9MM **Privately Held**
WEB: www.cpiwirecloth.com
SIC: 3496 Screening, woven wire: made
from purchased wire

(G-16551)
**CUSTOM COMPONENTS
INCORPORATED**
3446 S Main St (77581-4733)
PHONE..................................281 485-2200
Glenn Gault, *President*
EMP: 10
SQ FT: 800
SALES (est): 1.5MM **Privately Held**
WEB: www.customcomponentsinc.com
SIC: 3533 Oil field machinery & equipment

(G-16552)
DAVIS-LYNCH LLC (HQ)
2005 Garden Rd (77581-8738)
PHONE..................................281 485-8301
Carl A Davis, *President*
Frank Cole,
▼ **EMP:** 85 **EST:** 1947
SQ FT: 4,260
SALES (est): 704.3K **Publicly Held**
WEB: www.davis-lynch.com
SIC: 3533 Drilling tools for gas, oil or water
wells

(G-16553)
**DCG PARTNERSHIP I LIMITED
(PA)**
4170a S Main St (77581-6089)
PHONE..................................281 648-1894
David D'Agostaro, *Partner*
Louis Dagostaro, *Partner*
Jeffrey Werner, *COO*
Lori Bozdech, *Vice Pres*
Alexander Colton, *Production*
EMP: 23
SALES (est): 3MM **Privately Held**
WEB: www.dcgpartnership.com
SIC: 2911 3825 Petroleum refining; stan-
dards & calibrating equipment, laboratory

(G-16554)
DEEP SOUTH BARRELS LLC
2849 Miller Ranch Rd # 549 (77584-9724)
P.O. Box 18752, Sugar Land (77496-8752)
PHONE..................................713 340-3103
Miranda Knerr, *COO*
Randall Bentley, *Sales Dir*
Melissa Kloss, *Office Mgr*
Jonathan Emmons, *Officer*
EMP: 17
SALES (est): 2.3MM **Privately Held**
WEB: www.deepsouthbarrels.com
SIC: 2084 Wine cellars, bonded: engaged
in blending wines

(G-16555)
**DEERBORNE ENERGY
COMPANY**
2640 Broadway St Ste 102 (77581-4907)
PHONE..................................281 485-8705
Herman R Brown, *President*
EMP: 10
SQ FT: 2,000
SALES (est): 1.3MM **Privately Held**
SIC: 1389 Oil field services

(G-16556)
**DISTRIBUTED PWR SOLUTIONS
LLC**
4300 Rice Drier Rd (77581-2813)
PHONE..................................877 291-3354
Scott Milligan,
EMP: 20
SALES (est): 810K **Privately Held**
SIC: 3825 Energy measuring equipment,
electrical

(G-16557)
EA SERVICES INC (PA)
2800 Broadway St Ste C (77581-9503)
PHONE..................................866 711-1001
Kevin M Stern, *President*
Randall Pinson, *Vice Pres*
Russell A Naisbitt, *CFO*
◆ **EMP:** 61
SQ FT: 4,000

SALES (est): 12.1MM **Privately Held**
WEB: www.pearlandtx.gov
SIC: 2295 1623 1771 Sealing or insulating tape for pipe: coated fiberglass; pipeline wrapping; concrete repair

(G-16558)
EFFECTUS CORPORATION (PA)
10223 Broadway St P358 (77584-7880)
PHONE....................713 446-5275
Ricardo Duarte, *President*
▼ **EMP:** 10
SALES (est): 5MM **Privately Held**
WEB: www.effectuscorporation.com
SIC: 2821 Plastics materials & resins

(G-16559)
EMERSON ELECTRIC CO
3902 Magnolia Pkwy (77584-1910)
PHONE....................281 488-0788
Pamela Chittum, *Human Resources*
Paul Brown, *Technology*
Karen Greenough, *Admin Asst*
EMP: 43
SALES (corp-wide): 16.7B **Publicly Held**
WEB: www.emerson.com
SIC: 3823 Industrial instrmnts msrmnt display/control process variable
PA: Emerson Electric Co.
8000 West Florissant Ave
Saint Louis MO 63136
314 553-2000

(G-16560)
FIELDER ELECTRIC SUPPLY CO INC
2900 Manvel Rd (77584-7540)
PHONE....................281 485-6599
William J Fielder III, *President*
Luanna Fielder, *Vice Pres*
Mayra Reyes, *Sales Staff*
Amber White, *Sales Staff*
EMP: 26
SALES (est): 6.8MM **Privately Held**
WEB: www.fielderelectricsupply.net
SIC: 3699 3644 Electrical equipment & supplies; electric conduits & fittings

(G-16561)
FLOWBACK CHAMPION SERVICES LLC
3305 Beacon View Ct (77584-7933)
PHONE....................832 731-5783
Nakitta Taylor,
EMP: 12
SALES (est): 2.3MM **Privately Held**
WEB: www.championflowback.com
SIC: 1389 Oil field services

(G-16562)
G B INDUSTRY CO LP (PA)
Also Called: G B I
2019 County Road 124 (77581-6486)
P.O. Box 1622, Friendswood (77549-1622)
PHONE....................281 996-0020
Gert Bahlo, *President*
David Bahlo, *Principal*
◆ **EMP:** 18
SALES (est): 6MM **Privately Held**
WEB: www.gbindustry.com
SIC: 3533 Oil field machinery & equipment

(G-16563)
GARTNER COATINGS INC
2433 Reid Blvd (77581-7677)
PHONE....................281 997-3500
George Gartner III, *President*
Donna Gartner, *Admin Sec*
EMP: 38
SQ FT: 13,017
SALES (est): 5.5MM **Privately Held**
WEB: www.gartnercoatings.com
SIC: 3479 Coating of metals & formed products

(G-16564)
GATE PRECAST COMPANY
3201 Veterans Dr (77584-1602)
P.O. Box 38 (77588-0038)
PHONE....................281 485-3273
Pete Scowcroft, *Opers-Prdtn-Mfg*
Taylor Dubois, *Manager*
Jim Stini, *Manager*
Beth Sanford, *Administration*
EMP: 35

SALES (corp-wide): 708.1K **Privately Held**
WEB: www.gateprecast.com
SIC: 3272 Prestressed concrete products
HQ: Gate Precast Company
9540 San Jose Blvd
Jacksonville FL 32257
904 732-7668

(G-16565)
GE OIL & GAS LOGGING SVCS INC
3446 S Main St (77581-4733)
PHONE....................281 992-9676
Fax: 281 992-3960
EMP: 20
SQ FT: 21,780
SALES (corp-wide): 117.3B **Publicly Held**
SIC: 1389 Oil/Gas Field Services
HQ: Ge Oil & Gas Logging Services, Inc.
19416 Park Row Ste 100
Houston TX 77478

(G-16566)
GRAY GREEN BIOMEDICAL SVCS LLC
2911 Broadway St Ste 309 (77581-4681)
PHONE....................832 288-5958
Tommy Lear,
EMP: 9
SALES (est): 10MM **Privately Held**
WEB: www.graygreenbiomedservices.com
SIC: 7699 3826 7389 Hospital equipment repair services; medical equipment repair, non-electric; surgical instrument repair; laboratory instrument repair; environmental testing equipment; inspection & testing services

(G-16567)
HALF PRICE BKS REC MGZINES INC
2556 Smith Ranch Rd (77584-5235)
PHONE....................713 340-0094
Judy Huston, *Branch Mgr*
EMP: 15
SALES (corp-wide): 211.7MM **Privately Held**
WEB: www.becomegreen.info
SIC: 5942 2721 Books, religious; magazines: publishing & printing
PA: Half Price Books, Records, Magazines, Incorporated
5803 E Northwest Hwy
Dallas TX 75231
214 360-0833

(G-16568)
HENDRICKS BTS CORPORATION
2700 Cullen Blvd 1946 (77584-0239)
P.O. Box 841946 (77584-0027)
PHONE....................713 516-8716
Robert Hendricks, *President*
Darren Whitfield, *Managing Dir*
EMP: 12
SQ FT: 2,500
SALES (est): 1MM **Privately Held**
SIC: 8741 7371 7373 3572 Management services; custom computer programming services; computer systems analysis & design; computer storage devices

(G-16569)
HOUSTON TUBULARS INC (PA)
13600 Hatfield Rd (77581-2729)
PHONE....................281 485-4014
Dennis J Hayden, *President*
Kathy Hayden, *Vice Pres*
Claudio Cruz, *Opers Mgr*
Kelley Hayden, *Sales Staff*
Ken Cole, *Manager*
▲ **EMP:** 95
SQ FT: 6,000
SALES (est): 33.3MM **Privately Held**
SIC: 1389 Pipe testing, oil field service

(G-16570)
INTERFACE LGIC TECH DCMNTTION
11607 Bay Ledge Dr (77584-8189)
PHONE....................713 446-3560
Ora Lee, *CEO*
EMP: 10

SALES (est): 1MM **Privately Held**
WEB: www.interfacelogictechnology.com
SIC: 4213 7299 8999 2741 Automobiles, transport & delivery; personal document & information services; technical writing; technical manual preparation; technical manuals: publishing & printing; transportation equipment & supplies; warehousing, self-storage

(G-16571)
INTRINSIC SAFETY EQP TEXAS INC
Also Called: ISE-Mag Tech
3902 Magnolia Pkwy (77584-1910)
PHONE....................281 488-0788
Jolyon P Willson, *President*
▼ **EMP:** 100
SQ FT: 33,000
SALES (est): 12.8MM
SALES (corp-wide): 16.7B **Publicly Held**
WEB: www.emerson.com
SIC: 3823 Industrial instrmnts msrmnt display/control process variable
PA: Emerson Electric Co.
8000 West Florissant Ave
Saint Louis MO 63136
314 553-2000

(G-16572)
ISOTHRMAL PRTCTIVE CATINGS INC
Also Called: Acrylink G
1950 Oday Rd (77581-3161)
PHONE....................281 485-4440
Jim Turner, *President*
Gary Hollingshead, *Vice Pres*
EMP: 15 **EST:** 1981
SQ FT: 1,785
SALES (est): 3.2MM **Privately Held**
WEB: www.plioseal.com
SIC: 2851 Paints & allied products
PA: Edge Adhesives, Inc.
5117 Northeast Pkwy
Fort Worth TX 76106

(G-16573)
KEMLON PRODUCTS & DEV CO (PA)
1424 N Main St (77581-2215)
P.O. Box 2189 (77588-2189)
PHONE....................281 997-3300
Russell K Ring, *President*
Russel Ring, *Vice Pres*
William S Ring, *Vice Pres*
Dennis Ballard, *Purch Mgr*
Tyler Ring, *Marketing Staff*
▲ **EMP:** 265 **EST:** 1963
SQ FT: 80,000
SALES (est): 60.5MM **Privately Held**
WEB: www.kemlon.com
SIC: 3643 3561 Connectors & terminals for electrical devices; pumps & pumping equipment

(G-16574)
KOZA INC
2910 S Main St (77581-4710)
PHONE....................281 485-1462
Joseph D Koza Jr, *President*
John M Koza, *Vice Pres*
Janet Cole, *Treasurer*
Mysti Schild, *Marketing Mgr*
Terrie Flora, *Clerk*
▲ **EMP:** 50
SQ FT: 40,000
SALES (est): 4.8MM **Privately Held**
WEB: www.kozas.com
SIC: 2395 Emblems, embroidered

(G-16575)
L R WEST MANUFACTURING CO
13823 1945 N Htfeld Rd (77581)
P.O. Box 1728 (77588-1728)
PHONE....................281 485-6057
Kathleen M West, *President*
Larry D West, *Vice Pres*
EMP: 15
SQ FT: 50,000
SALES (est): 3.5MM **Privately Held**
SIC: 3444 Sheet metalwork

(G-16576)
LE BOUFS BINDERY INC
4101 Rice Drier Rd Ste E (77581-2817)
PHONE....................281 485-0332
EMP: 22
SALES (est): 2.4MM **Privately Held**
SIC: 2789 Bookbinding

(G-16577)
LEARNSAP A TEXAS LTD LBLTY CO
1927 County Road 129 (77581-6246)
PHONE....................832 419-7371
Khalid Khan, *CEO*
Rupal Patel, *Instructor*
EMP: 13
SALES (est): 991.2K **Privately Held**
WEB: www.learnsap.com
SIC: 7372 8243 Publishers' computer software; software training, computer

(G-16578)
LEMETRIX SOLUTIONS LLC
2800 Broadway St Ste C (77581-9503)
PHONE....................281 381-0714
Jillian Macy,
Jeff Tange,
EMP: 9 **Privately Held**
SIC: 3356 Nickel

(G-16579)
LIGHTING ETC INC
8575 County Rd 128 (77584)
P.O. Box 3403 (77588-3403)
PHONE....................281 992-8308
Sam Thomas, *President*
Denise Duncan, *General Mgr*
Kimberly Abel, *Project Mgr*
Eli Zukerman, *Purch Mgr*
Tim Egan, *VP Engrg*
EMP: 15
SQ FT: 10,000
SALES (est): 5.6MM **Privately Held**
WEB: www.lighting-etc.com
SIC: 3648 Lighting equipment

(G-16580)
MARKLOAD SYSTEMS INC
1118 N Main St Ste C (77581-2297)
PHONE....................281 485-8600
Jan S Roush, *Ch of Bd*
Bob Risma, *Admin Sec*
EMP: 14
SQ FT: 14,000
SALES (est): 1.5MM **Privately Held**
WEB: www.markload.com
SIC: 3625 Crane & hoist controls, including metal mill

(G-16581)
MCIP INDUSTRIAL ENTPS CORP
Also Called: Mosquedas Coml & Indus Pnt
1122 N Main St (77581-2210)
PHONE....................832 767-4006
Jose Perez, *General Mgr*
Miguel Mosqueda, *Principal*
EMP: 15
SALES (est): 1MM **Privately Held**
WEB: www.mcipcorp.net
SIC: 3498 Fabricated pipe & fittings

(G-16582)
MOORES MACHINE SHOP
3806 Fm 1128 Rd (77584-7518)
PHONE....................281 489-2925
Greg Arsement, *Owner*
EMP: 10
SQ FT: 2,500
SALES (est): 776.8K **Privately Held**
WEB: www.mooresmachineshop.com
SIC: 3599 Machine shop, jobbing & repair

(G-16583)
MULTALLOY LLC (HQ)
3730 S Main St (77581-5904)
PHONE....................713 943-3544
Scott Jackson, *Mng Member*
EMP: 24
SALES (est): 44.1MM
SALES (corp-wide): 318MM **Privately Held**
WEB: www.multalloy.com
SIC: 3351 Copper & copper alloy pipe & tube

PA: Texas Pipe And Supply Company, Ltd.
2330 Holmes Rd
Houston TX 77051
713 799-9235

(G-16584)
N & N SERVICES LLC
1502 Mykawa Rd (77581-2702)
PHONE.................................281 741-9714
Joshua Smith, *President*
Jennifer Smith, *Vice Pres*
EMP: 10
SQ FT: 2,500
SALES (est): 1.3MM **Privately Held**
WEB: www.nnfab.com
SIC: 3541 7692 Machine tools, metal cutting type; welding repair

(G-16585)
OTIS T DICKERSON
Also Called: Odeeco Ready Mix Concrete
2818 Wagon Trail Rd (77584-9089)
PHONE.................................713 988-2533
Otis T Dickerson, *Owner*
EMP: 11
SQ FT: 784
SALES (est): 550.6K **Privately Held**
SIC: 3273 4212 Ready-mixed concrete; local trucking, without storage

(G-16586)
PACKAGING SERVICE CO INC
1904 Mykawa Rd (77581-3210)
PHONE.................................281 485-1458
Jean Pierre Baizan, *President*
Hector Arreola, *Plant Supt*
Luis Delacruz, *Plant Mgr*
Michael Brantley, *Opers Mgr*
Stephen Craig, *Safety Mgr*
▲ **EMP:** 250
SQ FT: 300,000
SALES (est): 159.4MM **Privately Held**
WEB: www.latexagent.com
SIC: 3563 Spraying outfits: metals, paints & chemicals (compressor)

(G-16587)
PAULUHN ELECTRIC MFG LLP
1616 N Main St (77581-2897)
PHONE.................................281 485-4311
Will Bullock, *Partner*
John Darcy, *Partner*
Lawrence Neufeld, *General Mgr*
Tony Pham, *Engineer*
▲ **EMP:** 135
SQ FT: 165,000
SALES (est): 15.9MM **Privately Held**
SIC: 3647 3646 3645 Boat & ship lighting fixtures; commercial indusl & institutional electric lighting fixtures; residential lighting fixtures
HQ: Cooper Crouse-Hinds, Llc
1201 Wolf St
Syracuse NY 13208
315 477-7000

(G-16588)
PCC KLAD LLC
Also Called: Klad Manufacturing Company
1710 Mykawa Rd (77581-2706)
PHONE.................................713 433-5151
Mark Donegan, *President*
EMP: 20 **EST:** 2011
SALES (est): 4.5MM
SALES (corp-wide): 254.6B **Publicly Held**
WEB: www.pccforgedproducts.com
SIC: 3317 Conduit: welded, lock joint or heavy riveted
HQ: Precision Castparts Corp.
4650 Sw Mcdam Ave Ste 300
Portland OR 97239
503 946-4800

(G-16589)
PEARLAND ALTERNATOR INC
1221 N Main St (77581-2211)
P.O. Box 1482 (77588-1482)
PHONE.................................281 485-8871
Al Coker, *President*
Randy Coker, *Vice Pres*
Kollene Hyland, *Sales Staff*
▲ **EMP:** 22
SQ FT: 14,000

SALES (est): 2.9MM **Privately Held**
WEB: www.pearlandalternator.com
SIC: 3694 5015 5013 3714 Alternators, automotive; motors, starting: automotive & aircraft; motor vehicle parts, used; motor vehicle supplies & new parts; motor vehicle parts & accessories

(G-16590)
PEARLAND ARTS LEAGUE
3519 Liberty Dr (77581-5416)
PHONE.................................713 304-0672
Pat Riffel, *Manager*
Charles Vicktorin, *Director*
EMP: 16
SALES (est): 1MM **Privately Held**
WEB: www.pearlandartleague.com
SIC: 3952 Pastels, artists'

(G-16591)
PEARLAND MRI AND IMAGING CTR
8633 Broadway St Ste 209 (77584-8497)
PHONE.................................281 412-3916
Michelle Pope, *Office Mgr*
EMP: 10
SALES (est): 830.4K **Privately Held**
WEB: www.hcahoustonhealthcare.com
SIC: 3826 Magnetic resonance imaging apparatus

(G-16592)
PLANET RESOURCE RECOVERY INC
8815 Industrial Dr (77584-3559)
PHONE.................................281 996-5315
Kurt E Neubauer, *Ch of Bd*
W Frank Crane, *COO*
Kenneth D Wolcott, *Vice Pres*
EMP: 25
SQ FT: 4,100
SALES (est): 4.5MM **Privately Held**
WEB: www.planetresource.net
SIC: 2869 4959 7699 Antioxidants, rubber processing: cyclic or acyclic; oil spill cleanup; tank repair & cleaning services

(G-16593)
PLPS INC (PA)
8321 Industrial Dr (77584-3549)
P.O. Box 700 (77588-0700)
PHONE.................................866 992-7577
John Eckel Sr, *President*
James Wyman, *Opers Mgr*
EMP: 10
SALES (est): 6.6MM **Privately Held**
WEB: www.plpsinc.com
SIC: 1389 Oil field services

(G-16594)
POLYGLASS COATINGS LIMITED LLC
1616 N Main St (77581-2804)
PHONE.................................832 736-9243
Thomas Jamsson, *General Mgr*
EMP: 20 **EST:** 2008
SALES (est): 5.4MM
SALES (corp-wide): 20.7MM **Privately Held**
WEB: www.endurapaint.com
SIC: 2851 Paints & allied products
PA: Endura Manufacturing Company Limited
12425 149 St Nw
Edmonton AB T5L 2
780 451-4242

(G-16595)
ROCKMM MANUFACTURING INC
1620 N Main St (77581-2804)
PHONE.................................346 888-6188
Dennis Read, *President*
Farshad Hadaegh, *Treasurer*
EMP: 9
SQ FT: 37,500
SALES (est): 600K **Privately Held**
WEB: www.rockmm.com
SIC: 3599 Machine shop, jobbing & repair

(G-16596)
ROLLAC SHUTTER OF TEXAS INC
5331 W Orange St (77581-3237)
PHONE.................................281 485-1911

Walter Konrad, *President*
Eva Konrad, *Vice Pres*
Nina Konrad, *Opers Mgr*
Travis Willis, *Graphic Designe*
◆ **EMP:** 65
SQ FT: 105,000
SALES (est): 26.5MM **Privately Held**
WEB: www.rollac.com
SIC: 5039 2431 Awnings; awnings, blinds & shutters, wood

(G-16597)
RONALD L JORDAN COMPANY
Also Called: Intercontinental Machine
4271 Magnolia Pkwy (77584-1618)
PHONE.................................281 485-6626
Juanita Jordan, *Ch of Bd*
Ronald L Jordan, *President*
Thomas A Jordan, *Vice Pres*
Jordan Dearman, *Mfg Staff*
Tom Jordan, *Manager*
EMP: 20 **EST:** 1969
SQ FT: 12,500
SALES (est): 4.2MM **Privately Held**
WEB: www.intmachine.com
SIC: 3599 7692 Machine shop, jobbing & repair; welding repair

(G-16598)
SHAWCOR PIPE PROTECTION LLC
Also Called: Compression Coat
1122 N Main St (77582-2210)
PHONE.................................281 485-8321
Jerry Grigar, *Manager*
Brad Hext, *Info Tech Mgr*
EMP: 10
SALES (corp-wide): 1.1B **Privately Held**
WEB: www.shawcor.com
SIC: 3479 Coating or wrapping steel pipe
HQ: Shawcor Pipe Protection Llc
5875 N Sam Houston Pkwy W # 200
Houston TX 77086

(G-16599)
SHERMAN ROTO TANK LLC
8521 Industrial Dr (77584-3553)
PHONE.................................281 648-0909
Mark Adamson, *President*
Wade Sherman, *Admin Sec*
EMP: 23
SALES (est): 4.5MM **Privately Held**
WEB: www.sherman-tank.com
SIC: 3089 Plastic & fiberglass tanks

(G-16600)
SOLVCHEM INC (HQ)
1904 Mykawa Rd (77581-3210)
P.O. Box 490 (77588-0490)
PHONE.................................281 485-5377
◆ **EMP:** 35
SALES (est): 68.3MM
SALES (corp-wide): 75.4MM **Privately Held**
WEB: www.solvchem.com
SIC: 5169 2899 Chemicals, industrial & heavy; chemical preparations
PA: Sempre Avant Llc
1904 Mykawa Rd
Pearland TX 77581
281 485-5377

(G-16601)
TEXAS HONING INC (DH)
1710 Mykawa Rd (77581-2706)
PHONE.................................281 485-8339
▲ **EMP:** 49 **EST:** 1976
SQ FT: 90,000
SALES (est): 31.5MM
SALES (corp-wide): 254.6B **Publicly Held**
WEB: www.pccenergy.com
SIC: 3599 Machine shop, jobbing & repair
HQ: Berkshire Hathaway Auto Inc
8333 Royal Ridge Pkwy # 1
Irving TX 75063
972 536-2900

(G-16602)
TEXAS UNDERGROUND INC
1617 Garden Rd (77581-8730)
P.O. Box 2729 (77588-2729)
PHONE.................................281 485-9900
Thomas Stoneman, *President*
Lesy Stoneman, *Vice Pres*
Diane McMillan, *Controller*

Betty Stoneman, *Controller*
Diane McMillian, *Accounting Mgr*
▲ **EMP:** 60
SQ FT: 30,000
SALES (est): 18.9MM **Privately Held**
WEB: www.weatherford.com
SIC: 3715 3589 5084 Trailer bodies; sewer cleaning equipment, power; instruments & control equipment

(G-16603)
THI ACQUISITION INC
1710 Mykawa Rd (77581-2706)
PHONE.................................281 485-8339
Robert Steele, *President*
EMP: 110
SALES (est): 9.6MM
SALES (corp-wide): 254.6B **Publicly Held**
WEB: www.pccenergy.com
SIC: 3541 Boring mills
HQ: Precision Castparts Corp.
4650 Sw Mcdam Ave Ste 300
Portland OR 97239
503 946-4800

(G-16604)
THIRD COAST PACKAGING INC
Also Called: Third Coast Terminals
1871 Mykawa Rd (77581-3207)
PHONE.................................281 412-0275
Jim Clawson Jr, *President*
Grif Carnes, *Vice Pres*
Larry Rysavy, *Vice Pres*
Toni Randall, *Admin Sec*
◆ **EMP:** 40
SQ FT: 55,000
SALES (est): 19MM **Privately Held**
WEB: www.thirdcoastterminals.com
SIC: 4225 4783 2899 General warehousing & storage; packing goods for shipping; chemical preparations

(G-16605)
TREVINO INDUSTRIES INC
5302 Bailey Rd (77584-6034)
P.O. Box 1716 (77588-1716)
PHONE.................................281 489-1754
Frank Trevino Sr, *President*
EMP: 13
SQ FT: 3,600 **Privately Held**
WEB: www.trevinoindustries.com
SIC: 7692 Welding repair

(G-16606)
U S WEATHERFORD L P
3810 Magnolia Pkwy (77584-1608)
P.O. Box 899 (77588-0899)
PHONE.................................281 652-1300
Jim Slinkrad, *Principal*
Eric Josey, *Purch Agent*
EMP: 18 **Privately Held**
WEB: www.weatherford.com
SIC: 1389 Oil field services
HQ: U S Weatherford L P
179 Weatherford Dr
Schriever LA 70395
985 493-6100

(G-16607)
U S WEATHERFORD L P
3632 S Main St (77581-5944)
PHONE.................................281 485-1899
Hal Presley, *Branch Mgr*
EMP: 30
SQ FT: 43,560 **Privately Held**
WEB: www.weatherford.com
SIC: 1389 Oil field services
HQ: U S Weatherford L P
179 Weatherford Dr
Schriever LA 70395
985 493-6100

(G-16608)
U S WEATHERFORD L P
Also Called: Oil Field Rental Svc. Co.
3808 Magnolia Pkwy (77584-1608)
PHONE.................................281 485-0500
Randy Deweese, *Manager*
EMP: 12 **Privately Held**
WEB: www.weatherford.com
SIC: 1389 Oil field services
HQ: U S Weatherford L P
179 Weatherford Dr
Schriever LA 70395
985 493-6100

(G-16609)
VANS INC
11200 Broadway St # 1355 (77584-9785)
PHONE....................713 436-7925
Dewayne Long, *Asst Mgr*
EMP: 10
SALES (corp-wide): 10.4B **Publicly Held**
WEB: www.vans.com
SIC: 3021 Canvas shoes, rubber soled
HQ: Vans, Inc.
1588 S Coast Dr
Costa Mesa CA 92626
855 909-8267

(G-16610)
WEATHERFORD
INTERNATIONAL LLC
3632 S Main St Bldg 1 (77581-5944)
PHONE....................281 485-1899
Wesley Stoddard, *Project Mgr*
Darrell Hickey, *Branch Mgr*
Steven Shipley, *Supervisor*
EMP: 40 **Privately Held**
WEB: www.weatherford.com
SIC: 1389 Oil field services
HQ: Weatherford International, Llc
2000 Saint James Pl
Houston TX 77056
713 693-4000

(G-16611)
WOODLAND PUBLISHING INC
Also Called: Friendswood Reporter News
2407 Park Ave (77581-4233)
P.O. Box 954, Friendswood (77549-0954)
PHONE....................281 485-7501
Laura A Emmons, *President*
Randy Emmons, *General Mgr*
EMP: 27
SQ FT: 6,250
SALES (est): 1.6MM **Privately Held**
WEB: www.myreporternews.com
SIC: 2741 2711 Miscellaneous publishing;
newspapers

Pearsall
Frio County

(G-16612)
GRAND ISLE SHIPYARD INC
Also Called: Gis Oilfield Contractors
3300 Bus Interstate 35 E (78061)
P.O. Box 1109 (78061-1109)
PHONE....................830 334-2665
EMP: 93
SALES (corp-wide): 2.3B **Privately Held**
SIC: 1389 Oil/Gas Field Services
HQ: Grand Isle Shipyard Inc.
18838 Highway 3235
Galliano LA 70354
985 475-5238

(G-16613)
INGRAM READYMIX INC
Hwy 81 N (78061)
PHONE....................830 334-3622
Ruven Hernandez, *Manager*
EMP: 10
SALES (corp-wide): 125.6MM **Privately Held**
WEB: www.ingramreadymixinc.com
SIC: 5211 3273 Cement; ready-mixed concrete
PA: Ingram Readymix, Inc.
3580 Farm Market 482
New Braunfels TX 78132
830 625-9156

(G-16614)
RUTHERFORD OIL
CORPORATION
1825 Private Road 1500 (78061-6700)
PHONE....................830 334-8396
Bill Crain, *Manager*
EMP: 11
SALES (corp-wide): 11.4MM **Privately Held**
WEB: www.rutherfordoil.com
SIC: 1382 Oil & gas exploration services
PA: Rutherford Oil Corporation
8 Greenway Plz Ste 1400
Houston TX 77046
713 622-5555

(G-16615)
UVALDE LEADER NEWS
321 E San Marcos St (78061-3223)
P.O. Box 1208 (78061-1208)
PHONE....................830 334-3644
Craig Garnett, *Owner*
EMP: 17 **Privately Held**
WEB: www.uvaldeleadernews.com
SIC: 2711 Newspapers: publishing only, not printed on site
PA: The Uvalde Leader News
110 N East St
Uvalde TX 78801

Pecos
Reeves County

(G-16616)
B&C TEXAS LEASING LLC
2902 S Bickley Ave (79772-7217)
P.O. Box 898 (79772-0898)
PHONE....................432 362-0548
Curtis McKee, *Vice Pres*
EMP: 80
SQ FT: 1,200
SALES (est): 884.7K **Privately Held**
SIC: 1389 Oil field services

(G-16617)
BADGER BMB SERVICES INC
1724 S Bickley Ave (79772-4737)
P.O. Box 350 (79772-0350)
PHONE....................432 447-0498
Wally Moon, *President*
Nathan Blair, *President*
Criag Blair, *Vice Pres*
Tammy Moon, *Manager*
Steven Blair, *Admin Sec*
EMP: 57
SQ FT: 10,000
SALES (est): 8.9MM **Privately Held**
WEB: www.badgerbmbservices.com
SIC: 1389 Construction, repair & dismantling services

(G-16618)
BASIC ENERGY SERVICES INC
2307 S Bickley Ave (79772-6608)
P.O. Box 1811 (79772-1811)
PHONE....................432 445-2216
EMP: 30
SALES (corp-wide): 567.2MM **Publicly Held**
WEB: www.basices.com
SIC: 1389 Oil field services
PA: Basic Energy Services, Inc.
801 Cherry St Unit 2
Fort Worth TX 76102
817 334-4100

(G-16619)
CAPITOL AGGREGATES INC
7001 Hwy 17 S (79772)
P.O. Box 9024 (79772-9024)
PHONE....................432 447-9667
Danny Vasquez, *Branch Mgr*
EMP: 21 **Privately Held**
WEB: www.capitolaggregates.com
SIC: 1442 Gravel mining
HQ: Capitol Aggregates, Inc.
2330 N Loop 1604 W
San Antonio TX 78248
210 871-6100

(G-16620)
DUKES OUTDOOR
ADVERTISING
181 S Frontage Rd (79772-7202)
P.O. Box 911 (79772-0911)
PHONE....................432 447-2251
Kevin W Duke, *Owner*
EMP: 15
SALES (est): 1.3MM **Privately Held**
SIC: 3993 Signs & advertising specialties

(G-16621)
LA NORTENA INC
Also Called: La Nortena Factory
211 E 3rd St (79772-3217)
PHONE....................432 445-3273
David Castillo, *CEO*
EMP: 9

SALES (est): 322.5K **Privately Held**
WEB: www.lanortenatamales.com
SIC: 5812 2032 7371 Carry-out only (except pizza) restaurant; Mexican foods: packaged in cans, jars, etc.; computer software development & applications

(G-16622)
LA NORTENA TORTILLA
FACTORY
Also Called: La Nortena Restaurant
212 E 3rd St (79772-3204)
P.O. Box 896 (79772-0896)
PHONE....................432 445-3273
Miguel Castillo, *Owner*
EMP: 14
SQ FT: 1,500
SALES (est): 921.6K **Privately Held**
WEB: www.lanortenatamales.com
SIC: 2099 5812 5149 Tortillas, fresh or refrigerated; eating places; groceries & related products

(G-16623)
M & W HOT OIL INC (PA)
2902 Balmorhea Hwy (79772)
P.O. Box 69370, Odessa (79769-0370)
PHONE....................432 447-2108
Bruce McKee, *President*
Holly Key, *Vice Pres*
Curtis McKee, *Vice Pres*
Kenneth Winkles, *Shareholder*
EMP: 50
SQ FT: 9,000
SALES (est): 13.2MM **Privately Held**
WEB: www.mwhotoil.com
SIC: 4212 1389 Liquid transfer services; servicing oil & gas wells

(G-16624)
NEEDLEWORKS ETC (PA)
120 S Cedar St (79772-3207)
PHONE....................432 445-9313
Peggy Walker, *Owner*
EMP: 12
SQ FT: 1,600
SALES (est): 727.7K **Privately Held**
WEB: www.needleworksetc.com
SIC: 5621 2339 5137 Ready-to-wear apparel, women's; women's & misses' outerwear; women's & children's clothing

(G-16625)
PRIMEXX OPERATING
CORPORATION
2131 Barilla Rd (79772-7707)
PHONE....................432 445-7860
EMP: 22
SALES (corp-wide): 24.2MM **Privately Held**
WEB: www.primexx.com
SIC: 1311 Crude petroleum production
PA: Primexx Operating Corporation
4849 Grnvlle Ave Ste 1600
Dallas TX 75206
214 369-5909

(G-16626)
SELECT ENERGY SERVICES
INC
2400 Moore St (79772-7307)
P.O. Box 998 (79772-0998)
PHONE....................432 447-0602
EMP: 3302
SALES (corp-wide): 1.2B **Publicly Held**
WEB: www.selectenergyservices.com
SIC: 1389 Oil field services
PA: Select Energy Services, Inc.
1233 West Loop S Ste 1400
Houston TX 77027
713 235-9500

(G-16627)
TEXAS INDUSTRIAL CHOICE
LLC
2291 S Bickley Ave (79772-6609)
P.O. Box 64964, Lubbock (79464-4964)
PHONE....................432 231-7313
Taha Habib,
EMP: 32
SALES (est): 292.1K **Privately Held**
WEB: www.texasindustrialchoice.com
SIC: 1389 Pumping of oil & gas wells

Pendleton
Bell County

(G-16628)
EFCO MACHINE SHOP LLC
9740 Spur Rd 1237 (76564)
P.O. Box 59 (76564-0059)
PHONE....................254 778-7394
Mark Elliot, *Mng Member*
Byron Hamrick, *Manager*
Mark Elliott,
EMP: 14
SQ FT: 15,200
SALES (est): 4MM **Privately Held**
WEB: www.efcomachineshop.com
SIC: 3599 Machine shop, jobbing & repair

Penitas
Hidalgo County

(G-16629)
J & N WELDING AND
FABRICATORS
507 S Main St (78576-7415)
P.O. Box 1077 (78576-1077)
PHONE....................956 585-3992
Javier Cardenas, *CEO*
EMP: 20 EST: 2011
SQ FT: 25,000
SALES (est): 2MM **Privately Held**
WEB: www.jnweldingfab.com
SIC: 1791 3441 Structural steel erection; fabricated structural metal

(G-16630)
RIO VALLEY PIPE LLC
3100 N Tom Gill Rd (78576)
PHONE....................956 519-4960
Joe Villa Real, *Manager*
EMP: 50
SALES (corp-wide): 16MM **Privately Held**
WEB: www.capatexas.com
SIC: 3272 Pipe, concrete or lined with concrete
PA: Rio Valley Pipe Llc
3609 W Palma Vista Dr
Palmview TX 78572
956 580-3466

Perryton
Ochiltree County

(G-16631)
ALLRED CONSTRUCTION
COMPANY
302 Se 9th Ave (79070-3527)
P.O. Box 894 (79070-0894)
PHONE....................806 435-5817
Jerral Allred, *President*
Allred Perry, *Vice Pres*
Perry Alred, *Admin Sec*
EMP: 65 EST: 1965
SQ FT: 6,000
SALES (est): 3.6MM **Privately Held**
SIC: 1389 Roustabout service

(G-16632)
ALPAR ENERGY LP
320 Se 24th Ave (79070)
P.O. Box 1046 (79070-1046)
PHONE....................806 435-6566
Suzanne Willis, *Partner*
Jack M Allen, *Managing Dir*
Brent Allen, *Managing Dir*
Barry Willis, *Managing Dir*
Robert G Cunningham, *Controller*
EMP: 9
SQ FT: 8,000
SALES (est): 500K **Privately Held**
WEB: www.perrytonseniors.org
SIC: 1311 1382 Crude petroleum production; natural gas production; oil & gas exploration services

(G-16633)
ARKHOMA TRANSPORTS INC (PA)
102 S Juniper St (79070-2700)
P.O. Box 50659, Amarillo (79159-0659)
PHONE..................................806 435-2380
Charles Neas, *President*
Pam Neas, *Corp Secy*
EMP: 32
SQ FT: 2,640
SALES (est): 2.2MM Privately Held
SIC: 1389 Haulage, oil field; chemically treating wells

(G-16634)
BECKMAN WELL SERVICING COMPANY
1000 Ne 6th St (79070)
P.O. Box 769 (79070-0769)
PHONE..................................806 435-2543
Alfred L Hayden, *President*
EMP: 38
SQ FT: 6,000
SALES (est): 4.3MM Privately Held
SIC: 1389 Servicing oil & gas wells

(G-16635)
CHAPARRAL ENERGY LLC
12650 Fm 1267 (79070-6122)
P.O. Box 90 (79070-0090)
PHONE..................................806 435-7533
Steve Slaybaugh, *Branch Mgr*
EMP: 65 Privately Held
WEB: www.chaparralenergy.com
SIC: 1311 Crude petroleum production
HQ: Chaparral Energy, L.L.C.
701 Cedar Lake Blvd
Oklahoma City OK 73114
405 478-8770

(G-16636)
COURSON OIL & GAS INC
1800 S Main St (79070-5908)
P.O. Box 809 (79070-0809)
PHONE..................................806 435-2910
Harold Courson, *President*
Kirk Courson, *Treasurer*
David Hale, *Admin Sec*
EMP: 15
SQ FT: 12,500
SALES (est): 1.6MM Privately Held
WEB: www.coursonarchresearch.com
SIC: 1311 Crude petroleum production

(G-16637)
DAVID POND WELL SERVICE INC
606 S Juniper St (79070-2727)
P.O. Box 704 (79070-0704)
PHONE..................................806 435-2384
David Pond, *President*
Tony Pond, *Vice Pres*
Heather Dumcum, *Admin Sec*
EMP: 15
SALES (est): 1.4MM Privately Held
SIC: 1389 Oil field services

(G-16638)
JL BRYAN EQP & LEASE SVCS INC
806 S Industrial Hwy (79070-3636)
P.O. Box 669 (79070-0669)
PHONE..................................806 435-4511
Jerry Lynn Bryan, *President*
Jerry Bryan, *Info Tech Mgr*
EMP: 21
SQ FT: 3,375
SALES (est): 7.7MM
SALES (corp-wide): 13MM Privately Held
WEB: www.jlbryan.com
SIC: 5084 3491 Oil well machinery, equipment & supplies; gas valves & parts, industrial
PA: Tank Partners Holdings Llc
4320 Johnson Rd
Odessa TX 79764
803 433-4866

(G-16639)
LONS WELDING
522 N Main St (79070-2305)
P.O. Box 688 (79070-0688)
PHONE..................................806 435-2278
Budge Rawlins,

Jerry Denton,
EMP: 20 EST: 1970
SQ FT: 7,400
SALES (est): 1.8MM Privately Held
SIC: 1623 7692 Oil & gas pipeline construction; welding repair

(G-16640)
MEWBOURNE OIL COMPANY
143 E Loop Rd (79070)
P.O. Box 770 (79070-0770)
PHONE..................................806 435-6881
Brent Thurman, *Manager*
EMP: 31
SALES (corp-wide): 458.1MM Privately Held
WEB: www.mewbourne.net
SIC: 1382 Oil & gas exploration services
HQ: Mewbourne Oil Company
3620 Old Bullard Rd
Tyler TX 75701
903 561-2900

(G-16641)
N5 WIRELINE SERVICE LLC
1322 S Main St (79070-4710)
P.O. Box 836 (79070-0836)
PHONE..................................806 648-1505
Jose Najera, *Principal*
EMP: 15
SALES (est): 1.7MM Privately Held
WEB: www.n5wirelineservice.com
SIC: 1389 Removal of condensate gasoline from field (gathering) lines; oil field services

(G-16642)
NATURAL GAS ANADARKO COMPANY
1800 S Main St (79070-5908)
P.O. Box 809 (79070-0809)
PHONE..................................806 435-6818
Harold D Courson, *Partner*
David C Hale, *Partner*
Howard Skidgel, *Partner*
EMP: 30
SQ FT: 6,250
SALES (est): 2.2MM Privately Held
SIC: 1311 Crude petroleum production

(G-16643)
OMI OILFIELD INVESTMENTS LLC
Also Called: Elite Oilfield Services
1201 S Ash St (79070-4225)
P.O. Box 951 (79070-0951)
PHONE..................................806 648-4120
EMP: 12 EST: 2011
SALES (est): 1.2MM Privately Held
SIC: 1389 Oil field services

(G-16644)
PERRYTON FEEDERS LLC
13210 Highway 70 (79070-6760)
PHONE..................................806 435-5466
Ruth Farney, *Treasurer*
Chad Grimes, *Manager*
Amy Payton,
Bailey Payton,
EMP: 25
SALES (est): 1.9MM Privately Held
SIC: 3523 Cattle feeding, handling & watering equipment

(G-16645)
PHIL DOLLAR OILFIELD SERVICES
2025 W Hwy 15 (79070)
P.O. Box 744 (79070-0744)
PHONE..................................806 435-3373
Phil Dollar, *President*
Lori Dollar, *Vice Pres*
EMP: 10
SQ FT: 1,200
SALES (est): 1.3MM Privately Held
SIC: 1389 Oil field services

(G-16646)
RENCO TOOL CO INC
21 S Industrial Hwy (79070-2719)
P.O. Box 602 (79070-0602)
PHONE..................................806 648-2903
Ren Hensley, *President*
Tammie Hensley, *Corp Secy*
EMP: 11

SQ FT: 4,000
SALES (est): 600K Privately Held
WEB: www.rencotool.com
SIC: 1389 Oil & gas wells: building, repairing & dismantling

(G-16647)
ROBERSON WIRELINE INC
314 Se 9th Ave (79070-3527)
P.O. Box 1105 (79070-1105)
PHONE..................................806 435-3087
Dick Roberson, *President*
Bill Roberson, *Vice Pres*
Rhonda Roberson, *Treasurer*
Kim Roberson, *Admin Sec*
EMP: 25
SALES (est): 3.1MM Privately Held
WEB: www.robersonwireline.com
SIC: 1389 5084 Testing, measuring, surveying & analysis services; cleaning wells; swabbing wells; oil well machinery, equipment & supplies

(G-16648)
RUDD WELDING INC
12485 Spur 192 (79070-6731)
P.O. Box 341 (79070-0341)
PHONE..................................806 435-5501
Amanda Rudd, *President*
EMP: 11 EST: 2009
SALES (est): 1.6MM Privately Held
WEB: www.ruddwelding.com
SIC: 7692 Welding repair

(G-16649)
SAMSON RESOURCES COMPANY
922 Se 9th Ave (79070-3637)
P.O. Box 986, Elk City OK (73648-0986)
PHONE..................................806 435-7200
Fax: 806 435-7001
EMP: 27
SALES (corp-wide): 2.4B Privately Held
SIC: 1382 Oil/Gas Exploration Services
HQ: Samson Resources Company
2 W 2nd St Ste 1500
Tulsa OK 74103
918 583-1791

(G-16650)
TOTAL WELLHEAD & RENTL TLS LLC
401 S Juniper St (79070)
P.O. Box 1068 (79070-1068)
PHONE..................................806 435-3800
Clarke E Swinney,
EMP: 25
SQ FT: 10,000
SALES (est): 1.9MM Privately Held
WEB: www.totalwellhead.com
SIC: 1389 Oil field services

(G-16651)
WEATHERFORD INTERNATIONAL LLC
14425 E Loop 143 (79070)
P.O. Box 966 (79070-0966)
PHONE..................................806 435-6801
EMP: 16 Privately Held
WEB: www.weatherford.com
SIC: 1389 Oil field services
HQ: Weatherford International, Llc
2000 Saint James Pl
Houston TX 77056
713 693-4000

Petersburg
Hale County

(G-16652)
WYLIE & SON INC (PA)
Also Called: Wylie Sprayers of Amarillo
101 N Main St (79250)
PHONE..................................806 667-3566
Scot L Wylie, *President*
Loy L Wylie, *Chairman*
Mike Abbott, *Corp Secy*
John Baker, *Vice Pres*
Doug Mariott, *Vice Pres*
EMP: 76 EST: 1959
SQ FT: 50,000

SALES (est): 27MM Privately Held
WEB: www.wyliesprayers.com
SIC: 3523 3089 Sprayers & spraying machines, agricultural; plastic hardware & building products

Pettus
Bee County

(G-16653)
NELSON OIL FIELD EQP & SUP
Also Called: Yegua Well Service
Pns St (78146)
P.O. Box 117 (78146-0117)
PHONE..................................361 375-2105
James L Nelson, *Owner*
EMP: 13
SQ FT: 7,500
SALES (est): 1.5MM Privately Held
SIC: 7353 1311 3599 7699 Oil field equipment, rental or leasing; crude petroleum production; machine shop, jobbing & repair; machinery cleaning

(G-16654)
YEGUA OIL FIELD SERVICE INC
Also Called: Nelson Oilfield Equipment
S Hwy 181 And Pins St (78146)
P.O. Box 307 (78146-0307)
PHONE..................................361 375-2105
James Nelson, *President*
Nelson Richard, *Vice Pres*
Jerry Morris, *Treasurer*
Helen Nelson, *Admin Sec*
EMP: 10
SQ FT: 7,500
SALES (est): 924.3K Privately Held
SIC: 1389 Gas field services; oil field services

Pflugerville
Travis County

(G-16655)
365 CERTIFIED LOGISTICS LLC
819 Indian Run Dr (78660-3871)
PHONE..................................512 743-9304
Kristofor Fry, *President*
David Matthew Fry, *CFO*
EMP: 15 EST: 2013
SQ FT: 3,000
SALES (est): 600K Privately Held
SIC: 1389 5084 Oil field services; cleaning equipment, high pressure, sand or steam

(G-16656)
AI LONESTAR LLC
1009 W Wells Branch Pkwy (78660-3150)
PHONE..................................512 990-3999
Jim Laughlin, *General Mgr*
David Robinson, *General Mgr*
Charles Botti, *Co-President*
Robert Cattarin, *Co-President*
Jason Eastabrook, *Opers Staff*
EMP: 10
SQ FT: 15,000
SALES (est): 1.3MM
SALES (corp-wide): 20.1MM Privately Held
SIC: 3471 Finishing, metals or formed products
PA: Ai Industries, Llc
1725 E Byshore Rd Ste 101
Redwood City CA 94063
650 366-4099

(G-16657)
AMERICAN VAPOR COMPANY LLC
13400 Immanuel Rd Ste 2 (78660-8252)
PHONE..................................512 596-1892
Justin Suriff, *COO*
Carson Suriff,
EMP: 19
SALES (est): 3.6MM Privately Held
WEB: www.americanvaporcompany.com
SIC: 3999 7371 Manufacturing industries; computer software development & applications

▲ = Import ▼=Export
◆ =Import/Export

(G-16658)
ARMBRUST INC
3813a Helios Way 290 (78660-8371)
PHONE.....................512 807-0744
Lloyd Armbrust, *CEO*
EMP: 34
SALES (est): 10MM **Privately Held**
SIC: 2326 5047 Medical & hospital uniforms, men's; medical & hospital equipment

(G-16659)
AUSTIN PALLET COMPANY
1605 Century St (78660-3146)
PHONE.....................512 990-0090
David Campbell, *President*
EMP: 24
SQ FT: 1,400
SALES (est): 3.1MM **Privately Held**
WEB: www.austinpallet.com
SIC: 2448 Pallets, wood

(G-16660)
AVANT TECHNOLOGY INC (HQ)
828 New Meister Ln # 300 (78660-5829)
PHONE.....................512 651-5300
Tim Peddecord, *President*
Ken Bandy, *COO*
Trevor Majors, *Manager*
▲ **EMP:** 80
SQ FT: 55,000
SALES (est): 25.2MM
SALES (corp-wide): 49.5MM **Privately Held**
WEB: www.avanttechnology.com
SIC: 3674 8711 Computer logic modules; mechanical engineering
PA: All Components, Inc.
828 New Meister Ln # 300
Pflugerville TX 78660
512 651-5300

(G-16661)
BANISTER TOOL INCORPORATED
3009 A W Grimes Blvd (78660-5291)
P.O. Box 7769, Round Rock (78683-7769)
PHONE.....................512 258-8351
Ray Banister, *President*
Norma Kutch, *Admin Sec*
EMP: 42
SQ FT: 22,000
SALES (est): 6.3MM **Privately Held**
WEB: www.banistertool.com
SIC: 3599 Machine shop, jobbing & repair

(G-16662)
BURRELL PRINTING COMPANY INC
901 Fm 685 (78660-2802)
P.O. Box 1340 (78691-1340)
PHONE.....................512 990-1188
Mark Bolles, *Ch of Bd*
Carole Cearley, *Corp Secy*
Linda Krzesniak, *Accountant*
Donna Kilgore, *Executive Asst*
Kim Moreno,
EMP: 23 **EST:** 1960
SQ FT: 24,860
SALES (est): 3.4MM **Privately Held**
WEB: www.burrellprinting.com
SIC: 2759 2791 2752 Business forms: printing; typesetting; commercial printing, lithographic

(G-16663)
CASTLBERRY INSTRS AVIONICS LLC
13405 Immanuel Rd Ste 1a (78660-8338)
PHONE.....................512 251-5322
Alex Hodge, *Managing Prtnr*
John Semerjibashian, *General Mgr*
Ted Dunbar, *General Ptnr*
John Mounce, *General Ptnr*
Miranda Henson, *Sales Staff*
EMP: 21
SALES (est): 5.2MM **Privately Held**
WEB: www.ciamfg.com
SIC: 5599 3812 Aircraft instruments, equipment or parts; aircraft flight instruments

(G-16664)
CROSSLINK PWDR CTING ASTIN LTD
Also Called: Cross Link Powder Coating
2310 Patterson Indus Dr (78660-8303)
PHONE.....................512 989-6458
Jess Link, *Owner*
Renee Romelo, *Owner*
Mary Cay Link, *Co-Owner*
Jessica Gonzales, *Manager*
EMP: 9
SQ FT: 5,000
SALES (est): 649.3K **Privately Held**
WEB: www.crosslinktexas.com
SIC: 3479 Coating of metals & formed products

(G-16665)
CRUX MANUFACTURING INC
1421 W Wlls Br Pkwy Ste 3 (78660)
PHONE.....................512 619-6170
Tim Kelly, *President*
Willliam Heilveil, *Director*
Shane K Miller, *Director*
EMP: 12
SALES (est): 1.4MM **Privately Held**
WEB: www.cruxmanufacturing.com
SIC: 3544 Special dies, tools, jigs & fixtures

(G-16666)
CUMBERLAND ADDITIVE INC
1007 S Hthrwld Blvd (78660-5218)
PHONE.....................512 990-9100
Dawne Hickton, *Director*
EMP: 18
SALES (est): 4.6MM
SALES (corp-wide): 581.7K **Privately Held**
WEB: www.3dquote.rtiintl.com
SIC: 3841 Surgical & medical instruments
PA: Cumberland Additive Holdings, Llc
506 Hegner Way
Sewickley PA 15143
330 506-2457

(G-16667)
CUSTOM ELECTRONICS INC
102 W Pecan St (78660-2746)
P.O. Box 3103, Wimberley (78676-8003)
PHONE.....................512 454-8824
EMP: 10 **EST:** 1998
SALES (est): 1.5MM **Privately Held**
WEB: www.customelectronicsinc.com
SIC: 3651 5731 Household audio & video equipment; high fidelity stereo equipment

(G-16668)
EIEIO INC
Also Called: Coffee Legends
3813 Helios Way Ste 200 (78660-8373)
PHONE.....................512 342-8044
Cecil D Andrews, *CEO*
▲ **EMP:** 23 **EST:** 2000
SQ FT: 45,000
SALES (est): 2.3MM
SALES (corp-wide): 656MM **Privately Held**
WEB: www.eieio-inc.com
SIC: 7032 3523 Dude ranch; driers (farm): grain, hay & seed
HQ: Danone Us, Inc.
12002 Airport Way
Broomfield CO 80021
303 635-4500

(G-16669)
ELECTRONIC VISIONS SYSTEMS
400 S Heatherwilde Blvd (78660-3534)
PHONE.....................512 989-3000
Myranda Fredericks, *Manager*
EMP: 45
SALES (corp-wide): 23MM **Privately Held**
WEB: www.evsmetal.com
SIC: 3444 Sheet metalwork
PA: Electronic Visions Systems Inc
1 Kenner Ct
Riverdale NJ 07457
973 839-4432

(G-16670)
ESSENTIUM INC (PA)
Also Called: Essentium Materials
19025 N Hthrwld Blvd (78660-6193)
PHONE.....................210 616-1931
Edward Nevins, *Principal*
Blake Teipel, *Principal*
EMP: 49
SALES (est): 9.6MM **Privately Held**
WEB: www.essentium3d.com
SIC: 3531 Construction machinery

(G-16671)
EVS TEXAS INC
400 S Heatherwilde Blvd (78660-3534)
PHONE.....................512 989-3000
Scott Berkowitz, *President*
Wayne Bruck, *General Mgr*
Lee Grzywinski, *General Mgr*
Keith Tuthill, *General Mgr*
John Bingham, *Opers Mgr*
EMP: 60
SQ FT: 42,000
SALES (est): 9.5MM
SALES (corp-wide): 23MM **Privately Held**
WEB: www.evsmetal.com
SIC: 3444 Sheet metalwork
PA: Electronic Visions Systems Inc
1 Kenner Ct
Riverdale NJ 07457
973 839-4432

(G-16672)
FLEXTRONICS AMERICA LLC
Also Called: Flextronics Logistics USA
900 New Meister Ln (78660-5490)
PHONE.....................512 425-6180
EMP: 10 **Privately Held**
WEB: www.flex.com
SIC: 3672 Printed circuit boards
HQ: Flextronics America, Llc
6201 America Center Dr
San Jose CA 95002
408 576-7000

(G-16673)
FOUR PNTS PLTNUM INVSTMNTS LLC
Also Called: Four Pnts Pltnum Machining Mfg
2219 Patterson Indus Dr (78660-8315)
PHONE.....................512 588-7916
Tensay G Johnson,
EMP: 10
SQ FT: 900
SALES (est): 150K **Privately Held**
WEB: www.fourpointsplatinum.com
SIC: 8711 3599 Engineering services; machine shop, jobbing & repair

(G-16674)
GALLERY ONE POINT LLC
401 W Pecan St Ste E (78660-2714)
PHONE.....................512 428-5710
Haja Scott,
Lousie Harris,
EMP: 20
SALES (est): 966.9K **Privately Held**
WEB: www.galleryonepoint.com
SIC: 5651 5137 5621 7389 Unisex clothing stores; women's & children's clothing; ready-to-wear apparel, women's; textile & apparel services; customized clothing & apparel; service apparel (baker, barber, lab, etc.), washable: men's

(G-16675)
HILL COUNTRY INSULATION
20105 Algreg St (78660-6506)
PHONE.....................512 515-7707
Lee Morris, *President*
Jimmy Dimanoss, *Vice Pres*
Larry Scott, *Vice Pres*
Derek Dimanoff, *Opers Mgr*
EMP: 9
SQ FT: 10,000
SALES (est): 1.3MM **Privately Held**
WEB: www.hcinsulation.com
SIC: 1742 Insulation, buildings; gutters, sheet metal

(G-16676)
INTEGRATED FLOW SYSTEMS LLC
Also Called: Ifs
1007 S Heatherwilde Blvd (78660-5218)
PHONE.....................512 671-5002
Malcolm Gray, *General Mgr*
EMP: 65
SALES (corp-wide): 1B **Publicly Held**
SIC: 3823 3914 Industrial instrmnts msrmnt display/control process variable; holloware, stainless steel
HQ: Integrated Flow Systems, Llc
26462 Corporate Ave
Hayward CA

(G-16677)
JG MEDIA INC
Also Called: Community Impact Newspaper
16225 Impact Way Unit 1 (78660-4404)
PHONE.....................512 989-6808
John Garret, *President*
Jennifer Garrett, *Publisher*
Shawn Burrell, *General Mgr*
Phyllis Campos, *General Mgr*
Vicki Chen, *General Mgr*
EMP: 58
SALES (est): 558.4K **Privately Held**
WEB: www.communityimpact.com
SIC: 2711 Newspapers, publishing & printing

(G-16678)
JOHN ROBERTS ENTERPRISES INC
Also Called: John Roberts Designs
50063 Tictor Ste 100 (78660)
PHONE.....................512 252-0174
John Phillip Roberts, *President*
▲ **EMP:** 16
SQ FT: 6,000
SALES (est): 1.2MM **Privately Held**
SIC: 3229 Novelty glassware

(G-16679)
LIFELAST INC
3813 Helios Way Ste 190 (78660-8380)
PHONE.....................512 628-2112
Jeff Buratto, *President*
Stan Buratto, *Principal*
Mark Buratto, *Vice Pres*
Mary Grothe, *Info Tech Mgr*
Ian McFatridge, *Director*
EMP: 9
SQ FT: 4,800
SALES (est): 2.9MM **Privately Held**
WEB: www.lifelast.com
SIC: 3479 Coating of metals & formed products

(G-16680)
METRO OPTICS OF AUSTIN INC
Also Called: Metrosoft
15802 Vision Dr (78660-3184)
P.O. Box 81189, Austin (78708-1189)
PHONE.....................512 251-2386
Jim Webb, *President*
Lora Castle, *Vice Pres*
Steve Webb, *Vice Pres*
Kent Webb, *Treasurer*
Peggy Beutnagel, *Office Mgr*
EMP: 41
SQ FT: 12,000
SALES (est): 5.9MM **Privately Held**
WEB: www.metro-optics.com
SIC: 3851 5049 Contact lenses; optical goods

(G-16681)
MOTOR CITY TOOL & DIE CORP
20203 Algreg St (78660-6502)
PHONE.....................512 251-7700
Marin Andric, *President*
EMP: 13 **EST:** 2000
SQ FT: 15,000
SALES (est): 2.8MM **Privately Held**
WEB: www.motorcitytoolanddie.com
SIC: 3599 3544 3469 Machine shop, jobbing & repair; special dies & tools; metal stampings

(G-16682)
P T PRODUCTS & SERVICES INC
Also Called: George Howard
20109 Algreg St (78660-6506)
PHONE..............................512 251-3592
George M Howard, *President*
Larry Durham, *Vice Pres*
Pam Smith, *Purch Mgr*
▼ EMP: 25
SQ FT: 26,100
SALES (est): 2.3MM **Privately Held**
WEB: www.pt-products.com
SIC: 3484 3451 3599 3812 Small arms; screw machine products; machine & other job shop work; acceleration indicators & systems components, aerospace

(G-16683)
PARADIGM METALS INCORPORATED (PA)
Also Called: Austron
15811 Vision Dr (78660-3187)
PHONE..............................512 255-2622
Daniel J Chew, *President*
Steve Chew, *General Mgr*
Blain Ogea, *Vice Pres*
Carl Williams, *Buyer*
Robert Biebas, *QC Mgr*
▼ EMP: 25
SQ FT: 50,000
SALES (est): 19.6MM **Privately Held**
WEB: www.paradigmmetals.com
SIC: 3599 3444 Machine & other job shop work; sheet metalwork

(G-16684)
PENTA INDUSTRIES INC
20202 Mashburn St (78660-6500)
PHONE..............................512 834-2421
Jesus Padilla, *President*
Alex Padilla, *Vice Pres*
EMP: 10
SQ FT: 3,800
SALES (est): 550K **Privately Held**
WEB: www.pentaindustries.com
SIC: 3599 Machine shop, jobbing & repair

(G-16685)
PLATRON MANUFACTURING AND PLTG
13930 Immanuel Rd Ste A (78660-8256)
PHONE..............................512 989-1362
Peter Pham, *President*
Ha Vu, *COO*
Ha Pham, *CFO*
Mickey Corona, *Cust Mgr*
Darrel Dyson, *IT/INT Sup*
EMP: 35
SQ FT: 32,000
SALES (est): 5.8MM **Privately Held**
WEB: www.platronmfg.com
SIC: 3599 Machine shop, jobbing & repair

(G-16686)
REF MACHINING LTD PARTNR LLP
2210 Patterson Indus Dr (78660-8313)
P.O. Box 2085 (78691-2085)
PHONE..............................512 251-9954
Terry Bohm, *General Mgr*
Robert E Fritz, *General Ptnr*
EMP: 15
SALES (est): 2.4MM **Privately Held**
WEB: www.refmachining.com
SIC: 3599 Machine shop, jobbing & repair

(G-16687)
SEMES AMERICA INC
13400 Immanuel Rd Ste 1 (78660-8249)
PHONE..............................512 251-3188
Sun Joon Kim, *President*
EMP: 9 EST: 1998
SALES (est): 1MM **Privately Held**
WEB: www.semes.com
SIC: 3674 Semiconductors & related devices
HQ: Semes Co., Ltd.
77 4sandan 5-Gil, Jiksan-Eup Seobuk-Gu
Cheonan 31040

(G-16688)
SHARCO TECHNOLOGIES INC (PA)
1010 Old Austin Hutto Rd (78660-4218)
PHONE..............................512 258-0573
Sherry Walton, *President*
Monica Lassig, *Vice Pres*
Brian Milam, *Sales Staff*
EMP: 10
SQ FT: 1,300
SALES (est): 300K **Privately Held**
WEB: www.sharco.net
SIC: 8748 4899 7371 7372 Telecommunications consultant; data communication services; custom computer programming services; prepackaged software; security systems services

(G-16689)
TRAJAN SCIENTIFIC AMERICAS INC (DH)
Also Called: Trajan Scientific and Medical
1421 W Wlls Br Pkwy Ste 1 (78660)
PHONE..............................512 837-7190
Stephen Tomisich, *President*
Becky Thompson, *Corp Secy*
Glenn Clivaz, *Senior VP*
Brian Jackson, *Opers Mgr*
David Elks, *Mfg Mgr*
▲ EMP: 11
SQ FT: 7,350
SALES (est): 3MM **Privately Held**
WEB: www.sge.com
SIC: 3826 Analytical instruments

(G-16690)
UNIQUE CABINETS INC
16001 N Interstate 35 (78660-3195)
P.O. Box 335, Round Rock (78680-0335)
PHONE..............................512 251-3058
Kelly Kincaid, *President*
Kincaid N E, *Vice Pres*
EMP: 20 EST: 1973
SQ FT: 8,000
SALES (est): 1.4MM **Privately Held**
WEB: www.azuniquecabinets.com
SIC: 1751 2521 2517 2434 Cabinet building & installation; wood office furniture; wood television & radio cabinets; wood kitchen cabinets

(G-16691)
W B MASON CO INC
1215 W Wells Branch Pkwy (78660-3149)
PHONE..............................888 926-2766
EMP: 43
SALES (corp-wide): 1B **Privately Held**
WEB: www.wbmason.com
SIC: 5943 5712 2752 Office forms & supplies; office furniture; commercial printing, lithographic
PA: W. B. Mason Co., Inc.
59 Ctr St
Brockton MA 02301
508 586-3434

(G-16692)
WAUKESHA-PEARCE INDUSTRIES INC
16029 Ih 35 (78660-3195)
PHONE..............................512 989-4900
Rick Hutchens, *Manager*
EMP: 30
SALES (corp-wide): 396MM **Privately Held**
WEB: www.wpi.com
SIC: 7699 5082 3531 Industrial equipment services; contractors' materials; backhoes, tractors, cranes, plows & similar equipment
HQ: Waukesha-Pearce Industries, Llc
12320 Main St
Houston TX 77035
713 723-1050

(G-16693)
WORDYISMS INC
601 Olympic Dr (78660-4718)
PHONE..............................512 835-6695
Jean Garlick, *President*
David Garlick, *Vice Pres*
EMP: 12
SALES (est): 600K **Privately Held**
WEB: www.wordyisms.com
SIC: 2499 5999 Picture frame molding, finished; picture frames, ready made

Pharr
Hidalgo County

(G-16694)
BAKER HUGHES INCORPORATED
5510 N Cage Blvd (78577-1812)
PHONE..............................956 781-9133
EMP: 87
SALES (corp-wide): 24.5B **Publicly Held**
SIC: 3533 Mfg Equip & Provides Services For Oil And Gas Field
PA: Baker Hughes Incorporated
2929 Allen Pkwy Ste 2100
Houston TX 77073
713 439-8600

(G-16695)
C R BARD INC
Also Called: Bard Oprtion Ctr Reynosa Plant
201 W Anaya Rd (78577-9321)
PHONE..............................956 205-7100
Gabriel Cordova, *Engineer*
Juan Costellonos, *Engineer*
Gustavo Gallejos, *Manager*
Ismael Rodriguez, *Manager*
Ricardo Martinez, *Technology*
EMP: 2000
SALES (corp-wide): 17.1B **Publicly Held**
WEB: www.crbard.com
SIC: 3841 Surgical & medical instruments
HQ: C. R. Bard, Inc.
1 Becton Dr
Franklin Lakes NJ 07417
201 847-6800

(G-16696)
COMMERCIAL METALS COMPANY
Also Called: Rio Grande Steel
Hwy 281 And East Owassa (78577)
PHONE..............................956 702-4434
Cris Maldonado, *Branch Mgr*
EMP: 10
SALES (corp-wide): 5.4B **Publicly Held**
WEB: www.cmc.com
SIC: 3312 Blast furnaces & steel mills
PA: Commercial Metals Company
6565 N Macarthur Blvd # 800
Irving TX 75039
214 689-4300

(G-16697)
DE MAIZ TORTILLERIA L L C
700 W Sioux Rd (78577-7472)
P.O. Box 2826, McAllen (78502-2826)
PHONE..............................956 702-8855
EMP: 18
SALES (est): 3.5MM **Privately Held**
SIC: 2099 Mfg Food Preparations

(G-16698)
GIRL TALK BOUTIQUE & SPA LLC
807 S Jackson Rd Ste 3 (78577-6633)
PHONE..............................956 225-7898
Brenda Michelle Rivas, *Mng Member*
EMP: 10
SALES (est): 2.7MM **Privately Held**
SIC: 7991 5621 7372 Spas; women's clothing stores; application computer software

(G-16699)
GSW MANUFACTURING INC
500 Capote Central Ave # 400 (78577-1200)
PHONE..............................956 223-2644
EMP: 30 EST: 2012
SALES (est): 1.2MM **Privately Held**
SIC: 3999 Mfg Misc Products

(G-16700)
ILLINOIS TOOL WORKS INC
Also Called: ITW EF&c Mexico- US Trading
9601 International Blvd (78577-7279)
PHONE..............................956 215-2000
Max Castellon, *Branch Mgr*
EMP: 459
SALES (corp-wide): 14.1B **Publicly Held**
WEB: www.itw.com
SIC: 3089 3465 Automotive parts, plastic; body parts, automobile: stamped metal
PA: Illinois Tool Works Inc.
155 Harlem Ave
Glenview IL 60025
847 724-7500

(G-16701)
IXTAPA INC
Also Called: South Texas Neon Sign
1500 Mid Cities Dr (78577-2128)
PHONE..............................956 782-9601
Raul Gonzales, *President*
Jorge Munoz, *Production*
Stephany Gonzales, *Office Mgr*
Nereyda Bartolo, *
EMP: 24
SQ FT: 4,990
SALES (est): 3.9MM **Privately Held**
WEB: www.riotexneonsigns.com
SIC: 3993 Electric signs

(G-16702)
J-III CONCRETE CO
323 E Owassa Rd (78577)
PHONE..............................956 787-5518
Joe Covarrubias, *Manager*
EMP: 12
SALES (corp-wide): 9.8MM **Privately Held**
WEB: www.j3concrete.com
SIC: 3273 Ready-mixed concrete
PA: J-Iii Concrete Co
1700 E 28th St
Weslaco TX 78596
956 968-1371

(G-16703)
JA-EN ENTERPRISE INC
1305 Macco Dr (78577-1906)
PHONE..............................956 782-0085
Javier Chapa, *President*
EMP: 10 EST: 2000
SALES (est): 983.1K **Privately Held**
SIC: 2024 Ice cream & frozen desserts

(G-16704)
KERN-LIEBERS TEXAS INC
400 E Nolana Loop (78577-9608)
P.O. Box 5839, McAllen (78502-5839)
PHONE..............................956 781-6563
Torsten Buchwald, *President*
▲ EMP: 32
SALES (est): 7.4MM **Privately Held**
WEB: www.kern-liebers-north-america.com
SIC: 3495 Wire springs

(G-16705)
KIMBALL ELEC - MEXICO INC (DH)
Also Called: Kimball Electronics Group
9800 Intl Blvd Ste 120 (78577)
PHONE..............................956 205-4600
James C Thyen, *President*
Donald D Charron, *President*
R Gregory Kincer, *President*
Douglas A Habig, *Chairman*
John H Kahle, *Exec VP*
▲ EMP: 20
SQ FT: 1,000
SALES (est): 6MM
SALES (corp-wide): 1.2B **Publicly Held**
WEB: www.kimball.com
SIC: 2522 Office furniture, except wood

(G-16706)
LOZZ QUATEZZ LLC
Also Called: Sign Depot, The
105 E Interstate 2 Ste F (78577-6560)
PHONE..............................956 687-7446
Ruben Cepeda, *Mng Member*
Sophia Korren, *Admin Sec*
▲ EMP: 15
SALES (est): 2MM **Privately Held**
WEB: www.thesigndepot.com
SIC: 3993 7312 Signs & advertising specialties; outdoor advertising services

(G-16707)
MICHAEL EGAN ALLEN
Also Called: Hiway Neon Sign
1301 Macco Dr (78577-1906)
PHONE..............................956 702-0692

Mike Egan, *President*
EMP: 28 EST: 1950
SQ FT: 7,800
SALES (est): 4.1MM **Privately Held**
WEB: www.hiwayneonsigns.com
SIC: 3993 Neon signs

(G-16708)
MTX ELECTRONICS INC
100 S Austin Dr Ste A (78577-8659)
PHONE..............................956 781-3476
Stephen Butzer, *President*
Robert J Bowen, *Principal*
Bob Bowen, *Vice Pres*
EMP: 10
SALES (est): 2.9MM **Privately Held**
WEB: www.mtxelectronics.com
SIC: 3679 3694 Electronic circuits; harness wiring sets, internal combustion engines

(G-16709)
NORTH LEAN LTD
401 E Nolana Loop (78577-5839)
PHONE..............................956 781-2029
EMP: 10
SALES (est): 1.5MM **Privately Held**
WEB: www.printex-express.com
SIC: 2395 2396 Embroidery & art needlework; screen printing on fabric articles

(G-16710)
SOUTH TEXAS PAPER LLC
9102 Seguin Dr (78577-9734)
PHONE..............................956 239-1473
Jose Ibarra, *Mng Member*
Jose Iballa, *Mng Member*
EMP: 10 EST: 2016
SQ FT: 30,000
SALES (est): 1.3MM **Privately Held**
SIC: 2621 Packaging paper

(G-16711)
SPRINGS WINDOW FASHIONS LLC
9601 International Blvd (78577-7279)
PHONE..............................608 826-7052
EMP: 14
SALES (corp-wide): 3.1B **Privately Held**
WEB: www.springswindowfashions.com
SIC: 2591 Blinds vertical; curtain & drapery rods, poles & fixtures; window shade rollers & fittings
HQ: Springs Window Fashions, Llc
7549 Graber Rd
Middleton WI 53562
608 836-1011

(G-16712)
TECHNIMARK REYNOSA LLC
9600 International Blvd (78577-7294)
PHONE..............................336 498-4171
EMP: 10 **Privately Held**
WEB: www.technimark.com
SIC: 3089 Injection molding of plastics
HQ: Technimark Reynosa Llc
180 Commerce Pl
Asheboro NC 27203

(G-16713)
UNIVERSAL METAL PRODUCTS INC
101 W Eldora Rd (78577-7540)
PHONE..............................956 283-7200
David Shank, *Principal*
Jaime Martinez, *Plant Mgr*
Paul Sestokas, *Sales Staff*
Victor Trevino, *Manager*
EMP: 15
SALES (corp-wide): 60MM **Privately Held**
WEB: www.universalmetalproducts.com
SIC: 3469 Stamping metal for the trade
PA: Universal Metal Products, Inc.
29980 Lakeland Blvd
Wickliffe OH 44092
440 943-3040

(G-16714)
USI INTEGRATED TRNSP LLC
301 E Milano (78577)
PHONE..............................956 781-6606
Mike Castillo, *Mng Member*
EMP: 32
SQ FT: 3,179,880

SALES (est): 8MM **Privately Held**
SIC: 3715 Truck trailers

(G-16715)
VALLEY OUTDOOR POWER EQP INC
1012 E Ferguson St (78577-2616)
PHONE..............................956 787-0469
Pedro Cortina Jr, *President*
Ramiro Cortina, *Vice Pres*
EMP: 15
SQ FT: 6,000
SALES (est): 2.6MM **Privately Held**
WEB: www.vopeinc.com
SIC: 7699 5999 5261 5087 Engine repair & replacement, non-automotive; lawn mower repair shop; engine & motor equipment & supplies; lawnmowers & tractors; cleaning & maintenance equipment & supplies; cleaning equipment, high pressure, sand or steam; saws & sawing equipment

(G-16716)
WINDSOR MOLD USA INC (HQ)
Also Called: Windsor Mold Texas
9200 S Austin Dr (78577-0054)
P.O. Box 32523, Detroit MI (48232-0523)
PHONE..............................956 787-8737
Keith Henry, *President*
Greg Mahoney, *Corp Secy*
▲ EMP: 16
SALES (est): 3.3MM
SALES (corp-wide): 796K **Privately Held**
WEB: www.windsormoldgroup.com
SIC: 3089 Injection molding of plastics
PA: 873740 Ontario Inc
4035 Malden Rd
Windsor ON N9C 2
519 972-9032

(G-16717)
ZF PASSIVE SAFETY SYSTEMS US
Also Called: TRW Vssi
9600 International Blvd (78577-7294)
PHONE..............................956 566-7680
Allan Howe, *Materials Mgr*
Cookie Garcia, *Manager*
EMP: 25
SALES (corp-wide): 216.2K **Privately Held**
WEB: www.zf.com
SIC: 3714 5013 Connecting rods, motor vehicle engine; seat belts
HQ: Zf Passive Safety Systems Us Inc.
12001 Tech Center Dr
Livonia MI 48150

(G-16718)
ZF PASSIVE SAFETY US INC
9600 International Blvd (78577-7294)
PHONE..............................956 632-8100
Franz Kleiner, *President*
EMP: 10
SALES (corp-wide): 216.2K **Privately Held**
SIC: 3714 2399 Motor vehicle parts & accessories; seat belts, automobile & aircraft
HQ: Zf Passive Safety Us Inc.
12001 Tech Center Dr
Livonia MI 48150
734 855-2600

(G-16719)
ZF TRW AUTO HOLDINGS CORP
9600 Intl Blvd Docks 5/8 58 Docks (78577)
PHONE..............................956 632-8100
Jose Rios, *Prdtn Mgr*
Michael D Rankin, *Finance Mgr*
Adrian Davis, *Manager*
Cookie Garcia, *Manager*
EMP: 94
SALES (corp-wide): 216.2K **Privately Held**
WEB: www.zf.com
SIC: 3714 Motor vehicle parts & accessories
HQ: Zf Trw Automotive Holdings Corp.
12001 Tech Center Dr
Livonia MI 48150
734 855-2600

Pilot Point
Denton County

(G-16720)
3 STAR CUSTOM CABINETS INC
1297 N Saint James Rd (76258-2715)
PHONE..............................940 686-2124
Randy Pels, *President*
Kenneth Pels, *Vice Pres*
EMP: 10
SQ FT: 6,288
SALES (est): 1.2MM **Privately Held**
WEB: www.3starcustomcabinets.com
SIC: 2434 Wood kitchen cabinets

(G-16721)
ALL WOOD CUSTOM CABINETS INC
1217 N Highway 377 (76258-4040)
PHONE..............................940 686-2795
Dennis Hollar, *President*
EMP: 15
SQ FT: 10,500
SALES (est): 1MM **Privately Held**
WEB: www.tritexcabinets.com
SIC: 2434 1521 2511 Wood kitchen cabinets; single-family housing construction; wood household furniture

(G-16722)
BEAR CUSTOM MOULDING INC
1024 N Highway 377 (76258)
P.O. Box 1241 (76258-1241)
PHONE..............................940 686-5547
Jaime Bear, *President*
Alene Bear, *Admin Sec*
EMP: 17
SQ FT: 5,600
SALES (est): 1.8MM **Privately Held**
SIC: 2431 Millwork

(G-16723)
CUSTOM CABINET DOORS INC
924 N Industrial Blvd (76258-2936)
P.O. Box 580 (76258-0580)
PHONE..............................940 686-2808
Kevin Rider, *President*
EMP: 20
SQ FT: 30,000
SALES (est): 2.1MM **Privately Held**
WEB: www.customcabinetdoorsandmore.com
SIC: 5211 2434 Door & window products; wood kitchen cabinets

(G-16724)
CUSTOM DOOR COMPANY INC
10279 Fm 455 E Bldg 5 (76258-9253)
P.O. Box 607 (76258-0607)
PHONE..............................940 686-4500
Zebadiah Strickland, *President*
Billy J Gravley, *Director*
Mark McWhirter, *Director*
EMP: 25
SALES (est): 748.9K **Privately Held**
WEB: www.customdoorcompany.com
SIC: 2431 Doors, wood

(G-16725)
JOHNNYS CABINET SHOP INC
Also Called: Pilot Point Wood Design
301 W Broad St (76258-2618)
PHONE..............................940 686-2496
Wes Patterson, *President*
Johny Patterson, *Principal*
Gay Patterson, *Treasurer*
EMP: 10 EST: 1978
SQ FT: 8,000
SALES (est): 1.2MM **Privately Held**
WEB: www.ppwooddesigns.com
SIC: 2434 Wood kitchen cabinets

(G-16726)
NEU PLUMBING INC
1117 Foundation Dr (76258-2953)
P.O. Box 972, Gainesville (76241-0972)
PHONE..............................940 580-2200
Lorne Neu, *President*
Brad Reiter, *Vice Pres*
Tim Welch, *CFO*
River Mills, *Supervisor*
EMP: 65 EST: 2013
SQ FT: 2,100

SALES (est): 34.8MM **Privately Held**
WEB: www.neuplumbing.com
SIC: 1711 3433 3585 Plumbing contractors; gas infrared heating units; refrigeration & heating equipment

(G-16727)
REDDY ICE CORPORATION
309 Enterprise Dr (76258-4604)
PHONE..............................940 686-5259
Glen Carlton, *Manager*
EMP: 25 **Privately Held**
WEB: www.reddyice.com
SIC: 2097 5999 Manufactured ice; ice
HQ: Reddy Ice Corporation
5710 Lbj Fwy Ste 300
Dallas TX 75240
214 526-6740

(G-16728)
RS WELDING LLC
Also Called: Rockstar Welding
8490 Highway 377 (76258-6017)
P.O. Box 368, Aubrey (76227-0368)
PHONE..............................940 488-4144
Angela S Smith, *CEO*
Bill Smith, *President*
EMP: 10
SALES (est): 646K **Privately Held**
WEB: www.rockstarwelding.com
SIC: 7692 Welding repair

(G-16729)
STALEY STEEL INC
9620 Saint John Rd (76258-6618)
PHONE..............................940 686-6000
EMP: 50 EST: 1958
SQ FT: 70,000
SALES (est): 18.8MM **Privately Held**
WEB: www.staleysteel.com
SIC: 3441 Fabricated structural metal

(G-16730)
STURM WELDING INC
111 E Liberty St (76258-4518)
P.O. Box 572 (76258-0572)
PHONE..............................940 686-2492
Dale Dollar, *President*
Stanley Jones, *General Mgr*
Shawn Dollar, *Vice Pres*
Laura Riley, *Office Mgr*
EMP: 10
SQ FT: 5,500
SALES (est): 2.1MM **Privately Held**
WEB: www.sturmwelding.com
SIC: 3441 5084 7692 Fabricated structural metal; welding machinery & equipment; welding repair

(G-16731)
TRI-TEX CABINETS INC
900 N Highway 377 (76258-4045)
PHONE..............................940 686-2617
Shea Dane, *President*
Kelly Dane, *Corp Secy*
EMP: 60
SQ FT: 20,000
SALES (est): 5.3MM **Privately Held**
WEB: www.tritexcabinets.com
SIC: 2434 Wood kitchen cabinets

(G-16732)
UNIQUE WOODWORKS INC
1024 N Highway 377 (76258-4044)
P.O. Box 1267 (76258-1267)
PHONE..............................940 686-5547
Donald E Dean Jr, *Principal*
EMP: 20
SALES (est): 2.2MM **Privately Held**
WEB: www.unique-woodworks.com
SIC: 2431 Millwork

Pinehurst
Montgomery County

(G-16733)
DARTICAN LLC
37707 Millers Pass (77362-1925)
PHONE..............................281 645-6370
Michael Gerthe, *Opers Staff*
Michael B Gerthe,
Judy Gerthe,
EMP: 15

SALES (est): 1MM **Privately Held**
WEB: www.dartican.com
SIC: 7372 Prepackaged software

(G-16734)
EMISSIONS & SILENCER TECH INC
531 Goodson Loop (77362-2589)
P.O. Box 11046, Spring (77391-1046)
PHONE..................................281 259-9979
Robert Lindley, *President*
EMP: 10
SALES (est): 950K **Privately Held**
WEB: www.emissionsandsilencers.com
SIC: 3499 Fire- or burglary-resistive products

(G-16735)
T G INDUSTRIES INC
31714 Industrial Park Dr (77362-3809)
PHONE..................................281 356-2001
Betty Granhold, *President*
Trent Granhold, *Treasurer*
▲ EMP: 17
SQ FT: 1,700
SALES (est): 2MM **Privately Held**
WEB: www.tg-industries.com
SIC: 3471 3479 Anodizing (plating) of metals or formed products; etching on metals

(G-16736)
TPC ACQUISITION PARTNERS LP
Also Called: Texas Pit Crafters
31909 Decker Indus Dr (77362-3831)
P.O. Box 83, Tomball (77377-0083)
PHONE..................................281 356-2168
Michael Logan, *General Ptnr*
Wilma Logan, *Administration*
EMP: 14
SQ FT: 21,344
SALES (est): 2.1MM **Privately Held**
WEB: www.texaspitcrafters.com
SIC: 3631 Barbecues, grills & braziers (outdoor cooking)

(G-16737)
TURN-TECH INC
32007 Industrial Park Dr (77362-3894)
PHONE..................................281 356-1290
Murray D Jaeger, *President*
Don R Sanders, *Vice Pres*
Stephanie Feder, *Buyer*
Blake Urbanosky, *Purchasing*
EMP: 45
SQ FT: 25,000
SALES (est): 7.4MM **Privately Held**
WEB: www.turn-tech.com
SIC: 3599 3536 3441 Machine shop, jobbing & repair; hoists, cranes & monorails; fabricated structural metal

Pineland
Sabine County

(G-16738)
DON LANE LOGGING INC
Hwy 83 (75968)
P.O. Box 56 (75968-0056)
PHONE..................................409 584-2288
Don Lane, *President*
Debbie Lane, *Admin Sec*
EMP: 9
SALES (est): 500K **Privately Held**
SIC: 2411 Logging

(G-16739)
GEORGIA-PACIFIC LLC
105 Yellow Pine Hwy (75968)
P.O. Box 929 (75968-0929)
PHONE..................................409 584-4227
Mike Rogers, *Manager*
EMP: 15
SALES (corp-wide): 36.8B **Privately Held**
WEB: www.gp.com
SIC: 2435 Hardwood veneer & plywood
HQ: Georgia-Pacific Llc
133 Peachtree St Nw
Atlanta GA 30303
404 652-4000

(G-16740)
LETCO GROUP LLC
Also Called: Elliott's Agri-Service
U S Hwy 96 (75968)
P.O. Box 959 (75968-0959)
PHONE..................................409 584-2155
EMP: 42
SALES (corp-wide): 78.3MM **Privately Held**
WEB: www.livingearth.net
SIC: 2499 2875 Mulch, wood & bark; potting soil, mixed
PA: The Letco Group Llc
1901 Cal Crossing Rd
Dallas TX 75220
972 506-8575

Pipe Creek
Bandera County

(G-16741)
COACHWORKS LLC
Also Called: Texas Custom Coach
10498 State Highway 16 S (78063-5345)
PHONE..................................830 510-4224
David Miller, *General Mgr*
Steve Mauldin, *Project Mgr*
Dave Miller, *Mng Member*
William Stoner,
EMP: 20
SQ FT: 27,000
SALES (est): 2.6MM **Privately Held**
WEB: www.texascustomcoach.com
SIC: 3716 Motor homes

(G-16742)
T & H CONSTRUCTION INC
863 Roller Coaster (78063-5143)
PHONE..................................830 535-6111
EMP: 9
SALES (est): 600K **Privately Held**
SIC: 1389 Construction Company

Pittsburg
Camp County

(G-16743)
ANDRITZ SEPARATION INC
110 Dickson St (75686-1365)
PHONE..................................903 856-0445
Gary Dobbs, *Plant Mgr*
Steve Knight, *Safety Mgr*
Christian Bretterhofer, *Loan Officer*
Steve Raley, *Branch Mgr*
EMP: 43
SALES (corp-wide): 7.3B **Privately Held**
WEB: www.andritz.com
SIC: 3569 Centrifuges, industrial
HQ: Andritz Separation Inc.
1010 Commercial Blvd S
Arlington TX 76001
817 465-5611

(G-16744)
B & S HARDWARE INC (PA)
Also Called: True Value
112 N Greer Blvd (75686-1409)
PHONE..................................903 856-3552
Tim Spearman, *President*
Steve Spearman, *Admin Sec*
EMP: 22 EST: 1950
SQ FT: 20,000
SALES (est): 5.9MM **Privately Held**
WEB: www.truevalue.com
SIC: 5251 5211 5941 5072 Hardware; lumber & other building materials; sporting goods & bicycle shops; hardware; lumber, plywood & millwork; structural wood members

(G-16745)
JBS USA FOOD COMPANY
110 S Texas St (75686-1532)
P.O. Box 93 (75686-0093)
PHONE..................................903 434-1000
Craig Moucka, *Network Enginr*
EMP: 272 **Publicly Held**
WEB: www.jbssa.com
SIC: 2011 Boxed beef from meat slaughtered on site

HQ: Jbs Usa Food Company
1770 Promontory Cir
Greeley CO 80634
970 506-8000

(G-16746)
LOSPINOS RANCH VINEYARDS
658 County Road 1334 (75686-6302)
PHONE..................................903 855-1769
Gerald Jones, *Partner*
Jeffrey Sneed, *Principal*
Lesa Jones, *Marketing Staff*
Teresa Sais, *Teacher*
EMP: 11
SALES (est): 1.6MM **Privately Held**
WEB: www.lospinosranchvineyards.com
SIC: 2084 Wines

(G-16747)
M & S MECHANICAL INC
Also Called: M and S Mechanical
136 County Road 1309 (75686-6101)
P.O. Box 201 (75686-0201)
PHONE..................................318 755-2431
Daniel Mathis, *President*
Wade Stephens, *Vice Pres*
EMP: 20
SALES (est): 792K **Privately Held**
SIC: 1711 1389 0782 1796 Mechanical contractor; gas field services; highway lawn & garden maintenance services; millwright; welding repair

(G-16748)
PILGRIMS PRIDE CORPORATION
110 S Texas St (75686-1532)
P.O. Box 43 (75686-0043)
PHONE..................................919 774-7333
Glenn Barton, *Plant Mgr*
Karen Campbell, *VP Finance*
Kirk Leone, *Marketing Mgr*
Leda Martin, *Administration*
EMP: 293 **Publicly Held**
WEB: www.pilgrims.com
SIC: 2015 0254 Chicken, slaughtered & dressed; chicken hatchery
HQ: Pilgrim's Pride Corporation
1770 Promontory Cir
Greeley CO 80634
970 506-8000

(G-16749)
PILGRIMS PRIDE CORPORATION
Also Called: Walker Creek-Ppdc
4840 Us Highway 271 N (75686-4139)
PHONE..................................903 434-1000
Keith Arnold, *Vice Pres*
Steven Hughes, *Manager*
Kurt Crenwelge, *Technology*
EMP: 144 **Publicly Held**
WEB: www.pilgrims.com
SIC: 2015 Poultry slaughtering & processing
HQ: Pilgrim's Pride Corporation
1770 Promontory Cir
Greeley CO 80634
970 506-8000

(G-16750)
PITTSBURG STEEL LLC
3489 Fm 557 (75686-5391)
PHONE..................................903 855-7515
Wesley Baker, *Mng Member*
Tonya Baker, *Admin Sec*
EMP: 40
SQ FT: 75,000
SALES (est): 12.6MM **Privately Held**
WEB: www.pittsburgsteel.com
SIC: 3444 4225 Sheet metalwork; general warehousing & storage

Plainview
Hale County

(G-16751)
AZTECA MILLING LP
1388 County Road U (79072)
P.O. Box 620 (79073-0620)
PHONE..................................806 291-5633
Raul Gonzales, *Manager*
John Bickel, *Manager*

EMP: 260 **Privately Held**
WEB: www.aztecamilling.com
SIC: 0723 2034 Flour milling custom services; dehydrated fruits, vegetables, soups
HQ: Azteca Milling, L.P.
5601 Executive Dr Ste 650
Irving TX 75038
956 383-4911

(G-16752)
CARGILL MEAT SOLUTIONS CORP
Also Called: Country Fresh Meats
2226 F M 3183 (79072)
P.O. Box 579, Friona (79035-0579)
PHONE..................................806 293-5181
EMP: 20
SALES (corp-wide): 113.4B **Privately Held**
WEB: www.cargill.com
SIC: 5147 2013 2011 Meats & meat products; sausages & other prepared meats; meat packing plants
HQ: Cargill Meat Solutions Corp
151 N Main St Ste 900
Wichita KS 67202
316 291-2500

(G-16753)
CASA RICA LP
Also Called: Casa Rica Foods
105 N Interstate 27 (79072-6503)
PHONE..................................806 296-7582
Jose L Longoria, *President*
Bertha Longoria, *Vice Pres*
Israel Musquiz, *Vice Pres*
Juan C Lopez, *Opers Mgr*
Juan Lopez, *Opers Mgr*
EMP: 36
SQ FT: 40,000
SALES (est): 3.3MM **Privately Held**
WEB: www.casarica.com
SIC: 2099 Tortillas, fresh or refrigerated

(G-16754)
GAUNTLETT INC
Also Called: S & S Electric
2109 S Date St (79072-9390)
P.O. Box 490 (79073-0490)
PHONE..................................806 293-9849
Bruce Sisk, *President*
Linda Sisk, *Vice Pres*
EMP: 9
SQ FT: 3,200
SALES (est): 1.4MM **Privately Held**
WEB: www.sselectricplainview.com
SIC: 1731 7694 General electrical contractor; electric motor repair

(G-16755)
GREAT HOST INTERNATIONAL INC
Also Called: Andalucia Nuts
5205 N Interstate 27 (79072-0001)
PHONE..................................806 296-5455
Divid Fish, *Manager*
EMP: 144
SALES (corp-wide): 4.8MM **Privately Held**
WEB: www.andalucianuts.com
SIC: 2068 Nuts: dried, dehydrated, salted or roasted
PA: Great Host International, Inc.
3505 Bering Dr
Houston TX 77057
713 977-9090

(G-16756)
HEARSTCORPORATION
820 Broadway St (79072-7316)
PHONE..................................806 296-1300
Sandra Aven, *Principal*
Vernah Ransower, *Manager*
EMP: 45
SQ FT: 20,000
SALES (est): 2.9MM
SALES (corp-wide): 7.9B **Privately Held**
WEB: www.myplainview.com
SIC: 2711 Newspapers: publishing only, not printed on site
PA: The Hearst Corporation
300 W 57th St Fl 42
New York NY 10019
212 649-2000

(G-16757)
HIGH PLAINS CONCRETE COMPANY (PA)
Also Called: Tulia Ready Mix Concrete Co
3200 Canyon St (79072-1700)
PHONE..................................806 293-8313
Clinton Wall, *President*
T C Wall, *President*
Aaron Wall, *General Mgr*
Bert Wall, *Vice Pres*
EMP: 10
SQ FT: 5,000
SALES (est): 2.4MM **Privately Held**
SIC: 3273 Ready-mixed concrete

(G-16758)
IFCO SYSTEMS NORTH AMERICA INC
Also Called: Isco Systems
3800 N Quincy St (79072)
P.O. Box 458 (79073-0458)
PHONE..................................806 291-9024
EMP: 25 **Privately Held**
SIC: 2448 Mfg Pallets

(G-16759)
J & S RIDES INC
Also Called: Larson International
1933 State Highway 194 (79072-0806)
P.O. Box 638 (79073-0638)
PHONE..................................806 293-1353
Jeff Novotny, *President*
Lupe Castillo, *Accountant*
EMP: 38
SALES (est): 7.4MM **Privately Held**
WEB: www.larsonintl.com
SIC: 3599 Carnival machines & equipment, amusement park

(G-16760)
M HASTEY CONSTRUCTION CO INC
Also Called: Southwestern Diversified Lsg
101 E 24th St (79072-3101)
P.O. Box 339 (79073-0339)
PHONE..................................806 296-7444
Maurice Hastey, *President*
Stephen Hastey, *Vice Pres*
Ken Hastey, *Treasurer*
Eric Hastey, *Admin Sec*
EMP: 21
SQ FT: 4,200
SALES (est): 2.3MM **Privately Held**
WEB: www.mhastey.com
SIC: 3599 1541 Machine shop, jobbing & repair; grain elevator construction

(G-16761)
PLAINVIEW BIOENERGY LLC
2698 E Us Highway 70 (79072-0410)
PHONE..................................806 296-8000
Don Gales, *CEO*
EMP: 42
SALES (est): 2MM
SALES (corp-wide): 17.1MM **Privately Held**
SIC: 2869 Ethyl alcohol, ethanol
PA: White Energy Holding Company, Llc
2595 Dallas Pkwy Ste 310
Frisco TX 75034
972 715-6490

(G-16762)
ROTOM INC
Also Called: IMS
200 W 24th St (79072-3110)
PHONE..................................806 293-7331
Robert L Edwards, *President*
Tommy Bennett, *Vice Pres*
Walter Hall, *Purch Mgr*
Leta Bennett, *Admin Sec*
EMP: 24 **EST:** 1976
SQ FT: 10,000
SALES (est): 2.3MM **Privately Held**
WEB: www.imstexas.com
SIC: 3556 3599 7692 Meat processing machinery; machine shop, jobbing & repair; welding repair

(G-16763)
TEJAS INDUSTRIES INC
E Of City (79072)
P.O. Box 1698 (79073-1698)
PHONE..................................806 293-4431
John Cates, *Manager*

EMP: 45
SALES (corp-wide): 93.5B **Privately Held**
WEB: www.merrickpetcare.com
SIC: 3556 2048 Meat processing machinery; prepared feeds
HQ: Tejas Industries, Inc.
101 Se 11th Ave Ste 200
Amarillo TX 79101
806 322-2800

(G-16764)
TEXAS AGRI MACHINE & INDUS MFG
Also Called: Texas-Agri Mch Indus Manufact
1317 Andy Taylor Rd (79072-0803)
P.O. Box 343 (79073-0343)
PHONE..................................806 296-5765
Ronnie Shackleford, *Owner*
EMP: 24
SALES (est): 800K **Privately Held**
SIC: 3599 Machine shop, jobbing & repair

(G-16765)
THRASHER INC
Also Called: Thrasher Ready Mix
1209 E 24th St (79072-3401)
PHONE..................................806 296-2609
EMP: 29 **EST:** 1970
SQ FT: 5,600
SALES (est): 4MM **Privately Held**
WEB: www.thrashersinc.com
SIC: 5032 1442 1611 Brick, stone & related material; gravel & pebble mining; surfacing & paving

(G-16766)
TOMMY LEWIS INDUSTRIES
208 S Columbia St (79072-8550)
PHONE..................................806 291-4433
EMP: 30
SALES (est): 1.1MM **Privately Held**
SIC: 3999 Manufacturing industries

(G-16767)
WESTERN AG SALES CO INC
327 W 24th St (79072-3111)
P.O. Box 1538 (79073-1538)
PHONE..................................806 293-2517
Larry Hastings, *President*
W W Cantwell, *Chairman*
Janice Hastings, *Vice Pres*
EMP: 22
SQ FT: 2,000
SALES (est): 4.2MM **Privately Held**
SIC: 3084 Plastics pipe

Plano
Collin County

(G-16768)
ABB POWER ELECTRONICS INC (DH)
601 Shiloh Rd (75074-7210)
PHONE..................................972 244-9288
Jeffrey Schnitzer, *President*
Ryan Kane, *Treasurer*
Bridget Smith, *Admin Sec*
Charlie Higby, *Associate*
▲ **EMP:** 129 **EST:** 2000
SALES (est): 407.4MM
SALES (corp-wide): 27.9B **Privately Held**
SIC: 3661 Switching equipment, telephone
HQ: Abb Holdings Inc.
305 Gregson Dr
Cary NC 27511
919 856-2360

(G-16769)
ACCURATE CONNECTIONS INC
1700 Capital Ave Ste 100 (75074-1209)
PHONE..................................972 484-8500
Peggy Kovling, *President*
Richard Kovling, *Vice Pres*
Rick Kovling, *Vice Pres*
Scott Sundberg, *Regl Sales Mgr*
Rebecca Krause, *Sales Staff*
EMP: 33
SALES (est): 5MM **Privately Held**
WEB: www.accurateconnections.com
SIC: 2298 1731 Cable, fiber; fiber optic cable installation

(G-16770)
ADAPTIVE 3D TECHNOLOGIES LLC
608 Development Dr # 200 (75074-8345)
PHONE..................................469 573-0024
Kial Gramley, *VP Sales*
Walter Voit,
EMP: 29
SALES (est): 456.8K **Privately Held**
WEB: www.adaptive3d.com
SIC: 3087 Custom compound purchased resins

(G-16771)
ADELE CHARLES CORP
Also Called: Full of Grace Divine Design
2921 Falling Brook Dr (75023-1407)
PHONE..................................972 740-1028
Melissa A Woods, *Principal*
Melissa Woods, *Principal*
EMP: 9 **EST:** 2014
SALES (est): 1.1MM **Privately Held**
WEB: www.fullofgracedd.com
SIC: 3961 Costume jewelry

(G-16772)
ADVANCED INTEGRATION TECH INC
Also Called: Aint
2805 E Plano Pkwy Ste 300 (75074-7473)
PHONE..................................972 423-8354
Edward J Chalupa, *President*
Karl Williams, *COO*
Phil Check, *Vice Pres*
Jason McGahey, *Vice Pres*
Erica Moreno-Melton, *Vice Pres*
▲ **EMP:** 230
SQ FT: 18,000
SALES (est): 86MM **Privately Held**
WEB: www.aint.com
SIC: 3728 3544 Aircraft parts & equipment; industrial molds

(G-16773)
ADVANCED INTEGRATION TECH LP (PA)
2805 E Plano Pkwy Ste 300 (75074-7473)
PHONE..................................972 423-8354
Edward J Chalupa, *CEO*
Michael Wellham, *President*
James Gardner, *General Mgr*
Robert Reno, *Senior VP*
Stephen Dukich, *Project Mgr*
EMP: 65
SQ FT: 16,000
SALES (est): 13.3MM **Privately Held**
WEB: www.aint.com
SIC: 3728 3544 Aircraft parts & equipment; industrial molds

(G-16774)
ADVANCED MCRBIAL SOLUTIONS LLC
Also Called: Agricen
5601 Granite Pkwy Ste 740 (75024-6688)
P.O. Box 519, Pilot Point (76258-0519)
PHONE..................................800 787-3724
Michael Totora, *President*
EMP: 18
SALES (est): 2.8MM
SALES (corp-wide): 20B **Privately Held**
WEB: www.agricen.com
SIC: 0711 2873 Fertilizer application services; fertilizers: natural (organic), except compost
HQ: Loveland Products, Inc.
3005 Rocky Mountain Ave
Loveland CO 80538

(G-16775)
ADVANCED NRMDLTION SYSTEMS INC (DH)
Also Called: Ans-Plano-Manufacturing
6901 Preston Rd (75024-2508)
PHONE..................................972 309-8000
Eric S Fain, *President*
Craig Hoersten, *Counsel*
Alan Mock, *Vice Pres*
Gary Mink, *Prdtn Mgr*
Mike Campbell, *Engineer*
EMP: 300 **EST:** 1979
SQ FT: 143,000

SALES (est): 100.1MM
SALES (corp-wide): 31.9B **Publicly Held**
WEB: www.plano.gov
SIC: 3845 Electrotherapeutic apparatus
HQ: St. Jude Medical, Llc
1 St Jude Medical Dr
Saint Paul MN 55117
651 756-2000

(G-16776)
AEON PROCESS EQUIPMENT
Also Called: Halgo
811 E Plano Pkwy Ste 103 (75074-6860)
P.O. Box 7607, Shreveport LA (71137-7607)
PHONE..................................972 690-8200
Ron Goodman, *President*
Ron Sanchez, *COO*
Ken Mathews, *VP Engrg*
Reggie Porter, *Sales Staff*
Allen Fawcett, *Director*
EMP: 70
SALES (corp-wide): 14.9MM **Privately Held**
WEB: www.aeonpec.com
SIC: 3491 Process control regulator valves
PA: Aeon Process Equipment & Control Solutions, Inc.
505 Aero Dr
Shreveport LA 71107
318 221-0122

(G-16777)
AFFILIATED COMMUNICATIONS
800 Jupiter Rd Ste 200 (75074-3770)
PHONE..................................972 423-4222
Larry Carter, *President*
EMP: 45
SALES (est): 2.5MM **Privately Held**
WEB: www.affiliatedcom.com
SIC: 3661 Fiber optics communications equipment

(G-16778)
AGILEMESH INC
1825 Summit Ave Ste 206 (75074-8196)
PHONE..................................972 231-2122
Bill Dickerson, *President*
Dennis Smith, *COO*
Dennis K Smith, *Vice Pres*
Devin Lee, *Sales Staff*
▲ **EMP:** 10
SQ FT: 3,000
SALES (est): 1.2MM **Privately Held**
WEB: www.agilemesh.com
SIC: 3699 Security devices

(G-16779)
AIR DISTRIBUTION TECH INC (DH)
605 Shiloh Rd (75074-7210)
PHONE..................................972 943-6100
EMP: 31 **EST:** 2012
SALES (est): 377.3MM **Privately Held**
WEB: www.airdistribution.com
SIC: 3585 Refrigeration & heating equipment
HQ: Johnson Controls, Inc.
5757 N Green Bay Ave
Glendale WI 53209
800 382-2804

(G-16780)
AIR SYSTEM COMPONENTS INC (DH)
Also Called: A S C
605 Shiloh Rd (75074-7210)
PHONE..................................972 212-4888
Gordon Jones, *President*
Jon Muckley, *Vice Pres*
Marc R Szczerba, *Vice Pres*
◆ **EMP:** 190 **EST:** 1999
SQ FT: 28,800
SALES (est): 700.2MM **Privately Held**
WEB: www.airsysco.com
SIC: 3585 Air conditioning equipment, complete; heating equipment, complete
HQ: Johnson Controls, Inc.
5757 N Green Bay Ave
Glendale WI 53209
800 382-2804

(G-16781)
AIR SYSTEM COMPONENTS INC
Also Called: Pennbarry
605 Shiloh Rd (75074-7210)
PHONE.................................972 212-4700
EMP: 278 **Privately Held**
WEB: www.airsysco.com
SIC: 3585 Air conditioning equipment,
complete
HQ: Air System Components, Inc.
605 Shiloh Rd
Plano TX 75074
972 212-4888

(G-16782)
AIR SYSTEM COMPONENTS INC
Also Called: Superior Rex
605 Shiloh Rd (75074-7210)
PHONE.................................972 212-4800
EMP: 278 **Privately Held**
WEB: www.airsysco.com
SIC: 3585 Air conditioning equipment,
complete
HQ: Air System Components, Inc.
605 Shiloh Rd
Plano TX 75074
972 212-4888

(G-16783)
ALLIED BIOSCIENCE INC (PA)
7500 Dallas Pkwy Ste 800 (75024-4007)
PHONE.................................214 432-5580
Michael Ruley, *CEO*
George Peat, *Vice Chairman*
Alan Gessel, *COO*
Maha El-Sayed PHD, *Senior VP*
Howard Smith, *Vice Pres*
EMP: 50
SALES (est): 12.7MM **Privately Held**
WEB: www.alliedbioscience.com
SIC: 8731 2899 5169 2834 Antiseptics,
medicinal; biotechnical research, com-
mercial; chemical preparations; chemicals
& allied products

(G-16784)
AMDEC INC
4512 Bentley Dr (75093-7149)
PHONE.................................214 654-0560
Kathy Carmody, *President*
Laura Pena, *Prdtn Mgr*
▲ **EMP:** 89
SALES (est): 10MM **Privately Held**
WEB: www.amdecinc.com
SIC: 2759 Screen printing

(G-16785)
**AMERICAN BOTTLING
COMPANY (HQ)**
Also Called: Dr Pepper Snapple Group
5301 Legacy Dr (75024-3109)
PHONE.................................972 673-7000
Robert Gamgort, *CEO*
Tom Jacobberger, *Division Mgr*
Chris Siraco, *Regional Mgr*
Doug Hagan, *District Mgr*
Bruce Krause, *District Mgr*
▼ **EMP:** 224
SALES (est): 2.5B **Publicly Held**
WEB: www.dpsg.com
SIC: 2086 Soft drinks: packaged in cans,
bottles, etc.

(G-16786)
**AMERICAN CMNTY
NEWSPAPERS LLC**
624 Krona Dr Ste 170 (75074-8304)
P.O. Box 860248 (75086-0248)
PHONE.................................972 424-6565
Dan Wilson, *CFO*
Gene Carr,
EMP: 212
SALES (est): 6.6MM **Privately Held**
WEB: www.starlocalmedia.com
SIC: 2711 Newspapers, publishing & print-
ing

(G-16787)
**AMERICAN INDUS MFRS BLDG
MATE**
Also Called: Aim Building Materials
6505 W Park Blvd (75093-6208)
PHONE.................................214 254-4720
Andrew Hastings, *CEO*
Jane Hastings,

EMP: 220 **EST:** 2011
SALES (est): 16MM **Privately Held**
WEB: www.aimbuildingmaterials.com
SIC: 2952 2951 2891 2851 Asphalt felts
& coatings; asphalt paving mixtures &
blocks; adhesives & sealants; lacquers,
varnishes, enamels & other coatings

(G-16788)
**AMERICAN ROCKWOOL MFG
LLC (PA)**
1316 Village Creek Dr # 600 (75093-4487)
PHONE.................................214 882-1343
David D Martinez, *CEO*
Kent Kean, *President*
John Beck, *Sales Staff*
EMP: 22 **EST:** 2016
SQ FT: 100,000
SALES (est): 4MM **Privately Held**
WEB: www.americanrockwool.com
SIC: 3296 Insulation: rock wool, slag & sil-
ica minerals

(G-16789)
AMS SENSORS USA INC (HQ)
5556 Tennyson Pkwy (75024-3532)
PHONE.................................469 298-4252
▲ **EMP:** 68 **EST:** 1998
SQ FT: 10,000
SALES (est): 30.6MM
SALES (corp-wide): 2B **Privately Held**
WEB: www.ams.com
SIC: 3674 5065 Mfg Semiconductors/Re-
lated Devices Whol Electronic
Parts/Equipment
PA: Ams Ag
SchloB Premstatten, Tobelbader
StraBe 30
PremstAtten 8141
313 650-00

(G-16790)
**ANDERSON MERCHANDISERS
LLC (HQ)**
5601 Gran Pkwy Ste 1400 (75024)
PHONE.................................972 987-5516
Bill Lardie, *CEO*
Scott McDaniel, *President*
Floyd Christopher, *District Mgr*
Curtis Luper, *District Mgr*
Harry Miller, *District Mgr*
EMP: 150
SQ FT: 25,867
SALES (est): 171MM **Privately Held**
WEB: www.amerch.com
SIC: 7372 Business oriented computer
software

(G-16791)
**APPLIED OPTICAL SYSTEMS
INC**
Also Called: O C C
1700 Capital Ave Ste 150 (75074-1210)
PHONE.................................972 509-1500
Neil D Wilkin Jr, *President*
Sandra Williams, *Buyer*
Sandy Williams, *Buyer*
Raju Penumatcha, *Engineer*
Tracy G Smith, *CFO*
◆ **EMP:** 60
SQ FT: 35,000
SALES (est): 15.8MM
SALES (corp-wide): 55.2MM **Publicly
Held**
WEB: www.old.occfiber.com
SIC: 3357 Fiber optic cable (insulated)
PA: Optical Cable Corporation
5290 Concourse Dr
Roanoke VA 24019
540 265-0690

(G-16792)
ARCUBE OPTICAL MFG LLC
3817 Sandia Dr (75023-6125)
PHONE.................................972 267-1800
Mayurika C Damle,
Chintamani A Damle,
Ratheen C Damle,
EMP: 35
SALES (est): 3MM **Privately Held**
WEB: www.arcube.com
SIC: 3695 Computer software tape &
disks: blank, rigid & floppy

(G-16793)
ARROW ELECTRONICS INC
1820 Preston Park Blvd # 2800
(75093-3685)
PHONE.................................303 824-4000
EMP: 9
SALES (corp-wide): 28.6B **Publicly Held**
WEB: www.fiveyearsout.com
SIC: 7372 Application computer software
PA: Arrow Electronics, Inc.
9201 E Dry Creek Rd
Centennial CO 80112
303 824-4000

(G-16794)
ARUBA PETROLEUM INC (PA)
555 Republic Dr Ste 505 (75074-8865)
PHONE.................................972 312-9366
James L Poston, *CEO*
Michael McAlister, *Vice Pres*
D Michael McAllister, *Vice Pres*
Dwane Maxwell, *Foreman/Supr*
Joe Good, *Production*
EMP: 23
SQ FT: 7,000
SALES (est): 3.1MM **Privately Held**
WEB: www.arubapetroleum.com
SIC: 1311 Crude petroleum production

(G-16795)
**ASC SIGNAL CORPORATION
(HQ)**
1120 Jupiter Rd Ste 102 (75074-7069)
PHONE.................................214 291-7654
Keith Buckley, *President*
Troy Depuma, *CFO*
Bassem Mansour, *Treasurer*
◆ **EMP:** 40
SALES (est): 8.7MM **Publicly Held**
WEB: www.ascsignal.com
SIC: 3679 Antennas, satellite: household
use

(G-16796)
AUTO ELECTRIC SYSTEMS INC
2708 K Ave Ste B (75074-5371)
P.O. Box 59485, Dallas (75229-1485)
PHONE.................................972 241-2077
Jeff Andonian, *President*
Steve Tabanian, *Vice Pres*
Tabanian Minas, *Vice Pres*
EMP: 17
SQ FT: 6,000
SALES (est): 2.5MM **Privately Held**
WEB: www.autoelectricsystemsinc.com
SIC: 3621 7539 Generating apparatus &
parts, electrical; electrical services; alter-
nators & generators, rebuilding & repair

(G-16797)
BAARI INC
Also Called: Dynamo Paintball Company
7801 Alma Dr Ste 10516 (75025-3482)
PHONE.................................214 566-5165
Karim A Merchant, *President*
Nazakat Kerauala, *Vice Pres*
Eric Kerawala, *Vice Pres*
EMP: 17
SQ FT: 20,000
SALES (est): 2MM **Privately Held**
SIC: 3069 2077 Balls, rubber; animal fats,
oils & meals

(G-16798)
BARNES BARNETT LLC
5000 Legacy Dr Ste 300 (75024-3115)
PHONE.................................214 445-6800
John R Barnes,
EMP: 20
SQ FT: 10,000
SALES (est): 50MM **Privately Held**
SIC: 1382 Oil & gas exploration services
PA: Barnes Oil & Gas Llc
5000 Legacy Dr Ste 300
Plano TX 75024

(G-16799)
BARNES OIL & GAS LLC (PA)
5000 Legacy Dr Ste 300 (75024-3115)
P.O. Box 262289 (75026-2289)
PHONE.................................214 445-6800
John R Barnes, *CEO*
Charles Foster, *COO*
Brandy Barnes, *Vice Pres*
Robert W Barnes, *Vice Pres*
EMP: 12

SQ FT: 10,000
SALES (est): 50MM **Privately Held**
SIC: 1382 Oil & gas exploration services

(G-16800)
BAYER HEALTHCARE LLC
Also Called: Customer Care Division
5601 Granite Pkwy Ste 750 (75024-6687)
PHONE.................................972 377-1950
Bill Lowe, *Branch Mgr*
Christopher Maker, *Manager*
Chip Camiscione, *Director*
EMP: 40
SALES (corp-wide): 48.1B **Privately Held**
WEB: www.bayer.us
SIC: 2834 Pharmaceutical preparations
HQ: Bayer Healthcare Llc
100 Bayer Blvd
Whippany NJ 07981
862 404-3000

(G-16801)
**BEE BUILDERS SUPPLY INC
(PA)**
1300 Capital Ave (75074-8580)
PHONE.................................972 422-4960
Bobby E Edwards, *President*
Wilma J Edwards, *Corp Secy*
Nancy Arnold, *Vice Pres*
Randall E Edwards, *Vice Pres*
Cheryl Campbell, *Shareholder*
EMP: 50
SQ FT: 8,000
SALES (est): 7.1MM **Privately Held**
WEB: www.beebuilderssupply.com
SIC: 2431 5031 Door frames, wood; mill-
work

(G-16802)
BETTERA BRANDS LLC (PA)
5345 Towne Square Dr # 240
(75024-2448)
PHONE.................................800 344-6225
Jeff Partridge, *CEO*
EMP: 10
SALES (est): 6.1MM **Privately Held**
WEB: www.gimbalscandy.com
SIC: 2834 2064 Vitamin, nutrient & hema-
tinic preparations for human use; candy &
other confectionery products

(G-16803)
BI SOLUTIONS INC
5048 Tennyson Pkwy # 250 (75024-3081)
PHONE.................................469 287-5784
Saravanamagesh Ganesan, *President*
Nidhya Natarajan, *Vice Pres*
EMP: 20
SQ FT: 300
SALES (est): 2MM **Privately Held**
WEB: www.bi-sol.com
SIC: 7372 Business oriented computer
software

(G-16804)
BILLMYR ENTERPRISES INC
Also Called: Ad Pages
1705 K Ave Ste A (75074-6173)
PHONE.................................972 424-1980
William Squiric, *President*
Myrna Squiric, *Treasurer*
EMP: 35 **EST:** 1988
SQ FT: 4,496
SALES (est): 4MM **Privately Held**
WEB: www.adpages.com
SIC: 2741 Miscellaneous publishing

(G-16805)
BIO-RAD LABORATORIES INC
3201 Technology Dr (75074-7441)
PHONE.................................972 596-6165
Carrie Thompson, *Train & Dev Mgr*
Kyle Navel, *Accounts Mgr*
Jenny Throneberry, *Branch Mgr*
John Yundt-Pacheco, *Info Tech Mgr*
EMP: 60
SALES (corp-wide): 2.3B **Publicly Held**
WEB: www.bio-rad.com
SIC: 2835 7371 2899 Hemotology diag-
nostic agents; computer software devel-
opment; chemical preparations
PA: Bio-Rad Laboratories, Inc.
1000 Alfred Nobel Dr
Hercules CA 94547
510 724-7000

(G-16806)
BLUEJACK ENERGY SOLUTIONS LLC
5851 Legacy Cir Ste 600 (75024-5969)
PHONE..................................720 320-2709
Jeremiah Davidson, *Opers Mgr*
Ted Lopez,
Chris Valenti,
EMP: 20 EST: 2016
SQ FT: 3,000
SALES (est): 4MM **Privately Held**
WEB: www.bluejackenergy.com
SIC: 1382 Oil & gas exploration services

(G-16807)
BMC SOFTWARE INC
5000 Headquarters Dr (75024-5826)
PHONE..................................214 442-0397
Kent Landfield, *Branch Mgr*
EMP: 40
SALES (corp-wide): 1.4B **Privately Held**
WEB: www.bmc.com
SIC: 7372 Prepackaged software
PA: Bmc Software, Inc.
    2103 Citywest Blvd # 2100
    Houston TX 77042
    713 918-8800

(G-16808)
BOEING COMPANY
7221 Regency Ct (75024-4739)
PHONE..................................972 491-5442
EMP: 431
SALES (corp-wide): 58.1B **Publicly Held**
WEB: www.boeing.com
SIC: 3721 Aircraft
PA: The Boeing Company
    100 N Riverside Plz
    Chicago IL 60606
    312 544-2000

(G-16809)
BOGEY FREE LLC
Also Called: Rackmount Solutions
2805 E Plano Pkwy Ste 200 (75074-7473)
P.O. Box 451537, Garland (75045-1537)
PHONE..................................972 272-6631
John Baker, *VP Bus Dvlpt*
Kevin Viars, *Sales Staff*
Dennis T Currier,
Michell M Currier,
Laura Viars, *Advisor*
EMP: 18
SQ FT: 17,000
SALES (est): 7.2MM **Privately Held**
WEB: www.rackmountsolutions.net
SIC: 3572 Computer storage devices

(G-16810)
BRAINS4DRONES LLC
6524 Pheasant Run Rd (75023-1607)
PHONE..................................972 974-3476
Susan Rossbach, *CEO*
Goksel Dedeoglu,
EMP: 11
SALES (est): 1.1MM **Privately Held**
WEB: www.perceptonic.com
SIC: 3812 Search & navigation equipment

(G-16811)
BRESA TECH LLC
Also Called: Bresatech
6860 Dallas Pkwy Ste 200 (75024-4242)
PHONE..................................866 728-2889
Arvind Neredimili, *CEO*
Jessey Lee, *Chairman*
William Martin, *Security Dir*
EMP: 50 EST: 2017
SQ FT: 500
SALES (est): 1.1MM **Privately Held**
WEB: www.bresatech.com
SIC: 7361 7379 7372 8742 Employment agencies; computer related consulting services; prepackaged software; management consulting services; transportation consultant; programmed instruction service; computer integrated systems design; systems analysis & engineering consulting services

(G-16812)
BRIGADIER OIL & GAS LLC (PA)
5800 Granite Pkwy Ste 820 (75024-6612)
PHONE..................................469 209-0760
Frank Burke, *CEO*
Ryan Corbin, *Vice Pres*

Brent Roland, *Vice Pres*
Kurt Vanderyt, *Vice Pres*
Daniel Kimes, *CFO*
EMP: 13
SALES (est): 11.4MM **Privately Held**
WEB: www.brigadieroil.com
SIC: 1382 Oil & gas exploration services

(G-16813)
BRIGADIER OPERATING LLC
5800 Granite Pkwy Ste 860 (75024-6618)
PHONE..................................469 209-0760
Frank Burke, *CEO*
Kurt Vanderyt, *Vice Pres*
Daniel Kimes, *CFO*
EMP: 9
SALES (est): 1.4MM **Privately Held**
SIC: 1382 Oil & gas exploration services

(G-16814)
BROADAXIS INC
1400 Preston Rd Ste 400 (75093-5189)
PHONE..................................469 688-2272
Muhammad Tariq, *President*
EMP: 17 EST: 2014
SQ FT: 700
SALES (est): 228.9K **Privately Held**
WEB: www.broadaxis.com
SIC: 7371 7372 7373 7379 Computer software systems analysis & design, custom; application computer software; systems engineering, computer related; computer related consulting services; management consulting services

(G-16815)
BROADLEAF COMMERCE LLC (PA)
5550 Granite Pkwy Ste 155 (75024-3764)
PHONE..................................800 282-7443
EMP: 25 EST: 2009
SALES (est): 5MM **Privately Held**
WEB: www.broadleafcommerce.com
SIC: 7372 Application computer software

(G-16816)
CA INC
5465 Legacy Dr Ste 700 (75024-3194)
PHONE..................................972 577-3223
William E McCracken, *CEO*
Eugene Banks, *Partner*
Bala Panatpur, *Vice Pres*
Enrique Torres, *Vice Pres*
Mike Gierkey, *Sales Executive*
EMP: 500
SALES (corp-wide): 23.8B **Publicly Held**
WEB: www.broadcom.com
SIC: 7372 Application computer software
HQ: Ca, Inc.
    520 Madison Ave
    New York NY 10022
    800 225-5224

(G-16817)
CALAN GROUP INC
808 Stewart Dr (75074-8197)
PHONE..................................972 422-5808
Nand Kumar, *President*
Leonard Kilby, *President*
Bruce Carter, *Vice Pres*
Frank Langenecker, *Vice Pres*
John Lucido, *Project Mgr*
◆ EMP: 105
SQ FT: 213,000
SALES (est): 31MM **Privately Held**
WEB: www.stewart-systems.com
SIC: 3556 Food products machinery

(G-16818)
CAMTRON INCORPORATED
3101 Summit Ave Ste 300 (75074-7472)
PHONE..................................972 994-0000
David M Stout, *President*
EMP: 29
SQ FT: 70,000
SALES (est): 2.9MM **Privately Held**
WEB: www.camtroninc.com
SIC: 3599 Machine shop, jobbing & repair

(G-16819)
CAPSTONE METERING LLC
1600 Capital Ave Ste 200 (75074-8187)
PHONE..................................214 469-1065
Scott Williamson, *President*
James Rice, *COO*
Scott Corbitt, *VP Opers*

Scott Gunn, *CFO*
▲ EMP: 22
SQ FT: 5,000
SALES (est): 2.5MM **Privately Held**
WEB: www.intellih2o.com
SIC: 3824 Water meters

(G-16820)
CARBONYX INC (PA)
Also Called: Carbonyx Carbon Technologies
5513 Roberts Dr (75093-7630)
PHONE..................................972 943-3355
Dr Siddhartha Gaur, *CEO*
Rob McCrossan, *General Mgr*
Pablo Palomo, *General Mgr*
Vibha Bansal, *Vice Pres*
Dilip Assar, *Purchasing*
▲ EMP: 35
SALES (est): 7.7MM **Privately Held**
WEB: www.carbonyx.com
SIC: 3624 Carbon specialties for electrical use

(G-16821)
CATES CONTROL SYSTEMS INC
Also Called: Integrity Intgration Resources
4001 E Plano Pkwy Ste 500 (75074-1826)
PHONE..................................972 665-3200
Anshul Adkar, *Project Mgr*
Ron Davis, *Project Mgr*
Weldon Knighton, *Engineer*
Jennie Kunze, *Human Resources*
Jerry Smith, *Branch Mgr*
EMP: 65
SALES (corp-wide): 30MM **Privately Held**
WEB: www.cates.com
SIC: 3613 Control panels, electric
PA: Cates Control Systems, Inc.
    14221 Gulfstream Park Dr
    Webster TX 77598
    713 944-0101

(G-16822)
CHEVRON PHILLIPS CHEM CO LP
Performance Pipe Division
5085 W Park Blvd Ste 500 (75093-2591)
PHONE..................................972 599-6600
Victoria Wulfekammer, *Sales Mgr*
Misty Ross, *Sales Staff*
Debbie Haven, *Marketing Staff*
Dave Morgan, *Branch Mgr*
Jana Hazlewood, *Manager*
EMP: 120
SALES (corp-wide): 3.5B **Privately Held**
WEB: www.cpchem.com
SIC: 2821 Plastics materials & resins
HQ: Chevron Phillips Chemical Company Lp
    10001 Six Pines Dr
    The Woodlands TX 77380
    832 813-4100

(G-16823)
CISTERA NETWORKS INC (PA)
5045 Lorimar Dr Ste 180 (75093-5721)
PHONE..................................972 381-4699
Gregory T Royal, *President*
James T Miller, *President*
Linda Valentine, *Controller*
EMP: 15
SQ FT: 9,767
SALES (est): 1.7MM **Publicly Held**
WEB: www.cistera.com
SIC: 7371 7372 Computer software development; prepackaged software

(G-16824)
CITYON SYSTEMS INC
4120 W Spring Creek Pkwy (75024-5318)
PHONE..................................972 519-1673
Preet Kumar, *CEO*
Meena Kumar, *Vice Pres*
Sandy Kumar, *Vice Pres*
Baiju Nagori, *CTO*
Virendra Gupta, *Info Tech Dir*
EMP: 25
SQ FT: 2,400
SALES (est): 2.9MM **Privately Held**
WEB: www.cityonsystems.com
SIC: 7372 7379 Prepackaged software; computer related consulting services

(G-16825)
CLAIREX TECHNOLOGIES INC
Also Called: Clairex Semiconductor
1000 Jupiter Rd Ste 100 (75074-3727)
PHONE..................................972 265-4905
Laverne Catter, *CEO*
Malcolm Catter, *Exec VP*
David Catter Sr, *Vice Pres*
EMP: 16
SQ FT: 7,300
SALES (est): 1.5MM **Privately Held**
WEB: www.clairex.com
SIC: 3679 3674 3625 Electronic circuits; semiconductors & related devices; relays & industrial controls

(G-16826)
CLIENT CONNECT LLC (PA)
Also Called: Expedite Commerce
5700 Granite Pkwy Ste 200 (75024-6623)
PHONE..................................214 295-4940
Tyler Moini, *Mng Member*
Charlie Corbeill, *Director*
EMP: 20
SALES (est): 1.7MM **Privately Held**
WEB: www.expeditecommerce.com
SIC: 7372 8742 Prepackaged software; marketing consulting services

(G-16827)
CODEKKO INC
1820 Preston Park Blvd (75093-3656)
PHONE..................................214 919-0565
Andre Angel, *President*
EMP: 21
SALES (est): 1MM **Privately Held**
WEB: www.codekko.com
SIC: 7372 Application computer software

(G-16828)
COMFY CHOICE LLC
5725 Hathaway Pkwy # 9409 (75024-5678)
PHONE..................................972 302-8094
Debodrick Brooks,
EMP: 75
SALES (est): 2MM **Privately Held**
SIC: 2211 Apparel & outerwear fabrics, cotton

(G-16829)
COMPUTERIZED CUTTERS INC
2900 Guilder Dr (75074-8343)
PHONE..................................972 422-6900
Carl Ondracek, *President*
Victoria Robinson, *Office Mgr*
Leslie Donels, *Manager*
Jim Whitney, *Manager*
▼ EMP: 39
SALES (est): 7.4MM **Privately Held**
WEB: www.computerizedcutters.com
SIC: 3599 3545 Custom machinery; machine tool accessories; cutting tools for machine tools; machine tool attachments & accessories

(G-16830)
CPI SATCOM & ANTENNA TECH INC
1000 Klein Rd (75074-3756)
PHONE..................................972 852-5300
Christopher Marzilli, *President*
Mark Showah, *Vice Pres*
Brad McCreight, *Engineer*
Ronald Boyd, *Finance*
Brian Behrens, *Software Engr*
EMP: 116 **Privately Held**
WEB: www.gdmissionsystems.com
SIC: 3663 Antennas, transmitting & communications
HQ: Cpi Satcom & Antenna Technologies Inc.
    1700 Cable Dr Ne
    Conover NC 28613
    704 462-7330

(G-16831)
CREATION TECHNOLOGIES KENTUCKY
Also Called: Creation Tchnologies-Lexington
1001 Klein Rd Ste 100 (75074-3750)
PHONE..................................859 253-3066
Arthur R Tymos, *President*
Craig Schuster, *Vice Pres*
Michael Walsh, *Admin Sec*

▲ EMP: 325
SQ FT: 73,000
SALES (est): 67.8MM
SALES (corp-wide): 127.3MM **Privately Held**
WEB: www.creationtech.com
SIC: 3679 3672 Electronic circuits; printed circuit boards
PA: Creation Technologies Ltd.
　　8999 Fraserton Crt
　　Burnaby BC V5J 5

(G-16832)
CRITICAL SOLUTIONS INTL INC
821 Jupiter Rd Ste 406 (75074-7449)
PHONE..................................800 843-0000
Patrick Callahan, *CEO*
Camille Comire, *Vice Pres*
EMP: 31
SQ FT: 5,000
SALES (est): 1MM **Privately Held**
SIC: 3795 Specialized tank components, military

(G-16833)
CUSTOM CMPT CABLES AMER INC
1600 10th St Ste A (75074-8671)
PHONE..................................972 638-9309
Jay Chenault, *President*
Kenneth Atkins, *Exec VP*
Ken Atkins, *Vice Pres*
Robbie Chenault, *Vice Pres*
Vince Schlueter, *Vice Pres*
▲ EMP: 300
SQ FT: 18,000
SALES (est): 151.8MM **Privately Held**
WEB: www.cccoa.com
SIC: 5051 3357 Cable, wire; communication wire

(G-16834)
CUSTOM DIRECT INC
Also Called: Custom Direct International
5048 Tennyson Pkwy # 250 (75024-3081)
PHONE..................................201 934-4229
Mark I Stein, *President*
▲ EMP: 18
SQ FT: 1,200
SALES (est): 7.8MM **Privately Held**
SIC: 3161 3171 2672 Luggage; purses, women's; labels (unprinted), gummed: made from purchased materials

(G-16835)
CVE TECHNOLOGY GROUP INC
3000 E Plano Pkwy (75074-7421)
PHONE..................................972 424-6606
Edward Cho, *President*
Kyu Taek Cho, *President*
Sekwang OH, *Manager*
Angela Ho, *Asst Mgr*
▲ EMP: 700
SALES (est): 212.5MM **Privately Held**
SIC: 3663 Radio & TV communications equipment

(G-16836)
DAL-TILE CORPORATION
1300 E Plano Pkwy Ste A (75074-8546)
PHONE..................................972 578-1600
EMP: 13 **Publicly Held**
WEB: www.daltile.com
SIC: 5032 3253 Ceramic wall & floor tile; ceramic wall & floor tile
HQ: Dal-Tile Corporation
　　7834 C F Hawn Fwy
　　Dallas TX 75217
　　214 398-1411

(G-16837)
DELTA ELECTRONICS (USA) INC (HQ)
2925 E Plano Pkwy (75074-7419)
PHONE..................................469 330-9100
Allen Pitts, *President*
Barry Blair, *President*
Lance Christian, *Opers Staff*
Bob Wood, *Opers Staff*
Ricky McAllister, *Buyer*
◆ EMP: 130 EST: 2001
SQ FT: 18,000

SALES (est): 32.4MM **Privately Held**
WEB: www.eltek.com
SIC: 3621 3694 3679 3629 Inverters, rotating: electrical; rotary converters (electrical equipment); battery charging alternators & generators; static power supply converters for electronic applications; inverters, nonrotating: electrical; power conversion units, a.c. to d.c.: static-electric; rectifiers (electrical apparatus); electronic enclosures, stamped or pressed metal

(G-16838)
DENBURY INC (PA)
5851 Legacy Cir Ste 600 (75024-5969)
PHONE..................................972 673-2000
Christian S Kendall, *President*
Robbie Hudson, *Counsel*
Jim Matthews, *Senior VP*
Jenny Cochran, *Vice Pres*
Dan E Cole, *Vice Pres*
EMP: 9
SALES: 1.2B **Publicly Held**
WEB: www.denbury.com
SIC: 1311 Crude petroleum & natural gas production; crude petroleum production

(G-16839)
DENBURY MARINE LLC
5320 Legacy Dr (75024-3127)
PHONE..................................972 673-2000
Phil Rykhoek,
EMP: 26
SALES (est): 1MM
SALES (corp-wide): 1.2B **Publicly Held**
WEB: www.denbury.com
SIC: 1382 Oil & gas exploration services
PA: Denbury Inc.
　　5851 Legacy Cir Ste 600
　　Plano TX 75024
　　972 673-2000

(G-16840)
DENBURY ONSHORE LLC (HQ)
5320 Legacy Dr (75024-3127)
P.O. Box 251289 (75025-1289)
PHONE..................................972 673-2000
Brian Ehrmantraut, *Foreman/Supr*
Kevin Heider, *Foreman/Supr*
Jay King, *Foreman/Supr*
Brannon Ledbetter, *Foreman/Supr*
Chad Lofton, *Foreman/Supr*
▲ EMP: 150
SQ FT: 60,000
SALES (est): 554.9MM
SALES (corp-wide): 1.2B **Publicly Held**
WEB: www.denbury.com
SIC: 1382 1311 Oil & gas exploration services; crude petroleum production; crude petroleum & natural gas production
PA: Denbury Inc.
　　5851 Legacy Cir Ste 600
　　Plano TX 75024
　　972 673-2000

(G-16841)
DENBURY OPERATING COMPANY
5320 Legacy Dr (75024-3127)
PHONE..................................972 673-2000
Phil Rykhoek, *CEO*
EMP: 26
SALES (est): 1.5MM
SALES (corp-wide): 1.2B **Publicly Held**
WEB: www.denbury.com
SIC: 1382 Oil & gas exploration services
PA: Denbury Inc.
　　5851 Legacy Cir Ste 600
　　Plano TX 75024
　　972 673-2000

(G-16842)
DENBURY PIPELINE HOLDINGS LLC
5320 Legacy Dr (75024-3127)
PHONE..................................972 673-2000
Christian S Kendall,
EMP: 11 **EST: 2014**
SALES (est): 278.2K
SALES (corp-wide): 1.2B **Publicly Held**
WEB: www.denbury.com
SIC: 1382 Oil & gas exploration services

PA: Denbury Inc.
　　5851 Legacy Cir Ste 600
　　Plano TX 75024
　　972 673-2000

(G-16843)
DENBURY RESOURCES INC
5100 Tennyson Pkwy (75024-3524)
PHONE..................................972 378-4776
Robbie Hudson, *Counsel*
Eric Arnold, *Foreman/Supr*
Norman Harchar, *Controller*
Suzanne Grimes, *Asst Controller*
Alan Rhoades, *Asst Controller*
EMP: 15
SALES (corp-wide): 1.2B **Publicly Held**
WEB: www.denbury.com
SIC: 1382 Oil & gas exploration services
PA: Denbury Inc.
　　5851 Legacy Cir Ste 600
　　Plano TX 75024
　　972 673-2000

(G-16844)
DIODES FABTECH INC
Also Called: Fab Tech
4949 Hedgcoxe Rd Ste 100 (75024-3929)
PHONE..................................816 251-8800
Keh-Shew Lu, *President*
John Nguyen, *Opers Mgr*
Richard D White, *CFO*
▲ EMP: 250
SQ FT: 70,000
SALES (est): 72.8MM
SALES (corp-wide): 1.2B **Publicly Held**
WEB: www.diodes.com
SIC: 3674 Integrated circuits, semiconductor networks, etc.
PA: Diodes Incorporated
　　4949 Hedgcoxe Rd Ste 200
　　Plano TX 75024
　　972 987-3900

(G-16845)
DIODES INCORPORATED
4949 Hedgcoxe Rd (75024-3898)
PHONE..................................972 987-3900
Keh-Shew Lu, *Branch Mgr*
Andy Tsong, *Director*
EMP: 30
SALES (corp-wide): 1.2B **Publicly Held**
WEB: www.diodes.com
SIC: 3674 Semiconductors & related devices
PA: Diodes Incorporated
　　4949 Hedgcoxe Rd Ste 200
　　Plano TX 75024
　　972 987-3900

(G-16846)
DIODES INCORPORATED (PA)
4949 Hedgcoxe Rd Ste 200 (75024-3935)
PHONE..................................972 987-3900
Chung Hsiung Chen, *Vice Ch Bd*
Keh-Shew Lu, *President*
Ch Chen, *Vice Chairman*
Chung Chen, *Vice Chairman*
Neil Chadderton, *Business Mgr*
▲ EMP: 140
SQ FT: 41,780
SALES: 1.2B **Publicly Held**
WEB: www.diodes.com
SIC: 3674 Semiconductors & related devices; integrated circuits, semiconductor networks, etc.

(G-16847)
DMN INC
3900 W Plano Pkwy (75075-7807)
P.O. Box 655237, Dallas (75265-5237)
PHONE..................................214 977-6931
Karisa King, *Editor*
Patrick Walker, *Editor*
Bill May, *Vice Pres*
Jessica Baldwin, *Marketing Staff*
Mike Disen, *Manager*
EMP: 400 **Publicly Held**
WEB: www.dallasnews.com
SIC: 2711 Newspapers, publishing & printing
HQ: Dmn, Inc.
　　1954 Commerce St
　　Dallas TX 75201

PA: Denbury Inc.
　　5851 Legacy Cir Ste 600
　　Plano TX 75024
　　972 673-2000

(G-16848)
DPS HOLDINGS INC
5301 Legacy Dr (75024-3109)
P.O. Box 869077 (75086-9077)
PHONE..................................972 673-7000
Charles Pepper, *Principal*
EMP: 23
SALES (est): 9.2MM **Publicly Held**
WEB: www.keurigdrpepper.com
SIC: 2086 Carbonated beverages, nonalcoholic: bottled & canned
PA: Keurig Dr Pepper Inc.
　　53 South Ave
　　Burlington MA 01803

(G-16849)
DR PEPPER SNPPLE GROUP EMPLYEE
Also Called: D P S
5301 Legacy Dr (75024-3109)
P.O. Box 330999, Houston (77233-0999)
PHONE..................................972 673-7000
Larry D Young, *President*
Tina S Barry, *Exec VP*
James L Baldwin Jr, *Vice Pres*
Derry L Hobson, *Vice Pres*
Martin M Ellen, *CFO*
EMP: 145
SALES (est): 47.4MM **Publicly Held**
WEB: www.keurigdrpepper.com
SIC: 2086 Soft drinks: packaged in cans, bottles, etc.
PA: Keurig Dr Pepper Inc.
　　53 South Ave
　　Burlington MA 01803

(G-16850)
DR PEPPER/SEVEN UP INC (HQ)
5301 Legacy Dr Fl 1 (75024-3109)
P.O. Box 869077 (75086-9077)
PHONE..................................972 673-7000
Robert Gamgort, *CEO*
Douglas Tough, *President*
Taun Dimatteo, *Senior VP*
Tom Farrah, *Senior VP*
William M Nelson, *Senior VP*
◆ EMP: 450 EST: 1885
SQ FT: 200,000
SALES (est): 669.8MM **Publicly Held**
WEB: www.drpepper.com
SIC: 2087 Flavoring extracts & syrups

(G-16851)
DROPLETS INC
555 Republic Dr Ste 311 (75074-5418)
P.O. Box 600997, Dallas (75360-0997)
PHONE..................................214 969-9970
David Berberian, *CEO*
Ingo B Theuerkauf, *CFO*
Frank Leon Rose, *CTO*
EMP: 40
SALES (est): 1.6MM
SALES (corp-wide): 541.7MM **Publicly Held**
WEB: www.droplets.com
SIC: 7372 Prepackaged software
HQ: Vivox, Inc.
　　40 Speen St Ste 305
　　Framingham MA 01701

(G-16852)
DRUCKER LABS LP
1600 Capital Ave Ste 100 (75074-1200)
PHONE..................................972 881-2344
Richard Drucker, *Partner*
Shafiq Dharamsi, *Opers Staff*
Lisa McCauley, *CFO*
Allison Schwartz, *Marketing Mgr*
Mary Coker,
EMP: 20
SQ FT: 17,000
SALES (est): 5MM **Privately Held**
WEB: www.store.druckerlabs.com
SIC: 2833 2834 Vitamins, natural or synthetic: bulk, uncompounded; pharmaceutical preparations; vitamin, nutrient & hematinic preparations for human use; vitamin preparations

(G-16853)
DWELL APP LLC
3333 Premier Dr (75023-7141)
PHONE..................................214 417-9424
David Yount, *COO*
EMP: 10

SALES (est): 100K
SALES (corp-wide): 310.8K **Privately Held**
WEB: www.dwellapp.io
SIC: **7372** Prepackaged software
PA: Lea Little Llc
3333 Premier Dr
Plano TX

(G-16854)
DZS INC (HQ)
5700 Tennyson Pkwy # 400 (75024-3595)
PHONE..................................469 327-1531
Charlie Vogt, *CEO*
Min Woo Nam, *Ch of Bd*
Kai Uebach, *President*
Philip Yim, *COO*
Jay Hilbert, *Exec VP*
◆ EMP: 167 EST: 1997
SALES: 306.8MM **Publicly Held**
WEB: www.dasanzhone.com
SIC: **3661** 4813 Fiber optics communications equipment;

(G-16855)
ECOFUSION INC
6600 Chase Oaks Blvd (75023-2381)
P.O. Box 251408 (75025-1408)
PHONE..................................972 403-7449
Nikhil Kapadia, *President*
Minal N Kapadia, *Director*
▲ EMP: 9
SQ FT: 900
SALES: 6.1MM **Privately Held**
WEB: www.canagri.net
SIC: **2879** 3533 5169 5191 Agricultural disinfectants; derricks, oil or gas field; industrial chemicals; animal feeds

(G-16856)
ECOLOOP ENERGY INC
500 N Cent Expy Ste 266 (75074)
PHONE..................................972 885-5130
EMP: 20
SALES (est): 1MM **Privately Held**
WEB: www.ecoloopenergy.com
SIC: **1389** Cementing oil & gas well casings

(G-16857)
EDSHAH CAPITAL
500 N Central Expy (75074-6772)
P.O. Box 864902 (75086-4902)
PHONE..................................469 770-3740
Eddie Obajimi, *Mng Member*
EMP: 10
SALES (est): 180.6K **Privately Held**
WEB: www.edshahcapital.com
SIC: **7389** 7372 Financial services; educational computer software

(G-16858)
EDUPHORIA INCORPORATED
1700 Alma Dr Ste 410 (75075-6953)
PHONE..................................972 535-5570
Jeffrey L Rizzo, *CEO*
Timothy Smith, *Ch of Bd*
Blake Haller, *Marketing Staff*
Shanna James, *Manager*
Annette Hicks, *Director*
EMP: 36
SALES (est): 4.2MM **Privately Held**
WEB: www.eduphoria.net
SIC: **7372** Business oriented computer software

(G-16859)
EHMER PRODUCTION MACHINING CO
1135 E Plano Pkwy Ste 3 (75074-8576)
PHONE..................................972 422-2882
Paul G Ehmer, *President*
Roberta F Ehmer, *Vice Pres*
EMP: 12 EST: 1974
SQ FT: 2,200
SALES (est): 1.4MM **Privately Held**
WEB: www.localwombat.com
SIC: **3599** Machine shop, jobbing & repair

(G-16860)
ELUMENUS LIGHTING CORP INC
555 Republic Dr Ste 200 (75074-5469)
PHONE..................................214 392-2898
EMP: 10

SALES (corp-wide): 1.2MM **Privately Held**
SIC: **3641** Mfg Electric Lamps
PA: Elumenus Lighting Corporation Inc.
555 Republic Dr Ste 200
Plano TX
214 392-2898

(G-16861)
ENDTIME INC
Also Called: Politics & Religion Broadcast
2701 E President George B (75074-3774)
PHONE..................................972 422-0857
Irvin Baxter, *President*
Jana Robbins, *Office Mgr*
Gary McPeak, *Manager*
Vince Stegall, *Director*
EMP: 30
SQ FT: 8,000
SALES: 5.1MM **Privately Held**
WEB: www.endtime.com
SIC: **2721** 5961 Magazines: publishing only, not printed on site; religious merchandise, mail order

(G-16862)
ENSEO LLC
2201 10th St (75074-8019)
PHONE..................................972 234-2513
Vanessa Ogle, *CEO*
Omar Khan, *President*
Todd Helfer, *General Mgr*
Randy Eisenbach, *COO*
Ed Wolfe, *Senior VP*
▲ EMP: 45
SALES (est): 16.5MM **Privately Held**
WEB: www.enseo.com
SIC: **3577** Data conversion equipment, media-to-media: computer

(G-16863)
ENTERPRISE ESP SVC PRVIDER LLC
840 F Ave Ste 105 (75074-6864)
PHONE..................................469 619-3114
Clarence E Lindsey, *Mng Member*
Clarence Lindsey, *Info Tech Mgr*
EMP: 12
SALES (est): 950K **Privately Held**
WEB: www.enterprise-esp.com
SIC: **4899** 7629 4813 4812 Data communication services; telephone set repair; voice telephone communications; cellular telephone services; telephones & telephone apparatus

(G-16864)
ENTRY WAY PUBLISHING
6205 Oregon Ct (75023-4312)
PHONE..................................972 517-6513
EMP: 12
SALES (est): 510.4K **Privately Held**
SIC: **2741** Misc Publishing

(G-16865)
EPICOR SOFTWARE CORPORATION
2400 Dallas Pkwy (75093-4370)
PHONE..................................800 776-7438
Don Webb, *Principal*
Debbie Alvarado, *Sales Staff*
Doug Waite, *Sr Project Mgr*
Abhijeet Deshpande, *Manager*
Jeff Lilly, *Manager*
EMP: 73 **Privately Held**
WEB: www.epicor.com
SIC: **7372** Prepackaged software
PA: Epicor Software Corporation
804 Las Cimas Pkwy # 200
Austin TX 78746

(G-16866)
ESTECH SYSTEMS INC
Also Called: E S I
3701 E Plano Pkwy Ste 100 (75074-1809)
PHONE..................................972 422-9700
Eric Suder, *CEO*
Adrian Alvarado, *Partner*
Reah Donastorg-Josep, *Managing Dir*
Doug Boyd, *Principal*
George Platt, *Principal*
▲ EMP: 144
SQ FT: 20,000

SALES (est): 45.9MM **Privately Held**
WEB: www.esi-estech.com
SIC: **3661** Telephones & telephone apparatus

(G-16867)
EXCELENTE INC
Also Called: Safe PC Solutions
2701 W 15th St 513 (75075-7523)
PHONE..................................855 209-1970
Madinah S Ali, *President*
Ray Lenart, *CFO*
MSA Global, *Shareholder*
Toptel USA, *Shareholder*
EMP: 25
SALES (est): 8.5MM **Privately Held**
WEB: www.atlantagacomputerservices.com
SIC: **6799** 8748 7378 7372 Investors; business consulting; telecommunications consultant; computer maintenance & repair; computer & data processing equipment repair/maintenance; prepackaged software; computer related maintenance services; disk & diskette recertification service

(G-16868)
EXYTE AMERICAS HOLDING INC (DH)
Also Called: Mw Americas Inc.
1001 Klein Rd Ste 400 (75074-3751)
PHONE..................................972 535-7300
Gary C Baughman, *COO*
Christopher Craven, *Counsel*
Jose Rivas, *Vice Pres*
Jose M Rivas, *Vice Pres*
Mark Gilson, *Project Mgr*
EMP: 30
SQ FT: 23,000
SALES (est): 278.9MM
SALES (corp-wide): 242.1K **Privately Held**
WEB: www.mwgroup.net
SIC: **3433** 8712 8711 8741 Solar heaters & collectors; architectural services; architectural engineering; engineering services; construction & civil engineering; construction management
HQ: M+W Facility Engineering Gmbh
Lowentorbogen 9b
Stuttgart 70376
711 880-40

(G-16869)
FASHION WORKS INC
4609 Saxon Dr (75093-7143)
PHONE..................................972 596-5815
Cathy Kissler, *President*
Jerry Kissler, *Vice Pres*
▲ EMP: 12
SQ FT: 13,000 **Privately Held**
SIC: **2339** 2325 Women's & misses' athletic clothing & sportswear; men's & boys' trousers & slacks

(G-16870)
FASTSERV SUPPLY INC (PA)
Also Called: Eco Plus
4060 E Plano Pkwy (75074-1800)
PHONE..................................800 527-4126
Jon Kerr, *CEO*
Danny Anderson, *Vice Pres*
Jason Looft, *Vice Pres*
Diane Vanderbilt, *Vice Pres*
John Bacon, *CFO*
EMP: 32 EST: 2012
SALES (est): 9MM **Privately Held**
WEB: www.fastservsupply.com
SIC: **3452** 5072 5169 5251 Bolts, nuts, rivets & washers; bolts, nuts & screws; industrial chemicals; hardware

(G-16871)
FLEXTRONICS INTL USA INC
600 Shiloh Rd (75074-7209)
PHONE..................................817 837-5098
Michael McNamara, *Branch Mgr*
EMP: 365 **Privately Held**
WEB: www.flex.com
SIC: **3672** Printed circuit boards
HQ: Flextronics International Usa, Inc.
6201 America Center Dr
San Jose CA 95002

(G-16872)
FOXWORTH-GALBRAITH LUMBER CO (PA)
Also Called: Do It Best
4965 Preston Park Blvd # 400 (75093-5141)
P.O. Box 799002, Dallas (75379-9002)
PHONE..................................972 665-2400
Walter L Foxworth, *CEO*
Jack L Foxworth, *President*
J C Galbraith III, *President*
Rudy P Chanez, *General Mgr*
Brad Cooper, *General Mgr*
EMP: 95 EST: 1901
SQ FT: 20,000
SALES (est): 395.3MM **Privately Held**
WEB: www.foxgal.com
SIC: **5251** 5031 2439 2431 Hardware; lumber, plywood & millwork; trusses, except roof: laminated lumber; doors, wood

(G-16873)
FRITO-LAY INC (HQ)
7701 Legacy Dr (75024-4099)
PHONE..................................972 334-7000
Thomas Greco, *CEO*
Christine J Cioffe, *Vice Pres*
Corey Gottschalk, *Vice Pres*
Israel Kontorovsky, *Vice Pres*
John McIntyre, *Vice Pres*
EMP: 277
SALES (est): 243.9MM
SALES (corp-wide): 67.1B **Publicly Held**
WEB: www.fritolay.com
SIC: **2052** 2096 Cookies; potato chips & other potato-based snacks
PA: Pepsico, Inc.
700 Anderson Hill Rd
Purchase NY 10577
914 253-2000

(G-16874)
FRITO-LAY NORTH AMERICA INC (HQ)
Also Called: Pepsico Americas Foods
7701 Legacy Dr (75024-4099)
P.O. Box 660634, Dallas (75266-0634)
PHONE..................................972 334-7000
Albert P Carey, *CEO*
Oswald Barckhahn, *President*
Sam Alshawish, *Regional Mgr*
Anthony Evangelista, *District Mgr*
John Hart, *District Mgr*
◆ EMP: 3000
SALES (est): 12.8B
SALES (corp-wide): 67.1B **Publicly Held**
WEB: www.fritolay.com
SIC: **2086** 2013 5812 6794 Carbonated soft drinks, bottled & canned; snack sticks, including jerky: from purchased meat; fast-food restaurant, chain; chicken restaurant; franchises, selling or licensing; potato chips & other potato-based snacks
PA: Pepsico, Inc.
700 Anderson Hill Rd
Purchase NY 10577
914 253-2000

(G-16875)
FURNACE SYSTEMS INC
1209 Ave N Ste 15 (75074)
P.O. Box 941261 (75094-1261)
PHONE..................................972 423-7800
Terry F Smith, *President*
Terry Smith, *President*
EMP: 11
SQ FT: 8,000
SALES (est): 2.2MM **Privately Held**
WEB: www.furnacesystems.com
SIC: **3567** 1711 5085 5074 Industrial furnaces & ovens; boiler & furnace contractors; refractory material; gas burners

(G-16876)
FUTUREFAB INC
1209 Ave N Ste 12 (75074)
PHONE..................................972 423-6606
Derek Small, *President*
EMP: 10
SQ FT: 6,600
SALES (est): 2MM **Privately Held**
WEB: www.futurefab.com
SIC: **3674** 3089 Semiconductors & related devices; molding primary plastic

(G-16877)
G C INTERNATIONAL INC
1301 Precision Dr (75074-8636)
PHONE..................................972 422-2395
Susan Chen, *Principal*
EMP: 350
SQ FT: 27,000
SALES (est): 30MM **Privately Held**
SIC: 3629 Electronic generation equipment

(G-16878)
GE ZENITH CONTROLS INC (HQ)
601 Shiloh Rd (75074-7210)
PHONE..................................800 637-1738
▲ **EMP:** 280
SQ FT: 47,400
SALES (est): 57.4MM
SALES (corp-wide): 95.2B **Publicly Held**
SIC: 3613 Switchgear & switchgear accessories
PA: General Electric Company
5 Necco St
Boston MA 02210
617 443-3000

(G-16879)
GEOFORCE INC (PA)
5830 Gran Pkwy Ste 1200 (75024)
P.O. Box 3432, Coppell (75019-6403)
PHONE..................................972 546-3878
James Maclean III, *President*
Mark Slaughter, *Principal*
David Mordoh, *Regional Mgr*
Roopa S Misra, *Senior VP*
Richard Coffman, *Vice Pres*
EMP: 65
SQ FT: 3,000
SALES (est): 21.7MM **Privately Held**
WEB: www.geoforce.com
SIC: 7373 1382 Systems software development services; oil & gas exploration services

(G-16880)
GIRARD INVESTMENTS INC (PA)
Also Called: AlphaGraphics
601 W Plano Pkwy Ste 127 (75075-8968)
PHONE..................................972 423-0299
Craig Girard, *President*
Kristy Girard, *Vice Pres*
EMP: 9
SQ FT: 4,000
SALES (est): 1.7MM **Privately Held**
WEB: www.alphagraphics.com
SIC: 2752 7334 2789 2791 Commercial printing, lithographic; photocopying & duplicating services; bookbinding & repairing: trade, edition, library, etc.; typesetting, computer controlled

(G-16881)
GREN INDUSTRIES INC
Also Called: Service Rubber Group
740 Ave F Ste 300 (75074)
P.O. Box 701411, Dallas (75370-1411)
PHONE..................................972 881-2606
Brian E Greninger, *President*
Matt Greninger, *General Mgr*
Matthew Greninger, *Marketing Staff*
Cravan Dierckman, *Info Tech Mgr*
▲ **EMP:** 10
SQ FT: 5,200
SALES (est): 3MM **Privately Held**
WEB: www.servicerubber.com
SIC: 3061 Mechanical rubber goods

(G-16882)
GUIVERMAN INDUSTRIES LLC (PA)
5851 Legacy Cir Ste 600 (75024-5969)
PHONE..................................866 235-8057
William Verdaguer, *Mng Member*
Nicholas Barona,
Mary Chavarro,
Priscilla Pozo,
Angela Verdaguer,
EMP: 31
SALES (est): 2.5MM **Privately Held**
WEB: www.guiverman.com
SIC: 3589 5074 3559 Sewage & water treatment equipment; water purification equipment; pharmaceutical machinery

(G-16883)
HAPPYMECOM
6010 W Spring Creek Pkwy (75024-3569)
PHONE..................................972 503-4803
Gary Bourland, *Director*
EMP: 10
SALES (est): 372.1K **Privately Held**
WEB: www.happyme.com
SIC: 8049 2731 Psychotherapist, except M.D.; book publishing

(G-16884)
HARTFIEL AUTOMATION INC
2600 Tech Dr Ste 300 (75074)
PHONE..................................972 633-0000
Myron Moser, *Branch Mgr*
EMP: 19
SALES (corp-wide): 82.3MM **Privately Held**
WEB: www.hartfiel.com
SIC: 3594 5084 Motors, pneumatic; industrial machinery & equipment
PA: Hartfiel Automation, Inc.
6533 Flying Cloud Dr # 100
Eden Prairie MN 55344
952 974-2500

(G-16885)
HEMOTEK LLC
701 E Plano Pkwy Ste 500 (75074-6758)
PHONE..................................972 312-1609
John Woodmansee Jr, *CEO*
Rob Woodmansee, *Vice Pres*
EMP: 10
SQ FT: 2,400
SALES (est): 847K **Privately Held**
SIC: 2834 Powders, pharmaceutical

(G-16886)
HILTI OF AMERICA INC (DH)
7250 Dallas Pkwy Ste 1000 (75024-4998)
PHONE..................................800 879-8000
Cary Evert, *President*
Chris Beatt, *Partner*
Thomas Bail, *Regional Mgr*
Ed Selz, *Regional Mgr*
Tim Henry, *Project Mgr*
◆ **EMP:** 27
SQ FT: 341,105
SALES (est): 466.4MM
SALES (corp-wide): 157.2K **Privately Held**
WEB: www.hilti.com
SIC: 5084 3546 3825 Drilling equipment, excluding bits; drills & drilling tools; standards & calibration equipment for electrical measuring
HQ: Hilti Aktiengesellschaft
Feldkircherstrasse 100
Schaan 9494
423 234-2111

(G-16887)
HP INC
6901 Windcrest Dr (75024-4142)
PHONE..................................972 604-3355
Bill Janeshek, *Branch Mgr*
EMP: 500
SALES (corp-wide): 56.6B **Publicly Held**
WEB: www.hp.com
SIC: 3571 Personal computers (microcomputers)
PA: Hp Inc.
1501 Page Mill Rd
Palo Alto CA 94304
650 857-1501

(G-16888)
HUAWEI DEVICE USA INC (DH)
Also Called: Huawei Mobile USA
5700 Tennyson Pkwy # 300 (75024-3583)
PHONE..................................214 919-6688
Zhiqiang Xu, *President*
Jiangao Cui, *Principal*
Ailing Lin, *Treasurer*
▲ **EMP:** 108
SALES (est): 147MM
SALES (corp-wide): 7B **Privately Held**
SIC: 3663 Cellular radio telephone

(G-16889)
IDM GROUP LLC
2552 Summit Ave Ste 404 (75074-3722)
P.O. Box 1263, Grapevine (76099-1263)
PHONE..................................972 578-1010
Robert Heilbrun,

Mike Freitas,
Jeff Garrett,
Doug Laube,
▲ **EMP:** 13
SALES (est): 1.6MM **Privately Held**
SIC: 5251 3089 Tools; injection molding of plastics

(G-16890)
INFO-POWER INTERNATIONAL INC
3345 Silverstone Dr Ste B (75023-7836)
PHONE..................................972 424-4447
Zerrial Bass, *President*
Robert Cary Farrar, *Vice Pres*
Joe Bass, *Project Mgr*
EMP: 9
SQ FT: 7,500
SALES (est): 1.6MM **Privately Held**
WEB: www.abw.com
SIC: 7371 7372 Computer software development; business oriented computer software

(G-16891)
INOGEN INC
600 Shiloh Rd (75074-7209)
PHONE..................................972 616-5500
EMP: 519
SALES (corp-wide): 361.9MM **Publicly Held**
WEB: www.inogen.com
SIC: 7352 3841 Medical equipment rental; surgical & medical instruments
PA: Inogen, Inc.
326 Bollay Dr
Goleta CA 93117
805 562-0500

(G-16892)
INTEGER HOLDINGS CORPORATION (PA)
5830 Gran Pkwy Ste 1150 (75024)
PHONE..................................214 618-5243
Bill R Sanford, *Ch of Bd*
Joseph W Dziedzic, *President*
Joel Becker, *President*
Carter Houghton, *President*
Payman Khales, *President*
EMP: 91
SALES: 1.2B **Publicly Held**
WEB: www.integer.net
SIC: 3675 3692 3691 Electronic capacitors; primary batteries, dry & wet; storage batteries

(G-16893)
INTEL CORPORATION
5000 Headquarters Dr (75024-5826)
PHONE..................................972 987-2377
Paula Cook, *Branch Mgr*
Shameka Johnson, *Technology*
EMP: 12
SALES (corp-wide): 77.8B **Publicly Held**
WEB: www.intel.com
SIC: 3577 Computer peripheral equipment
PA: Intel Corporation
2200 Mission College Blvd
Santa Clara CA 95054
408 765-8080

(G-16894)
INTUIT INC
5601 Headquarters Dr (75024-5839)
PHONE..................................214 387-2000
Amy Bugh, *Partner*
Joel Hodges, *Chief*
Marilyn Jones, *Vice Pres*
Ravi Metta, *Vice Pres*
Patti Newcomer, *Vice Pres*
EMP: 39
SALES (corp-wide): 7.6B **Publicly Held**
WEB: www.intuit.com
SIC: 7372 Business oriented computer software
PA: Intuit Inc.
2700 Coast Ave
Mountain View CA 94043
650 944-6000

(G-16895)
IPCELERATE INC
6860 Dallas Pkwy Ste 200 (75024-4242)
PHONE..................................972 512-7100
Kevin Brown, *President*
Ric Reiff, *Sales Staff*

Alok Jain, *CTO*
Roger W Christopher, *Director*
EMP: 10
SALES (est): 2.2MM **Privately Held**
WEB: www.ipcelerate.com
SIC: 3695 Computer software tape & disks: blank, rigid & floppy

(G-16896)
JAGUAR HOSPITALITY SVCS CORP
6009 W Parker Rd 149-130 (75093-8120)
PHONE..................................214 295-3574
Roderick Edward Fruth, *President*
Karen Fisher, *Project Dir*
Karen Holland, *Project Dir*
Julie Miller, *Purchasing*
EMP: 10
SALES (est): 3.7MM **Privately Held**
WEB: www.jaguarhospitality.com
SIC: 2599 Restaurant furniture, wood or metal

(G-16897)
JAX LTD INC
3701 W Plano Pkwy Ste 100 (75075-7836)
PHONE..................................763 449-9699
Zelman Levine, *President*
Bruce Hilden, *Corp Secy*
Cindy Levine, *Vice Pres*
▲ **EMP:** 87
SALES (est): 12.8MM
SALES (corp-wide): 28.9MM **Privately Held**
WEB: www.jaxgames.com
SIC: 3944 Games, toys & children's vehicles
PA: Beryl Corporation
1850 Lake Lucy Rd
Excelsior MN 55331
763 449-9699

(G-16898)
JD MURCHISON INTERESTS INC (PA)
Also Called: Murchison Oil & Gas
7250 Dallas Pkwy (75024-4920)
PHONE..................................972 931-0700
J D Murchison, *Ch of Bd*
R J Penksa, *COO*
Dave B Marshall, *CFO*
Branka Daravong, *Office Mgr*
Monica Vasquez, *Office Mgr*
EMP: 30
SQ FT: 12,000
SALES (est): 10.9MM **Privately Held**
WEB: www.murchisonoil.com
SIC: 1311 1521 1522 1542 Crude petroleum production; new construction, single-family houses; multi-family dwelling construction; commercial & office building contractors

(G-16899)
JENKEM TECHNOLOGY USA INC
4105 W Spring Creek Pkwy (75024-5283)
PHONE..................................972 673-0603
Zhao Xuan, *President*
Lihong Guo, *Vice Pres*
EMP: 11
SALES (est): 1MM **Privately Held**
WEB: www.jenkemusa.com
SIC: 2822 Ethylene-propylene rubbers, EPDM polymers

(G-16900)
KAP TECHNOLOGIES INC
2500 Geiberger Dr (75025-5166)
PHONE..................................972 359-7060
RAO Alasakani, *President*
EMP: 11
SALES (est): 1MM **Privately Held**
SIC: 3826 Analytical instruments

(G-16901)
KEIL SOFTWARE INC (DH)
Also Called: Keil An Arm Company
4965 Preston Park Blvd # 650 (75093-8319)
PHONE..................................972 312-1107
SOO Hsien Tan, *President*
Tom Lantzsch, *Vice Pres*
Angela Williams, *Sales Mgr*
EMP: 12
SQ FT: 12,500

▲ = Import ▼=Export
◆ =Import/Export

SALES (est): 1MM **Privately Held**
WEB: www.keil.com
SIC: 3571 Electronic computers

(G-16902)
KINGSISLE ENTERTAINMENT INC (PA)
2745 Dallas Pkwy Ste 620 (75093-8760)
P.O. Box 5997, Round Rock (78683-5997)
PHONE..................................972 265-1900
Elie Akilian, *CEO*
David Nichols, *President*
Craig Beers, *Vice Pres*
Dave Rosen, *VP Mktg*
EMP: 32
SALES (est): 6.1MM **Privately Held**
WEB: www.kingsisle.com
SIC: 7372 Prepackaged software

(G-16903)
KODIAK NETWORKS INC (HQ)
1501 10th St Ste 130 (75074-8660)
PHONE..................................972 665-0200
John Vice, *President*
Ravi Ayyasamy, *Vice Pres*
John Dilley, *Vice Pres*
Tim Hall, *Vice Pres*
Brent Kohman, *Vice Pres*
◆ EMP: 15
SQ FT: 2,200
SALES (est): 23.4MM
SALES (corp-wide): 7.8B **Publicly Held**
WEB: www.motorolasolutions.com
SIC: 3663 Telephone Communications
PA: Motorola Solutions, Inc.
500 W Monroe St Ste 4400
Chicago IL 60661
847 576-5000

(G-16904)
KRYPTON SOLUTIONS LLC
3060 Summit Ave (75074-7200)
PHONE..................................972 424-3880
Suresh Patel, *CEO*
Vinay Naik, *General Mgr*
Mahesh Patel, *Principal*
Dipak Patel, *COO*
Chirag Bhingaradiya, *Prdtn Mgr*
◆ EMP: 180
SQ FT: 40,000
SALES (est): 26.3MM **Privately Held**
WEB: www.krypton-solutions.com
SIC: 3672 Printed circuit boards

(G-16905)
LA BLUE CRAB CO INC
1111 Jupiter Rd Ste 100e (75074-7042)
P.O. Box 251445 (75025-1445)
PHONE..................................972 422-7525
Joe Nguyen, *President*
EMP: 12
SALES (est): 1.6MM **Privately Held**
SIC: 2092 Crab meat, fresh: packaged in nonsealed containers

(G-16906)
LACERTE SOFTWARE CORPORATION
5601 Headquarters Dr (75024-5839)
PHONE..................................214 387-2000
Steve Benett, *President*
Karl Grass, *Vice Pres*
EMP: 250
SALES (est): 11.3MM
SALES (corp-wide): 7.6B **Publicly Held**
SIC: 7371 7372 Computer software development; prepackaged software
PA: Intuit Inc.
2700 Coast Ave
Mountain View CA 94043
650 944-6000

(G-16907)
LATTIMORE MATERIALS CORP
Also Called: Lattimore Ready Mix
1200 Ave N (75074)
PHONE..................................972 423-8359
Scott Barnhill, *Manager*
EMP: 26
SALES (corp-wide): 1.7B **Privately Held**
WEB: www.lafargeholcim.us
SIC: 3273 Ready-mixed concrete
HQ: Lattimore Materials Corp.
15900 Dooley Rd
Addison TX 75001
972 221-4646

(G-16908)
LHCN INC (PA)
Also Called: Plano Star Courier
624 Krona Dr Ste 170 (75074-8304)
P.O. Box 860248 (75086-0248)
PHONE..................................972 424-6565
Gene M Carr, *CEO*
Daniel J Wilson, *CFO*
▲ EMP: 100
SQ FT: 35,000
SALES (est): 10.2MM **Privately Held**
WEB: www.starlocalmedia.com
SIC: 2711 Newspapers, publishing & printing

(G-16909)
LIGHTING & POWER TECH LLC
7101 Whisperfield Dr (75024-7472)
PHONE..................................877 666-5267
Zhiquan Ou, *Mng Member*
Paul J Roth,
▲ EMP: 10
SALES (est): 2.1MM **Privately Held**
WEB: www.lightingandpowertech.com
SIC: 3646 Commercial indusl & institutional electric lighting fixtures

(G-16910)
LONG & LONG PIER DRILLING CO
1712 Ave N (75074)
PHONE..................................972 422-4084
Harold Long, *President*
Denny Long, *Vice Pres*
Georgia Long, *Treasurer*
EMP: 10
SALES (est): 500K **Privately Held**
WEB: www.longlongpierdrillingco.business.site
SIC: 3731 Drilling & production platforms, floating (oil & gas)

(G-16911)
LUMINATOR HOLDING LP (HQ)
Also Called: Luminator Aircraft Parts Div
900 Klein Rd (75074-3712)
PHONE..................................972 424-6511
Ramin Safavi, *President*
AVI Zisman, *Partner*
Gregg Evans, *Partner*
Rich Rosselet, *Partner*
Tina Morris, *Finance Dir*
▲ EMP: 190
SQ FT: 104,000
SALES (est): 36.6MM
SALES (corp-wide): 169.1MM **Privately Held**
WEB: www.luminator.com
SIC: 3648 3643 3646 3647 Arc lighting fixtures; current-carrying wiring devices; commercial indusl & institutional lighting fixtures; aircraft lighting fixtures; control equipment for electric buses & locomotives
PA: Luminator Technology Group, Llc
900 Klein Rd
Plano TX 75074
972 424-6511

(G-16912)
LUMINATOR TECHNOLOGY GROUP INC
900 Klein Rd (75074-3712)
PHONE..................................972 516-3154
Kirk Goins, *CEO*
EMP: 450
SALES (est): 4.7MM **Privately Held**
SIC: 4789 3663 Freight car loading & unloading; radio & TV communications equipment

(G-16913)
LUMINATOR TECHNOLOGY GROUP LLC (PA)
900 Klein Rd (75074-3712)
PHONE..................................972 424-6511
Kirk Goins, *CEO*
Thomas Lail, *Business Mgr*
April Johnson, *COO*
Bob Seidel, *CFO*
Werner Malcherek, *CTO*
▲ EMP: 200
SQ FT: 104,000

SALES (est): 169.1MM **Privately Held**
WEB: www.luminatoraerospace.com
SIC: 3643 3646 3647 3613 Current-carrying wiring devices; commercial indusl & institutional electric lighting fixtures; aircraft lighting fixtures; switchgear & switchboard apparatus; signs & advertising specialties; radio & TV communications equipment

(G-16914)
M-FILES INC
6400 Intl Pkwy Ste 2500 (75093)
PHONE..................................972 516-4210
Miika Makitalo, *CEO*
John Upham, *President*
Craig Hawker, *Partner*
Scott Erickson, *Chairman*
Greg Milliken, *Senior VP*
EMP: 500
SALES (est): 2.1MM
SALES (corp-wide): 69.9MM **Privately Held**
WEB: www.m-files.com
SIC: 7372 Business oriented computer software
PA: M-Files Oy
Hermiankatu 1b
Tampere 33720
331 387-500

(G-16915)
MACADAMIA BEAUTY LLC (PA)
Also Called: Macadamia Natural Oil
5340 Legacy Dr Ste 180 (75024-3359)
PHONE..................................800 807-3950
Henry Stein, *CEO*
Scott Hagstrom, *COO*
Lori Chase, *Vice Pres*
Jennifer Chang, *Buyer*
Christopher Stubbins, *Manager*
▲ EMP: 21
SQ FT: 6,500
SALES (est): 13.5MM **Privately Held**
WEB: www.macadamiahair.com
SIC: 2844 Hair preparations, including shampoos; shampoos, rinses, conditioners: hair; hair coloring preparations

(G-16916)
MACGMC LLC
Also Called: Lone Star Iron Doors
6121 W Park Blvd Ste C226 (75093-6263)
PHONE..................................214 774-4455
Matthew Clements, *Mng Member*
EMP: 10
SALES (est): 843.6K **Privately Held**
WEB: www.lonestarirondoors.com
SIC: 3442 5211 Shutters, door or window: metal; door & window products

(G-16917)
MACH SPEED HOLDINGS LLC
Also Called: Apollo Brands
7200 Bishop Rd Ste 280 (75024-3639)
PHONE..................................214 978-3800
Lawrence Mondry, *CEO*
Douglas Lane, *COO*
Jerry Kollar, *CFO*
Aaron Womack, *CFO*
Rick Baldwin,
EMP: 75 EST: 2011
SQ FT: 9,000
SALES (est): 1MM **Privately Held**
WEB: www.tcplp.com
SIC: 3679 5091 5065 Headphones, radio; sporting & recreation goods; electronic parts & equipment
PA: Transition Capital Partners Lp
2100 Mckinney Ave # 1501
Dallas TX 75201

(G-16918)
MANDERSCHEID INC
Also Called: Advantage Machine & Mfg
910 10th St (75074-6826)
PHONE..................................972 424-8701
Cari Manderscheid, *President*
Gregory Manderscheid, *Vice Pres*
EMP: 12
SQ FT: 10,000
SALES (est): 1.1MM **Privately Held**
WEB: www.advantagemachine.com
SIC: 3599 Machine shop, jobbing & repair

(G-16919)
MARTIN UAV LLC (PA)
5345 Towne Square Dr # 115 (75024-2449)
PHONE..................................972 381-2750
Ruben Martin, *CEO*
Tae Kim, *COO*
Mike Moody, *Engineer*
Erin Stanwix, *Human Res Mgr*
Wayne McAuliffe, *Surgery Dir*
EMP: 25
SQ FT: 18,000
SALES (est): 4.4MM **Privately Held**
WEB: www.martinuav.com
SIC: 3721 Motorized aircraft; research & development on aircraft by the manufacturer

(G-16920)
MAUI FOODS INTERNATIONAL INC
Also Called: Maxime International Foods
2901 Summit Ave Ste 400 (75074-7468)
PHONE..................................214 823-6284
Allan L Feinstein, *President*
Jeremy Scharf, *Vice Pres*
▼ EMP: 28
SALES (est): 5.6MM **Privately Held**
WEB: www.mauifoods.net
SIC: 2099 Food preparations

(G-16921)
MCAFEE LLC
5000 Headquarters Dr (75024-5826)
PHONE..................................972 963-7000
Doug Sabulsky, *Engineer*
Rick Moffitt, *Sales Staff*
David G Dewalt, *Branch Mgr*
Sailendra Mishra, *Manager*
Nick Pagnotta, *Manager*
EMP: 950 **Privately Held**
WEB: www.mcafee.com
SIC: 7372 Prepackaged software
HQ: Mcafee, Llc
6220 America Center Dr
San Jose CA 95002

(G-16922)
MCAFEE PUBLIC SECTOR LLC
5000 Headquarters Dr (75024-5826)
PHONE..................................972 963-7000
EMP: 11 **Privately Held**
WEB: www.intel.com
SIC: 7372 Application computer software
HQ: Mcafee Public Sector Llc
6220 America Center Dr
San Jose CA 95002
888 847-8766

(G-16923)
MCDOWELL PACKG & ADVG CO INC
Also Called: McDowell Label
2700 E Plano Pkwy (75074-7417)
PHONE..................................469 246-2700
Mike Apperson, *CEO*
John McDowell, *President*
Thomas Goode, *Prdtn Mgr*
Wendell Wendellskeen, *Manager*
Bobbi Foster, *Supervisor*
EMP: 52
SQ FT: 45,000
SALES (est): 12.9MM **Privately Held**
WEB: www.mcdowelllabel.com
SIC: 2672 2759 2679 2671 Labels (unprinted), gummed: made from purchased materials; tape, pressure sensitive: made from purchased materials; labels & seals: printing; labels, paper: made from purchased material; packaging paper & plastics film, coated & laminated; automotive & apparel trimmings
PA: Resource Label Group, Llc
147 Seaboard Ln
Franklin TN 37067

(G-16924)
MEDASSETS INC
5543 Legacy Dr (75024-3502)
PHONE..................................972 813-7500
EMP: 1000
SALES (corp-wide): 720.2MM **Publicly Held**
SIC: 7372 Prepackaged Software Services

PA: Medassets, Inc.
200 N Point Ctr E Ste 200
Alpharetta GA 75062
678 323-2500

(G-16925)
MEDHOST INC
6100 W Plano Pkwy # 3100 (75093-8342)
PHONE..............................972 560-3100
Craig Herrod, *President*
Dee Hubble, *Engineer*
Jeb Sims, *Engineer*
Tim Thomas, *Engineer*
Doug Stewart, *CFO*
EMP: 160
SQ FT: 13,000
SALES (est): 15.2MM **Privately Held**
WEB: www.medhost.com
SIC: 7372 Prepackaged software
PA: Healthtech Holdings, Inc.
3102 West End Ave Ste 400
Nashville TN 37203

(G-16926)
MI T FINE CAR WASH INC
1614 Custer Rd (75075-6632)
PHONE..............................972 422-0707
Belgie Luna, *Manager*
EMP: 20
SQ FT: 8,915
SALES (corp-wide): 11.7MM **Privately Held**
WEB: www.mitfinecarwash.com
SIC: 3589 7542 Car washing machinery; washing & polishing, automotive
PA: Mi T Fine Car Wash Inc
1902 Parkside Ave
Irving TX 75061
972 438-3416

(G-16927)
MICRON VISION CORPORATION
811 E Plano Pkwy Ste 113 (75074-6860)
PHONE..............................281 546-9632
Ying Ying Wood, *Principal*
EMP: 12
SALES (est): 1.6MM **Privately Held**
SIC: 3674 Semiconductors & related devices

(G-16928)
MICROTUNE INC (DH)
2201 10th St (75074-8019)
PHONE..............................972 673-1600
James A Fontaine, *President*
Barry F Koch, *Exec VP*
Robert S Kirk, *Vice Pres*
Justin M Chapman, *CFO*
Jennifer Clark, *Director*
▲ **EMP:** 18
SQ FT: 44,000
SALES (est): 17MM
SALES (corp-wide): 23.5B **Publicly Held**
WEB: www.microtune.com
SIC: 3674 Semiconductors & related devices
HQ: Zoran Corporation
1060 Rincon Cir
San Jose CA 95131
972 673-1600

(G-16929)
MINGTEL INC
Also Called: Azpen Innovation
4108 W Spring Creek Pkwy (75024-5233)
P.O. Box 261962 (75026-1962)
PHONE..............................972 378-5559
Yuet Ko Wu, *President*
Mike Glasscock, *Opers Staff*
Andy Alfaro, *Director*
▲ **EMP:** 10
SQ FT: 2,500
SALES (est): 9.4MM **Privately Held**
WEB: www.azpenpc.com
SIC: 3571 Personal computers (microcomputers)

(G-16930)
MINORITY OPPORTUNITY NEWS INC
1100 Summit Ave Ste 1201 (75074-8551)
P.O. Box 940226 (75094-0226)
PHONE..............................972 516-4191
Threman Jones, *President*
▲ **EMP:** 10 **EST:** 2001

SALES (est): 387.6K **Privately Held**
SIC: 2711 Newspapers, publishing & printing

(G-16931)
MITEL NETWORKS INC
5360 Legacy Dr Ste 300 (75024-3135)
PHONE..............................469 365-3000
Richard McBee, *Branch Mgr*
EMP: 21
SALES (corp-wide): 1B **Privately Held**
WEB: www.mitel.com
SIC: 3661 7629 Switching equipment, telephone; telecommunication equipment repair (except telephones)
HQ: Mitel Networks, Inc.
1146 N Alma School Rd
Mesa AZ 85201

(G-16932)
MOLSON COORS BEV CO USA LLC
7800 Dallas Pkwy Ste 400 (75024-0025)
PHONE..............................214 618-7400
Jeff Culver, *Vice Pres*
EMP: 182
SALES (corp-wide): 9.6B **Publicly Held**
WEB: www.molsoncoors.com
SIC: 2082 Beer (alcoholic beverage)
HQ: Molson Coors Beverage Company Usa Llc
250 S Wacker Dr Ste 800
Chicago IL 60606
312 496-2700

(G-16933)
MORGAN NEWTON COMPANY LP
3401 Wynwood Dr (75074-8306)
PHONE..............................972 212-8080
William Boyd, *President*
Morgan Newton Operating Compan, *Partner*
Jamey Boyd, *Vice Pres*
Gabriel Njoku, *Opers Mgr*
Ledayne Morris, *Production*
EMP: 78
SALES (est): 22.1MM **Privately Held**
WEB: www.morgannewton.com
SIC: 3672 Printed circuit boards

(G-16934)
MOTTS LLP (HQ)
Also Called: Motts
5301 Legacy Dr (75024-3109)
P.O. Box 869077 (75086-9077)
PHONE..............................972 673-8088
◆ **EMP:** 250 **EST:** 1994
SQ FT: 160,000
SALES (est): 216.4MM **Publicly Held**
WEB: www.motts.com
SIC: 2033 5149 2087 Fruit juices: packaged in cans, jars, etc.; apple sauce: packaged in cans, jars, etc.; beverage concentrates; cocktail mixes, nonalcoholic

(G-16935)
MPI MARKETING INC
Also Called: Mpi Wood
3308 Preston Rd Ste 350 (75093-7471)
PHONE..............................972 403-7801
Glenn R Kolodny, *President*
Katie Kolodny, *Vice Pres*
▲ **EMP:** 30 **EST:** 2000
SQ FT: 1,500
SALES (est): 8.5MM **Privately Held**
WEB: www.mpiwood.com
SIC: 2541 Display fixtures, wood

(G-16936)
MURCHISON OIL AND GAS INC
7250 Dallas Pkwy Ste 1400 (75024-5002)
PHONE..............................972 931-0700
Robert Pavewell Speer, *President*
J D Murchison, *Chairman*
Michael Daugherty, *COO*
Jack G Rankin, *Vice Pres*
Jack Rankin, *Vice Pres*
EMP: 33
SQ FT: 12,000
SALES (est): 8.7MM
SALES (corp-wide): 10.9MM **Privately Held**
WEB: www.murchisonoil.com
SIC: 1382 Oil & gas exploration services

PA: J.D. Murchison Interests, Inc.
7250 Dallas Pkwy
Plano TX 75024
972 931-0700

(G-16937)
MUSTANG TECHNOLOGY GROUP LP
Also Called: L-3 Mustang Technology
6900 K Ave (75074-2527)
PHONE..............................972 747-0707
EMP: 115 **EST:** 1999
SQ FT: 57,000
SALES (est): 28.2MM
SALES (corp-wide): 11.3B **Publicly Held**
WEB: www.l3t.com
SIC: 3812 Radar systems & equipment
HQ: L3 Technologies, Inc.
600 3rd Ave Fl 34
New York NY 10016
212 805-5234

(G-16938)
NACCO INDUSTRIES INC
5340 Legacy Dr Ste 300 (75024-3141)
PHONE..............................440 449-9600
Mary D Maloney, *Branch Mgr*
EMP: 30
SALES (corp-wide): 140.9MM **Publicly Held**
WEB: www.nacco.com
SIC: 3537 Industrial trucks & tractors
PA: Nacco Industries, Inc.
5875 Landerbrook Dr # 220
Cleveland OH 44124
440 229-5151

(G-16939)
NATURES FINEST LLC
4701 Old Shepard Pl Frnt (75093-5298)
PHONE..............................972 673-1526
▲ **EMP:** 30
SQ FT: 27,800
SALES (est): 3.4MM
SALES (corp-wide): 140.4MM **Privately Held**
SIC: 3999 Mfg Misc Products
PA: Rug Doctor, Llc
4701 Old Shepard Pl Frnt
Plano TX 75075
972 673-1400

(G-16940)
NAVISTAR INC
5850 Granite Pkwy Ste 760 (75024-6769)
PHONE..............................972 377-1217
Sean Carmichael, *Vice Pres*
EMP: 20
SALES (corp-wide): 7.5B **Publicly Held**
WEB: www.internationaltrucks.com
SIC: 3711 3713 Truck & tractor truck assembly; truck & bus bodies
HQ: Navistar, Inc.
2701 Navistar Dr
Lisle IL 60532
331 332-5000

(G-16941)
NEOSEN ENERGY LLC
2637 Summit Ave 301 (75074-7432)
PHONE..............................972 422-0722
Paul Garrity, *Mng Member*
EMP: 10 **EST:** 2014
SALES (est): 699.2K **Privately Held**
WEB: www.neosenenergy.com
SIC: 3661 Telephones & telephone apparatus

(G-16942)
NEOTEK ENERGY INC
2600 Tech Dr Ste 400 (75074)
PHONE..............................469 206-3344
Charles Stuewe, *CEO*
Lanny G Schoeling, *Vice Pres*
Lanny Schoeling, *Vice Pres*
Doug Weiner, *Vice Pres*
Scott Ito, *Mfg Staff*
EMP: 19 **EST:** 2011
SALES (est): 3.3MM **Privately Held**
WEB: www.neotekenergy.com
SIC: 8711 1389 Engineering services; testing, measuring, surveying & analysis services

(G-16943)
NETRAKE CORPORATION
1255 W 15th St Ste 200 (75075-7263)
PHONE..............................214 291-1000
Bruce Hill, *President*
Robert Maher, *Senior VP*
Mark Neider, *VP Mktg*
EMP: 70
SQ FT: 21,000
SALES (est): 7.1MM **Privately Held**
SIC: 3674 Computer logic modules

(G-16944)
NEWLINE INTERACTIVE INC (PA)
101 E Park Blvd Ste 807 (75074-8808)
PHONE..............................972 468-9728
Kevin Wang, *CEO*
Chris Bradford, *President*
Ty Hall, *Vice Pres*
Mark Schade, *Technical Mgr*
Chelsea Wolfe, *Accountant*
▲ **EMP:** 10
SQ FT: 5,000
SALES (est): 1.7MM **Privately Held**
WEB: www.newline-interactive.com
SIC: 3577 3679 3823 Graphic displays, except graphic terminals; liquid crystal displays (LCD); digital displays of process variables

(G-16945)
NITRO FIBER LLC
2801 Tech Dr Ste 157 (75074)
PHONE..............................888 906-4202
David M Juring, *Mng Member*
EMP: 11
SALES (est): 1.7MM **Privately Held**
WEB: www.nitrofiber.com
SIC: 3315 Barbed & twisted wire

(G-16946)
NORTH AMERICAN COAL CORP (HQ)
5340 Legacy Dr Ste 300 (75024-3141)
PHONE..............................972 448-5400
JC Butler Jr, *CEO*
Bob Benson, *President*
Alfred M Rankin, *Chairman*
Andy Hawkins, *Business Mgr*
Michael J Gregory, *Vice Pres*
▲ **EMP:** 55
SQ FT: 23,520
SALES (est): 596.1MM
SALES (corp-wide): 140.9MM **Publicly Held**
WEB: www.nacoal.com
SIC: 1221 Bituminous coal & lignite-surface mining
PA: Nacco Industries, Inc.
5875 Landerbrook Dr # 220
Cleveland OH 44124
440 229-5151

(G-16947)
NSG CORPORATION (PA)
Also Called: Cheerleader & Danzteam
640 Shiloh Rd 2 (75074-7256)
P.O. Box 660359, Dallas (75266-0359)
PHONE..............................972 840-1233
Jeff Webb, *President*
Buffy Duhon, *General Mgr*
John Nichols, *CFO*
Joel Hallford, *Controller*
Debra Garret, *Manager*
EMP: 135
SQ FT: 57,392
SALES (est): 39.1MM **Privately Held**
WEB: www.varsity.com
SIC: 2329 2339 Men's & boys' athletic uniforms; uniforms, athletic: women's, misses' & juniors'

(G-16948)
NTT DATA INC (DH)
7950 Legacy Dr Ste 900 (75024-0235)
PHONE..............................800 745-3263
EMP: 199 **EST:** 1967
SQ FT: 73,000
SALES (est): 1.3B **Privately Held**
WEB: www.nttdata.com
SIC: 7372 7379 7373 Prepackaged software; computer related consulting services; systems software development services

(G-16949)
NUVECTRA CORPORATION (PA)
Also Called: Algostim
5830 Gran Pkwy Ste 1100 (75024)
PHONE..................................214 474-3103
Fred B Parks, *CEO*
J Paul Hanchin, *President*
Jennifer Kosharek, *CFO*
Mike Hays, *Sales Dir*
Lyndsie Olson, *Business Anlyst*
EMP: 93
SALES: 48.8MM **Publicly Held**
WEB: www.nuvectramed.com
SIC: 3841 Surgical instruments & apparatus

(G-16950)
NUVINAIR LLC
5851 Legacy Cir Ste 600 (75024-5969)
PHONE..................................844 984-6247
Kyle A Bailey,
EMP: 20 EST: 2015
SALES (est): 2.4MM **Privately Held**
WEB: www.nuvinair.com
SIC: 2842 Automobile polish

(G-16951)
NUZEE INC
1401 Capital Ave Ste B (75074-1202)
PHONE..................................760 295-2408
Masateru Higashida, *Ch of Bd*
Travis Gorney, *President*
Shanoop Kothari, *COO*
EMP: 24
SALES: 1.4MM **Privately Held**
WEB: www.mynuzee.com
SIC: 2095 5499 Roasted coffee; coffee extracts; instant coffee; coffee

(G-16952)
OCTAL INC
4975 Preston Park Blvd # 850
(75093-3630)
PHONE..................................972 985-4370
William Barenberg, *COO*
Joe Barenberg, *COO*
Mark Hunt, *Vice Pres*
Sean Brown, *Opers Dir*
Marie Nduli, *Opers Staff*
▲ EMP: 13
SALES (est): 10.6MM
SALES (corp-wide): 11.3MM **Privately Held**
WEB: www.packexpo.com
SIC: 5162 2821 Plastics resins; acrylic resins
PA: Octal Holding
Next To Nissan Showroom, Al Rawaq Building Salalah Free Zone
Muscat 112
220 307-17

(G-16953)
OLD FRITO-LAY INC
7701 Legacy Dr (75024-4002)
P.O. Box 660634, Dallas (75266-0634)
PHONE..................................972 334-7000
Thomas Greco, *CEO*
Albert P Carey, *President*
Marc Guay, *President*
Ted Herrod, *Senior VP*
Ram Krishnan, *Senior VP*
◆ EMP: 39870
SQ FT: 550,000
SALES (est): 228.8MM
SALES (corp-wide): 67.1B **Publicly Held**
WEB: www.fritolay.com
SIC: 2096 2052 2013 5812 Potato chips & similar snacks; potato chips & other potato-based snacks; tortilla chips; corn chips & other corn-based snacks; cookies; snack sticks, including jerky: from purchased meat; fast-food restaurant, chain; chicken restaurant; franchises, selling or licensing; soft drinks: packaged in cans, bottles, etc.
HQ: Frito-Lay North America, Inc.
7701 Legacy Dr
Plano TX 75024

(G-16954)
ONEIL DIGITAL SOLUTIONS LLC (HQ)
Also Called: Oneil Data Systems
3100 E Plano Pkwy (75074-7423)
P.O. Box 941507 (75094-1507)
PHONE..................................972 881-1282
Elizabeth Smith, *Controller*
▲ EMP: 411 EST: 2011
SALES (est): 67.1MM
SALES (corp-wide): 254.6MM **Privately Held**
SIC: 7389 2752 5045 Mailbox rental & related service; commercial printing, lithographic; computer software
PA: Data Analysis Inc.
12655 Beatrice St
Los Angeles CA 90066
310 448-6800

(G-16955)
OPTECONN LP
Also Called: Optical Cabling Systems
2621 Summit Ave Ste 100 (75074-3705)
PHONE..................................972 331-4627
Rick Hobbs, *Senior VP*
Tom Carmody, *Accounts Mgr*
Kieran McGrath,
EMP: 139
SQ FT: 26,000
SALES (est): 19.5MM **Privately Held**
WEB: www.opticalcablingsys.com
SIC: 3229 Fiber optics strands

(G-16956)
OPTICAL CABLE CORPORATION
1700 Capital Ave (75074-1203)
PHONE..................................972 509-1500
Rick Hobbs, *Business Mgr*
Daniel Vance, *Sales Staff*
EMP: 30
SALES (corp-wide): 55.2MM **Publicly Held**
WEB: www.occfiber.com
SIC: 3357 3351 Fiber optic cable (insulated); wire, copper & copper alloy
PA: Optical Cable Corporation
5290 Concourse Dr
Roanoke VA 24019
540 265-0690

(G-16957)
OPTICAL CABLING SYSTEMS LC
2621 Summit Ave Ste 100 (75074-3705)
PHONE..................................972 331-4627
Kevin Ehringer, *President*
EMP: 45
SQ FT: 20,000
SALES (est): 4.4MM **Privately Held**
WEB: www.opticalcablingsys.com
SIC: 3229 3315 Fiber optics strands; steel wire & related products

(G-16958)
ORANO MED LLC
700 Klein Rd (75074-7440)
PHONE..................................301 841-1673
Patrick Bourdet, *President*
Alison Tise, *Project Mgr*
William Wilde,
EMP: 9 EST: 2009
SQ FT: 2,000
SALES (est): 1.6MM
SALES (corp-wide): 4.2MM **Privately Held**
WEB: www.macrocyclics.com
SIC: 2834 Pharmaceutical preparations
HQ: Framatome Inc.
3315 Old Forest Rd
Lynchburg VA 24501

(G-16959)
ORTHORX INC (DH)
Also Called: Texas Orthotics
5204 Tennyson Pkwy # 100 (75024-7116)
PHONE..................................214 501-0180
Tracy Peterson, *Principal*
EMP: 13
SALES (est): 4MM **Privately Held**
SIC: 3842 Orthopedic appliances
HQ: Viscent Orthpd Solutions Llc
2885 Loker Ave E
Carlsbad CA 92010
214 501-0180

(G-16960)
OWEN-BUNNELL INC
Also Called: Ob Cues
961 N Ave Ste 700 (75074-8683)
PHONE..................................972 578-9100
Shane Sinnott, *President*
EMP: 10
SALES (est): 1MM **Privately Held**
WEB: www.obcues.com
SIC: 3949 Billiard & pool equipment & supplies, general

(G-16961)
OWENS-BROCKWAY GLASS CONT INC
FIC Export
5200 Tennyson Pkwy # 100 (75024-7151)
PHONE..................................956 717-4200
Gerardo Cardenas, *Warehouse Mgr*
Ronald Hinojosa, *Traffic Mgr*
Jean Reynolds, *Inv Control Mgr*
Leigh Slade, *Credit Mgr*
Tabitha Burrus, *Hum Res Coord*
EMP: 21
SALES (corp-wide): 6.6B **Publicly Held**
WEB: www.o-i.com
SIC: 3221 Glass containers
HQ: Owens-Brockway Glass Container Inc.
1 Michael Owens Way
Perrysburg OH 43551

(G-16962)
OXIDOR CORPORATION INC
1825 E Plano Pkwy Ste 160 (75074-8570)
PHONE..................................972 424-6422
Terry Brown, *President*
Homer Youngblood, *Cust Mgr*
Chambless William, *Director*
Lonnie Buckaloo, *Technician*
EMP: 15
SQ FT: 12,000
SALES (est): 1.7MM **Privately Held**
WEB: www.oxidor.com
SIC: 8731 1081 Environmental research; metal mining services

(G-16963)
PACKAGING CORPORATION AMERICA
Also Called: PCA/Plano 374
1800 E Plano Pkwy (75074-8128)
P.O. Box 940089 (75094-0089)
PHONE..................................972 422-4270
Vance Moore, *Plant Mgr*
Julie Haynie, *Project Mgr*
Keith Strickland, *QC Mgr*
Nick Miller, *Branch Mgr*
EMP: 110
SQ FT: 35,000
SALES (corp-wide): 6.9B **Publicly Held**
WEB: www.packagingcorp.com
SIC: 2653 Boxes, corrugated: made from purchased materials
PA: Packaging Corporation Of America
1 N Field Ct
Lake Forest IL 60045
847 482-3000

(G-16964)
PAN-AMERICA HYPERBARICS INC
1607 Capital Ave (75074-8154)
P.O. Box 851104, Richardson (75085-1104)
PHONE..................................972 423-0377
Shin-Ban Tsai, *President*
Pauli Chang, *Sales Staff*
Barry Baker, *Mktg Dir*
◆ EMP: 14
SQ FT: 9,000
SALES (est): 1.5MM **Privately Held**
WEB: www.panamericahbo.com
SIC: 3841 Oxygen tents

(G-16965)
PAPER SOURCE INC
1900 Preston Rd Ste 211 (75093-5137)
PHONE..................................469 304-5168
EMP: 9
SALES (corp-wide): 64.3MM **Privately Held**
WEB: www.papersource.com
SIC: 5113 2621 Paper & products, wrapping or coarse; paper mills

HQ: Paper Source, Inc.
125 S Clark St Fl 15
Chicago IL 60603
888 727-3711

(G-16966)
PARSEC TECHNOLOGIES INC
820 Jupiter Rd (75074-7464)
PHONE..................................972 804-4600
Michael Neenan, *President*
Chris Friend, *Vice Pres*
Kim Kuiper, *CFO*
Jen Neenan, *Marketing Staff*
Jennifer Neenan, *Marketing Staff*
EMP: 15
SALES (est): 852.2K **Privately Held**
WEB: www.parsec-t.com
SIC: 3679 3663 Electronic circuits; antennas, transmitting & communications

(G-16967)
PEPSI LOGISTICS COMPANY INC
Also Called: Plci
5600 Headquarters Dr (75024-5838)
PHONE..................................972 963-1920
Philip Marineau, *President*
EMP: 135
SALES (est): 62.6MM
SALES (corp-wide): 67.1B **Publicly Held**
WEB: www.pepsilogistics.com
SIC: 2086 Carbonated soft drinks, bottled & canned
PA: Pepsico, Inc.
700 Anderson Hill Rd
Purchase NY 10577
914 253-2000

(G-16968)
PEPSI-COLA METRO BTLG CO INC
7701 Legacy Dr (75024-4002)
PHONE..................................972 801-1730
Christopher Mountain, *Finance*
Jim Richard, *Manager*
Sayaka Makishima, *Manager*
EMP: 45
SQ FT: 20,292
SALES (corp-wide): 67.1B **Publicly Held**
WEB: www.pepsico.com
SIC: 2086 Carbonated soft drinks, bottled & canned
HQ: Pepsi-Cola Metropolitan Bottling Company, Inc.
1111 Westchester Ave
White Plains NY 10604
914 767-6000

(G-16969)
PEPSICO INC
5600 Headquarters Dr (75024-5838)
PHONE..................................972 963-1000
Mohan Komanduri, *Vice Pres*
Karen Breuer, *Project Mgr*
Rob Coleman, *Project Mgr*
Ben Mayfield, *Project Mgr*
Lisa Stelly, *Project Mgr*
EMP: 58
SALES (corp-wide): 67.1B **Publicly Held**
WEB: www.pepsico.com
SIC: 2096 2087 2086 2037 Potato chips & similar snacks; corn chips & other corn-based snacks; potato chips & other potato-based snacks; cheese curls & puffs; flavoring extracts & syrups; syrups, drink; fruit juices: concentrated for fountain use; concentrates, drink; bottled & canned soft drinks; iced tea & fruit drinks, bottled & canned; soft drinks: packaged in cans, bottles, etc.; carbonated beverages, non-alcoholic: bottled & canned; fruit juices; cookies & crackers; cereal breakfast foods; oatmeal: prepared as cereal breakfast food
PA: Pepsico, Inc.
700 Anderson Hill Rd
Purchase NY 10577
914 253-2000

(G-16970)
PEPSICO INC
7701 Legacy Dr (75024-4002)
P.O. Box 660740, Dallas (75266-0740)
PHONE..................................972 334-4140
Kevin Rogers, *Business Mgr*
Azeem Ansari, *Vice Pres*

Tina Bigalke, *Vice Pres*
Guidry Chris, *Plant Mgr*
David Cody, *Mfg Spvr*
EMP: 58
SALES (corp-wide): 67.1B **Publicly Held**
WEB: www.pepsico.com
SIC: 2086 Carbonated soft drinks, bottled
& canned
PA: Pepsico, Inc.
700 Anderson Hill Rd
Purchase NY 10577
914 253-2000

(G-16971)
PETROTEL INC (PA)
Also Called: Petrotel USA
5240 Tennyson Pkwy # 207　(75024-3544)
PHONE..........................972 473-2767
Anil Chopra, *President*
Vishal Chopra, *Treasurer*
Marisol Chopra, *Financial Exec*
Arisol Chopra, *Director*
EMP: 14
SALES (est): 10.6MM **Privately Held**
WEB: www.petrotel.com
SIC: 1382 4925 Oil & gas exploration
services; gas production and/or distribu-
tion

(G-16972)
PLANO ACQUISITION LLC
3601 E Plano Pkwy Ste 200　(75074-1827)
PHONE..........................214 343-0131
Jeff Wanago, *Exec Dir*
Jeff Diora,
EMP: 142
SALES (est): 3.9MM
SALES (corp-wide): 59MM **Privately
Held**
SIC: 3672 Printed circuit boards
PA: Virtex Enterprises, Lp
12234 N Interstate 35
Austin TX 78753
512 835-6772

(G-16973)
PLANO DOOR SERVICE INC
1100 N Central Expy Ste A　(75074-6873)
PHONE..........................972 422-1695
Philip Mc Gregor, *President*
EMP: 11
SALES (est): 1.5MM **Privately Held**
WEB: www.planooverhead.com
SIC: 2434 7699 Wood kitchen cabinets;
general household repair services

(G-16974)
**PLANO SPORTS SOCCER INC
(PA)**
Also Called: Soccer Corner, The
1820 Coit Rd Ste 125　(75075-5035)
PHONE..........................972 519-0222
Donald Willard, *President*
Beth Brown-Smith, *Store Mgr*
Karen Meyer, *Marketing Staff*
Amy Harris, *Manager*
Mark Robinson, *Manager*
EMP: 15
SQ FT: 8,800
SALES: 10.8MM **Privately Held**
WEB: www.thesoccercorner.com
SIC: 5941 5091 2395 Soccer supplies;
sporting & recreation goods; embroidery
& art needlework

(G-16975)
PPG INDUSTRIES INC
Also Called: PPG 8331
909 W Spring Creek Pkwy # 330
(75023-4478)
PHONE..........................972 517-2226
Zakir Raza, *Branch Mgr*
EMP: 24
SALES (corp-wide): 15.3B **Publicly Held**
WEB: www.ppg.com
SIC: 2851 Paints & allied products
PA: Ppg Industries, Inc.
1 Ppg Pl
Pittsburgh PA 15272
412 434-3131

(G-16976)
PRECISION TECHNOLOGY INC
3601 E Plano Pkwy Ste 200　(75074-1827)
PHONE..........................214 343-0131
Atul Patel, *CEO*

Vithal Diora, *President*
Cynthia Form, *Project Mgr*
Gary Davis, *Sales Dir*
Johnnie Feathers, *Sales Dir*
▲ **EMP:** 142
SQ FT: 40,000
SALES (est): 20MM **Privately Held**
WEB: www.ptiassembly.com
SIC: 3672 Printed circuit boards

(G-16977)
PRINT PREMIUM
555 Republic Dr Ste 200　(75074-5469)
PHONE..........................972 292-7227
EMP: 39
SALES (est): 2.1MM **Privately Held**
SIC: 2752 Commercial printing, litho-
graphic

(G-16978)
**PRO CONNECT TECHNOLOGY
LLC**
1700 Capital Ave　(75074-1203)
PHONE..........................972 543-2603
Bret L Burdette,
EMP: 12
SALES (est): 1.1MM **Privately Held**
SIC: 3643 Current-carrying wiring devices

(G-16979)
PROCAM CONTROLS INC
Also Called: Filters Express
2605 Tech Dr Ste 300　(75074)
PHONE..........................972 422-1212
William C Overman, *CEO*
Roy Seibert, *President*
▼ **EMP:** 20
SALES (est): 12.7MM **Privately Held**
WEB: www.optipurewater.com
SIC: 5085 3589 Filters, industrial; water fil-
ters & softeners, household type
HQ: Aquion, Inc.
101 S Gary Ave Unit A
Roselle IL 60172

(G-16980)
PROCERA NETWORKS INC (HQ)
5800 Granite Pkwy Ste 170　(75024-6500)
PHONE..........................510 230-2777
Lyndon Cantor, *CEO*
Andrew Kowal, *President*
Mark Driedger, *COO*
Andy Lovit, *Senior VP*
Tom Carter, *Vice Pres*
▲ **EMP:** 47
SALES (est): 27.1MM **Privately Held**
WEB: www.proceranetworks.com
SIC: 7372 7371 Prepackaged software;
computer software development
PA: Kdr Holding, Inc.
47448 Fremont Blvd
Fremont CA 94538
510 230-2777

(G-16981)
PYSZ ENTERPRISES INC
Also Called: Signature Stair Parts
2305 Trellis Ln　(75075-3527)
PHONE..........................972 964-3980
Kenneth Pysz, *President*
Bernard Pysz, *Vice Pres*
EMP: 10 **EST:** 1991
SALES (est): 1MM **Privately Held**
SIC: 3446 Stairs, staircases, stair treads:
prefabricated metal

(G-16982)
R T L X LLC (DH)
6100 Tennyson Pkwy # 150　(75024-6101)
PHONE..........................214 778-6400
EMP: 50
SQ FT: 10,000
SALES (est): 6.4MM **Privately Held**
SIC: 7372 Computer Software And Profes-
sional Services

(G-16983)
R&D FUTURES LLC
Also Called: Wood House Bay Spa Plano
5760 Legacy Dr Ste B14　(75024-7199)
PHONE..........................214 473-9955
Robin Bray, *Mng Member*
EMP: 25
SALES (est): 1.7MM **Privately Held**
WEB: www.woodhousespas.com
SIC: 7991 2844 Spas; toilet preparations

(G-16984)
RAYTHEON COMPANY
1309 Harvest Glen Dr　(75023-6732)
PHONE..........................781 522-3000
Brian Moore, *Principal*
EMP: 170
SALES (corp-wide): 56.5B **Publicly Held**
WEB: www.rtx.com
SIC: 3812 Defense systems & equipment
HQ: Raytheon Company
870 Winter St
Waltham MA 02451
781 522-3000

(G-16985)
RAYTHEON COMPANY
3400 Louis Dr　(75023-1114)
PHONE..........................972 205-8846
EMP: 170
SALES (corp-wide): 56.5B **Publicly Held**
WEB: www.rtx.com
SIC: 3812 Defense systems & equipment
HQ: Raytheon Company
870 Winter St
Waltham MA 02451
781 522-3000

(G-16986)
RAYTHEON COMPANY
6600 Chase Oaks Blvd　(75023-2381)
PHONE..........................972 344-2591
William Swanson, *CEO*
EMP: 500
SALES (corp-wide): 56.5B **Publicly Held**
WEB: www.rtx.com
SIC: 3812 Defense systems & equipment
HQ: Raytheon Company
870 Winter St
Waltham MA 02451
781 522-3000

(G-16987)
RAYTHEON COMPANY
6625 Excellence Way　(75023-1201)
P.O. Box 660246, Dallas　(75266-0246)
PHONE..........................781 522-3000
Dan Perlman, *CEO*
Patricia Garcia, *Vice Pres*
Abbas Torabi, *Vice Pres*
Matthew Letterman, *Buyer*
Brandon Pillans, *Research*
EMP: 500
SALES (corp-wide): 56.5B **Publicly Held**
WEB: www.rtx.com
SIC: 3812 Sonar systems & equipment
HQ: Raytheon Company
870 Winter St
Waltham MA 02451
781 522-3000

(G-16988)
RAYTHEON COMPANY
4101 E Plano Pkwy　(75074-1814)
PHONE..........................877 291-9990
Brent Leppke, *Chief*
William Wilkinson, *Controller*
Stacy Chapman, *Human Res Mgr*
Bill Werner, *Branch Mgr*
Kenneth Wright, *Program Mgr*
EMP: 50
SALES (corp-wide): 56.5B **Publicly Held**
WEB: www.rtx.com
SIC: 3812 Defense systems & equipment
HQ: Raytheon Company
870 Winter St
Waltham MA 02451
781 522-3000

(G-16989)
RC DONUTS
700 W Spring Creek Pkwy　(75023-4623)
PHONE..........................972 422-3379
Seung C Lee, *Principal*
EMP: 9
SALES (est): 826.1K **Privately Held**
SIC: 2051 5461 Doughnuts, except
frozen; doughnuts

(G-16990)
**REGAL RESEARCH AND MFG
CO LLC**
Also Called: Solorider Golf Carts
1200 N Plano Pkwy　(75074-8522)
P.O. Box 940529　(75094-0529)
PHONE..........................972 494-0359
Gayle Glosser, *President*

Michael D Powell, *Exec VP*
Brian Imbler, *Vice Pres*
Gus Garcia, *Purch Mgr*
Phillip Speicher, *CFO*
◆ **EMP:** 200 **EST:** 1980
SQ FT: 193,000
SALES (est): 42.2MM **Privately Held**
WEB: www.regalresearch.com
SIC: 3679 3444 Electronic circuits; sheet
metalwork

(G-16991)
**REPUBLIC TITLE OF TEXAS INC
(DH)**
2701 W Plano Pkwy Ste 100　(75075-8211)
PHONE..........................972 578-8611
William A Kramer, *Ch of Bd*
Michelle Angelis, *President*
Evangela Furnace, *President*
Rosemary Grajeda, *President*
Jamar Lindsey, *President*
EMP: 175
SQ FT: 20,000
SALES (est): 171.1MM **Publicly Held**
WEB: www.republictitle.com
SIC: 6411 7372 6531 6541 Insurance
agents, brokers & service; prepackaged
software; real estate agents & managers;
title abstract offices
HQ: First American Title Insurance Com-
pany
1 First American Way
Santa Ana CA 92707
800 854-3643

(G-16992)
**REVENUE TECHNOLOGY SVCS
CORP (PA)**
Also Called: RTS
6404 Intl Pkwy 2000　(75093)
PHONE..........................972 573-1600
Pradeep Bandla, *Vice Pres*
Mukundh Parthasarathy, *Vice Pres*
Raja Kasilingam, *Director*
Jay Nanda, *Director*
EMP: 21
SQ FT: 4,500
SALES (est): 5.2MM **Privately Held**
WEB: www.rtscorp.com
SIC: 7372 Business oriented computer
software

(G-16993)
REVITALU INTERNATIONAL LLC
5830 Granite Pkwy Ste 110　(75024-6808)
PHONE..........................469 270-5533
Andrew McWilliams, *CEO*
EMP: 15
SALES (est): 4MM **Privately Held**
WEB: www.revitalu.com
SIC: 8742 7372 Marketing consulting
services; sales (including sales manage-
ment) consultant; application computer
software

(G-16994)
RICHARD ERIC LLC
1808 E Park Blvd　(75074-5143)
PHONE..........................214 477-5230
Akeem Phillips,
EMP: 10
SALES (est): 362.1K **Privately Held**
SIC: 3161 Clothing & apparel carrying
cases

(G-16995)
**ROCKY MOUNTAIN HIGH
BRANDS INC (PA)**
1000 Shiloh Rd Ste 200　(75074-7221)
PHONE..........................800 260-9062
Michael Welch, *Ch of Bd*
Charles Smith, *COO*
David Seeberger, *Vice Pres*
J Saldi, *VP Sls/Mktg*
Jens Mielke, *CFO*
EMP: 9
SALES: 205.2K **Publicly Held**
WEB: www.rockymountainhighbrands.com
SIC: 2086 Bottled & canned soft drinks;
iced tea & fruit drinks, bottled & canned;
fruit drinks (less than 100% juice): pack-
aged in cans, etc.

(G-16996)
ROLLING FRITO-LAY SALES LP
7701 Legacy Dr (75024-4002)
P.O. Box 1800, Winston Salem NC (27102-1800)
PHONE..............................972 334-2513
Tom Greco, *Partner*
Marc Kesselman, *Partner*
George Legge, *Partner*
EMP: 19
SALES (est): 5.3MM
SALES (corp-wide): 67.1B **Publicly Held**
SIC: 2096 Potato chips & other potato-based snacks
PA: Pepsico, Inc.
700 Anderson Hill Rd
Purchase NY 10577
914 253-2000

(G-16997)
RUBY AUTOMATION LLC
801 Klein Rd Ste 100 (75074-3703)
PHONE..............................972 881-9663
Rob George, *Branch Mgr*
EMP: 30
SALES (corp-wide): 763.7MM **Privately Held**
WEB: www.kaman.com
SIC: 5063 3613 5084 Motors, electric; time switches, electrical switchgear apparatus; industrial machinery & equipment
HQ: Ruby Automation, Llc
1 Vision Way
Bloomfield CT 06002
860 687-5000

(G-16998)
RUCKUS WIRELESS INC
101 E Park Blvd Ste 758 (75074-8825)
PHONE..............................972 546-1700
J F Rushing, *Sales/Mktg Mgr*
EMP: 20 **Publicly Held**
WEB: www.commscope.com
SIC: 3663 Modems
HQ: Ruckus Wireless, Inc.
350 W Java Dr
Sunnyvale CA 94089

(G-16999)
RUSHMAN DRAPERIES INC
8600 Preston Rd Ste 106 (75024-3313)
PHONE..............................214 943-1000
Kenneth Briggs Sr, *President*
EMP: 35
SALES (est): 3.2MM **Privately Held**
SIC: 3442 Shutters, door or window: metal

(G-17000)
SAMSUNG SDS GLOBL SCL AMER INC
3033 W Pres Grge Bush Pkw (75075)
PHONE..............................201 263-3000
EMP: 31 **Privately Held**
WEB: www.samsung.com
SIC: 7372 7371 Prepackaged software; computer software development
HQ: Samsung Sds Global Scl America, Inc.
100 Challenger Rd Ste 601
Ridgefield Park NJ 07660
201 807-5950

(G-17001)
SANWA ELECTRONICS USA CORP
4012 Preston Rd Ste 200 (75093-7350)
PHONE..............................972 503-3031
Takuji Ishii, *President*
Yasuo Ishii, *Vice Pres*
Akihito Ishikawa, *Treasurer*
EMP: 9
SQ FT: 1,200
SALES (est): 7MM **Privately Held**
WEB: www.sanwa-us.com
SIC: 3357 3699 Fiber optic cable (insulated); electrical equipment & supplies
PA: Sanwa Denki Kogyo Y.K.
19-1, Hiraicho
Tochigi TCG

(G-17002)
SANWA USA INC (HQ)
4012 Preston Rd Ste 200 (75093-7350)
PHONE..............................972 503-3031
Ryoichi Yamaji, *President*
Brian Bolton, *Principal*

◆ **EMP:** 23
SQ FT: 33,000
SALES (est): 744.1MM **Privately Held**
WEB: www.sanwa-us.com
SIC: 3442 2431 3699 3537 Garage doors, overhead: metal; doors, wood; door opening & closing devices, electrical; industrial trucks & tractors

(G-17003)
SIEMENS INDUSTRY SOFTWARE INC (DH)
5800 Granite Pkwy Ste 600 (75024-6612)
PHONE..............................972 987-3000
Anton S Huber, *Ch of Bd*
Charles C Grindstaff, *President*
Joan Franc S, *General Mgr*
Julie Brunett, *Counsel*
Stephen M Bashada, *Exec VP*
EMP: 200 **EST:** 1998
SQ FT: 43,800
SALES (est): 717.7MM
SALES (corp-wide): 67.4B **Privately Held**
WEB: www.new.siemens.com
SIC: 7372 Business oriented computer software
HQ: Siemens Industry, Inc.
1000 Deerfield Pkwy
Buffalo Grove IL 60089
847 215-1000

(G-17004)
SIEMENS INDUSTRY SOFTWARE INC
2805 Dallas Pkwy (75093-8719)
PHONE..............................972 391-2476
Joy Lin, *Assistant VP*
Rick Lloyd, *Engineer*
Kim Malott, *Branch Mgr*
EMP: 40
SQ FT: 500
SALES (corp-wide): 67.4B **Privately Held**
WEB: www.new.siemens.com
SIC: 7372 7371 7336 Educational computer software; custom computer programming services; commercial art & graphic design
HQ: Siemens Industry Software Inc.
5800 Granite Pkwy Ste 600
Plano TX 75024
972 987-3000

(G-17005)
SIERRA NEVADA CORPORATION
1100 Jupiter Rd Ste 200 (75074-7047)
PHONE..............................775 331-0222
Fatih Ozmen, *CEO*
Darlene Mims, *Buyer*
Al Venzon, *Manager*
Mark Cheney, *Software Engr*
EMP: 30
SALES (corp-wide): 1.9B **Privately Held**
WEB: www.sncorp.com
SIC: 3812 Search & navigation equipment
PA: Sierra Nevada Corporation
444 Salomon Cir
Sparks NV 89434
775 331-0222

(G-17006)
SIGNAZON CORPORATION
Also Called: Signazon.com
4000 E Plano Pkwy Ste A (75074-1830)
PHONE..............................214 296-0022
Richard Debus, *CEO*
Richard A Debus, *CEO*
Charles Mitchell, *Vice Pres*
Christian Vanderbeck, *Opers Staff*
Anita LI, *CFO*
EMP: 35
SALES (est): 3.8MM **Privately Held**
WEB: www.signazon.com
SIC: 2752 3993 Promotional printing, lithographic; signs & advertising specialties; signs, not made in custom sign painting shops

(G-17007)
SIGNS NOW CORPORATION
701 E Plano Pkwy Ste 113 (75074-6751)
PHONE..............................972 398-8648
Amy Lanksord, *Owner*
EMP: 11

SALES (corp-wide): 2.5MM **Privately Held**
WEB: www.alliancefranchisebrands.com
SIC: 3993 Signs & advertising specialties
PA: Signs Now Corporation
8681 Robert Fulton Dr
Columbia MD 21046
410 312-3600

(G-17008)
SOFF CORPORATION
2828 W Parker Rd Ste 101b (75075-9193)
P.O. Box 260757 (75026-0757)
PHONE..............................469 467-9700
Anwar Mahomed, *Branch Mgr*
EMP: 10
SALES (corp-wide): 2MM **Privately Held**
WEB: www.soff.com
SIC: 7372 Prepackaged software
PA: Soff Corporation
520 Central Pkwy E # 300
Plano TX 75074
469 467-9700

(G-17009)
SOFF CORPORATION (PA)
520 Central Pkwy E # 300 (75074-5527)
P.O. Box 260757 (75026-0757)
PHONE..............................469 467-9700
EMP: 10 **EST:** 1997
SQ FT: 1,000
SALES (est): 2MM **Privately Held**
WEB: www.soff.com
SIC: 7372 Prepackaged software

(G-17010)
SOUTHEAST PRTR CONNECTION LLC (PA)
2400 Dallas Pkwy Ste 230 (75093-4371)
PHONE..............................256 880-9991
Craig Cheek,
EMP: 20
SQ FT: 12,000
SALES (est): 1.5MM **Privately Held**
SIC: 3577 5045 5734 7378 Printers, computer; computers, peripherals & software; computer peripheral equipment; computer & data processing equipment repair/maintenance

(G-17011)
SPLUNK INC
5360 Legacy Dr Ste 250 (75024-3187)
PHONE..............................972 244-8806
Jim Apger, *Minister*
Jerry Fenerty, *Vice Pres*
Chip Winslow, *Vice Pres*
David Grubb, *Engineer*
Brandon Loehr, *Engineer*
EMP: 11
SALES (corp-wide): 2.3B **Publicly Held**
WEB: www.splunk.com
SIC: 7372 Prepackaged software
PA: Splunk Inc.
270 Brannan St
San Francisco CA 94107
415 848-8400

(G-17012)
SUCCESS PARTNERS HOLDING CO
5800 Democracy Dr (75024-4919)
PHONE..............................800 752-2030
Stuart Johnson, *President*
Marcia Mayhew, *Principal*
Tony Chaplin, *COO*
Lauren Lawley Head, *Senior VP*
Coy Moore, *Vice Pres*
▲ **EMP:** 250
SALES (est): 45.7MM
SALES (corp-wide): 979.9MM **Publicly Held**
WEB: www.successpartners.com
SIC: 7319 2721 Distribution of advertising material or sample services; magazines: publishing & printing; statistical reports (periodicals): publishing & printing
PA: Exp World Holdings, Inc.
2219 Rimland Dr Ste 301
Bellingham WA 98226
360 685-4206

(G-17013)
SUMMIT NIGHT VISION GROUP INC
Also Called: Summit Defense Systems Group
1845 Summit Ave Ste 403 (75074-8186)
PHONE..............................972 992-0046
Stefan Pryor, *CEO*
▼ **EMP:** 15
SQ FT: 5,000
SALES (est): 2.4MM **Privately Held**
WEB: www.summitnightvision.com
SIC: 3827 7699 Gun sights, optical; sighting & fire control equipment, optical; optical instrument repair; fire control (military) equipment repair

(G-17014)
SUNETICS INTL MKTG GROUP LLC
1700 Alma Dr Ste 400 (75075-6964)
PHONE..............................888 266-2232
EMP: 15 **EST:** 2010
SQ FT: 3,200
SALES: 2MM **Privately Held**
SIC: 3699 3845 5999 Mfg Electrical Equipment/Supplies Mfg Electromedical Equipment Ret Misc Merchandise

(G-17015)
SUPPLY SOLUTIONS INC
1800 Preston Park Blvd # 1 (75093-5188)
PHONE..............................214 766-6866
Roger Malmrose, *CEO*
EMP: 81
SALES (est): 13.5MM **Privately Held**
WEB: www.scrgww.com
SIC: 3999 Barber & beauty shop equipment

(G-17016)
SUSTAINABLE MODULAR MGT INC
7500 Dallas Pkwy Ste 175 (75024-0004)
PHONE..............................972 619-7300
Brian Schafer, *President*
Celine Jefferson, *Project Engr*
Dehn Smith, *CFO*
James Gladue, *Accountant*
Luke Mackie, *Accountant*
EMP: 13
SQ FT: 1,000
SALES (est): 6.5MM **Privately Held**
WEB: www.sustainablemodular.com
SIC: 2452 Prefabricated wood buildings

(G-17017)
SVTRONICS INC
3465 Technology Dr (75074-7433)
PHONE..............................214 440-1234
Jasmat Sutaria, *President*
Dhirajlal J Barbaria, *Vice Pres*
Barat Sutaria, *Vice Pres*
Bharat Sutaria, *Vice Pres*
Shweta Chaudhari, *Buyer*
▲ **EMP:** 130
SQ FT: 70,000
SALES (est): 22.5MM **Privately Held**
WEB: www.svtronics.com
SIC: 3672 3699 3643 Printed circuit boards; electrical equipment & supplies; current-carrying wiring devices

(G-17018)
SYSTUM INC
555 Republic Dr Ste 200 (75074-5469)
PHONE..............................406 600-3684
Dean Mansfield, *CEO*
Eric Borrmann, *CFO*
EMP: 10
SALES (est): 714.5K **Privately Held**
WEB: www.systum.com
SIC: 7371 7372 Computer software systems analysis & design, custom; business oriented computer software

(G-17019)
T-SYSTEM INC
6509 Windcrest Dr Ste 165 (75024-3403)
PHONE..............................972 503-8899
Roger Davis, *CEO*
Patrick Leonard, *President*
Tina Clark, *General Mgr*
Tim Swango, *COO*
Bradley Cordes, *Exec VP*
▲ **EMP:** 105

SALES (est): 15.9MM
SALES (corp-wide): 1B **Publicly Held**
WEB: www.tsystem.com
SIC: 2741 7372 Miscellaneous publishing; prepackaged software
HQ: T-System Holding, Inc.
4020 Mcewen Rd
Dallas TX 75244
972 503-8899

(G-17020)
TALLANNQUEST LLC
Also Called: Apogee Semiconductor
538 Haggard St Ste 406 (75074-5564)
PHONE............................972 423-8455
Anton Quiroz, *Principal*
Emily Donnelly, *Principal*
David Grant, *Principal*
Mark Hamlyn, *Principal*
Beth Woods, *Principal*
EMP: 9
SALES (est): 500K **Privately Held**
WEB: www.tallannquest.com
SIC: 8748 3674 Business consulting; microcircuits, integrated (semiconductor)

(G-17021)
TBK MATERIALS LLC (PA)
5208 Tennyson Pkwy # 130 (75024-7182)
PHONE............................214 239-4916
Brian Gatlin, *Marketing Staff*
Tina Rich, *Mng Member*
Diana Leyva, *Admin Mgr*
EMP: 30
SQ FT: 500
SALES (est): 8.1MM **Privately Held**
WEB: www.tbkmaterials.com
SIC: 3253 Quarry tile, clay

(G-17022)
TBX EMPLOYEE BENEFITS LLC
7500 Dallas Pkwy Ste 500 (75024-4022)
PHONE............................972 248-9030
Joe Fernandez, *CEO*
Belinda Maffei, *Sales Staff*
Marcel Mueller,
David Neel,
Patrick Wagner,
EMP: 30
SALES: 9.2MM **Privately Held**
WEB: www.tbxbenefits.com
SIC: 7372 Business oriented computer software

(G-17023)
TECH DOGS LLC
1200 Placid Ave Ste 500 (75074-8680)
PHONE............................972 985-4730
Christian Langseth, *Manager*
Roger Ramirez, *Officer*
Joselito Sison,
EMP: 15
SQ FT: 2,000
SALES (est): 3.3MM **Privately Held**
WEB: www.techdogsonline.com
SIC: 2759 7379 5943 Laser printing; computer related maintenance services; office forms & supplies

(G-17024)
TENTH STREET INDUSTRIES LP
901 10th St (75074-6801)
P.O. Box 940529 (75094-0529)
PHONE............................972 578-5155
Gayle Glosser, *President*
Mike Powerll, *Partner*
Phillip J Speicher, *CFO*
EMP: 20
SALES (est): 1.9MM **Privately Held**
WEB: www.enchantedcarecenter.com
SIC: 3471 Electroplating of metals or formed products

(G-17025)
TERADYNE INC
2701 W Plano Pkwy Ste 700 (75075-8202)
PHONE............................972 231-5384
Py Akin, *Sales/Mktg Mgr*
Mike Mills, *Info Tech Mgr*
EMP: 53
SALES (corp-wide): 2.3B **Publicly Held**
WEB: www.teradyne.com
SIC: 3643 3829 3674 Connectors & terminals for electrical devices; measuring & controlling devices; semiconductors & related devices

PA: Teradyne, Inc.
600 Riverpark Dr
North Reading MA 01864
978 370-2700

(G-17026)
TEXAKOMA FINANCIAL INC
5601 Granite Pkwy Ste 600 (75024-6679)
PHONE............................972 701-9106
Dean Kennedy, *President*
EMP: 42
SALES (est): 5.1MM **Privately Held**
WEB: www.texakoma.com
SIC: 6211 1382 Brokers, security; oil & gas exploration services

(G-17027)
TEXAKOMA OPERATING LP
5601 Granite Pkwy Ste 600 (75024-6679)
PHONE............................972 701-9106
Dean Kennedy, *Partner*
William Stapleton, *Principal*
Shanna Keaveny, *Vice Pres*
EMP: 49 **EST:** 1982
SQ FT: 12,000
SALES (est): 11.7MM **Privately Held**
WEB: www.texakoma.com
SIC: 1382 Oil & gas exploration services

(G-17028)
TEXAS 2 STITCH
3100 Independence Pkwy # 207
(75075-1996)
PHONE............................972 599-1717
Kari Scherf, *Owner*
EMP: 12
SALES (est): 69.8K **Privately Held**
WEB: www.texas2stitch.com
SIC: 2395 2261 5947 Embroidery products, except schiffli machine; printing of cotton broadwoven fabrics; gift shop

(G-17029)
TEXAS INSTRUMENTS INCORPORATED
4317 Brady Dr (75024-3472)
PHONE............................214 480-4691
James O Bondi, *Principal*
Corey Lewis, *Analyst*
EMP: 418
SALES (corp-wide): 14.4B **Publicly Held**
WEB: www.txwx.com
SIC: 3674 Microprocessors
PA: Texas Instruments Incorporated
12500 Ti Blvd
Dallas TX 75243
972 995-3773

(G-17030)
TEXAS INSTRUMENTS INCORPORATED
6500 Chase Oaks Blvd (75023-2308)
PHONE............................972 995-2011
Miller Adair, *General Mgr*
Ian Spencer, *VP Opers*
Leigh Harmon, *Project Mgr*
Faye Rainey, *Project Mgr*
Janine Spurgeon, *Project Mgr*
EMP: 35
SALES (corp-wide): 14.4B **Publicly Held**
WEB: www.txwx.com
SIC: 3674 Semiconductors & related devices
PA: Texas Instruments Incorporated
12500 Ti Blvd
Dallas TX 75243
972 995-3773

(G-17031)
TEXAS INSTRUMENTS INCORPORATED
6550 Chase Oaks Blvd (75023-2308)
P.O. Box 655012, Dallas (75265-5012)
PHONE............................214 567-9863
EMP: 27
SALES (corp-wide): 14.9B **Publicly Held**
SIC: 3674 Mfg Semiconductors & Related Devices
PA: Texas Instruments Incorporated
12500 Ti Blvd
Dallas TX 75243
214 479-3773

(G-17032)
THREADS IN MOTION
1240 Shiloh Rd Ste 200 (75074-7045)
PHONE............................972 422-4607
Mark D Case, *Owner*
David Kiser, *Manager*
EMP: 13
SALES (est): 800K **Privately Held**
WEB: www.threadsinmotion.com
SIC: 2395 Embroidery products, except schiffli machine; embroidery & art needlework

(G-17033)
TILLMAN LEARNING LLC
Also Called: Trainup.com
5700 W Plano Pkwy # 3200 (75093-2453)
PHONE............................866 540-9677
Jemery Tillman, *CEO*
Judie Hughes, *Accounting Mgr*
Wes Lanning, *Sales Dir*
Eric Jordan, *Manager*
EMP: 14
SQ FT: 3,600
SALES (est): 2MM **Privately Held**
WEB: www.jeremyblogs.com
SIC: 8249 7372 8331 8243 Business training services; educational computer software; job training & vocational rehabilitation services; software training, computer; human resource consulting services

(G-17034)
TOPPAN PHOTOMASKS INC
555 Republic Dr Ste 312 (75074-8857)
PHONE............................972 398-0411
Manoj K Chhabra, *Principal*
EMP: 49 **Privately Held**
WEB: www.photomask.com
SIC: 3559 Sewing machines & hat & zipper making machinery
HQ: Toppan Photomasks, Inc.
131 E Old Settlers Blvd
Round Rock TX 78664
512 310-6500

(G-17035)
TOYOTA MOTOR NORTH AMERICA INC
5360 Legacy Dr (75024-3130)
PHONE............................859 746-4351
EMP: 50
SALES (corp-wide): 275.7B **Privately Held**
SIC: 3714 5511 Mfg Motor Vehicle Parts/Accessories Ret New/Used Automobiles
HQ: Toyota Motor North America, Inc.
6565 Headquarters Dr
Plano TX 75024

(G-17036)
TOYOTA MOTOR NORTH AMERICA INC (HQ)
6565 Headquarters Dr (75024-5965)
P.O. Box 259001 (75025-9001)
PHONE............................469 292-4000
Yukitoshi Funo, *CEO*
David Finch, *President*
Mike Zielinski, *General Mgr*
Shigeru Hayakawa, *Vice Chairman*
Tetsuo Ogawa, *Exec VP*
◆ **EMP:** 29
SALES (est): 2.9B **Privately Held**
WEB: www.toyota.com
SIC: 5511 5012 3711 Automobiles, new & used; automobiles; motor vehicles & car bodies

(G-17037)
TOYOTA MTR ENGRG MFG N AMER IN (DH)
Also Called: T E M A
6565 Hdqtr Dr W1 3c 1 W (75024)
PHONE............................469 292-1074
Osamu Nagata, *CEO*
Shinichi Yasui, *President*
Rebecca Hill, *General Mgr*
Renee Robertson, *General Mgr*
Shawna Soper, *General Mgr*
◆ **EMP:** 200

SALES (est): 2.3B **Privately Held**
SIC: 5511 3713 8741 Automobiles, new & used; truck & bus bodies; management services

(G-17038)
TRADER SAM LLC
3928 Lost Creek Dr (75074-7768)
PHONE............................214 537-0885
Debbie Minardi, *Mng Member*
Raymond Minardi,
EMP: 11
SALES (est): 1MM **Privately Held**
SIC: 3621 Motors & generators

(G-17039)
TYLER TECHNOLOGIES INC (PA)
5101 Tennyson Pkwy (75024-3525)
PHONE............................972 713-3700
John S Marr Jr, *Ch of Bd*
H Lynn Moore Jr, *President*
Brad Green, *COO*
Elven Corder, *Vice Pres*
David Grossman, *Vice Pres*
EMP: 111 **EST:** 1966
SALES: 1B **Publicly Held**
WEB: www.tylertech.com
SIC: 7372 Prepackaged software

(G-17040)
TYLER TECHNOLOGIES INC
Software Group, The
6500 Intl Pkwy Ste 2000 (75093)
PHONE............................972 713-3700
Paige Cole, *Human Res Mgr*
Shelly Prewitt, *HR Admin*
Glenn Smith, *Branch Mgr*
Mike Fritz, *Supervisor*
EMP: 100
SALES (corp-wide): 1B **Publicly Held**
WEB: www.tylertech.com
SIC: 7372 Prepackaged software
PA: Tyler Technologies, Inc.
5101 Tennyson Pkwy
Plano TX 75024
972 713-3700

(G-17041)
UNICOM ENGINEERING INC
Also Called: Nei
3501 E Plano Pkwy (75074-7206)
PHONE............................972 673-1345
Robert Sheriff, *Vice Pres*
John Ryan, *Opers Staff*
Gerald Frisbie, *Purch Mgr*
Gilbert Flores, *Engineer*
Lisa Cliver, *Comms Mgr*
EMP: 100
SALES (corp-wide): 508.4MM **Privately Held**
WEB: www.unicomengineering.com
SIC: 3577 Computer peripheral equipment
HQ: Unicom Engineering, Inc.
25 Dan Rd
Canton MA 02021

(G-17042)
UNITED ADVG PUBLICATIONS INC
For Rent Media Solution
6500 Intl Pkwy Ste 1000 (75093)
PHONE............................214 269-0788
Tracy Slattely, *Vice Pres*
Griselle Garcia, *Sales Mgr*
Heidi Casertano, *Associate Dir*
EMP: 21 **Privately Held**
WEB: www.forrent.com
SIC: 2721 Magazines: publishing & printing
HQ: United Advertising Publications, Inc.
1331 L St Nw Ste 2
Washington DC 20005
210 377-3116

(G-17043)
URBAN OIL & GAS GROUP LLC (PA)
1000 14th St Fl 3 (75074-6205)
PHONE............................972 543-8800
Bonnie C Shea, *CEO*
Bonnie Shea, *Principal*
Fred Diem, *Vice Pres*
Mike Lemieux, *Foreman/Supr*
Mike Mercer, *VP Engrg*
EMP: 43

▲ = Import ▼=Export
◆ =Import/Export

SALES (est): 5.9MM **Privately Held**
WEB: www.urbanoilandgas.com
SIC: 1382 Oil & gas exploration services

(G-17044)
VENTURE RESEARCH INC
3001 Summit Ave Ste 100 (75074-7228)
PHONE....................469 246-4000
John Baker, *President*
Teri Baker, *Vice Pres*
Adnan Ali, *Electrical Engi*
John Kliewer, *Electrical Engi*
Jonathan Hall, *Marketing Staff*
EMP: 40
SQ FT: 52,500
SALES (est): 7.5MM **Privately Held**
WEB: www.ventureresearch.com
SIC: 3577 7371 Computer peripheral
equipment; computer software develop-
ment & applications

(G-17045)
VINE OIL & GAS LP (PA)
5800 Granite Pkwy Ste 550 (75024-6642)
P.O. Box 211370, Dallas (75211-4306)
PHONE....................469 606-0540
Eric D Marsh, *CEO*
David Elkin, *Exec VP*
Chris Williams, *Manager*
Branka Daravong, *Admin Mgr*
Caleb Smith, *IT/INT Sup*
EMP: 11 EST: 2014
SQ FT: 15,000
SALES (est): 12.4MM **Privately Held**
WEB: www.vineog.com
SIC: 1382 Oil & gas exploration services

(G-17046)
VISUAL BI SOLUTIONS INC
5920 Windhaven Pkwy # 200
(75093-8509)
PHONE....................972 232-2233
Gopal Krishnamurthy, *CEO*
Darby Solis, *Business Mgr*
Ulises Hubbard, *Vice Pres*
Karey Koscevic, *Opers Staff*
Clint Singleton, *Controller*
EMP: 45
SQ FT: 9,000
SALES (est): 16.2MM **Privately Held**
WEB: www.visualbi.com
SIC: 7371 7372 7373 7374 Computer
software development & applications;
business oriented computer software;
systems software development services;
computer graphics service

(G-17047)
VITALTECH AFFILIATES LLC
6652 Pinecrest Dr Ste 400 (75024-2957)
PHONE....................214 886-5249
James Hamilton,
EMP: 33 EST: 2017
SALES (est): 2.5MM **Privately Held**
WEB: www.vitaltech.com
SIC: 3841 Surgical & medical instruments

(G-17048)
VOOM GROUP INC
1825 E Plano Pkwy Ste 250 (75074-8599)
PHONE....................972 424-8887
Wendi Schlarb, *President*
Erich Schlarb, *Vice Pres*
EMP: 10
SQ FT: 7,000
SALES (est): 1.8MM **Privately Held**
WEB: www.voomgroup.com
SIC: 7336 2732 Graphic arts & related de-
sign; book printing

(G-17049)
VOTRONICS INC
1505 Capital Ave (75074-8152)
PHONE....................972 509-8494
David N Vo, *President*
Ha Vo, *Accountant*
EMP: 10
SQ FT: 4,000
SALES (est): 2.7MM **Privately Held**
WEB: www.votronicsinc.com
SIC: 3679 Microwave components

(G-17050)
WHOLESOME GROUP LLC
5850 Granite Pkwy Ste 150 (75024-0045)
PHONE....................214 937-4750

Cara Bonanno, *General Mgr*
Gabriel Delgado, *General Mgr*
Terence C Obrien, *Mng Member*
EMP: 120
SALES (est): 10.7MM **Privately Held**
WEB: www.eatwholesome.com
SIC: 2038 Breakfasts, frozen & packaged

(G-17051)
WINZER CORPORATION (HQ)
4060 E Plano Pkwy (75074-1800)
PHONE....................214 341-2122
Jon Kerr, *CEO*
John Burgess, *General Mgr*
Danny Anderson, *Vice Pres*
Paul Seibert, *Vice Pres*
Diane Vanderbilt, *Vice Pres*
▲ EMP: 130
SQ FT: 130,000
SALES (est): 81.8MM **Privately Held**
WEB: www.winzer.com
SIC: 5072 3452 5251 5169 Bolts, nuts &
screws; bolts, nuts, rivets & washers;
hardware; industrial chemicals; fran-
chises, selling or licensing
PA: Shoreview Industries Llc
222 S 9th St Ste 3300
Minneapolis MN 55402
612 436-0575

(G-17052)
WISHBONE GRAPHICS INC
Also Called: Plano Profile
1413 Gables Ct (75075-7643)
P.O. Box 861237 (75086-1237)
PHONE....................972 769-7272
Jean Ellis Newman, *President*
Philip Silvestri, *Publisher*
Barbara Walsh, *Publisher*
Mendy Lea, *Marketing Staff*
Susan Cunningham, *Office Mgr*
EMP: 11
SQ FT: 4,000
SALES (est): 1.5MM **Privately Held**
WEB: www.localprofile.com
SIC: 2721 Magazines: publishing only, not
printed on site

(G-17053)
WIZETRADE GROUP
6900 Dallas Pkwy Ste 600 (75024-4270)
PHONE....................407 206-6500
John Dankovchik, *Principal*
Joann Guillot, *Human Res Mgr*
EMP: 148
SALES (est): 7.8MM
SALES (corp-wide): 17.3MM **Privately
Held**
SIC: 7372 Prepackaged software
PA: Dynetech Corporation
2200 Lucien Way Ste 400
Maitland FL 32751
407 206-6500

(G-17054)
XENCOM ENERGY MANAGEMENT LLC
1609 Precision Dr # 3000 (75074-8675)
PHONE....................469 429-1111
Robert A Cross,
Karimen Melgar, *Advisor*
EMP: 15
SALES (est): 1MM **Privately Held**
WEB: www.xencom.com
SIC: 3822 Auto controls regulating residntl
& coml environmt & applncs

(G-17055)
XJIAN INC
4500 Staten Island Ct (75024-4712)
PHONE....................972 618-6096
Steve Shen, *President*
EMP: 12
SALES (est): 820.4K **Privately Held**
WEB: www.xjian.com
SIC: 2299 Textile goods

(G-17056)
Z FABULOUS INC
1700 Coit Rd (75075-6185)
PHONE....................972 385-0202
Kim Charlie, *CEO*
Amanda Otten, *Sales Staff*
▲ EMP: 20
SQ FT: 31,000

SALES (est): 5.8MM **Privately Held**
WEB: www.fabcz.com
SIC: 5094 3961 Jewelry; costume jewelry

(G-17057)
ZTI MERGER SUBSIDIARY III INC (DH)
5700 Tennyson Pkwy # 400 (75024-3583)
PHONE....................510 777-7000
Jeanette Symons, *Vice Pres*
Kirk Misaka, *Treasurer*
EMP: 11 EST: 1999
SALES (est): 19MM **Publicly Held**
WEB: www.dasanzhone.com
SIC: 5065 3661 Amateur radio communi-
cations equipment; telephone & telegraph
apparatus
HQ: Dzs Inc.
5700 Tennyson Pkwy # 400
Plano TX 75024
469 327-1531

Plantersville
Grimes County

(G-17058)
CREATIVE ALLOY PRODUCTS CO
17151 Highway 105 E (77363-1719)
PHONE....................936 894-2060
Chris W Lewis, *President*
William Lewis, *Vice Pres*
EMP: 22
SQ FT: 6,000
SALES (est): 2.9MM **Privately Held**
WEB: www.creativealloyproducts.com
SIC: 3441 Fabricated structural metal

(G-17059)
MERRIMAC MANUFACTURING INC
16749 Highway 105 E (77363-8201)
PHONE....................936 894-3900
James W Harris, *President*
James L McCulloch, *Senior VP*
Tom Simms, *Treasurer*
Denise Torgesen, *Asst Treas*
Rhonda Fenton, *Manager*
EMP: 49
SALES (est): 13.4MM **Publicly Held**
WEB: www.f-e-t.com
SIC: 3561 1389 Pumps, oil well & field;
servicing oil & gas wells; mud service, oil
field drilling
PA: Forum Energy Technologies, Inc.
10344 Sam Houston Park Dr # 300
Houston TX 77064

(G-17060)
PLANTEX MACHINE LLC
15622 Fm 1774 (77363-8609)
PHONE....................936 894-0226
Peter Joseph Imhoff,
Jeremy Grigsby,
EMP: 9
SALES (est): 1.3MM **Privately Held**
SIC: 3469 Machine parts, stamped or
pressed metal

Pleasanton
Atascosa County

(G-17061)
ANDERSON PERFORATING LTD
101055 Ih 37 (78064-6127)
PHONE....................830 569-1120
Chad Parrot, *Branch Mgr*
EMP: 20 **Privately Held**
WEB: www.apiperforating.com
SIC: 1389 Perforating well casings
PA: Anderson Perforating Services, Llc
124 Welco Rd
Albany TX 76430

(G-17062)
BAKER HGHES OLFLD OPRTIONS LLC
Also Called: Baker Hughes Solutions
6938 Fm 1784 (78064-6985)
PHONE....................361 692-3000
Carl Currie, *Branch Mgr*

EMP: 100 **Privately Held**
WEB: www.bakerhughes.com
SIC: 1389 Oil field services
PA: Baker Hughes Oilfield Operations Llc
2001 Rankin Rd
Houston TX 77073

(G-17063)
C & J EQUIPMENT MFG CORP
233 Corgey Rd (78064-6958)
PHONE....................830 569-1968
Chad Thornton, *CEO*
EMP: 35 **Privately Held**
WEB: www.cjemc.com
SIC: 3533 Oil & gas field machinery
PA: C & J Equipment Manufacturing Corpo-
ration
2250 N 1st St
Bloomfield NM 87413

(G-17064)
CACTUS ROPES INC
5116 E State Highway 97 (78064-5801)
P.O. Box 38 (78064-0038)
PHONE....................830 569-8744
D H Carroll, *President*
Michael Piland, *Vice Pres*
Gary J Minta, *Treasurer*
Thomas Z Hayward Jr, *Admin Sec*
▲ EMP: 32
SQ FT: 18,000
SALES (est): 4.7MM
SALES (corp-wide): 10.7MM **Privately
Held**
WEB: www.cactusropes.com
SIC: 2298 Nets, rope
PA: Pro Equine Group, Inc.
500 Lake Cook Rd Ste 430
Deerfield IL 60015
847 940-3535

(G-17065)
EAGLE PCO LLC
1189 County Road 429 (78064-6035)
PHONE....................361 756-0666
Jenniger Black, *Branch Mgr*
EMP: 10 **Privately Held**
WEB: www.trendservicesinc.com
SIC: 3533 1389 Oil field machinery &
equipment; oil field services
PA: Eagle Pco Llc
5808 Fm 3455 Rd
Navasota TX 77868

(G-17066)
EXPRESS ENERGY SVCS OPER LP
716 Eagle Ford Dr (78064-6972)
PHONE....................830 569-8606
Marcello Garcia, *Manager*
EMP: 42
SALES (corp-wide): 770.4MM **Privately
Held**
WEB: www.eeslp.com
SIC: 1389 Pipe testing, oil field service; oil
field services
PA: Express Energy Services Operating, Lp
9800 Richmond Ave Ste 500
Houston TX 77042
713 625-7400

(G-17067)
FLINT ENERGY SERVICES INC
756 Eagle Ford Dr (78064-6972)
PHONE....................830 569-8453
Tom Hogelin, *Branch Mgr*
EMP: 160
SALES (corp-wide): 13.2B **Publicly Held**
WEB: www.aecom.com
SIC: 1389 Haulage, oil field; roustabout
service
HQ: Flint Energy Services Inc.
6200 S Quebec St Ste 1
Greenwood Village CO 80111
918 294-3030

(G-17068)
FLINT ENERGY SERVICES INC
756 Eagle Ford Dr (78064-6972)
PHONE....................940 683-4181
Zach Johnson, *Principal*
EMP: 250
SALES (corp-wide): 13.2B **Publicly Held**
WEB: www.aecom.com
SIC: 1389 Construction, repair & disman-
tling services

HQ: Flint Energy Services Inc.
6200 S Quebec St Ste 1
Greenwood Village CO 80111
918 294-3030

(G-17069)
INDEPENDENCE OILFIELD CHEM LLC
472 Eagle Ford Dr (78064-7023)
PHONE...................210 888-0300
EMP: 9
SALES (corp-wide): 1.5B **Publicly Held**
WEB: www.innospecinc.com
SIC: 2899 Chemical preparations
HQ: Independence Oilfield Chemicals, Llc
2600 Tech Forest Blvd
The Woodlands TX 77381
713 936-4340

(G-17070)
INGRAM READYMIX INC
1710 W Oaklawn Rd (78064-4601)
PHONE...................830 569-2187
Rueben Hernandes, *Manager*
EMP: 10
SALES (corp-wide): 125.6MM **Privately Held**
WEB: www.ingramreadymixinc.com
SIC: 3273 Ready-mixed concrete
PA: Ingram Readymix, Inc.
3580 Farm Market 482
New Braunfels TX 78132
830 625-9156

(G-17071)
PINNERGY LTD
1012 W Oaklawn Rd Unit A (78064-3951)
PHONE...................830 569-1997
Lori Coteinas, *Branch Mgr*
EMP: 26 **Privately Held**
WEB: www.pinnergy.com
SIC: 1389 Oil field services
PA: Pinnergy, Ltd.
111 Congress Ave Ste 2020
Austin TX 78701

(G-17072)
RANGER ENERGY SERVICES INC
4740 County Road 430 (78064-6158)
PHONE...................830 569-1940
EMP: 25
SALES (corp-wide): 336.9MM **Publicly Held**
WEB: www.rangerenergy.com
SIC: 3533 Oil & gas drilling rigs & equipment
PA: Ranger Energy Services, Inc.
10350 Richmond Ave # 550
Houston TX 77042
713 935-8900

(G-17073)
SCHLUMBERGER TECHNOLOGY CORP
203 Wyoming Blvd (78064-4401)
PHONE...................830 569-8046
Jeff Ridley, *Branch Mgr*
EMP: 95 **Publicly Held**
SIC: 1389 Oil field services
HQ: Schlumberger Technology Corp
300 Schlumberger Dr
Sugar Land TX 77478
281 285-8500

(G-17074)
SCHLUMBERGER TECHNOLOGY CORP
Also Called: Schlumberger Well Services
206 Oil Rd (78064-4626)
PHONE...................956 744-4029
Sharif Aboelnaga, *Manager*
EMP: 70 **Publicly Held**
SIC: 1389 Oil field services
HQ: Schlumberger Technology Corp
300 Schlumberger Dr
Sugar Land TX 77478
281 285-8500

(G-17075)
SPARTAN ENERGY SERVICES LLC
511 Corgey Rd (78064-6997)
PHONE...................830 281-8505
Delmar Crushey, *Branch Mgr*

EMP: 70
SALES (corp-wide): 12MM **Privately Held**
WEB: www.spartansenergy.com
SIC: 1389 Oil field services
PA: Spartan Energy Services, L.L.C.
2901 Johnston St Ste 401
Lafayette LA 70503
337 406-1129

(G-17076)
W W WOOD INC
1799 Corgey Rd (78064-6941)
P.O. Box 398 (78064-0398)
PHONE...................830 569-2501
Jerry M Lawson, *President*
Ryan Lawson, *Vice Pres*
Jim Dominguez, *Opers Mgr*
Anthony Anderson, *Warehouse Mgr*
Pamela Youngblood, *Engineer*
EMP: 25
SALES (est): 5.9MM **Privately Held**
WEB: www.woodinc.com
SIC: 2421 Wood chips, produced at mill

(G-17077)
WARRIOR ENERGY SERVICES CORP
4541 County Road 430 (78064-6007)
PHONE...................830 569-2096
EMP: 15 **Publicly Held**
WEB: www.superiorenergy.com
SIC: 1389 Oil field services
HQ: Warrior Energy Services Corporation
5801 Highway 90 E
Broussard LA 70518
337 714-2400

(G-17078)
WILKERSON PUBLISHING COMPANY
Also Called: Pleasanton Express
114 W Goodwin St (78064-4126)
P.O. Box 880 (78064-0880)
PHONE...................830 281-2341
Sue Elizondo, *President*
Stephen Garcia, *Editor*
Erika Vela, *Editor*
David Wilkerson, *Corp Secy*
Judith Wilkerson, *Vice Pres*
EMP: 15 EST: 1955
SQ FT: 1,200
SALES (est): 1MM **Privately Held**
WEB: www.pleasantonexpress.com
SIC: 2711 Commercial printing & newspaper publishing combined; newspapers, publishing & printing

Point
Rains County

(G-17079)
DAL-AIR TOOL CO INC
Also Called: Dal-Air Investment Castings
Hwy 69 Nw Ste 591indus (75472)
P.O. Box 280 (75472-0280)
PHONE...................903 598-2226
Catheran Rhodes, *President*
Steve Rhodes, *Vice Pres*
▼ EMP: 48
SQ FT: 10,200
SALES (est): 11.9MM **Privately Held**
WEB: www.dalaircasting.com
SIC: 3324 Steel investment foundries

(G-17080)
RMS SOLUTIONS GROUP LLC
320 Rs County Road 4310 (75472-5606)
PHONE...................469 964-7127
Inna Reed, *President*
Price Reed, *Project Mgr*
EMP: 10
SALES (est): 93K **Privately Held**
WEB: www.rms.com
SIC: 1731 8711 3822 Electrical work; energy management controls; electrical or electronic engineering; refrigeration controls (pressure)

Point Comfort
Calhoun County

(G-17081)
ALCOA WORLD ALUMINA LLC
State Hwy 35 (77978)
P.O. Box 494 (77978-0494)
PHONE...................361 987-2631
R L Fischer, *Branch Mgr*
David Cano, *Manager*
Thomas Engelgau, *Manager*
Richard Ratliff, *Manager*
Andy Saenz, *IT/INT Sup*
EMP: 650
SALES (corp-wide): 10.4B **Publicly Held**
WEB: www.alcoa.com
SIC: 1081 Metal mining services
HQ: Alcoa World Alumina Llc
201 Isabella St Ste 500
Pittsburgh PA 15212

(G-17082)
FORMOSA HYDROCARBONS CO INC
103 Fannin Rd (77978)
P.O. Box 769 (77978-0769)
PHONE...................361 987-8900
Jack Wu, *President*
Y C W Ang, *Chairman*
Y T W Ang, *Chairman*
C T Lee, *Chairman*
C L Tseng, *Exec VP*
EMP: 39
SQ FT: 7,500
SALES (est): 2MM **Privately Held**
WEB: www.fpcusa.com
SIC: 2911 Gasoline; liquefied petroleum gases, LPG
HQ: Formosa Plastics Corporation, U.S.A.
9 Peach Tree Hill Rd
Livingston NJ 07039
973 992-2090

(G-17083)
FORMOSA INDUSTRIES CORPORATION
201 Formosa Dr (77978)
P.O. Box 700 (77978-0700)
PHONE...................361 987-7000
CT Lee, *Director*
King-Long Huang, *Director*
Jason Lin, *Director*
EMP: 26
SALES (est): 3.6MM **Privately Held**
WEB: www.fpcusa.com
SIC: 2821 Polyvinyl chloride resins (PVC)
PA: Formosa Plastics Corporation
100, Shuiguan Rd.,
Kaohsiung City 80660

(G-17084)
FORMOSA PLASTICS CORP AMERICA
201 Formosa Dr (77978)
P.O. Box 510 (77978-0510)
PHONE...................361 987-7000
Jason Lin, *President*
Ken Mounger, *Exec VP*
David Lin, *Senior VP*
▲ EMP: 73
SALES (est): 3.7MM **Privately Held**
WEB: www.fpcusa.com
SIC: 2821 Plastics materials & resins
HQ: Formosa Plastics Corporation, U.S.A.
9 Peach Tree Hill Rd
Livingston NJ 07039
973 992-2090

(G-17085)
FORMOSA PLASTICS CORP TEXAS (DH)
201 Formosa Dr (77978)
P.O. Box 700 (77978-0700)
PHONE...................361 987-7000
Jason Lin, *President*
Ken Mounger, *Exec VP*
David Gaskamp, *Production*
Chris Chen, *Engineer*
Jerry Chou, *Engineer*
◆ EMP: 300
SQ FT: 225,000

SALES (est): 113.9MM **Privately Held**
WEB: www.fpcusa.com
SIC: 2821 Polyvinyl chloride resins (PVC)
HQ: Formosa Plastics Corporation, U.S.A.
9 Peach Tree Hill Rd
Livingston NJ 07039
973 992-2090

(G-17086)
FORMOSA UTILITY VENTURE LTD
301 Formosa Dr (77978)
P.O. Box 700 (77978-0700)
PHONE...................361 987-7000
Jay Su, *Partner*
Randy Nichols, *Supervisor*
▲ EMP: 1500
SQ FT: 4,500
SALES (est): 228.8MM **Privately Held**
WEB: www.fpcusa.com
SIC: 2821 Plastics materials & resins

(G-17087)
JR SIMPLOT COMPANY
Also Called: Simplot Grower Solutions
2301 Farm Market 1593 S (77978)
P.O. Box 947, Hempstead (77445-0947)
PHONE...................361 987-2682
EMP: 46
SALES (corp-wide): 4.8B **Privately Held**
WEB: www.simplot.com
SIC: 2037 2874 2873 2879 Potato products, quick frozen & cold pack; phosphatic fertilizers; nitrogenous fertilizers; agricultural chemicals; beef cattle feedlots
PA: J. R. Simplot Company
1099 W Front St
Boise ID 83702
208 336-2110

(G-17088)
LAVACA PIPE LINE COMPANY
103 Fannin Rd (77978)
P.O. Box 769 (77978-0769)
PHONE...................361 987-8900
Jack Wu, *President*
EMP: 40
SALES (est): 2MM **Privately Held**
WEB: www.fpcusa.com
SIC: 2821 Plastics materials & resins
HQ: Formosa Plastics Corporation, U.S.A.
9 Peach Tree Hill Rd
Livingston NJ 07039
973 992-2090

(G-17089)
NEUMIN PRODUCTION CO
103 Fannin Rd (77978)
P.O. Box 769 (77978-0769)
PHONE...................361 987-8900
EMP: 39
SQ FT: 7,500
SALES (est): 2MM **Privately Held**
WEB: www.fpcusa.com
SIC: 1311 Crude petroleum production; natural gas production
HQ: Formosa Plastics Corporation, U.S.A.
9 Peach Tree Hill Rd
Livingston NJ 07039
973 992-2090

Pollok
Angelina County

(G-17090)
ACCENT ENVIRONMENTAL SERVICES
Also Called: Gas System
523 Fm 1819 (75969-3203)
P.O. Box 3289, Lufkin (75903-3289)
PHONE...................936 853-2264
Daniel W Brevard, *President*
David Brevard, *President*
Eric Brevard, *Vice Pres*
Jim Kennedy, *Exec Dir*
Daniel Brevard, *Bd of Directors*
EMP: 10
SQ FT: 2,000 **Privately Held**
WEB: www.accent-us.com
SIC: 3829 Geophysical & meteorological testing equipment

(G-17091)
ARBOR RESOURCES LLC
3921 W State Highway 7 (75969-2429)
PHONE..................................936 632-9914
Jason Nichols,
Tracy S Nichols,
EMP: 10
SALES (est): 400K **Privately Held**
WEB: www.arborresourcesllctx.com
SIC: 4212 3599 5191 Local trucking, without storage; amusement park equipment; fertilizers & agricultural chemicals

Ponder
Denton County

(G-17092)
ABAC LLC
Also Called: Lonestar Shelter Manufacturing
141 Seaborn Rd (76259-9789)
PHONE..................................940 479-9163
Barbara Choplick,
Andrien Choplick,
EMP: 15
SQ FT: 17,600
SALES (est): 1.6MM **Privately Held**
WEB: www.lonestarshelter.com
SIC: 3448 Buildings, portable: prefabricated metal

(G-17093)
ADVANCED AERO COATINGS LLC
3361 Amyx Hill Rd (76259-8053)
PHONE..................................940 367-5963
Rodney Pittman, *Principal*
EMP: 15 **Privately Held**
WEB: www.advancedaerocoatings.com
SIC: 3471 3999 Plating & polishing; atomizers, toiletry
PA: Advanced Aero Coatings, Llc
9004 Trinity Blvd
Hurst TX 76053

(G-17094)
BENCHMARK METAL SERVICE INC
155 Seaborn Rd (76259-9789)
P.O. Box 746, Krum (76249-0746)
PHONE..................................940 479-9134
John L Dast, *Principal*
EMP: 30
SQ FT: 8,000
SALES (est): 7.4MM **Privately Held**
SIC: 3441 Fabricated structural metal

(G-17095)
MILLS MACHINE SHOP
11619 Bois D Arc Ln (76259-5127)
PHONE..................................940 479-2194
William Edward Mills, *Owner*
Linda Mills, *Office Mgr*
EMP: 9
SALES (est): 450K **Privately Held**
WEB: www.millsmachineshop.com
SIC: 3599 Machine shop, jobbing & repair

(G-17096)
TEXAS INTEGRITY WASTE
Also Called: North Txas Intgrity Sptic Pmpg
7588 Fm 2449 (76259-8056)
P.O. Box 458 (76259-0458)
PHONE..................................940 479-0189
Joe Hernandez, *Owner*
EMP: 10
SQ FT: 5,000
SALES (est): 977.9K **Privately Held**
WEB: www.texasintegrityseptic.com
SIC: 7699 3443 Septic tank cleaning service; dumpsters, garbage

(G-17097)
TULSA ARSPC CMPNENT OVRHAUL RE
Also Called: Tacor
8086 Fm 2449 (76259-8047)
P.O. Box 309 (76259-0309)
PHONE..................................940 479-2000
Michael Norwood, *President*
Vinicius Rondon, *Sales Staff*
Alicia Norwood, *VP Mktg*
EMP: 9
SQ FT: 4,000
SALES (est): 1MM **Privately Held**
WEB: www.tacor.net
SIC: 3728 Aircraft parts & equipment

Pontotoc
Mason County

(G-17098)
SOUTHWEST EARTH RESOURCES
Hwy 501 (76869)
P.O. Box 219 (76869-0219)
PHONE..................................325 251-6598
Gary Shepherd, *President*
EMP: 13
SQ FT: 15,000
SALES (est): 913.4K **Privately Held**
SIC: 1081 Metal mining services

Poolville
Parker County

(G-17099)
WISE COUNTY POWER COMPANY LLC
800 Boones Creek Ln (76487-5042)
PHONE..................................940 374-9925
Andrew J Rosenlieb, *President*
Steven C McNeal, *Treasurer*
Thomas G Wagner, *Admin Sec*
EMP: 23
SQ FT: 4,700
SALES (est): 4.6MM
SALES (corp-wide): 11.8B **Publicly Held**
SIC: 3621 Generators & sets, electric
HQ: Vistra Intermediate Company Llc
601 Travis St Ste 1400
Houston TX 77002
713 507-6400

Port Aransas
Nueces County

(G-17100)
SOUTHERN PUBLISHING INC
Also Called: South Jetty
141 W Cotter Ave (78373-4034)
P.O. Box 1117 (78373-1117)
PHONE..................................361 749-5131
Murray Judson, *President*
Judson Mary Henkel, *Vice Pres*
Mary Judson, *Vice Pres*
EMP: 9 **EST:** 1959
SQ FT: 1,000
SALES (est): 618.6K **Privately Held**
WEB: www.portasouthjetty.com
SIC: 2711 Newspapers: publishing only, not printed on site

Port Arthur
Jefferson County

(G-17101)
BASF CORPORATION
Gate 66 State Hwy 366 (77643)
P.O. Box 2506 (77643-2506)
PHONE..................................409 960-5000
Ronald Piper, *Project Mgr*
Dwight Hines, *Manager*
Elise Mophett, *Manager*
Robert Grissom, *Analyst*
EMP: 15
SALES (corp-wide): 65.6B **Privately Held**
WEB: www.basf.com
SIC: 2869 Industrial organic chemicals
HQ: Basf Corporation
100 Park Ave
Florham Park NJ 07932
973 245-6000

(G-17102)
BGI CONTRACTORS INC
Also Called: United Marine Shipyard
2410 Coke Dock Rd (77642)
P.O. Box 22077, Beaumont (77720-2077)
PHONE..................................409 833-0303
Jimmy Jolivet,

A B Bernard Jr,
EMP: 185
SALES (est): 16.7MM **Privately Held**
WEB: www.bgitexas.us
SIC: 1629 8711 3443 Industrial plant construction; engineering services; industrial vessels, tanks & containers; pipe, large diameter: metal plate; cylinders, pressure: metal plate

(G-17103)
CAMIN CARGO CONTROL INC
1550 Industrial Park Dr (77640)
PHONE..................................409 729-3399
Rodney Broussard, *Manager*
EMP: 28
SALES (corp-wide): 67.5MM **Privately Held**
WEB: www.camincargo.com
SIC: 1389 Oil field services
PA: Camin Cargo Control, Inc.
230 Marion Ave
Linden NJ 07036
908 523-0616

(G-17104)
CHEVRON PHILLIPS CHEM CO LP
Also Called: Cpchem
2001 Gulfway Dr (77640-4534)
P.O. Box 1547 (77641-1547)
PHONE..................................409 985-0700
Mike Richard, *Maint Spvr*
Robert King, *Purch Agent*
Marian Ruiz, *Purch Agent*
Giacomo Figlia, *Project Engr*
Michael Nemeth, *Manager*
EMP: 280
SALES (corp-wide): 3.5B **Privately Held**
WEB: www.cpchem.com
SIC: 2821 Plastics materials & resins
HQ: Chevron Phillips Chemical Company Lp
10001 Six Pines Dr
The Woodlands TX 77380
832 813-4100

(G-17105)
CLIMATE CONTROL CONTAINERS
6648 Gulfway Dr (77642-0315)
PHONE..................................409 963-2137
EMP: 15
SQ FT: 20,000
SALES (est): 1.6MM **Privately Held**
SIC: 3412 Climate Controlled Shipping Containers

(G-17106)
ECHO MAINTENANCE LLC
6711 N Twin City Hwy (77642-6423)
P.O. Box 1915, Nederland (77627-1915)
PHONE..................................409 724-0456
Michael P Roebuck, *President*
Teddy Brisendine, *Superintendent*
Carroll Coco Fontenot, *Superintendent*
Denny Latiolais, *Superintendent*
Bruce Mays, *Superintendent*
EMP: 200
SQ FT: 8,000
SALES (est): 116.2MM **Privately Held**
WEB: www.echomaintenance.com
SIC: 1541 3498 1623 Industrial buildings, new construction; steel building construction; renovation, remodeling & repairs: industrial buildings; fabricated pipe & fittings; water, sewer & utility lines

(G-17107)
ECOWATER INDUSTRIES LLC
Also Called: Eco Werks
6200 Procter St Ext (77642)
P.O. Box 831986, Richardson (75083-1986)
PHONE..................................214 878-6527
Michael Laws, *President*
Joe Hollis, *General Mgr*
Heath Gaspard, *Facilities Mgr*
Hali Raggio, *Opers-Prdtn-Mfg*
Christine Casalas, *Director*
▲ **EMP:** 15
SQ FT: 8,000
SALES (est): 3.1MM **Privately Held**
WEB: www.ecowerks.com
SIC: 3589 Water treatment equipment, industrial

(G-17108)
FLOWSERVE CORPORATION
2220 Highway 365 (77640-1587)
PHONE..................................409 727-1476
Chad Gilchrist, *Sales Engr*
Stewart Shoefstall, *Manager*
EMP: 50
SALES (corp-wide): 3.9B **Publicly Held**
WEB: www.flowserve.com
SIC: 3561 Industrial pumps & parts
PA: Flowserve Corporation
5215 N Ocnnor Blvd Ste 23 Connor
Irving TX 75039
972 443-6500

(G-17109)
GULF COAST FABRICATORS INC (PA)
6711 N Twin City Hwy (77642-6423)
P.O. Box 1915, Nederland (77627-1915)
PHONE..................................409 727-2372
Phillip Roebuck, *President*
Mike Roebuck, *Vice Pres*
EMP: 50
SQ FT: 8,000
SALES (est): 11.5MM **Privately Held**
WEB: www.gulfcoastsheetmetal.com
SIC: 3441 Fabricated structural metal

(G-17110)
GULF COAST POWDR GELWORKS INC
Also Called: Gulf Coast Automotive
4141 32nd St (77642-2402)
P.O. Box 875, Groves (77619-0875)
PHONE..................................409 962-1211
Gabrielle Nessour, *President*
Frank Nessour, *Vice Pres*
EMP: 20
SQ FT: 2,800
SALES (est): 1.8MM **Privately Held**
SIC: 3479 Coating of metals & formed products

(G-17111)
GULF COPPER & MFG CORP (PA)
5700 Procter Ext (77642-0936)
PHONE..................................409 989-0300
Steve Hale, *President*
Eric Callarman, *General Mgr*
Burt Moorhouse, *General Mgr*
Carl Trent, *General Mgr*
Oscar Alberdin, *Superintendent*
▲ **EMP:** 15 **EST:** 1950
SQ FT: 18,000
SALES: 65.3MM **Privately Held**
WEB: www.gulfcopper.com
SIC: 3731 3599 3312 3732 Commercial cargo ships, building & repairing; machine shop, jobbing & repair; blast furnaces & steel mills; boat building & repairing; fabricated pipe & fittings; fabricated structural metal

(G-17112)
GULF COPPER & MFG CORP
Also Called: Machine Shop
2020 Gulfway Dr (77640-4533)
PHONE..................................409 982-6122
A Morris, *Principal*
EMP: 110
SALES (corp-wide): 65.3MM **Privately Held**
WEB: www.gulfcopper.com
SIC: 4493 7692 3731 1721 Boat yards, storage & incidental repair; welding repair; shipbuilding & repairing; painting & paper hanging
PA: Gulf Copper & Manufacturing Corporation
5700 Procter Ext
Port Arthur TX 77642
409 989-0300

(G-17113)
INEOS AMERICAS LLC
2001 Gulfway Dr (77640-4534)
PHONE..................................409 985-0863
Ray Walker, *Branch Mgr*
EMP: 34
SALES (corp-wide): 1.9MM **Privately Held**
WEB: www.ineos.com
SIC: 2821 Plastics materials & resins

HQ: Ineos Americas Llc
2600 S Shore Blvd Ste 500
League City TX 77573
251 535-6600

(G-17114)
JBS PACKING COMPANY INC
2170 Gulfway Dr (77640-4535)
P.O. Box 399 (77641-0399)
PHONE...................................409 982-5766
Mark Leckich, *Production*
EMP: 40
SALES (corp-wide): 45.3MM **Privately Held**
WEB: www.jbspackinginc.com
SIC: 5146 5812 5421 2092 Seafoods; seafood restaurants; fish & seafood markets; fresh or frozen packaged fish
PA: Jbs Packing Company, Inc.
101 Houston Ave
Port Arthur TX 77640
409 982-3216

(G-17115)
KT FOODS LLC
1520 Sabine Ave (77642-1652)
PHONE...................................409 293-3257
Jeff Roth,
▲ EMP: 85
SALES (est): 10.6MM **Privately Held**
SIC: 2033 Olives: packaged in cans, jars, etc.

(G-17116)
LIMA REFINING COMPANY
1801 Gulfway Dr (77640-4416)
PHONE...................................409 985-1000
Don Kinsley, *Branch Mgr*
EMP: 85
SALES (corp-wide): 1.6B **Privately Held**
WEB: www.huskyenergy.com
SIC: 5172 2911 Petroleum products; petroleum refining
HQ: Lima Refining Company
1150 S Metcalf St
Lima OH 45804
419 226-2300

(G-17117)
MAGNUM FABRICATIONS INC
Also Called: Magnum Fire & Safety Systems
6648 Gulfway Dr (77642-0315)
PHONE...................................409 963-0161
Kenneth Broussard, *CEO*
Jeanne Licatino, *President*
Mitsy May, *Buyer*
Linda Broussard, *Admin Sec*
▲ EMP: 20 EST: 1980
SQ FT: 60,000
SALES (est): 4MM **Privately Held**
WEB: www.magnumfire.com
SIC: 3569 Firefighting apparatus

(G-17118)
MBLH MARINE LLC
Also Called: Vessel Repair
5848 Procter Ext (77642-0900)
P.O. Box 965, Groves (77619-0965)
PHONE...................................409 962-1302
Ben Pate, *Project Mgr*
Keegan Guidry, *Human Resources*
Ron Moerbe, *Mng Member*
Mike Batson,
Wilson Lemaire,
EMP: 75
SQ FT: 270,000
SALES (est): 6MM **Privately Held**
SIC: 3731 Barges, building & repairing

(G-17119)
OLIVE PACKING COMPANY INC
Also Called: Olive Packing Company, The
1500 Sabine Ave (77642-1652)
PHONE...................................409 293-3257
Eric Moscahlaidis, *President*
Evee Moscahlaidis, *Vice Pres*
▲ EMP: 90
SQ FT: 35,000
SALES (est): 15.5MM
SALES (corp-wide): 46.7MM **Privately Held**
WEB: www.olivepackingcompany.com
SIC: 2033 Olives: packaged in cans, jars, etc.

(G-17120)
PAGE EAGLE INDUSTRIES INC
1520 Woodworth Blvd (77640-4655)
PHONE...................................409 960-4310
Don Page, *President*
EMP: 10 EST: 2015
SALES (est): 364.8K **Privately Held**
SIC: 3999 Manufacturing industries

(G-17121)
PAT TANK INC
2146 5th Ave (77642-5162)
P.O. Box L, Groves (77619-1259)
PHONE...................................409 982-7319
E L Ellerbee, *CEO*
Hans Jorgensen, *President*
David Hitt, *Vice Pres*
EMP: 100
SQ FT: 20,000
SALES: 19.4MM **Privately Held**
WEB: www.pattank.com
SIC: 1791 3443 Storage tanks, metal: erection; tanks, standard or custom fabricated: metal plate

(G-17122)
RAMSEY PROPERTIES LP
Also Called: Kmtex
2450 Gulfway Dr (77640-4541)
P.O. Box 1421 (77641-1421)
PHONE...................................409 985-4200
David Spotcheck, *Manager*
EMP: 25
SALES (corp-wide): 34.7MM **Privately Held**
WEB: www.kmcoinc.com
SIC: 4785 2879 Toll operations; agricultural chemicals
PA: Ramsey Properties, L.P.
16503 Ramsey Rd
Crosby TX 77532
281 328-3501

(G-17123)
ROBOGISTICS LLC
3451 57th St (77642-5902)
PHONE...................................713 364-4430
JC Caraway, *Branch Mgr*
EMP: 26
SQ FT: 36,000
SALES (corp-wide): 5.8MM **Privately Held**
WEB: www.txrobogistics.com
SIC: 3646 8731 Commercial indusl & institutional electric lighting fixtures; commercial research laboratory
PA: Robogistics Llc
363 N Sam Houston Pkwy E # 1100
Houston TX 77060
409 234-1033

(G-17124)
SANDIFERS LP GAS & SVC CO INC
5812 Gulfway Dr (77642-0307)
P.O. Box 3671 (77643-3671)
PHONE...................................409 963-1269
EMP: 11
SQ FT: 4,500
SALES (est): 3.7MM **Privately Held**
WEB: www.sandiferslp.com
SIC: 5984 7359 2911 5172 Propane gas, bottled; propane equipment rental; liquefied petroleum gases, LPG; gases, liquefied petroleum (propane)

(G-17125)
STANDARD ALLOYS INCORPORATED (DH)
201 Lakeshore Dr (77640-6421)
P.O. Box 969 (77641-0969)
PHONE...................................409 983-3201
Wolfgang Demmler, *Ch of Bd*
Richard Martinez, *President*
Jim Hewitt, *Vice Pres*
Larry Tagliabue, *Vice Pres*
Gary Scheff, *Plant Mgr*
EMP: 70 EST: 2010
SQ FT: 25,000
SALES: 17.4K
SALES (corp-wide): 144.1K **Privately Held**
WEB: www.ksb.com
SIC: 3322 3599 Malleable iron foundries; machine shop, jobbing & repair

(G-17126)
STEPHEN JONES
Also Called: S&K Residential Rmdlg Repr Co
4105 Ferndale Dr (77642-2547)
PHONE...................................409 460-8609
Stephen Jones, *Owner*
EMP: 12
SALES (est): 226.9K **Privately Held**
SIC: 1389 Construction, repair & dismantling services

(G-17127)
TAYLOR METAL WORKS & PIPE CO
215 W Highway 365 (77640-6936)
PHONE...................................409 736-3555
Thomas H Taylor, *President*
Charmain H Taylor, *Vice Pres*
Allan Ray, *Plant Mgr*
EMP: 50 EST: 1976
SQ FT: 15,000
SALES (est): 9MM **Privately Held**
WEB: www.taylormetalworks.com
SIC: 3444 Sheet metalwork

(G-17128)
TEAM FABRICATORS LLC
650 Main Ave (77642-0960)
PHONE...................................409 962-0266
John Panetti, *President*
Michael Mincks, *Vice Pres*
Timothy Monday, *Vice Pres*
Richard Stadelman, *Vice Pres*
EMP: 75
SALES (est): 14.8MM
SALES (corp-wide): 120.3MM **Privately Held**
WEB: www.teamind.com
SIC: 3498 3795 3441 3499 Fabricated pipe & fittings; tanks & tank components; fabricated structural metal; welding tips, heat resistant: metal
PA: Team Industries, Inc.
1200 Maloney Rd
Kaukauna WI 54130
920 766-7977

(G-17129)
TOTAL PTRCHEMICALS REF USA INC
Also Called: Port Arthur Refinery
Hwy 366 And 32nd St (77642)
P.O. Box 849 (77641-0849)
PHONE...................................409 963-6837
Alison Hills, *Vice Pres*
Hannah Sennett, *Safety Mgr*
Ryan Riffer, *Opers Staff*
Wouter Raemdonck, *Opers-Prdtn-Mfg*
Delbert Arendale, *Purch Mgr*
EMP: 450
SALES (corp-wide): 7B **Publicly Held**
WEB: www.totalpetrochemicalsrefiningusa.com
SIC: 2821 Plastics materials & resins
HQ: Total Petrochemicals & Refining Usa, Inc.
1201 La St Ste 1800
Houston TX 77002
713 483-5000

(G-17130)
TOTAL PTRCHEMICALS REF USA INC
7600 32nd St (77642-7901)
PHONE...................................409 963-6800
Stephen Focken, *Engineer*
Dan Durham, *Manager*
Ernest Anderson, *Manager*
EMP: 265
SALES (corp-wide): 7B **Publicly Held**
WEB: www.totalpetrochemicalsrefiningusa.com
SIC: 2911 2899 2869 Petroleum refining; chemical preparations; industrial organic chemicals

HQ: Total Petrochemicals & Refining Usa, Inc.
1201 La St Ste 1800
Houston TX 77002
713 483-5000

(G-17131)
UNITED INSUL SLS FBRCATION INC (DH)
Also Called: Black Hawk Specialty
6401 N Twin City Hwy (77642-6219)
P.O. Box 2228, Nederland (77627-8228)
PHONE...................................409 727-3191
Kathleen Brau, *President*
EMP: 15
SQ FT: 50,000
SALES (est): 5MM
SALES (corp-wide): 421MM **Privately Held**
WEB: www.franksinternational.com
SIC: 3296 5099 Mineral wool; safety equipment & supplies
HQ: Lecco Industries Inc
6401 N Twin City Hwy
Port Arthur TX 77642
409 727-3191

(G-17132)
VLS RECOVERY SERVICES LLC
Also Called: Vls Marine Services
8700 Yacht Club Rd (77642)
PHONE...................................409 962-8800
Eddie Van Huis, *Manager*
EMP: 100
SALES (corp-wide): 43.1MM **Privately Held**
WEB: www.vlsrs.com
SIC: 3731 Shipbuilding & repairing
PA: Vls Recovery Services, Llc
17020 Premium Dr
Hockley TX 77447
936 372-0464

(G-17133)
WILLIAMS FIRE HAZARD CTRL INC (DH)
9605 Richard Wycoff (77640-2038)
PHONE...................................409 745-3232
Dwight Williams, *President*
Roger Bower, *Principal*
Lindsey Boren, *Materials Mgr*
Troy Johnson, *Sales Mgr*
Thomas Jones, *Sales Staff*
EMP: 50
SQ FT: 10,000
SALES (est): 16.3MM **Privately Held**
WEB: www.williamsfire.com
SIC: 8711 7389 5099 3599 Fire protection engineering; designing: ship, boat, machine & product; fire protection service other than forestry or public; safety equipment & supplies; custom machinery
HQ: Tyco Fire Products Lp
1400 Pennbrook Pkwy
Lansdale PA 19446
215 362-0700

Port Bolivar
Galveston County

(G-17134)
ROYCE TOWER SERVICE INC
2323 Madison Ave (77650-1900)
P.O. Box 883 (77650-0883)
PHONE...................................409 684-1913
Ray Royce, *President*
Linda Royce, *Corp Secy*
EMP: 11
SALES (est): 1.3MM **Privately Held**
SIC: 3441 1623 Tower sections, radio & television transmission; transmitting tower (telecommunication) construction

Port Isabel
Cameron County

(G-17135)
BRYANT INDUSTRIAL SERVICES LLC
Also Called: Bryant Manufacturing
125 Taylor Ave (78578)
P.O. Box 2460, South Padre Island (78597-2460)
PHONE..................................956 838-5120
Daniel Bryant, *Mng Member*
EMP: 35
SALES (est): 5.8MM **Privately Held**
WEB: www.bryantindustrialservices.com
SIC: 1389 Construction, repair & dismantling services

(G-17136)
CEMEX CONSTRUCTION MTLS S LLC
Also Called: Port Isabel Rm
1250 Port Rd (78578-3704)
PHONE..................................956 943-2472
Victor Garza, *Manager*
EMP: 36 **Privately Held**
WEB: www.cemexusa.com
SIC: 3273 Ready-mixed concrete
HQ: Cemex Construction Materials South, Llc
2088 E 20th St
Yuma AZ 85365
928 343-4100

(G-17137)
NEW HORIZON PUBLISHERS
Also Called: Port Isabel Press
101 E Maxan St (78578-4504)
P.O. Box 308 (78578-0308)
PHONE..................................956 943-5545
Danno Wise, *President*
Logan Hawkes, *Editor*
EMP: 12
SQ FT: 2,934
SALES (est): 607.6K **Privately Held**
WEB: www.portisabelsouthpadre.com
SIC: 2711 Commercial printing & newspaper publishing combined

(G-17138)
TEXAS PACK INC
508 Port Rd (78578-3713)
P.O. Box 1643 (78578-1643)
PHONE..................................956 943-5461
Sammy Snodgrass, *President*
Dolby Linwood, *Vice Pres*
Carlton Reyes, *Treasurer*
Harley Londrie, *Admin Sec*
EMP: 385
SQ FT: 50,000
SALES (est): 45.6MM **Privately Held**
WEB: www.texaspack.net
SIC: 4222 2092 2037 Storage, frozen or refrigerated goods; shrimp, fresh: prepared; vegetables, quick frozen & cold pack, excl. potato products

(G-17139)
TEXGULMARCO CO INC
400 E Washington St (78578-4517)
PHONE..................................956 943-2673
Walter W Zimmerman, *President*
Londrie Harley, *Vice Pres*
Harley Londrie, *Vice Pres*
Patricia Zimmerman Assistant, *Admin Sec*
Cecil Moses, *Admin Sec*
EMP: 40
SALES (est): 2.7MM **Privately Held**
SIC: 3731 5551 0913 6799 Fishing vessels, large: building & repairing; marine supplies; shrimp, catching of; investors

(G-17140)
VECO PRINTING INC
33840 S Garcia St # 866 (78578-4361)
PHONE..................................956 968-1589
Clive W Roe Jr, *President*
Jeannette Roe, *Corp Secy*
Jeanette Sims, *Vice Pres*
EMP: 12

SALES (est): 2.3MM **Privately Held**
WEB: www.d2oh.com
SIC: 2679 2752 Labels, paper: made from purchased material; commercial printing, offset

Port Lavaca
Calhoun County

(G-17141)
ALAMO CONCRETE PRODUCTS LTD
Also Called: Alamo Ready Mix Concrete
2049 W Main St (77979-3651)
PHONE..................................361 552-9525
Bryan Ester, *Branch Mgr*
EMP: 11 **Privately Held**
SIC: 3273 Ready-mixed concrete
PA: Alamo Concrete Products, Ltd.
6055 W Green Mountain Rd
Austin TX 78744

(G-17142)
BRASKEM AMERICA INC
7501 State Hwy 185 N (77979)
P.O. Box 105 (77979-0105)
PHONE..................................215 841-3100
EMP: 9 **Privately Held**
WEB: www.braskem.com
SIC: 2821 2865 2869 Polypropylene resins; polyesters; acrylic resins; plasticizer/additive based plastic materials; cyclic crudes & intermediates; phenol, alkylated & cumene; aniline, nitrobenzene; diphenylamines; acetone, synthetic; alcohols, non-beverage
HQ: Braskem America, Inc.
1735 Market St Fl 28
Philadelphia PA 19103
215 841-3100

(G-17143)
CALHOUN CHEMICAL LLC
11674 State Highway 185 N (77979-7000)
PHONE..................................713 254-8974
EMP: 24
SALES (est): 315.7K **Privately Held**
WEB: www.calhounchemicals.com
SIC: 2899 Chemical preparations

(G-17144)
COASTAL PLAINS EXPLORATION LLC
323 Alcoa Dr (77979-3603)
PHONE..................................361 553-9000
King Tomlinson, *President*
John Foester, *Vice Pres*
Jim Gilstrap, *Vice Pres*
Priscilla Parsons, *Programmer Anys*
EMP: 12
SALES (est): 1.2MM **Privately Held**
WEB: www.coastal-plains.com
SIC: 1381 1781 Drilling water intake wells; directional drilling oil & gas wells; water well drilling

(G-17145)
EL PASO FIELD SERVICES LP
1234 Rosenbaum Rd (77979-5626)
PHONE..................................361 552-9601
Robert Shimek, *District Mgr*
EMP: 10 **Publicly Held**
WEB: www.kindermorgan.com
SIC: 4922 1389 Pipelines, natural gas; gas compressing (natural gas) at the fields
HQ: El Paso Field Services, L.P.
1001 Louisiana St
Houston TX 77002

(G-17146)
ENDEAVOUR MACHINE AND FAB INC
Also Called: Leverage Machine & Fabrication
2512 Fm 3084 (77979-6146)
P.O. Box 875, Palacios (77465-0875)
PHONE..................................361 551-2077
Greg Garcia, *Director*
Jaime Garcia, *Director*
Bryan Porche, *Director*
EMP: 10 EST: 2016
SQ FT: 10,000

SALES (est): 1.1MM **Privately Held**
SIC: 3441 Fabricated structural metal

(G-17147)
INEOS LLC
13050 Texas Hwy 185 (77979)
P.O. Box 659 (77979-0659)
PHONE..................................361 552-8205
Derrick Scott, *Opers Staff*
Paul Wachtendorf, *Engineer*
Carlos Ortiz, *Project Engr*
Jessica Lidiak, *Financial Analy*
Kathy Schuessler, *Sales Staff*
EMP: 131 **Privately Held**
WEB: www.ineos.com
SIC: 2821 Plastics materials & resins
PA: Ineos, L.L.C.
1900 Fort Amanda Rd
Lima OH 45804

(G-17148)
INEOS AMERICAS LLC
S Of Bloomington (77979)
P.O. Box 659 (77979-0659)
PHONE..................................361 552-8244
Sean Hockett, *Engineer*
Chrish Raju, *Manager*
EMP: 300
SALES (est): 1.9MM **Privately Held**
WEB: www.ineos.com
SIC: 2821 5172 Plastics materials & resins; petroleum products
HQ: Ineos Americas Llc
2600 S Shore Blvd Ste 500
League City TX 77573
251 535-6600

(G-17149)
INEOS NITRILES USA LLC
13050 State Highway 185 N (77979-7208)
P.O. Box 659 (77979-0659)
PHONE..................................361 552-8200
Paul Wachtendorf, *Branch Mgr*
Gerald Jurica, *Manager*
EMP: 200
SALES (corp-wide): 1.9MM **Privately Held**
WEB: www.ineos.com
SIC: 2869 2873 2899 Industrial organic chemicals; nitrogenous fertilizers; chemical preparations
HQ: Ineos Nitriles Usa Llc
2600 S Shore Blvd Ste 250
League City TX 77573

(G-17150)
INGRAM READYMIX INC
3627 State Highway 35 S (77979-5584)
PHONE..................................361 552-6071
Ken Cox, *Manager*
EMP: 20
SALES (corp-wide): 125.6MM **Privately Held**
WEB: www.ingramreadymixinc.com
SIC: 3273 Ready-mixed concrete
PA: Ingram Readymix, Inc.
3580 Farm Market 482
New Braunfels TX 78132
830 625-9156

(G-17151)
MILLER SEAFOOD CO INC (PA)
Also Called: Miller's Sea Food
1102 Broadway St (77979-2716)
PHONE..................................361 552-6423
Curtis Miller, *President*
Lisa Miller, *Corp Secy*
George W Miller Jr, *Vice Pres*
EMP: 25 EST: 1976
SQ FT: 1,200
SALES (est): 2.6MM **Privately Held**
WEB: www.millerseafoodportlavacatx.business.site
SIC: 5421 2032 Seafood markets; Mexican foods: packaged in cans, jars, etc.

(G-17152)
MOREMAN COMMUNITY GIN ASSN
10254 State Highway 35 S (77979-6270)
PHONE..................................361 552-9407
Richard Williams, *President*
Theodore Kallus, *General Mgr*
Michael W Hahn, *Vice Pres*
Mike Mutchler, *Admin Sec*

EMP: 35
SQ FT: 1,200
SALES (est): 3.6MM **Privately Held**
SIC: 2879 Pesticides, agricultural or household

(G-17153)
PALACIOS PROCESSORS INC
Also Called: Lighthouse Seafood
625 State Highway 316 (77979-5972)
P.O. Box 263, Palacios (77465-0263)
PHONE..................................361 552-1231
Ronald A Benner, *President*
EMP: 70 EST: 1992
SQ FT: 25,000
SALES (est): 5.2MM **Privately Held**
SIC: 2092 Seafoods, fresh: prepared

(G-17154)
PORT LAVACA WAVE
107 E Austin St (77979-4402)
P.O. Box 88 (77979-0088)
PHONE..................................361 552-9788
Tania French, *President*
William Hartman, *President*
Don Jones, *Corp Secy*
Clyde King, *Vice Pres*
EMP: 20
SQ FT: 3,200
SALES (est): 1.5MM
SALES (corp-wide): 32.2MM **Privately Held**
WEB: www.portlavacawave.com
SIC: 2711 2752 Newspapers, publishing & printing; commercial printing, lithographic
PA: Hartman Newspapers L.P.
1914 4th St
Rosenberg TX 77471
281 342-8691

(G-17155)
SEADRIFT COKE LP
8618 Hwy 185 N (77979)
P.O. Box 192 (77979-0192)
PHONE..................................361 552-8887
Hermanus L Pretorius, *President*
Jim Trigg Jr, *Partner*
John Bassett, *General Ptnr*
Eric Wheelock, *Vice Pres*
Larry Stone, *Maint Spvr*
EMP: 117
SALES (est): 28.5MM
SALES (corp-wide): 50.9B **Publicly Held**
WEB: www.seadriftcoke.com
SIC: 3312 Coke oven products (chemical recovery)
HQ: Graftech International Ltd.
982 Keynote Cir Ste 6
Brooklyn Heights OH 44131

(G-17156)
WELFAB INC
3839 Fm 2541 (77979-5977)
P.O. Box 103 (77979-0103)
PHONE..................................361 552-4033
Thomas L Crenshaw, *President*
Thomas Crenshaw, *President*
Sandra Crenshaw, *Vice Pres*
EMP: 50
SQ FT: 15,800
SALES (est): 4.2MM **Privately Held**
WEB: www.welfab.net
SIC: 1711 7692 Mechanical contractor; welding repair

Port Neches
Jefferson County

(G-17157)
AIR LIQUIDE AMERICA LP
2121 Park St (77651-3500)
P.O. Box 967 (77651-0967)
PHONE..................................409 720-4200
David Mullin, *Manager*
EMP: 14
SALES (corp-wide): 129.8MM **Privately Held**
WEB: www.industry.airliquide.us
SIC: 2813 5084 3533 4931 Industrial gases; industrial machinery & equipment; oil & gas field machinery; electric & other services combined

HQ: Air Liquide America L.P.
9811 Katy Fwy Ste 100
Houston TX 77024
713 624-8000

(G-17158)
ASHLAND LLC
Also Called: Isp Elastomers
1015 Main St (77651)
PHONE...................................973 628-3245
John M Clark, *Manager*
EMP: 219
SALES (corp-wide): 2.3B **Publicly Held**
WEB: www.ashland.com
SIC: 2869 Industrial organic chemicals
HQ: Ashland Llc
50 E Rivercenter Blvd # 16
Covington KY 41011
859 815-3333

(G-17159)
DUNN PALLET CO
Also Called: Groves Pallet Company
516 Orchard Ave (77651-3144)
PHONE...................................409 722-2933
Andrew W Dunn, *President*
Katherine E Dunn, *Corp Secy*
John D Dunn, *Vice Pres*
EMP: 48 EST: 1967
SQ FT: 53,000
SALES (est): 9.5MM **Privately Held**
WEB: www.grovespalletcompany.com
SIC: 2448 Pallets, wood

(G-17160)
FEATHERLITE CORP
1600 Main St (77651-3032)
P.O. Box 357 (77651-0357)
PHONE...................................409 727-8800
EMP: 23
SQ FT: 11,804
SALES (est): 1.9MM **Privately Held**
SIC: 3271 Mfg Concrete Block/Brick

(G-17161)
G V C HOLDINGS INC
1215 Main St (77651-3038)
PHONE...................................409 722-8321
Mahendra Parekh, *President*
EMP: 450
SALES (est): 24.2MM **Privately Held**
SIC: 2822 2895 3069 Chlorinated rubbers, synthetic; carbon black; latex, foamed

(G-17162)
HAUCK ENTERPRISES LTD (PA)
342 Twin City Hwy (77651-6203)
P.O. Box 70 (77651-0070)
PHONE...................................409 727-2227
James Hauck, *President*
EMP: 22
SQ FT: 2,000
SALES (est): 5.5MM **Privately Held**
WEB: www.hauckent.com
SIC: 3272 0782 Burial vaults, concrete or precast terrazzo; lawn services

(G-17163)
HUNTSMAN CORPORATION
Port Neches Operations Tio T Neches
Opera (77651)
P.O. Box 847 (77651-0847)
PHONE...................................409 722-8381
Karen Carnahan, *Sales Staff*
Eric Holdt, *Sales Staff*
David Harvick, *Branch Mgr*
Bob Townley-Smith, *Manager*
Bryan Collins, *Technology*
EMP: 215
SALES (corp-wide): 6.8B **Publicly Held**
WEB: www.ir.huntsman.com
SIC: 2821 Plastics materials & resins
PA: Huntsman Corporation
10003 Woodloch Forest Dr # 260
The Woodlands TX 77380
281 719-6000

(G-17164)
HUNTSMAN PETROCHEMICAL LLC
2701 Spur 136 (77651-4320)
P.O. Box 847 (77651-0847)
PHONE...................................409 722-8381
Chad Anderson, *Manager*
EMP: 600

SALES (corp-wide): 6.8B **Publicly Held**
WEB: www.huntsman.com
SIC: 2821 Plastics materials & resins
HQ: Huntsman Petrochemical Llc
500 S Huntsman Way
Salt Lake City UT 84108
801 584-5700

(G-17165)
HUNTSMAN PETROCHEMICAL LLC
6001 Highway 366 (77651-6304)
PHONE...................................409 724-4474
Steve Holland, *Branch Mgr*
EMP: 113
SALES (corp-wide): 6.8B **Publicly Held**
WEB: www.huntsman.com
SIC: 2821 Plastics materials & resins
HQ: Huntsman Petrochemical Llc
500 S Huntsman Way
Salt Lake City UT 84108
801 584-5700

(G-17166)
INEOS CALABRIAN CORPORATION
5500 Highway 366 (77651-6300)
PHONE...................................409 727-1471
Benny Deters, *Principal*
Roberto Gutierez, *Manager*
EMP: 40
SALES (corp-wide): 1.9MM **Privately Held**
WEB: www.ineoscalabrian.com
SIC: 2869 2819 Industrial organic chemicals; industrial inorganic chemicals
HQ: Ineos Calabrian Corporation
1521 Green Oak Pl Ste 200
Kingwood TX 77339
281 348-2303

(G-17167)
OSBORNE CABINETS & MILLWORK
Also Called: Osborne Cabinets Millwork
1420 Graham Ln (77651-5528)
PHONE...................................713 802-0092
Doyle Osborne, *Owner*
EMP: 25
SALES (corp-wide): 2.2MM **Privately Held**
WEB: www.osbornecabinets.com
SIC: 2434 5031 Wood kitchen cabinets; millwork
PA: Osborne Cabinets & Millwork Inc
8080 Eastex Fwy
Beaumont TX 77708
409 899-1191

(G-17168)
STERLING SHIPYARD LP
906 Main St (77651-2538)
PHONE...................................409 727-2009
Hary Murdock, *CEO*
Brad Taylor, *COO*
Sing W You, *CFO*
EMP: 35
SQ FT: 15,360
SALES (est): 9.3MM **Privately Held**
WEB: www.sterlingshipyard.net
SIC: 3731 Shipbuilding & repairing

(G-17169)
TEXAS PETROCHEMICALS LP
2102 Spur 136 (77651-4313)
PHONE...................................409 724-4857
Mike McDonald, *CEO*
Charles Graham, *Vice Pres*
Tony Wisenbaker, *Site Mgr*
Thomas Tidwell, *Engineer*
Koy Guilbeau, *Controller*
EMP: 158 **Privately Held**
WEB: www.tpcgrp.com
SIC: 2869 Industrial organic chemicals
HQ: Texas Petrochemicals Lp
500 Dallas St Ste 2000
Houston TX 77002
713 477-9211

Porter
Montgomery County

(G-17170)
ACACIA ORIGINALS LLC
17415 Louis Ln (77365-3373)
PHONE...................................877 565-5995
William L Fuller III, *Mng Member*
Loretta Hill, *Officer*
EMP: 17
SQ FT: 7,000
SALES (est): 3MM **Privately Held**
WEB: www.acaciaoriginals.com
SIC: 2514 2521 Metal household furniture; wood office furniture

(G-17171)
CALUMET BRANDED PRODUCTS LLC
Also Called: Royal Purple
1 Royal Purple Ln (77365-5143)
PHONE...................................281 354-8600
Dwight Wiggins, *Principal*
A Gustavsen, *Vice Pres*
Leigh McClellan, *Plant Mgr*
William Brooks, *Prdtn Mgr*
Veronica Baker, *Materials Mgr*
EMP: 68 **Publicly Held**
WEB: www.calumetspecialty.com
SIC: 2911 Lubricating oils
HQ: Calumet Branded Products, Llc
10411 Highway 1
Shreveport LA 71115

(G-17172)
CARBIDE SPECIALISTS INC
Also Called: Csi
21782 E Wallis Dr (77365-5365)
PHONE...................................281 354-5585
William E Algeo, *President*
Debra Algeo, *Treasurer*
EMP: 15 EST: 1981
SALES (est): 3.1MM **Privately Held**
SIC: 2819 Carbides

(G-17173)
CR MACHINE
23411 Albert Dr (77365-6007)
PHONE...................................281 354-4755
Carlos Rojas, *Owner*
EMP: 12
SALES (est): 2.3MM **Privately Held**
WEB: www.crmach.com
SIC: 3599 Machine shop, jobbing & repair

(G-17174)
DUNN ENTERPRISES INC (PA)
Also Called: Gulf States Abrasives
23438 Dunn Ln (77365-6401)
PHONE...................................713 869-4841
Freeman B Dunn, *President*
W T Dunn, *Exec VP*
Ronnie Archer, *Vice Pres*
Craig Dunn, *Vice Pres*
Thurman J Dunn, *Treasurer*
EMP: 46
SALES (est): 13.5MM **Privately Held**
SIC: 3291 5084 Abrasive products; welding machinery & equipment

(G-17175)
EAKIN INDUSTRIES LLC
24632 Hosford Meadows Dr (77365-3082)
P.O. Box 730 (77365-0730)
PHONE...................................281 620-8625
Damien Eakin,
▲ EMP: 9
SALES (est): 947K **Privately Held**
WEB: www.eakinindustries.com
SIC: 3999 Barber & beauty shop equipment

(G-17176)
FORD STEEL LLC
24800 Ford Rd (77365-5450)
PHONE...................................281 354-3011
Herbert Jeffries, *President*
Mary Jeffries, *Co-Owner*
Mark McElroy, *CFO*
Chad Jeffries, *Sales Staff*
Ross McGee, *Sales Staff*
▼ EMP: 70
SQ FT: 60,000

SALES (est): 20.4MM **Privately Held**
WEB: www.fordsteelllc.com
SIC: 3441 Building components, structural steel

(G-17177)
GULF STATES ABRASIVE MFG
Also Called: Dunn Welding Equipment
23438 Dunn Ln (77365-6401)
P.O. Box 7927, Houston (77270-7927)
PHONE...................................713 869-4841
Freeman B Dunn, *Owner*
Freeman Dunn, *Owner*
Bill Dunn, *Co-Owner*
EMP: 100 EST: 1964
SALES (est): 17.1MM **Privately Held**
WEB: www.gulfstatesabrasive.com
SIC: 3291 Abrasive products

(G-17178)
L & J TECHNOLOGY INC
22015 E Martin Dr (77365-5327)
PHONE...................................281 354-4800
Liviu Puiulet, *President*
Cristian Puiulet, *COO*
Silvia Puiulet, *CFO*
EMP: 14
SQ FT: 12,500
SALES (est): 2.2MM **Privately Held**
WEB: www.ljtechnology.com
SIC: 3599 Machine shop, jobbing & repair

(G-17179)
MIKEL MACHINE INC
24792 Ford Rd (77365-5448)
PHONE...................................281 354-2750
N Louise Quarles, *President*
Walter D Burnett, *Admin Sec*
EMP: 20
SQ FT: 6,200
SALES (est): 2.9MM **Privately Held**
WEB: www.mikelmachine.com
SIC: 3599 Machine shop, jobbing & repair

(G-17180)
PAN AMERICAN INDUSTRIES INC
20194 Alexander Ln (77365-3302)
P.O. Box 1996 (77365-1996)
PHONE...................................281 572-4842
Maria Martinez, *President*
Mark Novosad, *Sr Corp Ofcr*
Enrique Gutierrez, *Exec VP*
Michael Birchall, *Vice Pres*
Mike Birchall, *Vice Pres*
EMP: 9
SQ FT: 3,000
SALES (est): 1.3MM **Privately Held**
WEB: www.panamiris.com
SIC: 3533 7389 Oil & gas field machinery; purchasing service

(G-17181)
PORTER READY-MIX INC (PA)
25152 Loop 494 (77365-6100)
P.O. Box 981 (77365-0981)
PHONE...................................281 354-5181
Nathan Purkerson, *President*
Brenda Purkerson, *Corp Secy*
Larry Lee, *Vice Pres*
Bonnie Ward, *Executive*
EMP: 35
SQ FT: 3,000
SALES (est): 9.7MM **Privately Held**
WEB: www.porterreadymix.com
SIC: 3273 Ready-mixed concrete

(G-17182)
RIGHT SIGNS INC
Also Called: Ranger Signs
17218 Porter Ln (77365-3168)
P.O. Box 3028 (77365-8029)
PHONE...................................281 429-3683
Greg Gathright, *President*
▲ EMP: 10
SQ FT: 10,000
SALES (est): 1MM **Privately Held**
WEB: www.rightsigncompany.com
SIC: 3993 Electric signs

(G-17183)
TEXCON READY MIX INC
20783 Fm 1314 Rd (77365-3467)
PHONE...................................281 572-1712
Luis Solorzano, *Director*
Meng Zhang, *Director*

EMP: 95
SALES (est): 100.5K **Privately Held**
SIC: 3273 Ready-mixed concrete

(G-17184)
TOOLING DESIGNS INC
21790 E Wallis Dr (77365-5365)
PHONE.................................281 354-0421
William Algeo, *President*
Deborah Algeo, *Vice Pres*
EMP: 10
SQ FT: 3,000
SALES (est): 1.4MM **Privately Held**
WEB: www.toolingdesignsinc.com
SIC: 3544 Special dies & tools

Portland
San Patricio County

(G-17185)
CHANDLER SIGNS LLC
206 Doral Dr (78374-4003)
P.O. Box 125 (78374-0125)
PHONE.................................361 643-4115
Morton Jack, *Manager*
EMP: 92
SALES (corp-wide): 74MM **Privately Held**
WEB: www.chandlersigns.com
SIC: 3993 Electric signs
PA: Chandler Signs, Llc
14201 Sovereign Rd 101
Fort Worth TX 76155
214 902-2000

(G-17186)
CHARRO OPERATING LLC
321 5th St (78374-1701)
PHONE.................................361 643-5577
Mike R Richards, *Director*
EMP: 9 **EST:** 2012
SALES (est): 1.3MM **Privately Held**
SIC: 1382 Oil & gas exploration services

(G-17187)
SHORELINE INC
2361 Willow Dr (78374-3228)
PHONE.................................361 643-3135
Eddie Underwood, *Principal*
EMP: 15 **Privately Held**
WEB: www.shorelinetreatmentcenter.com
SIC: 2899 Chemical supplies for foundries
PA: Shoreline Inc.
1220 Gregory St
Taft TX 78390

(G-17188)
VOESTALPINE TEXAS LLC
2800 Kay Bley Htchison Rd (78374-7400)
PHONE.................................361 704-9000
Gottfried Simhoser, *Finance Dir*
Luis Cabrera, *Human Res Mgr*
Bernhard Schlattl, *Mng Member*
Gabriel Chapa, *Analyst*
Erich Tiffera,
◆ **EMP:** 23
SQ FT: 40,000
SALES (est): 12.2MM
SALES (corp-wide): 13.8B **Privately Held**
WEB: www.voestalpine.com
SIC: 3462 Iron & steel forgings
PA: Voestalpine Ag
Voest-Alpine-StraBe 1
Linz 4020
503 041-5

(G-17189)
WT LEASE SERVICES INC
1123 Orion Dr (78374-1922)
P.O. Box 1289, Premont (78375-1289)
PHONE.................................361 348-3525
Donald W Storck, *President*
Sara J Storck, *Admin Sec*
EMP: 34
SQ FT: 1,000
SALES (est): 3.3MM **Privately Held**
SIC: 1389 Construction, repair & dismantling services

Post
Garza County

(G-17190)
H & M DIRT CONTRACTORS INC
805 E Main St (79356-3448)
P.O. Box 459 (79356-0459)
PHONE.................................806 495-3293
Jack A Hair, *President*
Mike Hair, *Vice Pres*
Sharla Hair, *Admin Sec*
EMP: 30 **EST:** 1967
SQ FT: 4,100
SALES (est): 5MM **Privately Held**
SIC: 1389 1794 Oil field services; roustabout service; excavation work

(G-17191)
MASON BROTHERS CNSTR CO INC
119 N Avenue H (79356-3326)
P.O. Box 417 (79356-0417)
PHONE.................................806 495-3400
Joe Mason, *President*
Kelly Mason, *Vice Pres*
Brock Kraft, *Sales Mgr*
EMP: 30
SALES (est): 7.4MM **Privately Held**
SIC: 1542 1389 Commercial & office building, new construction; servicing oil & gas wells

(G-17192)
STRAWN TRANSPORT & ACID CO
1103 E Main St (79356-3241)
P.O. Box 458 (79356-0458)
PHONE.................................806 495-2422
Jay Strawn, *President*
Susan Strawn, *Vice Pres*
EMP: 13
SQ FT: 4,000
SALES (est): 1.4MM **Privately Held**
SIC: 4212 1389 1781 Liquid haulage, local; acidizing wells; water well servicing

Poteet
Atascosa County

(G-17193)
ATASCOSA STEEL INDUSTRIES INC
1275 Schuettig Rd (78065-4119)
PHONE.................................830 276-4322
James L Meyer Sr, *President*
Linda Adams, *Corp Secy*
Linda A Meyer, *Vice Pres*
EMP: 10 **EST:** 1993
SALES (est): 1.3MM **Privately Held**
SIC: 3441 Building components, structural steel

(G-17194)
CAMINO REAL COMMUNITY MHMR CTR
510 Ave Poteet (78065)
P.O. Box 123 (78065-0123)
PHONE.................................830 276-8578
Marvin Rubin, *CEO*
Jesse Ramirez, *Chairman*
Dan Byrd, *Director*
EMP: 18
SQ FT: 3,000
SALES (est): 1.2MM **Privately Held**
SIC: 2426 Chair seats, hardwood

Poth
Wilson County

(G-17195)
FELUX METAL WORKS & SUPPLY LP
Hwy 181 (78147)
P.O. Box 306 (78147-0306)
PHONE.................................830 484-3436
Gary Felux, *Principal*
EMP: 9

SALES (est): 1MM **Privately Held**
SIC: 3548 Welding apparatus

(G-17196)
WIATREK DUNN KUTAC INC
200 County Rd 220 (78147)
P.O. Box 518 (78147-0518)
PHONE.................................830 484-2888
David J Wiatrek, *President*
EMP: 30
SALES (est): 1.8MM **Privately Held**
WEB: www.wiatreksmeatmarket.com
SIC: 2011 Meat packing plants

Pottsboro
Grayson County

(G-17197)
JR SHELDON & COMPANY INC
136 Bent Oak Dr (75076-4861)
P.O. Box 2069, Pilot Point (76258-2069)
PHONE.................................940 368-5793
Alan Uptergrove, *President*
EMP: 12
SALES (est): 1.3MM **Privately Held**
SIC: 3589 Sewage & water treatment equipment

Powderly
Lamar County

(G-17198)
BZ & SONS SWEEPING & WSHG INC
5400 Us Highway 271 N (75473-4970)
PHONE.................................903 732-9882
Connie Stumpf, *President*
Bob Stumpf, *Vice Pres*
EMP: 9
SALES (est): 806.9K **Privately Held**
WEB: www.bzandsons.com
SIC: 6531 3991 0782 Real estate brokers & agents; brooms & brushes; lawn & garden services

(G-17199)
HOPE AGRI PRODUCTS OF TEXAS
6301 Us Highway 271 N (75473-4132)
P.O. Box 248 (75473-0248)
PHONE.................................903 732-3361
Tad Duncan, *President*
Tom Duncan, *Vice Pres*
EMP: 30
SALES (est): 2.9MM **Privately Held**
SIC: 2499 2873 Mulch, wood & bark; nitrogenous fertilizers

(G-17200)
REDDY ICE GROUP INC
89 County Road 35725 (75473-3148)
PHONE.................................903 732-3231
Pete Farmer, *Maint Spvr*
Clifford Farmer, *Manager*
EMP: 20 **Privately Held**
WEB: www.reddyice.com
SIC: 2097 Manufactured ice
HQ: Reddy Ice Group, Inc.
5720 Lbj Fwy Ste 200
Dallas TX 75240

Poynor
Henderson County

(G-17201)
GRIZZLY OPERATING LLC
1133 Fm 315 S (75782)
PHONE.................................903 876-2227
Owen Springfield, *Plant Mgr*
EMP: 36
SALES (corp-wide): 460.2MM **Publicly Held**
SIC: 2911 Mineral oils, natural
HQ: Grizzly Operating, Llc
5847 San Felipe St # 3000
Houston TX

(G-17202)
H G NICHOLS CONSTRUCTION CO
16760 Hwy 175 E (75782)
P.O. Box 232 (75782-0232)
PHONE.................................903 876-2527
Keith Bristow, *President*
Billie Nichols, *Corp Secy*
EMP: 13
SQ FT: 2,500
SALES (est): 940K **Privately Held**
SIC: 1389 Gas field services

Premont
Jim Wells County

(G-17203)
BASIC ENERGY SERVICES INC
1104 Fm 716 (78375-3728)
P.O. Box 1164 (78375-1164)
PHONE.................................361 348-3320
Danny Sanchez, *Manager*
EMP: 23
SALES (corp-wide): 567.2MM **Publicly Held**
WEB: www.basices.com
SIC: 1389 Servicing oil & gas wells; oil field services
PA: Basic Energy Services, Inc.
801 Cherry St Unit 2
Fort Worth TX 76102
817 334-4100

(G-17204)
RAYTHEON COMPANY
281 1 Mile S (78375)
PHONE.................................361 348-2712
EMP: 40
SALES (corp-wide): 56.5B **Publicly Held**
WEB: www.rtx.com
SIC: 3812 Radar systems & equipment
HQ: Raytheon Company
870 Winter St
Waltham MA 02451
781 522-3000

Princeton
Collin County

(G-17205)
CHARLEYS CONCRETE CO LTD
1134 Fm 982 (75407-5049)
PHONE.................................972 734-6300
Jose Saenz, *Plant Mgr*
Rich Szecsy, *Opers Staff*
Brent Pennington, *Branch Mgr*
EMP: 24
SALES (corp-wide): 39MM **Privately Held**
WEB: www.charleysconcrete.com
SIC: 3273 Ready-mixed concrete
PA: Charley's Concrete Co., Ltd.
11801 Katy Rd
Fort Worth TX 76244
817 431-3515

(G-17206)
CONTRACT FABRICATION
Also Called: Cfd
5427 Fm 546 (75407-4763)
PHONE.................................972 736-2260
Caleb Rankin, *QC Mgr*
David Dierks, *Engineer*
James Hardin, *Design Engr*
Ej Sanderson, *Mng Member*
Cindy Webb, *Manager*
EMP: 36
SQ FT: 8,400
SALES (est): 7.3MM **Privately Held**
WEB: www.cfdintl.com
SIC: 3728 Military aircraft equipment & armament

(G-17207)
DEDICATED CONTROLS LLC
9603 Private Road 5196 (75407-4119)
P.O. Box 100, Evant (76525-0100)
PHONE.................................972 632-8716
David Bounds, *President*
Brittney Bounds, *Manager*
EMP: 14

SALES (est): 2.3MM **Privately Held**
WEB: www.dedicatedcontrols.com
SIC: 3679 Transducers, electrical

(G-17208)
DNA STAT LLC
4388 County Road 444 (75407-4812)
PHONE.................................469 500-1137
Mitch Edland, *CEO*
EMP: 18
SALES (est): 4.2MM **Privately Held**
SIC: 2834 Chlorination tablets & kits (water purification)

(G-17209)
EXPRESS FABRICATION
3033 County Road 743 (75407-5164)
P.O. Box 652 (75407-0652)
PHONE.................................469 628-3960
Ronnie Welborn, *Principal*
EMP: 9
SALES (est): 1.1MM **Privately Held**
WEB: www.expfab.com
SIC: 3399 Primary metal products

(G-17210)
FABHAR MANUFACTURING LLC
Also Called: Fabhar Metal Works
524 E Hazelwood St (75407-5529)
PHONE.................................214 802-9400
Jim Hargis, *Owner*
Ray Shinske, *Project Mgr*
Jack Mize, *Opers Staff*
EMP: 21
SALES (est): 4.7MM **Privately Held**
WEB: www.fabhar.com
SIC: 3399 3444 3449 Metal powders, pastes & flakes; sheet metalwork; miscellaneous metalwork

(G-17211)
PURE RIVER LLC
1045 County Road 456 (75407-5515)
PHONE.................................469 853-4867
Daniel Caldwell, *Principal*
Danny Caldwell, *Mng Member*
Barbara Caldwell, *Mng Member*
Leland Caldwell, *Mng Member*
EMP: 10
SQ FT: 21,000
SALES (est): 620K **Privately Held**
SIC: 4212 1389 Petroleum haulage, local; oil field services

Prosper
Collin County

(G-17212)
ALLPAC INC
810 Buffalo Springs Dr (75078-8470)
P.O. Box 914, Van Alstyne (75495-0914)
PHONE.................................214 630-8804
Lawrence D Lakey, *President*
Jean Lakey, *Corp Secy*
EMP: 30
SQ FT: 22,000
SALES (est): 5.1MM **Privately Held**
SIC: 3565 Packaging machinery

(G-17213)
DAIRY MANUFACTURERS INC (PA)
Also Called: Dm
601 N Coleman St (75078-2333)
P.O. Box 639 (75078-0639)
PHONE.................................972 347-2878
Gerardo J Barrera, *President*
Jerry Barrera, *President*
Ramiro Trevino, *Vice Pres*
Enriguz Arredondo, *Engineer*
Murry Hicks, *Human Res Mgr*
▲ EMP: 17
SQ FT: 36,000
SALES (est): 3.4MM **Privately Held**
WEB: www.dairymanufacturers.com
SIC: 2048 5143 Prepared feeds; dairy products, except dried or canned

(G-17214)
LATTIMORE MATERIALS CORP
890 S Dallas Pkwy (75078)
PHONE.................................972 346-3002
David Williams, *General Mgr*
EMP: 21

SQ FT: 7,125
SALES (corp-wide): 1.7B **Privately Held**
WEB: www.lafargeholcim.us
SIC: 3273 Ready-mixed concrete
HQ: Lattimore Materials Corp.
　　15900 Dooley Rd
　　Addison TX 75001
　　972 221-4646

(G-17215)
ROCKIES ENVIRONMENTAL LLC
860 Dentwood Trl (75078-8454)
PHONE.................................469 715-2642
Jordan Muffler,
EMP: 12 **EST:** 2017
SALES (est): 296K **Privately Held**
SIC: 1382 Oil & gas exploration services

(G-17216)
STAIR SOLUTIONS LLC
474 N Hays Rd Ste 8 (75078-7002)
PHONE.................................972 347-5151
Timothy Paul Wilson, *Mng Member*
EMP: 10
SALES (est): 1.5MM **Privately Held**
WEB: www.stairsolutionsus.com
SIC: 2431 Millwork

Quanah
Hardeman County

(G-17217)
GEORGIA-PACIFIC LLC
5 Miles W Of Quanah On Us (79252)
P.O. Box 330 (79252-0330)
PHONE.................................940 663-6111
Stan Asbell, *Branch Mgr*
EMP: 130
SALES (corp-wide): 36.8B **Privately Held**
WEB: www.gp.com
SIC: 3275 Gypsum products
HQ: Georgia-Pacific Llc
　　133 Peachtree St Nw
　　Atlanta GA 30303
　　404 652-4000

Queen City
Cass County

(G-17218)
BEAKO MANUFACTURING CO LLC
304 Fm 74 (75572-8616)
P.O. Box 318 (75572-0318)
PHONE.................................903 796-5330
Malinda Hogue, *Corp Secy*
John Cullins, *Mng Member*
EMP: 10
SQ FT: 13,000
SALES (est): 680K **Privately Held**
SIC: 3999 Military insignia

(G-17219)
BMC INDUSTRY LLC
Also Called: Beaco Manufacturing
304 Fm 74 (75572-8616)
P.O. Box 316 (75572-0316)
PHONE.................................903 796-5330
John Cullins, *President*
Jeff Graham, *Engineer*
Malinda Faye Hogue, *Controller*
EMP: 15
SALES (est): 1.9MM **Privately Held**
WEB: www.bmcindustryllc.com
SIC: 3643 Current-carrying wiring devices

(G-17220)
GRAPHIC PACKAGING INTL LLC
Also Called: International Paper
9978 Fm 3129 (75572-5342)
PHONE.................................903 796-7101
EMP: 800 **Publicly Held**
WEB: www.graphicpkg.com
SIC: 2621 2631 2611 Paper mills; paperboard mills; pulp mills
HQ: Graphic Packaging International, Llc
　　1500 Riveredge Pkwy # 100
　　Atlanta GA 30328

(G-17221)
HEP MECHANICAL SERVICES LLC
295 County Road 3552 (75572-3823)
P.O. Box 1278, Atlanta (75551-1278)
PHONE.................................903 278-6826
H Gene Potter, *Owner*
Mike Thomas, *Sales Staff*
EMP: 10
SQ FT: 2,400
SALES (est): 1.3MM **Privately Held**
WEB: www.hepmechanical.com
SIC: 1796 3443 Installing building equipment; metal parts

Quemado
Maverick County

(G-17222)
KUNAFIN LLC
13955 N Highway 277 (78877-7837)
P.O. Box 190 (78877-0190)
PHONE.................................830 757-1181
Clifton Castle, *Sales Staff*
Frank Junfin,
Adele Junfin,
EMP: 10
SALES (est): 1.8MM **Privately Held**
WEB: www.kunafin.com
SIC: 2048 0721 Prepared feeds; crop related entomological services (insect control)

Quinlan
Hunt County

(G-17223)
J W DRILLING INC
10544 Kitsee Knoll Way (75474-5744)
PHONE.................................575 748-8704
Jerry Wilbanks, *President*
EMP: 75
SQ FT: 10,000
SALES (est): 4.4MM **Privately Held**
SIC: 1381 Drilling oil & gas wells

(G-17224)
METROPLEX CONVEYOR & SVCS LLC
5710 State Highway 34 S (75474-3240)
P.O. Box 8007, Greenville (75404-8007)
PHONE.................................972 584-0551
Matthew Panther,
EMP: 10 **EST:** 2013
SALES (est): 4.1MM **Privately Held**
WEB: www.metroplexconveyor.com
SIC: 3535 5084 Conveyors & conveying equipment; conveyor systems

(G-17225)
OGLETREE CUSTOM CABINETS
7183 County Road 2294 (75474-4025)
PHONE.................................903 356-2611
Gary Ogletree, *Owner*
EMP: 9
SQ FT: 4,000
SALES (est): 1MM **Privately Held**
WEB: www.ogletreescustomcabinets.com
SIC: 2434 Wood kitchen cabinets

(G-17226)
RELIABLE DESIGN SERVICES LP
5710 State Highway 34 S (75474-3240)
P.O. Box 8007, Greenville (75404-8007)
PHONE.................................972 584-0551
Matthew Panther, *Partner*
EMP: 10
SALES (est): 126.6K **Privately Held**
WEB: www.rds-web.com
SIC: 7389 3441 Design services; fabricated structural metal

(G-17227)
WW ELECTRONICS SOLUTIONS LLC
10167 County Road 3705 (75474-5510)
PHONE.................................214 396-6636
Richard Wilkinson, *CEO*
EMP: 11

SALES (est): 1.8MM **Privately Held**
WEB: www.wwelectronics.org
SIC: 1731 3669 3999 7382 Fire detection & burglar alarm systems specialization; fire alarm apparatus, electric; fire extinguishers, portable; fire alarm maintenance & monitoring; fire extinguisher servicing;

Quitman
Wood County

(G-17228)
PERFORMANCE METAL WORKS INC
Also Called: Pro-Form
Hwy 37 Quitman (75783)
P.O. Box 1338, Winnsboro (75494-1338)
PHONE.................................903 967-2622
Royce Patterson, *President*
Stacy Patterson, *Admin Sec*
▲ EMP: 60
SALES (est): 10.9MM **Privately Held**
WEB: www.proformtrailer.com
SIC: 3799 Trailer hitches

Rainbow
Somervell County

(G-17229)
SQUAW CREEK MATERIALS LP
4448 E Highway 67 (76077-2920)
P.O. Box 123 (76077-0123)
PHONE.................................254 897-3505
James Gosdin, *Partner*
Lindsey Upshaw, *Partner*
EMP: 12 **EST:** 1999
SALES (est): 640.9K **Privately Held**
SIC: 1241 Coal mining services

Randolph
Fannin County

(G-17230)
VERTEX AEROSPACE LLC
1851 5th St W Bldg 58 (75475)
PHONE.................................210 652-4541
William Linkenhoger, *Manager*
EMP: 15
SALES (corp-wide): 681.6MM **Privately Held**
WEB: www.vtxaero.com
SIC: 3721 Aircraft
HQ: Vertex Aerospace Llc
　　555 Industrial Dr S
　　Madison MS 39110
　　800 774-4927

Ranger
Eastland County

(G-17231)
R & B ENERGY LLC
2817 Highway 101 (76470-6207)
P.O. Box 38 (76470-0038)
PHONE.................................254 647-3358
Robert Beard,
Steve Hayes,
EMP: 9
SQ FT: 4,000
SALES (est): 1.3MM **Privately Held**
SIC: 1382 Oil & gas exploration services

Rankin
Upton County

(G-17232)
FLR OILFIELD SERVICES LLC
1010 W Us Highway 67 (79778-1019)
P.O. Box 321 (79778-0321)
PHONE.................................432 693-2245
Chris Fisher, *Vice Pres*
Jeffrey Lightsey,
EMP: 10 **EST:** 2018

SALES (est): 850K **Privately Held**
SIC: 1389 Oil field services

(G-17233)
TMR SERVICES LLC
1400 N Hwy 349 (79778)
P.O. Box 355 (79778-0355)
PHONE................................432 693-2175
EMP: 40
SALES (est): 5.6MM **Privately Held**
SIC: 1389 Oil/Gas Field Services

Ravenna
Fannin County

(G-17234)
TRUE GRIT WORKS
10236 Fm 274 (75476-3040)
PHONE................................978 604-4915
Blake Goode, *Principal*
EMP: 10
SALES (est): 801.5K **Privately Held**
WEB: www.truegritttransportation.com
SIC: 2899 Fluxes: brazing, soldering, galvanizing & welding

Raywood
Liberty County

(G-17235)
QUIKRETE COMPANIES LLC
Quikrete-Houston
203119 Highway 90 E (77582)
P.O. Box 158 (77582-0158)
PHONE................................936 587-4450
Al Simonson Jr, *General Mgr*
EMP: 80 **Privately Held**
WEB: www.quikrete.com
SIC: 3272 Concrete products
HQ: The Quikrete Companies Llc
5 Concourse Pkwy Ste 1900
Atlanta GA 30328
404 634-9100

Red Oak
Ellis County

(G-17236)
T&B BOILER INC
816 Vinson Ln (75154-7032)
PHONE................................972 576-1920
Tim Broadfoot, *President*
EMP: 16
SALES (est): 3MM **Privately Held**
WEB: www.tandbboiler.com
SIC: 3443 Boiler shop products: boilers, smokestacks, steel tanks

(G-17237)
TRIUMPH AEROSTRUCTURES
LLC (HQ)
300 Austin Blvd (75154-4608)
PHONE................................972 515-8276
Jeffry D Frisby, *President*
Richard C III, *Chairman*
Stephen A Davis, *Vice Pres*
Kevin P McGlinchey, *Vice Pres*
John B Wright II, *Vice Pres*
▲ EMP: 2000
SQ FT: 16,168
SALES (est): 1.2B **Publicly Held**
WEB: www.triumphgroup.com
SIC: 3721 3728 3812 3769 Aircraft; aircraft parts & equipment; search & navigation equipment; guided missile & space vehicle parts & auxiliary equipment

Red Rock
Bastrop County

(G-17238)
KAM-FAB LLC
1941 Fm 20 (78662-2617)
PHONE................................512 332-2252
Keith Helford, *President*
EMP: 15
SQ FT: 16,414

SALES (est): 650K **Privately Held**
WEB: www.kamfab.com
SIC: 3599 Machine shop, jobbing & repair

Refugio
Refugio County

(G-17239)
COPANO COMPANY
431 T C Oil Rd (78377)
PHONE................................361 526-2115
Steve Carter, *Manager*
EMP: 22
SALES (corp-wide): 1.5MM **Privately Held**
SIC: 1311 Crude petroleum & natural gas
PA: Copano Company
1 Oconnor Plz Ste 1100
Victoria TX 77901
361 578-6271

(G-17240)
DAECO LTD
703 W Commons St (78377-2464)
PHONE................................361 526-7017
Daryll Atkins, *Mng Member*
Jesse Cordova, *Supervisor*
William Perry, *Supervisor*
Tina Samford, *Admin Sec*
EMP: 30
SALES (est): 1.1MM **Privately Held**
WEB: www.daecoltd.com
SIC: 1389 Oil field services

(G-17241)
FESCO LTD
207 E Plasuela St (78377-3234)
PHONE................................361 526-4644
Brad Gillespie, *Manager*
EMP: 37
SALES (corp-wide): 201MM **Privately Held**
WEB: www.fescoinc.com
SIC: 1389 8711 Construction, repair & dismantling services; petroleum engineering
PA: Fesco, Ltd.
1000 Fesco Dr
Alice TX 78332
361 664-3479

(G-17242)
GRAY WIRELINE SERVICES
711 E Empresario St (78377-3118)
PHONE................................361 526-4729
EMP: 16
SALES (est): 595.3K **Privately Held**
SIC: 1389 Oil/Gas Field Services
HQ: Archer Well Company Inc.
10613 W Sh Pkwy N Ste 600
Houston TX 77041
713 856-4222

(G-17243)
J&P RAMIREZ SERVICES LLC
172 Highway 183 (78377-4486)
P.O. Box 853 (78377-0853)
PHONE................................361 526-2072
Johnny Ramirez, *CEO*
EMP: 30 EST: 2007
SALES (est): 2.6MM **Privately Held**
SIC: 4212 7353 1389 Liquid haulage, local; heavy construction equipment rental; oil field services; gas field services

(G-17244)
MIDCOAST LEASE SERVICE INC
1106 Old Brian Rd (78377)
P.O. Box 246 (78377-0246)
PHONE................................361 526-4636
EMP: 25 EST: 1974
SQ FT: 7,500
SALES (est): 3.4MM **Privately Held**
SIC: 1389 1382 Oil field services; oil & gas exploration services

(G-17245)
OAK LEASE SERVICE CO LLC
604 Osage St (78377-3229)
PHONE................................361 362-1429
Nancy Bellows, *Mng Member*
Mara Rivas, *Property Mgr*
Terry Bellows,
EMP: 15

SALES (est): 2.4MM **Privately Held**
SIC: 1389 Construction, repair & dismantling services

(G-17246)
RMOR ENERGY CORPORATION
116 Highway 183 (78377-4486)
P.O. Box 662 (78377-0662)
PHONE................................361 318-0151
Robby Stephenson, *President*
Kaleigh Silvas, *CFO*
EMP: 10 EST: 2014
SQ FT: 1,500
SALES (est): 400K **Privately Held**
WEB: www.rmorenergy.com
SIC: 1389 Oil field services

(G-17247)
SMITH SERVICES
INCORPORATED
103 Highway 183 (78377)
P.O. Box 1015 (78377-1015)
PHONE................................361 526-2615
Steven J Smith, *President*
Shirley Smith, *Corp Secy*
EMP: 15
SQ FT: 10,000
SALES: 804.6K **Privately Held**
SIC: 1389 Oil field services

(G-17248)
SOUTH TEXAS OIL FIELD MAINT
135 Fairgrounds Rd (78377-4420)
P.O. Box 460 (78377-0460)
PHONE................................361 526-2822
Randy Gumm, *President*
Brian Gumm, *Treasurer*
EMP: 36
SQ FT: 2,500
SALES (est): 7.1MM **Privately Held**
SIC: 1389 1611 1541 Oil field services; highway & street construction; industrial buildings & warehouses

(G-17249)
T-C OIL COMPANY
427 Fm 774 (78377-4546)
PHONE................................361 526-4693
Gary Childress, *CEO*
Joe Bland, *Executive*
EMP: 30
SALES (corp-wide): 67.9K **Privately Held**
WEB: www.tcoil.net
SIC: 1311 Crude petroleum production; natural gas production
PA: T-C Oil Company
1 Oconnor Plz Ste 1100
Victoria TX 77901
361 578-6271

(G-17250)
TEXAS STHWIND VNYRD
WINERY LLC
16375 Us 183 (78377)
P.O. Box 524 (78377-0524)
PHONE................................361 526-4662
Regina Staggs, *Mng Member*
EMP: 17
SALES (est): 2.5MM **Privately Held**
WEB: www.texassouthwind.com
SIC: 2084 Wines

Reno
Lamar County

(G-17251)
AGPRO INC
859 Airport Rd (75462-7151)
PHONE................................903 785-5531
D Joseph Gribble, *Ch of Bd*
Joann Gribble, *President*
Donald L Gribble, *Vice Pres*
Alvin Wofford, *Parts Mgr*
Shirley Vest, *Executive*
◆ EMP: 23
SQ FT: 12,000
SALES (est): 5.5MM **Privately Held**
WEB: www.agprousa.com
SIC: 3523 Dairy equipment (farm); hog feeding, handling & watering equipment

(G-17252)
RENO MACHINE WORKS LLC
275 Key West Rd (75462-7423)
PHONE................................903 224-6275
Donald Neisler, *President*
Melissa Neisler,
EMP: 10
SALES (est): 18.1K **Privately Held**
WEB: www.renomachineworks.com
SIC: 3599 3089 Machine shop, jobbing & repair

Rhome
Wise County

(G-17253)
CITY CONCRETE INC
90776 E Hwy 114 (76078)
P.O. Box 890 (76078-0890)
PHONE................................817 636-2690
Jim Foley, *President*
EMP: 12
SALES (est): 1.6MM **Privately Held**
WEB: www.cityconcreteinc.com
SIC: 3273 Ready-mixed concrete

(G-17254)
DIVERSIFIED PURE CHEM LLC
(DH)
11050 S Us Highway 287 (76078-4802)
PHONE................................817 677-9418
Monte Roach, *President*
Chris Oravetz, *Plant Mgr*
Scott Tibbs, *Maint Spvr*
Jessica Cumings, *Opers Staff*
Jason Zilles, *CFO*
EMP: 14 EST: 2012
SALES (est): 7.3MM **Privately Held**
WEB: www.divpc.com
SIC: 4953 3399 Chemical detoxification; reclaiming ferrous metals from clay
HQ: A-Gas Us Holdings Inc.
1100 Haskins Rd
Bowling Green OH 43402
419 867-8990

(G-17255)
DYSOL INC
Also Called: Socomore
5475 E State Hwy 114 (76078)
P.O. Box 664 (76078-0664)
PHONE................................817 335-1826
Andrew Leech, *President*
Phil Mawaka, *General Mgr*
Jason Klein, *Prdtn Mgr*
Danny Gehlhausen, *Opers Staff*
Becky Gregg, *Info Tech Mgr*
▲ EMP: 41
SQ FT: 15,000
SALES (est): 3.7MM
SALES (corp-wide): 2.3MM **Privately Held**
WEB: www.socomore.com
SIC: 2911 Solvents
HQ: Socomore Holdings Llc
5475 E State Hwy 114
Rhome TX 76078
817 335-1826

(G-17256)
KEYSTONE SYNERGY LLC
Also Called: Keystone Oilfield Fabrication
1870 Illinois St (76078-4280)
P.O. Box 136669, Fort Worth (76136-0669)
PHONE................................817 636-3300
Stacy Leverett, *Purch Agent*
Tifton Crist, *Sales Staff*
Janice Flory, *Office Mgr*
Larry Crist Jr,
Celia Crist,
EMP: 80 EST: 2009
SALES (est): 30.7MM **Privately Held**
WEB: www.keystonesynergy.com
SIC: 3533 5051 Oil field machinery & equipment; steel

(G-17257)
MAC TRAILER TEXAS INC
Also Called: Mac-T of Texas, Inc.
5940 E Hwy 114 (76078)
PHONE................................330 956-0171
Michael Conny, *President*
Jennifer Conny, *Director*

Randall Hunt, *Director*
EMP: 35 **EST:** 2017
SALES (est): 1.5MM **Privately Held**
SIC: 3715 Truck trailers
PA: Mac Trailer Manufacturing, Inc.
　14599 Commerce St Ne
　Alliance OH 44601

(G-17258)
MOBILE MINI INC
11042 S Us Hwy Ste 287 (76078)
PHONE.................................817 439-2288
Carla Bugas, *Branch Mgr*
EMP: 20
SALES (corp-wide): 1B **Publicly Held**
WEB: www.mobilemini.com
SIC: 3448 5411 Prefabricated metal build-
ings; convenience stores
HQ: Mobile Mini, Inc.
　4646 E Van Buren St # 400
　Phoenix AZ 85008
　480 894-6311

(G-17259)
**MODERN WELDING CO OF
TEXAS**
200 N Main St (76078-4484)
PHONE.................................817 636-2215
John Sandoval, *Vice Pres*
Jonathan Sandoval, *Purch Agent*
Wes Ramsey, *Sales Staff*
Bonnie Scroggins, *Manager*
EMP: 23
SQ FT: 160,000
SALES (est): 4.6MM
SALES (corp-wide): 131.1MM **Privately
Held**
WEB: www.modweldco.com
SIC: 3443 Hoppers, metal plate
PA: Modern Welding Company, Inc.
　2880 New Hartford Rd
　Owensboro KY 42303
　270 685-4400

(G-17260)
**SUMMIT METALS
CORPORATION**
3587 E Highway 114 (76078-3631)
P.O. Box 1845, Boyd (76023-1845)
PHONE.................................940 433-8788
Richard E Garrett Jr, *President*
EMP: 42
SQ FT: 10,000
SALES (est): 4.6MM **Privately Held**
WEB: www.summitmetalscorp.com
SIC: 3441 Fabricated structural metal

(G-17261)
TURNER COMPANY LLC
11049 S Us Hwy 287 (76078)
P.O. Box 885 (76078-0885)
PHONE.................................817 638-9053
Haylie Little, *Safety Mgr*
Andrea Stricklin, *CFO*
Sharon Gooding, *Sales Mgr*
Marty Anderson, *Sales Staff*
Bob Ballew, *Sales Staff*
EMP: 50
SALES (est): 16.1MM **Privately Held**
WEB: www.theturnerco.com
SIC: 3271 Sewer & manhole block, con-
crete

(G-17262)
**UNIFIED SUPPLY & SERVICES
CO**
124 Capital Ln (76078-2425)
PHONE.................................972 355-8299
Colin Sanburg, *President*
Blake Storms, *COO*
Tara Riggs, *Marketing Staff*
▼ **EMP:** 12
SQ FT: 10,000
SALES (est): 4.8MM **Privately Held**
WEB: www.unifiedsupply.com
SIC: 3535 Unit handling conveying sys-
tems

(G-17263)
UNITED METAL SERVICES INC
Also Called: Metal Fabrication
8333 S Us Highway 287 A (76078-3035)
P.O. Box 395, Paradise (76073-0395)
PHONE.................................817 932-3330
Jessica D Sims, *CEO*

Ted Sims, *Principal*
EMP: 11
SALES (est): 3.2MM **Privately Held**
WEB: www.united-metal.net
SIC: 3441 Building components, structural
steel

(G-17264)
**WELLFLEX ENRGY PRTNERS
FORT WR**
Also Called: Wellflex Energy Solutions
500 Randall St (76078-4469)
PHONE.................................817 730-5111
Mike Nathan, *COO*
Dale Moats, *Vice Pres*
Chris Cook, *Production*
Gina Hermes, *Purchasing*
Dan Patel, *Engineer*
EMP: 50
SALES (est): 4.2MM **Privately Held**
WEB: www.wellflex.com
SIC: 3533 Oil field machinery & equipment

Rice
Navarro County

(G-17265)
CASITA ENTERPRISES INC
Also Called: Castia
5029 Se Mckinney St # 1 (75155-9780)
PHONE.................................903 326-4717
John Lang, *President*
Robert Lang, *Vice Pres*
▼ **EMP:** 75
SALES (est): 14.1MM **Privately Held**
WEB: www.casitatraveltrailers.com
SIC: 3792 Travel trailers & campers

(G-17266)
**PRAIRIE PTFOOD INGREDIENTS
LLC**
3111 Se Mckinney St (75155-8500)
P.O. Box 194, Chatfield (75105-0194)
PHONE.................................469 383-5182
Collin Harwell, *Principal*
EMP: 11
SQ FT: 80,000
SALES (est): 1.8MM **Privately Held**
SIC: 2048 Prepared feeds

Richardson
Dallas County

(G-17267)
**AFFIRMED NTWRKS
CMMNCTONS TECH**
Also Called: Dallas R&D Center
2280 Campbell Creek Blvd (75082-4450)
PHONE.................................469 461-3101
Yoshihiro Kondo, *Principal*
EMP: 23 **Privately Held**
SIC: 3661 Telephone & telegraph appara-
tus
HQ: Affirmed Networks Communications
　Technologies
　3617 Parkway Ln
　Norcross GA 30092

(G-17268)
AIR SYSTEM COMPONENTS INC
Also Called: Tuttle & Bailey
1401 N Plano Rd (75081-2428)
PHONE.................................972 680-9128
EMP: 278 **Privately Held**
WEB: www.airsysco.com
SIC: 3585 Air conditioning equipment,
complete
HQ: Air System Components, Inc.
　605 Shiloh Rd
　Plano TX 75074
　972 212-4888

(G-17269)
**AMERICAN TRAILER WORLD
CORP (HQ)**
Also Called: American Trailer Works
1701 N Plano Rd Bldg 9 (75081-1915)
PHONE.................................855 289-0001
Jeff Scherer, *President*
EMP: 36 **EST:** 2017

SALES (est): 929MM
SALES (corp-wide): 8.8B **Privately Held**
WEB: www.atw.com
SIC: 3792 Travel trailers & campers
PA: Bain Capital, Lp
　200 Clarendon St
　Boston MA 02116
　617 516-2000

(G-17270)
APPLIED CONCEPTS INC
Also Called: Stalker Radar
855 E Collins Blvd (75081-2251)
PHONE.................................972 398-3750
Alan Mead, *CEO*
Diane Satoren, *Partner*
Bill Switzer, *Division Mgr*
Sharon Conner, *General Mgr*
Derek Stalker, *Principal*
◆ **EMP:** 150 **EST:** 1977
SQ FT: 36,000
SALES (est): 43.6MM **Privately Held**
WEB: www.stalkerradar.com
SIC: 3699 3812 5731 3824 Electrical
equipment & supplies; radar systems &
equipment; video cameras, recorders &
accessories; speed indicators &
recorders, vehicle

(G-17271)
APPLIED MATERIALS INC
1717 Firman Dr Ste 150 (75081-6781)
PHONE.................................469 340-7810
EMP: 100
SALES (corp-wide): 17.2B **Publicly Held**
WEB: www.appliedmaterials.com
SIC: 3674 Semiconductors & related de-
vices
PA: Applied Materials, Inc.
　3050 Bowers Ave Bldg 1
　Santa Clara CA 95054
　408 727-5555

(G-17272)
**APRIMA MEDICAL SOFTWARE
INC (HQ)**
Also Called: Aprima Financial Services
1010 E Arapaho Rd Ste 100 (75081-2362)
PHONE.................................214 466-8000
Michael Nissenbaum, *President*
Neil A Simon, *COO*
Mark L Richards, *Senior VP*
Jeanette Keith, *Controller*
Jeffrey Hyman, *Officer*
EMP: 24 **EST:** 2004
SALES (est): 8.8MM
SALES (corp-wide): 60.6MM **Privately
Held**
WEB: www.emds.com
SIC: 7372 Prepackaged software
PA: E-Mds, Inc.
　10901 Stonelake Blvd
　Austin TX 78759
　512 257-5200

(G-17273)
ARCUBE MULTIMEDIA INC (PA)
959 E Collins Blvd # 123 (75081-2261)
PHONE.................................972 267-1800
Chintamani A Damle, *President*
Tom Damle, *President*
Rita Bhat, *Vice Pres*
Mayurika C Damle, *Vice Pres*
EMP: 12
SALES (est): 2.8MM **Privately Held**
WEB: www.customcut.net
SIC: 3695 Computer software tape &
disks: blank, rigid & floppy

(G-17274)
**AUTOMATED CEILING
REGISTERS**
903 N Bowser Rd Ste 162 (75081-2858)
PHONE.................................972 509-2400
Fax: 469 509-2401
EMP: 10
SALES (est): 646.1K **Privately Held**
SIC: 3639 Mfg Household Appliances

(G-17275)
AXCELIS TECHNOLOGIES INC
870 N Dorothy Dr Ste 710 (75081-2771)
PHONE.................................214 377-7298
Jeff Bialecki, *Principal*
EMP: 400

SALES (corp-wide): 442.5MM **Publicly
Held**
WEB: www.axcelis.com
SIC: 3829 Ion chambers
PA: Axcelis Technologies, Inc.
　108 Cherry Hill Dr
　Beverly MA 01915
　978 787-4000

(G-17276)
AXENT MANUFACTURING INC
Also Called: Axiom Manufacturing
1226 Exchange Dr (75081-2313)
PHONE.................................972 437-3737
Gregory W Irvin, *President*
Roger Forrester, *Engineer*
Janet McCaffrey, *Manager*
EMP: 21
SQ FT: 7,500
SALES (est): 4.6MM **Privately Held**
WEB: www.axman.com
SIC: 3699 Electrical equipment & supplies

(G-17277)
BALONG TRUCKING LLC
110 W Cityline Dr # 3072 (75082-3263)
PHONE.................................408 471-1383
Emmanuel Chia,
EMP: 15
SALES (est): 823.5K **Privately Held**
SIC: 3537 Trucks: freight, baggage, etc.:
industrial, except mining

(G-17278)
BAYAN IMPORTS INC
Also Called: Sara's Mediterranean Foods
750 S Sherman St (75081-4028)
PHONE.................................972 437-1122
Walid Bayan, *President*
Khaloud Bayan, *Admin Sec*
EMP: 20
SQ FT: 15,000
SALES (est): 974.3K **Privately Held**
WEB: www.sarasmarketbakery.com
SIC: 5149 2051 Groceries & related prod-
ucts; bakery: wholesale or wholesale/re-
tail combined

(G-17279)
**BENNING POWER
ELECTRONICS INC**
1220 Presidential Dr # 100 (75081-2435)
PHONE.................................214 553-1444
Mario Barbaresso, *CEO*
Thomas Benning, *President*
David Almond, *COO*
Hardy Massoudi, *Vice Pres*
Daryll Rardon, *Vice Pres*
▲ **EMP:** 60
SQ FT: 70,000
SALES (est): 71.3K
SALES (corp-wide): 259MM **Privately
Held**
WEB: www.benning.de
SIC: 3679 Electronic circuits
PA: Benning Elektrotechnik Und Elektronik
　Gmbh & Co Kg
　Munsterstr. 135-137
　Bocholt 46397
　287 193-0

(G-17280)
BOEING COMPANY
3373 Breckinridge Blvd (75082-3511)
PHONE.................................972 344-7249
Keith Brown, *Engineer*
Kevin O'Brien, *Train & Dev Mgr*
Dennis Wise, *Program Mgr*
Kevin Ewbank, *Manager*
Katie Bouaphavong, *Info Tech Mgr*
EMP: 4518
SALES (corp-wide): 58.1B **Publicly Held**
WEB: www.boeing.com
SIC: 3721 Aircraft
PA: The Boeing Company
　100 N Riverside Plz
　Chicago IL 60606
　312 544-2000

(G-17281)
BRAZEN ANIMATION LLC
1210 E Campbell Rd # 110 (75081-1964)
PHONE.................................214 880-0101
Will Leonard, *Editor*
Jasmine Johnson, *Production*
Nicholas Prange, *Production*

▲ = Import ▼ =Export
◆ =Import/Export

Brian Cole, *CFO*
Paul Monroe, *Chief Mktg Ofcr*
EMP: 16
SALES (est): 2.5MM **Privately Held**
WEB: www.brazenanimation.com
SIC: 3861 Motion picture film

(G-17282)
CALIX INC
2350 Campbell Crk Ste 100 (75082-4435)
PHONE................................707 766-3000
Carl Russo, *President*
Jose Garcia, *Senior Mgr*
EMP: 9
SALES (corp-wide): 424.3MM **Publicly Held**
WEB: www.calix.com
SIC: 4899 7372 4813 Data communication services; prepackaged software;
PA: Calix, Inc.
2777 Orchard Pkwy
San Jose CA 95134
408 514-3000

(G-17283)
CAMERON MACHINE SHOP
404 N Bowser Rd (75081-2812)
PHONE................................972 235-8876
Wilburn P Cameron, *President*
Ron Cameron, *Corp Secy*
Porter P Cameron, *Vice Pres*
Katherine Ansley, *CFO*
EMP: 35
SQ FT: 15,000
SALES (est): 6.3MM **Privately Held**
WEB: www.cameronmachineshop.com
SIC: 3599 Machine shop, jobbing & repair

(G-17284)
CAPITALSOFT INC
1702 N Collins Blvd # 21 (75080-3566)
PHONE................................972 220-1560
Gary Slagel, *President*
EMP: 12
SQ FT: 2,000
SALES (est): 1.2MM **Privately Held**
WEB: www.capitalsoft.com
SIC: 7373 7371 8243 7372 Computer integrated systems design; systems software development services; computer software development; software training, computer; business oriented computer software

(G-17285)
CEMTECHNOLOGIES INC (PA)
1360 Presidential Dr # 140 (75081-2465)
P.O. Box 803067, Dallas (75380-3067)
PHONE................................972 238-3630
Gary L Bond, *President*
J Peterson, *President*
EMP: 15 **EST:** 2001
SQ FT: 1,200
SALES (est): 3.5MM **Privately Held**
WEB: www.cemtechnologies.com
SIC: 3672 3643 Printed circuit boards; current-carrying wiring devices

(G-17286)
CIRCUIT CHECK INC
Also Called: CCI
681 N Plano Rd Ste 101 (75081-2909)
PHONE................................972 480-0044
Shawn Reiler, *Vice Pres*
Craig Baker, *Manager*
EMP: 35 **Privately Held**
WEB: www.circuitcheck.com
SIC: 3825 Integrated circuit testers
HQ: Circuit Check, Inc.
6550 Wedgwood Rd N # 120
Maple Grove MN 55311
763 694-4100

(G-17287)
CISCO SYSTEMS INC
2300 E President Georger (75082-3582)
PHONE................................469 255-0000
Matt Daly, *Partner*
Kristina Hill, *Partner*
Chetan Saraogi, *Project Mgr*
Ben Kurtzer, *Opers Staff*
Joshua Beren, *Engineer*
EMP: 140
SALES (corp-wide): 49.3B **Publicly Held**
WEB: www.cisco.com
SIC: 3577 Computer peripheral equipment

PA: Cisco Systems, Inc.
170 W Tasman Dr
San Jose CA 95134
408 526-4000

(G-17288)
COBHAM ADVNCED ELCTRNIC SLTONS
405 Interntl Pkwy Ste 20 (75081-2854)
PHONE................................972 437-1049
Kirk Ashby, *Branch Mgr*
EMP: 21
SALES (corp-wide): 2MM **Privately Held**
WEB: www.cobham.com
SIC: 3812 Wafers (semiconductor devices); hybrid integrated circuits; integrated circuits, semiconductor networks, etc.
HQ: Cobham Advanced Electronic Solutions Inc.
305 Richardson Rd
Lansdale PA 19446

(G-17289)
COMMSCOPE TECHNOLOGIES LLC
2601 Telecom Pkwy (75082-3521)
PHONE................................214 267-5900
Elaine Louren On, *COO*
Philip Sorrells, *Vice Pres*
Matt Melester, *Manager*
EMP: 225 **Publicly Held**
WEB: www.commscope.com
SIC: 5063 3663 3661 8711 Telephone & telegraph wire & cable; radio & TV communications equipment; telephone & telegraph apparatus; engineering services
HQ: Commscope Technologies Llc
4 Westbrook Corporate Ctr
Westchester IL 60154
708 236-6600

(G-17290)
CONNECTIVITY SOLUTIONS MFG INC
Also Called: Commscope
2601 Telecom Pkwy (75082-3521)
PHONE................................972 792-3000
Chris Ewing, *President*
Marvin S Edwards Jr, *Principal*
Jean Gay, *Vice Pres*
Ernie Pickens, *Vice Pres*
Upendra Pingle, *Vice Pres*
EMP: 170
SALES (est): 35.4MM **Privately Held**
WEB: www.commscope.com
SIC: 3663 Radio & TV communications equipment

(G-17291)
CONTROLLED SYSTEMS SALES CO
1758 Firman Dr 200 (75081-1823)
PHONE................................972 234-6767
Patricia M Hodge, *President*
Doug Kuzanek, *Project Engr*
Frank Pazdric, *Sales Staff*
Jonathan Lewis, *Technology*
▲ **EMP:** 10
SALES (est): 2.8MM **Privately Held**
WEB: www.controlledsystems.us
SIC: 3621 3822 3625 Frequency converters (electric generators); temperature controls, automatic; motor starters & controllers, electric

(G-17292)
COPPELL WOODWORKS INC (PA)
633 W Belt Line Rd (75080-6114)
PHONE................................940 482-8900
Thomas H Schantz, *Principal*
EMP: 12 **EST:** 2008
SALES (est): 827.6K **Privately Held**
SIC: 2431 Millwork

(G-17293)
COWAN COOLANT MGT SVCS LLC
903 N Bowser Rd Ste 330 (75081-2868)
P.O. Box 835986 (75083-5986)
PHONE................................214 686-1010
Rex Cowan, *Owner*
EMP: 16

SALES (est): 1.7MM **Privately Held**
SIC: 3541 Machine tools, metal cutting type

(G-17294)
CRESCENT SYSTEMS INC
1155 E Collins Blvd # 10 (75081-2304)
PHONE................................972 437-0400
Clark Red, *President*
Brooke Buchanan, *Design Engr*
Gayle Red, *Treasurer*
Daniel Lewis, *Software Engr*
Richard Searle, *Sr Software Eng*
EMP: 45
SQ FT: 5,000
SALES (est): 1.6MM **Privately Held**
WEB: www.csitx.com
SIC: 7371 8731 3571 Computer software development; computer (hardware) development; electronic computers

(G-17295)
CUSTOM RODS & DRAPERIES
1225 N Plano Rd (75081-2424)
PHONE................................972 889-0580
Karen Hanson, *President*
EMP: 11
SALES (est): 886.4K **Privately Held**
WEB: www.customrodsanddraperies.com
SIC: 2391 5714 Draperies, plastic & textile: from purchased materials; draperies

(G-17296)
D4D TECHNOLOGIES LLC
Also Called: E4d Technologies
2920 Telecom Pkwy Ste 100 (75082-3524)
PHONE................................972 534-3101
Kala Cantu, *Buyer*
Andrew Hibma, *Engineer*
Mike Huneycutt, *Engineer*
Jinal Vora, *Engineer*
Brett Hetherington, *Finance*
◆ **EMP:** 120
SQ FT: 100,000
SALES (est): 41.1MM **Privately Held**
WEB: www.e4d.com
SIC: 3841 Surgical & medical instruments

(G-17297)
DALLAS CHINESE NEWS INC
Also Called: A-1 Printing
200 S Interurban St (75081-4165)
PHONE................................972 680-9577
Ralph Mak, *President*
EMP: 10
SQ FT: 3,800
SALES (est): 915.3K **Privately Held**
WEB: www.dallaschinesenews.com
SIC: 2759 2741 Commercial printing; miscellaneous publishing

(G-17298)
DELTA ELECTRONICS (USA) INC
1249 Commerce Dr (75081-2406)
PHONE................................469 330-9100
Paul Sullivan, *Branch Mgr*
EMP: 41 **Privately Held**
WEB: www.eltek.com
SIC: 3679 Static power supply converters for electronic applications
HQ: Delta Electronics (Usa) Inc.
2925 E Plano Pkwy
Plano TX 75074
469 330-9100

(G-17299)
DELTA V INSTRUMENTS INC
1870 Firman Dr (75081-1825)
PHONE................................972 644-6501
Robert Storey, *CEO*
James Crossland, *President*
Kenneth Bown, *Vice Pres*
Clint Wilson, *Vice Pres*
Kerry Cage, *Engineer*
EMP: 17
SQ FT: 11,000
SALES (est): 5MM **Privately Held**
WEB: www.delta-v.com
SIC: 3672 3825 Printed circuit boards; semiconductor test equipment

(G-17300)
DFA DAIRY BRANDS ICE CREAM LLC
400 N Grove Rd (75081-2738)
PHONE................................214 905-5003

David Ly, *Opers Staff*
EMP: 9
SALES (corp-wide): 15.8B **Privately Held**
SIC: 2024 Ice cream & ice milk
HQ: Dfa Dairy Brands Ice Cream, Llc
1405 N 98th St
Kansas City KS 66111
816 801-6455

(G-17301)
DFS FIRE SYSTEMS LLC
885 E Collins Blvd # 104 (75081-2296)
PHONE................................214 628-4061
Kimberly Davis,
Jeremy Davis,
EMP: 15
SALES (est): 2.4MM **Privately Held**
WEB: www.dfsfiresystems.com
SIC: 3569 Sprinkler systems, fire: automatic

(G-17302)
DRSK LIMITED PARTNERSHIP
Also Called: Recognition Express
113 E Polk St (75081-4132)
PHONE................................972 644-1490
Rick Perkins, *Owner*
Deana Perkins, *Partner*
Richard Perkins, *Human Res Mgr*
EMP: 13
SQ FT: 11,900
SALES (est): 946.3K **Privately Held**
WEB: www.bestbadge.com
SIC: 5999 3999 5947 7389 Trophies & plaques; plaques, picture, laminated; gifts & novelties; engraving service; badges

(G-17303)
DYNATRON SOFTWARE INC
2703 Telecom Pkwy Ste 140 (75082-3555)
PHONE................................972 488-0393
Doug Bradley, *Principal*
Amy Kelley, *Controller*
Donnie McLamb, *Regl Sales Mgr*
Michael Kotek, *Sales Executive*
Mike Hong, *Marketing Staff*
EMP: 18
SALES (est): 2.6MM **Privately Held**
WEB: www.dynatronsoftware.com
SIC: 7372 Prepackaged software

(G-17304)
EL DORADO PHARMACY LLC
1300 E Arapaho Rd Ste 210 (75081-2445)
PHONE................................214 329-4580
Austin Keyser, *Manager*
EMP: 9
SALES (est): 785.9K **Privately Held**
SIC: 2834 Pharmaceutical preparations

(G-17305)
ELECTRIC PWR SYSTEMS INTL INC
783 N Grove Rd Ste 101 (75081-2776)
PHONE................................972 907-3783
Thomas Thun, *Branch Mgr*
EMP: 20
SALES (corp-wide): 146MM **Privately Held**
WEB: www.epsii.com
SIC: 3699 1731 Electrical equipment & supplies; electric power systems contractors
PA: Electric Power Systems International, Inc.
15 Millpark Ct
Maryland Heights MO 63043
314 227-4800

(G-17306)
EXECUTIVE PRESS INC
1400 Presidential Dr # 110 (75081-2473)
PHONE................................214 217-7000
Tom Sadler, *President*
David Allen, *Vice Pres*
EMP: 11 **EST:** 1986
SQ FT: 11,000
SALES (est): 2.2MM **Privately Held**
WEB: www.executivepress.com
SIC: 2752 Commercial printing, offset

(G-17307)
EXFO AMERICA INC (HQ)
3400 Waterview Pkwy # 100 (75080-1472)
PHONE................................972 761-9271
Germain Lamonde, *CEO*

David Norman, *District Mgr*
Natalie Haycox, *Vice Pres*
Dorie Watkins, *Opers Staff*
Daniel Chiasson, *Mfg Staff*
EMP: 24
SQ FT: 1,200
SALES (est): 82.6MM
SALES (corp-wide): 266.6MM **Privately Held**
WEB: www.exfo.com
SIC: 3825 8734 Instruments to measure electricity; testing laboratories
PA: Exfo Inc
　　400 Av Godin
　　Quebec QC G1M 2
　　418 683-0211

(G-17308)
FAIRCHILD SEMICONDUCTOR CORP
2400 Lkeside Blvd Ste 700 (75082)
PHONE.................................972 910-8000
Ellen Goodloe, *Manager*
EMP: 20
SALES (corp-wide): 5.5B **Publicly Held**
WEB: www.onsemi.com
SIC: 3674 Integrated circuits, semiconductor networks, etc.
HQ: Fairchild Semiconductor Corporation
　　82 Running Hill Rd
　　South Portland ME 04106
　　207 775-8100

(G-17309)
FEI EFA INC
Also Called: Nano Instrs Div Dcg Systems
1321 N Plano Rd (75081-2426)
PHONE.................................972 792-1644
EMP: 10
SALES (corp-wide): 25.5B **Publicly Held**
WEB: www.fei.com
SIC: 3826 Analytical instruments
HQ: Fei Efa, Inc.
　　3400 W Warren Ave
　　Fremont CA 94538

(G-17310)
FOCUS WIRELESS INC
709 N Glenville Dr # 500 (75081-2479)
PHONE.................................586 907-5323
EMP: 15
SALES (est): 645K **Privately Held**
SIC: 3571 Mfg Electronic Computers

(G-17311)
FORUM COMMUNICATIONS SYSTEMS
Also Called: Forum Communications Intl
1223 N Glenville Dr (75081-2412)
PHONE.................................972 619-8603
Gayne Ek, *President*
T Raj Natarajan, *Vice Pres*
Kelly Grant, *Marketing Staff*
EMP: 15
SQ FT: 6,500
SALES (est): 4MM **Privately Held**
WEB: www.forum-com.com
SIC: 3663 5065 Radio & TV communications equipment; telephone equipment

(G-17312)
FOSSIL GROUP INC (PA)
901 S Central Expy (75080-7302)
PHONE.................................972 234-2525
Kosta N Kartsotis, *Ch of Bd*
Joy Baker, *District Mgr*
Amy Gebo, *District Mgr*
Jeff Boyer, *COO*
John A White, *COO*
◆ **EMP:** 277
SQ FT: 536,000
SALES: 2.2B **Publicly Held**
WEB: www.fossilgroup.com
SIC: 3873 5944 5094 5651 Watches, clocks, watchcases & parts; watches; watches & parts; family clothing stores; handbags

(G-17313)
FOSSIL PARTNERS LP
Kate Spade
901 S Central Expy (75080-7302)
PHONE.................................972 234-2525
EMP: 28

SALES (corp-wide): 2.2B **Publicly Held**
WEB: www.fossil.com
SIC: 3915 5944 5094 Jewel preparing: instruments, tools, watches & jewelry; watches; clocks, watches & parts
HQ: Fossil Partners, L.P.
　　901 S Central Expy
　　Richardson TX 75080

(G-17314)
FOSSIL PARTNERS LP
Also Called: Chaps
901 S Central Expy (75080-7302)
PHONE.................................972 234-2525
EMP: 351
SALES (corp-wide): 2.2B **Publicly Held**
SIC: 2339 5137 2389 Women's & misses' accessories; women's & children's accessories; men's miscellaneous accessories
HQ: Fossil Partners, L.P.
　　901 S Central Expy
　　Richardson TX 75080

(G-17315)
FOSSIL PARTNERS LP
Also Called: Sketchers
2280 N Greenville Ave (75082-4412)
PHONE.................................972 437-0452
Wendy Green, *Business Mgr*
Pam Harper, *Business Mgr*
Holly Pope, *Business Mgr*
Steve Evans, *Exec VP*
Dean Carter, *Vice Pres*
EMP: 9
SALES (corp-wide): 2.2B **Publicly Held**
WEB: www.fossil.com
SIC: 3021 3149 Shoes, rubber or plastic molded to fabric; athletic shoes, except rubber or plastic
HQ: Fossil Partners, L.P.
　　901 S Central Expy
　　Richardson TX 75080

(G-17316)
FOSSIL PARTNERS LP
Also Called: Diesel
2880 Greenville (75080)
PHONE.................................469 587-2627
Steve Bock, *Branch Mgr*
Diego Aviles, *Manager*
EMP: 351
SALES (corp-wide): 2.2B **Publicly Held**
WEB: www.shop.diesel.com
SIC: 2339 Women's & misses' accessories
HQ: Fossil Partners, L.P.
　　901 S Central Expy
　　Richardson TX 75080

(G-17317)
FOSSIL PARTNERS LP (HQ)
Also Called: Fossil Retrodome
901 S Central Expy (75080-7302)
P.O. Box 853914 (75085-3914)
PHONE.................................972 234-2525
Kosta Kartsotis, *Managing Prtnr*
Nickolaos Kon, *Partner*
Matt Deree, *Opers Dir*
Thomas Seguin-Cousinea, *Maint Spvr*
Jake Myers, *Sales Staff*
▲ **EMP:** 700
SALES (est): 532.8MM
SALES (corp-wide): 2.2B **Publicly Held**
SIC: 5137 2389 2339 5094 Women's & children's accessories; apparel belts, women's & children's; handbags; purses; men's miscellaneous accessories; women's & misses' accessories; jewelry
PA: Fossil Group, Inc.
　　901 S Central Expy
　　Richardson TX 75080
　　972 234-2525

(G-17318)
FUJITSU NTWRK CMMNICATIONS INC (HQ)
2801 Telecom Pkwy (75082-3599)
PHONE.................................972 479-6000
Nikito Kiname, *CEO*
Satoshi Ikeuchi, *President*
Kevin Dunsmore, *Partner*
David Berry, *Principal*
Femi Adeyemi, *Chief*
▲ **EMP:** 1000
SQ FT: 87,000

SALES (est): 332MM **Privately Held**
WEB: www.fujitsu.com
SIC: 3661 3663 Fiber optics communications equipment; cellular radio telephone

(G-17319)
GALAXY ELECTRONICS COMPANY
Also Called: Galaxy Fiber Optics and Elec
201 E Arapaho Rd (75081-6203)
PHONE.................................972 234-0065
Yueh S Yang, *President*
Shirley Fan, *Purchasing*
Laura Yang, *Treasurer*
◆ **EMP:** 19
SQ FT: 28,000
SALES (est): 1.8MM **Privately Held**
WEB: www.galaxyee.com
SIC: 3643 5045 5065 5063 Connectors & terminals for electrical devices; computers & accessories, personal & home entertainment; electronic parts & equipment; control & signal wire & cable, including coaxial; nonferrous wiredrawing & insulating

(G-17320)
GANTEN GROUP LLC
Also Called: Shower Doors of Dallas
1730 N Greenville Ave (75081-1808)
PHONE.................................214 530-5483
Monica Gantenbein, *Human Resources*
Jason Gantenbein,
EMP: 11 **EST:** 2010
SALES (est): 484.2K **Privately Held**
WEB: www.goframeless.com
SIC: 5211 3088 Bathroom fixtures, equipment & supplies; shower stalls, fiberglass & plastic

(G-17321)
GLAXOSMITHKLINE LLC
2425 N Central Expy # 470 (75080-2782)
PHONE.................................469 547-1722
Chuck Smith, *Branch Mgr*
EMP: 20
SALES (corp-wide): 43.6B **Privately Held**
WEB: www.us.gsk.com
SIC: 2834 5122 Pharmaceutical preparations; pharmaceuticals
HQ: Glaxosmithkline Llc
　　5 Crescent Dr
　　Philadelphia PA 19112
　　215 751-4000

(G-17322)
GLOBERANGER CORPORATION
1130 E Arapaho Rd Ste 450 (75081-2357)
PHONE.................................972 744-9977
George Brody, *President*
Joshua S Abelson, *Vice Pres*
Monty Cook, *Vice Pres*
Dominic Lanaway, *Vice Pres*
Guy G Mikel, *Vice Pres*
EMP: 43 **EST:** 2000
SQ FT: 16,800
SALES (est): 5.1MM **Privately Held**
WEB: www.globeranger.com
SIC: 7372 Business oriented computer software
HQ: Fujitsu Services Limited
　　22 Baker Street
　　London W1U 3
　　123 579-7711

(G-17323)
GO INDUSTRIES INC (PA)
420 N Grove Rd (75081-2784)
PHONE.................................972 783-7444
Robert J Orth Jr, *President*
Robert J Orth Sr, *Chairman*
Jeanne Orth, *Corp Secy*
Chris J Orth, *Vice Pres*
John Orth, *Vice Pres*
◆ **EMP:** 38
SQ FT: 50,000
SALES (est): 9.5MM **Privately Held**
WEB: www.goindustriesinc.com
SIC: 3714 Motor vehicle parts & accessories

(G-17324)
H E B & ASSOCIATES INC
Also Called: H E B Printing
1215 Commerce Dr (75081-2406)
PHONE.................................972 234-0347

Jared Danielson, *President*
EMP: 14
SQ FT: 5,000
SALES (est): 2.9MM **Privately Held**
WEB: www.hebprinting.com
SIC: 2752 Commercial printing, offset

(G-17325)
HALFF TRITEX LLC
1201 N Bowser Rd (75081-2220)
PHONE.................................214 217-6500
Mark Edwards,
Richard Jones,
EMP: 20
SQ FT: 1,200
SALES (est): 1.6MM **Privately Held**
WEB: www.halff.com
SIC: 1382 4922 Oil & gas exploration services; pipelines, natural gas

(G-17326)
HANSON AGGREGATES LLC
Also Called: Pioneer Concrete Plant
1250 Digital Dr (75081-1949)
PHONE.................................972 644-6415
Curtis Olins, *Manager*
EMP: 15
SALES (corp-wide): 20.8B **Privately Held**
WEB: www.heidelbergcement.com
SIC: 3273 Ready-mixed concrete
HQ: Hanson Aggregates Llc
　　8505 Freport Pkwy Ste 500
　　Irving TX 75063
　　469 417-1200

(G-17327)
HBS SYSTEMS INC
3400 Waterview Pkwy # 200 (75080-1472)
P.O. Box 832030 (75083-2030)
PHONE.................................972 234-4444
Chad Stone, *President*
G Lynn Reed, *Exec VP*
John Mathison, *CFO*
Alaina Jeanblanc, *Human Res Mgr*
EMP: 53
SQ FT: 24,274
SALES (est): 8.4MM **Privately Held**
WEB: www.hbssystems.com
SIC: 7372 5045 Prepackaged software; computer peripheral equipment

(G-17328)
HIGH TECH SERVICES INC
999 E Arapaho Rd Ste 200 (75081-2280)
PHONE.................................972 231-8037
Ken Abbott, *President*
Pat Abbott, *Vice Pres*
EMP: 14
SQ FT: 9,500
SALES (est): 2.8MM **Privately Held**
WEB: www.hightechservices.com
SIC: 3674 Semiconductors & related devices

(G-17329)
HONEYWELL INTERNATIONAL INC
830 E Arapaho Rd (75081-2241)
PHONE.................................972 792-1800
Amol Joshi, *Marketing Staff*
Paul Chapman, *Branch Mgr*
Steve Kordak, *Manager*
EMP: 450
SALES (corp-wide): 36.7B **Publicly Held**
WEB: www.honeywell.com
SIC: 3724 Aircraft engines & engine parts
PA: Honeywell International Inc.
　　300 S Tryon St
　　Charlotte NC 28202
　　704 627-6200

(G-17330)
IC ENABLE LLC
800 E Campbell Rd (75081-6706)
PHONE.................................214 575-9400
Ben Tranchina, *CEO*
Tim Snodgrass, *President*
Lisa Lawrence, *QA Dir*
Eva Bryan, *Manager*
Caitlin Mahoney, *Manager*
EMP: 48 **EST:** 2004
SALES (est): 2.6MM **Privately Held**
WEB: www.ic-enable.com
SIC: 3674 Microcircuits, integrated (semiconductor)

▲ = Import ▼=Export
◆ =Import/Export

(G-17331)
INDUSTRIAL NOISE CONTROL CORP
Also Called: Incc
1023 Sunningdale (75081-5161)
PHONE..............................972 494-1422
Bill Badgett, *President*
Kelly Crawley, *Vice Pres*
EMP: 40
SQ FT: 35,000
SALES (est): 7MM **Privately Held**
SIC: 2299 Acoustic felts

(G-17332)
INFOSYS LIMITED (HQ)
Also Called: Itl Infosys Limited
2400 N Glnvlle Dr Ste C15 (75082)
PHONE..............................214 306-2100
S D Shibulal, *CEO*
Mukul Awasthi, *Partner*
Vivek Bakshi, *Partner*
Erik Newlin, *Partner*
Dean Dastvar, *General Mgr*
EMP: 100
SALES (est): 78.5MM **Privately Held**
WEB: www.infosys.com
SIC: 7373 7379 7372 7371 Systems engineering, computer related; computer related consulting services; prepackaged software; computer software development

(G-17333)
INNOVATIVE SIGNAL ANALYSIS INC (PA)
Also Called: ISA
3301 E Renner Rd Ste 200 (75082-1802)
PHONE..............................972 231-5702
Stacy Kirk Kniffen, *President*
Karen Canterbury, *Business Mgr*
David Stevens, *Vice Pres*
Rachel Rivera, *Engineer*
Randy Reininger, *Technology*
EMP: 80
SQ FT: 35,000
SALES (est): 22.6MM **Privately Held**
WEB: www.signal-analysis.com
SIC: 3812 Search & navigation equipment

(G-17334)
INTELLIGENT EPITAXY TECH INC
Also Called: Intelliepi
1250 E Collins Blvd (75081-2401)
PHONE..............................972 234-0068
Yung Chung KAO, *President*
Jenn-Ming Kuo, *Vice Pres*
Kevin Vargason, *VP Opers*
David Ontiveros, *Prdtn Mgr*
Joe Middlebrooks, *Purchasing*
▲ EMP: 60
SQ FT: 26,000
SALES (est): 24.3MM **Privately Held**
WEB: www.intelliepi.com
SIC: 3674 Wafers (semiconductor devices); semiconductor circuit networks

(G-17335)
INTERFET CORPORATION
715 N Glenville Dr # 400 (75081-2879)
PHONE..............................972 238-9700
Dan E Roberts, *President*
Jerry McIntire, *Vice Pres*
Gladys Brantley, *CFO*
EMP: 16
SQ FT: 59,000
SALES (est): 2.7MM **Privately Held**
WEB: www.interfet.com
SIC: 3674 Transistors

(G-17336)
INTRUSION INC (PA)
1101 E Arapaho Rd Ste 200 (75081-2336)
PHONE..............................972 234-6400
Anthony J Levecchio, *Ch of Bd*
T Joe Head, *Vice Ch Bd*
Jack B Blount, *President*
Martin Koren, *Vice Pres*
Vittal Krishnamurthy, *Vice Pres*
EMP: 28
SQ FT: 23,000

SALES: 13.6MM **Publicly Held**
WEB: www.intrusion.com
SIC: 3577 7373 7371 Computer peripheral equipment; computer integrated systems design; local area network (LAN) systems integrator; custom computer programming services; computer software development & applications; computer software development

(G-17337)
ISLAMIC SERVICES FOUNDATION
Also Called: Brighter Horizons Academy
411 Industrial Dr Ste 105 (75081-2864)
P.O. Box 451623, Garland (75045-1623)
PHONE..............................972 414-5090
EMP: 70 EST: 1989
SQ FT: 50,000
SALES (est): 5.7MM **Privately Held**
WEB: www.islamicservices.org
SIC: 8299 2759 Educational services; publication printing

(G-17338)
K & L PRECISION PLASTICS INC
410 N Grove Rd (75081-2797)
PHONE..............................972 234-4231
Mark A Justice, *President*
Patrick Conley, *Vice Pres*
Mike L Justice, *Vice Pres*
Barbara Lane Justice-Conley, *Shareholder*
EMP: 10
SQ FT: 16,000
SALES (est): 1MM **Privately Held**
SIC: 3089 Injection molding of plastics

(G-17339)
KATHREIN HOLDING USA INC
2400 Lkeside Blvd Ste 650 (75082)
P.O. Box 111635, Carrollton (75011-1635)
PHONE..............................541 779-6500
Anton Kathrein, *President*
Ellis Feinstein, *Admin Sec*
◆ EMP: 100
SQ FT: 80,000
SALES (est): 10.6MM
SALES (corp-wide): 418.9K **Privately Held**
WEB: www.kathreinusa.com
SIC: 3663 Antennas, transmitting & communications
HQ: Kathrein Se
Anton-Kathrein-Str. 1-3
Rosenheim 83022
803 118-40

(G-17340)
KDL MEDICAL INC
Also Called: Chase Medical
885 E Collins Blvd # 110 (75081-2270)
PHONE..............................972 783-7005
Jackie D Lafollette, *President*
EMP: 12
SALES (est): 1.9MM **Privately Held**
WEB: www.chasemedical.com
SIC: 3841 Diagnostic apparatus, medical

(G-17341)
LEARJET INC
Also Called: Bombardier Flexjet
3400 Waterview Pkwy # 320 (75080-1472)
PHONE..............................972 720-2400
Eric Swanson, *Research*
Antonio Ficca, *Accounts Mgr*
Michael McClay, *Branch Mgr*
EMP: 750
SALES (corp-wide): 15.7B **Privately Held**
WEB: www.bombardier.com
SIC: 3721 Aircraft
HQ: Learjet Inc.
1 Learjet Way
Wichita KS 67209
316 946-2000

(G-17342)
LEEMAH CORPORATION
1001 E Arapaho Rd (75081-2327)
PHONE..............................214 570-7170
Dave Geferick, *Plant Mgr*
Thomas Mallow, *Manager*
EMP: 160
SQ FT: 53,028

SALES (corp-wide): 101MM **Privately Held**
WEB: www.leemah.com
SIC: 3672 Printed circuit boards
PA: Leemah Corporation
155 S Hill Dr
Brisbane CA 94005
415 394-1288

(G-17343)
LENNOX INTERNATIONAL INC (PA)
2140 Lake Park Blvd (75080-2252)
P.O. Box 799900, Dallas (75379-9900)
PHONE..............................972 497-5000
Todd M Bluedorn, *Ch of Bd*
Prakash Bedapudi, *Exec VP*
Gary S Bedard, *Exec VP*
Gary Bedard, *Exec VP*
Douglas L Young, *Exec VP*
▲ EMP: 200
SQ FT: 356,000
SALES (est): 3.8B **Publicly Held**
WEB: www.lennoxinternational.com
SIC: 3621 3585 Coils, for electric motors or generators; furnaces, warm air: electric

(G-17344)
LIBRA INDUSTRIES LLC
1250 American Pkwy (75081-2931)
PHONE..............................972 664-0900
Steve Schwaebler, *Branch Mgr*
EMP: 80
SALES (corp-wide): 144.3MM **Privately Held**
WEB: www.libraind.com
SIC: 3672 Printed circuit boards
HQ: Libra Industries, Llc
7770 Division Dr
Mentor OH 44060
440 974-7770

(G-17345)
LIQUID MOTORS INC
1755 N Collins Blvd # 109 (75080-3552)
PHONE..............................214 393-2323
Don R Daseke, *Ch of Bd*
Michael Daseke, *President*
Jill Givens, *Manager*
Steve Carson, *Software Dev*
EMP: 19
SALES (est): 2.5MM **Privately Held**
WEB: www.liquidmotors.com
SIC: 7372 Business oriented computer software

(G-17346)
LLC BATTLE BEAVER
Also Called: Battle Beaver Customs
1161 Executive Dr W (75081-2230)
PHONE..............................888 390-4363
David Bailey, *CEO*
David Christopher Bailey,
EMP: 52
SALES (est): 1.9MM **Privately Held**
WEB: www.battlebeavercustoms.com
SIC: 3944 7629 Video game machines, except coin-operated; electronic equipment repair

(G-17347)
LOJACK CORPORATION (HQ)
2400 N Glnvlle Dr Ste 225 (75082)
PHONE..............................781 302-4200
Randy L Ortiz, *President*
Elia De Leon, *General Mgr*
Kevin M Mullins, *General Mgr*
Jim Arnold, *Business Mgr*
Eryn McNearney, *Business Mgr*
▲ EMP: 99 EST: 1978
SALES (est): 91.5MM
SALES (corp-wide): 366.1MM **Publicly Held**
WEB: www.lojack.com
SIC: 3699 Security devices
PA: Calamp Corp.
15635 Alton Pkwy Ste 250
Irvine CA 92618
949 600-5600

(G-17348)
LOMA RENTALS LLC (PA)
433 Belle Grove Dr (75080-5200)
P.O. Box 832555 (75083-2555)
PHONE..............................817 964-1828
Lisa Farrell, *Vice Pres*

Doug Farrell, *Mng Member*
EMP: 15
SQ FT: 6,000
SALES (est): 3.7MM **Privately Held**
WEB: www.lomarentals.com
SIC: 1389 Oil field services

(G-17349)
LONG RANGE SYSTEMS LLC (PA)
Also Called: L R S
1155 Kas Dr Ste 150 (75081-7220)
PHONE..............................214 553-5308
John Weber, *CEO*
Kenneth Lovegreen, *Ch of Bd*
Marc Devinney, *Vice Pres*
Wayne Greene, *Vice Pres*
Jim Livingston, *Vice Pres*
◆ EMP: 46
SQ FT: 42,000
SALES (est): 8.1MM **Privately Held**
WEB: www.lrsus.com
SIC: 3663 5065 Pagers (one-way); paging & signaling equipment

(G-17350)
MACTRONIX INC
735 N Plano Rd 105 (75081-2944)
PHONE..............................972 690-0028
John Lau, *President*
Chuck Degeest, *Exec VP*
Deborah Lau, *Vice Pres*
Jay Reyes, *Technical Staff*
EMP: 32
SALES (est): 5.3MM **Privately Held**
WEB: www.mactronix.com
SIC: 3674 3825 Integrated circuits, semiconductor networks, etc.; semiconductor test equipment

(G-17351)
MARLIN ENVIRONMENTAL PRODUCTS
1406 Seminole Dr (75080-3737)
P.O. Box 5291, Kingwood (77325-5291)
PHONE..............................214 493-9128
Marty Zolton, *Ch of Bd*
Michael Zoltan, *President*
EMP: 11
SQ FT: 10,000
SALES (est): 1MM **Privately Held**
SIC: 8711 1541 3648 Engineering services; industrial buildings & warehouses; lighting equipment

(G-17352)
MAVENIR PRVATE HOLDINGS II LTD
1700 Intl Pkwy Ste 200 (75081)
PHONE..............................469 916-4393
Hubert De Pesquidoux, *Ch of Bd*
Pardeep Kohli, *President*
Bg Kumar, *President*
BJ Jalalizadeh, *Exec VP*
Ramnik Kamo, *Exec VP*
EMP: 2411
SQ FT: 58,635
SALES: 427.4MM **Privately Held**
SIC: 7372 Prepackaged software

(G-17353)
MCFADDEN & ASSOCIATES INC
515 N Interurban St # 103 (75081-3363)
PHONE..............................972 680-8333
John McFadden, *President*
EMP: 40
SALES (est): 6.6MM **Privately Held**
SIC: 3446 Stairs, staircases, stair treads: prefabricated metal

(G-17354)
MCFADDEN STAIRS INC
515 N Interurban St # 103 (75081-3363)
PHONE..............................972 680-8333
John McFadden, *Director*
EMP: 10
SALES (est): 760K **Privately Held**
WEB: www.dfwstairs.com
SIC: 2431 Staircases & stairs, wood

(G-17355)
MEDEANALYTICS INC (PA)
501 W President George Bu (75080-1131)
PHONE..............................469 476-5423
Paul Kaiser, *CEO*

Anthony McKeever, *CEO*
David Weiss, *Ch of Bd*
Scott Hampel, *President*
Kristen Aleksa Noftsger, *Senior VP*
EMP: 144
SQ FT: 25,078
SALES (est): 46MM **Privately Held**
WEB: www.medeanalytics.com
SIC: 7372 Business oriented computer
software

(G-17356)
METAPATH SOFTWARE INTL (DH)
Also Called: Mobile Systems International
1755 N Collins Blvd # 400 (75080-3562)
PHONE.........................972 907-3600
Clifford P Wagner, *Exec VP*
John Thornton, *Legal Staff*
EMP: 11
SALES (est): 14.8MM
SALES (corp-wide): 423.9K **Privately Held**
SIC: 8748 7372 4812 Systems analysis &
engineering consulting services; prepack-
aged software; cellular telephone services
HQ: Telent Limited
Point 3
Warwick CV34
192 669-3000

(G-17357)
MICREL LLC
2425 N Central Expy # 351 (75080-2756)
PHONE.........................972 235-9166
Billy Anderson, *Branch Mgr*
EMP: 250
SALES (corp-wide): 5.2B **Publicly Held**
WEB: www.microchip.com
SIC: 3674 Integrated circuits, semiconduc-
tor networks, etc.
HQ: Micrel, Llc
2355 W Chandler Blvd
Chandler AZ 85224
480 792-7200

(G-17358)
MIRACON TECHNOLOGIES LLC
401 S Sherman St Ste 101 (75081-4012)
PHONE.........................972 387-3099
Charles Welker, *President*
Martha Welker, *Mng Member*
EMP: 10
SQ FT: 4,000
SALES (est): 1.5MM **Privately Held**
WEB: www.miracontech.com
SIC: 2899 8731 Concrete curing & hard-
ening compounds; commercial physical
research

(G-17359)
MODUS TEST LLC
651 N Plano Rd Ste 419 (75081-2961)
P.O. Box 904, Laveen AZ (85339-0765)
PHONE.........................972 914-7866
Jay Williams, *Partner*
Tim Conner, *Engineer*
Woody Adams,
Micheal Bell,
Bruce Rogers,
EMP: 15
SALES (est): 1.1MM **Privately Held**
WEB: www.modustest.com
SIC: 3674 Semiconductors & related de-
vices

(G-17360)
MORGAN BUILDINGS & SPAS INC (HQ)
1651 N Glenville Dr (75081-7208)
P.O. Box 660280, Dallas (75266-0280)
PHONE.........................972 864-7300
Guy H Morgan, *President*
Karen Belans, *Principal*
Elisa Stevenson, *Principal*
Megan Spanitz, *Vice Pres*
Glenn Stevens, *Vice Pres*
EMP: 10
SQ FT: 32,000
SALES (est): 67.4MM **Privately Held**
WEB: www.morganusa.com
SIC: 5211 5999 5561 3448 Prefabricated
buildings; spas & hot tubs; swimming
pools, above ground; recreational vehicle
dealers; prefabricated metal buildings

(G-17361)
MULTI-QUEST INC (PA)
Also Called: Hightech Signs
1111 Commerce Dr (75081-2308)
PHONE.........................972 235-2356
Betty S Boyd, *President*
John G Boyd, *Vice Pres*
EMP: 12
SQ FT: 12,500
SALES (est): 2MM **Privately Held**
WEB: www.signs2k.com
SIC: 3993 2399 7336 5999 Signs, not
made in custom sign painting shops; ban-
ners, made from fabric; commercial art &
graphic design; banners

(G-17362)
NEOFIRMA INC
2100 Alamo Rd Ste T (75080-2738)
PHONE.........................214 233-7111
Steve Haglund, *President*
Eric Haig, *VP Bus Dvlpt*
Matt Malick, *Technology*
George Michael, *Director*
John Korb, *Education*
EMP: 10
SALES (est): 1MM **Privately Held**
WEB: www.neofirma.com
SIC: 7371 1382 7372 1311 Computer
software development; oil & gas explo-
ration services; prepackaged software;
crude petroleum & natural gas;

(G-17363)
NERVE SOFTWARE LLC
300 N Coit Rd Ste 1500 (75080-5460)
PHONE.........................972 231-4775
Matthew B James, *President*
Mason Lucas, *Vice Pres*
EMP: 9 EST: 2001
SALES (est): 939.7K **Privately Held**
WEB: www.nervesoftware.com
SIC: 7372 Application computer software

(G-17364)
NETWATCH SOLUTIONS INC
1101 E Arapaho Rd Ste 100 (75081-2355)
P.O. Box 831359 (75083-1359)
PHONE.........................214 446-8486
Peter Beasley, *President*
EMP: 15
SQ FT: 2,500
SALES (est): 1.2MM **Privately Held**
WEB: www.netwatchsolutions.com
SIC: 7372 Prepackaged software

(G-17365)
NEURO RESOURCE GROUP INTL INC
870 N Dorothy Dr Ste 708 (75081-2771)
PHONE.........................972 665-1810
Dave Turner, *Vice Pres*
EMP: 27
SALES (est): 2.7MM **Privately Held**
WEB: www.interx.com
SIC: 3841 Surgical & medical instruments

(G-17366)
NPI TECHNOLOGIES INC (PA)
1241 N Plano Rd (75081-2424)
PHONE.........................972 968-0400
Tony Thai, *President*
EMP: 27
SALES (est): 8MM **Privately Held**
WEB: www.npitechnologies.com
SIC: 3672 Printed circuit boards

(G-17367)
NVIDIA CORPORATION
740 E Campbell Rd Ste 300 (75081-6763)
PHONE.........................408 486-2000
Patti Simmons, *Branch Mgr*
EMP: 15 **Publicly Held**
WEB: www.nvidia.com
SIC: 3674 Semiconductors & related de-
vices
PA: Nvidia Corporation
2788 San Tomas Expy
Santa Clara CA 95051

(G-17368)
OPTEX SYSTEMS INC (HQ)
1420 Presidential Dr (75081-2439)
PHONE.........................972 764-5700
Danny Schoening, *Ch of Bd*

Stanley A Hirschman, *President*
Ernest Edwards, *Opers Staff*
Pam Hall, *Buyer*
Joe Aizpuru, *Engineer*
EMP: 53
SQ FT: 50,000
SALES (est): 14MM
SALES (corp-wide): 25.8MM **Publicly Held**
WEB: www.optexsys.com
SIC: 3827 Sighting & fire control equip-
ment, optical
PA: Optex Systems Holdings, Inc.
1420 Presidential Dr
Richardson TX 75081
972 764-5700

(G-17369)
OPTEX SYSTEMS HOLDINGS INC (PA)
1420 Presidential Dr (75081-2439)
PHONE.........................972 764-5700
Danny Schoening, *Ch of Bd*
Ron Stinedurf, *Mfg Mgr*
Jeff Balch, *QC Mgr*
Karen L Hawkins, *CFO*
Karen Hawkins, *CFO*
EMP: 58
SQ FT: 49,100
SALES: 25.8MM **Publicly Held**
WEB: www.optexsys.com
SIC: 3827 Sighting & fire control equip-
ment, optical

(G-17370)
PAMPILLONIA DESIGNS II INC
1740 N Collins Blvd (75080-3640)
PHONE.........................214 503-7272
Chris Pampillonia, *President*
Kathleen Pampillonia, *Vice Pres*
Claudia Stinnett, *QC Mgr*
◆ **EMP:** 70
SQ FT: 4,000
SALES (est): 1.2MM **Privately Held**
WEB: www.pampilloniadesigns.com
SIC: 3911 Jewelry, precious metal

(G-17371)
PAW DEPOT INCORPORATED
955 E Campbell Rd (75081-6794)
PHONE.........................214 440-6324
Julio Ferrari, *CEO*
Carolina De Paula, *COO*
◆ **EMP:** 10 EST: 2010
SQ FT: 1,400
SALES (est): 873.5K **Privately Held**
WEB: www.paw-depot.com
SIC: 5999 2047 Pets & pet supplies; dog
food

(G-17372)
PHASE DYNAMICS INC
1251 Columbia Dr (75081-2934)
PHONE.........................972 680-1550
Bentley Scott, *President*
Konrad Opitz, *COO*
Ramon Marquez, *Vice Pres*
Paul Morones, *Vice Pres*
Jeff Nelson, *Purch Mgr*
EMP: 20
SQ FT: 16,000
SALES (est): 4.7MM **Privately Held**
WEB: www.phasedynamics.com
SIC: 3825 8711 Instruments to measure
electricity; professional engineer

(G-17373)
PHOTODIGM INC
1155 E Collins Blvd # 20 (75081-2304)
PHONE.........................972 235-7584
John E Spencer, *President*
Jay Rawot, *COO*
Mark Eastin, *Engineer*
Preston Young, *Engineer*
Judith Nava, *Electrical Engi*
EMP: 25
SALES (est): 2.9MM **Privately Held**
WEB: www.photodigm.com
SIC: 3674 Semiconductors & related de-
vices

(G-17374)
POLYTRNIX MCHNING FBRCTION LLC (PA)
735 N Plano Rd 200 (75081-2944)
P.O. Box 852979 (75085-2979)
PHONE.........................972 436-0422
Randel Fry,
Jianlin LI,
EMP: 14
SQ FT: 22,000
SALES (est): 1.3MM **Privately Held**
WEB: www.poly-pmf.com
SIC: 3449 3724 3541 3441 Miscella-
neous metalwork; aircraft engines & en-
gine parts; machine tools, metal cutting
type; fabricated structural metal

(G-17375)
PRECISION POWER ASSOCIATES
1758 Firman Dr 200 (75081-1823)
PHONE.........................972 234-6165
Patricia M Hodge, *President*
EMP: 9
SALES (est): 1MM **Privately Held**
SIC: 5088 8741 3621 Transportation
equipment & supplies; management serv-
ices; phase or rotary converters (electrical
equipment)

(G-17376)
PRESSMAN TOY CORPORATION (DH)
1111 Digital Dr Ste 150 (75081-1948)
PHONE.........................732 562-1590
James Pressman, *CEO*
▲ **EMP:** 30 EST: 1976
SQ FT: 9,000
SALES (est): 6.6MM
SALES (corp-wide): 183.7K **Privately Held**
WEB: www.pressmantoy.com
SIC: 3944 Board games, children's &
adults'
HQ: Goliath Games Llc
1111 Digital Dr Ste 150
Richardson TX 75081
855 258-8214

(G-17377)
Q C GRAPHICS INC
Also Called: Qc Graphics
1501 N Plano Rd Ste 300 (75081-2562)
PHONE.........................972 931-4100
EMP: 45
SQ FT: 18,000
SALES (est): 7.8MM **Privately Held**
WEB: www.qcg.com
SIC: 7373 3672 7389 Computer-aided
design (CAD) systems service; wiring
boards; printed circuitry graphic layout

(G-17378)
QORVO TEXAS LLC
Also Called: Qorvo US
500 W Renner Rd (75080-1324)
P.O. Box 833938 (75083-3938)
PHONE.........................972 994-8200
Ralph G Quinsey, *Ch of Bd*
Robert A Bruggeworth, *President*
Peter Moon, *Partner*
Jon Alejandro, *Project Mgr*
Robert Dolphin, *Mfg Spvr*
▲ **EMP:** 1413
SQ FT: 120,000
SALES (est): 179.2MM
SALES (corp-wide): 3.2B **Publicly Held**
WEB: www.qorvo.com
SIC: 3674 Semiconductors & related de-
vices
PA: Qorvo, Inc.
7628 Thorndike Rd
Greensboro NC 27409
336 664-1233

(G-17379)
QUALITY CASES & CONTAINERS LLC
1800 Jay Ell Dr Ste 100 (75081-6726)
PHONE.........................972 690-9911
Jane Milligan, *Controller*
Edward Milligan,
Garrett Milligan, *Administration*
EMP: 18
SQ FT: 45,000

SALES (est): 4MM **Privately Held**
WEB: www.qualitycases.com
SIC: 5099 3086 Cases, carrying; cups & plates, foamed plastic

(G-17380)
QUICKFILTER TECHNOLOGIES INC
3103 Stonehenge Dr (75082-4075)
PHONE..................................972 442-3964
Edward Staiano, *CEO*
Edward Rocha, *Principal*
Tony Valentino, *CFO*
◆ **EMP:** 12
SQ FT: 6,500
SALES (est): 1.2MM **Privately Held**
WEB: www.quickfiltertech.com
SIC: 2741 Technical manual & paper publishing

(G-17381)
RADIATION SYS PREC CNTRLS
Also Called: RSI Precision Controls
1219 Digital Dr Ste 101 (75081-1975)
PHONE..................................972 907-9599
Fax: 972 907-0027
EMP: 1500
SQ FT: 42,000
SALES: 30MM
SALES (corp-wide): 31.4B **Publicly Held**
SIC: 3663 Designs Manufactures And Installs A Broad Range Of Earth Stations And Monitoring Control Systems
HQ: General Dynamics Satcom Technologies, Inc.
1700 Cable Dr Ne
Conover NC 28613
704 462-7330

(G-17382)
RAYTHEON COMPANY
2105 Belleview Ct (75082-4820)
PHONE..................................972 231-4931
Jack Lo, *Engineer*
Eric Nicholson, *Branch Mgr*
Victor Solorza, *Manager*
EMP: 170
SALES (corp-wide): 56.5B **Publicly Held**
WEB: www.rtx.com
SIC: 3812 Defense systems & equipment
HQ: Raytheon Company
870 Winter St
Waltham MA 02451
781 522-3000

(G-17383)
RAYTHEON COMPANY
1727 Cityline Dr (75082-3208)
P.O. Box 667061, Dallas (75266)
PHONE..................................915 771-5466
Barbara Johnson, *Vice Pres*
Bradley Whittington, *Chief Engr*
Mark Culross, *Engineer*
Chris Ditmer, *Engineer*
William Gilmore, *Engineer*
EMP: 132
SALES (corp-wide): 56.5B **Publicly Held**
WEB: www.rtx.com
SIC: 3812 Defense systems & equipment
HQ: Raytheon Company
870 Winter St
Waltham MA 02451
781 522-3000

(G-17384)
RAYTHEON COMPANY
1727 Cityline Dr (75082-3208)
P.O. Box 551299, Dallas (75355-1299)
PHONE..................................719 638-2756
Raymond Tsui, *Principal*
EMP: 450
SALES (corp-wide): 56.5B **Publicly Held**
WEB: www.rtx.com
SIC: 3812 Defense systems & equipment
HQ: Raytheon Company
870 Winter St
Waltham MA 02451
781 522-3000

(G-17385)
RAYTHEON COMPANY
1717 Cityline Dr (75082-3208)
P.O. Box 660023, Dallas (75266-0023)
PHONE..................................972 272-0515
John Soma, *Senior Mgr*
John D'Avanzo, *Technology*

Brian Tate, *Software Engr*
Dale Craig, *Director*
EMP: 75
SALES (corp-wide): 56.5B **Publicly Held**
WEB: www.rtx.com
SIC: 3812 Sonar systems & equipment
HQ: Raytheon Company
870 Winter St
Waltham MA 02451
781 522-3000

(G-17386)
RAYTHEON COMPANY
1601 N Plano Rd (75081-1913)
PHONE..................................972 344-8000
Susie Kempf, *General Mgr*
Heinrich Naumann, *Engineer*
Maria Coston, *Controller*
Nick Lindsay, *Sales Staff*
Paul Cocak, *Branch Mgr*
EMP: 200
SALES (corp-wide): 56.5B **Publicly Held**
WEB: www.rtx.com
SIC: 3812 Radar systems & equipment
HQ: Raytheon Company
870 Winter St
Waltham MA 02451
781 522-3000

(G-17387)
REALPAGE INC (PA)
2201 Lakeside Blvd (75082-4305)
PHONE..................................972 820-3000
Stephen T Winn, *Ch of Bd*
Ashley Glover, *COO*
Andrew Blount, *Exec VP*
Linda Alperin, *Vice Pres*
James Hilliard, *Vice Pres*
EMP: 800
SQ FT: 448,000
SALES: 988.1MM **Publicly Held**
WEB: www.realpage.com
SIC: 7372 Prepackaged software

(G-17388)
REEF EXPLORATION LP
Also Called: Reef Oil & Gas Companies
1901 N Cent Expy Ste 300 (75080)
PHONE..................................972 437-6792
Michael Mauceli, *CEO*
Paul Peck, *Vice Pres*
Skip Roberts, *Vice Pres*
Andrew Schenck, *Vice Pres*
Ronald Sentz, *Prdtn Mgr*
EMP: 38
SQ FT: 19,000
SALES (est): 11.4MM **Privately Held**
WEB: www.reefogc.com
SIC: 1382 1311 Oil & gas exploration services; crude petroleum production

(G-17389)
REEF OIL & GAS PARTNERS LLC
1901 N Central Expy Ste 3 (75080-3558)
PHONE..................................972 437-6792
Laura Kline, *COO*
Michael Mauceli,
EMP: 19
SALES (est): 1.8MM **Privately Held**
WEB: www.reefogc.com
SIC: 1382 1311 Oil & gas exploration services; crude petroleum production

(G-17390)
RICHARDSON TRIDENT COMPANY LLC (DH)
Also Called: Altair Company, The
1301 Apollo Rd (75081-3024)
P.O. Box 853900 (75085-3900)
PHONE..................................972 231-5176
David Martens, *President*
Dariel Garza, *General Mgr*
Karla Lewis, *Vice Pres*
Robert McPherson, *Vice Pres*
Silva Yeghyayan, *Vice Pres*
◆ **EMP:** 57 **EST:** 1962
SQ FT: 220,000
SALES (est): 95.6MM
SALES (corp-wide): 10.9B **Publicly Held**
WEB: www.trident-metals.com
SIC: 5051 5063 5085 3316 Nonferrous metal sheets, bars, rods, etc.; electrical fittings & construction materials; industrial supplies; cold finishing of steel shapes; electronic parts

(G-17391)
ROCKWELL COLLINS INC
Collins Aerospace
3200 E Renner Rd (75082-2402)
P.O. Box 833807 (75083-3807)
PHONE..................................972 705-3156
Jared Rahn, *Mfg Staff*
Mike Ambrose, *Engineer*
Jeffrey Box, *Engineer*
Kevin Carkin, *Engineer*
Manuel Diaz, *Engineer*
EMP: 944
SALES (corp-wide): 56.5B **Publicly Held**
WEB: www.rockwellcollins.com
SIC: 3812 3663 Search & navigation equipment; radio & TV communications equipment
HQ: Rockwell Collins, Inc.
400 Collins Rd Ne
Cedar Rapids IA 52498

(G-17392)
SAFETY-KLEEN SYSTEMS INC (HQ)
1651 N Glnvle Dr Ste 210 (75081)
PHONE..................................800 669-5740
Jerry E Correll, *President*
Roy Dean Bullinger, *President*
Dave Sprinkle, *President*
Jeff Covington, *General Mgr*
Brian Jantzen, *General Mgr*
◆ **EMP:** 322
SALES (est): 1B
SALES (corp-wide): 3.4B **Publicly Held**
WEB: www.safety-kleen.com
SIC: 4953 3559 4212 5172 Recycling, waste materials; degreasing machines, automotive & industrial; hazardous waste transport; petroleum products; industrial supplies; building scale models
PA: Clean Harbors, Inc.
42 Longwater Dr
Norwell MA 02061
781 792-5000

(G-17393)
SC-INTEGRITY INC
Also Called: Lojack Supply Chain Integrity
1301 W President George B (75080-1139)
PHONE..................................214 612-7000
EMP: 40
SALES (est): 5.2MM
SALES (corp-wide): 366.1MM **Publicly Held**
WEB: www.scioncommand.com
SIC: 3699 Security devices; security control equipment & systems
HQ: Lojack Corporation
2400 N Glnvle Dr Ste 225
Richardson TX 75082
781 302-4200

(G-17394)
SCIENTIFIC TEST INC
1110 E Collins Blvd # 130 (75081-2344)
PHONE..................................972 479-1300
John Bailey, *President*
Brandon Bailey, *Vice Pres*
Philip Halloran, *Treasurer*
Kathy Hernandez, *CIO*
Phillip Halloran, *Director*
▼ **EMP:** 10
SQ FT: 4,000
SALES (est): 2MM **Privately Held**
WEB: www.scitest.com
SIC: 3825 Test equipment for electronic & electrical circuits

(G-17395)
SELKIRK CORPORATION
Also Called: Air Mate Division
1301 Presidential Dr (75081-2438)
PHONE..................................972 943-6100
Ray Overbey, *Branch Mgr*
EMP: 500 **Privately Held**
WEB: www.selkirkcorp.com
SIC: 3444 3585 3564 3433 Ventilators, sheet metal; refrigeration & heating equipment; blowers & fans; heating equipment, except electric; blast furnaces & steel mills
HQ: Selkirk Corporation
5030 Corp Exch Blvd Se
Grand Rapids MI 49512

(G-17396)
SEMTECH CORPORATION
681 N Plano Rd Ste 121 (75081-2909)
PHONE..................................972 231-1606
Ross Teggatz, *Senior VP*
EMP: 33
SALES (corp-wide): 547.5MM **Publicly Held**
WEB: www.semtech.com
SIC: 3674 5065 Semiconductors & related devices; semiconductor devices
PA: Semtech Corporation
200 Flynn Rd
Camarillo CA 93012
805 498-2111

(G-17397)
SENTINEL MIDSTREAM LLC
740 E Campbell Rd Ste 200 (75081-1895)
PHONE..................................214 712-2141
Blair Mathews, *Mng Member*
EMP: 10
SALES (est): 409.5K **Privately Held**
WEB: www.sentinelmidstream.com
SIC: 2843 Oils & greases

(G-17398)
SIGNATURE CARDS LP
Also Called: Valerian Technologies
1299 Commerce Dr Bldg B (75081-2406)
PHONE..................................972 783-7600
Willard Hunter, *President*
Thomas Liskey, *Partner*
Ruth Rinehart, *Accounts Mgr*
Ethan Mayeux, *Sales Staff*
Angela Chang, *Mktg Coord*
▲ **EMP:** 55
SQ FT: 26,000
SALES (est): 12MM **Privately Held**
WEB: www.wp.valerian-tech.com
SIC: 3089 Identification cards, plastic

(G-17399)
SKYVEN TECHNOLOGIES INC
1201 Intl Pkwy Ste 300 (75081)
PHONE..................................972 861-0893
Arun Gupta, *CEO*
EMP: 50
SALES (est): 83.7K **Privately Held**
WEB: www.skyven.co
SIC: 3433 5074 8742 4911 Boilers, low-pressure heating: steam or hot water; solar heaters & collectors; heating equipment & panels, solar; management engineering; electric services; air purification equipment

(G-17400)
SOUTHERN GRAPHIC SYSTEMS LLC
Also Called: SGS
1101 E Arapaho Rd Ste 220 (75081-2309)
PHONE..................................214 565-9000
Jeff Slone, *Branch Mgr*
Tim Bellington, *Manager*
EMP: 35
SALES (corp-wide): 258.6MM **Privately Held**
WEB: www.sgsintl.com
SIC: 3555 2796 Printing trades machinery; plates & cylinders for rotogravure printing
HQ: Southern Graphic Systems, Llc
626 W Main St Ste 500
Louisville KY 40202
502 637-5443

(G-17401)
SPOTTED DOG PRINTING INC (PA)
Also Called: AlphaGraphics 103
1750 Alma Rd Ste 118 (75081-1863)
PHONE..................................972 234-3033
Toni Wilson, *President*
EMP: 12
SALES (est): 2.1MM **Privately Held**
WEB: www.alphagraphics.com
SIC: 2752 Commercial printing, lithographic

(G-17402)
STEVEN M RILEY
Also Called: Quality Ingredients
789 N Grove Rd Ste 113 (75081-2750)
PHONE..................................972 741-0971
Steven M Riley, *Owner*

EMP: 10 EST: 2011
SALES (est): 1MM **Privately Held**
SIC: 2099 Tortillas, fresh or refrigerated

(G-17403)
SUMMIT SPRINGS BOTTLED WATER
Also Called: Alpine Drinking Water
1501 N Plano Rd Ste 100　(75081-2493)
PHONE..................................559 277-1239
EMP: 9
SQ FT: 3,000
SALES (est): 918.6K **Privately Held**
SIC: 2086 Mfg Bottled/Canned Soft Drinks

(G-17404)
T G M INC
1810 N Glnvlle Dr Ste 108　(75081)
PHONE..................................972 761-9101
Richard Maccracken, *President*
Rebecca Jacobs, *Vice Pres*
Rachel Maccracken, *Director*
EMP: 13
SQ FT: 3,600
SALES (est): 665K **Privately Held**
WEB: www.tgm-incorporated.com
SIC: 3644 Insulators & insulation materials, electrical

(G-17405)
TELECORE INC
1600 Jay Ell Dr　(75081-1832)
PHONE..................................972 238-9000
Tim Moyers, *President*
Floyd Springfield, *Vice Pres*
Jeff Tsao, *Vice Pres*
Aaron Lesher, *Mfg Staff*
Michael McLaughlin, *Engineer*
EMP: 27
SQ FT: 25,000
SALES (est): 5.7MM **Privately Held**
WEB: www.telecore.com
SIC: 8711 3661 Electrical or electronic engineering; telephone & telegraph apparatus

(G-17406)
TESTRONICS CONSOLIDATED INC
903 N Bowser Rd Ste 300　(75081-2868)
PHONE..................................972 542-3111
Noel B Kelley, *President*
EMP: 30
SQ FT: 20,000
SALES (est): 5MM **Privately Held**
WEB: www.testronics.com
SIC: 3825 Test equipment for electronic & electrical circuits; integrated circuit testers

(G-17407)
TEXAS CAPITAL BANCSHARES INC
2350 Lakeside Blvd Frnt　(75082-4336)
PHONE..................................214 706-6780
Rebecca Conner, *Vice Pres*
Juan Ramirez, *Vice Pres*
Richard Rogers, *Vice Pres*
John Sullivan, *Vice Pres*
Anne Witherspoon, *Vice Pres*
EMP: 870
SALES (corp-wide): 1.2B **Publicly Held**
WEB: www.texascapitalbank.com
SIC: 1389 Construction, repair & dismantling services
PA: Texas Capital Bancshares, Inc.
　　2000 Mckinney Ave Ste 700
　　Dallas TX 75201
　　214 932-6600

(G-17408)
TEXAS INSTRUMENTS INCORPORATED
300 W Renner Rd　(75080-1319)
P.O. Box 660199, Dallas　(75266-0199)
PHONE..................................214 567-2075
David Larkin, *Design Engr*
Phillip Goines, *Branch Mgr*
EMP: 27

SALES (corp-wide): 14.4B **Publicly Held**
WEB: www.txwx.com
SIC: 3674 3613 3822 3578 Computer logic modules; memories, solid state; microcircuits, integrated (semiconductor); microprocessors; power circuit breakers; thermostats & other environmental sensors; calculators & adding machines
PA: Texas Instruments Incorporated
　　12500 Ti Blvd
　　Dallas TX 75243
　　972 995-3773

(G-17409)
TEXAS ROOF MANAGEMENT INC
728 Lingco Dr　(75081-4001)
P.O. Box 851975　(75085-1975)
PHONE..................................972 272-7663
Catherine Awtrey, *President*
Kelly Lea, *General Mgr*
Mike Cieri, *CFO*
Patricia Elliott, *Office Mgr*
EMP: 108
SQ FT: 6,094
SALES (est): 13.5MM **Privately Held**
WEB: www.texasroof.com
SIC: 1761 3444 Roofing contractor; roof deck, sheet metal

(G-17410)
THERMO FISHER SCIENTIFIC INC
900 Alpha Dr Ste 420　(75081-2800)
PHONE..................................972 437-3327
Roger Amos, *Manager*
Bill Maxson, *Technical Staff*
EMP: 13
SALES (corp-wide): 25.5B **Publicly Held**
WEB: www.thermofisher.com
SIC: 3826 Analytical instruments
PA: Thermo Fisher Scientific Inc.
　　168 3rd Ave
　　Waltham MA 02451
　　781 622-1000

(G-17411)
THOMPSON FAMILY PARTNERSHIP
Also Called: Sir Speedy
620 N Glenville Dr　(75081-2832)
PHONE..................................972 238-7664
Brook Thompson, *Partner*
Judi Thompson, *Partner*
EMP: 10
SQ FT: 2,200
SALES (est): 775.5K **Privately Held**
WEB: www.sirspeedy.com
SIC: 2752 Commercial printing, lithographic

(G-17412)
TOKYO SEIMITSU CO LTD (HQ)
Also Called: Accretech America
2280 Campbell Crk　(75082-4450)
PHONE..................................214 459-1688
Takeshi Kagamida, *President*
Koji Goto, *Controller*
EMP: 15
SALES (est): 2.6MM **Privately Held**
WEB: www.accretech.jp
SIC: 3825 Semiconductor test equipment

(G-17413)
TRITEX TECHNOLOGIES INC
1201 N Bowser Rd　(75081-2220)
PHONE..................................214 346-6200
Richard Jones, *President*
Dick Weinberger, *CFO*
EMP: 12
SALES (est): 867.5K
SALES (corp-wide): 155.4MM **Privately Held**
WEB: www.tritextech.com
SIC: 1382 Oil & gas exploration services
PA: Halff Associates, Inc.
　　1201 N Bowser Rd
　　Richardson TX 75081
　　214 346-6200

(G-17414)
TRUGLO INC
525 International Pkwy　(75081-2282)
PHONE..................................972 774-0300
Paul Lorocco, *Ch of Bd*

Antonio Velazquez, *Opers Staff*
Damon Coalson, *Engineer*
Dane Horton, *CFO*
Dean Horton, *CFO*
▲ EMP: 100
SQ FT: 13,000
SALES (est): 11MM **Privately Held**
WEB: www.truglo.com
SIC: 3949 Sporting & athletic goods

(G-17415)
TRUSTKEY SOLUTIONS INC
2100 Alamo Rd Ste T　(75080-2738)
PHONE..................................214 865-9354
Stephen OH, *CEO*
Andrew Jun, *Principal*
Jenny Jun, *Principal*
Mike Kwon, *Principal*
Brian Reynolds, *Principal*
EMP: 19
SALES (est): 869.7K **Privately Held**
WEB: www.trustkeysolutions.com
SIC: 3674 Semiconductors & related devices

(G-17416)
TURNAMATIC MACHINE INC
1725 Jay Ell Dr　(75081-1835)
PHONE..................................972 235-1923
Jimmie L Proctor, *President*
Kala Proctor Arguello, *President*
Frances A Proctor, *Corp Secy*
Mark Munnerlyn, *Vice Pres*
Frances Proctor, *Vice Pres*
EMP: 85
SQ FT: 50,000
SALES (est): 18.4MM **Privately Held**
WEB: www.turnamatic.com
SIC: 3599 Machine shop, jobbing & repair

(G-17417)
UHU TECHNOLOGIES LLC
1201 Executive Dr W　(75081-2232)
PHONE..................................972 523-2701
Jeffery C Sanders, *President*
William Broyles, *CFO*
Lawrence Simpson, *Info Tech Mgr*
EMP: 18 EST: 2013
SALES (est): 265.7K **Privately Held**
WEB: www.uhutechnologies.com
SIC: 3663

(G-17418)
VCE COMPANY LLC (DH)
Also Called: EMC Dell
1500 N Grnvlle Ave Ste 11　(75081)
PHONE..................................972 656-5300
David Goulden, *President*
Don Norbeck, *Chief*
Cathy Horan, *District Mgr*
Lauren Cathcart, *Counsel*
Trey Layton, *Senior VP*
EMP: 128
SALES (est): 312.9MM **Publicly Held**
WEB: www.vce.com
SIC: 3572 Computer storage devices
HQ: Emc Corporation
　　176 South St
　　Hopkinton MA 01748
　　508 435-1000

(G-17419)
VENT-A-HOOD LTD (PA)
Also Called: Vah Distributing
1000 N Greenville Ave　(75081-2799)
P.O. Box 830426　(75083-0426)
PHONE..................................888 557-8368
Blake Woodall, *Partner*
Miles Woodall III, *General Ptnr*
Michael J Collins, *Ltd Ptnr*
Nancy Fisher, *Ltd Ptnr*
Kirk Woodall, *Ltd Ptnr*
EMP: 136 EST: 1933
SQ FT: 145,000
SALES (est): 40.9MM **Privately Held**
WEB: www.ventahood.com
SIC: 3634 Fans, exhaust & ventilating, electric; household

(G-17420)
VERGE VENTURES LLC
49 Dunrobin　(75082-2675)
PHONE..................................972 200-1707
Srinivas Gorty, *President*
EMP: 16

SALES (est): 154.6K **Privately Held**
WEB: www.vergeventures.net
SIC: 7371 7372 7374 Computer software systems analysis & design, custom; computer software development & applications; software programming applications; prepackaged software; application computer software; data processing & preparation

(G-17421)
VERTICAL COMPUTER SYSTEMS INC (PA)
101 W Renner Rd Ste 200　(75082-2002)
PHONE..................................972 437-5200
Richard S Wade, *Ch of Bd*
Harold Frazier, *Director*
William K Mills, *Admin Sec*
EMP: 17
SQ FT: 4,000
SALES: 3.7MM **Publicly Held**
WEB: www.vcsy.com
SIC: 7372 Application computer software

(G-17422)
VIAVI SOLUTIONS INC
900 Alpha Dr Ste 420　(75081-2800)
PHONE..................................972 907-8882
Jeff Harmon, *Engineer*
Hollis Wende, *Sales Staff*
Jim Sago, *Manager*
EMP: 15
SALES (corp-wide): 1.1B **Publicly Held**
WEB: www.viavisolutions.com
SIC: 3674 Modules, solid state
PA: Viavi Solutions Inc.
　　6001 America Center Dr # 6
　　San Jose CA 95002
　　408 404-3600

(G-17423)
VISTECH CORPORATION
858 N Glenville Dr　(75081-2836)
PHONE..................................972 231-1746
Kuen Liu, *President*
Dennis Phillips, *Vice Pres*
Jack Wang, *Opers Mgr*
EMP: 16
SQ FT: 3,300
SALES (est): 2MM **Privately Held**
WEB: www.vistech-usa.com
SIC: 3699 Electrical equipment & supplies

(G-17424)
VLSIP TECHNOLOGIES INC (PA)
750 Presidential Dr　(75081-2929)
PHONE..................................972 437-5506
Lawrence Frauenheim, *President*
Gene W Wakefield, *President*
Rolf R Haberecht, *Chairman*
Robert N King, *Senior VP*
Cheri Curry, *Vice Pres*
EMP: 79
SQ FT: 6,618
SALES (est): 25.7MM **Privately Held**
WEB: www.vlsip.com
SIC: 3674 Integrated circuits, semiconductor networks, etc.

(G-17425)
WAGES WHITE LION INVSTMNTS LLC
Also Called: Triton Distribution
789 N Grove Rd Ste 111　(75081-2750)
PHONE..................................214 880-6440
Todd Wages,
EMP: 15
SALES (est): 2.2MM **Privately Held**
WEB: www.tritondistribution.com
SIC: 2899 Oils & essential oils

(G-17426)
WESTBROOK & ASSOCIATES INC
3309 Essex Dr Ste 100　(75082-9716)
PHONE..................................972 840-0858
Wayne Coll, *CEO*
Ray Durkin, *General Mgr*
EMP: 30 EST: 2010
SALES (est): 1.7MM **Privately Held**
SIC: 3843 Dental laboratory equipment

(G-17427)
WHITE ROCK NETWORKS INC A DE
1301 W Pres G Bush Hwy (75080)
PHONE................................972 543-6900
William L Martin III, *CEO*
Greg Lowe, *CTO*
EMP: 120
SQ FT: 76,000
SALES (est): 20.3MM **Privately Held**
WEB: www.whiterock.com
SIC: 3661 Telephone & telegraph apparatus

(G-17428)
WILSON ELECTRONICS LLC
750 International Pkwy (75081-2843)
PHONE................................800 204-4104
EMP: 114
SALES (corp-wide): 1.4MM **Privately Held**
WEB: www.weboost.com
SIC: 3669 Intercommunication systems, electric
PA: Wilson Electronics, Llc
2890 E Cottonwood Pkwy # 200
Cottonwood Heights UT 84121
435 673-5021

(G-17429)
WINDOW ON WALLSTREET INC
Also Called: Window On Wall Street
1820 N Glenville Dr # 100 (75081-7202)
PHONE................................972 727-3626
John R Jennings, *Ch of Bd*
T Keith Black, *President*
Sean M Davis, *Vice Pres*
David L Barnes, *Sales & Mktg St*
Alan Moore, *CFO*
EMP: 45
SQ FT: 14,000
SALES (est): 2.8MM **Privately Held**
SIC: 7371 7372 6289 Computer software development; prepackaged software; stock quotation service

(G-17430)
WINFIELD LABORATORIES INC
1221 W Campbell Rd # 201 (75080-2967)
P.O. Box 832297 (75083-2297)
PHONE................................972 234-0940
Janette Cummings, *President*
EMP: 20
SQ FT: 10,000
SALES (est): 2.2MM **Privately Held**
WEB: www.winfieldlabs.com
SIC: 3841 Surgical & medical instruments

(G-17431)
ZENTECH DALLAS LLC
1717 Firman Dr Ste 200 (75081-6781)
PHONE................................972 907-2727
Mark McCrocklin, *Vice Pres*
John Plank, *Prdtn Mgr*
Steve Fox, *QC Mgr*
Deanna Merriman, *Office Admin*
EMP: 30
SALES (est): 6MM
SALES (corp-wide): 56.8MM **Privately Held**
WEB: www.zentech.com
SIC: 3672 Printed circuit boards
PA: Zentech Manufacturing, Inc.
6980 Tudsbury Rd
Baltimore MD 21244
443 348-4500

(G-17432)
ZYVEX CORPORATION
1301 N Plano Rd (75081-2426)
PHONE................................972 235-7881
James R Von Ehr, *President*
John Randall, *Vice Pres*
Tim Gilmore, *CFO*
Joshua Ballard, *Director*
EMP: 600
SALES (est): 72.5MM **Privately Held**
WEB: www.zyvexlabs.com
SIC: 3545 Tools & accessories for machine tools

(G-17433)
ZYVEX INSTRUMENTS LLC
1321 N Plano Rd (75081-2426)
PHONE................................972 792-1625
James R Von Ehr II,

EMP: 24
SALES (est): 1.9MM
SALES (corp-wide): 25.5B **Publicly Held**
WEB: www.zyvexlabs.com
SIC: 3545 Tools & accessories for machine tools
HQ: Fei Efa, Inc.
3400 W Warren Ave
Fremont CA 94538

Richland Hills
Tarrant County

(G-17434)
ACCURATE METAL STAMPING LLC
7124 Belton St (76118-6804)
PHONE................................817 284-9444
Dave Carter, *General Mgr*
William G Rickett,
Tommy Thompson,
EMP: 40
SQ FT: 68,000
SALES (est): 8.6MM **Privately Held**
WEB: www.ams-metal.com
SIC: 3444 Sheet metalwork

(G-17435)
AMERICAN MAATCO LTD
2499 Austin Rd (76118-7008)
PHONE................................817 284-7222
Kelye Stites, *President*
Raymond Peralez, *Prdtn Mgr*
Stacy Watts, *Sales Staff*
EMP: 25
SALES (est): 3MM **Privately Held**
WEB: www.americanmaatco.com
SIC: 3272 Concrete products, precast

(G-17436)
BARTOS INDUSTRIES LTD
2901 Wesley Way (76118-6455)
PHONE................................800 858-8497
Suzanne Goldstein, *Branch Mgr*
EMP: 14
SALES (corp-wide): 18.6MM **Privately Held**
WEB: www.bartosindustries.com
SIC: 3999 Barber & beauty shop equipment
PA: Bartos Industries, Ltd.
10350 Olympic Dr
Dallas TX 75220
214 350-6871

(G-17437)
HAMILTON FORM CO LTD
7009 Midway Rd (76118-7099)
P.O. Box 99225, Fort Worth (76199-0225)
PHONE................................817 590-2111
Peter R Ollmann, *Managing Prtnr*
William F Daily, *Partner*
L Oliphant, *Partner*
Diego Rojas, *Mfg Mgr*
Taylor Slate, *Engineer*
▼ **EMP:** 80
SQ FT: 75,000
SALES (est): 22MM **Privately Held**
WEB: www.hamiltonform.com
SIC: 3559 3443 Concrete products machinery; fabricated plate work (boiler shop)

(G-17438)
INTERNATIONAL STEEL FRMNG LLC
7108 Burns St (76118-6808)
P.O. Box 20627, Boulder CO (80308-3627)
PHONE................................817 591-0507
EMP: 10
SALES (est): 1.4MM **Privately Held**
WEB: www.internationalsteelframing.com
SIC: 3442 3446 Metal doors, sash & trim; lintels light gauge steel

(G-17439)
KELYE B STITES INC (PA)
Also Called: Gametime
7115 Belton St (76118-6805)
PHONE................................817 284-3499
Kelye B Stites, *President*
Chance Pack, *VP Opers*
Kelye Stites, *Executive*

▲ **EMP:** 30
SQ FT: 35,000
SALES (est): 3.7MM **Privately Held**
WEB: www.championshuffleboard.com
SIC: 3999 5092 3949 Coin-operated amusement machines; toys & games; shuffleboards & shuffleboard equipment

(G-17440)
LOCKHEED MARTIN CORPORATION
3821 Ruth Rd (76118-5232)
PHONE................................817 655-8672
Tonya Barrett, *Manager*
EMP: 473 **Publicly Held**
WEB: www.lockheedmartin.com
SIC: 3812 Search & navigation equipment
PA: Lockheed Martin Corporation
6801 Rockledge Dr
Bethesda MD 20817

(G-17441)
MAXITROL COMPANY
Also Called: Paktronics Controls
7415 Whitehall St Ste 124 (76118-6427)
P.O. Box 185669, Fort Worth (76181-0669)
PHONE................................817 479-8505
David Sundberg, *Branch Mgr*
EMP: 23
SALES (corp-wide): 42.8MM **Privately Held**
WEB: www.maxitrol.com
SIC: 3822 3625 Temperature controls, automatic; relays & industrial controls
PA: Maxitrol Company
23555 Telegraph Rd
Southfield MI 48033
248 356-1400

(G-17442)
METROPLEX GRAPHICS & MKTG INC
Also Called: Metroplex Graphics and Svcs
7451 Tower St (76118-6425)
PHONE................................817 831-7215
Tony Bartolowits, *President*
Jim Schneider, *Vice Pres*
EMP: 21
SQ FT: 15,000
SALES (est): 3.2MM **Privately Held**
WEB: www.mgmprinting.com
SIC: 2752 Commercial printing, offset

(G-17443)
MODERN HEAT TREAT INC
2550 Austin Rd (76118-7032)
PHONE................................817 616-0333
Bradley F Luce, *President*
Rudy Saucedo, *Vice Pres*
John Saucedo, *Project Mgr*
EMP: 57
SQ FT: 2,700
SALES (est): 834.8K **Privately Held**
WEB: www.modernht.com
SIC: 3398 Metal heat treating

(G-17444)
NATIONWIDE PRESS LLC
Also Called: Nationwide Disc - Ntnwide Pres
7370 Dogwood Park Dr (76118-6403)
PHONE................................817 885-8855
Gary Lawrence, *Principal*
Richard L Horton, *Principal*
EMP: 19
SALES (est): 2.4MM **Privately Held**
WEB: www.nationwidepress.com
SIC: 2732 5734 2752 3577 Book printing; computer & software stores; advertising posters, lithographed; computer peripheral equipment

(G-17445)
PLASTI FAB INC
6430 Wuliger Way Ste J (76180-6042)
PHONE................................817 485-0156
Marshall Kelly Sligar, *President*
Larry Richardson, *CFO*
EMP: 23
SQ FT: 15,000
SALES (est): 4.5MM **Privately Held**
WEB: www.plastifaboftexas.com
SIC: 3089 Injection molding of plastics; plastic processing

(G-17446)
PLASTIC FORMING INC
2100 Reeves Pl (76118-7042)
PHONE................................817 284-7878
David Stepp, *President*
Jay Stevenson, *Vice Pres*
EMP: 39
SALES (est): 5MM **Privately Held**
WEB: www.plasticforminginc.com
SIC: 3089 Injection molding of plastics; plastic processing

(G-17447)
ROYAL BATHS MFG CO LTD
7112 Burns St (76118-6808)
PHONE................................817 589-7300
EMP: 30
SALES (corp-wide): 157.5MM **Privately Held**
SIC: 3842 Mfg Surgical Appliances/Supplies
PA: Royal Baths Manufacturing Company
14635 Chrisman Rd
Houston TX 77039
281 442-3400

(G-17448)
SIGNIT INC
Also Called: Fastsigns
3100 Handley Ederville Rd (76118-6464)
PHONE................................817 589-9988
Dan Boykin, *President*
Cynthia Boykin, *Vice Pres*
EMP: 20
SQ FT: 10,000
SALES (est): 9.5MM **Privately Held**
WEB: www.fastsigns.com
SIC: 3993 Signs & advertising specialties

Richmond
Fort Bend County

(G-17449)
3H MANUFACTURING INC
1318 Newlin Dr (77406-3921)
PHONE................................281 342-1478
John Girndt, *President*
Sherri Walstad, *CFO*
EMP: 20
SQ FT: 3,600 **Privately Held**
WEB: www.3hmanufacturing.com
SIC: 3643 Connectors & terminals for electrical devices

(G-17450)
AZAN INDUSTRIES INC
Also Called: Homeland Security Division
24811 Montclair Creek Ct (77406-3218)
PHONE................................832 310-4459
Azfar Syed, *President*
Muhammad Syed, *Principal*
EMP: 10
SALES (est): 188K **Privately Held**
SIC: 7381 3999 Guard services; manufacturing industries

(G-17451)
CAMPBELL CONCRETE & MTLS LP
Also Called: Gulf Coast Stabilized Mtls
10621 Sm 1464 (77469)
P.O. Box 1830, Sugar Land (77487-1830)
PHONE................................281 491-7376
Dana Osborne, *Manager*
Ruben Ruiz, *Executive*
EMP: 25
SALES (corp-wide): 20.8B **Privately Held**
WEB: www.michaeljames.com
SIC: 3273 Ready-mixed concrete
HQ: Campbell Concrete & Materials, L.P.
16155 Park Row Ste 120
Houston TX 77084
281 592-5201

(G-17452)
CARTER LEE PROPERTIES LLC
5560 Fm 1640 Rd (77406-6001)
P.O. Box 372 (77406-0010)
PHONE................................713 385-8092
Coetta Wilson, *Mng Member*
EMP: 12

SALES (est): 263.2K **Privately Held**
SIC: **6531** 6411 2599 5812 Real estate managers; professional standards services, insurance; food wagons, restaurant; restaurant, family: independent

(G-17453)
EFFICIENCY AGGREGATORS LLC (PA)
1207 Fm 359 Rd (77406-2015)
PHONE..............................832 862-1103
John Garcia, *Manager*
Chelsea Willis,
M Jared Willis,
EMP: 11
SQ FT: 2,400
SALES (est): 2.2MM **Privately Held**
WEB: www.efficiencyaggregators.com
SIC: **3646** 3674 3641 Commercial indusl & institutional electric lighting fixtures; semiconductors & related devices; electric lamps

(G-17454)
EOS WELL SERVICE INC
1860 Fm 359 Rd 328 (77406-1296)
P.O. Box 5298, Pasadena (77508-5298)
PHONE..............................281 914-2191
Jess L Moore, *President*
Ronald Moore, *Vice Pres*
EMP: 14
SQ FT: 1,000
SALES (est): 1.4MM **Privately Held**
SIC: **1382** Oil & gas exploration services

(G-17455)
ESIP GROUP LLC
19221 Beechnut St Apt 332 (77407-5212)
PHONE..............................281 965-4942
Emeka Chukwu,
EMP: 10
SALES (est): 362.1K **Privately Held**
SIC: **3161** Clothing & apparel carrying cases

(G-17456)
HANSON AGGREGATES LLC
19707 Fm 1093 Rd (77407-8547)
PHONE..............................281 238-4759
John Wingate, *Manager*
EMP: 17
SALES (corp-wide): 20.8B **Privately Held**
WEB: www.heidelbergcement.com
SIC: **3273** Ready-mixed concrete
HQ: Hanson Aggregates Llc
    8505 Freport Pkwy Ste 500
    Irving TX 75063
    469 417-1200

(G-17457)
JOHNSON CONTROLS INC
4701 Ave I (77406)
PHONE..............................281 633-5700
EMP: 50 **Privately Held**
WEB: www.johnsoncontrols.com
SIC: **3822** Auto controls regulating residntl & coml environmt & applncs
HQ: Johnson Controls, Inc.
    5757 N Green Bay Ave
    Glendale WI 53209
    800 382-2804

(G-17458)
JOREN
23031 S Waterlily Dr (77406-8623)
PHONE..............................713 300-0377
Johnny White, *Partner*
EMP: 10
SALES (est): 100K **Privately Held**
SIC: **2299** Textile goods

(G-17459)
KENT MOORE CABINETS LTD
1811 Frst Oaks St Ste 180 (77406)
PHONE..............................281 480-8883
Mark Shaver, *Branch Mgr*
EMP: 18
SALES (corp-wide): 81.4MM **Privately Held**
WEB: www.kmc.net
SIC: **2434** Wood kitchen cabinets
PA: Kent Moore Cabinets, Inc.
    1460 Fountain Ave
    Bryan TX 77801
    979 775-2906

(G-17460)
KLINE TECHNICAL CONSULTING LLC (PA)
Also Called: Ktc Global
19826 Quarry Stone Ln (77407-1910)
PHONE..............................505 310-2679
Charles R Kline, *Mng Member*
EMP: 22
SQ FT: 21,000
SALES (est): 2.5MM **Privately Held**
WEB: www.klinenm.com
SIC: **3699** Security control equipment & systems

(G-17461)
LETCO GROUP LLC
Also Called: Living Earth
1700 E Highway 90a (77406-2421)
PHONE..............................281 342-6113
Kevin M Mayo, *Site Mgr*
Kevin Mayo, *Manager*
EMP: 23
SALES (corp-wide): 78.3MM **Privately Held**
WEB: www.livingearth.net
SIC: **2499** 2875 Mulch, wood & bark; potting soil, mixed
PA: The Letco Group Llc
    1901 Cal Crossing Rd
    Dallas TX 75220
    972 506-8575

(G-17462)
LOGAN FARMS INC (PA)
Also Called: Logan Farms Honey Glazed Hams
1038 Winner Foster Rd (77406-8735)
PHONE..............................713 781-3773
James P Logan, *President*
Kimmi Logan, *Treasurer*
EMP: 20
SQ FT: 3,000
SALES (est): 2.5MM **Privately Held**
WEB: www.loganfarms.com
SIC: **5421** 6794 3556 5812 Meat markets, including freezer provisioners; franchises, selling or licensing; slicers, commercial, food; eating places

(G-17463)
NATIONAL PLASTIC MOLDERS INC
29313 Mckinnon Rd (77406-9799)
P.O. Box 1865, Gulfport MS (39502-1865)
PHONE..............................281 346-1942
EMP: 15 **EST:** 1982
SQ FT: 20,000
SALES (est): 1.6MM **Privately Held**
SIC: **3089** Mfg Injection Molding Of Plastics

(G-17464)
RANDOLPH PRODUCTS INC
Also Called: Marine Specialties
27110 Shamrock Ct (77406-8777)
P.O. Box 19094, Houston (77224-9094)
PHONE..............................713 468-6070
D Short, *President*
EMP: 10
SQ FT: 3,000
SALES (est): 1MM **Privately Held**
WEB: www.randolphproducts.com
SIC: **3944** Boat & ship models, toy & hobby

(G-17465)
RICHMOND MATERIALS INC
5251 Ransom Rd (77469-6328)
PHONE..............................281 238-5488
Roy Bekin, *President*
EMP: 20
SALES (est): 1.8MM **Privately Held**
WEB: www.richmondau.com
SIC: **3273** Ready-mixed concrete

(G-17466)
TARMAC MATERIALS LLC
6130 Fm 2218 Rd (77469-8970)
PHONE..............................281 342-9314
Cayetano Silva III,
EMP: 10
SALES (est): 1.2MM **Privately Held**
SIC: **2951** Asphalt paving mixtures & blocks

(G-17467)
WORLDWIDE DPWTER SOLUTIONS LLC
6023 Carolyn Ln (77406-8640)
PHONE..............................281 238-6000
Dan M Welch, *Mng Member*
EMP: 50
SALES (est): 6.2MM **Privately Held**
WEB: www.wdsonline.com
SIC: **3533** Oil & gas drilling rigs & equipment

Richwood
Brazoria County

(G-17468)
DRESSER LLC
Also Called: Dresser Measurement & Control
2024 Brazosport Blvd N (77531-2606)
PHONE..............................979 265-1309
Robert Cox, *Branch Mgr*
EMP: 10
SALES (corp-wide): 95.2B **Publicly Held**
WEB: www.dressergs.com
SIC: **3491** Industrial valves
HQ: Dresser, Llc
    4425 Westway Park Blvd
    Houston TX 77041
    262 549-2626

(G-17469)
MUELLER MANUFACTURING INC (PA)
Also Called: Mmi
2200 Brazosport Blvd N (77531-2308)
PHONE..............................979 265-8303
Ken Mueller, *President*
Sara Ottinger, *QC Mgr*
Dallas Vincent, *Manager*
Evelyn M Mueller, *Admin Sec*
EMP: 20
SQ FT: 53,578
SALES (est): 4.7MM **Privately Held**
WEB: www.muellermfg.com
SIC: **3599** Industrial valves

Riesel
Mclennan County

(G-17470)
TOTAL SPCALTY PUBLICATIONS LLC
5120 State Highway 6 (76682-3792)
PHONE..............................813 405-2610
Charles Broadhurst, *Exec VP*
EMP: 18 **Privately Held**
WEB: www.tspnational.com
SIC: **2741** Miscellaneous publishing
PA: Total Specialty Publications Llc
    1715 N West Shore Blvd # 266
    Tampa FL 33607

Rio Grande City
Starr County

(G-17471)
ERASMO LOPEZ JR
Also Called: Lopez Ready Mix
600 N West St (78582-3200)
PHONE..............................956 487-3366
Erasmo Lopez Jr, *Owner*
EMP: 25
SQ FT: 500
SALES (est): 2.2MM **Privately Held**
SIC: **4213** 3273 Trucking, except local; ready-mixed concrete

(G-17472)
GRANDE GARBAGE COLLECTN CO LLC (PA)
505 E Main St (78582-4543)
PHONE..............................956 487-4234
Patricio Hernandez,
EMP: 19

SALES (est): 2.5MM **Privately Held**
WEB: www.grandegarbagecollectionco.com
SIC: **3089** 4953 Garbage containers, plastic; garbage: collecting, destroying & processing

(G-17473)
MCKINLEY PAPER COMPANY
1 E Sauz St (78582-6371)
PHONE..............................956 487-7424
Ervin Flores, *Manager*
EMP: 20 **Privately Held**
WEB: www.biopappel.com
SIC: **2631** Paperboard mills
HQ: Mckinley Paper Company
    7850 Jefferson St Ne # 150
    Albuquerque NM 87109

Rio Hondo
Cameron County

(G-17474)
AAE MANUFACTURING CO INC
28764 Fm 106 (78583-3319)
PHONE..............................956 748-0033
John Matthew Eckert, *CEO*
Jose J Tovar, *Vice Pres*
EMP: 10 **EST:** 2004
SALES (est): 1.3MM **Privately Held**
WEB: www.aaemanufacturing.com
SIC: **2514** Cabinets, radio & television: metal

(G-17475)
ARGIO ROOFING & CNSTR LLLC (PA)
29729 Norman Rd (78583-3066)
PHONE..............................956 434-6411
Rogerio G Escobedo, *President*
Roger Escobedo, *Marketing Staff*
EMP: 18
SALES (est): 2.5MM **Privately Held**
WEB: www.argioroofing.com
SIC: **1521** 2952 Single-family housing construction; roofing felts, cements or coatings

(G-17476)
WILBUR-ELLIS COMPANY LLC
21204 Reynolds (78583)
P.O. Box 607 (78583-0607)
PHONE..............................956 748-2382
John Williams, *Manager*
EMP: 20
SQ FT: 53,846
SALES (corp-wide): 3.1B **Privately Held**
WEB: www.wilburellis.com
SIC: **5191** 2875 Insecticides; fertilizers, mixing only
HQ: Wilbur-Ellis Company Llc
    345 California St Fl 27
    San Francisco CA 94104
    415 772-4000

Rio Vista
Johnson County

(G-17477)
BS FAB & MECHANICAL INC
981 N Highway 174 (76093-3312)
P.O. Box 428 (76093-0428)
PHONE..............................817 373-2879
Bridget Tolbert, *President*
Debbie Barajas, *Finance Mgr*
EMP: 32
SQ FT: 3,600
SALES (est): 5.3MM **Privately Held**
WEB: www.bsfab.com
SIC: **3599** 1796 Custom machinery; machinery installation

Rising Star
Eastland County

(G-17478)
BIG COUNTRY LIVESTOCK EQP
804 W College St (76471-5249)
P.O. Box 460 (76471-0460)
PHONE..............................254 643-1119
Tim Evans, *President*
Melissa Evans, *Vice Pres*
EMP: 17 **EST:** 1996
SALES (est): 3.5MM **Privately Held**
WEB: www.corralpanels.com
SIC: 3523 Farm machinery & equipment

River Oaks
Tarrant County

(G-17479)
RIVER OAKS PRINTING CO INC
4706 Barbara Rd (76114-2994)
PHONE..............................817 738-5461
Alice Machos, *Vice Pres*
Mark Machos, *Vice Pres*
Barry Machos, *Treasurer*
Robert J Machos, *Sales Mgr*
Chuck Davis, *MIS Mgr*
EMP: 12 **EST:** 1951
SQ FT: 9,800
SALES (est): 1.5MM **Privately Held**
WEB: www.riveroaksprinting.com
SIC: 2752 2759 Lithographing on metal;
letterpress printing

Riverside
Walker County

(G-17480)
TALLENT ENTERPRISES INC
Also Called: Tallent Sausage and Grocery
3736 Hwy 19 (77367)
P.O. Box 165 (77367-0165)
PHONE..............................936 594-2591
Ron Tallent, *President*
Sharon Clayton, *Manager*
EMP: 25 **EST:** 1972
SQ FT: 8,000
SALES (est): 2.8MM **Privately Held**
WEB: www.tallentsausage.com
SIC: 5411 2013 Grocery stores, independent; sausages from purchased meat

(G-17481)
VALERO ENERGY CORPORATION
225 Hwy 19 (77367)
P.O. Box 410 (77367-0410)
PHONE..............................936 594-6233
Linda Frost, *Branch Mgr*
EMP: 11
SALES (corp-wide): 108.3B **Publicly Held**
WEB: www.valero.com
SIC: 2911 Petroleum refining
PA: Valero Energy Corporation
1 Valero Way
San Antonio TX 78249
210 345-2000

Roanoke
Denton County

(G-17482)
AUTOPOINT INC (DH)
1301 Solana Blvd Ste 2100 (76262-1675)
PHONE..............................888 335-5762
EMP: 26
SALES (est): 10.2MM
SALES (corp-wide): 760.7MM **Privately Held**
WEB: www.autopoint.com
SIC: 7372 Business oriented computer software

(G-17483)
BEHR PROCESS CORPORATION
701 Gateway Pkwy (76262-3308)
PHONE..............................817 837-2600
Robinson Don, *Superintendent*
Rick Tertzakian, *Plant Mgr*
Delettre David, *Inv Control Mgr*
Jeffrey D Filley, *Branch Mgr*
Geoffrey Ross, *Manager*
EMP: 96
SALES (corp-wide): 7.1B **Publicly Held**
WEB: www.behr.com
SIC: 2851 Paints & paint additives
HQ: Behr Process Corporation
1801 E Saint Andrew Pl
Santa Ana CA 92705

(G-17484)
CISCO SYSTEMS INC
724 Henrietta Creek Rd (76262-6398)
PHONE..............................817 490-6062
Bryan Harlow, *Engineer*
Phathutshedzo Thabane, *Engineer*
John Baca, *Marketing Mgr*
Brian Taler, *Manager*
Sam Asawa, *Technical Staff*
EMP: 691
SALES (corp-wide): 49.3B **Publicly Held**
WEB: www.cisco.com
SIC: 3577 Data conversion equipment, media-to-media: computer
PA: Cisco Systems, Inc.
170 W Tasman Dr
San Jose CA 95134
408 526-4000

(G-17485)
GENERAL MILLS INC
4901 Henrietta Creek Rd (76262-6313)
PHONE..............................817 490-6940
EMP: 12
SALES (corp-wide): 17.6B **Publicly Held**
WEB: www.generalmills.com
SIC: 2043 Cereal breakfast foods
PA: General Mills, Inc.
1 General Mills Blvd
Minneapolis MN 55426
763 764-7600

(G-17486)
LARWEL INDUSTRIES INC
3601 Haynes Rd (76262-6508)
P.O. Box 557, Bedford (76095-0557)
PHONE..............................817 491-1200
Larry Hoes, *President*
Cathryn Hoes, *Vice Pres*
Todd Howell, *Project Mgr*
EMP: 15
SQ FT: 15,000
SALES (est): 5.8MM **Privately Held**
WEB: www.larwel.com
SIC: 3441 Building components, structural steel

(G-17487)
LATTIMORE MATERIALS COMPANY LP
1689 N Highway 377 (76262-6168)
PHONE..............................817 491-2400
EMP: 30
SALES (corp-wide): 21.5B **Privately Held**
SIC: 3273 Mfg Ready-Mixed Concrete
HQ: Lattimore Materials Company Lp
15900 Dooley Rd
Addison TX 75001
972 221-4646

(G-17488)
LEVI STRAUSS & CO
Also Called: Levi Strauss North America
1600 Solana Blvd Ste 8200 (76262-1716)
PHONE..............................817 262-6314
Liz O'Neill, *President*
Marc Rosen, *President*
Tom Kasten, *Principal*
Venky Bettadapura, *Chairman*
Harmit Singh, *Exec VP*
EMP: 19
SQ FT: 3,229
SALES (corp-wide): 5.7B **Publicly Held**
WEB: www.levistrauss.com
SIC: 2325 Jeans: men's, youths' & boys'
PA: Levi Strauss & Co.
1155 Battery St
San Francisco CA 94111
415 501-6000

(G-17489)
LSI CORPORATION
905 Trophy Club Dr # 204 (76262-5572)
PHONE..............................817 430-5808
Nikki Hawkins, *Branch Mgr*
EMP: 49
SALES (corp-wide): 23.8B **Publicly Held**
WEB: www.broadcom.com
SIC: 3674 Microcircuits, integrated (semiconductor)
HQ: Lsi Corporation
1320 Ridder Park Dr
San Jose CA 95131
408 433-8000

(G-17490)
M & M ITALIAN STYLE FOODS INC
Also Called: Cinnamon Creek Wild Game Proc
13794 Old Denton Rd (76262-3857)
PHONE..............................817 439-8008
EMP: 70
SQ FT: 15,000
SALES (est): 9.5MM **Privately Held**
WEB: www.cinnamoncreekranch.com
SIC: 2013 5147 Sausages & other prepared meats; meats & meat products

(G-17491)
OLD NOCONA BOOT FACTORY LLC (PA)
304 N Oak St (76262-6613)
PHONE..............................682 237-7644
Craig Carter, *Mng Member*
Leigha Morgan,
EMP: 14
SALES (est): 5.8MM **Privately Held**
WEB: www.oldbootfactory.com
SIC: 5661 3069 Men's boots; women's boots; boot or shoe products, rubber

(G-17492)
P & L CAST STONE INC
Also Called: P & L Enterprises
210 James St (76262-9181)
P.O. Box 1751 (76262-1751)
PHONE..............................817 430-8114
Perry Rupp, *Owner*
EMP: 14
SQ FT: 5,890
SALES (est): 2.3MM **Privately Held**
WEB: www.pandlcaststone.com
SIC: 3272 Stone, cast concrete

(G-17493)
PFIZER INC
1301 Solana Blvd Ste 2330 (76262-1677)
PHONE..............................212 733-2323
James Nichols, *Branch Mgr*
Shannon Largent, *Oncology*
EMP: 146
SALES (corp-wide): 51.7B **Publicly Held**
WEB: www.pfizer.com
SIC: 2834 Pharmaceutical preparations
PA: Pfizer Inc.
235 E 42nd St Rm 107
New York NY 10017
212 733-2323

(G-17494)
PFIZER INC
7 Village Trl (76262-5220)
PHONE..............................817 491-8400
James Nichols, *Manager*
EMP: 100
SALES (corp-wide): 51.7B **Publicly Held**
WEB: www.pfizer.com
SIC: 2834 8999 Pharmaceutical preparations; information bureau
PA: Pfizer Inc.
235 E 42nd St Rm 107
New York NY 10017
212 733-2323

(G-17495)
REDROCK MICROSYSTEMS LLC
5230 Kelly Dr (76262-3611)
PHONE..............................817 490-1326
Sharon Falk, *Purch Agent*
Jamey Hurd,
EMP: 24
SALES (est): 3.6MM **Privately Held**
SIC: 3861 Photographic equipment & supplies

(G-17496)
TRENCH-TECH LTD (PA)
330 Benson Ln (76262-6353)
P.O. Box 99 (76262-0099)
PHONE..............................817 491-0621
Jerry Gilbert, *General Ptnr*
Kelly Ralls, *Sales Executive*
▲ **EMP:** 15
SALES (est): 2.4MM **Privately Held**
WEB: www.trenchtech.com
SIC: 3523 Farm machinery & equipment

Roaring Springs
Motley County

(G-17497)
T J MANUFACTURING CO
Also Called: Thacker Jewelry
200 Broadway St (79256)
P.O. Box 310 (79256-0310)
PHONE..............................806 348-7546
EMP: 18
SQ FT: 5,000
SALES (est): 1.6MM **Privately Held**
WEB: www.thackerjewelry.com
SIC: 3911 Jewelry, precious metal

Robert Lee
Coke County

(G-17498)
SANCO MATERIALS CO
Also Called: Ingram Sanco Materials
1681 Valley View Rd (76945-2823)
PHONE..............................325 453-2901
Richard Brian, *General Mgr*
EMP: 16
SALES (corp-wide): 1.4B **Publicly Held**
SIC: 1442 Construction sand & gravel
HQ: Sanco Materials Co
1040 Foster St
San Angelo TX 76903
325 655-7970

(G-17499)
SHERIDAN PRODUCTION CO LLC
900 Gas Plant Rd (76945-3247)
PHONE..............................325 453-2108
Lisa Stewart,
EMP: 83 **Privately Held**
WEB: www.sheridanproduction.com
SIC: 1382 Oil & gas exploration services
PA: Sheridan Production Company Llc
1360 Post Oak Blvd # 2500
Houston TX 77056

Robinson
Mclennan County

(G-17500)
FREEFLIGHT ACQUISITION CORP
Also Called: Freeflight Systems
7333 Interstate 35 S (76706-7130)
PHONE..............................254 662-7050
John Debusk, *Vice Pres*
Joey Huckabee, *Engineer*
Ashley Kelly, *Marketing Staff*
Dave Graham, *Manager*
Rene Masiongale, *Manager*
EMP: 35 **Privately Held**
WEB: www.freeflightsystems.com
SIC: 3812 Navigational systems & instruments
PA: Freeflight Acquisition Corporation
8080 Tristar Dr Ste 100
Irving TX 75063

(G-17501)
PLUMLEE PLACE LLC
Also Called: Custom Window Treatment
802 N Robinson Dr (76706-5052)
PHONE..............................254 662-4021
Mary Plumlee, *Owner*
Mary Ann Plumlee, *Principal*
EMP: 12

GEOGRAPHIC

SALES (est): 300K **Privately Held**
WEB: www.plumleeplace.com
SIC: 2394 2591 5719 Awnings, fabric: made from purchased materials; drapery hardware & blinds & shades; vertical blinds

(G-17502)
SOUTHWEST MAINTENANCE LLC
803 S Robinson Dr (76706-5625)
PHONE......................254 662-3966
Morris Wood, *Mng Member*
EMP: 12
SQ FT: 50,000
SALES (est): 740K **Privately Held**
WEB:
www.southwestmaintenancewaco.com
SIC: 1799 3271 Parking lot maintenance; paving blocks, concrete

Robstown
Nueces County

(G-17503)
ATLAS TUBULAR LLC (PA)
1710 S Highway 77 (78380-4550)
P.O. Box 431 (78380-0431)
PHONE......................361 387-7505
Ryan Kutzik, *Business Mgr*
Jason Hubbard, *Vice Pres*
David Coe, *QC Mgr*
Brent Birdwell, *CFO*
Tami Randel, *Accounting Mgr*
▲ **EMP:** 69
SQ FT: 9,500
SALES (est): 137.6MM **Privately Held**
WEB: www.atlastubular.com
SIC: 5051 3498 Pipe & tubing, steel; fabricated pipe & fittings

(G-17504)
CCB FABRICATORS INC
4515 Us Highway 77 (78380-6000)
P.O. Box 10398, Corpus Christi (78460-0398)
PHONE......................361 387-7900
Bill Blasingame, *CEO*
Daisy Mata, *Administration*
EMP: 50
SQ FT: 217,800
SALES (est): 18.3MM **Privately Held**
WEB: www.ccbfabricators.com
SIC: 3498 Tube fabricating (contract bending & shaping)

(G-17505)
CIRCLE 8 CRANE SERVICES LLC (PA)
3174 County Road 48 (78380-5945)
P.O. Box 260370, Corpus Christi (78426-0370)
PHONE......................361 933-0696
Phillip Bryson, *Ch of Bd*
Larry Worrell, *COO*
John Jalufka, *Assistant VP*
John Bradford, *Vice Pres*
Debbie Bryson, *Vice Pres*
EMP: 20
SQ FT: 12,000
SALES (est): 277.2MM **Privately Held**
WEB: www.circle8services.com
SIC: 1389 Oil field services

(G-17506)
CIRCLE 8 CRANE SERVICES LLC
4646 Daniel Dr (78380-6066)
PHONE......................361 442-0306
Phillip Bryson, *Branch Mgr*
EMP: 103
SALES (corp-wide): 277.2MM **Privately Held**
WEB: www.circle8services.com
SIC: 1389 Oil field services
PA: Circle 8 Crane Services Llc
3174 County Road 48
Robstown TX 78380
361 933-0696

(G-17507)
CUDD PRESSURE CONTROL INC
Also Called: Cudd Energy Service
1420 Highway 44 (78380-6173)
P.O. Box 10405, Corpus Christi (78460-0405)
PHONE......................361 387-8521
Phil Rocher, *Branch Mgr*
EMP: 50
SALES (corp-wide): 1.7B **Publicly Held**
WEB: www.cuddenergyservices.com
SIC: 1389 Oil field services
HQ: Cudd Pressure Control, Inc.
2828 Tech Forest Blvd
The Woodlands TX 77381
832 295-5555

(G-17508)
DD FLUIDS LLC (PA)
Also Called: Dynamic Drilling Fluids
2699 Highway 44 (78380-5965)
PHONE......................361 985-2600
Ray Gibson, *Principal*
Jason Ferguson, *Principal*
Wayne Newell, *Accounts Mgr*
Russell Austin, *Representative*
EMP: 35
SALES (est): 30.4MM **Privately Held**
WEB: www.ddfluids.net
SIC: 1389 Oil field services

(G-17509)
ETS OILFIELD SERVICES LP (PA)
15406 Northwest Blvd (78380-5865)
P.O. Box 53870, Midland (79710-3870)
PHONE......................361 767-4200
Devin W Nevilles, *Partner*
EMP: 45
SQ FT: 1,000
SALES (est): 12.7MM **Privately Held**
WEB: www.etsoilfield.com
SIC: 1389 Oil field services

(G-17510)
EXCEL PUMP & MACHINE INC
1450 Highway 44 (78380-6173)
P.O. Box 10039, Corpus Christi (78460-0039)
PHONE......................361 387-4508
Randy Hougton, *President*
Randy Houghton, *President*
EMP: 11
SALES (est): 1.3MM **Privately Held**
SIC: 3599 Machine shop, jobbing & repair

(G-17511)
FORTERRA PIPE & PRECAST LLC
Also Called: Hanson and Pipe Precast
1610 S Highway 77 (78380-4508)
P.O. Box 671 (78380-0671)
PHONE......................361 767-1060
EMP: 35
SALES (corp-wide): 1.5B **Publicly Held**
WEB: www.forterrabp.com
SIC: 3272 Precast terrazo or concrete products
HQ: Forterra Pipe & Precast, Llc
511 E John Carpenter Fwy
Irving TX 75062
469 458-7973

(G-17512)
FORUM ENERGY TECHNOLOGIES INC
Also Called: Forum Flow Equipment Mfg
4802 County Road 69 (78380-5806)
P.O. Box 1108, Sulphur OK (73086-8108)
PHONE......................361 664-6024
EMP: 82
SALES (corp-wide): 818.6MM **Publicly Held**
SIC: 3533 Mfg Oil/Gas Field Machinery
PA: Forum Energy Technologies, Inc.
920 Memorial City Way # 1000
Houston TX 77064
281 949-2500

(G-17513)
HUISACHE ENERGY SERVICES INC
4528 County Road 56 (78380-9313)
PHONE......................361 299-2815
EMP: 17 **EST:** 1997
SQ FT: 4,000
SALES (est): 1.5MM **Privately Held**
SIC: 1389 Oil/Gas Field Services

(G-17514)
NATIONAL OILWELL VARCO INC
3267 County Road 48 (78380-5959)
PHONE......................361 664-8013
Steven Isaacks, *Engineer*
Kc Otter, *Branch Mgr*
EMP: 20
SALES (corp-wide): 8.4B **Publicly Held**
WEB: www.nov.com
SIC: 1389 Oil field services
PA: National Oilwell Varco, Inc.
7909 Parkwood Circle Dr
Houston TX 77036
713 346-7500

(G-17515)
RAM-BRO CONTRACTING INC
904 Industrial Ave (78380-3836)
PHONE......................361 387-2795
Ricardo R Ramon, *President*
Raul Ramon, *Vice Pres*
Rene Ramon, *Vice Pres*
Minnie Duque, *Treasurer*
EMP: 39 **EST:** 1976
SQ FT: 8,000
SALES (est): 5.2MM **Privately Held**
SIC: 1771 2951 1794 1623 Concrete work; composition blocks for paving; excavation work; underground utilities contractor

(G-17516)
RODESSA OPERATING COMPANY INC (PA)
4085 Emil St (78380-6054)
P.O. Box 261029, Corpus Christi (78426-1029)
PHONE......................903 534-4765
Kenneth Talley, *President*
EMP: 9
SALES (est): 1.8MM **Privately Held**
SIC: 1382 Oil & gas exploration services

(G-17517)
STRIKE LLC
1130 S Highway 77 (78380-9502)
PHONE......................888 353-1444
Peter Nguyen, *Counsel*
Dario Deferrari, *Vice Pres*
Steve Barton, *Branch Mgr*
Jennifer Shoemaker, *Admin Asst*
EMP: 50
SALES (corp-wide): 1.4B **Privately Held**
WEB: www.strikeusa.com
SIC: 1389 Servicing oil & gas wells
PA: Strike, Llc
1800 Hughes Landing Blvd # 500
The Woodlands TX 77380
713 389-2400

(G-17518)
TOTAL OILFIELD EQP & SUP LLC
2653 Highway 44 (78380-5965)
P.O. Box 10367, Corpus Christi (78460-0367)
PHONE......................361 442-2922
George Todd Lowry, *Vice Pres*
Todd Lowry, *Vice Pres*
Sheri Jackson, *CFO*
Devary McWha, *Accounting Mgr*
Jerame Yaklin, *Sales Staff*
EMP: 30
SQ FT: 50,000
SALES (est): 4.1MM **Privately Held**
WEB: www.totaloilfield.net
SIC: 3533 7353 Oil field machinery & equipment; oil field equipment, rental or leasing

(G-17519)
WRIGHT MATERIALS INC
5706 Fm 3088 (78380-5248)
PHONE......................361 387-1511

Ruth Wright, *President*
Donald Wright Sr, *Vice Pres*
Gregg Truesdale, *Safety Dir*
Mark Truesdale, *Treasurer*
Milus G Wright, *Director*
EMP: 75 **EST:** 1939
SQ FT: 2,000
SALES (est): 17.8MM **Privately Held**
WEB: www.wrightmaterials.com
SIC: 1442 5211 Common sand mining; gravel mining; sand & gravel

(G-17520)
WS ENERGY SERVICES LLC
3913 Fm 1889 (78380)
PHONE......................361 348-3488
Troy J Williams,
EMP: 28
SALES (corp-wide): 6.4MM **Privately Held**
WEB: www.wseservices.com
SIC: 1389 Oil field services
PA: Ws Energy Services, Llc
445 County Road 425
Premont TX 78375
361 348-3488

(G-17521)
WT MINING COMPANY INC
Also Called: Wright Materials
5706 Fm 3088 (78380-5248)
PHONE......................361 767-4095
Gregg Truesdale, *President*
Milus Wright, *Admin Sec*
EMP: 18 **EST:** 1997
SQ FT: 1,000
SALES (est): 3.3MM **Privately Held**
WEB: www.wrightmaterials.com
SIC: 1442 Construction sand mining

Rochelle
Mcculloch County

(G-17522)
J & R CUSTOM PROCESSING LLC
507 County Road 476 (76872-3103)
PHONE......................325 456-1544
Jason Williams, *Mng Member*
EMP: 10
SALES (est): 150K **Privately Held**
SIC: 2011 Beef products from beef slaughtered on site

Rockdale
Milam County

(G-17523)
ALCOA LAKE CHARLES CARBN PLANT
4069 Chrles Mrtn Hall Ss (76567-3082)
PHONE......................845 334-7203
Klaus Kleinfeld, *Principal*
▲ **EMP:** 130
SQ FT: 40,000
SALES (est): 19.3MM **Privately Held**
SIC: 3452 Bolts, nuts, rivets & washers

(G-17524)
ALCOA USA CORP
3155 Charles Mrtn Hall Rd (76567)
P.O. Box 472 (76567-0472)
PHONE......................512 446-8681
EMP: 116
SALES (corp-wide): 10.4B **Publicly Held**
WEB: www.alcoa.com
SIC: 3355 Aluminum rolling & drawing
HQ: Alcoa Usa Corp.
201 Isabella St Ste 500
Pittsburgh PA 15212
212 518-5400

(G-17525)
LYONS DRILLING INC
120 E Bell Ave (76567-2908)
P.O. Box 260, Lyons (77863-0260)
PHONE......................979 596-1898
Bill May, *CEO*
EMP: 21
SALES (est): 20MM **Privately Held**
SIC: 1381 Drilling oil & gas wells

▲ = Import ▼=Export
◆ =Import/Export

GEOGRAPHIC

(G-17526)
ROCKDALE REPORTER INC
221225 E Cameron St (76567)
P.O. Box 552 (76567-0552)
PHONE...............................512 446-5838
EMP: 14
SQ FT: 7,500
SALES (est): 929.2K Privately Held
WEB: www.rockdalereporter.com
SIC: 2711 5943 2752 Newspapers: publishing only, not printed on site; office forms & supplies; commercial printing, offset

Rockport
Aransas County

(G-17527)
C CUSHIONS INC
206 Highway 35 S (78382-5050)
PHONE...............................361 729-1244
William N Coxwell, President
Thomas E Coxwell, Vice Pres
EMP: 16
SALES (est): 2.3MM Privately Held
WEB: www.ccushions.com
SIC: 2394 Canvas & related products

(G-17528)
CANVAS USA INC
Also Called: Canvas USA Manufacturing
1010 Hwy 35 S (78382-3910)
PHONE...............................361 729-0638
David Hays, President
EMP: 14
SQ FT: 8,000
SALES (est): 1.5MM Privately Held
WEB: www.canvasusa.com
SIC: 2394 5999 Canvas & related products; canvas products

(G-17529)
CK KUSTOMS IRON WORKS INC
2102 Picton Ln (78382-3448)
PHONE...............................281 850-6118
Cody Key, CEO
EMP: 12 EST: 2013
SALES (est): 193.7K Privately Held
SIC: 1799 3462 1389 3446 Welding on site; ornamental metal forgings, ferrous; construction, repair & dismantling services; gates, ornamental metal; steel building construction; fluxes: brazing, soldering, galvanizing & welding

(G-17530)
HARTMAN NEWSPAPERS LP
Also Called: Rockport Pilot
1002 E Wharf St (78382-2662)
P.O. Box 730 (78381-0730)
PHONE...............................361 729-9900
Mike Probst, Principal
EMP: 11
SALES (corp-wide): 32.2MM Privately Held
WEB: www.portlavacawave.com
SIC: 2711 Newspapers: publishing only, not printed on site
PA: Hartman Newspapers L.P.
1914 4th St
Rosenberg TX 77471
281 342-8691

(G-17531)
PROMAR LP (PA)
Also Called: Coastal Production Services
4305 Highway 35 S (78382-7172)
P.O. Box 1927 (78381-1927)
PHONE...............................361 727-3300
David Pilgrim, Partner
EMP: 145
SQ FT: 13,600
SALES (est): 12.5MM Privately Held
WEB: www.coastalcrewboats.com
SIC: 1389 Measurement of well flow rates, oil & gas; oil field services

(G-17532)
PRONAV INC (PA)
4305 Hwy 35 S (78382-7172)
P.O. Box 2197 (78381-2197)
PHONE...............................361 727-3300
David Pilgrim, President
Mike Arnold, Vice Pres

◆ EMP: 73
SALES (est): 18.9MM Privately Held
SIC: 3812 5063 Navigational systems & instruments; batteries

Rocksprings
Edwards County

(G-17533)
VALERO ENERGY CORPORATION
Also Called: Rocksprings Short Stop
Hwy 55 (78880)
P.O. Box 737 (78880-0737)
PHONE...............................325 347-6561
Betty Ann Lopez, Manager
EMP: 10
SALES (corp-wide): 108.3B Publicly Held
WEB: www.valero.com
SIC: 2911 Petroleum refining
PA: Valero Energy Corporation
1 Valero Way
San Antonio TX 78249
210 345-2000

Rockwall
Rockwall County

(G-17534)
31 GROUP LLC
3021 Ridge Rd Ste 156 (75032-5831)
PHONE...............................972 810-1031
Kris Freeman,
EMP: 28
SALES (est): 15MM Privately Held
WEB: www.31operating.com
SIC: 1382 Oil & gas exploration services

(G-17535)
31 OPERATING LLC
3021 Ridge Rd Ste 156 (75032-5831)
P.O. Box 1706 (75087-1706)
PHONE...............................972 810-1031
EMP: 12
SALES (est): 1MM Privately Held
WEB: www.31operating.com
SIC: 1382 Oil & gas exploration services

(G-17536)
ALFA LAVAL INC
7132 Hunt Ln (75087-7011)
P.O. Box 95156, Dallas (75395-0001)
PHONE...............................804 236-3106
EMP: 11
SALES (est): 1.3MM Privately Held
SIC: 3443 Fabricated plate work (boiler shop)

(G-17537)
ARCHER OPTX INC
1208 Sigma Ct (75087-4915)
PHONE...............................972 722-1064
William J Flannery, President
Kevin Mitchell, Director
▲ EMP: 35
SQ FT: 28,000
SALES (est): 7.5MM Privately Held
WEB: www.archeroptx.com
SIC: 3827 Optical instruments & apparatus

(G-17538)
ARIES ACRYLIC MFG INC
Also Called: Aries Spas
4176 E Interstate 30 (75087-2146)
PHONE...............................972 771-6286
Larry Williams, President
Marc Jenkins, General Mgr
Teresa Williams, Corp Secy
Lori Williams, Manager
EMP: 10
SALES (est): 1.3MM Privately Held
WEB: www.ariesspas.com
SIC: 3088 1521 3949 2439 Hot tubs, plastic or fiberglass; single & deck construction & repair; sporting & athletic goods; structural wood members

(G-17539)
ARKOMA BASIN RESOURCES LTD (PA)
Also Called: Arkoma Development
203 E Interstate 30 (75087-5402)
PHONE...............................972 771-6000
Mark S Kelldorf, President
Kelldorf Glenda G, Vice Pres
Malaga Fivash, Finance Dir
Kay-Lee Ogle, Director
Jason Steed, Director
EMP: 13
SQ FT: 5,000
SALES (est): 3.6MM Privately Held
WEB: www.arkomacompanies.com
SIC: 1382 Oil & gas exploration services

(G-17540)
BLUE RIBBON PRODUCTS INC
6 Austin Corners St (75032-9792)
PHONE...............................214 647-1825
Steven F Speed, President
Steve Speed, President
Edward Keith Speed, Corp Secy
EMP: 75
SQ FT: 9,000
SALES (est): 11.5MM Privately Held
SIC: 2099 2053 2045 Frosting mixes, dry: for cakes, cookies, etc.; frozen bakery products, except bread; prepared flour mixes & doughs

(G-17541)
BROADCAST YOUR VISION LLC
2931 Ridge Rd Ste 101-120 (75032-6670)
PHONE...............................972 984-0303
EMP: 17
SALES (est): 1.4MM Privately Held
WEB: www.bcyv.com
SIC: 3652 Pre-recorded records & tapes

(G-17542)
CHRYSO INC
1611 State Highway 276 (75032-9304)
P.O. Box 190 (75087-0190)
PHONE...............................972 772-6010
Lew Cook, President
Rod Thompson, Site Mgr
Steve Parker, Sales Mgr
◆ EMP: 45
SALES (est): 15MM
SALES (corp-wide): 7.5MM Privately Held
WEB: www.chrysoinc.com
SIC: 2869 3273 Industrial organic chemicals; ready-mixed concrete
HQ: Chryso
19 Place De La Resistance
Issy-Les-Moulineaux 92130
164 361-526

(G-17543)
COLUMBIA ALUM PROCESSORS CO JV
Also Called: Capco
1450 E Washington St (75087)
PHONE...............................972 771-7150
EMP: 50
SALES (est): 4.2MM Privately Held
SIC: 3353 3354 Aluminum Sheet, Plate, And Foil, Nsk

(G-17544)
COLUMBIA COML BLDG PDTS ACQSTI
Also Called: Columbia Commercial Bldg Pdts
1200 E Washington St (75087-4713)
PHONE...............................800 668-1645
Jimmy Wilson, General Mgr
Bill Brecker, Vice Pres
Jada Banks, Sales Staff
Lance Hamilton, Mng Member
▲ EMP: 100
SQ FT: 120,000
SALES (est): 22.5MM
SALES (corp-wide): 81.2MM Privately Held
WEB: www.ccbpwin.com
SIC: 3442 Window & door frames
PA: Consolidated Glass Holdings, Inc.
1 Gateway Blvd
Pedricktown NJ 08067
800 257-7827

(G-17545)
COOL CRUISERS OF TEXAS
512 Willow Springs Dr (75032-2098)
PHONE...............................972 772-5517
Steven McClung, Owner
EMP: 12
SALES (est): 1.2MM Privately Held
WEB: www.coolcruisers.com
SIC: 3089 Automotive parts, plastic

(G-17546)
DALLAS DECAL INC
Also Called: Touchtec
2317 Woodmont Cir (75032-1927)
PHONE...............................972 772-4641
Chris Clem, President
Nancy Clem, Treasurer
EMP: 15
SQ FT: 5,000
SALES (est): 1.3MM Privately Held
WEB: www.dallasdecal.com
SIC: 3625 2759 5999 Switches, electronic applications; decals: printing; decals

(G-17547)
EKJ ENTERPRISES LP
Also Called: Col Met Spray Booth
2975 Discovery Blvd (75032-6215)
PHONE...............................972 772-1919
Charles Cecil, President
C Eric Jones, General Ptnr
Anna Yeager, Sales Staff
Chet Sweatman, Manager
Paula Palmer, Admin Asst
▼ EMP: 154
SQ FT: 150,000
SALES (est): 26MM Privately Held
WEB: www.colmetsb.com
SIC: 3444 Booths, spray: prefabricated sheet metal

(G-17548)
FALCON FINE WIRE WIRE PDTS INC
2401 Discovery Blvd (75032-6200)
PHONE...............................214 771-3441
William D Lecount, President
James S Bunt, Vice Pres
William H Lecount, Vice Pres
Annette Lecount, Admin Sec
▲ EMP: 80 EST: 1978
SQ FT: 75,000
SALES: 25.1MM Privately Held
WEB: www.falconfinewire.com
SIC: 3496 Cable, uninsulated wire: made from purchased wire

(G-17549)
FUJI CERAMICS INC (PA)
Also Called: Fuji Ceramics Dental Lab
2686 S Goliad St (75032-6525)
P.O. Box 2 (75087-0002)
PHONE...............................972 722-1130
Kip Estep, President
Yuji Ono, Vice Pres
EMP: 35
SQ FT: 8,500
SALES (est): 3.3MM Privately Held
WEB: www.fujidentallab.com
SIC: 3843 8072 Dental equipment & supplies; dental laboratories

(G-17550)
INDEPENDENT TELE DIRCTRY CO (PA)
Also Called: Yellow Page Consultants
2860 State Highway 66 (75087-6849)
P.O. Box 86 (75087-0086)
PHONE...............................972 722-4796
Edward S Pogue, President
John Walsh, Corp Comm Staff
Viola Delhagen, Admin Sec
EMP: 11 EST: 1966
SQ FT: 1,200
SALES (est): 582.4K Privately Held
WEB: www.pobdirectory.com
SIC: 2741 Directories, telephone: publishing only, not printed on site

(G-17551)
KEVIN HALL
Also Called: Threshold Group
254 Ranch Trl (75032-6029)
PHONE...............................972 771-4246
Kevin Hall, Owner

Michelle Hall, *Co-Owner*
Mark Marks, *Foreman/Supr*
Ray Williams, *Manager*
EMP: 11
SQ FT: 4,000
SALES (est): 82.1K **Privately Held**
SIC: 2759 Screen printing

(G-17552)
L 3 CMNCATIONS INTGRTD
SYSTMS
1309 Ridge Rd (75087-4206)
P.O. Box 6056, Greenville (75403-6056)
PHONE....................................903 455-3450
John McNellis, *President*
S Gordon Walsh, *Exec VP*
EMP: 169
SALES (est): 55.4MM
SALES (corp-wide): 11.3B **Publicly Held**
WEB: www.l3.com
SIC: 3812 Aircraft/aerospace flight instruments & guidance systems
HQ: L3 Technologies, Inc.
   600 3rd Ave Fl 34
   New York NY 10016
   212 805-5234

(G-17553)
L3 TECHNOLOGIES INC
L3 Technologies Comcept Div
1700 Science Pl (75032-6282)
PHONE....................................972 722-7927
Alison Hartley, *President*
John Dodson, *Software Engr*
Eric Schulz, *Software Engr*
Mark Von Schwarz, *Program Dir*
EMP: 224
SALES (corp-wide): 11.3B **Publicly Held**
WEB: www.l3t.com
SIC: 3663 3812 3669 7373 Telemetering equipment, electronic; navigational systems & instruments; intercommunication systems, electric; computer integrated systems design; electrical or electronic engineering
HQ: L3 Technologies, Inc.
   600 3rd Ave Fl 34
   New York NY 10016
   212 805-5234

(G-17554)
L3HARRIS TECHNOLOGIES INC
1655 Science Pl (75032-6202)
PHONE....................................972 772-7501
Dan Zook, *Branch Mgr*
EMP: 1000
SALES (corp-wide): 11.3B **Publicly Held**
WEB: www.l3t.com
SIC: 3812 Aircraft control systems, electronic
PA: L3harris Technologies, Inc.
   1025 W Nasa Blvd
   Melbourne FL 32919
   321 727-9100

(G-17555)
LOCAL CUTS MEAT COMPANY
LLC
3620 Lakeside Dr (75087-5329)
PHONE....................................972 489-3832
Michael Crawford, *Principal*
Wayne Clark, *Principal*
Dan Stewart, *Principal*
Pamela Watkins, *Principal*
Hilton Wise, *Principal*
EMP: 10
SALES (est): 283.4K **Privately Held**
SIC: 2011 Meat packing plants

(G-17556)
MULTI-METAL & MFG CO INC
1500 E Interstate 30 (75087-6235)
PHONE....................................972 771-1376
Kevin Fite, *President*
Avos E Wicker, *Chairman*
Juan Carlos Luna, *Vice Pres*
Samuel Sanchez, *Purch Mgr*
Erin Walker, *CFO*
EMP: 97
SQ FT: 47,604
SALES (est): 18.8MM **Privately Held**
WEB: www.multi-metal.com
SIC: 3444 Sheet metal specialties, not stamped

(G-17557)
PACIFIC COLUMNS
6765 Horizon Rd (75032-7711)
PHONE....................................714 257-9600
EMP: 11
SALES (est): 1.4MM **Privately Held**
WEB: www.pacificcolumns.com
SIC: 2431 Millwork

(G-17558)
PEGASUS FOOD
1635 Innovation Dr (75032-6218)
PHONE....................................972 961-5200
Dan Trott, *CEO*
Angie Estrada, *Administration*
EMP: 15
SALES (est): 9.3MM **Privately Held**
WEB: www.pegasusfoodsinc.com
SIC: 2048 Feed concentrates

(G-17559)
PLOTTER DEPOT
CORPORATION
90 Windsor Dr (75032-7446)
PHONE....................................469 608-9747
Carlos Valencia, *President*
Stephanie Diane Cannon, *Vice Pres*
EMP: 10
SALES (est): 2.5MM **Privately Held**
WEB: www.theplotterdepot.com
SIC: 3829 Plotting instruments, drafting & map reading

(G-17560)
PRATT ROCKWALL
CORRUGATING LLC
3400 Discovery Blvd (75032-6257)
PHONE....................................770 918-5678
John Batts, *General Mgr*
Tori Skidmore, *Human Res Mgr*
EMP: 115
SALES (est): 16.1MM **Privately Held**
WEB: www.prattindustries.com
SIC: 2653 Boxes, corrugated: made from purchased materials

(G-17561)
PRECISION SHEET METAL
SHOP INC
Also Called: P S M S
2650 Observation Trl (75032-6204)
PHONE....................................972 771-1423
Thomas Jimenez, *President*
Jonathan Lopez, *General Mgr*
Leonardo Jimenez, *Treasurer*
EMP: 64
SQ FT: 10,000
SALES (est): 20.4MM **Privately Held**
WEB: www.precisionsmp.com
SIC: 3444 3083 Sheet metal specialties, not stamped; metal housings, enclosures, casings & other containers; plastic finished products, laminated

(G-17562)
PRISTINE CAST STONE INC
900 Sids Rd (75032-6512)
PHONE....................................972 772-9490
John Wheelock, *President*
EMP: 12
SALES (est): 1.4MM **Privately Held**
WEB: www.pristinecaststone.com
SIC: 3272 Stone, cast concrete

(G-17563)
ROCKWALL CHRYSLER DODGE
970 E Interstate 30 (75087-4823)
PHONE....................................469 698-2100
Ron Bailey, *General Mgr*
Christopher Miles, *Sales Staff*
EMP: 13
SALES (est): 2.5MM **Privately Held**
WEB: www.rockwalldodge.com
SIC: 5511 3537 5521 Automobiles, new & used; cars & trucks, for industrial mining; automobiles, used cars only

(G-17564)
S & A SYSTEMS INC
Also Called: Fleetwatch
992 Sids Rd (75032-6512)
P.O. Box 1928 (75087-2028)
PHONE....................................972 722-1009
EMP: 14
SQ FT: 2,800

SALES (est): 3.3MM **Privately Held**
WEB: www.fleetwatch.com
SIC: 3823 3824 Industrial flow & liquid measuring instruments; integrating & totalizing meters for gas & liquids

(G-17565)
SAN MARTINO WINERY &
VINEYARDS
12512 Highway 205 N (75087)
P.O. Box 2229 (75087-5929)
PHONE....................................972 772-6043
Amilio Ramof, *Owner*
Maria Ramof, *Co-Owner*
EMP: 15
SALES (est): 1.8MM **Privately Held**
WEB: www.sanmartinowinery.com
SIC: 2084 0172 Wines; grapes

(G-17566)
SPECIAL PRODUCTS & MFG INC
(PA)
2625 Discovery Blvd (75032-6226)
PHONE....................................972 771-8851
Robert J Grand-Lienard III, *CEO*
Edward Grand-Lienard, *Exec VP*
James Morris, *Vice Pres*
Bo Carroll, *Engineer*
Richard Scherer, *CFO*
▼ **EMP:** 100
SQ FT: 139,000
SALES (est): 38.7MM **Privately Held**
WEB: www.spmfg.com
SIC: 3444 Sheet metalwork

(G-17567)
STRATHMORE PRODUCTS INC
1250 Justin Rd (75087-4952)
PHONE....................................281 269-9658
Eric T Burr, *CEO*
William M Udovich, *President*
EMP: 21
SALES (est): 7MM **Privately Held**
WEB: www.strathmoreproducts.com
SIC: 2911 Solvents

(G-17568)
TEX-CO RESIN DISTRIBUTION
INC
Also Called: Tex Co
105 Industrial Blvd (75087-5416)
P.O. Box 2169 (75087-5069)
PHONE....................................972 722-8603
Joe Weissert, *President*
Diane Weissert, *Owner*
Derick Cook, *Accounts Mgr*
EMP: 17
SQ FT: 33,000
SALES (est): 20MM **Privately Held**
WEB: www.texcoresin.com
SIC: 2821 Plastics materials & resins

(G-17569)
TEXAS NOVA-CHEM
CORPORATION
Also Called: Pro Soap
2020 Industrial Blvd (75087-4907)
PHONE....................................972 771-1161
Katie Self, *President*
Katrina Lorenzen, *Sales Staff*
◆ **EMP:** 12 **EST:** 1975
SALES (est): 3.3MM **Privately Held**
WEB: www.prosoap.com
SIC: 2842 Cleaning or polishing preparations

(G-17570)
TEXAS ORTHOPAEDIC PDT
SVCS LLC
Also Called: Texas Orthopedic Products
805 Riding Club Rd (75087-2193)
P.O. Box 190, Fate (75132-0190)
PHONE....................................972 772-8776
George N Adbou, *Mng Member*
EMP: 10
SALES (est): 1.7MM **Privately Held**
WEB: www.topsproducts.com
SIC: 3842 Orthopedic appliances

(G-17571)
WHITMORE MANUFACTURING
COMPANY (HQ)
Also Called: Kats Coatings
930 Whitmore Dr (75087-4909)
PHONE....................................972 771-1000
Jeff Kilpatrick, *President*
Jeff Peterson, *President*
Randy Huff, *Corp Secy*
Rick Kusse, *Info Tech Dir*
◆ **EMP:** 13 **EST:** 1893
SQ FT: 200,000
SALES: 18.8MM
SALES (corp-wide): 62MM **Publicly Held**
WEB: www.katscoatings.com
SIC: 2851 2842 2992 Lacquers, varnishes, enamels & other coatings; specialty cleaning preparations; polishing preparations & related products; lubricating oils & greases
PA: Capital Southwest Corporation
   5400 Lyndon B Johnson Fwy
   Dallas TX 75240
   214 238-5700

(G-17572)
XCEL METAL FINISHING INC
2065 Kristy Ln (75032-6242)
PHONE....................................972 772-4440
Michael Moore, *President*
Denis B Boilard, *Managing Dir*
Marijane Moore, *Corp Secy*
Ashleigh Clark, *Admin Sec*
EMP: 15
SALES (est): 1.5MM **Privately Held**
WEB: www.xmfinc.com
SIC: 3479 Coating of metals & formed products

Rogers
Bell County

(G-17573)
ARCOSA AGGREGATES INC
5050 Reeds Lake Rd (76569)
PHONE....................................254 982-4158
Bill Ivey, *Manager*
EMP: 10
SALES (corp-wide): 1.7B **Publicly Held**
WEB: www.trinitymaterialsinc.com
SIC: 3273 Ready-mixed concrete
HQ: Arcosa Aggregates, Inc.
   401 N Interstate Hwy 45
   Ferris TX 75125
   972 544-5900

(G-17574)
SPECIALTY WOOOD
MOULDINGS INC
16999 E Us Highway 190 (76569-3687)
PHONE....................................254 642-3835
Fax: 254 642-3710
EMP: 10
SQ FT: 15,000
SALES: 707.9K **Privately Held**
SIC: 2431 Mfg Millwork

Rosenberg
Fort Bend County

(G-17575)
BENEDETTINI CABINETS LP
Also Called: Benedettini Cabinetry
533 Highway 36 N (77471-8742)
PHONE....................................281 633-8200
Stephen Benedettini, *Partner*
Ken Alexander, *Partner*
Mike Diclemente, *Opers Dir*
Pmp Martin, *Accounts Mgr*
Eugene Vargas, *Manager*
EMP: 200
SQ FT: 12,000
SALES (est): 43.4MM **Privately Held**
WEB: www.benedettinicabinetry.com
SIC: 2434 Wood kitchen cabinets

(G-17576)
BIOTICS BUILDING PARTNERSHIP
Also Called: Biotics Research
6801 Biotics Research Dr (77471-5755)
PHONE................................281 344-0909
Dennis Deluca, *Partner*
Daniel Deluca, *Partner*
Darrell Deluca, *Partner*
EMP: 95 EST: 1999
SALES (est): 9.4MM Privately Held
WEB: www.bioticsresearch.com
SIC: 2834 Pharmaceutical preparations

(G-17577)
BIOTICS RESEARCH CORPORATION (PA)
Also Called: Biotics Pharma
6801 Biotics Research Dr (77471-5755)
P.O. Box 36888, Houston (77236-6888)
PHONE................................281 344-0909
Dennis Deluca, *President*
Denis Deluca, *President*
Bill Sparks, *Corp Secy*
Dana Deluca, *Vice Pres*
Daryl Deluca, *Vice Pres*
▲ EMP: 65
SALES (est): 16MM Privately Held
WEB: www.bioticsresearch.com
SIC: 8731 2819 5122 8732 Food research; industrial inorganic chemicals; vitamins & minerals; commercial nonphysical research

(G-17578)
CASE HAFER INC
1018 Mulcahy St (77471-3234)
PHONE................................281 341-5070
William Hafer, *President*
Karen Hafer, *Vice Pres*
Don Drachenberg, *Admin Asst*
EMP: 15
SQ FT: 10,500
SALES (est): 3.1MM Privately Held
WEB: www.hafercase.com
SIC: 2655 Fiber cans, drums & containers

(G-17579)
CUSTOM FLAME CUTTING INC
1313 Daily Rd (77471)
PHONE................................281 342-3250
Mary Ann Montgomery, *CEO*
Timothy C Jansky, *President*
EMP: 15
SQ FT: 24,000
SALES (est): 3.6MM Privately Held
SIC: 3312 Plate, steel

(G-17580)
ENCAPSULITE INTERNATIONAL INC
1220 Bamore Rd (77471-3027)
P.O. Box 1086 (77471-1086)
PHONE................................281 239-0225
Mark Waumsley, *President*
Brian Pierson, *Vice Pres*
Sherry Calhoun, *Warehouse Mgr*
Nereyda Badillo, *Manager*
EMP: 15
SQ FT: 22,000
SALES (est): 4.1MM Privately Held
WEB: www.encapsulite.com
SIC: 3646 Fluorescent lighting fixtures, commercial

(G-17581)
ENGELBRECHT MANUFACTURING INC
708 Damascus St (77471-4263)
PHONE................................281 341-5110
Bryan Engelbrecht, *CEO*
Catherine Engelbrecht, *President*
EMP: 15
SQ FT: 22,000
SALES (est): 6.2MM Privately Held
WEB: www.engelbrechtmfg.com
SIC: 3599 Custom machinery; machine shop, jobbing & repair

(G-17582)
GEM FOOD SERVICES CORP
4310 Avenue H Ste 66 (77471-2848)
PHONE................................281 232-8013
Vicki Kennedy, *President*
EMP: 30

SQ FT: 2,400
SALES (est): 5.5MM Privately Held
WEB: www.gemfoodservices.com
SIC: 2099 Food preparations

(G-17583)
GUERRO READY MIX
770 Walsh Rd (77471-9114)
PHONE................................281 342-4022
Larry Guerro, *Owner*
EMP: 20
SALES (est): 1.7MM Privately Held
SIC: 2951 Concrete, asphaltic (not from refineries)

(G-17584)
GURECKY MANUFACTURING SVC INC
2420 3rd St (77471-5912)
PHONE................................281 342-5926
John Dorman, *President*
Joe M Gurecky, *Chairman*
Stephen Haas, *Vice Pres*
Robert Lorquet, *Vice Pres*
Chad Landry, *Purchasing*
EMP: 50
SQ FT: 29,000
SALES (est): 10.1MM Privately Held
WEB: www.gurecky.com
SIC: 3599 Machine shop, jobbing & repair

(G-17585)
HARTMAN NEWSPAPERS LP (PA)
1914 4th St (77471-5140)
PHONE................................281 342-8691
J W Hartman, *Partner*
Fred B Hartman, *Partner*
Fred Hartman, *Vice Chairman*
Donnis Baggett, *Exec VP*
EMP: 19
SQ FT: 5,000
SALES (est): 32.2MM Privately Held
WEB: www.portlavacawave.com
SIC: 2711 Newspapers, publishing & printing

(G-17586)
HARTMAN NEWSPAPERS LP
Also Called: Carols Crister
1902 4th St (77471-5140)
P.O. Box 1088 (77471-1088)
PHONE................................281 342-7304
Clyde King, *President*
Stefanie Bartlett, *Advt Staff*
EMP: 100
SALES (corp-wide): 32.2MM Privately Held
WEB: www.portlavacawave.com
SIC: 2711 Newspapers: publishing only, not printed on site
PA: Hartman Newspapers L.P.
1914 4th St
Rosenberg TX 77471
281 342-8691

(G-17587)
HARTMAN NEWSPAPERS LP
Also Called: Fort Bend Herald
1902 4th St (77471-5140)
P.O. Box 1088 (77471-1088)
PHONE................................281 232-3737
Marquita Griffin, *Publisher*
Denise Adams, *Pub Rel Staff*
David Lyons, *Branch Mgr*
Ron Depuy, *Manager*
Michelle Stroud, *Manager*
EMP: 50
SALES (corp-wide): 32.2MM Privately Held
WEB: www.portlavacawave.com
SIC: 7313 2711 2741 Newspaper advertising representative; newspapers; miscellaneous publishing
PA: Hartman Newspapers L.P.
1914 4th St
Rosenberg TX 77471
281 342-8691

(G-17588)
LAND OLAKES INC
825 Highway 36 N (77471-8744)
PHONE................................281 342-2493
Danny Farrell, *Manager*
Richard Haarala, *Manager*
Daniel Efigenio, *Representative*

EMP: 45
SALES (corp-wide): 6.1B Privately Held
WEB: www.landolakesinc.com
SIC: 2048 Prepared feeds
PA: Land O'lakes, Inc.
4001 Lexington Ave N
Arden Hills MN 55126
651 375-2222

(G-17589)
MAIN EVENT INC
2033 Avenue H (77471-2631)
P.O. Box 71 (77471-0071)
PHONE................................281 762-0854
Rosey Bartee, *President*
Ron Bartee, *Principal*
EMP: 9
SALES (est): 734.7K Privately Held
WEB: www.tmetexas.com
SIC: 2397 Schiffli machine embroideries

(G-17590)
MURPHY FW
Also Called: Frank W Murphy
2105 Randon Dyer Rd (77471-2468)
P.O. Box 1819 (77471-7819)
PHONE................................281 633-4500
Jack Maley, *Branch Mgr*
EMP: 60
SALES (corp-wide): 554.6MM Publicly Held
WEB: www.fwmurphy.com
SIC: 3829 5084 3823 3613 Measuring & controlling devices; instruments & control equipment; industrial instrmnts msrmnt display/control process variable; switchgear & switchboard apparatus; pumps & pumping equipment; machine tool accessories
HQ: Murphy Fw
4646 S Harvard Ave # 100
Tulsa OK 74135
918 317-4100

(G-17591)
O & C EQUIPMENT INC
Also Called: Open and Close Equipment
2808 Hartledge Rd (77471-9059)
PHONE................................281 232-4686
Julian Montemayor, *President*
EMP: 10
SALES (est): 1.3MM Privately Held
WEB: www.bopenandclose.com
SIC: 3533 1389 Oil field machinery & equipment; oil field services

(G-17592)
OCUSOFT INC
Also Called: Cynacon
30444 Southwest Fwy (77471-4871)
P.O. Box 429, Richmond (77406-0011)
PHONE................................281 342-3350
Cynthia L Barratt, *President*
Nat G Adkins Jr, *Chairman*
Thomas Mason, *Exec VP*
Stacy Foster, *Vice Pres*
Sue Herreth, *Vice Pres*
▲ EMP: 100
SQ FT: 11,000
SALES: 47.3MM Privately Held
WEB: www.ocusoft.com
SIC: 2841 2844 2834 5122 Soap & other detergents; toilet preparations; pharmaceutical preparations; dermatologicals; cosmetics

(G-17593)
PAVE/LOCK/PLUS LLC
1705 Cottonwood School Rd (77471-7125)
PHONE................................281 239-3033
Ted A Gillis, *
EMP: 10
SALES (est): 2MM Privately Held
WEB: www.pavelocplus.com
SIC: 3531 Pavers

(G-17594)
POWERHOUSE READY-MIX LLC
2710 W Eagle Dr (77471-9077)
PHONE................................832 620-1922
Ruben Ortega, *Principal*
EMP: 10
SALES (est): 110.5K Privately Held
SIC: 3273 Ready-mixed concrete

(G-17595)
PTP INCORPORATED
Also Called: Marathon Spa & Bath
1549 Highway 36 N (77471-8746)
PHONE................................281 342-8775
Larry Krolczyk, *President*
Betty Krolczyk, *Corp Secy*
EMP: 15
SQ FT: 15,000
SALES (est): 1.8MM Privately Held
WEB: www.marathonspaandbath.com
SIC: 3999 3431 5999 Hot tubs; bathtubs: enameled iron, cast iron or pressed metal; spas & hot tubs

(G-17596)
PURINA MILLS LLC
825 Highway 36 N (77471-8744)
PHONE................................281 342-6758
Ralph Hunn, *Opers-Prdtn-Mfg*
EMP: 12
SQ FT: 1,344
SALES (corp-wide): 6.1B Privately Held
WEB: www.purinamills.com
SIC: 2048 Prepared feeds
HQ: Purina Mills, Llc
555 Maryvle Univ Dr 200
Saint Louis MO 63141

(G-17597)
QUAINT SLUTIONS TRDG LTD LBLTY
Also Called: Quaint Energy
1201 Nantere Ct (77471-6164)
PHONE................................832 758-3074
Mobolaji Durodola, *CEO*
EMP: 15 EST: 2017
SALES (est): 755.8K Privately Held
SIC: 4911 8711 3519 1629 ; consulting engineer; parts & accessories, internal combustion engines; power plant construction

(G-17598)
UNIVERSAL RECTIFIERS INC
1631 Cottonwood School Rd (77471-8200)
P.O. Box 1640 (77471-1640)
PHONE................................281 342-8471
Robert Michael Speck Sr, *President*
Robert Michael Speck Jr, *Vice Pres*
Mary Speck, *Treasurer*
Mike Hill, *Marketing Staff*
Michael Llamas, *
EMP: 40
SQ FT: 20,000
SALES (est): 9.5MM Privately Held
WEB: www.universalrectifiers.com
SIC: 3629 Series capacitors

(G-17599)
VAIGN DESIGNER STREET AP LLC
1205 Blaydon Ct (77471-5687)
PHONE................................832 490-8510
Stanley Ike, *
EMP: 25
SALES (est): 750.2K Privately Held
SIC: 2211 Apparel & outerwear fabrics, cotton

Rosharon
Brazoria County

(G-17600)
CARBOLINE PRMIUM CUTNG TLS INC
1914 County Road 894 (77583-2320)
P.O. Box 1666, Pearland (77588-1666)
PHONE................................281 485-5505
Jarrod Richter, *President*
Rhonda E Richter, *Vice Pres*
EMP: 14
SQ FT: 6,720
SALES (est): 2MM Privately Held
WEB: www.carbolineusa.com
SIC: 3545 Cutting tools for machine tools

(G-17601)
CENTURY CONCRETE PARTNERS INC
8726 E Fm 1462 Rd (77583-7362)
P.O. Box 699, Alvin (77512-0699)
PHONE..................................281 585-5742
Candis Mixon, *CEO*
EMP: 9
SALES (est): 178K Privately Held
WEB: www.centuryconcretepartners.com
SIC: 3272 4789 Art marble, concrete;
pipeline terminal facilities, independently
operated

(G-17602)
CHEMICAL LIME-SOUTHWEST LLC
Also Called: Chemlime
5710 County Road 48 (77583-2816)
PHONE..................................281 431-0575
Joel Digiulio, *Manager*
EMP: 10
SALES (corp-wide): 2.6MM Privately Held
WEB: www.lhoist.com
SIC: 3274 Lime
HQ: Chemical Lime-Southwest, Llc
3700 Hulen St
Fort Worth TX 76107
817 732-8164

(G-17603)
CINCINNATI THERMAL SPRAY INC
4011 Chance Ln (77583-4377)
PHONE..................................281 431-1629
Shawn O'Hanlon, *Branch Mgr*
EMP: 18 Privately Held
WEB: www.cts-inc.net
SIC: 3479 Coating of metals & formed
products
PA: Cincinnati Thermal Spray, Inc.
10904 Deerfield Rd
Blue Ash OH 45242

(G-17604)
DMD PRODUCTS LLC
Also Called: Slinggrip
9973 Fm 521 Rd (77583-4511)
PHONE..................................281 778-2051
David Watts,
Michael Watts,
EMP: 9
SALES (est): 1.8MM Privately Held
WEB: www.lovehandle.com
SIC: 3069 5065 Grips or handles, rubber;
mobile telephone equipment

(G-17605)
FLOW-ZONE LLC (DH)
3504 Dwayne Rd (77583-2882)
PHONE..................................281 997-8899
Jim Franklin, *President*
San Angelo, *Store Mgr*
Curtis Shelor, *Purchasing*
Ameena Mingau, *Controller*
Jared Cano, *Sales Staff*
EMP: 17 EST: 1999
SALES (est): 26.1MM Privately Held
WEB: www.flow-zone.com
SIC: 1389 Oil field services

(G-17606)
JOEL G GIBBS INC
Also Called: Accurate Machine Shop
13730 County Road 48 (77583-6131)
P.O. Box 985, Alvin (77512-0985)
PHONE..................................281 595-3330
Joel G Gibbs, *President*
Robin Gibbs, *Admin Sec*
EMP: 10
SQ FT: 4,500
SALES (est): 1.8MM Privately Held
WEB: www.accuratemachineshops.com
SIC: 3599 7539 Machine shop, jobbing &
repair; machine shop, automotive

(G-17607)
LETCO GROUP LLC
16138 Highway 6 (77583-3224)
PHONE..................................281 431-3400
EMP: 59

SALES (corp-wide): 78.3MM Privately
Held
WEB: www.livingearth.net
SIC: 2875 Compost
PA: The Letco Group Llc
1901 Cal Crossing Rd
Dallas TX 75220
972 506-8575

(G-17608)
MAGNUM FEEDERS INC
Also Called: Magnum Hunting Products
6030 County Road 60 (77583-6360)
PHONE..................................281 261-0803
Samuel Jackson Arnold, *President*
Charlotte Kay Arnold, *Treasurer*
EMP: 10
SQ FT: 6,500
SALES (est): 1MM Privately Held
WEB: www.magnumhunting.com
SIC: 3949 5941 Hunting equipment; hunt-
ing equipment

(G-17609)
PALM INC
5725 County Road 121 (77583-5919)
PHONE..................................713 410-1331
Mark Chambers, *Owner*
EMP: 149 Privately Held
WEB: www.palmsource.com
SIC: 3663 Mobile communication equip-
ment
HQ: Palm, Inc.
950 W Maude Ave
Sunnyvale CA 94085

(G-17610)
R LUTE S INC
803 E Fm 1462 Rd (77583-7866)
P.O. Box 748 (77583-0748)
PHONE..................................281 595-3777
Kenneth Lute, *Owner*
EMP: 12
SALES (est): 1.8MM Privately Held
WEB: www.rlutesinc.com
SIC: 3441 Fabricated structural metal

(G-17611)
R LUTES INC (PA)
803 W Fm 1462 (77583-7959)
P.O. Box 748 (77583-0748)
PHONE..................................281 595-3777
Kenneth D Lute, *President*
Rebecca Lute, *Vice Pres*
EMP: 30
SALES (est): 5.6MM Privately Held
WEB: www.rlutesinc.com
SIC: 3449 Miscellaneous metalwork

(G-17612)
RPM SERVICES INC
Also Called: Texas R P M Services
27920 Highway 288 (77583-5224)
P.O. Box 747 (77583-0747)
PHONE..................................281 595-3165
Paul Martinuc, *President*
Tommy French, *Vice Pres*
Terry Schmidt, *Vice Pres*
Tim Bohac, *Opers Mgr*
Kristine Kulhanek, *Human Resources*
EMP: 100
SALES (est): 14.5MM Privately Held
WEB: www.rpm-services.com
SIC: 3599 Machine shop, jobbing & repair

(G-17613)
SCHLUMBERGER OMNES INC
14910 Airline Rd (77583-7900)
PHONE..................................281 285-5176
Moises E Smart, *Principal*
J-F Poupeau, *Exec VP*
John Schoellmann, *Engineer*
Xuedong Yang, *Electrical Engi*
Rick Brunson, *Software Dev*
EMP: 30 Publicly Held
SIC: 1389 Oil field services
HQ: Schlumberger Omnes, Inc.
5599 San Felipe St Fl 17
Houston TX 77056

(G-17614)
SCHLUMBERGER TECHNOLOGY CORP
Also Called: Schlumbrger Rsrvoir Cmpletions
14910 Airline Rd (77583-7900)
P.O. Box 1590 (77583-1590)
PHONE..................................281 285-5200
Ashish Sharma, *Design Engr*
Tom Zimmerman, *Branch Mgr*
Steve Solek, *Administration*
EMP: 150 Publicly Held
SIC: 1389 Oil field services
HQ: Schlumberger Technology Corp
300 Schlumberger Dr
Sugar Land TX 77478
281 285-8500

(G-17615)
TRINITY COATINGS LLC
25225 Hwy 288 Rosharon (77583)
PHONE..................................281 845-0022
Joseph Drury, *President*
Phillip Scott, *Vice Pres*
William Scott, *Vice Pres*
Jessie Scott, *Treasurer*
EMP: 11
SQ FT: 10,000
SALES (est): 315.6K Privately Held
WEB: www.trinity-coatings.com
SIC: 3479 Etching & engraving

(G-17616)
WISCO MORAN DRILLING CO INC
125 Post (77583-2113)
P.O. Box 939, Fresno (77545-0939)
PHONE..................................281 431-2600
Joel Bouldin Jr, *President*
Tommy Moore, *Superintendent*
Tim Eiler, *VP Admin*
Ron Townsend, *Vice Pres*
Bob Gowens, *CFO*
EMP: 75
SQ FT: 10,000
SALES (est): 13.8MM
SALES (corp-wide): 31.1MM Privately
Held
WEB: www.wiscomoran.com
SIC: 1381 Drilling oil & gas wells
PA: Wisco International, Inc.
125 Post
Rosharon TX 77583
281 431-2600

Ross
McLennan County

(G-17617)
TRAVIS SCOTT
Also Called: Lonestar Windmills
16629 N Interstate 35 (76684)
PHONE..................................254 829-0651
Travis Scott, *Owner*
Travis S Scott, *Manager*
EMP: 11 Privately Held
WEB: www.lonestarwindmills.com
SIC: 3523 Farm machinery & equipment
PA: Travis Scott
3339 Fort Graham Rd
Waco TX 76705

Rotan
Fisher County

(G-17618)
NG OPERATIONS LLC
National Gypsum of Texas
832 County Road 311 (79546-6923)
P.O. Box B (79546-0481)
PHONE..................................325 735-2221
Dale Miller, *Plant Mgr*
Buck Cashiola, *Manager*
Chuck Slanagan, *Manager*
EMP: 91
SALES (corp-wide): 478MM Privately
Held
WEB: www.nationalgypsum.com
SIC: 3275 Wallboard, gypsum
HQ: Proform Finishing Products, Llc
2001 Rexford Rd
Charlotte NC 28211

Round Mountain
Blanco County

(G-17619)
TEXAS FABCO SOLUTIONS INC
178 Ranch Road 962 E (78663-5000)
PHONE..................................979 255-3530
Brooks Pearce, *President*
EMP: 15
SQ FT: 3,200
SALES (est): 5.1MM Privately Held
WEB: www.texasfabco.com
SIC: 3533 Oil field machinery & equipment

Round Rock
Williamson County

(G-17620)
AKZO NOBEL INC
Also Called: Akzo Nobel Coatings
401 Texas Ave Ste B (78664-2494)
PHONE..................................512 244-9038
EMP: 34
SALES (corp-wide): 10.2B Privately Held
WEB: www.akzonobel.com
SIC: 2851 Paints & allied products
HQ: Akzo Nobel Inc.
535 Marriott Dr Ste 500
Nashville TN 37214

(G-17621)
ALK-ABELLO INC (DH)
Also Called: A L K
1700 Royston Ln (78664-9500)
PHONE..................................512 251-0037
Jens Bager, *President*
Jared Bates, *Business Mgr*
Steven Dietz, *Business Mgr*
Leslie Powell, *Business Mgr*
Bryan Romaine, *Business Mgr*
EMP: 90
SQ FT: 18,000
SALES (est): 56.2MM
SALES (corp-wide): 5B Privately Held
WEB: www.alk.net
SIC: 2834 Pharmaceutical preparations
HQ: Alk-Abello A/S
Boge Alle 6-8
Horsholm 2970
457 475-76

(G-17622)
ALWAYS INTEGRITY MACHINING LLC
16800 Radholme Ct Ste A (78664-8646)
PHONE..................................512 670-1010
Richard Muraoka,
Joseph Souza,
EMP: 10
SQ FT: 1,500
SALES (est): 558.7K Privately Held
WEB: www.aim-machining.com
SIC: 3599 Machine shop, jobbing & repair

(G-17623)
ASHLEY INDUSTRIES LLC
2541 S Interstate 35 (78664-7360)
PHONE..................................864 834-1167
Steve Wingard, *Mng Member*
EMP: 9
SQ FT: 3,000
SALES (est): 3.5MM Privately Held
SIC: 2833 3942 Medicinals & botanicals;
dolls & stuffed toys

(G-17624)
ASTRO MECHANICS INC
1411a Sam Bass Rd (78681-4141)
PHONE..................................512 246-9200
Tom Stacy, *President*
Angie Stacey, *Corp Secy*
EMP: 10
SALES (est): 1.7MM Privately Held
WEB: www.astromechanics.net
SIC: 3599 Machine shop, jobbing & repair

(G-17625)
AUSTIN DVD INC
3800 Julianas Way (78665-1151)
PHONE..................................512 246-8759
Ken Byrd, *President*

EMP: 12
SALES (est): 967.5K **Privately Held**
WEB: www.dvdaustin.com
SIC: 3652 Compact laser discs, prere-
corded

(G-17626)
BANNER SIGN GRAPHICS
607 Buckskin Dr (78681-6503)
PHONE..................................512 458-5348
Debbie Papst, *Owner*
EMP: 11
SALES (est): 849.9K **Privately Held**
WEB: www.bannersigngraphics.com
SIC: 3993 2759 Signs, not made in cus-
tom sign painting shops; screen printing

(G-17627)
BLUEBONNET BEER COMPANY LLC
1700 Bryant Dr Ste 107 (78664-3898)
PHONE..................................512 774-4258
Clare Hulama, *Principal*
EMP: 18
SALES (est): 2.7MM **Privately Held**
WEB: www.bluebonnetbeerco.com
SIC: 2082 Beer (alcoholic beverage)

(G-17628)
BOOMI INC
Also Called: Dell Boomi
1 Dell Way Ms (78682-7000)
PHONE..................................800 289-3355
EMP: 23 EST: 2008
SALES (est): 6.2MM **Publicly Held**
WEB: www.boomi.com
SIC: 3571 Electronic computers
PA: Dell Technologies Inc.
1 Dell Way
Round Rock TX 78682

(G-17629)
CEN-TEX MACHINING INC
1513 Sam Bass Rd (78681-2828)
P.O. Box 1479 (78680-1479)
PHONE..................................512 255-1477
Rich Phillips, *CEO*
Dennis Donovan, *Vice Pres*
EMP: 56
SQ FT: 22,000
SALES (est): 7.3MM **Privately Held**
WEB: www.centexmachining.com
SIC: 3841 3842 Surgical instruments &
apparatus; orthopedic appliances

(G-17630)
CENTEX MACHINE AND WELDING INC
1513 Sam Bass Rd (78681-2828)
PHONE..................................512 255-1477
Marcelo Draguicevich, *President*
EMP: 50
SALES (est): 1.5MM **Privately Held**
WEB: www.centexmachining.com
SIC: 3599 Custom machinery

(G-17631)
CENTURY TAPE & LABEL LLC
Also Called: Century Label
21 Cypress Blvd Ste 1120 (78665-1034)
PHONE..................................972 576-0826
EMP: 24
SQ FT: 25,000
SALES (est): 5.2MM **Privately Held**
WEB: www.hydeparklabel.com
SIC: 2679 Labels, paper: made from pur-
chased material

(G-17632)
CERILLIANT CORPORATION
811 Paloma Dr Ste A (78665-2402)
PHONE..................................512 238-9974
Sherri Pogue, *President*
Mitzi Rettinger, *Vice Pres*
Lara Sparks, *Vice Pres*
Richard Trammell, *Vice Pres*
Art Zisman, *Opers Mgr*
▲ EMP: 70
SQ FT: 32,500
SALES (est): 19.2MM
SALES (corp-wide): 17.8B **Privately Held**
WEB: www.cerilliant.com
SIC: 2869 Laboratory chemicals, organic

HQ: Sigma-Aldrich Corporation
3050 Spruce St
Saint Louis MO 63103
314 771-5765

(G-17633)
CLEARCORRECT OPERATING LLC
21 Cypress Blvd Ste 1010 (78665-1034)
PHONE..................................888 331-3323
Jarrett Pumphrey, *CEO*
Corey Johnson, *Vice Pres*
Jack Spradling, *Vice Pres*
Ashley Rogus, *Opers Staff*
Victoria Melchor, *Accounts Mgr*
EMP: 130 EST: 2007
SQ FT: 25,000
SALES (est): 30.1MM
SALES (corp-wide): 264.9MM **Privately Held**
WEB: www.straumann.com
SIC: 3843 Dental materials
HQ: Straumann Manufacturing, Inc.
60 Minuteman Rd
Andover MA 01810

(G-17634)
COMMERCIAL METALS COMPANY
16709 Central Commerce Dr (78664-8545)
PHONE..................................512 246-1424
Forrest Clark, *Branch Mgr*
EMP: 10
SALES (corp-wide): 5.4B **Publicly Held**
WEB: www.cmc.com
SIC: 3312 Blast furnaces & steel mills
PA: Commercial Metals Company
6565 N Macarthur Blvd # 800
Irving TX 75039
214 689-4300

(G-17635)
CONCURRENT MFG SOLUTIONS LLC
800 Paloma Dr Ste 240 (78665-2400)
PHONE..................................512 310-9139
EMP: 30
SALES (corp-wide): 47.8MM **Privately Held**
SIC: 3679 3672 Mfg Electronic Compo-
nents Mfg Printed Circuit Boards
HQ: Concurrent Manufacturing Solutions
Llc
2230 W 77th St
Hialeah FL 33178
305 556-9210

(G-17636)
CONNECTIONE LLC
Also Called: Trifusion
2550 N Mays St Ste B (78665-2410)
PHONE..................................512 310-1000
Corey Bell, *CEO*
Steve Savage, *COO*
Anurag Kumar,
EMP: 30
SALES (est): 2.3MM **Privately Held**
SIC: 7372 Prepackaged software

(G-17637)
CONSOLIDATED METAL TECH INC
Also Called: C M T
800 N Georgetown St (78664-4458)
PHONE..................................512 255-9296
Terry Burgess, *President*
Harry Bryant, *Office Mgr*
Cathie Sikorski, *Assistant*
EMP: 84
SQ FT: 26,000
SALES (est): 12MM **Privately Held**
WEB: www.cmtfinishing.com
SIC: 3471 Finishing, metals or formed
products

(G-17638)
CRAWFORD ELECTRIC SUP CO INC
2251 Picadilly Dr (78664-8653)
PHONE..................................512 593-4000
EMP: 20

SALES (corp-wide): 11.7MM **Privately Held**
WEB: www.crawfordelectricsupply.com
SIC: 5063 3699 1731 Electrical supplies;
electrical equipment & supplies; electrical
work
HQ: Crawford Electric Supply Company,
Inc.
7390 Northcourt Rd
Houston TX 77040
713 476-0788

(G-17639)
CREATIVE CUSTOM CABINETS INC
1500 W Industrial Blvd (78681-2950)
PHONE..................................512 821-0300
Jerry Penick, *President*
Kelly Penick, *Vice Pres*
EMP: 19
SALES (est): 3MM **Privately Held**
WEB: www.cabinets.cc
SIC: 2434 Wood kitchen cabinets

(G-17640)
CYBER DYNAMICS CORPORATION
3926 Harvey Penick Dr (78664-4049)
PHONE..................................818 706-3580
Lynn Schneider, *President*
EMP: 10 EST: 1997
SALES (est): 1MM **Privately Held**
SIC: 3669 Signaling apparatus, electric

(G-17641)
DELL AMERICA LATINA CORP (DH)
1 Dell Way (78682-7000)
PHONE..................................512 799-1022
Terry Wildenhaus, *Accounts Exec*
Kim Perry, *Technology*
Bruno Magalhaes, *Prgrmr*
EMP: 15
SALES (est): 3.8MM **Publicly Held**
WEB: www.dell.com
SIC: 3571 Electronic computers
HQ: Dell Inc.
1 Dell Way
Round Rock TX 78682
800 289-3355

(G-17642)
DELL INC (DH)
Also Called: Dell Computer
1 Dell Way (78682-7000)
P.O. Box 841392, Dallas (75284-1392)
PHONE..................................800 289-3355
Michael Dell, *Ch of Bd*
Jeffrey Clarke, *President*
Jason Cooke, *Partner*
Jeffrey W Clarke, *Vice Chairman*
Yvonne Gee, *Area Mgr*
◆ EMP: 2750
SALES (est): 33.1B **Publicly Held**
WEB: www.dell.com
SIC: 3572 3575 3577 7372 Computer
storage devices; computer terminals,
monitors & components; computer periph-
eral equipment; printers, computer; appli-
cation computer software; computer
related consulting services; computer re-
lated maintenance services; minicomput-
ers
HQ: Denali Intermediate Inc.
1 Dell Way
Round Rock TX 78682
713 627-0933

(G-17643)
DELL INC
Also Called: Dell Computer
501 Dell Center Blvd # 2 (78664-7306)
PHONE..................................512 324-0137
Jeffrey Mayder, *Branch Mgr*
EMP: 150 **Publicly Held**
WEB: www.dell.com
SIC: 3571 Personal computers (microcom-
puters)
HQ: Dell Inc.
1 Dell Way
Round Rock TX 78682
800 289-3355

(G-17644)
DELL MARKETING LP (DH)
1 Dell Way (78682-7000)
P.O. Box 676021, Dallas (75267-6021)
PHONE..................................512 513-9022
Michael S Dell, *Ch of Bd*
Eric Brown, *Vice Pres*
Richard Horton, *Engineer*
Travis Potter, *Senior Engr*
Giget Henderson, *Accounts Mgr*
▲ EMP: 241
SALES (est): 1.6B **Publicly Held**
WEB: www.dell.com
SIC: 3571 Electronic computers
HQ: Dell Inc.
1 Dell Way
Round Rock TX 78682
800 289-3355

(G-17645)
DELL PRODUCTS LP
1 Dell Way (78682-7000)
P.O. Box 149257, Austin (78714-9257)
PHONE..................................866 413-3355
Michael Dell, *Managing Prtnr*
Matthew Keck, *Counsel*
Helen He, *Production*
Jennifer Minarik, *Engineer*
Don Darden, *Accounts Exec*
◆ EMP: 1000
SALES (est): 205.9MM **Publicly Held**
WEB: www.dell.com
SIC: 3571 Electronic computers
HQ: Dell Inc.
1 Dell Way
Round Rock TX 78682
800 289-3355

(G-17646)
DELL TECHNOLOGIES INC (PA)
1 Dell Way (78682-7000)
PHONE..................................800 289-3355
Diego Puerta, *CEO*
Michael S Dell, *Ch of Bd*
Howard D Elias, *President*
William F Scannell, *President*
Michael Henderson, *Business Mgr*
EMP: 195
SALES: 92.1B **Publicly Held**
WEB: www.delltechnologies.com
SIC: 3571 3577 7372 Computers, digital,
analog or hybrid; computer peripheral
equipment; prepackaged software

(G-17647)
DELL USA LP (DH)
401 Dell Way (78664)
PHONE..................................512 725-1829
Michael S Dell, *Partner*
Jitin Aggarwal, *General Mgr*
Hartmut Lehmann, *Regional Mgr*
Andrew Deaton, *Business Mgr*
Niall Shanahan, *Project Mgr*
EMP: 80
SALES (est): 63.7MM **Publicly Held**
WEB: www.dell.com
SIC: 3571 Electronic computers
HQ: Dell Inc.
1 Dell Way
Round Rock TX 78682
800 289-3355

(G-17648)
DENALI INTERMEDIATE INC (HQ)
1 Dell Way (78682-7000)
PHONE..................................713 627-0933
Michael S Dell, *CEO*
EMP: 2750
SALES (est): 26.2B **Publicly Held**
WEB: www.delltechnologies.com
SIC: 3572 3577 7372 3571 Computer
storage devices; computer peripheral
equipment; printers, computer; application
computer software; minicomputers

(G-17649)
DIGITAL ALLIANCE MEDIA INC
1000 Heritage Center Cir (78664-4463)
PHONE..................................512 238-3014
Ben Mosley, *CEO*
Hoang L Nguyen, *President*
Renee Edwards, *Administration*
EMP: 21
SALES (est): 2.7MM **Privately Held**
SIC: 2741 Miscellaneous publishing

(G-17650)
DYNAMIC INTGRTONS CTRL SYSTEMS
475 Round Rock West Dr (78681-5009)
PHONE...................512 716-0817
Terry Ham, *Principal*
Butch Heth, *Info Tech Mgr*
Jared Travis, *Technology*
EMP: 17
SALES (est): 1.4MM **Privately Held**
WEB: www.dynamicintegrationsinc.com
SIC: 7382 1731 3651 Security systems services; telephone & telephone equipment installation; audio electronic systems; home entertainment equipment, electronic

(G-17651)
ELITE STAIRCASES LLC
836 Centerra Hills Cir (78665-5035)
PHONE...................512 466-6590
EMP: 10
SALES (est): 480K **Privately Held**
SIC: 2431 Millwork, Nsk

(G-17652)
ELLIOTT ELECTRIC SUPPLY INC
Also Called: Elliot Electric 29
445 Texas Ave (78664-2492)
PHONE...................512 246-8001
Mackenzie Alspaugh, *Project Mgr*
Chris Petty, *Manager*
EMP: 20
SALES (corp-wide): 1.1B **Privately Held**
WEB: www.elliottelectric.com
SIC: 5063 5084 3625 Electrical construction materials; industrial machinery & equipment; motor controls, electric
PA: Elliott Electric Supply, Inc.
2526 N Stallings Dr
Nacogdoches TX 75964
936 569-1184

(G-17653)
EMERSON AUTOMATION SOLUTIONS
1100 W Louis Henna Blvd (78681-9921)
PHONE...................512 835-2190
Lal Karsanbhai, *President*
EMP: 9
SALES (corp-wide): 16.7B **Publicly Held**
WEB: www.pentair.com
SIC: 3491 3625 3494 Industrial valves; relays & industrial controls; valves & pipe fittings
HQ: Emerson Automation Solutions Final Control Us Lp
10707 Clay Rd
Houston TX 77041

(G-17654)
EMERSON PROCESS MGT LLLP (DH)
1100 W Louis Henna Blvd (78681-9921)
P.O. Box 270626, Saint Louis MO (63127-0626)
PHONE...................512 835-2190
Steve Sonnenberg, *President*
Prathima Yakkanti, *Project Mgr*
Brian Capoccia, *Engineer*
Aaron John, *Engineer*
Cathie Tabor, *Project Engr*
EMP: 144
SALES (est): 142.1MM
SALES (corp-wide): 16.7B **Publicly Held**
WEB: www.emerson.com
SIC: 3823 Industrial instrmnts msrmnt display/control process variable

(G-17655)
ENTEGRIS PROF SOLUTIONS INC
700 Jeffrey Way Ste 400 (78665-2421)
PHONE...................512 244-5200
Allen Harvey, *Director*
EMP: 40
SALES (corp-wide): 1.8B **Publicly Held**
WEB: www.atmi.com
SIC: 3674 8731 Semiconductors & related devices; commercial physical research
HQ: Entegris Professional Solutions, Inc.
7 Commerce Dr
Danbury CT 06810
203 794-1100

(G-17656)
EQUALIZER INDUSTRIES INC
2611 Oakmont Dr (78665-1043)
PHONE...................512 388-7715
Eric Asbery, *President*
Gilbert Gutierrez, *Vice Pres*
Christina Flores, *Plant Mgr*
Bill Porter, *Production*
James Fatigate, *Purchasing*
◆ EMP: 30
SQ FT: 15,000
SALES (est): 15.2MM **Privately Held**
WEB: www.equalizer.com
SIC: 5013 5251 3423 Tools & equipment, automotive; tools; hand & edge tools

(G-17657)
FISHER-ROSEMOUNT SYSTEMS INC (HQ)
1100 W Louis Henna Blvd (78681-9921)
PHONE...................512 835-2190
Tom Snead, *President*
Deeann Delguzzi, *Opers Mgr*
Jesus Pineda, *Opers Mgr*
Dennis Lemker, *Purch Mgr*
Clint Griffin, *Engineer*
▲ EMP: 700
SALES (est): 468.2MM
SALES (corp-wide): 16.7B **Publicly Held**
WEB: www.emerson.com
SIC: 3625 3621 7699 Relays & industrial controls; motors & generators; industrial equipment services
PA: Emerson Electric Co.
8000 West Florissant Ave
Saint Louis MO 63136
314 553-2000

(G-17658)
FLUOROMED PRODUCTS LP
2350 Double Creek Dr (78664-3801)
PHONE...................512 255-6877
Tim Juhlke, *Partner*
Webb Bailey, *Partner*
Tom Bierschenk, *Partner*
Richard J Lagow, *Partner*
EMP: 10
SQ FT: 5,000
SALES (est): 1.5MM **Privately Held**
WEB: www.exfluor.com
SIC: 2833 Medicinals & botanicals

(G-17659)
GATE-MOLD INC
1413 Sam Bass Rd (78681-4141)
PHONE...................512 255-3470
Fax: 512 255-3813
EMP: 10
SQ FT: 7,600
SALES (est): 1.3MM **Privately Held**
SIC: 3544 3089 Mfg Dies/Tools/Jigs/Fixtures Mfg Plastic Products

(G-17660)
GENOMICS USA INC (PA)
2018 Westvalley Pl (78665-5011)
PHONE...................847 359-1032
Krishna Jayaraman, *President*
EMP: 12
SALES (est): 75K **Privately Held**
WEB: www.gmsbiotech.com
SIC: 3841 Medical instruments & equipment, blood & bone work

(G-17661)
HALF PRICE BKS REC MGZINES INC
1601 S I H 35 (78664-6041)
PHONE...................512 244-0203
Monica Schultz, *Manager*
EMP: 17
SALES (corp-wide): 211.7MM **Privately Held**
WEB: www.becomegreen.info
SIC: 2721 5735 5942 Magazines: publishing & printing; records; book stores
PA: Half Price Books, Records, Magazines, Incorporated
5803 E Northwest Hwy
Dallas TX 75231
214 360-0833

(G-17662)
HI-TECH PRODUCTS INC
1513 Brandi Ln (78681-4103)
PHONE...................512 450-1465
Michael Molina, *President*
Antoinette Yvonne Ojeda, *Admin Sec*
EMP: 14
SQ FT: 5,000
SALES (est): 1.9MM **Privately Held**
WEB: www.htpcadcam.com
SIC: 3599 7373 Machine shop, jobbing & repair; computer-aided design (CAD) systems service

(G-17663)
JACQUELINE THOMPSON
Also Called: JTL Suplies
104 Fred Couples Dr (78664-4036)
PHONE...................210 269-1548
Jacqueline Thompson, *Owner*
EMP: 11
SALES (est): 167K **Privately Held**
SIC: 3089 Automotive parts, plastic

(G-17664)
JOE BUSH & ASSOCIATES INC
Also Called: Bush and Associates
12 Indian Meadows Dr (78665-9419)
PHONE...................512 238-0450
Joe B Bush, *President*
Matthew C Bush, *Vice Pres*
Matthew Bush, *Vice Pres*
Jane E Bush, *Treasurer*
EMP: 11
SQ FT: 9,800
SALES (est): 2MM **Privately Held**
SIC: 1541 3441 Steel building construction; fabricated structural metal

(G-17665)
KEAL CASES INCORPORATED
1100 W Old Settlers Blvd (78681-2100)
P.O. Box 443 (78680-0443)
PHONE...................512 244-9100
Paul Keiser, *President*
Mike Maupin, *Vice Pres*
Eunice Keiser, *Office Mgr*
EMP: 25
SQ FT: 18,000
SALES (est): 3.4MM **Privately Held**
WEB: www.kealcases.com
SIC: 2448 3412 2449 Cargo containers, wood & metal combination; metal barrels, drums & pails; wood containers

(G-17666)
LASER SCIENTIFIC LLC
210a Commerce Blvd (78664-2116)
PHONE...................512 733-8709
John D Crownover, *President*
Mike Coufal, *Prdtn Mgr*
Ana Lobato, *Sales Mgr*
Walker Alsobrooks, *Manager*
EMP: 15
SALES (est): 2.4MM **Privately Held**
WEB: www.laserscientific.com
SIC: 3845 Laser systems & equipment, medical

(G-17667)
LAUREN CONCRETE INC
2001 Picadilly Dr (78664-9511)
PHONE...................512 233-1348
EMP: 26
SALES (est): 5.1MM **Privately Held**
WEB: www.laurenconcrete.com
SIC: 3273 Ready-mixed concrete

(G-17668)
LAUREN CONCRETE LP
Also Called: Circle B Ready-Mix
2001 Picadilly Dr (78664-9511)
PHONE...................512 389-2113
Ronald Klatt, *Partner*
Ronnie Klatt, *Partner*
Don Schulze, *CFO*
EMP: 18
SALES (est): 3.9MM **Privately Held**
WEB: www.laurenconcrete.com
SIC: 3273 Ready-mixed concrete

(G-17669)
LIBERTY SIGNS INC
1300 W Industrial Blvd B (78681-2964)
P.O. Box 1259, Liberty Hill (78642-1259)
PHONE...................512 255-3887
Mark Rocke, *President*
Kathy Records, *Accounting Mgr*
EMP: 12
SALES (est): 1.9MM **Privately Held**
WEB: www.libertysignstx.com
SIC: 3993 1799 Electric signs; sign installation & maintenance

(G-17670)
MAKERARM INC
4019 Galena Hills Dr (78681-2255)
PHONE...................512 553-8033
Zaib Iqtidar, *CEO*
EMP: 12
SALES (est): 532K **Privately Held**
WEB: www.makerarm.com
SIC: 3549 3559 Assembly machines, including robotic; synthetic filament extruding machines

(G-17671)
MECHANICAL TECHNICAL SVCS LP
Also Called: Mtech Comfort Systems
1720 Royston Ln (78664-9555)
PHONE...................512 929-7090
Bob Fabrizio, *President*
Ronald Fellers, *Partner*
Stan Henry, *Partner*
Edward Neal, *Partner*
Trent McKenna, *Vice Pres*
EMP: 50
SQ FT: 5,800
SALES (est): 4.7MM
SALES (corp-wide): 2.1B **Publicly Held**
WEB: www.mtechtexas.com
SIC: 1711 3585 Mechanical contractor; air conditioning equipment, complete
PA: Comfort Systems Usa, Inc.
675 Bering Dr Ste 400
Houston TX 77057
713 830-9600

(G-17672)
MI INC
2007 Lamar Dr (78664-2121)
PHONE...................512 244-3676
Nick Horn, *President*
Steve Orand, *President*
Robin Reiker, *Manager*
EMP: 20
SQ FT: 10,000
SALES (est): 2.8MM **Privately Held**
WEB: www.mi-inc.net
SIC: 3599 Machine shop, jobbing & repair

(G-17673)
MICROSS COMPONENTS-TX LLC
Also Called: Etech-Web
33 Cypress Blvd Ste 400 (78665-1010)
PHONE...................512 833-5868
Gregory Berry, *President*
Logan Willis, *Vice Pres*
James Waters, *Prdtn Mgr*
Sue Ellis, *Production*
Kim Steffenson, *Production*
EMP: 35
SALES (est): 6.5MM **Privately Held**
WEB: www.etech-web.com
SIC: 3672 Printed circuit boards

(G-17674)
NATIONAL ENERGETICS INC
2051 Gattis School Rd # 540 (78664-7441)
PHONE...................512 382-1894
Todd Ditmire, *President*
Nikki Chitwood, *General Mgr*
Mikael Martinez, *COO*
Randy Sanders, *Controller*
John King, *Manager*
EMP: 9
SALES (est): 1.8MM **Privately Held**
WEB: www.nationalenergetics.com
SIC: 3826 Analytical instruments

(G-17675)
NEXT TECHNOLOGIES INC
Also Called: Evodesk
2251 Picadilly Dr (78664-8653)
PHONE...................888 615-5721
EMP: 33

SALES (corp-wide): 6.7MM **Privately Held**
WEB: www.xdesk.com
SIC: 2521 2522 Wood office desks & tables; desks, office: except wood
PA: Next Technologies Inc.
2530 Shell Rd
Georgetown TX 78628
512 212-7758

(G-17676)
OPTICAL FILTER SOURCE LLC
16920 Joe Barbee Dr # 2 (78664-2374)
PHONE..................512 248-0605
Frank Calcagni, *Mng Member*
Jan Confalone, *Mng Member*
EMP: 10
SQ FT: 8,700
SALES (est): 1.8MM **Privately Held**
WEB: www.opticalfiltersource.com
SIC: 3827 Optical instruments & lenses

(G-17677)
PACIFICA T-SHIRTS INC
3000 Joe Dimaggio Blvd # 31
(78665-3994)
P.O. Box 2101, Tustin CA (92781-2101)
PHONE..................714 508-4848
Regine Lahde, *President*
Greg Lahde, *Vice Pres*
▲ **EMP:** 10
SQ FT: 12,900
SALES (est): 1.5MM **Privately Held**
WEB: www.pacificaracewear.com
SIC: 2759 5199 2834 Screen printing; advertising specialties; automotive & apparel trimmings

(G-17678)
PAYTON INTERESTS INC (PA)
Also Called: Round Rock Screen Printing
1609 Chisholm Trail Rd # 40 (78681-2912)
PHONE..................512 244-3221
Joseph Payton, *President*
Joe Looze, *Assistant VP*
EMP: 25
SQ FT: 7,000
SALES (est): 4MM **Privately Held**
WEB: www.rocksports.net
SIC: 5651 2759 Family clothing stores; screen printing

(G-17679)
PHD ENERGY INC
6026 Ronchamps Dr (78681-5330)
PHONE..................800 318-3639
Michael Xie, *CEO*
Harry Mkhitarian, *Principal*
Grace Xie, *Principal*
EMP: 50
SALES (est): 4MM **Privately Held**
WEB: www.phdenergy.com
SIC: 3694 Battery charging alternators & generators

(G-17680)
PPG INDUSTRIES INC
Also Called: PPG 8338
399 Texas Ave (78664-2142)
PHONE..................512 218-9551
Butch Duty, *Manager*
EMP: 24
SALES (corp-wide): 15.3B **Publicly Held**
WEB: www.ppg.com
SIC: 2851 Paints & allied products
PA: Ppg Industries, Inc.
1 Ppg Pl
Pittsburgh PA 15272
412 434-3131

(G-17681)
PREFERRED STAMPINGS OF TEXAS
1602 N A W Grimes Blvd (78665-3409)
PHONE..................512 255-7803
William B Rhodes, *President*
EMP: 50 **EST:** 1969
SQ FT: 52,000
SALES (est): 5.6MM **Privately Held**
SIC: 3469 3444 Stamping metal for the trade; sheet metalwork

(G-17682)
PRESIDIO CUSTOM METAL WORKS
903 Brandi Ln (78681-4105)
PHONE..................512 284-8549
Rodd Frank, *President*
EMP: 10
SALES (est): 303.5K **Privately Held**
WEB: www.presidiocustommetalworks.com
SIC: 3444 3312 1799 3446 Awnings & canopies; fence posts, iron & steel; fence construction; railings, bannisters, guards, etc.: made from metal pipe; gates, ornamental metal; curtain wall, metal

(G-17683)
PROPORTION FOODS LLC (PA)
101 Chisholm Trail Rd (78681-5001)
PHONE..................512 735-9800
David Howard, *Exec VP*
Marcela Salinas, *Human Res Mgr*
Brian Levy,
Todd Waldman,
Greg Wiviott,
▼ **EMP:** 350
SQ FT: 200,000
SALES (est): 111.8MM **Privately Held**
WEB: www.proportionfoods.com
SIC: 2099 Food preparations

(G-17684)
RELIABLE MANUFACTURING INC (PA)
1900 N A W Grimes Blvd (78665-3407)
P.O. Box 1165 (78680-1165)
PHONE..................512 255-6572
Michael M Murray, *President*
Ruby Murray, *Treasurer*
EMP: 15 **EST:** 1981
SQ FT: 15,000
SALES (est): 3MM **Privately Held**
WEB: www.reliable-mfg.com
SIC: 3599 3825 3643 Machine shop, jobbing & repair; instruments to measure electricity; current-carrying wiring devices

(G-17685)
ROSCO LABORATORIES INC
1600 Chisholm Trail Rd # 200
(78681-2936)
PHONE..................512 388-5299
Tom Dushaj, *General Mgr*
Joe Zserdin, *Branch Mgr*
EMP: 12 **Privately Held**
WEB: www.us.rosco.com
SIC: 3861 Motion picture apparatus & equipment
HQ: Rosco Laboratories, Inc.
52 Harbor View Ave
Stamford CT 06902
203 708-8900

(G-17686)
ROUND ROCK BAKERY LTD
Also Called: Lone Star Bakery
106 W Liberty St (78664-5122)
P.O. Box 1583 (78680-1583)
PHONE..................512 255-3629
Dale Cohrs, *Principal*
EMP: 12
SQ FT: 2,000
SALES (est): 1.4MM **Privately Held**
WEB: www.roundrockdonuts.com
SIC: 2051 Bakery: wholesale or wholesale/retail combined

(G-17687)
ROUND ROCK DNUTS - LIBERTY LLC
106 W Liberty Ave (78664-5122)
PHONE..................512 255-3629
Cathy Castleberry, *Mng Member*
EMP: 12
SALES (est): 1.8MM **Privately Held**
WEB: www.roundrockdonuts.com
SIC: 2051 Bread, cake & related products

(G-17688)
SABER SECURITY SYSTEMS INC
Also Called: Saber Systems
2111 Greenhill Dr Ste 100 (78664-2250)
PHONE..................512 341-8700
Matt Barber, *President*
Christy Barber, *Vice Pres*

EMP: 15
SQ FT: 2,500
SALES (est): 1.6MM **Privately Held**
WEB: www.sabersecurityinc.com
SIC: 3699 1711 Automotive driving simulators (training aids), electronic; heating & air conditioning contractors

(G-17689)
SABIO ENVIRONMENTAL LLC
21 Cypress Blvd Ste 1130 (78665-1034)
PHONE..................512 869-0544
Mike Gordy, *CEO*
Roger Jordan, *Senior Engr*
Tim Jackson, *Mng Member*
EMP: 25
SQ FT: 10,000
SALES (est): 2.5MM **Privately Held**
WEB: www.sabio.com
SIC: 3564 3829 Purification & dust collection equipment; measuring & controlling devices

(G-17690)
SIMPLY NUC INC
495 Round Rock West Dr (78681-5012)
PHONE..................512 766-0402
Aaron Rowsell, *CEO*
John Deatherage, *Chief Mktg Ofcr*
Daniel Knox,
EMP: 28 **EST:** 2015
SQ FT: 1,200
SALES (est): 5.4MM **Privately Held**
WEB: www.simplynuc.com
SIC: 3571 5045 Minicomputers; computers, peripherals & software

(G-17691)
SRI MONOGRAMMING INC
2303 County Road 172 (78681-7341)
P.O. Box 2383 (78680-2383)
PHONE..................512 388-4989
Charlotte O'Reilly, *President*
Mickey O'Reilley, *Vice Pres*
Mickey O'Riley, *Sales Staff*
Mickey Oriley, *Sales Staff*
Alan Johnston, *Manager*
EMP: 24
SQ FT: 4,000
SALES (est): 2.6MM **Privately Held**
WEB: www.srimonogramming.com
SIC: 7389 2395 Embroidering of advertising on shirts, etc.; embroidery products, except schiffli machine

(G-17692)
TEXAS HEAT TREATING INC (PA)
155 Texas Ave (78664-2138)
P.O. Box 1117 (78680-1117)
PHONE..................512 255-5884
C H Crossley Jr, *President*
Tony Pugh, *General Mgr*
Jim Filkowski, *Sales Engr*
Tito Correa, *Sales Staff*
Debbie Phillips, *Office Mgr*
EMP: 50
SQ FT: 4,200
SALES (est): 5.6MM **Privately Held**
WEB: www.texasheattreating.com
SIC: 3398 Metal heat treating

(G-17693)
TEXAS SEC & SURVEILLANCE INC (PA)
2111 Sam Bass Rd Ste 400a (78681-1872)
PHONE..................512 693-4003
Shawn McCown, *President*
Amy McCown, *Principal*
Stephanie Perez, *Opers Staff*
EMP: 20
SALES (est): 1.7MM **Privately Held**
WEB: www.texassecurity.net
SIC: 7382 7373 5063 1711 Burglar alarm maintenance & monitoring; systems integration services; fire alarm systems; fire sprinkler system installation; fire extinguisher servicing; fire extinguisher charges

(G-17694)
TOPPAN PHOTOMASKS INC
400 Texas Ave (78664-2492)
PHONE..................512 310-6000
Franklin Kalk, *Exec VP*
Gary Kasprzyk, *Vice Pres*

John Barker, *Vice Pres*
Colleen Weins, *Opers Mgr*
Dicky St Clair, *Facilities Mgr*
EMP: 140
SQ FT: 27,668 **Privately Held**
WEB: www.photomask.com
SIC: 3679 5065 Electronic circuits; semiconductor devices
HQ: Toppan Photomasks, Inc.
131 E Old Settlers Blvd
Round Rock TX 78664
512 310-6500

(G-17695)
TOPPAN PHOTOMASKS INC (HQ)
131 E Old Settlers Blvd (78664-2211)
PHONE..................512 310-6500
Michael Hadsell, *President*
Kent Green, *Business Mgr*
James W Boeckman, *Exec VP*
Dr Franklin Kalk, *Exec VP*
Barry Pomeroy, *Exec VP*
▲ **EMP:** 425
SQ FT: 1,770
SALES (est): 377.7MM **Privately Held**
WEB: www.photomask.com
SIC: 3559 Semiconductor manufacturing machinery

(G-17696)
TOWER ELEVATOR SYSTEMS INC
2000a Picadilly Dr (78664-8555)
PHONE..................512 266-6200
James Tiner, *CEO*
Todd Grovatt, *President*
EMP: 18
SQ FT: 6,000
SALES (est): 3.7MM **Privately Held**
WEB: www.towerelevators.com
SIC: 1796 3534 Elevator installation & conversion; elevators & equipment

(G-17697)
VERMEER EQUIPMENT TEXAS LLC
Also Called: Vermeer Texas-Louisiana
1945 Louis Henna Blvd (78664-7237)
PHONE..................512 244-0505
Scott Shuffield, *Sales Executive*
Terry Schexnayder, *Manager*
EMP: 10
SALES (corp-wide): 78.4MM **Privately Held**
WEB: www.vermeer.com
SIC: 3531 Construction machinery
PA: Vermeer Equipment Of Texas, Llc
3025 State Highway 161
Irving TX 75062
972 255-3500

(G-17698)
VIZZA WASH SERVICES LLC
1322 Round Rock Ave (78681-4900)
PHONE..................512 246-8822
Joe Atuilar, *Manager*
EMP: 24
SALES (corp-wide): 31.1MM **Privately Held**
WEB: www.washtub.com
SIC: 3589 7542 Car washing machinery; washing & polishing, automotive
PA: Vizza Wash Services, L.L.C.
2208 Nw Loop 410
San Antonio TX 78230
210 493-8822

(G-17699)
WILLIAMSON CONFERENCE CENTER
Also Called: Wingate Wllmson Conference Ctr
1209 N Interstate 35 (78664-2926)
PHONE..................512 341-7000
Michelle Williams, *Manager*
EMP: 20
SALES (est): 191.3K **Privately Held**
WEB: www.wingateroundrock.com
SIC: 7011 3669 Hotels; visual communication systems

(G-17700)
ZEBRA TECHNOLOGIES CORPORATION
3729 Galena Hills Loop (78681-1035)
PHONE....................................512 716-3088
Mike Johnson, *Principal*
EMP: 383
SALES (corp-wide): 4.4B **Publicly Held**
WEB: www.zebra.com
SIC: 3577 Bar code (magnetic ink) printers
PA: Zebra Technologies Corporation
3 Overlook Pt
Lincolnshire IL 60069
847 634-6700

Rowlett
Dallas County

(G-17701)
BEST AMERICAN MFG CORP
4821 Grisham Dr (75088-3950)
PHONE....................................972 475-0092
Larry Howell, *President*
Phillip Howell, *Vice Pres*
EMP: 12
SQ FT: 10,000
SALES (est): 1MM **Privately Held**
WEB: www.bestamericantrampolines.com
SIC: 3949 Track & field athletic equipment; gymnasium equipment

(G-17702)
BODIN CONCRETE LP (PA)
Also Called: Bodin Concrete Co
4810 Boyd Blvd (75088-3935)
P.O. Box 109 (75030-0109)
PHONE....................................972 463-7348
Perry Bodin, *Partner*
Charlotte Bodin, *Partner*
EMP: 43
SQ FT: 7,500
SALES (est): 15.2MM **Privately Held**
WEB: www.bodinconcrete.com
SIC: 3273 Ready-mixed concrete

(G-17703)
CENTENNIAL STEEL INC (PA)
5304 Dexham Rd (75088-3829)
P.O. Box 1486 (75030-1486)
PHONE....................................972 412-5144
Michael E Groves, *President*
Brenda S Groves, *Vice Pres*
Kimberly Stephens, *Vice Pres*
EMP: 20
SQ FT: 4,000
SALES (est): 5.7MM **Privately Held**
SIC: 5051 5072 3441 Steel; hand tools; fabricated structural metal

(G-17704)
DATATRONIC CONTROL CORPORATION
5130 Dexham Rd (75088-3827)
PHONE....................................972 475-7879
Stephen Kim, *President*
John Onstot, *COO*
Barbara Onstot, *Vice Pres*
Genevieve Ruble, *Marketing Staff*
Barbara Onstatt, *Manager*
▲ EMP: 48
SQ FT: 87,000
SALES (est): 5.6MM **Privately Held**
WEB: www.dcisign.com
SIC: 3993 3674 3577 Electric signs; semiconductors & related devices; computer peripheral equipment

(G-17705)
GLECO PLATING INC
2220 Grisham Dr (75088-3947)
PHONE....................................972 475-4300
Jeff D Fodge, *President*
Glenda S Fodge, *Corp Secy*
Jean Gurley, *Vice Pres*
Mike Fodge, *Manager*
Christopher Johnson, *Manager*
EMP: 100
SQ FT: 35,000
SALES (est): 10.2MM **Privately Held**
WEB: www.glecoplating.com
SIC: 3471 Electroplating of metals or formed products

(G-17706)
GUZMAN MFG INC
Also Called: Gz Manufacturing
4206 Industrial St (75088-7726)
PHONE....................................972 475-3003
Jorge Guzman, *President*
Sonia Guzman, *Vice Pres*
Annabelle Acuna, *Marketing Staff*
EMP: 14
SQ FT: 27,000
SALES (est): 2.8MM **Privately Held**
WEB: www.gzmetal.com
SIC: 3444 Sheet metal specialties, not stamped

(G-17707)
INTERIOR FIXTURE INSTALLATIONS
3714 Big A Rd (75089-4000)
PHONE....................................972 412-9773
David Maples, *President*
Jacky Maples, *Vice Pres*
Karen Windsor, *Admin Sec*
Cynthia Rozelle,
EMP: 25
SQ FT: 4,500
SALES (est): 2.4MM **Privately Held**
WEB: www.interiorfixture.com
SIC: 2434 Wood kitchen cabinets

(G-17708)
KENTUCKY FREIGHT SYSTEMS INC
8309 Concord Dr (75089-2001)
PHONE....................................972 475-6567
EMP: 16
SALES: 400K **Privately Held**
SIC: 3537 4731 Transportation General Freight And Auto Parts

(G-17709)
L & L PRODUCTS INC
3210 Century Dr (75088-4984)
PHONE....................................972 475-5202
Alan Lundquist, *President*
EMP: 14
SQ FT: 20,000
SALES (est): 2.6MM **Privately Held**
WEB: www.landlproducts.com
SIC: 3714 Exhaust systems & parts, motor vehicle

(G-17710)
PIVOT CORPORATION
Also Called: H&S Manufacturing Co
2913 Singleton St (75088-7513)
P.O. Box 1515 (75030-1515)
PHONE....................................972 475-4747
Bobby A Spruiell, *President*
William A Howard, *Corp Secy*
Drew Howard, *Vice Pres*
Doug McCormick, *Purch Agent*
EMP: 75
SQ FT: 43,560
SALES (est): 15.2MM **Privately Held**
WEB: www.hsmfg.com
SIC: 3444 3842 Sheet metalwork; sheet metal specialties, not stamped

(G-17711)
STORE DCOR INC - RTAILGRAPHICS
5050 Boyd Blvd (75088-3924)
PHONE....................................972 475-4404
Robert Potts, *President*
Robert P Potts, *President*
Joel Cook, *Vice Pres*
Julie L Evatt, *Vice Pres*
Gregg Sawyer, *Purch Agent*
▲ EMP: 100
SQ FT: 100,000
SALES (est): 32MM **Privately Held**
WEB: www.thestoredecor.com
SIC: 5049 3993 Scientific & engineering equipment & supplies; signs & advertising specialties

(G-17712)
TEXAS PHOTONICS INC
2202 Lkeview Pkwy Ste 106 (75088)
PHONE....................................972 412-7111
John Spor, *President*
◆ EMP: 9
SQ FT: 3,500
SALES (est): 533.9K **Privately Held**
WEB: www.texas-photonics.com
SIC: 3679 Antennas, receiving

(G-17713)
THREE D FINISHING INC
Also Called: 3-D Powder Coating
5020 Grisham Dr (75088-3953)
P.O. Box 462114, Garland (75046-2114)
PHONE....................................972 475-2726
Tom Darter Sr, *President*
Sylvia Darter, *Corp Secy*
Tommy Darter, *Sales Staff*
EMP: 11
SQ FT: 6,200
SALES (est): 900K **Privately Held**
WEB: www.3dpowdercoating.com
SIC: 3479 7336 Painting of metal products; silk screen design

Royse City
Rockwall County

(G-17714)
A SIGN OF QUALITY LLC
5707 State Highway 276 (75189-5747)
PHONE....................................972 722-4147
Jay Griner, *Mng Member*
Pam Griner,
EMP: 11
SQ FT: 4,000
SALES (est): 1.6MM **Privately Held**
WEB: www.asoq.com
SIC: 3993 Signs & advertising specialties

(G-17715)
BLAKO
1103 Walnut St (75189-2306)
PHONE....................................972 898-7772
Blair C Johnson, *President*
EMP: 11
SQ FT: 3,500
SALES (est): 250K **Privately Held**
SIC: 3645 3646 Residential lighting fixtures; commercial indusl & institutional electric lighting fixtures

(G-17716)
BROWN DIE CASTING & MFG INC
1209 Industrial Park Dr (75189)
P.O. Box 1179 (75189-1179)
PHONE....................................972 636-9575
Michael G Brown, *President*
EMP: 50
SQ FT: 20,000
SALES (est): 8MM **Privately Held**
WEB: www.bdcinc.com
SIC: 3363 Aluminum die-castings

(G-17717)
CAMERON KNIGHT
Also Called: Architechtual Design Mfg
9494 State Highway 276 (75189-6300)
PHONE....................................972 636-7172
Cameron Knight, *Owner*
Cameron R Knight, *Owner*
Kirk Knight, *Co-Owner*
EMP: 10
SQ FT: 8,000
SALES (est): 1MM **Privately Held**
WEB: www.architecturaldesigns.us
SIC: 2511 2434 Wood household furniture; vanities, bathroom: wood

(G-17718)
CAZAD INDUSTRIES INC
160 County Road 979 (75189-7730)
PHONE....................................972 635-2100
EMP: 16
SALES: 1.5MM **Privately Held**
SIC: 3599 Machine Shop

(G-17719)
DUST FREE LP
1112 Industrial Dr (75189-5407)
P.O. Box 519 (75189-0519)
PHONE....................................972 635-9565
Gregg Burnett, *Partner*
Jane L Burnett, *Partner*
Heather Burnett, *General Mgr*
Heather Pulis, *Engineer*
Josh Pulis, *Sales Staff*
▲ EMP: 45
SQ FT: 32,000
SALES (est): 19.2MM **Privately Held**
WEB: www.dustfree.com
SIC: 3564 Filters, air: furnaces, air conditioning equipment, etc.; air cleaning systems

(G-17720)
JTM TECHNOLOGIES INC
160 County Road 979 (75189-7730)
PHONE....................................972 635-6900
Keisha Joyce, *CEO*
James Joyce, *President*
Tammy Boughner, *Sales Mgr*
John Joyce, *Director*
▲ EMP: 15
SQ FT: 20,000
SALES (est): 2.6MM **Privately Held**
WEB: www.jtmtechnologies.com
SIC: 3674 Semiconductors & related devices

(G-17721)
K & K CHEMICAL COMPANY INC
1303 Industrial Dr (75189-5415)
P.O. Box 6434, McKinney (75071-5111)
PHONE....................................972 635-2482
Ken Kendall, *President*
Doug Charlton, *General Mgr*
◆ EMP: 28
SQ FT: 20,000
SALES (est): 5.5MM **Privately Held**
WEB: www.knkclean.com
SIC: 2819 5169 2842 Industrial inorganic chemicals; chemicals & allied products; specialty cleaning, polishes & sanitation goods

(G-17722)
POLAR CORPORATION
Also Called: Quality Running Gear
1012 Industrial Dr (75189-5401)
PHONE....................................972 635-2464
EMP: 77
SQ FT: 60,000
SALES: 9MM
SALES (corp-wide): 2.6B **Privately Held**
SIC: 3714 Axles, motor vehicle
HQ: Quality Trailer Products, Lp
604 W Main St
Azle TX 76020
817 444-4518

(G-17723)
PRECISION IRON FABRICATION LLC
Also Called: Precision Welding & Iron
1215 Industrial Dr (75189-5403)
P.O. Box 1289 (75189-1289)
PHONE....................................972 636-7581
Danny Edwards, *Owner*
David H Portnoy, *Mng Member*
EMP: 13
SALES (est): 1.3MM **Privately Held**
SIC: 7692 Welding repair

(G-17724)
PURSUIT SAFETY INC
4947 State Highway 276 (75189-5731)
PHONE....................................972 772-4747
Tony Edgemon, *President*
EMP: 12
SQ FT: 6,000
SALES (est): 1.1MM **Privately Held**
WEB: www.pursuitsafety.com
SIC: 3711 Patrol wagons (motor vehicles), assembly of

(G-17725)
RALPH CORDOVA COMPANY
131 Mark Ln (75189-5723)
P.O. Box 871 (75189-0871)
PHONE....................................972 771-7281
Ralph Cordova, *President*
Hilda Paredes, *Admin Asst*
EMP: 20
SALES (est): 1MM **Privately Held**
WEB: www.ralphcordovacompany.com
SIC: 3088 3281 5032 Plastics plumbing fixtures; cut stone & stone products; brick, stone & related material

(G-17726)
TEXAS MEDICAL INDUSTRIES INC
Also Called: Saf Evac
1409 Industrial Dr (75189-5405)
PHONE.....................972 636-9556
Susan Chambers, *President*
Danielle Robertson, *Manager*
EMP: 30
SQ FT: 38,000
SALES (est): 4.3MM **Privately Held**
WEB: www.tmiunited.com
SIC: 3842 Orthopedic appliances; traction apparatus

(G-17727)
USA MACHINE INC
2503 Circle Dr (75189-8556)
PHONE.....................972 636-7400
Jarrod Urban, *President*
Shelly Urban, *Vice Pres*
Dianna Woodruff, *Vice Pres*
EMP: 24
SQ FT: 26,000
SALES (est): 4.4MM **Privately Held**
WEB: www.usamachine.net
SIC: 3599 3444 3544 Machine shop, jobbing & repair; sheet metalwork; special dies & tools

Rule
Haskell County

(G-17728)
MATHIS & SON INC
Also Called: Mathis & Son Well Service
307 Amity Ave (79547-2022)
PHONE.....................940 997-2137
Terry Joe Mathis, *President*
Carolyn Mathis, *Treasurer*
EMP: 11
SALES (est): 993.9K **Privately Held**
WEB: www.mathisandsonsinc.com
SIC: 1389 Oil field services

Runge
Karnes County

(G-17729)
GISLER BROTHERS LOGGING CO
106 E Main St (78151)
P.O. Box 485 (78151-0485)
PHONE.....................830 239-4651
Mike Gisler, *President*
Richard Gisler, *Vice Pres*
Alfreda Gisler, *Treasurer*
EMP: 40
SQ FT: 6,000
SALES (est): 475K **Privately Held**
WEB: www.gislerbrotherslogging.com
SIC: 1389 Oil field services

Rusk
Cherokee County

(G-17730)
EASTEX FARMS
1975 County Road 1605 (75785-3654)
PHONE.....................903 683-5726
Bill Bradshaw, *Owner*
EMP: 40
SQ FT: 1,000
SALES (est): 2.7MM **Privately Held**
SIC: 2035 0171 Pickled fruits & vegetables; berry crops

(G-17731)
HUDSON BROTHERS MINING COMPANY
505 S Main St (75785-1344)
PHONE.....................903 876-4642
Comer H Hudson, *President*
Annette Kimbrell, *Corp Secy*
Nelda Hudson, *Vice Pres*
EMP: 13 EST: 1953
SQ FT: 1,800

SALES (est): 685.1K **Privately Held**
SIC: 1011 1629 1311 Iron ore mining; earthmoving contractor; crude petroleum production; natural gas production

(G-17732)
JAN PATE INC
120 Birmingham Forest Dr (75785-1452)
PHONE.....................903 683-5700
Jan E Pate, *President*
EMP: 10
SALES (est): 1.8MM **Privately Held**
SIC: 2411 5251 Logging camps & contractors; hardware

(G-17733)
WALLACE-THOMPSON COMPANY
Also Called: Funeral Home
514 Henderson St (75785)
PHONE.....................903 683-2223
James Thompson Sr, *Principal*
EMP: 15
SALES (corp-wide): 6.5MM **Privately Held**
WEB: www.wallacethompson.com
SIC: 3429 Manufactured hardware (general)
PA: Wallace-Thompson Company
   221 W 5th St
   Rusk TX 75785
   903 683-2222

Sachse
Dallas County

(G-17734)
RHINO RUSH 3GS LLC
7115 Lake Hill Trl (75048-5632)
PHONE.....................817 793-9400
Jesse McMullen, *General Mgr*
Nita Shinsky, *Director*
EMP: 15
SALES (est): 581.4K **Privately Held**
SIC: 2086 Carbonated beverages, nonalcoholic: bottled & canned

Saginaw
Tarrant County

(G-17735)
2ND CHANCE PALLETS LLC
213 E Mcleroy Blvd (76136)
P.O. Box 137087, Fort Worth (76136-1087)
PHONE.....................817 847-8005
Eric S George, *Mng Member*
EMP: 13 EST: 2013
SALES (est): 1.6MM **Privately Held**
WEB: www.2cpllc.com
SIC: 2448 4215 Pallets, wood; motorcycle delivery service

(G-17736)
ARCHER-DANIELS-MIDLAND COMPANY
Also Called: ADM
425 Fairmount St (76179-1608)
P.O. Box 79440, Fort Worth (76179-0440)
PHONE.....................817 917-2810
Chris Faust, *President*
Julie Leon, *Buyer*
EMP: 23
SALES (corp-wide): 64.6B **Publicly Held**
WEB: www.adm.com
SIC: 2041 Flour & other grain mill products
PA: Archer-Daniels-Midland Company
   77 W Wacker Dr Ste 4600
   Chicago IL 60601
   312 634-8100

(G-17737)
ARDENT MILLS LLC
Also Called: Flour Milling Division
401 E Industrial Ave (76131-2710)
P.O. Box 79370, Fort Worth (76179-0370)
PHONE.....................817 847-3400
Paul Wiest, *General Mgr*
Ruben Villalobos, *Engineer*
Greg Handy, *Human Resources*
Tj Tuetken, *Maintence Staff*
EMP: 100

SALES (corp-wide): 634.7MM **Privately Held**
WEB: www.ardentmills.com
SIC: 2041 1629 2099 Flour; railroad & subway construction; food preparations
PA: Ardent Mills, Llc
   1875 Lawrence St Ste 1400
   Denver CO 80202
   800 851-9618

(G-17738)
AVOMEX INC (HQ)
Also Called: Fresherized Foods
300 Burlington Rd (76179-1304)
PHONE.....................817 509-0626
Jeff Frank, *CEO*
Tracey Altman, *Vice Pres*
Ryan Michaelis, *Vice Pres*
Jeff Morris, *Vice Pres*
Gene Novak, *Warehouse Mgr*
◆ EMP: 50
SQ FT: 55,000
SALES (est): 14.4MM **Privately Held**
WEB: www.megamexfoodservice.com
SIC: 2035 Pickles, sauces & salad dressings

(G-17739)
BANA INC (PA)
Also Called: Bana Box
624 E Mcleroy Blvd (76179-4603)
P.O. Box 79290 (76179-0290)
PHONE.....................817 232-3750
David R Boenker, *President*
Beau Boenker, *Vice Pres*
Gregory T Boenker, *Vice Pres*
Angela Dill, *Vice Pres*
Linda D Wansing, *Vice Pres*
▲ EMP: 120
SQ FT: 175,000
SALES (est): 77.1MM **Privately Held**
WEB: www.banabox.com
SIC: 5085 2441 2448 Packing, industrial; boxes, wood; wood pallets & skids

(G-17740)
BOWLIN ENGINEERING CO
Also Called: Leland Southwest
600 Burlington Rd (76179-1310)
PHONE.....................817 232-2020
Bob P Bowlin, *President*
Loene Bowlin, *Treasurer*
EMP: 12 EST: 1967
SQ FT: 20,000
SALES (est): 3.1MM **Privately Held**
WEB: www.bowlinengineering.com
SIC: 3535 8711 Conveyors & conveying equipment; consulting engineer

(G-17741)
CFJ MANUFACTURING LP
Also Called: Collections Fine Jewelry
708 S Saginaw Blvd (76179-2109)
PHONE.....................817 232-9251
Kimberly Sissen, *Branch Mgr*
EMP: 77
SALES (corp-wide): 18.2MM **Privately Held**
WEB: www.cfjmanufacturinglp.com
SIC: 3911 3993 5094 5199 Jewelry, precious metal; signs & advertising specialties; jewelry; advertising specialties; jewelry, precious stones & precious metals
PA: Cfj Manufacturing, L.P.
   701 Eight Twenty Blvd # 145
   Fort Worth TX 76106
   817 625-9559

(G-17742)
CHM INDUSTRIES INC
Also Called: Chm Sports Lighting
700 E Mcleroy Blvd Ste A (76179-4628)
PHONE.....................682 286-0046
Thomas Ginsburg, *President*
Scott Engberg, *Vice Pres*
Ed Floyd, *Purch Mgr*
▲ EMP: 15
SQ FT: 9,000
SALES (est): 11MM **Privately Held**
WEB: www.chmindustries.com
SIC: 3644 Pole line hardware

(G-17743)
CTI ARLINGTON LLC
Also Called: CTI Foods
504 Sansom Blvd (76179-4622)
PHONE.....................817 869-1090
Misty Ramos, *Business Mgr*
Brad Brigham, *Vice Pres*
Bob Chudy, *Vice Pres*
Rajan Nagarajan, *Vice Pres*
Victor Gallardo, *Prdtn Mgr*
EMP: 200
SQ FT: 65,000
SALES (est): 50.4MM
SALES (corp-wide): 972MM **Privately Held**
WEB: www.ctifoods.com
SIC: 2032 Soups & broths: canned, jarred, etc.
HQ: Cti Foods, Llc
   22303 Highway 95
   Wilder ID 83676
   208 482-7844

(G-17744)
CTI SAGINAW I LLC
Also Called: Southwest Beanmakers
504 Sansom Blvd (76179-4622)
PHONE.....................817 869-1090
Robert Horowitz, *CEO*
Derick Glossup, *Accountant*
EMP: 100
SALES (est): 19.6MM
SALES (corp-wide): 972MM **Privately Held**
WEB: www.ctifoods.com
SIC: 2013 Sausages & other prepared meats
HQ: Cti Foods, Llc
   22303 Highway 95
   Wilder ID 83676
   208 482-7844

(G-17745)
D/FW PLASTICS INC
Also Called: Dfw Rotec
901 E Industrial Ave (76131-2715)
P.O. Box 648, Bedford (76095-0648)
PHONE.....................817 439-3600
Robert McKinnon, *President*
Carroll McKinnon, *President*
Bob McKinnon, *Vice Pres*
Thomas McKinnon, *Vice Pres*
James McKinnon, *Treasurer*
EMP: 18
SQ FT: 17,000
SALES (est): 4.7MM **Privately Held**
WEB: www.dfwplasticsinc.com
SIC: 3089 Fittings for pipe, plastic

(G-17746)
HOLLOWAY COMPANY INC (PA)
1200 Jarvis Rd (76179-5611)
P.O. Box 79577, Fort Worth (76179-0577)
PHONE.....................817 232-8663
Lynton Holloway, *President*
M Eugene Holloway, *Chairman*
Patricia J Holloway, *Corp Secy*
Terry Brown, *Vice Pres*
EMP: 32
SQ FT: 2,000
SALES (est): 5.4MM **Privately Held**
WEB: www.hollowaycompanyinc.com
SIC: 1791 3443 Storage tanks, metal: erection; tanks, standard or custom fabricated: metal plate

(G-17747)
L S W MFG INC
Also Called: Leland Southwest
600 Burlington Rd (76179-1310)
PHONE.....................817 232-4482
Bob P Bowlin, *President*
EMP: 15
SQ FT: 1,000
SALES (est): 3MM **Privately Held**
WEB: www.lelandsouthwest.com
SIC: 3556 Meat processing machinery; dough mixing machinery
PA: Saginaw Machine Company
   600 Burlington Rd
   Saginaw TX 76179

(G-17748)
LIGHTNING OILFIELD SVCS INC (PA)
11830 N Saginaw Blvd (76179)
P.O. Box 203, Haslet (76052-0203)
PHONE..........................817 439-5558
Mark S Waddell, *President*
Matt Riley, *Superintendent*
EMP: 52 EST: 2008
SALES (est): 25.7MM **Privately Held**
WEB: www.lightningos.com
SIC: 1389 Oil field services

(G-17749)
LONESTAR PIPE FABRICATION INC
211 Sansom Blvd (76179-4624)
P.O. Box 79230, Fort Worth (76179-0230)
PHONE..........................817 439-5575
Robert Jarvis, *President*
Steve Mackrodt, *President*
Steven M Machenrodt, *COO*
Tammy Mackenrodt, *Vice Pres*
EMP: 12
SALES (est): 7.5MM **Privately Held**
WEB: www.lonestarpipe.com
SIC: 3498 Tube fabricating (contract bending & shaping)

(G-17750)
METAL SPINNERS INC
1300 E Industrial Ave (76131-2709)
PHONE..........................817 847-0086
EMP: 24
SALES (corp-wide): 39.7MM **Privately Held**
WEB: www.samuel.com
SIC: 3441 Fabricated structural metal
PA: Metal Spinners, Inc.
914 Wohlert St
Angola IN 46703
260 665-2158

(G-17751)
MILLER MILLING COMPANY LLC
221 Fairmount St (76179-1604)
PHONE..........................817 847-8977
Hollis South, *Production*
Doug Olson, *Branch Mgr*
Melody Farahani, *Manager*
EMP: 36 **Privately Held**
WEB: www.millermilling.com
SIC: 2041 Flour & other grain mill products
HQ: Miller Milling Company, Llc
7808 Creekridge Cir # 100
Minneapolis MN 55439
952 826-6331

(G-17752)
NORTHWEST PIPE COMPANY
509 Burlington Rd (76179-1309)
PHONE..........................817 847-1402
Mark Woolsey, *Manager*
EMP: 40
SALES (corp-wide): 279.3MM **Publicly Held**
WEB: www.nwpipe.com
SIC: 3317 Pipes, wrought: welded, lock joint or heavy riveted
PA: Northwest Pipe Company
201 Ne Park Plaza Dr # 100
Vancouver WA 98684
360 397-6250

(G-17753)
NORTHWEST PIPE COMPANY
351 Longhorn Rd (76179-2404)
PHONE..........................817 847-1402
John Peterson, *Manager*
EMP: 100
SQ FT: 102,225
SALES (corp-wide): 279.3MM **Publicly Held**
WEB: www.nwpipe.com
SIC: 3432 3498 3312 Plumbing fixture fittings & trim; fabricated pipe & fittings; blast furnaces & steel mills
PA: Northwest Pipe Company
201 Ne Park Plaza Dr # 100
Vancouver WA 98684
360 397-6250

(G-17754)
PARKER-HANNIFIN CORPORATION
Also Called: Commercial Metal Forming
304 E Mcleroy Blvd (76179-4600)
PHONE..........................817 232-1040
Wayne Churlik, *Branch Mgr*
Jerome Wurst, *Manager*
EMP: 41
SALES (corp-wide): 13.7B **Publicly Held**
WEB: www.phtruck.com
SIC: 3443 4225 3444 3441 Tanks, lined: metal plate; general warehousing & storage; sheet metalwork; fabricated structural metal; blast furnaces & steel mills
PA: Parker-Hannifin Corporation
6035 Parkland Blvd
Cleveland OH 44124
216 896-3000

(G-17755)
RSG PRODUCTS INC
Also Called: Integrated Flight Systems
440 West Ln Ste 100 (76131-2146)
PHONE..........................817 624-6600
Ed Boldan, *President*
Daniel Dross, *Chairman*
EMP: 20
SQ FT: 38,000
SALES (est): 4MM **Privately Held**
WEB: www.rotorcraftservices.com
SIC: 3728 Aircraft parts & equipment
PA: Ranger Rotorcraft Group, Inc.
128 Millport Cir Ste 200
Greenville SC 29607

(G-17756)
SAGINAW MACHINE COMPANY (PA)
Also Called: Leland Southwest
600 Burlington Rd (76179-1310)
P.O. Box 79400 (76179-0400)
PHONE..........................817 232-4482
Paul Bowlin, *President*
EMP: 15
SQ FT: 20,000
SALES (est): 3MM **Privately Held**
WEB: www.lelandsouthwest.com
SIC: 3556 Food products machinery

(G-17757)
STYROCHEM CANADA
Also Called: Styrochem International
400 Minton Rd (76179-5609)
PHONE..........................817 847-8254
David Sands, *Branch Mgr*
EMP: 12
SALES (corp-wide): 21.3MM **Privately Held**
WEB: www.styrochem.com
SIC: 2821 Plastics foam products
PA: Styrochem Canada Ltd
19250 Av Clark-Graham
Baie-D'urfe QC H9X 3
514 457-3226

(G-17758)
VENTURA FOODS LLC
1100 Defiel Rd (76179-5699)
PHONE..........................817 232-5450
Vinced Vincent, *President*
Enri Bautista, *Research*
Greg Stuhler, *Director*
EMP: 89 **Privately Held**
WEB: www.venturafoods.com
SIC: 2079 2077 Edible fats & oils; animal & marine fats & oils
PA: Ventura Foods, Llc
40 Pointe Dr
Brea CA 92821

(G-17759)
WESTERN MARKETING INC
816 S Blue Mound Rd (76131-1023)
PHONE..........................817 232-8626
EMP: 9 **Privately Held**
WEB: www.reladyne.com
SIC: 2992 1382 Brake fluid (hydraulic): made from purchased materials; oil & gas exploration services
HQ: Western Marketing, Inc.
1010 S Access Rd
Tye TX 79563
800 588-4662

(G-17760)
WILLOW CREEK SIGNS INC
213 E Mcleroy Blvd (76179-1649)
P.O. Box 79326, Fort Worth (76179-0326)
PHONE..........................817 847-0571
David Flory, *President*
Thomas E Dennis III, *Vice Pres*
Cookie Cruz, *Manager*
EMP: 30
SALES (est): 1MM **Privately Held**
WEB: www.willowcreeksigns.com
SIC: 7389 1799 3993 Sign painting & lettering shop; sign installation & maintenance; signs & advertising specialties

Saint Hedwig
Bexar County

(G-17761)
ZAMO INC
Also Called: Concepts In Cabinetry
16102 E Lupon Rd (78152-3619)
PHONE..........................210 667-1717
Roy Zaiontz, *President*
Almira Zaiontz, *Treasurer*
EMP: 35
SQ FT: 22,000
SALES (est): 4.8MM **Privately Held**
WEB: www.conceptsincabinetry.com
SIC: 2434 2431 Wood kitchen cabinets; millwork

Saint Jo
Montague County

(G-17762)
BLUE OSTRICH WINERIES LLC
5611 Fm 2382 (76265-2582)
P.O. Box 119 (76265-0119)
PHONE..........................940 995-3100
Julie Whithead, *Managing Prtnr*
Patrick Whitehead, *Partner*
EMP: 11 EST: 2011
SALES (est): 1.6MM **Privately Held**
WEB: www.blueostrich.net
SIC: 2084 Wines

(G-17763)
JR THOMPSON INC
450 Rock Quarry Rd (76265-3001)
PHONE..........................940 995-2245
Johnny Thompson, *President*
EMP: 15
SALES (est): 846.8K **Privately Held**
SIC: 1422 Asphalt plant, including gravel-mix type

Salado
Bell County

(G-17764)
C&D ALLBRITTON HOLDINGS INC (PA)
14019 Blackberry Rd (76571-5406)
P.O. Box 1161 (76571-1161)
PHONE..........................833 227-2243
Damon Fogel, *CEO*
David Allbritton, *President*
EMP: 28
SALES (est): 6.1MM **Privately Held**
WEB: www.apache-stone.com
SIC: 3253 4213 Quarry tile, clay; trucking, except local

(G-17765)
KAMICO INSTRUCTIONAL MEDIA INC
4477 Fm 2843 (76571-5145)
P.O. Box 1143 (76571-1143)
PHONE..........................254 947-7283
Kathy Michael, *President*
EMP: 20
SALES (est): 2.7MM **Privately Held**
WEB: www.kamico.com
SIC: 2731 7372 8748 Textbooks: publishing only, not printed on site; textbooks: publishing & printing; educational computer software; educational consultant

Saltillo
Hopkins County

(G-17766)
MK PALLETS INC
12525 Interstate Hwy 30 E (75478-4422)
PHONE..........................903 537-2400
Michael Bangs, *President*
Keri Bangs, *Admin Sec*
EMP: 12 EST: 2014
SALES (est): 1MM **Privately Held**
WEB: www.mkpallets.com
SIC: 2448 Pallets, wood; pallets, wood & wood with metal

San Angelo
Tom Green County

(G-17767)
2V LED LLC
Also Called: Principal Led
3490 Venture Dr (76905-8534)
PHONE..........................325 227-4577
Jim Shaw, *COO*
Daryl Foreman, *Vice Pres*
Jerry Green, *VP Opers*
Todd REA, *Opers Mgr*
Derek Hopper, *Engineer*
▲ EMP: 85
SQ FT: 10,000
SALES: 30.1MM **Privately Held**
WEB: www.p-led.com
SIC: 3645 Residential lighting fixtures

(G-17768)
7 S PACKING LLC
Also Called: Texas Packing
1809 N Bell St (76903-3459)
PHONE..........................325 716-4047
Dean Yorton, *Mng Member*
Kristen Yorton, *Mng Member*
Jeremy Robinson,
EMP: 300 EST: 2013
SALES (est): 30MM **Privately Held**
WEB: www.texas-packing.com
SIC: 2011 Meat packing plants

(G-17769)
AB-TEX BEVERAGE LTD
Also Called: Pepsico
1023 Foster St (76903-8912)
PHONE..........................325 655-9588
Tim Gregory, *Sales & Mktg St*
Ryan Pina, *Sales Staff*
EMP: 40
SALES (corp-wide): 67.1B **Publicly Held**
WEB: www.pepsico.com
SIC: 2086 Carbonated soft drinks, bottled & canned
HQ: Ab-Tex Beverage, Ltd.
650 Colonial Dr
Abilene TX 79603
325 673-7171

(G-17770)
ACME BRICK COMPANY
4012 Arden Rd (76901-2606)
PHONE..........................325 949-7685
Brian Underwood, *Purch Mgr*
EMP: 81
SALES (corp-wide): 254.6B **Publicly Held**
WEB: www.brick.com
SIC: 3251 5032 5719 5211 Structural brick & blocks; brick, except refractory; fireplace equipment & accessories; brick
HQ: Acme Brick Company
3024 Acme Brick Plz
Fort Worth TX 76109

(G-17771)
AERMOTOR COMPANY
4277 Dan Hanks Ln (76904-2230)
P.O. Box 5110 (76902-5110)
PHONE..........................325 651-4951
Guy Morrow, *CEO*
▼ EMP: 24
SQ FT: 40,000
SALES (est): 5.6MM **Privately Held**
WEB: www.aermotorwindmill.com
SIC: 3523 Windmills for pumping water, agricultural

▲ = Import ▼=Export
◆ =Import/Export

(G-17772)
AIRWAY SERVICES INC
5001 Christoval Rd (76904-9622)
P.O. Box 60188 (76906-0188)
PHONE.....................................325 617-5813
Chase Hord, *CEO*
Tim Colliers, *President*
Charles Brooks, *Vice Pres*
Jonathan Click, *Vice Pres*
Ricky Corona, *Opers Mgr*
EMP: 150 **EST:** 2009
SQ FT: 2,600
SALES (est): 20MM **Privately Held**
WEB: www.airwayservicesinc.com
SIC: 3511 Hydraulic turbines

(G-17773)
ALL AMERICAN PUMP & MCH INC
1310 N Bell St (76903-3333)
PHONE.....................................325 653-6597
E J Bible, *President*
EMP: 10
SQ FT: 3,500
SALES (est): 860K **Privately Held**
WEB:
www.allamericanpumpandmachine.com
SIC: 7699 5251 5063 7629 Pumps &
pumping equipment repair; pumps &
pumping equipment; motors, electric;
electrical repair shops; rewinding services

(G-17774)
ALNC INC
2152 Fm Hwy 2105 (76902)
P.O. Box 669 (76902-0669)
PHONE.....................................325 658-3612
Kristin J Barta, *President*
Clint Barta, *Vice Pres*
EMP: 68
SQ FT: 10,000
SALES (est): 24MM **Privately Held**
WEB: www.alncsteelinc.com
SIC: 3441 Fabricated structural metal

(G-17775)
ALY CENTRIFUGE INC
5039 N Chadbourne St (76903-1333)
PHONE.....................................972 382-4400
EMP: 17
SALES (est): 1.2MM **Publicly Held**
SIC: 1381 Drilling Oil And Gas Wells
PA: Aly Energy Services, Inc.
3 Riverway Ste 920
Houston TX 77056

(G-17776)
ANGELO BOLT AND INDUS SUP INC
808 Warehouse Rd (76903-9323)
P.O. Box 61593 (76906-1593)
PHONE.....................................325 655-0075
Stephen J Fischer, *President*
Pete Fischer, *Vice Pres*
Kevin Okerstrom, *Sales Staff*
Beverly Fische, *Admin Sec*
EMP: 35
SQ FT: 10,000
SALES (est): 4MM **Privately Held**
WEB: www.angelobolt.com
SIC: 5251 5072 5085 3563 Builders'
hardware; hardware; miscellaneous fasteners; bolts; nuts (hardware); abrasives
& adhesives; air & gas compressors;
chemicals & allied products

(G-17777)
ANGELO PELLETS INC (PA)
Also Called: Angelo Pellets Feed Mill
1111 N Bell St (76903-3328)
P.O. Box 1876 (76902-1876)
PHONE.....................................325 655-5751
Tom Latham, *President*
Cody Cauley, *Vice Pres*
Vicki Latham, *Vice Pres*
EMP: 12 **EST:** 1963
SQ FT: 24,000
SALES (est): 2.2MM **Privately Held**
WEB: www.angelopellets.com
SIC: 2048 5083 Livestock feeds; farm &
garden machinery

(G-17778)
ARMANDO G MARTINEZ (PA)
Also Called: Mrs Rios Corn Products
215 W Avenue N (76903-8434)
PHONE.....................................325 653-5640
Armando G Martinez, *Owner*
EMP: 34
SQ FT: 26,000
SALES (est): 4.9MM **Privately Held**
WEB: www.mrsriostortilleria.com
SIC: 2099 6411 Tortillas, fresh or refrigerated; insurance agents, brokers & service

(G-17779)
ASSOCIATED PUBLISHING COMPANY
Also Called: Area Wide Phonebook
2825 Sherwood Way (76901-3513)
PHONE.....................................325 949-1910
Denny Fulks, *Manager*
EMP: 15
SALES (corp-wide): 7.9B **Privately Held**
SIC: 2741 Telephone & other directory
publishing
HQ: Associated Publishing Company, Inc
61 John Muir Dr
Buffalo NY 14228

(G-17780)
BEAVER GRAPHIX LLC
4722 Karsten Creek Dr (76904-1559)
PHONE.....................................325 227-3014
Wayne Paugh, *EMP:* 12
SALES (est): 474.9K **Privately Held**
SIC: 5136 5699 3552 Shirts, men's &
boys'; T-shirts, custom printed; silk
screens for textile industry

(G-17781)
BIG STAR LLC
4774 N Chadbourne St (76903-1328)
PHONE.....................................325 617-5731
James Wilson, *Mng Member*
Jessica Flint, *Agent*
EMP: 25
SALES (est): 691.5K **Privately Held**
SIC: 1389 Oil field services

(G-17782)
BLUE LINE DRILLING CO LLC
2102 Pecos St Ste 9 (76901-3061)
P.O. Box 3158 (76902-3158)
PHONE.....................................325 653-1891
Denise McDonald, *CFO*
Logan McDonald, *Human Res Mgr*
James R Phillips, *Mng Member*
Jerry D McDonald,
EMP: 75 **EST:** 2009
SQ FT: 800
SALES (est): 11.6MM **Privately Held**
WEB: www.bluelinedrilling.com
SIC: 1381 Directional drilling oil & gas
wells

(G-17783)
BOF SERVICES INC
2539 W Fm 2105 (76901-5410)
PHONE.....................................325 653-1755
EMP: 48
SALES (corp-wide): 14.7MM **Privately Held**
SIC: 1389 Oil/Gas Field Services
PA: B.O.F. Services, Inc.
2416 Erskine St
Lubbock TX 79415
806 741-1080

(G-17784)
BOLLMAN INDUSTRIES INC
928 Hughes St (76903-3315)
P.O. Box 1351 (76902-1351)
PHONE.....................................325 655-0112
Ladd Hughes, *Manager*
EMP: 40
SALES (corp-wide): 241.2MM **Privately Held**
WEB: www.bollmanhats.com
SIC: 2299 5199 2353 Scouring: wool, mohair & similar fibers; woolen & worsted
yarns; hats, caps & millinery
HQ: Bollman Industries Inc
110 E Main St
Adamstown PA 19501

(G-17785)
BORDER STATES INDUSTRIES INC
Simmons-Hggins A Div Brder Stt
425 Mrtin Lther King Blvd (76903-5763)
PHONE.....................................325 655-9163
Scott Dugger, *Branch Mgr*
EMP: 15
SALES (corp-wide): 2.4B **Privately Held**
WEB: www.borderstates.com
SIC: 5063 5065 5074 1711 Electrical
supplies; electronic parts & equipment;
plumbing & hydronic heating supplies;
plumbing, heating, air-conditioning contractors; plastics plumbing fixtures; vitreous plumbing fixtures
PA: Border States Industries, Inc.
2400 38th St S
Fargo ND 58104
701 293-5834

(G-17786)
BP SURFACE SOLUTIONS LLC
Also Called: Dorado Construction Group
424 S Chadbourne St (76903-6926)
P.O. Box 61791 (76906-1791)
PHONE.....................................325 387-3881
Clyde Butler, *COO*
Bryce Leggett, *CFO*
Casey Poynor, *Mng Member*
Marcus Fuchs, *Manager*
Shawn Poynor, *Director*
EMP: 83
SQ FT: 10,000
SALES (est): 13.7MM **Privately Held**
WEB: www.doradoconstructiongroup.com
SIC: 1389 1622 Construction, repair & dismantling services; tunnel construction

(G-17787)
CLEERECO SERVICES INC
14 E Beauregard Ave (76903-5885)
P.O. Box 5891 (76902-5891)
PHONE.....................................325 658-6533
Kirk Cleere, *President*
EMP: 10
SALES (est): 950K **Privately Held**
SIC: 1321 Propane (natural) production

(G-17788)
COMPANY PRINTING
3419 Knickerbocker Rd (76904-6816)
PHONE.....................................325 949-9941
Laurence Lasater, *Owner*
Mark Harrington, *General Mgr*
Rebecca Farley, *Graphic Designe*
EMP: 12
SALES (est): 1.4MM **Privately Held**
WEB: www.companyprinting.com
SIC: 5943 5099 2759 7331 Office forms
& supplies; signs, except electric; invitations: printing; mailing service; bookbinding & related work; commercial printing,
lithographic

(G-17789)
CONCHO BUSINESS SOLUTIONS INC
3302 Foster St (76903-9314)
PHONE.....................................325 653-1697
Marva Stephens, *President*
Roger Stephens, *Vice Pres*
EMP: 32
SQ FT: 6,000
SALES (est): 3MM **Privately Held**
WEB: www.longhornop.com
SIC: 5943 5712 2752 Office forms & supplies; office furniture; commercial printing,
offset

(G-17790)
CONCHO CONCRETE COMPANY INC
1040 Foster St (76903-8999)
PHONE.....................................325 653-3354
Jerry B Fraley, *Ch of Bd*
EMP: 31 **EST:** 1964
SALES (est): 3.8MM **Privately Held**
SIC: 3273 Ready-mixed concrete

(G-17791)
COVERLAY MANUFACTURING INC
4017 N Us Highway 67 (76905-4602)
PHONE.....................................325 659-4697
Paul Cornwall, *President*
Richard Thornesberry, *Corp Secy*
EMP: 30
SQ FT: 40,000
SALES (est): 4.2MM **Privately Held**
WEB: www.coverlaymfg.com
SIC: 3089 3083 Automotive parts, plastic;
laminated plastics plate & sheet

(G-17792)
CREATIVE SIGNWORKS INC
6861 S Us Highway 277 (76904-4109)
P.O. Box 3124 (76902-3124)
PHONE.....................................850 785-8899
Craig Nichols, *President*
Marsha Nichols, *Vice Pres*
EMP: 25
SQ FT: 17,000
SALES (est): 1.3MM **Privately Held**
SIC: 3993 7389 2396 5099 Signs, not
made in custom sign painting shops; sign
painting & lettering shop; automotive &
apparel trimmings; signs, except electric;
screen printing; sign installation & maintenance

(G-17793)
CSA MATERIALS INC
3001 Foster St (76903-9216)
P.O. Box 60693 (76906-0693)
PHONE.....................................325 655-4511
Jack Albert, *Ch of Bd*
Terrence Albert, *Exec VP*
EMP: 60
SQ FT: 30,000
SALES (est): 13.5MM **Privately Held**
WEB: www.csamaterials.com
SIC: 5032 2951 Asphalt mixture; paving
mixtures; asphalt & asphaltic paving mixtures (not from refineries)

(G-17794)
CUSTOM SKIN CO INC
2800 N Bell St (76903-3440)
PHONE.....................................325 655-9585
Bill J Cole, *President*
Sue Cole, *Corp Secy*
James Cole, *Vice Pres*
Vicki Lockwood, *Manager*
▼ **EMP:** 15 **EST:** 1970
SQ FT: 95,000
SALES (est): 1.5MM **Privately Held**
SIC: 3111 0752 Leather processing; animal specialty services

(G-17795)
DLH WENDLAND LLC
601 W 11th St (76903-5271)
P.O. Box 808 (76902-0808)
PHONE.....................................325 655-6778
David Hirschfeld, *Mng Member*
EMP: 24
SQ FT: 2,000
SALES (est): 3.6MM **Privately Held**
WEB: www.wendlandmfg.com
SIC: 3443 Tanks, standard or custom fabricated: metal plate

(G-17796)
DOUBLE BARREL FABRICATION INC
4605 Krupala Rd (76905-7412)
P.O. Box 60993 (76906-0993)
PHONE.....................................512 496-7448
Sam Janca, *President*
EMP: 11
SALES (est): 1.8MM **Privately Held**
WEB: www.doublebarrelfabrication.com
SIC: 3499 Fabricated metal products

(G-17797)
ETHICON INC
Ethicon Endo - Surgery
3348 Pulliam St (76905-4403)
PHONE.....................................325 482-5200
Adrian Ahmadi, *Opers Mgr*
Rudy Rodriguez, *Opers-Prdtn-Mfg*
Darryl Findley, *Sales Staff*
Jim Wescott, *Sales Staff*
EMP: 225
SALES (corp-wide): 82B **Publicly Held**
WEB: www.jnjmedicaldevices.com
SIC: 3842 Ligatures, medical

HQ: Ethicon Inc.
Us Route 22
Somerville NJ 08876
732 524-0400

(G-17798)
EW SCRIPPS COMPANY
Also Called: San Angelo Standard Times
34 W Harris Ave (76903-5838)
P.O. Box 511 (76902-0511)
PHONE..................................325 659-8200
EMP: 180
SALES (corp-wide): 715.6MM **Publicly Held**
SIC: 2711 Newspapers
PA: The E W Scripps Company
312 Walnut St Ste 2800
Cincinnati OH 45202
513 977-3000

(G-17799)
EXPRESS ENERGY SVCS OPER LP
1182 Gas Plant Rd (76904-9646)
PHONE..................................325 659-4412
EMP: 80
SALES (corp-wide): 1B **Privately Held**
SIC: 1389 As An Oil Field Service
PA: Express Energy Services Operating, Lp
9800 Richmond Ave Ste 500
Houston TX 77042
713 625-7400

(G-17800)
FRANKLIN-LEDDY CORPORATION
Also Called: Leddy, M L Boot & Saddlery
2200 W Beauregard Ave (76901-3702)
PHONE..................................325 653-3397
Sammy Farmer, *Manager*
EMP: 32
SALES (corp-wide): 9.7MM **Privately Held**
WEB: www.leddys.com
SIC: 3199 3172 3144 3143 Boots, horse; personal leather goods; women's footwear, except athletic; men's footwear, except athletic
PA: Franklin-Leddy Corporation
2455 N Main St
Fort Worth TX 76164
817 624-3149

(G-17801)
G AND G INVESTMENTS INC
Also Called: Gandy Ink
2027 Industrial Ave (76904-5507)
P.O. Box 62565 (76906-2565)
PHONE..................................325 949-7864
Phil Gandy, *CEO*
John Gandy, *Vice Pres*
Sean Carter, *Plant Mgr*
Misti Bedford, *Controller*
Shelby Alley, *Accountant*
EMP: 35
SQ FT: 5,000
SALES (est): 6.4MM **Privately Held**
WEB: www.gandyink.com
SIC: 2261 2395 2262 5699 Screen printing of cotton broadwoven fabrics; embroidery & art needlework; screen printing: manmade fiber & silk broadwoven fabrics; caps & gowns (academic vestments); advertising specialties; screen printing

(G-17802)
GEOSITE INC
5956 Side View Rd (76901-5449)
P.O. Box 590 (76902-0590)
PHONE..................................325 655-4356
Mark Hamilton, *President*
Terry Augustin, *Corp Secy*
Kyle Johnson, *Vice Pres*
Rhonda Robinson, *Office Mgr*
EMP: 48
SQ FT: 4,500
SALES (est): 3.8MM **Privately Held**
WEB: www.geosite.us
SIC: 1389 Oil field services

(G-17803)
HALL TREE ANTIQUES INC
Also Called: Olio
5213 Green Valley Trl (76904-7315)
PHONE..................................325 944-4794
Barbara Jean Riley, *President*

Morgan C Riley, *Principal*
Robin Bahlman, *Corp Secy*
Mark T Riley, *Vice Pres*
▲ EMP: 60
SQ FT: 67,000
SALES (est): 2.9MM **Privately Held**
SIC: 3999 5199 2841 Potpourri; candles; soap & other detergents

(G-17804)
HAMILTON OILFIELD SERVICES INC
3150 Executive Dr (76904-6802)
P.O. Box 60438 (76906-0438)
PHONE..................................325 944-2540
Ken Hamilton, *President*
Freeman Pickett III, *Vice Pres*
Diane G McAda, *Admin Sec*
EMP: 38
SQ FT: 3,500
SALES (est): 6.5MM **Privately Held**
WEB: www.hamiltonoilfieldservices.com
SIC: 1389 Fire fighting, oil & gas field; gas field services

(G-17805)
HIRSCHFELD HOLDINGS LP (PA)
Also Called: Hirschfeld Industries
112 W 29th St (76903-2553)
P.O. Box 3768 (76902-3768)
PHONE..................................325 486-4201
Joni Carter, *President*
Dennis Hirschfeld, *Partner*
John O Quinn, *Exec VP*
Jacob Balderas, *Senior VP*
Harry Jolly, *Vice Pres*
▼ EMP: 800
SQ FT: 1,690,000
SALES (est): 142.9MM **Privately Held**
WEB: www.hirschfeld.com
SIC: 1622 3441 Bridge construction; fabricated structural metal

(G-17806)
HIRSCHFELD OF NEVADA INC
112 W 29th St (76903-2553)
P.O. Box 3768 (76902-3768)
PHONE..................................325 486-4201
Dennis C Hirschfeld, *President*
Cody Carlisle, *Sales Staff*
EMP: 400
SALES (est): 43.4MM **Privately Held**
WEB: www.hirschfeld.com
SIC: 3441 Fabricated structural metal

(G-17807)
HOLLAND JEWELRY INC
501 W Beauregard Ave (76903-6330)
P.O. Box 1031 (76902-1031)
PHONE..................................325 655-3135
William S Holland, *CEO*
I J Chase Holland III, *President*
Brant Horner, *Treasurer*
Virginia H Holland, *Admin Sec*
EMP: 13
SQ FT: 5,800 **Privately Held**
WEB: www.hollandjewelry.com
SIC: 3911 5944 Jewelry, precious metal; jewelry mountings & trimmings; rings, finger: precious metal; silverware

(G-17808)
HTC INDUSTRIES INC
1812 N Bell St (76903-3460)
PHONE..................................325 949-0645
William Shirley, *President*
Jerry L Stokes, *Vice Pres*
EMP: 35
SQ FT: 11,000
SALES (est): 5.2MM **Privately Held**
SIC: 2077 Rendering
PA: Pascal Enterprises, Inc.
2621 State St
Dallas TX 75204

(G-17809)
INDECO-INDUSTRIAL ELECTRIC CO
65 E Avenue K (76903-7597)
PHONE..................................325 653-4255
Buster Peek, *President*
Kay Peek, *Vice Pres*
Sarah Entzminger, *Office Mgr*
Sarah Peek, *Admin Sec*
EMP: 13 EST: 1956
SQ FT: 16,000

SALES (est): 4MM **Privately Held**
WEB: www.indecousa.com
SIC: 5063 7694 Motors, electric; electric motor repair

(G-17810)
J I S MEASUREMENT & OPERATING (PA)
2412 College Hills Blvd (76904-8474)
PHONE..................................325 224-3036
Ronnie W Hord, *President*
EMP: 10
SALES (est): 1.5MM **Privately Held**
SIC: 1389 Oil field services

(G-17811)
JESSCO SOLUTIONS LLC
4477 Christoval Rd (76904-9616)
PHONE..................................325 227-4196
Jake Hall, *Regional Mgr*
Kris Mabry, *VP Opers*
David James, *Mng Member*
EMP: 19
SALES (est): 1.7MM **Privately Held**
WEB: www.jesscosolutions.com
SIC: 3822 5084 Vapor heating controls; pollution control equipment, air (environmental)

(G-17812)
JULIOS CORN CHIPS
1911 S Chadbourne St (76903-8553)
PHONE..................................325 486-9300
Jose Garcia, *Owner*
EMP: 18
SALES (est): 2.1MM **Privately Held**
WEB: www.julioschips.com
SIC: 5145 2099 Snack foods; tortillas, fresh or refrigerated

(G-17813)
LONE STAR BEEF PROCESSORS LP
2150 E 37th St (76903-3415)
PHONE..................................325 658-5555
John Cross, *Partner*
Burley Smith, *Partner*
Robby Smith, *Manager*
▼ EMP: 200
SQ FT: 105,000
SALES (est): 39.9MM **Privately Held**
WEB: www.lonestarbeef.net
SIC: 2011 Meat packing plants

(G-17814)
NABORS WELL SERVICES LTD
1214 Gas Plant Rd (76904-9687)
P.O. Box 61395 (76906-1395)
PHONE..................................325 651-9241
Jamey Tauerlein, *Branch Mgr*
EMP: 100 **Privately Held**
WEB: www.nabors.com
SIC: 1389 Oil field services
HQ: Nabors Well Services Ltd.
515 W Greens Rd Ste 1200
Houston TX 77067
281 874-0035

(G-17815)
NOBLE FLOW CONTROL LLC
5538 Club Park Way (76904-1905)
PHONE..................................432 638-5962
. Chris Griffin,
EMP: 15 EST: 2017
SALES (est): 698.5K **Privately Held**
SIC: 1389 Oil field services

(G-17816)
O TALK TEXAS BRANDS INC
1610 Roosevelt St (76905-6235)
P.O. Box 2091 (76902-2091)
PHONE..................................325 655-6077
Lawrence A Ricci, *President*
Mary Ricci Brow, *Vice Pres*
Cheryl S Ricci, *Admin Sec*
EMP: 21
SALES (est): 3.4MM **Privately Held**
WEB: www.talkotexas.com
SIC: 2033 Barbecue sauce: packaged in cans, jars, etc.

(G-17817)
ORIGINAL SERVICES INC
5986 Us Highway 87 N (76901-5466)
P.O. Box 62703 (76906-2703)
PHONE..................................325 617-7400
Zachery P Drennan, *Director*
EMP: 32 EST: 2010
SQ FT: 130,680
SALES (est): 7.3MM **Privately Held**
SIC: 1389 Oil field services

(G-17818)
PANCHITAS TORTILLA FACTORY
2504 N Chadbourne St (76903-2503)
PHONE..................................325 655-2138
Francis Pineda, *Owner*
EMP: 10
SALES (est): 417.3K **Privately Held**
SIC: 2099 Tortillas, fresh or refrigerated

(G-17819)
PATTERSON DRILLING COMPANY
4105 S Chadbourne St (76904-9152)
PHONE..................................325 651-6603
Cloyce Talbott, *Ch of Bd*
Glenn Patterson, *President*
EMP: 1400 EST: 1996
SALES (est): 432.3MM
SALES (corp-wide): 1.1B **Publicly Held**
WEB: www.patenergy.com
SIC: 1381 Directional drilling oil & gas wells
PA: Patterson-Uti Energy, Inc.
10713 W Sam Houston Pkwy
Houston TX 77064
281 765-7100

(G-17820)
PIONEER GAS PIPELINE INC
217 W Beauregard Ave (76903-5823)
P.O. Box 50, Christoval (76935-0050)
PHONE..................................325 655-3300
Philip Allard, *President*
Phillip Allard, *President*
Cindy Smith, *Vice Pres*
EMP: 12
SQ FT: 3,000
SALES (est): 1.9MM **Privately Held**
WEB: www.pioneergas.com
SIC: 1311 Crude petroleum & natural gas

(G-17821)
PITTS OILFIELD PDTS & SVCS LLC
2710 Smith Blvd (76905-4287)
PHONE..................................325 340-4401
Samantha Bobbitt, *CFO*
Curtis Pittman, *Mng Member*
EMP: 32 EST: 2015
SALES (est): 3MM **Privately Held**
WEB: www.pittsoilfield.com
SIC: 3443 Fuel tanks (oil, gas, etc.): metal plate

(G-17822)
POPS BAKERY INC
Also Called: Pop's Bkry/Grcias Trtlla Fctry
208 E Avenue J (76903-7551)
P.O. Box 60128 (76906-0128)
PHONE..................................325 655-1170
Antonio Garcia, *President*
Edward Garcia, *General Mgr*
Enoch Garcia, *Corp Secy*
Sara Garcia, *Vice Pres*
Rey Rubio, *Executive*
EMP: 24 EST: 1959
SQ FT: 6,000
SALES (est): 2.2MM **Privately Held**
SIC: 2099 5149 5142 2051 Tortillas, fresh or refrigerated; groceries & related products; packaged frozen goods; bread, cake & related products

(G-17823)
PREFERRED OILFIELD SERVICES
3027 Southwest Blvd (76904-5767)
PHONE..................................325 884-5700
Dwight Dowell, *Manager*
EMP: 14
SALES (est): 1.5MM **Privately Held**
WEB: www.oilfieldpros.com
SIC: 1389 Oil field services

▲ = Import ▼ =Export
◆ =Import/Export

(G-17824)
PRINCIPAL LIGHTING GROUP LLC
Also Called: Principal Led
3490 Venture Dr (76905-8534)
PHONE..............................325 227-4577
Blake Vincent, *Director*
Heather Hubbard, *Director*
John Vincent, *Director*
EMP: 72
SALES: 33.7MM **Privately Held**
SIC: 3645 Residential lighting fixtures

(G-17825)
S & S CABINET SHOP INC
3201 Lake Dr (76903-2396)
PHONE..............................325 655-6757
Larry Smith, *President*
Karl Smith, *Vice Pres*
Karen Banks, *Treasurer*
EMP: 11
SQ FT: 15,000
SALES (est): 775.6K **Privately Held**
SIC: 2434 2542 2541 Wood kitchen cabinets; partitions & fixtures, except wood; wood partitions & fixtures

(G-17826)
SCRIPPS TEXAS NEWSPAPERS LP
Also Called: The San Angelo Standard-Times
34 W Harris Ave (76903-5838)
PHONE..............................325 653-1221
Jack Pate, *Publisher*
EMP: 180
SALES (est): 7.8MM
SALES (corp-wide): 1.8B **Publicly Held**
WEB: www.gosanangelo.com
SIC: 2711 2752 Newspapers, publishing & printing; commercial printing, lithographic
HQ: Journal Media Group, Inc.
333 W State St
Milwaukee WI 53203
414 224-2000

(G-17827)
SELECT ENERGY SERVICES LLC
3001 W Harris Ave (76901-3509)
PHONE..............................325 949-0326
EMP: 58
SALES (corp-wide): 843.8MM **Privately Held**
HQ: Select Energy Services, Llc
1820 N Interstate 35
Gainesville TX 76240
940 668-1818

(G-17828)
STANDARDS TESTING LABS INC
Also Called: Transportation Testing
4321 S Chadbourne St (76904-9148)
P.O. Box 5697 (76902-5697)
PHONE..............................325 651-4946
Tina Wood, *Purch Agent*
Raymond Rico, *Manager*
Amy Yannayon, *Manager*
EMP: 60
SALES (corp-wide): 14MM **Privately Held**
WEB: www.stllabs.com
SIC: 3829 Testing equipment: abrasion, shearing strength, etc.
PA: Standards Testing Laboratories, Inc.
1845 Harsh Ave Se
Massillon OH 44646
330 833-8548

(G-17829)
T X P INC
3150 Executive Dr (76904-6802)
P.O. Box 60245 (76906-0245)
PHONE..............................325 944-9844
Freeman Pickett, *President*
EMP: 9
SALES (est): 810K **Privately Held**
WEB: www.txp.com
SIC: 1381 Drilling oil & gas wells

(G-17830)
TABORS OF SAN ANGELO INC
4816 Knickerbocker Rd (76904-7515)
PHONE..............................325 942-1696
Lydy Tabor, *President*

EMP: 20
SQ FT: 20,000
SALES (est): 1.8MM **Privately Held**
WEB: www.taborsofsanangelo.com
SIC: 7389 2392 Interior designer; comforters & quilts: made from purchased materials

(G-17831)
TALK OTEXAS BRANDS INC
1610 Roosevelt St (76905-6235)
P.O. Box 2091 (76902-2091)
PHONE..............................325 655-6077
Lawrence A Ricci, *President*
Cheryl S Power, *Corp Secy*
Lisa Robison, *Vice Pres*
EMP: 83 EST: 1955
SQ FT: 70,000
SALES (est): 8.8MM **Privately Held**
WEB: www.talkotexas.com
SIC: 2033 2035 Vegetables: packaged in cans, jars, etc.; pickles, sauces & salad dressings

(G-17832)
TAYLOR PUBLISHING COMPANY
3490 Venture Dr (76905-8534)
PHONE..............................325 486-5300
EMP: 140
SALES (corp-wide): 439.2MM **Privately Held**
SIC: 2731 Publish Books
HQ: Taylor Publishing Company
1550 W Mockingbird Ln
Dallas TX 75235
214 819-8321

(G-17833)
THE TERRILL MFG CO INC
2816 Mrtin Lther King Blv (76903-2500)
P.O. Box 10305, Lubbock (79408-3305)
PHONE..............................325 655-7133
Gary Rushin, *CEO*
Kent Terrill, *President*
Bill Hunter, *COO*
Weldon Riley, *Vice Pres*
Greg Douglas, *CFO*
EMP: 55 EST: 1945
SQ FT: 133,000
SALES (est): 2.5MM **Privately Held**
WEB: www.terrillmfg.com
SIC: 2431 Doors, wood; moldings, wood: unfinished & prefinished

(G-17834)
TIMECLOCK PLUS LLC (PA)
1 Time Clock Dr (76904-5917)
PHONE..............................325 223-9300
Eric Thurston, *CEO*
Wade Sorrells, *Business Mgr*
David Bray, *Vice Pres*
Jesse Gunder, *Vice Pres*
Cade Moorman, *Vice Pres*
EMP: 87
SQ FT: 94,000
SALES (est): 38.6MM **Privately Held**
WEB: www.timeclockplus.com
SIC: 7371 7372 Custom computer programming services; computer software writing services; application computer software; business oriented computer software

(G-17835)
TOASTMASTERS INTERNATIONAL
Also Called: Day Breakers
1819 Knickerbocker Rd (76904-5522)
PHONE..............................325 949-3782
Louise Korona, *Manager*
EMP: 20
SALES (corp-wide): 25.4MM **Privately Held**
WEB: www.toastmasters.org
SIC: 8299 2721 Educational service, non-degree granting: continuing educ.; magazines: publishing only, not printed on site
PA: Toastmasters International
9127 S Jamaica St Ste 400
Englewood CO 80112
949 858-8255

(G-17836)
VALLEY PROTEINS INC
8394 Fm 380 (76905-3315)
PHONE..............................325 653-3858

Ronnie Meine, *General Mgr*
EMP: 47
SALES (corp-wide): 142.4MM **Privately Held**
WEB: www.valleyproteins.com
SIC: 2077 Animal & marine fats & oils
PA: Valley Proteins, Inc.
151 Valpro Dr
Winchester VA 22603
540 877-2590

(G-17837)
WANT ADS OF SAN ANGELO INC
Also Called: Thrifty Nickel Want ADS
15 N Tyler St (76901-3105)
PHONE..............................325 944-7653
Pat Houston, *Owner*
EMP: 15
SQ FT: 6,000
SALES (est): 500K **Privately Held**
WEB: www.wacoamericanclassifieds.com
SIC: 2741 7313 Shopping news: publishing & printing; newspaper advertising representative

(G-17838)
WEST TEXAS STEEL AND SUP INC
6617 S Us Highway 277 (76904-4199)
PHONE..............................325 651-7322
Paul Wayne English, *President*
Stephen English, *Vice Pres*
EMP: 20
SQ FT: 32,000
SALES (est): 10MM **Privately Held**
WEB: www.wtxsteel.com
SIC: 3441 5051 Building components, structural steel; steel

(G-17839)
WEST TXAS LIGHTHOUSE FOR BLIND
2001 Austin St (76903-8705)
PHONE..............................325 653-4231
David Wells, *President*
Steve Cecil, *Vice Pres*
Barbra Rogers, *Vice Pres*
Steve Marx, *Treasurer*
Allen Adamson, *Manager*
▲ EMP: 54 EST: 1963
SQ FT: 15,800
SALES (est): 1.3MM **Privately Held**
WEB: www.lighthousefortheblind.org
SIC: 5199 3951 Bags, textile; ball point pens & parts

(G-17840)
WHEEL-A-RAMA INC
Also Called: Concho Bike Shop
2015 Austin St (76903-8705)
PHONE..............................325 655-7373
Randall Smith, *Manager*
EMP: 9
SALES (corp-wide): 4MM **Privately Held**
WEB: www.smithoutdoorpowerequipment.com
SIC: 3524 5083 7699 5084 Lawn & garden equipment; lawn machinery & equipment; lawn mower repair shop; engines, gasoline; generators; saws & sawing equipment
PA: Wheel-A-Rama, Inc.
1801 Butternut St
Abilene TX
325 672-6611

(G-17841)
WILBUR L ANDERSON INC
Also Called: Western Towers
320 W 26th St (76903-2824)
P.O. Box 2040 (76902-2040)
PHONE..............................325 658-6539
Charles Anderson, *President*
Courtney Beach, *General Mgr*
Daniel Anderson, *Vice Pres*
David Corbin, *Project Mgr*
Aaron Woods, *Safety Mgr*
EMP: 34
SQ FT: 8,000
SALES (est): 10.8MM **Privately Held**
WEB: www.westerntowers.com
SIC: 3441 4899 Tower sections, radio & television transmission; television antenna construction & rental

(G-17842)
WTX OILFIELD SERVICES
Also Called: Xqz
36 W Beauregard Ave # 604 (76903-5856)
PHONE..............................325 227-4656
Jim Raymond, *Owner*
Joe Sanchez, *Co-Owner*
EMP: 50
SALES (est): 4.3MM **Privately Held**
WEB: www.wtxoilfieldservices.com
SIC: 1389 Oil field services

(G-17843)
ZRC LTD
Also Called: Carol Turner Collection
1821 Knickerbocker Rd D (76904-5583)
PHONE..............................325 949-7625
Randy Turner, *Partner*
Carol Turner, *Partner*
Becky Cottle, *Credit Mgr*
EMP: 10
SALES (est): 1.9MM **Privately Held**
WEB: www.carolturnercollection.com
SIC: 2339 5621 Women's & misses' athletic clothing & sportswear; ready-to-wear apparel, women's

San Antonio
Bexar County

(G-17844)
1-FAST RSPNSE RNTALS OIL FELD
Also Called: Fast Response Transportation
6825 Us Highway 87 E C (78263-6035)
PHONE..............................210 437-2473
Fabian Corpus, *President*
Carlos Corpus,
EMP: 60 EST: 2013
SALES (est): 6.4MM **Privately Held**
SIC: 7538 5013 7532 3715 General truck repair; body repair or paint shop supplies, automotive; body shop, trucks; semitrailers for truck tractors

(G-17845)
4E BRANDS NORTHAMERICA LLC
17806 Ih 10 W Ste 300 (78257-8222)
PHONE..............................210 819-7385
Jorge Gonzalez Olvera, *Mng Member*
EMP: 1000
SALES (est): 6MM **Privately Held**
SIC: 2841 Soap & other detergents
PA: 4e De Mexico, S.A. De C.V.
Paseo Alexander Von Humboldt No. 43-A
Naucalpan EDOMEX.

(G-17846)
A & D CSTM WLDG & FABRICATION
7316 Ne Loop 410 (78219-1710)
PHONE..............................210 310-7610
Anthony Quinters, *President*
Donald Fischer, *Vice Pres*
Tammy Quinters, *Treasurer*
Vonda Fischer, *Admin Sec*
EMP: 10
SALES (est): 1.6MM **Privately Held**
WEB: www.adcustomwelding.com
SIC: 7692 Welding repair

(G-17847)
A PLUS THREE TRUCKING LLC
5886 Dzvala Rd Ste 102-47 (78249)
PHONE..............................210 852-9339
Aida Gomez, *Mng Member*
EMP: 10
SALES (est): 700K **Privately Held**
SIC: 3799 Trailers & trailer equipment

(G-17848)
A&A CONCEPTS
750 Merida St Ste 105 (78207-7208)
P.O. Box 830761 (78283-0761)
PHONE..............................210 435-1300
Nasario Gres Jr, *Principal*
Anthony Gres, *Principal*
EMP: 11
SALES (est): 1.3MM **Privately Held**
SIC: 2037 Frozen fruits & vegetables

(G-17849)
A&S NEW BRAUNFELS LLC
Also Called: Smartstyle
275 Landa Ave (78237-1646)
PHONE..............................832 206-4202
Anwar Bawani,
EMP: 40
SALES (est): 906.5K Privately Held
SIC: 2326 Service apparel (baker, barber, lab, etc.), washable; men's

(G-17850)
A-ACTION AIRE INC
7625 Us Highway 87 E (78263-2405)
P.O. Box 98, Adkins (78101-0098)
PHONE..............................210 648-3801
Robert O Skelton, President
Barbara J Skelton, Vice Pres
Roxsana Skelton, Admin Sec
EMP: 15
SQ FT: 5,000
SALES (est): 2.4MM Privately Held
WEB: www.a-actionaire.com
SIC: 1711 3822 Warm air heating & air conditioning contractor; air conditioning & refrigeration controls

(G-17851)
A-VOX SYSTEMS INC
12001 Network Blvd # 314 (78249-3351)
PHONE..............................210 695-8242
A P Shepherd, President
Melissa D Shepherd, Vice Pres
EMP: 10
SQ FT: 1,600
SALES (est): 634K Privately Held
WEB: www.avoxsystems.com
SIC: 3841 3826 Surgical & medical instruments; analytical instruments

(G-17852)
A-Z GRAPHICS LLC
Also Called: A Z Graphics.com
11908 Radium St (78216-2713)
PHONE..............................210 495-3468
Leland E Adkins,
EMP: 11
SALES (est): 1.3MM Privately Held
WEB: www.a-z-graphics.com
SIC: 2321 2331 2759 5136 Sport shirts, men's & boys': from purchased materials; T-shirts & tops, women's: made from purchased materials; screen printing; men's & boys' clothing

(G-17853)
ABACO OPERATING LLC
1020 Ne Loop 410 (78209-1204)
PHONE..............................210 828-4567
Erik G Hanson, Director
Clarence E Barter, Director
EMP: 9 EST: 2001
SQ FT: 4,000
SALES (est): 1MM Privately Held
SIC: 1382 Oil & gas exploration services

(G-17854)
ABBOTT TL INVESTMENTS LLC
Also Called: AlphaGraphics
2714 West Ave (78201-2238)
PHONE..............................210 344-5200
Aaron Grohs, President
Gay Burke, Chairman
Trent Lensch, Vice Pres
Tommy E Auger, CFO
Ryan Farris, Vice Pres
EMP: 12
SALES (est): 1.9MM Privately Held
WEB: www.agnortheast.com
SIC: 2752 Commercial printing, lithographic

(G-17855)
ABRAXAS PETROLEUM CORPORATION (PA)
18803 Meisner Dr (78258-4240)
PHONE..............................210 490-4788
Robert L G Watson, Ch of Bd
Peter Bommer, Vice Pres
Tod A Clarke, Vice Pres
Kenneth W Johnson, Vice Pres
G William Krog Jr, Vice Pres
EMP: 89 EST: 1990
SALES: 129.1MM Publicly Held
WEB: www.abraxaspetroleum.com
SIC: 1311 Crude petroleum production

(G-17856)
ACCENT DOOR CO INC
25010 Cloudy Crk (78255-9527)
PHONE..............................913 780-5800
John Noren, Ch of Bd
Jeff Griffith, President
Dean Gregg, Vice Pres
EMP: 20
SQ FT: 15,000
SALES (est): 3MM Privately Held
SIC: 1751 1799 5211 3699 Garage door, installation or erection; prefabricated fireplace installation; garage doors, sale & installation; door opening & closing devices, electrical

(G-17857)
ACCESS IMAGING SOLUTIONS LLC
4224 Centergate St (78217-4827)
PHONE..............................210 590-8338
Aaron Emery, Mng Member
EMP: 10
SQ FT: 2,300
SALES (est): 911.4K Privately Held
WEB: www.accessimagingsolutions.com
SIC: 7374 3577 Data processing & preparation; computer peripheral equipment

(G-17858)
ACE WELDING AND TRAILER CO (PA)
Also Called: Divison Alamo Industrial Group
9425 Saint Hedwig Rd (78263-1209)
P.O. Box 200426 (78220-0426)
PHONE..............................210 667-1171
Anthony H Koch, President
Marvin A Haas, Vice Pres
Alfred Villanueva, Purch Dir
Paul Perez, Parts Mgr
Debbie Adams, Accounts Mgr
EMP: 30
SQ FT: 30,890
SALES (est): 16.9MM Privately Held
WEB: www.aceweldingandtrailer.com
SIC: 5012 7692 7539 3713 Truck bodies; automotive welding; trailer repair; truck & bus bodies; industrial trucks & tractors

(G-17859)
ACELITY LP INC (HQ)
12930 W Interstate 10 (78249-2248)
PHONE..............................210 524-9000
R Andrew Eckert, CEO
Gaurav Agarwal, President
Rohit Kashyap, President
Byron Clark, General Mgr
Christopher McCurry, District Mgr
EMP: 49
SALES (est): 1.4B
SALES (corp-wide): 32.1B Publicly Held
WEB: www.acelity.com
SIC: 3841 2834 Surgical & medical instruments; pharmaceutical preparations
PA: 3m Company
3m Center
Saint Paul MN 55144
651 733-1110

(G-17860)
ACM HUB LLC
2643 Mossrock (78230-5169)
P.O. Box 40142 (78229-1142)
PHONE..............................210 248-9631
Cathy Song, President
EMP: 10 EST: 2014
SALES (est): 570.3K Privately Held
WEB: www.titansigncompany.com
SIC: 1731 3993 Electrical work; electric signs; letters for signs, metal

(G-17861)
ACME HOLDINGS INC (PA)
12015 Radium St (78216-2716)
PHONE..............................210 798-3460
Jeff Garvens, CEO
EMP: 20
SALES (est): 10.3MM Privately Held
SIC: 3471 Chromium plating of metals or formed products

(G-17862)
ACME SOAP INC
Also Called: Acme Soap Company
4351 Director Dr (78219-3203)
PHONE..............................210 731-9800
Barbara J Stratil, President
Thomas J Stratil, Treasurer
Brett Stratil, Info Tech Mgr
Lauren Delozier, Officer
EMP: 11
SALES (est): 3.1MM Privately Held
WEB: www.acmesoap.com
SIC: 2841 5087 Detergents, synthetic organic or inorganic alkaline; janitors' supplies

(G-17863)
ACOCK CONSULTING LLC
8610 N New Braunfels Ave # 517 (78217-6359)
P.O. Box 701687 (78270-1687)
PHONE..............................210 826-2553
Matthew Acock, Vice Pres
Kelle Acock,
EMP: 9
SQ FT: 3,000
SALES (est): 1.2MM Privately Held
WEB: www.aeaicc.com
SIC: 1382 Oil & gas exploration services

(G-17864)
ACT GLOBAL TECH INDUSTRIES
8666 Huebner Rd Ste 204 (78240-1837)
PHONE..............................210 651-2543
▲ EMP: 10 EST: 2012
SALES (est): 1.2MM Privately Held
WEB: www.indramat.net
SIC: 3999 Atomizers, toiletry

(G-17865)
ADELITA TORTILLA FACTORY
1130 Fresno (78201-4226)
PHONE..............................210 733-5352
Roberto Borrego Jr, Owner
EMP: 20
SQ FT: 3,000
SALES (est): 1.7MM Privately Held
WEB: www.adelitatamales.com
SIC: 2099 2032 Tortillas, fresh or refrigerated; tamales: packaged in cans, jars, etc.

(G-17866)
ADIENT US LLC
1 Lone Star Pass Bldg 41 (78264-3645)
PHONE..............................210 271-2428
Habib Ullah, Engineer
James D Conklin, Branch Mgr
EMP: 30 Privately Held
WEB: www.adient.com
SIC: 3714 Motor vehicle parts & accessories
HQ: Adient Us Llc
49200 Halyard Dr
Plymouth MI 48170
734 254-5000

(G-17867)
ADVANCED IMAGING SERVICES
5501 Grissom Rd Ste 101 (78238-3035)
P.O. Box 380552 (78268-7552)
PHONE..............................210 680-4749
Phillip Rathbun, President
Yvonne G Gutierrez, Administration
EMP: 10
SALES (est): 1.8MM Privately Held
WEB: www.ais.homestead.com
SIC: 3826 Magnetic resonance imaging apparatus

(G-17868)
ADVANCED INTEGRATION TECH LP
Also Called: Ait Aerospace Components Svcs
1900 1st Ave (78216-8509)
PHONE..............................210 762-3777
Brian Fuhrmann, Manager
EMP: 45
SQ FT: 320,000
SALES (corp-wide): 13.3MM Privately Held
WEB: www.aint.com
SIC: 3728 Aircraft parts & equipment
PA: Advanced Integration Technology, Lp
2805 E Plano Pkwy Ste 300
Plano TX 75074
972 423-8354

(G-17869)
ADVANCED INTEGRATION TECH SA
Also Called: Ait Aerospace Components Svcs
1900 1st Ave (78216-8509)
PHONE..............................210 762-3777
Edward J Chalupa, Partner
EMP: 60
SALES (est): 7.9MM
SALES (corp-wide): 13.3MM Privately Held
WEB: www.aint.com
SIC: 3728 Aircraft parts & equipment
PA: Advanced Integration Technology, Lp
2805 E Plano Pkwy Ste 300
Plano TX 75074
972 423-8354

(G-17870)
ADVANCED WINDOW AND GLASS MFG
1923 Capitol Ave (78201-4217)
PHONE..............................210 735-9959
Diane Abbott, President
Paula Griffith, Corp Secy
EMP: 9
SQ FT: 17,000
SALES (est): 1.7MM Privately Held
WEB: www.advancedwindowandglass.com
SIC: 5031 3211 Windows; window glass, clear & colored

(G-17871)
AEES INC
Also Called: Pkc Group
211 N Loop 1604 E Ste 290 (78232-1252)
P.O. Box 12090 (78212-0090)
PHONE..............................210 491-2600
Marty Hughes, VP Sales
William Collier, Branch Mgr
EMP: 63 Privately Held
WEB: www.aeesinc.com
SIC: 3679 Electronic loads & power supplies
HQ: Aees Inc.
36555 Corp Dr Ste 300
Farmington Hills MI 48331

(G-17872)
AERO-TECH METAL FINISHING INC
7927 Mainland Dr (78250-5101)
PHONE..............................210 522-0802
Rudy Muniz, President
Mary Muniz, Vice Pres
Mark Hubscher, Exec Dir
EMP: 12
SQ FT: 9,800
SALES (est): 1.5MM Privately Held
WEB: www.aerotechmfi.com
SIC: 3471 Electroplating of metals or formed products

(G-17873)
AEROSPACE PRODUCTS SE INC
913 Billy Mitchell Blvd (78226-2040)
PHONE..............................210 924-2907
Donald Joice, Branch Mgr
EMP: 18 Privately Held
WEB: www.apseinc.com
SIC: 3728 Aircraft parts & equipment
HQ: Aerospace Products, S.E. Inc.
2707 Artie St Sw
Huntsville AL 35805
256 837-8040

(G-17874)
AGGREGATE PLANT PRODUCTS CO (PA)
Also Called: Appco
7640 Us Highway 87 E (78263-2405)
P.O. Box 1198 (78294-1198)
PHONE..............................210 333-1111
Clay Williams, CEO
Glen Muenchow, CFO
EMP: 86 EST: 1955
SQ FT: 7,500

SALES (est): 16.3MM **Privately Held**
SIC: 3443 1442 1389 Fabricated plate work (boiler shop); construction sand & gravel; building oil & gas well foundations on site

(G-17875)

AHMSA INTERNATIONAL INC
5150 N Loop 1604 W (78249-1325)
PHONE...................................210 341-3777
Alonso Ancira, *CEO*
Alma Gloria, *Executive Asst*
EMP: 20
SALES (est): 9.5MM **Privately Held**
WEB: www.ahmsainternational.com
SIC: 3325 Rolling mill rolls, cast steel
HQ: Altos Hornos De Mexico, S.A.B. De C.V.
    Prol. Juarez S/N
    Monclova COAH. 25770

(G-17876)

AI ROOT COMPANY
918 S Laredo St (78204-3210)
PHONE...................................210 223-2948
Brad Root, *Owner*
EMP: 16
SALES (corp-wide): 34.8MM **Privately Held**
WEB: www.rootcandles.com
SIC: 3999 Candles
PA: The A I Root Company
    623 W Liberty St
    Medina OH 44256
    330 723-4359

(G-17877)

AIRCRAFT ON GROUND INC (PA)
11502 Jnes Maltsberger Rd (78216-2831)
PHONE...................................214 350-5334
Edwin Riner, *President*
David Watson, *Controller*
EMP: 20
SQ FT: 10,000
SALES (est): 8MM **Privately Held**
WEB: www.triumphgroup.com
SIC: 3728 Aircraft servicing & repairing

(G-17878)

AIRCRAFT TECHNOLOGIES INC
3650 Highpoint (78217-2892)
PHONE...................................210 590-6858
Edward H Riebesehl, *President*
Jon Riebesehl, *Vice Pres*
Jaxon Riebesehl, *Purchasing*
Mark Riebesehl, *Treasurer*
Edward Riebesehl, *IT/INT Sup*
▲ **EMP:** 25
SQ FT: 10,000
SALES (est): 4.2MM **Privately Held**
WEB: www.aircrafttech.com
SIC: 3728 Aircraft parts & equipment

(G-17879)

AKZO NOBEL INC
Also Called: ICI Paints Store
4211 Blanco Rd (78212-1174)
PHONE...................................210 520-6566
EMP: 34
SALES (corp-wide): 10.2B **Privately Held**
WEB: www.akzonobel.com
SIC: 2851 Paints & allied products
HQ: Akzo Nobel Inc.
    535 Marriott Dr Ste 500
    Nashville TN 37214

(G-17880)

ALAMO CITY COUNTER TOPS INC
940 W Laurel (78201-6425)
P.O. Box 100816 (78201-8816)
PHONE...................................210 732-4800
Jack Collier, *President*
Jeff Collier, *Corp Secy*
Richard Kline, *Vice Pres*
Stanley De Silva, *Manager*
EMP: 27
SQ FT: 20,000
SALES (est): 3.3MM **Privately Held**
SIC: 2541 2521 2434 Counter & sink tops; cabinets, office: wood; wood kitchen cabinets

(G-17881)

ALAMO CONCRETE PRODUCTS LTD
Also Called: Alamo Concrete Products L
7003 Lesli Rd (78254)
PHONE...................................210 208-1500
Richard Vega, *Manager*
EMP: 24 **Privately Held**
SIC: 3272 3273 Concrete products; ready-mixed concrete
PA: Alamo Concrete Products, Ltd.
    6055 W Green Mountain Rd
    Austin TX 78744

(G-17882)

ALAMO CONCRETE PRODUCTS LTD
6977 Evens Grv (78265)
P.O. Box 34807 (78265-4807)
PHONE...................................210 208-1880
Charlie Smith, *Owner*
EMP: 10 **Privately Held**
SIC: 3273 Ready-mixed concrete
PA: Alamo Concrete Products, Ltd.
    6055 W Green Mountain Rd
    Austin TX 78744

(G-17883)

ALAMO CONCRETE TILE INC
Also Called: Alamo Concrete Pavers
1008 Hoefgen Ave (78210-1772)
PHONE...................................210 534-8821
Richard J Penshorn, *Vice Pres*
Richard Penshorn, *Vice Pres*
Peggy Marie Penshorn, *Admin Sec*
EMP: 20
SQ FT: 3,000
SALES (est): 3.1MM **Privately Held**
WEB: www.alamopavers.net
SIC: 3272 3271 3253 2951 Concrete products, precast; concrete block & brick; ceramic wall & floor tile; asphalt paving mixtures & blocks

(G-17884)

ALAMO INDUSTRIAL GROUP INC
943 At And T Center Pkwy (78219-3107)
PHONE...................................210 223-6161
Anthony H Koch, *President*
Bill Bell, *Vice Pres*
Mark Sobotik, *VP Finance*
Robert Deleon, *Director*
EMP: 446
SQ FT: 400,000
SALES (est): 44.6MM **Privately Held**
WEB: www.aiwdirect.com
SIC: 5085 5084 5051 3599 Industrial supplies; industrial machinery & equipment; steel; machine shop, jobbing & repair

(G-17885)

ALAMO IRON WORKS INC
943 At And T Center Pkwy (78219-3134)
PHONE...................................210 223-6161
Duffy Shea, *President*
Larry Petron, *Store Mgr*
Mark Mc Burnett, *Human Resources*
Phil Jaskoviak, *Accounts Mgr*
Alex Martinez, *Accounts Mgr*
◆ **EMP:** 400
SQ FT: 400,000
SALES (est): 1.3MM
SALES (corp-wide): 11.7MM **Privately Held**
WEB: www.aiwdirect.com
SIC: 5051 3599 3321 3441 Steel; structural shapes, iron or steel; machine & other job shop work; cast iron pipe & fittings; ductile iron castings; fabricated structural metal; steel foundries; machine tools & metalworking machinery
HQ: Vallen Distribution, Inc.
    2100 The Oaks Pkwy
    Belmont NC 28012

(G-17886)

ALAMO PREMIUM DISTILLERY INC
Also Called: Alamo Distilling Company
2030 E Houston St (78202-2934)
PHONE...................................210 325-7853
Noel Burns, *President*
Daniel Taylor, *Vice Pres*

EMP: 12
SALES (est): 36.3K **Privately Held**
WEB: www.alamodistilling.com
SIC: 2085 Grain alcohol for beverage purposes

(G-17887)

ALAMO WATERPROOFING SVCS INC
4600 Boldt Rd (78222-3803)
PHONE...................................210 648-2100
Brandon Wilson, *President*
EMP: 10
SALES (est): 1.1MM **Privately Held**
WEB: www.alamowaterproofing.com
SIC: 2385 Waterproof outerwear

(G-17888)

ALAMO WELDING & BOILER WORK
816 N Flores St (78212-5102)
PHONE...................................210 227-6502
Jack Petty, *CEO*
EMP: 15 **EST:** 1927
SQ FT: 15,000
SALES (est): 1.6MM **Privately Held**
WEB: www.alamoboiler.net
SIC: 7699 5999 7692 Boiler repair shop; welding supplies; welding repair

(G-17889)

ALCOCER LLC
9521 Middlex Dr (78217-5915)
PHONE...................................210 930-4580
Mark Alcocer, *President*
Richard Garcia Jr,
EMP: 99
SALES (est): 3.7MM **Privately Held**
SIC: 3728 Aircraft parts & equipment

(G-17890)

ALCOR INC
Also Called: Alcor Aviation
300 Breesport St (78216-2601)
PHONE...................................210 349-6491
E Michael Hundere, *President*
Bhuvana Viswanathan, *QC Mgr*
Jesus Santos, *Admin Asst*
EMP: 15
SQ FT: 12,000
SALES (est): 1MM **Privately Held**
WEB: www.alcorinc.com
SIC: 3728 2899 Aircraft assemblies, sub-assemblies & parts; carbon removing solvent

(G-17891)

ALEXANDER PRODUCTION COMPANY
Also Called: Alexander Group
700 N Saint Marys St # 1200 (78205-3507)
PHONE...................................210 271-3691
John D Alexander Jr, *President*
EMP: 13
SQ FT: 3,000
SALES (est): 1.4MM **Privately Held**
SIC: 1311 6799 Crude petroleum production; natural gas production; investors

(G-17892)

ALL SEASONS FEEDERS INC
8424 Us Highway 87 E (78263-2228)
PHONE...................................210 648-0979
W Burnell Gates, *President*
EMP: 20
SALES (est): 5.5MM **Privately Held**
WEB: www.allseasonsfeeders.com
SIC: 3523 5191 Farm machinery & equipment; farm supplies

(G-17893)

ALL STAR CAPS INC
7939 Mainland Dr (78250-5101)
PHONE...................................210 509-9086
Kelly Thies, *President*
Karen Thies, *Vice Pres*
Larry Heiner, *Sales Staff*
Rosie Castilleja, *Admin Asst*
EMP: 10 **EST:** 1999
SQ FT: 2,000
SALES (est): 1MM **Privately Held**
WEB: www.allstarcaps.com
SIC: 2395 2759 7319 Embroidery & art needlework; screen printing; distribution of advertising material or sample services

(G-17894)

ALLEN AND ALLEN LLC (PA)
Also Called: Homehardwareoutlet.com
202 Culebra Rd (78201-6441)
P.O. Box 5140 (78201-0140)
PHONE...................................210 733-9191
Bobby J Miller, *President*
Coddy Pena, *Exec VP*
Wade Payne, *Vice Pres*
Carlos D Pena, *Vice Pres*
Michael McGinnis, *Controller*
EMP: 55 **EST:** 1931
SQ FT: 41,000
SALES (est): 16.2MM **Privately Held**
WEB: www.lumberhardware.com
SIC: 5211 3429 5031 2421 Door & window products; builders' hardware; cabinet hardware; lumber, plywood & millwork; lumber: rough, sawed or planed

(G-17895)

ALLEN AND ALLEN LLC
701 San Fernando St (78207-5042)
P.O. Box 5154 (78201-0154)
PHONE...................................210 733-9191
Chet Onken, *Sales Staff*
Buzz Miller, *Branch Mgr*
EMP: 11
SALES (corp-wide): 16.2MM **Privately Held**
WEB: www.lumberhardware.com
SIC: 4225 3442 General warehousing; metal doors
PA: Allen And Allen, Llc
    202 Culebra Rd
    San Antonio TX 78201
    210 733-9191

(G-17896)

ALLEN THARP LLC
16109 University Oak (78249-4017)
PHONE...................................210 878-0034
Allen Tharp,
▼ **EMP:** 650
SQ FT: 2,700
SALES (est): 20.5MM **Privately Held**
WEB: www.allentharp.com
SIC: 5812 2099 6794 Eating places; food preparations; franchises, selling or licensing

(G-17897)

ALLIED ADVERTISING AGENCY INC
Also Called: Allied Design & Graphics
1503 Stag Pt (78248-1345)
PHONE...................................210 732-7874
Patricia L A Herbots, *President*
John P Herbots, *President*
Mari Escobedo, *Purchasing*
EMP: 50
SQ FT: 30,000
SALES (est): 5.8MM **Privately Held**
WEB: www.alliedad.com
SIC: 7336 7312 3993 Silk screen design; billboard advertising; signs & advertising specialties

(G-17898)

ALLOSENSE INC
110 E Houston St Fl 7 (78205-2991)
PHONE...................................830 900-3080
EMP: 9 **EST:** 2015
SALES (est): 137.4K **Privately Held**
WEB: www.wavecasttech.com
SIC: 8711 3812 Engineering services; search & navigation equipment

(G-17899)

ALLSTREAM ENVMTL SVCS LLC
10004 Wurzbach Rd Pmb 273 (78230-2214)
PHONE...................................713 408-7237
Richard Alan Crosby,
Christina Maria Alonso,
EMP: 11
SALES (est): 249.1K **Privately Held**
SIC: 1389 Oil consultants

(G-17900)

ALSAY INCORPORATED
3359 Se Loop 410 (78222-3102)
PHONE...................................210 628-1090
Loren Slater, *Sales Staff*
Steve Bell, *Manager*
Charlie Liesberger, *Manager*

GEOGRAPHIC

EMP: 20
SQ FT: 4,956
SALES (corp-wide): 36MM **Privately Held**
WEB: www.alsaywater.com
SIC: 1781 7699 7694 Water well servicing; pumps & pumping equipment repair; electric motor repair
PA: Alsay Incorporated
　　6615 Gant Rd
　　Houston TX 77066
　　281 444-6960

(G-17901)
ALTERMAN ENERGY SERVICES INC
14703 Jones Maltsberger (78247-3713)
P.O. Box 700490 (78270-0490)
PHONE..................................210 496-6888
Greg Padalecki, *CEO*
Chris Thiel, *CFO*
EMP: 10
SALES (corp-wide): 109.3MM **Privately Held**
SIC: 1389 Construction, repair & dismantling services
PA: Alterman Group, Inc.
　　14703 Jnes Maltsberger Rd
　　San Antonio TX 78247
　　210 496-6888

(G-17902)
AMERICAN BOTTLING COMPANY
Also Called: Big Red 7 Up Btlg Co S Texas
4518 Seguin Rd (78219-1704)
P.O. Box 200243 (78220-0243)
PHONE..................................210 662-4400
Michael Grant, *Vice Pres*
Emmett Clemons, *Sales Staff*
Todd Wilkes, *Manager*
EMP: 200 **Publicly Held**
WEB: www.keurigdrpepper.com
SIC: 2086 5149 Soft drinks: packaged in cans, bottles, etc.; groceries & related products
HQ: The American Bottling Company
　　5301 Legacy Dr
　　Plano TX 75024

(G-17903)
AMERICAN COLOR LABS OF TEXAS
981 Isom Rd (78216-4136)
PHONE..................................210 308-0222
Cordell M Gardiner, *President*
Andrew Medina, *Vice Pres*
▲ **EMP:** 14
SQ FT: 3,200
SALES (est): 2.4MM **Privately Held**
WEB: www.saexhibits.com
SIC: 2752 Commercial printing, lithographic

(G-17904)
AMERICAN TRPHY HNTERS ASSN INC
326 Sterling Browning Rd # 101 (78232-1379)
PHONE..................................210 523-8500
EMP: 20 **EST:** 1975
SALES (est): 424.7K **Privately Held**
SIC: 7997 2721 Hunting club, membership; magazines: publishing only, not printed on site

(G-17905)
AMERICAN WLDG FABRICATION INC
2301 Ackerman Rd (78219-3021)
P.O. Box 200164 (78220-0164)
PHONE..................................210 661-4159
Clarence R Harding, *President*
Chris Geckler, *Senior VP*
Chris Macallister, *Vice Pres*
EMP: 17 **EST:** 1958
SQ FT: 14,000
SALES (est): 761.3K **Privately Held**
SIC: 7692 Welding repair

(G-17906)
AMPHION INC
999 E Basse Rd Ste 180 (78209-1807)
PHONE..................................210 771-8116
Marcel E Crettet, *CEO*

EMP: 14
SQ FT: 2,500
SALES (est): 84.4K **Privately Held**
SIC: 3731 3089 1629 3499 Submersible marine robots, manned or unmanned; plastic boats & other marine equipment; dams, waterways, docks & other marine construction; target drones, for use by ships: metal

(G-17907)
ANDEAVOR LLC (HQ)
19100 Ridgewood Pkwy (78259-1834)
P.O. Box 8016, Cary NC (27512-8016)
PHONE..................................210 626-6000
Gary R Heminger, *CEO*
Anthony R Kenney, *President*
Donald Templin, *President*
Erich Heitzmann, *Area Mgr*
Darren Snow, *Area Mgr*
◆ **EMP:** 177 **EST:** 1939
SALES (est): 34.9B **Publicly Held**
WEB: www.marathonpetroleum.com
SIC: 1311 5983 5984 2911 Crude petroleum & natural gas; crude petroleum production; natural gas production; fuel oil dealers; liquefied petroleum gas dealers; gasoline

(G-17908)
ANYTHING GOES ENTERPRISES LLC
1330 Pinnacle Fls (78260-2488)
PHONE..................................210 608-1741
Marcel Witter, *Principal*
EMP: 15
SALES (est): 214.1K **Privately Held**
WEB: www.anythinggoesenterprises.com
SIC: 4214 1389 4212 Household goods moving & storage, local; construction, repair & dismantling services; moving services

(G-17909)
APEX SOFTWARE SOLUTIONS INC
5139 Beckwith Blvd # 109 (78249-2390)
PHONE..................................210 699-6666
Mark Luketic, *Partner*
Randall Garrett, *General Ptnr*
Jeff Henderson, *COO*
Brian Woolard, *Marketing Staff*
Susan Coleman, *Administration*
EMP: 25
SQ FT: 10,000
SALES (est): 3.2MM **Privately Held**
WEB: www.apexwin.com
SIC: 7372 Application computer software

(G-17910)
APPLIED SOFTWARE TECH INC
10010 San Pedro Ave (78216-3862)
PHONE..................................210 732-9212
Matt Dillon, *Director*
EMP: 29
SALES (corp-wide): 16.9MM **Privately Held**
WEB: www.asti.com
SIC: 7372 Prepackaged software
PA: Applied Software Technology, Inc.
　　5901 Pchtree Dnwody Rd St
　　Atlanta GA
　　404 633-8660

(G-17911)
AQUA QUALITY WATER SYSTEMS
12015 Starcrest Dr (78247-4335)
PHONE..................................210 493-4545
Christopher Davie, *President*
James Davie, *Vice Pres*
Bruce Towler, *Technology*
Arlene Davie, *Admin Sec*
EMP: 9
SQ FT: 1,000
SALES (est): 420K **Privately Held**
WEB: www.aqualitywater.com
SIC: 3822 1711 Auto controls regulating residntl & coml environmt & applncs; plumbing, heating, air-conditioning contractors

(G-17912)
AR-CASE INC
Also Called: Architectural Caseworks of TX
1007 W Ashby Pl (78212-3814)
PHONE..................................210 735-5175
Marie Plata, *President*
Luis Perez, *Vice Pres*
Homer Plata, *Treasurer*
EMP: 15
SQ FT: 31,000
SALES (est): 2.2MM **Privately Held**
WEB: www.arcase.com
SIC: 2522 Office furniture, except wood

(G-17913)
ARCHITCTRAL INTERIORS BY SALAS
502 Riverside Dr (78223-2062)
PHONE..................................210 733-1269
Victor H Salas, *Co-Owner*
Sylvia Salas, *Co-Owner*
EMP: 10
SQ FT: 27,000
SALES (est): 650K **Privately Held**
WEB: www.artchitectural.com
SIC: 2431 Ornamental woodwork: cornices, mantels, etc.

(G-17914)
ARLON INC
6110 Rittiman Rd (78218-4715)
PHONE..................................210 798-1900
Randy Hockington, *Branch Mgr*
EMP: 35
SALES (corp-wide): 898.2MM **Publicly Held**
WEB: www.rogerscorp.com
SIC: 3089 Plastic hardware & building products
HQ: Arlon Llc
　　1100 Governor Lea Rd
　　Bear DE 19701

(G-17915)
ASG ENERGY LLC
11765 West Ave (78216-2559)
PHONE..................................210 610-0036
Chris Koehn, *CEO*
Keith McAslan, *Managing Prtnr*
Michael Repper, *CFO*
EMP: 25
SQ FT: 2,500
SALES (est): 2.3MM **Privately Held**
WEB: www.asgenergyllc.com
SIC: 3646 Commercial indusl & institutional electric lighting fixtures

(G-17916)
ASHLEY SALVAGE COMPANY
4918 Roosevelt Ave (78214-3296)
PHONE..................................210 922-7631
Wayne Ashley, *President*
Frank W Ashley, *President*
Carol Ashley, *Vice Pres*
Davy J Allen, *Treasurer*
Clyde Ross Allen, *Admin Sec*
EMP: 28
SQ FT: 4,000
SALES (est): 10.6MM **Privately Held**
WEB: www.ashleysalvage.net
SIC: 5093 3341 Ferrous metal scrap & waste; automotive wrecking for scrap; secondary nonferrous metals

(G-17917)
ASNA INC
1026 Central Pkwy S (78232-5021)
PHONE..................................210 408-0212
Carlos Valero, *CEO*
Eduardo Ross, *Vice Pres*
Abigail Cid, *Project Mgr*
Matthew Bowers, *Software Engr*
Rick Barron, *Director*
EMP: 50
SALES (est): 6.5MM **Privately Held**
WEB: www.asna.com
SIC: 7373 7372 Computer systems analysis & design; prepackaged software
PA: Modsys International Ltd
　　3 Hasadnaot
　　Herzliya

(G-17918)
ASPEN ENTERPRISES LTD
Also Called: Aspen Beverage Group
7015 Fairgrounds Pkwy (78238-4520)
PHONE..................................210 684-6363
Chad McNair, *President*
Steve Danforth, *Engineer*
Michael Goolsbee, *Engineer*
Jennifer Cervera, *Manager*
Leigh Brister, *IT/INT Sup*
EMP: 16
SQ FT: 14,000
SALES (est): 5MM
SALES (corp-wide): 13.5B **Privately Held**
WEB: www.aspenbeverage.com
SIC: 2095 Coffee extracts; instant coffee; coffee, ground: mixed with grain or chicory; freeze-dried coffee
HQ: Finlay Extracts & Ingredients Usa, Inc.
　　10 Blackstone Valley Pl
　　Lincoln RI 02865
　　800 288-6272

(G-17919)
ASSOCIATED CREDITORS INC (PA)
Also Called: Eagle Print
8938 Broadway (78217-6116)
P.O. Box 171170 (78217-8170)
PHONE..................................210 341-5642
Ramon G Trevino, *President*
Frances Trevino, *Consultant*
EMP: 14
SQ FT: 4,800
SALES (est): 3.7MM **Privately Held**
WEB: www.eagleprintsa.com
SIC: 7334 5943 2752 Mimeographing; office forms & supplies; commercial printing, offset

(G-17920)
ATHLETIC SEWING CENTER INC
7210 Eckhert Rd (78238-1244)
PHONE..................................210 681-9744
Cathy Barbatto, *President*
Gary Barbatto, *Treasurer*
John Barbatto, *Director*
Samuel D Barbatto, *Director*
▲ **EMP:** 10 **EST:** 1958
SQ FT: 13,200
SALES (est): 2.3MM **Privately Held**
WEB: www.athleticsewingcenter.com
SIC: 5136 2389 7389 7336 Shirts, men's & boys'; men's miscellaneous accessories; sewing contractor; silk screen design

(G-17921)
ATLAS SOUTHWEST PALLET CO INC (PA)
Also Called: Atlas Pallet
51 Essex St (78210-1843)
P.O. Box 10156 (78210-0156)
PHONE..................................210 532-5343
Edgar Lozano, *President*
EMP: 25
SQ FT: 23,200
SALES (est): 3.3MM **Privately Held**
SIC: 2448 Pallets, wood

(G-17922)
AUDIO AND PRFMCE SOLUTIONS LLC
6324 Bandera Rd (78238-1632)
PHONE..................................210 549-4242
Brad West, *President*
Paul Perry, *CFO*
EMP: 29
SALES (est): 214.1K **Privately Held**
WEB: www.performancehqtx.com
SIC: 5531 3441 Speed shops, including race car supplies; fabricated structural metal

(G-17923)
AUSTIN COCA-COLA BOTTLING CO (PA)
1 Coca Cola Pl (78219-3712)
PHONE..................................210 225-2601
Joan Aom, *President*
David Van Houten, *Vice Pres*
EMP: 295 **EST:** 1904
SQ FT: 28,513
SALES (est): 309.5MM **Privately Held**
SIC: 2086 Bottled & canned soft drinks

▲ = Import ▼=Export
◆ =Import/Export

(G-17924)
AUTOELECTRIC OF AMERICA INC (DH)
Also Called: Nexans
12500 San Pedro Ave # 30 (78216-2858)
PHONE..................................210 402-6003
Adrian Ardelean, *President*
Alicia Diaz, *Principal*
Edeltraud Fabianke, *Principal*
Werner Lexa, *Principal*
Diedrich Glaser, *Vice Pres*
▲ EMP: 14
SQ FT: 3,755
SALES (est): 6.6MM **Privately Held**
WEB: www.autoelectric.com
SIC: 3714 Automotive wiring harness sets
HQ: Nexans Autoelectric Gmbh
VohenstrauBer Str. 20
FloB 92685
960 320-0

(G-17925)
AXTON LLC
Also Called: Axton Fleet Systems
4844 Whirlwind Dr (78217-3715)
PHONE..................................210 637-7400
Troy Riegel, *COO*
Tommy Burrows,
Jeff Holt,
EMP: 14
SQ FT: 3,200
SALES (est): 4.2MM **Privately Held**
WEB: www.axtontruck.com
SIC: 3713 Truck bodies & parts

(G-17926)
AZAR DISTILLING LLC (PA)
222 Austin Hwy Ste 3 (78209-5373)
P.O. Box 90914 (78209-9092)
PHONE..................................210 403-5142
Trey Azar,
Kimberly Azar,
EMP: 10
SALES (est): 1.4MM **Privately Held**
SIC: 2085 Distilled & blended liquors

(G-17927)
AZZ GLVNZING - SAN ANTONIO LLC
5731 Fm 1346 (78220-1907)
PHONE..................................210 661-8574
Tom E Ferguson, *President*
Denise Golson, *Office Mgr*
EMP: 10
SALES (est): 872.4K
SALES (corp-wide): 1B **Publicly Held**
SIC: 3312 Iron & steel: galvanized, pipes, plates, sheets, etc.
PA: Azz Inc.
3100 W 7th St Ste 500
Fort Worth TX 76107
817 810-0095

(G-17928)
B B T INDUSTRIAL ENGINE SVC
5858 Bicentennial St (78219-3008)
PHONE..................................210 661-6703
Billy D Monroe, *President*
Barbara Sue Monroe, *Treasurer*
EMP: 11
SQ FT: 10,000
SALES (est): 1.5MM **Privately Held**
SIC: 3599 Machine shop, jobbing & repair

(G-17929)
B COMM CONSTRUCTORS LLC (PA)
1010 Creekview (78219-3330)
P.O. Box 200463 (78220-0463)
PHONE..................................210 257-0102
Bill Baldwin, *President*
Billy Baldwin, *Vice Pres*
Brian Adams, *Opers Mgr*
William Baldwin, *Manager*
Wanda Baldwin, *Admin Sec*
EMP: 50
SQ FT: 2,500
SALES (est): 5MM **Privately Held**
WEB: www.bcommconstructorsllc.com
SIC: 1623 3357 8748 1731 Cable television line construction; telephone & communication line construction; coaxial cable, nonferrous; telecommunications consultant; fiber optic cable installation

(G-17930)
B G METALS INC
8410 Us Highway 87 E (78263-2228)
PHONE..................................210 648-5071
W Burnell Gates, *President*
Laura Gates, *Corp Secy*
EMP: 30 EST: 1980
SQ FT: 45,000
SALES (est): 6.5MM **Privately Held**
WEB: www.bgmetals.com
SIC: 3499 3444 5039 Friction material, made from powdered metal; sheet metalwork; ducts, sheet metal; hoppers, sheet metal; vats, sheet metal; air ducts, sheet metal

(G-17931)
B IMPRESSED INC
Also Called: B C T
8610 Botts St (78217-6302)
PHONE..................................210 524-9229
Monta Frost, *President*
Cindy Hale, *President*
Darren Hale, *President*
Rick Harvey, *Principal*
Betty Barth, *Treasurer*
EMP: 21 EST: 1982
SQ FT: 5,000
SALES (est): 3MM **Privately Held**
WEB: www.bctsatx.com
SIC: 2752 2759 Commercial printing, offset; announcements: engraved; envelopes: printing

(G-17932)
B MARTINEZ & SONS COMPANY INC
623 S Leona St (78207-5016)
PHONE..................................210 226-6772
Ariel Berrueto Gonzales, *President*
David Garcia, *Vice Pres*
Richard Berrueto, *Treasurer*
EMP: 35 EST: 1896
SQ FT: 10,000
SALES (est): 750K **Privately Held**
SIC: 2041 2099 Corn flour; food preparations

(G-17933)
B PLAN INC
Also Called: P B I
1802 Shipman Dr (78219-2328)
PHONE..................................210 256-1700
Becky Bridges, *President*
Marcia Hyink, *Vice Pres*
Raul Teran, *Warehouse Mgr*
Bonnie Stone, *Admin Sec*
▲ EMP: 15
SQ FT: 33,000
SALES (est): 1.4MM **Privately Held**
WEB: www.planbinc.com
SIC: 7389 3559 Courier or messenger service; chemical machinery & equipment

(G-17934)
B R L CONSULTANTS INC
219 W Rhapsody Dr (78216-3107)
PHONE..................................210 341-3442
Debra I Lancon, *President*
Bryan Lancon, *Vice Pres*
EMP: 10
SQ FT: 5,000
SALES (est): 340K **Privately Held**
WEB: www.brlconsultants.com
SIC: 3721 8249 8734 Motorized aircraft; vocational schools; product testing laboratories

(G-17935)
BAKER HGHES OLFLD OPRTIONS LLC
Also Called: Baker Hughes Forum SPD
4302 Profit St (78219-2622)
PHONE..................................210 662-5650
Becky Eastwood, *Manager*
EMP: 31 **Privately Held**
WEB: www.bakerhughes.com
SIC: 1389 Oil field services
PA: Baker Hughes Oilfield Operations Llc
2001 Rankin Rd
Houston TX 77073

(G-17936)
BAKER HUGHES A GE COMPANY LLC
11245 Old Corpus Christi (78223-9306)
PHONE..................................210 662-5200
Steve Webb, *District Mgr*
Tara Butler, *Accounts Mgr*
David Cherry, *Manager*
Ryan Clevenger, *Manager*
EMP: 300
SALES (corp-wide): 23.8B **Publicly Held**
WEB: www.bhge.com
SIC: 1389 Oil field services
HQ: Baker Hughes Holdings Llc
17021 Aldine Westfield Rd
Houston TX 77073
713 439-8600

(G-17937)
BAKERY EQUIPMENT & SVC CO INC
Also Called: Besco Mfg
200 Lombrano St (78207-1804)
PHONE..................................210 734-5124
Robert Escamilla, *President*
Aaron Escamilla, *Vice Pres*
Rosie R Escamilla, *Vice Pres*
Ralph Elgesem, *Research*
Cesar Tercero, *Sales Staff*
EMP: 29
SQ FT: 60,000
SALES (est): 8MM **Privately Held**
WEB: www.bescomfg.com
SIC: 3556 5046 7699 Bakery machinery; bakery equipment & supplies; restaurant equipment & supplies; restaurant equipment repair

(G-17938)
BANKSON GROUP LTD
Also Called: Alamo Tees & Advertising
12814 Cogburn (78249-2230)
PHONE..................................210 699-3800
Michelle Richard, *Terminal Mgr*
Robin Hargett, *Accounts Mgr*
Matt Harris, *Payroll Mgr*
Art Santos, *Director*
Tom Knight,
EMP: 50
SQ FT: 35,000
SALES (est): 7.7MM **Privately Held**
WEB: www.alamotees.com
SIC: 3993 2759 Signs & advertising specialties; commercial printing

(G-17939)
BASIC ENERGY SERVICES INC
16500 San Pedro Ave # 400 (78232-2252)
PHONE..................................361 574-9512
Jay Copeland, *Manager*
EMP: 9
SALES (corp-wide): 567.2MM **Publicly Held**
WEB: www.basices.com
SIC: 1389 Oil field services
PA: Basic Energy Services, Inc.
801 Cherry St Unit 2
Fort Worth TX 76102
817 334-4100

(G-17940)
BASSETT FURNITURE INDS INC
Also Called: Bassett Furniture Direct
12720 W Ih 10 (78230-1046)
PHONE..................................210 641-0101
Tim Bryan, *Manager*
EMP: 19
SALES (corp-wide): 385.8MM **Publicly Held**
WEB: www.bassettfurniture.com
SIC: 2511 5021 Wood household furniture; furniture
PA: Bassett Furniture Industries Incorporated
3525 Fairystone Park Hwy
Bassett VA 24055
276 629-6000

(G-17941)
BAY VALLEY FOODS LLC
5342 Enrique M Barrera Pa (78227-2243)
PHONE..................................210 436-5551
Brien Kumbalek, *President*
Michael Beairsto, *Controller*
Robyn Gordon, *Human Res Mgr*

EMP: 25
SALES (corp-wide): 4.3B **Publicly Held**
WEB: www.bayvalleyfoods.com
SIC: 2099 Food preparations
HQ: Bay Valley Foods, Llc
3200 Riverside Dr Ste A
Green Bay WI 54301
800 558-4700

(G-17942)
BAY VALLEY FOODS LLC
San Antonio Fams
5310 Old Highway 90 W (78227)
PHONE..................................210 436-5551
Jack Kelly, *Division Pres*
EMP: 100
SALES (corp-wide): 4.3B **Publicly Held**
WEB: www.bayvalleyfoods.com
SIC: 2099 Food preparations
HQ: Bay Valley Foods, Llc
3200 Riverside Dr Ste A
Green Bay WI 54301
800 558-4700

(G-17943)
BECTON DICKINSON AND COMPANY
Also Called: Bd Medical Equipment & Sups
5859 Farinon Dr Ste 200 (78249-3461)
PHONE..................................210 526-5000
Phyllis Gallay, *Vice Pres*
Tina Solis, *Manager*
EMP: 11
SALES (corp-wide): 17.1B **Publicly Held**
WEB: www.bd.com
SIC: 3842 3826 3841 3821 Gloves, safety; surgical appliances & supplies; elastic hosiery, orthopedic (support); analytical instruments; blood testing apparatus; hemoglobinometers; hypodermic needles & syringes; IV transfusion apparatus; catheters; surgical knife blades & handles; laboratory apparatus & furniture; pipettes, hemocytometer
PA: Becton, Dickinson And Company
1 Becton Dr
Franklin Lakes NJ 07417
201 847-6800

(G-17944)
BEERNET COMMUNICATIONS
Also Called: Schuhmacher Publishing
909 Ne Loop 410 Ste 720 (78209-1303)
PHONE..................................210 805-8006
Jessica Lopez, *Admin Asst*
Jordan Driggers, *Associate*
EMP: 9
SALES (est): 338K **Privately Held**
WEB: www.beernet.com
SIC: 2721 Trade journals: publishing only, not printed on site

(G-17945)
BEN ADAMS PRECIOUS JEWELS (PA)
Also Called: Ben Adams
255 E Basse Rd Ste 1018 (78209-8338)
PHONE..................................210 826-6535
Ben Adams, *Owner*
EMP: 22 EST: 1977
SQ FT: 4,500
SALES (est): 2MM **Privately Held**
WEB: www.benadamspreciousjewels.com
SIC: 5944 5947 3911 Jewelry, precious stones & precious metals; gift shop; jewelry, precious metal

(G-17946)
BEN DUNN CORPORATION
Also Called: Excalibur Comics
7272 Wurzbach Rd Ste 204 (78240-4802)
PHONE..................................210 614-0396
Ben Y Dunn, *President*
Joe Dunn, *President*
▲ EMP: 10
SQ FT: 2,000
SALES (est): 901K **Privately Held**
WEB: www.antarctic-press.com
SIC: 2721 5092 5942 5945 Comic books: publishing only, not printed on site; toys & games; comic books; toys & games

G
E
O
G
R
A
P
H
I
C

(G-17947)
BENSON BOX INC
Also Called: Freight Mate
5810 Business Park (78218-5508)
PHONE................................210 662-6383
R L Bramble, *President*
Tom Benson, *Treasurer*
Richard Alvarado, *Accounts Mgr*
Miriam Benson, *Director*
Kevin Pendleton, *Planning*
EMP: 16
SQ FT: 20,000
SALES (est): 1.9MM **Privately Held**
WEB: www.bensonbox.com
SIC: 2653 Boxes, corrugated: made from
   purchased materials

(G-17948)
BERGSTROM CLIMATE
SYSTEMS LLC
202 Tayman St Ste 400b (78226-1378)
PHONE................................210 507-5670
Peter Schmit, *Branch Mgr*
EMP: 50
SALES (corp-wide): 464.1MM **Privately**
Held
WEB: www.bergstrominc.com
SIC: 3585 Air conditioning units, complete:
   domestic or industrial
HQ: Bergstrom Climate Systems L.L.C.
   2390 Blackhawk Rd
   Rockford IL 61109
   815 874-7821

(G-17949)
BERRIDGE MANUFACTURING
COMPANY (PA)
6515 Fratt Rd (78218-4415)
PHONE................................210 650-7056
Jack Berridge, *Ch of Bd*
Joel Leeeric Jesse, *President*
James Grant Gillum, *Exec VP*
Dwon Williams, *Opers Staff*
Derek Moczygemba, *Inv Control Mgr*
▼ EMP: 45
SQ FT: 60,000
SALES (est): 59.5MM **Privately Held**
WEB: www.berridge.com
SIC: 3479 3446 3444 Coating of metals &
   formed products; architectural metalwork;
   metal roofing & roof drainage equipment

(G-17950)
BEXAR CONCRETE WORKS I
LTD
19440 Judson Rd (78259-3706)
P.O. Box 700250 (78270-0250)
PHONE................................210 497-3773
Marylyn House, *CEO*
Hans Hofmann, *President*
Randall Hunter House, *Corp Secy*
Julius Thomas Jr, *Vice Pres*
Randy Frerich, *Plant Mgr*
EMP: 240
SQ FT: 3,200
SALES (est): 75.3MM **Privately Held**
SIC: 3272 Prestressed concrete products;
   piling, prefabricated concrete

(G-17951)
BEXAR MANUFACTURING &
TRDG CO
Also Called: Smocker's
1990 Cupples Rd (78226-1246)
P.O. Box 240370 (78224-0370)
PHONE................................210 977-9585
Brian A Rice, *CEO*
Veronica Deneve, *President*
EMP: 12
SALES (est): 511.6K **Privately Held**
WEB: www.smockers.com
SIC: 2329 Men's & boys' sportswear & ath-
   letic clothing

(G-17952)
BIELAS GLASS & ALUMINUM
PDTS
5585 Us Highway 87 E (78222-1501)
PHONE................................210 333-8040
Joe D Biela Jr, *President*
Karam Mary Jo, *Vice Pres*
Mary Biela, *Treasurer*
Maryjo Karam, *Admin Sec*
EMP: 23
SQ FT: 7,000

SALES (est): 3.4MM **Privately Held**
WEB: www.bielaglasstx.com
SIC: 1793 3442 3354 3231 Glass & glazing work; metal doors, sash & trim; aluminum extruded products; products of
   purchased glass; paint, glass & wallpaper; lumber & other building materials

(G-17953)
BIG STAR BRANDING INC
4009 Naco Perrin Blvd (78217-2582)
PHONE................................210 590-2662
Kathie Rowe, *CEO*
Kim Delagarza, *Bookkeeper*
Rebecca Peterson, *Sales Staff*
EMP: 32
SQ FT: 10,000
SALES (est): 9MM **Privately Held**
WEB: www.bigstarbranding.com
SIC: 5136 5137 2396 7336 Men's &
   boys' clothing; women's & children's
   clothing; fabric printing & stamping; com-
   mercial art & graphic design; signs & ad-
   vertising specialties

(G-17954)
BIONUMERIK
PHARMACEUTICALS INC
8023 Vantage Dr Ste L1 (78230-4790)
PHONE................................210 614-1701
Frederick H Hausheer, *Ch of Bd*
Harry Kochat, *Vice Pres*
David Margrave, *Vice Pres*
Steven W Reibel, *CFO*
EMP: 55
SQ FT: 21,000
SALES (est): 6.7MM **Privately Held**
WEB: www.bionumerik.com
SIC: 8731 2834 Medical research, com-
   mercial; pharmaceutical preparations

(G-17955)
BLACK RIFLE COFFEE
COMPANY LLC
355 Spencer Ln (78201-2019)
PHONE................................844 899-9330
EMP: 10
SALES (corp-wide): 10.5MM **Privately**
Held
WEB: www.blackriflecoffee.com
SIC: 2095 Instant coffee
PA: Black Rifle Coffee Company Llc
   1144 S 500 W
   Salt Lake City UT 84101
   844 899-9330

(G-17956)
BLACKBRUSH CNSLD
HOLDINGS LLC
18615 Tuscany Stone # 300 (78258-3486)
PHONE................................210 495-5577
Scott Martin,
EMP: 150
SALES (est): 5.2MM **Privately Held**
WEB: www.blackbrushenergy.com
SIC: 1382 Oil & gas exploration services

(G-17957)
BLACKBRUSH OIL & GAS LP
(PA)
Also Called: Blackbrush Texstar
18615 Tuscany Stone # 300 (78258-3505)
PHONE................................210 495-5577
Scott Martin, *CEO*
Mark A Norville, *Senior VP*
Farlyn Bowen, *Opers Staff*
Eric Friedrichs, *CFO*
John Ward, *Human Resources*
EMP: 60
SALES (est): 155.8MM **Privately Held**
WEB: www.blackbrushenergy.com
SIC: 1382 Oil & gas exploration services

(G-17958)
BLUE LINE CORPORATION (PA)
3443 E Commerce St (78220-1322)
PHONE................................210 225-0400
Jon Blumenthal, *President*
Mike Gretschel, *Plant Mgr*
Ken Stanton, *Prdtn Mgr*
Brandi Woods, *Production*
Belinda Riggs, *Purchasing*
◆ EMP: 36
SQ FT: 50,000

SALES (est): 8.3MM **Privately Held**
WEB: www.bluelinecorp.com
SIC: 2819 5169 Inorganic metal compounds or salts; chemicals & allied products

(G-17959)
BOBS MONOGRAM
EMBROIDERY
10646 Gulfdale St Ste 3 (78216-3654)
PHONE................................210 341-6700
Bob Schero, *Owner*
EMP: 10
SQ FT: 1,400
SALES (est): 300K **Privately Held**
WEB: www.budsembroidery.com
SIC: 2395 2759 Embroidery & art needle-
   work; screen printing

(G-17960)
BOEING AROSPC OPERATIONS
INC
375 Airlift Dr Ste 2 (78226-1977)
PHONE................................210 932-6990
Matthew Gomez, *Opers Staff*
Jeremy Willey, *Accountant*
Edward M Anderson, *Branch Mgr*
EMP: 2200
SALES (corp-wide): 58.1B **Publicly Held**
WEB: www.boeing.com
SIC: 3721 Aircraft
HQ: Boeing Aerospace Operations, Inc.
   6001 S A Depo Blvd Ste E
   Oklahoma City OK 73150
   405 622-6000

(G-17961)
BOEING COMPANY
7323 W Hwy 90 Ste 500 (78227)
PHONE................................210 677-0900
Doug Walters, *General Mgr*
Jimmy Allison, *Chief Engr*
Tim Shook, *Sr Software Eng*
EMP: 4518
SALES (corp-wide): 58.1B **Publicly Held**
WEB: www.boeing.com
SIC: 3721 Aircraft
PA: The Boeing Company
   100 N Riverside Plz
   Chicago IL 60606
   312 544-2000

(G-17962)
BOLNERS FIESTA PRODUCTS
INC (PA)
Also Called: Lynwood Farms
426 Menchaca St (78207-1295)
PHONE................................210 734-6404
Timothy J Bolner, *Principal*
Michael J Bolner, *Exec VP*
Christopher B Bolner, *Senior VP*
Michael Bolner, *Vice Pres*
Greg Bolner, *Plant Engr*
▲ EMP: 9
SALES (est): 2.1MM **Privately Held**
WEB: www.fiestaspices.com
SIC: 2099 Chili pepper or powder; season-
   ings: dry mixes; spices, including grinding

(G-17963)
BOULWARE & ANSON FAMILY
LTD
144 Park Hill Dr (78212-2573)
PHONE................................210 822-9245
A Ryland Howard, *Partner*
EMP: 9
SALES (est): 70K **Privately Held**
SIC: 3999 Manufacturing industries

(G-17964)
BRANDED
Also Called: Branded Tees
1720 S Presa St (78210-1791)
PHONE................................210 532-4212
George A Palacios, *Partner*
George Palacios, *Principal*
Anthony Trevino, *Principal*
EMP: 11 EST: 1997
SQ FT: 400
SALES (est): 1.5MM **Privately Held**
WEB: www.brandedts.com
SIC: 2759 Screen printing

(G-17965)
BRENHOLB INC
Also Called: Brenner Printing & Mailing
1234 Triplett St (78216-2859)
PHONE................................210 349-4024
Gene Brenner, *President*
Linda Weisel,
EMP: 44
SQ FT: 25,000
SALES (est): 7.9MM **Privately Held**
WEB: www.brennerprinting.com
SIC: 2752 2721 2791 2789 Commercial
   printing, offset; magazines: publishing
   only, not printed on site; comic books:
   publishing only, not printed on site; type-
   setting; bookbinding & related work; com-
   mercial printing

(G-17966)
BRET BROUSSARD INC
Also Called: Broussard Group
4985 Eisenhauer Rd # 103 (78218-2209)
PHONE................................210 224-6220
Bret Broussard Jr, *President*
Robert Gray, *Opers Staff*
Matt Tufono, *Opers Staff*
Shelley Moore, *Controller*
Shannon Moore, *Accounts Mgr*
EMP: 9
SQ FT: 54,000
SALES (est): 2.2MM **Privately Held**
WEB: www.broussardgroup.com
SIC: 2522 5021 Office furniture, except
   wood; office & public building furniture

(G-17967)
BRISTOL-MYERS SQUIBB
COMPANY
723 Larkwood Dr (78209-3002)
PHONE................................210 826-2999
Keri Roseberry, *Business Mgr*
EMP: 89
SALES (corp-wide): 42.5B **Publicly Held**
WEB: www.bms.com
SIC: 2834 Pharmaceutical preparations
PA: Bristol-Myers Squibb Company
   430 E 29th St Fl 14
   New York NY 10016
   212 546-4000

(G-17968)
BRITTANY ENERGY LLC
4040 Brdy Ste 305 (78209)
PHONE................................210 785-2893
Guy Robert Buschman, *Mng Member*
Richard Azar II,
Donnie Seay,
Frederick Wedell,
EMP: 52
SQ FT: 1,400
SALES (est): 1MM **Privately Held**
SIC: 1389 Cementing oil & gas well cas-
   ings

(G-17969)
BRUSHY RESOURCES INC (HQ)
300 E Sonterra Blvd # 122 (78258-3971)
PHONE................................210 999-5400
Michael Pawelek, *President*
Edward Shaw, *COO*
Thomas Saunders, *Opers Staff*
Kim Vo,
EMP: 13 EST: 2015
SALES (est): 7.7MM **Privately Held**
WEB: www.starboardresources.com
SIC: 1311 1382 Crude petroleum & natu-
   ral gas; oil & gas exploration services

(G-17970)
BUCKHEAD MEAT OF SAN
ANTONIO (DH)
Also Called: Texas Meat Purveyors
4241 Director Dr (78219-3201)
PHONE................................210 337-1011
Kevin Tulley, *Partner*
Ron Boatwright, *General Ptnr*
EMP: 63
SALES (est): 63MM
SALES (corp-wide): 52.8B **Publicly Held**
WEB: www.freedmanfoods.com
SIC: 2011 2013 Meat packing plants;
   sausages & other prepared meats

▲ = Import ▼=Export
◆ =Import/Export

HQ: Buckhead Meat & Seafood Of Houston, Inc.
10310 Grens Crossing Blvd
Houston TX 77038
281 405-3201

(G-17971)
BUDGET SIGNS LTD
2801 West Ave (78201-2241)
PHONE..................................210 349-7446
Paul Rohlfs, *Partner*
Sue Flippen, *COO*
Lanny Iwan, *Accounts Mgr*
Brandy Key, *Sales Staff*
Charles Gutierrez, *Marketing Staff*
EMP: 20 **EST:** 1978
SQ FT: 6,000
SALES (est): 2.3MM **Privately Held**
WEB: www.budsigns.com
SIC: 7389 5999 1799 3953 Sign painting
& lettering shop; banners, flags, decals &
posters; sign installation & maintenance;
marking devices

(G-17972)
**BUILDERS EXCHANGE OF
TEXAS (PA)**
4047 Naco Perrin Blvd # 100 (78217-2522)
P.O. Box 33009 (78265-3009)
PHONE..................................210 564-6900
EMP: 11 **EST:** 1900
SQ FT: 12,429
SALES (est): 858.2K **Privately Held**
WEB: www.virtualbx.com
SIC: 8611 2721 Contractors' association;
magazines: publishing only, not printed on
site

(G-17973)
BURKE TEXGALS LLC
Also Called: Water 2 Wine
16630 San Pedro Ave (78232-2242)
PHONE..................................210 344-9463
Karen L Westerman,
Nancy B Martin,
Patricia A McGarrity,
EMP: 13
SALES (est): 1.9MM **Privately Held**
WEB: www.straygrape.com
SIC: 2084 Wines

(G-17974)
**BUSINESS JRNL PUBLICATIONS
INC**
Also Called: San Antonio Business Journal
200 E Grayson St Ste 110 (78215-1269)
PHONE..................................210 341-3202
Kent Krauss, *Publisher*
Debi Slowik, *Manager*
EMP: 35
SALES (corp-wide): 5B **Privately Held**
SIC: 2711 Newspapers: publishing only,
not printed on site
HQ: Business Journal Publications, Inc.
4350 W Cypress St Ste 800
Tampa FL 33607

(G-17975)
C & F TOOL & DIE CO LLC
7202 Eckhert Rd Ste 6 (78238-1132)
PHONE..................................210 522-9310
Robert E Collier, *CEO*
Steve W Collier, *President*
Jason Collier, *Opers Staff*
Carlos Salazar, *QC Mgr*
Jennifer Debosier, *Manager*
EMP: 33
SQ FT: 10,000
SALES (est): 3.6MM **Privately Held**
WEB: www.c-ftool.com
SIC: 3728 7699 Aircraft parts & equipment; aircraft & heavy equipment repair
services

(G-17976)
CALIFORNIA STUCCO
2438 Wayne Dr (78222-1431)
PHONE..................................210 838-7433
Jesus Talamantes, *Officer*
EMP: 9 **EST:** 2008
SALES (est): 1MM **Privately Held**
SIC: 3299 Stucco

(G-17977)
**CAMBER DEF SEC SYSTEMS
SLTONS (DH)**
Also Called: Hii Mssion Drven Innvtive Slto
70 Ne Loop 410 Ste 400 (78216-5841)
PHONE..................................210 279-3608
Ronald E Moore, *President*
Bonita Foster, *Treasurer*
Gilbert Vazquez, *Admin Sec*
EMP: 41
SQ FT: 13,000
SALES (est): 13.7MM **Publicly Held**
WEB: www.hii-mdis.jobs
SIC: 7372 Prepackaged software

(G-17978)
CAMPBELL MILLWORK LLC
207 E Nakoma St (78216-2704)
PHONE..................................210 349-9294
Kelly Jan, *VP Opers*
John Bynum, *Controller*
Matthew Chapman,
EMP: 16 **EST:** 2013
SALES (est): 1.6MM **Privately Held**
WEB: www.campbellmillwork.com
SIC: 2431 Millwork

(G-17979)
CAPCO STEEL INC
Also Called: Capco General Contracting
9828 Lorene Ln (78216-4450)
PHONE..................................210 493-9992
Rodger Roycroft, *President*
Charles Plunkett, *COO*
Julie Plunkett, *Vice Pres*
EMP: 21
SQ FT: 7,200
SALES (est): 2.1MM **Privately Held**
WEB: www.capcosteel.com
SIC: 1542 1799 3448 4226 Exterior wall
system installation

(G-17980)
**CAPITAL HARDWOODS &
MLLWK LLC**
15421 Capital Prt (78249-1305)
PHONE..................................210 657-1200
Terry Harp, *Sales Associate*
Feline Jimenez, *Mng Member*
EMP: 13 **EST:** 2011
SALES (est): 2.5MM **Privately Held**
WEB: www.capitalhardwoods.com
SIC: 2431 Woodwork, interior & ornamental

(G-17981)
**CAPITOL AGGREGATES INC
(HQ)**
Also Called: Capitol Cement Division
2330 N Loop 1604 W (78248-4512)
P.O. Box 33240 (78265-3240)
PHONE..................................210 871-6100
David Zachry, *CEO*
Greg Hale, *President*
Leonard R Harral, *Senior VP*
Tim Watt, *Senior VP*
Timothy A Watt, *Senior VP*
▲ **EMP:** 215 **EST:** 1957
SQ FT: 10,000
SALES (est): 193.1MM **Privately Held**
WEB: www.capitolaggregates.com
SIC: 3241 1442 1422 2951 Portland cement; construction sand mining; gravel
mining; limestones, ground; asphalt & asphaltic paving mixtures (not from refineries); railroads, line-haul operating

(G-17982)
CAPITOL AGGREGATES INC
11551 Nacogdoches Rd (78217-2337)
P.O. Box 1206, Marble Falls (78654-1206)
PHONE..................................210 871-7228
Nicole Wyatt, *Manager*
EMP: 150 **Privately Held**
WEB: www.capitolaggregates.com
SIC: 3281 Stone, quarrying & processing
of own stone products
HQ: Capitol Aggregates, Inc.
2330 N Loop 1604 W
San Antonio TX 78248
210 871-6100

(G-17983)
**CARBONFREE CHEMICALS SPE
I LLC (PA)**
11839 Nacogdoches Rd (78217-2327)
PHONE..................................210 476-5906
Dave Law, *COO*
Laurel Danielson, *Finance*
EMP: 9
SALES (est): 546.3K **Privately Held**
WEB: www.carbonfreechem.com
SIC: 2819 Industrial inorganic chemicals

(G-17984)
**CARBONFREE CHEMICALS SPE
I LLC**
11503 Bulverde Rd (78217-2301)
PHONE..................................210 476-5906
Jeff Smith, *Branch Mgr*
EMP: 35
SALES (corp-wide): 546.3K **Privately
Held**
WEB: www.carbonfreechem.com
SIC: 2819 Industrial inorganic chemicals
PA: Carbonfree Chemicals Spe I Llc
11839 Nacogdoches Rd
San Antonio TX 78217
210 476-5906

(G-17985)
CARRIER CORPORATION
12029 Starcrest Dr (78247-4349)
PHONE..................................210 495-2600
Richard Lowery, *Manager*
EMP: 20
SALES (corp-wide): 17.4B **Publicly Held**
WEB: www.rtx.com
SIC: 3585 Air conditioning units, complete:
domestic or industrial
HQ: Carrier Corporation
13995 Pasteur Blvd
Palm Beach Gardens FL 33418
800 379-6484

(G-17986)
CASTEEL MFG INC
3747 Pitluk Ave (78211-3557)
PHONE..................................210 923-4558
Frank Castillo, *President*
Suzanne Walker, *Admin Sec*
EMP: 10
SQ FT: 8,000
SALES (est): 2MM **Privately Held**
WEB: www.casteelmfg.com
SIC: 3556 3444 Food products machinery;
sheet metalwork

(G-17987)
CATERPILLAR INC
4633 Perrin Crk (78217-3733)
PHONE..................................210 637-3700
Doug Herman, *Manager*
EMP: 80
SALES (corp-wide): 53.8B **Publicly Held**
WEB: www.caterpillar.com
SIC: 3599 3452 3545 3444 Machine
shop, jobbing & repair; nuts, metal; bolts,
metal; screws, metal; machine tool accessories; sheet metalwork; fabricated plate
work (boiler shop)
PA: Caterpillar Inc.
510 Lake Cook Rd Ste 100
Deerfield IL 60015
224 551-4000

(G-17988)
CAVALLINI CO INC
Also Called: Stained Glass Studio
4719 Blanco Rd (78212-1015)
PHONE..................................210 733-8161
Adrian J Cavallini, *President*
Debra A Cavallini, *Corp Secy*
Manlio Cavallini, *Vice Pres*
Debra Cavallini, *Admin Sec*
▲ **EMP:** 14
SQ FT: 6,700
SALES (est): 1.7MM **Privately Held**
WEB: www.cavallinistudios.com
SIC: 3231 5231 Stained glass: made from
purchased glass; mosaics, glass: made
from purchased glass; glass, leaded or
stained

(G-17989)
CELLISCO INC (PA)
Also Called: Accu-Print
3503 Crosspoint (78217-2889)
PHONE..................................210 692-1927
Dustin Ellis, *Ch of Bd*
Charles Headley, *Prdtn Mgr*
Charles F Ellis, *VP Bus Dvlpt*
Candace Ellis, *Treasurer*
Lindsay Ellis, *Sales Staff*
EMP: 26
SQ FT: 20,000
SALES (est): 3.6MM **Privately Held**
WEB: www.accu-print.com
SIC: 2791 2732 7334 2752 Typesetting;
textbooks: printing & binding, not publishing; mimeographing; photo-offset printing

(G-17990)
**CELONOVA BIOSCIENCES INC
(PA)**
8023 Vantage Dr Ste 1400 (78230-2204)
PHONE..................................210 489-4000
Dennert O Ware Sr, *Ch of Bd*
Martin J Landon, *President*
Eric Davis, *CFO*
Clifford James, *Technology*
◆ **EMP:** 120
SALES (est): 19.9MM **Privately Held**
WEB: www.celonova.com
SIC: 3841 Medical instruments & equipment, blood & bone work

(G-17991)
CEMEX MATERIALS LLC
Also Called: Rinker Materials Con Pipe Div
6145 Mechler Rd (78252)
PHONE..................................210 677-8191
Clay Braden, *Branch Mgr*
EMP: 20 **Privately Held**
SIC: 3273 Ready-mixed concrete
HQ: Cemex Materials Llc
1501 Belvedere Rd
West Palm Beach FL 33406
561 833-5555

(G-17992)
**CENTRAL TEXAS EX
METALWORK LLC**
Also Called: Express Contracting
304 El Paso St (78207-5000)
PHONE..................................210 337-2260
Kara Clayton, *President*
EMP: 20
SQ FT: 3,000
SALES (est): 10.3MM **Privately Held**
WEB: www.expressmetal.com
SIC: 1542 3441 Commercial & office building, new construction; fabricated structural metal

(G-17993)
CENTURION PALLET SERVICE
402 Tidewind St (78221-4152)
PHONE..................................210 823-3530
Manuel Lara, *Owner*
EMP: 11
SALES (est): 691.9K **Privately Held**
SIC: 2448 Pallets, wood & wood with metal

(G-17994)
CENVEO WORLDWIDE LIMITED
5101 S Zarzamora St (78211-2054)
PHONE..................................210 923-7591
George De Shaies, *Controller*
Carlos Lechuga, *Accounts Exec*
Gary Ferguson, *Branch Mgr*
EMP: 101
SQ FT: 50,660
SALES (corp-wide): 1B **Privately Held**
WEB: www.cenveo.com
SIC: 2752 2791 2789 2759 Commercial
printing, offset; typesetting; bookbinding &
related work; commercial printing
HQ: Cenveo Worldwide Limited
200 First Stamford Pl # 2
Stamford CT 06902
203 595-3000

(G-17995)
CFA SERVICES
3300 Nacogdoches Rd # 216
(78217-3373)
PHONE..................................210 758-5721
Arthur Perez, *Owner*

Fermin Alfaro, *Co-Owner*
EMP: 10
SALES (est): 1MM **Privately Held**
SIC: 1711 7372 Plumbing, heating, air-conditioning contractors; application computer software

(G-17996)
CFS FORMING STRUCTURE COMPANY
21120 Milsa Dr (78256-9615)
PHONE.................................210 698-9252
Vera Salvatore, *President*
Carlo Salvatore, *CFO*
EMP: 100
SALES (est): 24.3MM **Privately Held**
SIC: 3272 3444 Concrete products, pre-cast; sheet metalwork

(G-17997)
CH GUENTHER & SON LLC (PA)
Also Called: C H Guenther & Son
2201 Broadway St (78215-1135)
P.O. Box 118 (78291-0118)
PHONE.................................210 227-1401
Dale W Tremblay, *President*
Jim Phillipson, *District Mgr*
Rex Wilcken, *Business Mgr*
Tock McRae, *Vice Pres*
Chris Redkey, *Vice Pres*
▼ **EMP:** 300 **EST:** 1899
SALES (est): 758.5MM **Privately Held**
WEB: www.chg.com
SIC: 2041 2051 2045 2052 Flour mills, cereal (except rice); bread, cake & related products; biscuit mixes, prepared: from purchased flour; bakery products, dry; food preparations

(G-17998)
CHAMPION GROUP INC
Also Called: Delaware Champion Group
4416 Lockhill Selma Rd (78249-2078)
PHONE.................................210 490-1482
C David Gartley, *Branch Mgr*
EMP: 20
SALES (corp-wide): 7.4MM **Privately Held**
WEB: www.championgroup.com
SIC: 1382 Oil & gas exploration services
PA: The Champion Group Inc
5565 Maudlin St
Houston TX 77087
713 644-2181

(G-17999)
CHANDLER CONSULTANTS INC
Also Called: Presto Printing
2714 West Ave (78201-2238)
PHONE.................................210 344-5200
Wanda C Rohm, *President*
EMP: 15
SQ FT: 3,000
SALES (est): 900K **Privately Held**
WEB: www.presto-printing.com
SIC: 2752 Commercial printing, offset; cards, lithographed

(G-18000)
CHANDLER SIGNS LLC
17319 San Pedro Ave # 200 (78232-1411)
PHONE.................................210 349-3804
William Macrum, *Vice Pres*
Tony Quintero, *Manager*
EMP: 15
SALES (corp-wide): 74MM **Privately Held**
WEB: www.chandlersigns.com
SIC: 3993 Electric signs
PA: Chandler Signs, Llc
14201 Sovereign Rd 101
Fort Worth TX 76155
214 902-2000

(G-18001)
CHARLOTTES CONCRETE INC
4950 Lane Dr (78263-2410)
P.O. Box 200722 (78220-0722)
PHONE.................................210 648-4774
Dana Bishop, *President*
James Rice, *Chairman*
Brian Bishop, *Vice Pres*
EMP: 28
SQ FT: 35,000

SALES (est): 5.3MM **Privately Held**
WEB: www.charlottesconcrete.com
SIC: 3272 Manhole covers or frames, concrete

(G-18002)
CHEP (USA) INC
Also Called: Ifco Systems
5250 Tacco (78244-1007)
PHONE.................................210 662-7733
Kirby Schneider, *Manager*
Amy Perez, *Senior Mgr*
EMP: 72 **Privately Held**
WEB: www.chep.com
SIC: 2448 Pallets, wood
HQ: Chep (U.S.A.) Inc.
5897 Windward Pkwy
Alpharetta GA 30005
770 668-8100

(G-18003)
CHIRON HOLDINGS INC (DH)
12930 W Interstate 10 (78249-2248)
PHONE.................................210 524-9000
R Andrew Eckert, *CEO*
Vikram Bajaj, *Vice Pres*
Greg Garland, *Director*
EMP: 21
SALES (est): 1.2B
SALES (corp-wide): 32.1B **Publicly Held**
SIC: 2599 7352 Hospital beds; medical equipment rental
HQ: Acelity L.P. Inc.
12930 W Interstate 10
San Antonio TX 78249
210 524-9000

(G-18004)
CHISM COMPANY (PA)
8310 Broadway (78209-2007)
PHONE.................................210 824-6315
Roy Chism, *President*
Betty Chism, *Vice Pres*
Terry Chism, *Admin Sec*
EMP: 15 **EST:** 1965
SQ FT: 36,000
SALES (est): 2.1MM **Privately Held**
WEB: www.chismcompany.com
SIC: 3993 1799 3448 Signs, not made in custom sign painting shops; awning installation; carports: prefabricated metal

(G-18005)
CHROMALLOY COMPONENT SVCS INC
303 Industrial Park Rd (78226-1838)
P.O. Box 240280 (78224-0280)
PHONE.................................210 331-2300
David Ford, *General Mgr*
EMP: 243
SALES (corp-wide): 3.3B **Publicly Held**
WEB: www.chromalloy.com
SIC: 3714 Motor vehicle parts & accessories
HQ: Chromalloy Component Services, Inc.
303 Industrial Park Rd
San Antonio TX 78226
210 331-2300

(G-18006)
CHROMALLOY COMPONENT SVCS INC (DH)
303 Industrial Park Rd (78226-1838)
PHONE.................................210 331-2300
Martin Weinstein, *Ch of Bd*
Greg Baladjanian, *President*
Chris Richardson, *COO*
Kenneth Binder, *CFO*
Al Lopez, *Manager*
▲ **EMP:** 22
SQ FT: 177,500
SALES (est): 146.6MM
SALES (corp-wide): 3.3B **Publicly Held**
WEB: www.chromalloy.com
SIC: 7699 3724 Industrial equipment services; engine repair & replacement, non-automotive; aircraft engines & engine parts
HQ: Chromalloy Gas Turbine Llc
3999 Rca Blvd
Palm Beach Gardens FL 33410
561 935-3571

(G-18007)
CIRCLE C MILLWORK INC
9254 Us Highway 87 E (78263-9776)
P.O. Box 1119, Adkins (78101-1119)
PHONE.................................210 649-1228
Sandra Smith, *President*
Carl Smith, *Vice Pres*
Roy Wight, *Project Mgr*
EMP: 37
SQ FT: 4,000
SALES (est): 6.7MM **Privately Held**
WEB: www.circlecmillwork.com
SIC: 2431 Millwork

(G-18008)
CISCO SYSTEMS INC
18615 Tuscany Stone # 250 (78258-3486)
PHONE.................................210 357-2500
John N Stewart, *Senior VP*
Raul Arias, *Engineer*
Tony Beauford, *Engineer*
Jeff Carton, *Engineer*
Jeff Comer, *Engineer*
EMP: 691
SALES (corp-wide): 49.3B **Publicly Held**
WEB: www.cisco.com
SIC: 3577 Computer peripheral equipment
PA: Cisco Systems, Inc.
170 W Tasman Dr
San Jose CA 95134
408 526-4000

(G-18009)
CLARKE HARLAND CORP (DH)
15955 La Cantera Pkwy (78256-2589)
PHONE.................................830 609-5500
Jana Schmidt, *President*
Jared Carr, *Partner*
Rachel Bergman, *Senior VP*
Carrie Stapp, *Senior VP*
Geoff Thomas, *Senior VP*
◆ **EMP:** 1301 **EST:** 2007
SALES (est): 711MM **Publicly Held**
WEB: www.harlandclarke.com
SIC: 2782 2754 7389 Checkbooks; bank checkbooks & passbooks; commercial printing, gravure; telemarketing services; advertising, promotional & trade show services
HQ: Vericast Corp.
15955 La Cantera Pkwy
San Antonio TX 78256
210 697-8888

(G-18010)
CLAYTON HOMES INC
13700 Judson Rd Ofc (78233-4500)
PHONE.................................210 946-2222
Dorothy Hudson, *Manager*
EMP: 13
SALES (corp-wide): 254.6B **Publicly Held**
WEB: www.claytonhomes.com
SIC: 2451 Mobile homes
HQ: Clayton Homes, Inc.
5000 Clayton Rd
Maryville TN 37804
865 380-3000

(G-18011)
CLAYTON HOMES INC
1824 Sw Loop 410 (78227-2531)
PHONE.................................210 677-6100
Stephany Tebon, *Manager*
EMP: 13
SALES (corp-wide): 254.6B **Publicly Held**
WEB: www.claytonhomes.com
SIC: 2451 5271 6141 Mobile homes; mobile homes; installment sales finance, other than banks
HQ: Clayton Homes, Inc.
5000 Clayton Rd
Maryville TN 37804
865 380-3000

(G-18012)
CLEAR VISIONS INC (DH)
121 Interpark Blvd # 801 (78216-1848)
P.O. Box 790510 (78279-0510)
PHONE.................................210 496-6006
Joe R Davis, *CEO*
Michelle Hernandez, *President*
Andrew Kunczt, *Client Mgr*
Dave Falzareno, *Accounts Exec*
David Falzareno, *Accounts Exec*

EMP: 65 **EST:** 1995
SQ FT: 50,000
SALES (est): 23.4MM
SALES (corp-wide): 6.2B **Publicly Held**
WEB: www.clearvisionsinc.com
SIC: 2752 7331 2791 Commercial printing, offset; direct mail advertising services; typesetting; bookbinding & related work; commercial printing
HQ: Consolidated Graphics, Inc.
5858 Westheimer Rd # 200
Houston TX 77057
713 787-0977

(G-18013)
COAST TO COAST MINERALS LLC
Also Called: Diverse Minerals
5169 Randolph Blvd Bldg 1 (78233-6206)
PHONE.................................210 781-8505
Luis Estrada, *CEO*
EMP: 15
SQ FT: 1,300
SALES (est): 1.8MM **Privately Held**
SIC: 6221 1081 Commodity traders, contracts; mine development, metal

(G-18014)
COATES ENERGY TRUST
7373 Broadway Ste 406 (78209-3268)
PHONE.................................210 820-0113
George Stieren, *Trustee*
Barry Roberts, *Trustee*
Ed Boyle, *CFO*
EMP: 9 **EST:** 1930
SQ FT: 4,000
SALES (est): 20.2MM **Privately Held**
WEB: www.coatesenergy.com
SIC: 1311 Crude petroleum production; natural gas production

(G-18015)
COCA COLA BTLG CO OF SOUTHWEST
Also Called: Coca-Cola
1 Coca Cola Pl (78219-3712)
PHONE.................................210 229-0555
John R Alm, *President*
EMP: 170 **EST:** 1986
SALES (est): 21.6MM
SALES (corp-wide): 37.2B **Publicly Held**
SIC: 2086 Bottled & canned soft drinks
HQ: Coca-Cola Refreshments Usa, Inc.
2500 Windy Ridge Pkwy Se
Atlanta GA 30339
770 989-3000

(G-18016)
COHN SIGNS
21713 Us Highway 281 S (78264-4827)
P.O. Box 14653 (78214-0653)
PHONE.................................210 626-2157
Herbert Cohn, *Owner*
EMP: 9
SALES (est): 671.7K **Privately Held**
SIC: 3993 Signs & advertising specialties

(G-18017)
COLD KING INC
309 S Salado St (78207-4455)
P.O. Box 831412 (78283-1412)
PHONE.................................210 227-0264
EMP: 11
SQ FT: 9,000
SALES (est): 1.1MM **Privately Held**
SIC: 3632 3442 Household Refrigerators And Freezers

(G-18018)
COLUMBUS MCKINNON CORPORATION
2546 Boardwalk St (78217-4417)
PHONE.................................210 924-3700
David Euvino, *Branch Mgr*
EMP: 109
SALES (corp-wide): 809.1MM **Publicly Held**
WEB: www.columbusmckinnon.com
SIC: 3536 Hoists, cranes & monorails
PA: Columbus Mckinnon Corporation
205 Crosspoint Pkwy
Getzville NY 14068
716 689-5400

(G-18019)
COMEBACK BREWING INC (HQ)
Also Called: Bridgeport Brewing Company
14800 San Pedro Ave (78232-3733)
PHONE..............................210 490-9128
Carlos Alvarez, *President*
EMP: 10
SQ FT: 10,000
SALES (est): 23MM
SALES (corp-wide): 237.4MM **Privately Held**
SIC: 2082 Beer (alcoholic beverage)
PA: The Gambrinus Company
    14800 San Pedro Ave # 310
    San Antonio TX 78232
    210 483-5100

(G-18020)
COMEBACK BREWING II INC (PA)
Also Called: Trumer Brauerei
14800 San Pedro Ave Fl 3 (78232-3733)
PHONE..............................210 490-9128
Carlos Alvarez, *President*
Jim Bolz, *CFO*
▲ EMP: 80
SALES (est): 8.3MM **Privately Held**
WEB: www.trumer-international.com
SIC: 2082 Beer (alcoholic beverage); ale (alcoholic beverage)

(G-18021)
COMET SIGNS LLC (PA)
5003 Stout Dr (78219-4336)
PHONE..............................210 341-7244
Tim Edmonds, *General Mgr*
Estevan Medina, *General Mgr*
Kenneth Shelton, *General Mgr*
Robbie Justice, *Project Mgr*
Ben Calderon, *Production*
EMP: 119 EST: 2013
SALES (est): 38MM **Privately Held**
WEB: www.cometsigns.com
SIC: 3993 1799 Neon signs; sign installation & maintenance

(G-18022)
CONCORD OIL CO
100 W Houston St Ste 1500 (78205-1424)
PHONE..............................210 224-4455
Tom E Pawel, *President*
Reagan McCoy, *Vice Pres*
Nancy E Pawel, *Vice Pres*
EMP: 12 EST: 1956
SQ FT: 11,000
SALES (est): 2.3MM **Privately Held**
SIC: 6792 1311 Oil leases, buying & selling on own account; crude petroleum production; natural gas production

(G-18023)
CONETIC SOFTWARE SYSTEMS INC
10860 Gulfdale St (78216-3607)
PHONE..............................210 222-9621
Alfonso J Garza, *Ch of Bd*
Andres J Garza, *President*
EMP: 25
SALES (est): 1.7MM **Privately Held**
WEB: www.conetic.com
SIC: 3695 Magnetic & optical recording media

(G-18024)
CONSTRUCT CAPITAL LLC
Also Called: Perma-Pier Foundation Repair O
12050 Crwnpint Dr Ste 160 (78233)
PHONE..............................210 654-4400
Heather Claxton, *Sales Staff*
Barry Brickman, *Branch Mgr*
Stephen Gregory, *Director*
EMP: 74
SALES (corp-wide): 64.4MM **Privately Held**
WEB: www.permapier.com
SIC: 1629 1741 1381 Drainage system construction; foundation & retaining wall construction; service well drilling
PA: Construct Capital, Llc
    2821 E Randol Mill Rd
    Arlington TX 76011
    214 637-1444

(G-18025)
CONVERMEX USA CORP
4400 Tejasco Ste 120 (78218-5217)
PHONE..............................210 319-2972
Dave Fredrickson, *Vice Pres*
EMP: 26
SALES (est): 38MM **Privately Held**
WEB: www.convermex.com.mx
SIC: 2656 Paper cups, plates, dishes & utensils
HQ: Grupo Convermex, S.A. De C.V.
    Entronque No. 25
    Puebla PUE. 72300

(G-18026)
COPY CENTER LLC
Also Called: Texas Digital Copy and Print
20330 Huebner Rd Ste 104 (78258-3509)
PHONE..............................210 481-9305
Francis Mansfield, *CEO*
EMP: 20
SALES (est): 928.3K **Privately Held**
WEB: www.sundanceprintcenters1.com
SIC: 2752 Commercial printing, offset

(G-18027)
CORRECTIONS PRODUCTS CO LTD
5802 Rocky Pt (78249-3406)
PHONE..............................210 829-7951
Christian Hunter, *Partner*
Brooks Wooten, *Partner*
EMP: 10 EST: 1982
SQ FT: 18,000
SALES (est): 1.5MM **Privately Held**
WEB: www.correctionsproductsco.com
SIC: 3429 Manufactured hardware (general)

(G-18028)
COX MANUFACTURING COMPANY
Also Called: Comaco
5500 N Loop 1604 E (78247-4600)
PHONE..............................210 657-7731
Bill Cox, *President*
Mike Petrusch, *VP Mfg*
Jo Bal, *Buyer*
Nathan Echon, *Engineer*
Ygnacio Gutierrez, *Engineer*
EMP: 177 EST: 1956
SQ FT: 25,000
SALES (est): 48.1MM **Privately Held**
WEB: www.coxmanufacturing.com
SIC: 3451 Screw machine products

(G-18029)
CRAFCO TEXAS INC
102 Limestone Creek Rd (78232-3608)
PHONE..............................210 496-2070
Bill Frerichs, *President*
Judith G Frerichs, *Vice Pres*
EMP: 12
SALES (est): 468.8K **Privately Held**
WEB: www.crafco.com
SIC: 2951 Asphalt paving mixtures & blocks

(G-18030)
CRIMSTONE AAA OPERATING CO LP
Also Called: Pallet Logistics of America
5891 Fm 1346 (78220-1909)
PHONE..............................210 662-9400
Jim Suhwab, *Branch Mgr*
EMP: 15 **Privately Held**
WEB: www.plofa.com
SIC: 2448 Pallets, wood
PA: Crimstone Aaa Operating Company, Lp
    4100 Platinum Way
    Dallas TX 75237

(G-18031)
CROWN EQUIPMENT CORPORATION
Also Called: Crown Lift Trucks
4400 Ne Loop 410 Ste 140 (78218-5403)
PHONE..............................210 930-9360
Marc Davidson, *Manager*
EMP: 36
SALES (corp-wide): 3.7B **Privately Held**
WEB: www.crown.com
SIC: 3537 Lift trucks, industrial: fork, platform, straddle, etc.

PA: Crown Equipment Corporation
    44 S Washington St
    New Bremen OH 45869
    419 629-2311

(G-18032)
CRUISING KITCHENS LLC
Also Called: C K
14732 Bulverde Rd (78247-2626)
PHONE..............................210 920-2658
Cameron Davies, *President*
Sepulveda Dayna, *Director*
Joshua Davies, *Graphic Designe*
EMP: 9
SALES (est): 203K **Privately Held**
WEB: www.cruisingkitchens.com
SIC: 3713 1799 Truck bodies (motor vehicles); kitchen & bathroom remodeling

(G-18033)
CSI TECHS INC
Also Called: Csi Security
1247 Range Fld (78245-2879)
PHONE..............................210 875-7978
EMP: 56
SALES (est): 1.6MM **Privately Held**
WEB: www.csisanantonio.com
SIC: 3699 8243 1623 7373 Security control equipment & systems; repair training, computer; cable laying construction; local area network (LAN) systems integrator; computer installation; computer related consulting services

(G-18034)
CUDD PUMPING SERVICES INC
5251 Tacco (78244-1007)
P.O. Box 910, Pleasanton (78064-0910)
PHONE..............................210 310-1330
EMP: 17
SALES (corp-wide): 1.7B **Publicly Held**
WEB: www.cuddenergyservices.com
SIC: 1389 Oil field services
HQ: Cudd Pumping Services, Inc.
    2828 Tech Forest Blvd
    The Woodlands TX 77381

(G-18035)
CUMMINS SOUTHERN PLAINS LLC
Also Called: Southern Plains Power
6226 N Pan Am Expy (78218-4401)
P.O. Box 18385 (78218-0385)
PHONE..............................210 655-5420
Daniel Holbrook, *Manager*
EMP: 37
SQ FT: 10,000
SALES (corp-wide): 19.8B **Publicly Held**
WEB: www.cummins.com
SIC: 5084 3714 Engines & parts, diesel; motor vehicle parts & accessories
HQ: Cummins Southern Plains Llc
    600 N Watson Rd
    Arlington TX 76011
    817 640-6801

(G-18036)
CUSTOM CRUSHED STONE INC
8845 Leslie Rd (78254)
PHONE..............................210 688-3413
Zachary Tausch, *President*
Lloyd Tausch, *Treasurer*
Vernon Tausch, *Shareholder*
Dana Tausch, *Admin Sec*
EMP: 40 EST: 1999
SQ FT: 1,300
SALES (est): 6.2MM **Privately Held**
SIC: 1422 Crushed & broken limestone

(G-18037)
CUSTOM FAB INC
7030 Old Seal Rd (78252)
PHONE..............................210 923-3376
Tom Klingensmith, *Manager*
EMP: 16
SALES (corp-wide): 1.5B **Publicly Held**
WEB: www.uspipe.com
SIC: 3317 Steel pipe & tubes
HQ: Custom Fab, Inc.
    109 5th St
    Orlando FL 32824
    407 859-3954

(G-18038)
CUSTOM PIPING SYSTEMS LLC
4230 Milling Rd (78219-2707)
PHONE..............................210 867-6356
Barry Golobek, *President*
EMP: 50
SALES (est): 8.3MM **Privately Held**
WEB: www.custompipingsystems.com
SIC: 3498 Piping systems for pulp paper & chemical industries

(G-18039)
D & D MACHINERY AND SALES INC
2420 Wr Larson Rd (78261-2200)
P.O. Box 591730 (78259-0136)
PHONE..............................830 438-2309
David Martinez, *President*
Dolores Martinez, *Corp Secy*
Yolanda Bernal, *Vice Pres*
Brad Buchanan, *QC Mgr*
EMP: 15
SQ FT: 30,000
SALES (est): 3.8MM **Privately Held**
WEB: www.ddmach.com
SIC: 3724 Aircraft engines & engine parts

(G-18040)
D & D TWIN PRINT INC
6387 Babcock Rd (78240-2536)
PHONE..............................210 647-7576
Dawn Rangel, *President*
EMP: 10
SALES (est): 1.2MM **Privately Held**
WEB: www.ddtwinprint.com
SIC: 2752 Commercial printing, offset

(G-18041)
DAHILL OFFICE TECHNOLOGY CORP (DH)
8200 W Interstate 10 # 4 (78230-3876)
PHONE..............................210 805-8200
Bradley Rollins, *CEO*
Tony Damaini, *Vice Pres*
Robert Vandever, *CFO*
Tom Meagher, *Manager*
◆ EMP: 119
SQ FT: 35,000
SALES (est): 93.6MM
SALES (corp-wide): 9B **Publicly Held**
WEB: www.dahill.com
SIC: 5999 3861 2759 Business machines & equipment; photographic equipment & supplies; commercial printing

(G-18042)
DAVID LEE ROBERSON
Also Called: Kajun Kuisine
5935 Encanto Point Dr (78244-2501)
PHONE..............................210 662-8215
David Roberson, *Owner*
EMP: 14 EST: 2013
SALES (est): 1.1MM **Privately Held**
SIC: 2099 Food preparations

(G-18043)
DC CADD COMPANY (PA)
Also Called: Enceptia
10010 San Pedro Ave (78216-3862)
PHONE..............................210 732-9212
Fax: 210 525-1202
EMP: 12
SQ FT: 3,000
SALES (est): 8.6MM **Privately Held**
SIC: 7372 Prepackaged Software Services

(G-18044)
DE LA GARZA FENCE COMPANY
6475 Enrique M Barrera Pa (78227-3795)
PHONE..............................210 674-8302
Frank H De La Garza, *President*
Ruben J Solis, *COO*
Nick Dela Garza, *Project Mgr*
Cynthia De La Garza, *Treasurer*
EMP: 26
SQ FT: 30,000
SALES (est): 3.3MM **Privately Held**
WEB: www.delagarzafence.com
SIC: 3496 5039 Fencing, made from purchased wire; wire fence, gates & accessories

GEOGRAPHIC

(G-18045)
DEAN BALDWIN PNTG LTD PARTNR
9800 John Saunders (78216-4202)
PHONE..........................210 293-3528
Barbara Baldwin, *CEO*
Linda Anderson, *Admin Asst*
EMP: 20 **Privately Held**
WEB: www.deanbaldwinpainting.com
SIC: 3721 Aircraft
PA: Dean Baldwin Painting Limited Partnership
2395 Bulverde Rd Ste 105
Bulverde TX 78163

(G-18046)
DEANSTEEL MANUFACTURING CO
931 S Flores St (78204-1406)
PHONE..........................210 226-8271
John H Dean, *CEO*
Gary Rosetta, *President*
Claus Heide, *Exec VP*
Roy Canon, *Vice Pres*
Mike A Gittinger, *Vice Pres*
◆ EMP: 110 EST: 1958
SQ FT: 145,000
SALES: 10.5MM **Privately Held**
WEB: www.deansteel.com
SIC: 5712 3999 Beds & accessories; atomizers, toiletry

(G-18047)
DEFENSE LOGISTICS AGENCY
1014 Zbilly Mitchell Blvd # 1621 (78226)
PHONE..........................210 925-4455
EMP: 20 **Publicly Held**
WEB: www.dla.mil
SIC: 2869 Fuels
HQ: Defense Logistics Agency
8725 John J Kingman Rd # 2533
Fort Belvoir VA 22060

(G-18048)
DELRAY OIL INC (PA)
900 Ne Loop 410 Ste A107 (78209-1482)
PHONE..........................210 824-7214
Walter F Brown, *President*
Walter F Brown Jr, *Vice Pres*
Neeta Huey, *Treasurer*
Mary Lea Ryon, *Admin Sec*
EMP: 10
SQ FT: 7,744
SALES: 1MM **Privately Held**
SIC: 1311 Crude petroleum production

(G-18049)
DELRIO TORTILLA FACTORY (PA)
1402 Gillette Blvd (78224-2111)
PHONE..........................210 922-4810
Esta Perez, *Owner*
Paul Perez, *Co-Owner*
EMP: 24
SQ FT: 3,000
SALES (est): 1.8MM **Privately Held**
WEB: www.delriotortillas.com
SIC: 2099 Tortillas, fresh or refrigerated

(G-18050)
DELTA GRANITE AND MARBLE INC
2011 Sable Ln (78217-6331)
PHONE..........................210 829-7171
David Rymer, *President*
Michael Wiley, *Project Mgr*
Troy Loebel, *Prdtn Mgr*
Monica Gutierrez, *Human Res Dir*
Liz Flessner, *Human Res Mgr*
▲ EMP: 80
SQ FT: 12,000
SALES (est): 18.7MM **Privately Held**
WEB: www.deltagranite.com
SIC: 5032 1741 1743 3281 Granite building stone; marble building stone; ceramic wall & floor tile; stone, crushed or broken; marble masonry, exterior construction; stone masonry; tile installation, ceramic; cut stone & stone products

(G-18051)
DENTSPLY INTERNATIONAL INC
6415 Badcok Rd (78269)
P.O. Box 2846, York PA (17405-2846)
PHONE..........................800 877-0020

Allen McKee, *Sales Staff*
Brad Buss, *Manager*
EMP: 83 EST: 1969
SALES (est): 17.9MM **Privately Held**
WEB: www.dentsplysirona.com
SIC: 3843 Dental equipment & supplies

(G-18052)
DFA DAIRY BRANDS FLUID LLC
Also Called: Oak Farms Dairy
1314 Fredericksburg Rd (78201-5026)
P.O. Box 100507 (78201-8507)
PHONE..........................210 732-1111
Alan Bernon, *President*
Jeff Hulme, *General Mgr*
Raul Salinas, *Engineer*
Brandon Harjo, *Marketing Staff*
Jj Hernandez, *Manager*
EMP: 271
SQ FT: 12,000
SALES (corp-wide): 15.8B **Privately Held**
SIC: 2026 Fluid milk
HQ: Dfa Dairy Brands Fluid, Llc
1405 N 98th St
Kansas City KS 66111
816 801-6455

(G-18053)
DIAL-A-PICK CO
1207 Fulton Ave (78201-5104)
P.O. Box 5802 (78201-0802)
PHONE..........................210 736-1901
Sally Dev, *President*
EMP: 20 EST: 1975
SQ FT: 800
SALES (est): 1.6MM **Privately Held**
SIC: 2499 Toothpicks, wood

(G-18054)
DIAMANTE ENTERPRISES INC
Also Called: Diamond Metal Products
4427 Centergate St (78217-4826)
PHONE..........................210 655-9061
EMP: 16 EST: 1974
SQ FT: 6,000
SALES (est): 5.6MM **Privately Held**
WEB: www.diamondmetalproducts.com
SIC: 3441 5051 Fabricated structural metal; sheets, metal

(G-18055)
DIAMOND GREEN DIESEL LLC (JV) (PA)
1 Valero Way (78249-1616)
P.O. Box 696102 (78269-6102)
PHONE..........................210 345-2009
Gary Steckel, *Opers Mgr*
▲ EMP: 35
SALES (est): 13.8MM **Privately Held**
WEB: www.diamondgreendiesel.com
SIC: 2833 Animal oils, medicinal grade: refined or concentrated

(G-18056)
DIAMOND M DRLG EXPLORATION CO
8620 N New (78217)
PHONE..........................210 310-3135
James P Ford, *President*
Kyle R Ford, *Vice Pres*
Nancy M Ford, *Director*
EMP: 10
SALES (est): 342.4K **Privately Held**
SIC: 1311 5084 Crude petroleum & natural gas; petroleum industry machinery
PA: Ford Resources, Llc
8620 N New Braunfels Ave
San Antonio TX 78217

(G-18057)
DIAMOND SHAMROCK REF & MKTG CO (HQ)
6000 N Loop 1604 W (78249-1100)
P.O. Box 696000 (78269-6000)
PHONE..........................210 345-2000
William E Greehey, *CEO*
John D Gibbons, *Exec VP*
Gregory C King, *Exec VP*
William R Klesse, *Exec VP*
Gary L Arthur Jr, *Senior VP*
EMP: 3200
SQ FT: 115,000

SALES (est): 2.3B
SALES (corp-wide): 108.3B **Publicly Held**
WEB: www.ceodiamond-xpress.com
SIC: 5541 5171 2911 Filling stations, gasoline; petroleum bulk stations & terminals; petroleum refining
PA: Valero Energy Corporation
1 Valero Way
San Antonio TX 78249
210 345-2000

(G-18058)
DIEBOLD NIXDORF INCORPORATED
3453 N Ih 35 Ste 300 (78219-2339)
PHONE..........................210 242-6100
EMP: 10
SALES (corp-wide): 4.6B **Publicly Held**
SIC: 3578 Mfg Calculating Equipment
PA: Diebold Nixdorf, Incorporated
5995 Mayfair Rd
North Canton OH 44720
330 490-4000

(G-18059)
DIGITAL BANNER PLUS LLC
7107 Eckhert Rd Ste 1a (78238-1251)
PHONE..........................210 647-3124
Howard Benavides, *Vice Pres*
Howard A Benavides, *Vice Pres*
EMP: 9
SALES (est): 955K **Privately Held**
WEB: www.digitalbannersplus.com
SIC: 3993 Signs & advertising specialties

(G-18060)
DIGITECH SOLUTIONS GROUP LLC
2121 Mannix Dr (78217-5913)
PHONE..........................210 545-6000
Patric Coldewey, *Mng Member*
◆ EMP: 20
SQ FT: 18,000
SALES (est): 3.3MM **Privately Held**
WEB: www.digitechusa.com
SIC: 7389 5084 3555 Printers' services: folding, collating; printing trades machinery, equipment & supplies; printing trades machinery

(G-18061)
DIMENSION MILLWORKS INC
702 San Fernando St (78207-5041)
P.O. Box 830781 (78283-0781)
PHONE..........................210 281-0356
Ron Hodge, *President*
Barbara Hodge, *Corp Secy*
EMP: 35
SQ FT: 80,000
SALES (est): 3.8MM **Privately Held**
WEB: www.sanantoniomillworks.com
SIC: 2431 Millwork

(G-18062)
DIVERSIFIED PRINTING SVCS INC
1927 W Commerce St (78207-3834)
PHONE..........................210 226-2888
Gilbert Salinas, *President*
Rick Salinas, *General Mgr*
Belen Salinas, *Principal*
EMP: 9
SQ FT: 21,000
SALES (est): 1.2MM **Privately Held**
WEB: www.dpsfoil.com
SIC: 2759 Letterpress printing; embossing on paper

(G-18063)
DIXIE FLAG AND BANNER COMPANY
Also Called: Dixie Manufacturing Company
1930 N Interstate 35 (78208-1925)
P.O. Box 8618 (78208-0618)
PHONE..........................210 227-5039
Henry P Van De Putte Jr, *Ch of Bd*
Vanessa Van De Putte, *President*
Isabella Van De Putte, *Vice Pres*
Vanessa V Deputte, *Marketing Mgr*
Debbi Bevens, *Info Tech Mgr*
◆ EMP: 31
SQ FT: 20,000

SALES (est): 5.3MM **Privately Held**
WEB: www.dixieflag.com
SIC: 5999 2399 Flags; flags, fabric

(G-18064)
DLA DOCUMENT SERVICES
1531 Connally St # 6629 (78236-5512)
PHONE..........................210 671-1407
Lupe Alvarado, *Office Mgr*
EMP: 10 **Publicly Held**
WEB: www.documentservices.dla.mil
SIC: 2752 9711 Commercial printing, lithographic; national security
HQ: Dla Document Services
5450 Carlisle Pike Bldg 9
Mechanicsburg PA 17050
717 605-2362

(G-18065)
DOS CAROLINAS INC
2400 S Flores St (78204-2203)
PHONE..........................210 222-9117
Caroline Matthews, *President*
EMP: 48
SQ FT: 850
SALES (est): 1.3MM **Privately Held**
WEB: www.doscarolinas.com
SIC: 2321 5611 Men's & boys' furnishings; men's & boys' clothing stores

(G-18066)
DPT LABORATORIES LTD
8045 Lindbergh Lndg (78235)
PHONE..........................210 531-7100
Sylvia Hernandez, *Marketing Staff*
John Seik, *Manager*
EMP: 700 **Privately Held**
WEB: www.dptlabs.com
SIC: 2834 Pharmaceutical preparations
PA: Dpt Laboratories, Ltd.
318 Mccullough Ave
San Antonio TX 78215

(G-18067)
DPT LABORATORIES LTD
4040 Broadway Ste 401 (78209-6352)
PHONE..........................210 396-6252
Stacy London, *President*
EMP: 471 **Privately Held**
WEB: www.dptlabs.com
SIC: 2834 Pharmaceutical preparations
PA: Dpt Laboratories, Ltd.
318 Mccullough Ave
San Antonio TX 78215

(G-18068)
DPT LABORATORIES LTD (PA)
318 Mccullough Ave (78215-1833)
PHONE..........................866 225-5378
Paul H Johnson, *President*
Cindy Bertolami, *General Mgr*
Bicky O'Neal, *General Mgr*
Mark Fite, *Senior VP*
Rick Bentzinger, *Vice Pres*
▲ EMP: 105
SQ FT: 258,000
SALES (est): 437.7MM **Privately Held**
WEB: www.dptlabs.com
SIC: 2834 Pharmaceutical preparations

(G-18069)
DPT LABORATORIES LTD
307 E Josephine St (78215-1128)
PHONE..........................210 476-8100
Dan Donohue, *Branch Mgr*
EMP: 700 **Privately Held**
WEB: www.dptlabs.com
SIC: 2834 Pharmaceutical preparations
PA: Dpt Laboratories, Ltd.
318 Mccullough Ave
San Antonio TX 78215

(G-18070)
DPT LABORATORIES LTD
3300 Research Plz (78235-5151)
PHONE..........................210 531-7100
Paul Dorman, *Branch Mgr*
EMP: 700 **Privately Held**
WEB: www.dptlabs.com
SIC: 2834 Pharmaceutical preparations
PA: Dpt Laboratories, Ltd.
318 Mccullough Ave
San Antonio TX 78215

(G-18071)
DRAPERY MAN CORPORATION
Also Called: Royal Window Fashions
2911 Dason Ledge (78258-4591)
PHONE..................................210 733-5444
James Poole, *President*
Nancy Poole, *Vice Pres*
EMP: 26
SALES (est): 3.2MM **Privately Held**
WEB: www.royalwindowfashions.com
SIC: 2591 Blinds vertical

(G-18072)
DSA OPERATING COMPANY LLC
Also Called: Anthony Machine
1235 W Laurel (78201-6432)
PHONE..................................210 734-5121
Jerry McGee, *President*
Mark Gonzalez, *General Mgr*
Tom Menard, *General Mgr*
Eugene Ponomarev, *Engineer*
Johnny Sosa, *Accounts Mgr*
▲ EMP: 40 EST: 1955
SQ FT: 50,000
SALES (est): 11.8MM **Privately Held**
WEB: www.anthonymachine.com
SIC: 3491 3324 3532 Industrial valves;
automatic regulating & control valves;
steel investment foundries; commercial
investment castings, ferrous; mining ma-
chinery; cages, mine shaft

(G-18073)
DUFFIN ENGINE SERVICE
1227 Hallmark Dr (78216-6018)
PHONE..................................210 341-8183
Myrt Duffin, *President*
EMP: 10 EST: 1970
SQ FT: 6,500
SALES (est): 1.4MM **Privately Held**
WEB: www.duffinengine.com
SIC: 3599 Machine shop, jobbing & repair

(G-18074)
DURRSET AMIGOS LTD (PA)
Also Called: Amigos Canning
4669 W Us Highway 90 (78237-4014)
PHONE..................................210 798-5360
Clint McNew, *President*
W L Durrill,
Jerry Setlif,
EMP: 110
SQ FT: 120,000
SALES (est): 26.1MM **Privately Held**
WEB: www.amigosfoods.com
SIC: 2032 2096 Macaroni: packaged in
cans, jars, etc.; tortilla chips

(G-18075)
DYNAMIC DOWNHOLE SERVICES LLC
Also Called: Aqua Services
4714 College Park (78249-4008)
PHONE..................................210 881-9002
John Kelly Pease, *President*
Lincoln Talbert, *CFO*
Robyn Dominguez, *Office Mgr*
James G McClellen, *Mng Member*
EMP: 50
SALES (est): 9.9MM **Privately Held**
WEB: www.dynamicdownhole.com
SIC: 1389 Oil field services

(G-18076)
DYNATOUCH CORPORATION
9901 Broadway Ste 115 (78217-4916)
PHONE..................................210 828-8343
Thomas Mc Clelland, *President*
Tom Glassco, *Vice Pres*
Terri Martin, *Vice Pres*
Vincent Brown, *Sales Staff*
Paul Stahl, *Sales Staff*
EMP: 20
SQ FT: 6,500
SALES (est): 4.9MM **Privately Held**
WEB: www.dynatouch.com
SIC: 3577 Computer peripheral equipment

(G-18077)
E & E ENGINE MACHINE AND PARTS
1602 S Flores St (78204-1621)
PHONE..................................210 225-1141
Rod Eckert, *President*
EMP: 9

SQ FT: 13,000
SALES (est): 1.8MM **Privately Held**
WEB: www.eeengine.com
SIC: 5085 3714 Industrial supplies; re-
building engines & transmissions, factory
basis

(G-18078)
E J WARD INC (PA)
8620 N New Braunfels Ave # 200
(78217-6445)
PHONE..................................210 824-7383
EMP: 40 EST: 1974
SQ FT: 9,000
SALES (est): 13.4MM **Privately Held**
WEB: www.ejward.com
SIC: 3577 Computer peripheral equipment

(G-18079)
E TAMEZ COML RFRGN & AC INC
2403 N Zarzamora St (78201-5410)
P.O. Box 12093 (78212-0093)
PHONE..................................210 884-5059
Richard Tamez, *President*
Mari Tamez, *Vice Pres*
EMP: 9
SQ FT: 600
SALES (est): 900K **Privately Held**
WEB: www.tamezrefrigerationac.com
SIC: 7623 3585 Air conditioning repair; re-
frigerator repair service; refrigeration &
heating equipment

(G-18080)
E-SPECTRUM TECHNOLOGIES INC (PA)
Also Called: AES
12725 Spectrum Dr (78249-3400)
PHONE..................................210 696-8848
Ron Deichert, *General Mgr*
Robert Houston, *Vice Pres*
Roger Moore, *Engineer*
Greg Turner, *Sales Staff*
Daniel P Burris, *Director*
EMP: 15
SQ FT: 10,000
SALES (est): 3MM **Privately Held**
WEB: www.espectech.com
SIC: 8711 3826 Consulting engineer; envi-
ronmental testing equipment

(G-18081)
ECONTROLS LLC (DH)
5757 Farinon Dr (78249-3410)
PHONE..................................210 495-9772
Kennon Guglielmo, *President*
EMP: 300
SALES (est): 1.4MM
SALES (corp-wide): 554.6MM **Publicly Held**
WEB: www.econtrols.com
SIC: 3714 Motor vehicle engines & parts
HQ: Enovation Controls, Llc
5311 S 122nd East Ave
Tulsa OK 74146
918 317-4100

(G-18082)
ECONTROLS GROUP INC (PA)
5757 Farinon Dr (78249-3410)
PHONE..................................210 495-9772
Laura Guglielmo, *Ch of Bd*
Kennon Guglielmo, *President*
▲ EMP: 33
SALES (est): 27.6MM **Privately Held**
WEB: www.econtrols.com
SIC: 3714 8711 Motor vehicle engines &
parts; engineering services

(G-18083)
EDWARD BLOCH LTD
Also Called: Southwestern Wldg & Machining
2751 S Foster Rd (78220-5914)
PHONE..................................210 648-6011
Edward Bloch, *President*
Vicki Bloch, *Corp Secy*
Leonard Reinhard, *Vice Pres*
EMP: 14
SQ FT: 5,000
SALES (est): 1.7MM **Privately Held**
WEB: www.southwesternwelding.com
SIC: 7692 Welding repair

(G-18084)
EGM CLEANING & REMODELING
Also Called: Hinducar
10470 Culebra Rd (78251-3602)
PHONE..................................210 666-0234
Elvin A Varela, *Branch Mgr*
EMP: 9
SALES (corp-wide): 420.2K **Privately Held**
WEB: www.honducartexas.com
SIC: 3479 Painting of metal products
PA: Egm Cleaning & Remodeling
5007 Kallies Cir
San Antonio TX 78251
210 680-4294

(G-18085)
EJ USA INC
12019 Nacogdoches Rd B (78217-2332)
PHONE..................................210 946-3224
Val Velez, *Manager*
EMP: 12 **Privately Held**
WEB: www.eastjordancity.org
SIC: 3321 Pressure pipe & fittings, cast
iron
HQ: Ej Usa, Inc.
301 Spring St
East Jordan MI 49727
800 874-4100

(G-18086)
ELECTRO-COATINGS OF IOWA INC
12015 Radium St (78216-2716)
PHONE..................................800 806-6059
Mark S Freer, *President*
Shannon Sunderland, *CPA*
EMP: 9
SALES (est): 808.1K **Privately Held**
WEB: www.electro-coatings.com
SIC: 3479 Coating electrodes; coating of
metals & formed products

(G-18087)
ELIGIBILITY TRCKNG CALCULATORS
14607 San Pedro Ave # 250 (78232-4356)
PHONE..................................210 323-7846
Matt Scott, *Sales Staff*
Alicia Jordan Haff, *Mng Member*
Rhonny Rowden, *Office Admin*
Lisa Davis, *Consultant*
Kendra Stegemann, *Technology*
EMP: 40
SALES (est): 4.5MM **Privately Held**
WEB:
www.eligibilitytrackingcalculators.com
SIC: 3088 Meteorologic tracking systems

(G-18088)
ELLIOTT ELECTRIC SUPPLY INC
4306 Naco Patx Ste 101 (78217)
PHONE..................................210 646-6950
EMP: 30
SALES (corp-wide): 721.2MM **Privately Held**
SIC: 3699 5063 Electrical Equipment And
Supplies, Nec, N
PA: Elliott Electric Supply, Inc.
2526 N Stallings Dr
Nacogdoches TX 75964
936 569-1184

(G-18089)
EMBROIDERY CONCEPTS
5419 Bandera Rd Ste 701 (78238-1965)
PHONE..................................210 684-8362
Susan Yantis, *Owner*
EMP: 11
SALES (est): 732K **Privately Held**
SIC: 2395 Embroidery & art needlework

(G-18090)
ENGINEERING SPECTRUM INC
Also Called: E S I
5807 Sebastian Pl Ste 13 (78249-2228)
PHONE..................................210 697-8828
Rafael Gomez, *President*
EMP: 13 **Privately Held**
SIC: 3679 8711 Electronic circuits; engi-
neering services
PA: Engineering Spectrum, Incorporated
5920 100th St Sw Ste 1
Tacoma WA

(G-18091)
ENNIS INC
3463 E Commerce St (78220-1322)
PHONE..................................210 271-7971
EMP: 266
SALES (corp-wide): 438.4MM **Publicly Held**
WEB: www.ennis.com
SIC: 3544 Special dies, tools, jigs & fix-
tures
PA: Ennis, Inc.
2441 Presidential Pkwy
Midlothian TX 76065
972 775-9801

(G-18092)
ENTERPRISE HYDROCARBONS LP
1100 La St Fl 10 Flr 10 (78209)
PHONE..................................713 381-6500
Michael Creel, *CEO*
EMP: 69
SALES (est): 382MM
SALES (corp-wide): 32.7B **Publicly Held**
WEB: www.enterpriseproducts.com
SIC: 1389 Processing service, gas
HQ: Enterprise Products Operating Llc
1100 La St Ste Ste 1000
Houston TX 77002

(G-18093)
EOG RESOURCES INC
19100 Ridgewood Pkwy # 2 (78259-1834)
P.O. Box 592929 (78259-0196)
PHONE..................................210 403-7700
Don Gray, *Foreman/Supr*
Marissa Wright, *Opers Staff*
Geri Malcolm, *Opers-Prdtn-Mfg*
Colton Cobb, *Engineer*
Branden Keener, *Engineer*
EMP: 42
SALES (corp-wide): 17.3B **Publicly Held**
WEB: www.eogresources.com
SIC: 1382 1311 Oil & gas exploration serv-
ices; crude petroleum & natural gas
PA: Eog Resources, Inc.
1111 Bagby Sky Lbby 2
Houston TX 77002
713 651-7000

(G-18094)
EPIC Y-GRADE MARKETING LP
18615 Tuscany Stone # 30 (78258-3486)
PHONE..................................210 920-2285
Phil Mezey, *Partner*
Eric Friedrichs, *Partner*
Justin Gordon, *Partner*
Bob Smith, *Partner*
EMP: 50
SALES (est): 1.6MM **Privately Held**
WEB: www.epicmid.com
SIC: 1382 Oil & gas exploration services

(G-18095)
ESPEY SILICA SAND CO INC
Also Called: A-1 Sand Company
27265 Us Highway 281 S (78264-3749)
PHONE..................................210 626-2800
Edwin E Espey Jr, *President*
Espey Justin, *Vice Pres*
EMP: 10
SALES (est): 1.2MM **Privately Held**
WEB: www.sssand.com
SIC: 1446 Silica sand mining

(G-18096)
ESSKAY MANUFACTURING CO
122 Stribling (78204-1915)
P.O. Box 830068 (78283-0068)
PHONE..................................210 222-9585
Ray H Patterson, *President*
Hugh Patterson, *Vice Pres*
Sharon Beiter, *Controller*
▼ EMP: 100 EST: 1936
SQ FT: 65,000
SALES (est): 25MM **Privately Held**
SIC: 2311 2325 5136 Suits, men's &
boys': made from purchased materials;
trousers, dress (separate): men's, youths'
& boys'; shirts, men's & boys'

(G-18097)
EUCLID MEDIA GROUP LLC
Also Called: San Antonio Current
915 Dallas St (78215-1433)
PHONE..................................210 227-0044

Alejandra Lopez, *Editor*
Jenavie Aguilar, *Accounts Exec*
Ashley McLean, *Marketing Staff*
Joseph Rodriquez, *Marketing Staff*
Michael Wagner, *Manager*
EMP: 25
SALES (corp-wide): 3.8MM **Privately Held**
WEB: www.euclidmediagroup.com
SIC: 2711 Newspapers, publishing & printing
PA: Euclid Media Group Llc
737 Bolivar Rd
Cleveland OH 44115
216 241-7550

(G-18098)
EUREKA SHEET METAL INC
550 Delgado St (78207-1700)
PHONE.................................210 735-4426
Manuel Elizondo, *President*
Laura Elizondo, *Admin Sec*
EMP: 19
SQ FT: 12,000
SALES (est): 3.1MM **Privately Held**
SIC: 3444 Sheet metalwork

(G-18099)
EXIDE TECHNOLOGIES LLC
8569 Ne Loop 410 Ste 150 (78219-3322)
PHONE.................................210 662-8999
Kiki Hiatt, *Sales Staff*
Carlton Reed, *Manager*
EMP: 11
SALES (corp-wide): 2.1B **Privately Held**
WEB: www.exide.com
SIC: 5063 3629 Storage batteries, industrial; battery chargers, rectifying or nonrotating
PA: Exide Technologies, Llc
13000 Drfeld Pkwy Bldg 20
Milton GA 30004
678 566-9000

(G-18100)
EXPRESS INFO SYSTEMS INC (PA)
4115 Medical Dr Ste 604 (78229-5639)
P.O. Box 691261 (78269-1261)
PHONE.................................210 614-9410
Iris Etz Schimke, *President*
Cheryl Aceto, *Vice Pres*
Rana Camargo, *Sales Dir*
Stacey Campbell, *Accounts Mgr*
Jim Scarff, *Consultant*
EMP: 14
SQ FT: 25,000
SALES (est): 2.6MM **Privately Held**
WEB: www.expressinfo.com
SIC: 7372 Business oriented computer software

(G-18101)
EZNECTAR LLC
246 Early Trl (78228-3829)
PHONE.................................210 732-6400
David Hill, *CEO*
Kristie Hill, *VP Admin*
EMP: 10
SQ FT: 2,000
SALES (est): 700K **Privately Held**
WEB: www.eznectar.com
SIC: 2048 Canned pet food (except dog & cat)

(G-18102)
FABRICATION & MFG ALIANCE LLC
4614 Sinclair Rd (78222-2039)
PHONE.................................210 648-3131
Dale Patenaude, *Principal*
Trey Hall, *Principal*
Jorge Hernandez, *Principal*
EMP: 99
SALES (est): 5.2MM **Privately Held**
SIC: 3769 Guided missile & space vehicle parts & auxiliary equipment

(G-18103)
FALCON PROSOLUTIONS INC
16026 University Oak (78249-4013)
PHONE.................................210 547-2741
▲ **EMP:** 20 **EST:** 2009
SALES (est): 4.7MM **Privately Held**
WEB: www.efalcon-inc.com
SIC: 3589 Commercial cleaning equipment

(G-18104)
FAR SOUTH MINING LLC
8845 Leslie Rd (78254)
PHONE.................................210 688-2607
Zachary Tausch, *Principal*
EMP: 9
SALES (est): 1.6MM **Privately Held**
WEB: www.farsouthmining.com
SIC: 3273 Ready-mixed concrete

(G-18105)
FASSCO MANUFACTURING INC
3248 Northwestern (78238-4043)
PHONE.................................210 523-0800
Craig Swanson, *CEO*
EMP: 75 **EST:** 2001
SALES (est): 3.1MM **Privately Held**
WEB: www.taprite.com
SIC: 3999 Manufacturing industries

(G-18106)
FASTEEL LLC
4900 Center Park Blvd (78218-4407)
PHONE.................................210 661-2603
Luis Aranda, *Principal*
EMP: 9
SALES (est): 1.3MM **Privately Held**
WEB: www.fasteel.net
SIC: 3325 Steel foundries

(G-18107)
FEDEX OFFICE & PRINT SVCS INC
4418 Broadway (78209-6208)
PHONE.................................210 821-6911
EMP: 22
SALES (corp-wide): 69.2B **Publicly Held**
WEB: www.fedex.com
SIC: 7334 2789 2759 2752 Photocopying & duplicating services; bookbinding & related work; commercial printing; commercial printing, lithographic
HQ: Fedex Office And Print Services, Inc.
7900 Legacy Dr
Plano TX 75024
800 463-3339

(G-18108)
FEDEX OFFICE & PRINT SVCS INC
5755 Nw Loop 410 Ste 101 (78238-1662)
PHONE.................................210 521-8395
EMP: 15
SALES (corp-wide): 69.2B **Publicly Held**
WEB: www.fedex.com
SIC: 7334 3993 2759 Photocopying & duplicating services; signs & advertising specialties; commercial printing
HQ: Fedex Office And Print Services, Inc.
7900 Legacy Dr
Plano TX 75024
800 463-3339

(G-18109)
FENCECRETE AMERICA INC (PA)
15089 Tradesman (78249-1342)
PHONE.................................210 492-7911
Yuda Doliner, *President*
Jaime Rapaport, *Vice Pres*
Alexis Garcia, *Sales Staff*
Laura Sheffy, *Technology*
Leonard Holzman, *Admin Sec*
EMP: 120
SQ FT: 3,600
SALES (est): 32.8MM **Privately Held**
WEB: www.fencecrete.com
SIC: 1741 3272 Concrete block masonry laying; concrete products, precast

(G-18110)
FGF LLC (HQ)
Also Called: Fgf Texas
122 Stribling (78204-1915)
PHONE.................................210 475-9981
Ojus Ajmera, *CEO*
Tejus Ajmera, *Co-CEO*
EMP: 520
SQ FT: 283,000
SALES (est): 84.7MM
SALES (corp-wide): 1.2B **Privately Held**
WEB: www.fgfbrands.com
SIC: 2051 Bakery: wholesale or wholesale/retail combined

PA: Fgf Brands Inc
1295 Ormont Dr
Toronto ON M9L 2
905 761-3333

(G-18111)
FGF LLC
9910 Teal Ave (78224-3073)
PHONE.................................210 475-9981
Albert Salinas, *Branch Mgr*
EMP: 30
SALES (corp-wide): 1.2B **Privately Held**
WEB: www.fgfbrands.com
SIC: 2053 Frozen bakery products, except bread
HQ: Fgf Llc
122 Stribling
San Antonio TX 78204
210 475-9981

(G-18112)
FIBER GLASS SYSTEMS LP (HQ)
Also Called: Smith Fibercast
2425 Sw 36th St (78237-4026)
PHONE.................................210 477-7500
William Burnett, *President*
◆ **EMP:** 70 **EST:** 1968
SQ FT: 52,000
SALES (est): 44.1MM
SALES (corp-wide): 8.4B **Publicly Held**
WEB: www.nov.com
SIC: 3229 3084 3089 Glass fiber products; plastics pipe; fittings for pipe, plastic
PA: National Oilwell Varco, Inc.
7909 Parkwood Circle Dr
Houston TX 77036
713 346-7500

(G-18113)
FILESTACK
118 Broadway St Ste 627 (78205-1983)
PHONE.................................210 364-1833
Edward Byrne, *Principal*
Lew Moorman, *Principal*
Michael Dougherty, *CFO*
David Hoffman, *Marketing Staff*
EMP: 11
SALES (est): 318.2K **Privately Held**
WEB: www.filestack.com
SIC: 7372 Prepackaged software

(G-18114)
FILTRATION PRODUCTS LLC
1218 N Hackberry St (78202-1111)
PHONE.................................210 805-0200
David M Dilling, *Principal*
Keith Blessing, *Sales Staff*
Will Edger, *Mng Member*
EMP: 20
SALES (est): 2.9MM **Privately Held**
WEB: www.filtrationproducts.com
SIC: 3569 Filters

(G-18115)
FINCK CIGAR CO
12923 Jnes Maltsberger Rd (78247-4218)
PHONE.................................210 226-4191
Henry W Finck Sr, *President*
Felipe Gonzales, *General Mgr*
Henry W Finck Jr, *Treasurer*
Delia Quiroga, *Human Res Mgr*
Letty Molina, *Office Mgr*
◆ **EMP:** 80 **EST:** 1893
SALES (est): 13.2MM **Privately Held**
WEB: www.finckcigarcompany.com
SIC: 2121 5961 Cigars; catalog sales

(G-18116)
FLEXCON INDUSTRIAL LLC
6110 Rittiman Rd (78218-4715)
PHONE.................................210 798-1900
Neil McDonough, *President*
EMP: 27
SALES (corp-wide): 333.1MM **Privately Held**
WEB: www.flexconindustrial.com
SIC: 3999 Chairs, hydraulic, barber & beauty shop
HQ: Flexcon Industrial Llc
1 S Spencer Rd
Spencer MA 01562

(G-18117)
FLORENCIO VILLANUEVA
233 E Malone Ave (78214-1227)
PHONE.................................210 534-4879
Florencio Villanueva, *Owner*
EMP: 150
SALES (est): 5.8MM **Privately Held**
SIC: 3241 Masonry cement

(G-18118)
FLOWERS BKG CO SAN ANTONIO LLC (HQ)
Also Called: Butter Krust Thrift Shop
6000 Ne Loop 410 (78218-5424)
PHONE.................................210 661-2361
Ryan Barrios, *President*
Mark Poskon, *General Mgr*
Alberto Escobar, *Superintendent*
Martin Saldivar, *Superintendent*
Jeff Luce, *Corp Secy*
EMP: 290 **EST:** 1994
SQ FT: 250,000
SALES (est): 133.3MM
SALES (corp-wide): 4.1B **Publicly Held**
SIC: 2051 Bread, all types (white, wheat, rye, etc): fresh or frozen; buns, bread type: fresh or frozen
PA: Flowers Foods, Inc.
1919 Flowers Cir
Thomasville GA 31757
912 226-9110

(G-18119)
FMC TECHNOLOGIES INC
8620 N New Braunfels Ave (78217-4000)
PHONE.................................361 290-9795
Mario Lagunes, *Marketing Staff*
Jhonatan Gonzalez, *Branch Mgr*
EMP: 29
SALES (corp-wide): 13.4B **Privately Held**
WEB: www.technipfmc.com
SIC: 3533 Oil field machinery & equipment
HQ: Fmc Technologies, Inc.
11740 Katy Fwy Enrgy Twr
Houston TX 77079
281 591-4000

(G-18120)
FOOTPRINT MEDICAL INC
12727 Cimarron Path (78249-3405)
PHONE.................................210 226-2600
Robert Davis, *President*
Robert E Davis, *President*
Jeremy M Davis, *Senior VP*
Kevin B Mack, *Senior VP*
EMP: 35
SQ FT: 10,500
SALES (est): 1.4MM **Privately Held**
WEB: www.footprintmed.com
SIC: 3841 Surgical & medical instruments

(G-18121)
FORGE ENERGY LLC
15727 Anthem Pkwy Ste 501 (78249-4157)
PHONE.................................210 478-5950
Barry Winstead, *CEO*
Danny Boone, *Exec VP*
Arnold Nall, *Exec VP*
Matt Gentry, *Vice Pres*
Pat Laursen, *Vice Pres*
EMP: 35 **EST:** 2011
SALES (est): 26MM **Privately Held**
WEB: www.forgenergy.com
SIC: 1381 Drilling oil & gas wells

(G-18122)
FORMA AUTOMOTIVE LLC
1 Lone Star Pass Ste 1105 (78264-3638)
PHONE.................................210 212-4400
Rosa Santana, *CEO*
EMP: 19
SQ FT: 4,072
SALES (corp-wide): 5.7MM **Privately Held**
WEB: www.ihcus.com
SIC: 3714 Motor vehicle body components & frame
PA: Forma Automotive, Llc
45 Ne Loop 410 Ste 902
San Antonio TX 78216
210 888-0410

(G-18123)
FORMA AUTOMOTIVE LLC (PA)
45 Ne Loop 410 Ste 902 (78216-5831)
PHONE.................................210 888-0410

Rosa Santana, *CEO*
Fernando Peralta, *CFO*
Pat Franco, *Manager*
EMP: 13 EST: 2015
SALES (est): 5.7MM **Privately Held**
WEB: www.ihcus.com
SIC: 3714 Motor vehicle body components
& frame

(G-18124)
FORUM INDUSTRIES INC
Also Called: Forum-Direct
1400 Currency St (78219-2610)
P.O. Box 200025 (78220-0025)
PHONE...................................210 225-9600
Thomas McKown, *CEO*
Cindy Garza, *Materials Mgr*
Melanie McKown, *Treasurer*
Barbara Maus, *Controller*
George Weiss, *Sales Dir*
▲ **EMP:** 75 EST: 2001
SQ FT: 42,000
SALES (est): 8.8MM **Privately Held**
WEB: www.forum-direct.com
SIC: 7389 2385 Sewing contractor; water-
proof outerwear; raincoats, except vulcan-
ized rubber: purchased materials

(G-18125)
FRANKS MANUFACTURING CO
1336 W Blanco Rd (78232-1014)
PHONE...................................210 492-3222
James Franks, *President*
Linda Franks, *Vice Pres*
Douglas Franks, *Shareholder*
EMP: 10
SQ FT: 20,000
SALES (est): 2.1MM **Privately Held**
WEB: www.franksmanufacturing.com
SIC: 3089 Thermoformed finished plastic
products

(G-18126)
**FREDDYS FRZ CSTARD
STAKBURGERS**
5415 W Loop 1604 N (78253-7307)
PHONE...................................210 521-5400
Sean Kypke, *General Mgr*
EMP: 40 EST: 2012
SALES (est): 540.6K **Privately Held**
WEB: www.freddysusa.com
SIC: 5812 2024 Ice cream stands or dairy
bars; custard, frozen

(G-18127)
**FRITO-LAY NORTH AMERICA
INC**
4855 Greatland (78218-5380)
PHONE...................................210 662-2100
Carmen Bridges, *Business Mgr*
Sam Hernandez, *Project Mgr*
Elsa Delacruz, *Purch Mgr*
Wendy Agee, *Planning Mgr*
Kevin Brightwell, *Director*
EMP: 450
SQ FT: 181,566
SALES (corp-wide): 67.1B **Publicly Held**
WEB: www.fritolay.com
SIC: 2096 2099 Corn chips & other corn-
based snacks; potato chips & other po-
tato-based snacks; food preparations
HQ: Frito-Lay North America, Inc.
7701 Legacy Dr
Plano TX 75024

(G-18128)
FRONTIER SERVICES INC (PA)
21222 Gathering Oak # 102 (78260-3100)
P.O. Box 4037, Alice (78333-4037)
PHONE...................................210 520-1118
Richard McGehee, *President*
Denise Walker, *Vice Pres*
Denise Garza, *Manager*
EMP: 45
SQ FT: 8,000
SALES (est): 39.1MM **Privately Held**
WEB: www.frontierservicesinc.com
SIC: 1389 Testing, measuring, surveying &
analysis services; oil field services

(G-18129)
**FTS INTERNATIONAL SERVICES
LLC**
70 Ne Loop 410 (78216-5849)
PHONE...................................210 308-3400

EMP: 11 **Publicly Held**
WEB: www.ftsi.com
SIC: 3561 Pumps & pumping equipment
HQ: Fts International Services, Llc
777 Main St Ste 2900
Fort Worth TX 76102
817 862-2000

(G-18130)
FULLERS ALAMO SAFE & LOCK
3723 West Ave (78213-3641)
PHONE...................................210 344-4523
Melinda Fuller, *CEO*
Gilbert Cantu, *President*
Jonathan Fuller, *President*
Justin Fuller, *Vice Pres*
EMP: 9
SQ FT: 11,725
SALES (est): 1.4MM **Privately Held**
WEB: www.alamosafeandlock.com
SIC: 7699 3499 Locksmith shop; locks,
safe & vault: metal

(G-18131)
FURNITURE BY THURSTON
2 Winnco Dr (78218-5201)
P.O. Box 565821, Dallas (75356-5821)
PHONE...................................210 227-4747
Kelly L O'Donnell, *CEO*
◆ **EMP:** 105
SQ FT: 60,000
SALES (est): 13MM
SALES (corp-wide): 17.1MM **Privately
Held**
SIC: 2531 School furniture
PA: Kln Steel Products Company Llc
1161 Empire Central Dr
Dallas TX 75247
210 227-4747

(G-18132)
**FUTABA INDUSTRIAL TEXAS
CORP**
1 Lone Star Pass Bldg 34 (78264-3641)
PHONE...................................210 927-2288
Yoshikazu Kuwahara, *President*
Mike Nisshi, *President*
Lance Biddle, *Production*
Hiroshi Ishikawa, *Treasurer*
Miguel Jimenez, *Manager*
▲ **EMP:** 220
SQ FT: 566,300
SALES (est): 51.9MM **Privately Held**
WEB: www.futabasangyo.com
SIC: 3462 Automotive & internal combus-
tion engine forgings
HQ: Fic America Corp.
485 E Lies Rd
Carol Stream IL 60188

(G-18133)
GAMBRINUS COMPANY (PA)
Also Called: Shiner Bock
14800 San Pedro Ave # 310 (78232-3735)
PHONE...................................210 483-5100
Carlos Alvarez, *President*
James Bolz, *President*
John Horan, *Corp Secy*
Tess Liberto, *Opers Mgr*
James J O'Sullivan, *CFO*
▲ **EMP:** 80
SQ FT: 10,000
SALES (est): 237.4MM **Privately Held**
WEB: www.gambrinus.com
SIC: 5181 2082 Beer & other fermented
malt liquors; beer (alcoholic beverage)

(G-18134)
GAMEBREAKER INC
4404 N Interstate 35 (78218-5213)
PHONE...................................818 224-7424
EMP: 12
SALES (corp-wide): 2.7MM **Privately
Held**
WEB: www.gamebreaker.com
SIC: 3949 Sporting & athletic goods
PA: Gamebreaker, Inc.
31324 Via Colinas Ste 102
Westlake Village CA 91362
818 224-7424

(G-18135)
GANDY ENGINEERING LLC
Also Called: Gandy Digital
5750 Northwest Pkwy # 850 (78249-3367)
PHONE...................................210 338-8303

James Gandy, *President*
Satish Semwal, *Engineer*
David Doyle, *Human Res Dir*
Cristian Valdiviezo, *Sales Staff*
Ann Robaye, *Office Mgr*
EMP: 10
SQ FT: 7,500
SALES (est): 7.7MM **Privately Held**
WEB: www.gandydigital.com
SIC: 3555 Printing trade parts & attach-
ments

(G-18136)
GARCIA FOODS INC
Also Called: Andy Garcia Foods
1802 Jackson Keller Rd (78213-2517)
PHONE...................................210 349-6262
Louis R Garcia, *President*
Yvonne Gottwald, *President*
Andy Garcia, *Principal*
Andrew E Garcia, *Corp Secy*
Kenneth D Garcia, *Vice Pres*
EMP: 120 EST: 1956
SQ FT: 40,000
SALES (est): 1.4MM **Privately Held**
WEB: www.garciafoods.com
SIC: 2032 Mexican foods: packaged in
cans, jars, etc.

(G-18137)
**GENERAL DYNMICS MSSION
SYSTEMS**
389 E Ramsey Rd (78216-4636)
PHONE...................................210 524-8200
Fred Santos, *Mfg Staff*
Joseph Frias, *Purchasing*
Stan Bottoms, *Chief Engr*
Don Boulanger, *Engineer*
Ted Dacosta, *Engineer*
EMP: 120
SALES (corp-wide): 37.9B **Publicly Held**
WEB: www.gdmissionsystems.com
SIC: 3571 Electronic computers
HQ: General Dynamics Mission Systems,
Inc.
12450 Fair Lakes Cir
Fairfax VA 22033
877 449-0600

(G-18138)
GENERAL LED OPCO LLC (PA)
Also Called: Agilight
1074 Arion Cir Ste 116 (78216-3085)
P.O. Box 461689 (78246-1689)
PHONE...................................210 360-1444
Steven Mayo, *CEO*
Bradley Philip, *CFO*
Stephanie Irwin, *Credit Mgr*
Gray Lankford, *Manager*
EMP: 13
SALES (est): 7.7MM **Privately Held**
WEB: www.genledbrands.com
SIC: 3674 Light emitting diodes

(G-18139)
GEORGE W COX & SONS INC
Also Called: Autotest
5347 Dietrich Rd (78219-2909)
PHONE...................................210 661-8661
Robert Cox, *Ch of Bd*
Zhang Ling-Ling, *General Mgr*
Reeves Moore, *General Mgr*
Michael McGregor, *Vice Pres*
Robert Moyer, *Vice Pres*
EMP: 25
SQ FT: 11,600
SALES (est): 5MM **Privately Held**
WEB: www.autotest.com
SIC: 3825 Test equipment for electronic &
electrical circuits

(G-18140)
GILES EFTON
8523 Ne Loop 410 (78219-3333)
P.O. Box 700928 (78270-0928)
PHONE...................................210 662-2800
Efton Giles, *Owner*
Kim Evans, *Co-Owner*
EMP: 45
SALES (est): 3.6MM **Privately Held**
SIC: 2429 Special product sawmills

(G-18141)
GL AUTOMOTIVE LLC
13602 Applewhite Rd (78224-3173)
PHONE...................................925 360-3937

Scott Granneman,
EMP: 12
SALES (est): 458.2K **Privately Held**
SIC: 3089 Automotive parts, plastic

(G-18142)
**GLASS SAMUELS COMPANY
LLC (PA)**
3011 Ne Loop 410 Ste 120 (78218-1567)
PHONE...................................210 227-2481
Gary Haverda, *President*
Jenni Haverda, *Vice Pres*
Martha Samuels, *Vice Pres*
Andy Rapstine, *Project Mgr*
EMP: 57 EST: 1914
SQ FT: 78,000
SALES (est): 10.7MM **Privately Held**
WEB: www.samuelsglass.com
SIC: 3231 5039 3229 3442 Products of
purchased glass; glass construction ma-
terials; pressed & blown glass; window &
door frames; glass

(G-18143)
GLAXOSMITHKLINE LLC
12522 Wandering Trl (78249-2111)
PHONE...................................210 627-0572
EMP: 26
SALES (corp-wide): 43.6B **Privately Held**
WEB: www.us.gsk.com
SIC: 2834 Pharmaceutical preparations
HQ: Glaxosmithkline Llc
5 Crescent Dr
Philadelphia PA 19112
215 751-4000

(G-18144)
**GLO-JO ELECTRICAL
PRODUCTS INC**
Also Called: Epi
10000 W Commerce St (78227-1300)
PHONE...................................210 673-3583
EMP: 25 EST: 1967
SQ FT: 20,000
SALES (est): 4.5MM **Privately Held**
SIC: 3625 3699 Mfg Relays/Industrial
Controls Mfg Electrical Equipment/Sup-
plies

(G-18145)
GLOBAL 360 BGS INC
10537 Gulfdale St (78216-3602)
PHONE...................................210 826-5501
Rob Allen, *Manager*
EMP: 50
SALES (corp-wide): 3.1B **Privately Held**
WEB: www.opentext.com
SIC: 3537 Platforms, stands, tables, pallets
& similar equipment
PA: Open Text Corporation
275 Frank Tompa Dr
Waterloo ON N2L 0
519 888-7111

(G-18146)
GLOBAL DISPENSE
6203 Krempen Ave 102 (78233-4585)
PHONE...................................210 310-2337
Ron Finnerty, *Principal*
Francisco Lopez, *Vice Pres*
▲ **EMP:** 11
SALES (est): 1.2MM **Privately Held**
WEB: www.globaldispense.com
SIC: 2086 Carbonated beverages, nonal-
coholic: bottled & canned

(G-18147)
GLOBAL MANUFACTURING LLC
Also Called: 900 Global Manufacturing
1303 Rilling Rd (78214-3200)
PHONE...................................210 598-4100
John W Chrisman III, *Mng Member*
▲ **EMP:** 20
SALES (est): 2.5MM **Privately Held**
WEB: www.900global.com
SIC: 3949 Bowling balls

(G-18148)
**GLOBAL OPERATIONS TEXAS
LP**
Also Called: Dahill Industries
8200 W Interstate 10 # 400 (78230-3876)
PHONE...................................915 595-2250
Michelle Hartman, *Vice Pres*
Joe Ramirez, *Opers Mgr*

David Reynosa, *Facilities Mgr*
Estella Lazar, *Purchasing*
Pam Murphy, *Accountant*
EMP: 17
SALES (corp-wide): 12.3MM **Privately Held**
WEB: www.southwest.xeroxbusinesssolutions.com
SIC: 3999 Atomizers, toiletry
PA: Global Operations Texas, L.P.,
8200 W Interstate 10 # 4
San Antonio TX 78230
210 805-8200

(G-18149)
GLOBAL PLUS TRADING CO LLC
7100 San Pedro Ave # 310 (78216-6218)
PHONE..........................210 807-0190
Felix Mellado,
EMP: 10
SALES (est): 896.2K **Privately Held**
WEB: www.globalplustrading.com
SIC: 2672 Coated & laminated paper

(G-18150)
GLOBALSCAPE INC (DH)
4500 Lockhill Selma Rd (78249-3552)
PHONE..........................210 308-8267
Robert H Alpert, *Ch of Bd*
Leah Webb, *Partner*
Paul Judkins, *Business Mgr*
Mark C Hood, *COO*
Michael P Canavan, *Exec VP*
EMP: 82
SQ FT: 21,000
SALES: 40.3MM
SALES (corp-wide): 350.9MM **Privately Held**
WEB: www.globalscape.com
SIC: 7372 Prepackaged software
HQ: Help/Systems, Llc
6455 City West Pkwy
Eden Prairie MN 55344
952 933-0609

(G-18151)
GOODMAN FINE ART INC
4226 Blanco Rd (78212-1100)
PHONE..........................210 733-0190
William Goodman, *President*
EMP: 11
SALES (est): 900K **Privately Held**
WEB: www.goodmansignart.com
SIC: 3993 Signs & advertising specialties

(G-18152)
GREAT TEXAS COMPRESSION LLC
18615 Tuscany Stone # 39 (78258-3486)
PHONE..........................210 569-6742
Martin Kaler, *President*
EMP: 10
SALES (est): 1.3MM **Privately Held**
WEB: www.greattexascompression.com
SIC: 1389 Gas compressing (natural gas) at the fields

(G-18153)
GREEN WOOD MILLING LLC
3510 Barrington St (78217-4650)
P.O. Box 1626, Converse (78109-6126)
PHONE..........................210 544-5777
Dacia II Napier,
EMP: 10
SALES (est): 1.2MM **Privately Held**
WEB: www.greenwoodmilling.com
SIC: 2431 Millwork

(G-18154)
GRUMA CORPORATION
Also Called: Mission Foods
4340 Dividend (78219-2614)
PHONE..........................210 304-6700
Arnold Olivarez, *Sales Staff*
Sergio Paez, *Manager*
EMP: 120 **Privately Held**
WEB: www.missionfoods.com
SIC: 2096 2099 Tortilla chips; food preparations
HQ: Gruma Corporation
5601 Executive Dr Ste 800
Irving TX 75038
972 232-5000

(G-18155)
GUENTHER FAMILY LP
153 Treeline Park Ste 300 (78209-1880)
PHONE..........................210 829-1800
EMP: 9 EST: 1999
SALES (est): 702.3K **Privately Held**
WEB: www.guentherhouse.com
SIC: 1381 Drilling oil & gas wells

(G-18156)
GULF BUSINESS FORMS SYSTEMS
434 W Nakoma St (78216-2623)
PHONE..........................210 265-1620
Mike Morgan, *VP Bus Dvlpt*
James Burkhalter, *Branch Mgr*
EMP: 10
SALES (corp-wide): 3MM **Privately Held**
WEB: www.gulfbusinessprinting.com
SIC: 2752 Commercial printing, offset
PA: Gulf Business Forms Systems Inc
6317 Harwick Dr
Corpus Christi TX 78417
361 853-9877

(G-18157)
GW PLASTICS SAN ANTONIO INC
901 Paulsun St (78219-3125)
PHONE..........................210 225-1516
Brenan Riehlk, *President*
Arthur Bennert, *Vice Pres*
John Hellsten, *Opers Mgr*
Ed Immel, *Safety Mgr*
Kenneth Werdebaugh, *Opers Spvr*
▲ **EMP:** 200
SQ FT: 30,000
SALES (est): 54.5MM
SALES (corp-wide): 821.9MM **Privately Held**
WEB: www.gwplastics.com
SIC: 3089 Injection molding of plastics
HQ: Nolato Gw, Inc.
239 Pleasant St
Bethel VT 05032
802 234-9941

(G-18158)
H W D CASINGS INC
5010 Interstate 10 E (78219-3300)
PHONE..........................210 661-6161
Howard W Dewied, *President*
George Burt, *Vice Pres*
Aaron Gage, *VP Sales*
Jorge Iparraguirre, *Prgrmr*
Chad Baumgartner, *Representative*
◆ **EMP:** 65 **EST:** 1932
SQ FT: 25,600
SALES (est): 19.4MM **Privately Held**
WEB: www.dewied.net
SIC: 2013 Sausage casings, natural

(G-18159)
HARRISON GYPSUM LLC
Also Called: Acg Materials
302 Casa Blanca (78215-1234)
PHONE..........................210 225-9502
Barbara Nunez, *Administration*
EMP: 10
SALES (corp-wide): 1.7B **Publicly Held**
WEB: www.arcosaspecialtymaterials.com
SIC: 1442 1382 Construction sand & gravel; oil & gas exploration services
HQ: Harrison Gypsum, Llc
1550 Double C Dr
Norman OK 73069
405 366-9500

(G-18160)
HAWKINS RMOTE SNSING EXPLRTION
8531 N New Braunfels Ave # 201 (78217-6387)
PHONE..........................210 829-5330
Alf Hawkins, *Owner*
EMP: 30
SALES (est): 1.1MM **Privately Held**
SIC: 1382 7389 Oil & gas exploration services; photogrammatic mapping

(G-18161)
HEARST CORPORATION
Also Called: San Antonio Light
420 Broadway St (78205-1928)
P.O. Box 161 (78291-0161)
PHONE..........................210 271-2700
George B Irish, *Publisher*
Salvatore Del Giudice, *General Mgr*
Amy L Smith, *Editor*
Kevin J Johnson, *Opers Staff*
Gilbert Alfaro, *Purch Mgr*
EMP: 700
SALES (corp-wide): 7.9B **Privately Held**
WEB: www.hearst.com
SIC: 2711 Newspapers, publishing & printing
PA: The Hearst Corporation
300 W 57th St Fl 42
New York NY 10019
212 649-2000

(G-18162)
HEARST CORPORATION
Also Called: San Antonio Express News
301 Avenue E (78205-2006)
P.O. Box 2171 (78297-2171)
PHONE..........................210 250-3000
John C McKeon, *President*
Ellen Koskinas, *Managing Dir*
Henry Krausse, *Editor*
Audrey Lee, *Editor*
Nora Lopez, *Editor*
EMP: 800
SALES (corp-wide): 7.9B **Privately Held**
WEB: www.hearst.com
SIC: 2711 Newspapers, publishing & printing
PA: The Hearst Corporation
300 W 57th St Fl 42
New York NY 10019
212 649-2000

(G-18163)
HEB PLUS
8219 Marbach Rd (78227-1652)
PHONE..........................210 673-4900
Mary Bernie, *Principal*
EMP: 35
SALES (est): 3.5MM **Privately Held**
SIC: 2099 Food preparations

(G-18164)
HELMY ASSOCIATES & CO INC
7334 Caribou (78238-1230)
PHONE..........................210 681-0101
Mona T Helmy, *President*
Ruben Castro, *Manager*
Abel Trinidad, *Maintence Staff*
EMP: 22
SQ FT: 45,000
SALES (est): 3.9MM **Privately Held**
WEB: www.helmyplastics.com
SIC: 3089 Plastic containers, except foam; injection molding of plastics

(G-18165)
HERO ASSEMBLERS LP
1 Lone Star Pass Ste 1101 (78264-3439)
PHONE..........................210 628-4800
Ray Romero, *Partner*
Frank Herrera Jr, *Partner*
EMP: 21
SALES (est): 12.1MM **Privately Held**
SIC: 3549 Assembly machines, including robotic

(G-18166)
HIGH LINE RANCH LLC
8526 N New Braunfels Ave (78217-6304)
PHONE..........................830 875-5386
Travis Davis, *President*
Ryan Acker, *Vice Pres*
Walt Dyer, *Opers Staff*
Wayne Schroeder, *CFO*
Frank W Davis II,
EMP: 70
SQ FT: 2,000
SALES (est): 41MM **Privately Held**
SIC: 1311 Crude petroleum & natural gas

(G-18167)
HIGUCHI MANUFACTURING AMER LLC
Also Called: Higuchi International
14901 Southton Rd (78223)
PHONE..........................210 633-2877

Nariie Higuchi, *President*
▲ **EMP:** 130
SALES (est): 28.2MM **Privately Held**
WEB: www.hig-jp.net
SIC: 3829 3545 3089 3548 Measuring & controlling devices; tools & accessories for machine tools; injection molding of plastics; welding & cutting apparatus & accessories
HQ: Higuchi International Corporation
14901 Southton Rd
Elmendorf TX 78112
210 633-2877

(G-18168)
HIROKO INTERNATIONAL INC
6185 Camp Bullis Rd (78257-9730)
PHONE..........................210 590-4411
John Booten, *President*
EMP: 10
SQ FT: 25,000
SALES (est): 1.2MM **Privately Held**
SIC: 3536 5082 7694 7629 Cranes, industrial plant; construction & mining machinery; electric motor repair; generator repair

(G-18169)
HOBART SALES AND SERVICE INC
5407 Bandera Rd Ste 110 (78238-1961)
PHONE..........................210 829-5663
Mike Tight, *Branch Mgr*
EMP: 50
SALES (corp-wide): 14.1B **Publicly Held**
WEB: www.hobartservice.com
SIC: 3589 5046 Commercial cooking & foodwarming equipment; commercial cooking & food service equipment
HQ: Hobart Sales And Service, Inc.
701 S Ridge Ave
Troy OH 45373
937 332-3000

(G-18170)
HOLLIMON OIL CORPORATION
Also Called: Hollimon, J Charles
8833 Tradeway St (78217-6114)
PHONE..........................210 829-8822
J Charles Hollimon, *President*
EMP: 17
SALES (est): 4.6MM **Privately Held**
SIC: 1382 Oil & gas exploration services

(G-18171)
HOLT TEXAS LTD (PA)
5665 Se Loop 410 (78222-3903)
P.O. Box 207916 (78220-7916)
PHONE..........................210 648-1111
Peter M Holt, *CEO*
Allyn Archer, *President*
Don Myrick, *General Mgr*
Trevor Coleman, *Principal*
Marshall Crum, *Principal*
◆ **EMP:** 450 **EST:** 1961
SQ FT: 100,000
SALES (est): 780.9MM **Privately Held**
WEB: www.holttruckcenters.com
SIC: 3531 5082 7353 7699 Dozers, tractor mounted: material moving; road construction & maintenance machinery; excavating machinery & equipment; heavy construction equipment rental; construction equipment repair

(G-18172)
HOLVERSTOTT NAJEE
6435 Crestway Rd Lot 13 (78239-2864)
PHONE..........................210 769-5246
EMP: 10 EST: 2016
SALES (est): 124.8K **Privately Held**
SIC: 7349 1389 0781 Building maintenance services; janitorial service, contract basis; construction, repair & dismantling services; landscape services

(G-18173)
HORMEL FOODS CORP SVCS LLC
16414 San Pedro Ave # 50 (78232-2277)
PHONE..........................210 495-0764
Mike Kinney, *Manager*
EMP: 15
SALES (corp-wide): 9.6B **Publicly Held**
WEB: www.hormelfoods.com
SIC: 2099 Food preparations

HQ: Hormel Foods Corporate Services, Llc
1 Hormel Pl
Austin MN 55912

(G-18174)
HUB INTRNTNAL TRNSP INSUR SVCS
70 Ne Loop 410 Ste 425 (78216-5852)
PHONE....................800 369-9010
Laura Rodriguez, *Accounts Mgr*
Maria Stephens, *Accounts Mgr*
Roxanne Dalrymple, *Manager*
Joanne Constantin, *Manager*
EMP: 16 Privately Held
WEB: www.hubtransportation.com
SIC: 3711 6411 Wreckers (tow truck), assembly of; insurance agents & brokers
HQ: Hub International Transportation Insurance Services Inc.
75 W Towne Ridge Pkwy # 4
Sandy UT 84070
801 943-2600

(G-18175)
HUDSONS EMBROIDERY
330 Culebra Rd (78201-6415)
PHONE....................210 224-5504
Robert Hudson, *Owner*
EMP: 30
SALES (est): 2MM Privately Held
SIC: 2395 Embroidery & art needlework

(G-18176)
HURD ENTERPRISES LTD
7373 Broadway Ste 200 (78209-3265)
PHONE....................210 829-5255
Cliff Hurd, *President*
J Rhurd, *Chairman*
John Hurd, *General Ptnr*
McCutchen Dana, *Production*
James Kuster, *Controller*
EMP: 19 EST: 1982
SQ FT: 6,500
SALES (est): 3.7MM Privately Held
WEB: www.hurdenterprises.com
SIC: 1311 6211 Crude petroleum production; natural gas production; investment firm, general brokerage

(G-18177)
HYDRADYNE LLC
4235 S Ww White Rd (78222-5206)
PHONE....................210 661-4378
Jesse Touchette, *General Mgr*
Randy Steed, *Branch Mgr*
EMP: 17
SALES (corp-wide): 371.3MM Privately Held
WEB: www.hydradynellc.com
SIC: 3612 5084 7699 Transformers, except electric; hydraulic systems equipment & supplies; hydraulic equipment repair
HQ: Hydradyne, Llc
15050 Faa Blvd
Fort Worth TX 76155
817 391-1547

(G-18178)
ICP INDUSTRIES LLC (HQ)
100 Business Park Ave (78204)
P.O. Box 10176 (78210-0176)
PHONE....................210 226-1261
Gary E Smith, *Mng Member*
EMP: 16
SALES (est): 4.3MM
SALES (corp-wide): 424.6MM Privately Held
WEB: www.icp-sa.com
SIC: 3471 Chromium plating of metals or formed products
PA: Innovative Chemical Products Group, Llc
150 Dascomb Rd
Andover MA 01810
978 623-9980

(G-18179)
IMOGENE WAGNER COMPANY INC
Also Called: Wagner Materials & Cnstr
30520 Smithson Valley Rd (78261-2973)
P.O. Box 1167, Spring Branch (78070-1167)
PHONE....................210 669-8927
Stephen J Wagner, *President*

Marcella F Wagner, *Vice Pres*
Siegred M Ahr, *Treasurer*
EMP: 22
SQ FT: 2,500
SALES (est): 8.1MM Privately Held
WEB: www.rockmilling.net
SIC: 1611 3531 Concrete construction: roads, highways, sidewalks, etc.; hammer mills (rock & ore crushing machines), portable

(G-18180)
IMPACT RECOVERY SYSTEMS INC
4955 Stout Dr (78219-4333)
P.O. Box 12637 (78212-0637)
PHONE....................210 736-4477
Greg Hannah, *President*
Barbara Cheatham, *Purchasing*
Tracy Wencka, *Cust Mgr*
Herbert Gruen, *Shareholder*
▲ EMP: 20
SQ FT: 17,000
SALES (est): 5.3MM Privately Held
WEB: www.impactrecovery.com
SIC: 3669 3993 Transportation signaling devices; signs & advertising specialties

(G-18181)
INDO-MIM INC (DH)
3902 Sw 36th St Ste 101 (78226-4403)
PHONE....................609 580-9745
Krishna Chivukula Jr, *Ch of Bd*
Jagadamba Chadrasekhar, *Director*
Raj Chivukula, *Director*
EMP: 150 EST: 2016
SQ FT: 100,000
SALES (est): 32.2MM Privately Held
WEB: www.indo-mim.com
SIC: 3499 Friction material, made from powdered metal

(G-18182)
INFORMATION MGT SOLUTIONS LLC
Also Called: IMS
2416 Brockton St Ste 105 (78217-4909)
PHONE....................210 826-4994
K Henry Minten, *Mng Member*
Cindy Green, *Supervisor*
John Reed, *Executive*
T Kelly Dowe, *Executive*
EMP: 22
SALES (est): 2.7MM Privately Held
WEB: www.imsprintingandmailing.com
SIC: 2621 7331 Printing paper; mailing service

(G-18183)
INGRAM READYMIX INC
9703 S Us Highway 181 (78223-5082)
PHONE....................210 633-9161
Robert Mendoza, *Branch Mgr*
EMP: 20
SALES (corp-wide): 125.6MM Privately Held
WEB: www.ingramreadymixinc.com
SIC: 3273 Ready-mixed concrete
PA: Ingram Readymix, Inc.
3580 Farm Market 482
New Braunfels TX 78132
830 625-9156

(G-18184)
INGRAM READYMIX INC
8963 State Highway 211 (78254-1885)
PHONE....................210 798-2676
Philip Shaw, *General Mgr*
EMP: 21
SALES (corp-wide): 125.6MM Privately Held
WEB: www.ingramreadymixinc.com
SIC: 3273 Ready-mixed concrete
PA: Ingram Readymix, Inc.
3580 Farm Market 482
New Braunfels TX 78132
830 625-9156

(G-18185)
INGRAM READYMIX INC
18679 Nw Military Hwy (78257-9712)
PHONE....................210 492-8851
Kevin Peace, *Manager*
EMP: 50

SALES (corp-wide): 125.6MM Privately Held
WEB: www.ingramreadymixinc.com
SIC: 3273 Ready-mixed concrete
PA: Ingram Readymix, Inc.
3580 Farm Market 482
New Braunfels TX 78132
830 625-9156

(G-18186)
INGRAM READYMIX INC
10400 W Loop 1604 S (78252-2651)
PHONE....................210 622-5621
Kat Rodriguez, *Manager*
EMP: 30
SQ FT: 6,463
SALES (corp-wide): 125.6MM Privately Held
WEB: www.ingramreadymixinc.com
SIC: 5172 3273 Petroleum products; ready-mixed concrete
PA: Ingram Readymix, Inc.
3580 Farm Market 482
New Braunfels TX 78132
830 625-9156

(G-18187)
INNER HEALTH GROUP INC
Also Called: Michaels Naturopathic Programs
6003 Randolph Blvd (78233-5719)
PHONE....................210 661-8311
Michael Schwartz, *President*
David Rhodes, *Marketing Staff*
Aaron Gosnell, *Supervisor*
Brian Goldsmith, *Graphic Designe*
EMP: 50
SALES (est): 11.1MM Privately Held
WEB: www.michaelshealth.com
SIC: 2844 5122 2834 Cosmetic preparations; suntan lotions & oils; vitamins & minerals; pharmaceutical preparations

(G-18188)
INNOVATIVE SFTWR SOLUTIONS INC
27212 S Glenrose Rd (78260-5329)
PHONE....................830 265-6835
Richard Carrier, *President*
EMP: 10 EST: 1993
SALES (est): 65.2K Privately Held
WEB: www.innsoftinc.com
SIC: 7372 Prepackaged software

(G-18189)
INSPIRED ELEARNING LLC
4630 N Loop 1604 W # 401 (78249-1374)
PHONE....................210 579-0224
Kyle Metcalf, *CEO*
Lenore Martinez, *Vice Pres*
Erin Kerr, *Opers Staff*
Marie Cackler, *Controller*
Stuart Breslow, *Benefits Mgr*
EMP: 80
SALES (est): 7.9MM
SALES (corp-wide): 1.3B Publicly Held
WEB: www.inspiredelearning.com
SIC: 7373 7372 Computer integrated systems design
PA: J2 Global, Inc.
6922 Hollywood Blvd # 50
Los Angeles CA 90028
323 860-9200

(G-18190)
INTEGRATED TAX SOLUTIONS LLC
8015 Bandera Rd Ste 103 (78250-5136)
PHONE....................855 792-6657
Stephen Pennington, *Manager*
EMP: 10
SALES (est): 112.2K
SALES (corp-wide): 450K Privately Held
SIC: 7291 8721 7372 Tax return preparation services; accounting, auditing & bookkeeping; billing & bookkeeping service; business oriented computer software
PA: Nonprofit Financial Services
10130 San Pedro Ave # 10
San Antonio TX 78216
210 306-4445

(G-18191)
INTERAV INC
106 E Rhapsody Dr (78216-3112)
P.O. Box 792228 (78279-2228)
PHONE....................210 344-2785

Eric Buschfort, *President*
EMP: 10
SQ FT: 8,000
SALES (est): 600K Privately Held
WEB: www.inter-av.com
SIC: 3821 Laboratory equipment: fume hoods, distillation racks, etc.

(G-18192)
INTERNATIONAL AERIAL MAPPING
2118 Mannix Dr (78217-5914)
PHONE....................210 826-8681
Edward H Sokolowski, *President*
Louis A Rizzo, *Exec VP*
Robert Gonzales, *Treasurer*
Charles Percival, *Admin Sec*
EMP: 20
SALES (est): 1MM Privately Held
WEB: www.iamap.com
SIC: 7389 2752 Mapmaking or drafting, including aerial; maps, lithographed

(G-18193)
INTERNATIONAL PAPER COMPANY
1111 At&T Center Pkwy (78219)
PHONE....................210 225-2901
Michael Sandheinrich, *Controller*
Vernon Williams, *Clerk*
EMP: 21
SALES (corp-wide): 22.3B Publicly Held
WEB: www.internationalpaper.com
SIC: 2621 Paper mills
PA: International Paper Company
6400 Poplar Ave
Memphis TN 38197
901 419-9000

(G-18194)
INTERNATIONAL PAPER COMPANY
610 Pop Gunn St (78219-4322)
P.O. Box 200206 (78220-0206)
PHONE....................210 661-8543
Robin Carrera, *Opers-Prdtn-Mfg*
Archie Marinas, *Plant Engr*
Roger Calandres, *Controller*
Michael Sandheinrich, *Controller*
Dugald Winter, *Sales Mgr*
EMP: 125
SALES (corp-wide): 22.3B Publicly Held
WEB: www.internationalpaper.com
SIC: 2621 Paper mills
PA: International Paper Company
6400 Poplar Ave
Memphis TN 38197
901 419-9000

(G-18195)
ITRON NETWORKED SOLUTIONS INC
Also Called: Silver Spring Networks
300 Convent St Ste 1200 (78205-1323)
PHONE....................210 762-4400
EMP: 14
SALES (corp-wide): 2.5B Publicly Held
WEB: www.itron.com
SIC: 4899 7372 Communication signal enhancement network system; prepackaged software
HQ: Itron Networked Solutions, Inc.
230 W Tasman Dr
San Jose CA 95134
669 770-4000

(G-18196)
IWC OIL & REFINERY LLC
8610 N New Braunfels Ave # 3 (78217-6370)
PHONE....................210 900-9928
Marco Aparicio, *General Mgr*
Claudia Aparicio,
EMP: 35
SQ FT: 1,871
SALES: 6.6MM Privately Held
WEB: www.iwcgroupinc.com
SIC: 1382 2911 1311 Oil & gas exploration services; petroleum refining; crude petroleum & natural gas

(G-18197)
J & B SAUSAGE COMPANY INC
10221 Desert Sands St # 302
(78216-3959)
PHONE..................210 344-2212
Pat O'Higgins, *Manager*
EMP: 10
SALES (corp-wide): 83.8MM **Privately Held**
WEB: www.jbfoods.com
SIC: 2011 Sausages from meat slaughtered on site
PA: J & B Sausage Company, Inc.
100 Main
Waelder TX 78959
830 788-7661

(G-18198)
JADCAP MACHINE WORKS INC
3621 Sw Military Dr (78211-3512)
P.O. Box 241086 (78224-8086)
PHONE..................210 932-1019
Joe A Perez, *President*
Aida D Cortez-Perez, *Vice Pres*
Ivan Alvarado, *Engineer*
Jonathan Vasquez, *Engineer*
Juan Reyes, *Manager*
EMP: 12
SQ FT: 4,500
SALES (est): 2.9MM **Privately Held**
WEB: www.jadcap.com
SIC: 3599 Machine shop, jobbing & repair

(G-18199)
JEFF BONNER R & D INC
Also Called: Jeff Bonner Research & Dev Co
10525 Mopac Dr (78217-3827)
PHONE..................210 590-3133
Jeff Bonner, *President*
Dave Castiglione, *Vice Pres*
Ed Harris, *Vice Pres*
Jordan Endsley, *Project Mgr*
Bruce V Hoose, *Buyer*
EMP: 120
SQ FT: 21,000
SALES (est): 15.9MM **Privately Held**
WEB: www.jbrnd.com
SIC: 3728 8731 Research & dev by manuf., aircraft parts & auxiliary equip; commercial physical research

(G-18200)
JEH-EAS INC
Also Called: Stars Information Solutions
12813 Wetmore Rd (78247-3628)
PHONE..................210 490-9156
David L Granato, *Vice Pres*
David Petteys, *Opers Mgr*
Cameron Granato, *Manager*
EMP: 9
SQ FT: 4,600
SALES (est): 924.5K **Privately Held**
WEB: www.starstek.com
SIC: 7374 3861 7378 7372 Optical scanning data service; microfilm equipment: cameras, projectors, readers, etc.; computer & data processing equipment repair/maintenance; application computer software; business oriented computer software; document & office records storage

(G-18201)
JF FILTRATION INC
4707 Nw Industrial (78238-1977)
PHONE..................210 946-1688
Will Fawcett, *Manager*
EMP: 15 **Privately Held**
WEB: www.joeflyco.com
SIC: 5075 3564 Air filters; filters, air: furnaces, air conditioning equipment, etc.
PA: Jf Filtration, Inc.
4820 Memphis St
Dallas TX 75207

(G-18202)
JOES INDUSTRIAL MCH SP INC
1837 Rigsby Ave (78210-3323)
PHONE..................210 359-7500
Jimmy Garza, *Director*
Sandra Garza, *Director*
EMP: 11
SALES (est): 865.1K **Privately Held**
WEB: www.joesindustrialmachineshop.com
SIC: 3599 Machine shop, jobbing & repair

(G-18203)
JOEY RECORDS INC
Also Called: Joey Records International
6703 W Commerce St (78227-1599)
PHONE..................210 432-7893
Joe S Lopez Sr, *President*
Raquel Lopez, *Vice Pres*
Dinah Perez, *Treasurer*
EMP: 33
SQ FT: 180,000
SALES (est): 3.8MM **Privately Held**
SIC: 3652 Pre-recorded records & tapes

(G-18204)
JOHN H SOROLA INC
523 W Cypress St (78212-4684)
PHONE..................210 224-8597
Loren F Brown, *President*
John H Sorola, *Vice Pres*
Margarette M Brown, *Vice Pres*
Sorola Ramona C, *Vice Pres*
Jaclyn Hanover, *Treasurer*
EMP: 17
SQ FT: 12,500
SALES (est): 1.3MM **Privately Held**
WEB: www.sorolas.com
SIC: 3519 Internal combustion engines

(G-18205)
JOHNNIES PLASTICS INC
725 Florida St (78210-1847)
P.O. Box 10367 (78210-0367)
PHONE..................210 533-8463
Tommy J Barnes, *President*
Cindy Barnes, *Corp Secy*
Johnnie Barnes Jr, *Vice Pres*
EMP: 22
SQ FT: 20,000
SALES (est): 1MM **Privately Held**
SIC: 3083 1799 2542 2541 Plastic finished products, laminated; counter top installation; partitions & fixtures, except wood; counter & sink tops; plastics materials & resins

(G-18206)
JON HART DESIGN CO
220 Burleson (78202-1803)
PHONE..................210 226-8544
Douglas Smith, *President*
Mark Risien, *Vice Pres*
Thomas Wood, *Opers Mgr*
Hannah Blakeney, *Purchasing*
Kyle Jaster, *CFO*
▲ EMP: 35
SALES (est): 6.9MM **Privately Held**
WEB: www.jonhartdesign.com
SIC: 3161 2339 3171 Luggage; women's & misses' accessories; sportswear, women's; women's handbags & purses

(G-18207)
JONES HOLT ENTERPRISES INC
Also Called: San Antonio Foam Fabricators
13715 Topper Cir (78233-4032)
PHONE..................210 657-5917
Jeff Jones, *Vice Pres*
EMP: 30 **EST**: 1976
SQ FT: 26,000
SALES (est): 4.9MM **Privately Held**
WEB: www.sanantoniofoam.com
SIC: 3086 3993 3053 2675 Packaging & shipping materials, foamed plastic; signs & advertising specialties; gaskets, packing & sealing devices; die-cut paper & board

(G-18208)
JOSE ALFONSIN
Also Called: Mainteniruav
10511 Sunflower Ln (78213-1622)
PHONE..................210 717-2306
Jose Alfonsin, *Owner*
EMP: 10 **EST**: 2016
SALES (est): 402.8K **Privately Held**
SIC: 3728 7389 5734 7371 Target drones, ; computer software & accessories; software programming applications

(G-18209)
JOSEPHS STOREHOUSE BAKING CO
3420 N Saint Marys St # 105 (78212-3169)
PHONE..................405 253-0669
Michele McCurdy, *President*
Patrick McCurdy, *President*
EMP: 20
SQ FT: 2,500
SALES (est): 772.7K **Privately Held**
WEB: www.josephs-storehouse.com
SIC: 5812 2051 Eating places; breads, rolls & buns

(G-18210)
JOYSON SFETY SYSTEMS ACQSTION
Also Called: Takata Seat Belts
4611 Wiseman Blvd (78251-4202)
P.O. Box 982146, El Paso (79998-2146)
PHONE..................210 250-5000
Darin Duffy, *Manager*
EMP: 30
SALES (corp-wide): 2.2B **Privately Held**
WEB: www.joysonsafety.com
SIC: 3199 Seat belts, leather
PA: Joyson Safety Systems Acquisition Llc
2500 Innovation Dr
Auburn Hills MI 48326
248 373-8040

(G-18211)
JRN MANAGEMENT LP
726 Probandt (78204-2342)
P.O. Box 830808 (78283-0808)
PHONE..................210 222-9511
John Newell, *Partner*
Tom Harlan, *Data Proc Exec*
Carlton Nichols,
EMP: 100
SQ FT: 22,000
SALES (est): 22.8MM **Privately Held**
WEB: www.cmcrecycling.com
SIC: 3341 5093 Secondary nonferrous metals; ferrous metal scrap & waste

(G-18212)
JULIE KECK
Also Called: Starline Costumes
1286 Bandera Rd (78228-4030)
PHONE..................210 435-3535
EMP: 15 **EST**: 1920
SQ FT: 10,000
SALES (est): 672.3K **Privately Held**
WEB: www.starlinecostumes.com
SIC: 7299 3961 5699 Costume rental; costume novelties; costumes, masquerade or theatrical

(G-18213)
JV INDUSTRIAL COMPANIES LTD (DH)
Also Called: JV Piping
527 Logwood Ave (78221-1738)
PHONE..................713 568-2600
John B Zachry, *CEO*
Joe Vardell, *Partner*
Justin Graham, *Superintendent*
Robert Hemler, *Superintendent*
Shannon Venglar, *Superintendent*
◆ EMP: 100 **EST**: 2002
SALES (est): 710.9MM **Privately Held**
WEB: www.jvic.com
SIC: 3441 7692 8711 Building components, structural steel; welding repair; construction & civil engineering

(G-18214)
K W D MANUFACTURING INC
2230 W Southcross Blvd (78211-1956)
PHONE..................210 924-5999
Patricia R Deane, *Ch of Bd*
John E Deane, *President*
EMP: 40
SQ FT: 50,000
SALES: 5.2MM **Privately Held**
WEB: www.kwdmfg.com
SIC: 3728 3537 Aircraft parts & equipment; industrial trucks & tractors

(G-18215)
KADENCE COLLECTIVE LLC
118 Broadway St Ste 627 (78205-1983)
PHONE..................888 901-5343
Robert Martinez, *CEO*

EMP: 18
SALES (est): 198.4K **Privately Held**
WEB: www.hirekadence.com
SIC: 3652 Pre-recorded records & tapes

(G-18216)
KALLE ENTERPRISES INC
Also Called: Allegra Marketing-Print-Mail
11811 Warfield St (78216-3214)
PHONE..................210 340-1841
Garry Lundberg, *President*
John Giannola, *Partner*
EMP: 12
SQ FT: 5,200
SALES (est): 1.7MM **Privately Held**
WEB: www.allegramarketingprint.com
SIC: 2752 Commercial printing, offset

(G-18217)
KATHLEEN SOMMERS DESIGNS INC
818 E Myrtle St (78212-4136)
PHONE..................210 271-7118
Fax: 210 271-7146
▲ EMP: 11
SALES (est): 970K **Privately Held**
SIC: 2335 2339 Mfg Women's/Misses' Dresses Mfg Women's/Misses' Outerwear

(G-18218)
KAUTEX INC
1 Lone Star Pass Bldg 3 (78264-3629)
PHONE..................210 229-2300
Ricardo Tenorio, *Branch Mgr*
EMP: 34
SALES (corp-wide): 13.6B **Publicly Held**
WEB: www.kautex.de
SIC: 3714 Motor vehicle parts & accessories
HQ: Kautex Inc.
750 Stephenson Hwy # 200
Troy MI 48083
248 616-5100

(G-18219)
KCI INTERNATIONAL INC (DH)
12930 W Interstate 10 (78249-2248)
P.O. Box 659508 (78265-9508)
PHONE..................210 524-9000
Martin J Landon, *President*
Robert Jackson, *District Mgr*
Allen Sexton, *District Mgr*
Lesley Fronio, *Vice Pres*
Stephen D Seidel, *Vice Pres*
EMP: 40
SALES (est): 48.7MM
SALES (corp-wide): 32.1B **Publicly Held**
WEB: www.mykci.com
SIC: 2599 7352 Beds, not household use; medical equipment rental
HQ: Kinetic Concepts, Inc.
12930 W Interstate 10
San Antonio TX 78249
800 531-5346

(G-18220)
KCI USA INC (DH)
Also Called: 3M Medical Solutions
12930 W Interstate 10 (78249-2248)
P.O. Box 659508 (78265-9508)
PHONE..................800 275-4524
Todd Fruchterman, *President*
Brett Kraemer, *Principal*
Charles Colby, *Vice Pres*
Rosa Gomez, *Vice Pres*
Steven Jackson, *Vice Pres*
▲ EMP: 121
SQ FT: 700,000
SALES (est): 70.4MM
SALES (corp-wide): 32.1B **Publicly Held**
WEB: www.mykci.com
SIC: 7352 3842 5047 Medical equipment rental; surgical appliances & supplies; medical & hospital equipment
HQ: Acelity, Inc.
12930 W Interstate 10
San Antonio TX 78249
210 255-6838

(G-18221)
KCM CABINETS INC
5748 Grey Rock Dr (78228-6527)
PHONE..................210 695-2213
Connie Moore, *President*
Kenneth Moore, *Treasurer*
EMP: 10

SQ FT: 10,500
SALES (est): 1.7MM **Privately Held**
SIC: 2542 Cabinets: show, display or storage: except wood; partitions for floor attachment, prefabricated: except wood

(G-18222)
KELLER ADVG & MEDIA SVCS
Also Called: Keller Custom Signs & Designs
1234 San Francisco (78201-4638)
P.O. Box 690970 (78269-0970)
PHONE....................210 695-8767
Dudley Keller, *President*
Angelo Grizzaffi, *Vice Pres*
Corey Keller, *Vice Pres*
Mike Santos, *Opers Staff*
Steve Grothues, *Sales Staff*
EMP: 30
SQ FT: 30,000
SALES (est): 4.3MM **Privately Held**
WEB: www.kellercustomsigns.com
SIC: 3993 Electric signs

(G-18223)
KENNEDY WIRE ROPE & SLING CO
4202 Dividend (78219-2612)
PHONE....................210 527-0555
Toll Free:....................877 -
Gonzalo Ferniz, *Sales Staff*
Frank Garcia, *Manager*
EMP: 16
SALES (corp-wide): 48MM **Privately Held**
WEB: www.kwrs.com
SIC: 3496 Miscellaneous fabricated wire products
PA: Kennedy Wire Rope & Sling Co Inc
302 Flato Rd
Corpus Christi TX 78405
361 289-1444

(G-18224)
KEYMEX LLC
915 Cormorant (78245-1398)
PHONE....................210 300-7056
Ubaldo Anton Velasco Torr, *CEO*
EMP: 10 EST: 2016
SALES (est): 807.6K **Privately Held**
WEB: www.keymexllc.com
SIC: 3429 Keys, locks & related hardware

(G-18225)
KINETIC CONCEPTS INC (DH)
Also Called: Kci
12930 W Interstate 10 (78249-2248)
P.O. Box 659508 (78265-9508)
PHONE....................800 531-5346
Ronald A Matricaria, *Ch of Bd*
Catherine M Burzik, *President*
Stephen D Seidel, *President*
Joseph Woody, *President*
Michelle Peterson, *Principal*
▲ EMP: 450
SQ FT: 156,400
SALES (est): 1.2B
SALES (corp-wide): 32.1B **Publicly Held**
WEB: www.mykci.com
SIC: 3842 Surgical appliances & supplies
HQ: Chiron Holdings Inc.
12930 W Interstate 10
San Antonio TX 78249
210 524-9000

(G-18226)
KINGDOM CAPTAIN OF TEXAS LLC
Also Called: Bud's Custom EMB & Screen Prtg
222 W Nakoma St (78216-2619)
PHONE....................210 535-9480
Badr Sinno,
Fayza Sinno,
EMP: 12
SQ FT: 6,000
SALES (est): 1MM **Privately Held**
WEB: www.budsembroidery.com
SIC: 2395 7336 Embroidery products, except schiffli machine; commercial art & graphic design

(G-18227)
KIOLBASSA PROVISION COMPANY
1325 S Brazos St (78207-6931)
PHONE....................210 226-8127
Robert A Kiolbassa, *CEO*
Michael R Kiolbassa, *President*
Barbara K Britton, *Corp Secy*
Bob Cohen, *Adv Board Mem*
Charles Harris, *Vice Pres*
EMP: 260 EST: 1949
SQ FT: 25,000
SALES (est): 75MM **Privately Held**
WEB: www.kiolbassa.com
SIC: 2013 Sausages from purchased meat; frankfurters from purchased meat

(G-18228)
KOCH RANCHES INC
Also Called: Koch Ranches Gourmet Cntry Str
1999 Gulfmart St Ste 512 (78217-6325)
P.O. Box 38, Yancey (78886-0038)
PHONE....................210 858-9795
Anthony Koch, *President*
Bret Koch, *Treasurer*
Cheryl Ludwick, *Admin Sec*
EMP: 15
SALES (est): 479K **Privately Held**
WEB: www.kochranches.net
SIC: 0291 5148 2048 5142 General farms, primarily animals; fresh fruits & vegetables; frozen pet food (except dog & cat); meat, frozen: packaged; gourmet food stores; food crops

(G-18229)
KTA SERVICES
12296 S Us Highway 181 # 3 (78223-9658)
P.O. Box 1319, East Bernard (77435-1319)
PHONE....................832 368-0138
Kenneth Aubushon, *President*
EMP: 12
SALES (est): 1.7MM **Privately Held**
WEB: www.ebairandheat.com
SIC: 3315 Fence gates posts & fittings: steel

(G-18230)
KUEST CORPORATION
10909 N Interstate 35 (78233-5704)
P.O. Box 33007 (78265-3007)
PHONE....................210 655-1220
Albert R Kuest, *President*
Kristina Mistry, *Engineer*
Frank E Connolly, *Treasurer*
Frank Connolly, *Treasurer*
Juliana Kuest Connolly, *Treasurer*
EMP: 40 EST: 1963
SQ FT: 100,000
SALES (est): 8.9MM **Privately Held**
WEB: www.kuestcorp.com
SIC: 3444 Sheet metalwork

(G-18231)
L & M SHTMTL & STL FABRICATORS
1202 Saltillo St (78207-6656)
PHONE....................210 433-7131
Pablo C Lomas, *President*
Joe M Medina, *Vice Pres*
EMP: 25
SQ FT: 22,000
SALES (est): 4.2MM **Privately Held**
SIC: 3441 Fabricated structural metal

(G-18232)
LA AUTENTICA INC
17806 W Interstate 10 (78257-8221)
P.O. Box 52, Midlothian VA (23113-0052)
PHONE....................202 415-6979
Armando Leonides, *President*
EMP: 16 EST: 2015
SALES (est): 860K **Privately Held**
WEB: www.autenticahub.com
SIC: 5411 5145 2032 2043 Grocery stores; snack foods; Mexican foods: packaged in cans, jars, etc.; cereal breakfast foods

(G-18233)
LA FRONTERA MOLINA
727 Enrique M Barrera Pkw (78237-2309)
PHONE....................210 432-0855

Manuel Menchaca, *Owner*
EMP: 10 EST: 1973
SQ FT: 2,100
SALES (est): 510.8K **Privately Held**
SIC: 2099 5812 Tortillas, fresh or refrigerated; eating places

(G-18234)
LA LUZ MARKETING GROUP INC
12001 Network Blvd # 115 (78249-3355)
PHONE....................210 202-1800
EMP: 12 EST: 2012
SALES (est): 222K **Privately Held**
WEB: www.laluzmarketing.com
SIC: 8742 2759 Marketing consulting services; commercial printing

(G-18235)
LA REGIA TORTILLA FACTORY LLC
1615 N Laredo St Ste 105 (78207-1861)
PHONE....................210 971-9190
Jose Luis Heredia,
Jorge Contreras Trujano,
EMP: 25
SALES (est): 906.4K **Privately Held**
WEB: www.laregiatortillafactory.com
SIC: 2099 Tortillas, fresh or refrigerated

(G-18236)
LANCER CORPORATION (DH)
Also Called: Industrias Lancermex SA De Cv
6655 Lancer Blvd (78219-4735)
PHONE....................210 310-7250
Luis Alvarez, *President*
E J Morrow, *President*
David Ewing, *Vice Pres*
Richard Laughlin, *Vice Pres*
Victor Orduna, *Export Mgr*
◆ EMP: 400
SQ FT: 346,000
SALES (est): 142MM **Privately Held**
WEB: www.lancercorp.com
SIC: 3585 Ice making machinery; soda fountain & beverage dispensing equipment & parts; beer dispensing equipment; carbonators, soda water
HQ: Hoshizaki America, Inc.
618 Highway 74 S
Peachtree City GA 30269
770 487-2331

(G-18237)
LASER PRTRS & MAILING SVCS LLC
8701 Perrin Beitel Rd (78217-4820)
PHONE....................210 590-6565
William White, *Accounts Exec*
Catherine Milward,
EMP: 10
SALES (est): 1.4MM **Privately Held**
WEB: www.lpmsi.com
SIC: 2759 7331 Laser printing; mailing service

(G-18238)
LAWE INDUSTRIES LLC (PA)
24165 W Interstate 10 (78257-1449)
PHONE....................210 833-9497
Daniel Lee, *Director*
EMP: 21
SALES (est): 8.5MM **Privately Held**
SIC: 3999 Barber & beauty shop equipment

(G-18239)
LCW AUTOMOTIVE CORP
1102 N Cherry St (78202-1103)
PHONE....................210 732-5466
Todd Boyar, *Principal*
Adam Boyar, *Vice Pres*
Fernando Montalvo, *Human Res Mgr*
Gilberto Cossio, *Shareholder*
EMP: 55
SQ FT: 60,000
SALES (est): 9.3MM **Privately Held**
WEB: www.lcwlimo.com
SIC: 3711 Automobile bodies, passenger car, not including engine, etc.

(G-18240)
LEAR SIEGLER LOGISTICS INTL (PA)
333 Morris Witt Ste 1 (78226-1879)
PHONE....................210 490-0267
Patrick Hawkins, *Manager*
EMP: 10
SALES (est): 799.6K **Privately Held**
SIC: 3714 Motor vehicle parts & accessories

(G-18241)
LEE CUSTOM WORKS INC
501 Culebra Rd (78201-6420)
P.O. Box 6997 (78209-0997)
PHONE....................210 432-1911
Dan Lee, *President*
Diane Lee, *Vice Pres*
EMP: 14
SQ FT: 11,000
SALES (est): 1.5MM **Privately Held**
SIC: 2521 2522 Wood office furniture; office furniture, except wood

(G-18242)
LEGACY VULCAN LLC
Southwest Division
800 Isom Rd Ste 300 (78216-4053)
P.O. Box 791550 (78279-1550)
PHONE....................210 349-3311
Demitri Hatzi, *Plant Mgr*
EMP: 50 **Publicly Held**
WEB: www.vulcanmaterials.com
SIC: 3273 Ready-mixed concrete
HQ: Legacy Vulcan, Llc
1200 Urban Center Dr
Vestavia AL 35242
205 298-3000

(G-18243)
LEGACY VULCAN LLC
Also Called: Huebner Road Quarry and Rdymx
12307 Huebner Rd (78230-1552)
PHONE....................210 492-1053
Paul Obar, *Manager*
EMP: 60 **Publicly Held**
WEB: www.vulcanmaterials.com
SIC: 1442 3273 1422 Construction sand & gravel; ready-mixed concrete; crushed & broken limestone
HQ: Legacy Vulcan, Llc
1200 Urban Center Dr
Vestavia AL 35242
205 298-3000

(G-18244)
LEHMBERG ENTERPRISES INC
Also Called: Olympic Trophy Center
919 Sw Military Dr # 100 (78221-1579)
PHONE....................210 924-6811
David Lehmberg, *President*
EMP: 11
SQ FT: 2,000
SALES (est): 1.6MM **Privately Held**
WEB: www.olympiatrophyandapparel.com
SIC: 5999 3479 Trophies & plaques; etching & engraving

(G-18245)
LEIDOS INC
1777 Ne Loop 410 Ste 912 (78217-5217)
PHONE....................210 731-1438
Christine Vargas, *Branch Mgr*
EMP: 31 **Publicly Held**
WEB: www.leidos.com
SIC: 3679 3674 Recording & playback apparatus, including phonograph; integrated circuits, semiconductor networks, etc.
HQ: Leidos, Inc.
1750 Presidents St
Reston VA 20190
571 526-6000

(G-18246)
LENNOX INTERNATIONAL INC
10610 Sentinel St (78217-3812)
PHONE....................210 646-2399
Fred Thomas, *Branch Mgr*
EMP: 547
SALES (corp-wide): 3.8B **Publicly Held**
WEB: www.lennoxinternational.com
SIC: 3585 Refrigeration & heating equipment

PA: Lennox International Inc.
2140 Lake Park Blvd
Richardson TX 75080
972 497-5000

(G-18247)
LEONARD & HARRAL PACKING CO (HQ)
Also Called: L&H Packing
2001 S Laredo St (78207-7023)
P.O. Box 831368 (78283-1368)
PHONE..................................210 532-3241
Kenneth E Leonard, *CEO*
K E Leonard, *Ch of Bd*
Justin Still, *President*
Marvin Eggleston, *Corp Secy*
Neal Leonard, *COO*
EMP: 300
SQ FT: 9,000
SALES (est): 67.5MM **Privately Held**
WEB: www.lhpacking.net
SIC: 2011 5147 2077 2048 Meat by-products from meat slaughtered on site; meats, fresh; animal & marine fats & oils; prepared feeds

(G-18248)
LEONARD HOLDING COMPANY (HQ)
2001 S Laredo St (78207-7023)
P.O. Box 831368 (78283-1368)
PHONE..................................210 532-3241
Kenneth E Leonard, *President*
Clay Davis, *Managing Dir*
Cory Simmons, *Info Tech Dir*
Terry L Black, *Admin Sec*
EMP: 16
SALES (est): 68.8MM **Privately Held**
WEB: www.leonardhc.com
SIC: 2013 Prepared beef products from purchased beef

(G-18249)
LEWIS PETRO PROPERTIES INC
Also Called: Olmos Drilling Co
10101 Reunion Pl Ste 1000 (78216-4157)
P.O. Box 180, Encinal (78019-0180)
PHONE..................................210 384-3200
Rodney R Lewis, *President*
Kimberly S Lewis, *Vice Pres*
EMP: 75
SQ FT: 2,600
SALES (est): 10.3MM **Privately Held**
WEB: www.lewisenergy.com
SIC: 1321 1382 1381 Natural gasoline production; oil & gas exploration services; drilling oil & gas wells
PA: Lewis Energy Group, L.P.
10101 Reunion Pl Ste 1000
San Antonio TX 78216

(G-18250)
LIBERTO MANAGEMENT CO INC
Also Called: Liberto Fun Foods
830 S Presa St (78210-1375)
PHONE..................................210 226-4167
Frank G Liberto, *CEO*
Tony Liberto, *President*
Jeremy Powledge, *CFO*
Patricia Ann Liberto, *Treasurer*
Travis Pilat, *Accounting Mgr*
EMP: 40
SALES (est): 8.6MM
SALES (corp-wide): 68.8MM **Privately Held**
WEB: www.ricos.com
SIC: 3589 Popcorn machines, commercial
PA: Liberto Specialty Company Inc
830 S Presa St
San Antonio TX 78210
210 222-1415

(G-18251)
LIBERTY A&A
24385 Wilderness Oak (78258-7900)
PHONE..................................213 221-8110
Jamie Vega, *Ch of Bd*
EMP: 10
SALES (est): 177K **Privately Held**
SIC: 8744 3484 8711 Facilities support services; small arms; engineering services

(G-18252)
LINDE GAS NORTH AMERICA LLC
Also Called: Life Gas
5810 Rocky Pt (78249-3406)
PHONE..................................210 287-9788
Kat Klumpp, *Branch Mgr*
EMP: 19 **Privately Held**
WEB: www.praxair.com
SIC: 2813 Nitrogen; oxygen, compressed or liquefied
HQ: Linde Gas North America Llc
10 Riverview Dr
Danbury CT 06810

(G-18253)
LINDE INC
Also Called: Praxair
1077 Central Pkwy S # 600 (78232-5079)
P.O. Box 44, Tonawanda NY (14151-0044)
PHONE..................................210 489-5800
EMP: 9 **Privately Held**
WEB: www.praxair.com
SIC: 2813 Industrial gases
HQ: Linde Inc.
10 Riverview Dr
Danbury CT 06810
203 837-2000

(G-18254)
LITHO PRESS INC
4334 Milling Rd (78219-2721)
PHONE..................................210 333-1711
Thomas F Murray, *President*
Margie Peak, *Vice Pres*
Mark Mayfield, *Marketing Staff*
EMP: 35 **EST:** 1961
SQ FT: 15,000
SALES (est): 6.3MM **Privately Held**
WEB: www.lithopress.net
SIC: 2752 Commercial printing, offset

(G-18255)
LITHOGRAPHICS INC
Also Called: Accurate Litho & Printing Co
500 N Alamo St (78215-1807)
PHONE..................................210 226-1722
Arthur L Richter, *CEO*
Steve Richter, *President*
Bryan Dugger, *Vice Pres*
Nancy Dugger, *Vice Pres*
EMP: 9
SQ FT: 7,200
SALES (est): 1.2MM **Privately Held**
WEB: www.accuratelithoandprintingco.com
SIC: 2752 2791 2789 2759 Commercial printing, offset; typesetting; bookbinding & related work; commercial printing

(G-18256)
LOBO VENTURES LTD
Also Called: Precision Mold TI Gvrnment Div
12027 Warfield St (78216-3231)
PHONE..................................210 525-9595
Letty N Whittaker, *Controller*
Todd Wulfe, *Manager*
EMP: 32
SQ FT: 26,000
SALES (est): 3.8MM **Privately Held**
WEB: www.pmtgov.com
SIC: 3724 Aircraft engines & engine parts

(G-18257)
LOCKHEED MARTIN CORPORATION
4243 E Piedras Dr Ste 100 (78228-1416)
PHONE..................................210 736-6461
Don Braton, *Branch Mgr*
EMP: 435 **Publicly Held**
WEB: www.lockheedmartin.com
SIC: 3812 Search & navigation equipment
PA: Lockheed Martin Corporation
6801 Rockledge Dr
Bethesda MD 20817

(G-18258)
LOCKHEED MARTIN CORPORATION
1777 Ne Loop 410 Ste 912 (78217-5217)
PHONE..................................210 581-6100
Adalberto Martinez, *Principal*
Steven Allen, *Branch Mgr*
Sylvia Watts, *Sr Software Eng*
Richard McDaniel, *Director*
EMP: 458 **Publicly Held**

WEB: www.lockheedmartin.com
SIC: 3812 Search & navigation equipment
PA: Lockheed Martin Corporation
6801 Rockledge Dr
Bethesda MD 20817

(G-18259)
LOCKHEED MARTIN CORPORATION
3203 General Hudnell Dr (78226-1424)
PHONE..................................210 729-8600
Adalberto Martinez, *Principal*
EMP: 80 **Publicly Held**
WEB: www.lockheedmartin.com
SIC: 3761 Space vehicles, complete
PA: Lockheed Martin Corporation
6801 Rockledge Dr
Bethesda MD 20817

(G-18260)
LOCKHEED MARTIN CORPORATION
485 Quentin Roosevelt Rd (78226-1845)
PHONE..................................210 445-5628
Peter Duren, *Manager*
EMP: 20 **Publicly Held**
WEB: www.lockheedmartin.com
SIC: 3812 Search & navigation equipment
PA: Lockheed Martin Corporation
6801 Rockledge Dr
Bethesda MD 20817

(G-18261)
LOCKHEED MARTIN CORPORATION
1777 Ne Loop 410 Ste 300 (78217-5216)
PHONE..................................210 581-6100
Lee R Heiser, *Manager*
EMP: 65 **Publicly Held**
WEB: www.lockheedmartin.com
SIC: 3812 Search & navigation equipment
PA: Lockheed Martin Corporation
6801 Rockledge Dr
Bethesda MD 20817

(G-18262)
LOGO MASTERS LLC
11031 Wye Dr Ste 108 (78217-2625)
PHONE..................................830 822-8390
EMP: 12 **EST:** 2010
SQ FT: 1,100
SALES (est): 350K **Privately Held**
SIC: 2211 Apparel & outerwear fabrics, cotton

(G-18263)
LONE STAR SPECIAL TEES LLC
Also Called: Logo Pro
1011 N Frio St (78207-1811)
PHONE..................................210 402-0091
Elaine Wilson-Blain, *CEO*
David Rakowitz, *Purchasing*
Laurie Leach, *CFO*
Johnny Villanueva, *Accounts Exec*
◆ **EMP:** 26
SQ FT: 40,000
SALES (est): 3.6MM
SALES (corp-wide): 175.8MM **Privately Held**
WEB: www.lonestartees.com
SIC: 2396 7389 Screen printing on fabric articles; embroidering of advertising on shirts, etc.
PA: Pmg International, Ltd.
1011 N Frio St
San Antonio TX 78207
210 226-6820

(G-18264)
LONESTAR FENCING AND WLDG LLC
7014 Valley Trl (78250-1739)
PHONE..................................210 992-0441
David Castillo, *Manager*
EMP: 9
SALES (est): 188.5K **Privately Held**
WEB: www.lsfencingandwelding.com
SIC: 7692 Welding repair

(G-18265)
LOPEZ PRINTING INCORPORATED
Also Called: Lopez Printing & Bindery Svc
427 Lombrano St (78207-1222)
PHONE..................................210 732-3232

Leonard Lopez Jr, *President*
Connie Lopez, *Vice Pres*
Roger Lopez, *Vice Pres*
Leonard Lopez, *Director*
EMP: 18
SQ FT: 16,000
SALES (est): 3.7MM **Privately Held**
WEB: www.lopezprint.com
SIC: 2752 Commercial printing, offset

(G-18266)
LORENTA NUTS LLC
2564 Macarthur Vw 101 (78217-4448)
PHONE..................................361 876-7570
Sam Henselijn, *Mng Member*
Samuel S Henselijn, *Administration*
EMP: 10 **EST:** 2017
SALES (est): 752.1K
SALES (corp-wide): 5MM **Privately Held**
WEB: www.lorentanuts.com
SIC: 2068 Salted & roasted nuts & seeds
PA: Hocorn Holding B.V.
Ellermanstraat 27
Duivendrecht 1115

(G-18267)
LULUS DESSERT CORPORATION
Also Called: Lulus Dessert Factory
1031 Hot Wells Blvd (78223-2731)
P.O. Box 23090 (78223-0090)
PHONE..................................210 399-3767
Maria De Lourdes Sobrino, *CEO*
EMP: 70
SQ FT: 25,000
SALES (est): 10.2MM **Privately Held**
SIC: 2099 5149 Gelatin dessert preparations; bakery products

(G-18268)
M & M METALS INC
103 Braniff Dr (78216-3399)
PHONE..................................210 341-1313
EMP: 69
SQ FT: 18,000
SALES (est): 11.2MM **Privately Held**
WEB: www.mmmet.com
SIC: 1761 3599 Sheet metalwork; machine & other job shop work

(G-18269)
M2 GLOBAL TECHNOLOGY LTD
5714 Epsilon (78249-3407)
PHONE..................................210 561-4800
Douglas F Carlberg, *CEO*
Zeniff Segura, *Buyer*
Gene Garcia, *Engineer*
Patti K Meisetschleager, *CFO*
Bill Blessing, *Controller*
EMP: 10
SQ FT: 23,000
SALES (est): 2.4MM
SALES (corp-wide): 5.2MM **Privately Held**
WEB: www.m2global.com
SIC: 3549 3663 Metalworking machinery; microwave communication equipment
PA: M2 Global Inc.
5714 Epsilon
San Antonio TX 78249
210 561-4800

(G-18270)
M3 TOOLING LLC
Also Called: Window Gang
218 Roan Spg (78258-4872)
PHONE..................................210 946-4264
Martha Mercereau,
EMP: 11 **EST:** 2013
SALES (est): 1.1MM **Privately Held**
WEB: www.m3tooling.com
SIC: 3544 Special dies, tools, jigs & fixtures

(G-18271)
MAGNUM CUSTOM TRLR MFG CO INC
Also Called: Magnum Trlrs Parts Equipments
11210 N Ih 35 (78233-5709)
PHONE..................................512 258-4101
Charlie McLemore, *Branch Mgr*
EMP: 13

SALES (corp-wide): 15MM **Privately Held**
WEB: www.magnumtrailers.com
SIC: **3715** 5531 7539 7538 Truck trailers; trailer hitches, automotive; trailer repair; recreational vehicle repairs; utility trailers
PA: Magnum Custom Trailer Mfg. Co., Inc.
10806 N Fm 620 Rd
Austin TX 78726
512 258-4101

(G-18272)
MALIM INC
Also Called: Fresh From Texas
3602 Highpoint (78217-2864)
PHONE..................................210 654-3963
Judy Clark, *CEO*
Mark A Miller, *President*
Phil Huebner, *COO*
Lisa Miller, *Vice Pres*
Rick Mangum, *CFO*
▲ EMP: 150
SQ FT: 60,000
SALES (est): 5.5MM **Privately Held**
WEB: www.freshfromtx.com
SIC: 2099 Salads, fresh or refrigerated

(G-18273)
MANI LITTLE & WORTMANN
300 Austin Hwy Ste 150 (78209-5338)
PHONE..................................210 403-9461
Philip C Mani, *President*
EMP: 20
SALES (est): 1.7MM **Privately Held**
WEB: www.mlwenergylaw.com
SIC: 1382 Oil & gas exploration services

(G-18274)
MARATHON OIL EF LLC
5253 Prue Rd Ste 230 (78240-1759)
P.O. Box 22165, Tulsa OK (74121-2165)
PHONE..................................713 209-2458
Bruce Smith, *Opers Spvr*
Joshua Callahan, *Corp Comm Staff*
Blanche Roberston, *Mng Member*
Dwayne Derry, *Administration*
Edward Balderrama, *Technician*
EMP: 14
SALES (est): 2.5MM
SALES (corp-wide): 5.1B **Publicly Held**
WEB: www.marathonoil.com
SIC: 1382 Oil & gas exploration services
PA: Marathon Oil Corporation
5555 San Felipe St
Houston TX 77056
713 629-6600

(G-18275)
MARBROS L L C
Also Called: El Rancho Food Service
623 New Laredo Hwy (78211-1929)
PHONE..................................210 922-8383
Ruben E Martinez, *Mng Member*
Renato Martinez,
EMP: 15 EST: 1996
SQ FT: 7,560
SALES (est): 2.3MM **Privately Held**
SIC: 2099 Tortillas, fresh or refrigerated

(G-18276)
MARK/TRECE INC
3453 N Panam Expy Ste 203 (78219-2338)
PHONE..................................210 281-8348
Jon Lawson, *General Mgr*
Mark Trece, *Principal*
EMP: 26
SALES (corp-wide): 33.5MM **Privately Held**
WEB: www.marktrece.com
SIC: 3555 Printing trades machinery
PA: Mark/Trece, Inc.
2001 Stockton Rd
Joppa MD 21085
410 879-0060

(G-18277)
MARKLE MFG CO SAN ANTONIO INC
Also Called: Markle Mfg Co
10619 N Interstate 35 (78233-6627)
P.O. Box 18384 (78218-0384)
PHONE..................................210 655-7130
Siegfried Friese, *President*
Roland Friese, *Vice Pres*
EMP: 64

SALES (est): 14.1MM **Privately Held**
WEB: www.marklemfg.com
SIC: 3441 Fabricated structural metal

(G-18278)
MARTIN MARIETTA MATERIALS INC
Also Called: Martin Mrietta San Antonio Dst
5710 W Hausman Rd Ste 121 (78249-1646)
PHONE..................................210 208-4400
David Hagerman, *Manager*
EMP: 10 **Publicly Held**
WEB: www.martinmarietta.com
SIC: **1423** Crushed & broken granite
PA: Martin Marietta Materials Inc
2710 Wycliff Rd
Raleigh NC 27607

(G-18279)
MARTIN MARIETTA MATERIALS INC
Also Called: O'Connor Ready Mix Plant
4303 N Loop 1604 E (78247-5909)
PHONE..................................210 495-6224
Roberta Meader, *Manager*
EMP: 20 **Publicly Held**
WEB: www.martinmarietta.com
SIC: **1422** Crushed & broken limestone
PA: Martin Marietta Materials Inc
2710 Wycliff Rd
Raleigh NC 27607

(G-18280)
MARTIN MRTTA MTLS SUTHWEST LLC (HQ)
5710 W Hausman Rd Ste 121 (78249-1646)
PHONE..................................210 208-4400
Howard C Nye, *President*
Roselyn R Bar, *Senior VP*
Daniel L Grant, *Senior VP*
Dana F Guzzo, *Senior VP*
W D Bankston, *Vice Pres*
▲ EMP: 400 EST: 1934
SQ FT: 10,000
SALES (est): 888.1MM **Publicly Held**
WEB: www.chenega.com
SIC: **1422** 3273 2951 3274 Crushed & broken limestone; ready-mixed concrete; concrete, asphaltic (not from refineries); hydrated lime; quicklime; construction sand & gravel

(G-18281)
MARYFIELD ENTERPRISES LP (PA)
Also Called: Arrowwood Cabinetry
2161 Nw Loop 410 (78213-2324)
PHONE..................................210 344-4151
Bryce Maryfield, *Partner*
Diane Maryfield, *Partner*
EMP: 100
SQ FT: 105,000
SALES (est): 6.2MM **Privately Held**
SIC: 2434 5031 1751 Wood kitchen cabinets; kitchen cabinets; cabinet building & installation

(G-18282)
MASSENGALE ARMATURE WORKS INC
1031 Basse Rd (78212-1002)
PHONE..................................210 732-5168
Michael Massengale, *President*
Terry Massengale, *Vice Pres*
John Massengale, *Admin Sec*
EMP: 16
SQ FT: 10,000
SALES (est): 1.8MM **Privately Held**
WEB: www.massengale.works
SIC: 7694 Electric motor repair; coil winding service

(G-18283)
MATHESON TRI-GAS INC
3566 N Panam Expy (78219-2319)
PHONE..................................210 225-3151
EMP: 13
SQ FT: 10,000 **Privately Held**
WEB: www.mathesongas.com
SIC: 2813 5084 Industrial gases; welding machinery & equipment

HQ: Matheson Tri-Gas, Inc.
3 Mountainview Rd Ste 3 # 3
Warren NJ 07059
908 991-9200

(G-18284)
MATTHIESEN EQUIPMENT CO
Also Called: Mathiesen
566 N Ww White Rd (78219-2816)
PHONE..................................210 333-1510
Pete Ruiz, *General Mgr*
John Murphy, *Vice Pres*
▼ EMP: 19
SALES (est): 5MM **Privately Held**
WEB: www.matthiesenequipment.com
SIC: 3585 Refrigeration & heating equipment

(G-18285)
MAXIM INTEGRATED PRODUCTS INC
9651 Westover Hills Blvd (78251-2700)
PHONE..................................210 522-7000
David Ledvina, *Manager*
Bill York, *Manager*
EMP: 528
SALES (corp-wide): 2.1B **Publicly Held**
WEB: www.maximintegrated.com
SIC: 3674 Microcircuits, integrated (semiconductor)
PA: Maxim Integrated Products, Inc.
160 Rio Robles
San Jose CA 95134
408 601-1000

(G-18286)
MDI SECURITY LLC
Also Called: Monitor Dynamics
6800 Alamo Downs Pkwy (78238-4515)
PHONE..................................210 477-5400
Mark Garrett, *General Mgr*
Troy Paddock, *Principal*
Sanjay Prasad, *Vice Pres*
Derk Wallace, *Sales Staff*
Tim Rohrbach, *CTO*
EMP: 18
SALES (est): 950K **Privately Held**
WEB: www.mdisecure.com
SIC: 3679 Electronic circuits

(G-18287)
MEDCOGNITION INC
21750 Hardy Oak Blvd (78258-4925)
PHONE..................................210 960-0930
Kevin King, *CEO*
Brian Dedmon, *CFO*
Roland Paquette, *Agent*
John Quarles, *Director*
Hector Caraballo, *Admin Sec*
EMP: 11 EST: 2016
SALES (est): 171.6K **Privately Held**
WEB: www.medcognition.com
SIC: 7372 Application computer software; educational computer software

(G-18288)
MEDIA DISPLAYS INC
14731 Bulverde Rd (78247-2627)
PHONE..................................210 495-6338
Emmett R Womack, *President*
Rhonda Wall, *Exec VP*
Sherry Welge, *Admin Sec*
EMP: 14
SQ FT: 2,000
SALES (est): 1.1MM **Privately Held**
WEB: www.mediaoutdoordisplays.com
SIC: 3993 7629 Electric signs; electronic equipment repair

(G-18289)
MEDIANA TECHNOLOGIES CORP
23510 Canyon Golf Rd # 103 (78258-4945)
PHONE..................................425 406-2262
Peter Hsu, *CEO*
Moon Jong Khil, *Chairman*
Fernando Flores, *CFO*
Chuck Crisafulli, *Marketing Staff*
Keng Hean Lim, *Manager*
▲ EMP: 21
SQ FT: 45,000

SALES (est): 2.2MM **Privately Held**
WEB: www.medianatech.com
SIC: **3845** 3841 5047 Patient monitoring apparatus; blood pressure apparatus; medical & hospital equipment
PA: Mediana.Co.Ltd
132 Donghwagongdan-Ro, Munmak-Eup
Wonju 26365

(G-18290)
MEDTRONIC USA INC
613 Nw Loop 410 Ste 660 (78216-5507)
PHONE..................................210 395-5769
David Trapp, *District Mgr*
EMP: 28 **Privately Held**
WEB: www.medtronic.com
SIC: 3841 Surgical & medical instruments
HQ: Medtronic Usa, Inc.
710 Medtronic Pkwy
Minneapolis MN 55432
763 514-4000

(G-18291)
MELET PLASTICS USA INC
210 Laramie Dr (78209-2346)
PHONE..................................210 822-0460
Andrew T Burchfield, *President*
EMP: 10
SALES (est): 139.9K **Privately Held**
SIC: 3089 Injection molding of plastics

(G-18292)
MESA ORTHOPEDIC SUPPLIES
Also Called: Medical External Support Appls
7319 Caribou (78238-1231)
PHONE..................................210 699-6911
David R Jones, *President*
EMP: 36
SALES (est): 4.8MM **Privately Held**
SIC: 3842 Orthopedic appliances

(G-18293)
METALSA LIGHT TRUCK INC (HQ)
1 Lone Star Pass Bldg 4 (78264-3630)
PHONE..................................210 242-3403
Jesus Theurel, *CEO*
Enrique Cambrana, *President*
Guillermo Zambran Lozano, *President*
Jose Alejo Cantu, *CFO*
Nicolas Villarreal, *Admin Sec*
EMP: 13
SALES (est): 2.9MM **Privately Held**
WEB: www.metalsa.com
SIC: 3714 Motor vehicle parts & accessories

(G-18294)
METOKOTE CORPORATION
1 Lone Star Pass Bldg 37 (78264-3642)
PHONE..................................210 628-1955
James Bender, *General Mgr*
Jaime Gonzalez, *Plant Mgr*
EMP: 15
SALES (corp-wide): 15.3B **Publicly Held**
WEB: www.metokote.com
SIC: 3479 Coating of metals & formed products
HQ: Metokote Corporation
1340 Neubrecht Rd
Lima OH 45801
419 996-7800

(G-18295)
METSO MINERALS INDUSTRIES INC
11451 Jnes Maltsberger Rd (78216-2830)
PHONE..................................210 491-9521
Marcelo Farah, *Vice Pres*
Andrea Vallejo, *Purch Agent*
Maggie Cox, *Engineer*
Webb Schoenfeld, *Engineer*
Felipe Gonzalez, *Design Engr*
EMP: 30
SALES (corp-wide): 1.3B **Privately Held**
WEB: www.metso.com
SIC: **3321** 3069 3561 3535 Ductile iron castings; linings, vulcanizable rubber; hard rubber products; pumps & pumping equipment; bulk handling conveyor systems; crushing, pulverizing & screening equipment

HQ: Metso Outotec Usa Inc.
20965 Crossroads Cir
Waukesha WI 53186
262 717-2500

(G-18296)
MEYER INDUSTRIES INC
Also Called: Meyer Machine Company
3528 Fredericksburg Rd (78201-3849)
P.O. Box 5460 (78201-0460)
PHONE..................................210 736-1811
Stan Poortinga, *President*
Jack Wilson, *Design Engr*
Julia O'Meara, *Accounting Mgr*
◆ EMP: 75 EST: 1945
SQ FT: 100,000
SALES (est): 23.2MM
SALES (corp-wide): 176.3MM **Privately Held**
WEB: www.meyer-industries.com
SIC: 3556 3535 Food products machinery; belt conveyor systems, general industrial use
PA: Precision, Inc.
300 Se 14th St
Pella IA 50219
641 628-3115

(G-18297)
MG BUILDING MATERIALS LTD
Mg Building Materials Truss
9405 New Laredo Hwy (78211-5301)
PHONE..................................210 798-0650
Staton Douthit, *Principal*
Gilbert Trejo, *Buyer*
EMP: 9
SQ FT: 5,884
SALES (corp-wide): 332.4MM **Privately Held**
WEB: www.mgbuildingmaterials.com
SIC: 2439 3448 Trusses, wooden roof; prefabricated metal buildings; trusses & framing: prefabricated metal
HQ: Mg Building Materials, Ltd.
2651 Sw Military Dr
San Antonio TX 78224

(G-18298)
MG BUILDING MATERIALS LTD (HQ)
Also Called: Mg Truck Sales
2651 Sw Military Dr (78224-1048)
PHONE..................................210 924-8604
Allan Grothues, *Partner*
David Grothues, *Partner*
Larry E Grothues, *Partner*
Thomas Grothues, *Partner*
Tom Lyda, *Controller*
EMP: 390
SALES (est): 332.4MM **Privately Held**
WEB: www.mgbuildingmaterials.com
SIC: 2421 4212 5211 Sawmills & planing mills, general; lumber (log) trucking, local; lumber & other building materials
PA: Grothues Brothers Holdings, Ltd.
2651 Sw Military Dr
San Antonio TX 78224
830 569-1131

(G-18299)
MICHELSON ENERGY COMPANY (PA)
7709 Broadway Apt 106 (78209-3203)
P.O. Box 6027 (78209-0027)
PHONE..................................210 826-0681
Calvin Michelson, *President*
Mitch Michelson, *Vice Pres*
Robert L Fannin, *Treasurer*
EMP: 12
SALES (est): 12.8MM **Privately Held**
WEB: www.bengalenergy.com
SIC: 4923 1389 1382 1311 Gas transmission & distribution; servicing oil & gas wells; oil & gas exploration services; crude petroleum production; natural gas production

(G-18300)
MICRO-TES INC
12500 Network Blvd # 201 (78249-3307)
PHONE..................................210 558-4757
Bill Botto, *President*
Richard Geisler, *Vice Pres*
Karen Shutes, *Office Mgr*
EMP: 10
SQ FT: 2,800

SALES (est): 1.9MM **Privately Held**
WEB: www.liventia.net
SIC: 2836 8748 Biological products, except diagnostic; business consulting

(G-18301)
MICROSOFT CORPORATION
401 E Sonterra Blvd # 300 (78258-4315)
PHONE..................................210 402-0577
Edwin Rodriguez, *Manager*
EMP: 103
SALES (corp-wide): 143B **Publicly Held**
WEB: www.microsoft.com
SIC: 7372 Application computer software
PA: Microsoft Corporation
1 Microsoft Way
Redmond WA 98052
425 882-8080

(G-18302)
MICROSOFT CORPORATION
5150 Rogers Rd (78251-3660)
PHONE..................................210 346-2500
Roland Spencer, *Sales Staff*
Eddie Reed, *Branch Mgr*
EMP: 75
SALES (corp-wide): 143B **Publicly Held**
WEB: www.microsoft.com
SIC: 3577 Application computer software
PA: Microsoft Corporation
1 Microsoft Way
Redmond WA 98052
425 882-8080

(G-18303)
MICROTEQ ENGINEERING INC
3003 Aniol St Ste 112 (78219-3610)
P.O. Box 5802 (78201-0802)
PHONE..................................210 736-2611
Vaishali P Dev, *President*
Arturo Ramirez, *General Mgr*
EMP: 12
SALES (est): 986.8K **Privately Held**
WEB: www.microteq1.wpengine.com
SIC: 3441 Fabricated structural metal

(G-18304)
MIDCOAST OPERATING LP
10101 Reunion Pl Ste 200 (78216-4163)
PHONE..................................210 321-8000
Bill Waldrip, *Vice Pres*
EMP: 50
SALES (corp-wide): 1.2B **Privately Held**
WEB: www.midcoastenergy.com
SIC: 1321 Natural gasoline production
HQ: Midcoast Energy, Llc
1501 Mckinney St Ste 600
Houston TX 77010
713 821-2000

(G-18305)
MIDSTREAM NAVARRO SERVICES LLC
10101 Reunion Pl Ste 1000 (78216-4157)
PHONE..................................956 728-6000
Craig Rosensterin, *President*
EMP: 900
SALES (est): 23.8MM **Privately Held**
SIC: 1382 Oil & gas exploration services
PA: Lewis Energy Group, L.P.
10101 Reunion Pl Ste 1000
San Antonio TX 78216

(G-18306)
MILESTONE INTERNATIONAL INC
Also Called: Press Stop
1403 E Commerce St (78205-3321)
PHONE..................................210 226-2122
EMP: 9 EST: 2010
SALES (est): 560.4K **Privately Held**
SIC: 2741 Miscellaneous publishing

(G-18307)
MILLENNIUM EXPLORATION CO LLC
211 N Loop 1604 E Ste 220 (78232-1242)
PHONE..................................210 960-1000
Richard Monroy, *CEO*
Gary Hand, *Vice Pres*
Theo Johns, *Vice Pres*
Jaime Ramirez, *Vice Pres*
Bob Stinziano, *VP Opers*
EMP: 12

SALES (est): 2MM **Privately Held**
WEB: www.millenniumpetrocapital.com
SIC: 8748 1311 Business consulting; crude petroleum & natural gas

(G-18308)
MINOM INC
200 Lombrano St (78207-1804)
PHONE..................................210 734-5124
Robert Escamilla, *President*
EMP: 18
SQ FT: 5,500 **Privately Held**
WEB: www.minom.com
SIC: 2099 Food preparations

(G-18309)
MISSION CITY PRESS INC
115 N Loop 1604 E Ste 220 (78232-1398)
PHONE..................................210 614-7051
Sandi Shelton, *President*
▲ EMP: 10
SALES (est): 986.2K **Privately Held**
SIC: 2731 8661 Book publishing; religious organizations

(G-18310)
MISSION CYCLEPLEX LLC
9800 San Pedro Ave (78216-4434)
PHONE..................................210 250-0057
Ryan Martin, *Manager*
EMP: 10 EST: 2016
SALES (est): 139.4K **Privately Held**
WEB: www.missionmitsubishi.com
SIC: 7694 7699 Motor repair services; motorcycle repair service

(G-18311)
MISSION OIL COMPANY
100 W Houston St Ste 1500 (78205-1424)
PHONE..................................210 224-4455
Tom E Pawel, *President*
Reagan McCoy, *Vice Pres*
Nancy E Pawel, *Vice Pres*
EMP: 13
SALES (est): 1.4MM **Privately Held**
SIC: 1311 Crude petroleum production

(G-18312)
MISSION PHARMACAL COMPANY (PA)
10999 W Interstate 10 (78230-1300)
PHONE..................................210 696-8400
Neill B Walsdorf Sr, *Ch of Bd*
Neill B Walsdorf Jr, *President*
Mark Celeste, *Senior VP*
Tom Dooley, *CFO*
Linda Marsh, *Treasurer*
◆ EMP: 60 EST: 1946
SQ FT: 18,000
SALES: 180.5MM **Privately Held**
WEB: www.missionpharmacal.com
SIC: 2834 Vitamin preparations

(G-18313)
MISSION PHARMACAL COMPANY
1325 E Cesar E Chavez Blv (78210-1724)
P.O. Box 786099 (78278-6099)
PHONE..................................210 696-8400
Neill Walsdorf, *President*
Kash Walsdorf, *Plant Mgr*
Douglas Leonard, *Production*
Daniela Alessia, *Sales Staff*
Pamela Crispino, *Sales Staff*
EMP: 30
SQ FT: 33,316
SALES (corp-wide): 180.5MM **Privately Held**
WEB: www.missionpharmacal.com
SIC: 7311 2834 4225 Advertising consultant; pharmaceutical preparations; general warehousing & storage
PA: Mission Pharmacal Company
10999 W Interstate 10
San Antonio TX 78230
210 696-8400

(G-18314)
MISSION SOLAR ENERGY LLC
8303 S New Braunfels (78235-1068)
PHONE..................................210 531-8600
Alex Kim, *President*
Brad Miles, *Exec VP*
Frank Pham, *Plant Mgr*
John Deleon, *Mfg Mgr*
Sam Martens, *Opers Staff*

▲ EMP: 60 EST: 2012
SALES (est): 31.5MM **Privately Held**
WEB: www.missionsolar.com
SIC: 3674 Photovoltaic devices, solid state; solar cells; silicon wafers, chemically doped
HQ: Oci Solar Power Llc
8000 W Interstate 10 # 1201
San Antonio TX 78230

(G-18315)
MODERN FABRICATING INC
Also Called: Matthiesen
566 N Ww White Rd (78219-2816)
P.O. Box 11340, Cincinnati OH (45211-0340)
PHONE..................................800 543-1581
Gary E Jerow, *President*
John Murphy, *Vice Pres*
EMP: 14
SQ FT: 1,000
SALES (est): 1.9MM **Privately Held**
WEB: www.matthiesenequipment.com
SIC: 3444 Sheet metalwork
PA: Modern Ice Equipment And Supply Company
5709 Harrison Ave
Cincinnati OH 45248

(G-18316)
MOHAWK INDUSTRIES INC
4602 Perrin Crk Ste 1240 (78217-3734)
PHONE..................................210 564-8849
Andrew Love, *Manager*
EMP: 156 **Publicly Held**
WEB: www.mohawkind.com
SIC: 2273 Finishers of tufted carpets & rugs
PA: Mohawk Industries, Inc.
160 S Industrial Blvd
Calhoun GA 30701

(G-18317)
MONTECARLO FOODS LLC
6421 Broadway (78209-4563)
PHONE..................................206 304-6771
Gabriel Martinez, *President*
EMP: 10
SQ FT: 1,490
SALES: 186.4K **Privately Held**
SIC: 2024 Ice cream, bulk

(G-18318)
MONTERREY IRON & METAL LTD
Also Called: Toucan Recycling
2300 Frio City Rd (78226-1520)
P.O. Box 241509 (78224-8509)
PHONE..................................210 927-2727
Jack Vexler, *CEO*
Jordan Vexler, *COO*
David Vexler, *Manager*
EMP: 55
SQ FT: 30,000
SALES (est): 36.7MM **Privately Held**
WEB: www.monterreyiron.com
SIC: 5093 2611 Metal scrap & waste materials; pulp mills, mechanical & recycling processing

(G-18319)
MONTERREY PRODUCTS COMPANY
Also Called: Texan Accent
803 S Zarzamora St (78207-5363)
PHONE..................................210 435-2872
Ernest De Los Santos, *President*
Sylvia De Los Santos, *Treasurer*
EMP: 10 EST: 1948
SQ FT: 5,000
SALES (est): 1.6MM **Privately Held**
WEB: www.monterreyproducts.com
SIC: 5149 2064 Seasonings, sauces & extracts; candy & other confectionery products

(G-18320)
MORTON PRINTERS INC
814 N Alamo St (78215-1535)
PHONE..................................210 223-4258
Kevin J Morton, *President*
EMP: 13 EST: 1947
SQ FT: 6,000
SALES (est): 1.6MM **Privately Held**
SIC: 2752 Commercial printing, offset

(G-18321)
MOTHER EARTH LABS INC
24165 Ih 10 W (78257-1449)
PHONE..................................210 695-3535
Careylyn Carter, *President*
EMP: 9
SQ FT: 6,000
SALES (est): 929.7K Privately Held
WEB: www.motherearthlabs.com
SIC: 2833 Vitamins, natural or synthetic: bulk, uncompounded

(G-18322)
MPS GROUP (PA)
Also Called: Printer Solutions
12020 Warfield St (78216-3217)
PHONE..................................210 344-0332
James Thomas, *President*
Yvette Thomas, *Vice Pres*
▲ EMP: 12
SQ FT: 4,200
SALES (est): 1.7MM Privately Held
WEB: www.meyertorg.com
SIC: 7699 2893 Printing trades machinery & equipment repair; printing ink

(G-18323)
MSF ELECTRIC INC
15500 Tradesman (78249-1330)
PHONE..................................210 781-4112
Jon Edwards, *Division Mgr*
Ernest Pierce, *Superintendent*
Alex Adarmes, *CFO*
Jon Turner, *Supervisor*
EMP: 72 Privately Held
WEB: www.msfelectric.com
SIC: 3699 1731 Electrical equipment & supplies; electrical work
PA: Msf Electric, Inc.
    10455 Fountaingate Dr
    Stafford TX 77477

(G-18324)
MT TEXAS LLC
3614 Highpoint (78217-2892)
PHONE..................................210 599-0060
Terry O'Leary, *Opers Staff*
Debbie Sexton, *Manager*
Mark Faulkner,
Ricardo Cortez,
Monica Reyes,
EMP: 43
SALES (est): 5.1MM Privately Held
WEB: www.meyertool.com
SIC: 3724 Aircraft engines & engine parts

(G-18325)
MULBERRY HEART I LTD (PA)
Also Called: Painted Pony
118 Irvington Dr (78209-4218)
PHONE..................................210 377-3335
Katherine R Hoermann, *Partner*
Grady Hoermann, *Partner*
Kathy Hoermann, *Partner*
EMP: 12
SQ FT: 7,500
SALES (est): 1.8MM Privately Held
SIC: 2335 Dresses, paper: cut & sewn

(G-18326)
MULTICOPY PRINTING COMPANY
516 New Laredo Hwy (78211-1928)
PHONE..................................210 923-8373
Carmen Gugliemo, *President*
Pat Sorriano, *Director*
EMP: 16
SALES (est): 1.8MM Privately Held
WEB: www.multicopyprinting.com
SIC: 2752 Commercial printing, offset

(G-18327)
N D NOLEN DRILLING LLC
300 Convent St Ste 1330 (78205-1357)
PHONE..................................210 585-1966
Brian Nolen,
Austin Gard,
EMP: 12
SQ FT: 3,000
SALES (est): 250K Privately Held
SIC: 1382 Oil & gas exploration services

(G-18328)
NAILIT MILLWORK INC
Also Called: Nailit Millwork Installation
205 E Nakoma St (78216-2704)
PHONE..................................210 633-4659
Michael K Mansfield, *CEO*
EMP: 12 EST: 2011
SALES (est): 559.8K Privately Held
WEB: www.nailitmillworks.com
SIC: 2431 Millwork

(G-18329)
NAKENT LLC
25755 Velvet Crk (78255-4419)
PHONE..................................619 212-2277
EMP: 12 EST: 2017
SALES (est): 33.8K Privately Held
SIC: 7389 2033 Business services; fruits & fruit products in cans, jars, etc.

(G-18330)
NALCO COMPANY LLC
3523 Oakfort St (78247-3196)
PHONE..................................210 493-0379
EMP: 9
SALES (corp-wide): 13.8B Publicly Held
SIC: 2899 Mfg Chemical Preparations
HQ: Nalco Company Llc
    11177 S Stadium Dr
    Sugar Land TX 77478
    281 632-6500

(G-18331)
NANO COAT LP
750 Rittiman Rd (78209-5500)
PHONE..................................281 217-5265
Ed Thompson, *Principal*
EMP: 10
SALES (est): 598.5K Privately Held
WEB: www.nanocoatlp.com
SIC: 3479 Metal coating & allied service

(G-18332)
NAPCO PRECAST LLC (PA)
6949 Low Bid Ln (78250-4632)
PHONE..................................210 424-4371
Todd Davidson, *President*
Jorge Londono, *Vice Pres*
Cipriano Deluna, *Plant Mgr*
Isaac A Rodriguez, *Materials Mgr*
Frank Mitchel, *Opers Staff*
▲ EMP: 230
SQ FT: 3,000
SALES (est): 40.6MM Privately Held
WEB: www.napcosa.com
SIC: 1791 3271 3272 Precast concrete structural framing or panels, placing of; blocks, concrete: landscape or retaining wall; concrete products, precast; concrete stuctural support & building material; pre-stressed concrete products

(G-18333)
NATIONAL OILWELL VARCO INC
7640 Us Highway 87 E (78263-2405)
PHONE..................................210 572-4012
Shawn Dewey, *Project Engr*
Bill Silner, *Sales Staff*
EMP: 32
SALES (corp-wide): 8.4B Publicly Held
WEB: www.nov.com
SIC: 3533 Oil & gas field machinery
PA: National Oilwell Varco, Inc.
    7909 Parkwood Circle Dr
    Houston TX 77036
    713 346-7500

(G-18334)
NATIONAL OILWELL VARCO LP
Also Called: National Olwell Vrco - Fibr GL
17115 San Pedro Ave # 20 (78232-2685)
PHONE..................................210 477-7500
Joe Factor, *Superintendent*
Calvin Dickenson, *Plant Mgr*
EMP: 35
SALES (corp-wide): 8.4B Publicly Held
WEB: www.nov.com
SIC: 1389 Oil field services
HQ: National Oilwell Varco, L.P.
    7909 Parkwood Circle Dr
    Houston TX 77036
    713 375-3700

(G-18335)
NATIONS CABINETRY LLC
4600 Timco E (78238-1968)
PHONE..................................210 681-8477
EMP: 22
SALES (corp-wide): 4.1MM Privately Held
WEB: www.nationscabinetry.com
SIC: 2434 Wood kitchen cabinets
PA: Nation's Cabinetry, Llc
    4600 W Us Highway 90
    San Antonio TX 78237
    210 684-1611

(G-18336)
NATIONWIDE PHARMACEUTICAL LLC
Also Called: Valor Built
1270 N Loop 1604 E # 1306 (78232-1393)
PHONE..................................800 697-3329
Joseph Lawrence, *CEO*
Kyle Lavelle, *Accounts Mgr*
Joseph B Lawrence, *Mng Member*
Marc Young, *Officer*
Jeremy W Briggs,
EMP: 12
SALES (est): 3.2MM Privately Held
WEB: www.nationwidepharmaceutical.com
SIC: 1542 2834 Commercial & office building, new construction; pills, pharmaceutical

(G-18337)
NATIONWIDE PNNANT FLAG MFG INC
Also Called: Nap
7325 Reindeer Trl (78238-1214)
PHONE..................................210 684-3524
Donald W Engelhardt, *President*
Rose Engelhardt, *Vice Pres*
Doug Peterson, *Safety Mgr*
Mary Quiroga, *Human Res Mgr*
EMP: 120
SQ FT: 54,000
SALES (est): 14.9MM Privately Held
WEB: www.napmfg.com
SIC: 2399 Pennants; banners, made from fabric; flags, fabric

(G-18338)
NCP SOLUTIONS LLC
15955 La Cantera Pkwy (78256-2589)
PHONE..................................210 694-1528
EMP: 19
SALES (est): 3.4MM Privately Held
WEB: www.ncpsolutions.com
SIC: 2752 Commercial printing, lithographic

(G-18339)
NCR CORPORATION
1077 Central Pkwy S # 800 (78232-5079)
PHONE..................................210 366-2959
Terry Miyata, *IT/INT Sup*
EMP: 10
SALES (corp-wide): 6.9B Publicly Held
WEB: www.ncr.com
SIC: 3575 3578 7379 7374 Computer terminals; point-of-sale devices; computer related maintenance services; data processing & preparation; custom computer programming services; software programming applications
PA: Ncr Corporation
    864 Spring St Nw
    Atlanta GA 30308
    937 445-1936

(G-18340)
NCS PEARSON INC
Also Called: Pearson Company
19500 Bulverde Rd Ste 100 (78259-3768)
PHONE..................................210 339-5000
Kevin Brueggeman, *President*
Mary Hanson, *Research*
Keisha Phillips, *Research*
Myesha Soukup, *Human Resources*
Michael Cook, *Info Tech Mgr*
EMP: 99
SALES (corp-wide): 5B Privately Held
WEB: www.pearsonassessments.com
SIC: 3577 7372 7374 Optical scanning devices; application computer software; tabulating service; optical scanning data service

HQ: Ncs Pearson Inc
    5601 Green Valley Dr # 220
    Bloomington MN 55437
    952 681-3000

(G-18341)
NEIGHBORHOOD NEWS INC
3740 Colony Dr Ste Ll100 (78230-2290)
PHONE..................................210 558-3160
Susan Schopp, *President*
EMP: 10 EST: 2000
SALES (est): 1MM Privately Held
WEB: www.neighborhoodnews.com
SIC: 2711 Newspapers

(G-18342)
NERIUM BIOTECHNOLOGY INC (PA)
Also Called: Nerium Skincare
11467 Huebner Rd Ste 175 (78230-1074)
PHONE..................................210 822-7908
Dennis Knocke, *CEO*
Joseph Nester, *CFO*
Joseph B Nester, *Admin Sec*
EMP: 12
SQ FT: 2,400
SALES: 2.8MM Privately Held
WEB: www.nbiresearch.com
SIC: 2819 8731 Industrial inorganic chemicals; commercial physical research

(G-18343)
NEWELL LTD
726 Probandt (78204-2342)
P.O. Box 830808 (78283-0808)
PHONE..................................210 222-9511
John R Newell, *General Ptnr*
John Newell, *General Ptnr*
EMP: 27 EST: 1976
SQ FT: 150,000
SALES (est): 6MM Privately Held
SIC: 3341 7389 Recovery & refining of nonferrous metals; metal cutting services

(G-18344)
NEWTEK INC
5131 Beckwith Blvd (78249-2256)
PHONE..................................210 370-8000
Andrew Cross, *President*
Chuck Silber, *COO*
Brian Olson, *Vice Pres*
Rex Olson, *Vice Pres*
Warren Bishop, *Plant Mgr*
EMP: 50
SALES (est): 11.1MM
SALES (corp-wide): 166.6MM Privately Held
WEB: www.newtek.com
SIC: 7372 Prepackaged software
HQ: Vizrt Group As
    Lars Hilles Gate 30
    Bergen 5008

(G-18345)
NEWTEK PARTNERS LP
5131 Beckwith Blvd (78249-2256)
PHONE..................................210 370-8000
Tim Jenison, *Partner*
Will Waters, *Vice Pres*
EMP: 75 EST: 1997
SALES (est): 3.6MM Privately Held
WEB: www.newtek.com
SIC: 7372 7373 3825 Prepackaged software; computer integrated systems design; instruments to measure electricity

(G-18346)
NITROCISION LLC
6766 Culebra Rd (78238-4700)
PHONE..................................210 254-4100
Bob Copp, *President*
Ronald R Warnecke, *CFO*
◆ EMP: 12
SALES (est): 2MM Privately Held
WEB: www.ihiswt.com
SIC: 3569 Generators: steam, liquid oxygen or nitrogen
HQ: Iia Nuclear Services, Inc.
    6766 Culebra Rd
    San Antonio TX 78238
    210 256-4102

(G-18347)
NOAH TECHNOLOGIES CORP TEXAS
Also Called: Noah Chemical
1 Noah Park (78249-3419)
PHONE.................................210 691-2000
Jamie Hong, *CEO*
Sonya Blumenthal, *President*
Bob Blumenthal, *Vice Pres*
John Meyers, *Treasurer*
Yvonne Lopez, *Sales Staff*
▲ EMP: 100
SQ FT: 85,000
SALES (est): 21.2MM **Privately Held**
WEB: www.noahtech.com
SIC: 2819 2899 2865 Chemicals, high purity: refined from technical grade; chemical preparations; cyclic crudes & intermediates

(G-18348)
NOAHMAYA CANDLE CO
Also Called: Scent Chips
13702 Chittim Woods (78232-5460)
PHONE.................................210 341-7373
Tanya Clark, *President*
EMP: 10
SQ FT: 2,000
SALES (est): 1MM **Privately Held**
WEB: www.scentchips.com
SIC: 3999 Candles

(G-18349)
NOISY TRUMPET LLC
7550 W Interstate 10 (78229-5803)
PHONE.................................210 852-0505
Fran Yanity, *CEO*
EMP: 10
SALES (est): 1MM **Privately Held**
WEB: www.noisytrumpet.com
SIC: 2741 7379 8743 ; computer related maintenance services; public relations services

(G-18350)
NORTH AMERICAN PRECAST COMPANY
6949 Low Bid Ln (78250-4632)
PHONE.................................210 509-9100
Jaime Iragorri, *President*
Jorge Londono, *Vice Pres*
Jose Luis Pliego, *Engineer*
Sabrina Murillo, *Human Res Dir*
EMP: 200
SQ FT: 1,000
SALES (est): 34.9MM **Privately Held**
WEB: www.napcosa.com
SIC: 3272 1791 Concrete products, precast; precast concrete structural framing or panels, placing of

(G-18351)
NORTONLIFELOCK INC
Also Called: Symantec
911 Central Pkwy N # 300 (78232-5052)
PHONE.................................210 403-7800
Greg Adams, *Branch Mgr*
EMP: 80
SALES (corp-wide): 4.7B **Publicly Held**
WEB: www.broadcom.com
SIC: 3674 Prepackaged software
PA: Nortonlifelock Inc.
60 E Rio Salado Pkwy # 1
Tempe AZ 85281
650 527-8000

(G-18352)
NTW SERVICES INC
Also Called: A 2nd To None
4507 Lakebend West Dr (78244-1704)
PHONE.................................210 885-8637
James Ramon, *President*
EMP: 9
SALES (est): 50K **Privately Held**
SIC: 1761 2842 7299 Roofing contractor; cleaning or polishing preparations; personal financial services

(G-18353)
NUSTAR GP LLC
19003 W Interstate 10 (78257-9518)
PHONE.................................210 370-2000
Curtis V Anastasio, *CEO*
James R Bluntzer, *Vice Pres*
Clayton E Killinger, *Vice Pres*

Jerry D McVicker, *Vice Pres*
Rodney L Reese, *Vice Pres*
EMP: 1226
SALES (est): 50.5MM **Publicly Held**
SIC: 3533 Oil & gas field machinery
HQ: Nustar Gp Holdings, Llc
19003 Ih 10 W
San Antonio TX 78257

(G-18354)
OLDCASTLE INFRASTRUCTURE INC
1900 Rilling Rd (78214-3240)
PHONE.................................210 922-7306
Konner Everhard, *Branch Mgr*
EMP: 30
SQ FT: 18,080
SALES (corp-wide): 30.6B **Privately Held**
WEB: www.oldcastleinfrastructure.com
SIC: 3272 Concrete products, precast
HQ: Oldcastle Infrastructure, Inc.
7000 Central Pkwy Ste 800
Atlanta GA 30328
470 602-2000

(G-18355)
ONCKEN & SONS CABINET SHOP
203 Seale Rd (78219-2712)
PHONE.................................210 333-4611
Irene Oncken, *President*
Norwin K Oncken, *Chairman*
Alton Oncken, *Vice Pres*
EMP: 19
SQ FT: 12,000
SALES (est): 1MM **Privately Held**
WEB: www.onckenandsons.com
SIC: 2434 Wood kitchen cabinets

(G-18356)
ORACLE AMERICA INC
Also Called: Sun Microsystems
613 Nw Loop 410 Ste 1000 (78216-5593)
PHONE.................................650 506-7000
Steve Dali, *Manager*
EMP: 10
SALES (corp-wide): 39B **Publicly Held**
WEB: www.ea.com
SIC: 7372 Prepackaged software
HQ: Oracle America, Inc.
500 Oracle Pkwy
Redwood City CA 94065
650 506-7000

(G-18357)
OSBORN HEIRS COMPANY LTD
1250 Ne Loop 410 Ste 1100 (78209-1525)
P.O. Box 17968 (78217-0968)
PHONE.................................210 826-0700
Albert Biedenharn, *Principal*
Albert M Biedenharn III, *Principal*
Charles Osborn Biedenharn, *Principal*
Jewel Biedenharn Crosswell, *Principal*
Tom Gish, *Principal*
EMP: 40 EST: 1997
SQ FT: 14,500
SALES (est): 11.9MM **Privately Held**
WEB: www.osbornheirs.com
SIC: 1382 1311 Oil & gas exploration services; crude petroleum production; natural gas production

(G-18358)
OSBURN SAND CO
Also Called: Osburn Materials
215 Wellesley Loop (78231-2266)
PHONE.................................210 626-2045
Clay M Tooke, *President*
Robert L Tooke, *Treasurer*
EMP: 15
SALES (est): 1.9MM **Privately Held**
WEB: www.osburnmaterials.com
SIC: 1446 Silica sand mining

(G-18359)
P2ES HOLDINGS LLC
1355 Central Pkwy S # 500 (78232-5055)
PHONE.................................210 402-5900
Thomas W Neubert, *Manager*
Vaishali Kumar, *Software Engr*
EMP: 99 **Privately Held**
WEB: www.p2energysolutions.com
SIC: 7372 Prepackaged software

HQ: P2es Holdings, Llc
1670 Broadway Ste 2800
Denver CO 80202
303 292-0990

(G-18360)
P3 IMAGING SOLUTIONS LLC
1211 Safari St (78216-2855)
PHONE.................................210 494-9998
Jennifer J Mery, *President*
Kellie Mery, *Business Mgr*
Jordan Mery, *Prdtn Mgr*
Paul K Mery, *Accounts Mgr*
Almendarez Armando, *Manager*
EMP: 23
SQ FT: 1,300
SALES (est): 3.6MM **Privately Held**
WEB: www.p3is.com
SIC: 2752 Commercial printing, lithographic

(G-18361)
PABST BREWING COMPANY LLC
110 E Houston St Fl 3 (78205-2991)
P.O. Box 792627 (78279-2627)
PHONE.................................210 299-6708
Gigi Waymack, *Partner*
Kevin Osborn, *General Mgr*
Adam Powers, *General Mgr*
Ed Prike, *Vice Pres*
Margaret Chiti, *Traffic Mgr*
EMP: 48 **Privately Held**
WEB: www.pabst.com
SIC: 2082 Beer (alcoholic beverage)
PA: Pabst Brewing Company, Llc
10635 Santa Monica Blvd
Los Angeles CA 90025

(G-18362)
PACKAGING CORPORATION AMERICA
Also Called: PCA
4671 W Us Highway 90 (78237-4000)
PHONE.................................210 798-1700
EMP: 103
SALES (corp-wide): 6.9B **Publicly Held**
WEB: www.packagingcorp.com
SIC: 2653 Boxes, corrugated: made from purchased materials
PA: Packaging Corporation Of America
1 N Field Ct
Lake Forest IL 60045
847 482-3000

(G-18363)
PAISANO EDUCATIONAL TRUST
Also Called: PAISANO STUDENT NEWSPAPER
14547 Roadrunner Way (78249-1515)
PHONE.................................210 690-9301
Meena Thiru, *Director*
EMP: 25
SALES: 104.6K **Privately Held**
WEB: www.paisano-online.com
SIC: 2711 Newspapers: publishing only, not printed on site

(G-18364)
PALLET OPS - SAN ANTONIO LLC
Also Called: Alamo Wood
514 Merida St Ste 1 (78207-7645)
PHONE.................................210 225-7882
Michael McDonald, *Mng Member*
EMP: 10
SQ FT: 13,000
SALES (est): 1.4MM **Privately Held**
WEB: www.alamo.edu
SIC: 2448 Pallets, wood

(G-18365)
PANAMERICAN INDUS SVCS CO INC
5290 New Sulphur Sprng Rd (78222-4043)
PHONE.................................210 666-3542
Jose P Cantu, *President*
EMP: 10 EST: 1998
SALES (est): 812.6K **Privately Held**
WEB: www.panamericanindustrial.com
SIC: 1389 Oil field services

(G-18366)
PAPA GRANDE GOURMET FOODS LLC
Also Called: Garcia Foods
3444 E Commerce St (78220-1323)
P.O. Box 13280 (78213-0280)
PHONE.................................210 349-6262
Hilda Garcia, *President*
EMP: 250
SQ FT: 39,000
SALES (est): 17.8MM **Privately Held**
WEB: www.garciafoods.com
SIC: 2013 Sausages & other prepared meats

(G-18367)
PARLEVEL SYSTEMS INC
114 E Cevallos (78204-1721)
PHONE.................................210 200-8873
Luis P Gonzalez, *CEO*
Gabriel Senior, *COO*
Jennifer Ortiz, *Opers Staff*
Alan Munson, *Ch Credit Ofcr*
Jeremy Brice, *Manager*
EMP: 25
SQ FT: 1,000
SALES (est): 1.7MM **Privately Held**
WEB: www.parlevelsystems.com
SIC: 7372 Business oriented computer software

(G-18368)
PCCS PRINTING SOLUTIONS INC
Also Called: Allegra Marketing Print Mail
11811 Warfield St (78216-3214)
PHONE.................................210 340-1841
Petra McCann, *President*
Henry C McCann, *Vice Pres*
Chuck McCann, *Opers Mgr*
Sandy Reynoso, *Accounts Mgr*
Tamara Urbach, *Accounts Mgr*
EMP: 25
SALES (est): 4.7MM **Privately Held**
WEB: www.allegramarketingprint.com
SIC: 2752 2759 Commercial printing, offset; advertising literature: printing; circulars: printing; invitation & stationery printing & engraving; announcements: engraved

(G-18369)
PEPSI BEVERAGES COMPANY
6100 Ne Loop 410 (78218-5409)
PHONE.................................210 661-5311
▲ EMP: 9
SALES (est): 1.6MM **Privately Held**
WEB: www.pepsico.com
SIC: 2086 Carbonated soft drinks, bottled & canned

(G-18370)
PEPSI BOTTLING COMPANY
6100 Ne Loop 410 (78218-5409)
PHONE.................................210 662-3418
Wade Worthy, *QC Mgr*
EMP: 11
SALES (est): 1.4MM **Privately Held**
WEB: www.pepsico.com
SIC: 2086 Carbonated soft drinks, bottled & canned

(G-18371)
PEPSI-COLA METRO BTLG CO INC
6100 Ne Loop 410 (78218-5409)
PHONE.................................210 661-5311
Tyrone Sapenter, *Plant Mgr*
David Harris, *VP Human Res*
Steve Milnovitch, *Manager*
Chris Vieyra, *Executive*
Sam Hernadez, *Technician*
EMP: 220
SQ FT: 10,000
SALES (corp-wide): 67.1B **Publicly Held**
WEB: www.pepsico.com
SIC: 2086 Carbonated soft drinks, bottled & canned
HQ: Pepsi-Cola Metropolitan Bottling Company, Inc.
1111 Westchester Ave
White Plains NY 10604
914 767-6000

(G-18372)
PHILIP MORRIS USA INC
84 Ne Loop 410 (78216-5802)
PHONE......................................210 530-7100
Steve Olsen, *Branch Mgr*
EMP: 69
SALES (corp-wide): 25.1B **Publicly Held**
WEB: www.philipmorrisusa.com
SIC: 2111 Cigarettes
HQ: Philip Morris Usa Inc.
6601 W Brd St
Richmond VA 23230
804 274-2000

(G-18373)
PHOENIX FUND INC
8626 Tesoro Dr Ste 801 (78217-6279)
PHONE......................................210 828-4373
O Crandell Addington, *President*
EMP: 10
SQ FT: 2,500
SALES (est): 648.6K **Privately Held**
SIC: 1311 Crude petroleum production;
natural gas production

(G-18374)
PICTSWEET COMPANY
4231 Profit St Ste C (78219-2604)
PHONE......................................210 833-9618
EMP: 90
SALES (corp-wide): 403.3MM **Privately
Held**
WEB: www.pictsweetfarms.com
SIC: 2037 4213 Vegetables, quick frozen
& cold pack, excl. potato products; truck-
ing, except local
PA: The Pictsweet Company
10 Pictsweet Dr
Bells TN 38006
731 663-7600

(G-18375)
PIERCE CORPORATION (PA)
Also Called: Pierce Manufacturing Company
3407 Steen St (78219-2331)
PHONE......................................541 998-0300
Cecil Rock, *President*
Jenny Rogers, *CFO*
John Phebus, *Admin Sec*
▲ **EMP:** 30
SALES (est): 8.8MM **Privately Held**
WEB: www.piercecorporation.com
SIC: 3523 Irrigation equipment, self-pro-
pelled

(G-18376)
**PILGRIMS PRIDE
CORPORATION**
11850 Center Rd Frzr 4 4 Freezer (78223)
PHONE......................................210 633-2412
Kelli Rowell, *Manager*
EMP: 293 **Publicly Held**
WEB: www.pilgrims.com
SIC: 2015 Chicken, slaughtered & dressed
HQ: Pilgrim's Pride Corporation
1770 Promontory Cir
Greeley CO 80634
970 506-8000

(G-18377)
**PIONEER DRILLING SERVICES
LTD (HQ)**
1250 Ne Loop 410 Ste 1000 (78209-1560)
PHONE......................................210 828-7689
Wm Stacy Locke, *CEO*
Franklin C West, *Exec VP*
William Hibbetts, *Senior VP*
Carlos R Pena, *Senior VP*
Scott Keenen, *Vice Pres*
▼ **EMP:** 50
SQ FT: 12,500
SALES (est): 407.8MM
SALES (corp-wide): 575.7MM **Privately
Held**
WEB: www.pioneeres.com
SIC: 1381 Drilling oil & gas wells
PA: Pioneer Energy Services Corp.
1250 Ne Loop 410 Ste 1000
San Antonio TX 78209
855 884-0575

(G-18378)
**PIONEER ENERGY SERVICES
CORP (PA)**
1250 Ne Loop 410 Ste 1000 (78209-1560)
PHONE......................................855 884-0575
Matt Porte, *CEO*
Dean A Burkhardt, *Ch of Bd*
Stanley Fields, *Division Mgr*
William C Preston, *Principal*
Brian L Tucker, *COO*
▼ **EMP:** 109
SALES: 575.7MM **Privately Held**
WEB: www.pioneeres.com
SIC: 1382 7353 Oil & gas exploration
services; oil well drilling equipment, rental
or leasing

(G-18379)
**PIONEER WIRELINE SERVICES
LLC (HQ)**
1250 Ne Loop 410 Ste 1000 (78209-1560)
PHONE......................................210 828-7689
Joe Eustace, *President*
Kurt Forkheim, *Vice Pres*
Martin O'Neil, *Vice Pres*
David Armbruster, *Engineer*
Scott Pfeil, *Asst Controller*
EMP: 77
SALES (est): 167.9MM
SALES (corp-wide): 575.7MM **Privately
Held**
WEB: www.pioneeres.com
SIC: 1381 Drilling oil & gas wells
PA: Pioneer Energy Services Corp.
1250 Ne Loop 410 Ste 1000
San Antonio TX 78209
855 884-0575

(G-18380)
PIXELWORKS CORPORATION
Also Called: San Antonio Woman
8603 Botts St (78217-6301)
PHONE......................................210 826-5375
J Michael Gaffney, *President*
EMP: 20
SQ FT: 3,000
SALES (est): 2MM **Privately Held**
WEB: www.pixelworksonline.com
SIC: 2721 Magazines: publishing only, not
printed on site

(G-18381)
**PLASTCOS ARCO IRIS OF SAN
ANTN**
Also Called: Plasscon
2819 Woodcliffe St # 100 (78230-5143)
P.O. Box 780234 (78278-0234)
PHONE......................................210 308-6500
Sergio Bueno Ramirez, *CEO*
EMP: 25
SALES (est): 1.6MM **Privately Held**
SIC: 3085 Plastics bottles

(G-18382)
**PLASTIC VACUUM FORMING
INC**
Also Called: Pvf Extruders
104 Trailcrest St (78232-1319)
PHONE......................................210 344-8531
Joe Franks, *President*
Dan Sargent, *Vice Pres*
Debra Sargent, *Treasurer*
Hazel Franks, *Admin Sec*
EMP: 10 **EST:** 1970
SALES (est): 1.7MM **Privately Held**
WEB: www.blynd.com
SIC: 3089 Injection molding of plastics

(G-18383)
PLUS ONE ROBOTICS INC
311 N Frank Luke Dr # 101 (78226-1827)
PHONE......................................937 287-5060
Erik Nieves, *CEO*
Paul Hvass, *COO*
Bill Kitchel, *CFO*
David Scheffrahn, *VP Sales*
Shaun Edwards, *CTO*
EMP: 12
SQ FT: 5,000
SALES (est): 486.5K **Privately Held**
WEB: www.plusonerobotics.com
SIC: 7372 3559 Operating systems com-
puter software; robots, molding & forming
plastics

(G-18384)
POPES CLEANERS LLC (PA)
6218 S Flores St (78214-2622)
PHONE......................................210 923-7785
Melody Cooper, *President*
Walter S Pope, *Owner*
Helen Payne, *Manager*
EMP: 11
SQ FT: 2,800
SALES (est): 200K **Privately Held**
WEB: www.popecleaners.com
SIC: 7218 7216 7212 7219 Industrial
equipment launderers; cleaning & dyeing,
except rugs; laundry & drycleaner agents;
garment making, alteration & repair;
ironers, commercial laundry & drycleaning

(G-18385)
**POWERTECH COMPONENTS
INC**
403 E Ramsey Rd Ste 205 (78216-4662)
PHONE......................................210 521-0799
Charles Emig, *President*
Josh Villegas, *Sales Staff*
▼ **EMP:** 12
SALES (est): 2.1MM **Privately Held**
WEB: www.powertechcomponents.com
SIC: 3549 Assembly machines, including
robotic

(G-18386)
**PRECISION HELICOPTER SVCS
INC**
12027 Warfield St (78216-3231)
PHONE......................................210 525-9595
Todd Wulfe, *President*
Naum Royberg, *Research*
EMP: 50 **EST:** 1997
SQ FT: 8,000
SALES (est): 7.5MM **Privately Held**
SIC: 3728 Aircraft parts & equipment

(G-18387)
PRECISION READY MIX LTD
3714 Fossil Crk (78261-3002)
PHONE......................................210 872-6053
Marc Wulf, *Mng Member*
EMP: 11
SALES (est): 10MM **Privately Held**
SIC: 3273 Ready-mixed concrete

(G-18388)
**PREMCOR REFINING GROUP
INC (HQ)**
Also Called: Valero Port Arthur
1 Valero Way (78249-1616)
PHONE......................................210 345-2000
Bill Klesse, *CEO*
Joe Gorder, *President*
Tom Laven, *Engineer*
Lee Brown, *Director*
▲ **EMP:** 9
SALES (est): 1.5MM
SALES (corp-wide): 108.3B **Publicly
Held**
WEB: www.valero.com
SIC: 2911 Petroleum refining
PA: Valero Energy Corporation
1 Valero Way
San Antonio TX 78249
210 345-2000

(G-18389)
**PREMIER ANTIQUE STUCCO
LLC**
1114 Delgado St (78207-1506)
PHONE......................................210 602-8054
Ruby Ann Sanchez,
Jorge Sanchez,
EMP: 37
SALES (est): 1MM **Privately Held**
SIC: 3299 Stucco

(G-18390)
PREMIER DIGITAL DESIGN LLC
8523 Speedway Dr (78230-5330)
PHONE......................................210 774-5456
Nolvia Ramos, *Mng Member*
EMP: 9
SALES (est): 300K **Privately Held**
WEB: www.premierdigitaldesigns.com
SIC: 7371 7372 Computer software devel-
opment & applications; software program-
ming applications; application computer
software

(G-18391)
**PREMIER EMBLEM & INSIGNIA
INC**
2111 West Ave (78201-2822)
PHONE......................................210 253-3406
Vernon Thompson, *President*
Sterling L Thompson, *Vice Pres*
▲ **EMP:** 17
SQ FT: 24,000
SALES (est): 1.6MM **Privately Held**
WEB: www.premier-emblem.com
SIC: 2399 Aprons, breast (harness)
PA: Premier Uniform, Inc.
2111 West Ave
San Antonio TX 78201
210 253-3406

(G-18392)
PREMIER UNIFORM INC (PA)
Also Called: Premier Emblem
2111 West Ave (78201-2822)
PHONE......................................210 253-3406
EMP: 14 **EST:** 1990
SQ FT: 62,000
SALES (est): 1.6MM **Privately Held**
WEB: www.premier-emblem.com
SIC: 2399 Emblems, badges & insignia

(G-18393)
**PRESCOTTS LIMBS & BRACES
(PA)**
Also Called: Galveston Brace & Limb
6715 San Pedro Ave (78216-7232)
PHONE......................................210 224-0726
Gary Prescott, *President*
Pat Prescott, *Treasurer*
EMP: 28
SQ FT: 8,500
SALES (est): 3.6MM **Privately Held**
SIC: 5999 3842 Artificial limbs; surgical
appliances & supplies

(G-18394)
**PRESSURE SYSTEMS
INTERNATIONAL**
Also Called: P.S.i
4323 Interstate Way (78219-1717)
PHONE......................................210 222-1926
Tim Musgrave, *President*
Steve Otteman, *General Mgr*
Jonathan Gravell, *Vice Pres*
Jim Herzog, *Opers Mgr*
Steve Miller, *VP Engrg*
EMP: 90
SQ FT: 12,000
SALES (est): 22MM
SALES (corp-wide): 151.7MM **Privately
Held**
WEB: www.psitireinflation.com
SIC: 3714 Motor vehicle parts & acces-
sories
PA: Berry Gp, Inc.
1414 Corn Product Rd
Corpus Christi TX 78409
361 693-2100

(G-18395)
PRIME TIME LLC
301 Avenue E (78205-2006)
PHONE......................................210 250-3000
Susan Pape, *COO*
EMP: 195 **EST:** 2007
SALES (est): 28.6K
SALES (corp-wide): 7.9B **Privately Held**
SIC: 2711 Newspapers: publishing only,
not printed on site
PA: The Hearst Corporation
300 W 57th St Fl 42
New York NY 10019
212 649-2000

(G-18396)
PRINTED SUPPLIES INC
10530 Sentinel St (78217-3822)
P.O. Box 171245 (78217-8245)
PHONE......................................210 946-2977
Debbie B Wenzel, *President*
Amy Wenzel, *Vice Pres*
▲ **EMP:** 25
SQ FT: 4,500
SALES (est): 3.7MM **Privately Held**
WEB: www.printedsupplies.com
SIC: 2759 Screen printing

(G-18397)
PRISM ENTERPRISES (DH)
Also Called: Prism Technologies
6952 Fairgrounds Pkwy (78238-4528)
PHONE..................................210 520-8051
Merle Smith, *President*
◆ EMP: 13
SQ FT: 17,000
SALES (est): 2MM
SALES (corp-wide): 2.4B **Publicly Held**
SIC: 3999 Heating pads, nonelectric

(G-18398)
PRISTECH PRODUCTS INC
6952 Fairgrounds Pkwy # 107
(78238-4528)
PHONE..................................210 520-8051
Mark Smith, *CEO*
Grant Hassmann, *President*
Monica Reyes, *Associate*
▲ EMP: 35
SQ FT: 30,000
SALES (est): 6.1MM **Privately Held**
WEB: www.pristech.com
SIC: 3561 Pumps & pumping equipment

(G-18399)
PROMPT PRINTERS INC
503 Chestnut St (78202-2196)
P.O. Box 47866 (78265-8866)
PHONE..................................210 223-9177
Charles M Cytrin, *President*
EMP: 12 EST: 1922
SQ FT: 8,000
SALES (est): 1.1MM **Privately Held**
SIC: 2752 Commercial printing, offset

(G-18400)
PSI CONCRETE CONSTRUCTION LLC
130 Talavera Pkwy # 1032 (78232-1067)
PHONE..................................210 204-1529
Eric Ryles, *Principal*
EMP: 10 EST: 2017
SALES (est): 376.7K **Privately Held**
WEB: www.psiconcretes.com
SIC: 1611 1771 3272 3271 Highway &
street construction; patio construction,
concrete; fountains, concrete; slabs,
crossing: concrete; pier footings, prefabri-
cated concrete; blocks, concrete: land-
scape or retaining wall

(G-18401)
PURE PARTY ICE LP
1902 S Laredo St Bldg 5 (78207-7047)
PHONE..................................210 223-6400
Mark Biediger, *General Ptnr*
EMP: 35
SALES (est): 5.6MM **Privately Held**
WEB: www.purepartyice.com
SIC: 2097 Manufactured ice

(G-18402)
PYRAMID STONE CO INC
9011 Old Crpus Chrsti Hwy (78223-4307)
P.O. Box 10248 (78210-0248)
PHONE..................................210 533-3511
Frank Monaco Jr, *President*
EMP: 17 EST: 1946
SQ FT: 2,400
SALES (est): 1.8MM **Privately Held**
SIC: 3272 Cast stone, concrete; terrazzo
products, precast

(G-18403)
QSFIRST INC
10203 Kotzebue St Ste 106 (78217-4447)
PHONE..................................210 362-1983
Deryck Yeung, *CEO*
EMP: 16
SALES (est): 875.2K **Privately Held**
WEB: www.comfort-air.com
SIC: 1711 3724 ; aircraft engines & en-
gine parts

(G-18404)
QUACITO LLC (PA)
Also Called: 1 Quacito
11802 Warfield St (78216-3213)
PHONE..................................210 695-0795
Nitesh Jain, *CEO*
Sonal Jain, *President*
Nick Mehta, *Executive*
EMP: 15

SQ FT: 1,800
SALES (est): 86K **Privately Held**
WEB: www.quacito.com
SIC: 8748 7372 7371 7378 Business
consulting; application computer software;
custom computer programming services;
computer & data processing equipment
repair/maintenance; graphic arts & related
design

(G-18405)
QUADRANGLE PRESS INC
9111 Broadway (78217-6118)
P.O. Box 17927 (78217-0927)
PHONE..................................210 828-8191
James P Fahrenthold, *President*
Lisa Maggiani, *Purch Agent*
Lana Fahrenthold, *Treasurer*
Joe Baker, *Manager*
EMP: 35
SQ FT: 13,200
SALES (est): 5.5MM **Privately Held**
WEB: www.quadp.com
SIC: 2752 2791 2789 2759 Commercial
printing, offset; typesetting; bookbinding &
related work; commercial printing

(G-18406)
QUALTEX LABORATORIES
6211 W Interstate 10 (78201-2023)
PHONE..................................210 736-8952
Linda Myers, *CEO*
Dirk Johnson, *COO*
Kelli Riggins, *Vice Pres*
Donna Respondek, *CFO*
EMP: 23
SALES (est): 122.8MM
SALES (corp-wide): 20.9MM **Privately
Held**
WEB: www.qualtexlabs.org
SIC: 2836 Biological products, except diag-
nostic
HQ: South Texas Blood & Tissue Center
6211 W Interstate 10
San Antonio TX 78201
210 731-5555

(G-18407)
R D MOXIE LLC (PA)
13515 Blue Wing Rd (78223-5446)
PHONE..................................210 633-2300
Jack Heinesh,
Robert R Lininger Jr,
EMP: 9
SALES (est): 300K **Privately Held**
SIC: 3547 Rolling mill machinery

(G-18408)
R D SCREW MACHINE PRODUCTS INC
1054 Grubb St (78219-3227)
PHONE..................................210 337-8942
Robert Flores, *President*
Greg Flores, *Vice Pres*
EMP: 17
SQ FT: 10,000
SALES (est): 1MM **Privately Held**
WEB: www.rdscrewmachineproducts.com
SIC: 3451 Screw machine products

(G-18409)
RAST IRON WORK COMPANY INC
6430 Railway (78244-1716)
P.O. Box 591786 (78259-0139)
PHONE..................................210 659-6704
Glenn B Boggs Jr, *President*
Betty Boggs, *Corp Secy*
Patrick McShane, *Vice Pres*
Cynthia Briones, *Project Mgr*
Kevin Heinze, *Project Mgr*
EMP: 20 EST: 1976
SQ FT: 12,500
SALES (est): 7.1MM **Privately Held**
WEB: www.rastironworks.com
SIC: 3441 Fabricated structural metal

(G-18410)
RAYTHEON TECHNOLOGIES CORP
6948 Fairgrounds Pkwy (78238-4527)
PHONE..................................210 680-0283
EMP: 255

SALES (corp-wide): 56.5B **Publicly Held**
WEB: www.rtx.com
SIC: 3724 Aircraft engines & engine parts
PA: Raytheon Technologies Corporation
870 Winter St
Waltham MA 02451
781 522-3000

(G-18411)
RAZOR SPECIALTIES LLC
4553 N Loop 1604 W # 1227 (78249-1366)
PHONE..................................888 578-9656
John A Kaler II,
EMP: 9
SALES (est): 906.5K **Privately Held**
WEB: www.razorspecialtiesrentals.com
SIC: 3533 Oil & gas field machinery

(G-18412)
RBC MUSIC COMPANY
Also Called: Rbc/H & H Sheet Music Centers
4415 Centerview (78228-1403)
PHONE..................................210 736-6902
Tom Rhodes, *President*
Donald Bierschenk, *Treasurer*
Tony Klamm, *Technology*
EMP: 18
SQ FT: 16,000
SALES (est): 2.1MM **Privately Held**
WEB: www.jwpepper.com
SIC: 5736 5199 2741 Sheet music; sheet
music; music, sheet: publishing only, not
printed on site

(G-18413)
REAL ESTATE FORECLOSURES
Also Called: First Position Publications
2007 Candlelight Ln (78213-3149)
P.O. Box 13085 (78213-0085)
PHONE..................................210 733-4262
Greg Stanley, *President*
EMP: 12
SALES (est): 670K **Privately Held**
SIC: 6531 2759 Real estate brokers &
agents; advertising literature: printing

(G-18414)
REAL GRANITE INC
848 W Rhapsody Dr (78216-2600)
PHONE..................................210 732-8350
Roland Martinez, *President*
▲ EMP: 20
SQ FT: 14,000
SALES (est): 2.9MM **Privately Held**
SIC: 3281 1743 Granite, cut & shaped;
terrazzo, tile, marble, mosaic work

(G-18415)
REDDY ICE CORPORATION
1106 E Cesar E Chavez Blv (78210-1768)
PHONE..................................210 532-3232
Robert Martinez, *Plant Mgr*
Lavon Washington, *Manager*
EMP: 35
SQ FT: 2,000 **Privately Held**
WEB: www.reddyice.com
SIC: 2097 Manufactured ice
HQ: Reddy Ice Corporation
5710 Lbj Fwy Ste 300
Dallas TX 75240
214 526-6740

(G-18416)
REDEMPTION OIL & GAS LLC
401 E Sonterra Blvd # 165 (78258-4317)
PHONE..................................210 572-2988
Bill Pennington, *CFO*
James Bookout, *Mng Member*
Mark Macaluso,
EMP: 52
SALES (est): 1.2MM **Privately Held**
WEB: www.redemptionong.com
SIC: 1382 Oil & gas exploration services

(G-18417)
REED CANDLE COMPANY
Also Called: Mission Candle Company
1531 W Poplar St (78207-1236)
P.O. Box 7261 (78207-0261)
PHONE..................................210 737-7156
Sister S Reed, *CEO*
Peter N Reed, *Chairman*
EMP: 190 EST: 1937
SQ FT: 125,000

SALES (est): 26.7MM **Privately Held**
WEB: www.reedcandlecompany.com
SIC: 3999 Candles

(G-18418)
REFRESCO BEVERAGES US INC
4238 Director Dr (78219-3202)
PHONE..................................210 333-4310
Luis Urrea, *Production*
Kim Brennan, *Senior Buyer*
Troy Nievaard, *Branch Mgr*
Omar Al-Saigh, *Technical Staff*
EMP: 160
SALES (corp-wide): 1.3B **Privately Held**
WEB: www.primowatercorp.com
SIC: 2086 Carbonated beverages, nonal-
coholic: bottled & canned
HQ: Refresco Beverages Us Inc.
8112 Woodland Center Blvd
Tampa FL 33614

(G-18419)
REGAL PLASTIC SUPPLY CO INC
4041 Rittiman Rd (78218-4344)
PHONE..................................210 599-8291
Javior Garcia, *Sales/Mktg Mgr*
Joe Alonzo, *Sales Staff*
EMP: 13
SQ FT: 24,000
SALES (corp-wide): 69.3MM **Privately
Held**
WEB: www.regal-plastics.com
SIC: 5162 3089 Plastics products; plastic
processing
PA: Regal Plastic Supply Company, Inc.
9200 N Royal Ln Ste 120
Irving TX 75063
800 441-1553

(G-18420)
REQUEJO CONSTRUCTION SVCS LLC
820 County Road 3822 (78253-6881)
PHONE..................................210 459-5161
Robert Requejo,
EMP: 15 EST: 2015
SALES (est): 545.7K **Privately Held**
WEB:
www.requejoconstructionservices.com
SIC: 1522 1771 1542 1751 Apartment
building construction; patio construction,
concrete; commercial & office building,
new construction; lightweight steel framing (metal stud) installation; electric
housewares & fans; commercial painting

(G-18421)
RESCUE RESCUE LLC
6223 Us Highway 87 E (78222-1821)
P.O. Box 94, Adkins (78101-0094)
PHONE..................................210 648-2722
Scott Young,
◆ EMP: 10
SQ FT: 2,000
SALES (est): 1MM **Privately Held**
WEB: www.rescue-rescue.com
SIC: 3711 Fire department vehicles (motor
vehicles), assembly of

(G-18422)
RESONANT TECH PARTNERS LLC
16103 University Oak # 100 (78249-4017)
PHONE..................................210 477-3671
EMP: 14 EST: 2018
SALES (est): 1.6MM **Privately Held**
WEB:
www.resonanttechnologypartners.com
SIC: 2752 Commercial printing, litho-
graphic

(G-18423)
REYES AUTOMOTIVE GROUP LLC
1 Lone Star Pass Bldg 28 (78264-3639)
PHONE..................................210 228-2500
Fernando Reyes,
▲ EMP: 190
SQ FT: 98,000
SALES (est): 64.9MM **Privately Held**
WEB: www.reyesautomotivegroup.com
SIC: 3714 Motor vehicle body components
& frame

(G-18424)
REYES AUTOMOTIVE GROUP II LLC
1 Lone Star Pass Bldg 28 (78264-3639)
PHONE...................................210 228-2500
Reyes Fernando, *Mng Member*
Kamsickas Jim,
Ritz Mark,
Jason Reyes,
EMP: 190
SALES (est): 36.7MM **Privately Held**
WEB: www.reyesautomotivegroup.com
SIC: 3714 Motor vehicle parts & accessories

(G-18425)
REYES-AMTEX AUTOMOTIVE LLC (PA)
1 Lone Star Pass Bldg 30 (78264-3639)
PHONE...................................210 628-4900
Fernando Reyes, *Principal*
Jason Reyes,
▲ **EMP:** 28
SALES (est): 8.1MM **Privately Held**
WEB: www.reyesamtexautomotive.com
SIC: 2273 1731 Automobile floor coverings, except rubber or plastic; safety & security specialization

(G-18426)
RICOS PRODUCTS CO INC (HQ)
830 S Presa St (78210-1375)
PHONE.......................•.............210 222-1415
Tony Liberto, *Principal*
Ron Mulholland, *Vice Pres*
Kara Boggess, *Buyer*
Clem Martinez, *Credit Staff*
Mike McGuire, *Sales Staff*
▼ **EMP:** 125
SALES: 44.6MM
SALES (corp-wide): 68.8MM **Privately Held**
WEB: www.ricos.com
SIC: 5046 5145 2099 2096 Commercial cooking & food service equipment; confectionery; food preparations; potato chips & similar snacks; flavoring extracts & syrups
PA: Liberto Specialty Company Inc
830 S Presa St
San Antonio TX 78210
210 222-1415

(G-18427)
RIVER CITY READY MIX INC
5745 Easterling (78251-3604)
P.O. Box 681085 (78268-1085)
PHONE...................................210 520-1941
Art Lopez, *President*
EMP: 11 **EST:** 1996
SQ FT: 2,000
SALES (est): 1.7MM **Privately Held**
WEB: www.river-city-ready-mix.business.site
SIC: 3273 Ready-mixed concrete

(G-18428)
RIVERCITY WATERJET INC
Also Called: River City Industries
11734 Nacogdoches Rd (78217-2302)
PHONE...................................210 590-0300
Steven Jones, *President*
Chris Jones, *Vice Pres*
EMP: 14
SQ FT: 15,000
SALES (est): 3.6MM **Privately Held**
WEB: www.rivercity-industries.com
SIC: 3699 3086 Laser welding, drilling & cutting equipment; packaging & shipping materials, foamed plastic

(G-18429)
RIVERSIDE ENGINEERING INC (PA)
121 Interpark Blvd # 604 (78216-1842)
PHONE...................................210 227-9090
Jim Olson, *CEO*
Randy Brace, *President*
Matthew Crowe, *Business Mgr*
Kurtis Wilcox, *Purch Mgr*
Jesus Reyna, *Engineer*
◆ **EMP:** 15
SQ FT: 10,000

SALES (est): 5.1MM **Privately Held**
WEB: www.rsengr.com
SIC: 3589 Shredders, industrial & commercial

(G-18430)
ROES OF SAN ANTONIO LLC
Also Called: San Antonio Packing Company
1922 S Laredo St (78207-7020)
P.O. Box 7265 (78207-0265)
PHONE...................................210 224-5441
Thomas J Roe,
Jennifer Roe,
EMP: 50
SQ FT: 30,000
SALES (est): 7.5MM **Privately Held**
WEB: www.sanantoniopacking.com
SIC: 2011 Meat packing plants

(G-18431)
ROTARY EXPLORATION INC
19276 Redland Rd (78259-3341)
P.O. Box 680981 (78268-0981)
PHONE...................................210 248-9892
Mark Wynne, *CEO*
Karen Wynne, *Admin Sec*
EMP: 16
SALES (est): 2.9MM **Privately Held**
SIC: 1381 Drilling oil & gas wells

(G-18432)
ROTHE ENTERPRISES INC (PA)
4535 E Houston St (78220-1701)
P.O. Box 200443 (78220-0443)
PHONE...................................210 310-0447
Trey Th Hall III, *President*
Colleen M Koenig, *Corp Secy*
Eduardo Guerrero, *Vice Pres*
Richard M Owens, *Vice Pres*
Dale C Patenaude, *Vice Pres*
EMP: 16
SQ FT: 12,000
SALES (est): 2.3MM **Privately Held**
WEB: www.rothesites.com
SIC: 3451 Computer maintenance & repair

(G-18433)
ROTHE JOINT VENTURE LP (PA)
4614 Sinclair Rd (78222-2039)
PHONE...................................210 648-3131
W D Rothe, *General Mgr*
EMP: 9
SALES (est): 5.7MM **Privately Held**
WEB: www.rxjv-alliant.com
SIC: 3812 Aircraft/aerospace flight instruments & guidance systems

(G-18434)
ROTO-FLEX OVEN CO
135 E Cevallos (78204-1795)
PHONE...................................210 222-2278
Richard Dunfield, *President*
E P Dunfield, *Corp Secy*
Allen Kieny, *Manager*
▼ **EMP:** 12
SQ FT: 25,000
SALES (est): 1.9MM **Privately Held**
WEB: www.rotoflexoven.com
SIC: 3556 Ovens, bakery

(G-18435)
ROYBERG INC (PA)
Also Called: Precision Mold & Tool Group
315 N Park Dr (78216-2726)
PHONE...................................210 525-0094
Maya Royberg, *CEO*
Naum Royberg, *President*
▲ **EMP:** 50
SQ FT: 22,000
SALES (est): 11.1MM **Privately Held**
WEB: www.precision-group.com
SIC: 3541 3089 3544 2679 Machine tool replacement & repair parts, metal cutting types; molding primary plastic; special dies, tools, jigs & fixtures; pressed fiber & molded pulp products except food products

(G-18436)
RPC INC
5251 Tacco (78244-1007)
PHONE...................................210 310-1330
EMP: 20

SALES (corp-wide): 1.7B **Publicly Held**
WEB: www.rpc.net
SIC: 1389 Construction, repair & dismantling services
PA: Rpc, Inc.
2801 Buford Hwy Ne # 300
Brookhaven GA 30329
404 321-2140

(G-18437)
RUBRIX LLC
Also Called: Telefuel
110 E Houston St (78205-2990)
PHONE...................................512 581-5513
John Adams, *CEO*
EMP: 25
SALES (est): 367.8K **Privately Held**
WEB: www.acalibre.com
SIC: 8322 5047 9661 7371 First aid service; medical equipment & supplies; ; computer software development & applications; application computer software

(G-18438)
RUDYS CUSTOM UPHL & DESIGN
4334 Mccullough Ave (78212-1909)
PHONE...................................210 821-5156
Rudy De Leon, *President*
Anne De Leon, *Corp Secy*
EMP: 10
SQ FT: 6,000
SALES (est): 760.1K **Privately Held**
WEB: www.uthscsa.edu
SIC: 7641 5131 2512 Upholstery work; piece goods & other fabrics; upholstered household furniture

(G-18439)
RYC FOODS LLC
7700 Broadway Ste 200 (78209-3260)
PHONE...................................210 731-8854
Jose Ramon Lozano, *President*
Roseo Sotelo, *Office Mgr*
EMP: 30
SQ FT: 5,000
SALES: 16.2MM **Privately Held**
WEB: www.rycfoods.com
SIC: 2099 Food preparations

(G-18440)
SA QUALITY FENCE LTD
Also Called: Quality Steel Fab
13115 Wetmore Rd (78247-3634)
PHONE...................................210 545-6767
Bruce Johnston, *Vice Pres*
Jordon Brown, *Mktg Coord*
Scott Peck, *Branch Mgr*
Craig A Noto,
EMP: 70
SQ FT: 25,000
SALES (est): 12.9MM **Privately Held**
WEB: www.saqualityfence.com
SIC: 1799 3446 3499 Fence construction; architectural metalwork; boxes for packing & shipping, metal

(G-18441)
SAFETY SUPPLY INC
11827 Tech Com Rd Ste 114 (78233-6015)
PHONE...................................210 650-9033
Michael Wacaser, *President*
Kenneth Wacaser, *Managing Dir*
Horace Wacaser, *Principal*
E W Stafford, *Vice Pres*
Sean Williams, *Regl Sales Mgr*
▲ **EMP:** 12
SQ FT: 10,000
SALES (est): 10.7MM **Privately Held**
WEB: www.safetysupplyinc.com
SIC: 5084 2311 2326 Safety equipment; firemen's uniforms: made from purchased materials; policemen's uniforms: made from purchased materials; work apparel, except uniforms; work uniforms

(G-18442)
SAFZONE FIELD SERVICES LLC
18615 Tuscany Stone # 38 (78258-3486)
PHONE...................................210 569-6699
Wade Ingle, *Mng Member*
Julie Clark, *Manager*
Ryan Flores, *Manager*
Niki Kastner, *Manager*
Tristan Knight, *Manager*

EMP: 50 **EST:** 2009
SALES (est): 5.9MM **Privately Held**
WEB: www.safzone.com
SIC: 1389 Cementing oil & gas well casings

(G-18443)
SAGE ENERGY COMPANY (PA)
100 Ne Loop 410 Ste 1300 (78216-4736)
PHONE...................................210 404-2828
Jesse Minor, *President*
Ron Amini, *Managing Dir*
Michael Amini, *Exec VP*
Rex Amini, *Exec VP*
Stanley A Paris, *Vice Pres*
EMP: 27 **EST:** 1977
SQ FT: 1,450
SALES (est): 6.7MM **Privately Held**
WEB: www.sage-energy.com
SIC: 1311 1382 1381 Crude petroleum production; natural gas production; oil & gas exploration services; drilling oil & gas wells

(G-18444)
SAN ANTNIO LGHTHOUSE FOR BLIND (PA)
2305 Roosevelt Ave (78210-4920)
PHONE...................................210 533-5195
Mike Gilliam, *President*
Roslyn Vogel, *General Mgr*
Jose Ireta, *Vice Pres*
Joe Langley, *Vice Pres*
Alex Gonzales, *Store Mgr*
EMP: 215 **EST:** 1933
SQ FT: 59,679
SALES: 76.6MM **Privately Held**
WEB: www.salighthouse.org
SIC: 8331 3823 3951 Vocational rehabilitation agency; analyzers, industrial process type; pens & mechanical pencils

(G-18445)
SAN ANTONIO ARMATURE WORKS INC
1015 N Colorado St (78207-1759)
PHONE...................................210 227-0291
Elaine E Staglik, *Ch of Bd*
Steven Staglik, *President*
Dein Inger, *CFO*
Tim Horan, *Accounts Mgr*
John Liuzzi, *Sales Staff*
EMP: 36
SQ FT: 35,000
SALES (est): 9.8MM **Privately Held**
WEB: www.saarmature.com
SIC: 7694 5063 Electric motor repair; motors, electric

(G-18446)
SAN ANTONIO BROOM FACTORY INC
Also Called: Sabfi
3535 N Panam Expy Ste 117 (78219-1815)
P.O. Box 7053 (78207-0053)
PHONE...................................210 226-9762
Gary L Northway, *President*
EMP: 20 **EST:** 1919
SALES (est): 2.2MM **Privately Held**
SIC: 2392 3991 4215 Mops, floor & dust; brooms; courier services, except by air

(G-18447)
SAN ANTONIO REFINERY LLC
7811 S Presa St (78223-3547)
PHONE...................................512 350-7898
EMP: 43
SALES (corp-wide): 10.7MM **Privately Held**
WEB: www.calumetspecialty.com
SIC: 2911 Petroleum refining
PA: The San Antonio Refinery Llc
1 Bda Xing Ste 100
San Antonio TX 78235
210 918-7436

(G-18448)
SAN ANTONIO REFINERY LLC (PA)
1 Bda Xing Ste 100 (78235-1022)
PHONE...................................210 918-7436
F William Grube, *CEO*
Jennifer Straumins, *President*
Dave Ross, *Buyer*
R Patrick Murray, *CFO*

Debby Neubauer, *Marketing Staff*
EMP: 34 **EST:** 2012
SALES (est): 10.7MM **Privately Held**
WEB: www.calumetspecialty.com
SIC: 2911 Petroleum refining

(G-18449)
SAN ANTONIO SHOE INC
101 Alamo Plz (78205-2655)
PHONE..................210 223-0166
EMP: 11
SALES (corp-wide): 272.2MM **Privately Held**
WEB: www.sasshoes.com
SIC: 3131 Footwear cut stock
PA: San Antonio Shoe, Inc.
　　1717 Sas Dr
　　San Antonio TX 78224
　　877 727-7463

(G-18450)
SAN ANTONIO SHOE INC
Also Called: S A S
1717 Sas Dr 2 (78224-1042)
PHONE..................210 921-8274
David Curtis, *Manager*
EMP: 9
SALES (corp-wide): 272.2MM **Privately Held**
WEB: www.sasshoes.com
SIC: 3144 5661 5139 Women's footwear, except athletic; women's shoes; footwear
PA: San Antonio Shoe, Inc.
　　1717 Sas Dr
　　San Antonio TX 78224
　　877 727-7463

(G-18451)
SANI-SAFE PRODUCTS INC (PA)
2723 Old Ranch Rd (78217-5853)
PHONE..................210 826-1344
Sharon Nunn, *President*
Gene Nunn, *Vice Pres*
James Ryan Nunn, *Shareholder*
EMP: 10 **EST:** 1989
SALES (est): 1MM **Privately Held**
SIC: 2221 Acrylic broadwoven fabrics

(G-18452)
SANI-SAFE PRODUCTS INC
11311 Wayland Way (78233-5789)
PHONE..................210 646-6706
Sharon Nunn, *President*
EMP: 25
SALES (est): 2.9MM **Privately Held**
WEB: www.sanisafeusa.com
SIC: 2821 Acrylic resins

(G-18453)
SANITARY TORTILLA MFG CO
623 Urban Loop (78204-3117)
PHONE..................210 226-9209
Jesse Villarreal Sr, *President*
EMP: 30
SQ FT: 6,000
SALES (est): 3.4MM **Privately Held**
WEB: www.sanitarytortillacompany.com
SIC: 2099 2096 Tortillas, fresh or refrigerated; potato chips & similar snacks

(G-18454)
SANTIN AUTO AND TRUCK REPR CTR
9822 Perrin Beitel Rd (78217-3527)
PHONE..................210 648-4100
Esteban Santin, *President*
EMP: 22
SALES (est): 902.5K **Privately Held**
WEB: www.santinautomotive.com
SIC: 7538 7699 7692 7539 Recreational vehicle repairs; general truck repair; miscellaneous automotive repair services; welding repair; trailer repair

(G-18455)
SCANTRON CORPORATION
15955 La Cantera Pkwy (78256-2589)
PHONE..................770 593-5050
Kevin Brueggeman, *CEO*
EMP: 13
SALES (corp-wide): 434MM **Privately Held**
WEB: www.scantron.com
SIC: 3577 Optical scanning devices

HQ: Scantron Corporation
　　1313 Lone Oak Rd
　　Eagan MN 55121
　　651 683-6000

(G-18456)
SCENTCHIPS INC
Also Called: Puff & Stuff Candles
301 Breesport St (78216-2602)
PHONE..................210 341-7373
Kenneth Moore, *CEO*
Kathy Moore, *President*
Barbara Muzney, *Bookkeeper*
EMP: 9
SALES (est): 22.2K **Privately Held**
WEB: www.scentchips.com
SIC: 3999 Candles

(G-18457)
SCHLEMMER USA INC (DH)
4709 Marco Dr (78218-5422)
P.O. Box 591310 (78259-0115)
PHONE..................210 491-4800
Josef Minster, *CEO*
Christian Von Derlinde, *CFO*
Joanna Perdomo, *Human Resources*
Jim Hilker, *Sales Mgr*
▲ **EMP:** 60
SQ FT: 14,000
SALES (est): 13MM
SALES (corp-wide): 331.9MM **Privately Held**
WEB: www.schlemmerusa.com
SIC: 3089 Automotive parts, plastic
HQ: Schlemmer Gmbh
　　Einsteinring 10
　　Aschheim 85609
　　812 180-40

(G-18458)
SCHLUMBERGER TECHNOLOGY CORP
6415 Babcock Rd (78249-2980)
PHONE..................312 237-2810
EMP: 202 **Publicly Held**
SIC: 1382 Geophysical exploration, oil & gas field; geological exploration, oil & gas field
HQ: Schlumberger Technology Corp
　　300 Schlumberger Dr
　　Sugar Land TX 77478
　　281 285-8500

(G-18459)
SCHLUMBERGER TECHNOLOGY CORP
Also Called: Schlumberger Oilfield Services
777 E Sonterra Blvd # 200 (78258-4246)
PHONE..................210 824-7921
George Lange, *Manager*
EMP: 100 **Publicly Held**
SIC: 1389 Oil field services
HQ: Schlumberger Technology Corp
　　300 Schlumberger Dr
　　Sugar Land TX 77478
　　281 285-8500

(G-18460)
SCHUHMACHER PUBLISHING CO INC
909 Ne Loop 410 Ste 720 (78209-1303)
PHONE..................210 805-8006
Harry Schuhmacher, *President*
Kimberly Nelson, *General Mgr*
Kimberly Griffin, *Principal*
EMP: 9 **EST:** 2013
SALES (est): 306.9K **Privately Held**
WEB: www.beernet.com
SIC: 2741 Newsletter publishing

(G-18461)
SEASON GROUP USA LLC
Also Called: Xytronics
8001 Mainland Dr (78250-5112)
PHONE..................210 522-1116
David Chavez, *Principal*
Michael Cox, *Director*
EMP: 40
SALES (corp-wide): 50.5MM **Privately Held**
WEB: www.seasongroup.com
SIC: 3559 Electronic component making machinery

PA: Season Group Usa, Llc
　　8001 Mainland Dr
　　San Antonio TX 78250
　　210 522-1116

(G-18462)
SEASON GROUP USA LLC (PA)
8001 Mainland Dr (78250-5112)
PHONE..................210 522-1116
Patrick Hung, *Mng Member*
Ricky Wong, *Program Mgr*
Carl Hung,
▲ **EMP:** 98 **EST:** 2010
SQ FT: 600,000
SALES (est): 50.5MM **Privately Held**
WEB: www.seasongroup.com
SIC: 3679 Electronic circuits

(G-18463)
SECURE CONTROL SYSTEMS INC
16103 University Oak (78249-4017)
P.O. Box 780009 (78278-0009)
PHONE..................210 530-5245
Brian Mikiten, *President*
EMP: 30
SQ FT: 3,672
SALES (est): 6.2MM **Privately Held**
WEB: www.securecontrolsystems.com
SIC: 3699 Security control equipment & systems

(G-18464)
SEE YOU AT THE TOP INC
17422 Oconnor Rd Ste 200 (78247-5680)
PHONE..................210 556-5452
Erik J Bernal, *President*
Katalina Cabello, *VP Opers*
EMP: 15
SALES (est): 1.5MM **Privately Held**
SIC: 3589 Water treatment equipment, industrial

(G-18465)
SEGUNDO NAVARRO DRILLING LTD
10101 Reunion Pl Ste 1000 (78216-4157)
PHONE..................210 384-3200
Rod Lewis, *Partner*
Duane Lewis, *Partner*
EMP: 40
SALES (est): 106.2MM **Privately Held**
SIC: 1382 4925 Oil & gas exploration services; gas production and/or distribution
PA: Lewis Energy Group, L.P.
　　10101 Reunion Pl Ste 1000
　　San Antonio TX 78216

(G-18466)
SENO MEDICAL INSTRUMENTS INC
8023 Vantage Dr Ste 1000 (78230-2436)
PHONE..................210 615-6501
Tom Umbel, *CEO*
Thomas Miller, *President*
Bryan Clingman, *Vice Pres*
Steve Miller, *Vice Pres*
George Lamberson, *Engineer*
EMP: 50
SQ FT: 12,641
SALES (est): 9.8MM **Privately Held**
WEB: www.senomedical.com
SIC: 3841 5047 Diagnostic apparatus, medical; medical equipment & supplies

(G-18467)
SEVEN Q SEVEN LTD
11827 Tech Com Rd Ste 220 (78233-6014)
PHONE..................210 930-4040
Ulick McEvaddy, *Managing Prtnr*
Desmond McEvaddy, *Partner*
▲ **EMP:** 45
SALES (est): 9.8MM **Privately Held**
SIC: 3721 3724 4581 Aircraft; research & development on aircraft engines & parts; aircraft maintenance & repair services

(G-18468)
SHANNON DUNN
Also Called: Page's Printing
1810 N Pine St (78208-1037)
PHONE..................210 653-7222
Shannon Dunn, *Owner*
EMP: 17

SQ FT: 5,500
SALES (est): 1MM **Privately Held**
WEB: www.pagesprinting.com
SIC: 2752 Commercial printing, offset

(G-18469)
SHAYNE FOODS INCORPORATED
Also Called: Shayne Foods Market
4225 Gatecrest (78217-4807)
PHONE..................210 442-8776
EMP: 10
SQ FT: 3,000
SALES: 400K **Privately Held**
SIC: 5149 2099 Whol Groceries Mfg Food Preparations

(G-18470)
SHORT-LINE CORPORATION
Also Called: American Signal Company
1206 W Blanco Rd (78232-1013)
P.O. Box 700961 (78270-0961)
PHONE..................210 492-6088
Tom Short, *Owner*
EMP: 14
SQ FT: 8,616
SALES (est): 3MM **Privately Held**
WEB: www.americansignalequipment.com
SIC: 3669 7359 1611 Transportation signaling devices; sign rental; highway & street maintenance

(G-18471)
SHWEIKI MEDIA INC (PA)
Also Called: Study Breaks Magazine
4954 Space Center Dr (78218-5326)
PHONE..................210 804-0390
Gal Shweiki, *President*
Elizabeth Castro, *Accounting Mgr*
April Key, *Cust Mgr*
Jennifer Mueller, *Executive*
Cynthia Hinojosa,
EMP: 20
SQ FT: 12,000
SALES (est): 5MM **Privately Held**
WEB: www.shweiki.com
SIC: 2721 7313 Magazines: publishing & printing; printed media advertising representatives

(G-18472)
SIERRA INDUSTRIES LTD
1770 Skyplace Blvd (78216-3145)
PHONE..................210 805-3188
Mark Huffstutler, *CEO*
Gary Buchanan, *COO*
Cynthia King, *Mfg Staff*
Bill Micale, *CFO*
Patrick Carter, *Sales Staff*
▲ **EMP:** 55
SALES (est): 10.8MM **Privately Held**
WEB: www.skyway-mro.com
SIC: 3724 3721 4522 3443 Air scoops, aircraft; airplanes, fixed or rotary wing; air cargo carriers, nonscheduled; air coolers, metal plate; package delivery, private air; aircraft training equipment
PA: The Skyway Group Inc
　　122 Howard Langford Dr
　　Uvalde TX 78801

(G-18473)
SIERRA NEVADA CORPORATION
4801 Nw Loop 410 Ste 250 (78229-5343)
PHONE..................210 523-6500
Nate Titus, *Manager*
Jason Lawson, *Software Engr*
EMP: 257
SALES (corp-wide): 1.9B **Privately Held**
WEB: www.sncorp.com
SIC: 3812 Search & navigation equipment
PA: Sierra Nevada Corporation
　　444 Salomon Cir
　　Sparks NV 89434
　　775 331-0222

(G-18474)
SIGNATURE MLDNGS MILLWORKS INC (PA)
Also Called: Signature Moulding & Millworks
1400 Currency St (78219-2610)
P.O. Box 200450 (78220-0450)
PHONE..................210 967-8400
Terry Allen Mason, *President*
Robert Earl Adams, *Director*
▲ **EMP:** 20

SQ FT: 200,000
SALES (est): 5MM **Privately Held**
WEB: www.signaturepartnersltd.com
SIC: 2431 Moldings & baseboards, ornamental & trim

(G-18475)
SIGNATURE PARTNERS LTD
Also Called: Signature Molding
4234 Profit St (78219-2617)
P.O. Box 200450 (78220-0450)
PHONE...................210 967-8400
Terry Mason, *Partner*
Damen Hardis, *Partner*
EMP: 20
SALES (est): 14.9MM **Privately Held**
WEB: www.signaturepartnersltd.com
SIC: 2431 Moldings & baseboards, ornamental & trim

(G-18476)
SIMPLEX TIME RECORDER LLC
1070 Arion Cir Ste 102 (78216-2839)
PHONE...................210 402-6311
Vince Baker, *Branch Mgr*
EMP: 80 **Privately Held**
WEB: www.simplex-fire.com
SIC: 3669 Fire detection systems, electric
HQ: Simplex Time Recorder Llc
    50 Technology Dr
    Westminster MA 01441

(G-18477)
SIMPLYFRESCO LLC
12867 Wetmore Rd (78247-3628)
PHONE...................210 494-8443
Nichole Stroman, *Sales Staff*
Michael Kennedy, *Mng Member*
▲ EMP: 20
SQ FT: 9,600
SALES (est): 4.1MM **Privately Held**
WEB: www.cocinafresca.com
SIC: 2033 Tomato sauce: packaged in cans, jars, etc.; spaghetti & other pasta sauce: packaged in cans, jars, etc.

(G-18478)
SKYLIGHTS OVER TEXAS LLC (PA)
319 E Nakoma St Ste 1 (78216-2706)
PHONE...................210 402-0500
Glenn J Ovidio Flores Jr,
Glenn J Flores,
EMP: 13
SQ FT: 10,000
SALES (est): 3MM **Privately Held**
WEB: www.skylightsovertexas.com
SIC: 3211 1761 3083 Skylight glass; skylight installation; window sheeting, plastic

(G-18479)
SKYWAY AVIATION GROUP LLC
1770 Skyplace Blvd (78216-2869)
PHONE...................830 278-4481
EMP: 90
SALES (est): 3.4MM **Privately Held**
SIC: 3365 Aluminum Foundry

(G-18480)
SMART CONTROL SYSTEMS LLC
Also Called: Hotsy Equipment Company
3005 Interstate Dr (78219-1708)
P.O. Box 8262 (78208-0262)
PHONE...................210 224-4906
Joanne Loftus,
EMP: 14
SQ FT: 6,000
SALES (est): 1.9MM **Privately Held**
WEB: www.hotsysouthtexas.com
SIC: 5084 7699 3589 Cleaning equipment, high pressure, sand or steam; industrial machinery & equipment repair; high pressure cleaning equipment

(G-18481)
SOFTEST DESIGNS CORPORATION
5807 Sebastian Pl (78249-2228)
PHONE...................210 697-8828
Paul Bernhard, *President*
Victor Gomez, *Engineer*
Norma Galvan, *Sales Executive*
Brian Keller, *CTO*
Gent David W, *Director*

EMP: 22
SQ FT: 12,000
SALES (est): 5.1MM **Privately Held**
WEB: www.softestdesigns.com
SIC: 3825 7372 Sweep oscillators; prepackaged software

(G-18482)
SON BEVERAGE COMPANY
Also Called: Jell-Craft Products
6896 Fairgrounds Pkwy (78238-4539)
PHONE...................210 733-7761
Charles Timothy Son, *President*
Mary Wendland Son, *Senior VP*
Tim Son, *Vice Pres*
EMP: 12
SQ FT: 10,000
SALES (est): 1.8MM **Privately Held**
WEB: www.sonbeverage.com
SIC: 2086 Bottled & canned soft drinks

(G-18483)
SONATEST INC
12775 Cogburn (78249-2239)
PHONE...................210 697-0335
Norman Ng, *President*
Jason Schulz, *Opers Mgr*
Bobbie Thompson, *Controller*
▲ EMP: 9
SQ FT: 1,900
SALES (est): 1.7MM
SALES (corp-wide): 11.3MM **Privately Held**
WEB: www.sonatestinc.com
SIC: 3829 Ultrasonic testing equipment
HQ: Sonatest Ltd
    Dickens Road
    Milton Keynes BUCKS MK12
    190 831-6345

(G-18484)
SONTERRA GRP ZPPELINN ENRGY LP
901 Ne Loop 410 Ste 500 (78209-1306)
PHONE...................210 930-3111
Roger Festor, *Principal*
EMP: 11
SALES (est): 1.5MM **Privately Held**
SIC: 1382 Oil & gas exploration services

(G-18485)
SORCERERS APPRENTICE INC
10839 Vandale St (78216-3626)
PHONE...................210 377-1212
Martin Alcala, *President*
Connie Hedrick, *Treasurer*
Cheryl Long, *Admin Sec*
EMP: 9
SALES (est): 962.8K **Privately Held**
SIC: 2752 Commercial printing, offset

(G-18486)
SOUTH TEXAS BINDERY
9914 Mccullough Ave (78216-4611)
PHONE...................210 340-1110
EMP: 12
SQ FT: 3,700
SALES (est): 1.1MM **Privately Held**
SIC: 2759 Printing Services

(G-18487)
SOUTHERN FLGER DTNTION EQP LLC
4634 S Presa St (78223-1058)
P.O. Box 2021 (78297-2021)
PHONE...................210 533-1231
Donald G Halloran, *President*
John Legros, *General Mgr*
Michael Chike, *Regional Mgr*
James W Harris, *Vice Pres*
Sal Aceves, *Senior Buyer*
◆ EMP: 250
SALES (est): 36.6MM **Privately Held**
WEB: www.southernfolger.com
SIC: 3429 Locks or lock sets

(G-18488)
SOUTHWEST NIPPLE COMPANY INC
2831 S Ww White Rd (78222-2809)
P.O. Box 200022 (78220-0022)
PHONE...................210 333-3720
Vernon Vaughan, *President*
EMP: 13 EST: 1950
SQ FT: 3,900

SALES (est): 440K **Privately Held**
WEB: www.swnippleco.com
SIC: 3498 Fabricated pipe & fittings

(G-18489)
SOUTHWEST SIGN GROUP INC (PA)
Also Called: Apex Sign Group
7208 S Ww White Rd (78222-5204)
PHONE...................210 648-3221
Charles Jones, *President*
Donald Blanton, *Vice Pres*
Gregory Burkette, *Vice Pres*
Samantha Vasquez, *Project Mgr*
Stephanie Garza, *Purch Agent*
EMP: 73 EST: 1946
SQ FT: 70,000
SALES (est): 13.8MM **Privately Held**
WEB: www.southwestsigns.com
SIC: 7629 3993 Electrical repair shops; signs & advertising specialties

(G-18490)
SPACE ENTERPRISES LLC (PA)
Also Called: Ambiente Home Decor
26310 Oak Rdg Ste 38 (78229)
PHONE...................800 559-2923
EMP: 15 EST: 2009
SQ FT: 10,763
SALES (est): 1.1MM **Privately Held**
WEB: www.ambientehomedecor.com
SIC: 2033 3431 5023 Fruit juices: packaged in cans, jars, etc.; sinks: enameled iron, cast iron or pressed metal; home furnishings

(G-18491)
SPFM LP (PA)
Also Called: Tiendas Sindicales
4310 West Ave (78213-3033)
PHONE...................210 805-8931
Fred M Battah, *Partner*
Mike Battah, *Partner*
Shalimar Maakar, *Partner*
Raul Garza, *Controller*
Randy Soowal, *VP Finance*
▲ EMP: 97
SQ FT: 40,000
SALES (est): 197.8MM **Privately Held**
WEB: www.distromex.com
SIC: 5122 5149 2834 2833 Cosmetics, perfumes & hair products; specialty food items; pharmaceutical preparations; medicinals & botanicals; soap & other detergents; toilet preparations

(G-18492)
SPIRIT AEROSYSTEMS INC
1900 1st Ave (78216-8509)
PHONE...................316 523-4221
Bridget Thomas, *President*
EMP: 99
SALES (est): 11MM **Privately Held**
SIC: 3728 Aircraft parts & equipment

(G-18493)
STAKEHOLDER GAS UTILITY LLC
401 E Sonterra Blvd (78258-4073)
PHONE...................210 444-9664
Robert Liddell, *CEO*
Gaylon Gray, *COO*
Shannon Neill, *Vice Pres*
Marvin Webb, *CFO*
EMP: 40
SQ FT: 8,800
SALES (est): 2MM **Privately Held**
WEB: www.stakeholdermidstream.com
SIC: 1382 Pipelines, natural gas

(G-18494)
STAKEHOLDER MIDSTREAM LLC
401 E Sonterra Blvd # 215 (78258-4314)
PHONE...................210 444-9664
Robert Liddell, *CEO*
Gaylon Gray, *Co-CEO*
Josh J Roberts, *COO*
Shannon Neill, *Vice Pres*
Marvin Webb, *CFO*
EMP: 12
SQ FT: 2,800

SALES (est): 802K **Privately Held**
WEB: www.stakeholdermidstream.com
SIC: 1389 4612 4922 Gas compressing (natural gas) at the fields; crude petroleum pipelines; pipelines, natural gas

(G-18495)
STAMP SHOP INC
Also Called: A1 Engravers
8800 Broadway Ste 106 (78217-6346)
PHONE...................210 824-7373
Lee Coley, *President*
EMP: 10
SQ FT: 3,000
SALES (est): 730K **Privately Held**
SIC: 3953 3993 7389 Marking devices; signs & advertising specialties; engraving service

(G-18496)
STANDARD WASTE SERVICES LLC
5610 Fm 1346 (78220-1906)
PHONE...................210 619-7962
Robert Edler, *Mng Member*
EMP: 10 EST: 2008
SALES (est): 910K **Privately Held**
SIC: 4953 5082 3639 Recycling, waste materials; front end loaders; garbage disposal units, household

(G-18497)
STAR DELTA MOTOR CONTROLS INC
11135 Iota Dr (78217-2611)
PHONE...................210 479-3550
EMP: 20 EST: 1997
SQ FT: 7,500
SALES (est): 1.3MM **Privately Held**
SIC: 3089 5063 Mfg Plastic Products Whol Electrical Equipment

(G-18498)
STEELHEAD INC
Also Called: True Integration Limited
10322 Moursund Blvd (78221-9671)
P.O. Box 240487 (78224-0487)
PHONE...................210 628-1066
Alan Pyle, *President*
John C Cooke, *Chairman*
Allison Pyle, *Corp Secy*
◆ EMP: 22 EST: 1990
SQ FT: 17,000
SALES (est): 5.8MM **Privately Held**
WEB: www.steelheadinc.com
SIC: 3589 3441 Commercial cooking & foodwarming equipment; fabricated structural metal

(G-18499)
STEELTRON METAL WORKS
402 Kraft St (78220-1031)
PHONE...................210 774-4127
Jim Cardenas, *Owner*
Jim Cardenan, *Owner*
EMP: 11
SQ FT: 15,000
SALES (est): 500K **Privately Held**
WEB: www.steeltron.com
SIC: 3444 Sheet metal specialties, not stamped

(G-18500)
STEP ENERGY SERVICES USA LTD (HQ)
Also Called: Step Energy Services USA Ltd.
70 Ne Loop 410 Ste 1070 (78216-8420)
PHONE...................210 477-1517
Brock Duhon, *President*
Mike Burvill, *COO*
Brad McFarlane, *CFO*
Mike Kelly, *Treasurer*
EMP: 15
SQ FT: 4,000
SALES (est): 406.9MM
SALES (corp-wide): 501.9MM **Privately Held**
WEB: www.stepenergyservices.com
SIC: 1389 Servicing oil & gas wells
PA: Step Energy Services Ltd
    205 5 Ave Sw Suite 1200
    Calgary AB T2P 2
    403 457-1772

(G-18501)
STEP ENERGY SVCS HOLDINGS LTD
70 Ne Loop 410 Ste 1070 (78216-8420)
PHONE.................................918 423-4300
Wayne Tucker, *President*
Matt Merriott, *Supervisor*
EMP: 19
SALES (corp-wide): 501.9MM **Privately Held**
WEB: www.tuckerenergy.com
SIC: 1389 3533 Oil consultants; well logging equipment
HQ: Step Energy Services Holdings Ltd.
　480 Wildwood Forest Dr
　Spring TX 77380

(G-18502)
STERLING BV INC
Also Called: Sterling Foods
1075 Arion Pkwy (78216-2883)
PHONE.................................210 490-1669
John Likovich, *CEO*
Carrie Romeo, *Vice Pres*
Jill Meyers, *Sales Staff*
Peter Woods, *Sales Staff*
EMP: 99 EST: 2016
SALES (est): 5MM **Privately Held**
WEB: www.sterling-fd.com
SIC: 2052 2051 Cookies; bread, cake & related products

(G-18503)
STERLING FOODS LLC (DH)
1075 Arion Pkwy (78216-2883)
PHONE.................................210 490-1669
John D Likovich, *President*
Elva Charles, *Senior VP*
Johnny Cisneros, *Vice Pres*
Paul Miller, *Vice Pres*
Liz Thomas, *Vice Pres*
▲ EMP: 183 EST: 1974
SQ FT: 85,000
SALES (est): 123.1MM **Privately Held**
WEB: www.sterlingfoodsusa.com
SIC: 2051 2052 Bread, cake & related products; cookies

(G-18504)
STERLING FOODS II INC (HQ)
1075 Arion Pkwy (78216-2883)
PHONE.................................210 490-1669
Lori Houlihan, *CEO*
John D Likovich, *President*
Jyostna Bhatt, *General Mgr*
Kellie Long, *Principal*
Nick Davis, *COO*
EMP: 42
SALES (est): 123.1MM **Privately Held**
WEB: www.sterling-fd.com
SIC: 2052 2051 Cookies; cakes, bakery: except frozen

(G-18505)
STEVES & SONS INC
Also Called: Steves Doors & Windows
211 New Laredo Hwy (78211-1905)
PHONE.................................210 921-1400
Edward G Steves, *CEO*
▲ EMP: 270
SALES (corp-wide): 226MM **Privately Held**
WEB: www.stevesdoors.com
SIC: 3442 Window & door frames; sash, door or window: metal
PA: Steves & Sons, Inc.
　203 Humble Ave
　San Antonio TX 78225
　210 924-5111

(G-18506)
STEVES & SONS INC
113 Humble Ave (78225)
PHONE.................................210 924-5111
EMP: 60
SALES (corp-wide): 226MM **Privately Held**
WEB: www.stevesdoors.com
SIC: 2431 Doors, wood
PA: Steves & Sons, Inc.
　203 Humble Ave
　San Antonio TX 78225
　210 924-5111

(G-18507)
STREAMLINE INNOVATIONS INC (PA)
21252 Gathering Oak # 101 (78260-3458)
PHONE.................................888 787-6569
Dave Sisk, *CEO*
Matt Lewis, *CFO*
John Bourdon, *CTO*
Katie Turner, *Administration*
EMP: 21 EST: 2016
SQ FT: 5,300
SALES (est): 20.6MM **Privately Held**
WEB: www.streamlineinnovations.com
SIC: 1389 Detection & analysis service, gas

(G-18508)
STREAMLINE INNOVATIONS INC
20079 Stone Oak Pkwy (78258-6942)
PHONE.................................888 787-6569
Dave Sisk, *CEO*
EMP: 9
SALES (corp-wide): 20.6MM **Privately Held**
WEB: www.streamlineinnovations.com
SIC: 1311 Crude petroleum & natural gas
PA: Streamline Innovations, Inc.
　21252 Gathering Oak # 101
　San Antonio TX 78260
　888 787-6569

(G-18509)
STRIKE LLC
5436 Old Pearsall Rd (78242-2332)
PHONE.................................888 353-1444
Sam Anaya, *Principal*
EMP: 35
SALES (corp-wide): 1.4B **Privately Held**
WEB: www.strikeusa.com
SIC: 1389 Servicing oil & gas wells
PA: Strike, Llc
　1800 Hughes Landing Blvd # 500
　The Woodlands TX 77380
　713 389-2400

(G-18510)
SUMITOMO ELC WIRG SYSTEMS INC
6903 Ne Loop 410 (78219-1715)
PHONE.................................210 507-3395
Martin Pena, *Opers Spvr*
Andreas Martinez, *Asst Mgr*
EMP: 20 **Privately Held**
WEB: www.sewsus.com
SIC: 3694 Distributors, motor vehicle engine
HQ: Sumitomo Electric Wiring Systems, Inc.
　1018 Ashley St
　Bowling Green KY 42103
　270 782-7397

(G-18511)
SUNBELT DESIGN & DEV INC
730 Perez St (78207-2318)
PHONE.................................210 227-9162
Ruben Solis, *President*
Tim Midlane, *Vice Pres*
EMP: 52
SQ FT: 32,000
SALES: 3.4MM **Privately Held**
WEB: www.sunbeltdesign.com
SIC: 3764 3829 3724 3537 Rocket motors, guided missiles; measuring & controlling devices; research & development on aircraft engines & parts; industrial trucks & tractors; drafting service, except temporary help

(G-18512)
SUNBELT DESIGN HOLDINGS LLC
730 Perez St (78207-2318)
PHONE.................................210 227-9162
Daniel Wheeler,
EMP: 43
SALES (est): 1.4MM **Privately Held**
SIC: 3728 Aircraft parts & equipment

(G-18513)
SUNTERRA INTERNATIONAL LLC
21720 Hardy Oak Blvd (78258-4835)
PHONE.................................210 501-9510
Enrique Valdes, *Mng Member*

EMP: 60
SQ FT: 100,000
SALES (est): 1.5MM **Privately Held**
WEB: www.sunterraoutdoor.com
SIC: 3446 Grillwork, ornamental metal

(G-18514)
SUPERIOR SIGNS
6606 Topper Rd (78233)
PHONE.................................210 646-7799
Ernest Ledesma, *Owner*
EMP: 9
SQ FT: 5,400
SALES (est): 900K **Privately Held**
SIC: 3993 Signs & advertising specialties

(G-18515)
SUPERIOR SILICA SANDS LLC
Also Called: Osburn Materials
215 Wellesley Loop (78231-2266)
PHONE.................................210 626-2045
EMP: 12
SALES (corp-wide): 313.5MM **Privately Held**
WEB: www.sssand.com
SIC: 1446 Silica sand mining
HQ: Superior Silica Sands Llc
　6500 West Fwy Ste 800
　Fort Worth TX 76116
　817 841-8070

(G-18516)
SURLEAN MEAT COMPANY (DH)
Also Called: Surlean Foods
1545 S San Marcos (78207-7033)
P.O. Box 831449 (78283-1449)
PHONE.................................210 227-4370
Kenneth E Leonard, *Ch of Bd*
Darryl Scott, *President*
Terry Black, *Vice Pres*
Robbie Laporte, *Vice Pres*
Harry Spahn, *Vice Pres*
▲ EMP: 157 EST: 1979
SQ FT: 21,000
SALES (est): 68.8MM **Privately Held**
WEB: www.surleanfoods.net
SIC: 2013 Prepared beef products from purchased beef

(G-18517)
SYNERGY TELECOM SERVICE CO INC
12126 El Sendero St (78233-6720)
PHONE.................................210 599-7743
John Crawford, *President*
Charles Slaughter, *Vice Pres*
Ginger Smith, *Consultant*
Dennis Evans, *Director*
EMP: 10
SALES (est): 1.4MM **Privately Held**
WEB: www.synergyinmatephones.com
SIC: 4813 3663 Telephone communication, except radio;

(G-18518)
SYSTAGENIX WOUND MGT US INC
12930 W Interstate 10 (78249-2248)
PHONE.................................617 774-5500
Ernest Waaser, *CEO*
Robert Waaser, *President*
Steve Atkinson, *Principal*
David J Milner, *Treasurer*
Ray Derise, *Admin Sec*
▲ EMP: 90
SQ FT: 3,700
SALES (est): 6.4MM
SALES (corp-wide): 32.1B **Publicly Held**
WEB: www.acelity.com
SIC: 3841 Surgical & medical instruments
HQ: Kinetic Concepts, Inc.
　12930 W Interstate 10
　San Antonio TX 78249
　800 531-5346

(G-18519)
TAKUMI STAMPING INC
1930 Hormel Dr (78219-2324)
PHONE.................................210 380-1087
Roger De Luna, *General Mgr*
EMP: 40 **Privately Held**
WEB: www.takumitx.com
SIC: 3465 Automotive stampings
HQ: Takumi Stamping Inc.
　1 Lone Star Pass Bldg 40
　San Antonio TX 78264

(G-18520)
TAKUMI STAMPING INC (DH)
1 Lone Star Pass Bldg 40 (78264-3644)
PHONE.................................210 924-3110
Katsumi Naruse, *President*
Takatoshi Kurotani, *Vice Pres*
Luna Jr Roger, *Vice Pres*
Renee Hernandez, *Purchasing*
Miguel Hernandez, *Engineer*
▲ EMP: 300
SQ FT: 87,460
SALES (est): 125.8MM **Privately Held**
WEB: www.takumitx.com
SIC: 3469 Stamping metal for the trade

(G-18521)
TALON/LPE LTD
13111 Lookout Way (78233-5171)
PHONE.................................210 253-7200
Doug Millsaps, *Vice Pres*
EMP: 12
SALES (corp-wide): 24.7MM **Privately Held**
WEB: www.talonlpe.com
SIC: 8748 1799 1542 1389 Environmental consultant; antenna installation; commercial & office building contractors; cementing oil & gas well casings
PA: Talon/Lpe, Ltd.
　921 N Bivins St
　Amarillo TX 79107
　806 467-0607

(G-18522)
TAPRITE INC (HQ)
3248 Northwestern (78238-4043)
PHONE.................................210 523-0800
◆ EMP: 37
SQ FT: 21,000
SALES (est): 14.6MM
SALES (corp-wide): 3.1B **Privately Held**
WEB: www.taprite.com
SIC: 3499 3444 3443 3429 Metal household articles; sheet metalwork; fabricated plate work (boiler shop); manufactured hardware (general); partitions & fixtures, except wood
PA: Aalberts N.V.
　Stadsplateau 18
　Utrecht
　303 079-300

(G-18523)
TECHNICAL COMPOSITE CORP
2107 Danbury St (78217-5909)
PHONE.................................210 832-0200
Louis Martin, *President*
▲ EMP: 30
SALES (est): 2.6MM **Privately Held**
WEB: www.techcomposites.com
SIC: 3999 Manufacturing industries

(G-18524)
TEJAS PRECISION METALFABRICATN
Also Called: Tejas PMS
2818 Se Loop 410 (78222-2202)
PHONE.................................210 648-1555
Bryce T Baker,
Sharon K Baker,
Sharon E Buchta,
EMP: 55
SQ FT: 15,000
SALES (est): 10.3MM **Privately Held**
WEB: www.sheet-metal-contractors.cmac.ws
SIC: 3599 Machine & other job shop work

(G-18525)
TEJAS SUPREME MEAT
Also Called: Supreme Meat Purveyors
222 E Cevallos (78204-1723)
PHONE.................................210 224-9672
Lynn Moondy, *Partner*
James Worth, *Ltd Ptnr*
EMP: 30
SALES (est): 3.6MM **Privately Held**
SIC: 2011 Meat packing plants

(G-18526)
TEJONES OPERATING CORPORATION
17 Bitterblue Ln (78218-1791)
P.O. Box 17925 (78217-0925)
PHONE.................................210 824-5957

▲ = Import ▼=Export
◆ =Import/Export

Tom M Gouger III, *President*
EMP: 9
SQ FT: 2,000
SALES (est): 1MM **Privately Held**
SIC: 1382 Oil & gas exploration services

(G-18527)
TELESPACE LLC
1354 N Loop 1604 E # 103 (78232-1342)
PHONE..................................210 489-6600
Brian Fox, *CEO*
Sean Nelson, *President*
James Goodman, *Chairman*
Cathy Kincy, *CFO*
EMP: 9
SALES (est): 1.5MM **Privately Held**
WEB: www.telespace.com
SIC: 3315 Wire products, ferrous/iron: made in wiredrawing plants

(G-18528)
TENNECO AUTOMOTIVE OPER CO INC
1 Lone Star Pass (78264-3638)
PHONE..................................210 304-9390
Ernesto Zepeda, *Branch Mgr*
EMP: 45
SALES (corp-wide): 17.4B **Publicly Held**
SIC: 3714 Shock absorbers, motor vehicle
HQ: Tenneco Automotive Operating Company, Inc.
500 N Field Dr
Lake Forest IL 60045
847 482-5000

(G-18529)
TESORO LGSTICS NW PIPELINE LLC
19100 Ridgewood Pkwy (78259-1834)
P.O. Box 8016, Cary NC (27512-8016)
PHONE..................................210 249-9123
EMP: 39
SALES: 72.6MM
SALES (corp-wide): 9B **Publicly Held**
SIC: 1311 Crude petroleum production
HQ: Andeavor Logistics Lp
200 E Hardin St
Findlay OH 45840

(G-18530)
TESORO REFINING & MKTG CO LLC (DH)
19100 Ridgewood Pkwy (78259-1834)
P.O. Box 599701 (78259-9701)
PHONE..................................210 828-8484
Gregory J Goff, *President*
Keith Casey, *Exec VP*
Charles S Parrish, *Exec VP*
Steven Sterin, *Exec VP*
Cynthia Warner, *Exec VP*
▲ **EMP:** 200
SQ FT: 150,000
SALES (est): 970MM **Publicly Held**
WEB: www.marathonpetroleum.com
SIC: 2911 5541 Petroleum refining; gasoline service stations
HQ: Andeavor Llc
19100 Ridgewood Pkwy
San Antonio TX 78259
210 626-6000

(G-18531)
TEXAN WASTE EQUIPMENT INC
503 Pop Gunn St (78219-4303)
PHONE..................................210 224-5800
Mike Dugi, *Branch Mgr*
EMP: 10
SALES (corp-wide): 40MM **Privately Held**
WEB: www.heiloftexas.com
SIC: 3713 Garbage, refuse truck bodies
PA: Texan Waste Equipment, Inc.
5900 Wheeler St
Houston TX 77023
713 923-7600

(G-18532)
TEXAS AIR PRODUCTS LTD (PA)
Also Called: T A P
11122 Gordon Rd (78216-2825)
PHONE..................................210 495-8100
Robert Stinson Pe, *CEO*
John Delgado, *Engineer*
Sandra Pina, *Controller*

Aaron Caldwell, *Sales Staff*
Clint Doege, *Sales Staff*
EMP: 19
SQ FT: 25,000
SALES (est): 10.4MM **Privately Held**
WEB: www.txap.com
SIC: 3585 Air conditioning equipment, complete; heating equipment, complete

(G-18533)
TEXAS ARMORING CORPORATION
4323 Factory Hill St (78219-2702)
PHONE..................................210 333-0211
Ronald T Kimball, *President*
Javier Garza, *Prdtn Mgr*
Larry Kosub, *Sales Staff*
Trish Dukes, *Mktg Dir*
Rick Ryan, *Marketing Staff*
▼ **EMP:** 15
SQ FT: 7,500
SALES (est): 3.9MM **Privately Held**
WEB: www.texasarmoring.com
SIC: 3711 Motor vehicles & car bodies

(G-18534)
TEXAS AVIATION TECH LLC
1731 S San Marcos # 912 (78207-7062)
PHONE..................................210 680-8181
Luis Nieves, *President*
EMP: 19
SALES (est): 1.8MM **Privately Held**
SIC: 3728 Aircraft parts & equipment

(G-18535)
TEXAS BIG GAME PROCESSING INC
15603 Legend Springs Dr (78247-5563)
PHONE..................................210 366-0638
EMP: 10
SALES (est): 1MM **Privately Held**
SIC: 2011 Meat Packing Plant

(G-18536)
TEXAS EIFS LLC (PA)
Also Called: Teifs Wall Systems
220 Burleson (78202-1803)
PHONE..................................210 472-2935
Dale Fairbanks,
EMP: 10
SALES (est): 2.3MM **Privately Held**
SIC: 3272 Building materials, except block or brick: concrete

(G-18537)
TEXAS LANDFILL MANAGEMENT LLC
Garden-Ville
14080 Nacogdoches Rd # 314 (78247-1944)
PHONE..................................210 651-6115
Jim Doersam, *General Mgr*
Kimberly McGill, *Site Mgr*
Jaquin Salazar, *Sales Staff*
Mark Haley, *Manager*
Kenneth McClusky, *Supervisor*
EMP: 30
SALES (corp-wide): 421.8MM **Privately Held**
WEB: www.texasdisposal.com
SIC: 2875 5261 5083 2873 Fertilizers, mixing only; lawn & garden supplies; top soil; landscaping equipment; nitrogenous fertilizers
HQ: Texas Landfill Management, L.L.C.
12200 Carl Rd
Creedmoor TX 78610

(G-18538)
TEXAS NEON ADVERTISING COMPANY
245 W Josephine St (78212-4153)
P.O. Box 15245 (78212-8445)
PHONE..................................210 734-6694
George Ryan, *President*
Barbara Ryan, *Admin Sec*
EMP: 16 **EST:** 1925
SQ FT: 12,000
SALES (est): 2.1MM **Privately Held**
WEB: www.texasneonadvertisingco.com
SIC: 1799 8712 3993 Lightning conductor erection; architectural services; signs & advertising specialties; neon signs

(G-18539)
TEXAS NOM LIMITED PARTNERSHIP
Also Called: Garrison
6002 Camp Bullis Rd (78257-9738)
PHONE..................................210 687-1900
Martin O Neil, *Partner*
EMP: 20
SALES (est): 1.6MM **Privately Held**
SIC: 1311 Crude petroleum & natural gas

(G-18540)
TEXAS OIL GROUP LTD CO
17806 W Interstate 10 (78257-8221)
PHONE..................................281 645-9398
Michael Phipps, *Mng Member*
EMP: 15
SQ FT: 5,000
SALES (est): 1MM **Privately Held**
WEB: www.texasoilgroup.com
SIC: 2992 Re-refining lubricating oils & greases

(G-18541)
TEXAS PIPELINE WEBB
Also Called: Eagle Ford Gathering System
17806 Ih 10 W Ste 210 (78257-8222)
PHONE..................................210 298-2222
Steven B Huckaby, *President*
Nicholas O Thomas, *Exec VP*
J Stacey Horn, *Vice Pres*
William S Dickey, *CFO*
EMP: 26
SALES (est): 7.4MM **Privately Held**
WEB: www.howardenergypartners.com
SIC: 1382 1389 Oil & gas exploration services; oil field services
HQ: Howard Midstream Energy Partners, Llc
16211 La Cantera Pkwy
San Antonio TX 78256

(G-18542)
TEXAS SCENIC COMPANY INC (PA)
8053 Potranco Rd (78251-2915)
P.O. Box 680008 (78268-0008)
PHONE..................................210 684-0091
Richard Mecke, *President*
Steve G Surratt, *General Mgr*
Glenn C Martin III, *Principal*
Stephen G Surratt, *COO*
Hien Van Luong, *Vice Pres*
▲ **EMP:** 85 **EST:** 1963
SALES (est): 36.3MM **Privately Held**
WEB: www.texasscenic.com
SIC: 5049 3999 Theatrical equipment & supplies; theatrical scenery

(G-18543)
TEXAS STAR ENVELOPE INC
610 Lanark Dr Ste 204 (78218-1844)
PHONE..................................210 293-8820
Javier Fernandez, *CEO*
Frederico Toca, *President*
Carlos Fernandez, *Vice Pres*
Leopoldo Fernandez, *Vice Pres*
Ferando Toca, *Vice Pres*
EMP: 35
SALES (est): 11MM **Privately Held**
WEB: www.texasstar.protacto.com
SIC: 2759 Commercial printing
PA: Arpapel, S.A. De C.V.
Calzada De La Naranja No. 140
Naucalpan EDOMEX. 53370

(G-18544)
TEXAS TOOLMAKERS INC
11411 E Coker Loop (78216-2810)
PHONE..................................210 494-3651
John P Bishop, *President*
Michael L Ridgway, *Vice Pres*
Cheryl D Castillo, *Treasurer*
Steve Gayer, *Manager*
Gilbert Lopez, *Supervisor*
EMP: 38 **EST:** 1975
SQ FT: 33,000
SALES (est): 6.9MM **Privately Held**
WEB: www.txtoolmakers.com
SIC: 3599 3544 3444 3441 Machine shop, jobbing & repair; special dies, tools, jigs & fixtures; sheet metalwork; fabricated structural metal

(G-18545)
TEXAS TROPHIES INC (PA)
2525 Renwick Dr (78227-3675)
PHONE..................................210 674-6099
Jessie Pope, *President*
EMP: 14
SQ FT: 6,000
SALES (est): 812K **Privately Held**
WEB: www.texastrophies.com
SIC: 5999 3914 Trophies & plaques; trophies

(G-18546)
TEXTRON INC
1 Lone Star Pass Bldg 3 (78264-3629)
PHONE..................................210 229-2303
EMP: 64
SALES (corp-wide): 13.6B **Publicly Held**
WEB: www.textron.com
SIC: 3721 Aircraft
PA: Textron Inc.
40 Westminster St
Providence RI 02903
401 421-2800

(G-18547)
THE SAN ANTONIO TRUSS COMPANY
1010 Culebra Rd (78201-6119)
PHONE..................................210 736-9629
Felix Guerra III, *President*
Roodolso Guerra, *Admin Sec*
EMP: 9
SQ FT: 4,900
SALES (est): 1.3MM **Privately Held**
WEB: www.satruss.com
SIC: 2439 Trusses, wooden roof; trusses, except roof: laminated lumber

(G-18548)
THOMAS REPROGRAPHICS INC
1223 Arion Pkwy (78216-2822)
PHONE..................................210 829-7000
Phil Burgess, *Production*
Paul Mery Jr, *Manager*
Jake Markey, *Manager*
Alexi Garza,
Wendy Hildebrandt,
EMP: 55
SALES (corp-wide): 62.7MM **Privately Held**
WEB: www.thomasprintworks.com
SIC: 2752 7334 7374 5199 Commercial printing, offset; photocopying & duplicating services; computer processing services; architects' supplies (non-durable); bookbinding & related work; commercial printing
PA: Thomas Reprographics, Inc.
600 N Central Expy
Richardson TX 75080
972 231-7227

(G-18549)
THOMPSON BUSINESS FORMS INC
Also Called: Thompson Print Solutions
5818 Rocky Pt (78249-3406)
PHONE..................................210 734-5356
David Thompson, *President*
EMP: 30 **EST:** 1964
SQ FT: 13,000
SALES (est): 8.1MM **Privately Held**
WEB: www.thompsonprintsolutions.com
SIC: 5943 2782 2752 Office forms & supplies; account books; commercial printing, lithographic

(G-18550)
THOR ENERGY GROUP INC
710 Lightstone Dr (78258-2305)
PHONE..................................210 277-0368
EMP: 10 **EST:** 2008
SALES: 2.5MM **Privately Held**
SIC: 1311 Crude Petroleum/Natural Gas Production

(G-18551)
THORNE ELECTRIC COMPANY
Also Called: Koblend
610 Lanark Dr Ste 205 (78218-1844)
P.O. Box 18363 (78218-0363)
PHONE..................................210 590-1226
Michele Folks, *Manager*
EMP: 10

SALES (corp-wide): 3.3MM **Privately Held**
WEB: www.koblenz.com
SIC: 3639 Floor waxers & polishers, electric: household
PA: Thorne Electric Company
1558 Candish Ln
Chesterfield MO 63017

(G-18552)
TK HOLDINGS INC (HQ)
4611 Wiseman Blvd (78251-4202)
PHONE..................................210 509-0762
Yoshiyasu Kikuchi, *CEO*
Robert Fisher, *President*
Teresa Clark, *Vice Pres*
Andrew James, *Purchasing*
Phillip Maguire, *Engineer*
▲ EMP: 60
SALES (est): 202.4MM
SALES (corp-wide): 2.2B **Privately Held**
SIC: 2399 Seat belts, automobile & aircraft; seat covers, automobile
PA: Joyson Safety Systems Acquisition Llc
2500 Innovation Dr
Auburn Hills MI 48326
248 373-8040

(G-18553)
TNG GP
5130 Commerce Pkwy (78218-5523)
PHONE..................................210 226-9333
Bob Kilgore, *Branch Mgr*
EMP: 3700
SALES (corp-wide): 1.3B **Privately Held**
WEB: www.tng.com
SIC: 2721 Periodicals
PA: Tng Gp
100 Galleria Pkwy Se # 13
Atlanta GA 30339
770 863-9000

(G-18554)
TOWER SEMICDTR SAN ANTONIO INC
9651 Westover Hills Blvd (78251-2700)
PHONE..................................210 522-7000
Rafi Mor, *Director*
Eric Clark, *Director*
EMP: 500
SALES (est): 1MM **Privately Held**
WEB: www.towersemi.com
SIC: 3674 Semiconductors & related devices
HQ: Tower Us Holdings Inc.
4321 Jamboree Rd
Newport Beach CA 92660

(G-18555)
TOYODA GOSEI
15800 Applewhite Rd (78264-3638)
PHONE..................................210 628-1337
Kathleen Toyoda, *Principal*
EMP: 13
SALES (est): 1.7MM **Privately Held**
WEB: www.toyodagosei.com
SIC: 3465 Body parts, automobile: stamped metal

(G-18556)
TOYODA GOSEI TEXAS LLC
1 Lone Star Pass Bldg 31 (78264-3640)
PHONE..................................210 302-4600
Mototsugu Sugeyama, *CEO*
Kuniyoshi Kojima, *President*
Akid Narano, *Vice Pres*
Hipcki Fuzui, *Treasurer*
Toru Koyama, *Director*
▲ EMP: 220
SALES (est): 37.9MM **Privately Held**
SIC: 3714 Motor vehicle parts & accessories
HQ: Toyoda Gosei North America Corporation
1400 Stephenson Hwy
Troy MI 48083
248 280-2100

(G-18557)
TOYOTETSU TEXAS INC
Also Called: Ttna
1 Lone Star Pass Bldg 38 (78264-3643)
PHONE..................................210 231-5515
Tetsuji Hatano, *President*
Takehiro Maruyama, *Principal*
Seiji Horiguchi, *Vice Pres*

Kenji Takamatsu, *Vice Pres*
Gregory Polston, *Production*
EMP: 56
SALES (est): 23.3MM **Privately Held**
WEB: www.ttna.com
SIC: 3465 3714 3429 Automotive stampings; motor vehicle parts & accessories; manufactured hardware (general)
PA: Toyoda Iron Works Co.,Ltd.
4-50, Hosoyacho
Toyota AIC 471-0

(G-18558)
TRADE-MARK INDUSTRIAL LLC
1 Lone Star Pass Lot C12 (78264-3648)
PHONE..................................519 650-7444
Mark Mitchell, *Sales Staff*
Russell Straus, *Mng Member*
David Straus,
EMP: 100 EST: 2009
SQ FT: 800
SALES (est): 8.5MM **Privately Held**
WEB: www.trade-markllc.com
SIC: 3499 1799 Aerosol valves, metal; dock equipment installation, industrial

(G-18559)
TRANE US INC
Also Called: Trane Technologies
9535 Ball St (78217-3751)
PHONE..................................210 657-0901
Jeffrey Watson, *Vice Pres*
Ray Merchant, *Sales Mgr*
Daniel Dornier, *Accounts Mgr*
Mario Trejo, *Accounts Mgr*
Scott Naab, *Accounts Exec*
EMP: 75 **Privately Held**
WEB: www.trane.com
SIC: 3585 Refrigeration & heating equipment
HQ: Trane U.S. Inc.
3600 Pammel Creek Rd
La Crosse WI 54601
608 787-2000

(G-18560)
TRANS TOOL LLC
110 Connelly St (78203-1706)
PHONE..................................210 225-6745
Robert I Safstrom, *Mng Member*
EMP: 14
SQ FT: 25,000
SALES (est): 1.5MM **Privately Held**
WEB: www.atoztool.com
SIC: 5251 3423 3589 Tools; mechanics' hand tools; commercial cleaning equipment

(G-18561)
TRANS-TEL CENTRAL INC
10930 Wye Dr Ste 104 (78217-2648)
PHONE..................................405 447-5025
Scott Jackson, *Manager*
Courtney Caraway, *Executive Asst*
EMP: 14
SALES (corp-wide): 28.2MM **Privately Held**
WEB: www.trans-tel.com
SIC: 1731 4813 1522 1623 Fiber optic cable installation; telephone/video communications; renovation, hotel/motel; communication line & transmission tower construction; industrial plant construction; mine development, nonmetallic minerals
PA: Trans-Tel Central, Inc.
2851 N Flood Ave
Norman OK 73069
405 447-5025

(G-18562)
TRANS-TEX FABRICATING CO INC (PA)
Also Called: Bexar Steel Company
549 Heimer Rd Ste 100 (78232-5111)
PHONE..................................210 924-4431
John C Schuepbach, *CEO*
John W Schuepbach, *Ch of Bd*
Charlotte Schuepbach, *Chairman*
EMP: 20
SQ FT: 100,000
SALES (est): 7.5MM **Privately Held**
WEB: www.skylinesteeldetailing.com
SIC: 3312 Structural & rail mill products

(G-18563)
TRANSPLANT TECHNOLOGY INC (PA)
Also Called: Bone Bank Allografts
5335 Castroville Rd (78227-4237)
P.O. Box 690988 (78269-0988)
PHONE..................................210 696-7616
Joe M Mims Jr, *CEO*
Donna D'Lynn Mims, *President*
John W Lee, *COO*
Joel Davis, *Opers Staff*
John McDougall, *Mfg Staff*
EMP: 27
SQ FT: 8,500
SALES (est): 4.4MM **Privately Held**
WEB: www.bonebank.com
SIC: 3841 Surgical & medical instruments

(G-18564)
TRAVIS MILLWORK INC
Also Called: Vision Openings
235 W Turbo Dr (78216-3313)
PHONE..................................210 525-8088
John E Travis, *President*
Juan Castaneda, *Superintendent*
Scot Farber, *Project Mgr*
Veronica Gonzales, *Project Mgr*
Robin Qualls, *Project Mgr*
EMP: 50
SALES (est): 7.5MM **Privately Held**
WEB: www.traviscompanies.com
SIC: 2599 1721 2431 Cabinets, factory; painting & paper hanging; millwork

(G-18565)
TRI-COR INDUSTRIES INC
2929 Mossrock Ste 105 (78230-5141)
PHONE..................................210 979-0552
Al Greenough, *Branch Mgr*
EMP: 30
SALES (corp-wide): 33.1MM **Privately Held**
WEB: www.tricorind.com
SIC: 7373 7374 3571 3577 Systems integration services; data processing service; electronic computers; computer peripheral equipment
PA: Tri-Cor Industries, Inc.
1818 Library St Ste 500
Reston VA 20190
571 458-3824

(G-18566)
TRIANGLE REPRODUCTIONS OF SAN
2203 Ceegee St (78217-6368)
P.O. Box 17214 (78217-0214)
PHONE..................................713 780-0236
Edgar A Christy III, *President*
EMP: 24
SQ FT: 2,500
SALES (est): 2.5MM **Privately Held**
WEB: www.triangle-sa.com
SIC: 2752 5999 Commercial printing, offset; drafting equipment & supplies

(G-18567)
TRINITY MILLENNIUM GROUP INC
2424 Babcock Rd Ste 300 (78229-6031)
PHONE..................................210 615-1606
David M Garza, *President*
EMP: 110
SQ FT: 15,000
SALES (est): 11.1MM **Privately Held**
WEB: www.tringroup.com
SIC: 7373 7372 Systems software development services; prepackaged software

(G-18568)
TRINITY SPECIALTY PRODUCTS INC
647 N Ww White Rd (78219-2817)
PHONE..................................210 304-2100
EMP: 9
SALES (est): 1.2MM
SALES (corp-wide): 3B **Publicly Held**
SIC: 3441 Fabricated structural metal
PA: Trinity Industries, Inc.
14221 Dallas Pkwy Ste 11
Dallas TX 75254
214 631-4420

(G-18569)
TRIPLE AIM VENTURES LLC
Also Called: Tavhealth
100 Ne Loop 410 Ste 100 # 100 (78216-4719)
P.O. Box 690008 (78269-0008)
PHONE..................................210 417-4170
Melinda Floros, *Vice Pres*
Allison Halley, *Vice Pres*
Heather Whitaker, *HR Admin*
Lia Ahchu, *Director*
James Rubin,
EMP: 25
SALES (est): 2.1MM
SALES (corp-wide): 37.4MM **Privately Held**
WEB: www.tavhealth.com
SIC: 7372 Application computer software
PA: Signify Health, Llc
4055 Valley View Ln # 400
Dallas TX 75244
972 715-3800

(G-18570)
TRULITE GL ALUM SOLUTIONS LLC
5807 Business Park # 100 (78218-5525)
PHONE..................................210 653-7790
Ed Bator, *Manager*
Mateo Ramirez, *Maintence Staff*
EMP: 40 **Privately Held**
WEB: www.trulite.com
SIC: 3211 5039 3231 Tempered glass; exterior flat glass: plate or window; products of purchased glass
PA: Trulite Glass & Aluminum Solutions, Llc
403 Westpark Ct Ste 201
Peachtree City GA 30269

(G-18571)
TURBO MACH R & D II INC
143 W Rhapsody Dr (78216-3105)
PHONE..................................210 340-4773
EMP: 15
SQ FT: 28,000
SALES (est): 1.8MM **Privately Held**
SIC: 3728 Mfg Aircraft Body Parts

(G-18572)
TURBOMASTERS INC
Also Called: Test Engineering
12718 Cimarron Path (78249-3423)
PHONE..................................210 690-1958
John W Knight, *President*
Shirley F Knight, *Treasurer*
Derek Grosch, *Technical Staff*
EMP: 11
SQ FT: 10,000
SALES (est): 3.4MM **Privately Held**
WEB: www.tei-net.com
SIC: 3569 8711 Lubricating equipment; consulting engineer

(G-18573)
TWC ARCHITECTURAL MOLDINGS LTD
8523 Ne Loop 410 (78219-3333)
PHONE..................................210 662-2800
Efton Giles, *Partner*
Kim Evans, *Partner*
David Atkinson, *Manager*
John Solter, *Exec Dir*
EMP: 43
SQ FT: 30,000
SALES (est): 4.7MM **Privately Held**
WEB: www.twcmouldings.com
SIC: 2431 Millwork

(G-18574)
TXSYN INT LLC
Also Called: Txsyn Labs Stsfy Lqds / Pur La
7232 Eckhert Rd (78238-1244)
P.O. Box 5804 (78201-0804)
PHONE..................................210 884-3895
Mark Rivera, *Mng Member*
Kabir Adatia, *Mng Member*
Aamir Ajani, *Mng Member*
Alexander Wong, *Mng Member*
EMP: 25
SALES (est): 1.8MM **Privately Held**
WEB: www.txsynlabs.com
SIC: 2844 Toilet preparations

(G-18575)
ULTRAFRYER SYSTEMS INC
302 Spencer Ln (78201-2018)
P.O. Box 5369 (78201-0369)
PHONE...........................210 731-5000
Edward T Odmark, *President*
William A Collins, *Vice Pres*
Mark Escalera, *Engineer*
Wendy Kane, *Sales Staff*
EMP: 103
SQ FT: 85,000
SALES (est): 36MM
SALES (corp-wide): 604.5MM **Publicly Held**
WEB: www.ultrafryer.com
SIC: 3589 Commercial cooking & food-warming equipment
PA: Standex International Corporation
23 Keewaydin Dr Ste 300
Salem NH 03079
603 893-9701

(G-18576)
ULTRAMAR INC (HQ)
1 Valero Way (78249-1616)
P.O. Box 696000 (78269-6000)
PHONE...........................210 345-2000
William R Klesse, *CEO*
Kimberly S Bowers, *Exec VP*
Jay D Browning, *Senior VP*
Anthony D Jones, *Senior VP*
Cheryl L Thomas, *Vice Pres*
EMP: 800
SQ FT: 500,000
SALES (est): 415.1MM
SALES (corp-wide): 108.3B **Publicly Held**
SIC: 2911 5172 5541 Petroleum refining; gasoline; filling stations, gasoline
PA: Valero Energy Corporation
1 Valero Way
San Antonio TX 78249
210 345-2000

(G-18577)
UNITED ENERGEX INC (HQ)
7709 Broadway St Apt 106 (78209-3203)
P.O. Box 6027 (78209-0027)
PHONE...........................210 826-0681
Calvin Michelson, *President*
Robert Fannin, *Vice Pres*
Mitch Michelson, *Vice Pres*
Karl Knox, *Finance*
EMP: 35
SQ FT: 3,517
SALES (corp-wide): 12.8MM **Privately Held**
SIC: 1389 Servicing oil & gas wells
PA: Michelson Energy Company
7709 Broadway Apt 106
San Antonio TX 78209
210 826-0681

(G-18578)
UNITED METRO MEDIA LLC
4242 Woodcock Dr Ste 202 (78228-1325)
PHONE...........................210 315-6046
EMP: 10
SALES (corp-wide): 13.6MM **Privately Held**
WEB: www.jobnewsusa.com
SIC: 2711 Newspapers, publishing & printing
PA: United Metro Media Llc
118 E Main St Ste 500
Louisville KY 40202
502 412-7500

(G-18579)
UNIVERSAL PEN & PRINT INC
Also Called: Cubie Co
5351 Brewster St (78233-5723)
PHONE...........................210 656-4000
Dee Hernandez, *President*
Roland Hernandez, *Corp Secy*
EMP: 13
SQ FT: 1,250
SALES (est): 2.3MM **Privately Held**
WEB: www.cubie.co
SIC: 5943 2752 Office forms & supplies; commercial printing, lithographic

(G-18580)
US DEPT OF THE AIR FORCE
Also Called: Sa-Alc/Ldae-adtic
404 Greig St 178 (78226-1844)
PHONE...........................210 925-4401
Dan Booth, *Branch Mgr*
EMP: 254 **Publicly Held**
WEB: www.af.mil
SIC: 9711 3728 Air Force; military aircraft equipment & armament
HQ: United States Department Of The Air Force
1000 Air Force Pentagon
Washington DC 20330

(G-18581)
US PIPE FABRICATION
7030 Old Pearsall Rd (78252-2702)
PHONE...........................817 232-5858
EMP: 10 **EST:** 2013
SALES (est): 1.6MM **Privately Held**
SIC: 3498 Mfg Fabricated Pipe/Fittings

(G-18582)
USDATWING AERIAL ANALYTICS LLC
18615 Tuscany Stone # 200 (78258-3502)
PHONE...........................210 495-5577
Wade Ingle,
Scott Martin,
Phil Mezey,
Gayle Muench,
Clay Smith,
EMP: 14
SALES (est): 332.3K **Privately Held**
WEB: www.datawingglobal.com
SIC: 7374 7389 1389 8713 Data processing & preparation; ; mapmaking or drafting, including aerial; oil field services;

(G-18583)
VALERO ENERGY CORPORATION (PA)
1 Valero Way (78249-1616)
P.O. Box 696000 (78269-6000)
PHONE...........................210 345-2000
Joseph W Gorder, *Ch of Bd*
R Lane Riggs, *President*
Sherena Shawrieh, *Counsel*
Jason W Fraser, *Exec VP*
Daniel Collier, *Vice Pres*
▲ **EMP:** 550 **EST:** 1980
SALES (est): 108.3B **Publicly Held**
WEB: www.valero.com
SIC: 2911 Gasoline

(G-18584)
VALERO REF COMPANY-CALIFORNIA (DH)
1 Valero Way (78249-1616)
P.O. Box 696000 (78269-6000)
PHONE...........................210 345-2000
Bill Klesse, *CEO*
William E Greehey, *Ch of Bd*
Joe Gorder, *President*
Gregory C King, *Exec VP*
Michael S Ciskowski, *Senior VP*
▲ **EMP:** 132
SQ FT: 1,800
SALES (est): 857.5MM
SALES (corp-wide): 108.3B **Publicly Held**
SIC: 2911 Petroleum refining
HQ: Valero Refining-New Orleans, L.L.C.
1 Valero Way
San Antonio TX 78249
210 345-2000

(G-18585)
VALERO REF COMPANY-NEW JERSEY (DH)
1 Valero Way (78249-1616)
P.O. Box 696000 (78269-6000)
PHONE...........................210 345-2000
Bill Klesse, *President*
Joe Gorder, *President*
Mike Ciskowski, *Exec VP*
Gene Edwards, *Exec VP*
Gary Arthur Jr, *Vice Pres*
◆ **EMP:** 400

SALES (est): 117.5MM
SALES (corp-wide): 108.3B **Publicly Held**
WEB: www.valero.com
SIC: 2911 6163 Petroleum refining; loan brokers
HQ: Valero Refining-New Orleans, L.L.C.
1 Valero Way
San Antonio TX 78249
210 345-2000

(G-18586)
VALERO REFINING COMPANY (HQ)
1 Valero Way (78249-1616)
P.O. Box 696000 (78269-6000)
PHONE...........................210 345-2000
William E Greehey, *Ch of Bd*
Joe Gorder, *President*
Bill Klesse, *Chairman*
George E Kain, *Senior VP*
Kirk Saffell, *Senior VP*
EMP: 53
SALES (est): 657MM
SALES (corp-wide): 108.3B **Publicly Held**
WEB: www.valero.com
SIC: 2911 Gasoline
PA: Valero Energy Corporation
1 Valero Way
San Antonio TX 78249
210 345-2000

(G-18587)
VALERO REFINING-TEXAS LP (DH)
1 Valero Way (78249-1616)
P.O. Box 691847 (78269-1847)
PHONE...........................210 345-2000
Joe Gorder, *CEO*
Bill Klesse, *Ch of Bd*
Christopher Quinn, *President*
John Duenckel, *Superintendent*
Joe Bateman, *Fire Chief*
◆ **EMP:** 331
SALES (est): 578.6MM
SALES (corp-wide): 108.3B **Publicly Held**
WEB: www.valero.com
SIC: 5541 2911 Filling stations, gasoline; gasoline blending plants
HQ: Valero Refining-New Orleans, L.L.C.
1 Valero Way
San Antonio TX 78249
210 345-2000

(G-18588)
VALERO RENEWABLE FUELS CO LLC (HQ)
1 Valero Way (78249-1616)
P.O. Box 696000 (78269-6000)
PHONE...........................210 345-2000
William R Klesse, *Chairman*
James Satel, *Counsel*
Kimberly S Bowers, *Exec VP*
Michael S Ciskowski, *Exec VP*
S Eugene Edwards, *Exec VP*
EMP: 70
SALES (est): 111.3MM
SALES (corp-wide): 108.3B **Publicly Held**
WEB: www.valero.com
SIC: 2911 Petroleum refining
PA: Valero Energy Corporation
1 Valero Way
San Antonio TX 78249
210 345-2000

(G-18589)
VALERO RFINING-NEW ORLEANS LLC (HQ)
1 Valero Way (78249-1616)
P.O. Box 696000 (78269-6000)
PHONE...........................210 345-2000
Jay D Browning, *Managing Prtnr*
S Eugene Edwards, *Managing Prtnr*
John D Gibbons, *Managing Prtnr*
John F Hohnholt, *Managing Prtnr*
Gregory C King, *Managing Prtnr*
◆ **EMP:** 250
SALES (est): 1.5B
SALES (corp-wide): 108.3B **Publicly Held**
SIC: 2911 Petroleum refining

PA: Valero Energy Corporation
1 Valero Way
San Antonio TX 78249
210 345-2000

(G-18590)
VALERO SERVICES INC
1 Valero Way (78249-1616)
P.O. Box 696000 (78269-6000)
PHONE...........................210 345-2000
Bill Klesse, *CEO*
Joe Gorder, *President*
Kirk Saffell, *Senior VP*
Ellen Williams, *Vice Pres*
Guy Young, *Vice Pres*
EMP: 2400
SALES (corp-wide): 108.3B **Publicly Held**
SIC: 2911 5172 5411 Petroleum refining; petroleum products; convenience stores
PA: Valero Energy Corporation
1 Valero Way
San Antonio TX 78249
210 345-2000

(G-18591)
VERICAST CORP (DH)
15955 La Cantera Pkwy (78256-2589)
PHONE...........................210 697-8888
Chuck Dawson, *CEO*
Charles T Dawson, *President*
Dan Singleton, *President*
Martin Wexler, *Vice Pres*
Gary Yeats, *Vice Pres*
▲ **EMP:** 85 **EST:** 2005
SQ FT: 90,000
SALES (est): 2.4B **Publicly Held**
WEB: www.harlandclarke.com
SIC: 2754 7389 2782 Commercial printing, gravure; telemarketing services; advertising, promotional & trade show services; bank checkbooks & passbooks

(G-18592)
VIANT SAN ANTONIO INC
Also Called: C L T
7027 Fairgrounds Pkwy (78238-4544)
PHONE...........................210 684-7553
Paul A Muller, *President*
David Huff, *COO*
EMP: 200
SALES (est): 35MM
SALES (corp-wide): 458.7MM **Privately Held**
WEB: www.cltsa.com
SIC: 3841 Surgical & medical instruments
HQ: Viant Medical, Llc
2 Hampshire St
Foxborough MA 02035

(G-18593)
VIOLET CARE LLC
14603 Bassett Ln (78231-1705)
P.O. Box 470366, Fort Worth (76147-0366)
PHONE...........................210 482-0237
Theodore McAlister, *Partner*
John Harris, *Principal*
Daniel White, *Principal*
Kay Lowe,
EMP: 11
SALES (est): 707.8K **Privately Held**
SIC: 3842 Bandages & dressings

(G-18594)
VIPER PETROLEUM LLC
13423 Blanco Rd 348 (78216-2187)
P.O. Box 460068 (78246-0068)
PHONE...........................832 917-5804
Rhonda Mills, *CEO*
Michael Andrews, *Superintendent*
John Tate, *COO*
Sylvester Ekeh, *Vice Pres*
Rodney Smith, *CFO*
EMP: 12 **EST:** 2014
SQ FT: 4,500
SALES (est): 511K **Privately Held**
SIC: 1381 1389 Drilling oil & gas wells; servicing oil & gas wells

(G-18595)
VISION PRODUCTS INC (PA)
12726 Cimarron Path (78249-3423)
PHONE...........................830 755-4719
George Wolff, *Ch of Bd*
Kirk B Wolff, *President*
Bruce Parker, *Corp Secy*

Gary Wolff, *CFO*
◆ **EMP:** 215
SQ FT: 5,500
SALES (est): 11.7MM **Privately Held**
SIC: 2431 8741 Window sashes, wood;
management services

(G-18596)
VISIONWORKS OF AMERICA INC (HQ)
175 E Houston St (78205-2255)
PHONE..........................800 669-1183
Peter Bridgeman, *CEO*
Billy Chamberlin, *General Mgr*
Robert Allison, *Vice Pres*
Stuart Bolerjack, *Vice Pres*
J Llanes, *Vice Pres*
▲ **EMP:** 600
SQ FT: 65,000
SALES (est): 977MM
SALES (corp-wide): 6.1B **Privately Held**
WEB: www.visionworks.com
SIC: 5995 3851 Optical goods stores; eye-
glasses, prescription; eyeglasses, lenses
& frames
PA: Vision Service Plan, Inc.
3333 Quality Dr
Rancho Cordova CA 95670
916 851-5000

(G-18597)
VISTECH MFG SOLUTIONS LLC
3345b N Panam Expy (78219-2313)
PHONE..........................210 225-9900
Marisol Hollenbeck, *Branch Mgr*
EMP: 20
SALES (corp-wide): 55.8MM **Privately Held**
WEB: www.vistechmfg.com
SIC: 3565 Packaging machinery
HQ: Vistech Manufacturing Solutions, Llc
1156 Scenic Dr Ste 120
Modesto CA 95350
209 544-9333

(G-18598)
VIVACE INTERNATIONAL CORP
22211 W Interstate 10 (78257-1699)
PHONE..........................504 613-4329
EMP: 26 **Privately Held**
WEB: www.vivace.com
SIC: 3761 Guided missiles & space vehi-
cles
PA: Vivace International Corp
13800 Old Gentilly Rd
New Orleans LA 70129

(G-18599)
VOLCANO CORPORATION
12829 Wetmore Rd (78247-3628)
PHONE..........................210 582-5820
Christopher Banas, *Vice Pres*
EMP: 14
SALES (corp-wide): 21.5B **Privately Held**
WEB: www.usa.philips.com
SIC: 3845 Electromedical equipment
HQ: Volcano Corporation
3721 Vly Cntre Dr Ste 500
San Diego CA 92130
800 228-4728

(G-18600)
VP RACING FUELS INC (HQ)
204 E Rhapsody Dr (78216-3114)
P.O. Box 47878 (78265-8878)
PHONE..........................210 635-7744
Andrew S Burns Jr, *President*
Anna Crowder, *QC Mgr*
Fred Turza, *Research*
Jessica Schuemann, *Controller*
Brad Horton, *Regl Sales Mgr*
◆ **EMP:** 60
SQ FT: 30,000
SALES (est): 32.8MM **Privately Held**
WEB: www.vpracingfuels.com
SIC: 2911 5172 Gasoline blending plants;
fuel oil

(G-18601)
VTECH COMMUNICATIONS INC
Distribution Center
1143 At&T Center Pkwy (78219)
PHONE..........................210 244-0600
Erni Levenson, *Division Mgr*
Paige Huff, *Marketing Staff*
Sylvia Evans, *Manager*

Roberto Salgado, *Manager*
EMP: 23 **Privately Held**
WEB: www.vtechphones.com
SIC: 3661 Telephone & telegraph appara-
tus
HQ: Vtech Communications, Inc.
9020 Sw Washngtn Sq Rd # 555
Portland OR 97223
503 596-1200

(G-18602)
VULCAN CONSTRUCTION MTLS LLC
12307 Huebner Rd (78230-1552)
PHONE..........................210 492-1053
Stewert Tally, *Branch Mgr*
EMP: 16 **Publicly Held**
WEB: www.vulcanmaterials.com
SIC: 3273 Ready-mixed concrete
HQ: Vulcan Construction Materials, Llc
1200 Urban Center Dr
Vestavia AL 35242
205 298-3000

(G-18603)
VULCAN MATERIALS COMPANY
Vulcan Cnstr Southwest Div
800 Isom Rd Ste 300 (78216-4053)
P.O. Box 791550 (78279-1550)
PHONE..........................210 349-3311
Stan Bass, *President*
April Montanez, *Buyer*
Scott Kremm, *Project Engr*
Linda Alvarado, *Human Res Mgr*
Ronnie Burris, *Manager*
EMP: 17 **Publicly Held**
WEB: www.vulcanmaterials.com
SIC: 1423 2951 1442 3273 Crushed &
broken granite; asphalt paving mixtures &
blocks; construction sand & gravel; sand
mining; gravel & pebble mining; ready-
mixed concrete; concrete products; lime-
stones, ground
PA: Vulcan Materials Company
1200 Urban Center Dr
Vestavia AL 35242

(G-18604)
VULCAN MATERIALS COMPANY
Also Called: 1604 Plant
4303 N Loop 1604 E (78247-5909)
PHONE..........................210 494-9555
John Cybriwsky, *Opers Staff*
Alvaro Montemayor, *Manager*
Darrell Erwin, *Executive*
EMP: 17 **Publicly Held**
WEB: www.vulcanmaterials.com
SIC: 1423 2951 1442 3273 Crushed &
broken granite; asphalt paving mixtures &
blocks; construction sand & gravel; sand
mining; gravel & pebble mining; ready-
mixed concrete; concrete products; lime-
stones, ground
PA: Vulcan Materials Company
1200 Urban Center Dr
Vestavia AL 35242

(G-18605)
VUTEX INC
1 Lone Star Pass Ste 1102 (78264-3439)
PHONE..........................210 476-1700
Sean Yanagawa, *President*
Adrian Garcia, *Production*
Rachel Oaks, *Accounting Mgr*
Yvette Cavazos, *Senior Mgr*
Ken Mahnke, *Info Tech Mgr*
EMP: 150
SQ FT: 35,000
SALES (est): 34.8MM **Privately Held**
WEB: www.toyotatexas.com
SIC: 3711 Automobile assembly, including
specialty automobiles
PA: Vuteq Corporation
9-30-3, Umetsubocho
Toyota AIC 471-0

(G-18606)
VYSK COMMUNICATIONS INC
13750 San Pedro Ave # 27 (78232-4375)
P.O. Box 120174 (78212-9374)
PHONE..........................210 832-8322
Victor Cocchia, *CEO*
David Rocha, *Vice Pres*
Lisa Shaw, *Vice Pres*
Kevin Mundy, *Engineer*
Davis Eberhart, *Director*

EMP: 34
SQ FT: 8,000
SALES (est): 5.8MM **Privately Held**
WEB: www.vysk.com
SIC: 3661 Telephones & telephone appara-
tus

(G-18607)
W B OSBORN OIL GAS OPRTONS L
Also Called: W.B. Osborn Oil Gas Operations
1250 Ne Loop 410 Ste 600 (78209-1536)
P.O. Box 8c (78217-8199)
PHONE..........................210 826-8654
Diana T Morehouse, *Partner*
Estate Robert F Townsend III, *Partner*
W B Osborn III, *General Ptnr*
James Douglas Schueneman, *CFO*
EMP: 11
SQ FT: 10,722
SALES (est): 15.8MM **Privately Held**
SIC: 1311 Crude petroleum production

(G-18608)
WALLS ACROSS TEXAS I LTD
10203 Kotzebue St Ste 120 (78217-4447)
PHONE..........................210 826-4123
Robert Lynch, *Partner*
EMP: 40
SQ FT: 2,100
SALES (est): 3MM **Privately Held**
SIC: 1742 3446 Drywall; acoustical & ceil-
ing work; acoustical suspension systems,
metal

(G-18609)
WALTON SIGNAGE LTD
10101 Reunion Pl Ste 200 (78216-4163)
PHONE..........................210 886-0644
Renee Davis, *CEO*
Gary Walton, *Partner*
Darian Beachy, *Vice Pres*
Jack Day, *Vice Pres*
Brittany Peavy, *Vice Pres*
EMP: 110
SALES (est): 35.8MM **Privately Held**
WEB: www.waltonsignage.com
SIC: 3993 Signs & advertising specialties

(G-18610)
WATERFLEET LLC
5110 Se Loop 410 (78222-3937)
PHONE..........................855 744-5222
Alan R Pyle, *President*
Brad Murdock, *Opers Dir*
Bradj Murdock, *Opers Dir*
Allison Pyle, *CFO*
Allisonc Pyle, *CFO*
EMP: 23 **EST:** 2014
SALES (est): 7.1MM **Privately Held**
WEB: www.waterfleet.com
SIC: 3321 Water pipe, cast iron

(G-18611)
WATERMARK GROUP INC
4271 Gatecrest (78217-4807)
PHONE..........................210 599-0400
Bob Bryant, *President*
Al Esquivel, *Production*
Don Crumrine, *Accounts Exec*
Tom Kamp, *Accounts Exec*
Mark Mendez, *Accounts Exec*
EMP: 35
SQ FT: 28,500
SALES (est): 5.9MM **Privately Held**
WEB: www.thewatermarkgroup.com
SIC: 2752 7331 2759 Commercial print-
ing, offset; mailing service; mailing list
brokers; laser printing

(G-18612)
WATTS WTR QULTY COND PDTS INC
Also Called: Watts Water Qulty & Cond Pdts
13700 W Us Highway 90 (78245-9513)
PHONE..........................210 677-0618
Neil Delettre, *Branch Mgr*
EMP: 62
SALES (corp-wide): 1.6B **Publicly Held**
WEB: www.watts.com
SIC: 5074 3589 Water heaters & purifica-
tion equipment; sewage & water treat-
ment equipment

HQ: Watts Water Quality And Conditioning
Products, Inc.
815 Chestnut St
North Andover MA 01845
978 688-1811

(G-18613)
WELDER EXPLORATION & PROD INC (PA)
100 W Olmos Dr (78212-1988)
PHONE..........................210 354-1515
Raymond J Welder III, *President*
John Langdon, *CFO*
Katharine Welder, *Human Res Dir*
C Clark Welder, *Admin Sec*
Deborah Condon, *Analyst*
EMP: 16 **EST:** 1997
SQ FT: 6,000
SALES (est): 3.9MM **Privately Held**
WEB: www.weldergroup.com
SIC: 1382 Oil & gas exploration services

(G-18614)
WESSELY-THOMPSON HARDWARE INC
102 Interloop Rd (78216-7042)
PHONE..........................210 344-3081
Norma Thompson, *President*
R Larry Thompson Sr, *Corp Secy*
Terry Thompson, *Vice Pres*
EMP: 27
SQ FT: 20,000
SALES (est): 3.9MM **Privately Held**
WEB: www.wessely-thompson.com
SIC: 2431 5251 Door frames, wood;
builders' hardware

(G-18615)
WESTERN REF CNAN GATHERING LLC
19100 Ridgewood Pkwy (78259-1834)
PHONE..........................210 626-6000
EMP: 15
SALES: 39MM
SALES (corp-wide): 9B **Publicly Held**
SIC: 1311 Crude petroleum production
HQ: Andeavor Logistics Lp
200 E Hardin St
Findlay OH 45840

(G-18616)
WHEEL RACK
6127 San Pedro Ave (78216-7225)
PHONE..........................210 342-0333
Andrew Perez, *Owner*
EMP: 11
SALES (est): 1.2MM **Privately Held**
WEB: www.online.flippingbook.com
SIC: 3842 Wheelchairs

(G-18617)
WHEELS AND FITNESS IN MOTION
Also Called: Fitness In Motion South Texas
8522 Broadway Ste 101 (78217-6377)
PHONE..........................210 828-4542
Paul Cuevas,
EMP: 18
SALES (est): 1.8MM **Privately Held**
WEB: www.fitnessinmotionsouthtexas.com
SIC: 3949 Dumbbells & other weightlifting
equipment

(G-18618)
WHITEWATER RESOURCES LLC
Also Called: White Water Resources
8700 Crownhill Blvd # 408 (78209-1128)
PHONE..........................210 290-9005
Scott Stabler,
EMP: 13 **EST:** 2012
SALES (est): 2.9MM **Privately Held**
WEB: www.whitewaterresources.com
SIC: 3822 Auto controls regulating residntl
& coml environmt & applncs

(G-18619)
WILBERT FUNERAL SERVICES INC
Also Called: Wilbert of San Antonio
5111 Se Loop 410 (78222-3936)
PHONE..........................210 922-2122
Jessica Ibarra, *Branch Mgr*
EMP: 13
SQ FT: 24,900

SALES (corp-wide): 9B **Publicly Held**
WEB: www.greensborowilbert.com
SIC: 3272 Burial vaults, concrete or pre-cast terrazzo
HQ: Wilbert Funeral Services, Inc.
10965 Granada Ln Ste 300
Overland Park KS 66211
913 345-2120

(G-18620)
WILBORN STEEL COMPANY
2315 Dan Ct (78223-3541)
P.O. Box 10208 (78210-0208)
PHONE..................210 532-6852
Ernest Wilborn, *Managing Prtnr*
EMP: 20
SQ FT: 24,000
SALES (est): 5.9MM **Privately Held**
WEB: www.wilborn-steel-company-ltd-in-san-antonio-tx.cityfos.com
SIC: 3441 Building components, structural steel

(G-18621)
WILLIAMS PRINTING
4733 Rittiman Rd (78218-4631)
PHONE..................210 599-6204
Patricia Williams, *Owner*
EMP: 18
SALES (est): 761.1K **Privately Held**
SIC: 2752 Commercial printing, offset

(G-18622)
WINGS SPORTSWEAR INC
12814 Cogburn (78249-2230)
PHONE..................210 696-1824
Thomas Knight, *President*
John Lawson, *Vice Pres*
Leo Saavedra, *Vice Pres*
Michael Anderson, *Director*
James Lawson, *Director*
EMP: 70
SQ FT: 35,000
SALES (est): 8.3MM **Privately Held**
WEB: www.alamotees.com
SIC: 2396 5137 5136 Screen printing on fabric articles; sportswear, women's & children's; sportswear, men's & boys'

(G-18623)
WINSUPPLY SAN ANTONIO
10000 Iota Dr (78217-2628)
PHONE..................210 481-8123
CJ Hooper, *President*
EMP: 15
SALES (est): 15MM **Privately Held**
SIC: 3585 Air conditioning equipment, complete

(G-18624)
WOODCO MILLWORK LTD
1210 Arion Pkwy (78216-2907)
P.O. Box 65206 (78265-5206)
PHONE..................210 298-9663
Peter George, *Managing Prtnr*
Gareth George, *Partner*
Jacqueline George, *Partner*
Warwick George, *Partner*
▲ **EMP:** 14 **EST:** 2000
SQ FT: 44,000
SALES (est): 1.6MM **Privately Held**
WEB: www.woodco.com
SIC: 2426 5031 Flooring, hardwood; lumber, plywood & millwork

(G-18625)
WORLDWIDE STFFING SLUTIONS LLC
11502 Jnes Maltsberger Rd (78216-2831)
PHONE..................210 293-3600
Scott Hagler, *CEO*
Ed Ubry, *QC Mgr*
Stephen Pierce, *CFO*
EMP: 10
SALES (est): 1.8MM **Privately Held**
SIC: 2821 Plastics materials & resins

(G-18626)
XELLA AIRCRETE NORTH AMER INC
833 Isom Rd (78216-4035)
PHONE..................229 896-1593
John Blackwelder, *CEO*
Michael Bundschuh, *Vice Pres*
Slawomir Horodyski, *CFO*
Geert Rombaut, *CTO*

▲ **EMP:** 50
SALES (est): 6.5MM
SALES (corp-wide): 2.1MM **Privately Held**
WEB: www.hebel-usa.com
SIC: 3272 Concrete products
HQ: Xella Baustoffe Gmbh
Dusseldorfer Landstr. 395
Duisburg 47259
203 608-800

(G-18627)
XENEX DISINFECTION SVCS INC (PA)
1074 Arion Cir Ste 116 (78216-3085)
PHONE..................800 553-0069
Morris Miller, *CEO*
Roy M Martin Jr, *Ch of Bd*
Nita Schweitzer, *General Mgr*
Paul Froutan, *COO*
Enda Flynn, *Exec VP*
EMP: 137
SALES (est): 26.7MM **Privately Held**
WEB: www.xenex.com
SIC: 3842 Sterilizers, hospital & surgical

(G-18628)
XGRAFX LLC (PA)
2643 Mossrock Ste 1 (78230-5170)
P.O. Box 5278 (78201-0278)
PHONE..................210 681-7177
Kong Song, *President*
Marco Garcia, *General Mgr*
Frank Maldonado, *Sales Mgr*
Cathy Song, *Consultant*
EMP: 19
SALES (est): 3MM **Privately Held**
WEB: www.xgrafx.com
SIC: 3993 Electric signs

(G-18629)
YBARRA GROUP INC
Also Called: Service Shade Shop
10104 Huebner Rd (78240-1319)
PHONE..................210 533-5323
Larry J Ybarra, *President*
Aida Ybarra, *Vice Pres*
Patricia Kneuper, *Administration*
Trish Kneuper, *Assistant*
EMP: 13
SQ FT: 4,350
SALES (est): 2.6MM **Privately Held**
WEB: www.serviceshade.com
SIC: 2591 5719 7699 Window shades; venetian blinds; window blind repair services

(G-18630)
ZACHRY CONSOLIDATED LLC
527 Logwood Ave (78221-1738)
P.O. Box 240130 (78224-0130)
PHONE..................210 588-5000
John B Zachry, *CEO*
Mark Mills, *President*
Henry B Zachry Jr, *President*
Jeffery D Hatfield, *Business Mgr*
D Kirk McDonald Sr, *Exec VP*
◆ **EMP:** 20000
SQ FT: 100,000
SALES (est): 2.3MM **Privately Held**
WEB: www.zachrygroup.com
SIC: 1611 1622 1623 1629 General contractor, highway & street construction; bridge construction; pipeline construction; dam construction; portland cement; construction sand mining

(G-18631)
ZACHRY CONSTRUCTION & MTLS INC (PA)
2330 N Loop 1604 W (78248-4512)
P.O. Box 33240 (78265-3240)
PHONE..................210 479-1027
David S Zachry, *CEO*
Timothy A Watt, *Senior VP*
Jean J Abiassi, *Vice Pres*
Max Frailey, *Vice Pres*
Greg W Hale, *Vice Pres*
EMP: 75
SQ FT: 100,000
SALES (est): 1.1B **Privately Held**
SIC: 1611 1622 1623 1629 General contractor, highway & street construction; bridge construction; pipeline construction; dam construction; nonresidential construction; portland cement

(G-18632)
ZACHRY HOLDINGS INC (PA)
527 Logwood Ave (78221-1738)
P.O. Box 240130 (78224-0130)
PHONE..................210 588-5000
John Zachry, *CEO*
Suzanne Johnson, *CEO*
Steven K Brauer, *President*
Gerald P Burke, *President*
Duane Bunce, *General Mgr*
EMP: 600
SQ FT: 150,000
SALES (est): 3.8B **Privately Held**
WEB: www.zachrygroup.com
SIC: 6719 7692 8711 3441 Investment holding companies, except banks; welding repair; construction & civil engineering; building components, structural steel

(G-18633)
ZAMORANO ENTERPRISES INC
8603 S Flores St (78221-3004)
PHONE..................210 924-2320
Pedro Zamorano, *President*
Hector Zamorano, *Vice Pres*
EMP: 9
SQ FT: 9,800
SALES (est): 1MM **Privately Held**
SIC: 3599 Machine shop, jobbing & repair

San Antonio
Comal County

(G-18634)
ACTION FUELS LP
23090 Fm 3009 (78266-2625)
PHONE..................210 651-9308
Brian Williams, *Managing Prtnr*
EMP: 13 **EST:** 2009
SALES (est): 3.1MM **Privately Held**
WEB: www.action-fuels.com
SIC: 2869 Fuels

(G-18635)
ALAMO CEMENT COMPANY (HQ)
6055 W Green Mountain Rd (78266-1705)
P.O. Box 34807 (78265-4807)
PHONE..................210 208-1880
Massimo Toso, *CEO*
Allen Walsh, *President*
Rick Couch, *Manager*
▲ **EMP:** 116
SALES (est): 53.1MM
SALES (corp-wide): 395.5MM **Privately Held**
SIC: 3241 Cement, hydraulic
PA: Buzzi Unicem Spa
Via Luigi Buzzi 6
Casale Monferrato AL 15033
014 241-6111

(G-18636)
ALAMO CONCRETE PRODUCTS LTD
Also Called: Barlite
6981 E Evans Rd (78266-2805)
PHONE..................210 208-1580
Kurt Taylor, *President*
EMP: 50 **Privately Held**
SIC: 3273 3271 Ready-mixed concrete; blocks, concrete or cinder: standard
PA: Alamo Concrete Products, Ltd.
6055 W Green Mountain Rd
Austin TX 78744

(G-18637)
ALAMO CONCRETE PRODUCTS CO (PA)
6981 E Evans Rd (78266-2805)
PHONE..................210 208-1500
Massino Toso, *CEO*
Kirk Taylor, *Corp Secy*
EMP: 30
SALES (est): 345.6K **Privately Held**
SIC: 3272 Concrete products

(G-18638)
ALAMO OUTDOOR STRUCTURES INC
18860 Goll St (78266-2792)
PHONE..................210 651-0425

Kyle Jividen, *President*
EMP: 14 **EST:** 1997
SQ FT: 13,000
SALES (est): 1.5MM **Privately Held**
WEB: www.alamooutdoor.com
SIC: 3993 Signs, not made in custom sign painting shops

(G-18639)
ARROWALL COMPANY (PA)
18985 Goll St (78266-2878)
PHONE..................713 462-1751
William D Morris Jr, *President*
William Morris, *COO*
Mark D Harrelson, *Vice Pres*
Rod Pistokache, *Project Mgr*
David Harkins, *Safety Mgr*
▲ **EMP:** 100
SQ FT: 45,000
SALES (est): 30.7MM **Privately Held**
WEB: www.arrowall.com
SIC: 1793 3231 Glass & glazing work; products of purchased glass

(G-18640)
CODY COMPANY INC
7951 E Evans Rd (78266-2811)
PHONE..................210 651-5305
John R Cody, *Branch Mgr*
EMP: 30
SQ FT: 68,008
SALES (corp-wide): 795.7MM **Privately Held**
WEB: www.codycompany.com
SIC: 3444 Sheet metalwork
HQ: Cody Company, Llc
4200 N Interstate Hwy 45
Ennis TX 75119
972 875-5884

(G-18641)
EDWARDS MICHAEL CUSTOM
18975 Marbach Ln Ste 900 (78266-2213)
PHONE..................210 651-3800
Michael Swintek, *President*
Theatra Swintek, *Vice Pres*
EMP: 40
SALES (est): 4.6MM **Privately Held**
WEB: www.mecctx.com
SIC: 2431 Millwork

(G-18642)
GATES MCH & FABRICATION INC
8025 Jethro Ln (78266-2174)
PHONE..................210 651-6567
Gary Gates, *President*
EMP: 48
SQ FT: 30,000
SALES (est): 4MM **Privately Held**
WEB: www.gates-mfg.com
SIC: 3599 Machine shop, jobbing & repair

(G-18643)
INSTALLED BUILDING PDTS INC
Also Called: Key Insulation
8135 Bracken Crk (78266-2121)
PHONE..................210 937-1082
Ross E Bacon, *Branch Mgr*
EMP: 50
SALES (corp-wide): 1.5B **Publicly Held**
WEB: www.installedbuildingproducts.com
SIC: 2493 2621 1742 Insulation board, cellular fiber; insulation siding, paper; plastering, drywall & insulation
PA: Installed Building Products, Inc.
495 S High St Ste 50
Columbus OH 43215
614 221-3399

(G-18644)
QUIKRETE
6981 E Evans Rd (78266-2805)
PHONE..................210 208-1511
EMP: 9 **EST:** 2018
SALES (est): 1.9MM **Privately Held**
WEB: www.quikrete.com
SIC: 2952 Roofing felts, cements or coatings

(G-18645)
SOUTHEASTERN METALS MFG CO INC
Also Called: DOT Metals Products
18757 Bracken Dr (78266-2142)
PHONE..................210 651-6331

Vincent Rodriguez, *Principal*
Dan Graves, *Vice Pres*
Leila Avila, *Buyer*
James Lea, *Manager*
EMP: 60
SALES (corp-wide): 1B **Publicly Held**
WEB: www.semetals.com
SIC: 3444 Metal roofing & roof drainage equipment
HQ: Southeastern Metals Manufacturing Company, Inc.
　　11801 Industry Dr
　　Jacksonville FL 32218
　　904 757-4200

(G-18646)
TEJAS SIGNS WETZ
Also Called: A 1 Signs
20286 Fm 2252 (78266-2612)
PHONE.....................830 609-6246
Bill Wetz, *Owner*
EMP: 12 **EST:** 1983
SQ FT: 1,094
SALES (est): 1MM **Privately Held**
WEB: www.a1signstexas.com
SIC: 3993 Signs & advertising specialties

(G-18647)
VALRO-K LLC
Also Called: Key Insulation
8135 Bracken Crk (78266-2121)
PHONE.....................210 937-1082
Preston Bacon, *General Mgr*
Brad Bochat, *Area Mgr*
Abraham Nevarez, *Vice Pres*
Derek Albright, *Opers Staff*
Cory Nickodam, *Production*
EMP: 50
SALES (est): 8.9MM **Privately Held**
WEB: www.keyinsulation.com
SIC: 2493 2621 1742 Insulation board, cellular fiber; insulation siding, paper; plastering, drywall & insulation; acoustical & insulation work; exterior insulation & finish (EIFS) applicator; insulation, buildings

(G-18648)
VINTAGE AIR INC
18865 Goll St (78266-2792)
PHONE.....................210 296-2302
Jack L Chisenhall, *President*
Rick Love, *Exec VP*
Richard Love, *Vice Pres*
Mark Colwell, *Purch Mgr*
Stephen Walton, *Buyer*
▲ **EMP:** 88
SQ FT: 45,000
SALES (est): 26.8MM **Privately Held**
WEB: www.vintageair.com
SIC: 3585 5531 3714 Refrigeration & heating equipment; automobile air conditioning equipment, sale, installation; air conditioner parts, motor vehicle

(G-18649)
WETZ SIGN & LIGHTING SERVICE
Also Called: A-1 Signs and Tejas
20286 Fm 2252 (78266-2612)
PHONE.....................830 609-6246
Bill Wetz, *Owner*
EMP: 10
SALES (est): 638.3K **Privately Held**
WEB: www.a1signstexas.com
SIC: 3993 Signs & advertising specialties

San Augustine
San Augustine County

(G-18650)
ATTOYAC ROCK LLC
1450 Eddings Ln (75972-6404)
PHONE.....................936 275-3636
Robert Birdwell,
Kelly Birdwell,
EMP: 11
SALES (est): 549.6K **Privately Held**
SIC: 1429 Boulder, crushed & broken-quarrying

(G-18651)
L & R TIMBER COMPANY INC
240 Fm 3451 (75972-4247)
P.O. Box 599 (75972-0599)
PHONE.....................936 275-9701
Mike Lout, *President*
Barry Lout, *Treasurer*
Rick Lout, *Admin Sec*
EMP: 20 **EST:** 1981
SQ FT: 4,500
SALES (est): 4.2MM **Privately Held**
SIC: 2421 Wood chips, produced at mill

(G-18652)
PINEY FOREST PRODUCTS LLC
201 Farm Market 3451 (75972)
P.O. Box 575 (75972-0575)
PHONE.....................936 275-9751
Warlow Oliver,
Thomas Oliver,
Wardlow Oliver,
EMP: 63
SALES (est): 6.9MM **Privately Held**
WEB: www.pineyforestproducts.com
SIC: 2491 Poles, posts & pilings: treated wood

San Benito
Cameron County

(G-18653)
AG III CONTRACTORS LLC
22414 W Us Highway 281 (78586-8106)
PHONE.....................956 456-0628
Alberto Garza III, *Mng Member*
EMP: 10
SALES (est): 840.2K **Privately Held**
SIC: 1442 Construction sand & gravel

(G-18654)
AGE INDUSTRIES LTD
1701 Amistad Dr (78586-7737)
PHONE.....................956 399-8279
Maxine Guerrero, *Purchasing*
Cruz Guerrero, *Manager*
EMP: 35
SALES (corp-wide): 140.8MM **Privately Held**
WEB: www.ageindustries.com
SIC: 2653 2449 5113 2679 Boxes, corrugated: made from purchased materials; wood containers; corrugated & solid fiber boxes; corrugated paper: made from purchased material
PA: Age Industries, Ltd.
　　3601 County Road 316c
　　Cleburne TX 76031
　　817 477-5266

(G-18655)
CENTRAL READY MIX CONCRETE CO
2101 Utex Dr (78586-7788)
PHONE.....................956 541-6082
Richard Linn, *Manager*
EMP: 30
SQ FT: 1,920
SALES (corp-wide): 6.9MM **Privately Held**
SIC: 3273 Ready-mixed concrete
PA: Central Ready Mix Concrete Co Inc
　　304 W Railroad St
　　San Juan TX 78589
　　956 383-2261

(G-18656)
DUTCH MARBLE CREATIONS
901 S Williams Rd (78586-2768)
P.O. Box 663, Combes (78535-0663)
PHONE.....................956 399-6767
Larry Onderdonk, *Owner*
EMP: 17
SQ FT: 6,125
SALES (est): 1.2MM **Privately Held**
SIC: 3281 2541 2434 Bathroom fixtures, cut stone; wood partitions & fixtures; wood kitchen cabinets

(G-18657)
GALVAN NATIONAL CARRIERS LLC
34005 La Brecha Dr (78586)
P.O. Box 1235, Los Fresnos (78566-1235)
PHONE.....................956 346-7095
Edgar G Galvan, *President*
EMP: 18
SALES (est): 1.9MM **Privately Held**
SIC: 3537 Trucks: freight, baggage, etc.: industrial, except mining

(G-18658)
GULF COAST SIGN INC
951 Falcon Blvd (78586-7733)
P.O. Box 1270, Olmito (78575-1270)
PHONE.....................956 399-0755
Angel Arce, *Principal*
EMP: 20
SQ FT: 5,000
SALES (est): 3.5MM **Privately Held**
WEB: www.gulfcoastsigncompany.com
SIC: 1799 3993 Sign installation & maintenance; signs & advertising specialties

(G-18659)
LORENTSON MANUFACTURING CO
Also Called: LORENTSON MANUFACTURING COMPANY, INC.
2101 Amistad Dr (78586-8585)
PHONE.....................956 399-8902
Porfirio Cantu, *Prdtn Mgr*
Bethany Quinn, *Comptroller*
Tom Straka, *Branch Mgr*
EMP: 30
SALES (corp-wide): 8.9MM **Privately Held**
WEB: www.lorentson.com
SIC: 3544 Industrial molds; special dies & tools
PA: Lorentson Manufacturing Company, Inc
　　1111 Rank Pkwy
　　Kokomo IN 46901
　　765 452-4425

(G-18660)
LORENTSON MFG CO SOUTHWEST INC
2101 Amistad Dr (78586-8585)
PHONE.....................956 399-8902
Christina Lorentson, *President*
John Routt, *COO*
Porfirio Cantu, *Prdtn Mgr*
EMP: 34
SALES (est): 6MM **Privately Held**
WEB: www.lorentson-southwest.com
SIC: 3089 Injection molding of plastics

(G-18661)
NEW HORIZON PUBLISHERS INC
Also Called: San Benito News
356 N Sam Houston Blvd (78586-4657)
P.O. Box 1791 (78586-0017)
PHONE.....................956 399-2436
Broward E Ratliff, *President*
EMP: 32
SQ FT: 4,677
SALES (est): 1MM **Privately Held**
WEB: www.sbnewspaper.com
SIC: 2711 2752 Newspapers: publishing only, not printed on site; commercial printing, lithographic

(G-18662)
ONE WIND SERVICES (US) INC
2684 Shafer Rd (78586-7673)
PHONE.....................902 482-8687
Paul Pynn, *President*
Grayson Swan, *Vice Pres*
Jordan Beaton, *Accountant*
Ben Emodi, *Manager*
EMP: 13
SALES (est): 694.1K **Privately Held**
WEB: www.onewindinc.com
SIC: 3621 Windmills, electric generating

(G-18663)
REEF INDUSTRIES INC
1951 Amistad Dr (78586-7734)
PHONE.....................956 399-1352
Adan Rodriguez, *Plant Mgr*
Jack Davis, *Manager*
EMP: 75

SALES (corp-wide): 21.6MM **Privately Held**
WEB: www.reefindustries.com
SIC: 3083 2394 Plastic finished products, laminated; canvas & related products
PA: Reef Industries, Inc.
　　9209 Almeda Genoa Rd
　　Houston TX 77075
　　713 507-4200

(G-18664)
RIO GRANDE STEEL LTD
1980 E Business Rd 77 (78586)
P.O. Box 1411 (78586-0049)
PHONE.....................956 361-4443
Cris Maldonado, *Vice Pres*
Frank Maldonado, *Store Mgr*
Gene Espinoza, *Sales Mgr*
Mirta Guajardo, *Office Mgr*
Juan Aguilar, *Branch Mgr*
EMP: 50 **Privately Held**
WEB: www.riograndesteel.com
SIC: 3312 Blast furnaces & steel mills
PA: Rio Grande Steel, Ltd.
　　213 E Owassa Rd
　　Edinburg TX 78542

(G-18665)
ROYAL METAL BLDG COMPONENTS (PA)
Also Called: Royal Metal Bldg Components
2031 Amistad Dr (78586-7732)
PHONE.....................956 399-2271
Pat L Pace Jr, *Partner*
Bill Conner, *Vice Pres*
Michael D Conner, *Vice Pres*
Martin Olivares, *Technical Staff*
William M Conner, *Admin Sec*
EMP: 21 **EST:** 1994
SQ FT: 35,000
SALES (est): 9.4MM **Privately Held**
WEB: www.royalmbc.com
SIC: 3272 Concrete products

(G-18666)
SAN BENITO TEXTILE INC
201 N Travis St (78586-4532)
PHONE.....................956 361-0282
Carlos Sanchez, *President*
Jennifer Sanchez, *General Mgr*
Dolores Sanchez, *Admin Sec*
EMP: 15
SQ FT: 21,000
SALES (est): 2.4MM **Privately Held**
WEB: www.sanbenitotextiles.com
SIC: 2299 Batting, wadding, padding & fillings

(G-18667)
SAUCEDAS PRCISION GRINDING INC
2800 E Business 77 (78586-5418)
PHONE.....................956 399-1572
Jesse Sauceda, *President*
Jaime Sauceda, *Vice Pres*
Frances Sauceda, *Treasurer*
Brenda S Garcia, *Admin Sec*
EMP: 20
SQ FT: 3,100
SALES (est): 2.7MM **Privately Held**
WEB: www.spginc.us
SIC: 3545 3544 Machine tool accessories; special dies, tools, jigs & fixtures

(G-18668)
SSP DEVELOPERS INC
420 Jay St (78586-3049)
PHONE.....................956 456-4415
Sergio O Anguiano, *President*
EMP: 12
SALES (est): 357K **Privately Held**
SIC: 1799 1389 Construction site cleanup; construction, repair & dismantling services

San Diego
Duval County

(G-18669)
WESTWATER RESOURCES INC
3021 County Road 333 (78384-4576)
PHONE.....................361 279-3307
Joel Alamarza, *Manager*

EMP: 30
SALES (corp-wide): 12.8MM Publicly
Held
WEB: www.westwaterresources.net
SIC: 1094 Uranium-radium-vanadium ores
PA: Westwater Resources, Inc.
6950 S Potomac St Ste 300
Centennial CO 80112
303 531-0516

San Juan
Hidalgo County

(G-18670)
ALFONSO HINOSTROZA
Also Called: Hinostroza Cabinet Shop
1806 N Raul Longoria Rd (78589-3432)
P.O. Box 51 (78589-0051)
PHONE..................................956 781-1845
Alfonso Hinostroza, Owner
EMP: 21
SQ FT: 13,000
SALES (est): 2.3MM Privately Held
SIC: 5712 1751 2431 Cabinet work, custom; cabinet & finish carpentry; millwork

(G-18671)
AZTECA TORTILLA FACTORY
1800 N Raul Longoria Rd (78589-3400)
PHONE..................................956 702-7395
Carlos Cepeda, Owner
EMP: 20
SALES (est): 1MM Privately Held
SIC: 2099 Tortillas, fresh or refrigerated

(G-18672)
**CENTRAL READY MIX
CONCRETE CO (PA)**
304 W Railroad St (78589-2715)
P.O. Box 143 (78589-0143)
PHONE..................................956 383-2261
Lyle M Linn, President
Richard Linn, Vice Pres
EMP: 25 EST: 1948
SQ FT: 5,000
SALES (est): 6.9MM Privately Held
SIC: 3273 5023 Ready-mixed concrete;
pottery

(G-18673)
EMERSON ELECTRIC CO
2216 Olmo St (78589-4163)
PHONE..................................956 702-2389
Jaime Anguiano, Principal
EMP: 39
SALES (corp-wide): 16.7B Publicly Held
WEB: www.emerson.com
SIC: 3823 Industrial instrmnts msrmnt display/control process variable
PA: Emerson Electric Co.
8000 West Florissant Ave
Saint Louis MO 63136
314 553-2000

(G-18674)
GILSA NORTH AMERICA LLC
801 E Expy 83 (78589-4508)
PHONE..................................956 223-2900
Ricardo Dorbecker,
EMP: 18
SALES (est): 2.4MM Privately Held
WEB: www.gilsa.us
SIC: 3253 Enamel tile, floor or wall: clay

(G-18675)
TORTILLAS OLIVO LLC
502 S San Antonio Ave (78589-2477)
PHONE..................................956 702-8388
Kathy Morales, Mng Member
EMP: 10
SQ FT: 1,600
SALES (est): 450K Privately Held
SIC: 2099 Tortillas, fresh or refrigerated

San Marcos
Hays County

(G-18676)
3NINE USA INC
Also Called: M Grill
4768 N State Highway 123 (78666-9419)
P.O. Box 1046 (78667-1046)
PHONE..................................512 667-6146
James Pate, President
Christian Grill, President
Sven Wachter, Sales Staff
Cliff Betty, Director
Leonard Pate, Director
▲ EMP: 13 EST: 2009
SQ FT: 2,000
SALES (est): 4MM
SALES (corp-wide): 314.5MM Privately
Held
WEB: www.3nine.us
SIC: 3564 Air cleaning systems; air purification equipment
HQ: 3 Nine Ab
Cylindervagen 12
Nacka Strand 131 5

(G-18677)
**AMERIDRIVES INTERNATIONAL
LLC**
Also Called: Ameridrives Power Transmission
2000 Clovis Barker Rd (78666-9792)
PHONE..................................512 353-4000
Jack Pederson, General Mgr
Lisa Olmsted, Controller
Heather Putnam, Accountant
Bill Major, Manager
Jesus Hernandez, Prgrmr
▲ EMP: 30
SQ FT: 83,000
SALES (est): 37.9MM
SALES (corp-wide): 1.8B Publicly Held
WEB: www.ameridrives.com
SIC: 3568 Shafts, flexible; couplings; shaft:
rigid, flexible, universal joint, etc.
PA: Altra Industrial Motion Corp.
300 Granite St Ste 201
Braintree MA 02184
781 917-0600

(G-18678)
AVEY PLASTICS
251 Uhland Rd (78666-2558)
P.O. Box 808 (78667-0808)
PHONE..................................512 784-7047
Terry Avey, President
Jerry Avey, Corp Secy
Ray G Avey, Vice Pres
EMP: 14 EST: 1945
SQ FT: 15,000
SALES (est): 1.6MM Privately Held
SIC: 3083 3544 Plastic finished products,
laminated; forms (molds), for foundry &
plastics working machinery

(G-18679)
BASLER PLASTICS LLC
201 Center Point Rd (78666-6454)
PHONE..................................512 392-2800
Daniel Kelley, Manager
EMP: 9
SALES (est): 1.2MM
SALES (corp-wide): 180.5MM Privately
Held
WEB: www.basler.com
SIC: 3089 Injection molded finished plastic
products; injection molding of plastics
PA: Basler Electric Company
12570 State Route 143
Highland IL 62249
618 654-2341

(G-18680)
BAY ENERGY BLANKET INC
111 E Mccarty Ln (78666-6416)
PHONE..................................512 353-4064
Daniel A Schmidt, CEO
Ronn C Kleinschmidt, Vice Pres
Gloria J Schmidt, Vice Pres
EMP: 11
SALES (est): 1.4MM Privately Held
SIC: 5033 2493 3296 Insulation materials; insulation & roofing material, reconstituted wood; mineral wool

PA: Aws/Gb Corporation
2929 Walker Dr
Green Bay WI 54311

(G-18681)
BECERRA CORP
201 S Lbj Dr (78666-5575)
PHONE..................................512 787-2755
Ruben Becerra, Director
EMP: 10 EST: 2015
SQ FT: 2,000
SALES (est): 342.9K Privately Held
SIC: 2051 Breads, rolls & buns

(G-18682)
**COMMUNITY NEWSPAPERS
HOLDINGS**
Also Called: San Marcos Daily Record
1910 S Interstate 35 (78666-5901)
P.O. Box 1109 (78667-1109)
PHONE..................................512 392-6143
Guy Trimble, President
Mike Meek, Manager
EMP: 55
SQ FT: 3,500
SALES (est): 3.2MM
SALES (corp-wide): 23.7B Privately Held
WEB: www.sanmarcosrecord.com
SIC: 2711 5994 Commercial printing &
newspaper publishing combined; news
dealers & newsstands
HQ: Cnhi, Llc
445 Dexter Ave Ste 7000
Montgomery AL 36104

(G-18683)
CWR MANAGEMENT LLC
Also Called: Clear Water Resources
101 Uhland Rd Ste 212 (78666-6630)
P.O. Box 2700 (78667-2700)
PHONE..................................512 212-9737
Jason Roberts,
Charles Manning,
EMP: 24
SQ FT: 217,800
SALES (est): 10MM
SALES (corp-wide): 10.7MM Privately
Held
WEB: www.clearwaterresources.com
SIC: 1389 Servicing oil & gas wells
PA: Clearwater Holdco Llc
101 Uhland Rd Ste 212
San Marcos TX 78666
512 212-9737

(G-18684)
DK OIL FIELD SERVICES LLC
101 Uhland Rd Ste 205 (78666-6681)
PHONE..................................830 857-6339
Barron Cudney, President
Jason Robert, President
EMP: 17 EST: 2014
SALES (est): 1.5MM Privately Held
SIC: 3533 Oil & gas drilling rigs & equipment

(G-18685)
EL MILAGRO OF TEXAS INC
400 Barnes Dr (78666-5900)
PHONE..................................512 477-6476
Rafael Lopez, President
Paz Ramirez, General Mgr
Manuel Lopez, Vice Pres
Paz R Ramirez, Executive
Jesus Lopez, Admin Sec
EMP: 49
SQ FT: 8,705
SALES (est): 7.1MM Privately Held
WEB: www.elmilagro.com
SIC: 2099 2096 Tortillas, fresh or refrigerated; potato chips & similar snacks

(G-18686)
EMBER INDUSTRIES INC
321 Carlson Cir (78666-6756)
PHONE..................................512 396-1911
Thomas F Leonardis, President
Rob Leonardis, COO
Frank Leonardis, Vice Pres
Robert T Leonardis, Vice Pres
George Ranft, Purchasing
EMP: 35
SQ FT: 14,500
SALES (est): 9.3MM Privately Held
WEB: www.emberindustries.com
SIC: 3672 Printed circuit boards

(G-18687)
**FEDEX OFFICE & PRINT SVCS
INC**
Also Called: Fedex Office Print & Ship Ctr
303 N Edward Gary St (78666-5711)
PHONE..................................512 396-1559
EMP: 20
SALES (corp-wide): 69.2B Publicly Held
WEB: www.fedex.com
SIC: 7334 2752 Photocopying & duplicating services; commercial printing, lithographic
HQ: Fedex Office And Print Services, Inc.
7900 Legacy Dr
Plano TX 75024
800 463-3339

(G-18688)
FOUNTAIN PEOPLE INC
4600 N State Highway 123 (78666-9408)
P.O. Box 807 (78667-0807)
PHONE..................................512 392-1155
Jerry B Elbel, Vice Pres
Steve Case, Vice Pres
Luke Cavanaugh, Vice Pres
Preston A Tatum, Vice Pres
Ken Krauskopf, Mfg Mgr
◆ EMP: 58
SQ FT: 30,000
SALES (est): 23.2MM Privately Held
WEB: www.fountainpeople.com
SIC: 3272 5084 Fountains, concrete;
pumps & pumping equipment
HQ: Playcore Holdings, Inc.
544 Chestnut St
Chattanooga TN 37402
877 762-7563

(G-18689)
GENLYTE THOMAS GROUP LLC
GENLYTE THOMAS GROUP LLC
1611 Clovis R Barker Rd (78666-5177)
PHONE..................................512 392-5821
EMP: 9
SALES (corp-wide): 6.9B Privately Held
SIC: 3648 Lighting equipment
HQ: Genlyte Thomas Group Llc
200 Franklin Square Dr
Somerset NJ 08873

(G-18690)
GOODRICH CORPORATION
2005 Technology Way (78666-8501)
PHONE..................................512 754-3658
Bruce Tifft, Manager
EMP: 168
SALES (corp-wide): 56.5B Publicly Held
WEB: www.collinsaerospace.com
SIC: 3728 Aircraft parts & equipment
HQ: Goodrich Corporation
2730 W Tyvola Rd
Charlotte NC 28217
704 423-7000

(G-18691)
GULF BUSINESS FORMS INC
2460 S Ih 35 (78666-5921)
P.O. Box 1073 (78667-1073)
PHONE..................................512 353-8313
Ross D Doane Jr, CEO
Allan Doane, President
Linda Porterfield, Vice Pres
Ray Konecney, Plant Mgr
Ray Konecny, Sales Mgr
EMP: 70
SQ FT: 23,000
SALES (est): 10.9MM Privately Held
WEB: www.gulfforms.com
SIC: 2759 2761 Commercial printing; continuous forms, office & business

(G-18692)
H T A AEROSTRUCTURES INC
2005 Technology Way (78666-8501)
PHONE..................................512 754-3600
▲ EMP: 200
SQ FT: 168,000
SALES (est): 25.1MM
SALES (corp-wide): 56.1B Publicly Held
SIC: 3728 Mfg Aircraft Parts/Equipment
HQ: Rohr, Inc
850 Lagoon Dr
Chula Vista CA 91910
619 691-4111

(G-18693)
HALF PRICE BKS REC MGZINES INC
900 Bugg Ln Ste 301124 (78666-8086)
PHONE...................................512 805-7503
Bryan Eanes, *Manager*
EMP: 17
SALES (corp-wide): 211.7MM **Privately Held**
WEB: www.becomegreen.info
SIC: 2721 5735 5932 Magazines: publishing & printing; compact discs; book stores, secondhand
PA: Half Price Books, Records, Magazines, Incorporated
5803 E Northwest Hwy
Dallas TX 75231
214 360-0833

(G-18694)
HELDENFELS ENTERPRISES INC (PA)
5700 S I h 35 (78666-9505)
PHONE...................................512 396-2376
Fred W Heldenfels III, *President*
Paul Elrod, *General Mgr*
Ronald G Reich, *Vice Pres*
Kurt R Schriefer, *Vice Pres*
Blaine R Withers, *Vice Pres*
EMP: 160
SQ FT: 3,200
SALES (est): 41.6MM **Privately Held**
WEB: www.heldenfels.com
SIC: 3272 Concrete products

(G-18695)
HUNTER INDUSTRIES LTD (PA)
Also Called: Colorado Materials
4501 Hunter Rd (78666-9204)
P.O. Box 2109 (78667-2109)
PHONE...................................512 353-7757
John R Weisman, *Ch of Bd*
Ronnie Jones, *Vice Pres*
Mark D Reininger, *Vice Pres*
Walter Ulbricht, *Treasurer*
Maxwell A Robert, *Director*
▲ EMP: 500
SQ FT: 100,000
SALES (est): 150MM **Privately Held**
WEB: www.coloradomaterialsltd.com
SIC: 1611 2951 1442 General contractor, highway & street construction; asphalt & asphaltic paving mixtures (not from refineries); gravel mining

(G-18696)
INGRAM READYMIX INC
3830 S I h 35 (78666-9365)
PHONE...................................512 396-3136
Doug Permot, *Branch Mgr*
EMP: 22
SALES (corp-wide): 125.6MM **Privately Held**
WEB: www.ingramreadymixinc.com
SIC: 3273 Ready-mixed concrete
PA: Ingram Readymix, Inc.
3580 Farm Market 482
New Braunfels TX 78132
830 625-9156

(G-18697)
LUCKY BRAND DUNGAREES LLC
3939 S Interstate 35 # 1250 (78666-5857)
PHONE...................................512 393-2002
Lisa Ramos, *Branch Mgr*
EMP: 15
SALES (corp-wide): 109.7MM **Privately Held**
WEB: www.luckybrand.com
SIC: 2325 5136 Dungarees: men's, youths' & boys'; men's & boys' clothing
PA: Lucky Brand Dungarees, Llc
540 S Santa Fe Ave
Los Angeles CA 90013

(G-18698)
MENSOR LP
201 Barnes Dr (78666-5994)
PHONE...................................512 396-4200
Alexander Wiegand, *CEO*
Dan Fenger, *Principal*
Tom Turner, *COO*
Keith Carnes, *Site Mgr*
Terry Bullock, *Opers Staff*
EMP: 70
SQ FT: 25,000
SALES (est): 19.5MM
SALES (corp-wide): 545.6MM **Privately Held**
WEB: www.mensor.com
SIC: 3823 Pressure measurement instruments, industrial; controllers for process variables, all types
HQ: Wika Holding, Lp
1000 Wiegand Blvd
Lawrenceville GA 30043
770 513-8200

(G-18699)
MICROPOWER GLOBAL CORPORATION
3055 Hunter Rd (78666-6460)
PHONE...................................512 245-8976
Tom Zirkle, *CTO*
Tristan Lewinsohn, *Director*
Max Lewinsohn, *Director*
Ali Murdoch, *Director*
Eric L Robinson, *Director*
EMP: 10
SALES (est): 1.3MM **Privately Held**
WEB: www.micropower-global.com
SIC: 3674 Semiconductors & related devices

(G-18700)
NEWSPAPER HOLDING INC
Also Called: San Marcos Daily Record
1910 S Interstate 35 (78666-5901)
PHONE...................................512 392-2458
EMP: 38
SALES (corp-wide): 23.7B **Privately Held**
WEB: www.oskaloosa.com
SIC: 2711 Newspapers: publishing only, not printed on site
HQ: Newspaper Holding, Inc.
425 Locust St
Johnstown PA 15901
814 532-5102

(G-18701)
NICKEL ROCK LLC
2206 Old Ranch Road 12 D (78666-2543)
PHONE...................................512 395-7416
Bryan Nichols, *Mng Member*
EMP: 14
SALES (est): 4.6MM **Privately Held**
WEB: www.nickelrockllc.com
SIC: 3356 Nickel

(G-18702)
PATHMARK TRAFFIC EQUIPMENT LLC
4435 Hunter Rd (78666-9203)
P.O. Box 1066 (78667-1066)
PHONE...................................512 392-2090
Tom Short,
EMP: 20
SALES (est): 808.5K **Privately Held**
WEB: www.pathmark.net
SIC: 3669 Pedestrian traffic control equipment

(G-18703)
PAVESTONE LLC
1900 Clovis Barker Rd (78666-9704)
P.O. Box 947 (78667-0947)
PHONE...................................512 558-7283
Toll Free:...................................866   -
David Hasness, *Business Mgr*
Cheryl Pape, *Human Res Dir*
EMP: 50 **Privately Held**
WEB: www.pavestone.com
SIC: 3271 5211 5032 1741 Paving blocks, concrete; masonry materials & supplies; paving materials; retaining wall construction; concrete products
HQ: Pavestone, Llc
5 Concourse Pkwy Ste 1900
Atlanta GA 30328
404 926-3167

(G-18704)
PVH CORP
Also Called: Van Heusen
4015 S I h 35 Ste 1050 (78666-5991)
PHONE...................................512 392-2036
Ester Juarez, *Manager*
EMP: 9

SALES (corp-wide): 9.9B **Publicly Held**
WEB: www.pvh.com
SIC: 2321 Men's & boys' dress shirts; sport shirts, men's & boys': from purchased materials; blouses, women's & juniors': made from purchased material; shirts, women's & juniors': made from purchased materials
PA: Pvh Corp.
200 Madison Ave
New York NY 10016
212 381-3500

(G-18705)
QUALITY LIGHTING
1611 Clovis R Barker Rd (78666-5177)
PHONE...................................512 799-2341
John Campsmith, *Principal*
▲ EMP: 9
SALES (est): 1.6MM **Privately Held**
SIC: 3648 Lighting equipment

(G-18706)
QUANTUM MATERIALS CORP
3055 Hunter Rd (78666-6460)
PHONE...................................512 245-6646
Stephen Squires, *President*
David Doderer, *Vice Pres*
Robin Squires, *Vice Pres*
Robert Phillips, *CFO*
E Jamie Schloss, *Controller*
EMP: 9
SALES: 20.1K **Privately Held**
WEB: www.qmcdots.com
SIC: 3674 Semiconductors & related devices; integrated circuits, semiconductor networks, etc.; solar cells

(G-18707)
RIVERCITY SPORTSWEAR LLC (PA)
Also Called: Designs On Garments
1705 S I 35 Exit 202 (78666)
PHONE...................................512 754-8039
Anthony Heath, *Opers Mgr*
Adrian Duran, *Prdtn Mgr*
Rosa Sepulveda, *Prdtn Mgr*
Ricky Sandate, *Opers Staff*
Crystal Campbell, *Finance*
▲ EMP: 38
SQ FT: 24,000
SALES (est): 10MM **Privately Held**
WEB: www.welogoit.com
SIC: 2395 2759 5699 Embroidery & art needlework; commercial printing; letterpress & screen printing; customized clothing & apparel

(G-18708)
S H LEGGITT COMPANY (PA)
Also Called: Marshall Brass
1000 Civic Center Loop (78666-9568)
P.O. Box 2640 (78667-2640)
PHONE...................................956 504-6440
Don C Leggitt Sr, *Ch of Bd*
Don C Leggitt Jr, *President*
J Mark Ross, *Vice Pres*
Ross L Miller, *Treasurer*
Al Horn, *Asst Treas*
▲ EMP: 150
SQ FT: 60,000
SALES (est): 53.6MM **Privately Held**
WEB: www.shleggitt.com
SIC: 3491 3451 3082 Gas valves & parts, industrial; screw machine products; tubes, unsupported plastic

(G-18709)
SAN MARCOS PUBLISHING LP
Also Called: San Marcos Daily Record
1910 S I h 35 (78666-5901)
P.O. Box 1109 (78667-1109)
PHONE...................................512 392-2458
Don Moore, *Owner*
EMP: 40
SALES (corp-wide): 3.6MM **Privately Held**
WEB: www.sanmarcosrecord.com
SIC: 2711 Newspapers, publishing & printing
PA: San Marcos Publishing, Lp
105 E Main St Ste 109a
Brenham TX 77833
512 392-2458

(G-18710)
SIGN CRAFTERS INC
Also Called: Access Drilling
2401 S Interstate 35 (78666-5922)
PHONE...................................512 392-0900
Scott Vaughan, *President*
Kai Jensen, *Engineer*
Allen Tyson, *Accounts Exec*
Lorraine Croy, *Administration*
EMP: 15
SQ FT: 6,500
SALES (est): 1.7MM **Privately Held**
WEB: www.signcrafters.net
SIC: 7389 2499 Sign painting & lettering shop; signboards, wood

(G-18711)
SIGNIFY NORTH AMERICA CORP
1611 Clovis Barker Rd (78666-5177)
P.O. Box 606 (78667-0606)
PHONE...................................800 235-2314
Ben Kozlowski, *Engineer*
EMP: 11
SALES (corp-wide): 6.9B **Privately Held**
WEB: www.colorkinetics.com
SIC: 3646 Commercial indusl & institutional electric lighting fixtures
HQ: Signify North America Corporation
200 Franklin Square Dr # 4
Somerset NJ 08873
732 563-3000

(G-18712)
TB WOODS INCORPORATED
2000 Clovis Barker Rd (78666-9792)
PHONE...................................512 352-4000
William Fejes, *Branch Mgr*
EMP: 60
SALES (corp-wide): 1.8B **Publicly Held**
WEB: www.tbwoods.com
SIC: 3568 Power transmission equipment
HQ: Tb Wood's Incorporated
440 5th Ave
Chambersburg PA 17201
717 264-7161

(G-18713)
TB WOODS INCORPORATED
2000 Clovis R Barker Rd (78666-9792)
PHONE...................................512 353-4000
Pat Kelly, *Principal*
Edward Chivington, *Engineer*
Bill Juergens, *Sales Staff*
EMP: 13
SALES (est): 2.5MM
SALES (corp-wide): 1.8B **Publicly Held**
WEB: www.tbwoods.com
SIC: 3568 Power transmission equipment
PA: Altra Industrial Motion Corp.
300 Granite St Ste 201
Braintree MA 02184
781 917-0600

(G-18714)
TEXAS STATE UNIVERSITY
Also Called: University Star, The
203 Pleasant St (78666)
PHONE...................................512 245-3487
Laura Krantz, *Branch Mgr*
Susan Weill, *Med Doctor*
Krystle Zuniga, *Med Doctor*
Shuying Sun, *Assoc Prof*
EMP: 17
SALES (corp-wide): 878.7MM **Privately Held**
WEB: www.txstate.edu
SIC: 2711 Newspapers, publishing & printing
HQ: Texas State University
601 University Dr
San Marcos TX 78666
512 245-2111

(G-18715)
THERMON INC (HQ)
100 Thermon Dr (78666-5947)
P.O. Box 609 (78667-0609)
PHONE...................................512 396-5801
Rodney L Bingham, *President*
Michelle Watson, *President*
Bill Roeder, *Regional Mgr*
Geni Silvey, *COO*
Rodney Bingham, *Sr Exec VP*
◆ EMP: 240 EST: 1954
SQ FT: 200,000

SALES (est): 67.6MM **Publicly Held**
WEB: www.thermon.com
SIC: 3643 3612 Current-carrying wiring devices; power transformers, electric

(G-18716)
THERMON INDUSTRIES INC
100 Thermon Dr (78666-5947)
P.O. Box 609 (78667-0609)
PHONE.................................512 396-5801
Rodney Dingham, *CEO*
Mark Burdick, *President*
Linda Dietert, *President*
Felipe Barrientos, *General Mgr*
Alisa Harrison, *COO*
◆ EMP: 500
SQ FT: 160,000
SALES (est): 68.5MM **Publicly Held**
WEB: www.thermon.com
SIC: 3643 Current-carrying wiring devices
PA: Thermon Group Holdings, Inc.
7171 Sw Pkwy Bldg 300
Austin TX 78735

San Saba
San Saba County

(G-18717)
HOYT DERYL
Also Called: San Saba Printing
2404 W Wallace St (76877-3822)
P.O. Box 696 (76877-0696)
PHONE.................................325 372-3825
Deryl Hoyt, *Owner*
EMP: 14 EST: 1976
SQ FT: 3,300
SALES (est): 1.6MM **Privately Held**
WEB: www.sansabaprinting.com
SIC: 2752 2759 5943 Commercial printing, offset; imprinting; office forms & supplies

(G-18718)
MORVEN PARTNERS LP
Also Called: San Saba Pecan
2803 W Wallace St (76877-3838)
PHONE.................................325 372-5727
Keith Shahan, *Partner*
EMP: 12 **Privately Held**
WEB: www.oliverpecan.com
SIC: 5145 5441 2068 Nuts, salted or roasted; nuts; salted & roasted nuts & seeds
PA: Morven Partners, L.P.
11 Leigh Fisher Blvd
El Paso TX 79906

(G-18719)
TEXAS ARCHTCTRAL AGGREGATE INC (PA)
Hwy 190 E (76877)
P.O. Box 608 (76877-0608)
PHONE.................................325 372-5105
Joe R Williams, *President*
Louise Williams, *Treasurer*
David Williams, *Admin Sec*
▼ EMP: 35 EST: 1960
SQ FT: 1,300
SALES (est): 14.5MM **Privately Held**
WEB: www.texarcagg.com
SIC: 5032 3281 1442 Stone, crushed or broken; cut stone & stone products; construction sand & gravel

(G-18720)
VANGUARD RESOURCES INC
606 E Wallace St (76877-3605)
PHONE.................................325 372-3142
Ricky Powers, *Principal*
EMP: 10
SALES (corp-wide): 42.6MM **Privately Held**
WEB: www.vanguardresources.com
SIC: 2353 Baseball caps
PA: Vanguard Resources, Inc.
6500 Us Highway 281 N
Spring Branch TX 78070
210 495-1950

(G-18721)
WEDDING OAK WINERY LLC
301 E Wallace St Ste 205 (76877-3541)
PHONE.................................325 372-4050
Michael McHenry, *Managing Prtnr*

Dyana Pemberton, *Opers Staff*
EMP: 10
SALES (est): 610.5K **Privately Held**
WEB: www.weddingoakwinery.com
SIC: 2084 Wines

Sandy Point
Brazoria County

(G-18722)
BLSR OPERATING LTD
11160 Fm 521 Rd (77583-5114)
PHONE.................................281 369-2032
John H Caldwell Jr, *Partner*
Jack Taylor, *Controller*
EMP: 26
SQ FT: 1,200
SALES (est): 1.5MM **Privately Held**
WEB: www.blsroperating.com
SIC: 1389 Oil field services

Sanger
Denton County

(G-18723)
A&W PRODUCTIONS INC
1002 Cowling Rd (76266-9080)
P.O. Box 1924, Denton (76202-1924)
PHONE.................................940 458-4190
Dwayne Waters, *President*
EMP: 70
SALES (est): 9.1MM **Privately Held**
WEB: www.aandwproductions.com
SIC: 3559 Foundry machinery & equipment

(G-18724)
CONCIERGE RENOVATION COMPANY
Also Called: Latham Stairs & Millworks
1850 N Stemmons St (76266-8730)
PHONE.................................940 458-3075
David Todd Greenwood, *President*
EMP: 40
SALES (est): 6.4MM **Privately Held**
WEB: www.lathamstairsandcabinets.com
SIC: 2431 Millwork

(G-18725)
DOZIER CABINET WORKS INC
2742 Milam Rd E (76266-7502)
P.O. Box 554, Denton (76202-0554)
PHONE.................................940 566-5315
Kevin Dozier, *President*
Craig Gossett, *Purchasing*
Jerri Eayllr, *Admin Sec*
EMP: 33
SQ FT: 24,000
SALES (est): 4.6MM **Privately Held**
WEB: www.doziercabinetworks.com
SIC: 2434 Wood kitchen cabinets

(G-18726)
MARSHALL PRCSION MACHINING INC
403 Acker St (76266-8725)
PHONE.................................940 320-4240
Beth Marshall, *President*
Mark Marshall, *Vice Pres*
EMP: 10
SQ FT: 5,800
SALES (est): 1.2MM **Privately Held**
WEB: www.marshallprecisionmanufacturing.com
SIC: 3541 Machine tools, metal cutting type

(G-18727)
NATIONAL FRAME RAIL INC
11919 Interstate 35 N (76266-7413)
PHONE.................................940 482-9494
Matthew C Elkins, *President*
▲ EMP: 20
SQ FT: 50,000
SALES (est): 4.8MM **Privately Held**
SIC: 3449 Miscellaneous metalwork

(G-18728)
NORTH TEXAS PLASTICS INC
Also Called: North Texas Tool and Machine
503 W Chapman Dr (76266-9038)
P.O. Box 1018 (76266-1018)
PHONE.................................940 458-7954
Howard C Ashcraft, *President*
Freida Ashcraft, *Vice Pres*
▲ EMP: 30 EST: 1978
SQ FT: 25,000
SALES (est): 4.8MM **Privately Held**
WEB: www.northtexasplastics.com
SIC: 3089 3544 Injection molded finished plastic products; special dies, tools, jigs & fixtures

(G-18729)
PANTHEON CONSTRUCTION INC
7880 Rector Rd (76266-7320)
PHONE.................................940 458-9183
Linda Byrom, *CEO*
Robert Byrom, *Vice Pres*
Toni Walker, *Administration*
EMP: 27
SALES (est): 6MM **Privately Held**
WEB: www.pantheonconstruction.net
SIC: 1389 Gas field services

(G-18730)
SQS NDT LP
1641 Melton Rd (76266-3558)
PHONE.................................940 726-1107
Michael Lewis, *Partner*
EMP: 28
SALES (corp-wide): 3.5MM **Privately Held**
WEB: www.sqsndtlp.com
SIC: 1389 Testing, measuring, surveying & analysis services
PA: Sqs Ndt, Lp
2600 W I 20
Odessa TX 79763
432 614-9920

(G-18731)
TRICOUNTY MATERIALS & SVCS LP
14459 Intrstate 35 Frntag (76266)
PHONE.................................972 446-1816
Russ Williams, *Partner*
EMP: 17
SQ FT: 540
SALES (est): 4.9MM **Privately Held**
WEB: www.tricountymaterials.com
SIC: 1442 5032 1522 5211 Construction sand & gravel; aggregate; residential construction; sand & gravel

(G-18732)
WALLACE MARINE OF TEXAS INC
Also Called: Lake Ray Roberts Marina
1399 Marina Cir (76266-5847)
PHONE.................................940 458-7343
Michael D Wallace, *President*
Sue Wallace, *Marketing Mgr*
EMP: 20
SALES (est): 2.1MM **Privately Held**
WEB: www.rayrobertsmarina.com
SIC: 4493 3732 Boat yards, storage & incidental repair; boat building & repairing

Santa Fe
Galveston County

(G-18733)
CRAWFORD INDUSTRIAL SVCS LLC
3811 1/2 Fm 646 Rd N (77510-6104)
PHONE.................................409 925-9580
Custer Crawford, *President*
Tiffany Tillery, *Manager*
EMP: 50
SALES (est): 3.2MM **Privately Held**
WEB: www.crawfordindustrialservices.com
SIC: 1389 Building oil & gas well foundations on site

(G-18734)
GATES FUEL SERVICES LLC
3813 Fm 646 Rd N (77510-6104)
P.O. Box 1315 (77510-1315)
PHONE.................................409 925-8897
Steven R Nathanson,
David Delaureal,
Dennis A Pasentine,
John Pasentine,
EMP: 40
SQ FT: 45,000
SALES (est): 35MM **Privately Held**
WEB: www.gatesfuelservices.com
SIC: 1389 3731 Processing service, gas; barges, building & repairing

(G-18735)
IPC FABRICATORS LLC
12221 Highway 6 Unit C (77510-7703)
PHONE.................................409 935-8800
James C Hertenberger, *President*
James Chad Griffis, *Vice Pres*
Tamara Bailey, *CFO*
EMP: 65
SALES (est): 15.3MM **Privately Held**
SIC: 3496 Miscellaneous fabricated wire products

(G-18736)
LEE TECH LLC
5215 Fm 646 Rd S (77510-2075)
P.O. Box 1034 (77517-1034)
PHONE.................................409 925-0553
Kevin Lee, *Mng Member*
EMP: 10
SQ FT: 3,000
SALES (est): 1.5MM **Privately Held**
SIC: 3679 7389 Electronic circuits; artists' agents & brokers

Santa Rosa
Cameron County

(G-18737)
RIO GRANDE VLY SUG GROWERS INC
Also Called: Rgvsg
2.5 Miles W Hwy 107 (78593)
P.O. Box 459 (78593-0459)
PHONE.................................956 636-1411
James Russell, *CEO*
Steven Bearden, *President*
Dale Murden, *Chairman*
Tudor Uhlhorn, *Corp Secy*
Randy Rolando, *Treasurer*
▲ EMP: 500 EST: 1970
SQ FT: 5,000
SALES (est): 136.3MM **Privately Held**
WEB: www.rgvsugar.com
SIC: 2061 Raw cane sugar

Santo
Palo Pinto County

(G-18738)
PREMIUM WELD SERVICES INC
16119 S Fm 4 (76472-3435)
P.O. Box 422 (76472-0422)
PHONE.................................940 329-0222
Clinton R Dobyns, *President*
Aaron Adams, *Regional Mgr*
EMP: 10
SALES (est): 1.4MM **Privately Held**
WEB: www.hstrial-debbie-tangen-72982.homestead.com
SIC: 1799 3441 Welding on site; fabricated structural metal

(G-18739)
TEXAS BEST PROTEINS LP
Also Called: Kennedy Sausage Company
5775 Fm 2201 (76472-3285)
P.O. Box 517 (76472-0517)
PHONE.................................940 769-2028
Lou Profera, *Partner*
EMP: 30
SALES (est): 8.3MM **Privately Held**
WEB: www.texasbestproteins.com
SIC: 3826 2011 2013 Protein analyzers, laboratory type; meat packing plants; sausages & other prepared meats

Saratoga
Hardin County

(G-18740)
BASILS OILFIELD SERVICE INC
F M 787 (77585)
P.O. Box 93 (77585-0093)
PHONE..................................936 274-5575
Billy Tomlinson, *President*
Ruth Tomlinson, *Corp Secy*
EMP: 31 **EST:** 1961
SQ FT: 23,000
SALES (est): 2.9MM **Privately Held**
SIC: 1389 Swabbing wells; bailing wells;
lease tanks, oil field: erecting, cleaning &
repairing

Savoy
Fannin County

(G-18741)
SUPER SACK BAG INC
512 Hwy 56 (75479)
PHONE..................................903 965-7713
Dyrle Whipple, *Manager*
EMP: 15 **Privately Held**
WEB: www.bagcorp.com
SIC: 4225 2674 Miniwarehouse, ware-
housing; bags: uncoated paper & multi-
wall
PA: Super Sack Bag Inc
11510 Data Dr
Dallas TX 75218

Schertz
Guadalupe County

(G-18742)
ADVANCED BIOMECHANICS
4500 Cascade Dr (78154-1126)
PHONE..................................956 971-8200
Alan Inman, *Principal*
Sara Inman, *Principal*
EMP: 21
SALES (est): 950K **Privately Held**
SIC: 3842 Prosthetic appliances

(G-18743)
AER MANUFACTURING INC
5915 Corridor Pkwy (78154-3215)
PHONE..................................972 417-2582
Bob McGraw, *President*
EMP: 400
SALES (est): 31.6MM **Privately Held**
SIC: 3714 Motor vehicle engines & parts

(G-18744)
ARMORTEX INC
5926 Corridor Pkwy (78154-3201)
PHONE..................................800 880-8306
Javier Trevino, *President*
Tom E Turner Jr, *Director*
Jon R Turner, *Admin Sec*
▼ **EMP:** 48
SALES (est): 8.9MM **Privately Held**
WEB: www.armortex.com
SIC: 3842 Personal safety equipment

(G-18745)
BOA STUDIO LLC
117 Pecan Dr (78154-1733)
P.O. Box 691247, San Antonio (78269-
1247)
PHONE..................................210 314-4547
Mary Ryan,
Colleen Ryan,
Donald E Ryan Jr,
EMP: 16
SALES (est): 3.9MM **Privately Held**
WEB: www.maderamillwork.com
SIC: 2431 Millwork

(G-18746)
C3 ENVIRONMENTAL SPC LP
130 Nell Deane Blvd (78154-1500)
PHONE..................................210 653-7801
EMP: 21 **Privately Held**
WEB: www.c3environmental.com

SIC: 3822 Auto controls regulating residntl
& coml environmt & applncs
PA: C3 Environmental Specialties, Lp
132 Nell Deane Blvd
Schertz TX 78154

(G-18747)
CADILLAC PRODUCTS INC
Also Called: Cadillac Products Auto Co
6389 Fm 3009 Ste B203 (78154-3230)
PHONE..................................248 813-8200
George Bellairs, *Principal*
Mikesha Shaw, *Production*
EMP: 15
SALES (corp-wide): 155.2MM **Privately
Held**
WEB: www.cadprod.com
SIC: 3714 Motor vehicle parts & acces-
sories
PA: Cadillac Products, Inc.
5800 Crooks Rd Ste 100
Troy MI 48098
248 813-8200

(G-18748)
**COMPLEMENTARY COATINGS
CORP**
Also Called: Coronado Paint Products
7451 Fm 3009 (78154-3249)
PHONE..................................210 651-6996
Fax: 210 651-0247
EMP: 30
SALES (corp-wide): 162.4B **Publicly
Held**
SIC: 5198 2851 Whol Paints/Varnishes
Mfg Paints/Allied Products
HQ: Complementary Coatings Corp.
101 Paragon Dr
Montvale NJ 07645
845 786-5000

(G-18749)
EVESTRA INC (PA)
6410 Tri County Pkwy (78154-3202)
PHONE..................................210 673-3300
Shifra Birnbaum, *Research*
Laura Condel, *Research*
Michael Oettel, *Research*
John Tobler, *Research*
Daniel Anzak, *Finance*
EMP: 18
SALES (est): 2.3MM **Privately Held**
WEB: www.evestra.com
SIC: 2834 8731 Druggists' preparations
(pharmaceuticals); biological research

(G-18750)
INSTRUMENTS TECH MCHY INC
Also Called: I T M
5925 Corridor Pkwy (78154-3215)
PHONE..................................210 651-9066
Klaus D Weiswurm, *CEO*
Andrew Petterson, *President*
Pat Cheatham, *Partner*
Charla Weiswurm, *Corp Secy*
Jeff Weaver, *Engineer*
EMP: 30
SQ FT: 21,000
SALES (est): 9.7MM **Privately Held**
WEB: www.itm-texas.com
SIC: 3569 3599 Filter elements, fluid, hy-
draulic line; machine shop, jobbing & re-
pair

(G-18751)
KEACO ENTERPRISES INC
1006 Assembly Cir (78154-3231)
PHONE..................................210 651-6688
Mark F Keatts, *President*
Lori L Keatts, *Vice Pres*
L K Ding, *Shareholder*
▲ **EMP:** 13
SQ FT: 13,000
SALES (est): 3.3MM **Privately Held**
WEB: www.keaco-smt.com
SIC: 3565 Packaging machinery

(G-18752)
MAIN GLASS & MIRROR CO
17341 Bell North Dr (78154-3326)
P.O. Box 776 (78154-0776)
PHONE..................................210 637-1011
Robin Stewart, *President*
George Tilotta, *President*
William D Burnside, *Vice Pres*
EMP: 16

SALES (est): 2.4MM **Privately Held**
WEB: www.mainglasssa.net
SIC: 3231 Products of purchased glass

(G-18753)
MANCO STRUCTURES LTD
6106 Fm 3009 (78154-3205)
PHONE..................................210 690-1705
Carlos D Cerna, *President*
EMP: 90
SQ FT: 12,000
SALES (est): 15.4MM **Privately Held**
WEB: www.manco-satx.com
SIC: 3272 Concrete products, precast

(G-18754)
**MANUFACTURED CONCRETE
LTD**
6106 Fm 3009 (78154-3205)
P.O. Box 690250, San Antonio (78269-
0250)
PHONE..................................210 690-1705
Carlos D Cerna, *President*
EMP: 150
SQ FT: 10,000
SALES (est): 13.7MM **Privately Held**
SIC: 3272 Prestressed concrete products

(G-18755)
**MAVERICK DOOR AND
MILLWORK INC**
124 Pecan Dr (78154-1734)
PHONE..................................210 659-5553
Karl L Mayer, *President*
Craig Montgomery, *Treasurer*
Jackie Baer, *Office Mgr*
EMP: 18
SALES (est): 2.5MM **Privately Held**
WEB: www.maverickdoor.com
SIC: 2431 Doors, wood

(G-18756)
MERIDIAN BRICK LLC
21455 Fm 2252 (78154-9406)
PHONE..................................830 980-7071
Alvin Rodriquez, *Manager*
EMP: 50
SALES (corp-wide): 441MM **Privately
Held**
WEB: www.meridianbrick.com
SIC: 3271 3251 Concrete block & brick;
brick & structural clay tile
PA: Meridian Brick Llc
6455 Shiloh Rd D
Alpharetta GA 30005
770 645-4500

(G-18757)
**NATIONAL OPTCL & SCIENTFIC
INS**
6508 Tri County Pkwy (78154-3474)
PHONE..................................210 590-9010
Stephen P Y Chan, *President*
▲ **EMP:** 18
SQ FT: 4,000
SALES (est): 4.1MM **Privately Held**
WEB: www.nationaloptical.com
SIC: 3827 Optical instruments & lenses

(G-18758)
**NATIONWIDE APPLICATIONS
LLC**
17324 Bell North Dr (78154-3325)
PHONE..................................210 651-0202
James H Morgan, *President*
Melissa Morgan, *Admin Sec*
EMP: 20
SALES (est): 2.8MM **Privately Held**
WEB: www.naisignagesolutions.com
SIC: 3993 Signs & advertising specialties

(G-18759)
PRATT INDUSTRIES INC
Also Called: Converting Division
6389 Fm 3009 Ste 100 (78154-3230)
PHONE..................................210 651-6309
Eddie Canales, *General Mgr*
Iliana Labiste, *Opers Mgr*
Jennifer Smith, *Buyer*
Elizabeth Mc Caig, *Controller*
EMP: 66 **Privately Held**
WEB: www.prattindustries.com
SIC: 2653 Boxes, corrugated: made from
purchased materials

PA: Pratt Industries, Inc.
1800 Sarasot Bus Pkwy Ne S
Conyers GA 30013

(G-18760)
PSP INDUSTRIES INC (HQ)
Also Called: Psp Engineering
9885 Doerr Ln (78154-9408)
PHONE..................................210 651-9595
Michael Senneway, *President*
Bennie Ray Hooper, *President*
Brad Hooper, *Vice Pres*
Dennis Stirm, *Vice Pres*
Roy Stokes, *Vice Pres*
EMP: 15 **EST:** 1956
SALES (est): 163.9MM
SALES (corp-wide): 221.8MM **Privately
Held**
WEB: www.pspindustries.com
SIC: 3533 3531 3564 3532 Oil & gas
field machinery; construction machinery;
air purification equipment; mining machin-
ery; refinery, chemical processing & simi-
lar machinery
PA: The Herrick Corporation
3003 E Hammer Ln
Stockton CA 95212
209 956-4751

(G-18761)
**ROLLTCHS SPCIALTY VEHICLES
LLC**
Also Called: Shook Mobile Technology
7451 Fm 3009 (78154-3249)
PHONE..................................210 651-5700
John P Heaney, *CEO*
Tony Beigel, *Exec VP*
Ron Laurence, *VP Sales*
◆ **EMP:** 31
SQ FT: 79,400
SALES (est): 5MM **Privately Held**
WEB: www.shook-usa.com
SIC: 3663 Mobile communication equip-
ment

(G-18762)
**SIGMA INDUSTRIAL AUTOMTN
INC (PA)**
5450 Fm 1103 (78108-2110)
PHONE..................................210 659-5000
Kathleen Chinni, *President*
Rick Curcio, *Engineer*
Guy Gibson, *Engineer*
Erik Frost, *Manager*
Doug Lansdowne, *Info Tech Mgr*
EMP: 10
SQ FT: 14,500
SALES: 3.5MM **Privately Held**
WEB: www.sigma-usa.com
SIC: 3577 Computer peripheral equipment

(G-18763)
TAYLOR PUBLISHING COMPANY
1136 Berry Creek Dr (78154-2798)
PHONE..................................210 659-7505
Kathi Hopkins, *Branch Mgr*
EMP: 44 **Privately Held**
WEB: www.balfour.com
SIC: 2731 Books: publishing only
HQ: Taylor Publishing Company
1550 W Mockingbird Ln
Dallas TX 75235
214 637-2800

(G-18764)
TECHNOS INC
7016 Fm 3009 (78154-3220)
PHONE..................................210 651-9393
Phillip Neal, *President*
Michael Hatfield, *Superintendent*
Sabina Neal, *Vice Pres*
Derrick Dowden, *Purch Mgr*
Dave Tomme, *Purch Mgr*
EMP: 50
SQ FT: 15,000
SALES (est): 12.8MM **Privately Held**
WEB: www.technosfans.com
SIC: 3564 7699 Blowers & fans; balancing
service

(G-18765)
TWE NONWOVENS US INC
Also Called: Vita Nonwovens Texas Plant
6389 Fm 3009 Ste B202 (78154-3230)
PHONE..................................210 651-3735
Art Perez, *Manager*

▲ = Import ▼=Export
◆ =Import/Export

EMP: 22
SALES (corp-wide): 359.8MM Privately Held
WEB: www.vitanonwovens.com
SIC: 2297 Nonwoven fabrics
HQ: Twe Nonwovens Us, Inc.
2215 Shore St
High Point NC 27263
336 431-7187

(G-18766)
UFP SCHERTZ LLC
Also Called: Universal Forest Products
21700 Fm 2252 (78154-9407)
P.O. Box 786 (78154-0786)
PHONE.................................830 606-4300
Kaleb Hensley, Production
Mark Novall, Branch Mgr
▼ EMP: 50
SALES (est): 5.9MM
SALES (corp-wide): 4.4B Publicly Held
WEB: www.ufpi.com
SIC: 2449 2448 2491 2499 Rectangular
boxes & crates, wood; wood pallets &
skids; wood preserving; fencing, wood
PA: Ufp Industries, Inc.
2801 E Beltline Ave Ne
Grand Rapids MI 49525
616 364-6161

(G-18767)
UNIFIED SCREENING &
CRUSHING -
Also Called: Texas Wire
9235 Margies Ln (78154-1283)
PHONE.................................210 946-6900
Andy Hamilton, Branch Mgr
EMP: 12
SALES (corp-wide): 18.7MM Privately
Held
WEB: www.unifiedscreening.com
SIC: 3496 Miscellaneous fabricated wire
products
PA: Unified Screening & Crushing - Ca, Inc.
8300 W Elowin Ct
Visalia CA 93291
559 651-3737

(G-18768)
VESTAL STEEL SPECIALTIES
INC
17993 Red Iron (78154-3212)
PHONE.................................210 651-4333
Walter J Vestal, Owner
Don Vestal, Corp Secy
Tommy Vestal Sr, Vice Pres
Lloyd Respondek, Purch Dir
EMP: 25
SQ FT: 4,400
SALES (est): 8.1MM Privately Held
WEB: www.vestalsteel.com
SIC: 3315 3441 Steel wire & related prod-
ucts; fabricated structural metal

(G-18769)
W P MURPHY INC
Also Called: Murphy's Readymix Concrete
11695 E Fm 1518 N (78108-3323)
P.O. Box 8, Converse (78109-0008)
PHONE.................................210 658-4947
Kelly T Murphy-Perez, President
Kelly Murphy-Perez, Vice Pres
EMP: 15
SQ FT: 4,000
SALES (est): 2.5MM Privately Held
WEB:
www.murphysreadymixsanantonio.com
SIC: 3273 1611 Ready-mixed concrete;
highway & street construction; concrete
construction: roads, highways, sidewalks,
etc.; resurfacing contractor

Schulenburg
Fayette County

(G-18770)
3-D BELT COMPANY LP
1001 Huser Blvd (78956-5665)
PHONE.................................979 743-4567
Stephen E Dees, Managing Prtnr
Roger Schuster, Partner
Martha White, Natl Sales Mgr
Jackie Machac, VP Sales
◆ EMP: 35

SQ FT: 25,000
SALES (est): 3.8MM Privately Held
WEB: www.3dbelt.com
SIC: 2387 3172 Apparel belts; personal
leather goods

(G-18771)
AMERICAN KART MFG LLC
707 Demel Ave (78956-1715)
P.O. Box 547 (78956-0547)
PHONE.................................979 505-5076
Kurt Vedder, Principal
EMP: 16 EST: 2017
SALES (est): 48K Privately Held
WEB: www.akm-tugs.com
SIC: 3999 Manufacturing industries

(G-18772)
BKH ENTERPRISES LLC
633 Oakland Rd (78956-5274)
P.O. Box 5 (78956-0005)
PHONE.................................979 743-6577
Ben Hercik, President
EMP: 52
SQ FT: 42,000
SALES (est): 10.4MM Privately Held
WEB: www.primehdpe.com
SIC: 3085 Plastics bottles

(G-18773)
BWI COMPANIES INC
Also Called: B W I of Schulenburg
100 N Main St (78956-1636)
P.O. Box 459 (78956-0459)
PHONE.................................979 743-4581
Dennis Brower, Manager
EMP: 100
SALES (corp-wide): 270.1MM Privately
Held
WEB: www.bwicompanies.com
SIC: 5191 3423 Greenhouse equipment &
supplies; hand & edge tools
PA: Bwi Companies, Inc.
1355 N Kings Hwy
Nash TX 75569
903 838-8561

(G-18774)
CONTECH ENGNERED
SOLUTIONS LLC
232 Oakland Rd (78956-5275)
P.O. Box 26 (78956-0026)
PHONE.................................979 743-4123
Royce Shimek, Production
Philip Guenther, Opers-Prdtn-Mfg
EMP: 15 Privately Held
WEB: www.conteches.com
SIC: 3443 Fabricated plate work (boiler
shop)
HQ: Contech Engineered Solutions Llc
9025 Centre Pointe Dr # 400
West Chester OH 45069
513 645-7000

(G-18775)
DAIRY FARMERS AMERICA INC
801 James Ave (78956-1916)
P.O. Box 176 (78956-0176)
PHONE.................................979 743-4161
Jeff Hurley, Vice Pres
Anthony Nix, Maint Spvr
Bruce Dameworth, Opers Spvr
Michael Zweschper, Human Res Mgr
Steven Fiss, Manager
EMP: 85
SQ FT: 20,000
SALES (corp-wide): 15.8B Privately Held
WEB: www.dfamilk.com
SIC: 2026 Fluid milk
PA: Dairy Farmers Of America, Inc.
1405 N 98th St
Kansas City KS 66111
816 801-6455

(G-18776)
MAREMONT EXHAUST
PRODUCTS INC
423 Bird House Hill Rd (78956-5238)
PHONE.................................865 458-4681
Kenneth Banks, President
▲ EMP: 250
SQ FT: 50,000

SALES (est): 27.4MM Publicly Held
WEB: www.maremont.com
SIC: 3714 5013 Exhaust systems & parts,
motor vehicle; exhaust systems (mufflers,
tail pipes, etc.)
PA: Meritor, Inc.
2135 W Maple Rd
Troy MI 48084

(G-18777)
PRIME PRODUCTS INC
601 S Main St (78956-2025)
P.O. Box 100 (78956-0100)
PHONE.................................979 743-6555
Elgin R Kristinik, President
Andy Bosl, Vice Pres
Nick Patalik, QC Mgr
Ron Vyvial, Controller
Paul Gonzales, Manager
◆ EMP: 100
SQ FT: 25,000
SALES (est): 11.7MM Privately Held
WEB: www.primeproductsinc.net
SIC: 3089 5085 Air mattresses, plastic; in-
jection molding of plastics; plastic bottles

(G-18778)
SCHULENBURG PRTG OFF
SUPS INC
Also Called: Profile Labels & Tags
705 Upton Ave (78956-1565)
P.O. Box 429 (78956-0429)
PHONE.................................979 743-4511
Randy J Proske, President
Chris Proske, Vice Pres
Christopher Proske, Vice Pres
Jeff Proske, Treasurer
Susie Behlen, Accounts Exec
EMP: 30
SQ FT: 12,000
SALES (est): 4.9MM Privately Held
WEB: www.schulenburgprinting.com
SIC: 2752 5943 2679 Commercial print-
ing, offset; office forms & supplies; labels,
paper; made from purchased material

(G-18779)
SCHULENBURGH STICKER INC
405 N Main St (78956-1561)
P.O. Box 160 (78956-0160)
PHONE.................................979 743-3450
Maxine Vyvjala, President
Darrell Vyvjala, Vice Pres
Carla Ricicar, Adv Mgr
Diane Paruse, Admin Sec
EMP: 10
SQ FT: 1,000
SALES (est): 200K Privately Held
WEB: www.schulenburgsticker.com
SIC: 2711 Commercial printing & newspa-
per publishing combined

(G-18780)
TENTH FRAME INC
233 College St (78956-1603)
P.O. Box 45 (78956-0045)
PHONE.................................979 743-6585
EMP: 20 EST: 1999
SALES (est): 1.3MM Privately Held
WEB: www.schulenburgrvpark.com
SIC: 3949 Bowling alleys & accessories

Scottsville
Harrison County

(G-18781)
W A NEEL CO INC
2199 Farm Rd I 20 20 I (75688)
P.O. Box 340 (75688-0340)
PHONE.................................903 503-5834
W A Neel, President
Art Neel, President
Russel Neel, Vice Pres
Jorene Neel, Treasurer
EMP: 12
SALES (est): 1.9MM Privately Held
SIC: 3823 Computer interface equipment
for industrial process control

Scurry
Kaufman County

(G-18782)
B T S PRECISION MACHINE
8615 County Road 4074 (75158-4703)
P.O. Box 455 (75158-0455)
PHONE.................................903 498-7501
Glenda Bradley, Owner
EMP: 9
SQ FT: 3,000
SALES (est): 953.8K Privately Held
SIC: 3565 7699 Packaging machinery; in-
dustrial machinery & equipment repair

(G-18783)
PAPPYS SAND & GRAVEL INC
13851 Hwy 34 W (75158)
P.O. Box 307 (75158-0307)
PHONE.................................972 486-4400
John Reeder, President
EMP: 45
SQ FT: 1,500
SALES (est): 1MM Privately Held
SIC: 5032 1442 Sand, construction;
gravel; construction sand & gravel

Seabrook
Harris County

(G-18784)
BARITE LOGISTICS LLC
2301 Pin Hook Ct (77586-3349)
PHONE.................................281 635-0584
John Michael Solt, President
EMP: 14
SQ FT: 4,000
SALES (est): 60MM Privately Held
WEB: www.baritelogistics.com
SIC: 1479 Barite mining

(G-18785)
GULF COAST LIMESTONE INC
(PA)
1402 3rd St (77586-3519)
P.O. Box 66 (77586-0066)
PHONE.................................281 474-4124
EMP: 15
SQ FT: 2,000
SALES (est): 49.6MM Privately Held
WEB: www.gcli.com
SIC: 1411 1422 1423 1481 Dimension
stone; crushed & broken limestone;
crushed & broken granite; nonmetallic
mineral services; igneous rock, crushed &
broken-quarrying

(G-18786)
JACKSON PROMOTIONS INC
Also Called: Signquick
1908 Hialeah Dr Ste A (77586-3061)
PHONE.................................281 474-1313
Larry W Bouley, President
Lisa J Bouley, Vice Pres
Lisa Bouley, Vice Pres
EMP: 10
SQ FT: 3,600
SALES (est): 1MM Privately Held
WEB: www.signquick.com
SIC: 3993 Signs & advertising specialties

(G-18787)
KIWO HOLDINGS INC (DH)
1929 Marvin Cir (77586-2813)
P.O. Box 1009 (77586-1009)
PHONE.................................281 474-9777
R David Eisenbeiss, President
Clark King, Vice Pres
Sean Chism, Manager
EMP: 20
SQ FT: 13,000
SALES (est): 8MM
SALES (corp-wide): 1MM Privately Held
WEB: www.kiwo.com
SIC: 2842 2899 5199 Specialty cleaning
preparations; chemical preparations; art
goods

HQ: Kissel & Wolf Gesellschaft Mit
Beschrankter Haftung
In Den Ziegelwiesen 6
Wiesloch 69168
622 257-80

(G-18788)
PAN CONTINENTAL RESOURCES (PA)
2600 Red Bluff Rd (77586-1509)
PHONE....................281 291-8100
Y S Pan, *CEO*
EMP: 23
SQ FT: 14,000
SALES (est): 3.6MM **Privately Held**
SIC: 5082 1479 8748 Mining machinery & equipment, except petroleum; mineral pigment mining; business consulting

(G-18789)
POLYONE CORPORATION
5306 Highway 146 (77586-1516)
P.O. Box 478 (77586-0478)
PHONE....................281 474-2831
Jim Griffeth, *Opers-Prdtn-Mfg*
Jim Griffith, *Branch Mgr*
Sandra Lin, *Bd of Directors*
EMP: 145
SQ FT: 10,000 **Publicly Held**
WEB: www.polyone.com
SIC: 3087 3084 2821 Custom compound purchased resins; plastics pipe; plastics materials & resins
PA: Avient Corporation
33587 Walker Rd
Avon Lake OH 44012

(G-18790)
POLYONE CORPORATION
5110 Hwy 146 (77586)
PHONE....................281 474-2831
Jim Griffith, *Branch Mgr*
EMP: 240 **Publicly Held**
WEB: www.polyone.com
SIC: 2821 Plastics materials & resins
PA: Avient Corporation
33587 Walker Rd
Avon Lake OH 44012

(G-18791)
SEABROOK MARINA INC
Also Called: Seabrook Shipyard
1900 Shipyard Dr (77586-3469)
PHONE....................281 694-0001
Steve Evnochides, *Ch of Bd*
Albert Fay Jr, *President*
Carolyn Grant Faye, *Vice Pres*
Marion Fay Monsen, *Treasurer*
Katherine Faye-Smith, *Admin Sec*
EMP: 13 EST: 1939
SQ FT: 2,000
SALES (est): 1.9MM **Privately Held**
WEB: www.seabrookmarinacenter.com
SIC: 7699 4493 3732 Boat repair; boat yards, storage & incidental repair; boat building & repairing

(G-18792)
TECHNICAL AUTOMTN SVCS CO LTD (PA)
Also Called: Vivicom
2000 Nasa Pkwy (77586-3420)
PHONE....................281 474-3232
John Burkland, *President*
Jacquelyn Hurry, *Technician*
EMP: 82
SQ FT: 70,000
SALES (est): 35.7MM **Privately Held**
WEB: www.tascorp.com
SIC: 8731 8711 3829 3823 Commercial physical research; consulting engineer; measuring & controlling devices; industrial instrmnts msrmnt display/control process variable

(G-18793)
USA SCREEN PRINTING CHEM INC
1929 Marvin Cir (77586-2813)
P.O. Box 1009 (77586-1009)
PHONE....................281 474-9777
R David Eisenbeiss, *President*
Gary Gayton, *Vice Pres*
Clark King, *Vice Pres*
Mona Farid, *Admin Sec*

▲ EMP: 30
SQ FT: 27,000
SALES (est): 4.7MM
SALES (corp-wide): 1MM **Privately Held**
SIC: 2899 2842 5199 3555 Chemical preparations; specialty cleaning preparations; art goods; printing trades machinery
HQ: Kiwo Holdings, Inc
1929 Marvin Cir
Seabrook TX 77586
281 474-9777

(G-18794)
WELL BODY PURIFY LLC
3663 Nasa Pkwy Apt 706 (77586-6319)
PHONE....................443 847-6501
Joseph Terzo, *COO*
Mike O'Heir, *CFO*
EMP: 12
SALES (est): 910.8K **Privately Held**
SIC: 2842 Sanitation preparations, disinfectants & deodorants

Seadrift
Calhoun County

(G-18795)
COASTLINE TRAILER MFG INC
306 S Main St (77983-3730)
P.O. Box 97 (77983-0097)
PHONE....................361 785-4073
Marvin F Strakos, *President*
EMP: 10
SALES (est): 1.2MM **Privately Held**
WEB: www.coastlinetrailermfg.com
SIC: 3799 Boat trailers; trailers & trailer equipment

(G-18796)
JC CUSTOM BOATS INC
478 Cemetery Rd (77983-3824)
P.O. Box 2476, Aransas Pass (78335-2476)
PHONE....................361 785-6035
Julie Coulter, *President*
EMP: 10
SQ FT: 3,500
SALES (est): 1MM **Privately Held**
WEB: www.hayniebayboats.com
SIC: 3732 Boat building & repairing

(G-18797)
UNION CARBIDE CORPORATION
7501 State Hwy 185 N (77983)
P.O. Box 210279, Dallas (75211-0279)
PHONE....................361 553-2000
Patrick E Gottschalk, *Principal*
G E Barnett, *Principal*
EMP: 56
SALES (corp-wide): 38.5B **Publicly Held**
WEB: www.unioncarbide.com
SIC: 2869 2821 Industrial organic chemicals; plastics materials & resins
HQ: Union Carbide Corporation
1254 Enclave Pkwy
Houston TX 77077
281 966-2727

Seagoville
Dallas County

(G-18798)
ARCOSA AGGREGATES INC
3829 Bilindsay Rd (75159)
P.O. Box 373, Ferris (75125-0373)
PHONE....................972 287-4343
EMP: 15
SQ FT: 1,500
SALES (corp-wide): 1.7B **Publicly Held**
WEB: www.trinitymaterialsinc.com
SIC: 3273 Ready-mixed concrete
HQ: Arcosa Aggregates, Inc.
401 N Interstate Hwy 45
Ferris TX 75125
972 544-5900

(G-18799)
B & B READY MIX INC
4240 S Belt Line Rd (75159-3916)
PHONE....................972 287-9998
Ronny G Brown, *President*
Scotty Brown, *Vice Pres*

Shannon Sewell, *Treasurer*
Twana J Brown, *Admin Sec*
EMP: 20
SALES (est): 6MM **Privately Held**
WEB: www.bbreadymix.com
SIC: 3273 Ready-mixed concrete

(G-18800)
FEDERAL PRISON INDUSTRIES
Also Called: Unicor
2113 N Highway 175 (75159-2237)
PHONE....................972 287-4040
EMP: 18 **Publicly Held**
WEB: www.bop.gov
SIC: 2353 9223 Hats, caps & millinery; correctional institutions
HQ: Federal Prison Industries, Inc
320 1st St Nw
Washington DC 20534

(G-18801)
KENNYMAC LLC
Also Called: Mygi's Desserts
704 Smith Ln (75159-1829)
PHONE....................214 732-4759
EMP: 10
SALES (est): 450K **Privately Held**
SIC: 2051 Mfg Bread/Related Products

(G-18802)
PRECISION-HAYES INTL INC (HQ)
704 W Simonds Rd (75159-3227)
PHONE....................972 287-2390
Chris Mitchell, *Vice Pres*
Cindy Myers, *Human Res Mgr*
Bobby Baker, *Info Tech Mgr*
Alexander Thornton, *Analyst*
◆ EMP: 110
SQ FT: 70,000
SALES (est): 152MM
SALES (corp-wide): 493.2MM **Publicly Held**
WEB: www.precision-hayes.com
SIC: 3272 Prestressed concrete products
PA: Enerpac Tool Group Corp.
N86 W12500 Wstbrook Crssi St N 86
Menomonee Falls WI 53051
262 293-1500

Seagraves
Gaines County

(G-18803)
ENVENTIVES LLC
2945 Old Seagraves Rd (79359-8123)
P.O. Box 1203 (79359-1203)
PHONE....................612 930-1977
Jay D Cowan, *CEO*
Michael J Kilchrist,
EMP: 20 EST: 2015
SALES (est): 594.2K **Privately Held**
WEB: www.enventives.com
SIC: 2992 Transmission fluid: made from purchased materials

Sealy
Austin County

(G-18804)
ALPHA LUBRICANTS LLC
415 Walker St (77474-2421)
PHONE....................214 971-1170
Husam Mutawe, *Manager*
EMP: 10
SALES (est): 3MM **Privately Held**
SIC: 2899 Corrosion preventive lubricant

(G-18805)
AUSTIN COUNTY MACHINE SHOP INC
9364 Fm 1458 Rd (77474-7723)
PHONE....................979 885-3716
Albert J Sodolak, *President*
Doris K Sodolak, *Corp Secy*
Laura R Bartholomaus, *Vice Pres*
Brian G Sodolak, *Vice Pres*
EMP: 9
SQ FT: 10,000

SALES (est): 1.3MM **Privately Held**
WEB: www.austincountymachine.com
SIC: 3599 Machine shop, jobbing & repair

(G-18806)
BLENCOR LLC
2324 Fm 3013 Rd (77474-9602)
P.O. Box 1728 (77474-6728)
PHONE....................979 627-7801
Eulogio Fernandini, *CEO*
Javier Vitro, *Principal*
Miguel Calatayud, *Admin Sec*
Jorge Fernandini,
▲ EMP: 102 EST: 2008
SQ FT: 120,000
SALES (est): 28.7MM **Privately Held**
WEB: www.blencor.com
SIC: 2037 Fruits, quick frozen & cold pack (frozen); frozen fruits & vegetables

(G-18807)
CEMEX MATERIALS LLC
Rinker Materials
2735 Highway 36 (77474-5956)
P.O. Box 1088 (77474-1088)
PHONE....................979 885-7403
Chad Holden, *Manager*
EMP: 50 **Privately Held**
SIC: 3272 Concrete products
HQ: Cemex Materials Llc
1501 Belvedere Rd
West Palm Beach FL 33406
561 833-5555

(G-18808)
HYDRO CONDUIT OF TEXAS LP
Also Called: Sealy - Precast
2735 Highway 36 (77474-5956)
PHONE....................979 885-7403
Chad Holden, *Branch Mgr*
EMP: 34 **Privately Held**
WEB: www.rinkerpipe.com
SIC: 3272 Concrete products
HQ: Hydro Conduit Of Texas, Lp
6560 Langfield Rd 3-H
Houston TX 77092

(G-18809)
HYDRO CONDUIT OF TEXAS LP
Also Called: Rinker Materials
2839 Highway 36 (77474-8271)
PHONE....................979 885-7403
Oscar Yeps, *Plant Mgr*
EMP: 50 **Privately Held**
WEB: www.rinkerpipe.com
SIC: 3272 Concrete products used to facilitate drainage
HQ: Hydro Conduit Of Texas, Lp
6560 Langfield Rd 3-H
Houston TX 77092

(G-18810)
INTERNATIONAL PAPER COMPANY
1485 Silliman St (77474-4007)
PHONE....................979 885-4191
Urmila Jhattu, *Human Res Mgr*
John Parent, *Branch Mgr*
EMP: 110
SQ FT: 160,000
SALES (corp-wide): 22.3B **Publicly Held**
WEB: www.internationalpaper.com
SIC: 2621 Paper mills
PA: International Paper Company
6400 Poplar Ave
Memphis TN 38197
901 419-9000

(G-18811)
JUSTIN INDUSTRIES INC
6005 Peters San Felipe Rd (77474-5925)
P.O. Box 397 (77474-0397)
PHONE....................979 885-4124
Bob Boling, *Opers-Prdtn-Mfg*
EMP: 90
SALES (corp-wide): 254.6B **Publicly Held**
WEB: www.brick.com
SIC: 5211 3251 Brick; brick & structural clay tile
HQ: Justin Industries, Inc.
3024 Acme Brick Plz
Fort Worth TX 76109
817 332-4101

(G-18812)
MASTER WALL INC
914 Bartlett Rd (77474-5901)
PHONE...............................979 885-6905
Leo Crowell, *Branch Mgr*
Ryan Whiting, *Manager*
EMP: 12
SALES (corp-wide): 7.7MM **Privately
Held**
WEB: www.masterwall.com
SIC: 3299 Stucco
PA: Master Wall, Inc.
6975 Flat Rock Rd
Midland GA 31820
706 569-0092

(G-18813)
**MFS PIPING AND INDUS SVCS
LLC**
910 Columbus Rd (77474-1718)
PHONE...............................979 472-7658
Joe Craft, *Mng Member*
Steve Hopkins, *Mng Member*
Will Hopkins, *Mng Member*
Nick Magoulianos, *Mng Member*
EMP: 49
SQ FT: 38,000
SALES (est): 2.6MM **Privately Held**
WEB: www.mfspipingandindustrial.com
SIC: 3498 Piping systems for pulp paper &
chemical industries

(G-18814)
PENCCO INC (PA)
831 Bartlett Rd (77474-9518)
P.O. Box 600, San Felipe (77473-0600)
PHONE...............................979 885-0005
Ron L Horne, *President*
Sarah Duffy, *Sales Staff*
Aline Horne, *Admin Sec*
EMP: 32
SQ FT: 4,000
SALES (est): 13.9MM **Privately Held**
WEB: www.pencco.com
SIC: 2899 5169 2819 Water treating com-
pounds; chemicals & allied products; in-
dustrial inorganic chemicals

(G-18815)
QUALITY MACHINE SHOP LLC
3213 Highway 36 (77474-5957)
P.O. Box 425 (77474-0425)
PHONE...............................979 885-6932
Dorothy Sklar, *Mng Member*
Andrew F Sowa,
▼ **EMP:** 34
SQ FT: 32,000
SALES (est): 6.5MM **Privately Held**
SIC: 3599 Machine shop, jobbing & repair

(G-18816)
**REACTIVE & ALLOY MTLS INDS
INC**
Also Called: Ram
829 Bartlett Rd (77474-9518)
P.O. Box 786 (77474-0786)
PHONE...............................979 885-2244
Michael P Hicks Jr, *President*
Daniel Aguilar, *General Mgr*
Scott Meredith, *Vice Pres*
Rachel Hicks, *Office Mgr*
EMP: 10 **EST:** 2000
SQ FT: 12,500
SALES (est): 1.8MM **Privately Held**
WEB: www.reactivealloy.com
SIC: 3441 Fabricated structural metal

(G-18817)
RYDAR INC (PA)
979 Brazos Crossing Ln (77474-9117)
PHONE...............................979 877-0703
William Whiting, *President*
EMP: 23
SQ FT: 18,000
SALES (est): 2.1MM **Privately Held**
WEB: www.accentstucco.com
SIC: 3299 Stucco

(G-18818)
SEALY CONCRETE INC
4460 Ne I 10 Frontage Rd (77474-9088)
PHONE...............................281 391-3435
William J Schaffner, *President*
David R Nelson, *Corp Secy*
EMP: 28

SQ FT: 6,000
SALES: 11.4MM **Privately Held**
WEB: www.sealyconcreteinc.com
SIC: 3273 5211 Ready-mixed concrete;
sand & gravel

(G-18819)
**SEALY PRECISION MACHINING
INC**
2060 Highway 90 W (77474-9510)
P.O. Box 664 (77474-0664)
PHONE...............................979 885-7380
EMP: 15
SQ FT: 12,000
SALES (est): 2MM **Privately Held**
WEB: www.austincountymachine.com
SIC: 3599 Machine shop, jobbing & repair

(G-18820)
**TOPS WELL SERVICES LLC
(PA)**
3077 Outlet Center Dr (77474-8205)
PHONE...............................979 627-7434
Billy Rushing,
EMP: 56
SALES (est): 41.7MM **Privately Held**
WEB: www.topswellservices.com
SIC: 3533 Drilling tools for gas, oil or water
wells

(G-18821)
TRANSCOM PACKAGING INC
2893 Fm 1094 Rd (77474-4363)
PHONE...............................979 885-1800
James Mansouri, *President*
▼ **EMP:** 12
SQ FT: 14,000
SALES (est): 2.6MM **Privately Held**
WEB: www.liquiset.com
SIC: 2655 Containers, laminated phenolic
& vulcanized fiber; containers, liquid tight
fiber: from purchased material

Seguin
Guadalupe County

(G-18822)
ALAMO GROUP (TX) INC
1502 E Walnut St (78155-5202)
P.O. Box 549 (78156-0549)
PHONE...............................800 882-5762
Ronald A Robinson, *CEO*
James B Skaggs, *Ch of Bd*
Ian Burden, *President*
Dan E Malone, *Exec VP*
Robert H George, *Treasurer*
▲ **EMP:** 275
SQ FT: 230,000
SALES (est): 24.6MM
SALES (corp-wide): 1.1B **Publicly Held**
WEB: www.alamo-group.com
SIC: 3523 Grounds mowing equipment
HQ: Alamo Group (Usa) Inc.
1627 E Walnut St
Seguin TX 78155
830 379-1480

(G-18823)
ALAMO SALES CORP
1502 E Walnut St (78155-5202)
P.O. Box 549 (78156-0549)
PHONE...............................800 882-5762
Ronald A Robinson, *President*
Jimmy Garcia, *Sales Staff*
Kraig A Niebuhr, *Manager*
Mike Pereny, *Manager*
Sharon Rice, *Admin Sec*
EMP: 63
SQ FT: 230,000
SALES (est): 5.6MM
SALES (corp-wide): 1.1B **Publicly Held**
WEB: www.alamo-industrial.com
SIC: 3523 Farm machinery & equipment
HQ: Alamo Group (Usa) Inc.
1627 E Walnut St
Seguin TX 78155
830 379-1480

(G-18824)
ALX IMAGING LLC
Also Called: Newpro
7000 Fm 466 (78155-7759)
PHONE...............................210 651-5000

Stefan A Rohach, *Principal*
Stefan Rohach, *Director*
Stefan A Rohach,
EMP: 30 **EST:** 2011
SALES (est): 524.4K **Privately Held**
WEB: www.alximaging.com
SIC: 5734 2893 5112 Computer periph-
eral equipment; printing ink; photocopying
supplies; laserjet supplies

(G-18825)
**AMERITEX PIPE & PRODUCTS
LLC**
3960 E Us Highway 90 (78155-2077)
P.O. Box 150 (78156-0150)
PHONE...............................830 372-2300
Kevin M Thompson, *Owner*
Steve Bakonyi, *Principal*
Rocky Lorenz, *COO*
Nicholas Archila, *Project Mgr*
Armando Ortiz, *Controller*
▲ **EMP:** 64
SALES (est): 24MM **Privately Held**
WEB: www.ameritexpipe.com
SIC: 3317 Steel pipe & tubes

(G-18826)
**BERRIDGE MANUFACTURING
COMPANY**
2201 Rudeloff Rd (78155-0175)
PHONE...............................830 401-5200
Bulmaro Chapa, *Manager*
Brian Schmidt, *Manager*
EMP: 30
SALES (corp-wide): 59.5MM **Privately
Held**
WEB: www.berridge.com
SIC: 3444 3429 3448 Metal roofing & roof
drainage equipment; manufactured hard-
ware (general); prefabricated metal build-
ings
PA: Berridge Manufacturing Company, Inc
6515 Fratt Rd
San Antonio TX 78218
210 650-7056

(G-18827)
**C M C STEEL FABRICATORS
INC (DH)**
Also Called: CMC Rbar San Antnio E Loca-
tion
1 Steel Mill Dr (78155-7510)
P.O. Box 911 (78156-0911)
PHONE...............................830 372-8200
Tracy Porter, *President*
Ben Tschirhart, *Mfg Staff*
Bryan Creswell, *Purchasing*
Luke Garcia, *Electrical Engi*
Paul Lawrence, *Treasurer*
◆ **EMP:** 840 **EST:** 1978
SALES (est): 472.3MM
SALES (corp-wide): 5.4B **Publicly Held**
WEB: www.cmc.com
SIC: 3312 3441 Structural shapes & pil-
ings, steel; fabricated structural metal
HQ: Cmc Steel Holding Company
802 N West St Ste 302
Wilmington DE 19801
302 691-6200

(G-18828)
CARCHALK INC
5075 N State Highway 123 (78155-0350)
P.O. Box 1110, Boerne (78006-1110)
PHONE...............................210 667-3890
Joseph Daniel, *President*
Tracy Daniel, *Vice Pres*
EMP: 12
SQ FT: 22,000
SALES (est): 2.3MM **Privately Held**
WEB: www.glasschalk.com
SIC: 2851 Paints & allied products

(G-18829)
CATERPILLAR INC
1720 W Kingsbury St (78155-3109)
PHONE...............................830 401-5600
EMP: 23
SALES (corp-wide): 53.8B **Publicly Held**
WEB: www.caterpillar.com
SIC: 3452 Nuts, metal; bolts, metal;
screws, metal
PA: Caterpillar Inc.
510 Lake Cook Rd Ste 100
Deerfield IL 60015
224 551-4000

(G-18830)
**COMMERCIAL DIESL PARTS
SVC LTD**
Also Called: John Deere Authorized Dealer
1900 E Us Highway 90 (78155-1226)
PHONE...............................830 372-1594
Charles Loftin, *Owner*
Angie Loftin, *CFO*
EMP: 23
SALES (est): 3.7MM **Privately Held**
WEB: www.cdpstexas.com
SIC: 1389 7699 5084 Construction, repair
& dismantling services; industrial equip-
ment services; construction equipment re-
pair; industrial machine parts

(G-18831)
**COMMERCIAL METALS
COMPANY**
Also Called: CMC Metals Recycling
100 Steel Mill Dr (78155-7517)
P.O. Box 911 (78156-0911)
PHONE...............................830 372-8200
Robert Guido, *Branch Mgr*
Lorrie Rangel, *Manager*
EMP: 10
SALES (corp-wide): 5.4B **Publicly Held**
WEB: www.cmc.com
SIC: 3312 Bars & bar shapes, steel, hot-
rolled
PA: Commercial Metals Company
6565 N Macarthur Blvd # 800
Irving TX 75039
214 689-4300

(G-18832)
**CONE BIOPRODUCTS SEGUIN
LLC (PA)**
1012 N Austin St (78155-4518)
PHONE...............................830 379-0197
William K Cone, *President*
Mary B Cone, *Vice Pres*
Todd Bush, *Opers Mgr*
EMP: 15
SQ FT: 10,000
SALES (est): 2.7MM **Privately Held**
WEB: www.conebio.com
SIC: 2836 Biological products, except diag-
nostic

(G-18833)
**CONTINENTAL AUTO SYSTEMS
INC**
3740 N Austin St (78155-7359)
PHONE...............................830 372-7000
John Cowey, *Mfg Staff*
Michael Nowacki, *QC Mgr*
Arturo Vargas, *QC Mgr*
Jorge Contreras, *Engineer*
Chad Darlington, *Engineer*
EMP: 2000
SALES (corp-wide): 49.2B **Privately Held**
WEB: www.continental-automotive.com
SIC: 3674 3714 Semiconductors & related
devices; motor vehicle parts & acces-
sories
HQ: Continental Automotive Systems, Inc.
1 Continental Dr
Auburn Hills MI 48326
248 393-5300

(G-18834)
CRISP INDUSTRIES INC
4547 W Interstate 10 (78155-1411)
PHONE...............................830 372-1110
John I Crisp, *Branch Mgr*
EMP: 51
SALES (corp-wide): 78.5MM **Privately
Held**
WEB: www.crispindustries.com
SIC: 7692 5084 1542 Welding repair;
conveyor systems; nonresidential con-
struction
PA: Crisp Industries, Inc.
323 Energy Way
Bridgeport TX 76426
940 683-4070

(G-18835)
D&D RETAIL LP
Also Called: True Value
516 Intrstate 10 Frmtage (78155)
PHONE...............................830 379-7340
Lyle Heidemann, *CEO*
Charles Kevin Ferrell, *Partner*

Cathy Anderson, *Vice Pres*
EMP: 50
SQ FT: 25,000
SALES (est): 14.7MM **Privately Held**
WEB: www.d-dfarmranch.com
SIC: 5651 5599 3751 Family clothing stores; utility trailers; saddles & seat posts, motorcycle & bicycle

(G-18836)
DRAGONFLY GARMENT DESIGN CORP
217 S River St Ste 202 (78155-6104)
PHONE.....................830 549-5113
Carolina Brueggemann, *President*
Dale Brueggemann, *Vice Pres*
EMP: 9
SALES (est): 600K **Privately Held**
WEB: www.dragonflygarment.com
SIC: 2395 2759 3993 Embroidery products, except schiffli machine; letterpress & screen printing; signs & advertising specialties

(G-18837)
FUJIREBIO DIAGNOSTICS INC
940 Crossroads Blvd (78155-7801)
PHONE.....................830 372-1391
Alicia Ember, *General Mgr*
Andre Hepburn, *Project Mgr*
Todd Rider, *Safety Mgr*
Michael McClellan, *Engineer*
Mark Difelice, *Info Tech Dir*
EMP: 25 **Privately Held**
WEB: www.fujirebio.com
SIC: 2835 In vitro & in vivo diagnostic substances
HQ: Fujirebio Diagnostics, Inc.
201 Great Valley Pkwy
Malvern PA 19355
610 240-3800

(G-18838)
GLASS CHALK
5075 N State Highway 123 (78155-0350)
PHONE.....................830 379-1814
Jay Daniel, *Owner*
EMP: 9
SALES (est): 1.3MM **Privately Held**
WEB: www.glasschalk.com
SIC: 3951 Markers, soft tip (felt, fabric, plastic, etc.)

(G-18839)
GUNCKEL ARCHTECTURAL MILLWORKS
404 W Kingsbury St (78155-2630)
P.O. Box 2400 (78156-2400)
PHONE.....................830 303-0688
Forrest Gunckel, *President*
Val Schultze, *Admin Sec*
EMP: 23
SQ FT: 7,000
SALES (est): 3MM **Privately Held**
SIC: 2541 2434 2431 Counters or counter display cases, wood; cabinets, except refrigerated: show, display, etc.: wood; wood kitchen cabinets; vanities, bathroom: wood; windows, wood

(G-18840)
GUSTAVS TOOL & DIE INC
Also Called: Eisen Gustav Tool & Die Works
1503 N Austin St (78155-2615)
P.O. Box 1226 (78156-1226)
PHONE.....................830 379-3551
Gerd Haeussler, *President*
Allison Haeussler, *Vice Pres*
EMP: 10
SQ FT: 5,624
SALES (est): 1.2MM **Privately Held**
WEB: www.gustavstoolanddieinc.com
SIC: 3544 Special dies & tools

(G-18841)
HELMERICH & PAYNE INC
567 E Ih 10 (78155-1421)
PHONE.....................830 379-5858
EMP: 9
SALES (corp-wide): 3.7B **Publicly Held**
SIC: 1381 Oil/Gas Well Drilling
PA: Helmerich & Payne, Inc.
1437 S Boulder Ave # 1400
Tulsa OK 74119
918 742-5531

(G-18842)
HELMERICH & PAYNE INTL DRLG CO
Also Called: H & P Drilling
4074 N State Highway 123 (78155-8802)
PHONE.....................361 664-0114
Jim Schlieper, *Branch Mgr*
EMP: 210
SALES (corp-wide): 1.7B **Publicly Held**
WEB: www.hpinc.com
SIC: 1381 Drilling oil & gas wells
HQ: Helmerich & Payne International Drilling Co Inc
1437 S Boulder Ave # 1400
Tulsa OK 74119
918 742-5531

(G-18843)
HEXCEL REINFORCEMENTS CORP (HQ)
1913 N King St (78155-2115)
PHONE.....................830 379-1580
David E Berges, *President*
Joseph H Shaulson, *President*
Rodney P Jenks Jr, *Vice Pres*
Ira J Krakower, *Vice Pres*
Wayne C Pensky, *Vice Pres*
▲ **EMP:** 65 **EST:** 2001
SALES (est): 40.9MM
SALES (corp-wide): 1.5B **Publicly Held**
WEB: www.hexcel.com
SIC: 2821 Plastics materials & resins; plasticizer/additive based plastic materials
PA: Hexcel Corporation
281 Tresser Blvd Fl 16
Stamford CT 06901
203 969-0666

(G-18844)
INGRAM READYMIX INC
1316 N Bowie St (78155-2618)
PHONE.....................830 379-2765
Mike Garcia, *Branch Mgr*
EMP: 18
SQ FT: 8,925
SALES (corp-wide): 125.6MM **Privately Held**
WEB: www.ingramreadymixinc.com
SIC: 3273 Ready-mixed concrete
PA: Ingram Readymix, Inc.
3580 Farm Market 482
New Braunfels TX 78132
830 625-9156

(G-18845)
ITW MINIGRIP INC
1650 N Heideke St (78155-2823)
PHONE.....................830 372-4400
Jim Koho, *President*
◆ **EMP:** 210
SQ FT: 47,000
SALES (est): 27.6MM
SALES (corp-wide): 14.1B **Publicly Held**
SIC: 3089 3083 2673 Plastic kitchenware, tableware & houseware; laminated plastics plate & sheet; bags: plastic, laminated & coated
PA: Illinois Tool Works Inc.
155 Harlem Ave
Glenview IL 60025
847 724-7500

(G-18846)
KEISER MANUFACTURING INC
3501 N Hwy 123 Byp (78155-7328)
PHONE.....................830 303-3397
Fred Keiser, *President*
EMP: 9 **EST:** 1976
SQ FT: 12,600
SALES (est): 1.6MM **Privately Held**
WEB: www.keiser-mfg.com
SIC: 3491 3714 3556 Industrial valves; motor vehicle engines & parts; smokers, food processing equipment

(G-18847)
KING TERRAIN CORPORATION
1502 E Walnut St (78155-5297)
P.O. Box 549 (78156-0549)
PHONE.....................830 379-1480
Ian Burden, *President*
Keith Vinyard, *Corp Secy*
George Murphy, *Vice Pres*
Jim Robertson, *Vice Pres*
Blake Johnson, *Sales Staff*

EMP: 150
SQ FT: 176,000
SALES (est): 13.4MM
SALES (corp-wide): 1.1B **Publicly Held**
WEB: www.terrainking.com
SIC: 3531 Construction machinery
HQ: Alamo Group (Usa) Inc.
1627 E Walnut St
Seguin TX 78155
830 379-1480

(G-18848)
KOEHLER CO
1404 N Camp St (78155-2600)
P.O. Box 1290 (78156-1290)
PHONE.....................830 303-6256
Charles Koehler, *Ch of Bd*
Steve Koehler, *President*
Rodney Bargfrede, *Superintendent*
Doug Mannel, *Superintendent*
Greg Koehler, *Vice Pres*
EMP: 50
SQ FT: 30,000
SALES (est): 11.3MM **Privately Held**
WEB: www.thekoehlercompany.com
SIC: 1521 1542 2431 New construction, single-family houses; commercial & office building contractors; millwork

(G-18849)
LIBERTY LABEL COMPANY INC
964 E Kingsbury St (78155-2128)
PHONE.....................830 549-5459
Fax: 830 303-0985
EMP: 10 **EST:** 1998
SALES: 1MM **Privately Held**
SIC: 2679 Mfg Converted Paper Products

(G-18850)
LONGHORN DRILLING AND EQP CO
1200 J Bar K Ln (78155-2555)
PHONE.....................830 372-1910
EMP: 15
SALES: 2MM **Privately Held**
SIC: 1381 Oil/Gas Well Drilling

(G-18851)
MEDICAL COMPONENTS OF AMERICA
292 Navarro Dr (78155-2234)
PHONE.....................830 237-6405
Chris Morton, *President*
EMP: 9
SALES (est): 3.5MM **Privately Held**
SIC: 2821 3089 3829 Thermoplastic materials; injection molding of plastics; medical diagnostic systems, nuclear

(G-18852)
P M P E LTD (PA)
2251 Rudeloff Rd (78155-0175)
P.O. Box 447 (78156-0447)
PHONE.....................830 303-0056
Clinton A Plant, *President*
Richard Basquez, *Purch Mgr*
Alex Sanches, *Engineer*
Sharon Plant, *Human Res Mgr*
John Webber, *Manager*
EMP: 56
SQ FT: 60,000
SALES (est): 13.9MM **Privately Held**
WEB: www.epmp.com
SIC: 3444 Sheet metal specialties, not stamped

(G-18853)
PAK-MOR LTD
2191 Rudeloff Rd (78155)
P.O. Box 389 (78156-0389)
PHONE.....................830 303-6238
Jason Berridge, *Partner*
Vikki Matthews, *Purch Agent*
Ben Hund, *Technology*
▼ **EMP:** 25
SQ FT: 25,000
SALES (est): 8.7MM **Privately Held**
WEB: www.pakmor.com
SIC: 3713 Truck & bus bodies

(G-18854)
PAMROD PRODUCTS COMPANY
2511 N Heideke St (78155-7480)
P.O. Box 1897 (78156-8897)
PHONE.....................830 372-1500
Richard La Pierre, *President*

▼ **EMP:** 25
SQ FT: 24,000
SALES (est): 2.9MM **Privately Held**
SIC: 3296 Fiberglass insulation

(G-18855)
PBR INC
Also Called: Skaps Matrix
1903 N Austin St (78155-1903)
PHONE.....................830 401-4523
Don Hudson, *Branch Mgr*
EMP: 29 **Privately Held**
WEB: www.skaps.com
SIC: 2399 Emblems, badges & insignia
PA: Pbr, Inc.
335 Athena Dr
Athens GA 30601

(G-18856)
PROPER STORAGE SYSTEMS LLC
2200 E Us Highway 90 (78155-1234)
P.O. Box 803 (78156-0803)
PHONE.....................830 372-1380
Clint Murphy, *Engineer*
Mikal Harn, *Mng Member*
EMP: 9
SQ FT: 20,000
SALES (est): 1.3MM **Privately Held**
WEB: www.properstorage.com
SIC: 2542 Shelving, office & store: except wood

(G-18857)
PURE & GENTLE INC
2460 Crossroads Blvd (78155-7400)
PHONE.....................830 379-1937
John Blount, *President*
▲ **EMP:** 50
SQ FT: 25,000
SALES (est): 2.9MM **Privately Held**
WEB: www.pureandgentlesoap.com
SIC: 2841 Soap: granulated, liquid, cake, flaked or chip

(G-18858)
QUALITY BIORESOURCES INC
Also Called: Quality Biologicals
1015 N Austin St (78155-4517)
PHONE.....................830 372-4797
Cara Vela, *QC Mgr*
Marc Henriquez, *Treasurer*
Jeff Johnson, *Director*
EMP: 38
SQ FT: 7,000
SALES (est): 6.3MM **Privately Held**
WEB: www.qualbio.com
SIC: 2834 2835 3841 Pharmaceutical preparations; in vitro & in vivo diagnostic substances; in vitro diagnostics; veterinary diagnostic substances; surgical & medical instruments

(G-18859)
RANEWS TEXAS INCORPORATED
940 Best Dr (78155-2525)
PHONE.....................770 229-5090
Lester Ranew, *President*
J Bryant Beeland, *CFO*
William Yancy, *Sales Staff*
EMP: 30
SALES (est): 3.8MM **Privately Held**
WEB: www.thefirminator.com
SIC: 3523 Farm machinery & equipment

(G-18860)
RAVE GEAR LLC
Also Called: Rave Gears
425 Strempel St (78155-7319)
PHONE.....................830 421-3295
Nick Patel, *CEO*
Pankaj Patel, *COO*
Vinay Shah, *COO*
Cary Rolfing, *Vice Pres*
Melissa Bauer, *QC Mgr*
EMP: 65
SQ FT: 21,500
SALES (est): 4.7MM **Privately Held**
WEB: www.ravegears.com
SIC: 3566 3728 Speed changers, drives & gears; beaching gear, aircraft

(G-18861)
REYNOLDS SCRAPERS LLC
2191 Rudeloff Rd (78155)
PHONE................................830 303-0794
Jason Berridge, *Mng Member*
EMP: 25
SALES (est): 4.6MM **Privately Held**
WEB: www.reynoldsinternational.com
SIC: 3531 Scrapers, graders, rollers & similar equipment

(G-18862)
SCHWARZE INDUSTRIES INC
1627 E Walnut St (78155-5259)
P.O. Box 549 (78156-0549)
PHONE................................830 379-1480
Greg Heyer, *Vice Pres*
EMP: 10 **EST:** 2011
SALES (est): 2.5MM
SALES (corp-wide): 1.1B **Publicly Held**
SIC: 3523 3531 Farm machinery & equipment; construction machinery attachments
PA: Alamo Group Inc.
1627 E Walnut St
Seguin TX 78155
830 379-1480

(G-18863)
SEGUINS BUDGET AUTO INC
Also Called: Seguin Fiberglass
1440 N King St (78155-2106)
PHONE................................830 372-1790
Chris Hampe, *President*
Karen Crow, *Sales Mgr*
EMP: 14 **EST:** 1977
SALES (est): 1.5MM **Privately Held**
WEB: www.seguinfiberglassco.com
SIC: 3296 3443 6512 Fiberglass insulation; tanks, standard or custom fabricated: metal plate; nonresidential building operators

(G-18864)
SOUTHERN NEWSPAPERS INC
Also Called: Seguin Gazette Enterprises
1012 Schriewer (78155-7473)
P.O. Box 1200 (78156-1200)
PHONE................................830 379-5402
Jeff Fowler, *Publisher*
Dalondo Moultrie, *Editor*
Sam Hilton, *District Mgr*
Mary Luensmann, *District Mgr*
Patty Castillo, *Bookkeeper*
EMP: 20
SALES (corp-wide): 140.3MM **Privately Held**
WEB: www.sninews.com
SIC: 2711 2752 Newspapers, publishing & printing; commercial printing, lithographic
PA: Southern Newspapers, Inc.
5701 Woodway Dr Ste 131
Houston TX 77057
713 266-5481

(G-18865)
STAR MANUFACTURING LTD
1001 Crossroads Blvd (78155-7469)
PHONE................................830 401-5951
Jacob Gray, *CEO*
Michael Lovay, *Partner*
▲ **EMP:** 30
SQ FT: 15,000
SALES (est): 6.9MM **Privately Held**
WEB: www.starmfgtx.com
SIC: 3469 Perforated metal, stamped

(G-18866)
STRUCTURAL METALS INC
Also Called: CMC Steel Texas
1 Steel Mill Dr (78155-7510)
P.O. Box 911 (78156-0911)
PHONE................................830 372-8200
Joseph Alvarado, *CEO*
Tracy Porter, *President*
Carey Dubois, *Treasurer*
Paul Kirkpatrick, *Admin Sec*
▼ **EMP:** 885 **EST:** 1947
SQ FT: 58,000
SALES (est): 228.8MM
SALES (corp-wide): 5.4B **Publicly Held**
WEB: www.cmc.com
SIC: 3441 3462 3312 Fabricated structural metal; iron & steel forgings; bars & bar shapes, steel, hot-rolled

PA: Commercial Metals Company
6565 N Macarthur Blvd # 800
Irving TX 75039
214 689-4300

(G-18867)
TEJAS ALLOYS LLC
Also Called: Geronimo Alloys
285 Navarro Dr (78155-2234)
PHONE................................830 303-4422
Kirk E Williamson, *Mng Member*
EMP: 22 **EST:** 2010
SALES (est): 5.5MM **Privately Held**
WEB: www.geronimoalloys.com
SIC: 3312 Tool & die steel & alloys

(G-18868)
TH PRECISION LLC
Also Called: Precision Iron
2579 Old Lehmann Rd (78155-8694)
PHONE................................830 549-5864
Anthony D Hatcher, *President*
Amber Hatcher, *Principal*
Eric Kuntz, *Principal*
EMP: 32 **EST:** 2009
SALES (est): 8.4MM **Privately Held**
WEB: www.thprecisioniron.com
SIC: 3441 1791 Fabricated structural metal; structural steel erection; iron work, structural

(G-18869)
TQI LLC
Also Called: Tecni-Quip Carts
960 Crossroads Blvd (78155-7801)
P.O. Box 2050 (78156-9050)
PHONE................................830 401-4400
Jo Beth Clement-Reilly, *Partner*
Michael T Reilly, *General Ptnr*
Dave Papayanopolus, *Engineer*
Lesa Akeroyd, *Controller*
Ryan Freudenberg, *Natl Sales Mgr*
EMP: 30 **EST:** 1961
SQ FT: 35,000
SALES (est): 6.3MM **Privately Held**
WEB: www.tqind.com
SIC: 2599 3569 Carts, restaurant equipment; filters, general line: industrial

(G-18870)
TRYTON TOOLS USA INC
3517 W Us Highway 90 (78155-1385)
PHONE................................830 372-2755
Randy Berryman, *Manager*
EMP: 16
SALES (corp-wide): 1.7MM **Privately Held**
WEB: www.trytontoolservices.com
SIC: 1389 Construction, repair & dismantling services
PA: Tryton Tools Usa Inc.
20329 State Highway 249 # 125
Houston TX 77070
832 717-7125

(G-18871)
TYSON FOODS INC
1200 W Kingsbury St (78155-3495)
P.O. Box 2228 (78156-2228)
PHONE................................830 401-8800
William Jay, *Safety Dir*
Gloria Shields, *Purch Dir*
Billy Wade Lovette, *Manager*
Jesse Cruz, *Supervisor*
Edmo Benavides, *Clerk*
EMP: 800
SALES (corp-wide): 43.1B **Publicly Held**
WEB: www.tysonfoods.com
SIC: 2015 Poultry slaughtering & processing
PA: Tyson Foods, Inc.
2200 W Don Tyson Pkwy
Springdale AR 72762
479 290-4000

(G-18872)
VITESCO TECHNOLOGIES USA LLC
3740 N Austin St (78155-7359)
PHONE................................830 379-8850
Scott Williams, *Branch Mgr*
EMP: 1500
SALES (corp-wide): 8.6B **Privately Held**
SIC: 3714 Motor vehicle parts & accessories

HQ: Vitesco Technologies Usa, Llc
2400 Executive Hills Dr
Auburn Hills MI 48326
248 209-4000

(G-18873)
WESTERN READY MIX LLC
6411 Ih 10 W (78155)
PHONE................................830 433-1963
James D Woodruff, *Manager*
EMP: 10
SALES (est): 395.4K **Privately Held**
SIC: 3274 Concrete products

(G-18874)
WIRELINE TRUCK FAB LP
2200 Ilka Switch (78155-1588)
P.O. Box 142 (78156-0142)
PHONE................................830 372-3626
Billy Smith, *Partner*
Ricky Smith, *Webmaster*
EMP: 12 **EST:** 2006
SALES (est): 2.4MM **Privately Held**
WEB: www.wirelinetruckfab.com
SIC: 1389 Oil field services

(G-18875)
XERXES CORPORATION
2001 Proform Rd (78155-2238)
PHONE................................830 372-0090
Mike Miller, *Enginr/R&D Mgr*
EMP: 35
SALES (corp-wide): 1.1B **Privately Held**
WEB: www.zcl.com
SIC: 3089 3714 Plastic processing; motor vehicle parts & accessories
HQ: Xerxes Corporation
7901 Xerxes Ave S Ste 201
Minneapolis MN 55431
952 887-1890

Selma
Guadalupe County

(G-18876)
KAREL MANUFACTURING INC
16742 Pawlin Dr (78154-1239)
P.O. Box 621, Schertz (78154-0621)
PHONE................................210 651-6643
Davorin Jordan, *President*
Martin Jordan, *COO*
Roland Aubert, *Vice Pres*
Mario O Ergang, *CFO*
Mario Ergang, *CFO*
EMP: 85
SQ FT: 7,000
SALES (est): 17.7MM **Privately Held**
WEB: www.karelmfg.com
SIC: 3444 Sheet metalwork

(G-18877)
MAGI FOODS LLC
Also Called: Louisiana Purchase Foods
17750 Lookout Rd Ste 205 (78154-2195)
P.O. Box 120008, San Antonio (78212-9208)
PHONE................................210 590-1308
Charles Matthew Mayes, *President*
Doug Herber,
George Karutz,
Robert Miggins,
Dacia Hammerick Napier,
EMP: 10
SQ FT: 10,000
SALES (est): 2.3MM **Privately Held**
WEB: www.magifoods.com
SIC: 2099 2043 Rice, uncooked: packaged with other ingredients; desserts, ready-to-mix; rice: prepared as cereal breakfast food

(G-18878)
MUNTERS CORPORATION
16900 Jordan (78154-1272)
PHONE................................210 651-5018
EMP: 95
SQ FT: 60,000
SALES (corp-wide): 760.6MM **Privately Held**
WEB: www.munters.us
SIC: 3585 1711 Humidifiers & dehumidifiers; heating & air conditioning contractors

HQ: Munters Corporation
79 Monroe St
Amesbury MA 01913

(G-18879)
MUNTERS CORPORATION
Munters Dry Cool
16900 Jordan (78154-1272)
PHONE................................210 651-5018
Skip King, *COO*
Jeff Mills, *Engineer*
Robert Untz, *Engineer*
EMP: 95
SALES (corp-wide): 760.6MM **Privately Held**
WEB: www.munters.us
SIC: 3634 5075 1799 Dehumidifiers, electric: room; air conditioning & ventilation equipment & supplies; post-disaster renovations
HQ: Munters Corporation
79 Monroe St
Amesbury MA 01913

Seminole
Gaines County

(G-18880)
APACHE PACKERS LLC
344 County Road 306 (79360-5913)
P.O. Box 1963 (79360-1963)
PHONE................................432 758-6202
EMP: 34
SQ FT: 900
SALES (est): 3MM **Privately Held**
SIC: 1389 Oil field services

(G-18881)
BASIC ENERGY SERVICES LP
W Hwy 180 & Cr 209 (79360)
P.O. Box 425 (79360-0425)
PHONE................................432 758-9215
H H Wommack III, *President*
EMP: 14
SALES (corp-wide): 567.2MM **Publicly Held**
WEB: www.basices.com
SIC: 1389 Oil field services
HQ: Basic Energy Services, L.P.
801 Cherry St Unit 2
Fort Worth TX 76102

(G-18882)
FAITH DRILLING LLC
191 Us Highway 180 E (79360-6049)
P.O. Box 1378 (79360-1378)
PHONE................................432 758-6352
EMP: 29
SQ FT: 5,000
SALES (est): 2.7MM **Privately Held**
SIC: 1381 Oil/Gas Well Drilling

(G-18883)
FEHRS INDUSTRIAL MFG LLC
Also Called: Fim Cranes
373 County Road 307 (79360-5736)
P.O. Box 780 (79360-0780)
PHONE................................432 758-0068
Fred Elias, *General Mgr*
Willie Penner, *Project Mgr*
David Mutter, *Safety Mgr*
Ben Loewen, *Engineer*
Henry Dyck, *Sales Mgr*
EMP: 65
SALES (est): 19MM **Privately Held**
WEB:
www.fehrsindustrialmanufacturing.com
SIC: 3448 3536 7389 3446 Prefabricated metal buildings; hoists, cranes & monorails; inspection & testing services; ladders, for permanent installation: metal

(G-18884)
JD KING INC
1300 Sw 2nd St (79360-5462)
P.O. Box 1254 (79360-1254)
PHONE................................800 805-6302
Chad King, *Principal*
Josie King, *Opers Mgr*
Lorene Ramirez,
EMP: 130

GEOGRAPHIC

SALES (est): 26MM **Privately Held**
WEB: www.jdkingcorp.com
SIC: 4959 1794 1389 1629 Environmental cleanup services; excavation work; construction, repair & dismantling services; cutting of right-of-way; land preparation construction; oil refinery construction; curb & sidewalk contractors

(G-18885)
JIMS MACHINE SERVICE INC
102 County Road 402 (79360-6050)
P.O. Box 7 (79360-0007)
PHONE..........................432 758-2611
James F Wood, *President*
Gail Wood, *Vice Pres*
EMP: 12
SQ FT: 7,400
SALES (est): 1.3MM **Privately Held**
SIC: 3599 Machine shop, jobbing & repair

(G-18886)
PATE TRUCKING CO INC
104 N Hwy 214 (79360)
PHONE..........................432 758-2166
Melvon Seay, *Branch Mgr*
EMP: 15
SALES (corp-wide): 23.1MM **Privately Held**
WEB: www.patetrucking.com
SIC: 1389 Cementing oil & gas well casings
PA: Pate Trucking Co., Llc
2763 Highway 214
Denver City TX 79323
806 592-2772

(G-18887)
SPEEDWAY LLC
100 Nw 7th St (79360-3438)
PHONE..........................432 758-6700
Dan Farris, *Manager*
Nicki Wiley, *Manager*
Rebecca Rickman, *Admin Asst*
Stephanie Biernat, *Analyst*
Stacie Ericson, *Assistant*
EMP: 10 **Publicly Held**
WEB: www.speedway.com
SIC: 1311 1382 Crude petroleum production; oil & gas exploration services
HQ: Speedway Llc
500 Speedway Dr
Enon OH 45323
937 864-3000

(G-18888)
WT FIBER LINK LLC
Also Called: W T Fiber Link Company
807 Se Avenue P (79360-5618)
P.O. Box 1685 (79360-1685)
PHONE..........................432 758-2700
Erika Alvidrez, *Office Mgr*
Hector Alvidrez,
EMP: 98 **EST:** 2010
SALES (est): 1.5MM **Privately Held**
SIC: 7371 3229 1731 Custom computer programming services; fiber optics strands; electrical work

Seymour
Baylor County

(G-18889)
CONTECH ENGNERED SOLUTIONS LLC
1100 N Main St (76380-4235)
P.O. Box 112 (76380-0112)
PHONE..........................940 888-3871
David Horton, *Plant Mgr*
EMP: 35 **Privately Held**
WEB: www.conteches.com
SIC: 3444 5082 Culverts, sheet metal; blades for graders, scrapers, dozers & snow plows
HQ: Contech Engineered Solutions Llc
9025 Centre Pointe Dr # 400
West Chester OH 45069
513 645-7000

Shallowater
Lubbock County

(G-18890)
GORMAN OUTDOOR INC
7212 N Fm 179 (79363-3617)
PHONE..........................806 832-0159
Brett Gorman, *President*
EMP: 15 **EST:** 2013
SALES (est): 1.3MM **Privately Held**
WEB: www.gormanoutdoor.com
SIC: 3524 Grass catchers, lawn mower

Shamrock
Wheeler County

(G-18891)
JAMES RENEAU SEED COMPANY
119 S Main St (79079-2519)
P.O. Box 40 (79079-0040)
PHONE..........................806 256-3216
Patricia Arnold, *President*
James Royce Reneau, *President*
Rebecca Pena, *Treasurer*
◆ **EMP:** 15
SQ FT: 25,000
SALES (est): 2.7MM **Privately Held**
SIC: 1311 5191 Crude petroleum production; natural gas production; seeds: field, garden & flower

(G-18892)
LUBRICATION TECHNOLOGIES INC
Also Called: Chem-Tech
6194 Us Highway 83 (79079-6924)
PHONE..........................806 256-1600
EMP: 14
SALES (corp-wide): 164.7MM **Privately Held**
SIC: 1389 Oil/Gas Field Services
PA: Lubrication Technologies, Inc.
900 Mendelssohn Ave N
Minneapolis MN 55427
763 545-0707

(G-18893)
VINYARD WATER SERVICE
709 E 11 St (79079)
P.O. Box 190 (79079-0190)
PHONE..........................806 256-2766
Winnie Faye Vinyard, *Owner*
Darwin Vinyard, *Co-Owner*
Paul Vinyard, *Co-Owner*
Philip Vinyard, *Co-Owner*
EMP: 24
SALES (est): 2.1MM **Privately Held**
SIC: 1389 7692 Oil field services; welding repair

Shelbyville
Shelby County

(G-18894)
AFI UNLIMITED LLC
Also Called: Neuville
114 Fm 417 W (75973)
P.O. Box 246 (75973-0246)
PHONE..........................936 591-9300
Chance David, *Principal*
EMP: 20
SALES (est): 12MM **Privately Held**
SIC: 1389 Oil field services

Shenandoah
Montgomery County

(G-18895)
BLACK SAIL HOLDINGS CORP
250 Ed English Dr (77385-8020)
PHONE..........................281 315-4955
David Lomas, *President*
EMP: 15
SALES (est): 416.6K **Privately Held**
WEB: www.blacksailholding.com
SIC: 1381 Drilling oil & gas wells

(G-18896)
EPCON INDUSTRIAL SYSTEMS LP
17777 Interstate 45 S (77385-8732)
P.O. Box 7060, The Woodlands (77387-7060)
PHONE..........................936 273-1774
▲ **EMP:** 60
SQ FT: 250,000
SALES (est): 18.2MM **Privately Held**
WEB: www.epconlp.com
SIC: 3444 3567 3433 3443 Sheet metalwork; industrial furnaces & ovens; heating equipment, except electric; finned tubes, for heat transfer; pollution control engineering

(G-18897)
HMT LLC (PA)
19241 David Memorial Dr # 150 (77385-8786)
PHONE..........................281 681-7000
Millard H Jones, *CEO*
S Kent Rockwell, *CEO*
Gary E Tesch, *President*
John Hazel, *General Mgr*
John Soderman, *General Mgr*
◆ **EMP:** 30
SQ FT: 13,200
SALES (est): 113MM **Privately Held**
WEB: www.hmttank.com
SIC: 7699 3443 7389 1791 Tank repair; fuel tanks (oil, gas, etc.): metal plate; industrial & commercial equipment inspection service; storage tanks, metal: erection

(G-18898)
SANTTE LABS LLC
Also Called: Santte Foods
250 Ed English Dr Ste C (77385-8019)
PHONE..........................832 585-1862
EMP: 15 **EST:** 2010
SALES (est): 4MM **Privately Held**
SIC: 2052 Testing Laboratory

Shepherd
San Jacinto County

(G-18899)
AGRI-TEX WOOD SHAVINGS CO LLC
200 Industrial Blvd (77371-6270)
P.O. Box 519 (77371-0519)
PHONE..........................936 628-1950
Chris Molton, *Sales Mgr*
H Ross Arnold III, *Mng Member*
R Michael Webb,
EMP: 19
SALES (est): 3.6MM **Privately Held**
WEB: www.agri-tex.com
SIC: 2421 Sawdust & shavings

(G-18900)
CLEVELAND ASPHALT PRODUCTS INC
Hwy 59 N (77371)
P.O. Box 1449 (77371-1449)
PHONE..........................936 628-6200
Murray Moore, *President*
Scott M Moore, *Vice Pres*
EMP: 30
SQ FT: 1,500
SALES (est): 12.6MM **Privately Held**
SIC: 2951 Asphalt & asphaltic paving mixtures (not from refineries)

(G-18901)
COTTON UTILITY CONSTRUCTORS
5101 Fm 2666 Rd (77371-2631)
PHONE..........................281 659-5707
Laurence Murphy, *President*
Susan Murphy, *Corp Secy*
EMP: 15
SALES (est): 2.1MM **Privately Held**
SIC: 3643 1623 Power line cable; electric power line construction

Sheppard Afb
Wichita County

(G-18902)
PAE AVATION TECHNICAL SVCS LLC
Also Called: Ds2
235 9th Ave Bldg 140 (76311-3304)
PHONE..........................940 257-2836
EMP: 13
SALES (corp-wide): 311.4MM **Publicly Held**
WEB: www.pae.com
SIC: 3728 Aircraft parts & equipment
HQ: Pae Aviation And Technical Services Llc
1320 N Courthouse Rd # 700
Arlington VA 22201
856 866-2200

Sheridan
Colorado County

(G-18903)
B & D SERVICES INC
Hwy 90 (77475)
P.O. Box 1123, Columbus (78934-1123)
PHONE..........................979 733-9938
Bruce Tesch, *President*
Donna Tesch, *Vice Pres*
EMP: 22
SQ FT: 5,000
SALES (est): 3.2MM **Privately Held**
SIC: 1389 Oil field services

Sherman
Grayson County

(G-18904)
ACTITECH LP
301 W Fm 1417 (75092-8005)
PHONE..........................903 893-2551
Hal Rose, *Partner*
Michael Bhisop, *General Ptnr*
Tonya McWhorter, *Controller*
John Labonte, *Technical Staff*
EMP: 65
SALES (est): 21.5MM **Privately Held**
WEB: www.actitech.com
SIC: 2834 Ointments

(G-18905)
ALTIUM PACKAGING
4201 S Us Highway 75 (75090-9305)
PHONE..........................903 870-7080
Lisa Phillips, *Human Res Mgr*
Donald Brumett, *Manager*
EMP: 20
SALES (corp-wide): 12.5B **Publicly Held**
WEB: www.altiumpkg.com
SIC: 3089 Plastic containers, except foam
HQ: Altium Packaging Llc
2500 Windy Ridge Pkwy Se # 1400
Atlanta GA 30339
678 742-4600

(G-18906)
AMERICAN BOTTLING COMPANY
Also Called: Dr Pepper Bottling Co In Texas
1915 Us Highway 82 E (75090-2403)
PHONE..........................903 893-6536
Tin Bowling, *Manager*
EMP: 45 **Publicly Held**
WEB: www.keurigdrpepper.com
SIC: 2086 Soft drinks: packaged in cans, bottles, etc.
HQ: The American Bottling Company
5301 Legacy Dr
Plano TX 75024

(G-18907)
BALL DPF LLC
Also Called: Nature's Source
307 E Mulberry St (75090-5905)
PHONE..........................888 839-8722
Anna C Ball, *President*
Anne Leventry, *Exec VP*
Cornelis A Boonman, *Vice Pres*

W Todd Billings, *CFO*
Todd P Frauendorfer, *Treasurer*
▼ EMP: 25
SQ FT: 22,000
SALES (est): 3MM
SALES (corp-wide): 623.5MM **Privately Held**
WEB: www.naturessourceplantfood.com
SIC: 2874 Plant foods, mixed: from plants making phosphatic fertilizer
PA: Ball Horticultural Company
622 Town Rd
West Chicago IL 60185
630 231-3600

(G-18908)
BRECO TRUCKING INC
Also Called: Breco Wood Products
620 E Pecan St (75090-6051)
PHONE..................................903 870-0396
Bob Edwards, *President*
Leta Edwards, *Corp Secy*
EMP: 27
SQ FT: 18,000
SALES (est): 7.9MM Privately Held
WEB: www.brecowoodproducts.com
SIC: 2421 Building & structural materials, wood

(G-18909)
CITY OF SHERMAN
243 La Cima Rd (75092-6609)
P.O. Box 1106 (75091-1106)
PHONE..................................903 892-7258
Dwayne Sutherland, *Principal*
Willie Steele, *Mayor*
Joanna Curry, *Supervisor*
EMP: 22
SALES (corp-wide): 42.8MM **Privately Held**
WEB: www.ci.sherman.tx.us
SIC: 3589 Water treatment equipment, industrial
PA: City Of Sherman
220 W Mulberry St
Sherman TX 75090
903 892-7200

(G-18910)
CLAY PRECISION LTD
1102 Fm 1417 Ne (75090-2704)
PHONE..................................903 891-9022
Julia Spencer, *President*
Joe W Ayers, *Vice Pres*
Joe Ayers, *Info Tech Dir*
EMP: 20
SQ FT: 12,000
SALES (est): 3.3MM Privately Held
WEB: www.clayprecision.com
SIC: 3599 Machine shop, jobbing & repair

(G-18911)
COCA-COLA REFRESHMENTS USA INC
1820 N Frisco Rd (75090-2646)
PHONE..................................903 893-0194
Eddie Brown, *Branch Mgr*
EMP: 50
SALES (corp-wide): 37.2B **Publicly Held**
WEB: www.coca-colacompany.com
SIC: 2086 Bottled & canned soft drinks
HQ: Coca-Cola Refreshments Usa, Inc.
2500 Windy Ridge Pkwy Se
Atlanta GA 30339
770 989-3000

(G-18912)
COMMISSARY EXPRESS INC
609 E Pecan St (75090-6050)
PHONE..................................903 357-5670
Sam Loria, *CEO*
EMP: 17 EST: 2017
SALES (est): 2.6MM Privately Held
SIC: 2033 Vegetables: packaged in cans, jars, etc.

(G-18913)
COOPER B-LINE INC
4901 Marshall St (75090-2002)
PHONE..................................903 813-1746
Kristi Patterson, *Manager*
Carrie Williams, *Personnel Assit*
EMP: 135 Privately Held
WEB: www.eaton.com

SIC: 3441 3443 3699 3644 Fabricated structural metal; fabricated plate work (boiler shop); electrical equipment & supplies; noncurrent-carrying wiring services
HQ: Cooper B-Line, Inc.
509 W Monroe St
Highland IL 62249
618 654-2184

(G-18914)
FISHER CONTROLS INTL LLC
4725 S Us Highway 75 (75090-9495)
P.O. Box 1658 (75091-1658)
PHONE..................................903 868-3200
EMP: 290
SALES (corp-wide): 16.7B **Publicly Held**
WEB: www.emersonprocess.com
SIC: 3823 Industrial instrmnts msrmnt display/control process variable
HQ: Fisher Controls International Llc
205 S Center St
Marshalltown IA 50158
641 754-3011

(G-18915)
FRITO-LAY NORTH AMERICA INC
4809 Marshall St (75090-2075)
PHONE..................................903 868-2657
Brian Trapp, *Manager*
EMP: 15
SALES (corp-wide): 67.1B **Publicly Held**
WEB: www.fritolay.com
SIC: 5145 2096 Snack foods; potato chips & similar snacks
HQ: Frito-Lay North America, Inc.
7701 Legacy Dr
Plano TX 75024

(G-18916)
GLOBITECH INCORPORATED
200 W Fm 1417 (75092-8002)
PHONE..................................903 957-1999
EMP: 150 EST: 1998
SQ FT: 125,000
SALES (est): 168.6MM Privately Held
WEB: www.globitech.com
SIC: 3674 Integrated circuits, semiconductor networks, etc.
PA: Sino-American Silicon Products Lnc.
4f, 8, Industrial E. 2nd Rd., Hsinchu Science-Based Ind. Park,
Hsinchu City 30075

(G-18917)
HERALD DEMOCRAT (DH)
Also Called: Db Texas Holdings, Inc.
603 S Sam Rayburn Fwy (75090-7258)
P.O. Box 1128 (75091-1128)
PHONE..................................903 893-8181
Kirk Davis, *CEO*
EMP: 19
SALES (est): 4.5MM
SALES (corp-wide): 1.8B **Publicly Held**
WEB: www.heralddemocrat.com
SIC: 2711 2752 Newspapers: publishing only, not printed on site; commercial printing, lithographic
HQ: Gatehouse Media, Llc
175 Sullys Trl Fl 3
Pittsford NY 14534
585 598-0030

(G-18918)
KAISER ALUMINUM FAB PDTS LLC
4300 S Us Highway 75 (75090-9311)
P.O. Box 1215 (75091-1215)
PHONE..................................903 868-1556
Larry Beam, *Safety Mgr*
Carolyn Bartholomew, *Branch Mgr*
Julio Garza, *Manager*
Arnold Holley, *Supervisor*
Eddie Carver, *Info Tech Mgr*
EMP: 190
SQ FT: 76,000
SALES (corp-wide): 1.5B **Publicly Held**
SIC: 3341 3354 3334 Aluminum smelting & refining (secondary); aluminum extruded products; primary aluminum
HQ: Kaiser Aluminum Fabricated Products, Llc
27422 Portola Pkwy # 200
Foothill Ranch CA 92610

(G-18919)
KEYSTONE CONSOLIDATED INDS
Also Called: Sherman Wire, West Plant
428 Gibbons Rd (75092-8390)
PHONE..................................903 893-0191
Greg Lecheler, *Manager*
EMP: 100
SALES (corp-wide): 928.5K **Privately Held**
WEB: www.kci-corp.com
SIC: 3315 3496 3429 3357 Wire, ferrous/iron; wire, steel: insulated or armored; miscellaneous fabricated wire products; manufactured hardware (general); nonferrous wiredrawing & insulating
HQ: Keystone Consolidated Industries, Inc.
5430 Lyndon B Johnson Fwy
Dallas TX 75240
800 441-0308

(G-18920)
LATTIMORE MATERIALS CORP
6102 Theresa Dr (75090-2108)
PHONE..................................903 868-9585
Dennis Powers, *Manager*
EMP: 15
SALES (corp-wide): 1.7B **Privately Held**
WEB: www.lafargeholcim.us
SIC: 3273 Ready-mixed concrete
HQ: Lattimore Materials Corp.
15900 Dooley Rd
Addison TX 75001
972 221-4646

(G-18921)
MIDWEST PROVISIONS INC
4700 S Us Highway 75 (75090-3476)
PHONE..................................903 891-6213
EMP: 115 Privately Held
WEB: www.midwestprovisions.com
SIC: 2011 Meat packing plants
PA: Midwest Provisions, Inc
3608 Se Ave
Sioux Falls SD

(G-18922)
MODERN EXPLORATION INC (PA)
4900 Texoma Pkwy (75090-5974)
PHONE..................................903 893-1129
Gary Yost, *President*
Charles Holcomb, *Vice Pres*
Heath Yost, *Vice Pres*
Amy Yost, *Web Dvlpr*
EMP: 15
SQ FT: 8,500
SALES (est): 5.3MM Privately Held
WEB: www.modernexploration.com
SIC: 1311 1381 Crude petroleum production; natural gas production; drilling oil & gas wells

(G-18923)
MONITOR CANOPIES INC
200 Elliott Rd (75092-8322)
P.O. Box 1315 (75091-1315)
PHONE..................................903 893-6336
Stoney Russell, *Director*
EMP: 15
SALES (est): 2.3MM Privately Held
WEB: www.monitorinc.com
SIC: 3339 Precious metals

(G-18924)
MUELLER CONSTRUCTION COMPANY
5100 Marshall St (75090-2104)
PHONE..................................903 868-3585
Larry Mueller, *Partner*
Michael Mueller, *Partner*
EMP: 30
SQ FT: 96,000
SALES (est): 6.7MM Privately Held
WEB: www.muellerc.com
SIC: 1796 3535 1742 3441 Millwright; conveyors & conveying equipment; insulation, buildings; fabricated structural metal

(G-18925)
MUELLER SUPPLY COMPANY INC
110 E Hwy 82 (75092)
P.O. Box 1174 (75091-1174)
PHONE..................................903 892-6222
Brad Bryan, *Manager*
EMP: 12
SALES (corp-wide): 180.3MM **Privately Held**
WEB: www.muellerinc.com
SIC: 3448 Prefabricated metal buildings
PA: Mueller Supply Company, Inc.
1913 Hutchins Ave
Ballinger TX 76821
325 365-3555

(G-18926)
PEPSI-COLA METRO BTLG CO INC
Also Called: Pepsico
4817 Marshall St (75090-2075)
P.O. Box 1185 (75091-1185)
PHONE..................................903 892-3030
Christine Terry, *Sales Staff*
David Derfelt, *Manager*
EMP: 22
SALES (corp-wide): 67.1B **Publicly Held**
WEB: www.pepsico.com
SIC: 2086 5149 Bottled & canned soft drinks; groceries & related products
HQ: Pepsi-Cola Metropolitan Bottling Company, Inc.
1111 Westchester Ave
White Plains NY 10604
914 767-6000

(G-18927)
PRECISION SPECIALTIES COMPANY
Also Called: Presco
1201 E Pecan St (75090-6227)
P.O. Box 226467, Dallas (75222-6467)
PHONE..................................800 527-3295
Waymon E McMackin, *President*
Becky Brussow, *Purchasing*
Gayle Telker, *Purchasing*
David Chisum, *CFO*
Clayton Chancy, *Marketing Staff*
▲ EMP: 20
SALES (est): 1.6MM Privately Held
WEB: www.presco.com
SIC: 2821 6722 Polypropylene resins; management investment, open-end
PA: River Associates Llc
633 Chestnut St Ste 1640
Chattanooga TN 37450

(G-18928)
PRENGLER LTD
Also Called: National Carport Industries
14871 State Highway 56 (75092-4621)
P.O. Box 2323 (75091-2323)
PHONE..................................972 965-5188
Aaron Prengler, *Principal*
Craig Prengler, *Treasurer*
Cinthia Prengler, *Shareholder*
Jackie Prengler, *Admin Sec*
EMP: 14
SQ FT: 20,000
SALES (est): 4.4MM Privately Held
WEB: www.prenglerproducts.com
SIC: 3448 Carports: prefabricated metal

(G-18929)
PRESCO POLYMERS OPCO INC
1201 E Pecan St (75090-6227)
PHONE..................................903 957-2263
David Chisum, *CFO*
EMP: 208
SALES (est): 13.8MM Privately Held
WEB: www.presco.com
SIC: 2671 Plastic film, coated or laminated for packaging

(G-18930)
ROYAL CASE COMPANY INC (PA)
419 E Lamar St (75090-7017)
P.O. Box 2231 (75091-2231)
PHONE..................................903 868-0288
▲ EMP: 150 EST: 1982
SQ FT: 80,000

SALES: 55.9MM **Privately Held**
WEB: www.royalcase.com
SIC: 3172 3161 Personal leather goods;
cases, carrying

(G-18931)
ROYAL CASE COMPANY INC
309 E Houston St (75090-5936)
PHONE..................................903 328-3371
EMP: 9
SALES (corp-wide): 55.9MM **Privately
Held**
WEB: www.royalcase.com
SIC: 3089 Air mattresses, plastic
PA: Royal Case Company, Inc.
419 E Lamar St
Sherman TX 75090
903 868-0288

(G-18932)
SHERMAN MACHINE INC
1622 S First St (75090-8400)
P.O. Box 102 (75091-0102)
PHONE..................................903 892-2889
Richard Harris, *President*
Douglas Lamb, *Vice Pres*
Mike Garner, *Purchasing*
Michelle Prutch, *Treasurer*
Doug Lamb, *Sales Executive*
EMP: 20
SQ FT: 9,000
SALES (est): 3.7MM **Privately Held**
WEB: www.shermanmachine.com
SIC: 3599 Machine shop, jobbing & repair

(G-18933)
STARR AIRCRAFT PRODUCTS
INC
5236 N Hwy 1417 (75092)
P.O. Box 158 (75091-0158)
PHONE..................................903 893-1106
Shelby Barnett, *President*
Joe Blanton, *Principal*
Les McConnell, *Vice Pres*
Mike Dunn, *Safety Mgr*
Cathy Erbay, *Purch Mgr*
▲ **EMP:** 250
SQ FT: 28,000
SALES (est): 31.4MM **Privately Held**
WEB: www.starraircraft.com
SIC: 2393 3728 Cushions, except spring &
carpet: purchased materials; aircraft parts
& equipment

(G-18934)
STRUCTURAL FABRICATIONS
INC
111 Cody Ln (75092-8335)
P.O. Box 2145 (75091-2145)
PHONE..................................903 868-2979
Roy Spears, *President*
Neil Scoggins, *Vice Pres*
EMP: 26
SQ FT: 35,000
SALES (est): 7.4MM **Privately Held**
WEB: www.structuralfabrications.com
SIC: 3441 Building components, structural
steel

(G-18935)
SUNNY DELIGHT BEVERAGES
CO
300 W Fm 1417 (75092-8004)
PHONE..................................903 893-5764
John Henry, *Manager*
EMP: 100
SALES (corp-wide): 1.1B **Privately Held**
WEB: www.sunnyd.com
SIC: 2033 Fruit juices: fresh
HQ: Sunny Delight Beverage Co
10300 Alliance Rd Ste 500
Blue Ash OH 45242
513 483-3300

(G-18936)
TEXAS PRIMING LLC
14989 State Highway 56 (75092-4605)
PHONE..................................903 893-6200
Cynthia L Diaz, *Treasurer*
EMP: 9
SALES (est): 1.3MM **Privately Held**
SIC: 2421 Sawmills & planing mills, general

(G-18937)
TYSON FOODS INC
4700 S Us Highway 75 (75090-3476)
PHONE..................................903 891-6001
Jessie Liles, *Asst Controller*
Cassandra Carey, *Human Res Mgr*
Mike Gerleman, *Branch Mgr*
EMP: 1150
SALES (corp-wide): 43.1B **Publicly Held**
WEB: www.tysonfoods.com
SIC: 2011 Beef products from beef slaugh-
tered on site; pork products from pork
slaughtered on site
PA: Tyson Foods, Inc.
2200 W Don Tyson Pkwy
Springdale AR 72762
479 290-4000

(G-18938)
WIRE SALES INC
Also Called: Wire Products Supply
4707 Gibbons Rd (75092-6418)
P.O. Box 911568 (75091-1568)
PHONE..................................903 892-9473
Patricia J Moore, *President*
Rick Broyles, *Accounts Mgr*
Danna Blaylock, *Sales Staff*
▲ **EMP:** 30
SALES (est): 8.5MM **Privately Held**
WEB: www.wiresalesinc.com
SIC: 3496 Miscellaneous fabricated wire
products

Shiner
Lavaca County

(G-18939)
D S D SERVICES INC
Also Called: Shiner Candy Company
723 N Avenue E (77984-7108)
P.O. Box 1449 (77984-1449)
PHONE..................................361 594-4114
Rennie Joe Overton Jr, *President*
Denise Overton III, *Manager*
EMP: 13
SQ FT: 20,000
SALES (est): 2.1MM **Privately Held**
WEB: www.dsd-services.com
SIC: 2096 5145 Potato sticks; snack foods

(G-18940)
GAMBRINUS COMPANY
Also Called: Shiner Beer
603 E Brewery St (77984)
P.O. Box 368 (77984-0368)
PHONE..................................361 594-3383
Jimmy Mauric, *COO*
Takacs Peter, *Vice Pres*
Peter Takacs, *Vice Pres*
Bob Darilek, *Maintence Staff*
Tracy Pavelka, *Maintence Staff*
EMP: 53
SALES (corp-wide): 237.4MM **Privately
Held**
WEB: www.gambrinus.com
SIC: 2082 Beer (alcoholic beverage)
PA: The Gambrinus Company
14800 San Pedro Ave # 310
San Antonio TX 78232
210 483-5100

(G-18941)
KASPAR DIE & TOOL INC
959 State Highway 95 N (77984-5883)
P.O. Box 667 (77984-0667)
PHONE..................................361 594-3327
Don G Kaspar, *President*
Douglas D Kaspar, *Principal*
David C Kaspar, *Vice Pres*
Dan A Kaspar, *Treasurer*
Dennis G Kaspar, *Admin Sec*
EMP: 14
SQ FT: 7,000
SALES (est): 1.6MM **Privately Held**
WEB: www.kasparmfg.com
SIC: 3599 Special dies & tools

(G-18942)
KASPAR RANCH HAND EQP LLC
(DH)
Also Called: Ranch Hand Truck Accessories
959 State Highway 95 N (77984-5883)
P.O. Box 667 (77984-0667)
PHONE..................................361 594-4608
Dan Kaspar, *Partner*
David Kaspar, *Partner*
Dennis Kaspar, *Partner*
Douglas Kaspar, *Partner*
Jerry Courtney, *Vice Pres*
EMP: 121
SALES (est): 49.9MM
SALES (corp-wide): 71.2MM **Privately
Held**
WEB: www.ranchhand.com
SIC: 5013 3714 Truck parts & acces-
sories; motor vehicle parts & accessories
HQ: Kaspar Ranch Hand Inc.
959 State Highway 95 N
Shiner TX 77984
361 594-3327

(G-18943)
KASPAR WIRE WORKS INC (PA)
Also Called: Kaspar Manufacturing
959 State Highway 95 N (77984-5883)
P.O. Box 667 (77984-0667)
PHONE..................................361 594-3327
Dan A Kaspar, *President*
David C Kaspar, *Vice Pres*
Douglas Kaspar, *VP Opers*
Douglas D Kaspar, *Treasurer*
Lori Malina, *Controller*
▲ **EMP:** 50
SQ FT: 500,000
SALES (est): 106.7MM **Privately Held**
WEB: www.kasparwireworks.com
SIC: 3496 Miscellaneous fabricated wire
products

(G-18944)
KASPAR WIRE WORKS INC
Also Called: Sho Rack
1127 Shorack (77984-5884)
P.O. Box 1127 (77984-1127)
PHONE..................................361 594-3327
Tarek Saab, *COO*
Chris N Stluka, *Finance Mgr*
Tricia Knezek, *Human Res Dir*
David Kaspar, *Branch Mgr*
Martha Gold, *Supervisor*
EMP: 600
SALES (corp-wide): 106.7MM **Privately
Held**
WEB: www.kasparwireworks.com
SIC: 5046 3581 3496 2542 Vending ma-
chines, coin-operated; automatic vending
machines; miscellaneous fabricated wire
products; partitions & fixtures, except
wood
PA: Kaspar Wire Works, Inc.
959 State Highway 95 N
Shiner TX 77984
361 594-3327

(G-18945)
MILLER MECHANICAL GROUP
7824 Fm 443 (77984-5364)
P.O. Box 987 (77984-0987)
PHONE..................................361 594-8080
Gina Miller, *Principal*
EMP: 11
SALES (est): 1.1MM **Privately Held**
WEB: www.millermechanicalgroup.com
SIC: 7623 1711 3822 Air conditioning re-
pair; heating & air conditioning contrac-
tors; air flow controllers, air conditioning &
refrigeration

(G-18946)
PATEK GROCERY AND MARKET
224 S Avenue E (77984-5714)
P.O. Box 635 (77984-0635)
PHONE..................................361 594-3171
Robert J Patek, *President*
Paul R Patek, *Vice Pres*
EMP: 14 **EST:** 1932
SQ FT: 6,000
SALES (est): 1.5MM **Privately Held**
SIC: 5411 2011 Grocery stores, independ-
ent; meat packing plants

(G-18947)
POLYFAB INC
Also Called: Preferred Plastics
514 W Runk St (77984-5692)
P.O. Box 577 (77984-0577)
PHONE..................................361 594-3535
Paul Panus, *President*
Sheri Panus, *Vice Pres*
EMP: 9
SQ FT: 12,000
SALES (est): 1MM **Privately Held**
WEB: www.preferredplasticsinc.com
SIC: 3599 Machine shop, jobbing & repair

(G-18948)
PREFERRED PLASTICS INC
514 W Runk St (77984-5692)
P.O. Box 577 (77984-0577)
PHONE..................................361 594-3535
Paul Panus, *President*
EMP: 11
SQ FT: 9,500
SALES (est): 2.5MM **Privately Held**
WEB: www.preferredplasticsinc.com
SIC: 3089 Injection molding of plastics

Silsbee
Hardin County

(G-18949)
APACHE PRODUCTS INC
Also Called: Acme Skid
1012 John Hare Rd (77656)
P.O. Box 187 (77656-0187)
PHONE..................................409 385-7021
Brook Gilchriest, *President*
Jamie Pridemore, *Sales Staff*
Gillum Gilchriest, *Shareholder*
Lanita Gilchriest, *Shareholder*
EMP: 85
SQ FT: 54,000
SALES (est): 13.1MM **Privately Held**
WEB: www.acmeskid.com
SIC: 2448 2441 Cargo containers, wood;
cargo containers, wood & metal combina-
tion; pallets, wood; skids, wood; nailed
wood boxes & shook

(G-18950)
CARAUSTAR INDUSTRIAL AND
CON
Also Called: Silsbee Tube Plant
932 John Hare Rd (77656-6126)
PHONE..................................409 898-6600
James Yancey, *Manager*
EMP: 24
SALES (corp-wide): 4.5B **Publicly Held**
WEB: www.greif.com
SIC: 2655 5113 Tubes, for chemical or
electrical uses: paper or fiber; paper
tubes & cores
HQ: Caraustar Industrial And Consumer
Products Group Inc
5000 Austell Powder Ste
Austell GA 30106
803 548-5100

(G-18951)
CLEAR VIEW UNLIMITED LLC
3417 Old Spurger Hwy (77656-7235)
PHONE..................................409 782-3594
Sammy Crawford,
Corliss Crawford, *Administration*
EMP: 15
SALES (est): 266.3K **Privately Held**
SIC: 1389 Oil & gas field services

(G-18952)
CURTIS OILFIELD SERVICES
LLC
Also Called: Curtis Welding Service
4779 Highway 96 Byp (77656-6596)
P.O. Box 1236 (77656-1236)
PHONE..................................409 385-2937
Pat Burrell, *Buyer*
Eddie Curtis, *Manager*
Buford Curtis,
EMP: 22
SQ FT: 6,000
SALES (est): 2.9MM **Privately Held**
WEB: www.curtisoilfield.com
SIC: 7692 Welding repair

(G-18953)
LOCAL PHONE BOOK
1250 Highway 96 S (77656-6406)
P.O. Box 8070, Lumberton (77657-0070)
PHONE.....................................409 386-2244
Shelly Wilson, *President*
Gerry Spring, *Vice Pres*
EMP: 10
SALES (est): 766.6K **Privately Held**
SIC: 2759 Directories, telephone: printing

(G-18954)
RENEAU PUBLISHING INC
Also Called: Silsbee Bee
404 Highway 96 S (77656-4810)
PHONE.....................................409 385-5278
Danny Reneau, *President*
EMP: 9 **EST:** 1919
SQ FT: 2,800
SALES (est): 428.6K **Privately Held**
WEB: www.silsbeebee.com
SIC: 2711 5943 Newspapers: publishing
only, not printed on site; office forms &
supplies

(G-18955)
SHERROD RV CENTER INC
1000 Highway 327 E (77656-5118)
PHONE.....................................409 385-5689
Robert Sherrod, *President*
Deborah J Sherrod, *Corp Secy*
Gary Post, *Consultant*
EMP: 12
SALES (est): 2.4MM **Privately Held**
WEB: www.sherrodrvcenter.com
SIC: 3799 5561 Recreational vehicles;
recreational vehicle dealers

(G-18956)
SOUTH HAMPTON RESOURCES INC (HQ)
7752 Fm 418 (77656-8943)
P.O. Box 1636 (77656-1636)
PHONE.....................................409 385-1400
Nick Carter, *President*
Nicholas Carter, *COO*
Richard Crain, *Vice Pres*
Mark Williamson, *Vice Pres*
John Cook, *Prdtn Mgr*
◆ **EMP:** 30
SQ FT: 15,300
SALES (est): 13.5MM
SALES (corp-wide): 258.9MM **Publicly Held**
WEB: www.southhamptonr.com
SIC: 2911 4612 Solvents; crude petroleum pipelines
PA: Trecora Resources
1650 Highway 6 Ste 190
Sugar Land TX 77478
281 980-5522

(G-18957)
TEXAS OIL & CHEMICAL CO II INC
7752 Fm 418 (77656-8943)
PHONE.....................................409 385-1400
Nicholas N Carter, *President*
Connie Cook, *Controller*
EMP: 57 **EST:** 1978
SQ FT: 15,000
SALES (est): 918.5K
SALES (corp-wide): 258.9MM **Publicly Held**
WEB: www.southhamptonr.com
SIC: 2911 Gasoline
PA: Trecora Resources
1650 Highway 6 Ste 190
Sugar Land TX 77478
281 980-5522

(G-18958)
WESTROCK MWV LLC
4594 Old Evadale Rd (77656-5890)
PHONE.....................................409 276-3000
Glen Richards, *Manager*
EMP: 77
SALES (corp-wide): 17.5B **Publicly Held**
WEB: www.westrock.com
SIC: 2631 2675 2672 Linerboard; die-cut
paper & board; coated & laminated paper
HQ: Westrock Mwv, Llc
501 S 5th St
Richmond VA 23219
804 444-1000

(G-18959)
WOODEN PALLETS LTD
3840 Henry Reed Rd (77656)
P.O. Box 555 (77656-0555)
PHONE.....................................409 385-1234
Ed T Worthey, *Mng Member*
Robert Worthey,
EMP: 165
SQ FT: 100,000
SALES (est): 33.1MM **Privately Held**
WEB: www.woodenpalletsltd.com
SIC: 2448 Pallets, wood

Sinton
San Patricio County

(G-18960)
A F C LEASE SERVICE INC
1200 Railroad Ave (78387-3662)
P.O. Box 776 (78387-0776)
PHONE.....................................361 364-2547
April Strum, *President*
Ashley Yeats, *Vice Pres*
EMP: 35
SALES (est): 3.6MM **Privately Held**
SIC: 1389 Construction, repair & dismantling services

(G-18961)
DOUBLE O FIELD SERVICES
2000 S San Patricio St (78387-3526)
PHONE.....................................361 364-2673
Oscar Israel, *President*
EMP: 12
SALES (est): 928.6K **Privately Held**
WEB: www.downsouthfs.com
SIC: 1389 Oil field services

(G-18962)
DUGGA BOYS INC
Also Called: H & K Vacuum Trucks
1010 Sodville St (78387-3822)
P.O. Box 1340 (78387-1340)
PHONE.....................................361 364-4311
Frank E Brandenburg, *President*
EMP: 20
SALES (est): 3.1MM **Privately Held**
SIC: 1389 Haulage, oil field

(G-18963)
LA COPA FIELD SERVICES INC
500 W Fulton St (78387-2440)
P.O. Box 336 (78387-0336)
PHONE.....................................361 364-1608
William Petrus, *President*
EMP: 60
SALES (est): 7.9MM **Privately Held**
WEB: www.lacopafs.com
SIC: 1389 Oil field services

(G-18964)
SAN PATRICIO CO DRAIN
701 S San Patricio St (78387-3501)
PHONE.....................................361 364-4268
Deborah Baron, *President*
EMP: 25
SALES (est): 1.5MM **Privately Held**
WEB: www.sanpatcad.org
SIC: 1481 Pumping or draining, nonmetallic mineral mines

(G-18965)
SAN PATRICIO PUBLISHING CO INC (PA)
Also Called: Taft Tribune
117 S Rachal St (78387-2545)
PHONE.....................................361 364-1270
John Tracy, *President*
EMP: 14
SQ FT: 7,500
SALES (est): 1.4MM **Privately Held**
WEB: www.mysoutex.com
SIC: 2711 2759 Newspapers, publishing &
printing; commercial printing

(G-18966)
TENNESSEE PIPELINE CNSTR INC
917 S San Patricio St (78387-3505)
P.O. Box 250 (78387-0250)
PHONE.....................................361 364-2703
Kevin Gregory, *President*
Matt Adair, *Vice Pres*

Dorothy Adair, *Admin Sec*
EMP: 200
SQ FT: 7,000
SALES (est): 24.2MM
SALES (corp-wide): 151.7MM **Privately Held**
WEB: www.tennpipe.com
SIC: 1623 1389 Oil & gas pipeline construction; oil field services
PA: Berry Gp, Inc.
1414 Corn Product Rd
Corpus Christi TX 78409
361 693-2100

(G-18967)
WELDER ROB & BESSIE WILDLIFE
10429 Welder Wildlife (78387)
P.O. Box 1400 (78387-1400)
PHONE.....................................361 364-2643
EMP: 13
SALES (corp-wide): 360.2K **Privately Held**
WEB: www.welderwildlife.org
SIC: 0971 1311 0212 Game preserve;
crude petroleum production; beef cattle
except feedlots
PA: Welder, Rob & Bessie Wildlife Foundation
503 Frst Victoria Nat Bnk
Victoria TX 77901
361 573-9722

Slaton
Lubbock County

(G-18968)
ARCHER-DANIELS-MIDLAND COMPANY
Also Called: ADM
7414 E County Road 7500 (79364-6809)
PHONE.....................................806 828-3948
Jerry Batenhorst, *Branch Mgr*
EMP: 49
SALES (corp-wide): 64.6B **Publicly Held**
WEB: www.adm.com
SIC: 2041 Flour & other grain mill products
PA: Archer-Daniels-Midland Company
77 W Wacker Dr Ste 4600
Chicago IL 60601
312 634-8100

(G-18969)
BACK TO NATURE INC
5407 E Highway 84 (79364-6987)
P.O. Box 190 (79364-0190)
PHONE.....................................806 745-3559
Wayne Schilling, *President*
Mary Schilling, *Corp Secy*
EMP: 20
SALES (est): 3.1MM **Privately Held**
WEB: www.backtonaturecompost.com
SIC: 2875 Compost

(G-18970)
BRAZOS OFFSET PRINTERS INC
9th & Industrial St (79364)
P.O. Box 773, Canyon (79015-0773)
PHONE.....................................806 828-5681
Wendell Tooley, *President*
Bobby Morman, *Vice Pres*
Terry Reeves, *Manager*
Stephen Henry, *Admin Sec*
EMP: 12
SQ FT: 7,100
SALES (est): 1MM **Privately Held**
SIC: 2752 Commercial printing, offset

(G-18971)
GRANVILLE R DAMRON TRUCKING (PA)
8602 Fm 400 (79364-7548)
PHONE.....................................806 842-3519
Michael Damron Jr, *President*
Justin Damron, *Vice Pres*
EMP: 20 **EST:** 1952
SQ FT: 1,120
SALES (est): 3.1MM **Privately Held**
SIC: 1442 0212 Common sand mining;
gravel mining; beef cattle except feedlots

(G-18972)
GRANVILLE R DAMRON TRUCKING
8602 Hwy 400 (79364)
PHONE.....................................806 842-3519
Michael Damron Jr, *Manager*
EMP: 18
SALES (corp-wide): 3.1MM **Privately Held**
SIC: 1442 0212 Common sand mining;
beef cattle except feedlots
PA: Damron Granville R Trucking Sand &
Gravel Co Inc
8602 Fm 400
Slaton TX 79364
806 842-3519

(G-18973)
SIKES MACHINE SHOP INC
265 N Terry Dr (79364-3644)
P.O. Box 370 (79364-0370)
PHONE.....................................806 828-6568
James A Sikes, *President*
Donald R Sikes, *Vice Pres*
EMP: 9
SALES (est): 850.8K **Privately Held**
SIC: 3599 Machine shop, jobbing & repair

(G-18974)
SOUTH PLAINS COMPOST INC
5407 E Highway 84 (79364-6987)
P.O. Box 9 (79364-0009)
PHONE.....................................806 745-3559
Wayne Schilling, *President*
Mary Schilling, *Corp Secy*
EMP: 22
SQ FT: 2,750
SALES (est): 8MM **Privately Held**
WEB: www.backtonaturecompost.com
SIC: 5191 2875 Fertilizer & fertilizer materials; fertilizers, mixing only

---

Smithville
Bastrop County

(G-18975)
BASTROP CNTY PRCNCT 2 RD BRDGE
911 Se Mrtn Lther King Rd (78957-2535)
P.O. Box 676, Bastrop (78602-0676)
PHONE.....................................512 360-4224
Claire Beckett, *Commissioner*
EMP: 13
SALES (est): 1.5MM **Privately Held**
WEB: www.co.bastrop.tx.us
SIC: 2491 Railroad cross bridges & switch
ties, treated wood

(G-18976)
CEN-TEX MARINE FABRICATORS (PA)
1100 Ne 1st St (78957-2000)
PHONE.....................................512 237-2496
Alvin Ulrich, *President*
Gene Hinnant, *Vice Pres*
Aaron Blackwell, *Manager*
Richard Hurst, *Manager*
Karen Badders, *Info Tech Mgr*
EMP: 49
SQ FT: 35,000
SALES (est): 5.9MM **Privately Held**
WEB: www.centexmarine.com
SIC: 3441 Fabricated structural metal

(G-18977)
K & H FABRICATORS INC
170 Loop Rd (78957-1232)
P.O. Box 695 (78957-0695)
PHONE.....................................512 237-5020
EMP: 32 **EST:** 2011
SALES (est): 7MM **Privately Held**
WEB: www.khfab.com
SIC: 3549 Wiredrawing & fabricating machinery & equipment, ex. die

(G-18978)
TEXAS NATURAL RAINWTR HRVSTNG
125 Kellar Rd (78957-5762)
PHONE.....................................512 772-1981
David M Schraub, *Principal*
EMP: 10

SALES (est): 860K **Privately Held**
WEB: www.texas-rain.net
SIC: 2086 Bottled & canned soft drinks

(G-18979)
WOLF & SONS DESIGN INC
Also Called: Patricia Wolf Designs
314 Main St (78957-1427)
P.O. Box 807 (78957-0807)
PHONE..................................512 237-3388
William S Wolfensen, *President*
William Wolfenson, *President*
Patricia Wolfenson, *Vice Pres*
EMP: 23
SQ FT: 5,500
SALES (est): 2.1MM **Privately Held**
WEB: www.patriciawolf.com
SIC: 2386 2211 Coats & jackets, leather &
sheep-lined; apparel & outerwear fabrics,
cotton

(G-18980)
ZAPCO INC
403 Zapalac Rd (78957-2134)
PHONE..................................512 237-5521
Steve Zapalac, *President*
Sharon Zapalac, *Corp Secy*
Shawn Zapalac, *Marketing Mgr*
EMP: 25
SALES (est): 2.6MM **Privately Held**
WEB: www.zapcopaper.com
SIC: 2621 5113 2675 Paper mills; indus-
trial & personal service paper; die-cut
paper & board

Snook
Burleson County

(G-18981)
SLOVACEK FOODS LP
Also Called: Slovacek Sausage
Hwy 60 W (77878)
PHONE..................................979 272-8625
Timothy Rabroker, *Partner*
Ray Rabroker, *Plant Mgr*
Cydney Mathis, *Opers Staff*
Michael Trojacek, *Inv Control Mgr*
Laura Doskocil, *CFO*
EMP: 42
SQ FT: 22,000
SALES (est): 15.6MM **Privately Held**
WEB: www.slovacek.com
SIC: 5147 2013 Meats, cured or smoked;
meats, fresh; sausages & other prepared
meats

Snyder
Scurry County

(G-18982)
**ARROW CONSTRUCTION CO
INC (PA)**
2700 21st St (79549-2329)
P.O. Box 576 (79550-0576)
PHONE..................................325 573-3571
Rickey Daniell, *President*
EMP: 40
SQ FT: 1,500
SALES (est): 3.8MM **Privately Held**
SIC: 3471 Sand blasting of metal parts

(G-18983)
BAKER HUGHES
311 Old Lubbock (79549)
P.O. Box 85 (79550-0085)
PHONE..................................432 385-7861
Mark Dorty, *Branch Mgr*
EMP: 170
SALES (corp-wide): 23.8B **Publicly Held**
WEB: www.bakerhughes.com
SIC: 1389 Oil field services
HQ: Baker Hughes Holdings Llc
17021 Aldine Westfield Rd
Houston TX 77073
713 439-8600

(G-18984)
BASIC ENERGY SERVICES INC
Also Called: G & L Tool
213 N College Ave (79549-8421)
PHONE..................................325 573-8837

Tommy Clayton, *Manager*
EMP: 130
SALES (corp-wide): 567.2MM **Publicly
Held**
WEB: www.basices.com
SIC: 1389 Oil field services
PA: Basic Energy Services, Inc.
801 Cherry St Unit 2
Fort Worth TX 76102
817 334-4100

(G-18985)
CAMERON SOLUTIONS INC
Also Called: Natco
720 N Fm 1611 (79549-8540)
PHONE..................................325 573-8521
Tommy Green, *Manager*
EMP: 11 **Publicly Held**
SIC: 1389 2911 Gas field services; gases
& liquefied petroleum gases
HQ: Cameron Solutions Inc.
3600 Briarpark Dr
Houston TX 77042
713 849-7500

(G-18986)
CARRIZO WELL SERVICE LLC
1105 Old Lubbock Hwy (79549)
PHONE..................................325 574-6291
Lee Staiger,
EMP: 16
SALES (est): 363.8K **Privately Held**
SIC: 1382 Oil & gas exploration services

(G-18987)
CIRCLE M WELDING & SVCS INC
7393 W Us Highway 180 (79549-0257)
P.O. Box 1069 (79550-1069)
PHONE..................................325 573-8005
James Michael Merrill, *President*
EMP: 60
SQ FT: 1,200
SALES (est): 7MM **Privately Held**
SIC: 7692 1794 Welding repair; excava-
tion & grading, building construction

(G-18988)
CML EXPLORATION LLC
1105 Old Lubbock Hwy (79549)
P.O. Box 890 (79550-0890)
PHONE..................................325 573-0750
Donna Hartman, *CFO*
EMP: 22 **Privately Held**
WEB: www.cmlexploration.com
SIC: 1382 Oil & gas exploration services
PA: Cml Exploration, Llc
Barton Oaks Plz 1 Ste 430
Austin TX 78746

(G-18989)
**DIAMOND D SLICKLINE SVC CO
INC**
2006 N Us Highway 84 (79549-7930)
P.O. Box 216 (79550-0216)
PHONE..................................325 573-0220
Dee Carr, *Owner*
EMP: 10
SALES (est): 325K **Privately Held**
WEB: www.diamonddslickline.com
SIC: 1389 Oil field services

(G-18990)
**ELECTRIC SUBMERSIBLE PUMP
INC**
2507 25th St (79549-2317)
P.O. Box 916 (79550-0916)
PHONE..................................325 573-8101
Joe Mederano, *Manager*
EMP: 17
SALES (est): 885.3K **Privately Held**
SIC: 1731 1799 1389 Electrical work; ath-
letic & recreation facilities construction;
construction, repair & dismantling serv-
ices

(G-18991)
**EZELL-KEY GRAIN COMPANY
INC (PA)**
Also Called: Ezell-Key Feed & Seed
3101 Us Hwy 84 (79550)
PHONE..................................325 573-9373
Weldon Key, *President*
Monty Key, *Corp Secy*
Roland Key, *Vice Pres*
EMP: 28 **EST:** 1955

SQ FT: 1,800
SALES (est): 3.5MM **Privately Held**
SIC: 2048 Livestock feeds

(G-18992)
G & W TRUCKING INC
2111 Avenue Z (79549-7788)
P.O. Box 10383, Midland (79702-7383)
PHONE..................................325 573-6338
Dennis Downing, *President*
Robin Downing, *Vice Pres*
EMP: 20 **EST:** 1977
SALES (est): 2.4MM **Privately Held**
WEB: www.gwtrucking.com
SIC: 1389 Haulage, oil field

(G-18993)
**MACHINE TECH SERVICES INC
(PA)**
2708 25th St (79549-2404)
P.O. Box 170 (79550-0170)
PHONE..................................325 573-1741
Joe Roemisch, *President*
Mike Gobel, *Vice Pres*
EMP: 18
SALES (est): 1.4MM **Privately Held**
WEB: www.westechmachine.com
SIC: 3599 Machine shop, jobbing & repair

(G-18994)
MCDONALD WELDING CO
1110 College Ave (79549-1598)
PHONE..................................325 573-5329
Jack McDonald, *Owner*
EMP: 11
SALES (est): 1.2MM **Privately Held**
SIC: 7692 5599 5169 5084 Welding re-
pair; utility trailers; oxygen; welding ma-
chinery & equipment; steel

(G-18995)
MESQUITE OIL TOOLS INC (PA)
815 S County Road 221 (79549-7959)
P.O. Box 668 (79550-0668)
PHONE..................................325 573-1705
Justin Pechacek, *President*
EMP: 43
SALES (est): 18.7MM **Privately Held**
WEB: www.mesquiteoiltools.com
SIC: 1389 Oil field services

(G-18996)
NABORS WELL SERVICES LTD
2857 W Us Highway 180 (79549-7845)
P.O. Box 889 (79550-0889)
PHONE..................................325 573-2621
Ramon Valadez, *Vice Pres*
Ciston Holmes, *Sales/Mktg Mgr*
EMP: 60 **Privately Held**
WEB: www.nabors.com
SIC: 1389 Oil field services
HQ: Nabors Well Services Ltd.
515 W Greens Rd Ste 1200
Houston TX 77067
281 874-0035

(G-18997)
**NATIONAL OILWELL VARCO
INC**
2004 84 Byp (79549)
PHONE..................................325 573-2665
L T Hood, *Branch Mgr*
EMP: 12
SALES (corp-wide): 8.4B **Publicly Held**
WEB: www.nov.com
SIC: 1389 Pipe testing, oil field service
PA: National Oilwell Varco, Inc.
7909 Parkwood Circle Dr
Houston TX 77036
713 346-7500

(G-18998)
**PATTERSN-UTI DRLG SVCS LP
LLLP (HQ)**
Also Called: Norton Drilling
4500 Lamesa Hwy (79549)
PHONE..................................325 573-1104
Sherman H Norton, *CEO*
Douglas J Wall, *President*
S H Norton, *Partner*
David Ridley, *Partner*
EMP: 100
SQ FT: 4,000

SALES (est): 41.3MM
SALES (corp-wide): 1.1B **Publicly Held**
WEB: www.patenergy.com
SIC: 1381 Drilling oil & gas wells
PA: Patterson-Uti Energy, Inc.
10713 W Sam Houston Pkwy
Houston TX 77064
281 765-7100

(G-18999)
**PATTERSON-UTI DRILLING CO
LLC**
4510 Lamesa Hwy (79549)
PHONE..................................325 574-6300
James M Holcomb, *President*
Curtis Mann, *General Mgr*
Kyle Brocious, *Engineer*
John E Volimer III, *CFO*
Danny Brumley, *VP Mktg*
EMP: 41
SALES (est): 12.6MM
SALES (corp-wide): 1.1B **Publicly Held**
WEB: www.patenergy.com
SIC: 1381 Service well drilling
PA: Patterson-Uti Energy, Inc.
10713 W Sam Houston Pkwy
Houston TX 77064
281 765-7100

(G-19000)
PATTERSON-UTI MGT SVCS LLC
4510 Lamesa Hwy (79549)
P.O. Box 1416 (79550-1416)
PHONE..................................325 574-6300
William A Hendricks Jr, *President*
Seth D Wexler, *Director*
EMP: 10
SALES (est): 3MM
SALES (corp-wide): 1.1B **Publicly Held**
WEB: www.patenergy.com
SIC: 1381 Drilling oil & gas wells
PA: Patterson-Uti Energy, Inc.
10713 W Sam Houston Pkwy
Houston TX 77064
281 765-7100

(G-19001)
PEAK COMPLETION TECH INC
1802 Mccowen St (79549)
PHONE..................................325 574-1170
Fred Clem, *Principal*
Randy Kirchberg, *District Mgr*
Charles Hurst, *Human Res Dir*
Don Wells, *Branch Mgr*
EMP: 40
SALES (corp-wide): 104.3MM **Privately
Held**
WEB: www.peakcompletions.com
SIC: 1389 Oil field services
PA: Peak Completion Technologies, Inc.
7710 W Highway 80
Midland TX 79706
432 617-0178

(G-19002)
PRODUCTION LOGGING INC
2268 N State Highway 208 (79549-8745)
P.O. Box 707 (79550-0707)
PHONE..................................325 573-4441
Gerald R Gunset, *President*
Eloise Gunset, *Corp Secy*
EMP: 12 **EST:** 1979
SQ FT: 2,500
SALES (est): 1MM **Privately Held**
SIC: 1389 Well logging

(G-19003)
REEF SERVICES LLC
Also Called: Rock Water Energy
1600th Ave Q (79549)
P.O. Box 1109 (79550-1109)
PHONE..................................325 573-1133
Glen Barton, *Branch Mgr*
EMP: 20
SALES (corp-wide): 1.2B **Publicly Held**
WEB: www.reefcorp.com
SIC: 3533 Oil & gas drilling rigs & equip-
ment
HQ: Reef Services, Llc
1515 W Sam Houston Pkwy N
Houston TX 77043

(G-19004)
ROBERT EARLY WELDING
5140 County Road 475 (79549-1018)
PHONE..................................325 573-0029

Robert Early, *Owner*
EMP: 32
SALES (est): 1.5MM **Privately Held**
SIC: 7692 Welding repair

(G-19005)
RPC INC
2545 County Road 226 (79549-7924)
PHONE...................................325 573-7022
Max Hildebrand, *District Mgr*
EMP: 28
SALES (corp-wide): 1.7B **Publicly Held**
WEB: www.rpc.net
SIC: 1389 Oil field services; pumping of oil
& gas wells; servicing oil & gas wells; fire
fighting, oil & gas field
PA: Rpc, Inc.
2801 Buford Hwy Ne # 300
Brookhaven GA 30329
404 321-2140

(G-19006)
SMITH VACUUM SERVICE
3642 W Us Highway 180 (79549-7980)
PHONE...................................325 573-7437
Gary P Smith, *Owner*
EMP: 14
SALES (est): 1.2MM **Privately Held**
SIC: 1389 4959 Impounding & storing salt
water, oil & gas field; oil spill cleanup

(G-19007)
SNYDER DAILY NEWS
3600 College Ave (79549-4637)
P.O. Box 949 (79550-0949)
PHONE...................................325 573-5486
Bill Crest, *President*
Walter Buckel, *Corp Secy*
William Beecher Mc Cormick, *Vice Pres*
EMP: 28 **EST:** 1951
SALES (est): 1.5MM **Privately Held**
WEB: www.thesnydernews.com
SIC: 2711 Newspapers, publishing & print-
ing

(G-19008)
SNYDER IRON METAL
208 N Old Post Rd (79549-6523)
PHONE...................................325 573-6862
Chris Maxfield, *Owner*
EMP: 16
SALES (est): 1.1MM **Privately Held**
WEB:
www.metalrecyclingcentersnydertx.com
SIC: 5051 2611 Metal wires, ties, cables &
screening; pulp mills, mechanical & recy-
cling processing

(G-19009)
SOLVAY USA INC
Also Called: Chemplex Solvay Group
506 County Road 137 (79549-8610)
P.O. Box 1071 (79550-1071)
PHONE...................................325 515-7609
Michael Lacey, *President*
EMP: 131
SALES (corp-wide): 13.8MM **Privately
Held**
WEB: www.solvay.us
SIC: 2899 2869 2821 2087 Chemical
preparations; fluorinated hydrocarbon
gases; silicones; plastics materials &
resins; flavoring extracts & syrups; phe-
nol, alkylated & cumene; diphenylamines;
isocyanates
HQ: Solvay Usa Inc.
504 Carnegie Ctr
Princeton NJ 08540
609 860-4000

(G-19010)
STEVEN C RICH LLC
Also Called: Richco Acidizing Services
1345 N College Ave (79549-8011)
P.O. Box 143 (79550-0143)
PHONE...................................325 573-6653
Steve Rich,
Janell Rich,
EMP: 19 **EST:** 1997
SQ FT: 1,200
SALES (est): 3.9MM **Privately Held**
SIC: 1389 Acidizing wells

(G-19011)
SUITS DRILLING COMPANY (HQ)
4510 Lamesa Way (79549)
PHONE...................................325 573-1104
Colloce Talbitt, *CEO*
Mark Seagle, *Ch of Bd*
EMP: 13
SQ FT: 13,000
SALES (est): 5.2MM
SALES (corp-wide): 1.1B **Publicly Held**
SIC: 1381 Drilling oil & gas wells
PA: Patterson-Uti Energy, Inc.
10713 W Sam Houston Pkwy
Houston TX 77064
281 765-7100

(G-19012)
TOMBSTONE WELDING
1015 N Avenue M (79549-8117)
P.O. Box 140 (79550-0140)
PHONE...................................325 573-8446
Ruben Marles, *Owner*
Elaine Marles, *Co-Owner*
EMP: 15
SALES (est): 1.1MM **Privately Held**
SIC: 7692 Welding repair

(G-19013)
UNIVERSAL WELL SVC HOLDINGS
3704 W Highway 180 (79549-7856)
P.O. Box 610 (79550-0610)
PHONE...................................325 573-6209
EMP: 137
SALES (corp-wide): 12.2MM **Privately
Held**
SIC: 3533 Mfg Oil/Gas Field Machinery
PA: Universal Well Service Holdings Inc
301 Commerce St Ste 1450
Fort Worth TX 76102
325 573-6209

(G-19014)
WL PLASTICS CORPORATION
2160 S Hwy Bus 84 (79549)
PHONE...................................325 574-6100
Jody Hair, *Branch Mgr*
EMP: 35 **Privately Held**
WEB: www.wlplastics.com
SIC: 3084 Plastics pipe
PA: W.L. Plastics Corporation
3575 Lone Star Cir Ste 30
Fort Worth TX 76177

(G-19015)
WSI CASED HOLE SPECIALIST INC
4668 Fm 1607 (79549-0934)
P.O. Box 670 (79550-0670)
PHONE...................................800 658-9674
Treva Moore, *President*
Roger Weaver, *Director*
Treva Hawthorne, *Director*
Stephanie Martin, *Director*
EMP: 45
SQ FT: 3,240
SALES (est): 11.1MM **Privately Held**
WEB: www.wsicasedhole.com
SIC: 1389 1382 Perforating well casings;
well logging; oil & gas exploration serv-
ices

Socorro
El Paso County

(G-19016)
3M COMPANY
11751 Alameda Ave Ste A (79927-3247)
PHONE...................................915 860-5408
EMP: 25
SALES (corp-wide): 32.1B **Publicly Held**
WEB: www.3m.com
SIC: 3841 Surgical instruments & appara-
tus
PA: 3m Company
3m Center
Saint Paul MN 55144
651 733-1110

(G-19017)
OTW-EP INC (PA)
Also Called: Oasis Tires & Wheels
757 Horizon Blvd (79927-4414)
PHONE...................................915 858-0448
Genaro Gonzalez, *President*
Olga Martinez, *Vice Pres*
EMP: 31
SALES (est): 12.5MM **Privately Held**
WEB: www.oasistires.com
SIC: 3691 5085 Batteries, rechargeable;
bearings, bushings, wheels & gears

(G-19018)
Q CABINETS INC
10050 N Loop Dr (79927-5051)
PHONE...................................915 859-5252
Enrique A Quintanilla, *President*
Quintanilla Maria A, *Vice Pres*
EMP: 14
SALES (est): 1.3MM **Privately Held**
SIC: 2434 Wood kitchen cabinets

(G-19019)
TECHNICOLOR USA INC
Also Called: El Paso Tce
11751 Alameda Ave (79927-3247)
PHONE...................................915 841-7233
Al Minjarez, *Branch Mgr*
EMP: 200
SALES (corp-wide): 59.7MM **Privately
Held**
SIC: 3651 Household audio & video equip-
ment
HQ: Technicolor Usa, Inc.
6040 W Sunset Blvd
Hollywood CA 90028
317 587-4287

(G-19020)
WERNER CO
Also Called: Werner - North Coast Logistics
11751 Alameda Ave Ste C (79927-3247)
PHONE...................................915 851-4933
Miguel Crispin, *Business Anlyst*
George Resemedz, *Manager*
EMP: 26 **Privately Held**
WEB: www.wernerco.com
SIC: 3499 Aerosol valves, metal
HQ: Werner Co.
93 Werner Rd
Greenville PA 16125

Somerset
Bexar County

(G-19021)
TEXAS STUD WELDING LLC
7780 Fm 3175 (78069-3781)
PHONE...................................210 300-2500
Gary Harvey, *Principal*
EMP: 9
SALES (est): 488.2K **Privately Held**
WEB: www.texasstudwelding.com
SIC: 7692 Welding repair

Somerville
Burleson County

(G-19022)
KOPPERS INC
Koppers RR & Utility Pdts Div
Hwy 36 N And Cntry Rd 423 (77879)
P.O. Box 189 (77879-0189)
PHONE...................................979 596-1321
David Shaw, *General Mgr*
EMP: 85 **Publicly Held**
WEB: www.koppers.com
SIC: 2491 2421 Poles, posts & pilings:
treated wood; railroad cross bridges &
switch ties, treated wood; railroad cross-
ties, treated wood; sawmills & planing
mills, general
HQ: Koppers Inc.
436 7th Ave
Pittsburgh PA 15219
412 227-2001

(G-19023)
RHODES BUILDING SYSTEMS INC
Also Called: Diamonds 88
1607 Ave E Thor (77879)
P.O. Box 39 (77879-0039)
PHONE...................................979 596-1451
Michael Rhodes, *President*
Jason Rhodes, *President*
Ben Schroeder, *Vice Pres*
Joey Brock, *Treasurer*
EMP: 25 **EST:** 1974
SQ FT: 19,000
SALES (est): 4.1MM **Privately Held**
WEB: www.rbstx.com
SIC: 1541 1542 3448 Industrial buildings,
new construction; commercial & office
building, new construction; prefabricated
metal buildings

Sonora
Sutton County

(G-19024)
CHARLES HOWARD CONSTRUCTION
601 W 8th St (76950-6011)
P.O. Box 1426 (76950-1426)
PHONE...................................325 387-3093
Robert Hard, *President*
Debbie Hard, *Vice Pres*
EMP: 17 **EST:** 1971
SALES (est): 2.5MM **Privately Held**
SIC: 1389 Oil field services

(G-19025)
COMPASS WELL SERVICES LLC
1930 Highway 277 S (76950-9203)
PHONE...................................325 387-2940
EMP: 24
SALES (corp-wide): 80MM **Privately
Held**
WEB: www.compasswellservices.com
SIC: 1389 Cementing oil & gas well cas-
ings
PA: Compass Well Services, Llc
4100 Intl Plz Ste 500
Fort Worth TX 76109
817 244-2555

(G-19026)
HIGHMOUNT EXPLORATION PROD LLC
Highway 277 S 209 Pr 4489 (76950)
PHONE...................................325 387-3588
Danny Eaton, *Branch Mgr*
EMP: 9 **Privately Held**
SIC: 1382 Oil & gas exploration services
HQ: Highmount Exploration & Production
Llc
1001 Fannin St Ste 800
Houston TX 77002

(G-19027)
LUTHER M CREEK
Also Called: Creek's Welding
912 S Crockett Ave (76950-7838)
P.O. Box 453 (76950-0453)
PHONE...................................325 387-3295
Luther Creek, *Owner*
EMP: 75 **EST:** 1985
SALES (est): 1.3MM **Privately Held**
SIC: 1389 1382 Oil field services; oil &
gas exploration services

(G-19028)
NABORS WELL SERVICES LTD
Hwy 277 S (76950)
PHONE...................................325 387-2884
EMP: 71 **Privately Held**
WEB: www.nabors.com
SIC: 1389 1382 Oil field services; oil &
gas exploration services
HQ: Nabors Well Services Ltd.
515 W Greens Rd Ste 1200
Houston TX 77067
281 874-0035

(G-19029)
OL SONORA TRADING COMPANY (PA)
1203 End Of E 2nd St (76950)
P.O. Box 1150 (76950-1150)
PHONE..................................325 387-2524
Carl James Cahill III, *President*
Kelly Cahill Owens, *Corp Secy*
EMP: 13
SALES (est): 5.4MM **Privately Held**
WEB: www.texasdirtcontractor.com
SIC: **1389** Oil field services

(G-19030)
SUTTON BROS INC
210 E Pecan St (76950-2623)
PHONE..................................325 387-2053
Quade Sutton, *President*
Jeffrey Sutton, *Vice Pres*
Elizabeth Sutton, *Treasurer*
EMP: 19 EST: 1980
SQ FT: 1,000
SALES (est): 1.1MM **Privately Held**
SIC: **1389** 1382 Oil field services; oil & gas exploration services

(G-19031)
U S WEATHERFORD L P
3269 Selfservice Rd (76950)
PHONE..................................325 387-3280
EMP: 30 **Privately Held**
WEB: www.weatherford.com
SIC: **1389** Oil field services
HQ: U S Weatherford L P
179 Weatherford Dr
Schriever LA 70395
985 493-6100

(G-19032)
WALSH WELDING INC (PA)
1603 S Crockett Ave (76950-8805)
P.O. Box 1343 (76950-1343)
PHONE..................................325 387-2357
David Walsh, *Owner*
EMP: 15
SALES (est): 1.2MM **Privately Held**
WEB: www.walshwelding.com
SIC: **7692** Welding repair

Sour Lake
Hardin County

(G-19033)
RADCO OPERATIONS LP
165 S Merchant St (77659-2901)
P.O. Box 1017 (77659-1017)
PHONE..................................409 287-1277
Radley Corp, *Partner*
Ashley Harvey, *Manager*
EMP: 11 EST: 2000
SQ FT: 2,000
SALES (est): 7MM **Privately Held**
SIC: **1381** Drilling oil & gas wells

(G-19034)
RADLEY ELECTRIC INC
Also Called: Ros Vacuum Services
105 S Fannin St (77659-7753)
P.O. Box 2027 (77659-2027)
PHONE..................................409 781-7172
Guy Gatewood, *Manager*
EMP: 14
SALES (corp-wide): 4.6MM **Privately Held**
WEB: www.radleyelectric.com
SIC: **7629** 5082 1389 Electrical repair shops; oil field equipment; oil field services
PA: Radley Electric, Inc.
22942 Highway 105
Sour Lake TX 77659
409 287-3401

(G-19035)
RHEACO OIL COMPANY LTD
395 Highway 105 W (77659-9522)
P.O. Box 555 (77659-0555)
PHONE..................................409 287-1225
Rhea Radley, *Partner*
Steven Radley, *Partner*
EMP: 10
SALES (est): 656.5K **Privately Held**
SIC: **1389** Oil field services

South Houston
Harris County

(G-19036)
A & M PLASTICS INC
1502 Alabama St (77587-5446)
P.O. Box 285 (77587-0285)
PHONE..................................713 941-1033
Katherine Mason, *President*
Teri Bieterman, *Corp Secy*
Arthur Mason, *Vice Pres*
Jacquelyn Abella, *Admin Sec*
EMP: 9
SQ FT: 16,000
SALES (est): 1.3MM **Privately Held**
WEB: www.anmplastics.com
SIC: **3089** Injection molded finished plastic products; injection molding of plastics

(G-19037)
ALLIED MCROBIAL INVESTIGATIONS
1309 Illinois St (77587-5418)
PHONE..................................713 941-9200
Loretta Riddle, *President*
Darryl Riddle, *General Mgr*
Kim Riddle, *Admin Sec*
EMP: 20
SALES (est): 1.5MM **Privately Held**
SIC: **2835** Microbiology & virology diagnostic products

(G-19038)
ENGINE SERVICE INC
531 Georgia St (77587-3448)
PHONE..................................713 473-4167
Belinda Youngdale, *President*
Mike Morgan, *Vice Pres*
EMP: 12
SQ FT: 8,000
SALES (est): 900K **Privately Held**
WEB: www.southhoustonengine.com
SIC: **3519** Diesel engine rebuilding

(G-19039)
FULLERS MACHINING CENTER INC
701 Dumont St (77587-3302)
PHONE..................................713 943-0228
Jimmy Fuller, *President*
EMP: 10
SQ FT: 6,000
SALES (est): 1.5MM **Privately Held**
WEB: www.fullersmci.com
SIC: **3599** Machine shop, jobbing & repair

(G-19040)
GLOBALTECH SUBSEA INC
1016 Indiana St (77587-4015)
PHONE..................................713 504-0331
Thomas Vu, *Exec Dir*
EMP: 14
SALES (est): 3.4MM **Privately Held**
WEB: www.globaltechsubsea.com
SIC: **3533** Oil & gas field machinery

(G-19041)
GREEN MACHINE & TOOL INC
1007 Pennsylvania St (77587-4036)
P.O. Box 87785, Houston (77287-7785)
PHONE..................................713 943-0402
Shane Churchill, *President*
EMP: 12 EST: 1982
SQ FT: 26,600
SALES (est): 2.6MM **Privately Held**
SIC: **3599** 7692 Machine shop, jobbing & repair; welding repair

(G-19042)
GULF STATES ASPHALT COMPANY LP (PA)
300 Christi Pl (77587-5165)
PHONE..................................713 941-4410
Reba H Bramble, *Partner*
Luis X Pena, *General Ptnr*
EMP: 87 EST: 1947
SQ FT: 10,000
SALES (est): 9MM **Privately Held**
WEB: www.themartincompanies.com
SIC: **2891** 2951 Sealants; adhesives; asphalt & asphaltic paving mixtures (not from refineries)

(G-19043)
GULFEX HOLDINGS
401 State St (77587-3025)
P.O. Box 12720, Houston (77217-2720)
PHONE..................................713 946-6614
Greg Bregstone, *CEO*
Wb Sheehy, *President*
David Tilley, *President*
W B Sheehy, *Partner*
Aubrey Davis, *Vice Pres*
▲ EMP: 55 EST: 1966
SQ FT: 52,000
SALES (est): 21.5MM **Privately Held**
WEB: www.gulfexlp.com
SIC: **3441** Fabricated structural metal

(G-19044)
HAYES CARPENTRY L L C
Also Called: Hayes Company
1404 Illinois St (77587-5421)
PHONE..................................713 944-2608
EMP: 40
SQ FT: 13,000
SALES (est): 1.7MM **Privately Held**
WEB: www.hayescarpentry.com
SIC: **2499** 2431 Decorative wood & woodwork; millwork

(G-19045)
HERNDON FABRICATION WORKS
911 Pennsylvania St (77587-4034)
P.O. Box 971 (77587-0971)
PHONE..................................713 941-3785
Jerry D Herndon, *Owner*
EMP: 10
SQ FT: 5,000
SALES (est): 916.2K **Privately Held**
SIC: **3441** Fabricated structural metal

(G-19046)
HOUSTON PLATING & COATINGS LLC
1311 Georgia St (77587-3924)
PHONE..................................713 946-8920
William Howard Jr, *Branch Mgr*
Cynthia Turner, *Manager*
EMP: 75
SALES (corp-wide): 35MM **Privately Held**
WEB: www.houstonplating.com
SIC: **3471** Electroplating of metals or formed products
PA: Houston Plating & Coatings, Llc
1301 Georgia St
South Houston TX 77587
713 946-8920

(G-19047)
HOUSTON PLATING & COATINGS LLC (PA)
Also Called: Hpc Plating Company
1301 Georgia St (77587-3924)
P.O. Box 418 (77587-0418)
PHONE..................................713 946-8920
William Howard Jr, *Ch of Bd*
Ian Fellow, *President*
Eric Turner, *COO*
Alberto Landois, *Vice Pres*
Joe Stankovich, *Vice Pres*
EMP: 125
SALES (est): 35MM **Privately Held**
WEB: www.houstonplating.com
SIC: **3471** Plating of metals or formed products

(G-19048)
JIM RAY COMPANY INC
Also Called: Specialty Products Division
1207 Indiana St (77587-4018)
PHONE..................................713 941-2275
Rudy Villarrieal, *Manager*
EMP: 12
SQ FT: 4,080
SALES (corp-wide): 3.6MM **Privately Held**
WEB: www.jimray.com
SIC: **3053** Gaskets, all materials
PA: Jim Ray Company, Inc.
10645 Richmond Ave # 130
Houston TX 77042
713 785-5055

(G-19049)
MCAPS INC
Also Called: McAps Automation and Power
102 Main St (77587-3044)
PHONE..................................713 941-1300
Gary Kelley, *President*
Rebecca Ball, *Office Mgr*
▲ EMP: 10
SALES (est): 2.2MM **Privately Held**
WEB: www.mcaps-inc.com
SIC: **3625** 5063 Motor controls & accessories; circuit breakers

(G-19050)
MIDWAY MACHINE & INSTR CO INC
701 Oregon St Ste B (77587-4934)
PHONE..................................713 947-1312
John MAI, *President*
David Kirkley, *Opers Mgr*
Donna Guidry, *CFO*
EMP: 28
SQ FT: 4,800
SALES (est): 6MM **Privately Held**
WEB: www.midway-machine.com
SIC: **3599** Machine shop, jobbing & repair

(G-19051)
MONTES MACHINE WORKS LLC
706 Nebraska St (77587-3135)
PHONE..................................346 320-4960
Jose Mario Montes Jr, *Mng Member*
EMP: 10
SALES (est): 450K **Privately Held**
SIC: **3499** Machine bases, metal

(G-19052)
SOUTHWEST SIGNAL SUPPLY INC
1107 Jackson St (77587-3910)
P.O. Box 125 (77587-0125)
PHONE..................................713 946-7162
Clarence A Rice, *President*
Michael Nash, *Vice Pres*
Roxanne Nash, *Vice Pres*
Charlene Rice, *Vice Pres*
Brenda Boren, *Treasurer*
EMP: 17
SQ FT: 2,400
SALES: 5.7MM **Privately Held**
WEB: www.swsignal.net
SIC: **3669** Traffic signals, electric

(G-19053)
UNISORB CORPORATION
1310 Genoa St (77587-5415)
P.O. Box 388 (77587-0388)
PHONE..................................713 943-3753
Larry Thomas, *President*
Julie Gallington, *Purch Mgr*
Glenda Thomas, *Treasurer*
Laura Thomas, *Controller*
EMP: 15
SQ FT: 12,800
SALES (est): 3.2MM **Privately Held**
WEB: www.unisorbcorporation.com
SIC: **3564** 3599 Filters, air: furnaces, air conditioning equipment, etc.; gasoline filters, internal combustion engine, except auto

(G-19054)
VALVES AND CONTROL SYSTEMS INC
1202 Washington St (77587-4557)
PHONE..................................713 378-0311
Sharon McCall, *President*
Laura McCall, *Corp Secy*
Bill McCall, *Director*
▲ EMP: 10 EST: 2012
SQ FT: 30,000
SALES (est): 1.2MM **Privately Held**
WEB: www.controlvalvesystems.com
SIC: **3491** 7699 Process control regulator valves; valve repair, industrial

(G-19055)
VU ENTERPRISE INC
1016 Virginia St (77587-3966)
PHONE..................................713 944-0384
Thomas Vu, *President*
Vivian Vo, *Treasurer*
Chris Vu, *Accounting Mgr*
▲ EMP: 46 EST: 1999
SQ FT: 10,000

SALES (est): 9.1MM Privately Held
WEB: www.vuenterprise.com
SIC: 3599 Machine shop, jobbing & repair

(G-19056)
W T PORTER CORP
1211 Virginia St (77587-3947)
P.O. Box 715 (77587-0715)
PHONE..................713 946-4174
Gary James Wenzel, *President*
EMP: 9
SQ FT: 7,500
SALES (est): 1MM Privately Held
WEB: www.wtporterhydraulics.com
SIC: 7699 3721 7359 5599 Construction
   equipment repair; aircraft; aircraft rental;
   aircraft dealers

Southlake
Tarrant County

(G-19057)
ACERTS INC
1801 Native Dancer Pl (76092-6931)
PHONE..................866 938-5599
Gary Carlsen,
Jimmy Ahmed,
Jagtar Khera,
EMP: 10
SALES (est): 690.3K Privately Held
SIC: 3728 Aircraft parts & equipment

(G-19058)
**AMERICAN TRAILER WORKS
INC (DH)**
180 State St Ste 230 (76092-7619)
PHONE..................817 328-3686
Curt Howell, *CEO*
Ray Dulin, *President*
Douglas Clark, *CFO*
EMP: 12
SALES (est): 448.1MM
SALES (corp-wide): 8.8B Privately Held
WEB: www.southlakeequity.com
SIC: 3715 Truck trailers
HQ: American Trailer World Corp.
   1701 N Plano Rd Bldg 9
   Richardson TX 75081
   855 289-0001

(G-19059)
CJHORAK ENTERPRISES INC
Also Called: Priority Signs and Graphics
2838 Market Loop Ste 104 (76092-9179)
P.O. Box 32, Grapevine (76099-0032)
PHONE..................817 260-0700
Curtis Horak, *President*
Janice Horak, *Vice Pres*
EMP: 9
SALES (est): 1.1MM Privately Held
WEB: www.prioritysignsandgraphics.com
SIC: 3993 Signs & advertising specialties

(G-19060)
CODA GLOBAL LLC
550 Reserve St Ste 190 (76092-1546)
PHONE..................844 366-8250
Sam Fatigato, *CEO*
Sharan Gurunathan, *Managing Prtnr*
Terry Cain, *Partner*
Terence Goodwin, *General Mgr*
Troy Vetter, *COO*
EMP: 23 EST: 2015
SALES (corp-wide): 3B Privately Held
WEB: www.coda.global
SIC: 7371 7372 7373 Computer software
   systems analysis & design, custom; appli-
   cation computer software; business ori-
   ented computer software; value-added
   resellers, computer systems
HQ: Presidio, Inc.
   1 Penn Plz Ste 2832
   New York NY 10119

(G-19061)
**CONNOR SPORTS FLOORING
LLC**
1160 Highland Oaks Dr (76092-8586)
PHONE..................817 944-0269
EMP: 10

SALES (corp-wide): 533.7K Privately
Held
WEB: www.connorsports.com
SIC: 2426 5031 2439 Flooring, hardwood;
   lumber: rough, dressed & finished; struc-
   tural wood members
HQ: Connor Sports Flooring, Llc
   595 Supreme Dr
   Bensenville IL 60106

(G-19062)
DISTINCTIVE GRAPHICS INC
Also Called: Identitec
2840 Market Loop (76092-9178)
P.O. Box 93555 (76092-0114)
PHONE..................817 329-0411
John Pichler, *President*
Sherry Pichler, *Corp Secy*
EMP: 12
SQ FT: 7,000
SALES (est): 1.5MM Privately Held
SIC: 3993 Signs, not made in custom sign
   painting shops; electric signs

(G-19063)
**DISTRIBUTION MANAGEMENT
CO INC**
Also Called: Flow Software
1121 S Carroll Ave # 120 (76092-8708)
P.O. Box 93416 (76092-0113)
PHONE..................817 421-3311
Stacy Tate, *President*
Abbie Hasse, *Partner*
Tina Tate, *Treasurer*
Neel Price, *Software Dev*
EMP: 12
SQ FT: 6,000
SALES (est): 202.3K Privately Held
WEB: www.flowtrac.com
SIC: 7372 Prepackaged software

(G-19064)
DOWNEY PUBLISHING INC (PA)
2545 E Southlake Blvd (76092-6609)
PHONE..................817 416-6661
Wallace Downey, *President*
Margaret Downey, *Corp Secy*
Stephanie Potter, *Sales Mgr*
Ryan Duncan, *Accounts Exec*
Karen Holderfield, *Accounts Exec*
EMP: 12
SQ FT: 2,000
SALES (est): 3.9MM Privately Held
WEB: www.downeypublishing.com
SIC: 2741 8748 Directories, telephone:
   publishing only, not printed on site; pub-
   lishing consultant

(G-19065)
**ECOCLEAN SUPPLY &
SERVICES LLC**
950 E State Highway 114 # 1 (76092-5240)
PHONE..................800 245-9896
Andrew Sternke, *CEO*
EMP: 10
SALES (est): 276.1K Privately Held
SIC: 5999 2842 Cleaning equipment &
   supplies; specialty cleaning preparations

(G-19066)
ECOSTREAM LLC
2140 E Southlake Blvd L203 (76092-6516)
PHONE..................832 429-5317
Tyler Radbourne,
EMP: 50
SQ FT: 1,000
SALES (est): 261.7K Privately Held
SIC: 1389 Impounding & storing salt water,
   oil & gas field

(G-19067)
EKLUNDS INC (PA)
2860 Market Loop Ste 200 (76092-9149)
P.O. Box 1566, Grapevine (76099-1566)
PHONE..................817 949-2030
Beth K Cunningham, *President*
James B Eklund, *Principal*
Bunny Eklund, *Corp Secy*
Heath Cunningham, *Vice Pres*
Bradley Eklund, *Vice Pres*
▲ EMP: 40
SQ FT: 30,000

SALES (est): 21.5MM Privately Held
WEB: www.eklunds.com
SIC: 1542 3534 5084 Commercial & office buildings, renovation & repair; elevators & equipment; elevators

(G-19068)
**FAIRWAY RSRCES PRTNERS III
LLC**
538 Silicon Dr Ste 101 (76092-7517)
PHONE..................817 416-1946
Matthew A Eagleston, *President*
Lester K Stephens, *CFO*
EMP: 23 EST: 2016
SALES (est): 519.2K Privately Held
WEB: www.fairwayresources.com
SIC: 1311 Crude petroleum & natural gas

(G-19069)
FROG STREET PRESS LLC
530 S Nolen Dr (76092-9165)
PHONE..................817 251-0510
Ronald Chase, *CEO*
Charles Pierson, *President*
Madalyn Martin, *Vice Pres*
William Hunt, *VP Opers*
Brenda Claborn, *CFO*
▲ EMP: 35
SQ FT: 11,000
SALES (est): 5.3MM
SALES (corp-wide): 198.7MM Privately
Held
WEB: www.frogstreet.com
SIC: 3999 Education aids, devices & sup-
   plies
PA: Excellingence Learning Corporation
   20 Ryan Ranch Rd Ste 200
   Monterey CA 93940
   831 333-2000

(G-19070)
FSI APPAREL INC
1080 S Kimball Ave # 130 (76092-1507)
PHONE..................562 906-3000
Kathryn Del Calvo, *President*
Leo Del Calvo Sr, *Vice Pres*
Kristin Garcia, *Admin Sec*
◆ EMP: 30
SQ FT: 35,000
SALES (est): 23.2MM Privately Held
SIC: 2339 Women's & misses' outerwear

(G-19071)
GENERAL ELECTRIC COMPANY
914 Independence Pkwy (76092-8483)
PHONE..................412 469-6080
John Anderson, *Opers-Prdtn-Mfg*
EMP: 70
SALES (corp-wide): 95.2B Publicly Held
WEB: www.ge.com
SIC: 7629 7694 3462 Electrical equip-
   ment repair, high voltage; electrical
   household appliance repair; armature
   rewinding shops; iron & steel forgings
PA: General Electric Company
   5 Necco St
   Boston MA 02210
   617 443-3000

(G-19072)
**GEORGIA SANDWICH COMPANY
INC**
276 Pine Dr (76092-7402)
PHONE..................770 426-5678
Michael Gordon, *President*
EMP: 50
SALES (est): 7.7MM Privately Held
SIC: 2099 Sandwiches, assembled &
   packaged: for wholesale market

(G-19073)
H P CREATIONS
Also Called: Pieter Andries Jewelries
2525 E Southlake Blvd (76092-6609)
PHONE..................817 749-4367
Pieter Andries Hye, *Owner*
Marilyn Hye, *Co-Owner*
Janice AGS-Csa, *Exec VP*
Janice Gaddie, *Exec VP*
Carrie Philion, *Sales Staff*
EMP: 25
SQ FT: 7,000

SALES (est): 2.6MM Privately Held
WEB: www.pieterandries.com
SIC: 3911 5094 5944 3873 Jewelry, precious metal; precious stones (gems); jewelry, precious stones & precious metals;
   watches, clocks, watchcases & parts

(G-19074)
HKN INC (HQ)
180 State St Ste 200 (76092-7619)
PHONE..................817 424-2424
EMP: 14 EST: 1973
SQ FT: 5,826
SALES (est): 9.3MM Publicly Held
WEB: www.hkninc.com
SIC: 1311 Crude petroleum production

(G-19075)
INSIGHT EQUITY A P X L P (PA)
Also Called: Vision-Ease Lens
1400 Civic Pl Ste 250 (76092-7647)
PHONE..................817 488-7775
Robert J Conner,
EMP: 19
SQ FT: 150,000
SALES (est): 85.7MM Privately Held
WEB: www.insightequity.com
SIC: 6722 3441 3443 3556 Management
   investment, open-end; bridge sections,
   prefabricated highway; tanks, lined:
   metal plate; food products machinery;
   motor vehicle parts & accessories; petro-
   leum terminals

(G-19076)
INSIGHT EQUITY LP (HQ)
1400 Civic Pl Ste 250 (76092-7647)
PHONE..................817 488-7775
Ted Beneski, *Managing Prtnr*
Warren Bonham, *Partner*
Eliot Kerlin, *Partner*
Victor L Vescovo, *Partner*
Andrew Boisseau, *Senior VP*
EMP: 24
SALES (est): 346.8MM Privately Held
WEB: www.insightequity.com
SIC: 6722 3441 3443 3556 Management
   investment, open-end; bridge sections,
   prefabricated highway; tanks, lined:
   metal plate; food products machinery;
   motor vehicle parts & accessories; petro-
   leum terminals; petroleum bulk stations

(G-19077)
JAUNT AIR MOBILITY LLC
2820 Rainforest Ct (76092-5544)
PHONE..................817 692-3030
Martin Alex Peryea, *CEO*
Kaydon Stanzione, *CEO*
EMP: 12
SALES (est): 113.3K Privately Held
WEB: www.jauntairmobility.com
SIC: 3812 Aircraft/aerospace flight instru-
   ments & guidance systems

(G-19078)
JWTMBG ENTERPRISE LLC
1256 Main St Ste 210 (76092-7636)
PHONE..................817 230-2513
Bob Greene, *Purch Mgr*
Scott Netherton, *VP Bus Dvlpt*
Brendon Graft,
John Willbanks III,
▲ EMP: 12
SALES (est): 4.4MM Privately Held
SIC: 3446 Gratings, tread: fabricated metal

(G-19079)
**MULLINS WHITE EXPLORATION
INC**
100 S Village Center Dr (76092-7910)
PHONE..................817 442-5259
Rick Mullins, *President*
Theresa Mullins, *Admin Sec*
EMP: 62
SQ FT: 10,000
SALES (est): 5.9MM Privately Held
SIC: 1382 Oil & gas exploration services

(G-19080)
NCI GROUP INC
Also Called: Mesco Building Solutions
400 N Kimball Ave 114 (76092-6898)
P.O. Box 20, Grapevine (76099-0020)
PHONE..................817 481-2501
Kim Wells, *President*

Page Deanne, *Manager*
EMP: 130
SALES (corp-wide): 4.8B **Publicly Held**
WEB: www.cornerstonebuildingbrands.com
SIC: 3448 3444 Buildings, portable: pre-fabricated metal; metal roofing & roof drainage equipment
HQ: Nci Group, Inc.
10943 N Sam Huston Pkwy W
Houston TX 77064
281 897-7788

(G-19081)
PETROH2O RECOVERY LLC
2225 W Southlake Blvd (76092-6750)
PHONE....................817 778-8413
EMP: 22 **EST:** 2013
SALES (est): 783.1K **Privately Held**
WEB: www.petroh2o.com
SIC: 1389 Gas field services

(G-19082)
SWEDISH MATCH NORTH AMER LLC
541 Silicon Dr Ste 100 (76092-7565)
PHONE....................817 416-7017
Chuck Pavona, *Regional Mgr*
EMP: 194
SALES (corp-wide): 1.5B **Privately Held**
WEB: www.swedishmatch.com
SIC: 2131 5199 5194 Chewing tobacco; smoking tobacco; lighters, cigarette & cigar; tobacco & tobacco products
HQ: Swedish Match North America Llc
1021 E Cary St Ste 1600
Richmond VA 23219
804 787-5100

(G-19083)
VARIOSYSTEMS INC (DH)
901 S Kimball Ave (76092-9006)
PHONE....................817 416-7535
▲ **EMP:** 150 **EST:** 1998
SQ FT: 18,000
SALES (est): 31.2MM
SALES (corp-wide): 7.5MM **Privately Held**
WEB: www.variosystems.com
SIC: 3672 Circuit boards, television & radio printed
HQ: Variosystems Ag
Amperestrasse 5
Steinach SG 9323
714 478-700

(G-19084)
YADBLUE LLC
1716 Water Lily Dr (76092-5860)
PHONE....................214 542-6140
Siva Nandigam, *Partner*
Srinivas Nandigam, *Partner*
EMP: 12
SALES (est): 927.6K **Privately Held**
WEB: www.yadblue.com
SIC: 7371 7372 7373 7389 Computer software systems analysis & design, custom; computer software development & applications; application computer software; educational computer software; systems software development services;

Spearman
Hansford County

(G-19085)
DCP MIDSTREAM LLC
11300 Fm 281 (79081-5816)
PHONE....................806 228-6241
Gary Garrison, *Manager*
EMP: 21
SALES (corp-wide): 1.9B **Privately Held**
WEB: www.dcpmidstream.com
SIC: 1311 Crude petroleum production
PA: Dcp Midstream, Llc
370 17th St Ste 2500
Denver CO 80202
303 633-2900

(G-19086)
H & H WATER WELL SERVICE INC
Gruver Hwy W (79081)
P.O. Box 158 (79081-0158)
PHONE....................806 659-5577
Jerry Holton, *President*
Steve Holton, *Corp Secy*
Elizabeth Holton, *Vice Pres*
EMP: 9
SALES (est): 2.6MM **Privately Held**
WEB: www.handhwaterwellserviceinc.com
SIC: 5083 3599 7699 Irrigation equipment; machine shop, jobbing & repair; agricultural equipment repair services

(G-19087)
SPEARTEX GRAIN COMPANY
405 Collard St (79081-2045)
P.O. Box 248 (79081-0248)
PHONE....................806 659-3711
Mary Dixon, *Manager*
EMP: 30
SQ FT: 2,000
SALES (est): 2.5MM **Privately Held**
SIC: 1311 0111 0212 Crude petroleum production; natural gas production; wheat; beef cattle except feedlots

(G-19088)
TEXAS 28 LLC
Also Called: Sportzone, The
719 W 7th Ave (79081-3432)
P.O. Box 997 (79081-0997)
PHONE....................806 644-9663
Chad Riggins, *
EMP: 12
SALES (est): 965.9K **Privately Held**
WEB: www.thesportzonestore.net
SIC: 2261 2759 2395 3993 Screen printing of cotton broadwoven fabrics; promotional printing; embroidery & art needlework; signs & advertising specialties

(G-19089)
TRENCOR ENTERPRISES INC
1103 W 7th (79081)
P.O. Box 773 (79081-0773)
PHONE....................806 659-3911
Ricky White, *President*
EMP: 12
SALES (est): 810K **Privately Held**
WEB: www.trencorenterprisesinc.com
SIC: 1799 1389 Welding on site; oil field services

Spicewood
Travis County

(G-19090)
ABRACON LLC (PA)
5101 Hidden Creek Ln (78669-6951)
PHONE....................512 371-6159
Michael Calabria, *President*
Amy Keller, *Vice Pres*
Anitha Govind, *Senior Engr*
Rosa Calabria, *CFO*
Marla Alacali, *Sales Staff*
▲ **EMP:** 17
SQ FT: 30,000
SALES (est): 11.6MM **Privately Held**
WEB: www.abracon.com
SIC: 3679 3677 Electronic crystals; oscillators; inductors, electronic

(G-19091)
ADAPTIVE SWITCH LABORATORIES
125 Spur 191 Ste C (78669-4134)
P.O. Box 636 (78669-0636)
PHONE....................440 329-6276
Gerald B Blouch, *President*
▲ **EMP:** 11
SQ FT: 12,000
SALES (est): 1.8MM
SALES (corp-wide): 927.9MM **Publicly Held**
WEB: www.asl-inc.com
SIC: 3842 Orthopedic appliances

PA: Invacare Corporation
1 Invacare Way
Elyria OH 44035
440 329-6000

(G-19092)
CUVEE COFFEE LLC
22601 Hwy 71 W (78669-6466)
PHONE....................512 264-1479
Michael McKim, *Principal*
Rashelle McKim, *Controller*
Michelle Diaz, *Sales Staff*
EMP: 11
SALES (est): 493.8K **Privately Held**
WEB: www.cuveecoffee.com
SIC: 2095 Roasted coffee

(G-19093)
REHME CUSTOM DOORS & LTG INC
Also Called: Rehme Steel Windows & Doors
3914 Crawford Rd (78669-6408)
PHONE....................512 916-0511
Peter Rehme, *President*
EMP: 28
SQ FT: 13,820
SALES (est): 1.7MM **Privately Held**
WEB: www.rehmesteel.com
SIC: 3442 Window & door frames

(G-19094)
SCOUT GOODS & DESIGN LLC
Also Called: Scout Lightning and Design
4819 R O Dr Ste 202 (78669-6513)
PHONE....................512 865-8775
Tara Camp, *Mng Member*
EMP: 10
SALES (est): 750K **Privately Held**
WEB: www.scoutlightingatx.com
SIC: 3645 Chandeliers, residential

(G-19095)
SPILLAR WELDING INC
Also Called: Spillar Boatdocks & Boatlifts
Rr 3 (78669)
PHONE....................512 264-0351
Fax: 512 264-1081
EMP: 20 **EST:** 1948
SALES (est): 1.4MM **Privately Held**
SIC: 7692 1629 Welding Repair Heavy Construction

Splendora
Montgomery County

(G-19096)
KENNEDY FABRICATING INC
25370 Fm 2090 Rd (77372-3721)
P.O. Box 1357 (77372-1357)
PHONE....................281 399-3008
Jeremy Want, *CEO*
Kevin Kenndy, *President*
John Coleman, *COO*
Joe Hnatek, *Vice Pres*
Kevin Kennedy, *Vice Pres*
▲ **EMP:** 135
SQ FT: 34,000
SALES (est): 48.5MM **Privately Held**
WEB: www.kennedyfab.com
SIC: 3441 Fabricated structural metal

Spring
Harris County

(G-19097)
ABRASIVE CONTOUR TECH LLC
2731 Spring Stuebner Rd (77389-4826)
PHONE....................281 288-8800
Chip Morander, *Mng Member*
EMP: 14
SALES (est): 1.9MM **Privately Held**
SIC: 3312 Tool & die steel

(G-19098)
ACTION WEAR PLUS INC
Also Called: Action Trophies
18610 Klein Church Rd (77379-4936)
PHONE....................281 376-4300
Kathy A Howard, *Owner*
David Howard, *COO*
David M Howard, *Treasurer*

Alissa McWhorter, *Sales Staff*
EMP: 12
SALES (est): 847K **Privately Held**
WEB: www.actionwearplus.com
SIC: 2396 5699 2261 5999 Screen printing on fabric articles; sports apparel; embossing cotton broadwoven fabrics; trophies & plaques; screen printing; embroidery products, except schiffli machine

(G-19099)
ALPHAGRAPHICS WILLOWBROOK
17126 Stuebner Airline Rd (77379-6213)
PHONE....................281 890-0200
EMP: 12 **EST:** 2011
SALES (est): 1.7MM **Privately Held**
SIC: 2752 Lithographic Commercial Printing

(G-19100)
APPLIED TRAINING RESOURCES INC
Also Called: Atr
6405 Cypresswood Dr # 250 (77379-8066)
PHONE....................281 370-9540
Grace M Lander, *President*
Elliott Lander, *Managing Dir*
Daniel Kossman, *Business Mgr*
Royce Burnett, *Vice Pres*
Elliott P Lander, *Vice Pres*
EMP: 48
SQ FT: 18,946
SALES (est): 3.6MM **Privately Held**
WEB: www.atrco.com
SIC: 7372 Prepackaged software

(G-19101)
ARMAMENTARIUM INC (PA)
22317 Gosling Rd (77389-4409)
PHONE....................281 528-5700
Urmas Riig, *President*
Jonathan Lang, *Regional Mgr*
Chris David, *Opers Mgr*
Alex Menchaca, *Engineer*
John P Nail, *Treasurer*
EMP: 9
SQ FT: 4,500
SALES (est): 4.3MM **Privately Held**
WEB: www.armamentarium.com
SIC: 5047 3841 Physician equipment & supplies; surgical & medical instruments

(G-19102)
BAYOU ARMS INC
Also Called: Spring Guns and Ammo
4401 Spring Cypress Rd (77388-4468)
PHONE....................281 475-4470
Chris Rhodes, *Director*
EMP: 20 **EST:** 2010
SALES (est): 4.5MM **Privately Held**
WEB: www.springgunsandammo.com
SIC: 3484 Small arms

(G-19103)
BIG 4 STEEL SERVICES LP
27444 E Hardy Rd (77373-2701)
PHONE....................281 353-5333
Henry Hoke, *Mng Member*
▼ **EMP:** 30
SALES (est): 11.7MM **Privately Held**
SIC: 3441 Fabricated structural metal

(G-19104)
CEMEX CONSTRUCTION MTLS S LLC
Also Called: Spring Rm Dual
1115 W Riley Fuzzel Rd (77373-8202)
PHONE....................281 651-6426
Richard Benner, *Manager*
EMP: 21 **Privately Held**
WEB: www.cemexusa.com
SIC: 3241 Portland cement
HQ: Cemex Construction Materials South, Llc
2088 E 20th St
Yuma AZ 85365
928 343-4100

(G-19105)
CENTREX INTERNATIONAL LLC
18334 Stuebner Airline Rd (77379-5466)
PHONE....................281 370-0720
Greg Dyer,
Dale Benditz,

Daniel Benditz,
EMP: 22
SALES (est): 194.8K **Privately Held**
WEB: www.contalloy.com
SIC: 3599 Machine shop, jobbing & repair

(G-19106)
COASTAL HYDRAULIC CRANES INC
9723 Sotherloch Lake Dr (77379-3687)
PHONE....................................281 448-8998
Timothy J Coiner, *President*
Michelle Joiner, *Vice Pres*
▲ **EMP:** 13
SQ FT: 16,000
SALES (est): 3MM **Privately Held**
SIC: 3531 Cranes

(G-19107)
COLACO CONSULTANTS INC
8523 Delachase Cir (77379-6782)
PHONE....................................281 370-2948
Titus J Colaco, *President*
Miguel Cirbi, *Director*
Megan Dodd, *Officer*
▲ **EMP:** 15
SALES (est): 225K **Privately Held**
SIC: 1389 Testing, measuring, surveying & analysis services; oil consultants

(G-19108)
COVESTRO LLC
2400 Spring Stuebner Rd (77389-4819)
P.O. Box 1509 (77383-1509)
PHONE....................................281 350-9000
Walker Bob, *Top Exec*
Scott Kearns, *Manager*
EMP: 40
SALES (corp-wide): 13.7B **Privately Held**
WEB: www.covestro.us
SIC: 2822 2821 Synthetic rubber; plastics materials & resins
HQ: Covestro Llc
1 Covestro Cir
Pittsburgh PA 15205
866 540-0753

(G-19109)
DDI MACHINE INC
21422 Holzwarth Rd (77388-3453)
P.O. Box 1593 (77383-1593)
PHONE....................................281 353-3721
Kent Rives, *President*
Patti Rives, *Admin Sec*
EMP: 11
SQ FT: 16,200
SALES (est): 2.4MM **Privately Held**
SIC: 3599 Machine shop, jobbing & repair

(G-19110)
DDI MACHINE INC
1806 Fm 2920 Rd (77388-3463)
P.O. Box 1593 (77383-1593)
PHONE....................................281 353-5108
Kent Rives, *President*
EMP: 11
SALES (est): 1.1MM **Privately Held**
SIC: 3599 Machine shop, jobbing & repair

(G-19111)
DORSTENER WIRE TECH INC (HQ)
19994 Hickory Twig Way (77388-6211)
P.O. Box 3019 (77383-3019)
PHONE....................................281 651-6226
Ruediger Tushaus, *President*
Billee Eisenhart, *Regional Mgr*
Gary Cobden, *Vice Pres*
Pat McGrenera, *Vice Pres*
Samuel Wilhelm, *QC Mgr*
▲ **EMP:** 13
SQ FT: 10,000
SALES (est): 3.3MM
SALES (corp-wide): 34.1MM **Privately Held**
WEB: www.dwt-inc.com
SIC: 3496 5051 Concrete reinforcing mesh & wire; reinforcement mesh, wire
PA: Dorstener Drahtwerke H. W. Brune & Co. Gesellschaft Mit Beschrankter Haftung
Marler Str. 109
Dorsten 46282
236 220-990

(G-19112)
DOWNHOLE WELL SOLUTIONS LLC
18300 Strack Dr Ste 900 (77379-8799)
PHONE....................................832 761-5111
Taylor Janca, *Mng Member*
Morgan Psullmann, *Manager*
EMP: 10
SALES (est): 520.8K **Privately Held**
WEB: www.downholewellsolutions.com
SIC: 1321 Natural gas liquids production

(G-19113)
ESSENTIAL SAFETY PPE LLC
22936 Kuykendahl Rd (77389-4325)
PHONE....................................844 372-3377
Chad Hawkins,
Robert Lee McPheron IV,
EMP: 88
SALES (est): 3.4MM **Privately Held**
WEB: www.esppe.com
SIC: 2389 Hospital gowns

(G-19114)
EVEREST COATINGS INC
2400 Spring Stuebner Rd (77389-4819)
P.O. Box 1509 (77383-1509)
PHONE....................................281 350-9800
EMP: 10
SQ FT: 20,000
SALES (est): 2MM **Privately Held**
SIC: 2952 Mfg Asphalt Felts/Coatings

(G-19115)
EXXON MOBIL FUELS MARKETING CO (HQ)
Also Called: Jana's Ministry
22777 Sprngwoods Vlg Pkwy (77389-1425)
PHONE....................................703 846-3000
Jana L Stevens, *Owner*
▲ **EMP:** 14
SALES (est): 36.3MM
SALES (corp-wide): 264.9B **Publicly Held**
WEB: www.corporate.exxonmobil.com
SIC: 1311 Crude petroleum & natural gas
PA: Exxon Mobil Corporation
5959 Las Colinas Blvd
Irving TX 75039
972 940-6000

(G-19116)
EXXONMOBIL CHEMICAL COMPANY (HQ)
Also Called: Exxonmobil Lubr & Petro Spc
22777 Sprngwoods Vlg Pkwy (77389-1425)
PHONE....................................800 243-9966
Karen McKee, *President*
◆ **EMP:** 275
SALES (est): 957.4MM
SALES (corp-wide): 264.9B **Publicly Held**
WEB: www.exxonmobilchemical.com
SIC: 2821 Plastics materials & resins
PA: Exxon Mobil Corporation
5959 Las Colinas Blvd
Irving TX 75039
972 940-6000

(G-19117)
EXXONMOBIL PIPELINE COMPANY (DH)
22777 Sprngwoods Vlg Pkwy (77389-1425)
P.O. Box 9677 (77387-6677)
PHONE....................................713 656-3636
Mike P Tudor, *President*
▲ **EMP:** 145 **EST:** 1941
SQ FT: 54,746
SALES: 248.2MM
SALES (corp-wide): 264.9B **Publicly Held**
WEB: www.exxonmobilpipeline.com
SIC: 4612 4613 2911 Crude petroleum pipelines; gasoline pipelines (common carriers); petroleum refining
HQ: Exxon Pipeline Holdings, Inc.
800 Bell St Rm 2441
Houston TX 77002
713 656-3636

(G-19118)
EXXONMOBIL RESEARCH & ENGRG CO
22777 Sprngwoods Vlg Pkwy (77379-1425)
PHONE....................................815 521-7411
Darren W Woods, *Ch of Bd*
EMP: 25
SALES (est): 8.2MM
SALES (corp-wide): 264.9B **Publicly Held**
SIC: 2821 Plastics materials & resins
PA: Exxon Mobil Corporation
5959 Las Colinas Blvd
Irving TX 75039
972 940-6000

(G-19119)
EXXONMOBIL SALES AND SUP LLC (HQ)
Also Called: Exxon Trading Interamerica
22777 Sprngwoods Vlg Pkwy (77389-1425)
PHONE....................................800 243-9966
Lance E Johnson, *President*
James Rouse, *Vice Pres*
◆ **EMP:** 202
SALES (est): 86.2MM
SALES (corp-wide): 264.9B **Publicly Held**
WEB: www.corporate.exxonmobil.com
SIC: 2911 Petroleum refining
PA: Exxon Mobil Corporation
5959 Las Colinas Blvd
Irving TX 75039
972 940-6000

(G-19120)
F-1 FIREARMS LLC
5045 Fm 2920 Rd (77388-3114)
PHONE....................................832 299-6100
Dion Podgurny, *CEO*
Mick Okrzesik, *President*
Nate Harper, *Sales Staff*
Sierra Kimbrell, *Office Mgr*
▲ **EMP:** 23
SQ FT: 15,000
SALES (est): 1MM **Privately Held**
WEB: www.f-1firearms.com
SIC: 3484 5941 Guns (firearms) or gun parts, 30 mm. & below; firearms

(G-19121)
FISHER HAM AND MEAT CO
5023 Spring Cypress Rd (77379-3442)
PHONE....................................281 376-1644
William K Fisher, *Director*
EMP: 10
SALES (est): 1.1MM **Privately Held**
WEB: www.fisherhamandmeat.com
SIC: 0751 2011 5147 5421 Slaughtering: custom livestock services; sausages from meat slaughtered on site; meats, fresh; meat & fish markets

(G-19122)
FLO PURA CORP
6717 Klein Cemetary Rd G (77379-4214)
P.O. Box 690447, Houston (77269-0447)
PHONE....................................281 320-9547
Rocky Rasberry, *President*
Mitzi Schultz, *Vice Pres*
Robert B Grossman, *Treasurer*
Claudia Brambila, *Sales Mgr*
EMP: 20
SQ FT: 10,000
SALES (est): 3.7MM **Privately Held**
WEB: www.mypuraflo.com
SIC: 3589 5074 5999 7359 Water purification equipment, household type; water purification equipment; water purification equipment; equipment rental & leasing; industrial equipment services

(G-19123)
FOODER LLC
20311 Sienna Pines Ct (77379-2526)
PHONE....................................832 953-8944
Timothy Andis,
EMP: 10
SALES (est): 221.8K **Privately Held**
SIC: 7372 Application computer software

(G-19124)
GEMSTAR STONEWORKS INC
Also Called: Gemstar Group USA
17819 Theiss Mail Rt Rd (77379-6110)
PHONE....................................281 257-6500
Gianpaolo Garrone, *President*
Eddie Caruthers, *General Mgr*
Lidia Garrone, *Purchasing*
Joe Enriquez, *Manager*
◆ **EMP:** 20
SALES (est): 3.6MM **Privately Held**
WEB: www.gemstargroupusa.com
SIC: 7311 3281 Advertising agencies; granite, cut & shaped

(G-19125)
GLOBAL REMOTE TECHNOLOGIES LLC (HQ)
Also Called: Grt
21617 Rhodes Rd (77388-3026)
PHONE....................................888 381-3222
Chris Dorris, *CEO*
Kane Smith, *President*
EMP: 35
SQ FT: 6,000
SALES (est): 2.3MM
SALES (corp-wide): 15.1K **Privately Held**
SIC: 1389 7373 7389 Oil field services; systems integration services; inspection & testing services
PA: Extreme Vehicle Battery Technologies Corp
625 Howe St Suite 1200
Vancouver BC V6C 2
604 681-1269

(G-19126)
GLOBAL TECHNICAL SOLUTIONS USA
6114 Windrose Hollow Ln (77379-8905)
PHONE....................................832 410-4488
Guillermo Garcia, *Principal*
EMP: 10 **EST:** 2014
SALES (est): 101.2K **Privately Held**
SIC: 8712 8748 3612 Architectural engineering; systems engineering consultant, ex. computer or professional; current limiting reactors, electrical

(G-19127)
H & W MANUFACTURING CO LTD
2731 Spring Stuebner Rd H (77389-4826)
P.O. Box 1414 (77383-1414)
PHONE....................................281 353-9079
Lee Ann Hilderbrandt, *Partner*
Karl Valleskey, *QC Mgr*
Heather Davis, *Accounts Mgr*
Anthony Hilderbrandt,
EMP: 40 **EST:** 1978
SQ FT: 30,000
SALES (est): 7.6MM **Privately Held**
WEB: www.hwmfg.com
SIC: 3599 Machine shop, jobbing & repair

(G-19128)
HARSCO CORPORATION
1514 S Sheldon Rd (77373)
PHONE....................................713 378-3900
Tony Moulds, *Vice Pres*
EMP: 43
SALES (corp-wide): 1.5B **Publicly Held**
WEB: www.harsco.com
SIC: 3446 5051 Open flooring & grating for construction; steel decking
PA: Harsco Corporation
350 Poplar Church Rd
Camp Hill PA 17011
717 763-7064

(G-19129)
HEWLETT-PACKARD DEV CO LP
10300 Energy Dr (77389-1864)
PHONE....................................281 370-0670
Dion Weisler, *President*
EMP: 10
SALES (est): 1.7MM
SALES (corp-wide): 56.6B **Publicly Held**
WEB: www.hp.com
SIC: 3575 Computer terminals, monitors & components
PA: Hp Inc.
1501 Page Mill Rd
Palo Alto CA 94304
650 857-1501

(G-19130)
HITECH FIRE DETECTION CORP
Also Called: Hitech Integrated Solutions
18315 Trace Forest Dr (77379-3966)
PHONE..................................281 475-7289
Dan Cooley, *CEO*
Eric Cooley, *President*
Wesley D Cooley, *Director*
Paula Cooley, *Admin Sec*
EMP: 57
SQ FT: 8,000
SALES (est): 17.3MM **Privately Held**
SIC: 5065 5087 5099 3669 Security control equipment & systems; sprinkler systems; fire extinguishers; smoke detectors

(G-19131)
HOUSTON WIFI C/HSTON CNSTR SVC
18703 White Candle Dr (77388-5870)
PHONE..................................832 444-8300
Ray Gutierrez, *President*
EMP: 10
SALES (est): 950K **Privately Held**
WEB: www.thehoustonwifi.com
SIC: 7379 1771 1541 1542 ; concrete work; steel building construction; commercial & office building contractors; glass & glazing work; fabricated structural metal

(G-19132)
HP INC
10300 Energy Dr (77389-1864)
PHONE..................................541 360-4763
Bob Tesh, *Partner*
Lorena Kubera, *Vice Pres*
Michael Frick, *Project Mgr*
Cory Nguyen, *Project Mgr*
Julia West-Boyt, *Project Mgr*
EMP: 1000
SALES (corp-wide): 56.6B **Publicly Held**
WEB: www.hp.com
SIC: 3571 7372 Personal computers (microcomputers); prepackaged software
PA: Hp Inc.
　1501 Page Mill Rd
　Palo Alto CA 94304
　650 857-1501

(G-19133)
HUNTING ENERGY SERVICES LLC
7211 Spring Cypress Rd (77379-3216)
PHONE..................................281 379-4289
Marcia Preston, *Branch Mgr*
EMP: 75
SALES (corp-wide): 960MM **Privately Held**
WEB: www.hunting-intl.com
SIC: 1389 Oil field services
HQ: Hunting Energy Services, Llc
　16825 Northchase Dr # 600
　Houston TX 77060

(G-19134)
INSECT CONTROL SOLUTIONS INC
612 Spring Cypress Rd (77373-2526)
PHONE..................................832 299-2400
Dave Glaffelc, *President*
Dave Lester Glassel, *Director*
EMP: 15 **EST:** 2013
SALES (est): 68MM **Privately Held**
SIC: 2879 Insecticides & pesticides

(G-19135)
INTEL CORPORATION
6518 Castle Pine Ln (77379-4202)
PHONE..................................281 370-9355
Jon Milburn, *Principal*
Jarrad Brenek, *Sales Staff*
EMP: 60
SALES (corp-wide): 77.8B **Publicly Held**
WEB: www.intel.com
SIC: 3577 Computer peripheral equipment
PA: Intel Corporation
　2200 Mission College Blvd
　Santa Clara CA 95054
　408 765-8080

(G-19136)
JARVIS INDUSTRIES INC
23924 Lenze Rd (77389-3507)
P.O. Box 1417, Tomball (77377-1417)
PHONE..................................281 370-5455
Beverly Jarvis, *President*
Jennifer Grissom, *Mktg Dir*
▲ **EMP:** 9
SQ FT: 10,000
SALES (est): 1.3MM **Privately Held**
WEB: www.jarvisonline.com
SIC: 3931 Musical instruments

(G-19137)
JBL OIL & GAS OPERATING LLC
8500 Cypresswood Dr # 10 (77379-7105)
PHONE..................................281 516-3137
Jason Lane,
EMP: 14
SALES (est): 278.8K **Privately Held**
SIC: 1389 Oil & gas wells: building, repairing & dismantling

(G-19138)
JIM R REYNOLDS & ASSOC INC
25702 Aldine Westfield Rd (77373-5978)
PHONE..................................832 257-2312
Jim R Reynolds, *President*
Steve Holte, *Opers Staff*
Richard Otwell, *CFO*
EMP: 22
SQ FT: 12,000
SALES (est): 3.2MM **Privately Held**
WEB: www.jimrreynolds.com
SIC: 2434 Wood kitchen cabinets

(G-19139)
KECA METAL PRODUCTS INC
1227 Pine Walk Trl (77388-5435)
P.O. Box 10 (77383-0010)
PHONE..................................713 249-3392
Jeffrey Robbins, *President*
EMP: 15
SQ FT: 7,500 **Privately Held**
SIC: 3599 Machine shop, jobbing & repair

(G-19140)
LAND & SEA INDUSTRIES LLC
19321 Stuebner Airline Rd (77379-5446)
PHONE..................................832 622-4216
Wade D Schindewolf, *Mng Member*
EMP: 17 **EST:** 2014
SALES (est): 4.2MM **Privately Held**
WEB: www.landandseaindustries.com
SIC: 3496 Chain, welded

(G-19141)
LIQUIDMTAL CTNGS SOLUTIONS LLC (PA)
20404 Whitewood Dr (77373-5691)
PHONE..................................281 359-1283
Larry Buffington, *CEO*
David Cole, *Vice Pres*
Lora Sigglin, *Controller*
Valee Malone, *Accounting Mgr*
Christoph Brandt, *Manager*
▼ **EMP:** 10
SALES (est): 1.5MM **Privately Held**
WEB: www.liquidmetal-coatings.com
SIC: 3479 Coating of metals & formed products

(G-19142)
LONE STAR FASTENERS LLC (DH)
24131 W Hardy Rd (77373-5769)
PHONE..................................281 353-1191
◆ **EMP:** 190 **EST:** 1985
SQ FT: 60,000
SALES (est): 36.6MM **Privately Held**
WEB: www.lonestargroup.com
SIC: 3452 Bolts, nuts, rivets & washers
HQ: Ameribolt, Inc.
　18060 Al Hwy 21
　Sycamore AL 35149
　256 249-6979

(G-19143)
LUBCHEM INC
23609 W Hardy Rd (77373-5713)
P.O. Box 2626 (77383-2626)
PHONE..................................281 350-9600
H D Riney, *CEO*
R G Riney, *President*
S G Riney, *Vice Pres*
EMP: 10 **EST:** 1950
SQ FT: 18,000
SALES (est): 2.9MM **Privately Held**
WEB: www.lubchem.com
SIC: 2992 2819 Lubricating oils & greases; industrial inorganic chemicals

(G-19144)
MARTIN PEDRAZA
24202 Hampton Oaks Dr (77389-3542)
PHONE..................................281 814-3916
Martin Pedraza, *Owner*
EMP: 11
SALES (est): 1.1MM **Privately Held**
SIC: 2431 Interior & ornamental woodwork & trim

(G-19145)
MEDCO MANUFACTURING LLC
8319 Thora Ln Hngr A1 (77379-3153)
PHONE..................................281 379-3100
Elaine Martin, *Principal*
EMP: 9
SALES (est): 904.2K **Privately Held**
WEB: www.medcomanufacturing.com
SIC: 3089 Plastics products

(G-19146)
MLC OPERATING LP
8900 Eastloch Dr Ste 235 (77379-2341)
PHONE..................................713 255-6200
Mike Mount, *Managing Prtnr*
EMP: 50
SALES (est): 4.2MM **Privately Held**
SIC: 1381 Drilling oil & gas wells

(G-19147)
MONICO MONITORING INC
18530 Klein Church Rd (77379-4925)
PHONE..................................281 350-8751
Doyle Taylor, *CEO*
EMP: 12 **EST:** 1986
SALES (est): 1.5MM **Privately Held**
WEB: www.monicoinc.com
SIC: 5088 3621 Marine propulsion machinery & equipment; motor generator sets

(G-19148)
MORGAN PERFORMANCE
6715 Klein Cemetary Rd (77379-4258)
P.O. Box 11816 (77391-1816)
PHONE..................................281 370-2465
Charlie Kalef, *CFO*
Mark Morgan, *CFO*
▼ **EMP:** 19
SQ FT: 15,000
SALES (est): 3.7MM **Privately Held**
WEB: www.morganperformance.com
SIC: 3599 Machine shop, jobbing & repair

(G-19149)
MOTIVE WIRELESS LTD LBLTY CO
8765 Spring Cypress Rd (77379-3194)
PHONE..................................214 500-9242
Marquis Wallace, *Mng Member*
EMP: 10
SALES (est): 419K **Privately Held**
SIC: 3661 Communication headgear, telephone

(G-19150)
MPACT BEVERAGE SOLUTIONS LLC (PA)
Also Called: Mpact Beverage Company
21240 Foster Rd (77388-4248)
PHONE..................................832 260-2342
Greg Johnson, *CEO*
Gregory Johnson, *CEO*
Brock Johnson, *Manager*
▲ **EMP:** 14
SQ FT: 20,000
SALES (est): 3.6MM **Privately Held**
WEB: www.mpactbeverage.com
SIC: 2085 Cocktails, alcoholic

(G-19151)
NAPCO CHEMICAL COMPANY INC
2830 Spring Cypress Rd (77388-4633)
P.O. Box 1239 (77383-1239)
PHONE..................................281 651-6800
Pamela Manning, *CEO*
Mike Manning, *President*
Jay Judge, *Sales Staff*
▲ **EMP:** 28
SQ FT: 25,000
SALES (est): 11.7MM **Privately Held**
WEB: www.napcochemical.com
SIC: 2819 Industrial inorganic chemicals

(G-19152)
NATIONAL MAIL ADVERTISING INC
Also Called: Magazine Fulfillment Service
6706 River Lodge Dr (77379-5007)
P.O. Box 2687, Houston (77252-2687)
PHONE..................................713 869-8551
Ronald D Garrow, *President*
EMP: 125 **EST:** 1967
SQ FT: 65,000
SALES (est): 11.8MM **Privately Held**
WEB: www.nationalmail.com
SIC: 7331 2752 Mailing service; mailing list compilers; addressing service; commercial printing, lithographic

(G-19153)
NAUTICAL CONTROL SOLUTIONS LP
Also Called: Fueltrax
20358 Whitewood Dr (77373-5552)
PHONE..................................281 209-3480
Anthony George, *Partner*
Brian Doyle, *Engineer*
Gloria Mejia, *Office Mgr*
Sara Edmonds, *Administration*
EMP: 20
SALES (est): 2.9MM **Privately Held**
WEB: www.fueltrax.com
SIC: 3812 Nautical instruments

(G-19154)
NEB PRODUCTS LLC
3336 Spring Stuebner Rd O (77389-4782)
PHONE..................................281 528-9428
Neil Edward Broesche, *Mng Member*
EMP: 9
SQ FT: 3,000
SALES (est): 995.6K **Privately Held**
WEB: www.neb.com
SIC: 3069 Molded rubber products

(G-19155)
NEW CENTURY EXPLORATION INC
20008 Champion Forest Dr # 701 (77379-8696)
PHONE..................................832 698-1374
Phil Martin, *President*
Narda Martin, *Vice Pres*
Martin Stutes, *Vice Pres*
Scandas Ter Haar, *Administration*
EMP: 10
SQ FT: 3,500
SALES (est): 4.2MM **Privately Held**
WEB: www.newcenturyexp.com
SIC: 1382 Oil & gas exploration services

(G-19156)
NUCOR CORPORATION
Also Called: Vulcraft
16000 Stuebner Airline Rd # 520 (77379-7363)
PHONE..................................281 251-8857
Nichole Sanchez, *Sales Staff*
Michael Griffith, *Branch Mgr*
EMP: 9
SALES (corp-wide): 22.5B **Publicly Held**
WEB: www.nucor.com
SIC: 3449 3444 Joists, fabricated bar; roof deck, sheet metal
PA: Nucor Corporation
　1915 Rexford Rd Ste 400
　Charlotte NC 28211
　704 366-7000

(G-19157)
PERFECT INK INC
Also Called: AlphaGraphics
17126 Stuebner Airline Rd (77379-6213)
PHONE..................................281 376-4781
Jerry Hays, *President*
David Vaughan, *Vice Pres*
EMP: 11
SQ FT: 6,000

SALES (est): 1.4MM **Privately Held**
WEB: www.kkbc117.com
SIC: 2752 Commercial printing, litho-
graphic

(G-19158)
PIVOT3 INC
6605 Cypresswood Dr (77379-7708)
PHONE.................................281 516-6000
Ben Bolles, *Vice Pres*
EMP: 23
SALES (corp-wide): 77MM **Privately
Held**
WEB: www.pivot3.com
SIC: 7372 Prepackaged software
PA: Pivot3, Inc.
361 Centennial Pkwy # 230
Louisville CO 80027
512 807-2666

(G-19159)
**PML EXPLORATION SERVICES
LLC (PA)**
19059 Champion Forest Dr # 103
(77379-8596)
PHONE.................................405 606-2701
Jim Fletcher, *General Mgr*
EMP: 110
SQ FT: 5,000
SALES (est): 8MM **Privately Held**
WEB: www.pmles.com
SIC: 1389 Mud service, oil field drilling

(G-19160)
POROUS METAL FILTERS INC
19994 Hickory Twig Way (77388-6211)
P.O. Box 3019 (77383-3019)
PHONE.................................866 288-2522
Rick Kenney, *Vice Pres*
Sam Wilhelm, *QC Mgr*
EMP: 15
SALES (est): 483.5K **Privately Held**
WEB: www.pmfilter.net
SIC: 3569 Filters

(G-19161)
**RADIAL DRILLING SERVICES
INC (PA)**
Also Called: RDS
4921 Spring Cypress Rd (77379-3444)
PHONE.................................281 374-7507
Henk H Jelsma, *President*
Patrick L Jelsma, *Vice Pres*
Luis Hernandez, *Warehouse Mgr*
Daniel Wandurraga, *Opers Spvr*
Sergey Faerman, *Opers Staff*
▲ EMP: 41
SQ FT: 12,000
SALES (est): 35.4MM **Privately Held**
WEB: www.radialdrilling.com
SIC: 1381 Reworking oil & gas wells

(G-19162)
REDBUD E&P INC (PA)
16000 Stuebner Airline Rd # 320
(77379-7363)
PHONE.................................832 698-4234
Thomas Kaetzer, *CEO*
EMP: 23
SALES (est): 5.3MM **Privately Held**
WEB: www.redbudinc.com
SIC: 1382 Oil & gas exploration services

(G-19163)
RTI ENERGY SYSTEMS INC
Also Called: Weld-Tech Engineering
7211 Spring Cypress Rd (77379-3216)
P.O. Box 12329 (77391-2329)
PHONE.................................281 379-4289
Mike Foley, *Engineer*
Chris Caldwell, *Info Tech Mgr*
Chad Whalen, *Admin Sec*
Marcia Preston, *Planning*
◆ EMP: 21
SQ FT: 87,000
SALES (est): 228.8MM
SALES (corp-wide): 14.1B **Publicly Held**
WEB: www.rtiintl.com
SIC: 3533 3498 Oil field machinery &
equipment; fabricated pipe & fittings
HQ: Rmi Titanium Company, Llc
1000 Warren Ave
Niles OH 44446
330 652-9952

(G-19164)
SANDAY CORPORATION
9111 Memorial Grove Dr (77379-2967)
PHONE.................................832 717-4412
Roger Smith, *CEO*
EMP: 10
SQ FT: 7,500
SALES (est): 780.4K
SALES (corp-wide): 1MM **Privately Held**
WEB: www.cannabisfundinggrouplp.com
SIC: 1382 Oil & gas exploration services
PA: Smart Ventures Inc.
9111 Memorial Grove Dr
Spring TX 77379
832 717-4412

(G-19165)
SES FOAM LLC (PA)
2400 Spring Stuebner Rd (77389-4819)
PHONE.................................713 239-0252
Charles Valentine, *CEO*
Mark Assise, *CFO*
Steve Fortin, *Regl Sales Mgr*
EMP: 30
SALES (est): 12.6MM **Privately Held**
WEB: www.sesfoam.com
SIC: 3086 5169 Insulation or cushioning
material, foamed plastic; polyurethane
products

(G-19166)
SOCCER 4 ALL INC
6700 Louetta Rd Ste C (77379-7569)
PHONE.................................281 376-7890
Anita Thompson, *Branch Mgr*
EMP: 10
SALES (corp-wide): 5.4MM **Privately
Held**
WEB: www.soccer4all.com
SIC: 5941 2759 Soccer supplies; screen
printing
PA: Soccer 4 All, Inc.
1306 Fm 1092 Rd Ste 101
Missouri City TX 77459
281 499-6665

(G-19167)
**SOUTHWESTERN ENERGY
COMPANY (PA)**
10000 Energy Dr (77389-4954)
P.O. Box 12359 (77391-2359)
PHONE.................................832 796-1000
William J Way, *President*
E Kelsey Ridpath, *General Mgr*
Kevin Cotton, *Superintendent*
Clayton A Carrell, *COO*
J David Cecil, *Exec VP*
EMP: 82 EST: 1929
SALES: 3B **Publicly Held**
WEB: www.swn.com
SIC: 1311 1382 Crude petroleum produc-
tion; oil & gas exploration services

(G-19168)
**SUPERIOR PATTERN WORKS
INC**
21614 Tophill Dr (77388-2952)
PHONE.................................281 442-1422
Ted Keen, *President*
Patricia Keen, *Corp Secy*
Jesse Stinson, *Manager*
EMP: 10
SQ FT: 4,200
SALES (est): 1.5MM **Privately Held**
SIC: 3543 Foundry patternmaking

(G-19169)
**SUPPLY CHAIN SOLUTIONS
LTD**
Also Called: Antares U S A
4503 Spring Cypress Rd (77388-4566)
PHONE.................................281 288-0658
Steve Michell, *President*
Miguel Ludena, *Business Mgr*
EMP: 10
SALES (est): 2.5MM **Privately Held**
WEB: www.antares-usa-ltd.com
SIC: 3533 Oil field machinery & equipment

(G-19170)
**SWIRE OILFIELD SERVICES LLC
(PA)**
28420 Hardy Toll Rd # 100 (77373-8665)
PHONE.................................281 210-5598
Lyall Dochard, *CEO*

Steve Hardwick, *President*
Mike Perera, *General Mgr*
Chris Wasson, *Vice Pres*
Gunnar Asland, *Opers Staff*
EMP: 26
SALES (est): 13.4MM **Privately Held**
WEB: www.swireos.com
SIC: 1389 Oil field services

(G-19171)
SWN INTERNATIONAL LLC
10000 Energy Dr (77389-4954)
PHONE.................................832 796-1000
William Way, *President*
Jayme Negvesky, *Manager*
Ira Canoy, *IT/INT Sup*
Ann Barrett, *Director*
Rick Ogle, *General Counsel*
EMP: 1469 EST: 2010
SALES (est): 10.2MM
SALES (corp-wide): 3B **Publicly Held**
WEB: www.swn.com
SIC: 1311 1382 Crude petroleum produc-
tion; oil & gas exploration services
PA: Southwestern Energy Company Inc
10000 Energy Dr
Spring TX 77389
832 796-1000

(G-19172)
**SWN PRODUCTION
(ARKANSAS) LLC**
10000 Energy Dr (77389-4954)
PHONE.................................832 796-1000
William J Way, *President*
EMP: 1469
SALES (est): 9.3MM
SALES (corp-wide): 3B **Publicly Held**
SIC: 1311 1382 Crude petroleum produc-
tion; oil & gas exploration services
PA: Southwestern Energy Company Inc
10000 Energy Dr
Spring TX 77389
832 796-1000

(G-19173)
**SWN PRODUCTION COMPANY
LLC (HQ)**
Also Called: Sepco
10000 Energy Dr (77389-4954)
PHONE.................................832 796-1000
EMP: 14
SALES (est): 4MM
SALES (corp-wide): 3B **Publicly Held**
WEB: www.swn.com
SIC: 1389 Lease tanks, oil field: erecting,
cleaning & repairing
PA: Southwestern Energy Company Inc
10000 Energy Dr
Spring TX 77389
832 796-1000

(G-19174)
TAMS INDUSTRIES LLC (HQ)
8303 Thora Ln (77379-3160)
PHONE.................................281 370-3087
Wade Schindewolf, *President*
Jimmy Hancock, *General Mgr*
Jairo Parra, *CFO*
▲ EMP: 61 EST: 2006
SQ FT: 30,000
SALES (est): 18.8MM **Privately Held**
WEB: www.houston-websites.net
SIC: 3533 Oil & gas drilling rigs & equip-
ment

(G-19175)
TECHMAR INDUSTRIES LLC
5510 Spring Stuebner Rd (77389-4570)
P.O. Box 11930 (77391-1930)
PHONE.................................832 246-6200
Elias Abdallah, *Principal*
Jesus Finol, *Principal*
Roger Rodriguez, *Sales Executive*
Rayner Diaz, *Director*
EMP: 18
SALES (est): 4.5MM **Privately Held**
SIC: 3441 3599 3448 3443 Fabricated
structural metal; machine & other job
shop work; prefabricated metal buildings;
plate work for the metalworking trade; air-
craft engines & engine parts

(G-19176)
TELECOM MANAGEMENT CORP
1110 Arden Forest Dr (77379-2985)
PHONE.................................281 404-5610
James Pintkowski, *President*
EMP: 10
SALES (est): 1.2MM **Privately Held**
WEB: www.phonetmc.com
SIC: 3661 5065 Communication head-
gear, telephone; electronic parts & equip-
ment

(G-19177)
TEXAS COUPLINGS
1835 Old Holzwarth Rd (77388-4802)
PHONE.................................281 350-2494
Jim Rizzo, *Partner*
EMP: 12 EST: 1982
SALES (est): 2.8MM **Privately Held**
WEB: www.texascouplings.com
SIC: 3533 Oil field machinery & equipment

(G-19178)
**TEXAS EXTRUSION SERVICE
INC**
20803 Sunshine Ln (77388-4838)
P.O. Box 2807 (77383-2807)
PHONE.................................281 350-2288
David C Kores Jr, *President*
Sharon Kores, *Vice Pres*
Korey Lowry, *Foreman/Supr*
Stephen Arnold, *Engineer*
Morgan Keen, *Mktg Dir*
▲ EMP: 11
SQ FT: 10,000
SALES (est): 2.9MM **Privately Held**
WEB: www.texasextrusion.com
SIC: 3542 3559 1796 Extruding machines
(machine tools), metal; rubber working
machinery, including tires; plastics work-
ing machinery; machinery installation

(G-19179)
**TONATCO CRYOGENIC
SERVICES**
1906 Old Holzwarth Rd (77388-4803)
PHONE.................................281 651-0305
Bonnie Yough, *President*
Alfred Yough, *Vice Pres*
Nathan Yough, *Treasurer*
Todd Yough, *Admin Sec*
EMP: 10
SQ FT: 6,800
SALES (est): 1.6MM **Privately Held**
WEB: www.tonatcocryogenic.com
SIC: 3443 Cryogenic tanks, for liquids &
gases

(G-19180)
TOPGOLF INTERNATIONAL INC
560 Spring Park Ctr Blvd (77373-8177)
PHONE.................................832 200-0106
EMP: 11
SALES (corp-wide): 214.3MM **Privately
Held**
WEB: www.topgolf.com
SIC: 3949 Driving ranges, golf, electronic
PA: Topgolf International, Inc.
8750 N Cntl Expy Ste 1200
Dallas TX 75231
214 377-0663

(G-19181)
**TOTAL MACHINING SOLUTIONS
LLC (PA)**
19129 Northpine Dr (77388-4440)
PHONE.................................281 355-7700
Mark Law,
Daniel Taggart,
EMP: 9
SALES (est): 772K **Privately Held**
SIC: 3599 Machine shop, jobbing & repair

(G-19182)
TRIX & KIX DANNYS
3400 Fm 2920 Rd (77388-4115)
P.O. Box 1835 (77383-1835)
PHONE.................................281 353-6618
Danny Gurganus, *Owner*
EMP: 10
SQ FT: 7,818

SALES (est): 489.9K **Privately Held**
WEB: www.dannystrixkix.com
SIC: 5947 3089 3999 Novelties; novelties, plastic; magic equipment, supplies & props

(G-19183)
UVC MANUFACTURING GROUP LLC
3430 Rolling Terrace Dr (77388-5159)
PHONE...................................281 969-6059
Scott Blue, *Principal*
Binish Ali, *Principal*
Isabella Ali, *Principal*
William Condrey, *Principal*
Paul Fairchild, *Principal*
EMP: 9
SALES (est): 302.1K **Privately Held**
SIC: 3999 Manufacturing industries

(G-19184)
VANGUARD DEFENSE INDS LLC
2455 Fm 2920 Rd Ste A (77388-3418)
PHONE...................................281 298-6672
EMP: 13
SQ FT: 11,000
SALES (est): 1.7MM **Privately Held**
SIC: 3721 3724 3728 3812 Mfg Aircraft, Mfg Aircraft Engine/Part Mfg Aircraft Parts/Equip Mfg Search/Navgatn Equip

(G-19185)
VANGUARD PHARMACEUTICAL MCHY
21755 Interstate 45 # 6 (77388-3621)
PHONE...................................281 528-8885
David Van, *President*
Cathryn Fan, *Principal*
Helena K K, *Exec VP*
Loyd Bowman, *Sales Dir*
▲ **EMP:** 10
SQ FT: 16,500
SALES (est): 1.9MM **Privately Held**
WEB: www.pharmaceutical-equipment.com
SIC: 3559 5047 Pharmaceutical machinery; medical equipment & supplies

(G-19186)
VOGLER SHEET METAL COMPANY
1331 Lemm Road 1 (77373-5738)
PHONE...................................713 861-1154
James Kaiser, *President*
EMP: 22 **EST:** 1904
SALES (est): 8.3MM **Privately Held**
WEB: www.voglermetals.com
SIC: 3444 1761 Sheet metalwork; gutter & downspout contractor

(G-19187)
WELD REVOLUTION LLC
19511 Wied Rd (77388-4589)
PHONE...................................832 585-1244
Eric M Christofferson, *Principal*
Bryan George, *Business Dir*
EMP: 11
SALES (est): 1MM **Privately Held**
WEB: www.weldrevolution.com
SIC: 7692 Welding repair

(G-19188)
XTO ENERGY INC (HQ)
22777 Sprngwoods Vlg Pkwy (77389-1425)
PHONE...................................817 870-2800
Randy J Cleveland, *CEO*
Rett Storm, *President*
John Woolverton, *Superintendent*
Ronnie Blackwell, *Counsel*
Timothy L Petrus, *Exec VP*
EMP: 300
SALES (est): 7.1B
SALES (corp-wide): 264.9B **Publicly Held**
WEB: www.xtoenergy.com
SIC: 1311 Crude petroleum production; natural gas production
PA: Exxon Mobil Corporation
5959 Las Colinas Blvd
Irving TX 75039
972 940-6000

(G-19189)
XTREME LASHES LLC
24127 W Hardy Rd Ste C (77373-5761)
PHONE...................................281 907-0689
Joumana Mousselli, *CEO*
Rex Deguzman, *Sales Executive*
Jessica Cahalen, *Marketing Staff*
Kelly Fischer, *Director*
Adam Weddington, *Technician*
▲ **EMP:** 35
SQ FT: 5,000
SALES (est): 4.5MM **Privately Held**
WEB: www.xtremelashes.com
SIC: 3999 Eyelashes, artificial

Spring
Montgomery County

(G-19190)
A SPECLZED APPRACH TO PRSTHTIC
Also Called: Asaprosthetics
500 Spring Hill Dr # 200 (77386-6023)
PHONE...................................832 813-5278
Craig Saravo, *President*
Brandon Smith, *Director*
EMP: 16
SALES (est): 380.2K **Privately Held**
WEB: www.asaprosthetics.com
SIC: 3842 Limbs, artificial

(G-19191)
ADVANCED FABRIC TECH LLC
2441 High Timbers Dr # 400 (77380-1051)
PHONE...................................281 872-7272
David O'Keefe,
EMP: 10
SQ FT: 4,000
SALES (est): 1MM **Privately Held**
WEB: www.advancedfabrictechnology.com
SIC: 2299 8711 2298 Upholstery filling, textile; engineering services; blasting mats, rope

(G-19192)
AFREN USA INC
Also Called: Afren Resources USA
10001 Woodloch Forest Dr (77380-1923)
PHONE...................................281 363-8600
Toby Hayward, *CEO*
Egbert Imomoh, *Chairman*
Douglas J Barrie, *Director*
Osman Shahenshah, *Director*
Shahid Ullah, *Director*
▼ **EMP:** 28 **EST:** 2008
SALES (est): 9.7MM **Privately Held**
SIC: 1382 Oil & gas exploration services
PA: Afren Plc
8th Floor
Manchester M2 4W

(G-19193)
AFTON CHEMICAL CORPORATION
Also Called: Ethyl
4526 Res Frest Dr Ste 375 (77381)
PHONE...................................281 475-1040
Michael Nieman, *Engineer*
John Boerner, *Manager*
EMP: 15
SALES (corp-wide): 2.1B **Publicly Held**
WEB: www.aftonchemical.com
SIC: 2899 Chemical preparations
HQ: Afton Chemical Corporation
500 Spring St
Richmond VA 23219
804 788-5800

(G-19194)
AJR MEDIA GROUP LLC
Also Called: Tourtexas.com
25132 Oakhurst Dr Ste 201 (77386-1443)
PHONE...................................713 942-7676
Nelson Gumm, *CEO*
Laura Baker, *Sales Staff*
EMP: 18
SQ FT: 2,010
SALES (est): 2.3MM **Privately Held**
WEB: www.ajrmediagroup.com
SIC: 7374 2741 7313 Computer graphics service; miscellaneous publishing; radio, television, publisher representatives; radio advertising representative

(G-19195)
APERGY ARTFL LIFT INTL LLC (HQ)
Also Called: Norris Production Solutions
2445 Tech Frest Blvd Ste (77381)
PHONE...................................281 403-5742
Robert A Livingston, *CEO*
William C Johnson, *President*
Kevin P Buchanan, *Vice Pres*
Brad M Cerepak, *CFO*
John S Anderson, *Admin Sec*
◆ **EMP:** 28
SALES (est): 565.9MM
SALES (corp-wide): 1.1B **Publicly Held**
SIC: 3559 3535 3533 3561 Automotive related machinery; bulk handling conveyor systems; oil field machinery & equipment; industrial pumps & parts
PA: Championx Corporation
2445 Tech Frest Blvd Bldg
The Woodlands TX 77381
281 403-5772

(G-19196)
APERGY ARTFL LIFT INTL LLC
Norris Production Solutions
2445 Tech Forest Blvd (77381-5259)
PHONE...................................281 602-2176
Kelli Haider, *Branch Mgr*
EMP: 11
SALES (corp-wide): 1.1B **Publicly Held**
SIC: 3531 Construction machinery
HQ: Apergy Artificial Lift International, Llc
2445 Tech Frest Blvd Ste
Spring TX 77381
281 403-5742

(G-19197)
ATCO STRCTRES LGISTICS USA INC
480 Wildwood Forest Dr (77380-3491)
PHONE...................................208 242-3804
Dave Cook, *Manager*
EMP: 9
SALES (corp-wide): 3.5B **Privately Held**
WEB: www.atco.com
SIC: 2452 Modular homes, prefabricated, wood
HQ: Atco Structures & Logistics (Usa) Inc.
480 Wildwood Forest Dr
Spring TX 77380
936 829-2325

(G-19198)
ATCO STRCTRES LGISTICS USA INC (HQ)
480 Wildwood Forest Dr (77380-3491)
PHONE...................................936 829-2325
George Lidgett, *President*
Michael M Shaw, *President*
Henry G Wilmot, *President*
Chad Gareau, *Vice Pres*
Rolando Sepulveda, *Sales Staff*
▼ **EMP:** 70
SQ FT: 100,000
SALES (est): 20.5MM
SALES (corp-wide): 3.5B **Privately Held**
WEB: www.atco.com
SIC: 2452 Modular homes, prefabricated, wood
PA: Atco Ltd
5302 Forand St Sw
Calgary AB T3E 8
403 292-7500

(G-19199)
ATTENTUS MEDICAL SALES INC
10101 Woodloch Forest Dr (77380-1975)
PHONE...................................281 776-5188
Jason Jodway, *President*
Jason J Jodway, *President*
▲ **EMP:** 9
SALES (est): 5.3MM
SALES (corp-wide): 231B **Publicly Held**
WEB: www.attentusmedical.com
SIC: 5047 3841 Medical equipment & supplies; surgical & medical instruments
HQ: Medical Specialties Distributors, Llc
800 Technology Center Dr # 3
Stoughton MA 02072
781 344-6000

(G-19200)
BENCHMARK COMPLETIONS LLC (PA)
Also Called: Antelope Oil Tools & Mfg Co
1400 Woodloch Forest Dr (77380-1100)
PHONE...................................281 537-8483
Bill Kelley, *CEO*
Iain Levie, *Vice Pres*
Greg Roger, *Vice Pres*
Warren Smith, *Engineer*
Abbas Udawala, *CFO*
EMP: 26 **EST:** 2013
SALES (est): 8.1MM **Privately Held**
WEB: www.aot-llc.com
SIC: 3499 3599 Stabilizing bars (cargo), metal; machine & other job shop work

(G-19201)
BJ HOOKERS DISTILLERIES LLC
23 Chestnut Hill Ct (77380-4617)
PHONE...................................713 249-2022
EMP: 11 **EST:** 2012
SALES (est): 1MM **Privately Held**
SIC: 2085 Distilled & blended liquors

(G-19202)
CAZA OIL & GAS INC (PA)
Also Called: Caza Petroleum
200 Valley Wood Dr B200 (77380-5408)
PHONE...................................281 363-4442
W Michael Ford, *CEO*
Richard R Albro, *Vice Pres*
EMP: 10
SALES (est): 999.7K **Privately Held**
WEB: www.cazapetro.com
SIC: 1382 Oil & gas exploration services

(G-19203)
CENTRAX INTERNATIONAL CORP (PA)
8505 Tech Frest Pl Ste 70 (77381)
PHONE...................................281 465-0781
EMP: 22 **EST:** 1974
SQ FT: 5,000
SALES (est): 13.2MM **Privately Held**
SIC: 3829 1389 7371 Testing equipment: abrasion, shearing strength, etc.; testing, measuring, surveying & analysis services; computer software development & applications

(G-19204)
CUDD WELL CONTROL
2828 Tech Forest Blvd (77381-3907)
PHONE...................................713 849-2769
Dan Edy, *Principal*
Bhavesh Ranka, *Opers Mgr*
Robert Langford, *Engineer*
Mark Spitz, *Engineer*
Robert Rooney, *Sales Staff*
EMP: 20
SALES (est): 1.3MM **Privately Held**
WEB: www.cuddwellcontrol.com
SIC: 1389 Oil field services

(G-19205)
CYPRESS TELECOMMUNICATIONS
Also Called: Cytel
1511 Sungail Dr (77386-2632)
PHONE...................................281 449-4000
Roger Scott, *President*
EMP: 21
SQ FT: 6,000
SALES (est): 2.2MM **Privately Held**
WEB: www.cytrexus.com
SIC: 4813 7375 7372 Long distance telephone communications; information retrieval services; prepackaged software

(G-19206)
CYTEC INDUSTRIES INC
25227 Grogans Mill Rd # 125 (77380-2951)
PHONE...................................281 296-1622
James Wallis, *Branch Mgr*
EMP: 66
SALES (corp-wide): 13.8MM **Privately Held**
WEB: www.solvay.com
SIC: 2899 Chemical preparations
HQ: Cytec Industries Inc.
4500 Mcginnis Ferry Rd
Alpharetta GA 30005

(G-19207)
DUNNS VALVE TESTERS INC
1827 Riley Fuzzel Rd # 2 (77386-3708)
P.O. Box 489 (77383-0489)
PHONE..................................281 350-4767
Emmett L Dunn, *President*
Faye Dunn, *Vice Pres*
Elsie F Dunn, *Admin Sec*
EMP: 12 **EST:** 1980
SQ FT: 7,000
SALES (est): 1.8MM **Privately Held**
WEB: www.dunnsvalvetesters.com
SIC: 3829 Measuring & controlling devices

(G-19208)
DURANGO MIDSTREAM LLC
(HQ)
10077 Grogans Mill Rd # 300
(77380-1032)
PHONE..................................346 351-2787
Richard Cargile, *President*
David Stone, *CFO*
Christina Lyons, *Commercial*
EMP: 21
SALES (est): 150MM
SALES (corp-wide): 2.1MM **Privately Held**
WEB: www.durangomidstream.com
SIC: 1321 Natural gas liquids production
PA: Durango Investment Holdings Llc
2002 Timberloch Pl # 110
The Woodlands TX 77380
346 351-2787

(G-19209)
E & E POLARIS SERVICES INC
2700 Res Frest Dr Ste 100 (77381)
PHONE..................................281 367-6000
William Sutley, *President*
Patrick Klem, *Vice Pres*
Patrick Lam, *Vice Pres*
William Strange, *Treasurer*
Chris Sutlay, *Manager*
EMP: 9
SQ FT: 4,200
SALES (est): 1.3MM **Privately Held**
WEB: www.polarisdata.com
SIC: 1382 8999 Geophysical exploration, oil & gas field; geophysical consultant

(G-19210)
ECO SERVICES OPERATIONS
LLC
2002 Timberloch Pl # 300 (77380-1171)
PHONE..................................800 642-4200
James Harton, *Ch of Bd*
David Garza, *Maint Spvr*
Joseph Lacasella, *Engineer*
Russell Wasden, *Controller*
Cameron Alfier, *VP Finance*
EMP: 500 **EST:** 2011
SALES (est): 390.8MM **Privately Held**
WEB: www.pqcorp.com
SIC: 2819 Sulfuric acid, oleum

(G-19211)
ETS ZONE
2170 Buckthorne Pl # 250 (77380-1775)
PHONE..................................713 559-1400
Giuliana Kendall, *Principal*
Matt Duszynski, *CTO*
John Stautner,
EMP: 10
SALES (est): 1MM **Privately Held**
WEB: www.etszone.com
SIC: 7371 7372 7374 Custom computer programming services; word processing computer software; computer graphics service

(G-19212)
FULL CIRCLE ENTERPRISES
INC (PA)
3 Gabled Pines Pl (77382-1517)
PHONE..................................936 441-0101
Donald Branham, *President*
Charlotte Branham, *Vice Pres*
Thomas Branham, *Vice Pres*
Linda Crawford, *Admin Sec*
EMP: 35
SALES (est): 8MM **Privately Held**
WEB: www.fceus.com
SIC: 3533 Oil field machinery & equipment

(G-19213)
GRENADIER ENERGY
PARTNERS LLC
24 Waterway Ave Ste 875 (77380-3389)
PHONE..................................281 907-4120
Patrick J Noyes, *President*
Robert Hallett, *President*
E Byron Hailey III, *Vice Pres*
Lenny Lilja, *Vice Pres*
George Moretti Jr, *Vice Pres*
EMP: 15
SALES (est): 2MM **Privately Held**
WEB: www.grenadierenergy.com
SIC: 1382 Oil & gas exploration services

(G-19214)
HALLIBURTON COMPANY
445 Woodline Dr (77386-1977)
PHONE..................................281 297-1200
Michael Kohlhauff, *Vice Pres*
Hern Lorraine, *Senior Mgr*
Pranay Asthana, *Professor*
EMP: 24 **Publicly Held**
WEB: www.halliburton.com
SIC: 1389 1382 1381 8711 Oil field services; cementing oil & gas well casings; well logging; perforating well casings; oil & gas exploration services; drilling oil & gas wells; petroleum, mining & chemical engineers
PA: Halliburton Company
3000 N Sam Houston Pkwy E
Houston TX 77032

(G-19215)
HIGH GRADE PRODUCTS LLC
25700 Interstate 45 # 121 (77386-1364)
PHONE..................................832 381-3455
Darryl Tramonte, *President*
EMP: 18
SQ FT: 2,500
SALES (est): 1.9MM **Privately Held**
WEB: www.woodlandsonline.com
SIC: 2099 Food preparations

(G-19216)
HOKULIA SHAVE ICE OF
HUMBLE
3540 Rayford Rd (77386-4343)
PHONE..................................832 527-2820
Randy Hall, *Owner*
EMP: 10 **EST:** 2015
SALES (est): 218.8K **Privately Held**
WEB: www.humbleisd.net
SIC: 2024 Ices, flavored (frozen dessert)

(G-19217)
INNOSPEC INC
Also Called: Innospec Oilfield Services
2600 Tech Forest Blvd (77381-3904)
PHONE..................................832 748-0284
EMP: 15
SALES (corp-wide): 1.5B **Publicly Held**
WEB: www.innospecinc.com
SIC: 2911 Fuel additives
PA: Innospec Inc.
8310 S Valley Hwy Ste 350
Englewood CO 80112
303 792-5554

(G-19218)
INTERNATIONAL LAB SUP LTD
Also Called: Interlab
26018 Budde Rd (77380-2014)
P.O. Box 130549 (77393-0549)
PHONE..................................281 298-9410
Joseph P Perez, *Partner*
Ann H Perez, *Partner*
Peggy Morrison, *Manager*
EMP: 20
SALES (est): 3.8MM **Privately Held**
WEB: www.interlabsupply.com
SIC: 2836 Biological products, except diagnostic

(G-19219)
INTERTEK CNSLTING TRNING
USA I (DH)
Also Called: Randy Smith Training Solutions
25025 Interstate 45 # 30 (77380-3036)
PHONE..................................337 235-4493
Greg Anderson, *President*
Eric Guidry, *COO*
Robert Suggs, *Vice Pres*
Brooke West, *Accounts Mgr*

Michael Lebla, *Consultant*
◆ **EMP:** 20
SALES (est): 5.4MM
SALES (corp-wide): 3.8B **Privately Held**
WEB: www.intertek.com
SIC: 8748 1389 Business consulting; safety training service; oil field services
HQ: Intertek Inspection Services Uk Limited
Academy Place
Brentwood CM14
127 722-3400

(G-19220)
INTERTEK USA INC
25025 Interstate 45 (77380-3036)
PHONE..................................281 364-2800
Renier Van Wyk, *Branch Mgr*
EMP: 19
SALES (corp-wide): 3.8B **Privately Held**
WEB: www.intertek.com
SIC: 7389 1389 Automobile recovery service; construction, repair & dismantling services
HQ: Intertek Usa Inc.
200 Westlake Park Blvd # 400
Houston TX 77079
713 543-3600

(G-19221)
INWELL INC
504 Spring Hill Dr # 300 (77386-6028)
PHONE..................................281 443-7614
Danny Mullens, *President*
Stephen G Allums, *President*
Danny Mullen, *President*
Chris Lemaster, *Opers Staff*
Leah Reeves,
EMP: 16
SQ FT: 2,150
SALES (est): 3.8MM **Privately Held**
WEB: www.inwell.com
SIC: 1381 Directional drilling oil & gas wells

(G-19222)
ISOMERIC INDUSTRIES INC (PA)
3400 Res Forest Dr Ste B4 (77381)
PHONE..................................678 713-4275
Chris A Harken, *CEO*
Brian Robertson, *Vice Pres*
▲ **EMP:** 24 **EST:** 2012
SALES (est): 9.9MM **Privately Held**
WEB: www.isomericindustries.com
SIC: 3999 Barber & beauty shop equipment

(G-19223)
J E F FABRICATION INC
25803 Oak Ridge Dr (77380-2015)
PHONE..................................281 367-2032
EMP: 10 **EST:** 1990
SALES (est): 1.6MM **Privately Held**
WEB: www.jef-fabrication.com
SIC: 3441 Fabricated structural metal

(G-19224)
KERR-MCGEE (NEVADA) LLC
(DH)
9950 Woodloch Forest Dr (77380-3991)
PHONE..................................303 321-0683
Karl F Kurz, *President*
Barth E Whitham, *President*
Grant W Henderson, *Exec VP*
Howard L Boigon, *Vice Pres*
Lon McCain, *CFO*
EMP: 90
SALES (est): 44.8MM
SALES (corp-wide): 21.2B **Publicly Held**
SIC: 1311 1382 Crude petroleum & natural gas; oil & gas exploration services
HQ: Kerr-Mcgee Corp
9950 Woodloch Forest Dr
Spring TX 77380
832 636-1000

(G-19225)
KOVACH ENCLOSURE
SYSTEMS LLC
1118 Sawdust Rd (77380-2154)
PHONE..................................480 926-9292
EMP: 70

SALES (est): 1.4MM
SALES (corp-wide): 66.4MM **Privately Held**
SIC: 1761 1793 3211 Roofing, siding & sheet metal work; glass & glazing work; flat glass
PA: Kovach Enclosure Systems, Llc
3195 W Armstrong Pl
Chandler AZ 85286
480 926-9292

(G-19226)
LAYNE CHRISTENSEN
COMPANY (HQ)
9303 New Trils Dr Ste 200 (77381)
PHONE..................................281 475-2600
Michael J Caliel, *President*
Gary Hanks, *General Mgr*
Terry Heiliger, *General Mgr*
Audie Medhurst, *General Mgr*
Joseph Patronik, *Superintendent*
▲ **EMP:** 65 **EST:** 1882
SALES (est): 475.5MM **Publicly Held**
WEB: www.layne.com
SIC: 1623 5084 1481 8748 Water, sewer & utility lines; materials handling machinery; nonmetallic minerals development & test boring; environmental consultant; water well servicing

(G-19227)
LINDE INC
Also Called: Praxair
1585 Sawdust Rd Ste 300 (77380-2095)
PHONE..................................281 203-3600
Ramchandra Watwe, *Research*
John McDonald, *Engineer*
Sheila Lang, *Credit Mgr*
Tom Richard, *Cust Mgr*
Kara Stout, *Sales Staff*
EMP: 20 **Privately Held**
WEB: www.praxair.com
SIC: 2813 3569 Industrial gases; gas producers (machinery)
HQ: Linde Inc.
10 Riverview Dr
Danbury CT 06810
203 837-2000

(G-19228)
LUCIAS OAKS LP
1908 Sawdust Rd (77380-2140)
PHONE..................................832 616-3306
Jose Villamediana, *Partner*
Marco Borges, *Financial Analy*
Christian Morales, *Supervisor*
EMP: 14
SALES (est): 5.1MM **Privately Held**
WEB: www.luciasoaks.com
SIC: 2499 Decorative wood & woodwork

(G-19229)
LYONDLLBSELL ADVNCED
PLYMERS I
24624 Interstate 45 (77386-4084)
PHONE..................................832 663-3104
A John Knapp Jr, *CEO*
EMP: 124
SALES (corp-wide): 34.9B **Privately Held**
WEB: www.lyondellbasell.com
SIC: 2821 Molding compounds, plastics
HQ: Lyondellbasell Advanced Polymers Inc.
1221 Mckinney St Ste 300
Houston TX 77010
713 309-7200

(G-19230)
MAVERICK DIRECTIONAL
SERVICES (PA)
25615 Oakhurst Dr (77386-1437)
P.O. Box 8429, The Woodlands (77387-8429)
PHONE..................................281 364-1212
Mark Hollier, *President*
Daniel Anthony, *Vice Pres*
W R Springer, *Vice Pres*
EMP: 26
SALES (est): 8.3MM **Privately Held**
WEB: www.maverickdirectional.com
SIC: 1381 Directional drilling oil & gas wells

(G-19231)
MECOR USA INC (HQ)
Also Called: Mecor Group
1776 Woodstead Ct Ste 109 (77380-1450)
P.O. Box 1881, Vidor (77670-1881)
PHONE................................713 817-0683
Ricardo Rausseo, *President*
EMP: 17
SQ FT: 3,000
SALES (est): 3.2MM **Privately Held**
SIC: 8711 3317 Petroleum, mining &
chemical engineers; welded pipe & tubes

(G-19232)
MOHAVE OIL AND GAS
CORPORATION (PA)
24 Waterway Ave Ste 350 (77380-3197)
PHONE................................713 975-1725
Patric Monteleone, *President*
EMP: 10
SQ FT: 6,000
SALES (est): 973.5K **Privately Held**
SIC: 1382 Oil & gas exploration services

(G-19233)
MOHF MANUFACTURING INC
31 Roundtop Pl (77381-4006)
PHONE................................346 317-3618
Juan Aramburu, *President*
EMP: 16
SALES (est): 418.9K **Privately Held**
SIC: 3999 Manufacturing industries

(G-19234)
MOVENTAS GEARS INC (DH)
2002 Timberloch Pl # 200 (77380-1182)
PHONE................................503 247-6107
Arto Lahtela, *CEO*
Pedro Figueiras, *Vice Pres*
Jari Mononen, *Opers Mgr*
Jessica Hesse, *Production*
Mick Heither, *Buyer*
▲ **EMP:** 30
SALES (est): 5.9MM
SALES (corp-wide): 970.5K **Privately
Held**
WEB: www.moventas.com
SIC: 3462 Iron & steel forgings
HQ: Moventas Gears Oy
Etelaportintie 17
Jyvaskyla 40530
201 847-000

(G-19235)
MULTI-SEAL CORPORATION
407 Alana Ln (77386-1221)
PHONE................................281 591-0111
Donald Webb, *President*
David Macrae, *VP Opers*
Ken Olson, *Plant Mgr*
Margaret D Webb, *Shareholder*
Tiffany Sicinski, *Clerk*
▲ **EMP:** 10 **EST:** 1998
SQ FT: 18,000
SALES (est): 2.2MM **Privately Held**
WEB: www.multiseal.us
SIC: 5531 3011 2891 Automotive tires;
tire sundries or tire repair materials, rub-
ber; sealants

(G-19236)
NEWFIELD EXPLORATION
COMPANY
24 Waterway Ave Ste 900 (77380-3197)
PHONE................................281 847-6000
EMP: 70
SALES (corp-wide): 1.7B **Publicly Held**
SIC: 1382 1311 Oil/Gas Exploration Serv-
ices Crude Petroleum/Natural Gas Pro-
duction
PA: Newfield Exploration Company
4 Waterway Square Pl # 100
The Woodlands TX 77380
281 210-5100

(G-19237)
NEWPARK DRLG FLIDS
PRSONNEL SE
9320 Lakeside Blvd (77381-1200)
PHONE................................405 721-0207
EMP: 12
SALES (est): 781.1K **Privately Held**
WEB: www.newpark.com
SIC: 1389 Oil field services

(G-19238)
OXBOW CALCINING LLC (DH)
Also Called: Oxbow Carbon Minerals
1450 Lake Robbins Dr # 500 (77380-3252)
PHONE................................281 907-9425
Steve Fried, *Exec VP*
Zachary Shipley, *CFO*
T J Estep, *Human Res Mgr*
◆ **EMP:** 22
SALES (est): 14.3MM
SALES (corp-wide): 446.2MM **Privately
Held**
SIC: 2911 Coke, petroleum

(G-19239)
PACIFIC VALVES
Also Called: Crane Co
4526 Res Frest Dr Ste 400 (77381)
PHONE................................562 426-2531
Mark Controls Corporation, *Owner*
Anthony Duncan, *Principal*
Bradley Ellis, *Vice Pres*
▲ **EMP:** 78
SALES (est): 1MM **Privately Held**
WEB: www.cranecpe.com
SIC: 3491 Industrial valves

(G-19240)
PIETRO FIORENPINI
10077 Grogans Mill Rd # 275
(77380-1000)
PHONE................................832 299-6075
David Watkins, *President*
Watkins David, *Vice Pres*
Lee Mayhew, *Vice Pres*
Alex Vera, *Engineer*
Pietro Cerami, *Marketing Mgr*
EMP: 16
SALES (est): 1.1MM **Privately Held**
WEB: www.fiorentini.com
SIC: 3491 Industrial valves

(G-19241)
POLLUTION SYSTEM
SOLUTIONS INC
Also Called: Pollution Systems
2170 Buckthorne Pl # 160 (77380-1775)
PHONE................................713 574-6661
Richard Corcoran, *President*
Kevin Stevens, *Corp Secy*
Karl Harris, *Project Mgr*
Donnie Timmons, *Regl Sales Mgr*
Al Duff, *Technical Staff*
EMP: 11
SALES (est): 2.5MM **Privately Held**
WEB: www.pollutionsystems.com
SIC: 8711 3567 3564 Pollution control en-
gineering; ; purification & dust collection
equipment

(G-19242)
PRO OILFIELD SERVICES LLC
(PA)
25700 Interstate 45 # 460 (77386-4702)
PHONE................................281 496-5810
J Darrell Brewer, *CEO*
Vinko Maurac, *Vice Pres*
Scott McMahon, *CFO*
Montana Cormier, *Human Resources*
Miriam Garza, *Office Mgr*
EMP: 200 **EST:** 2011
SALES (est): 205.4MM **Privately Held**
WEB: www.pro-ogs.com
SIC: 1389 Oil field services

(G-19243)
PRO-JECT CHEMICALS INC
1800 Hughes Landing Blvd (77380-1682)
PHONE................................832 403-2560
Robert Ayres, *President*
Ben Vavra, *General Mgr*
Chris Williamson, *COO*
Dusty Bryant, *Opers Staff*
Jim Bonsall, *Controller*
EMP: 32
SALES (est): 3.8MM **Privately Held**
WEB: www.pro-jectchemicals.com
SIC: 1389 Oil field services

(G-19244)
PRODUCTIONEERED
PRODUCTS CO
25531 Richards Rd (77386-2640)
P.O. Box 7734, The Woodlands (77387-
7734)
PHONE................................281 364-1086
Phil Rummell, *Owner*
Terry Swan, *Engineer*
Diane Williamson, *Office Mgr*
Katherine Rummell, *Manager*
EMP: 28
SQ FT: 15,000
SALES (est): 4.5MM **Privately Held**
WEB: www.productioneered.com
SIC: 3563 Air & gas compressors

(G-19245)
PYRAMID TUBULAR PRODUCTS
LLC
Also Called: Master Tubulars Ptp
480 Wildwood Forest Dr # 700
(77380-4121)
PHONE................................281 405-8090
Kathy Walton, *Partner*
Erik Skoy, *Exec VP*
Steve Gilbert, *Vice Pres*
Kelly Griffin, *Vice Pres*
Mike Syrko, *VP Opers*
▲ **EMP:** 30
SQ FT: 2,800
SALES (est): 5.1MM **Privately Held**
WEB: www.pyramidtubular.com
SIC: 3317 Steel pipe & tubes
HQ: Sumitomo Corporation Of Americas
300 Madison Ave
New York NY 10017
212 207-0700

(G-19246)
QUALITY FUR DRESSING
Also Called: Quality For Dressing Co
1012 Rayford Rd Ste E (77386-2619)
PHONE................................281 292-2617
Fred Sweisthal Jr, *President*
Vicky Schmitt, *Office Mgr*
EMP: 12
SQ FT: 5,000
SALES (est): 2MM **Privately Held**
WEB: www.qualityfurdressing.com
SIC: 3111 Leather tanning & finishing

(G-19247)
REPSOL OIL & GAS USA LLC
(DH)
2455 Tech Forest Blvd (77381-5205)
PHONE................................832 442-1000
James F O'Driscoll, *President*
Frank Dompnier, *Vice Pres*
April Callihan, *Human Resources*
Jason Archuleta, *Manager*
Dawson Lindauere, *Manager*
EMP: 57
SALES (est): 140.9MM
SALES (corp-wide): 6.7B **Privately Held**
WEB: www.repsol.com
SIC: 1311 Natural gas production
HQ: Repsol Oil & Gas Canada Inc
888 3 St Sw Suite 2000
Calgary AB T2P 5
403 237-1234

(G-19248)
RIO OIL AND GAS LLC
3 Waterway Square Pl # 500 (77380-3898)
PHONE................................832 616-3717
Alan Clemens, *Chairman*
Myer Ballesteros, *Administration*
EMP: 25
SALES (est): 2.3MM **Privately Held**
WEB: www.riooilandgas.net
SIC: 1382 Oil & gas exploration services

(G-19249)
SENTRY WELLHEAD SYSTEMS
LLC (PA)
1780 Hughes Landing Blvd # 675
(77380-4024)
PHONE................................281 210-0070
Jimmy Enriquez, *CEO*
James Johnson, *Senior VP*
Dibbon Rowe, *CFO*
Christian Galindo, *Controller*
Chris Keene, *Manager*
EMP: 40

SQ FT: 30,000
SALES (est): 13.5MM **Privately Held**
WEB: www.sentrywellhead.com
SIC: 1389 Oil & gas wells: building, repair-
ing & dismantling

(G-19250)
SIGMA-GENOSYS OF TEXAS
LLC
9186 Six Pines Dr Ste 100 (77380-3677)
PHONE................................281 363-3693
Tish Creasey, *Partner*
Theresa Creasey, *Vice Pres*
Jason Perez, *Engineer*
Craig McKenzie, *Empl Rel Mgr*
Tina Rodgers, *Technical Staff*
EMP: 150
SQ FT: 7,634
SALES (est): 26.1MM
SALES (corp-wide): 17.8B **Privately Held**
SIC: 2833 2836 Medicinals & botanicals;
biological products, except diagnostic
HQ: Sigma-Aldrich Corporation
3050 Spruce St
Saint Louis MO 63103
314 771-5765

(G-19251)
SOS ENVIRONMENTAL INC
719 Sawdust Rd Ste 331 (77380-2916)
P.O. Box 2157, Conroe (77305-2157)
PHONE................................281 723-8282
EMP: 12
SQ FT: 1,500
SALES (est): 10MM **Privately Held**
WEB: www.sosenvironmental.com
SIC: 8744 0711 8999 2819 ; soil chemi-
cal treatment services; scientific consult-
ing; chemicals, high purity: refined from
technical grade

(G-19252)
SOUTH BY MIDWEST RET
PARTNERS
9595 Six Pines Dr # 1035 (77380-1531)
PHONE................................281 465-8480
EMP: 10
SQ FT: 100
SALES (est): 717K **Privately Held**
SIC: 3961 Costume Jewelry, Nsk

(G-19253)
SPARTAN ENERGY PARTNERS
LP
9595 Six Pines Dr (77380-1531)
P.O. Box 24 Waterway Ave, The Woodlands
(77380)
PHONE................................281 466-3310
EMP: 9
SQ FT: 3,000
SALES (corp-wide): 18.8MM **Privately
Held**
SIC: 1321 Natural Gas Liquids Production
PA: Spartan Energy Partners Lp
9595 Six Pines Dr # 4000
The Woodlands TX 77380
281 466-3310

(G-19254)
STEP ENERGY SVCS HOLDINGS
LTD (DH)
Also Called: Tucker Technologies
480 Wildwood Forest Dr (77380-3491)
PHONE................................281 606-3600
Brock Duhon, *President*
Dexter Farray, *General Mgr*
Mike Burvill, *COO*
Sean Tucker, *Vice Pres*
Mikhail Barcellos, *Opers Spvr*
◆ **EMP:** 10
SQ FT: 3,850
SALES (est): 447.6MM
SALES (corp-wide): 501.9MM **Privately
Held**
WEB: www.tuckerenergy.com
SIC: 1389 Hydraulic fracturing wells
HQ: Step Energy Services (Usa) Ltd.
70 Ne Loop 410 Ste 1070
San Antonio TX 78216
210 477-1517

(G-19255)
STORE FRONT PRINTERS INC
25723 Lake Lawn Dr (77380-2040)
PHONE................................281 367-3373

EMP: 9
SQ FT: 1,600
SALES (est): 1.1MM **Privately Held**
SIC: 2752 Lithographic Commercial Printing

(G-19256)
STRATA CONTROL SERVICES INC
1450 Lake Robbins Dr # 400 (77380-3263)
PHONE................................337 785-0000
Patrick Williams, *President*
Thomas Entwistle, *Exec VP*
Ian Cleminson, *CFO*
Diane Cleminson, *Treasurer*
Richard L Jenkins, *Director*
▼ **EMP:** 22
SQ FT: 10,000
SALES (est): 12MM
SALES (corp-wide): 1.5B **Publicly Held**
SIC: 1389 2899 Oil field services; chemical preparations
PA: Innospec Inc.
    8310 S Valley Hwy Ste 350
    Englewood CO 80112
    303 792-5554

(G-19257)
SUPERLIFE PRODUCTS INC (PA)
25143 Melda Rd Bldg A (77380-3887)
P.O. Box 521, Dobbin (77333-0521)
PHONE................................281 298-5550
James Andrew Hassenger, *Director*
EMP: 14
SALES (est): 4.4MM **Privately Held**
WEB: www.superlifeproducts.net
SIC: 2834 Vitamin, nutrient & hematinic preparations for human use; vitamin preparations

(G-19258)
TARSCO CONSTRUCTION CORP (HQ)
25000 Pitkin Rd Ste 100 (77386-1990)
PHONE................................515 225-3003
Terrence F Warren, *President*
Carlos Gutierrez, *Vice Pres*
Ron Shambro, *Vice Pres*
Jeff Hill, *Project Mgr*
Rosemarie Estrada, *Purchasing*
EMP: 150
SALES (est): 55.8MM
SALES (corp-wide): 63.5MM **Privately Held**
WEB: www.tfwarren.com
SIC: 3731 Tankers, building & repairing
PA: T.F. Warren Group Corporation
    12900 Saddlebrook Cir
    Fairhope AL 36532
    519 754-3710

(G-19259)
TEJAS MACHINES INC
2115 Riley Fuzzel Rd (77386-2729)
P.O. Box 1325 (77383-1325)
PHONE................................281 350-8890
Debra Jackson, *President*
Juanita Jackson, *Treasurer*
Debbie Jackson, *Sales Staff*
Terri Jackson, *Admin Sec*
EMP: 23
SQ FT: 10,000
SALES (est): 1.5MM **Privately Held**
SIC: 1389 Construction, repair & dismantling services

(G-19260)
TRITON EQUIPMENT & SERVICES
2847 W Wildwind Cir (77380-1383)
PHONE................................281 681-9797
Scott L Jovien, *CEO*
EMP: 15
SALES (est): 653K **Privately Held**
WEB: www.tritonequipment.net
SIC: 1389 Oil field services

(G-19261)
UNIVAR SOLUTIONS USA INC
3 Waterway Square Pl # 1000 (77380-3488)
PHONE................................281 297-0678
David A Bradley, *CEO*
Ronald Labuschewsky, *Vice Pres*

Kristina Smith, *Vice Pres*
Linda Huckaba, *Senior Buyer*
Ashley Isaacs, *Buyer*
EMP: 26
SALES (corp-wide): 9.2B **Publicly Held**
WEB: www.univarsolutions.com
SIC: 5191 5169 2822 2821 Chemicals, agricultural; silicon lubricants; ethylene-propylene rubbers, EPDM polymers; thermoplastic materials; gasoline; antioxidants, rubber processing: cyclic or acyclic; ethylene glycols
HQ: Univar Solutions Usa Inc.
    3075 Highland Pkwy # 200
    Downers Grove IL 60515
    331 777-6000

(G-19262)
WOODLAND MIDSTREAM II LLC
24 Waterway Ave Ste 1460 (77380-3292)
PHONE................................832 592-1202
Mattew East, *Principal*
Richard H Wright III, *Mng Member*
Darin Aucoin, *Mng Member*
EMP: 45
SALES (est): 98.6MM **Privately Held**
WEB: www.woodlandmidstream.com
SIC: 1321 Natural gas liquids production

(G-19263)
WORLD WIDE CELEBRITY MAG LLP
846 Rayford Rd (77386-1926)
PHONE................................832 305-8716
Kassim Lawal, *CEO*
EMP: 10
SALES (est): 50K **Privately Held**
SIC: 2741

(G-19264)
WRIGHTS WELL CONTROL SVCS LLC
28019 Buena Way (77386-2819)
PHONE................................337 502-4160
David Wright, *Mng Member*
Monique Wright,
EMP: 45
SALES (est): 7.6MM **Privately Held**
WEB: www.wrightswell.com
SIC: 1389 Oil field services

Spring Branch
Comal County

(G-19265)
AIRTRONIC USA LLC
21155 State Highway 46 W (78070-6791)
PHONE................................830 980-9788
George Salof, *CEO*
Richard Vandiver, *President*
Bruce McNabb, *CFO*
EMP: 25
SQ FT: 5,000
SALES (est): 4.7MM **Privately Held**
WEB: www.airtronic-usa.com
SIC: 3484 Small arms

(G-19266)
ASTERIA LEARNING INC
116 Kestrel Dr (78070-6167)
PHONE................................210 960-3855
Mary Jo Eldridge, *CEO*
EMP: 25
SALES (est): 799.4K **Privately Held**
SIC: 3999 Education aids, devices & supplies

(G-19267)
BELL EXPERIMENTAL GROUP INC
Also Called: Bell Engineering Group
203 Kestrel Dr (78070-6145)
PHONE................................830 438-2890
Courtland Bell, *President*
Mary Bell, *Vice Pres*
EMP: 9
SQ FT: 7,000
SALES (est): 300K **Privately Held**
WEB: www.bellengineering.net
SIC: 3714 Motor vehicle engines & parts

(G-19268)
BELL INTERCOOLERS LLC
247 Kestrel Dr (78070-6145)
PHONE................................830 438-6150
Michael Stewart, *President*
David Gomez, *President*
Gehard M Schruf, *Corp Secy*
EMP: 16
SALES (est): 3.7MM **Privately Held**
WEB: www.bellintercoolers.com
SIC: 3443 Heat exchangers: coolers (after, inter), condensers, etc.

(G-19269)
DISTRIBUIDORA COMERCIAL LLC
5140 Us Highway 281 N (78070-6824)
PHONE................................830 438-3877
Joe Gomez, *President*
EMP: 10
SALES (est): 375K **Privately Held**
SIC: 3999 Manufacturing industries

(G-19270)
HILL COUNTRY CABINET SHOP INC
18200 State Highway 46 W (78070-6836)
PHONE................................830 228-5062
Theron K Flowers, *President*
Doug Flowers, *Vice Pres*
Flowers Ora Mae, *Vice Pres*
EMP: 15
SALES (est): 1.7MM **Privately Held**
WEB: www.hillcountrycabinetshop.com
SIC: 2434 2521 Wood kitchen cabinets; cabinets, office: wood

Springtown
Parker County

(G-19271)
ALTECH MACHINE SHOP INC
396 Goshen Rd (76082-2619)
P.O. Box 137073, Fort Worth (76136-1073)
PHONE................................817 718-8824
Raul Martinez, *Director*
EMP: 9
SALES (est): 1MM **Privately Held**
WEB: www.altechms.com
SIC: 3599 Machine shop, jobbing & repair

(G-19272)
COMPLETE SYS FABRICATION LLC
4948 E Highway 199 (76082-7371)
P.O. Box 2340, Azle (76098-2340)
PHONE................................817 682-0729
Anthony Keeton, *President*
Michael Keeton,
EMP: 27
SQ FT: 31,000
SALES (est): 14.5MM **Privately Held**
WEB: www.csftx.com
SIC: 3441 Fabricated structural metal

(G-19273)
DEERSKIN MFG INC
4078 W Highway 199 (76082-5221)
P.O. Box 127 (76082-0127)
PHONE................................817 220-5535
Kenny Deskins, *President*
EMP: 10
SQ FT: 10,000
SALES (est): 2MM **Privately Held**
WEB: www.deerskinmfg.com
SIC: 3713 5012 Specialty motor vehicle bodies; utility truck bodies; recreational vehicles, motor homes & trailers

(G-19274)
OREGON RESOURCES CORPORATION
764 Salt Creek Rd (76082-3932)
PHONE................................541 266-0875
Philip J Garratt, *President*
John Mears, *President*
George Gabriel, *CFO*
James Randall, *Admin Sec*
EMP: 68
SALES (est): 10.1MM **Privately Held**
WEB: www.oregon-resources.com
SIC: 1446 Industrial sand

PA: Idm International Ltd

6158

(G-19275)
RLN CONSULTING ENTERPRISES LLC
Also Called: Rln Fabricators
2791 E Highway 199 (76082-6838)
P.O. Box 467 (76082-0467)
PHONE................................713 515-3638
Randy Nix, *President*
EMP: 12 **EST:** 2013
SQ FT: 35,000
SALES (est): 2.5MM **Privately Held**
SIC: 3441 Building components, structural steel

(G-19276)
RWN CONTRACTORS LLC
8700 W Highway 199 (76082-5066)
PHONE................................817 523-7900
Robert Naron, *President*
Walter McKey, *Opers Mgr*
▲ **EMP:** 60
SQ FT: 2,000
SALES (est): 18.1MM **Privately Held**
WEB: www.rwncontractors.net
SIC: 3441 Fabricated structural metal

(G-19277)
WASHITA VALLEY ENTERPRISES INC
3064 W Highway 199 (76082-5242)
P.O. Box 471 (76082-0471)
PHONE................................817 220-0450
Ashlee Waller, *Sales Staff*
Monique Martinez, *Assistant*
EMP: 10
SALES (corp-wide): 41.8MM **Privately Held**
WEB: www.wvei.com
SIC: 1389 Oil field services
PA: Washita Valley Enterprises, Inc.
    1705 Se 59th St
    Oklahoma City OK 73129
    405 670-5338

Spurger
Tyler County

(G-19278)
JEFFCOAT PRODUCTION SERVICE
11555 Fm 92 (77660)
P.O. Box 451 (77660-0451)
PHONE................................409 429-5900
Lamar Jeffcoat, *Owner*
EMP: 10
SQ FT: 1,600
SALES (est): 813.8K **Privately Held**
SIC: 1389 Oil consultants; oil field services

Stafford
Fort Bend County

(G-19279)
A & W WELDING INC
Also Called: Affordable Neighbor Homes
1403 Moore Rd (77477-6842)
PHONE................................281 499-4332
Raul Casarez, *President*
EMP: 9
SQ FT: 3,840
SALES (est): 788K **Privately Held**
SIC: 7692 Welding repair

(G-19280)
ABUATA ENTERPRISES INC
Also Called: Jericho Woodworks
425 Summer Park Dr (77477-5577)
PHONE................................281 969-7947
Nidal Abuata, *President*
Cinthya A Toledo, *Vice Pres*
EMP: 20
SQ FT: 20,000
SALES (est): 2.6MM **Privately Held**
WEB: www.educationalcasework.net
SIC: 2431 Interior & ornamental woodwork & trim

(G-19281)
ACCESSESP LLC
Also Called: Artificial Lift Company
13215 N Promenade Blvd (77477-3957)
PHONE......................................713 589-2599
David Malone, *President*
Samer Cheblak, *Business Mgr*
Greg Nutter, *Vice Pres*
Todd Wray, *Vice Pres*
Dan Theriault, *Mfg Mgr*
▲ EMP: 30
SALES (est): 6.6MM **Privately Held**
WEB: www.accessesp.com
SIC: 1389 Oil consultants

(G-19282)
AIR STARTER COMPONENTS INC (PA)
13935 Stafford Rd (77477-5009)
P.O. Box 986 (77497-0986)
PHONE......................................281 261-7939
Jack H Heck, *President*
Ray Morris, *Principal*
Gary Ackman, *Sales Staff*
▲ EMP: 43
SQ FT: 15,000
SALES (est): 5.9MM **Privately Held**
WEB: www.ascairstarter.com
SIC: 3621 3625 Starters, for motors; relays & industrial controls

(G-19283)
ALPHA CIRCUITS INCORPORATED
4855 Alpine Dr Ste 100 (77477-4141)
PHONE......................................281 980-2800
Mark Kisner, *CEO*
Rickey Williams, *Vice Pres*
Jeffrey Behrendt, *CFO*
Michael Baudler, *Admin Sec*
▲ EMP: 63
SQ FT: 60,000
SALES (est): 11.6MM **Privately Held**
WEB: www.alpha-circuits.com
SIC: 3672 Printed circuit boards

(G-19284)
ALPHA TECH INTERNATIONAL INC
12701 Executive Dr # 604 (77477-4000)
PHONE......................................281 240-8989
Amar Amancharla, *President*
Frank Clinch, *Vice Pres*
EMP: 550
SQ FT: 39,000
SALES (est): 43.9MM **Privately Held**
SIC: 3823 1389 3829 7375 Pressure measurement instruments, industrial; testing, measuring, surveying & analysis services; seismoscopes; information retrieval services

(G-19285)
ALUMINUM TECHNIQUES INC
Also Called: Sun Fun Enclosures
13302 Redfish Ln (77477-4422)
PHONE......................................281 499-9026
Gerard Van Deursen, *President*
David Deursen, *Superintendent*
Daniel Van Deursen, *Vice Pres*
EMP: 17
SQ FT: 10,000
SALES (est): 1.1MM **Privately Held**
WEB: www.aluminumtechniques.com
SIC: 3441 Fabricated structural metal

(G-19286)
ANOVA INDUSTRIALS
10905 Cash Rd (77477-4301)
PHONE......................................281 494-8896
Jeff Wu, *Vice Pres*
▲ EMP: 25
SALES (est): 2.9MM **Privately Held**
WEB: www.chemyx.com
SIC: 3823 Temperature measurement instruments, industrial

(G-19287)
ASHCRFT-UROPEAN BKY LTD PARTNR
Also Called: Ashcraft/European Bakery
220 Murphy Rd (77477-5412)
PHONE......................................281 403-5040
Ronald M Weil, *Partner*
Roger Saa, *Partner*

Fani Fiscal, *Sales Staff*
Carlos Parra, *Sales Staff*
▲ EMP: 60 EST: 1953
SQ FT: 20,000
SALES (est): 11.4MM **Privately Held**
WEB: www.ashcraftbakery.com
SIC: 2052 2051 Cookies; bread, all types (white, wheat, rye, etc): fresh or frozen

(G-19288)
ASPHWAX INC
Also Called: Kosta Oil Field Technologies
12972 Sugar Ridge Blvd (77477-3147)
PHONE......................................281 568-8415
Kosta Leontaritis, *President*
Sophia Leontaritis, *Vice Pres*
Justin Merryman, *QC Mgr*
EMP: 9
SALES (est): 648.1K **Privately Held**
WEB: www.asphwax.com
SIC: 1389 Oil field services

(G-19289)
ATEC INC (PA)
12600 Executive Dr (77477-3698)
PHONE......................................281 276-2700
Howard F Lederer, *CEO*
Paul Finley, *President*
Dan Carley, *Senior VP*
Brian Durbin, *Vice Pres*
Mike Rigdon, *Vice Pres*
◆ EMP: 130
SQ FT: 50,000
SALES (est): 38.8MM **Privately Held**
WEB: www.atec.com
SIC: 3599 3829 3592 Machine & other job shop work; measuring & controlling devices; aircraft & motor vehicle measurement equipment; surveying & drafting equipment; valves

(G-19290)
ATEC RESOURCES INC
12600 Executive Dr (77477-3698)
PHONE......................................281 276-2700
Howard F Lederer, *Director*
EMP: 40
SALES (est): 1.4MM
SALES (corp-wide): 38.8MM **Privately Held**
SIC: 3599 Machine & other job shop work
PA: Atec, Inc.
12600 Executive Dr
Stafford TX 77477
281 276-2700

(G-19291)
BK/JA HOLDINGS INC
Also Called: Ja Electronic Manufacturing Co
13715 N Promenade Blvd (77477-4033)
PHONE......................................281 879-9903
Jessie Marion, *President*
James Schulte, *President*
Brent Bertrand, *Vice Pres*
John Parkins, *Vice Pres*
CM Nelson, *Treasurer*
EMP: 20
SQ FT: 10,000
SALES (est): 3.2MM
SALES (corp-wide): 11.1MM **Privately Held**
WEB: www.jaelectronics.com
SIC: 3679 3643 3625 Power supplies, all types: static; rectifiers, electronic; current-carrying wiring devices; relays & industrial controls
PA: Integrated Corrosion Companies, Inc.
601 Century Plaza Dr
Houston TX 77073
713 789-9181

(G-19292)
CARLISLE SYSTEMS INC
12814 Murphy Rd (77477-3902)
PHONE......................................713 703-9256
Ian Hamlin, *Vice Pres*
EMP: 9
SALES (est): 369.2K **Privately Held**
SIC: 3999 Manufacturing industries

(G-19293)
CES INDUSTRIAL LLC
13802 Murphy Rd (77477-4904)
P.O. Box 1984 (77497-1984)
PHONE......................................281 615-5621
Eric Medford, *Mng Member*

David Medford,
James Webster,
EMP: 10 EST: 2015
SQ FT: 303,550
SALES (est): 352.9K **Privately Held**
WEB: www.cesindustrial.com
SIC: 5063 5074 3585 Hanging & fastening devices, electrical; heating equipment (hydronic); air conditioning units, complete: domestic or industrial

(G-19294)
CHEMPLAST INC
1002 Fm 2234 Rd Ste A (77477-6482)
PHONE......................................281 208-2585
Alexander Kudakkachira, *President*
Annie Parakattel, *Vice Pres*
Kc Alexander, *Engineer*
George Kallingakudiyil, *Treasurer*
▲ EMP: 36
SQ FT: 40,000
SALES (est): 13.6MM **Privately Held**
WEB: www.chemplastinc.com
SIC: 3089 3542 Injection molding of plastics; die casting machines

(G-19295)
CHEMYX INC
10905 Cash Rd (77477-4301)
P.O. Box 121 (77497-0121)
PHONE......................................281 277-5499
Jeff Wu, *President*
Jeff CA, *Engineer*
Natalie Vixen, *Marketing Staff*
Joana Arheober, *Manager*
▲ EMP: 20
SALES (est): 800K **Privately Held**
WEB: www.chemyx.com
SIC: 3821 Laboratory apparatus & furniture

(G-19296)
COAST GRAPHICS & SIGNS INC
12999 Murphy Rd Ste E1 (77477-3943)
P.O. Box 546, Rosharon (77583-0546)
PHONE......................................281 499-9721
Ken Siegrist, *President*
EMP: 20
SQ FT: 8,750
SALES (est): 2.4MM **Privately Held**
WEB: www.coastsigns.net
SIC: 3993 Electric signs

(G-19297)
COASTLINE INDUS COATINGS INC
3401 5th St (77477-6605)
P.O. Box 941688, Houston (77094-8688)
PHONE......................................281 499-0633
Harry M Main, *President*
H Macgregor Main, *Exec VP*
Quint Hinson, *Site Mgr*
Macgregor Main, *Purchasing*
▼ EMP: 15
SQ FT: 50,000
SALES (est): 3.6MM **Privately Held**
WEB: www.coastlinecoatings.com
SIC: 2851 Paints & allied products

(G-19298)
CYNCO SPECIALTY INC
226 Brand Ln (77477-4804)
P.O. Box 553 (77497-0553)
PHONE......................................281 499-0519
James E Hitt, *President*
EMP: 9 EST: 1978
SQ FT: 5,000
SALES (est): 1.1MM **Privately Held**
WEB: www.cyncospecialty.com
SIC: 3541 3471 2759 Chemical milling machines; anodizing (plating) of metals or formed products; engraving

(G-19299)
D & R SIGNS LLC (PA)
12999 Murphy Rd Ste J1 (77477-3949)
PHONE......................................281 988-9995
David S Lepine, *Partner*
Susan Lepine, *Partner*
Ralph Vantassell, *Partner*
EMP: 14
SQ FT: 7,000
SALES (est): 3.1MM **Privately Held**
WEB: www.d-r-signs.com
SIC: 3993 Signs & advertising specialties

(G-19300)
DE YOUNG MACHINE WORKS INC
12999 Murphy Rd Ste G1 (77477-3944)
PHONE......................................832 328-1500
Shannon De Young, *President*
Jason Deyoung, *Vice Pres*
EMP: 30
SALES (est): 4.3MM **Privately Held**
WEB: www.deyoungmw.com
SIC: 3599 Machine shop, jobbing & repair

(G-19301)
DENMARK MANUFACTURING INC
10700 Corp Dr Ste 110 (77477)
PHONE......................................281 494-1527
Den Phan, *President*
EMP: 11
SQ FT: 8,000 **Privately Held**
WEB: www.denmarkmanufacturing.com
SIC: 3672 Printed circuit boards

(G-19302)
DETECTACHEM INC
4100 Greenbriar Dr # 180 (77477-3962)
PHONE......................................855 573-3537
Travis Kisner, *COO*
Thea Milan, *Marketing Staff*
Aaron Sanders, *Manager*
Mark Kisner, *Info Tech Mgr*
Don Michlin,
EMP: 21
SQ FT: 10,000
SALES (est): 3.1MM **Privately Held**
WEB: www.detectachem.com
SIC: 3826 Analytical instruments

(G-19303)
DEYOUNG MACHINE WORKS INC
12999 Murphy Rd Bldg G (77477-3955)
PHONE......................................832 328-1500
Richard Deyoung, *Owner*
Jason D De Young, *Purch Mgr*
Shannon Young, *Manager*
EMP: 14
SALES (est): 2.4MM **Privately Held**
WEB: www.deyoungmw.com
SIC: 3599 Machine shop, jobbing & repair

(G-19304)
DICKEY-WEBB INC
Also Called: Dickey Manufacturing
12999 Murphy Rd Bldg G (77477-3955)
P.O. Box 847 (77497-0847)
PHONE......................................281 933-5400
Terry R Dickey, *President*
Sandra J Dickey, *Corp Secy*
Sandra Dickey, *Admin Sec*
EMP: 12
SQ FT: 7,400
SALES (est): 1.5MM **Privately Held**
WEB: www.dickeymfg.com
SIC: 3444 Sheet metalwork

(G-19305)
DISHAKA LLC
Also Called: Dishaka U S A
13843 Stafford Rd (77477-5007)
PHONE......................................713 988-2900
Andrea Noboa, *Manager*
Kawal Oberoi,
Dhiraj Oberoi,
Kiran Oberoi,
Sudhir Oberoi,
◆ EMP: 78
SQ FT: 208,000
SALES (est): 41.2MM **Privately Held**
WEB: www.dishaka.com
SIC: 5149 5153 2096 Pasta & rice; seasonings, sauces & extracts; spices & seasonings; pickles, preserves, jellies & jams; field beans; potato chips & similar snacks

(G-19306)
DIVERSITY INDUSTRIES INC
Also Called: Kwikool
10404 Mula Rd (77477-3111)
PHONE......................................713 667-9595
Michael Volle, *President*
◆ EMP: 20
SQ FT: 10,000

▲ = Import ▼=Export
◆ =Import/Export

SALES (est): 5.1MM **Privately Held**
WEB: www.kwikool.com
SIC: 3585 Air conditioning equipment, complete

(G-19307)
DYNAMIC VOICE DATA INC
4403 Greenbriar Dr (77477-3801)
PHONE......................800 838-5070
Shangju Yang, *President*
Tina Greenfield, *Treasurer*
Jeff Koopman, *Sales Mgr*
Mena Kader, *Accounts Mgr*
▲ EMP: 16
SQ FT: 18,000
SALES (est): 3.5MM **Privately Held**
WEB: www.dvd-inc.com
SIC: 3661 5065 Telephones & telephone apparatus; telephone & telegraphic equipment

(G-19308)
ELGIN SPRTION SLTONS INDSTRALS (DH)
10050 Cash Rd (77477-4407)
PHONE......................281 261-5778
Michael Anderson, *President*
Jon Domingue, *Business Mgr*
Steve Cross, *Sales Staff*
Alvin Grose, *Sales Staff*
Steve Powell, *Sales Staff*
◆ EMP: 83
SALES (est): 23.6MM
SALES (corp-wide): 1.5B **Privately Held**
WEB: www.elginseparationsolutions.com
SIC: 3533 Oil & gas drilling rigs & equipment

(G-19309)
EMERSON AUTOMATION SOLUTIONS
3950 Greenbriar Dr (77477-3919)
PHONE......................281 274-4400
Calvin Deng, *Engineer*
Alan Alberts, *Manager*
Hank Cornett, *Manager*
EMP: 20
SALES (corp-wide): 16.7B **Publicly Held**
WEB: www.pentair.com
SIC: 3491 Industrial valves
HQ: Emerson Automation Solutions Final Control Us Lp
10707 Clay Rd
Houston TX 77041

(G-19310)
EMERSON AUTOMATION SOLUTIONS
Also Called: Pentair Valves & Controls
3950 Greenbriar Dr (77477-3919)
PHONE......................281 274-4400
John Ward, *Plant Mgr*
David Moore, *Project Mgr*
Adam Attig, *Engineer*
Arthur Grahmann, *Engineer*
Rochelle Fontana, *Marketing Staff*
EMP: 347
SALES (corp-wide): 16.7B **Publicly Held**
WEB: www.pentair.com
SIC: 3491 5084 Industrial valves; industrial machinery & equipment
HQ: Emerson Automation Solutions Final Control Us Lp
10707 Clay Rd
Houston TX 77041

(G-19311)
ENERSYS CORPORATION
12875 Capricorn St (77477-3915)
P.O. Box 131525, Houston (77219-1525)
PHONE......................281 598-7100
Russel W Treat, *President*
Philip Jones, *Purchasing*
Jeff Mak, *Project Engr*
Dale Schafer, *VP Bus Dvlpt*
Megan Ikerd, *Manager*
EMP: 15
SALES (est): 1.9MM **Privately Held**
WEB: www.enersyscorp.com
SIC: 1389 Gas field services

(G-19312)
ENPRO INDUSTRIES INC
CPI
4410 Greenbriar Dr (77477-3802)
PHONE......................281 207-4600
Ray Davis, *Vice Pres*
Daniel Hoffmann, *Engineer*
Lisha Betancourt, *Human Res Mgr*
Marie Doran, *Marketing Staff*
Anthony Gioffredi, *Manager*
EMP: 80
SALES (corp-wide): 1.2B **Publicly Held**
WEB: www.safety-culture-training.com
SIC: 3053 Gaskets & sealing devices
PA: Enpro Industries, Inc.
5605 Carnegie Blvd # 500
Charlotte NC 28209
704 731-1500

(G-19313)
FISERV SOLUTIONS LLC
13100 N Promenade Blvd (77477-3900)
PHONE......................281 242-8569
Erick Herring, *Manager*
EMP: 200
SALES (corp-wide): 10.1B **Publicly Held**
WEB: www.fiserv.com
SIC: 2759 2752 7374 Commercial printing; commercial printing, lithographic; data processing & preparation
HQ: Fiserv Solutions, Llc
575 Brick Church Pkwy Dr
Nashville TN 37207
615 227-6245

(G-19314)
FOAMPACK US
13630 Dublin Ct (77477-4317)
PHONE......................281 565-9619
Jack Zhaw, *General Mgr*
Isabel Fu, *Manager*
▲ EMP: 26
SALES (est): 2.6MM **Privately Held**
WEB: www.foampakus.com
SIC: 3086 Plastics foam products

(G-19315)
FOGLE MANUFACTURING SVCS LP
10101 Mula Rd (77477-3313)
P.O. Box 1309 (77497-1309)
PHONE......................281 495-1828
Allen H Fogle, *Partner*
Dorothy Fogle, *Partner*
EMP: 52
SQ FT: 59,000
SALES (est): 16.6MM **Privately Held**
SIC: 3533 Bits, oil & gas field tools: rock

(G-19316)
FORT BEND BUSINESS JOURNAL
Also Called: Fort Bend South West Star
4655 Techniplex Dr # 300 (77477-3867)
PHONE......................281 690-4200
Michael Fredericksen, *Owner*
EMP: 10
SALES (est): 709.8K **Privately Held**
WEB: www.fortbendstar.com
SIC: 2711 Newspapers, publishing & printing

(G-19317)
FORT BEND PUBLISHING GROUP
Also Called: Houston Lifestyles & Homes
10707 Corp Dr Ste 170 (77477)
PHONE......................281 240-2445
EMP: 14
SQ FT: 1,400
SALES (est): 1.1MM **Privately Held**
SIC: 2721 Periodicals-Publishing/Printing

(G-19318)
FORWARD SCIENCE HOLDING INC
10401 Greenbough Dr 100 (77477-5014)
PHONE......................855 696-7254
Robert Whitman, *CEO*
Brian Pikkula, *Principal*
Daniel Llerena, *Vice Pres*
EMP: 18
SQ FT: 19,000

SALES (est): 815.2K **Privately Held**
WEB: www.forwardscience.com
SIC: 3843 Dental equipment

(G-19319)
FORWARD SCIENCE TECH LLC (PA)
Also Called: Biored
10401 Greenbough Dr 100 (77477-5014)
PHONE......................855 696-7254
Kelly Kunkel, *Natl Sales Mgr*
Bonnie Phillips, *Natl Sales Mgr*
Amanda Carter, *Accounts Exec*
Brian Pikkula, *Mng Member*
William Burelsmith, *Creative Dir*
EMP: 10 EST: 2013
SALES (est): 1.1MM **Privately Held**
WEB: www.forwardscience.com
SIC: 3843 Dental equipment

(G-19320)
G & S ASPHALT INC
Also Called: American Materials
10126 Cash Rd (77477-4409)
P.O. Box 1338 (77497-1338)
PHONE......................281 499-1551
Jeff W Greene, *President*
EMP: 12
SQ FT: 4,950
SALES (est): 3.2MM **Privately Held**
SIC: 2951 Asphalt paving mixtures & blocks

(G-19321)
GENERAL TECHNOLOGIES INC (PA)
Also Called: Gti
13022 Trinity Dr (77477-4218)
P.O. Box 1503 (77497-1503)
PHONE......................281 240-0550
Felix Sorkin, *President*
Joe Harrison, *Vice Pres*
Larry Krauser, *Vice Pres*
Carlos Melendez, *Vice Pres*
Virginia Solis, *Cust Mgr*
◆ EMP: 45
SALES (est): 11.2MM **Privately Held**
WEB: www.gti-usa.net
SIC: 3089 Injection molded finished plastic products; injection molding of plastics; molding primary plastic

(G-19322)
GI CIRCUITS INC
12701 Royal Dr (77477-4207)
PHONE......................281 495-2100
Jack Xu, *Principal*
Frank Chen, *Vice Pres*
EMP: 20
SALES (est): 3.9MM **Privately Held**
WEB: www.gicircuits.com
SIC: 3672 Printed circuit boards

(G-19323)
GI ELECTROTECH INC
Also Called: GI Circuits
12701 Royal Dr (77477-4207)
PHONE......................832 886-4997
Jack Xu, *President*
Frank Chen, *Vice Pres*
Dave Chow, *VP Mktg*
EMP: 48
SALES (est): 5.1MM **Privately Held**
WEB: www.gicircuits.com
SIC: 3672 Printed circuit boards

(G-19324)
GROTH CORPORATION
13650 N Promenade Blvd (77477-3972)
P.O. Box 952170, Saint Louis MO (63195-2170)
PHONE......................913 952-8114
C J Hagemann, *Vice Pres*
Andrea Johnson, *Purch Mgr*
Anton David, *Project Engr*
Mark Taylor, *CFO*
Linda Glaspie, *Controller*
◆ EMP: 95 EST: 1960
SQ FT: 60,000
SALES (est): 21.4MM **Privately Held**
WEB: www.grothcorp.com
SIC: 3491 3498 Industrial valves; fabricated pipe & fittings

HQ: Continental Disc Corporation
3160 W Heartland Dr
Liberty MO 64068
816 792-1500

(G-19325)
HEXION INC
12650 Dirs Dr Ste 100 (77477)
PHONE......................281 325-3368
Marvin Schlanger, *Branch Mgr*
EMP: 34
SALES (corp-wide): 1.5B **Privately Held**
WEB: www.hexion.com
SIC: 2869 Industrial organic chemicals
HQ: Hexion Inc.
180 E Broad St Fl 26
Columbus OH 43215
614 225-4000

(G-19326)
HOUSTON GEAR USA INC
12810 Mula Ln (77477-3317)
P.O. Box 1787 (77497-1787)
PHONE......................281 495-8274
Frank Garza, *President*
Joe Garza, *Director*
EMP: 15
SQ FT: 13,750
SALES (est): 1.5MM **Privately Held**
WEB: www.houstongear.com
SIC: 3462 Gears, forged steel

(G-19327)
HUNTING ENERGY SERVICES INC
1316 Staffordshire Rd (77477-6321)
PHONE......................281 499-2583
Dennis Proctor, *CEO*
Bryan Farley, *Accounts Mgr*
EMP: 72
SALES (corp-wide): 960MM **Privately Held**
WEB: www.hunting-intl.com
SIC: 1389 Oil field services
HQ: Hunting Energy Services, Llc
16825 Northchase Dr # 600
Houston TX 77060

(G-19328)
INDUSTRIAL PIPE FITTINGS LLC (PA)
Also Called: Ipf
10707 Corp Dr Ste 220 (77477)
PHONE......................800 241-4175
Phillip Ford, *CEO*
Tracey Mooneyhan, *Maint Spvr*
Terry Schillaci, *CFO*
Thomas Saju, *Asst Controller*
Lesli Snowden, *Sales Staff*
◆ EMP: 14
SALES (est): 27.1MM **Privately Held**
WEB: www.plassonusa.com
SIC: 3084 Plastics pipe

(G-19329)
INSTRUMENT PRODUCTS INC
3727 Greenbriar Dr # 108 (77477-3954)
P.O. Box 1680, Sugar Land (77487-1680)
PHONE......................281 491-0237
Milton Carroll, *President*
Cindy Carroll, *CFO*
EMP: 13 EST: 1977
SQ FT: 5,000
SALES (est): 1.5MM **Privately Held**
SIC: 3317 Steel pipe & tubes

(G-19330)
ION EXPLORATION PDTS USA INC
Also Called: Input/Output
12300 Parc Crest Dr (77477-2419)
PHONE......................281 933-3339
Tim Probert, *President*
Robert P Brindley, *President*
Brian Hanson, *President*
Greg Heinlein, *Vice Pres*
Charles Ledet, *Vice Pres*
▲ EMP: 9
SQ FT: 55,060
SALES (est): 2.4MM
SALES (corp-wide): 180MM **Publicly Held**
WEB: www.iongeo.com
SIC: 1382 Oil & gas exploration services

PA: Ion Geophysical Corporation
2105 Citywest Blvd # 100
Houston TX 77042
281 933-3339

(G-19331)
**ION GEOPHYSICAL
CORPORATION**
12300 Parc Crest Dr (77477-2419)
PHONE.....................281 552-3000
Richard Hill, *Vice Pres*
Rick Middaugh, *Vice Pres*
Dennard Rupp Gray, *Investment Ofcr*
Robert Peebler, *Branch Mgr*
Albert Zarate, *Manager*
EMP: 100
SALES (corp-wide): 180MM **Publicly
Held**
WEB: www.iongeo.com
SIC: 7372 Application computer software
PA: Ion Geophysical Corporation
2105 Citywest Blvd # 100
Houston TX 77042
281 933-3339

(G-19332)
ION SCIENCE INC
4153 Bluebonnet Dr (77477-3909)
PHONE.....................877 864-7710
Duncan Johns, *Ch of Bd*
Terry Deeds, *General Mgr*
Patricia Ruiz, *Manager*
EMP: 12
SQ FT: 600
SALES (est): 1.2MM
SALES (corp-wide): 1.8MM **Privately
Held**
WEB: www.ionscience.com
SIC: 3829 5046 Geophysical & meteoro-
logical testing equipment; store fixtures &
display equipment
HQ: Ion Science Limited
The Way
Royston HERTS SG8 7
176 320-8503

(G-19333)
ISO MACHINE INC
13050 Sugar Ridge Blvd (77477-3145)
P.O. Box 1031 (77497-1031)
PHONE.....................281 568-1700
Robert J Glaser, *President*
Barbara Glaser, *Vice Pres*
EMP: 12
SQ FT: 10,000
SALES (est): 1.9MM **Privately Held**
WEB: www.isomachinehouston.com
SIC: 3599 Machine shop, jobbing & repair

(G-19334)
ITT BORNEMANN USA INC
12510 Sugar Ridge Blvd (77477-3146)
PHONE.....................832 320-2500
Gero Fon De Wense, *CEO*
Robert Triscoli, *General Mgr*
Friedrich Harten, *Vice Pres*
Hajo Hartmann, *CFO*
▲ **EMP:** 10
SQ FT: 3,800
SALES (est): 1.4MM
SALES (corp-wide): 242.1K **Privately
Held**
SIC: 3561 5084 Pumps & pumping equip-
ment; pumps & pumping equipment
HQ: Itt Bornemann Gmbh
Industriestr. 2
Obernkirchen 31683
572 439-00

(G-19335)
ITT LLC
12510 Sugar Ridge Blvd (77477-3146)
PHONE.....................281 504-6300
Farruk Hafeez, *Manager*
John Martin, *Manager*
EMP: 16
SALES (corp-wide): 2.8B **Publicly Held**
WEB: www.itt.com
SIC: 3594 Fluid power pumps & motors
HQ: Itt Llc
1133 Westchester Ave N-100
White Plains NY 10604
914 641-2000

(G-19336)
JOHNNYS CUSTOM CABINET
9947 Mula Rd Ste 101 (77477-3400)
P.O. Box 1867 (77497-1867)
PHONE.....................281 498-8950
Johnny Guerrero, *Owner*
EMP: 10
SALES (est): 921.9K **Privately Held**
SIC: 2434 1751 Wood kitchen cabinets;
cabinet & finish carpentry

(G-19337)
JOSAN CORPORATION
Also Called: Sunbelt Laboratories
1209 Moore Rd (77477-6823)
P.O. Box 1563 (77497-1563)
PHONE.....................281 261-4747
EMP: 16 **EST:** 1982
SALES (est): 3.8MM **Privately Held**
WEB: www.sunbelt-labs.com
SIC: 2842 Industrial plant disinfectants or
deodorants

(G-19338)
KAMMA GROUP INC
335 Staffordshire Rd # 6 (77477-5600)
P.O. Box 711278, Houston (77271-1278)
PHONE.....................281 499-5888
Emmanuel Nadozie, *President*
Chevelle Bosier, *Office Mgr*
EMP: 9
SALES (est): 500K **Privately Held**
WEB: www.31042.net
SIC: 2434 5211 5712 Wood kitchen cabi-
nets; cabinets, kitchen; cabinet work, cus-
tom

(G-19339)
**KEM-TRON TECHNOLOGIES
INC**
10404 Cash Rd Ste B (77477-4425)
PHONE.....................281 261-5778
Zarir Choksy, *Controller*
EMP: 30
SALES (corp-wide): 1.5B **Privately Held**
WEB: www.elginseparationsolutions.com
SIC: 2819 Chemicals, reagent grade: re-
fined from technical grade
HQ: Elgin Separation Solutions Industrials
Llc
10050 Cash Rd
Stafford TX 77477

(G-19340)
KESTRAN INC
12600 Executive Dr (77477-3604)
PHONE.....................281 276-2700
Howard Lederer, *Director*
EMP: 41
SQ FT: 34,000
SALES (est): 6MM
SALES (corp-wide): 38.8MM **Privately
Held**
SIC: 3533 3599 Well surveying equip-
ment; machine shop, jobbing & repair
PA: Atec, Inc.
12600 Executive Dr
Stafford TX 77477
281 276-2700

(G-19341)
**KOBELCO WELDING OF
AMERICA**
4755 Alpine Dr Ste 250 (77477-4129)
PHONE.....................281 240-5600
Yoshiki Kawaue, *President*
Jerry Whiteley, *Regl Sales Mgr*
▲ **EMP:** 9
SQ FT: 24,500
SALES (est): 232.2K **Privately Held**
WEB: www.kobelcowelding.com
SIC: 7692 Welding repair
HQ: Kobe Steel Usa Holdings Inc.
535 Madison Ave Fl 5
New York NY 10022

(G-19342)
KPR & RSW INVESTMENTS INC
Also Called: Southwest Machine
811 Success Ct Ste 400 (77477-5575)
P.O. Box 2505, League City (77574-2505)
PHONE.....................281 499-2910
Kenneth P Rannals, *CEO*
Randall S Walker, *CFO*
EMP: 11

SQ FT: 10,300
SALES (est): 1.9MM **Privately Held**
WEB: www.s-w-m.com
SIC: 3441 Fabricated structural metal

(G-19343)
LADDS CORPORATION
12670 Jebbia Ln (77477-3302)
PHONE.....................281 495-5200
Noorali Hussain, *President*
◆ **EMP:** 10
SQ FT: 55,000
SALES (est): 2.5MM **Privately Held**
WEB: www.laddscorp.com
SIC: 5023 2392 Linens, table; pillowcases;
sheets, textile; towels; blankets, com-
forters & beddings; pillowcases: made
from purchased materials; sheets, fabric:
made from purchased materials; towels,
fabric & nonwoven: made from purchased
materials

(G-19344)
LAMOT CORPORATION
13650 N Promenade Blvd (77477-3972)
PHONE.....................816 792-1500
Dave Brown, *President*
Ken Shaw, *President*
Lindsey Markham, *Sales Staff*
▲ **EMP:** 65 **EST:** 1964
SALES (est): 11.7MM **Privately Held**
WEB: www.lamot.com
SIC: 3533 Oil field machinery & equipment
HQ: Continental Disc Corporation
3160 W Heartland Dr
Liberty MO 64068
816 792-1500

(G-19345)
**LAREDO CONSTRUCTION INC
(HQ)**
13385 Murphy Rd (77477-4305)
PHONE.....................281 499-4333
Robert R Springob, *CEO*
Tarn M Springbob, *President*
Waltraud K Springob, *Corp Secy*
Nadja Knoulton, *Vice Pres*
Tim McConnell, *VP Opers*
EMP: 12
SQ FT: 4,000
SALES (est): 9.3MM
SALES (corp-wide): 14.7MM **Privately
Held**
WEB: www.laredogroup.org
SIC: 1629 1389 Marine construction; oil
field services
PA: Springob Enterprises, Inc.
13385 Murphy Rd
Stafford TX 77477
281 499-4333

(G-19346)
LASER SHOT INC (PA)
4214 Bluebonnet Dr (77477-2911)
PHONE.....................281 240-1122
◆ **EMP:** 75
SQ FT: 25,000
SALES (est): 21.3MM **Privately Held**
WEB: www.lasershot.com
SIC: 3699 Laser systems & equipment

(G-19347)
**LEEDO MANUFACTURING CO
LP**
Also Called: Leedo Cabinetry
10707 Corp Dr Ste 250 (77477)
PHONE.....................866 995-3336
EMP: 349
SALES (corp-wide): 112.1MM **Privately
Held**
WEB: www.leedocabinetry.com
SIC: 2434 Vanities, bathroom: wood
PA: Leedo Manufacturing Co., L.P.
16856 Cabinet Rd
East Bernard TX 77435
866 465-3336

(G-19348)
**LONE STAR MEDICAL
PRODUCTS INC**
11211 Cash Rd (77477-4310)
PHONE.....................281 340-6000
Jim Fowler, *President*
Xavier Adame, *Director*
EMP: 50 **EST:** 1979

SQ FT: 35,000
SALES (est): 6.3MM **Privately Held**
SIC: 3841 Surgical & medical instruments

(G-19349)
LOOKOUT SERVICES INC
4134 Bluebonnet Dr # 110 (77477-3983)
P.O. Box 1692 (77497-1692)
PHONE.....................713 668-6200
Arden Morley, *CEO*
Alisha Campos, *Opers Staff*
EMP: 12
SQ FT: 5,000
SALES (est): 900K **Privately Held**
WEB: www.lookoutservices.net
SIC: 7372 Business oriented computer
software

(G-19350)
MAKITSO USA LLC
12850 Sugar Ridge Blvd (77477-3117)
PHONE.....................281 495-1300
Can Li, *Mng Member*
EMP: 15
SALES (est): 626.4K **Privately Held**
WEB: www.makitsodisplays.com
SIC: 3993 5046 Signs & advertising spe-
cialties; signs, electrical

(G-19351)
**MASTERPIECE MACHINE AND
MFG CO**
10245 W Airport Blvd (77477-3300)
PHONE.....................713 952-4102
Michael Cheatwood, *General Mgr*
Abbas Arian, *Co-Owner*
Trevor Goodchild, *Co-Owner*
Georgios Varsamis, *Co-Owner*
Laurence Wisniewski, *Co-Owner*
▼ **EMP:** 87
SQ FT: 117
SALES (est): 25.1MM **Privately Held**
WEB: www.masterpiecemachine.com
SIC: 3531 Construction machinery

(G-19352)
MATHESON TRI-GAS INC
13045 Murphy Rd (77477-3905)
PHONE.....................281 498-2310
Roger Chapman, *Manager*
EMP: 15 **Privately Held**
WEB: www.mathesongas.com
SIC: 2813 5084 5984 Industrial gases;
welding machinery & equipment; propane
gas, bottled
HQ: Matheson Tri-Gas, Inc.
3 Mountainview Rd Ste 3 # 3
Warren NJ 07059
908 991-9200

(G-19353)
**MICROWAVE NETWORKS INC
(HQ)**
4000 Greenbriar Dr # 100 (77477-4026)
PHONE.....................281 263-6500
Aviad Gefen, *CEO*
Vikram Bala, *COO*
Alvin Aurelio, *Vice Pres*
Jerry Hulburt, *Vice Pres*
Ben Lee, *Vice Pres*
◆ **EMP:** 30 **EST:** 1998
SQ FT: 44,000 **Privately Held**
WEB: www.microwavenetworks.com
SIC: 3663 Microwave communication
equipment

(G-19354)
MLI SUPPLY INC
3776 Greenbriar Dr (77477-3924)
PHONE.....................713 266-1400
Ron Daniels, *President*
EMP: 10
SALES (est): 456.3K **Privately Held**
WEB: www.mlisupply.com
SIC: 3841 Surgical & medical instruments

(G-19355)
MOTION GEAR WORKS LLC
10511 Wndsor Ln Bldg A St (77477)
PHONE.....................713 585-5245
Mike Thompson, *General Mgr*
EMP: 16
SALES (est): 580.7K **Privately Held**
SIC: 3599 Machine shop, jobbing & repair

(G-19356)
NATIONAL COUPLING COMPANY INC
Also Called: Hunting Energy Services
1316 Staffordshire Rd (77477-6321)
PHONE...................................281 499-2583
Dane Tipton, *President*
Dennis Proctor, *President*
Gary G Weathers, *President*
Jim Johnson, *Senior VP*
Craig Kirchner, *Purchasing*
▲ **EMP:** 162
SQ FT: 95,000
SALES (est): 32.8MM
SALES (corp-wide): 960MM **Privately Held**
SIC: 1389 Oil field services
HQ: Hunting Energy Services, Llc
16825 Northchase Dr # 600
Houston TX 77060

(G-19357)
NEWAY VALVE USA LP
9757 Stafford Centre Dr (77477-5030)
PHONE...................................281 969-5500
Mc McDonald, *Partner*
Jonathan Lenz, *Sales Mgr*
Godwin Cheng, *Manager*
▲ **EMP:** 25
SALES (est): 5.3MM **Privately Held**
WEB: www.newayvalve.com
SIC: 3491 Industrial valves

(G-19358)
NEWCO VALVES LLC
Also Called: Newmans
4655 Wright Rd Ste 250 (77477-4134)
PHONE...................................832 944-5930
James Pease, *President*
Jim Hartnel, *Manager*
EMP: 16 **Publicly Held**
WEB: www.qrcvalves.com
SIC: 3592 Valves
HQ: Newco Valves, Llc
13127 Trinity Dr
Stafford TX 77477
281 325-0041

(G-19359)
NEWCO VALVES LLC (DH)
Also Called: Newmans
13127 Trinity Dr (77477-4297)
PHONE...................................281 325-0041
Steve Mitchell, *Director*
Charles M Sledge, *Director*
James E Wright, *Director*
◆ **EMP:** 55
SQ FT: 160,000
SALES (est): 32.4MM **Publicly Held**
WEB: www.qrcvalves.com
SIC: 3494 5085 Valves & pipe fittings;
valves & fittings

(G-19360)
NUVO ATHLETIC LLC
3727 Greenbriar Dr # 111 (77477-3954)
PHONE...................................281 808-7650
Orlando Moore, *Manager*
EMP: 9
SALES (est): 116.8K **Privately Held**
WEB: www.nuvoathletic.com
SIC: 5699 2339 Sports apparel; sportswear, women's

(G-19361)
ON SITE DECALS LLC
12807 Royal Dr Ste 101 (77477-4222)
PHONE...................................281 994-9000
EMP: 13 **EST:** 2014
SQ FT: 5,000
SALES (est): 1.7MM **Privately Held**
WEB: www.onsitedecals.com
SIC: 2759 Decals: printing

(G-19362)
OUTPUT ACQUISITION CORP
Also Called: Opex
11104 W Airport Blvd # 160 (77477-3035)
PHONE...................................281 879-3609
James E Sigmon, *President*
Gary Grinsfelder, *General Mgr*
P Mark Stark, *CFO*
EMP: 16
SQ FT: 7,000
SALES (est): 1.1MM **Privately Held**
SIC: 1382 Oil & gas exploration services

(G-19363)
PBV-USA INC
Also Called: Pbv Valve
12735 Dairy Ashford Rd (77477-3612)
PHONE...................................800 231-3530
▲ **EMP:** 100
SQ FT: 18,000
SALES (est): 36.7K
SALES (corp-wide): 818.6MM **Publicly Held**
SIC: 3491 Mfg Industrial Valves
HQ: Forum Us, Inc.
10344 Sam Houston Park Dr
Houston TX 77064
713 351-7900

(G-19364)
PUFFER-SWEIVEN LP INC
4230 Greenbriar Dr (77477-3917)
PHONE...................................281 240-2000
Albert Grobmyer, *President*
Keith Erskine, *Vice Pres*
Aaron Griffin, *Sales Associate*
◆ **EMP:** 20
SALES (est): 4.6MM **Privately Held**
WEB: www.puffer.com
SIC: 3823 Industrial process control instruments

(G-19365)
QUALITY TABLE LINEN INC
Also Called: Jack The Ripper Table Skirts
4003 Greenbriar Dr Ste A (77477-4014)
P.O. Box 20248, Houston (77225-0248)
PHONE...................................281 240-1024
Bernardine Franklin, *President*
EMP: 25
SQ FT: 11,000
SALES (est): 2.3MM **Privately Held**
SIC: 2392 Tablecloths & table settings

(G-19366)
QUILTERS EMPORIUM LLC
11925 Ste 11 Sw Fwy (77477)
PHONE...................................281 491-0016
Rose Ann Cook, *Principal*
EMP: 10
SQ FT: 1,600
SALES (est): 813.6K **Privately Held**
WEB: www.quiltersemporium.com
SIC: 2395 Quilting & quilting supplies

(G-19367)
R C TECHNICAL WELDING & FABR
Also Called: R C Technical
12814 Mula Ln (77477-3317)
PHONE...................................281 933-6004
Robert Cone, *President*
James Norman, *President*
Valerie Cone, *Corp Secy*
EMP: 45
SQ FT: 54,000
SALES (est): 11.5MM **Privately Held**
WEB: www.rctfab.com
SIC: 3443 3354 3559 8711 Industrial vessels, tanks & containers; aluminum pipe & tube; frame straighteners, automobile (garage equipment); engineering services; welding repair; welding on site

(G-19368)
REGIONAL ACID PRODUCTION LP
Also Called: Rap
4755 Alpine Dr Ste 150b (77477-4129)
PHONE...................................281 381-7866
Edward Stribling, *President*
EMP: 100
SQ FT: 4,000
SALES (est): 5.7MM **Privately Held**
SIC: 2869 Industrial organic chemicals

(G-19369)
RESERVOIR GROUP
12950 S Kirkwood Rd # 160 (77477-3863)
PHONE...................................281 776-5300
EMP: 10
SALES (est): 1.3MM **Privately Held**
WEB: www.reservoirgroup.com
SIC: 1389 Oil field services

(G-19370)
RH TAMLYN & SONS (PA)
13623 Pike Rd (77477-5103)
PHONE...................................281 499-9604
Randy Tamlyn, *Partner*
Ronald H Tamlyn Jr, *Partner*
Rusty Tamlyn, *Partner*
Tom Tamlyn, *General Ptnr*
Joshua Godkin, *Regional Mgr*
▲ **EMP:** 40 **EST:** 1971
SQ FT: 60,000
SALES: 23.3MM **Privately Held**
WEB: www.tamlyn.com
SIC: 3444 5031 5169 3441 Sheet metalwork; building materials, exterior; building materials, interior; adhesives & sealants; fabricated structural metal

(G-19371)
ROCA PRECISION MFG INC
Also Called: Roca Printed Circuits
12830 Century Dr (77477-4204)
PHONE...................................281 240-2020
Barry L Finberg, *President*
Monica Barrow, *Vice Pres*
EMP: 16
SQ FT: 16,000
SALES (est): 1.3MM **Privately Held**
WEB: www.rocacircuits.com
SIC: 3672 Circuit boards, television & radio printed

(G-19372)
ROSEMOUNT INC
12603 Southwest Fwy # 400 (77477-3818)
PHONE...................................281 240-2000
Chris Sokol, *Manager*
EMP: 40
SALES (corp-wide): 16.7B **Publicly Held**
WEB: www.rosemount.com
SIC: 3823 Manometers, industrial process type
HQ: Rosemount Inc.
8200 Market Blvd
Chanhassen MN 55317
952 906-8888

(G-19373)
SAM&M GROUP LLC (PA)
Also Called: Context Home and Garden
1112 Staffordshire Rd (77477-6218)
PHONE...................................346 204-5786
Davud Mushin Ozcan, *Principal*
Salih Volkan, *Principal*
EMP: 11
SALES (est): 1.3MM **Privately Held**
SIC: 2273 5023 2211 5963 Rugs, machine woven; rugs; towels & toweling, cotton; appliance sales, house-to-house; commercial & office building contractors

(G-19374)
SATAKE USA INC (HQ)
10900 Cash Rd (77477-4300)
PHONE...................................281 276-3600
Junjiro Naoki, *President*
Toshiko Satake, *Chairman*
Peter Cawthorne, *Vice Pres*
Jerry Brum, *VP Mfg*
Paul Cardiel, *Engineer*
▲ **EMP:** 99
SALES (est): 55.3MM **Privately Held**
WEB: www.satake-usa.com
SIC: 5084 3556 Food product manufacturing machinery; food products machinery

(G-19375)
SCANLIN SIGN SERVICE INC
13123 Mula Ct (77477-3321)
PHONE...................................281 561-9924
Ed Scanlin, *President*
David Scanlin, *Vice Pres*
EMP: 20
SQ FT: 10,000
SALES (est): 2MM **Privately Held**
WEB: www.scanlinsigns.com
SIC: 3993 Electric signs

(G-19376)
SGM CORPORATION
Also Called: V-J Electronic Assemblies
12831 Royal Dr (77477-4209)
PHONE...................................281 313-6111
Shanker Patel, *President*
Manaji Thakor, *Vice Pres*
Girish Parikh, *Admin Sec*
EMP: 40
SQ FT: 3,200
SALES (est): 5.6MM **Privately Held**
WEB: www.vjassemblies.com
SIC: 3672 Printed circuit boards

(G-19377)
SHANY ENTERPRISES INC
Also Called: Shany Cosmetics
10302 Mula Rd (77477-3110)
P.O. Box 421037, Houston (77242-1037)
PHONE...................................713 772-1345
Payam Pourmeh, *CEO*
Assad Pourmehr, *Opers Staff*
▲ **EMP:** 21
SQ FT: 25,000
SALES (est): 3.6MM **Privately Held**
WEB: www.shanycosmetics.com
SIC: 2844 Cosmetic preparations

(G-19378)
SHUTTER SOURCE INC
Also Called: Mark Morales Shutter Source
10404 Cash Rd Ste B (77477-4425)
PHONE...................................281 403-2012
Mark Morales, *President*
EMP: 15
SALES (est): 1.8MM **Privately Held**
WEB: www.shuttersourcehouston.com
SIC: 5023 2431 Window furnishings; millwork

(G-19379)
SIMPLY 7 SNACKS LLC
13843 Stafford Rd (77477-5007)
P.O. Box 710543, Houston (77271-0543)
PHONE...................................713 988-2900
Kawal Oberoi, *CEO*
Dhiraj Oberoi, *Chairman*
Mark Jackson, *Sales Staff*
Sang Owen, *Manager*
Kiran Oberoi, *Admin Sec*
EMP: 20
SQ FT: 5,000
SALES (est): 17.8MM **Privately Held**
WEB: www.simply7snacks.com
SIC: 2096 Potato chips & similar snacks

(G-19380)
SUNBELT MACHINE WORKS CORP
13411 Redfish Ln (77477-4420)
PHONE...................................281 499-0051
C Frank Scantlin, *President*
Chris Scantlin, *General Mgr*
Cecil Craig Scantlin, *Vice Pres*
J Brent Scantlin, *Vice Pres*
Peter Woukoun, *Sales Staff*
EMP: 40 **EST:** 1978
SQ FT: 55,000
SALES: 7.8MM **Privately Held**
WEB: www.sunbeltmachine.com
SIC: 3599 Machine shop, jobbing & repair

(G-19381)
SUNRGY LLC
Also Called: Sunrgy Solar Distribution
12763 Capricorn St # 100 (77477-3994)
PHONE...................................832 786-5051
Neel Desai,
EMP: 21 **EST:** 2019
SALES (est): 657.2K **Privately Held**
WEB: www.sunrgy.com
SIC: 3674 3613 5722 5074 Semiconductors & related devices; solar cells; panel & distribution boards & other related apparatus; distribution boards, electric; household appliance stores; heating equipment & panels, solar

(G-19382)
TECH POWER INTERNATIONAL CO
4147 Greenbriar Dr (77477-3907)
PHONE...................................281 494-4242
Jasbir Dhindsa, *President*
EMP: 70
SQ FT: 1,500
SALES (est): 10MM **Privately Held**
WEB: www.techpowerinternational.com
SIC: 3679 3625 Electronic circuits; electric controls & control accessories, industrial

(G-19383)
TECHNIPLEX CONFERENCE CENTER
Also Called: Ballroom
4810 Techniplex Dr (77477-3827)
PHONE....................281 565-5566
EMP: 9 EST: 2014
SALES (est): 276.5K **Privately Held**
WEB: www.thetuscanyballroom.com
SIC: 1389 Building oil & gas well foundations on site

(G-19384)
TEX STYLES INTERNATIONAL INC
12725 Royal Dr (77477-4207)
PHONE....................713 787-9955
Robert Lary, *President*
EMP: 20
SQ FT: 11,000
SALES (est): 1.6MM **Privately Held**
WEB: www.texstyles.com
SIC: 2395 Embroidery products, except schiffli machine

(G-19385)
TEXAS INDUSTRIES INC
Also Called: T X I
13908 Pike Rd (77477)
PHONE....................281 261-0790
JD Stanley, *Manager*
EMP: 43 **Publicly Held**
WEB: www.martinmarietta.com
SIC: 1442 Sand mining; gravel mining
HQ: Texas Industries, Inc.
1503 Lyndon B Johnson Fwy
Dallas TX 75234
972 647-6700

(G-19386)
TEXAS INSTRUMENTS INCORPORATED
12201 Southwest Fwy (77477-3006)
P.O. Box 1443, Houston (77251-1443)
PHONE....................972 995-2011
Gang Hua, *Engineer*
Waqar Mehmood, *Engineer*
Jason Peck, *Engineer*
Brian Hargraves, *Program Mgr*
Gregg Delagi, *Manager*
EMP: 20
SALES (corp-wide): 14.4B **Publicly Held**
WEB: www.txwx.com
SIC: 3674 Semiconductors & related devices
PA: Texas Instruments Incorporated
12500 Ti Blvd
Dallas TX 75243
972 995-3773

(G-19387)
TRI TOOL INC
13330 Pike Rd (77477-5105)
PHONE....................281 499-1188
EMP: 51
SALES (corp-wide): 74.9MM **Privately Held**
WEB: www.tritool.com
SIC: 3541 5084 3548 Machine tools, metal cutting type; industrial machinery & equipment; welding apparatus
HQ: Tri Tool Inc.
3041 Sunrise Blvd
Rancho Cordova CA 95742
916 288-6100

(G-19388)
TRIBOCOR TECHNOLOGIES INC
12950 Royal Dr (77477-4217)
PHONE....................281 277-7200
Phillip Koshy, *President*
Bruce Weisman, *Prdtn Mgr*
Alexander Groth, *Senior Engr*
Ruth Flores, *Manager*
Vijay Koshy, *Manager*
▲ EMP: 16
SALES (est): 6.2MM **Privately Held**
WEB: www.tribocor.com
SIC: 3533 5082 Oil field machinery & equipment; oil field equipment

(G-19389)
TRS DISTRIBUTION LLC
Also Called: Texas Roofing Supply
12002 Southwest Fwy (77477-3030)
P.O. Box 1486, Rosenberg (77471-1486)
PHONE....................281 372-8479
Brian Slay, *CEO*
Ted Gillis, *CFO*
Austin Hill, *CFO*
EMP: 13
SQ FT: 34,000
SALES (est): 8.7MM **Privately Held**
WEB: www.texasroofingsupply.com
SIC: 2821 Plastics materials & resins

(G-19390)
TTL SUBSEA INC
10700 Corp Dr Ste 108 (77477)
PHONE....................713 960-3655
John Blair, *Director*
EMP: 9
SALES (est): 402.6K **Privately Held**
WEB: www.ttlsubsea.com
SIC: 1389 Oil field services

(G-19391)
U S ALLOY CO
Also Called: Washington Alloy
4855 Alpine Dr Ste 100 (77477-4141)
PHONE....................877 711-9274
Tom Hill, *Branch Mgr*
EMP: 23
SALES (corp-wide): 35MM **Privately Held**
WEB: www.weldingwire.com
SIC: 3548 Welding wire, bare & coated
PA: U. S. Alloy Co.
8885 White Oak Ave Ste 10
Rancho Cucamonga CA 91730
800 830-9033

(G-19392)
UMBILICALS INTERNATIONAL INC
Also Called: Geocables Systems
10711 Cash Rd (77477-4431)
PHONE....................281 275-6600
Colin Zak, *CEO*
Joaquin Medina, *Vice Pres*
Marcel Wolring, *Vice Pres*
Raul Lara, *Production*
John Pazzanese, *Finance*
◆ EMP: 70 EST: 1996
SQ FT: 100,000
SALES (est): 21MM **Privately Held**
WEB: www.umbilicals.com
SIC: 3357 3643 Nonferrous wiredrawing & insulating; current-carrying wiring devices

(G-19393)
UNITRA INC
12601 Exchange Dr Ste 100 (77477-3600)
PHONE....................281 240-1500
Sara Sukun, *President*
◆ EMP: 28
SQ FT: 35,500
SALES (est): 7MM **Privately Held**
WEB: www.unitrainc.com
SIC: 3561 3589 Pumps, domestic: water or sump; water purification equipment, household type

(G-19394)
VANCO RING GSKET SPCLTY CORP I
10138 Cash Rd (77477-4409)
PHONE....................281 499-1543
Brooke E Beierle, *President*
Kelly V Dries, *Vice Pres*
Elizabeth Pekar, *Admin Sec*
EMP: 11
SQ FT: 28,000
SALES (est): 2.1MM **Privately Held**
WEB: www.vancoring.com
SIC: 3053 Gaskets, all materials

(G-19395)
VICTAULIC COMPANY
Also Called: Victaulic Co of America
13833 N Promenade Blvd # 500 (77477-4043)
PHONE....................281 494-5000
Ben Hudson, *Sales Staff*
Chris Smith, *Sales Staff*
Randy Plost, *Manager*

Michael Acero, *Manager*
EMP: 15
SALES (corp-wide): 637.9MM **Privately Held**
WEB: www.victaulic.com
SIC: 3999 Barber & beauty shop equipment
PA: Victaulic Company
4901 Kesslersville Rd
Easton PA 18040
610 559-3300

(G-19396)
VOGT VALVES INC
13800 N Promenade Blvd (77477-4042)
PHONE....................346 304-2566
Simone Brevi, *President*
Adam Enloe, *Natl Sales Mgr*
EMP: 52
SALES (est): 2.5MM **Privately Held**
WEB: www.vogtvalves.com
SIC: 3491 Industrial valves

(G-19397)
W R WATSON CORPORATION
12902 Mula Ln (77477-3318)
PHONE....................281 495-2800
Wade Watson, *President*
Shade Watson, *Accounting Mgr*
EMP: 30 EST: 1992
SQ FT: 15,000
SALES (est): 642.4K **Privately Held**
WEB: www.wrwatson.com
SIC: 2434 Wood kitchen cabinets

(G-19398)
WHITEHILL MANUFACTURING INC
12603 Executive Dr # 810 (77477-3611)
PHONE....................281 240-2003
Robert White, *Ch of Bd*
Robert Lepple, *President*
Dale Brown, *President*
Ira Hill, *Mktg Dir*
Joe Mc Vaigh, *Administration*
EMP: 15
SQ FT: 10,000
SALES (est): 2.6MM **Privately Held**
SIC: 3843 8021 Dental equipment & supplies; offices & clinics of dentists

(G-19399)
WIRELESS SEISMIC INC (PA)
12503 Exchange Dr Ste 500 (77477-3607)
PHONE....................832 532-5080
Michael Lambert, *CEO*
Lionel Lhommet, *Chairman*
Keith Elder, *Vice Pres*
Travis Ohnesorge, *Vice Pres*
John Smith, *Vice Pres*
▲ EMP: 30
SALES (est): 6.4MM **Privately Held**
WEB: www.wirelessseismic.com
SIC: 3829 Measuring & controlling devices

(G-19400)
WRISTBANDS WITH A MESSAGE INC
10200 W Airport Blvd # 100 (77477-3333)
P.O. Box 2494 (77497-2494)
PHONE....................281 494-2424
Darla Farmer, *President*
EMP: 13
SALES (est): 1.5MM **Privately Held**
WEB: www.wristbandswithamessage.com
SIC: 3961 Bracelets, except precious metal

Stagecoach
Montgomery County

(G-19401)
JDM DESIGNS INC
Also Called: Custom Wood Designs & Mfg
14135 Stagecoach Rd (77355-8402)
PHONE....................281 356-6131
Jim McDonald, *President*
Sheryl McDonald, *Vice Pres*
EMP: 20

SALES (est): 2.4MM **Privately Held**
WEB: www.jdmdesigns.com
SIC: 2511 3993 7336 Wood household furniture; signs & advertising specialties; graphic arts & related design

Stamford
Jones County

(G-19402)
WALCOTT ENTERPRISES INC
Also Called: Walcott Drywall
211 N Swenson St (79553-4117)
P.O. Box 26 (79553-0026)
PHONE....................325 773-5212
Barry Walcott, *President*
Kelly Williamson, *Vice Pres*
EMP: 30
SALES (est): 3MM **Privately Held**
SIC: 1742 1711 2434 Drywall; plumbing contractors; wood kitchen cabinets

Stanton
Martin County

(G-19403)
M & M METER SERVICE INC
Also Called: M & M Disposal
108 N St Peter (79782)
P.O. Box 3608 I 20 E
PHONE....................432 756-2801
Roger Burch, *President*
EMP: 15 EST: 1969
SQ FT: 4,000
SALES (est): 792K **Privately Held**
WEB: www.mmdisposal.com
SIC: 3825 7629 Meters: electric, pocket, portable, panelboard, etc.; electrical measuring instrument repair & calibration

(G-19404)
REAGENT CHEMICAL & RES INC
2833 Ih 20 South Svc Rd (79782)
P.O. Box 1253 (79782-1253)
PHONE....................432 458-3403
Arthur Ruiz, *Manager*
EMP: 16
SALES (corp-wide): 376.8MM **Privately Held**
WEB: www.prosysfill.com
SIC: 2819 3949 Sulfur, recovered or refined, incl. from sour natural gas; targets, archery & rifle shooting
PA: Reagent Chemical & Research, Inc.
115 Rte 202
Ringoes NJ 08551
908 284-2800

(G-19405)
TEXAS 21ST CENTURY TRANSPORT &
Also Called: Texas 21st Century Trnsp
708 N Lamesa Hwy (79782)
PHONE....................432 607-2071
Refugio Gutierrez, *President*
Billie McGuire,
Walt Haislip, *Administration*
EMP: 110
SQ FT: 1,800
SALES (est): 26.5MM **Privately Held**
SIC: 1389 1381 Oil & gas wells: building, repairing & dismantling; drilling oil & gas wells

Stephenville
Erath County

(G-19406)
APPLETON GRP LLC
2150 W South Loop (76401-3922)
PHONE....................254 968-6071
Ricky Files, *Plant Mgr*
Dustin Keith, *Maint Spvr*
Jeanie Shelton, *Human Res Dir*
Jim Johnson, *Manager*
EMP: 90

SALES (corp-wide): 16.7B **Publicly Held**
WEB: www.emerson.com
SIC: 3823 Industrial instrmnts msrmnt display/control process variable
HQ: Appleton Grp Llc
9377 W Higgins Rd
Rosemont IL 60018
847 268-6000

(G-19407)
BADJ INC
Also Called: Cabinet Concepts
139 Private Road 1705 (76401-1295)
PHONE..................................254 918-5397
Billy Wilson, *President*
EMP: 10 **EST:** 2009
SALES (est): 700K **Privately Held**
SIC: 2514 Kitchen cabinets: metal

(G-19408)
CHILDS READY-MIX CONCRETE CO
Also Called: Ingram Ready Mix
1375 N Bates St (76401-2705)
P.O. Box 181 (76401-0024)
PHONE..................................254 968-4755
James Cockrum, *Site Mgr*
Russell Haynes, *Opers-Prdtn-Mfg*
Ron Gray, *Executive*
EMP: 10
SALES (corp-wide): 1.4B **Publicly Held**
WEB: www.ingramconcrete.com
SIC: 3273 1771 Ready-mixed concrete; concrete work
HQ: Childs Ready-Mix Concrete Company
4301 Danhil Dr
Brownwood TX 76801
325 646-6518

(G-19409)
DAY NIGHT SIGNS INC
Also Called: Signs and Designs
1715 N Graham St (76401-2201)
PHONE..................................254 965-9000
Morris Duree, *President*
Sherri Duree, *Vice Pres*
▲ **EMP:** 10
SALES (est): 942.9K **Privately Held**
WEB: www.day-nightsigns.com
SIC: 3993 Neon signs

(G-19410)
ERATH PUBLISHERS INC
Also Called: Stephenville Empire Tribune
702 E South Loop (76401-5314)
P.O. Box 958 (76401-0009)
PHONE..................................254 965-3124
Rochelle Stidham, *President*
James Stevenson, *Principal*
Shelton Prince, *Vice Pres*
Raymond M Mathieu, *CFO*
Robert C Tanner, *Admin Sec*
EMP: 69 **EST:** 1969
SQ FT: 12,000
SALES (est): 3.9MM
SALES (corp-wide): 1.8B **Publicly Held**
WEB: www.yourstephenvilletx.com
SIC: 2711 Newspapers, publishing & printing
HQ: Gatehouse Media, Llc
175 Sullys Trl Fl 3
Pittsford NY 14534
585 598-0030

(G-19411)
FIBERGRATE COMPOSITE
840 Airport Rd (76401-5420)
PHONE..................................254 977-1302
Ken Miller, *Purch Mgr*
Windell Hollingworth, *Branch Mgr*
Bob Dmytro, *Manager*
EMP: 78
SALES (corp-wide): 5.5B **Publicly Held**
WEB: www.fibergrate.com
SIC: 3089 Plastic hardware & building products
HQ: Fibergrate Composite Structures Incorporated
5151 Belt Line Rd Ste 700
Dallas TX 75254

(G-19412)
FIBERGRATE COMPOSITE
900 Fm 205 (76401-4688)
P.O. Box 208 (76401-0003)
PHONE..................................254 965-3148

Justin Boles, *Project Mgr*
Darryl MBA, *Mfg Staff*
Beverly Salter, *Purch Mgr*
Rodney Teten, *Purchasing*
Delia Speriatu, *Controller*
EMP: 115
SALES (corp-wide): 5.5B **Publicly Held**
WEB: www.fibergrate.com
SIC: 3089 Fiberglass doors
HQ: Fibergrate Composite Structures Incorporated
5151 Belt Line Rd Ste 700
Dallas TX 75254

(G-19413)
FMC TECHNOLOGIES INC
Also Called: FMC Subsea Systems
2825 W Washington St (76401-3706)
PHONE..................................254 968-2181
Jayton Fair, *Warehouse Mgr*
Jason Thames, *Purchasing*
Lee Witte, *Engineer*
Larry Morrow, *Regl Sales Mgr*
Dean Walker, *Marketing Mgr*
EMP: 15
SALES (corp-wide): 13.4B **Privately Held**
WEB: www.technipfmc.com
SIC: 3533 Oil field machinery & equipment
HQ: Fmc Technologies, Inc.
11740 Katy Fwy Enrgy Twr
Houston TX 77079
281 591-4000

(G-19414)
FMC TECHNOLOGIES INC
FMC Fluid Control
2825 W Washington St (76401-3706)
P.O. Box 1377 (76401-0014)
PHONE..................................254 968-2181
John Moore, *Branch Mgr*
Pat Young, *Manager*
Richard Clarke, *Prgrmr*
EMP: 29
SALES (corp-wide): 13.4B **Privately Held**
WEB: www.technipfmc.com
SIC: 3533 Oil field machinery & equipment
HQ: Fmc Technologies, Inc.
11740 Katy Fwy Enrgy Twr
Houston TX 77079
281 591-4000

(G-19415)
FMC TECHNOLOGIES INC
2830 W Frey St (76401-1905)
PHONE..................................254 968-2181
Alejandro Ramos, *Research*
EMP: 14
SALES (corp-wide): 13.4B **Privately Held**
WEB: www.technipfmc.com
SIC: 3533 Oil field machinery & equipment
HQ: Fmc Technologies, Inc.
11740 Katy Fwy Enrgy Twr
Houston TX 77079
281 591-4000

(G-19416)
HOKA HEY INC
Also Called: Hoka Hey Fine Arts Foundry
1405 Parkwood Ct (76401-1618)
P.O. Box 88, Dublin (76446-0088)
PHONE..................................254 445-2017
Richard Cowan Jr, *President*
Patricia Cowan, *Corp Secy*
Richard Wade Cowan, *Vice Pres*
EMP: 12 **EST:** 1977
SALES (est): 1.6MM **Privately Held**
SIC: 3366 Castings (except die): bronze

(G-19417)
OUTLAW CONVERSIONS INC
Also Called: Emerald Luxury Coaches
1000 Airport Rd (76401-5402)
P.O. Box 154 (76401-0002)
PHONE..................................254 968-5733
JB Garrett, *Partner*
John Walker, *Principal*
Patricia Harrington, *Mfg Staff*
Sarah Decker, *Human Res Dir*
David Johnson, *Sales Staff*
▲ **EMP:** 190
SQ FT: 35,000
SALES (est): 32.9MM **Privately Held**
WEB: www.outlawconversions.com
SIC: 3799 Horse trailers, except fifth-wheel type

(G-19418)
PAL-CON LLC
Also Called: PAL- LEASE & MANAGEMENT
12425 N Hwy 377 (76401)
P.O. Box 1338 (76401-0013)
PHONE..................................254 968-3335
Randy Thompson, *President*
Wayne Campbell, *Superintendent*
Tamela Mund, *General Ptnr*
Tracy Tuck, *Project Mgr*
Josh Raymond, *Purch Mgr*
EMP: 50
SQ FT: 75,000
SALES: 17.4MM **Privately Held**
WEB: www.palconltd.com
SIC: 3511 Gas turbine generator set units, complete

(G-19419)
POWDER FINISHES INC (PA)
645 W Lingleville Rd (76401-2225)
PHONE..................................254 968-5601
Dan Malone, *President*
EMP: 33
SQ FT: 15,000
SALES (est): 2.8MM **Privately Held**
SIC: 3479 Coating of metals & formed products

(G-19420)
RIGGS MACHINE AND WELDING INC
307 East Rd (76401-4517)
PHONE..................................254 965-3910
J C Riggs, *President*
Jean V Riggs, *Vice Pres*
EMP: 17
SQ FT: 110,000
SALES (est): 2.2MM **Privately Held**
WEB: www.riggsmachineandwelding.com
SIC: 3599 7692 5531 Machine shop, jobbing & repair; welding repair; automobile & truck equipment & parts

(G-19421)
SAINT-GOBAIN ABRASIVES INC
Also Called: Coated Abrasive Division
2770 W Washington St (76401-3702)
PHONE..................................254 918-2307
EMP: 600
SALES (corp-wide): 328.4MM **Privately Held**
WEB: www.saint-gobain.com
SIC: 3291 Abrasive products
HQ: Saint-Gobain Abrasives, Inc.
1 New Bond St
Worcester MA 01606
508 795-5000

(G-19422)
SHINN AND GREGORY INC
Also Called: Gregory Pile Driving
3237 N Us Highway 281 (76401-9077)
P.O. Box 344 (76401-0005)
PHONE..................................254 965-7585
Eldon Gregory, *President*
Jimmy Shinn, *Admin Sec*
EMP: 9
SQ FT: 5,000
SALES (est): 1.8MM **Privately Held**
SIC: 1629 1771 1081 Pile driving contractor; foundation & footing contractor; preparing shafts or tunnels, metal mining

(G-19423)
SQUARE ONE MACHINE INC
6420 S Us Highway 377 (76401-8618)
P.O. Box 836 (76401-0029)
PHONE..................................254 968-5600
Kenneth K Laughlin, *President*
Morris Greenhaw, *Admin Sec*
EMP: 12
SALES (est): 2MM **Privately Held**
WEB: www.sq1machine.com
SIC: 3599 Machine shop, jobbing & repair

(G-19424)
STEPHENVILLE PRINTING COMPANY (PA)
1193 W South Loop (76401-5201)
PHONE..................................254 965-5012
Tommy Cochran, *President*
Jennifer Grandpre, *Opers Staff*
EMP: 10 **EST:** 1942
SQ FT: 4,800

SALES (est): 2MM **Privately Held**
WEB: www.spcotx.com
SIC: 2752 7336 2395 Commercial printing, offset; lithographing on metal; silk screen design; embroidery & art needlework

(G-19425)
STEPHENVILLE PRINTING COMPANY
Also Called: Coyote Designs
1193 W South Loop (76401-5201)
PHONE..................................254 968-3115
Tom Cochran, *President*
EMP: 20
SALES (corp-wide): 2MM **Privately Held**
WEB: www.spcotx.com
SIC: 2395 Embroidery products, except schiffli machine
PA: Stephenville Printing Company Inc
1193 W South Loop
Stephenville TX 76401
254 965-5012

(G-19426)
TEJAS TUBULAR PRODUCTS INC
600 Caporal Dr (76401-3931)
P.O. Box 1728 (76401-0017)
PHONE..................................254 965-5162
EMP: 103 **Privately Held**
WEB: www.tejastubular.com
SIC: 3317 Steel pipe & tubes
PA: Tejas Tubular Products, Inc.
8799 North Loop E Ste 300
Houston TX 77029

Stinnett
Hutchinson County

(G-19427)
JOHN OATES COMPANY INC
10398 S Stinnett Hwy (79083)
P.O. Box 1189 (79083-1189)
PHONE..................................806 878-3338
Jack Oates, *President*
Terry Dougherty, *Vice Pres*
Colby Oates, *Treasurer*
EMP: 9
SQ FT: 4,000
SALES (est): 1.2MM **Privately Held**
WEB: www.johnoatescompany.com
SIC: 1389 1311 Acidizing wells; crude petroleum production; natural gas production

(G-19428)
SERVICE DRILLING SOUTHWEST LLC
Hwy 152 (79083)
PHONE..................................806 878-2052
EMP: 13
SALES (corp-wide): 854.2K **Publicly Held**
SIC: 1381 Oil Well Drilling Co
HQ: Service Drilling Southwest, L.L.C.
301 W 6th St Ste 301
Borger TX 79007

Stockdale
Wilson County

(G-19429)
KOTARA MFG INC
8855 State Highway 123 S (78160-6565)
PHONE..................................830 745-9007
Jason Kotara, *President*
Dorothy Kotara, *Admin Sec*
EMP: 9
SALES (est): 777.5K **Privately Held**
SIC: 3999 Farm equipment & supplies

Stonewall
Gillespie County

(G-19430)
WOODROSE WINERY INC
662 Woodrose Ln (78671-3704)
PHONE..................................830 644-2539

Michael S Guilette, *President*
Jerri Guilette, *Vice Pres*
EMP: 10
SQ FT: 2,000
SALES (est): 895.1K **Privately Held**
WEB: www.woodrosewinery.com
SIC: 2084 Wines

Stowell
Chambers County

(G-19431)
SEABREEZE CULVERT INC
3836 State Hwy 124 (77661)
P.O. Box 6 (77661-0006)
PHONE.............................409 296-4098
Lamont Meaux, *President*
Edward Meaux, *Vice Pres*
Chip Privette, *Sales Engr*
Coy Sewell, *Manager*
Kim Credeur, *Admin Sec*
EMP: 10 **EST:** 1976
SALES (est): 2.1MM **Privately Held**
WEB: www.seabreeze-culvert.com
SIC: 3444 Sheet metalwork

Strawn
Palo Pinto County

(G-19432)
RED DOG TRACK INC
Also Called: Rdt General Contracters
3271 State Highway 108 (76475-2706)
PHONE.............................254 672-5261
EMP: 25
SQ FT: 6,000
SALES (est): 2.1MM **Privately Held**
WEB: www.reddogtracks.com
SIC: 3281 1442 Cut stone & stone products; construction sand & gravel

(G-19433)
TEXAS BUILDING PRODUCTS INC
3261 State Highway 108 (76475-2706)
PHONE.............................254 672-5262
James D Hopkins, *President*
Robert T Dolson, *Vice Pres*
Tim Jenkins, *Vice Pres*
Donny Wells, *Opers Mgr*
EMP: 48
SQ FT: 35,000
SALES (est): 11.5MM **Privately Held**
WEB: www.texasbuildingproducts.com
SIC: 3271 Blocks, concrete or cinder: standard

Streetman
Freestone County

(G-19434)
KURT LUPO
Also Called: Rustic Creations
118 Main St (75859)
PHONE.............................903 599-3181
Kurt Lupo, *Owner*
EMP: 16 **EST:** 1991
SALES (est): 1.6MM **Privately Held**
WEB: www.rustic-creations.com
SIC: 2431 Millwork

(G-19435)
LEGEND MARINE MANGEMENT LLC
107 Fm 3059 (75859-4003)
PHONE.............................870 481-6750
Randy Qualls,
EMP: 25
SALES (est): 6MM **Privately Held**
SIC: 3732 Fishing boats: lobster, crab, oyster, etc.: small

Sugar Land
Fort Bend County

(G-19436)
ACCREDO PACKAGING INC
Also Called: API
12682 Cardinal Mdw (77478-6195)
PHONE.............................713 580-4800
Hank Nguyen, *CEO*
Matthew Tomasello, *President*
Chinh Nguyen, *COO*
Rex Varn, *Exec VP*
Janak Sheth, *CFO*
▼ **EMP:** 88
SALES (est): 42.5MM **Privately Held**
WEB: www.accredopackaging.com
SIC: 2671 3089 Plastic film, coated or laminated for packaging; laminating of plastic

(G-19437)
ADVANCE POLYBAG (NEVADA) INC
12682 Cardinal Mdw (77478-6195)
PHONE.............................702 642-1110
Hank Duc Nguyen, *President*
▲ **EMP:** 10
SALES (est): 1.7MM **Privately Held**
WEB: www.apicorp.com
SIC: 2673 Plastic bags: made from purchased materials

(G-19438)
ADVANCE POLYBAG (TEXAS) INC (PA)
12682 Cardinal Mdw (77478-6195)
PHONE.............................713 580-4800
Chinh T Nugyen, *President*
◆ **EMP:** 50
SQ FT: 1,200
SALES (est): 22.4MM **Privately Held**
WEB: www.apicorp.com
SIC: 2673 Plastic bags: made from purchased materials

(G-19439)
ADVANCE POLYBAG NORTH EAST INC (PA)
12682 Cardinal Mdw (77478-6195)
PHONE.............................410 796-8551
Hank Nguyen, *CEO*
▲ **EMP:** 10
SALES (est): 8.4MM **Privately Held**
WEB: www.apicorp.com
SIC: 2673 Plastic bags: made from purchased materials

(G-19440)
ADVANCED GEOPHYSICAL TECH INC
14100 Southwest Fwy # 110 (77478-4566)
PHONE.............................281 888-6789
Rob Yorke, *CEO*
J Jerry Yuan, *President*
Wenyi Hu, *Vice Pres*
Xijing Lian, *Vice Pres*
Lijian Tan, *Vice Pres*
EMP: 12
SALES (est): 1.2MM **Privately Held**
WEB: www.agtgeo.com
SIC: 1382 Oil & gas exploration services

(G-19441)
ALPHA PLASTICS INC
5819 Mogo Creek Ln (77479-4916)
PHONE.............................281 564-8838
Gary Chen, *President*
Flora Wang, *Vice Pres*
▲ **EMP:** 28
SALES (est): 5.5MM **Privately Held**
WEB: www.johnnychenseo.com
SIC: 3089 Injection molding of plastics

(G-19442)
AMERIPOWER LLC (PA)
2808 Grants Lake Blvd (77479-1379)
P.O. Box 16206 (77496-6206)
PHONE.............................281 240-0405
Tejbir Singh, *Mng Member*
Veronica Saenz,
Ted Singh, *Representative*
EMP: 10
SQ FT: 10,000

SALES (est): 1.3MM **Privately Held**
WEB: www.ameripower.com
SIC: 3625 Relays, electric power

(G-19443)
AMRAN INC
Also Called: Amran Instrument Transformers
12320 Cardinal Mdw # 100 (77478-6236)
PHONE.............................281 243-2200
Kevin Coulter, *Production*
Huong Vuong, *Accounting Mgr*
Nicholas Zuniga, *Sales Staff*
Michelle Seni, *Office Mgr*
Scott McCloskey, *Info Tech Mgr*
◆ **EMP:** 160
SQ FT: 15,000
SALES (est): 27.6MM **Privately Held**
WEB: www.amranit.com
SIC: 3612 Voltage regulating transformers, electric power

(G-19444)
ANDEAVOR RIO HOLDINGS LLC (DH)
2150 Town Square Pl # 700 (77479-1465)
PHONE.............................281 566-3000
Christopher W Keene, *President*
Paul Broker, *COO*
Rafael Colaco, *Vice Pres*
Bobby Arp, *Manager*
EMP: 11
SALES (est): 17MM **Publicly Held**
WEB: www.rangelandenergy.com
SIC: 1389 Gas field services
HQ: Tesoro Refining & Marketing Company Llc
19100 Ridgewood Pkwy
San Antonio TX 78259
210 828-8484

(G-19445)
APPLIED OPTOELECTRONICS INC (PA)
Also Called: Aoi
13139 Jess Pirtle Blvd (77478-2856)
PHONE.............................281 295-1800
Chih-Hsiang Lin, *Ch of Bd*
Hung-Lun Chang, *Senior VP*
Shu-Hua Yeh, *Senior VP*
Fred Chang, *Vice Pres*
David C Kuo, *Vice Pres*
▲ **EMP:** 150
SQ FT: 139,450
SALES: 190.8MM **Publicly Held**
WEB: www.ao-inc.com
SIC: 3674 3827 3699 Semiconductors & related devices; optical instruments & lenses; electrical equipment & supplies

(G-19446)
ARGOS USA LLC
Also Called: Southern Star
620 Sartartia Rd (77479-9616)
PHONE.............................713 273-2700
Gary Bullock, *CEO*
EMP: 13
SQ FT: 2,000 **Privately Held**
WEB: www.argos-us.com
SIC: 3273 Ready-mixed concrete
HQ: Argos Usa Llc
3015 Windward Plz Ste 300
Alpharetta GA 30005
678 368-4300

(G-19447)
BAKER HUGHES A GE COMPANY LLC
Also Called: New Phase Technologies
12645 W Airport Blvd (77478-6120)
PHONE.............................281 276-5400
Jim Sheridan, *Business Mgr*
Adam Bettwy, *Opers Staff*
Donald Prejean, *VP Finance*
Amy Redfearn, *Admin Asst*
EMP: 87
SALES (corp-wide): 23.8B **Publicly Held**
WEB: www.bhge.com
SIC: 1389 Oil field services
HQ: Baker Hughes Holdings Llc
17021 Aldine Westfield Rd
Houston TX 77073
713 439-8600

(G-19448)
BAKER PETROLITE LLC (HQ)
Also Called: New Phase Technologies
12645 W Airport Blvd (77478-6120)
P.O. Box 5050 (77487-5050)
PHONE.............................281 276-5400
Jerry Basconi, *Vice Pres*
David Clifton, *Plant Mgr*
Joe Valencia, *Foreman/Supr*
Reed J McDonald, *Project Engr*
Leo Castro, *Senior Engr*
◆ **EMP:** 450 **EST:** 1930
SALES (est): 996.7MM **Privately Held**
WEB:
www.bakerhughesdirect.lookchem.com
SIC: 2899 2869 Water treating compounds; industrial organic chemicals

(G-19449)
BEYOND INTERNATIONAL INC
711 Julie Rivers Dr (77478-2871)
PHONE.............................281 277-4352
Andy Hsu, *CEO*
Samuel Brooks, *CFO*
◆ **EMP:** 22
SQ FT: 40,000
SALES (est): 2.6MM **Privately Held**
WEB: www.beyonddent.com
SIC: 3843 Compounds, dental

(G-19450)
BIOSUITE LLC
12625 W Airport Blvd (77478-6201)
PHONE.............................713 849-5319
Edward Corrin,
Michael Harless,
EMP: 10
SALES (est): 1.9MM
SALES (corp-wide): 1.5B **Publicly Held**
WEB: www.biosuitegroup.com
SIC: 2899 Chemical supplies for foundries
PA: Innospec Inc.
8310 S Valley Hwy Ste 350
Englewood CO 80112
303 792-5554

(G-19451)
BLUEBONNET NUTRACEUTICAL LTD
Also Called: Bluebonnet Nutrition
12915 Dairy Ashford Rd (77478-3101)
PHONE.............................281 340-0322
EMP: 25
SQ FT: 30,000
SALES (est): 6.1MM **Privately Held**
WEB: www.bluebonnetnutrition.com
SIC: 2833 Vitamins, natural or synthetic: bulk, uncompounded

(G-19452)
BLUEBONNET NUTRITION CORP
12915 Dairy Ashford Rd (77478-3101)
PHONE.............................281 240-3332
Gary Barrows, *President*
Joyce Barrows, *Corp Secy*
Steven Barrows, *Vice Pres*
Willie Yang, *Director*
Robert Lee Barrows, *Executive*
EMP: 85
SQ FT: 60,000
SALES (est): 36.2MM **Privately Held**
WEB: www.bluebonnetnutrition.com
SIC: 2834 5122 2833 Pharmaceutical preparations; drugs, proprietaries & sundries; medicinals & botanicals

(G-19453)
CAMPBELL CONCRETE & MTLS LP
14011 Fm 1464 Rd (77498-9601)
PHONE.............................281 277-0022
Charles E Campbell, *Ch of Bd*
EMP: 15
SQ FT: 6,500
SALES (corp-wide): 20.8B **Privately Held**
WEB: www.michaeljames.com
SIC: 3273 Ready-mixed concrete
HQ: Campbell Concrete & Materials, L.P.
16155 Park Row Ste 120
Houston TX 77084
281 592-5201

(G-19454)
CENTENNIAL RESOURCE DEV INC
2245 Texas Dr Ste 490 (77479-1679)
PHONE...................................281 302-5048
EMP: 39
SALES (corp-wide): 944.3MM **Publicly Held**
WEB: www.cdevinc.com
SIC: 1311 Crude petroleum production
PA: Centennial Resource Development, Inc.
1001 17th St Ste 1800
Denver CO 80202
720 499-1400

(G-19455)
CHAMPIONX LLC (HQ)
11177 S Stadium Dr (77478)
PHONE...................................281 632-6500
Darrell Brown, *President*
Leonel Lizarazo, *General Mgr*
Carolina Diaz-Rodriguez, *Principal*
Rich Lancaster, *District Mgr*
Deric Bryant, *Exec VP*
◆ EMP: 1155
SQ FT: 417,000
SALES (est): 1.1B **Publicly Held**
WEB: www.championx.com
SIC: 3559 2899 2992 2891 Chemical machinery & equipment; corrosion preventive lubricant; lubricating oils; adhesives; water pump, motor vehicle
PA: Championx Corporation
2445 Tech Frest Blvd Bldg
The Woodlands TX 77381
281 403-5772

(G-19456)
CHRISTIAN FORT BEND ACADEMY
Also Called: Fort Bend County Road & Bridge
12919 1/2 Dar Ashford Rd (77478-3101)
PHONE...................................281 980-3724
Roby Tate, *Principal*
EMP: 50 **Privately Held**
WEB: www.fortbendchristian.org
SIC: 3531 Road construction & maintenance machinery
PA: Christian Fort Bend Academy
1250 7th St
Sugar Land TX 77478

(G-19457)
CHROMA ENERGY INC (PA)
13135 Dairy Ashford Rd # 290 (77478-3680)
PHONE...................................281 340-6100
Steven H Mikel, *CEO*
George R Morris, *COO*
EMP: 13
SQ FT: 6,388
SALES (est): 1.8MM **Privately Held**
SIC: 1382 Geological exploration, oil & gas field

(G-19458)
CITGO PETROLEUM CORPORATION
220 Terminal Ln (77498-5750)
PHONE...................................832 486-5900
EMP: 10 **Privately Held**
WEB: www.citgolubes.com
SIC: 5541 2911 Filling stations, gasoline; gasoline
HQ: Citgo Petroleum Corporation
1293 Eldridge Pkwy
Houston TX 77077
832 486-4000

(G-19459)
COCA-COLA COMPANY
2105 Town Square Pl # 400 (77479-1277)
PHONE...................................281 302-4317
Gary Fayard, *Exec VP*
Richard Villanueva, *Director*
EMP: 99
SALES (corp-wide): 37.2B **Publicly Held**
WEB: www.coca-colacompany.com
SIC: 2086 2037 Bottled & canned soft drinks; frozen fruits & vegetables
PA: The Coca-Cola Company
1 Coca Cola Plz Nw
Atlanta GA 30313
404 676-2121

(G-19460)
COCA-COLA REFRESHMENTS USA INC
Also Called: Minute Maid Co, The
2150 Town Square Pl # 400 (77479-1465)
PHONE...................................800 438-2653
EMP: 11
SALES (corp-wide): 37.2B **Publicly Held**
WEB: www.coca-colacompany.com
SIC: 2086 Bottled & canned soft drinks
HQ: Coca-Cola Refreshments Usa, Inc.
2500 Windy Ridge Pkwy Se
Atlanta GA 30339
770 989-3000

(G-19461)
COFCO AMERICAS RESOURCES CORP
Cofco Agri-Cotton Division
16190 City Walk Ste 200 (77479-6586)
PHONE...................................832 944-6359
Dwayne Morgan, *Branch Mgr*
EMP: 137 **Privately Held**
WEB: www.cofcointernational.com
SIC: 2211 Drills, cotton
PA: Cofco Americas Resources Corp.
4 Stamford Plz
Stamford CT 06902

(G-19462)
COFFEYVILLE RESOURCES LLC (HQ)
2277 Plaza Dr Ste 500 (77479-6602)
PHONE...................................281 207-3200
Jack Lipinski, *President*
Edmund Gross, *President*
Robert W Haugen, *Exec VP*
John R Walter, *Senior VP*
Susan M Ball, *CFO*
▲ EMP: 65
SQ FT: 11,400
SALES (est): 494MM **Publicly Held**
WEB: www.cvrenergy.com
SIC: 2911 Gasoline

(G-19463)
COFFEYVILLE RESOURCES LLC
Also Called: Coffeyville Resources Nitrogen
2277 Plaza Dr Ste 500 (77479-6602)
PHONE...................................281 207-7711
Katherine Scott, *Branch Mgr*
EMP: 15 **Publicly Held**
WEB: www.cvrenergy.com
SIC: 2911 Petroleum refining
HQ: Coffeyville Resources, Llc
2277 Plaza Dr Ste 500
Sugar Land TX 77479
281 207-3200

(G-19464)
COFFEYVILLE RESOURCES TRML LLC
2277 Plaza Dr Ste 500 (77479-6602)
PHONE...................................281 207-3200
Philip Rinaldi, *CEO*
Stanley Riemann, *COO*
James Rens, *CFO*
Brian Walz, *Manager*
EMP: 19
SALES (est): 3.2MM **Publicly Held**
SIC: 5171 2951 Petroleum bulk stations & terminals; asphalt paving mixtures & blocks
HQ: Cvr Refining, Llc
2277 Plaza Dr Ste 500
Sugar Land TX 77479
281 207-3200

(G-19465)
COFFEYVLLE RSRCES REF MKTG LLC (DH)
2277 Plaza Dr Ste 500 (77479-6602)
P.O. Box 410420, Kansas City MO (64141-0420)
PHONE...................................281 207-3200
Jack Lipinski, *President*
David L Landreth, *President*
Patrick J Quinn, *President*
John R Walter, *President*
Edmund S Gross, *Exec VP*
EMP: 20
SQ FT: 11,400

SALES (est): 115.4MM **Publicly Held**
WEB: www.cvrenergy.com
SIC: 2911 Petroleum refining
HQ: Cvr Refining, Llc
2277 Plaza Dr Ste 500
Sugar Land TX 77479
281 207-3200

(G-19466)
COMPETITIVE ENERGY - TEXAS LP
Also Called: Cetx Energy Agency
1 Sugar Creek Center Blvd # 700 (77478-3560)
PHONE...................................713 957-9948
EMP: 9
SALES (est): 600.5K
SALES (corp-wide): 2.5B **Publicly Held**
SIC: 3621 Mfg Motors/Generators
HQ: Amerex Brokers Llc
1 Sugar Creek Ln
Sugar Land TX 77478
281 340-5200

(G-19467)
CONTINENTAL POLY INC
Also Called: Continental Poly Bags
767 Industrial Blvd (77478-2821)
PHONE...................................281 277-6550
George X Zhang, *President*
Carol Zhang, *Vice Pres*
George Zhong, *Executive*
▲ EMP: 40
SQ FT: 20,000
SALES (est): 14.1MM **Privately Held**
WEB: www.continentalpoly.com
SIC: 2673 Plastic bags: made from purchased materials

(G-19468)
CPT INTERNATIONAL (USA) LLC
12950 Executive Dr (77478-4500)
PHONE...................................713 747-4773
Abdulghaffar Omeri, *General Mgr*
Abdulghaffar Al-Omeri, *Mng Member*
▼ EMP: 60
SQ FT: 9,000
SALES (est): 8.1MM
SALES (corp-wide): 22.5MM **Privately Held**
WEB: www.cptuk.com
SIC: 2064 5145 5141 Candy & other confectionery products; confectionery; groceries, general line
PA: Cpt International (Uk) Limited
Unit 27-28
Birmingham W MIDLANDS B9 4N
121 766-6422

(G-19469)
CROWN CORK & SEAL USA INC
12910 Jess Pirtle Blvd (77478-2850)
PHONE...................................281 240-4838
Judy Otell, *Purch Agent*
Judy Gordon, *Branch Mgr*
Billy Davis, *Manager*
EMP: 155
SQ FT: 167,000
SALES (corp-wide): 11.6B **Publicly Held**
WEB: www.crowncork.com
SIC: 3411 3354 Metal cans; aluminum extruded products
HQ: Crown Cork & Seal Usa, Inc.
770 Township Line Rd # 100
Yardley PA 19067
215 698-5100

(G-19470)
CSTOREPRO TECHNOLOGIES INC
77 Sugar Creek Center Blv (77478-3688)
PHONE...................................866 265-5826
Jimmy Frangis, *CEO*
EMP: 253 **EST:** 1997
SALES (est): 201.6K
SALES (corp-wide): 62.3MM **Privately Held**
WEB: www.pdicstoreessentials.com
SIC: 7372 Prepackaged software
HQ: Professional Datasolutions, Inc.
11675 Rainwater Dr # 350
Alpharetta GA 30009

(G-19471)
CUBIC ITS INC (HQ)
Also Called: Trafficware
522 Gillingham Blvd (77478-5900)
PHONE...................................281 240-7233
Jon Newhard, *President*
Jeff Contreras, *Vice Pres*
Charles Gwirtsman, *Vice Pres*
Alen Bishop, *CFO*
Greg Freel, *Sales Engr*
EMP: 130 **EST:** 1979
SQ FT: 18,000
SALES (est): 34.1MM
SALES (corp-wide): 1.4B **Publicly Held**
WEB: www.trafficware.com
SIC: 3669 Highway signals, electric
PA: Cubic Corporation
9333 Balboa Ave
San Diego CA 92123
858 277-6780

(G-19472)
CVR ENERGY INC (PA)
2277 Plaza Dr Ste 500 (77479-6602)
PHONE...................................281 207-3200
Sunghwan Cho, *Ch of Bd*
David L Lamp, *President*
Sean White, *Superintendent*
Michael Brooks, *COO*
Christopher Stauffer, *Trustee*
EMP: 65
SALES: 6.3B **Publicly Held**
WEB: www.cvrenergy.com
SIC: 2911 2873 Petroleum refining; nitrogenous fertilizers

(G-19473)
CVR PARTNERS LP (HQ)
2277 Plaza Dr Ste 500 (77479-6602)
PHONE...................................281 207-3200
Mark A Pytosh, *President*
Cvr GP, *General Ptnr*
Christopher Gswanberg, *Vice Pres*
Tracy D Jackson, *CFO*
Khyati Chothani, *Manager*
EMP: 144
SALES: 404.1MM **Publicly Held**
WEB: www.cvrpartners.com
SIC: 2873 Nitrogenous fertilizers

(G-19474)
CVR REFINING LP (HQ)
2277 Plaza Dr Ste 500 (77479-6602)
PHONE...................................281 207-3200
David L Lamp, *President*
Robert Haugen, *Exec VP*
Tracy Jackson, *Exec VP*
Mike Howard, *Vice Pres*
Calen Gibbs, *Maint Spvr*
EMP: 14
SALES: 5.6B **Publicly Held**
WEB: www.cvrrefining.com
SIC: 2911 4612 Petroleum refining; crude petroleum pipelines

(G-19475)
CVR REFINING HOLDINGS LLC (DH)
2277 Plaza Dr Ste 500 (77479-6602)
PHONE...................................281 207-3200
John J Lipinski, *President*
Stanley A Riemann, *COO*
Keith Kuehn, *Opers Mgr*
EMP: 428 **EST:** 2012
SALES (est): 89.8MM **Publicly Held**
WEB: www.cvrenergy.com
SIC: 2911 4612 Petroleum refining; crude petroleum pipelines
HQ: Coffeyville Resources, Llc
2277 Plaza Dr Ste 500
Sugar Land TX 77479
281 207-3200

(G-19476)
CYANCO INTERNATIONAL LLC
2245 Texas Dr Ste 500 (77479-1102)
PHONE...................................832 590-3641
Jeffrey Davis, *President*
Jeffrey Jdavis, *President*
Paul Rostek, *President*
Greg Mitch, *Vice Pres*
Bob Warriner, *Vice Pres*
▼ EMP: 22

GEOGRAPHIC

SALES (est): 4.8MM **Privately Held**
WEB: www.cyanco.com
SIC: 1481 Mine development, nonmetallic minerals
PA: Cyanco Holding Corp.
  1920 Country Place Pkwy # 400
  Pearland TX 77584

(G-19477)
DE NORA WATER TECHNOLOGIES LLC
1110 Industrial Blvd (77478-2832)
PHONE....................281 240-6770
Robert Campbell, *Branch Mgr*
EMP: 60 **Privately Held**
WEB: www.denora.com
SIC: 3589 Water treatment equipment, industrial
HQ: De Nora Water Technologies Llc
  3000 Advance Ln
  Colmar PA 18915
  215 997-4000

(G-19478)
DESIGN WOODWORKS
Also Called: Custom Home Builder
2603 Hodges Bend Cir (77479-1406)
PHONE....................713 478-7397
Sergio Jimenez, *Principal*
EMP: 30 **EST:** 2011
SALES (est): 126K **Privately Held**
SIC: 2431 Millwork

(G-19479)
DIE & TOOL SERVICE INC
9431 Gaines Rd (77498-9711)
PHONE....................281 498-3317
Lidia Musil, *President*
Ivan Musil, *Vice Pres*
Carina Betzel, *Office Mgr*
EMP: 12
SQ FT: 26,000
SALES (est): 3.3MM **Privately Held**
WEB: www.die-tool.com
SIC: 3544 7692 3444 Special dies & tools; welding repair; sheet metalwork

(G-19480)
DTM PRECISION MACHINING INC
15117 Aurora St (77498-1329)
PHONE....................281 564-7997
T Manh Do, *President*
EMP: 10
SALES (est): 1.7MM **Privately Held**
WEB: www.dtmus.com
SIC: 3599 Machine shop, jobbing & repair

(G-19481)
E B R ENERGY LP
245 Commerce Green Blvd # 165 (77478-3775)
PHONE....................281 265-6500
Mark Ely, *Partner*
Terry Boening, *Partner*
EMP: 11
SQ FT: 7,000
SALES (est): 4.5MM **Privately Held**
SIC: 1382 1311 Oil & gas exploration services; crude petroleum & natural gas production

(G-19482)
EXCELL TECHNOLOGIES INTL CORP
Also Called: Exceltec
1110 Industrial Blvd (77478-2832)
PHONE....................281 240-6770
Leonard F Graziano, *President*
EMP: 70
SQ FT: 40,000
SALES (est): 11MM **Privately Held**
WEB: www.denora.com
SIC: 3589 Water treatment equipment, industrial

(G-19483)
FIFTH ROCK SOFTWARE INC
Also Called: Powersource
3707 Adonia Pl (77479-2804)
PHONE....................281 265-0944
Sue Ellen Millone Strapp, *CEO*
Thomas Strapp, *President*
EMP: 30

SALES (est): 1.8MM **Privately Held**
WEB: www.powersource.com
SIC: 7372 Application computer software

(G-19484)
GAUGING SYSTEMS INC
910 Industrial Blvd Ste A (77478-2987)
P.O. Box 680 (77487-0680)
PHONE....................281 980-3999
Alan Westmoreland, *President*
John Hoben, *Vice Pres*
Edgar Dohmann, *Project Mgr*
Terry Guidry, *Prdtn Mgr*
Julian Caliandro, *Engineer*
EMP: 27
SQ FT: 34,000
SALES (est): 4.6MM **Privately Held**
WEB: www.gaugingsystemsinc.com
SIC: 3545 3823 Gauges (machine tool accessories); transmitters of process variables, stand. signal conversion

(G-19485)
GE OIL & GAS LOGGING SVCS INC (DH)
13000 Executive Dr (77478-4506)
P.O. Box 849, Lufkin (75902-0849)
PHONE....................281 579-9879
John Paul Jones, *President*
Marco Rossi, *President*
Grant Johnston, *Vice Pres*
Jon Piantez, *CFO*
James Renfro, *Director*
▼ **EMP:** 20
SQ FT: 13,000
SALES (est): 381MM
SALES (corp-wide): 95.2B **Publicly Held**
WEB: www.bhge.com
SIC: 1389 4789 Oil field services; cargo loading & unloading services
HQ: Ge Energy Manufacturing, Inc.
  1333 West Loop S Ste 700
  Houston TX 77027
  713 803-0900

(G-19486)
GEWI NORTH AMERICA LLC (PA)
19901 Southwest Fwy (77479-6538)
PHONE....................713 446-6902
Jim O'Neill, *CEO*
Rainer Klockmann, *Director*
EMP: 30
SALES (est): 950K **Privately Held**
WEB: www.gewi.com
SIC: 3799 Transportation equipment

(G-19487)
GLOBAL CASEWORK MFG INC
910 Industrial Blvd Ste D (77478-2987)
PHONE....................281 494-6181
Joseph Abuata, *President*
George Abuata, *Vice Pres*
EMP: 21
SQ FT: 23,000
SALES (est): 4.8MM **Privately Held**
WEB: www.globalcasework.com
SIC: 2434 Wood kitchen cabinets

(G-19488)
GLOBAL OILFIELD SERVICES INC (HQ)
Also Called: International Tool & Supply
2150 Town Square Pl # 410 (77479-1465)
PHONE....................713 977-5900
Wayne Richards, *President*
Stuart Spence, *CFO*
Gary Kasper, *Treasurer*
▲ **EMP:** 20
SALES (est): 67.9MM **Publicly Held**
WEB: www.gos-inc.com
SIC: 3561 Pumps, domestic: water or sump

(G-19489)
GR ENERGY SERVICES MGT LP
2150 Town Square Pl # 410 (77479-1465)
PHONE....................281 201-6812
Wayne Richards, *Managing Prtnr*
James Morgan, *District Mgr*
Joshua Bentsen, *Business Mgr*
Kevin Kennett, *VP Opers*
James Backest, *Engineer*
EMP: 50
SQ FT: 10,000

SALES (est): 1.3MM **Privately Held**
WEB: www.grenergyservices.com
SIC: 8741 1389 Management services; oil field services

(G-19490)
HAYES HOLDINGS INC
14030 Florence Rd Ste E (77498-3356)
P.O. Box 1665, Stafford (77497-1665)
PHONE....................281 565-8111
Norris O Hayes, *President*
Bobby Field, *Vice Pres*
Mike Rios, *Facilities Mgr*
▼ **EMP:** 125
SQ FT: 75,000
SALES (est): 22.7MM **Privately Held**
SIC: 3089 Injection molding of plastics

(G-19491)
HERCULES FILMS LLC (PA)
12600 Cardinal Mdw (77478-6195)
PHONE....................920 284-0796
Ricardo Alarcon, *Sales Mgr*
EMP: 9
SQ FT: 4,000
SALES (est): 2.4MM **Privately Held**
WEB: www.herculesfilmsusa.com
SIC: 3081 5199 Plastic film & sheet; packaging materials

(G-19492)
HERCULES FILMS LLC
12510 Cardinal Mdw (77478-6194)
PHONE....................920 284-0796
EMP: 16
SALES (corp-wide): 2.4MM **Privately Held**
WEB: www.herculesfilmsusa.com
SIC: 3081 5199 Plastic film & sheet; packaging materials
PA: Hercules Films, Llc
  12600 Cardinal Mdw
  Sugar Land TX 77478
  920 284-0796

(G-19493)
HONS INTERNATIONAL INC
14835 Walbrook Dr (77498-1019)
PHONE....................281 940-9184
Uche Animadu, *President*
Henry Nemkembe, *Vice Pres*
EMP: 65
SQ FT: 13,000
SALES (est): 25MM **Privately Held**
SIC: 1382 Oil & gas exploration services

(G-19494)
HOUSTON READY MIX LLC
140 Eldridge Rd Ste D (77478-4550)
PHONE....................832 532-7408
Gerardo Calderon, *President*
EMP: 10 **EST:** 2015
SALES (est): 3.6MM **Privately Held**
WEB: www.texasconcretereadymix.com
SIC: 3273 Ready-mixed concrete

(G-19495)
IMPERIAL OUTDOOR POWER EQP
Also Called: Imperial Outdoor Power Eqp
7822 Us 90 Alt Ste B (77498)
PHONE....................832 939-9838
Andrew Bolivar, *Director*
EMP: 10
SALES (est): 600K **Privately Held**
WEB: www.imperialoutdoorequipment.stihldealer.net
SIC: 3648 Outdoor lighting equipment

(G-19496)
IMPERIAL SUGAR COMPANY (DH)
Also Called: Imperial - Savannah
3 Sugar Creek Center Blvd # 500 (77478-2216)
P.O. Box 9 (77487-0009)
PHONE....................281 491-9181
John C Sheptor, *CEO*
Michael Gorrell, *President*
Louis T Bolognini, *Senior VP*
George Muller, *Vice Pres*
Jeffrey Zanchelli, *Vice Pres*
◆ **EMP:** 150 **EST:** 1905

SALES (est): 81MM
SALES (corp-wide): 34.5B **Privately Held**
WEB: www.imperialsugarcompany.com
SIC: 2062 5149 Granulated cane sugar from purchased raw sugar or syrup; sugar, refined

(G-19497)
IMPERIAL SUGAR COMPANY
8016 Highway 90a (77478-2961)
PHONE....................281 491-9181
Darrell D Swank, *CFO*
Natalie Lilley, *Director*
EMP: 190
SALES (corp-wide): 34.5B **Privately Held**
WEB: www.imperialsugarcompany.com
SIC: 2063 Beet sugar
HQ: Imperial Sugar Company
  3 Sugar Creek Center Blvd # 500
  Sugar Land TX 77478
  281 491-9181

(G-19498)
INDUSTRIAL INFO RESOURCES INC (PA)
2277 Plaza Dr Ste 300 (77479-6601)
P.O. Box 42442, Houston (77242-2442)
PHONE....................713 783-5147
Edward Lewis, *President*
Tom Fordham, *President*
Tony Sandoval, *Managing Dir*
Ed Fox, *COO*
Edward Fox, *COO*
EMP: 91
SQ FT: 20,860
SALES (est): 22.1MM **Privately Held**
WEB: www.industrialinfo.com
SIC: 8732 8742 2741 Market analysis or research; industry specialist consultants; technical manuals: publishing & printing

(G-19499)
INOVA GEOPHYSICAL INC (DH)
13000 Executive Dr (77478-4506)
PHONE....................281 568-2000
Glenn Hauer, *President*
Tim Hladik, *Senior VP*
Carey Mogdan, *Senior VP*
Keith Witt, *Senior VP*
Arjun Selvakumar, *Vice Pres*
◆ **EMP:** 48
SQ FT: 110,000
SALES (est): 55MM **Privately Held**
WEB: www.inovageo.com
SIC: 3829 Measuring & controlling devices

(G-19500)
JAMES L REMBERT JR INC
Also Called: Venture Products Co
12832 Park One Dr (77478-2521)
P.O. Box 996 (77487-0996)
PHONE....................281 240-7070
EMP: 15 **EST:** 1950
SQ FT: 9,000
SALES (est): 2.6MM **Privately Held**
WEB: www.vpcgasket.com
SIC: 3053 5084 Gaskets, all materials; compressors, except air conditioning

(G-19501)
KALSI ENGINEERING INCORPORATED
745 Park Two Dr (77478-2885)
PHONE....................281 240-6500
Manmohan S Kalsi, *President*
Mital Mistry, *Software Engr*
Nancy Richey, *Director*
Marieluise Kalsi Ward, *Officer*
Marieluise S Kalsi, *Admin Sec*
◆ **EMP:** 32 **EST:** 1979
SQ FT: 13,000
SALES (est): 7.9MM **Privately Held**
WEB: www.kalsi.com
SIC: 3053 8711 8734 Gaskets & sealing devices; consulting engineer; testing laboratories

(G-19502)
KW INDUSTRIES INC
909 Industrial Blvd (77478-2887)
PHONE....................281 240-0909
E A Kostelnik, *Ch of Bd*
James A White, *President*
Sam Hennie, *Plant Mgr*
Albert Perez, *Opers Mgr*
Laura Estle, *Treasurer*

▲ EMP: 143
SQ FT: 60,000
SALES (est): 36.9MM **Privately Held**
WEB: www.kwindustries.com
SIC: 3648 Public lighting fixtures

(G-19503)
LAVERSAB INC
. 505 Gillingham Blvd (77478-5901)
PHONE.....................281 325-8300
P D Balsaver, *President*
Neeta Balsaver, *Vice Pres*
Vinoth Kumar, *Engineer*
Aravind Kotcherlakota, *Sales Mgr*
Tushar Bajaj, *Manager*
▲ EMP: 30
SQ FT: 40,000
SALES (est): 8MM **Privately Held**
WEB: www.laversab.com
SIC: 3571 3829 Electronic computers;
    measuring & controlling devices

(G-19504)
**LIGHT HOUSE CANDLES LLC
(HQ)**
Also Called: Light House Home Products
1601 Gillingham Ln # 120 (77478-2901)
PHONE.....................713 467-4774
Tom Gaines, *Mng Member*
Jackie Garlitz,
▲ EMP: 45
SALES (est): 4.9MM **Privately Held**
SIC: 3999 Candles

(G-19505)
LOTUS MIDSTREAM LLC (PA)
2150 Town Square Pl # 395 (77479-1465)
PHONE.....................713 234-7865
Mike Prince, *CEO*
Pete Gvazdauskas, *CFO*
Jill Eppes, *Controller*
Phillip Criniti, *Finance*
Liz Condreay, *Manager*
EMP: 9
SALES (est): 275.2MM **Privately Held**
WEB: www.lotusmidstream.com
SIC: 1382 Oil & gas exploration services

(G-19506)
MAYORS MACHINE WORKS INC
Also Called: Open and Closed Equipment
2620 Charles Ln (77498-1702)
PHONE.....................281 242-0636
Julian Montemayor, *President*
Lidia Montemayor, *Vice Pres*
EMP: 50
SQ FT: 24,000
SALES (est): 8.2MM **Privately Held**
WEB: www.mayorsmachine.com
SIC: 3599 Machine shop, jobbing & repair

(G-19507)
MECO INC
12505 Reed Rd Ste 100 (77478-2876)
PHONE.....................281 276-7600
Van Gallinghouse, *Vice Pres*
Lauren Haislup, *Project Mgr*
Ted Gussett, *Mfg Staff*
Jerry Garza, *Buyer*
Will Brown, *Engineer*
EMP: 27 EST: 2011
SALES (est): 5.1MM **Privately Held**
WEB: www.meco.com
SIC: 3589 Water treatment equipment, in-
    dustrial

(G-19508)
**MYLAN BERTEK
PHARMACEUTICALS**
12720 Dairy Ashford Rd (77478-2844)
P.O. Box 5047 (77487-5047)
PHONE.....................281 240-1000
Hazel Davison, *General Mgr*
David Satter, *Exec VP*
Sheela Vadavalli, *VP Legal*
Jeffrey Smith, *Vice Pres*
Sanjay Gautam, *Assoc VP*
EMP: 50 EST: 2003
SALES (est): 9.6MM **Privately Held**
SIC: 2834 Druggists' preparations (phar-
    maceuticals)

(G-19509)
MYLAN INSTITUTIONAL INC
12720 Dairy Ashford Rd (77478-2844)
PHONE.....................281 240-1000
David Ainsworth, *Engineer*
Brian Mahoney, *Regl Sales Mgr*
Gretchen Rachles, *Regl Sales Mgr*
Kelsey Flood, *Sales Staff*
Dwayne Dickey, *Branch Mgr*
EMP: 58
SALES (corp-wide): 6.2B **Privately Held**
WEB: www.mylan.com
SIC: 2834 5122 7389 Pharmaceutical
    preparations; pharmaceuticals; packaging
    & labeling services
HQ: Mylan Institutional Inc.
    1718 Northrock Ct
    Rockford IL 61103
    815 282-1201

(G-19510)
**NATIONAL OILWELL VARCO
INC**
100 Gillingham Ln (77478-3135)
PHONE.....................713 237-3766
EMP: 32
SALES (corp-wide): 8.4B **Publicly Held**
WEB: www.nov.com
SIC: 3533 Oil & gas field machinery
PA: National Oilwell Varco, Inc.
    7909 Parkwood Circle Dr
    Houston TX 77036
    713 346-7500

(G-19511)
NEON SYSTEMS INC (HQ)
Also Called: Datadirect Technologies
14100 Southwest Fwy # 500 (77478-3466)
PHONE.....................281 276-5900
Mark Cresswell, *President*
EMP: 72
SQ FT: 19,400
SALES (est): 7.2MM
SALES (corp-wide): 442.1MM **Publicly
Held**
SIC: 7372 Prepackaged software
PA: Progress Software Corporation
    14 Oak Park Dr
    Bedford MA 01730
    781 280-4000

(G-19512)
NEWAGE CASTING LP
12630 W Arprt Blvd Ste 10 (77478)
PHONE.....................281 565-0928
Bikram Singh, *Partner*
Bhupinder Singh, *Partner*
Taran Singh, *Partner*
Tony Ferrer, *Manager*
Aslyn Aguilar, *Representative*
▲ EMP: 26
SQ FT: 55,000
SALES (est): 1.7MM **Privately Held**
WEB: www.newagecasting.com
SIC: 3321 Cast iron pipe & fittings

(G-19513)
NOBLE DRILLING (US) INC (DH)
13135 Dairy Ashford Rd (77478-3680)
PHONE.....................281 276-6100
James C Day, *President*
William C Hofman, *Vice Pres*
Michael Lamb, *Treasurer*
▲ EMP: 100
SALES (est): 195.9MM
SALES (corp-wide): 1.3B **Privately Held**
WEB: www.noblecorp.com
SIC: 1381 Drilling oil & gas wells
HQ: Noble Drilling Corporation
    13135 Dairy Ashford Rd # 700
    Sugar Land TX 77478
    281 276-6100

(G-19514)
**NOBLE DRILLING
CORPORATION (DH)**
13135 Dairy Ashford Rd # 700
(77478-3680)
PHONE.....................281 276-6100
James C Day, *Ch of Bd*
Mark A Jackson, *President*
Mike Tino, *Superintendent*
Robert D Campbell, *Senior VP*
Julie J Robertson, *Senior VP*
◆ EMP: 300

SQ FT: 20,000
SALES (est): 1B
SALES (corp-wide): 1.3B **Privately Held**
WEB: www.noblecorp.com
SIC: 1381 8711 Drilling oil & gas wells; pe-
    troleum engineering
HQ: Noble Holding (U.S.) Corporation
    3135 S Dairy Ashford
    Sugar Land TX 77478
    281 276-6100

(G-19515)
NOBLE DRILLING HOLDING LLC
13135 Dairy Ashford Rd (77478-3680)
PHONE.....................281 276-6100
David W Williams, *Chairman*
Scott Marks, *Senior VP*
Amanda Joiner, *Recruiter*
EMP: 23
SALES (est): 32.6MM
SALES (corp-wide): 1.3B **Privately Held**
WEB: www.noblecorp.com
SIC: 1381 Drilling oil & gas wells
PA: Noble Holding Corporation Plc
    3rd Floor
    Altrincham WA14

(G-19516)
NOBLE DRILLING SERVICES INC
13135 Dairy Ashford Rd # 800
(77478-3698)
PHONE.....................281 276-6100
David W Williams, *President*
James C Day, *President*
Dennis J Lubojacky, *President*
Bob Campbell, *Vice Pres*
Robert Eifler, *Vice Pres*
◆ EMP: 500
SQ FT: 20,000
SALES (est): 46.6MM
SALES (corp-wide): 1MM **Privately Held**
WEB: www.noblecorp.com
SIC: 1381 Drilling oil & gas wells
HQ: Noble Holding (U.S.) Llc
    13135 Dar Ashford Ste 800
    Sugar Land TX

(G-19517)
**NOBLE HOLDING US
CORPORATION (DH)**
3135 S Dairy Ashford (77478)
PHONE.....................281 276-6100
David W Williams, *Principal*
Milton Watson, *Opers Staff*
Smith Kevin, *Purch Agent*
Tim Matal, *Engineer*
Jermaine Gibbs, *Technology*
◆ EMP: 200
SALES: 3.3B
SALES (corp-wide): 1.3B **Privately Held**
WEB: www.noblecorp.com
SIC: 1381 Drilling oil & gas wells

(G-19518)
**NOBLE INTERNATIONAL
FINANCE CO**
13135 Dairy Ashford Rd (77478-3680)
PHONE.....................281 276-6142
David W Williams, *Principal*
EMP: 15
SALES (est): 1.7MM
SALES (corp-wide): 1.3B **Privately Held**
WEB: www.noblecorp.com
SIC: 1381 Drilling oil & gas wells
HQ: Noble Corporation
    C/O Maples Corporate Services Lim-
    ited
    George Town GR CAYMAN

(G-19519)
NPI TECHNOLOGIES 2 INC
12144 Dairy Ashford Rd (77478-6211)
PHONE.....................281 265-2815
Tony Thai, *President*
Dinh Doan, *Shareholder*
Tuan Doan, *Shareholder*
Kiet Ngo, *Shareholder*
Lethu Thai, *Shareholder*
EMP: 15
SQ FT: 10,000
SALES (est): 2.9MM **Privately Held**
WEB: www.npitechnologies.com
SIC: 3672 Printed circuit boards

(G-19520)
NUCERA SOLUTIONS LLC
12645 W Airport Blvd (77478-6120)
PHONE.....................281 275-7473
EMP: 48
SALES (corp-wide): 177.9K **Privately
Held**
SIC: 2822 Ethylene-propylene rubbers,
    EPDM polymers
HQ: Nucera Solutions Llc
    430 Park Ave
    New York NY 10022
    203 258-3970

(G-19521)
OILFIELD AUDIT SERVICES INC
Also Called: Oas
1933 Country Club Blvd (77478-3909)
PHONE.....................281 242-9521
Roy Sareen, *Owner*
Ashwani Kumar, *COO*
Abhinav Himani, *Vice Pres*
EMP: 12
SQ FT: 1,800
SALES (est): 977.1K **Privately Held**
WEB: www.oasinc.com
SIC: 1389 Oil field services

(G-19522)
OMNI FLOW COMPUTERS INC
12320 Cardinal Mdw # 180 (77478-6236)
PHONE.....................281 240-6161
Alan L McCartney, *CEO*
Ken Elledge, *Business Mgr*
Phillip Cates, *Vice Pres*
Mark Godfrey, *Vice Pres*
Helen Pei, *Vice Pres*
▲ EMP: 15
SQ FT: 17,000
SALES (est): 4.2MM **Privately Held**
WEB: www.omniflow.com
SIC: 3823 8711 Flow instruments, indus-
    trial process type; electrical or electronic
    engineering

(G-19523)
PAMELA PRINTING CO
550 Jlie Rvers Dr Ste 310 (77478)
PHONE.....................281 240-1313
Ann Smith, *President*
David Smith, *Treasurer*
Patricia Smith, *Director*
EMP: 13
SQ FT: 6,500
SALES (est): 1MM **Privately Held**
WEB: www.pamelaprinting.com
SIC: 5084 2752 Printing trades machinery,
    equipment & supplies; commercial print-
    ing, offset

(G-19524)
PEM-TECH INC
12144 Dairy Ashford Rd # 200
(77478-6212)
PHONE.....................281 494-2079
Rizwan Mistry, *President*
EMP: 9
SQ FT: 7,500
SALES (est): 2.2MM **Privately Held**
WEB: www.pem-tech.com
SIC: 3829 Measuring & controlling devices

(G-19525)
PETROCHEM ENERGY LLC
13914 Abbey Ln (77498-6302)
PHONE.....................713 234-7814
Adejoke Otegbola, *CEO*
Michael Otegbola, *Officer*
EMP: 10 EST: 2010
SALES (est): 575.5K **Privately Held**
WEB: www.petrochemenergy.com
SIC: 3544 7389 Special dies, tools, jigs &
    fixtures;

(G-19526)
**PETRONASH AMERICAS LLC
(HQ)**
12633 Reed Rd (77478-2839)
PHONE.....................281 566-6600
Venkata Jetty, *CEO*
Venkata Uma Maheswara RAO Jett,
    President
Patrick Chandna, *Mng Member*
▲ EMP: 22
SQ FT: 180,000

SALES (est): 2.2MM **Privately Held**
SIC: 3533 Oil & gas field machinery

(G-19527)
POTBELLY CORPORATION
1815 Highway 6 (77478-4964)
PHONE...................................281 277-2515
Robert Couch, *General Mgr*
EMP: 20
SALES (corp-wide): 409.7MM **Publicly Held**
WEB: www.potbelly.com
SIC: 5812 2099 Sandwiches & submarines shop; ready-to-eat meals, salads & sandwiches
PA: Potbelly Corporation
　111 N Canal St Ste 850
　Chicago IL 60606
　312 951-0600

(G-19528)
PPG INDUSTRIES INC
Also Called: PPG 8328
2601 Cordes Dr (77479-1353)
PHONE...................................281 265-5333
Robert Moore, *Branch Mgr*
EMP: 24
SALES (corp-wide): 15.3B **Publicly Held**
WEB: www.ppg.com
SIC: 2851 Paints & allied products
PA: Ppg Industries, Inc.
　1 Ppg Pl
　Pittsburgh PA 15272
　412 434-3131

(G-19529)
PRIME MOMENTO LLC
19901 Southwest Fwy # 124 (77479-6538)
PHONE...................................832 643-4605
Hector Villegas, *CEO*
EMP: 15
SALES (est): 2.5MM **Privately Held**
WEB: www.primemomento.com
SIC: 3559 2611 4953 Recycling machinery; pulp mills, mechanical & recycling processing; recycling, waste materials

(G-19530)
PRINCE PLASTICS INC
455 Julie Rivers Dr (77478-3146)
PHONE...................................281 240-6400
Firozali M Roopani, *President*
◆ EMP: 25
SQ FT: 54,000
SALES (est): 5.5MM **Privately Held**
SIC: 2673 Plastic & pliofilm bags

(G-19531)
QUANTUM FITNESS CORPORATION
126 Eldridge Rd Ste B (77478-3794)
P.O. Box 460, Cedar Park (78630-0460)
PHONE...................................281 495-3003
William Brooke Ayton, *President*
◆ EMP: 55
SQ FT: 37,705
SALES (est): 7.6MM **Privately Held**
WEB: www.quantumfitness.com
SIC: 3949 5941 Exercise equipment; exercise equipment

(G-19532)
QUVA PHARMA INC (PA)
1075 W Park One Dr # 100 (77478-2576)
PHONE...................................888 339-0874
Stuart Hinchen, *Principal*
Mike Rutkowski, *Vice Pres*
Mark Sheppard, *Vice Pres*
David Short, *Vice Pres*
Lauren Pham, *Opers Staff*
EMP: 55
SALES (est): 3MM **Privately Held**
WEB: www.quvapharma.com
SIC: 2834 Pharmaceutical preparations

(G-19533)
RESERVOIR MARINE LLC
13313 Southwest Fwy # 285 (77478-3669)
PHONE...................................281 277-7575
Alton Warren, *President*
EMP: 20
SALES (est): 752.6K **Privately Held**
WEB: www.reservoirmarinellc.com
SIC: 1382 Oil & gas exploration services

(G-19534)
RETRO LTG & CONSERVATION LC
3407 Autumn Bend Dr (77479-3040)
PHONE...................................281 302-6431
EMP: 20 EST: 1999
SALES (est): 2.6MM **Privately Held**
WEB: www.retrolightinginc.com
SIC: 3646 Commercial indusl & institutional electric lighting fixtures

(G-19535)
RHEONICS INC
3 Sugar Creek Center Blvd (77478-2210)
PHONE...................................713 364-5427
Dr Sunil Kumar, *CEO*
Vijoya SA, *COO*
Joe Goodbread, *Vice Pres*
Bernhard Zybach, *Opers Staff*
Bill Befeld, *Director*
EMP: 35 EST: 2010
SALES (est): 695.8K **Privately Held**
WEB: www.rheonics.com
SIC: 3823 Industrial instrmnts msrmnt display/control process variable

(G-19536)
ROGERS MANUFACTURING CORP
4223 Rocky Bend Dr (77479-5115)
PHONE...................................901 301-4936
Derek Moody, *Branch Mgr*
EMP: 24
SALES (corp-wide): 53.2MM **Privately Held**
WEB: www.rogersmfg.com
SIC: 2439 Trusses, wooden roof
PA: Rogers Manufacturing Corporation
　801 Industrial Pkwy
　West Monroe LA 71291
　318 396-5700

(G-19537)
ROMTEX ENTERPRISES INC
16322 W Bellfort St (77498-8531)
PHONE...................................281 494-0373
Edward Golik, *President*
Sebastian Bartnik, *Mfg Mgr*
Jo Diehl, *Admin Asst*
Richard Witek, *Master*
EMP: 70
SQ FT: 42,000
SALES (est): 14MM **Privately Held**
WEB: www.romtexinc.com
SIC: 3599 Machine shop, jobbing & repair

(G-19538)
ROYWELL LLC (HQ)
1600 Highway 6 Ste 220 (77478-4956)
PHONE...................................713 661-4747
Richard Mascorro, *General Mgr*
George Crawford, *Mng Member*
EMP: 28
SALES (est): 7.5MM
SALES (corp-wide): 7.8MM **Privately Held**
WEB: www.roywell.com
SIC: 1389 8731 4212 5169 Cementing oil & gas well casings; energy research; liquid transfer services; acids
PA: Catapult Energy Services Group, Llc
　3050 Post Oak Blvd Ste 65
　Houston TX 77056
　832 615-3660

(G-19539)
SAGO CHRISTIE LP
14090 Southwest Fwy # 460 (77478-3677)
PHONE...................................281 240-8444
Kendall Purgason, *Partner*
EMP: 9
SALES (est): 439.8K
SALES (corp-wide): 3.9MM **Privately Held**
SIC: 1311 Natural gas production
PA: Sago Energy Llc
　211 N Colorado St
　Midland TX 79701
　432 682-6311

(G-19540)
SAIGE USA INC
Also Called: Kentec Composites
3202 Deer Creek Dr (77478-4042)
PHONE...................................281 980-8393

Weiping Gu, *President*
Thomas Fujita, *Vice Pres*
Aaron Uy, *Vice Pres*
▲ EMP: 14
SALES (est): 249K **Privately Held**
SIC: 3291 5131 Abrasive metal & steel products; fiberglass fabrics

(G-19541)
SARTARTIA FABRICATION INC
730 Sartartia Rd (77479-9682)
PHONE...................................281 240-1222
Alan T Winslette, *President*
Paige T Manard, *Vice Pres*
EMP: 23
SQ FT: 4,800
SALES (est): 2.1MM **Privately Held**
SIC: 3443 Air coolers, metal plate

(G-19542)
SCHLUMBERGER TECHNOLOGY CORP (DH)
Also Called: Schlumberger Oilfield Services
300 Schlumberger Dr (77478-3155)
PHONE...................................281 285-8500
Paal Kibsgaard, *CEO*
Simon Ayat, *Exec VP*
Ashok Belani, *Exec VP*
Satish Pai, *Exec VP*
Jean-Franois Poupeau, *Exec VP*
◆ EMP: 1957
SALES (est): 25B **Publicly Held**
SIC: 1382 1389 3825 3824 Geophysical exploration, oil & gas field; geological exploration, oil & gas field; well logging; cementing oil & gas well casings; pumping of oil & gas wells; oil field services; instruments to measure electricity; meters: electric, pocket, portable, panelboard, etc.; fluid meters & counting devices; counters, revolution; oil & gas field machinery; measuring & dispensing pumps

(G-19543)
SCHLUMBERGER TECHNOLOGY CORP
Also Called: Schlumberger Oilfield Services
121 Industrial Blvd (77478-3127)
PHONE...................................281 285-8500
David Mullen, *Branch Mgr*
EMP: 40 **Publicly Held**
SIC: 1389 Oil field services
HQ: Schlumberger Technology Corp
　300 Schlumberger Dr
　Sugar Land TX 77478
　281 285-8500

(G-19544)
SCHLUMBERGER TECHNOLOGY CORP
Also Called: Schlumberger Recruiting
12808 W Airport Blvd (77478-6184)
PHONE...................................281 285-7400
Andre Orban, *Manager*
EMP: 43 **Publicly Held**
SIC: 1389 Oil field services
HQ: Schlumberger Technology Corp
　300 Schlumberger Dr
　Sugar Land TX 77478
　281 285-8500

(G-19545)
SCHLUMBERGER TECHNOLOGY CORP
Also Called: Schlumberger Oilfield Services
300 Schlumberger Dr (77478-3155)
PHONE...................................281 285-8400
Saul Laureles, *Counsel*
Kirk Flight, *Project Mgr*
McFrancis Idemudia, *Project Mgr*
Robert Krush, *Project Mgr*
Valerie Lafitte, *Project Mgr*
EMP: 40 **Publicly Held**
SIC: 1382 Geophysical exploration, oil & gas field; geological exploration, oil & gas field
HQ: Schlumberger Technology Corp
　300 Schlumberger Dr
　Sugar Land TX 77478
　281 285-8500

(G-19546)
SCHLUMBERGER TECHNOLOGY CORP
105 Industrial Blvd (77478-3127)
PHONE...................................281 285-8500
EMP: 209 **Publicly Held**
SIC: 1389 Oil field services
HQ: Schlumberger Technology Corp
　300 Schlumberger Dr
　Sugar Land TX 77478
　281 285-8500

(G-19547)
SCHLUMBERGER TECHNOLOGY CORP
Also Called: Sugar Land Product Center
200 Gillingham Ln (77478-3136)
PHONE...................................281 285-4823
Loong Tam, *Engineer*
Thang Tran, *Engineer*
Ken Havelineck, *Branch Mgr*
EMP: 40 **Publicly Held**
SIC: 1389 Oil field services
HQ: Schlumberger Technology Corp
　300 Schlumberger Dr
　Sugar Land TX 77478
　281 285-8500

(G-19548)
SCHLUMBERGER TECHNOLOGY CORP
Also Called: Dowell Schlumberger
110 Schlumberger Dr (77478-3154)
PHONE...................................281 285-6370
Andre Garnier, *Branch Mgr*
EMP: 10 **Publicly Held**
SIC: 1389 Oil field services
HQ: Schlumberger Technology Corp
　300 Schlumberger Dr
　Sugar Land TX 77478
　281 285-8500

(G-19549)
SCHLUMBERGER TECHNOLOGY CORP
555 Industrial Blvd (77478-2817)
PHONE...................................281 285-8500
Paal Kibsgaard, *CEO*
Daneille Garate, *General Mgr*
Annette Jenkins, *General Mgr*
Prakash Gururajan, *Business Mgr*
Izegbua Okonya, *Counsel*
EMP: 139 **Publicly Held**
SIC: 1382 1389 3824 3825 Geological exploration, oil & gas field; geophysical exploration, oil & gas field; cementing oil & gas well casings; oil field services; pumping of oil & gas wells; well logging; controls, revolution & timing instruments; gauges for computing pressure temperature corrections; measuring instruments & meters, electric; meters: electric, pocket, portable, panelboard, etc.; oil & gas field machinery; measuring & dispensing pumps
HQ: Schlumberger Technology Corp
　300 Schlumberger Dr
　Sugar Land TX 77478
　281 285-8500

(G-19550)
SCHLUMBERGER TECHNOLOGY CORP
Also Called: Schlumberger Nam Financial Ctr
100 Gillingham Ln (77478-3135)
PHONE...................................281 285-8226
Nancy Russel, *Branch Mgr*
EMP: 50 **Publicly Held**
SIC: 1382 Geophysical exploration, oil & gas field; geological exploration, oil & gas field
HQ: Schlumberger Technology Corp
　300 Schlumberger Dr
　Sugar Land TX 77478
　281 285-8500

(G-19551)
SCHLUMBERGER TECHNOLOGY CORP
150 Gillingham Ln Md1 (77478-3135)
PHONE...................................281 285-8500
Attilio Tisoni, *Branch Mgr*
EMP: 2000 **Publicly Held**
SIC: 1389 Oil field services

HQ: Schlumberger Technology Corp
300 Schlumberger Dr
Sugar Land TX 77478
281 285-8500

(G-19552)
SCHLUMBERGER TECHNOLOGY CORP
Also Called: Dowell Schlumberger
225 Schlumberger Dr (77478-3156)
PHONE..................................281 285-4551
Larry Brumit, *Vice Pres*
EMP: 90 **Publicly Held**
WEB: www.myclacademy.com
SIC: 1389 Cementing oil & gas well casings
HQ: Schlumberger Technology Corp
300 Schlumberger Dr
Sugar Land TX 77478
281 285-8500

(G-19553)
SCHLUMBERGER TECHNOLOGY CORP
Also Called: Dowell Schlumberger
145 Industrial Blvd (77478-3169)
P.O. Box 4288 (77478)
PHONE..................................281 285-8500
EMP: 50 **Publicly Held**
SIC: 1389 Oil field services
HQ: Schlumberger Technology Corp
300 Schlumberger Dr
Sugar Land TX 77478
281 285-8500

(G-19554)
SERENITY CANDLES
226 Scarlet Maple Dr (77479-5010)
PHONE..................................281 565-0130
Lori Harpst, *Owner*
EMP: 10
SALES (est): 428K **Privately Held**
SIC: 3999 Candles

(G-19555)
SERVOMEX COMPANY
12300 Dairy Ashford Rd # 400
(77478-6234)
PHONE..................................281 295-5800
Shelly Moore, *Branch Mgr*
EMP: 50
SALES (corp-wide): 2.1B **Privately Held**
WEB: www.servomex.com
SIC: 3826 Gas analyzing equipment
HQ: Servomex Company
12300 Dar Ashford Ste 400
Sugar Land TX 77478
281 295-5800

(G-19556)
SIGGA USA LLC
13135 Dairy Ashford Rd # 525
(77478-3689)
PHONE..................................855 744-4287
EMP: 12
SALES (est): 1.5MM **Privately Held**
WEB: www.sigga.com
SIC: 7372 Application computer software
PA: Wbr Consultoria S/A
Av. Dos Andradas 3002
Belo Horizonte MG 30260

(G-19557)
SOLARCRAFT INC
12300 Dairy Ashford Rd (77478-6233)
PHONE..................................281 340-1224
Darrell Haun, *President*
Tim Morehead, *Business Mgr*
Fredi Mendez, *Prdtn Mgr*
Blaine Sweatt, *Technician*
▲ EMP: 35
SQ FT: 36,000
SALES (est): 11.4MM **Privately Held**
WEB: www.solarcraft.net
SIC: 3621 Generating apparatus & parts, electrical

(G-19558)
SRI ENERGY INC
12565 W Airport Blvd (77478-6190)
PHONE..................................832 742-7500
Radha Sundararajan, *President*
Jason Correa, *Business Mgr*
EMP: 14 EST: 2013

SALES (est): 2.5MM **Privately Held**
WEB: www.srienergy.com
SIC: 3533 Bits, oil & gas field tools: rock

(G-19559)
SUPPLY PRO SORBENTS LLC
4102 Ivymist Ct (77479-5307)
PHONE..................................713 672-9080
Harmon K Fine, *President*
Scott Mitchell, *Vice Pres*
Hermon K Fine,
EMP: 21 EST: 2013
SALES (est): 2.9MM **Privately Held**
SIC: 2297 2679 Nonwoven fabrics; paper products, converted

(G-19560)
SYSTEL INC
1655 Industrial Blvd (77478-2579)
PHONE..................................281 207-7619
Vimal Kothari, *CEO*
Michael Ponder, *Business Mgr*
Jacob Evans, *VP Opers*
Jaykrishna Patel, *Purch Agent*
David D Anderson, *VP Engrg*
EMP: 50
SQ FT: 30,000
SALES (est): 18.9MM **Privately Held**
WEB: www.systelusa.com
SIC: 3571 7371 3577 Computers, digital, analog or hybrid; computer software systems analysis & design, custom; computer peripheral equipment

(G-19561)
TARQUIN POLYMERS & COLORS INC
13313 Southwest Fwy # 194 (77478-3660)
PHONE..................................281 240-0202
Fred C Kramer, *President*
John Hay, *Principal*
Rita Kramer, *CFO*
Lorie Johannessen, *Controller*
EMP: 9
SQ FT: 1,500
SALES (est): 20MM **Privately Held**
WEB: www.tpcplastic.com
SIC: 2821 Plastics materials & resins

(G-19562)
TEXAS INSTRUMENTS INCORPORATED
13905 University Blvd (77479-3694)
PHONE..................................832 939-2000
Todd Hiers, *Engineer*
EMP: 11
SALES (corp-wide): 14.4B **Publicly Held**
WEB: www.txwx.com
SIC: 3674 Semiconductors & related devices
PA: Texas Instruments Incorporated
12500 Ti Blvd
Dallas TX 75243
972 995-3773

(G-19563)
TEXAS PRECISION METALCRAFT INC
810 Industrial Blvd (77478-2826)
P.O. Box 1329 (77487-1329)
PHONE..................................281 240-9191
Jerry Conner, *President*
Steve Jaroszewski, *Principal*
Constance Kuykendall, *Principal*
Brad Desplinter, *Vice Pres*
John Talbert, *Engineer*
◆ EMP: 25
SQ FT: 14,000
SALES (est): 6.5MM **Privately Held**
WEB: www.txpm.com
SIC: 3324 Commercial investment castings, ferrous

(G-19564)
THERMO PROCESS INSTRUMENTS LP
Also Called: Thermo Flow Systems
12320 Cardinal Mdw # 150 (77478-6235)
PHONE..................................713 272-0404
Karen Coakley, *Sales Staff*
Peiyun Wu, *Software Engr*
EMP: 10

SALES (est): 1.3MM
SALES (corp-wide): 25.5B **Publicly Held**
WEB: www.thermofisher.com
SIC: 3823 Industrial flow & liquid measuring instruments; flow instruments, industrial process type
PA: Thermo Fisher Scientific Inc.
168 3rd Ave
Waltham MA 02451
781 622-1000

(G-19565)
THINK PLASTICS LLC
602 Piedmont St (77478-3318)
PHONE..................................713 771-7700
Christine Klatt, *Mng Member*
EMP: 10
SALES (est): 1.1MM **Privately Held**
SIC: 3089 Injection molding of plastics

(G-19566)
THRUBIT LLC
Also Called: Schlumberger
150 Gillingham Ln (77478-3135)
PHONE..................................713 874-9600
Cindy Thomas, *Administration*
EMP: 50 **Privately Held**
WEB: www.thrubit.com
SIC: 1389 Oil field services
PA: Thrubit Llc
150 Gillingham Ln
Sugar Land TX 77478

(G-19567)
THRUBIT LLC (PA)
Also Called: Thrubit Logging Solutions
150 Gillingham Ln (77478-3135)
PHONE..................................713 538-9500
James Aivalis, *CEO*
Chris Cashion, *CFO*
EMP: 92
SQ FT: 9,000
SALES (est): 57.7MM **Privately Held**
WEB: www.thrubit.com
SIC: 1389 Oil field services

(G-19568)
TRECORA RESOURCES (PA)
1650 Highway 6 Ste 190 (77478-4926)
P.O. Box 1636, Silsbee (77656-1636)
PHONE..................................281 980-5522
Karen A Twitchell, *Ch of Bd*
Patrick D Quarles, *President*
Michael Humby, *Exec VP*
Joseph M Tanner, *Vice Pres*
S Sami Ahmad, *CFO*
EMP: 25
SALES: 258.9MM **Publicly Held**
WEB: www.trecora.com
SIC: 2911 2999 5172 Petroleum refining; waxes, petroleum: not produced in petroleum refineries; petroleum products

(G-19569)
TUBULAR RESOURCE INC
1108 Soldiers Field Dr (77479-4053)
PHONE..................................281 240-3343
Timothy W King, *President*
Don Kreitz, *Vice Pres*
◆ EMP: 11
SQ FT: 3,750
SALES (est): 2.1MM **Privately Held**
WEB: www.tubularresource.com
SIC: 3449 Miscellaneous metalwork

(G-19570)
UPSTREAM INTERNATIONAL LLC
15140 Southwest Fwy Ste C (77478-5023)
PHONE..................................281 265-0033
Bryan Anderson, *Vice Pres*
Travis Buchanan, *Opers Mgr*
Matt Kehnemund, *Opers Staff*
Cody Pope, *Opers Staff*
Susie Juarez, *Opers-Prdtn-Mfg*
EMP: 370
SQ FT: 4,600
SALES (est): 80MM **Privately Held**
WEB: www.upstreaminternational.com
SIC: 1389 Oil consultants

(G-19571)
WELKER INC
13839 W Bellfort St (77498-1671)
PHONE..................................281 491-2331
◆ EMP: 90 EST: 1954

SQ FT: 45,000
SALES (est): 24.7MM **Privately Held**
WEB: www.welker.com
SIC: 3823 3829 3492 3533 Industrial process measurement equipment; measuring & controlling devices; control valves, fluid power: hydraulic & pneumatic; oil & gas field machinery

(G-19572)
WESTERN CONTAINER CORPORATION (DH)
2277 Plaza Dr Ste 270 (77478-6703)
PHONE..................................346 309-3238
Eric Scott, *CEO*
Mike Andrysiak, *President*
Kathi Tysor, *Principal*
Gregg Johnson, *Vice Pres*
Roger Kerr, *Vice Pres*
▲ EMP: 290
SQ FT: 192,000
SALES (est): 111MM
SALES (corp-wide): 37.2B **Publicly Held**
WEB: www.westerncontainercoke.com
SIC: 3085 Plastics bottles
HQ: Coca-Cola Refreshments Usa, Inc.
2500 Windy Ridge Pkwy Se
Atlanta GA 30339
770 989-3000

(G-19573)
WFMS INC
13901 W Bellfort St (77498-1678)
P.O. Box 138 (77487-0138)
PHONE..................................281 491-2445
▼ EMP: 20 EST: 1996
SQ FT: 15,000
SALES (est): 6.1MM **Privately Held**
WEB: www.wfmsinc.com
SIC: 3823 Combustion control instruments

(G-19574)
WYNNEWOOD ENERGY COMPANY LLC
2277 Plaza Dr Ste 500 (77479-6602)
PHONE..................................281 207-3200
John J Lipinski, *President*
John R Walter, *Senior VP*
Susan M Ball, *CFO*
Martin J Power, *Ch Credit Ofcr*
EMP: 290
SALES (est): 22.4MM **Publicly Held**
WEB: www.cvrenergy.com
SIC: 2911 Gasoline
HQ: Cvr Refining, Llc
2277 Plaza Dr Ste 500
Sugar Land TX 77479
281 207-3200

(G-19575)
WYNNEWOOD REFINING COMPANY LLC (DH)
2277 Plaza Dr Ste 500 (77479-6602)
P.O. Box 305, Wynnewood OK (73098-0305)
PHONE..................................281 207-3444
John J Lipinski, *President*
Martin J Power, *COO*
Robert W Haugen, *Exec VP*
David L Landreth, *Senior VP*
Patrick J Quinn, *Senior VP*
▲ EMP: 70
SALES (est): 65.8MM **Publicly Held**
SIC: 2911 Petroleum refining
HQ: Cvr Refining, Llc
2277 Plaza Dr Ste 500
Sugar Land TX 77479
281 207-3200

(G-19576)
YOKOGAWA CORPORATION AMERICA (HQ)
12530 W Airport Blvd (77478-6189)
PHONE..................................281 340-3800
Shuji Mori, *President*
Roger Van Nuis, *General Mgr*
Cynthia Keith, *Vice Pres*
Shubun Mizuki, *Vice Pres*
Richard Westerfield, *Vice Pres*
▼ EMP: 50 EST: 1989
SQ FT: 48,000

SALES (est): 40.5MM **Privately Held**
WEB: www.yokogawa.com
SIC: 3825 3577 5084 Measuring instruments & meters, electric; meters: electric, pocket, portable, panelboard, etc.; electrical energy measuring equipment; computer peripheral equipment; meters, consumption registering

Sullivan City
Hidalgo County

(G-19577)
SOUTH TEXAS CONCRETE
Also Called: Texas Gravel Co
122 El Faro Rd (78595-1337)
P.O. Box 531808, Harlingen (78553-1808)
PHONE..............................956 485-2301
Jonny Chise, *Manager*
EMP: 30
SALES (corp-wide): 15.6MM **Privately Held**
WEB: www.j3concrete.com
SIC: 1442 3273 Gravel & pebble mining; ready-mixed concrete
PA: South Texas Concrete
1420 S 28th Ave
Edinburg TX 78542
956 381-9886

Sulphur Springs
Hopkins County

(G-19578)
AEROSTAR INTERNATIONAL INC
186 Heritage Ct (75482-3605)
PHONE..............................903 885-0728
Loren Seely, *Branch Mgr*
EMP: 29
SQ FT: 65,000
SALES (corp-wide): 406.6MM **Publicly Held**
WEB: www.ravenaerostar.com
SIC: 2329 3721 3761 3089 Men's & boys' leather, wool & down-filled outerwear; aircraft; guided missiles & space vehicles, research & development; plastic processing
HQ: Aerostar International, Inc.
1001 W Algonquin St
Sioux Falls SD 57104
605 331-3500

(G-19579)
API INDUSTRIES INC
Also Called: Aluf Plastics Texas Division
1212 Elm St (75482-4459)
PHONE..............................845 365-2200
Kristi Hooten, *Manager*
James Thompson, *Manager*
Jonathan Richey, *Maintence Staff*
EMP: 203
SALES (corp-wide): 80.6MM **Privately Held**
WEB: www.alufplastics.com
SIC: 2673 Plastic bags: made from purchased materials
PA: Api Industries, Inc.
2 Glenshaw St
Orangeburg NY 10962
845 365-2200

(G-19580)
BANKERS PRODUCTS & PRINTING
216 Jackson St N (75482-2641)
P.O. Box 1369 (75483-1369)
PHONE..............................903 438-0500
Gail Niergarth, *Owner*
EMP: 9
SQ FT: 2,500
SALES (est): 1.2MM **Privately Held**
WEB: www.bankersproducts.net
SIC: 2752 Commercial printing, offset

(G-19581)
BELL CONCRETE PRODUCTS CO
625 7th St (75482-2066)
P.O. Box 479 (75483-0479)
PHONE..............................903 885-3126
Glenn Bell, *President*
Talley Bell, *President*
Don Bell, *Vice Pres*
EMP: 16 EST: 1946
SQ FT: 1,500
SALES (est): 3.8MM **Privately Held**
WEB: www.bellconcreteinc.com
SIC: 3273 Ready-mixed concrete

(G-19582)
CATOCON INC
739 County Road 1183 (75482-8471)
PHONE..............................903 348-3350
Sandra I Pickett, *President*
Joe C Pickett, *Vice Pres*
Jarred Pickett, *Treasurer*
Jerrod Pickett, *Treasurer*
EMP: 50
SALES (est): 5.6MM **Privately Held**
SIC: 1311 0211 1794 Crude petroleum & natural gas production; beef cattle feedlots; excavation & grading, building construction

(G-19583)
CMH MANUFACTURING INC
2600 Main St (75482-3688)
P.O. Box 1310 (75483-1310)
PHONE..............................903 439-0242
Michael Duncon, *Manager*
EMP: 165
SALES (corp-wide): 254.6B **Publicly Held**
WEB: www.claytonhomes.com
SIC: 2451 Mobile homes
HQ: Cmh Manufacturing, Inc.
5000 Clayton Rd
Maryville TN 37804
865 380-3000

(G-19584)
CONTECH ENGNERED SOLUTIONS LLC
1009 Como St S (75482-4522)
P.O. Box 95 (75483-0095)
PHONE..............................903 885-0673
Jeff Caldwell, *Plant Mgr*
David Horton, *Manager*
Cheryl Potter, *Clerk*
EMP: 12 **Privately Held**
WEB: www.conteches.com
SIC: 3443 Fabricated plate work (boiler shop)
HQ: Contech Engineered Solutions Llc
9025 Centre Pointe Dr # 400
West Chester OH 45069
513 645-7000

(G-19585)
ECHO COMMERCIAL PRINTING INC
401 Church St (75482-2645)
P.O. Box 598 (75483-0598)
PHONE..............................903 885-0861
Scott Keys, *President*
Dan Smith, *General Mgr*
Jim Butler, *Vice Pres*
EMP: 83 EST: 1954
SALES (est): 3.5MM **Privately Held**
SIC: 2759 2752 Letterpress printing; commercial printing, lithographic

(G-19586)
ECHO PUBLISHING COMPANY (PA)
Also Called: Hopkins County Echo
401 Church St Ste B (75482-2633)
P.O. Box 598 (75483-0598)
PHONE..............................903 885-2030
Scott Keys, *President*
Carolyn Keys, *Treasurer*
Bob Spillers, *Advt Staff*
EMP: 50 EST: 1876
SQ FT: 20,500
SALES (est): 11.8MM **Privately Held**
WEB: www.ssecho.com
SIC: 2711 2752 Commercial printing & newspaper publishing combined; commercial printing, offset

(G-19587)
FLOWSERVE CORPORATION
1511 Jefferson St E (75482-3008)
PHONE..............................903 439-3324
Chuck Askins, *General Mgr*
Tony Flippin, *Production*
Chris Clement, *Engineer*
Tim Potts, *Engineer*
Robert Pazin, *Senior Engr*
EMP: 200
SALES (corp-wide): 3.9B **Publicly Held**
WEB: www.flowserve.com
SIC: 3491 Industrial valves
PA: Flowserve Corporation
5215 N Ocnnor Blvd Ste 23 Connor
Irving TX 75039
972 443-6500

(G-19588)
GARY SANVIG
Also Called: Sanvig Sawmill
1317 Jefferson St E (75482-3007)
PHONE..............................903 885-7956
Gary Sanvig, *Owner*
EMP: 9
SALES (est): 1.1MM **Privately Held**
WEB: www.sanvigsawmill.com
SIC: 2421 Lumber: rough, sawed or planed

(G-19589)
GSC ENTERPRISES INC
Fidelity Express-Entronics
1301 Main St (75482-3806)
P.O. Box 768 (75483-0768)
PHONE..............................903 885-1283
Lonnita Finnie, *Credit Staff*
Troy Schmidt, *Sales Staff*
Brad Shaw, *Sales Staff*
Pat Odom, *Branch Mgr*
Kristen Van De Laar, *Prgrmr*
EMP: 30
SALES (corp-wide): 375.1MM **Privately Held**
WEB: www.grocerysupply.com
SIC: 6099 2752 Money order issuance; commercial printing, lithographic
PA: Gsc Enterprises, Inc.
130 Hillcrest Dr
Sulphur Springs TX 75482
903 885-7621

(G-19590)
JELD-WEN INC
Jeld-Wen Doors
902 N Hillcrest Dr (75482-2084)
PHONE..............................903 885-0660
Keith Kultgen, *Branch Mgr*
Rhonda Harry,
EMP: 105 **Publicly Held**
WEB: www.jeld-wen.com
SIC: 3442 Metal doors
HQ: Jeld-Wen, Inc.
2645 Silver Crescent Dr
Charlotte NC 28273
800 535-3936

(G-19591)
LEGEND AIRCRAFT MFG LP
Also Called: American Legend Aircraft
1810 Piper Ln (75482-5437)
P.O. Box 1220 (75483-1220)
PHONE..............................903 885-7000
Darin Hart, *Partner*
R Timothy Elliott, *Partner*
Bob Thomas, *Engineer*
▲ EMP: 25
SALES (est): 1.3MM **Privately Held**
WEB: www.legend.aero
SIC: 3721 5599 Aircraft; aircraft dealers

(G-19592)
MILLENNIUM SHOPPER
115 Jefferson St E (75482-2642)
P.O. Box 1037 (75483-1037)
PHONE..............................903 885-9966
Joy Wilson, *Owner*
Jim Wilson, *Co-Owner*
EMP: 13
SALES (est): 483.2K **Privately Held**
WEB: www.millenniumshopper.com
SIC: 2711 Newspapers: publishing only, not printed on site

(G-19593)
NORTHEAST TEXAS HYDRAULICS
11339 Texas Highway 11 W (75482-1890)
PHONE..............................903 582-2692
Frank Littlefield, *President*
Beverly Littlefield, *Treasurer*
EMP: 13
SQ FT: 12,000
SALES (est): 1.4MM **Privately Held**
SIC: 3714 7699 Cylinder heads, motor vehicle; hydraulic equipment repair

(G-19594)
OCEAN SPRAY CRANBERRIES INC
419 Industrial Dr E (75482-4883)
PHONE..............................903 885-8676
Joshua Houston, *Opers Spvr*
Kim Keaton, *QC Mgr*
Brian McMillan, *Engineer*
Debbie Johnson, *Human Res Mgr*
Craig Miller, *Manager*
EMP: 175
SALES (corp-wide): 1B **Privately Held**
WEB: www.oceanspray.com
SIC: 2033 Fruit juices: packaged in cans, jars, etc.
PA: Ocean Spray Cranberries, Inc.
1 Ocean Spray Dr
Middleboro MA 02349
508 946-1000

(G-19595)
PCI MANUFACTURING LLC
906 N Hillcrest Dr (75482-2084)
PHONE..............................903 439-1080
EMP: 33
SALES (corp-wide): 34.3MM **Privately Held**
SIC: 3999 Mfg Misc Products
PA: Pci Manufacturing, Llc
903 I 30 E
Sulphur Springs TX 75482
903 885-6772

(G-19596)
PCI MANUFACTURING LLC
903 I 30 E (75482-6192)
P.O. Box 296 (75483-0296)
PHONE..............................903 885-6772
Matthew Hanna,
EMP: 35
SALES (est): 12.2MM **Privately Held**
SIC: 3731 Tankers, building & repairing

(G-19597)
SAPUTO DAIRY FOODS USA LLC
300 Industrial Dr E (75482-4800)
P.O. Box 488 (75483-0488)
PHONE..............................903 885-0881
Joe Wallace, *Plant Mgr*
Scott U Brown, *Site Mgr*
Aaron Parada, *Manager*
Mike Stoltenberg, *Executive*
EMP: 40
SALES (corp-wide): 3.7B **Privately Held**
WEB: www.saputo.com
SIC: 2026 Milk processing (pasteurizing, homogenizing, bottling)
HQ: Saputo Dairy Foods Usa, Llc
2711 N Haskell Ave # 370
Dallas TX 75204
214 863-2300

(G-19598)
SAPUTO DAIRY FOODS USA LLC
Also Called: Distribution Center 1
1107 Como St S (75482-4501)
PHONE..............................214 433-3978
Clevon Alexander, *Manager*
EMP: 104
SALES (corp-wide): 3.7B **Privately Held**
WEB: www.saputo.com
SIC: 2023 Cream substitutes
HQ: Saputo Dairy Foods Usa, Llc
2711 N Haskell Ave # 370
Dallas TX 75204
214 863-2300

(G-19599)
SULTA MANUFACTURING COMPANY
159 Putman St (75482-2833)
P.O. Box 597 (75483-0597)
PHONE................................903 885-2139
EMP: 20 EST: 1974
SQ FT: 7,000
SALES (est): 6.3MM Privately Held
WEB: www.sultamfg.com
SIC: 3441 3443 5084 Building components, structural steel; fabricated plate work (boiler shop); industrial machinery & equipment

(G-19600)
SUMMIT ENERGY EQUIPMENT
41 Pioneer Pkwy (75482-6637)
PHONE................................903 951-1217
EMP: 14
SALES (est): 4.5MM Privately Held
WEB: www.summitenergyequipment.com
SIC: 3533 Oil & gas field machinery

(G-19601)
SUNBELT CUSTOM MINERAL LLC
79 County Road 2306 (75482-8001)
PHONE................................903 438-2340
Michael Mazoch, CEO
EMP: 16
SQ FT: 17,000
SALES (est): 3MM Privately Held
WEB: www.sunbeltcustommineral.com
SIC: 2048 Mineral feed supplements

(G-19602)
TEMPLES TRAILER SALES INC
3964 Texas Highway 154 S (75482-7582)
PHONE................................903 885-7301
Judy Temples, President
EMP: 14
SQ FT: 32,000
SALES (est): 1.4MM Privately Held
WEB: www.templestrailers.com
SIC: 7692 5599 Welding repair; snowmobiles

(G-19603)
TMD MANUFACTURING INC
46 Pioneer Pkwy (75482-6638)
PHONE................................903 919-0600
Tim Dollison, President
EMP: 10
SALES (est): 311.4K Privately Held
WEB: www.tmdmanufacturing.com
SIC: 3999 Manufacturing industries

(G-19604)
WESTWAY FEED PRODUCTS LLC
206 League St N (75482-2342)
P.O. Box 403 (75483-0403)
PHONE................................903 885-5541
Matt Kitten, Manager
EMP: 11
SALES (corp-wide): 7.7B Privately Held
WEB: www.contanda.com
SIC: 2048 Prepared feeds
HQ: Westway Feed Products Llc
365 Canal St Ste 2929
New Orleans LA 70130
504 934-1850

(G-19605)
XTREME STRCTRES FBRICATION LLC
300 Cmh (75482-6605)
P.O. Box 915 (75483-0915)
PHONE................................903 438-1100
Mark Newlin, Vice Pres
Terry Williams, VP Sales
Linda Eastep, Executive
Michael Wells,
Polyester Wells,
EMP: 26
SALES (est): 9.5MM Privately Held
WEB: www.xsftruss.com
SIC: 3441 Fabricated structural metal

Sumner
Lamar County

(G-19606)
BUCK DANDY CO
12900 Farm Road 79 (75486-5227)
PHONE................................903 784-6362
David Michael, President
Brad Michael, Vice Pres
Gain Michael, Vice Pres
EMP: 25
SQ FT: 30,000
SALES (est): 4.4MM Privately Held
WEB: www.buckdandy.net
SIC: 3715 7539 5599 5531 Truck trailers; trailer repair; utility trailers; automotive tires; industrial trucks & tractors

(G-19607)
MICHAEL ROY
Also Called: Dandi Co
12900 Farm Road 79 (75486-5227)
PHONE................................903 784-6362
David Michael, CEO
Roy Michael, Owner
EMP: 17
SALES (est): 626.2K Privately Held
WEB: www.michaelroy.com
SIC: 3792 Trailer coaches, automobile

(G-19608)
NORTHEAST GATE CO INC
20364 Farm Road 79 (75486-3667)
P.O. Box 60 (75486-0060)
PHONE................................903 739-8778
Roger Knowles, President
Randy Knowles, Admin Sec
EMP: 10
SQ FT: 700,000
SALES (est): 990K Privately Held
WEB: www.netxgates.com
SIC: 3446 3699 Gates, ornamental metal; door opening & closing devices, electrical

(G-19609)
SUMMIT MECHANICAL
5200 County Road 31100 (75486-5729)
PHONE................................903 267-7949
Brian Collard, Principal
EMP: 20
SALES (est): 2.5MM Privately Held
SIC: 2141 Tobacco thrashing (mechanical stemming)

Sundown
Hockley County

(G-19610)
AGGIETECH ENERGY SERVICES LLC
Also Called: Big Bear-Aggietech
690 W Richardson (79372)
PHONE................................806 229-6129
Mark Bales, President
EMP: 28
SALES (corp-wide): 29.3MM Privately Held
WEB: www.aggietechoil.com
SIC: 3599 7699 7692 Machine shop, jobbing & repair; industrial machinery & equipment repair; welding repair
PA: Aggietech Energy Services, Llc
5101 W Interstate 20
Midland TX 79706
432 682-3131

(G-19611)
APACHE CORPORATION
3749 Sagebrush Rd (79372)
P.O. Box 1150 (79372-1150)
PHONE................................806 229-3010
Tony Chenault, Manager
EMP: 13
SALES (corp-wide): 6.4B Publicly Held
WEB: www.apachecorp.com
SIC: 1311 Crude petroleum production
PA: Apache Corporation
2000 Post Oak Blvd Ste 10
Houston TX 77056
713 296-6000

(G-19612)
BAKER PETROLITE LLC
E Hwy 301 (79372)
PHONE................................806 229-8121
Vern Disney, Manager
EMP: 10 Privately Held
WEB:
www.bakerhughesdirect.lookchem.com
SIC: 1389 Oil field services
HQ: Baker Petrolite Llc
12645 W Airport Blvd
Sugar Land TX 77478
281 276-5400

(G-19613)
OCCIDENTAL PERMIAN LTD
4 Miles West Fm 301 (79372)
PHONE................................806 229-2501
Jim Richardson, Manager
EMP: 50
SALES (corp-wide): 21.2B Publicly Held
WEB: www.oxy.com
SIC: 1311 Crude petroleum & natural gas production
HQ: Occidental Permian Ltd.
5 Greenway Plz Ste 110
Houston TX 77046

(G-19614)
SUNDOWN OPERATING INC
304 Richardson (79372)
P.O. Box 938 (79372-0938)
PHONE................................806 229-6102
Clyde Wilson, President
EMP: 85
SQ FT: 4,000
SALES (est): 10MM Privately Held
SIC: 1389 1382 Oil field services; oil & gas exploration services

Sunnyvale
Dallas County

(G-19615)
VINCE HAGAN COMPANY (PA)
330 Clay Rd (75182-9711)
PHONE................................214 330-4601
Carol Hagan, President
Randy Haddox, Principal
Chris Toedt, Vice Pres
Glen Garner, Opers Staff
Ricardo Hernandez, Purch Mgr
▼ EMP: 13 EST: 1956
SALES (est): 56.8MM Privately Held
WEB: www.vincehagan.com
SIC: 5084 3444 3443 3441 Industrial machinery & equipment; sheet metalwork; fabricated plate work (boiler shop); fabricated structural metal; concrete plants

Sunray
Moore County

(G-19616)
CONTINENTAL CARBON COMPANY
11702 Carbon Black Rd (79086-2003)
PHONE................................806 935-4174
Larry Parrish, Opers Mgr
Steve Brown, Branch Mgr
Jonathan Petty, Maintence Staff
EMP: 50 Privately Held
WEB: www.continentalcarbon.com
SIC: 2819 Industrial inorganic chemicals
HQ: Continental Carbon Company
16850 Park Row
Houston TX 77084
281 647-3700

(G-19617)
FORTAY INC
7525 Fm 119 (79086-2210)
P.O. Box 670 (79086-0670)
PHONE................................806 948-4166
Shelby Taylor, President
Scott Peeples, Vice Pres
EMP: 10
SALES (est): 1.5MM Privately Held
SIC: 1389 Servicing oil & gas wells

(G-19618)
GEAR DRIVE SERVICE PUMP DIV
100 Highway Ave 281w (79086-1623)
P.O. Box 895 (79086-0895)
PHONE................................806 948-5366
Wayne Carrell, President
Theressa Carrell, Corp Secy
EMP: 10
SQ FT: 3,600
SALES (est): 1.4MM Privately Held
SIC: 3599 5083 Machine shop, jobbing & repair; irrigation equipment

(G-19619)
HIGH PLAINS HYDRO CARBON
Hwy 119 (79086)
P.O. Box 670 (79086-0670)
PHONE................................806 948-4166
Shelby Taylor, Partner
EMP: 9
SQ FT: 6,875
SALES (est): 296.2K Privately Held
SIC: 1382 Oil & gas exploration services

(G-19620)
L C BURKETT DRILLING
Fm 119 (79086)
P.O. Box 630 (79086-0630)
PHONE................................806 948-4252
L C Burkett, Owner
EMP: 15
SQ FT: 6,875
SALES (est): 1.1MM Privately Held
SIC: 1781 5084 3599 Water well drilling; pumps & pumping equipment; machine shop, jobbing & repair

(G-19621)
TAYLOR OIL CO LTD PARTNERSHIP (PA)
Also Called: Taylor, Gordon Oil Co
Fm 119 Fm 1 St (79086)
PHONE................................806 948-4166
Dorothy Taylor, Managing Prtnr
Shelby Taylor, General Ptnr
Mitch Taylor, Ltd Ptnr
Mitzie Taylor, Ltd Ptnr
Dorothy Taylor Marital Trust, Ltd Ptnr
EMP: 9
SQ FT: 6,000
SALES (est): 1.5MM Privately Held
SIC: 1311 Crude petroleum production; natural gas production

(G-19622)
TAYLOR OIL INC
Also Called: Taylor Oil Field Supply
Fm 119 (79086)
P.O. Box 670 (79086-0670)
PHONE................................806 948-4166
Shelby Taylor, General Ptnr
Dorothy Taylor, General Ptnr
EMP: 10
SQ FT: 6,000
SALES (est): 1.4MM Privately Held
SIC: 1389 5084 5085 Oil field services; oil well machinery, equipment & supplies; valves & fittings

(G-19623)
VALERO ENERGY CORPORATION
Also Called: Valero McKee Refinery
6701 Fm 119 (79086-2013)
PHONE................................806 935-1307
Sal Viscontini, Vice Pres
Lauren Bird, Plant Mgr
Ronnie Hatter, Opers Mgr
James Muir, Terminal Mgr
Barry Glasgow, Engineer
EMP: 450
SALES (corp-wide): 108.3B Publicly Held
WEB: www.valero.com
SIC: 2911 Petroleum refining
PA: Valero Energy Corporation
1 Valero Way
San Antonio TX 78249
210 345-2000

Sunset
Montague County

(G-19624)
CHRIS BURNS WELDING LLC
264 Sunset School Rd (76270-7184)
P.O. Box 9 (76270-0009)
PHONE..........................940 845-4945
Chris Ray Burns, *Mng Member*
Malynn Burns, *Mng Member*
EMP: 9
SALES (est): 1.3MM **Privately Held**
SIC: 7692 Welding repair

(G-19625)
MEGALODON SERVICES INC
565 County Road 1591 (76270-5302)
P.O. Box 1959, Decatur (76234-6154)
PHONE..........................941 882-3108
James Covin, *President*
Misty Covin, *Vice Pres*
EMP: 45
SALES: 3.9MM **Privately Held**
WEB: www.megalodonservices.com
SIC: 1389 Oil field services

Sunset Valley
Travis County

(G-19626)
M PATEL ENTERPRISES INC
Also Called: Party Pig Superstore
5601 Brodie Ln Ste 1000 (78745-2540)
PHONE..........................512 892-2721
Rick Alvarado, *Manager*
EMP: 20
SALES (corp-wide): 4.7MM **Privately Held**
SIC: 5947 7389 7299 5999 Party favors; balloons, novelty & toy; costume rental; banners; invitations: printing
PA: M. Patel Enterprises, Inc.
11150 Res Blvd Ste 100b
Austin TX 78759
512 343-8181

Sweeny
Brazoria County

(G-19627)
HILCORP ENERGY COMPANY
10201 County Road 359 (77480-9678)
PHONE..........................979 548-2144
Ashley Washington, *Manager*
EMP: 18
SQ FT: 1,650 **Privately Held**
WEB: www.hilcorp.com
SIC: 1382 1311 Oil & gas exploration services; crude petroleum production
PA: Hilcorp Energy Company
1111 Travis St
Houston TX 77002

(G-19628)
J & S CONTRACTORS INC (PA)
212 N Main St (77480-3008)
P.O. Box 4003, Brazoria (77422-4003)
PHONE..........................979 647-0040
Johnnie D Glick, *President*
Scott Glick, *Vice Pres*
EMP: 18
SQ FT: 32,670
SALES (est): 2.4MM **Privately Held**
WEB: www.jscontractorsinc.com
SIC: 1629 1794 1791 3441 Marine construction; excavation work; structural steel erection; fabricated structural metal

Sweetwater
Nolan County

(G-19629)
EMA ELECTROMECHANICS INC
16 Industrial St (79556-6200)
P.O. Box 785 (79556-0785)
PHONE..........................325 235-8000
Eduardo Montich, *President*

Joao Pinheiro, *Principal*
◆ **EMP:** 30
SQ FT: 22,000
SALES (est): 6.3MM **Privately Held**
WEB: www.emaelectromechanics.com
SIC: 3613 Power circuit breakers
PA: Ema Electromecanica S.A.
Avenida San Martin 4970
Florida BUE B1604

(G-19630)
GLOBAL FBRGLS SLTONS TEXAS LLC
13 Industrial St (79556-6221)
PHONE..........................425 483-1303
Ronald Albrecht, *COO*
EMP: 21
SALES (corp-wide): 7MM **Privately Held**
WEB: www.globalfiberglassinc.com
SIC: 2519 Fiberglass & plastic furniture
PA: Global Fiberglass Solutions Of Texas, Llc
16212 Bothell Everett Hwy
Mill Creek WA 98012
425 320-9044

(G-19631)
HORIZON PUBLICATIONS INC
Also Called: Sweetwater Reporter
112 W 3rd St (79556-4430)
P.O. Box 1431, Big Spring (79721-1431)
PHONE..........................325 236-6677
Carol Bond, *CFO*
EMP: 23
SALES (corp-wide): 71.5MM **Privately Held**
WEB: www.horizonpublicationsinc.com
SIC: 2711 Newspapers: publishing only, not printed on site
PA: Horizon Publications, Inc.
1120 N Carbon St Ste 100
Marion IL 62959
618 993-1711

(G-19632)
KEY ENERGY SERVICES INC
2210 W Broadway St (79556-4276)
PHONE..........................325 236-6611
Gayland Bond, *Manager*
EMP: 24
SALES (corp-wide): 413.8MM **Publicly Held**
WEB: www.keyenergy.com
SIC: 1389 Oil field services
PA: Key Energy Services, Inc.
1301 Mckinney St Ste 1800
Houston TX 77010
713 651-4300

(G-19633)
LUDLUM MEASUREMENTS INC (PA)
501 Oak St (79556-3209)
P.O. Box 810 (79556-0810)
PHONE..........................325 235-5494
Donald G Ludlum, *President*
Larry Place, *General Mgr*
Larry M Ludlum, *Vice Pres*
Jamie Witt, *Vice Pres*
Mark Mims, *Opers Dir*
EMP: 400
SQ FT: 7,000
SALES (est): 83.6MM **Privately Held**
WEB: www.ludlums.com
SIC: 3829 3826 3824 3823 Nuclear radiation & testing apparatus; analytical instruments; fluid meters & counting devices; industrial instrmnts msrmnt display/control process variable

(G-19634)
LUDLUM MEASUREMENTS INC
Adit
300 Crane St (79556-4602)
PHONE..........................325 235-1418
John Spaulding, *General Mgr*
Charlie Hurlbut, *General Mgr*
Dianne Hethcoat, *Purch Mgr*
Gary Watson, *Purch Mgr*
Larry Hillis, *Human Res Mgr*
EMP: 98

SALES (corp-wide): 83.6MM **Privately Held**
WEB: www.ludlums.com
SIC: 3829 3674 3671 Measuring & controlling devices; semiconductors & related devices; electron tubes
PA: Ludlum Measurements, Inc.
501 Oak St
Sweetwater TX 79556
325 235-5494

(G-19635)
LUDLUM MEASUREMENTS INC
Also Called: Eljen Technology
1300 W Broadway St (79556-4264)
PHONE..........................325 235-4276
Charles Hurldut, *General Mgr*
EMP: 80
SALES (corp-wide): 83.6MM **Privately Held**
WEB: www.ludlums.com
SIC: 3829 Nuclear radiation & testing apparatus
PA: Ludlum Measurements, Inc.
501 Oak St
Sweetwater TX 79556
325 235-5494

(G-19636)
M & B OILFIELD CONSTRUCTION
2700 E Broadway St (79556-2818)
P.O. Box 26 (79556-0026)
PHONE..........................325 235-2514
Steven Mahaffey, *President*
Randy Brown, *Vice Pres*
EMP: 20
SALES (est): 2.2MM **Privately Held**
SIC: 1389 Oil field services

(G-19637)
SWEETWATER MACHINE AND WELDING
711 W Broadway St (79556-4307)
P.O. Box 1296 (79556-1296)
PHONE..........................325 235-2922
Richard Porter, *President*
Dewwy R Baxter, *Vice Pres*
Darold Little, *Vice Pres*
EMP: 27 EST: 1975
SQ FT: 12,000
SALES (est): 3.3MM **Privately Held**
WEB: www.sweetwatermachine.com
SIC: 3444 3599 7692 Sheet metalwork; machine shop, jobbing & repair; welding repair

(G-19638)
SWEETWATER READY-MIX CON CO (PA)
105 W 12th St (79556-3110)
P.O. Box 1196 (79556-1196)
PHONE..........................325 236-6200
Bill C Burwick, *President*
Greg Burwick, *Vice Pres*
EMP: 10 EST: 1958
SQ FT: 2,000
SALES (est): 1.9MM **Privately Held**
WEB: www.sweetwaterreporter.com
SIC: 3273 5032 1442 Ready-mixed concrete; sand, construction; gravel; construction sand & gravel

(G-19639)
WIND ENERGY TURBINE SERVICES
Also Called: Wets
2503 E Broadway St (79556-2813)
P.O. Box 862 (79556-0862)
PHONE..........................325 235-1555
James McCasland, *President*
Mark Meneses, *Vice Pres*
Larry Martin, *Treasurer*
Jason Hasner, *Admin Sec*
EMP: 60
SALES (est): 9.2MM **Privately Held**
WEB: www.wetsinc.net
SIC: 3511 Turbines & turbine generator sets & parts

Taft
San Patricio County

(G-19640)
COX TANK CONSTRUCTION CO INC
Us Hwy 181 (78390)
P.O. Box 147, Portland (78374-0147)
PHONE..........................361 528-3524
Don J Cox Sr, *President*
Linda Cox, *Corp Secy*
Jack H Cox, *Shareholder*
EMP: 25 EST: 1975
SQ FT: 60,000
SALES (est): 3.4MM **Privately Held**
WEB: www.coxtank.com
SIC: 1629 3443 Dams, waterways, docks & other marine construction; fabricated plate work (boiler shop)

Tahoka
Lynn County

(G-19641)
KNOX JR LEIGHTON
1683 Cr 29 (79373)
P.O. Box 914 (79373-0914)
PHONE..........................806 327-5420
Leighton Knox Jr, *Owner*
EMP: 30
SQ FT: 15,500
SALES (est): 2MM **Privately Held**
SIC: 3523 5084 3949 3563 Sprayers & spraying machines, agricultural; industrial machinery & equipment; sporting & athletic goods; air & gas compressors; partitions & fixtures, except wood

(G-19642)
WILDCAT MANUFACTURING INC
1683 County Rd 29 (79373)
P.O. Box 914 (79373-0914)
PHONE..........................806 327-5602
Leighton Knox, *President*
Starr Bray, *Office Mgr*
EMP: 30
SALES (est): 2MM **Privately Held**
WEB: www.wildcatmfg.net
SIC: 3423 3523 Hand & edge tools; farm machinery & equipment

Tarpley
Bandera County

(G-19643)
HEADWATERS INCORPORATED
5555 Fellowship Ln Spg Spring (78883)
PHONE..........................830 562-3239
Claudia Hudson, *President*
Steven Allen, *Maintence Staff*
EMP: 18 **Privately Held**
WEB: www.flyash.com
SIC: 3272 Siding, precast stone
HQ: Headwaters Incorporated
10701 S River Front Pkwy # 300
South Jordan UT 84095

Tatum
Rusk County

(G-19644)
KIM R SMITH LOGGING INC
1155 E Johnson St (75691-1908)
PHONE..........................903 947-6242
Kim R Smith, *President*
Pam Smith, *Treasurer*
EMP: 45
SALES (est): 2.5MM **Privately Held**
SIC: 2411 Logging camps & contractors

(G-19645)
SIERRA DUST CONTROL LLC (PA)
1155 E Johnson St (75691-1908)
PHONE..........................903 836-4642
Kim R Smith,
Pamela Smith,

▲ = Import ▼=Export
◆ =Import/Export

EMP: 10
SALES (est): 4.2MM **Privately Held**
WEB: www.sierrafracsand.com
SIC: 2865 2869 Dyes & pigments; high
purity grade chemicals; organic

Taylor
Williamson County

(G-19646)
A & B SHEET METAL INC
4804 W 2nd St (76574-4643)
P.O. Box 105 (76574-0105)
PHONE.....................512 365-7870
Bill Albert, *Principal*
EMP: 9 EST: 2010
SALES (est): 757.5K **Privately Held**
WEB: www.ab-roofing.com
SIC: 5211 3444 1761 Lumber & other
building materials; sheet metal special-
ties, not stamped; roofing contractor

(G-19647)
ACCURATE INC (PA)
Also Called: Accurate Coatings
207 Allison (76574-3805)
P.O. Box 1296 (76574-6296)
PHONE.....................512 352-5278
Henry Hutcherson, *CEO*
Hank Hutcherson, *President*
Rick Commander, *Sales Staff*
Beatrice Kruse, *Manager*
◆ EMP: 83
SQ FT: 25,000
SALES (est): 30.2MM **Privately Held**
WEB: www.accuratecoatings.com
SIC: 3479 Coating of metals & formed
products; painting, coating & hot dipping

(G-19648)
BABECO INC
Also Called: Texas Ammo
1101 Crlos Parker Blvd Nw (76574-7061)
PHONE.....................512 352-5355
David Mucha, *Vice Pres*
Cody Montgomery, *Purchasing*
Glen Buchhorn, *Sales Staff*
Steven Hubnik, *Mng Member*
Mary Jo Tschoerner, *Manager*
EMP: 35
SQ FT: 47,000
SALES (est): 6MM **Privately Held**
WEB: www.babecoinc.com
SIC: 3599 Machine shop, jobbing & repair

(G-19649)
BASLER ELECTRIC COMPANY
Also Called: Basler Electric Circuits Div
204 Highland Dr (76574-1811)
P.O. Box 1165 (76574-1165)
PHONE.....................512 352-3154
Millie Wyatt, *Buyer*
Roberto Flores, *Engineer*
Kenneth Parker, *VP Finance*
Sherry McKinley, *Accountant*
Tom Harnetiaux, *VP Sales*
EMP: 25
SQ FT: 18,000
SALES (corp-wide): 180.5MM **Privately Held**
WEB: www.basler.com
SIC: 3672 Printed circuit boards
PA: Basler Electric Company
12570 State Route 143
Highland IL 62249
618 654-2341

(G-19650)
BLACKLANDS PUBLICATIONS INC (PA)
Also Called: Taylor Daily Press
211 W 3rd St (76574-3518)
P.O. Box 1040 (76574-1040)
PHONE.....................512 352-8535
EMP: 20
SQ FT: 4,185
SALES (est): 1.7MM **Privately Held**
WEB: www.printablepress.com
SIC: 2711 Commercial printing & newspa-
per publishing combined

(G-19651)
CARPENTER CO
Also Called: Carpenter Co Morning Glory Div
302 Highland Dr (76574-1847)
PHONE.....................512 365-5833
Randall Fisher, *Branch Mgr*
EMP: 83
SQ FT: 111,340
SALES (corp-wide): 1.8B **Privately Held**
WEB: www.carpenterftp.com
SIC: 2392 Cushions & pillows
PA: Carpenter Co.
5016 Monument Ave
Richmond VA 23230
804 359-0800

(G-19652)
CENTEX MEAT COMPANY LP
Also Called: Taylor Meat Company
2211 W 2nd St (76574-2130)
P.O. Box 670 (76574-0670)
PHONE.....................512 352-6357
Ron Ivy, *Partner*
EMP: 25 EST: 1947
SQ FT: 9,200
SALES (est): 1.8MM **Privately Held**
WEB: www.taylormeat.com
SIC: 5421 5147 2011 Meat markets, in-
cluding freezer provisioners; meats, fresh;
meats, cured or smoked; meat packing
plants

(G-19653)
DYNALYST CORPORATION
1008 Crlos Parker Blvd Sw (76574-4511)
PHONE.....................512 365-1203
Craig Takacs, *CEO*
Mike Moore, *CFO*
Joe Schaefer, *Controller*
EMP: 30
SALES (est): 4.5MM **Privately Held**
WEB: www.dynalyst.com
SIC: 3672 Circuit boards, television & radio
printed

(G-19654)
DYNALYST MANUFACTURING CORP
1008 Crlos Parker Blvd Sw (76574-4511)
PHONE.....................512 365-1230
David Cox, *General Mgr*
Mark Bouril, *Engineer*
Debbie Iselt, *Technical Staff*
Maria Miralles,
EMP: 38
SQ FT: 29,694
SALES (corp-wide): 6MM **Privately Held**
WEB: www.dynalyst.com
SIC: 3672 Circuit boards, television & radio
printed
PA: Dynalyst Manufacturing Corporation
738 Highway 6 S Ste 230
Houston TX 77079

(G-19655)
FACILITIES REHAB INC
716 N Main St Ste 3 (76574-3234)
PHONE.....................512 352-6035
German Ramirez, *President*
▲ EMP: 15 EST: 2008
SALES (est): 3.2MM **Privately Held**
SIC: 3321 1623 Manhole covers, metal;
water, sewer & utility lines

(G-19656)
GEMINI INCORPORATED
102 Wagner Way (76574-3809)
PHONE.....................512 352-5207
Frank Hamilton, *Branch Mgr*
EMP: 100
SQ FT: 19,200
SALES (corp-wide): 94.6MM **Privately Held**
WEB: www.geminisignproducts.com
SIC: 5162 3953 Plastics products; mark-
ing devices
PA: Gemini, Incorporated
103 Mensing Way
Cannon Falls MN 55009
507 263-3957

(G-19657)
GRANITE PUBLICATIONS LLC (PA)
211 W 3rd St (76574-3518)
P.O. Box 1010 (76574-1010)
PHONE.....................512 352-8285
Ashley Tompkins, *Opers Staff*
James Chionsini, *Mng Member*
Tia Stone, *Manager*
Ruby Vazquez, *Supervisor*
Julie Rydell, *Graphic Designe*
EMP: 10
SALES (est): 1.5MM **Privately Held**
WEB: www.granitepublications.com
SIC: 2711 Commercial printing & newspa-
per publishing combined; newspapers,
publishing & printing

(G-19658)
JIM MCNABB INC (PA)
Also Called: Art Office Signs
201 W 2nd St (76574-3512)
PHONE.....................512 365-2010
Jim Mc Nabb, *President*
Joel Cecil, *General Mgr*
Donna Mc Nab, *Principal*
Randy Meeks, *CFO*
David Jones, *Sales Staff*
EMP: 12
SQ FT: 6,000 **Privately Held**
WEB: www.artofficesigns.com
SIC: 3993 Signs & advertising specialties

(G-19659)
K AND M MANUFACTURING CO INC
Also Called: Hay King
628 E Lake Dr (76574-1818)
PHONE.....................512 352-2588
Darrell Malish, *Vice Pres*
Kerry Malish, *Vice Pres*
Judy Malish, *Treasurer*
Cheryl Barron, *Finance Mgr*
Cheryl Malish-Barron, *Admin Sec*
◆ EMP: 22 EST: 1980
SQ FT: 16,000
SALES (est): 3MM **Privately Held**
WEB: www.hayking.com
SIC: 3523 Balers, farm: hay, straw, cotton,
etc.; loaders, farm type: manure, general
utility

(G-19660)
MOEHNKE CUSTOM CABINETRY
2210 W 2nd St (76574-2131)
PHONE.....................512 352-6506
EMP: 10
SALES (est): 399.3K **Privately Held**
WEB: www.cabinetsbeautiful.com
SIC: 2434 1751 Vanities, bathroom: wood;
cabinet & finish carpentry

(G-19661)
NOREN PRODUCTS INC (PA)
205 S Edmond St (76574-2320)
PHONE.....................650 322-9500
Cheryl Webster, *CEO*
EMP: 32
SQ FT: 30,000
SALES (est): 5MM **Privately Held**
WEB: www.norenthermal.com
SIC: 3585 Evaporative condensers, heat
transfer equipment

(G-19662)
TAYLOR CRAFT CABINET & DOOR
1353 W 2nd St (76574-2434)
PHONE.....................512 352-6355
Sherman Burrows, *Owner*
Heath Till, *COO*
EMP: 50
SALES (est): 3.9MM **Privately Held**
WEB: www.taylorcraftdoor.com
SIC: 2434 Wood kitchen cabinets

(G-19663)
TAYLOR IRON-MACHINE WORKS
208 Bland St (76574-4102)
P.O. Box 188 (76574-0188)
PHONE.....................512 365-3646
Curtis Hickman, *President*
Arnold C Cuba Jr, *Corp Secy*
Bob Holmquist, *VP Bus Dvlpt*
EMP: 13 EST: 1920

SQ FT: 28,000
SALES (est): 3.5MM **Privately Held**
WEB: www.tayloriron.com
SIC: 3599 7699 Machine shop, jobbing &
repair; welding equipment repair

Teague
Freestone County

(G-19664)
COTHRAN AG SERVICES LLC
402 Fm 1451 (75860-3063)
P.O. Box 509 (75860-0509)
PHONE.....................254 625-1715
Leonard W Cothran, *Principal*
EMP: 10 EST: 2010
SALES (est): 1.7MM **Privately Held**
SIC: 1389 Construction, repair & disman-
tling services

Telephone
Fannin County

(G-19665)
B MAYFIELD MCCRAW
Also Called: McCraw Materials
3765 County Road 2135 (75488-3009)
P.O. Box 9 (75488-0009)
PHONE.....................903 664-2332
Mayfield McCraw, *Owner*
Lynn Gibbs, *Manager*
Pam Gibbs, *Admin Sec*
EMP: 75
SALES (est): 9.5MM **Privately Held**
WEB: www.hopeplantationturf.com
SIC: 3273 0191 Ready-mixed concrete;
general farms, primarily crop

Temple
Bell County

(G-19666)
ACER AMERICA CORPORATION
1394 Eberhardt Rd (76504-8832)
P.O. Box 6137 (76503-6137)
PHONE.....................254 298-4000
EMP: 145 **Privately Held**
WEB: www.acer.com
SIC: 3571 7378 Electronic computers;
computer maintenance & repair
HQ: Acer America Corporation
1730 N 1st St Ste 400
San Jose CA 95112
408 533-7700

(G-19667)
ADVANCED LASER MATERIALS LLC
Also Called: Eos North America
3115 Lucius Mccelvey Dr (76504-1213)
PHONE.....................254 773-3080
Caleb Ferrell, *General Mgr*
Catherine Mertz, *General Mgr*
Michael Conner, *Vice Pres*
Ankit Saharan, *Mfg Staff*
Kristi Cochran, *Manager*
▲ EMP: 16
SALES (est): 4.4MM **Privately Held**
WEB: www.alm-llc.com
SIC: 2821 Plastics materials & resins

(G-19668)
AMERICAN CLASSIFIEDS (PA)
Also Called: Thrifty Nickel
2905 W Adams Ave (76504-2862)
P.O. Box 1608 (76503-1608)
PHONE.....................254 771-2777
Chip Treese, *President*
Carol Treese, *Corp Secy*
Harry Treese, *Vice Pres*
Dave Nelson, *Sales Staff*
EMP: 15
SQ FT: 3,300
SALES (est): 1.8MM **Privately Held**
WEB: www.ac-tnol.com
SIC: 2741 Shopping news: publishing &
printing

(G-19669)
AMERICAN PRINTING & OFF PDTS
4106 Eagle Rd (76502-1138)
PHONE.....................................254 771-2422
B J Donaldson, *President*
Janet Donaldson, *Vice Pres*
EMP: 10 EST: 1920
SQ FT: 6,600
SALES (est): 1.5MM Privately Held
WEB: www.amerprint.com
SIC: 2752 Commercial printing, offset

(G-19670)
BAE SYSTEMS LAND ARMAMENTS LP
3831 Lucius Mccelvey Dr (76504-1208)
PHONE.....................................408 504-1877
Doug Lorenz, *Manager*
EMP: 56
SALES (corp-wide): 23.6B Privately Held
WEB: www.baesystems.com
SIC: 3812 Search & navigation equipment
HQ: Bae Systems Land & Armaments L.P.
   2941 Frview Pk Dr Ste 100
   Falls Church VA 22042
   571 461-6000

(G-19671)
BLIND DOG PRODUCTIONS LTD
Also Called: Izone
2526 Charter Oak Dr # 100 (76502-4864)
P.O. Box 368 (76503-0368)
PHONE.....................................254 778-0722
Michael Maceachern, *CEO*
Grady Brown, *President*
Cindy King, *Business Mgr*
Michael Dean, *Accounts Mgr*
Sheryl Teetz, *Mktg Coord*
EMP: 40
SQ FT: 57,280
SALES (est): 4.9MM Privately Held
WEB: www.izoneimaging.com
SIC: 3993 2672 Signs & advertising specialties; coated & laminated paper

(G-19672)
CALDWELL UPFITTERS LLC (PA)
4715 S General Bruce Dr (76502-1420)
PHONE.....................................254 773-1959
Juan Villalovan,
EMP: 15
SALES (est): 1.6MM Privately Held
WEB: www.capfleetupfitters.com
SIC: 3465 Body parts, automobile: stamped metal

(G-19673)
CARGILL INCORPORATED
251 Berger Rd (76501-6674)
PHONE.....................................254 774-9022
Pat Fullack, *Manager*
EMP: 18
SALES (corp-wide): 113.4B Privately Held
WEB: www.peterschocolate.com
SIC: 2048 Prepared feeds
PA: Cargill, Incorporated
   15407 Mcginty Rd W
   Wayzata MN 55391
   952 742-7575

(G-19674)
CARPENTER CO
2611 N General Bruce Dr (76501-1362)
P.O. Box 1007 (76503-1007)
PHONE.....................................254 778-0131
Mark Willard, *Division Mgr*
EMP: 96
SQ FT: 450,000
SALES (corp-wide): 1.8B Privately Held
WEB: www.carpenterftp.com
SIC: 3086 2824 Insulation or cushioning material, foamed plastic; organic fibers, noncellulosic
PA: Carpenter Co.
   5016 Monument Ave
   Richmond VA 23230
   804 359-0800

(G-19675)
CENTRIFUGAL CASTINGS INC
3320 Parkway Dr (76504-1241)
P.O. Box 210 (76503-0210)
PHONE.....................................254 773-9068
Gary D Smith, *President*
Cameron Reynolds, *Maint Spvr*
Scott Kruppa, *Opers Staff*
Julie Nagy, *Treasurer*
Ashley Botts, *Sales Staff*
EMP: 50
SQ FT: 37,000
SALES (est): 12.6MM Privately Held
WEB: www.centrifugal.net
SIC: 3325 3369 Alloy steel castings, except investment; nonferrous foundries

(G-19676)
CLARIOS
Also Called: Johnson Controls
18 S Main St (76501-7652)
PHONE.....................................254 774-9287
EMP: 94 Privately Held
WEB: www.johnsoncontrols.com
SIC: 2531 Seats, automobile
HQ: Johnson Controls, Inc.
   5757 N Green Bay Ave
   Glendale WI 53209
   800 382-2804

(G-19677)
COMPASS CONVERSIONS LLC
1822 Industrial Blvd (76504-1005)
PHONE.....................................254 771-9909
Gena Goodwin, *Principal*
Clark McDaniel,
Glenda McDaniel,
EMP: 25
SALES (est): 3.4MM Privately Held
WEB: www.compassconversions.com
SIC: 3715 Trailers or vans for transporting horses

(G-19678)
DANHIL CONTAINERS II LTD (HQ)
3715 Lucius Mccelvey Dr (76504-1203)
P.O. Box 2089 (76503-2089)
PHONE.....................................254 773-0704
E J Daniel, *Partner*
Jeff Daniel, *Partner*
Darin Taylor, *Partner*
Brian Wilkinson, *Partner*
Gary Kenney, *Plant Mgr*
EMP: 120
SQ FT: 220,000
SALES (est): 59.3MM
SALES (corp-wide): 134.1MM Privately Held
WEB: www.danhilcontainers.com
SIC: 2653 Boxes, corrugated: made from purchased materials
PA: Danhil Containers, Inc.
   3715 Lucius Mccelvey Dr
   Temple TX 76504
   254 773-0704

(G-19679)
DELTA CENTRIFUGAL LLC
3402 Center St (76504-1207)
P.O. Box 1043 (76503-1043)
PHONE.....................................254 773-9055
Robert Rose, *President*
Matt Greenfield, *COO*
Chris Anderson, *Vice Pres*
Mark Anderson, *Vice Pres*
Hope Luther, *Vice Pres*
▲ EMP: 140
SQ FT: 110,000
SALES (est): 88MM Privately Held
WEB: www.deltacentrifugal.com
SIC: 5051 3325 3369 Sheets, galvanized or other coated; alloy steel castings, except investment; nonferrous foundries

(G-19680)
E R CARPENTER LP (PA)
2611 N General Bruce Dr (76501-1362)
PHONE.....................................804 359-0800
Dick Davidson, *Partner*
Stanley F Pauley, *General Ptnr*
◆ EMP: 175
SQ FT: 10,111

SALES (est): 54.6MM Privately Held
WEB: www.carpenter.com
SIC: 3086 1311 2869 2297 Carpet & rug cushions, foamed plastic; insulation or cushioning material, foamed plastic; padding, foamed plastic; crude petroleum & natural gas; industrial organic chemicals; bonded-fiber fabrics, except felt; household furnishings

(G-19681)
HEART OF TEXAS MUSIC INC (PA)
Also Called: Heart of Texas Music Temple
808 S 31st St (76504-5209)
P.O. Box 522, Leander (78646-0522)
PHONE.....................................254 778-7422
Ray Hennig, *President*
Mary Henning, *Admin Sec*
EMP: 10
SQ FT: 7,000
SALES (est): 1.7MM Privately Held
WEB: www.heartoftexasmusic.com
SIC: 5736 3651 Pianos; speaker systems

(G-19682)
IMPAC SYSTEMS ENGINEERING LLP
319 S 1st St (76504-5500)
PHONE.....................................713 784-3500
Carl Rose, *President*
Scot Andrews, *VP Engrg*
Bob Gilman, *Accounts Exec*
Michelle Saindon, *Accounts Exec*
Kelly Knake, *Sales Executive*
EMP: 15
SALES (est): 2.6MM Privately Held
WEB: www.impacsystems.com
SIC: 8711 7371 7372 Engineering services; custom computer programming services; prepackaged software

(G-19683)
JUPE FEEDS INC
Also Called: Wendland's Farm Products
405 S 2nd St (76504-5862)
P.O. Box 40 (76503-0040)
PHONE.....................................254 773-5211
Mark Jupe, *Vice Pres*
Darren Jupe, *Treasurer*
EMP: 35
SQ FT: 5,200
SALES (est): 19MM Privately Held
WEB: www.wendlands.com
SIC: 2048 Poultry feeds; livestock feeds

(G-19684)
LINDE GAS NORTH AMERICA LLC
Also Called: Lifegas
3301 Charter Oak Dr (76502-5854)
PHONE.....................................254 718-5124
Billy Miles, *Branch Mgr*
EMP: 19 Privately Held
WEB: www.praxair.com
SIC: 2813 Nitrogen
HQ: Linde Gas North America Llc
   10 Riverview Dr
   Danbury CT 06810

(G-19685)
LJT TEXAS LLC
3601 Eberhardt Rd (76504-2600)
PHONE.....................................254 771-2253
Mark Richner, *Plant Mgr*
Kenny Brown, *Safety Mgr*
EMP: 75 Privately Held
WEB: www.ljtube.com
SIC: 3317 Tubes, wrought: welded or lock joint
HQ: Ljt Texas Llc
   515 W Ireland Rd
   South Bend IN 46614

(G-19686)
LOCK JOINT TUBE LLC
3601 Eberhardt Rd (76504-2600)
PHONE.....................................254 771-2253
EMP: 126 Privately Held
WEB: www.ljtube.com
SIC: 3317 Welded pipe & tubes
HQ: Lock Joint Tube Llc
   515 W Ireland Rd
   South Bend IN 46614

(G-19687)
MARS PETCARE US INC
3401 Eberhardt Rd (76504-2604)
PHONE.....................................254 771-3366
Tom Smolen, *Manager*
EMP: 100
SALES (corp-wide): 45B Privately Held
WEB: www.williamsonchamber.com
SIC: 2047 Dog food
HQ: Mars Petcare Us, Inc.
   2013 Ovation Pkwy
   Franklin TN 37067
   615 807-4626

(G-19688)
MATERIALS TRANSPORTATION CO (PA)
1408 S Commerce St (76504)
P.O. Box 1358 (76503-1358)
PHONE.....................................800 433-3110
Kenneth Alessi, *CEO*
Bob Neil, *Vice Pres*
Leonard Pate, *Vice Pres*
Peter Denharder, *Plant Mgr*
Peter Harder, *Mfg Staff*
◆ EMP: 142
SQ FT: 100,000
SALES (est): 30MM Privately Held
WEB: www.gomtc.com
SIC: 3559 3556 Automotive related machinery; food products machinery

(G-19689)
METAL SALES MANUFACTURING CORP
3838 N General Bruce Dr (76501-6505)
PHONE.....................................254 791-6650
Shaun Herron, *Production*
Nate Cheeley, *Inv Control Mgr*
Tanya Rexroat, *Asst Controller*
Frank Gigliotti, *Sales Staff*
Chris Glazik, *Sales Staff*
EMP: 30
SQ FT: 47,064
SALES (corp-wide): 390.6MM Privately Held
WEB: www.metalsales.us.com
SIC: 3444 Roof deck, sheet metal; siding, sheet metal
HQ: Metal Sales Manufacturing Corporation
   545 S 3rd St Ste 200
   Louisville KY 40202
   502 855-4300

(G-19690)
MIDWEST FOLDING PRODUCTS CORP (HQ)
1302 Industrial Blvd (76504-1126)
PHONE.....................................312 666-3366
Sam Thomas, *Vice Pres*
◆ EMP: 180
SQ FT: 200,000
SALES (est): 21.7MM
SALES (corp-wide): 2.2B Publicly Held
WEB: www.midwestfolding.com
SIC: 2531 5021 6512 5064 Public building & related furniture; public building furniture; shopping center, property operation only; electric household appliances
PA: Hni Corporation
   600 E 2nd St
   Muscatine IA 52761
   563 272-7400

(G-19691)
MOORECO INC (HQ)
Also Called: Balt Best Rite
2885 Lorraine Ave (76501-7402)
PHONE.....................................254 778-4727
Gregory C Moore, *CEO*
Naomi Lewis, *Regional Mgr*
Brian Wilkinson, *COO*
Jeanne Swift, *Vice Pres*
Trudy Vollmer, *Vice Pres*
▲ EMP: 116
SALES (est): 31.1MM Privately Held
WEB: www.moorecoinc.com
SIC: 2522 Office furniture, except wood

(G-19692)
MUELLER SUPPLY COMPANY INC
6910 N General Bruce Dr (76501-6617)
P.O. Box 1044 (76503-1044)
PHONE................................254 742-2754
Rodney Tedrow, *Branch Mgr*
EMP: 18
SQ FT: 37,750
SALES (corp-wide): 180.3MM **Privately Held**
WEB: www.muellerinc.com
SIC: 3448 Prefabricated metal buildings
PA: Mueller Supply Company, Inc.
    1913 Hutchins Ave
    Ballinger TX 76821
    325 365-3555

(G-19693)
PACTIV LLC
3000 Pegasus Dr (76501-6682)
PHONE................................254 770-4100
Tom Devito, *President*
Ron Figgins, *Plant Mgr*
Andrew J Eller, *QC Mgr*
Steve Corse, *Human Res Mgr*
Patrick Oneill, *Human Res Mgr*
EMP: 9 **Publicly Held**
WEB: www.pactiv.com
SIC: 2621 3086 2673 Paper mills; plastics
    foam products; bags: plastic, laminated &
    coated
HQ: Pactiv Llc
    1900 W Field Ct
    Lake Forest IL 60045
    847 482-2000

(G-19694)
PANEL SPECIALISTS INC
Topstone
3601 Range Rd (76504-1200)
PHONE................................254 774-9197
Carl Stein, *Division Mgr*
Ray E Schiller, *Vice Pres*
Dorothy Granfor, *Manager*
Todd Jones, *Manager*
EMP: 22
SALES (corp-wide): 9.5B **Publicly Held**
WEB: www.panelspec.com
SIC: 2531 3281 Public building & related
    furniture; granite, cut & shaped
HQ: Panel Specialists, Inc.
    3115 Range Rd
    Temple TX 76504

(G-19695)
PANEL SPECIALISTS INC (DH)
Also Called: PSI
3115 Range Rd (76504-1240)
P.O. Box 968 (76503-0968)
PHONE................................254 774-9800
Elliot Germany, *CEO*
Kurt E Toliver, *Principal*
Ray Schiller, *Exec VP*
Gary Kosel, *CFO*
Jason Yelverton, *Director*
▲ **EMP:** 60
SQ FT: 75,000
SALES (est): 41MM
SALES (corp-wide): 9.5B **Publicly Held**
WEB: www.panelspec.com
SIC: 2531 2452 2541 3083 Public build-
    ing & related furniture; panels & sections,
    prefabricated, wood; cabinets, lockers &
    shelving; laminated plastics plate & sheet

(G-19696)
PAPERGRAPHICS LTD (PA)
904 S 31st St (76504-5208)
PHONE................................254 526-4303
Dennis Smith, *Partner*
Smith-Ink Lc, *General Ptnr*
Gena Smith, *Controller*
Lisa Smith, *Webmaster*
EMP: 12
SQ FT: 6,000
SALES (est): 1.3MM **Privately Held**
WEB: www.papergraphicsltd.com
SIC: 2752 7334 7331 Commercial print-
    ing, offset; photocopying & duplicating
    services; mailing service

(G-19697)
PECHAL CABINETS LLC
18451 Se H K Dodgen Loop (76501-6821)
PHONE................................254 773-4460

Helen J Tepera, *Treasurer*
William J Tepera, *Mng Member*
John Dillard,
EMP: 12 **EST:** 1949
SQ FT: 21,000
SALES (est): 1.9MM **Privately Held**
SIC: 2434 Wood kitchen cabinets

(G-19698)
PECHAL PALLETS LLC
3205 E Adams Ave (76501-9619)
PHONE................................254 773-4460
Richard Tepera, *CEO*
William Tepera, *Mng Member*
EMP: 40
SQ FT: 21,694
SALES (est): 4.4MM **Privately Held**
SIC: 2448 Pallets, wood

(G-19699)
PERMOCAST CORPORATION
3110 Center St (76504-1227)
P.O. Box 1063 (76503-1063)
PHONE................................254 778-5216
Matthew Curry, *President*
Florine Curry, *Shareholder*
EMP: 28 **EST:** 1966
SQ FT: 30,000
SALES (est): 6MM **Privately Held**
WEB: www.permocast.com
SIC: 3366 Copper foundries

(G-19700)
QUVA PHARMA INC
5920 S General Bruce Dr # 100
(76502-5804)
PHONE................................201 306-4412
Travis Leeah, *Vice Pres*
Brett Coverdale, *CFO*
Shawna Maedgen, *Manager*
Joel Martinez, *Senior Mgr*
Alicia Ashford, *Director*
EMP: 50
SALES (corp-wide): 3MM **Privately Held**
WEB: www.quvapharma.com
SIC: 2834 Pharmaceutical preparations
PA: Quva Pharma, Inc.
    1075 W Park One Dr # 100
    Sugar Land TX 77478
    888 339-0874

(G-19701)
REYNOLDS CONSUMER PRODUCTS LLC
3000 Pegasus Dr (76501-6682)
PHONE................................254 770-4100
Gregory Alan Cole, *President*
Helen Dorothy Golding, *Vice Pres*
Cindi Alison Lefari, *Vice Pres*
EMP: 19
SALES (est): 4.9MM **Publicly Held**
WEB:
www.reynoldsconsumerproducts.com
SIC: 2671 2673 3842 Plastic film, coated
    or laminated for packaging; food storage
    & frozen food bags, plastic; swabs, sani-
    tary cotton
HQ: Reynolds Consumer Products Inc.
    1900 W Field Ct
    Lake Forest IL 60045
    800 879-5067

(G-19702)
SAGUS INTERNATIONAL INC (HQ)
1302 Industrial Blvd (76504-1126)
PHONE................................630 413-5540
Darryl Rosser, *President*
Len Farrell, *CFO*
EMP: 12
SQ FT: 4,000
SALES (est): 26.8MM
SALES (corp-wide): 2.2B **Publicly Held**
SIC: 2531 School furniture
PA: Hni Corporation
    600 E 2nd St
    Muscatine IA 52761
    563 272-7400

(G-19703)
STARCORR SHEETS LLC
4515 Wendland Rd (76504-2617)
PHONE................................254 598-7800
EMP: 54 **EST:** 2014

SALES (est): 7.6MM **Privately Held**
WEB: www.starcorrsheets.com
SIC: 2653 Solid fiber boxes, partitions, dis-
    play items & sheets

(G-19704)
SUNBELT TRANSFORMER LTD
1922 S Martin Luther King (76504-8611)
PHONE................................713 481-5500
Kyle Williams, *Branch Mgr*
EMP: 9
SALES (corp-wide): 34.2MM **Privately Held**
WEB: www.sunbeltusa.com
SIC: 3612 Power & distribution transform-
    ers
PA: Sunbelt Transformer, Ltd.
    1922 S Mrtn Lther King Jr
    Temple TX 76504
    800 433-3128

(G-19705)
SUNBELT TRANSFORMER LTD (PA)
1922 S Mrtn Lther King Jr (76504-8611)
PHONE................................800 433-3128
Dan Sweeney, *President*
Jim Gentry, *COO*
Eric Johnson, *Exec VP*
Bill Sparks, *Project Mgr*
Jason Tigner, *Opers Staff*
◆ **EMP:** 22 **EST:** 2001
SQ FT: 80,000
SALES (est): 34.2MM **Privately Held**
WEB: www.sunbeltusa.com
SIC: 3612 5063 Power & distribution
    transformers; transformers, electric

(G-19706)
TEMPLE BOTTLING COMPANY LTD (PA)
3510 Parkway Dr (76504-1243)
P.O. Box 308 (76503-0308)
PHONE................................254 773-3376
Elizabeth Floca, *Partner*
Kathryn Floca, *Partner*
T F Floca, *General Ptnr*
Bruce Connor, *Vice Pres*
Terri Sisk, *Controller*
EMP: 85
SQ FT: 130,000
SALES (est): 16.6MM **Privately Held**
WEB: www.templebot.com
SIC: 2086 5149 Soft drinks: packaged in
    cans, bottles, etc.; groceries & related
    products

(G-19707)
TEMPLE FREIGHTLINER LP
4848 N General Bruce Dr (76501-9722)
PHONE................................254 770-1422
Clay Corley, *Principal*
EMP: 35
SALES (est): 963.6K **Privately Held**
WEB: www.ltgtemple.com
SIC: 3713 Truck bodies & parts

(G-19708)
TEMPLE GENERATION I LLC
2892 Panda Dr (76501-6838)
PHONE................................254 598-3700
Anuradha Sen, *VP Finance*
Daniel Hudson, *Mng Member*
EMP: 33
SALES (est): 11.5MM **Privately Held**
WEB: www.templegenerationi.com
SIC: 1382 Oil & gas exploration services
PA: Panda Power Funds
    5001 Spring Valley Rd 1150w
    Dallas TX 75244
    972 361-2000

(G-19709)
TEMPLE MACHINE SHOP INC
1401 N 14th St (76501-2076)
P.O. Box 576 (76503-0576)
PHONE................................254 774-8099
Stewart Fettig, *President*
Michelle Fettig, *Corp Secy*
Lisa Ortiz, *Opers Staff*
▲ **EMP:** 70
SQ FT: 45,000

SALES (est): 18.5MM **Privately Held**
WEB: www.tmshydraulics.com
SIC: 3593 3599 Fluid power cylinders, hy-
    draulic or pneumatic; machine shop, job-
    bing & repair

(G-19710)
TEMPLE TAG II LTD
1110 Industrial Blvd (76504-1130)
P.O. Box 369 (76503-0369)
PHONE................................254 982-4212
Roger Hinds, *Ch of Bd*
Bill McCoy, *President*
▲ **EMP:** 52
SQ FT: 20,000
SALES (est): 14.2MM **Privately Held**
WEB: www.datamarsna.com
SIC: 3089 Injection molding of plastics

(G-19711)
TEMPLE WATER TREATMENT
4820 Parkside Dr (76502-5704)
PHONE................................254 939-2161
EMP: 16 **EST:** 1910
SALES (est): 1.7MM **Privately Held**
SIC: 3589 Sewage & water treatment
    equipment

(G-19712)
TEXAS HYDRAULICS INC (HQ)
Also Called: Precise Hard Chrome
3410 Range Rd (76504-1237)
P.O. Box 1067 (76503-1067)
PHONE................................254 778-4701
Patrick Taylor, *CEO*
Matthew Fangman, *Principal*
Chris Shelton, *Vice Pres*
Carl Troy, *Buyer*
Jeremy Karnowski, *Engineer*
▲ **EMP:** 700
SQ FT: 100,000
SALES (est): 336.9MM
SALES (corp-wide): 53.4MM **Privately Held**
WEB: www.texashydraulics.com
SIC: 3593 3443 Fluid power cylinders, hy-
    draulic or pneumatic; industrial vessels,
    tanks & containers
PA: Texas Hydraulics Holdings, Inc.
    3410 Range Rd
    Temple TX 76504
    254 778-4701

(G-19713)
TOM LANHAM SOFTWARE
2801 W Avenue T (76504-6430)
P.O. Box 360, Belton (76513-0360)
PHONE................................254 773-2513
Tom Lanham, *Owner*
EMP: 9
SQ FT: 3,000
SALES (est): 848.3K **Privately Held**
SIC: 7372 Prepackaged software

(G-19714)
VIRON INTERNATIONAL CORP
3100 Lucius Mccelvey Dr (76504-1201)
PHONE................................254 773-9292
Terry Gregoricka, *Manager*
EMP: 90
SALES (corp-wide): 17.8MM **Privately Held**
WEB: www.vironintl.com
SIC: 3564 Air purification equipment
PA: Viron International Corporation
    505 N Hintz Rd
    Owosso MI 48867
    989 773-9292

(G-19715)
WILSONART INTL HOLDINGS INC
2400 Wilson Pl (76504-5131)
PHONE................................254 207-7000
John Krenicki, *President*
EMP: 30 **EST:** 1995
SALES (est): 6.1MM **Privately Held**
WEB: www.wilsonart.com
SIC: 2821 Plastics materials & resins

(G-19716)
WILSONART INTL HOLDINGS LLC (DH)
2501 Wilsonart Dr (76504-1232)
P.O. Box 6110 (76503-6110)
PHONE................................254 207-7000

Terry Jackson, *Production*
Nicole Kepler, *Human Resources*
Tammy Weadock, *Pub Rel Staff*
Sathish Iyer, *IT/INT Sup*
Kevin Sweeney, *Director*
EMP: 89
SALES (est): 259.9MM
SALES (corp-wide): 4.9B **Privately Held**
WEB: www.wilsonart.com
SIC: 2541 Counters or counter display cases, wood; display fixtures, wood; office fixtures, wood

(G-19717)
WILSONART INTL HOLDINGS LLC
10501 Nw H K Dodgen Loop (76504-6805)
PHONE.................................254 207-6000
David Craven, *Branch Mgr*
EMP: 31
SALES (corp-wide): 4.9B **Privately Held**
WEB: www.wilsonart.com
SIC: 2821 2541 Plastics materials & resins; table or counter tops, plastic laminated
HQ: Wilsonart International Holdings Llc
　　2501 Wilsonart Dr
　　Temple TX 76504
　　254 207-7000

(G-19718)
WILSONART INTL HOLDINGS LLC
2400 Wilson Pl (76504-5131)
P.O. Box 6110 (76503-6110)
PHONE.................................254 207-7000
Cathy Chester, *Manager*
EMP: 40
SALES (corp-wide): 4.9B **Privately Held**
WEB: www.wilsonart.com
SIC: 2821 2541 Plastics materials & resins; table or counter tops, plastic laminated
HQ: Wilsonart International Holdings Llc
　　2501 Wilsonart Dr
　　Temple TX 76504
　　254 207-7000

(G-19719)
WILSONART LLC (DH)
Also Called: Wilsonart Engineered Surfaces
2501 Wilsonart Dr (76504-1232)
P.O. Box 6110 (76503-6110)
PHONE.................................254 207-7000
Timothy J Obrien, *CEO*
Susie Klein, *Regional Mgr*
Mike Locke, *Regional Mgr*
Wayne Irmiter, *Vice Pres*
John Siemon, *Vice Pres*
EMP: 15
SALES (est): 60.2MM
SALES (corp-wide): 4.9B **Privately Held**
WEB: www.wilsonart.com
SIC: 2541 Counters or counter display cases, wood; display fixtures, wood; office fixtures, wood
HQ: Wilsonart International Holdings Llc
　　2501 Wilsonart Dr
　　Temple TX 76504
　　254 207-7000

(G-19720)
WILSONART LLC
2400 Wilson Pl (76504-5131)
PHONE.................................254 742-2451
Connor Rankin, *Sales Staff*
Julie Mattson, *Manager*
John Hubbard, *Manager*
EMP: 45
SQ FT: 138,240
SALES (corp-wide): 4.9B **Privately Held**
WEB: www.wilsonart.com
SIC: 2821 2541 Plastics materials & resins; table or counter tops, plastic laminated
HQ: Wilsonart Llc
　　2501 Wilsonart Dr
　　Temple TX 76504
　　254 207-7000

(G-19721)
WILSONART LLC
1110 Industrial Blvd (76504-1130)
PHONE.................................254 207-7000
Regina Gallia, *Branch Mgr*
EMP: 12

SQ FT: 27,600
SALES (corp-wide): 4.9B **Privately Held**
WEB: www.wilsonart.com
SIC: 2541 Counter & sink tops
HQ: Wilsonart Llc
　　2501 Wilsonart Dr
　　Temple TX 76504
　　254 207-7000

(G-19722)
WILSONART LLC
500 E Ridge Blvd (76502-4068)
P.O. Box 6110 (76503-6110)
PHONE.................................254 207-0207
Lisa Palomino, *Manager*
EMP: 23
SALES (corp-wide): 4.9B **Privately Held**
WEB: www.wilsonart.com
SIC: 2821 2541 Plastics materials & resins; table or counter tops, plastic laminated
HQ: Wilsonart Llc
　　2501 Wilsonart Dr
　　Temple TX 76504
　　254 207-7000

Tenaha
Shelby County

(G-19723)
BASIC ENERGY SERVICES INC
724 84 Hwy E (75974)
P.O. Box 379 (75974-0379)
PHONE.................................936 248-2788
Robbie Hale, *Manager*
EMP: 34
SALES (corp-wide): 567.2MM **Publicly Held**
WEB: www.basices.com
SIC: 1389 Oil field services
PA: Basic Energy Services, Inc.
　　801 Cherry St Unit 2
　　Fort Worth TX 76102
　　817 334-4100

(G-19724)
PILGRIMS PRIDE CORPORATION
Also Called: Tenaha Feed Mill
Hwy 59 (75974)
PHONE.................................936 248-5600
Jim Jacobs, *Manager*
Chad Norton, *Manager*
EMP: 29 **Publicly Held**
WEB: www.pilgrims.com
SIC: 2015 Chicken, slaughtered & dressed
HQ: Pilgrim's Pride Corporation
　　1770 Promontory Cir
　　Greeley CO 80634
　　970 506-8000

(G-19725)
TYSON FOODS INC
7665 Us Highway 96 N (75974-2564)
PHONE.................................936 248-2081
John Rittenberry, *Manager*
EMP: 30
SALES (corp-wide): 43.1B **Publicly Held**
WEB: www.tysonfoods.com
SIC: 2011 2048 Meat packing plants; prepared feeds
PA: Tyson Foods, Inc.
　　2200 W Don Tyson Pkwy
　　Springdale AR 72762
　　479 290-4000

Tennessee Colony
Anderson County

(G-19726)
PINNACLE GAS TREATING LLC
1760 An County Road 2608 (75861-3304)
PHONE.................................903 928-1200
Bill Buckley, *Branch Mgr*
EMP: 10
SALES (corp-wide): 21.2B **Publicly Held**
WEB: www.oxy.com
SIC: 1382 Oil & gas exploration services
HQ: Pinnacle Gas Treating Llc
　　1201 Lake Robbins Dr
　　The Woodlands TX 77380
　　832 636-1000

(G-19727)
WINKEL & SON INC
1159 Fm 645 (75861-2355)
PHONE.................................903 928-2560
Todd Winkel, *President*
EMP: 20
SALES (est): 2.1MM **Privately Held**
SIC: 1389 1629 Excavating slush pits & cellars; railroad & railway roadbed construction

Terrell
Kaufman County

(G-19728)
BINGHAM MANUFACTURING INC
Also Called: Bingham Industries
2000 Airport Rd (75160-5213)
PHONE.................................360 863-1170
Gary Bingham, *President*
Jeremy Bingham, *President*
▼ **EMP:** 9
SALES (est): 1.6MM **Privately Held**
WEB: www.binghamindustries.com
SIC: 3589 Water treatment equipment, industrial

(G-19729)
BUBBACO
2031 Dogpatch Dr (75161-8111)
PHONE.................................972 768-0282
Wilfred Berbeaux, *Partner*
Sandra Berbeaux, *Partner*
EMP: 10
SALES (est): 976.9K **Privately Held**
SIC: 3499 Fire- or burglary-resistive products

(G-19730)
CARLISLE CONSTRUCTION MTLS LLC
10 Rexel Ct (75160)
PHONE.................................214 515-5200
Brandi Hendrix, *Human Resources*
Jay Rector, *Manager*
EMP: 30
SALES (corp-wide): 4.2B **Publicly Held**
WEB: www.carlisleconstructionmaterials.com
SIC: 3086 Insulation or cushioning material, foamed plastic
HQ: Carlisle Construction Materials, Llc
　　1285 Ritner Hwy
　　Carlisle PA 17013

(G-19731)
COMPLIANT PAINT BOOTHS LLC
6 Skyline Dr (75160-5413)
PHONE.................................800 609-6408
Teresa Owens, *Engineer*
Donnie Montgomery, *Mng Member*
EMP: 14
SQ FT: 15,000
SALES (est): 2.9MM **Privately Held**
WEB: www.compliantpaintbooths.com
SIC: 2851 Paints & allied products

(G-19732)
ECS REFINING TEXAS LLC
106 Tejas Dr (75160-6573)
PHONE.................................972 524-1075
Jim Taggart, *CEO*
Ken Taggart, *Exec VP*
Bill McGeever, *Vice Pres*
Mark Robards, *Vice Pres*
Monica Hushen, *CFO*
▲ **EMP:** 35
SALES (est): 7.3MM **Privately Held**
WEB: www.bigtimeshirt.com
SIC: 3341 4953 Secondary nonferrous metals; recycling, waste materials

(G-19733)
FACTORY MOTORHOMES INC
11394 County Road 2312 (75160-8948)
PHONE.................................214 830-2910
Teddy D Moody, *President*
EMP: 15
SQ FT: 10,000

SALES (est): 1.5MM **Privately Held**
SIC: 3715 3716 Truck trailers; motor homes

(G-19734)
FINE LINE MET FABRICATORS INC
Also Called: Fine Line Metalfab
3975 Tem Tex Blvd (75160-6659)
PHONE.................................972 524-6248
Brian S Whitehead, *President*
Carl L Morgan, *Vice Pres*
Carl Morgan, *Vice Pres*
Monte Morrish, *Treasurer*
Steve W Whitehead, *Admin Sec*
EMP: 35
SQ FT: 31,000
SALES (est): 8.7MM **Privately Held**
WEB: www.finelinemetal.net
SIC: 3441 Fabricated structural metal

(G-19735)
GH CRANES & COMPONENTS USA INC
Also Called: F&G Cranes
14891 Hwy 205 (75160-0905)
P.O. Box 704 (75160-0013)
PHONE.................................972 563-8333
Sergio Robledo, *President*
Delmar G Garrett, *President*
Gene Garrett, *President*
Carolyn Burns, *Buyer*
Rodney Lance, *Sales Staff*
▲ **EMP:** 40
SQ FT: 33,000
SALES: 11.5MM **Privately Held**
WEB: www.fgcranes.com
SIC: 3536 7699 7389 5084 Cranes & monorail systems; hoists; industrial equipment services; crane & aerial lift service; hoists
HQ: Industrias Electromecanicas G H Sa
　　Apartado De Correos 27 (Bo Salbatore Auzoa)
　　Beasain 20200
　　943 805-660

(G-19736)
HALO FBRICATION METALWORKS LLC
203 Metro Dr (75160-9170)
PHONE.................................972 587-0788
Tammy Horton, *President*
Bobby Horton, *General Mgr*
EMP: 25
SALES (est): 3MM **Privately Held**
SIC: 3441 Fabricated structural metal

(G-19737)
HARTMAN NEWSPAPERS LP
Also Called: Terrell Tribune
150 9th St (75160-3061)
P.O. Box 669 (75160-0012)
PHONE.................................972 563-6476
Michael Gresham, *Manager*
EMP: 12
SQ FT: 6,000
SALES (corp-wide): 32.2MM **Privately Held**
WEB: www.portlavacawave.com
SIC: 2711 7313 Newspapers: publishing only, not printed on site; newspaper advertising representative
PA: Hartman Newspapers L.P.
　　1914 4th St
　　Rosenberg TX 77471
　　281 342-8691

(G-19738)
INNOCOR FOAM TECH - ACP INC
501 Industrial Blvd (75160-5403)
PHONE.................................972 563-1559
Chris Lacorata, *CEO*
EMP: 14 **Privately Held**
WEB: www.innocorfoamtechnologies.com
SIC: 3086 Plastics foam products
HQ: Innocor Foam Technologies - Acp, Inc.
　　200 Schulz Dr Ste 2
　　Red Bank NJ 07701
　　732 945-6222

(G-19739)
LONGHORN FABRICATION INC
3200 Airport Rd (75160-5212)
PHONE................................972 225-6800
Eric Sullins, *Owner*
EMP: 70
SQ FT: 19,056
SALES (est): 17.3MM **Privately Held**
WEB: www.longhornfab.com
SIC: 3441 Fabricated structural metal

(G-19740)
MADIX INC (PA)
500 Airport Rd (75160-5200)
P.O. Box 729 (75160-9001)
PHONE................................214 515-5400
Alan H Sharaway, *Ch of Bd*
Thomas A Satterfield, *President*
Joyce Weinstein, *Principal*
Mike Huey, *Vice Pres*
Mark Pugh, *Plant Supt*
◆ EMP: 1400
SQ FT: 925,000
SALES: 307.8MM **Privately Held**
WEB: www.madixinc.com
SIC: 2542 2541 Fixtures, store: except wood; wood partitions & fixtures; display fixtures, wood

(G-19741)
MC HONE METAL FABRICATORS INC
10300 County Road 304 (75160-6574)
PHONE................................972 524-7775
Wil Mc Hone, *President*
Marie Perry, *Info Tech Mgr*
Tony R Dirickson, *Admin Sec*
EMP: 10
SQ FT: 1,580
SALES (est): 1.4MM **Privately Held**
WEB: www.mchonemetalfabricators.com
SIC: 3444 Sheet metal specialties, not stamped

(G-19742)
MECHANICAL SHEET METAL INC
3002 Tem Tex Blvd (75160-6593)
P.O. Box 127 (75160-0003)
PHONE................................972 524-6200
Jerry W Langley, *President*
Cory Langley, *Vice Pres*
Gary Langley, *Vice Pres*
Shane Langley, *Vice Pres*
Corry Langley, *Executive*
EMP: 32
SQ FT: 21,000
SALES (est): 12.1MM **Privately Held**
WEB: www.msmmechanical.com
SIC: 3444 Sheet metal specialties, not stamped

(G-19743)
NATURAL TECHNOLOGY INC
Also Called: Naturetech
350 Apache Trl (75160-6592)
P.O. Box 795788, Dallas (75379-5788)
PHONE................................972 551-2563
Jeff Svendsen, *CEO*
Benjamin Baume, *CFO*
EMP: 20
SQ FT: 36,000
SALES (est): 5.5MM **Privately Held**
SIC: 5122 2844 Cosmetics; hair preparations, including shampoos

(G-19744)
NUCOR BLDG SYSTEMS SLS CORP
600 Apache Trl (75160-6512)
PHONE................................972 524-5407
Jeff Carmean, *President*
Kelechi Emelogu, *Design Engr*
Brett Ullom, *Controller*
Jonathan Pikett, *Sales Mgr*
Jose Cavazos, *Manager*
EMP: 250
SALES (est): 51.1MM
SALES (corp-wide): 22.5B **Publicly Held**
WEB: www.nucorbuildingsystems.com
SIC: 3448 Prefabricated metal buildings
PA: Nucor Corporation
1915 Rexford Rd Ste 400
Charlotte NC 28211
704 366-7000

(G-19745)
NUCOR CORPORATION
Also Called: Nucor Building Systems Texas
600 Apache Trl (75160-6512)
PHONE................................972 524-5407
Ray Napolitan, *General Mgr*
Shawn Cornett, *Safety Dir*
Kelly Lengacher, *Purch Mgr*
Briana Abernathy, *Buyer*
Melanie Sisk, *Buyer*
EMP: 103
SALES (corp-wide): 22.5B **Publicly Held**
WEB: www.nucor.com
SIC: 3312 3316 Blast furnaces & steel mills; cold finishing of steel shapes
PA: Nucor Corporation
1915 Rexford Rd Ste 400
Charlotte NC 28211
704 366-7000

(G-19746)
OLDCASTLE BUILDINGENVELOPE INC
Also Called: Oldcastle Glass
803 Airport Rd (75160-5224)
P.O. Box 629 (75160-0011)
PHONE................................972 551-6100
Eric Villanueva, *Purchasing*
Alan Stewart, *Plant Engr*
Shelley Carpenter, *Accountant*
Mark Lehman, *Sales Mgr*
Michael Zaremba, *Program Mgr*
EMP: 900
SALES (corp-wide): 30.6B **Privately Held**
WEB: www.obe.com
SIC: 3442 3354 3448 5039 Metal doors, sash & trim; aluminum extruded products; panels for prefabricated metal buildings; prefabricated structures; metals service centers & offices; prefabricated wood buildings
HQ: Oldcastle Buildingenvelope, Inc.
5005 Lyndon B Johnson Fwy # 1050
Dallas TX 75244
214 273-3400

(G-19747)
OLDCASTLE GL ENGNERED PDTS INC
Also Called: Vistawall
803 Airport Rd (75160-5224)
PHONE................................972 563-2627
Edwin B Hathaway, *CEO*
EMP: 150
SALES (est): 27.9MM
SALES (corp-wide): 30.6B **Privately Held**
SIC: 3271 Architectural concrete: block, split, fluted, screen, etc.
HQ: Oldcastle Buildingenvelope, Inc.
5005 Lyndon B Johnson Fwy # 1050
Dallas TX 75244
214 273-3400

(G-19748)
R & R DESIGN INC
1112 S Virginia St (75160-4507)
P.O. Box 220 (75160-0004)
PHONE................................972 524-1789
Clifford Rabal, *President*
Robert Rabal, *Treasurer*
EMP: 50
SQ FT: 15,000
SALES (est): 13.7MM **Privately Held**
WEB: www.mrd.com
SIC: 3444 3732 Sheet metal specialties, not stamped; boat building & repairing

(G-19749)
RENFRO INDUSTRIES INC
102 Metro Dr (75160-9104)
P.O. Box 773 (75160-0015)
PHONE................................972 563-4295
Richard L Renfro, *President*
Wanda F Renfro, *Admin Sec*
▲ EMP: 81
SQ FT: 300,000
SALES (est): 16.1MM **Privately Held**
WEB: www.renfroindustries.com
SIC: 3578 3589 3496 Point-of-sale devices; commercial cooking & foodwarming equipment; grilles & grillework, woven wire

(G-19750)
SOLAR ACCESSORIES CORPORATION
109 Silent Wings Blvd (75160-5422)
P.O. Box 725 (75160-0014)
PHONE................................972 524-2099
Dennis Yarborough, *CEO*
Darren Yarborough, *Vice Pres*
EMP: 10
SQ FT: 26,000
SALES (est): 1MM **Privately Held**
WEB: www.solaraccessoriescorp.com
SIC: 3444 Skylights, sheet metal

(G-19751)
SOUTHLAND ATHLETIC MFG CO
714 E Grove St (75160-3746)
P.O. Box 280 (75160-0005)
PHONE................................972 563-3321
William C Sturgeon, *President*
James M Warlick Jr, *Chairman*
Paul J Themer, *Vice Pres*
EMP: 75
SQ FT: 30,000
SALES (est): 5.3MM **Privately Held**
WEB: www.southland-athletic.com
SIC: 2339 2329 2326 Uniforms, athletic: women's, misses' & juniors'; men's & boys' athletic uniforms; men's & boys' work clothing

(G-19752)
STEELWAY INTERNATIONAL LLC
2990 Tem Tex Blvd (75160-6584)
PHONE................................972 563-2000
Kirk Hagler, *Mng Member*
Willy Hagler, *Technology*
Mike Baker, *Director*
Eric Sides,
EMP: 32
SALES (est): 6.6MM **Privately Held**
WEB: www.steelwayintl.com
SIC: 3449 Bars, concrete reinforcing: fabricated steel

(G-19753)
TOWSLEY AND BAILEY INC
10415 County Road 305 (75160-6515)
PHONE................................972 563-5400
Vernon Towsley, *President*
David Bailey, *Treasurer*
EMP: 9
SALES (est): 903.2K **Privately Held**
SIC: 3496 Grilles & grillework, woven wire

(G-19754)
VAN TONE CREATIVE FLAVORS INC
200 Metro Dr (75160-9169)
PHONE................................972 563-2600
B David Hinds, *President*
Christy Johnson, *Purchasing*
Lisa Devore, *Finance*
Christy Henderson, *Admin Sec*
EMP: 20
SQ FT: 37,000
SALES (est): 3MM **Privately Held**
WEB: www.vantonecf.com
SIC: 2087 Extracts, flavoring

(G-19755)
VEKA SOUTH INC
107 Metrocrest Way (75160-6565)
PHONE................................972 551-2030
Joachim Peilert, *President*
James H Druschel, *Vice Pres*
Glenn H Taborski, *Treasurer*
Verne Welch, *Sales Mgr*
◆ EMP: 22
SALES (est): 4MM
SALES (corp-wide): 1.2B **Privately Held**
WEB: www.vekainc.com
SIC: 3089 Extruded finished plastic products
HQ: Veka Holdings, Inc.
100 Veka Dr
Fombell PA 16123

Texarkana
Bowie County

(G-19756)
BAPTIST SUNDAY SCHL COMMITTEE
Also Called: Baptist Book Store
4605 N State Line Ave (75503-2916)
PHONE................................903 792-2783
Wayne Sewell, *Principal*
David Butimore, *Principal*
Steve Butler, *Principal*
Neal Clark, *Principal*
Mark Harris, *Principal*
▲ EMP: 50 EST: 1904
SQ FT: 60,000
SALES (est): 5.2MM **Privately Held**
WEB:
www.baptistbookstoreintexarkana.com
SIC: 5942 2721 Books, religious; periodicals: publishing & printing

(G-19757)
BRUCE KENNEDY SAND & GRAVEL CO (PA)
Also Called: Kennedy Construction Co
1201 S Robison Rd (75501)
PHONE................................903 838-3377
Gloria Kennedy, *Owner*
EMP: 10 EST: 1946
SALES (est): 3.1MM **Privately Held**
SIC: 5211 1442 Sand & gravel; construction sand & gravel

(G-19758)
CARAUSTAR INDUSTRIES INC
Also Called: Texarkana Recycling Plant
112 S Lelia Ave (75501-6972)
PHONE................................903 793-6231
Sharon Straun, *General Mgr*
Danny Wicker, *Plant Mgr*
EMP: 50
SALES (corp-wide): 4.5B **Publicly Held**
WEB: www.greif.com
SIC: 2679 2655 2673 3275 Paperboard products, converted; tubes, fiber or paper: made from purchased material; cores, fiber: made from purchased material; bags: plastic, laminated & coated; gypsum products; wallboard, gypsum; injection molded finished plastic products; extruded finished plastic products; folding boxboard
HQ: Caraustar Industries, Inc.
5000 Austell Powder Sprin
Austell GA 30106
770 948-3101

(G-19759)
COCA-COLA REFRESHMENTS USA INC
1930 New Boston Rd (75501-3506)
PHONE................................903 276-1295
Scott McCallister, *Branch Mgr*
EMP: 80
SALES (corp-wide): 37.2B **Publicly Held**
WEB: www.coca-colacompany.com
SIC: 2086 Bottled & canned soft drinks
HQ: Coca-Cola Refreshments Usa, Inc.
2500 Windy Ridge Pkwy Se
Atlanta GA 30339
770 989-3000

(G-19760)
COLGATE-PALMOLIVE COMPANY
303 Falvey Ave (75501-6620)
PHONE................................903 832-8615
Robert Goergen, *Branch Mgr*
EMP: 279
SALES (corp-wide): 15.6B **Publicly Held**
WEB: www.colgate.com
SIC: 2844 Toilet preparations
PA: Colgate-Palmolive Company
300 Park Ave Fl 8
New York NY 10022
212 310-2000

(G-19761)
COMMERCIAL MFG CO INC
1713 W 24th St (75501-3672)
P.O. Box 1836 (75504-1836)
PHONE................................903 794-1321

W Robert Pickens, *President*
EMP: 18
SQ FT: 25,000
SALES (est): 800K **Privately Held**
WEB: www.cmcfinishing.com
SIC: 3471 7389 Finishing, metals or formed products; metal slitting & shearing

(G-19762)
DOUBLE S SIGNS LLC
Also Called: Hightech Signs
3502 New Boston Rd (75501-3140)
PHONE.................................903 838-8999
Jared Russell Sparks, *President*
Bill Shepherd, *Vice Pres*
Lee Shepherd,
EMP: 10
SALES (est): 321K **Privately Held**
SIC: 3993 Signs & advertising specialties

(G-19763)
FIRMIN PRINTING & OFF EQP CO (PA)
Also Called: Firmin's Office City
2217 N State Line Ave (75501-3924)
P.O. Box 951 (75504-0951)
PHONE.................................903 793-5566
Chuck Firmin, *President*
Kenneth Williams, *Business Mgr*
Charles Firmin Jr, *Vice Pres*
Judie Firmin, *Treasurer*
EMP: 25
SQ FT: 15,000
SALES (est): 7.8MM **Privately Held**
WEB: www.firmins.com
SIC: 5943 2759 5712 Office forms & supplies; commercial printing; office furniture

(G-19764)
HANSON AGGREGATES LLC
2515 W 7th St (75501-6417)
PHONE.................................903 794-6161
Darrel Youngblood, *Manager*
EMP: 35
SALES (corp-wide): 20.8B **Privately Held**
WEB: www.heidelbergcement.com
SIC: 5032 5211 3273 Concrete & cinder block; lumber & other building materials; ready-mixed concrete
HQ: Hanson Aggregates Llc
　　8505 Freport Pkwy Ste 500
　　Irving TX 75063
　　469 417-1200

(G-19765)
HOWMET AEROSPACE INC
300 Alumax Dr (75501-0209)
PHONE.................................903 832-8471
Ann Whitty, *Branch Mgr*
EMP: 316
SALES (corp-wide): 14.1B **Publicly Held**
WEB: www.howmet.com
SIC: 3353 Aluminum sheet & strip
PA: Howmet Aerospace Inc.
　　201 Isabella St Ste 200
　　Pittsburgh PA 15212
　　412 553-1940

(G-19766)
HUMCO HOLDING GROUP INC (HQ)
7400 Alumax Rd (75501-0282)
PHONE.................................903 831-7808
Gregory C Pulido, *President*
Shane Meador, *Exec VP*
Terry Bird, *Vice Pres*
Lana Carmeli, *Vice Pres*
Carissa Clack, *Vice Pres*
◆ **EMP:** 102
SQ FT: 121,000
SALES (est): 47.5MM **Privately Held**
WEB: www.humco.com
SIC: 2834 2899 2844 Pharmaceutical preparations; chemical preparations; toilet preparations

(G-19767)
KELLEY INSTRUMENT MACHINE INC
120 Fairway St (75501-9533)
P.O. Box 5368 (75505-5368)
PHONE.................................903 832-3332
William T Kelley, *President*
William Kelley, *Vice Pres*
Angela Law, *Admin Sec*

▲ **EMP:** 29
SQ FT: 9,450
SALES (est): 700K **Privately Held**
WEB: www.kelleyplates.com
SIC: 3533 3824 Oil field machinery & equipment; fluid meters & counting devices

(G-19768)
LEDWELL & SON ENTERPRISES INC (PA)
Also Called: Ledwell Office Solutions
3300 Waco St (75501-6645)
P.O. Box 1106 (75504-1106)
PHONE.................................903 838-6531
Stephen H Ledwell, *President*
Steven Ledwell, *Corp Secy*
Mary Elizabeth Ledwell, *Exec VP*
Gary Gathright, *Engineer*
Michael Brackins, *Manager*
◆ **EMP:** 214 **EST:** 1946
SQ FT: 192,000
SALES (est): 38.2MM **Privately Held**
WEB: www.ledwell.com
SIC: 3715 5013 Truck trailers; trailer parts & accessories

(G-19769)
MAYO MFG CORPORATION
4101 Terry St (75501-6759)
P.O. Box 5338 (75505-5338)
PHONE.................................903 838-0518
Mike Delisle, *General Mgr*
Michael L Mayo, *Principal*
Patrick J Mayo, *Vice Pres*
Patrick Mayo, *Vice Pres*
Stephen Mayo, *Vice Pres*
◆ **EMP:** 130 **EST:** 1965
SQ FT: 156,000
SALES (est): 21.7MM **Privately Held**
WEB: www.mayofurniture.com
SIC: 2512 Living room furniture: upholstered on wood frames

(G-19770)
P-AMERICAS LLC
Also Called: Pepsico
3005 Magnolia St (75503-3720)
PHONE.................................903 794-3883
Carol Boze, *Manager*
EMP: 43
SALES (corp-wide): 67.1B **Publicly Held**
SIC: 2086 Carbonated soft drinks, bottled & canned
HQ: P-Americas Llc
　　1 Pepsi Way
　　Somers NY 10589
　　336 896-5740

(G-19771)
PRECISION DEF COMPONENTS LLC
5911 Richmond Rd Apt 4103 (75503-1201)
PHONE.................................870 949-8590
Matt Baraga, *Principal*
EMP: 12 **EST:** 2016
SALES (est): 469K **Privately Held**
SIC: 3599 3728 Machine shop, jobbing & repair; research & dev by manuf., aircraft parts & auxiliary equip

(G-19772)
SIDCO MINERALS INC
2801 Richmond Rd Ste 51 (75503-2123)
P.O. Box 51 (75504-0051)
PHONE.................................903 838-4493
Bill Fuerst, *President*
Marjorie Fuerst, *President*
EMP: 15
SQ FT: 5,000
SALES (est): 2.2MM **Privately Held**
WEB: www.sidcominerals.com
SIC: 3295 Minerals, ground or treated

(G-19773)
SIGN TECHNOLOGIES INC
Also Called: Hightech Signs
3502 New Boston Rd (75501-3140)
PHONE.................................903 838-8999
Barbara K Adcock, *President*
EMP: 12
SQ FT: 6,000

SALES (est): 715K **Privately Held**
WEB: www.hightechsign.com
SIC: 3993 7389 5999 1799 Signs, not made in custom sign painting shops; engraving service; banners, flags, decals & posters; sign installation & maintenance

(G-19774)
SPORTS MAGIC INC
8523 S Lake Dr (75501-9093)
PHONE.................................903 832-1975
Roger Sheppard, *President*
Lindsey Tilgreen, *Vice Pres*
Debra Sheppard, *Admin Sec*
EMP: 11
SQ FT: 8,400
SALES (est): 1.4MM **Privately Held**
WEB: www.sportsmagicinc.com
SIC: 2396 7389 2759 2395 Screen printing on fabric articles; fund raising organizations; screen printing; embroidery products, except schiffli machine

(G-19775)
STERNO GROUP LLC
303 Falvey Ave (75501-6620)
PHONE.................................903 223-3400
Reggie Moss, *Branch Mgr*
EMP: 145 **Publicly Held**
WEB: www.sternopro.com
SIC: 3589 Commercial cooking & food-warming equipment
HQ: Sterno Products, Llc
　　1880 Compton Ave Ste 101
　　Corona CA 92881

(G-19776)
STEWART STEVENSON PWR PDTS LLC
80 Bilek Dr (75501-1362)
PHONE.................................903 838-9966
EMP: 17
SALES (corp-wide): 2.8B **Publicly Held**
WEB: www.stewartandstevenson.com
SIC: 5999 1389 Engine & motor equipment & supplies; construction, repair & dismantling services
HQ: Stewart & Stevenson Power Products, Llc
　　55 Waugh Dr Ste 800
　　Houston TX 77007

(G-19777)
TEXARKANA DOOR & WINDOW INC
6509 Farmers Ln (75503-1899)
PHONE.................................903 793-6011
Larry Walls, *President*
Kerry Cook, *Purch Agent*
EMP: 15
SQ FT: 14,000
SALES (est): 3.2MM **Privately Held**
WEB: www.tdwdoor.net
SIC: 5211 2431 Lumber & other building materials; doors, wood

(G-19778)
TEXARKANA EMB & GRAPHICS
21 Lambeth Rd (75503-2557)
PHONE.................................903 792-1144
EMP: 10
SQ FT: 2,260
SALES: 750K **Privately Held**
SIC: 2395 Pleating/Stitching Services

(G-19779)
TEXARKANA MACHINE INC
277 White Rd E (75503-5077)
PHONE.................................903 831-4355
Stephen Petty Sr, *President*
Randy Crocker, *Production*
Rebecca Harris, *Finance Mgr*
Kerri Crocker, *Office Mgr*
EMP: 13
SQ FT: 23,500
SALES (est): 860K **Privately Held**
WEB: www.texarkanamachine.com
SIC: 3554 3599 Paper mill machinery: plating, slitting, waxing, etc.; machine shop, jobbing & repair

(G-19780)
TEXAS MUSIC MAGAZINE
120 Cherokee Trl Apt 5 (75501-9553)
PHONE.................................903 838-3838
Bill Chapman, *Owner*

Stewart Ramser, *Director*
EMP: 22
SALES (est): 965.3K **Privately Held**
SIC: 2721 Magazines: publishing only, not printed on site

(G-19781)
TRINITY SERVICES GROUP INC
2819 W 7th St (75501-6423)
PHONE.................................903 277-7128
EMP: 111
SQ FT: 1,200
SALES (corp-wide): 437.4MM **Privately Held**
WEB: www.trinityservicesgroup.com
SIC: 7694 7692 7699 1542 Motor repair services; welding repair; engine repair & replacement, non-automotive; nonresidential construction
HQ: Trinity Services Group, Inc.
　　477 Commerce Blvd
　　Oldsmar FL 34677

(G-19782)
TRONOX INCORPORATED
2513 Buchanan Rd (75501-7543)
P.O. Box 690 (75504-0690)
PHONE.................................903 794-5169
John Getz, *Branch Mgr*
EMP: 72
SALES (corp-wide): 2.6B **Privately Held**
WEB: www.tronox.com
SIC: 1311 Crude petroleum production
HQ: Tronox Incorporated
　　1 Stamford Plz
　　Stamford CT 06901
　　203 705-3800

(G-19783)
W W METAL PRODUCTS INC
1226 N Fm 2148 (75501-0371)
PHONE.................................903 838-4329
Randal Walker, *President*
Wilma Walker, *Corp Secy*
Jim Rubey, *Plant Supt*
EMP: 25
SQ FT: 35,000
SALES (est): 6.2MM **Privately Held**
WEB: www.wwmetalproducts.com
SIC: 3443 3599 Fabricated plate work (boiler shop); machine shop, jobbing & repair

(G-19784)
WHITES WOOD GROUP INC
Also Called: Whites Trucking
2723 W 7th St (75501-6421)
PHONE.................................903 793-1603
Fax: 903 793-0923
EMP: 20
SQ FT: 5,000
SALES (est): 2.2MM **Privately Held**
SIC: 2499 Mfg Wood Products

Texas City
Galveston County

(G-19785)
AIRTRUST INTL SYSTEMS CORP (PA)
1201 N Logan St Ste 100 (77590-5178)
P.O. Box 2159 (77592-2159)
PHONE.................................713 491-4455
EMP: 15
SQ FT: 2,274
SALES (est): 3.9MM **Privately Held**
SIC: 8711 8748 5052 1389 Consulting engineer; telecommunications consultant; coal & other minerals & ores; oil field services; land subdividers & developers, commercial

(G-19786)
CERTISPEC SERVICES INC
1448 Texas Ave (77590-8445)
PHONE.................................409 945-3338
Wayne Todd, *President*
Richard Smith, *Vice Pres*
Carol Fairchild, *Opers Staff*
Charles Wu, *Controller*
▼ **EMP:** 15

▲ = Import ▼ =Export
◆ =Import/Export

SALES (est): 3MM **Privately Held**
WEB: www.certispec.com
SIC: 2999 Waxes, petroleum: not produced in petroleum refineries

(G-19787)
D & V DAY INVESTMENTS CORP
Also Called: Post Newspaper, The
501 6th St N (77590-7855)
P.O. Box 1686 (77592-1686)
PHONE......................409 943-4265
David S Day, *President*
Virginia N Day, *Vice Pres*
EMP: 17
SALES (est): 1.2MM **Privately Held**
WEB: www.thepostnewspaper.net
SIC: 2711 2721 Newspapers, publishing & printing; magazines: publishing only, not printed on site

(G-19788)
DOW CHEMICAL COMPANY
3301 5th Ave S (77590-8121)
PHONE......................409 948-5886
John Cooper, *Principal*
Ann Brown, *Technical Staff*
EMP: 75
SALES (corp-wide): 38.5B **Publicly Held**
WEB: www.dow.com
SIC: 2819 Industrial inorganic chemicals
HQ: The Dow Chemical Company
2211 H H Dow Way
Midland MI 48642
989 636-1000

(G-19789)
EASON PROPERTIES I LLC
Also Called: Hoffman Lumber Company
915 6th Ave N (77590-7420)
P.O. Box 99 (77592-0099)
PHONE......................409 945-4416
Robert Eason, *Mng Member*
EMP: 9
SALES (est): 1.3MM **Privately Held**
SIC: 2421 Building & structural materials, wood

(G-19790)
EASTMAN CHEMICAL COMPANY
201 Bay St S (77590-8779)
P.O. Box 1311 (77592-1311)
PHONE......................409 942-3532
Terry Moore, *Executive*
EMP: 911 **Publicly Held**
WEB: www.eastman.com
SIC: 2821 Plastics materials & resins
PA: Eastman Chemical Company
200 S Wilcox Dr
Kingsport TN 37660

(G-19791)
EASTMAN CHEMICAL TEXAS CY INC (HQ)
201 Bay St S (77590-8779)
P.O. Box 431, Kingsport TN (37662-0431)
PHONE......................409 942-3307
John V Genova, *President*
Heidi F Barnes, *President*
Kenneth M Hale, *Senior VP*
Walter B Treybig, *Senior VP*
Matthew A Stevens, *Vice Pres*
▼ EMP: 35 EST: 1996
SALES (est): 37.8MM **Publicly Held**
WEB: www.eastman.com
SIC: 2865 2821 2869 2861 Styrene; ethylbenzene; toluene; acrylonitrile-butadiene-styrene resins (ABS resins); plasticizer/additive based plastic materials; industrial organic chemicals; acetic & chloroacetic acid & metallic salts; plasticizers, organic: cyclic & acyclic; methanol, natural (wood alcohol); sodium & potassium compounds, exc. bleaches, alkalies, alum.; cyanides

(G-19792)
EASTMAN CHEMICAL TEXAS CY INC
201 Bay St S (77590-8779)
P.O. Box 1311 (77592-1311)
PHONE......................409 945-4431
Tom Gillespie, *Principal*
Robert Bannon, *VP Opers*
K V Hammer, *Engineer*
Georgina Winningham, *Engineer*
Walter Treybig, *Manager*

EMP: 185 **Publicly Held**
WEB: www.eastman.com
SIC: 2821 Plastics materials & resins
HQ: Eastman Chemical Texas City, Inc.
201 Bay St S
Texas City TX 77590
409 942-3307

(G-19793)
EVCO PARTNERS LP
Also Called: Burgoon Company
2701 Palmer Hwy Ste B (77590-6938)
P.O. Box 290 (77592-0290)
PHONE......................409 766-1900
Donna Hanson, *Owner*
Scott Hanson, *VP Business*
Robert Rangel, *Accounts Mgr*
Anthony Romagnoli, *Accounts Mgr*
Marvin Dawson, *Sales Staff*
EMP: 35
SQ FT: 3,000
SALES: 38.5MM **Privately Held**
WEB: www.burgooncompany.com
SIC: 5049 5047 5169 5099 Laboratory equipment, except medical or dental; scientific & engineering equipment & supplies; medical laboratory equipment; chemicals & allied products; safety equipment & supplies; industrial machinery & equipment; electrical equipment & supplies; accelerating waveguide structures

(G-19794)
HAGGAR CLOTHING CO
5885 Gulf Fwy Ste 715 (77591-7056)
PHONE......................214 352-8481
Shahid Gandi, *Manager*
EMP: 253 **Privately Held**
WEB: www.haggar.com
SIC: 2325 2311 2321 5611 Men's & boys' trousers & slacks; men's & boys' suits & coats; men's & boys' furnishings; men's & boys' clothing stores; family clothing stores
HQ: Haggar Clothing Co.
1507 Lyndon B Johnson Fwy # 100
Farmers Branch TX 75234
214 352-8481

(G-19795)
INTEGRAWOOD INC
Also Called: Woodshop of Texas
6001 E Lowery (77591)
PHONE......................713 329-9949
Leslie D Hurd, *President*
Terry Hurd, *Vice Pres*
EMP: 23
SQ FT: 18,000
SALES (est): 2.2MM **Privately Held**
WEB: www.antiquewoods.net
SIC: 2499 Decorative wood & woodwork

(G-19796)
LINDE INC
Also Called: Praxair
2800s Loop 197 N (77590-4621)
PHONE......................409 943-9280
Clay Norwood, *Production*
Ramiro Fernandez, *Manager*
Barry Labbe, *Technician*
EMP: 25 **Privately Held**
WEB: www.praxair.com
SIC: 2813 Industrial gases
HQ: Linde Inc.
10 Riverview Dr
Danbury CT 06810
203 837-2000

(G-19797)
MAINLAND CONCRETE INC
5501 Century Blvd (77592)
P.O. Box 906, Dickinson (77539-0906)
PHONE......................281 337-7400
Larry Burks, *President*
EMP: 35
SALES (est): 5.9MM **Privately Held**
WEB: www.mainlandconcrete.com
SIC: 5999 3273 Concrete products, precast; ready-mixed concrete

(G-19798)
MIRROR PUBLISHERS INC
7500 Fm 1765 (77591-3672)
P.O. Box 628, Galveston (77553-0628)
PHONE......................281 486-6558
Jake S Propp, *President*

Billie Propp, *Corp Secy*
Atchison Billie, *Vice Pres*
EMP: 14 EST: 1967
SQ FT: 11,000
SALES (est): 1.7MM **Privately Held**
WEB: www.mirrorpub.com
SIC: 2741 Miscellaneous publishing

(G-19799)
OILTANKING TEXAS CITY LP
2800 Loop 197 S (77592)
PHONE......................409 797-1710
Alex Degeest, *Opers Mgr*
Anita Hocke, *Opers Staff*
Richard Dikkers, *Finance*
Nancy De Groof, *Director*
Rance Fromme, *Executive*
◆ EMP: 11
SALES (est): 4.3MM
SALES (corp-wide): 14.2B **Privately Held**
WEB: www.texas-city-tx.org
SIC: 2899 Chemical supplies for foundries
HQ: Oiltanking Gmbh
Koreastr. 7
Hamburg 20457
403 709-90

(G-19800)
SAYBOLT LP
220 Texas Ave (77590-8755)
PHONE......................409 948-3166
Henry Roenne, *General Mgr*
Chris Baiamomte, *Manager*
EMP: 13
SALES (corp-wide): 668.2MM **Privately Held**
WEB: www.corelab.com
SIC: 1389 Oil field services
HQ: Saybolt Lp
6316 Windfern Rd
Houston TX 77040
713 328-2673

(G-19801)
SEA LION INC
5700 Century Blvd (77591-5009)
P.O. Box 1807 (77592-1807)
PHONE......................409 948-4351
Malcolm Colditz, *President*
Bernard F Jungman, *Admin Sec*
▲ EMP: 65
SQ FT: 10,000
SALES (est): 9.4MM **Privately Held**
SIC: 2869 Industrial organic chemicals

(G-19802)
SIKES FABRICATING CO INC
3416 3rd Ave S (77590-8012)
P.O. Box 3078 (77592-3078)
PHONE......................409 941-0727
EMP: 10 EST: 1973
SQ FT: 16,000
SALES (est): 1.4MM **Privately Held**
WEB: www.sikesfabricating.com
SIC: 3443 3441 Pipe, standpipe & culverts; fabricated structural metal

(G-19803)
TEXAS CITY NEWSPAPERS INC
Also Called: Texas City Sun, The
7800 Emmett F Lowry Expy (77591-2456)
P.O. Box 2249 (77592-2249)
PHONE......................409 945-3441
EMP: 687 EST: 1912
SQ FT: 17,000
SALES (est): 22.7MM
SALES (corp-wide): 140.3MM **Privately Held**
WEB: www.galvnews.com
SIC: 2711 2752 Newspapers, publishing & printing; commercial printing, lithographic
HQ: Galveston Newspapers, Inc.
8522 Teichman Rd
Galveston TX 77554
409 683-5200

(G-19804)
TREY INDUSTRIES INC
5201 Emmett F Lowry Expy (77591-2607)
P.O. Box 3834 (77592-3834)
PHONE......................409 948-8891
Ea Tholcken Jr, *President*
Chuck Horne, *Purch Mgr*
Laura Wilks, *Office Mgr*
EMP: 105
SQ FT: 1,150

SALES (est): 21.6MM **Privately Held**
WEB: www.treyindustries.com
SIC: 1629 3498 Oil refinery construction; fabricated pipe & fittings

(G-19805)
UNITED SERVICE ALLIANCE INC
Also Called: U S A
5245 Emmett F Lowry Expy (77591-2607)
PHONE......................409 935-9500
Douglas Temple, *President*
John Bennett, *Vice Pres*
Teresa Antley, *Office Mgr*
▼ EMP: 20
SQ FT: 20,000
SALES (est): 5.1MM **Privately Held**
WEB: www.usallianceinc.net
SIC: 3533 3599 Oil & gas field machinery; machine & other job shop work

(G-19806)
VALERO REFINING-TEXAS LP
1301 Loop 197 S (77590)
P.O. Box 3429 (77592-3429)
PHONE......................409 945-4451
Christopher Pettit, *Engineer*
Marcus Self, *Engineer*
Bob Gregory, *Manager*
Robert Copeland, *Analyst*
EMP: 400
SQ FT: 6,400
SALES (corp-wide): 108.3B **Publicly Held**
WEB: www.valero.com
SIC: 2911 Petroleum refining
HQ: Valero Refining-Texas, L.P.
1 Valero Way
San Antonio TX 78249
210 345-2000

(G-19807)
WOODSHOP OF TEXAS LTD
6001 Emmett F Lowry Expy (77591-2640)
PHONE......................409 938-7875
Terry Hurd, *Partner*
EMP: 26
SALES (est): 2.6MM **Privately Held**
WEB: www.antiquewoods.net
SIC: 2431 Millwork

Texline
Dallam County

(G-19808)
POOLE CHEMICAL CO INC (PA)
111 N 1st St (79087)
P.O. Box 8 (79087-0008)
PHONE......................806 362-4261
Danny Poole, *President*
Karen Poole, *Corp Secy*
Jayme Poole Rittenberry, *Vice Pres*
John Kay, *Plant Mgr*
Brad Riley, *Sales Staff*
EMP: 72
SALES (est): 35MM **Privately Held**
WEB: www.poolechemical.com
SIC: 2875 5191 Fertilizers, mixing only; fertilizer & fertilizer materials

The Colony
Denton County

(G-19809)
APEX CUSTOM SOFTWARE INC
Also Called: Perigee Health
3512 Balbirnie Ct (75056-6601)
PHONE......................214 725-9792
Pamela Renshaw, *President*
Thomas Renshaw, *Vice Pres*
EMP: 9
SALES (est): 228K **Privately Held**
WEB: www.apexcustomsoftware.com
SIC: 7373 7372 Systems software development services; application computer software

(G-19810)
EXCALIBUR LLC
5532 Big River Dr (75056-3778)
P.O. Box 560908 (75056-0908)
PHONE.....................................214 632-0161
Jason Skidmore, *Mng Member*
EMP: 9
SALES (est): 1MM **Privately Held**
WEB: www.excaliburshutters.com
SIC: 3272 Irrigation pipe, concrete

(G-19811)
GENESIS ENTITAI LLC
303 5733 Sh 121 Ste 210 (75056)
PHONE.....................................904 803-2457
Andres Marquez,
EMP: 20
SALES (est): 382.7K **Privately Held**
SIC: 7372 Application computer software

(G-19812)
RCW ENERGY SERVICES LLC
(HQ)
Also Called: R C W
6270 Morning Star Dr # 100 (75056-4588)
PHONE.....................................972 394-1000
Brian Green, *President*
Joseph Alaimo, *General Mgr*
Patrick Marburger, *Senior VP*
Brent Barrs, *Vice Pres*
Terry Mauboule, *Vice Pres*
EMP: 21 EST: 2012
SALES (est): 15.9MM **Privately Held**
WEB: www.rcwenergyservices.com
SIC: 1389 4941 Impounding & storing salt
water, oil & gas field; water supply
PA: Zackat, Inc.
6270 Mrnngstar Dr Ste 100
The Colony TX 75056
972 939-9200

(G-19813)
RUTH VENDING INC
Also Called: Tuffronts
6300 Fallwater Trl # 100 (75056-2625)
P.O. Box 560850 (75056-0850)
PHONE.....................................972 905-3523
Robert Liva, *President*
Justin Liva, *COO*
Robert Liva II, *CFO*
EMP: 12
SQ FT: 9,000
SALES (est): 1.3MM **Privately Held**
WEB: www.graphicsthatpop.com
SIC: 2821 Molding compounds, plastics

(G-19814)
SMOOTHIE KING
Also Called: Smoothie King
4770 State Highway 121 (75056-2913)
PHONE.....................................214 469-1552
EMP: 9 EST: 2014
SALES (est): 179.6K **Privately Held**
WEB: www.smoothieking.com
SIC: 5812 2086 Ice cream, soft drink &
soda fountain stands; fruit drinks (less
than 100% juice): packaged in cans, etc.

(G-19815)
TAG HOLDINGS INC (DH)
883 Trinity Dr (75056-5297)
PHONE.....................................214 469-3300
Donald Young, *President*
Walter Bearden, *President*
Norman Goldberg, *President*
Cindy McKotch, *Vice Pres*
EMP: 125
SQ FT: 200,000
SALES (est): 109.3MM **Privately Held**
SIC: 2321 2339 2369 Men's & boys'
dress shirts; women's & misses' outer-
wear; girls' & children's outerwear

(G-19816)
TMI LLC
2324 Barton Creek Blvd (75056-4878)
PHONE.....................................469 231-6918
Tim McElwain, *President*
Carmen McElwain, *Vice Pres*
▲ EMP: 10
SALES (est): 1.7MM **Privately Held**
SIC: 3645 Residential lighting fixtures

(G-19817)
TOP GOLF USA INC
3760 Blair Oaks Dr (75056-2700)
PHONE.....................................214 494-6310
Brian Riesenberg, *General Mgr*
Joseph Alfieri, *Opers Staff*
Lana Aleixo, *Sales Staff*
Stephanie Farrell, *Sales Staff*
Shelby Rushing, *Sales Staff*
EMP: 188
SALES (corp-wide): 214.3MM **Privately
Held**
WEB: www.topgolf.com
SIC: 3949 Sporting & athletic goods
HQ: Top Golf Usa Inc.
8750 N Cntl Expy Ste 1200
Dallas TX 75231

The Hills
Travis County

(G-19818)
FISHER-ROSEMOUNT SYSTEMS
INC
6 Cloverbrook Ct (78738-1324)
PHONE.....................................512 418-7400
Grant Wilson, *Vice Pres*
Ryan Malone, *Sales Staff*
John Nettle, *Manager*
EMP: 255
SALES (corp-wide): 16.7B **Publicly Held**
WEB: www.emerson.com
SIC: 3823 Industrial instrmnts msrmnt dis-
play/control process variable
HQ: Fisher-Rosemount Systems, Inc.
1100 W Louis Henna Blvd
Round Rock TX 78681

The Woodlands
Harris County

(G-19819)
ACEROS TURIA INC (PA)
25219 Kuykendahl Rd # 290 (77375-3425)
PHONE.....................................832 791-5479
Kristin Jennifer, *Manager*
Luis Barrenechea, *Director*
Jordi Barrenechea, *Director*
Rafael Barrenechea, *Director*
Jose Ignacio Sala Sr, *Director*
EMP: 21
SALES (est): 208.2MM **Privately Held**
WEB: www.wmc.us.com
SIC: 3496 Miscellaneous fabricated wire
products

(G-19820)
OPTIMUS STEEL LLC (DH)
25219 Kuykendahl Rd # 290 (77375-3425)
P.O. Box 3869, Beaumont (77704-3869)
PHONE.....................................800 303-9543
James R Kerkvliet, *President*
Luis Barrenechea, *Exec VP*
Rafael Barrenechea, *Exec VP*
EMP: 30
SALES (est): 448.8K
SALES (corp-wide): 208.2MM **Privately
Held**
WEB: www.optimus-steelusa.com
SIC: 3312 5051 Wire products, steel or
iron; metals service centers & offices
HQ: Turia Holdings, Lp
25219 Kuykendahl Rd # 290
The Woodlands TX 77375
706 922-5179

(G-19821)
WIRE MESH SALES LLC (DH)
25219 Kuykendahl Rd # 290 (77375-3425)
PHONE.....................................706 922-5179
Luis Barrenechea, *President*
Jordi Barrenechea,
Rafael Barrenechea,
EMP: 20
SALES (est): 11.8MM
SALES (corp-wide): 208.2MM **Privately
Held**
WEB: www.wmc-us.com
SIC: 3496 Concrete reinforcing mesh &
wire

HQ: Wmc Holdings, Lp
25219 Kuykendahl Rd Ste 2
The Woodlands TX 77375
904 751-4301

The Woodlands
Montgomery County

(G-19822)
AIM WORLD SERVICES INC
9450 Grogans Mill Rd # 1 (77380-3626)
PHONE.....................................281 847-2000
Michael Child, *President*
Michael R Child, *Exec VP*
Dawn Child, *Vice Pres*
Spencer Child, *Manager*
EMP: 50
SQ FT: 3,000
SALES (est): 47MM
SALES (corp-wide): 1.9MM **Privately
Held**
SIC: 7361 1382 8744 Employment agen-
cies; oil & gas exploration services; facili-
ties support services
PA: Aim Group (Alberta) Inc, The
340 Midpark Way Se Suite 170
Calgary AB T2X 1
403 303-2881

(G-19823)
ALOTERRA ENERGY LLC (PA)
2002 Timberloch Pl # 420 (77380-1171)
PHONE.....................................713 412-5311
Scott Coye-Huhn, *Mng Member*
Mark Griswold,
EMP: 19
SALES (est): 9.6MM **Privately Held**
WEB: www.aloterraenergy.com
SIC: 5211 8731 3999 Energy conserva-
tion products; agricultural research; bar-
ber & beauty shop equipment

(G-19824)
ALOTERRA PACKAGING LLC
(PA)
2002 Timberloch Pl # 420 (77380-1171)
PHONE.....................................440 689-0986
Scott Coye-Huhn, *Mng Member*
EMP: 15
SQ FT: 18,000
SALES (est): 6.3MM **Privately Held**
SIC: 2679 Food dishes & utensils, from
pressed & molded pulp

(G-19825)
AMERICAN FLUORITE INC
Also Called: Geo Southern Energy
1425 Lake Front Cir # 200 (77380-3610)
PHONE.....................................281 363-9161
George H Bishop, *CEO*
EMP: 22
SALES (est): 1.7MM
SALES (corp-wide): 11.9MM **Privately
Held**
SIC: 1382 Oil & gas exploration services
PA: Us Exploration Inc
1425 Lake Front Cir # 200
The Woodlands TX 77380
281 363-9161

(G-19826)
AMERICAS STYRENICS LLC
(HQ)
Also Called: Amsty
24 Waterway Ave Ste 1200 (77380-3289)
PHONE.....................................832 616-7800
Randy Pogue, *CEO*
Peter Ott, *VP Opers*
Christina Guice, *Opers Mgr*
Dan Bialkowski, *CFO*
Joe Hulett, *VP Human Res*
◆ EMP: 75
SALES (est): 304.9MM
SALES (corp-wide): 3.5B **Privately Held**
WEB: www.amsty.com
SIC: 2821 2865 Polystyrene resins;
styrene
PA: Chevron Phillips Chemical Company
Llc
10001 Six Pines Dr
The Woodlands TX 77380
832 813-4100

(G-19827)
ANADARKO ALGERIA
CORPORATION
1201 Lake Robbins Dr (77380-1124)
P.O. Box 1330, Houston (77251-1330)
PHONE.....................................832 636-1000
James Hackett, *Ch of Bd*
Charles Moley, *Vice Pres*
Albert L Richey, *Vice Pres*
Al Walker, *CFO*
Robert J Allison Jr, *Director*
EMP: 300
SALES (est): 5.5MM
SALES (corp-wide): 21.2B **Publicly Held**
WEB: www.oxy.com
SIC: 1382 Oil & gas exploration services
HQ: Anadarko Petroleum Corporation
1201 Lake Robbins Dr
The Woodlands TX 77380
832 636-1000

(G-19828)
ANADARKO E&P ONSHORE LLC
(DH)
1201 Lake Robbins Dr (77380-1124)
PHONE.....................................832 636-1000
Charles A Meloy, *President*
Stephen Eubank, *Counsel*
Matt Hartford, *Counsel*
Craig Olsen, *Counsel*
Sue Hollcroft, *Project Mgr*
EMP: 11
SALES (est): 4.6MM
SALES (corp-wide): 21.2B **Publicly Held**
WEB: www.oxy.com
SIC: 2911 Petroleum refining
HQ: Anadarko Petroleum Corporation
1201 Lake Robbins Dr
The Woodlands TX 77380
832 636-1000

(G-19829)
ANADARKO ENERGY SERVICES
CO
1201 Lake Robbins Dr (77380-1124)
P.O. Box 1330, Houston (77251-1330)
PHONE.....................................832 636-1000
R A Walker, *President*
Richard J Sharples, *President*
Robert P Daniels, *Exec VP*
Robert G Gwin, *Exec VP*
James J Kleckner, *Exec VP*
▲ EMP: 65
SQ FT: 127,000
SALES (est): 5.9MM
SALES (corp-wide): 21.2B **Publicly Held**
WEB: www.oxy.com
SIC: 1382 Oil & gas exploration services
HQ: Anadarko Petroleum Corporation
1201 Lake Robbins Dr
The Woodlands TX 77380
832 636-1000

(G-19830)
ANADARKO PETROLEUM
CORPORATION (HQ)
1201 Lake Robbins Dr (77380-1124)
P.O. Box 1330, Houston (77251-1330)
PHONE.....................................832 636-1000
R A Walker, *Ch of Bd*
Robert G Gwin, *President*
Ronnie Carman, *Superintendent*
Amanda M McMillian, *Exec VP*
Christopher O Champion, *Senior VP*
◆ EMP: 141
SALES (est): 13.3B
SALES (corp-wide): 21.2B **Publicly Held**
WEB: www.oxy.com
SIC: 1311 4924 5171 1382 Crude petro-
leum production; natural gas production;
natural gas distribution; petroleum bulk
stations; oil & gas exploration services
PA: Occidental Petroleum Corporation
5 Greenway Plz Ste 110
Houston TX 77046
713 215-7000

(G-19831)
ANADARKO US OFFSHORE
CORP
1201 Lake Robbins Dr (77380-1124)
PHONE.....................................832 636-1000
Ra Walker, *President*
EMP: 50

▲ = Import ▼=Export
◆ =Import/Export

SALES (est): 5.6MM
SALES (corp-wide): 21.2B **Publicly Held**
WEB: www.oxy.com
SIC: **1382** Oil & gas exploration services
HQ: Kerr-Mcgee Corp
9950 Woodloch Forest Dr
Spring TX 77380
832 636-1000

(G-19832)
ARENA OFFSHORE LP
2103 Res Frest Dr Ste 200 (77380)
PHONE..................................218 210-3138
Mike McCauley, *Prdtn Mgr*
Joey Choate, *Production*
Kilil Ackal, *Manager*
Allen White, *Manager*
Mike Minarovic,
EMP: 60
SQ FT: 8,000
SALES (est): 24.5MM **Privately Held**
WEB: www.arenaoffshore.com
SIC: **1382** Aerial geophysical exploration
oil & gas

(G-19833)
**BAKER HGHES OLFLD
OPRTIONS LLC**
Hughes Christenson
9110 Grogans Mill Rd (77380-3615)
P.O. Box 2539, Houston (77252-2539)
PHONE..................................281 363-6000
Douglas Wall, *Division Pres*
Jimmy Ehn, *Mfg Staff*
Chris Perez, *Manager*
Juan Vidal, *Technology*
Marie Geist, *Analyst*
EMP: 300 **Privately Held**
WEB: www.bakerhughes.com
SIC: **5084 3545** Derricks; drilling bits; machine tool accessories
PA: Baker Hughes Oilfield Operations Llc
2001 Rankin Rd
Houston TX 77073

(G-19834)
**BAKER HUGHES A GE
COMPANY LLC**
Also Called: Hughes Christenson
9110 Grogans Mill Rd (77380-3615)
P.O. Box 2539, Houston (77252-2539)
PHONE..................................281 363-6000
Charles Wolley, *President*
Scot Elder, *Senior Buyer*
Anthony Phillips, *Engineer*
Shelley Zaiser, *Manager*
Sophie Hovland, *Senior Mgr*
EMP: 300
SALES (corp-wide): 23.8B **Publicly Held**
WEB: www.bhge.com
SIC: **1389** Oil field services
HQ: Baker Hughes Holdings Llc
17021 Aldine Westfield Rd
Houston TX 77073
713 439-8600

(G-19835)
**BENDEL TANK HEAT
EXCHNGER CORP**
27 W Misty Morning Trce (77381-3859)
PHONE..................................832 436-4626
EMP: 35
SALES (corp-wide): 15.7MM **Privately Held**
WEB: www.bendelcorp.com
SIC: **3443** Tanks, standard or custom fabricated: metal plate
PA: Bendel Tank & Heat Exchanger, Corp.
4823 N Graham St
Charlotte NC 28269
704 596-5112

(G-19836)
BEUSA ENERGY LLC
Also Called: Beusa Energy, Inc
1780 Hughes Landing Blvd # 100
(77380-4023)
PHONE..................................281 296-1500
Jeffrey G Morris, *CEO*
EMP: 30
SQ FT: 7,900
SALES (est): 6.1MM **Privately Held**
WEB: www.beusaenergy.com
SIC: **1382** Oil & gas exploration services

PA: Bc Energy Investments Corp
C/O Tmf (B.V.I.) Ltd
Road Town

(G-19837)
**C TREAT OFFSHORE
WATERMAKERS**
Also Called: C'Treat
309 Briar Rock Rd (77380-3529)
PHONE..................................281 367-2800
Victor Jaroch, *President*
Ronny Teoh, *Sr Project Mgr*
▼ EMP: 28
SALES (est): 8.8MM **Privately Held**
WEB: www.ctreat.com
SIC: **5074 2086 5149 2899** Water purification equipment; water, pasteurized: packaged in cans, bottles, etc.; mineral or spring water bottling; water treating compounds

(G-19838)
CANTERA ENERGY LLC (PA)
10001 Woodloch Forest Dr # 400
(77380-1952)
PHONE..................................832 246-6100
John Kelly, *President*
Nico Garza, *COO*
James Abney, *Vice Pres*
David Balusek, *Vice Pres*
Michael R Hill, *Vice Pres*
EMP: 20 **EST:** 2013
SALES (est): 50MM **Privately Held**
WEB: www.canteraenergy.com
SIC: **1381 1311** Drilling oil & gas wells; crude petroleum & natural gas production

(G-19839)
CANTERA OPERATING LLC
10001 Woodloch Forest Dr # 400
(77380-1952)
PHONE..................................832 246-6100
John Kelly, *President*
David Garza, *COO*
Robert L Roberts, *CFO*
James Carlson,
Nico Garza,
EMP: 14 **EST:** 2012
SALES (est): 4.7MM
SALES (corp-wide): 50MM **Privately Held**
SIC: **1381 1311** Drilling oil & gas wells; crude petroleum & natural gas production
PA: Cantera Energy Llc
10001 Woodloch Forest Dr # 400
The Woodlands TX 77380
832 246-6100

(G-19840)
**CHAMPIONX CORPORATION
(PA)**
2445 Tech Frest Blvd Bldg (77381)
PHONE..................................281 403-5772
Daniel W Rabun, *Ch of Bd*
Sivasankaran Somasundaram, *President*
Robert K Galloway, *President*
Paul E Mahoney, *President*
Deric Bryant, *COO*
EMP: 106
SALES: 1.1B **Publicly Held**
WEB: www.championx.com
SIC: **3533 5084** Gas field machinery & equipment; oil & gas drilling rigs & equipment; oil field machinery & equipment; oil refining machinery, equipment & supplies

(G-19841)
CHART INDUSTRIES INC
8665 New Trils Dr Ste 100 (77381)
PHONE..................................281 364-8700
Elise Winslow, *Business Mgr*
Jerome Beguerie, *Vice Pres*
Brian Snover, *Project Mgr*
Joe Tardiff, *Project Mgr*
Erich Wetzel, *Project Mgr*
EMP: 235 **Publicly Held**
WEB: www.chartindustries.com
SIC: **3443 3559 3569** Heat exchangers: coolers (after, inter), condensers, etc.; tanks for tank trucks, metal plate; vessels, process or storage (from boiler shops): metal plate; cryogenic machinery, industrial; gas producers, generators & other gas related equipment; generators: steam, liquid oxygen or nitrogen

PA: Chart Industries, Inc.
3055 Torrington Dr
Ball Ground GA 30107

(G-19842)
CHEMEX GLOBAL INC
24 Waterway Ave Ste 900 (77380-3197)
PHONE..................................346 388-6100
David C Kehoe, *President*
Brian D Swearingen, *Vice Pres*
EMP: 200
SALES (est): 2.9MM **Privately Held**
SIC: **1382** Oil & gas exploration services

(G-19843)
**CHEVRON PHILLIPS CHEM CO
LLC (PA)**
10001 Six Pines Dr (77380-1498)
P.O. Box 4910 (77387-4910)
PHONE..................................832 813-4100
Mark Lashier, *CEO*
Peter L Cella, *President*
Ron Corn, *President*
Bill Strain, *General Mgr*
Jennifer Bauer, *Superintendent*
◆ EMP: 600
SALES (est): 3.5B **Privately Held**
WEB: www.cpchem.com
SIC: **2821** Plastics materials & resins

(G-19844)
**CHEVRON PHILLIPS CHEM CO
LP**
Performance Pipe Div Chevron
10001 Six Pines Dr (77380-1498)
P.O. Box 4920 (77387-4920)
PHONE..................................832 813-4100
EMP: 51
SALES (corp-wide): 3.5B **Privately Held**
WEB: www.cpchem.com
SIC: **2821** Plastics materials & resins
HQ: Chevron Phillips Chemical Company
Lp
10001 Six Pines Dr
The Woodlands TX 77380
832 813-4100

(G-19845)
**CHEVRON PHILLIPS CHEM CO
LP (HQ)**
Also Called: Cpchem
10001 Six Pines Dr (77380-1498)
P.O. Box 4910 (77387-4910)
PHONE..................................832 813-4100
Peter Cella, *CEO*
Mark Amelunke, *General Mgr*
Bob Rhoades, *General Mgr*
Jim Fiedler, *Superintendent*
Micah Sperling, *Superintendent*
▲ EMP: 600
SQ FT: 200,000
SALES (est): 3.1B
SALES (corp-wide): 3.5B **Privately Held**
WEB: www.cpchem.com
SIC: **5169 3084 3089 3292** Chemicals & allied products; plastics pipe; plastic hardware & building products; tubing & piping, asbestos & asbestos cement; aromatic chemical products; plumbing fixture fittings & trim
PA: Chevron Phillips Chemical Company
Llc
10001 Six Pines Dr
The Woodlands TX 77380
832 813-4100

(G-19846)
CLARIANT CORPORATION
Clariant Oil & Mining Services
2645 Technology Frst (77381-3910)
PHONE..................................281 465-9100
Mike Urbano, *Opers Mgr*
Keith Pennington, *Opers Staff*
Thomas Hammer, *Engineer*
Larry Dyen, *Senior Engr*
Jean Finnerty, *Sales Mgr*
EMP: 30
SALES (corp-wide): 4.4B **Privately Held**
WEB: www.clariant.com
SIC: **1222 1382** Bituminous coal-underground mining; oil & gas exploration services
HQ: Clariant Corporation
4000 Monroe Rd
Charlotte NC 28205
704 331-7000

(G-19847)
**COMPLETE INTELLIGENCE
TECH INC**
8111 Ashlane Way Ste 211 (77382-2337)
PHONE..................................281 710-9131
Robert Bryngelson, *COO*
James Langston, *Vice Pres*
EMP: 10
SALES (est): 320K **Privately Held**
WEB: www.completeintel.com
SIC: **7372** Prepackaged software

(G-19848)
**COVIA HOLDINGS
CORPORATION**
2829 Tech Frest Blvd Ste (77381)
PHONE..................................281 298-8088
Leann Wright, *Officer*
EMP: 31
SALES (corp-wide): 125.5MM **Privately
Held**
WEB: www.coviacorp.com
SIC: **1446** Silica mining
HQ: Covia Holdings Corporation
3 Summit Park Dr Ste 700
Independence OH 44131
440 214-3284

(G-19849)
CROSSFIRE LLC
1800 Hughes Landing Blvd (77380-1682)
PHONE..................................970 884-4869
Jonathan Nielson, *Branch Mgr*
EMP: 40
SALES (corp-wide): 1.4B **Privately Held**
WEB: www.crossfire-llc.com
SIC: **1389** Oil field services
HQ: Crossfire, Llc
820 Airport Rd
Durango CO 81303
970 884-4869

(G-19850)
CSI COMPRESSCO LP (PA)
24955 Interstate 45 (77380-3055)
PHONE..................................281 367-1983
Timothy A Knox, *President*
Owen Serjeant, *President*
Elijio Serrano, *Partner*
Charles Benge, *Vice Pres*
Matthew Pitcock, *Vice Pres*
EMP: 290
SALES: 476.5MM **Publicly Held**
WEB: www.csicompressco.com
SIC: **1389 3533** Oil field services; gas field services; gas field machinery & equipment

(G-19851)
**CUDD PUMPING SERVICES INC
(HQ)**
Also Called: Cudd Energy Services
2828 Tech Forest Blvd (77381-3907)
PHONE..................................832 295-5555
Robert Talk, *Exec VP*
Clint Walker, *Vice Pres*
Dan Bohannon, *Vice Pres*
Johnny Brady, *Opers Mgr*
Francisco Valinhas, *Maint Spvr*
▲ EMP: 10
SQ FT: 10,000
SALES (est): 125.7MM
SALES (corp-wide): 1.7B **Publicly Held**
WEB: www.cuddenergyservices.com
SIC: **1389** Oil field services
PA: Rpc, Inc.
2801 Buford Hwy Ne # 300
Brookhaven GA 30329
404 321-2140

(G-19852)
**DRILLCHEM DRLG SOLUTIONS
LLC**
8701 New Trils Dr Ste 100 (77381)
PHONE..................................281 713-8941
Dustin Zeigenbein, *President*
Brandon J Hayes, *General Mgr*
Albert Castaneda, *Project Engr*
Amber Tawse, *CFO*
Clay Croasdale, *Sales Staff*
EMP: 9
SALES (est): 3.2MM **Privately Held**
WEB: www.drillchem.com
SIC: **1381** Directional drilling oil & gas
wells

(G-19853)
DRILLING SPECIALTIES CO LLC
Also Called: Drilling Specialties Company
10001 Six Pines Dr (77380-1498)
PHONE...............................800 423-3985
Peter Cella, *CEO*
Joe R Prather, *President*
Peggy Colsman, *Vice Pres*
Tim Hill, *Vice Pres*
Joe R McKee, *Vice Pres*
◆ EMP: 18
SALES (est): 5MM
SALES (corp-wide): 3.5B **Privately Held**
WEB: www.cpchem.com
SIC: 2821 Plastics materials & resins
HQ: Chevron Phillips Chemical Company
　Lp
　10001 Six Pines Dr
　The Woodlands TX 77380
　832 813-4100

(G-19854)
DUNPHY GRAPHICS SOLUTIONS INC
Also Called: AlphaGraphics
2319 Timberloch Pl Ste A (77380-1040)
PHONE...............................281 363-9261
Paula Dunphy, *President*
EMP: 9 EST: 2010
SALES (est): 1.2MM **Privately Held**
WEB: www.txagprinting.com
SIC: 2752 Commercial printing, lithographic

(G-19855)
DYCEM CORPORATION
1725 Hughes Landing Blvd # 865
(77380-3875)
PHONE...............................832 447-1420
Lauren Wright, *Vice Pres*
EMP: 10
SALES (corp-wide): 6.3MM **Privately Held**
WEB: www.dycem-ns.com
SIC: 2426 Flooring, hardwood
HQ: Dycem Corporation
　33 Appian Way
　Smithfield RI 02917
　401 738-4420

(G-19856)
DYNA THERM CORPORATION
10077 Grogans Mill Rd # 300
(77380-1032)
PHONE...............................832 616-3094
Scott Lyons Jr, *President*
Joan Townsend, *Vice Pres*
Debra Lyons, *Admin Sec*
EMP: 10 EST: 1962
SQ FT: 10,000
SALES (est): 2.1MM **Privately Held**
WEB: www.dyna-therm.com
SIC: 3443 8711 Separators, industrial process: metal plate; industrial engineers

(G-19857)
EARTHSTONE ENERGY INC (PA)
1400 Woodloch Forest Dr # 300
(77380-1197)
PHONE...............................281 298-4246
EMP: 16
SQ FT: 19,600
SALES: 191.2MM **Publicly Held**
WEB: www.earthstoneenergy.com
SIC: 1382 Oil & gas exploration services

(G-19858)
EARTHSTONE ENERGY HOLDINGS LLC (HQ)
1400 Woodloch Forest Dr # 300
(77380-1197)
PHONE...............................281 298-4246
Steve Collins, *Exec VP*
Francis Mury, *Exec VP*
Shannon Klier, *Engineer*
EMP: 49
SALES (corp-wide): 191.2MM **Publicly Held**
WEB: www.earthstoneenergy.com
SIC: 6719 1382 Oil & gas exploration services

PA: Earthstone Energy, Inc.
　1400 Woodloch Forest Dr # 300
　The Woodlands TX 77380
　281 298-4246

(G-19859)
EARTHSTONE OPERATING LLC
1400 Woodloch Forest Dr (77380-1100)
PHONE...............................281 298-4246
Frank Lodzinski, *CEO*
Neil Cohen, *Treasurer*
EMP: 50 EST: 2011
SQ FT: 20,000
SALES (est): 50MM
SALES (corp-wide): 191.2MM **Publicly Held**
WEB: www.earthstoneenergy.com
SIC: 1382 Oil & gas exploration services
PA: Earthstone Energy, Inc.
　1400 Woodloch Forest Dr # 300
　The Woodlands TX 77380
　281 298-4246

(G-19860)
ECO SERVICES OPERATIONS CORP
2002 Timberloch Pl (77380-1171)
PHONE...............................844 812-1812
Megan Barkalow, *Production*
EMP: 13
SALES (corp-wide): 1.5B **Publicly Held**
SIC: 2819 Sulfuric acid, oleum
HQ: Eco Services Operations Corp.
　300 Lindenwood Dr
　Malvern PA 19355
　610 251-9118

(G-19861)
ENERCORP ENGNRED SOLUTIONS LLC (HQ)
Also Called: Enercorp Sand Solutions, LLC
25700 I 45 N Ste 110 (77386)
PHONE...............................832 791-1276
James Pung, *President*
Kenny Platt, *VP Sales*
EMP: 11
SALES (est): 9.3MM
SALES (corp-wide): 41MM **Privately Held**
WEB: www.enercorpsandsolutions.com
SIC: 1389 Oil field services
PA: Enercorp Sand Solutions Partnership
　520 3 Ave Sw Unit 530
　Calgary AB T2P 0
　403 217-1332

(G-19862)
EPSILYTE LLC
1330 Lake Robbins Dr # 310 (77380-3266)
PHONE...............................815 224-1525
Dan Bialkowski, *Mng Member*
Brad Crocker,
EMP: 115
SALES (est): 11.1MM **Privately Held**
SIC: 2821 Plastics materials & resins

(G-19863)
EXIDE TECHNOLOGIES LLC
22 Windledge Pl (77381-4642)
PHONE...............................678 566-9000
EMP: 13
SALES (corp-wide): 2.1B **Privately Held**
WEB: www.exide.com
SIC: 5063 3691 3629 Batteries; storage batteries; battery chargers, rectifying or nonrotating
PA: Exide Technologies, Llc
　13000 Drfeld Pkwy Bldg 20
　Milton GA 30004
　678 566-9000

(G-19864)
FEDEX OFFICE & PRINT SVCS INC
479 Sawdust Rd (77380-2263)
PHONE...............................281 364-7898
EMP: 11
SALES (corp-wide): 69.2B **Publicly Held**
WEB: www.fedex.com
SIC: 7334 2752 Photocopying & duplicating services; commercial printing, lithographic

HQ: Fedex Office And Print Services, Inc.
　7900 Legacy Dr
　Plano TX 75024
　800 463-3339

(G-19865)
FLINT HILLS RESOURCES LP
1330 Lake Robbins Dr # 400 (77380-3203)
PHONE...............................281 363-7200
Matt Figueroa, *Terminal Mgr*
Francis Murphy, *Branch Mgr*
Stephanie Bowen, *Director*
EMP: 50
SALES (corp-wide): 36.8B **Privately Held**
WEB: www.fhr.com
SIC: 2911 Petroleum refining
HQ: Flint Hills Resources, Lp
　4111 E 37th St N
　Wichita KS 67220
　800 292-3133

(G-19866)
GEOSOUTHERN ENERGY CORPORATION (PA)
1425 Lake Front Cir # 200 (77380-3631)
PHONE...............................281 363-9161
George Bishop, *President*
Larry Gregory, *General Mgr*
Steve Hanks, *General Mgr*
Donald Hausen, *General Mgr*
Russell Buehrle, *Counsel*
EMP: 30 EST: 1981
SALES (est): 47.7MM **Privately Held**
SIC: 1311 Crude petroleum production

(G-19867)
GEP HAYNESVILLE LLC
1425 Lake Front Cir (77380-3610)
PHONE...............................281 363-9161
Margaret Molleston, *CEO*
Richard Borstmayer, *COO*
Steve Hanks, *CFO*
EMP: 40
SALES (est): 230.3K **Privately Held**
SIC: 3569 1382 1389 Gas producers, generators & other gas related equipment; oil & gas exploration services; cementing oil & gas well casings

(G-19868)
GLOBAL SHOP SOLUTIONS INC (PA)
975 Evergreen Cir (77380-3637)
PHONE...............................281 681-1959
H Richard Alexander, *President*
Tom Proctor, *Vice Pres*
Kim Bellini, *Project Mgr*
Daniel Carranco, *Project Mgr*
Silas Fulsom, *Project Mgr*
EMP: 61
SQ FT: 12,000
SALES (est): 16.9MM **Privately Held**
WEB: www.globalshopsolutions.com
SIC: 7372 8748 7371 Prepackaged software; business consulting; computer software development

(G-19869)
GMA GARNET (USA) CORP (HQ)
1780 Hughes Landing Blvd # 725
(77380-4052)
PHONE...............................832 243-9300
Rod Liebeck, *President*
Arnold Salinas Jr, *Vice Pres*
Ajay Thanki, *Sales Mgr*
Ellen Lambert, *Sales Staff*
Ernie McDaniel, *Sales Staff*
◆ EMP: 138
SALES (est): 20.3MM **Privately Held**
WEB: www.gmagarnet.com
SIC: 1499 Garnet mining

(G-19870)
GPS INTERNATIONAL LLC (PA)
4200 Res Frest Dr Ste 110 (77381)
PHONE...............................832 319-1730
Faith Quirk, *VP Finance*
Alicia Heiskell, *Mng Member*
EMP: 16
SQ FT: 2,500

SALES (est): 7.8MM **Privately Held**
WEB: www.gpsinc.com
SIC: 7363 8742 8748 2899 Engineering help service; employee leasing service; industrial & labor consulting services; business consulting; fire extinguisher charges; fire retardant chemicals

(G-19871)
GRENADIER ENRGY PRTNERS II LLC
24 Waterway Ave Ste 875 (77380-3389)
PHONE...............................281 907-4120
Patrick J Noyes, *President*
EMP: 19
SALES (est): 99.1K **Privately Held**
WEB: www.grenadierenergy.com
SIC: 1382 Oil & gas exploration services

(G-19872)
HMC CAPITAL INC (PA)
27601 Commerce Oaks Dr (77385-4405)
PHONE...............................936 441-2666
Ruth Simms, *CFO*
EMP: 9
SQ FT: 20,000
SALES (est): 7.7MM **Privately Held**
WEB: www.hsi-power.com
SIC: 3511 1799 5999 Hydraulic turbines; hydraulic equipment, installation & service; engine & motor equipment & supplies

(G-19873)
HOWELL CORPORATION (DH)
1201 Lake Robbins Dr (77380-1181)
P.O. Box 1330, Houston (77251-1330)
PHONE...............................832 636-1000
William D Sullivan, *President*
James R Larson, *Senior VP*
Michael E Rose, *CFO*
Albert L Richey, *Treasurer*
EMP: 70 EST: 1955
SQ FT: 52,900
SALES (est): 37.6MM
SALES (corp-wide): 21.2B **Publicly Held**
WEB: www.oxy.com
SIC: 1311 Crude petroleum production
HQ: Anadarko Petroleum Corporation
　1201 Lake Robbins Dr
　The Woodlands TX 77380
　832 636-1000

(G-19874)
HOWMET AEROSPACE INC
25025 I 45 N Ste 575 (77380)
PHONE...............................866 385-2137
EMP: 427
SALES (corp-wide): 14.1B **Publicly Held**
WEB: www.howmet.com
SIC: 3334 Primary aluminum
PA: Howmet Aerospace Inc.
　201 Isabella St Ste 200
　Pittsburgh PA 15212
　412 553-1940

(G-19875)
HUNTING PLC USA (HQ)
24 Waterway Ave Ste 700 (77380-3391)
PHONE...............................713 595-2950
Dennis Proctor, *CEO*
Jim Johnson, *COO*
Bobby Blankenship, *Technical Staff*
EMP: 581
SALES (est): 118.5MM
SALES (corp-wide): 960MM **Privately Held**
WEB: www.huntingplc.com
SIC: 1382 Oil & gas exploration services
PA: Hunting Plc
　5 Hanover Square
　London W1S 1
　207 321-0123

(G-19876)
HUNTSMAN ADVNCED MTLS AMRCAS L (DH)
10003 Woodloch Forest Dr # 260
(77380-1955)
PHONE...............................281 719-6000
Peter R Huntsman, *President*
Landis Alday, *Plant Mgr*
◆ EMP: 10
SQ FT: 85,000

SALES (est): 97.9MM
SALES (corp-wide): 6.8B **Publicly Held**
WEB: www.huntsman.com
SIC: 2821 Plastics materials & resins
HQ: Huntsman Advanced Materials Llc
500 S Huntsman Way
Salt Lake City UT 84108
801 584-5700

(G-19877)
HUNTSMAN CORPORATION (PA)
10003 Woodloch Forest Dr # 260
(77380-1955)
PHONE....................281 719-6000
Anthony P Hankins, *CEO*
Peter R Huntsman, *Ch of Bd*
Nolan D Archibald, *Vice Ch Bd*
Michael Meador, *General Mgr*
Monica R Fisher, *Principal*
▲ EMP: 20
SALES (est): 6.8B **Publicly Held**
WEB: www.ir.huntsman.com
SIC: 2821 3081 2869 2816 Polystyrene
resins; polyethylene film; ethylene; propy-
lene, butylene; titanium dioxide, anatase
or rutile (pigments); dyes & pigments

(G-19878)
HUNTSMAN INTERNATIONAL LLC (HQ)
10003 Woodloch Forest Dr # 260
(77380-1955)
PHONE....................281 719-6000
Peter R Huntsman, *Ch of Bd*
Rohit Aggarwal, *Division Pres*
Monte G Edlund, *Division Pres*
Anthony P Hankins, *Division Pres*
David M Stryker, *Exec VP*
◆ EMP: 100 EST: 1970
SALES (est): 6.8B **Publicly Held**
WEB: www.huntsman.com
SIC: 2821 3081 2869 2816 Polystyrene
resins; polyethylene film; ethylene; tita-
nium dioxide, anatase or rutile (pigments);
dyes & pigments
PA: Huntsman Corporation
10003 Woodloch Forest Dr # 260
The Woodlands TX 77380
281 719-6000

(G-19879)
HUNTSMAN INTL TRDG CORP
8600 Gosling Rd (77381-4845)
PHONE....................281 719-7400
Brad Lamont, *Engineer*
Brian Pellon, *Branch Mgr*
Joann Lacheny, *Info Tech Mgr*
Eva Lok, *Analyst*
EMP: 41
SALES (corp-wide): 6.8B **Publicly Held**
WEB: www.huntsman.com
SIC: 2821 Plastics materials & resins
HQ: Huntsman International Trading Corpo-
ration
10003 Woodloch Forest Dr # 260
The Woodlands TX 77380

(G-19880)
HUNTSMAN INTL TRDG CORP (DH)
10003 Woodloch Forest Dr # 260
(77380-1955)
PHONE....................281 719-6000
Peter R Huntsman, *CEO*
Jon M Huntsman, *Chairman*
Sean Douglas, *Exec VP*
Jan Verstraeten, *Exec VP*
R Wade Rogers, *Senior VP*
◆ EMP: 20
SQ FT: 108,000
SALES (est): 95.5MM
SALES (corp-wide): 6.8B **Publicly Held**
WEB: www.huntsman.com
SIC: 2821 Plastics materials & resins
HQ: Huntsman Petrochemical Llc
500 S Huntsman Way
Salt Lake City UT 84108
801 584-5700

(G-19881)
HYDRAULIC SYSTEMS INC (HQ)
27601 Commerce Oaks Dr (77385-4405)
P.O. Box 132004, Spring (77393-2004)
PHONE....................832 791-5000
James Bement, *CEO*
S Charles Maurice, *Ch of Bd*

Chris Vincer, *VP Opers*
Ron Lunceford, *Warehouse Mgr*
Gordon Novotny, *Purchasing*
◆ EMP: 43
SQ FT: 20,000
SALES (est): 7.7MM **Privately Held**
WEB: www.hsi-power.com
SIC: 1799 3511 5999 Hydraulic equip-
ment, installation & service; turbines &
turbine generator sets; engine & motor
equipment & supplies
PA: Hmc Capital, Inc.
27601 Commerce Oaks Dr
The Woodlands TX 77385
936 441-2666

(G-19882)
INDEPENDENCE OILFIELD CHEM LLC (HQ)
2600 Tech Forest Blvd (77381-3904)
PHONE....................713 936-4340
Jeff Hibbeler, *President*
Matt Hancock, *Business Mgr*
Jaime De Los Santos, *Exec VP*
Jeff Dawson, *Senior VP*
Jeffrey C Dawson, *Senior VP*
▲ EMP: 26 EST: 2012
SQ FT: 6,000
SALES (est): 109.2MM
SALES (corp-wide): 1.5B **Publicly Held**
WEB: www.innospecinc.com
SIC: 2899 5169 Chemical preparations;
chemicals & allied products
PA: Innospec Inc.
8310 S Valley Hwy Ste 350
Englewood CO 80112
303 792-5554

(G-19883)
INDORAMA VENTURES OXIDES LLC
24 Waterway Ave Ste 1100 (77380-3445)
PHONE....................346 365-6056
Valerie Flannigan, *Purch Mgr*
Sn Mohta,
DK Agarwal,
Joel Saltzman,
EMP: 735
SALES (est): 25MM **Privately Held**
SIC: 2899 5169 Oxidizers, inorganic;
chemicals & allied products
HQ: Indorama Ventures Usa Holdings Lp
2610 Lake Cook Rd
Riverwoods IL 60015

(G-19884)
INDUSTRIAL SAFETY TECH LLC
4055 Tech Forest Blvd (77381-2007)
PHONE....................713 559-9200
Adam Markin, *CEO*
Dave Rutter, *CEO*
Kevin McKeigue, *Vice Pres*
EMP: 560
SALES (est): 30.6MM
SALES (corp-wide): 32.1B **Publicly Held**
WEB: www.teledynegasandflamedetec-
tion.com
SIC: 3829 3812 Gas detectors; search &
detection systems & instruments
HQ: Scott Technologies, Inc.
4320 Goldmine Rd
Monroe NC 28110
704 291-8300

(G-19885)
IPR INDUSTRIAL LLC
9400 Grogans Mill Rd # 205 (77380-3642)
PHONE....................281 362-1131
Joe Cutillo, *President*
EMP: 25
SALES (est): 4.5MM **Privately Held**
SIC: 3996 1794 1623 8999 Asphalted-
felt-base floor coverings: linoleum, carpet;
excavation & grading, building construc-
tion; pipeline construction; earth science
services
PA: Inland Pipe Rehabilitation, Llc
1510 Klondike Rd Sw # 40
Conyers GA 30094

(G-19886)
ISOMERIC INDUSTRIES INC
3400 Research Forest Dr B4 (77381-4247)
PHONE....................832 491-8106
Huiguang Zhu, *Branch Mgr*
EMP: 40

SALES (corp-wide): 9.9MM **Privately Held**
WEB: www.isomericindustries.com
SIC: 2851 Paints & paint additives
PA: Isomeric Industries Incorporated
3400 Res Forest Dr Ste B4
Spring TX 77381
678 713-4275

(G-19887)
ITT LLC
ITT C Treat Offshore
309 Briar Rock Rd (77380-3529)
PHONE....................281 367-2800
Tom Banden Haubel, *General Mgr*
Beverly Corley, *Export Mgr*
Ronny Teoh, *Project Engr*
EMP: 25
SALES (corp-wide): 2.8B **Publicly Held**
WEB: www.itt.com
SIC: 3625 Control equipment, electric
HQ: Itt Llc
1133 Westchester Ave N-100
White Plains NY 10604
914 641-2000

(G-19888)
JARVANTECH INC
2219 Sawdust Rd Ste 401 (77380-2576)
PHONE....................832 742-7220
Mahesh Vandanam, *President*
Libby Hotard, *Accounting Mgr*
Paige Falgoust, *Cust Mgr*
EMP: 11
SALES (est): 142.1K **Privately Held**
WEB: www.jarvantech.com
SIC: 8748 7373 7372 7371 Business
consulting; systems software develop-
ment services; application computer soft-
ware; software programming applications

(G-19889)
JEFFERSON REFINERY LLC (PA)
Also Called: Jefferson Energy Company
9595 Six Pines Dr # 6370 (77380-1647)
PHONE....................281 677-4900
Marty Reynolds, *VP Admin*
Carrie Chase, *Vice Pres*
Sally Shaw, *Vice Pres*
Chris Robbins, *CFO*
Katy Rivers, *Human Res Mgr*
▲ EMP: 15
SQ FT: 3,700
SALES (est): 7.3MM **Privately Held**
WEB: www.jeffersonenergyco.com
SIC: 1382 Oil & gas exploration services

(G-19890)
KEANE GROUP HOLDINGS LLC
Also Called: Research and Development
8301 New Trils Dr Ste 151 (77381)
PHONE....................281 719-7200
Caren Erwin, *Office Mgr*
EMP: 41
SALES (corp-wide): 1.8B **Publicly Held**
WEB: www.nextierofs.com
SIC: 1389 Oil field services
HQ: Keane Group Holdings, Llc
3990 Rogerdale Rd
Houston TX 77042
713 960-0381

(G-19891)
KERR-MCGEE OIL GAS ONSHORE LP
1201 Lake Robbins Dr (77380-1181)
PHONE....................832 636-1000
EMP: 140
SALES (est): 7.4MM
SALES (corp-wide): 18.9B **Publicly Held**
SIC: 1311 1382 Crude Petroleum And
Natural Gas, Nsk
HQ: Kerr-Mcgee Corp
1201 Lake Robbins Dr
The Woodlands TX 77380
832 636-1000

(G-19892)
MAXUS US EXPLORATION COMPANY
1330 Lake Robbins Dr # 300 (77380-3203)
PHONE....................281 681-7200
Guzman Solana, *President*
Jose D Rico, *Principal*

Wendy Weber-Francis, *Manager*
EMP: 20
SQ FT: 15,000
SALES (est): 943.8K **Privately Held**
SIC: 1381 Drilling oil & gas wells
HQ: Maxus Energy Corporation
10333 Richmond Ave # 1050
Houston TX 77042
281 681-7200

(G-19893)
MCC HOLDINGS INC (DH)
Also Called: Crane Energy Flow Solutions
4526 Res Frest Dr Ste 400 (77381)
PHONE....................936 271-6500
Alex Alcala, *President*
Louis V Pinkham, *President*
Kevin Olsen, *COO*
Ray Sherwood, *Vice Pres*
Kevin Burke, *CFO*
◆ EMP: 68
SALES (est): 458.8MM
SALES (corp-wide): 3.2B **Publicly Held**
WEB: www.craneenergy.com
SIC: 3491 7699 Industrial valves; valve re-
pair, industrial

(G-19894)
MICROBES INC
1544 Sawdust Rd Ste 505 (77380-2905)
PHONE....................281 367-7500
Bryan W Pusch, *President*
Alan Warren, *Principal*
Forrest Dietrich, *Exec VP*
EMP: 45
SQ FT: 6,300
SALES (est): 3.6MM **Privately Held**
WEB: www.microbesbiosciences.com
SIC: 8711 2835 Professional engineer; mi-
crobiology & virology diagnostic products

(G-19895)
NEWPARK INDUS BLNDING SLTONS L
9320 Lkeside Blvd Ste 100 (77381)
PHONE....................713 898-3829
Matthew Lanigan,
EMP: 38
SALES (est): 1.4MM **Privately Held**
SIC: 2899 Chemical preparations

(G-19896)
NEWPARK MATS INTGRTED SVCS LLC (HQ)
9320 Lkeside Blvd Ste 100 (77381)
PHONE....................281 362-6800
Paul L Howes, *CEO*
Jeff L Juergens, *President*
Mark J Airola, *Senior VP*
Gregg Piontek, *CFO*
▼ EMP: 10 EST: 2007
SALES (est): 102.5MM
SALES (corp-wide): 747.7MM **Publicly Held**
WEB: www.newpark.com
SIC: 1389 Oil field services; excavating
slush pits & cellars
PA: Newpark Resources Inc.
9320 Lkeside Blvd Ste 100
The Woodlands TX 77381
281 362-6800

(G-19897)
NEWPARK RESOURCES INC (PA)
9320 Lkeside Blvd Ste 100 (77381)
PHONE....................281 362-6800
Paul L Howes, *President*
Matthew S Lanigan, *President*
David Paterson, *President*
Chad Erdice, *Superintendent*
Bruce Smith, *Exec VP*
▲ EMP: 40 EST: 1932
SALES: 747.7MM **Publicly Held**
WEB: www.newpark.com
SIC: 1389 4959 4953 2273 Construction,
repair & dismantling services; excavating
slush pits & cellars; testing, measuring,
surveying & analysis services; cleaning
wells; environmental cleanup services;
non-hazardous waste disposal sites; recy-
cling, waste materials; mats & matting

(G-19898)
OILWELL HYDRAULICS INC
2002 Timberloch Pl Ste 50 (77380-1171)
PHONE...........................281 602-8170
EMP: 10 Privately Held
SIC: 1389 Oil/Gas Field Services
PA: Oilwell Hydraulics, Inc.
1460 Windway
Odessa TX 79763

(G-19899)
OVINTIV EXPLORATION INC (DH)
Also Called: Newfield
4 Waterway Square Pl # 100 (77380-2664)
PHONE...........................281 210-5100
Lee K Boothby, Ch of Bd
Michael G McAllister, President
W Allen Donaldson, Vice Pres
Edward Haas, Vice Pres
John Jasek, Vice Pres
▲ EMP: 160
SALES (est): 1.7B
SALES (corp-wide): 9.3M Publicly Held
WEB: www.newfield.com
SIC: 1382 Aerial geophysical exploration
oil & gas
HQ: Ovintiv Canada Ulc
500 Centre St Se
Calgary AB T2G 1
403 645-2000

(G-19900)
PENNAR GLOBAL INC
21 Waterway Ave Ste 300 (77380-3099)
PHONE...........................281 362-2707
Eric Brown, CEO
EMP: 10
SALES (est): 1.3MM Privately Held
WEB: www.pennarglobal.com
SIC: 3312 8711 3593 Tubes, steel & iron;
engineering services; fluid power cylin-
ders, hydraulic or pneumatic

(G-19901)
PETRA LAND LLC
10200 Grogans Mill Rd # 125 (77380-1174)
PHONE...........................832 791-5495
Ryan Hawkins, Mng Member
EMP: 10
SALES (est): 114K Privately Held
WEB: www.petralandllc.com
SIC: 1382 Aerial geophysical exploration
oil & gas

(G-19902)
PHILLIPS SMIKA PLYPRPYLENE LLC (PA)
10001 Six Pines Dr (77380-1498)
PHONE...........................832 813-4100
Dennis Holtermann, President
Ron Gallo, Principal
John Watson, Exec VP
Mike Minor, Exec Dir
Jean Steele, Director
◆ EMP: 140
SALES (est): 14.1MM Privately Held
WEB: www.cpchem.com
SIC: 2821 2673 Polypropylene resins;
bags: plastic, laminated & coated

(G-19903)
POLSYS SERVICES INC
2170 Buckthorne Pl # 165 (77380-1775)
PHONE...........................713 999-1100
Richard Corcoran, President
Kevin Stevens, Co-Owner
▲ EMP: 11
SALES (est): 8MM Privately Held
WEB: www.polsys.com
SIC: 8711 7359 3564 7699 Pollution con-
trol engineering; equipment rental & leas-
ing; blowers & fans; dust or fume
collecting equipment, industrial; industrial
machinery & equipment repair

(G-19904)
PRESTON EXPLORATION LTD LBLTY
1717 Woodstead Ct Ste 207 (77380-1448)
P.O. Box 7520 (77387-7520)
PHONE...........................281 367-8697
Arthur F Preston,
William J Preston,
EMP: 16 EST: 1994
SQ FT: 13,000

SALES (est): 1.9MM Privately Held
SIC: 1382 Geophysical exploration, oil &
gas field

(G-19905)
PRESTON OIL COMPANY LP
1717 Woodstead Ct Ste 207 (77380-1448)
P.O. Box 7520 (77387-7520)
PHONE...........................281 367-8697
William J Preston, Partner
Arthur F Preston, Partner
EMP: 26 EST: 1980
SQ FT: 5,000
SALES (est): 1.5MM Privately Held
SIC: 1311 Crude petroleum production;
natural gas production

(G-19906)
PROMICOM INC (PA)
Also Called: Microbes
1544 Sawdust Rd Ste 301 (77380-2904)
PHONE...........................832 544-0855
Carlos Girault, President
Enrique Franco, Vice Pres
Jose P Girault, Admin Sec
EMP: 9
SQ FT: 6,000
SALES (est): 1.8MM Privately Held
WEB: www.promicom.com
SIC: 8732 3316 3317 Research services,
except laboratory; bars, steel, cold fin-
ished, from purchased hot-rolled; tubes,
seamless steel

(G-19907)
R360 ENVMTL SOLUTIONS LLC (DH)
3 Waterway Square Pl # 110 (77380-3487)
PHONE...........................281 872-7360
William Werdenberg, General Ptnr
Les Elliott, District Mgr
Gabriel Rio, Exec VP
Gary Wallace, Exec VP
Robert Nielsen, Vice Pres
EMP: 9
SALES (est): 6.6MM
SALES (corp-wide): 5.3B Privately Held
WEB:
www.r360environmentalsolutions.com
SIC: 1389 Oil field services

(G-19908)
REPSOL ENERGY NORTH AMER CORP (HQ)
2455 Tech Forest Blvd (77381-5205)
PHONE...........................832 442-1000
Phil Ribbeck, President
Martin Safronchik, Human Res Mgr
Dean Manuel, Manager
Enrique Resina, Info Tech Mgr
Sanjay Panjwani, Technology
◆ EMP: 700
SALES (est): 746.9MM
SALES (corp-wide): 6.7B Privately Held
WEB: www.repsol.com
SIC: 1382 Oil & gas exploration services
PA: Repsol Sa.
Calle Mendez Alvaro 44
Madrid 28045
917 538-100

(G-19909)
REPSOL SERVICES COMPANY
2455 Tech Forest Blvd (77381-5205)
PHONE...........................832 442-1000
Antonia Brufau, CEO
Ramon Hernan, President
Isaac Alvarez, Principal
Chris David, Vice Pres
Melissa Kruse, Project Mgr
▲ EMP: 243
SALES (est): 57.6MM
SALES (corp-wide): 6.7B Privately Held
WEB: www.repsol.com
SIC: 1382 Oil & gas exploration services
PA: Repsol Sa.
Calle Mendez Alvaro 44
Madrid 28045
917 538-100

(G-19910)
RHIZOGEN LLC (PA)
4200 Res Frest Dr Ste 100 (77381)
PHONE...........................281 367-7500
Karen Doig, Accountant
Alan Warren, Mng Member

EMP: 15
SALES (est): 2.7MM Privately Held
WEB: www.microbesbiosciences.com
SIC: 2875 Fertilizers, mixing only

(G-19911)
RIGAKU AMERICAS CORPORATION (DH)
Also Called: Molecular Structure
9009 New Trails Dr (77381-5209)
PHONE...........................281 362-2300
Paul Swepston, CEO
Hikaru Shimura, Ch of Bd
Yasuhiro Sugiyama, President
Mark Benson, General Mgr
Jessica Miller, COO
▲ EMP: 12
SQ FT: 16,000
SALES (est): 52.7MM Privately Held
WEB: www.rigaku.com
SIC: 3844 3826 5049 X-ray apparatus &
tubes; analytical instruments; analytical
instruments
HQ: Rigaku Americas Holding, Inc
9009 New Trails Dr
The Woodlands TX 77381
281 362-2300

(G-19912)
RIO OIL AND GAS II LLC
3 Waterway Square Pl # 500 (77380-3487)
PHONE...........................832 616-3726
Stacey A Cude,
EMP: 11 EST: 2014
SALES (est): 532.5K Privately Held
WEB: www.rioog.com
SIC: 1382 Oil & gas exploration services

(G-19913)
ROLDAN DRILLING FLUIDS R&D
3600 College Park Dr # 10206
(77384-4814)
PHONE...........................832 918-6267
Javier G Roldan, Principal
EMP: 10
SALES (est): 216.3K Privately Held
WEB: www.roldanco.com
SIC: 1389 Oil & gas field services

(G-19914)
ROLDAN MIDSTREAM SERVICES LLC
123 N Misty Dawn Dr (77385-3650)
PHONE...........................832 918-6267
Javier Gerardo Roldan, CEO
EMP: 9
SALES (est): 200.6K Privately Held
WEB: www.roldanco.com
SIC: 1389 Oil & gas field services

(G-19915)
SAGE SURFACES LLC
6700 The Wdlnds Pkwy Ste (77382)
PHONE...........................281 907-8766
Christopher Althouse, Sales Staff
Jeff Stiles, Sales Staff
Thomas G Schneider, Mng Member
John P Pinsoneault, Mng Member
Cassie Jensen, Technical Staff
EMP: 14
SQ FT: 3,000
SALES (est): 2.3MM Privately Held
WEB: www.sagesurfaces.com
SIC: 1411 1799 Granite dimension stone;
counter top installation

(G-19916)
SARAIS SPREADS SUPERFOOD LLC
2202 Timberloch Pl # 133 (77380-1149)
PHONE...........................552 163-6178
Sara Mizrahi Mustri,
EMP: 17
SALES (est): 586.7K Privately Held
SIC: 2099 Food preparations

(G-19917)
SAVANNA ENERGY SVCS USA CORP (DH)
2445 Tech Frest B Ste 200 (77381)
PHONE...........................281 907-4800
Ken Mullen, CEO
Johnny Day, Superintendent
George Chow, Exec VP
John Cooper, Exec VP

Darcy Draudson, Exec VP
EMP: 10
SQ FT: 6,000
SALES (est): 116.5MM
SALES (corp-wide): 568.8MM Privately Held
WEB: www.savannaenergy.com
SIC: 1381 1389 Drilling oil & gas wells;
bailing, cleaning, swabbing & treating of
wells
HQ: Savanna Energy Services Corp
311 6 Ave Sw Suite 800
Calgary AB T2P 3
403 503-9990

(G-19918)
SMART SAND INC (PA)
1725 Hughes Landing Blvd # 800
(77380-4314)
PHONE...........................281 231-2660
Charles E Young, CEO
Jose E Feliciano, Ch of Bd
Andrew Speaker, Ch of Bd
William John Young, COO
Robert Kiszka, Exec VP
EMP: 21
SALES: 233MM Publicly Held
WEB: www.smartsand.com
SIC: 1446 Silica sand mining

(G-19919)
SMARTDRAW SOFTWARE LLC
1780 Hughes Landing Blvd (77380-4021)
PHONE...........................858 225-3300
Paul Stannard, CEO
J Anthony Patterson, COO
Jeff Anderson, Vice Pres
Dan Hoffman, Vice Pres
Linda Kaechele, Vice Pres
EMP: 42
SQ FT: 14,567
SALES (est): 14.5MM Privately Held
WEB: www.smartdraw.com
SIC: 7372 Application computer software

(G-19920)
SMITH PRODUCTION INC
8708 Tech Forest Pl 15 (77381-1179)
PHONE...........................281 296-5600
Glenn R Smith, President
EMP: 30
SQ FT: 1,000
SALES (est): 9.1MM Privately Held
WEB: www.smithproduction.com
SIC: 1382 Oil & gas exploration services

(G-19921)
SOLVAY USA INC
2645 Tech Forest Blvd (77381-3910)
PHONE...........................281 882-4700
Michael Lacey, Branch Mgr
EMP: 9
SALES (corp-wide): 13.8MM Privately Held
WEB: www.solvay.us
SIC: 2819 Industrial inorganic chemicals
HQ: Solvay Usa Inc.
504 Carnegie Ctr
Princeton NJ 08540
609 860-4000

(G-19922)
SOUTH BAY SOLUTIONS INC
2600 Tech Forest Blvd (77381-3904)
PHONE...........................936 494-0180
Adam Drewniany, Branch Mgr
EMP: 30 Privately Held
WEB: www.southbaysolutions.com
SIC: 3599 Machine shop, jobbing & repair
PA: South Bay Solutions, Inc.
37399 Centralmont Pl
Fremont CA 94536

(G-19923)
SPACE ENTERPRISES LLC
26310 Oak Ridge Dr Ste 38 (77380-3777)
PHONE...........................281 846-9613
EMP: 34
SALES (corp-wide): 1.1MM Privately Held
WEB: www.ambientehomedecor.com
SIC: 2033 3431 5023 Fruit juices: pack-
aged in cans, jars, etc.; sinks: enameled
iron, cast iron or pressed metal; home fur-
nishings

PA: Space Enterprises, Llc
26310 Oak Rdg Ste 38
San Antonio TX 78229
800 559-2923

(G-19924)
SPARTAN OPERATING COMPANY LLC
Also Called: Sep Operating Company
24 Waterway Ave Ste 850 (77380-3292)
PHONE..........................281 466-3310
John E Jackson, *President*
Stephen P York, *Vice Pres*
David Edelmaier, *CFO*
Jonathan W Byers, *Admin Sec*
EMP: 22
SALES (est): 296.2K
SALES (corp-wide): 7.8MM **Privately Held**
WEB: www.spartanep.com
SIC: 1321 Natural gas liquids production
PA: Spartan Energy Partners Lp
9595 Six Pines Dr # 4000
Spring TX 77380
281 466-3310

(G-19925)
STUART PRESSURE CONTROL
10077 Grogans Mill Rd # 100
(77380-1000)
PHONE..........................713 678-0154
Kirk Yariger, *CEO*
Brian Shoemaker, *Vice Pres*
Stephen Norris, *VP Opers*
Michael Gonzalez, *Opers Staff*
Bruce P Koch, *CFO*
EMP: 14
SALES (est): 2.7MM **Privately Held**
WEB: www.stuartpressurecontrol.com
SIC: 3321 Pressure pipe & fittings, cast iron

(G-19926)
TELEDYNE DETCON INC
4055 Tech Frest Blvd Ste (77381)
P.O. Box 360072, Pittsburgh PA (15251-6072)
PHONE..........................281 367-4100
Michael William Ryan, *President*
Patty Bakke, *Vice Pres*
Tony Liberti, *Regl Sales Mgr*
Matthew Tanzer, *Admin Sec*
▲ EMP: 105
SQ FT: 24,500
SALES (est): 29.6MM
SALES (corp-wide): 3.1B **Publicly Held**
WEB: www.teledynegasandflamedetection.com
SIC: 3829 Gas detectors
PA: Teledyne Technologies Inc
1049 Camino Dos Rios
Thousand Oaks CA 91360
805 373-4545

(G-19927)
TETRA PRODUCTION TSTG SVCS LLC
24955 Interstate 45 (77380-3055)
PHONE..........................281 367-1983
Phillip N Longorio, *President*
EMP: 329
SALES (est): 12.3MM
SALES (corp-wide): 1B **Publicly Held**
WEB: www.tetratec.com
SIC: 1389 Oil consultants
PA: Tetra Technologies, Inc.
24955 Interstate 45
The Woodlands TX 77380
281 367-1983

(G-19928)
TETRA TECHNOLOGIES INC (PA)
24955 Interstate 45 (77380-3055)
PHONE..........................281 367-1983
Brady M Murphy, *CEO*
William D Sullivan, *Ch of Bd*
Terrell Jensen, *District Mgr*
Brandon Mitchell, *District Mgr*
Bass C Wallace Jr, *Senior VP*
EMP: 150 EST: 1981

SALES: 1B **Publicly Held**
WEB: www.tetratec.com
SIC: 2819 1389 Brine; calcium chloride & hypochlorite; oil & gas wells: building, repairing & dismantling; well plugging & abandoning, oil & gas; testing, measuring, surveying & analysis services

(G-19929)
TEXAS MARKING PRODUCTS INC
26019 Interstate 45 (77380-3531)
PHONE..........................281 364-7100
Jerry Jackson, *President*
Dee Jackson, *Vice Pres*
EMP: 12
SALES (est): 1.3MM **Privately Held**
WEB: www.texasmarkingproducts.com
SIC: 3993 Signs & advertising specialties

(G-19930)
TOPSAIL ENERGY MKTG GROUP LLC
25775 Oak Ridge Dr # 150 (77380-2075)
PHONE..........................832 823-2380
Walt Fintch, *Vice Pres*
EMP: 10
SALES (est): 285.7K **Privately Held**
WEB: www.topsailenergy.com
SIC: 1311 Crude petroleum & natural gas production

(G-19931)
TRUTH CHEMICAL LLC
2170 Buckthorne Pl # 400 (77380-1775)
PHONE..........................281 292-6900
Dan Russel, *President*
Steve Baklund, *Vice Pres*
Mia McGinty-Sherno, *Vice Pres*
Amber Tawse, *CFO*
Joe D Newcomb,
◆ EMP: 14
SQ FT: 1,300
SALES (est): 12.7MM **Privately Held**
WEB: www.truthind.com
SIC: 5169 1479 Industrial chemicals; fertilizer mineral mining
PA: The Plaza Group Inc
1177 West Loop S Ste 1450
Houston TX 77027

(G-19932)
URMAN INC
8350 Ashlane Way Ste 104 (77382-2341)
PHONE..........................832 246-8810
Manuel Del Castillo, *CEO*
Karla Castrejon, *Vice Pres*
Sandra Martinez, *Sales Staff*
▲ EMP: 11
SALES (est): 1.3MM **Privately Held**
WEB: www.urman.com
SIC: 2678 Notebooks: made from purchased paper

(G-19933)
USER FRIENDLY PHONE BOOK LLC (PA)
10200 Grogans Mill Rd # 440 (77380-1134)
PHONE..........................281 465-5400
Ben Robbins, *Manager*
Bruce Howard,
John Henning,
EMP: 36
SALES (est): 94.2MM **Privately Held**
WEB: www.userfriendlymedia.com
SIC: 2741 Telephone & other directory publishing

(G-19934)
VALENCE SURFACE TECH LLC (PA)
1790 Hughes Landing Blvd (77380-1689)
PHONE..........................855 370-5920
Tracy Glende, *CEO*
Tim Mickael, *Exec VP*
Chris Urtnowski, *Opers Mgr*
James Mitchell, *CFO*
Amber Bauer, *Human Res Mgr*
EMP: 10 EST: 2014 **Privately Held**
WEB: www.valencesurfacetech.com
SIC: 3471 Electroplating of metals or formed products

(G-19935)
VENATOR AMERICAS LLC (HQ)
Also Called: Huntsman Pigments & Additives
10001 Woodloch Forest Dr (77380-1923)
PHONE..........................281 465-6700
Peter Huntsman, *Ch of Bd*
Jon Huntsman, *Chairman*
◆ EMP: 80
SQ FT: 50,000
SALES (est): 2.7MM
SALES (corp-wide): 6.8B **Publicly Held**
WEB: www.huntsman.com
SIC: 2299 5169 2816 Yarn, metallic, ceramic or paper fibers; chemicals & allied products; concrete additives; zinc pigments: zinc oxide, zinc sulfide; chrome pigments: chrome green, chrome yellow, zinc yellow; iron oxide pigments (ochers, siennas, umbers)
PA: Huntsman Corporation
10003 Woodloch Forest Dr # 260
The Woodlands TX 77380
281 719-6000

(G-19936)
VENATOR AMERICAS LLC
10003 Woodloch Forest Dr (77380-1913)
PHONE..........................281 719-6000
EMP: 17
SALES (corp-wide): 6.8B **Publicly Held**
WEB: www.huntsman.com
SIC: 2895 2816 2299 5169 Carbon black; zinc pigments: zinc oxide, zinc sulfide; yarn, metallic, ceramic or paper fibers; chemicals & allied products
HQ: Venator Americas Llc
10001 Woodloch Forest Dr
The Woodlands TX 77380
281 465-6700

(G-19937)
VENATOR MATERIALS LLC
10003 Woodloch Forest Dr (77380-1913)
PHONE..........................281 465-6700
Simon Turner, *President*
Russ R Stolle, *Exec VP*
Mahomed Maiter, *Vice Pres*
Kurt D Ogden, *CFO*
Russ R Stolle, *Ch Credit Ofcr*
EMP: 4500
SALES (est): 228.8MM
SALES (corp-wide): 2.1B **Privately Held**
WEB: www.venatorcorp.com
SIC: 2816 2865 5198 Titanium dioxide, anatase or rutile (pigments); zinc pigments: zinc oxide, zinc sulfide; iron oxide pigments (ochers, siennas, umbers); black pigments; color pigments, organic; colors & pigments
PA: Venator Materials Plc
Titanium House Hanzard Drive
Billingham TS22
174 060-8246

(G-19938)
VHSC CEMENT LLC (PA)
2204 Timberloch Pl # 248 (77380-1164)
PHONE..........................281 419-2422
Clinton W Pike, *President*
Marry Best, *Treasurer*
▲ EMP: 12
SALES (est): 1.8MM **Privately Held**
WEB: www.pozzoslag.com
SIC: 2674 Cement bags: made from purchased materials

(G-19939)
VITRUVIAN II WOODFORD LLC
4 Waterway Square Pl # 400 (77380-2664)
PHONE..........................832 458-3100
Richard Lane, *Principal*
John Thaeler, *COO*
Brian L Rickmers, *CFO*
EMP: 60
SQ FT: 24,000
SALES (est): 9MM **Privately Held**
WEB: www.vexpl.com
SIC: 1382 Oil & gas exploration services

(G-19940)
WESTERN MIDSTREAM PARTNERS LP (PA)
9950 Woodloch Forest Dr (77380-3991)
PHONE..........................832 636-6000
Michael P Ure, *President*
Catherine A Green, *General Ptnr*

Craig W Collins, *COO*
Charles G Griffie, *Senior VP*
Jaime R Casas, *CFO*
EMP: 13
SALES: 2.9B **Publicly Held**
WEB: www.westernmidstream.com
SIC: 1311 7371 Crude petroleum & natural gas; computer software development & applications

(G-19941)
WRIGHTS PRINTING & MKTG LLP
2407 Timberloch Pl Ste A (77380-1039)
PHONE..........................281 367-6060
Richard Wright, *Managing Prtnr*
Scott Barnes, *CFO*
Charles Hill, *Manager*
David Felts, *Director*
Laurel Robinson, *Graphic Designe*
EMP: 15
SALES (est): 2.7MM **Privately Held**
WEB: www.wrightsprinting.com
SIC: 2752 Commercial printing, offset

(G-19942)
XOMOX CORPORATION (DH)
Also Called: Tufline
4526 Res Frest Dr Ste 400 (77381)
PHONE..........................936 271-6500
William C Hayes, *President*
Dale Friemoth, *General Mgr*
William Metz, *Vice Pres*
Dustin Poteat, *Engineer*
Ashton Drenner, *Sales Staff*
◆ EMP: 120 EST: 1956
SQ FT: 144,000
SALES (est): 190.1MM
SALES (corp-wide): 3.2B **Publicly Held**
WEB: www.cranecpe.com
SIC: 3491 3593 3494 Process control regulator valves; fluid power cylinders & actuators; valves & pipe fittings
HQ: Mcc Holdings, Inc.
4526 Res Frest Dr Ste 400
The Woodlands TX 77381
936 271-6500

Thornton
Limestone County

(G-19943)
SHERROD SERVICES LLC
311 Lcr 730 (76687-2216)
PHONE..........................254 729-3177
Daniel R Sherrod, *President*
Wendy S Sherrod, *Vice Pres*
Keith Sherrod, *Supervisor*
EMP: 35
SALES (est): 7.3MM **Privately Held**
WEB: www.sherrodservices.com
SIC: 1794 1389 1711 4212 Excavation work; oil & gas wells: building, repairing & dismantling; septic system construction; dump truck haulage;

Three Rivers
Live Oak County

(G-19944)
DIAMOND SHAMROCK REF & MKTG CO
301 Leeroy St (78071)
P.O. Box 490 (78071-0490)
PHONE..........................361 786-2536
Ron Eaves, *Project Engr*
Harry Wright, *Manager*
EMP: 300
SALES (corp-wide): 108.3B **Publicly Held**
WEB: www.valero.com
SIC: 2911 2992 2899 2875 Gases & liquefied petroleum gases; lubricating oils & greases; chemical preparations; fertilizers, mixing only; industrial inorganic chemicals
HQ: Diamond Shamrock Refining And Marketing Company
6000 N Loop 1604 W
San Antonio TX 78249
210 345-2000

(G-19945)
EAGLE FORD RECLAMATION CO LLC
119 N Hwy 281a 281 A (78071)
PHONE..................................361 786-3960
Charles R Richesin, *Mng Member*
David Gatewood,
Thomas P Jones,
EMP: 40 **EST:** 2012
SALES (est): 2.9MM **Privately Held**
WEB: www.shalegasservices.com
SIC: 1389 Gas field services; oil field services
PA: Shale Gas Services, Llc
　1901 Napa Valley Dr # 201
　Little Rock AR 72212
　501 687-9191

Throckmorton
Throckmorton County

(G-19946)
RO MAC OIL CO INC
104 W High St (76483-5087)
P.O. Box 99 (76483-0099)
PHONE..................................940 849-2261
Ross Mc Knight, *President*
EMP: 10
SALES (est): 1MM **Privately Held**
SIC: 1382 Oil & gas exploration services

Tilden
Mcmullen County

(G-19947)
ZEOTECH CORPORATION
Hwy 72 W (78072)
PHONE..................................361 274-3357
Mark Hrbacek, *Manager*
EMP: 18
SALES (corp-wide): 586.4K **Privately Held**
WEB: www.zeotechcorp.com
SIC: 1459 Clays, except kaolin & ball
PA: Zeotech Corporation
　3815 Lisbon St Ste 100
　Fort Worth TX 76107
　817 335-4261

Timpson
Shelby County

(G-19948)
FOREST NIX INDUSTRIES INC
14732 State Highway 87 N (75975-4114)
P.O. Box 190 (75975-0190)
PHONE..................................936 254-2441
Jerry B Nix, *President*
Linda Kay Nix, *Corp Secy*
Milt Nix, *Vice Pres*
EMP: 50 **EST:** 1931
SQ FT: 1,200
SALES (est): 10.4MM **Privately Held**
WEB: www.nixforestindustries.com
SIC: 2421 Sawmills & planing mills, general

(G-19949)
ROSS LUMBER LTD
2770 Fm 1645 (75975-4017)
P.O. Box 900 (75975-0900)
PHONE..................................936 254-2575
Mike Ross, *President*
Linda Collins, *Corp Secy*
Lois Ross, *Shareholder*
EMP: 39 **EST:** 1964
SQ FT: 1,000
SALES (est): 6.7MM **Privately Held**
SIC: 2421 Sawmills & planing mills, general

Tokio
Yoakum County

(G-19950)
XTO ENERGY INC
888 County Road 121 (79376-2303)
PHONE..................................806 367-1047
Merit Marquiss, *Principal*
EMP: 71
SALES (corp-wide): 264.9B **Publicly Held**
WEB: www.xtoenergy.com
SIC: 1311 Crude petroleum production
HQ: Xto Energy Inc.
　22777 Sprngwoods Vlg Pkwy
　Spring TX 77389

Tom Bean
Grayson County

(G-19951)
ELLIS TOOL & MACHINE INC
310 Luby Dr (75090-5669)
P.O. Box 719 (75489-0719)
PHONE..................................903 546-6540
David Ellis, *President*
A J Ellis, *President*
Jean Ellis, *Corp Secy*
EMP: 22
SQ FT: 19,000
SALES (est): 3.9MM **Privately Held**
SIC: 3599 3829 3545 Machine shop, jobbing & repair; measuring & controlling devices; machine tool accessories

Tomball
Harris County

(G-19952)
365 MACHINE INC
27830 Commercial Park Rd (77375-6533)
PHONE..................................281 378-7811
Richard W Draper, *Principal*
Kevin McBride, *VP Opers*
EMP: 18 **EST:** 2014
SALES (est): 2.8MM **Privately Held**
WEB: www.365-machine.com
SIC: 3599 Machine shop, jobbing & repair

(G-19953)
A&T STEEL FABRICATORS INC
Also Called: Power Steel
14608 Union St (77377-7528)
P.O. Box 1307 (77377-1307)
PHONE..................................281 351-7650
Gabriel Aguirre, *President*
Laura Lohbeck, *Treasurer*
EMP: 30
SQ FT: 5,500
SALES (est): 5.5MM **Privately Held**
SIC: 3441 Fabricated structural metal

(G-19954)
ADVANCED PRECISION SERVICES LP
Also Called: APS Plastics
701 S Persimmon St Ste 50 (77375-6876)
PHONE..................................281 290-9950
Scott Johnson, *Partner*
David Mitchell, *Partner*
Peter Goldsmith, *General Ptnr*
Johnny Matsoukas, *Branch Mgr*
▲ **EMP:** 15
SQ FT: 12,000
SALES (est): 2.2MM **Privately Held**
WEB: www.apsplastics.com
SIC: 3599 Machine shop, jobbing & repair

(G-19955)
ALERT CONTROL TECHNOLOGIES LLC
9421 Fm 2920 Rd (77375-8947)
PHONE..................................281 288-1321
John Mayard, *President*
Dahleen Mayard,
EMP: 9
SQ FT: 1,600

SALES (est): 1.6MM **Privately Held**
WEB: www.alertcontrol.com
SIC: 1389 Oil field services

(G-19956)
ALLIED OFS LLC (PA)
11211 Fm 2920 Rd (77375-8927)
PHONE..................................832 482-3730
Eric Snell, *CEO*
Tammy Sharp, *Controller*
EMP: 13
SALES (est): 29.6MM **Privately Held**
WEB: www.bjservices.com
SIC: 1389 Oil field services

(G-19957)
AMERICAN COATINGS LP
10625 Mahaffey Rd (77375-6980)
P.O. Box 1426 (77377-1426)
PHONE..................................281 351-1776
Jim Adams, *Owner*
Jim Morrison,
▼ **EMP:** 50
SQ FT: 25,000
SALES (est): 17.6MM **Privately Held**
WEB: www.americancoatings.com
SIC: 2851 Paints & paint additives

(G-19958)
AMERICAN NATIONAL CARBIDE CO
915 S Cherry St (77375-6669)
PHONE..................................281 351-7165
D Greg Stroud, *President*
Donald Stroud, *Chairman*
Jack Leared, *Vice Pres*
Pam Smith, *CFO*
Wes Wedelich, *Sales Staff*
▲ **EMP:** 80
SQ FT: 45,000
SALES (est): 25.7MM **Privately Held**
WEB: www.anconline.com
SIC: 3541 3545 Machine tools, metal cutting type; machine tool accessories

(G-19959)
APS PLASTICS LP
701 Suth Persimmon Ste 85 (77375)
PHONE..................................281 290-9950
David Mitchell, *Partner*
EMP: 11
SALES (est): 1.5MM **Privately Held**
WEB: www.apsplastics.com
SIC: 3559 Plastics working machinery

(G-19960)
APS PRESSURE SYSTEMS LLC (DH)
Also Called: Advanced Pressure Systems
701 S Persimmon St Ste 85 (77375-6876)
PHONE..................................281 290-9950
Peter J Goldsmith, *Principal*
David L Mitchell, *Principal*
▲ **EMP:** 29
SALES (est): 6.9MM
SALES (corp-wide): 179MM **Privately Held**
WEB: www.advancedpressuresystems.com
SIC: 3589 High pressure cleaning equipment
HQ: Shape Technologies Group, Inc.
　23500 64th Ave S
　Kent WA 98032
　253 246-3200

(G-19961)
ASSOCIATED STL FABRICATORS INC
25234 Fm 2978 Rd (77375-2504)
PHONE..................................281 516-0909
Craig Drachman, *President*
Salina Ramirez, *Manager*
EMP: 16
SQ FT: 1,750
SALES (est): 8.3MM **Privately Held**
WEB: www.associatedsteelfab.com
SIC: 3441 Building components, structural steel

(G-19962)
B & C COATING INC
826 S Persimmon St (77375-6812)
PHONE..................................281 351-4773
Carolyn Johnson, *President*
EMP: 10

SALES (est): 73.8K **Privately Held**
SIC: 3471 Finishing, metals or formed products

(G-19963)
B J SERVICES COMPANY USA
11211 Fm 2920 Rd (77375-8927)
PHONE..................................281 357-2700
EMP: 28 **Privately Held**
SIC: 1389 Oil/Gas Field Services

(G-19964)
BAKER HGHES OLFLD OPRTIONS LLC
Also Called: BJ Unichem Chemical Services
11211 Fm 2920 Rd (77375-8927)
PHONE..................................281 351-8131
Bongben Kigham, *Branch Mgr*
EMP: 42 **Privately Held**
WEB: www.bakerhughes.com
SIC: 1389 Cementing oil & gas well casings; hydraulic fracturing wells; acidizing wells; construction, repair & dismantling services
PA: Baker Hughes Oilfield Operations Llc
　2001 Rankin Rd
　Houston TX 77073

(G-19965)
BAKER HUGHES A GE COMPANY LLC
Also Called: BJ Services Co
11211 Fm 2920 Rd (77375-8927)
P.O. Box 4442, Houston (77210-4442)
PHONE..................................281 351-8131
Bill Stuart, *Principal*
Michael Kelly, *Opers Staff*
Alejandro Hernandez, *Marketing Staff*
Robert Comer, *Manager*
Gail Nsofor, *Manager*
EMP: 128
SALES (corp-wide): 23.8B **Publicly Held**
WEB: www.bakerhughes.com
SIC: 1389 Oil field services
HQ: Baker Hughes Holdings Llc
　17021 Aldine Westfield Rd
　Houston TX 77073
　713 439-8600

(G-19966)
BJ SERVICES LLC (PA)
11211 Fm 2920 Rd (77375-8927)
PHONE..................................281 408-2361
Warren Zemlack, *President*
Caleb Barclay, *COO*
Lesa Carter, *Vice Pres*
Scott Danby, *Vice Pres*
Brent Savage, *Vice Pres*
◆ **EMP:** 34
SALES (est): 33.9MM **Privately Held**
WEB: www.bjservices.com
SIC: 1389 Oil field services

(G-19967)
BL TECHNOLOGY INC (PA)
1730 S Cherry St (77375-6820)
PHONE..................................832 698-8000
Deborah Lee, *President*
Vince Nussbaumer, *Division Mgr*
Robert Lee, *Vice Pres*
Camille Havelka, *Controller*
Karen Fishbeck, *Human Res Mgr*
EMP: 37
SQ FT: 17,000
SALES (est): 7.1MM **Privately Held**
WEB: www.blti.com
SIC: 3625 7382 3823 3613 Relays & industrial controls; security systems services; industrial instrmnts msrmnt display/control process variable; switchgear & switchboard apparatus; emergency alarms

(G-19968)
BREAUX MACHINE WORKS LP
13842 Hirschfield Rd (77377-6208)
P.O. Box 152 (77377-0152)
PHONE..................................281 351-4042
Dorothy Breaux, *Partner*
Thomas Breaux, *Partner*
Leslie Guynes, *Buyer*
Kurt Van Laningham, *Sales Executive*
Bill Spring, *Officer*
EMP: 85 **EST:** 2005
SQ FT: 46,000

▲ = Import ▼=Export
◆ =Import/Export

SALES (est): 14.3MM **Privately Held**
WEB: www.breauxmachine.com
SIC: 3599 Machine shop, jobbing & repair

(G-19969)
CHALLENGER DRILLING INC
Also Called: CDI Products
14102 Pine Meadow Ln (77377-6265)
P.O. Box 1988 (77377-1988)
PHONE.................................281 290-8335
Jeffrey Lutz, *President*
Danny Tweedel, *Vice Pres*
Gary Carville, *Safety Dir*
Susan C Lutz, *CFO*
Evonne Riddle, *Manager*
EMP: 18 **EST:** 1998
SQ FT: 3,000
SALES (est): 5.2MM **Privately Held**
WEB: www.challengerdrilling.com
SIC: 1381 1781 1623 Directional drilling
oil & gas wells; water well drilling; water,
sewer & utility lines

(G-19970)
CHALLENGER EQP & TL CO INC
12814 Old Boudreaux Ln (77375)
PHONE.................................281 351-4247
Wayne E Hawkins, *President*
Chad Hawkins, *Vice Pres*
Jennifer A Hawkins,
◆ **EMP:** 20
SALES (est): 5.1MM **Privately Held**
WEB: www.challengerequipment.com
SIC: 7353 3533 Oil field equipment, rental
or leasing; drill rigs

(G-19971)
COMPASS INSTRUMENTS LLC
321 S Persimmon St (77375-6801)
PHONE.................................832 698-2047
Cary Wilson, *Vice Pres*
Joseph Wilson,
EMP: 18
SALES (est): 950K **Privately Held**
WEB: www.compassinstruments.com
SIC: 3823 Electrolytic conductivity instruments, industrial process

(G-19972)
CROWN AEROSPACE INC
611 S Persimmon St (77375-6807)
PHONE.................................281 351-7068
Amber C Thomas, *President*
EMP: 10
SALES (est): 627.3K **Privately Held**
SIC: 3728 Aircraft parts & equipment

(G-19973)
DEEP IMAGING TECHNOLOGIES INC
990 Village Square Dr A (77375-4269)
PHONE.................................281 290-0492
David Moore, *CEO*
Trevor Pugh, *President*
John Ughetta, *Exec VP*
Alex Kalish, *Vice Pres*
Mary Helen Threlkeld-O'lea, *Vice Pres*
EMP: 19
SALES (est): 1.5MM **Privately Held**
WEB: www.deepimaging.com
SIC: 1389 7389 Surveying wells; measurement of well flow rates, oil & gas;

(G-19974)
DYNAMIC SIGNS SYSTEMS MKTG LLC
24501 Hufsmth Kohrvll 4 (77375-6932)
P.O. Box 131956, The Woodlands (77393-1956)
PHONE.................................281 255-0420
Nathan Nevedal,
EMP: 10
SQ FT: 3,000
SALES (est): 600K **Privately Held**
WEB: www.dssmllc.com
SIC: 3993 Signs & advertising specialties

(G-19975)
EAGLE GASKET AND PACKING CO
Also Called: Eagle Gaskets
1110 Ulrich Rd (77375-4326)
P.O. Box 749 (77377-0749)
PHONE.................................713 290-8811
Jean S Faires, *President*

Ronald E Blumick, *Vice Pres*
Matthew Cooper, *Vice Pres*
Randy S Ledbetter, *CFO*
Wade Gaddis, *Accounts Mgr*
▲ **EMP:** 22
SQ FT: 35,000
SALES (est): 4.4MM **Privately Held**
WEB: www.eaglegasket.com
SIC: 3053 5085 Gaskets, all materials;
gaskets

(G-19976)
ENERGY OPERATORS INC
1431 Graham Dr Ste 203 (77375-6452)
P.O. Box 1357, Cypress (77410-1357)
PHONE.................................281 351-1780
Sam Oliver, *President*
Larry R Oliver, *Chairman*
EMP: 130
SQ FT: 1,500
SALES (est): 6.8MM **Privately Held**
WEB: www.energyoperators.com
SIC: 1389 Oil consultants

(G-19977)
ENERGY SOLUTIONS INC
17210 Leeside Dr (77377-8063)
PHONE.................................281 257-2994
Jeff Stagg, *President*
EMP: 10
SALES (est): 409.7K **Privately Held**
WEB: www.energy-solutions.com
SIC: 1389 Oil consultants

(G-19978)
ENTHUSIASTIC SALES LLC
Also Called: Sol Marketing
9421 Fm 2920 Rd Bldg 10a (77375-8949)
P.O. Box 520 (77377-0520)
PHONE.................................832 698-1608
Shawn Cromack, *Mng Member*
EMP: 18
SALES (est): 4.5MM **Privately Held**
SIC: 2253 Beachwear, knit

(G-19979)
FOSTERS POINT INC (PA)
23810 Fm 2978 Rd (77375-5034)
PHONE.................................281 353-6696
Don Foster Jr, *President*
Jacqueline Foster, *Vice Pres*
Matthew Collins, *Opers Staff*
Jonathan Foster, *Treasurer*
Josh Floyd, *Marketing Staff*
◆ **EMP:** 40
SALES (est): 3.3MM **Privately Held**
WEB: www.fosterspoint.com
SIC: 3999 5999 Artificial flower arrangements; artificial flowers

(G-19980)
GRIMES INDUSTRIAL INC
929 E Main St (77375-6724)
PHONE.................................713 921-0000
Jody Grimes, *President*
Aaron Lambeth, *Engineer*
EMP: 23
SQ FT: 90,000
SALES (est): 1.9MM **Privately Held**
WEB: www.grimes-industrial.com
SIC: 3441 Fabricated structural metal

(G-19981)
HIGH-TECH FABRICATION INC
22206 Kobs Rd (77377-3604)
PHONE.................................281 351-0882
Kent Stephenson, *President*
Timmy Savoy, *Vice Pres*
EMP: 20
SALES (est): 4.4MM **Privately Held**
SIC: 3443 8711 Tanks, standard or custom
fabricated: metal plate; engineering services

(G-19982)
HOELSCHER WEATHERSTRIP MFG INC
2400 S Persimmon St (77375-5741)
PHONE.................................713 869-6466
Derek L Hoelscher, *President*
Charles H Hoelscher, *Vice Pres*
Mark A Hoelscher, *Vice Pres*
Ann Thom, *Credit Mgr*
Erika Gianni, *Sales Staff*
▲ **EMP:** 60

SALES (est): 7.8MM **Privately Held**
WEB: www.hoelscherweatherstrip.com
SIC: 1799 3442 Weather stripping; metal
doors, sash & trim

(G-19983)
HOLE SPECIALISTS INC
27950 Commercial Park Rd (77375-6535)
PHONE.................................281 290-7770
Larry A Robinson, *President*
Anthony Fite, *Finance Mgr*
Tony Fite, *Marketing Staff*
Donna Kleppel, *Office Mgr*
Jack Huitt, *Manager*
EMP: 39
SQ FT: 35,000
SALES (est): 8.8MM **Privately Held**
WEB: www.holespecialists.net
SIC: 3599 Machine shop, jobbing & repair

(G-19984)
HOUSTON NORTH MACHINE INC
14202 Pine Meadow Ln (77377-2404)
P.O. Box 1647 (77377-1647)
PHONE.................................281 351-8108
Tim Johnson, *President*
Mike Mannen, *Vice Pres*
▼ **EMP:** 18
SQ FT: 9,400
SALES (est): 1MM **Privately Held**
WEB: www.northhoustonmachine.com
SIC: 3599 Flexible metal hose, tubing &
bellows; machine shop, jobbing & repair

(G-19985)
INDUSTRIAL OLFLD MAR CMPNNTS I
Also Called: Iom Components
906 S Persimmon St (77375-6814)
PHONE.................................713 266-1900
EMP: 10
SALES (est): 1.7MM **Privately Held**
WEB: www.iomcomponents.com
SIC: 3625 3533 Mfg Relays/Industrial
Controls Mfg Oil/Gas Field Machinery

(G-19986)
M3 DISTRIBUTION INC
25116 Stanolind Rd (77375-2557)
P.O. Box 654 (77377-0654)
PHONE.................................281 357-0604
Kelly Bell, *President*
Fred Murphy, *Vice Pres*
Kathleen Murphy, *Vice Pres*
Christian Bell, *Opers Staff*
Elena Aaron, *Mfg Staff*
EMP: 12
SQ FT: 18,000
SALES (est): 6.1MM **Privately Held**
WEB: www.m3distribution.com
SIC: 5065 3679 3444 Electronic parts;
harness assemblies for electronic use:
wire or cable; sheet metalwork

(G-19987)
MICRON SEMICONDUCTOR PDTS INC
16510 Avenplace Rd (77377-8479)
PHONE.................................281 970-3202
Tim Emery, *Branch Mgr*
EMP: 14
SALES (corp-wide): 21.4B **Publicly Held**
WEB: www.micron.com
SIC: 3674 Semiconductors & related devices
HQ: Micron Semiconductor Products, Inc.
8000 S Federal Way
Boise ID 83716
208 368-4000

(G-19988)
MISCELLANEOUS SPECIALTIES INC
11024 Mahaffey Rd (77375-6906)
P.O. Box 2401, Spring (77383-2401)
PHONE.................................281 351-1177
Donna Caswell, *President*
Robert Caswell, *Admin Sec*
EMP: 10
SQ FT: 8,000
SALES (est): 2.3MM **Privately Held**
SIC: 3441 Fabricated structural metal

(G-19989)
MITCHELL MANUFACTURING INC
22806 Commercial Ln (77375-6969)
P.O. Box 289 (77377-0289)
PHONE.................................281 351-9641
Gene Mitchell, *President*
Nicki Mitchell, *Vice Pres*
EMP: 27
SQ FT: 25,000
SALES (est): 4.5MM **Privately Held**
WEB: www.mitchellmfg.com
SIC: 3599 7699 3441 3545 Machine
shop, jobbing & repair; welding equipment
repair; fabricated structural metal; machine tool accessories; machine tools,
metal cutting type; oil & gas field machinery

(G-19990)
MSP DRILEX INC
21227 Hfsmith Khrvil Rd (77375-7218)
PHONE.................................281 377-4393
Hongwei Lu, *General Mgr*
▲ **EMP:** 21
SALES (est): 4.3MM **Privately Held**
WEB: www.msp-drilex.us.com
SIC: 3491 Industrial valves

(G-19991)
NATIONAL OILWELL VARCO INC
Also Called: National Oilwell-Pft Div
10906 Fm 2920 Rd (77375-8934)
PHONE.................................281 351-2222
Hayley Skie, *Buyer*
Jimmy Owens, *QC Mgr*
Randall Hinson, *Manager*
Ken Colson, *Manager*
Timothy Rackel, *Representative*
EMP: 20
SALES (corp-wide): 8.4B **Publicly Held**
WEB: www.nov.com
SIC: 3533 Oil field machinery & equipment
PA: National Oilwell Varco, Inc.
7909 Parkwood Circle Dr
Houston TX 77036
713 346-7500

(G-19992)
NORTHWEST ADVANTAGE INC
Also Called: Signs By Tomorrow
8802 W Rayford Rd (77375-5150)
PHONE.................................713 622-4888
Thor A Holder, *President*
EMP: 12
SALES (est): 1.3MM **Privately Held**
WEB: www.signsbytomorrow.com
SIC: 3993 Signs & advertising specialties

(G-19993)
NRG MANUFACTURING INC (HQ)
11311 Holderrieth Rd # 100 (77375-7385)
PHONE.................................281 320-2525
Mark Terry, *President*
Tom Giles, *Vice Pres*
Tim Rodabough, *Vice Pres*
Jason Bludau, *Project Mgr*
Curtis Myrick, *Project Mgr*
EMP: 81
SQ FT: 60,000
SALES (est): 65.8MM
SALES (corp-wide): 118.9MM **Privately Held**
WEB: www.afglobalcorp.com
SIC: 3449 3441 Miscellaneous metalwork;
fabricated structural metal
PA: Afg Holdings, Inc.
945 Bunker Hill Rd # 500
Houston TX 77024
713 393-4200

(G-19994)
OLD DF INC
20322 Hfsmth Khrville Rd (77375-7422)
PHONE.................................281 590-5467
Robert Lindley, *President*
Eric Politte, *Vice Pres*
Todd Yaunches, *Executive*
EMP: 36
SQ FT: 36,000
SALES (est): 6MM **Privately Held**
SIC: 3443 Tanks for tank trucks, metal
plate; vessels, process or storage (from
boiler shops): metal plate

G E O G R A P H I C

(G-19995)
PACKERS PLUS ENRGY SVCS USA IN (HQ)
11415 Spell Rd (77375-7216)
PHONE.....................281 872-6999
Daniel Themig, *President*
Erin Scott, *General Mgr*
Ken Paltzat, *Corp Secy*
Jeremy Ragan, *Mfg Spvr*
Chris Desranleau, *Engineer*
EMP: 110
SALES (est): 85.4MM
SALES (corp-wide): 47MM **Privately Held**
WEB: www.packersplus.com
SIC: 1389 Pumps & pumping equipment
PA: Packers Plus Energy Services Inc
205 5 Ave Sw Suite 2200
Calgary AB T2P 2
403 263-7587

(G-19996)
PENSPEN CORPORATION (PA)
122 N Holderrieth Blvd (77375-4256)
PHONE.....................713 953-7007
John D Patton, *President*
Michael Kneale, *Vice Pres*
Jeff Powers, *CFO*
Sarah Howell, *Marketing Staff*
Brenda Hallford, *Manager*
EMP: 13
SALES (est): 90.9MM **Privately Held**
WEB: www.penspen.com
SIC: 1389 Gas field services

(G-19997)
PETROLEUM PRODUCTS & SVCS INC (PA)
Also Called: Wellhead Distributors Intl
23518 Coons Rd (77375-8202)
PHONE.....................281 448-1000
Alejandro Kiss, *President*
Balazs Horvath, *Mfg Mgr*
Jimmy Schultz, *Sales Staff*
Thad Crawford, *Manager*
Gabriel Ibarra, *Manager*
◆ EMP: 12
SQ FT: 55,000
SALES (est): 6.2MM **Privately Held**
WEB: www.wellheaddistributors.com
SIC: 7699 3533 5082 Industrial machinery & equipment repair; oil field machinery & equipment; oil field equipment

(G-19998)
PIGS UNLIMITED INTL INC
15719 Treichel Rd (77377-2503)
PHONE.....................281 351-2749
Allen A Pennington, *President*
Joel Jeansonne, *General Mgr*
John Pennington, *Vice Pres*
A Keith Wagner, *Vice Pres*
Ashley Gunter, *Sales Staff*
◆ EMP: 33
SALES (est): 10.3MM **Privately Held**
WEB: www.pigsunlimited.com
SIC: 3334 Pigs, aluminum

(G-19999)
PIONEER ENERGY SERVICES CORP
16430 N Eldridge Pkwy E (77377-9144)
PHONE.....................281 880-9988
EMP: 66
SALES (corp-wide): 575.7MM **Privately Held**
WEB: www.pioneeres.com
SIC: 1381 Drilling oil & gas wells
PA: Pioneer Energy Services Corp.
1250 Ne Loop 410 Ste 1000
San Antonio TX 78209
855 884-0575

(G-20000)
PPG INDUSTRIES INC
Also Called: PPG 8304
24914 Tomball Pkwy # 160 (77375-7690)
PHONE.....................281 357-0455
Ali Abidi, *Manager*
EMP: 24
SALES (corp-wide): 15.3B **Publicly Held**
WEB: www.ppg.com
SIC: 2851 Paints & allied products

PA: Ppg Industries, Inc.
1 Ppg Pl
Pittsburgh PA 15272
412 434-3131

(G-20001)
PRECISION FLUOROCARBON INC
Also Called: Pfi
9930 Fm 2920 Rd (77375-8915)
PHONE.....................281 351-4070
Howard L Frank, *President*
Helen J Frank, *Corp Secy*
Stephen H Frank, *Senior VP*
Elizabeth Frank, *Vice Pres*
Steve Frank, *Vice Pres*
EMP: 49
SQ FT: 38,500
SALES (est): 10.1MM **Privately Held**
WEB: www.pfi-plastics.com
SIC: 3089 Injection molding of plastics

(G-20002)
PROXIMITY SYSTEMS INC
11301 Boudreaux Rd (77375-7431)
P.O. Box 690371, Houston (77269-0371)
PHONE.....................281 370-5004
Jeremy Goza, *CEO*
Roger Goza, *President*
Denver Kryder, *Vice Pres*
Mike Schwab, *Vice Pres*
Jonathan Goza, *VP Mfg*
▲ EMP: 50
SALES (est): 8.6MM **Privately Held**
WEB: www.proximitysystems.com
SIC: 2521 Wood office desks & tables

(G-20003)
QTRCO INC
13120 Theis Ln (77375-6502)
PHONE.....................281 516-0277
Ed Holtgraver, *CEO*
Shawn Hughes, *President*
Steve Bursmith, *Vice Pres*
Tim Sumner, *Vice Pres*
James Howard, *Engineer*
▲ EMP: 12
SQ FT: 11,000
SALES (est): 3MM **Privately Held**
WEB: www.qtrco.com
SIC: 3593 Fluid power actuators, hydraulic or pneumatic

(G-20004)
QUICK TURN MACHINING INC
428 S Persimmon St (77375-6804)
PHONE.....................281 355-8876
Johnny Khalaf, *President*
EMP: 11
SQ FT: 1,250
SALES (est): 1.5MM **Privately Held**
WEB: www.quickturnmachininginc.com
SIC: 2079 Edible oil products, except corn oil

(G-20005)
RAC MATERIALS LLC
Also Called: Russell's Maintenance
31350 Sh 249 (77375)
PHONE.....................281 255-8500
Russell Denina, *Mng Member*
Frank Denina,
EMP: 12
SALES (est): 753.9K **Privately Held**
WEB: www.racmaterials.com
SIC: 1442 Sand mining; gravel mining

(G-20006)
RHINO MACHINE SHOP INC
402 Carrell St (77375-4803)
PHONE.....................281 290-7858
Terrance E Reddell, *President*
Cary D Williams, *Vice Pres*
Alan Lewandowski, *Admin Sec*
EMP: 9 EST: 1996
SQ FT: 7,800
SALES (est): 800K **Privately Held**
SIC: 3599 Machine shop, jobbing & repair

(G-20007)
SAI POWER SYSTEMS INC
Also Called: S A I
11311 Holderrieth Rd # 200 (77375-7388)
PHONE.....................281 516-3130
Ken Shutts, *President*
Deborah Blue, *Controller*

Kimberly Gauthier, *Admin Asst*
Kimberly Trafton, *Admin Asst*
EMP: 12
SQ FT: 5,000
SALES (est): 2.8MM **Privately Held**
WEB: www.saipower.com
SIC: 3621 Motors & generators

(G-20008)
SIGNTEX IMAGING INC
1225 Alma St Ste C (77375-4793)
PHONE.....................281 351-2776
Luther M Field Jr, *President*
Mike Martin, *General Mgr*
EMP: 30
SALES (est): 3.6MM **Privately Held**
WEB: www.stigraphics.com
SIC: 3993 Advertising artwork

(G-20009)
SIGNTEX OUTDOOR INC
1225 Alma St Ste D (77375-4793)
PHONE.....................281 351-8023
Darlene Feild-Smith, *President*
Dwain Wiedemann, *Vice Pres*
▲ EMP: 11
SQ FT: 7,500
SALES (est): 1.5MM **Privately Held**
WEB: www.stigraphics.com
SIC: 3993 7389 Signs & advertising specialties; sign painting & lettering shop

(G-20010)
SOLIDWOOD FOREST LTD (PA)
Also Called: Tomball Forest
16801 Fm 2920 Rd (77377-6018)
PHONE.....................281 351-0271
Vincent M Goodman, *Partner*
Doug Griffith, *Purchasing*
Dan Hudson, *Sales Staff*
EMP: 33
SALES (est): 25.2MM **Privately Held**
WEB: www.tomballforest.com
SIC: 2491 Structural lumber & timber, treated wood

(G-20011)
STI GRAPHICS INC
1225 Alma St Ste C (77375-4793)
PHONE.....................281 351-2776
Luther M Field Jr, *President*
EMP: 9
SALES (est): 1.1MM **Privately Held**
WEB: www.stigraphics.com
SIC: 3993 Signs & advertising specialties

(G-20012)
T & S RANDALL AND SONS LP
27760 Commercial Park Rd (77375-6531)
P.O. Box 41896, Houston (77241-1896)
PHONE.....................713 466-6951
Tim Randall, *General Ptnr*
▼ EMP: 9
SQ FT: 12,500
SALES (est): 1.9MM
SALES (corp-wide): 70MM **Privately Held**
WEB: www.jamisonproducts.com
SIC: 3569 Filters & strainers, pipeline
HQ: T.F. Hudgins, Incorporated
10344 Sam Houston Park Dr # 110
Houston TX 77064
713 682-3651

(G-20013)
TECPAC PLASTICS & SEALS LLC
22955 State Highway 249 # 25 (77375-8294)
P.O. Box 1011, Pinehurst (77362-1011)
PHONE.....................281 547-0620
David Florian, *Partner*
Zak Christen, *Partner*
Scott Johnson, *Partner*
EMP: 10
SQ FT: 4,200
SALES (est): 1.5MM **Privately Held**
WEB: www.tecpac.com
SIC: 2821 Plastics materials & resins

(G-20014)
THERMAL SOLUTIONS TEXAS LLC
14306 Mary Jane Ln (77377-6297)
PHONE.....................281 351-4328
Ryan Kraus, *Accounts Mgr*

Jeff D Peterson,
EMP: 17
SALES (est): 3.3MM **Privately Held**
WEB: www.thermalsolutionsoftexas.com
SIC: 3585 Heating equipment, complete

(G-20015)
VULCAN FINNED TUBES LP
27951 Commercial Park Rd (77375-6536)
PHONE.....................281 255-4775
Michael Soulant, *President*
Rob Faucett, *Sales Staff*
▲ EMP: 23
SQ FT: 30,000
SALES (est): 6MM **Privately Held**
WEB: www.vulcanfinnedtubes.com
SIC: 3317 Steel pipe & tubes

Trenton
Fannin County

(G-20016)
GUDGEL & SONS INC
Also Called: Trenton Plastics
300 S Us Highway 69 (75490-4106)
P.O. Box 68 (75490-0068)
PHONE.....................903 989-2232
John Gudgel, *CEO*
Zach Hightower, *QC Mgr*
Lisa Powell, *CFO*
Tom Jeffrey, *Manager*
▼ EMP: 35
SQ FT: 35,000
SALES: 5.1MM **Privately Held**
WEB: www.trentonplastics.com
SIC: 3089 Injection molding of plastics

(G-20017)
JB COMMERCIAL MILLWORK INC
Also Called: J & M Fixtures
402 W Saunders St (75490-2105)
P.O. Box 126 (75490-0126)
PHONE.....................903 989-2241
Jeff Barnes, *President*
Mike Boydston, *Prdtn Mgr*
EMP: 22
SQ FT: 13,000
SALES (est): 2.6MM **Privately Held**
WEB: www.jbmillwork.com
SIC: 2434 Wood kitchen cabinets

(G-20018)
PLBENNETT ENTP & INV FUND A
Also Called: Groundzeroprecision Com
15732 S State Hwy 121 (75490)
P.O. Box 3 (75490-0003)
PHONE.....................903 405-1940
Philip Bennett, *CEO*
EMP: 9
SQ FT: 6,500
SALES (est): 1.1MM **Privately Held**
WEB: www.groundzeroprecision.com
SIC: 3484 Guns (firearms) or gun parts, 30 mm. & below

Trinity
Trinity County

(G-20019)
PATRIOT TRINITY LLC
104 Industrial Blvd (75862)
P.O. Box 1760 (75862-1760)
PHONE.....................936 594-5948
Charlie Scocin, *Branch Mgr*
EMP: 36
SALES (corp-wide): 9.2MM **Privately Held**
WEB: www.trinitysteel.com
SIC: 3441 Building components, structural steel
PA: Patriot Trinity Llc
205 Pine Valley Dr
Trinity TX 75862
281 379-5373

(G-20020)
XG VENTURES LLC
Also Called: National Oilfield Fabricators
101 Martin Ct (75862-3805)
PHONE..................................936 744-1800
EMP: 30 **EST:** 2011
SALES (est): 400K **Privately Held**
SIC: 3448 3443 3423 Prefabricated metal
buildings; fabricated plate work (boiler
shop); hand & edge tools

Trophy Club
Denton County

(G-20021)
**SOFTWARE DEVELOPMENT
TECH**
Also Called: Software Consulting
10 Rochester Ct (76262-5589)
PHONE..................................650 906-6135
Catherine F Baldwin, *COO*
EMP: 40
SALES (est): 155.9K **Privately Held**
SIC: 7372 Prepackaged software

Troup
Smith County

(G-20022)
C DIAMOND F INC
Also Called: Neckover Trailer
938 S Railroad St (75789-2600)
P.O. Box 306 (75789-0306)
PHONE..................................903 842-3107
James Czajkoski, *President*
EMP: 50
SALES (est): 11MM **Privately Held**
WEB: www.neckovermfg.com
SIC: 3523 Farm machinery & equipment

(G-20023)
CARL R MCEVER
Also Called: McEver Machine Works
8198 Fm 2064 N (75789-7728)
PHONE..................................903 842-2555
Carl R Mc Ever, *Owner*
EMP: 10
SQ FT: 12,000
SALES (est): 900K **Privately Held**
SIC: 3599 Machine shop, jobbing & repair

(G-20024)
**CHALLENGER PROCESS
SYSTEMS CO**
21249 State Highway 110 S (75789-5700)
P.O. Box 249, Whitehouse (75791-0249)
PHONE..................................903 839-7291
David Spindle, *President*
Charles K Fischer, *General Mgr*
Roy John Bracken, *Vice Pres*
David Martin, *Vice Pres*
Sandra M Bitz, *Admin Sec*
EMP: 110 **EST:** 1981
SQ FT: 31,000
SALES (est): 29.2MM
SALES (corp-wide): 7.1B **Publicly Held**
WEB: www.acceleratedps.com
SIC: 3443 1791 3533 Tanks, standard or
custom fabricated: metal plate; storage
tanks, metal: erection; oil & gas field ma-
chinery
PA: Dover Corporation
3005 Highland Pkwy # 200
Downers Grove IL 60515
630 541-1540

(G-20025)
MCELROY PLASTICS INC
725 Arp Dr (75789-2903)
P.O. Box 668 (75789-0668)
PHONE..................................903 842-2180
EMP: 30
SQ FT: 35,000
SALES (est): 8.5MM **Privately Held**
WEB: www.mcelroyplastics.com
SIC: 3089 Injection molding of plastics

(G-20026)
MOTOR TRIKE INC
22667 Fm 15 (75789-6221)
P.O. Box 611 (75789-0611)
PHONE..................................903 842-3094
Jeffrey L Vey, *President*
Diane D Vey, *Corp Secy*
Diane Vey, *Treasurer*
Rachel Escanlar, *Marketing Staff*
▲ **EMP:** 132
SALES (est): 26.9MM **Privately Held**
WEB: www.motortrike.com
SIC: 3621 3751 Motors & generators; mo-
torcycles, bicycles & parts

Troy
Bell County

(G-20027)
ANDERTON CASTINGS LLC
222 Lely Dr (76579-3714)
PHONE..................................254 938-2541
Hugh Holstine, *Engineer*
Celia Martinez, *Human Resources*
Charles Hinkle, *Mng Member*
Camille Lecoutre,
EMP: 300 **EST:** 2014
SALES (est): 97.2MM
SALES (corp-wide): 40.5MM **Privately
Held**
WEB: www.andertoncastings.com
SIC: 3465 Body parts, automobile:
stamped metal
HQ: Anderton Intermediate Company
222 Lely Dr
Troy TX 76579
248 430-6650

(G-20028)
ARIES BUILDING SYSTEMS LLC
1919 Mueller Ln (76579-3733)
P.O. Box 548 (76579-0548)
PHONE..................................254 938-0800
Rich Brewer, *Director*
EMP: 108
SALES (corp-wide): 24.6MM **Privately
Held**
WEB: www.ariesbuildings.com
SIC: 2452 Modular homes, prefabricated,
wood
PA: Aries Building Systems, Llc
12621 Featherwood Dr # 300
Houston TX 77034
254 938-0800

(G-20029)
**LELY TANK WASTE SOLUTIONS
LLC**
111 Lely Dr (76579-3739)
P.O. Box 1026, Temple (76503-1026)
PHONE..................................800 367-5359
Coydette Jones, *Vice Pres*
William A Jones III, *Mng Member*
Tim Counts, *Regional*
EMP: 15
SALES (est): 3MM **Privately Held**
WEB: www.atcvacuumtruck.com
SIC: 3563 3443 Vacuum pumps, except
laboratory; industrial vessels, tanks &
containers

(G-20030)
LIDE INDUSTRIES LLC
Also Called: Permin Tanks
114 W Hillyard Rd (76579-3631)
P.O. Box 547 (76579-0547)
PHONE..................................254 562-0233
Justin Day, *Manager*
EMP: 15
SALES (corp-wide): 99.4MM **Privately
Held**
WEB: www.lideindustries.com
SIC: 3795 Tanks & tank components
HQ: Lide Industries, Llc
2701 W Interstate 20
Odessa TX 79766
254 562-0233

(G-20031)
MPCK MACHINING INC
1709 Church Ave (76579-2743)
PHONE..................................254 938-7555
Marlon D Goates, *President*

◆ **EMP:** 13
SALES (est): 2.2MM **Privately Held**
SIC: 3599 Machine shop, jobbing & repair

(G-20032)
PAVLISKA CABINETS INC
Also Called: Kopriva Cabinets
I-35 N Pendleton Rd (76579)
P.O. Box 407 (76579-0407)
PHONE..................................254 773-4461
Julius Pavliska, *President*
Betty Pavliska, *Corp Secy*
Ronnie Harrison, *Vice Pres*
EMP: 12 **EST:** 1964
SQ FT: 18,000
SALES (est): 961.5K **Privately Held**
SIC: 2431 2434 Millwork; vanities, bath-
room: wood

Tuleta
Bee County

(G-20033)
DIRNETT INC
Also Called: Rw Dirk Engineering
Hwy 181 (78162)
P.O. Box 200 (78162-0200)
PHONE..................................361 375-2194
R W Dirks, *President*
Eula Mae Dirks, *Vice Pres*
Susan Dirks, *Vice Pres*
EMP: 11
SQ FT: 1,500
SALES (est): 200K **Privately Held**
WEB: www.rwdirkspetroleum.com
SIC: 1311 Crude petroleum production

Tulia
Swisher County

(G-20034)
D/A MFG CO INC
7574 Highway 86 (79088-6333)
P.O. Box T (79088-0920)
PHONE..................................806 995-2316
Donald L Adams, *President*
Dexter Adams, *Vice Pres*
Freba Adams, *Admin Sec*
▼ **EMP:** 26
SQ FT: 26,700
SALES (est): 4.7MM **Privately Held**
WEB: www.d-a-mfg.com
SIC: 3492 3494 Control valves, fluid
power: hydraulic & pneumatic; valves &
pipe fittings

(G-20035)
**KBG MANAGEMENT COMPANY
LP**
3071 Highway 86 (79088-2909)
PHONE..................................806 627-4276
Keith Birkenseld, *Partner*
Bob Birkenfeld, *Partner*
Greg Birkenfeld, *Partner*
EMP: 9
SALES (est): 926K **Privately Held**
SIC: 2875 Compost

(G-20036)
KENNETH WYATT GALLERIES
Also Called: Y 8 Foundry
310 Comanche Trl (79088-3110)
PHONE..................................806 995-2239
EMP: 19 **EST:** 1974
SQ FT: 6,400
SALES (est): 1.6MM **Privately Held**
WEB: www.kennethwyatt.com
SIC: 5999 4225 3299 Art dealers; general
warehousing & storage; architectural
sculptures: gypsum, clay, papier mache,
etc.

(G-20037)
**ROLL-A-CONE MFG DISTRG CO
LTD**
7655 Roll A Cone Rd (79088-6107)
PHONE..................................806 668-4722
Dan C Byrd, *Vice Pres*
▲ **EMP:** 40
SQ FT: 95,000

SALES (est): 17.3MM **Privately Held**
SIC: 5083 3523 Farm equipment parts &
supplies; farm machinery & equipment

(G-20038)
SOIL MENDER PRODUCTS L P
3071 Highway 86 (79088-2909)
PHONE..................................806 627-4276
Greg Birkenfeld, *Partner*
EMP: 22
SALES (corp-wide): 9MM **Privately Held**
WEB: www.soilmender.com
SIC: 2875 Compost
PA: Soil Mender Products, L. P.
7355 Fm 928
Tulia TX 79088
806 627-4276

(G-20039)
**SOIL MENDER PRODUCTS L P
(PA)**
7355 Fm 928 (79088-3524)
PHONE..................................806 627-4276
Greg Birkenfeld, *Partner*
Keith Birkenfeld, *Vice Pres*
Robert Birkenfeld, *Vice Pres*
EMP: 40
SALES (est): 9MM **Privately Held**
WEB: www.soilmender.com
SIC: 2875 Compost

(G-20040)
**TOP SHELF INDUSTRIES OPER
LTD**
907 E Service Rd (79088-1127)
P.O. Box 797 (79088-0797)
PHONE..................................806 995-2224
EMP: 10
SALES (corp-wide): 982.7K **Privately
Held**
SIC: 3999 Atomizers, toiletry
PA: Top Shelf Industries Operating, Ltd.
16333 Prairie Garden Rd
Canyon TX 79015
806 729-7882

Tye
Taylor County

(G-20041)
**BULLZEYE OILFIELD SERVICE
LLC**
581 County Road 307 (79563-2635)
P.O. Box 368, Merkel (79536-0368)
PHONE..................................325 665-0220
Zackry Maxey, *President*
Keith Maxey, *Vice Pres*
Misti Maxey, *Vice Pres*
EMP: 16
SALES (est): 3MM **Privately Held**
WEB: www.bullzeyewireline.com
SIC: 1389 Oil field services

Tyler
Smith County

(G-20042)
3P INDUSTRIES LLC
11942 Laney Rd (75708-2422)
PHONE..................................903 877-3960
Jamie Rivers, *Purchasing*
Dennis M McInnis,
EMP: 40
SQ FT: 57,000
SALES (est): 5.7MM **Privately Held**
WEB: www.3pindustries.com
SIC: 3479 Coating of metals & formed
products

(G-20043)
ABLES-LAND INC (PA)
420-428 S Fannin Ave (75702)
P.O. Box 7933 (75711-7933)
PHONE..................................903 593-8407
Scott King, *Corp Secy*
Julie Ables, *Vice Pres*
Gary Ables, *Vice Pres*
Nicole Cox, *Marketing Staff*
Kerry Hannah, *Department Mgr*
EMP: 31 **EST:** 1963
SQ FT: 14,040

SALES (est): 3MM **Privately Held**
WEB: www.shop.ablesland.com
SIC: 5943 5712 2752 Office forms & supplies; office furniture; commercial printing, offset

(G-20044)
AFFORDABLE ASPHALT PAVING INC
Also Called: Affordable Concrete
5696 County Road 1143 (75704-8405)
PHONE..................903 596-7003
Lea Kastmo, *President*
Jan-Harry Kastmo, *Vice Pres*
EMP: 10
SALES (est): 1.3MM **Privately Held**
WEB: www.vikingreadymix.com
SIC: 5211 1611 3273 Concrete & cinder block; concrete construction: roads, highways, sidewalks, etc.; ready-mixed concrete

(G-20045)
AG-JAX LTD
6775 Old Jacksonville Hwy (75703-6049)
PHONE..................903 705-0625
David Ronca, *General Mgr*
Ronnie Swink,
James R Swink,
Todd Swink,
EMP: 9
SALES (est): 547.7K **Privately Held**
SIC: 1382 Oil & gas exploration services

(G-20046)
ANA-LOG INC
11067 Hwy 848 (75707)
P.O. Box 6404 (75711-6404)
PHONE..................903 597-6341
Katie J Jordan, *President*
Chris Major, *Engineer*
EMP: 20
SQ FT: 8,000
SALES (est): 1.2MM **Privately Held**
WEB: www.hpinc.com
SIC: 1389 Oil field services

(G-20047)
APERGY ARTFL LIFT INTL LLC
Ferguson Beauregard
12424 Hwy 64 W (75704-8018)
PHONE..................903 266-3552
Jack Rogers, *President*
EMP: 28
SALES (corp-wide): 1.1B **Publicly Held**
WEB: www.apergy.com
SIC: 1389 Oil field services
HQ: Apergy Artificial Lift International, Llc
2445 Tech Frest Blvd Ste
Spring TX 77381
281 403-5742

(G-20048)
ARK-LA-TEX SHREDDING CO INC
12405 State Highway 155 N (75708-2443)
P.O. Box 5227, Longview (75608-5227)
PHONE..................903 877-3734
Beth Fouse, *President*
Robert Fouse, *Vice Pres*
Robert Lynn Fouse, *Vice Pres*
W D Chrisner, *Shareholder*
EMP: 18
SQ FT: 10,800
SALES (est): 1.8MM **Privately Held**
WEB: www.altshred.com
SIC: 7389 3589 Document & office record destruction; shredders, industrial & commercial

(G-20049)
ASHCRAFT-SOUTHERN MARBLE CO
13822 State Highway 155 S (75703-6630)
PHONE..................903 581-5501
Charles D Ashcraft Jr, *President*
EMP: 30
SQ FT: 12,800
SALES (est): 3.8MM **Privately Held**
WEB: www.ashcraftmarble.com
SIC: 3281 7389 Marble, building: cut & shaped; engraving service

(G-20050)
ASTRO MACHINE & TOOL WORKS LLC
8044 County Road 313 E (75706-3902)
PHONE..................903 595-6655
Tanner Smith, *Prgrmr*
Warren Woodcock,
Andrew Evalds,
Jerry Rawlinson,
Hazen Thomas Smith III,
EMP: 16
SQ FT: 14,000
SALES (est): 1.5MM **Privately Held**
WEB: www.astromachinetools.com
SIC: 3599 Machine shop, jobbing & repair

(G-20051)
ATHLETIC BAG COMPANY LP (PA)
Also Called: R Y N O
316 S Glenwood Blvd (75702-6936)
PHONE..................903 520-3343
Brandon Steel, *CEO*
Mr Joe Hebb, *Co-Owner*
Andrea Steele, *Vice Pres*
▲ **EMP:** 34 **EST:** 1996
SQ FT: 25,000
SALES (est): 4.3MM **Privately Held**
WEB: www.ryno.com
SIC: 2393 3949 2394 Duffle bags, canvas: made from purchased materials; sporting & athletic goods; canvas & related products

(G-20052)
ATLAS BUILDING SYSTEMS INC (PA)
5511 State Highway 31 W (75709-9731)
PHONE..................903 597-4211
William Downs Jr, *President*
Roy Davis, *Sales Staff*
▲ **EMP:** 14
SQ FT: 2,500
SALES (est): 5.2MM **Privately Held**
WEB: www.atlasbackyardsheds.com
SIC: 2452 3448 1522 3444 Prefabricated buildings, wood; buildings, portable: prefabricated metal; garages, portable: prefabricated metal; residential construction; roof deck, sheet metal

(G-20053)
AUSTIN COCA-COLA BOTTLING CO
3200 W Gentry Pkwy (75702-1311)
PHONE..................903 597-9325
Scott Plankenashie, *Branch Mgr*
EMP: 60
SALES (corp-wide): 309.5MM **Privately Held**
SIC: 2086 Bottled & canned soft drinks
PA: Austin Coca-Cola Bottling Company
1 Coca Cola Pl
San Antonio TX 78219
210 225-2601

(G-20054)
B & B BOX AND LUMBER COMPANY
2800 Sunnybrook Dr (75701-5353)
PHONE..................903 592-7369
David Brooks, *President*
Rachel Pierce, *Corp Secy*
EMP: 32 **EST:** 1978
SQ FT: 7,500
SALES (est): 6MM **Privately Held**
SIC: 2448 2449 Skids, wood; pallets, wood; rectangular boxes & crates, wood

(G-20055)
B W ENERGY CONSULTANTS INC
516 S Spring Ave (75702-8140)
PHONE..................903 593-1173
Bob Washmon, *President*
Wade Washmon, *Vice Pres*
EMP: 12
SALES (est): 1.6MM **Privately Held**
WEB: www.bwecland.com
SIC: 1382 Oil & gas exploration services

(G-20056)
BAKER & COMPANY CNSTR LLC
4955 Profit Dr (75707-1838)
PHONE..................903 561-1763
Bradley Baker, *President*
Smith Reid, *Vice Pres*
Charles Reid, *Admin Sec*
EMP: 21
SALES (est): 348.1K **Privately Held**
WEB: www.bakercompanyllc.com
SIC: 1799 3317 3446 1611 Fence construction; pipes, seamless steel; gratings, open steel flooring; fences or posts, ornamental iron or steel; highway & street construction

(G-20057)
BAKER HGHES OLFLD OPRTIONS LLC
11047 Fm 14 (75706-6317)
PHONE..................940 626-4169
David Grizzell, *Branch Mgr*
EMP: 21 **Privately Held**
WEB: www.bakerhughes.com
SIC: 1389 Oil field services
PA: Baker Hughes Oilfield Operations Llc
2001 Rankin Rd
Houston TX 77073

(G-20058)
BASIN DRILLING LP
Also Called: Basin Drilling 2
1121 E Se Loop 323 # 218 (75701-9694)
PHONE..................903 561-8211
Jeff Kraker, *President*
Scott Martin, *President*
Kathy Geddie, *General Mgr*
David Chatelain, *Safety Dir*
Linda Herrington, *Manager*
EMP: 60
SALES (est): 9.4MM **Privately Held**
WEB: www.basindrilling.com
SIC: 1382 Oil & gas exploration services

(G-20059)
BLACKSHEEP INC
3220 W Gentry Pkwy (75702-1300)
PHONE..................903 592-3853
Bob Archer, *President*
▲ **EMP:** 500
SQ FT: 45,000
SALES (est): 42MM
SALES (corp-wide): 159.8MM **Privately Held**
SIC: 3842 3949 2399 3429 Life preservers, cork & inflatable; cases, gun & rod (sporting equipment); cartridge belts, sporting type; pet collars, leashes, etc.: non-leather; manufactured hardware (general); luggage; plastics foam products
PA: Kent Water Sports, Llc
433 Park Ave
New London OH 44851
419 929-7021

(G-20060)
BRIDES & BELLES OF TYLER
109 E 7th St (75701-4203)
PHONE..................903 581-8211
Jo Ann Owers, *Owner*
Joanne Owers, *Owner*
EMP: 9
SQ FT: 6,600
SALES (est): 702.4K **Privately Held**
WEB: www.bridesbellestyler.com
SIC: 5621 5661 2759 Bridal shops; shoes, orthopedic; invitations: printing

(G-20061)
BRITEC SOLUTIONS INC
3709 Westway St 1-A (75703-6465)
PHONE..................903 707-7471
Brian K Cochran, *President*
EMP: 9
SALES (est): 375K **Privately Held**
WEB: www.britecsolutions.com
SIC: 2821 Plasticizer/additive based plastic materials

(G-20062)
BURTON OIL SVC OPERATIONS LLC
102 N College Ave # 1036 (75702-7277)
PHONE..................713 805-2934
Trevor Morris, *General Mgr*

Michael Aaron, *Sales Staff*
Ben Burton,
Preston Burton,
EMP: 12
SALES (est): 2.3MM **Privately Held**
WEB: www.burtonoil.com
SIC: 1389 Oil field services

(G-20063)
CARRIER CORPORATION
1700 E Duncan St (75702-2430)
P.O. Box 2010 (75710-2010)
PHONE..................903 510-7300
EMP: 120
SALES (corp-wide): 59.8B **Publicly Held**
SIC: 3585 3567 3564 Mfg Refrigeration/Heating Equipment Mfg Industrial Furnaces/Ovens Mfg Blowers/Fans
HQ: Carrier Corporation
13995 Pasteur Blvd
Palm Beach Gardens FL 33418
800 379-6484

(G-20064)
CATES CASTSTONE CO INC
3901 S Southwest Loop 323 (75701-9233)
P.O. Box 576, Whitehouse (75791-0576)
PHONE..................903 839-0309
Morris Cates, *President*
EMP: 14
SALES (est): 1.7MM **Privately Held**
WEB: www.catescaststone.com
SIC: 3272 Stone, cast concrete

(G-20065)
CATES MACHINE SHOP INC
12198 State Highway 64 W (75704-6966)
PHONE..................903 592-2015
Kip Cates, *President*
Eddie Cates, *Vice Pres*
▲ **EMP:** 13
SQ FT: 7,320
SALES (est): 2MM **Privately Held**
WEB: www.catesmachineshop.com
SIC: 7699 3599 Industrial equipment services; machine shop, jobbing & repair

(G-20066)
CHEMFOUNDRY INC
Also Called: Engineered Fluids
4845 Cantina Dr (75708-6610)
PHONE..................725 218-1955
Gary Testa, *CEO*
Bash Derti, *CFO*
Cynthia Wynn, *Manager*
David Sundin, *Officer*
EMP: 10
SQ FT: 7,500
SALES (est): 950.5K **Privately Held**
WEB: www.engineeredfluids.com
SIC: 3644 Insulators & insulation materials, electrical

(G-20067)
CLEMENTS FLUIDS BUFFALO LTD
701 Old Bllard Rd Pmb 20 (75703)
PHONE..................903 581-5110
Megan Tarrant, *Partner*
Clement Fluids Managment LLC, *General Ptnr*
EMP: 25
SALES (est): 1.2MM **Privately Held**
WEB: www.clementsfluids.com
SIC: 1389 Oil field services

(G-20068)
CLEMENTS FLUIDS HENDERSON LTD
5201 S Broadway Ave # 212 (75703-3748)
PHONE..................903 581-5110
Mike Clements, *Partner*
Tyler Russell, *District Mgr*
Link Abraham, *Opers Mgr*
Jeremy Davis, *Sales Staff*
David Shubert, *Sales Staff*
EMP: 30
SALES (est): 1.6MM **Privately Held**
WEB: www.clementsfluids.com
SIC: 1389 Servicing oil & gas wells

(G-20069)
COKER ENTERPRISES
7106 Us Highway 271 (75708-5710)
PHONE..................903 533-8894

▲ = Import ▼=Export
◆ =Import/Export

Sally Coker, *Owner*
EMP: 15
SQ FT: 6,000
SALES (est): 2.4MM **Privately Held**
WEB: www.generalimp.com
SIC: 3537 5084 5561 Truck trailers, used in plants, docks, terminals, etc.; industrial machinery & equipment; recreational vehicle dealers

(G-20070)
CONCOTE CORPORATION
Also Called: Insul-Fab of Tyler
2340 E Erwin St (75702-6421)
PHONE...................903 581-0697
Cheng Peng, *Sales Engr*
Rocky Jacobs, *Branch Mgr*
EMP: 10
SALES (corp-wide): 29.4MM **Privately Held**
WEB: www.concote.com
SIC: 3086 5085 3471 2675 Plastics foam products; adhesives; tape & plasters; electroplating of metals or formed products; die-cut paper & board
PA: Concote Corporation
600 Freeport Pkwy Ste 150
Coppell TX 75019
214 956-0077

(G-20071)
CONTRACT MANUFACTURERS INC
729 N Fleishel Ave (75702-6078)
P.O. Box 2034 (75710-2034)
PHONE...................903 597-8297
Robert S Burch, *President*
Lori Burch, *Vice Pres*
EMP: 45
SQ FT: 133,000
SALES (est): 10.1MM **Privately Held**
WEB: www.cmitx.net
SIC: 3585 Parts for heating, cooling & refrigerating equipment; air conditioning units, complete: domestic or industrial; furnaces, warm air: electric

(G-20072)
CONTRACTORS SUPPLIES INC
1601 John Carney Dr (75701-2537)
PHONE...................903 597-1308
Chris Sonnamaker, *Vice Pres*
Crystal Garrett, *Office Mgr*
Jim Caldwell, *Director*
EMP: 25
SALES (corp-wide): 30.6MM **Privately Held**
WEB: www.csiconcrete.com
SIC: 3273 Ready-mixed concrete
PA: Contractor's Supplies, Inc.
304 Webber St
Lufkin TX 75904
936 634-3341

(G-20073)
CORNERSTONE APPAREL INC
4601 S Broadway Ave C08 (75703-1332)
PHONE...................903 939-0188
EMP: 44
SALES (corp-wide): 212.9MM **Privately Held**
SIC: 2299 Mfg Textile Goods
PA: Cornerstone Apparel, Inc.
5807 Smithway St
Commerce CA 90040
323 724-3600

(G-20074)
DANWAL INC
Also Called: Designer Graphics
12404 State Highway 155 S (75703-6446)
PHONE...................903 581-0777
Dan Miller, *CEO*
Rick Perry, *President*
Brenda Suberbielle, *MIS Mgr*
EMP: 40
SQ FT: 20,000
SALES (est): 4.3MM **Privately Held**
WEB: www.designergraphics.com
SIC: 7389 2759 Sign painting & lettering shop; screen printing

(G-20075)
DESIGN CENTER SIGNS INC
2971 Elkton Trl (75703-0675)
PHONE...................903 561-4995

Nita Peterson Ingle, *President*
James Paul Ingle Jr, *Vice Pres*
Paul Ingle, *Vice Pres*
Molly Brown, *Manager*
Sheena Keenan, *Consultant*
EMP: 17
SALES (est): 2.4MM **Privately Held**
WEB: www.designcentersigns.com
SIC: 3993 2399 Signs, not made in custom sign painting shops; banners, made from fabric

(G-20076)
DIAMOND WIRE SPRING COMPANY
4501 Candy Ln (75701-8410)
PHONE...................903 581-2358
Karl Schnack, *General Mgr*
Frank E Fazio, *Vice Pres*
Nina Williams, *Sales Executive*
EMP: 20
SALES (corp-wide): 10.7MM **Privately Held**
WEB: www.diamondwire.com
SIC: 3493 5051 Steel springs, except wire; metals service centers & offices
PA: Diamond Wire Spring Company Inc
1479 Glenn Ave
Glenshaw PA 15116
412 684-1201

(G-20077)
DIXON SERVICES INC
12559 County Road 192 (75703-6411)
P.O. Box 6602 (75711-6602)
PHONE...................903 579-9300
Larry R Dixon, *President*
Tom Ridley, *General Ptnr*
Libby Dixon, *Vice Pres*
John Champion, *Project Mgr*
EMP: 13
SALES (est): 1MM **Privately Held**
WEB: www.dsityler.com
SIC: 1389 8711 Oil consultants; engineering services

(G-20078)
DYNA-MIX INC
Also Called: Dyna-Mix Texas
705 S Lyons Ave Ste A (75702-6857)
P.O. Box 4726 (75712-4726)
PHONE...................903 593-7387
Angela Harris, *Clerk*
EMP: 10
SALES (corp-wide): 84.4MM **Privately Held**
WEB: www.dyna-mix.com
SIC: 3069 Rubberized fabrics
HQ: Dyna-Mix, Inc.
1879 Country Club Rd
Grafton WV 26354

(G-20079)
EAST TEXAS CONTAINERS INC
Also Called: E T C
10235 County Road 489 (75706-6023)
P.O. Box 4357 (75712-4357)
PHONE...................903 595-6444
EMP: 45
SQ FT: 50,000
SALES (est): 14.8MM **Privately Held**
SIC: 2653 Boxes, corrugated: made from purchased materials

(G-20080)
EAST TEXAS MUNICPL UTILITY DST
12162 State Highway 155 N (75708-2436)
PHONE...................903 877-3644
Tommy Vice, *CEO*
EMP: 13
SALES (est): 2.7MM **Privately Held**
WEB: www.etmud.com
SIC: 4941 2842 Water supply; sanitation preparations

(G-20081)
EAST TEXAS SMOKER COMPANY
10228 County Road 290 (75707-3870)
PHONE...................903 245-0039
Clint E Shockey, *Corp Secy*
EMP: 9

SALES (est): 57.8K **Privately Held**
WEB: www.easttexassmokercompany.com
SIC: 3556 Smoking or roasting machinery, including ovens

(G-20082)
EAST TXAS LIGHTHOUSE FOR BLIND
Also Called: Horizon Industries
500 N Bois D Arc Ave (75702-5310)
PHONE...................903 595-3444
David J Huffman, *President*
Lee Tillson, *General Mgr*
Michael G Hubbard, *Vice Pres*
Michael Hubbard, *VP Finance*
Habibatou Diallo, *Accountant*
EMP: 95
SQ FT: 100,000
SALES: 20.3MM **Privately Held**
WEB: www.tylerlighthouse.org
SIC: 2676 2392 2211 Towels, napkins & tissue paper products; towels, paper: made from purchased paper; cleansing tissues: made from purchased paper; household furnishings; broadwoven fabric mills, cotton

(G-20083)
EDUCATION ADVANCED INC (PA)
2702 E 5th St Ste 372 (75701-5021)
PHONE...................903 858-4497
Eli Crow, *CEO*
Misti Rasure, *Vice Pres*
Alkesh Patel, *Software Dev*
Travis Prince, *Officer*
EMP: 9
SALES (est): 250K **Privately Held**
WEB: www.educationadvanced.com
SIC: 7372 7389 Educational computer software;

(G-20084)
ETHEREDGE ELC CO TYLER INC
11698 Fm 3270 (75708-3269)
P.O. Box 133024 (75713-3024)
PHONE...................903 877-4774
Mike Etheredge, *President*
Brad Bennett, *COO*
Allen Findley, *Vice Pres*
R Allen Findley, *Vice Pres*
James Burt Grubbs, *Vice Pres*
EMP: 25
SQ FT: 2,000
SALES (est): 4.8MM
SALES (corp-wide): 13.6MM **Privately Held**
WEB: www.eecmotor.com
SIC: 7694 Electric motor repair; rebuilding motors, except automotive
PA: Etheredge Electric Company, Llc
6719 Woolworth Rd
Shreveport LA 71129
318 688-5351

(G-20085)
FAULCONER ENERGY JOINT VENTR S
1001 E Se Loop 323 # 160 (75701-9664)
P.O. Box 7995 (75711-7995)
PHONE...................903 581-4382
Vernon E Faulconer, *Principal*
EMP: 75
SQ FT: 16,000
SALES (est): 4.4MM **Privately Held**
WEB: www.vefinc.com
SIC: 1311 Crude petroleum production; natural gas production

(G-20086)
FAULCONER RESOURCES CORP
1001 E Se Loop 323 # 160 (75701-9664)
P.O. Box 7995 (75711-7995)
PHONE...................903 581-4382
David J Enright, *President*
EMP: 10
SALES (est): 259.7K **Privately Held**
SIC: 1311 Crude petroleum production

(G-20087)
FE SAWYER BLDG SYSTEMS INC
Also Called: Sawyer Metal
12562 State Highway 64 W (75704-8020)
PHONE...................903 531-0182
Clinton B Sawyer, *President*
F E Sawyer, *Vice Pres*
EMP: 20
SALES (est): 5.5MM **Privately Held**
WEB: www.sawyermetal.com
SIC: 3448 Prefabricated metal buildings

(G-20088)
FLOWERS BAKING CO TYLER LLC (DH)
Also Called: Flowers Bakery
1200 W Erwin St (75702-6907)
P.O. Box 360 (75710-0360)
PHONE...................903 595-2421
Bobby Harrison, *President*
Ray Kirkland, *Vice Pres*
Philip Wright, *Purch Agent*
Pamela Cosper, *Treasurer*
Billy Luck, *Manager*
EMP: 160 EST: 1956
SQ FT: 36,000
SALES (est): 30MM
SALES (corp-wide): 4.1B **Publicly Held**
WEB: www.flowersfoods.com
SIC: 2051 Bread, all types (white, wheat, rye, etc): fresh or frozen; buns, bread type: fresh or frozen

(G-20089)
FLUIDS CLEMENTS MANAGEMENT LLC
4710 Kinsey Dr Ste 200 (75703-1009)
PHONE...................903 581-5110
Michael T Clements, *President*
EMP: 9 EST: 2006
SALES (est): 825.5K **Privately Held**
WEB: www.clementsfluids.com
SIC: 1389 Oil field services

(G-20090)
GLENWOOD BLIND & AWNING CO INC
3025 Spur 124 (75707-3251)
PHONE...................903 597-2088
Albert Lee Tindall, *President*
Lee Tindall, *Principal*
Douglas Lynn Tindall, *Corp Secy*
EMP: 9
SQ FT: 6,250
SALES (est): 762.4K **Privately Held**
WEB: www.glenwoodblindandawning.com
SIC: 7299 2591 1521 Home improvement & renovation contractor agency; venetian blinds; single-family home remodeling, additions & repairs

(G-20091)
GREENBERG SMOKED TURKEYS INC
221 Mcmurrey Dr (75702-6396)
P.O. Box 4818 (75712-4818)
PHONE...................903 595-0725
Sam Greenberg, *President*
Joyce Greenberg, *Treasurer*
Larry Barnes, *Sales Executive*
EMP: 20
SQ FT: 20,000
SALES (est): 3.4MM **Privately Held**
WEB: www.gobblegobble.com
SIC: 2015 5144 Turkey, slaughtered & dressed; poultry products

(G-20092)
H3 MEDIA LLC
Also Called: Bscene Magazine
3650 Old Bullard Rd # 110 (75701-8665)
PHONE...................903 581-4237
Shawn Hanney,
EMP: 12
SALES (est): 153.1K **Privately Held**
WEB: www.bscenemag.com
SIC: 2721 Magazines: publishing only, not printed on site

(G-20093)
HARRIS N COMPUTER CORPORATION
Imsoftech
3800 Paluxy Dr Ste 540 (75703-1664)
PHONE...................................903 535-8222
Ponder Wright, *General Mgr*
Neeraja Dubagunta, *Analyst*
EMP: 17
SALES (corp-wide): 3.4B **Privately Held**
WEB: www.harriscomputer.com
SIC: 7371 7372 Computer software systems analysis & design, custom; prepackaged software
HQ: N. Harris Computer Corporation
1 Antares Dr Suite 400
Nepean ON K2E 8
613 226-5511

(G-20094)
HARWOOD INDUSTRIES INC
17833 State Highway 31 E (75705-4733)
PHONE...................................903 566-6001
Gary B Harwood, *President*
Ricky Seagroves, *Graphic Designe*
EMP: 30
SQ FT: 80,000
SALES (est): 5.9MM **Privately Held**
WEB: www.eharwood.com
SIC: 3711 3714 Automobile bodies, passenger car, not including engine, etc.; chassis, motor vehicle; motor vehicle parts & accessories

(G-20095)
HERD PRODUCING CO INC
3901 Manhatton Dr (75701-9403)
P.O. Box 9340 (75711-9340)
PHONE...................................903 509-3456
Bob L Herd, *President*
A W Fears, *Exec VP*
EMP: 29 EST: 1964
SQ FT: 15,000
SALES (est): 2.6MM **Privately Held**
SIC: 1311 8741 6282 Crude petroleum production; management services; investment advice

(G-20096)
HERFF JONES LLC
107 W 6th St (75701-4015)
PHONE...................................903 592-3800
Michael Tidwell, *Branch Mgr*
EMP: 9
SALES (corp-wide): 1.1B **Privately Held**
WEB: www.yearbookdiscoveries.com
SIC: 2752 Commercial printing, lithographic
HQ: Herff Jones, Llc
4501 W 62nd St
Indianapolis IN 46268
800 419-5462

(G-20097)
HERITAGE WIRE LINE SERVICES
Hwy 155 South 10 Miles (75703)
P.O. Box 6904 (75711-6904)
PHONE...................................903 534-0671
Paul Myrick, *President*
Isha Myrick, *Corp Secy*
EMP: 9
SQ FT: 7,200
SALES (est): 1.5MM **Privately Held**
SIC: 1389 Servicing oil & gas wells; perforating well casings

(G-20098)
HILAND DAIRY FOODS COMPANY LLC
Also Called: Hiland Dairy Packaging
200 N Fuller Ave (75702-6209)
PHONE...................................903 565-0288
Barry Beaman, *Branch Mgr*
EMP: 100
SALES (corp-wide): 1.5B **Privately Held**
WEB: www.hilanddairy.com
SIC: 2026 Milk processing (pasteurizing, homogenizing, bottling)
HQ: Hiland Dairy Foods Company., Llc
1133 E Kearney St
Springfield MO 65803
417 862-9311

(G-20099)
HILLMAN GROUP INC
Also Called: St Fastening Systems
6357 Reynolds Rd (75708-6016)
P.O. Box 4515 (75712-4515)
PHONE...................................903 592-2826
David Quel, *Manager*
EMP: 75
SALES (corp-wide): 472MM **Privately Held**
WEB: www.hillmangroup.com
SIC: 5085 3452 Fasteners, industrial: nuts, bolts, screws, etc.; bolts, nuts, rivets & washers
HQ: The Hillman Group Inc
10590 Hamilton Ave
Cincinnati OH 45231
513 851-4900

(G-20100)
HOOD FLEXIBLE PACKAGING CORP (PA)
2410 N Lyndon Ave (75702-2539)
P.O. Box 818 (75710-0818)
PHONE...................................903 593-1793
Robert Morris, *President*
Gulam Harji, *Principal*
John Johnson, *Vice Pres*
R J More, *VP Human Res*
◆ EMP: 75
SQ FT: 200,000
SALES (est): 29.7MM **Privately Held**
WEB: www.hoodpkg.com
SIC: 2673 2671 3089 Plastic bags: made from purchased materials; packaging paper & plastics film, coated & laminated; blow molded finished plastic products

(G-20101)
IMPRESSIVE IMAGE WORKS INC (PA)
2901 Teague Dr (75701-3753)
P.O. Box 131013 (75713-1013)
PHONE...................................903 597-4599
Dale Eppler, *President*
EMP: 23
SQ FT: 8,200
SALES (est): 1.6MM **Privately Held**
WEB: www.impressiveimageworks.com
SIC: 2761 2782 2752 Computer forms, manifold or continuous; checkbooks; commercial printing, lithographic

(G-20102)
INTEGRATED FLOW SOLUTIONS LLC (HQ)
Also Called: I F S
6461 Reynolds Rd (75708-6017)
P.O. Box 7095 (75711-7095)
PHONE...................................903 595-6511
Lourdes Aguilar, *Project Mgr*
Troy Urbantke, *Project Mgr*
Daniel Leal, *Engineer*
Maria Quijada, *Engineer*
Roger Pugh, *Electrical Engi*
◆ EMP: 64
SQ FT: 70,000
SALES (est): 24.9MM **Publicly Held**
WEB: www.ifsolutions.com
SIC: 3561 Pumps & pumping equipment

(G-20103)
INTENSE WIRELINE SOLUTIONS LLC
100 Independence Pl # 405 (75703-1318)
P.O. Box 3242, Flint (75762-3250)
PHONE...................................903 630-5440
Tony Wiggins, *Mng Member*
EMP: 57
SALES (est): 3.7MM **Privately Held**
WEB: www.intensewireline.com
SIC: 1389 5082 Oil field services; oil field equipment

(G-20104)
JOHN SOULES FOODS INC (PA)
10150 Fm 14 (75706-7145)
P.O. Box 4579 (75712-4579)
PHONE...................................903 592-9800
John E Soules II, *CEO*
Mark D Soules, *CEO*
John E Soules Sr, *Ch of Bd*
Thomas L Ellis, *Exec VP*
Krystal Pelayo, *Production*
◆ EMP: 207

SQ FT: 220,000
SALES (est): 265.3MM **Privately Held**
WEB: www.johnsoulesfoods.com
SIC: 2013 2015 5147 Sausages & other prepared meats; poultry slaughtering & processing; meats & meat products

(G-20105)
JV INDUSTRIAL COMPANIES LTD
Also Called: JV Tyler Engineers
1001 E Northst Lp 323 2 (75708)
PHONE...................................903 579-8900
EMP: 16 **Privately Held**
SIC: 7692 8711 Welding Repair Engineering Services
HQ: J.V. Industrial Companies, Ltd.
4040 Red Bluff Rd
Pasadena TX 78221
713 568-2600

(G-20106)
KARIS RESOURCES LLC
3626 Rock Creek Dr (75707-1634)
PHONE...................................903 595-0900
Pamela Greer, *CEO*
David Melton, *President*
EMP: 24
SALES (est): 6MM **Privately Held**
SIC: 3533 Oil & gas field machinery

(G-20107)
KEEN SOLUTIONS GROUP INC
110 N College Ave Ste 203 (75702-7221)
PHONE...................................903 253-0476
Joshua Norris, *Mng Member*
Joshua A Norris,
EMP: 21 EST: 2012
SALES (est): 3MM **Privately Held**
WEB: www.keensg.com
SIC: 7373 7372 7371 Systems engineering, computer related; systems integration services; value-added resellers, computer systems; business oriented computer software; computer software systems analysis & design, custom

(G-20108)
KENT SPORTING GOODS CO INC
Also Called: Blacksheep
3220 W Gentry Pkwy (75702-1311)
PHONE...................................903 592-3853
Hank Wiggins, *General Mgr*
Jeff Carlson, *Branch Mgr*
EMP: 200
SALES (corp-wide): 159.8MM **Privately Held**
WEB: www.kentwatersports.com
SIC: 3949 Sporting & athletic goods
PA: Kent Water Sports, Llc
433 Park Ave
New London OH 44851
419 929-7021

(G-20109)
KLUBER LUBRICATION N AMER LP
Also Called: Summit Industrial Products
9010 County Road 2120 (75707-5400)
P.O. Box 131359 (75713-1359)
PHONE...................................903 534-8021
Rodney Rushing, *Vice Pres*
Scott Burns, *Purch Mgr*
Tim Merrell, *Purch Mgr*
Kelly Starr, *Human Res Mgr*
Dennis Bland, *Regl Sales Mgr*
EMP: 60
SALES (corp-wide): 10.5B **Privately Held**
WEB: www.klueber.com
SIC: 2992 Lubricating oils & greases
HQ: Kluber Lubrication Na Lp
32 Industrial Dr
Londonderry NH 03053
603 647-4104

(G-20110)
KLUBER LUBRICATION NA LP
Also Called: Summit Industrial Products
9010 County Road 2120 (75707-5400)
P.O. Box 131359 (75713-1359)
PHONE...................................903 534-8021
Alfred R Pate III, *President*
Kent Brandon, *Vice Pres*
Dwight Evans, *Vice Pres*

Tim Merrell, *Purch Mgr*
Kelly Star, *CFO*
EMP: 9
SQ FT: 100,000
SALES (est): 2.6MM
SALES (corp-wide): 10.5B **Privately Held**
WEB: www.klsummit.com
SIC: 2992 Lubricating oils & greases
HQ: Kluber Lubrication Na Lp
32 Industrial Dr
Londonderry NH 03053
603 647-4104

(G-20111)
KNIGHT MANUFACTURING CO INC
Also Called: Creme Lure
5401 Kent Dr (75707-1947)
P.O. Box 6162 (75711-6162)
PHONE...................................903 561-0522
L Wayne Kent, *President*
Judith Carol Kent, *Vice Pres*
▲ EMP: 60
SQ FT: 29,000
SALES (est): 6.1MM **Privately Held**
WEB: www.cremelure.com
SIC: 3949 Lures, fishing: artificial

(G-20112)
LEONS SIGNS INC
851 E Northeast Loop 323 (75708-1023)
P.O. Box 4788 (75712-4788)
PHONE...................................903 597-7731
Phil Sulser, *President*
Matt Nellenback, *Vice Pres*
Kathy Nellenback, *Admin Sec*
EMP: 20
SQ FT: 24,000
SALES (est): 2.4MM **Privately Held**
WEB: www.leonssignsinc.com
SIC: 3993 Electric signs

(G-20113)
LILLY MACHINERY INC
10259 County Road 2213 (75707-5407)
P.O. Box 130655 (75713-0655)
PHONE...................................903 561-6733
Roy H Lilly, *President*
Theresa Lilly, *Corp Secy*
Ann tJ Lilly, *Vice Pres*
Ann Lilly, *Vice Pres*
EMP: 20
SQ FT: 18,000
SALES (est): 3.9MM **Privately Held**
WEB: www.lillymachinery.com
SIC: 3599 Machine shop, jobbing & repair

(G-20114)
LINDE GAS NORTH AMERICA LLC
Also Called: Lifegas
2107 Broussard St (75701-8408)
PHONE...................................903 939-0613
Kelly Burns, *Branch Mgr*
EMP: 14 **Privately Held**
WEB: www.praxair.com
SIC: 2813 Nitrogen; oxygen, compressed or liquefied
HQ: Linde Gas North America Llc
10 Riverview Dr
Danbury CT 06810

(G-20115)
LOGGINS MEAT COMPANY INC
1908 E Erwin St (75702-6413)
P.O. Box 7369 (75711-7369)
PHONE...................................903 595-1011
Bobby G Loggins, *Ch of Bd*
Randy Parker, *Director*
Virginia McKelvey, *Admin Sec*
EMP: 61 EST: 1942
SQ FT: 54,000
SALES (est): 21.3MM **Privately Held**
WEB: www.logginsrestaurant.com
SIC: 5142 2011 Frozen fish, meat & poultry; meat packing plants

(G-20116)
M B & G OILFLD FABRICATION INC
2611 Us Highway 271 (75708-6449)
P.O. Box 120399 (75712-0399)
PHONE...................................903 593-0400
Larry Moore, *President*
Leslie Moore, *Vice Pres*

EMP: 14
SQ FT: 10,000
SALES (est): 3.8MM **Privately Held**
SIC: 3533 Oil & gas field machinery

(G-20117)
M H C X-PLORATION CORPORATION
14609 Hwy 64 W (75704-6423)
P.O. Box 7405 (75711-7405)
PHONE..................................903 595-4323
Kathleen Collum, *President*
James K Collum, *Vice Pres*
EMP: 13
SQ FT: 2,000
SALES (est): 1.8MM **Privately Held**
WEB: www.mhcxploration.com
SIC: 1241 1781 1382 1799 Exploration, bituminous or lignite mining; water well drilling; geophysical exploration, oil & gas field; core drilling & cutting

(G-20118)
M P INDUSTRIES INC
4939 Profit Dr (75707-1838)
P.O. Box 130579 (75713-0579)
PHONE..................................903 561-4232
Monroe Mirsky, *President*
Phil Phelps, *Vice Pres*
▲ **EMP:** 36 **EST:** 1977
SQ FT: 50,000
SALES (est): 5.5MM **Privately Held**
WEB: www.mpioiltool.com
SIC: 3061 3533 Oil & gas field machinery rubber goods (mechanical); oil & gas field machinery

(G-20119)
MADDOX ENTERPRISES INC (PA)
Also Called: Maddox Residential & Coml Svcs
125 S Bonner Ave (75702-7118)
P.O. Box 12157, Austin (78711-2157)
PHONE..................................903 592-6531
Edwin T Maddox, *Ch of Bd*
Tom Maddox, *President*
Erby Eikner, *Business Mgr*
Larry Walker, *Supervisor*
Carol C Maddox, *Director*
EMP: 49
SQ FT: 15,000
SALES (est): 9.8MM **Privately Held**
WEB: www.maddoxac.com
SIC: 3585 1711 3822 1731 Refrigeration & heating equipment; mechanical contractor; auto controls regulating residntl & coml environmt & applncs; general electrical contractor

(G-20120)
MARTIN-DECKER TOTCO INC
4912 Hightech Dr (75703-2625)
PHONE..................................903 534-3677
Alan Patterson, *Manager*
EMP: 12
SALES (corp-wide): 8.4B **Publicly Held**
WEB: www.nov.com
SIC: 1389 Measurement of well flow rates, oil & gas
HQ: Martin-Decker Totco, Inc.
1200 Cypress Creek Rd
Cedar Park TX 78613

(G-20121)
MCMT LLC
Also Called: Woody's Accessories & Off-Road
1810 W Southwest Loop 323 (75701-8425)
PHONE..................................903 592-9663
Matthew R Denson,
EMP: 12 **EST:** 2011
SALES (est): 2MM **Privately Held**
WEB: www.woodystruck.com
SIC: 7538 3714 7549 General automotive repair shops; pickup truck bed liners; glass tinting, automotive

(G-20122)
MCWANE INC
Tyler Union
11910 County Road 492 (75706-5840)
PHONE..................................800 527-8478
Dale Garrett, *Superintendent*
Jonathan Pollard, *Plant Mgr*
Tom Berry, *Materials Mgr*
Rick Thompson, *Materials Mgr*

Chris Hyche, *Plant Engr Mgr*
EMP: 376
SALES (corp-wide): 970.3MM **Privately Held**
WEB: www.mcwane.com
SIC: 3491 Water works valves
PA: Mcwane, Inc.
2900 Highway 280 S # 300
Birmingham AL 35223
205 414-3100

(G-20123)
MCWANE INC (HQ)
Also Called: Tyler Pipe Company
11910 County Road 492 (75706-5840)
PHONE..................................800 527-8478
Ruffner Page, *President*
Harold Golden, *Superintendent*
Victor Hatcher, *Regional Mgr*
Bill Bliss, *Vice Pres*
Jennie Shephard, *Safety Dir*
◆ **EMP:** 128
SQ FT: 250,000
SALES (est): 107.9MM
SALES (corp-wide): 970.3MM **Privately Held**
WEB: www.tylerpipe.com
SIC: 3321 Sewer pipe, cast iron
PA: Mcwane, Inc.
2900 Highway 280 S # 300
Birmingham AL 35223
205 414-3100

(G-20124)
MCWANE INC
Tyler Pipe Company
11721 Us Highway 69 N (75706-5637)
P.O. Box 2027 (75710-2027)
PHONE..................................903 882-5511
Bill Shockley, *Sales Staff*
Rick Tatman, *Branch Mgr*
Jennifer Wickliffe, *Manager*
EMP: 1000
SALES (corp-wide): 970.3MM **Privately Held**
WEB: www.mcwane.com
SIC: 3321 Gray & ductile iron foundries
PA: Mcwane, Inc.
2900 Highway 280 S # 300
Birmingham AL 35223
205 414-3100

(G-20125)
MEWBORNE ENRGY PRTNERS 04-A LP
Also Called: Mewbourne Oil Company
3901 S Broadway Ave (75701-8716)
PHONE..................................903 561-2900
Alan Clark, *Treasurer*
EMP: 100
SALES: 768.3K **Privately Held**
WEB: www.mewbourne.net
SIC: 1382 Oil & gas exploration services

(G-20126)
MEWBOURNE HOLDINGS INC (PA)
3901 S Broadway Ave (75701-8716)
P.O. Box 7698 (75711-7698)
PHONE..................................903 561-2900
Kenneth Waits, *CEO*
Kenneth S Waits, *CEO*
Curtis Mewbourne, *Founder*
Roe Buckley, *CFO*
Alan Clark, *Treasurer*
EMP: 40
SQ FT: 20,000
SALES (est): 458.1MM **Privately Held**
WEB: www.mewbourne.net
SIC: 1311 Crude petroleum production

(G-20127)
MEWBOURNE OIL COMPANY (HQ)
3620 Old Bullard Rd (75701-8644)
P.O. Box 7698 (75711-7698)
PHONE..................................903 561-2900
Curtis W Mewbourne, *President*
Joseph F Odom, *Vice Pres*
Monty Whetstone, *Vice Pres*
Job Gutierrez, *Foreman/Supr*
Kelly Westby, *Foreman/Supr*
EMP: 35
SQ FT: 20,000

SALES (est): 503.8MM
SALES (corp-wide): 458.1MM **Privately Held**
WEB: www.mewbourne.net
SIC: 1311 Crude petroleum production; natural gas production
PA: Mewbourne Holdings, Inc.
3901 S Broadway Ave
Tyler TX 75701
903 561-2900

(G-20128)
MICROTEK MEDICAL INC
Also Called: Ecolab
2319 E Erwin St (75702-6422)
PHONE..................................903 597-2568
Pat Nicklson, *Principal*
EMP: 30
SQ FT: 10,000
SALES (corp-wide): 14.9B **Publicly Held**
WEB: www.ecolab.com
SIC: 3841 Surgical & medical instruments
HQ: Microtek Medical Inc.
512 N Lehmberg Rd
Columbus MS 39702
662 327-1863

(G-20129)
MILLENNIUM SIGNS AMERICA LLC
1832 W Gentry Pkwy (75702-3928)
PHONE..................................903 944-7981
Shawn Dawkins, *Mng Member*
EMP: 400
SALES (est): 1.2MM **Privately Held**
WEB: www.texasdigitaldisplay.com
SIC: 3993 Letters for signs, metal

(G-20130)
MILLER POWER EQUIPMENT CO LLC
3227 Old Jacksonville Rd (75701-7505)
PHONE..................................903 592-7201
Fax: 903 592-7248
EMP: 9
SQ FT: 8,000
SALES: 100K **Privately Held**
SIC: 3524 Mfg Lawn/Garden Equipment

(G-20131)
MOORE ASPHALT CO INC
5509 Old Jacksonville Hwy (75703-3379)
PHONE..................................903 561-1321
Joe C Moore, *President*
Moore Robert S, *Vice Pres*
Damaris Moore, *Admin Sec*
EMP: 25
SQ FT: 1,500
SALES (est): 2.1MM **Privately Held**
SIC: 5032 2951 Asphalt mixture; asphalt paving mixtures & blocks

(G-20132)
NATIONAL DENTEX CORPORATION
Also Called: Stern Empire Dental Laboratory
114 Jordan Plaza Blvd # 300 (75704-2056)
PHONE..................................903 597-3198
Missy Miller, *Branch Mgr*
EMP: 10
SALES (corp-wide): 144.6MM **Privately Held**
WEB: www.nationaldentex.com
SIC: 3843 8072 Dental equipment & supplies; dental laboratories
HQ: National Dentex, Llc
11601 Kew Gardens Ave # 200
Palm Beach Gardens FL 33410
561 537-8300

(G-20133)
NBR SAND LLC
905 Interstate 20 W (75706-5351)
PHONE..................................903 593-3311
Bryan Shinn, *President*
EMP: 11
SALES (est): 395.5K
SALES (corp-wide): 1.4B **Publicly Held**
WEB: www.nbrsand.com
SIC: 1442 Sand mining
HQ: Tyler Silica Company
6316 Design Dr
Greenville WI 54942
888 388-3224

(G-20134)
NRI INC
218 N College Ave (75702-5715)
PHONE..................................903 526-5800
Harold E McGowen III, *President*
Dwayne Thomson, *Controller*
M S Smith, *Manager*
EMP: 11
SQ FT: 10,000
SALES (est): 870K **Privately Held**
WEB: www.bluedge.com
SIC: 1381 Drilling oil & gas wells

(G-20135)
OIL STATES ENERGY SERVICES LLC
9019 Us Highway 271 (75708-4134)
PHONE..................................903 526-4777
Allen Carter, *Owner*
EMP: 35
SALES (corp-wide): 1B **Publicly Held**
WEB: www.oses.com
SIC: 5082 3533 Oil field equipment; oil field machinery & equipment
HQ: Oil States Energy Services, L.L.C.
333 Clay St Ste 2100
Houston TX 77002
713 425-2400

(G-20136)
ORS FLUIDS LLC
809 E Erwin St (75702-7536)
PHONE..................................903 535-9992
EMP: 28 **EST:** 2013
SALES (est): 3.1MM **Privately Held**
SIC: 1382 Oil/Gas Exploration Services

(G-20137)
PACO LABEL SYSTEMS INC
1 Hombre Dr (75707)
P.O. Box 6502 (75711-6502)
PHONE..................................903 561-2125
Kyle Eldred, *CEO*
Rowe Anderson, *President*
EMP: 15 **EST:** 1967
SQ FT: 25,000
SALES (est): 2.3MM
SALES (corp-wide): 18MM **Privately Held**
WEB: www.pacolabel.com
SIC: 3069 2754 Tape, pressure sensitive: rubber; labels: gravure printing
PA: Frankston Packaging Company, Llc
699 N Frankston Hwy
Frankston TX 75763
903 876-2550

(G-20138)
PATTERSON-UTI ENERGY INC
Also Called: Patterson-Uti Drilling
11940 Constantine Ave (75708-3253)
PHONE..................................903 877-3659
Mike Holcomb, *Opers Staff*
Curtis Mana, *Branch Mgr*
EMP: 50
SALES (corp-wide): 1.1B **Publicly Held**
WEB: www.patenergy.com
SIC: 1381 Directional drilling oil & gas wells
PA: Patterson-Uti Energy, Inc.
10713 W Sam Houston Pkwy
Houston TX 77064
281 765-7100

(G-20139)
PENDLETON WOOLEN MILLS INC
909 E Northeast Loop 323 (75708-1025)
PHONE..................................903 581-7742
Jim Pendleton, *Principal*
EMP: 11
SALES (corp-wide): 126.1MM **Privately Held**
WEB: www.pendleton-usa.com
SIC: 2337 Women's & misses' suits & coats
PA: Pendleton Woolen Mills, Inc.
220 Nw Broadway
Portland OR 97209
503 226-4801

(G-20140)
PETERSEN ALUMINUM CORPORATION
10551 Pac Rd (75707-5470)
PHONE.................................903 581-6228
Mark Humphrey, *Sales Staff*
Eric Davis, *Sales Associate*
Joshua Jacobi, *Sales Executive*
Chris Headley, *Comms Dir*
Andrea Burrow, *Office Mgr*
EMP: 20
SALES (corp-wide): 4.2B **Publicly Held**
WEB: www.pac-clad.com
SIC: 5051 1521 3444 Aluminum bars, rods, ingots, sheets, pipes, plates, etc.; single-family housing construction; sheet metalwork
HQ: Petersen Aluminum Corporation
1005 Tonne Rd
Elk Grove Village IL 60007
847 228-7150

(G-20141)
PETRO LAND GROUP INC
3400 G E Dr (75701-7336)
P.O. Box 389 (75710-0389)
PHONE.................................903 595-4293
Terry Fowler, *President*
Philip Nobles, *Vice Pres*
Kim Whisenhunt, *Manager*
Doye Carroll, *Administration*
EMP: 20
SALES (est): 1.4MM **Privately Held**
WEB: www.petroland.com
SIC: 1382 Oil & gas exploration services

(G-20142)
PI TAPE TEXAS LLC (PA)
10235 Robinson Dr (75703-3416)
PHONE.................................903 266-9204
Harold Phillips, *President*
▲ **EMP:** 18
SQ FT: 10,000
SALES (est): 2.5MM **Privately Held**
WEB: www.pitape.com
SIC: 3544 Special dies, tools, jigs & fixtures

(G-20143)
PICO SALES AND DIST LLC
Also Called: Pico Technology
320 N Glenwood Blvd (75702-5427)
PHONE.................................800 591-2796
Craig Schoenberger, *President*
Craig Wheeler, *Business Mgr*
Richard Boyd, *Sales Staff*
EMP: 13
SALES (est): 1.1MM **Privately Held**
WEB: www.picotech.com
SIC: 3825 Digital test equipment, electronic & electrical circuits; pulse (signal) generators; test equipment for electronic & electrical circuits; oscillographs & oscilloscopes

(G-20144)
R J REYNOLDS TOBACCO COMPANY
Also Called: Lorillard Tobacco
5400 University Dr (75707-2131)
PHONE.................................877 703-0386
EMP: 251
SALES (corp-wide): 33.4B **Privately Held**
WEB: www.rjrt.com
SIC: 2111 Cigarettes
HQ: R. J. Reynolds Tobacco Company
401 N Main St
Winston Salem NC 27101
336 741-5000

(G-20145)
REDCO PALLET INC
413 Top Hill Dr (75703-3678)
P.O. Box 7373 (75711-7373)
PHONE.................................903 561-2075
John T Acker Jr, *President*
Justin R Acker, *Vice Pres*
EMP: 20
SALES (est): 3MM **Privately Held**
SIC: 2448 Pallets, wood

(G-20146)
REX-HIDE INCORPORATED (PA)
705 S Lyons Ave (75702-6857)
P.O. Box 4726 (75712-4726)
PHONE.................................903 593-7387
Brad J Hoeffner, *President*
Tjkav Hoeffnek, *President*
Dale Wagner, *Vice Pres*
Chris McCurry, *Treasurer*
Delores Thurston, *Treasurer*
◆ **EMP:** 10 **EST:** 1917
SQ FT: 60,000
SALES (est): 84.4MM **Privately Held**
WEB: www.rex-hideinc.com
SIC: 3061 3069 2891 6799 Automotive rubber goods (mechanical); rubber automotive products; adhesives; investors

(G-20147)
REX-HIDE INDUSTRIES INC (HQ)
705 S Lyons Ave (75702-6857)
P.O. Box 4726 (75712-4726)
PHONE.................................903 593-7387
Brad Hoeffner, *President*
David Mohr, *President*
Chris Mc Curry, *Corp Secy*
Allen Snyder, *Info Tech Dir*
Brian Cook, *Information Mgr*
EMP: 100
SQ FT: 55,000
SALES (est): 41.1MM
SALES (corp-wide): 84.4MM **Privately Held**
WEB: www.rex-hide.com
SIC: 3061 Automotive rubber goods (mechanical)
PA: Rex-Hide Incorporated
705 S Lyons Ave
Tyler TX 75702
903 593-7387

(G-20148)
SCAN DRILLING COMPANY INC
9395 Fm 2767 (75708-7820)
PHONE.................................903 597-5368
Ricky Perkins, *Superintendent*
Neil Pierce, *VP Opers*
John Arvy, *Manager*
EMP: 15
SALES (corp-wide): 111.3MM **Privately Held**
WEB: www.scandrill.com
SIC: 1389 Oil field services
PA: Scan Drilling Company, Inc.
11777 Katy Fwy Ste 300
Houston TX 77079
281 496-5571

(G-20149)
SCHLUMBERGER TECHNOLOGY CORP
Also Called: Schlumberger Wireline & Tstg
9965 State Highway 31 E (75705-2332)
PHONE.................................903 590-4500
Lance Hudson, *Branch Mgr*
William Gardner, *Manager*
EMP: 82 **Publicly Held**
SIC: 1389 Well logging; oil field services
HQ: Schlumberger Technology Corp
300 Schlumberger Dr
Sugar Land TX 77478
281 285-8500

(G-20150)
SDS ENERGY SERVICES LLC
1406 Rice Rd Ste 400 (75703-3267)
PHONE.................................903 747-3837
Scott Stovall,
EMP: 20
SALES (est): 72K **Privately Held**
SIC: 1389 Oil & gas field services

(G-20151)
SEPRA-CHEM CORPORATION
10975 Spur 248 (75707-4683)
P.O. Box 132100 (75713-2100)
PHONE.................................478 788-9789
Jerry Hamilton, *President*
Bob Stephenson, *Vice Pres*
Robert Stephenson, *Vice Pres*
Alek Hamilton, *Senior Engr*
Cindy Stephenson, *Treasurer*
EMP: 10
SQ FT: 5,000

SALES (est): 2.1MM **Privately Held**
WEB: www.seprachem.com
SIC: 3564 3569 3443 Filters, air: furnaces, air conditioning equipment, etc.; gas separators (machinery); separators for steam, gas, vapor or air (machinery); industrial vessels, tanks & containers; separators, industrial process: metal plate

(G-20152)
SMARTDRONE CORPORATION
2014 Deerbrook Dr (75703-5967)
PHONE.................................443 655-5556
Robert Cammack, *CEO*
EMP: 12
SALES (est): 1.5MM **Privately Held**
SIC: 3728 Target drones

(G-20153)
SMITH TANK & EQUIPMENT COMPANY
9887 Us Highway 271 (75708-4101)
P.O. Box 2014 (75710-2014)
PHONE.................................903 597-5541
James W Blair, *President*
Dick Counts, *Vice Pres*
Mike Hogue, *Vice Pres*
Richard Amason, *Purch Mgr*
Tammy Blair, *Controller*
EMP: 29 **EST:** 1929
SQ FT: 97,000
SALES (est): 8.9MM **Privately Held**
WEB: www.smithtank.com
SIC: 3443 2656 Tanks for tank trucks, metal plate; tanks, standard or custom fabricated: metal plate; sanitary food containers

(G-20154)
SOUTHERN UTILITIES COMPANY
Also Called: Dixon Farms
218 N Broadway Ave Frnt (75702-5791)
PHONE.................................903 593-2588
Royce E Wisenbaker Jr, *Branch Mgr*
EMP: 20
SALES (corp-wide): 17.1MM **Privately Held**
WEB: www.southernutilitiesco.com
SIC: 1311 Crude petroleum production
PA: Southern Utilities Company Inc
218 N Broadway Ave
Tyler TX 75702
903 593-2588

(G-20155)
SPRAYING SYSTEMS CO
15592 Timberline Dr (75703-6975)
PHONE.................................903 535-5036
Suzanne R Smith, *Principal*
EMP: 48
SALES (corp-wide): 350.3MM **Privately Held**
WEB: www.spray.com
SIC: 3499 Nozzles, spray: aerosol, paint or insecticide
PA: Spraying Systems Co.
200 W North Ave
Glendale Heights IL 60139
630 665-5000

(G-20156)
SPUR MACHINE WORKS INC
3182 Spur 124 (75707-3252)
PHONE.................................903 597-8757
Susie Leon, *President*
Murchison Nickie, *Vice Pres*
EMP: 10
SQ FT: 15,000
SALES (est): 1.6MM **Privately Held**
SIC: 3599 Machine shop, jobbing & repair

(G-20157)
STAINLESS STL FABRICATORS LTD
11967 State Highway 64 W (75704-6939)
P.O. Box 4549 (75712-4549)
PHONE.................................903 595-6625
Greg King, *General Ptnr*
EMP: 20
SALES (est): 4.1MM **Privately Held**
WEB: www.ssftexas.com
SIC: 3441 Fabricated structural metal

(G-20158)
SURFACE WELL CONTROL LLC (PA)
6290b Reynolds Rd (75708-6010)
P.O. Box 1737, Chandler (75758-1737)
PHONE.................................903 526-2522
Dennis Willard, *President*
Dusty Willard, *Manager*
EMP: 18 **EST:** 2007
SALES (est): 3.3MM **Privately Held**
WEB: www.surfacewellcontrolllc.listandfound.com
SIC: 1389 Oil & gas wells: building, repairing & dismantling

(G-20159)
SWORD COMPANY
19981 Us Highway 69 S (75703-8711)
P.O. Box 6365 (75711-6365)
PHONE.................................903 561-1921
Michael Sword, *President*
EMP: 23
SQ FT: 11,300
SALES (est): 8MM **Privately Held**
WEB: www.swordco.com
SIC: 5072 3264 5074 Builders' hardware; knobs, porcelain; plumbing & hydronic heating supplies

(G-20160)
TANOS ENERGY LLC
821 E Se Loop 323 Ste 400 (75701-9613)
PHONE.................................903 597-7667
Mark Brandon, *Mng Member*
Genevieve Jordan, *Analyst*
EMP: 13 **EST:** 2007
SQ FT: 4,000
SALES (est): 261.8K **Privately Held**
WEB: www.tanosexp.com
SIC: 1382 Oil & gas exploration services

(G-20161)
TEXAS RESPONSIBLE ENERGY &
705 Sutherland Dr (75703-4627)
PHONE.................................903 266-9103
Phil Parks, *President*
EMP: 16
SALES (est): 1.6MM **Privately Held**
WEB: www.gotreepower.com
SIC: 3433 Heating equipment, except electric

(G-20162)
THRYV INC
1001 E Se Loop 323 # 420 (75701-9664)
PHONE.................................903 593-5400
Jeffrey W Brown, *Branch Mgr*
EMP: 42
SALES (corp-wide): 1.4B **Publicly Held**
WEB: www.thryv.com
SIC: 2741 Telephone & other directory publishing
HQ: Thryv, Inc.
2200 W Airfield Dr
Dfw Airport TX 75261
972 453-7000

(G-20163)
TRANE TECHNOLOGIES COMPANY LLC
Also Called: Ingersoll-Rand
6200 Troup Hwy (75707-1948)
PHONE.................................903 730-4000
Paparao Kodali, *President*
Michael Pryor, *Production*
James Alvarado, *Engineer*
Valerie Shepard, *Finance Mgr*
Andrew Wong, *Accountant*
EMP: 26 **Privately Held**
WEB: www.ingersollrand.com
SIC: 3561 3429 3546 3563 Pumps & pumping equipment; furniture builders' & other household hardware; keys, locks & related hardware; power-driven handtools; air & gas compressors including vacuum pumps; winches
HQ: Trane Technologies Company Llc
800 Beaty St
Davidson NC 28036
704 655-4000

(G-20164)
TRANE US INC
Trane Company, The
6200 Troup Hwy (75707-1948)
P.O. Box 9010 (75711-9010)
PHONE..................903 581-3200
EMP: 40 **Privately Held**
WEB: www.trane.com
SIC: **3585** Mfg Refrigeration/Heating
 Equipment
HQ: Trane U.S. Inc.
 3600 Pammel Creek Rd
 La Crosse WI 54601
 608 787-2000

(G-20165)
TRANE US INC
1211 Woodland Hills Dr (75701-8523)
P.O. Box 9010 (75711-9010)
PHONE..................903 316-8033
Doug Hunsley, *Branch Mgr*
EMP: 63 **Privately Held**
WEB: www.trane.com
SIC: **3585** Refrigeration & heating equip-
 ment
HQ: Trane U.S. Inc.
 3600 Pammel Creek Rd
 La Crosse WI 54601
 608 787-2000

(G-20166)
TW STAMPING & TOOL INC
Also Called: Regal Machine, Mfg
10893 Us Highway 271 (75708-3120)
P.O. Box 176, Winona (75792-0176)
PHONE..................903 877-2353
Terry Warren, *President*
Vicki Warren, *Corp Secy*
Blake Warren, *Vice Pres*
Phil Liggett, *Sales Mgr*
EMP: 32
SQ FT: 35,000
SALES (est): 8.8MM **Privately Held**
WEB: www.regalmfg.com
SIC: **3498** 3444 3469 Fabricated pipe &
 fittings; sheet metalwork; metal stampings

(G-20167)
TYLER BUILDING SYSTEMS LP (PA)
3535 Shiloh Rd (75707-1909)
P.O. Box 130819 (75713-0819)
PHONE..................903 561-3000
William E Curtis Jr, *Managing Prtnr*
Robert C Curtis, *Partner*
Hubert M Sherrell, *Partner*
David Weatherford, *Safety Mgr*
Jessica Davlin, *Purch Mgr*
EMP: 34
SQ FT: 85,000
SALES: 16.4MM **Privately Held**
WEB: www.tylerbuilding.com
SIC: **3448** 1542 Prefabricated metal build-
 ings; nonresidential construction

(G-20168)
TYLER CANDLE COMPANY LLC
11733 State Highway 155 N (75708-3245)
PHONE..................903 877-2298
Eric Horton, *President*
Mary Katherine Martinez, *Vice Pres*
Priscilla Floyd, *Supervisor*
Amy Surber, *Executive Asst*
Katherine Martinez,
▲ EMP: 16 EST: 1999
SALES (est): 2MM **Privately Held**
WEB: www.tylercandles.com
SIC: **3999** Candles

(G-20169)
TYLER CORRUGATED BOX INC
5710 Reed Rd (75707-1968)
P.O. Box 8502 (75711-8502)
PHONE..................903 581-4950
Richard Greg Patterson, *President*
Larry Patterson, *President*
Jean Patterson, *Corp Secy*
Greg Patterson, *Vice Pres*
Teri Westerheide, *Vice Pres*
EMP: 32
SQ FT: 57,000
SALES (est): 8.6MM **Privately Held**
WEB: www.tylerbox.com
SIC: **2653** Boxes, corrugated: made from
 purchased materials

(G-20170)
TYLER IRON & METAL LTD
1630 W Northwest Loop 323 (75702-1148)
P.O. Box 4536 (75712-4536)
PHONE..................903 592-8144
Tommy G Salome, *Partner*
Melvin A Lipsitz Jr, *Partner*
EMP: 23
SQ FT: 10,000
SALES (est): 3.4MM **Privately Held**
WEB: www.tylerironandmetal.com
SIC: **5093** 3341 Ferrous metal scrap &
 waste; secondary nonferrous metals

(G-20171)
TYLER PACKING CO INC
Also Called: Tiptop Quality
2209 E Erwin St Ste 11 (75702-6420)
P.O. Box 1116 (75710-1116)
PHONE..................903 593-9592
Herbert C Buie, *CEO*
EMP: 15
SQ FT: 30,000
SALES (est): 2MM **Privately Held**
WEB: www.tylerpaper.com
SIC: **2013** Pork, cured: from purchased
 meat; cured meats from purchased meat

(G-20172)
TYLER PRODUCTS SALES INC
10383 Spur 164 (75709-5116)
P.O. Box 605, Chandler (75758-0605)
PHONE..................903 593-8633
John Redfern, *President*
Lynn P White, *Vice Pres*
Kim Redfern, *Treasurer*
Susan Case, *Admin Asst*
EMP: 32
SQ FT: 1,800
SALES (est): 5.6MM **Privately Held**
WEB: www.tylerproductssales.com
SIC: **3272** 1711 5211 Precast terrazo or
 concrete products; septic system con-
 struction; masonry materials & supplies

(G-20173)
US FABRICATION EAST TEXAS INC
5624 American Legion Rd (75708-6115)
PHONE..................903 531-0000
James Ray Barrow, *President*
Brandon James Barrow, *Vice Pres*
Bill Compton, *Vice Pres*
EMP: .4
SQ FT: 15,384
SALES (est): 1.5MM **Privately Held**
WEB: www.usffab.com
SIC: **3443** Industrial vessels, tanks & con-
 tainers

(G-20174)
VERNON E FAULCONER INC (PA)
1001 E Se Loop 323 # 160 (75701-9663)
P.O. Box 7995 (75711-7995)
PHONE..................903 581-4382
Vernon E Faulconer, *CEO*
Grant Faulconer, *CEO*
David J Enright, *President*
Jean Crowley, *Vice Pres*
David Chace, *Foreman/Supr*
EMP: 40
SQ FT: 19,000
SALES (est): 93.2MM **Privately Held**
WEB: www.vefinc.com
SIC: **1311** Crude petroleum production;
 natural gas production

(G-20175)
VESUVIUS U S A CORPORATION
1812 E Duncan St (75702-2409)
P.O. Box 4080, Champaign IL (61824-
 4080)
PHONE..................903 597-7237
Jim Waddell, *Manager*
Darla Bury, *Technology*
EMP: 64
SALES (corp-wide): 2.2B **Privately Held**
WEB: www.vesuvius.com
SIC: **3297** Graphite refractories: carbon
 bond or ceramic bond
HQ: Vesuvius U S A Corporation
 1404 Newton Dr
 Champaign IL 61822
 217 351-5000

(G-20176)
VINCENT GRAPHICS & SUPPLY INC (PA)
Also Called: Key Products, The
12979 State Highway 110 N (75704-2435)
PHONE..................903 882-3123
Harvey Vincent, *President*
Brenda Vincent, *Corp Secy*
EMP: 20
SQ FT: 6,300
SALES (est): 3.1MM **Privately Held**
WEB: www.vgs-express.com
SIC: **2752** 5943 2521 Commercial print-
 ing, lithographic; office forms & supplies;
 wood office furniture

(G-20177)
WORLD RESEARCH COMPANY INC (PA)
4926 Profit Dr (75707-1837)
P.O. Box 578, Whitehouse (75791-0578)
PHONE..................903 581-3720
Clyde Connell, *CEO*
Colleen Hayes, *President*
Juanita Connell, *Corp Secy*
EMP: 20
SQ FT: 5,000
SALES (est): 1.3MM **Privately Held**
SIC: **3999** 2493 Education aids, devices &
 supplies; hardboard, tempered

(G-20178)
XTO ENERGY INC
6141 Paluxy Dr (75703-5976)
PHONE..................903 939-1200
Bob Simpson, *Principal*
Tony Long, *Engineer*
Adam Pope, *Controller*
Gordan Holloway, *Prgrmr*
EMP: 75
SALES (corp-wide): 264.9B **Publicly Held**
WEB: www.xtoenergy.com
SIC: **1311** Crude petroleum production;
 natural gas production
HQ: Xto Energy Inc.
 22777 Sprngwoods Vlg Pkwy
 Spring TX 77389

(G-20179)
ZDSCADA LP
1918 Sybil Ln (75703-1858)
PHONE..................903 526-1100
Fred Haberle, *Partner*
Eddie Baker, *Vice Pres*
EMP: 12
SQ FT: 4,000
SALES (est): 403.2K **Privately Held**
WEB: www.zdscada.com
SIC: **1389** Measurement of well flow rates,
 oil & gas

Tynan
Bee County

(G-20180)
BCCA LLC
410 1st St (78391)
P.O. Box 128 (78391-0128)
PHONE..................361 547-3341
Aaron Salge, *Manager*
EMP: 9
SALES (est): 506.8K **Privately Held**
SIC: **2041** Flour & other grain mill products

Universal City
Bexar County

(G-20181)
CELLRIGHT TECHNOLOGIES LLC
1808 Universal City Blvd (78148-3356)
PHONE..................210 659-9353
Daniel Lee, *President*
Robin Sullivan, *Vice Pres*
Tina Tremble, *Vice Pres*
EMP: 45 EST: 2011
SQ FT: 10,000

SALES (est): 6.5MM
SALES (corp-wide): 16.8MM **Privately Held**
WEB: www.tissueregenix.com
SIC: **3841** 5047 Surgical & medical instru-
 ments; instruments, surgical & medical;
 surgical equipment & supplies
PA: Tissue Regenix Group Plc
 Unit 3
 Leeds

(G-20182)
IATID INC
Also Called: Supa Doors
1732 Universal City Blvd (78148-3351)
PHONE..................210 698-8500
David Fisher, *CEO*
Ian Fisher, *President*
◆ EMP: 50
SQ FT: 80,000
SALES (est): 12.4MM
SALES (corp-wide): 276.6MM **Privately Held**
WEB: www.supadoor.com
SIC: **2431** Doors & door parts & trim, wood
PA: V-T Industries Inc.
 1000 Industrial Park
 Holstein IA 51025
 712 368-4381

(G-20183)
JANA INC (PA)
1717 Universal City Blvd (78148-3348)
PHONE..................210 616-0083
Evelyn Niland, *Ch of Bd*
Edward A Niland, *President*
Arty Niland, *General Mgr*
Jan Marshall, *COO*
Martha J Niland-Marshall, *Exec VP*
EMP: 60
SQ FT: 40,000
SALES (est): 12.5MM **Privately Held**
WEB: www.janacorp.com
SIC: **2741** Technical manuals: publishing
 only, not printed on site

(G-20184)
PPG INDUSTRIES INC
Also Called: PPG 8314
1705 Pat Booker Rd # 223 (78148-3524)
PHONE..................210 656-5541
Frank Sanchez, *Manager*
EMP: 24
SALES (corp-wide): 15.3B **Publicly Held**
WEB: www.ppg.com
SIC: **2851** Paints & allied products
PA: Ppg Industries, Inc.
 1 Ppg Pl
 Pittsburgh PA 15272
 412 434-3131

(G-20185)
VERTEX AEROSPACE LLC
5th St Hngr 7 (78148)
PHONE..................210 652-6717
Roger Ryder, *Manager*
EMP: 35
SALES (corp-wide): 681.6MM **Privately Held**
WEB: www.vtxaero.com
SIC: **3721** Aircraft
HQ: Vertex Aerospace Llc
 555 Industrial Dr S
 Madison MS 39110
 800 774-4927

(G-20186)
ZUBIE WEAR
1516 Universal City Blvd (78148-3318)
PHONE..................210 590-8892
Oscar Zubiate, *CEO*
Jennifer Forga, *Accounts Exec*
Kimberly Kellogg, *Accounts Exec*
EMP: 20
SALES (est): 3.1MM **Privately Held**
WEB: www.zubiewear.com
SIC: **2759** 7389 Screen printing; design
 services

Utopia
Uvalde County

(G-20187)
ADAMS EVIDENCE GRADE TECH INC
4123 N Little Creek Rd (78884)
P.O. Box 1217 (78884-1217)
PHONE..................................830 966-4210
Bernard Adams, *President*
Doris U Adams, *Treasurer*
▲ EMP: 11
SQ FT: 4,000
SALES (est): 1.6MM **Privately Held**
WEB: www.evidencegrade.com
SIC: 3652 5065 Pre-recorded records & tapes; security control equipment & systems

Uvalde
Uvalde County

(G-20188)
BLADES GROUP LLC
Also Called: Road Rescue
3 Fm 1403 (78801-7722)
PHONE..................................830 278-1211
John S Blades, *CEO*
Christina Zamora, *Manager*
EMP: 12 EST: 2011
SALES (est): 1MM **Privately Held**
WEB: www.roadrescueasphalt.com
SIC: 2911 Asphalt or asphaltic materials, made in refineries

(G-20189)
EAGLE CREEK INC (DH)
Also Called: Eagle Creek Travel Gear
510 Crystal City Hwy # 5 (78801-6180)
PHONE..................................760 431-6400
Steve Barker, *President*
Dale Penk, *Senior VP*
Ricky Schlesinger, *Senior VP*
Bert Fenenga, *CFO*
◆ EMP: 98 EST: 1975
SALES (est): 56.5MM
SALES (corp-wide): 10.4B **Publicly Held**
WEB: www.eaglecreek.com
SIC: 3161 Traveling bags
HQ: Vf Outdoor, Llc
2701 Harbor Bay Pkwy
Alameda CA 94502
855 500-8639

(G-20190)
LEGACY VULCAN LLC
Also Called: Vulcan Materials Plant 363
Hwy 90 W Fm 1022 (78801)
P.O. Box 149 (78802-0149)
PHONE..................................830 278-6205
Chris Hazelka, *Manager*
EMP: 45 **Publicly Held**
WEB: www.vulcanmaterials.com
SIC: 1442 1422 Construction sand & gravel; crushed & broken limestone
HQ: Legacy Vulcan, Llc
1200 Urban Center Dr
Vestavia AL 35242
205 298-3000

(G-20191)
MARSHA KITCHENS
Also Called: Lyfe Tyme Products
504 W Fannin St (78801-3201)
PHONE..................................830 278-7262
Marsha Kitchens, *Owner*
Gary Carlson, *MIS Dir*
EMP: 18
SALES (est): 785K **Privately Held**
WEB: www.lyfetyme.com
SIC: 3631 Barbecues, grills & braziers (outdoor cooking)

(G-20192)
MARTIN MARIETTA MATERIALS INC
Also Called: Black Spur Quarry
4483 Ranch Road 1022 (78801-4579)
PHONE..................................830 591-1887
Dan Persyn, *Manager*
EMP: 20 **Publicly Held**

WEB: www.martinmarietta.com
SIC: 1422 Crushed & broken limestone
PA: Martin Marietta Materials Inc
2710 Wycliff Rd
Raleigh NC 27607

(G-20193)
MID-COAST ELECTRIC SUPPLY INC
2022 E Main St (78801-4852)
PHONE..................................830 333-7030
EMP: 23
SALES (corp-wide): 58.6MM **Privately Held**
WEB: www.mcesi.com
SIC: 5063 5051 3699 Fuses & accessories; metal wires, ties, cables & screening; electrical equipment & supplies
PA: Mid-Coast Electric Supply, Inc.
1801 Stolz St
Victoria TX 77901
361 575-6311

(G-20194)
PAT AND GAIL JACKOWSKI
Also Called: Uvalde Meat Processing Plant
508 S Wood St (78801-5653)
PHONE..................................830 278-6247
Pat Jackowski, *Owner*
Gail Jackowski, *Co-Owner*
EMP: 15 EST: 1988
SALES (est): 2.1MM **Privately Held**
WEB: www.uvaldemeat.com
SIC: 2011 5147 5421 Meat packing plants; meats, fresh; meat markets, including freezer provisioners

(G-20195)
SCOTTS MIRACLE-GRO COMPANY
90 Fm 1403 (78801-7722)
PHONE..................................830 591-0299
Jim King, *Exec VP*
Adam Haney, *Foreman/Supr*
John Longshore, *Production*
Alex Soucek, *Auditor*
Kristine Ernst, *Human Res Mgr*
EMP: 29
SALES (corp-wide): 4.1B **Publicly Held**
WEB: www.scottsmiraclegro.com
SIC: 2873 2048 Fertilizers: natural (organic), except compost; stock feeds, dry
PA: The Scotts Miracle-Gro Company
14111 Scottslawn Rd
Marysville OH 43040
937 644-0011

(G-20196)
SKYWAY GROUP INC (PA)
122 Howard Langford Dr (78801-6904)
PHONE..................................830 278-4481
Mark Huffstutler, *CEO*
EMP: 12
SALES (est): 13.6MM **Privately Held**
SIC: 3721 8741 Aircraft; management services

(G-20197)
TIMS SOUTH TEXAS LLC (PA)
4055 E Main St (78801-6408)
P.O. Box 1555 (78802-1555)
PHONE..................................830 278-3368
Tim Ligocky, *President*
EMP: 12
SQ FT: 2,500
SALES (est): 1MM **Privately Held**
WEB: www.timssouthtexas.com
SIC: 5999 3799 Welding supplies; trailers & trailer equipment

(G-20198)
UVALDE CONCRETE INC (PA)
3043 Fm 1052 Benson Rd (78801)
P.O. Box 819 (78802-0819)
PHONE..................................830 278-9200
Nick Ayala, *President*
Irma Ayala, *Vice Pres*
EMP: 25
SQ FT: 500
SALES (est): 4.9MM **Privately Held**
SIC: 3273 Ready-mixed concrete

(G-20199)
VF OUTDOOR LLC
510 S Highway 83 (78801-6157)
PHONE..................................830 278-2535

Brad Balentine, *Manager*
EMP: 300
SALES (corp-wide): 10.4B **Publicly Held**
WEB: www.dickies.com
SIC: 2339 2325 2326 Slacks: women's, misses' & juniors'; slacks, dress: men's, youths' & boys'; men's & boys' work clothing
HQ: Vf Outdoor, Llc
2701 Harbor Bay Pkwy
Alameda CA 94502
855 500-8639

Valley Mills
Bosque County

(G-20200)
BYFORD MACHINE-TOOL INC
2038 State Hwy 6 N (76689)
P.O. Box 646 (76689-0646)
PHONE..................................254 932-6111
Robert Hoffmann, *President*
John Erickson, *General Mgr*
EMP: 20
SQ FT: 36,000
SALES (est): 4.5MM **Privately Held**
WEB: www.byfordmachine.com
SIC: 3599 Machine shop, jobbing & repair

(G-20201)
JDH IRON DESIGNS LLC
9685 N Lone Star Pkwy (76689-3034)
PHONE..................................254 486-9150
Lori Holmes, *Mng Member*
Jimmy Don Holmes, *Mng Member*
EMP: 18
SALES (est): 2.3MM **Privately Held**
WEB: www.jdhirondesigns.com
SIC: 3471 5999 Decorative plating & finishing of formed products; decals

Valley View
Cooke County

(G-20202)
DDM MATERIALS INC
807 N Frontage Rd (76272-9747)
P.O. Box 245 (76272-0245)
PHONE..................................970 726-1122
Jamie Markwardt, *President*
EMP: 15
SALES (est): 2.3MM **Privately Held**
WEB: www.ddmmaterials.com
SIC: 3273 Ready-mixed concrete

(G-20203)
JBM SPECIALTIES LLC
Also Called: Whiskey Hollow
302 W Obuch St (76272-5431)
PHONE..................................214 604-7646
Leslie R Beasley, *Principal*
Brian Beasley,
Mathew Beasley,
John Crisp,
Tim Felderhoff,
EMP: 13 EST: 2014
SALES (est): 1.1MM **Privately Held**
SIC: 2085 Distilled & blended liquors

(G-20204)
M&M PRCSION MTAL FBRCATION INC
12757 I 35 Frontage Rd (76272)
PHONE..................................940 726-3379
Mark Allan Moore, *President*
Anthony Moore, *Director*
Mary Moore, *Admin Sec*
EMP: 15
SALES (est): 210K **Privately Held**
WEB:
www.mmprecisionmetalfabrication.com
SIC: 3441 Fabricated structural metal

Van
Van Zandt County

(G-20205)
AL ROWAN
Also Called: Rowan Oil Operator
160 W Main St (75790-2882)
P.O. Box 605 (75790-0605)
PHONE..................................903 963-7036
Polly Rowan, *President*
Mike Rowan, *Assistant VP*
Susan Hardy, *Vice Pres*
Pat Rowan, *Vice Pres*
EMP: 70
SALES (est): 12.3MM **Privately Held**
SIC: 1311 Crude petroleum production; natural gas production

(G-20206)
CHEVRON CORPORATION
Also Called: Unocal
108 Vz County Rd Ste 1417 (75790)
PHONE..................................903 963-8631
Robert Wright, *Manager*
EMP: 31
SQ FT: 15,000
SALES (corp-wide): 146.5B **Publicly Held**
WEB: www.chevron.com
SIC: 1311 1321 Crude petroleum production; natural gasoline production
PA: Chevron Corporation
6001 Bollinger Canyon Rd
San Ramon CA 94583
925 842-1000

(G-20207)
ENERGY DEVICES OF TEXAS INC (PA)
Also Called: Edi Oilfield Pumps and Sups
303 Park Row St (75790-3865)
PHONE..................................903 963-7906
Larry Corbett, *President*
Monta Sewell, *Corp Secy*
EMP: 31
SALES (est): 3.2MM **Privately Held**
WEB: www.edisupply.com
SIC: 5082 3561 Oil field equipment; pumps & pumping equipment

(G-20208)
KEY ENERGY SERVICES INC
202 S Main (75790)
PHONE..................................903 963-5208
Ricky Nolan, *Branch Mgr*
EMP: 50
SALES (corp-wide): 413.8MM **Publicly Held**
WEB: www.keyenergy.com
SIC: 1389 1381 Oil field services; drilling oil & gas wells
PA: Key Energy Services, Inc.
1301 Mckinney St Ste 1800
Houston TX 77010
713 651-4300

(G-20209)
ROCO DRILLING AND SERVICE INC
160 W Main St (75790-2882)
P.O. Box 605 (75790-0605)
PHONE..................................903 963-7036
EMP: 72
SQ FT: 5,000
SALES (est): 7.1MM **Privately Held**
WEB: www.rocodrilling.com
SIC: 1381 1389 Drilling oil & gas wells; servicing oil & gas wells

(G-20210)
THE PALLET PLACE INC
303 Park Row St (75790-3865)
PHONE..................................903 963-4026
Daniel Nipp, *President*
Dennis Nipp, *Vice Pres*
Crystal Nipp, *Treasurer*
Mary Nipp, *Admin Sec*
EMP: 38
SALES (est): 6.7MM **Privately Held**
SIC: 2448 Pallets, wood; pallets, wood & wood with metal

▲ = Import ▼=Export
◆ =Import/Export

Van Alstyne
Grayson County

(G-20211)
MUSTANG MANUFACTURING CORP
461 Martin Duke Rd (75495-2811)
P.O. Box 35 (75495-0035)
PHONE...................................903 482-5666
Roy Watson, *President*
▲ EMP: 30
SALES (est): 2.9MM **Privately Held**
WEB: www.mustangmfg.net
SIC: 2399 Horse & pet accessories, textile

(G-20212)
RITESCREEN COMPANY LLC
787 E Village Pkwy (75495-2822)
PHONE...................................903 482-9200
Jorge Loza, *Office Mgr*
EMP: 110
SALES (corp-wide): 125.1MM **Privately Held**
WEB: www.ritescreen.com
SIC: 3442 Screen & storm doors & windows
PA: The Ritescreen Company Llc
4314 State Route 209
Elizabethville PA 17023
717 362-7483

Van Horn
Culberson County

(G-20213)
BLUE ORIGIN TEXAS LLC
35961 State Hwy 54 (79855)
PHONE...................................253 437-9300
Stephanie Koster, *Treasurer*
EMP: 50
SALES (est): 3.4MM **Privately Held**
SIC: 3761 Guided missiles & space vehicles
PA: Blue Origin, Llc
21719 84th Ave S
Kent WA 98032

(G-20214)
HEATH TRANSIT MIX CONCRETE CO (PA)
Also Called: Heath Auto Supply
401 W Broadway St (79855)
PHONE...................................432 283-2127
Don R Heath, *President*
Jennie Heath, *Treasurer*
EMP: 13
SQ FT: 7,000
SALES (est): 943.3K **Privately Held**
SIC: 3273 Ready-mixed concrete

(G-20215)
NATURAL MINERALS INC
12900 E Interstate 10 (79855)
PHONE...................................432 283-2330
Steve Harms, *General Mgr*
EMP: 20
SALES (corp-wide): 1.2MM **Privately Held**
WEB: www.naturalminerals.com
SIC: 1499 Talc mining
PA: Natural Minerals, Inc.
5959 Gateway Blvd W # 570
El Paso TX 79925
432 283-2330

Vega
Oldham County

(G-20216)
WILDERADO WIND LLC
Also Called: Wilderado Wind Ranch
6798 County Rd 42 (79092)
P.O. Box 55 (79092-0055)
PHONE...................................806 267-0746
Brad Christopher,
EMP: 10
SALES (est): 1.2MM **Privately Held**
SIC: 3621 Windmills, electric generating

Venus
Johnson County

(G-20217)
ADVANCED INDUSTRIES INC
Also Called: A I
1014 S Fm 157 (76084-3806)
PHONE...................................972 366-9000
David Brown, *President*
Kelly Brightwell, *Senior VP*
Ben Avery, *Vice Pres*
Mike Hajer, *Branch Mgr*
EMP: 30
SALES (est): 2.1MM **Privately Held**
WEB: www.advindustries.com
SIC: 3498 Pipe fittings, fabricated from purchased pipe

(G-20218)
HUGHES TANK COMPANY INC
157 South Hwy (76084)
P.O. Box 570 (76084-0570)
PHONE...................................972 366-8684
Vickie Hughes, *President*
EMP: 12
SALES (est): 3.4MM **Privately Held**
WEB: www.hughestankcompany.com
SIC: 3443 7389 Fuel tanks (oil, gas, etc.): metal plate; business services

(G-20219)
INTERNTNAL PRTEIN COLLOIDS INC
370 English Trl (76084-3237)
P.O. Box 2300, Mansfield (76063-0047)
PHONE...................................817 795-7744
David Walsh, *President*
Tom Walsh, *Vice Pres*
Terry Cowhey, *Marketing Staff*
▲ EMP: 11
SALES (est): 1.4MM **Privately Held**
WEB: www.proteincolloids.com
SIC: 2077 Animal fats, oils & meals

(G-20220)
K-T GALVANIZING CO INC
2500 Chambers St (76084-3314)
PHONE...................................817 477-4434
Alfred Peck Jr, *Data Proc Staff*
Tad Peck, *Executive*
EMP: 25
SALES (corp-wide): 5.8MM **Privately Held**
WEB: www.ktgalvanizing.com
SIC: 3479 3547 3312 Galvanizing of iron, steel or end-formed products; galvanizing lines (rolling mill equipment); blast furnaces & steel mills
PA: K-T Galvanizing Co., Inc.
5105 3rd St
Katy TX 77493
281 391-9201

(G-20221)
PRESTIGE KITCHEN INC
1404 S Fm 157 (76084-3814)
PHONE...................................972 366-3322
Fax: 972 366-3198
EMP: 10
SQ FT: 6,000
SALES: 1MM **Privately Held**
SIC: 3312 Blast Furnace-Steel Works

(G-20222)
SOUTHERN PETROLEUM LABS INC
Also Called: Southern Patrolling Labs
2440 Chambers St Unit A (76084-3346)
PHONE...................................817 539-2168
Christopher Brown, *Branch Mgr*
EMP: 15
SALES (corp-wide): 157.5MM **Privately Held**
WEB: www.spl-inc.com
SIC: 1311 Crude petroleum production
PA: Southern Petroleum Laboratories, Inc.
8850 Interchange Dr
Houston TX 77054
713 660-0901

(G-20223)
STEELTEX FABRICATORS LLC
6840 N Fm 157 (76084-3293)
PHONE...................................817 225-0973
Jason Ladd,
Meehan Development,
Tony Meehan,
EMP: 28
SQ FT: 30,000
SALES (est): 8MM
SALES (corp-wide): 164.4MM **Privately Held**
WEB: www.utexind.com
SIC: 3533 Oil & gas field machinery
HQ: Utex Industries, Inc.
10810 Katy Fwy Ste 100
Houston TX 77043
713 467-1000

(G-20224)
UNITED WORTH HYDROCHEM CORP
350 English Trl Ste C (76084-3367)
P.O. Box 366, Fort Worth (76101-0366)
PHONE...................................682 518-6200
Roy Coleman, *President*
Dan Coleman, *Treasurer*
EMP: 15 EST: 1946
SQ FT: 6,000
SALES (est): 1.5MM **Privately Held**
WEB: www.worthhydrochem.com
SIC: 2899 7699 Water treating compounds; industrial equipment services

(G-20225)
UTEX INDUSTRIES INC
6840 N Fm 157 (76084-3293)
PHONE...................................713 559-0203
EMP: 9
SALES (corp-wide): 164.4MM **Privately Held**
WEB: www.utexind.com
SIC: 3053 Gaskets, packing & sealing devices
HQ: Utex Industries, Inc.
10810 Katy Fwy Ste 100
Houston TX 77043
713 467-1000

(G-20226)
VENUS FABRICATION INC
Also Called: V Fab
18901 County Road 620 (76084-3708)
PHONE...................................972 366-3565
Randy Gore, *President*
EMP: 17
SQ FT: 4,000
SALES (est): 2.7MM **Privately Held**
WEB: www.stainlesssteelfabricators.net
SIC: 3914 Stainless steel ware

Vernon
Wilbarger County

(G-20227)
KINLAU SHEET METAL WORKS INC
2522 Frontage Rd (76384-3408)
P.O. Box 1515 (76385-1515)
PHONE...................................940 552-5311
Leslie Miller, *President*
Stephen Miller, *Vice Pres*
Donna Muse, *Finance Mgr*
Leslie M Miller, *Manager*
EMP: 10
SQ FT: 15,150
SALES (est): 1.2MM **Privately Held**
WEB: www.kinlau.com
SIC: 3444 0191 Sheet metal specialties, not stamped; general farms, primarily crop

(G-20228)
OK CONCRETE COMPANY
Also Called: O K Concrete
1620 Frontage Rd (76384-3629)
P.O. Box 1354 (76385-1354)
PHONE...................................940 552-5162
David Litteken, *Branch Mgr*
EMP: 10
SALES (corp-wide): 5.5MM **Privately Held**
WEB: www.okconcreteco.com
SIC: 3273 Ready-mixed concrete
PA: Ok Concrete Company
2304 Sheppard Access Rd
Wichita Falls TX 76306
940 723-4324

(G-20229)
PEARSONS INC
Also Called: Pearson's Livestock Equipment
122 Wilbarger St (76384-3926)
PHONE...................................308 645-2231
David R Rater, *President*
Richard D Rater, *Vice Pres*
Richard Rater, *Director*
EMP: 20
SALES: 2.9MM **Privately Held**
WEB: www.pearsonlivestockeq.com
SIC: 3523 Cattle feeding, handling & watering equipment

(G-20230)
SOLVAY USA INC
201 Harrison St (76384-3327)
PHONE...................................940 552-9911
Jim Trafton, *Plant Mgr*
Dana Ponciroli, *Corp Comm Staff*
David Hardin, *Manager*
EMP: 90
SALES (corp-wide): 13.8MM **Privately Held**
WEB: www.solvay.us
SIC: 2819 2812 2865 2869 Alkali metals: lithium, cesium, francium, rubidium; boric acid; soda ash, sodium carbonate (anhydrous); phenol, alkylated & cumene; diphenylamines; isocyanates; fluorinated hydrocarbon gases; silicones; plastics materials & resins; flavoring extracts & syrups
HQ: Solvay Usa Inc.
504 Carnegie Ctr
Princeton NJ 08540
609 860-4000

(G-20231)
TYSON FOODS INC
700 Wheeler St (76384-3431)
PHONE...................................940 553-1811
Marc Killebrew, *Vice Pres*
Belinda Jove, *Parts Mgr*
Kirk Eggleston, *Engineer*
Dane Bonfy, *Plant Engr*
William Ley, *Controller*
EMP: 15
SALES (corp-wide): 43.1B **Publicly Held**
WEB: www.tysonfoods.com
SIC: 2015 2032 2048 2011 Chicken slaughtering & processing; ethnic foods: canned, jarred, etc.; tortillas: packaged in cans, jars etc.; feeds from meat & from meat & vegetable meals; beef products from beef slaughtered on site
PA: Tyson Foods, Inc.
2200 W Don Tyson Pkwy
Springdale AR 72762
479 290-4000

(G-20232)
W T WAGGONER ESTATE
Also Called: Waggoner Ranch
1700 Deaf Smith St (76384-4629)
P.O. Box 2130 (76385-2130)
PHONE...................................940 552-2521
A B Wharton, *Ch of Bd*
Joel R Lovelady, *Corp Secy*
Gene Willingham, *Director*
EMP: 135 EST: 1870
SQ FT: 46,000
SALES (est): 18.9MM **Privately Held**
WEB: www.waggonerranch.com
SIC: 1311 0212 0111 6211 Crude petroleum production; beef cattle except feedlots; wheat; investment firm, general brokerage

Victoria
Victoria County

(G-20233)
A SKLAR COMPANY INC
Also Called: Golden Crescent Construction
5274 State Highway 185 (77905-2103)
PHONE....................................361 573-5775
Allan Sklar II, *President*
Angela Sklar, *Treasurer*
Clayton Kenne, *Sales Staff*
EMP: 22 EST: 1998
SQ FT: 14,000
SALES (est): 7.1MM **Privately Held**
WEB: www.gccbuildings.com
SIC: 3449 1521 Miscellaneous metalwork;
single-family housing construction

(G-20234)
ACI WORLDWIDE CORP
Also Called: T S A
1501 E Mockingbird Ln (77904-2155)
PHONE....................................361 579-4800
Wayne Kroll, *President*
EMP: 10 **Publicly Held**
WEB: www.aciworldwide.com
SIC: 7372 Business oriented computer
software
HQ: Aci Worldwide Corp.
6060 Coventry Dr
Elkhorn NE 68022
402 390-7600

(G-20235)
ACME TRUCK LINE INC
6811 Us Highway 59 N (77905-5807)
PHONE....................................361 576-2934
Tricia Parker, *Manager*
EMP: 13
SALES (corp-wide): 707.4MM **Privately
Held**
WEB: www.acmetruck.com
SIC: 4213 1389 Heavy hauling; haulage,
oil field
PA: Acme Truck Line, Inc.
200 Westbank Expy
Gretna LA 70053
504 368-2510

(G-20236)
**ALAMO CONCRETE PRODUCTS
LTD**
10006 Holletsville Hwy (77904)
P.O. Box 1546 (77902-1546)
PHONE....................................361 572-0231
Nick Hinojosa, *Manager*
EMP: 18 **Privately Held**
SIC: 5031 5032 5211 5251 Lumber:
rough, dressed & finished; brick, stone &
related material; lumber & other building
materials; builders' hardware; ready-
mixed concrete
PA: Alamo Concrete Products, Ltd.
6055 W Green Mountain Rd
Austin TX 78744

(G-20237)
**ALAMO CONCRETE PRODUCTS
LTD**
10006 Halletsville Hwy (77904)
P.O. Box 1546 (77902-1546)
PHONE....................................361 578-9678
Nick Hinajosa, *Branch Mgr*
EMP: 15 **Privately Held**
SIC: 3273 Ready-mixed concrete
PA: Alamo Concrete Products, Ltd.
6055 W Green Mountain Rd
Austin TX 78744

(G-20238)
**ALTMAN & NELSON PRTG CO
INC**
Also Called: Mortin Printing
2407 N Laurent St (77901-4119)
P.O. Box 3602 (77903-3602)
PHONE....................................361 575-3118
Tom Murrah, *President*
William Todd, *Corp Secy*
Ronald Bingham, *Vice Pres*
EMP: 10
SQ FT: 8,000

SALES (est): 1.2MM **Privately Held**
WEB: www.dbsofvictoria.net
SIC: 2752 Commercial printing, offset

(G-20239)
ARCHROCK INC
8193 Lone Tree Rd (77905-3792)
PHONE....................................361 572-9904
Russell Scogin, *Principal*
Michaela Munoz, *Purchasing*
David Ridgway, *Purchasing*
EMP: 20 **Publicly Held**
WEB: www.archrock.com
SIC: 1389 5084 7699 Gas compressing
(natural gas) at the fields; processing &
packaging equipment; industrial machin-
ery & equipment repair
PA: Archrock, Inc.
9807 Katy Fwy Ste 100
Houston TX 77024

(G-20240)
AWESOME PAGING INC (PA)
3902 Houston Hwy (77904-4706)
P.O. Box 7106 (77903-7106)
PHONE....................................361 576-2255
James Young, *President*
James Bennett, *Vice Pres*
EMP: 9
SQ FT: 2,500
SALES (est): 766.8K **Privately Held**
SIC: 5999 5065 4813 3663 Telephone
equipment & systems; electronic parts &
equipment; ; radio broadcasting & com-
munications equipment

(G-20241)
**BACKWOODS
COMMUNICATIONS LLC**
918 Conti Ln (77904-1200)
P.O. Box 3721 (77903-3721)
PHONE....................................361 652-6900
Derick Ross, *CEO*
EMP: 11
SALES (est): 132.7K **Privately Held**
WEB: www.txbackwoods.com
SIC: 3669 5065 7622 Intercommunication
systems, electric; intercommunication
equipment, electronic; intercommunica-
tion equipment repair

(G-20242)
**BAKER HGHES OLFLD
OPRTIONS LLC**
Also Called: Baker Atlas
4206 N Main St (77901-2614)
PHONE....................................361 573-2493
Trey Clark, *Manager*
EMP: 28 **Privately Held**
WEB: www.bakerhughes.com
SIC: 1389 1382 Oil field services; seismo-
graph surveys
PA: Baker Hughes Oilfield Operations Llc
2001 Rankin Rd
Houston TX 77073

(G-20243)
**BAKER HUGHES A GE
COMPANY LLC**
Also Called: Baker Atlas
4206 N Main St (77901-2614)
PHONE....................................361 573-2493
Tonia Dunlap, *Purch Mgr*
Bill Huppered, *Branch Mgr*
EMP: 80
SALES (corp-wide): 23.8B **Publicly Held**
WEB: www.bhge.com
SIC: 1389 1382 Oil field services; well log-
ging; seismograph surveys
HQ: Baker Hughes Holdings Llc
17021 Aldine Westfield Rd
Houston TX 77073
713 439-8600

(G-20244)
BASIC ENERGY SERVICES INC
1303 E Constitution St (77901-8475)
PHONE....................................361 578-3503
EMP: 29
SALES (corp-wide): 1.3B **Publicly Held**
SIC: 1389 Oil/Gas Field Services
PA: Basic Energy Services, Inc.
801 Cherry St Unit 2
Fort Worth TX 76102
817 334-4100

(G-20245)
BC OILFIELD SERVICES INC
110 Moller Rd (77905)
P.O. Box 5033 (77903-5033)
PHONE....................................361 573-6354
Robert N Croft, *President*
Joellen Adams, *Principal*
Brandon Norman, *Purchasing*
Cassie Edwards, *Office Mgr*
Jo Ellen Adams, *Manager*
EMP: 15
SQ FT: 6,000
SALES (est): 3.9MM **Privately Held**
WEB: www.bcoilfield.com
SIC: 7699 3533 Industrial equipment serv-
ices; oil field machinery & equipment

(G-20246)
BERRY GLOBAL INC
202 John Stockbauer Dr (77901-3763)
PHONE....................................361 575-9565
Harold Reed, *CFO*
EMP: 127 **Publicly Held**
WEB: www.berryplastics.com
SIC: 3089 Plastic containers, except foam
HQ: Berry Global, Inc.
101 Oakley St
Evansville IN 47710

(G-20247)
**BKG MACHINE & FABRICATION
INC**
5509 State Highway 185 (77905-2111)
PHONE....................................361 575-9592
Robert J Klimitchek, *President*
Virginia Klimitchek, *Vice Pres*
EMP: 18 EST: 1979
SQ FT: 4,200
SALES (est): 430.8K **Privately Held**
WEB: www.bkgmachine.com
SIC: 3599 3533 Machine shop, jobbing &
repair; oil field machinery & equipment

(G-20248)
BORDER SWABBING INC
5903 Us Highway 59 N (77905-5514)
PHONE....................................361 575-7852
Cynthia Pozzi, *President*
EMP: 16
SALES (est): 1.5MM **Privately Held**
SIC: 1389 Swabbing wells; oil field serv-
ices

(G-20249)
BOSS OIL FIELD SERVICE INC
2307 Fm 2615 (77905-5550)
P.O. Box 3112 (77903-3112)
PHONE....................................361 574-7939
EMP: 10
SALES (est): 750K **Privately Held**
SIC: 1389 Oil/Gas Field Services

(G-20250)
**C M C STEEL FABRICATORS
INC**
255 Skytop Rd (77905-5469)
PHONE....................................361 575-4561
Jeff Garrelts, *Sales/Mktg Mgr*
EMP: 163
SALES (corp-wide): 5.4B **Publicly Held**
WEB: www.cmc.com
SIC: 5051 3498 3441 Steel; fabricated
pipe & fittings; fabricated structural metal
HQ: C M C Steel Fabricators, Inc.
1 Steel Mill Dr
Seguin TX 78155
830 372-8200

(G-20251)
CARBON SILICA PARTNERS LP
Also Called: Diamond Fiberglass
1036 Industrial Park Dr (77905-0701)
PHONE....................................361 572-4040
William G Porr Sr, *Partner*
Paul A Cohen, *Partner*
Mike Merrick, *Business Mgr*
Cody Rath, *Project Mgr*
▲ EMP: 70
SQ FT: 23,000
SALES (est): 27.6MM **Privately Held**
WEB: www.diamondfiberglass.com
SIC: 3089 Plastic & fiberglass tanks

(G-20252)
CATERPILLAR INC
7300 Lone Tree Rd (77905-5484)
PHONE....................................361 580-5600
Roger Montalvan, *Manager*
EMP: 22
SALES (corp-wide): 53.8B **Publicly Held**
WEB: www.caterpillar.com
SIC: 3531 Construction machinery
PA: Caterpillar Inc.
510 Lake Cook Rd Ste 100
Deerfield IL 60015
224 551-4000

(G-20253)
CLEGG INDUSTRIES INC
16400 Nw Zac Lentz Pkwy (77905-4070)
PHONE....................................361 578-0291
Judy Clegg, *President*
John Bradley Clegg, *Vice Pres*
John Henry Clegg III, *Vice Pres*
Richard Mollicone, *QC Mgr*
Chana Clegg, *Admin Asst*
EMP: 30
SQ FT: 40,000
SALES (est): 6.2MM **Privately Held**
WEB: www.cleggind.com
SIC: 7532 5271 3799 Customizing serv-
ices, non-factory basis; mobile homes;
trailers & trailer equipment

(G-20254)
COPANO COMPANY (PA)
1 Oconnor Plz Ste 1100 (77901-6549)
PHONE....................................361 578-6271
Ralph Gilster, *CEO*
Robert J Hewitt, *Principal*
Kathrine O'Conner, *Principal*
EMP: 30
SQ FT: 3,000
SALES (est): 1.5MM **Privately Held**
SIC: 1311 Crude petroleum & natural gas

(G-20255)
COWBOY CONTAINMENTS INC
3802 E Rio Grande St (77901-1726)
PHONE....................................361 576-9550
Michael Browning, *President*
Charles Trice, *Vice Pres*
EMP: 12
SALES (est): 1MM **Privately Held**
WEB: www.cowboycontainment.com
SIC: 2911 Oils, fuel

(G-20256)
CSI COMPRESSCO SUB INC
11503 Us Highway 59 N (77905-4416)
PHONE....................................361 576-6827
Larry Skelton, *Manager*
EMP: 35
SALES (corp-wide): 1B **Publicly Held**
WEB: www.csicompressco.com
SIC: 7359 3563 Equipment rental & leas-
ing; air & gas compressors
HQ: Csi Compressco Sub Inc.
24955 I 45 N
The Woodlands TX 77380
832 482-1399

(G-20257)
DANIEL H BRAMAN JR ESTATE
1 Oconnor Plz Ste 1100 (77901-6549)
PHONE....................................361 578-6271
D H Braman Jr, *Owner*
Wanda Ulrey, *Principal*
EMP: 20
SQ FT: 7,000
SALES (est): 2.3MM **Privately Held**
SIC: 1311 Crude petroleum & natural gas

(G-20258)
DH BRAMAN III
201 E Santa Rosa St (77901-8124)
P.O. Box 400 (77902-0400)
PHONE....................................361 578-6271
EMP: 20 EST: 2013
SALES (est): 1.5MM **Privately Held**
SIC: 1381 Drilling oil & gas wells

(G-20259)
E I DU PONT DE NEMOURS & CO
Also Called: Dupont Victoria Plant
2697 Old Bloomington Rd N (77905)
P.O. Box 526 (77902-0526)
PHONE....................................361 572-1330
EMP: 100

SALES (corp-wide): 36B **Publicly Held**
SIC: 2822 Mfg Synthetic Rubber
PA: E. I. Du Pont De Nemours And Company
1007 Market St
Wilmington DE 19805
302 774-1000

(G-20260)
E I DU PONT DE NEMOURS & CO
2695 Old Bloomington Rd N (77905-1840)
P.O. Box 2626 (77902-2626)
PHONE....................................361 572-1330
Bruce Chinn, *Manager*
EMP: 333
SALES (corp-wide): 14.2B **Publicly Held**
WEB: www.dupont.com
SIC: 2821 Nylon resins; polyethylene resins
HQ: E. I. Du Pont De Nemours And Company
974 Centre Rd Bldg 735
Wilmington DE 19805
302 485-3000

(G-20261)
EQUISTAR CHEMICALS LP
2695 Old Bloomington Rd N (77905-1840)
PHONE....................................361 572-2547
EMP: 9
SALES (corp-wide): 34.9B **Privately Held**
WEB: www.lyondellbasell.com
SIC: 2869 Industrial organic chemicals
HQ: Equistar Chemicals, Lp
1221 Mckinney St Ste 300
Houston TX 77010

(G-20262)
ESPADA OILFIELD SERVICES LLC
1501 E Mockingbird Ln # 211 (77904-2155)
PHONE....................................361 894-1810
Michael C Martinez,
Mike Martinez,
EMP: 10
SALES (est): 457.2K **Privately Held**
SIC: 1389 Oil field services

(G-20263)
FESCO LTD
4906 Houston Hwy (77901-3782)
PHONE....................................361 575-7533
Joe Gray, *District Mgr*
Travis Findley, *Marketing Staff*
EMP: 15
SALES (corp-wide): 201MM **Privately Held**
WEB: www.fescoinc.com
SIC: 8711 1389 Petroleum engineering; oil field services
PA: Fesco, Ltd.
1000 Fesco Dr
Alice TX 78332
361 664-3479

(G-20264)
FORDYCE HOLDINGS INC
210 W Juan Linn St (77901-8002)
P.O. Box 1417 (77902-1417)
PHONE....................................361 573-4309
Keith Henke, *CFO*
EMP: 99
SALES (est): 15.9MM **Privately Held**
WEB: www.briggsranches.com
SIC: 1442 Construction sand & gravel

(G-20265)
FREDDYS WELL SERVICE INC
Old Goliad Rd (77902)
P.O. Box 124 (77902-0124)
PHONE....................................361 578-4559
Richard Flores, *President*
John Fuentes, *Vice Pres*
Emma Flores, *Treasurer*
Diana Flores, *Exec Dir*
EMP: 12
SQ FT: 1,600
SALES (est): 1MM **Privately Held**
WEB: www.freddyswellservice.com
SIC: 1389 Oil field services

(G-20266)
GEMCO OF PORT LAVACA INC
Also Called: Gemco Plltizing Dies Machining
6611 Lone Tree Rd (77905-5467)
PHONE....................................361 570-6611

Denis Burns, *President*
Donna Pridgen, *Vice Pres*
Joanna M Jacobs, *Admin Sec*
▼ EMP: 30 EST: 1950
SQ FT: 30,000
SALES (est): 4MM **Privately Held**
WEB: www.gemcodies.com
SIC: 3544 Dies, plastics forming; extrusion dies

(G-20267)
GENES MACHINE INC
235 Leeper Ln (77904-4901)
PHONE....................................361 573-7146
Gene Pratka, *President*
Gail Pratka, *Corp Secy*
Tim Hall, *Info Tech Mgr*
Sherry Chase, *Admin Sec*
EMP: 90 EST: 1979
SQ FT: 33,000
SALES (est): 18.1MM **Privately Held**
WEB: www.genesmachine.com
SIC: 3599 7692 Machine shop, jobbing & repair; welding repair

(G-20268)
GMU DOWNHOLE TOOL CORPORATION
1602 La Valliere St (77901-7364)
P.O. Box 3504 (77903-3504)
PHONE....................................361 573-5100
Russell W Doerr, *President*
EMP: 9
SALES (est): 1.7MM **Privately Held**
WEB: www.gmudownholetools.com
SIC: 3533 Oil & gas field machinery

(G-20269)
GOLDEN CRESCENT COMMUNICATIONS
103 John Stockbauer Dr (77901-3761)
P.O. Box 3246 (77903-3246)
PHONE....................................361 578-4091
Johnny Jank, *Owner*
EMP: 10
SQ FT: 2,500
SALES (est): 946K **Privately Held**
WEB: www.gccs-online.com
SIC: 5999 3663 Telephone & communication equipment; radio broadcasting & communications equipment

(G-20270)
GULF COAST CASING INC
833 Lower Mission Vly Rd (77905-3543)
PHONE....................................361 575-5488
Jessie Armstrong, *President*
Janice Armstrong, *Admin Sec*
EMP: 20
SQ FT: 1,500
SALES (est): 1.7MM **Privately Held**
WEB: www.gulfcoastcasing.com
SIC: 1389 Oil field services

(G-20271)
HALLIBURTON COMPANY
101 Holt Rd (77905-5876)
PHONE....................................210 621-1800
Anibal Alfaro, *Foreman/Supr*
Brett McBride, *Foreman/Supr*
Russell Wittig, *Opers Staff*
Aaron Steuart, *Engineer*
Wesley Hawkins, *Manager*
EMP: 20 **Publicly Held**
WEB: www.halliburton.com
SIC: 1389 Oil field services
PA: Halliburton Company
3000 N Sam Houston Pkwy E
Houston TX 77032

(G-20272)
HOFFMAN INDUSTRIAL ELECTRIC (PA)
301 W Convent St (77901-8013)
P.O. Box 1306 (77902-1306)
PHONE....................................361 573-6365
Tim Hoffman, *President*
EMP: 9
SQ FT: 7,000
SALES (est): 425.1K **Privately Held**
SIC: 7694 5063 Electric motor repair; electrical apparatus & equipment

(G-20273)
INGRAM READYMIX INC
4905 Houston Hwy (77901-3783)
PHONE....................................361 575-6358
Alfred Perez, *Manager*
EMP: 15
SQ FT: 5,000
SALES (corp-wide): 125.6MM **Privately Held**
WEB: www.ingramreadymixinc.com
SIC: 3273 5171 Ready-mixed concrete; petroleum bulk stations
PA: Ingram Readymix, Inc.
3580 Farm Market 482
New Braunfels TX 78132
830 625-9156

(G-20274)
INVISTA CAPITAL MANAGEMENT LLC
Also Called: Invista Sarl - Victoria
2695 Old Bloomington Rd N (77905-1840)
P.O. Box 2626 (77902-2626)
PHONE....................................361 572-1111
Drew Ruterbories, *Facilities Mgr*
Wyn Steadman, *Engineer*
Roy Balerio, *Manager*
Samuel Booth, *Manager*
Danny L Ballard, *Supervisor*
EMP: 700
SALES (corp-wide): 36.8B **Privately Held**
WEB: www.invista.com
SIC: 2824 2296 Nylon fibers; tire cord & fabrics
HQ: Invista Capital Management, Llc
2801 Centerville Rd
Wilmington DE 19808
302 683-3000

(G-20275)
J-W OPERATING COMPANY
4607 E Juan Linn St (77901-1507)
PHONE....................................361 570-2788
Ken Kirkpatrick, *General Mgr*
EMP: 48 **Privately Held**
WEB: www.jwpower.net
SIC: 1311 1389 Crude petroleum production; oil field services
HQ: J-W Operating Company
15505 Wright Brothers Dr
Addison TX 75001
972 233-8191

(G-20276)
JAKS MACHINE INC
3302 Houston Hwy (77901-4606)
P.O. Box 3874 (77903-3874)
PHONE....................................361 575-2312
Douglas C Wuest, *President*
Betty J Bireley, *Vice Pres*
Deborah Wuest, *Admin Sec*
EMP: 11 EST: 2001
SALES (est): 1.6MM **Privately Held**
WEB: www.jaksmachine.com
SIC: 3592 Valves

(G-20277)
JET MAINTENANCE INC
4301 Houston Hwy (77901-4789)
P.O. Box 5026 (77903-5026)
PHONE....................................361 576-3226
Jim West, *President*
EMP: 20
SALES (est): 6MM **Privately Held**
WEB: www.jetmaintenanceinc.com
SIC: 1389 Oil field services

(G-20278)
K & K REPAIR SERVICE LLC
Also Called: John Deere Authorized Dealer
4855 Us Highway 87 S (77905-5593)
P.O. Box 427, Telferner (77988-0427)
PHONE....................................361 573-5027
Brandun K Knocke, *President*
Mike Anderson, *General Mgr*
Steve Uresti, *QC Mgr*
Joe Ordanis, *Sales Executive*
Holly Jhahn, *Office Mgr*
EMP: 20 EST: 1999
SQ FT: 5,000
SALES (est): 11.2MM **Privately Held**
WEB: www.kkrepair.net
SIC: 1389 5082 Oil field services; construction & mining machinery

(G-20279)
K & N PERFORATORS INC
508 Profit Dr (77901-7348)
P.O. Box 3327 (77903-3327)
PHONE....................................361 578-8851
Don Keeney, *President*
EMP: 15 EST: 1976
SALES (est): 1.1MM **Privately Held**
SIC: 1389 Servicing oil & gas wells; well logging; perforating well casings

(G-20280)
KEN GARNER MFG - VTO INC
Also Called: Kgm-Vto
203 Wayne Watkins Rd (77905-4398)
PHONE....................................361 485-0541
Ken Garner Jr, *Ch of Bd*
John Garner, *Project Mgr*
EMP: 12
SALES (est): 169.7K **Privately Held**
WEB: www.kgarnermfg.com
SIC: 3548 3531 Resistance welders, electric; excavators: cable, clamshell, crane, derrick, dragline, etc.; construction machinery attachments

(G-20281)
KLEAN CORP INTERNATIONAL
601 John Stockbauer Dr (77901-3794)
PHONE....................................361 578-1524
Robby Burdge, *CEO*
Al Bump, *Vice Pres*
Tami Burdge, *Vice Pres*
Dale Jones, *Vice Pres*
EMP: 26
SALES (est): 1.6MM **Privately Held**
WEB: www.kleancorp.com
SIC: 7349 2819 Chemical cleaning services; industrial inorganic chemicals

(G-20282)
LA ORIGINAL TORTILLA CO INC
302 Profit Dr (77901-7367)
PHONE....................................361 570-8905
Ray Bazan, *President*
EMP: 30
SQ FT: 4,000
SALES (est): 1.4MM **Privately Held**
WEB: www.laoriginaltortilla.com
SIC: 2099 Tortillas, fresh or refrigerated

(G-20283)
LAWRENCE FURNITURE CO INC
400 Warehouse Rd (77905-0512)
PHONE....................................361 572-3710
Craig Lawrence, *President*
EMP: 13
SALES (est): 900K **Privately Held**
WEB: www.lawrencefurnitureco.com
SIC: 2434 Wood kitchen cabinets

(G-20284)
LYONDELL CHEMICAL COMPANY
Old Bloomington Hwy (77901)
P.O. Box 513 (77902-0513)
PHONE....................................361 572-2500
Dale Friedrichs, *Manager*
EMP: 83
SALES (corp-wide): 34.9B **Privately Held**
WEB: www.lyondellbasell.com
SIC: 2869 Butadiene (industrial organic chemical)
HQ: Lyondell Chemical Company
1221 Mckinney St Ste 300
Houston TX 77010
713 309-7200

(G-20285)
MORGAN KINDER TREATING LP (DH)
407 Holt Rd (77905-5575)
PHONE....................................361 578-1312
Sam Rhodes, *General Mgr*
Evan Herrera, *Opers Staff*
Kimberly A Dang, *CFO*
Ted A Gardner, *Director*
Gary L Hultquist, *Director*
EMP: 55
SALES (est): 21.2MM **Publicly Held**
WEB: www.kindermorgantreating.com
SIC: 1311 Gas & hydrocarbon liquefaction from coal

HQ: Kinder Morgan Energy Partners, L.P.
1001 La St Ste 1000
Houston TX 77002
713 369-9000

(G-20286)
MUELLER SUPPLY COMPANY INC
9502 Us Highway 59 N (77905-5570)
PHONE..........................361 580-1427
Mark Murphy, *Branch Mgr*
EMP: 10
SALES (corp-wide): 180.3MM **Privately Held**
WEB: www.muellerinc.com
SIC: 3444 Sheet metalwork
PA: Mueller Supply Company, Inc.
1913 Hutchins Ave
Ballinger TX 76821
325 365-3555

(G-20287)
NATIONAL OILWELL VARCO INC
508 Mallard Rd (77905-0615)
P.O. Box 3494 (77903-3494)
PHONE..........................361 576-3161
Raquel Cardenas, *Sales Staff*
Carl Gilbert, *Manager*
EMP: 43
SALES (corp-wide): 8.4B **Publicly Held**
WEB: www.nov.com
SIC: 5084 3536 3533 Industrial machinery & equipment; hoists, cranes & monorails; oil & gas field machinery
PA: National Oilwell Varco, Inc.
7909 Parkwood Circle Dr
Houston TX 77036
713 346-7500

(G-20288)
NATURAL GAS PIPELINE AMER LLC
9819 State Highway 185 S (77905-1700)
PHONE..........................361 897-1022
K Simnacher, *Branch Mgr*
EMP: 18 **Publicly Held**
WEB: www.kindermorgan.com
SIC: 4922 1311 Pipelines, natural gas; crude petroleum & natural gas
HQ: Natural Gas Pipeline Company Of America Llc
1001 Louisiana St
Houston TX 77002
713 369-9000

(G-20289)
OIL PATCH GROUP INC
991 Industrial Park Dr (77905-0679)
PHONE..........................361 576-0300
Diana Alles, *Principal*
Danette Mares, *Manager*
EMP: 24 **Privately Held**
WEB: www.oilpatchgroup.com
SIC: 1389 Construction, repair & dismantling services
HQ: Oil Patch Group, Inc.
12012 Wickchester Ln # 475
Houston TX 77079
832 300-0000

(G-20290)
PATRIOT OILFIELD SERVICES LLC (PA)
1 Oconnor Plz Ste 300 (77901-6695)
P.O. Box 65, Louise (77455-0065)
PHONE..........................979 648-2416
Scott Jaynes,
EMP: 20
SALES (est): 4.2MM **Privately Held**
WEB: www.patriotofs.com
SIC: 4212 1389 Petroleum haulage, local; mud service, oil field drilling

(G-20291)
PATTERSN-UTI DRLG SVCS LP LLLP
844 Bob White Rd (77905-0618)
P.O. Box 1416, Snyder (79550-1416)
PHONE..........................361 576-6896
Keith Morris, *Manager*
EMP: 30
SALES (corp-wide): 1.1B **Publicly Held**
WEB: www.patenergy.com
SIC: 1381 Drilling oil & gas wells

HQ: Patterson-Uti Drilling Services Lp, Lllp
4500 Lamesa Hwy
Snyder TX 79549
325 573-1104

(G-20292)
PATTERSON WELL SERVICE CO LLC
1501 E Mockingbird Ln # 3 (77904-2155)
P.O. Box 3867 (77903-3867)
PHONE..........................361 575-9600
Linda H Patterson, *Principal*
EMP: 13 EST: 2007
SALES (est): 2.3MM **Privately Held**
WEB: www.pattersonwellservice.com
SIC: 3533 Oil & gas drilling rigs & equipment

(G-20293)
PEAK COMPLETION TECH INC
159 Enterprise Dr (77905-3273)
PHONE..........................361 668-8383
Raymond Hofman, *President*
EMP: 40
SALES (corp-wide): 104.3MM **Privately Held**
WEB: www.peakcompletions.com
SIC: 1389 Oil field services
PA: Peak Completion Technologies, Inc.
7710 W Highway 80
Midland TX 79706
432 617-0178

(G-20294)
PEPSI-COLA METRO BTLG CO INC
Also Called: Pepsico
3811 E Rio Grande St (77901-1727)
PHONE..........................361 575-2661
Edward Ortiz, *Manager*
EMP: 15
SALES (corp-wide): 67.1B **Publicly Held**
WEB: www.pepsico.com
SIC: 2086 5149 Soft drinks: packaged in cans, bottles, etc.; groceries & related products
HQ: Pepsi-Cola Metropolitan Bottling Company, Inc.
1111 Westchester Ave
White Plains NY 10604
914 767-6000

(G-20295)
PETROLEUM COLLEGE INTL
3302 N Ben Wilson St (77901-5742)
PHONE..........................361 575-4882
Frank Klepper, *President*
EMP: 11
SALES (est): 892.2K **Privately Held**
WEB: www.petroleumcollege.com
SIC: 1389 Oil field services

(G-20296)
PRO FIELD SERVICES INC
22905 Nw Zac Lentz Pkwy (77905)
PHONE..........................361 575-0348
Billy Hahn, *Branch Mgr*
EMP: 16
SALES (corp-wide): 29.6MM **Privately Held**
WEB: www.profieldservices.com
SIC: 1389 Haulage, oil field
PA: Pro Field Services, Inc.
212 E 2nd St
Hallettsville TX 77964
361 798-5552

(G-20297)
QES PRESSURE CONTROL LLC
Also Called: Archer
376 Enterprise Dr (77905-3276)
PHONE..........................361 580-5400
EMP: 80
SALES (corp-wide): 1B **Privately Held**
WEB: www.quintanaenergyservices.com
SIC: 1389 Oil field services
HQ: Qes Pressure Control Llc
4500 Se 59th St
Oklahoma City OK 73135

(G-20298)
QUAIL TOOLS LP
7701 Us Highway 59 N (77905-5579)
P.O. Box 3250 (77903-3250)
PHONE..........................361 579-0244
Daniel Derouen, *Manager*

EMP: 50
SALES (corp-wide): 571MM **Publicly Held**
WEB: www.quailtools.com
SIC: 1389 Oil field services
HQ: Quail Tools, L.P.
3713 Highway 14
New Iberia LA 70560
337 365-8154

(G-20299)
REDDY ICE CORPORATION
507 E Sabine St (77901-5268)
PHONE..........................361 578-3032
Mark M Niell, *General Mgr*
EMP: 11 **Privately Held**
WEB: www.reddyice.com
SIC: 2097 Manufactured ice
HQ: Reddy Ice Corporation
5710 Lbj Fwy Ste 300
Dallas TX 75240
214 526-6740

(G-20300)
REGAL MARBLE CO
2498 Guadalupe Rd (77905-2004)
PHONE..........................361 572-8498
Ken Crawford, *President*
Audrey Crawford, *Corp Secy*
EMP: 14
SQ FT: 10,000
SALES (est): 1.5MM **Privately Held**
WEB: www.marketplacevictoria.com
SIC: 3281 1522 1799 Marble, building: cut & shaped; residential construction; counter top installation

(G-20301)
RIGAMONTI WELDING SERVICES
Also Called: Rigamonti Trailer Parts
5180 Hanselman Rd (77905-5522)
PHONE..........................361 578-0397
Charles Rigamonti, *President*
Gary Rigamonti, *Vice Pres*
EMP: 9
SQ FT: 5,000
SALES (est): 999.6K **Privately Held**
SIC: 1389 Welding repair

(G-20302)
SCHROEDER WELDING & CNSTR
2303 Lone Tree Rd (77901-7228)
P.O. Box 123 (77902-0123)
PHONE..........................361 573-4322
Robert G Schroeder, *President*
Debbie Valenta, *Corp Secy*
EMP: 50 EST: 1951
SQ FT: 1,300
SALES (est): 1MM **Privately Held**
SIC: 1389 1799 Oil field services; welding on site

(G-20303)
SCHROEDER WELDING & CNSTR
3112 Pleasant Green Dr (77901-1478)
P.O. Box 123 (77902-0123)
PHONE..........................361 575-4992
Bobby Schroeder, *Vice Pres*
EMP: 20
SALES (est): 1.1MM **Privately Held**
SIC: 1389 Oil field services

(G-20304)
SPARKMAN INDUSTRIES INC
Also Called: Victoria Well Service
169 Aviation Dr (77904-3706)
PHONE..........................361 573-0001
Jack Brown, *COO*
Melissa Proctor, *CFO*
Robert Sparkman, *Manager*
Kyle Brady, *Technology*
Robert T Sparkman Jr, *Director*
▲ **EMP:** 100
SALES (est): 21MM **Privately Held**
WEB: www.sparkmanindustries.com
SIC: 3599 1389 Machine shop, jobbing & repair; construction, repair & dismantling services; gas compressing (natural gas) at the fields

(G-20305)
SPARKMAN WELL SERVICE INC (PA)
Also Called: American Pumping & Trucking
6811 Us Highway 59 N (77905-5807)
P.O. Box 312580, New Braunfels (78131-2580)
PHONE..........................361 572-4833
Bennie Sparkman, *President*
Carrie Sparkman, *Vice Pres*
EMP: 110
SALES (est): 11.7MM **Privately Held**
SIC: 1381 1389 4212 Directional drilling oil & gas wells; oil field equipment; oil field services; local trucking, without storage

(G-20306)
STALLION OILFIELD SERVICES
10205 Us Highway 59 N (77905-5827)
P.O. Box 4469 (77903-4469)
PHONE..........................361 578-7500
Craig Johnson, *CEO*
Steve Wood, *Vice Pres*
EMP: 20
SALES (est): 1.8MM **Privately Held**
WEB: www.stallionoilfield.com
SIC: 1389 Oil field services

(G-20307)
TEJAS PRODUCTION SERVICES INC
7303 Houston Hwy (77901-5488)
P.O. Box 3368 (77903-3368)
PHONE..........................361 572-3127
Jerry Bang, *President*
Gary Ford, *General Mgr*
Tom Lempa, *Corp Secy*
Hunter Follett, *CFO*
Elton Calhoun, *Shareholder*
▼ **EMP:** 14
SQ FT: 6,000
SALES (est): 6.2MM **Privately Held**
WEB: www.tejasproduction.com
SIC: 1389 Oil & gas wells: building, repairing & dismantling; oil field services

(G-20308)
TEXAS CONCRETE PARTNERS LP
4702 N Vine St (77904-4015)
P.O. Box 1070 (77902-1070)
PHONE..........................361 573-9145
Paul M Guthrie, *President*
Larry Mikulec, *CFO*
EMP: 200 EST: 1947
SQ FT: 2,500
SALES (est): 48.8MM
SALES (corp-wide): 61.1MM **Privately Held**
WEB: www.texasconcrete.com
SIC: 3272 Prestressed concrete products
PA: Texas Concrete Partners, L.P.
1690 Mesquite Tree Rd
Elm Mott TX 76640
254 822-1351

(G-20309)
TEXAS SAMPLING INC
3706 E Rio Grande St (77901-1815)
P.O. Box 4866, Spartanburg SC (29305-4866)
PHONE..........................361 575-8087
A William Higgins, *President*
Susan M McCuaig, *President*
James Blose, *Vice Pres*
Richard A Broughton, *Vice Pres*
Alan J Glass, *Vice Pres*
◆ **EMP:** 18
SQ FT: 12,000
SALES (est): 3.1MM
SALES (corp-wide): 1.1B **Publicly Held**
WEB: www.texassampling.com
SIC: 3829 Measuring & controlling devices
PA: Circor International, Inc.
30 Corporate Dr Ste 200
Burlington MA 01803
781 270-1200

(G-20310)
THOMAS KURTZ
Also Called: Kurtz Printing Co
102 Cozzi Cir (77901-2629)
PHONE..........................361 578-2594
Thomas Kurtz, *Owner*

▲ = Import ▼=Export
◆ =Import/Export

EMP: 12
SQ FT: 5,000
SALES (est): 1.4MM **Privately Held**
WEB: www.thomaskurtz.com
SIC: 2752 Commercial printing, offset

(G-20311)
TOTAL PRODUCTION SERVICES INC
2501 E Real Grant (77901)
P.O. Box 5215 (77903-5215)
PHONE..................361 572-0484
Fax: 361 572-0489
EMP: 103
SQ FT: 25,000
SALES (est): 4.6MM **Privately Held**
SIC: 1389 Oil/Gas Field Services

(G-20312)
TYCO INTERNATIONAL MGT CO LLC
202 John Stockbauer Dr (77901-3763)
PHONE..................361 575-9565
Kevin Larang, *Manager*
EMP: 250 **Privately Held**
WEB: www.tyco.com
SIC: 3089 5162 2673 Garbage containers, plastic; plastics materials; bags: plastic, laminated & coated
HQ: Tyco International Management Company, Llc
9 Roszel Rd Ste 2
Princeton NJ 08540
609 720-4200

(G-20313)
VICTORIA ADVOCATE NEWS BUREAU
1 Oconnor Plz Ste 1200 (77901-6549)
PHONE..................361 575-1451
John Roberts, *Publisher*
Richard Vargas Jr, *Principal*
Steve McHaney, *Vice Pres*
EMP: 160
SALES (est): 3.8MM **Privately Held**
WEB: www.victoriaadvocate.com
SIC: 2711 Newspapers: publishing only, not printed on site

(G-20314)
VICTORIA ADVOCATE PUBG CO (PA)
1 Oconnor Plz Ste 1200 (77901-6549)
P.O. Box 1518 (77902-1518)
PHONE..................361 575-1451
John M Roberts, *President*
Michael Cloud, *Publisher*
Jerry Pye, *Publisher*
Tyler M Telegraph, *Publisher*
Tony Balandran, *Editor*
EMP: 61 **EST:** 1846
SALES (est): 16.1MM **Privately Held**
WEB: www.victoriaadvocate.com
SIC: 2711 Newspapers: publishing only, not printed on site

(G-20315)
VISION OIL FIELD SERVICES LC
1908 N Laurent St Ste 200 (77901-5458)
P.O. Box 3506 (77903-3506)
PHONE..................361 578-1901
John Gayle, *Manager*
Mr John R Gayle, *Manager*
Sandra Gayle,
EMP: 10
SALES (est): 944.5K **Privately Held**
SIC: 1389 Oil field services

(G-20316)
VITEX WIRELINE SERVICES INC
3802 E Rio Grande St (77901-1726)
P.O. Box 3411 (77903-3411)
PHONE..................361 575-1233
David Simek, *President*
Debbie Simek, *Corp Secy*
EMP: 9
SQ FT: 10,000
SALES (est): 859.6K **Privately Held**
SIC: 1389 Oil field services

(G-20317)
VMC SIGNS INC
102 E Mockingbird Ln (77904-2046)
P.O. Box 3944 (77903-3944)
PHONE..................361 575-0548

Tom Willis, *President*
Nancy Hayward, *General Mgr*
Richard Willis, *Manager*
EMP: 17
SQ FT: 6,000
SALES (est): 1.3MM **Privately Held**
WEB: www.vmcsigns.com
SIC: 1799 3993 Sign installation & maintenance; electric signs

(G-20318)
WANT ADS OF COLORADO SPRINGS
Also Called: Thrifty Nckel Want ADS Vctoria
2708 N Ben Wilson St (77901-5729)
PHONE..................361 575-6400
Rhonda Kalich, *Vice Pres*
EMP: 10
SALES (est): 600K **Privately Held**
WEB: www.victoriaamclass.com
SIC: 2711 Newspapers: publishing only, not printed on site

(G-20319)
WATERMARK GRAPHICS INC (PA)
9201 Us Highway 59 N (77905-5573)
PHONE..................361 576-6874
Jason Elder, *CEO*
Sharon Elder, *President*
Todd Elder, *Vice Pres*
William Charles, *Project Mgr*
Lisa Manning, *Project Mgr*
EMP: 13
SQ FT: 5,000
SALES (est): 3.2MM **Privately Held**
WEB: www.watermarkgraphics.com
SIC: 2752 2396 Offset & photolithographic printing; promotional printing, lithographic; screen printing on fabric articles

(G-20320)
WEATHERFORD INTERNATIONAL LLC
435 Leeper Ln (77904-4924)
P.O. Box 4711 (77903-4711)
PHONE..................361 576-5641
EMP: 9 **Privately Held**
WEB: www.weatherford.com
SIC: 1389 Oil field services
HQ: Weatherford International, Llc
2000 Saint James Pl
Houston TX 77056
713 693-4000

(G-20321)
YELLOWJACKET OILFIELD SVCS LLC
5500 Sw Moody St (77905-4080)
PHONE..................361 485-0625
EMP: 75
SALES (corp-wide): 25.4MM **Privately Held**
SIC: 1389 Oil/Gas Field Services
PA: Yellowjacket Oilfield Services, L.L.C.
200 N Loraine St Ste 1150
Midland TX 79701
432 242-7570

(G-20322)
ZARSKY LUMBER COMPANY INC (DH)
604 E Rio Grande St (77901-6035)
P.O. Box 2527 (77902-2527)
PHONE..................361 573-2479
Phillip Steffy, *President*
Helen Winter, *COO*
Michael Trice, *Credit Mgr*
Chip Wagenhauser, *Sales Staff*
Ernest Vasquez, *Manager*
EMP: 35
SQ FT: 8,000
SALES (est): 30.5MM
SALES (corp-wide): 137.6MM **Privately Held**
WEB: www.zarsky.com
SIC: 5211 1389 Lumber & other building materials; mud service, oil field drilling
HQ: Kodiak Gypsum Llc
1745 Shea Center Dr # 130
Highlands Ranch CO 80129
720 336-0083

(G-20323)
ZEDI US INC
3001 N Cameron St (77901-3942)
PHONE..................361 575-4528
Gary Edwards, *Manager*
EMP: 22
SALES (corp-wide): 16.7B **Publicly Held**
WEB: www.zedisolutions.com
SIC: 1389 Oil field services
HQ: Zedi Us Inc.
101 Ibex Ln
Broussard LA 70518
337 233-2066

Vidor
Orange County

(G-20324)
ASI PIPING LLC
Also Called: A S I Piping
3530 Lakeview Cutoff St (77662-9092)
PHONE..................409 786-1080
Clyde Williamson,
EMP: 50
SQ FT: 7,000
SALES (est): 7.9MM **Privately Held**
WEB: www.asipiping.com
SIC: 3498 7692 Fabricated pipe & fittings; welding repair

(G-20325)
BUNA ELECTRIC MOTOR SVC INC
Also Called: Bems
465 S Main St (77662-5747)
P.O. Box 1088 (77670-1088)
PHONE..................409 769-5402
Asa Brad Mansfield, *President*
Brad Mansfield, *Principal*
Clifford R Mansfield, *Corp Secy*
Faron B Wilson, *Vice Pres*
Faron Wilson, *VP Opers*
EMP: 44
SALES (est): 8.1MM **Privately Held**
WEB: www.bunaelectric.com
SIC: 7694 Electric motor repair

(G-20326)
DIVERSIFIED METAL WORKS INC
4810 Evangeline Dr (77662-7501)
P.O. Box 1297 (77670-1297)
PHONE..................409 769-1146
Paul L Peveto, *President*
Jerry A Jones, *Vice Pres*
Bruce W Weaver, *Vice Pres*
EMP: 18
SALES (est): 2.8MM **Privately Held**
SIC: 3444 Sheet metalwork

(G-20327)
ISM INDUSTRIES INC (PA)
16645 Ih 10 (77662-2464)
PHONE..................409 769-7841
Jack Tindel Sr, *President*
Jack Tindel Jr, *Vice Pres*
EMP: 54
SQ FT: 3,000
SALES (est): 11.8MM **Privately Held**
WEB: www.ismfab.com
SIC: 8711 3441 Construction & civil engineering; fabricated structural metal

(G-20328)
JUDYS IRON & METAL INC (PA)
6755 N Highway 105 (77662-7127)
PHONE..................409 681-0500
Michael J Judy, *President*
EMP: 23
SALES (est): 1.7MM **Privately Held**
WEB: www.j3metals.com
SIC: 7692 Welding repair

(G-20329)
LNC FABRICATION LLC
17970 Ih 10 (77662-2385)
P.O. Box 270 (77670-0270)
PHONE..................409 769-0403
Herb Lutz, *Mng Member*
EMP: 14 **EST:** 2012
SALES (est): 3.3MM **Privately Held**
WEB: www.lncfabrication.com
SIC: 3312 Bars, iron: made in steel mills

(G-20330)
ORANGE COUNTY PUBLISHING CO
Also Called: Vidorian, The
450 W Bolivar St (77662-4724)
P.O. Box 1236 (77670-1236)
PHONE..................409 769-5428
Albert M Luker, *Ch of Bd*
Randell Luker, *President*
EMP: 15 **EST:** 1953
SQ FT: 10,000
SALES (est): 1MM **Privately Held**
WEB: www.thevidorian.com
SIC: 2711 Commercial printing & newspaper publishing combined

(G-20331)
REAGENT CHEMICAL & RES INC
18950 Ih 10 (77662-2393)
PHONE..................409 962-1116
Linda Cornet, *Vice Pres*
David Stewart, *Branch Mgr*
Gary Morse, *Manager*
EMP: 35
SALES (corp-wide): 376.8MM **Privately Held**
WEB: www.prosysfill.com
SIC: 2819 3949 Sulfur, recovered or refined, incl. from sour natural gas; targets, archery & rifle shooting
PA: Reagent Chemical & Research, Inc.
115 Rte 202
Ringoes NJ 08551
908 284-2800

(G-20332)
SOUTHEAST TEXAS INDUSTRIES INC
Also Called: STI Group
635 Old Highway 90 W (77662-4740)
PHONE..................409 783-0009
David Cude, *Project Mgr*
Brett Horn, *Manager*
Robert Woodard, *Supervisor*
Blain Dugas, *Executive*
Terri Freeman, *Executive*
EMP: 198 **Privately Held**
WEB: www.setxind.com
SIC: 3441 Fabricated structural metal
PA: Southeast Texas Industries, Inc.
35911 Us Highway 96 S
Buna TX 77612

(G-20333)
STANDARD ALLOYS INCORPORATED
22389 Ih 10 (77662-2567)
PHONE..................409 769-7850
Jeffrey Smith, *President*
EMP: 9
SALES (corp-wide): 144.1K **Privately Held**
WEB: www.ksb.com
SIC: 3599 Machine shop, jobbing & repair
HQ: Standard Alloys Incorporated
201 Lakeshore Dr
Port Arthur TX 77640
409 983-3201

(G-20334)
STRONGARM INDUSTRIES INC
790 Highway 1131 (77662-8913)
P.O. Box 1119 (77670-1119)
PHONE..................409 835-1330
EMP: 15
SALES (est): 4.2MM **Privately Held**
SIC: 3569 Mfg General Industrial Machinery

(G-20335)
SUMMIT SEALS INC
760 Archie St (77662-4502)
P.O. Box 209 (77670-0209)
PHONE..................409 769-8151
Dode White, *President*
Ed Molanders, *Vice Pres*
Dean Fredericks, *Regl Sales Mgr*
EMP: 12
SALES (est): 1.7MM **Privately Held**
SIC: 1791 3441 Storage tanks, metal: erection; fabricated structural metal

(G-20336)
TUBAL CAIN INDUSTRIES INC (PA)
Also Called: Tubal-Cain
5665 N Main St (77662-8123)
P.O. Box 2393, Beaumont (77704-2393)
PHONE..........................409 786-1783
Edward Van Huis IV, *President*
Charles Miller, *COO*
Stuart Simpson, *COO*
Deborah J Van Huis, *Vice Pres*
Tim Huis, *Project Mgr*
EMP: 55
SQ FT: 55,000
SALES (est): 13.6MM **Privately Held**
WEB: www.tubal-cain.com
SIC: 3449 3452 5051 3444 Bars, concrete reinforcing: fabricated steel; bolts, metal; metals service centers & offices; sheet metalwork

Village Mills
Hardin County

(G-20337)
INTEGRATED PIPE & SUPPLY LLC
13604 Highway 69 (77663)
PHONE..........................409 834-6123
Michael D Renick, *Mng Member*
EMP: 10
SALES (est): 2.8MM **Privately Held**
WEB: www.integratedpipe.com
SIC: 3312 3317 Pipes, iron & steel; steel pipe & tubes

(G-20338)
MC MANUS INSTRUMENT CO INC
5088 Fm 3063 (77663)
P.O. Box 829 (77663-0829)
PHONE..........................409 834-2419
EMP: 12
SQ FT: 12,000
SALES (est): 600K **Privately Held**
WEB: www.mcmanusinstruments.com
SIC: 3599 3841 3812 Machine shop, jobbing & repair; surgical & medical instruments; search & navigation equipment

(G-20339)
STREAMLINE PRODUCTION SVCS INC
13604 Hwy 69 N (77663)
P.O. Box 609 (77663-0609)
PHONE..........................409 834-6096
Mike Renick, *President*
Jill Renick, *Vice Pres*
EMP: 55 EST: 2014
SALES (est): 10MM **Privately Held**
SIC: 1389 Oil field services

Vinton
El Paso County

(G-20340)
BOWDEN SADDLE TREE COMPANY INC
8227 Doniphan Dr (79821-9322)
PHONE..........................915 877-3191
Francis Bowden, *President*
Betty Bowden, *Corp Secy*
Arlen Bowden, *Vice Pres*
EMP: 15
SQ FT: 10,000
SALES (est): 1.8MM **Privately Held**
WEB: www.saddletree.com
SIC: 2499 5941 Saddle trees, wood; sporting goods & bicycle shops

(G-20341)
TEWA LLC
251 Valley Chili Rd (79821-9323)
P.O. Box 938, Canutillo (79835-0938)
PHONE..........................915 886-9973
John Bernard, *Mng Member*
Carl W Bonner,
Joshua Ziegler,
EMP: 29
SQ FT: 44,000
SALES (est): 7MM **Privately Held**
SIC: 2431 Moldings, wood: unfinished & prefinished

(G-20342)
VINTON STEEL LLC
Also Called: Metal Processing
8100 Border Steel Rd (79821)
P.O. Box 12843, El Paso (79913-0843)
PHONE..........................915 886-2000
Masahiro Kitada, *President*
Juan Delgado, *Vice Pres*
Miguel Franco, *Vice Pres*
▼ EMP: 450
SQ FT: 10,000
SALES (est): 221.8MM **Privately Held**
WEB: www.vintonsteel.com
SIC: 5051 3312 3449 3316 Metals service centers & offices; bars & bar shapes, steel, hot-rolled; miscellaneous metalwork; cold finishing of steel shapes
PA: Kyoei Steel Ltd.
1-4-16, Dojimahama, Kita-Ku
Osaka OSK 530-0

(G-20343)
W SILVER INC
Also Called: W S I
9059 Doniphan Dr (79821-9372)
PHONE..........................915 886-3553
Luis Garcia, *President*
Mark Fenenbock, *Chairman*
Javier Valtierrez, *Prdtn Mgr*
Gary Manoni, *Controller*
Gabriel Santana, *Accounting Mgr*
▲ EMP: 135 EST: 1969
SQ FT: 74,528
SALES (est): 60.7MM **Privately Held**
WEB: www.wsilverinc.com
SIC: 3312 3462 Bar, rod & wire products; iron & steel forgings

Voca
Mcculloch County

(G-20344)
CADRE MATERIAL PRODUCTS LLC
153 County Rd 220 (76887)
PHONE..........................325 400-2793
Jerry McGee,
Rick Dowd,
Rex Tucker,
EMP: 105
SALES (est): 58.9MM
SALES (corp-wide): 1.4B **Publicly Held**
SIC: 2819 Industrial inorganic chemicals
PA: U.S. Silica Holdings, Inc.
24275 Katy Fwy Ste 600
Katy TX 77494
281 258-2170

Von Ormy
Bexar County

(G-20345)
AREPET INDUSTRIES LLC
3603 Speedway Run (78073-3833)
PHONE..........................210 628-1622
Sam Lopez, *Plant Mgr*
EMP: 20
SALES (corp-wide): 6.4MM **Privately Held**
WEB: www.arepexpress.com
SIC: 1311 Oil sand mining
PA: Arepet Industries, Llc
3900 N 10th St Ste 1010
Mcallen TX 78501
956 686-1039

(G-20346)
CHAMPION FOOD SERVICE 2 INC
15326 Watson Rd (78073-3812)
PHONE..........................210 736-2190
Lucas Gonzalez, *President*
Marcelino Cordero, *Vice Pres*
EMP: 17
SALES (est): 880.8K **Privately Held**
SIC: 5812 3556 Contract food services; food products machinery

(G-20347)
DREADNAUGHT INDUSTRIES
1648 Palo Alto Dr (78073-5923)
P.O. Box 562, Zephyr (76890-0562)
PHONE..........................210 601-8149
Alex Wakal, *President*
Liota Wakal, *Exec Dir*
EMP: 9
SALES (est): 338.7K **Privately Held**
WEB: www.dreadnaught-industries.com
SIC: 8011 3484 8299 Specialized medical practitioners, except internal; guns (firearms) or gun parts, 30 mm. & below; self-defense & athletic instruction

(G-20348)
PETROSAURUS INC
20905 State Highway 16 S (78073-4768)
P.O. Box 130, Somerset (78069-0130)
PHONE..........................210 624-2750
Catherine Garret, *President*
Ruben Prado, *Principal*
Sergio Castaneda, *Vice Pres*
Ruben Smith, *Opers Mgr*
Antonio Prado, *Officer*
EMP: 16 EST: 1997
SALES (est): 2.2MM **Privately Held**
WEB: www.petrosaurus-inc.com
SIC: 1311 Crude petroleum production

(G-20349)
SANMINA CORPORATION
10501 Fischer Rd (78073-2809)
PHONE..........................210 623-5081
Richard Vinas, *Branch Mgr*
EMP: 200 **Publicly Held**
WEB: www.sanmina.com
SIC: 3672 Printed circuit boards
PA: Sanmina Corporation
2700 N 1st St
San Jose CA 95134

(G-20350)
SCHLUMBERGER TECHNOLOGY CORP
10310 Fischer Rd (78073-2837)
PHONE..........................210 623-4975
EMP: 74 **Publicly Held**
SIC: 1389 Oil field services
HQ: Schlumberger Technology Corp
300 Schlumberger Dr
Sugar Land TX 77478
281 285-8500

(G-20351)
SCHLUMBERGER TECHNOLOGY CORP
10625 Fischer Rd (78073-2830)
PHONE..........................210 623-9400
Ronnie Prior, *General Mgr*
EMP: 74 **Publicly Held**
SIC: 1389 Construction, repair & dismantling services
HQ: Schlumberger Technology Corp
300 Schlumberger Dr
Sugar Land TX 77478
281 285-8500

(G-20352)
SMURFIT KAPPA BATES LLC
10600 Fischer Rd (78073-2814)
P.O. Box 1359 (78073-1359)
PHONE..........................210 436-7777
Bob Schroeter, *General Mgr*
Mike Hernandez, *Opers Staff*
EMP: 60 **Privately Held**
WEB: www.batescontainer.com
SIC: 2653 5113 Boxes, corrugated: made from purchased materials; bags, paper & disposable plastic
HQ: Smurfit Kappa Bates, Llc
6433 Davis Blvd
North Richland Hills TX 76182
817 498-3200

Waco
Mclennan County

(G-20353)
A & R ENERGY SERVICES CORP
517 Jancy St Waco (76706)
P.O. Box 23606 (76702-3606)
PHONE..........................254 732-7759
Andrew Schnizer, *President*
EMP: 13
SALES (est): 2.9MM **Privately Held**
WEB: www.ar-energyservices.com
SIC: 7699 1389 Pumps & pumping equipment repair; oil field services; gas field services

(G-20354)
ACME BRICK COMPANY
1620 W Loop 340 (76712-6838)
PHONE..........................254 662-9846
Becky Bray, *Manager*
EMP: 81
SALES (corp-wide): 254.6B **Publicly Held**
WEB: www.brick.com
SIC: 3251 Brick & structural clay tile
HQ: Acme Brick Company
3024 Acme Brick Plz
Fort Worth TX 76109

(G-20355)
ADVANCED SHEET METAL LLC
2901 E Industrial Blvd (76705-2453)
P.O. Box 154187 (76715-4187)
PHONE..........................254 772-0134
Barry Kirk, *CEO*
EMP: 20 EST: 2016
SALES (est): 2.7MM **Privately Held**
WEB: www.advancedshm.com
SIC: 3444 3441 Sheet metalwork; fabricated structural metal

(G-20356)
AGRI WOOD PRODUCTS INC
8102 Knottingham Dr (76712-3406)
P.O. Box 149, Crawford (76638-0149)
PHONE..........................254 709-6584
Michael Neal, *Owner*
EMP: 9 EST: 2000
SALES (est): 1.3MM **Privately Held**
WEB: www.agri-wood.com
SIC: 2421 Sawdust, shavings & wood chips

(G-20357)
ALAMO STRUCTURAL STEEL LLC
Also Called: Alamo Structural Steel Co
2784 Old Dallas Rd (76705-1771)
P.O. Box 154849 (76715-4849)
PHONE..........................254 799-2471
Kurt Langsenkamp, *Manager*
Timothy Burns, *Manager*
Marcel Dutil, *Manager*
EMP: 70
SQ FT: 248,085
SALES (est): 80MM
SALES (corp-wide): 1B **Privately Held**
WEB: www.alamosteel.com
SIC: 3441 Fabricated structural metal
HQ: Fabsouth Llc
721 Ne 44th St
Oakland Park FL 33334
954 938-5800

(G-20358)
ALLERGAN SALES LLC
8301 Mars Dr (76712-6578)
P.O. Box 2675 (76702-2675)
PHONE..........................254 666-3331
Mari Zamrazil, *General Mgr*
Danielle Caprino, *District Mgr*
Tami Gray, *Business Mgr*
Kimberly Metts, *Business Mgr*
Donna Urick, *Business Mgr*
EMP: 51 **Privately Held**
WEB: www.allergan.com
SIC: 2834 Pharmaceutical preparations
HQ: Allergan Sales, Llc
2525 Dupont Dr
Irvine CA 92612

(G-20359)
AMA PRINTING / FINISHING INC (PA)
Also Called: Creative Communications
920 N Valley Mills Dr (76710-4754)
P.O. Box 7535 (76714-7535)
PHONE..........................254 776-8860
Randy Slechta, *CEO*
Marsh Shaw, *President*
Linda Stone, *COO*
Eugene R Franklin, *Vice Pres*
Deborah Hansen, *CFO*

▲ **EMP:** 36 **EST:** 1970
SQ FT: 2,700
SALES (est) 7.6MM **Privately Held**
WEB: www.amanystrom.com
SIC: 3652 7389 5065 2782 Pre-recorded records & tapes; recording studio, non-commercial records; cassettes, recording; blankbooks & looseleaf binders; commercial printing, lithographic

(G-20360)
AMERICAN BOTTLING COMPANY
Also Called: 7 Up Bottling Co
100 Aviation Pkwy (76705-4962)
PHONE..................254 412-1900
George Page, *Branch Mgr*
EMP: 144 **Publicly Held**
WEB: www.keurigdrpepper.com
SIC: 2086 5149 Soft drinks: packaged in cans, bottles, etc.; groceries & related products
HQ: The American Bottling Company
5301 Legacy Dr
Plano TX 75024

(G-20361)
ANDERTON GROUP II LTD (PA)
Also Called: Integ
700 W Loop 340 (76712-6866)
P.O. Box 23007 (76702-3007)
PHONE..................254 751-1012
David Anderton, *CEO*
Debbie Anderton, *Principal*
Kali Newcom, *Human Res Mgr*
Kyle Dewitt, *Manager*
EMP: 15
SQ FT: 46,000
SALES (est): 4.5MM **Privately Held**
WEB: www.integdoes.com
SIC: 7334 2759 7331 Photocopying & duplicating services; commercial printing; direct mail advertising services

(G-20362)
ANDERTON GROUP INC (PA)
Also Called: Integ
700 W Loop 340 (76712-6866)
P.O. Box 23007 (76702-3007)
PHONE..................254 751-1012
David R Anderton, *President*
Russell Landry, *Prdtn Mgr*
Kelly Balderrama, *Marketing Staff*
Wendy Seward, *Office Mgr*
Gary McWilliams, *Manager*
EMP: 50
SQ FT: 46,000
SALES (est): 13.3MM **Privately Held**
WEB: www.integdoes.com
SIC: 7331 2759 5136 Mailing service; commercial printing; men's & boys' clothing

(G-20363)
AQUILA & PRISCILLA TENTMAKERS
Also Called: Tent Rental
398 Cherokee Trl (76712-2555)
PHONE..................254 848-4432
Janelle Rogers, *President*
EMP: 15
SQ FT: 15,745
SALES (est): 1.5MM **Privately Held**
WEB: www.aptents.com
SIC: 7359 2394 Tent & tarpaulin rental; tents: made from purchased materials

(G-20364)
ARCOSA AGGREGATES INC
544 Rosenfeld Rd (76706-7334)
PHONE..................254 662-1025
Jody Perkins, *Manager*
EMP: 30
SALES (corp-wide): 1.7B **Publicly Held**
WEB: www.trinitymaterialsinc.com
SIC: 3273 Ready-mixed concrete
HQ: Arcosa Aggregates, Inc.
401 N Interstate Hwy 45
Ferris TX 75125
972 544-5900

(G-20365)
AXION STRL INNOVATIONS LLC
501 Old Hewitt Rd (76712-6684)
PHONE..................254 420-2078
James Walker, *Mng Member*

EMP: 70
SALES (corp-wide): 18.4MM **Privately Held**
WEB: www.axionsi.com
SIC: 3089 Extruded finished plastic products
PA: Axion Structural Innovations Llc
1100 Brandywine Blvd H
Zanesville OH 43701
740 452-2500

(G-20366)
BALCONES DISTILLING LLC (PA)
225 S 11th St (76701-1806)
PHONE..................254 755-6003
Michael Rockafellow, *Principal*
Greg Allen, *Principal*
Mark Allen, *Principal*
Jeff Liebhardt, *Vice Pres*
Alex Elrod, *Sales Staff*
▲ **EMP:** 27
SALES (est): 4.5MM **Privately Held**
WEB: www.balconesdistilling.com
SIC: 2085 Distilled & blended liquors

(G-20367)
BETBAN INVESTMENTS LLC
22003 Bush Dr (76712-8502)
P.O. Box 23131 (76702-3131)
PHONE..................254 776-2243
Mike Betke, *Mng Member*
Ken Irvin,
EMP: 12
SQ FT: 8,000
SALES (est): 1.3MM **Privately Held**
SIC: 2431 Doors & door parts & trim, wood

(G-20368)
BIMBO BAKERIES USA INC
225 S 17th St (76701-1735)
PHONE..................254 750-2500
Charlie Busch, *Manager*
EMP: 10 **Privately Held**
WEB: www.arnoldbread.com
SIC: 2051 Bakery: wholesale or wholesale/retail combined
HQ: Bimbo Bakeries Usa, Inc
255 Business Center Dr # 200
Horsham PA 19044
215 347-5500

(G-20369)
BLACKHAWK MODIFICATIONS INC
7601 Karl May Dr (76708-5570)
PHONE..................254 755-6711
Jim Allmon, *President*
David Gee, *President*
Matt Shieman, *Chairman*
Donnie Holder, *Vice Pres*
Micky Bitcon, *CFO*
EMP: 22 **EST:** 2008
SALES (est): 7.1MM **Privately Held**
WEB: www.blackhawk.aero
SIC: 3728 Aircraft parts & equipment

(G-20370)
BRAZOS OAKS LTD
6408 Gholson Rd (76705-5329)
PHONE..................254 399-0505
Warren Owen, *President*
▲ **EMP:** 30
SQ FT: 12,000
SALES (est): 4.6MM **Privately Held**
WEB: www.brazos-walking-sticks.com
SIC: 5023 5999 3842 Frames & framing, picture & mirror; picture frames, ready made; surgical appliances & supplies

(G-20371)
BRAZOS WALKING STICKS
6408 Gholson Rd (76705-5329)
PHONE..................254 799-7119
Warren Owen, *Owner*
▲ **EMP:** 30
SALES (est): 1.1MM **Privately Held**
WEB: www.brazos-walking-sticks.com
SIC: 2499 Decorative wood & woodwork

(G-20372)
C & C COATING INC
225 S 12th St (76701-1811)
P.O. Box 4684, Midland (79704-4684)
PHONE..................432 682-7201
Sonny Etheredge, *President*

EMP: 25
SQ FT: 300
SALES (est): 1.8MM **Privately Held**
WEB: www.coating-construction.com
SIC: 1389 1382 Oil field services; oil & gas exploration services

(G-20373)
C M C STEEL FABRICATORS INC
Also Called: CMC Alamo Steel
2784 Old Dallas Rd (76705-1771)
P.O. Box 154849 (76715-4849)
PHONE..................254 799-2471
Marvin Turner, *General Mgr*
EMP: 87
SALES (corp-wide): 5.4B **Publicly Held**
WEB: www.cmc.com
SIC: 3441 Expansion joints (structural shapes), iron or steel
HQ: C M C Steel Fabricators, Inc.
1 Steel Mill Dr
Seguin TX 78155
830 372-8200

(G-20374)
C M TRAUTSCHOLD MILLWORK CO
1500 Franklin Ave (76701-1718)
P.O. Box 175 (76703-0175)
PHONE..................254 752-6547
Michiel Sheedy, *Partner*
Lynne Bowerman, *Project Mgr*
Mike Sheedy, *Sales Executive*
Lynn Bowerman, *Manager*
EMP: 35
SQ FT: 30,450
SALES (est): 5.2MM **Privately Held**
WEB: www.trautscholdmillwork.com
SIC: 2431 Doors, wood

(G-20375)
CARGILL INCORPORATED
2510 E Lake Shore Dr (76705-1788)
P.O. Box 20788 (76702-0788)
PHONE..................254 799-6211
Aaron Waits, *QA Dir*
Wesley Carter, *Branch Mgr*
Joey Charanza, *Manager*
EMP: 650
SALES (corp-wide): 113.4B **Privately Held**
WEB: www.peterschocolate.com
SIC: 5142 2015 2011 0253 Poultry, frozen: packaged; poultry slaughtering & processing; meat packing plants; turkey egg farm
PA: Cargill, Incorporated
15407 Mcginty Rd W
Wayzata MN 55391
952 742-7575

(G-20376)
CATERPILLAR INC
2100 Orchard Ln Unit C (76705-3370)
PHONE..................254 752-3456
EMP: 330
SALES (corp-wide): 53.8B **Publicly Held**
WEB: www.caterpillar.com
SIC: 3531 Construction machinery
PA: Caterpillar Inc.
510 Lake Cook Rd Ste 100
Deerfield IL 60015
224 551-4000

(G-20377)
CATERPILLAR INC
2901 Gateway Blvd (76712-8899)
PHONE..................309 675-1000
Danny Phillipi, *Branch Mgr*
EMP: 1000
SALES (corp-wide): 53.8B **Publicly Held**
WEB: www.caterpillar.com
SIC: 3531 3519 3511 Construction machinery; engines, diesel & semi-diesel or dual-fuel; gas turbine generator set units, complete
PA: Caterpillar Inc.
510 Lake Cook Rd Ste 100
Deerfield IL 60015
224 551-4000

(G-20378)
CATERPILLAR WORK TOOLS INC
2000 Texas Central Pkwy (76712-6945)
PHONE..................254 297-2321
Travis Hegle, *Engineer*
Annette Miller, *Accountant*
Bob Hunter, *Branch Mgr*
Nick Phillips, *Technician*
EMP: 81
SQ FT: 13,107
SALES (corp-wide): 53.8B **Publicly Held**
WEB: www.cat.com
SIC: 3089 5082 Buckets, plastic; construction & mining machinery
HQ: Caterpillar Work Tools, Inc.
400 Work Tool Rd
Wamego KS 66547
785 456-2224

(G-20379)
CENTEX MANUFACTURING CO
3718 Franklin Ave (76710-7330)
P.O. Box 2183 (76703-2183)
PHONE..................254 752-2531
Martin Schwartz, *CEO*
Ken Bennett, *General Mgr*
John Schwartz, *Vice Pres*
John N Schwartz, *Vice Pres*
Jewell Stroble, *Office Mgr*
EMP: 13
SQ FT: 10,000
SALES (est): 2.1MM **Privately Held**
WEB: www.centexmfg.com
SIC: 5199 5072 2394 Canvas products; hardware; awnings, fabric: made from purchased materials

(G-20380)
CENTRAL TEXAS CORRUGATED INC
Also Called: Ctc
7200 Mars Dr (76712-6634)
P.O. Box 21539 (76702-1539)
PHONE..................254 776-6902
A V Lamendola, *President*
Steve Barrett, *COO*
Randy Vanek, *Exec VP*
D W Parks, *Vice Pres*
Clay Cooper, *Manager*
▲ **EMP:** 130
SQ FT: 132,000
SALES (est): 37.3MM **Privately Held**
WEB: www.ctcwaco.com
SIC: 2653 Boxes, corrugated: made from purchased materials

(G-20381)
CENTRAL TEXAS PRINTING INC
1522 Washington Ave (76701-1133)
PHONE..................254 754-4653
David Anderson, *President*
A Lane Price, *President*
Joyce Farar,
EMP: 28
SQ FT: 14,500
SALES (est): 3.5MM **Privately Held**
SIC: 2752 2791 2789 2759 Commercial printing, offset; typesetting; bookbinding & related work; commercial printing

(G-20382)
CERTAINTEED CORPORATION
Also Called: Plastic Pipe Plant
501 Hewitt Dr (76712-6411)
P.O. Box 21147 (76702-1147)
PHONE..................800 233-8990
Frank Partin, *Branch Mgr*
EMP: 100
SALES (corp-wide): 328.4MM **Privately Held**
WEB: www.certainteed.com
SIC: 3084 Plastics pipe
HQ: Certainteed Llc
20 Moores Rd
Malvern PA 19355
610 893-5000

(G-20383)
CLARKE PRODUCTS INC
2100 Orchard Ln Unit B (76705-3370)
PHONE..................972 660-1992
Don Clarke, *Principal*
▲ **EMP:** 14

SALES (est): 3.2MM **Privately Held**
SIC: 5074 5999 3432 Plumbing fittings &
supplies; swimming pools, hot tubs &
sauna equipment & supplies; plumbing
fixture fittings & trim

(G-20384)
CLAYTON HOMES INC
9000 Chapel Rd (76712-8740)
PHONE.....................................254 666-9570
Carlton Crittenden, *Branch Mgr*
EMP: 13
SALES (corp-wide): 254.6B **Publicly
Held**
WEB: www.claytonhomes.com
SIC: 2451 Mobile homes
HQ: Clayton Homes, Inc.
5000 Clayton Rd
Maryville TN 37804
865 380-3000

(G-20385)
CLAYTON HOMES INC
7001 Imperial Dr (76712-6815)
PHONE.....................................254 772-1808
Dave Stewart, *General Mgr*
Richard Benvenutti, *General Mgr*
Mitchell Berry, *Vice Pres*
Bob Blakney, *Purch Agent*
Keith Baker, *Sales Mgr*
EMP: 145
SALES (corp-wide): 254.6B **Publicly
Held**
WEB: www.claytonhomes.com
SIC: 2451 Mobile homes
HQ: Clayton Homes, Inc.
5000 Clayton Rd
Maryville TN 37804
865 380-3000

(G-20386)
CLIFTON UPHOLSTERY CO INC
416 Mary Ave (76701-2119)
PHONE.....................................254 753-0211
W Pat Armstrong Jr, *President*
Bob Strickland, *President*
Carol Strickland, *Vice Pres*
Tamara S Armstrong, *Treasurer*
EMP: 18
SQ FT: 23,000
SALES (est): 1.2MM **Privately Held**
SIC: 2515 2512 Mattresses, containing
felt, foam rubber, urethane, etc.; uphol-
stered household furniture

(G-20387)
CMH MANUFACTURING INC
9000 Van American Dr (76712-8181)
PHONE.....................................254 666-3534
Bob Wallace, *Manager*
EMP: 20
SALES (corp-wide): 254.6B **Publicly
Held**
WEB: www.claytonhomes.com
SIC: 2451 Mobile homes, except recre-
ational
HQ: Cmh Manufacturing, Inc.
5000 Clayton Rd
Maryville TN 37804
865 380-3000

(G-20388)
COCA-COLA COMPANY
8400 Imperial Dr (76712-6509)
PHONE.....................................254 666-5500
David Reck, *Plant Mgr*
Robert Biggerstaff, *Production*
Nicholas Polak, *Maintence Staff*
EMP: 100
SALES (corp-wide): 37.2B **Publicly Held**
WEB: www.coca-colacompany.com
SIC: 2086 Bottled & canned soft drinks
PA: The Coca-Cola Company
1 Coca Cola Plz Nw
Atlanta GA 30313
404 676-2121

(G-20389)
COMPOSTOLOGY LLC
747 Fort Graham Rd (76705-5711)
PHONE.....................................318 787-7442
EMP: 10 EST: 2019
SALES (est): 289.9K **Privately Held**
WEB: www.compostology.us
SIC: 5046 2875 Commercial equipment;
fertilizers, mixing only

(G-20390)
CORD COMMUNICATIONS INC
Also Called: CCI Publishing
4901 Bosque Blvd Fl 2 (76710-2800)
P.O. Box 21689 (76702-1689)
PHONE.....................................254 776-1822
Piers Bateman, *President*
Ronald Schwartinsky, *Treasurer*
EMP: 9
SQ FT: 31,000
SALES (est): 1.2MM
SALES (corp-wide): 2MM **Privately Held**
WEB: www.cordcommunications.com
SIC: 2721 2752 Periodicals; commercial
printing, lithographic
PA: Center For Occupational Research And
Development, Inc.
4901 Bosque Blvd Ste 200
Waco TX 76710
254 772-8756

(G-20391)
CREATIVE EDUCATION INST INC
4567 Lake Shore Dr (76710-1814)
P.O. Box 7306 (76714-7306)
PHONE.....................................254 751-1188
Terry Irwin, *President*
Paul Myers, *Vice Pres*
Deborah Hansen, *Admin Sec*
EMP: 67
SQ FT: 50,000
SALES (est): 5.3MM **Privately Held**
WEB: www.ceilearning.com
SIC: 7372 Educational computer software

(G-20392)
D E SHIPP BELTING COMPANY
123 S Industrial Dr (76710-6925)
P.O. Box 20035 (76702-0035)
PHONE.....................................254 776-0493
Greg Ogden, *President*
Dale Macfarland, *Regional Mgr*
Shannon Kinslow, *Vice Pres*
Mert Ferguson, *Sales Staff*
Teresa Kopp, *Sales Staff*
▲ EMP: 16
SQ FT: 25,000
SALES (est): 3.9MM **Privately Held**
WEB: www.shippbelting.com
SIC: 3052 Rubber & plastics hose & belt-
ings

(G-20393)
**DAVIS BROTHERS PUBG CO
LTD**
Also Called: Texian Press
4500 Speight Ave (76711-1799)
P.O. Box 1684 (76703-1684)
PHONE.....................................254 754-5636
Earl R Davis, *President*
Mary Ann Davis, *General Ptnr*
Allen Chick, *Vice Pres*
Barbara Roscher, *IT/INT Sup*
EMP: 41 EST: 1928
SQ FT: 45,000
SALES (est): 6.1MM **Privately Held**
WEB: www.integdoes.com
SIC: 2721 Magazines: publishing & print-
ing; periodicals: publishing & printing

(G-20394)
**EASY GARDENER PRODUCTS
INC (PA)**
Also Called: Jobe's Company, The
400 Austin Ave Ste 1101 (76701-2142)
P.O. Box 21025 (76702-1025)
PHONE.....................................254 753-5353
David Jackson, *President*
James Herrmann, *Opers Mgr*
Tracy Small, *Materials Mgr*
Jocelyn Angelo, *Purchasing*
Esmeralda Reyes, *Human Resources*
◆ EMP: 100
SALES (est): 44.4MM **Privately Held**
WEB: www.jobescompany.com
SIC: 2879 2875 Agricultural chemicals;
fertilizers, mixing only

(G-20395)
ECD ACQUISITIONS INC (PA)
Also Called: Englander Dzignpak
701 Texas Central Pkwy (76712-6507)
P.O. Box 22067 (76702-2067)
PHONE.....................................254 776-2360
Toll Free:.....................................888 -

Marty Englander, *President*
Louis Englander, *Chairman*
Jack Dunn, *COO*
Steve Hager, *Exec VP*
Perry Gilbert, *Vice Pres*
EMP: 70
SQ FT: 100,000
SALES (est): 31.6MM **Privately Held**
WEB: www.englanderdzp.com
SIC: 2653 Boxes, corrugated: made from
purchased materials

(G-20396)
ESCO INDUSTRIES INC
4901 Steinbeck Bend Dr (76708-5236)
PHONE.....................................254 296-0500
Vicki Olivo, *Office Mgr*
Harnia Young, *Manager*
EMP: 40
SALES (corp-wide): 32.1MM **Privately
Held**
WEB: www.escoindustries.com
SIC: 7389 2672 Laminating service;
coated & laminated paper
PA: Esco Industries, Inc.
185 Sink Hole Rd
Douglas GA 31533
912 384-1417

(G-20397)
ESCO LAMINATING TEXAS INC
4901 Steinbeck Bend Dr (76708-5236)
P.O. Box 5678 (76708-0678)
PHONE.....................................254 296-0500
Randy Crook, *Manager*
EMP: 60 **Privately Held**
WEB: www.escoindustries.com
SIC: 2439 Structural wood members
PA: Esco Laminating Texas, Inc
185 Sink Hole Rd
Douglas GA 31533

(G-20398)
EST OF JAMES T JONES
117 Virginia Rd (76705-1192)
PHONE.....................................254 799-4515
Barbara Jones, *Owner*
EMP: 30
SALES (est): 1.9MM **Privately Held**
SIC: 3441 Fabricated structural metal

(G-20399)
EVANS ENTERPRISES INC
Also Called: Evans Electric
201 S Industrial Dr (76710-6927)
PHONE.....................................254 772-4710
Jeremy McKee, *Accounts Mgr*
Larry Williams, *Manager*
Felipe Vega, *Supervisor*
EMP: 16
SALES (corp-wide): 132.7MM **Privately
Held**
WEB: www.goevans.com
SIC: 7694 7629 7699 5063 Rebuilding
motors, except automotive; electric motor
repair; electrical repair shops; compressor
repair; industrial equipment services; mo-
tors, electric; controlling instruments & ac-
cessories; compressors, except air
conditioning; cranes, industrial
PA: Evans Enterprises, Inc.
6707 N Interstate Dr
Norman OK 73069
405 631-1344

(G-20400)
EYEMASTERS 13 INC
6001 W Waco Dr Ste 612 (76710-6303)
PHONE.....................................254 751-0010
Joel Files, *General Mgr*
EMP: 12
SALES (est): 1MM **Privately Held**
SIC: 3827 Optical instruments & apparatus

(G-20401)
**FEDEX OFFICE & PRINT SVCS
INC**
1821 S Valley Mills Dr # 140 (76711-2118)
PHONE.....................................254 776-7763
EMP: 23
SALES (corp-wide): 69.2B **Publicly Held**
WEB: www.fedex.com
SIC: 7334 2791 2789 2759 Photocopying
& duplicating services; typesetting; book-
binding & related work; commercial print-
ing

HQ: Fedex Office And Print Services, Inc.
7900 Legacy Dr
Plano TX 75024
800 463-3339

(G-20402)
FIRMIN BUSINESS FORMS INC
202 Deb Ave (76712-6707)
P.O. Box 23587 (76702-3587)
PHONE.....................................254 776-5742
George Firmin Jr, *President*
Sally Firmin, *Corp Secy*
Firmin Sara M, *Vice Pres*
EMP: 12
SQ FT: 5,000
SALES (est): 1.8MM **Privately Held**
WEB: www.firmin.com
SIC: 5943 2752 7389 5999 Office forms
& supplies; commercial printing, offset;
engraving service; trophies & plaques;
blankbooks & looseleaf binders

(G-20403)
FLAMCO OF TEXAS INC
2525 Gholson Rd (76704-1103)
PHONE.....................................254 799-4936
Lee B Jones IV, *President*
EMP: 10 **Privately Held**
WEB: www.flamco.com
SIC: 3444 Sheet metalwork
HQ: Flamco Of Texas, Inc
6940 Stuart Ave
Jacksonville FL 32254
904 783-8400

(G-20404)
FRITEL & ASSOCIATES LLC
Also Called: Diversified Product Dev
1001 Webster Ave (76706-1545)
PHONE.....................................254 757-1177
Raymond Fritel, *President*
Christopher Fritel, *Vice Pres*
Judy Goble, *Purchasing*
Mark Blanpied, *Engineer*
Justin Branch, *Engineer*
EMP: 45
SQ FT: 8,000
SALES (est): 8MM **Privately Held**
WEB: www.diversifiedproduct.com
SIC: 3699 8711 Electrical equipment &
supplies; designing: ship, boat, machine
& product

(G-20405)
G G A INC
Also Called: G G A Pest Management Serv-
ices
6802 Broad Ave (76712-6703)
PHONE.....................................254 732-1701
Fred Huffman, *President*
Michael Holt, *Manager*
EMP: 10
SQ FT: 1,200
SALES (est): 1MM **Privately Held**
WEB: www.ggapest.com
SIC: 7342 2842 Exterminating & fumigat-
ing; specialty cleaning, polishes & sanita-
tion goods

(G-20406)
**GARNER & GOLDING
CORPORATION**
Also Called: Texas Tape & Label
500 S 26th St (76706-2708)
P.O. Box 365 (76703-0365)
PHONE.....................................254 753-8061
Junius Davis Metz Jr, *President*
EMP: 11
SQ FT: 6,500
SALES (est): 725K **Privately Held**
WEB: www.txlabel.com
SIC: 2754 2752 Labels: gravure printing;
commercial printing, offset

(G-20407)
GRAHAM EMBROIDERY CO INC
300 S Valley Mills Dr (76710-7348)
P.O. Box 20637 (76702-0637)
PHONE.....................................254 772-7020
Ray Pareya, *President*
Steve Martinez, *Vice Pres*
EMP: 77 EST: 1949
SQ FT: 15,000

SALES (est): 1.3MM **Privately Held**
WEB: www.grahamembroidery.com
SIC: **2395** Embroidery products, except schiffli machine; embroidery & art needle-work

(G-20408)
H & B PACKING CO INC
702 Forrest St (76704-2730)
P.O. Box 2344 (76703-2344)
PHONE.............................254 752-2506
J K Bauer, *President*
Simone Bauer, *Corp Secy*
Benjy Bauer, *Vice Pres*
David Bauer, *Vice Pres*
Richard Bauer, *Vice Pres*
EMP: 80
SQ FT: 12,000
SALES (est): 13.8MM **Privately Held**
WEB: www.h-bpacking.com
SIC: **2013** 2011 Sausages & other pre-pared meats; sausages from meat slaughtered on site

(G-20409)
H & H SIGN CO INC (PA)
2611 S Univ Parks Dr (76706-6431)
P.O. Box 206 (76703-0206)
PHONE.............................254 752-1801
Earl L Haberman Jr, *President*
James Richard Haberman, *Principal*
Clara Haberman, *Treasurer*
Kathy Coffer, *Admin Sec*
EMP: 20
SQ FT: 26,000
SALES (est): 2.7MM **Privately Held**
SIC: **3993** 1799 1611 Signs & advertising specialties; sign installation & mainte-nance; highway & street construction

(G-20410)
HEART OF TEXAS BISCUITS INC
Also Called: Hot Biscuits
204 Deb Ave (76712-6707)
PHONE.............................254 753-0046
Scott Corbin, *President*
Scott W Corbin, *President*
EMP: 10
SALES (est): 900K **Privately Held**
WEB: www.hotbiscuitsinc.com
SIC: **2045** Biscuit dough, prepared: from purchased flour

(G-20411)
HIGHWOOD MACHINE TOOL LLC
600 Research Pkwy (76705-2651)
P.O. Box 154069 (76715-4069)
PHONE.............................254 412-0512
John Galanis, *Purch Mgr*
Corey Petersen, *Engineer*
Dan Birdsall, *Electrical Engi*
Tonya Burson, *Accounting Mgr*
Michael J Sullivan, *Mng Member*
▲ EMP: 12
SQ FT: 40,000 **Privately Held**
WEB: www.tmiusa.com
SIC: **3541** 8711 Machine tools, metal cut-ting type; machine tool design

(G-20412)
HOBBS BONDED FIBERS LLC (PA)
200 Commerce Dr (76710-6975)
PHONE.............................254 741-0040
Larry Hobbs, *President*
Norman Brings, *Vice Pres*
Greg Gerald, *Vice Pres*
Steve Watson, *Inv Control Mgr*
Kathy Brinkman, *Controller*
EMP: 49 EST: 2015
SALES (est): 101.4MM **Privately Held**
WEB: www.hobbsbondedfibers.com
SIC: **2297** 2299 Bonded-fiber fabrics, ex-cept felt; apparel filling: cotton waste, kapok & related material; batts & batting: cotton mill waste & related material

(G-20413)
HOBBS BONDED FIBERS NA LLC (HQ)
200 Commerce Dr (76710-6975)
PHONE.............................254 741-0040
Larry Hobbs, *President*
Jim Freeman, *CFO*

◆ EMP: 56 EST: 1953
SQ FT: 171,440
SALES (est): 64.2MM
SALES (corp-wide): 101.4MM **Privately Held**
WEB: www.hobbsbondedfibers.com
SIC: **2297** 2299 Bonded-fiber fabrics, ex-cept felt; apparel filling: cotton waste, kapok & related material; batts & batting: cotton mill waste & related material
PA: Hobbs Bonded Fibers, Llc
200 Commerce Dr
Waco TX 76710
254 741-0040

(G-20414)
HOMESTEAD CRAFTSMEN LLC (PA)
Also Called: Heritage Restorations
308 Dry Creek Rd (76705)
P.O. Box 869, Elm Mott (76640-0869)
PHONE.............................254 754-9600
Zain Dumont, *Manager*
Curtis Brown, *Director*
Abraham Adams, *Director*
Kevin Durkin, *Director*
Tony Salmeri, *Director*
EMP: 100
SQ FT: 15,000
SALES (est): 20.9MM **Privately Held**
WEB: www.homesteadheritage.com
SIC: **1542** 1521 5712 2511 Nonresiden-tial construction; single-family housing construction; furniture stores; wood household furniture; eating places; gen-eral farms, primarily crop

(G-20415)
HOMESTEAD GRISTMILL LLC
800 Dry Creek Rd (76705-5409)
PHONE.............................254 829-2135
Shahar Yarden,
EMP: 20
SQ FT: 4,672
SALES (est): 739K **Privately Held**
WEB: www.homesteadgristmill.com
SIC: **2041** Flour & other grain mill products

(G-20416)
HOMESTEAD HERITAGE
Also Called: Homestead Maintenance Serv-ices
800 Dry Creek Rd (76705-5409)
PHONE.............................254 754-9665
Kevin Durkin, *President*
Carl Ballerino, *Treasurer*
EMP: 23
SQ FT: 2,656
SALES (est): 1.5MM **Privately Held**
WEB: www.texasbcs.com
SIC: **7549** 0212 5947 2013 High per-formance auto repair & service; beef cat-tle except feedlots; gift shop; calf's foot jelly from purchased meat; residential construction; millwork

(G-20417)
HUCK INTERNATIONAL INC
Also Called: Alcoa Fastening Systems
8001 Imperial Dr (76712-6522)
PHONE.............................254 751-5283
Bart Preston, *Director*
EMP: 352
SALES (corp-wide): 14.1B **Publicly Held**
WEB: www.alcoa.com
SIC: **3399** Metal fasteners
HQ: Huck International, Inc.
3724 E Columbia St
Tucson AZ 85714
520 519-7400

(G-20418)
ICS JAIL SUPPLIES INC
Also Called: I C S
5804 Franklin Ave (76710-6938)
P.O. Box 21056 (76702-1056)
PHONE.............................254 751-1566
Todd Bogan, *President*
Michelle Markum Gwin, *Opers Staff*
James M Bogan III, *Treasurer*
▲ EMP: 35
SQ FT: 130,000
SALES (est): 7.5MM **Privately Held**
WEB: www.icswaco.com
SIC: **2311** 5136 Men's & boys' uniforms; uniforms, men's & boys'

(G-20419)
J&J WEAVER CO (PA)
Also Called: Pickup Outfitters
500 S Valley Mills Dr (76711-1176)
PHONE.............................254 756-2139
Jeff Weaver, *President*
EMP: 25 EST: 1946
SQ FT: 67,000
SALES (est): 3.9MM **Privately Held**
SIC: **3523** 3714 5531 Farm machinery & equipment; motor vehicle parts & acces-sories; pickup truck bed liners; truck equipment & parts

(G-20420)
JONES MANUFACTURING INC
640 Ruby Ave (76710-6037)
PHONE.............................254 399-8940
Bradley T Jones, *President*
Barbara S Jones, *Corp Secy*
Timothy Judge, *Sales Mgr*
EMP: 15 EST: 1978
SQ FT: 30,000
SALES (est): 293.5K **Privately Held**
WEB: www.jonesmfg.com
SIC: **7692** Welding repair

(G-20421)
JR3 WEBSMART LLC
925 Columbus Ave (76701-1240)
P.O. Box 1067 (76703-1067)
PHONE.............................254 759-1902
Robert Clemons, *Mng Member*
David Hankins,
Jim Payne,
EMP: 24 EST: 2006
SALES (est): 720.1K
SALES (corp-wide): 3.4B **Privately Held**
WEB: www.jr3online.com
SIC: **7372** Educational computer software
HQ: Prosoft Technologies, Inc.
2000 Oxford Dr Ste 610
Bethel Park PA 15102
412 835-6217

(G-20422)
KASPAR MACHINE LLC
Also Called: Kormachine
12431 Wortham Bend Rd (76708-7023)
PHONE.............................254 836-1564
Colter Kaspar, *President*
EMP: 20
SQ FT: 15,000
SALES (est): 119.3K **Privately Held**
WEB: www.kormachine.com
SIC: **3451** 3728 Screw machine products; aircraft parts & equipment; aircraft assem-blies, subassemblies & parts

(G-20423)
KUNKA ENTERPRISES LLC
Also Called: Red Express Pallet Company
7314 Bagby Ave (76712-6923)
PHONE.............................254 666-3576
EMP: 16 EST: 1998
SQ FT: 15,000
SALES (est): 3.1MM **Privately Held**
WEB: www.redexpresspallet.com
SIC: **2448** Pallets, wood

(G-20424)
L3HARRIS TECHNOLOGIES INC
7500 Maehr Rd (76705-1632)
PHONE.............................254 799-5533
James Burkhardt, *Branch Mgr*
Julie Sahm, *Director*
EMP: 2000
SALES (corp-wide): 11.3B **Publicly Held**
WEB: www.l3t.com
SIC: **3728** Aircraft parts & equipment
PA: L3harris Technologies, Inc.
1025 W Nasa Blvd
Melbourne FL 32919
321 727-9100

(G-20425)
LEHIGH CEMENT COMPANY LLC
100 Wickson Rd (76712-8514)
P.O. Box 2576 (76702-2576)
PHONE.............................254 776-7162
William Miller, *Vice Pres*
Charles W Moore Jr, *Plant Mgr*
EMP: 54
SQ FT: 7,690

SALES (corp-wide): 20.8B **Privately Held**
WEB: www.lehighwhitecement.com
SIC: **3273** Ready-mixed concrete
HQ: Lehigh Cement Company Llc
300 E John Carpenter Fwy
Irving TX 75062
877 534-4442

(G-20426)
LEHIGH CEMENT COMPANY LLC
Also Called: White Cement
100 Wickson Rd (76712-8514)
PHONE.............................254 772-9350
Jeffery Shannon, *Vice Pres*
EMP: 75
SALES (corp-wide): 20.8B **Privately Held**
WEB: www.lehighwhitecement.com
SIC: **3273** Ready-mixed concrete
HQ: Lehigh Cement Company Llc
300 E John Carpenter Fwy
Irving TX 75062
877 534-4442

(G-20427)
LETS GEL INC
501 Precision Dr (76710-6972)
PHONE.............................512 628-1709
Will Jones, *Vice Pres*
Terri Dawson, *Production*
Clinton Teders, *Sales Mgr*
Erika Ison, *Manager*
Ty Morley, *Representative*
EMP: 15 **Privately Held**
WEB: www.gelpro.com
SIC: **3996** Hard surface floor coverings
PA: Let's Gel, Inc.
11525b Stnholw Dr 200
Austin TX 78758

(G-20428)
LOWE PRECAST INC
24000 Woodway Dr (76712-7508)
PHONE.............................254 776-9690
Martha Lowe, *President*
Charles R Lowe, *Senior VP*
Brenner Lowe, *QC Mgr*
Greg Menning, *Chief Engr*
EMP: 50
SQ FT: 6,000
SALES (est): 8.8MM **Privately Held**
WEB: www.loweprecast.com
SIC: **3272** Concrete products, precast

(G-20429)
MANITOU NORTH AMERICA INC
6401 Imperial Dr (76712-6803)
PHONE.............................254 799-0232
Herva Rochet, *Exec VP*
Martin Simard, *Plant Mgr*
Marco Iotti, *Purch Mgr*
Kenneth Carothers, *Engineer*
Bill Coleman, *Engineer*
▲ EMP: 86
SQ FT: 10,000
SALES (est): 16.8MM
SALES (corp-wide): 1.6B **Privately Held**
WEB: www.manitou.com
SIC: **3523** 3537 3593 3524 Turf equip-ment, commercial; forklift trucks; lift trucks, industrial: fork, platform, straddle, etc.; fluid power cylinders & actuators; lawn & garden equipment
PA: Manitou Bf
Aubiniere
Ancenis 44150

(G-20430)
MARATHONNORCO AEROSPACE INC
8301 Imperial Dr (76712-6524)
PHONE.............................254 776-0650
Sergio Rodriguez, *President*
Prima Ponce-Zapata, *Prdtn Mgr*
Spencer McNiel, *Production*
Elliott Spence, *Production*
Jason Vandevelde, *Chief Engr*
EMP: 115
SQ FT: 108,000
SALES (est): 51.4MM
SALES (corp-wide): 5.1B **Publicly Held**
WEB: www.mnaerospace.com
SIC: **3728** Aircraft/aerospace flight instru-ments & guidance systems
HQ: Transdigm, Inc.
4223 Monticello Blvd
Cleveland OH 44121

(G-20431)
MARATHONNORCO
AEROSPACE INC
Also Called: Marathon Battery
8301 Imperial Dr (76712-6524)
P.O. Box 8233 (76714-8233)
PHONE..........................254 315-7524
Raymond F Laubenthal, *CEO*
Jill Recio, *CEO*
Sergio Rodriguez, *President*
Kenton Van Harten, *CFO*
Gregory Rufus, *Treasurer*
EMP: 115
SQ FT: 215,000
SALES: 77.9MM
SALES (corp-wide): 5.1B **Publicly Held**
WEB: www.mptc.com
SIC: 3812 Acceleration indicators & systems components, aerospace
HQ: Transdigm, Inc.
4223 Monticello Blvd
Cleveland OH 44121

(G-20432)
MARATHONNORCO
AEROSPACE INC
8301 Imperial Dr (76712-6524)
PHONE..........................254 772-7358
Sergio Rodriguez, *President*
Jennifer Wu, *Accountant*
Yichun Wu, *Accountant*
Gary McMurtrey, *Director*
EMP: 90
SALES (est): 2.4MM **Privately Held**
WEB: www.mnaerospace.com
SIC: 3812 Aircraft/aerospace flight instruments & guidance systems

(G-20433)
MARS CHOCOLATE NORTH
AMER LLC
Also Called: Mars Snackfood US
1001 Texas Central Pkwy (76712-6508)
P.O. Box 7955 (76714-7955)
PHONE..........................254 776-2100
Michael Linch, *Principal*
Ron Ordner, *Technical Staff*
Dan Braswell, *Director*
EMP: 589
SALES (corp-wide): 45B **Privately Held**
WEB: www.snickers.tumblr.com
SIC: 2064 2066 Candy & other confectionery products; chocolate & cocoa products
HQ: Mars Chocolate North America, Llc
800 High St
Hackettstown NJ 07840
908 852-1000

(G-20434)
MARS WRIGLEY CONF US LLC
1001 Texas Central Pkwy (76712-6508)
PHONE..........................254 751-5404
Tracey Massey, *President*
EMP: 24
SALES (corp-wide): 45B **Privately Held**
SIC: 2064 Candy & other confectionery products
HQ: Mars Wrigley Confectionery Us, Llc
800 High St
Hackettstown NJ 07840
908 852-1000

(G-20435)
MERCURY TOOL AND MACHINE
INC
7420 Karl May Dr (76708-5533)
P.O. Box 5190 (76708-0190)
PHONE..........................254 752-1639
Jack A Peck, *President*
Janice Braswell, *Vice Pres*
Ed Jasek, *Purch Agent*
Norman Hoffman, *Treasurer*
Jeff Nors, *Accountant*
▲ **EMP:** 55 **EST:** 1949
SQ FT: 71,000
SALES (est): 6.2MM **Privately Held**
WEB: www.mercurytool.com
SIC: 3599 Machine shop, jobbing & repair; machine & other job shop work

(G-20436)
MERRICK ENGINEERING INC
7325 Imperial Dr (76712-6602)
PHONE..........................254 741-6330

Elizabeth Sanchez, *Vice Pres*
Roy Jergenson, *Manager*
Olie Jawady, *Manager*
EMP: 200
SALES (corp-wide): 88.8MM **Privately**
Held
WEB: www.merrickengineering.com
SIC: 3496 Miscellaneous fabricated wire products
PA: Merrick Engineering, Inc.
1275 Quarry St
Corona CA 92879
951 737-6040

(G-20437)
NEARLY ME TECHNOLOGIES
LLC
200 N Industrial Dr (76710-7030)
P.O. Box 21475 (76702-1475)
PHONE..........................254 662-1752
Deborah Harris, *Vice Pres*
Pam Strahl, *Opers Mgr*
Melissa Hardin, *Sales Staff*
Rt Gray, *Mng Member*
David Kilgore, *Info Tech Dir*
▲ **EMP:** 44
SQ FT: 20,400
SALES (est): 6.2MM **Privately Held**
WEB: www.nearlyme.org
SIC: 3842 Surgical appliances & supplies

(G-20438)
NORTHERN & NYE PRINTING
INC
Also Called: Franklin's Printing
3115 Robinson Dr (76706-4424)
PHONE..........................254 662-2292
Randy Northern, *President*
Blake Northern, *Vice Pres*
Jerry Nye, *Vice Pres*
EMP: 15
SALES (est): 2.2MM **Privately Held**
WEB: www.northernnye.com
SIC: 2752 2759 5112 Commercial printing, offset; letterpress printing; office supplies

(G-20439)
OFLAHERTY HOLDINGS INC
(PA)
7601 Imperial Dr (76712-6608)
P.O. Box 20368 (76702-0368)
PHONE..........................254 399-2100
Stephen N O'Flaherty, *CEO*
Nigel O'Flaherty, *Ch of Bd*
David Post, *Corp Secy*
Tom O'Dowd, *Vice Pres*
Michael P O'Flaherty, *Vice Pres*
◆ **EMP:** 330
SQ FT: 190,000
SALES (est): 39.6MM **Privately Held**
WEB: www.timemfg.com
SIC: 3534 Elevators & equipment

(G-20440)
OHENRY PRODUCTIONS INC
3859 Chappel Hill Rd (76705-3701)
PHONE..........................254 714-1103
J D Henry, *President*
Jessica Renner, *Sales Associate*
Lacey Peterson, *Receptionist*
Jessica Foddrell, *Real Est Agnt*
EMP: 10
SQ FT: 10,000
SALES (est): 2.1MM **Privately Held**
WEB: www.ohenrytents.com
SIC: 5999 2394 Tents; tents: made from purchased materials

(G-20441)
PACKAGING CORPORATION
AMERICA
701 Texas Central Pkwy (76712-6507)
PHONE..........................254 776-2360
Mark W Kowlzan, *Ch of Bd*
EMP: 160
SALES (corp-wide): 6.9B **Publicly Held**
WEB: www.packagingcorp.com
SIC: 2631 2653 Container board; container, packaging & boxboard; corrugated & solid fiber boxes
PA: Packaging Corporation Of America
1 N Field Ct
Lake Forest IL 60045
847 482-3000

(G-20442)
PACKAGING CORPORATION
AMERICA
Also Called: Pca/Regional Design Center
9200 Old Mcgregor Rd (76712-6438)
PHONE..........................254 776-8890
Jason Bahnsen, *Vice Pres*
Jing Sheng, *Design Engr*
Kathy Hoffmeyer, *Controller*
Michael Mehler, *Controller*
Michael Savana, *Sales Staff*
EMP: 105
SALES (corp-wide): 6.9B **Publicly Held**
WEB: www.packagingcorp.com
SIC: 2653 Boxes, corrugated: made from purchased materials
PA: Packaging Corporation Of America
1 N Field Ct
Lake Forest IL 60045
847 482-3000

(G-20443)
PACKLESS METAL HOSE INC
(PA)
Also Called: Packless Industries
8401 Imperial Dr (76712-6525)
PHONE..........................254 666-7700
L Robert Zifferer, *President*
Doris Zifferer, *Vice Pres*
Scott C Zifferer, *Vice Pres*
Edward Reed, *Plant Mgr*
Alicia Arroyo, *CFO*
◆ **EMP:** 100 **EST:** 1934
SQ FT: 205,000
SALES (est): 25.3MM **Privately Held**
WEB: www.packless.com
SIC: 3585 Parts for heating, cooling & refrigerating equipment; air conditioning condensers & condensing units

(G-20444)
PATRICK INDUSTRIES INC
Also Called: Custom Vinyl Division
1500 Fort Graham Rd (76705-5712)
PHONE..........................254 799-5717
Don Williamson, *Sales/Mktg Mgr*
EMP: 10
SALES (corp-wide): 2.3B **Publicly Held**
WEB: www.patrickind.com
SIC: 2295 Coated fabrics, not rubberized
PA: Patrick Industries, Inc.
107 W Franklin St
Elkhart IN 46516
574 294-7511

(G-20445)
PERRYMAN GROUP INC (PA)
Also Called: Texas Economic Publishers
510 N Vly Mills Dr # 300 (76710-6076)
PHONE..........................254 751-9595
M Ray Perryman, *President*
Elodia Cavazos, *Research*
Richard Cox, *Manager*
Cristin Hulyk, *Consultant*
Pete Tamez, *Technology*
▲ **EMP:** 23
SALES (est): 3.2MM **Privately Held**
WEB: www.perrymangroup.com
SIC: 8748 2741 8732 2721 Economic consultant; business service newsletters: publishing & printing; commercial nonphysical research; periodicals

(G-20446)
PILGRIMS PRIDE
CORPORATION
Also Called: Pilgrims Pride Prpred Fods Div
2500 E Lake Shore Dr (76705-1788)
PHONE..........................254 412-5800
EMP: 700
SQ FT: 132,694 **Publicly Held**
WEB: www.pilgrims.com
SIC: 2015 Chicken, slaughtered & dressed
HQ: Pilgrim's Pride Corporation
1770 Promontory Cir
Greeley CO 80634
970 506-8000

(G-20447)
PLASTIC SPECIALTIES & TECH
INC
Also Called: Colorite Plastics
700 Jewell Dr (76712-6616)
PHONE..........................254 772-6979
Don Linnstaedter, *Manager*

EMP: 100
SALES (corp-wide): 1B **Privately Held**
WEB: www.tekni-plex.com
SIC: 3083 Laminated plastics plate & sheet
HQ: Plastic Specialties And Technologies
Inc.
101 Railroad Ave
Ridgefield NJ 07657
201 941-2900

(G-20448)
POWERS EMBROIDERY INC
2825 Gholson Rd (76704-1110)
PHONE..........................254 754-2498
Jay Powers, *General Mgr*
Marilyn Atwood, *Manager*
David Gooch, *Manager*
▲ **EMP:** 95
SQ FT: 16,000
SALES (est): 6.4MM **Privately Held**
WEB: www.powersembroidery.com
SIC: 2395 7389 2211 2399 Emblems, embroidered; swiss loom embroideries; embroidering of advertising on shirts, etc.; blankets & blanketings, cotton; banners, made from fabric; broadwoven fabric mills, manmade
HQ: Taylor Publishing Company
1550 W Mockingbird Ln
Dallas TX 75235
214 637-2800

(G-20449)
PRECISE HARD CHROME
6613 N 19th St (76708)
P.O. Box 5660 (76708-0660)
PHONE..........................254 756-6879
Jim Hale, *Principal*
EMP: 14
SALES (est): 3.1MM **Privately Held**
WEB: www.precisechrome.com
SIC: 3471 Electroplating of metals or formed products

(G-20450)
PRUF ENERGY SOLUTIONS LLC
Also Called: Led Illumination II
215 Cotton Dr (76712-6724)
P.O. Box 22047 (76702-2047)
PHONE..........................254 870-0400
Chris Sadler, *CEO*
Frank Jennings, *CFO*
EMP: 17
SALES (est): 9MM **Privately Held**
WEB: www.prufenergysolutions.com
SIC: 5063 3641 Lighting fixtures; electric lamps

(G-20451)
QTI APPAREL & PROMOTIONS
LLC
Also Called: Qti Apparel and Promotions
300 S Valley Mills Dr (76710-7348)
P.O. Box 50550, Austin (78763-0550)
PHONE..........................254 662-3076
Jeffrey Paul, *Senior VP*
Corinne Carroll, *Vice Pres*
Randy Cox, *Mng Member*
Nancy Cox, *Mng Member*
EMP: 28
SQ FT: 7,500
SALES (est): 290.9K **Privately Held**
WEB: www.qtipromo.com
SIC: 7299 5699 3545 T-shirts, custom printed; stitching, custom; chucks: drill, lathe or magnetic (machine tool accessories)

(G-20452)
QTI PROMOTIONS AND
APPAREL INC
Also Called: Bear Cotton
300 S Valley Mills Dr (76710-7348)
P.O. Box 50550, Austin (78763-0550)
PHONE..........................254 756-4444
Patricia Winstanley, *President*
Dennis Phipps, *Executive*
EMP: 20
SQ FT: 56,000
SALES (est): 1.3MM **Privately Held**
WEB: www.qtipromo.com
SIC: 2759 2395 3993 2399 Screen printing; embroidery & art needlework; signs & advertising specialties; banners, pennants & flags; gifts & novelties

PA: Aztec Promotional Group, L.P.
1616 W 5th St
Austin TX 78703

(G-20453)
QTI-POWERS INC
300 S Valley Mills Dr (76710-7348)
PHONE..............................254 662-3076
Nancy Cox, *President*
Randy Cox, *Vice Pres*
Jay C Power, *Vice Pres*
EMP: 49 **EST:** 2010
SQ FT: 60,000
SALES (est): 5MM **Privately Held**
WEB: www.qtipromo.com
SIC: 2759 Promotional printing; screen printing

(G-20454)
REINFORCED EARTH COMPANY
136 Waco Sand Rd (76708-7082)
PHONE..............................254 836-1847
Johnson Chemplavil, *General Mgr*
Cenaido Jaimes, *Plant Mgr*
Jessie Ullerich, *Plant Mgr*
Lawrence Charles, *Project Mgr*
Robert Saucedo, *Opers Staff*
EMP: 75
SALES (corp-wide): 22.1MM **Privately Held**
WEB: www.reinforcedearth.com
SIC: 3272 Panels & sections, prefabricated concrete
HQ: The Reinforced Earth Company
45610 Woodland Rd Ste 200
Sterling VA 20166
703 547-8797

(G-20455)
ROBINSON MEDIA COMPANY LLC
Also Called: Waco Tribune-Herald
900 Franklin Ave (76701-1906)
P.O. Box 2588 (76702-2588)
PHONE..............................254 757-5757
Steve Boggs, *Editor*
Ricky George, *Editor*
Carl Hoover, *Editor*
Freda Jackson, *Editor*
Kevin Marshall, *District Mgr*
EMP: 16
SALES (est): 1.2MM **Privately Held**
WEB: www.wacotrib.com
SIC: 2711 Newspapers, publishing & printing

(G-20456)
SAFETY-KLEEN SYSTEMS INC
22006 Woodway Dr (76712-7517)
PHONE..............................254 772-4419
Paul Darnell, *Branch Mgr*
EMP: 11
SALES (corp-wide): 3.4B **Publicly Held**
WEB: www.safety-kleen.com
SIC: 3559 Degreasing machines, automotive & industrial
HQ: Safety-Kleen Systems, Inc.
42 Longwater Dr
Norwell MA 02061
972 265-2000

(G-20457)
SANDERSON FARMS INC
Also Called: Processing Division
301 Aviation Pkwy (76705-5468)
PHONE..............................254 412-3800
Todd Ormon, *Manager*
EMP: 1200
SALES (corp-wide): 3.5B **Publicly Held**
WEB: www.sandersonfarms.com
SIC: 2015 Poultry slaughtering & processing
PA: Sanderson Farms, Inc.
127 Flynt Rd
Laurel MS 39443
601 649-4030

(G-20458)
SONOCO PRODUCTS COMPANY
Sonoco Flexible Packaging Div
6501 Texas Central Pkwy (76712-6947)
PHONE..............................254 666-4777
Walter Yakich, *CEO*
EMP: 100
SQ FT: 132,694

SALES (corp-wide): 5.3B **Publicly Held**
WEB: www.sonoco.com
SIC: 3081 2671 Packing materials, plastic sheet; packaging paper & plastics film, coated & laminated
PA: Sonoco Products Company
1 N 2nd St
Hartsville SC 29550
843 383-7000

(G-20459)
SOUTHERN CABINETS
405 N Lacy Dr (76705-1004)
PHONE..............................254 799-2271
Eugene Hefelfinger, *Owner*
EMP: 9
SQ FT: 6,000
SALES (est): 690.9K **Privately Held**
WEB: www.southerncabinets.net
SIC: 2434 7641 Wood kitchen cabinets; furniture refinishing; reupholstery

(G-20460)
SPECIALTY COMPOSITES GROUP LLC
Also Called: Waco Composites
302 S 27th St (76710-7454)
P.O. Box 20008 (76702-0008)
PHONE..............................254 752-3622
EMP: 35 **EST:** 2001
SQ FT: 50,000
SALES (est): 10.5MM **Privately Held**
WEB: www.specialtycompositesgroup.com
SIC: 2221 Plastic containers, except foam

(G-20461)
SWAN PRODUCTS LLC
700 Jewell Dr (76712-6616)
PHONE..............................254 772-6979
Mark Bewley, *Plant Mgr*
Doug Shelton, *QC Mgr*
Joseph Saganski, *Manager*
EMP: 200 **Privately Held**
WEB: www.swanhose.com
SIC: 3052 Garden hose, plastic
HQ: Swan Products, Llc
7840 Rswell Rd Bldg 100s
Sandy Springs GA 30350
470 294-2650

(G-20462)
T SQUARED MFG INC
7400 Imperial Dr (76712-6605)
PHONE..............................254 732-9039
Deborah Townsend, *CEO*
Barclay Townsend, *President*
Deborah L Townsend, *Exec Dir*
EMP: 24
SALES (est): 448.7K **Privately Held**
WEB: www.tsquaredmfg.com
SIC: 3599 Machine shop, jobbing & repair

(G-20463)
TATEX INC
Also Called: Tatex Thermographers
2800 Gholson Rd (76704-1109)
PHONE..............................254 799-4911
Mike Scherr, *General Mgr*
Don Oliver, *Safety Mgr*
Bruce Walrath, *Sales Staff*
Rene Kolar, *Manager*
Bob McKeon, *Info Tech Mgr*
EMP: 195
SALES (est): 19.5MM
SALES (corp-wide): 2.5B **Privately Held**
WEB: www.theoccasionsgroup.com
SIC: 2759 Thermography
HQ: The Occasions Group Inc
1750 Tower Blvd
North Mankato MN 56003

(G-20464)
TELEOMETRICS INTERNATIONAL
4567 Lake Shore Dr (76710-1814)
PHONE..............................254 776-2060
David Byrd, *President*
Bill Moyer, *Exec VP*
Tony Stiglianl, *Exec VP*
Randy Wiggins, *Vice Pres*
EMP: 11
SQ FT: 10,000

SALES (est): 660K **Privately Held**
WEB: www.teleometrics-my-tyme.myshopify.com
SIC: 2741 8299 Miscellaneous publishing; educational services

(G-20465)
TEXAS FARM BUREAU
Also Called: Texas Neighbors
7420 Fish Pond Rd (76710-1010)
P.O. Box 2689 (76702-2689)
PHONE..............................254 751-2251
Vernie Glasson, *Exec Dir*
EMP: 500
SALES (corp-wide): 23.6MM **Privately Held**
WEB: www.texasfarmbureau.org
SIC: 2721 Periodicals
PA: Texas Farm Bureau
7420 Fish Pond Rd
Waco TX 76710
254 772-3030

(G-20466)
TEXAS HYDRAULICS INC
Also Called: Precise Hard Chrome
6613 N 19th St (76708)
P.O. Box 5660 (76708-0660)
PHONE..............................254 756-6879
David Boothby, *Branch Mgr*
EMP: 35
SQ FT: 22,500
SALES (corp-wide): 53.4MM **Privately Held**
WEB: www.texashydraulics.com
SIC: 3599 3471 Machine shop, jobbing & repair; plating & polishing
HQ: Texas Hydraulics, Inc.
3410 Range Rd
Temple TX 76504
254 778-4701

(G-20467)
TEXAS METER AND DEVICE CO LLC
Also Called: T M D
300 S 8th St (76701-1916)
P.O. Box 154099 (76715-4099)
PHONE..............................254 732-1305
Steven Swenke, *CEO*
Josh Kovar, *Division Mgr*
Layton Lively, *Exec VP*
Richard Guerra, *Vice Pres*
Rick Guerra, *Vice Pres*
▲ **EMP:** 75 **EST:** 1937
SQ FT: 23,000
SALES (est): 21.6MM **Privately Held**
WEB: www.tmd-llc.com
SIC: 3825 3613 7629 Meters: electric, pocket, portable, panelboard, etc.; switchgear & switchboard apparatus; electrical repair shops

(G-20468)
TYMCO INTERNATIONAL INC
225 E Industrial Blvd (76705-9415)
P.O. Box 2368 (76703-2368)
PHONE..............................254 799-5546
Chris Ivy, *Engineer*
Don Blasche, *Marketing Staff*
Kenneth J Young, *Director*
Gary B Young, *Director*
Norman Gilbert, *Technician*
EMP: 130
SQ FT: 100,000
SALES (est): 31.9MM **Privately Held**
WEB: www.tymco.com
SIC: 3711 7699 Street sprinklers & sweepers (motor vehicles), assembly of; aircraft & heavy equipment repair services

(G-20469)
ULTRAMATION INC
221 Cotton Dr (76712-6724)
P.O. Box 20428 (76702-0428)
PHONE..............................254 772-4860
William C Sandlin, *President*
Jane Sandlin, *Vice Pres*
Priscilla Sandlin, *Admin Sec*
EMP: 9
SQ FT: 16,000
SALES (est): 2.4MM **Privately Held**
WEB: www.ultramation.com
SIC: 3625 Actuators, industrial

(G-20470)
UNITED AMERCN ACQUISITION CORP
Also Called: Easy Gardener
400 Austin Ave (76701-2138)
P.O. Box 21025 (76702-1025)
PHONE..............................859 987-5389
Karen Bettege, *CEO*
David Jackson, *President*
◆ **EMP:** 31
SALES (est): 86MM **Privately Held**
WEB: www.jobescompany.com
SIC: 2211 0782 3423 2875 Canvas & other heavy coarse fabrics: cotton; lawn & garden services; hand & edge tools; fertilizers, mixing only

(G-20471)
VANTRAN INDUSTRIES INC
Also Called: Vantran Transformers
7711 Imperial Dr (76712-6501)
P.O. Box 20128 (76702-0128)
PHONE..............................254 772-9740
Alpha E Bolin, *CEO*
Nancy Kral, *President*
Shirley Bolin, *Corp Secy*
Charles A Parsons, *Vice Pres*
Kenny Thigpen, *Opers Mgr*
◆ **EMP:** 50 **EST:** 1963
SQ FT: 50,000
SALES (est): 15.7MM **Privately Held**
WEB: www.vantran.com
SIC: 3612 5063 Power transformers, electric; electrical apparatus & equipment

(G-20472)
VERSALIFT EAST LLC (HQ)
7601 Imperial Dr (76712-6608)
PHONE..............................254 399-2100
Keith Joseph, *President*
David Post, *Corp Secy*
Jay Jeffrey, *Vice Pres*
Gary Lerch, *Prdtn Mgr*
Jon Funk, *Opers Staff*
EMP: 105
SALES (est): 120.4MM
SALES (corp-wide): 200.1MM **Privately Held**
WEB: www.east.versalift.com
SIC: 3711 Automobile assembly, including specialty automobiles
PA: Time Manufacturing Company
7601 Imperial Dr
Waco TX 76712
254 399-2100

(G-20473)
VERSALIFT SOUTHWEST LLC (HQ)
1200 Texas Central Pkwy (76712-6579)
P.O. Box 21415 (76702-1415)
PHONE..............................254 399-2100
Dave Whitby, *President*
Jerry Hatley, *Vice Pres*
Robert Martz, *Vice Pres*
Mike Jefferson, *Opers Mgr*
Greg Sandidge, *Opers Mgr*
EMP: 70
SALES (est): 7MM
SALES (corp-wide): 200.1MM **Privately Held**
WEB: www.southwest.versalift.com
SIC: 3531 Aerial work platforms: hydraulic/elec. truck/carrier mounted
PA: Time Manufacturing Company
7601 Imperial Dr
Waco TX 76712
254 399-2100

(G-20474)
W PROMOTIONS
906 Austin Ave (76701-1902)
PHONE..............................254 753-3411
Trent Weber, *Owner*
Brian Ginsburg, *Manager*
Theresa Nickel, *Graphic Designe*
EMP: 30
SALES (est): 2.7MM **Privately Held**
WEB: www.wpromotions.net
SIC: 2759 Screen printing

(G-20475)
WACO COMPOSITES
302 S 27th St (76710-7454)
PHONE..............................866 688-3088

Bob Simons, *Principal*
Juan Naranjo, *Prdtn Mgr*
Justin Clark, *Sales Staff*
EMP: 25 **EST:** 2017
SALES (est): 2.9MM **Privately Held**
WEB: www.wacocomposites.com
SIC: 3089 Plastics products

(G-20476)
WACO PUBLICATIONS INC
Also Called: American Classifieds
3901 W Waco Dr (76710-7107)
P.O. Box 8575 (76714-8575)
PHONE..........................254 752-0334
Harry Treese, *President*
Carol Treese, *Treasurer*
Kenny Gregg, *Sales Staff*
Amy Gasetric, *Admin Sec*
EMP: 26
SALES (est): 1.3MM **Privately Held**
WEB: www.wacoamericanclassifieds.com
SIC: 2711 2741 7311 Newspapers: pub-
lishing only, not printed on site; miscella-
neous publishing; advertising agencies

(G-20477)
WELLCO HOLDINGS INC
Also Called: Wells Cargo Texas Div
600 Texas Central Pkwy (76712-6514)
P.O. Box 7128 (76714-7128)
PHONE..........................254 772-1740
Jimmy Davis, *Executive*
EMP: 100
SALES (corp-wide): 847.8MM **Privately
Held**
WEB: www.wellscargo.com
SIC: 3715 Truck trailers
HQ: Wellco Holdings, Inc.
1503 Mcnaughton Ave
Elkhart IN 46514
574 264-9661

(G-20478)
WEQ BRITCO LP
1101 Foundation Dr (76712-6825)
P.O. Box 20875 (76702-0875)
PHONE..........................254 741-6701
Douglas B Morgan, *President*
Darcy Hall, *Vice Pres*
EMP: 20
SQ FT: 100,000
SALES (est): 1.9MM
SALES (corp-wide): 838.7K **Privately
Held**
SIC: 2452 Modular homes, prefabricated,
wood
PA: Modular Holdings Llp
21690 Glover Rd
Langley BC
604 888-2000

(G-20479)
WMC WACO HOLDINGS INC
1801 W Waco Dr (76707-3579)
PHONE..........................254 753-7301
Jeffrey Wolf, *CEO*
Abbye Silver, *President*
Russell Crane, *Corp Secy*
Shawnette Petty, *Controller*
◆ **EMP:** 50 **EST:** 1946
SQ FT: 150,000
SALES (est): 11.1MM **Privately Held**
WEB: www.worldsbesttravelpillows.com
SIC: 2211 2392 Blankets & blanketings,
cotton; cushions & pillows

(G-20480)
WRS GROUP LTD
624 Texas Central Pkwy (76712-6568)
P.O. Box 21207 (76702-1207)
PHONE..........................254 776-6461
Scott Salmans, *Branch Mgr*
EMP: 75
SALES (corp-wide): 16.1MM **Privately
Held**
WEB: www.healthedco.com
SIC: 3999 Education aids, devices & sup-
plies
PA: Wrs Group, Ltd.
624 Texas Central Pkwy
Waco TX 76712
254 776-6461

(G-20481)
WRS GROUP LTD (PA)
Also Called: Childbirth Graphics
624 Texas Central Pkwy (76712-6568)
P.O. Box 21207 (76702-1207)
PHONE..........................254 776-6461
Scott Salmans, *CEO*
Victoria Nimmo, *Editor*
Cynthia Peterson, *COO*
Mike Mulholland, *Plant Mgr*
Nathan Foster, *Production*
▲ **EMP:** 29
SQ FT: 30,000
SALES (est): 16.1MM **Privately Held**
WEB: www.healthedco.com
SIC: 2761 3993 3999 Manifold business
forms; signs & advertising specialties; ed-
ucation aids, devices & supplies

Waelder
Gonzales County

(G-20482)
C & C WOOD COMPANY INC
4710 Jeddo Rd (78959-5109)
P.O. Box 230, Weimar (78962-0230)
PHONE..........................361 865-3444
Frank Kainer, *President*
Genevieve Kainer, *Corp Secy*
EMP: 15
SALES (est): 1.7MM **Privately Held**
SIC: 5052 2421 Coal & other minerals &
ores; wood chips, produced at mill

(G-20483)
CAL-MAINE FOODS INC
Also Called: Cal-Maine Farms
1680 County Road 431 (78959-5096)
PHONE..........................830 540-4105
Reggie Otho, *Manager*
EMP: 50
SALES (corp-wide): 1.3B **Publicly Held**
WEB: www.calmainefoods.com
SIC: 5144 2015 Eggs; poultry slaughtering
& processing
PA: Cal-Maine Foods, Inc.
3320 W Woodrow Wilson Ave
Jackson MS 39209
601 948-6813

(G-20484)
**J & B SAUSAGE COMPANY INC
(PA)**
Also Called: J Bar B Foods
100 Main (78959-5329)
P.O. Box 7 (78959-0007)
PHONE..........................830 788-7661
Danny Janecka, *CEO*
Noreen Janecka, *Corp Secy*
Lyndell Bisbee, *Vice Pres*
Travis Holmes, *Vice Pres*
Danny Janecka II, *Vice Pres*
▲ **EMP:** 325 **EST:** 1969
SQ FT: 100,000
SALES (est): 83.8MM **Privately Held**
WEB: www.jbfoods.com
SIC: 2011 5147 2013 Sausages from
meat slaughtered on site; meats & meat
products; sausages & other prepared
meats

Wake Village
Bowie County

(G-20485)
C-L & ASSOCIATES INC
Also Called: Fay-J Packaging Division
616 S Wake Village Rd (75501-6606)
P.O. Box 6043, Texarkana (75505-6043)
PHONE..........................903 831-4311
Fay J Durant, *President*
Jack Coltharp, *Vice Pres*
Martin P Lewis, *Vice Pres*
Derreck Durrant, *Controller*
Gail Coltharp, *Human Res Mgr*
▲ **EMP:** 49
SQ FT: 70,000

SALES (est): 11.4MM **Privately Held**
WEB: www.fayjpackaging.com
SIC: 2674 5162 2673 Paper bags: made
from purchased materials; plastics materials; bags: plastic, laminated & coated

(G-20486)
**INDUSTRIAL MILL MAINT SUP
INC (PA)**
4401 Waco St (75501-6666)
P.O. Box 6188, Texarkana (75505-6188)
PHONE..........................800 537-1218
Arthur Scott Tipton, *President*
Alex Tipton, *Vice Pres*
EMP: 24
SQ FT: 23,000
SALES (est): 12.1MM **Privately Held**
WEB: www.industrialmill.com
SIC: 5085 5084 3541 Valves & fittings;
mill supplies; safety equipment; machine
tools, metal cutting type

(G-20487)
**PARKS METAL FABRICATORS
INC**
5702 W 7th St (75501-5940)
P.O. Box 6006, Texarkana (75505-6006)
PHONE..........................903 838-0535
Jack L Allensworth, *President*
Cynthia Allensworth, *Treasurer*
EMP: 16 **EST:** 1967
SQ FT: 35,000
SALES (est): 3.3MM **Privately Held**
WEB: www.parksmetalfabricators.com
SIC: 3441 Fabricated structural metal

Walburg
Williamson County

(G-20488)
CPI PRODUCTS INTL INC
4100 Fm 1105 (78673)
P.O. Box 510 (78673-0510)
PHONE..........................512 868-0346
Ken Lucas, *President*
Bruce Kaldenbach, *Controller*
EMP: 42
SQ FT: 55,000
SALES (est): 8.3MM **Privately Held**
WEB: www.cpiproducts.com
SIC: 2519 Furniture, household: glass,
fiberglass & plastic

Waller
Harris County

(G-20489)
A J FOYT ENTERPRISES INC
19480 Stokes Rd (77484-8785)
PHONE..........................936 372-3698
A J Foyt Jr, *President*
Anne Fornoro, *Marketing Staff*
EMP: 62
SQ FT: 2,500
SALES (est): 22.8MM **Privately Held**
WEB: www.foytracing.com
SIC: 3711 7948 Automobile assembly, in-
cluding specialty automobiles; race car
owners

(G-20490)
ALEGACY EQUIPMENT LLC
1475 Alegacy Pl (77484-2096)
P.O. Box 1804 (77484-1804)
PHONE..........................832 916-3700
Allen Caldwell, *CEO*
Robert C Nickles Jr, *Principal*
Don Ray, *Vice Pres*
Kyle Manzer, *Project Mgr*
Pete Salazar, *Buyer*
EMP: 22
SALES (est): 20.7MM
SALES (corp-wide): 42.5MM **Privately
Held**
WEB: www.alegacy.biz
SIC: 3563 Air & gas compressors
PA: Alegacy Group, Llc
1475 Alegacy Pl
Waller TX 77484
832 916-3700

(G-20491)
ALPHA FOODS CO
Also Called: Sgt. Pepperoni's
19802 G H Cir (77484-8285)
PHONE..........................936 372-5858
George A Sarandos, *CEO*
Athena Sarandos, *President*
Arist Sarandos, *Vice Pres*
Maria Vowen, *Vice Pres*
Jeanie Anderson, *Treasurer*
EMP: 40
SQ FT: 120,000
SALES (est): 12.1MM **Privately Held**
WEB: www.alphafoodsco.com
SIC: 2045 Pizza mixes: from purchased
flour

(G-20492)
**ARKOS FIELD SERVICES LP
(HQ)**
19750 Fm 362 Rd Ste 100 (77484-5067)
PHONE..........................832 783-5400
Ray Cox, *Superintendent*
David Pennington, *Superintendent*
Marcel Pawlicek, *General Ptnr*
Lee Sumrall, *General Ptnr*
Duane Childress, *District Mgr*
EMP: 16
SQ FT: 10,000
SALES (est): 271.6MM
SALES (corp-wide): 644MM **Privately
Held**
WEB: www.arkos.com
SIC: 1382 Oil & gas exploration services
PA: Burckhardt Compression Holding Ag
Franz-Burckhardt-Strasse 5
Winterthur ZH 8404
522 625-500

(G-20493)
ASHTER CONSTRUCTION LLC
36417 Richard Frey Rd (77484-5285)
PHONE..........................832 786-0053
Huzefa Amiji,
EMP: 20
SALES (est): 629.3K **Privately Held**
SIC: 3993 Electric signs

(G-20494)
**BROAD-OCEAN MOTOR
HOUSTON LLC**
18140 Kickapoo Rd (77484-9288)
PHONE..........................713 353-0100
Joann Liu, *Opers Dir*
Charles Lu, *Mng Member*
EMP: 25 **EST:** 2016
SALES (est): 1MM **Privately Held**
SIC: 3585 Refrigeration & heating equip-
ment

(G-20495)
**CAMERON INTERNATIONAL
CORP**
Also Called: Cooper Energy Services Div
20110 Gh Cir (77484)
PHONE..........................713 571-3100
Norm Shade, *General Mgr*
Jean Smith, *Business Mgr*
Austin Jochetz, *Buyer*
Marty Lafleur, *Buyer*
Shawn Carter, *Engineer*
EMP: 25
SQ FT: 149,349 **Publicly Held**
WEB: www.products.slb.com
SIC: 3533 3563 Oil field machinery &
equipment; air & gas compressors
HQ: Cameron International Corporation
4646 W Sam Houston Pkwy N
Houston TX 77041

(G-20496)
COTTON CONSTRUCTION INC
30505 Betka Rd (77484-5077)
PHONE..........................936 931-2510
Bobby C Cotton Jr, *President*
Sherry Cotton, *Vice Pres*
EMP: 12
SALES (est): 500K **Privately Held**
SIC: 3448 Prefabricated metal buildings

(G-20497)
FAB SERVICES LTD
2405 Washington St (77484-8368)
P.O. Box 1277 (77484-1277)
PHONE..........................936 931-1004

▲ = Import ▼=Export
◆ =Import/Export

Michael H Newton, *President*
Randy Newton, *President*
Jacob Farris, *Superintendent*
Joey Speegle, *Opers Mgr*
Luke Thomason, *Sales Mgr*
EMP: 25
SQ FT: 8,750
SALES (est): 4.2MM **Privately Held**
WEB: www.fabservices.net
SIC: 3441 Fabricated structural metal

(G-20498)
FJW MACHINE INC
43313 Old Houston Hwy (77484-5630)
PHONE..................................936 931-5507
Felix Worchesik, *President*
EMP: 13
SQ FT: 3,500
SALES (est): 585.6K **Privately Held**
WEB: www.fjwco.com
SIC: 3599 Machine shop, jobbing & repair

(G-20499)
GARZO INC
Also Called: Engine & Compressor ACC
42146 Hwy 290 Business (77484-8173)
PHONE..................................936 931-5631
Thomas M Pafford, *President*
Bill Pafford, *Vice Pres*
Mary Pafford, *Treasurer*
EMP: 45
SQ FT: 9,000
SALES (est): 18.7MM **Privately Held**
WEB: www.garzoproducts.com
SIC: 3533 Oil field machinery & equipment

(G-20500)
GOODMAN GLOBAL HOLDINGS INC (HQ)
19001 Kermier Rd (77484-8810)
PHONE..................................713 861-2500
Charles A Carroll, *President*
Ben D Campbell, *Exec VP*
Donald R King, *Exec VP*
Lawrence M Blackburn, *CFO*
Mark M Dolan, *Treasurer*
▲ **EMP:** 10
SALES (est): 1B **Privately Held**
WEB: www.goodmanmfg.com
SIC: 3585 3564 Air conditioning equipment, complete; heating equipment, complete; heating & air conditioning combination units; blowers & fans

(G-20501)
GOODMAN MANUFACTURING CO LP
19001 Kermier Rd (77484-8810)
PHONE..................................936 372-5224
Shel Dail, *General Mgr*
EMP: 10 **Privately Held**
WEB: www.goodmanmfg.com
SIC: 5075 3999 3585 Air conditioning equipment, except room units; barber & beauty shop equipment; air conditioning equipment, complete
HQ: Goodman Manufacturing Company, Lp
19001 Kermier Rd
Waller TX 77484
713 861-2500

(G-20502)
GOODMAN MANUFACTURING CO LP (HQ)
Also Called: Goodman A Cndtioners Coolg Htg
19001 Kermier Rd (77484-8810)
PHONE..................................713 861-2500
Takeshi Ebisu, *CEO*
Bradley Snyder, *President*
David Swift, *President*
Jeffrey Ellingham, *Vice Pres*
Hank Nolin, *Engineer*
◆ **EMP:** 250 **EST:** 1975
SALES (est): 1.5B **Privately Held**
WEB: www.goodmanmfg.com
SIC: 3585 Air conditioning units, complete: domestic or industrial

(G-20503)
GREEN-SPAN PROFILES LP
21200 Fm 362 Rd (77484-5900)
P.O. Box 730 (77484-0730)
PHONE..................................281 807-7400
Kelly Ginn, *Principal*

Brian N Jaks, *Vice Pres*
Thad Wilson, *Plant Mgr*
Jesse Cobarrubias, *Project Mgr*
Chris Tolen, *Design Engr*
▲ **EMP:** 13
SALES (est): 7.3MM **Privately Held**
WEB: www.greenspanprofiles.com
SIC: 3448 Panels for prefabricated metal buildings

(G-20504)
MOHAWK MACHINE & WELDING INC
19111 Fm 362 Rd (77484-5073)
PHONE..................................936 372-5103
Jim Bittikoffer, *Principal*
John E Thompson, *Principal*
John Fallon, *Admin Sec*
Paula Thompson, *Administration*
EMP: 30 **EST:** 1970
SQ FT: 11,630
SALES (est): 4.6MM **Privately Held**
WEB: www.mohawkmachine.com
SIC: 3599 Machine shop, jobbing & repair

(G-20505)
NRG MANUFACTURING INC
18703 G H Cir (77484-8275)
PHONE..................................281 320-2525
EMP: 10
SALES (corp-wide): 118.9MM **Privately Held**
WEB: www.afglobalcorp.com
SIC: 3449 3441 Miscellaneous metalwork; fabricated structural metal
HQ: Nrg Manufacturing Inc
11311 Holderrieth Rd # 100
Tomball TX 77375
281 320-2525

(G-20506)
PICCO COATINGS CO
20738 Stokes Rd (77484-5428)
PHONE..................................281 447-8877
Gary Phillips, *CEO*
Rocky Tornberg, *President*
Barry Burke, *Vice Pres*
Aaron Vance, *Plant Engr*
Cody Tornburg, *CFO*
EMP: 41
SQ FT: 12,500
SALES (est): 16MM **Privately Held**
WEB: www.piccocoatings.com
SIC: 2851 Enamels

(G-20507)
PREMIER COIL SOLUTIONS INC
18993 G H Cir (77484-1589)
P.O. Box 1909 (77484-1909)
PHONE..................................713 677-0209
Brett Witte, *President*
Tyler Parker, *General Mgr*
Javier Sauceda, *General Mgr*
John Arango, *Prdtn Mgr*
Brenda Rodriguez, *Buyer*
EMP: 50
SQ FT: 70,000
SALES (est): 19.7MM **Privately Held**
WEB: www.premiercoil.com
SIC: 3549 5251 Coiling machinery; pumps & pumping equipment

(G-20508)
TEXAS STEEL FABRICATORS INC
28306 Fm 2920 Rd (77484-8073)
P.O. Box 1512, Cypress (77410-1512)
PHONE..................................936 372-1616
Osiel Lopez, *President*
Norma Rosales, *Admin Sec*
EMP: 16
SQ FT: 15,250
SALES (est): 4.1MM **Privately Held**
WEB: www.txsteelfabricators.com
SIC: 3441 Fabricated structural metal

(G-20509)
WHITE STAR PUMP COMPANY LLC
41499 Cyrus Ln (77484-5446)
PHONE..................................281 357-4999
Bruce Suggs, *President*
Shawn Michael White, *Mng Member*
▼ **EMP:** 18

SALES (est): 3.9MM **Privately Held**
WEB: www.whitestarpump.com
SIC: 3561 Pumps & pumping equipment

Wallis
Austin County

(G-20510)
WALLIS CONCRETE LLC
646 Wallis Concrete Rd (77485-9480)
P.O. Box 789 (77485-0789)
PHONE..................................979 478-6734
EMP: 15
SQ FT: 40,000
SALES (est): 2.7MM **Privately Held**
WEB: www.wallisconcrete.com
SIC: 3272 5074 Precast terrazo or concrete products; pipes & fittings, plastic

Wallisville
Chambers County

(G-20511)
COWBOYS READY MIX LLC
24015 Interstate 10 (77597-3032)
PHONE..................................281 972-7000
Keith Joseph Jannise, *Principal*
EMP: 45 **EST:** 2014
SALES (est): 4.6MM **Privately Held**
WEB: www.cowboysreadymix.com
SIC: 3273 Ready-mixed concrete

(G-20512)
KB STRUCTURES INC
23 Rd 602 I 10 (77597)
P.O. Box 217 (77597-0217)
PHONE..................................713 875-1024
Kevin D Boyer, *President*
Kevin Boyer, *President*
EMP: 13
SALES (est): 1.6MM **Privately Held**
WEB: www.kbstructures.net
SIC: 3291 Abrasive metal & steel products

Warda
Fayette County

(G-20513)
WOLF OIL FIELD SERVICES INC
Hwy 77 (78960)
P.O. Box 41 (78960-0041)
PHONE..................................979 242-5341
Arnold Wolfe, *President*
EMP: 15 **EST:** 1981
SQ FT: 8,000
SALES (est): 600K **Privately Held**
SIC: 1389 Oil field services

Waskom
Harrison County

(G-20514)
AZTEC MNFCTURING-WASKOM PARTNR
Also Called: Aztec Galvanizing Services
990 E Texas Ave (75692-3672)
P.O. Box 728 (75692-0728)
PHONE..................................903 687-3943
L C Martin, *General Ptnr*
Jimmy Williams, *Plant Mgr*
Peggy Hanson, *Office Mgr*
EMP: 35
SALES (est): 4.3MM **Privately Held**
WEB: www.azz.com
SIC: 3479 3547 Galvanizing of iron, steel or end-formed products; galvanizing lines (rolling mill equipment)

(G-20515)
BADGER PRESSURE CONTROL LLC (PA)
1197 Magnolia Rd Ste B (75692-5217)
P.O. Box 1246, Woodward OK (73802-1246)
PHONE..................................903 687-4100
Timothy Crain, *Mng Member*
Kelly Miller,

EMP: 31
SQ FT: 12,000
SALES (est): 6.2MM **Privately Held**
SIC: 1389 Oil sampling service for oil companies

(G-20516)
BASS ENERGY SERVICES LLC (PA)
1197 Magnolia Rd Ste B (75692-5217)
P.O. Box 1890 (75692-1890)
PHONE..................................903 687-1800
Steven L Johnston, *President*
Michael White, *Chairman*
Ryan Ferrell, *Foreman/Supr*
Timothy Crain, *Treasurer*
Leslie Starr, *Accounting Mgr*
EMP: 74
SALES (est): 113.7MM **Privately Held**
WEB: www.bassenergyservices.com
SIC: 1389 Oil field services

(G-20517)
BLACK GOLD OPER & CNSTR INC
119 County Road 335 (75692-2521)
P.O. Box 161, Panola (75685-0161)
PHONE..................................903 766-3636
Terry Stephens, *President*
Maxanna Stephens, *Vice Pres*
EMP: 29
SALES (est): 2.8MM **Privately Held**
SIC: 1389 Oil field services

(G-20518)
LATX OILFIELD SERVICES LLC (PA)
13927 Us Highway 80 E (75692-3829)
P.O. Box 704 (75692-0704)
PHONE..................................903 934-8263
Celeste St Amant, *Manager*
Jonathan Owen St Amant,
Richard W Darouse,
Derek Jason St Amant,
Jefferey Ryan St Amant,
EMP: 27
SALES (est): 11.1MM **Privately Held**
WEB: www.latxoperations.com
SIC: 1389 Oil field services

(G-20519)
LATX OPERATIONS LLC
13927 Us Highway 80 E (75692-3829)
P.O. Box 704 (75692-0704)
PHONE..................................903 927-2091
Scotty Collins, *Controller*
EMP: 90
SALES (est): 14.1MM **Privately Held**
WEB: www.latxoperations.com
SIC: 1389 Oil field services
PA: Sta Operations, Llc
13927 Us Highway 80 E
Waskom TX 75692
903 927-1446

(G-20520)
RATEC INC
Also Called: Specialty Wldg & Fabrication
935 W Texas Ave (75692-3690)
P.O. Box 132 (75692-0132)
PHONE..................................903 687-3811
L Rhea Haston, *President*
EMP: 12
SQ FT: 6,000
SALES (est): 1.7MM **Privately Held**
WEB: www.familymattersfinancial.com
SIC: 3441 7692 Fabricated structural metal; welding repair

(G-20521)
RED DIAMOND OILFLD SVCS L L C
1268 Magnolia Rd (75692-5258)
PHONE..................................903 687-4000
Kenneth J Whitehurst, *Mng Member*
EMP: 29
SALES (est): 5.5MM **Privately Held**
WEB: www.reddiamondofs.com
SIC: 1389 Oil field services

(G-20522)
RED DIAMOND PRESSURE CTRL LLC
1268 Magnolia Rd (75692-5258)
PHONE..................................903 687-4000

Ricky Palmer,
EMP: 16
SQ FT: 16,000
SALES (est): 4.8MM **Privately Held**
WEB: www.reddiamondofs.com
SIC: 1389 Oil field services

(G-20523)
TRI RESOURCES INC
Also Called: Dynegy
155 Private Rd Ste 1133 (75692)
PHONE.................................903 687-2513
Bobby Lawrence, *Manager*
EMP: 11 **Publicly Held**
WEB: www.triresources.com
SIC: 1321 Natural gas liquids
HQ: Tri Resources Inc.
811 Louisiana St Ste 2100
Houston TX 77002
713 584-1000

(G-20524)
TRINITY SERVICES LLC
Also Called: Trinity Services LLC-Admin
18149 Us Highway 80 E (75692-5013)
PHONE.................................903 687-4350
Newton Dorset, *Mng Member*
EMP: 60
SQ FT: 10,000
SALES (est): 3MM **Publicly Held**
SIC: 1389 Oil field services
PA: Smg Industries Inc.
710 N Post Oak Rd Ste 400
Houston TX 77024

(G-20525)
WASKOM GAS PROCESSING COMPANY
155 Private Road 1133 (75692-5037)
PHONE.................................903 687-2513
David Favors, *Branch Mgr*
EMP: 37
SALES (corp-wide): 847.1MM **Publicly Held**
WEB: www.waskomisd.net
SIC: 1311 Gas & hydrocarbon liquefaction from coal
HQ: Waskom Gas Processing Company
2350 Airport Fwy
Bedford TX

Waxahachie
Ellis County

(G-20526)
ALTEC INDUSTRIES INC
1001 Solon Rd (75165-5097)
PHONE.................................972 937-8284
Dwayne Reeder, *Manager*
Danny Wright, *Administration*
EMP: 15
SALES (corp-wide): 1.1B **Privately Held**
WEB: www.altec.com
SIC: 3531 Construction machinery
HQ: Altec Industries, Inc.
210 Inverness Center Dr
Birmingham AL 35242
205 991-7733

(G-20527)
ARCHITECTURAL WOOD DESIGNS
408 Higgins Rd (75167-8398)
PHONE.................................972 935-0222
EMP: 10
SQ FT: 10,000
SALES: 329.1K **Privately Held**
SIC: 2541 Mfg Cabinets

(G-20528)
AUTOMATED FOOD SYSTEMS INC
Also Called: A F S
1000 Lofland Dr (75165-6200)
PHONE.................................469 517-0470
Glenn Walser, *Ch of Bd*
Robert D Walser, *President*
Charles Stone, *Prdtn Mgr*
Robin Williams, *Purchasing*
Phineas Henshaw, *Engineer*
▲ **EMP:** 11 **EST:** 1976
SQ FT: 12,000

SALES (est): 3.1MM **Privately Held**
WEB: www.afstexas.com
SIC: 3556 Food products machinery

(G-20529)
BERRY GLOBAL FILMS LLC
6250 N I Hwy 35 E (75165-5602)
PHONE.................................972 576-8193
Paul Vegliante, *Vice Pres*
Bob Pierce, *Natl Sales Mgr*
Arnie Pedersen, *Manager*
EMP: 140
SQ FT: 101,345 **Publicly Held**
WEB: www.berryplastics.com
SIC: 3089 3081 2673 2671 Plastic containers, except foam; unsupported plastics film & sheet; bags: plastic, laminated & coated; packaging paper & plastics film, coated & laminated
HQ: Berry Global Films, Llc
95 Chestnut Ridge Rd
Montvale NJ 07645
201 641-6600

(G-20530)
BUFFALO CREEK MILLWORK INC
509 N Interstate Hwy 35 E (75165-5231)
P.O. Box 813 (75168-0813)
PHONE.................................972 938-2392
Demetre Koutros, *President*
EMP: 20
SQ FT: 18,000
SALES (est): 2.4MM **Privately Held**
WEB: www.buffalocreekmillwork.com
SIC: 2431 Millwork

(G-20531)
BULLDOG IRONWORKS LLC
2561 S Highway 77 (75165-7688)
P.O. Box 642 (75168-0642)
PHONE.................................972 935-0575
Crystal Copeland, *Office Mgr*
Angela Copeland,
James Copeland,
Nick Copeland,
EMP: 12
SQ FT: 30,000
SALES (est): 4.2MM **Privately Held**
WEB: www.bulldogironworksllc.com
SIC: 3441 Fabricated structural metal

(G-20532)
C M C STEEL FABRICATORS INC
Also Called: CMC Construction Services
4100 N I Hwy 35 E (75165-6614)
PHONE.................................972 938-9500
EMP: 100
SALES (corp-wide): 5.4B **Publicly Held**
WEB: www.cmc.com
SIC: 3441 Fabricated structural metal
HQ: C M C Steel Fabricators, Inc.
1 Steel Mill Dr
Seguin TX 78155
830 372-8200

(G-20533)
CARDINAL GLASS INDUSTRIES INC
Also Called: Cardinal Ig
201 Cardinal Rd (75165-6230)
PHONE.................................972 937-4969
Drew Berry, *Superintendent*
David Bunce, *Opers Staff*
John Dicken, *Sales Mgr*
Eric Showquist, *Manager*
Jeanne Curtis, *Executive*
EMP: 98
SALES (corp-wide): 1B **Privately Held**
WEB: www.cardinalcorp.com
SIC: 3231 3211 Insulating glass: made from purchased glass; tempered glass: made from purchased glass; flat glass
PA: Cardinal Glass Industries Inc
775 Pririe Ctr Dr Ste 200
Eden Prairie MN 55344
952 229-2600

(G-20534)
CARDINAL GLASS INDUSTRIES INC
203 Cardinal Rd (75165-6230)
PHONE.................................972 937-1708
Mike Deidrich, *Plant Mgr*

Erik Shoquist, *Plant Mgr*
Mike Tilley, *Opers Mgr*
Patrick Adams, *Purchasing*
Anthony Lopez, *Manager*
EMP: 171
SALES (corp-wide): 1B **Privately Held**
WEB: www.cardinalcorp.com
SIC: 3231 3211 Insulating glass: made from purchased glass; tempered glass: made from purchased glass; flat glass
PA: Cardinal Glass Industries Inc
775 Pririe Ctr Dr Ste 200
Eden Prairie MN 55344
952 229-2600

(G-20535)
CASTELL LP
Also Called: Texcorr
200 Butcher Rd (75165-6076)
PHONE.................................972 938-2739
Kevin Brower, *General Mgr*
James Jones, *Plant Mgr*
Tony Morgan, *Controller*
◆ **EMP:** 62
SQ FT: 50,000
SALES (est): 23.1MM **Privately Held**
WEB: www.texcorr.com
SIC: 2679 Corrugated paper: made from purchased material

(G-20536)
CMCABCO LLC (PA)
Also Called: C & M Manufacturing
3637 N Highway 77 (75165-0025)
P.O. Box 1277, Red Oak (75154-1277)
PHONE.................................972 617-8605
Carey Paquin, *Mng Member*
EMP: 12
SALES (est): 900K **Privately Held**
WEB: www.cmcabco.com
SIC: 2434 Wood kitchen cabinets

(G-20537)
COAST TO COAST TOWER SVC INC
753 Arrowhead Rd (75167-8597)
PHONE.................................972 923-9504
Todd Jackson, *President*
Mary Faulkenberry, *Office Mgr*
Mike J Jackson, *Manager*
Angie Jackson, *Admin Sec*
EMP: 15
SALES (est): 2.3MM **Privately Held**
WEB: www.ctctower.com
SIC: 3441 Fabricated structural metal

(G-20538)
COMMERCIAL METALS COMPANY
4100 N I 35 (75165-6614)
PHONE.................................972 938-9500
Tom Carry, *Engineer*
Mark Newman, *Director*
EMP: 145
SQ FT: 79,900
SALES (corp-wide): 5.4B **Publicly Held**
WEB: www.cmc.com
SIC: 3441 Fabricated structural metal
PA: Commercial Metals Company
6565 N Macarthur Blvd # 800
Irving TX 75039
214 689-4300

(G-20539)
CREEKSIDE MIRROR AND GLASS LLC
Also Called: Creekside Mirror & Glass
3811 S Us Highway 287 (75165-7452)
P.O. Box 1890, Red Oak (75154-1568)
PHONE.................................972 617-9805
Steve McCloud, *Mng Member*
EMP: 11
SALES (est): 944.3K **Privately Held**
WEB: www.creeksidemirrorandglass.com
SIC: 3229 5231 Glass furnishings & accessories; glass

(G-20540)
DRUG PREVENTION RESOURCES INC
201 Ferris Ave Ste G (75165-3660)
PHONE.................................972 518-1821
Rebecca Vance, *CEO*
Sherri Ansley, *CFO*
Phillip Watson, *Director*

EMP: 14
SALES: 1.4MM **Privately Held**
WEB: www.drugfreegeneration.org
SIC: 2731 8322 Pamphlets: publishing only, not printed on site; individual & family services

(G-20541)
ELLIS COUNTY CHRONICLE
200 W Marvin Ave (75165-3040)
PHONE.................................972 937-3310
Rick Stark, *President*
Neil White, *Principal*
EMP: 40
SQ FT: 1,000
SALES (est): 930.5K **Privately Held**
WEB: www.elliscountychronicle.com
SIC: 2711 Newspapers, publishing & printing

(G-20542)
ESPINOZA CAST STONE INC
4743 N Intrstate Hwy 35 E (75165-5706)
PHONE.................................214 396-5280
Jose Espinoza, *President*
EMP: 17
SALES (est): 987.8K **Privately Held**
WEB: www.espinozacaststone.com
SIC: 3272 Concrete products

(G-20543)
GEORGIA-PACIFIC LLC
5800 N Intrstate Hwy 35 E (75165-5717)
PHONE.................................972 937-8804
Charlie Martin, *Manager*
EMP: 135
SALES (corp-wide): 36.8B **Privately Held**
WEB: www.gp.com
SIC: 2653 Boxes, corrugated: made from purchased materials
HQ: Georgia-Pacific Llc
133 Peachtree St Nw
Atlanta GA 30303
404 652-4000

(G-20544)
GUARDIAN SOUTHWEST STRING TAG
Also Called: Guardian Tag & Label
300 N Rogers St (75165-3354)
PHONE.................................972 938-0123
Wally Szymczak, *President*
Walter Szymczak, *Info Tech Mgr*
EMP: 12
SQ FT: 9,876
SALES (est): 1.1MM **Privately Held**
WEB: www.guardiansouthwest.com
SIC: 2269 2672 2752 Finishing plants; adhesive papers, labels or tapes: from purchased material; labels (unprinted), gummed: made from purchased materials; commercial printing, offset

(G-20545)
INTERNATIONAL ALUMINUM CORP
Also Called: International Extrusion Co
202 Singleton Rd (75165-5012)
PHONE.................................972 937-7032
Dick Almy, *CEO*
James P Baione, *President*
Kent Estes, *Vice Pres*
Mitch Whitehead, *Plant Mgr*
Clois Carter, *Purch Mgr*
EMP: 179
SALES (est): 1.3MM **Privately Held**
WEB: www.intlextrusion.com
SIC: 3354 Aluminum extruded products
HQ: Universal Molding Extrusion Company, Inc.
9151 Imperial Hwy
Downey CA 90242
562 401-1015

(G-20546)
J & G CONCRETE LP
1220 Solon Rd (75167-5821)
P.O. Box 10, Paris (75461-0010)
PHONE.................................972 937-9200
John Greb, *Partner*
Rick Johnson, *Partner*
Larry J Greb, *General Ptnr*
EMP: 48
SQ FT: 1,000

SALES (est): 20MM **Privately Held**
SIC: 3271 5039 Brick, concrete; air ducts, sheet metal

(G-20547)
JAMES HARDIE BUILDING PDTS INC
2425 N Highway 77 (75165-6222)
PHONE...................................972 923-9300
Adam Graham, *Plant Mgr*
Bob Grove, *Human Resources*
Aaron George, *Regl Sales Mgr*
Kevin Yelle, *Manager*
Conrad Adkins, *Legal Staff*
EMP: 176 **Privately Held**
WEB: www.jameshardie.com
SIC: 5031 3241 Building materials, exterior; cement, hydraulic
HQ: James Hardie Building Products Inc.
231 S La Salle St # 2000
Chicago IL 60604
312 291-5072

(G-20548)
KINRO COMPOSTIES
101 Mushroom Rd (75165-6103)
PHONE...................................800 262-8827
Fredric M Zinn, *CEO*
William Mitchell, *President*
▲ EMP: 105
SQ FT: 90,000
SALES (est): 17.4MM
SALES (corp-wide): 2.3B **Publicly Held**
WEB: www.lci1.com
SIC: 3088 3211 Tubs (bath, shower & laundry), plastic; window glass, clear & colored
HQ: Kinro Manufacturing, Inc.
3501 County Road 6 E
Elkhart IN 46514
574 535-1125

(G-20549)
LARKIN PRODUCTS INC
1620 E Main St (75165-4454)
PHONE...................................972 937-3640
Jean Shannon, *General Mgr*
EMP: 27
SQ FT: 36,000 **Privately Held**
WEB: www.larkinproductsinc.com
SIC: 5084 3533 Oil well machinery, equipment & supplies; oil & gas field machinery
PA: Larkin Products, Llc
3105 Charles Page Blvd
Tulsa OK 74127

(G-20550)
LAWN MASTER OUTDOOR LIVING LLC (PA)
3841 S Intrstate Hwy 35 E (75165-5418)
P.O. Box 837 (75168-0837)
PHONE...................................972 938-7100
Bryan Keith Johnson, *Mng Member*
Michael Shane Leath,
John Leslie Sanders III,
EMP: 35
SALES (est): 4.9MM **Privately Held**
WEB: www.lawn-master.com
SIC: 2491 Structural lumber & timber; treated wood

(G-20551)
LIFOAM INDUSTRIES LLC
1600 W Hwy 287 Byp (75165-5068)
PHONE...................................972 937-6512
Ike Knight, *Branch Mgr*
EMP: 100
SALES (corp-wide): 9.7B **Publicly Held**
WEB: www.lifoam.com
SIC: 2821 3086 Polystyrene resins; plastics foam products
HQ: Lifoam Industries, Llc
121 Bata Blvd
Belcamp MD 21017
866 770-3626

(G-20552)
LIPPERT COMPONENTS INC
101 Mushroom Rd (75165-6103)
PHONE...................................972 232-3119
EMP: 59
SALES (corp-wide): 2.3B **Publicly Held**
WEB: www.lci1.com
SIC: 3711 Motor vehicles & car bodies

HQ: Lippert Components, Inc.
3501 County Road 6 E
Elkhart IN 46514
574 535-1125

(G-20553)
NATIONAL WHOLESALE SUPPLY INC
3500 S Intrstate Hwy 35 E (75165-5426)
PHONE...................................469 517-0600
EMP: 14
SALES (corp-wide): 91.2MM **Privately Held**
WEB: www.nationalwholesalesupply.com
SIC: 5074 3432 Plumbing & hydronic heating supplies; plumbing fixture fittings & trim
PA: National Wholesale Supply, Inc.
1972 Cal Crossing Rd
Dallas TX 75220
972 331-7770

(G-20554)
OWENS CORNING SALES LLC
3700 N Ih 35 E (75165-6699)
P.O. Box 837 (75168-0837)
PHONE...................................972 937-1340
Wayne Powers, *Branch Mgr*
EMP: 400 **Publicly Held**
WEB: www.owenscorning.com
SIC: 3296 Insulation, buildings
HQ: Owens Corning Sales, Llc
1 Owens Corning Pkwy
Toledo OH 43659
419 248-8000

(G-20555)
REDOX CHEMICALS LLC
116 N Rogers St (75165-3798)
PHONE...................................972 923-7734
EMP: 17 **Privately Held**
WEB: www.redoxgrows.com
SIC: 2819 Industrial inorganic chemicals
PA: Redox Chemicals, Llc
130 S 100 W
Burley ID 83318

(G-20556)
REFRIGERATION DESIGN INC
Also Called: Refrigeration Design Tech
1808 Fm 66 (75167-5507)
PHONE...................................972 937-3240
Randall Deyess, *President*
Brent Deyess, *Vice Pres*
EMP: 20
SALES (est): 1.7MM **Privately Held**
WEB: www.rdtonline.com
SIC: 3585 3999 Refrigeration equipment, complete; manufacturing industries

(G-20557)
SCOTT TRAFFIC LLC
Also Called: Websiteradiotraffic.com
307 Brown St (75165-2616)
PHONE...................................972 937-6040
Bob Meadows, *Vice Pres*
David J Blyth,
Karen Blyth,
Richard Gross,
EMP: 11
SALES (est): 1.2MM **Privately Held**
WEB: www.marketron.com
SIC: 7372 Prepackaged software

(G-20558)
SON-LAN INDUSTRIES INC
419 E Madison St (75165-3720)
P.O. Box 7 (75168-0007)
PHONE...................................972 937-8162
Sonny Atkins, *President*
Clark Langford, *Vice Pres*
Guy Windshields, *Manager*
Guy Atkins, *Admin Sec*
EMP: 9
SQ FT: 13,500
SALES (est): 1.1MM **Privately Held**
SIC: 3449 3479 Bars, concrete reinforcing: fabricated steel; aluminum coating of metal products

(G-20559)
SOUND BRIDGE ACOUSTIC LABS INC
3501 S Intrstate Hwy 35 E (75165-5429)
PHONE...................................972 937-2030
Chris Cole, *President*

Troy Tuttle, *COO*
Ethan Rumfield, *Project Mgr*
Michael Pajak, *CFO*
Regina Alexander, *Bookkeeper*
◆ EMP: 35
SQ FT: 60,000
SALES (est): 10.5MM **Privately Held**
WEB: www.soundbridge.com
SIC: 7812 3651 Motion picture & video production; audio-visual program production; household audio & video equipment

(G-20560)
SOUTHERN FRAC LLC
1805 Howard Rd (75165-4225)
P.O. Box 2779 (75168-8779)
PHONE...................................877 576-0821
Shane Boston,
Nathan Bennett, *Maintence Staff*
G Martin Haight,
EMP: 250
SALES (est): 52.8MM **Publicly Held**
WEB: www.southernfrac.com
SIC: 3441 Fabricated structural metal
PA: General Finance Corporation
39 E Union St Ste 206
Pasadena CA 91103

(G-20561)
SOUTHERN WELDING LLC
300 Howard Rd Ste 100 (75165-4205)
PHONE...................................469 517-0410
Shane Boston, *Owner*
Chris Gowins, *Superintendent*
Jake Hinds, *Purchasing*
Alexa Gibbs, *Office Mgr*
EMP: 14
SALES (est): 2.1MM **Privately Held**
SIC: 7692 Welding repair

(G-20562)
SOUTHWEST INDEX TAB CO INC
300 N Rogers St (75165-3354)
PHONE...................................972 228-8227
Gail Szymczak, *President*
Micheal Anderson, *Vice Pres*
Michael Anderson, *Vice Pres*
Mike Anderson, *Vice Pres*
EMP: 30
SALES (est): 6.5MM **Privately Held**
SIC: 2675 2671 Index cards, die-cut: made from purchased materials; packaging paper & plastics film, coated & laminated

(G-20563)
STELCO INDUSTRIES INC
1313 N Intrstate Hwy 35 E (75165-5213)
PHONE...................................972 923-3603
Stella Fischer, *President*
Clifford P Fischer, *Exec VP*
EMP: 12
SQ FT: 12,000
SALES (est): 2.6MM **Privately Held**
WEB: www.stelco-industries-inc.sbcontract.com
SIC: 3399 Nails: aluminum, brass or other nonferrous metal or wire

(G-20564)
TAYLOR COML FOODSERVICE INC
2275 N Highway 77 (75165-6218)
P.O. Box 597 (75168-0597)
PHONE...................................972 937-1820
Gwen Johnson, *Branch Mgr*
EMP: 500
SALES (corp-wide): 2.7B **Publicly Held**
WEB: www.taylor-company.com
SIC: 3585 Refrigeration equipment, complete
HQ: Taylor Commercial Foodservice, Llc
750 N Blackhawk Blvd
Rockton IL 61072
815 624-8333

(G-20565)
TEXAS BOOK COMPANY
1123 Sycamore St (75165-2342)
PHONE...................................972 825-4781
EMP: 54
SALES (corp-wide): 155.7MM **Privately Held**
WEB: www.texasbook.com
SIC: 2731 Books: publishing only

PA: Texas Book Company
8501 Technology Cir
Greenville TX 75402
903 455-6937

(G-20566)
TOP QUALITY SPINDLES LLC
Also Called: J B Leasing
2650 Fm 878 (75165-9232)
P.O. Box 741 (75168-0741)
PHONE...................................972 937-2126
J B Hurn, *Mng Member*
Jetty Hurn, *Mng Member*
Mary Hurn, *Mng Member*
EMP: 10
SQ FT: 10,000
SALES (est): 2.1MM **Privately Held**
WEB: www.topqualityspindles.com
SIC: 3714 5015 5999 Axle housings & shafts, motor vehicle; motor vehicle parts, used; alcoholic beverage making equipment & supplies

(G-20567)
WABASH NATIONAL TRLR CTRS INC
4675 N I 35 (75165-5705)
PHONE...................................972 923-2200
Jerry Dumont, *Branch Mgr*
EMP: 12
SALES (corp-wide): 2.2B **Publicly Held**
WEB: www.wabashnational.com
SIC: 3715 Truck trailers
HQ: Wabash National Trailer Centers, Inc.
1000 Sagamore Pkwy S
Lafayette IN 47905
765 771-5300

(G-20568)
WESCO CHEMICALS INC
103 Industrial Dr (75165-6105)
P.O. Box 2506 (75168-8506)
PHONE...................................972 938-0913
Gene Kirk Saunders, *President*
Sam Villarreal, *Opers Spvr*
Keith Hall, *Consultant*
Cody Wylie, *Representative*
EMP: 10
SQ FT: 20,000
SALES (est): 1.8MM **Privately Held**
WEB: www.wescochemicals.com
SIC: 2899 3589 Antiscaling compounds, boiler; corrosion preventive lubricant; metal treating compounds; water treating compounds; water treatment equipment, industrial

(G-20569)
WEST-REEVES, LTD.
Also Called: Cabinet Specialists
1616 E Main St (75165-4454)
P.O. Box 718 (75168-0718)
PHONE...................................972 938-9623
EMP: 240 **Privately Held**
WEB: www.cabinetspecialists.com
SIC: 2434 Vanities, bathroom: wood

(G-20570)
WHITAKER METAL DECK SALES
800 Fm 879 (75165-8606)
P.O. Box 551 (75168-0551)
PHONE...................................972 938-1445
Michael Bradshaw, *President*
Deatra Bradshaw, *Vice Pres*
EMP: 10
SQ FT: 18,368
SALES (est): 4.6MM **Privately Held**
WEB: www.whitakermetaldecksales.com
SIC: 3444 Sheet metalwork

Weatherford
Parker County

(G-20571)
37 BUILDING PRODUCTS LTD
3133 Ranger Hwy (76088-8419)
PHONE...................................817 341-3130
Leigh Anne Jones, *President*
Ken Vickers, *Technical Mgr*
EMP: 140
SQ FT: 4,000

GEOGRAPHIC

SALES (est): 30.3MM **Privately Held**
WEB: www.37bp.com
SIC: 3272 1791 Art marble, concrete; concrete reinforcement, placing of

(G-20572)
A BETTER FABRICATION LLC
220 Adams Dr (76086-6333)
PHONE..................................817 629-8908
Russell Berrier II,
EMP: 28
SALES (est): 1.4MM **Privately Held**
WEB: www.abetterfabrication.com
SIC: 3441 Fabricated structural metal

(G-20573)
ABSOLUTE ACSTIC NOISE CTRL LLC (PA)
Also Called: Absolute Noise Control
3208 Fm 920 (76088-6814)
P.O. Box 3110 (76086-0019)
PHONE..................................817 594-4446
Casey Duncan, *Regional Mgr*
Dalton Gribble, *Foreman/Supr*
Manuel Alfaro, *Project Engr*
Jason Davis, *Marketing Staff*
Ruben Espitia, *Manager*
EMP: 11
SQ FT: 3,200
SALES (est): 3.1MM **Privately Held**
WEB: www.absolutenoisecontrol.com
SIC: 3822 Auto controls regulating residntl & coml environmt & applncs

(G-20574)
AES INDUSTRIES INC
1831 Barnett Dr (76087-9441)
P.O. Box 781147, Tallassee AL (36078-0012)
PHONE..................................817 341-7250
Tony Taylor, *Manager*
EMP: 20 **Privately Held**
WEB: www.aescurb.com
SIC: 3444 3441 Metal roofing & roof drainage equipment; fabricated structural metal
PA: Aes Industries, Inc.
2171 Al Highway 229 S
Tallassee AL 36078

(G-20575)
AMERI-FAB LLC
6364 W Interstate 20 (76088-8285)
PHONE..................................817 458-4262
Shelley Chester, *President*
Zack Chester, *Vice Pres*
Chris Taylor, *Project Mgr*
Ken Laye, *CFO*
Hilary Mask, *Office Mgr*
EMP: 65
SQ FT: 140,000
SALES (est): 23.3MM **Privately Held**
WEB: www.amerifabllc.com
SIC: 3533 3498 Oil & gas field machinery; pipe sections fabricated from purchased pipe

(G-20576)
ATKORE PLASTIC PIPE CORP (DH)
1202 N Bowie Dr (76086-1539)
PHONE..................................817 594-8791
EMP: 63
SALES (est): 1.1MM **Publicly Held**
SIC: 3547 Pipe & tube mills

(G-20577)
ATKORE PLASTIC PIPE CORP
Also Called: Heritage Plas An Atkore Intl
1202 N Bowie Dr (76086-1539)
PHONE..................................817 594-8791
Jack Hunt, *Plant Mgr*
EMP: 95 **Publicly Held**
SIC: 3699 Electrical equipment & supplies
HQ: Atkore Plastic Pipe Corporation
1202 N Bowie Dr
Weatherford TX 76086
817 594-8791

(G-20578)
BIG TEX WELL SERVICES LLC
327 N Denton St Ste 100 (76086-2615)
PHONE..................................817 599-6155
Tommy Robertson, *Mng Member*
EMP: 49 **EST:** 2013

SALES (est): 3.3MM **Privately Held**
SIC: 1381 Drilling oil & gas wells

(G-20579)
BROOKS & BROOKS SERVICES INC
Also Called: Benchmark Signs
1826 Barnett Dr (76087-9440)
PHONE..................................817 560-9965
Janis Brooks, *CEO*
Carl L Brooks, *President*
April Carney, *Project Mgr*
EMP: 9
SALES (est): 750K **Privately Held**
WEB: www.benchmarksigns.biz
SIC: 3993 Signs & advertising specialties

(G-20580)
BRYCON INC
Also Called: Brashear Custom Cabinets
400 Mary Dr (76085-8043)
P.O. Box 530, Azle (76098-0530)
PHONE..................................817 444-2724
Dewey Brashear, *President*
EMP: 40
SQ FT: 13,000
SALES (est): 5.2MM **Privately Held**
SIC: 5712 2431 Cabinet work, custom; millwork

(G-20581)
CALVIN ALLEN SADDLERY
Also Called: Allen Calvin Sad & Wstn Wr
3830 E I 20 Exit 415 (76087)
PHONE..................................817 598-0505
G Calvin Allen, *President*
Calvin Allen, *Owner*
EMP: 14
SQ FT: 5,000
SALES (est): 1.8MM **Privately Held**
WEB: www.calvinallensaddlery.com
SIC: 5699 3199 Western apparel; saddles or parts

(G-20582)
COMMUNITY VENTURES INC
Also Called: Community News
5190 E I 20 Svc Rd S (76087)
P.O. Box 1031, Aledo (76008-1031)
PHONE..................................817 441-7661
Randy Keck, *President*
EMP: 10
SALES (est): 726.9K **Privately Held**
WEB: www.community-news.com
SIC: 2711 Commercial printing & newspaper publishing combined; newspapers, publishing & printing

(G-20583)
COOL CITY INC
Also Called: Cool City Motor Company
10655 Mineral Wells Hwy (76088-6721)
PHONE..................................940 682-1122
James L Irwin, *President*
EMP: 15 **EST:** 2000
SALES (est): 1.8MM **Privately Held**
SIC: 3711 Chassis, motor vehicle

(G-20584)
CYCLONE SERVICES LLC
220 Overton Ridge Cir (76088-7848)
P.O. Box 275, Peaster (76485-0275)
PHONE..................................817 594-5571
Michael Spindler,
EMP: 12
SALES (est): 1.6MM **Privately Held**
WEB: www.cycloneservicesllc.com
SIC: 1389 Oil field services

(G-20585)
DALE NICHOLS MARBLE INC
2927 Greenlee Park (76088-7842)
PHONE..................................817 341-8970
Mike Nichols, *President*
EMP: 15
SALES (est): 686.2K **Privately Held**
WEB: www.dalenicholsmarble.com
SIC: 2541 Counter & sink tops

(G-20586)
DALTONS WELDING SERVICE INC
467 Rawhide Trl (76088-0802)
PHONE..................................940 682-7237
Dalton Leatherman, *President*

Linda Dalder, *Principal*
Theresa Leatherman, *Corp Secy*
Brian Leatherman, *Vice Pres*
EMP: 12
SALES (est): 1MM **Privately Held**
WEB: www.daltonswelding.com
SIC: 1791 7692 Structural steel erection; welding repair

(G-20587)
DOBBS COATING SYSTEMS INC (PA)
1888 Mineral Wells Hwy (76088-8316)
PHONE..................................817 341-1777
Wendell Dobbs, *President*
Alvin Warwick, *Opers Mgr*
Lisa Lowery, *Manager*
EMP: 15
SQ FT: 1,700
SALES (est): 2.8MM **Privately Held**
WEB: www.dobbscoatingsystems.com
SIC: 3479 Coating of metals & formed products

(G-20588)
DRALCO SYSTEMS LLC (PA)
1219 Fort Worth Hwy (76086-4556)
PHONE..................................817 599-7335
James Gopffarth, *Mng Member*
Michael S Manson, *Mng Member*
EMP: 53
SALES (est): 22.4MM **Privately Held**
WEB: www.dralco.com
SIC: 3444 Sheet metal specialties, not stamped

(G-20589)
ENLINK MIDSTREAM PARTNERS LP
410 Pearson Ranch Rd (76087-7080)
PHONE..................................817 599-3492
Dean Mueller, *Vice Pres*
EMP: 12
SALES (corp-wide): 6B **Publicly Held**
WEB: www.enlink.com
SIC: 1311 Pipelines, natural gas
HQ: Enlink Midstream Partners, Lp
1722 Routh St Ste 1300
Dallas TX 75201

(G-20590)
EOG RESOURCES INC
395 Jones Rd (76088-8649)
PHONE..................................817 598-8300
Preston Shade, *Manager*
EMP: 40
SALES (corp-wide): 17.3B **Publicly Held**
WEB: www.eogresources.com
SIC: 1382 Oil & gas exploration services
PA: Eog Resources, Inc.
1111 Bagby Sky Lbby 2
Houston TX 77002
713 651-7000

(G-20591)
FIVE STAR FIELD SERVICES LLC
Also Called: 5 Star Measurement
217 W Intersta (76087)
P.O. Box 442 (76086-0442)
PHONE..................................817 594-9799
Keith Stone, *Mng Member*
William Cook III,
Eugene Swindell,
EMP: 60
SALES (est): 17.6MM **Privately Held**
SIC: 1389 Measurement of well flow rates, oil & gas

(G-20592)
FMC TECHNOLOGIES INC
1822 Ranger Hwy (76088-9138)
PHONE..................................817 599-3337
Fax: 817 599-3337
EMP: 24
SALES (corp-wide): 7.9B **Publicly Held**
SIC: 3533 Mfg Oil/Gas Field Machinery
PA: Fmc Technologies, Inc.
5875 N Sam Houston Pkwy W
Houston TX 77079
281 591-4000

(G-20593)
FORT WORTH CRUSHED STONE LLC
4313 Bethel Rd (76087-9318)
PHONE..................................817 596-5512
Jerry Keen, *Manager*
EMP: 12
SALES (corp-wide): 2.6MM **Privately Held**
SIC: 3281 5032 Cut stone & stone products; stone, crushed or broken
PA: Fort Worth Crushed Stone Llc
3312 Joyce Dr
Fort Worth TX 76116
817 244-6024

(G-20594)
FRANKENSTEIN RACING HEADS LLC
Also Called: Frankenstein Engine Dynamics
2410 Ranger Hwy (76088-9181)
PHONE..................................817 556-2434
Chris Frank, *CEO*
EMP: 23
SALES (est): 1.2MM **Privately Held**
WEB: www.frankensteined.net
SIC: 3714 Cylinder heads, motor vehicle

(G-20595)
GENERAL AVIATION INDS INC
415 Jones Rd (76088-9121)
PHONE..................................817 598-4848
Paul Mauldin, *President*
Kenneth Onken, *Vice Pres*
William Sessum, *Opers Staff*
Jodi Hadley, *Purch Mgr*
Lisa Ellerbrook, *Buyer*
EMP: 43
SQ FT: 40,000
SALES (est): 10.4MM **Privately Held**
WEB: www.gaiinc.com
SIC: 3728 3537 Military aircraft equipment & armament; platforms, stands, tables, pallets & similar equipment; platforms, cargo

(G-20596)
INNOVATIVE HINGE PRODUCTS
415 Jones Rd (76088-9121)
PHONE..................................817 598-4846
Don Roach, *Owner*
EMP: 30
SALES (est): 2.4MM **Privately Held**
WEB: www.gaiinc.net
SIC: 3429 Door opening & closing devices, except electrical

(G-20597)
J MORCO INCORPORATED
Also Called: Manufacturing
6650 Mineral Wells Hwy (76088-6011)
PHONE..................................817 596-3989
Joe Morton, *President*
Joseph Morton, *President*
EMP: 25
SQ FT: 10,000
SALES (est): 3.8MM **Privately Held**
WEB: www.jmorco.net
SIC: 3535 3011 Conveyors & conveying equipment; tires, cushion or solid rubber

(G-20598)
JAMAK FABRICATION-TEX LTD
1401 N Bowie Dr (76086-1599)
PHONE..................................817 594-8771
EMP: 13
SALES (est): 1.6MM **Privately Held**
WEB: www.jamak.com
SIC: 3061 3053 2822 Mechanical rubber goods; gaskets, packing & sealing devices; synthetic rubber

(G-20599)
JMK INTERNATIONAL INC (PA)
1401 N Bowie Dr (76086-1503)
PHONE..................................817 737-3703
Alfred M Micallef, *President*
Patricia Post, *CFO*
Cathy Snotee, *Admin Sec*
▲ EMP: 30
SQ FT: 10,000
SALES (est): 60.5MM **Privately Held**
WEB: www.jmkint.com
SIC: 3061 Appliance rubber goods (mechanical)

(G-20600)
LONE STAR INSTRMNTTN&ELCTRC
1577 Ranger Hwy (76086-9210)
PHONE................................817 458-9347
Rick Flanagan, *Branch Mgr*
EMP: 49
SALES (corp-wide): 26.6MM **Privately Held**
WEB: www.lonestarcorporation.com
SIC: 3699 Electrical equipment & supplies
PA: Lone Star Instrumentation & Electric
Corporation
2222 W 42nd St
Odessa TX 79764
432 368-7827

(G-20601)
M K S NATURAL GAS COMPANY
200 Cochran Rd (76085-6845)
P.O. Box 1209 (76086-1209)
PHONE................................817 599-9477
Richard F Williamson, *President*
EMP: 45
SALES (est): 5MM **Privately Held**
SIC: 1381 Drilling oil & gas wells

(G-20602)
MABCO EQUIPMENT LTD
1219 Fort Worth Hwy (76086-4556)
PHONE................................817 599-7335
Mike Lang, *President*
Brian Lang, *Vice Pres*
EMP: 35
SQ FT: 50,000
SALES (est): 3.5MM **Privately Held**
SIC: 3444 3499 Sheet metal specialties,
not stamped; mail chutes, sheet metal;
metal ventilating equipment; fire- or bur-
glary-resistive products

(G-20603)
MACLASKEY OIL FIELD SERVICES
12600 Cleburne Hwy (76086)
P.O. Box 2378 (76086-7378)
PHONE................................817 594-8073
Kelly Maclaskey, *CEO*
Stacy Maclaskey, *Corp Secy*
EMP: 73 EST: 2012
SQ FT: 58,000
SALES (est): 3.1MM **Privately Held**
WEB: www.maclaskey.com
SIC: 1389 Oil field services

(G-20604)
MCDONALD EXTRUSION TOOLING
Also Called: McDonald Mch & Fabrications
116 Price Ln (76085-8875)
PHONE................................817 594-1290
David McDonald, *President*
▼ EMP: 10
SALES (est): 1.2MM **Privately Held**
SIC: 3599 Machine shop, jobbing & repair

(G-20605)
MOEIN INC
Also Called: Furniture Land
1816 Barnett Dr (76087-9440)
PHONE................................817 341-1414
Hossein Moein, *President*
EMP: 10
SQ FT: 10,000
SALES (est): 100K **Privately Held**
SIC: 2512 2511 Upholstered household
furniture; living room furniture: uphol-
stered on wood frames; novelty furniture:
wood

(G-20606)
NEW RAILHEAD MANUFACTURING LLC
1405 Mineral Wells Hwy (76086-9219)
P.O. Box 2409 (76086-7409)
PHONE................................817 594-6663
Ralph Edwards, *Sales Staff*
Don Putman, *Branch Mgr*
EMP: 10
SALES (corp-wide): 348K **Privately Held**
WEB: www.railhead.com
SIC: 3533 3532 Oil & gas field machinery;
drills & drilling equipment, mining (except
oil & gas)

PA: New Railhead Manufacturing Llc
5750 N Riverside Dr
Fort Worth TX 76137
817 847-6647

(G-20607)
NEWSPAPER HOLDING INC
Also Called: Weatherford Democrat
512 Palo Pinto St (76086-4128)
PHONE................................817 594-7440
Jim Wilson, *Manager*
EMP: 37
SALES (corp-wide): 23.7B **Privately Held**
WEB: www.oskaloosa.com
SIC: 2711 2752 Newspapers, publishing &
printing; commercial printing, lithographic
HQ: Newspaper Holding, Inc.
425 Locust St
Johnstown PA 15901
814 532-5102

(G-20608)
OMEGA CHEMICAL PRODUCTS INC
688 Hiner Rd (76087-9501)
PHONE................................219 208-0500
Jerry Kaisetz, *President*
EMP: 25
SALES (est): 2.6MM **Privately Held**
WEB: www.omegachemical.com
SIC: 2841 2842 Soap & other detergents;
specialty cleaning, polishes & sanitation
goods

(G-20609)
PIPERS WELDING SERVICE INC
Also Called: Pied Piper Animal Trap
445 Garner Adell Rd (76088-7192)
PHONE................................940 682-4663
Margie Piper, *President*
EMP: 12 EST: 1987
SQ FT: 4,960
SALES (est): 2.1MM **Privately Held**
WEB: www.piedpipertraps.com
SIC: 3496 Traps, animal & fish

(G-20610)
POWER SERVICE PRODUCTS INC (PA)
513 Peaster Hwy (76086)
P.O. Box 1089 (76086-1089)
PHONE................................817 599-9486
Ed M Kramer, *President*
Kramer Jeff, *Vice Pres*
Jeff Kramer, *Vice Pres*
Patricia Kramer, *Vice Pres*
Bob Sellers, *Vice Pres*
◆ EMP: 34
SQ FT: 11,000
SALES (est): 15.7MM **Privately Held**
WEB: www.powerservice.com
SIC: 2899 Fuel treating compounds

(G-20611)
PPG INDUSTRIES INC
Also Called: PPG 8362
2201 Tin Top Rd Ste 375 (76087-4431)
PHONE................................817 613-1860
Clint Gray, *Manager*
EMP: 24
SALES (corp-wide): 15.3B **Publicly Held**
WEB: www.ppg.com
SIC: 2851 Paints & allied products
PA: Ppg Industries, Inc.
1 Ppg Pl
Pittsburgh PA 15272
412 434-3131

(G-20612)
PROVIMI NORTH AMERICA INC
1050 Vigortone Blvd (76086-1554)
PHONE................................817 594-9628
Dave Rozendall, *Branch Mgr*
EMP: 9
SALES (corp-wide): 113.4B **Privately Held**
WEB: www.provimius.com
SIC: 2048 Prepared feeds
HQ: Provimi North America, Inc.
10 Nutrition Way
Brookville OH 45309
937 770-2400

(G-20613)
RADIUS HDD DIRECT LLC
2525 Ranger Hwy (76088-9110)
P.O. Box 3106 (76086-0019)
PHONE................................800 892-9114
John Szabuniewicz, *Director*
Pamela Summers, *Director*
EMP: 42
SALES (est): 10MM
SALES (corp-wide): 3.3B **Publicly Held**
WEB: www.radiushdd.com
SIC: 3546 Drills & drilling tools
HQ: The Charles Machine Works Inc
1959 W Fir St
Perry OK 73077
580 572-2693

(G-20614)
RAWLINS MONUMENT INC
111 Palo Pinto St (76086-4325)
P.O. Box 237 (76086-0237)
PHONE................................817 594-2726
Nancy L Deison, *President*
Mark R Littleton, *Corp Secy*
Deison David, *Vice Pres*
EMP: 10
SQ FT: 3,000
SALES (est): 1MM **Privately Held**
WEB: www.rawlinsmonuments.net
SIC: 3281 Monuments, cut stone (not fin-
ishing or lettering only)

(G-20615)
READY SEAL INC
Also Called: Ready Products Resaw Mill
801 W Interstate 20 (76087-8587)
PHONE................................817 594-8198
Don Mauldin, *Branch Mgr*
EMP: 20 **Privately Held**
WEB: www.readyseal.com
SIC: 2851 Paints & allied products
PA: Ready Seal, Incorporated
1440 S State Highway 121 # 3
Lewisville TX 75067

(G-20616)
REEVES ROOFING EQUIPMENT CO
1025 Forest Park Dr (76087-2815)
PHONE................................210 695-3567
Joe S Reeves Jr, *President*
Amy Edison, *Corp Secy*
John Reeves, *Vice Pres*
EMP: 27
SQ FT: 1,600
SALES (est): 4MM
SALES (corp-wide): 14.4MM **Privately Held**
WEB: www.hecousa.com
SIC: 3531 Roofing equipment
PA: Reves Equipment Company
1025 Forest Park Dr
Weatherford TX 76087
210 215-1666

(G-20617)
RIM MANUFACTURING LLC
901 W Interstate 20 (76087-8588)
PHONE................................817 599-6521
Steve Harms, *CEO*
Scott Frost, *President*
Eddie McSwain, *Opers Staff*
EMP: 50 EST: 1979
SQ FT: 35,000
SALES (est): 8.1MM **Privately Held**
WEB: www.reactioninjectionmolding.com
SIC: 3089 Injection molded finished plastic
products; injection molding of plastics

(G-20618)
RYAN MANUFACTURING COMPANY INC
213 Old Agnes Rd (76088-8210)
PHONE................................817 613-1890
Mary Ryan Kimbrell, *President*
▲ EMP: 12
SQ FT: 5,000
SALES (est): 730K **Privately Held**
SIC: 3599 Machine shop, jobbing & repair

(G-20619)
S2W CONTRACTING LLC
Also Called: S2w Field Services
136 Miramar Cir (76085-2827)
P.O. Box 422, Clarks Summit PA (18411-0422)
PHONE................................940 745-1421
Holly Stratton Withee,
Charles Emmery Withee,
EMP: 30
SALES (est): 11MM **Privately Held**
WEB: www.s2wcontracting.com
SIC: 1389 Processing service, gas

(G-20620)
SELECT ENERGY SERVICES LLC
Also Called: Impact Energy Services
6150 N Fm 51 (76085-9360)
PHONE................................817 523-0136
Russel Bezner, *Branch Mgr*
EMP: 30
SALES (corp-wide): 1.2B **Publicly Held**
WEB: www.selectenergyservices.com
SIC: 1389 Oil field services
HQ: Select Energy Services, Llc
1820 N I 35
Gainesville TX 76240
940 668-1818

(G-20621)
SPOTTED LAKES LLC
Also Called: 1845 Oil Field Services
1995 Ranger Hwy (76088-9104)
PHONE................................817 441-9900
Timothy M Buffington, *President*
Chad Hall, *Vice Pres*
Nathan Kurland, *VP Opers*
Kenny Webster, *Natl Sales Mgr*
EMP: 146
SQ FT: 4,000
SALES (est): 8.8MM **Privately Held**
WEB: www.1845.com
SIC: 3715 Truck trailers

(G-20622)
STANDARD INDUS MFG PRTNERS LLC
3600 N Fm 51 (76085-6802)
PHONE................................817 598-1500
EMP: 9
SALES (corp-wide): 27.2MM **Privately Held**
WEB: www.standardpumpparts.com
SIC: 3561 Pump jacks & other pumping
equipment
PA: Standard Industrial
901 W 3rd St
Odessa TX 79763
432 332-5955

(G-20623)
STRC OILFIELD TECHNOLOGY LLC
327 N Denton St Ste 100 (76086-2615)
PHONE................................817 599-6155
Tommy Robertson, *Mng Member*
EMP: 28
SALES (est): 5.7MM **Privately Held**
WEB: www.strcoilfieldtechnology.com
SIC: 1389 Oil field services

(G-20624)
SUN WEST MUD COMPANY INC
112 W Scenic Trl (76088-8405)
PHONE................................817 594-9758
Malcolm Outlaw, *Principal*
EMP: 15
SALES (corp-wide): 19.1MM **Privately Held**
WEB: www.sunwestfluids.com
SIC: 1389 Oil field services
PA: Sun West Mud Company, Inc
3002 W Front St
Midland TX 79701
432 689-0777

(G-20625)
TEXAS INDUSTRIES INC
Also Called: T X I
5211 New Tin Top Rd (76087-7438)
PHONE................................817 596-4307
Gary Williams, *Opers-Prdtn-Mfg*
Kery Marlett, *CPA*
EMP: 20 **Publicly Held**

WEB: www.martinmarietta.com
SIC: 1442 Sand mining; gravel mining
HQ: Texas Industries, Inc.
  1503 Lyndon B Johnson Fwy
  Dallas TX 75234
  972 647-6700

(G-20626)
TEXAS STEEL TECH LLC
6620 Mineral Wells Hwy (76088-6011)
PHONE....................817 894-7041
EMP: 10
SALES (corp-wide): 649K **Privately Held**
SIC: 3462 Mfg Light Steel And Engineering Services
PA: Texas Steel Tech Llc
  220 Fort Worth Hwy # 850
  Weatherford TX 76086
  817 894-7041

(G-20627)
TUFFYS AC & HTG SVC INC
4017 Azle Hwy (76085-8419)
PHONE....................817 596-0150
Janice Roberts Gilliland, *President*
Becky McCollough, *Manager*
Jef Branon, *Shareholder*
Alan Gilliland, *Shareholder*
EMP: 10
SALES (est): 1MM **Privately Held**
WEB: www.tuffysac.net
SIC: 7623 3086 Air conditioning repair; plastics foam products

(G-20628)
VALERUS COMPRESSION SVCS LP
1303 Azle Hwy (76085-9561)
PHONE....................817 598-1600
Mike Griffin, *Manager*
EMP: 30
SALES (est): 967.8K **Privately Held**
SIC: 1389 Oil field services

(G-20629)
WEATHERFORD ADVERTISING INC
Also Called: Parker County Shopper
512 Palo Pinto St (76086-4128)
PHONE....................817 594-7440
Mike Thornberry, *Principal*
Martin Paul, *Vice Pres*
Michelle Roberts, *Advt Staff*
Dale Gosser, *Manager*
EMP: 40
SQ FT: 2,500
SALES (est): 2.3MM **Privately Held**
WEB: www.weatherforddemocrat.com
SIC: 2711 Newspapers: publishing only, not printed on site

(G-20630)
WEATHERFORD AEROSPACE INC
610 W 3rd St (76086-2037)
PHONE....................817 598-0044
Charles Paris Sr, *Branch Mgr*
EMP: 150
SALES (corp-wide): 166.5MM **Privately Held**
WEB: www.weatherfordaerospace.com
SIC: 3728 Aircraft parts & equipment
HQ: Weatherford Aerospace, Inc.
  1020 E Columbia St
  Weatherford TX 76086

(G-20631)
WEATHERFORD AEROSPACE INC (HQ)
1020 E Columbia St (76086-4522)
PHONE....................817 594-5464
Charles Paris Jr, *President*
EMP: 79
SQ FT: 300,000
SALES (est): 32.5MM
SALES (corp-wide): 166.5MM **Privately Held**
WEB: www.weatherfordaerospace.com
SIC: 3728 Aircraft parts & equipment
PA: Novaria Group, L.L.C.
  6300 Ridglea Pl Ste 800
  Fort Worth TX 76116
  817 381-3810

Webster
Harris County

(G-20632)
ALIMAK GROUP USA INC (DH)
12552 Galveston Rd (77598)
PHONE....................713 640-8500
Dale Stoddard, *President*
Tom Dunn, *Vice Pres*
Ed Gibbs, *Vice Pres*
Rico Thomas, *Production*
Philip Caltabiano, *Purch Mgr*
▲ **EMP:** 100
SQ FT: 10,000
SALES (est): 68.3MM **Privately Held**
WEB: www.alimak.us
SIC: 5084 7699 3535 3534 Elevators; elevators: inspection, service & repair; conveyors & conveying equipment; elevators & moving stairways
HQ: Alimak Group Sweden Ab
  Stenbacka
  Skelleftea 931 4
  910 870-00

(G-20633)
ASTROTECH CORPORATION (PA)
555 Forge River Rd # 100 (77598-4369)
PHONE....................512 485-9530
Thomas B Pickens III, *Ch of Bd*
Rajesh Mellacheruvu, *COO*
Eric N Stober, *CFO*
Eric Stober, *CFO*
Vincent Gomez, *Controller*
EMP: 9
SQ FT: 5,219
SALES: 488K **Publicly Held**
WEB: www.astrotechcorp.com
SIC: 3826 2836 Automatic chemical analyzers; vaccines

(G-20634)
BEST PUBLICATIONS LLP
1199 W Nasa Pkwy (77598-4944)
PHONE....................281 488-8300
Kathy Denim, *Manager*
EMP: 21
SALES (corp-wide): 6.5MM **Privately Held**
WEB: www.bpyp.com
SIC: 2741 Telephone & other directory publishing
PA: Best Publications Llp
  5107 Catalpa Ln
  Amarillo TX 79110
  806 352-8993

(G-20635)
CENTURY ELEVATORS INC
12130 Galveston Rd Bldg 5 (77598)
PHONE....................281 667-3000
Walter P Manning Jr, *President*
Kevin Lavorgna, *Vice Pres*
Paula R Manning, *Vice Pres*
Steve Gwaltney, *VP Opers*
Lee Brantley, *VP Sales*
EMP: 13
SQ FT: 2,500
SALES (est): 5.1MM **Privately Held**
WEB: www.centuryelevators.com
SIC: 3534 7359 Elevators & moving stairways; equipment rental & leasing

(G-20636)
CLEAR LK PROGRAM SOLUTIONS LLC
18422 Highway 3 (77598-5406)
PHONE....................713 784-0111
Steven Jones, *Principal*
EMP: 10
SQ FT: 1,700
SALES (est): 512.9K **Privately Held**
SIC: 3369 Aerospace castings, nonferrous: except aluminum

(G-20637)
DERMATLGICAL ASSN OF TEXAS LLP (PA)
451 N Texas Ave (77598-4927)
PHONE....................281 333-3376
Stephen K Tyring, *Principal*
Deborah Yetman, *Manager*

Ivonne Kizilkaya, *Assistant*
EMP: 14
SALES (est): 2.4MM **Privately Held**
WEB: www.dermtexas.com
SIC: 2834 Dermatologicals

(G-20638)
GHG CORP
960 Clear Lake City Blvd (77598-6604)
PHONE....................281 461-6533
Israel Galvan, *CEO*
Joseph Willhelm, *President*
Kim Patton, *General Mgr*
Kimberly Patton, *Vice Pres*
Sheila Rolland, *QC Mgr*
EMP: 340
SQ FT: 12,000
SALES (est): 39.6MM **Privately Held**
WEB: www.ghgcorp.com
SIC: 7372 8711 8731 Application computer software; engineering services; engineering laboratory, except testing

(G-20639)
INDUS INSTRUMENTS
721 Tristar Dr Ste C (77598-1302)
PHONE....................281 286-1130
Sridhar Madala, *Owner*
Walter Caro, *Vice Pres*
Blair Poetschke, *Vice Pres*
Juan Tovar, *Mfg Mgr*
Michael Weneck, *Info Tech Mgr*
EMP: 14
SQ FT: 7,800
SALES (est): 1.7MM **Privately Held**
WEB: www.indusinstruments.com
SIC: 3679 Electronic circuits

(G-20640)
MACAULAY CONTROLS COMPANY (PA)
13920 Osprey Ct Ste E (77598-1615)
P.O. Box 890231, Houston (77289-0231)
PHONE....................281 282-0100
Kari Hollway, *President*
James Hollway, *Vice Pres*
Jim Hollway, *Vice Pres*
Cheryl Diegelman, *Sales Staff*
Sarah Guzman, *Sales Staff*
EMP: 10
SQ FT: 3,000
SALES (est): 7.1MM **Privately Held**
WEB: www.macaulaycontrols.com
SIC: 5085 3829 Pistons & valves; instrumentation for reactor controls, auxiliary

(G-20641)
NANORACKS LLC
503 Forge River Rd (77598-4357)
PHONE....................832 632-7754
Jeffrey Manber, *CEO*
Stephanie Purgerson, *COO*
Ronald Goedendorp, *Vice Pres*
Rich Pournelle, *Vice Pres*
Richard Pournelle, *Vice Pres*
EMP: 53
SALES (est): 8.3MM
SALES (corp-wide): 8.2MM **Privately Held**
WEB: www.nanoracks.com
SIC: 8731 3761 Biotechnical research, commercial; guided missiles & space vehicles, research & development
PA: Xo Markets Holdings, Inc.
  503 Forge River Rd
  Webster TX 77598
  281 984-4040

(G-20642)
PATTON ENTERPRISES INC
Also Called: Protec
12130 Highway 3 Bldg 4 (77598-1550)
PHONE....................832 619-1890
Fax: 281 339-1269
EMP: 20
SALES (corp-wide): 3.6MM **Privately Held**
SIC: 1389 Oil/Gas Field Services
PA: Patton Enterprises Inc.
  7136 S Yale Ave Ste 200
  Tulsa OK 74136
  918 493-6101

(G-20643)
ROBERT J JENKINS CO
906 W Medical Center Blvd (77598-4010)
PHONE....................281 332-3566
Robert J Jenkins, *President*
Juli Sullivan, *Manager*
▲ **EMP:** 35
SQ FT: 5,000
SALES (est): 3.5MM **Privately Held**
WEB: www.rjjenkins.com
SIC: 3255 Clay refractories

(G-20644)
SCHNEIDER ELECTRIC SYSTEMS USA
17146 Feathercraft Ln (77598-4364)
PHONE....................281 709-1200
Steve Brotzman, *Engineer*
David Brown, *Engineer*
Mark Allen, *Controller*
Alynn Burk, *Marketing Mgr*
James Austin, *Manager*
EMP: 80
SALES (corp-wide): 177.9K **Privately Held**
WEB: www.se.com
SIC: 3823 Industrial instrmnts msrmnt display/control process variable
HQ: Schneider Electric Systems Usa, Inc.
  10900 Equity Dr
  Houston TX 77041
  713 329-1600

(G-20645)
SGT LLC
17155 Feathercraft Ln # 100 (77598-4417)
PHONE....................281 751-1071
Mark Greeley, *Branch Mgr*
EMP: 80 **Publicly Held**
WEB: www.kbr.com
SIC: 3812 Search & navigation equipment
HQ: Sgt, Llc
  7701 Greenbelt Rd Ste 400
  Greenbelt MD 20770

(G-20646)
SIGN CITY INC
1851 Fm 528 Rd (77598-4501)
PHONE....................281 338-1203
Praveen Gohel, *President*
EMP: 9
SALES (est): 1MM **Privately Held**
WEB: www.signcityhouston.com
SIC: 3993 Electric signs

(G-20647)
STANDARD INDUSTRIAL PDTS CO (PA)
Also Called: Sipco
12610 Galveston Rd (77598)
P.O. Box 890325, Houston (77289-0325)
PHONE....................281 280-0147
Raul A Martinez, *President*
Maria Esther Martinez, *Human Res Dir*
Maria Almandoz Martinez, *Admin Sec*
▲ **EMP:** 25
SQ FT: 18,000
SALES (est): 14.9MM **Privately Held**
WEB: www.sipco-mls.com
SIC: 5085 3714 5999 5063 Power transmission equipment & apparatus; transmissions, motor vehicle; engine & motor equipment & supplies; power transmission equipment, electric; iron & steel forgings; gray & ductile iron foundries

(G-20648)
TRI-SEN SYSTEMS CORPORATION (HQ)
Also Called: North American Engineering Ctr
109 Magellan Cir (77598-2033)
PHONE....................832 632-1211
William Barkovitz, *President*
Jim Jacoby, *Vice Pres*
Tim Pieszchala, *Vice Pres*
Kimball R Smith, *Vice Pres*
Michael Wrenn, *Project Engr*
▲ **EMP:** 28
SQ FT: 5,000
SALES (est): 5.7MM **Privately Held**
WEB: www.tri-sen.com
SIC: 3543 Industrial patterns

▲ = Import ▼ =Export
◆ =Import/Export

Weimar
Colorado County

(G-20649)
J & B SAUSAGE COMPANY INC
1078 Highway 90 (78962-4402)
PHONE..................................979 725-6661
EMP: 168
SALES (corp-wide): 83.8MM **Privately Held**
WEB: www.jbfoods.com
SIC: 2011 Sausages from meat slaughtered on site
PA: J & B Sausage Company, Inc.
100 Main
Waelder TX 78959
830 788-7661

(G-20650)
KASPERS MEAT MARKET INC (PA)
Also Called: Kasper Packing
119 E Post Office St (78962-1631)
PHONE..................................979 725-8227
Maurice Kasper, President
Kasper Barney, Vice Pres
Jean Kasper Blaha, Treasurer
Jean Blaha, Treasurer
EMP: 21
SQ FT: 2,500
SALES (est): 1.9MM **Privately Held**
WEB: www.weimartexas.net
SIC: 5421 2011 2013 Meat markets, including freezer provisioners; beef products from beef slaughtered on site; sausages & other prepared meats

(G-20651)
UTEX INDUSTRIES INC
605 Utex Dr (78962-3310)
P.O. Box 901 (78962-0901)
PHONE..................................979 725-8503
Chuck Rankin, VP Opers
Mike Vacek, Production
Tom Goedrich, QC Mgr
Tom Hobbs, Engineer
Carolyn Klam, Sales Staff
EMP: 300
SQ FT: 175,000
SALES (corp-wide): 164.4MM **Privately Held**
WEB: www.utexind.com
SIC: 3053 3061 2822 Packing: steam engines, pipe joints, air compressors, etc.; gaskets, all materials; mechanical rubber goods; synthetic rubber
HQ: Utex Industries, Inc.
10810 Katy Fwy Ste 100
Houston TX 77043
713 467-1000

(G-20652)
WEIMAR INDUSTRIES INC
Also Called: Weimar Manufacturing
505 S Eagle St (78962-2901)
P.O. Box 777 (78962-0777)
PHONE..................................979 725-8503
Frank Macaulay, President
Richard C Macaulay, President
Frances Macaulay, Corp Secy
EMP: 9
SQ FT: 12,750
SALES (est): 1.2MM **Privately Held**
WEB: www.weimartexas.net
SIC: 3822 Auto controls regulating residntl & coml environmt & applncs

(G-20653)
WHISTLING DUCK VNEYARDS WINERY
1241 County Road 212 (78962-3739)
PHONE..................................512 913-4813
John Cooke, Mng Member
Stan Johnson,
EMP: 9
SALES (est): 200K **Privately Held**
WEB: www.whistlingduckwinery.com
SIC: 5921 2084 Wine; wines

Welch
Dawson County

(G-20654)
APACHE CORPORATION
1811 County Road 690 (79377-4102)
PHONE..................................806 755-2231
Paul Bedwell, Manager
EMP: 11
SALES (corp-wide): 6.4B **Publicly Held**
WEB: www.apachecorp.com
SIC: 1311 Crude petroleum production
PA: Apache Corporation
2000 Post Oak Blvd Ste 10
Houston TX 77056
713 296-6000

(G-20655)
KEY ENERGY SERVICES INC
Hwy 137 S (79377)
P.O. Box 130 (79377-0130)
PHONE..................................806 489-7452
Mike Slaughter, Manager
EMP: 27
SALES (corp-wide): 413.8MM **Publicly Held**
WEB: www.keyenergy.com
SIC: 1389 1382 Servicing oil & gas wells; oil & gas exploration services
PA: Key Energy Services, Inc.
1301 Mckinney St Ste 1800
Houston TX 77010
713 651-4300

Wellington
Collingsworth County

(G-20656)
PLAS MAC INC
3696 Us Highway 83 (79095-4817)
PHONE..................................806 447-0065
Roger Wilhelm, President
Lisa Wilhelm, Vice Pres
EMP: 16
SQ FT: 21,000
SALES (est): 1.2MM **Privately Held**
WEB: www.plas-mac.com
SIC: 3089 Plastic & fiberglass tanks; pontoons, nonrigid: plastic

Wells
Cherokee County

(G-20657)
GREENHEAD INDUSTRIES INC
Hwy 69 N (75976)
PHONE..................................936 867-4801
Nona Baily, CEO
Blake Baily, President
▲ EMP: 16
SALES (est): 180.6K **Privately Held**
SIC: 2221 Textile mills, broadwoven: silk & manmade, also glass

(G-20658)
W C HODGES LOGGING
County Rd 2707 (75976)
P.O. Box 568 (75976-9005)
PHONE..................................936 867-4550
William C Hodges, Owner
EMP: 12
SALES (est): 500K **Privately Held**
SIC: 2411 Logging

Weslaco
Hidalgo County

(G-20659)
EXTREME WELL TESTING LLC
2401 E Expressway 83 (78599-5512)
PHONE..................................956 969-4452
Bob Grooms, CFO
Edwin M Payne, Mng Member
Beatriz N Saenz,
EMP: 50
SALES (est): 3MM **Privately Held**
SIC: 1389 Servicing oil & gas wells

(G-20660)
INTERNATIONAL WOOD LLC
2300 N Sugar Sweet Ave (78596)
PHONE..................................956 969-8666
▲ EMP: 150 EST: 2005
SALES (est): 14.2MM **Privately Held**
SIC: 2431 Mfg Millwork

(G-20661)
J-III CONCRETE CO (PA)
1700 E 28th St (78596-8245)
PHONE..................................956 968-1371
A C Cuellar III, President
J Cuellar, Vice Pres
EMP: 36
SQ FT: 2,500
SALES (est): 9.8MM **Privately Held**
WEB: www.j3concrete.com
SIC: 3273 Ready-mixed concrete

(G-20662)
JORGE TREVINO
Also Called: Moltroq International
1115 E 20th St (78596-8259)
PHONE..................................956 376-7114
Jorge Trevino, Owner
EMP: 10
SALES (est): 391.5K **Privately Held**
SIC: 3544 Industrial molds

(G-20663)
LA ABUELA MEXICAN FOODS INC
1904 Joe Stephens Ave (78599-3702)
PHONE..................................956 447-8289
Cristina Ardila, President
EMP: 46
SQ FT: 10,000
SALES (est): 7.9MM **Privately Held**
WEB: www.la-abuela.com
SIC: 2099 Tortillas, fresh or refrigerated

(G-20664)
MARDEL SOUZA INC
Also Called: American Made Solar Wind Tech
611 S International Blvd (78596-9108)
PHONE..................................956 459-3504
Alejandro Rodriguez, CEO
Alejandro Pena, CEO
EMP: 30
SQ FT: 1,500
SALES (est): 3MM **Privately Held**
WEB: www.mardelsouza.com
SIC: 3674 5074 Solar cells; heating equipment & panels, solar

(G-20665)
MID-VALLEY NEWSPAPERS INC
Also Called: Mid-Valley Towncrier
401 S Kansas Ave Ste C2 (78596-6382)
PHONE..................................956 969-2543
Fax: 956 968-0855
EMP: 31 EST: 1982
SQ FT: 3,000
SALES (est): 1.6MM
SALES (corp-wide): 103.4MM **Privately Held**
SIC: 2711 Newspapers-Publishing/Printing
PA: Aim Media Texas Operating, Llc
1400 E Nolana Ave
Mcallen TX 78504
956 683-4000

(G-20666)
MONTES TORTILLA FACTORY
7536 N Fm 88 (78599-4263)
PHONE..................................956 969-5792
Gilberto Rodriguez, Owner
EMP: 10 EST: 2008
SALES (est): 590K **Privately Held**
SIC: 2099 Tortillas, fresh or refrigerated

(G-20667)
R GUERRA CONSTRUCTION INC
6700 N Mile 3 1/2 W (78599-1479)
PHONE..................................956 854-4038
EMP: 15
SALES: 500K **Privately Held**
SIC: 0782 3444 Landscape Contractors & Guard Rail Contractors

(G-20668)
RIO GRANDE CONTAINER INC
1405 E Expressway 83 (78599-4520)
PHONE..................................956 447-5949
Harold Jones, President
Mark Gibbs, Vice Pres
EMP: 33
SQ FT: 60,000
SALES (est): 9.8MM **Privately Held**
WEB: www.riograndecontainer.com
SIC: 2653 Boxes, corrugated: made from purchased materials

(G-20669)
TRANE COMPANY
1240 Vo Tech Dr (78599-5173)
PHONE..................................956 968-6425
James Trane, Branch Mgr
EMP: 39 **Privately Held**
WEB: www.trane.com
SIC: 3585 Refrigeration & heating equipment
HQ: The Trane Company
3600 Pammel Creek Rd
La Crosse WI 54601
608 787-2000

(G-20670)
TYR USA LLC
3800 Canan (78596)
PHONE..................................956 274-9380
Arturo Palacios Medina, Mng Member
Martha Patricia Marquez,
EMP: 20
SQ FT: 3,000
SALES (est): 879.6K **Privately Held**
SIC: 2673 Bags: plastic, laminated & coated

(G-20671)
WOODCRAFTERS HOME PRODUCTS LLC (DH)
3700 Camino De Verdad Rd (78596-7531)
P.O. Box 8242 (78599-8242)
PHONE..................................956 565-6329
Rick Vasquez, President
Ricardo Villareal, President
Steve Strasevicz, Exec VP
Rocio Tanus, Exec VP
Sissy Navarrete, Prdtn Mgr
◆ EMP: 97
SQ FT: 360,000
SALES (est): 285.6MM
SALES (corp-wide): 5.7B **Publicly Held**
WEB: www.woodcrafters-tx.com
SIC: 2434 Vanities, bathroom: wood

West
McLennan County

(G-20672)
WESTEX WELDING COMPANY
210 Cottonwood Rd (76691-1801)
PHONE..................................254 826-5343
Raymond R Matus, Owner
EMP: 15
SQ FT: 12,000
SALES (est): 1.3MM **Privately Held**
WEB: www.westexfire.com
SIC: 3713 Truck bodies (motor vehicles)

West Columbia
Brazoria County

(G-20673)
ALAMO CONCRETE PRODUCTS LTD
County Rd 437 (77486)
P.O. Box 366 (77486-0366)
PHONE..................................979 345-4631
Henry Havel, Manager
EMP: 13 **Privately Held**
SIC: 3273 Ready-mixed concrete
PA: Alamo Concrete Products, Ltd.
6055 W Green Mountain Rd
Austin TX 78744

(G-20674)
ALAMO CONCRETE PRODUCTS LTD
Also Called: Alamo Ready Mix Concrete
Hwy 35 E (77486)
P.O. Box 366 (77486-0366)
PHONE..................................979 849-6378
Henry Havel, *Branch Mgr*
EMP: 10 **Privately Held**
SIC: 3273 Ready-mixed concrete
PA: Alamo Concrete Products, Ltd.
6055 W Green Mountain Rd
Austin TX 78744

(G-20675)
BRAZORIA COUNTY NEWS (PA)
Also Called: Gulf Coast Tribune
113 E Bernard St (77486-3213)
PHONE..................................979 345-3127
Carlene Toney, *President*
David E Toney, *President*
EMP: 10 **EST:** 1962
SQ FT: 8,851
SALES (est): 1.5MM **Privately Held**
WEB: www.brazoriacountynews.com
SIC: 2711 Newspapers, publishing & printing

West Lake Hills
Travis County

(G-20676)
ACE HARDWOOD FLOORING INC
4238 Bee Caves Rd (78746-6412)
PHONE..................................512 719-3555
Mark Szeneri, *President*
▲ **EMP:** 17
SALES (est): 2.5MM **Privately Held**
WEB: www.acehardwood.com
SIC: 1752 2426 5023 Wood floor installation & refinishing; flooring, hardwood; wood flooring

(G-20677)
APOLLO ENDOSURGERY INC (PA)
1120 S Capital Of Texas H (78746-6715)
PHONE..................................512 279-5100
Todd Newton, *CEO*
Donald Jones, *Owner*
Lane Baumberger, *District Mgr*
John Molesphini, *Exec VP*
Mary League, *Vice Pres*
EMP: 45
SQ FT: 18,388
SALES (est): 50.7MM **Publicly Held**
WEB: www.apolloendo.com
SIC: 3845 Endoscopic equipment, electromedical

(G-20678)
ASPYR MEDIA INC
1250 S Cpitl Of Txas Hwy (78746-6446)
PHONE..................................512 708-8100
Michael Rogers, *CEO*
EMP: 18
SALES (est): 2.3MM **Privately Held**
WEB: www.aspyr.com
SIC: 7372 Publishers' computer software

(G-20679)
COHERENT LOGIX INCORPORATED
1120 S Capital Of Texas H (78746-4485)
PHONE..................................512 382-8961
Michael Doerr, *President*
David Gibson, *Project Mgr*
Tony Jarnigan, *Engineer*
Viet Ngo, *Engineer*
Martin Hunt, *Program Mgr*
EMP: 50
SALES (est): 1.6MM **Privately Held**
WEB: www.coherentlogix.com
SIC: 3674 Semiconductors & related devices

(G-20680)
CONSISTENT REASONING INC
1120 S Cpitl Of Tx 3 200 (78746-7137)
PHONE..................................512 382-8940
Michael Doerr, *President*

Donald Gorsuch, *Vice Pres*
Viet Ngo, *Engineer*
Dave Townsend, *Software Engr*
EMP: 33
SQ FT: 2,200
SALES (est): 6.5MM **Privately Held**
WEB: www.coherentlogix.com
SIC: 3674 Semiconductors & related devices

(G-20681)
EVERI GAMES HOLDING INC (HQ)
206 Wild Basin Rd Bldg B (78746-3343)
PHONE..................................512 334-7500
Michael D Rumbolz, *President*
Linda V Trinh, *Vice Pres*
Robert Wallis, *Opers Staff*
Randy L Taylor, *CFO*
Smith Trevor, *Manager*
▲ **EMP:** 56
SQ FT: 65,000
SALES (est): 62.4MM
SALES (corp-wide): 533.2MM **Publicly Held**
WEB: www.everi.com
SIC: 3944 Electronic game machines, except coin-operated; video game machines, except coin-operated
PA: Everi Holdings Inc.
7250 S Tenaya Way Ste 100
Las Vegas NV 89113
800 833-7110

(G-20682)
HMT HIGH MEDICAL TECH USA INC
Also Called: Healthtronics
1301 S Cptl Of Tx Hwy 2 (78746-6574)
PHONE..................................512 721-4700
Stan Johnson, *CEO*
Julie Dusek, *Managing Dir*
Manfred Menzi, *COO*
Andy Greuling, *Exec VP*
Richard Rusk, *Vice Pres*
▲ **EMP:** 20
SQ FT: 1,000
SALES (est): 2.2MM **Privately Held**
WEB: www.healthtronics.com
SIC: 3845 Ultrasonic scanning devices, medical

(G-20683)
LIGHTSIDE GAMES INC
1250 S Capital Of Texas H (78746-6446)
PHONE..................................650 814-0293
Brent Dusing, *CEO*
EMP: 9
SALES (est): 623.6K **Privately Held**
WEB: www.lightsidegames.com
SIC: 7372 Business oriented computer software

(G-20684)
LONESTAR LOGOS MGT CO LLC
3701 Bee Caves Rd Ste 202 (78746-5886)
PHONE..................................512 462-1310
Matt Johnston, *Principal*
Vince Hazen, *COO*
David Alley, *Vice Pres*
Susan Aragon, *Accountant*
Allison Crutchfield, *Accounts Exec*
EMP: 32
SALES (est): 8.1MM **Privately Held**
WEB: www.lone-starlogos.com
SIC: 3993 Signs & advertising specialties

(G-20685)
MOONTOWER RESOURCES LLC
303 Camp Craft Rd Ste 360 (78746-6510)
PHONE..................................432 400-2445
Joseph Magoto, *President*
EMP: 15
SALES (est): 519K **Privately Held**
WEB: www.chargeroil.com
SIC: 1389 Oil field services

(G-20686)
NUBOCAM LLC
4611 Bee Caves Rd Ste 202 (78746-5283)
PHONE..................................512 473-0500
Ruben Castilla,
EMP: 25

SALES (est): 899.6K **Privately Held**
SIC: 3699 Security devices

(G-20687)
RENESAS ELECTRONICS AMER INC
900 S Cpitl Of Txas Hwy S (78746-5469)
PHONE..................................408 432-8888
Brian Wong, *Manager*
EMP: 30 **Privately Held**
WEB: www.intersil.com
SIC: 3674 Semiconductors & related devices
HQ: Renesas Electronics America Inc.
1001 Murphy Ranch Rd
Milpitas CA 95035
408 432-8888

(G-20688)
SIGMASENSE
3939 Bee Caves Rd Ste A6 (78746-6429)
PHONE..................................844 248-9081
Rick Seger, *CEO*
Shawn Gray, *COO*
Rudy Prince, *CFO*
EMP: 40
SALES (est): 1.9MM **Privately Held**
WEB: www.sigmasense.com
SIC: 3674 Semiconductors & related devices

(G-20689)
TEKVOX INC
108 Wild Basin Rd Ste 215 (78746-3311)
PHONE..................................512 808-0845
EMP: 10
SALES (est): 1.5MM **Privately Held**
SIC: 3695 Mfg Magnetic/Optical Recording Media

(G-20690)
TEXAS INSTRUMENTS INCORPORATED
108 Wild Basin Rd (78746-3326)
PHONE..................................512 434-1560
Artem Aginskiy, *Business Mgr*
Denard Andrews, *Engineer*
Ranita Bera, *Engineer*
Heath Chambers, *Engineer*
Abhijit Das, *Engineer*
EMP: 27
SALES (corp-wide): 14.4B **Publicly Held**
WEB: www.txww.com
SIC: 3674 Microprocessors
PA: Texas Instruments Incorporated
12500 Ti Blvd
Dallas TX 75243
972 995-3773

(G-20691)
TINY PIES LLC
3736 Bee Caves Rd Ste 8b (78746-5378)
P.O. Box 5205, Austin (78763-5205)
PHONE..................................512 297-2690
Kit Seay, *Mng Member*
EMP: 10
SALES (est): 900.7K **Privately Held**
WEB: www.tinypies.com
SIC: 2051 Cakes, pies & pastries

West Orange
Orange County

(G-20692)
AKROTEX FILMS INC
1804 Austin St (77630-6552)
PHONE..................................409 886-0063
Rick Keszeg, *Branch Mgr*
EMP: 30
SALES (corp-wide): 35.4MM **Privately Held**
SIC: 3081 5162 4213 4214 Unsupported plastics film & sheet; plastics materials & basic shapes; trucking, except local; local trucking with storage
PA: Akrotex Films, Inc.
1301 S Childers Rd
Orange TX 77630
409 886-0111

(G-20693)
BEACON MARITIME INC (PA)
Also Called: Beacon Offshore
505 Highway 87 S (77630-8304)
P.O. Box 3053, Orange (77631-3053)
PHONE..................................409 670-1060
Russell Covington, *President*
Guy Covington, *Vice Pres*
Elizabeth Jackson, *Vice Pres*
◆ **EMP:** 550
SALES (est): 50.9MM **Privately Held**
WEB: www.beaconmaritime.com
SIC: 1629 3731 Marine construction; shipbuilding & repairing

(G-20694)
HOGAN STEEL ERECTORS INC (PA)
Also Called: Hogan, C H Drafting Service
605 Dayton St (77630-6553)
P.O. Box 1051, Orange (77631-1051)
PHONE..................................409 883-8208
Cleon H Hogan Jr, *President*
C H Hogan Jr, *President*
Claudine Hogan, *Corp Secy*
EMP: 35 **EST:** 1963
SALES (est): 5.1MM **Privately Held**
SIC: 3449 Bars, concrete reinforcing: fabricated steel

(G-20695)
INVISTA CAPITAL MANAGEMENT LLC
2020 Western Ave (77630-6441)
PHONE..................................409 886-5080
Nicole Harper, *Branch Mgr*
EMP: 517
SALES (corp-wide): 36.8B **Privately Held**
WEB: www.invista.com
SIC: 2821 Polyethylene resins
HQ: Invista Capital Management, Llc
2801 Centerville Rd
Wilmington DE 19808
302 683-3000

Westlake
Denton County

(G-20696)
IOWA FOOD GROUP LLC
1205 Perdenalas Trl (76262-4820)
PHONE..................................712 600-3663
EMP: 12 **EST:** 2018
SALES (est): 1.7MM **Privately Held**
SIC: 2011 Meat by-products from meat slaughtered on site

(G-20697)
VIRBAC CORPORATION (HQ)
Also Called: Virbac Animal Health
1301 Solana Blvd Ste 2400 (76262-1679)
PHONE..................................800 338-3659
Stan Gabriel, *Regional Mgr*
Douglas Monnin, *Regional Mgr*
Pierre Pags, *COO*
Mike O'Bryan, *Exec VP*
Laurent Cesar, *Exec VP*
◆ **EMP:** 130
SQ FT: 127,000
SALES (est): 69.2MM
SALES (corp-wide): 305.5MM **Privately Held**
WEB: www.us.virbac.com
SIC: 2834 5122 Veterinary pharmaceutical preparations; animal medicines
PA: Virbac
Lid
Le Broc 06510
492 087-100

Wharton
Wharton County

(G-20698)
CAROLS MCH & FABRICATION INC
Also Called: CMF
841 Fm 102 Rd (77488-3773)
P.O. Box 223, Hungerford (77448-0223)
PHONE..................................713 921-7266
Carol Huddleston, *President*

▲ = Import ▼=Export
◆ =Import/Export

John Huddleston, *Vice Pres*
EMP: 26
SQ FT: 28,000
SALES (est): 4.5MM **Privately Held**
WEB: www.carolsmachine.com
SIC: 3599 2899 3312 Machine shop, jobbing & repair; fluxes: brazing, soldering, galvanizing & welding; black plate

(G-20699)
DR PEPPER/SEVEN UP INC
Also Called: Pepsico
505 Rugeley Ln (77488-3733)
PHONE..................................979 532-8801
Avery Hughs, *Branch Mgr*
EMP: 150 **Publicly Held**
WEB: www.drpepper.com
SIC: 2086 Carbonated soft drinks, bottled & canned
  HQ: Dr Pepper/Seven Up, Inc.
    5301 Legacy Dr Fl 1
    Plano TX 75024
    972 673-7000

(G-20700)
J-M MANUFACTURING COMPANY INC
Also Called: JM Eagle
10807 Us 59 Hwy (77488-7219)
PHONE..................................979 532-5640
Dan Wimberly, *Branch Mgr*
EMP: 66
SALES (corp-wide): 998.2MM **Privately Held**
WEB: www.jmeagle.com
SIC: 2821 Polyvinyl chloride resins (PVC)
  PA: J-M Manufacturing Company, Inc.
    5200 W Century Blvd
    Los Angeles CA 90045
    800 621-4404

(G-20701)
KOENIG WELDING SERVICE INC
2305 N Richmond Rd (77488-2401)
PHONE..................................979 532-4161
Gary Koenig, *President*
Carol Koenig, *Vice Pres*
Ronnie Koenig, *Treasurer*
Greg Koenig, *Admin Sec*
EMP: 20
SQ FT: 18,500
SALES (est): 3MM **Privately Held**
SIC: 3599 3441 Machine shop, jobbing & repair; fabricated structural metal

(G-20702)
NAN YA PLASTICS CORP AMERICA
2081 Fm 102 Rd (77488-8790)
PHONE..................................979 532-5494
EMP: 384 **Privately Held**
WEB: www.npcam.com
SIC: 2821 Plastics materials & resins
  HQ: Nan Ya Plastics Corporation, America
    9 Peach Tree Hill Rd
    Livingston NJ 07039

(G-20703)
NAN YA PLASTICS CORP AMERICA
Also Called: Nan Ya Plstic Corp Tpei Taiwan
706 F M 102 (77488)
PHONE..................................281 727-7300
Y C Wang, *Ch of Bd*
Sheila Koudela, *Admin Sec*
▲ **EMP:** 160
SALES (est): 18.3MM **Privately Held**
WEB: www.npcusa.com
SIC: 2821 Plastics materials & resins

(G-20704)
NAN YA PLASTICS CORP USA
2081 Fm 102 Rd (77488-8790)
PHONE..................................979 532-5494
W T Lin, *Manager*
EMP: 200 **Privately Held**
WEB: www.npcusa.com
SIC: 3081 Plastic film & sheet
  HQ: Nan Ya Plastics Corporation, America
    9 Peach Tree Hill Rd
    Livingston NJ 07039
    973 992-1775

(G-20705)
PW EAGLE INC
Also Called: JM Eagle
10807 Us 59 Hwy (77488-7219)
PHONE..................................979 532-5640
EMP: 50
SQ FT: 1,160
SALES (corp-wide): 978.3MM **Privately Held**
SIC: 3084 Mfg Plastic Pipe
  HQ: Pw Eagle, Inc.
    5200 W Century Blvd
    Los Angeles CA 90045
    800 621-4404

(G-20706)
SCHLUMBERGER
Also Called: M-I Swacor
1506 N Alabama Rd (77488-3271)
PHONE..................................979 531-8141
EMP: 10
SALES (est): 410K **Privately Held**
SIC: 1389 Oil/Gas Field Services

(G-20707)
TEXAS ENTERPRISE MFG & MCH
2505 County Road 235 (77488-4665)
P.O. Box 907 (77488-0907)
PHONE..................................281 342-0027
Roy Kurtz, *President*
Barbara Kurtz, *Vice Pres*
Betty Ensof, *Office Mgr*
EMP: 10
SQ FT: 20,000
SALES (est): 1.4MM **Privately Held**
SIC: 3599 Machine shop, jobbing & repair

Wheeler
Wheeler County

(G-20708)
ENERFLEX ENERGY SYSTEMS INC
120 W Texas Ave (79096)
PHONE..................................806 826-0126
Doug Adams, *Manager*
EMP: 11
SALES (corp-wide): 1.5B **Privately Held**
WEB: www.enerflex.com
SIC: 3585 7623 7699 3563 Refrigeration equipment, complete; compressors for refrigeration & air conditioning equipment; refrigeration repair service; compressor repair; air & gas compressors
  HQ: Enerflex Energy Systems Inc.
    10815 Telge Rd
    Houston TX 77095
    281 345-9300

White Deer
Carson County

(G-20709)
FREEMAN BROTHERS INC
Also Called: Clint & Sons Processing
115 W 3rd St (79097)
P.O. Box 426 (79097-0426)
PHONE..................................806 883-7831
Johnny Freeman, *President*
Freeman Joe David, *Vice Pres*
Joe Freeman, *Vice Pres*
EMP: 10
SQ FT: 2,000
SALES (est): 850K **Privately Held**
WEB: www.clintandsons.com
SIC: 5421 3556 Meat markets, including freezer provisioners; meat processing machinery

(G-20710)
PRAXIS FABRICATION INC
Also Called: Scarab
1475 County Rd W (79097-3004)
PHONE..................................806 883-7621
Marvin Urbanczyk, *President*
Janet Urbanczyk, *Admin Sec*
EMP: 12
SQ FT: 50,000

SALES (est): 1.1MM **Privately Held**
WEB: www.scarabmfg.com
SIC: 3599 Custom machinery

(G-20711)
SCARAB INTERNATIONAL LLLP
1475 County Rd W (79097-3004)
PHONE..................................806 883-7621
Mark Urbanczyk, *Partner*
Marvin Urbanczyk, *Partner*
Sheri Urbanczyk, *Partner*
Richard Miller, *Sales Staff*
EMP: 25
SALES (est): 5MM **Privately Held**
WEB: www.scarabmfg.com
SIC: 2875 Fertilizers, mixing only

White Oak
Gregg County

(G-20712)
CHEROKEE STEEL FABRICATORS INC
2001 Cherokee Trce (75693-3517)
PHONE..................................903 759-3844
EMP: 30 **EST:** 1974
SQ FT: 45,000
SALES (est): 4.8MM **Privately Held**
WEB: www.cherokeesteelfabricators.com
SIC: 3441 Building components, structural steel

(G-20713)
D C G MACHINE INC
1001 Cherokee Trce (75693-3501)
PHONE..................................903 297-2053
David C Grotheim, *President*
Margaret Grotheim, *Corp Secy*
Frank Young, *QC Mgr*
EMP: 40
SQ FT: 40,000
SALES (est): 7MM **Privately Held**
WEB: www.dcgmachineinc.com
SIC: 3599 3533 3369 Machine shop, jobbing & repair; oil & gas field machinery; nonferrous foundries

(G-20714)
GREAT AMERICAN COIL LLC
1704 Cherokee Trce (75693-3510)
P.O. Box 127 (75693-0127)
PHONE..................................903 297-4700
Dion Faucheux, *President*
Scott Nichols, *Vice Pres*
Tony Barber, *Purch Mgr*
Kim Raglin, *Human Res Dir*
Nichols Scott, *Sales Mgr*
▲ **EMP:** 75
SQ FT: 29,000
SALES (est): 23.8MM **Privately Held**
WEB: www.greatamericancoil.com
SIC: 3585 Refrigeration & heating equipment

(G-20715)
J L RUSHING INC
Also Called: Rushing Machine Shop
1106 Cherokee Trce (75693-3533)
P.O. Box 609 (75693-0609)
PHONE..................................903 759-6000
EMP: 30
SQ FT: 15,200
SALES (est): 4.8MM **Privately Held**
WEB: www.rushingmachine.com
SIC: 3599 Machine shop, jobbing & repair

(G-20716)
KALAMAR INDUSTRIES USA INC
Also Called: Magnum Terminal Tractor Div
1301 Cherokee Trce (75693-3530)
PHONE..................................903 759-5490
Gilbert Pilz, *Principal*
EMP: 75
SALES (est): 11.4MM **Privately Held**
SIC: 3537 5084 Industrial trucks & tractors; industrial machinery & equipment

(G-20717)
MID SOUTH MANUFACTURING LLC
1301 Cherokee Trce (75693-3530)
PHONE..................................903 759-5490
Greg Hulett, *Mng Member*

Karen Hulett,
Jerry Newman,
EMP: 80
SALES (est): 1.9MM **Privately Held**
SIC: 3999 Manufacturing industries

(G-20718)
O & D MANUFACTURING INC
1103 Cherokee Trce (75693-3503)
P.O. Box 277 (75693-0277)
PHONE..................................903 295-2057
Lewis E Orms, *President*
Janet Orms, *Corp Secy*
EMP: 54
SQ FT: 50,000
SALES (est): 9.1MM **Privately Held**
WEB: www.odmfg.com
SIC: 3463 3366 Bearing & bearing race forgings, nonferrous; copper foundries; bronze foundry; bushings & bearings, bronze (nonmachined)

(G-20719)
SAT-LITE TECHNOLOGIES LTD
1969 Willow Lk (75693-2266)
PHONE..................................903 295-3400
Darin Beakley, *Partner*
Jeremy Bartell, *Partner*
Matt Collier, *Production*
Michelle Raymond, *Buyer*
Chris Callow, *Sales Staff*
EMP: 15
SQ FT: 16,000
SALES (est): 3.5MM **Privately Held**
WEB: www.sat-litetech.com
SIC: 3663 Digital encoders

(G-20720)
TOP CAT WELL TRANSPORT
513 S Sun Camp Rd (75693-1439)
PHONE..................................903 295-7000
Johnny Mumphrey, *General Mgr*
Ali Sheikh, *Principal*
Patrick Bowles, *Business Mgr*
EMP: 16
SALES (est): 1.1MM **Privately Held**
WEB: www.topcatws.com
SIC: 1389 Oil field services

(G-20721)
WELL-PRO SERVICES LP
1907 E Us Highway 80 (75693-2338)
P.O. Box 486 (75693-0486)
PHONE..................................903 759-6071
Greg May, *Partner*
Dan Mitchel, *Partner*
Tom Worley, *Partner*
Rick May, *Principal*
Richard May, *General Ptnr*
EMP: 41
SQ FT: 1,000
SALES (est): 6.6MM **Privately Held**
SIC: 1389 Oil field services

(G-20722)
WINSTON/ROYAL GUARD CORP (PA)
1604 Cherokee Trce (75693-3506)
P.O. Box 1145 (75693-6145)
PHONE..................................903 757-7341
John W Kinsel Jr, *President*
Mary O Neal, *Corp Secy*
Robin Strobridge, *Purch Mgr*
Steven Wendel, *QC Mgr*
Deana Beavers, *Sales Mgr*
▼ **EMP:** 40 **EST:** 1965
SQ FT: 30,000
SALES (est): 6.1MM **Privately Held**
WEB: www.winston-royalguard.com
SIC: 3624 3569 3564 3443 Carbon & graphite products; filters; blowers & fans; fabricated plate work (boiler shop)

(G-20723)
WREN OILFIELD SERVICES INC
1500 Cherokee Trce (75693-3526)
P.O. Box 334 (75693-0334)
PHONE..................................903 759-3086
Joe Wren, *President*
Christopher Wren, *Vice Pres*
EMP: 11
SQ FT: 4,700
SALES (est): 2MM **Privately Held**
SIC: 1389 Well logging; perforating well casings

Whiteface
Cochran County

(G-20724)
DEVON ENERGY CORPORATION
2560 Farm Rd Ste 301 (79379)
PHONE......................806 229-6300
Roy Hanigan, *Branch Mgr*
EMP: 12
SALES (corp-wide): 6.2B **Publicly Held**
WEB: www.devonenergy.com
SIC: 1311 Natural gas production
PA: Devon Energy Corporation
333 W Sheridan Ave
Oklahoma City OK 73102
405 235-3611

Whitehouse
Smith County

(G-20725)
APACHE CONSTRUCTION INC
905 State Highway 110 N (75791-3031)
PHONE......................903 839-2242
Ronald Gilbert, *President*
EMP: 14
SQ FT: 5,000
SALES (est): 2MM **Privately Held**
WEB: www.apacheconstruction.com
SIC: 3448 1521 Buildings, portable: pre-
fabricated metal; single-family housing
construction

(G-20726)
ONE TEN WELDING INC
14762 State Highway 110 S (75791-9338)
PHONE......................903 561-8549
Walter Mathis, *President*
Jason Wade, *Vice Pres*
Doris M Mathis, *Admin Sec*
EMP: 9
SQ FT: 6,400
SALES (est): 1.4MM **Privately Held**
WEB: www.onetenwelding.com
SIC: 3446 Architectural metalwork

Whitesboro
Grayson County

(G-20727)
K W UTILITY CONS INC
26097 State Highway 56 (76273-7915)
P.O. Box 32 (76273-0032)
PHONE......................903 564-5771
Keary Williams, *President*
Julie Williams, *Vice Pres*
Patty Sammons, *Admin Sec*
EMP: 30
SALES (est): 3.2MM **Privately Held**
SIC: 1389 Oil field services

Whitewright
Grayson County

(G-20728)
ROYAL CASE COMPANY INC
124 E Grand St (75491-2225)
P.O. Box 833 (75491-0833)
PHONE......................903 364-5231
Larry Henderson, *Branch Mgr*
EMP: 40
SALES (corp-wide): 55.9MM **Privately
Held**
WEB: www.royalcase.com
SIC: 3172 Checkbook covers
PA: Royal Case Company, Inc.
419 E Lamar St
Sherman TX 75090
903 868-0288

(G-20729)
**TIGER RIDGE MANUFACTURING
INC**
12656 State Highway 11 (75491-5285)
P.O. Box 1087 (75491-1087)
PHONE......................903 364-1810
John Williams, *President*

David Ellis, *Vice Pres*
Brenda Williams, *Office Mgr*
EMP: 21
SQ FT: 40,000
SALES (est): 2.9MM **Privately Held**
WEB: www.tigerridgemfg.com
SIC: 3599 3089 Machine & other job shop
work; blow molded finished plastic prod-
ucts; injection molded finished plastic
products; molding primary plastic

Whitney
Hill County

(G-20730)
**LONE STAR STONE TEXAS INC
(PA)**
1073 Fm 1713 (76692-3085)
P.O. Box 2125 (76692-5125)
PHONE......................254 694-6613
Steve Weick, *President*
Scott Pelham, *Sales Dir*
Sergio Montes, *Manager*
Seth Weick, *Info Tech Mgr*
Elaine Cardoso, *Executive*
EMP: 30
SALES (est): 5MM **Privately Held**
WEB: www.lonestarstone.com
SIC: 3272 Stone, cast concrete

(G-20731)
**MILLER MACHINE & WELDING
LLC**
256 Fm 3050 (76692-3527)
P.O. Box 991, Hillsboro (76645-0991)
PHONE......................254 582-2185
F Todd Miller,
Ruth Ann Miller,
EMP: 40
SQ FT: 25,000
SALES (est): 2.7MM **Privately Held**
WEB: www.miller-machine.com
SIC: 1799 3444 7692 3053 Welding on
site; forming machine work, sheet metal;
welding repair; gaskets, packing & sealing
devices

(G-20732)
R & C MACHINE LLC
1104 Hwy 22 (76692)
P.O. Box 2377 (76692-5377)
PHONE......................254 694-9278
Roy Maul,
EMP: 12 EST: 1999
SQ FT: 9,625
SALES (est): 1.2MM **Privately Held**
SIC: 3599 Hose, flexible metallic; machine
shop, jobbing & repair

(G-20733)
TRX INDUSTRIES INC
1130 Fm 1713 (76692-9447)
PHONE......................254 694-6256
Joseph Elkin, *President*
Alan Elkin, *Corp Secy*
Truman Choate, *Vice Pres*
EMP: 16
SQ FT: 24,000
SALES (est): 2.5MM **Privately Held**
SIC: 3533 Oil & gas field machinery

Wichita Falls
Wichita County

(G-20734)
3-T EXPLORATION INC
3707 Maplewood Ave # 100 (76308-2100)
PHONE......................940 691-5091
Thomas T Thacker, *President*
Billy R Thacker, *Corp Secy*
W M Thacker Jr, *Vice Pres*
EMP: 12
SALES (est): 2.8MM **Privately Held**
WEB: www.3texplorationinc.com
SIC: 1311 Crude petroleum production;
natural gas production

(G-20735)
**A & E VENETIAN BLIND
COMPANY**
Also Called: A & E Blind and Awning Co
3601 Sheridan Rd (76302-2814)
PHONE......................940 767-1449
Tyra L Elam, *President*
John R Ketner, *Vice Pres*
Randy Ketner, *Vice Pres*
Callie Elam, *Director*
EMP: 10 EST: 1939
SQ FT: 10,000
SALES: 748.5K **Privately Held**
WEB: www.aeblind.com
SIC: 2591 3444 2431 3442 Venetian
blinds; awnings, sheet metal; window
shutters, wood; storm doors or windows,
metal

(G-20736)
AB-TEX BEVERAGE LTD
1100 7th St (76301-2302)
PHONE......................940 322-5416
John Cox, *Branch Mgr*
EMP: 50
SALES (corp-wide): 67.1B **Publicly Held**
WEB: www.pepsico.com
SIC: 2086 Soft drinks: packaged in cans,
bottles, etc.; water, pasteurized: pack-
aged in cans, bottles, etc.
HQ: Ab-Tex Beverage, Ltd.
650 Colonial Dr
Abilene TX 79603
325 673-7171

(G-20737)
**ADVANCED HYDRSTATIC SVCS
L L C**
5514 Northwest Fwy (76305-5342)
PHONE......................940 337-7950
Marc Moore, *Mng Member*
EMP: 20 EST: 2006
SALES (est): 912.8K **Privately Held**
SIC: 1389 Pipe testing, oil field service

(G-20738)
APAC INTERNATIONAL INC
6308 Seymour Hwy (76310-1512)
P.O. Box 9303 (76308-9303)
PHONE......................940 696-2525
Steve Soule, *President*
EMP: 10
SQ FT: 32,000
SALES (est): 1.2MM **Privately Held**
WEB: www.apacinternational.com
SIC: 3498 3479 Pipe fittings, fabricated
from purchased pipe; coating or wrapping
steel pipe

(G-20739)
AQUILA DRILLING CO LP
2525 Kell Blvd Ste 405 (76308-1060)
PHONE......................940 761-3153
Pat S Bolin, *CEO*
David Fuchik, *General Mgr*
Warren T Ayres, *Exec VP*
Stan Laukhuf, *Vice Pres*
Marvin Stuckey, *Human Res Mgr*
EMP: 140
SQ FT: 1,000
SALES (est): 16.5MM **Privately Held**
WEB: www.aquiladrilling.com
SIC: 1381 Drilling oil & gas wells

(G-20740)
ARMOR PETROLEUM INC
4245 Kemp Blvd Ste 910 (76308-2828)
P.O. Box 4625 (76308-0625)
PHONE......................940 692-5001
Doyle Bentley, *President*
Carroll Laing, *Vice Pres*
EMP: 9
SALES (est): 1.6MM **Privately Held**
SIC: 1311 Crude petroleum production

(G-20741)
B & C PRINTING INC
600 Ohio Ave (76301-2517)
P.O. Box 484 (76307-0484)
PHONE......................940 766-0033
Robert Mayfield, *President*
Brenda Mayfield, *Vice Pres*
EMP: 19
SQ FT: 1,300

SALES (est): 350K **Privately Held**
WEB: www.bandcprinting.com
SIC: 2752 Commercial printing, offset

(G-20742)
B W SINCLAIR INC
13923 Us Highway 287 N (76310-8178)
P.O. Box 1111 (76307-1111)
PHONE......................940 766-2556
Danny Bretschneider, *President*
Bobby W Sinclair, *Vice Pres*
Jerry Sinclair, *Purch Mgr*
Adrian Sinclair, *Purchasing*
Brian Chance, *Sales Mgr*
◆ EMP: 33
SQ FT: 36,000
SALES (est): 6MM **Privately Held**
WEB: www.bwsinclair.com
SIC: 3535 3444 Belt conveyor systems,
general industrial use; bucket type con-
veyor systems; sheet metalwork

(G-20743)
BEACON LIGHTHOUSE INC
Also Called: Beacon Lighthouse For Blind
300 7th St (76301-1699)
PHONE......................940 767-0888
A W Edgemon, *President*
Dan Browning, *Purch Agent*
Judy Koetter, *CFO*
Bryan Edgemon, *Manager*
Deanna Dockman, *Executive Asst*
EMP: 63 EST: 1975
SQ FT: 40,000
SALES: 2.8MM **Privately Held**
WEB: www.beaconwf.com
SIC: 8322 2842 Association for the handi-
capped; cleaning or polishing prepara-
tions

(G-20744)
**BELL PROCESSING
INCORPORATED (PA)**
Also Called: City Iron & Metal Co
1326 Burkburnett Rd (76306-6002)
P.O. Box 2604 (76307-2604)
PHONE......................940 322-8621
EMP: 63 EST: 1967
SQ FT: 2,000
SALES (est): 15.1MM **Privately Held**
WEB: www.bellprocessing.com
SIC: 5093 2611 Metal scrap & waste ma-
terials; pulp mills

(G-20745)
**BIG STATE WELDING &
MACHINE LC**
3015 Old Jacksboro Hwy (76302-1094)
PHONE......................940 766-0191
Micheal Sheppard, *Mng Member*
EMP: 13 EST: 2004
SQ FT: 10,000
SALES (est): 141.9K **Privately Held**
SIC: 7692 Welding repair

(G-20746)
BLOCK DIVISION INC
618 Front St (76301-1012)
P.O. Box 6115, McKinney (75071-5103)
PHONE......................940 723-7308
◆ EMP: 10 EST: 1960
SQ FT: 10,000
SALES (est): 1.9MM **Privately Held**
WEB: www.blockdivision.com
SIC: 3429 Tackle blocks, metal; pulleys
metal

(G-20747)
**BRIDWELL OIL MANAGEMENT
LLC (PA)**
810 8th St (76301-3303)
P.O. Box 1830 (76307-1830)
PHONE......................940 723-4351
Steve Ginnings, *General Mgr*
J S Bridwell Trust, *Principal*
Mark Henderson, *Mng Member*
Alison Gale Dehan,
Bonnie Lynn Whities,
EMP: 10 EST: 1910
SQ FT: 10,000
SALES (est): 5.5MM **Privately Held**
SIC: 1389 Oil field services

(G-20748)
BURK ROYALTY CO LTD (PA)
4245 Kemp Blvd Ste 600 (76308-2829)
P.O. Box 94903 (76308-0903)
PHONE.....................................940 397-8600
David A Kimbell Sr, *Ch of Bd*
Jon Bear, *Vice Pres*
Jonathan Bear, *Vice Pres*
Mike Elyea, *Vice Pres*
Pat Hensley, *Vice Pres*
EMP: 32 **EST:** 2001
SQ FT: 15,000
SALES (est): 49.3MM **Privately Held**
WEB: www.burkroyalty.com
SIC: 1311 1389 6512 Crude petroleum
production; natural gas production; gas
compressing (natural gas) at the fields;
nonresidential building operators

(G-20749)
**CANNEDY CONTEMPORARY
SVCS INC**
Also Called: Ray Cannedy SEC Investigations
1912 Kemp Blvd (76309-3960)
P.O. Box 4727 (76308-0727)
PHONE.....................................940 322-3856
Joe Viavattene, *Principal*
Jimmy Don Seigler, *Senior VP*
Ty Cannedy, *Admin Sec*
EMP: 40
SQ FT: 3,800
SALES (est): 682K **Privately Held**
WEB: www.cannedysecurity.com
SIC: 7381 7389 3578 Armored car services; security guard service; courier or
messenger service; automatic teller machines (ATM)

(G-20750)
CARTER AEROSPACE DEV LLC
2730 Commerce St Ste 500 (76301-8000)
PHONE.....................................940 691-0819
EMP: 10 **EST:** 2011
SALES (est): 499.1K **Privately Held**
WEB: www.carteraero.com
SIC: 3721 Aircraft

(G-20751)
CECIL MACHINE SHOP INC
526 Front St (76301-1027)
P.O. Box 2186 (76307-2186)
PHONE.....................................940 322-4072
Jon Michael Cecil, *President*
Carol E Cecil, *Vice Pres*
Michael Wayne Cecil, *Director*
EMP: 10 **EST:** 1947
SQ FT: 8,300
SALES (est): 1.5MM **Privately Held**
SIC: 3599 Machine shop, jobbing & repair

(G-20752)
CERTAINTEED CORPORATION
211 Randy Dr (76306-5324)
P.O. Box 937 (76307-0937)
PHONE.....................................940 723-5998
Ron Provonche, *Manager*
EMP: 38
SALES (corp-wide): 328.4MM **Privately Held**
WEB: www.certainteed.com
SIC: 2221 Fiberglass fabrics
HQ: Certainteed Llc
20 Moores Rd
Malvern PA 19355
610 893-5000

(G-20753)
CHANDLER MFG LLC
2701 Business Hwy 287j E (76305-8926)
P.O. Box 4684 (76308-0684)
PHONE.....................................940 763-1528
Ronald L Chandler, *President*
Jonathan Holub, *General Mgr*
Sharon A Chandler, *Vice Pres*
Dion King, *Director*
Reanna Jones, *Officer*
EMP: 70
SALES (est): 7.5MM **Privately Held**
WEB: www.chandlermfg.com
SIC: 1389 Oil field services

(G-20754)
**COBRA OIL & GAS
CORPORATION (PA)**
2201 Kell Blvd (76308-1000)
P.O. Box 8206 (76307-8206)
PHONE.....................................940 723-4331
Arvin R Dillard Jr, *CEO*
Jeff R Dillard, *President*
Speedy Shairrick, *Asst Supt*
Robert W Osborne, *Vice Pres*
Charlie Gibson, *Opers Mgr*
EMP: 35 **EST:** 1981
SALES (est): 22.7MM **Privately Held**
WEB: www.cobraogc.com
SIC: 1382 1311 Oil & gas exploration services; crude petroleum & natural gas

(G-20755)
**COCA-COLA REFRESHMENTS
USA INC**
1512 Lamar St (76301-7035)
PHONE.....................................940 720-3907
Brent Tincher, *Manager*
EMP: 60
SALES (corp-wide): 37.2B **Publicly Held**
WEB: www.coca-colacompany.com
SIC: 2086 Bottled & canned soft drinks
HQ: Coca-Cola Refreshments Usa, Inc.
2500 Windy Ridge Pkwy Se
Atlanta GA 30339
770 989-3000

(G-20756)
CONLOOP INC (PA)
1411 Twin Oaks St (76302-2723)
PHONE.....................................940 322-2206
Bruce Parker, *President*
Steve Jones, *Business Mgr*
Lanny Keith Star, *Corp Secy*
Mark Augustine, *Vice Pres*
Jason Talbot, *Electrical Engi*
EMP: 18
SQ FT: 7,500
SALES (est): 17.2MM **Privately Held**
WEB: www.shermco.com
SIC: 7371 3613 3625 Custom computer
programming services; control panels,
electric; relays & industrial controls

(G-20757)
COVERCRAFT INDUSTRIES INC
2720 Market St (76301-8053)
PHONE.....................................940 763-2535
Roger Bassar, *Plant Mgr*
EMP: 90
SALES (corp-wide): 141MM **Privately
Held**
WEB: www.covercraft.com
SIC: 2394 3714 Canvas & related products; motor vehicle parts & accessories
PA: Covercraft Industries, Llc
100 Enterprise
Pauls Valley OK 73075
405 238-9651

(G-20758)
CRYOVAC LLC
3800 Central Fwy (76306-2397)
PHONE.....................................940 851-6060
Gayle Thomas, *Manager*
EMP: 10
SALES (corp-wide): 4.7B **Publicly Held**
WEB: www.sealedair.com
SIC: 3086 Packaging & shipping materials,
foamed plastic
HQ: Cryovac, Llc
2415 Cascade Pointe Blvd
Charlotte NC 28208
980 430-7000

(G-20759)
DILLARD KAY R & ESTATE AR D
2201 Kell Blvd (76308-1000)
PHONE.....................................940 716-5100
Jeff Dillard, *Principal*
EMP: 25
SALES (est): 880.7K **Privately Held**
WEB: www.dillards.com
SIC: 1381 Drilling oil & gas wells

(G-20760)
**DR PPPER BTLG WICHITA FLS
INC**
1100 7th St (76301-2302)
PHONE.....................................940 322-5416

Kirk Massey, *President*
EMP: 55 **EST:** 1966
SALES (est): 4MM
SALES (corp-wide): 67.1B **Publicly Held**
SIC: 5149 2086 Soft drinks; bottled &
canned soft drinks
HQ: Ab-Tex Beverage, Ltd.
650 Colonial Dr
Abilene TX 79603
325 673-7171

(G-20761)
E & A MATERIALS INC
6007 Seymour Hwy (76310-1503)
P.O. Box 365 (76307-0365)
PHONE.....................................940 692-3290
John Pitts, *President*
Carmen Roy, *Office Mgr*
Robert Pitts, *Shareholder*
EMP: 21 **EST:** 1954
SQ FT: 2,500
SALES (est): 3.8MM **Privately Held**
WEB: www.eandamaterials.com
SIC: 5032 1442 Sand, construction;
gravel; construction sand & gravel

(G-20762)
EAGLE OIL & GAS CO (HQ)
2525 Kell Blvd Ste 510 (76308-1061)
PHONE.....................................940 723-7322
Pat S Bolin, *President*
Darrell S Lohoefer, *President*
Warren Ayres, *Exec VP*
Stan Laukhuf, *Vice Pres*
▲ **EMP:** 15 **EST:** 1976
SQ FT: 4,800
SALES (est): 4.8MM **Privately Held**
WEB: www.eagleog.com
SIC: 1311 1382 Crude petroleum production; natural gas production; oil & gas exploration services

(G-20763)
ECHOMETER COMPANY
5001 Ditto Ln (76302-3597)
PHONE.....................................940 767-4334
James N McCoy, *President*
A Drake, *Vice Pres*
Lynn Rowlan, *Vice Pres*
Jenny Pruner, *Office Mgr*
Janis Weseman, *Manager*
EMP: 25 **EST:** 1962
SQ FT: 10,000
SALES (est): 6.6MM **Privately Held**
WEB: www.echometer.com
SIC: 3829 Geophysical & meteorological
testing equipment; dynamometer instruments; pressure transducers

(G-20764)
EVANS ENTERPRISES INC
Also Called: Evans Electric
2707 Central Fwy E (76302-5804)
PHONE.....................................940 723-7466
Steve Campbell, *Branch Mgr*
Brandon Kent, *Manager*
EMP: 15
SQ FT: 10,800
SALES (corp-wide): 132.7MM **Privately
Held**
WEB: www.goevans.com
SIC: 7694 Electric motor repair
PA: Evans Enterprises, Inc.
6707 N Interstate Dr
Norman OK 73069
405 631-1344

(G-20765)
G A JO INC
Also Called: Delta Precision Products
363 Us Highway 281 (76310-0544)
PHONE.....................................940 767-2340
Gary Adams, *President*
Jolynn Adams, *Admin Sec*
EMP: 9
SQ FT: 4,500
SALES (est): 800K **Privately Held**
SIC: 3599 Machine shop, jobbing & repair

(G-20766)
G9GRAPHIX
4517 Southwest Pkwy (76308-3335)
PHONE.....................................940 268-1411
James Gullage, *Manager*
EMP: 9

SALES (est): 412.1K **Privately Held**
WEB: www.g9graphix.net
SIC: 2759 Screen printing

(G-20767)
GENESIS GRANITE INC
7635 Seymour Hwy Ste B (76310-6863)
P.O. Box 4456 (76308-0456)
PHONE.....................................940 692-0611
William G Streich, *President*
Susan S Hill, *Treasurer*
EMP: 19
SQ FT: 900
SALES (est): 2MM **Privately Held**
WEB: www.wilbertprecast.com
SIC: 3272 Concrete products

(G-20768)
GRACE IV ALBERT THOMAS
Also Called: G&S Suzuki
1001 Scott Ave (76301-3417)
PHONE.....................................940 500-4323
Albert Grace IV, *Owner*
EMP: 10
SALES (est): 1.8MM **Privately Held**
WEB: www.suzuki.com
SIC: 5511 3692 5063 Automobiles, new &
used; primary batteries, dry & wet; batteries; batteries, dry cell; storage batteries,
industrial; flashlights

(G-20769)
GUNN OIL COMPANY
811 6th St Ste 100 (76301-2535)
P.O. Box 97508 (76307-7508)
PHONE.....................................940 723-5585
Robert D Gunn, *Ch of Bd*
Donald Hupp, *President*
Terry Caves, *Vice Pres*
Bill Gunn, *Vice Pres*
Bill Stephens, *Vice Pres*
EMP: 18
SQ FT: 25,000
SALES (est): 5MM **Privately Held**
WEB: www.gunnoil.com
SIC: 1311 Crude petroleum production;
natural gas production

(G-20770)
**HANNA-WICHITA TOOL SUPPLY
CO**
104 Oak St (76301-4709)
P.O. Box 5185 (76307-5185)
PHONE.....................................940 766-3151
Cletha Hanna, *President*
Marsha May, *Treasurer*
Debbie Hanna-Bigot, *Admin Sec*
EMP: 10 **EST:** 1942
SQ FT: 6,820
SALES (est): 1.2MM **Privately Held**
SIC: 3599 Machine shop, jobbing & repair

(G-20771)
**HOWMET CASTINGS &
SERVICES INC**
Also Called: Alcoa Howmet, Wichita Falls
6200 Central Fwy (76305-6605)
PHONE.....................................940 855-8100
Monty Gillespie, *Branch Mgr*
EMP: 331
SALES (corp-wide): 14.1B **Publicly Held**
WEB: www.alcoa.com
SIC: 3324 Aerospace investment castings,
ferrous
HQ: Howmet Castings & Services, Inc.
1616 Harvard Ave
Newburgh Heights OH 44105
216 641-4400

(G-20772)
INTELLIGEN
3808b Kemp Blvd 308 (76308-2150)
PHONE.....................................940 692-3334
Russell Jennings, *President*
EMP: 25
SALES (est): 922.1K **Privately Held**
SIC: 3999 Atomizers, toiletry

(G-20773)
J R & ADAM SEITZ LTD
813 8th St Ste 720 (76301-3356)
P.O. Box 1700 (76307-1700)
PHONE.....................................940 723-7303
Charles McBride, *Partner*
R W Mc Bride, *Partner*
J R Sietz Jr, *Partner*

EMP: 11 EST: 1945
SALES (est): 1MM Privately Held
SIC: 1311 Crude petroleum production

(G-20774)
JOHNSON & ERNST OPERATING CO
807 8th St Ste 1200 (76301-3308)
P.O. Box 1551 (76307-1551)
PHONE..............................940 723-8127
Randolph B Johnson, *President*
Paul D Ernst, *Vice Pres*
Greg H Johnson, *Vice Pres*
EMP: 20
SALES (est): 3.8MM Privately Held
SIC: 6792 1311 Oil royalty traders; crude petroleum & natural gas

(G-20775)
KALCO MACHINE & MFG CO
5000 Cntl Fwy Wichita Fls (76306)
PHONE..............................940 761-1060
David Kulbeth, *President*
Tres Ward, *Purchasing*
Becky Roberson, *Human Resources*
Wayne Barnett, *Manager*
Mike Bledsoe, *Manager*
EMP: 55
SQ FT: 14,000
SALES (est): 9.4MM Privately Held
WEB: www.kalcomachine.com
SIC: 3531 3545 Construction machinery; machine tool accessories

(G-20776)
KENNYS ALL PURPOSE SEASONING
Also Called: Kenny's Seasonings
5930 Us Highway 281 (76310-0636)
P.O. Box 16, Scotland (76379-0016)
PHONE..............................940 733-2200
Kenny Humpert, *President*
EMP: 10
SALES (est): 100K Privately Held
WEB: www.kennysseasonings.com
SIC: 2099 Seasonings & spices

(G-20777)
KRUGER ALUMINUM & BRASS FNDRY
Also Called: Kruger Aluminum & Brass Fndry
1233 36th St (76302-1709)
PHONE..............................940 767-0432
Mike Kruger, *President*
George H Kruger, *President*
Sybil Kruger, *Admin Sec*
EMP: 10
SQ FT: 2,400
SALES (est): 1.2MM Privately Held
SIC: 3363 3364 3543 Aluminum die-castings; brass & bronze die-castings; industrial patterns

(G-20778)
LAKE ROAD WELDING CO
Also Called: L R W Fabricators
5615 State Highway 79 S (76310-5402)
P.O. Box 4711 (76308-0711)
PHONE..............................940 692-4988
Donald R Morgan, *President*
Jerry Don Morgan, *Vice Pres*
EMP: 20
SQ FT: 20,000
SALES (est): 4.6MM Privately Held
WEB: www.lrwfab.com
SIC: 3441 7692 3541 Fabricated structural metal; welding repair; machine tools, metal cutting type

(G-20779)
LOADRITE INC
3014 Seymour Rd (76309-3137)
PHONE..............................940 322-1003
John Hooker, *President*
Jim Johnston, *Vice Pres*
Kay Hooker, *Admin Sec*
EMP: 16
SQ FT: 25,000
SALES (est): 1.6MM Privately Held
SIC: 2448 Pallets, wood

(G-20780)
LUIG ENERGY SERVICES LLC
Also Called: Mustang Wireline Services
8039 Seymour Hwy (76306-6855)
P.O. Box 9080 (76308-9080)
PHONE..............................940 264-6188
Ty Luig, *President*
Clint Luig, *Vice Pres*
Ken Luig, *Shareholder*
EMP: 16
SQ FT: 1,000
SALES (est): 5.5MM Privately Held
SIC: 1382 Oil & gas exploration services

(G-20781)
MACHINING SOLUTIONS LLC (PA)
Also Called: Arrow Manufactured Products
5000 Central Fwy (76306-1502)
P.O. Box 8145 (76307-8145)
PHONE..............................940 761-3030
Danny Perry, *General Mgr*
Josh Anderson, *Engineer*
Eric Vandonge, *Prgrmr*
Michael Bernhardt,
Matt Maness,
EMP: 23
SALES (est): 11.1MM Privately Held
WEB: www.arrowmp.com
SIC: 3599 Machine shop, jobbing & repair

(G-20782)
MEADOR PRODUCTS INC
Also Called: Taylor Foundry
1901 Broday Rd (76305-2942)
PHONE..............................940 767-8541
Charles Meador, *President*
Sheila Meador, *Vice Pres*
EMP: 53 EST: 1925
SQ FT: 14,240
SALES (est): 11.1MM Privately Held
WEB: www.taylorfoundry.com
SIC: 3321 Gray iron castings

(G-20783)
MEDDERS OIL COMPANY
4245 Kemp Blvd Ste 904 (76308-2828)
PHONE..............................940 692-6626
EMP: 9 EST: 1918
SALES (est): 981.6K Privately Held
SIC: 1311 Crude petroleum production

(G-20784)
MPP INVESTMENTS LLC
Also Called: McBride Distribution
4517 Southwest Pkwy (76308-3335)
P.O. Box 4703 (76308-0703)
PHONE..............................940 691-0014
Mike Shallenberger,
Steve Hanger,
Ford Swanson,
EMP: 139
SALES (est): 2.8MM Privately Held
SIC: 5812 2011 Eating places; meat packing plants

(G-20785)
NATIONAL OILWELL VARCO INC
Nov Gill
803 E Scott Ave (76301-5914)
PHONE..............................940 761-2333
Paul Gill, *Manager*
Liming Chen, *Manager*
EMP: 23
SALES (corp-wide): 8.4B Publicly Held
WEB: www.nov.com
SIC: 1389 5084 Oil field services; oil well machinery, equipment & supplies
PA: National Oilwell Varco, Inc.
7909 Parkwood Circle Dr
Houston TX 77036
713 346-7500

(G-20786)
NITROUS EXPRESS INC
5411 Seymour Hwy (76310-1203)
PHONE..............................940 767-7694
Mike Wood, *President*
Fred Smith, *General Mgr*
Lori Wood, *Treasurer*
Mike Abney, *Natl Sales Mgr*
Ryan Lewis, *Marketing Mgr*
▲ **EMP:** 15
SQ FT: 10,000

SALES (est): 5MM Privately Held
WEB: www.nitrousexpress.com
SIC: 3714 Fuel systems & parts, motor vehicle

(G-20787)
NORTH AMERICAN PIPE CORP
Also Called: Napco,
3348 Industrial Dr (76306-3735)
PHONE..............................940 855-4100
Andre Battistin, *Mfg Staff*
Maurice Azevedo, *Manager*
Christine Rushing, *Executive*
EMP: 80 Publicly Held
WEB: www.napcopipe.com
SIC: 3354 3498 3084 Pipe, extruded, aluminum; fabricated pipe & fittings; plastics pipe
HQ: North American Pipe Corporation
2801 Post Oak Blvd # 600
Houston TX 77056

(G-20788)
NOTTUS ENERGY RESOURCES INC
900 8th St Ste 916 (76301-6810)
P.O. Box 22 (76307-0022)
PHONE..............................940 687-5304
Mark Sutton, *President*
Sam Sutton, *Vice Pres*
Travis Yandel, *Vice Pres*
Sheri Sutton, *Treasurer*
EMP: 10 EST: 2006
SQ FT: 3,000
SALES (est): 799K Privately Held
WEB: www.texasalliance.org
SIC: 1382 Oil & gas exploration services

(G-20789)
NUCO CONTROLS LLC
1008 7th St (76301-2405)
PHONE..............................940 257-7092
Fred Rougier, *Mfg Spvr*
Mark Reynolds, *Manager*
Chad Konermann,
Randy Beaver,
John Bridgman,
▲ **EMP:** 17
SQ FT: 22,500
SALES (est): 5MM Privately Held
WEB: www.nucocontrols.com
SIC: 3625 Control equipment, electric

(G-20790)
OK CONCRETE COMPANY (PA)
2304 Sheppard Access Rd (76306-5321)
PHONE..............................940 723-4324
David R Litteken, *President*
Brandon Litteken, *General Mgr*
Janis Toth, *General Mgr*
Mike Gilmore, *Vice Pres*
Arthur Litteken, *Vice Pres*
EMP: 20
SQ FT: 2,100
SALES (est): 5.5MM Privately Held
WEB: www.okconcreteco.com
SIC: 3273 Ready-mixed concrete

(G-20791)
OWENS CORNING
219 Randy Dr (76306-5324)
PHONE..............................940 723-5998
EMP: 12 Publicly Held
WEB: www.owenscorning.com
SIC: 3296 Fiberglass insulation
PA: Owens Corning
1 Owens Corning Pkwy
Toledo OH 43659

(G-20792)
P M W VENTURES INC
Also Called: Precision Machine Works
9142 Powell Rd (76305-6358)
PHONE..............................940 855-6100
Jeff W Barfield, *President*
Donnie Shepard, *Admin Sec*
EMP: 10
SQ FT: 8,000
SALES (est): 750K Privately Held
SIC: 3599 Machine shop, jobbing & repair

(G-20793)
PARAMOUNT RENTAL SERVICES LLC
900 8th St Ste 1002 (76301-6811)
PHONE..............................940 264-8379

EMP: 15 EST: 2018
SALES (est): 64.6K Privately Held
SIC: 7359 1389 Equipment rental & leasing; oil & gas field services

(G-20794)
PITTS SAND & GRAVEL INC
6007 Seymour Hwy (76310-1503)
P.O. Box 365 (76307-0365)
PHONE..............................940 692-3290
Michael Pitts, *President*
John Pitts Jr, *Vice Pres*
Roberta Pitts, *Admin Sec*
EMP: 22
SALES (est): 744.4K Privately Held
WEB: www.pittsstoneyard.com
SIC: 1442 Construction sand & gravel

(G-20795)
POWER SEAL
701 Pleasant View Dr (76306-5903)
PHONE..............................940 767-5566
Patrick Powers, *President*
Rafael Barreto, *President*
David Rhone, *Regional Mgr*
Taylor Kilcrease, *Purch Mgr*
Matthew Havens, *Engineer*
◆ **EMP:** 75
SALES (est): 10.5MM Privately Held
WEB: www.powerseal.com
SIC: 3441 Fabricated structural metal

(G-20796)
POWERSEAL PIPELINE PDTS CORP
701 Pleasant View Dr (76306-5903)
P.O. Box 2014 (76307-2014)
PHONE..............................940 767-5566
Patrick F Powers, *President*
Steve Kilcrease, *Vice Pres*
Ricky Chavez, *Personnel*
Mary F Powers, *Shareholder*
◆ **EMP:** 65
SALES (est): 21.5MM Privately Held
WEB: www.powerseal.com
SIC: 3089 3432 3498 Fittings for pipe, plastic; plumbing fixture fittings & trim; fabricated pipe & fittings

(G-20797)
PPG INDUSTRIES INC
Also Called: PPG 9714
1810 9th St (76301-5030)
PHONE..............................940 322-5201
Jimmy Howard, *Branch Mgr*
EMP: 24
SALES (corp-wide): 15.3B Publicly Held
WEB: www.ppg.com
SIC: 2851 Paints & allied products
PA: Ppg Industries, Inc.
1 Ppg Pl
Pittsburgh PA 15272
412 434-3131

(G-20798)
PRODUCTION MACHINE & TOOL LP
2450 Burkburnett Rd (76306-5305)
PHONE..............................940 767-9400
Mark McMullen, *Partner*
Neil McMullen, *Partner*
Lance Morton, *Purchasing*
Jerry Burns, *Engineer*
Lois Lutteringer, *Human Resources*
EMP: 45
SALES (est): 20MM Privately Held
WEB: www.production-machine.com
SIC: 3599 3451 Machine shop, jobbing & repair; screw machine products

(G-20799)
PRODUCTION MCH & TL MGT LLC
2450 Burkburnett Rd (76306-5305)
PHONE..............................940 767-9400
Neil McMullen, *Managing Prtnr*
Markham N McMullen, *Partner*
David Morton, *Engineer*
Ronnie Thomas, *Engineer*
EMP: 75
SQ FT: 52,000
SALES (est): 15.9MM Privately Held
WEB: www.production-machine.com
SIC: 3599 Machine shop, jobbing & repair

(G-20800)
QUATRO OIL AND GAS INC
700 Lamar St (76301-6823)
PHONE..................................940 767-4443
John W Bradley, *President*
Corkey Cummings, *President*
EMP: 12
SQ FT: 2,800
SALES (est): 3.1MM **Privately Held**
SIC: 1311 Crude petroleum & natural gas

(G-20801)
RAYTHEON TECHNOLOGIES CORP
Also Called: P & W C
3101 Hammon Rd (76310-7501)
PHONE..................................940 761-9200
Deborah Wells, *Branch Mgr*
EMP: 207
SALES (corp-wide): 56.5B **Publicly Held**
WEB: www.rtx.com
SIC: 3724 Turbines, aircraft type
PA: Raytheon Technologies Corporation
870 Winter St
Waltham MA 02451
781 522-3000

(G-20802)
REDDING MACHINE SHOP INC
5720 Seymour Hwy (76310-1210)
PHONE..................................940 691-5218
Paul Redding, *President*
Nancy B Redding, *Vice Pres*
EMP: 15
SQ FT: 9,000
SALES (est): 1.8MM **Privately Held**
SIC: 3599 7692 Machine shop, jobbing & repair; welding repair

(G-20803)
RELIABLE WELL SVC N TEXAS LLC (PA)
7774 Seymour Hwy (76310-6846)
P.O. Box 4153 (76308-0153)
PHONE..................................940 692-9511
William McBroom, *Partner*
William N Owens, *Partner*
Curtis Wheeler, *Safety Mgr*
William Mc Broom,
EMP: 15
SQ FT: 960
SALES (est): 6MM **Privately Held**
SIC: 1389 Oil field services

(G-20804)
SAFETY DESIGN USA INC
Also Called: Sdtx
3029 Cromwell Ave (76309-4711)
PHONE..................................940 757-0238
Felix Torrent, *President*
Jose Torrent, *CFO*
EMP: 26 EST: 2014
SALES (est): 525.9K **Privately Held**
SIC: 1389 Pipe testing, oil field service

(G-20805)
SAUDER MANAGEMENT CO (PA)
900 8th St Ste 202 (76301-6803)
P.O. Box 8546 (76307-8546)
PHONE..................................940 723-8125
John Saunder, *President*
Kerry Graham, *Corp Secy*
EMP: 10
SQ FT: 4,500
SALES (est): 1MM **Privately Held**
WEB: www.saudermgmt.com
SIC: 1311 Crude petroleum production

(G-20806)
SEALED AIR CORPORATION
3800 Central Fwy (76306-2304)
PHONE..................................940 851-6060
Greg Williams, *Opers Mgr*
Gus Olivarez, *Sales Staff*
Deanna Barfield, *Sales Executive*
Vian Stephanie, *Branch Mgr*
Brandon Hiracheta, *Info Tech Mgr*
EMP: 64
SALES (corp-wide): 4.7B **Publicly Held**
WEB: www.sealedair.com
SIC: 3086 Packaging & shipping materials, foamed plastic

PA: Sealed Air Corporation
2415 Cascade Pointe Blvd
Charlotte NC 28208
980 221-3235

(G-20807)
SELECT INDUSTRIES INC
4163 Airport Dr (76305-5708)
P.O. Box 2450 (76307-2450)
PHONE..................................940 855-0461
William G Harrison, *President*
Eddie Huber, *Vice Pres*
Cindy Nosser, *Treasurer*
EMP: 25
SQ FT: 20,000
SALES (est): 8.9MM **Privately Held**
WEB: www.selectindustries.com
SIC: 2819 Industrial inorganic chemicals

(G-20808)
SERVA CORPORATION
1500 Fisher Rd Ste A (76305-8928)
P.O. Box 8121 (76307-8121)
PHONE..................................940 761-3361
Bill Ladd, *President*
Michael Bernhardt, *Vice Pres*
Charles Miller, *Supervisor*
Pete Seitz, *Shareholder*
Marsha Bernhardt, *Admin Sec*
◆ EMP: 17
SALES (est): 16.7MM **Privately Held**
WEB: www.servagroup.com
SIC: 3533 5084 Oil field machinery & equipment; industrial machinery & equipment

(G-20809)
SHARP IRON GROUP LLC
4140 Reilly Rd (76305-5424)
PHONE..................................940 855-2710
Michael Matthews, *Purchasing*
Ted Turner, *Branch Mgr*
EMP: 27
SALES (corp-wide): 20.5MM **Privately Held**
WEB: www.sharpirongroup.com
SIC: 7692 Welding repair
PA: Sharp Iron Group, Llc
1206 Hatton Rd
Wichita Falls TX 76302
940 766-4545

(G-20810)
SHARP IRON GROUP LLC (PA)
Also Called: Bw Fabricators
1206 Hatton Rd (76302-3002)
PHONE..................................940 766-4545
Kristin Gonzales, *Principal*
Cindy Press, *Principal*
Michael Stanford, *Principal*
Paulo Santos, *Opers Mgr*
James Frank, *Mng Member*
EMP: 60
SQ FT: 100,000
SALES (est): 20.5MM **Privately Held**
WEB: www.sharpirongroup.com
SIC: 3549 7692 Metalworking machinery; welding repair

(G-20811)
SHERMCO SYSTEM INTEGRATION LLC
1411 Twin Oaks St (76302-2723)
PHONE..................................940 322-2206
Mike Henricks, *President*
Mark Selz, *Admin Sec*
EMP: 104
SQ FT: 23,400
SALES (est): 2.9MM **Privately Held**
SIC: 3613 3625 Control panels, electric; relays & industrial controls
HQ: Shermco Industries, Inc.
2425 E Pioneer Dr
Irving TX 75061
972 793-5523

(G-20812)
STEPHENS & JOHNSON OPER CO
Also Called: Sjoc
811 6th St Ste 300 (76301-2509)
P.O. Box 2249 (76307-2249)
PHONE..................................940 723-2166
T Frederick Stephens, *President*
Bob Gilmore, *Engineer*
Jeff Ritchie, *Engineer*

Jim Tull, *Engineer*
Sheila McGaughey, *Manager*
EMP: 50
SQ FT: 18,000
SALES (est): 6.6MM **Privately Held**
WEB: www.sjoc.net
SIC: 1389 Pumping of oil & gas wells

(G-20813)
SWANNER PROPERTIES
2608 Kemp Blvd Ste E (76309-5351)
PHONE..................................940 723-7714
Roger Swanner, *Owner*
EMP: 9 EST: 1922
SALES (est): 580K **Privately Held**
SIC: 1311 Crude petroleum production

(G-20814)
TALALAY GLOBAL INC
8600 Central Fwy N (76305-5917)
PHONE..................................940 851-0107
Christopher Miller, *Branch Mgr*
EMP: 65
SALES (corp-wide): 4.6MM **Privately Held**
WEB: www.talalayglobal.com
SIC: 2392 5021 Mattress pads; mattresses
PA: Talalay Global, Inc.
510 River Rd
Shelton CT 06484
203 924-0700

(G-20815)
TEXAS AUSTRALIAN POWER INC
5018 Ditto Ln (76302-3502)
P.O. Box 9005 (76308-9005)
PHONE..................................940 723-4122
Tommy Isbell, *President*
John Thomas, *Vice Pres*
R L Bolin, *Shareholder*
EMP: 25
SQ FT: 4,000
SALES (est): 5MM **Privately Held**
WEB: www.texauspower.com
SIC: 1381 1382 4911 Drilling oil & gas wells; oil & gas exploration services; generation, electric power

(G-20816)
TEXAS KENWORTH CO
Also Called: Mhc Kenworth- Wichita Falls
1901 Central Fwy E (76302-1425)
P.O. Box 5924 (76302)
PHONE..................................940 767-0001
David Douglas, *Branch Mgr*
EMP: 9
SALES (corp-wide): 1B **Privately Held**
WEB: www.texastrucksales.com
SIC: 3715 3713 5531 6159 Truck trailer chassis; truck bodies (motor vehicles); automobile & truck equipment & parts; truck finance leasing; trucking, except local
HQ: Texas Kenworth Co.
4040 Irving Blvd
Dallas TX 75247
214 920-7300

(G-20817)
TEXON PARTNERS
7645 Seymour Hwy (76310-6863)
PHONE..................................940 264-3019
EMP: 15
SALES (est): 596.8K **Privately Held**
SIC: 1389 Oil/Gas Field Services

(G-20818)
TITANIUM EMERGENCY GROUP LLP
1600 11th St (76301-4300)
P.O. Box 206676, Dallas (75320-6676)
PHONE..................................940 613-2653
Rodrigo X Menchaca, *Partner*
EMP: 9
SALES (est): 1MM **Privately Held**
WEB: www.unitedregional.org
SIC: 3356 Titanium

(G-20819)
TRANTER INC (DH)
1900 Old Burk Hwy (76306-5904)
P.O. Box 2289 (76307-2289)
PHONE..................................940 723-7125
Henrik Johansson, *President*

Jack Dinello, *Vice Pres*
Mika Penttinen, *CFO*
Stephanie Chavez, *Accountant*
Cathy Singer, *Accountant*
◆ EMP: 204
SQ FT: 620,000
SALES (est): 33.2MM **Privately Held**
WEB: www.tranter.com
SIC: 3443 Nuclear core structurals, metal plate

(G-20820)
TRC RECREATION LP (PA)
Also Called: Super Soft
908 N Beverly Dr (76306-3529)
P.O. Box 539 (76307-0539)
PHONE..................................940 322-4463
Matt Iles, *President*
Lee Lasseter, *Purchasing*
Mary Elizabeth Pearce, *Human Res Mgr*
Vicki Powell, *Manager*
Joel Hastings, *Technical Staff*
◆ EMP: 40 EST: 1957
SQ FT: 67,500
SALES (est): 14.4MM **Privately Held**
WEB: www.texasrec.com
SIC: 3086 Plastics foam products

(G-20821)
TRITAN PRODUCTZ LTD
2006 Avondale St (76308-1307)
PHONE..................................940 224-1575
Dennis Harris, *COO*
Stephen Santellana, *Vice Pres*
EMP: 9
SALES (est): 343.9K **Privately Held**
SIC: 3449 Miscellaneous metalwork

(G-20822)
TRYER PROCESS EQUIPMENT LTD
1730 City View Dr (76306-4623)
P.O. Box 3456 (76301-0456)
PHONE..................................940 432-0130
Tom Tryer, *General Ptnr*
Jonathan Tryer, *Engineer*
▼ EMP: 40
SQ FT: 65,000
SALES (est): 11.4MM **Privately Held**
WEB: www.tryerpe.com
SIC: 3533 3443 Oil & gas field machinery; industrial vessels, tanks & containers

(G-20823)
UNITED ELECTRIC COMPANY LP
Also Called: Magic Aire
501 Galveston St (76301-5906)
PHONE..................................940 397-2100
Ron Duncan, *Partner*
Victor Moreno, *Vice Pres*
Dick Stearns, *Vice Pres*
Richard Stearns, *Vice Pres*
Brian Francis, *Engineer*
▼ EMP: 250 EST: 1932
SQ FT: 143,300
SALES (est): 90.8MM **Privately Held**
WEB: www.magicaire.com
SIC: 3585 Air conditioning condensers & condensing units; compressors for refrigeration & air conditioning equipment; condensers, refrigeration
PA: Ma Acquisition Co., Llc
501 Galveston St
Wichita Falls TX 76301

(G-20824)
VITRO ARCHITECTURAL GLASS
7400 Central Fwy N (76305-6656)
PHONE..................................940 851-4374
Phil Trivette, *Principal*
James Biroscak, *Sales Staff*
Jim Bray, *Sales Staff*
Paul Dicesare, *Sales Staff*
Mike Dishmon, *Sales Staff*
EMP: 14 EST: 2017
SALES (est): 3.2MM **Privately Held**
WEB: www.vitroglazings.com
SIC: 2851 Paints & allied products

(G-20825)
VITRO FLAT GLASS LLC
7400 Central Fwy N (76305-6656)
PHONE..................................940 855-3804
Bill Haley, *Branch Mgr*
Joseph Shadwick, *Supervisor*

Katie Leckie,
EMP: 300 Privately Held
WEB: www.vitroglazings.com
SIC: 3231 Products of purchased glass
HQ: Vitro Flat Glass Llc
400 Guys Run Rd
Cheswick PA 15024
412 820-8500

(G-20826)
WALKER-NEER MANUFACTURING CO
Also Called: Walker Neer
1520 Old Iowa Park Rd (76306-5929)
P.O. Box 2490 (76307-2490)
PHONE..................................940 723-0711
Clyde A Willis, *President*
EMP: 14 EST: 1921
SALES (est): 1MM **Privately Held**
SIC: 1389 Pipe testing, oil field service

(G-20827)
WARNER ELECTRIC LLC
2800 Fisher Rd (76302-5917)
PHONE..................................940 767-2000
Carl R Christenson, *CEO*
Mark Stuebe, *General Mgr*
Christian Storch, *Vice Pres*
Marvin Vincent, *Engineer*
Donnie Nall, *Info Tech Dir*
▲ **EMP:** 100
SQ FT: 85,000
SALES (est): 16.3MM
SALES (corp-wide): 1.8B **Publicly Held**
WEB: www.wichitaclutch.com
SIC: 3568 3625 Clutches, except vehicular; brakes, electromagnetic
PA: Altra Industrial Motion Corp.
300 Granite St Ste 201
Braintree MA 02184
781 917-0600

(G-20828)
WARNER ELECTRIC LLC
Also Called: Wichita Clutch
2800 Fisher Rd (76302-5917)
PHONE..................................940 723-3400
Eric Micheli, *Plant Mgr*
Scotty Francisco, *Mfg Spvr*
Terry McShan, *Senior Buyer*
Kitty Nguyen, *Buyer*
Steve Law, *Engrg Mgr*
EMP: 86
SALES (corp-wide): 1.8B **Publicly Held**
WEB: www.warnerelectric.com
SIC: 3714 Motor vehicle brake systems & parts
HQ: Warner Electric Llc
449 Gardner St
South Beloit IL 61080
815 389-4300

(G-20829)
WESTERN TRUCK & EQUIPMENT
2213 East Rd 79s (76305)
PHONE..................................940 723-2555
Ed Spragins, *Owner*
EMP: 20
SALES (est): 466.6K **Privately Held**
SIC: 1389 Servicing oil & gas wells

(G-20830)
WESTERN WELL SERVICE INC
Also Called: Western Rental and Fishing Tls
2213 East Rd 79s (76305-6622)
P.O. Box 4417 (76308-0417)
PHONE..................................940 723-2550
EMP: 30 EST: 1975
SQ FT: 1,200
SALES (est): 4MM **Privately Held**
WEB: www.westernwellproductionservices.com
SIC: 1381 Reworking oil & gas wells

(G-20831)
WICHITA FALLS MFG INC
2000 Old Burk Hwy (76306-5340)
P.O. Box 5326 (76307-5326)
PHONE..................................940 322-4491
Richard Jeter, *President*
Lester Wright, *Vice Pres*
Robby West, *Sales Executive*
EMP: 50
SQ FT: 77,000

SALES (est): 11.3MM **Privately Held**
WEB: www.wfmtx.com
SIC: 3364 2822 3544 Nonferrous die-castings except aluminum; synthetic rubber; special dies, tools, jigs & fixtures

(G-20832)
WICHITA FALLS TIMES RECORD
1301 Lamar St (76301-7032)
P.O. Box 120 (76307-0120)
PHONE..................................940 767-8341
Andy Newberry, *Editor*
Russell Arbuckle, *Director*
Adam Symson,
EMP: 26 EST: 2012
SALES (est): 2.4MM **Privately Held**
WEB: www.timesrecordnews.com
SIC: 2711 Newspapers, publishing & printing

(G-20833)
WICHITA METAL PRODUCTS INC (PA)
1020 Vermont St (76306-6735)
P.O. Box 4162 (76308-0162)
PHONE..................................940 322-9611
Thomas G Ruddy, *President*
Roscoe Perkins, *Vice Pres*
Carroll Harrell, *Manager*
EMP: 26
SALES (est): 5.4MM **Privately Held**
SIC: 3441 Building components, structural steel

(G-20834)
WICHITA TANK MFG INC
8321 Seymour Hwy (76310-6858)
PHONE..................................940 692-5791
David Tanner, *President*
EMP: 75 EST: 1996
SALES (est): 12.4MM **Privately Held**
WEB: www.wichitatank.com
SIC: 3443 Fabricated plate work (boiler shop)

(G-20835)
WORK SERVICES CORPORATION (PA)
1343 Hatton Rd (76302-3007)
PHONE..................................940 766-3207
David Toogood, *President*
Ben Ezzell, *Vice Pres*
Jessica Traw, *Vice Pres*
Nancy K Cupit, *CFO*
Amy Brown, *Human Resources*
EMP: 82
SQ FT: 75,000
SALES: 25.2MM **Privately Held**
WEB: www.workservicescorp.com
SIC: 8331 3496 0782 Sheltered workshop; miscellaneous fabricated wire products; lawn services

(G-20836)
WORLDWIDE SPANISH LITERATURE
4212 Fairway Blvd (76308-2453)
P.O. Box 4650 (76308-0650)
PHONE..................................940 692-4933
EMP: 10
SQ FT: 5,830
SALES: 276K **Privately Held**
WEB: www.spanliterature.com
SIC: 2752 8399 Commercial printing, offset; fund raising organization, non-fee basis

(G-20837)
WPT POWER CORPORATION
1600 Fisher Rd (76305-8907)
P.O. Box 8148 (76307-8148)
PHONE..................................940 761-1971
Lane Brock, *President*
Karen Brock, *Treasurer*
Byron Baber, *Sales Mgr*
Marcia Bernhardt, *Admin Sec*
▲ **EMP:** 30
SQ FT: 8,000
SALES (est): 7.9MM **Privately Held**
WEB: www.wptpower.com
SIC: 3568 Bearings, bushings & blocks

(G-20838)
ZACK BURKETT CO
Also Called: Zack Burkett Co Asp Plant 1
2600 Old Burk Hwy (76306-4334)
PHONE..................................940 322-2101
Gerry Lee, *Branch Mgr*
EMP: 50
SALES (corp-wide): 35.4MM **Privately Held**
WEB: www.zackburkettco.com
SIC: 2951 Asphalt & asphaltic paving mixtures (not from refineries)
HQ: Zack Burkett Co.
105 Industrial Blvd
Graham TX 76450
940 549-0436

Wickett
Ward County

(G-20839)
JV ROUSTABOUT INC
400 Houston (79788)
PHONE..................................432 943-2999
EMP: 10 EST: 2012
SALES (est): 490K **Privately Held**
SIC: 1389 Oil/Gas Field Services

Wiergate
Newton County

(G-20840)
RED WATSON LOGGING INC
Hwy 63 E (75977)
P.O. Box 236 (75977-0236)
PHONE..................................409 565-2484
James Watson, *President*
EMP: 17
SALES (est): 2.3MM **Privately Held**
SIC: 2411 Logging camps & contractors

Willis
Montgomery County

(G-20841)
ALLAN BANKS
Also Called: Asian2u.com
14414 Lake Vista Ct (77318-5230)
P.O. Box 181, Montgomery (77356-0181)
PHONE..................................936 337-4020
Allan A Banks, *Owner*
◆ **EMP:** 15
SALES (est): 714.1K **Privately Held**
SIC: 7379 8748 3648 5812 Computer related consulting services; educational consultant; public lighting fixtures; steak & barbecue restaurants; foreign trade consultant

(G-20842)
AMERITEX MACHINE AND FAB LLC
13391 E Fm 1097 Rd (77378-4337)
P.O. Box 280 (77378-0280)
PHONE..................................936 228-5070
Lawrence B Fennell, *President*
Mike Wolf, *Foreman/Supr*
Jeffrey Miller, *Controller*
Roman Williams, *Sales Mgr*
Ryan Gibson, *Sales Staff*
EMP: 50
SQ FT: 40,000
SALES (est): 20.5MM **Privately Held**
WEB: www.ameritexllc.com
SIC: 3441 Fabricated structural metal

(G-20843)
APACHE REFINERY SVCS INTL LLC
10301 Farrell Rd (77378-6115)
PHONE..................................936 890-8586
David Nunez Sr, *President*
Sandra Nunez, *Opers Staff*
EMP: 55
SQ FT: 13,000
SALES (est): 18.5MM **Privately Held**
WEB: www.apacherefineryservices.com
SIC: 3559 Petroleum refinery equipment

(G-20844)
CHEMTEC ENERGY SERVICES LLC
11745 Cude Cemetery Rd (77318-6413)
P.O. Box 1165, Montgomery (77356-1165)
PHONE..................................936 856-1704
Milton Page, *CEO*
Chris Winn, *Business Mgr*
▼ **EMP:** 45
SALES (est): 2MM
SALES (corp-wide): 655MM **Publicly Held**
WEB: www.lbfoster.com
SIC: 3533 3559 2911 5084 Oil & gas field machinery; refinery, chemical processing & similar machinery; gasoline blending plants; fuel injection systems
PA: L. B. Foster Company
415 Holiday Dr Ste 1
Pittsburgh PA 15220
412 928-3400

(G-20845)
ELEET CRYOGENICS INC
17301 E Fm 1097 Rd (77378-3959)
PHONE..................................936 856-6549
EMP: 25 Privately Held
WEB: www.eleetcryogenics.com
SIC: 3795 7699 Tanks & tank components; tank repair
PA: Eleet Cryogenics, Inc.
11132 Industrial Pkwy Nw
Bolivar OH 44612

(G-20846)
ELLIOTT CONTROL COMPANY LTD
13344 N Highway 75 (77378-3408)
P.O. Box 467 (77378-0467)
PHONE..................................713 589-3102
Ric Fennell, *Partner*
Joel Stubbs, *Vice Pres*
EMP: 10 EST: 2001
SQ FT: 30,000
SALES (est): 2.1MM **Privately Held**
WEB: www.emotorcontrol.com
SIC: 3625 Relays & industrial controls

(G-20847)
H & R MFG AND SUPPLY INC
12400 Rose Rd (77378-4762)
P.O. Box 3183, Conroe (77305-3183)
PHONE..................................936 856-5529
Harvey L Hivnor, *President*
Diane Hivnor, *Treasurer*
Omar Reyna, *Sales Executive*
Kyle Jackson, *Director*
Christa Hamm, *Executive Asst*
EMP: 39
SQ FT: 30,000
SALES (est): 9MM **Privately Held**
WEB: www.hrmfg.com
SIC: 3599 Machine shop, jobbing & repair

(G-20848)
INKJET INC (PA)
Also Called: Community Chemical
11111 Inkjet Way (77378-4936)
PHONE..................................936 856-6600
Jeane Schalm, *CEO*
Patricia Quinlan, *Ch of Bd*
Dana Nordman, *Regional Mgr*
Deanne Biles, *Project Mgr*
Jose Octaviano, *Prdtn Mgr*
◆ **EMP:** 80
SQ FT: 50,000
SALES (est): 17.7MM **Privately Held**
WEB: www.inkjetinc.com
SIC: 2893 Printing ink

(G-20849)
INKJET INC
11111 Inkjet Way (77378-4936)
PHONE..................................936 856-6600
Jim Burge, *General Mgr*
EMP: 30 Privately Held
WEB: www.inkjetinc.com
SIC: 2899 2893 Ink or writing fluids; printing ink
PA: Inkjet, Inc.
11111 Inkjet Way
Willis TX 77378

(G-20850)
INTERNATIONAL COATING SERVICES
Also Called: Icsi
18150 Interstate 45 N (77318-6919)
PHONE...................................936 344-9494
Roy R Brock, *President*
William X Hearn Jr, *Vice Pres*
Peter Twidal, *Vice Pres*
EMP: 50
SQ FT: 50,000 **Privately Held**
SIC: 3731 Shipbuilding & repairing

(G-20851)
J&A TRUCKING CO
15911 Rogers Rd (77378-3851)
PHONE...................................713 854-0226
EMP: 10 EST: 1999
SALES (est): 782.9K **Privately Held**
SIC: 3537 Industrial trucks & tractors

(G-20852)
KONGSBERG PWR PROD SYSTEMS I
Also Called: Kongsberg Automotive
300 S Cochran St (77378-9034)
P.O. Box 588 (77378-0588)
PHONE...................................936 856-2971
Rachel Baxter, *President*
Larry Lyng, *Exec VP*
Chris Farnsworth, *Plant Mgr*
Joel Blunt, *Engineer*
John Colville, *Engineer*
▲ **EMP:** 123
SQ FT: 100,000
SALES: 40.5MM
SALES (corp-wide): 1.2B **Privately Held**
WEB: www.kongsbergautomotive.com
SIC: 3714 Anti-sway devices, motor vehicle
HQ: Kongsberg Holding Iii, Inc
  27275 Haggerty Rd Ste 610
  Novi MI 48377

(G-20853)
LB FOSTER BALL WINCH INC
Also Called: Ball Winch Pipeline Services
15786 N Highway 75 (77378-3456)
PHONE...................................936 228-0077
Merry L Brumbaugh, *President*
Thomas A Ball, *Engineer*
EMP: 77 EST: 2013
SALES (est): 527.9K
SALES (corp-wide): 655MM **Publicly Held**
WEB: www.lbfoster.com
SIC: 3479 Coating or wrapping steel pipe
PA: L. B. Foster Company
  415 Holiday Dr Ste 1
  Pittsburgh PA 15220
  412 928-3400

(G-20854)
LOOP TECH INTERNATIONAL LTD
Also Called: Looptech
13802 N Highway 75 (77378-3418)
P.O. Box 1609, New Waverly (77358-1609)
PHONE...................................936 295-7038
Gl Ross, *Ch of Bd*
Russell Buras, *Principal*
Michael Ross, *Chairman*
▼ **EMP:** 27
SQ FT: 1,200
SALES (est): 6.7MM **Privately Held**
WEB: www.looptech.net
SIC: 3585 Heat pumps, electric

(G-20855)
MUELLER SUPPLY COMPANY INC
16355 N Highway 75 (77378-3407)
PHONE...................................936 344-9057
Mark Jones, *Branch Mgr*
EMP: 60
SALES (corp-wide): 180.3MM **Privately Held**
WEB: www.muellerinc.com
SIC: 3448 Prefabricated metal components; prefabricated metal buildings
PA: Mueller Supply Company, Inc.
  1913 Hutchins Ave
  Ballinger TX 76821
  325 365-3555

(G-20856)
NATIONAL OILWELL VARCO LP
Also Called: Nov
10586 N Highway 75 (77378-5715)
PHONE...................................817 203-8302
EMP: 11
SALES (corp-wide): 7.3B **Publicly Held**
SIC: 3533 Oil/Gas Field Machinery
HQ: National Oilwell Varco, L.P.
  7909 Parkwood Circle Dr
  Houston TX 77036
  713 960-5100

(G-20857)
OREILLY AUTOMOTIVE STORES INC
12275 N Highway 75 (77378-5749)
PHONE...................................936 856-2409
Ray Davison, *Manager*
EMP: 10 **Publicly Held**
SIC: 5999 5531 5063 3692 Batteries, non-automotive; automotive parts; batteries, dry cell; primary batteries, dry & wet
HQ: O'reilly Automotive Stores, Inc.
  233 S Patterson Ave
  Springfield MO 65802
  417 862-2674

(G-20858)
RANGER OILFIELD PRODUCTS INC
224 Longstreet Rd (77378-9265)
PHONE...................................936 856-4182
Ricci Harughty, *President*
Gerri Young, *Treasurer*
EMP: 17
SALES (est): 1.2MM **Privately Held**
WEB: www.rangeroilfieldproducts.com
SIC: 1389 Oil field services

(G-20859)
RFR VERTEX LLC
11355 Fm 830 Rd (77318-5627)
PHONE...................................713 851-2060
David Riggs, *Manager*
EMP: 11
SALES (est): 1.9MM **Privately Held**
WEB: www.rfrvertex.com
SIC: 3599 Machine shop, jobbing & repair

(G-20860)
RIG QA INTERNATIONAL INC (PA)
12725 Cude Cemetery Rd (77318-6468)
PHONE...................................936 856-5614
Darrel L Grumbles, *Principal*
Donna Fox, *Vice Pres*
Miranda Grumbles, *Opers Mgr*
Benny Mason, *Manager*
Jami Dixon, *Executive*
EMP: 16
SALES (est): 1.9MM **Privately Held**
WEB: www.rigqa.com
SIC: 1389 Oil field services

(G-20861)
ROBBINS & MYERS INC (HQ)
10586 Highway 75 N (77378-1600)
PHONE...................................936 890-1064
Peter C Wallace, *President*
Clay C Williams, *President*
Saeid Rahimian, *Senior VP*
Craig C Goss, *Vice Pres*
Daniel L Molinaro, *Vice Pres*
◆ **EMP:** 45
SALES (est): 528.5MM
SALES (corp-wide): 8.4B **Publicly Held**
WEB: www.robn.com
SIC: 3533 3443 3823 5084 Oil & gas field machinery; reactor containment vessels, metal plate; industrial process control instruments; hydraulic systems equipment & supplies
PA: National Oilwell Varco, Inc.
  7909 Parkwood Circle Dr
  Houston TX 77036
  713 346-7500

(G-20862)
ROBBINS MYERS ENRGY SYSTEMS LP
Also Called: R&M Energy Systems
10586 N Highway 75 (77378-5715)
PHONE...................................936 890-1064
Saeid Rahimian, *President*

Joseph M Rigot, *Partner*
◆ **EMP:** 400
SQ FT: 4,320
SALES (est): 127.9MM
SALES (corp-wide): 8.4B **Publicly Held**
SIC: 3491 3533 Industrial valves; oil & gas field machinery
HQ: Robbins & Myers, Inc.
  10586 Highway 75 N
  Willis TX 77378
  936 890-1064

(G-20863)
S F L INC
Also Called: Lone Star Fabrication
410 Lindley Dr (77378-9050)
PHONE...................................936 856-1433
Michael R Willis, *President*
EMP: 30
SQ FT: 5,425
SALES (est): 4.9MM **Privately Held**
WEB: www.lonestarfabrication.com
SIC: 3446 3441 Railings, prefabricated metal; stairs, staircases, stair treads: prefabricated metal; fabricated structural metal

(G-20864)
SCHMIDT TOOL & MFG CO
13967 Fm 1097 Rd W (77318-4962)
PHONE...................................936 856-5897
William Schmidt, *President*
Gloria Schmidt, *Corp Secy*
James Schmidt, *Vice Pres*
Kristen Schmidt, *Vice Pres*
EMP: 24
SQ FT: 20,000
SALES: 2.5MM **Privately Held**
WEB: www.steadyrest.net
SIC: 3599 3544 Machine shop, jobbing & repair; special dies, tools, jigs & fixtures

(G-20865)
SHORELINE SERVICES INC
Also Called: Marine Construction
12435 Fm 830 Rd (77318-5564)
PHONE...................................936 856-4880
Vernon B Miller, *President*
Carol Rainer, *Consultant*
Cristin Cash, *Real Est Agnt*
EMP: 13
SQ FT: 8,400
SALES (est): 1.7MM **Privately Held**
WEB: www.shorelinecompanies.com
SIC: 3732 Boat building & repairing

(G-20866)
TEXAS TECHNICAL CERAMICS INC
303 Industrial Park Ln (77378-3038)
P.O. Box 1440 (77378-1440)
PHONE...................................936 856-2903
Terry Lassinger, *President*
Jeffrey Lassinger, *Vice Pres*
EMP: 20
SQ FT: 25,000
SALES (est): 2.1MM **Privately Held**
WEB: www.texastechnicalceramics.com
SIC: 3255 3299 3264 Clay refractories; ceramic fiber; porcelain electrical supplies

(G-20867)
UNI-FAB LLC
15890 N Highway 75 (77378-3458)
PHONE...................................936 344-2800
Joey Adams, *Principal*
Robert Gibbens, *Principal*
Michael Maraist, *Principal*
Jason Mizibrocky, *Principal*
Kevin Tomczak, *Principal*
EMP: 11
SALES (est): 510.9K **Privately Held**
WEB: www.unifabinc.com
SIC: 7692 Welding repair

(G-20868)
UNLIMITED SUPPLY INC
Also Called: Specialty Sup Installation Co
12511 Fm 830 Rd (77318-5565)
P.O. Box 1047, Conroe (77305-1047)
PHONE...................................936 890-8997
Dennis Norman, *President*
Norman Stephen C, *Vice Pres*
Wilda Norman, *Project Leader*
EMP: 22

SALES (est): 2.8MM **Privately Held**
WEB: www.theseatingpros.com
SIC: 2531 5021 3949 Stadium furniture; school desks; sporting & athletic goods

(G-20869)
WILDKAT PRECISION LLC
14357 N Highway 75 (77378-3429)
P.O. Box 1196 (77378-1196)
PHONE...................................936 890-9572
Charles Landry Butler, *President*
George Simmons, *Vice Pres*
EMP: 16 EST: 2010
SALES (est): 4MM **Privately Held**
WEB: www.wildkatprecision.com
SIC: 3533 Oil & gas field machinery

Willow City
Gillespie County

(G-20870)
BELL MOUNTAIN VINEYARDS INC
463 Bell Mountain Rd (78675-8501)
PHONE...................................830 685-3297
Robert Oberhelman, *President*
Evelyn Oberhellmann, *Admin Sec*
EMP: 9
SQ FT: 24,000
SALES (est): 958K **Privately Held**
WEB: www.wildharebistrocafe.com
SIC: 2084 Wines

(G-20871)
SANITZ ENTERPRISES INC
Also Called: American Patriot Sales & Svcs
2054 Willow City Loop (78675-2122)
P.O. Box 2333, Fredericksburg (78624-1920)
PHONE...................................719 439-2183
Tommy E Sanitz, *CEO*
EMP: 11
SQ FT: 9,500
SALES (est): 10.2MM **Privately Held**
SIC: 7382 5251 3429 Security systems services; hardware; aircraft & marine hardware, inc. pulleys & similar items

Willow Park
Parker County

(G-20872)
CHILDS READY-MIX CONCRETE CO
Also Called: Weatherford Concrete
6222 E Interstate 20 (76008-2647)
P.O. Box 874, Weatherford (76086-0874)
PHONE...................................817 594-3832
Jorge Torres, *Manager*
EMP: 17
SALES (corp-wide): 1.4B **Publicly Held**
WEB: www.ingramconcrete.com
SIC: 3273 Ready-mixed concrete
HQ: Childs Ready-Mix Concrete Company
  4301 Danhil Dr
  Brownwood TX 76801
  325 646-6518

Wills Point
Van Zandt County

(G-20873)
ATLAS BUILDING SYSTEMS INC
23370 Interstate 20 (75169-7454)
PHONE...................................903 865-1153
Dale Conkion, *Manager*
EMP: 25
SALES (corp-wide): 5.2MM **Privately Held**
WEB: www.atlasbackyardsheds.com
SIC: 2452 3448 1522 Prefabricated buildings, wood; buildings, portable: prefabricated metal; residential construction
PA: Atlas Building Systems, Inc.
  5511 State Highway 31 W
  Tyler TX 75709
  903 547-4211

(G-20874)
BRAZOS TRAILER MFG LLC (PA)
22488 I 20 Svc Rd Wlls Pt (75169)
PHONE...........................903 873-8130
Nathan Bullard,
Chris Bullard,
James Bullard,
EMP: 26
SALES (est): 7.8MM Privately Held
WEB: www.brazostrailers.com
SIC: 3799 3715 Trailers & trailer equipment; semitrailers for truck tractors

(G-20875)
GRIFFIN PRODUCTS INC
303 Bluebird Pkwy (75169-8811)
P.O. Box 90 (75169-0090)
PHONE...........................903 873-6388
Shane W Griffin, President
Kenneth E Fritcher, Vice Pres
Steve Gipson, Plant Mgr
Mike Whitus, Sales Executive
EMP: 20
SQ FT: 45,000
SALES (est): 4.7MM Privately Held
WEB: www.griffinproducts.com
SIC: 3441 3431 Fabricated structural metal; metal sanitary ware

(G-20876)
R&R MILLWORK INC
304 Bluebird Pkwy (75169-8810)
PHONE...........................903 873-6600
Ron Hoover, President
Donna Asbill, Human Res Mgr
EMP: 50
SQ FT: 20,000
SALES (est): 7.7MM Privately Held
WEB: www.randrmillwork.com
SIC: 2431 Millwork

(G-20877)
R-5 METAL FABRICATORS INC
21121 Us Highway 80 (75169-6435)
P.O. Box 605 (75169-0605)
PHONE...........................903 873-2633
Gary Rabal, President
EMP: 15
SQ FT: 14,000
SALES (est): 3MM Privately Held
WEB: www.r5metalfabinc.com
SIC: 3599 3469 Machine & other job shop work; stamping metal for the trade

(G-20878)
TEXAS INDUSTRIES INC
Also Called: T X I
201 Vz County Road 3805 (75169-5664)
PHONE...........................903 873-2849
Chris Mayfield, General Mgr
EMP: 50 Publicly Held
WEB: www.martinmarietta.com
SIC: 3273 3271 Ready-mixed concrete; blocks, concrete or cinder: standard
HQ: Texas Industries, Inc.
1503 Lyndon B Johnson Fwy
Dallas TX 75234
972 647-6700

(G-20879)
TEXAS MACHINERY CO
451 Vz County Road 3803 (75169-5982)
PHONE...........................972 792-0166
Andy Plassenthal, President
EMP: 10 EST: 2009
SALES (est): 1.2MM Privately Held
WEB: www.billor.com
SIC: 3531 Construction machinery

(G-20880)
VAN ZANDT NEWSPAPERS LLC (PA)
Also Called: First Monday Directory
109 N 5th St (75169-2058)
P.O. Box 60 (75169-0060)
PHONE...........................903 567-4000
John Buzzetta,
EMP: 23
SALES (est): 1.9MM Privately Held
WEB: www.vanzandtnews.com
SIC: 2711 Newspapers, publishing & printing

Wimberley
Hays County

(G-20881)
HILL COUNTRY LAND IMPROVEMENT
801 Carney Ln (78676-4802)
PHONE...........................512 766-8122
Chris Lawson, CEO
EMP: 20 EST: 2015
SALES (est): 41.1K Privately Held
WEB: www.hillcountrylandimprovement.com
SIC: 0781 1794 3446 1629 Landscape counseling & planning; excavation & grading, building construction; fences, gates, posts & flagpoles; land preparation construction

(G-20882)
HILLBURN DEFENSE SYSTEMS INC
310 W View Dr (78676-3332)
PHONE...........................512 636-8498
Ray Hilburn, CEO
Lash L McGee, Vice Pres
Jason Stelle, Administration
EMP: 9
SALES (est): 470.8K Privately Held
SIC: 2851 Paints, asphalt or bituminous

(G-20883)
RUPERT NEVE DESIGNS LLC
511 Flite Acres Rd (78676-5416)
P.O. Box 1969 (78676-6869)
PHONE...........................512 847-3013
Lucas Burden, Design Engr
Cindy Thornburg, Accounts Mgr
Greg Addington, Sales Staff
Tristan Rhodes, Marketing Staff
Martin Arthurs, Manager
EMP: 13
SQ FT: 4,000
SALES (est): 2.6MM Privately Held
WEB: www.rupertneve.com
SIC: 3651 Audio electronic systems

(G-20884)
TEXAS LEHIGH CEMENT COMPANY LP
336 Scenic Way (78676-3304)
PHONE...........................512 434-9330
EMP: 71
SALES (corp-wide): 1.4B Publicly Held
WEB: www.texaslehigh.com
SIC: 3241 Portland cement
HQ: Texas Lehigh Cement Company Lp
1000 Jack C Hays Trl
Buda TX 78610
512 295-6111

(G-20885)
TORRENT ENERGY SERVICES LLC
173 Fm 3237 Ste B (78676-5373)
PHONE...........................512 722-3439
Lance Perryman, Principal
EMP: 25
SALES (est): 127.4K
SALES (corp-wide): 336.9MM Publicly Held
SIC: 1382 Oil & gas exploration services
PA: Ranger Energy Services, Inc.
10350 Richmond Ave # 550
Houston TX 77042
713 935-8900

Windthorst
Archer County

(G-20886)
STEINBERGER DRILLING COMPANY
10063 State Highway 25 E (76389-4300)
P.O. Box 250 (76389-0250)
PHONE...........................940 423-6900
Charles Steinberger, President
Justin Steinberger, Vice Pres
EMP: 24

SALES (est): 3.4MM Privately Held
WEB: www.steinbergerdrilling.com
SIC: 1381 Directional drilling oil & gas wells

Wink
Winkler County

(G-20887)
GARCIAS WELL SERVICING INC
203 Ashby Ave (79789)
P.O. Box 803 (79789-0803)
PHONE...........................432 527-3748
Martin Garcia, President
Stacey Garcia, Admin Sec
EMP: 40 EST: 1998
SALES (est): 3.2MM Privately Held
SIC: 1381 Service well drilling

Winnie
Chambers County

(G-20888)
LARRY PRTERS CSTM INTR DSGNS I
480 Broadway (77665-7718)
P.O. Box 536 (77665-0536)
PHONE...........................409 296-3868
Larry Porter, President
EMP: 10 EST: 2004
SALES (est): 539.6K Privately Held
SIC: 2599 Cabinets, factory

(G-20889)
S & S OPERATING CO INC
46436 Interstate 10 (77665-9067)
P.O. Box 1250 (77665-1250)
PHONE...........................409 296-9571
Scott D Jones, President
John S Leger, Vice Pres
Sissy Leger, Treasurer
Tinker Adams, Office Mgr
Monica Jones, Admin Sec
EMP: 10
SQ FT: 800
SALES (est): 1MM Privately Held
SIC: 1389 Oil field services

(G-20890)
SASOL CHEMICALS (USA) LLC
14322 Rollins Rd (77665)
PHONE...........................409 296-9091
John Riekert, Manager
EMP: 9
SALES (corp-wide): 10.7MM Privately Held
WEB: www.sasolnorthamerica.com
SIC: 2869 2819 Industrial organic chemicals; industrial inorganic chemicals
HQ: Sasol Chemicals (Usa) Llc
12120 Wickchester Ln
Houston TX 77079
281 588-3000

(G-20891)
SEABREEZE CULVERT
3836 Texas 124 (77665)
P.O. Box 6, Stowell (77661-0006)
PHONE...........................409 296-4675
Lamont Meaux, Partner
EMP: 17
SALES (est): 840.4K Privately Held
WEB: www.seabreeze-culvert.com
SIC: 5993 3499 Pipe store; fabricated metal products

(G-20892)
VORTECH CONTRACTING INC
42408 Ih 10 (77665-1309)
P.O. Box 2279 (77665-2279)
PHONE...........................409 296-3219
John Frank Abalos, President
Craig Wayne, Vice Pres
Steve Abalos, CFO
EMP: 186
SQ FT: 2,500
SALES (est): 38.1MM Privately Held
WEB: www.vortechcontracting.com
SIC: 1389 Oil & gas wells: building, repairing & dismantling

(G-20893)
WIN-TEX LEASE SERVICES INC
18195 County Line Rd (77665)
P.O. Box 658 (77665-0658)
PHONE...........................409 296-4194
Jimmy Cossey, President
EMP: 10
SQ FT: 800
SALES (est): 2.1MM Privately Held
SIC: 1389 Oil field services

(G-20894)
WINNIE WLDG WORKS & CNSTR INC
25949 Highway 73 (77665-8226)
P.O. Box 237 (77665-0237)
PHONE...........................409 296-2953
EMP: 30
SQ FT: 1,800
SALES (est): 3MM Privately Held
WEB: www.andconstruction.com
SIC: 7692 Welding repair

Winnsboro
Wood County

(G-20895)
AIRBORN INTERCONNECT INC
Also Called: Airborn Connectors
Fm 312 S St (75494)
P.O. Box 685 (75494-0685)
PHONE...........................903 629-7821
Lisa Kraniske, General Mgr
Sandy RAO, COO
Brian Kerns, Purch Mgr
Sue Salvog, Buyer
Jessamy Czerniecki, Purchasing
EMP: 25
SALES (corp-wide): 221.1MM Privately Held
WEB: www.airborn.com
SIC: 3089 3544 Injection molding of plastics; special dies, tools, jigs & fixtures
PA: Airborn Interconnect, Inc.
3500 Airborn Cir
Georgetown TX 78626
512 863-5585

(G-20896)
B & T DIRECTIONAL DRILLING INC
4581 N Fm 2869 (75494-7477)
P.O. Box 790 (75494-0790)
PHONE...........................903 629-3406
Tommy J Steele, President
Ted Ford, Vice Pres
David McCreary, Vice Pres
Deborah Nimmo, Treasurer
Cassie Steele, Admin Sec
EMP: 10
SALES (est): 4MM Privately Held
WEB: www.dgdirectional.com
SIC: 1381 Directional drilling oil & gas wells

(G-20897)
ITEC MANUFACTURING LLC
400 All Star Dr (75494-3532)
P.O. Box 325 (75494-0325)
PHONE...........................903 365-6390
Michael R Wilson, Mng Member
Charlotte C Wilson,
EMP: 17
SQ FT: 48,000
SALES (est): 2MM Privately Held
WEB: www.itecems.com
SIC: 3841 Surgical & medical instruments

(G-20898)
JEB SALES COMPANY INC
Also Called: Jeb Originals
103 E Coke Rd (75494-3211)
P.O. Box 592 (75494-0592)
PHONE...........................903 342-3112
Jim Herlocker, President
EMP: 9
SQ FT: 4,000
SALES (est): 1.4MM Privately Held
WEB: www.jebsalescompany.com
SIC: 2759 Screen printing

(G-20899)
KELLERS CREAMERY LLC
1015 E Broadway St (75494-2901)
PHONE..................................903 347-4250
Larry Merchant, *Manager*
EMP: 50
SALES (corp-wide): 15.8B **Privately Held**
WEB: www.kellerscreamery.com
SIC: 2021 2023 Creamery butter; dry, con-
densed, evaporated dairy products
HQ: Keller's Creamery, L.L.C.
855 Maple Ave
Harleysville PA 19438

(G-20900)
NEW CONCEPT SERVICES INC
100 Park St (75494-3524)
PHONE..................................903 342-5523
EMP: 18 **EST:** 1998
SALES (est): 1.3MM **Privately Held**
SIC: 3714 3357 Automotive wiring har-
ness sets; nonferrous wiredrawing & insu-
lating

(G-20901)
USA HARNESS INC
1201 E Coke Rd (75494-3519)
P.O. Box 691342, Tulsa OK (74169-1342)
PHONE..................................903 342-3767
Lawrence Chambly, *President*
Brett Miller, *Vice Pres*
Kim Scott, *Vice Pres*
Mary Smith, *Vice Pres*
Debbie Thompson, *Vice Pres*
◆ **EMP:** 100
SQ FT: 75,000
SALES (est): 15.2MM
SALES (corp-wide): 25.3MM **Privately
Held**
WEB: www.optronicsinc.com
SIC: 3694 Harness wiring sets, internal
combustion engines
PA: Optronics International, Llc
5115 S 122nd East Ave # 20
Tulsa OK 74146
918 286-1288

(G-20902)
**WINNSBORO SPCLTY PRTS
INTL INC**
Also Called: Alexander's Tractor Parts
301 Park St (75494-3529)
P.O. Box 28 (75494-0028)
PHONE..................................903 342-3551
Xerlene Alexander, *President*
◆ **EMP:** 25
SQ FT: 60,000
SALES (est): 5.3MM **Privately Held**
WEB: www.alexandertractorparts.com
SIC: 5083 3519 Tractors, agricultural; farm
equipment parts & supplies; diesel engine
rebuilding

Winona
Smith County

(G-20903)
CRISP AIR
10330 County Road 3168 (75792-6920)
PHONE..................................903 530-4385
Dave Pool, *Owner*
EMP: 20
SALES (est): 2.5MM **Privately Held**
SIC: 3822 Air conditioning & refrigeration
controls

Winters
Runnels County

(G-20904)
**COLLINS ROUSTABOUT & WELL
SVC**
7726 State Highway 153 (79567-7353)
P.O. Box 284 (79567-0284)
PHONE..................................325 754-4237
Louie Collins, *President*
EMP: 10
SQ FT: 480
SALES (est): 779.4K **Privately Held**
SIC: 1389 Roustabout service

(G-20905)
MAC OIL FIELD COMPANY INC
1007 W Dale St (79567-4915)
P.O. Box 669 (79567-0669)
PHONE..................................325 754-5565
Allen Belk, *President*
Jerry Lloyd, *Corp Secy*
Michelle Belk, *Admin Sec*
EMP: 15
SQ FT: 4,500
SALES (est): 1.6MM **Privately Held**
SIC: 1389 Oil field services

Wolfe City
Hunt County

(G-20906)
ENNIS INC
Also Called: Ennis Tag & Label
118 E Main St (75496-3107)
P.O. Box D (75496-0190)
PHONE..................................903 496-2244
Al Lemieux, *Manager*
EMP: 170
SALES (corp-wide): 438.4MM **Publicly
Held**
WEB: www.ennis.com
SIC: 2752 2679 2672 2671 Tags, litho-
graphed; tags, paper (unprinted): made
from purchased paper; coated & lami-
nated paper; packaging paper & plastics
film, coated & laminated; paper mills
PA: Ennis, Inc.
2441 Presidential Pkwy
Midlothian TX 76065
972 775-9801

Wolfforth
Lubbock County

(G-20907)
**DAILY OFFRNGS COF
ROASTERY LLC**
Also Called: Roastery, The
1106 Preston Trl (79382-1758)
PHONE..................................805 423-7410
Kristy Kotze,
EMP: 10
SALES (est): 20.4K **Privately Held**
SIC: 2095 5812 Roasted coffee; coffee
shop

(G-20908)
**HERITAGE EQUIPMENT
COMPANY INC**
10312 Fm 41 (79382-4820)
PHONE..................................806 745-4451
David Braune, *President*
Sue Braune, *Vice Pres*
EMP: 62
SALES (est): 7.7MM **Privately Held**
SIC: 3523 5999 Loaders, farm type: ma-
nure, general utility; farm equipment &
supplies

(G-20909)
OUTERWEAR USA
726 Donald Preston Dr (79382-5402)
PHONE..................................806 792-8891
Steven Peterson, *Principal*
EMP: 19
SALES (est): 1.4MM **Privately Held**
WEB: www.outerwearusa.com
SIC: 2759 Commercial printing

(G-20910)
**PLUNKETT ENERGY &
INDUSTRIAL S**
Also Called: Plunkett Oil & Energy Svc Co
9723 Highway 62 (79382-5108)
P.O. Box 910 (79382-0910)
PHONE..................................806 395-3205
John Plunkett, *Mng Member*
Derek Plunkett, *Officer*
Dylan Plunkett,
EMP: 14
SQ FT: 7,500
SALES (est): 1.5MM **Privately Held**
SIC: 1382 Oil & gas exploration services

(G-20911)
**REHAB PLUS THRAPEUTIC
PDTS INC**
Also Called: RPS Manufacturing Solutions
726 Donald Preston Dr (79382-5402)
PHONE..................................806 791-2288
Ronnie Bilbo, *President*
David Foster, *Vice Pres*
Greg Mason, *CFO*
◆ **EMP:** 11
SQ FT: 40,000
SALES (est): 3.8MM **Privately Held**
WEB: www.rpssolutions.net
SIC: 3842 Elastic hosiery, orthopedic (sup-
port)
PA: Rehabplus Safety, S.A. De C.V.
Carr. Presa De La Amistad No. 990
Cd. Acuna COAH. 26230

(G-20912)
SCOTT MANUFACTURING INC
10609 Fm 1585 (79382-4625)
P.O. Box 10232, Lubbock (79408-3232)
PHONE..................................806 747-3395
Rickie Scott, *President*
Billie Daly, *Director*
▲ **EMP:** 150
SQ FT: 250,000
SALES (est): 38.5MM **Privately Held**
WEB: www.scottmanufacturing.com
SIC: 3441 3443 Fabricated structural
metal; fabricated plate work (boiler shop)

(G-20913)
SIGN PRO OF LUBBOCK LTD
110 E Highway 62 (79382-2251)
P.O. Box 53263, Lubbock (79453-3263)
PHONE..................................806 798-7446
Valton Cooper, *President*
EMP: 12
SQ FT: 600
SALES (est): 1.5MM **Privately Held**
WEB: www.signprolubbock.com
SIC: 3993 Electric signs

Woodville
Tyler County

(G-20914)
AMERIFORGE GROUP INC
Texas Metal Works
Hwy 69 (75979)
P.O. Box 2070 (75979-2070)
PHONE..................................409 283-8138
Michael Watts, *Plant Supt*
EMP: 40
SALES (corp-wide): 252.3MM **Privately
Held**
WEB: www.afglobalcorp.com
SIC: 3462 3494 Flange, valve & pipe fit-
ting forgings, ferrous; valves & pipe fit-
tings
PA: Ameriforge Group Inc.
945 Bunker Hill Rd # 500
Houston TX 77024
713 393-4200

(G-20915)
AZT WOOD LLC
950 N Pine St (75979-4114)
P.O. Box 2279 (75979-2279)
PHONE..................................409 283-5355
Lonnie Grissom Jr,
Bobbie Breaux,
Harry Carnes Jr,
EMP: 10
SALES (est): 1.8MM **Privately Held**
SIC: 3537 Trucks: freight, baggage, etc.:
industrial, except mining

(G-20916)
POLK COUNTY PUBLISHING CO
Also Called: Tyler County Booster
205 W Bluff St (75979-5221)
P.O. Box 339 (75979-0339)
PHONE..................................409 283-2516
Kelli Barnes, *Manager*
EMP: 12
SALES (corp-wide): 6MM **Privately Held**
WEB: www.easttexasnews.com
SIC: 2711 7313 Newspapers, publishing &
printing; newspaper advertising represen-
tative

PA: Polk County Publishing Co.
100 E Calhoun St
Livingston TX 77351
936 327-4357

(G-20917)
SPURLOCK LOGGING INC
201 Sutton St (75979-4827)
PHONE..................................409 429-4333
Charles F Spurlock, *President*
Kay Spurlock, *Vice Pres*
EMP: 30
SQ FT: 1,000
SALES (est): 2.2MM **Privately Held**
SIC: 2411 Logging camps & contractors

(G-20918)
**TEMPLE PRECISION ENTERPISE
INC**
Also Called: Precision Enterprise
1036 Hwy 69 N (75979)
P.O. Box 429 (75979-0429)
PHONE..................................409 283-8163
Greg Temple, *President*
Colleen Temple, *Admin Sec*
EMP: 12
SALES (est): 1.7MM **Privately Held**
SIC: 3559 Electronic component making
machinery

(G-20919)
WARRIOR G INDUSTRIES
1008 N Nellius St (75979-4204)
PHONE..................................409 594-5258
Izene Sheffield, *Partner*
EMP: 10
SALES (est): 561.3K **Privately Held**
SIC: 3492 Fluid power valves & hose fit-
tings

(G-20920)
WOODVILLE HARDWOODS
4937 Us Highway 69 S (75979-6273)
P.O. Box 2144 (75979-2144)
PHONE..................................409 283-6106
Mack Anthony, *Owner*
EMP: 20
SALES (est): 2.5MM **Privately Held**
SIC: 2421 Sawmills & planing mills, gen-
eral

Woodway
Mclennan County

(G-20921)
**JACKSON SIGN AND LIGHTING
INC**
22007 Bush Industrial Par (76712)
P.O. Box 23087, Waco (76702-3087)
PHONE..................................254 751-0390
Wendell Jackson, *President*
Ruth Jackson, *Corp Secy*
Phil Jackson, *Vice Pres*
EMP: 9
SQ FT: 10,000
SALES (est): 1MM **Privately Held**
WEB: www.jacksonsigntx.com
SIC: 3993 1799 Electric signs; sign instal-
lation & maintenance

Wortham
Freestone County

(G-20922)
**CPI SATCOM & ANTENNA TECH
INC**
1004 N Mrtn Lther King Av (76693)
P.O. Box 428 (76693-0428)
PHONE..................................254 765-3304
Christopher Marzilli, *President*
Sean Boyer, *General Mgr*
David Gregory, *Branch Mgr*
EMP: 81 **Privately Held**
WEB: www.gdmissionsystems.com
SIC: 3731 3663 Radar towers, floating;
antennas, transmitting & communications
HQ: Cpi Satcom & Antenna Technologies
Inc.
1700 Cable Dr Ne
Conover NC 28613
704 462-7330

Wylie
Collin County

(G-20923)
72ND & THORNHILL LLC
306 Trenton Dr (75098-7418)
PHONE..................................469 318-5087
Jacoby Stewart,
EMP: 10
SALES (est): 600K **Privately Held**
SIC: 2599 Food wagons, restaurant

(G-20924)
ALL STATE FIRE EQP TEXAS INC
1307 Century Way (75098-4072)
PHONE..................................972 412-0770
Yvonne Damon, *President*
Ken Damon, *Vice Pres*
Randy Payne, *Opers Mgr*
EMP: 15
SQ FT: 1,500
SALES (est): 3MM **Privately Held**
WEB: www.asfefleetsolutions.com
SIC: 7389 3585 Fire extinguisher servicing; air conditioning equipment, complete

(G-20925)
ALUMA GRAPHICS LP (PA)
103 Security Ct (75098-4943)
PHONE..................................972 442-3299
Ray Crockett, *President*
Randal Williams, *Senior VP*
Randy Kearby, *Vice Pres*
Bill Smith, *Vice Pres*
Carla Harris, *Manager*
EMP: 46
SQ FT: 45,700
SALES (est): 6.9MM **Privately Held**
WEB: www.alumagraphics.com
SIC: 2796 2759 3993 2671 Photoengraving plates, linecuts or halftones; screen printing; signs & advertising specialties; packaging paper & plastics film, coated & laminated

(G-20926)
AMERICAN STEAM INC
49 Steel Rd (75098-7048)
P.O. Box 1149 (75098-1149)
PHONE..................................972 442-4499
Carlos Diaz, *President*
Dwan Diaz, *Corp Secy*
Jim Houser, *Regional*
EMP: 30 **EST:** 1981
SQ FT: 27,500
SALES (est): 4.1MM **Privately Held**
WEB: www.americansteam.com
SIC: 7699 3433 3823 5074 Boiler & heating repair services; boiler repair shop; boilers, low-pressure heating: steam or hot water; gas-oil burners, combination; combustion control instruments; boilers, power (industrial); boilers, steam; gas burners; controlling instruments & accessories

(G-20927)
BEST CIRCUIT BOARDS INC (HQ)
Also Called: Global Innovation
901 Hensley Ln (75098-4909)
PHONE..................................214 291-1427
Brad Jacoby, *President*
Brent Nolan, *COO*
Manny Ortiz, *Purch Mgr*
Brad Peters, *CFO*
Charla Riner, *Director*
EMP: 56
SQ FT: 101,000
SALES (est): 26.4MM
SALES (corp-wide): 34MM **Privately Held**
WEB: www.lscpcbs.com
SIC: 3672 Circuit boards, television & radio printed
PA: Global Innovation Corp.
901 Hensley Ln
Wylie TX 75098
214 291-1427

(G-20928)
C & S MEDIA INC
Also Called: The Wylie News
110 N Ballard Ave (75098-4467)
P.O. Box 369 (75098-0369)
PHONE..................................972 442-5515
Chad Engbrock, *President*
Duggan Sonia A, *Vice Pres*
EMP: 9
SQ FT: 3,625
SALES (est): 679.4K **Privately Held**
WEB: www.csmediatexas.com
SIC: 2711 7313 Newspapers: publishing only, not printed on site; newspaper advertising representative

(G-20929)
CARLISLE CTNGS WTRPROOFING INC (DH)
900 Hensley Ln (75098-4908)
PHONE..................................972 442-6545
John W Altmeyer, *President*
Steven J Ford, *Vice Pres*
Robert L Stout, *Vice Pres*
Mark Wodek, *Materials Mgr*
Keith Rivers, *Cust Mgr*
◆ **EMP:** 70
SALES (est): 56MM
SALES (corp-wide): 4.2B **Publicly Held**
WEB: www.carlisleccw.com
SIC: 2899 2851 2295 Waterproofing compounds; polyurethane coatings; tape, varnished: plastic & other coated (except magnetic)

(G-20930)
CARMIES KITCHEN INC
Also Called: Pepper Springs Spice Co
210 Windco Cir (75098-5203)
PHONE..................................972 442-1337
Carmie Randack, *CEO*
Jerry Randack, *President*
EMP: 10
SQ FT: 3,100
SALES (est): 1.1MM **Privately Held**
WEB: www.carmieskitchen.com
SIC: 2099 5149 Seasonings: dry mixes; spices & seasonings

(G-20931)
CUSTOM EXTRUSIONS HOLDINGS LLC (PA)
1405 Martinez Ln (75098-4075)
PHONE..................................972 442-7200
Jeff Hull, *Mng Member*
Mark Blanchat, *Mng Member*
Alex Guiva, *Mng Member*
William Retterath, *Mng Member*
EMP: 14
SALES (est): 13.7MM **Privately Held**
SIC: 3355 8741 Extrusion ingot, aluminum: made in rolling mills; administrative management

(G-20932)
DCU INC
2774 Capital Street Wylie (75098)
P.O. Box 155 (75098-0155)
PHONE..................................972 816-6667
Mark H Hambelton, *Owner*
Ed Wales, *Senior VP*
EMP: 10
SQ FT: 4,000
SALES (est): 1.4MM **Privately Held**
WEB: www.dcumodels.com
SIC: 3089 2221 1799 2499 Plastic processing; fiberglass fabrics; welding on site; food handling & processing products, wood

(G-20933)
DISTINCTIVE DOORS INC
933 Hensley Ln (75098-4909)
PHONE..................................972 487-6680
Pat Meyer, *Principal*
▲ **EMP:** 10 **EST:** 2007
SQ FT: 88,279
SALES (est): 1.5MM **Privately Held**
WEB: www.maidoors.com
SIC: 2431 Millwork

(G-20934)
DUEL PRODUCTS INC
702 Cooper Dr (75098-3949)
PHONE..................................972 429-5607

Louise Nation, *President*
Rodger Nation, *Vice Pres*
Mike Nation, *Sales Staff*
EMP: 10
SQ FT: 9,300
SALES (est): 1.4MM **Privately Held**
SIC: 3599 Machine shop, jobbing & repair

(G-20935)
EXCO EXTRUSION DIES TEXAS INC
911 Hensley Ln (75098-4909)
P.O. Box 2925 (75098-2925)
PHONE..................................972 442-3131
Bonnie Cartwright, *President*
EMP: 19
SALES (est): 5.6MM
SALES (corp-wide): 311.7MM **Privately Held**
WEB: www.etsdies.com
SIC: 3544 Special dies & tools
PA: Exco Technologies Limited
130 Spy Crt
Markham ON L3R 5
905 477-3065

(G-20936)
GIFFORD MONUMENT WORKS INC (PA)
77 Paul Wilson Rd (75098-4552)
P.O. Box 4243, Alamogordo NM (88311-4243)
PHONE..................................972 544-6305
Cleve Kurz, *President*
Nick Kurz, *Vice Pres*
Judy Kurz, *Director*
▲ **EMP:** 10
SALES (est): 1.3MM **Privately Held**
WEB: www.giffordmonument.com
SIC: 5999 1542 3272 Monuments, finished to custom order; mausoleum construction; monuments & grave markers, except terrazo

(G-20937)
INHERENT SOFTWARE LLC
2209 Lakeridge Ln (75098-7491)
PHONE..................................817 379-0328
Jane Fuhrman, *Mng Member*
EMP: 10
SALES (est): 300K **Privately Held**
SIC: 7372 Prepackaged software

(G-20938)
J C ORNAMENTAL IRONWORKS INC
130 Kristen Ln (75098-4032)
P.O. Box 1239 (75098-1239)
PHONE..................................972 442-6293
EMP: 15
SALES (est): 2.5MM **Privately Held**
SIC: 3446 Mfg Architectural Metalwork

(G-20939)
KEN ROSS INC
Also Called: Ken Ross International
703 Cooper Dr (75098-3950)
P.O. Box 116 (75098-0116)
PHONE..................................972 442-3523
Dan Ross, *President*
Mary M Ross, *Corp Secy*
EMP: 10
SQ FT: 18,000
SALES (est): 2MM **Privately Held**
SIC: 3089 Molding primary plastic

(G-20940)
LUTZ WOODWORKS LLC
700 Parker Rd (75098-4712)
PHONE..................................972 429-5521
Tom Bartlett, *General Mgr*
Vickie Lutz, *Principal*
Greg Lutz, *Vice Pres*
Gregory Lutz, *Vice Pres*
Mike West, *Project Mgr*
EMP: 30
SQ FT: 12,000
SALES (est): 2.9MM **Privately Held**
WEB: www.lutzwoodworks.com
SIC: 2431 2521 Millwork; wood office desks & tables

(G-20941)
MULTI-MACHINING CO INC
701 Business Way (75098-3961)
PHONE..................................972 429-6111
Tony Linduff, *President*
Jane Watson, *Sales Executive*
EMP: 28
SQ FT: 30,000
SALES (est): 2.4MM **Privately Held**
WEB: www.multi-machining.com
SIC: 3599 Machine shop, jobbing & repair

(G-20942)
PERFORMAX CUSTOM TRAILERS
Also Called: Performax Custom Accessories
1825 E Fm 544 (75098-6765)
PHONE..................................972 442-3527
Ronnie Young, *President*
Dee Young, *Vice Pres*
EMP: 15
SQ FT: 10,000
SALES (est): 2.2MM **Privately Held**
WEB: www.bluemaxracing.net
SIC: 3715 Truck trailers

(G-20943)
PRECISION M/C MFG INC
700 Sanden Blvd (75098-4945)
PHONE..................................972 429-6200
Pamela Patrick, *President*
EMP: 13
SQ FT: 12,000
SALES (est): 1.6MM **Privately Held**
WEB: www.precisionmc.net
SIC: 3444 Metal housings, enclosures, casings & other containers; hoods, range: sheet metal

(G-20944)
PRECISION M/C PRODUCTS INC
700 Sanden Blvd (75098-4945)
PHONE..................................972 429-6200
Sue Patrick, *President*
Chris Gartman, *Vice Pres*
Barry Patrick, *Vice Pres*
EMP: 13
SQ FT: 12,000
SALES (est): 2.2MM **Privately Held**
WEB: www.precisionmc.net
SIC: 3441 3699 7692 Fabricated structural metal; laser welding, drilling & cutting equipment; welding repair

(G-20945)
PSDE LLC
Also Called: CPI Communications
941 Hensley Ln (75098-4909)
PHONE..................................972 429-7160
Phil Easterling, *President*
Pat Easterling, *Corp Secy*
Perry W Easterling, *Vice Pres*
Harvey Branton, *Opers Mgr*
Lesley Joyce, *Chief Acct*
EMP: 12
SQ FT: 14,000
SALES (est): 1.5MM **Privately Held**
WEB: www.uk-cpi.com
SIC: 3825 Radio apparatus analyzers

(G-20946)
RWG INCORPORATED
Also Called: Gemco Manufacturing
2807 Capital St (75098-7003)
PHONE..................................972 461-1920
Robert Geckler, *President*
EMP: 15
SQ FT: 8,000
SALES (est): 2.2MM **Privately Held**
WEB: www.gemco-mfg.com
SIC: 3599 Machine shop, jobbing & repair

(G-20947)
SAF-HOLLAND INC
Also Called: Holland Hitch
1301 Martinez Ln (75098-4023)
PHONE..................................972 442-3556
David Tackett, *Facilities Mgr*
Franklin Healey, *Mfg Staff*
Tino Lara, *Production*
Debbie Pollock, *Purch Mgr*
Carl Harris, *Engineer*
EMP: 130
SQ FT: 133,008

▲ = Import ▼=Export
◆ =Import/Export

SALES (corp-wide): 355.8K **Privately Held**
WEB: www.safholland.us
SIC: 3714 3713 Motor vehicle parts & accessories; truck & bus bodies
HQ: Saf-Holland, Inc.
 1950 Industrial Blvd
 Muskegon MI 49442
 231 773-3271

(G-20948)
SANDEN INTERNATIONAL USA INC (DH)
601 Sanden Blvd (75098-4923)
PHONE 972 442-8400
◆ EMP: 735 EST: 1974
SQ FT: 385,000
SALES (est): 206.5MM **Privately Held**
WEB: www.sanden.com
SIC: 3714 1711 3585 3563 Air conditioner parts, motor vehicle; plumbing, heating, air-conditioning contractors; refrigeration & heating equipment; air & gas compressors
HQ: Sanden Of America Inc
 601 Sanden Blvd
 Wylie TX 75098
 972 442-8400

(G-20949)
SAVAGE PRCSION FABRICATION INC
1415 Martinez Ln (75098-4075)
P.O. Box 2049 (75098-2049)
PHONE 972 429-0993
Jo Ann Gardner, President
Dave Owen, Business Mgr
Chris Foster, Prdtn Mgr
Rodger Goodwin, QC Mgr
Ashley Hannigan, Human Resources
EMP: 35
SQ FT: 60,000
SALES (est): 4.1MM **Privately Held**
WEB: www.savage-precision.com
SIC: 3599 Machine shop, jobbing & repair

(G-20950)
SLOCUM PRINTING INCORPORATED
909 Lorene Dr (75098-4808)
PHONE 214 748-2238
Barbara Slocum, Owner
William Slocum III, Vice Pres
EMP: 12
SQ FT: 20,000
SALES (est): 1.8MM **Privately Held**
WEB: www.slocumprinting.com
SIC: 2752 Commercial printing, offset

(G-20951)
SPECIALTY DEVICES INCORPORATED
Also Called: S D I
2905 Capital St (75098-7058)
PHONE 972 429-7240
Paul D Higley, President
Leann J Johnson, COO
Jane Higley, Vice Pres
▼ EMP: 11
SQ FT: 5,250
SALES (est): 850K **Privately Held**
WEB: www.specialtydevices.com
SIC: 8711 3533 Consulting engineer; oil & gas drilling rigs & equipment

(G-20952)
TOWER EXTRUSIONS LTD
930 Hensley Ln (75098-4908)
PHONE 972 442-3535
EMP: 340
SQ FT: 200,000
SALES (corp-wide): 123.3MM **Privately Held**
WEB: www.towerextrusion.com
SIC: 3354 Aluminum extruded products
PA: Tower Extrusions Ltd
 1003 State Highway 79 S
 Olney TX 76374
 940 564-5681

(G-20953)
TOWER EXTRUSIONS LTD
1405 Martinez Ln (75098-4075)
PHONE 972 442-7200
Mark L McClelland, Manager

EMP: 140
SALES (corp-wide): 123.3MM **Privately Held**
WEB: www.towerextrusion.com
SIC: 3354 Aluminum extruded products
PA: Tower Extrusions Ltd
 1003 State Highway 79 S
 Olney TX 76374
 9?0 564-5681

(G-20954)
VILLATORO CONSTRUCTION LLC
2851 Whiteley Rd (75098-6206)
PHONE 214 350-7900
Miguel A Villatoro, Mng Member
Ana A Perez,
EMP: 25
SALES (est): 2.2MM **Privately Held**
SIC: 1731 1381 Fiber optic cable installation; drilling oil & gas wells

(G-20955)
VLJ INC
Also Called: Smith Tool & Manufacturing
116 Regency Dr (75098-7016)
PHONE 972 442-4673
Vicki Lewis, President
Laura Eppler, Vice Pres
Jim Palmer, Vice Pres
EMP: 17
SQ FT: 40,000
SALES (est): 2MM **Privately Held**
WEB: www.smithtoolmfg.com
SIC: 3444 3545 Sheet metal specialties, not stamped; precision tools, machinists'

(G-20956)
XL TECHNOLOGY LLC
210 Security Ct (75098-4910)
PHONE 972 369-1359
Richard F Parker, Mng Member
▲ EMP: 10
SQ FT: 4,500
SALES (est): 1MM **Privately Held**
WEB: www.xl-t.com
SIC: 3674 5999 7629 Semiconductors & related devices; electronic parts & equipment; electronic equipment repair

Yoakum
Lavaca County

(G-20957)
AA&E LEATHERCRAFT LLC
208 Industrial Loop (77995-4871)
PHONE 361 293-6366
Shannon Blaschke, Mng Member
Marvin Kremling,
▲ EMP: 9
SQ FT: 9,375
SALES (est): 250K **Privately Held**
WEB: www.aaeleathercraft.com
SIC: 3111 Leather tanning & finishing

(G-20958)
ADVANCED DRAINAGE SYSTEMS INC
Also Called: Hancor
801 Hickey Rd (77995-5193)
PHONE 361 293-6313
Mark Halepeska, Manager
EMP: 14
SALES (corp-wide): 1.6B **Publicly Held**
WEB: www.ads-pipe.com
SIC: 3089 Plastic hardware & building products
PA: Advanced Drainage Systems, Inc.
 4640 Trueman Blvd
 Hilliard OH 43026
 800 821-6710

(G-20959)
ASHER OIL FIELD SPECIALTY
1001 Us Highway 77a N (77995-2400)
PHONE 361 293-0562
Steve Asher, Mng Member
EMP: 12
SALES (est): 416.2K **Privately Held**
SIC: 1389 Oil field services

(G-20960)
BRUSHY CREEK BELT & BUCKLE CO
204 Industrial Loop (77995-4871)
P.O. Box 129 (77995-0129)
PHONE 361 293-2345
Jon E Ballard, President
Gerald Jay Ballard, Treasurer
EMP: 12 EST: 1975
SQ FT: 18,000
SALES (est): 1.2MM **Privately Held**
WEB: www.brushycreekbeltco.com
SIC: 2387 3172 Apparel belts; personal leather goods

(G-20961)
CIRCLE Y SADDLES INC
1708 N South St (77995-3802)
P.O. Box 271 (77995-0271)
PHONE 361 293-3501
Steve Tucker, President
Diane Broussard, Prdtn Mgr
Charles Proschko, CFO
▲ EMP: 10
SALES (est): 1.7MM **Privately Held**
WEB: www.circley.com
SIC: 2387 3199 Apparel belts; boots, horse

(G-20962)
DOUBLE D RANCHWEAR INC
120 W Grand Ave (77995-2612)
P.O. Box 754 (77995-0754)
PHONE 361 293-9239
Audrey Farns, General Mgr
Mitchell Franz, Associate
EMP: 19 **Privately Held**
WEB: www.doubledranch.com
SIC: 2339 Women's & misses' outerwear
PA: Double D Ranchwear, Inc.
 122 W Grand Ave
 Yoakum TX 77995

(G-20963)
DOUBLE D RANCHWEAR INC (PA)
122 W Grand Ave (77995-2612)
P.O. Box 754 (77995-0754)
PHONE 361 293-2394
Margie Mc Mullen, President
Audrey Franz, Corp Secy
Cheryl Matusek, Vice Pres
Lynita Brown, Representative
▲ EMP: 10
SALES (est): 5.3MM **Privately Held**
WEB: www.doubledranch.com
SIC: 2329 2339 Men's & boys' sportswear & athletic clothing; women's & misses' outerwear

(G-20964)
DOUBLE J SADDLERY INC
2243 Us Highway 77a S (77995-5305)
P.O. Box 3 (77995-0003)
PHONE 361 293-6364
John Debord, President
Nancy Debord, Corp Secy
▲ EMP: 70
SQ FT: 6,000
SALES (est): 8.5MM **Privately Held**
WEB: www.doublejsaddlery.com
SIC: 3171 5941 2386 3199 Handbags, women's; saddlery & equestrian equipment; leather & sheep-lined clothing; equestrian related leather articles

(G-20965)
EDDY PACKING CO INC (PA)
404 Airport Rd (77995-4801)
P.O. Box 392 (77995-0392)
PHONE 361 580-3800
Jim Reed, CEO
John M Fortino Jr, President
Robert Summers, President
Dean Sanders, Exec VP
Bryan Blackmon, Purch Mgr
▲ EMP: 400 EST: 1953
SQ FT: 24,975
SALES (est): 252.4MM **Privately Held**
WEB: www.eddypacking.com
SIC: 2011 2013 Meat packing plants; sausages & other prepared meats

(G-20966)
FRIEDEL DRILLING CO
555 City Of Hochheim Rd (77995-4824)
PHONE 361 293-5545
Edmund Friedel Jr, President
Margaret Friedel, Executive Asst
EMP: 10
SQ FT: 4,000
SALES (est): 1.6MM **Privately Held**
WEB: www.friedeldrilling.com
SIC: 1781 1381 Water well drilling; drilling oil & gas wells

(G-20967)
HANCOR INC
801 Hickey Rd (77995-5193)
PHONE 361 293-6313
Steve Farrow, Manager
EMP: 50
SALES (corp-wide): 1.6B **Publicly Held**
WEB: www.hancor.com
SIC: 3084 3082 Plastics pipe; unsupported plastics profile shapes
HQ: Hancor, Inc.
 4640 Trueman Blvd
 Hilliard OH 43026
 614 658-0050

(G-20968)
MECHANISM EXCHANGE & REPR INC
210 E Hochheim St (77995-3206)
P.O. Box 311 (77995-0311)
PHONE 361 293-6452
Bruce Card, President
John Valis, Vice Pres
Dorothy Card, Admin Sec
EMP: 25
SQ FT: 27,480
SALES (est): 2MM **Privately Held**
WEB: www.mernewsrack.com
SIC: 7699 3581 Printing trades machinery & equipment repair; dental instrument repair; automatic vending machines; mechanisms for coin-operated machines

(G-20969)
MERCHANTS MOVING & STORAGE INC
Also Called: Ranger Gate Company
4701 Us Highway 77a S (77995-5313)
P.O. Box 350 (77995-0350)
PHONE 361 293-7202
David Jahn, President
Geraldine Jahn, Shareholder
James Jahn, Shareholder
Nicky Jahn, Admin Sec
EMP: 25 EST: 1937
SQ FT: 7,000
SALES (est): 5MM **Privately Held**
WEB: www.rangergate.com
SIC: 3446 4213 Fences, gates, posts & flagpoles; trucking, except local

(G-20970)
MERCHANTS MOVING AND STOR INC
Also Called: Ranger Gate Company
4701 Us Highway 77a S (77995-5313)
P.O. Box 350 (77995-0350)
PHONE 361 293-7202
Covey Morrow, Owner
Frank Bates, Buyer
Rick Jahn, Sales Executive
David Jahn, Director
EMP: 80
SALES (est): 11.8MM **Privately Held**
WEB: www.rangergate.com
SIC: 3317 Steel pipe & tubes

(G-20971)
MERIT ENERGY COMPANY LLC
22629 Us Highway 77 S (77995-7013)
PHONE 361 293-3586
EMP: 15 **Privately Held**
WEB: www.meritenergy.com
SIC: 1311 Crude petroleum production
PA: Merit Energy Company, Llc
 13737 Noel Rd Ste 1200
 Dallas TX 75240

(G-20972)
NAEGLES INDUSTRIAL LEA MCHY CO
Also Called: Campbell Bosworth Machinery Co
405 Fm 3083 (77995)
PHONE..................................361 293-7015
▲ EMP: 13
SQ FT: 14,000
SALES (est): 2.9MM **Privately Held**
SIC: 3559 Repair And Manufacturer Of Leather Machinery

(G-20973)
TEX TAN WESTERN CO YOAKUM INC
Also Called: Tex Tan Western Leather Co
601 Hickey St (77995-2800)
PHONE..................................361 293-2314
Don Motsenbocker, *Ch of Bd*
Jay Cassell, *President*
EMP: 10
SQ FT: 700,000
SALES (est): 1.1MM
SALES (corp-wide): 7.4MM **Privately Held**
WEB: www.actioncompany.com
SIC: 3199 Saddles or parts; equestrian related leather articles; leather belting & strapping
PA: Action, Inc
　　1425 N Tennessee St
　　Mckinney TX 75069
　　972 542-8700

(G-20974)
TUCKER SADDLERY INC
Also Called: Tucker Saddlery & Western AP
201 W Morris St (77995-3052)
P.O. Box 271 (77995-0271)
PHONE..................................361 293-3501
Steven Tucker, *President*
▲ EMP: 20
SQ FT: 10,000
SALES (est): 2.3MM **Privately Held**
WEB: www.tuckersaddlery.com
SIC: 3199 5699 Saddles or parts; western apparel

(G-20975)
YOAKUM HERALD-TIMES INC (PA)
Also Called: Yoakum Herald Times
312 Lott St (77995-2798)
P.O. Box 798 (77995-0798)
PHONE..................................361 293-5266
Lawrence M Preuss III, *President*
Frank Kasper, *Corp Secy*
EMP: 16 EST: 1970
SALES (est): 967.8K **Privately Held**
WEB: www.cityofyoakum.org
SIC: 2711 Newspapers, publishing & printing

Yorktown
Dewitt County

(G-20976)
BAKER HGHES OLFLD OPRTIONS LLC
Also Called: Baker Oil Tools
714 N Riedel St (78164-1800)
PHONE..................................800 441-0535
Ken Wright, *Manager*
EMP: 150 **Privately Held**
WEB: www.bakerhughes.com
SIC: 3569 1389 3643 3533 Centrifuges, industrial; oil field services; current-carrying wiring devices; oil & gas field machinery
PA: Baker Hughes Oilfield Operations Llc
　　2001 Rankin Rd
　　Houston TX 77073

(G-20977)
DLUGOSCH III LLC (PA)
507 E Main St (78164-2067)
P.O. Box 338 (78164-0338)
PHONE..................................361 564-9504
Brian Dlugosch, *President*
EMP: 131 EST: 2010
SQ FT: 5,000

SALES: 18.4MM **Privately Held**
SIC: 3494 7353 Valves & pipe fittings; oil field equipment, rental or leasing

(G-20978)
NITRO DOWNHOLE LLC
6001 Fm 240 (78164-3496)
P.O. Box 595 (78164-0595)
PHONE..................................361 564-9282
EMP: 12
SALES (est): 1.4MM **Privately Held**
SIC: 1389 Construction, repair & dismantling services

Zapata
Zapata County

(G-20979)
CAMINO AGAVE INC
N Hwy 83 (78076)
P.O. Box 1067 (78076-1067)
PHONE..................................956 765-4635
EMP: 60
SALES (corp-wide): 55MM **Privately Held**
SIC: 1389 Oil/Gas Field Services
PA: Camino Agave, Inc.
　　144 County Road 150
　　Kenedy TX 78114
　　956 723-1701

(G-20980)
CHAPAS OILFIELD SERVICES LLC
811 Zapata Ave (78076-4188)
P.O. Box 963 (78076-0963)
PHONE..................................956 847-6460
Joel Chapa,
EMP: 12 EST: 2012
SALES (est): 1.6MM **Privately Held**
SIC: 1389 4789 4212 Oil field services; cargo loading & unloading services; local trucking, without storage

(G-20981)
COSI ENERGY SERVICES LLC
3050 S Us Highway 83 (78076)
P.O. Box 157 (78076-0157)
PHONE..................................956 765-6729
EMP: 40
SALES (est): 1.8MM **Privately Held**
SIC: 1389 Oil/Gas Field Services

(G-20982)
GTZ SERVICES LLC
202 Carla St (78076-3114)
P.O. Box 1360 (78076-1360)
PHONE..................................956 750-6147
Maria F Gutierrez,
EMP: 12
SALES (est): 333K **Privately Held**
SIC: 1389 Oil field services

(G-20983)
JOSE LUIS VILLARREAL
Also Called: Villarreal Production Service
641 Fm 496 E (78076-3547)
P.O. Box 947 (78076-0947)
PHONE..................................956 765-5535
Jose Luis Villarreal, *Co-Owner*
Edula Villarreal, *Co-Owner*
EMP: 42
SALES (est): 3.6MM **Privately Held**
SIC: 1389 Well logging

(G-20984)
MED-LOZ LEASE SERVICE INC
Also Called: Med-Loz Oil Field Supply
3050 N Us Highway 83 (78076-0207)
P.O. Box 627 (78076-0627)
PHONE..................................956 765-6029
Juan A Medina, *President*
Delfino Lozano III, *Exec VP*
Minerva Lozano, *Treasurer*
Dolores Medina, *Admin Sec*
EMP: 160
SQ FT: 3,600
SALES (est): 24.3MM **Privately Held**
SIC: 1389 1382 Excavating slush pits & cellars; oil & gas exploration services

(G-20985)
UMPHRES PRODUCTION SERVICES
607 Falcon Ave (78076-3109)
P.O. Box 928 (78076-0928)
PHONE..................................956 765-8409
EMP: 10
SALES (est): 752.1K **Privately Held**
SIC: 1389 Oil/Gas Field Services

SIC INDEX

Standard Industrial Classification Alphabetical Index

SIC NO	PRODUCT

A

3291 Abrasive Prdts
2891 Adhesives & Sealants
3563 Air & Gas Compressors
3585 Air Conditioning & Heating Eqpt
3721 Aircraft
3724 Aircraft Engines & Engine Parts
3728 Aircraft Parts & Eqpt, NEC
2812 Alkalies & Chlorine
3363 Aluminum Die Castings
3354 Aluminum Extruded Prdts
3365 Aluminum Foundries
3355 Aluminum Rolling & Drawing, NEC
3353 Aluminum Sheet, Plate & Foil
3483 Ammunition, Large
3826 Analytical Instruments
2077 Animal, Marine Fats & Oils
2389 Apparel & Accessories, NEC
2387 Apparel Belts
3446 Architectural & Ornamental Metal Work
7694 Armature Rewinding Shops
3292 Asbestos products
2952 Asphalt Felts & Coatings
3822 Automatic Temperature Controls
3581 Automatic Vending Machines
3465 Automotive Stampings
2396 Automotive Trimmings, Apparel Findings, Related Prdts

B

2673 Bags: Plastics, Laminated & Coated
2674 Bags: Uncoated Paper & Multiwall
3562 Ball & Roller Bearings
2836 Biological Prdts, Exc Diagnostic Substances
1221 Bituminous Coal & Lignite: Surface Mining
1222 Bituminous Coal: Underground Mining
2782 Blankbooks & Looseleaf Binders
3312 Blast Furnaces, Coke Ovens, Steel & Rolling Mills
3564 Blowers & Fans
3732 Boat Building & Repairing
3452 Bolts, Nuts, Screws, Rivets & Washers
2732 Book Printing, Not Publishing
2789 Bookbinding
2731 Books: Publishing & Printing
3131 Boot & Shoe Cut Stock & Findings
2342 Brassieres, Girdles & Garments
2051 Bread, Bakery Prdts Exc Cookies & Crackers
3251 Brick & Structural Clay Tile
3991 Brooms & Brushes
3995 Burial Caskets
2021 Butter

C

3578 Calculating & Accounting Eqpt
2064 Candy & Confectionery Prdts
2033 Canned Fruits, Vegetables & Preserves
2032 Canned Specialties
2394 Canvas Prdts
3624 Carbon & Graphite Prdts
2895 Carbon Black
3955 Carbon Paper & Inked Ribbons
3592 Carburetors, Pistons, Rings & Valves
2273 Carpets & Rugs
2823 Cellulosic Man-Made Fibers
3241 Cement, Hydraulic
3253 Ceramic Tile
2043 Cereal Breakfast Foods
2022 Cheese
1479 Chemical & Fertilizer Mining
2899 Chemical Preparations, NEC
2361 Children's & Infants' Dresses & Blouses
3261 China Plumbing Fixtures & Fittings
3262 China, Table & Kitchen Articles
2066 Chocolate & Cocoa Prdts
2111 Cigarettes
2121 Cigars
3255 Clay Refractories
1459 Clay, Ceramic & Refractory Minerals, NEC
1241 Coal Mining Svcs
3479 Coating & Engraving, NEC
2095 Coffee
3316 Cold Rolled Steel Sheet, Strip & Bars
3582 Commercial Laundry, Dry Clean & Pressing Mchs
2759 Commercial Printing
2754 Commercial Printing: Gravure
2752 Commercial Printing: Lithographic
3646 Commercial, Indl & Institutional Lighting Fixtures

3669 Communications Eqpt, NEC
3577 Computer Peripheral Eqpt, NEC
3572 Computer Storage Devices
3575 Computer Terminals
3271 Concrete Block & Brick
3272 Concrete Prdts
3531 Construction Machinery & Eqpt
1442 Construction Sand & Gravel
2679 Converted Paper Prdts, NEC
3535 Conveyors & Eqpt
2052 Cookies & Crackers
3366 Copper Foundries
1021 Copper Ores
2298 Cordage & Twine
2653 Corrugated & Solid Fiber Boxes
3961 Costume Jewelry & Novelties
2261 Cotton Fabric Finishers
2211 Cotton, Woven Fabric
2074 Cottonseed Oil Mills
3466 Crowns & Closures
1311 Crude Petroleum & Natural Gas
1423 Crushed & Broken Granite
1422 Crushed & Broken Limestone
1429 Crushed & Broken Stone, NEC
3643 Current-Carrying Wiring Devices
2391 Curtains & Draperies
3087 Custom Compounding Of Purchased Plastic Resins
3281 Cut Stone Prdts
3421 Cutlery
2865 Cyclic-Crudes, Intermediates, Dyes & Org Pigments

D

3843 Dental Eqpt & Splys
2835 Diagnostic Substances
2675 Die-Cut Paper & Board
3544 Dies, Tools, Jigs, Fixtures & Indl Molds
1411 Dimension Stone
2047 Dog & Cat Food
3942 Dolls & Stuffed Toys
2591 Drapery Hardware, Window Blinds & Shades
2381 Dress & Work Gloves
2034 Dried Fruits, Vegetables & Soup
1381 Drilling Oil & Gas Wells

E

3634 Electric Household Appliances
3641 Electric Lamps
3694 Electrical Eqpt For Internal Combustion Engines
3629 Electrical Indl Apparatus, NEC
3699 Electrical Machinery, Eqpt & Splys, NEC
3845 Electromedical & Electrotherapeutic Apparatus
3313 Electrometallurgical Prdts
3675 Electronic Capacitors
3677 Electronic Coils & Transformers
3679 Electronic Components, NEC
3571 Electronic Computers
3678 Electronic Connectors
3676 Electronic Resistors
3471 Electroplating, Plating, Polishing, Anodizing & Coloring
3534 Elevators & Moving Stairways
3431 Enameled Iron & Metal Sanitary Ware
2677 Envelopes
2892 Explosives

F

2241 Fabric Mills, Cotton, Wool, Silk & Man-Made
3499 Fabricated Metal Prdts, NEC
3498 Fabricated Pipe & Pipe Fittings
3443 Fabricated Plate Work
3069 Fabricated Rubber Prdts, NEC
3441 Fabricated Structural Steel
2399 Fabricated Textile Prdts, NEC
2295 Fabrics Coated Not Rubberized
2297 Fabrics, Nonwoven
3523 Farm Machinery & Eqpt
3965 Fasteners, Buttons, Needles & Pins
1061 Ferroalloy Ores, Except Vanadium
2875 Fertilizers, Mixing Only
2655 Fiber Cans, Tubes & Drums
2091 Fish & Seafoods, Canned & Cured
2092 Fish & Seafoods, Fresh & Frozen
3211 Flat Glass
2087 Flavoring Extracts & Syrups
2045 Flour, Blended & Prepared
2041 Flour, Grain Milling
3824 Fluid Meters & Counters

3593 Fluid Power Cylinders & Actuators
3594 Fluid Power Pumps & Motors
3492 Fluid Power Valves & Hose Fittings
2657 Folding Paperboard Boxes
3556 Food Prdts Machinery
2099 Food Preparations, NEC
3149 Footwear, NEC
2053 Frozen Bakery Prdts
2037 Frozen Fruits, Juices & Vegetables
2038 Frozen Specialties
2371 Fur Goods
2599 Furniture & Fixtures, NEC

G

3944 Games, Toys & Children's Vehicles
3524 Garden, Lawn Tractors & Eqpt
3053 Gaskets, Packing & Sealing Devices
2369 Girls' & Infants' Outerwear, NEC
3221 Glass Containers
3231 Glass Prdts Made Of Purchased Glass
1041 Gold Ores
3321 Gray Iron Foundries
2771 Greeting Card Publishing
3769 Guided Missile/Space Vehicle Parts & Eqpt, NEC
3764 Guided Missile/Space Vehicle Propulsion Units & parts
3761 Guided Missiles & Space Vehicles
2861 Gum & Wood Chemicals
3275 Gypsum Prdts

H

3423 Hand & Edge Tools
3425 Hand Saws & Saw Blades
3171 Handbags & Purses
3429 Hardware, NEC
2426 Hardwood Dimension & Flooring Mills
2435 Hardwood Veneer & Plywood
2353 Hats, Caps & Millinery
3433 Heating Eqpt
3536 Hoists, Cranes & Monorails
2252 Hosiery, Except Women's
2392 House furnishings: Textile
3639 Household Appliances, NEC
3651 Household Audio & Video Eqpt
3631 Household Cooking Eqpt
2519 Household Furniture, NEC
3633 Household Laundry Eqpt
3632 Household Refrigerators & Freezers
3635 Household Vacuum Cleaners

I

2097 Ice
2024 Ice Cream
2819 Indl Inorganic Chemicals, NEC
3823 Indl Instruments For Meas, Display & Control
3569 Indl Machinery & Eqpt, NEC
3567 Indl Process Furnaces & Ovens
3537 Indl Trucks, Tractors, Trailers & Stackers
2813 Industrial Gases
2869 Industrial Organic Chemicals, NEC
3543 Industrial Patterns
1446 Industrial Sand
3491 Industrial Valves
2816 Inorganic Pigments
3825 Instrs For Measuring & Testing Electricity
3519 Internal Combustion Engines, NEC
3462 Iron & Steel Forgings
1011 Iron Ores

J

3915 Jewelers Findings & Lapidary Work
3911 Jewelry: Precious Metal

K

1455 Kaolin & Ball Clay
2253 Knit Outerwear Mills
2259 Knitting Mills, NEC

L

3821 Laboratory Apparatus & Furniture
2258 Lace & Warp Knit Fabric Mills
1031 Lead & Zinc Ores
3952 Lead Pencils, Crayons & Artist's Mtrls
2386 Leather & Sheep Lined Clothing
3151 Leather Gloves & Mittens
3199 Leather Goods, NEC
3111 Leather Tanning & Finishing
3648 Lighting Eqpt, NEC

SIC NO	PRODUCT
3274	Lime
3996	Linoleum & Hard Surface Floor Coverings, NEC
2085	Liquors, Distilled, Rectified & Blended
2411	Logging
2992	Lubricating Oils & Greases
3161	Luggage

M

SIC NO	PRODUCT
2098	Macaroni, Spaghetti & Noodles
3545	Machine Tool Access
3541	Machine Tools: Cutting
3542	Machine Tools: Forming
3599	Machinery & Eqpt, Indl & Commercial, NEC
3322	Malleable Iron Foundries
2082	Malt Beverages
2761	Manifold Business Forms
3999	Manufacturing Industries, NEC
3953	Marking Devices
2515	Mattresses & Bedsprings
3829	Measuring & Controlling Devices, NEC
3586	Measuring & Dispensing Pumps
2011	Meat Packing Plants
3568	Mechanical Power Transmission Eqpt, NEC
2833	Medicinal Chemicals & Botanical Prdts
2329	Men's & Boys' Clothing, NEC
2323	Men's & Boys' Neckwear
2325	Men's & Boys' Separate Trousers & Casual Slacks
2321	Men's & Boys' Shirts
2311	Men's & Boys' Suits, Coats & Overcoats
2322	Men's & Boys' Underwear & Nightwear
2326	Men's & Boys' Work Clothing
3143	Men's Footwear, Exc Athletic
3412	Metal Barrels, Drums, Kegs & Pails
3411	Metal Cans
3442	Metal Doors, Sash, Frames, Molding & Trim
3398	Metal Heat Treating
2514	Metal Household Furniture
1081	Metal Mining Svcs
3469	Metal Stampings, NEC
3549	Metalworking Machinery, NEC
2026	Milk
2023	Milk, Condensed & Evaporated
2431	Millwork
3296	Mineral Wool
3295	Minerals & Earths: Ground Or Treated
3532	Mining Machinery & Eqpt
3496	Misc Fabricated Wire Prdts
2741	Misc Publishing
3449	Misc Structural Metal Work
1499	Miscellaneous Nonmetallic Mining
2451	Mobile Homes
3061	Molded, Extruded & Lathe-Cut Rubber Mechanical Goods
3716	Motor Homes
3714	Motor Vehicle Parts & Access
3711	Motor Vehicles & Car Bodies
3751	Motorcycles, Bicycles & Parts
3621	Motors & Generators
3931	Musical Instruments

N

SIC NO	PRODUCT
1321	Natural Gas Liquids
2711	Newspapers: Publishing & Printing
2873	Nitrogenous Fertilizers
3297	Nonclay Refractories
3644	Noncurrent-Carrying Wiring Devices
3364	Nonferrous Die Castings, Exc Aluminum
3463	Nonferrous Forgings
3369	Nonferrous Foundries: Castings, NEC
3357	Nonferrous Wire Drawing
3299	Nonmetallic Mineral Prdts, NEC
1481	Nonmetallic Minerals Svcs, Except Fuels

O

SIC NO	PRODUCT
2522	Office Furniture, Except Wood
3579	Office Machines, NEC
1382	Oil & Gas Field Exploration Svcs
1389	Oil & Gas Field Svcs, NEC
3533	Oil Field Machinery & Eqpt
3851	Ophthalmic Goods
3827	Optical Instruments
3489	Ordnance & Access, NEC
3842	Orthopedic, Prosthetic & Surgical Appliances/Splys

P

SIC NO	PRODUCT
3565	Packaging Machinery
2851	Paints, Varnishes, Lacquers, Enamels
2671	Paper Coating & Laminating for Packaging
2672	Paper Coating & Laminating, Exc for Packaging
3554	Paper Inds Machinery

SIC NO	PRODUCT
2621	Paper Mills
2631	Paperboard Mills
2542	Partitions & Fixtures, Except Wood
2951	Paving Mixtures & Blocks
3951	Pens & Mechanical Pencils
2844	Perfumes, Cosmetics & Toilet Preparations
2721	Periodicals: Publishing & Printing
3172	Personal Leather Goods
2879	Pesticides & Agricultural Chemicals, NEC
2911	Petroleum Refining
2834	Pharmaceuticals
3652	Phonograph Records & Magnetic Tape
2874	Phosphatic Fertilizers
3861	Photographic Eqpt & Splys
2035	Pickled Fruits, Vegetables, Sauces & Dressings
3085	Plastic Bottles
3086	Plastic Foam Prdts
3083	Plastic Laminated Plate & Sheet
3084	Plastic Pipe
3088	Plastic Plumbing Fixtures
3089	Plastic Prdts
3082	Plastic Unsupported Profile Shapes
3081	Plastic Unsupported Sheet & Film
2821	Plastics, Mtrls & Nonvulcanizable Elastomers
2796	Platemaking & Related Svcs
2395	Pleating & Stitching For The Trade
3432	Plumbing Fixture Fittings & Trim, Brass
3264	Porcelain Electrical Splys
1474	Potash, Soda & Borate Minerals
2096	Potato Chips & Similar Prdts
3269	Pottery Prdts, NEC
2015	Poultry Slaughtering, Dressing & Processing
3546	Power Hand Tools
3612	Power, Distribution & Specialty Transformers
3448	Prefabricated Metal Buildings & Cmpnts
2452	Prefabricated Wood Buildings & Cmpnts
7372	Prepackaged Software
2048	Prepared Feeds For Animals & Fowls
3229	Pressed & Blown Glassware, NEC
3692	Primary Batteries: Dry & Wet
3399	Primary Metal Prdts, NEC
3339	Primary Nonferrous Metals, NEC
3334	Primary Production Of Aluminum
3331	Primary Smelting & Refining Of Copper
3672	Printed Circuit Boards
2893	Printing Ink
3555	Printing Trades Machinery & Eqpt
2999	Products Of Petroleum & Coal, NEC
2531	Public Building & Related Furniture
2611	Pulp Mills
3561	Pumps & Pumping Eqpt

R

SIC NO	PRODUCT
3663	Radio & T V Communications, Systs & Eqpt, Broadcast/Studio
3671	Radio & T V Receiving Electron Tubes
3743	Railroad Eqpt
3273	Ready-Mixed Concrete
2493	Reconstituted Wood Prdts
3695	Recording Media
3625	Relays & Indl Controls
3645	Residential Lighting Fixtures
2044	Rice Milling
3547	Rolling Mill Machinery & Eqpt
3351	Rolling, Drawing & Extruding Of Copper
3356	Rolling, Drawing-Extruding Of Nonferrous Metals
3021	Rubber & Plastic Footwear
3052	Rubber & Plastic Hose & Belting

S

SIC NO	PRODUCT
2068	Salted & Roasted Nuts & Seeds
2656	Sanitary Food Containers
2676	Sanitary Paper Prdts
2013	Sausages & Meat Prdts
2421	Saw & Planing Mills
3596	Scales & Balances, Exc Laboratory
2397	Schiffli Machine Embroideries
3451	Screw Machine Prdts
3812	Search, Detection, Navigation & Guidance Systs & Instrs
3341	Secondary Smelting & Refining Of Nonferrous Metals
3674	Semiconductors
3589	Service Ind Machines, NEC
2652	Set-Up Paperboard Boxes
3444	Sheet Metal Work
3731	Shipbuilding & Repairing
2079	Shortening, Oils & Margarine
3993	Signs & Advertising Displays
2262	Silk & Man-Made Fabric Finishers
2221	Silk & Man-Made Fiber
1044	Silver Ores

SIC NO	PRODUCT
3914	Silverware, Plated & Stainless Steel Ware
3484	Small Arms
3482	Small Arms Ammunition
2841	Soap & Detergents
2086	Soft Drinks
2436	Softwood Veneer & Plywood
2075	Soybean Oil Mills
2842	Spec Cleaning, Polishing & Sanitation Preparations
3559	Special Ind Machinery, NEC
2429	Special Prdt Sawmills, NEC
3566	Speed Changers, Drives & Gears
3949	Sporting & Athletic Goods, NEC
2678	Stationery Prdts
3511	Steam, Gas & Hydraulic Turbines & Engines
3325	Steel Foundries, NEC
3324	Steel Investment Foundries
3317	Steel Pipe & Tubes
3493	Steel Springs, Except Wire
3315	Steel Wire Drawing & Nails & Spikes
3691	Storage Batteries
3259	Structural Clay Prdts, NEC
2439	Structural Wood Members, NEC
2063	Sugar, Beet
2061	Sugar, Cane
2062	Sugar, Cane Refining
2843	Surface Active & Finishing Agents, Sulfonated Oils
3841	Surgical & Medical Instrs & Apparatus
3613	Switchgear & Switchboard Apparatus
2824	Synthetic Organic Fibers, Exc Cellulosic
2822	Synthetic Rubber (Vulcanizable Elastomers)

T

SIC NO	PRODUCT
3795	Tanks & Tank Components
3661	Telephone & Telegraph Apparatus
2393	Textile Bags
2269	Textile Finishers, NEC
2299	Textile Goods, NEC
3552	Textile Machinery
2284	Thread Mills
2296	Tire Cord & Fabric
3011	Tires & Inner Tubes
2141	Tobacco Stemming & Redrying
2131	Tobacco, Chewing & Snuff
3799	Transportation Eqpt, NEC
3792	Travel Trailers & Campers
3713	Truck & Bus Bodies
3715	Truck Trailers
2791	Typesetting

U

SIC NO	PRODUCT
1094	Uranium, Radium & Vanadium Ores

V

SIC NO	PRODUCT
3494	Valves & Pipe Fittings, NEC
2076	Vegetable Oil Mills
3647	Vehicular Lighting Eqpt

W

SIC NO	PRODUCT
3873	Watch & Clock Devices & Parts
2385	Waterproof Outerwear
3548	Welding Apparatus
7692	Welding Repair
2046	Wet Corn Milling
2084	Wine & Brandy
3495	Wire Springs
2331	Women's & Misses' Blouses
2335	Women's & Misses' Dresses
2339	Women's & Misses' Outerwear, NEC
2337	Women's & Misses' Suits, Coats & Skirts
3144	Women's Footwear, Exc Athletic
2341	Women's, Misses' & Children's Underwear & Nightwear
2441	Wood Boxes
2449	Wood Containers, NEC
2511	Wood Household Furniture
2512	Wood Household Furniture, Upholstered
2434	Wood Kitchen Cabinets
2521	Wood Office Furniture
2448	Wood Pallets & Skids
2499	Wood Prdts, NEC
2491	Wood Preserving
2517	Wood T V, Radio, Phono & Sewing Cabinets
2541	Wood, Office & Store Fixtures
3553	Woodworking Machinery
2231	Wool, Woven Fabric

X

SIC NO	PRODUCT
3844	X-ray Apparatus & Tubes

Y

SIC NO	PRODUCT
2281	Yarn Spinning Mills
2282	Yarn Texturizing, Throwing, Twisting & Winding Mills

SIC INDEX

SIC NO	PRODUCT

10 metal mining

1011 Iron Ores
1021 Copper Ores
1031 Lead & Zinc Ores
1041 Gold Ores
1044 Silver Ores
1061 Ferroalloy Ores, Except Vanadium
1081 Metal Mining Svcs
1094 Uranium, Radium & Vanadium Ores

12 coal mining

1221 Bituminous Coal & Lignite: Surface Mining
1222 Bituminous Coal: Underground Mining
1241 Coal Mining Svcs

13 oil and gas extraction

1311 Crude Petroleum & Natural Gas
1321 Natural Gas Liquids
1381 Drilling Oil & Gas Wells
1382 Oil & Gas Field Exploration Svcs
1389 Oil & Gas Field Svcs, NEC

14 mining and quarrying of nonmetallic minerals, except fuels

1411 Dimension Stone
1422 Crushed & Broken Limestone
1423 Crushed & Broken Granite
1429 Crushed & Broken Stone, NEC
1442 Construction Sand & Gravel
1446 Industrial Sand
1455 Kaolin & Ball Clay
1459 Clay, Ceramic & Refractory Minerals, NEC
1474 Potash, Soda & Borate Minerals
1479 Chemical & Fertilizer Mining
1481 Nonmetallic Minerals Svcs, Except Fuels
1499 Miscellaneous Nonmetallic Mining

20 food and kindred products

2011 Meat Packing Plants
2013 Sausages & Meat Prdts
2015 Poultry Slaughtering, Dressing & Processing
2021 Butter
2022 Cheese
2023 Milk, Condensed & Evaporated
2024 Ice Cream
2026 Milk
2032 Canned Specialties
2033 Canned Fruits, Vegetables & Preserves
2034 Dried Fruits, Vegetables & Soup
2035 Pickled Fruits, Vegetables, Sauces & Dressings
2037 Frozen Fruits, Juices & Vegetables
2038 Frozen Specialties
2041 Flour, Grain Milling
2043 Cereal Breakfast Foods
2044 Rice Milling
2045 Flour, Blended & Prepared
2046 Wet Corn Milling
2047 Dog & Cat Food
2048 Prepared Feeds For Animals & Fowls
2051 Bread, Bakery Prdts Exc Cookies & Crackers
2052 Cookies & Crackers
2053 Frozen Bakery Prdts
2061 Sugar, Cane
2062 Sugar, Cane Refining
2063 Sugar, Beet
2064 Candy & Confectionery Prdts
2066 Chocolate & Cocoa Prdts
2068 Salted & Roasted Nuts & Seeds
2074 Cottonseed Oil Mills
2075 Soybean Oil Mills
2076 Vegetable Oil Mills
2077 Animal, Marine Fats & Oils
2079 Shortening, Oils & Margarine
2082 Malt Beverages
2084 Wine & Brandy
2085 Liquors, Distilled, Rectified & Blended
2086 Soft Drinks
2087 Flavoring Extracts & Syrups
2091 Fish & Seafoods, Canned & Cured
2092 Fish & Seafoods, Fresh & Frozen
2095 Coffee
2096 Potato Chips & Similar Prdts
2097 Ice

2098 Macaroni, Spaghetti & Noodles
2099 Food Preparations, NEC

21 tobacco products

2111 Cigarettes
2121 Cigars
2131 Tobacco, Chewing & Snuff
2141 Tobacco Stemming & Redrying

22 textile mill products

2211 Cotton, Woven Fabric
2221 Silk & Man-Made Fiber
2231 Wool, Woven Fabric
2241 Fabric Mills, Cotton, Wool, Silk & Man-Made
2252 Hosiery, Except Women's
2253 Knit Outerwear Mills
2258 Lace & Warp Knit Fabric Mills
2259 Knitting Mills, NEC
2261 Cotton Fabric Finishers
2262 Silk & Man-Made Fabric Finishers
2269 Textile Finishers, NEC
2273 Carpets & Rugs
2281 Yarn Spinning Mills
2282 Yarn Texturizing, Throwing, Twisting & Winding Mills
2284 Thread Mills
2295 Fabrics Coated Not Rubberized
2296 Tire Cord & Fabric
2297 Fabrics, Nonwoven
2298 Cordage & Twine
2299 Textile Goods, NEC

23 apparel and other finished products made from fabrics and similar material

2311 Men's & Boys' Suits, Coats & Overcoats
2321 Men's & Boys' Shirts
2322 Men's & Boys' Underwear & Nightwear
2323 Men's & Boys' Neckwear
2325 Men's & Boys' Separate Trousers & Casual Slacks
2326 Men's & Boys' Work Clothing
2329 Men's & Boys' Clothing, NEC
2331 Women's & Misses' Blouses
2335 Women's & Misses' Dresses
2337 Women's & Misses' Suits, Coats & Skirts
2339 Women's & Misses' Outerwear, NEC
2341 Women's, Misses' & Children's Underwear & Nightwear
2342 Brassieres, Girdles & Garments
2353 Hats, Caps & Millinery
2361 Children's & Infants' Dresses & Blouses
2369 Girls' & Infants' Outerwear, NEC
2371 Fur Goods
2381 Dress & Work Gloves
2385 Waterproof Outerwear
2386 Leather & Sheep Lined Clothing
2387 Apparel Belts
2389 Apparel & Accessories, NEC
2391 Curtains & Draperies
2392 House furnishings: Textile
2393 Textile Bags
2394 Canvas Prdts
2395 Pleating & Stitching For The Trade
2396 Automotive Trimmings, Apparel Findings, Related Prdts
2397 Schiffli Machine Embroideries
2399 Fabricated Textile Prdts, NEC

24 lumber and wood products, except furniture

2411 Logging
2421 Saw & Planing Mills
2426 Hardwood Dimension & Flooring Mills
2429 Special Prdt Sawmills, NEC
2431 Millwork
2434 Wood Kitchen Cabinets
2435 Hardwood Veneer & Plywood
2436 Softwood Veneer & Plywood
2439 Structural Wood Members, NEC
2441 Wood Boxes
2448 Wood Pallets & Skids
2449 Wood Containers, NEC
2451 Mobile Homes
2452 Prefabricated Wood Buildings & Cmpnts
2491 Wood Preserving
2493 Reconstituted Wood Prdts
2499 Wood Prdts, NEC

25 furniture and fixtures

2511 Wood Household Furniture
2512 Wood Household Furniture, Upholstered
2514 Metal Household Furniture
2515 Mattresses & Bedsprings
2517 Wood T V, Radio, Phono & Sewing Cabinets
2519 Household Furniture, NEC
2521 Wood Office Furniture
2522 Office Furniture, Except Wood
2531 Public Building & Related Furniture
2541 Wood, Office & Store Fixtures
2542 Partitions & Fixtures, Except Wood
2591 Drapery Hardware, Window Blinds & Shades
2599 Furniture & Fixtures, NEC

26 paper and allied products

2611 Pulp Mills
2621 Paper Mills
2631 Paperboard Mills
2652 Set-Up Paperboard Boxes
2653 Corrugated & Solid Fiber Boxes
2655 Fiber Cans, Tubes & Drums
2656 Sanitary Food Containers
2657 Folding Paperboard Boxes
2671 Paper Coating & Laminating for Packaging
2672 Paper Coating & Laminating, Exc for Packaging
2673 Bags: Plastics, Laminated & Coated
2674 Bags: Uncoated Paper & Multiwall
2675 Die-Cut Paper & Board
2676 Sanitary Paper Prdts
2677 Envelopes
2678 Stationery Prdts
2679 Converted Paper Prdts, NEC

27 printing, publishing, and allied industries

2711 Newspapers: Publishing & Printing
2721 Periodicals: Publishing & Printing
2731 Books: Publishing & Printing
2732 Book Printing, Not Publishing
2741 Misc Publishing
2752 Commercial Printing: Lithographic
2754 Commercial Printing: Gravure
2759 Commercial Printing
2761 Manifold Business Forms
2771 Greeting Card Publishing
2782 Blankbooks & Looseleaf Binders
2789 Bookbinding
2791 Typesetting
2796 Platemaking & Related Svcs

28 chemicals and allied products

2812 Alkalies & Chlorine
2813 Industrial Gases
2816 Inorganic Pigments
2819 Indl Inorganic Chemicals, NEC
2821 Plastics, Mtrls & Nonvulcanizable Elastomers
2822 Synthetic Rubber (Vulcanizable Elastomers)
2823 Cellulosic Man-Made Fibers
2824 Synthetic Organic Fibers, Exc Cellulosic
2833 Medicinal Chemicals & Botanical Prdts
2834 Pharmaceuticals
2835 Diagnostic Substances
2836 Biological Prdts, Exc Diagnostic Substances
2841 Soap & Detergents
2842 Spec Cleaning, Polishing & Sanitation Preparations
2843 Surface Active & Finishing Agents, Sulfonated Oils
2844 Perfumes, Cosmetics & Toilet Preparations
2851 Paints, Varnishes, Lacquers, Enamels
2861 Gum & Wood Chemicals
2865 Cyclic-Crudes, Intermediates, Dyes & Org Pigments
2869 Industrial Organic Chemicals, NEC
2873 Nitrogenous Fertilizers
2874 Phosphatic Fertilizers
2875 Fertilizers, Mixing Only
2879 Pesticides & Agricultural Chemicals, NEC
2891 Adhesives & Sealants
2892 Explosives
2893 Printing Ink
2895 Carbon Black
2899 Chemical Preparations, NEC

29 petroleum refining and related industries

2911 Petroleum Refining

S I C

SIC NO	PRODUCT

2951 Paving Mixtures & Blocks
2952 Asphalt Felts & Coatings
2992 Lubricating Oils & Greases
2999 Products Of Petroleum & Coal, NEC

30 rubber and miscellaneous plastics products

3011 Tires & Inner Tubes
3021 Rubber & Plastic Footwear
3052 Rubber & Plastic Hose & Belting
3053 Gaskets, Packing & Sealing Devices
3061 Molded, Extruded & Lathe-Cut Rubber Mechanical Goods
3069 Fabricated Rubber Prdts, NEC
3081 Plastic Unsupported Sheet & Film
3082 Plastic Unsupported Profile Shapes
3083 Plastic Laminated Plate & Sheet
3084 Plastic Pipe
3085 Plastic Bottles
3086 Plastic Foam Prdts
3087 Custom Compounding Of Purchased Plastic Resins
3088 Plastic Plumbing Fixtures
3089 Plastic Prdts

31 leather and leather products

3111 Leather Tanning & Finishing
3131 Boot & Shoe Cut Stock & Findings
3143 Men's Footwear, Exc Athletic
3144 Women's Footwear, Exc Athletic
3149 Footwear, NEC
3151 Leather Gloves & Mittens
3161 Luggage
3171 Handbags & Purses
3172 Personal Leather Goods
3199 Leather Goods, NEC

32 stone, clay, glass, and concrete products

3211 Flat Glass
3221 Glass Containers
3229 Pressed & Blown Glassware, NEC
3231 Glass Prdts Made Of Purchased Glass
3241 Cement, Hydraulic
3251 Brick & Structural Clay Tile
3253 Ceramic Tile
3255 Clay Refractories
3259 Structural Clay Prdts, NEC
3261 China Plumbing Fixtures & Fittings
3262 China, Table & Kitchen Articles
3264 Porcelain Electrical Splys
3269 Pottery Prdts, NEC
3271 Concrete Block & Brick
3272 Concrete Prdts
3273 Ready-Mixed Concrete
3274 Lime
3275 Gypsum Prdts
3281 Cut Stone Prdts
3291 Abrasive Prdts
3292 Asbestos products
3295 Minerals & Earths: Ground Or Treated
3296 Mineral Wool
3297 Nonclay Refractories
3299 Nonmetallic Mineral Prdts, NEC

33 primary metal industries

3312 Blast Furnaces, Coke Ovens, Steel & Rolling Mills
3313 Electrometallurgical Prdts
3315 Steel Wire Drawing & Nails & Spikes
3316 Cold Rolled Steel Sheet, Strip & Bars
3317 Steel Pipe & Tubes
3321 Gray Iron Foundries
3322 Malleable Iron Foundries
3324 Steel Investment Foundries
3325 Steel Foundries, NEC
3331 Primary Smelting & Refining Of Copper
3334 Primary Production Of Aluminum
3339 Primary Nonferrous Metals, NEC
3341 Secondary Smelting & Refining Of Nonferrous Metals
3351 Rolling, Drawing & Extruding Of Copper
3353 Aluminum Sheet, Plate & Foil
3354 Aluminum Extruded Prdts
3355 Aluminum Rolling & Drawing, NEC
3356 Rolling, Drawing-Extruding Of Nonferrous Metals
3357 Nonferrous Wire Drawing
3363 Aluminum Die Castings
3364 Nonferrous Die Castings, Exc Aluminum
3365 Aluminum Foundries
3366 Copper Foundries
3369 Nonferrous Foundries: Castings, NEC
3398 Metal Heat Treating
3399 Primary Metal Prdts, NEC

34 fabricated metal products, except machinery and transportation equipment

3411 Metal Cans
3412 Metal Barrels, Drums, Kegs & Pails
3421 Cutlery
3423 Hand & Edge Tools
3425 Hand Saws & Saw Blades
3429 Hardware, NEC
3431 Enameled Iron & Metal Sanitary Ware
3432 Plumbing Fixture Fittings & Trim, Brass
3433 Heating Eqpt
3441 Fabricated Structural Steel
3442 Metal Doors, Sash, Frames, Molding & Trim
3443 Fabricated Plate Work
3444 Sheet Metal Work
3446 Architectural & Ornamental Metal Work
3448 Prefabricated Metal Buildings & Cmpnts
3449 Misc Structural Metal Work
3451 Screw Machine Prdts
3452 Bolts, Nuts, Screws, Rivets & Washers
3462 Iron & Steel Forgings
3463 Nonferrous Forgings
3465 Automotive Stampings
3466 Crowns & Closures
3469 Metal Stampings, NEC
3471 Electroplating, Plating, Polishing, Anodizing & Coloring
3479 Coating & Engraving, NEC
3482 Small Arms Ammunition
3483 Ammunition, Large
3484 Small Arms
3489 Ordnance & Access, NEC
3491 Industrial Valves
3492 Fluid Power Valves & Hose Fittings
3493 Steel Springs, Except Wire
3494 Valves & Pipe Fittings, NEC
3495 Wire Springs
3496 Misc Fabricated Wire Prdts
3498 Fabricated Pipe & Pipe Fittings
3499 Fabricated Metal Prdts, NEC

35 industrial and commercial machinery and computer equipment

3511 Steam, Gas & Hydraulic Turbines & Engines
3519 Internal Combustion Engines, NEC
3523 Farm Machinery & Eqpt
3524 Garden, Lawn Tractors & Eqpt
3531 Construction Machinery & Eqpt
3532 Mining Machinery & Eqpt
3533 Oil Field Machinery & Eqpt
3534 Elevators & Moving Stairways
3535 Conveyors & Eqpt
3536 Hoists, Cranes & Monorails
3537 Indl Trucks, Tractors, Trailers & Stackers
3541 Machine Tools: Cutting
3542 Machine Tools: Forming
3543 Industrial Patterns
3544 Dies, Tools, Jigs, Fixtures & Indl Molds
3545 Machine Tool Access
3546 Power Hand Tools
3547 Rolling Mill Machinery & Eqpt
3548 Welding Apparatus
3549 Metalworking Machinery, NEC
3552 Textile Machinery
3553 Woodworking Machinery
3554 Paper Inds Machinery
3555 Printing Trades Machinery & Eqpt
3556 Food Prdts Machinery
3559 Special Ind Machinery, NEC
3561 Pumps & Pumping Eqpt
3562 Ball & Roller Bearings
3563 Air & Gas Compressors
3564 Blowers & Fans
3565 Packaging Machinery
3566 Speed Changers, Drives & Gears
3567 Indl Process Furnaces & Ovens
3568 Mechanical Power Transmission Eqpt, NEC
3569 Indl Machinery & Eqpt, NEC
3571 Electronic Computers
3572 Computer Storage Devices
3575 Computer Terminals
3577 Computer Peripheral Eqpt, NEC
3578 Calculating & Accounting Eqpt
3579 Office Machines, NEC
3581 Automatic Vending Machines
3582 Commercial Laundry, Dry Clean & Pressing Mchs
3585 Air Conditioning & Heating Eqpt
3586 Measuring & Dispensing Pumps
3589 Service Ind Machines, NEC
3592 Carburetors, Pistons, Rings & Valves

3593 Fluid Power Cylinders & Actuators
3594 Fluid Power Pumps & Motors
3596 Scales & Balances, Exc Laboratory
3599 Machinery & Eqpt, Indl & Commercial, NEC

36 electronic and other electrical equipment and components, except computer

3612 Power, Distribution & Specialty Transformers
3613 Switchgear & Switchboard Apparatus
3621 Motors & Generators
3624 Carbon & Graphite Prdts
3625 Relays & Indl Controls
3629 Electrical Indl Apparatus, NEC
3631 Household Cooking Eqpt
3632 Household Refrigerators & Freezers
3633 Household Laundry Eqpt
3634 Electric Household Appliances
3635 Household Vacuum Cleaners
3639 Household Appliances, NEC
3641 Electric Lamps
3643 Current-Carrying Wiring Devices
3644 Noncurrent-Carrying Wiring Devices
3645 Residential Lighting Fixtures
3646 Commercial, Indl & Institutional Lighting Fixtures
3647 Vehicular Lighting Eqpt
3648 Lighting Eqpt, NEC
3651 Household Audio & Video Eqpt
3652 Phonograph Records & Magnetic Tape
3661 Telephone & Telegraph Apparatus
3663 Radio & T V Communications, Systs & Eqpt, Broadcast/Studio
3669 Communications Eqpt, NEC
3671 Radio & T V Receiving Electron Tubes
3672 Printed Circuit Boards
3674 Semiconductors
3675 Electronic Capacitors
3676 Electronic Resistors
3677 Electronic Coils & Transformers
3678 Electronic Connectors
3679 Electronic Components, NEC
3691 Storage Batteries
3692 Primary Batteries: Dry & Wet
3694 Electrical Eqpt For Internal Combustion Engines
3695 Recording Media
3699 Electrical Machinery, Eqpt & Splys, NEC

37 transportation equipment

3711 Motor Vehicles & Car Bodies
3713 Truck & Bus Bodies
3714 Motor Vehicle Parts & Access
3715 Truck Trailers
3716 Motor Homes
3721 Aircraft
3724 Aircraft Engines & Engine Parts
3728 Aircraft Parts & Eqpt, NEC
3731 Shipbuilding & Repairing
3732 Boat Building & Repairing
3743 Railroad Eqpt
3751 Motorcycles, Bicycles & Parts
3761 Guided Missiles & Space Vehicles
3764 Guided Missile/Space Vehicle Propulsion Units & parts
3769 Guided Missile/Space Vehicle Parts & Eqpt, NEC
3792 Travel Trailers & Campers
3795 Tanks & Tank Components
3799 Transportation Eqpt, NEC

38 measuring, analyzing and controlling instruments; photographic, medical an

3812 Search, Detection, Navigation & Guidance Systs & Instrs
3821 Laboratory Apparatus & Furniture
3822 Automatic Temperature Controls
3823 Indl Instruments For Meas, Display & Control
3824 Fluid Meters & Counters
3825 Instrs For Measuring & Testing Electricity
3826 Analytical Instruments
3827 Optical Instruments
3829 Measuring & Controlling Devices, NEC
3841 Surgical & Medical Instrs & Apparatus
3842 Orthopedic, Prosthetic & Surgical Appliances/Splys
3843 Dental Eqpt & Splys
3844 X-ray Apparatus & Tubes
3845 Electromedical & Electrotherapeutic Apparatus
3851 Ophthalmic Goods
3861 Photographic Eqpt & Splys
3873 Watch & Clock Devices & Parts

39 miscellaneous manufacturing industries

3911 Jewelry: Precious Metal
3914 Silverware, Plated & Stainless Steel Ware
3915 Jewelers Findings & Lapidary Work

SIC INDEX

SIC

SIC SECTION

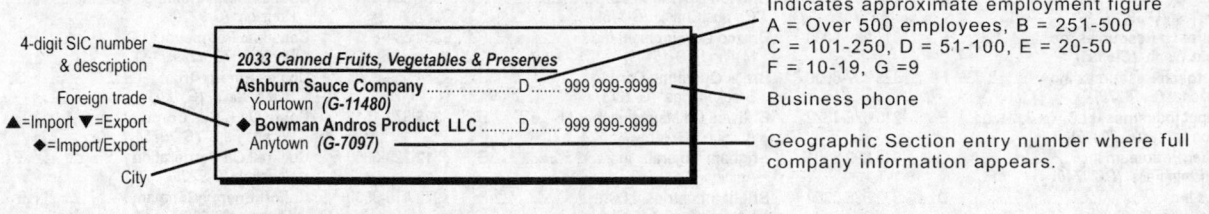

10 METAL MINING

1011 Iron Ores

◆ **BHP Minerals International LLC** ....B 713 961-8500
Houston *(G-8878)*
Hudson Brothers Mining Company ......F 903 876-4642
Rusk *(G-17731)*

1021 Copper Ores

◆ **BHP Minerals International LLC** ....B 713 961-8500
Houston *(G-8878)*
Freeport Minerals Corporation ....C 915 778-9881
El Paso *(G-5774)*

1031 Lead & Zinc Ores

▲ **Nexa Resources Us Inc** ....F 832 726-0160
Houston *(G-11043)*

1041 Gold Ores

Battle Mountain Dominian Repub ....E 713 655-1742
Houston *(G-8830)*

1044 Silver Ores

Battle Mountain Dominian Repub ....E 713 655-1742
Houston *(G-8830)*
Rio Grande Mining Company ....D 432 229-4737
Marfa *(G-14754)*

1061 Ferroalloy Ores, Except Vanadium

▲ **Nexa Resources Us Inc** ....F 832 726-0160
Houston *(G-11043)*

1081 Metal Mining Svcs

Alcoa World Alumina LLC ....A 361 987-2631
Point Comfort *(G-17081)*
Coast To Coast Minerals LLC ....F 210 781-8505
San Antonio *(G-18013)*
Coastal Gulf & Intl Inc ....D 713 740-9800
Pasadena *(G-16411)*
Health Care Temporaries Inc ....A 713 631-7106
Houston *(G-10143)*
Holsey Mining Inc ....F 936 545-1021
Crockett *(G-3719)*
Itafos Services LLC ....B 713 242-8446
Houston *(G-10430)*
Keller North America Inc ....E 817 443-1465
Fort Worth *(G-6755)*
Oxidor Corporation Inc ....F 972 424-6422
Plano *(G-16962)*
Shinn and Gregory Inc ....G 254 965-7585
Stephenville *(G-19422)*
Southwest Earth Resources ....F 325 251-6598
Pontotoc *(G-17098)*
▲ **Superior Shot Peening Inc** ....D 281 449-6559
Houston *(G-12119)*

1094 Uranium, Radium & Vanadium Ores

Mestena Uranium LLC ....G 361 884-2191
Corpus Christi *(G-3577)*
South Texas Mining Venture LLP ....E 361 888-8235
Corpus Christi *(G-3624)*
Uranium Energy Corp ....E 361 888-8235
Corpus Christi *(G-3648)*
Westwater Resources Inc ....E 361 279-3307
San Diego *(G-18669)*

12 COAL MINING

1221 Bituminous Coal & Lignite: Surface Mining

Caddo Creek Resources Co LLC ....G 903 927-1130
Marshall *(G-14767)*
El Paso CNG Company LLC ....F 713 420-2600
Houston *(G-9586)*
Knife River Corporation ....D 979 361-2900
Bryan *(G-2488)*
Natural Resource Partners LP ....E 713 751-7507
Houston *(G-11010)*
▲ **North American Coal Corp** ....D 972 448-5400
Plano *(G-16946)*
North American Coal Corp ....C 830 784-3545
Christine *(G-3059)*
Nrp (gp) LP ....B 713 751-7507
Houston *(G-11092)*
Nrp (operating) LLC ....F 713 751-7507
Houston *(G-11093)*
▲ **Sabine Mining Company** ....C 903 660-4200
Hallsville *(G-8130)*
▲ **Williams Gas Pipeline-Transco** ....C 713 215-2000
Houston *(G-12670)*

1222 Bituminous Coal: Underground Mining

American Natural Resources Co ....E 832 320-5000
Houston *(G-8603)*
BHP Mineral Resources Inc ....D 713 961-8500
Houston *(G-8877)*
◆ **BHP Minerals International LLC** ....B 713 961-8500
Houston *(G-8878)*
Clariant Corporation ....E 281 465-9100
The Woodlands *(G-19846)*
▲ **Williams Gas Pipeline-Transco** ....C 713 215-2000
Houston *(G-12670)*

1241 Coal Mining Svcs

Enerquest Resources LLC ....E 432 685-3116
Midland *(G-15219)*
▼ **Far East Energy Corporation** ....F 832 598-0470
Houston *(G-9762)*
Hunt Dominion Corporation ....C 214 880-8400
Dallas *(G-4472)*
Isco Industries Inc ....E 817 477-2900
Mansfield *(G-14683)*
Kingdom Coal LLC ....F 817 840-6646
Irving *(G-13077)*
M H C X-Ploration Corporation ....F 903 595-4323
Tyler *(G-20117)*
P&G Mining LLC ....F 682 500-8986
Grand Prairie *(G-7943)*
▲ **Sabine Mining Company** ....C 903 660-4200
Hallsville *(G-8130)*
Savage Companies ....E 806 381-0261
Amarillo *(G-461)*
Squaw Creek Materials LP ....F 254 897-3505
Rainbow *(G-17229)*
▲ **Texas Westmoreland Coal Co** ....D 903 626-5485
Jewett *(G-13309)*

13 OIL AND GAS EXTRACTION

1311 Crude Petroleum & Natural Gas

3-T Exploration Inc ....F 940 691-5091
Wichita Falls *(G-20734)*
Abraxas Petroleum Corporation ....D 210 490-4788
San Antonio *(G-17855)*

Abraxas Petroleum Corporation ....G 325 573-6010
Ira *(G-12912)*
Adams Resources & Energy Inc ....E 713 881-3600
Houston *(G-8475)*
▲ **Addax Petro Cameroon Co LLC** ....C 713 245-1263
Houston *(G-8477)*
Adexco Operating Company ....G 817 332-3891
Fort Worth *(G-6345)*
Aix Energy Inc ....F 214 292-3482
Dallas *(G-3913)*
Al Rowan ....D 903 963-7036
Van *(G-20205)*
Alexander Production Company ....F 210 271-3691
San Antonio *(G-17891)*
Allar Company ....G 940 549-0077
Graham *(G-7775)*
Allied Natural Gas Corporation ....F 713 658-1144
Houston *(G-8550)*
Alpar Energy LP ....G 806 435-6566
Perryton *(G-16632)*
American Natural Resources Co ....E 832 320-5000
Houston *(G-8603)*
Amplify Acquisitionco Inc ....E 713 490-8900
Houston *(G-8628)*
Amplify Energy Holdings LLC ....F 713 490-8900
Houston *(G-8630)*
▲ **Anadarko Holding Company** ....E 832 636-7200
Houston *(G-8633)*
Anadarko Petroleum Corporation ....E 432 684-2800
Midland *(G-15115)*
◆ **Anadarko Petroleum Corporation** ....C 832 636-1000
The Woodlands *(G-19830)*
Anadarko Petroleum Corporation ....E 979 828-1668
Franklin *(G-7163)*
Anadarko Petroleum Corporation ....F 979 567-7013
Caldwell *(G-2626)*
◆ **Andeavor LLC** ....C 210 626-6000
San Antonio *(G-17907)*
Anderson Oil Ltd ....F 713 652-5746
Houston *(G-8641)*
▲ **Apache Corporation** ....A 713 296-6000
Houston *(G-8650)*
Apache Corporation ....F 432 524-2277
Andrews *(G-536)*
Apache Corporation ....F 713 296-6000
Midland *(G-15116)*
Apache Corporation ....E 325 835-2323
Mertzon *(G-15019)*
Apache Corporation ....E 432 558-2065
Crane *(G-3697)*
Apache Corporation ....F 432 558-2572
Crane *(G-3698)*
Apache Corporation ....E 800 272-2434
Houston *(G-8651)*
Apache Corporation ....F 713 296-6000
Houston *(G-8652)*
Apache Corporation ....F 806 229-3010
Sundown *(G-19611)*
Apache Corporation ....F 806 755-2231
Welch *(G-20654)*
Apache Corporation ....F 806 234-2058
Lubbock *(G-14362)*
Apache Corporation ....F 979 543-4391
El Campo *(G-5610)*
Apache Crude Oil Marketing ....F 713 296-6000
Houston *(G-8653)*
Apache Deepwater LLC ....E 713 296-6000
Houston *(G-8654)*
Apache Gathering Company ....A 713 296-6000
Houston *(G-8657)*

SIC

Apache International LLC	E	713 296-6000	
Houston (G-8659)			
Apollo Resources Intl Inc	E	214 389-9800	
Dallas (G-3952)			
Approach Resources Inc	E	817 989-9000	
Fort Worth (G-6395)			
Approach Resources Inc	E	325 392-8900	
Ozona (G-16278)			
Arepet Industries LLC	E	210 628-1622	
Von Ormy (G-20345)			
Armor Petroleum Inc	G	940 692-5001	
Wichita Falls (G-20740)			
Aroc Inc	D	832 538-0300	
Houston (G-8702)			
Aruba Petroleum Inc	F	940 466-9438	
Decatur (G-5241)			
Aruba Petroleum Inc	E	972 312-9366	
Plano (G-16794)			
Athlon Energy Inc	E	817 984-8200	
Fort Worth (G-6407)			
Atlas Energy Group LLC	E	412 489-0006	
Fort Worth (G-6408)			
Atlas Growth Partners Gp LLC	E	412 489-0006	
Fort Worth (G-6409)			
Atropos Exploration Company	F	214 691-2377	
Dallas (G-3985)			
Axess North America Inc	E	281 994-0364	
Houston (G-8758)			
Azure Midstream Company LLC	F	281 680-4300	
Houston (G-8767)			
B B L Ltd	E	254 559-3355	
Breckenridge (G-2220)			
B D Production Co Inc	D	361 888-4741	
Corpus Christi (G-3478)			
Badger Midstream Energy LP	E	713 395-6111	
Houston (G-8788)			
Bainbridge Uinta LLC	F	214 580-2059	
Dallas (G-3998)			
◆ Baker Hghes Olfld Oprtions LLC	F	713 879-1000	
Houston (G-8796)			
Baker Operating Inc	G	432 367-5808	
Odessa (G-15924)			
Ballard Exploration Co Inc	E	713 651-0181	
Houston (G-8810)			
Basa Resources Inc	F	936 655-2477	
Kennard (G-13494)			
Basa Resources Inc	E	254 559-3366	
Breckenridge (G-2221)			
Bass Enterprises Production Co	E	432 586-2563	
Kermit (G-13509)			
Battalion Oil Corporation	E	832 538-0300	
Houston (G-8826)			
Belvan Partners LP	F	432 682-4349	
Midland (G-15137)			
Bennett Production Corp	F	940 872-1183	
Bowie (G-2191)			
Berry Corporation (bry)	E	661 616-3900	
Dallas (G-4021)			
Beta Operating Company LLC	E	562 628-8900	
Houston (G-8864)			
Bettis Boyle & Stovall Inc	E	940 549-0780	
Graham (G-7777)			
◆ Bg Brasilia LLC	F	713 599-4000	
Houston (G-8868)			
▲ BHP Billiton Petro N Amer Inc	C	713 961-8500	
Houston (G-8875)			
Big Bear Oil Company Inc	F	915 775-1945	
El Paso (G-5662)			
Bison Development Company	F	806 355-8253	
Amarillo (G-481)			
Black Stone Energy Company LLC	E	713 658-0647	
Houston (G-8906)			
Blue Bell Energy LLC	F	713 661-1040	
Houston (G-8917)			
Blue Mountain Midstream LLC	F	281 377-8770	
Houston (G-8919)			
Blue Star Ltd	E	281 893-6035	
Houston (G-8920)			
Bluescape Resources Co LLC	F	469 398-2202	
Dallas (G-4033)			
BP America Production Company	F	903 927-8999	
Hallsville (G-8127)			
◆ BP Corporation North Amer Inc	A	281 366-2000	
Houston (G-8965)			
BP Corporation North Amer Inc	A	281 366-2000	
Houston (G-8967)			
◆ BP Exploration & Prod Inc	E	800 333-3991	
Houston (G-8969)			
Bpz Resources Inc	E	281 556-6200	
Houston (G-8973)			

Bradley Operating Company	F	806 665-7130	
Pampa (G-16316)			
Brayton Operating Corp	F	361 884-8741	
Corpus Christi (G-3489)			
Brazco Development Inc	F	432 684-8031	
Midland (G-15149)			
Breck Operating Corp	F	254 559-3355	
Breckenridge (G-2223)			
Bridwell Oil Management LLC	E	325 672-1512	
Abilene (G-24)			
Brigham Minerals Inc	F	512 220-6350	
Austin (G-1007)			
Bright Industries LLC	E	972 410-6500	
Lewisville (G-110)			
Broken Hill Propty USA Inc	D	713 961-8500	
Houston (G-8992)			
Brown Fndtion Repr In Cnslting	F	972 271-2621	
Dallas (G-4060)			
Brown Oil & Gas Co Inc	F	254 562-2818	
Mexia (G-15087)			
Browning Offshore Inc	F	214 739-3481	
Dallas (G-4061)			
Browning Oil Company Inc	F	214 739-3481	
Dallas (G-4062)			
Bruce A Wilbanks Company Inc	F	432 682-7582	
Midland (G-15152)			
Brushy Resources Inc	F	210 999-5400	
San Antonio (G-17969)			
Buck Production	F	940 567-3005	
Jacksboro (G-13217)			
Buffco Production Inc	F	903 988-8199	
Longview (G-14204)			
Burk Royalty Co Ltd	F	940 397-8600	
Wichita Falls (G-20748)			
▲ Burlington Resources LLC	C	281 293-1000	
Houston (G-9020)			
Burnett Oil Co Inc	E	817 332-5108	
Fort Worth (G-6479)			
Cabot Oil & Gas Corporation	C	281 589-4600	
Houston (G-9041)			
Caelus Energy Alaska LLC	E	214 368-6050	
Dallas (G-4077)			
Callon Petroleum Company	D	281 589-5200	
Houston (G-9051)			
▲ Callon Petroleum Operating Co	E	601 442-1601	
Houston (G-9053)			
◆ Cameron LNG Holdings LLC	E	832 783-5500	
Houston (G-9075)			
Cantera Energy LLC	E	832 246-6100	
The Woodlands (G-19838)			
Cantera Operating LLC	E	832 246-6100	
The Woodlands (G-19839)			
Caprock Permian Processing LLC	F	832 914-1679	
Humble (G-12752)			
Catocon Inc	E	903 348-3350	
Sulphur Springs (G-19582)			
Centennial Resource Dev Inc	E	281 302-5048	
Sugar Land (G-19454)			
Centurion Pipeline LP	E	713 215-7000	
Houston (G-9140)			
Channel Brfinery Terminals LLC	F	713 965-4150	
Houston (G-9161)			
Chaparral Energy LLC	D	806 435-7533	
Perryton (G-16635)			
Chesapeake Energy Corporation	E	817 502-5000	
Fort Worth (G-6512)			
Chesapeake Operating LLC	E	806 273-5820	
Borger (G-2167)			
Chevron Corporation	E	903 963-8631	
Van (G-20206)			
Chevron Corporation	C	907 276-7600	
Houston (G-9177)			
Chevron Corporation	B	713 754-3998	
Houston (G-9178)			
CHI Energy Inc	G	432 685-5001	
Midland (G-15163)			
Chief Oil & Gas LLC	F	214 265-9590	
Dallas (G-4112)			
Choctaw II Oil & Gas Ltd	F	713 632-0222	
Houston (G-9184)			
Cholla Petroleum Inc	E	214 692-7052	
Dallas (G-4113)			
Citation Oil & Gas Corp	F	432 262-7600	
Midland (G-15167)			
Citation Oil & Gas Corp	C	281 891-1000	
Houston (G-9199)			
Citation Oil & Gas Corp	G	956 248-5741	
Lyford (G-14571)			
Clajon Holding Corp	C	432 682-6324	
Midland (G-15168)			

Clear Fork Incorporated	F	325 677-1309	
Abilene (G-31)			
Cnooc Energy Holdings USA Inc	E	713 380-4800	
Houston (G-9220)			
Coastline Petroleum LLC	F	281 844-4272	
Houston (G-9229)			
Coates Energy Trust	G	210 820-0113	
San Antonio (G-18014)			
Cobra Oil & Gas Corporation	E	940 723-4331	
Wichita Falls (G-20754)			
Cockrell Oil Corporation	E	713 209-7300	
Houston (G-9235)			
Cohort Energy Company	E	972 233-8191	
Addison (G-110)			
Comstock Oil & Gas Llc	E	972 668-8800	
Frisco (G-7273)			
Comstock Resources Inc	D	972 668-8800	
Frisco (G-7274)			
Concho Oil & Gas LLC	C	432 683-7443	
Midland (G-15175)			
Concho Resources Inc	E	432 221-0400	
Midland (G-15176)			
Concho Resources Inc	B	432 683-7443	
Midland (G-15177)			
Concord Oil Co	F	210 224-4455	
San Antonio (G-18022)			
Conocophillips	A	281 293-1000	
Houston (G-9272)			
Contango Oil & Gas Company	E	713 236-7400	
Houston (G-9282)			
Continental Operating Co	F	713 209-1110	
Houston (G-9287)			
Copano Company	F	361 578-6271	
Victoria (G-20254)			
Copano Company	E	361 526-2115	
Refugio (G-17239)			
Corporate Texas Co LLC	F	940 549-1400	
Graham (G-7778)			
Courson Oil & Gas Inc	E	806 435-2910	
Perryton (G-16636)			
Covey Park II LLC	D	214 548-6000	
Frisco (G-7276)			
Crawford Energy Inc	F	713 626-2637	
Houston (G-9335)			
Crimson Exploration Inc	E	713 236-7400	
Houston (G-9344)			
Cw Resources Inc	F	903 759-8822	
Longview (G-14218)			
Dale Operating Company	E	214 979-9010	
Dallas (G-4208)			
Dallas Production Inc	F	940 328-1241	
Mineral Wells (G-15524)			
Dallas Production Inc	E	214 369-9266	
Dallas (G-4224)			
Daniel H Braman Jr Estate	E	361 578-6271	
Victoria (G-20257)			
Dcp Midstream LLC	E	806 228-6241	
Spearman (G-19085)			
Dcp Midstream LLC	E	361 584-8500	
Bishop (G-2106)			
◆ Dcp NGL Services LP	F	713 735-3600	
Houston (G-9416)			
Dcp Operating Company LP	C	361 584-8509	
Bishop (G-2107)			
Delaware River Swd LLC	D	432 683-7443	
Midland (G-15189)			
Delray Oil Inc	F	210 824-7214	
San Antonio (G-18048)			
Delta Oil & Gas Ltd	E	254 559-9841	
Breckenridge (G-2228)			
Denbury Inc	G	972 673-2000	
Plano (G-16838)			
Denbury Onshore LLC	F	281 482-7581	
Alvin (G-358)			
▲ Denbury Onshore LLC	C	972 673-2000	
Plano (G-16840)			
Devon Energy Corporation	F	903 693-7196	
Carthage (G-2906)			
Devon Energy Corporation	F	806 229-6300	
Whiteface (G-20724)			
Devon Permian Corporation	C	432 685-0727	
Midland (G-15191)			
Diamond M Drlg Exploration Co	F	210 310-3135	
San Antonio (G-18056)			
Diamondback Energy Inc	E	432 221-7400	
Midland (G-15193)			
Dirnett Inc	F	361 375-2194	
Tuleta (G-20033)			
Djh Services LLC	F	325 392-3671	
Ozona (G-16281)			

Djh Services LLC ....E 713 228-5911
Houston (G-9485)

Dorado Oil Company ....E 361 241-3200
Corpus Christi (G-3516)

Dorchester Minerals LP ....E 214 559-0300
Dallas (G-4273)

Double Eagle Lone Star LLC ....F 817 928-3260
Fort Worth (G-6591)

Doyle Hartman Oil Producer ....F 432 684-4011
Midland (G-15196)

Dstj Corporation ....F 936 447-1174
Montgomery (G-15632)

▲ Dubai Petroleum Company ......A 281 293-1000
Houston (G-9537)

Duncan Drilling Company ....G 432 263-7721
Big Spring (G-2081)

Durham Inc ....F 432 684-5557
Midland (G-15198)

Dynamic Inc ....E 817 838-1800
Fort Worth (G-6597)

Dynamic Production ....E 817 838-1800
Fort Worth (G-6598)

Dyne Oil & Gas Inc ....F 806 274-2952
Borger (G-2176)

E & H Drilling Co ....F 940 549-0370
Graham (G-7781)

E B R Energy LP ....F 281 265-6500
Sugar Land (G-19481)

◆ E R Carpenter LP ....C 804 359-0800
Temple (G-19680)

▲ Eagle Oil & Gas Co ....F 940 723-7322
Wichita Falls (G-20762)

Eagle Rock Energy G&P LLC ......F 281 408-1200
Houston (G-9561)

Eagle Rock Energy Partners LP ....D 281 408-1200
Houston (G-9562)

Eagle Rock Field Services LP ......F 806 323-5381
Canadian (G-2648)

Eagle Rock Pipeline LP ....E 281 408-1200
Houston (G-9565)

Eaglehawk Field Services LLC .....C 832 204-2700
Houston (G-9568)

Eastland Oil Co ....F 432 683-6293
Midland (G-15205)

Eclipse Resources Holdings LP ....F 814 308-9754
Irving (G-13006)

Eclipse Resources I LP ....F 814 308-9754
Irving (G-13007)

Ecostim Inc ....D 281 531-7200
Katy (G-13399)

Edmar Company LLC ....F 432 686-8888
Midland (G-15206)

◆ El Paso Cgp Company LLC ....E 713 420-2600
Houston (G-9585)

El Paso CNG Company LLC ....F 713 420-2600
Houston (G-9586)

Elevation Resources LLC............G 432 686-7500
Midland (G-15208)

Elgie Company Inc ....F 214 691-6216
Dallas (G-4310)

Elm Ridge Resources Inc ....F 972 889-2100
Dallas (G-4316)

Emerald Gathering & Trnsp LLC ....F 713 621-2242
Houston (G-9611)

Emerge Energy Services LP ....E 817 618-4020
Fort Worth (G-6610)

▲ Endeavor Energy Resources LP ....E 432 687-1575
Midland (G-15210)

Endeavor Energy Resources LP ....D 432 221-9300
Midland (G-15211)

Endeavor Energy Resources LP ....F 432 687-1575
Midland (G-15213)

▲ Endeavour International Corp ....E 713 307-8700
Houston (G-9627)

Energen Corporation ....F 205 326-2700
Midland (G-15216)

Energen Resources Corporation ....F 432 687-1155
Midland (G-15217)

Energy Xxi Gulf Coast Inc ....F 713 351-3000
Houston (G-9640)

Energy Xxi Ltd ....F 713 351-3000
Houston (G-9641)

Enervest Ltd ....D 713 659-3500
Houston (G-9643)

Eni Petroleum US LLC ....C 713 393-6100
Houston (G-9648)

Enlink Midstream Inc ....E 214 953-9500
Dallas (G-4324)

Enlink Midstream Partners LP ....F 817 599-3492
Weatherford (G-20589)

Enlink N Texas Gathering LP ....E 432 221-9757
Midland (G-15220)

Eog Resources Inc ....E 979 245-2201
Bay City (G-1772)

Eog Resources Inc ....C 713 651-7000
Houston (G-9671)

Eog Resources Inc ....E 830 879-4614
Cotulla (G-3690)

Eog Resources Inc ....D 361 866-4300
Corpus Christi (G-3519)

Eog Resources Inc ....E 210 403-7700
San Antonio (G-18093)

Eog Resources Inc ....D 432 686-3600
Midland (G-15223)

Eog Resources Inc ....E 940 696-6000
Bowie (G-2194)

Ep Energy Corporation..............F 713 997-1000
Houston (G-9673)

Ep Energy LLC ....F 713 997-1200
Houston (G-9675)

Equinor Exploration Company ......F 512 427-3300
Austin (G-1135)

Esenjay Petroleum Corporation ....F 361 883-7464
Corpus Christi (G-3521)

Etc Intrastate Procurement LLC ......A 713 989-2688
Houston (G-9703)

Excel Production Co ....F 806 665-0366
Pampa (G-16322)

Exco Holdings Inc ....B 214 368-2084
Dallas (G-4343)

Exterran Corporation ....E 281 836-7000
Houston (G-9735)

▲ Exxon Mobil Fuels Marketing Co......F 703 846-3000
Spring (G-19115)

Fairway Rsrces Prtners III LLC ......E 817 416-1946
Southlake (G-19068)

Falcon Seaboard Holdings LLC......E 713 622-0055
Houston (G-9755)

▼ Far East Energy Corporation ....F 832 598-0470
Houston (G-9762)

Farmers Oil Co ....E 281 874-2101
Houston (G-9764)

Faulconer Energy Joint Ventr S ......D 903 581-4382
Tyler (G-20085)

Faulconer Resources Corp ....F 903 581-4382
Tyler (G-20086)

Fayetteville-Floyd Gas Company ....D 432 682-6685
Midland (G-15229)

Federal Royalty Partners Ltd ....E 713 529-3729
Houston (G-9771)

Five - Jab Inc ....D 281 356-7767
Magnolia (G-14607)

Foothills Resources Inc ....F 713 621-9408
Houston (G-9831)

Fortson Oil Company ....F 817 335-5641
Fort Worth (G-6645)

Founders Oil & Gas Oper LLC ......F 817 390-1800
Arlington (G-680)

Four Sevens Operating Co Ltd ......F 817 870-9088
Fort Worth (G-6647)

Fred Brown Methanol Inc ....F 806 665-0034
Pampa (G-16323)

Freedom Oil & Gas Inc ....F 832 783-5700
Houston (G-9859)

Frostwood Energy LLC ....G 713 623-7133
Houston (G-9871)

Fuller Production Inc ....F 432 683-5661
Midland (G-15233)

G S Petroleum Inc ....E 936 336-4114
Liberty (G-14118)

Galveston Bay Gathering LLC ......F 281 408-1200
Houston (G-9896)

Garvon Inc ....E 214 691-0711
Dallas (G-4392)

Gas Acquisition & Supply Inc ......F 940 872-1183
Bowie (G-2195)

Gene Powell Investments Inc ....F 903 234-1155
Longview (G-14240)

Geo Halcon Holdings LLC............D 832 538-0300
Houston (G-9932)

Georesources Inc ....E 832 538-0300
Houston (G-9940)

George R Brown Partnership........E 713 652-4901
Houston (G-9942)

Geosouthern Energy Corporation ....E 281 363-9161
The Woodlands (G-19866)

Gip II Blue Holding Partnr LP ....C 713 496-4200
Houston (G-9959)

▼ Glen Rose Petroleum Corp ....F 832 437-0701
Houston (G-9964)

Global Marine Inc ....D 713 232-7500
Houston (G-9974)

Glori Energy Inc ....E 713 237-8880
Houston (G-8383)

Gmt Exploration Co Texas LLC ......F 713 334-6001
Houston (G-9988)

Golden Oil Company ....F 713 626-1110
Houston (G-9993)

Goldston Oil Corporation ....E 713 355-3408
Houston (G-9995)

Goodrich Petroleum Company LLC ....D 713 780-9494
Houston (G-10002)

▲ Goodrich Petroleum Corporation ......C 713 780-9494
Houston (G-10003)

GP II Energy Inc ....F 432 684-4748
Midland (G-15238)

Granite Operating Company ....E 806 323-9118
Canadian (G-2651)

Grizzly Energy LLC ....F 832 327-2255
Houston (G-10047)

GSM Enterprises Inc ....E 806 358-6894
Amarillo (G-430)

Gunn Oil Company ....F 940 723-5585
Wichita Falls (G-20769)

H L Brown Jr ....F 432 683-5216
Midland (G-15243)

H R Stasney & Sons Ltd ....F 325 762-3311
Albany (G-189)

Halcon Gulf States LLC ....E 832 538-0300
Houston (G-10091)

Halcon Holdings Inc ....F 832 538-0300
Houston (G-10092)

Halcon Operating Co Inc ....D 832 538-0300
Houston (G-10093)

Hallwood Petroleum LLC ....E 214 528-5588
Dallas (G-4431)

Halres LLC ....C 832 538-0300
Houston (G-10111)

▲ Hamill Resources Inc ....F 281 556-9581
Houston (G-10112)

Haynes International Inc ....F 713 937-7597
Houston (G-10138)

Headington Oil Company ....E 214 696-0606
Dallas (G-4442)

Headington Oil Limited 1993 LP ....D 214 696-0606
Dallas (G-4443)

Headingtron Oil LP ....E 214 696-0606
Dallas (G-4444)

◆ Helix Enrgy Slutions Group Inc ....C 281 618-0400
Houston (G-10150)

Hep El Dorado LLC ....F 214 871-3555
Dallas (G-4451)

Herd Producing Co Inc ....E 903 509-3456
Tyler (G-20095)

Hesco Gathering Company L L C ......F 361 883-8398
Corpus Christi (G-3547)

Hess Midstream GP LP ....C 713 496-4200
Houston (G-10165)

High Line Ranch LLC ....D 830 875-5386
San Antonio (G-18166)

▲ Hilcorp Energy Company ....F 713 209-2400
Houston (G-10182)

Hilcorp Energy Company ....F 979 548-2144
Sweeny (G-19627)

Hkn Inc ....F 817 424-2424
Southlake (G-19074)

Hopewell Operating Inc ....F 214 691-6216
Dallas (G-4467)

Horseshoe Operating Inc ....F 432 683-1448
Midland (G-15249)

◆ Houston Opicoil Inc ....F 713 840-7171
Houston (G-10242)

Howell Corporation...................F 832 636-1000
The Woodlands (G-19873)

Howell Oil & Gas Inc ....F 903 935-0999
Marshall (G-14782)

Howell Petroleum Corporation ......D 281 320-9096
Houston (G-10269)

Hudson Brothers Mining Company......F 903 876-4642
Rusk (G-17731)

Hughes Dan A Company Lp ....E 361 358-3752
Beeville (G-1985)

Hunt Nlson Bnker Trust Estt-T............F 214 979-9072
Dallas (G-4471)

Hunt Dominion Corporation ....E 214 880-8400
Dallas (G-4472)

Hunt Petroleum Corporation ....E 214 880-8400
Fort Worth (G-6710)

Hunt Petroleum Corporation ....E 713 871-3400
Houston (G-10280)

Hurd Enterprises Ltd ....F ...... 210 829-5255 San Antonio (G-18176)	Legacy Investments Inc ....E ...... 214 750-1522 Dallas (G-4587)	Michelson Energy Company ....F ...... 210 826-0681 San Antonio (G-18299)
Hyperion Energy LP ....F ...... 214 750-3820 Dallas (G-4478)	Legacy Reserves Inc ....F ...... 432 689-5200 Midland (G-15274)	Midcoast Energy Partners LP ....F ...... 713 821-2000 Houston (G-10872)
Hyperion Resources Inc ....F ...... 214 750-1522 Dallas (G-4479)	Legacy Reserves LP ....D ...... 432 689-5200 Midland (G-15276)	Midland Energy Inc ....E ...... 432 683-6686 Midland (G-15301)
Iacx Energy LLC ....F ...... 972 960-3210 Dallas (G-4483)	Lenoir M Josey Inc ....G ...... 713 526-3844 Houston (G-10624)	Millennium Exploration Co LLC ....F ...... 210 960-1000 San Antonio (G-18307)
Ibex Inc ....E ...... 254 559-3355 Breckenridge (G-2229)	Lewis Operating Co ....F ...... 940 723-0266 Holliday (G-8352)	Mineral Technologies Inc ....F ...... 432 685-3520 Midland (G-15305)
Inpex Corporation ....F ...... 713 850-8480 Houston (G-10374)	Lime Rock Resources Iv-A LP ....C ...... 713 292-9500 Houston (G-10643)	Miranda Energy Corporation ....F ...... 432 685-1953 Midland (G-15306)
Inpex Eagle Ford LLC ....D ...... 713 850-8480 Houston (G-10375)	Linnco LLC ....A ...... 281 840-4000 Houston (G-10653)	Mission Oil Company ....F ...... 210 224-4455 San Antonio (G-18311)
Isramco Inc ....F ...... 713 621-3882 Houston (G-10427)	▲ LNG Freeport Development L P ......E ...... 713 980-2888 Houston (G-10659)	Mobil Producing Texas and NM ....A ...... 713 871-5000 Houston (G-10898)
Iwc Oil & Refinery LLC ....E ...... 210 900-9928 San Antonio (G-18196)	Lone Star Oil & Gas Inc ....E ...... 432 686-9390 Midland (G-15284)	Modern Exploration Inc ....F ...... 903 893-1129 Sherman (G-18922)
J & L Partners ....E ...... 972 417-3977 Dallas (G-4516)	Lonestar Resources US Inc ....E ...... 817 921-1889 Fort Worth (G-6800)	Moncrief Partners LP ....E ...... 817 336-7232 Fort Worth (G-6849)
J Cleo Thmpson Jmes Cleo Thmp .....F ...... 432 550-8887 Dallas (G-4517)	Long Trusts ....F ...... 903 984-5017 Kilgore (G-13564)	Moncries Faxel Oil Interests ....F ...... 817 335-5656 Fort Worth (G-6850)
J R & Adam Seitz Ltd ....F ...... 940 723-7303 Wichita Falls (G-20773)	Lrr Energy LP ....C ...... 713 292-9510 Houston (G-10693)	Monterey Oil & Gas Corporation ....E ...... 832 985-8723 Houston (G-10913)
J-W Energy Company ....D ...... 972 233-8191 Addison (G-137)	Lynx Energy Company Inc ....F ...... 214 969-5555 Dallas (G-4614)	Montex Drilling Company ....E ...... 817 336-7232 Fort Worth (G-6851)
▲ J-W Operating Company ....D ...... 972 233-8191 Addison (G-138)	M P Energy Inc ....F ...... 281 350-6350 Houston (G-10719)	Morgan Kinder Treating LP ....D ...... 361 578-1312 Victoria (G-20285)
J-W Operating Company ....E ...... 361 570-2788 Victoria (G-20275)	M-C Production and Drlg Co Inc ....E ...... 903 297-2251 Longview (G-14273)	Morgan Kinder Treating LP ....F ...... 432 563-2766 Odessa (G-16083)
Jackal Merger Sub A LLC ....D ...... 737 704-2300 Austin (G-1248)	Magnum Engineering Company ....G ...... 361 882-3858 Corpus Christi (G-3568)	MRC Global (us) Inc ....E ...... 432 620-0059 Midland (G-15307)
Jagee Petro Inc ....F ...... 817 335-5881 Fort Worth (G-6734)	Magnum Producing LP ....F ...... 361 882-3858 Corpus Christi (G-3569)	◆ Murphy Exploration Prod - USA ......B ...... 281 675-9000 Houston (G-10942)
James Lee Davis ....D ...... 432 682-6311 Midland (G-15258)	Maralo LLC ....E ...... 713 622-5420 Houston (G-10751)	Mustang Exploration Co Inc ....F ...... 979 648-2641 Louise (G-14353)
◆ James Reneau Seed Company ....F ...... 806 256-3216 Shamrock (G-18891)	Maralo LLC ....F ...... 512 322-0041 Austin (G-1326)	N D Stovall & Son ....G ...... 940 549-2616 Graham (G-7787)
◆ Jamex Inc ....F ...... 214 265-7141 Lewisville (G-14058)	◆ Marathon Oil Company ....A ...... 713 629-6600 Houston (G-10754)	N M L Inc of Texas ....D ...... 713 753-1448 Houston (G-10948)
JD Murchison Interests Inc ....E ...... 972 931-0700 Plano (G-16898)	◆ Marathon Oil Corporation ....A ...... 713 629-6600 Houston (G-10756)	Nacero Inc ....D ...... 346 200-7706 Houston (G-10959)
Jet Oil Producers Inc ....F ...... 936 653-3379 Coldspring (G-3166)	Mariner Gulf of Mexico LLC ....D ...... 713 954-5500 Houston (G-10767)	Natural Gas Anadarko Company ....E ...... 806 435-6818 Perryton (G-16642)
Jetta Operating Company Inc ....D ...... 817 335-1179 Fort Worth (G-6739)	Marshall & Winston Inc ....F ...... 432 684-6373 Midland (G-15293)	Natural Gas Pipeline Amer LLC ....A ...... 713 369-9000 Houston (G-11007)
Jetta Production Company Inc ....E ...... 817 335-1179 Fort Worth (G-6740)	Marshall R Young Oil Co ....F ...... 817 335-1216 Fort Worth (G-6812)	Natural Gas Pipeline Amer LLC ....E ...... 903 758-0154 Longview (G-14283)
JM Cox Resources LP ....F ...... 432 682-9435 Midland (G-15259)	▲ Marubeni Oil & Gas (usa) LLC ....E ...... 832 379-1100 Houston (G-10781)	Natural Gas Pipeline Amer LLC ....F ...... 361 897-1022 Victoria (G-20288)
John H Hendrix Corporation ....G ...... 432 684-6631 Midland (G-15261)	Matador Resources Company ....E ...... 972 371-5200 Dallas (G-4650)	Nbl Permian LLC ....E ...... 979 542-5571 Midland (G-15312)
John H Young Inc ....F ...... 713 236-8303 Houston (G-10481)	Matthews-Daniel Holdings Inc ....D ...... 713 622-1633 Houston (G-10798)	Nbl Permian LLC ....F ...... 979 764-4030 College Station (G-3195)
John Oates Company Inc ....G ...... 806 878-3338 Stinnett (G-19427)	Maverick Field Services LLC ....F ...... 432 685-5021 Midland (G-15294)	Nearburg Producing Company ....F ...... 214 739-1778 Dallas (G-4718)
Johnson & Ernst Operating Co ....E ...... 940 723-8127 Wichita Falls (G-20774)	▲ Maxus Energy Corporation ....E ...... 281 681-7200 Houston (G-10806)	Nearburg Producing Company ....F ...... 432 686-8235 Midland (G-15315)
Jpm Eoc Opal LLC ....E ...... 303 861-8140 Houston (G-10486)	MB Robinson Inc ....E ...... 432 267-5277 Big Spring (G-2087)	Nelson Oil Field Eqp & Sup ....F ...... 361 375-2105 Pettus (G-16653)
Karper Oil & Gas Corporation ....F ...... 940 549-0606 Graham (G-7785)	McBee Operating Company LLC ....F ...... 214 526-1500 Dallas (G-4658)	Neofirma Inc ....F ...... 214 233-7111 Richardson (G-17362)
KCS Resources LLC ....C ...... 832 204-2700 Houston (G-10505)	McGrew Energy Corporation ....G ...... 214 265-1135 Dallas (G-4661)	Neumin Production Co ....E ...... 361 987-8900 Point Comfort (G-17089)
Kerr-Mcgee (nevada) LLC ....D ...... 303 321-0683 Spring (G-19224)	Medallion Oil Company Inc ....F ...... 713 654-0144 Houston (G-10815)	Newfield Exploration Company ....D ...... 281 847-6000 Spring (G-19236)
Kerr-Mcgee Oil Gas Onshore LP ....C ...... 832 636-1000 The Woodlands (G-19891)	Medders Oil Company ....G ...... 940 692-6626 Wichita Falls (G-20783)	Newman Operating Co ....D ...... 361 394-5516 Freer (G-7231)
▼ Key Energy Services Inc ....C ...... 713 651-4300 Houston (G-10522)	Melvin Hammon ....F ...... 806 665-2667 Pampa (G-16328)	Nexen Petroleum USA Inc ....E ...... 972 450-4600 Houston (G-11045)
Killam Oil Co Ltd ....E ...... 956 724-7141 Laredo (G-13902)	Merit Energy Company LLC ....E ...... 940 683-4059 Gainesville (G-7347)	Nexus Capacity Services Ulc ....C ...... 713 627-5040 Houston (G-11050)
Kinder Morgan (delaware) Inc ....C ...... 806 272-3309 Muleshoe (G-15677)	Merit Energy Company LLC ....E ...... 956 728-6206 Laredo (G-13912)	◆ Noble Energy Inc ....C ...... 281 872-3100 Houston (G-11064)
King Ranch Holdings Inc ....E ...... 832 681-5700 Houston (G-10535)	Merit Energy Company LLC ....F ...... 903 923-7300 Hallsville (G-8129)	Noble Energy Inc ....D ...... 800 234-3867 Houston (G-11063)
Klabzuba Oil & Gas Inc ....F ...... 817 336-5757 Fort Worth (G-6765)	Merit Energy Company LLC ....F ...... 361 293-3586 Yoakum (G-20971)	Nortex Corporation ....G ...... 713 658-1142 Houston (G-11071)
Koch Industries Inc ....F ...... 806 347-2645 Matador (G-14816)	Merit Energy Company LLC ....F ...... 956 842-3649 Edinburg (G-5596)	Nuevo Energy Company ....B ...... 713 579-6000 Houston (G-11097)
KSA Industries Inc ....D ...... 713 881-3400 Houston (G-10569)	▲ Merit Energy Company LLC ....C ...... 972 701-8377 Dallas (G-4666)	Oasis Petroleum Inc ....D ...... 281 404-9500 Houston (G-11109)
L C S Production Company ....D ...... 325 692-3903 Abilene (G-55)	Mesquite Energy Inc ....E ...... 713 756-2700 Houston (G-10840)	Oasis Petroleum LLC ....F ...... 281 404-9500 Houston (G-11110)
L T D Explorations Inc ....G ...... 361 664-9108 Freer (G-7230)	Mewbourne Holdings Inc ....F ...... 903 561-2900 Tyler (G-20126)	Oasis Petroleum North Amer LLC ....D ...... 281 404-9500 Houston (G-11111)
Lamar Hunt Trust Estate Inc ....D ...... 214 720-1600 Dallas (G-4579)	Mewbourne Oil Company ....F ...... 281 580-6608 Houston (G-10859)	◆ Occidental Oil and Gas Corp ....E ...... 713 215-7000 Houston (G-11114)
Langley Energy ....F ...... 214 221-2669 Dallas (G-4581)	Mewbourne Oil Company ....E ...... 903 561-2900 Tyler (G-20127)	Occidental Oil and Gas Corp ....B ...... 432 685-5600 Midland (G-15323)

Occidental Permian Ltd F 432 523-7556
Andrews *(G-555)*
Occidental Permian Ltd E 806 592-3777
Denver City *(G-5422)*
Occidental Permian Ltd E 806 229-2501
Sundown *(G-19613)*
◆ **Occidental Permian Ltd** C 713 215-7000
Houston *(G-11115)*
Occidental Petroleum Corp A 713 215-7000
Houston *(G-11116)*
Occidental Petroleum Corp G 325 574-8567
Ira *(G-12913)*
Occidental Petroleum Corp E 713 640-7500
Houston *(G-11117)*
Occidntal Intl Explration Prod B 713 215-7600
Houston *(G-11118)*
Ohs Energy Corp G 832 871-5088
Houston *(G-11149)*
Oil & Gas Producers Inc F 214 696-2393
Dallas *(G-4756)*
Omimex Canada Ltd E 817 460-7777
Fort Worth *(G-6877)*
Omimex Energy Inc F 817 460-7777
Fort Worth *(G-6878)*
Omimex Resources Inc F 817 460-7777
Fort Worth *(G-6880)*
One Gas Inc E 830 672-2921
Gonzales *(G-7760)*
One Gas Inc E 830 672-2256
Gonzales *(G-7761)*
Osborn Heirs Company Ltd E 210 826-0700
San Antonio *(G-18357)*
OXY Inc F 432 685-5600
Midland *(G-15334)*
▲ **OXY Inc** C 713 215-7000
Houston *(G-11209)*
OXY Inc E 956 728-6200
Laredo *(G-13918)*
OXY USA Inc F 432 634-2247
Big Spring *(G-2091)*
OXY USA Inc C 713 215-7000
Houston *(G-11210)*
OXY USA Inc C 956 429-0600
McAllen *(G-14897)*
OXY USA Inc C 806 637-5965
Loop *(G-14340)*
P-R-O Management Inc E 972 720-1475
Dallas *(G-4776)*
Palo Petroleum Inc F 214 691-3676
Dallas *(G-4781)*
Palo Verde Oil Company D 214 692-7052
Dallas *(G-4782)*
Pantera Energy Company D 806 376-6625
Amarillo *(G-451)*
Par Pacific Holdings Inc D 281 899-4800
Houston *(G-11235)*
Par Petroleum LLC G 281 899-4800
Houston *(G-11236)*
Parallel Petroleum LLC E 432 684-3727
Midland *(G-15336)*
Parsley Energy Inc D 737 704-2300
Austin *(G-1398)*
Parsley Energy LLC E 432 818-2100
Midland *(G-15337)*
Partee Enterprises F 432 263-0632
Big Spring *(G-2092)*
Parten Operating Inc F 281 874-2101
Houston *(G-11248)*
Patriot Resources Inc F 432 686-9801
Midland *(G-15340)*
Patterson-Uti Energy Inc F 432 682-9401
Midland *(G-15343)*
Patterson-Uti Energy Inc D 281 765-7100
Houston *(G-11262)*
▲ **Penn Virginia Mc Corporation** D 713 722-6500
Houston *(G-11278)*
Perdure Petroleum LLC F 281 668-8488
Allen *(G-291)*
Petco Petroleum Corporation D 806 669-3947
Pampa *(G-16334)*
Peter Paul Petroleum Company E 713 209-1100
Houston *(G-11295)*
Petro Harvester Oper Co LLC D 214 618-7600
Dallas *(G-4798)*
Petro-Hunt LLC E 903 629-3205
Como *(G-3249)*
Petro-Hunt LLC D 214 880-8400
Dallas *(G-4799)*
Petrohawk Energy Corporation G 713 961-8500
Houston *(G-11303)*
▲ **Petrosantander Inc** F 713 784-8700
Houston *(G-11311)*
Petrosaurus Inc F 210 624-2750
Von Ormy *(G-20348)*
◆ **Phillips 66** C 281 293-6600
Houston *(G-11324)*
Phillips 66 Partners LP F 855 283-9237
Houston *(G-11326)*
Phoenix Fund Inc F 210 828-4373
San Antonio *(G-18373)*
Phoenix Hydrocarbons Operating F 936 258-2646
Dayton *(G-5234)*
Pickens Company Inc F 214 369-7471
Dallas *(G-4803)*
Pickens Energy Corporation F 214 503-1271
Dallas *(G-4804)*
Pioneer Drilling Services Ltd C 361 289-9241
Corpus Christi *(G-3591)*
Pioneer Exploration Company E 281 893-9400
Houston *(G-11334)*
Pioneer Gas Pipeline Inc F 325 655-3300
San Angelo *(G-17820)*
Pioneer Natural Resources Co B 972 444-9001
Irving *(G-13144)*
Pioneer Natural Resources Co C 432 571-2800
Midland *(G-15355)*
Pioneer Natural Resources Co D 432 535-2444
Midkiff *(G-15096)*
Pioneer Ntral Rsources USA Inc D 432 683-4768
Midland *(G-15356)*
Pioneer Ntral Rsources USA Inc F 361 456-7201
Pawnee *(G-16534)*
Pioneer Water Management LLC F 800 242-2607
Irving *(G-13147)*
Pitcock Inc F 940 549-3344
Graham *(G-7788)*
Pitts Oil Company LLC F 214 369-9266
Dallas *(G-4806)*
Plains Resources Inc G 713 579-5000
Houston *(G-11344)*
Preston Oil Company LP E 281 367-8697
The Woodlands *(G-19905)*
Prime Natural Resources LLC F 713 953-3200
Houston *(G-11415)*
Primeenergy Corporation E 713 735-0000
Houston *(G-11417)*
Primexx Operating Corporation F 214 369-5909
Dallas *(G-4824)*
Primexx Operating Corporation E 432 445-7860
Pecos *(G-16625)*
▲ **Prosep Technologies Inc** E 281 504-2040
Houston *(G-11454)*
Pxp Gulf Coast Inc C 713 579-6000
Houston *(G-11477)*
Q-West Energy Company G 972 233-8191
Addison *(G-157)*
Quantum Investment Group Inc E 281 994-5400
Houston *(G-11507)*
Quatro Oil and Gas Inc F 940 767-4443
Wichita Falls *(G-20800)*
Quicksilver Resources Inc D 817 665-5000
Fort Worth *(G-6928)*
Quintana Energy Services Inc A 832 518-4094
Houston *(G-11515)*
Quintana Minerals Brazil LLC F 713 751-7500
Houston *(G-11517)*
R A Beaird Oil Co F 325 928-5220
Merkel *(G-15016)*
Range Production Parent Co E 817 870-2601
Fort Worth *(G-6939)*
Ray Mac Energy F 806 274-5881
Borger *(G-2184)*
Red Mountain Resources Inc E 214 871-0400
Dallas *(G-4869)*
Reef Exploration LP E 972 437-6792
Richardson *(G-17388)*
Reef Oil & Gas Partners LLC F 972 437-6792
Richardson *(G-17389)*
Regency Crude Marketing LLC D 806 665-3491
Pampa *(G-16337)*
Regency Desoto-Hesco Svcs LLC E 281 408-1200
Houston *(G-11584)*
Reliance Energy Inc E 432 683-4816
Midland *(G-15380)*
Remnant Oil Company LLC F 432 695-6997
Midland *(G-15381)*
Remora Royalties Inc E 512 579-3590
Austin *(G-1458)*
Renaissance Offshore LLC E 832 333-7700
Houston *(G-11598)*
Repsol Oil & Gas Usa LLC D 832 442-1000
Spring *(G-19247)*
Republic Energy Inc E 214 369-4800
Dallas *(G-4889)*
Ridge Oil Company Inc F 254 559-2297
Breckenridge *(G-2236)*
Ring Energy Inc E 432 682-7464
Midland *(G-15385)*
Ring Energy Inc F 432 682-7464
Midland *(G-15386)*
Rk Petroleum Corp F 432 683-4319
Midland *(G-15387)*
Rockcliff Energy MGT LLC E 713 351-0525
Houston *(G-11650)*
▼ **Rosewood Resources Inc** E 214 849-9300
Dallas *(G-4912)*
Royal Production Company Inc F 361 888-4792
Corpus Christi *(G-3611)*
Royalty Well Service Inc D 432 547-2926
Grandfalls *(G-8000)*
Rsp Permian Inc F 432 683-7443
Midland *(G-15390)*
▲ **Rutherford Oil Corporation** F 713 622-5555
Houston *(G-11701)*
Sabine Investor Holdings LLC B 832 242-9600
Houston *(G-11716)*
Sabine Oil & Gas Corporation F 832 242-9600
Houston *(G-11717)*
Sabine Oil & Gas LLC F 832 242-9600
Houston *(G-11718)*
Sable Natural Resources Corp F 972 770-4700
Dallas *(G-4925)*
Saga Petro Ltd Lblty Co Colo F 432 687-6200
Midland *(G-15392)*
Sage Energy Company F 979 567-7629
Caldwell *(G-2634)*
Sage Energy Company E 210 404-2828
San Antonio *(G-18443)*
Sago Christie LP G 281 240-8444
Sugar Land *(G-19539)*
Sago Energy LLC D 325 473-5161
Bronte *(G-2306)*
Sahara Operating Company F 432 697-0967
Midland *(G-15393)*
Samedan Oil Corporation F 580 223-4110
Houston *(G-11739)*
San Mateo Midstream LLC F 972 371-5203
Dallas *(G-4930)*
Sanchez Oil & Gas Corporation D 210 208-1300
Catarina *(G-2933)*
Sandalwood Oil & Gas Inc F 713 759-6095
Houston *(G-11746)*
Saracen Energy Advisors LP F 713 285-2900
Houston *(G-11750)*
Saratoga Resources Inc F 713 458-1560
Houston *(G-11751)*
Sauder Management Co F 940 723-8125
Wichita Falls *(G-20805)*
Savant Alaska LLC E 907 868-1258
Houston *(G-11759)*
Schlachter Operating Corp G 214 692-1567
Dallas *(G-4940)*
Scout Energy Management LLC F 972 277-1397
Dallas *(G-4945)*
Sea Eagle Ford LLC E 720 390-6244
Houston *(G-11795)*
Seaboard Oil Co F 432 684-7005
Midland *(G-15401)*
Sellers Lease Service Inc F 361 865-2142
Flatonia *(G-6234)*
Sentry Oil & Gas LLC E 212 753-6367
Mico *(G-15094)*
Sg Interests I Ltd F 713 951-0100
Houston *(G-11843)*
◆ **Shell Oil Company** A 713 241-6161
Houston *(G-11860)*
Shenandoah Petroleum Corp F 432 685-1964
Midland *(G-15406)*
Siana Oil & Gas Co LLC F 713 568-1082
Houston *(G-11876)*
Sidwell Operating Company LP G 806 371-7513
Amarillo *(G-463)*
Sienergy LP F 281 778-6250
Lakeway *(G-13819)*
Silverbow Resources Inc D 281 874-2700
Houston *(G-11899)*
SM Energy Company D 432 688-1700
Midland *(G-15411)*
SM Energy Company F 281 677-2800
Houston *(G-11916)*

Employee Codes: A=Over 500 employees, B=251-500
C=101-250, D=51-100, E=20-50, F=10-19, G=9
2021 Harris Texas
Manufacturers Directory
881

Smalley Drilling & Trckg Corp ....E 325 762-3409
Albany *(G-193)*

▲ Smith Energy Company ....F 713 651-9102
Houston *(G-11922)*

Sn Operating LLC ....E 713 951-0233
Houston *(G-11929)*

Snw Operating Company Inc ....F 806 273-2667
Borger *(G-2185)*

Socorro Exploration Inc ....G 806 798-2790
Lubbock *(G-14483)*

Sojitz Energy Venture Inc ....F 713 963-9101
Houston *(G-11933)*

Sojourner Drilling Corporation ....E 325 672-2832
Abilene *(G-81)*

Southcross Gathering Ltd ....F 214 979-3700
Dallas *(G-4983)*

Southcross Marketing Co Ltd ....F 214 979-3700
Dallas *(G-4984)*

Southeast Land Services LLC ....F 724 256-9259
Little Elm *(G-14142)*

Southern Petroleum Labs Inc ....F 817 539-2168
Venus *(G-20222)*

Southern Utilities Company ....E 903 593-2588
Tyler *(G-20154)*

Southwest Resources ....F 979 836-5500
Brenham *(G-2273)*

Southwest Royalties Inc ....E 325 573-4977
Ira *(G-12915)*

Southwestern Energy Company ....D 832 796-1000
Spring *(G-19167)*

Sowell & Co LP ....E 214 871-3320
Dallas *(G-4994)*

Speartex Grain Company ....E 806 659-3711
Spearman *(G-19087)*

Speedway LLC ....D 713 943-9002
Houston *(G-12011)*

Speedway LLC ....E 432 758-6700
Seminole *(G-18887)*

Speedway LLC ....F 713 496-4000
Houston *(G-12013)*

Spindletop Oil & Gas Co ....E 972 644-2581
Dallas *(G-4998)*

Spruiell Drilling Co ....F 940 592-5471
Iowa Park *(G-12911)*

States Inc ....E 254 559-3355
Breckenridge *(G-2239)*

Statoil Oil & Gas Services Inc ....D 512 427-3300
Austin *(G-1533)*

Strand Energy LC ....F 713 658-8096
Houston *(G-12074)*

Streamline Innovations Inc ....G 888 787-6569
San Antonio *(G-18508)*

Sulphur River Exploration Inc ....F 214 373-1091
Dallas *(G-5021)*

Sulphur River Exploration Inc ....F 903 734-7248
Gilmer *(G-7714)*

▲ Summit Midstream Partners LP .....E 832 413-4770
Houston *(G-12094)*

Superior Processing Service ....E 713 759-6900
Houston *(G-12118)*

Swanner Properties ....G 940 723-7714
Wichita Falls *(G-20813)*

Swn International LLC ....A 832 796-1000
Spring *(G-19171)*

Swn Production (arkansas) LLC ....A 832 796-1000
Spring *(G-19172)*

Swn Production Company LLC ....E 281 618-4700
Houston *(G-12133)*

Synergy Oil & Gas LP ....F 713 827-9988
Houston *(G-12135)*

Synthesis Energy Systems Inc ....F 713 579-0600
Houston *(G-12138)*

T-C Oil Company ....E 361 526-4693
Refugio *(G-17249)*

Talos Energy Inc ....C 713 328-3000
Houston *(G-12150)*

Talos Ert LLC ....F 281 618-0590
Houston *(G-12152)*

Talos Production LLC ....G 713 328-3000
Houston *(G-12154)*

Targa Gas Marketing LLC ....F 713 584-1000
Houston *(G-12159)*

Tauber Exploration & Prod Co ....F 713 869-5656
Houston *(G-12164)*

Taylor Oil Co Ltd Partnership ....G 806 948-4166
Sunray *(G-19621)*

Tep Barnett Usa LLC ....C 817 720-1130
Fort Worth *(G-7043)*

Tepee Petroleum Company Inc ....G 713 659-8300
Houston *(G-12206)*

Terra Energy Partners LLC ....E 281 936-0355
Houston *(G-12209)*

Tesoro Lgstics NW Pipeline LLC ......E 210 249-9123
San Antonio *(G-18529)*

Texas Crude Energy Inc ....F 713 599-9900
Houston *(G-12228)*

Texas Crude Energy LLC ....E 713 599-9900
Houston *(G-12229)*

Texas Gas Service Company ....A 956 444-3900
Harlingen *(G-8205)*

Texas Nom Limited Partnership ....E 210 687-1900
San Antonio *(G-18539)*

Thompson & Thompson ....E 214 953-1177
Dallas *(G-5086)*

Thompson & Thompson ....E 214 953-1177
Odessa *(G-16177)*

Thompson & Thompson ....F 325 392-3721
Ozona *(G-16287)*

Thompson Petroleum Corporation .....F 214 953-1177
Dallas *(G-5087)*

Thor Energy Group Inc ....F 210 277-0368
San Antonio *(G-18550)*

Three P Operating Company ....F 940 846-3326
Newcastle *(G-15863)*

Threshold Development Company ......F 817 870-1483
Fort Worth *(G-7060)*

Tidal Energy Marketing US LLC ....C 713 650-8900
Houston *(G-12288)*

Tom McGee Corp ....G 806 658-4591
Booker *(G-2159)*

Topsail Energy Mktg Group LLC ....F 832 823-2380
The Woodlands *(G-19930)*

Tortuga Operating Co ....F 713 680-3600
Houston *(G-12325)*

◆ Total E&P Usa Inc ....C 713 647-3000
Houston *(G-12330)*

◆ Total Holdings Usa Inc ....F 713 483-5000
Houston *(G-12331)*

Transamerican Natural Gas Corp ......C 281 372-5304
Houston *(G-12346)*

Transatlantic Petroleum Ltd ....E 214 220-4323
Addison *(G-170)*

Transworld Worldwide Inc ....B 713 232-7500
Houston *(G-12355)*

Trend Gathering & Treating LP ....F 817 885-2524
Fort Worth *(G-7073)*

Tri Resources Inc ....E 432 558-3996
Crane *(G-3703)*

Triple Crown Resources LLC ....F 972 444-8808
Dallas *(G-5115)*

Tronox Incorporated ....D 903 794-5169
Texarkana *(G-19782)*

Tronox Incorporated ....F 432 263-4301
Big Spring *(G-2101)*

U S Companies Inc ....F 214 891-3300
Dallas *(G-3854)*

Unit Corporation ....G 806 658-2262
Booker *(G-2160)*

United Oil Corporation ....F 303 856-6444
Austin *(G-1608)*

Unity Hunt Inc ....E 214 720-1600
Dallas *(G-5140)*

Upham Oil & Gas Company LP ....F 940 325-4491
Mineral Wells *(G-15544)*

US Sand LLC ....F 713 333-3001
Houston *(G-12488)*

V-F Petroleum Inc ....F 432 683-3344
Midland *(G-15459)*

Vaalco Energy Inc ....F 713 623-0801
Houston *(G-12514)*

Valence Operating Company ....E 281 359-3659
Kingwood *(G-13659)*

Van Operating Ltd ....E 325 762-3353
Albany *(G-195)*

Vastar Resources Inc ....A 281 584-6000
Houston *(G-12539)*

Verado Energy Inc ....F 214 368-5322
Dallas *(G-5159)*

Verdad Oil & Gas Corporation ....E 214 357-0333
Dallas *(G-5162)*

Vernon E Faulconer Inc ....E 903 581-4382
Tyler *(G-20174)*

Viper Energy Partners LP ....C 432 221-7400
Midland *(G-15462)*

Virtex Holdings LLP ....F 361 882-3046
Corpus Christi *(G-3652)*

◆ Vitol Americas Corp ....D 713 230-1000
Houston *(G-12576)*

W B Osborn Oil Gas Oprtons L ....F 210 826-8654
San Antonio *(G-18607)*

W T Waggoner Estate ....C 940 552-2521
Vernon *(G-20232)*

W&T Offshore Inc ....C 713 626-8525
Houston *(G-12588)*

Wagner & Brown Ltd ....D 432 682-7936
Midland *(G-15463)*

Wagner Oil Company ....E 817 335-2222
Fort Worth *(G-7116)*

Walsh and Watts Inc ....D 817 335-5417
Fort Worth *(G-7120)*

Walsh Company ....E 817 335-3741
Fort Worth *(G-7121)*

Walsh F Howard Jr Oper Co Inc ....D 817 336-2062
Fort Worth *(G-7122)*

Walsh Oil Co ....E 817 336-2062
Fort Worth *(G-7123)*

Walsh Petroleum Inc ....F 432 684-5937
Midland *(G-15464)*

▼ Walter Oil & Gas Corporation ....E 713 659-1221
Houston *(G-12597)*

Wapiti Operating LLC ....D 713 365-8500
Houston *(G-12598)*

Waskom Gas Processing Company ....E 903 687-2513
Waskom *(G-20525)*

Wcs Oil & Gas Corporation ....F 979 542-0021
Giddings *(G-7704)*

Welder Rob & Bessie Wildlife ....F 361 364-2643
Sinton *(G-18967)*

Wes Tex Drilling Company LLC ....F 325 677-9121
Abilene *(G-93)*

Westerly Exploration Inc ....F 817 738-1917
Fort Worth *(G-7138)*

Westerly Exploration Inc ....F 713 524-7755
Houston *(G-12640)*

Western Midstream Partners LP ....F 832 636-6000
The Woodlands *(G-19940)*

Western Ref Cnan Gathering LLC ......F 210 626-6000
San Antonio *(G-18615)*

William L Arrington ....G 806 669-3324
Pampa *(G-16345)*

Williams Field Services Co LLC ....E 979 843-7724
Bay City *(G-1777)*

Winn Exploration Co Inc ....F 361 844-6900
Corpus Christi *(G-3657)*

Winston Land & Cattle Co Inc ....F 936 634-6321
Lufkin *(G-14557)*

WO Energy of Nevada Inc ....G 806 665-8298
Pampa *(G-16346)*

Wtg Gas Processing LP ....E 325 473-5161
Bronte *(G-2307)*

Xto Energy Inc ....E 817 885-2195
Fort Worth *(G-7154)*

Xto Energy Inc ....E 817 870-2800
Houston *(G-12708)*

Xto Energy Inc ....C 432 682-8873
Midland *(G-15474)*

Xto Energy Inc ....D 806 367-1047
Tokio *(G-19950)*

Xto Energy Inc ....E 979 828-1963
Bryan *(G-2516)*

Xto Energy Inc ....D 903 939-1200
Tyler *(G-20178)*

Xto Energy Inc ....D 903 553-3800
Longview *(G-14339)*

Xto Energy Inc ....B 817 870-2800
Spring *(G-19188)*

Xto Energy Inc ....G 903 983-8800
Kilgore *(G-13605)*

Xto Energy Inc ....F 432 524-6545
Andrews *(G-562)*

Xto Energy Inc ....E 936 858-3533
Alto *(G-320)*

Xto Energy Inc ....E 713 871-3453
Fort Worth *(G-7156)*

Xto Energy Inc ....E 817 740-0488
Dallas *(G-5206)*

Zackson Resources Inc ....F 713 782-1075
Houston *(G-12720)*

Zevex Corporation ....F 512 322-9039
Austin *(G-1685)*

Zion Oil & Gas Inc ....F 214 221-4610
Dallas *(G-5209)*

1321 Natural Gas Liquids

▲ Anadarko Holding Company ....F 832 636-7200
Houston *(G-8633)*

Arbor Renewable Gas LLC ....F 281 849-9834
Houston *(G-8676)*

▲ Bg Energy Merchants LLC ....B 713 599-4000
Houston *(G-8869)*

▲ Bg LNG Services LLC ....D 713 599-4000
Houston (G-8870)

BP America Production Company.........F 903 927-8999
Hallsville (G-8127)

Bridgeline Holdings LP ....F 713 432-6000
Bellaire (G-1991)

Cailip Gas Marketing LLC ....E 281 833-4217
Houston (G-9046)

◆ Cameron LNG Holdings LLC ....E 832 783-5500
Houston (G-9075)

Cheniere Cch Holdco II LLC ....A 713 375-5000
Houston (G-9174)

Cheniere Energy Inc ....D 713 375-5000
Houston (G-9175)

Chevron Corporation......................E 432 523-7950
Andrews (G-543)

Chevron Corporation......................E 903 963-8631
Van (G-20206)

Chevron Corporation......................B 713 754-3998
Houston (G-9178)

Cleereco Services Inc ....F 325 658-6533
San Angelo (G-17787)

Coronado Midstream LLC ....E 432 684-3870
Midland (G-15179)

Corpus Christi Pipeline GP LLC ....C 713 375-5000
Gregory (G-8100)

Dcp Midstream LLC ....E 361 584-8500
Bishop (G-2106)

Dcp Midstream LLC ....E 432 693-2204
Midkiff (G-15095)

◆ Dcp NGL Services LP ....F 713 735-3600
Houston (G-9416)

Downhole Well Solutions LLC ....F 832 761-5111
Spring (G-19112)

Durango Midstream LLC ....E 346 351-2787
Spring (G-19208)

Eagle Rock Energy Partners LP ....D 281 408-1200
Houston (G-9562)

Eagle Rock Field Services LP ....E 281 408-1200
Houston (G-9563)

Eagle Rock Operating LP ....F 281 408-1200
Houston (G-9564)

El Paso Field Services LP ....F 210 621-2031
Elmendorf (G-6068)

Energen Corporation......................F 205 326-2700
Midland (G-15216)

Enterprise Gas Processing LLC ....E 713 381-4068
Houston (G-9661)

◆ Enterprise Products Company.........C 713 381-6500
Houston (G-9663)

Enterprise Products Company ....E 432 221-7700
Midland (G-15221)

Enterprise Products Company ....E 432 686-5421
Midland (G-15222)

Ep Energy Management LLC ....E 713 997-1000
Houston (G-9676)

Finley Resources Inc ....D 817 336-1924
Fort Worth (G-6631)

Hiland Gp LLC ....E 713 369-9000
Houston (G-10180)

Hiland Partners Holdings LLC ....D 713 369-9000
Houston (G-10181)

Irion County Plant ....G 432 682-6311
Midland (G-15256)

J L Davis Company........................E 432 399-4575
Coahoma (G-3165)

JP Energy Partners LP ....E 972 444-0300
Irving (G-13069)

Lacy Operations Ltd ....E 903 693-3501
Beckville (G-1971)

Lewis Petro Properties Inc ....D 210 384-3200
San Antonio (G-18249)

Lone Star NGL Pipeline LP ....F 210 403-7300
Houston (G-10679)

Lone Star NGL Rfinery Svcs LLC ....F 210 403-7300
Houston (G-10680)

Markwest Enrgy E Texas Gas LP.........E 903 694-2225
Carthage (G-2914)

Martin Midstream GP LLC ....A 903 983-6200
Kilgore (G-13568)

Martin Midstream Partners LP ....D 903 983-6200
Kilgore (G-13569)

Martin Midstream Partners LP ....F 281 471-2211
La Porte (G-13774)

Midcoast Operating LP ....E 210 321-8000
San Antonio (G-18304)

Midlothian Lng LLC ....F 818 450-3668
Midlothian (G-15486)

Midstream Hess Operations LP...........F 713 496-4200
Houston (G-10874)

Morgan Kinder Treating LP ....F 432 563-2766
Odessa (G-16083)

◆ Natural Gas Vehicles Texas Inc ....F 214 630-1000
Dallas (G-4717)

Nextdecade Corporation ....E 713 574-1880
Houston (G-11047)

Oneok Inc ....E 915 680-7200
El Paso (G-5902)

Panhandle Eastrn Pipe Line LP.........F 713 627-5400
Houston (G-11233)

Pioneer Exploration Company ....E 281 893-9400
Houston (G-11334)

Pioneer Natural Resources Co ....D 432 535-2444
Midkiff (G-15096)

Plains GP Holdings LP ....F 713 646-4100
Houston (G-11343)

Process Recovery Systems Inc ....F 281 448-8180
Houston (G-11432)

Prometheus Energy Group Inc ....F 832 456-6500
Houston (G-11448)

Quicksilver Resources Inc ....D 817 665-5000
Fort Worth (G-6928)

R T M Interests LLC ....F 432 683-7700
Midland (G-15376)

Regency Energy Partners LP ....F 806 665-2551
Pampa (G-16338)

Regency Energy Partners LP ....D 214 750-1771
Dallas (G-4881)

Sabine Hub Services LLC ....E 214 721-9474
Houston (G-11715)

Sentry Oil & Gas LLC ....E 212 753-6367
Mico (G-15094)

Sg Interests I Ltd ....F 713 951-0100
Houston (G-11843)

Southcross Ccng Gathering Ltd...........F 214 953-9500
Dallas (G-4982)

Southcross Enrgy Prtners GP LL ....B 214 979-3792
Houston (G-11970)

Spartan Energy Partners LP ....E 281 466-3310
Spring (G-19253)

Spartan Operating Company LLC ....E 281 466-3310
The Woodlands (G-19924)

Stabilis Energy Inc ....D 832 456-6500
Houston (G-12035)

Stabilis Energy LLC ....E 409 833-1115
Houston (G-12036)

Taylor Distributing Co Inc ....E 817 831-0601
Fort Worth (G-7037)

Tellurian Investments Inc ....F 832 962-4000
Houston (G-12194)

▲ Texaco Exploration & Prod Inc ....B 800 962-1223
Houston (G-12218)

Trans-Pecos Pipeline LLC................E 713 989-2606
Houston (G-12344)

Tri Resources Inc ....E 432 558-3996
Crane (G-3703)

Tri Resources Inc ....F 432 688-0555
Midland (G-15445)

Tri Resources Inc ....C 281 385-3200
Mont Belvieu (G-15623)

Tri Resources Inc ....G 806 323-9125
Canadian (G-2655)

Tri Resources Inc ....E 940 549-8340
Breckenridge (G-2240)

Tri Resources Inc ....F 903 687-2513
Waskom (G-20523)

Tri Resources Inc ....F 254 559-7533
Breckenridge (G-2241)

Tri Resources Inc ....E 940 644-2233
Chico (G-3054)

◆ Tri Resources Inc ....E 713 584-1000
Houston (G-12362)

Twin Eagle Sand Logistics LLC ....E 713 341-7300
Houston (G-12414)

W&T Offshore Inc.........................C 713 626-8525
Houston (G-12588)

Western Gas Resources Inc ....F 432 693-2302
Midkiff (G-15098)

Western Gas Resources Inc ....E 432 395-2448
Fort Stockton (G-6331)

▲ Williams Gas Pipeline-Transco ....C 713 215-2000
Houston (G-12670)

Woodland Midstream II LLC ....E 832 592-1202
Spring (G-19262)

Wtg Gas Processing LP ....E 432 682-4349
Midland (G-15471)

Wtg Gas Processing LP ....E 325 473-5161
Bronte (G-2307)

1381 Drilling Oil & Gas Wells

5 Elements Drilling LLC ....E 281 203-0405
Houston (G-8413)

Acme Energy Services Inc ....A 432 561-5271
Midland (G-15104)

◆ AES Drilling Fluids LLC ....C 888 556-4533
Houston (G-8499)

Aim Directional Services LLC ....E 432 934-0628
Midland (G-15110)

Aim Directional Services LLC ....D 361 653-6500
Corpus Christi (G-3467)

Air Drilling Associates Inc ....F 832 957-6093
Houston (G-8505)

Aly Centrifuge Inc ....F 972 382-4400
San Angelo (G-17775)

▲ Applied Drilling Tech Inc ....D 281 925-7100
Houston (G-8667)

Aquila Drilling Co LP ....C 940 761-3153
Wichita Falls (G-20739)

▲ Archer Well Company Inc ....D 713 856-4222
Houston (G-8682)

Aries One LLC ....F 832 564-3628
Houston (G-8695)

Athens Group Holdings LLC ....G 512 345-0600
Austin (G-945)

Atlantic Maritime Services LLC ....F 713 621-7800
Houston (G-8739)

▲ Atlantica Management USA Inc ....E 832 494-2200
Houston (G-8741)

Atlas Ptro Explrtion Worldwide ....E 281 579-5200
Houston (G-8745)

Atlas Well Service LLC ....E 432 683-3835
Midland (G-15123)

▲ Ats Drilling LP ....D 817 498-0040
Haltom City (G-8132)

▲ Atwood Oceanics Management LLC F 281 749-7800
Houston (G-8747)

Austral Integrated Services ....F 936 266-0945
Conroe (G-3259)

Axis Energy Services LLC ....F 903 643-3700
Longview (G-14198)

Axon Ep Inc ....E 281 855-3200
Houston (G-8762)

Axxis Drilling Inc ....E 985 868-6969
Houston (G-8765)

B & T Directional Drilling Inc ....F 903 629-3406
Winnsboro (G-20896)

◆ Baker Hghes Olfld Oprtions LLC ....F 713 879-1000
Houston (G-8796)

Baker Hughes A GE Company LLC ....B 713 625-4200
Houston (G-8801)

Big 6 Drilling Company ....E 713 783-2300
Houston (G-8880)

Big Red Engineering LLC ....E 817 539-9560
Fort Worth (G-6450)

Big Rock Energy Services Inc ....E 432 235-8509
Midland (G-15141)

Big Tex Well Services LLC ....E 817 599-6155
Weatherford (G-20578)

Bill Smalley Drilling & Trckg ....E 325 762-3409
Albany (G-185)

Bison Drlg & Field Svcs LLC ....C 405 463-6912
Odessa (G-15935)

Black Diamond Energy Inc...............E 307 684-2910
Katy (G-13352)

Black Sail Holdings Corp ....F 281 315-4955
Shenandoah (G-18895)

Blue Line Drilling Co LLC ....D 325 653-1891
San Angelo (G-17782)

Bluff Creek Petroleum LLC ....F 325 676-5557
Abilene (G-17)

Bmlcrude Inc ....F 325 676-3355
Abilene (G-20)

BP America Production Company.........D 806 935-8810
Dumas (G-5519)

Brucemark Petroleum Inc ....F 630 339-5490
Addison (G-108)

Busters Well Service Inc ....D 432 586-2533
Kermit (G-13510)

C&D Bobcat and Backhoe LLC...........F 512 358-0163
Austin (G-1018)

Cantera Energy LLC ....E 832 246-6100
The Woodlands (G-19838)

Cantera Operating LLC...................F 832 246-6100
The Woodlands (G-19839)

Capital Well Service LLC ....E 830 767-2036
Jourdanton (G-13329)

Cathedral Energy Services Inc ....E 303 825-1001
Houston (G-9102)

Cavern Solutions Inc ....F .... 713 393-7733 Houston (G-9103)	◆ Ensco International Inc ....D .... 800 423-8006 Houston (G-9652)	Inpex Eagle Ford LLC ....D .... 713 850-8480 Houston (G-10375)
Challenger Drilling Inc ....F .... 281 290-8335 Tomball (G-19969)	▼ Ensign United States Drlg Inc ....E .... 303 292-1206 Houston (G-9657)	Integrity Services LLC ....D .... 432 682-0703 Midland (G-15253)
Charger Services LLC ....E .... 432 218-7674 Midland (G-15158)	Ensign US Southern Drlg LLC ....E .... 303 292-1206 Houston (G-9658)	▲ Interwell US LLC ....E .... 832 461-1500 Houston (G-10408)
▲ Coastal Drilling Company L L C ....C .... 361 852-6195 Corpus Christi (G-3503)	Enterprise Offshore Drlg LLC ....B .... 832 399-6500 Houston (G-9662)	Intrepid Drctnal Drlg Spclsts ....E .... 432 617-0593 Midland (G-15254)
Coastal Plains Exploration LLC ....F .... 361 553-9000 Port Lavaca (G-17144)	Envirotech Drilling Services ....F .... 832 493-8063 Houston (G-9670)	Inwell Inc ....F .... 281 443-7614 Spring (G-19221)
▲ Construct Capital LLC ....C .... 214 637-1444 Arlington (G-645)	Epic Energy Resources Inc ....C .... 281 419-3742 Houston (G-9681)	J & S Construction LLC ....E .... 903 322-4942 Buffalo (G-2544)
Construct Capital LLC ....D .... 713 322-6714 Houston (G-9278)	Erin Energy Corporation ....D .... 713 797-2940 Houston (G-9692)	J B Oil & Gas Well Service ....F .... 830 378-5586 Dilley (G-5482)
Construct Capital LLC ....D .... 210 654-4400 San Antonio (G-18024)	Estill Inc ....G .... 806 789-1548 Lubbock (G-14408)	J W Drilling Inc ....D .... 575 748-8704 Quinlan (G-17223)
Copan Corporation ....G .... 806 665-1267 Pampa (G-16319)	Exceed Drilling Tech LLC ....F .... 512 656-9669 Austin (G-1144)	J W Resources Inc ....G .... 806 935-0185 Dumas (G-5523)
Crescent Directional Drlg LP ....D .... 281 668-9500 Houston (G-9342)	▼ Exxonmobil Development Company ....E .... 713 656-3636 Houston (G-9740)	J-W Energy Company ....D .... 972 233-8191 Addison (G-137)
Crimson Exploration Inc ....F .... 713 236-7400 Houston (G-9344)	Faith Drilling LLC ....E .... 432 758-6352 Seminole (G-18882)	◆ Jamex Inc ....F .... 214 265-7141 Lewisville (G-14058)
Cude Oilfield Contractors Inc ....F .... 281 298-0600 Conroe (G-3288)	Falcon Seaboard Oil & Gas LLC ....F .... 713 622-0055 Houston (G-9756)	JF Construction Inc ....E .... 214 272-1902 Frisco (G-7293)
D & S Drilling Ltd ....F .... 806 794-8866 Lubbock (G-14400)	Ferza Company LLC ....G .... 956 686-7100 Hidalgo (G-8307)	Johnson Burns Co ....F .... 806 372-5869 Amarillo (G-494)
Dallas Directional Drlg Inc ....F .... 214 254-6985 Dallas (G-4215)	Finley Resources Inc ....D .... 817 336-1924 Fort Worth (G-6631)	Jp3 Measurement LLC ....E .... 512 537-8450 Austin (G-1262)
Dallas Oil ....E .... 214 638-9055 Dallas (G-4223)	Flocap Injection Services LLC ....F .... 432 614-1609 Midland (G-15232)	Keane Frac Tx LLC ....F .... 713 960-0381 Houston (G-10507)
Deen Drilling Company ....F .... 940 574-2561 Archer City (G-595)	Forge Energy LLC ....E .... 210 478-5950 San Antonio (G-18121)	Keane Group Holdings LLC ....D .... 713 960-0381 Houston (G-10510)
Deepwell Energy Services LLC ....E .... 337 780-8297 Beaumont (G-1882)	Fox Nde ....E .... 325 690-1633 Abilene (G-41)	Kelford Energy LLC ....F .... 817 615-0263 Fort Worth (G-6754)
Deepwell Energy Services LLC ....E .... 817 796-9970 Grapevine (G-8027)	Foxxe Energy Services LLC ....D .... 713 960-0381 Houston (G-9868)	Kenner Well Svc of Palestine ....E .... 903 729-3196 Palestine (G-16300)
Denbury Onshore LLC ....E .... 281 482-7581 Alvin (G-358)	Friedel Drilling Co ....F .... 361 293-5545 Yoakum (G-20966)	Keppel Letourneau Usa Inc ....E .... 281 677-4482 Houston (G-10518)
Devon Energy Corporation ....F .... 903 693-7196 Carthage (G-2906)	▼ Frontera Resources Corporation ....F .... 713 585-3200 Houston (G-9868)	Key Energy Drilling Inc ....E .... 432 639-2534 Iraan (G-12919)
Dewbre Petroleum Corporation ....F .... 361 888-7978 Corpus Christi (G-3512)	Garcias Well Servicing Inc ....E .... 432 527-3748 Wink (G-20887)	Key Energy Drilling Inc ....G .... 713 651-4300 Kilgore (G-13560)
DH Braman III ....E .... 361 578-6271 Victoria (G-20258)	Global Marine Inc ....D .... 713 232-7500 Houston (G-9974)	Key Energy Services Inc ....F .... 432 570-7440 Midland (G-15270)
Dhw Well Service Inc ....C .... 830 876-9615 Carrizo Springs (G-2685)	Global Santa Fe Drilling Co ....D .... 281 925-6821 Houston (G-9976)	▼ Key Energy Services Inc ....C .... 713 651-4300 Houston (G-10522)
◆ Diamond Offshore Company ....C .... 281 492-5300 Houston (G-9452)	Global Santa Fe Inc ....B .... 281 925-6000 Houston (G-9977)	Key Energy Services Inc ....D .... 432 586-2591 Odessa (G-16048)
◆ Diamond Offshore Drilling Inc ....C .... 281 492-5300 Houston (G-9453)	Goodrich Drillers LLC ....F .... 713 659-3680 Houston (G-10000)	Key Energy Services Inc ....E .... 432 561-5682 Odessa (G-16049)
Diamond Offshore Drlg Svcs Inc ....E .... 281 492-5300 Houston (G-9454)	Guenther Family LP ....G .... 210 829-1800 San Antonio (G-18155)	Key Energy Services Inc ....E .... 432 267-5291 Big Spring (G-2086)
Diamond Offshore Finance Co ....B .... 281 492-5300 Barker (G-1746)	H & K Well Service LLC ....F .... 361 394-7165 Freer (G-7226)	Key Energy Services Inc ....E .... 713 651-4300 Houston (G-10523)
Diamond Offshore General Co ....B .... 281 492-5300 Houston (G-9455)	Halliburton Company ....E .... 281 297-1200 Spring (G-19214)	Key Energy Services Inc ....D .... 903 538-2280 Palestine (G-16301)
Diamond Offshore Management Co ....B .... 281 492-5300 Houston (G-9456)	Halliburton Company ....C .... 281 297-1200 Houston (G-10100)	Key Energy Services Inc ....D .... 806 872-8331 Lamesa (G-13827)
Diamond Offshore Nthrlands B U ....B .... 281 492-5300 Houston (G-9457)	◆ Halliburton Company ....E .... 281 871-2699 Houston (G-10107)	Key Energy Services Inc ....E .... 903 963-5208 Van (G-20208)
Dillard Kay R & Estate AR D ....E .... 940 716-5100 Wichita Falls (G-20759)	Halliburton International Inc ....A .... 214 759-2600 Dallas (G-4429)	Kodiak Production Ltd ....E .... 325 884-2040 Big Lake (G-2058)
Directional Prj Support Inc ....G .... 281 259-7819 Magnolia (G-14601)	Hayhurst Bros Drilling Co ....F .... 325 340-1865 Abilene (G-47)	Lauson Drilling Services Inc ....E .... 979 733-0345 Alleyton (G-310)
Djh Services LLC ....F .... 713 228-5911 Houston (G-9485)	Hazelett Drilling and Sup Corp ....E .... 512 398-6682 Lockhart (G-14169)	Lewis Petro Properties Inc ....D .... 210 384-3200 San Antonio (G-18249)
Don H Wilson Inc ....F .... 903 478-3860 Elkhart (G-6059)	Hb2 Energy Inc ....E .... 713 377-9860 Houston (G-10140)	Lindemann Drilling Co Inc ....F .... 940 691-1344 Archer City (G-596)
Double K Drilling LLC ....F .... 940 567-2855 Jacksboro (G-13218)	Hdd Rotary Sales LLC ....E .... 936 446-1200 Houston (G-10141)	Logan International Inc ....E .... 832 386-2500 Houston (G-10670)
Double K Well Service LP ....F .... 940 567-2855 Jacksboro (G-13219)	Heart Land Petroleum Corp ....D .... 325 437-8430 Abilene (G-48)	Longhorn Drilling and Eqp Co ....F .... 830 372-1910 Seguin (G-18850)
Downhole Energy LLC ....G .... 469 250-7179 Garland (G-7481)	Helmerich & Payne Inc ....E .... 830 379-5858 Seguin (G-18841)	Lottco Inc ....E .... 832 773-4345 Humble (G-12785)
Drillchem Drlg Solutions LLC ....G .... 281 713-8941 The Woodlands (G-19852)	Helmerich & Payne Intl Drlg Co ....C .... 361 664-0114 Seguin (G-14534)	Lovelady Directional Drilling ....F .... 936 675-4598 Lufkin (G-14534)
Duffco Oil Tools Inc ....D .... 325 672-2446 Abilene (G-39)	Helmerich & Payne Intl Drlg Co ....B .... 832 782-6800 Houston (G-10151)	Lynco Well Service Inc ....E .... 936 336-7332 Liberty (G-14123)
E & H Drilling Co ....E .... 940 549-0370 Graham (G-7781)	Hercules Drilling Company LLC ....A .... 713 350-5100 Houston (G-10157)	Lyons Drilling Inc ....E .... 979 596-1898 Rockdale (G-17525)
Eagle Oilfield Welding ....E .... 830 965-4255 Dilley (G-5480)	◆ Hercules Offshore Inc ....A .... 713 350-5100 Houston (G-10158)	M K S Natural Gas Company ....E .... 817 599-9477 Weatherford (G-20601)
Edf Trading North America LLC ....F .... 830 351-5075 Luling (G-14560)	Hess Jerry Operating Company ....F .... 940 759-4791 Muenster (G-15670)	M P Energy Inc ....E .... 281 350-6350 Houston (G-10719)
EGI Resources Inc ....F .... 432 687-6560 Midland (G-15207)	Ht Energy LLC ....E .... 806 771-7769 Lubbock (G-14419)	M3p Directional Services Ltd ....F .... 432 561-8801 Midland (G-15289)
◆ Emas Chiyoda Subsea Inc ....D .... 832 487-7300 Houston (G-9607)	◆ Impact Fluid Solutions LP ....F .... 713 964-7736 Houston (G-10333)	◆ Maersk Drilling USA Inc ....D .... 713 972-3300 Houston (G-10733)
Energy Reserves Group LLC ....E .... 713 659-7800 Houston (G-9636)	Independence Contract Drlg Inc ....D .... 281 598-1230 Houston (G-10338)	Martinez Oil & Gas LLC ....E .... 361 384-9500 Orange Grove (G-16268)

Maverick Directional Services	E	281 364-1212	Spring (G-19230)
Maxus US Exploration Company	E	281 681-7200	The Woodlands (G-19892)
MB Robinson Inc	E	432 267-5277	Big Spring (G-2087)
McClinton Energy Group L L C	C	432 563-5500	Midland (G-15296)
McClinton Energy Group L L C	E	432 563-5500	Odessa (G-16077)
Medallion Oil Company Inc	F	713 654-0144	Houston (G-10815)
Mhwirth Inc	F	281 371-2424	Houston (G-10864)
Midstar Energy LP	E	281 940-3022	Katy (G-13425)
Miramar Wf LLC	F	940 626-4309	Alvord (G-389)
Mlc Operating LP	E	713 255-6200	Spring (G-19146)
Modern Exploration Inc	F	903 893-1129	Sherman (G-18922)
Morningstar Partners LP	E	817 334-7800	Fort Worth (G-6852)
Ms Directional LLC	D	936 442-2500	Conroe (G-3332)
Mudsmith Ltd	F	432 687-6837	Midland (G-15308)
Muenster Drilling Company	F	940 759-4949	Muenster (G-15671)
Mustang Well Service LLC	F	432 524-6112	Andrews (G-553)
Nabors Corporate Services Inc	C	281 874-0035	Houston (G-10950)
◆ Nabors Drilling Tech USA Inc	C	281 874-0035	Houston (G-10952)
Nabors Drilling Tech USA Inc	E	281 462-1730	Crosby (G-3738)
◆ Nabors Industries Inc	C	281 874-0035	Houston (G-10953)
◆ Nabors International Inc	E	281 874-0035	Houston (G-10954)
▲ Nabors Offshore Corporation	E	281 874-0406	Houston (G-10955)
Nicklos Drilling Company	D	713 224-5959	Houston (G-11052)
Nitrogen Services LLC	C	925 336-1560	Midland (G-15320)
▲ Noble Drilling (us) Inc	D	281 276-6100	Sugar Land (G-19513)
◆ Noble Drilling Corporation	B	281 276-6100	Sugar Land (G-19514)
Noble Drilling Holding LLC	E	281 276-6100	Sugar Land (G-19515)
◆ Noble Drilling Services Inc	B	281 276-6100	Sugar Land (G-19516)
◆ Noble Holding US Corporation	C	281 276-6100	Sugar Land (G-19517)
Noble International Finance Co	F	281 276-6142	Sugar Land (G-19518)
Noram Drilling Company	E	281 598-9200	Houston (G-11068)
◆ Northern Offshore Ltd	E	281 649-2600	Houston (G-11078)
Nova Directional Inc	E	281 246-1149	Houston (G-11089)
Nova Drilling Technologies Inc	F	713 726-0151	Houston (G-11090)
Nri Inc	F	903 526-5800	Tyler (G-20134)
Nzone Guidance LLC	F	512 778-5353	Liberty Hill (G-14128)
Oasis Midstream Partners LP	C	281 404-9500	Houston (G-11108)
Octane Energy Consulting LLC	F	432 685-7736	Midland (G-15324)
Odyssea Marine Holdings Inc	A	713 260-1100	Houston (G-11135)
Oil Field Supply Pty Ltd	F	281 877-0049	Houston (G-11152)
◆ Pacific Drilling Services Inc	D	713 334-6662	Houston (G-11217)
◆ Parker Drilling Company	C	281 406-2000	Houston (G-11241)
◆ Parker Drilling MGT Svcs Ltd	C	281 406-2000	Houston (G-11242)
Parker Drilling Offshr Co LLC	F	281 406-2000	Houston (G-11243)
Parkerlane Directional Drlg LP	E	817 235-4050	Euless (G-6152)
Particle Drilling Tech Inc	F	713 223-3031	Houston (G-11249)
Pattersn-Uti Drlg Svcs LP Lllp	D	325 573-1104	Snyder (G-18998)
Pattersn-Uti Drlg Svcs LP Lllp	E	361 576-6896	Victoria (G-20291)
Patterson Drilling Company	A	325 651-6603	San Angelo (G-17819)
▲ Patterson-Uti Acquisition LLC	B	432 561-9382	Midland (G-15341)
Patterson-Uti Drilling Co LLC	E	325 574-6300	Snyder (G-18999)
Patterson-Uti Drlg Intl Inc	D	214 765-5530	Houston (G-11261)
Patterson-Uti Energy Inc	D	432 561-9382	Midland (G-15342)
Patterson-Uti Energy Inc	D	281 765-7100	Houston (G-11262)
Patterson-Uti Energy Inc	F	903 877-3659	Tyler (G-20138)
Patterson-Uti Energy Inc	F	432 682-9401	Midland (G-15343)
Patterson-Uti MGT Svcs LLC	F	325 574-6300	Snyder (G-19000)
Permian H2o Solutions LLC	F	432 214-4520	Odessa (G-16117)
Petroleum Engineers Intl	E	337 984-2603	Houston (G-11306)
Petroplex Energy Inc	F	432 687-2222	Midland (G-15349)
Phoenix Technology Svcs USA	F	713 337-0600	Houston (G-11330)
Piedra Operating LLC	F	432 685-9005	Midland (G-15351)
▼ Pioneer Drilling Services Ltd	E	210 828-7689	San Antonio (G-18377)
Pioneer Drilling Services Ltd	F	432 684-7360	Midland (G-15353)
Pioneer Drilling Services Ltd	C	361 289-9241	Corpus Christi (G-3591)
Pioneer Energy Services Corp	D	281 880-9988	Tomball (G-19999)
Pioneer Wireline Services LLC	D	210 828-7689	San Antonio (G-18379)
Precision Directional Svcs Inc	F	713 975-1209	Houston (G-11389)
Precision Drilling Company LP	E	817 396-4714	Cresson (G-3711)
▲ Precision Drilling Company LP	D	713 435-6100	Houston (G-11390)
◆ Precision Drilling Corporation	A	713 435-6100	Houston (G-11391)
◆ Precision Tech	D	281 227-5750	Houston (G-11395)
Premier Directional Drlg LP	E	281 673-4000	Houston (G-11400)
Price Drilling Company Inc	D	361 256-3363	Benavides (G-2035)
Primera Energy LLC	F	210 490-8200	Longview (G-14290)
Professnal Drctional Entps Inc	C	936 441-7266	Conroe (G-3354)
Progress Drilling Inc	E	830 875-3442	Luling (G-14563)
Propetro Services Inc	F	432 685-0059	Midland (G-15367)
Qes Pressure Control LLC	F	903 643-0700	Longview (G-14291)
▲ Qri International LLC	F	713 485-8800	Houston (G-11487)
Quintana Energy Services LP	F	832 518-4094	Houston (G-11516)
Radco Operations LP	F	409 287-1277	Sour Lake (G-19033)
▲ Radial Drilling Services Inc	E	281 374-7507	Spring (G-19161)
Resource Energy Service Corp	D	713 953-5300	Houston (G-11608)
Rfc Drilling LLC	C	432 276-3505	Odessa (G-16138)
RG Exploration LLC	G	405 650-1207	Midland (G-15384)
Ringo Drilling I Lp	C	325 232-5807	Dallas (G-4900)
Robinson Drilling Texas Ltd	C	432 267-5277	Big Spring (G-2096)
Roco Drilling and Service Inc	D	903 963-7036	Van (G-20209)
Rotary Components Intl Inc	F	281 590-6484	Houston (G-11668)
Rotary Exploration Inc	F	210 248-9892	San Antonio (G-18431)
◆ Rowan Companies LLC	C	713 621-7800	Houston (G-11676)
▲ Rowan Drilling Company Inc	E	713 621-7800	Houston (G-11677)
Rowan Marine Drilling Inc	E	713 621-7800	Houston (G-11678)
Rowan Petroleum Inc	E	713 621-7800	Houston (G-11679)
Roxwell Performance Drlg LLC	F	432 617-0419	Midland (G-15389)
Rutherford-Moran Exploration		859 254-4775	Houston (G-11702)
Sage Energy Company	F	979 567-7629	Caldwell (G-2634)
Sage Energy Company		210 404-2828	San Antonio (G-18443)
▼ Savanna Drilling LLC	F	432 614-1055	Odessa (G-16150)
Savanna Energy Svcs USA Corp	F	281 907-4800	The Woodlands (G-19917)
▼ Saxon Drilling LP	E	281 712-4529	Katy (G-13439)
Schlumberger Limited		713 513-2000	Houston (G-11767)
Schlumberger Limited		713 513-2000	Houston (G-11768)
◆ Scientific Drilling Intl Inc		281 443-3300	Houston (G-11786)
Scientific Drilling Intl Inc		281 214-7600	Houston (G-11787)
Scientific Drilling Intl Inc		432 563-1339	Midland (G-15399)
◆ Seadrill Americas Inc	D	713 407-8900	Houston (G-11799)
▲ Seahawk Drilling Inc	F	713 369-7300	Houston (G-11803)
Sentry Energy Production LLC	F	972 380-1600	Addison (G-162)
Sentry Oil & Gas LLC	E	212 753-6367	Mico (G-15094)
Service Drilling Southwest LLC	F	806 878-2052	Stinnett (G-19428)
SES Operating Inc	E	432 687-6560	Midland (G-15404)
Sidewinder Drilling Inc	D	832 320-7600	Houston (G-11877)
Smalley Drilling & Trckg Corp	E	325 762-3409	Albany (G-193)
Snyder Drilling Corp	F	325 762-2389	Albany (G-194)
▼ Songa Offshore	E	713 781-0670	Houston (G-11952)
Sparkman Well Service Inc	F	361 572-4833	Victoria (G-20305)
Spruiell Drilling Co	F	940 592-5471	Iowa Park (G-12911)
Steinberger Drilling Company	E	940 423-6900	Windthorst (G-20886)
Sterling Drlg Fund 1983-1 LP	C	203 358-5700	Houston (G-12059)
Steward Energy II LLC	F	214 297-0500	Frisco (G-7314)
Suits Drilling Company	F	325 573-1104	Snyder (G-19011)
Sunset Well Service Inc	E	432 561-8600	Odessa (G-16169)
Surge Operating LLC	F	832 333-2300	Houston (G-12125)
Swans Production Inc	F	940 567-3147	Jacksboro (G-13223)
Synergy Oil & Gas LP	F	713 827-9988	Houston (G-12135)
T X P Inc	G	325 944-9844	San Angelo (G-17829)
Tally Energy Services	F	832 530-4880	Houston (G-12149)
Talon/Lpe Ltd	F	806 467-0607	Amarillo (G-466)
◆ Tesco Corporation (us)	D	713 359-7000	Houston (G-12212)
Texas 21st Century Transport &	C	432 607-2071	Stanton (G-19405)
Texas Australian Power Inc	E	940 723-4122	Wichita Falls (G-20815)
Texokan Operating Inc	F	214 484-2322	Dallas (G-5080)
Texstar Energy Corporation	G	830 875-5919	Luling (G-14565)

TNT Directional Drilling Inc ....F 972 333-3410
  Garland (G-7602)
Tomcat Drilling LLC ....D 316 262-8554
  Corsicana (G-3686)
◆ Total E&P Usa Inc ....C 713 647-3000
  Houston (G-12330)
Total Operations Prod Svcs LLC ....F 432 332-9777
  Midland (G-15440)
Trans-Gulf Drilling Svcs Inc ....G 903 759-0010
  Longview (G-14320)
◆ Transcean Offshore Dpwter Drlg ....G 713 232-7500
  Houston (G-12349)
Transcend Drilling Company Inc ....D 432 618-1100
  Midland (G-15443)
◆ Transocean Inc ....C 713 232-7500
  Houston (G-12352)
◆ Transocean Offshore USA Inc ....D 713 232-7500
  Houston (G-12353)
◆ Transworld Worldwide Inc ....B 713 232-7500
  Houston (G-12355)
Trey Resources Inc ....E 432 570-6898
  Midland (G-15444)
◆ Tri Resources Inc ....E 713 584-1000
  Houston (G-12362)
Trinity River Energy LLC ....F 817 872-7898
  Houston (G-12375)
Tsar Operating Company ....F 817 731-9595
  Fort Worth (G-7085)
▲ Tuboscope (holding US) LLC ....F 713 799-5100
  Houston (G-12401)
Turn Right Tools LLC ....E 432 704-5490
  Midland (G-15449)
▲ Txco Resources Inc ....F 210 822-8864
  Dallas (G-5124)
Union Drilling Inc ....C 432 682-6111
  Midland (G-15454)
Unit Drilling Company ....E 713 960-8870
  Houston (G-12443)
Universal Pressure Pumping Inc ....F 432 699-3205
  Midland (G-15457)
Universal Pressure Pumping Inc ....D 432 221-7000
  Houston (G-12463)
◆ Vaalco Gabon (etame) Inc ....E 713 623-0801
  Houston (G-12515)
Vantage Driller I Co ....E 281 404-4700
  Houston (G-12531)
◆ Vantage Drilling Intl Inc ....E 281 404-4700
  Houston (G-12532)
Vantage Energy Services Inc ....E 281 404-4700
  Houston (G-12533)
▲ Varel Energy Solutions ....F 972 242-1160
  Houston (G-12537)
◆ Varel International Ind LLC ....D 281 272-6000
  Houston (G-12538)
Villatoro Construction LLC ....E 214 350-7900
  Wylie (G-20954)
Viper Petroleum LLC ....F 832 917-5804
  San Antonio (G-18594)
Viper Well Services LLC ....E 979 541-5262
  El Campo (G-5628)
Weatherford International Inc ....G 713 836-4000
  Houston (G-12620)
Weatherford International Ltd ....E 713 836-4000
  Houston (G-12621)
West Texas Energy Sevices LLC ....F 432 267-3126
  Big Spring (G-2102)
Western Well Service Inc ....E 940 723-2550
  Wichita Falls (G-20830)
Wil Call Services Ltd ....D 903 322-2911
  Buffalo (G-2549)
Wisco Moran Drilling Co Inc ....D 281 431-2600
  Rosharon (G-17616)
XCL Resources LLC ....E 346 335-1081
  Houston (G-12705)
Yohawk Energy LLC ....G 817 484-9642
  Fort Worth (G-7157)
Zarsky Lumber Company Inc ....E 361 882-2575
  Corpus Christi (G-3658)

1382 Oil & Gas Field Exploration Svcs

31 Group LLC ....E 972 810-1031
  Rockwall (G-17534)
31 Operating LLC ....F 972 810-1031
  Rockwall (G-17535)
686 Inc ....F 830 876-5541
  Carrizo Springs (G-2683)
Abaco Operating LLC ....G 210 828-4567
  San Antonio (G-17853)
Accelerate Resources Oper LLC ....E 214 292-8960
  Dallas (G-3881)

Acock Consulting LLC ....G 210 826-2553
  San Antonio (G-17863)
Adams Resources & Energy Inc ....E 713 881-3600
  Houston (G-8475)
▼ Adams Resources Marketing Ltd ....F 281 902-4100
  Houston (G-8476)
▲ Addax Petro Cameroon Co LLC ....C 713 245-1263
  Houston (G-8477)
Addison Oil LLC ....F 972 239-2400
  Addison (G-100)
Advance Energy Partners Llc ....F 832 672-4700
  Houston (G-8481)
Advanced Geophysical Tech Inc ....F 281 888-6789
  Sugar Land (G-19440)
Adventure Explrtion Prtners LL ....F 432 684-8006
  Midland (G-15107)
Aegis Chemical Solutions LLC ....D 281 258-4095
  Houston (G-8497)
Aegis Oil Limited Ventures LLC ....F 214 431-5201
  Dallas (G-3895)
Aethon Energy Management LLC ....E 214 750-3820
  Dallas (G-3898)
Aethon Energy Operating LLC ....C 214 750-3833
  Dallas (G-3899)
▼ Afren Usa Inc ....E 281 363-8600
  Spring (G-19192)
Ag-Jax Ltd ....G 903 705-0625
  Tyler (G-20045)
Aggietech Oil Ltd ....F 432 682-3131
  Midland (G-15109)
Aim World Services Inc ....E 281 847-2000
  The Woodlands (G-19822)
Alamo Resources LLC ....F 281 398-9500
  Houston (G-8524)
Alexander & Co ....G 325 677-1309
  Abilene (G-12)
Alliance Energy Corporation ....F 713 333-4000
  Houston (G-8545)
Alliance Petroleum Interests ....F 469 249-8985
  Dallas (G-3925)
Alloy Carbide Company ....E 713 923-2700
  Houston (G-8557)
Alpar Energy LP ....E 806 435-6566
  Perryton (G-16632)
Alta Marcellus Development LLC ....F 713 759-1155
  Houston (G-8564)
Alta Mesa Holdings LP ....G 281 530-0991
  Houston (G-8565)
Alta Mesa Resources Inc ....F 214 647-7630
  Dallas (G-3932)
Alta Resources LLC ....F 713 759-1155
  Houston (G-8566)
Alta Resources Development LLC ....E 713 759-1155
  Houston (G-8567)
American Fluorite Inc ....E 281 363-9161
  The Woodlands (G-19825)
Americo Energy Resources LLC ....E 713 984-9700
  Houston (G-8614)
Ameritex Petroleum LLC ....F 972 528-6644
  Dallas (G-3946)
Amplify Energy Corp ....E 713 490-8900
  Houston (G-8629)
Anadarko Algeria Corporation ....B 832 636-1000
  The Woodlands (G-19827)
▲ Anadarko Energy Services Co ....E 832 636-1000
  The Woodlands (G-19829)
Anadarko Petroleum Corporation ....E 903 389-3814
  Buffalo (G-2542)
Anadarko Petroleum Corporation ....F 817 877-7449
  Fort Worth (G-6388)
Anadarko Petroleum Corporation ....E 830 491-3300
  Carrizo Springs (G-2684)
◆ Anadarko Petroleum Corporation ....C 832 636-1000
  The Woodlands (G-19830)
Anadarko US Offshore Corp ....E 832 636-1000
  The Woodlands (G-19831)
Apache Foundation ....E 713 296-6000
  Houston (G-8656)
Apache Instrumentations & Gas ....E 432 336-7755
  Fort Stockton (G-6327)
Apex Intl Enrgy MGT LLC ....F 832 770-6900
  Houston (G-8663)
Apex/Fcc ....F 830 875-2429
  Luling (G-14559)
Approach Mdstream Holdings LLC ....F 817 989-9000
  Fort Worth (G-6393)
Approach Resources I LP ....F 817 989-9000
  Fort Worth (G-6394)
Approach Resources Inc ....F 817 989-9000
  Fort Worth (G-6395)

Approach Resources Inc ....F 325 392-8900
  Ozona (G-16278)
Approach Services LLC ....F 817 989-9000
  Fort Worth (G-6396)
Aqua Transfer & Enrgy Svcs LLC ....E 903 874-4946
  Corsicana (G-3661)
Arcooil Corp ....E 940 549-4444
  Graham (G-7776)
Arcturus Corporation ....F 214 720-0075
  Dallas (G-3963)
Ard Operating LLC ....E 713 759-1155
  Houston (G-8687)
Arena Offshore LP ....D 218 210-3138
  The Woodlands (G-19832)
Arkoma Basin Resources Ltd ....F 972 771-6000
  Rockwall (G-17539)
Arkos Field Services LP ....E 832 783-5400
  Waller (G-20492)
Arrington Oil & Gas Oper LLC ....D 432 682-6685
  Midland (G-15119)
Arrowhead Operating Inc ....F 432 683-9700
  Midland (G-15120)
Aspen Operating Company LLC ....E 817 882-9063
  Fort Worth (G-6405)
Atlantic Operating Inc ....F 432 683-3272
  Midland (G-15122)
Atlas Oilfield Cnstr Co LLC ....F 325 428-0552
  Abilene (G-14)
Atropos Exploration Company ....F 214 691-2377
  Dallas (G-3985)
Autoseis Inc ....F 972 332-3388
  Dallas (G-3989)
Axess North America Inc ....E 281 994-0364
  Houston (G-8758)
B & E Roustabout Inc ....E 432 393-5672
  Big Spring (G-2070)
B W Energy Consultants Inc ....F 903 593-1173
  Tyler (G-20055)
B-29 Investments LP ....D 940 665-4373
  Gainesville (G-7334)
Bailey & Harley Services LLC ....E 409 994-5857
  Buna (G-2560)
Baker Hghes Olfld Oprtions LLC ....F 713 879-3760
  Houston (G-8793)
Baker Hghes Olfld Oprtions LLC ....E 432 694-7761
  Midland (G-15129)
Baker Hghes Olfld Oprtions LLC ....E 361 573-2493
  Victoria (G-20242)
Baker Hghes Olfld Oprtions LLC ....E 432 694-9517
  Midland (G-15130)
Baker Hghes Olfld Oprtions LLC ....D 972 466-2673
  Carrollton (G-2701)
Baker Hughes A GE Company LLC ....D 361 573-2493
  Victoria (G-20243)
Baker Hughes A GE Company LLC ....D 979 826-3621
  Hempstead (G-8249)
Ballard Exploration Co Inc ....E 713 651-0181
  Houston (G-8810)
Barnes Barnett LLC ....E 214 445-6800
  Plano (G-16798)
Barnes Oil & Gas LLC ....E 214 445-6800
  Plano (G-16799)
Barrera Contractors Inc ....F 432 639-2516
  Iraan (G-12916)
▲ Basa Resources Inc ....E 214 580-5203
  Dallas (G-4008)
Basic Energy Services LP ....D 432 530-0907
  Odessa (G-15928)
Basin Drilling LP ....D 903 561-8211
  Tyler (G-20058)
Basin Oil & Gas LLC ....F 817 820-8910
  Fort Worth (G-6436)
▲ Bass Enterprises Production Co ....C 817 698-0200
  Fort Worth (G-6438)
Bayou Bouillon Operating LLC ....F 346 802-3134
  Houston (G-8833)
Baytex Energy (usa) Inc ....E 713 402-1920
  Houston (G-8840)
Bc Operating Inc ....E 432 684-9696
  Midland (G-15136)
BCM & Associates Inc ....E 432 580-7161
  Odessa (G-15931)
Beacon Offshore Enrgy Oper LLC ....G 346 867-0509
  Houston (G-8845)
Benton Oil Co ....F 806 763-5302
  Lubbock (G-14370)
Bergstein Enterprises Ltd ....E 806 741-1080
  Lubbock (G-14371)
Beusa Energy LLC ....E 281 296-1500
  The Woodlands (G-19836)

▲ **BHP Billton Petro Deepwater Inc** F 713 961-8500
Houston *(G-8876)*
Big Star Oil & Gas LLC E 432 687-4900
Midland *(G-15142)*
Black Diamond Minerals LLC G 720 341-2212
Houston *(G-8901)*
Black Mountain Sand LLC F 817 698-9901
Fort Worth *(G-6454)*
Black Mtn Royalty I 2009 LP F 888 698-9901
Fort Worth *(G-6455)*
Black Stone Energy Company LLC E 713 658-0647
Houston *(G-8906)*
Black Stone Minerals LP E 713 445-3200
Houston *(G-8907)*
Black Stone Minerals Co LP F 713 658-0647
Houston *(G-8908)*
Black Stone Ntral Rsources MGT F 713 445-3241
Houston *(G-8909)*
Blackbrush Cnsld Holdings LLC C 210 495-5577
San Antonio *(G-17956)*
Blackbrush Oil & Gas LP D 210 495-5577
San Antonio *(G-17957)*
Blade Energy Partners Ltd E 972 712-8407
Frisco *(G-7271)*
Blue Racer Finance Corp E 214 580-3700
Dallas *(G-4032)*
Blue Ridge Mtn Resources Inc E 469 444-1647
Irving *(G-12949)*
Bluecrest Energy Inc E 817 731-0066
Fort Worth *(G-6459)*
Bluejack Energy Solutions LLC E 720 320-2709
Plano *(G-16806)*
Boaz Energy II LLC F 432 253-7074
Midland *(G-15144)*
BOF Services Inc E 806 741-1080
Lubbock *(G-14377)*
Bold Energy II LLC F 432 686-1100
Midland *(G-15146)*
Borets US Inc F 254 559-5502
Breckenridge *(G-2222)*
Bowmans Oilfield Service LLC E 903 657-0698
Henderson *(G-8258)*
◆ **BP Energy Company** C 281 366-2000
Houston *(G-8968)*
◆ **BP Exploration & Prod Inc** E 800 333-3991
Houston *(G-8969)*
BP International Ltd C 281 366-2000
Houston *(G-8970)*
Braden Exploration LLC F 817 717-7020
Fort Worth *(G-6466)*
Braden Exploration II LLC F 817 717-7020
Fort Worth *(G-6467)*
Brayton Operating Corp F 361 884-8741
Corpus Christi *(G-3489)*
Brazos Delaware Gas LLC F 817 332-6800
Fort Worth *(G-6470)*
Brazos Mdstream Hldings II LLC E 817 332-6800
Fort Worth *(G-6471)*
BRC Operating Company LLC E 214 855-2260
Dallas *(G-4048)*
Breckenridge Exploration Co E 254 559-7566
Breckenridge *(G-2225)*
Bri Consulting Group Inc F 713 468-6813
Houston *(G-8983)*
Brigadier Oil & Gas LLC F 469 209-0760
Plano *(G-16812)*
Brigadier Operating LLC G 469 209-0760
Plano *(G-16813)*
Broadspectrum Downstream Servi A 713 964-2800
Houston *(G-8989)*
Brothers Well Service Ltd E 979 543-6851
El Campo *(G-5613)*
Browning Offshore Inc F 214 739-3481
Dallas *(G-4061)*
Browning Oil Company Inc F 214 739-3481
Dallas *(G-4062)*
Bruin E&P Operating LLC C 713 456-3000
Houston *(G-8998)*
Bruin E&P Partners LLC F 713 456-3000
Houston *(G-8999)*
Brushy Resources Inc F 210 999-5400
San Antonio *(G-17969)*
Buckhead Midstream LLC E 832 752-4526
Houston *(G-9008)*
Buffco Production Inc F 903 988-8199
Longview *(G-14204)*
Burnett Oil Co Inc E 817 332-5108
Fort Worth *(G-6479)*
C & C Coating Inc E 432 682-7201
Waco *(G-20372)*

Caballo Loco Midstream LLC F 432 262-1011
Midland *(G-15154)*
Caiman Energy LLC E 214 580-3700
Dallas *(G-4078)*
Callon Petroleum Company D 713 328-1000
Houston *(G-9052)*
Callon Petroleum Company E 432 218-2800
Midland *(G-15155)*
Calyx Energy LLC E 918 949-4224
Houston *(G-9056)*
Camac International Corp E 713 965-5100
Houston *(G-9059)*
Camterra Rsources Partners Ltd E 903 938-9949
Marshall *(G-14769)*
Canyon Midstream Partners LLC E 713 655-9500
Houston *(G-9087)*
Cardinal Midstream II LLC E 214 468-0700
Dallas *(G-4084)*
Carrizo Well Service LLC F 325 574-6291
Snyder *(G-18986)*
Castex Energy Inc E 281 447-8601
Houston *(G-9096)*
Caza Oil & Gas Inc F 281 363-4442
Spring *(G-19202)*
Cdw Consultant Group LLC E 361 237-9339
Bloomington *(G-2111)*
Celero Energy G 817 708-3800
Fort Worth *(G-6503)*
Celero Energy II LP E 817 708-3800
Fort Worth *(G-6504)*
Central Management Inc F 713 961-9777
Houston *(G-9138)*
Cgg Marine (us) Inc F 713 369-5600
Houston *(G-9148)*
◆ **Cgg Services (us) Inc** B 832 351-8300
Houston *(G-9149)*
Champion Group Inc E 210 490-1482
San Antonio *(G-17998)*
Charro Operating LLC G 361 643-5577
Portland *(G-17186)*
Chem Rock Technologies LLC F 432 940-2299
Midland *(G-15160)*
Chemex Global Inc C 346 388-6100
The Woodlands *(G-19842)*
Cherokee Horn Production LP F 619 435-8950
Dallas *(G-4111)*
Chevron Corporation C 907 276-7600
Houston *(G-9177)*
Chevron Corporation B 713 754-3998
Houston *(G-9178)*
Chevron Midcontinent LP C 432 498-8600
Midland *(G-15161)*
Chevron USA Inc C 432 687-7100
Midland *(G-15162)*
Chisholm Energy Operating LLC F 817 953-6063
Fort Worth *(G-6514)*
Choate Co Inc E 432 687-5977
Midland *(G-15165)*
Choice Exploration Inc E 817 633-7777
Arlington *(G-641)*
Christeros Services LLC E 325 884-1100
Big Lake *(G-2055)*
Chroma Energy Inc F 281 340-6100
Sugar Land *(G-19457)*
Cimarex Energy Co E 432 571-7800
Midland *(G-15166)*
Cimarex Energy Co D 432 634-1674
Iraan *(G-12917)*
Cinco Energy MGT Group LLC F 713 463-6009
Houston *(G-9192)*
Cinco Natural Resources Corp E 214 520-7727
Dallas *(G-4117)*
Cinco Oil & Gas LLC E 214 520-7727
Dallas *(G-4118)*
Cinco Resources Inc G 214 520-7727
Dallas *(G-4119)*
Citation Oil & Gas Corp C 281 891-1000
Houston *(G-9199)*
CL&f Offshore LLC F 281 873-9378
Houston *(G-9204)*
CL&f Operating LLC F 281 873-9378
Houston *(G-9205)*
CL&f Resources LP E 281 873-9378
Houston *(G-9206)*
Clariant Corporation E 281 465-9100
The Woodlands *(G-19846)*
Clearfork Petroleum Inc E 806 763-5625
Lubbock *(G-14394)*
Clearly Petroleum Opco LLC E 281 781-0412
Houston *(G-9213)*

Clementson Inc E 956 631-9121
McAllen *(G-14848)*
Cml Exploration LLC E 325 573-0750
Snyder *(G-18988)*
Cml Exploration LLC E 512 328-8085
Austin *(G-1053)*
Cnooc Petroleum Offshr USA Inc C 972 450-4600
Dallas *(G-4132)*
▲ **Cnpc USA Corporation** E 713 465-7382
Houston *(G-9222)*
▼ **Cobalt International Energy LP** D 713 452-2322
Houston *(G-9231)*
Cobalt International Enrgy Inc E 713 579-9100
Houston *(G-9232)*
Cobra Oil & Gas Corporation E 940 723-4331
Wichita Falls *(G-20754)*
Cockrell Oil Corporation E 713 209-7300
Houston *(G-9235)*
Cog Operating LLC C 432 685-0727
Midland *(G-15169)*
Cogent Midstream Westex LLC E 469 290-4100
Dallas *(G-4140)*
Cohort Energy Company E 972 233-8191
Addison *(G-110)*
Colgate Energy LLC E 432 695-4222
Midland *(G-15171)*
Colgate Energy Partners LLC F 432 695-4222
Midland *(G-15172)*
Compass Well Services LLC D 817 244-2555
Fort Worth *(G-6532)*
Compass Well Services LLC E 432 561-5970
Midland *(G-15173)*
Concho Resources Inc D 713 739-7561
Houston *(G-9267)*
Confab Oilfield Contractors F 817 992-6563
Burleson *(G-2576)*
Conocophillips A 281 293-1000
Houston *(G-9272)*
◆ **Conocophillips Company** A 281 293-1000
Houston *(G-9273)*
Contango Oil & Gas Company E 713 236-7400
Houston *(G-9282)*
Continental Land & Fur Co Inc F 281 873-9378
Houston *(G-9286)*
Coronado Resources GP LLC F 214 651-6245
Dallas *(G-4169)*
Cortez Resources LLC G 214 628-9155
Dallas *(G-4174)*
Covey Park Energy Holdings LLC G 214 548-6000
Dallas *(G-4176)*
Cowboys Resources Corp G 432 686-7797
Midland *(G-15181)*
Cox Oil LLC F 214 420-7710
Dallas *(G-4177)*
Cox Operating LLC F 504 267-9138
Dallas *(G-4178)*
Crawford Energy Inc F 713 626-2637
Houston *(G-9335)*
Crimson Exploration Inc E 713 236-7400
Houston *(G-9344)*
Crown Exploration Ltd F 972 395-1133
Carrollton *(G-2861)*
Crown Oil Partners LP F 432 683-2950
Midland *(G-15182)*
Crownquest Operating LLC D 432 818-0300
Midland *(G-15183)*
Crownrock LP C 432 818-0300
Midland *(G-15184)*
Crusader Energy Group LLC E 512 328-2953
Austin *(G-1075)*
Cudd Pressure Control Inc C 903 988-2161
Kilgore *(G-13542)*
Cudd Pumping Services Inc B 432 580-3544
Odessa *(G-15972)*
◆ **Current Power Solutions Inc** D 281 943-7700
Houston *(G-9359)*
Cw Resources Inc F 903 759-8822
Longview *(G-14218)*
D & L Well Service Inc F 432 336-8101
Fort Stockton *(G-6329)*
Dale Operating Company E 214 979-9010
Dallas *(G-4208)*
Dalla Compress Ener Solutio LL E 214 265-0400
Dallas *(G-4209)*
Danick Resources E 214 827-2222
Dallas *(G-4234)*
Datagration Solutions Inc E 713 568-4580
Houston *(G-9405)*
Dataseismic Corporation E 713 650-3200
Houston *(G-9406)*

Davis Chemical Services LLC...............C...... 903 938-3800
Marshall *(G-14772)*

Davis Coiled Tubing Svcs LLC..............D...... 903 927-5555
Marshall *(G-14773)*

Davis Offshore LP...............................F...... 713 933-0064
Houston *(G-9409)*

◆ Davoil Inc.....................................F...... 817 737-6678
Fort Worth *(G-6578)*

Dawson Geophysical Company.............F...... 713 917-6772
Houston *(G-9410)*

Dawson Geophysical Company.............C...... 432 684-3000
Midland *(G-15187)*

Deep Gulf Energy II LLC.....................D...... 281 596-0933
Houston *(G-9421)*

▲ Deep Gulf Energy LP......................F...... 281 596-0933
Houston *(G-9422)*

Denbury Marine LLC.............................E...... 972 673-2000
Plano *(G-16839)*

Denbury Onshore LLC...........................E...... 409 729-0211
Nederland *(G-15751)*

▲ Denbury Onshore LLC....................C...... 972 673-2000
Plano *(G-16840)*

Denbury Operating Company................E...... 972 673-2000
Plano *(G-16841)*

Denbury Pipeline Holdings LLC............F...... 972 673-2000
Plano *(G-16842)*

Denbury Resources Inc........................F...... 972 378-4776
Plano *(G-16843)*

Devon Energy Corporation..................E...... 817 396-4000
Cresson *(G-3707)*

Devon Energy Corporation..................F...... 903 693-7196
Carthage *(G-2906)*

Diamondback E&P LLC.........................D...... 866 531-3667
Midland *(G-15192)*

Discovery Acquisition Svcs LLC...........E...... 281 371-2700
Katy *(G-13395)*

Diversity Petroleum LP........................F...... 972 772-6025
Mesquite *(G-15040)*

◆ Dof Subsea Usa Inc.......................C...... 713 896-2500
Houston *(G-9491)*

Dome Energy Inc................................G...... 281 558-8585
Houston *(G-9494)*

Double Eagle Energy Oper LLC............E...... 817 928-3260
Fort Worth *(G-6590)*

Downunder Gosolutions Amer LLC........G...... 832 582-3221
Houston *(G-9510)*

Draco Technologies LLC......................F...... 432 213-5626
Big Spring *(G-2080)*

Drilling Info Inc...................................D...... 512 477-9200
Austin *(G-1101)*

DTE Gas Resources LLC.....................E...... 817 302-4600
Fort Worth *(G-6595)*

Dtn LLC..E...... 713 430-7100
Houston *(G-9535)*

Dunagin Transport Company................F...... 325 928-5253
Aspermont *(G-816)*

Dynamic Inc......................................E...... 817 838-1800
Fort Worth *(G-6597)*

E & E Polaris Services Inc..................G...... 281 367-6000
Spring *(G-19209)*

E B R Energy LP................................F...... 281 265-6500
Sugar Land *(G-19481)*

E T C Company.................................E...... 210 403-6402
Dallas *(G-4285)*

E2 Energy Services LLC.....................E...... 214 365-3200
Dallas *(G-4288)*

Eagle Gas & Oil Co Inc......................F...... 214 369-1545
Dallas *(G-4291)*

Eagle Geophysical Inc........................E...... 713 881-2800
Houston *(G-9557)*

▲ Eagle Oil & Gas Co........................F...... 940 723-7322
Wichita Falls *(G-20762)*

Eagle Vly Enrgy Partners LLC.............F...... 512 413-7140
Austin *(G-1110)*

Eagleclaw Midstream Svcs LLC...........E...... 432 789-1333
Midland *(G-15204)*

Eagleridge Energy LLC.......................F...... 214 295-6704
Dallas *(G-4293)*

Earthstone Energy Inc........................F...... 281 298-4246
The Woodlands *(G-19857)*

Earthstone Energy Holdings LLC..........E...... 281 298-4246
The Woodlands *(G-19858)*

Earthstone Operating LLC...................E...... 281 298-4246
The Woodlands *(G-19859)*

Eastex Crude Company.......................E...... 903 856-2401
Leesburg *(G-13999)*

Eastex Crude Trucking LLC.................B...... 800 443-8580
Leesburg *(G-14000)*

Easton Energy LLC............................F...... 214 712-2141
Houston *(G-9571)*

Eclipse Resources I LP.......................F...... 814 308-9754
Irving *(G-13007)*

Eclipse Resources-Pa LP.....................F...... 814 409-7006
Irving *(G-13008)*

◆ Ecopetrol America Inc....................D...... 713 634-3800
Houston *(G-9581)*

Ejr Consulting Services Inc................F...... 432 634-2905
Odessa *(G-15986)*

El Paso CNG Company LLC.................F...... 713 420-2600
Houston *(G-9586)*

Eland Energy Inc...............................E...... 214 368-6100
Dallas *(G-4308)*

Element Markets LLC..........................E...... 281 207-7200
Houston *(G-9598)*

Elevate Midstream Partners LLC...........F...... 214 215-9298
Houston *(G-9599)*

Elite Wellsite Services LLC..................F...... 940 393-2116
Bridgeport *(G-2292)*

Elm Ridge Exploration Co LLC.............E...... 972 889-2100
Dallas *(G-4315)*

Elm Ridge Resources Inc....................E...... 972 889-2100
Dallas *(G-4316)*

Encino Energy LLC.............................E...... 281 254-7070
Houston *(G-9624)*

Endeavor Natural Gas LLC..................E...... 713 658-8555
Houston *(G-9626)*

Endurance Resources LLC...................E...... 214 996-0900
Addison *(G-121)*

Enduro Resource Partners LLC.............E...... 817 744-8200
Fort Worth *(G-6612)*

Energen Resources Corporation...........D...... 205 326-2700
Midland *(G-15218)*

Energy Explration Partners Inc............E...... 817 789-6712
Fort Worth *(G-6613)*

Energy Management Company..............F...... 972 885-6799
Dallas *(G-4323)*

Energy Precision Tstg Lab LLC.............F...... 806 665-0750
Amarillo *(G-422)*

Energy Xxi Gom LLC..........................E...... 713 659-2100
Houston *(G-9639)*

Energy Xxi USA Inc............................C...... 713 351-3000
Houston *(G-9642)*

Enersol Group Inc.............................E...... 830 387-4011
New Braunfels *(G-15790)*

Enervest Ltd.....................................D...... 713 659-3500
Houston *(G-9643)*

Enervest Operating LLC......................E...... 979 542-2054
Giddings *(G-7694)*

Enervest Operating LLC......................E...... 940 683-1966
Bridgeport *(G-2293)*

Enervest Operating LLC......................E...... 713 659-3500
Houston *(G-9644)*

▲ Eni USA Inc................................B...... 713 393-6100
Houston *(G-9649)*

Ensosoft LLC....................................F...... 713 360-4841
Houston *(G-9660)*

Enven Energy Ventures LLC................E...... 713 335-7000
Houston *(G-9666)*

Eog Resources Inc.............................E...... 830 879-4614
Cotulla *(G-3690)*

Eog Resources Inc.............................D...... 361 866-4300
Corpus Christi *(G-3519)*

Eog Resources Inc.............................E...... 210 403-7700
San Antonio *(G-18093)*

Eog Resources Inc.............................E...... 432 586-9141
Kermit *(G-13512)*

Eog Resources Inc.............................D...... 432 686-3600
Midland *(G-15223)*

Eog Resources Inc.............................C...... 817 339-9380
Fort Worth *(G-6616)*

Eog Resources Inc.............................E...... 940 567-9777
Jacksboro *(G-13220)*

Eog Resources Inc.............................E...... 325 392-3782
Ozona *(G-16282)*

Eog Resources Inc.............................E...... 940 696-6000
Bowie *(G-2194)*

Eog Resources Inc.............................E...... 817 212-3100
Alvarado *(G-330)*

Eog Resources Inc.............................E...... 817 598-8300
Weatherford *(G-20590)*

Eog Resources Investments Inc............F...... 713 651-6914
Houston *(G-9672)*

Eos Well Service Inc..........................F...... 281 914-2191
Richmond *(G-17454)*

Ep Energy E&P Company LP................D...... 713 997-1200
Houston *(G-9674)*

Epic Y-Grade Marketing LP.................E...... 210 920-2285
San Antonio *(G-18094)*

Epl Oil & Gas Inc..............................F...... 713 228-0711
Houston *(G-9682)*

Epsilon Energy Usa Inc......................F...... 281 670-0002
Houston *(G-9684)*

Equinor Energy LP.............................D...... 512 427-3300
Austin *(G-1134)*

Equinor Gulf of Mexico LLC.................F...... 713 918-8200
Houston *(G-9686)*

▲ Equinor US Operations LLC.............E...... 713 918-8200
Houston *(G-9687)*

▲ Equinor USA E&P Inc.....................E...... 713 918-8200
Houston *(G-9688)*

Equinor USA Properties Inc................G...... 713 918-8200
Austin *(G-1136)*

Erg Resources LLC............................E...... 713 812-1800
Houston *(G-9690)*

Erhc Energy Inc................................G...... 713 626-4700
Houston *(G-9691)*

Erskine Energy LLC............................E...... 281 225-7223
Houston *(G-9694)*

Escondido Resources II MGT LLC..........F...... 713 662-0332
Katy *(G-13401)*

Eseis Inc...E...... 281 531-1447
Houston *(G-9696)*

Esenjay Exploration Inc......................E...... 361 883-7464
Corpus Christi *(G-3520)*

Eureka Midstream LLC........................E...... 832 203-4544
Houston *(G-9711)*

Ev Energy Partners LP.......................F...... 713 659-3500
Houston *(G-9714)*

Exco Operating Company LP................E...... 214 368-2084
Dallas *(G-4344)*

▲ Exco Resources Inc......................C...... 214 368-2084
Dallas *(G-4345)*

Exl Petroleum LP..............................F...... 432 686-8080
Midland *(G-15225)*

Exl Petroleum Management LLC...........E...... 432 686-8080
Midland *(G-15226)*

Exl Petroleum Operating Inc...............F...... 432 686-8080
Midland *(G-15227)*

Exploitation Company LLP....................C...... 713 351-3000
Houston *(G-9727)*

Exploration Center Building.................E...... 806 353-9123
Amarillo *(G-487)*

F F Foster & Associates Inc................E...... 713 266-2883
Houston *(G-9744)*

◆ Fairfield Industries Inc....................C...... 281 275-7500
Houston *(G-9752)*

Fairways Exploration Prod LLC.............F...... 713 622-3492
Houston *(G-9753)*

Fairways Offshore Expl.......................E...... 713 622-3492
Houston *(G-9754)*

Falcon Bay Energy L L C.....................F...... 432 682-7424
Midland *(G-15228)*

Falcon Seaboard Holdings LLC.............E...... 713 622-0055
Houston *(G-9755)*

▼ Far East Energy Corporation.............F...... 832 598-0470
Houston *(G-9762)*

FE Hill Co LLP...................................F...... 903 389-3616
Fairfield *(G-6173)*

Ferus LP...E...... 832 709-0750
Houston *(G-9778)*

Fervid Group LLC..............................F...... 713 364-3378
Houston *(G-9779)*

Finley Co..E...... 830 816-2107
Boerne *(G-2120)*

Finley Resources Inc..........................D...... 817 336-1924
Fort Worth *(G-6631)*

Fivestones Energy LLC........................F...... 432 618-9929
Midland *(G-15230)*

Flint Hills Resources LP......................C...... 361 241-4811
Corpus Christi *(G-3531)*

Flow Control Division Cameron.............F...... 713 513-3300
Houston *(G-9807)*

Flying A Pumping Services LLC.............E...... 325 794-1667
Albany *(G-188)*

Focus Exploration LLC........................F...... 713 435-0021
Houston *(G-9830)*

Foothills Resources Inc......................F...... 713 621-9408
Houston *(G-9831)*

▲ Forum Us Inc...............................C...... 713 351-7900
Houston *(G-9844)*

Foundation Energy MGT LLC................E...... 972 707-2500
Addison *(G-127)*

Franks International LLC.....................D...... 281 331-1501
Alvin *(G-362)*

◆ Franks International LLC..................D...... 281 966-7300
Houston *(G-9857)*

Freeman & Curiel Engineers LLP............F...... 713 895-8668
Houston *(G-9861)*

▲ Freeport-Mcmoran Oil & Gas LLC.....C...... 713 579-6000
Houston *(G-9862)*

Company	Code	Phone	G-ref
Frontline Geoservices Ltd	E	281 371-2800	
Katy (G-13406)			
Fts International Services LLC	E	817 862-2000	
Aledo (G-198)			
Fts International Services LLC	E	817 862-2000	
Fort Worth (G-6656)			
Gaither Petroleum Corporation	E	281 579-5200	
Houston (G-9892)			
Gardner Denver Inc	G	817 248-4510	
Fort Worth (G-6662)			
Gas Sensing Technology Corp	E	307 742-6340	
Houston (G-9902)			
Gas Ventures Ltd Liability Co	G	307 864-3754	
Houston (G-9903)			
Gastar Exploration Inc	E	713 739-1800	
Houston (G-9904)			
Gavstar Services	E	817 657-4020	
Arlington (G-686)			
▲ Genesis Crude Oil LP	C	713 860-2500	
Houston (G-9931)			
Geo Mesa Analysis LLC	E	443 637-2436	
Addison (G-130)			
Geoforce Inc	D	972 546-3878	
Plano (G-16879)			
▲ Geokinetics Acquisition Co	E	281 509-8000	
Houston (G-9934)			
◆ Geokinetics Inc	E	713 850-7600	
Houston (G-9935)			
▲ Geolog Americas Inc	F	281 984-7078	
Houston (G-9936)			
Geophyscal Explrtion Technolgy	D	713 979-9900	
Houston (G-9939)			
Geosouthern Energy Corporation	F	979 836-5203	
Brenham (G-2255)			
Gep Haynesville LLC	E	281 363-9161	
The Woodlands (G-19867)			
Ggm Exploration Inc	E	817 338-1137	
Fort Worth (G-6667)			
Glass Mountain Pipeline LLC	E	214 880-6000	
Dallas (G-4408)			
Glori Energy Inc	E	713 237-8880	
Houston (G-8383)			
Gmt Exploration Co Texas LLC	F	713 334-6001	
Houston (G-9988)			
Goldston Oil Corporation	E	713 355-3408	
Houston (G-9995)			
Goodrich Petroleum Co La LLC	D	713 780-9494	
Houston (G-10001)			
▲ Goodrich Petroleum Corporation	C	713 780-9494	
Houston (G-10003)			
Gordy Gas Corporation	E	979 922-1313	
Houston (G-10004)			
Gordy Oil Company	E	713 951-0100	
Houston (G-10005)			
Grand Energy Inc	E	972 788-2080	
Addison (G-132)			
Gravity Midstream LLC	F	832 426-3302	
Houston (G-10020)			
Grayson Mill Energy LLC	E	832 271-8050	
Houston (G-10022)			
Great Basin Petroleum Svcs LP	D	432 561-9702	
Odessa (G-16018)			
Green Vly Oil Svcs Free Zone	F	936 242-0603	
Houston (G-10031)			
Grenadier Energy Partners LLC	F	281 907-4120	
Spring (G-19213)			
Grenadier Enrgy Prtners II LLC	F	281 907-4120	
The Woodlands (G-19871)			
Grierson Springs Midstream LLC	E	713 655-9500	
Houston (G-10042)			
Griffith Land Services Inc	G	713 465-3273	
Houston (G-10046)			
Grizzly Energy LLC	E	832 327-2255	
Houston (G-10047)			
Gryphon Production Co LLC	E	806 688-9697	
Pampa (G-16324)			
Gulf Coast Western LLC	E	972 284-0600	
Dallas (G-4421)			
H E & D Operating Inc	E	713 650-8008	
Houston (G-10083)			
H J Gruy and Associates Inc	F	713 739-1000	
Bellaire (G-1997)			
H L Brown Jr	F	432 683-5216	
Midland (G-15243)			
◆ H Power I LLC	D	214 978-8943	
Dallas (G-4425)			
Halff Tritex LLC	E	214 217-6500	
Richardson (G-17325)			
Hall-Houston Exploration LP	G	713 333-0975	
Houston (G-10095)			
Hall-Houston Exploration II LP	F	713 333-0930	
Houston (G-10096)			
Halliburton Company	E	281 297-1200	
Spring (G-19214)			
Halliburton Company	E	281 575-5000	
Corpus Christi (G-3544)			
Halliburton Company	C	281 297-1200	
Houston (G-10100)			
◆ Halliburton Company	E	281 871-2699	
Houston (G-10107)			
▲ Hamill Resources Inc	F	281 556-9581	
Houston (G-10112)			
Harding Energy Partners LLC	F	214 723-5112	
Dallas (G-4435)			
Harrison Gypsum LLC	F	210 225-9502	
San Antonio (G-18159)			
▼ Harvest Natural Resources Inc	E	281 899-5700	
Dallas (G-4439)			
Harvest Pipeline Company	E	830 334-3280	
Houston (G-10135)			
Hawkins Rmote Snsing Explrtion	E	210 829-5330	
San Antonio (G-18160)			
Hawkwood Energy East Texas LLC	A	303 823-4175	
Dallas (G-4441)			
Hb2 Energy Inc	E	713 377-9860	
Houston (G-10140)			
Headington Energy Partners LLC	E	214 307-5400	
McKinney (G-14946)			
Headington Oil Limited 1993 LP	F	361 885-0110	
Corpus Christi (G-3546)			
Henry Oil LC	F	214 696-5150	
Dallas (G-4449)			
Henry Resources LLC	E	432 694-3000	
Midland (G-15245)			
Hep Services LLC	F	210 278-1563	
Houston (G-10156)			
Hess Corporation	F	713 496-4000	
Houston (G-10163)			
Hess Investments ND LLC	C	713 496-4000	
Houston (G-10164)			
Hibernia Energy III LLC	F	713 728-7911	
Houston (G-10173)			
High Plains Hydro Carbon	G	806 948-4166	
Sunray (G-19619)			
Highmount Exploration Prod LLC	G	325 387-3588	
Sonora (G-19026)			
Highmount Exploration Prod LLC	C	281 873-1500	
Houston (G-10177)			
Highpeak Energy Partners LP	E	817 850-9200	
Fort Worth (G-6696)			
Hilcorp Energy Company	F	979 548-2144	
Sweeny (G-19627)			
▲ Hilcorp Energy Company	F	713 209-2400	
Houston (G-10182)			
Hilcorp Energy I LP	F	713 209-2400	
Houston (G-10183)			
Hilcorp Energy I LP	F	713 209-2400	
Houston (G-10184)			
Hilcorp Finance Company	C	713 209-2400	
Houston (G-10185)			
Hilltop Energy LLC	F	972 686-0369	
Dallas (G-4459)			
HK Energy Operating LLC	C	281 537-9920	
Houston (G-10188)			
Hollimon Oil Corporation	E	210 829-8822	
San Antonio (G-18170)			
Hons International Inc	D	281 940-9184	
Sugar Land (G-19493)			
Horizon Production & Oper LLC	F	713 522-5800	
Houston (G-10206)			
Horizon Resources LP	F	713 522-5800	
Houston (G-10207)			
Houston Energy LP	F	713 650-8008	
Houston (G-10232)			
Howell Oil & Gas Inc	F	903 935-0999	
Marshall (G-14782)			
Hunt Nlson Bnker Trust Estt-T	F	214 979-9072	
Dallas (G-4471)			
Hunt Dominion Corporation	C	214 880-8400	
Dallas (G-4472)			
▲ Hunt Exploration Mining Co	F	214 979-9072	
Dallas (G-4473)			
Hunt Marcellus LLC	F	214 978-8000	
Dallas (G-4474)			
Hunt Oil Company	E	214 978-8000	
Dallas (G-4475)			
Hunt Petroleum Corporation	C	214 880-8400	
Fort Worth (G-6710)			
Hunt Petroleum Corporation	F	713 871-3400	
Houston (G-10280)			
Hunting PLC USA	A	713 595-2950	
The Woodlands (G-19875)			
Hydrocrbon Exploration Dev LLC	F	281 453-5700	
Houston (G-10306)			
Independence Resources MGT LLC	E	832 916-2300	
Houston (G-10339)			
Independence Resources MGT LLC	E	832 916-2300	
Midland (G-15252)			
Indigo Minerals LLC	C	713 237-5000	
Houston (G-10342)			
Infrastructure Networks Inc	E	832 598-6600	
Houston (G-10361)			
Innovtive Trnround Contrls Ltd	C	281 998-9547	
Pasadena (G-16460)			
Interctive Explrtion Solutions	F	713 993-0676	
Houston (G-10394)			
Intermoor Inc	E	832 399-5000	
Houston (G-10397)			
▲ Ion Exploration Pdts USA Inc	G	281 933-3339	
Stafford (G-19330)			
Ipr Transoil Corporation	F	972 257-1900	
Irving (G-13065)			
Ips International LLC	F	936 521-1981	
Conroe (G-3311)			
Iron Hrse Olfled Svc Group LLC	F	832 224-4430	
Houston (G-10419)			
Ironroc Energy Partners LLC	E	713 377-9860	
Houston (G-10422)			
Ironwood Oil & Gas LLC	E	281 873-9378	
Houston (G-10423)			
Iskandia Energy Operating Inc	E	832 209-8240	
Houston (G-10426)			
Isramco Energy LLC	E	713 456-7892	
Houston (G-10428)			
Iwc Oil & Refinery LLC	E	210 900-9928	
San Antonio (G-18196)			
J & X Trucking LLC	E	830 583-0611	
Kenedy (G-13488)			
J-W Gathering Company	F	903 643-3413	
Longview (G-14255)			
Jagged Peak Energy MGT LLC	E	720 215-3700	
Austin (G-1249)			
▲ Jaguar Exploration Inc	F	281 920-2668	
Katy (G-13366)			
James Fisher Subsea Excav Inc	F	713 466-1233	
Houston (G-10451)			
Jay Management Company LLC	G	936 258-2646	
Dayton (G-5232)			
▲ Jefferson Refinery LLC	F	281 677-4900	
The Woodlands (G-19889)			
Jgc Energy Development USA Inc	F	832 487-9965	
Houston (G-10473)			
Joy Glbal Lngview Oprtions LLC	A	903 237-7000	
Longview (G-14258)			
K&L Contractors Inc	E	936 591-8333	
Center (G-3001)			
Kap Project Services Ltd	D	877 527-7762	
La Porte (G-13761)			
Kelman Technologies Inc	E	281 529-3204	
Houston (G-10514)			
Kerr Energy Companies LLC	G	713 501-9555	
Houston (G-10520)			
Kerr-Mcgee (nevada) LLC	D	303 321-0683	
Spring (G-19224)			
Kerr-Mcgee Oil Gas Onshore LP	C	832 636-1000	
The Woodlands (G-19891)			
Key Energy Drilling Inc	E	432 639-2534	
Iraan (G-12919)			
Key Energy Services Inc	D	979 542-3344	
Giddings (G-7698)			
Key Energy Services Inc	E	806 489-7452	
Welch (G-20655)			
Keystone Exploration Ltd	F	817 820-7029	
Fort Worth (G-6758)			
Kgh Intermediate Holdco II LLC	F	432 563-1708	
Midland (G-15271)			
Khanty Mansiysk Oil Corp	A	713 629-6600	
Houston (G-10529)			
Killam Oil Co Ltd	E	956 724-7141	
Laredo (G-13902)			
Killam Oil Co Ltd	E	361 394-7680	
Freer (G-7229)			
Kinder Morgan (delaware) Inc	C	806 272-3309	
Muleshoe (G-15677)			
King Operating Corporation	F	214 420-3000	
Dallas (G-4556)			
King Pipeline Services LLC	E	903 530-8667	
Fort Worth (G-6762)			
Kokomo Energy Inc	F	940 683-1102	
Bridgeport (G-2296)			

▲ Kosmos Energy LLC ....F 214 445-9600
Dallas *(G-4565)*

Kosmos Energy Ltd ....G 214 445-9600
Dallas *(G-4566)*

Kraken Oil & Gas LLC ....F 713 360-7705
Houston *(G-10562)*

Lacy Operations Ltd ....E 903 758-8276
Longview *(G-14262)*

Lamar Hunt Trust Estate Inc ....D 214 720-1600
Dallas *(G-4579)*

Lambda Energy Resources LLC ....D 231 258-6425
Houston *(G-10587)*

Laredo Energy IV Gp LLC ....F 713 600-6000
Houston *(G-10600)*

Laredo Petroleum Inc ....E 432 684-9955
Midland *(G-15272)*

Layline Petroleum LLC ....E 713 465-4100
Houston *(G-10608)*

Layton Energy Inc ....F 713 590-2820
Houston *(G-10609)*

Legacy Offshore LLC ....F 281 334-2266
League City *(G-13968)*

Legacy Reserves LP ....E 432 967-3490
Midland *(G-15275)*

Legacy Reserves Oper GP LLC ....C 432 689-5200
Midland *(G-15277)*

Lewis Energy Group LP ....A 956 728-6000
Encinal *(G-6086)*

Lewis Petro Properties Inc ....D 210 384-3200
San Antonio *(G-18249)*

Lilis Energy Inc ....F 817 585-9001
Fort Worth *(G-6789)*

Lime Rock Resources A LP ....E 713 292-9510
Houston *(G-10642)*

Limestone Exploration II LLC ....F 432 695-6970
Midland *(G-15282)*

Linn Acquisition Company LLC ....C 281 840-4000
Houston *(G-10648)*

Linn Energy Inc ....E 281 840-4000
Houston *(G-10649)*

Linn Energy Inc ....C 405 241-2200
Houston *(G-10650)*

Linn Energy Finance Corp ....E 281 840-4000
Houston *(G-10651)*

Linn Energy Holdings LLC ....E 806 274-3074
Houston *(G-10652)*

Llano Operating Corporation ....F 972 677-7690
Dallas *(G-4598)*

Llog Exploration Company LLC ....D 281 752-1100
Houston *(G-10656)*

Longfellow Energy LP ....E 972 590-9900
Addison *(G-146)*

Lotus Midstream LLC ....G 713 234-7865
Sugar Land *(G-19505)*

Lowe Offshore Inc ....D 281 894-5454
Houston *(G-10690)*

LPC Crude Oil Inc ....D 432 682-8555
Midland *(G-15287)*

▲ Lr Energy Inc ....E 214 691-5800
Dallas *(G-4608)*

Lucid Energy Group LLC ....E 575 810-6025
Dallas *(G-4610)*

Lucid Energy Group II LLC ....F 214 420-4950
Dallas *(G-4611)*

Luig Energy Services LLC ....F 940 264-6188
Wichita Falls *(G-20780)*

◆ Lukoil Intl Upstream W Inc ....E 713 877-8544
Houston *(G-10700)*

Luther M Creek ....D 325 387-3295
Sonora *(G-19027)*

M H C X-Ploration Corporation ....F 903 595-4323
Tyler *(G-20117)*

M3 Midstream LLC ....F 713 783-3000
Houston *(G-10727)*

M5 Louisiana Gathering LLC ....E 713 783-3000
Houston *(G-10728)*

Magnolia Oil & Gas Oper LLC ....D 713 842-9050
Houston *(G-10736)*

Magseis Ff LLC ....C 281 275-7500
Houston *(G-10737)*

Mallard Completions LLC ....D 432 381-8508
Midland *(G-15292)*

Mani Little & Wortmann ....E 210 403-9461
San Antonio *(G-18273)*

Manti Operating Company ....E 361 888-7708
Corpus Christi *(G-3572)*

Manti Resources Inc ....E 361 888-7708
Houston *(G-10746)*

Manti Tarka Permian LP ....G 832 460-0046
Houston *(G-10747)*

Marathon International Oil Co ....D 713 629-6600
Houston *(G-10753)*

Marathon Oil Ef LLC ....F 713 209-2458
San Antonio *(G-18274)*

Mariner Gulf of Mexico LLC ....D 713 954-5500
Houston *(G-10767)*

Marion Energy Inc ....F 435 789-6959
McKinney *(G-14957)*

Matador Production Company ....E 972 371-5200
Dallas *(G-4649)*

▲ Mathew Marine Inc ....F 877 508-4004
Houston *(G-10795)*

Maverick Trmnals Three Rvers L ....F 956 371-6530
Brownsville *(G-2382)*

McX Gulf of Mexico LLC ....G 713 953-9292
Houston *(G-10814)*

Med-Loz Lease Service Inc ....F 956 765-6029
Zapata *(G-20984)*

Medallion Delaware Basin LLC ....C 972 746-4401
Irving *(G-13103)*

Medallion Midstream LLC ....E 972 746-4401
Irving *(G-13104)*

Medallion Oil Company Inc ....F 713 654-0144
Houston *(G-10815)*

Melissa Renewables LLC ....E 432 563-0447
Melissa *(G-14998)*

Mentor IMC (usa) Inc ....E 713 425-6307
Houston *(G-10829)*

Mercury Operating LLC ....F 214 935-1698
Irving *(G-13107)*

Meridian Energy Group Inc ....E 281 291-0510
Pasadena *(G-16482)*

Mewborne Enrgy Prtners 04-A LP .....D 903 561-2900
Tyler *(G-20125)*

Mewbourne Oil Company ....F 432 682-3715
Midland *(G-15298)*

Mewbourne Oil Company ....F 806 435-6881
Perryton *(G-16640)*

Mexico Pacific Limited LLC ....F 713 425-6500
Houston *(G-10860)*

Meyer Energy Services LLC ....E 830 377-1099
Midland *(G-15299)*

Meyer Energy Services LLC ....D 830 377-1099
Midland *(G-15300)*

Michelson Energy Company ....F 210 826-0681
San Antonio *(G-18299)*

▲ Microseismic Inc ....D 713 781-2323
Houston *(G-10869)*

Midcoast Energy LLC ....F 806 663-7700
Pampa *(G-16329)*

Midcoast Lease Service Inc ....E 361 526-4636
Refugio *(G-17244)*

Midstream Energy Holdings LLC ....G 713 403-6460
Houston *(G-10873)*

Midstream Navarro Services LLC ....A 956 728-6000
San Antonio *(G-18305)*

Midstream Noble Services LLC ....E 281 872-3100
Houston *(G-10875)*

Milagro Exploration Gp LLC ....F 713 750-1600
Houston *(G-10880)*

Minergy LLC ....A 832 800-6336
Houston *(G-10887)*

▲ Mitsui E&P USA LLC ....E 713 960-0023
Houston *(G-10893)*

Moda Midstream LLC ....E 832 930-4838
Houston *(G-10901)*

Modena Operating LLC ....F 713 592-5000
Houston *(G-10903)*

Mohave Oil and Gas Corporation ....F 713 975-1725
Spring *(G-19232)*

Momentum Operating Co Inc ....E 325 762-3331
Albany *(G-191)*

Moncrief Oil International Inc ....F 817 348-8454
Fort Worth *(G-6848)*

Moyes & Co Inc ....E 214 623-6700
Dallas *(G-4694)*

MRC Energy Company ....E 972 371-5200
Dallas *(G-4700)*

Mudsmith Ltd ....F 432 687-6837
Midland *(G-15308)*

Mullins White Exploration Inc ....D 817 442-5259
Southlake *(G-19079)*

Murchison Oil and Gas Inc ....E 972 931-0700
Plano *(G-16936)*

Murex Petroleum Corporation ....E 281 590-3313
Houston *(G-10940)*

Murphy Exploration & Prod Co ....F 281 675-9000
Houston *(G-10941)*

◆ Murphy Exploration Prod - USA ....B 281 675-9000
Houston *(G-10942)*

Mustang Extreme Envmtl Svcs LL ......F 830 393-1034
Fort Worth *(G-6858)*

N D Nolen Drilling LLC ....F 210 585-1966
San Antonio *(G-18327)*

Nabors Well Services Ltd ....D 325 387-2884
Sonora *(G-19028)*

Nabors Well Services Ltd ....E 432 836-4332
Iraan *(G-12920)*

Nacogdoches Oil and Gas Inc ....F 936 560-4747
Nacogdoches *(G-15705)*

National Enrgy Svcs Rnted Corp ....G 832 925-3777
Houston *(G-10967)*

Navco Oilfield Services LLC ....G 956 542-4426
Brownsville *(G-2386)*

Nbl Permian LLC ....C 281 872-3100
Houston *(G-11012)*

Nbl Permian LLC ....F 432 688-3430
Midland *(G-15313)*

Nbl Permian LLC ....F 979 764-4030
College Station *(G-3195)*

Nbl Texas LLC ....E 281 872-3100
Houston *(G-11013)*

Nelson Hunt Bunker ....F 214 979-9072
Dallas *(G-4720)*

Neofirma Inc ....F 214 233-7111
Richardson *(G-17362)*

◆ Neste Oil Services Inc ....F 713 407-4411
Houston *(G-11026)*

Neste Petroleum Inc ....F 713 407-4400
Houston *(G-11027)*

Nettlecombe Oil Co Inc ....F 713 652-4040
Houston *(G-11038)*

New Century Exploration Inc ....F 832 698-1374
Spring *(G-19155)*

New Ventures Leasing LLC ....F 940 577-7789
Bowie *(G-2198)*

Newfield Exploration Company ....D 281 847-6000
Spring *(G-19236)*

Newpark Mats Intgrted Svcs LLC ....D 979 245-3894
Bay City *(G-1775)*

Newpark Mats Intgrted Svcs LLC ....E 409 752-5800
Beaumont *(G-1934)*

Nexen Energy Services USA Inc ....E 832 714-5000
Houston *(G-11044)*

Nexen Petroleum USA Inc ....E 972 450-4600
Houston *(G-11045)*

Noble Energy Inc ....D 800 234-3867
Houston *(G-11063)*

◆ Noble Energy Inc ....C 281 872-3100
Houston *(G-11064)*

◆ North American Interpipe Inc ....E 713 333-0333
Houston *(G-11072)*

Northstar Interests LC ....F 713 626-9696
Houston *(G-11079)*

Nottus Energy Resources Inc ....F 940 687-5304
Wichita Falls *(G-20788)*

Nrpc Operating LLC ....G 512 428-4753
Dallas *(G-4745)*

O-Tex Pumping LLC ....D 432 685-9901
Midland *(G-15322)*

▲ Occidental Energy Mktg Inc ....C 713 215-7000
Houston *(G-11113)*

◆ Occidental Permian Ltd ....C 713 215-7000
Houston *(G-11115)*

Occidental Petroleum Corp ....A 713 215-7000
Houston *(G-11116)*

Occidental Petroleum Corp ....G 325 574-8567
Ira *(G-12913)*

Occidental Petroleum Corp ....G 713 640-7500
Houston *(G-11117)*

Odl Inc ....G 281 647-8300
Houston *(G-11131)*

Offshore Express Inc ....D 985 868-1438
Houston *(G-11141)*

Oginfocom LLC ....E 361 904-0071
Corpus Christi *(G-3583)*

Ogp Operating Inc ....G 214 696-2393
Dallas *(G-4755)*

Ohs Energy Corp ....G 832 871-5088
Houston *(G-11149)*

Oil & Gas Consultants Intl Inc ....F 832 426-1200
Katy *(G-13374)*

Oil & Gas Technology Fund Inc ....F 281 671-7142
League City *(G-13973)*

Oil Data Inc ....E 713 461-7178
Houston *(G-11150)*

Oil Spill Response USA Inc ....F 832 431-3191
Houston *(G-11153)*

Oklahoma Pacific Ltd ....E 713 209-1100
Houston *(G-11166)*

Omimex Energy Inc	F	817 460-7777
Fort Worth (G-6878)		
Omimex Resources Inc	F	817 460-7777
Fort Worth (G-6880)		
Opal Resources LLC	G	713 647-7300
Houston (G-11183)		
Ors Fluids LLC	E	903 535-9992
Tyler (G-20136)		
Oryx Midstream Services LLC	E	432 684-4272
Midland (G-15330)		
Oryx Sthern Del Oil Gthring Tr	F	432 684-4272
Midland (G-15331)		
Osborn Heirs Company Ltd	E	210 826-0700
San Antonio (G-18357)		
Otcr Inc	F	713 685-3600
Houston (G-11199)		
Output Acquisition Corp	F	281 879-3609
Stafford (G-19362)		
Overflow Energy LLC	E	806 658-7832
Booker (G-2157)		
▲ Ovintiv Exploration Inc	C	281 210-5100
The Woodlands (G-19899)		
▲ OXY Inc	C	713 215-7000
Houston (G-11209)		
OXY USA Wtp LP	D	713 366-5303
Houston (G-11211)		
◆ OXY Vinyls LP	F	877 699-8465
Dallas (G-4775)		
Palo Petroleum Inc	F	214 691-3676
Dallas (G-4781)		
Paloma Partners III LLC	F	713 650-8500
Houston (G-11225)		
Panda Pwr Gnrtion Infrstrcture	E	972 361-2000
Dallas (G-4784)		
Parabellum Energy LLC	E	832 460-6521
Houston (G-11237)		
Paragon Offshore PLC	F	832 783-4000
Houston (G-11240)		
Parallel Petroleum LLC	E	432 684-3727
Midland (G-15336)		
Parsley Energy Operations LLC	D	432 818-2100
Midland (G-15338)		
Parten Operating Inc	E	936 624-3100
Crockett (G-3721)		
Patara Oil & Gas LLC	D	214 295-6704
Dallas (G-4790)		
Pcore Exploration Prod II LLC	F	469 802-1400
Dallas (G-4792)		
Peba Oil & Gas Co	F	940 825-4825
Nocona (G-15870)		
Penn Virginia Corporation	E	713 722-6500
Houston (G-11277)		
Penn Virginia Mc Energy LLC	E	713 722-6500
Houston (G-11279)		
Penn Virginia Oil & Gas LP	F	713 722-6500
Houston (G-11280)		
Penn Virginia Oil & Gas Corp	F	610 687-8900
Houston (G-11281)		
Penn Virginia Oil & Gas GP LLC	E	713 722-6500
Houston (G-11282)		
Penntex Midstream Partners LLC	D	214 981-0700
Houston (G-11283)		
Pentagon Energy LLC	E	203 451-8382
Houston (G-11285)		
Perdure Petroleum LLC	F	281 668-8488
Allen (G-291)		
Peregrine Petroleum LLC	E	214 231-6800
Dallas (G-4796)		
Peregrine Petroleum LLC	E	713 630-8965
Houston (G-11289)		
Permian Basin Joint Ventr LLC	E	713 296-6000
Houston (G-11292)		
Permian Petroleum Services Inc	E	432 682-0434
Midland (G-15345)		
Peter Paul Petroleum Company	E	713 209-1100
Houston (G-11295)		
Petra Land LLC	E	832 791-5495
The Woodlands (G-19901)		
Petro Land Group Inc	E	903 595-4293
Tyler (G-20141)		
Petrobal Omega 1 LLC	E	972 284-5120
Irving (G-13142)		
Petrolegacy Energy II LLC	E	512 735-9000
Austin (G-1414)		
Petroleum Exploration Co Ltd	E	254 559-5453
Breckenridge (G-2233)		
▲ Petroleum Geo-Services Inc	C	281 509-8000
Houston (G-11307)		
Petrolima LLC	E	432 695-9989
Midland (G-15347)		

Petrotel Inc	F	972 473-2767
Plano (G-16971)		
Pgs Americas Inc	D	512 670-8700
Manor (G-14648)		
▲ Pgs Americas Inc	D	281 509-8000
Houston (G-11317)		
Pgs Imaging Inc	B	281 509-8000
Houston (G-11319)		
Pinnacle Gas Treating LLC	F	903 928-1200
Tennessee Colony (G-19726)		
▼ Pioneer Energy Services Corp	C	855 884-0575
San Antonio (G-18378)		
Pioneer Natural Resources Co	E	432 683-4768
Midland (G-15354)		
Pioneer Natural Resources Co	C	432 571-2800
Midland (G-15355)		
Pioneer Ntral Rsources USA Inc	D	432 684-0023
Midland (G-15357)		
Piranha Scientific LLC	F	855 585-5200
Midland (G-15359)		
Pitts Oil Company LLC	F	214 369-9266
Dallas (G-4806)		
Plains Exploration & Prod Co	F	713 579-6000
Houston (G-11342)		
Platinum Energy Resources Inc	D	713 364-7822
Houston (G-11348)		
Plunkett Energy & Industrial S	F	806 395-3205
Wolfforth (G-20910)		
Plunkett Research Ltd	E	713 932-0000
Houston (G-11351)		
◆ Pluspetrol International Inc	F	713 961-1095
Houston (G-11352)		
Polaris Exploration Corp	F	361 857-7176
Beeville (G-1987)		
Polk Production Tech Inc	F	361 815-1245
Corpus Christi (G-3593)		
Pool Energy Corporation	F	512 249-9252
Austin (G-1425)		
Post Oak Energy Capital LP	F	713 571-9393
Houston (G-11369)		
Presidio Petroleum LLC	G	814 589-3550
Fort Worth (G-6914)		
Preston Exploration Ltd Lblty	F	281 367-8697
The Woodlands (G-19904)		
Prime Natural Resources Inc	F	832 531-8555
Houston (G-11414)		
Prime Operating Company	E	830 876-2441
Carrizo Springs (G-2687)		
Prime Operating Company	E	713 735-0000
Houston (G-11416)		
Pro-Test Inc	E	903 986-8404
Kilgore (G-13584)		
Probity Energy Partners LLC	E	432 570-1122
Midland (G-15363)		
◆ Procurement Services Del Inc	E	832 243-6330
Houston (G-11434)		
Propel Energy LLC	G	713 463-6500
Houston (G-11449)		
Propetro Holding Corp	F	432 688-0012
Midland (G-15366)		
▲ Propetro Services Inc	D	432 688-0012
Midland (G-15368)		
Protege Energy III LLC	F	918 728-3092
Houston (G-11463)		
Providence Energy Corporation	E	214 522-9131
Dallas (G-4833)		
PSI Midstream Partners LP	E	713 554-2880
Houston (G-11469)		
Pursuit Oil & Gas LLC	F	832 706-2299
Houston (G-11475)		
Pxp Offshore LLC	F	713 579-6000
Houston (G-11478)		
Pyramid Gom Inc	E	281 822-0801
Houston (G-11479)		
Python Pressure Pumping LLC	E	940 549-6900
Cleburne (G-3106)		
Qae Inc	D	281 436-5500
Houston (G-11482)		
Quail Well Service Inc	E	325 677-0323
Abilene (G-67)		
Quantum Investment Group Inc	E	281 994-5400
Houston (G-11507)		
Quintana Minerals Brazil LLC	F	713 751-7500
Houston (G-11517)		
Quintana Minerals Corporation	E	713 751-7500
Houston (G-11518)		
R & B Energy LLC	G	254 647-3358
Ranger (G-17231)		
R Lacy Inc	F	903 758-8276
Longview (G-14293)		

R Lacy Services Ltd	E	903 758-8276
Longview (G-14294)		
Range Resources - La Inc	E	713 588-8300
Fort Worth (G-6940)		
Range Resources Corporation	D	817 870-2601
Fort Worth (G-6941)		
Range Resources Corporation	C	817 870-2601
Fort Worth (G-6942)		
Recon Exploration Inc	F	972 960-8600
Addison (G-158)		
Red Arrow Energy LLC	E	713 580-7250
Houston (G-11566)		
Red Rock Oilfield Service LLC	F	325 933-0224
Colorado City (G-3226)		
Red Technology Alliance LLC	E	713 839-4689
Houston (G-11570)		
Red Willow Offshore LLC	D	281 822-7500
Houston (G-11571)		
Redbud E&P Inc	E	832 698-4234
Spring (G-19162)		
Redcliff Midstream LLC	E	713 655-9500
Houston (G-11572)		
Redemption Oil & Gas LLC	D	210 572-2988
San Antonio (G-18416)		
Redman Energy Corporation	G	713 782-2870
Houston (G-11575)		
Redwine Resources Inc	E	214 691-5800
Dallas (G-4879)		
Reef Exploration LP	F	972 437-6792
Richardson (G-17388)		
Reef Oil & Gas Partners LLC	F	972 437-6792
Richardson (G-17389)		
Remington Oil and Gas Corp	F	281 618-0400
Houston (G-11594)		
Remora Energy Management LLC	F	832 325-2300
Houston (G-11596)		
◆ Repsol Energy North Amer Corp	A	832 442-1000
The Woodlands (G-19908)		
▲ Repsol Services Company	C	832 442-1000
The Woodlands (G-19909)		
Republic Energy Inc	E	214 369-4800
Dallas (G-4889)		
Reservoir Marine LLC	E	281 277-7575
Sugar Land (G-19533)		
Resmetrics LLC	E	832 592-1900
Houston (G-11607)		
Resolute Natural Resources LLC	E	432 684-7475
Midland (G-15382)		
Resource Royalty LLC	F	214 691-5234
Dallas (G-4891)		
Ridgewood Energy Corporation	E	281 293-8488
Houston (G-11620)		
Rife Energy Operating Inc	G	940 964-2822
Forestburg (G-6300)		
◆ Ril USA Inc	F	713 430-8700
Houston (G-11623)		
Riley Exploration Group LLC	D	512 481-7676
Austin (G-1466)		
Rimrock Energy LLC	E	303 308-1300
Fort Worth (G-6959)		
Rio Oil and Gas II LLC	E	832 616-3726
The Woodlands (G-19912)		
Rio Oil and Gas LLC	E	832 616-3717
Spring (G-19248)		
Rio Petroleum	F	806 356-8033
Amarillo (G-458)		
Riviera Operating LLC	D	713 227-1868
Houston (G-11631)		
Riviera Resources Inc	E	281 840-4000
Houston (G-11632)		
Rk Petroleum Corp	F	432 683-4319
Midland (G-15387)		
Ro Mac Oil Co Inc	F	940 849-2261
Throckmorton (G-19946)		
Rockall Energy LLC	D	214 618-7600
Dallas (G-4908)		
Rockies Environmental LLC	F	469 715-2642
Prosper (G-17215)		
Rodessa Operating Company Inc	G	903 534-4765
Robstown (G-17516)		
Rosetta Resources Offshore LLC	C	713 335-2400
Houston (G-11666)		
Rosetta Resources Operating LP	C	281 872-3100
Houston (G-11667)		
Royalty Clearinghouse Ltd	F	800 877-5122
Austin (G-1474)		
Rsp Permian LLC	F	432 818-1300
Midland (G-15391)		
Rsp Permian LLC	E	214 252-2700
Dallas (G-4916)		

▲ Rutherford Oil Corporation ....F ...713 622-5555	Seneca Resources Corporation ....D.....713 374-6300	Stratum Energy Romania LLC..........F ...832 813-8947
Houston *(G-11701)*	Houston *(G-11830)*	Montgomery *(G-15642)*
Rutherford Oil Corporation ....F ...830 334-8396	Sentry Oil & Gas LLC.......................F ...212 753-6367	Strong Services LP ....D...903 693-3966
Pearsall *(G-16614)*	Mico *(G-15094)*	Carthage *(G-2922)*
Rutherford-Moran Exploration ....E ...859 254-4775	SHD Oil & Gas LLC ....F ...713 595-4274	Summit Petroleum LLC ....E ...432 682-9800
Houston *(G-11702)*	Houston *(G-11854)*	Midland *(G-15423)*
S K Resources Inc ....F ...713 782-1075	Shearwater Geoservices Inc ....F ...281 921-8000	Sun Energy Services LLC..................F ...432 701-9000
Houston *(G-11711)*	Houston *(G-11855)*	Midland *(G-15424)*
Sabalo Explrtion Operating LLC.......E ...361 888-7708	Shell Gulf of Mexico Inc ....F ...713 241-6161	Sundown Operating Inc ....D...806 229-6102
Corpus Christi *(G-3614)*	Houston *(G-11859)*	Sundown *(G-15614)*
Sable Permian Resources LLC.........E ...713 579-8000	Shell Oil Company ....F ...713 241-6471	Superior Pipeline Company ....D...806 323-8145
Houston *(G-11719)*	Houston *(G-11861)*	Canadian *(G-2654)*
Sable Prmian Resources Fin LLC ....F ...713 579-8000	Sheridan Prod Partners I-A LP ....C ...432 683-5271	Surgitech Inc ....E ...800 975-6850
Houston *(G-11720)*	Midland *(G-15407)*	Houston *(G-12126)*
Saexploration Holdings Inc ....F ...281 258-4400	Sheridan Prod Partners I-A LP ....F ...713 548-1000	Sutton Bros Inc ....F ...325 387-2053
Houston *(G-11723)*	Houston *(G-11866)*	Sonora *(G-19030)*
Sage Energy Company ....E ...210 404-2828	Sheridan Production Co LLC ....D...806 842-3521	Swn International LLC ....A ...832 796-1000
San Antonio *(G-18443)*	Lorenzo *(G-14345)*	Spring *(G-19171)*
Samson Resources Company ....E ...806 435-7200	Sheridan Production Co LLC ....D...432 263-4301	Swn Production (arkansas) LLC........A ...832 796-1000
Perryton *(G-16649)*	Big Spring *(G-2098)*	Spring *(G-19172)*
Sanare Energy Partners LLC ....F ...713 626-9696	Sheridan Production Co LLC ....D...325 453-2108	Swn Production Company LLC...........E ...281 618-4700
Houston *(G-11741)*	Robert Lee *(G-17499)*	Houston *(G-12133)*
Sanchez Oil & Gas Corporation........C ...713 783-8000	Sheridan Production Co LLC ....C ...713 548-1000	Sylvan Energy LLC ....D...412 222-9600
Houston *(G-11742)*	Houston *(G-11867)*	Houston *(G-12134)*
Sanchez Oil & Gas Corporation........E ...713 783-8000	Sheridan Production Co LLC ....F ...979 567-7629	Synergy Oil & Gas LP ....F ...713 827-9988
Houston *(G-11743)*	Caldwell *(G-2635)*	Houston *(G-12135)*
Sandalwood Exploration LP ....F ...713 759-6095	Shorthorn Resources Inc ....F ...713 668-0550	Talon Oil & Gas LLC ....F ...214 323-8360
Houston *(G-11745)*	Houston *(G-11874)*	Dallas *(G-5034)*
Sandalwood Oil & Gas Inc ....F ...713 759-6095	Siana Oil & Gas Co LLC ....F ...713 568-1082	Talos Energy Inc ....C ...713 328-3000
Houston *(G-11746)*	Houston *(G-11876)*	Houston *(G-12150)*
Sanday Corporation...........................F ...832 717-4412	Sierra Resources LLC ....F ...713 365-6100	Talos Energy LLC ....E ...713 328-3000
Spring *(G-19164)*	Houston *(G-11881)*	Houston *(G-12151)*
Saratoga Resources Inc ....F ...713 458-1560	Sigmund Kane & Hatch Inc ....F ...713 782-1075	Talos Petroleum LLC ....F ...281 872-1999
Houston *(G-11751)*	Houston *(G-11888)*	Houston *(G-12153)*
Sasol (usa) Corporation ....F ...281 588-3000	Signal Peak Silica LLC ....C ...281 822-4568	Talos Production LLC ....G ...713 328-3000
Houston *(G-11753)*	Houston *(G-11892)*	Houston *(G-12154)*
Saxet Petroleum Inc ....F ...713 783-4883	Silver Creek Oil & Gas LLC ....D...972 573-1630	Tana Exploration Company LLC.........D...469 276-8262
Houston *(G-11760)*	Irving *(G-13180)*	Dallas *(G-5035)*
Saybolt LP ....D...281 478-1300	Silver Hill Enrgy Partners LLC ....E ...214 865-6555	Tanos Energy LLC ....F ...903 597-7667
Deer Park *(G-5294)*	Dallas *(G-4964)*	Tyler *(G-20160)*
◆ Sbm Offshore Usa Inc ....B ...281 848-6000	Sinochem Petroleum USA LP ....F ...832 742-8670	▲ Taos Resources Oper Co LLC ....F ...713 993-0774
Houston *(G-11762)*	Houston *(G-11906)*	Houston *(G-12157)*
Schlumberger Limited ....E ...713 513-2000	▲ Site Safe Solutions Ltd ....D...940 612-2286	Targa Resources Corp.......................E ...713 584-1053
Houston *(G-11767)*	Gainesville *(G-7368)*	Channelview *(G-3042)*
Schlumberger Limited ....F ...713 513-2000	◆ Sk Gc Americas Inc ....F ...713 341-5820	Tauren Exploration Inc ....F ...972 681-8047
Houston *(G-11768)*	Houston *(G-11911)*	Dallas *(G-5036)*
Schlumberger Omnes Inc ....B ...713 375-3400	Skh Management LP ....F ...713 782-1075	Taurus Oil Inc ....F ...432 685-3520
Houston *(G-11770)*	Houston *(G-11914)*	Midland *(G-15432)*
◆ Schlumberger Technology Corp .....A ...281 285-8500	SM Energy Company ....E ...281 677-2800	Tecpetrol Corporation ....E ...713 974-3322
Sugar Land *(G-19542)*	Houston *(G-11915)*	Houston *(G-12181)*
Schlumberger Technology Corp ....E ...281 285-8400	SM Energy Company ....D...432 688-1700	Tejones Operating Corporation ....G ...210 824-5957
Sugar Land *(G-19545)*	Midland *(G-15411)*	San Antonio *(G-18526)*
Schlumberger Technology Corp ....C ...312 237-2810	SM Energy Company ....F ...281 677-2800	Tellurian Inc ....E ...832 962-4000
San Antonio *(G-18458)*	Houston *(G-11916)*	Houston *(G-12193)*
Schlumberger Technology Corp ....C ...832 310-2155	▲ Smith Energy Company ....F ...713 651-9102	Tema Oil and Gas Company ....E ...281 829-3206
Houston *(G-11772)*	Houston *(G-11922)*	Houston *(G-12196)*
Schlumberger Technology Corp ....C ...281 285-8500	▲ Smith Production Inc ....E ...281 583-0196	Temple Generation I LLC ....E ...254 598-3700
Sugar Land *(G-19549)*	Houston *(G-11924)*	Temple *(G-19708)*
Schlumberger Technology Corp ....E ...281 285-8226	Smith Production Inc ....E ...281 296-5600	Tepee Petroleum Company Inc..........G ...713 659-8300
Sugar Land *(G-19550)*	The Woodlands *(G-19920)*	Houston *(G-12206)*
Schlumberger Technology Corp ....C ...281 285-3501	Sn Midstream LLC ....E ...713 783-8000	Terra Energy Partners LLC ....E ...281 936-0355
Houston *(G-11779)*	Houston *(G-11928)*	Houston *(G-12209)*
Schlumberger Technology Corp ....C ...281 285-8500	Snd Operating LLC ....E ...214 691-3072	Terrace Energy LLC ....F ...817 546-7490
Houston *(G-11780)*	Dallas *(G-4972)*	Fort Worth *(G-7044)*
Schlumberger Technology Corp ....E ...432 694-0000	Sonterra Grp Zppelinn Enrgy LP ....F ...210 930-3111	Tetra Technologies Inc ....E ...903 693-9500
Midland *(G-15396)*	San Antonio *(G-18484)*	Carthage *(G-2923)*
Scorpion Flowback LLC ....F ...432 302-1628	South Bay Resources LLC ....F ...713 785-8700	Texakoma Financial Inc ....E ...972 701-9106
Midland *(G-15400)*	Houston *(G-11959)*	Plano *(G-17026)*
Sea Eagle Ford LLC ....E ...720 390-6244	Southwestern Energy Company........D...832 796-1000	Texakoma Operating LP ....E ...972 701-9106
Houston *(G-11795)*	Spring *(G-19167)*	Plano *(G-17027)*
Seabed Geosolutions (us) Inc ....E ...713 904-2244	Spectraseis Inc ....E ...303 658-9171	Texas Australian Power Inc................E ...940 723-4122
Houston *(G-11796)*	Houston *(G-12006)*	Wichita Falls *(G-20815)*
Segundo Navarro Drilling Ltd ....E ...210 384-3200	Speedway LLC ....B ...877 609-4255	Texas Coastal Energy Co LLC ....E ...214 429-3700
San Antonio *(G-18465)*	Houston *(G-12012)*	Dallas *(G-5057)*
Seidler Oil & Gas LP ....G ...817 259-1777	Speedway LLC ....F ...432 758-6700	Texas Energy Holdings Inc ....E ...214 231-4000
Alvarado *(G-345)*	Seminole *(G-18887)*	Dallas *(G-5059)*
◆ Seismic Eqp Solutions Inc ....E ...832 288-4427	Spindletop Drilling Company ....F ...972 644-2581	Texas Geologic Services LLC............E ...979 542-3893
Houston *(G-11815)*	Dallas *(G-4997)*	Giddings *(G-7702)*
◆ Seismic Exchange Inc ....E ...832 590-5100	Spindletop Oil & Gas Co ....E ...972 644-2581	Texas Intl Gas & Oil Co.....................F ...915 860-8803
Houston *(G-11816)*	Dallas *(G-4998)*	El Paso *(G-5999)*
Seitel ....D...832 295-8300	Spire Marketing Inc ....E ...346 308-7549	Texas Pipeline Webb ....E ...210 298-2222
Houston *(G-11817)*	Houston *(G-12016)*	San Antonio *(G-18541)*
▲ Seitel Inc ....E ...713 881-8900	Square Mile Energy LLC ....E ...713 266-3685	Texla Energy Management Inc...........F ...713 655-9900
Houston *(G-11818)*	Houston *(G-12029)*	Houston *(G-12260)*
Seitel Management Inc ....D...713 881-8900	Stakeholder Gas Utility LLC ....E ...210 444-9664	Texod Energy LLC ....F ...214 998-5360
Houston *(G-11819)*	San Antonio *(G-18493)*	Dallas *(G-5079)*
Selman & Associates Ltd ....C ...432 563-0084	▲ Steward Enterprises Inc ....C ...432 687-2553	Texseis Inc ....G ...713 465-3181
Midland *(G-15403)*	Midland *(G-15420)*	Houston *(G-12263)*
Seneca Resources Company LLC.....E ...713 654-2600	Strand Energy LC..............................F ...713 658-8096	◆ Tgs-Nopec Geophysical Company ...D...713 860-2100
Houston *(G-11829)*	Houston *(G-12074)*	Houston *(G-12268)*

Tgs-Nopec Geophysical Company........E 281 319-4944
Humble (G-12803)

The Cumming Company Inc ....F 817 737-2393
Fort Worth (G-7053)

Thomas Reprographics Inc ....F 281 875-2500
Houston (G-12276)

Three Rivers Operating Co LLC ....F 512 600-3190
Austin (G-1577)

Three Span Oil & Gas Inc ....F 432 684-6511
Midland (G-15437)

Three Streams Energy LLC ....F 469 917-1777
Dallas (G-5088)

Timekeepers Inc ....D 830 331-1224
Boerne (G-2142)

Top Coat Inc ....E 979 233-9558
Freeport (G-7216)

Torrent Energy Services LLC ....E 512 722-3439
Wimberley (G-20885)

◆ Total E&P Usa Inc ....C 713 647-3000
Houston (G-12330)

◆ Total Holdings Usa Inc ....E 713 483-5000
Houston (G-12331)

Tradewinds Petrotrade LLC ....F 713 465-7590
Houston (G-12341)

Transamerican Natural Gas Corp ....C 281 372-5304
Houston (G-12346)

Transatlantic Petro USA Corp ....F 214 220-4323
Addison (G-169)

Transatlantic Petroleum Ltd ....F 214 220-4323
Addison (G-170)

Transcanada USA Services Inc ....E 832 320-5000
Houston (G-12348)

Transtex LLC ....F 832 369-6986
Irving (G-13197)

Travis Peak Resources LLC ....F 512 814-0345
Houston (G-12357)

Trek Resources Inc ....F 214 373-0318
Dallas (G-5107)

◆ Tri Resources Inc ....E 713 584-1000
Houston (G-12362)

Tri-Star Petroleum Company ....G 713 222-0011
Houston (G-12364)

Trinity River Energy Oper LLC ....G 817 872-7800
Houston (G-12376)

Triple Diamond Energy Oper LLC ....F 972 267-8600
Dallas (G-3853)

Triple N Services Inc ....E 432 687-1994
Midland (G-15446)

Tritex Technologies Inc ....F 214 346-6200
Richardson (G-17413)

Triton Data Services Inc ....E 281 578-9700
Houston (G-12381)

Triumph Energy Partners LLC ....G 918 986-8283
Dallas (G-5119)

TRT Holdings Inc ....E 214 283-8500
Dallas (G-5121)

Trwa Inc...............................D 817 361-8839
Fort Worth (G-7083)

Trwa Inc...............................E 817 361-8839
Fort Worth (G-7084)

Twilight Services LLC ....F 817 326-4806
Granbury (G-7815)

▲ Txco Resources Inc ....F 210 822-8864
Dallas (G-5124)

Tzc Services LLC ....F 432 517-1212
Midland (G-15451)

U S Energy Development Corp ....F 682 305-2868
Arlington (G-807)

Unit Corporation ....D 432 362-0901
Odessa (G-16188)

Unit Petroleum Company ....F 713 960-8870
Houston (G-12444)

United Shtdown Sfety Texas Inc ....F 877 805-5155
Pasadena (G-16522)

Unitex Oil & Gas LLC ....F 432 685-0014
Midland (G-15456)

Universal Valve Company Inc ....E 432 689-6341
Midland (G-15458)

Upham Oil & Gas Company LP ....E 940 325-4491
Mineral Wells (G-15544)

Urban Oil & Gas Group LLC ....E 972 543-8800
Plano (G-17043)

Ursa Resources Group II LLC ....F 713 456-3000
Houston (G-12480)

US Operating Inc ....F 214 393-3992
Dallas (G-3856)

◆ Vaalco Gabon (etame) Inc ....E 713 623-0801
Houston (G-12515)

Valence Midstream Ltd ....E 281 359-3659
Kingwood (G-13658)

◆ Valerus Feld Sltons Hldngs LLC ....E 713 744-6100
Houston (G-12520)

▼ Valerus Field Solutions LP ....E 877 983-7500
Houston (G-12521)

Vanguard Permian LLC ....F 432 362-2209
Odessa (G-16195)

Vantage Energy Services Inc ....E 281 404-4700
Houston (G-12533)

Vaughn Energy Services ....F 936 539-9096
Conroe (G-3382)

Vector Seismic Data Processing ....F 303 571-1515
Houston (G-12543)

Venado Oil & Gas LLC ....F 512 518-2900
Austin (G-1628)

Venado Oil & Gas LLC ....F 512 518-2900
Charlotte (G-3049)

Verado Energy Inc ....F 214 368-5322
Dallas (G-5159)

Verado Oil and Gas Corporation ....F 214 368-5322
Dallas (G-5160)

Verdun Oil Company LLC ....E 713 554-4577
Houston (G-12550)

Viceroy Petroleum LP ....E 832 783-5790
College Station (G-3209)

Viking International Limited ....E 214 220-4323
Dallas (G-5167)

Vine Oil & Gas LP ....F 469 606-0540
Plano (G-17045)

Vitruvian Exploration II LLC ....F 832 458-3100
Cypress (G-3825)

Vitruvian Exploration IV LLC ....E 832 458-3100
Cypress (G-3826)

Vitruvian II Woodford LLC ....D 832 458-3100
The Woodlands (G-19939)

Vog Palo Verde LP ....E 512 518-2900
Austin (G-1643)

▼ Walter Oil & Gas Corporation ....E 713 659-1221
Houston (G-12597)

Wapiti Operating LLC ....D 713 365-8500
Houston (G-12598)

Warren Resources Inc ....E 214 393-9688
Dallas (G-5172)

◆ Wartsila North America Inc ....C 281 233-6200
Houston (G-12600)

Waterford Operating LLC ....F 713 255-6200
Houston (G-12604)

Weatherford Fracturing Tech ....F 817 882-9955
Fort Worth (G-7130)

Weatherford International LLC ....G 817 443-3000
Benbrook (G-2048)

Welder Exploration & Prod Inc ....F 210 354-1515
San Antonio (G-18613)

Western Atlas Intl Inc ....B 713 972-4000
Houston (G-12641)

Western Gas Resources Inc ....F 432 395-2973
Fort Stockton (G-6332)

Western Marketing Inc ....G 817 232-8626
Saginaw (G-17759)

◆ Westerngeco LLc ....A 713 789-9600
Houston (G-12644)

White Oak Operating Co LLC ....F 281 876-2025
Houston (G-12662)

Wildcat Midstream Oper LLC ....E 214 310-1213
Dallas (G-5186)

Wildhorse Resources LLC ....E 713 568-4910
Houston (G-12666)

William L Arrington ....G 806 669-3324
Pampa (G-16345)

Wilson County Holdings LLC ....F 512 402-7273
Austin (G-1669)

Winn Exploration Co Inc ....F 361 844-6900
Corpus Christi (G-3657)

▲ Woodside Energy (usa) Inc ....C 713 963-8490
Houston (G-12690)

Wsh Land Inc ....F 713 622-4823
Houston (G-12700)

Wsi Cased Hole Specialist Inc ....E 800 658-9674
Snyder (G-19015)

Xog Operating LLC ....E 432 683-3171
Midland (G-15473)

Xstar Resources LLC ....F 817 495-9306
Jacksboro (G-13224)

Xto Energy Inc ....F 505 333-3100
Fort Worth (G-7155)

Zarvona Energy LLC ....F 713 600-0600
Houston (G-12721)

Zaza Energy LLC ....F 713 595-1900
Houston (G-12722)

Zaza Energy Corporation ....F 713 595-1900
Houston (G-12723)

Zion Oil & Gas Inc ....F 214 221-4610
Dallas (G-5209)

1389 Oil & Gas Field Svcs, NEC

212 Resources LLC ....D 303 892-5616
Houston (G-8404)

2w Services LLC ....F 361 645-1010
Goliad (G-7746)

3 Amorez LLC ....F 432 269-4199
Midland (G-15099)

365 Certified Logistics LLC ....F 512 743-9304
Pflugerville (G-16655)

3s Team LLC ....D 918 396-4155
Pasadena (G-16375)

4-A Oilfield Enterprises ....F 903 668-3815
Longview (G-14186)

4I Oilfield Services LLC ....E 830 879-5300
Cotulla (G-3689)

5I Energy Services LLC ....F 936 539-1232
Conroe (G-3251)

A & M Tubular Maintenance Inc ....E 903 983-1007
Kilgore (G-13529)

A & R Energy Services Corp ....F 254 732-7759
Waco (G-20353)

A and M Services Inc ....F 432 290-5536
Andrews (G-532)

A E & Sons LLC ....F 281 898-4021
Pearland (G-16535)

A F C Lease Service Inc ....E 361 364-2547
Sinton (G-18960)

A&E Oilfield Services LLC ....D 956 380-5098
Mission (G-15547)

◆ Abasco LLC ....E 281 446-1500
Humble (G-12742)

Abshier Energy LLC ....G 432 352-4338
Bowie (G-2189)

Absolute Roustabout Svc LLC ....D 432 488-8788
Midland (G-15103)

▲ Accessesp LLC ....E 713 589-2599
Stafford (G-19281)

Accurate Pmpg Contractings Inc ....F 254 562-9747
Mexia (G-15086)

Ace Energy Solutions Inc ....F 281 394-9989
Katy (G-13347)

Acid and Cementing Svcs Inc ....E 903 729-2500
Palestine (G-16294)

Acme Energy Services Inc ....A 432 561-5271
Midland (G-15104)

Acme Truck Line Inc ....F 361 576-2934
Victoria (G-20235)

Acuren Inspection Inc ....A 281 228-0000
La Porte (G-13716)

Adobe Oilfield Ltd ....G 432 337-3731
Odessa (G-15902)

Advance Hydrocarbon Corp ....F 979 778-8100
Bryan (G-2451)

Advance Hydrocarbon Corp ....F 979 542-1520
Giddings (G-7690)

Advance Hydrocarbon Corp ....F 979 690-2226
Houston (G-8483)

Advanced Cementing Svcs Inc ....F 979 921-0356
Hempstead (G-8248)

Advanced Hydrstatic Svcs L L C ....E 940 337-7950
Wichita Falls (G-20737)

Advanced Stimulation Tech Inc ....D 432 617-3250
Midland (G-15106)

Affirm Oilfield Services LLC ....A 817 644-3360
Fort Worth (G-6354)

Afi Unlimited LLC ....E 936 591-9300
Shelbyville (G-18894)

Aggregate Plant Products Co ....D 210 333-1111
San Antonio (G-17874)

Aguilar Oilfield Services ....E 432 230-2548
Odessa (G-15904)

Aim Oilfield Services ....F 281 814-9787
Pearland (G-16537)

Airtrust Intl Systems Corp ....F 713 491-4455
Texas City (G-19785)

▲ Aker Solutions Inc ....C 713 685-5700
Houston (G-8519)

Alamo Pressure Pumping LLC ....B 432 695-6210
Midland (G-15111)

Alert Control Technologies LLC ....G 281 288-1321
Tomball (G-19955)

Alinet Oilfield Services Corp ....F 903 984-2307
Kilgore (G-13531)

All City Well Service ....F 432 332-8863
Odessa (G-15908)

◆ All Points Equipment Co LLC ....F 337 369-6314
Houston (G-8540)

Allamon Tool Company Inc ....E .... 936 449-5433 Montgomery *(G-15625)*	Astrimar Consultants LLC ....E .... 281 994-7816 Houston *(G-8729)*	◆ Baker Hghes Olfld Oprtions LLC ....F .... 713 879-1000 Houston *(G-8796)*
Alliance Field Services LLC ....D .... 432 332-4308 Midland *(G-15113)*	Astrimar Consultants LLC ....E .... 281 994-7816 Houston *(G-8730)*	Baker Hghes Prcess Ppline Svcs ....G .... 832 519-2000 Houston *(G-8798)*
Allied Ofs LLC ....F .... 832 482-3730 Tomball *(G-19956)*	Atk Oilfield Trnsp USA Inc ....D .... 432 452-3550 Odessa *(G-15920)*	Baker Hughes ....F .... 806 273-6531 Borger *(G-2162)*
Allied Oil Field Mch Pump LLC ....D .... 806 894-7263 Levelland *(G-14003)*	◆ Atlantic Pacific Marine Corp ....F .... 713 346-4300 Houston *(G-8740)*	Baker Hughes ....C .... 432 385-7861 Snyder *(G-18983)*
Allied Well Service Inc ....F .... 361 664-6122 Alice *(G-204)*	Atx Oil and More LLC ....E .... 512 660-0696 Austin *(G-947)*	Baker Hughes A GE Company LLC ....C .... 281 351-8131 Tomball *(G-19965)*
Allied Wireline Services LLC ....F .... 713 343-7280 Houston *(G-8555)*	Auto Dril Inc ....F .... 432 561-8455 Midland *(G-15125)*	Baker Hughes A GE Company LLC ....D .... 713 580-9700 Houston *(G-8799)*
Allpoints Oilfield Svcs LLC ....F .... 713 393-4200 Houston *(G-8558)*	Auto Fire and Safety Cons ....G .... 832 585-0423 Conroe *(G-3260)*	Baker Hughes A GE Company LLC ....G .... 361 883-1591 Corpus Christi *(G-3480)*
Allred Construction Company ....D .... 806 435-5817 Perryton *(G-16631)*	Avk Construction Group Inc ....F .... 972 255-9464 Irving *(G-12939)*	Baker Hughes A GE Company LLC ....E .... 432 685-8900 Midland *(G-15131)*
Allstream Envmtl Svcs LLC ....F .... 713 408-7237 San Antonio *(G-17899)*	▼ Axiom Technologies LLC ....E .... 281 931-0907 Houston *(G-8760)*	Baker Hughes A GE Company LLC ....B .... 432 248-3000 Odessa *(G-15923)*
Alpha Tech International Inc ....A .... 281 240-8989 Stafford *(G-19284)*	Axis Well Services LLC ....D .... 903 759-0082 Longview *(G-14199)*	Baker Hughes A GE Company LLC ....C .... 713 625-4200 Houston *(G-8800)*
Alterman Energy Services Inc ....F .... 210 496-6888 San Antonio *(G-17901)*	Axis Well Services LLC ....D .... 432 333-1111 Odessa *(G-15921)*	Baker Hughes A GE Company LLC ....D .... 956 383-0142 Edinburg *(G-5578)*
Altus Intervention USA Inc ....E .... 346 231-0060 Houston *(G-8573)*	Azar Services LLC ....F .... 956 717-0023 Laredo *(G-13864)*	Baker Hughes A GE Company LLC ....B .... 210 662-5200 San Antonio *(G-17936)*
American Safety Services Inc ....C .... 432 552-7625 Odessa *(G-15914)*	B & B Roustabout Inc ....D .... 806 872-7276 Lamesa *(G-13822)*	Baker Hughes A GE Company LLC ....B .... 936 336-7218 Liberty *(G-14114)*
Amerig Solutions LLC ....F .... 713 960-6606 Houston *(G-8617)*	B & D Services Inc ....F .... 979 733-9938 Sheridan *(G-18903)*	Baker Hughes A GE Company LLC ....E .... 903 690-0026 Carthage *(G-2899)*
Ana-Log Inc ....E .... 903 597-6341 Tyler *(G-20046)*	B & E Roustabout Inc ....E .... 432 393-5672 Big Spring *(G-2070)*	Baker Hughes A GE Company LLC ....E .... 956 791-0466 Laredo *(G-13866)*
Anadrill Directional Svcs Inc ....F .... 281 745-6983 Houston *(G-8634)*	B & J Vacuum Tank Service Inc ....G .... 936 536-6148 Daisetta *(G-3832)*	Baker Hughes A GE Company LLC ....D .... 361 573-2493 Victoria *(G-20243)*
Analytic Stress Relieving Inc ....D .... 281 471-9600 La Porte *(G-13724)*	B & S Services Inc ....F .... 281 342-1052 Boling *(G-2146)*	Baker Hughes A GE Company LLC ....E .... 972 550-3933 Irving *(G-12942)*
Andeavor Rio Holdings LLC ....F .... 281 566-3000 Sugar Land *(G-19444)*	B J Services Company USA ....A .... 713 625-4200 Houston *(G-8775)*	Baker Hughes A GE Company LLC ....D .... 281 276-5400 Sugar Land *(G-19447)*
Anderson Mud Logging Service ....F .... 903 693-5817 Carthage *(G-2898)*	B J Services Company USA ....E .... 281 357-2700 Tomball *(G-19963)*	Baker Hughes A GE Company LLC ....E .... 432 681-8300 Midland *(G-15132)*
Anderson Perforating Ltd ....E .... 830 569-1120 Pleasanton *(G-17061)*	B J Services Company USA ....A .... 713 879-1727 Houston *(G-8776)*	Baker Hughes A GE Company LLC ....B .... 281 363-6000 The Woodlands *(G-19834)*
Anything Goes Enterprises LLC ....F .... 210 608-1741 San Antonio *(G-17908)*	B J Services Company USA ....A .... 713 439-8600 Houston *(G-8777)*	Baker Hughes A GE Company LLC ....G .... 979 826-3621 Hempstead *(G-8249)*
Anzures Welding Roustabout A ....G .... 432 385-4122 Odessa *(G-15916)*	B&C Texas Leasing LLC ....D .... 432 362-0548 Pecos *(G-16616)*	Baker Hughes A GE Company LLC ....B .... 713 625-4200 Houston *(G-8801)*
Apache Packers LLC ....E .... 432 758-6202 Seminole *(G-18880)*	B-P Supply Inc ....E .... 806 872-9169 Lamesa *(G-13823)*	Baker Hughes Financing LLC ....D .... 713 439-8600 Houston *(G-8804)*
Apergy Artfl Lift Intl LLC ....E .... 903 266-3552 Tyler *(G-20047)*	Badger Bmb Services Inc ....D .... 432 447-0498 Pecos *(G-16617)*	Baker Hughes Holdings LLC ....E .... 956 285-2002 Laredo *(G-13867)*
Apollo Perforators Inc ....E .... 432 563-0891 Odessa *(G-15917)*	Badger Pressure Control LLC ....E .... 903 687-4100 Waskom *(G-20515)*	Baker Hughes Holdings LLC ....D .... 325 853-2553 Eldorado *(G-6044)*
Applied US Energy Inc ....E .... 713 466-1538 Houston *(G-8669)*	Bailey & Harley Services LLC ....E .... 409 994-5857 Buna *(G-2560)*	Baker Hughes Holdings LLC ....F .... 713 625-4200 Houston *(G-8805)*
Applied US Energy Inc ....F .... 432 689-0102 Midland *(G-15117)*	Baker Hghes Olfld Oprtions Inc ....F .... 806 665-5786 Pampa *(G-16315)*	Baker Hughes Holdings LLC ....D .... 713 439-8600 Houston *(G-8808)*
Aransas Fuel LLC ....E .... 361 992-5223 Corpus Christi *(G-3474)*	Baker Hghes Olfld Oprtions LLC ....E .... 432 685-8900 Midland *(G-15128)*	Baker Hughes Holdings LLC ....D .... 806 637-4745 Brownfield *(G-2329)*
ARC Pressure Data Inc ....F .... 432 563-2371 Aubrey *(G-846)*	Baker Hghes Olfld Oprtions LLC ....F .... 281 456-5300 Houston *(G-8792)*	Baker Hughes Holdings LLC ....D .... 817 426-7080 Burleson *(G-2568)*
Archer Prod Cmpletion Svcs LLC ....E .... 281 951-4038 Houston *(G-8681)*	Baker Hghes Olfld Oprtions LLC ....F .... 713 879-3760 Houston *(G-8793)*	Baker Petrolite ....E .... 432 498-9191 Odessa *(G-15925)*
Archrock Inc ....C .... 281 836-8000 Houston *(G-8685)*	Baker Hghes Olfld Oprtions LLC ....E .... 940 626-4169 Tyler *(G-20057)*	Baker Petrolite ....E .... 903 984-0251 Kilgore *(G-13533)*
Archrock Inc ....F .... 432 567-1050 Midland *(G-15118)*	Baker Hghes Olfld Oprtions LLC ....C .... 713 923-9351 Houston *(G-8794)*	Baker Petrolite LLC ....G .... 940 658-3574 Knox City *(G-13662)*
Archrock Inc ....F .... 432 336-8632 Fort Stockton *(G-6328)*	Baker Hghes Olfld Oprtions LLC ....E .... 432 694-7761 Midland *(G-15129)*	Baker Petrolite LLC ....F .... 979 567-9859 Caldwell *(G-2627)*
Archrock Inc ....E .... 361 572-9904 Victoria *(G-20239)*	Baker Hghes Olfld Oprtions LLC ....E .... 361 573-2493 Victoria *(G-20242)*	Baker Petrolite LLC ....D .... 940 626-4436 Decatur *(G-5243)*
Archrock Inc ....F .... 903 389-5666 Fairfield *(G-6168)*	Baker Hghes Olfld Oprtions LLC ....E .... 432 694-9517 Midland *(G-15130)*	Baker Petrolite LLC ....F .... 361 394-7544 Freer *(G-7222)*
Archrock Inc ....D .... 806 669-8900 Pampa *(G-16314)*	Baker Hghes Olfld Oprtions LLC ....D .... 361 692-3000 Pleasanton *(G-17062)*	Baker Petrolite LLC ....F .... 409 935-2248 La Marque *(G-13706)*
Arctic Pipe Insptn Inc Texas ....D .... 281 456-8300 Houston *(G-8686)*	Baker Hghes Olfld Oprtions LLC ....E .... 210 662-5650 San Antonio *(G-17935)*	Baker Petrolite LLC ....F .... 806 229-8121 Sundown *(G-19612)*
Arguijo Oilfield Services Inc ....E .... 432 550-5650 Odessa *(G-15918)*	Baker Hghes Olfld Oprtions LLC ....D .... 713 466-1322 Houston *(G-8795)*	Bakken Express LLC ....F .... 281 359-8382 Kingwood *(G-13638)*
Ark La Tex Surveying Co Inc ....F .... 903 938-9939 Marshall *(G-14762)*	Baker Hghes Olfld Oprtions LLC ....D .... 972 466-2673 Carrollton *(G-2701)*	Balderas Welding Services LLC ....F .... 432 661-3164 Odessa *(G-15926)*
Arkhoma Transports Inc ....E .... 806 435-2380 Perryton *(G-16633)*	Baker Hghes Olfld Oprtions LLC ....E .... 432 563-1900 Odessa *(G-15922)*	Banks Petroleum Inc ....E .... 512 478-0059 Austin *(G-974)*
Arpco Valves & Controls LLC ....F .... 903 834-7007 Kilgore *(G-13532)*	Baker Hghes Olfld Oprtions LLC ....G .... 832 519-2000 Houston *(G-8797)*	Barnett Gathering LLC ....F .... 817 870-2800 Fort Worth *(G-6427)*
Array Coating Technology LLC ....E .... 936 321-7000 Houston *(G-8703)*	Baker Hghes Olfld Oprtions LLC ....E .... 817 806-3200 Fort Worth *(G-6421)*	Barrera Contractors Inc ....F .... 432 639-2516 Iraan *(G-12916)*
Artesia Ecoscience LLC ....F .... 281 978-2521 Houston *(G-8710)*	Baker Hghes Olfld Oprtions LLC ....E .... 281 351-8131 Tomball *(G-19964)*	Barrilleaux Inc ....D .... 903 545-2280 Oakwood *(G-15892)*
Asher Oil Field Specialty ....F .... 361 293-0562 Yoakum *(G-20959)*	Baker Hghes Olfld Oprtions LLC ....E .... 361 289-0373 Corpus Christi *(G-3479)*	Basic Energy Services Inc ....E .... 361 348-3320 Premont *(G-17203)*
Asphwax Inc ....G .... 281 568-8415 Stafford *(G-19288)*	Baker Hghes Olfld Oprtions LLC ....C .... 800 441-0535 Yorktown *(G-20976)*	Basic Energy Services Inc ....D .... 817 334-4100 Fort Worth *(G-6429)*

Basic Energy Services Inc ....E 817 645-0853
Fort Worth (G-6430)

Basic Energy Services Inc ....E 918 225-1111
Fort Worth (G-6431)

Basic Energy Services Inc ....F 432 523-4251
Andrews (G-537)

Basic Energy Services Inc ....E 432 445-2216
Pecos (G-16618)

Basic Energy Services Inc ....E 361 578-3503
Victoria (G-20244)

Basic Energy Services Inc ....E 432 620-5500
Midland (G-15134)

Basic Energy Services Inc ....F 940 683-5484
Bridgeport (G-2288)

Basic Energy Services Inc ....C 432 586-2586
Kermit (G-13508)

Basic Energy Services Inc ....E 979 733-0488
El Campo (G-5612)

Basic Energy Services Inc ....D 254 442-2200
Fort Worth (G-6432)

Basic Energy Services Inc ....E 903 295-0817
Longview (G-14201)

Basic Energy Services Inc ....E 903 895-4448
Overton (G-16275)

Basic Energy Services Inc ....D 325 884-5901
Big Lake (G-2054)

Basic Energy Services Inc ....F 432 267-8885
Big Spring (G-2072)

Basic Energy Services Inc ....E 936 248-2788
Tenaha (G-19723)

Basic Energy Services Inc ....E 325 762-2239
Albany (G-184)

Basic Energy Services Inc ....E 432 620-0880
Midland (G-15135)

Basic Energy Services Inc ....C 325 573-8837
Snyder (G-18984)

Basic Energy Services Inc ....G 361 574-9512
San Antonio (G-17939)

Basic Energy Services Inc ....F 432 580-8821
Odessa (G-15927)

Basic Energy Services LP ....D 432 264-1212
Big Spring (G-2073)

Basic Energy Services LP ....D 432 530-0907
Odessa (G-15928)

Basic Energy Services LP ....F 432 758-9215
Seminole (G-18881)

Basic Energy Services LP ....D 806 592-4287
Denver City (G-5416)

Basic Energy Services LP ....E 817 334-4100
Fort Worth (G-6433)

Basic Energy Services LP ....E 361 358-2505
Beeville (G-1982)

Basic Energy Services LP ....F 903 657-8171
Henderson (G-8257)

Basic Energy Services LP ....E 903 643-1140
Fort Worth (G-6434)

Basic Energy Services LP ....E 409 842-6262
Dayton (G-5221)

Basic Esa Inc ....D 817 334-4100
Knox City (G-13663)

Basic Marine Services Inc ....C 817 334-4100
Fort Worth (G-6435)

Basils Oilfield Service Inc ....E 936 274-5575
Saratoga (G-18740)

Basin Pipeline LLC ....E 817 460-7777
Fort Worth (G-6437)

Bass Energy Services LLC ....D 903 687-1800
Waskom (G-20516)

Bassler Energy Services Inc ....E 979 535-4593
Caldwell (G-2628)

Bastion Technologies Inc ....E 281 283-9330
Houston (G-8823)

Bb Chemicals Inc ....E 432 381-2595
Odessa (G-15929)

Bbb Tank Services LLC ....C 832 695-2132
Baytown (G-1808)

Bc Johnson Assoc LLC ....E 281 489-4894
Houston (G-8841)

BCM & Associates Inc ....F 432 580-7161
Odessa (G-15930)

BCM & Associates Inc ....E 432 580-7161
Odessa (G-15931)

Beagle Steam Service Inc ....G 806 274-6892
Borger (G-2163)

Beck Bros Inc ....D 361 289-6082
Beeville (G-1983)

Beckman Well Servicing Company ......E 806 435-2543
Perryton (G-16634)

Bedrock Production LLC ....E 281 786-0220
Houston (G-8850)

BEg Liquid Mud Services Corp ....F 979 542-7000
Giddings (G-7692)

Belarco Indus Clg Odessa LLC ....E 432 381-0999
Odessa (G-15932)

Bep Oilfield Ltd ....F 281 873-9100
Houston (G-8859)

Bergstein Well Servicing LLC ....E 806 741-1095
Lubbock (G-14372)

▲ Bico Drilling Tools Inc ....E 832 598-9200
Houston (G-8879)

Big 4 Inc ....E 409 787-2733
Hemphill (G-8245)

Big C Rentals LLC ....G 432 266-8834
Andrews (G-538)

Big D Equipment Company Ltd ....D 432 682-1664
Midland (G-15139)

Big E Services LLC ....F 432 550-2443
Odessa (G-15934)

Big Lake Services Company LLC ......F 432 686-0475
Midland (G-15140)

Big Shot LLC ....E 504 877-2335
Lancaster (G-13840)

Big Spring Cat Cnstr Inc ....F 432 394-4161
Coahoma (G-3164)

Big Star LLC ....E 325 617-5731
San Angelo (G-17781)

Big Tom Construction Inc ....G 903 752-1008
Overton (G-16276)

Billy R Coats Inc ....E 432 523-3861
Andrews (G-539)

Bioremediation Contrs Cons Inc ....F 806 771-8033
Lubbock (G-14374)

Birch Operations Inc ....E 832 701-1776
Houston (G-8890)

Bisn Oil Tools LLC ....E 832 919-7500
Houston (G-8893)

Bison Energy Partners Inc ....E 281 873-9100
Houston (G-8894)

◆ BJ Services LLC ....E 281 408-2361
Tomball (G-19966)

Black Elk Energy LLC ....E 281 507-7652
Houston (G-8902)

Black Elk Energy Offshore Oper ....F 832 973-4230
Houston (G-8903)

Black Gold Oper & Cnstr Inc ....F 903 766-3636
Waskom (G-20517)

Black Horse Test Services ....F 903 938-8554
Marshall (G-14764)

Black Sheep Oilfield Svcs LLC ....F 940 644-1720
Chico (G-3051)

Black Widow Energy LLC ....F 956 378-5363
Edinburg (G-5579)

Blackgold Services Inc ....F 936 336-9600
Liberty (G-14115)

Blackstar Envmtl Indus Svcs LL ....F 713 280-0590
Houston (G-8911)

Blakely Construction Co Inc ....C 432 363-6650
Odessa (G-15937)

Blaxtone Energy LLC ....F 432 250-9039
Odessa (G-15938)

Blaze Sales and Service Inc ....F 713 828-1685
Houston (G-8913)

Bless Oilfield Services Inc ....E 281 227-3300
Houston (G-8915)

Blsr Operating Ltd ....E 281 369-2032
Sandy Point (G-18722)

Blue Quail Energy Services LLC ....E 432 684-0999
Midland (G-15143)

Bmf Oil & Gas Services Inc ....F 832 443-2089
Houston (G-8926)

Bml Inc ....E 325 676-3355
Abilene (G-19)

▲ Bobbitt Construction Inc ....E 903 769-4513
Hawkins (G-8228)

Bobcat Contracting LLC ....C 254 582-0205
Hillsboro (G-8322)

BOF Services Inc ....E 806 741-1080
Lubbock (G-14377)

BOF Services Inc ....D 432 523-2110
Andrews (G-540)

BOF Services Inc ....E 325 653-1755
San Angelo (G-17783)

Bold Production Services LLC ....G 281 615-6799
Houston (G-8945)

Boots & Coots LLC ....E 281 931-8884
Houston (G-8953)

◆ Boots & Coots LLC ....E 281 871-2699
Houston (G-8954)

Boots & Coots Services LLC ....E 281 931-8884
Houston (G-8955)

Boots & Coots Services Inc ....F 281 931-8884
Houston (G-8956)

◆ BOP Products LLC ....F 281 955-6321
Houston (G-8957)

Border Lease Services Inc ....D 956 728-1959
Laredo (G-13868)

Border Swabbing Inc ....E 361 575-7852
Victoria (G-20248)

Border Well Services Inc ....D 956 753-7540
Laredo (G-13869)

Borets US Inc ....E 432 697-1900
Midland (G-15148)

Boss Oil Field Service Inc ....F 361 574-7939
Victoria (G-20249)

BP Surface Solutions LLC ....D 325 387-3881
San Angelo (G-17786)

Brammer Petroleum Inc ....F 940 665-4807
Gainesville (G-7335)

▲ Brammer Pipe and Steel Inc ....F 940 665-4807
Gainesville (G-7336)

Brandt A Varco Company ....F 940 683-6286
Bridgeport (G-2289)

Breakwater Energy Partners LLC ....D 281 648-1268
Houston (G-8980)

Breckenridge Exploration Co ....F 254 559-7566
Breckenridge (G-2225)

Bridgeport Tank Trucks LLC ....D 940 683-9440
Bridgeport (G-2290)

◆ Bridges Equipment Ltd ....F 432 333-9741
Odessa (G-15943)

Bridges Holdings Inc ....F 817 396-4340
Cresson (G-3706)

Bridwell Oil Management LLC ....F 940 723-4351
Wichita Falls (G-20747)

Brinkerhoff Inspection Inc ....F 432 924-2915
Midland (G-15150)

Brinkerhoff Inspection Inc ....E 432 770-4626
Midland (G-15151)

Britt Dirt Contracting Inc ....F 806 872-5194
Lamesa (G-13824)

Brittany Energy LLC ....D 210 785-2893
San Antonio (G-17968)

Broncs Inc ....F 432 614-8305
Odessa (G-15945)

Brothers Well Service Ltd ....E 979 543-6851
El Campo (G-5613)

Brown and Anthony Inc ....F 806 762-1975
Lubbock (G-14384)

Bryant Industrial Services LLC ....E 956 838-5120
Port Isabel (G-17135)

Bulldog Wireline Inc ....F 936 399-3999
North Zulch (G-15884)

Bulldog Wireline Inc ....F 979 260-9034
College Station (G-3179)

Bullet Production Services LLC ....E 361 504-4200
Corpus Christi (G-3491)

Bullzeye Oilfield Service LLC ....F 325 665-0220
Tye (G-20041)

Burk Royalty Co Ltd ....F 940 397-8600
Wichita Falls (G-20748)

Burns Welding Works Inc ....F 432 682-0495
Midland (G-15153)

Burnsco Blowt Prvntr RPR & Srv ....F 432 367-5329
Odessa (G-15946)

Burton Oil Svc Operations LLC ....F 713 805-2934
Tyler (G-20062)

Butchs Oilfield Services Inc ....E 956 381-8409
Edinburg (G-5580)

Butchs Rat Hole Anchr Svc Inc ....E 806 894-6294
Levelland (G-14004)

Bws Construction LLC ....F 254 562-6820
Mexia (G-15088)

Byrd Oilfield Services LLC ....F 432 385-7635
Odessa (G-15948)

▲ Byrd Oilfield Services LLC ....E 325 690-0053
Abilene (G-27)

C & A Contractors Inc ....F 817 441-4178
Aledo (G-197)

C & C Coating Inc ....E 432 682-7201
Waco (G-20372)

C & C Logging ....F 903 895-4738
New London (G-15849)

C Automation Inc ....E 832 467-4644
Houston (G-9026)

▲ C Hinton Enterprises Inc ....E 432 339-0411
Odessa (G-15950)

C P Bailey Cnstr Co Inc ....G 936 348-3627
Madisonville (G-14585)

C&J Well Services Inc ....E 817 573-3550
Granbury (G-7794)

Company		Phone	Location (ID)
C&S Lease Service LC	E	903 988-8642	Kilgore (G-13534)
C2 Pipeline Services LLC	E	713 253-6980	Conroe (G-3271)
◆ Cactus Wellhead LLC	C	713 626-8800	Houston (G-9044)
Cadena Services LLC	F	956 727-9391	Laredo (G-13872)
Cagle Fishing & Rental Tls Inc	F	432 381-3061	Odessa (G-15952)
Calfrac Well Services Corp	C	210 268-0800	Converse (G-3391)
CAM Field Solutions LLC	E	832 533-2706	Houston (G-9057)
CAM Services Inc	F	254 629-8561	Eastland (G-5561)
Camac International Corp	E	713 965-5100	Houston (G-9059)
Cameron International Corp	E	361 289-1455	Corpus Christi (G-3494)
Cameron International Corp	A	713 939-2211	Houston (G-9067)
Cameron International Corp	E	281 391-4600	Katy (G-13355)
Cameron International Corp	E	713 946-2122	Houston (G-9069)
Cameron International Corp	B	713 939-2650	Houston (G-9070)
Cameron International Corp	E	713 849-7500	Houston (G-9071)
▼ Cameron International Holding	F	713 513-3300	Houston (G-9074)
Cameron Solutions Inc	F	325 573-8521	Snyder (G-18985)
◆ Cameron Solutions Inc	C	713 849-7500	Houston (G-9079)
Camin Cargo Control Inc	E	409 729-3399	Port Arthur (G-17103)
Camin Cargo Control Inc	F	361 884-3922	Corpus Christi (G-3495)
Camino Agave Inc	C	830 393-1051	Floresville (G-6246)
Camino Agave Inc	D	956 765-4635	Zapata (G-20979)
Canary LLC	C	432 563-1970	Odessa (G-15954)
Canden Resources Ltd	E	403 473-8786	Austin (G-1022)
Canon Safety Services Ltd	F	903 984-5928	Kilgore (G-13535)
Canrig Drilling Technology Ltd	F	281 443-1414	Houston (G-9085)
▲ Canyon Offshore Inc	D	713 856-6010	Houston (G-9088)
Capps Construction and Gas Co	F	903 693-2580	Carthage (G-2900)
Car-Tex Transport & Vacuum Svc	D	903 693-6271	Carthage (G-2901)
Carber Holdings Inc	E	281 837-8003	Deer Park (G-5263)
Carber Holdings Inc	E	713 797-2859	Houston (G-9089)
Catalyst Oilfld Svcs 2016 LLC	D	432 563-0727	Gardendale (G-7420)
Cavern Solutions Inc	F	713 393-7733	Houston (G-9103)
Cbg Corporation	E	512 491-7541	Austin (G-1032)
CDI Vessel Holdings LLC	A	713 361-2600	Houston (G-9113)
CDK Perforating	E	817 945-1051	Fort Worth (G-6500)
CDK Perforating LLC	C	817 945-1051	Fort Worth (G-6501)
CDK Perforating Holdings Inc	C	817 945-1051	Fort Worth (G-6502)
CDM Resource Management LLC	D	281 376-2980	Houston (G-9114)
Cec Corrosion Services LLC	F	361 883-6930	Corpus Christi (G-3498)
Ceda International Inc	F	281 478-2600	League City (G-13952)
▲ Central Texas Oilfield Sup Co	G	254 562-5522	Mexia (G-15089)
Centrax International Corp	E	281 465-0781	Spring (G-19203)
Cetco Energy Services Co LLC	D	281 578-8911	Houston (G-9147)
Chachos Lease Service Inc	F	361 661-1143	Alice (G-205)
Chalk Mountain Svcs Texas LLC	E	817 473-1931	Mansfield (G-14661)
Champion Drilling Fluids Inc	F	580 225-3450	Houston (G-9156)
Champion Oilfield Services LLC	E	512 327-3300	Austin (G-1043)
Chandler Mfg LLC	D	940 763-1528	Wichita Falls (G-20753)
Chapas Oilfield Services LLC	F	956 847-6460	Zapata (G-20980)
Charles Howard Construction	E	325 387-3093	Sonora (G-19024)
Charts Ltd	E	432 697-7801	Midland (G-15159)
▼ Chemex Modular LLC	D	801 565-8099	New Waverly (G-15856)
Chemical Service Company	E	432 523-5290	Andrews (G-542)
Chemical Tracers Inc	F	936 564-1866	Nacogdoches (G-15691)
Cheyenne Services Inc	E	713 937-7733	Houston (G-9182)
Chief Oilfield Tech LLC	F	432 614-4481	Midland (G-15164)
Chisholm Trail Oilfield Svc	F	979 567-4943	Caldwell (G-2630)
Choat Enterprises Inc	F	432 367-8459	Odessa (G-15960)
Choctaw Lease Service LLC	F	361 449-3506	George West (G-7623)
CIC Construction Inc	D	979 648-2968	Louise (G-14351)
Cierra Tank Services LLC	E	713 568-4028	Houston (G-8375)
Cimarron Energy Holding Co LLC	D	701 352-9620	Houston (G-9189)
Circle 8 Crane Services LLC	E	361 933-0696	Robstown (G-17505)
Circle 8 Crane Services LLC	D	432 332-6900	Odessa (G-15962)
Circle 8 Crane Services LLC	C	361 442-0306	Robstown (G-17506)
Cjr Contractors Inc	C	806 592-2232	Denver City (G-5417)
CK Kustoms Iron Works Inc	F	281 850-6118	Rockport (G-17529)
CL&f Offshore LLC	E	281 873-9378	Houston (G-9204)
CL&f Operating LLC	F	281 873-9378	Houston (G-9205)
Clean Combustion Inc	E	832 333-7800	Dayton (G-5223)
◆ Clean Harbors San Leon Inc	D	281 339-1352	Dickinson (G-5473)
Clean Hrbors Expirtion Svcs In	F	281 478-2600	Deer Park (G-5264)
Clear View Unlimited LLC	F	409 782-3594	Silsbee (G-18951)
Clements Fluids Buffalo Ltd	E	903 581-5110	Tyler (G-20067)
Clements Fluids Henderson Ltd	E	903 581-5110	Tyler (G-20068)
Cline Construction Inc	E	432 267-6006	Big Spring (G-2075)
Cnooc Marketing USA Inc	D	713 380-4800	Houston (G-9221)
Coastal Flow Measurement Inc	D	713 477-1956	Houston (G-9225)
Coastal Wireline Services Inc	E	281 485-6548	Pearland (G-16546)
Cogent Energy Services LLC	E	713 554-1200	Houston (G-9238)
Coil Tubing Partners LLC	E	432 201-4111	Midland (G-15170)
Coil Tubing Technology Inc	E	281 651-0200	Houston (G-9240)
Cokinos Oil Company	F	713 974-0101	Houston (G-9242)
▲ Colaco Consultants Inc	F	281 370-2948	Spring (G-19107)
Collins Roustabout & Well Svc	F	325 754-4237	Winters (G-20904)
Collins Surveying and Mapping	E	903 234-8051	Longview (G-14210)
Colt Services LP	E	409 842-6929	Beaumont (G-1874)
▼ Colt Services LP	E	281 471-9099	La Porte (G-13729)
Comac Well Service Inc	E	806 274-2259	Borger (G-2170)
Commercial Diesl Parts Svc Ltd	E	830 372-1594	Seguin (G-18830)
Compass Drctional Guidance Inc	F	281 442-7484	Houston (G-9255)
Compass Drctional Guidance Inc	E	281 442-7484	Houston (G-9256)
Compass Well Services LLC	E	325 387-2940	Sonora (G-19025)
Compass Well Services LLC	D	817 244-2555	Fort Worth (G-6532)
Compass Well Services LLC	E	432 561-5970	Midland (G-15173)
Complete Energy Services Inc	E	940 668-5186	Gainesville (G-7340)
Complete Energy Services Inc	A	940 665-4373	Gainesville (G-7341)
Complete Pipe Services LLC	E	903 988-1124	Kilgore (G-13537)
◆ Complete Production Svcs Inc	E	281 372-2300	Houston (G-9260)
Complete Solids Control LLC	F	817 372-2702	Fort Worth (G-6533)
Completion Technologies Inc	F	936 760-2734	Conroe (G-3279)
Compliance Group Inc	F	936 447-6100	Montgomery (G-15628)
Comprssion Contrls Rentals LLC	F	903 643-7970	Longview (G-14212)
Concho Oilfield Services LLC	E	325 762-3300	Albany (G-186)
Concho Services LLC	F	325 869-5242	Eden (G-5571)
Conner Machine and Welding Inc	C	806 274-2281	Borger (G-2171)
Consolidated Wellsite Svcs LLC	E	903 983-9811	Haslet (G-8218)
Continental Laboratories Inc	E	713 460-0780	Houston (G-9285)
Continental Prod Svcs Inc	E	281 431-0502	Houston (G-9288)
Convoy Servicing Co	F	214 638-3050	Irving (G-12979)
Cooper Oil Company Inc	F	817 332-7755	Fort Worth (G-6546)
Copan Corporation	G	806 665-1267	Pampa (G-16319)
Copano/Operations Inc	F	361 668-8580	Alice (G-207)
Copperbeck Energy Partners LLC	E	214 238-4881	Dallas (G-4166)
Core Laboratories (texas) LLC	B	713 328-2673	Houston (G-9315)
Core Laboratories Holding Inc	B	713 328-2673	Houston (G-9316)
Core Laboratories LP	D	432 687-5797	Midland (G-15178)
Core Laboratories LP	D	903 984-4223	Kilgore (G-13538)
◆ Core Laboratories LP	B	713 328-2673	Houston (G-9317)
Cornerstone Synergy LLC	F	806 679-9178	Panhandle (G-16347)
Corrosion Ltd	E	432 561-8504	Odessa (G-15969)
Cosi Energy Services LLC	E	956 765-6729	Zapata (G-20981)
Cothran AG Services LLC	F	254 625-1715	Teague (G-19664)
Cottons Inspection Service Inc	E	432 366-2631	Odessa (G-15970)
Coyote Roustabout LLC	F	325 455-0090	Hawley (G-8230)
Crab Ventures LLC	E	979 571-0258	Bryan (G-2467)
Craft Wireline Services Inc	F	432 943-5150	Monahans (G-15603)
Crawford Industrial Svcs LLC	E	409 925-9580	Santa Fe (G-18733)
Crest Pumping Technologies LLC	D	817 484-5100	Fort Worth (G-6560)
Cretic Energy Corp	F	713 922-3784	Montgomery (G-15630)
Crossfire LLC	E	970 884-4869	The Woodlands (G-19849)
Crowder Construction Co Inc	E	254 629-1688	Eastland (G-5562)
Crowder Services Inc	E	325 853-2852	Eldorado (G-6045)
◆ Crown Energy Technologies Inc	F	403 215-5300	Houston (G-9347)

Company	Code	Phone
Crudechem Technology LLC	F	832 206-0790
Pattison (G-16531)		
Cs Well Service LLC	F	325 242-2438
Colorado City (G-3224)		
Csi Compressco LP	B	281 367-1983
The Woodlands (G-19850)		
Cudd Pressure Control Inc	E	361 387-8521
Robstown (G-17507)		
Cudd Pressure Control Inc	D	432 580-3544
Odessa (G-15971)		
Cudd Pressure Control Inc	C	903 988-2161
Kilgore (G-13542)		
Cudd Pumping Services Inc	F	210 310-1330
San Antonio (G-18034)		
▲ Cudd Pumping Services Inc	F	832 295-5555
The Woodlands (G-19851)		
Cudd Well Control	E	713 849-2769
Spring (G-19204)		
CW Ford Rentals LP	F	903 935-7608
Kilgore (G-13543)		
Cwr Management LLC	E	512 212-9737
San Marcos (G-18683)		
Cyclone Construction LLC	F	512 288-0430
Austin (G-859)		
Cyclone Services LLC	F	817 594-5571
Weatherford (G-20584)		
D & D Swabbing LLC	F	903 729-7922
Palestine (G-16298)		
D & L Well Service Inc	E	432 336-8101
Fort Stockton (G-6329)		
D & R Casing Services Inc	F	432 263-8900
Big Spring (G-2078)		
D Courtney Construction Inc	B	903 694-2911
Carthage (G-2905)		
D M Glover Incorporated	F	325 392-2561
Ozona (G-16279)		
D-Js Well Svc Roustabout Inc	E	806 273-2667
Borger (G-2172)		
Daeco Ltd	E	361 526-7017
Refugio (G-17240)		
Dan Blocker Petroleum Cons	D	903 234-2093
Longview (G-14222)		
Daniel Mike Construction Inc	E	903 389-2595
Fairfield (G-6172)		
Danos LLC	C	985 219-3313
Midland (G-15186)		
Dapco Services Inc	F	281 482-1479
Alvin (G-357)		
Daves Tubing Testing &HOt Oil	E	432 263-1747
Big Spring (G-2079)		
David Keels	E	409 316-9265
Hitchcock (G-8336)		
David Pond Well Service Inc	F	806 435-2384
Perryton (G-16637)		
David R Rogers Cnstr Inc	C	940 549-6374
Graham (G-7779)		
Davis Energy Services LLC	C	903 935-9269
Marshall (G-14774)		
Dcaf Inc	E	956 286-9177
Laredo (G-13877)		
Dcp Midstream LLC	E	432 343-7112
Coyanosa (G-3695)		
Dd Fluids LLC	E	361 985-2600
Robstown (G-17508)		
De Laune Drilling Service Ltd	F	361 664-0106
Alice (G-208)		
Deep Imaging Technologies Inc	F	281 290-0492
Tomball (G-19973)		
Deep Well Tubular Service Inc	F	432 699-6675
Midland (G-15188)		
▲ Deepsea Technologies Inc	F	713 849-5555
Houston (G-9424)		
Deepwater Subsea LLC	E	832 356-6781
Katy (G-13359)		
Deer Park Cnstr Assoc Inc	E	281 839-0020
Baytown (G-1815)		
Deerborne Energy Company	F	281 485-8705
Pearland (G-16555)		
Delmar Systems Inc	E	832 252-7100
Houston (G-9427)		
Delta Marine Technologies	F	936 582-7237
Montgomery (G-15631)		
▲ Delta Seaboard LLC	G	713 782-1468
Houston (G-9435)		
Dennis Energy Services Inc	F	956 712-1114
Laredo (G-13878)		
Desert Ndt LLC	E	325 864-6547
Abilene (G-37)		
Desert Ndt LLC	E	580 225-2108
Houston (G-9441)		

Company	Code	Phone
Detsco Inc	F	713 999-5260
Jersey Village (G-13298)		
Devonian Dirt Works LLC	G	432 253-7777
Odessa (G-15975)		
DFI Piling Inc	F	877 334-7453
Conroe (G-3291)		
Dfw Oilfield Services Inc	E	972 893-8025
Irving (G-12999)		
Dialog Wireline Services L L C	E	903 988-2311
Kilgore (G-13544)		
Dialog Wireline Services L L C	F	936 264-3847
Conroe (G-3292)		
Diamante Construction & Design	F	361 449-7072
Laredo (G-13880)		
Diamond D Slickline Svc Co Inc	E	325 573-0220
Snyder (G-18989)		
Diamond P Lease & Well Svc Inc	E	979 567-1919
Caldwell (G-2631)		
Diamond P Lease & Well Svc Inc	D	979 884-6111
Dime Box (G-5484)		
Diamond Refractory Svcs LLC	E	713 378-9200
Houston (G-9458)		
Diamond Tank Rental Inc	E	432 337-0011
Odessa (G-15976)		
Digco Utility Construction LP	F	281 833-2000
Houston (G-9468)		
Dixon Services Inc	F	903 579-9300
Tyler (G-20077)		
Dnv GL Noble Denton Usa LLC	B	281 396-1000
Katy (G-13396)		
◆ Dof Subsea Usa Inc	C	713 896-2500
Houston (G-9491)		
Don Brock Distributor Inc	D	361 592-5126
Kingsville (G-13626)		
Don Spencer Co	C	817 389-4413
Godley (G-7735)		
◆ Don-Nan Pump and Supply Co Inc	C	432 682-7742
Midland (G-15194)		
Don-Nan Pump and Supply Co Inc	F	432 530-1925
Odessa (G-15978)		
Doris Usa Inc	E	713 973-2520
Houston (G-9500)		
Dorsal Services Inc	E	361 394-6300
Alice (G-209)		
Dossey Oilfield Services LLC	F	325 928-0001
Merkel (G-15014)		
▲ Double Barrel Downhole Tech	F	281 495-1200
Houston (G-9501)		
Double D Tongs Inc	E	432 381-0602
Odessa (G-15979)		
Double O Field Services	F	361 364-2673
Sinton (G-18961)		
Double R Construction Inc	E	903 452-7890
Kilgore (G-13545)		
Double T Oilfield Service LLC	F	325 315-2370
Midland (G-15195)		
Downhole Innovations LLC	F	936 537-4640
Houston (G-9508)		
▼ Downhole Technology LLC	D	281 820-2545
Houston (G-9509)		
Downing Well Service Inc	F	830 665-4923
Devine (G-5449)		
Drag N Fly Trucking	F	903 987-0027
Kilgore (G-13546)		
Drilltools	F	903 986-3745
Kilgore (G-13547)		
▲ Drover Energy Services LLC	E	903 986-8911
Kilgore (G-13548)		
Drum Equipment Inc	G	936 336-9256
Liberty (G-14117)		
Ds Oilfield Construction LLC	F	361 396-0089
Alice (G-210)		
Dugga Boys LLC	E	361 364-4311
Sinton (G-18962)		
Dunagin Transport Company	E	325 928-5253
Merkel (G-15015)		
Dunn Services Inc	E	361 275-3952
Cuero (G-3760)		
◆ Duoline Technologies LLC	E	903 734-1371
Gilmer (G-7706)		
Duphil Inc	E	409 883-8550
Orange (G-16238)		
Dupr Energy Services LLC	F	713 231-9000
Houston (G-9538)		
Duval Well Service Inc	E	361 394-7079
Freer (G-7223)		
Dve Management Inc	E	214 957-1095
Greenville (G-8071)		
▲ Dynaenergetics Us Inc	D	512 327-2043
Houston (G-9544)		

Company	Code	Phone
Dynamic Downhole Services LLC	E	210 881-9002
San Antonio (G-18075)		
Dynamic Fishing & Rentals LLC	F	432 684-3898
Midland (G-15199)		
Dynasty Wireline Services LLC	E	432 363-3100
Midland (G-15200)		
E L Farmer & Company	E	432 366-2010
Odessa (G-15981)		
E T C Company	E	210 403-6402
Dallas (G-4285)		
E Z Roustabout	F	432 556-8419
Midland (G-15201)		
E&R Vacuum Truck Services LLC	F	956 618-9590
Edinburg (G-5585)		
Eagle Completion Usa Ltd	E	432 561-7000
Odessa (G-15982)		
Eagle Ford Reclamation Co LLC	E	361 786-3960
Three Rivers (G-19945)		
Eagle Pco LLC	E	432 400-2771
Midland (G-15202)		
Eagle Pco LLC	F	361 756-0666
Pleasanton (G-17065)		
Eagle Pco LLC	D	817 678-8998
Navasota (G-15731)		
East Texas Pipe Service Inc	F	903 639-2541
Hughes Springs (G-12739)		
Eastern Oil Well Service Corp	E	203 358-5700
Houston (G-9570)		
Eastham Drilling Inc	C	713 661-6890
Bellaire (G-1995)		
Ecoloop Energy Inc	E	972 885-5130
Plano (G-16856)		
Ecostream LLC	E	832 429-5317
Southlake (G-19066)		
Edge Integrity Services LLC	G	817 585-1007
Fort Worth (G-6605)		
Edge Specialty Services Inc	E	361 668-3343
Alice (G-211)		
El Paso Field Services LP	F	361 552-9601
Port Lavaca (G-17145)		
Electric Submersible Pump Inc	F	325 573-8101
Snyder (G-18990)		
Elite Upstream LLC	F	832 674-3050
Houston (G-9603)		
Emerge Energy Services LP	E	817 618-4020
Fort Worth (G-6610)		
Empire Tubing Tongs Inc	E	432 366-7702
Odessa (G-15988)		
Empire Wireline LLC	F	985 264-7746
League City (G-13955)		
Empirica LLC	E	713 466-7400
Houston (G-9620)		
Ems Usa Inc	C	713 595-7600
Pasadena (G-16427)		
◆ En-Fab Inc	D	713 225-4913
Houston (G-9623)		
Encore Wellhead Systems LLC	F	832 742-1350
Houston (G-9625)		
Encore Wellhead Systems LLC	E	832 742-1325
Angleton (G-571)		
Encore Wellhead Systems LLC	E	903 983-4481
Kilgore (G-13550)		
Endeavor Energy Resources LP	E	432 683-4292
Midland (G-15212)		
Endeavor Energy Resources LP	E	432 563-5000
Midland (G-15214)		
Endurance Lift Solutions LLC	D	281 269-6880
Gainesville (G-7343)		
Endurance Roustabout	E	432 697-1300
Midland (G-15215)		
Enercorp Engnred Solutions LLC	F	832 791-1276
The Woodlands (G-19861)		
Energes Oilfield Solutions LLC	F	830 769-1484
Jourdanton (G-13330)		
Energes Services LLC	C	432 307-0650
Odessa (G-15989)		
Energy Facility Services Inc	E	281 286-8500
Houston (G-9634)		
Energy Fishing & Rental Svc	F	361 668-8000
Alice (G-212)		
Energy Fishing Rentl Svcs Inc	F	713 433-5506
Houston (G-9635)		
Energy Operators Inc	E	281 351-1780
Tomball (G-19976)		
Energy Solutions Inc	F	281 257-2994
Tomball (G-19977)		
Enersys Corporation	E	281 598-7100
Stafford (G-19311)		
Enertech Industries Inc	E	432 550-0543
Odessa (G-15991)		

Company	Location		Phone
Enserco Midstream LLC	Houston (G-9654)	F	713 341-7378
Ensign Intl Enrgy Svcs Inc	Houston (G-9655)	E	281 872-7770
Ensign Management LLC	Houston (G-9656)	E	281 403-6304
Enterprise Hydrocarbons LP	San Antonio (G-18092)	D	713 381-6500
Entrec Corporation	Odessa (G-15992)	D	432 301-2794
Environmental Floors Inc	Georgetown (G-7651)	F	713 956-5526
Epic Energy Services LLC	Odem (G-15895)	C	361 222-1226
Epica Applied Technologies LLC	Converse (G-3392)	E	281 367-1983
Epica Applied Technologies LLC	Converse (G-3393)	E	210 310-7710
◆ Eproduction Solutions LLC	Kingwood (G-13641)	B	281 348-1000
Erhc Energy Inc	Houston (G-9691)	G	713 626-4700
Espada Oilfield Services LLC	Victoria (G-20262)	F	361 894-1810
Espinoza Services Inc	Denver City (G-5418)	F	806 592-8463
Estis Compression LLC	Kilgore (G-13552)	E	318 397-5557
Etech Envmtl Safety Solutions	Odessa (G-15993)	E	432 563-2200
Etos Inc	New London (G-15850)	D	903 895-2220
Ets Oilfield Services LP	Robstown (G-17509)	E	361 767-4200
Everett LLC	Odessa (G-15994)	F	432 381-5700
Evers and Sons Inc	Caldwell (G-2632)	D	979 596-2139
Excalibar Minerals LLC	Corpus Christi (G-3523)	F	361 883-5227
Express Energy Services GP LLC	Houston (G-9729)	A	713 625-7400
Express Energy Svcs Oper LP	San Angelo (G-17799)	D	325 659-4412
Express Energy Svcs Oper LP	Odessa (G-15995)	C	432 530-1111
Express Energy Svcs Oper LP	Houston (G-9730)	E	713 625-7400
Express Energy Svcs Oper LP	Bryan (G-2472)	E	979 589-2255
Express Energy Svcs Oper LP	Mission (G-15552)	E	713 625-7403
Express Energy Svcs Oper LP	Pleasanton (G-17066)	E	830 569-8606
Express Energy Svcs Oper LP	Iowa Park (G-12905)	F	940 592-4391
Expro Americas LLC	Longview (G-14233)	E	903 753-2003
Expro Americas LLC	Houston (G-9733)	E	281 977-2600
Extech Consulting LLC	Henrietta (G-8280)	E	940 613-6461
Exterran Corporation	Houston (G-9735)	E	281 836-7000
◆ Exterran Energy Solutions LP	Houston (G-9736)	C	281 836-7000
▲ Exterran Trinidad LLC	Houston (G-9737)	B	281 921-9337
Extreme Well Testing LLC	Weslaco (G-20659)	E	956 969-4452
Farm & Ranch Construction LLC	Iredell (G-12921)	E	254 364-2226
Fasterra Group LP	Argyle (G-600)	C	940 240-5800
FDL Operating LLC	Irving (G-13023)	E	469 453-7346
Fesco Ltd	Laredo (G-13884)	E	956 724-7501
Fesco Ltd	Corpus Christi (G-3527)	E	361 882-4124
Fesco Ltd	Alice (G-213)	D	361 661-1538
Fesco Ltd	Lufkin (G-14527)	D	936 632-7036
Fesco Ltd	Canadian (G-2649)	F	361 661-7000
Fesco Ltd	Kilgore (G-13553)	E	903 984-4814
Fesco Ltd	El Campo (G-5618)	E	979 543-9451
Fesco Ltd	Bryan (G-2473)	F	979 775-1825
Fesco Ltd	Edinburg (G-5588)	E	956 383-8378
Fesco Ltd	Odessa (G-16000)	E	432 332-3211
Fesco Ltd	Refugio (G-17241)	E	361 526-4644
Fesco Ltd	Victoria (G-20263)	E	361 575-7533
Fesco Ltd	Ozona (G-16283)	E	325 392-3773
Fesco Ltd	Beaumont (G-1893)	E	409 842-3000
Fieldco Energy Services Inc	Carthage (G-2907)	F	903 693-5900
First Energy Services Company	Fort Worth (G-6633)	B	817 334-4100
Fisher Construction	Odessa (G-16001)	E	432 332-7532
Fisher Lease Service Inc	Big Lake (G-2056)	E	325 884-2701
Fisk/MEI Inspection Svcs Inc	Houston (G-9793)	C	281 436-5500
Five Star Consolidated Co Ltd	Denver City (G-5419)	C	806 592-3113
Five Star Field Services LLC	Weatherford (G-20591)	D	817 594-9799
Five Star Roustabouts LLC	O Brien (G-15888)	E	940 657-4778
Fla Safety & Prod Svcs Inc	Charlotte (G-3047)	E	830 570-7286
Flat Creek Resources LLC	Fort Worth (G-6637)	F	817 310-8570
Flatrock Compression Ltd	Houston (G-9798)	E	281 517-3680
Fleaux Services Louisiana LLC	Midland (G-15231)	F	432 694-0004
Flint Energy Services Inc	Mission (G-15554)	F	956 585-9779
Flint Energy Services Inc	Pleasanton (G-17067)	C	830 569-8453
Flint Energy Services Inc	George West (G-7624)	C	361 449-2405
Flint Energy Services Inc	Pleasanton (G-17068)	C	940 683-4181
Flint Energy Services Inc	Fairfield (G-6174)	D	903 389-8716
Flo Trend Systems Inc	Houston (G-9804)	E	713 699-0152
Flow-Zone LLC	Rosharon (G-17605)	F	281 997-8899
Flowback Champion Services LLC	Pearland (G-16561)	F	832 731-5783
Flowback Green Services LLC	Beaumont (G-1894)	E	409 217-1482
Flr Oilfield Services LLC	Rankin (G-17232)	F	432 693-2245
Fluid Disposal Specialties Inc	Marshall (G-14777)	F	903 927-2050
Fluids Clements Management LLC	Tyler (G-20089)	G	903 581-5110
FMC Technologies Offshore LLC	Houston (G-9828)	E	713 341-7742
Forbes Energy Services Ltd	Alice (G-215)	F	361 664-0549
Fortay Inc	Sunray (G-19617)	F	806 948-4166
Forum Energy Technologies Inc	Odessa (G-16008)	D	432 550-9000
Forum Energy Technologies Inc	Argyle (G-601)	F	817 602-1174
Foster Testing Co Inc	Farnsworth (G-6227)	E	806 435-6876
Four K Services Inc	Canadian (G-2650)	F	806 323-8560
Fowlerton Energy Services LLC	Fowlerton (G-7161)	G	830 570-4507
Frac Fuel Solutions LLC	Cypress (G-3792)	E	713 907-4371
▲ Framework Offshore LLC	Katy (G-13405)	E	281 610-1078
◆ Franklin Howard Intl LLC	Houston (G-9856)	F	281 815-1527
Franks International LLC	Bryan (G-2474)	D	979 778-8700
Freddys Well Service Inc	Victoria (G-20265)	F	361 578-4559
Freeze Technology Intl	Amarillo (G-425)	E	806 371-8854
▲ Freudenberg Oil & Gas LLC	Houston (G-9867)	D	281 233-1400
Frontier Services Inc	Alice (G-216)	E	361 668-1188
Frontier Services Inc	San Antonio (G-18128)	E	210 520-1118
Frontline Energy Inc	Houston (G-9870)	F	713 228-3577
Fts International Inc	Flint (G-6237)	B	903 590-2440
Fts International Inc	Fort Worth (G-6652)	E	817 862-2000
Fulfer Vanek Well Servicing Co	Iowa Park (G-12906)	E	940 438-2276
Fulkrum Tchnical Resources Inc	Houston (G-9873)	D	713 485-4519
Fun Da Mentals For Educatn LLC	Houston (G-9874)	E	832 368-3345
G & W Trucking Inc	Snyder (G-18992)	E	325 573-6338
G E Oil Technology Inc	Houston (G-9886)	E	713 774-0340
Garrison Contractors Inc	Iraan (G-12918)	E	432 639-2811
Gates Fuel Services LLC	Santa Fe (G-18734)	E	409 925-8897
Gds International LLC	Houston (G-9910)	E	713 623-1449
Gdsware	Houston (G-9912)	F	832 350-1166
GE Oil & Gas Logging Svcs Inc	Corpus Christi (G-3534)	E	361 299-9457
GE Oil & Gas Logging Svcs Inc	Pearland (G-16565)	E	281 992-9676
▼ GE Oil & Gas Logging Svcs Inc	Sugar Land (G-19485)	E	281 579-9879
GE Oil & Gas Pressure Ctrl LP	Midland (G-15235)	D	432 686-0720
Gel Technologies Corp	Midland (G-15236)	F	432 683-1881
Gem Services LLP	McAllen (G-14865)	E	210 863-2020
Genco Energy Services Inc	McAllen (G-14866)	E	956 380-3710
Geonix Operating LP	Kilgore (G-13556)	E	903 983-3249
George Bartee Cnstr Co Inc	Grapeland (G-8005)	E	936 687-4811
Geoservices Incorporated	Houston (G-9944)	F	281 443-3370
Geosite Inc	San Angelo (G-17802)	E	325 655-4356
Gep Haynesville LLC	The Woodlands (G-19867)	E	281 363-9161
▲ Gibbons Inc	Bowie (G-2196)	F	940 872-2452
Giddings Volunteer Fire Dept	Giddings (G-7695)	E	979 492-1156
Gisler Brothers Logging Co	Runge (G-17729)	E	830 239-4651
▲ Global Am-Tx, Inc.	Alvin (G-364)	F	281 331-0200
Global Industries Inc	Carrollton (G-2745)	G	972 236-1366
Global Remote Technologies LLC	Spring (G-19125)	E	888 381-3222
Globalogix Inc	Aledo (G-199)	F	817 441-5570
Globalogix Inc	Houston (G-9982)	E	713 987-7630
Globe Well Service Inc	Big Lake (G-2057)	D	325 884-3091
Glover Inc	Ozona (G-16284)	F	325 392-2561
GM Oilfield & Trckg Svcs LLC	Midland (G-15237)	E	432 934-6525
Gmp Energy LLC	Houston (G-9987)	F	713 963-4600
Gobbato Builders LLC	Austin (G-1185)	F	737 843-4327
Gonco Oilfield Services LLC	Odessa (G-16016)	G	432 208-2389
▲ Gowell International LLC	Houston (G-10007)	E	713 909-2555
Gr Energy Services MGT LP	Sugar Land (G-19489)	E	281 201-6812
Grace Shursen Moore Assoc Inc	Amarillo (G-429)	G	806 358-6894
Graco Fishing & Rental Tls Inc	Frisco (G-7289)	F	214 618-3930

Graco Fishing & Rental Tls Inc	F	432 943-5019	Monahans (G-15604)
Grand Isle Shipyard Inc	D	432 362-0019	Odessa (G-16017)
Grand Isle Shipyard Inc	D	830 334-2665	Pearsall (G-16612)
Grand Operating Inc	G	972 788-2080	Addison (G-133)
Gravity Oilfield Services Inc	E	432 218-7888	Midland (G-15239)
Gravity Oilfield Services LLC	D	830 203-5210	Gonzales (G-7753)
Gravity Oilfield Services LLC	E	806 894-3151	Levelland (G-14007)
Gravity Oilfield Services LLC	D	817 558-9194	Cleburne (G-3092)
▼ Gravity Oilfield Services LLC	C	432 218-7889	Midland (G-15240)
Gray Energy Services LLC	A	806 894-6008	Levelland (G-14008)
Gray Wireline Services	F	361 526-4729	Refugio (G-17242)
Great Basin Petroleum Svcs LP	D	432 561-9702	Odessa (G-16018)
Great Texas Compression LLC	F	210 569-6742	San Antonio (G-18152)
Green & Hansen LLC	E	210 289-2482	Jourdanton (G-13331)
Green Energy Oilfield Svcs LLC	C	210 904-3400	Fairfield (G-6175)
▲ Greenes Energy Group LLC	E	337 232-1830	Houston (G-10035)
Greenwell Energy Solutions LLC	F	713 993-7772	Houston (G-10037)
Greenwell Energy Solutions LLC	F	432 381-2595	Odessa (G-16019)
Griffith Oil Field Services	G	409 246-8530	Kountze (G-13671)
Gryphon Oilfield Solutions LLC	F	281 738-3110	Houston (G-10051)
Gt Oilfield Repair Inc	E	361 782-7300	Edna (G-5606)
Gtz Services LLC	F	956 750-6147	Zapata (G-20982)
Guardian Wellhead Protection	D	432 368-5449	Odessa (G-16020)
Gulf Coast Casing Inc	E	361 575-5488	Victoria (G-20270)
▲ Gulf Island Fabrication Inc	B	713 714-6100	Houston (G-10065)
Gw Marine (usa) LLC	E	281 809-6213	Houston (G-10077)
Gyrodata Incorporated	F	432 561-8458	Midland (G-15242)
◆ Gyrodata Incorporated	D	713 461-3146	Houston (G-10078)
Gyrodata Incorporated	D	361 289-1031	Corpus Christi (G-3541)
H & M Dirt Contractors Inc	E	806 495-3293	Post (G-17190)
H and L Crimp Inc	F	325 672-9282	Abilene (G-45)
H G Nichols Construction Co	F	903 876-2527	Poynor (G-17202)
H2o Greenworks LLC	F	817 884-7788	Arlington (G-694)
Hacker Brothers Well Service	G	940 759-4196	Muenster (G-15669)
Halliburton Company	E	361 527-2780	Dilley (G-5481)
Halliburton Company	E	281 297-1200	Spring (G-19214)
Halliburton Company	E	972 418-3221	Carrollton (G-2751)
Halliburton Company	E	281 575-5000	Corpus Christi (G-3544)
Halliburton Company	E	281 575-3000	Houston (G-10097)
Halliburton Company	E	281 871-6875	Houston (G-10098)
Halliburton Company	A	281 871-2908	Houston (G-10099)
Halliburton Company	C	281 297-1200	Houston (G-10100)
Halliburton Company	E	972 418-3000	Carrollton (G-2752)
Halliburton Company	C	281 871-4000	Houston (G-10101)
Halliburton Company	F	713 455-9547	Houston (G-10102)

Halliburton Company	E	936 442-4700	Conroe (G-3300)
Halliburton Company	E	903 981-7032	Longview (G-14246)
Halliburton Company	E	210 621-1800	Victoria (G-20271)
Halliburton Company	G	713 839-2000	Houston (G-10103)
Halliburton Company	F	281 986-4400	Houston (G-10104)
Halliburton Company	F	903 389-9275	Fairfield (G-6176)
Halliburton Company	E	281 871-4482	Houston (G-10105)
Halliburton Company	E	281 871-4000	Houston (G-10106)
◆ Halliburton Company	E	281 871-2699	Houston (G-10107)
Halliburton Company	E	432 571-8600	Odessa (G-16024)
Halliburton Company	E	713 455-9547	Baytown (G-1790)
▲ Halliburton Delaware Inc	E	713 759-2600	Houston (G-10108)
◆ Halliburton Energy Svcs Inc	E	281 871-4000	Houston (G-10109)
Halliburton Energy Svcs Inc	D	281 871-4482	Houston (G-10110)
Halliburton International Inc	A	214 759-2600	Dallas (G-4429)
Hamilton Oilfield Services Inc	E	325 944-2540	San Angelo (G-17804)
Hamm Well Service Co	F	940 549-4769	Graham (G-7783)
Hammer Construction Inc	D	940 683-3131	Bridgeport (G-2294)
Hard Band Industries Inc	F	432 563-3752	Odessa (G-16027)
Hawkins Lease Service Inc	D	281 331-2739	Alvin (G-365)
Healthtronics Service Ctr LLC	B	512 328-2892	Austin (G-1697)
◆ Helix Enrgy Slutions Group Inc	C	281 618-0400	Houston (G-10150)
◆ Hercules Offshore Inc	A	713 350-5100	Houston (G-10158)
Heritage Wire Line Services	G	903 534-0671	Tyler (G-20097)
Hernandez Sandblasting	F	361 701-2522	Freer (G-7227)
High Roller Wells LLc	E	936 598-5577	Center (G-2999)
High Tide Oilfield Svcs LLC	G	361 394-1731	Freer (G-7228)
Hilliard Energy Inc	E	432 683-9100	Midland (G-15247)
Hli Resources LLC	C	817 240-4361	Cleburne (G-3095)
HM Roustabout Service Inc	F	830 563-5449	Eldorado (G-6046)
Holloman Corporation	E	281 878-2600	Houston (G-10194)
Holman Well Service LLC	D	806 665-3355	Pampa (G-16325)
Holverstott Najee	F	210 769-5246	San Antonio (G-18172)
Hooken R LLC	E	817 304-7645	Cuero (G-3761)
Horsepower Services LLC	E	713 582-2105	Houston (G-10209)
◆ Hotwell Us LLC	F	281 598-9990	Houston (G-10213)
Houston Business & Fincl Svcs	F	713 398-6314	Houston (G-10218)
Houston Casing Specialities	F	713 433-3940	Houston (G-10223)
Houston North Remodel	F	936 314-4654	Montgomery (G-15634)
▲ Houston Tubulars Inc	D	281 485-4014	Pearland (G-16569)
◆ Houston Well Screen Company	D	281 449-7261	Houston (G-10263)
Howard Measurement Co Inc	E	903 677-0700	Athens (G-827)
Hub City Industries	E	903 938-8554	Marshall (G-14783)
Huisache Energy Services Inc	F	361 299-2815	Robstown (G-17513)
Hulk Oilfield Services Inc	F	432 803-7060	Monahans (G-15605)

Hunting Energy Services Inc	D	281 821-5577	Houston (G-10281)
Hunting Energy Services Inc	F	281 328-1400	Crosby (G-3734)
Hunting Energy Services Inc	D	281 499-2583	Stafford (G-19327)
Hunting Energy Services Inc	E	832 902-2266	Baytown (G-1791)
Hunting Energy Services Inc	E	281 569-3620	Houston (G-10282)
Hunting Energy Services LLC	E	281 379-4289	Spring (G-19133)
◆ Hunting Energy Services LLC	E	281 820-3838	Houston (G-10283)
Hunting Titan Inc	F	281 463-5881	Houston (G-10285)
Hurd Oil Field Service Inc	E	940 567-3131	Jacksboro (G-13221)
Hutchins Oil and Lube	E	972 225-0846	Hutchins (G-12867)
Hydessco LLC	F	903 983-2021	Kilgore (G-13559)
Ic-I Remediate LLC	F	432 213-7813	Big Spring (G-2083)
Icon Oilfield Services LLC	F	214 758-0315	Dallas (G-4484)
Ili Technologies 2002 USA	F	713 960-0811	Houston (G-10322)
Infrastructure Networks Inc	E	832 598-6600	Houston (G-10361)
Innovex Downhole Solutions Inc	C	281 602-7815	Houston (G-10373)
Inspectorate America Corp	E	281 291-9000	Pasadena (G-16461)
Integrated Advantage Group LP	F	806 367-8031	Amarillo (G-493)
Integrated Production Svcs Inc	E	281 774-6700	Houston (G-10385)
Intense Wireline Solutions LLC	D	903 630-5440	Tyler (G-20103)
International Energy Svcs LLC	E	281 973-9462	Houston (G-10402)
International Well Testers	F	361 358-1990	Beeville (G-1986)
Interstate Explorations LLC	E	254 442-1057	Cisco (G-3067)
▼ Interstate Treating Inc	D	432 362-9291	Odessa (G-16034)
◆ Intertek Cnslting Trning USA I	E	337 235-4493	Spring (G-19219)
Intertek USA Inc	E	281 364-2800	Spring (G-19220)
▲ Interwell US LLC	E	832 461-1500	Houston (G-10408)
Ios/Pci LLC	E	281 310-5357	Houston (G-10414)
Ironhorse Unlimited Inc	C	903 489-2075	Malakoff (G-14635)
J & M Energy Services LP	E	432 943-7770	Monahans (G-15606)
J & P Services Inc	F	979 542-0500	Giddings (G-7697)
J & R Valley Oilfield Svcs Inc	F	956 581-7235	Mission (G-15556)
▲ J & W Services & Equipment Co	D	432 689-3947	Midland (G-15257)
J & X Trucking LLC	E	830 583-0611	Kenedy (G-13488)
J Connor Consulting Inc	E	281 578-3388	Houston (G-10436)
J I S Measurement & Operating	F	325 224-3036	San Angelo (G-17810)
J Patrick Services LLC	F	432 214-5443	Odessa (G-16035)
J Rollins Construction Inc	D	936 258-3485	Dayton (G-5231)
J&P Ramirez Services LLC	E	361 526-2072	Refugio (G-17243)
J-W Operating Company	E	432 332-0111	Odessa (G-16037)
J-W Operating Company	D	281 592-2351	Cleveland (G-3129)
J-W Operating Company	E	361 570-2788	Victoria (G-20275)
Jab Rentals Inc	E	432 296-6464	Odessa (G-16038)
Jade Services Inc	E	806 870-3883	Lamesa (G-13825)
Jag Energy Usa Inc	E	361 449-1400	George West (G-7625)

Jaguar Energy Services LLC ....F 337 250-4030	Katco Vacuum Truck Service LP ....E 361 527-4421	Khudairi Group Incorporated ....E 713 782-1080
Marion (G-14757)	Hebbronville (G-8235)	Houston (G-10530)
Jaguar Energy Services LLC ....E 337 250-4030	Kc Field Services Inc ....F 903 322-9353	Kil-Tex Oilfield Services LLC ....G....... 903 736-5051
Bryan (G-2480)	Buffalo (G-2545)	Kilgore (G-13561)
Jamco Services LLC ....D 432 242-6051	Keane Frac Tx LLC ....F 281 929-0370	King Pipeline Services LLC ....E 903 530-8667
Dallas (G-4523)	Houston (G-10508)	Fort Worth (G-6762)
Janssen Lease Service Inc ....E 361 771-3556	Keane Frac Tx LLC ....E 281 929-0370	King Well Service Inc ....D 806 323-6664
Ganado (G-7415)	Houston (G-10509)	Canadian (G-2652)
Jbl Oil & Gas Operating LLC ....F 281 516-3137	Keane Group Holdings LLC ....D 903 247-1053	King Workover Service Inc ....F 979 543-5464
Spring (G-19137)	Longview (G-14259)	El Campo (G-5620)
JCs Marine Oilfield Svc Inc ....E 281 338-7835	Keane Group Holdings LLC ....E 281 719-7200	Kingfisher Midstream LLC ....F 281 655-3200
League City (G-13967)	The Woodlands (G-19890)	Dallas (G-4557)
JD King Inc ....C 800 805-6302	Keane Group Holdings LLC ....C 432 488-3800	Kiva Construction & Engrg Inc ....E 409 252-3211
Seminole (G-18884)	Odessa (G-16044)	Anahuac (G-526)
Jdw Services Inc ....E 903 845-5586	Keane Group Holdings LLC ....A 281 716-9152	Kixx Rentals & Services LLC ....E 830 437-2959
Gladewater (G-7723)	Houston (G-10511)	Gonzales (G-7758)
Je Oilfield Services LLC ....F 361 701-1324	Kel-Tech Inc ....E 432 684-4700	Kizer Energy Inc ....E 281 712-2047
Alice (G-218)	Midland (G-15266)	Houston (G-10539)
Jeffcoat Production Service ....F 409 429-5900	◆ Kellogg Brown & Root Intl Inc ....F 713 753-2000	Kj Energy LLC ....F 214 297-5013
Spurger (G-19278)	Houston (G-10512)	Dallas (G-4559)
Jensco Transport Services LLC ....F 325 234-1412	Kellogg Brown Root ....E 361 758-2554	Kj Rustic Designs LLC ....D 832 477-6545
Eola (G-6124)	Aransas Pass (G-593)	Bryan (G-2486)
Jet Maintenance Inc ....E 361 576-3226	Kelman Technologies Inc ....E 281 529-3204	Klx Energy Services LLC ....D 832 844-1015
Victoria (G-20277)	Houston (G-10514)	Houston (G-10542)
JGB Oilfield Services LLC ....F 806 789-2796	Kenergy Oilfield Solutions LLC ....E 830 263-9951	Knight Energy Holdings LLC ....E 713 466-6660
Lubbock (G-14430)	Nixon (G-15867)	Houston (G-10547)
Jgt Services ....E 432 553-5167	▲ Kenjer Inc ....F 281 897-8600	▲ Knight Energy Services LLC ....E 832 678-8585
Andrews (G-545)	Houston (G-10516)	Houston (G-10548)
Jk Red Dirt Rentals LLC ....D 214 530-3922	Kenner Well Svc of Palestine ....E 903 729-3196	Knight Oil Tools LLC ....E 432 530-1010
Granbury (G-7801)	Palestine (G-16300)	Odessa (G-16054)
JM Construction ....E 956 518-2113	▲ Keppel Amfels Inc ....A 956 838-3110	Knight Oil Tools LLC ....F 361 668-8065
Brownsville (G-2370)	Brownsville (G-2374)	Alice (G-223)
Jmd Oilfield & Rig Service LLC ....E 469 261-2415	Kerr Oilfield Company ....E 940 327-0447	Koch Industries Inc ....E 903 693-5172
Odessa (G-16040)	Mineral Wells (G-15530)	Carthage (G-2911)
Jmd Oilfield and Rig Svc LLC ....E 432 208-9941	Key Energy Drilling Inc ....E 903 693-2622	Kodiak Gas Services LLC ....B 936 539-3300
Odessa (G-16041)	Carthage (G-2910)	Montgomery (G-15635)
Jmi Machine LLC ....E 361 664-2848	▲ Key Energy Drilling Inc ....D 432 620-0300	Kuykendall Btm Hole Pressure ....E 432 563-5231
Alice (G-219)	Houston (G-10521)	Odessa (G-16056)
Jmr Industries Ltd ....F 432 557-9721	Key Energy Drilling Inc ....G 713 651-4300	L & C Safety Inc ....D 432 653-0393
Midland (G-15260)	Kilgore (G-13560)	Odessa (G-16057)
Jodys Oilfield Service Inc ....F 432 523-6866	Key Energy Services Inc ....D 979 542-3344	L G Pump Inc ....E 432 550-3445
Andrews (G-546)	Giddings (G-7698)	Odessa (G-16058)
John Linder Operating Co LLC ....E 903 845-4240	Key Energy Services Inc ....E 361 668-1526	L R G Services Inc ....F 713 504-4470
Gladewater (G-7724)	Alice (G-220)	New Caney (G-15843)
John Oates Company Inc ....G 806 878-3338	Key Energy Services Inc ....E 432 381-1301	La Copa Field Services Inc ....D 361 364-1608
Stinnett (G-19427)	Odessa (G-16047)	Sinton (G-18963)
Johnson Cnstr Clearing LLC ....E 281 659-1428	Key Energy Services Inc ....D 432 523-5155	Lang & Mitchell Contrs Inc ....F 903 876-2882
Huntsville (G-12815)	Andrews (G-547)	Frankston (G-7167)
Johnson Matthey Inc ....D 281 291-7769	Key Energy Services Inc ....F 432 620-0300	Langford Roustabout Svcs LLC ....F 940 864-3490
Pasadena (G-16465)	Midland (G-15269)	Haskell (G-8213)
Jordan Spooling Service Inc ....E 432 366-6040	Key Energy Services Inc ....E 361 578-9975	Laredo Construction Inc ....F 281 499-4333
Odessa (G-16042)	Edna (G-5608)	Stafford (G-19345)
Jorn Well Service ....F 432 943-5699	Key Energy Services Inc ....D 713 651-4300	Lariat Construction Services ....G 361 318-9104
Monahans (G-15607)	El Campo (G-5619)	Pawnee (G-16533)
Jose Luis Villarreal ....E 956 765-5535	Key Energy Services Inc ....D 361 668-1818	Larry & Matt Inc ....D 806 665-4418
Zapata (G-20983)	Alice (G-221)	Pampa (G-16326)
JP Tubular Services Inc ....E 281 426-8596	▼ Key Energy Services Inc ....C 713 651-4300	Larry McHorse Services LLC ....F 361 275-4978
Crosby (G-3737)	Houston (G-10522)	Cuero (G-3762)
Jp3 Measurement LLC ....E 512 537-8450	Key Energy Services Inc ....D 432 586-2591	Latx Oilfield Services LLC ....E 903 934-8263
Austin (G-1262)	Odessa (G-16048)	Waskom (G-20518)
Jspaz Guardian Energy Svcs LLC ....E 432 606-5003	Key Energy Services Inc ....E 432 561-5682	Latx Operations LLC ....D 903 927-2091
Big Spring (G-2085)	Odessa (G-16049)	Waskom (G-20519)
JT Swabbing Services Inc ....F 956 580-8954	Key Energy Services Inc ....E 432 267-5291	Laverton Oilfield Services LLC ....F 325 899-3556
Mission (G-15557)	Big Spring (G-2086)	Albany (G-190)
Jta Service ....F 432 556-0091	Key Energy Services Inc ....E 432 488-2800	Leam Drilling Systems LLC ....E 936 539-1351
Midland (G-15262)	Odessa (G-16050)	Conroe (G-3318)
JV Roustabout Inc ....F 432 943-2999	Key Energy Services Inc ....C 432 558-3574	Leemak LP ....B 281 492-9555
Wickett (G-20839)	Crane (G-3699)	Houston (G-10619)
Jwb Consulting Service Inc ....F 817 675-6419	Key Energy Services Inc ....E 713 651-4300	Leeson Energy Services LLC ....F 432 689-7000
Midland (G-15263)	Houston (G-10523)	Midland (G-15273)
K & K Repair Service LLC ....E 361 573-5027	Key Energy Services Inc ....E 806 872-6688	Legacy Field Services LLC ....D 903 694-9445
Victoria (G-20278)	Lamesa (G-13826)	Carthage (G-2912)
K & N Perforators Inc ....E 361 578-8851	Key Energy Services Inc ....E 979 589-2594	Legend Energy Services LLC ....E 432 523-6585
Victoria (G-20279)	Bryan (G-2483)	Andrews (G-549)
K D M Hot Oil Service Inc ....G 432 683-0831	Key Energy Services Inc ....E 325 236-6611	Lengston Corporation ....F 713 757-1331
Midland (G-15264)	Sweetwater (G-19632)	Houston (G-10623)
K W Utility Cons Inc ....E 903 564-5771	Key Energy Services Inc ....D 903 538-2280	Lenoir Water Transfer Inc ....D 432 686-8200
Whitesboro (G-20727)	Palestine (G-16301)	Midland (G-15278)
K&B Oilfield Services Inc ....F 903 392-8213	Key Energy Services Inc ....E 806 489-7452	Lenorah Operators LLC ....E 432 684-9822
Henderson (G-8266)	Welch (G-20655)	Midland (G-15279)
K&F Equipment LLC ....F 432 664-0758	Key Energy Services Inc ....D 806 872-8331	Lewis Casing Crews Inc ....F 432 366-8077
Midland (G-15265)	Lamesa (G-13827)	Odessa (G-16061)
K&P Oilfield Solutions ....G 254 290-4862	Key Energy Services Inc ....D 979 778-1800	Liberty Fishing Rentl Tls Inc ....E 432 381-0551
Cypress (G-3806)	Bryan (G-2484)	Odessa (G-16062)
K-3 Resources LP ....D 281 585-2817	Key Energy Services Inc ....E 903 963-5208	▲ Liberty Lift Solutions LLC ....E 713 575-2300
Alvin (G-370)	Van (G-20208)	Houston (G-10633)
K-C Lease Service Inc ....E 979 323-9911	Key Energy Services Inc ....E 432 523-5155	Lightning Fluid Services Inc ....F 361 396-0801
Louise (G-14352)	Andrews (G-548)	Alice (G-224)
Kasper Pro Vac Service Inc ....E 956 796-0765	Key Energy Services Inc ....E 361 661-0488	Lightning Oilfield Svcs Inc ....D 817 439-5558
Laredo (G-13901)	Alice (G-222)	Midland (G-15281)

Lightning Oilfield Svcs Inc............D...... 817 439-5558
  Saginaw (G-17748)
Lilly Construction Inc...................E...... 325 392-2669
  Ozona (G-16285)
◆ Lindsayca Inc..............................D...... 713 467-9560
  Houston (G-10646)
Line Quest LLC..............................E...... 432 218-4980
  Midland (G-15283)
Lloyds Register Drilling Inte...........B...... 281 675-3100
  Houston (G-10658)
Lobo Tubing Tester Inc.................G...... 432 943-5441
  Monahans (G-15608)
◆ Logan Oil Tools Inc....................C...... 281 219-6613
  Houston (G-10671)
Logic Services LLC........................F...... 832 617-0805
  Houston (G-10672)
Loma Rentals LLC.........................F...... 817 964-1828
  Richardson (G-17348)
Longhorn Services Inc..................E...... 956 655-2360
  Edinburg (G-5593)
Loss Oil Field Services LLC..........E...... 432 695-6914
  Midland (G-15286)
Lowe Offshore Inc.........................D...... 281 894-5454
  Houston (G-10690)
Lsri LLC...D...... 817 770-0937
  Burleson (G-2588)
Lubrication Technologies Inc.......F...... 806 256-1600
  Shamrock (G-18892)
Lucere LLc....................................E...... 281 240-7355
  Missouri City (G-15582)
Lufkin Gears LLC...........................C...... 936 634-2211
  Lufkin (G-14540)
Lufkin Ils......................................E...... 281 445-7676
  Houston (G-10699)
Lufkin Industries LLC....................E...... 806 592-2586
  Denver City (G-5420)
Lufkin Industries LLC....................E...... 903 986-9080
  Kilgore (G-13565)
Lufkin Industries LLC....................E...... 903 984-3875
  Kilgore (G-13566)
Lufkin Industries LLC....................E...... 936 634-2211
  Lufkin (G-14542)
Luling Well Service........................F...... 830 875-9181
  Luling (G-14562)
Luther M Creek..............................D...... 325 387-3295
  Sonora (G-19027)
Lynx Well Service Inc....................F...... 409 735-2604
  Orangefield (G-16271)
M & B Oilfield Construction...........E...... 325 235-2514
  Sweetwater (G-19636)
M & D Companies Inc...................E...... 936 347-2138
  Garrison (G-7613)
M & G Development LP..................F...... 361 664-6122
  Alice (G-226)
M & Q Oilfield Service Inc.............F...... 806 894-4025
  Levelland (G-14010)
M & S Mechanical Inc....................E...... 318 755-2431
  Pittsburg (G-16747)
M & W Hot Oil Inc..........................E...... 432 447-2108
  Pecos (G-16623)
M-I LLC...E...... 361 886-3400
  Corpus Christi (G-3567)
◆ M-I LLC.....................................B...... 281 561-1300
  Houston (G-10725)
M-I LLC...E...... 409 763-2249
  Galveston (G-7403)
Mac Oil Field Company Inc............F...... 325 754-5565
  Winters (G-20905)
Maclaskey Oil Field Services.........D...... 817 594-8073
  Weatherford (G-20603)
Madden Systems Inc.....................F...... 432 332-0255
  Odessa (G-16069)
Madisonville Service Contr LP.......F...... 936 348-5506
  Madisonville (G-14589)
Maersk Oil Houston Inc.................C...... 713 346-5800
  Houston (G-10734)
Magnum Producing LP....................F...... 361 882-3858
  Corpus Christi (G-3569)
Majestic Petroleum Svcs LLC........D...... 432 686-2023
  Midland (G-15291)
Mako Oilfield Services LLC............E...... 832 680-1300
  Houston (G-10742)
Mangums Oilfield Services............E...... 979 234-7327
  Eagle Lake (G-5542)
Mangums Oilfield Services Ltd......E...... 979 234-5203
  East Bernard (G-5560)
Manufacturing Global Resources...F...... 361 668-0111
  Alice (G-227)
◆ Map Oil Tools Inc.......................F...... 337 560-8559
  Houston (G-10750)

Marco Services Inc.......................F...... 806 344-4784
  Hereford (G-8293)
Marine Well Containment Co LLC...E...... 281 820-8800
  Houston (G-10766)
Markwest Enrgy E Texas Gas LP...E...... 903 694-2225
  Carthage (G-2914)
Markwest Javelina Company LLC...D...... 361 289-4900
  Corpus Christi (G-3573)
Martex Well Services LLP..............D...... 903 938-3574
  Marshall (G-14792)
Martin Underground Storage.........D...... 903 983-1551
  Kilgore (G-13571)
Martin-Decker Totco Inc...............F...... 903 534-3677
  Tyler (G-20120)
Martins Fishing Tls & Rentals........F...... 432 524-7456
  Andrews (G-550)
Martins Fishing Tools....................E...... 432 524-7456
  Andrews (G-551)
Mash Oilfield Services LP..............F...... 940 549-6152
  Graham (G-7786)
Mason Brothers Cnstr Co Inc........E...... 806 495-3400
  Post (G-17191)
Mathis & Son Inc...........................E...... 940 997-2137
  Rule (G-17728)
Maverick Companies LLC...............C...... 817 334-4100
  Fort Worth (G-6820)
Maverick Solutions LLC.................C...... 817 334-4100
  Fort Worth (G-6821)
Maverick Well Pluggers LLC...........E...... 432 458-3780
  Midland (G-15295)
Maverick Well Service LLC.............F...... 903 983-6050
  Kilgore (G-13572)
McCamey Well Service Inc............F...... 432 208-2769
  Mc Camey (G-14819)
McCurdy Services Inc....................E...... 903 729-5681
  Palestine (G-16303)
McDermott International Inc...........B...... 281 588-6600
  Houston (G-10810)
McGuire Industries Inc..................F...... 979 968-5131
  La Grange (G-13698)
McMillan Welding...........................D...... 432 687-4625
  Midland (G-15297)
MCR Oil Tools LLC........................E...... 817 704-6677
  Arlington (G-730)
MD Construction Inc......................C...... 903 389-2595
  Fairfield (G-6178)
Measurement Services Inc.............F...... 361 227-4998
  Alice (G-228)
Meco Construction Company LLC...E...... 817 975-4599
  Fort Worth (G-6825)
Med-Loz Lease Service Inc.............C...... 956 765-6029
  Zapata (G-20984)
Mega Oil Corporation....................E...... 903 984-7050
  Kilgore (G-13573)
Megalodon Services Inc.................E...... 941 882-3108
  Sunset (G-19625)
Mercer Well Service Inc.................D...... 940 567-5991
  Jacksboro (G-13222)
Merco Solutions Corporation.........E...... 830 519-4260
  Gonzales (G-7759)
Merit Energy Partners F-I LP..........F...... 972 701-8377
  Dallas (G-4667)
Merrell Lease Service Inc..............D...... 361 643-6911
  Gregory (G-8101)
Merrimac Manufacturing Inc..........E...... 936 894-3900
  Plantersville (G-17059)
Mesa Drilling Inc...........................G...... 713 993-7082
  Lago Vista (G-13807)
Mesa Wireline LLC.........................E...... 970 257-0458
  Houston (G-10839)
Mesquite Oil Tools Inc...................E...... 325 573-1705
  Snyder (G-18995)
Mesquite Services LLC...................E...... 806 368-7726
  Lubbock (G-14446)
Mexssub International Inc...............C...... 713 278-2175
  Houston (G-10861)
Michelson Energy Company...........F...... 210 826-0681
  San Antonio (G-18299)
Mid-West Truck Center Inc.............D...... 432 523-3451
  Andrews (G-552)
Midcoast Energy LLC.....................C...... 713 821-2000
  Houston (G-10871)
Midcoast Lease Service Inc...........E...... 361 526-4636
  Refugio (G-17244)
Midland Roustabout Service Inc....D...... 432 682-5017
  Midland (G-15302)
Midway Oilfield Constrs Inc...........C...... 817 389-2525
  Godley (G-7736)
Midway Oilfield Constrs Inc...........D...... 936 348-3721
  Midway (G-15499)

Midwestern Services Inc...............D...... 325 573-6666
  Houston (G-10876)
Millennium Resources LP...............E...... 432 687-4074
  Midland (G-15304)
▲ Mitchell Well Service Inc...........E...... 281 576-5007
  Baytown (G-1797)
MO Vac Service Co of Alice...........F...... 361 668-8203
  Alice (G-229)
Mo-Vac Service Company...............D...... 956 682-6381
  Edinburg (G-5597)
Mo-Vac Service Company...............F...... 830 583-3622
  Kenedy (G-13489)
Mobley Oilfield Services LP...........E...... 903 234-2179
  Longview (G-14279)
Moffitt & Assoc Inc........................F...... 361 884-9273
  Corpus Christi (G-3578)
Momentum Operating Co Inc.........E...... 325 762-3331
  Albany (G-191)
▲ Momentum Pressure Control LLC....E...... 903 643-3700
  Longview (G-14280)
Montecito Oilfield Svcs LLC...........F...... 956 337-6082
  Laredo (G-13914)
Moontower Resources LLC.............F...... 432 400-2445
  West Lake Hills (G-20685)
Morrison Energy Group LLC...........A...... 713 344-9233
  Houston (G-10924)
Moses Envmtl & Cnstr Svcs LLC....E...... 806 418-8525
  Amarillo (G-448)
Mpact Strategic Consulting LLC.....E...... 866 361-7611
  Houston (G-10929)
Ms Directional LLC........................D...... 936 442-2500
  Conroe (G-3332)
MSA Industries Inc........................E...... 432 337-6062
  Odessa (G-16084)
Mtlv Properties LLC........................E...... 361 946-6145
  Corpus Christi (G-3580)
◆ Mud King Products Inc...............E...... 281 645-4158
  Houston (G-10934)
Mudsmith.......................................F...... 214 370-9535
  Dallas (G-4703)
◆ Multi-Chem Inc............................D...... 281 442-1222
  Houston (G-10937)
▲ Multi-Chem Group LLC...............E...... 281 871-4000
  Houston (G-10938)
Mustang Gas Compression LLC.....D...... 903 218-4459
  Kilgore (G-13576)
Mustang Oilfield Services LLC.......E...... 903 389-4200
  Fairfield (G-6179)
N5 Wireline Service LLC.................F...... 806 648-1505
  Perryton (G-16641)
Nabors Corporate Services Inc......C...... 281 874-0035
  Houston (G-10950)
Nabors Drilling International...........D...... 281 775-8506
  Houston (G-10951)
Nabors Drilling Tech USA Inc..........C...... 281 874-0035
  Odessa (G-16085)
Nabors Drilling Tech USA Inc..........B...... 281 259-8887
  Magnolia (G-14619)
Nabors Drilling Tech USA Inc..........E...... 281 462-1730
  Crosby (G-3738)
◆ Nabors Industries Inc.................C...... 281 874-0035
  Houston (G-10953)
▲ Nabors Offshore Corporation......E...... 281 874-0406
  Houston (G-10955)
▼ Nabors Well Services Co.............D...... 281 874-0035
  Houston (G-10956)
Nabors Well Services Co.................D...... 325 884-2536
  Big Lake (G-2059)
Nabors Well Services Co.................D...... 817 396-4310
  Cresson (G-3710)
Nabors Well Services Co.................D...... 940 626-3735
  Decatur (G-5249)
Nabors Well Services Co.................E...... 281 775-8506
  Houston (G-10957)
Nabors Well Services Ltd...............D...... 432 523-4420
  Andrews (G-554)
Nabors Well Services Ltd...............D...... 325 387-2884
  Sonora (G-19028)
Nabors Well Services Ltd...............D...... 325 573-2621
  Snyder (G-18996)
Nabors Well Services Ltd...............D...... 432 943-2227
  Monahans (G-15610)
Nabors Well Services Ltd...............E...... 281 874-0035
  Houston (G-10958)
Nabors Well Services Ltd...............E...... 432 683-5000
  Midland (G-15309)
Nabors Well Services Ltd...............E...... 806 592-9128
  Denver City (G-5421)
Nabors Well Services Ltd...............D...... 325 651-9241
  San Angelo (G-17814)

SIC

Nabors Well Services Ltd .... F 325 392-2313
Ozona **(G-16286)**

Nabors Well Services Ltd .... E 432 836-4332
Iraan **(G-12920)**

Nalco Champion Wellchem .... F 432 366-0971
Odessa **(G-16086)**

Nason Services LLC .... F 940 495-2558
Electra **(G-6048)**

◆ Natco Group Inc .... F 713 849-7500
Houston **(G-10964)**

▲ National Coupling Company Inc .... C 281 499-2583
Stafford **(G-19356)**

National Enrgy Svcs Rnted Corp .... G 832 925-3777
Houston **(G-10967)**

National Oilwell Varco Inc .... F 432 333-4196
Odessa **(G-16087)**

National Oilwell Varco Inc .... E 432 528-4354
Odessa **(G-16088)**

National Oilwell Varco Inc .... F 432 563-2150
Odessa **(G-16089)**

National Oilwell Varco Inc .... F 713 799-8198
Houston **(G-10972)**

National Oilwell Varco Inc .... D 713 466-7999
Houston **(G-10973)**

National Oilwell Varco Inc .... D 713 983-9281
Houston **(G-10974)**

National Oilwell Varco Inc .... E 361 664-8013
Robstown **(G-17514)**

National Oilwell Varco Inc .... E 713 896-9115
Houston **(G-10977)**

National Oilwell Varco Inc .... F 325 573-2665
Snyder **(G-18997)**

National Oilwell Varco Inc .... E 713 375-3700
Houston **(G-10979)**

National Oilwell Varco Inc .... E 713 482-0500
Houston **(G-10985)**

National Oilwell Varco Inc .... B 281 456-0751
Houston **(G-10989)**

National Oilwell Varco Inc .... E 940 761-2333
Wichita Falls **(G-20785)**

National Oilwell Varco Inc .... F 817 389-2444
Godley **(G-7737)**

National Oilwell Varco Inc .... F 281 209-4840
Houston **(G-10994)**

National Oilwell Varco Inc .... D 409 842-2114
Beaumont **(G-1933)**

National Oilwell Varco Inc .... E 325 884-2556
Big Lake **(G-2060)**

National Oilwell Varco LP .... E 210 477-7500
San Antonio **(G-18334)**

National Oilwell Varco LP .... E 936 777-6200
Conroe **(G-3339)**

Natural Gas Services Group Inc .... C 432 262-2700
Midland **(G-15311)**

Natural Gas Sltions N Amer LLC .... A 832 590-2303
Houston **(G-11008)**

Ncs Multistage Holdings Inc .... F 281 453-2222
Houston **(G-11020)**

Neotek Energy Inc .... F 469 206-3344
Plano **(G-16942)**

Newpark Drilling Fluids LLC .... E 903 297-2210
Longview **(G-14284)**

Newpark Drlg Flids Prsonnel SE .... F 405 721-0207
Spring **(G-19237)**

Newpark Environmental Svcs LLC ..... E 432 682-5411
Midland **(G-15317)**

▼ Newpark Mats Intgrted Svcs LLC .... F 281 362-6800
The Woodlands **(G-19896)**

Newpark Mats Intgrted Svcs LLC ...... D 979 245-3894
Bay City **(G-1775)**

Newpark Mats Intgrted Svcs LLC ...... E 409 752-5800
Beaumont **(G-1934)**

▲ Newpark Resources Inc .... E 281 362-6800
The Woodlands **(G-19897)**

Nexgen Wtr Solutions Ltd Lblty .... E 830 583-9915
Kenedy **(G-13490)**

Nexgen Wtr Solutions Ltd Lblty .... F 432 234-8404
Midland **(G-15318)**

Nextier Cmpltion Solutions Inc .... F 830 277-1200
Charlotte **(G-3048)**

Nextier Cmpltion Solutions Inc .... E 713 325-6000
Houston **(G-11048)**

Nextier Oilfield Solutions Inc .... D 713 325-6000
Houston **(G-11049)**

Nibletts Oilfield Services Inc .... E 325 853-2521
Eldorado **(G-6047)**

Nine Energy Service Inc .... D 281 730-5100
Houston **(G-11058)**

Nine Energy Service Inc .... F 903 469-3922
Murchison **(G-15680)**

Nine Energy Service Inc .... F 903 479-3155
Athens **(G-836)**

Nitro Downhole LLC .... F 361 564-9282
Yorktown **(G-20978)**

Nitro Fluids LLC .... E 361 938-5300
Nordheim **(G-15872)**

Nitro Well Service LLC .... F 432 617-1128
Midland **(G-15319)**

Noahs Service & Supply LLC .... G 903 218-6888
Kilgore **(G-13578)**

Noble Flow Control LLC .... F 432 638-5962
San Angelo **(G-17815)**

Non-Typical Pipeline Llc .... E 281 622-5002
Cleveland **(G-3132)**

Noral Holding Company .... E 972 392-7780
Dallas **(G-4742)**

Norm Pipe Inc .... D 903 702-8966
Marshall **(G-14795)**

Normans Well Service Inc .... F 940 668-8201
Gainesville **(G-7354)**

North Amercn Tubular Svcs LLC .... F 903 984-0625
Kilgore **(G-13579)**

North Basin Coating Inc .... E 806 894-1531
Levelland **(G-14011)**

North Texas Compression .... F 940 683-5025
Bridgeport **(G-2297)**

Nova Consulting .... F 281 445-6393
Houston **(G-11088)**

Novak Commercial Cnstr LLC .... F 512 688-5644
Georgetown **(G-7668)**

◆ Novomet Usa Inc .... F 832 437-5998
Katy **(G-13430)**

Novosad Enterprises Inc .... F 979 272-9203
Caldwell **(G-2633)**

Nutech Energy Alliance Ltd .... D 281 812-4030
Houston **(G-11101)**

O & B Tank Co Inc .... D 806 624-3431
Darrouzett **(G-5214)**

O & B Tank Co Inc .... F 806 624-4781
Darrouzett **(G-5215)**

O & C Equipment Inc .... E 281 232-4686
Rosenberg **(G-17591)**

O M C International LLC .... E 281 398-4281
Houston **(G-11106)**

O S & S Operating Inc .... G 940 495-3645
Electra **(G-6049)**

O-Tex Pumping LLC .... E 806 665-0552
Pampa **(G-16330)**

Oak Lease Service Co LLC .... F 361 362-1429
Refugio **(G-17245)**

◆ Oceaneering International Inc .... C 713 329-4500
Houston **(G-11124)**

Oceaneering International Inc .... C 713 939-3682
Houston **(G-11125)**

Oceaneering International Inc .... F 713 329-4318
Houston **(G-11126)**

Oceaneering International Inc .... E 713 466-8853
Houston **(G-11127)**

Oceaneering International Inc .... F 713 856-9375
Jersey Village **(G-13303)**

Oceaneering International Inc .... F 361 776-7251
Ingleside **(G-12898)**

Octane Energy Consulting LLC .... C 432 685-7736
Midland **(G-15324)**

Ods International Inc .... D 713 782-6767
Houston **(G-11133)**

Oes Oilfield Services USA Inc .... D 713 960-1339
Houston **(G-11139)**

Offshore Express Inc .... D 985 868-1438
Houston **(G-11141)**

▲ Offshore Spclty Fbricators LLC .... C 985 868-1438
Houston **(G-11144)**

Ofs Inc .... E 281 456-0052
Houston **(G-11146)**

Ofs Global Inc .... F 832 786-4728
Houston **(G-11147)**

Ofs International LLC .... B 281 452-3036
Houston **(G-11148)**

Oil & Gas Consultants Intl Inc .... F 832 426-1200
Katy **(G-13374)**

Oil Field Dev Engrg LLC .... D 281 679-9060
Houston **(G-11151)**

Oil Patch Group Inc .... E 361 576-0300
Victoria **(G-20289)**

Oil States Energy Services LLC .... E 281 331-1800
Alvin **(G-376)**

Oil States Energy Services LLC .... F 432 943-2556
Monahans **(G-15611)**

Oil States Industries Inc .... D 817 468-1400
Arlington **(G-741)**

Oil States Industries Inc .... F 713 920-9800
Houston **(G-11156)**

Oil States Industries Inc .... D 713 510-2200
Houston **(G-11158)**

◆ Oil States Industries Inc .... C 817 548-4200
Arlington **(G-743)**

Oil States Industries Inc .... F 281 247-7400
Houston **(G-11159)**

Oil States Industries Inc .... C 713 445-2200
Houston **(G-11160)**

◆ Oil States Systems Inc .... D 713 445-2210
Arlington **(G-744)**

Oil Well Chemical Co Inc .... F 940 592-2012
Iowa Park **(G-12907)**

Oilfield Anchor Company Inc .... D 903 723-2833
Palestine **(G-16306)**

Oilfield Audit Services Inc .... F 281 242-9521
Sugar Land **(G-19521)**

Oilfield Services & Tech LLC .... F 281 452-3036
Houston **(G-11164)**

Oilfield Water Logistics LLC .... D 214 292-2011
Dallas **(G-4757)**

Oilwell Hydraulics Inc .... F 281 602-8170
The Woodlands **(G-19898)**

Oilwell Tubular Consultants .... E 281 328-6220
Crosby **(G-3740)**

Ol Sonora Trading Company .... F 325 387-2524
Sonora **(G-19029)**

OMI Oilfield Investments LLC .... E 806 648-4120
Perryton **(G-16643)**

Omimex Petroleum Inc .... F 817 460-7777
Fort Worth **(G-6879)**

Omni Air & Nitrogen Ltd .... F 432 288-9087
Midland **(G-15327)**

Omni Energy Services Corp .... E 936 591-8598
Center **(G-3003)**

On Shore Qlty Ctrl Spclist LLC .... D 512 443-3582
Austin **(G-1383)**

ONeal Oil Company .... F 940 825-3716
Nocona **(G-15869)**

Online Construction LP .... F 361 445-6161
George West **(G-7627)**

Onward LLC .... F 281 535-2739
Kemah **(G-13478)**

Onyx Contractors Operations LP .... D 432 561-8900
Midland **(G-15328)**

Operations Rod Permian L C .... E 432 367-4149
Odessa **(G-16102)**

Opportune LP .... D 713 772-0664
Houston **(G-11184)**

Origin Bio Solutions LLC .... F 432 570-4081
Midland **(G-15329)**

Original Services Inc .... E 325 617-7400
San Angelo **(G-17817)**

▲ Orteq Energy Technologies LLC ..... E 940 665-2316
Gainesville **(G-7356)**

Outlaws Oilfield Service LLC .... E 432 445-0005
Midland **(G-15333)**

Overton Energy LLC .... F 713 580-7250
Houston **(G-11207)**

P & C Oil Field Service LLC .... E 956 581-1725
Mission **(G-11561)**

P & W Sales Incorporated .... G 817 244-6565
Fort Worth **(G-6887)**

Pacific Mwd Inc .... E 713 466-1616
Houston **(G-11218)**

Pacific Sensor LLC .... F 972 242-5750
Carrollton **(G-2788)**

▲ Packard International Inc .... F 281 399-8771
Conroe **(G-3346)**

Packers Plus Enrgy Svcs USA In .... C 281 872-6999
Tomball **(G-19995)**

Paisano Service & Supply Inc .... E 361 572-0322
Cuero **(G-3765)**

Palmetto Services LLC .... D 903 655-0900
Henderson **(G-8269)**

Paloma Lease Service Inc .... E 361 449-2815
George West **(G-7628)**

Panamerican Indus Svcs Co Inc .... F 210 666-3542
San Antonio **(G-18365)**

Panola Equipment Inc .... F 903 633-2545
Panola **(G-16349)**

Panola Wire Line Services Inc .... F 903 693-3966
Carthage **(G-2915)**

Pantheon Construction Inc .... E 940 458-9183
Sanger **(G-18729)**

Paragon Directional Drlg LLC .... F 903 880-7398
Granbury **(G-7804)**

Paramount Rental Services LLC .... F 940 264-8379
Wichita Falls **(G-20793)**

Company	Code	Phone
Paris Construction LLC Cypress *(G-3810)*	F	832 752-5271
Parman Capital Group LLC Houston *(G-11247)*	A	713 751-2700
Partners Specialties Inc Houston *(G-11251)*	E	281 922-9102
Partrac Geomarine Inc Houston *(G-11252)*	F	713 338-3495
Pason Systems USA Corp Houston *(G-11256)*	D	713 693-8700
Pate Trucking Co Inc Seminole *(G-18886)*	F	432 758-2166
Pate Trucking Co LLC Lubbock *(G-14458)*	E	575 392-4441
Patriot Oilfield Services LLC Victoria *(G-20290)*	E	979 648-2416
Patterson Tubular Services Inc Channelview *(G-3032)*	E	281 452-5443
Patterson-Uti Energy Inc Cleburne *(G-3105)*	E	817 556-5300
Patterson-Uti Energy Inc Houston *(G-11262)*	D	281 765-7100
Patton Enterprises Inc Webster *(G-20642)*	E	832 619-1890
Paul Musslewhite Trckg Co LLC Levelland *(G-14012)*	A	806 894-3151
Pcs Oilfield Services LLC Canadian *(G-2653)*	E	806 323-8007
Peak Completion Tech Inc Victoria *(G-20293)*	E	361 668-8383
Peak Completion Tech Inc Fort Worth *(G-6899)*	E	817 529-2030
Peak Completion Tech Inc Snyder *(G-19001)*	F	325 574-1170
▲ Peak Industrial Services Inc Nederland *(G-15758)*	F	409 729-0345
Peak Oilfield Services LLC Bridgeport *(G-2298)*	E	940 683-1627
Peak Pressure Control LLC Midland *(G-15344)*	E	432 563-5800
Pegasus Optmztion Managers LLC Montgomery *(G-15638)*	C	979 213-4101
Penspen Corporation Tomball *(G-19996)*	F	713 953-7007
Peregrine Stimulation Svcs LLC Fulshear *(G-7329)*	F	713 201-6787
Performance Pressure Pumping Beaumont *(G-1940)*	F	409 980-8188
Permian Anchors Inc Odessa *(G-16111)*	E	432 563-0205
Permian Basin Derrick Svcs LP Odessa *(G-16112)*	G	432 332-2315
Permian Ndt Inc Houston *(G-11293)*	E	432 563-3638
Permian Petroleum Services Inc Midland *(G-15345)*	E	432 682-0434
Permian Power Tong Inc Gardendale *(G-7421)*	E	432 550-7386
Peterson Drilling and Tstg Inc Amarillo *(G-453)*	E	806 342-4911
Petro Mechanical Services LLC Odessa *(G-16120)*	D	800 727-1398
Petro-Tech Environmental LLC Houston *(G-11301)*	G	713 926-9986
◆ Petrochem Field Services Inc Humble *(G-12792)*	D	281 441-2550
Petrofuels Quality Mktg LP Nederland *(G-15759)*	F	409 722-6880
Petroh2o Recovery LLC Southlake *(G-19081)*	E	817 778-8413
Petroleum College Intl Victoria *(G-20295)*	F	361 575-4882
◆ Petroleum Elastomers Inc Houston *(G-11305)*	E	281 591-1500
Petroleum Financial Inc Fort Worth *(G-6904)*	E	817 339-1075
Petroleum Industry Inspectors Houston *(G-11308)*	E	713 377-2637
Petroplex Acidizing Inc Midland *(G-15348)*	E	432 563-1299
Petroplex Pipe & Cnstr Inc Midland *(G-15350)*	D	432 697-4540
Petrostar Services LLC Longview *(G-14289)*	F	903 247-6390
Petrustech Oil & Gas LLC Houston *(G-11312)*	F	281 781-0020
Pfm LLC Houston *(G-11315)*	F	713 664-7767
Phil Dollar Oilfield Services Perryton *(G-16645)*	F	806 435-3373
Phillip E Mosley & Associates Houston *(G-11322)*	F	281 496-1249
Pierce Construction Inc Beckville *(G-1972)*	D	903 678-3748
Pinnergy Ltd Pleasanton *(G-17071)*	E	830 569-1997
Pinnergy Ltd Carthage *(G-2916)*	D	903 693-6300
Pinnergy Ltd Godley *(G-7739)*	C	817 389-2105
Pinnergy Ltd Austin *(G-1417)*	D	512 343-8880
Pinnergy Ltd Carthage *(G-2917)*	D	903 693-8400
Pioneer Ntral Rsrces Pmpg Svcs Irving *(G-13145)*	F	972 444-9001
Pioner Ntrl Rsrc Wll Srvcs LLC Irving *(G-13148)*	E	972 969-3670
Pipe Pros LLC Corpus Christi *(G-3592)*	E	361 289-9090
▲ Pipeline Technique LLC Humble *(G-12794)*	C	281 570-1363
Pirate Oilfield Services Inc Midland *(G-15360)*	E	432 260-9040
Plank Coatings Inc Odessa *(G-16123)*	F	432 530-1234
Platinum Pressure Services Inc Decatur *(G-5250)*	E	866 943-2204
PLPS Inc Pearland *(G-16593)*	F	866 992-7577
Pml Exploration Services LLC Spring *(G-19159)*	C	405 606-2701
Power Line Infrstrcture Svcs I Kermit *(G-13514)*	E	432 586-2518
◆ Precision Energy Services Inc Houston *(G-11393)*	C	713 693-4000
Precision Well Logging Inc Houston *(G-11396)*	E	713 681-3435
◆ Preco Turbine Comprsr Svcs Inc Houston *(G-11397)*	C	281 821-9620
Preferred Oilfield Services San Angelo *(G-17823)*	F	325 884-5700
Premier Oilfield Group LLC Houston *(G-11402)*	F	713 492-2057
▼ Premier Pipe LLC Houston *(G-11403)*	F	832 300-8100
Premier Worldwide Inc Montgomery *(G-15640)*	F	281 752-0014
Premiere Inc Granbury *(G-7805)*	F	817 326-3500
Premiere Well Service Pampa *(G-16335)*	F	806 669-3227
▲ Premium Oilfield Tech LLC Houston *(G-11405)*	D	281 670-5200
Prime Operating Company Houston *(G-11416)*	E	713 735-0000
Primed Up Nitrogen Svcs LLC Anahuac *(G-527)*	F	361 543-0747
Primeenergy Corporation Carrizo Springs *(G-2688)*	F	830 876-2441
Pro Field Services Inc Hallettsville *(G-8125)*	E	361 798-5552
Pro Field Services Inc Victoria *(G-20296)*	F	361 575-0348
Pro Inspection Inc Odessa *(G-16126)*	F	432 362-2247
Pro Oilfield Services LLC Spring *(G-19242)*	E	281 496-5810
Pro Tech Mwd Services Inc Fort Worth *(G-6918)*	F	817 568-1038
Pro-Ject Chemicals Inc Spring *(G-19243)*	F	832 403-2560
Producers Midstream LP Dallas *(G-4832)*	F	214 238-5740
Product Quality Management LLC Pasadena *(G-16498)*	F	713 538-3028
Production Downhole Svcs Inc Denver City *(G-5423)*	F	806 592-0032
Production Facilities Eqp Inc Magnolia *(G-14621)*	E	281 356-1107
Production Lift Systems Inc Midland *(G-15364)*	E	432 699-1200
Production Logging Inc Snyder *(G-19002)*	F	325 573-4441
Production Meter & Testing Breckenridge *(G-2234)*	F	254 559-7271
◆ Production Tech & Svcs Inc Houston *(G-11437)*	F	281 498-7399
Professional Projects Inc Cypress *(G-3814)*	D	281 351-6315
Professional Rental Tools LLC Houston *(G-11439)*	E	713 808-9756
Professnal Drctional Entps Inc Conroe *(G-3354)*	C	936 441-7266
Professnal Drctional Entps Inc Midland *(G-15365)*	E	432 695-6152
Promar LP Rockport *(G-17531)*	C	361 727-3300
▲ Proptester Incorporated Cypress *(G-3815)*	F	281 256-8880
Proserv Operations Inc Houston *(G-11456)*	B	337 984-8054
Proserv Operations Inc Houston *(G-11459)*	F	713 983-7222
Proserv Operations Inc Houston *(G-11460)*	B	281 807-2100
Protechnics Houston *(G-11462)*	F	713 328-2320
Protorque Energy Inc Midland *(G-15369)*	E	432 208-1404
Puffer-Sweiven Holdings Inc Corpus Christi *(G-3599)*	F	361 883-6215
Pumpco Inc Giddings *(G-7700)*	C	979 542-9054
Pure River LLC Princeton *(G-17211)*	F	469 853-4867
Purity Oilfield Services LLC Dallas *(G-4836)*	E	214 880-8400
Purity Oilfield Services LLC Midland *(G-15371)*	D	844 221-1500
Q2 Artificial Lift Svcs LLC Midland *(G-15372)*	D	903 983-1432
Qes Pressure Control LLC Victoria *(G-20297)*	D	361 580-5400
Qes Wireline LLC Longview *(G-14292)*	F	903 720-8805
Qes Wireline LLC Fort Worth *(G-6925)*	F	817 546-4970
Qes Wireline LLC Cresson *(G-3712)*	F	432 813-6088
▼ QMax America Inc Houston *(G-11483)*	E	817 732-2423
QMax Solutions Inc Houston *(G-11484)*	F	832 672-4459
QO Inc Houston *(G-11485)*	F	713 224-7823
▲ Qri International LLC Houston *(G-11487)*	F	713 485-8800
Quail Energy Services LP Andrews *(G-557)*	E	432 523-3742
Quail Tools LP Victoria *(G-20298)*	E	361 579-0244
Quail Tools LP Houston *(G-11490)*	D	281 445-1777
Quail Well Service Inc Abilene *(G-67)*	E	325 677-0323
Quality Foundation Repair Inc Austin *(G-1443)*	F	512 363-7769
Quality Logging Inc Midland *(G-15373)*	D	432 682-7168
◆ Quality Mat Company Beaumont *(G-1944)*	C	409 898-1170
Quantum Reservoir Impact LLC Houston *(G-11508)*	E	713 485-8800
Quasar Energy Services Inc Gainesville *(G-7359)*	F	940 612-3336
▲ Quell Petroleum Services Inc Monahans *(G-15612)*	E	432 943-8400
Quintana Energy Services Inc Houston *(G-11515)*	A	832 518-4094
Quintana Energy Services LP Houston *(G-11516)*	F	832 518-4094
R & R Lease Service Inc Alice *(G-230)*	F	361 562-8379
R & R Oilfield Services Inc Corpus Christi *(G-3604)*	D	361 289-5892
R A Beaird Oil Co Merkel *(G-15016)*	F	325 928-5220
R A D Roustabout Service LLC Midland *(G-15375)*	G	432 664-2430
R B Testers Inc Odessa *(G-16129)*	F	432 582-2500
R Construction Company Buffalo *(G-2547)*	C	903 322-4639
R-Tex Services LLC Joshua *(G-13324)*	D	817 774-3333
R360 Envmtl Solutions LLC The Woodlands *(G-19907)*	G	281 872-7360
Radley Electric Inc Sour Lake *(G-19034)*	F	409 781-7172

◆ Rae Energy Inc ....C.. 281 578-6523
  Katy *(G-13434)*

Raider Services LP ....C.. 830 996-0016
  Gordon *(G-7769)*

Ramco Roustabout Inc ....E.. 325 884-5734
  Big Lake *(G-2061)*

Randall & Dewey Jefferis ....D.. 281 774-2000
  Houston *(G-11542)*

Ranger Energy Services Inc ....D.. 713 935-8900
  Houston *(G-11545)*

Ranger Energy Services LLC ....B.. 713 461-9000
  Houston *(G-11546)*

Ranger Oilfield Products Inc ....F.. 936 856-4182
  Willis *(G-20858)*

Rapid Service Inc ....F.. 432 367-7283
  Odessa *(G-16133)*

Rathole Drilling Inc ....E.. 361 664-9995
  Alice *(G-232)*

Raydon Inc ....E.. 254 559-5012
  Breckenridge *(G-2235)*

Rcw Energy Services LLC ....E.. 972 394-1000
  The Colony *(G-19812)*

RDG Real Estate & Construction .....F.. 469 629-9919
  Dallas *(G-4865)*

Rdt Inc ....D.. 979 387-3223
  Beasley *(G-1845)*

Rebuilding Tgether El Paso Inc ....F.. 915 342-3882
  El Paso *(G-5932)*

Reclamation Contractors Texas ....E.. 903 895-4584
  New London *(G-15851)*

Recovered Water Industries LLC .....E.. 940 668-8200
  Gainesville *(G-7360)*

Red Diamond Energy Svcs Inc ....E.. 325 690-0053
  Abilene *(G-69)*

Red Diamond Oilfld Svcs L L C ....E.. 903 687-4000
  Waskom *(G-20521)*

Red Diamond Pressure Ctrl LLC ......F.. 903 687-4000
  Waskom *(G-20522)*

Red Energy Services LP ....F.. 432 943-2746
  Monahans *(G-15613)*

Red Rock Oilfield Service LLC ....F.. 325 933-0224
  Colorado City *(G-3226)*

Redi Services ....E.. 432 272-1583
  Odessa *(G-16134)*

Redzone Coil Tubing LLC ....D.. 936 632-2645
  Lufkin *(G-14548)*

Redzone Holdco LLC ....F.. 936 632-2645
  Lufkin *(G-14549)*

Reed-Hycalog ....D.. 832 422-4070
  Houston *(G-11576)*

Reef Chemical Corporation Inc ....C.. 432 560-5600
  Midland *(G-15379)*

Relentless Oilfield Svcs LLC ....F.. 432 242-1160
  Odessa *(G-16136)*

Reliable Well Svc N Texas LLC ....F.. 940 692-9511
  Wichita Falls *(G-20803)*

Reliable Wireline LLC ....E.. 713 280-7995
  Houston *(G-11592)*

Renaissance Offshore LLC ....E.. 832 333-7700
  Houston *(G-11598)*

Renco Tool Co Inc ....F.. 806 648-2903
  Perryton *(G-16646)*

Renegade Well Services LLC ....E.. 940 626-4498
  Decatur *(G-5252)*

Renegade Well Services LLC ....E.. 830 378-5977
  Dilley *(G-5483)*

Renegade Well Services LLC ....E.. 817 389-2496
  Godley *(G-7740)*

Renegade Well Services LLC ....E.. 682 936-4466
  Granbury *(G-7807)*

▲ Repcon Inc ....B.. 361 289-6342
  Corpus Christi *(G-3609)*

Reserve Analysts Assoc Inc ....F.. 281 438-3000
  Missouri City *(G-15588)*

Reserve Compression Corp ....E.. 713 783-8851
  Houston *(G-11605)*

Reserve Equipment Inc ....E.. 713 939-8988
  Houston *(G-11606)*

Reservoir Group ....F.. 281 776-5300
  Stafford *(G-19369)*

Rh Well Service ....F.. 432 393-5305
  Big Spring *(G-2095)*

Rheaco Oil Company Ltd ....F.. 409 287-1225
  Sour Lake *(G-19035)*

Rhos Inc ....F.. 979 542-5420
  Giddings *(G-7701)*

Riddles Dehi & Chem Svc Co LLC ....F.. 903 986-3904
  Kilgore *(G-13587)*

Rig Qa International Inc ....F.. 936 856-5614
  Willis *(G-20860)*

Rig Technology Inc ....E.. 432 362-2789
  Odessa *(G-16139)*

Rig Testers Inc ....G.. 325 673-2771
  Abilene *(G-72)*

Rigamonti Welding Services ....G.. 361 578-0397
  Victoria *(G-20301)*

Rkt Operating LLC ....E.. 903 686-0284
  Longview *(G-14299)*

Rmor Energy Corporation ....F.. 361 318-0151
  Refugio *(G-17246)*

Ro SA Vacuum Trucks Inc ....F.. 956 584-8685
  Edinburg *(G-5600)*

Roberson Wireline Inc ....E.. 806 435-3087
  Perryton *(G-16647)*

Robert Marshall Cnstr Inc ....F.. 361 747-5253
  Bruni *(G-2450)*

ROC Service Company LLC ....C.. 940 683-0159
  Bridgeport *(G-2300)*

Roco Drilling and Service Inc ....D.. 903 963-7036
  Van *(G-20209)*

Rods Service LLC ....E.. 979 775-5000
  Bryan *(G-2502)*

Roldan Drilling Fluids R&D ....F.. 832 918-6267
  The Woodlands *(G-19913)*

Roldan Midstream Services LLC ....F.. 832 918-6267
  The Woodlands *(G-19914)*

Ross Co Services Company Inc ....F.. 806 894-1511
  Levelland *(G-14013)*

Rotary Components Intl Inc ....F.. 281 590-6484
  Houston *(G-11668)*

Roto-Versal Compression Svcs ....E.. 713 538-2800
  Houston *(G-11671)*

Rover Oilfield Services LLC ....F.. 979 533-7195
  Abilene *(G-76)*

Rovop Inc ....F.. 281 231-2626
  Houston *(G-11675)*

Royalty Well Service Inc ....D.. 432 547-2926
  Grandfalls *(G-8000)*

Roywell LLC ....E.. 713 661-4747
  Sugar Land *(G-19538)*

Roywell LLC ....E.. 432 332-0703
  Odessa *(G-16144)*

Rpc Inc ....E.. 817 689-7660
  Fort Worth *(G-6968)*

Rpc Inc ....E.. 210 310-1330
  San Antonio *(G-18436)*

Rpc Inc ....E.. 325 573-7022
  Snyder *(G-19005)*

Rpc Inc ....E.. 361 289-7088
  Corpus Christi *(G-3612)*

Rt Technical Solutions LLC ....E.. 409 721-9100
  Nederland *(G-15760)*

Ruben Arispe Jr ....F.. 512 543-3444
  Austin *(G-1475)*

Rubicon Olfld Intl Hldings LLC ....F.. 832 386-2500
  Houston *(G-11693)*

Rusk County Well Service Inc ....E.. 903 984-5017
  Kilgore *(G-13588)*

Russian-American Quality ....E.. 713 522-0453
  Houston *(G-11700)*

Rustex Inc ....E.. 979 778-7551
  Bryan *(G-2503)*

Rwls LLC ....E.. 806 897-0231
  Levelland *(G-14014)*

Rwls LLC ....E.. 432 664-0020
  Odessa *(G-16146)*

S & G Disposal ....F.. 806 894-6044
  Levelland *(G-14015)*

S & S Contract Pumping Svc Inc ....F.. 956 386-0211
  Edinburg *(G-5601)*

S & S Operating Co Inc ....F.. 409 296-9571
  Winnie *(G-20889)*

S & V Well Service Inc ....E.. 940 872-3535
  Bowie *(G-2200)*

S L P Backhoe Service ....F.. 903 643-8258
  Longview *(G-14300)*

S O A Pump & Supply Inc ....F.. 432 381-2380
  Odessa *(G-16147)*

S R Hill and Assoc Intl Inc ....F.. 713 960-6617
  Houston *(G-11713)*

S&M Energy Services LLC ....F.. 318 210-5166
  Gary *(G-7616)*

S2w Contracting LLC ....F.. 940 745-1421
  Weatherford *(G-20619)*

Sabine Mud Logging Inc ....F.. 903 693-2912
  Carthage *(G-2918)*

Safety Design Usa Inc ....E.. 940 757-0238
  Wichita Falls *(G-20804)*

Safzone Field Services LLC ....E.. 210 569-6699
  San Antonio *(G-18442)*

◆ Saipem America Inc ....C.. 281 552-5600
  Houston *(G-11732)*

Salazar Service and Trckg Corp ....E.. 432 523-9658
  Midland *(G-15394)*

Salt Creek Midstream LLC ....F.. 281 655-3200
  Houston *(G-11734)*

Saltel-Industries Inc ....F.. 432 238-1076
  Midland *(G-15395)*

Sancus Energy and Power LLC ....E.. 832 460-1000
  Houston *(G-11744)*

Santos CMI Inc (usa) ....F.. 713 273-4140
  Houston *(G-11749)*

Sardisco Enterprises Inc ....F.. 281 419-9229
  Oak Ridge North *(G-15890)*

▼ Savanna Drilling LLC ....F.. 432 614-1055
  Odessa *(G-16150)*

Savanna Energy Svcs USA Corp ......F.. 281 907-4800
  The Woodlands *(G-19917)*

Saybolt LP ....D.. 281 478-1300
  Deer Park *(G-5294)*

Saybolt LP ....F.. 409 948-3166
  Texas City *(G-19800)*

Scan Drilling Company Inc ....F.. 903 597-5368
  Tyler *(G-20148)*

Schlumberger ....F.. 979 531-8141
  Wharton *(G-20706)*

Schlumberger International ....A.. 713 747-4000
  Houston *(G-11766)*

Schlumberger Limited ....E.. 713 513-2000
  Houston *(G-11767)*

Schlumberger Limited ....F.. 713 513-2000
  Houston *(G-11768)*

Schlumberger Omnes Inc ....E.. 281 285-5176
  Rosharon *(G-17613)*

Schlumberger Omnes Inc ....B.. 713 375-3400
  Houston *(G-11770)*

Schlumberger Technology Corp ....E.. 281 285-8500
  Sugar Land *(G-19543)*

Schlumberger Technology Corp ....D.. 361 210-6200
  Alice *(G-233)*

Schlumberger Technology Corp ....E.. 281 285-7400
  Sugar Land *(G-19544)*

Schlumberger Technology Corp ....C.. 281 285-5200
  Rosharon *(G-17614)*

Schlumberger Technology Corp ....D.. 830 569-8046
  Pleasanton *(G-17073)*

Schlumberger Technology Corp ....E.. 432 694-0000
  Midland *(G-15396)*

Schlumberger Technology Corp ....D.. 210 623-4975
  Von Ormy *(G-20350)*

Schlumberger Technology Corp ....D.. 956 744-4029
  Pleasanton *(G-17074)*

Schlumberger Technology Corp ....C.. 940 442-6566
  Frisco *(G-7310)*

Schlumberger Technology Corp ....C.. 713 482-0700
  Houston *(G-11773)*

Schlumberger Technology Corp ....D.. 210 623-9400
  Von Ormy *(G-20351)*

Schlumberger Technology Corp ....C.. 281 285-8500
  Sugar Land *(G-19546)*

Schlumberger Technology Corp ....E.. 281 285-4823
  Sugar Land *(G-19547)*

Schlumberger Technology Corp ....F.. 817 870-9040
  Fort Worth *(G-6978)*

Schlumberger Technology Corp ....F.. 325 692-1930
  Abilene *(G-78)*

Schlumberger Technology Corp ....B.. 713 513-2000
  Houston *(G-11774)*

Schlumberger Technology Corp ....D.. 903 590-4500
  Tyler *(G-20149)*

Schlumberger Technology Corp ....E.. 903 297-0222
  Longview *(G-14304)*

Schlumberger Technology Corp ....E.. 713 513-2000
  Houston *(G-11775)*

Schlumberger Technology Corp ....F.. 281 285-6370
  Sugar Land *(G-19548)*

Schlumberger Technology Corp ....E.. 281 369-3800
  Angleton *(G-578)*

Schlumberger Technology Corp ....D.. 210 824-7921
  San Antonio *(G-18459)*

Schlumberger Technology Corp ....C.. 432 683-0047
  Midland *(G-15397)*

Schlumberger Technology Corp ....C.. 361 664-3458
  Alice *(G-234)*

Schlumberger Technology Corp ....C.. 903 297-0222
  Longview *(G-14305)*

Schlumberger Technology Corp ....D.. 432 571-4600
  Midland *(G-15398)*

Schlumberger Technology Corp ....E.. 713 747-4000
  Houston *(G-11777)*

Schlumberger Technology Corp ....A....... 281 285-8500
Sugar Land *(G-19551)*
Schlumberger Technology Corp ....D....... 281 285-4551
Sugar Land *(G-19552)*
Schlumberger Technology Corp ....E....... 281 285-8500
Sugar Land *(G-19553)*
Schlumberger Technology Corp ....D....... 281 285-1300
Houston *(G-11778)*
◆ Schlumberger Technology Corp ....A....... 281 285-8500
Sugar Land *(G-19542)*
Schlumberger Technology Corp ....C....... 281 285-8500
Sugar Land *(G-19549)*
Schlumberger Technology Corp ....C....... 281 285-8500
Houston *(G-11780)*
Schroeder Welding & Cnstr ....E....... 361 573-4322
Victoria *(G-20302)*
Schroeder Welding & Cnstr ....E....... 361 575-4992
Victoria *(G-20303)*
Schwob Energy Services LLC ....D....... 469 917-9023
Dallas *(G-4941)*
◆ Scientific Drilling Intl Inc ....C....... 281 443-3300
Houston *(G-11786)*
◆ Scomi Equipment Inc.........................E....... 281 260-6016
Houston *(G-11788)*
▲ Scotia Group Inc ....F....... 281 448-6188
Houston *(G-11790)*
Scott Environmental Svcs Inc ....E....... 903 663-4635
Longview *(G-14306)*
Scott Measurement Service Inc.............E....... 817 326-2361
Granbury *(G-7809)*
▲ Scout Downhole Inc...........................F....... 936 756-3255
Conroe *(G-3362)*
Scurry Midstream LLC..........................F....... 214 238-5740
Dallas *(G-4946)*
SDS Energy Services LLC.....................E....... 903 747-3837
Tyler *(G-20150)*
Seaboard Operating Inc ....E....... 432 684-7005
Midland *(G-15402)*
Seah Steel California LLC ....F....... 281 873-7800
Houston *(G-11801)*
Seawolf Rswd Resources LP.................F....... 713 518-1763
Houston *(G-11809)*
Seawolf Transport LP ....F....... 713 518-1763
Houston *(G-11810)*
Secco Inc...G....... 361 289-1722
Corpus Christi *(G-3619)*
Seguro Well Service Inc........................F....... 830 672-8025
Gonzales *(G-7764)*
Select Energy Services Inc....................A....... 432 447-0602
Pecos *(G-16626)*
Select Energy Services Inc....................D....... 713 235-9500
Houston *(G-11821)*
Select Energy Services Inc....................A....... 903 766-2600
Gainesville *(G-7363)*
Select Energy Services LLC..................C....... 956 286-7100
Laredo *(G-13932)*
Select Energy Services LLC..................F....... 713 296-1000
Houston *(G-11822)*
Select Energy Services LLC..................D....... 940 668-1818
Gainesville *(G-7364)*
Select Energy Services LLC..................E....... 817 523-0136
Weatherford *(G-20620)*
Select Energy Services LLC..................E....... 361 701-8465
Bryan *(G-2508)*
Select Energy Services LLC..................D....... 325 949-0326
San Angelo *(G-17827)*
Select Energy Services LLC..................D....... 318 949-5080
De Berry *(G-5235)*
Select Energy Services LLC..................E....... 940 665-8223
Gainesville *(G-7365)*
Select Energy Services LLC..................D....... 940 665-1767
Gainesville *(G-7366)*
Select Energy Services LLC..................D....... 956 723-4900
Laredo *(G-13933)*
Select Energy Services LLC..................C....... 830 457-2215
Big Wells *(G-2104)*
Select Energy Services LLC..................D....... 940 627-2066
Decatur *(G-5254)*
Sellers Lease Service Inc......................F....... 361 865-2142
Flatonia *(G-6234)*
Selman & Associates Ltd......................C....... 432 563-0084
Midland *(G-15403)*
Sentry Oil & Gas LLC............................E....... 212 753-6367
Mico *(G-15094)*
Sentry Wellhead Systems LLC ....E....... 281 210-0070
Spring *(G-19249)*
Sentry Wellhead Systems LLC ....F....... 432 661-5810
Odessa *(G-16151)*
Seven Construction Inc..........................G....... 806 894-5685
Levelland *(G-14016)*

Shale Flow Specialties LLC ....E....... 903 218-6120
Kilgore *(G-13589)*
Sharidge Inc ....E....... 325 573-4242
Ira *(G-12914)*
Sharp Oilfield Services LLC..................D....... 877 742-7784
Gainesville *(G-7367)*
Sharp Roustabout & Cnstr LLC............E....... 432 528-6360
Midland *(G-15405)*
Shekinah Oilfield Services Inc..............F....... 325 762-2205
Albany *(G-192)*
Sherman Branson Construction............D....... 432 684-4740
Midland *(G-15408)*
Sherrod Services LLC ....E....... 254 729-3177
Thornton *(G-19943)*
Shoco Production LP ....F....... 903 759-0082
Longview *(G-14308)*
Shortes Inc ....E....... 940 658-3576
Knox City *(G-13665)*
Silvertip Completion Svcs LLC.............E....... 432 701-9020
Midland *(G-15409)*
Sitepro LLC..D....... 806 687-5326
Lubbock *(G-14481)*
Sitton Enterprises LLC..........................F....... 817 737-8500
Fort Worth *(G-6991)*
Slaughter & Stanley Cnstr Inc ....F....... 432 264-0031
Midland *(G-15410)*
Sloan Energy Services LLC ....E....... 432 653-0205
Odessa *(G-16154)*
Smco L & M LP......................................E....... 432 550-7116
Odessa *(G-16155)*
Smith Energy Services Inc.....................C....... 903 693-8872
Carthage *(G-2919)*
Smith Industries Inc...............................E....... 432 683-9722
Midland *(G-15412)*
Smith International Inc ....E....... 409 724-2471
Beaumont *(G-1950)*
Smith International Inc ....E....... 432 337-5541
Odessa *(G-16156)*
Smith International Inc ....F....... 254 697-4488
Missouri City *(G-15594)*
Smith International Inc ....F....... 903 693-2596
Carthage *(G-2920)*
Smith International Inc ....E....... 432 550-6909
Odessa *(G-16157)*
Smith Oilfield Services Inc.....................E....... 940 683-5722
Bridgeport *(G-2301)*
Smith Services Incorporated ....F....... 361 526-2615
Refugio *(G-17247)*
Smith Services Red Baron.....................F....... 361 396-0521
Alice *(G-235)*
Smith Vacuum Service ....F....... 325 573-7437
Snyder *(G-19006)*
Snap Oilfield Services LLC ....E....... 956 322-1210
McAllen *(G-14908)*
Snelson Oilfield Ltg Co Inc....................G....... 713 937-3600
Houston *(G-11930)*
Snyder Drilling Corp...............................F....... 325 762-2389
Albany *(G-194)*
Soc Industries LLC ....E....... 432 620-0040
Midland *(G-15413)*
Solaris Oilfield Tech LLC........................B....... 281 501-3070
Houston *(G-11936)*
Solaris Olfld Infrstrcture Inc ....F....... 281 501-3070
Houston *(G-11937)*
Sonic Surveys Ltd..................................F....... 281 385-6500
Baytown *(G-1802)*
Sooner Pipe LLC....................................E....... 281 328-4877
Crosby *(G-3743)*
◆ South Coast Terminals LP ....D....... 713 672-2401
Houston *(G-11963)*
South Texas Oil Field Maint ....E....... 361 526-2822
Refugio *(G-17248)*
South Texas Oilfield Svcs LLC ....D....... 361 701-7064
Freer *(G-7232)*
South Txas Olfld Solutions LLC............D....... 361 396-1777
Alice *(G-237)*
Southern Lease Service Ltd...................F....... 361 449-3048
George West *(G-7629)*
Southern Petroleum Labs Inc.................E....... 903 693-6242
Carthage *(G-2921)*
▲ Sparkman Industries Inc ....D....... 361 573-0001
Victoria *(G-20304)*
Sparkman Well Service Inc ....C....... 361 572-4833
Victoria *(G-20305)*
Spartan Energy Services LLC................D....... 830 281-8505
Pleasanton *(G-17075)*
Specialized Cnstr Svcs LLC...................E....... 210 262-7263
Converse *(G-3403)*
Spirit Globl Enrgy Sltions Inc ....E....... 432 522-2288
Odessa *(G-16161)*

Sqs Ndt LP..E....... 940 726-1107
Sanger *(G-18730)*
Sqs Ndt LP..F....... 432 614-9920
Odessa *(G-16163)*
Srh Tools LLC...E....... 432 686-1058
Midland *(G-15416)*
Ss Equipment Services II LLC ....E....... 830 483-0187
Cotulla *(G-3691)*
SSP Developers Inc................................F....... 956 456-4415
San Benito *(G-18668)*
Stabil Drill Specialties LLC ....E....... 281 583-0127
Houston *(G-12034)*
Stage 3 Separation LLC.........................D....... 713 868-4040
Houston *(G-12037)*
Stakeholder Midstream LLC ....F....... 210 444-9664
San Antonio *(G-18494)*
Stallion Oilfield Cnstr LLC ....E....... 713 528-5544
Houston *(G-12040)*
Stallion Oilfield Holdings Ltd..................E....... 713 528-5544
Houston *(G-12041)*
Stallion Oilfield Services........................E....... 361 578-7500
Victoria *(G-20306)*
Stallion Oilfield Services Ltd ....E....... 830 583-6927
Kenedy *(G-13491)*
Stallion Oilfield Services Ltd ....D....... 713 528-5544
Houston *(G-12042)*
Stanco Marine Inc ....F....... 979 233-1614
Freeport *(G-7214)*
Standard E&S LLC.................................E....... 806 741-1080
Lubbock *(G-14487)*
Steady Flow Testers Llc ....F....... 432 258-1184
Midland *(G-15419)*
Stealth Oilwell Services LLC..................D....... 432 333-3600
Odessa *(G-16165)*
Steel Insulator Group LLC ....F....... 409 284-4407
Beaumont *(G-1954)*
Stellar Automation Inc ....F....... 432 517-4502
Big Spring *(G-2099)*
Step Energy Services USA Ltd ....F....... 210 477-1517
San Antonio *(G-18500)*
Step Energy Svcs Holdings Ltd.............F....... 918 423-4300
San Antonio *(G-18501)*
◆ Step Energy Svcs Holdings Ltd ....F....... 281 606-3600
Spring *(G-19254)*
Stephen Jones ....F....... 409 460-8609
Port Arthur *(G-17126)*
Stephens & Johnson Oper Co ....E....... 940 723-2166
Wichita Falls *(G-20812)*
Sterlings Vacuum Service......................F....... 979 657-4633
Boling *(G-2148)*
Steven C Rich LLC.................................F....... 325 573-6653
Snyder *(G-19010)*
◆ Stewart Stevenson Pwr Pdts LLC.....C....... 713 751-2600
Houston *(G-12065)*
Stewart Stevenson Pwr Pdts LLC ....F....... 903 838-9966
Texarkana *(G-19776)*
Stone Well Service Inc...........................E....... 361 874-4211
Lolita *(G-14177)*
Stork Technical Svcs USA Inc ....D....... 832 781-5700
Houston *(G-12073)*
Straight Line Construction Inc ....E....... 361 394-7656
Freer *(G-7233)*
▼ Strata Control Services Inc ....E....... 337 785-0000
Spring *(G-19256)*
Strawn Transport & Acid Co ....F....... 806 495-2422
Post *(G-17192)*
Strc Oilfield Technology LLC.................E....... 817 599-6155
Weatherford *(G-20623)*
Streamline Energy Services LLC...........F....... 361 852-0907
Corpus Christi *(G-3630)*
Streamline Innovations Inc ....E....... 888 787-6569
San Antonio *(G-18507)*
Streamline Prod Systems Inc ....D....... 800 780-4011
Kountze *(G-13673)*
Streamline Production Svcs Inc............D....... 409 834-6096
Village Mills *(G-20339)*
Strike LLC...E....... 888 353-1444
Odessa *(G-16167)*
Strike LLC...E....... 888 353-1444
Robstown *(G-17517)*
Strike LLC...E....... 888 353-1444
San Antonio *(G-18509)*
Strike LLC...E....... 888 353-1444
Edinburg *(G-5603)*
Strike LLC...D....... 888 353-1444
Fort Worth *(G-7020)*
Strike LLC...B....... 888 353-1444
Baytown *(G-1837)*
▲ Submersible Oil Services Inc.............C....... 432 699-1506
Midland *(G-15422)*

S
I
C

Company		Phone
▲ Subsea Company, Houston (G-12087)	E	281 324-0558
▼ Subsea Technology Inc, Houston (G-12089)	D	281 498-7399
Sulphur River Exploration Inc, Dallas (G-5021)	F	214 373-1091
Sulphur River Exploration Inc, Gilmer (G-7714)	F	903 734-7248
Summa Group LLC, Pasadena (G-16514)	G	713 524-2768
Summit Pump & Safety Inc, Caldwell (G-2637)	E	979 567-7867
Sun Coast Resources Inc, Houston (G-12097)	C	713 844-9600
Sun West Mud Company Inc, Midland (G-15425)	F	432 689-0777
Sun West Mud Company Inc, Weatherford (G-20624)	F	817 594-9758
Sundown Operating Inc, Sundown (G-19614)	D	806 229-6102
Super Heaters Inc, Houston (G-12105)	E	713 952-5533
Superior Energy Services Inc, Houston (G-12111)	E	281 784-5717
Superior Energy Services Inc, Gainesville (G-7370)	F	940 668-5100
Superior Energy Services Inc, Houston (G-12112)	D	713 654-2200
Superior Energy Services LLC, Odessa (G-16171)	E	432 385-3000
Superior Energy Services LLC, Houston (G-12114)	D	281 784-5700
Superior Energy Services LLC, Brookshire (G-2326)	E	281 934-2181
Superior Energy Services LLC, Houston (G-12113)	E	281 999-0047
Superior Optimization Ltd, Fort Worth (G-7024)	F	817 244-4900
Superior Tubing Tester, Alice (G-238)	F	361 668-4611
Surface Well Control LLC, Tyler (G-20158)	F	903 526-2522
Sutton Bros Inc, Sonora (G-19030)	F	325 387-2053
Swabco Inc, Levelland (G-14017)	F	806 894-1511
Swat Inc, Floresville (G-6250)	E	409 296-4976
Swd Enterprises LLC, Houston (G-12129)	E	281 846-6851
▲ Sweco, Grand Prairie (G-7979)	F	817 202-0350
Swiftwater Energy Services LLC, Midland (G-15427)	G	405 203-5419
Swire Oilfield Services LLC, Spring (G-19170)	E	281 210-5598
Swn Production Company LLC, Spring (G-19173)	F	832 796-1000
Systems International Inc, Anahuac (G-528)	F	281 424-2700
T & H Construction, Pipe Creek (G-16742)	G	830 535-6111
T & L Lease Service Ltd, Alvin (G-381)	C	281 331-8221
T & T Marine Salvage Inc, Galveston (G-7410)	F	409 621-4500
T & T Testers Inc, Midland (G-15428)	F	432 682-5456
T & T Transports Inc, Colorado City (G-3227)	F	325 728-2669
T Hill Production Svcs Inc, Big Lake (G-2062)	F	325 884-2670
T-P Rentals LLC, Crane (G-3701)	E	432 558-7218
T-Rey Properties Inc, Midland (G-15429)	E	432 570-6822
Talajak Inc, Mertzon (G-15021)	F	325 632-5341
Tall City Well Service Co LP, Midland (G-15430)	F	432 618-9937
Talon/Lpe Ltd, Amarillo (G-465)	F	806 372-6600
Talon/Lpe Ltd, San Antonio (G-18521)	F	210 253-7200
Talos Ert LLC, Houston (G-12152)	F	281 618-0590
Talos Production LLC, Houston (G-12154)	G	713 328-3000
Tan Boots LLC, Austin (G-1713)	F	512 921-0720

Company		Phone
Targa Ppline Mid-Continent LLC, Midkiff (G-15097)	D	432 535-2484
Targa Resources GP LLC, Houston (G-12160)	E	713 873-1000
Target Well Services Inc, Canyon Lake (G-2681)	F	361 883-8100
Taylor Industries LLC, Fort Worth (G-7038)	D	918 266-7301
Taylor Oil Inc, Sunray (G-19622)	F	806 948-4166
TCO Field Service Inc, Midland (G-15433)	E	432 682-5355
Tdr Services Inc, Midland (G-15434)	D	422 606-6084
Tdw Services Inc, Pasadena (G-16517)	F	281 291-8156
Team Inc, Beaumont (G-1957)	E	409 840-9955
Techniplex Conference Center, Stafford (G-19383)	G	281 565-5566
▲ Technologies Alliance Inc, Houston (G-12176)	E	281 442-8825
Teems Rig Manufacturing LLC, Amarillo (G-513)	F	806 379-6904
Tegraexcel Energy Services LLC, Midland (G-15435)	F	412 508-0690
Tejas Machines Inc, Spring (G-19259)	E	281 350-8890
▼ Tejas Production Services Inc, Victoria (G-20307)	F	361 572-3127
Tejas Trucking Inc, Andrews (G-560)	G	432 523-5786
Tejas Utility Construction Inc, Humble (G-12802)	F	281 299-5097
Tejon Exploration Co, Abilene (G-86)	G	325 673-6429
◆ Tendeka Inc, Houston (G-12202)	D	832 827-4211
Tennessee Pipeline Cnstr Inc, Sinton (G-18966)	C	361 364-2703
▲ Tercel Oilfield Pdts USA LLC, Houston (G-12207)	E	832 386-2500
Tervita LLC, Houston (G-12210)	D	832 399-4500
Tervita LLC, Alvarado (G-346)	F	817 783-2777
◆ Tesco Corporation (us), Houston (G-12212)	D	713 359-7000
Tesco Services Inc, Kilgore (G-13596)	D	903 983-1007
Testco Well Services LLC, Laredo (G-13937)	D	361 396-0626
Testmasters Inc, Houston (G-12214)	E	713 896-1885
Tetra Production Tstg Svcs LLC, The Woodlands (G-19927)	B	281 367-1983
Tetra Technologies Inc, Carthage (G-2923)	E	903 693-9500
Tetra Technologies Inc, The Woodlands (G-19928)	E	281 367-1983
Texas 21st Century Transport &, Stanton (G-19405)	C	432 607-2071
Texas Capital Bancshares Inc, Richardson (G-17407)	A	214 706-6780
Texas Cementing Services Inc, Kingsville (G-13635)	F	361 516-1127
Texas Energy Services LP, Alice (G-240)	B	361 664-5020
Texas Global Systems Inc, Houston (G-12233)	F	832 403-4238
Texas Hot Oilers Inc, Giddings (G-7703)	F	979 542-9341
Texas Industrial Choice LLC, Pecos (G-16627)	E	432 231-7313
Texas Ine Inc, Houston (G-12236)	D	281 601-4884
Texas Lumber Construction, Columbus (G-3234)	F	979 732-2063
Texas Oiltech Laboratories Inc, Houston (G-12242)	E	281 495-2400
Texas Perforators Inc, Kingsville (G-13636)	F	361 516-0541
Texas Pipeline Webb, San Antonio (G-18541)	F	210 298-2222
Texas Tank Trucks Co, Granbury (G-7812)	F	254 559-5404
▼ Texas Wireline Mfg LLC, Fort Worth (G-7051)	F	817 546-0772
Texforce Restoration Svcs LLC, North Richland Hills (G-15882)	F	817 775-3556

Company		Phone
Texland Petroleum LP, Lubbock (G-14495)	E	806 894-4657
Texoil Services, La Grange (G-13702)	F	979 242-5571
Texon Partners, Wichita Falls (G-20817)	F	940 264-3019
Thomas Lease Service, Amarillo (G-514)	F	806 202-1800
Thomas Oilfield Services LLC, Longview (G-14319)	D	855 778-5940
Thomas Oilfield Services LLC, Odessa (G-16176)	D	903 806-0582
Thompson & Thompson, Ozona (G-16287)	F	325 392-3721
Threading & Precision Mfg LLC, Houston (G-12282)	C	281 452-3036
Thru Tubing Solutions Inc, Corpus Christi (G-3641)	F	361 883-4600
Thrubit LLC, Sugar Land (G-19566)	E	713 874-9600
Thrubit LLC, Sugar Land (G-19567)	D	713 538-9500
Thurmond-Mcglothlin LLC, Pampa (G-16341)	G	806 665-5700
Tidal Logistics Inc, Fort Worth (G-7063)	C	940 668-1818
Tierra Lease Service LLC, Kenedy (G-13492)	B	830 583-3717
Tillery & Parks Company LP, Odessa (G-16179)	F	432 366-2700
Timco Services Inc, Carthage (G-2924)	E	903 693-9400
Tmr Services LLC, Rankin (G-17233)	E	432 693-2175
TOFS LLC, Lubbock (G-14496)	F	806 543-9833
Tom Thorp Transports, Ozona (G-16288)	E	325 392-8323
Tomdao Llc, Arlington (G-800)	F	817 888-6167
Tomlinson Oilfield Service, La Vernia (G-13803)	F	956 802-0030
Top Cat Well Transport, White Oak (G-20720)	F	903 295-7000
Top O Texas Oilfield Services, Pampa (G-16342)	E	806 665-2501
▼ Top-Co Cementing Products Inc, Houston (G-12321)	C	832 300-3660
Torcsill Foundations LLC, Houston (G-12323)	D	281 825-5200
Tornado Production Svcs LLC, Orange Grove (G-16270)	D	361 384-9020
Total Production Services Inc, Victoria (G-20311)	C	361 572-0484
Total Sand Services LLC, Fort Worth (G-7067)	G	817 420-7474
Total Wellhead & Rentl Tls LLC, Perryton (G-16650)	E	806 435-3800
Tracker Energy Services Inc, New Braunfels (G-15829)	E	830 837-0806
▲ Trans-Tex Cementing Svcs LLC, Midland (G-15442)	D	432 699-4400
Transcontinental Energy Corp, Houston (G-12351)	G	713 856-6755
Transtar Oilfield Services LLC, Houston (G-12354)	E	281 456-7822
TRC Consultants Lc, Boerne (G-2144)	F	830 249-9968
Trencor Enterprises Inc, Spearman (G-19089)	F	806 659-3911
Trend Services Inc, Alice (G-241)	G	361 396-0048
Trendsetter Construction Inc, Gladewater (G-7728)	C	903 759-4955
Trey Trucks Ltd, Crane (G-3702)	D	432 558-7966
Tri Capital Energy Corporation, Dallas (G-5108)	F	972 996-7486
Tri Leaf Industries LLC, Missouri City (G-15596)	D	830 742-3700
Tri Resources Inc, Houston (G-12361)	F	713 584-1000
Tri Resources Inc, Gladewater (G-7729)	F	903 845-2617
Triangle Well Servicing Co, Pampa (G-16343)	F	806 665-8459
▼ Trican Well Service LP, Houston (G-12368)	A	281 716-9152
Trident Water Services LLC, Benbrook (G-2046)	E	817 889-4334

Trifecta Oilfield Services LLC	C	930 730-4800	Floresville (G-6254)
Trinity Environmental Svcs LLC	F	512 582-8050	Austin (G-1594)
Trinity Envmtl Ctarina Swd LLC	E	512 524-7281	Austin (G-1595)
Trinity Services LLC	D	903 687-4350	Waskom (G-20524)
Trinitys Covenant LLC	F	210 620-3694	Laredo (G-13939)
Triple D Services LLC	F	512 750-6052	Cedar Park (G-2989)
Triple J Oilfield Services Inc	D	956 585-1949	Mission (G-15570)
Triple R Welding LLC	E	432 336-5289	Fort Stockton (G-6330)
Triple S Onshore Oprations LLC	E	903 658-0489	Bullard (G-2552)
Tripp Construction Inc	E	432 381-2440	Odessa (G-16182)
Tristar Globl Enrgy Sltons Inc	F	713 463-9200	Houston (G-12378)
Tristream Energy LLC	E	281 240-8444	Houston (G-12380)
Triton Equipment & Services	F	281 681-9797	Spring (G-19260)
Triumph Inc	F	361 946-4658	Corpus Christi (G-3643)
Trucoastal Oil and Gas Svcs	F	432 413-9950	Midland (G-15448)
True Grit Transportation Inc	E	682 708-5847	Burleson (G-2599)
Trupoint Well Services LLC	E	940 683-2871	Longview (G-14323)
Tryton Tools USA Inc	F	830 372-2755	Seguin (G-18870)
Tryton Tools USA Inc	E	832 717-7125	Houston (G-12393)
Tsunami Rig Wash LLC	E	512 280-1649	Austin (G-1599)
Ttl Subsea Inc	G	713 960-3655	Stafford (G-19390)
Tubing Testers Inc	E	940 574-2177	Archer City (G-597)
Tuboscope Pipeline Svcs Inc	F	432 337-1570	Odessa (G-16184)
Tuboscope Pipeline Svcs Inc	F	936 870-3680	Navasota (G-15745)
Tubular Makeup Technology Inc	E	281 452-5211	Highlands (G-8315)
Tubular Services LLC	E	713 675-6212	Houston (G-12404)
Tubular Services LLC	C	281 452-4353	Houston (G-12405)
▲ Turbeco Inc	F	713 849-9911	Houston (G-12407)
Turnbow Oil Field Services LLC	F	817 880-3833	Lubbock (G-14501)
Turner Energy Services LLC	F	806 323-8844	Canadian (G-2656)
Twbm Holding Co Inc	F	469 916-9430	Dallas (G-5123)
Twisted R Oilfield Svcs LLC	F	432 312-3110	Midland (G-15450)
Twisted S Services Inc	E	817 473-6959	Mansfield (G-14724)
U S Weatherford L P	F	903 729-2106	Kilgore (G-13598)
U S Weatherford L P	F	817 293-5192	Fort Worth (G-7090)
U S Weatherford L P	E	281 331-5505	Alvin (G-383)
U S Weatherford L P	F	281 674-6500	Houston (G-12422)
U S Weatherford L P	E	361 289-1551	Corpus Christi (G-3645)
U S Weatherford L P	E	806 592-3407	Denver City (G-5425)
U S Weatherford L P	E	903 984-5541	Kilgore (G-13599)
U S Weatherford L P	D	432 550-9297	Odessa (G-16185)
U S Weatherford L P	F	281 348-1000	Kingwood (G-13655)
U S Weatherford L P	E	713 983-5000	Houston (G-12424)
U S Weatherford L P	E	281 652-1300	Pearland (G-16606)
U S Weatherford L P	G	832 590-4130	Houston (G-12425)
U S Weatherford L P	C	832 424-0000	Katy (G-13453)
U S Weatherford L P	D	361 289-5111	Corpus Christi (G-3646)
U S Weatherford L P	E	281 485-1899	Pearland (G-16607)
U S Weatherford L P	E	432 530-4900	Odessa (G-16186)
U S Weatherford L P	E	940 626-4698	Decatur (G-5255)
U S Weatherford L P	E	936 435-8118	Huntsville (G-12827)
U S Weatherford L P	F	432 682-7321	Midland (G-15453)
U S Weatherford L P	F	281 449-1383	Houston (G-12426)
U S Weatherford L P	E	325 387-3280	Sonora (G-19031)
U S Weatherford L P	E	936 295-0080	Huntsville (G-12828)
U S Weatherford L P	C	281 847-0121	Houston (G-12427)
U S Weatherford L P	F	325 392-3715	Ozona (G-16290)
U S Weatherford L P	F	281 485-0500	Pearland (G-16608)
Udelhoven Inc	D	210 635-8833	Floresville (G-6255)
Umphres Production Services	F	956 765-8409	Zapata (G-20985)
Underwriters Indemnity	E	713 961-1300	Houston (G-12432)
United Casing Incorporated	F	281 456-0212	Houston (G-12445)
United Casing Tubular Services	E	281 456-0212	Houston (G-12446)
United Energex Inc	E	254 629-8560	Cisco (G-3069)
United Energex Inc	E	210 826-0681	San Antonio (G-17577)
United Petro Transports Inc	E	817 540-6178	Euless (G-6165)
Universal Ensco Inc	E	713 425-6000	Houston (G-12461)
Universal Oilfield Services	F	936 636-2324	Lovelady (G-14355)
Universal Valve Company Inc	E	432 689-6341	Midland (G-15458)
Universal Wllhead Svcs Hldngs	F	361 299-1100	Corpus Christi (G-3647)
Unlimited Frac Sand Llc	E	800 560-1246	Odessa (G-16191)
Upstream International LLC	B	281 265-0033	Sugar Land (G-19570)
▲ US Joiner LLC	E	713 330-1700	Houston (G-12484)
US Well Services Inc	F	832 562-3730	Houston (G-12492)
USA Compression Partners LLC	F	512 369-1380	Austin (G-1618)
USA Compression Partners LP	E	512 473-2662	Austin (G-1619)
▲ USA Rock Bit Inc	G	940 574-2238	Archer City (G-598)
Usac Leasing 2 LLC	C	512 473-2662	Austin (G-1620)
Usdatwing Aerial Analytics LLC	F	210 495-5577	San Antonio (G-18582)
Uv Logistics LLC	G	281 436-2310	Houston (G-12508)
V P Sales & Company LP	E	361 664-2999	Alice (G-243)
Vac-U-Rat Oilfield Svcs LLC	F	214 850-1042	Dallas (G-5149)
Valerus Compression Svcs LP	E	817 598-1600	Weatherford (G-20628)
Varco LP	E	432 550-6802	Odessa (G-16196)
◆ Varco LP	C	713 799-5272	Houston (G-12534)
Varco LP	E	432 362-0581	Odessa (G-16197)
Varco LP	E	361 854-1167	Corpus Christi (G-3650)
Venables Construction Inc	C	806 381-2121	Amarillo (G-520)
◆ Versabar Inc	C	713 937-3100	Houston (G-12554)
Vfl Energy Technologies Inc	F	713 466-9883	Houston (G-12560)
Viking Coil Tubing LLC	D	432 580-7555	Odessa (G-16201)
Vinyard Water Service	E	806 256-2766	Shamrock (G-18893)
Viper Blasting & Coating Inc	F	432 337-9711	Odessa (G-16202)
Viper Drilling International	D	832 917-5804	Houston (G-12570)
Viper Petroleum LLC	F	832 917-5804	San Antonio (G-18594)
Vision Oil Field Services Lc	E	361 578-1901	Victoria (G-20315)
Vitex Wireline Services Inc	G	361 575-1233	Victoria (G-20316)
Viva Well Servicing Company LP	E	432 552-0800	Odessa (G-16203)
Viva Well Servicing II L P	F	432 524-2781	Andrews (G-561)
Volks Resources LLC	F	972 636-1880	Frisco (G-7324)
Vortech Contracting Inc	C	409 296-3219	Winnie (G-20892)
W E Hayden Lease Service Inc	E	361 771-3684	Ganado (G-7416)
W L Flowers Mch Wldg Co Inc	D	361 664-6527	Alice (G-244)
W M Greens Construction Svcs	E	713 692-2291	Houston (G-12585)
Waggoner Land Services	E	817 763-8112	Fort Worth (G-7115)
Walker-Neer Manufacturing Co	F	940 723-0711	Wichita Falls (G-20826)
Ward Mc Carty Inc	E	936 336-3132	Liberty (G-14127)
Warrior Energy Services Corp	F	903 984-9093	Kilgore (G-13601)
Warrior Energy Services Corp	F	972 687-9057	Dallas (G-5173)
Warrior Energy Services Corp	E	830 569-2096	Pleasanton (G-17077)
Warrior Energy Services Corp	F	504 220-8080	Dallas (G-3859)
Warrior Energy Services Corp	F	817 237-9223	Alice (G-245)
Warrior Technologies LLC	G	432 818-0498	Midland (G-15465)
Washita Valley Enterprises Inc	F	817 220-0450	Springtown (G-19277)
Waters & Waters Services Inc	D	432 827-3354	Goldsmith (G-7743)
Wayne Fueling Systems LLC	F	512 388-8311	Austin (G-1652)
Wcc Energy LLC	E	432 208-2839	Anson (G-587)
WCI Construction Inc	F	432 530-4009	Odessa (G-16204)
Weatherford Artificia	E	817 882-9955	Fort Worth (G-7129)
Weatherford Artificia	F	432 550-6118	Odessa (G-16205)
Weatherford Artificia	E	432 368-3865	Odessa (G-16206)
Weatherford International LLC	E	903 353-9700	Longview (G-14333)
Weatherford International LLC	E	281 652-1300	Houston (G-12612)
Weatherford International LLC	B	985 493-6100	Huntsville (G-12829)
Weatherford International LLC	E	713 693-4000	Huntsville (G-12830)
Weatherford International LLC	E	281 485-1899	Pearland (G-16610)
Weatherford International LLC	E	817 568-0282	Fort Worth (G-7131)
Weatherford International LLC	E	210 306-3431	Elmendorf (G-6074)
Weatherford International LLC	D	432 332-1318	Odessa (G-16207)
◆ Weatherford International LLC	A	713 693-4000	Houston (G-12613)
Weatherford International LLC	G	361 576-5641	Victoria (G-20320)
Weatherford International LLC	E	281 759-5100	Houston (G-12614)
Weatherford International LLC	F	806 435-6801	Perryton (G-16651)
Weatherford International LLC	G	817 443-3000	Benbrook (G-2048)
Weatherford International LLC	E	832 955-0000	Houston (G-12615)

S
I
C

Weatherford International LLC ....E 661 589-2146
Greenville (G-8095)

Weatherford International LLC ....E 832 590-4000
Houston (G-12616)

Weatherford International LLC ....E 281 260-5700
Houston (G-12617)

◆ Weatherford International LLC ....G 281 460-7863
Houston (G-12618)

Weatherford International LLC ....C 281 260-2707
Houston (G-12619)

Weatherford International LLC ....D 432 563-0598
Odessa (G-16208)

Weatherford International Ltd ....G 210 626-0831
Elmendorf (G-6076)

Weatherford US LP ....E 210 306-3400
Elmendorf (G-6077)

Weathrford Artfl Lift Systems ....D 432 334-4500
Odessa (G-16209)

Weathrford Artfl Lift Systems ....E 903 663-1966
Longview (G-14334)

Weathrford Artfl Lift Systems ....E 432 586-3883
Kermit (G-13515)

Wedge Measurement & Control LP ....C 713 490-9555
Houston (G-12624)

Wedge Measurement Systems LLC ....C 713 490-9444
Houston (G-12625)

Well-Foam Inc ....C 432 276-3290
Odessa (G-16210)

Well-Pro Services LP ....E 903 759-6071
White Oak (G-20721)

Wellbore Fishing Rentl Tls LLC ....F 432 563-1478
Midland (G-15467)

◆ Welldynamics Inc ....E 281 297-1211
Houston (G-12631)

Wellhead Control Products Inc ....E 713 475-2283
Pasadena (G-16525)

Wells Family Holding Co LLC ....E 903 756-5656
Linden (G-14137)

▲ Welltec Inc ....E 281 371-1200
Katy (G-13455)

West Texas Anchor Inc ....E 325 884-3402
Big Lake (G-2063)

Westbrook Hot Shot Service Inc ....G 903 987-1400
Kilgore (G-13602)

Western Atlas Intl Inc ....B 713 972-4000
Houston (G-12641)

Western Chemical Trading LLC ....F 405 923-4211
Corpus Christi (G-3654)

Western Truck & Equipment ....E 940 723-2555
Wichita Falls (G-20829)

White Wing Inspection Inc ....E 979 421-8255
Brenham (G-2279)

Whitewater Midstream LLC ....E 512 953-2100
Austin (G-1661)

Whitney Oil & Gas LLC ....F 504 218-2929
Houston (G-12665)

Wildcat Minerals Holdings LLC ....E 214 706-3553
Dallas (G-5187)

Wildcat Oil Tools LLC ....E 432 332-4241
Odessa (G-16212)

Wildcat Wireline ....D 830 879-5100
Cotulla (G-3692)

Wiley Lease Co Ltd ....E 830 277-0112
Jourdanton (G-13336)

Willbnks Fncl Cnslting Group L ....F 469 444-0170
Dallas (G-3860)

Willda Beast LLC ....F 979 268-6760
Iola (G-12901)

Williams Companies Inc ....F 281 444-6441
Houston (G-12669)

Win-Tex Lease Services Inc ....F 409 296-4194
Winnie (G-20893)

Winkel & Son Inc ....E 903 928-2560
Tennessee Colony (G-19727)

Wireline Incorporated ....E 903 663-1963
Longview (G-14338)

Wireline Truck Fab LP ....F 830 372-3626
Seguin (G-18874)

Wolf Oil Field Services Inc ....F 979 242-5341
Warda (G-20513)

Wood County Energy LLC ....E 281 994-5400
Houston (G-12684)

◆ Wood Group Management Svcs Inc .E 281 828-3500
Houston (G-12685)

Wood Group Usa Inc ....F 281 647-8300
Houston (G-12688)

◆ Wood Group Usa Inc ....A 832 809-8000
Houston (G-12687)

Woolley Fishing Tool Inc ....E 903 984-3553
Kilgore (G-13603)

Woolley Tool Inc ....F 903 984-3553
Kilgore (G-13604)

Workover Solutions Inc ....E 361 947-8695
Houston (G-12691)

Wp Resources LLC ....F 512 913-7234
New Braunfels (G-15833)

Wren Oilfield Services Inc ....F 903 759-3086
White Oak (G-20723)

Wrights Well Control Svcs LLC ....E 337 502-4160
Spring (G-19264)

Ws Energy Services LLC ....E 361 348-3488
Robstown (G-17520)

Wsi Cased Hole Specialist Inc ....E 800 658-9674
Snyder (G-19015)

Wt Lease Services Inc ....E 361 348-3525
Portland (G-17189)

Wte Services LLC ....E 432 547-2300
Monahans (G-15615)

Wtg Suth Permian Midstream LLC ....F 432 682-4349
Midland (G-15472)

Wtx Oilfield Services ....E 325 227-4656
San Angelo (G-17842)

Ww Wireline Co Inc ....E 956 712-9473
Laredo (G-13940)

Wwt International Inc ....F 281 345-8019
Houston (G-12701)

▲ Wwt International Inc ....F 281 345-8019
Houston (G-12702)

Xl Oilfield Services LLC ....E 830 672-6644
Gonzales (G-7767)

Xterra Fishing & Rental Tls Co ....E 817 334-4100
Fort Worth (G-7153)

Xxtreme Pipe Storage LLC ....E 281 452-9015
Houston (G-12712)

Xytex Inc ....F 361 394-5524
Freer (G-7235)

Yegua Oil Field Service Inc ....F 361 375-2105
Pettus (G-16654)

Yellowjacket Oilfield Svcs LLC ....E 432 523-3692
Andrews (G-563)

Yellowjacket Oilfield Svcs LLC ....D 361 485-0625
Victoria (G-20321)

Yellowjacket Oilfield Svcs LLC ....E 432 381-0104
Houston (G-12716)

Yellowjacket Oilfield Svcs LLC ....E 432 242-7615
Levelland (G-14018)

Zarsky Lumber Company Inc ....E 361 882-2575
Corpus Christi (G-3658)

Zarsky Lumber Company Inc ....E 361 573-2479
Victoria (G-20322)

Zarvona Energy LLC ....F 713 600-0600
Houston (G-12721)

Zdscada LP ....F 903 526-1100
Tyler (G-20179)

Zedi US Inc ....E 830 876-2777
Carrizo Springs (G-2689)

Zedi US Inc ....F 361 575-4528
Victoria (G-20323)

Zedi US Inc ....G 713 527-9591
Houston (G-12724)

Zephyr Gas Services LLC ....E 281 376-2980
Houston (G-12725)

14 MINING AND QUARRYING OF NONMETALLIC MINERALS, EXCEPT FUELS

1411 Dimension Stone

Alkusari Texas Limestone Corp ....F 512 339-2299
Bertram (G-2050)

Arrow Crushed Stone Inc ....F 817 423-1337
Fort Worth (G-6402)

Chemical Lime-Southwest LLC ....C 254 675-8668
Clifton (G-3142)

Continental Quarries ....F 325 228-4180
Lueders (G-14517)

Custom Crete Inc ....F 713 937-3966
Houston (G-9369)

Dietz Memorial Company Inc ....F 512 451-1983
Austin (G-1091)

Espinoza Stone Inc ....D 830 629-2530
New Braunfels (G-15791)

Gulf Coast Limestone Inc ....F 281 474-4124
Seabrook (G-18785)

Lithic Industries Inc ....E 254 793-3791
Florence (G-6240)

Lueders Limestone LP ....D 325 228-4370
Florence (G-6241)

Pb Materials Holdings Inc ....E 432 563-8036
Odessa (G-16106)

Sage Surfaces LLC ....F 281 907-8766
The Woodlands (G-19915)

Salado Operations LLC ....C 254 793-3355
Florence (G-6243)

Simpson Stone Company ....E 512 746-2204
Jarrell (G-13272)

Target Stone LLC ....E 832 827-8663
Houston (G-12161)

▲ Texastone Quarries LLC ....E 432 354-2569
Garden City (G-7417)

Vgcm LLC ....F 713 455-1465
Houston (G-12562)

▲ Zemer International LLC ....E 214 227-2320
Midlothian (G-15497)

1422 Crushed & Broken Limestone

Arrow Crushed Stone Inc ....F 817 423-1337
Fort Worth (G-6402)

▲ Capitol Aggregates Inc ....C 210 871-6100
San Antonio (G-17981)

Caprock Materials LLC ....F 806 778-0343
Lubbock (G-14390)

Cemex Construction Mtls S LLC ....D 830 608-3556
New Braunfels (G-15779)

Cemex Construction Mtls S LLC ....A 713 650-6200
Houston (G-9128)

Chemical Lime-Southwest LLC ....C 254 675-8668
Clifton (G-3142)

Chico Stone Inc ....E 972 276-2284
Garland (G-7456)

Cooke County Crushed Stone ....F 940 759-4104
Muenster (G-15668)

Custom Crushed Stone Inc ....E 210 688-3413
San Antonio (G-18036)

Frost Crushed Stone Co Inc ....C 254 587-2472
Kosse (G-13666)

Gulf Coast Limestone Inc ....F 281 474-4124
Seabrook (G-18785)

Hanson Aggregates LLC ....E 512 756-8255
Burnet (G-2609)

Hanson Aggregates LLC ....D 210 658-7461
New Braunfels (G-15801)

Hanson Aggregates LLC ....F 210 658-3533
New Braunfels (G-15802)

Hanson Lehigh Inc ....E 281 616-0700
Houston (G-10120)

◆ Hanson Lehigh Inc ....B 972 653-5500
Irving (G-13052)

Jr Thompson Inc ....F 940 995-2245
Saint Jo (G-17763)

Kirby Stone Company LLC ....E 281 427-7990
Baytown (G-1824)

▲ Lattimore Materials Corp ....C 972 221-4646
Addison (G-143)

Legacy Vulcan LLC ....E 830 278-6205
Uvalde (G-20190)

Legacy Vulcan LLC ....E 325 646-8526
Brownwood (G-2435)

Legacy Vulcan LLC ....D 210 492-1053
San Antonio (G-18243)

▲ Lhoist North America Ala LLC ....D 817 732-8164
Fort Worth (G-6785)

Lhoist North America Tenn Inc ....E 254 486-2105
Crawford (G-3704)

Lhoist North America Tenn Inc ....E 817 732-8164
Fort Worth (G-6787)

Lhoist North America Texas Ltd ....E 254 698-6610
Nolanville (G-15871)

Live Oak Materials Inc ....E 361 775-0065
Ingleside (G-12896)

M E Ruby Jr Inc ....E 512 258-1601
Cedar Park (G-2977)

Marietta Martin Materials Inc ....F 979 758-3960
Garwood (G-7615)

Martin Marietta Materials Inc ....E 210 495-6224
San Antonio (G-18279)

Martin Marietta Materials Inc ....E 972 350-8200
Dallas (G-4640)

Martin Marietta Materials Inc ....E 830 591-1887
Uvalde (G-20192)

▲ Martin Mrtta Mtls Suthwest LLC ....B 210 208-4400
San Antonio (G-18280)

Martin Mrtta Mtls Suthwest LLC ....D 940 644-5084
Chico (G-3053)

Martin Mrtta Mtls Suthwest LLC ....C 956 381-1459
Edinburg (G-5595)

Mezger Enterprises Ltd ....D 254 547-8174
Kempner (G-13486)

North Texas Crushed Stone ....F 940 665-9100
  Gainesville *(G-7355)*
Patara Stone Inc ....E 713 681-2301
  Houston *(G-11257)*
Rock Crushers Inc ....F 979 289-3768
  Burton *(G-2620)*
Rock Solid Crushed Stone Inc ....F 903 587-3448
  Leonard *(G-14002)*
Superior Stone Inc ....E 512 327-4509
  Austin *(G-1550)*
Superior Stone Inc ....F 512 746-2608
  Jarrell *(G-13273)*
▲ Texas Crushed Stone Company ....C ... 512 255-4405
  Georgetown *(G-7684)*
Texas Lime Company ....E 972 385-1335
  Dallas *(G-5075)*
Texas Lime Company ....D 817 641-4433
  Cleburne *(G-3114)*
▲ Texastone Quarries LLC ....E 432 354-2569
  Garden City *(G-7417)*
Thompson Jr Inc ....E 940 665-2533
  Gainesville *(G-7372)*
United States Lime & Mnrl Inc ....E 972 991-8400
  Dallas *(G-5138)*
Vantacore Partners LLC ....F 215 751-1403
  Houston *(G-12530)*
Vulcan Materials Company ....E 830 624-4944
  New Braunfels *(G-15831)*
Vulcan Materials Company ....E 940 683-4996
  Bridgeport *(G-2304)*
Vulcan Materials Company ....F 210 349-3311
  San Antonio *(G-18603)*
Vulcan Materials Company ....F 210 494-9555
  San Antonio *(G-18604)*
Word Constructors LLC ....F 830 693-2933
  Marble Falls *(G-14752)*

1423 Crushed & Broken Granite

Cactus Cyn Quarries of Texas ....F 830 693-4331
  Marble Falls *(G-14740)*
Gulf Coast Limestone Inc ....F 281 474-4124
  Seabrook *(G-18785)*
Hanson Lehigh Inc ....E 281 616-0700
  Houston *(G-10120)*
◆ Hanson Lehigh Inc ....B 972 653-5500
  Irving *(G-13052)*
Martin Marietta Materials Inc ....F 210 208-4400
  San Antonio *(G-18278)*
Martin Marietta Materials Inc ....E 713 896-8683
  Houston *(G-10776)*
Vulcan Materials Company ....F 210 349-3311
  San Antonio *(G-18603)*
Vulcan Materials Company ....F 210 494-9555
  San Antonio *(G-18604)*

1429 Crushed & Broken Stone, NEC

Attoyac Rock LLC ....F 936 275-3636
  San Augustine *(G-18650)*
Avila Stone LLC ....E 956 453-4747
  Donna *(G-5487)*
Cactus Cyn Quarries of Texas ....F 830 693-4331
  Marble Falls *(G-14740)*
Caprock Materials LLC ....F 806 778-0343
  Lubbock *(G-14390)*
Colorado Materials Ltd ....D 512 396-1555
  New Braunfels *(G-15785)*
Desert Rock Co ....F 915 859-5969
  El Paso *(G-5721)*
Gulf Coast Limestone Inc ....F 281 474-4124
  Seabrook *(G-18785)*
Hard Rock Crushing ....F 806 383-1721
  Amarillo *(G-433)*
Hillstone Company ....E 512 746-5544
  Jarrell *(G-13270)*
Killeen Crushed Stone ....E 254 526-2526
  Killeen *(G-13611)*
M & T Natural Stone ....F 817 556-2107
  Joshua *(G-13321)*
Ultra Fine Silica LP ....F 936 444-7338
  Conroe *(G-3377)*
Yarrington Road Materials ....D 512 754-3573
  Kyle *(G-13689)*

1442 Construction Sand & Gravel

Ace Sand and Gravel ....F 432 290-1205
  Fort Stockton *(G-6326)*
AG III Contractors LLC ....F 956 456-0628
  San Benito *(G-18653)*
Aggregate Plant Products Co ....D 210 333-1111
  San Antonio *(G-17874)*

Alamo Concrete Products Ltd ....E 361 289-9200
  Corpus Christi *(G-3471)*
Arcosa Aggregates Inc ....E 972 544-5900
  Ferris *(G-6229)*
Associated Group Investment Co ....F 806 794-9507
  Lubbock *(G-14364)*
Atlas Sand Company LLC ....E 432 276-3990
  Austin *(G-946)*
B&B Aggregates Inc ....F 281 659-9004
  Cleveland *(G-3120)*
Barco Industries ....F 979 732-2086
  Columbus *(G-3229)*
Bruce Kennedy Sand & Gravel Co ....F 903 838-3377
  Texarkana *(G-19757)*
Capitol Aggregates Inc ....E 432 447-9667
  Pecos *(G-16619)*
Capitol Aggregates Inc ....F 830 693-3533
  Marble Falls *(G-14741)*
▲ Capitol Aggregates Inc ....C 210 871-6100
  San Antonio *(G-17981)*
Cemex El Paso Inc ....C 915 564-8400
  El Paso *(G-5692)*
Cemex El Paso Inc ....C 915 565-4681
  El Paso *(G-5691)*
Centex Materials LLC ....E 512 251-5106
  Austin *(G-1038)*
Centex Materials LLC ....E 512 444-9591
  Austin *(G-1039)*
▲ Centex Materials LLC ....F 512 460-3003
  Austin *(G-1040)*
Challenger Services Inc ....F 361 874-4433
  Lolita *(G-14174)*
Childs Ready-Mix Concrete Co ....E 817 477-5151
  Cleburne *(G-3083)*
Colorado Cnty Sand Grav L L C ....F 979 543-3791
  El Campo *(G-5614)*
Costello Doab Enterprises LLC ....E 512 364-1708
  Austin *(G-1068)*
Crockett Sand and Gravel Inc ....E 936 545-1021
  Crockett *(G-3716)*
Desert Rock Co ....F 915 859-5969
  El Paso *(G-5721)*
E & A Materials Inc ....E 940 692-3290
  Wichita Falls *(G-20761)*
Earth Haulers Inc ....F 817 540-2777
  Euless *(G-6141)*
Ellinger Materials LLC ....F 281 227-6233
  Houston *(G-9604)*
Erna Frac Sand LC ....E 325 265-4400
  Mason *(G-14813)*
Fordyce Ltd ....E 956 581-0672
  Palmview *(G-16310)*
Fordyce Holdings Inc ....D 361 573-4309
  Victoria *(G-20264)*
Fun Da Mentals For Educatn LLC ....F 832 368-3345
  Houston *(G-9874)*
Granville R Damron Trucking ....E 806 842-3519
  Slaton *(G-18971)*
Granville R Damron Trucking ....E 806 842-3519
  Slaton *(G-18972)*
H J G Trucking Inc ....F 817 834-7181
  Fort Worth *(G-6683)*
Hanson Aggregates LLC ....D 940 683-4294
  Bridgeport *(G-2295)*
Hanson Aggregates LLC ....E 979 758-3662
  Garwood *(G-7614)*
Hanson Lehigh Inc ....B 972 653-3735
  Mineral Wells *(G-15528)*
Hanson Lehigh Inc ....E 281 616-0700
  Houston *(G-10120)*
◆ Hanson Lehigh Inc ....B 972 653-5500
  Irving *(G-13052)*
Harrison Gypsum LLC ....F 210 225-9502
  San Antonio *(G-18159)*
▲ Hi-Crush Inc ....E 713 980-6200
  Houston *(G-10170)*
Hi-Crush Permian Sand LLC ....E 713 960-4777
  Dallas *(G-4455)*
Hi-Crush Wyeville Oper LLC ....E 608 372-4705
  Houston *(G-10171)*
Howell Sand Company Inc ....D 806 383-1721
  Amarillo *(G-436)*
▲ Hunter Industries Ltd ....B 512 353-7757
  San Marcos *(G-18695)*
I 35 Sandpit Inc ....E 817 790-2772
  Alvarado *(G-335)*
Johnny Baulch ....F 409 938-8971
  Hitchcock *(G-8338)*
Katy Stone & Gravel Inc ....F 281 371-3003
  Katy *(G-13417)*

Knife River Corp - South ....F 979 361-2900
  College Station *(G-3191)*
Knife River Corporation ....D 979 361-2900
  Bryan *(G-2488)*
Knights Landscaping LLC ....E 972 971-4213
  Mesquite *(G-15057)*
▲ Lattimore Materials Corp ....C 972 221-4646
  Addison *(G-143)*
Legacy Vulcan LLC ....E 325 646-8526
  Brownwood *(G-2435)*
Legacy Vulcan LLC ....E 830 278-6205
  Uvalde *(G-20190)*
Legacy Vulcan LLC ....E 325 529-3785
  Abilene *(G-58)*
Legacy Vulcan LLC ....D 210 492-1053
  San Antonio *(G-18243)*
Liberty Sand & Gravel Inc ....F 972 924-8065
  Anna *(G-584)*
▲ Martin Mrtta Mtls Suthwest LLC ....B 210 208-4400
  San Antonio *(G-18280)*
Metroplex Sand & Gravel Ltd ....D 817 589-9001
  Fort Worth *(G-6833)*
Multisources Ltd ....F 979 247-4305
  La Grange *(G-13699)*
Murphy & Murphy Inc ....F 940 325-2666
  Mineral Wells *(G-15533)*
Nbr Sand LLC ....F 903 593-3311
  Tyler *(G-20133)*
Pappys Sand & Gravel Inc ....E 972 486-4400
  Scurry *(G-18783)*
Pb Materials Holdings Inc ....E 432 563-8036
  Odessa *(G-16106)*
Permian Basin Materials LLC ....E 432 614-6201
  Odessa *(G-16114)*
Pitts Sand & Gravel Inc ....E 940 692-3290
  Wichita Falls *(G-20794)*
Platinum Underground LLC ....E 512 770-9410
  Georgetown *(G-7670)*
R E Janes Gravel Co ....E 325 736-5008
  Merkel *(G-15017)*
RAC Materials LLC ....F 281 255-8500
  Tomball *(G-20005)*
Red Dog Track Inc ....E 254 672-5261
  Strawn *(G-19432)*
Redco Endeavors Inc ....F 832 421-8549
  Gilmer *(G-7711)*
Rickett Ricky Sand & Gravel ....F 281 356-3103
  Magnolia *(G-14624)*
River Aggregates LLC ....E 936 446-2000
  Conroe *(G-3358)*
Sanco Materials Co ....F 325 453-2901
  Robert Lee *(G-17498)*
Signal Peak Silica LLC ....C 281 822-4568
  Houston *(G-11892)*
Silver Creek Materials Inc ....E 817 246-2426
  Fort Worth *(G-6989)*
Solid Rocks Properties LLC ....F 940 779-3700
  Graford *(G-7773)*
Sorrell Cnstr Eqp & Mtls LLC ....D 979 233-6655
  Freeport *(G-7213)*
South Texas Concrete ....E 956 485-2301
  Sullivan City *(G-19577)*
Sweetwater Ready-Mix Con Co ....F 325 236-6200
  Sweetwater *(G-19638)*
▼ Texas Archtctral Aggregate Inc ....E 325 372-5105
  San Saba *(G-18719)*
▲ Texas Crushed Stone Company ....C 512 255-4405
  Georgetown *(G-7684)*
Texas Industries Inc ....F 817 596-4307
  Weatherford *(G-20625)*
Texas Industries Inc ....E 940 969-6021
  Paradise *(G-16354)*
Texas Industries Inc ....F 281 261-0790
  Stafford *(G-19385)*
Texas Lumber Construction ....F 979 732-2063
  Columbus *(G-3234)*
Thompson Jr Inc ....E 940 665-2533
  Gainesville *(G-7372)*
Thrasher Inc ....E 806 296-2609
  Plainview *(G-16765)*
Tricounty Materials & Svcs LP ....F 972 446-1816
  Sanger *(G-18731)*
▲ Txi Operations LP ....C 972 647-6700
  Dallas *(G-5125)*
US Lbm Holdings LLC ....C 713 650-6200
  Houston *(G-12485)*
Vernor Material & Eqp Co Inc ....D 409 233-3366
  Freeport *(G-7221)*
Vista Proppants Logistics LLC ....A 817 563-3500
  Fort Worth *(G-7109)*

SIC

Vulcan Materials Company ....F 210 349-3311
San Antonio *(G-18603)*

Vulcan Materials Company ....F 210 494-9555
San Antonio *(G-18604)*

Weir Brothers Contracting LLC ....F 940 440-2931
Aubrey *(G-852)*

Word Constructors LLC ....F 830 693-2933
Marble Falls *(G-14752)*

Wright Materials Inc ....D 361 387-1511
Robstown *(G-17519)*

Wt Mining Company Inc ....F 361 767-4095
Robstown *(G-17521)*

Yarrington Road Materials ....D 512 754-3573
Kyle *(G-13689)*

Yarrington Road Materials LP ....F 512 306-7800
Austin *(G-1678)*

◆ Zachry Consolidated LLC ....A 210 588-5000
San Antonio *(G-18630)*

1446 Industrial Sand

Covia Holdings Corporation ....E 281 298-8088
The Woodlands *(G-19848)*

Covia Holdings Corporation ....E 254 897-4408
Cleburne *(G-3084)*

Custom Abrasives LLC ....F 281 286-7200
Houston *(G-9362)*

Espey Silica Sand Co Inc ....F 210 626-2800
San Antonio *(G-18095)*

Frac Sand Services LLC ....F 713 668-6766
Houston *(G-9851)*

Ggc USS Holdings LLC ....A 800 345-6170
Katy *(G-13362)*

Hauling & Excavating Casco ....E 713 433-6209
Houston *(G-10136)*

Hermitage Operating LLC ....F 337 852-0001
Houston *(G-10161)*

Industrial Sand Products LLC ....F 832 838-8095
Highlands *(G-8312)*

Innovative Sand Solutions LLC ....F 817 421-7428
Fort Worth *(G-6722)*

Lonestar Prospects Ltd ....E 817 279-1660
Fort Worth *(G-6799)*

Oregon Resources Corporation ....D 541 266-0875
Springtown *(G-19274)*

Osburn Sand Co. ....F 210 626-2045
San Antonio *(G-18358)*

Pioneer Sands LLC ....G 325 597-0721
Brady *(G-2216)*

Pioneer Sands LLC ....D 972 444-9001
Irving *(G-13146)*

Signal Peak Silica LLC ....C 281 822-4568
Houston *(G-11892)*

Silver Creek Materials Inc ....E 817 246-2426
Fort Worth *(G-6989)*

Smart Sand Inc ....E 281 231-2660
The Woodlands *(G-19918)*

Specialty Sand Company ....G 979 234-7431
Eagle Lake *(G-5543)*

▲ Specialty Sand Company Inc ....E 281 456-9553
Houston *(G-12001)*

Superior Silica Sands LLC ....F 210 626-2045
San Antonio *(G-18515)*

◆ U S Silica Company ....E 301 682-0600
Katy *(G-13381)*

U S Silica Company ....E 254 375-2225
Kosse *(G-13667)*

Unlimited Frac Sand Llc ....E 800 560-1246
Odessa *(G-16191)*

US Silica Holdings Inc ....E 281 258-2170
Katy *(G-13382)*

US Silica Holdings Inc ....F 281 258-2170
Houston *(G-12490)*

1455 Kaolin & Ball Clay

◆ U S Silica Company ....E 301 682-0600
Katy *(G-13381)*

1459 Clay, Ceramic & Refractory Minerals, NEC

Mid Tex Minerals Inc ....F 361 865-3530
Flatonia *(G-6233)*

▼ Milwhite Inc ....E 956 547-1970
Brownsville *(G-2383)*

◆ U S Silica Company ....E 301 682-0600
Katy *(G-13381)*

Zemer International MO Inc ....E 214 227-2320
Midlothian *(G-15498)*

Zeotech Corporation ....F 361 274-3357
Tilden *(G-19947)*

1474 Potash, Soda & Borate Minerals

Natural Resource Partners LP ....E 713 751-7507
Houston *(G-11010)*

◆ Solvay Chemicals Inc ....C 713 525-6800
Houston *(G-11945)*

Solvay Chemicals Inc ....D 713 307-3800
La Porte *(G-13789)*

1479 Chemical & Fertilizer Mining

▼ Agrifos LLC ....C 713 920-5300
Pasadena *(G-16379)*

Barite Logistics LLC ....F 281 635-0584
Seabrook *(G-18784)*

Pan Continental Resources ....E 281 291-8100
Seabrook *(G-18788)*

Texas United Corporation ....E 713 877-1793
Houston *(G-12258)*

◆ Truth Chemical LLC ....F 281 292-6900
The Woodlands *(G-19931)*

United Salt Baytown LLC ....E 936 372-3931
Hockley *(G-8350)*

United Salt Baytown LLC ....E 281 303-1101
Baytown *(G-1804)*

United Salt Carlsbad LLC ....E 713 877-2600
Houston *(G-12454)*

United Salt Hockley LLC ....E 713 877-2781
Hockley *(G-8351)*

1481 Nonmetallic Minerals Svcs, Except Fuels

▼ Cyanco International LLC ....E 832 590-3641
Sugar Land *(G-19476)*

Gulf Coast Limestone Inc ....F 281 474-4124
Seabrook *(G-18785)*

▲ Hi-Crush Inc ....E 713 980-6200
Houston *(G-10170)*

Keane Group Holdings LLC ....A 281 716-9152
Houston *(G-10511)*

▲ Layne Christensen Company ....D 281 475-2600
Spring *(G-19226)*

Maximum Industries Inc ....E 214 614-6936
Irving *(G-13099)*

Nigen International LLC ....E 713 956-8022
Houston *(G-11053)*

San Patricio Co Drain ....E 361 364-4268
Sinton *(G-18964)*

Texas Rapid LLC ....E 432 837-1049
Alpine *(G-312)*

Trans-Tel Central Inc ....F 405 447-5025
San Antonio *(G-18561)*

▼ Trican Well Service LP ....A 281 716-9152
Houston *(G-12368)*

US American Resources Inc ....E 972 662-9070
Dallas *(G-3855)*

1499 Miscellaneous Nonmetallic Mining

American Gilsonite Company ....F 713 400-7600
Houston *(G-8597)*

American Quartz LLC ....D 214 243-6676
Dallas *(G-3945)*

Big 4 Inc ....E 409 787-2733
Hemphill *(G-8245)*

Continental Quarries ....F 325 228-4180
Lueders *(G-14517)*

Evans Sons Prtble Rock Crshing ....F 830 214-3629
Euless *(G-6144)*

Georgia-Pacific Bldg Pdts LLC ....F 830 997-4341
Fredericksburg *(G-7181)*

◆ Gma Garnet (usa) Corp ....C 832 243-9300
The Woodlands *(G-19869)*

Natural Energy Resources Inc ....D 832 631-5013
Katy *(G-13426)*

Natural Minerals Inc ....F 432 283-2330
Van Horn *(G-20215)*

Rlf Salado Quarries LLC ....E 254 793-3355
Florence *(G-6242)*

Sun Gro Horticulture Dist Inc ....E 903 938-7348
Marshall *(G-14804)*

Wes-Tex Pure Minerals Inc ....F 432 250-7010
McAllen *(G-14919)*

20 FOOD AND KINDRED PRODUCTS

2011 Meat Packing Plants

7 S Packing LLC ....B 325 716-4047
San Angelo *(G-17768)*

ABF Packing Inc ....D 254 968-4919
Dublin *(G-5514)*

Bay Deer Processing Inc ....F 713 472-6000
Pasadena *(G-16395)*

Boggs Enterprises Inc ....F 903 572-8722
Mount Pleasant *(G-15647)*

Buckhead Meat of San Antonio ....D 210 337-1011
San Antonio *(G-17970)*

Buckhead Mt Safood Houston Inc ....D 281 405-3201
Houston *(G-9009)*

Caddo Packing Co Inc ....G 903 935-2211
Marshall *(G-14768)*

Cargill Incorporated ....A 254 799-6211
Waco *(G-20375)*

Cargill Meat Solutions Corp ....E 806 295-8393
Friona *(G-7252)*

Cargill Meat Solutions Corp ....E 806 295-8243
Friona *(G-7253)*

Cargill Meat Solutions Corp ....E 806 293-5181
Plainview *(G-16752)*

Caviness Beef Packers Ltd ....B 806 372-5781
Amarillo *(G-412)*

Caviness Beef Packers Ltd ....B 806 372-5781
Amarillo *(G-413)*

Caviness Packing Company Inc ....C 806 357-2443
Hereford *(G-8286)*

Centex Meat Company LP ....E 512 352-6357
Taylor *(G-19652)*

Columbia Packing Co Inc ....E 214 946-8171
Dallas *(G-4144)*

Deen Wholesale Meat Co ....E 817 335-2257
Fort Worth *(G-6582)*

Ditta Meat Company ....D 281 487-2010
Pasadena *(G-16417)*

Double B Foods Inc ....C 254 435-6187
Meridian *(G-15013)*

Double R Brand Mfg LLC ....D 979 289-3421
Brenham *(G-2252)*

Dutchmans Market Inc ....F 830 997-5693
Fredericksburg *(G-7177)*

Dziuk Meat Market Inc ....F 830 538-3082
Castroville *(G-2928)*

▲ Eddy Packing Co Inc ....B 361 580-3800
Yoakum *(G-20965)*

Fisher Ham and Meat Co ....F 281 376-1644
Spring *(G-19121)*

Glens Packing Company Inc ....F 361 798-2601
Hallettsville *(G-8122)*

H & B Packing Co Inc ....D 254 752-2506
Waco *(G-20408)*

Harvest House Farms ....F 830 868-7253
Johnson City *(G-13312)*

Hayes Farm ....E 817 477-1661
Mansfield *(G-14681)*

Hlc Custom Processing LLC ....F 432 556-2443
Andrews *(G-544)*

Hormel Foods Corp Svcs LLC ....F 817 465-4735
Arlington *(G-698)*

Huse Processing Inc ....G 254 533-2205
Malone *(G-14638)*

Iowa Food Group LLC ....F 712 600-3663
Westlake *(G-20696)*

▲ J & B Sausage Company Inc ....B 830 788-7661
Waelder *(G-20484)*

J & B Sausage Company Inc ....F 210 344-2212
San Antonio *(G-18197)*

J & B Sausage Company Inc ....C 979 725-6661
Weimar *(G-20649)*

J & R Custom Processing LLC ....F 325 456-1544
Rochelle *(G-17522)*

Janak Packing Inc ....G 361 798-2985
Hallettsville *(G-8123)*

Jbs USA Food Company ....B 817 306-9900
Fort Worth *(G-6736)*

Jbs USA Food Company ....B 903 434-1000
Pittsburg *(G-16745)*

Jbs USA Food Company ....D 806 966-5103
Cactus *(G-2622)*

Jbs USA Food Company ....B 956 632-3800
McAllen *(G-14877)*

K & C Meat Processing ....F 936 825-6944
Navasota *(G-15738)*

Kaspers Meat Market Inc ....E 979 725-8227
Weimar *(G-20650)*

Leonard & Harral Packing Co ....B 210 532-3241
San Antonio *(G-18247)*

Local Cuts Meat Company LLC ....F 972 489-3832
Rockwall *(G-17555)*

Loggins Meat Company Inc ....D 903 595-1011
Tyler *(G-20115)*

▼ Lone Star Beef Processors LP ....C 325 658-5555
San Angelo *(G-17813)*

▲ MARTIN PREFERRED FOODS LP ....C 713 869-6191
Houston (G-10777)

Midwest Provisions Inc ....C 903 891-6213
Sherman (G-18921)

Mineola Packing Company ....E 903 569-5355
Mineola (G-15510)

Mpp Investments LLC ....C 940 691-0014
Wichita Falls (G-20784)

Pat and Gail Jackowski ....F 830 278-6247
Uvalde (G-20194)

Patek Grocery and Market ....F 361 594-3171
Shiner (G-18946)

Pederson Natural Farms Inc ....E 254 386-4790
Hamilton (G-8169)

Pilgrims Pride Corporation ....C 936 564-3306
Nacogdoches (G-15709)

Plains Meat Co Ltd ....E 806 765-5595
Lubbock (G-14462)

Preferred Beef Group LP ....C 806 658-4561
Booker (G-2158)

Ranch House Meat Company LLC ......F 325 396-4536
Menard (G-15000)

Roes of San Antonio LLC ....E 210 224-5441
San Antonio (G-18430)

▼ Stx Beef Company LLC ....A 361 241-5000
Corpus Christi (G-3632)

Tasman Industries Inc ....E 806 372-3850
Amarillo (G-512)

Tejas Supreme Meat ....E 210 224-9672
San Antonio (G-18525)

Texana Feeders Ltd ....E 830 947-3396
Floresville (G-6253)

Texas Best Proteins LP ....E 940 769-2028
Santo (G-18739)

Texas Big Game Processing Inc ....F 210 366-0638
San Antonio (G-18535)

Thompsons Cstm Meats & Proc LP ......E 254 445-4180
Dublin (G-5517)

Tyson Foods Inc ....B 903 859-4030
Arp (G-813)

Tyson Foods Inc ....C 214 331-1010
Dallas (G-5126)

Tyson Foods Inc ....E 936 248-2081
Tenaha (G-19725)

Tyson Foods Inc ....A 903 891-6001
Sherman (G-18937)

Tyson Foods Inc ....F 940 553-1811
Vernon (G-20231)

Tyson Foods Inc ....B 713 678-1893
Houston (G-12421)

Tyson Fresh Meats Inc ....E 806 335-7492
Amarillo (G-469)

Tyson Fresh Meats Inc ....A 806 335-7322
Amarillo (G-470)

Tyson Fresh Meats Inc ....E 806 335-2301
Amarillo (G-471)

Union Slaughter House Inc ....E 830 774-0065
Del Rio (G-5327)

West Phalia Market Inc ....F 512 846-1155
Hutto (G-12888)

Wiatrek Dunn Kutac Inc ....E 830 484-2888
Poth (G-17196)

2013 Sausages & Meat Prdts

B&G Foods Inc ....F 281 821-6680
Houston (G-8779)

▲ Bear Creek Smokehouse LLC ....E 903 935-5217
Marshall (G-14763)

Bridgford Industries Inc ....E 214 428-1535
Dallas (G-4053)

Buckhead Meat of San Antonio ....D 210 337-1011
San Antonio (G-17970)

Cargill Meat Solutions Corp ....E 806 293-5181
Plainview (G-16752)

Carlton Foods Corp ....D 830 625-7583
Houston (G-9093)

Chorizo De San Manuel Guer ....F 956 383-8751
Edinburg (G-5582)

Columbia Packing Co Inc ....E 214 946-8171
Dallas (G-4144)

CTI Saginaw I LLC ....D 817 869-1090
Saginaw (G-17744)

Dankworth Packing Co Inc ....E 325 365-3552
Ballinger (G-1740)

Ditta Meat Company ....D 281 487-2010
Pasadena (G-16417)

Double B Foods Inc ....C 254 435-6187
Meridian (G-15013)

Double R Brand Foods LLC ....E 713 868-0030
Houston (G-9502)

Dutchmans Market Inc ....F 830 997-5693
Fredericksburg (G-7177)

Dziuk Meat Market Inc ....F 830 538-3082
Castroville (G-2928)

▲ Eddy Packing Co Inc ....B 361 580-3800
Yoakum (G-20965)

◆ Fortis Foods International LP ....E 214 472-6400
Frisco (G-7286)

Frenchys Sausage Co Inc ....F 713 862-2299
Houston (G-9863)

◆ Frito-Lay North America Inc ....A 972 334-7000
Plano (G-16874)

H & B Packing Co Inc ....D 254 752-2506
Waco (G-20408)

◆ H W D Casings Inc ....D 210 661-6161
San Antonio (G-18158)

Hill Country Provisions LLC ....F 512 564-3013
Austin (G-1204)

Hillshire Brands Company ....E 817 427-7700
Fort Worth (G-6700)

Hillshire Brands Company ....B 972 556-0392
Irving (G-13057)

Hillshire Brands Company ....B 972 416-4395
Carrollton (G-2760)

Homestead Heritage ....E 254 754-9665
Waco (G-20416)

Huse Processing Inc ....G 254 533-2205
Malone (G-14638)

Intercarnes Texas Corporation ....D 281 360-3825
El Paso (G-5812)

▲ J & B Sausage Company Inc ....B 830 788-7661
Waelder (G-20484)

◆ John Soules Foods Inc ....C 903 592-9800
Tyler (G-20104)

Kaspers Meat Market Inc ....E 979 725-8227
Weimar (G-20650)

Kiolbassa Provision Company ....B 210 226-8127
San Antonio (G-18227)

Kubys Sausage House Inc ....F 214 363-2231
Dallas (G-4572)

Leonard Holding Company ....F 210 532-3241
San Antonio (G-18248)

▲ Leons Fine Foods Inc ....C 972 529-5050
McKinney (G-14953)

M & M Italian Style Foods Inc ....D 817 439-8008
Roanoke (G-17490)

Milton Bernhard Meat Proc ....F 830 367-2995
Kerrville (G-13523)

Nueces Canyon Companies ....F 979 289-5600
Brenham (G-2266)

◆ Old Frito-Lay Inc ....A 972 334-7000
Plano (G-16953)

Papa Grande Gourmet Foods LLC ......C 210 349-6262
San Antonio (G-18366)

Pederson Kronseder LLC ....E 254 386-4790
Hamilton (G-8168)

Plains Meat Co Ltd ....E 806 765-5595
Lubbock (G-14462)

Praseks Hillje Smokehouse ....D 979 543-8312
El Campo (G-5626)

Prause Market LLC ....F 979 968-3259
La Grange (G-13700)

▲ Quality Sausage Company Inc ....C 214 634-3400
Dallas (G-4845)

Quality Sausage Company Inc ....C 214 634-3400
Dallas (G-4846)

Ranch House Jerky LLC ....E 512 347-8999
Austin (G-1452)

Rudolphs Market & Sausage Co ....F 214 741-1874
Dallas (G-4920)

Singleton ML Inc ....F 409 755-0893
Lumberton (G-14570)

Slovacek Foods LP ....E 979 272-8625
Snook (G-18981)

Squares Distributing Inc ....F 325 692-4797
Abilene (G-82)

▲ Standard Meat Company LLC ....C 214 561-0561
Dallas (G-5005)

▲ Surlean Meat Company ....C 210 227-4370
San Antonio (G-18516)

Tallent Enterprises Inc ....E 936 594-2591
Riverside (G-17480)

Texas Best Proteins LP ....E 940 769-2028
Santo (G-18739)

Tyler Packing Co Inc ....F 903 593-9592
Tyler (G-20171)

Tyson Foods Inc ....B 817 656-5507
Fort Worth (G-7089)

Tyson Fresh Meats Inc ....A 806 335-7322
Amarillo (G-470)

Usm Manufacturing LLC ....E 806 791-0220
Lubbock (G-14505)

V & V Products Inc ....F 361 865-3841
Flatonia (G-6235)

2015 Poultry Slaughtering, Dressing & Processing

Bally United Produce Ltd ....E 972 487-7788
Garland (G-7447)

Bc Wetlands Ltd ....G 903 718-1530
Denison (G-5335)

Bridgford Industries Inc ....E 214 428-1535
Dallas (G-4053)

Buddys Natural Chickens Inc ....D 830 672-6262
Gonzales (G-7749)

Buddys Natural Chickens Inc ....D 830 305-0553
Gonzales (G-7750)

Cal-Maine Foods Inc ....E 830 540-4105
Waelder (G-20483)

Cargill Incorporated ....A 254 799-6211
Waco (G-20375)

Dallas USA Foods Inc ....D 214 905-1511
Dallas (G-4229)

Davis Applicators LLC ....E 830 857-3222
Gonzales (G-7751)

Gold Taste Foods Inc ....D 713 378-0198
Houston (G-9991)

Golden Duck Inc ....E 713 222-9262
Houston (G-9992)

Greenberg Smoked Turkeys Inc ....E 903 595-0725
Tyler (G-20091)

Holmes Foods Inc ....E 830 582-1551
Nixon (G-15866)

Holmes Foods Inc ....F 830 437-5555
Gonzales (G-7755)

Holmes Foods Inc ....F 830 437-2555
Gonzales (G-7756)

Ideal Plty Breeding Farms Inc ....E 254 697-6677
Cameron (G-2642)

◆ John Soules Foods Inc ....C 903 592-9800
Tyler (G-20104)

Lion Share LLP ....D 281 888-5383
Houston (G-10654)

Lone Star Poultry Inc ....D 713 868-3888
Houston (G-10681)

▲ MARTIN PREFERRED FOODS LP ....C 713 869-6191
Houston (G-10777)

Pilgrims Pride Corporation ....D 936 598-3356
Center (G-3004)

Pilgrims Pride Corporation ....A 903 575-1000
Mt Pleasant (G-15667)

Pilgrims Pride Corporation ....C 936 564-3306
Nacogdoches (G-15709)

Pilgrims Pride Corporation ....E 254 412-5800
Waco (G-20446)

Pilgrims Pride Corporation ....E 936 560-3901
Nacogdoches (G-15710)

Pilgrims Pride Corporation ....A 936 639-1174
Lufkin (G-14545)

Pilgrims Pride Corporation ....E 214 565-8600
Dallas (G-4805)

Pilgrims Pride Corporation ....D 903 575-3540
Mount Pleasant (G-15657)

Pilgrims Pride Corporation ....E 936 248-5600
Tenaha (G-19724)

Pilgrims Pride Corporation ....B 919 774-7333
Pittsburg (G-16748)

Pilgrims Pride Corporation ....B 903 575-3403
Mount Pleasant (G-15658)

Pilgrims Pride Corporation ....C 903 434-1000
Pittsburg (G-16749)

Pilgrims Pride Corporation ....B 210 633-2412
San Antonio (G-18376)

Pilgrims Pride Corporation ....B 903 575-3748
Mount Pleasant (G-15659)

▲ Rio Star Foods Inc ....D 214 630-4455
Dallas (G-4901)

Sanderson Farms Inc ....D 903 723-2112
Palestine (G-16308)

Sanderson Farms Inc ....A 254 412-3800
Waco (G-20457)

Sanderson Farms Inc Proc Div ....A 979 361-3410
Bryan (G-2504)

Sanderson Farms Inc Prod Div ....A 979 778-5730
Bryan (G-2505)

▲ Saputo Dairy Foods Usa LLC ....C 214 863-2300
Dallas (G-4934)

Tig Real Estate Services Inc ....E 972 661-0232
Dallas (G-5092)

SIC

Tyson Farms of Texas Inc ....A 936 598-2474
Center **(G-3010)**

Tyson Foods Inc ....A 817 485-8912
North Richland Hills **(G-15883)**

Tyson Foods Inc ....D 936 569-7967
Nacogdoches **(G-15717)**

Tyson Foods Inc ....A 903 297-4200
Carthage **(G-2925)**

Tyson Foods Inc ....C 830 672-6548
Gonzales **(G-7766)**

Tyson Foods Inc ....A 830 401-8800
Seguin **(G-18871)**

Tyson Foods Inc ....F 940 553-1811
Vernon **(G-20231)**

Tyson Foods Inc ....C 817 568-9000
Fort Worth **(G-7088)**

Tyson Foods Inc ....B 713 678-1893
Houston **(G-12421)**

2021 Butter

Ingenia Polymers Inc ....E 281 862-2111
Houston **(G-10363)**

Kellers Creamery LLC ....E 903 347-4250
Winnsboro **(G-20899)**

New Dairy Trademark Holdg LLC ...F 803 297-7342
Dallas **(G-4727)**

2022 Cheese

Bridgford Industries Inc ....E 214 428-1535
Dallas **(G-4053)**

Castro Cheese Company Inc ....E 713 460-0329
Houston **(G-9097)**

Cheesemakers Inc ....E 281 593-1319
Cleveland **(G-3122)**

Fountain Valley Foods Inc ....F 281 592-0610
Livingston **(G-14156)**

M Sosa White Cheese La Pintita ....G 956 546-7078
Brownsville **(G-2379)**

Mondelez Global LLC ....C 847 943-4000
El Paso **(G-5883)**

Mozzarella Company ....E 214 741-4072
Dallas **(G-4695)**

2023 Milk, Condensed & Evaporated

Ajooo Inc ....F 469 494-7317
Dallas **(G-3914)**

Bio Trust Nutrition LLC ....E 800 766-5086
Dallas **(G-4025)**

Bristol-Myers Squibb Company ......E 212 546-4000
Houston **(G-8986)**

Cheers Health Inc ....E 518 379-6133
Houston **(G-9168)**

Compass Alpha LLC ....E 512 557-9138
Austin **(G-1059)**

Cosmax Nbt Usa Inc ....C 469 661-9700
Garland **(G-7466)**

▲ Cosmax Nbt USA Inc ....D 469 298-2222
Garland **(G-7467)**

Dean Foods Company ....B 214 303-3400
Dallas **(G-4242)**

▲ Dean Holding Company ....E 214 303-3400
Dallas **(G-4243)**

Dfa Dairy Brands Distrg N LLC ......E 214 303-3400
Dallas **(G-4250)**

Dfa Dairy Brands Distrg S LLC ......E 214 303-3400
Dallas **(G-4251)**

Dfa Dairy Brands Distrg W LLC .....E 214 303-3400
Dallas **(G-4252)**

Dfa Dairy Brands Ip LLC ....C 214 303-3400
Dallas **(G-4253)**

Dfa Dairy Brands Trnsp LLC ....C 214 303-3400
Dallas **(G-4254)**

Eagle Family Foods Group LLC ....C 915 584-7189
El Paso **(G-5729)**

Europa Sports Products Inc ....F 214 388-7444
Mesquite **(G-15041)**

Formulife Inc ....C 214 221-4911
Allen **(G-269)**

▲ JW Nutritional LLC ....D 214 221-0404
Allen **(G-281)**

◆ Kaneka North America LLC ....C 281 474-7084
Pasadena **(G-16468)**

Kellers Creamery LLC ....E 903 347-4250
Winnsboro **(G-20899)**

Lala US Inc ....B 469 804-3850
Dallas **(G-4578)**

Lone Star Dairy Products LLC ....D 806 567-5623
Canyon **(G-2673)**

Naturelab Corp ....G 972 417-3000
Carrollton **(G-2784)**

Nestle Usa Inc ....C 817 420-9971
Fort Worth **(G-6864)**

Nestle Usa Inc ....C 817 491-5500
Fort Worth **(G-6865)**

New Dairy Madisonville LLC ....F 863 297-7342
Dallas **(G-4723)**

New Dairy Ndh Transport LLC ....F 214 459-1100
Dallas **(G-4724)**

New Dairy Opco LLC ....D 972 619-1535
Dallas **(G-4725)**

New Dairy Texas LLC ....F 214 459-1100
Dallas **(G-4726)**

New Diry Clims Adjsting Svcs L ....F 863 297-7342
Dallas **(G-4728)**

New National Dairy LLC ....F 863 297-7342
Dallas **(G-4730)**

Op2 Labs LLC ....A 888 448-8468
Euless **(G-6151)**

Premark Health Science Inc ....E 972 894-0020
Irving **(G-13155)**

Saputo Dairy Foods Usa LLC ....C 214 433-3978
Sulphur Springs **(G-19598)**

▲ Saputo Dairy Foods Usa LLC ......C 214 863-2300
Dallas **(G-4934)**

Specktrum ....F 832 892-0863
Houston **(G-12004)**

◆ Usplabs LLC ....E 469 484-1927
Dallas **(G-5148)**

Valley Herbal Products Inc ....F 956 631-8869
McAllen **(G-14914)**

◆ Yogurt Technologies LLC ....F 409 621-2060
Galveston **(G-7414)**

2024 Ice Cream

▲ Authentic Gelato LLC ....F 214 654-9501
Dallas **(G-3986)**

Blue Bell Creameries LP ....F 806 749-9005
Lubbock **(G-14375)**

Candy Kings Inc ....F 409 762-6100
Galveston **(G-7391)**

Country Fresh LLC ....B 616 243-0173
Dallas **(G-4175)**

Dairy Queen ....F 281 481-8505
Houston **(G-9396)**

Dfa Dairy Brands Ice Cream LLC .....G 214 905-5003
Richardson **(G-17300)**

Epic Source Food Company LLC .....F 214 407-7154
Frisco **(G-7283)**

Freddys Frz Cstard Stakburgers ......E 210 521-5400
San Antonio **(G-18126)**

Gelu Italian Ice LLC ....F 970 986-9535
Houston **(G-9919)**

Gooeys ....F 832 788-9644
Cypress **(G-3798)**

Hokulia Shave Ice of Humble ....F 832 527-2820
Spring **(G-19216)**

Ja-En Enterprise Inc ....F 956 782-0085
Pharr **(G-16703)**

Joseph McSweeny Entps LLC ....G 214 334-8181
Justin **(G-13345)**

Kathy & Janes Co ....E 817 605-9335
Colleyville **(G-3215)**

Kaurinas LLC ....F 972 888-9990
Dallas **(G-4545)**

Kk Meier Co LLC ....F 281 256-7366
Cypress **(G-3807)**

▲ La Brisa Ice Cream Company LLC ..E 713 926-3450
Houston **(G-10579)**

Marble Slab Creamery No 152 ....F 713 455-5786
Houston **(G-10760)**

Montecarlo Foods LLC ....F 206 304-6771
San Antonio **(G-18317)**

Paleteria El Pibe ....F 281 541-8777
Houston **(G-11223)**

Pop Star LLC ....F 214 244-2502
Dallas **(G-4812)**

Sweet Ritual LLC ....G 512 923-1930
Austin **(G-1552)**

2026 Milk

▲ Affiliated Foods Inc ....C 806 372-3851
Amarillo **(G-476)**

Borden Dairy Company ....E 855 311-1583
Dallas **(G-4042)**

Borden Transport Co Ohio LLC ....D 214 459-1100
Dallas **(G-4043)**

Country Fresh LLC ....B 616 243-0173
Dallas **(G-4175)**

Dairy Farmers America Inc ....D 979 743-4161
Schulenburg **(G-18775)**

Dairy Farmers America Inc ....E 817 410-4500
Grapevine **(G-8025)**

▲ Daisy Brand LLC ....C 972 726-0800
Dallas **(G-4207)**

Daisy Brand LLC ....D 972 271-7314
Garland **(G-7475)**

Danone Us LLC ....C 817 336-2320
Fort Worth **(G-6576)**

Danone Us LLC ....C 817 332-1264
Fort Worth **(G-6577)**

Dean Foods Company ....C 214 944-4960
Fort Worth **(G-6580)**

Dean Foods Company ....B 214 303-3400
Dallas **(G-4242)**

Dean Foods Company ....B 817 684-3600
Fort Worth **(G-6581)**

Dean Intllctual Prprty Svcs II ....A 214 303-3400
Dallas **(G-4244)**

Dfa Dairy Brands Distrg N LLC ....E 214 303-3400
Dallas **(G-4250)**

Dfa Dairy Brands Distrg S LLC ....E 214 303-3400
Dallas **(G-4251)**

Dfa Dairy Brands Distrg W LLC ....E 214 303-3400
Dallas **(G-4252)**

Dfa Dairy Brands Fluid LLC ....B 210 732-1111
San Antonio **(G-18052)**

Dfa Dairy Brands Fluid LLC ....F 361 854-4561
Corpus Christi **(G-3513)**

Dfa Dairy Brands Fluid LLC ....E 956 722-1718
Laredo **(G-13879)**

Dfa Dairy Brands Fluid LLC ....E 512 755-6015
Austin **(G-1089)**

Dfa Dairy Brands Fluid LLC ....D 806 765-8833
Lubbock **(G-14404)**

Dfa Dairy Brands Fluid LLC ....F 972 542-9391
McKinney **(G-14936)**

Dfa Dairy Brands Fluid LLC ....B 713 223-5296
Houston **(G-9448)**

Dfa Dairy Brands Fluid LLC ....G 956 686-0511
McAllen **(G-14853)**

Dfa Dairy Brands Fluid LLC ....G 903 758-8211
Longview **(G-14224)**

Dfa Dairy Brands Ip LLC ....C 214 303-3400
Dallas **(G-4253)**

Dfa Dairy Brands Trnsp LLC ....C 214 303-3400
Dallas **(G-4254)**

Gh Dairy ....C 915 790-2609
El Paso **(G-5785)**

Hiland Dairy Foods Company LLC .....D 903 565-0288
Tyler **(G-20098)**

Kady International LLC ....E 210 860-1637
Helotes **(G-8240)**

Kroger Co ....C 817 698-4357
Fort Worth **(G-6773)**

Lala US Inc ....B 469 804-3850
Dallas **(G-4578)**

▲ Plains Dairy LLC ....A 806 374-0385
Amarillo **(G-455)**

Saputo Dairy Foods Usa LLC ....E 903 885-0881
Sulphur Springs **(G-19597)**

▲ Saputo Dairy Foods Usa LLC ......C 214 863-2300
Dallas **(G-4934)**

SFG Management Ltd Lblty Co ....A 214 824-8163
Dallas **(G-4950)**

▼ Southern Foods Group LLC ....C 214 824-8163
Dallas **(G-4986)**

Southern Foods Group LLC ....D 214 941-0302
Dallas **(G-4987)**

▲ Vital Farms Inc ....C 877 455-3063
Austin **(G-1641)**

2032 Canned Specialties

Adelita Tortilla Factory ....E 210 733-5352
San Antonio **(G-17865)**

Bruce Foods Corporation ....F 915 821-2500
El Paso **(G-5674)**

▲ CGJ Enterprises Inc ....F 281 575-8801
Houston **(G-9151)**

Creative Spclty Fd Sltions LLC ....D 713 864-7777
Houston **(G-9341)**

CTI Arlington LLC ....C 817 869-1090
Saginaw **(G-17743)**

Cuatro Cinco Enterprises LLC ....E 713 647-2846
Houston **(G-9355)**

Dallas Tortillas Inc ....F 214 943-7681
Dallas **(G-4228)**

Durrset Amigos Ltd ....C 210 798-5360
San Antonio **(G-18074)**

Fortune One Foods Inc ....E 713 426-1133
Houston **(G-9840)**

Garcia Foods Inc ....C..... 210 349-6262
San Antonio (G-18136)

Guar Resources LLC ....E..... 806 637-4662
Brownfield (G-2331)

▲ Houston Calco Inc ....G..... 713 236-8668
Houston (G-10221)

International Do Foods Idf Inc ....F..... 713 222-0598
Houston (G-10401)

La Autentica Inc ....F..... 202 415-6979
San Antonio (G-18232)

La Nortena Inc ....G..... 432 445-3273
Pecos (G-16621)

▲ Lechi Foods ....E..... 281 470-6200
La Porte (G-13767)

Miller Seafood Co Inc ....E..... 361 552-6423
Port Lavaca (G-17151)

Mr Nams Foods Incorporated ....F..... 214 689-4688
Dallas (G-4698)

Odessa Tortilla & Tamale Fctry ....E..... 432 332-6676
Odessa (G-16098)

Palacios & Sons LLC ....G..... 713 463-5851
Houston (G-11222)

Rd Food Manufacturing Inc ....E..... 915 594-4488
El Paso (G-5930)

Renfro Foods Inc ....E..... 817 336-3849
Fort Worth (G-6955)

Rodriguez Foods Ltd ....E..... 817 626-3961
Fort Worth (G-6964)

Southern Noodle Company ....F..... 281 988-7778
Houston (G-11976)

▼ Teasdale Foods Inc ....C..... 209 358-5616
Flower Mound (G-6287)

Texas Titos Inc ....F..... 830 626-1123
New Braunfels (G-15828)

Triple Nickel Inc ....F..... 806 272-5589
Muleshoe (G-15679)

Tyson Foods Inc ....F..... 940 553-1811
Vernon (G-20231)

Tyson Foods Inc ....B..... 713 678-1893
Houston (G-12421)

2033 Canned Fruits, Vegetables & Preserves

Agrana Fruit Us Inc ....D..... 817 625-9053
Fort Worth (G-6355)

▼ Aloe Farms Inc ....F..... 956 425-1289
Harlingen (G-8177)

▲ Bartush-Schnitzius Foods Co ....E..... 972 219-1270
Lewisville (G-14026)

Borden Dairy Company ....B..... 855 311-1583
Dallas (G-4042)

Bruce Foods Corporation ....F..... 915 821-2500
El Paso (G-5674)

Campbell Soup Company ....C..... 903 784-3341
Paris (G-16359)

Claudes Sauces Inc ....F..... 915 858-4299
El Paso (G-5697)

Commissary Express Inc ....F..... 903 357-5670
Sherman (G-18912)

Dean Foods Company ....B..... 817 684-3600
Fort Worth (G-6581)

Del Monte Foods Inc ....B..... 830 374-3451
Crystal City (G-3756)

Dfa Dairy Brands Fluid LLC ....B..... 713 223-5296
Houston (G-9448)

F and B Holdings LLC ....E..... 956 424-7775
Mission (G-15553)

Gooch Investments Inc ....F..... 325 677-5904
Abilene (G-44)

Good Flow Honey & Juice Co ....F..... 512 472-6714
Austin (G-1188)

Good Flow Juice Company LLC ....F..... 512 472-6714
Austin (G-1189)

Gourmet Grdns Spclty Foods Inc ....E..... 903 284-6215
Jacksonville (G-13241)

Herb Hilltop Farm & Restaurant ....D..... 832 397-4020
Cleveland (G-3128)

▲ Jardine Foods Inc ....E..... 512 295-4600
Buda (G-2531)

Jensar Corporation ....G..... 817 542-4327
Fort Worth (G-6738)

Juiceus LLC ....E..... 956 667-0153
Brownsville (G-2372)

Kraft Heinz Company ....B..... 972 272-7511
Garland (G-7534)

Kraft Heinz Foods Company ....B..... 847 646-2000
Irving (G-13079)

Kraft Heinz Foods Company ....E..... 817 837-4100
Fort Worth (G-6772)

▲ Kt Foods LLC ....D..... 409 293-3257
Port Arthur (G-17115)

◆ Motts LLP ....C..... 972 673-8088
Plano (G-16934)

Nakent LLC ....F..... 619 212-2277
San Antonio (G-18329)

National Food and Beverage Inc ....D..... 214 905-9700
Dallas (G-4715)

New Canaan Farms Inc ....F..... 512 858-7669
Dripping Springs (G-5509)

O Talk Texas Brands Inc ....E..... 325 655-6077
San Angelo (G-17816)

Ocean Spray Cranberries Inc ....C..... 903 885-8676
Sulphur Springs (G-19594)

▲ Olive Packing Company Inc ....D..... 409 293-3257
Port Arthur (G-17119)

▼ One World Foods Inc ....F..... 512 480-0203
Austin (G-1387)

▲ Plains Dairy LLC ....A..... 806 374-0385
Amarillo (G-455)

◆ Riviana Foods Inc ....C..... 713 529-3251
Houston (G-11629)

▲ Simplyfresco LLC ....E..... 210 494-8443
San Antonio (G-18477)

▲ Sneaky Chef Foods LLC ....F..... 203 768-5654
Austin (G-1514)

Space Enterprises LLC ....F..... 800 559-2923
San Antonio (G-18490)

Space Enterprises LLC ....E..... 281 846-9613
The Woodlands (G-19923)

Sunny Delight Beverages Co ....D..... 903 893-5764
Sherman (G-18935)

Talk OTexas Brands Inc ....D..... 325 655-6077
San Angelo (G-17831)

Teasdale Foods Inc ....B..... 915 821-2500
El Paso (G-5994)

◆ Texas Citrus Exchange ....C..... 956 585-8321
Mission (G-15567)

Texas Rib Rangers Product ....E..... 940 565-1983
Denton (G-5406)

TJ Blackburn Syrup Works Inc ....D..... 903 665-2541
Jefferson (G-13289)

Wonderful Citrus Packing LLC ....F..... 956 205-7300
Mission (G-15574)

2034 Dried Fruits, Vegetables & Soup

Azteca Milling LP ....B..... 806 291-5633
Plainview (G-16751)

Epic Provisions LLC ....F..... 512 944-8502
Austin (G-1129)

Frito-Lay North America Inc ....D..... 817 649-3266
Arlington (G-681)

▼ Teasdale Foods Inc ....C..... 209 358-5616
Flower Mound (G-6287)

2035 Pickled Fruits, Vegetables, Sauces & Dressings

Apolo Commercial LLC ....F..... 956 688-8207
New Braunfels (G-15774)

◆ Avomex Inc ....E..... 817 509-0626
Saginaw (G-17738)

▲ Bartush-Schnitzius Foods Co ....E..... 972 219-1270
Lewisville (G-14026)

Bruce Foods Corporation ....F..... 915 821-2500
El Paso (G-5674)

▲ Daltons Best Maid Products Inc ....C..... 800 447-3581
Fort Worth (G-6574)

Del Monte Foods Inc ....B..... 830 374-3451
Crystal City (G-3756)

▼ Del Sol Food Company Inc ....E..... 979 836-5978
Brenham (G-2251)

Eastex Farms ....E..... 903 683-5726
Rusk (G-17730)

First Place Foods LLC ....E..... 972 272-1111
Garland (G-7490)

Food Group Ventures LLC ....G..... 936 327-4443
Livingston (G-14153)

▲ Food Source Inc ....D..... 972 548-9001
McKinney (G-14944)

Frankie VS Kitchen LLC ....D..... 214 303-9910
Dallas (G-4377)

Frito-Lay North America Inc ....D..... 817 649-3266
Arlington (G-681)

Gourmet Grdns Spclty Foods Inc ....E..... 903 284-6215
Jacksonville (G-13241)

Gruma Corporation ....C..... 972 232-5000
Irving (G-13043)

◆ Heritage Fmly Spclty Foods Inc ....E..... 972 660-6511
Grand Prairie (G-7889)

▲ Jardine Foods Inc ....E..... 512 295-4600
Buda (G-2531)

Kraft Heinz Company ....B..... 972 272-7511
Garland (G-7534)

Mexi-Snax Corporation ....E..... 915 779-5709
El Paso (G-5874)

National Food and Beverage Inc ....D..... 214 905-9700
Dallas (G-4715)

Nueces Canyon Companies ....F..... 979 289-5600
Brenham (G-2266)

Renfro Foods Inc ....E..... 817 336-3849
Fort Worth (G-6955)

Richard E Colgin I Ltd ....E..... 214 951-8687
Dallas (G-4897)

Talk OTexas Brands Inc ....D..... 325 655-6077
San Angelo (G-17831)

2037 Frozen Fruits, Juices & Vegetables

A&A Concepts ....F..... 210 435-1300
San Antonio (G-17848)

▲ Blencor LLC ....C..... 979 627-7801
Sealy (G-18806)

Citrolim Inc ....F..... 281 453-5150
Houston (G-9202)

Coca-Cola Company ....D..... 281 302-4317
Sugar Land (G-19459)

JR Simplot Company ....C..... 361 987-2682
Point Comfort (G-17087)

JR Simplot Company ....D..... 979 826-8063
Hempstead (G-8253)

Mibo Fresh Foods LLC ....E..... 817 882-9600
Fort Worth (G-6835)

Pepsico Inc ....D..... 972 963-1000
Plano (G-16969)

Pictsweet Company ....E..... 210 833-9618
San Antonio (G-18374)

▲ Precision Formulations LLC ....D..... 972 393-7170
Dallas (G-4819)

Texas Pack Inc ....E..... 956 943-5461
Port Isabel (G-17138)

Usm Manufacturing LLC ....E..... 806 791-0220
Lubbock (G-14505)

2038 Frozen Specialties

1st Original Texas Chili Inc ....G..... 817 626-0983
Fort Worth (G-6333)

◆ Amy Food Inc ....D..... 713 910-5860
Houston (G-8631)

Austin Ventures LP ....D..... 512 485-1900
Austin (G-963)

Beetnik Foods LLC ....F..... 512 584-8228
Austin (G-986)

▲ Bottom Line Fd Processors Inc ....E..... 512 218-3500
Austin (G-1003)

Bridgford Foods Corporation ....D..... 214 428-1535
Dallas (G-4051)

Bridgford Industries Inc ....D..... 214 428-1535
Dallas (G-4053)

Campbell Soup Company ....C..... 903 784-3341
Paris (G-16359)

▲ Choiers Company ....E..... 817 312-1364
Hurst (G-12843)

▲ Chungs Products LP ....C..... 713 741-2118
Houston (G-9186)

▲ Food Source Inc ....D..... 972 548-9001
McKinney (G-14944)

▲ Garland Ventures Ltd ....E..... 972 485-8878
Garland (G-7496)

Good Fat Co Ltd ....E..... 512 300-8391
Austin (G-1187)

Gourmet Cuisine Inc ....E..... 972 289-7441
Mesquite (G-15045)

Gruma Corporation ....C..... 972 232-5000
Irving (G-13043)

▲ Isabella Foods Inc ....D..... 915 590-1899
El Paso (G-5818)

Kaiser Foodline LLC ....E..... 972 705-9595
Garland (G-7529)

Night Hawk Frozen Foods Inc ....D..... 800 580-4166
Buda (G-2533)

Pretzels Inc ....E..... 972 416-3660
Carrollton (G-2795)

▲ Quality Star Products Ltd ....D..... 214 680-7448
Garland (G-7574)

Sfc Global Supply Chain Inc ....B..... 713 740-7200
Pasadena (G-16505)

Sfc Global Supply Chain Inc ....B..... 713 740-7536
Deer Park (G-5295)

Super Seed Foods LLC ....E..... 512 698-7907
Austin (G-1547)

Texpac Foods LLC ....F..... 713 780-4876
Houston (G-12261)

Usm Manufacturing LLC ....E 806 791-0220
Lubbock *(G-14505)*

▲ Van Oriental Food Inc ....D 214 630-0333
Dallas *(G-5153)*

WEI-Chuan USA Inc ....F 713 690-3677
Houston *(G-12626)*

Wholesome Group LLC ....C 214 937-4750
Plano *(G-17050)*

Yellowstone Brands Ltd ....G 713 650-0065
Houston *(G-12717)*

2041 Flour, Grain Milling

ADM Milling Co ....E 830 625-2301
New Braunfels *(G-15772)*

Andersons Inc ....F 913 748-4401
Lytle *(G-14572)*

Archer-Daniels-Midland Company ...... E 325 356-2511
Comanche *(G-3235)*

Archer-Daniels-Midland Company ...... E 817 917-2810
Saginaw *(G-17736)*

Archer-Daniels-Midland Company ...... D 806 723-5117
Lubbock *(G-14363)*

Archer-Daniels-Midland Company ...... F 806 364-4732
Hereford *(G-8283)*

Archer-Daniels-Midland Company ...... F 214 357-3331
Dallas *(G-3957)*

Archer-Daniels-Midland Company ...... E 806 828-3948
Slaton *(G-18968)*

Ardent Mills LLC ....E 512 789-5165
Galena Park *(G-7377)*

Ardent Mills LLC ....D 817 847-3400
Saginaw *(G-17737)*

Azteca Milling LP ....C 806 258-7704
Dawn *(G-5216)*

▲ Azteca Milling LP ....C 956 383-4911
Irving *(G-12940)*

Azteca Milling LP ....F 972 232-5363
Irving *(G-12941)*

Azteca Milling LP ....C 956 383-4911
Edinburg *(G-5577)*

B Martinez & Sons Company Inc ...... E 210 226-6772
San Antonio *(G-17932)*

Bcca LLC ....G 361 547-3341
Tynan *(G-20180)*

Bcw Food Products Inc ....E 214 350-3320
Dallas *(G-4010)*

Bridgford Foods Corporation ....D 214 428-1535
Dallas *(G-4051)*

Bunge Milling Southwest Inc ....F 806 799-3755
Lubbock *(G-14385)*

▲ Bunge Milling Southwest Inc ....D 800 852-8291
Muleshoe *(G-15676)*

CH Guenther & Son LLC ....C 972 298-4281
Duncanville *(G-5529)*

▼ CH Guenther & Son LLC ....B 210 227-1401
San Antonio *(G-17997)*

Collingwood Grain Inc ....F 254 582-5344
Hillsboro *(G-8324)*

General Mills Inc ....E 972 892-4100
Addison *(G-129)*

Hbreaux Companies Inc ....F 409 792-9212
Bridge City *(G-2284)*

Homestead Gristmill LLC ....E 254 829-2135
Waco *(G-20415)*

Miller Milling Company LLC ....E 817 847-8977
Saginaw *(G-17751)*

▲ Morrison Milling Company ....D 940 387-6111
Denton *(G-5382)*

Panhandle Milling LLC ....E 806 243-4211
Dawn *(G-5217)*

Panhandle Milling LLC ....F 806 258-7253
Dawn *(G-5218)*

R Ibarras Inc ....D 817 625-8962
Fort Worth *(G-6931)*

Richardson Milling Inc ....F 806 258-7227
Dawn *(G-5219)*

Riviana Foods Inc ....B 713 529-3251
Houston *(G-11628)*

▲ Riviana International Inc ....C 713 529-3251
Houston *(G-11630)*

Snow Flake Bakery ....E 281 427-4423
Baytown *(G-1834)*

Southern Noodle Company ....F 281 988-7778
Houston *(G-11976)*

Sunbelt Mixes Inc ....F 972 529-5155
McKinney *(G-14980)*

2043 Cereal Breakfast Foods

General Mills Inc ....F 817 490-6940
Roanoke *(G-17485)*

General Mills Inc ....D 281 890-0784
Houston *(G-9925)*

Holly Yaupon Tea LLC ....G 512 677-4907
Cat Spring *(G-2930)*

Kellogg Company ....A 830 438-2254
Bulverde *(G-2555)*

La Autentica Inc ....F 202 415-6979
San Antonio *(G-18232)*

Magi Foods LLC ....F 210 590-1308
Selma *(G-18877)*

Nsh Services Inc ....F 817 961-5045
Fort Worth *(G-6873)*

Pepsico Inc ....D 972 963-1000
Plano *(G-16969)*

2044 Rice Milling

◆ American Rice Inc ....E 281 272-8800
Houston *(G-8606)*

American Rice Inc ....C 979 233-8248
Freeport *(G-7191)*

Barton Springs Mill Inc ....F 512 554-5981
Dripping Springs *(G-5501)*

Beaumont Rice Mills Inc ....E 409 832-2521
Beaumont *(G-1862)*

Bu Growers Ltd ....E 979 245-2043
Bay City *(G-1769)*

▼ Colorado County Rice Mill Inc ...... F 979 234-5554
Eagle Lake *(G-5540)*

Doguets Rice Milling Company ....E 409 866-2297
Beaumont *(G-1883)*

Ebrofrost North America Inc ....E 281 727-8139
Houston *(G-9573)*

◆ Gulf Pacific Rice Co Inc ....E 713 464-0606
Houston *(G-10066)*

◆ Gulf Rice Milling Inc ....D 713 464-0606
Houston *(G-10070)*

◆ Ricetec Inc ....C 281 756-3300
Alvin *(G-379)*

Riviana Foods Inc ....B 713 529-3251
Houston *(G-11628)*

◆ Riviana Foods Inc ....C 713 529-3251
Houston *(G-11629)*

▲ Riviana International Inc ....C 713 529-3251
Houston *(G-11630)*

▲ SOS Cuetara USA Inc ....C 281 272-8800
Houston *(G-11956)*

TLC Tonerland LP ....F 713 692-6650
Houston *(G-12306)*

Wenglar Services Inc ....F 979 648-2225
Louise *(G-14354)*

2045 Flour, Blended & Prepared

Alpha Foods Co ....E 936 372-5858
Waller *(G-20491)*

Bcw Food Products Inc ....E 214 350-3320
Dallas *(G-4010)*

Blue Ribbon Products Inc ....D 214 647-1825
Rockwall *(G-17540)*

Bridgford Industries Inc ....E 214 428-1535
Dallas *(G-4053)*

▼ CH Guenther & Son LLC ....B 210 227-1401
San Antonio *(G-17997)*

Das Brot Inc ....E 972 243-8443
Carrollton *(G-2721)*

Dawn Food Products Inc ....E 972 485-8004
Garland *(G-7477)*

Heart of Texas Biscuits Inc ....F 254 753-0046
Waco *(G-20410)*

Sfc Global Supply Chain Inc ....B 713 740-7200
Pasadena *(G-16505)*

Tiger Construction ....F 915 999-1260
El Paso *(G-6005)*

Vicky Cakes Pancake Mix LLC ....G 469 573-2773
Farmers Branch *(G-6218)*

2046 Wet Corn Milling

◆ Interntional Grains Cereal LLC ...... E 903 554-1003
Greenville *(G-8077)*

Kmr Group LLC ....G 713 932-6988
Houston *(G-10543)*

2047 Dog & Cat Food

Bark To Basics LLC ....F 913 825-1760
Irving *(G-12944)*

Mars Petcare Us Inc ....D 254 771-3366
Temple *(G-19687)*

◆ Paw Depot Incorporated ....F 214 440-6324
Richardson *(G-17371)*

Pethonesty LLC ....F 909 435-6574
Austin *(G-1413)*

Prairie Dog Pet Products LLC ....B 972 606-9050
Grand Prairie *(G-7951)*

Summma International LLC ....F 630 519-3632
Laredo *(G-13936)*

Tejas Industries Inc ....E 806 322-2822
Hereford *(G-8295)*

◆ Texas Farm Products Company ...... C 936 564-3711
Nacogdoches *(G-15715)*

Valley Proteins (de) Inc ....E 806 379-6001
Amarillo *(G-519)*

2048 Prepared Feeds For Animals & Fowls

Abilene AG Service & Sup Inc ....D 325 677-4371
Abilene *(G-4)*

American Dehydrated Foods Inc ....G 903 838-0366
Hooks *(G-8360)*

Angelo Pellets Inc ....F 325 655-5751
San Angelo *(G-17777)*

◆ Animal Science Products Inc ....E 936 560-0003
Nacogdoches *(G-15685)*

Archer-Daniels-Midland Company ...... D 806 723-5117
Lubbock *(G-14363)*

Behrends Feed & Fertilizer LLC ....E 830 997-3410
Fredericksburg *(G-7172)*

Bryant Grain Co ....E 817 441-9782
Aledo *(G-196)*

Cargill Incorporated ....F 806 364-3891
Hereford *(G-8285)*

Cargill Incorporated ....E 325 672-3271
Abilene *(G-29)*

Cargill Incorporated ....E 254 774-9022
Temple *(G-19673)*

◆ Contanda LLC ....E 832 699-4001
Houston *(G-9281)*

Crystal Feed Mills Inc ....E 903 488-3261
Como *(G-3247)*

▲ Dairy Manufacturers Inc ....F 972 347-2878
Prosper *(G-17213)*

Darling Ingredients Inc ....D 313 928-7400
Irving *(G-12993)*

Darling Ingredients Inc ....E 214 948-7501
Dallas *(G-4238)*

E Barr Feeds Inc ....F 830 672-6515
Gonzales *(G-7752)*

East Bernard Milling Co LLC ....G 979 335-7554
East Bernard *(G-5557)*

Economy Mills Ltd ....F 806 765-5547
Lubbock *(G-14406)*

Ezell-Key Grain Company Inc ....E 325 573-9373
Snyder *(G-18991)*

Eznectar LLC ....F 210 732-6400
San Antonio *(G-18101)*

Feeders Supply ....F 806 889-3391
Lubbock *(G-14409)*

◆ Global Animal Products Inc ....E 806 622-9600
Amarillo *(G-489)*

Gorman Milling Co Inc ....D 254 734-2252
Gorman *(G-7772)*

Hamlin Pet Worx LLC ....F 855 430-9888
Hamlin *(G-8170)*

International Ingredient Corp ....F 817 645-1328
Cleburne *(G-3096)*

▼ J M Saddler Inc ....G 979 693-5114
College Station *(G-3188)*

John B Smith ....C 830 620-9090
New Braunfels *(G-15806)*

Jupe Feeds Inc ....E 254 773-5211
Temple *(G-19683)*

Koch Ranches Inc ....F 210 858-9795
San Antonio *(G-18228)*

Kunafin LLC ....F 830 757-1181
Quemado *(G-17222)*

Land OLakes Inc ....E 281 342-2493
Rosenberg *(G-17588)*

Leonard & Harral Packing Co ....B 210 532-3241
San Antonio *(G-18247)*

Livengood Feeds Inc ....E 512 398-2351
Lockhart *(G-14170)*

Mahard Feed Mill Inc ....G 903 523-4455
Gordonville *(G-7770)*

Marshall Minerals Inc ....E 903 938-8301
Marshall *(G-14789)*

MB Nutritional Sciences LLC ....G 806 778-2697
Lubbock *(G-14444)*

▼ Mid-America Pet Food LLC ....E 903 572-5900
Mount Pleasant *(G-15655)*

Mr Bird ....F 830 620-9090
New Braunfels *(G-15814)*

▲ Norel Animal Nutrition USA Inc	F	281 741-8211	
Pasadena (G-16490)			
Nutri-Feeds Inc	E	806 357-2288	
Hereford (G-8294)			
Nutrition Plus LLP	G	806 655-0505	
Canyon (G-2675)			
Pegasus Food	F	972 961-5200	
Rockwall (G-17558)			
Prairie Ptfood Ingredients LLC	F	469 383-5182	
Rice (G-17266)			
Precision Joint Solution Inc	F	972 351-0470	
Austin (G-1429)			
Protocol Technologies Inc	F	940 683-8123	
Bridgeport (G-2299)			
Provimi North America Inc	G	817 594-9628	
Weatherford (G-20612)			
Purina Animal Nutrition LLC	E	817 492-9159	
Fort Worth (G-6922)			
Purina Animal Nutrition LLC	D	817 878-0280	
Fort Worth (G-6923)			
Purina Animal Nutrition LLC	E	830 672-6565	
Gonzales (G-7762)			
Purina Animal Nutrition LLC	F	806 761-7200	
Lubbock (G-14466)			
Purina Animal Nutrition LLC	E	254 840-3276	
Mc Gregor (G-14822)			
Purina Mills LLC	F	281 342-6758	
Rosenberg (G-17596)			
Purina Mills LLC	D	830 672-6565	
Gonzales (G-7763)			
R J Mangold Grain Co Inc	F	830 985-3323	
La Coste (G-13690)			
R J Smelley Company Inc	F	817 295-4241	
Burleson (G-2595)			
Reconserve of Texas Inc	E	214 339-4755	
Dallas (G-4868)			
Red River Commodities Inc	E	806 763-9747	
Lubbock (G-14471)			
Ridley USA Inc	F	903 322-4228	
Buffalo (G-2548)			
Ridley USA Inc	F	817 625-6680	
Fort Worth (G-6958)			
Scotts Miracle-Gro Company	E	830 591-0299	
Uvalde (G-20195)			
Sooner Trading Inc	F	806 235-3904	
Channing (G-3045)			
Sunbelt Custom Mineral LLC	F	903 438-2340	
Sulphur Springs (G-19601)			
Tejas Industries Inc	E	806 293-4431	
Plainview (G-16763)			
TX Quality Products LLC	F	979 234-7979	
Eagle Lake (G-5546)			
Tyson Foods Inc	E	936 248-2081	
Tenaha (G-19725)			
Tyson Foods Inc	F	940 553-1811	
Vernon (G-20231)			
Tyson Foods Inc	B	713 678-1893	
Houston (G-12421)			
Valley Feed Mill Inc Paris	E	903 785-3501	
Paris (G-16373)			
Valley Proteins (de) Inc	E	806 379-6001	
Amarillo (G-519)			
Volume Feed & Seed Inc	G	325 676-3302	
Abilene (G-90)			
Westway Feed Products LLC	F	903 885-5541	
Sulphur Springs (G-19604)			
Westway Feed Products LLC	E	713 514-1000	
Houston (G-12659)			
Westway Feed Products LLC	F	806 364-5200	
Hereford (G-8298)			
Wilbur-Ellis Nutrition LLC	F	979 849-6757	
Angleton (G-582)			

2051 Bread, Bakery Prdts Exc Cookies & Crackers

AB Mauri Food Inc	E	903 454-3891	
Greenville (G-8061)			
Adem Ruman Inc	G	713 266-8584	
Houston (G-8478)			
▲ Affiliated Foods Inc	C	806 372-3851	
Amarillo (G-476)			
▲ Ashcrft-Uropean Bky Ltd Partnr	D	281 403-5040	
Stafford (G-19287)			
Ashley Donuts & Ice Cream Inc	F	281 486-5644	
Houston (G-8719)			
Bairds Mrs Bakeries Bus Tr	B	713 996-5000	
Houston (G-8791)			
Bakery Express Centl Texas LP	D	972 221-8394	
Lewisville (G-14025)			

Bakeryworks LLC	E	972 250-1818	
Farmers Branch (G-6190)			
Bayan Imports Inc	E	972 437-1122	
Richardson (G-17278)			
Becerra Corp	F	512 787-2755	
San Marcos (G-18681)			
Bimbo Bakeries Usa Inc	F	254 750-2500	
Waco (G-20368)			
Bimbo Bakeries Usa Inc	A	903 785-6401	
Paris (G-16358)			
Bluebonnet Bakery Inc	F	817 731-4233	
Fort Worth (G-6458)			
Bridgford Foods Corporation	D	214 428-1535	
Dallas (G-4051)			
Brill Inc	C	214 343-4816	
Dallas (G-4055)			
Bryan Baking Inc	C	979 778-6600	
Bryan (G-2461)			
Bryan Baking Company LLC	B	979 778-6600	
Bryan (G-2462)			
C & K Management Co Inc	F	713 774-7429	
Houston (G-9025)			
Cake Craft Factory LLC	F	469 782-2500	
Garland (G-7452)			
Campbell Soup Company	C	903 784-3341	
Paris (G-16359)			
Capt Nemos Steak Submarines	F	972 438-7777	
Irving (G-12959)			
CCS Cupcake Heaven	F	817 732-2993	
Fort Worth (G-6499)			
▼ CH Guenther & Son LLC	B	210 227-1401	
San Antonio (G-17997)			
▲ Cheesecake Royale Inc	E	214 328-9102	
Dallas (G-4107)			
Churro Factory LLC	G	214 566-5894	
Dallas (G-4116)			
Dallas Gourmet Bakery Inc	F	972 247-9835	
Frisco (G-7279)			
David	E	713 357-6393	
Houston (G-9407)			
Dessert Dreams Inc	E	972 313-2138	
Irving (G-12996)			
Dibella Baking Company LLC	F	281 987-8985	
Houston (G-9461)			
Dmv Wicks Inc	F	713 520-0340	
Houston (G-9488)			
▲ Droubis Bakery & Deli Inc	F	713 988-5897	
Houston (G-9532)			
Empire Baking Company L P	F	972 851-5677	
Dallas (G-4320)			
Epic Source Food Company LLC	F	214 407-7154	
Frisco (G-7283)			
Exquisita Tortillas Inc	E	956 383-3011	
Edinburg (G-5587)			
Fgf LLC	A	210 475-9981	
San Antonio (G-18110)			
Flowers Bakeries LLC	E	915 533-8434	
El Paso (G-5771)			
Flowers Bakeries LLC	E	361 814-0558	
Corpus Christi (G-3532)			
Flowers Baking Co Denton LLC	F	214 343-6796	
Dallas (G-4371)			
Flowers Baking Co Denton LLC	E	972 263-3363	
Grand Prairie (G-7876)			
Flowers Baking Co Denton LLC	C	940 383-5280	
Denton (G-5366)			
Flowers Baking Co El Paso LLC	F	915 533-8434	
El Paso (G-5772)			
Flowers Baking Co Houston LLC	E	713 869-5701	
Houston (G-9812)			
Flowers Baking Co Tyler LLC	C	903 595-2421	
Tyler (G-20088)			
Flowers Baking Co Tyler LLC	F	903 758-2369	
Longview (G-14236)			
Flowers Baking Co Tyler LLC	C	903 677-2455	
Athens (G-826)			
Flowers Bkg Co San Antonio LLC	B	210 661-2361	
San Antonio (G-18118)			
Fr Hruska Store	E	979 378-2333	
Ellinger (G-6062)			
Frito-Lay North America Inc	B	214 331-7000	
Dallas (G-4381)			
Fxm International LLC	F	832 886-0003	
Houston (G-9880)			
H & M Baking LLC	G	713 568-5674	
Houston (G-10079)			
H E Butt Grocery Company	C	956 702-2289	
Alamo (G-179)			
Hillarys Sweet Temptations Inc	F	972 485-1005	
Garland (G-7514)			

James Skinner Co	F	903 784-7174	
Paris (G-16362)			
Josephs Storehouse Baking Co	E	405 253-0669	
San Antonio (G-18209)			
Kennymac LLC	F	214 732-4759	
Seagoville (G-18801)			
▲ Lawler Foods Ltd	C	281 446-0059	
Humble (G-12783)			
Lawler Foods Ltd	C	281 540-3321	
Humble (G-12784)			
▲ Lone Star Bakery Inc	E	210 648-6400	
China Grove (G-3057)			
Lua Br LLC	G	404 610-0118	
Austin (G-1307)			
Marick Foods Inc	D	915 593-2271	
El Paso (G-5867)			
Martech Foods Inc	F	713 692-0077	
Houston (G-10775)			
Mary and Megan Food Co LLC	E	972 921-9618	
Dallas (G-4642)			
Mary of Puddin Hill Inc	F	903 455-2651	
Palestine (G-16302)			
Merrills Southern Maid	G	409 755-2400	
Lumberton (G-14568)			
▲ Mrs Bairds Bakeries Bus Tr	B	800 355-1260	
Fort Worth (G-6857)			
Mygis Empire LLC	F	972 674-9758	
Arlington (G-735)			
New York Bagles Inc	F	713 723-5879	
Houston (G-11038)			
Ohara Valente	F	830 775-8769	
Del Rio (G-5321)			
Pattty Brinlee	F	940 600-0878	
Corinth (G-3461)			
Pops Bakery Inc	E	325 655-1170	
San Angelo (G-17822)			
RC Donuts	G	972 422-3379	
Plano (G-16989)			
Reyniers French Bakery Inc	F	972 401-3600	
Dallas (G-4894)			
Rise n Shine Donuts	F	806 745-5282	
Lubbock (G-14473)			
Rock Island Donut Shop	F	972 254-5069	
Irving (G-13166)			
Round Rock Bakery Ltd	F	512 255-3629	
Round Rock (G-17686)			
Round Rock Dnuts - Liberty LLC	F	512 255-3629	
Round Rock (G-17687)			
Russells Bakery and Coffee Bar	F	512 419-7877	
Austin (G-1477)			
Shipley Do - Nuts	F	281 499-5234	
Missouri City (G-15593)			
Shipley Do-Nut Flour Sup Inc	G	281 575-1766	
Houston (G-11871)			
Shipley Do-Nut Flour Sup Inc	G	713 728-9366	
Houston (G-11872)			
Shipley Do-Nut Flour Sup Inc	F	713 729-2381	
Houston (G-11873)			
Simply Donuts	F	281 955-6374	
Houston (G-11904)			
Souza Bakery	F	214 631-0669	
Dallas (G-4993)			
Spiral Diners	F	817 332-8834	
Fort Worth (G-7012)			
Sterling Bv Inc	D	210 490-1669	
San Antonio (G-18502)			
▲ Sterling Foods LLC	C	210 490-1669	
San Antonio (G-18503)			
Sterling Foods II Inc	E	210 490-1669	
San Antonio (G-18504)			
Sugar Krystles LLC	F	817 368-6869	
Dallas (G-5019)			
Swiss Pastry Shop	F	817 732-5661	
Fort Worth (G-7025)			
Three Brothers Bakery Inc	F	713 666-2253	
Houston (G-12283)			
Tiny Pies LLC	F	512 297-2690	
West Lake Hills (G-20691)			
Tootie Pie Company Inc	D	210 737-6600	
Boerne (G-2143)			
Upper Crust Bakery Inc	E	512 467-0102	
Austin (G-1614)			
Voss Catering Inc	D	713 257-9898	
Bellaire (G-2004)			
Willow Bend Bakery Inc	F	214 353-0889	
Dallas (G-5190)			

2052 Cookies & Crackers

ABC Ingredients Corp	F	972 602-2427	
Grand Prairie (G-7819)			

▲ Ashcrft-Uropean Bky Ltd Partnr ......D 281 403-5040
Stafford *(G-19287)*

Bluebonnet Bakery Inc ....F 817 731-4233
Fort Worth *(G-6458)*

Campbell Soup Company ....C 903 784-3341
Paris *(G-16359)*

▼ CH Guenther & Son LLC ....B 210 227-1401
San Antonio *(G-17997)*

Dgg Group LLC ....F 512 398-4523
Lockhart *(G-14166)*

Ellard John ....F 214 352-5946
Dallas *(G-4314)*

Food Group Ventures LLC ....G 936 327-4443
Livingston *(G-14153)*

Frito-Lay Inc ....B 972 334-7000
Plano *(G-16873)*

Fxm International LLC ....F 832 886-0003
Houston *(G-9880)*

Hillarys Sweet Temptations Inc ....F 972 485-1005
Garland *(G-7514)*

Keebler Company ....E 817 868-2800
Fort Worth *(G-6753)*

▲ Lwc Brands Inc ....E 214 630-9101
Dallas *(G-4613)*

Mondelez Global LLC ....A 713 749-0400
Houston *(G-10910)*

◆ Old Frito-Lay Inc ....A 972 334-7000
Plano *(G-16953)*

Pepperidge Farm Incorporated ....E 713 385-2010
Houston *(G-11287)*

Pepsico Inc ....D 972 963-1000
Plano *(G-16969)*

Pretzels Inc ....E 972 416-3660
Carrollton *(G-2795)*

◆ Riviana Foods Inc ....C 713 529-3251
Houston *(G-11629)*

Santte Labs LLC ....F 832 585-1862
Shenandoah *(G-18898)*

Southern Noodle Company ....F 281 988-7778
Houston *(G-11976)*

Sterling Bv Inc ....D 210 490-1669
San Antonio *(G-18502)*

▲ Sterling Foods LLC ....C 210 490-1669
San Antonio *(G-18503)*

Sterling Foods II Inc ....E 210 490-1669
San Antonio *(G-18504)*

Tiffs Treats Rbd Inc ....E 512 614-3200
Austin *(G-1579)*

Tifs Treats ....E 512 473-2600
Austin *(G-1580)*

2053 Frozen Bakery Prdts

Blue Ribbon Products Inc ....D 214 647-1825
Rockwall *(G-17540)*

Fgf LLC ....E 210 475-9981
San Antonio *(G-18111)*

▲ Lawler Foods Ltd ....C 281 446-0059
Humble *(G-12783)*

▲ Lone Star Bakery Inc ....B 210 648-6400
China Grove *(G-3057)*

Lone Star Bakery Inc ....C 210 648-6400
China Grove *(G-3058)*

Newberry Bakers Inc ....D 281 987-8985
Houston *(G-11039)*

Newberry Bakers Inc ....C 281 987-8985
Houston *(G-11040)*

Pepperidge Farm Incorporated ....E 713 385-2010
Houston *(G-11287)*

Pretzels Inc ....E 972 416-3660
Carrollton *(G-2795)*

▲ Quality Bakery Products Inc ....D 281 449-4977
Houston *(G-11492)*

Rich Products Corporation ....F 281 835-7100
Missouri City *(G-15590)*

Rich Products Corporation ....C 281 410-6600
Missouri City *(G-15591)*

▲ Sweet ....F 713 647-9338
Houston *(G-12131)*

Tootie Pie Company Inc ....D 210 737-6600
Boerne *(G-2143)*

Whipped Up Inc ....G 361 248-4639
Corpus Christi *(G-3655)*

2061 Sugar, Cane

▲ Rio Grande Vly Sug Growers Inc ......B 956 636-1411
Santa Rosa *(G-18737)*

2062 Sugar, Cane Refining

◆ Imperial Sugar Company ....C 281 491-9181
Sugar Land *(G-19496)*

2063 Sugar, Beet

Imperial Sugar Company ....C 281 491-9181
Sugar Land *(G-19497)*

2064 Candy & Confectionery Prdts

Amplify Snack Brands Inc ....E 512 600-9893
Austin *(G-920)*

B & G Inc ....F 713 944-1200
Houston *(G-8772)*

Bearded Brothers LLC ....F 940 367-8256
Austin *(G-983)*

Bettera Brands LLC ....F 800 344-6225
Plano *(G-16802)*

Candy Kings Inc ....F 409 762-6100
Galveston *(G-7391)*

CPT International (usa) LLC ....D 713 747-4773
Sugar Land *(G-19468)*

Cyclone Cotton Candy LLC ....E 281 748-9163
Houston *(G-9383)*

Elamex Usa Corp ....A 915 298-3061
El Paso *(G-5748)*

Goodart Candy Inc ....D 806 747-2600
Lubbock *(G-14418)*

Jacksonville Candy Co Inc ....E 903 586-8334
Jacksonville *(G-13244)*

Katysweet Confectioners Inc ....E 979 242-5172
La Grange *(G-13697)*

Kraft Heinz Company ....B 972 272-7511
Garland *(G-7534)*

Lammes Candies Since 1885 Inc ....F 512 310-1885
Austin *(G-1280)*

Mars Chocolate North Amer LLC ....A 254 776-2100
Waco *(G-20433)*

Mars Wrigley Conf US LLC ....E 254 751-5404
Waco *(G-20434)*

Mary of Puddin Hill Inc ....F 903 455-2651
Palestine *(G-16302)*

Monterrey Products Company ....F 210 435-2872
San Antonio *(G-18319)*

Mount Franklin Foods LLC ....B 800 351-8178
El Paso *(G-5885)*

North Blue Oak Inc ....F 844 778-2336
Missouri City *(G-15585)*

Quintessential Chocolates Inc ....F 830 990-9382
Fredericksburg *(G-7187)*

Red River Commodities Inc ....E 806 763-9747
Lubbock *(G-14471)*

Ricos Manufacturing Co Inc ....E 210 226-4168
Lewisville *(G-14088)*

Snyders-Lance Inc ....E 214 638-2378
Dallas *(G-4974)*

▲ Susies South Forty Confections ......D 432 570-4040
Midland *(G-15426)*

Uptown Popcorn LLC ....F 972 291-4767
Dallas *(G-5145)*

2066 Chocolate & Cocoa Prdts

Candy Kings Inc ....F 409 762-6100
Galveston *(G-7391)*

Good Fat Co Ltd ....E 512 300-8391
Austin *(G-1187)*

La India Packing Co ....E 956 723-3772
Laredo *(G-13903)*

Mars Chocolate North Amer LLC ....A 254 776-2100
Waco *(G-20433)*

▲ Susies South Forty Confections ......D 432 570-4040
Midland *(G-15426)*

Wiseman House Companies Inc ....F 254 796-2565
Hico *(G-8303)*

2068 Salted & Roasted Nuts & Seeds

◆ Austinuts Wholesale Inc ....E 512 272-8007
Manor *(G-14645)*

Birdsong Corporation ....E 254 734-2266
Gorman *(G-7771)*

Birdsong Corporation ....F 806 637-7200
Brownfield *(G-2330)*

Chase Pecan LP ....D 706 556-6216
Fort Worth *(G-6511)*

Clements Nut Co Inc ....E 972 436-4596
Lewisville *(G-14038)*

Elamex Usa Corp ....A 915 298-3061
El Paso *(G-5748)*

Garnea Llc ....E 512 398-4523
Lockhart *(G-14168)*

Golden Peanut Company LLC ....D 254 893-2034
De Leon *(G-5238)*

Great Host International Inc ....C 806 296-5455
Plainview *(G-16755)*

◆ Great Host International Inc ....D 713 977-9090
Houston *(G-10026)*

LOrenta Nuts LLC ....F 361 876-7570
San Antonio *(G-18266)*

Morven Partners LP ....F 325 372-5727
San Saba *(G-18718)*

Ramirez Pecan Farm LLC ....F 915 851-2003
Clint *(G-3147)*

Sungold Foods Inc ....F 806 748-2500
Lubbock *(G-14489)*

▲ Texas Star Nut and Food Co Inc ......D 830 249-8300
Boerne *(G-2140)*

Universal Blanchers LLC ....E 254 445-4021
Dublin *(G-5518)*

2074 Cottonseed Oil Mills

Delta and Pine Land Company ....F 806 839-2491
Hale Center *(G-8118)*

Pyco Industries Inc ....C 806 747-3434
Lubbock *(G-14467)*

2075 Soybean Oil Mills

Gruma Corporation ....C 972 232-5000
Irving *(G-13043)*

2076 Vegetable Oil Mills

Archer-Daniels-Midland Company ....D 806 723-5117
Lubbock *(G-14363)*

Bunge Oils Inc ....D 817 568-4900
Fort Worth *(G-6478)*

Darling Ingredients Inc ....D 313 928-7400
Irving *(G-12993)*

Noircroxx Biologicals LLC ....E 406 471-0671
Arlington *(G-739)*

2077 Animal, Marine Fats & Oils

American Commodities Inc ....E 817 740-8326
Fort Worth *(G-6379)*

Baari Inc ....E 214 566-5165
Plano *(G-16797)*

▼ Darling Ingredients Inc ....C 972 717-0300
Irving *(G-12992)*

Darling Ingredients Inc ....D 313 928-7400
Irving *(G-12993)*

Darling Ingredients Inc ....F 512 303-2571
Bastrop *(G-1753)*

Darling Ingredients Inc ....F 979 778-0298
Bryan *(G-2469)*

Darling Ingredients Inc ....C 972 717-0300
Irving *(G-12994)*

Darling Ingredients Inc ....E 713 224-0438
Houston *(G-9404)*

Darling Ingredients Inc ....E 214 948-7501
Dallas *(G-4238)*

HTC Industries Inc ....E 325 949-0645
San Angelo *(G-17808)*

Inland Products Inc ....E 956 627-5700
McAllen *(G-14872)*

▲ Interntnal Prtein Colloids Inc ....F 817 795-7744
Venus *(G-20219)*

Jacob Stern & Sons Inc ....E 713 926-8386
Houston *(G-10448)*

Leonard & Harral Packing Co ....B 210 532-3241
San Antonio *(G-18247)*

Nutri-Feeds Inc ....E 806 357-2288
Hereford *(G-8294)*

Omega Protein Corporation ....C 713 940-6100
Houston *(G-11174)*

Texas By-Products Partnership ....F 214 871-0600
Dallas *(G-5055)*

Triton Products LLC ....F 940 455-2800
Argyle *(G-604)*

Valley By Products Inc ....E 915 877-3131
Canutillo *(G-2667)*

Valley Proteins Inc ....D 432 334-0449
Odessa *(G-16193)*

Valley Proteins Inc ....E 325 653-3858
San Angelo *(G-17836)*

Valley Proteins (de) Inc ....D 469 580-0864
Dallas *(G-5152)*

Valley Proteins (de) Inc ....D 540 247-2798
Amarillo *(G-518)*

Valley Proteins (de) Inc ....E 806 379-6001
Amarillo *(G-519)*

Ventura Foods LLC ....D 817 232-5450
Saginaw *(G-17758)*

2079 Shortening, Oils & Margarine

American Commodities Inc ....E 817 740-8326
Fort Worth *(G-6379)*

Archer-Daniels-Midland Company .....D 806 723-5117
Lubbock *(G-14363)*

Bright Initiatives LLC ....F 512 466-4734
Austin *(G-1008)*

Inland Products Inc ....E 956 627-5700
McAllen *(G-14872)*

Jst Global LLC ....F 713 926-8386
Houston *(G-10488)*

Quick Turn Machining Inc ....F 281 355-8876
Tomball *(G-20004)*

Stratas Foods LLC ....G 713 671-0057
Houston *(G-12075)*

Ventura Foods LLC ....D 817 232-5450
Saginaw *(G-17758)*

2082 Malt Beverages

Anheuser-Busch LLC ....C 713 670-1629
Houston *(G-8644)*

Anheuser-Busch LLC ....C 713 675-2311
Houston *(G-8645)*

Big Buck Brewery & Steakhouse ....D 972 691-5100
Grapevine *(G-8014)*

Bluebonnet Beer Company LLC ....F 512 774-4258
Round Rock *(G-17627)*

Brazos Valley Brewing Co LLC ....F 979 353-5361
Brenham *(G-2244)*

C Villanueva Company LLc ....F 281 974-2361
Houston *(G-9035)*

Comeback Brewing Inc ....F 210 490-9128
San Antonio *(G-18019)*

▲ **Comeback Brewing II Inc** ....D 210 490-9128
San Antonio *(G-18020)*

▲ **Deep Ellum Brewing Company LLC** .E 214 888-3322
Dallas *(G-4245)*

Fredericksburg Brewing Company ......D 830 997-1646
Fredericksburg *(G-7178)*

Gambrinus Company ....D 361 594-3383
Shiner *(G-18940)*

▲ **Gambrinus Company** ....D 210 483-5100
San Antonio *(G-18133)*

Goliad Brewing Company Inc ....F 936 441-6100
Goliad *(G-7747)*

Guadalupe Brewing Company LLC ......G 512 878-9214
New Braunfels *(G-15798)*

▲ **Live Oak Brewing Company LLC** .....E 512 385-2299
Del Valle *(G-5332)*

Lorelei Brewing Company LLC ....G 361 445-1084
Corpus Christi *(G-3564)*

Lost Falls LLC ....F 737 300-1965
Austin *(G-1303)*

Manhattan Project LLC ....E 469 678-8870
Dallas *(G-4631)*

▲ **Miller Brewing** ....E 817 551-3300
Fort Worth *(G-6841)*

Molson Coors Bev Co USA LLC ....C 214 618-7400
Plano *(G-16932)*

Molson Coors Bev Co USA LLC ....D 817 551-3300
Fort Worth *(G-6847)*

Pabst Brewing Company LLC ....E 210 299-6708
San Antonio *(G-18361)*

Refresco Beverages US Inc ....D 817 359-4500
Fort Worth *(G-6951)*

▲ **Saint Arnold Brewing Company** ......G 713 686-9494
Houston *(G-11731)*

◆ **Southern Glazers Wine and Sp** ......C 972 277-2000
Farmers Branch *(G-6215)*

▲ **Sway Water Inc** ....F 512 693-7588
Austin *(G-1551)*

▲ **Texas Ingredient Corporation** ......D 817 645-1328
Cleburne *(G-3113)*

▲ **Treaty Oak Brewing Distlg LLC** .....E 512 680-1606
Dripping Springs *(G-5513)*

2084 Wine & Brandy

1851 Vineyards LLC ....E 830 391-8510
Fredericksburg *(G-7168)*

2018 Kidwell LLC ....E 214 824-9463
Dallas *(G-3864)*

Ambiente Opco LLC ....F 512 835-2299
Austin *(G-910)*

Augusta Vin LLC ....E 830 307-1007
Fredericksburg *(G-7170)*

Barons Creek Vineyards LLC ....F 830 304-3000
Fredericksburg *(G-7171)*

Bell Mountain Vineyards Inc ....G 830 685-3297
Willow City *(G-20870)*

Blue Ostrich Wineries LLC ....F 940 995-3100
Saint Jo *(G-17762)*

Bobby G Smith Do ....F 817 481-9463
Grapevine *(G-8015)*

Burke Texgals LLC ....F 210 344-9463
San Antonio *(G-17973)*

C K Higgs ....F 713 666-5739
Bellaire *(G-1992)*

▲ **Cap Rock Winery Inc** ....F 806 863-2704
Lubbock *(G-14388)*

Crossroads Winery ....G 817 421-2999
Grapevine *(G-8024)*

Deep South Barrels LLC ....F 713 340-3103
Pearland *(G-16554)*

Delaney Vineyards Inc ....F 817 421-0950
Grapevine *(G-8028)*

◆ **Dionysus Group LLLP** ....F 512 572-7000
Florence *(G-6239)*

Driftwood Estate Winery LLC ....E 512 692-6229
Driftwood *(G-5500)*

▲ **Firestone Robertson Distlg LLC** ....F 817 840-9140
Fort Worth *(G-6632)*

Future Proof Brands LLC ....E 512 790-9967
Austin *(G-1174)*

Gcv Enterprise LLC ....F 830 644-2710
Fredericksburg *(G-7180)*

Georgetown Winery LLC ....G 512 869-8600
Georgetown *(G-7652)*

Kuhlman Cellars LLC ....E 512 920-2675
Austin *(G-1275)*

La Bella Vida Inc ....F 806 744-3600
Lubbock *(G-14434)*

▲ **Llano Estacado Winery Inc** ....E 806 745-2258
Lubbock *(G-14439)*

Lospinos Ranch Vineyards ....F 903 855-1769
Pittsburg *(G-16746)*

McPherson Cellars Inc ....F 806 687-9463
Lubbock *(G-14445)*

▲ **Messina Hof Wine Cellars Inc** ......E 979 778-9463
Bryan *(G-2493)*

Patrick S Molak Corp ....F 830 606-0093
New Braunfels *(G-15818)*

San Martino Winery & Vineyards ......F 972 772-6043
Rockwall *(G-17565)*

Specs Family Partners Ltd ....F 713 669-1722
Houston *(G-12005)*

Texas Hills Vineyard Inc ....F 830 868-2321
Johnson City *(G-13313)*

Texas Sthwind Vnyrd Winery LLC ......F 361 526-4662
Refugio *(G-17250)*

Torr NA Lochs LLC ....F 832 606-7575
Burnet *(G-2617)*

Wedding Oak Winery LLC ....F 325 372-4050
San Saba *(G-18721)*

Whistling Duck Vneyards Winery ......G 512 913-4813
Weimar *(G-20653)*

Woodrose Winery Inc ....F 830 644-2539
Stonewall *(G-19430)*

Yamhill Valley Vineyards Inc ....F 281 822-9463
Houston *(G-12713)*

2085 Liquors, Distilled, Rectified & Blended

Alamo Premium Distillery Inc ....F 210 325-7853
San Antonio *(G-17886)*

Azar Distilling LLC ....F 210 403-5142
San Antonio *(G-17926)*

▲ **Balcones Distilling LLC** ....E 254 755-6003
Waco *(G-20366)*

Barmac LLC ....G 903 454-3166
Greenville *(G-8064)*

Bendt Distilling LLC ....E 214 814-0545
Lewisville *(G-14027)*

BJ Hookers Distilleries LLC ....F 713 249-2022
Spring *(G-19201)*

▲ **Buzzballz LLC** ....D 972 242-3777
Carrollton *(G-2707)*

C Villanueva Company LLc ....F 281 974-2361
Houston *(G-9035)*

Ckl Distilling LLC ....E 512 963-2373
Driftwood *(G-5499)*

Diageo North America Inc ....E 972 716-7700
Addison *(G-117)*

▲ **Firestone Robertson Distlg LLC** ....E 817 840-9140
Fort Worth *(G-6632)*

Jbm Specialties LLC ....F 214 604-7646
Valley View *(G-20203)*

▲ **Mpact Beverage Solutions LLC** ......F 832 260-2342
Spring *(G-19150)*

Riazul Imports LLC ....F 713 894-9177
Houston *(G-11616)*

▲ **Russian Spirit Inc** ....F 214 334-3018
Dallas *(G-4921)*

Southwest Dist & Winery LLC ....F 214 440-4144
Dallas *(G-4990)*

Spirited Cocktails Corporation ......F 512 256-0150
Austin *(G-1528)*

Tahwahkaro Distilling Co LLC ....G 479 871-2565
Grapevine *(G-8056)*

▲ **Treaty Oak Brewing Distlg LLC** .....E 512 680-1606
Dripping Springs *(G-5513)*

Trinity River Distillery LLC ....F 214 293-6011
Fort Worth *(G-7077)*

William Price Distlg Co LLC ....G 713 364-9225
Houston *(G-12667)*

Windy Hill Spirits Inc ....F 615 678-4785
Austin *(G-1673)*

2086 Soft Drinks

Ab-Tex Beverage Ltd ....E 830 775-1543
Del Rio *(G-5304)*

Ab-Tex Beverage Ltd ....E 325 655-9588
San Angelo *(G-17769)*

Ab-Tex Beverage Ltd ....C 325 673-7171
Abilene *(G-3)*

Ab-Tex Beverage Ltd ....E 956 722-9934
Laredo *(G-13853)*

Ab-Tex Beverage Ltd ....E 940 322-5416
Wichita Falls *(G-20736)*

American Bottling Company ....D 956 423-2705
Harlingen *(G-8180)*

American Bottling Company ....C 210 662-4400
San Antonio *(G-17902)*

American Bottling Company ....E 512 385-4477
Austin *(G-915)*

American Bottling Company ....D 972 579-1024
Irving *(G-12928)*

American Bottling Company ....C 903 893-6536
Sherman *(G-18906)*

American Bottling Company ....C 254 412-1900
Waco *(G-20360)*

American Bottling Company ....C 972 721-8197
Irving *(G-12929)*

American Bottling Company ....E 214 330-0491
Dallas *(G-3938)*

American Bottling Company ....D 361 851-9977
Corpus Christi *(G-3472)*

American Bottling Company ....D 713 799-1024
Houston *(G-8590)*

American Bottling Company ....E 409 842-6061
Beaumont *(G-1851)*

American Bottling Company ....C 903 874-5666
Corsicana *(G-3660)*

▼ **American Bottling Company** ....C 972 673-7000
Plano *(G-16785)*

Apani Southwest Inc ....E 325 690-1550
Abilene *(G-13)*

Austin Coca-Cola Bottling Co ....D 979 543-2522
El Campo *(G-5611)*

Austin Coca-Cola Bottling Co ....E 512 832-2652
Austin *(G-953)*

Austin Coca-Cola Bottling Co ....E 713 799-7296
Houston *(G-8749)*

Austin Coca-Cola Bottling Co ....B 210 225-2601
San Antonio *(G-17923)*

Austin Coca-Cola Bottling Co ....E 409 899-5080
Beaumont *(G-1855)*

Austin Coca-Cola Bottling Co ....D 903 597-9325
Tyler *(G-20053)*

Austin Coca-Cola Bottling Co ....A 817 232-8600
Fort Worth *(G-6410)*

Austin Coca-Cola Bottling Co ....D 713 805-9722
Houston *(G-8750)*

Austin Coca-Cola Bottling Co ....E 512 836-0870
Austin *(G-954)*

Beaumont Coca-Cola Bottling Co ......C 409 899-5080
Beaumont *(G-1860)*

Beer Dudes Canning Co LLC ....F 972 342-4819
Denton *(G-5353)*

Big Red Inc ....G 713 791-9886
Houston *(G-8884)*

▼ **Birch B LLC** ....F 646 942-8058
Houston *(G-8889)*

▼ **C Treat Offshore Watermakers** ......E 281 367-2800
The Woodlands *(G-19837)*

Coca Cola Btlg Co of Southwest ......C 210 229-0555
San Antonio *(G-18015)*

▲ **Coca Cola Btlg of Shreveport** ......C 214 902-2600
Dallas *(G-4134)*

Coca Cola Btlg of Shreveport ....D 956 632-3773
McAllen *(G-14849)*

Coca-Cola Bottling Co ....G...... 830 775-8561
Del Rio (G-5313)
Coca-Cola Company ....D...... 281 302-4317
Sugar Land (G-19459)
Coca-Cola Company ....B...... 817 847-3000
Fort Worth (G-6526)
Coca-Cola Company ....C...... 713 799-7332
Houston (G-9234)
Coca-Cola Company ....C...... 214 351-4797
Dallas (G-4135)
Coca-Cola Company ....D...... 254 666-5500
Waco (G-20388)
Coca-Cola Enterprises ....E...... 817 232-8600
Fort Worth (G-6527)
Coca-Cola Enterprises Bottling ....C...... 214 253-5747
Dallas (G-4136)
Coca-Cola Refreshments USA Inc ....E...... 903 893-0194
Sherman (G-18911)
Coca-Cola Refreshments USA Inc ....F...... 800 438-2653
Sugar Land (G-19460)
Coca-Cola Refreshments USA Inc ....D...... 214 253-5600
Dallas (G-4137)
Coca-Cola Refreshments USA Inc ....D...... 281 452-7635
Channelview (G-3016)
Coca-Cola Refreshments USA Inc ....D...... 325 672-3232
Abilene (G-33)
Coca-Cola Refreshments USA Inc ....D...... 903 276-1295
Texarkana (G-19759)
Coca-Cola Refreshments USA Inc ....D...... 806 324-5300
Amarillo (G-417)
Coca-Cola Refreshments USA Inc ....E...... 806 472-3200
Lubbock (G-14395)
Coca-Cola Refreshments USA Inc ....D...... 325 437-5000
Abilene (G-34)
Coca-Cola Refreshments USA Inc ....D...... 940 720-3907
Wichita Falls (G-20755)
Coca-Cola Southwest Bevs LLC ....C...... 214 902-2600
Dallas (G-4138)
Coca-Cola Southwest Bevs LLC ....B...... 214 388-6000
Dallas (G-4139)
Culligan Southeast Texas Water ....E...... 409 838-6261
Beaumont (G-1879)
Dps Holdings Inc ....E...... 972 673-7000
Plano (G-16848)
Dr Pepper Snpple Group Emplyee ....C...... 972 673-7000
Plano (G-16849)
Dr Pepper/Seven Up Inc ....C...... 979 532-8801
Wharton (G-20699)
Dr Ppper Btlg Wichita FLS Inc ....D...... 940 322-5416
Wichita Falls (G-20760)
Drink A Pak Inc ....F...... 325 690-1550
Abilene (G-38)
Ds Services of America Inc ....E...... 281 391-3770
Katy (G-13360)
Ds Services of America Inc ....E...... 713 947-1900
Houston (G-9533)
Dublin Bottling Works Inc ....E...... 254 445-3939
Dublin (G-5515)
Essence Bottling Co Texas Inc ....F...... 806 993-1391
Lubbock (G-14407)
Ewb International Inc ....F...... 972 764-5252
Addison (G-122)
◆ Frito-Lay North America Inc ....A...... 972 334-7000
Plano (G-16874)
▲ Global Dispense ....F...... 210 310-2337
San Antonio (G-18146)
H2eco Bulk LLC ....F...... 713 812-8400
Houston (G-10087)
Heyday Beverage Company LLC ....F...... 512 387-2399
Austin (G-1201)
◆ Impreso Inc ....D...... 972 462-0100
Coppell (G-3421)
▼ International Beverage Inc ....F...... 956 727-2995
Laredo (G-13897)
Kalil Bottling Co ....E...... 915 778-4413
El Paso (G-5825)
▲ Kristen Distributing Co ....E...... 979 775-6322
Bryan (G-2489)
Laredo Coca-Cola Bottling Co ....C...... 956 726-2671
Laredo (G-13905)
Laredo Coca-Cola Bottling Co ....F...... 361 693-4200
Corpus Christi (G-3562)
Laredo Coca-Cola Bottling Co ....C...... 956 686-8827
McAllen (G-14884)
Live Soda LLC ....F...... 512 888-9959
Austin (G-1295)
Llanos Altos LLC ....F...... 806 934-4534
Dumas (G-5524)
Lufkin Coca Cola Bottling Co ....D...... 936 639-2355
Lufkin (G-14536)

Magnolia Coca-Cola Bottling Co ....E...... 915 593-2653
El Paso (G-5859)
Marsmith Enterprises Inc ....F...... 972 488-9339
Dallas (G-4638)
Mason Bottling Company ....F...... 325 347-5150
Mason (G-14815)
▲ Mountain Pure TX LLC ....E...... 903 723-1362
Palestine (G-16304)
Nacogdoches Coca Cola Btlg Co ....D...... 936 564-0268
Nacogdoches (G-15704)
Odwalla Inc ....G...... 281 925-0189
Houston (G-11134)
◆ Old Frito-Lay Inc ....A...... 972 334-7000
Plano (G-16953)
▲ One Water Source LLC ....F...... 512 347-9280
Lakeway (G-13818)
Oneta Company ....C...... 361 853-0123
Corpus Christi (G-3585)
P-Americas LLC ....E...... 361 853-0123
Corpus Christi (G-3588)
P-Americas LLC ....E...... 903 794-3883
Texarkana (G-19770)
▲ Pepsi Beverages Company ....G...... 210 661-5311
San Antonio (G-18369)
Pepsi Bottling Company ....F...... 210 662-3418
San Antonio (G-18370)
▲ Pepsi Bottling Group ....D...... 214 324-8500
Mesquite (G-15069)
Pepsi Cola Bottling Co Laredo ....E...... 956 722-9934
Laredo (G-13920)
▲ Pepsi Cola Sales & Dist ....G...... 909 472-4060
Grand Prairie (G-7945)
Pepsi Logistics Company Inc ....F...... 972 963-1920
Plano (G-16967)
Pepsi-Cola Bottling Group ....E...... 254 953-7433
Killeen (G-13616)
Pepsi-Cola Btlg Crpus Chrsti V ....C...... 361 853-0123
Corpus Christi (G-3590)
Pepsi-Cola Metro Btlg Co Inc ....E...... 409 842-2111
Beaumont (G-1939)
Pepsi-Cola Metro Btlg Co Inc ....D...... 817 640-4445
Arlington (G-750)
Pepsi-Cola Metro Btlg Co Inc ....C...... 210 661-5311
San Antonio (G-18371)
Pepsi-Cola Metro Btlg Co Inc ....F...... 361 575-2661
Victoria (G-20294)
Pepsi-Cola Metro Btlg Co Inc ....C...... 214 324-8500
Mesquite (G-15070)
Pepsi-Cola Metro Btlg Co Inc ....E...... 979 779-6324
Bryan (G-2497)
Pepsi-Cola Metro Btlg Co Inc ....E...... 806 745-7711
Lubbock (G-14460)
Pepsi-Cola Metro Btlg Co Inc ....E...... 972 801-1730
Plano (G-16968)
Pepsi-Cola Metro Btlg Co Inc ....C...... 713 645-4111
Houston (G-11288)
Pepsi-Cola Metro Btlg Co Inc ....C...... 817 625-4101
Fort Worth (G-6901)
Pepsi-Cola Metro Btlg Co Inc ....D...... 936 522-4400
Conroe (G-3348)
Pepsi-Cola Metro Btlg Co Inc ....E...... 806 372-8717
Amarillo (G-452)
Pepsi-Cola Metro Btlg Co Inc ....E...... 979 836-3755
Brenham (G-2268)
Pepsi-Cola Metro Btlg Co Inc ....E...... 361 798-3651
Hallettsville (G-8124)
Pepsi-Cola Metro Btlg Co Inc ....D...... 915 590-6965
El Paso (G-5908)
Pepsi-Cola Metro Btlg Co Inc ....E...... 903 892-3030
Sherman (G-18926)
Pepsi-Cola Sales and Dist Inc ....D...... 817 640-4445
Arlington (G-751)
Pepsico Inc ....F...... 972 334-4140
Plano (G-16970)
Pepsico Inc ....D...... 972 963-1000
Plano (G-16969)
Pickle Juice Company ....F...... 972 755-0289
Mesquite (G-15071)
▲ Plains Dairy LLC ....A...... 806 374-0385
Amarillo (G-455)
Quaker Oats Company ....C...... 214 333-1200
Dallas (G-4842)
Refresco Beverages US Inc ....C...... 210 333-4310
Mercedes (G-18418)
Rhino Rush 3gs LLC ....F...... 817 793-9400
Sachse (G-17734)
Rocky Mountain High Brands Inc ....G...... 800 260-9062
Plano (G-16995)
Ruiz Distributing Co ....F...... 713 682-7008
Houston (G-11696)

Shasta Beverages Inc ....E...... 713 634-0094
Houston (G-11847)
Smoothie King ....G...... 214 469-1552
The Colony (G-19814)
Son Beverage Company ....F...... 210 733-7761
San Antonio (G-18482)
Southwest Canners Texas Inc ....D...... 936 569-9737
Nacogdoches (G-15714)
Specktrum ....F...... 832 892-0863
Houston (G-12004)
Summit Springs Bottled Water ....G...... 559 277-1239
Richardson (G-17403)
▲ Sunny Sky Products LLC ....D...... 713 683-9399
Houston (G-12102)
Temple Bottling Company Ltd ....D...... 254 773-3376
Temple (G-19706)
Temple Bottling Company Ltd ....G...... 979 778-1203
Bryan (G-2510)
Texas Natural Rainwtr Hrvstng ....F...... 512 772-1981
Smithville (G-18978)
Tropical Fusions Inc ....E...... 830 203-5116
Gonzales (G-7765)
◆ Tst/Impreso Inc ....D...... 972 462-0100
Coppell (G-3451)
Water Event Gulf Coast LLC ....E...... 713 937-8630
Carrollton (G-2846)
Waterloo Sparkling Water Corp ....F...... 512 910-8990
Austin (G-1649)

2087 Flavoring Extracts & Syrups

▲ Adams Flvors Fods Ingrdnts LLC ....C...... 830 672-1850
Gonzales (G-7748)
Agrana Fruit Us Inc ....B...... 817 625-9053
Fort Worth (G-6355)
Aloe Laboratories Inc ....D...... 956 428-8416
Harlingen (G-8178)
American Bottling Company ....D...... 713 799-1024
Houston (G-8590)
▲ Bartush-Schnitzius Foods Co ....E...... 972 219-1270
Lewisville (G-14026)
Bcw Food Products Inc ....E...... 214 350-3320
Dallas (G-4010)
Brook Sara Enterprises Inc ....F...... 713 522-9999
Houston (G-8995)
Chameleon Cold Brew LLC ....E...... 512 323-0345
Austin (G-1042)
▼ Chemicals Incorporated ....D...... 281 576-5000
Baytown (G-1813)
Coca-Cola Company ....C...... 214 351-4797
Dallas (G-4135)
Coca-Cola Refreshments USA Inc ....E...... 806 472-3200
Lubbock (G-14395)
Coca-Cola Southwest Bevs LLC ....C...... 214 902-2600
Dallas (G-4138)
Collins Gold Label Inc ....G...... 972 960-7346
Addison (G-111)
Consolidated Mills Inc ....E...... 713 896-4196
Houston (G-9276)
◆ Dr Pepper/Seven Up Inc ....B...... 972 673-7000
Plano (G-16850)
Drafft Root Beer Inc ....F...... 214 638-8442
Dallas (G-4278)
Epic Bottling LLC ....E...... 512 947-8608
Coppell (G-3416)
▲ Flotek Industries Inc ....E...... 713 849-9911
Houston (G-9806)
ICEE Company ....F...... 713 937-9496
Houston (G-10313)
▼ Illes Food Ingredients Ltd ....D...... 800 683-4553
Carrollton (G-2764)
John Hogan Interests Inc ....E...... 214 637-0214
Dallas (G-4537)
Mmmix Ltd ....E...... 830 336-4252
Bergheim (G-2049)
Mooala Brands LLC ....F...... 214 206-1902
Dallas (G-4687)
◆ Motts LLP ....C...... 972 673-8088
Plano (G-16934)
North American Beverages Ltd ....F...... 512 501-3890
Austin (G-1368)
◆ O D C L Inc ....F...... 940 566-9914
Denton (G-5385)
O D C L Inc ....E...... 956 565-3131
Mercedes (G-15009)
Pepsico Inc ....D...... 972 963-1000
Plano (G-16969)
▼ Ricos Products Co Inc ....C...... 210 222-1415
San Antonio (G-18426)
Solvay USA Inc ....C...... 325 515-7609
Snyder (G-19009)

Solvay USA Inc......................................D...... 940 552-9911
  Vernon (G-20230)

TJ Blackburn Syrup Works Inc............D...... 903 665-2541
  Jefferson (G-13289)

Van Tone Creative Flavors Inc............E...... 972 563-2600
  Terrell (G-19754)

2091 Fish & Seafoods, Canned & Cured

La India Packing Co..............................E...... 956 723-3772
  Laredo (G-13903)

▲ Lt Seafood LP...................................F...... 713 328-1999
  Houston (G-10697)

2092 Fish & Seafoods, Fresh & Frozen

Farm Ctch Ctfish Prcessors Inc...........D...... 903 639-2394
  Hughes Springs (G-12740)

Hillman Shrimp & Oyster Co.................B...... 281 339-1506
  Dickinson (G-5474)

▼ Hillman Shrimp and Oyster Co.........B...... 281 339-1506
  Dickinson (G-5475)

Jbs Packing Company Inc.....................E...... 409 982-5766
  Port Arthur (G-17114)

La Blue Crab Co Inc.............................F...... 972 422-7525
  Plano (G-16905)

North Texas Packing Inc.......................F...... 972 660-2800
  Grand Prairie (G-7937)

Palacios Processors Inc........................D...... 361 552-1231
  Port Lavaca (G-17153)

Rich Products Corporation....................B...... 956 542-0001
  Brownsville (G-2399)

Seabrook Seafood Inc..........................E...... 281 334-2546
  Kemah (G-13479)

Tex-Mex Cold Storage Inc....................C...... 956 831-4531
  Brownsville (G-2409)

Texas Pack Inc....................................B...... 956 943-5461
  Port Isabel (G-17138)

William B Sides...................................F...... 512 385-3826
  Austin (G-1667)

2095 Coffee

Aspen Enterprises Ltd..........................F...... 210 684-6363
  San Antonio (G-17918)

◆ Atlantic Cof Indus Sltions LLC.........B...... 713 228-9501
  Houston (G-8738)

Black Rifle Coffee Company LLC..........F...... 844 899-9330
  San Antonio (G-17955)

Candy Kings Inc..................................F...... 409 762-6100
  Galveston (G-7391)

Chameleon Cold Brew LLC...................E...... 512 323-0345
  Austin (G-1042)

Coffee Traders Inc..............................E...... 512 476-2279
  Austin (G-1056)

▲ CPI Importers Inc...........................F...... 214 353-0328
  Dallas (G-4179)

Cuvee Coffee LLC................................F...... 512 264-1479
  Spicewood (G-19092)

Daily Offrngs Cof Roastery LLC...........F...... 805 423-7410
  Wolfforth (G-20907)

Farmer Bros Co....................................C...... 682 549-6767
  Northlake (G-15885)

Farmer Bros Co....................................F...... 682 549-6600
  Northlake (G-15886)

Farmer Bros Co....................................E...... 817 640-8111
  Arlington (G-675)

Farmer Bros Co....................................F...... 713 864-1487
  Houston (G-9763)

▲ Fresh Brew Group Usa LP................E...... 281 847-2222
  Houston (G-9864)

Grand Coffees of Texas LLC.................F...... 281 530-8321
  Houston (G-10014)

Hillshire Brands Company....................C...... 713 928-6281
  Houston (G-10186)

Indies Productions LLC.........................G...... 281 508-3920
  League City (G-13959)

La Creme Inc......................................F...... 214 352-8090
  Irving (G-13081)

Metro Coffee Grouppe Inc....................F...... 972 263-8744
  Grand Prairie (G-7927)

▲ Mother Parkers Tea Cof USA Ltd......C...... 817 551-5500
  Fort Worth (G-6855)

Nuzee Inc...E...... 760 295-2408
  Plano (G-16951)

Perkup Coffees LLC.............................E...... 281 445-6744
  Houston (G-11291)

Royal Cup Inc.....................................F...... 817 261-7527
  Arlington (G-775)

Texas Coffee Company.........................E...... 409 835-3434
  Beaumont (G-1958)

Wicked Voodoo Espresso LLC...............E...... 360 631-1447
  New Braunfels (G-15832)

2096 Potato Chips & Similar Prdts

Amplify Snack Brands Inc.....................E...... 512 600-9893
  Austin (G-920)

Arte Sano LLC.....................................D...... 512 400-8743
  Austin (G-935)

Aus-Mex Company Inc..........................D...... 432 561-8866
  Midland (G-15124)

Campbell Soup Company.......................C...... 903 784-3341
  Paris (G-16359)

D S D Services Inc..............................F...... 361 594-4114
  Shiner (G-18939)

Dallas Tortillas Inc..............................F...... 214 943-7681
  Dallas (G-4228)

◆ Dishaka LLC....................................D...... 713 988-2900
  Stafford (G-19305)

Double Jj Corporation..........................E...... 214 353-0230
  Dallas (G-4274)

Durrset Amigos Ltd.............................C...... 210 798-5360
  San Antonio (G-18074)

El Milagro of Texas Inc........................E...... 512 477-6476
  San Marcos (G-18685)

Evans Foods Inc.................................F...... 817 640-5626
  Arlington (G-674)

Exquisita Tortillas Inc..........................E...... 956 383-3011
  Edinburg (G-5587)

Frito-Lay Inc......................................B...... 972 334-7000
  Plano (G-16873)

Frito-Lay North America Inc..................A...... 972 579-2543
  Irving (G-13036)

Frito-Lay North America Inc..................B...... 210 662-2100
  San Antonio (G-18127)

Frito-Lay North America Inc..................E...... 817 649-3266
  Arlington (G-681)

Frito-Lay North America Inc..................E...... 214 631-8485
  Dallas (G-4379)

Frito-Lay North America Inc..................D...... 214 944-5238
  Dallas (G-4380)

Frito-Lay North America Inc..................F...... 903 868-2657
  Sherman (G-18915)

Frito-Lay North America Inc..................B...... 214 331-7000
  Dallas (G-4381)

◆ Frito-Lay North America Inc.............A...... 972 334-7000
  Plano (G-16874)

Gruma Corporation..............................B...... 972 709-1217
  Dallas (G-4419)

Gruma Corporation..............................C...... 956 380-4090
  Edinburg (G-5589)

Gruma Corporation..............................C...... 210 304-6700
  San Antonio (G-18154)

▲ Gruma Corporation.........................C...... 972 232-5000
  Irving (G-13044)

Gruma Corporation..............................C...... 972 232-5000
  Irving (G-13043)

▲ Isabella Foods Inc..........................D...... 915 590-1899
  El Paso (G-5818)

Ixpalia Inc...E...... 512 389-0389
  Austin (G-1245)

Lopez Tortilla Foods Inc.......................E...... 214 353-9538
  Dallas (G-4606)

Lunas Tortillas Factory.........................F...... 214 747-2661
  Dallas (G-4612)

Mexi-Snax Corporation.........................E...... 915 779-5709
  El Paso (G-5874)

▼ Mexican Snacks Inc.........................E...... 956 440-9127
  Harlingen (G-8195)

Odessa Tortilla & Tamale Fctry............E...... 432 332-6676
  Odessa (G-16098)

◆ Old Frito-Lay Inc.............................A...... 972 334-7000
  Plano (G-16953)

Pepsico Inc..D...... 972 963-1000
  Plano (G-16969)

Pretzels Inc.......................................E...... 972 416-3660
  Carrollton (G-2795)

Ricos Manufacturing Co Inc..................E...... 210 226-4168
  Lewisville (G-14088)

▼ Ricos Products Co Inc......................C...... 210 222-1415
  San Antonio (G-18426)

Rolling Frito-Lay Sales LP.....................F...... 972 334-2513
  Plano (G-16996)

Rudolph Foods Company Inc.................D...... 214 638-2204
  Dallas (G-4919)

Sanitary Tortilla Mfg Co.......................E...... 210 226-9209
  San Antonio (G-18453)

Simply 7 Snacks LLC............................E...... 713 988-2900
  Stafford (G-19379)

Tortillas Santos LLC............................G...... 956 712-3800
  Laredo (G-13938)

Tyson Foods Inc..................................B...... 713 678-1893
  Houston (G-12421)

▲ Xochitl Inc.....................................E...... 214 800-3551
  Irving (G-13211)

2097 Ice

Country Fresh LLC...............................B...... 616 243-0173
  Dallas (G-4175)

Dean Foods Company...........................B...... 817 684-3600
  Fort Worth (G-6581)

Debes Ice Company.............................F...... 409 835-4431
  Beaumont (G-1881)

Emergency Ice Inc...............................F...... 972 988-0577
  Dallas (G-4318)

Heath Inc...E...... 979 822-6924
  Bryan (G-2476)

Hipple Ice Company............................E...... 325 692-0101
  Abilene (G-50)

Kfl Promotions LLC..............................F...... 817 822-9116
  Colleyville (G-3216)

Nacogdoches Coca Cola Btlg Co...........B...... 936 564-0268
  Nacogdoches (G-15704)

Polar Ice Inc.......................................F...... 979 830-1954
  Brenham (G-2269)

Pure Party Ice LP................................E...... 210 223-6400
  San Antonio (G-18401)

Reddy Ice Corporation.........................E...... 956 428-6666
  Harlingen (G-8199)

Reddy Ice Corporation.........................F...... 956 723-3838
  Laredo (G-13923)

Reddy Ice Corporation.........................E...... 940 686-5259
  Pilot Point (G-16727)

Reddy Ice Corporation.........................E...... 210 532-3232
  San Antonio (G-18415)

Reddy Ice Corporation.........................F...... 361 578-3032
  Victoria (G-20299)

Reddy Ice Corporation.........................D...... 972 296-4271
  Dallas (G-4872)

Reddy Ice Corporation.........................E...... 713 691-2773
  Houston (G-11574)

Reddy Ice Corporation.........................F...... 214 526-6740
  Dallas (G-4873)

Reddy Ice Corporation.........................F...... 432 943-4541
  Monahans (G-15614)

Reddy Ice Corporation.........................D...... 214 526-6740
  Dallas (G-4874)

Reddy Ice Corporation.........................E...... 361 289-0276
  Corpus Christi (G-3607)

Reddy Ice Corporation.........................F...... 817 654-9020
  Fort Worth (G-6948)

Reddy Ice Corporation.........................E...... 915 532-2495
  El Paso (G-5933)

Reddy Ice Group Inc............................G...... 254 753-7378
  Jefferson (G-13287)

Reddy Ice Group Inc............................E...... 903 732-3231
  Powderly (G-17200)

Reddy Ice Group Inc............................F...... 972 263-4359
  Dallas (G-4875)

▼ Reddy Ice Group Inc........................F...... 877 295-0024
  Dallas (G-4876)

Reddy Ice Holdings Inc.........................F...... 214 526-6740
  Dallas (G-4877)

Trevino Jr Gustavo..............................G...... 956 585-2522
  Mission (G-15569)

2098 Macaroni, Spaghetti & Noodles

Baily International Inc..........................C...... 713 673-0080
  Houston (G-8790)

▲ Food Source Inc.............................D...... 972 548-9001
  McKinney (G-14944)

Southern Noodle Company....................F...... 281 988-7778
  Houston (G-11976)

2099 Food Preparations, NEC

AB Mauri Food Inc..............................E...... 903 454-3891
  Greenville (G-8061)

◆ Abimar Foods Inc...........................A...... 325 691-5425
  Abilene (G-8)

Acj Produce & Spices LLC.....................E...... 956 627-4246
  McAllen (G-14831)

▲ Adams Flvors Fods Ingrdnts LLC.......C...... 830 672-1850
  Gonzales (G-7748)

Adelita Tortilla Factory.........................E...... 210 733-5352
  San Antonio (G-17865)

Alamo Tamale Company LP....................D...... 713 228-6445
  Houston (G-8525)

▼ Allen Tharp LLC..............................A...... 210 878-0034
  San Antonio (G-17896)

Ameripack Foods LLC...........................E...... 903 639-4007
  Hughes Springs (G-12738)

Amplify Snack Brands Inc.....................E...... 512 600-9893
  Austin (G-920)

Ardent Mills LLC D 817 847-3400 Saginaw *(G-17737)*
Armando G Martinez E 325 653-5640 San Angelo *(G-17778)*
Asiel Enterprises Inc D 361 765-6670 Corpus Christi *(G-3476)*
Aspire Food Group Usa Inc E 512 645-0700 Austin *(G-941)*
Aus-Mex Company Inc D 432 561-8866 Midland *(G-15124)*
Azteca Tortilla Factory E 956 702-7395 San Juan *(G-18671)*
B Martinez & Sons Company Inc E 210 226-6772 San Antonio *(G-17932)*
Barton Table LLC G 512 791-2260 Austin *(G-976)*
▲ Bartush-Schnitzius Foods Co E 972 219-1270 Lewisville *(G-14026)*
Bay Valley Foods LLC E 210 436-5551 San Antonio *(G-17941)*
Bay Valley Foods LLC D 210 436-5551 San Antonio *(G-17942)*
Bee Delightful LLC E 253 722-3018 Austin *(G-984)*
Birdsong Corporation E 254 734-2266 Gorman *(G-7771)*
Birdsong Corporation F 806 637-7200 Brownfield *(G-2330)*
Blue Ribbon Products Inc D 214 647-1825 Rockwall *(G-17540)*
▲ Bolners Fiesta Products Inc G 210 734-6404 San Antonio *(G-17962)*
▼ Breedlove Foods Inc E 806 741-0404 Lubbock *(G-14382)*
Bridgford Food Proc Texas LP D 214 428-1535 Dallas *(G-4050)*
Bridgford Foods Corporation E 214 631-7970 Dallas *(G-4052)*
Bridgford Foods Corporation D 214 428-1535 Dallas *(G-4051)*
Bridgford Industries Inc E 214 428-1535 Dallas *(G-4053)*
Bridgford Marketing Company D 214 428-1535 Dallas *(G-4054)*
▲ Cain Food Industries Inc E 214 630-4511 Dallas *(G-4079)*
▲ Calco Taiwan Marketing Service F 713 247-9918 Houston *(G-9048)*
Capistran Tortilla Factory E 956 541-3053 Brownsville *(G-2343)*
Carmies Kitchen Inc F 972 442-1337 Wylie *(G-20930)*
Carnicria Y Tortilleria El Sol G 915 877-5553 El Paso *(G-5684)*
Casa Rica LP E 806 296-7582 Plainview *(G-16753)*
▼ CH Guenther & Son LLC B 210 227-1401 San Antonio *(G-17997)*
Circle U Foods Inc F 817 626-6918 Fort Worth *(G-6520)*
City Tortilla Factory Inc F 361 776-3578 Ingleside *(G-12892)*
▲ Classic Foods LP F 817 332-1071 Burleson *(G-2574)*
Clements Nut Co Inc E 972 436-4596 Lewisville *(G-14038)*
Commonwealth Urology E 281 372-1112 Houston *(G-9254)*
Conagra Brands Inc D 817 210-1600 Fort Worth *(G-6539)*
Consolidated Mills Inc E 713 896-4196 Houston *(G-9276)*
Cookies-N-Milk Inc F 214 491-6370 McKinney *(G-14932)*
Dallas Tortillas Inc F 214 943-7681 Dallas *(G-4228)*
Das Brot Inc E 972 243-8443 Carrollton *(G-2721)*
David Lee Roberson F 210 662-8215 San Antonio *(G-18042)*
De Maiz Tortilleria L L C F 956 702-8855 Pharr *(G-16697)*
Delrio Tortilla Factory E 210 922-4810 San Antonio *(G-18049)*
Double R Brnd Prmium Fd Pdts L D 713 868-0030 Lufkin *(G-14524)*
E A Sween Company D 972 219-0566 Lewisville *(G-14046)*
El Milagro of Texas Inc E 512 477-6476 San Marcos *(G-18685)*
▲ El Venado Foods E 713 692-0688 Houston *(G-9587)*
Epd Inc E 979 239-1917 Angleton *(G-572)*
Evans Foods Inc F 817 640-5626 Arlington *(G-674)*
Exel N Amercn Logistics Inc B 972 647-1101 Grand Prairie *(G-7867)*
Exquisita Tortillas Inc C 956 383-6712 Edinburg *(G-5586)*
Exquisita Tortillas Inc E 956 383-3011 Edinburg *(G-5587)*
▲ Figueroa Brothers Inc E 214 351-9060 Irving *(G-13026)*
▲ Five Star Custom Foods Ltd E 682 647-2700 Fort Worth *(G-6635)*
Frito-Lay North America Inc A 972 579-2543 Irving *(G-13036)*
Frito-Lay North America Inc B 210 662-2100 San Antonio *(G-18127)*
Frito-Lay North America Inc E 214 631-8485 Dallas *(G-4379)*
Frito-Lay North America Inc B 214 331-7000 Dallas *(G-4381)*
Frito-Lay North America Inc D 817 649-3266 Arlington *(G-681)*
Frito-Lay North America Inc D 214 944-5238 Dallas *(G-4380)*
G Tacos Inc D 806 371-0411 Amarillo *(G-427)*
Garden State Salsa Inc F 512 242-4534 Austin *(G-1178)*
Gem Food Services Corp E 281 232-8013 Rosenberg *(G-17582)*
Georgia Sandwich Company Inc E 770 426-5678 Southlake *(G-19072)*
Good Flow Honey & Juice Co F 512 472-6714 Austin *(G-1188)*
Great American Marketing Co D 713 682-6471 Houston *(G-10024)*
Gruma Corporation C 972 232-5000 Irving *(G-13043)*
Gruma Corporation C 210 304-6700 San Antonio *(G-18154)*
Gruma Corporation D 832 441-5982 Houston *(G-10050)*
▲ Gruma Corporation C 972 232-5000 Irving *(G-13044)*
Gruma Corporation B 972 709-1217 Dallas *(G-4419)*
GSC Chipotle Texas Ltd E 915 769-0097 Fort Hancock *(G-6321)*
Han-D-Pac Products Inc E 915 595-2212 El Paso *(G-5793)*
Heb Plus E 210 673-4900 San Antonio *(G-18163)*
High Grade Products LLC F 832 381-3455 Spring *(G-19215)*
Hillshire Brands Company C 713 928-6281 Houston *(G-10186)*
Hormel Foods Corp Svcs LLC F 210 495-0764 San Antonio *(G-18173)*
▲ Houston Calco Inc G 713 236-8668 Houston *(G-10221)*
▲ Houston Sysco Inc E 713 672-8080 Houston *(G-10254)*
▼ Illes Food Ingredients Ltd D 800 683-4553 Carrollton *(G-2764)*
▲ Intermex Products Usa Ltd E 972 660-2071 Grand Prairie *(G-7894)*
▲ Isabella Foods Inc D 915 590-1899 El Paso *(G-5818)*
Ixpalia Inc E 512 389-0389 Austin *(G-1245)*
J Leals Food Inc E 214 412-3158 Grand Prairie *(G-7898)*
▲ Jardine Foods Inc E 512 295-4600 Buda *(G-2531)*
Jgr Enterprises LLC E 817 335-4629 Fort Worth *(G-6741)*
John Hogan Interests Inc E 214 637-0214 Dallas *(G-4537)*
Julios Corn Chips F 325 486-9300 San Angelo *(G-17812)*
Kennys All Purpose Seasoning F 940 733-2200 Wichita Falls *(G-20776)*
La Abuela Mexican Foods Inc E 956 447-8289 Weslaco *(G-20663)*
La Espiga De Oro - Georgia Inc C 713 861-4200 Houston *(G-10580)*
La Fama Foods Inc D 903 968-4500 Ore City *(G-16274)*
La Famosa Tortilla F 361 592-5596 Kingsville *(G-13633)*
La Frontera Molina F 210 432-0855 San Antonio *(G-18233)*
La Hacenda Mexican Fd Pdts Inc E 214 353-0230 Dallas *(G-4575)*
La Hacienda Tortilla Factory F 830 773-9151 Eagle Pass *(G-5548)*
La India Packing Co E 956 723-3772 Laredo *(G-13903)*
La Mexicana Tortilla Fctry Inc D 214 943-7770 Duncanville *(G-5532)*
La Nortena Tortilla Factory F 432 445-3273 Pecos *(G-16622)*
La Nueva Riograndese Inc E 817 921-0440 Fort Worth *(G-6777)*
La Original Tortilla Co Inc E 361 570-8905 Victoria *(G-20282)*
La Paloma Tortilla Factory F 956 316-1515 Edinburg *(G-5592)*
La Ranchera Inc F 713 699-4400 Houston *(G-10582)*
La Regia Tortilla Factory LLC E 210 971-9190 San Antonio *(G-18235)*
La Rotativa Tortilla Inc G 915 533-2317 El Paso *(G-5834)*
La Superior Foods Inc F 682 703-1165 Fort Worth *(G-6778)*
La Tapatia Inc E 915 859-9616 El Paso *(G-5835)*
Lapaz Tortilla Factory G 432 337-7735 Odessa *(G-16060)*
▲ Leons Fine Foods Inc C 972 529-5050 McKinney *(G-14953)*
▲ Lobo Tortilla Factory Inc C 972 388-8000 Dallas *(G-4599)*
Lopez Efrain F 713 921-0057 Houston *(G-10688)*
Lulus Dessert Corporation D 210 399-3767 San Antonio *(G-18267)*
Lunas Tortillas Factory F 214 747-2661 Dallas *(G-4612)*
Magi Foods LLC F 210 590-1308 Selma *(G-18877)*
▲ Malim Inc C 210 654-3963 San Antonio *(G-18272)*
Marbros L L C F 210 922-8383 San Antonio *(G-18275)*
Marroquin Tortilla Factory F 361 883-7051 Corpus Christi *(G-3574)*
▼ Maui Foods International Inc E 214 823-6284 Plano *(G-16920)*
McCormick & Company Inc D 972 721-9318 Irving *(G-13100)*
McCormick & Company Inc C 214 329-7044 Irving *(G-13101)*
Meditrrnean Spcialty Foods LLC D 214 680-8820 Dallas *(G-4664)*
Mexi-Snax Corporation E 915 779-5709 El Paso *(G-5874)*
Micor Inc E 281 476-0808 Deer Park *(G-5286)*
Minom Inc F 210 734-5124 San Antonio *(G-18308)*
Mizkan America Inc D 214 339-5551 Dallas *(G-4679)*
Mizkan Americas Inc E 214 339-5551 Dallas *(G-4680)*
Montega Ltd D 713 692-1400 Houston *(G-10912)*
Montes Tortilla Factory F 956 969-5792 Weslaco *(G-20666)*
▲ Mother Parkers Tea Cof USA Ltd C 817 551-5500 Fort Worth *(G-6855)*
National Food and Beverage Inc D 214 905-9700 Dallas *(G-4715)*
National Vinegar Company E 713 223-4214 Houston *(G-11004)*
Newly Weds Foods Inc E 903 577-3200 Mount Pleasant *(G-15656)*
North Texas Ingredients Inc F 817 270-2397 Azle *(G-1727)*
Nuevo Leon Tortilla Factory E 972 721-1984 Irving *(G-13129)*
Odessa Tortilla & Tamale Fctry E 432 332-6676 Odessa *(G-16098)*
Panchitas Tortilla Factory F 325 655-2138 San Angelo *(G-17818)*

Papa Bears Pizza ....E 512 351-5421
  Cedar Park *(G-2982)*

Paper Plate Incorporated ....D 972 296-7888
  Desoto *(G-5439)*

Peached Tortilla Mobile LLC ....F 512 297-8635
  Austin *(G-1403)*

Pepperidge Farm Incorporated ....E 713 385-2010
  Houston *(G-11287)*

Perfectfitmeals LLC ....F 713 868-5300
  Houston *(G-11290)*

Piedras Negras Tortilla Fctry ....G 830 773-6706
  Eagle Pass *(G-5553)*

▲ Pioneer Frozen Foods Inc ....A 972 298-4281
  Duncanville *(G-5536)*

◆ Pita Pal Industries Inc ....F 713 777-7482
  Houston *(G-11339)*

Pops Bakery Inc ....E 325 655-1170
  San Angelo *(G-17822)*

Potbelly Corporation ....E 281 277-2515
  Sugar Land *(G-19527)*

Precise Food Ingredients Inc ....E 972 323-4951
  Carrollton *(G-2882)*

Pretzels Inc ....E 972 416-3660
  Carrollton *(G-2795)*

▼ Proportion Foods LLC ....B 512 735-9800
  . Round Rock *(G-17683)*

Pulido Associates Inc ....E 817 249-6728
  Benbrook *(G-2045)*

▲ Quality Bakery Products Inc ....D 281 449-4977
  Houston *(G-11492)*

Quiktrip Corporation ....E 817 378-8410
  Fort Worth *(G-6929)*

R Ibarras Inc ....E 817 625-8962
  Fort Worth *(G-6931)*

Red River Tea Company ....F 214 956-0373
  Dallas *(G-4870)*

Regal Interests Inc ....E 713 222-8231
  Houston *(G-11583)*

▲ Riba Foods Inc ....D 713 975-7001
  Houston *(G-11617)*

▼ Ricos Products Co Inc ....C 210 222-1415
  San Antonio *(G-18426)*

Riviana Foods Inc ....B 713 529-3251
  Houston *(G-11628)*

Rudolph Foods Company Inc ....D 214 638-2204
  Dallas *(G-4919)*

Russell E Womack Inc ....E 806 747-2581
  Lubbock *(G-14474)*

Ryc Foods LLC ....E 210 731-8854
  San Antonio *(G-18439)*

Sanitary Tortilla Mfg Co ....E 210 226-9209
  San Antonio *(G-18453)*

Sarais Spreads Superfood LLC ....F 552 163-6178
  The Woodlands *(G-19916)*

Select Butter & Packaging LLC ....F 214 568-9000
  Littlefield *(G-14149)*

Sfc Global Supply Chain Inc ....B 713 740-7200
  Pasadena *(G-16505)*

Shayne Foods Incorporated ....F 210 442-8776
  San Antonio *(G-18469)*

▲ Sneaky Chef Foods LLC ....F 203 768-5654
  Austin *(G-1514)*

Southwest Spice Company LLC ....G 713 860-5300
  Houston *(G-11984)*

Steven M Riley ....F 972 741-0971
  Richardson *(G-17402)*

Super Lopez Tortillas LLC ....D 713 921-1237
  Houston *(G-12107)*

Taco & Tortilla Factory Inc ....F 713 706-3233
  Houston *(G-12146)*

Teasdale Foods Inc ....C 952 854-0903
  Flower Mound *(G-6288)*

Teasdale Foods Inc ....C 915 821-2500
  El Paso *(G-5994)*

Texas Automatic Foods Inc ....E 713 432-1331
  Bellaire *(G-2003)*

Texas Coffee Company ....E 409 835-3434
  Beaumont *(G-1958)*

Texas Food Solutions LLC ....D 713 579-5634
  Katy *(G-13449)*

TJ Blackburn Syrup Works Inc ....D 903 665-2541
  Jefferson *(G-13289)*

Todays Children Food Program ....F 214 562-4702
  Desoto *(G-5445)*

Tortillas Olivo LLC ....F 956 702-8388
  San Juan *(G-18675)*

Tortilleria Cuauhtemoc ....F 915 886-4480
  Canutillo *(G-2666)*

Tortilria Monterrey Groceries ....F 956 544-7222
  Brownsville *(G-2415)*

Trinidad Benham Holding Co ....D 903 569-2283
  Mineola *(G-15514)*

Tyson Foods Inc ....B 817 656-5507
  Fort Worth *(G-7089)*

Universal Blanchers LLC ....E 254 445-4021
  Dublin *(G-5518)*

US Citrus LLC ....E 956 252-3101
  Hargill *(G-8171)*

Usm Manufacturing LLC ....E 806 791-0220
  Lubbock *(G-14505)*

▲ Van Oriental Food Inc ....D 214 630-0333
  Dallas *(G-5153)*

Veggie Noodle Co LLC ....D 512 200-3337
  Austin *(G-1626)*

Ventura Foods LLC ....F 817 232-6800
  Fort Worth *(G-7097)*

Warabeya Texas Inc ....D 972 219-7110
  Lewisville *(G-14110)*

West Phalia Market Inc ....F 512 846-1155
  Hutto *(G-12888)*

▲ Wonton Food Corporation ....D 832 366-1280
  Houston *(G-12682)*

▲ Woo Kee Foods Inc ....F 832 818-6988
  Houston *(G-12683)*

▲ Xochitl Inc ....E 214 800-3551
  Irving *(G-13211)*

Zilks Foods LLC ....F 512 633-8904
  Austin *(G-1687)*

21 TOBACCO PRODUCTS

2111 Cigarettes

Permian Basin Eqp & Sup LLC ....E 432 563-1044
  Odessa *(G-16113)*

Philip Morris USA Inc ....D 210 530-7100
  San Antonio *(G-18372)*

R J Reynolds Tobacco Company ....B 877 703-0386
  Tyler *(G-20144)*

2121 Cigars

◆ Finck Cigar Co ....D 210 226-4191
  San Antonio *(G-18115)*

2131 Tobacco, Chewing & Snuff

Swedish Match North Amer LLC ....C 817 416-7017
  Southlake *(G-19082)*

2141 Tobacco Stemming & Redrying

Summit Mechanical ....E 903 267-7949
  Sumner *(G-19609)*

22 TEXTILE MILL PRODUCTS

2211 Cotton, Woven Fabric

▲ A Lakhany International Inc ....C 713 266-8799
  Houston *(G-8427)*

▲ Alteca LLC ....F 956 423-1885
  Harlingen *(G-8179)*

Censored Soles ....F 832 443-4365
  Houston *(G-9135)*

Climax Investors LLC ....E 832 582-9622
  Dallas *(G-4130)*

Cofco Americas Resources Corp ....C 832 944-6359
  Sugar Land *(G-19461)*

Comfy Choice LLC ....D 972 302-8094
  Plano *(G-16828)*

Custom Filter Supply Inc ....F 713 947-8147
  Houston *(G-9371)*

Denimatrix LLC ....E 806 385-6401
  Littlefield *(G-14144)*

Diaper Sports Group LLC ....F 214 871-5131
  Dallas *(G-4257)*

East Txas Lighthouse For Blind ....D 903 595-3444
  Tyler *(G-20082)*

Fiberco Inc ....F 682 647-1332
  Fort Worth *(G-6628)*

Fresh Meadows Industries Inc ....E 713 464-9554
  Houston *(G-9865)*

▼ Ggs Wiping Products LLC ....E 713 672-7200
  Houston *(G-9948)*

▲ Home Treasures Inc ....E 713 937-7716
  Houston *(G-10198)*

▼ Innova Supply Inc ....E 713 473-3345
  Pasadena *(G-16459)*

J Lewis Partners LP ....A 972 702-7390
  Dallas *(G-4519)*

Lauras Carousel Inc ....F 940 365-1875
  Aubrey *(G-850)*

▲ Levan Group I LP ....F 713 528-3838
  Houston *(G-10628)*

Logo Masters LLC ....F 830 822-8390
  San Antonio *(G-18262)*

Medical Textiles Inc ....E 214 744-1246
  Dallas *(G-4662)*

Medline Industries Inc ....C 281 574-6200
  Katy *(G-13371)*

Mount Vernon Mills Inc ....C 361 275-2393
  Cuero *(G-3764)*

Mount Vernon Mills Inc ....B 979 836-5255
  Brenham *(G-2265)*

N 2 The World ....E 817 424-0799
  Grapevine *(G-8046)*

▲ Powers Embroidery Inc ....D 254 754-2498
  Waco *(G-20448)*

SAM&m Group LLC ....F 346 204-5786
  Stafford *(G-19373)*

▲ Southwest Cutters LLC ....D 915 858-2200
  El Paso *(G-5971)*

Texas Wipers & Rags LLC ....C 956 554-7500
  Brownsville *(G-2411)*

Tri-Tex Enterprises Inc ....D 214 744-1246
  Eastland *(G-5569)*

◆ United Amercn Acquisition Corp ....E 859 987-5389
  Waco *(G-20470)*

V Respect ....G 281 780-6267
  Houston *(G-12511)*

Vaign Designer Street AP LLC ....E 832 490-8510
  Rosenberg *(G-17599)*

◆ Wmc Waco Holdings Inc ....E 254 753-7301
  Waco *(G-20479)*

Wolf & Sons Design Inc ....E 512 237-3388
  Smithville *(G-18979)*

2221 Silk & Man-Made Fiber

A & M Composites Corporation ....E 432 267-6525
  Big Spring *(G-2068)*

Best Made Designs LLC ....E 432 943-9995
  Monahans *(G-15600)*

Casting Designs Inc ....C 817 551-7373
  Fort Worth *(G-6496)*

Certainteed Corporation ....E 940 723-5998
  Wichita Falls *(G-20752)*

Dcu Inc ....F 972 816-6667
  Wylie *(G-20932)*

▲ F & F Composite Group Inc ....E 817 379-4411
  Fort Worth *(G-6622)*

Fiberglass Specialties Inc ....D 903 657-6522
  Henderson *(G-8263)*

▲ Greenhead Industries Inc ....F 936 867-4801
  Wells *(G-20657)*

▲ Hallwood Group Incorporated ....E 214 528-5588
  Dallas *(G-4430)*

Hc Interiors Inc ....E 214 350-0468
  Carrollton *(G-2754)*

J Lewis Partners LP ....A 972 702-7390
  Dallas *(G-4519)*

Jones-Bell LLC ....E 254 933-2270
  Belton *(G-2026)*

Kerick Industries ....F 214 432-2446
  Dallas *(G-4552)*

Liftex Corporation ....E 713 863-0900
  Houston *(G-10639)*

Lycra Company LLC ....F 218 842-4613
  La Porte *(G-13770)*

Mount Vernon Mills Inc ....B 979 836-5255
  Brenham *(G-2265)*

Mount Vernon Mills Inc ....C 361 275-2393
  Cuero *(G-3764)*

Ortegas Custom Interiors Inc ....F 214 341-4003
  Dallas *(G-4769)*

▲ Ply-Tech Inc ....F 830 625-3913
  New Braunfels *(G-15819)*

◆ Polytex Fibers Corp ....C 713 690-9055
  Houston *(G-11362)*

▲ Powers Embroidery Inc ....D 254 754-2498
  Waco *(G-20448)*

Quest and Sons Inc ....E 806 744-2351
  Lubbock *(G-14468)*

RPS Composites Alabama Inc ....F 979 265-4262
  Clute *(G-3158)*

Sani-Safe Products Inc ....F 210 826-1344
  San Antonio *(G-18451)*

Specialty Composites Group LLC ....E 254 752-3622
  Waco *(G-20460)*

The Texas A&M University Sys ....C 979 845-3414
  College Station *(G-3205)*

United Aviation ACC Inc ....E 817 447-8000
  Burleson *(G-2600)*

▲ Winzen Film Inc ....E 214 340-7060
Dallas (G-5198)

2231 Wool, Woven Fabric

Carruth Nursery Irrigation ....F 903 236-7555
Longview (G-14208)

Ingrids Custom Hand Woven ....F 325 732-4370
Paint Rock (G-16291)

ISO Covers LLC ....F 972 221-4410
Lewisville (G-14057)

Roddie Wool Scouring Inc ....F 325 597-2138
Brady (G-2217)

Standard Textile Co Inc ....D 956 831-9040
Brownsville (G-2407)

Texas Eagle Star MGT Inc ....F 915 858-3144
El Paso (G-5998)

2241 Fabric Mills, Cotton, Wool, Silk & Man-Made

Cheryl L McDaniel ....F 281 814-0533
New Waverly (G-15857)

Guardian Insptn Tbular MGT LLC ....F 403 233-7561
Midland (G-15241)

▼ Stewart Tubular Products LLC ......F 713 682-1486
Dallas (G-12066)

2252 Hosiery, Except Women's

▲ Celeste Stein Designs Inc ....F 409 763-1009
Galveston (G-7392)

Sand Socks ....F 512 284-7706
Buda (G-2536)

Sock Club Enterprises LLC ....G 919 619-4981
Austin (G-1515)

2253 Knit Outerwear Mills

◆ Bio World Merchandising Inc ....C 972 488-0655
Irving (G-12948)

Body Language Fashions Inc ....F 713 974-0960
Houston (G-8936)

Brazos Running Company LLC ....G 979 485-9830
College Station (G-3178)

Enthusiastic Sales LLC ....F 832 698-1608
Tomball (G-19978)

Gall Art Novelties LLC ....F 956 290-3124
Laredo (G-13888)

▲ Haggar Womens Wear Ltd ....C 214 637-5300
Dallas (G-4427)

▲ Headcovers Unlimited Inc ....F 281 334-4287
League City (G-13958)

Hg Tshirt Design Company ....F 469 776-4995
Grand Prairie (G-7890)

Virtual Realities ....F 409 599-7863
Dickinson (G-5479)

2258 Lace & Warp Knit Fabric Mills

▲ Texas Leather Trim Inc ....E 817 535-5883
Fort Worth (G-7049)

2259 Knitting Mills, NEC

▲ Center-Line Curtains Inc ....F 972 299-5902
Cedar Hill (G-2937)

2261 Cotton Fabric Finishers

Action Wear Plus Inc ....F 281 376-4300
Spring (G-19098)

Adrian Scott Industries Inc ....F 713 941-3300
Pasadena (G-16377)

G and G Investments Inc ....E 325 949-7864
San Angelo (G-17801)

Global Chemliquidations LLC ....E 832 539-3969
Houston (G-9968)

J Harding & Co ....F 713 862-9855
Houston (G-10440)

▲ JC Viramontes Inc ....F 915 857-4545
El Paso (G-5820)

Kampus Books ....F 936 560-0033
Nacogdoches (G-15700)

Kelly B Pitts Jr ....F 713 923-5555
Houston (G-10513)

Protective Concepts Inc ....F 832 843-7619
Cypress (G-3816)

Ritchie-Vincent Inc ....F 432 337-5133
Odessa (G-16142)

Sam Group Inc ....F 817 481-1968
Grapevine (G-8053)

Schneider-Banks Inc ....F 903 675-1440
Athens (G-838)

Summit Sportswear Inc ....G 281 335-5370
League City (G-13980)

Texas 2 Stitch ....F 972 599-1717
Plano (G-17028)

Texas 28 LLC ....F 806 644-9663
Spearman (G-19088)

Texas Flameproofing Inc ....F 214 630-1088
Dallas (G-5061)

Versa Printing Inc ....E 972 243-5353
Dallas (G-5163)

2262 Silk & Man-Made Fabric Finishers

Adrian Scott Industries Inc ....F 713 941-3300
Pasadena (G-16377)

G and G Investments Inc ....E 325 949-7864
San Angelo (G-17801)

Promos Distributors Inc ....D 972 478-7298
Carrollton (G-2799)

Protective Concepts Inc ....F 832 843-7619
Cypress (G-3816)

Schneider-Banks Inc ....E 903 675-1440
Athens (G-838)

Sports Wear Graphics Inc ....G 817 870-9900
Fort Worth (G-7014)

Ttc Trammell Co Inc ....F 713 921-7121
Houston (G-12399)

Zspace LLC ....F 713 662-3123
Houston (G-12733)

2269 Textile Finishers, NEC

Alecom Technologies Group Inc ......G 972 870-9400
Flower Mound (G-6259)

Anchor Graphics Inc ....E 972 422-4300
McKinney (G-14923)

G & A Label Inc ....E 915 544-1766
El Paso (G-5777)

Guardian Southwest String Tag ......F 972 938-0123
Waxahachie (G-20544)

2273 Carpets & Rugs

▲ Al Knoch Interiors Inc ....F 915 886-5800
Canutillo (G-2662)

Clover Group Inc ....E 915 590-2525
El Paso (G-5698)

Curse of Good Taste Inc ....F 512 327-9660
Austin (G-1078)

East Texas Acoustical Inc ....F 903 663-3820
Longview (G-14226)

◆ El Paso Saddleblanket Co LP ......E 915 544-1000
El Paso (G-5741)

Elk Corporation of Texas ....C 972 875-9611
Ennis (G-6095)

▼ Elk Corporation of Texas ....D 972 851-0500
Dallas (G-4312)

Exclusive Oriental Rugs Inc ....F 214 747-5557
Dallas (G-4342)

Gormans Uniform Rental Inc ....D 713 467-5424
Houston (G-10006)

▲ Great Rug Company ....F 713 789-3666
Houston (G-10028)

Gunns Restoration ....F 281 645-2260
Houston (G-10075)

Ingrids Custom Hand Woven ....F 325 732-4370
Paint Rock (G-16291)

◆ Lets Gel Inc ....E 512 628-1700
Austin (G-1289)

◆ Loloi Inc ....C 972 503-5656
Dallas (G-4602)

Metro Mats ....E 817 640-6287
Arlington (G-732)

Michaels Companies Inc ....D 972 409-1300
Irving (G-13108)

Mohawk Industries Inc ....C 210 564-8849
San Antonio (G-18316)

Mohawk Industries Inc ....C 956 630-4709
McAllen (G-14891)

Mohawk Industries Inc ....F 972 874-5820
Flower Mound (G-6272)

Mohawk Industries Inc ....E 214 309-4848
Dallas (G-4683)

▲ Newpark Resources Inc ....E 281 362-6800
The Woodlands (G-19897)

▲ R S Global Inc ....D 972 406-2930
Dallas (G-4857)

▲ Reyes-Amtex Automotive LLC ......E 210 628-4900
San Antonio (G-18425)

SAM&m Group LLC ....E 346 204-5786
Stafford (G-19373)

United Aviation ACC Inc ....F 817 447-8000
Burleson (G-2600)

▼ United Rtorcraft Solutions LLC ......E 940 627-0626
Decatur (G-5256)

2281 Yarn Spinning Mills

▼ Celanese Acetate LLC ....A 972 443-4000
Dallas (G-4093)

Cramer Computer Supplies Ltd ....E 806 371-7310
Amarillo (G-485)

Liberty Mask LLC ....E 214 915-2133
Midland (G-15280)

Lorenzo Textile Mills Inc ....E 806 634-5506
Lorenzo (G-14344)

▲ Southwest Textiles Inc ....D 806 687-4001
Lubbock (G-14485)

2282 Yarn Texturizing, Throwing, Twisting & Winding Mills

Alliance Carpet Cushion Co ....D 903 886-4153
Commerce (G-3241)

Carrion Enterprises Inc ....F 915 593-1338
El Paso (G-5686)

▲ Winzen Film Inc ....E 214 340-7060
Dallas (G-5198)

2284 Thread Mills

Texas Thread Manufacturing Co ......G 956 412-4999
Harlingen (G-8206)

2295 Fabrics Coated Not Rubberized

Ace Hanger Strap Inc ....F 214 742-8585
Dallas (G-3882)

◆ Carlisle Ctngs Wtrproofing Inc ......D 972 442-6545
Wylie (G-20929)

◆ Ea Services Inc ....D 866 711-1001
Pearland (G-16557)

▲ Hanitatek LLC ....G 214 351-5818
Carrollton (G-2753)

▲ Houston Wiper & Mill Supply Co .....F 713 672-0571
Houston (G-10264)

▲ Muncaster Capital Texas Inc ....E 214 515-5000
Ennis (G-6111)

Patrick Industries Inc ....F 254 799-5717
Waco (G-20444)

Pipe Coatings Intl LLC ....E 979 387-3150
Beasley (G-1843)

▲ Polyguard Products Inc ....E 972 875-8421
Ennis (G-6114)

Rvo Manufacturing LLC ....E 832 229-5114
Houston (G-11703)

▲ Westlake Pvc Corporation ....C 713 960-9111
Houston (G-12653)

2296 Tire Cord & Fabric

Invista Capital Management LLC ......A 361 572-1111
Victoria (G-20274)

▲ Jadtis Industries LP ....D 214 905-9566
Farmers Branch (G-6204)

Lone Star Molding Inc ....E 936 539-0008
Conroe (G-3324)

2297 Fabrics, Nonwoven

◆ E R Carpenter LP ....C 804 359-0800
Temple (G-19680)

Fiberco Inc ....F 682 647-1332
Fort Worth (G-6628)

Hobbs Bonded Fibers LLC ....E 254 741-0040
Waco (G-20412)

◆ Hobbs Bonded Fibers Na LLC ......D 254 741-0040
Waco (G-20413)

▲ NW Fabrics LLC ....F 832 895-1110
Houston (G-11103)

Supply Pro Sorbents LLC ....E 713 672-9080
Sugar Land (G-19559)

Twe Nonwovens Us Inc ....E 210 651-3735
Schertz (G-18765)

2298 Cordage & Twine

Accurate Connections Inc ....E 972 484-8500
Plano (G-16769)

Advanced Fabric Tech LLC ....E 281 872-7272
Spring (G-19191)

▲ Cactus Ropes Inc ....E 830 569-8744
Pleasanton (G-17064)

▲ Cargo Systems Inc ....E 512 837-1300
Austin (G-1029)

Delta Rigging & Tools Inc ....D 877 889-8833
Hurst (G-12844)

◆ Delta Rigging & Tools Inc ....C 713 512-1700
Houston *(G-9433)*

▲ Equibrand Products Group LP ....D 817 573-1884
Granbury *(G-7796)*

▲ Fast Back Rope Mfg ....F 817 279-1851
Granbury *(G-7798)*

Federal Prison Industries ....C 432 466-2300
Big Spring *(G-2082)*

HWC Wire & Cable Company ....C 713 453-8518
Houston *(G-10293)*

Kevin M Ehringer Entps Inc ....D 972 620-4997
Dallas *(G-4553)*

▲ Ls Rope LLC ....E 903 322-6580
Buffalo *(G-2546)*

▲ Ma-Tex Wire Rope Co Inc ....E 903 984-9691
Kilgore *(G-13567)*

Parker Systems Inc ....F 800 262-4891
Houston *(G-11245)*

Pedley Nets Inc ....F 940 328-0448
Mineral Wells *(G-15537)*

◆ Southwest Ocean Services Inc ....E 713 671-9101
Houston *(G-11982)*

2299 Textile Goods, NEC

Addison Collection LP ....G 817 921-4450
Fort Worth *(G-6344)*

Advanced Fabric Tech LLC ....F 281 872-7272
Spring *(G-19191)*

Advanced Ocean Shipping ....E 281 300-0191
Houston *(G-8489)*

◆ Ascend Performance Mtls Inc ....F 713 315-5700
Houston *(G-8713)*

◆ Ascend Prfmce Mtls Hldings Inc ......E 713 315-5700
Houston *(G-8714)*

Bollman Industries Inc ....E 325 655-0112
San Angelo *(G-17784)*

Capital City Processors LLC ....E 405 232-5511
Dallas *(G-4080)*

Cornerstone Apparel Inc ....E 903 939-0188
Tyler *(G-20073)*

◆ Fred Clark Felt Co Beaumont ....E 409 842-5080
Beaumont *(G-1897)*

Hobbs Bonded Fibers LLC ....E 254 741-0040
Waco *(G-20412)*

◆ Hobbs Bonded Fibers Na LLC ....D 254 741-0040
Waco *(G-20413)*

Industrial Noise Control Corp ....E 972 494-1422
Richardson *(G-17331)*

Insituform Technologies Inc ....F 636 530-8020
Houston *(G-10378)*

▲ John Cole Chemical Corporation ......E 512 443-1037
Austin *(G-1257)*

Joren ....F 713 300-0377
Richmond *(G-17458)*

Knit Rags LLC ....F 713 249-9478
Houston *(G-10549)*

▲ M & L Rose Enterprises Inc ....F 214 637-8000
Dallas *(G-4617)*

▲ Reclaimed Textiles Co ....E 214 638-7551
Dallas *(G-4867)*

Rockpoint Apparel Company ....F 713 699-9896
Houston *(G-11651)*

Roddie Wool Scouring Inc ....F 325 597-2138
Brady *(G-2217)*

San Benito Textile Inc ....F 956 361-0282
San Benito *(G-18666)*

Sigma Corporation ....E 281 987-1200
Houston *(G-11883)*

Startex Linen Co ....F 713 782-4419
Houston *(G-12050)*

Team Pvf LLC ....E 281 714-1582
Houston *(G-12173)*

◆ Venator Americas LLC ....D 281 465-6700
The Woodlands *(G-19935)*

Venator Americas LLC ....F 281 719-6000
The Woodlands *(G-19936)*

Warner Bailey Inc ....F 936 867-4801
Alto *(G-318)*

Wesco Industries Inc ....E 817 551-7063
Fort Worth *(G-7137)*

Xjian Inc ....F 972 618-6096
Plano *(G-17055)*

23 APPAREL AND OTHER FINISHED PRODUCTS MADE FROM FABRICS AND SIMILAR MATERIAL

2311 Men's & Boys' Suits, Coats & Overcoats

▲ Advantage Supplies Inc ....F 972 250-1339
Carrollton *(G-2854)*

▲ Directors Assistant LLC ....F 972 816-5553
Dallas *(G-4261)*

El Paso Lighthouse For Blind ....E 915 532-4495
El Paso *(G-5736)*

▼ Esskay Manufacturing Co ....D 210 222-9585
San Antonio *(G-18096)*

◆ Haggar Clothing Co ....B 214 352-8481
Farmers Branch *(G-6199)*

Haggar Clothing Co ....B 214 352-8481
Texas City *(G-19794)*

◆ Haggar Corp ....A 214 352-8481
Farmers Branch *(G-6200)*

▲ Ics Jail Supplies Inc ....E 254 751-1566
Waco *(G-20418)*

Ingamia Inc ....F 214 828-1660
Dallas *(G-4499)*

Marlo Sales Inc ....F 972 721-9755
Irving *(G-13095)*

Neosensory Inc ....F 401 257-9460
Houston *(G-11025)*

◆ Readyone Industries Inc ....A 915 858-7277
El Paso *(G-5931)*

Red The Uniform Tailor ....E 972 660-8433
Grand Prairie *(G-7963)*

Roicom Usa LLC ....E 915 471-3071
El Paso *(G-5944)*

Rvg Prodirect LLC ....F 956 627-6161
McAllen *(G-14903)*

▲ Safety Supply Inc ....F 210 650-9033
San Antonio *(G-18441)*

Texas Clothing Holding Corp ....E 214 956-4494
Dallas *(G-5056)*

Tom James Company ....F 325 695-0190
Abilene *(G-88)*

◆ Walls Industries LLC ....D 844 259-2557
Fort Worth *(G-7118)*

2321 Men's & Boys' Shirts

A-Z Graphics LLC ....F 210 495-3468
San Antonio *(G-17852)*

◆ Apparel Group Ltd ....C 214 469-3300
Lewisville *(G-14022)*

Asics America Corporation ....E 972 678-0200
Allen *(G-252)*

▲ Bond Clothier Inc ....E 713 784-7121
Houston *(G-8949)*

Business Print Center Inc ....E 505 864-3553
Converse *(G-3390)*

Dos Carolinas Inc ....E 210 222-9117
San Antonio *(G-18065)*

Earls Apparel Inc ....D 936 544-5521
Crockett *(G-3717)*

◆ Haggar Clothing Co ....B 214 352-8481
Farmers Branch *(G-6199)*

Haggar Clothing Co ....B 214 352-8481
Texas City *(G-19794)*

◆ Haggar Corp ....A 214 352-8481
Farmers Branch *(G-6200)*

Hamilton Shirt Interests Ltd ....E 713 780-8222
Houston *(G-10113)*

▲ J & G Trybus Corporation ....F 214 331-5248
Desoto *(G-5435)*

Pvh Corp ....F 512 392-2036
San Marcos *(G-18704)*

Rockpoint Apparel Company ....F 713 699-9896
Houston *(G-11651)*

▲ Ruddock Manufacturing Co Inc ....C 915 544-3530
El Paso *(G-5949)*

Ruddock Manufacturing Co Inc ....C 915 544-3530
El Paso *(G-5950)*

Tag Holdings Inc ....C 214 469-3300
The Colony *(G-19815)*

Texas Clothing Holding Corp ....E 214 956-4494
Dallas *(G-5056)*

◆ Vf Sagebrush Enterprises LLC ....E 817 336-7201
Fort Worth *(G-7103)*

▲ Westmoor Corp ....E 817 625-2841
Fort Worth *(G-7142)*

▲ Westmoor Mfg Co ....E 817 625-2841
Fort Worth *(G-7143)*

2322 Men's & Boys' Underwear & Nightwear

▲ Inzer Advance Designs Inc ....E 903 236-4012
Longview *(G-14253)*

▲ J & G Trybus Corporation ....F 214 331-5248
Desoto *(G-5435)*

▲ New Icm LP ....F 979 578-0543
El Campo *(G-5623)*

2323 Men's & Boys' Neckwear

Cortwear Sports AP & Eqp LLC ....F 361 728-1868
Kingsville *(G-13624)*

2325 Men's & Boys' Separate Trousers & Casual Slacks

Aalfs Manufacturing Inc ....B 972 991-3945
Dallas *(G-3874)*

Ameri-Tech Dist Inc ....E 915 772-9090
El Paso *(G-5643)*

Bellagio Menswear LLC ....G 512 496-8322
Austin *(G-988)*

Earls Apparel Inc ....D 936 544-5521
Crockett *(G-3717)*

▼ Esskay Manufacturing Co ....D 210 222-9585
San Antonio *(G-18096)*

▲ Excel Garment Mfg Ltd ....E 915 544-5006
El Paso *(G-5760)*

▲ Fashion Works Inc ....F 972 596-5815
Plano *(G-16869)*

▼ Glen Oaks Industries Inc ....F 214 631-1340
Dallas *(G-4409)*

Guess Inc ....E 915 877-1948
Canutillo *(G-2664)*

Haggar Clothing Co ....B 214 352-8481
Texas City *(G-19794)*

◆ Haggar Clothing Co ....B 214 352-8481
Farmers Branch *(G-6199)*

◆ Haggar Corp ....A 214 352-8481
Farmers Branch *(G-6200)*

▲ J & G Trybus Corporation ....F 214 331-5248
Desoto *(G-5435)*

Levi Strauss & Co ....F 817 262-6314
Roanoke *(G-17488)*

Lucky Brand Dungarees LLC ....F 512 393-2002
San Marcos *(G-18697)*

Stanley Jeans Corp ....D 936 544-5521
Crockett *(G-3724)*

Stitches Inc ....E 915 591-9260
El Paso *(G-5981)*

Texas Clothing Holding Corp ....E 214 956-4494
Dallas *(G-5056)*

Vf Industrial Park Inc ....E 979 826-8277
Hempstead *(G-8256)*

Vf Outdoor LLC ....B 830 278-2535
Uvalde *(G-20199)*

◆ Vf Sagebrush Enterprises LLC ....E 817 336-7201
Fort Worth *(G-7103)*

2326 Men's & Boys' Work Clothing

A&S New Braunfels LLC ....E 832 206-4202
San Antonio *(G-17849)*

Armbrust Inc ....E 512 807-0744
Pflugerville *(G-16658)*

Ashley Worldwide Inc ....E 956 383-0636
Edinburg *(G-5575)*

▲ Asti Manufacturing Corp Inc ....E 972 241-3055
Farmers Branch *(G-6189)*

Aztec Fr Apparel Inc ....B 830 422-1775
Del Rio *(G-5306)*

Blue Medical Services Inc ....E 954 417-5442
Cypress *(G-3781)*

▲ Border Apparel Laundry Ltd ....E 915 772-7170
El Paso *(G-5666)*

Earls Apparel Inc ....D 936 544-5521
Crockett *(G-3717)*

Gallery One Point LLC ....E 512 428-5710
Pflugerville *(G-16674)*

▲ Guard-Line Inc ....C 903 796-4111
Atlanta *(G-843)*

◆ Handgards LLC ....C 915 779-6606
El Paso *(G-5794)*

▲ Le Stitch N Designs Inc ....E 214 340-1592
Dallas *(G-4586)*

▲ Maquilaplex LLC ....F 956 542-4138
Brownsville *(G-2380)*

◆ Med Couture Inc ....E 214 231-2500
Farmers Branch *(G-6207)*

▲ Medical Uniform Mfg Inc ....G 713 838-2233
Bellaire *(G-1998)*

Medline Industries Inc ....C 281 574-6200
Katy *(G-13371)*

Newinn Inc ....F 713 473-8188
Pasadena *(G-16488)*

▲ Radia Enterprises Inc ....E 713 645-3600
Houston *(G-11530)*

REr Apparel Inc ....E 417 673-5786
Dallas *(G-3851)*

▲ Ruddock Manufacturing Co Inc ......C 915 544-3530
El Paso *(G-5949)*

▲ Safety Supply Inc ....F 210 650-9033
San Antonio *(G-18441)*

Schaefer Ventures LLC ....G 800 426-2074
Fort Worth *(G-6977)*

Southland Athletic Mfg Co ....D 972 563-3321
Terrell *(G-19751)*

▲ Stanco Manufacturing Inc ....D 903 796-7936
Atlanta *(G-845)*

Stanley Jeans Corp ....D 936 544-5521
Crockett *(G-3724)*

Stitches Inc ....E 915 591-9260
El Paso *(G-5981)*

Texas Sewing Inc ....G 713 271-5466
Houston *(G-12248)*

▲ Twin Hill Acquisition Co Inc ....E 888 206-0699
Houston *(G-12415)*

Unifirst Corporation ....E 281 261-9632
Missouri City *(G-15597)*

Uniforms Inc ....F 214 630-0924
Dallas *(G-5132)*

Vf Industrial Park Inc ....E 936 327-7881
Livingston *(G-14163)*

Vf Outdoor LLC ....A 817 336-7201
Fort Worth *(G-7100)*

Vf Outdoor LLC ....C 817 810-4401
Fort Worth *(G-7101)*

Vf Outdoor LLC ....E 817 491-4949
Fort Worth *(G-7102)*

Vf Outdoor LLC ....B 817 348-0567
Fort Worth *(G-7099)*

Vf Outdoor LLC ....B 830 278-2535
Uvalde *(G-20199)*

◆ Walls Industries LLC ....D 844 259-2557
Fort Worth *(G-7118)*

Walls Industries LLC ....E 817 357-8040
Fort Worth *(G-7119)*

2329 Men's & Boys' Clothing, NEC

1 Play Away LLC ....E 972 532-6226
Desoto *(G-5426)*

8228 Corporation ....E 713 465-1303
Houston *(G-8417)*

▲ Advantage Supplies Inc ....F 972 250-1339
Carrollton *(G-2854)*

Aerostar International Inc ....E 903 885-0728
Sulphur Springs *(G-19578)*

▲ Baw Athletic Wear LP ....F 281 391-3335
Katy *(G-13389)*

Bexar Manufacturing & Trdg Co ......F 210 977-9585
San Antonio *(G-17951)*

Dilly Letter Jackets ....F 713 334-3232
Houston *(G-9473)*

▲ Double D Ranchwear Inc ....F 361 293-2394
Yoakum *(G-20963)*

Ennis Inc ....A 972 775-9801
Midlothian *(G-15480)*

Gmyp Manufacturing LLC ....F 682 313-3023
Farmers Branch *(G-6197)*

H & H T-Shirt Printing Inc ....G 254 628-1453
Belton *(G-2023)*

H & R Black Mfg Co LLC ....F 806 364-2040
Hereford *(G-8290)*

Hurley International LLC ....C 972 912-3040
Allen *(G-277)*

Hurley International LLC ....C 956 514-1700
Mercedes *(G-15006)*

▲ Inzer Advance Designs Inc ....E 903 236-4012
Longview *(G-14253)*

▲ J & G Trybus Corporation ....F 214 331-5248
Desoto *(G-5435)*

Lululemon Athletica ....F 713 863-1280
Houston *(G-10701)*

Nsg Corporation ....C 972 840-1233
Plano *(G-16947)*

Required Team Gear LLC ....E 817 922-8448
Fort Worth *(G-6957)*

▲ Roka Sports Inc ....E 877 985-7652
Austin *(G-1470)*

S N D Manufacturing Ltd ....D 214 340-1592
Dallas *(G-4923)*

Southland Athletic Mfg Co ....D 972 563-3321
Terrell *(G-19751)*

▼ Trademarks Promotional Pdts LP ...D 713 255-6506
Houston *(G-12340)*

◆ Vf Sagebrush Enterprises LLC ......E 817 336-7201
Fort Worth *(G-7103)*

2331 Women's & Misses' Blouses

A-Z Graphics LLC ....F 210 495-3468
San Antonio *(G-17852)*

Chapman Shameka ....F 281 507-8790
Pearland *(G-16543)*

Circle T Western Wear Ltd ....F 214 808-1100
Dallas *(G-4121)*

David McNeff Inc ....F 972 562-0607
McKinney *(G-14935)*

Ennis Inc ....A 972 775-9801
Midlothian *(G-15480)*

Moll McNeill Inc ....G 214 748-7272
Dallas *(G-4684)*

Pvh Corp ....G 512 392-2036
San Marcos *(G-18704)*

◆ Readyone Industries Inc ....A 915 858-7277
El Paso *(G-5931)*

◆ Treska Inc ....E 682 647-0352
Fort Worth *(G-7074)*

◆ Vf Sagebrush Enterprises LLC ......E 817 336-7201
Fort Worth *(G-7103)*

▲ Westmoor Corp ....E 817 625-2841
Fort Worth *(G-7142)*

▲ Westmoor Mfg Co ....E 817 625-2841
Fort Worth *(G-7143)*

2335 Women's & Misses' Dresses

David McNeff Inc ....F 972 562-0607
McKinney *(G-14935)*

G-III Apparel Group Ltd ....F 281 256-3661
Cypress *(G-3794)*

▲ Kathleen Sommers Designs Inc ......F 210 271-7118
San Antonio *(G-18217)*

Moll McNeill Inc ....G 214 748-7272
Dallas *(G-4684)*

Mulberry Heart I Ltd ....F 210 377-3335
San Antonio *(G-18325)*

▲ Sharon Young Inc ....E 214 349-1891
Dallas *(G-4953)*

Terry Costa Inc ....E 972 385-6100
Dallas *(G-5050)*

2337 Women's & Misses' Suits, Coats & Skirts

▲ Career Concepts Inc ....E 972 276-9332
Garland *(G-7453)*

Circle T Western Wear Ltd ....F 214 808-1100
Dallas *(G-4121)*

Ensemble Theatre ....F 713 520-0055
Houston *(G-9653)*

Leonard Sloan & Associates Inc ......F 214 350-2440
Dallas *(G-4591)*

▲ LEtoile Apparel Inc ....E 972 701-8916
Dallas *(G-3848)*

Moll McNeill Inc ....G 214 748-7272
Dallas *(G-4684)*

Pendleton Woolen Mills Inc ....F 903 581-7742
Tyler *(G-20139)*

2339 Women's & Misses' Outerwear, NEC

8228 Corporation ....E 713 465-1303
Houston *(G-8417)*

◆ Apparel Group Ltd ....C 214 469-3300
Lewisville *(G-14022)*

Asics America Corporation ....E 972 678-0200
Allen *(G-252)*

◆ B & J Accessories Inc ....E 972 494-6939
Frisco *(G-7269)*

B Bad Sports Inc ....E 713 664-3838
Houston *(G-8773)*

Boone Industries ....F 940 325-6215
Mineral Wells *(G-15519)*

▼ Charles De Vuae Inc ....E 713 789-8485
Houston *(G-9164)*

▲ Cheerleading Company Inc ....E 800 411-4105
Dallas *(G-4106)*

Conversation Pieces Inc ....G 409 762-2799
Galveston *(G-7394)*

Couture American Lifestyle ....F 972 487-1641
Garland *(G-7469)*

David McNeff Inc ....F 972 562-0607
McKinney *(G-14935)*

▲ Directors Assistant LLC ....F 972 816-5553
Dallas *(G-4261)*

Double D Ranchwear Inc ....F 361 293-9239
Yoakum *(G-20962)*

▲ Double D Ranchwear Inc ....F 361 293-2394
Yoakum *(G-20963)*

▲ Excel Garment Mfg Ltd ....C 915 544-5006
El Paso *(G-5760)*

▲ Fashion Works Inc ....F 972 596-5815
Plano *(G-16869)*

Fossil Partners LP ....B 972 234-2525
Richardson *(G-17314)*

Fossil Partners LP ....B 469 587-2627
Richardson *(G-17316)*

▲ Fossil Partners LP ....A 972 234-2525
Richardson *(G-17317)*

◆ FSI Apparel Inc ....E 562 906-3000
Southlake *(G-19070)*

Gmyp Manufacturing LLC ....F 682 313-3023
Farmers Branch *(G-6197)*

▲ Helens Heart LLC ....F 972 247-1414
Dallas *(G-4447)*

▲ I&G Designs and Logistics LLC ......F 214 543-4461
Dallas *(G-4481)*

▲ J Suzette & Company Inc ....F 972 359-0001
Allen *(G-279)*

▲ Jerell Clothing Company LLC ......F 214 349-1891
Dallas *(G-4532)*

▲ Jon Hart Design Co ....E 210 226-8544
San Antonio *(G-18206)*

▲ Kathleen Sommers Designs Inc ......F 210 271-7118
San Antonio *(G-18217)*

▲ LEtoile Apparel Inc ....E 972 701-8916
Dallas *(G-3848)*

Lululemon Athletica ....F 713 863-1280
Houston *(G-10701)*

Moll McNeill Inc ....G 214 748-7272
Dallas *(G-4684)*

Needleworks Etc ....F 432 445-9313
Pecos *(G-16624)*

Nsg Corporation ....C 972 840-1233
Plano *(G-16947)*

Nuvo Athletic LLC ....G 281 808-7650
Stafford *(G-19360)*

Rai of Sunshine LLC ....D 832 271-0144
Houston *(G-11534)*

REr Apparel Inc ....E 417 673-5786
Dallas *(G-3851)*

▲ Roka Sports Inc ....E 877 985-7652
Austin *(G-1470)*

▲ Ruddock Manufacturing Co Inc ......C 915 544-3530
El Paso *(G-5949)*

Southland Athletic Mfg Co ....D 972 563-3321
Terrell *(G-19751)*

Stitches Inc ....E 915 591-9260
El Paso *(G-5981)*

Tag Holdings Inc ....C 214 469-3300
The Colony *(G-19815)*

▲ Team Go Figure LLP ....E 972 276-6700
Dallas *(G-5043)*

Vf Outdoor LLC ....B 817 348-0567
Fort Worth *(G-7099)*

Vf Outdoor LLC ....B 830 278-2535
Uvalde *(G-20199)*

Vf Outdoor LLC ....A 817 336-7201
Fort Worth *(G-7100)*

Vf Outdoor LLC ....E 817 491-4949
Fort Worth *(G-7102)*

◆ Vf Sagebrush Enterprises LLC ......E 817 336-7201
Fort Worth *(G-7103)*

▲ Westmoor Corp ....E 817 625-2841
Fort Worth *(G-7142)*

▲ Westmoor Mfg Co ....E 817 625-2841
Fort Worth *(G-7143)*

World of Jeans & Tops ....F 806 788-1233
Lubbock *(G-14514)*

Zrc Ltd ....F 325 949-7625
San Angelo *(G-17843)*

2341 Women's, Misses' & Children's Underwear & Nightwear

Body Language Fashions Inc ....F 713 974-0960
Houston *(G-8936)*

▲ New Icm LP ....F 979 578-0543
El Campo *(G-5623)*

New ICM L P ....C 979 578-0543
El Campo *(G-5624)*

Shame Lingerie ....F 214 823-1454
Dallas *(G-4952)*

2342 Brassieres, Girdles & Garments

◆ Ce Soir Lingerie Co Inc ....D 512 953-4500
   Austin *(G-1035)*

Hanesbrands Inc ....F 254 582-7541
   Hillsboro *(G-8326)*

2353 Hats, Caps & Millinery

▲ Ahc Western Hatters Ltd Lblty ....E 940 872-2404
   Bowie *(G-2190)*

▲ Arena Brands Inc ....F 972 494-7133
   Garland *(G-7441)*

◆ Bio World Merchandising Inc ....C 972 488-0655
   Irving *(G-12948)*

Bollman Industries Inc ....E 325 655-0112
   San Angelo *(G-17784)*

C & C Western Wear Inc ....F 903 753-8991
   Longview *(G-14206)*

▲ Choice Cap Inc ....F 832 251-9551
   Houston *(G-9185)*

▲ Circle R Embroidery Co Inc ....E 214 741-1555
   Dallas *(G-4120)*

City Hatz/City Flagz ....D 214 376-2589
   Dallas *(G-4122)*

Federal Prison Industries ....F 972 287-4040
   Seagoville *(G-18800)*

Federal Prison Industries ....B 512 321-3903
   Bastrop *(G-1757)*

▲ Guard-Line Inc ....C 903 796-4111
   Atlanta *(G-843)*

▲ Master Hatters of Texas Inc ....F 972 864-5523
   Garland *(G-7544)*

Rhe Hatco Inc ....C 903 753-2631
   Longview *(G-14297)*

▲ Rhe Hatco Inc ....B 972 494-0511
   Garland *(G-7578)*

Rhe Hatco Inc ....B 972 494-0511
   Garland *(G-7579)*

Rockpoint Apparel Company ....F 713 699-9896
   Houston *(G-11651)*

Vanguard Resources Inc ....F 325 372-3142
   San Saba *(G-18720)*

2361 Children's & Infants' Dresses & Blouses

▲ Caseros Imports Inc ....F 972 247-1991
   Dallas *(G-4089)*

Ingamia Inc ....F 214 828-1660
   Dallas *(G-4499)*

Paty Investments Inc ....F 713 688-7686
   Houston *(G-11263)*

▲ Quatrefoil Partners LLC ....F 214 631-7117
   Dallas *(G-4848)*

Universal Kids LLC ....E 832 374-1082
   Kingwood *(G-13657)*

2369 Girls' & Infants' Outerwear, NEC

Asics America Corporation ....E 972 678-0200
   Allen *(G-252)*

Dallas Bias Fabrics Inc ....F 214 824-2036
   Dallas *(G-4212)*

▲ Excel Garment Mfg Ltd ....C 915 544-5006
   El Paso *(G-5760)*

▲ Headcovers Unlimited Inc ....F 281 334-4287
   League City *(G-13958)*

Ingamia Inc ....F 214 828-1660
   Dallas *(G-4499)*

▲ LEtoile Apparel Inc ....E 972 701-8916
   Dallas *(G-3848)*

Paty Investments Inc ....E 713 688-7686
   Houston *(G-11263)*

Tag Holdings Inc ....C 214 469-3300
   The Colony *(G-19815)*

▲ Team Go Figure LLP ....E 972 276-6700
   Dallas *(G-5043)*

◆ Vf Sagebrush Enterprises LLC ....E 817 336-7201
   Fort Worth *(G-7103)*

◆ Walls Industries LLC ....D 844 259-2557
   Fort Worth *(G-7118)*

▲ Westmoor Corp ....E 817 625-2841
   Fort Worth *(G-7142)*

▲ Westmoor Mfg Co ....E 817 625-2841
   Fort Worth *(G-7143)*

2371 Fur Goods

Europa Designs ....F 972 792-0997
   Dallas *(G-4336)*

2381 Dress & Work Gloves

▲ Guard-Line Inc ....C 903 796-4111
   Atlanta *(G-843)*

▲ Innovative Gloves & Safety LLC ....F 281 582-0700
   Houston *(G-10371)*

Premier Board Inc ....F 361 883-6553
   Corpus Christi *(G-3596)*

▲ Stanco Manufacturing Inc ....D 903 796-7936
   Atlanta *(G-845)*

2385 Waterproof Outerwear

Alamo Waterproofing Svcs Inc ....F 210 648-2100
   San Antonio *(G-17887)*

▲ Forum Industries Inc ....D 210 225-9600
   San Antonio *(G-18124)*

◆ Handgards LLC ....C 915 779-6606
   El Paso *(G-5794)*

Orc Industries Inc ....D 956 831-0618
   Brownsville *(G-2389)*

Precision Frac LLC ....F 855 967-1023
   Midland *(G-15362)*

◆ Walls Industries LLC ....D 844 259-2557
   Fort Worth *(G-7118)*

2386 Leather & Sheep Lined Clothing

C N A Inc ....E 915 533-2425
   El Paso *(G-5675)*

Distinctive Inds Texas Inc ....E 512 491-3500
   Austin *(G-1096)*

▲ Double J Saddlery Inc ....D 361 293-6364
   Yoakum *(G-20964)*

Wolf & Sons Design Inc ....E 512 237-3388
   Smithville *(G-18979)*

2387 Apparel Belts

◆ 3-D Belt Company LP ....E 979 743-4567
   Schulenburg *(G-18770)*

Brushy Creek Belt & Buckle Co ....F 361 293-2345
   Yoakum *(G-20960)*

▲ Circle Y Saddles Inc ....E 361 293-3501
   Yoakum *(G-20961)*

Cowtown Western Belt Inc ....E 817 625-4411
   Fort Worth *(G-6554)*

Lagarto Inc ....E 915 598-2668
   El Paso *(G-5837)*

Mallorys Western & Leather Sup ....F 817 558-0804
   Joshua *(G-13322)*

Maxims Imports Inc ....F 915 577-9228
   El Paso *(G-5870)*

Stallion Boot Co Inc ....E 915 532-6268
   El Paso *(G-5974)*

▲ Travis Assn For The Blind ....C 512 442-2329
   Austin *(G-1590)*

2389 Apparel & Accessories, NEC

▲ Athletic Sewing Center Inc ....E 210 681-9744
   San Antonio *(G-17920)*

▲ Band Mans Co Southwest Inc ....F 214 350-0631
   Dallas *(G-4003)*

Best Made Designs LLC ....E 432 943-9995
   Monahans *(G-15600)*

▲ Border Opprtnity Sver Systems ....E 830 775-1225
   Del Rio *(G-5308)*

▲ Bric Mc Mann Industries Inc ....F 830 775-9153
   Del Rio *(G-5309)*

▲ Cheerleading Company Inc ....E 800 411-4105
   Dallas *(G-4106)*

Claudia Rodriguez ....F 956 381-0845
   Edinburg *(G-5583)*

Cowan Costumes Inc ....F 817 641-3126
   Cleburne *(G-3085)*

▲ Directors Assistant LLC ....F 972 816-5553
   Dallas *(G-4261)*

Encompass Group LLC ....F 972 732-7694
   Addison *(G-120)*

Essential Safety Ppe LLC ....D 844 372-3377
   Spring *(G-19113)*

▲ Fossil Partners LP ....A 972 234-2525
   Richardson *(G-17317)*

Fossil Partners LP ....B 972 234-2525
   Richardson *(G-17314)*

Game Day Sports Apparel LLC ....E 214 499-0028
   Grapevine *(G-8037)*

▲ Gavson Inc ....E 214 341-0440
   Dallas *(G-4394)*

Guess Inc ....E 915 877-1948
   Canutillo *(G-2664)*

McCartney Investment Corp ....F 214 521-8410
   Dallas *(G-4659)*

▲ MJM Sourcing LLC ....F 214 769-7881
   Dallas *(G-4681)*

▲ Montana West USA ....F 972 241-9998
   Dallas *(G-4686)*

▲ MTC Marketing Inc ....E 972 488-0577
   Carrollton *(G-2782)*

New Purple LLC ....E 713 499-0422
   Houston *(G-11036)*

▲ Overton Enterprises LLC ....E 512 394-6089
   Austin *(G-1395)*

Parker School Uniforms LLC ....E 713 465-1635
   Houston *(G-11244)*

Privileged Culture LLC ....F 682 252-5173
   Arlington *(G-760)*

Radtke Jenna ....F 512 444-2002
   Austin *(G-1450)*

▲ Rebel Athletic Inc ....F 972 418-0827
   Carrollton *(G-2803)*

Rita Barber Inc ....F 325 698-0111
   Abilene *(G-73)*

Stitches Inc ....E 915 591-9260
   El Paso *(G-5981)*

▲ Techstyles Inc ....E 972 732-7694
   Addison *(G-167)*

Tripp Research Inc ....F 512 321-9445
   Bastrop *(G-1764)*

Vikay Group LLC ....F 512 291-8234
   Austin *(G-1634)*

Vlgc LLC ....E 817 926-5209
   Fort Worth *(G-7110)*

World of Jeans & Tops ....F 806 788-1233
   Lubbock *(G-14514)*

2391 Curtains & Draperies

Ascot Enterprises Inc ....F 254 582-1970
   Hillsboro *(G-8321)*

Austin Window Fashion Inc ....F 512 836-3388
   Austin *(G-967)*

▲ Bkbl Holdings Ltd ....F 214 436-4161
   Frisco *(G-7270)*

Boriack Interiors Inc ....E 214 376-1814
   Dallas *(G-4044)*

▼ CFS Brands LLC ....E 972 466-1030
   Flower Mound *(G-6262)*

Custom Drapery Company Inc ....D 713 225-9221
   Houston *(G-9370)*

Custom Rods & Draperies ....F 972 889-0580
   Richardson *(G-17295)*

Custom Work Room Services ....F 214 631-2795
   Dallas *(G-4197)*

D & D Drapery Company ....F 713 522-1643
   Houston *(G-9386)*

▲ Display Products Inc ....D 972 406-1221
   Dallas *(G-4262)*

Fresh Meadows Industries Inc ....E 713 464-9554
   Houston *(G-9865)*

Garland Drapery Inc ....F 972 276-5297
   Garland *(G-7493)*

Hc Interiors Inc ....F 214 350-0468
   Carrollton *(G-2754)*

Heines Custom Draperies Inc ....D 281 391-3103
   Katy *(G-13363)*

Horton Draperies of Texas Inc ....F 713 774-7477
   Houston *(G-10210)*

Kites Draperies Inc ....E 817 336-1027
   Fort Worth *(G-6764)*

Nsec LLC ....F 254 756-0651
   Lorena *(G-14343)*

Party Props Inc ....E 713 868-5433
   Houston *(G-11253)*

Perfect Windows Inc ....F 817 277-0014
   Arlington *(G-752)*

▲ Roland Curtains Inc ....F 817 607-0080
   Arlington *(G-772)*

◆ Tri-Tex Enterprises Inc ....E 214 744-1246
   Dallas *(G-5109)*

Tri-Tex Enterprises Inc ....D 214 744-1246
   Eastland *(G-5569)*

2392 House furnishings: Textile

American Dawn Inc ....F 713 670-8505
   Houston *(G-8593)*

Arden Companies Inc ....C 806 335-1147
   Amarillo *(G-400)*

Banyan Industries Inc ....E 817 413-7945
   Fort Worth *(G-6426)*

▲ Blazing Needles LP ....E 817 831-2668
   Fort Worth *(G-6457)*

Bronx Industries Inc ....G 713 467-6155
   Houston *(G-8994)*

Brunton International Inc ....E 214 638-4600
Dallas *(G-4063)*

Carpenter Co ....D 512 365-5833
Taylor *(G-19651)*

▼ CFS Brands LLC ....E 972 466-1030
Flower Mound *(G-6262)*

Childress Furniture & Fabr Inc ....E 214 565-0900
Addison *(G-109)*

▲ Clark Pillow Company ....E 409 842-5767
Beaumont *(G-1870)*

Creative MENus&folders LLC ....F 254 653-2775
Olden *(G-16219)*

▲ Display Products Inc ....D 972 406-1221
Dallas *(G-4262)*

◆ E R Carpenter LP ....C 804 359-0800
Temple *(G-19680)*

East Txas Lighthouse For Blind ....D 903 595-3444
Tyler *(G-20082)*

Easy Way Leisure Corporation ....C 956 831-6442
Brownsville *(G-2352)*

Encompass Group LLC ....F 972 732-7694
Addison *(G-120)*

◆ Glen Kammerman Enterprises Inc ...D 713 666-0602
Houston *(G-9963)*

Hobby Lobby Stores Inc ....F 214 872-3184
Frisco *(G-7290)*

▲ Home Treasures Inc ....E 713 937-7716
Houston *(G-10198)*

▲ Houston Wiper & Mill Supply Co ......F 713 672-0571
Houston *(G-10264)*

Ingrids Custom Hand Woven ....F 325 732-4370
Paint Rock *(G-16291)*

KS Little Shop ....F 214 371-4113
Dallas *(G-4571)*

◆ Ladds Corporation ....F 281 495-5200
Stafford *(G-19343)*

◆ Langes Legacy Home Ltd ....F 972 712-3949
Allen *(G-284)*

Le Ragge Ruggs Inc ....E 512 858-4186
Dripping Springs *(G-5508)*

◆ Loloi Inc ....C 972 503-5656
Dallas *(G-4602)*

Medline Industries Inc ....C 281 574-6200
Katy *(G-13371)*

Mozaic Company ....E 972 386-3332
Arlington *(G-733)*

◆ Nielsen & Bainbridge LLC ....E 512 506-3900
Austin *(G-1367)*

▲ Peacock Alley Inc ....D 214 744-0399
Dallas *(G-4793)*

Quality Table Linen Inc ....E 281 240-1024
Stafford *(G-19365)*

Quickie Manufacturing Corp ....D 915 859-2522
El Paso *(G-5923)*

S N D Manufacturing Ltd ....E 214 340-1592
Dallas *(G-4923)*

San Antonio Broom Factory Inc ....E 210 226-9762
San Antonio *(G-18446)*

Shelbis Stuff Inc ....F 903 450-1300
Greenville *(G-8091)*

▲ Sweet Dreams Inc ....D 956 687-2737
McAllen *(G-14909)*

Tabors of San Angelo Inc ....E 325 942-1696
San Angelo *(G-17830)*

Talalay Global Inc ....D 940 851-0107
Wichita Falls *(G-20814)*

▲ Techstyles Inc ....E 972 732-7694
Addison *(G-167)*

◆ Tri-Tex Enterprises Inc ....E 214 744-1246
Dallas *(G-5109)*

Tri-Tex Enterprises Inc ....D 214 744-1246
Eastland *(G-5569)*

Unifirst Corporation ....D 817 834-7386
Haltom City *(G-8160)*

◆ Wmc Waco Holdings Inc ....E 254 753-7301
Waco *(G-20479)*

2393 Textile Bags

▲ Athletic Bag Company LP ....E 903 520-3343
Tyler *(G-20051)*

▲ Bags Elite Inc ....E 972 279-7798
Mesquite *(G-15029)*

◆ Flying Circle Bag Co ....E 830 249-2480
Boerne *(G-2121)*

▲ Gulf Coast Bag Inc ....E 281 556-8500
Houston *(G-10057)*

◆ Kenneth Fox Supply Company ....C 956 682-6176
McAllen *(G-14882)*

Kerick Industries ....F 214 432-2446
Dallas *(G-4552)*

▲ Landes Inc ....E 713 665-0655
Houston *(G-10593)*

McAllen Bag & Supply Company ....F 956 686-6571
McAllen *(G-14887)*

◆ Polytex Fibers Corp ....C 713 690-9055
Houston *(G-11362)*

Southast Vcational Aliance Inc ....D 713 847-0697
Houston *(G-11969)*

▲ Starr Aircraft Products Inc ....C 903 893-1106
Sherman *(G-18933)*

2394 Canvas Prdts

All American Awnings Inc ....E 214 388-5444
Dallas *(G-3919)*

American Canvas Products Inc ....F 817 429-3108
Fort Worth *(G-6378)*

Aquila & Priscilla Tentmakers ....F 254 848-4432
Waco *(G-20363)*

Associated Canvas Pdts I Ltd ....F 281 457-1480
Channelview *(G-3012)*

▲ Athletic Bag Company LP ....E 903 520-3343
Tyler *(G-20051)*

◆ Awntech Corporation ....E 817 354-9600
Euless *(G-6132)*

C Cushions Inc ....F 361 729-1244
Rockport *(G-17527)*

C H V Corporation ....F 713 526-1347
Houston *(G-9029)*

Campbell Trailers & Leasing ....F 806 250-3611
Friona *(G-7251)*

Canvas USA Inc ....F 361 729-0638
Rockport *(G-17528)*

Carports Childers & Structures ....F 713 460-2181
Houston *(G-9094)*

Centex Manufacturing Co ....F 254 752-2531
Waco *(G-20379)*

▲ Coronet Enterprises Inc ....E 214 630-1116
Dallas *(G-4170)*

◆ Corradi USA Inc ....E 972 466-0721
Carrollton *(G-2860)*

Covercraft Industries Inc ....D 940 763-2535
Wichita Falls *(G-20757)*

Double C Canvas & Repairs Inc ....G 972 723-8000
Midlothian *(G-15479)*

Festive Tents LP ....F 713 468-3687
Houston *(G-9780)*

▲ Guard-Line Inc ....C 903 796-4111
Atlanta *(G-843)*

◆ Hendee Enterprises Inc ....D 713 796-2322
Houston *(G-10153)*

Hi-Plains Canvas Products Inc ....E 806 352-5345
Amarillo *(G-492)*

▲ Houston Canvas and Awning Co ......E 713 789-8712
Houston *(G-10222)*

Houston Truck Tarps LLC ....F 346 571-1832
Houston *(G-10259)*

Inpro Fabrication Ltd ....E 817 926-5050
Forest Hill *(G-6297)*

John C Maudlin Inc ....F 281 334-7224
Kemah *(G-13476)*

Jones Aluminum ....F 409 866-5585
Beaumont *(G-1913)*

Lift-All Company Inc ....E 281 445-2256
Houston *(G-10638)*

Lisco LLP ....F 806 762-5126
Lubbock *(G-14437)*

Marygrove Awning LLC ....E 713 697-0156
Houston *(G-10782)*

Matson Inc ....E 817 478-1800
Fort Worth *(G-6818)*

Mike Sandone Productions Inc ....E 800 652-5635
Dallas *(G-4677)*

Modern Shade LLC ....F 512 385-4100
Austin *(G-1349)*

Ohenry Productions Inc ....F 254 714-1103
Waco *(G-20440)*

Orc Industries Inc ....E 956 831-0618
Brownsville *(G-2389)*

Plumlee Place LLC ....F 254 662-4021
Robinson *(G-17501)*

Quest and Sons Inc ....E 806 744-2351
Lubbock *(G-14468)*

Reef Industries Inc ....D 956 399-1352
San Benito *(G-18663)*

Richmonds American Svc Ctr Inc ....F 972 681-2222
McKinney *(G-14971)*

Roche Rouge Company L L C ....F 512 326-1670
Austin *(G-1469)*

Shade Structures Inc ....G 214 905-9500
Dallas *(G-4951)*

Sign & Awning Services Inc ....E 817 926-7270
Fort Worth *(G-6987)*

Southwest Canvas Mfg Co ....F 806 747-0201
Lubbock *(G-14484)*

Southwest Tactical LLC ....C 915 726-0634
El Paso *(G-5972)*

Tarps LLC ....E 833 469-8277
Austin *(G-1714)*

Tent Company LLC ....E 832 623-8958
Houston *(G-12204)*

▲ Tents of Southwest Inc ....E 713 692-8565
Houston *(G-12205)*

Victory Awning Inc ....E 817 759-1600
Fort Worth *(G-7104)*

2395 Pleating & Stitching For The Trade

2logo Inc ....F 214 350-2505
Dallas *(G-3866)*

8228 Corporation ....E 713 465-1303
Houston *(G-8417)*

Action Screen Graphics ....F 512 478-6248
Austin *(G-886)*

Action Wear Plus Inc ....F 281 376-4300
Spring *(G-19098)*

Airmark Industries Inc ....E 325 641-1999
Brownwood *(G-2424)*

All Star Caps Inc ....E 210 509-9086
San Antonio *(G-17893)*

American Screen Graphics & EMB ......F 281 354-2581
Houston *(G-8609)*

Bear Paw Custom Embroidery LLC ...G 903 394-0722
Centerville *(G-3011)*

Bertrand Enterprises Inc ....F 409 833-0922
Beaumont *(G-1864)*

Bobs Monogram Embroidery ....F 210 341-6700
San Antonio *(G-17959)*

Bronx Industries Inc ....E 713 467-6155
Houston *(G-8994)*

▲ CC Creations Ltd ....C 979 693-9664
College Station *(G-3181)*

Century Graphics & Sign Inc ....E 432 686-8244
Midland *(G-15157)*

▲ Circle R Embroidery Co Inc ....E 214 741-1555
Dallas *(G-4120)*

Co Co MO Joes ....F 409 212-9892
Beaumont *(G-1871)*

Creative Stitches Inc ....E 817 284-0061
Fort Worth *(G-6559)*

Custom Chenille Embroidery Inc ....E 214 343-0888
Dallas *(G-4194)*

Davids Apparel Inc ....F 915 590-3744
El Paso *(G-5715)*

Dbs Group Inc ....F 817 453-8386
Grapevine *(G-8026)*

Doyle & Hamilton Inc ....F 817 882-8080
Fort Worth *(G-6592)*

Dragonfly Garment Design Corp ....G 830 549-5113
Seguin *(G-18836)*

Embroidery Concepts ....F 210 684-8362
San Antonio *(G-18089)*

Fiberco Inc ....F 682 647-1332
Fort Worth *(G-6628)*

Firestick Productions ....E 817 360-7740
Arlington *(G-679)*

G and G Investments Inc ....E 325 949-7864
San Angelo *(G-17801)*

Ghashim Capital Ventures Corp ....F 713 266-1888
Houston *(G-9949)*

Graham Embroidery Co Inc ....D 254 772-7020
Waco *(G-20407)*

H & R Black Mfg Co LLC ....F 806 364-2040
Hereford *(G-8290)*

Hudsons Embroidery ....E 210 224-5504
San Antonio *(G-18175)*

Innovative Impressions Inc ....E 817 838-6466
Fort Worth *(G-6721)*

J Harding & Co ....F 713 862-9855
Houston *(G-10440)*

Jj of Dallas Manufacturing Inc ....E 972 866-9866
Addison *(G-141)*

Jovi Printing ....F 713 467-4980
Houston *(G-10485)*

Kingdom Captain of Texas LLC ....F 210 535-9480
San Antonio *(G-18226)*

▲ Koza Inc ....G 281 485-1462
Pearland *(G-16574)*

Lamont Brands Inc ....G 281 286-7553
Houston *(G-10590)*

Leonard Sloan & Associates Inc ....F 214 350-2440
Dallas *(G-4591)*

Lugra Inc ....F 956 986-0958
Brownsville (G-2378)

McAllen Sports Inc ....E 956 687-5500
McAllen (G-14889)

▲ Miller Uniforms & Emblems Inc ......E 512 302-5541
Austin (G-1345)

Monograms & More ....F 979 693-7773
College Station (G-3194)

Mooney Saenger Enterprises ....F 512 869-0979
Georgetown (G-7665)

North Lean Ltd ....F 956 781-2029
Pharr (G-16709)

Plano Sports Soccer Inc ....F 972 519-0222
Plano (G-16974)

▲ Powers Embroidery Inc ....D 254 754-2498
Waco (G-20448)

Pro Digi Embroidery ....F 713 339-4373
Houston (G-11424)

Qti Promotions and Apparel Inc ....F 254 756-4444
Waco (G-20452)

Quilters Emporium LLC ....F 281 491-0016
Stafford (G-19366)

▲ Rivercity Sportswear LLC ....E 512 754-8039
San Marcos (G-18707)

San Bay Studio Inc ....F 940 387-4466
Denton (G-5399)

Sasch Inc ....F 214 388-7000
Dallas (G-4935)

Screened Images Inc ....F 979 260-9891
Bryan (G-2506)

SMA Distributors ....F 281 442-0890
Houston (G-11917)

Sports Magic Inc ....F 903 832-1975
Texarkana (G-19774)

SRI Monogramming Inc ....E 512 388-4989
Round Rock (G-17691)

Stephenville Printing Company ....E 254 968-3115
Stephenville (G-19425)

Stephenville Printing Company ....F 254 965-5012
Stephenville (G-19424)

Stitch Gallery Inc ....F 956 412-3087
Harlingen (G-8203)

Stitch Gallery Inc ....F 512 550-6172
Lakeway (G-13820)

Summit Sportswear Inc ....G 281 335-5370
League City (G-13980)

Tex Styles International Inc ....E 713 787-9955
Stafford (G-19384)

Texarkana EMB & Graphics ....F 903 792-1144
Texarkana (G-19778)

Texas 2 Stitch ....F 972 599-1717
Plano (G-17028)

Texas 28 LLC ....F 806 644-9663
Spearman (G-19088)

Threads In Motion ....F 972 422-4607
Plano (G-17032)

Uniform Concepts Inc ....F 512 345-5793
Austin (G-1607)

Uniforms Inc ....F 214 630-0924
Dallas (G-5132)

▲ Unlimited Custom Embroidery ....F 713 773-0111
Houston (G-12470)

Wearables Etc Inc ....F 713 339-1373
Houston (G-12609)

2396 Automotive Trimmings, Apparel Findings, Related Prdts

A 1 Distributors Sign Supply ....D 432 682-0083
Midland (G-15100)

Action Wear Plus Inc ....F 281 376-4300
Spring (G-19098)

Arcanum Corp ....F 214 507-3433
Carrollton (G-2857)

Austin Screen Printing Inc ....E 512 454-6249
Austin (G-961)

Beeville Publishing Company ....F 361 358-2550
Beeville (G-1984)

Bertrand Enterprises Inc ....F 409 833-0922
Beaumont (G-1864)

Big Star Branding Inc ....E 210 590-2662
San Antonio (G-17953)

Brammers Athletic Wearhouse LP ......F 281 391-1441
Katy (G-13390)

Brooks Industrial Coatings Inc ....F 512 990-5333
Austin (G-1012)

Campus Design Incorporated ....F 806 744-9998
Lubbock (G-14387)

Cenikor Foundation ....F 817 921-2771
Arlington (G-640)

Creative Signworks Inc ....E 850 785-8899
San Angelo (G-17792)

Dallas Bias Fabrics Inc ....E 214 824-2036
Dallas (G-4212)

Davids Apparel Inc ....F 915 590-3744
El Paso (G-5715)

Dcl America Inc ....F 281 651-5900
Conroe (G-3290)

▲ F & H Ribbon Company Inc ....D 817 283-5891
Euless (G-6145)

Fineline Sportswear Inc ....F 512 832-1441
Austin (G-1156)

Ghashim Capital Ventures Corp ....F 713 266-1888
Houston (G-9949)

▲ Grafikshop Corporation ....F 713 977-2555
Houston (G-10012)

Harvey Dupriest & Sons Inc ....D 214 337-4731
Dallas (G-4440)

Jackie Todaro ....F 281 354-2581
Kingwood (G-13646)

Jaropamex ....F 830 774-5920
Del Rio (G-5318)

Jj of Dallas Manufacturing Inc ....F 972 866-9866
Addison (G-141)

▲ Landes Inc ....E 713 665-0655
Houston (G-10593)

◆ Lone Star Special Tees LLC ....F 210 402-0091
San Antonio (G-18263)

◆ Lorente International LLC ....E 877 281-6469
Farmers Branch (G-6206)

▲ M & M Designs Inc ....F 936 295-2682
Huntsville (G-12817)

▲ M W Periscope Inc ....E 972 247-4202
Dallas (G-4622)

Mc Creless Company ....F 432 332-1213
Odessa (G-16076)

McDowell Packg & Advg Co Inc ....D 469 246-2700
Plano (G-16923)

Military Customs LLC ....F 254 699-8106
Harker Heights (G-8172)

ML Industries Inc ....G 956 279-8678
Fredericksburg (G-7186)

Monograms & More ....F 979 693-7773
College Station (G-3194)

North Lean Ltd ....F 956 781-2029
Pharr (G-16709)

▲ Pacifica T-Shirts Inc ....F 714 508-4848
Round Rock (G-17677)

Pan Ector Industries LLC ....F 940 566-1414
Denton (G-5389)

Pb Unlimited LLC ....F 817 831-4336
Haltom City (G-8156)

Positive Marketing (usa) Inc ....F 877 284-4488
Dallas (G-4813)

Revolution Screening Inc ....F 916 712-4458
Katy (G-13436)

Ritchie-Vincent Inc ....F 432 337-5133
Odessa (G-16142)

Screened Images Inc ....F 979 260-9891
Bryan (G-2506)

▲ Semasys Inc ....C 713 869-8331
Houston (G-11825)

Sports Magic Inc ....F 903 832-1975
Texarkana (G-19774)

Srg Ventures LLC ....E 281 214-8560
Houston (G-12030)

TNT Printing ....G 281 449-9090
Houston (G-12315)

▲ TST NA Trim Llc ....A 956 843-3500
Hidalgo (G-8310)

Uniforms Inc ....F 214 630-0924
Dallas (G-5132)

Versa Printing Inc ....F 972 243-5353
Dallas (G-5163)

W & W Silkscreening Inc ....E 817 590-4479
Fort Worth (G-7112)

Watermark Graphics Inc ....F 361 576-6874
Victoria (G-20319)

Wings Sportswear Inc ....D 210 696-1824
San Antonio (G-18622)

Your Ideas Inc ....F 325 673-5860
Abilene (G-96)

2397 Schiffli Machine Embroideries

Fiesta Graphics ....F 956 546-1722
Brownsville (G-2356)

Main Event Inc ....G 281 762-0854
Rosenberg (G-17589)

2399 Fabricated Textile Prdts, NEC

A B C Flag Acquisition Corp ....E 817 335-2548
Fort Worth (G-6336)

Armor Industrial Fabricators ....E 281 573-2777
Baytown (G-1779)

Banner Supply Inc ....F 713 802-2225
Houston (G-8814)

▲ Blacksheep Inc ....B 903 592-3853
Tyler (G-20059)

Complete Reprographics Inc ....F 915 779-5000
El Paso (G-5702)

▲ Dalco Athletic Lettering Inc ....D 903 201-6244
Corsicana (G-3669)

Dallas Flag & Flagpole Co Lc ....F 972 607-0958
Dallas (G-4216)

Design Center Signs Inc ....F 903 561-4995
Tyler (G-20075)

◆ Dixie Flag and Banner Company ......E 210 227-5039
San Antonio (G-18063)

▲ F & H Ribbon Company Inc ....D 817 283-5891
Euless (G-6145)

Houston North Sleep Center ....F 713 688-3188
Houston (G-10240)

Joyson Safety Systems ....E 830 703-7191
Del Rio (G-5319)

Kammok Gear LLC ....G 512 947-7344
Austin (G-1264)

▲ Mfi International Mfg LLC ....A 915 858-0971
El Paso (G-5876)

Military Customs LLC ....F 254 699-8106
Harker Heights (G-8172)

Multi-Quest Inc ....F 972 235-2356
Richardson (G-17361)

▲ Mustang Manufacturing Corp ....F 903 482-5666
Van Alstyne (G-20211)

Nationwide Pnnant Flag Mfg Inc ....C 210 684-3524
San Antonio (G-18337)

Pbr Inc ....E 830 401-4523
Seguin (G-18855)

▲ Powers Embroidery Inc ....D 254 754-2498
Waco (G-20448)

▲ Premier Emblem & Insignia Inc ....E 210 253-3406
San Antonio (G-18391)

Premier Uniform Inc ....F 210 253-3406
San Antonio (G-18392)

Qti Promotions and Apparel Inc ....F 254 756-4444
Waco (G-20452)

▲ Reliance Industries LLC ....E 281 930-8000
Deer Park (G-5290)

Screen Play Promotions Inc ....G 817 788-8608
Hurst (G-12858)

Sumehr Inc ....F 713 849-5528
Houston (G-12093)

Symonds Flags & Poles Inc ....E 214 596-1900
Fort Worth (G-7026)

▲ Texas Auto Trim ....F 713 661-5557
Houston (G-12221)

▲ Tk Holdings Inc ....D 210 509-0762
San Antonio (G-18552)

▲ Willingham Systems LLC ....D 713 928-3936
Houston (G-12671)

▲ Yj USA Corp ....F 877 927-8777
Addison (G-175)

ZF Passive Safety US Inc ....F 956 632-8100
Pharr (G-16718)

ZF Passive Safety US Inc ....B 734 582-1139
El Paso (G-6043)

24 LUMBER AND WOOD PRODUCTS, EXCEPT FURNITURE

2411 Logging

Batson Lumber Company LLC ....E 936 262-8000
Batson (G-1766)

Brocks Logging Inc ....E 281 593-1531
Cleveland (G-3121)

Cdw Consultant Group LLC ....E 361 237-9339
Bloomington (G-2111)

Cecil Phillips Lumber Mill ....F 903 684-3516
De Kalb (G-5236)

Colvin Timber Company LC ....F 936 563-4404
Livingston (G-14151)

Cypress River Logging Corp ....F 903 236-7696
Longview (G-14219)

D & L Timber Inc ....E 936 422-3153
Huntington (G-12809)

David Hatton Logging Inc ....G 409 656-8535
Hillister (G-8318)

S I C

Dean Due Logging Inc ... F ... 936 642-2782
Groveton *(G-8112)*
Dennis W Oates Logging LLC ... E ... 936 526-2700
Diboll *(G-5464)*
Dewayne Rogers Logging Inc ... F ... 936 831-2060
Apple Springs *(G-591)*
Don Lane Logging Inc ... G ... 409 584-2288
Pineland *(G-16738)*
Douglassville Timber Co ... G ... 903 796-7691
Atlanta *(G-842)*
Eld Operations LLC ... D ... 630 338-5425
Kermit *(G-13511)*
Flurry and Son Logging Contr ... F ... 409 384-5441
Jasper *(G-13275)*
Forrest Hodges Operations ... E ... 936 867-4910
Alto *(G-315)*
G & G Logging LLC ... E ... 936 269-9086
Joaquin *(G-13310)*
Hicks Post Co Inc ... E ... 936 858-4228
Alto *(G-316)*
Hlh Timber Company LLC ... E ... 936 269-4199
Joaquin *(G-13311)*
▲ Hollman Inc ... C ... 972 815-4000
Irving *(G-13058)*
Howard Croft ... F ... 936 258-3321
Dayton *(G-5229)*
Jan Pate Inc ... F ... 903 683-5700
Rusk *(G-17732)*
Jml Management Inc ... F ... 936 591-9782
Center *(G-3000)*
Keith Carrell Logging Inc ... E ... 936 422-3375
Huntington *(G-12810)*
Kim R Smith Logging Inc ... E ... 903 947-6242
Tatum *(G-19644)*
King Roy Jr Logging Inc ... F ... 936 563-4899
Livingston *(G-14158)*
Lindsay Forest Products Inc ... F ... 903 693-7526
Carthage *(G-2913)*
Ms Logging Inc ... F ... 409 382-2424
Bon Wier *(G-2149)*
Porterfield Timber Harvesting ... G ... 936 598-4203
Center *(G-3007)*
Procella Logging ... F ... 409 787-2325
Hemphill *(G-8247)*
Randy L Gardner Inc ... F ... 409 837-5111
Colmesneil *(G-3222)*
Red Watson Logging Inc ... F ... 409 565-2484
Wiergate *(G-20840)*
Renfro Logging I Ltd ... E ... 936 208-6177
Lufkin *(G-14550)*
Rhonda Griffin ... F ... 936 715-0735
Nacogdoches *(G-15712)*
Spurlock Logging Inc ... E ... 409 429-4333
Woodville *(G-20917)*
Stetson International LP ... G ... 281 592-4788
Cleveland *(G-3137)*
Teer Logging Inc ... F ... 936 632-6862
Lufkin *(G-14554)*
Texas Timberjack Inc ... D ... 409 397-4221
Bon Wier *(G-2151)*
W C Hodges Logging ... F ... 936 867-4550
Wells *(G-20658)*
Weyerhaeuser Company ... C ... 940 230-4670
Denton *(G-5412)*
Williams Logging ... F ... 936 632-6891
Lufkin *(G-14556)*

2421 Saw & Planing Mills

Adam Nerren Ltd ... G ... 936 422-4800
Huntington *(G-12808)*
Agri Wood Products Inc ... G ... 254 709-6584
Waco *(G-20356)*
Agri-Tex Wood Shavings Co LLC ... F ... 936 628-1950
Shepherd *(G-18899)*
Allen and Allen LLC ... D ... 210 733-9191
San Antonio *(G-17894)*
Allied Truss LLC ... E ... 903 586-1982
Jacksonville *(G-13225)*
American Wholesale Lbr & Mfg ... E ... 281 342-7020
Needville *(G-15762)*
American Wood Fibers Inc ... E ... 903 923-8700
Marshall *(G-14761)*
Breco Trucking Inc ... E ... 903 870-0396
Sherman *(G-18908)*
Builders Firstsource Inc ... E ... 956 755-0301
Mercedes *(G-15004)*
Builders Firstsource Inc ... E ... 214 880-3500
Dallas *(G-4066)*
Builders Firstsource-Ohio Vall ... C ... 214 880-3500
Dallas *(G-4067)*
▲ Bwf Enterprises Inc ... D ... 972 875-8391
Ennis *(G-6089)*
C & C Wood Company Inc ... F ... 361 865-3444
Waelder *(G-20482)*
Cadre Timber Products Inc ... E ... 409 246-3573
Kountze *(G-13669)*
Cal-Tex Lumber Company Inc ... C ... 936 564-6426
Nacogdoches *(G-15688)*
Carrizo Wood Products Inc ... E ... 936 569-0582
Nacogdoches *(G-15690)*
Carthage Hardwoods LLC ... F ... 903 693-9300
Carthage *(G-2903)*
Cecil Phillips Lumber Mill ... F ... 903 684-3516
De Kalb *(G-5236)*
Cedar Supply Inc ... E ... 972 242-6561
Carrollton *(G-2711)*
Clw Inc ... D ... 281 592-4691
Cleveland *(G-3123)*
Conner Industries Inc ... E ... 817 439-3555
Fort Worth *(G-6541)*
Conner Industries Inc ... E ... 956 781-0215
Alamo *(G-178)*
Cypress Lumber Company Inc ... F ... 903 572-6561
Mount Pleasant *(G-15649)*
Eason Properties I LLC ... G ... 409 945-4416
Texas City *(G-19789)*
Fivepayne LLC ... F ... 817 310-0907
Mansfield *(G-14673)*
Forest Nix Industries Inc ... E ... 936 254-2441
Timpson *(G-19948)*
Forest Ogletree Products Inc ... E ... 936 327-2424
Livingston *(G-14155)*
G & S Lumber Co Inc ... E ... 936 564-7676
Nacogdoches *(G-15699)*
G D Edgar Lumber Co Inc ... F ... 409 787-2452
Hemphill *(G-8246)*
Gary Sanvig ... G ... 903 885-7956
Sulphur Springs *(G-19588)*
Georgia-Pacific LLC ... C ... 817 625-9091
Fort Worth *(G-6665)*
Georgia-Pacific LLC ... D ... 940 205-9558
Denton *(G-5368)*
Georgia-Pacific WD Pdts S LLC ... A ... 936 398-2511
Camden *(G-2638)*
Hicks Post Co Inc ... E ... 936 858-4228
Alto *(G-316)*
Idaho Timber of Texas LLC ... D ... 817 293-1001
Fort Worth *(G-6714)*
K L Barton & Sons Tie Co ... F ... 936 347-2744
Garrison *(G-7611)*
Koppers Inc ... D ... 979 596-1321
Somerville *(G-19022)*
L & R Timber Company Inc ... E ... 936 275-9701
San Augustine *(G-18651)*
Lincoln Lumber LLC ... E ... 409 384-2587
Jasper *(G-13278)*
Lincoln Lumber LLC ... D ... 936 539-4421
Conroe *(G-3321)*
Long Beach Shavings Co Inc ... F ... 936 231-4400
Conroe *(G-3325)*
▲ Lufkin Creosoting Co Inc ... D ... 936 634-2211
Lufkin *(G-14537)*
Mg Building Materials Ltd ... B ... 210 924-8604
San Antonio *(G-18298)*
Oliver Brothers Sawmill ... G ... 936 295-0931
Huntsville *(G-12821)*
Quality Mill of Texas LLC ... F ... 409 722-4594
Beaumont *(G-1945)*
Rocla Concrete Tie Inc ... E ... 806 383-7071
Amarillo *(G-459)*
Rogers Lumber Co Inc ... E ... 409 745-1953
Orange *(G-16258)*
Ross Lumber Ltd ... E ... 936 254-2575
Timpson *(G-19949)*
Sawmill Partners LLC ... E ... 214 358-2314
Dallas *(G-4939)*
▲ Snider Industries LLP ... D ... 903 938-9221
Marshall *(G-14803)*
Southern Forest Products LLC ... D ... 409 634-3365
Bon Wier *(G-2150)*
Spivey Stake & Supply Inc ... E ... 903 822-3888
Mount Enterprise *(G-15645)*
Steely Lumber Co Inc ... D ... 936 295-5898
Huntsville *(G-12824)*
Texas Priming LLC ... G ... 903 893-6200
Sherman *(G-18936)*
Texas Timberjack Inc ... D ... 409 397-4221
Bon Wier *(G-2151)*
Thick n Thin Lumber Co Inc ... F ... 281 592-0437
Cleveland *(G-3139)*
W W Wood Inc ... E ... 830 569-2501
Pleasanton *(G-17076)*
Warner Bailey Inc ... F ... 936 867-4801
Alto *(G-318)*
West Fraser Inc ... C ... 903 657-4575
Henderson *(G-8277)*
West Fraser Inc ... C ... 903 628-2506
New Boston *(G-15770)*
Woodville Hardwoods ... E ... 409 283-6106
Woodville *(G-20920)*

2426 Hardwood Dimension & Flooring Mills

▲ Ace Hardwood Flooring Inc ... F ... 512 719-3555
West Lake Hills *(G-20676)*
▲ Ameripro Partnership LP ... F ... 713 526-3936
Houston *(G-8620)*
Brazos Forest Products LP ... E ... 512 443-0777
Austin *(G-1006)*
Building Plastics Inc ... E ... 713 896-9001
Houston *(G-9015)*
C & L Millwork Inc ... G ... 817 605-0002
Haltom City *(G-8133)*
Camino Real Community Mhmr Ctr ... F ... 830 276-8578
Poteet *(G-17194)*
Caney Creek Moulding Inc ... E ... 936 560-1331
Nacogdoches *(G-15689)*
Cecil Phillips Lumber Mill ... F ... 903 684-3516
De Kalb *(G-5236)*
Clarks Hardwood Lumber Co LP ... F ... 713 862-6628
Houston *(G-9211)*
Conner Industries Inc ... E ... 956 781-0215
Alamo *(G-178)*
Connor Sports Flooring LLC ... F ... 817 944-0269
Southlake *(G-19061)*
▲ Custom Floors Unlimited Inc ... D ... 713 861-4139
Houston *(G-9372)*
▲ Diamond Living LLC ... F ... 281 766-1600
Magnolia *(G-14600)*
Dycem Corporation ... F ... 832 447-1420
The Woodlands *(G-19855)*
◆ Elkcorp ... E ... 972 851-0500
Dallas *(G-4313)*
G & S Lumber Co Inc ... E ... 936 564-7676
Nacogdoches *(G-15699)*
G D Edgar Lumber Co Inc ... F ... 409 787-2452
Hemphill *(G-8246)*
Industrial Lumber and Box Inc ... F ... 713 928-2096
Houston *(G-10351)*
Jellison Inc ... E ... 512 282-5256
Manchaca *(G-14639)*
K L Barton & Sons Tie Co ... F ... 936 347-2744
Garrison *(G-7611)*
Lindseys NW Off Furn Inc ... E ... 713 957-2424
Houston *(G-10647)*
◆ MJB Wood Group LLC ... E ... 972 401-0005
Coppell *(G-3428)*
Plano Synergy Holding Inc ... E ... 469 733-1868
Grand Prairie *(G-7946)*
Quality Mat Company ... F ... 713 455-3990
Houston *(G-11496)*
▲ Rbt Industries LLC ... F ... 512 600-5994
Austin *(G-1453)*
▲ Regal Hardwoods Inc ... F ... 972 620-8833
Carrollton *(G-2804)*
▼ Rodco-Brandt Manufacturing ... E ... 817 477-4118
Mansfield *(G-14713)*
Southern Forest Products LLC ... D ... 409 634-3365
Bon Wier *(G-2150)*
Ually LLC ... E ... 936 252-7476
Euless *(G-6164)*
▼ Ufp New Waverly LLC ... D ... 936 295-3411
New Waverly *(G-15861)*
Unique Wood Products Inc ... F ... 713 462-5045
Houston *(G-12441)*
Venetian Blind Flr Cvg Sp Ltd ... E ... 713 528-2404
Houston *(G-12546)*
▲ Walls & Forms Inc ... D ... 972 745-0800
Fort Worth *(G-7117)*
West Fraser Inc ... C ... 903 628-2506
New Boston *(G-15770)*
▲ Woodco Millwork Ltd ... F ... 210 298-9663
San Antonio *(G-18624)*
▲ Woodwright Hardwood Flr Co Inc ... E ... 214 630-8811
Dallas *(G-5202)*

2429 Special Prdt Sawmills, NEC

American Excelsior Company ... E ... 817 385-4300
Arlington *(G-616)*
Giles Efton ... E ... 210 662-2800
San Antonio *(G-18140)*

2431 Millwork

A & E Venetian Blind Company ....F 940 767-1449
Wichita Falls *(G-20735)*

A C N Millwork Corp ....F 713 649-6015
Houston *(G-8425)*

A E S Custom Wood Inc ....G 972 262-0755
Grand Prairie *(G-7816)*

AAA Woodwork ....F 713 935-0002
Houston *(G-8437)*

Abilene Mill Work ....F 325 677-8856
Abilene *(G-5)*

Abuata Enterprises Inc ....E 281 969-7947
Stafford *(G-19280)*

Aim Solar Screens Inc ....F 281 997-1543
Pearland *(G-16538)*

Alexander Moulding Mill Co ....D 254 386-3187
Hamilton *(G-8164)*

Alfonso Hinostroza ....E 956 781-1845
San Juan *(G-18670)*

Allstar Door & Maintenance LP ....F 817 748-0667
Colleyville *(G-3210)*

American Eagle Enteprise ....F 972 494-3357
Garland *(G-7434)*

Architctral Interiors By Salas ....F 210 733-1269
San Antonio *(G-17913)*

Artisans Cabinetry & Woodwork ....D 512 626-7311
Georgetown *(G-7636)*

▲ Atrium Windows and Doors Inc ....D 214 583-1840
Dallas *(G-3983)*

Austins Cabinets & Cnstr ....F 281 987-3308
Houston *(G-8751)*

Autumnwood Millworks LLC ....F 936 344-9784
New Waverly *(G-15853)*

AW Installers Inc ....E 210 649-1618
Adkins *(G-176)*

◆ Awntech Corporation ....E 817 354-9600
Euless *(G-6132)*

▲ Basileia Investments Inc ....C 806 765-5791
Lubbock *(G-14365)*

Bear Custom Moulding Inc ....F 940 686-5547
Pilot Point *(G-16722)*

Bee Builders Supply Inc ....E 972 422-4960
Plano *(G-16801)*

Betban Investments LLC ....F 254 776-2243
Waco *(G-20367)*

▲ Blue Streak LLC ....G 940 440-2105
Aubrey *(G-848)*

BMC Millwork ....F 512 456-2000
Cedar Park *(G-2962)*

BMC Stock Holdings Inc ....C 972 606-6200
Grand Prairie *(G-7847)*

BMC West LLC ....E 806 747-1580
Lubbock *(G-14376)*

BMC West LLC ....E 817 952-3124
Hurst *(G-12840)*

BMC West LLC ....D 325 698-4465
Abilene *(G-18)*

Boa Studio LLC ....F 210 314-4547
Schertz *(G-18745)*

Bochelle Inc ....F 972 837-1080
McKinney *(G-14928)*

Brownsvlle Architectural Mllwk ....E 956 592-5423
Brownsville *(G-2341)*

Brycon Inc ....E 817 444-2724
Weatherford *(G-20580)*

Buda Woodworks LLC ....D 512 312-0550
Buda *(G-2521)*

Buffalo Creek Millwork Inc ....E 972 938-2392
Waxahachie *(G-20530)*

Builders Firstsource Inc ....E 956 755-0301
Mercedes *(G-15004)*

◆ Builders Firstsource - SE Grp ....D 214 880-3500
Dallas *(G-4065)*

Builders Firstsource Inc ....E 214 880-3500
Dallas *(G-4066)*

Builders Firstsource-Ohio Vall ....C 214 880-3500
Dallas *(G-4067)*

C M Trautschold Millwork Co ....E 254 752-6547
Waco *(G-20374)*

Campbell Millwork LLC ....F 210 349-9294
San Antonio *(G-17978)*

Capital Hardwoods & Mllwk LLC ....F 210 657-1200
San Antonio *(G-17980)*

Cedar Mill Co Inc ....E 713 984-2600
Houston *(G-9116)*

Centerpoint Productions Inc ....E 214 905-0000
Carrollton *(G-2712)*

Central Hardwoods Inc ....E 972 241-3571
Dallas *(G-4098)*

Central Millwork LLC ....E 925 963-5448
Dallas *(G-4100)*

Century Millwork LLC ....E 281 821-0191
Houston *(G-9142)*

Circle c Millwork Inc ....E 210 649-1228
San Antonio *(G-18007)*

Clarks Hardwood Lumber Co LP ....F 713 862-6628
Houston *(G-9211)*

Classic Doors Systems Co ....F 214 678-9555
Dallas *(G-4128)*

▲ Claytex Trophies Inc ....C 940 538-6521
Henrietta *(G-8279)*

▼ Clifton Moulding Corp ....D 877 882-1803
Clifton *(G-3143)*

Cmcs Group LLC ....F 972 647-6260
Grand Prairie *(G-7854)*

Coen Furniture Inc ....E 281 983-0100
Houston *(G-9237)*

Cokers Doors & Mouldings Inc ....F 409 727-4600
Nederland *(G-15750)*

Coleman Wood Products Inc ....E 940 440-2300
Aubrey *(G-849)*

Complete Woodworks Inc ....G 830 992-3163
Fredericksburg *(G-7174)*

Computerized Millwork Svcs Inc ....F 281 575-1699
Houston *(G-9265)*

Concierge Renovation Company ....F 940 458-3075
Sanger *(G-18724)*

Cook & Boardman Group LLC ....E 214 630-3965
Dallas *(G-4165)*

Coppell Woodworks Inc ....F 940 482-8900
Richardson *(G-17292)*

◆ Corradi USA Inc ....E 972 466-0721
Carrollton *(G-2860)*

Crc/Mastercraft Inc ....E 281 897-8880
Houston *(G-9338)*

Creative Wood Concepts Inc ....F 972 539-2555
Dallas *(G-4184)*

Custom Door Company Inc ....E 940 686-4500
Pilot Point *(G-16724)*

Custom Shutters Inc ....E 903 488-3224
Como *(G-3248)*

Dallas Fort Wrth Fyrestone LLC ....E 817 429-0999
Fort Worth *(G-6573)*

Daniels Terry Cstm Trim Mllwk ....F 817 295-6750
Fort Worth *(G-6575)*

Delta Millwork ....E 713 849-2281
Houston *(G-9432)*

Denton Door Company Inc ....F 940 891-0600
Denton *(G-5358)*

Design Woodworks ....E 713 478-7397
Sugar Land *(G-19478)*

Detering Company of Houston LP ....C 713 869-3761
Houston *(G-9446)*

Devos Custom Woodworking ....F 512 894-0464
Dripping Springs *(G-5504)*

Dimension Millworks Inc ....E 210 281-0356
San Antonio *(G-18061)*

▲ Distinctive Doors Inc ....E 972 487-6680
Wylie *(G-20933)*

Door Center ....F 713 932-9343
Houston *(G-9497)*

Door Sa-Lutions Inc ....F 915 781-0664
El Paso *(G-5723)*

Dovetail Custom Woodworks Inc ....E 512 501-6717
Del Valle *(G-5330)*

Edwards Michael Custom ....E 210 651-3800
San Antonio *(G-18641)*

El Paso Wood Products Inc ....F 915 545-2974
El Paso *(G-5747)*

Elite Staircases LLC ....F 512 466-6590
Round Rock *(G-17651)*

◆ Elkcorp ....E 972 851-0500
Dallas *(G-4313)*

Evans Cabinet and Door Ltd ....E 979 836-6934
Brenham *(G-2253)*

Faifer Arlin D Woodmill Co ....F 830 216-4189
Floresville *(G-6247)*

◆ Faubion Associates Inc ....C 214 565-1000
Dallas *(G-4355)*

FC Dsigns Qulty WD Work Corp ....F 713 462-1442
Houston *(G-9767)*

Fox John ....E 915 755-0080
El Paso *(G-5773)*

Foxworth-Galbraith Lumber Co ....D 972 665-2400
Plano *(G-16872)*

Freedom Architectural Millwork ....F 281 592-5377
Cleveland *(G-3125)*

Genesis Millwork LLC ....E 469 402-3940
Garland *(G-7501)*

Georgetown Woodworks LLC ....E 512 868-9048
Georgetown *(G-7653)*

Georgia-Pacific LLC ....D 940 205-9558
Denton *(G-5368)*

▲ Glasscraft Door Mfg Corp ....C 713 690-8282
Houston *(G-9962)*

Green Wood Milling LLC ....E 210 544-5777
San Antonio *(G-18153)*

Grenier Service Company Llc ....E 512 335-7441
Cedar Park *(G-2972)*

Growth-Holdings LLC ....E 972 241-9535
Dallas *(G-4418)*

Gunckel Archtectural Millworks ....E 830 303-0688
Seguin *(G-18839)*

Gunter Lumber Company Inc ....E 903 433-1303
Gunter *(G-8115)*

Hardwood Products & Doors Inc ....F 512 259-3094
Leander *(G-13991)*

Hayes Carpentry L L C ....F 713 944-2608
South Houston *(G-19044)*

Hoffman Ventures Inc ....F 281 339-2812
Bacliff *(G-1732)*

Homestead Heritage ....E 254 754-9665
Waco *(G-20416)*

▲ House of Forgings LLC ....E 281 443-4848
Houston *(G-10216)*

▲ Houston Shutters LLC ....B 713 723-7100
Houston *(G-10251)*

Hull Historical Inc ....E 817 332-1495
Fort Worth *(G-6708)*

Hunter Millworks Inc ....E 806 792-4864
Lubbock *(G-14421)*

◆ Iatid Inc ....E 210 698-8500
Universal City *(G-20182)*

Ikg Usa LLC ....D 281 452-6637
Houston *(G-10320)*

Independent Door Co Inc ....F 972 487-0511
Garland *(G-7518)*

Innovative Millwork Systems ....E 972 869-9892
Dallas *(G-4503)*

▲ International Wood LLC ....C 956 969-8666
Weslaco *(G-20660)*

J & H Manufacturing Inc ....E 830 665-5230
Devine *(G-5450)*

J Waters Inc ....F 502 896-0850
Ennis *(G-6108)*

◆ Jackson Deerfield Mfg Corp ....E 972 233-7513
Dallas *(G-4521)*

▲ Jason Jones ....F 903 753-6045
Longview *(G-14256)*

JC Millwork Inc ....C 469 702-2570
Flower Mound *(G-6269)*

Jeld-Wen Inc ....D 972 623-1727
Grand Prairie *(G-7902)*

Jeld-Wen Inc ....E 972 272-3667
Garland *(G-7526)*

Jenkins Fabco Inc ....F 806 372-4336
Amarillo *(G-443)*

Ken Jordan Shutters Inc ....F 972 241-7776
Dallas *(G-4549)*

Kikers Machine Works Inc ....F 432 381-8142
Odessa *(G-16052)*

Kings Ltd ....E 830 990-0565
Fredericksburg *(G-7185)*

Kitchen Bath Cbinets Doors Inc ....E 915 852-0499
El Paso *(G-5830)*

Koehler Co ....E 830 303-6256
Seguin *(G-18848)*

Kurt Lupo ....F 903 599-3181
Streetman *(G-19434)*

L J Smith Inc ....F 713 462-4653
Houston *(G-10574)*

Latham Stairs & Millworks Inc ....E 940 458-3075
Fort Worth *(G-6781)*

Legant Interior Inc ....E 713 784-2647
Houston *(G-10621)*

Liberty Company ....E 817 921-0218
Fort Worth *(G-6788)*

Luna Piena Inc ....E 512 926-6346
Austin *(G-1311)*

Lundy Services LLC ....E 972 494-2554
Garland *(G-7539)*

Lutz Woodworks Llc ....E 972 429-5521
Wylie *(G-20940)*

Maintenance Builders Sup Ltd ....E 713 462-8213
Houston *(G-10741)*

Martin Pedraza ....E 281 814-3916
Spring *(G-19144)*

Martinez Millworks Inc ....F 281 988-9334
Houston *(G-10779)*

S I C

▲ Masonite International ....G...... 972 686-5500
Mesquite (G-15061)

Masonite International Corp ....E...... 903 454-9500
Greenville (G-8084)

Masonite International Corp ....D...... 972 686-5500
Dallas (G-4643)

Masons Mill & Lumber Co Inc ....D...... 713 462-6975
Houston (G-10785)

Maverick Door and Millwork Inc ....F...... 210 659-5553
Schertz (G-18755)

McCoy Corporation ....E...... 956 618-3104
McAllen (G-14890)

McFadden Stairs Inc ....F...... 972 680-8333
Richardson (G-17354)

Megatrend Designs Inc ....F...... 713 675-8838
Houston (G-10823)

Mg Doors & More LLC ....F...... 972 291-4389
Cedar Hill (G-2948)

Mgc Inc ....C...... 713 800-7300
Houston (G-10863)

▲ Millsource Inc ....F...... 281 372-0311
Houston (G-10884)

Millwork Solutions Ltd ....E...... 817 473-3934
Mansfield (G-14696)

Morgan Trim Inc ....F...... 806 655-9777
Canyon (G-2674)

Mpr Products Inc ....F...... 713 493-0252
Houston (G-10930)

Nailit Millwork Inc ....E...... 210 633-4659
San Antonio (G-18328)

NC Group Inc ....E...... 281 459-9418
Houston (G-11014)

Nfs Inc ....F...... 915 584-1440
El Paso (G-5895)

Nightngale Archtctral Dors Inc ....G...... 972 875-1134
Ennis (G-6113)

▲ Nmg Workspace Solutions LLC .....E...... 281 240-1007
Houston (G-11061)

◆ Overhead Door Corporation ....C...... 469 549-7100
Lewisville (G-14080)

Overhead Door Corporation ....B...... 361 884-6640
Corpus Christi (G-3586)

Overhead Door Corporation ....D...... 214 630-4669
Dallas (G-4773)

Pacific Columns ....F...... 714 257-9600
Rockwall (G-17557)

Panel-Tech Incorporated ....E...... 713 896-6900
Houston (G-11230)

Paramount Millwork Corporation ....E...... 817 429-1145
Fort Worth (G-6894)

▲ Patterson Manufacturing Inc ....F...... 903 757-0523
Longview (G-14288)

Patton Manufactured Pdts LP ....E...... 512 918-3737
Austin (G-1401)

Pavliska Cabinets Inc ....F...... 254 773-4461
Troy (G-20032)

Petroplex Cabinets Inc ....G...... 432 333-2025
Odessa (G-16121)

Phoenix Millwork LLC ....D...... 281 388-2211
Alvin (G-377)

Pioneer Mill Works Inc ....F...... 806 622-3201
Amarillo (G-505)

Pioneer Millwork Inc ....F...... 806 622-3100
Amarillo (G-506)

Plumbline Inc ....F...... 713 462-9500
Houston (G-11350)

Ply Gem Industries Inc ....C...... 979 361-3514
Bryan (G-2498)

Progressive Components Inc ....F...... 972 775-6932
Midlothian (G-15491)

Progressive Millworks Inc ....D...... 512 832-0551
Austin (G-1436)

R&R Millwork Inc ....E...... 903 873-6600
Wills Point (G-20876)

RDHS Inc ....F...... 361 852-4094
Corpus Christi (G-3606)

▲ Renlita Doors North Amer LLC ....E...... 903 583-7500
Bonham (G-2154)

Robert K Dean ....F...... 713 681-2218
Houston (G-11642)

Robert Shaw Mfg Co Inc ....E...... 817 927-2557
Fort Worth (G-6962)

◆ Rollac Shutter of Texas Inc ....D...... 281 485-1911
Pearland (G-16596)

◆ Sanwa Usa Inc ....E...... 972 503-3031
Plano (G-17002)

Sasa Molding LLC ....E...... 915 726-9290
El Paso (G-5952)

Saw Custom Millwork Inc ....E...... 972 288-2118
Mesquite (G-15076)

▲ Screenfab LLC ....E...... 972 438-2860
Irving (G-13173)

Select Millwork Inc ....F...... 972 445-8287
Irving (G-13175)

Shade Shop Inc ....G...... 713 623-0750
Houston (G-11844)

Shepherd Shutter Company Inc ....G...... 806 799-3458
Lubbock (G-14478)

Showcase Windows & Doors Inc ....F...... 713 926-8500
Houston (G-11875)

Shutter Source Inc ....F...... 281 403-2012
Stafford (G-19378)

Signature Arch & Blind ....E...... 281 469-2500
Houston (G-11893)

▲ Signature Mldngs Millworks Inc .....E...... 210 967-8400
San Antonio (G-18474)

Signature Partners Ltd ....E...... 210 967-8400
San Antonio (G-18475)

Singleton Mouldings Inc ....F...... 254 559-7541
Breckenridge (G-2237)

South Texas Moulding Inc ....F...... 361 857-7770
Corpus Christi (G-3625)

South Texas Moulding Inc ....F...... 956 464-0560
Donna (G-5492)

Southern Forest Products LLC ....D...... 409 634-3365
Bon Wier (G-2150)

Specialty Woood Mouldings Inc ....F...... 254 642-3835
Rogers (G-17574)

Stair Solutions LLC ....F...... 972 347-5151
Prosper (G-17216)

▼ Stairways Inc ....E...... 713 680-3110
Houston (G-12039)

Steve Gibson ....F...... 713 937-8838
Houston (G-12061)

Steves & Sons Inc ....D...... 210 924-5111
San Antonio (G-18506)

Sunshine Custom Cabinets Inc ....F...... 817 572-5201
Fort Worth (G-7023)

Tewa LLC ....E...... 915 886-9973
Vinton (G-20341)

Texarkana Door & Window Inc ....F...... 903 793-6011
Texarkana (G-19777)

Texas Cabinet Inc ....F...... 972 293-2450
Cedar Hill (G-2953)

▲ Texas Fixtures and Interiors ....D...... 512 846-1998
Hutto (G-12886)

Texas Home & Projects LLC ....G...... 956 546-8400
Brownsville (G-2410)

Texas Timberjack Inc ....D...... 409 397-4221
Bon Wier (G-2151)

The Terrill Mfg Co Inc ....D...... 325 655-7133
San Angelo (G-17833)

Titan Solutions ....F...... 281 973-9653
Houston (G-12298)

Travis Millwork Inc ....F...... 210 525-8088
San Antonio (G-18564)

Trimco Master Millwork Inc ....F...... 915 855-8501
El Paso (G-6016)

Trinity Stairs Inc ....F...... 972 335-0700
Frisco (G-7320)

TWC Architectural Moldings Ltd ....F...... 210 662-2800
San Antonio (G-18573)

Unique Woodworks Inc ....E...... 940 686-5547
Pilot Point (G-16732)

US Remodelers Inc ....E...... 214 488-6300
Lewisville (G-14103)

◆ Vision Products Inc ....C...... 830 755-4719
San Antonio (G-18595)

Water Street Millworks Inc ....G...... 512 321-5741
Bastrop (G-1765)

Wessely-Thompson Hardware Inc ....E...... 210 344-3081
San Antonio (G-18614)

West Texas Chaptr of Archtctrl ....E...... 915 833-9922
El Paso (G-6030)

▲ Window Outfitters LP ....E...... 469 619-0892
Dallas (G-5193)

Wingate Archtectural Millworks ....E...... 936 560-1040
Nacogdoches (G-15718)

Woodhaus Inc ....D...... 972 245-8117
Carrollton (G-2850)

Woodshop of Texas Ltd ....E...... 409 938-7875
Texas City (G-19807)

Zamo Inc ....E...... 210 667-1717
Saint Hedwig (G-17761)

2434 Wood Kitchen Cabinets

3 L Designs Inc ....E...... 214 920-9223
Dallas (G-3867)

3 Star Custom Cabinets Inc ....F...... 940 686-2124
Pilot Point (G-16720)

34 Oaks Fine Cabinetry LLC ....D...... 469 533-0730
Dallas (G-3868)

A & C Cabinet Co ....E...... 817 244-4303
Fort Worth (G-6334)

Alamo City Counter Tops Inc ....E...... 210 732-4800
San Antonio (G-17880)

All Wood Custom Cabinets Inc ....F...... 940 686-2795
Pilot Point (G-16721)

American Woodmark Corporation ....C...... 469 635-1960
Coppell (G-3409)

Americana Cabinets LLC ....G...... 281 973-8255
Humble (G-12746)

B & W Remodeling Inc ....E...... 817 485-0444
North Richland Hills (G-15874)

Bassett Woodworks ....F...... 915 855-2144
El Paso (G-5659)

Benedettini Cabinets LP ....C...... 281 633-8200
Rosenberg (G-17575)

Bentwood Companies Inc ....D...... 972 227-6855
Lancaster (G-13839)

Brandom Holdings LLC ....C...... 800 366-8001
Hillsboro (G-8323)

Builders Firstsource-Ohio Vall ....C...... 214 880-3500
Dallas (G-4067)

C K Higgs ....E...... 713 666-5739
Bellaire (G-1992)

Cabinet Creation Inc ....E...... 830 709-4116
Lytle (G-14573)

Cabinettech Inc ....F...... 325 670-0414
Abilene (G-28)

Cameron Knight ....F...... 972 636-7172
Royse City (G-17717)

Central Renovation Solutions ....F...... 469 567-2400
Lancaster (G-13842)

Champion Custom Cabinets Inc ....F...... 817 834-8552
Fort Worth (G-6507)

Classic Millwork and Products ....E...... 915 833-9922
El Paso (G-5696)

Cmcabco LLC ....F...... 972 617-8605
Waxahachie (G-20536)

Coleman Wood Products Inc ....E...... 940 440-2300
Aubrey (G-849)

Colony Cabinets Inc ....E...... 903 753-2488
Longview (G-14211)

Creative Custom Cabinets Inc ....F...... 512 821-0300
Round Rock (G-17639)

Creative Wood Concepts Inc ....F...... 972 539-2555
Dallas (G-4184)

Custom Cabinet Doors Inc ....E...... 940 686-2808
Pilot Point (G-16723)

D & H Quality Cabinets ....F...... 903 882-0274
Lindale (G-14134)

Daycor Enterprises Inc ....F...... 972 838-2700
Melissa (G-14996)

Delta Millwork ....E...... 713 849-2281
Houston (G-9432)

Donovan White Cabinets Inc ....F...... 903 569-5611
Mineola (G-15506)

Dozier Cabinet Works Inc ....E...... 940 566-5315
Sanger (G-18725)

Dunlaps Custom Cabinets Inc ....F...... 254 829-2279
Elm Mott (G-6063)

Dutch Marble Creations ....F...... 956 399-6767
San Benito (G-18656)

E & A Ventures LLC ....E...... 903 297-0829
Longview (G-14225)

Elite Cabinets & Closets ....F...... 903 737-0848
Paris (G-16361)

Encore Cabinets Ltd ....E...... 979 968-9482
La Grange (G-13694)

Espitias Cabinet & Door Makers ....E...... 713 329-9515
Houston (G-9699)

Evans Cabinet and Door Ltd ....E...... 979 836-6934
Brenham (G-2253)

Fixture Exchange Corporation ....E...... 817 429-2496
Joshua (G-13320)

Global Casework Mfg Inc ....E...... 281 494-6181
Sugar Land (G-19487)

Gracy Cabinets ....F...... 972 843-3123
Lavon (G-13943)

Graham Custom Cabinets LLC ....F...... 940 549-4311
Graham (G-7782)

Greenhaw Cabinets Inc ....F...... 325 646-8319
Brownwood (G-2430)

Growth Holdings LLC ....E...... 972 241-9535
Dallas (G-4418)

Gulf Coast Cabinet Doors LLC ....F...... 979 265-1519
Clute (G-3155)

Gunckel Archtectural Millworks ....E...... 830 303-0688
Seguin (G-18839)

Hartsfield & Pierce Cabinet Co ....F 972 288-5487
Irving *(G-13053)*

Heartland Furniture Inc ....E 817 483-6161
Arlington *(G-695)*

Hill Country Cabinet Shop Inc ....F 830 228-5062
Spring Branch *(G-19270)*

▼ Home Mart Inc ....F 956 724-4521
Laredo *(G-13892)*

◆ Homeart Designs Inc ....F 956 724-4412
Laredo *(G-13893)*

Hornbeek Enterprises Inc ....F 817 478-2447
Arlington *(G-699)*

Hornsbys Custom Cabinets ....F 830 693-2420
Marble Falls *(G-14744)*

Houston Cabinets Inc ....E 713 349-0848
Houston *(G-10220)*

Interior Fixture Installations ....E 972 412-9773
Rowlett *(G-17707)*

▼ J-Kraft Inc ....E 281 876-2535
Humble *(G-12780)*

JB Commercial Millwork Inc ....E 903 989-2241
Trenton *(G-20017)*

Jim R Reynolds & Assoc Inc ....F 832 257-2312
Spring *(G-19138)*

Johnnys Cabinet Shop Inc ....F 940 686-2496
Pilot Point *(G-16725)*

Johnnys Custom Cabinet ....F 281 498-8950
Stafford *(G-19336)*

Johnson Cabinets & Woodworking ....F 512 266-7099
Austin *(G-1258)*

Jormac Aerospace Inc ....E 972 436-7069
Coppell *(G-3424)*

Kamma Group Inc ....E 281 499-5888
Stafford *(G-19338)*

Keeling Homes Inc ....F 806 655-2071
Canyon *(G-2671)*

Kenneth M Burgin ....F 903 636-4086
Big Sandy *(G-2065)*

Kent Moore Cabinets Inc ....E 979 775-2906
Bryan *(G-2482)*

Kent Moore Cabinets Ltd ....F 281 480-8883
Richmond *(G-17459)*

Killeen Marble ....E 254 699-3408
Killeen *(G-13612)*

Knot Hole LLC ....E 254 634-0773
Killeen *(G-13614)*

Lawrence Furniture Co Inc ....F 361 572-3710
Victoria *(G-20283)*

▲ Leedo Manufacturing Co LP ....C 866 465-3336
East Bernard *(G-5559)*

Leedo Manufacturing Co LP ....B 866 995-3336
Stafford *(G-19347)*

Lundy Services LLC ....E 972 494-2554
Garland *(G-7539)*

Manufacturing Group Amer Inc ....A 214 467-4444
Dallas *(G-4633)*

Maryfield Enterprises LP ....D 210 344-4151
San Antonio *(G-18281)*

Masco Cabinetry LLC ....C 972 725-4298
Duncanville *(G-5533)*

▲ Master Woodcraft Cabinetry LLC ....D 903 935-0500
Marshall *(G-14793)*

Mastercraft Wood Products LP ....B 903 935-0500
Marshall *(G-14794)*

▲ Metroplex Cabinets Inc ....D 940 321-5151
Corinth *(G-3457)*

Metroplex Millworks Inc ....F 214 358-1770
Dallas *(G-4672)*

Mikada Cabinets LLC ....D 713 681-6116
Houston *(G-10878)*

Mike Conkles Custom Cabinets ....E 817 483-9658
Kennedale *(G-13499)*

Millwood Cabinets LLP ....E 903 567-3333
Canton *(G-2658)*

◆ MJB Wood Group LLC ....E 972 401-0005
Coppell *(G-3428)*

Moehnke Custom Cabinetry ....F 512 352-6506
Taylor *(G-19660)*

Morrow Cabinets Inc ....F 972 221-7551
Lewisville *(G-14070)*

Nations Cabinetry LLC ....E 210 681-8477
San Antonio *(G-18335)*

New Saw Inc ....E 972 288-2117
Mesquite *(G-15064)*

OBrien Hogman Associates LLC ....F 972 823-1900
Irving *(G-13130)*

Ogletree Custom Cabinets ....G 903 356-2611
Quinlan *(G-17225)*

Oncken & Sons Cabinet Shop ....F 210 333-4611
San Antonio *(G-18355)*

Osborne Cabinets & Millwork ....E 713 802-0092
Port Neches *(G-17167)*

Osborne Cabinets & Millwork ....E 409 899-1191
Beaumont *(G-1936)*

▲ Patterson Manufacturing Inc ....F 903 757-0523
Longview *(G-14288)*

Pavliska Cabinets Inc ....F 254 773-4461
Troy *(G-20032)*

Pechal Cabinets LLC ....F 254 773-4460
Temple *(G-19697)*

Petroplex Cabinets Inc ....G 432 333-2025
Odessa *(G-16121)*

Plano Door Service Inc ....F 972 422-1695
Plano *(G-16973)*

Prestige Custom Cabinetry ....G 832 674-8074
Cypress *(G-3813)*

Procraft Cabinetry Inc ....F 832 203-5736
Houston *(G-11433)*

Procraft Cabinetry Dallas LLC ....E 469 607-2588
Dallas *(G-4831)*

Progressive Millworks Inc ....D 512 832-0551
Austin *(G-1436)*

▲ Prorock Granite & Cabinets Inc ......F 832 486-9414
Houston *(G-11451)*

Q Cabinets Inc ....F 915 859-5252
Socorro *(G-19018)*

Qsi Custom Cabinets LP ....E 512 443-3303
Austin *(G-1440)*

R & R Custom Cabinets Inc ....F 972 247-4697
Carrollton *(G-2883)*

▲ Republic Nat Inds Texas LP ....C 903 935-3680
Marshall *(G-14800)*

Republic National Cabinet Corp ....F 903 935-3680
Marshall *(G-14801)*

Rick Triplett ....F 214 823-2830
Dallas *(G-4899)*

River City Cabinets Inc ....F 512 442-9990
Austin *(G-1467)*

Robert V Johns & Associates ....F 214 741-1912
Dallas *(G-4905)*

RWS Cabinets LLC ....F 936 760-2407
Conroe *(G-3360)*

S & S Cabinet Shop Inc ....F 325 655-6757
San Angelo *(G-17825)*

Skyline Cabinetry Inc ....F 972 620-8880
Farmers Branch *(G-6214)*

Skyline Cabinetry Inc ....F 972 620-8880
Dallas *(G-4970)*

Southern Cabinets ....G 254 799-2271
Waco *(G-20459)*

Square Cabinetry LLC ....E 214 838-2225
Dallas *(G-5000)*

Sunshine Custom Cabinets Inc ....F 817 572-5201
Fort Worth *(G-7023)*

Taylor Craft Cabinet & Door ....E 512 352-6355
Taylor *(G-19662)*

Texas Home & Projects LLC ....G 956 546-8400
Brownsville *(G-2410)*

▲ Thom-Bat-Ler Enterprises ....F 972 660-4056
Grand Prairie *(G-7982)*

Tri-Tex Cabinets Inc ....D 940 686-2617
Pilot Point *(G-16731)*

Unique Cabinets Inc ....E 512 251-3058
Pflugerville *(G-16690)*

US Remodelers Inc ....E 214 488-6300
Lewisville *(G-14103)*

W R Watson Corporation ....E 281 495-2800
Stafford *(G-19397)*

Walcott Enterprises Inc ....F 325 773-5212
Stamford *(G-19402)*

West-Reeves, Ltd. ....C 972 938-9623
Waxahachie *(G-20569)*

▲ Western Cabinets Inc ....C 469 916-5350
Dallas *(G-5181)*

Western Cabinets Inc ....E 972 293-2450
Cedar Hill *(G-2955)*

◆ Woodcrafters Home Products LLC ...D 956 565-6329
Weslaco *(G-20671)*

Zamo Inc ....E 210 667-1717
Saint Hedwig *(G-17761)*

2435 Hardwood Veneer & Plywood

C & H Hardwoods Inc ....F 817 561-7711
Fort Worth *(G-6482)*

Century Millwork LLC ....E 281 821-0191
Houston *(G-9142)*

Georgia-Pacific LLC ....F 409 584-4227
Pineland *(G-16739)*

Georgia-Pacific LLC ....B 866 924-1397
El Paso *(G-5784)*

Georgia-Pacific WD Pdts S LLC ....A 936 398-2511
Camden *(G-2638)*

▲ Hollman Inc ....C 972 815-4000
Irving *(G-13058)*

Masons Mill & Lumber Co Inc ....D 713 462-6975
Houston *(G-10785)*

Metro Gate & Mfg Co Inc ....E 903 785-8911
Paris *(G-16365)*

2436 Softwood Veneer & Plywood

Corelite Inc ....F 214 905-4359
Dallas *(G-4167)*

Georgia-Pacific WD Pdts S LLC ....A 936 398-2511
Camden *(G-2638)*

M & H Crates Inc ....D 903 683-5351
Jacksonville *(G-13248)*

2439 Structural Wood Members, NEC

All Truss Building Systems Inc ....F 817 247-7671
Dallas *(G-3922)*

Allied Truss LLC ....E 903 586-1982
Jacksonville *(G-13225)*

American Truss Systems Inc ....E 281 442-4584
Houston *(G-8613)*

Aries Acrylic Mfg Inc ....F 972 771-6286
Rockwall *(G-17538)*

▼ Associated Truss Company ....D 972 226-1973
Mesquite *(G-15028)*

B & S Hardware Inc ....E 903 856-3552
Pittsburg *(G-16744)*

BMC West LLC ....D 325 698-4465
Abilene *(G-18)*

Builders Firstsource Inc ....D 972 621-2233
Irving *(G-12953)*

Builders Firstsource Inc ....E 817 625-1200
Fort Worth *(G-6476)*

Builders Firstsource-Ohio Vall ....C 214 880-3500
Dallas *(G-4067)*

Case Hill Group Inc ....F 903 657-7000
Henderson *(G-8260)*

Claussen Inc ....F 512 556-2180
Lampasas *(G-13833)*

Colonial Truss Co LLC ....E 469 320-1000
Dallas *(G-4142)*

Component Structures Inc ....E 940 566-1166
Denton *(G-5356)*

Connor Sports Flooring LLC ....F 817 944-0269
Southlake *(G-19061)*

Contractors Service Ltd ....F 325 692-4317
Abilene *(G-36)*

East Texas Truss LLC ....F 409 283-3728
Hillister *(G-8319)*

El Paso Truss Inc ....D 915 751-0025
El Paso *(G-5745)*

Esco Laminating Texas Inc ....D 254 296-0500
Waco *(G-20397)*

Foxworth-Galbraith Lumber Co ....D 972 665-2400
Plano *(G-16872)*

Lockhart Truss Co Inc ....F 512 398-5300
Lockhart *(G-14171)*

Loredo Truss Company Inc ....E 512 926-1782
Austin *(G-1301)*

Mg Building Materials Ltd ....G 210 798-0650
San Antonio *(G-18297)*

Noltex Truss Big Spring Inc ....F 254 216-0904
Gatesville *(G-7621)*

Noltex Truss Big Spring Inc ....F 432 267-4700
Big Spring *(G-2089)*

Noltex Truss Dfw Inc ....E 817 866-3333
Grandview *(G-8002)*

Noltex Truss Gatesville LP ....D 713 926-7715
Houston *(G-11066)*

Noltex Truss Littlefield LP ....E 432 687-1241
Midland *(G-15321)*

Noltex Truss Littlefield LP ....E 806 385-5533
Littlefield *(G-14147)*

North Texas Truss ....E 806 385-5533
Littlefield *(G-14148)*

Panel Truss of Longview Inc ....F 903 657-7000
Henderson *(G-8270)*

Panel Truss Texas Inc ....D 903 657-7000
Henderson *(G-8271)*

Rio Truss LP ....F 956 682-9822
McAllen *(G-14902)*

Rogers Manufacturing Corp ....E 901 301-4936
Sugar Land *(G-19536)*

Rushin Truss Ltd ....F 972 442-3544
Nevada *(G-15766)*

Sand Creek Timber Frames LLC ....E 210 698-6156
Boerne *(G-2135)*

SIC

Steel Building Supply Inc ....E 936 598-6373
  Center (G-3009)
Stock Building Sup Texas LLC ....B 512 444-3172
  Austin (G-1537)
Textruss Component Bldg Inc ....E 512 836-4830
  Austin (G-1571)
The San Antonio Truss Company ....G 210 736-9629
  San Antonio (G-18547)
Truss Ops North LLC ....G 479 824-8787
  Henderson (G-8276)
Trussway LLC Central ....F 713 691-6900
  Houston (G-12387)
Trussway LLC East ....F 713 691-6900
  Houston (G-12388)
Trussway Holdings Inc ....F 713 691-6900
  Houston (G-12389)
Trussway Manufacturing Inc ....C 719 322-9662
  Houston (G-12390)
Trussway Transportation Inc ....A 713 691-6900
  Houston (G-12391)
▼ Ufp New Waverly LLC ....D 936 295-3411
  New Waverly (G-15861)
Unifix Inc ....E 817 645-3435
  Cleburne (G-3116)
Wood Shed Truss ....F 903 569-2147
  Mineola (G-15515)
Wood Shed Trusse ....F 903 569-2147
  Mineola (G-15516)

2441 Wood Boxes

Apache Products Inc ....D 409 385-7021
  Silsbee (G-18949)
▲ Bana Inc ....C 817 232-3750
  Saginaw (G-17739)
Bell Wooden Products Inc ....E 214 388-5421
  Dallas (G-4016)
Corsicana Box Company Inc ....F 903 874-5615
  Corsicana (G-3665)
Erwin Containers Inc ....E 817 295-5256
  Burleson (G-2578)
Ifco Systems North America Inc ....E 713 937-9311
  Houston (G-10318)
Industrial Lumber and Box Inc ....F 713 928-2096
  Houston (G-10351)
▼ Kainer Export Crating Inc ....F 713 641-2345
  Houston (G-10499)
▲ Main Gate ....E 409 832-1546
  Beaumont (G-1924)
◆ Morris Export Crating Company ....D 713 675-9101
  Houston (G-10922)
▲ Nefab Companies Inc ....E 866 332-4425
  Coppell (G-3430)
◆ Nefab Packaging Inc ....E 469 444-5264
  Coppell (G-3431)
Pallet & Crating Co Inc ....E 903 463-5786
  Denison (G-5344)
Pierce Packaging Co ....E 815 636-5656
  Houston (G-11331)
Schry-Way Cases ....F 806 622-0066
  Amarillo (G-511)
Serious Cigars Llc ....G 281 397-9800
  Houston (G-11837)
Superior Pllet Wichita FLS Ltd ....F 940 569-5244
  Burkburnett (G-2564)
◆ Trident Crating & Services Inc ....E 281 227-3999
  Houston (G-12372)

2448 Wood Pallets & Skids

2nd Chance Pallets LLC ....F 817 847-8005
  Saginaw (G-17735)
A & A Pallet and Lumber Co ....F 713 462-4575
  Houston (G-8420)
A & A Pallet Co ....F 713 480-9861
  Houston (G-8421)
Age Industries Ltd ....E 915 852-9099
  Horizon City (G-8361)
Age Industries Ltd ....D 210 659-1301
  Cibolo (G-3060)
Alamo Pallet Recyclers Inc ....F 972 296-2090
  Dallas (G-3917)
Aldersgate Enrichment Center ....D 325 646-2566
  Early (G-5556)
Allied Pallet & Eqp Co LLC ....F 281 850-8090
  Houston (G-8551)
Apache Products Inc ....D 409 385-7021
  Silsbee (G-18949)
Arrington Lbr & Pallet Co Inc ....C 903 586-4070
  Jacksonville (G-13226)
Arrington Sawmill Inc ....C 903 586-4070
  Jacksonville (G-13227)

Atlas Southwest Pallet Co Inc ....E 210 532-5343
  San Antonio (G-17921)
Austin Pallet Company ....E 512 990-0090
  Pflugerville (G-16659)
AZ Pallet Exchange ....E 713 332-6145
  Houston (G-8766)
B & B Box and Lumber Company ....E 903 592-7369
  Tyler (G-20054)
▲ Bana Inc ....C 817 232-3750
  Saginaw (G-17739)
Bell Wooden Products Inc ....E 214 388-5421
  Dallas (G-4016)
Border Pallets Inc ....E 915 852-3939
  El Paso (G-5669)
Cargo Crating Company Ltd ....F 713 699-0172
  Houston (G-9092)
Carrizo Wood Products Inc ....E 936 569-0582
  Nacogdoches (G-15690)
Central Pallets No 2 ....F 956 726-4023
  Laredo (G-13873)
Centurion Pallet Service ....F 210 823-3530
  San Antonio (G-17993)
Champion Pallet & Packaging ....E 972 551-2474
  Irving (G-12968)
Chep (usa) Inc ....D 214 688-4108
  Dallas (G-4109)
Chep (usa) Inc ....E 806 577-4447
  Lubbock (G-14392)
Chep (usa) Inc ....E 806 553-5655
  Amarillo (G-415)
Chep (usa) Inc ....D 210 662-7733
  San Antonio (G-18002)
Conner Industries Inc ....F 713 944-6766
  Houston (G-9270)
◆ Consolidated Wood Products Inc ....E 903 894-7745
  Bullard (G-2551)
Corr-Wood Mfg Inc ....D 817 467-5525
  Arlington (G-648)
Cougar Pallet Inc ....D 281 442-1177
  Houston (G-9330)
Crimstone AAA Operating Co LP ....F 210 662-9400
  San Antonio (G-18030)
Custom Crates & Pallets Ltd ....D 915 886-4985
  Canutillo (G-2663)
D&D Pallets Inc ....F 817 625-7966
  Fort Worth (G-6571)
Dfw A-1 Pallet Inc ....D 972 401-3502
  Irving (G-12998)
Dunn Pallet Co ....E 409 722-2933
  Port Neches (G-17159)
Entech Technology Inc ....F 972 542-0210
  Dallas (G-4325)
Fivepayne LLC ....D 817 310-0147
  Grapevine (G-8035)
Flores Pallets LLC ....F 713 645-1022
  Houston (G-9805)
Four Way Pallet Co ....F 713 675-7788
  Houston (G-9847)
G & A Pallet LLC ....E 713 670-8118
  Houston (G-9881)
G & A Pallet Co ....F 713 670-8118
  Houston (G-9882)
◆ Gps-Global Pallets Svcs LLC ....E 281 862-9244
  Houston (G-10008)
Ifco Systems North America Inc ....D 214 637-4840
  Dallas (G-4485)
Ifco Systems North America Inc ....E 806 335-1746
  Amarillo (G-437)
Ifco Systems North America Inc ....E 806 291-9024
  Plainview (G-16758)
Industrial Lumber and Box Inc ....F 713 928-2096
  Houston (G-10351)
Intermdal Repr Mdfcation Trckg ....F 713 674-2179
  Houston (G-10396)
K L Barton & Sons Tie Co ....F 936 347-2744
  Garrison (G-7611)
Kastros Wood Pallets Inc ....F 915 855-8011
  El Paso (G-5826)
Keal Cases Incorporated ....E 512 244-9100
  Round Rock (G-17665)
Kunka Enterprises LLC ....F 254 666-3576
  Waco (G-20423)
L & L Pallet Supply Inc ....E 806 272-5041
  Muleshoe (G-15678)
L & L Pallet Supply Inc ....F 806 272-5041
  Amarillo (G-497)
L L Pallets ....F 469 916-7552
  Dallas (G-4573)
La Pallet Recyclers ....F 281 469-6070
  Houston (G-10581)

Leonard Ray Vaught ....E 903 572-0352
  Cookville (G-3405)
Loadrite Inc ....F 940 322-1003
  Wichita Falls (G-20779)
M & H Crates Inc ....D 903 683-5351
  Jacksonville (G-13248)
M & T Pallet Company Inc ....E 409 866-8136
  Beaumont (G-1921)
Mayco Inc ....F 214 638-4848
  Dallas (G-4657)
McAllen Bag & Supply Company ....F 956 686-6571
  McAllen (G-14887)
Metroplex Wood Products Ltd ....E 817 538-0375
  Fort Worth (G-6834)
Miller Waste Mills Inc ....D 817 293-6163
  Fort Worth (G-6842)
Mk Pallets Inc ....F 903 537-2400
  Saltillo (G-17766)
MPW Enterprises LLC ....E 713 671-9560
  Houston (G-10932)
▲ Nefab Companies Inc ....E 866 332-4425
  Coppell (G-3430)
◆ Nefab Packaging Inc ....E 469 444-5264
  Coppell (G-3431)
Neopal LLC ....E 281 219-9600
  Houston (G-11024)
Pal-Serv of Dallas LLC ....F 214 631-4600
  Balch Springs (G-1738)
Pallet & Crating Co Inc ....E 903 463-5786
  Denison (G-5344)
Pallet Advisor LLC ....E 817 271-4840
  Dallas (G-4780)
Pallet Depot ....F 972 336-0006
  Grand Prairie (G-7944)
Pallet King Enterprises Inc ....F 972 723-3249
  Midlothian (G-15490)
Pallet Ops LLC ....E 713 554-6972
  Houston (G-11224)
Pallet Ops - San Antonio LLC ....F 210 225-7882
  San Antonio (G-18364)
Pallet Repair Services Inc ....D 972 913-1110
  Hutchins (G-12870)
Palletone Inc ....D 903 427-3030
  Clarksville (G-3077)
▲ Palletone of Texas LP ....C 903 628-5695
  New Boston (G-15768)
Pallets911 LLC ....F 956 203-2671
  Brownsville (G-2390)
Pechal Pallets LLC ....E 254 773-4460
  Temple (G-19698)
Pleasant Fencing & Cnstr ....E 903 572-0352
  Cookville (G-3406)
Rashidah LLC ....G 281 469-5277
  Houston (G-11551)
Redco Pallet Inc ....E 903 561-2075
  Tyler (G-20145)
S and S Pallets ....F 972 382-8142
  Celina (G-2994)
Saifee Corporation ....E 713 674-2000
  Houston (G-11730)
Select Mat Inc ....F 833 205-1515
  Magnolia (G-14627)
South East Pallet Inc ....G 713 645-6131
  Houston (G-11964)
Springhill Pallets LLC ....F 903 297-6090
  Longview (G-14311)
Stephens A-1 Lbr & Pallet Inc ....E 281 440-6444
  Houston (G-12058)
Superior Pllet Wichita FLS Ltd ....F 940 569-5244
  Burkburnett (G-2564)
The Pallet Place Inc ....E 903 963-4026
  Van (G-20210)
Threet Pallet LLC ....E 972 489-6887
  Ennis (G-6119)
Total Pallet Solutions LLC ....E 817 783-5565
  Alvarado (G-347)
Traeger Wood Pellets ....G 409 384-5331
  Jasper (G-13282)
▼ Ufp Schertz LLC ....E 830 606-4300
  Schertz (G-18766)
Wooden Pallets Ltd ....C 409 385-1234
  Silsbee (G-18959)

2449 Wood Containers, NEC

Age Industries Ltd ....E 956 399-8279
  San Benito (G-18654)
Age Industries Ltd ....D 210 659-1301
  Cibolo (G-3060)
B & B Box and Lumber Company ....E 903 592-7369
  Tyler (G-20054)

Bell Wooden Products Inc .... E 214 388-5421
Dallas *(G-4016)*

Cargo Crating Company Ltd .... F 713 699-0172
Houston *(G-9092)*

Conner Industries Inc .... E 817 439-3555
Fort Worth *(G-6541)*

Cougar Pallet Inc .... D 281 442-1177
Houston *(G-9330)*

◆ DMd Custom Crates & Bxs Inc ..... F 915 849-1744
Horizon City *(G-8364)*

Ics Enterprises LLP .... B 915 239-9256
El Paso *(G-5808)*

Ifco Systems North America Inc .... E 713 937-9311
Houston *(G-10318)*

Industrial Lumber and Box Inc .... F 713 928-2096
Houston *(G-10351)*

Keal Cases Incorporated .... E 512 244-9100
Round Rock *(G-17665)*

Leonard Ray Vaught .... E 903 572-0352
Cookville *(G-3405)*

▲ Nefab Companies Inc .... E 866 332-4425
Coppell *(G-3430)*

◆ Nefab Packaging Inc .... E 469 444-5264
Coppell *(G-3431)*

Pallet & Crating Co Inc .... E 903 463-5786
Denison *(G-5344)*

▲ Relocation Systems Inc .... E 972 241-2300
Irving *(G-13164)*

Solid Crate LLC .... F 713 475-9926
Pasadena *(G-16507)*

Superior Pllet Wichita FLS Ltd .... F 940 569-5244
Burkburnett *(G-2564)*

Ufp Dallas LLC .... E 817 825-6512
Dallas *(G-5127)*

▼ Ufp Schertz LLC .... E 830 606-4300
Schertz *(G-18766)*

▲ W T Harris Company Inc .... E 325 646-7521
Brownwood *(G-2448)*

Western Industries Corporation .... D 214 503-8322
Carrollton *(G-2848)*

2451 Mobile Homes

Al/Tex Homes Inc .... C 817 847-1355
Fort Worth *(G-6361)*

American Homestar Corporation ...... E 281 334-9700
League City *(G-13946)*

American Homestar Lancaster LP ..... E 281 334-9700
League City *(G-13947)*

Atomic Container Homes Inc .... E 915 433-4817
El Paso *(G-5653)*

Bristlecone Ventures 2 LLC .... E 512 231-9603
Manor *(G-14646)*

▲ Centex Corporation .... C 214 981-5000
Dallas *(G-4097)*

Clayton Homes Inc .... F 254 666-9570
Waco *(G-20384)*

Clayton Homes Inc .... F 210 946-2222
San Antonio *(G-18010)*

Clayton Homes Inc .... C 254 772-1808
Waco *(G-20385)*

Clayton Homes Inc .... F 210 677-6100
San Antonio *(G-18011)*

CMH Manufacturing Inc .... C 903 439-0242
Sulphur Springs *(G-19583)*

CMH Manufacturing Inc .... E 254 666-3534
Waco *(G-20387)*

CMH Manufacturing Inc .... C 800 445-3516
Bonham *(G-2152)*

G-Con LLC .... F 214 220-4303
College Station *(G-3184)*

Mobile Toys Inc .... F 979 268-6066
College Station *(G-3193)*

▼ Teton Buildings LLC .... E 307 473-7543
Houston *(G-12215)*

2452 Prefabricated Wood Buildings & Cmpnts

Amtex Corp .... D 972 276-7626
Garland *(G-7437)*

Aries Building Systems LLC .... C 254 938-0800
Troy *(G-20028)*

Aries Building Systems LLC .... F 254 938-0800
Houston *(G-8694)*

Atco Strctres Lgistics USA Inc .... G 208 242-3804
Spring *(G-19197)*

▼ Atco Strctres Lgistics USA Inc ...... D 936 829-2325
Spring *(G-19198)*

▲ Atlas Building Systems Inc .... F 903 597-4211
Tyler *(G-20052)*

Atlas Building Systems Inc .... E 903 865-1153
Wills Point *(G-20873)*

Boxx Modular Inc .... F 972 492-4040
Fort Worth *(G-6464)*

Component Structures Inc .... E 940 566-1166
Denton *(G-5356)*

Cook Sales Inc .... E 512 321-2888
Bastrop *(G-1751)*

General Shlters of Bvlle Texas .... E 936 598-3389
Center *(G-2998)*

Gfrc 360 LLC .... E 972 494-9000
Garland *(G-7503)*

Hawk Portable Buildings Inc .... E 325 893-5120
Clyde *(G-3163)*

Indicom Buildings Inc .... D 817 447-1213
Burleson *(G-2582)*

Langford Construction Inc .... F 817 478-0218
Arlington *(G-718)*

Morgan Building & Spa Mfg Corp ..... D 254 629-1599
Eastland *(G-5568)*

Morgan Building Transport .... E 972 864-7300
Dallas *(G-4688)*

Murray Building & Crane Inds .... D 713 464-6506
Houston *(G-10944)*

▲ Neon Electric Corporation .... D 281 987-1144
Houston *(G-11023)*

Neopod Systems LLC .... F 954 603-3100
New Braunfels *(G-15816)*

Oldcastle Buildingenvelope Inc .... A 972 551-6100
Terrell *(G-19746)*

Palomar Modular Buildings LLC .... C 469 727-0727
Desoto *(G-5438)*

▲ Panel Specialists Inc .... D 254 774-9800
Temple *(G-19695)*

◆ Pilot Plastics LLC .... G 800 918-6765
Fort Worth *(G-6907)*

Ramtech Building Systems Inc .... E 817 473-9376
Mansfield *(G-14707)*

Raul Gonzalez .... F 956 793-5359
Elsa *(G-6080)*

Rmd Manufacturing Ltd .... E 817 477-5321
Mansfield *(G-14712)*

Satterwhite Companies Inc .... D 903 663-1729
Longview *(G-14303)*

Sustainable Modular MGT Inc .... F 972 619-7300
Plano *(G-17016)*

Tuff Shed Inc .... F 903 236-9126
Longview *(G-14324)*

Weq Britco LP .... E 254 741-6701
Waco *(G-20478)*

2491 Wood Preserving

Bastrop Cnty Prcnct 2 Rd Brdge ...... F 512 360-4224
Smithville *(G-18975)*

Bayou City Lumber Company .... F 713 991-2377
Houston *(G-8834)*

▼ Building Products Plus LLC .... E 713 946-7939
Houston *(G-9016)*

Chicago Flameproof WD Spc Corp .... F 817 534-9800
Fort Worth *(G-6513)*

Fowler Post Co Inc .... G 903 966-2417
Bagwell *(G-1735)*

Green Bay Packaging Inc .... E 915 822-9700
El Paso *(G-5791)*

Hixson Lumber Sales Inc .... E 903 527-4010
Caddo Mills *(G-2624)*

Koppers Inc .... D 979 596-1321
Somerville *(G-19022)*

Lawn Master Outdoor Living LLC ...... E 972 938-7100
Waxahachie *(G-20550)*

Leo Hicks Creosoting Co Inc .... F 936 858-4419
Alto *(G-317)*

LLC Huber Land .... F 936 347-2744
Garrison *(G-7612)*

▲ Lufkin Creosoting Co Inc .... D 936 634-2211
Lufkin *(G-14537)*

Menard Industries LLC .... E 512 628-1058
Houston *(G-10828)*

Morgan Cabinetry Inc .... F 972 278-8836
Garland *(G-7555)*

Newton Pole Co Inc .... F 409 379-2715
Newton *(G-15865)*

North American Tech Group Inc .... F 972 996-5750
Marshall *(G-14796)*

Piney Forest Products LLC .... D 936 275-9751
San Augustine *(G-18652)*

Russell Marine LLC .... C 281 860-0011
Channelview *(G-3034)*

Select Mat LLC .... F 833 205-1515
Magnolia *(G-14627)*

Solidwood Forest Ltd .... E 281 351-0271
Tomball *(G-20010)*

Southeast Wood Treating Inc .... F 903 569-9441
Mineola *(G-15512)*

Stock Building Sup Texas LLC .... B 512 444-3172
Austin *(G-1537)*

Texas Electric Coops Inc .... E 512 454-0311
Austin *(G-1567)*

Texas Electric Coops Inc .... D 512 868-8610
Georgetown *(G-7685)*

Texas Electric Coops Inc .... E 409 384-4633
Jasper *(G-13281)*

▼ Ufp New Waverly LLC .... D 936 295-3411
New Waverly *(G-15861)*

▼ Ufp Schertz LLC .... E 830 606-4300
Schertz *(G-18766)*

2493 Reconstituted Wood Prdts

Bay Energy Blanket Inc .... F 512 353-4064
San Marcos *(G-18680)*

Cedar Fiber Company Inc .... D 325 446-2571
Junction *(G-13338)*

Conner Industries Inc .... E 817 439-3555
Fort Worth *(G-6541)*

Corrigan Osb LLC .... E 318 448-0405
Corrigan *(G-3659)*

Digital Communication Svcs Inc .... F 682 478-2134
Fort Worth *(G-6586)*

Georgia-Pacific LLC .... C 800 231-6060
Diboll *(G-5465)*

Georgia-Pacific LLC .... C 936 829-5511
Diboll *(G-5466)*

Gregg Indus Insulators Inc .... B 903 757-5754
Longview *(G-14243)*

Installed Building Pdts Inc .... E 210 937-1082
San Antonio *(G-18643)*

Jci Roofing LLC .... F 956 227-1745
McAllen *(G-14878)*

Laminate Works Inc .... E 713 955-1310
Houston *(G-10588)*

Laminate Works Inc .... E 913 281-7474
Dallas *(G-4580)*

Louisiana-Pacific Corporation .... D 409 383-0767
Jasper *(G-13279)*

◆ Norbord Texas LP .... A 936 568-8009
Jefferson *(G-13285)*

Norbord Texas Nacogdoches Inc ...... C 936 568-8000
Nacogdoches *(G-15707)*

▲ Paragon Furniture Inc .... D 817 633-3242
Arlington *(G-749)*

Standard Industries Inc .... C 972 851-0460
Dallas *(G-5004)*

Target Stone LLC .... E 832 827-8663
Houston *(G-12161)*

Ufp Dallas LLC .... C 972 232-1711
Dallas *(G-5128)*

Valro-K LLC .... E 210 937-1082
San Antonio *(G-18647)*

World Research Company Inc .... E 903 581-3720
Tyler *(G-20177)*

Zilkha Biomass Fuels I LLC .... E 713 979-9961
Houston *(G-12729)*

2499 Wood Prdts, NEC

American Wood Fibers Inc .... E 903 923-8700
Marshall *(G-14761)*

▲ Arne Distributors Inc .... F 713 869-8321
Houston *(G-8700)*

B & B Stake Co .... G 936 327-2161
Livingston *(G-14150)*

Bowden Saddle Tree Company Inc .... F 915 877-3191
Vinton *(G-20340)*

▲ Brazos Walking Sticks .... E 254 799-7119
Waco *(G-20371)*

Classic Picture Company Inc .... F 972 225-7590
Hutchins *(G-12864)*

Comac Fixtures Inc .... F 806 376-4511
Amarillo *(G-418)*

Crescent Reel Manufacturing Co ...... F 713 695-4587
Houston *(G-9343)*

Dcu Inc .... F 972 816-6667
Wylie *(G-20932)*

Dial-A-Pick Co .... E 210 736-1901
San Antonio *(G-18053)*

Eggemeyer Land Clearing LLC .... E 210 366-4100
New Braunfels *(G-15789)*

Enrud Resources Inc .... F 713 943-1600
Pasadena *(G-16429)*

▲ Framecrafters Inc .... E 713 973-1333
Houston *(G-9852)*

G4 Spatial Technologies LLC ....E 512 447-9879
Austin (G-1176)

Greater Southwest Art Center ....G 915 566-2410
El Paso (G-5790)

Harris Cabinet & Wdwkg Inc ....G 817 561-2959
Fort Worth (G-6690)

Hayes Carpentry L L C ....E 713 944-2608
South Houston (G-19044)

Hope Agri Products of Texas ....E 903 732-3361
Powderly (G-17199)

Hoyafam Holdings Ltd ....F 281 447-0447
Houston (G-10270)

Hw Holdco LLC ....E 972 536-6300
Irving (G-13061)

Image Furnishings Inc ....F 806 747-6500
Lubbock (G-14424)

Integrawood Inc ....E 713 329-9949
Texas City (G-19795)

◆ International Innovations Inc ....D 512 600-4517
Austin (G-1238)

▲ Jamieson Manufacturing Co ....E 214 339-8384
Dallas (G-4524)

Jemasco Inc ....E 903 784-3014
Paris (G-16363)

Jml Services Inc ....F 713 582-9500
Crosby (G-3736)

John D Blankenship ....E 214 752-9191
Dallas (G-4535)

Kitchen Bath Cbinets Doors Inc ....E 915 852-0499
El Paso (G-5830)

Larson-Juhl US LLC ....E 713 895-0296
Houston (G-10602)

Letco Group LLC ....F 817 490-6655
Double Oak (G-5496)

Letco Group LLC ....F 972 274-2835
Lancaster (G-13844)

Letco Group LLC ....E 409 584-2155
Pineland (G-16740)

Letco Group LLC ....E 281 342-6113
Richmond (G-17461)

Letco Group LLC ....F 281 537-2377
Houston (G-10627)

Liberty Company ....E 817 921-0218
Fort Worth (G-6788)

Lucias Oaks LP ....F 832 616-3306
Spring (G-19228)

▲ Magnolia Brush Mfrs Inc ....D 903 427-2261
Clarksville (G-3074)

Mark Prestigious ....F 210 820-0093
New Braunfels (G-15812)

Masterwerkes ....F 214 315-6479
Garland (G-7545)

McWhirter Wood Products Inc ....F 713 861-1437
Houston (G-10813)

Metropolex Wood Specialty ....E 214 339-5115
Dallas (G-4673)

National Art Service Co Inc ....F 713 869-5861
Houston (G-10965)

Natures Way Resources Inc ....F 936 273-1200
Conroe (G-3341)

◆ Nielsen & Bainbridge LLC ....E 512 506-3900
Austin (G-1367)

▲ P Diamond Enterprises Inc ....F 325 643-5629
Brownwood (G-2441)

R M S Inc ....G 713 467-2043
Houston (G-11523)

Ramrod Enterprises LLC ....E 936 756-4846
Conroe (G-3356)

Randy Wrecker Service Inc ....F 713 690-4000
Houston (G-11543)

▲ RE Watson & Associates Inc ....E 817 478-4401
Kennedale (G-13501)

Reel-Logix LLC ....E 713 369-3139
Houston (G-11581)

Roy C Garrett Inc ....F 210 659-6701
Cibolo (G-3064)

S W Galleries Corp ....E 972 788-2743
Dallas (G-4924)

Sabine River & Northern RR Co ....E 409 746-2453
Orange (G-16260)

Screen Play Promotions Inc ....G 817 788-8608
Hurst (G-12858)

Sign Crafters Inc ....F 512 392-0900
San Marcos (G-18710)

Smith Design and Mfg Inc ....F 903 433-4444
Gunter (G-8116)

▲ Smith Wood Products Inc ....E 817 581-5200
Fort Worth (G-6997)

Sorensen Industries Inc ....E 940 365-9999
Crossroads (G-3750)

Spivey Stake & Supply Inc ....E 903 822-3888
Mount Enterprise (G-15645)

Spooltech LLC ....E 281 861-6800
Houston (G-12022)

Srg Ventures LLC ....E 281 214-8560
Houston (G-12030)

Tach Services Inc ....E 254 547-7121
Copperas Cove (G-3456)

Texas Electric Coops Inc ....D 409 384-4633
Jasper (G-13281)

▼ Ufp New Waverly LLC ....D 936 295-3411
New Waverly (G-15861)

▼ Ufp Schertz LLC ....E 830 606-4300
Schertz (G-18766)

Villpac Inc ....F 713 672-1255
Houston (G-12568)

Vrt Investments Inc ....F 972 226-1981
Forney (G-6316)

Whites Wood Group Inc ....E 903 793-1603
Texarkana (G-19784)

Wordyisms Inc ....F 512 835-6695
Pflugerville (G-16693)

Zachry Holdings Inc ....F 806 322-4100
Amarillo (G-525)

Zspace LLC ....F 713 662-3123
Houston (G-12733)

25 FURNITURE AND FIXTURES

2511 Wood Household Furniture

3 L Designs Inc ....E 214 920-9223
Dallas (G-3867)

▲ Alan Charles Incorporated ....E 817 922-9834
Fort Worth (G-6362)

All Wood Custom Cabinets Inc ....F 940 686-2795
Pilot Point (G-16721)

Bassett Furniture Inds Inc ....F 210 641-0101
San Antonio (G-17940)

Cabinets Deluxe By Dale Inc ....D 512 259-2531
Freeport (G-7195)

Cabinettech Inc ....F 325 670-0414
Abilene (G-28)

Cameron Knight ....F 972 636-7172
Royse City (G-17717)

Care Products Inc ....E 956 383-6049
McAllen (G-14846)

Carlton Mfg Inc ....D 903 537-4591
Mount Vernon (G-15666)

Coleman Wood Products Inc ....E 940 440-2300
Aubrey (G-849)

Dickson Furniture Mfrs LLC ....F 713 747-0341
Houston (G-9463)

Dickson Furniture Mfrs LLC ....E 281 299-6197
Houston (G-9464)

▲ Feinkind Inc ....E 914 591-5868
Austin (G-1153)

Homestead Craftsmen LLC ....D 254 754-9600
Waco (G-20414)

Industrial Lumber and Box Inc ....F 713 928-2096
Houston (G-10351)

Inwood Furniture Manufacturing ....D 972 564-4444
Forney (G-6311)

JDM Designs Inc ....E 281 356-6131
Stagecoach (G-19401)

Kerr Collection ....E 817 572-4663
Burleson (G-2584)

Keys Corporation ....F 713 864-7299
Houston (G-10525)

Little Green Apples Inc ....F 956 668-0028
McAllen (G-14885)

Manheim Companies Inc ....E 972 387-4578
Dallas (G-4632)

▲ Mfi International Mfg LLC ....A 915 858-0971
El Paso (G-5876)

Moein Inc ....E 817 341-1414
Weatherford (G-20605)

Mozaic Company ....F 972 386-3332
Arlington (G-733)

Pallas Archtctral Wodworks LLC ....F 214 741-1125
Dallas (G-4779)

▲ Patio One Furniture LP ....F 713 789-8080
Houston (G-11260)

Patton Manufactured Pdts LP ....E 512 918-3737
Austin (G-1401)

Precision Wood Products Inc ....D 972 293-2252
Cedar Hill (G-2951)

R Jones and Associates Inc ....E 214 951-0091
Dallas (G-4854)

▼ Rack Solutions Inc ....F 903 453-0800
Greenville (G-8088)

Renever Inc ....F 214 761-1882
Dallas (G-4887)

Reynolds Mfg Corp Inc ....E 325 698-7300
Abilene (G-71)

▼ Rodco-Brandt Manufacturing ....E 817 477-4118
Mansfield (G-14713)

Solano Furniture Incorporated ....F 713 849-4855
Houston (G-11934)

▼ Tables Manufacturing Inc ....B 972 932-4148
Kaufman (G-13464)

▲ Trosby of Georgia Inc ....G 713 526-7332
Houston (G-12382)

▲ Woodard—Cm LLC ....E 972 393-3800
Coppell (G-3453)

2512 Wood Household Furniture, Upholstered

◆ Al Legacy Partners Inc ....B 972 296-9599
Dallas (G-3916)

▲ Alan Charles Incorporated ....E 817 922-9834
Fort Worth (G-6362)

American Lea Operations LLC ....B 972 296-8016
Dallas (G-3944)

Carl Kisabeth Co Inc ....F 817 281-7560
Haltom City (G-8134)

Carlton Mfg Inc ....D 903 537-4591
Mount Vernon (G-15666)

Clifton Upholstery Co Inc ....F 254 753-0211
Waco (G-20386)

▲ Dbljs7 Inc ....F 440 746-1200
Horseshoe Bay (G-8366)

Delatorre Inc ....F 713 522-5833
Houston (G-9426)

Diamond Modern Furniture LLC ....G 877 349-5003
Houston (G-9451)

Double L Leather LLC ....E 888 643-5117
Denton (G-5361)

J&D Interiors Inc ....F 817 626-2365
Fort Worth (G-6731)

Keys Corporation ....F 713 864-7299
Houston (G-10525)

M & M Upholstery Inc ....E 214 391-2666
Dallas (G-4618)

Marroquin Custom Upholstery ....E 214 905-0461
Dallas (G-4637)

Massoud Furniture Mfg Co ....D 214 388-8655
Dallas (G-4644)

◆ Mayo Mfg Corporation ....C 903 838-0518
Texarkana (G-19769)

Moein Inc ....F 817 341-1414
Weatherford (G-20605)

▲ Noahs Manufacturing Inc ....D 713 926-3500
Houston (G-11062)

R Jones and Associates Inc ....E 214 951-0091
Dallas (G-4854)

Rudys Custom Uphl & Design ....F 210 821-5156
San Antonio (G-18438)

Solano Furniture Incorporated ....F 713 849-4855
Houston (G-11934)

Swiftex Manufacturing Corp ....F 512 321-2574
Bastrop (G-1761)

Texas Office Pdts & Sup Inc ....F 512 472-1340
Austin (G-1569)

▲ United Leather Usa Inc ....D 214 698-8270
Dallas (G-5135)

2514 Metal Household Furniture

AAe Manufacturing Co Inc ....F 956 748-0033
Rio Hondo (G-17474)

Acacia Originals LLC ....F 877 565-5995
Porter (G-17170)

Amweld International LLC ....D 888 775-2397
Dallas (G-3948)

▲ Asmar Custom Cabinets Inc ....F 972 241-7676
Dallas (G-3971)

Badj Inc ....F 254 918-5397
Stephenville (G-19407)

Cmp Express LLC ....F 469 348-2272
Grand Prairie (G-7855)

Colonial Art Inc ....F 713 697-8407
Houston (G-9245)

Dickson Furniture Mfrs LLC ....F 713 747-0341
Houston (G-9463)

Felipe Arreazola ....F 956 334-3136
Laredo (G-13883)

Hickory Springs Mfg Co ....F 817 831-1785
Fort Worth (G-6695)

Jormac Aerospace Inc ....E 972 436-7069
Coppell (G-3424)

◆ Kessler Industries Inc ....E 915 591-8161
  El Paso (G-5828)
◆ Kln Manufacturing LLC ....C 210 227-4747
  Dallas (G-4560)
▲ Kln Steel Products Company LLC ...C 210 227-4747
  Dallas (G-4561)
Living Company Holdings LLC ....E 469 687-8991
  Garland (G-7538)
Mantua Manufacturing Co ....E 713 672-9811
  Houston (G-10748)
Peck & Company ....E 713 526-2590
  Houston (G-11268)
◆ Rangaire Manufacturing Co LP ......D 817 556-6500
  Cleburne (G-3107)
Robert F Herndon Corporation ....F 915 779-7905
  El Paso (G-5942)
▲ Sibbitt and Lott Inc ....G 214 742-6949
  Dallas (G-4958)

2515 Mattresses & Bedsprings

Apartment Furnishings Co Inc ....E 817 568-2002
  Fort Worth (G-6390)
Cantwell Mattress Company ....F 361 883-8525
  Corpus Christi (G-3496)
Clifton Upholstery Co Inc ....F 254 753-0211
  Waco (G-20386)
◆ Continntal Silverline Pdts LLC ......D 713 222-7394
  Houston (G-9291)
Corsicana Bedding LLC ....D 903 872-2591
  Corsicana (G-3663)
◆ Corsicana Bedding LLC ....E 800 323-4349
  Dallas (G-4173)
Corsicana Bedding LLC ....E 903 257-3360
  Corsicana (G-3664)
Dormae Products Inc ....B 512 398-2650
  Lockhart (G-14167)
▲ Dynasty Consolidated Inds Inc ......D 214 630-3132
  Fort Worth (G-6599)
◆ Golden Pedic Inc ....E 214 630-5588
  Dallas (G-4412)
Leggett & Platt Incorporated ....E 817 378-0108
  Fort Worth (G-6782)
Leggett & Platt Incorporated ....E 817 626-6690
  Fort Worth (G-6783)
Leggett & Platt Incorporated ....E 214 391-3181
  Dallas (G-4590)
Leggett & Platt Incorporated ....B 972 875-8401
  Ennis (G-6109)
National Bedding Company LLC ....D 281 345-6237
  Houston (G-10966)
▲ Noahs Manufacturing Inc ....D 713 926-3500
  Houston (G-11062)
Quality Mattress Company Inc ....F 713 433-9155
  Houston (G-11497)
▲ Quatrefoil Partners LLC ....F 214 631-7117
  Dallas (G-4848)
Restline Bedding Products Inc ....F 713 921-1900
  Houston (G-11613)
◆ Royal Sleep Products Ltd ....D 817 834-7522
  Fort Worth (G-6967)
Ssb Manufacturing Company ....B 972 874-9666
  Grapevine (G-8055)
Texas Dept Criminal Justice ....A 936 295-6371
  Huntsville (G-12825)
▲ Texas Pocket Springs Tech Inc ......D 817 645-7666
  Keene (G-13465)
Ultimate Comfort Manufacturing ....E 713 641-0100
  Houston (G-12428)

2517 Wood T V, Radio, Phono & Sewing Cabinets

Cabinets Deluxe By Dale Inc ....D 512 259-2531
  Freeport (G-7195)
▲ Clearmediaone Inc ....E 713 622-9393
  Houston (G-9214)
Knot Hole LLC ....E 254 634-0773
  Killeen (G-13614)
Texas Home & Projects LLC ....G 956 546-8400
  Brownsville (G-2410)
Unique Cabinets Inc ....E 512 251-3058
  Pflugerville (G-16690)

2519 Household Furniture, NEC

Akcorp Inc ....F 409 833-8002
  Beaumont (G-1848)
▲ Allan Knight & Associates Inc ....F 214 741-2227
  Dallas (G-3923)
CPI Products Intl Inc ....E 512 868-0346
  Walburg (G-20488)

▲ Delta Composites LLC ....D 281 907-0619
  Houston (G-9430)
Global Fbrgls Sltons Texas LLC ....E 425 483-1303
  Sweetwater (G-19630)
Kerr Collection ....F 817 572-4663
  Burleson (G-2584)
LP & M Group Inc ....E 972 458-9393
  Dallas (G-4607)
▲ Patio One Furniture LP ....F 713 789-8080
  Houston (G-11260)
Regency Purchasing Inc ....F 713 973-0315
  Houston (G-11585)
▲ Wingate Partners LP ....F 214 720-1313
  Dallas (G-5195)

2521 Wood Office Furniture

A E S Custom Wood Inc ....G 972 262-0755
  Grand Prairie (G-7816)
Acacia Originals LLC ....F 877 565-5995
  Porter (G-17170)
Alamo City Counter Tops Inc ....E 210 732-4800
  San Antonio (G-17880)
Aris Designs Inc ....F 361 881-8131
  Corpus Christi (G-3475)
▲ Asmar Custom Cabinets Inc ....F 972 241-7676
  Dallas (G-3971)
Cabinet Creation Inc ....E 830 709-4116
  Lytle (G-14573)
Cabinets By Michael Inc ....F 817 485-1962
  Fort Worth (G-6485)
Cabinets Deluxe By Dale Inc ....D 512 259-2531
  Freeport (G-7195)
Classic Millwork and Products ....E 915 833-9922
  El Paso (G-5696)
▲ Cube Solutions LLC ....F 972 783-4880
  Dallas (G-4191)
◆ Evosite LLC ....E 713 365-3900
  Houston (G-9721)
Growth Holdings LLC ....E 972 241-9535
  Dallas (G-4418)
Hayes Building Service Inc ....F 940 484-7775
  Crossroads (G-3748)
Herman Miller Inc ....F 214 855-0200
  Dallas (G-4453)
Hill Country Cabinet Shop Inc ....F 830 228-5062
  Spring Branch (G-19270)
▲ Indeco Sales Inc ....E 254 939-5742
  Belton (G-2025)
Interntonal Laminating Systems ....F 713 645-0383
  Houston (G-10406)
J C Manufacturing Inc ....F 903 473-3770
  Emory (G-6083)
K & J Woodworks LLC ....D 512 668-4237
  Kyle (G-13683)
Kerr Collection ....F 817 572-4663
  Burleson (G-2584)
Keystone Millwork Inc ....E 979 823-4846
  Bryan (G-2485)
Knoll Inc ....F 713 629-5665
  Houston (G-10550)
Knoll Inc ....F 214 741-5819
  Dallas (G-4562)
Kuba-Tech Industries LLC ....F 817 924-5520
  Fort Worth (G-6775)
Lee Custom Works Inc ....F 210 432-1911
  San Antonio (G-18241)
Lindseys NW Off Furn Inc ....E 713 957-2424
  Houston (G-10647)
Lundy Services LLC ....E 972 494-2554
  Garland (G-7539)
Lutz Woodworks Llc ....E 972 429-5521
  Wylie (G-20940)
◆ Marco Dsplay Specialists GP Lc .....C 817 244-8300
  Fort Worth (G-6810)
Nevins LLC ....E 713 230-2100
  Cat Spring (G-2931)
Next Technologies Inc ....E 888 615-5721
  Round Rock (G-17675)
▲ Next Technologies Inc ....F 512 212-7758
  Georgetown (G-7666)
Office Furn Cmpanies Texas LLC ....F 281 724-1533
  League City (G-13970)
▲ Paragon Furniture Inc ....D 817 633-3242
  Arlington (G-749)
Pencil Cup Office Products Inc ....F 915 838-0026
  El Paso (G-5907)
Petroplex Cabinets Inc ....G 432 333-2025
  Odessa (G-16121)
▲ Proximity Systems Inc ....E 281 370-5004
  Tomball (G-20002)

Rick Triplett ....F 214 823-2830
  Dallas (G-4899)
Robert Shaw Mfg Co Inc ....F 817 927-2557
  Fort Worth (G-6962)
Saw Custom Millwork Inc ....E 972 288-2118
  Mesquite (G-15076)
▲ Smith System Manufacturing Co .....C 800 328-1061
  Carrollton (G-2816)
Solano Furniture Incorporated ....F 713 849-4855
  Houston (G-11934)
▲ Southwest Cabinet Corporation ......D 817 460-8681
  Pantego (G-16352)
Srg Ventures LLC ....E 281 214-8560
  Houston (G-12030)
Stella Hasegawa ....F 915 594-7633
  El Paso (G-5977)
▲ Ultra Seating Company ....E 469 865-2010
  Grand Prairie (G-7989)
Unique Cabinets Inc ....E 512 251-3058
  Pflugerville (G-16690)
Vincent Graphics & Supply Inc ....E 903 882-3123
  Tyler (G-20176)
▲ Wingate Partners LP ....F 214 720-1313
  Dallas (G-5195)

2522 Office Furniture, Except Wood

Ar-Case Inc ....F 210 735-5175
  San Antonio (G-17912)
▲ Bandy Incorporated ....F 972 276-6516
  Garland (G-7448)
Bret Broussard Inc ....G 210 224-6220
  San Antonio (G-17966)
▲ Caco Manufacturing Corporation ....F 713 644-0170
  Houston (G-9042)
Computer Comforts Inc ....F 281 535-2288
  Kemah (G-13472)
Dakota Cabinets Inc ....F 281 741-7695
  Houston (G-9397)
▲ Ergotect Corporation ....E 214 747-3746
  Dallas (G-4331)
◆ Evosite LLC ....E 713 365-3900
  Houston (G-9721)
Herman Miller Inc ....F 214 855-0200
  Dallas (G-4453)
Hilltop Texas Inc ....E 214 430-1311
  Allen (G-275)
▲ Kimball Elec - Mexico Inc ....E 956 205-4600
  Pharr (G-16705)
Lee Custom Works Inc ....F 210 432-1911
  San Antonio (G-18241)
◆ M J M International Corp ....E 956 781-5000
  Edinburg (G-5594)
▲ Mooreco Inc ....C 254 778-4727
  Temple (G-19691)
▲ Neutral Posture Inc ....D 979 778-0502
  Bryan (G-2494)
Nevins LLC ....E 713 230-2100
  Cat Spring (G-2931)
Next Technologies Inc ....E 888 615-5721
  Round Rock (G-17675)
▲ Next Technologies Inc ....F 512 212-7758
  Georgetown (G-7666)
Office Furn Cmpanies Texas LLC ....F 281 724-1533
  League City (G-13970)
▲ Paragon Furniture Inc ....D 817 633-3242
  Arlington (G-749)
Peck & Company ....E 713 526-2590
  Houston (G-11268)
▲ Sibbitt and Lott Inc ....G 214 742-6949
  Dallas (G-4958)
▲ Smith System Manufacturing Co .....C 800 328-1061
  Carrollton (G-2816)
Spaceman Home & Office Inc ....F 713 688-8808
  Houston (G-11991)
▲ Tesco Industries Lp ....D 979 865-2163
  Bellville (G-2012)
Tigua Enterprises Inc ....E 915 298-0700
  El Paso (G-6006)

2531 Public Building & Related Furniture

Adient Clanton Inc ....B 956 525-4515
  Brownsville (G-2334)
▲ Alan Charles Incorporated ....E 817 922-9834
  Fort Worth (G-6362)
American Grand Stand Inc ....F 214 638-7007
  Dallas (G-3942)
Capitol Seating Company ....E 254 939-1853
  Belton (G-2022)
Clarios ....D 254 774-9287
  Temple (G-19676)

SIC

Clarios	D	817 733-4326	
Fort Worth (G-6522)			
Clarios	C	281 518-8053	
Houston (G-9208)			
Dickson Furniture Mfrs LLC	F	713 747-0341	
Houston (G-9463)			
◆ Discovery Green Conservancy	E	713 400-7336	
Houston (G-9478)			
Discovery Green Conservancy	E	713 529-5534	
Houston (G-9479)			
Fellfab Corporation	E	817 595-7408	
Fort Worth (G-6627)			
Fleming & Son Corporation	E	972 263-1713	
Grand Prairie (G-7873)			
◆ Furniture By Thurston	C	210 227-4747	
San Antonio (G-18131)			
Herman Miller Inc	F	214 855-0200	
Dallas (G-4453)			
▲ Indeco Sales Inc	E	254 939-5742	
Belton (G-2025)			
Johnson Controls Inc	D	713 934-2400	
Houston (G-10482)			
Johnson Controls Inc	F	281 821-0121	
Houston (G-10483)			
Little Green Apples Inc	F	956 668-0028	
McAllen (G-14885)			
▲ Llebroc Industries Inc	E	817 831-3158	
Fort Worth (G-6791)			
▲ Maco Manufacturing Inc	E	254 939-5742	
Belton (G-2027)			
◆ Midwest Folding Products Corp	C	312 666-3366	
Temple (G-19690)			
▲ Neon Electric Corporation	D	281 987-1144	
Houston (G-11023)			
Pan Inc	E	713 589-6850	
Houston (G-11228)			
Panel Specialists Inc	E	254 774-9197	
Temple (G-19694)			
▲ Panel Specialists Inc	D	254 774-9800	
Temple (G-19695)			
▼ Rodco-Brandt Manufacturing	E	817 477-4118	
Mansfield (G-14713)			
Safespace Concepts Inc	F	713 956-0820	
Houston (G-11725)			
Sagus International Inc	F	630 413-5540	
Temple (G-19702)			
Sanbar Balls & Seats Inc	F	432 332-3755	
Odessa (G-16149)			
Schultz Industries Inc	D	254 666-5155	
Hewitt (G-8300)			
▲ Smith System Manufacturing Co	C	800 328-1061	
Carrollton (G-2816)			
▲ Southern Bleacher Company Inc	C	940 549-0733	
Graham (G-7789)			
▲ Stadium Chair Co LLC	F	432 682-4682	
Midland (G-15418)			
T R W Modernfold Company Inc	F	214 357-2572	
Lewisville (G-14096)			
▲ Tesco Industries Lp	D	979 865-2163	
Bellville (G-2012)			
▲ Texwood Ltd	D	888 388-3224	
Cameron (G-2644)			
▲ Ultra Seating Company	F	469 865-2010	
Grand Prairie (G-7989)			
United Aviation ACC Inc	F	817 447-8000	
Burleson (G-2600)			
▼ United Rtorcraft Solutions LLC	E	940 627-0626	
Decatur (G-5256)			
Unlimited Supply Inc	E	936 890-8997	
Willis (G-20868)			

2541 Wood, Office & Store Fixtures

77 Stone	F	915 590-0770	
El Paso (G-5631)			
Ace Automatics Inc	F	903 852-3004	
Ben Wheeler (G-2030)			
▲ Advanced Fixtures Inc	C	972 784-8800	
Farmersville (G-6220)			
Aircraft Composite Inc	F	214 638-0138	
Dallas (G-3909)			
Alamo City Counter Tops Inc	C	210 732-4800	
San Antonio (G-17880)			
Amarillo Plstic Fbricators Ltd	F	806 372-1207	
Amarillo (G-397)			
Ameritek Design Inc	E	281 442-7767	
Houston (G-8621)			
Architectural Wood Designs	F	972 935-0222	
Waxahachie (G-20527)			
Arismendy Josias	E	817 353-1244	
Fort Worth (G-6401)			

Bentwood Companies Inc	D	972 227-6855	
Lancaster (G-13839)			
Bmp & Associates Inc	E	713 779-8677	
Houston (G-8927)			
Cabfixco Inc	E	214 389-1520	
Dallas (G-4075)			
Cabinet Creation Inc	E	830 709-4116	
Lytle (G-14573)			
Center Fixtures	D	936 598-2247	
Center (G-2996)			
Dale Nichols Marble Inc	F	817 341-8970	
Weatherford (G-20585)			
Daryan Design Inc	F	214 905-6022	
Dallas (G-4239)			
Diesel Displays & Interior LLC	D	800 747-4417	
Carrollton (G-2865)			
Dutch Marble Creations	F	956 399-6767	
San Benito (G-18656)			
E and H Originals In Wood Inc	F	832 203-7629	
Houston (G-9552)			
F C Designs Inc	E	713 462-1442	
Houston (G-9743)			
Falcon Wood Products 2 Ltd	E	936 295-9381	
Huntsville (G-12811)			
◆ Faubion Associates Inc	C	214 565-1000	
Dallas (G-4355)			
Fixture Exchange Corporation	E	817 429-2496	
Joshua (G-13320)			
Greenhaw Cabinets Inc	F	325 646-8319	
Brownwood (G-2430)			
Gunckel Archtectural Millworks	E	830 303-0688	
Seguin (G-18839)			
Herman Miller Inc	F	214 855-0200	
Dallas (G-4453)			
▲ Hollman Inc	C	972 815-4000	
Irving (G-13058)			
Idx Dallas LLC	D	972 637-1525	
Cedar Hill (G-2944)			
Incounters Inc	E	325 675-5909	
Abilene (G-51)			
Irving Counter Inc	E	972 438-4343	
Irving (G-13066)			
J & H Manufacturing Inc	E	830 665-5230	
Devine (G-5450)			
Jay H Fixtures Inc	E	972 223-2245	
De Soto (G-5239)			
Johnnies Plastics Inc	E	210 533-8463	
San Antonio (G-18205)			
Johns Dovetail Shop	F	972 557-0775	
Mesquite (G-15055)			
K & J Woodworks LLC	D	512 668-4237	
Kyle (G-13683)			
K & K Langham Ltd	D	512 835-5100	
Austin (G-1263)			
Kamal Incorporated	D	210 695-2678	
Helotes (G-8241)			
Keystone Millwork Inc	E	979 823-4846	
Bryan (G-2485)			
Kitchen Cabinets Inc	D	972 660-6304	
Grand Prairie (G-7905)			
▲ Legacy Housing Corporation	C	817 799-4900	
Bedford (G-1976)			
▲ Legacy Lockers LLC	E	972 937-1088	
Dallas (G-4588)			
Leggett & Platt Incorporated	C	817 922-5000	
Fort Worth (G-6784)			
Liberty Company	E	817 921-0218	
Fort Worth (G-6788)			
▲ Maco Manufacturing Inc	E	254 939-5742	
Belton (G-2027)			
◆ Madix Inc	A	214 515-5400	
Terrell (G-19740)			
◆ Marco Display Specialists LP	B	817 244-8300	
Fort Worth (G-6809)			
◆ Marco Dsplay Specialists GP Lc	C	817 244-8300	
Fort Worth (G-6810)			
Mike Davis and Associates Inc	E	512 836-8442	
Austin (G-1343)			
Morgan Cabinetry Inc	F	972 278-8836	
Garland (G-7555)			
▲ Mpi Marketing Inc	E	972 403-7801	
Plano (G-16935)			
Panel Processing Texas Inc	F	903 586-2423	
Jacksonville (G-13255)			
▲ Panel Specialists Inc	D	254 774-9800	
Temple (G-19695)			
Quality Case & Fixture Inc	F	409 832-3200	
Beaumont (G-1943)			
R & R Custom Cabinets Inc	F	972 247-4697	
Carrollton (G-2883)			

▲ Republic Nat Inds Texas LP	C	903 935-3680	
Marshall (G-14800)			
Robert Shaw Mfg Co Inc	E	817 927-2557	
Fort Worth (G-6962)			
◆ Rodgers-Wade Mfg Co Inc	E	903 739-2500	
Paris (G-16367)			
S & S Cabinet Shop Inc	F	325 655-6757	
San Angelo (G-17825)			
Shioleno Industries Inc	F	817 465-9361	
Arlington (G-780)			
Southwest Solutions Group Inc	E	972 250-1970	
Lewisville (G-14091)			
▲ Stonefab Intl LLC	G	806 352-3416	
Amarillo (G-464)			
Sunrise Woods Designs	D	972 842-3579	
Ferris (G-6232)			
▲ Texas Fixtures and Interiors	D	512 846-1998	
Hutto (G-12886)			
US Surface Warehouse	E	866 433-2229	
Austin (G-1617)			
V T I of Texas Inc	E	979 778-2804	
Bryan (G-2515)			
Venus Marble Co Inc	D	972 223-8008	
Desoto (G-5447)			
▲ Walls & Forms Inc	D	972 745-0800	
Fort Worth (G-7117)			
Wilsonart Intl Holdings LLC	D	254 207-7000	
Temple (G-19716)			
Wilsonart Intl Holdings LLC	E	254 207-6000	
Temple (G-19717)			
Wilsonart Intl Holdings LLC	E	254 207-7000	
Temple (G-19718)			
Wilsonart LLC	F	254 207-7000	
Temple (G-19719)			
Wilsonart LLC	F	254 207-7000	
Temple (G-19721)			
Wilsonart LLC	E	254 742-2451	
Temple (G-19720)			
Wilsonart LLC	E	254 207-0207	
Temple (G-19722)			
Wilsonart LLC	F	713 576-5500	
Houston (G-12676)			

2542 Partitions & Fixtures, Except Wood

American Egle Mailbox Mfr Corp	F	214 358-2873	
Dallas (G-3939)			
▲ BAC Products Inc	E	832 230-1463	
Houston (G-8785)			
Cabfixco Inc	E	214 389-1520	
Dallas (G-4075)			
Cedra Pharmacy Houston LLC	E	713 621-0621	
Houston (G-9117)			
Center Fixtures	D	936 598-2247	
Center (G-2996)			
Classic Millwork and Products	E	915 833-9922	
El Paso (G-5696)			
Custom Delis Equipment Co Inc	E	817 831-7080	
Fort Worth (G-6567)			
◆ Displays By Martin Paul Inc	E	940 458-7976	
Denton (G-5360)			
Empire Electric Inc	E	713 688-0151	
Houston (G-9619)			
◆ Ets-Lindgren Inc	E	512 531-6400	
Cedar Park (G-2968)			
Fab-Tex Fixture & Mfg Co	E	972 660-6304	
Grand Prairie (G-7868)			
◆ Faubion Associates Inc	C	214 565-1000	
Dallas (G-4355)			
◆ G2 Automated Technologies LLC	E	972 479-0699	
Dallas (G-4390)			
Growth Holdings LLC	E	972 241-9535	
Dallas (G-4418)			
Herman Miller Inc	E	214 855-0200	
Dallas (G-4453)			
◆ Houston Wire Works Inc	F	713 946-2920	
Houston (G-10265)			
Hufcor Inc	F	972 850-2200	
Dallas (G-4470)			
Hull Supply Company Inc	E	512 385-1262	
Austin (G-1213)			
Hutchins Oil and Lube	E	972 225-0846	
Hutchins (G-12867)			
Idx Corporation	C	314 739-4120	
Cedar Hill (G-2943)			
Idx Dallas LLC	D	972 637-1525	
Cedar Hill (G-2944)			
Incounters Inc	E	325 675-5909	
Abilene (G-51)			
Interlake Mecalux Inc	E	972 245-3910	
Dallas (G-4506)			

▲ Intrapack Corporation ....E 214 348-7105
Dallas *(G-4509)*

J & H Manufacturing Inc ....F 830 665-5230
Devine *(G-5450)*

Jim Dandy Boxes Inc ....E 817 608-9180
Grand Prairie *(G-7903)*

Johnnies Plastics Inc ....E 210 533-8463
San Antonio *(G-18205)*

Kaspar Wire Works Inc ....A 361 594-3327
Shiner *(G-18944)*

Kcm Cabinets Inc ....F 210 695-2213
San Antonio *(G-18221)*

Knickerbocker Partition Corp ....F 972 438-5330
Irving *(G-13078)*

Knox Jr Leighton ....E 806 327-5420
Tahoka *(G-19641)*

Lamrite ....F 512 385-4455
Austin *(G-1281)*

Liberty Company ....E 817 921-0218
Fort Worth *(G-6788)*

▲ Loftwall Inc ....F 214 239-3162
Grand Prairie *(G-7916)*

◆ Madix Inc ....A 214 515-5400
Terrell *(G-19740)*

Martin Paul Inc ....F 940 458-7976
Denton *(G-5380)*

Performance Companies LP ....C 214 665-1000
Dallas *(G-4797)*

Proper Storage Systems LLC ....E 830 372-1380
Seguin *(G-18856)*

Quality Store Equipment Inc ....F 713 278-8634
Houston *(G-11501)*

R & R Custom Cabinets Inc ....F 972 247-4697
Carrollton *(G-2883)*

R C T Inc ....E 972 231-9698
Dallas *(G-4853)*

Rj & RC Associates LLC ....E 214 352-4690
Dallas *(G-4903)*

S & S Cabinet Shop Inc ....F 325 655-6757
San Angelo *(G-17825)*

▲ Semasys Inc ....C 713 869-8331
Houston *(G-11825)*

Shioleno Industries Inc ....F 817 465-9361
Arlington *(G-780)*

▲ South Txas Lghthouse For Blind ....C 361 883-6553
Corpus Christi *(G-3627)*

Southwest Solutions Group Inc ....E 972 250-1970
Lewisville *(G-14091)*

Sullys Lone Star Office Pdts ....F 512 835-9506
Austin *(G-1544)*

◆ Taprite Inc ....E 210 523-0800
San Antonio *(G-18522)*

▲ Thom-Bat-Ler Enterprises ....F 972 660-4056
Grand Prairie *(G-7982)*

United Office Interiors Inc ....D 214 381-0101
Dallas *(G-5136)*

Universal Display & Fixs Co ....B 972 221-5157
Lewisville *(G-14100)*

Universal Display & Fixs Co ....C 972 829-2366
Coppell *(G-3452)*

◆ Universal Display and Fix Co ....C 972 434-8067
Lewisville *(G-14101)*

Universal Display and Fix Co ....C 972 221-5157
Flower Mound *(G-6291)*

V T I of Texas Inc ....E 979 778-2804
Bryan *(G-2515)*

◆ Vira Insight LLC ....C 800 366-2345
Lewisville *(G-14107)*

Vira Insight LLC ....D 800 366-2345
Lewisville *(G-14108)*

2591 Drapery Hardware, Window Blinds & Shades

A & E Venetian Blind Company ....F 940 767-1449
Wichita Falls *(G-20735)*

Academy Venetian Blinds Co Inc ....F 361 852-6088
Corpus Christi *(G-3465)*

Alpha Door and Rail Inc ....F 817 358-8687
Aurora *(G-853)*

Aramco Home Improvement LLC ....F 409 762-9652
Galveston *(G-7387)*

◆ Awntech Corporation ....E 817 354-9600
Euless *(G-6132)*

Boriack Interiors Inc ....E 214 376-1814
Dallas *(G-4044)*

Custom Drapery Company Inc ....D 713 225-9221
Houston *(G-9370)*

Drapery Man Corporation ....E 210 733-5444
San Antonio *(G-18071)*

◆ Fleuron Enterprises Inc ....D 214 678-0805
Dallas *(G-4369)*

Glenwood Blind & Awning Co Inc ....G 903 597-2088
Tyler *(G-20090)*

Hc Interiors Inc ....E 214 350-0468
Carrollton *(G-2754)*

K & S Products Inc ....F 972 820-0007
Carrollton *(G-2772)*

Kites Draperies Inc ....E 817 336-1027
Fort Worth *(G-6764)*

Piw Ventures Ltd ....F 713 932-9311
Houston *(G-11340)*

Plantation Shutter ....F 214 341-3677
Dallas *(G-4809)*

Plumlee Place LLC ....F 254 662-4021
Robinson *(G-17501)*

Ral & Associates Inc ....E 903 833-5191
Ben Wheeler *(G-2034)*

Satori Home Limited LLC ....E 855 472-8674
Dallas *(G-4937)*

▲ Sibbitt and Lott Inc ....G 214 742-6949
Dallas *(G-4958)*

Springs Window Fashions LLC ....F 608 826-7052
Pharr *(G-16711)*

Tex Sun Manufacturing Co ....F 830 393-5186
Floresville *(G-6251)*

Tex-Sun Shade Specialties Inc ....F 972 279-0132
Dallas *(G-5053)*

Texton ....D 972 494-5941
Garland *(G-7600)*

◆ Timber Blinds Mfg Ltd ....B 972 569-9100
McKinney *(G-14982)*

Vertical Nerve Inc ....F 800 330-9450
Dallas *(G-5164)*

▲ Window Outfitters LP ....E 469 619-0892
Dallas *(G-5193)*

▲ Worldwide Wndows Tratments LLC ....E 718 893-9370
Dallas *(G-5203)*

Yates Carpet Incorporated ....E 806 795-9942
Lubbock *(G-14516)*

Ybarra Group Inc ....F 210 533-5323
San Antonio *(G-18629)*

2599 Furniture & Fixtures, NEC

72nd & Thornhill LLC ....E 469 318-5087
Wylie *(G-20923)*

◆ Avteq Inc ....G 214 905-9001
Dallas *(G-3994)*

BBA&j&v inc ....F 469 998-0660
Frisco *(G-7256)*

Bianco Brothers ....F 817 922-0885
Fort Worth *(G-6449)*

▲ C H Industries Inc ....D 972 416-1304
Carrollton *(G-2709)*

Cabinettech Inc ....F 325 670-0414
Abilene *(G-28)*

Carter Lee Properties LLC ....F 713 385-8092
Richmond *(G-17452)*

Chef Units LLC ....F 713 589-2613
Houston *(G-9169)*

◆ Chippenhook Corporation ....E 800 527-5866
Lewisville *(G-14036)*

Chiron Holdings Inc ....E 210 524-9000
San Antonio *(G-18003)*

Complete Restaurant Svcs Inc ....E 214 350-1110
Dallas *(G-4150)*

Dickson Furniture Mfrs LLC ....F 713 747-0341
Houston *(G-9463)*

Doiy LLC ....F 469 513-4159
Dallas *(G-4270)*

Formaspace LP ....E 512 279-2576
Austin *(G-1165)*

◆ G2 Automated Technologies LLC ....E 972 479-0699
Dallas *(G-4390)*

Image Furnishings Inc ....F 806 747-6500
Lubbock *(G-14424)*

Jaguar Hospitality Svcs Corp ....E 214 295-3574
Plano *(G-16896)*

Joe Garcia ....F 361 436-2130
George West *(G-7626)*

Kci International Inc ....E 210 524-9000
San Antonio *(G-18219)*

Kuba-Tech Industries LLC ....F 817 924-5520
Fort Worth *(G-6775)*

La Paleteria ....D 214 887-8278
Dallas *(G-4576)*

Larry Prters Cstm Intr Dsgns I ....F 409 296-3868
Winnie *(G-20888)*

▲ Lmt Rustic & Western Imports ....F 972 641-6700
Grand Prairie *(G-7913)*

MBS Construction I Ltd ....E 817 473-0328
Mansfield *(G-14693)*

Metroplex Millworks Inc ....F 214 358-1770
Dallas *(G-4672)*

▼ Onepointe Solutions LLC ....D 866 222-7494
Elgin *(G-6056)*

Provence Hardware Corporation ....F 817 572-4663
Burleson *(G-2594)*

Robinson Aerospace Inc ....F 817 253-0639
Dallas *(G-4906)*

Shioleno Industries Inc ....F 817 465-9361
Arlington *(G-780)*

Solano Furniture Incorporated ....F 713 849-4855
Houston *(G-11934)*

Srg Ventures LLC ....E 281 214-8560
Houston *(G-12030)*

▼ Tables Manufacturing Inc ....B 972 932-4148
Kaufman *(G-13464)*

Texas Metal Equipment Co Ltd ....E 713 466-8722
Houston *(G-12241)*

Tqi LLC ....E 830 401-4400
Seguin *(G-18869)*

Transitions Industries LLC ....F 806 698-6200
Lubbock *(G-14497)*

Travis Millwork Inc ....E 210 525-8088
San Antonio *(G-18564)*

26 PAPER AND ALLIED PRODUCTS

2611 Pulp Mills

Akrotex Films Inc ....E 409 886-0632
Orange *(G-16229)*

Aldersgate Enrichment Center ....D 325 646-2566
Early *(G-5556)*

Bell Processing Incorporated ....D 940 322-8621
Wichita Falls *(G-20744)*

◆ BLUE CUBE OPERATIONS LLC ....F 979 238-2011
Freeport *(G-7192)*

Delta Paper Stock Corp ....E 713 666-1440
Bellaire *(G-1993)*

Graphic Packaging Intl LLC ....A 903 796-7101
Queen City *(G-17220)*

Greenstar North Amer Holdings ....A 713 965-0005
Houston *(G-10036)*

Master Fibers Inc ....D 915 544-2299
El Paso *(G-5868)*

Monterrey Iron & Metal Ltd ....A 210 927-2727
San Antonio *(G-18318)*

One Source Recycling Inc ....D 512 549-2812
Austin *(G-1386)*

Packaging One Inc ....F 713 674-0302
Houston *(G-11220)*

Pratt Industries USA Inc ....E 940 387-7291
Denton *(G-5393)*

Prime Momento LLC ....F 832 643-4605
Sugar Land *(G-19529)*

Snyder Iron Metal ....F 325 573-6862
Snyder *(G-19008)*

2621 Paper Mills

▲ Ampersand Art Supply Inc ....E 512 322-0278
Buda *(G-2519)*

▼ Build A Sign LLC ....C 512 374-9850
Austin *(G-1015)*

Creative Molded Packaging LLC ....F 915 881-8401
El Paso *(G-5705)*

Domtar Industries LLC ....C 972 929-3565
Irving *(G-13001)*

Domtar Paper Company LLC ....C 972 929-8581
Irving *(G-13002)*

Duro Bag Manufacturing Company ....C 956 843-6607
Hidalgo *(G-8305)*

Ennis Inc ....C 903 496-2244
Wolfe City *(G-20906)*

Garland Independent School Dst ....D 972 494-8580
Garland *(G-7494)*

Georgia-Pacific LLC ....D 940 205-9558
Denton *(G-5368)*

Gipson Group LLC ....G 512 931-2211
Georgetown *(G-7654)*

GL Brands Inc ....F 888 811-4367
Fort Worth *(G-6670)*

Gold Bond Building Pdts LLC ....F 830 864-4100
Harper *(G-8209)*

Graphic Packaging Intl LLC ....A 903 796-7101
Queen City *(G-17220)*

Halbert Mill Company Texas Inc ....F 903 683-2788
Jacksonville *(G-13243)*

Howred Corporation ....C 956 712-1003
Laredo *(G-13894)*

Information MGT Solutions LLC ....E 210 826-4994
San Antonio *(G-18182)*

Inservio LLC ....E 713 344-1214
Houston *(G-10377)*

Inservio3 LLC ....G 213 439-9656
Georgetown *(G-7658)*

Installed Building Pdts Inc ....E 210 937-1082
San Antonio *(G-18643)*

International Paper Company ....C 972 512-0400
Carrollton *(G-2767)*

International Paper Company ....C 956 383-3811
Edinburg *(G-5590)*

International Paper Company ....E 713 996-9877
Houston *(G-10405)*

International Paper Company ....C 956 387-8100
Edinburg *(G-5591)*

International Paper Company ....E 210 225-2901
San Antonio *(G-18193)*

International Paper Company ....C 210 661-8543
San Antonio *(G-18194)*

International Paper Company ....C 915 858-8877
El Paso *(G-5815)*

International Paper Company ....C 979 885-4191
Sealy *(G-18810)*

International Paper Company ....E 972 416-8680
Carrollton *(G-2768)*

International Paper Company ....D 972 602-9880
Grand Prairie *(G-7895)*

International Paper Company ....C 817 338-4000
Fort Worth *(G-6725)*

International Paper Company ....C 972 641-2972
Grand Prairie *(G-7896)*

James D Vossler ....F 281 376-6420
Cypress *(G-3804)*

Kimberly-Clark Corporation ....A 903 737-5100
Paris *(G-16364)*

Kimberly-Clark Corporation ....F 817 847-0211
Fort Worth *(G-6761)*

◆ Kimberly-Clark Corporation ....B 972 281-1200
Irving *(G-13075)*

Koch Pulp & Paper Trading LLC ....F 713 544-5070
Houston *(G-10554)*

Longhorn Paper Converting LLC ......E 214 988-3251
Grand Prairie *(G-7918)*

Miller Paper Company ....E 806 353-0317
Amarillo *(G-502)*

Pactiv LLC ....G 254 770-4100
Temple *(G-19693)*

Paper Source Inc ....G 469 304-5168
Plano *(G-16965)*

R W Gonzalez Office Pdts Inc ....F 512 300-2300
Austin *(G-1448)*

Sample House & Resale Shop Inc ....E 214 688-0751
Dallas *(G-4929)*

South Texas Paper LLC ....F 956 239-1473
Pharr *(G-16710)*

▲ Specialty Packaging Inc ....C 817 922-9727
Fort Worth *(G-7010)*

▲ Sunshine Paper Corp ....F 956 283-9999
Donna *(G-5493)*

▲ Texas Envelope Company ....E 214 358-5661
Dallas *(G-5060)*

◆ Texas Tissue Converting LLC ....D 281 821-0429
Houston *(G-12257)*

Valro-K LLC ....E 210 937-1082
San Antonio *(G-18647)*

Versa Printing Inc ....E 972 243-5353
Dallas *(G-5163)*

▲ Wingate Partners LP ....F 214 720-1313
Dallas *(G-5195)*

Zapco Inc ....E 512 237-5521
Smithville *(G-18980)*

2631 Paperboard Mills

Age Industries Ltd ....E 915 852-9099
Horizon City *(G-8361)*

Caraustar Industries Inc ....E 903 799-5100
Atlanta *(G-841)*

Caraustar Industries Inc ....E 903 793-6231
Texarkana *(G-19758)*

Creative Molded Packaging LLC ......F 915 881-8401
El Paso *(G-5705)*

Custom Box Solutions LLC ....F 888 376-8061
Houston *(G-9366)*

Envirotainer Inc ....F 972 831-3800
Irving *(G-13016)*

Georgia-Pacific LLC ....D 940 205-9558
Denton *(G-5368)*

Graphic Packaging Intl LLC ....A 903 796-7101
Queen City *(G-17220)*

Green Bay Packaging Inc ....E 915 822-9700
El Paso *(G-5791)*

International Paper Company ....C 956 682-9406
McAllen *(G-14874)*

International Paper Company ....D 806 381-0121
Amarillo *(G-439)*

McKinley Paper Company ....E 956 487-7424
Rio Grande City *(G-17473)*

Packaging Corporation America ....C 254 776-2360
Waco *(G-20441)*

Packaging Corporation America ....D 469 568-7000
Carrollton *(G-2789)*

Packaging One Inc ....F 713 674-0302
Houston *(G-11220)*

RTS Packaging LLC ....D 214 331-6555
Dallas *(G-4917)*

Sctray Company ....D 817 473-0233
Mansfield *(G-14716)*

Sheldon Industries Inc ....F 713 398-2427
Houston *(G-11856)*

Sonoco Products Company ....D 903 665-3966
Jefferson *(G-13288)*

Stratas Foods LLC ....F 469 341-7055
Dallas *(G-5015)*

Thompson Paper Pdts Texas Inc ....E 713 869-6636
Houston *(G-12278)*

Western Pulp Products Co ....C 903 586-3608
Jacksonville *(G-13266)*

Westrock Mwv LLC ....D 409 276-3000
Silsbee *(G-18958)*

Westrock Rkt LLC ....D 903 455-0147
Greenville *(G-8096)*

2652 Set-Up Paperboard Boxes

Abox Paperboard Company ....D 972 932-9800
Forney *(G-6301)*

2653 Corrugated & Solid Fiber Boxes

101 Products LLC ....F 832 247-7979
Houston *(G-8400)*

Accurate Die Cutting Inc ....E 972 562-7921
McKinney *(G-14922)*

▲ Action Box Co Inc ....C 713 869-7701
Houston *(G-8469)*

Age Industries Ltd ....E 254 939-5828
Belton *(G-2017)*

Age Industries Ltd ....E 956 399-8279
San Benito *(G-18654)*

Age Industries Ltd ....D 817 477-5266
Cleburne *(G-3079)*

Age Industries Ltd ....D 210 659-1301
Cibolo *(G-3060)*

Age Industries Ltd ....E 713 460-3060
Houston *(G-8502)*

Age Industries Ltd ....E 915 852-9099
Horizon City *(G-8361)*

All Star Corrugated ....E 817 551-5580
Fort Worth *(G-6371)*

All Star Corrugated ....D 817 454-8640
Burleson *(G-2566)*

Amarillo Custom Box Co ....E 806 371-9111
Amarillo *(G-393)*

▲ America Empack Inc ....E 956 618-3922
McAllen *(G-14837)*

American Carton Company Inc ....E 817 473-2992
Mansfield *(G-14655)*

▲ Amerisource Companies LP ....E 972 380-2000
Carrollton *(G-2856)*

Apple Corrugated Packaging Inc ....E 214 331-9000
Duncanville *(G-5528)*

Benson Box Inc ....F 210 662-6383
San Antonio *(G-17947)*

Buckeye Corrugated Inc ....E 713 869-9121
Houston *(G-9006)*

▲ Capital City Container Corp ....F 512 312-1222
Buda *(G-2523)*

▲ Central Texas Corrugated Inc ......C 254 776-6902
Waco *(G-20380)*

Corrugated Concepts Packg Inc ....E 713 462-5600
Houston *(G-9326)*

Corrugated Services Garland ....G 972 494-4059
Garland *(G-7465)*

D & S Container Inc ....D 214 637-7957
Dallas *(G-4199)*

Danhil Containers II Ltd ....E 254 773-0704
Temple *(G-19678)*

Durabox Corrugated Pdts Inc ....F 915 440-4409
El Paso *(G-5725)*

East Texas Containers Inc ....E 903 595-6444
Tyler *(G-20079)*

Ecd Acquisitions Inc ....D 254 776-2360
Waco *(G-20395)*

Edi Weyerhaeuser McAllen ....G 956 682-9406
McAllen *(G-14855)*

Fairbanks Packaging LLC ....G 817 849-1366
Grand Prairie *(G-7869)*

Georgia-Pacific LLC ....C 972 937-8804
Waxahachie *(G-20543)*

Green Bay Packaging Inc ....C 817 551-1934
Fort Worth *(G-6675)*

Green Bay Packaging Inc ....E 915 822-9700
El Paso *(G-5791)*

Hager Containers L P ....D 972 417-7660
Carrollton *(G-2750)*

Harris Packaging Corporation ....D 817 429-6262
Haltom City *(G-8148)*

Herman Packaging Co Inc ....E 713 462-0228
Houston *(G-10159)*

◆ Hurley Packaging Texas Inc ....E 806 687-6179
Lubbock *(G-14422)*

Ics Enterprises LLP ....B 915 239-9256
El Paso *(G-5808)*

International Paper Company ....C 972 417-1350
Carrollton *(G-2766)*

International Paper Company ....D 806 381-0121
Amarillo *(G-439)*

International Paper Company ....C 956 682-9406
McAllen *(G-14874)*

International Paper Company ....C 972 641-2972
Grand Prairie *(G-7896)*

Jim Dandy Boxes Inc ....E 817 608-9180
Grand Prairie *(G-7903)*

Kessler Packaging Inc ....E 915 591-8161
El Paso *(G-5829)*

▲ Liberty Carton Co - Texas ....C 817 577-6100
Haltom City *(G-8151)*

◆ Lone Star Container Sales Corp ....F 972 579-1551
Irving *(G-13088)*

▲ Lone Star Corrugated Cont Corp ...C 972 579-1551
Irving *(G-13089)*

Menasha Packaging Company LLC ....E 330 419-3505
Lewisville *(G-14064)*

Mick & David Enterprises Inc ....F 214 350-5765
Dallas *(G-4674)*

▲ National Cnverting Fulfillment ......E 972 875-5096
Ennis *(G-6112)*

Ok-Go Packaging Inc ....E 915 440-2500
El Paso *(G-5900)*

Orora North America ....E 972 724-2828
Grapevine *(G-8050)*

Orora Packaging Solutions ....D 281 517-8600
Houston *(G-11193)*

Packaging Corporation America ....C 210 798-1700
San Antonio *(G-18362)*

Packaging Corporation America ....C 972 422-4270
Plano *(G-16963)*

Packaging Corporation America ....C 214 227-5124
Garland *(G-7565)*

Packaging Corporation America ....E 817 640-1888
Arlington *(G-746)*

Packaging Corporation America ....C 254 776-8890
Waco *(G-20442)*

Packaging Corporation America ....D 956 464-5664
Donna *(G-5489)*

Packaging Corporation America ....E 915 779-1291
El Paso *(G-5903)*

Packaging Corporation America ....C 254 776-2360
Waco *(G-20441)*

Packaging Corporation America ....D 469 568-7000
Carrollton *(G-2789)*

Perennial Design LLC ....F 512 387-1582
Austin *(G-1410)*

Pratt Industries Inc ....E 972 296-2900
Dallas *(G-4816)*

Pratt Industries Inc ....D 210 651-6309
Schertz *(G-18759)*

Pratt Rockwall Corrugating LLC ....C 770 918-5678
Rockwall *(G-17560)*

Rio Grande Container Inc ....E 956 447-5949
Weslaco *(G-20668)*

▲ Sbu Group LP ....F 281 564-6464
Houston *(G-11763)*

▲ Smurfit Kappa Bates LLC ....C 817 498-3200
North Richland Hills *(G-15881)*

Smurfit Kappa Bates LLC ....F 903 234-1100
Longview *(G-14309)*

Smurfit Kappa Bates LLC ....D 210 436-7777
Von Ormy *(G-20352)*

Smurfit Kappa North Amer LLC ....B 214 515-6400
Forney *(G-6314)*

▲ Smurfit Kappa North Amer LLC ....B 800 306-8326
Irving *(G-13182)*

Smurfit Kappa North Amer LLC ....E 713 869-5900
Houston *(G-11926)*

Starcorr Sheets LLC ....D 254 598-7800
Temple *(G-19703)*

Supplynet Inc ....D 214 637-0160
Dallas *(G-5029)*

Taylormade Pllets Lgistics LLC ....E 210 566-3833
Boerne *(G-2139)*

▼ Technology Container Corp ....E 972 228-1617
Desoto *(G-5444)*

Texas Corrugated Box Packg LLC ....E 817 454-2037
Fort Worth *(G-7046)*

Titan Corrugated Inc ....E 214 513-2691
Flower Mound *(G-6289)*

Tyler Corrugated Box Inc ....E 903 581-4950
Tyler *(G-20169)*

Unipal Intl Ltd Co Texas ....F 850 232-5586
Pasadena *(G-16521)*

US Corrugated Mesquite LLC ....F 801 798-7331
Mesquite *(G-15083)*

Ward Packaging of Fort Worth ....E 817 334-0484
Fort Worth *(G-7126)*

▲ West Texas Container Corp ....E 915 859-6712
El Paso *(G-6031)*

Westrock Container LLC ....D 972 285-8865
Mesquite *(G-15085)*

Westrock Cp LLC ....B 915 778-7350
El Paso *(G-6037)*

Westrock Cp LLC ....C 817 568-0918
Fort Worth *(G-7144)*

Westrock Cp LLC ....D 281 830-0131
Houston *(G-12657)*

Westrock Cp LLC ....E 281 893-8918
Houston *(G-12658)*

Westrock Cp LLC ....E 915 778-7350
El Paso *(G-6038)*

Westrock Mwv LLC ....C 409 276-3243
Evadale *(G-6167)*

Westrock Rkt LLC ....C 214 941-3400
Dallas *(G-5184)*

Weyerhaeuser Company ....C 972 641-3891
Grand Prairie *(G-7992)*

Wrkco Inc ....F 817 624-8000
Fort Worth *(G-7152)*

2655 Fiber Cans, Tubes & Drums

Age Industries Ltd ....D 817 477-5266
Cleburne *(G-3079)*

Age Industries Ltd ....E 915 852-9099
Horizon City *(G-8361)*

Allegiant Industrial LLC ....E 409 782-7963
Beaumont *(G-1849)*

Caraustar Industrial and Con ....E 409 898-6600
Silsbee *(G-18950)*

Caraustar Industries Inc ....E 903 793-6231
Texarkana *(G-19758)*

Caraustar Industries Inc ....E 903 799-5100
Atlanta *(G-841)*

Case Hafer Inc ....F 281 341-5070
Rosenberg *(G-17578)*

▲ Custom Ppr Tube Southwest Inc ......F 817 385-5367
Arlington *(G-656)*

▲ Drilltec Technologies Inc ....D 713 895-9852
Houston *(G-9531)*

▼ Dtc P&T Liquidating Co ....F 713 996-8802
Houston *(G-9534)*

Equipment Storage Service Inc ....F 214 374-3995
Dallas *(G-4329)*

▲ Greif Inc ....F 281 573-6380
Baytown *(G-1788)*

Greif Inc ....E 281 470-4469
La Porte *(G-13740)*

Greif Inc ....E 817 834-6333
Haltom City *(G-8144)*

Greif Inc ....F 281 470-4400
La Porte *(G-13741)*

Greif Inc ....E 817 222-0413
Haltom City *(G-8145)*

Greif Inc ....E 713 462-0073
Houston *(G-10039)*

Impact Composite Tech Ltd ....E 806 385-1015
Littlefield *(G-14146)*

▲ Paper Tubes & Sales Co ....E 214 631-0973
Dallas *(G-4787)*

Schutz Container Systems Inc ....C 281 474-5200
Pasadena *(G-16503)*

Sonoco Products Company ....E 817 461-5616
Irving *(G-13184)*

Sonoco Products Company ....D 972 416-2595
Carrollton *(G-2817)*

Sonoco Products Company ....D 903 665-3966
Jefferson *(G-13288)*

▼ Transcom Packaging Inc ....F 979 885-1800
Sealy *(G-18821)*

Western Pulp Products Co ....F 903 586-3608
Jacksonville *(G-13266)*

2656 Sanitary Food Containers

Convermex USA Corp ....E 210 319-2972
San Antonio *(G-18025)*

▲ Gca Products Inc ....G 972 506-3196
Dallas *(G-4395)*

Georgia-Pacific WD Pdts S LLC ....A 936 398-2511
Camden *(G-2638)*

Huhtamaki Inc ....B 903 427-5711
Clarksville *(G-3073)*

MANS Distributors Inc ....E 972 930-0330
Carrollton *(G-2777)*

Smith Tank & Equipment Company ......E 903 597-5541
Tyler *(G-20153)*

Tetra Pak Materials LP ....C 940 565-8800
Denton *(G-5405)*

Various Fields LLC ....F 512 788-2228
Austin *(G-1624)*

2657 Folding Paperboard Boxes

Abox Paperboard Company ....D 972 932-9800
Forney *(G-6301)*

Age Industries Ltd ....E 915 852-9099
Horizon City *(G-8361)*

Ics Enterprises Ltd ....E 915 539-5415
El Paso *(G-5807)*

Morgan Truck Body LLC ....D 903 872-7445
Corsicana *(G-3679)*

P & A Graphics LLC ....F 972 632-2100
McKinney *(G-14961)*

Sctray Company ....D 817 473-0233
Mansfield *(G-14716)*

Smurfit Kappa North Amer LLC ....B 214 515-6400
Forney *(G-6314)*

▲ Smurfit Kappa North Amer LLC ....B 800 306-8326
Irving *(G-13182)*

Westrock Rkt LLC ....C 903 455-0147
Greenville *(G-8096)*

2671 Paper Coating & Laminating for Packaging

▼ Accredo Packaging Inc ....D 713 580-4800
Sugar Land *(G-19436)*

Age Industries Ltd ....D 817 477-5266
Cleburne *(G-3079)*

Aluma Graphics LP ....E 972 442-3299
Wylie *(G-20925)*

American Excelsior Company ....E 817 385-4300
Arlington *(G-616)*

Bayou Imaging Products LLC ....F 713 923-8300
Houston *(G-8835)*

Berry Global Films LLC ....C 972 576-8193
Waxahachie *(G-20529)*

Charta Group Inc ....E 310 327-0244
Austin *(G-1044)*

Dac Labels & Graphic Spc ....F 214 340-2055
Dallas *(G-4205)*

Dalpack ....F 972 446-8101
Haltom City *(G-8137)*

Darling Quick Print Inc ....F 915 858-5055
El Paso *(G-5714)*

Ennis Inc ....C 903 496-2244
Wolfe City *(G-20906)*

▼ Formtex Plastics Corporation ....E 713 493-6628
Houston *(G-9836)*

Greif Inc ....F 346 263-2639
Baytown *(G-1789)*

▲ Greif Flexibles USA Inc ....F 713 461-0840
Houston *(G-10040)*

◆ Hood Flexible Packaging Corp ....D 903 593-1793
Tyler *(G-20100)*

▲ Idea Planet LP ....E 972 380-9867
Dallas *(G-3844)*

Industrial Tape & Label Corp ....F 713 748-3105
Houston *(G-10354)*

▲ Label Products Inc ....E 713 869-2959
Houston *(G-10584)*

LSI Integrated Graphics LP ....C 713 744-4100
Houston *(G-10696)*

McDowell Packg & Advg Co Inc ....D 469 246-2700
Plano *(G-16923)*

Norkol Inc ....E 832 644-1481
Humble *(G-12790)*

▼ Orion Pacific Inc ....D 432 332-0058
Odessa *(G-16103)*

▲ Orrex Plastics Company LLC ....E 432 332-1229
Odessa *(G-16104)*

Pactiv LLC ....E 817 608-9009
Arlington *(G-747)*

Presco Polymers Opco Inc ....C 903 957-2263
Sherman *(G-18929)*

Printpack Inc ....E 972 602-8421
Grand Prairie *(G-7955)*

◆ Rextac LLC ....C 432 332-0058
Odessa *(G-16137)*

Reynolds Consumer Products LLC ....F 254 770-4100
Temple *(G-19701)*

Reynolds Presto Products Inc ....B 972 416-6500
Carrollton *(G-2807)*

Sealed Air Corporation ....D 817 540-2020
Grand Prairie *(G-7972)*

Signode Industrial Group LLC ....E 409 745-2600
Orange *(G-16263)*

Smurfit Kappa North Amer LLC ....B 214 515-6400
Forney *(G-6314)*

▲ Smurfit Kappa North Amer LLC ....B 800 306-8326
Irving *(G-13182)*

Sonoco Products Company ....D 254 666-4777
Waco *(G-20458)*

Southwest Index Tab Co Inc ....E 972 228-8227
Waxahachie *(G-20562)*

◆ Tetra Pak Inc ....C 940 565-8800
Denton *(G-5404)*

Tetra Pak Materials LP ....C 940 565-8800
Denton *(G-5405)*

Transcendia Inc ....E 800 659-4254
Carrollton *(G-2838)*

Tru-Vision Plastics Inc ....F 979 836-1091
Brenham *(G-2276)*

Vf Outdoor LLC ....E 817 491-4949
Fort Worth *(G-7102)*

Western Pulp Products Co ....F 903 586-3608
Jacksonville *(G-13266)*

2672 Paper Coating & Laminating, Exc for Packaging

3M Company ....E 512 984-2708
Austin *(G-871)*

Advantage Marking & Labeling ....E 214 638-5225
Dallas *(G-3894)*

Associated Label & Tape Co ....E 214 744-1662
Dallas *(G-3972)*

Avery Dennison Corporation ....E 972 919-6900
Carrollton *(G-2699)*

Blind Dog Productions Ltd ....E 254 778-0722
Temple *(G-19671)*

Cash Engraving Co ....E 817 831-8585
Fort Worth *(G-6495)*

▲ Custom Direct Inc ....F 201 934-4229
Plano *(G-16834)*

Diversfied Lbling Slutions Inc ....E 817 471-1310
Arlington *(G-664)*

Ennis Inc ....C 903 496-2244
Wolfe City *(G-20906)*

Esco Industries Inc ....E 254 296-0500
Waco *(G-20396)*

Fedex Office & Print Svcs Inc ....E 713 521-9465
Houston *(G-9772)*

Global Plus Trading Co LLC ....E 210 807-0190
San Antonio *(G-18149)*

Green Bay Packaging Inc ....E 915 822-9700
El Paso *(G-5791)*

Guardian Southwest String Tag ....F 972 938-0123
Waxahachie *(G-20544)*

His Company Inc ....F 713 934-1600
Houston *(G-10187)*

▲ Label Products Inc ....E 713 869-2959
Houston *(G-10584)*

Longer Protective LLC ....F 832 987-1790
Missouri City *(G-15581)*

McDowell Packg & Advg Co Inc ....D 469 246-2700
Plano *(G-16923)*

Miller Products Inc ....E 972 988-0983
Grand Prairie *(G-7929)*

Paul Smoke ....F 281 422-4228
Baytown *(G-1831)*

◆ Performance Label Company ....F 806 763-1663
Lubbock *(G-14461)*

Tape Innovations LLC ....E 817 568-1212
Fort Worth *(G-7034)*

SIC

Trpg Inc .... F 713 477-6995
Pasadena *(G-16520)*

Westrock Mwv LLC .... D 409 276-3000
Silsbee *(G-18958)*

▲ Wingate Partners LP .... F 214 720-1313
Dallas *(G-5195)*

2673 Bags: Plastics, Laminated & Coated

▲ Advance Polybag (nevada) Inc .... F 702 642-1110
Sugar Land *(G-19437)*

◆ Advance Polybag (texas) Inc .... E 713 580-4800
Sugar Land *(G-19438)*

▲ Advance Polybag North East Inc .... F 410 796-8551
Sugar Land *(G-19439)*

▲ Agribag Inc .... F 713 847-8008
Houston *(G-8504)*

▲ American Film & Printing Ltd .... D 817 783-7600
Alvarado *(G-323)*

API Industries Inc .... C 845 365-2200
Sulphur Springs *(G-19579)*

Berry Global Films LLC .... C 972 576-8193
Waxahachie *(G-20529)*

▲ Better Bags Inc .... E 713 864-8200
Houston *(G-8866)*

▲ C-L & Associates Inc .... E 903 831-4311
Wake Village *(G-20485)*

Caraustar Industries Inc .... E 903 793-6231
Texarkana *(G-19758)*

◆ Cardet Wholesale Inc .... D 713 266-9834
Brookshire *(G-2312)*

Command Packaging LLC .... F 903 984-8596
Kilgore *(G-13536)*

▲ Continental Poly Inc .... E 281 277-6550
Sugar Land *(G-19467)*

El Chilito Foods Inc .... F 512 391-0550
Austin *(G-1118)*

▲ Express Plastic Corporation .... F 713 664-9588
Houston *(G-9732)*

Global Empire Incorporated .... F 713 503-5545
Houston *(G-9971)*

Global Entp Worldwide LLC .... F 713 260-9687
Houston *(G-9972)*

◆ Handgards LLC .... C 915 779-6606
El Paso *(G-5794)*

◆ Hood Flexible Packaging Corp .... D 903 593-1793
Tyler *(G-20100)*

Houston Custom Packaging LLC .... F 713 827-1427
Houston *(G-10227)*

▲ Houston D&J International Inc .... F 713 678-7888
Houston *(G-10228)*

▲ Integrity Plastics Inc .... E 281 575-6688
Houston *(G-10387)*

Interglobal Plastics Inc .... F 713 672-6055
Houston *(G-10395)*

◆ ITW Minigrip Inc .... C 830 372-4400
Seguin *(G-18845)*

▲ Momentum Plastics LLC .... C 713 678-7741
Houston *(G-10909)*

Novolex Inc .... C 972 686-5090
Dallas *(G-4744)*

Pactiv LLC .... G 254 770-4100
Temple *(G-19693)*

◆ Phillips Smika Plyprpylene LLC .... C 832 813-4100
The Woodlands *(G-19902)*

▲ Poly Sac Inc .... E 713 978-7888
Houston *(G-11356)*

◆ Poly-America LP .... A 972 337-7100
Grand Prairie *(G-7948)*

◆ Prince Plastics Inc .... E 281 240-6400
Sugar Land *(G-19530)*

Printpack Inc .... C 409 883-9325
Orange *(G-16257)*

Printpack Inc .... C 972 602-8421
Grand Prairie *(G-7955)*

Printpack Inc .... E 972 641-4421
Grand Prairie *(G-7956)*

Pro-Plastics Inc .... D 713 690-9000
Houston *(G-11428)*

▲ Pro-Plastics Inc .... E 713 690-9000
Houston *(G-11429)*

▲ Republic Mfg Group Inc .... D 713 847-7542
Houston *(G-11602)*

Reynolds Consumer Products LLC ...... F 254 770-4100
Temple *(G-19701)*

Reynolds Presto Products Inc .... B 972 416-6500
Carrollton *(G-2807)*

S & G Plastics Inc .... E 713 467-8766
Houston *(G-11705)*

Sealed Air Corporation .... D 940 592-2111
Iowa Park *(G-12910)*

Starpak Plastics Inc .... D 713 329-9183
Houston *(G-12049)*

◆ Super Sack Bag Inc .... F 214 340-7060
Dallas *(G-5024)*

▲ Superbag USA Corp .... B 713 462-1173
Houston *(G-12108)*

Superbag USA Corp .... C 713 462-1173
Houston *(G-12109)*

Supplynet Inc .... E 484 582-1004
Dallas *(G-5028)*

Supplynet Inc .... D 214 637-0160
Dallas *(G-5029)*

▲ Texas Poly Inc .... E 817 540-2351
Euless *(G-6162)*

Titex Inc .... E 713 678-8890
Houston *(G-12302)*

◆ Tristar Packaging Inc .... F 281 540-2613
Humble *(G-12806)*

Tyco International MGT Co LLC .... C 361 575-9565
Victoria *(G-20312)*

Tyr Usa LLC .... E 956 274-9380
Weslaco *(G-20670)*

Unistar Plastics LLC .... D 713 242-8377
Houston *(G-12442)*

▲ United Plastics Inc .... E 713 222-2186
Houston *(G-12452)*

Walming Inc .... E 713 690-9000
Houston *(G-12596)*

◆ Westlake Polymers LLC .... C 713 960-9111
Houston *(G-12652)*

▲ Winzen Film Inc .... E 214 340-7060
Dallas *(G-5198)*

2674 Bags: Uncoated Paper & Multiwall

B & H Bag Company .... E 713 641-0921
Brookshire *(G-2310)*

▲ C-L & Associates Inc .... E 903 831-4311
Wake Village *(G-20485)*

Knight Corporation .... E 281 933-5363
Houston *(G-10546)*

▲ Mosites Rubber Company Inc .... E 817 335-3451
Fort Worth *(G-6854)*

Protective Packaging Corp Inc .... E 972 446-2247
Carrollton *(G-2800)*

Super Sack Bag Inc .... F 903 965-7713
Savoy *(G-18741)*

◆ Tristar Packaging Inc .... F 281 540-2613
Humble *(G-12806)*

▲ Vhsc Cement LLC .... F 281 419-2422
The Woodlands *(G-19938)*

Westx Packaging Company .... F 806 686-4447
Lubbock *(G-14511)*

2675 Die-Cut Paper & Board

Abco Inc .... D 214 428-8996
Dallas *(G-3878)*

Accurate Die Cutting Inc .... E 972 562-7921
McKinney *(G-14922)*

American Railcar Inds Inc .... D 936 365-2679
Goodrich *(G-7768)*

Caraustar Industries Inc .... E 903 799-5100
Atlanta *(G-841)*

◆ Concote Corporation .... C 214 956-0077
Coppell *(G-3412)*

Concote Corporation .... F 903 581-0697
Tyler *(G-20070)*

Creative MENus&folders LLC .... F 254 653-2775
Olden *(G-16219)*

Fedex Office & Print Svcs Inc .... F 806 359-9684
Amarillo *(G-488)*

HFS Holding Corporation .... F 214 634-8600
Dallas *(G-4454)*

Jones Holt Enterprises Inc .... E 210 657-5917
San Antonio *(G-18207)*

JPS Alliance Inc .... E 817 534-0044
Fort Worth *(G-6746)*

Smead Manufacturing Company .... F 956 631-1418
McAllen *(G-14907)*

Southern Champion Tray LP .... F 817 477-3485
Mansfield *(G-14719)*

Southwest Index Tab Co Inc .... E 972 228-8227
Waxahachie *(G-20562)*

Tape Innovations LLC .... E 817 568-1212
Fort Worth *(G-7034)*

Thompson Paper Pdts Texas Inc .... E 713 869-6636
Houston *(G-12278)*

▲ Trumed Technologies Inc .... E 952 882-0611
Mesquite *(G-15082)*

Westrock Mwv LLC .... D 409 276-3000
Silsbee *(G-18958)*

Zapco Inc .... E 512 237-5521
Smithville *(G-18980)*

2676 Sanitary Paper Prdts

▲ Abiie LLC .... F 512 514-6325
Austin *(G-876)*

East Txas Lighthouse For Blind .... D 903 595-3444
Tyler *(G-20082)*

Georgia-Pacific LLC .... G 434 283-6202
El Paso *(G-5783)*

◆ Kimberly-Clark Corporation .... B 972 281-1200
Irving *(G-13075)*

Kimberly-Clark Corporation .... A 903 737-5100
Paris *(G-16364)*

Kimberly-Clark Corporation .... F 817 847-0211
Fort Worth *(G-6761)*

Kimberly-Clark Worldwide Inc .... F 972 281-1200
Irving *(G-13076)*

Omganics Inc .... A 512 560-3262
Austin *(G-1379)*

Solo Cup Operating Corporation .... A 214 339-3131
Dallas *(G-4977)*

◆ Texas Tissue Converting LLC .... D 281 821-0429
Houston *(G-12257)*

2677 Envelopes

Blumbergexcelsior Inc .... E 817 462-1530
Arlington *(G-632)*

Cenveo Worldwide Limited .... C 972 729-5700
Dallas *(G-4102)*

Eric Industries Inc .... E 972 248-8009
Dallas *(G-3841)*

▲ Goelzer Industries Inc .... D 214 524-6700
Grand Prairie *(G-7883)*

Motion Envelope Inc .... E 214 634-2131
Dallas *(G-4690)*

Nev Holdings LLC .... A 972 731-1100
Frisco *(G-7301)*

R R Donnelley & Sons Company .... D 972 353-6130
Lewisville *(G-14086)*

Signature Envelope Company Inc .... F 713 538-1177
Coldspring *(G-3167)*

▲ Texas Envelope Company .... E 214 358-5661
Dallas *(G-5060)*

2678 Stationery Prdts

B and D Index Inc .... E 817 261-8227
Arlington *(G-628)*

Blumbergexcelsior Inc .... E 817 462-1530
Arlington *(G-632)*

▲ Urman Inc .... F 832 246-8810
The Woodlands *(G-19932)*

2679 Converted Paper Prdts, NEC

Accent Mercantile Inc .... F 817 579-6076
Granbury *(G-7792)*

Advantage Marking & Labeling .... E 214 638-5225
Dallas *(G-3894)*

Age Industries Ltd .... E 956 399-8279
San Benito *(G-18654)*

Alecom Technologies Group Inc .... G 972 870-9400
Flower Mound *(G-6259)*

Aloterra Packaging LLC .... F 440 689-0986
The Woodlands *(G-19824)*

Altlite LLC .... F 469 767-1959
Dallas *(G-3935)*

▲ Aztec Imports Inc .... E 915 858-2287
El Paso *(G-5657)*

Caraustar Industries Inc .... E 903 793-6231
Texarkana *(G-19758)*

Caraustar Industries Inc .... E 903 799-5100
Atlanta *(G-841)*

Carlton Industries LP .... E 979 242-5055
La Grange *(G-13693)*

◆ Castell LP .... D 972 938-2739
Waxahachie *(G-20535)*

Century Tape & Label LLC .... E 972 576-0826
Round Rock *(G-17631)*

Classic Corrugated Inc .... D 940 381-0137
Denton *(G-5354)*

◆ Cole & Ashcroft LP .... F 713 937-8657
Houston *(G-9243)*

Dac Labels & Graphic Spc .... F 214 340-2055
Dallas *(G-4205)*

Dallas Label and Packaging Inc .... F 972 487-6064
Farmers Branch *(G-6192)*

▲ Dallco Marketing Inc .... E 214 217-7800
Dallas *(G-4231)*

Dietzgen Corporation ....F 713 937-1632
Houston *(G-9467)*

Diversfied Lbling Slutions Inc ....E 817 471-1310
Arlington *(G-664)*

Ennis Inc ....C 903 496-2244
Wolfe City *(G-20906)*

Fortis Solutions Group LLC ....F 512 302-0204
Austin *(G-1169)*

Graphic Converting Ltd ....E 972 554-8000
Carrollton *(G-2747)*

Halbert Mill Company Texas Inc ......F 903 683-2788
Jacksonville *(G-13243)*

HFS Holding Corporation ....F 214 634-8600
Dallas *(G-4454)*

Imperial Bag & Paper Co LLC ....E 713 223-5050
Houston *(G-10334)*

◆ Impreso Inc ....D 972 462-0100
Coppell *(G-3421)*

▲ Inchbug LLC ....E 512 837-1010
Austin *(G-1227)*

Industrial Pipe Fittings LLC ....F 800 241-4175
Houston *(G-10353)*

Industrial Pipe Fittings LLC ....E 903 872-7890
Corsicana *(G-3674)*

▲ Ki Memories Inc ....E 972 333-3015
Dallas *(G-4554)*

▲ Label Products Inc ....E 713 869-2959
Houston *(G-10584)*

▲ Labelmax Inc ....D 956 718-3961
Laredo *(G-13904)*

Lakeland Paper Corporation ....E 817 840-5470
Arlington *(G-716)*

Liberty Label Company Inc ....F 830 549-5459
Seguin *(G-18849)*

Lighthouse Distribution Inc ....F 214 630-1630
Dallas *(G-4595)*

Marking Services Inc ....F 281 424-6710
Baytown *(G-1828)*

Marking Systems Inc ....D 972 475-0770
Garland *(G-7543)*

▲ Maxwell Papers LP ....D 214 631-5550
Dallas *(G-4655)*

◆ Maxwell Papers Holdings LLP ....F 214 631-5550
Dallas *(G-4656)*

Mayfield Paper Company Inc ....F 432 580-4118
Odessa *(G-16075)*

McDowell Packg & Advg Co Inc ....D 469 246-2700
Plano *(G-16923)*

Medek L L C ....F 956 800-4366
Alamo *(G-180)*

Miller Products Inc ....E 972 988-0983
Grand Prairie *(G-7929)*

Partners Converting Inc ....F 469 568-5000
Carrollton *(G-2790)*

Power Pipe and Tank LLC ....E 417 447-4508
Amarillo *(G-508)*

RB Converting Inc ....E 800 543-7690
Dallas *(G-4863)*

Rios Packaging Corp ....F 214 920-9851
Dallas *(G-4902)*

▲ Royberg Inc ....E 210 525-0094
San Antonio *(G-18435)*

RTS Packaging LLC ....D 214 331-6555
Dallas *(G-4917)*

Schulenburg Prtg Off Sups Inc ....E 979 743-4511
Schulenburg *(G-18778)*

Smurfit Kappa North Amer LLC ....E 713 869-5900
Houston *(G-11926)*

Solo Cup Operating Corporation ......A 214 339-3131
Dallas *(G-4977)*

Southern Champion Tray LP ....E 512 442-2337
Austin *(G-1522)*

Superior Label Systems Inc ....F 214 330-7770
Dallas *(G-5026)*

Supply Pro Sorbents LLC ....E 713 672-9080
Sugar Land *(G-19559)*

▼ Technology Container Corp ......E 972 228-1617
Desoto *(G-5444)*

◆ Tst/Impreso Inc ....D 972 462-0100
Coppell *(G-3451)*

Veco Printing Inc ....F 956 968-1589
Port Isabel *(G-17140)*

Voidform Products Inc ....E 817 429-0888
Fort Worth *(G-7111)*

▲ Wbc Media LP ....F 214 764-2000
Dallas *(G-5176)*

Western Pulp Products Co ....E 903 586-3608
Jacksonville *(G-13266)*

27 PRINTING, PUBLISHING, AND ALLIED INDUSTRIES

2711 Newspapers: Publishing & Printing

21st Century Fox America Inc ....F 214 981-0800
Dallas *(G-3865)*

A H Belo Corporation ....D 214 977-8222
Dallas *(G-3871)*

Ad Sack Inc ....E 361 854-0137
Corpus Christi *(G-3466)*

Aim Media Texas LLC ....C 432 337-4661
Odessa *(G-15905)*

▲ Aim Media Texas Operating LLC ...B 956 683-4000
McAllen *(G-14833)*

Aim Media Texas Operating LLC ....C 956 430-6200
Harlingen *(G-8174)*

Alice Newspapers Inc ....E 361 664-6588
Alice *(G-203)*

Alm Media LLC ....E 214 744-9300
Dallas *(G-3928)*

Alvin Sun & Advertiser Inc ....E 281 331-4421
Alvin *(G-351)*

American Classifieds ....F 806 376-8663
Amarillo *(G-480)*

American Cmnty Newspapers LLC ......C 972 424-6565
Plano *(G-16786)*

Andrews County News ....F 432 523-2085
Andrews *(G-533)*

Arbol Publishing LP ....F 512 476-8636
Austin *(G-929)*

Asp Westward LP ....D 713 256-0953
Houston *(G-8723)*

Asp Westward LP ....E 903 845-2235
Gladewater *(G-7718)*

Asp Westward LP ....F 903 237-7700
Longview *(G-14197)*

Associated Texas Newspapers ....F 830 426-3346
Hondo *(G-8353)*

Assocted Bldrs Cntrs Grter Hst ......F 713 523-6222
Houston *(G-8727)*

Austin Chronicle Corporation ....D 512 454-5766
Austin *(G-952)*

Azle Tri-County Advertiser ....F 817 270-3340
Azle *(G-1720)*

Barton Publications Inc ....E 512 262-1110
Kyle *(G-13679)*

Bay City Tribune ....F 979 245-2920
Bay City *(G-1768)*

Bcs Eagle ....F 979 776-4444
Bryan *(G-2456)*

Beeville Publishing Company ....E 361 358-2550
Beeville *(G-1984)*

Belo Corp ....C 979 776-4444
Bryan *(G-2457)*

Belton Newspaper Inc ....F 254 939-5754
Belton *(G-2021)*

Bernie Star Newspaper ....F 830 249-2441
Boerne *(G-2115)*

Bjhr Inc ....E 409 735-5305
Bridge City *(G-2280)*

Blacklands Publications Inc ....E 512 352-8535
Taylor *(G-19650)*

Bowie News Inc ....F 940 872-2247
Bowie *(G-2193)*

Brady Standard Herald Inc ....F 325 597-2959
Brady *(G-2211)*

Brazoria County News ....F 979 345-3127
West Columbia *(G-20675)*

Bridwell Publishing Company ....F 940 683-4021
Bridgeport *(G-2291)*

Briggs News Alliance LLC ....G 432 943-4313
Monahans *(G-15601)*

Business Jrnl Publications Inc ....E 210 341-3202
San Antonio *(G-17974)*

C & S Media Inc ....G 972 442-5515
Wylie *(G-20928)*

Caller-Times Publishing Co ....B 361 883-1111
Corpus Christi *(G-3493)*

City Newspapers Management LLC ......C 214 739-2244
Dallas *(G-4123)*

Cnhi LLC ....E 806 273-5611
Borger *(G-2169)*

Cnhi LLC ....E 432 263-7331
Big Spring *(G-2076)*

Cnhi LLC ....E 940 665-5511
Gainesville *(G-7339)*

Community Newspapers Holdings ....D 512 392-6143
San Marcos *(G-18682)*

Community Ventures Inc ....F 817 441-7661
Weatherford *(G-20582)*

Connor Media Group LLC ....E 817 336-8300
Fort Worth *(G-6542)*

Cox Texas Newspapers LP ....D 512 445-3500
Austin *(G-1069)*

Cox Texas Newspapers LP ....C 903 237-7777
Longview *(G-14215)*

▲ Cox Texas Newspapers LP ....D 512 445-3500
Austin *(G-1070)*

D & V Day Investments Corp ....F 409 943-4265
Texas City *(G-19787)*

D F W Elite News ....G 214 372-6500
Campbell *(G-2645)*

D J Young Publishing ....F 361 238-4188
Ingleside *(G-12893)*

Daily Commercial Record Inc ....E 214 741-6366
Dallas *(G-4206)*

Daily Court Review Inc ....F 713 869-5434
Houston *(G-9394)*

Daily DOT LLC ....F 512 420-9403
Austin *(G-1084)*

Daily Sentinel ....G 936 631-2607
Nacogdoches *(G-15694)*

Dalhart Publishing Co ....F 806 244-4511
Dalhart *(G-3833)*

Dallas Observer LP ....E 214 757-9000
Dallas *(G-4222)*

Denton Publishing Company ....C 940 387-3811
Denton *(G-5359)*

Dmn Inc ....E 214 745-8383
Garland *(G-7480)*

▲ Dmn Inc ....A 214 977-8222
Dallas *(G-4267)*

Dmn Inc ....B 214 977-6931
Plano *(G-16847)*

Dow Jones & Company Inc ....A 214 951-7251
Dallas *(G-4275)*

Drc Media LLC ....F 817 336-8300
Fort Worth *(G-6594)*

Eagle Printing Company ....C 979 776-4444
Bryan *(G-2471)*

East Dllas-Lakewood People Inc ......E 214 823-5885
Dallas *(G-4294)*

Eastland County Newspaper Inc ....F 254 629-1707
Eastland *(G-5564)*

Eastland County Newspaper Inc ....F 254 442-2000
Cisco *(G-3066)*

Echo Publishing Company ....E 903 885-2030
Sulphur Springs *(G-19586)*

El Campo Newspapers Inc ....F 979 543-3363
El Campo *(G-5616)*

El Extra Spnish Lngage Newsppr ......F 214 309-0990
Dallas *(G-4305)*

El Heraldo News Incorporated ....E 214 827-9700
Dallas *(G-4306)*

El Manana Inc ....F 956 712-1122
Laredo *(G-13882)*

El Paso Times Charitable Corp ....B 915 546-6100
El Paso *(G-5743)*

El Periodico U S A Inc ....F 956 631-5628
McAllen *(G-14856)*

El Tejano Hispanic Community ....F 361 884-2238
Corpus Christi *(G-3518)*

Ellis Co Newspapers ....E 972 875-3801
Ennis *(G-6096)*

Ellis County Chronicle ....C 972 937-3310
Waxahachie *(G-20541)*

Ellis County Newspapers Inc ....E 972 872-9113
Ennis *(G-6097)*

Embossed Graphics Inc ....F 713 667-0034
Houston *(G-9608)*

Epochtimes Public Media Inc ....E 713 790-0815
Houston *(G-9683)*

Erath Publishers Inc ....D 254 965-3124
Stephenville *(G-19410)*

Euclid Media Group LLC ....E 210 227-0044
San Antonio *(G-18097)*

EW Scripps Company ....C 325 659-8200
San Angelo *(G-17798)*

EW Scripps Company ....C 361 886-3652
Corpus Christi *(G-3522)*

Examiner Corporation ....F 409 833-1755
Beaumont *(G-1889)*

Examiner Newspaper Group Inc ....F 713 526-3617
Houston *(G-9722)*

Facts ....F 979 237-0100
Clute *(G-3154)*

Fannin County Leader LLC ....F 903 583-3280
Bonham *(G-2153)*

Fayette County Record Inc ....G..... 979 968-3155
La Grange (G-13695)

Flightsafety International Inc ....C..... 817 571-5925
Fort Worth (G-6638)

Floyd County Hesperian-Beacon ....F..... 888 400-1083
Floydada (G-6293)

Focus Newspapers of Dfw Inc ....E..... 972 223-9175
Desoto (G-5431)

Fort Bend Business Journal ....F..... 281 690-4200
Stafford (G-19316)

Forward Times Publishing Co ....E..... 713 526-4727
Houston (G-9845)

Frank Mayborn Enterprises Inc ....C..... 254 501-7499
Killeen (G-13607)

Frank Mayborn Enterprises Inc ....C..... 254 634-6666
Killeen (G-13608)

Fredericksburg Publishing Co ....E..... 830 997-2155
Fredericksburg (G-7179)

Galveston Newspapers Inc ....D..... 409 683-5200
Galveston (G-7398)

Gatehouse Media LLC ....F..... 956 546-5113
Brownsville (G-2358)

Granite Publications LLC ....F..... 512 352-8285
Taylor (G-19657)

Greeneway Enterprises Inc ....F..... 903 843-2503
Gilmer (G-7707)

Guadalupe Valley Publishing Co ....G..... 830 672-2861
Gonzales (G-7754)

Hartman Newspapers LP ....F..... 281 342-8691
Rosenberg (G-17585)

Hartman Newspapers LP ....F..... 361 729-9900
Rockport (G-17530)

Hartman Newspapers LP ....F..... 972 563-6476
Terrell (G-19737)

Hartman Newspapers LP ....F..... 936 336-3611
Liberty (G-14119)

Hartman Newspapers LP ....D..... 281 342-7304
Rosenberg (G-17586)

Hartman Newspapers LP ....E..... 281 232-3737
Rosenberg (G-17587)

Hearst Corporation ....A..... 210 271-2700
San Antonio (G-18161)

Hearst Corporation ....C..... 956 728-2500
Laredo (G-13890)

Hearst Corporation ....C..... 432 682-5311
Midland (G-15244)

Hearst Corporation ....F..... 409 384-3441
Jasper (G-13277)

Hearst Corporation ....A..... 210 250-3000
San Antonio (G-18162)

Hearst Newspapers LLC ....C..... 713 220-7171
Houston (G-10144)

Hearst Newspapers LLC ....C..... 713 220-7171
Houston (G-10145)

Hearstcorporation ....E..... 806 296-1300
Plainview (G-16756)

Helen Gordon Interests Ltd ....C..... 713 371-3500
Houston (G-10149)

Helen Gordon Interests Ltd ....D..... 214 853-6088
Dallas (G-4446)

Henderson Newspapers Inc ....E..... 903 657-2501
Henderson (G-8265)

Herald Democrat ....F..... 903 893-8181
Sherman (G-18917)

Hereford Brand Inc ....E..... 806 364-2030
Hereford (G-8291)

Hill Country News ....F..... 512 259-4449
Cedar Park (G-2973)

Hill Country Publishing Co ....E..... 512 556-6262
Lampasas (G-13834)

Hill County Press Inc ....F..... 254 582-3431
Hillsboro (G-8327)

Hillsboro Reporter Inc ....F..... 254 582-3431
Hillsboro (G-8328)

Hockley County Publishing Co ....F..... 806 894-3121
Levelland (G-14009)

Hood County News Inc ....D..... 817 573-7066
Granbury (G-7800)

Horizon Publications Inc ....E..... 325 236-6677
Sweetwater (G-19631)

Houston Business Journals Inc ....E..... 214 696-5959
Dallas (G-4468)

Houston Business Journals Inc ....E..... 713 688-8811
Houston (G-10219)

Houston Chronicle ....A..... 713 362-7171
Houston (G-10225)

Houston Defender Newspaper Inc ....F..... 713 663-6996
Houston (G-10229)

Houston Press LP ....E..... 713 280-2400
Houston (G-10247)

Informacion Publishing Co Inc ....E..... 713 272-0100
Houston (G-10357)

International Daily News Inc ....F..... 713 270-4855
Houston (G-10400)

▲ Investor Publications Inc ....E..... 915 534-4422
El Paso (G-5817)

Irent ....F..... 956 592-4061
Brownsville (G-2366)

Itexaspolitics LLC ....G..... 512 200-4035
Colleyville (G-3214)

Jackson County Herald Tribune ....F..... 361 782-2131
Edna (G-5607)

Jewish Herald Voice Inc ....F..... 713 630-0391
Houston (G-10472)

JG Media Inc ....D..... 512 989-6808
Pflugerville (G-16677)

K P A N Broadcasters ....F..... 806 364-1860
Hereford (G-8292)

▼ King Ranch Inc ....E..... 832 681-5700
Houston (G-10534)

Kingsville Publishing Company ....F..... 361 592-4304
Kingsville (G-13631)

Krenek Printing Company ....F..... 281 463-8649
Houston (G-10568)

La Subasta Incorporated ....E..... 214 951-9500
Dallas (G-4577)

▲ La Subasta Incorporated ....E..... 713 777-1010
Houston (G-10583)

Lake County Newspaper ....F..... 254 559-5412
Breckenridge (G-2231)

Lamesa Reporter Inc ....G..... 806 872-2177
Lamesa (G-13828)

Lfn LLC ....F..... 956 330-6838
Los Fresnos (G-14347)

▲ Lhcn Inc ....D..... 972 424-6565
Plano (G-16908)

Libredigital Inc ....F..... 512 334-5100
Austin (G-1291)

Light & Champion Publishing ....E..... 936 598-3377
Center (G-3002)

Longview News Journal ....F..... 903 237-7711
Longview (G-14271)

Los Angles Tmes Cmmnctions LLC ......C..... 512 476-7777
Austin (G-1302)

Marcos N Suarez ....F..... 214 357-2186
Dallas (G-4634)

Marshall News Messenger Inc ....E..... 903 935-7914
Marshall (G-14790)

Media Palmer Inc ....E..... 903 572-1705
Mount Pleasant (G-15654)

Messenger Publishing Co Inc ....F..... 254 865-5212
Gatesville (G-7620)

Mid-Valley Newspapers Inc ....E..... 956 969-2543
Weslaco (G-20665)

Milam Broadcasting Co Inc ....F..... 254 697-6633
Cameron (G-2643)

Millennium Shopper ....F..... 903 885-9966
Sulphur Springs (G-19592)

▲ Minority Opportunity News Inc ....F..... 972 516-4191
Plano (G-16930)

Minority Print Media ....F..... 713 748-6300
Houston (G-10888)

Monitor ....F..... 903 887-4511
Mabank (G-14580)

Moore County News Press ....F..... 806 935-4111
Dumas (G-5526)

Morris Communications Co LLC ....C..... 806 376-4488
Amarillo (G-447)

National Oil & Lube News Inc ....F..... 806 762-4464
Lubbock (G-14449)

Neighborhood News Inc ....F..... 210 558-3160
San Antonio (G-18341)

New Century Enterprises Inc ....E..... 972 926-6062
Garland (G-7562)

New Horizon Publishers ....F..... 956 943-5545
Port Isabel (G-17137)

New Horizon Publishers Inc ....F..... 956 399-2436
San Benito (G-18661)

News Gram ....F..... 830 773-8610
Eagle Pass (G-5551)

▲ News Korea Texas Inc ....E..... 972 247-9111
Dallas (G-4733)

News Publications Inc ....F..... 713 668-9293
Bellaire (G-1999)

Newspaper Holding Inc ....E..... 817 645-2441
Cleburne (G-3102)

Newspaper Holding Inc ....D..... 903 729-0281
Palestine (G-16305)

Newspaper Holding Inc ....F..... 903 586-2236
Jacksonville (G-13253)

Newspaper Holding Inc ....E..... 817 594-7440
Weatherford (G-20607)

Newspaper Holding Inc ....E..... 903 675-5626
Athens (G-835)

Newspaper Holding Inc ....E..... 903 455-4220
Greenville (G-8085)

Newspaper Holding Inc ....E..... 936 295-5407
Huntsville (G-12820)

Newspaper Holding Inc ....E..... 903 886-3196
Commerce (G-3244)

Newspaper Holding Inc ....E..... 512 392-2458
San Marcos (G-18700)

Orange County Publishing Co ....F..... 409 769-5428
Vidor (G-20330)

Paisano Educational Trust ....E..... 210 690-9301
San Antonio (G-18363)

Paso Del Norte Publishing Inc ....D..... 915 838-1601
El Paso (G-5905)

Polk County Publishing Co ....F..... 409 283-2516
Woodville (G-20916)

Polk County Publishing Co ....E..... 936 327-4357
Livingston (G-14160)

Polk County Publishing Co ....F..... 936 544-0540
Crockett (G-3722)

Port Lavaca Wave ....E..... 361 552-9788
Port Lavaca (G-17154)

Post Up Town Inc ....G..... 214 965-6565
Dallas (G-4814)

Prime Time LLC ....C..... 210 250-3000
San Antonio (G-18395)

Progrssive Mdia Communications ....F..... 254 675-3336
Clifton (G-3146)

Pts Inc ....F..... 806 669-2525
Pampa (G-16336)

Rains County Leader ....G..... 903 473-2653
Emory (G-6085)

Rambler Newspapers Inc ....F..... 972 870-1992
Irving (G-13162)

Recorder Publishing Co Inc ....F..... 817 926-5351
Fort Worth (G-6947)

Reneau Publishing Inc ....G..... 409 385-5278
Silsbee (G-18954)

Rio Grande Valley Business ....E..... 956 546-5113
Brownsville (G-2400)

Robinson Media Company LLC ....F..... 254 757-5757
Waco (G-20455)

Rockdale Reporter Inc ....F..... 512 446-5838
Rockdale (G-17526)

San Marcos Publishing LP ....E..... 512 392-2458
San Marcos (G-18709)

San Patricio Publishing Co Inc ....F..... 361 364-1270
Sinton (G-18965)

Schulenburgh Sticker Inc ....F..... 979 743-3450
Schulenburg (G-18779)

Scripps Texas Newspapers LP ....C..... 325 653-1221
San Angelo (G-17826)

Scripps Texas Newspapers LP ....C..... 325 673-4271
Abilene (G-79)

Snyder Daily News ....E..... 325 573-5486
Snyder (G-19007)

South Belt Press Inc ....F..... 281 484-4337
Houston (G-11960)

▲ Southern Chnese Nwspapers Pubg .F..... 281 498-4310
Houston (G-11973)

Southern Newspapers Inc ....E..... 830 896-7000
Kerrville (G-13526)

Southern Newspapers Inc ....F..... 830 625-5232
New Braunfels (G-15824)

Southern Newspapers Inc ....E..... 830 625-9144
New Braunfels (G-15825)

Southern Newspapers Inc ....E..... 830 379-5402
Seguin (G-18864)

Southern Newspapers Inc ....E..... 281 422-8302
Baytown (G-1835)

Southern Newspapers Inc ....D..... 979 237-0100
Clute (G-3160)

Southern Newspapers Inc ....D..... 936 632-6631
Lufkin (G-14552)

Southern Newspapers Inc ....E..... 903 785-6900
Paris (G-16370)

Southern Publishing Inc ....G..... 361 749-5131
Port Aransas (G-17100)

Star-Telegram Operating Ltd ....B..... 817 215-2100
Fort Worth (G-7015)

Star-Telegram Operating Ltd ....A..... 817 390-7400
Fort Worth (G-7016)

Sun Newspapers ....F..... 940 497-4141
Lake Dallas (G-13811)

Sun-Times Media Group Inc ....F..... 254 562-2868
Mexia (G-15091)

Texas Catholic Herald Inc ....F 713 659-5461
   Houston *(G-12224)*

Texas City Newspapers Inc ....A 409 945-3441
   Texas City *(G-19803)*

Texas Community Media LLC ....C 903 757-3311
   Longview *(G-14315)*

Texas Jewish Post Ltd ....F 972 458-7283
   Dallas *(G-5074)*

Texas State University ....F 512 245-3487
   San Marcos *(G-18714)*

Thrifty Nckel Want ADS Crpus C ....F 361 980-0008
   Corpus Christi *(G-3640)*

Thrifty Nickel Want Ads Inc ....F 915 751-3494
   El Paso *(G-6003)*

Tristar Web Graphics Inc ....C 713 691-0001
   Houston *(G-12379)*

United Metro Media LLC ....F 210 315-6046
   San Antonio *(G-18578)*

University of Houston System ....F 713 221-8192
   Houston *(G-12468)*

University of Texas At Austin ....E 512 471-1865
   Austin *(G-1610)*

USA Printing Corporation ....F 281 498-4310
   Houston *(G-12500)*

Uvalde Leader News ....F 830 334-3644
   Pearsall *(G-16615)*

Val Verde Publishing LLC ....F 830 774-2198
   Del Rio *(G-5328)*

Valley Media Inc ....E 956 546-5113
   Brownsville *(G-2419)*

Van Zandt Newspapers LLC ....E 903 567-4000
   Wills Point *(G-20880)*

Versa Printing Inc ....E 972 243-5353
   Dallas *(G-5163)*

Victoria Advocate News Bureau ....C 361 575-1451
   Victoria *(G-20313)*

Victoria Advocate Pubg Co ....D 361 575-1451
   Victoria *(G-20314)*

Voice Media Group Inc ....D 713 280-2400
   Houston *(G-12580)*

Voice Publishing Co Inc ....F 214 754-8710
   Dallas *(G-5168)*

Waco Publications Inc ....E 254 752-0334
   Waco *(G-20476)*

Want ADS of Colorado Springs ....F 361 575-6400
   Victoria *(G-20318)*

Want ADS of Fort Worth Inc ....F 817 870-0055
   Fort Worth *(G-7124)*

Wcn Inc ....E 830 216-4519
   Floresville *(G-6258)*

Weatherford Advertising Inc ....E 817 594-7440
   Weatherford *(G-20629)*

West Texas Want Ads Inc ....F 325 673-4521
   Abilene *(G-94)*

Wichita Falls Times Record ....E 940 767-8341
   Wichita Falls *(G-20832)*

Wilkerson Publishing Company ....F 830 281-2341
   Pleasanton *(G-17078)*

Williamson County Sun Inc ....E 512 930-3072
   Georgetown *(G-7689)*

Wise County Messenger Inc ....E 940 627-5987
   Decatur *(G-5257)*

Woodland Publishing Inc ....E 281 485-7501
   Pearland *(G-16611)*

World Journal La LLC ....F 713 771-4363
   Houston *(G-12692)*

Yoakum Herald-Times Inc ....F 361 293-5266
   Yoakum *(G-20975)*

2721 Periodicals: Publishing & Printing

20 Spc Inc ....D 972 687-6700
   Dallas *(G-3863)*

Absolute Multimedia Inc ....E 512 892-8682
   Austin *(G-879)*

Advertisers Dynmc Svcs Co Inc ....F 972 392-9722
   Carrollton *(G-2691)*

AMC Publishing LLC ....E 512 380-1611
   Austin *(G-914)*

▲ American Paint Horse Assn ....C 817 834-2742
   Fort Worth *(G-6382)*

American Trphy Hnters Assn Inc ....E 210 523-8500
   San Antonio *(G-17904)*

ART&quilt Magazine ....G 713 975-7140
   Houston *(G-8709)*

Associated Locksmiths Amer Inc ....F 214 819-9733
   Dallas *(G-3973)*

Austin Fit Magazine LP ....F 512 407-8383
   Austin *(G-955)*

Avid Media Venture Inc ....E 972 550-9000
   Irving *(G-12937)*

Avid Media Ventures Inc ....F 972 550-9000
   Irving *(G-12938)*

▲ Baptist Sunday Schl Committee ....E 903 792-2783
   Texarkana *(G-19756)*

Beckett Collectibles Inc ....D 855 777-2325
   Dallas *(G-4011)*

▲ Beckett Media LLC ....C 972 991-6657
   Dallas *(G-4012)*

Beernet Communications ....G 210 805-8006
   San Antonio *(G-17944)*

▲ Ben Dunn Corporation ....F 210 614-0396
   San Antonio *(G-17946)*

Blue Thumb Inc ....E 713 523-6523
   Houston *(G-8921)*

▲ Boy Scouts of America ....A 972 580-2000
   Irving *(G-12950)*

Brenholb Inc ....E 210 349-4024
   San Antonio *(G-17965)*

Briggs News Alliance LLC ....G 432 943-4313
   Monahans *(G-15601)*

Builders Exchange of Texas ....F 210 564-6900
   San Antonio *(G-17972)*

Celebrity Group Magazine ....E 956 579-2020
   Brownsville *(G-2345)*

Chemical Data LLC ....F 713 683-3900
   Houston *(G-9170)*

Chip McCormick Custom LLC ....E 830 798-2863
   Bogata *(G-2145)*

Clarion Events Inc ....C 713 963-6220
   Houston *(G-9207)*

Cord Communications Inc ....G 254 776-1822
   Waco *(G-20390)*

Cowboy Publishing Group ....E 817 737-6397
   Fort Worth *(G-6551)*

Currid & Company ....F 713 893-8401
   Houston *(G-9360)*

D & V Day Investments Corp ....F 409 943-4265
   Texas City *(G-19787)*

D Magazine Partners LP ....E 214 939-3636
   Dallas *(G-4203)*

Davis Brothers Pubg Co Ltd ....E 254 754-5636
   Waco *(G-20393)*

Ddsep LLC ....D 972 931-8000
   Carrollton *(G-2722)*

East Dllas-Lakewood People Inc ....E 214 823-5885
   Dallas *(G-4294)*

El Extra Spnish Lngage Newsppr ....F 214 309-0990
   Dallas *(G-4305)*

Elite Publications Inc ....F 713 263-9476
   Houston *(G-9602)*

Endtime Inc ....E 972 422-0857
   Plano *(G-16861)*

Falchion Publications LLC ....F 214 244-9645
   Frisco *(G-7285)*

Fort Bend Publishing Group ....F 281 240-2445
   Stafford *(G-19317)*

▲ Gamestop Corp ....C 817 424-2000
   Grapevine *(G-8038)*

Gamestop Holdings Corp ....B 817 424-2159
   Grapevine *(G-8039)*

Georgia Tre Magazine LLC ....E 770 755-5420
   Garland *(G-7502)*

GP Tm Acquisition LLC ....D 512 320-6900
   Austin *(G-1190)*

Gulf Publishing Company ....E 713 529-4301
   Houston *(G-10067)*

Gulf Publishing Company ....E 713 529-4301
   Houston *(G-10068)*

H3 Media LLC ....F 903 581-4237
   Tyler *(G-20092)*

Half Price Bks Rec Mgzines Inc ....F 512 244-0203
   Round Rock *(G-17661)*

Half Price Bks Rec Mgzines Inc ....F 512 805-7503
   San Marcos *(G-18693)*

Half Price Bks Rec Mgzines Inc ....F 281 540-3950
   Humble *(G-12774)*

Half Price Bks Rec Mgzines Inc ....F 713 340-0094
   Pearland *(G-16567)*

Half Price Bks Rec Mgzines Inc ....F 817 295-8560
   Burleson *(G-2580)*

Hart Energy Publishing LLC ....D 713 993-9320
   Houston *(G-10130)*

Hart Energy Publishing Lllp ....D 713 993-9320
   Houston *(G-10132)*

Herald of Truth Ministries ....F 325 698-4370
   Abilene *(G-49)*

Hussy Media LLC ....E 832 906-5816
   Austin *(G-1079)*

Iiat Services Company ....E 512 476-6281
   Austin *(G-1222)*

Indochinese Culture Center ....F 713 522-7799
   Houston *(G-10343)*

International Business Publs ....F 713 626-5369
   Houston *(G-10399)*

JDC Enterprises Inc ....E 972 550-1880
   Irving *(G-13068)*

Journal Air Law Commerce ....E 214 768-2570
   Dallas *(G-4540)*

Katy Magazine LLC ....F 281 579-9840
   Katy *(G-13415)*

Latina Style Inc ....E 214 357-2186
   Dallas *(G-4584)*

Lauren Publications Inc ....F 214 628-9720
   Addison *(G-144)*

Left Right Media LLC ....E 972 897-6578
   Austin *(G-1287)*

Leopard Media LLC ....E 713 993-9320
   Houston *(G-10625)*

Loomis Publishing Services ....F 281 829-6825
   Houston *(G-10687)*

Maquila Magazine Inc ....E 915 544-5845
   El Paso *(G-5863)*

North Texas Farm & Ranch ....F 940 872-5922
   Bowie *(G-2199)*

Now Magazines LLC ....F 972 937-8447
   Corsicana *(G-3680)*

Open Sky Media Inc ....D 512 263-9133
   Austin *(G-1388)*

Pearson Education Inc ....F 866 565-4879
   Austin *(G-1405)*

Permian Bsin Hmes Land Mag LLC ......F 737 256-0799
   Odessa *(G-16115)*

▲ Perryman Group Inc ....E 254 751-9595
   Waco *(G-20445)*

Pixelworks Corporation ....E 210 826-5375
   San Antonio *(G-18380)*

Promotional Products Assn Intl ....D 972 252-0404
   Irving *(G-13160)*

Publictions Communications Inc ....E 512 250-9023
   Austin *(G-1437)*

Red News Inc ....F 281 888-1448
   Houston *(G-11567)*

Sales R Up Media Inc ....E 817 326-3282
   Granbury *(G-7808)*

Shawdashian Group LLC ....E 832 649-3800
   Houston *(G-11853)*

Shopper ....G 940 872-6186
   Bowie *(G-2201)*

Shweiki Media Inc ....E 210 804-0390
   San Antonio *(G-18471)*

Silent Partners Inc ....E 512 458-1191
   Austin *(G-1503)*

Sport Source Inc ....F 972 509-5707
   McKinney *(G-14978)*

Style Publications ....E 713 748-6300
   Houston *(G-12085)*

Style Publishing Group LLC ....F 972 335-1181
   Frisco *(G-7315)*

▲ Success Partners Holding Co ....C 800 752-2030
   Plano *(G-17012)*

Tanglewood Moms LLC ....F 817 247-1474
   Fort Worth *(G-7033)*

Texas Dental Association Inc ....E 512 443-3675
   Austin *(G-1565)*

Texas Department Trnsp ....E 512 486-5887
   Austin *(G-1566)*

Texas Farm Bureau ....B 254 751-2251
   Waco *(G-20465)*

▲ Texas Fish Game Pubg Co L L C ......F 281 227-3001
   Houston *(G-12230)*

Texas Music Magazine ....E 903 838-3838
   Texarkana *(G-19780)*

Thomson Rters Tax Accnting Inc ....B 800 431-9025
   Carrollton *(G-2833)*

Tng GP ....A 210 226-9333
   San Antonio *(G-18553)*

Toastmasters International ....E 325 949-3782
   San Angelo *(G-17835)*

Travelhost Printing Inc ....E 972 556-0541
   Irving *(G-13198)*

United Advg Publications Inc ....E 214 269-0788
   Plano *(G-17042)*

Up & Out Communications ....F 713 520-7237
   Houston *(G-12473)*

Urban Publishers Inc ....G 214 521-3439
   Dallas *(G-5146)*

Urban Publishers Inc ....E 713 524-0606
   Houston *(G-12477)*

Vacation Publications Inc ....B 713 974-6903
   Houston *(G-12516)*

W V Grant Intl Ministries ....F 214 333-2176
Dallas (G-5171)

Waterfront Publishing Inc ....F 281 334-2202
Kemah (G-13482)

Western Horseman Magazine ....E 817 737-6397
Fort Worth (G-7140)

Wishbone Graphics Inc ....F 972 769-7272
Plano (G-17052)

2731 Books: Publishing & Printing

▲ Abrams & Company Publs Inc ....E 800 227-9120
Austin (G-878)

Aha Process Inc ....E 281 426-5300
Highlands (G-8311)

Associated Publishing Company ....E 432 687-1756
Midland (G-15121)

Behavioral Science Res Press ....F 972 243-8543
Dallas (G-4015)

▲ Benbella Books Inc ....F 214 750-3600
Dallas (G-4017)

Brightleaf Group Inc ....F 512 795-8900
Austin (G-1010)

◆ Brownlow Publishing Company ....E 817 831-3831
Fort Worth (G-6473)

Cambium Learning Inc ....F 214 932-9500
Dallas (G-3840)

Clarion Events Inc ....C 713 963-6220
Houston (G-9207)

Creative MENus&folders LLC ....F 254 653-2775
Olden (G-16219)

Currid & Company ....F 713 893-8401
Houston (G-9360)

Drug Prevention Resources Inc ....F 972 518-1821
Waxahachie (G-20540)

Edmonds Pubg & Media Group LLC .....F 214 460-7560
Colleyville (G-3213)

Flightsafety International Inc ....C 817 571-5925
Fort Worth (G-6638)

Foreclosure Listing Service ....F 972 250-0993
Addison (G-125)

Formulary Productions LLC ....F 901 767-3000
Austin (G-1167)

▲ Future Horizons Inc ....E 817 277-0727
Arlington (G-683)

▲ Gods Word In Time Inc ....F 713 466-6799
Houston (G-9989)

◆ Graphic Image Inc ....E 563 285-5214
Flower Mound (G-6267)

◆ Greenleaf Book Group LLC ....E 512 891-6100
Austin (G-1193)

Gulf Publishing Company ....E 713 529-4301
Houston (G-10068)

Happymecom ....F 972 503-4803
Plano (G-16883)

Hmh Supplemental Publishers ....C 512 721-7000
Austin (G-1206)

Houghton Mifflin Harcourt Pubg ....C 817 302-0006
Fort Worth (G-6705)

I Do It With Ink ....G 817 715-0681
Fort Worth (G-6712)

John Wiley & Sons Inc ....D 972 245-0480
Carrollton (G-2875)

Kamico Instructional Media Inc ....E 254 947-7283
Salado (G-17765)

Knowles Publishing Inc ....D 817 838-0202
Colleyville (G-3217)

Laser Printing Inc ....G 972 235-2488
Garland (G-7536)

Living Stream ....G 972 257-1166
Irving (G-13087)

▲ M Brown Books Pubg Group Inc ......F 972 381-0009
Dallas (G-4619)

Mancomm Inc ....E 563 323-6245
Austin (G-1321)

▲ Mission City Press Inc ....F 210 614-7051
San Antonio (G-18309)

Mometrix Media LLC ....E 888 248-1219
Beaumont (G-1931)

Newpoint Media Group LLC ....D 770 962-7220
Austin (G-1365)

Online Training Solutions Inc ....E 888 308-6874
Argyle (G-602)

Paradigm Bks Lecture Notes Ltd ....F 217 344-4433
Austin (G-1396)

Paradigm Concept LLC ....F 817 896-7729
Mansfield (G-14700)

Pearson Education Inc ....E 281 496-0657
Houston (G-11267)

Pearson Education Inc ....E 512 989-5300
Austin (G-1404)

Pearson Education Inc ....F 972 870-1048
Irving (G-13140)

Pritchett LP ....E 214 239-9600
Dallas (G-4828)

Sales R Up Media Inc ....F 817 326-3282
Granbury (G-7808)

Stone-Cmpbell Rest Mvment Pubg ......D 325 674-2720
Abilene (G-83)

▲ Taylor Publishing Company ....A 214 637-2800
Dallas (G-5039)

Taylor Publishing Company ....G 325 486-5300
San Angelo (G-17832)

Taylor Publishing Company ....F 210 659-7505
Schertz (G-18763)

Texas Book Company ....D 972 825-4781
Waxahachie (G-20565)

▲ Texas State Historical Assn ....E 512 471-2600
Austin (G-1570)

The Texas A&M University Sys ....E 979 845-1436
College Station (G-3206)

The Texas A&M University Sys ....F 979 845-6601
College Station (G-3207)

▼ Thinkwell Corporation ....F 888 416-8880
Austin (G-1575)

Thomson Reuters Corporation ....D 972 250-7000
Carrollton (G-2832)

TM Luckett Enterprises LLC ....F 866 216-7278
Houston (G-12307)

Trinity Fellowship ....C 806 355-8955
Amarillo (G-515)

University of Houston System ....E 713 743-2841
Houston (G-12469)

University of Texas At Austin ....E 800 252-3206
Austin (G-1609)

Up & Out Communications ....F 713 520-7237
Houston (G-12473)

Vacation Publications Inc ....B 713 974-6903
Houston (G-12516)

Viserv Inc ....F 512 454-7403
Austin (G-1637)

Whitley & Siddons ....F 512 477-9491
Austin (G-1662)

Zinepak LLC ....F 212 706-8621
Austin (G-1688)

2732 Book Printing, Not Publishing

▲ Bob Lillys Prof Mktg Group Inc ....E 214 231-2082
Garland (G-7449)

C & R Bindery Inc ....F 214 688-5258
Dallas (G-4072)

Capital Printing LLC ....D 512 442-1415
Austin (G-1027)

Cellisco Inc ....E 210 692-1927
San Antonio (G-17989)

Creative Handworks Inc ....E 214 682-2090
Arlington (G-650)

Cyclone Production Inc ....F 713 979-1101
Houston (G-9384)

Finishing & Mailing Center LLC ....E 214 747-6244
Dallas (G-4362)

Gipson Group LLC ....G 512 931-2211
Georgetown (G-7654)

Hill Print Solutions Ltd ....E 214 826-0092
Dallas (G-4458)

Nationwide Press LLC ....F 817 885-8855
Richland Hills (G-17444)

▲ Taylor Publishing Company ....A 214 637-2800
Dallas (G-5039)

The Texas A&M University Sys ....F 979 845-6601
College Station (G-3207)

Tops Printing Inc ....E 979 779-1234
Bryan (G-2512)

Voom Group Inc ....F 972 424-8887
Plano (G-17048)

2741 Misc Publishing

360 Press Solutions LLC ....E 512 381-2360
Cedar Park (G-2957)

A T D Austin ....F 512 288-6215
Austin (G-873)

▲ Abrams & Company Publs Inc ....E 800 227-9120
Austin (G-878)

ABS Printing Services ....E 806 747-3702
Lubbock (G-14356)

▲ Access Intelligence Events LLC ....D 832 242-1969
Houston (G-8458)

Actual Seo Media Inc ....E 832 834-0661
Houston (G-8472)

Afam Capital Inc ....E 512 354-7041
Austin (G-900)

Ajr Media Group LLC ....F 713 942-7676
Spring (G-19194)

Alex Esolutions Inc ....C 512 305-6500
Austin (G-907)

Aliento Inc ....E 214 302-6580
Duncanville (G-5527)

▲ American Achievement Corp ....E 512 444-0571
Dallas (G-3937)

American Classifieds ....F 254 771-2777
Temple (G-19668)

Argus Media Inc ....E 713 968-0000
Houston (G-8691)

Associated Publishing Company ....F 325 949-1910
San Angelo (G-17779)

Associated Publishing Company ....E 432 687-1756
Midland (G-15121)

Associated Telephone ....E 512 288-6215
Kyle (G-13677)

AT&T Inc ....A 210 821-4105
Dallas (G-3978)

Bernadette Debrango ....F 806 342-0606
Amarillo (G-408)

Best Publications LLP ....E 281 488-8300
Webster (G-20634)

Bilingual Yellow Pages ....G 214 823-4384
Dallas (G-4024)

Billmyr Enterprises Inc ....E 972 424-1980
Plano (G-16804)

Black Lemon Media Inc ....E 832 666-6600
Houston (G-8905)

Brightleaf Group Inc ....F 512 795-8900
Austin (G-1010)

Cactus Express LP ....D 936 632-3031
Lufkin (G-14521)

Cev Multimedia Ltd ....E 806 745-8820
Lubbock (G-14391)

Champions Printing & Pubg Inc ....E 281 583-7661
Houston (G-9160)

Circle A Xpress Inc ....F 956 547-9393
Harlingen (G-8185)

College Port Enterprises Inc ....F 979 848-3070
Angleton (G-568)

Comanche Moon Publishing LLC ....E 325 572-3339
Buffalo Gap (G-2550)

▲ Coole School Inc ....G 713 552-1600
Houston (G-9302)

Creative MENus&folders LLC ....E 254 653-2775
Olden (G-16219)

Dallas Chinese News Inc ....F 972 680-9577
Richardson (G-17297)

Deep Vellum Publishing Inc ....F 972 638-7741
Dallas (G-4246)

▲ Defense Solutions Group Inc ....F 800 382-7571
Cleburne (G-3087)

Digital Alliance Media Inc ....E 512 238-3014
Round Rock (G-17649)

Digital Marketer Labs LLC ....E 512 892-3022
Austin (G-1093)

Dirt Road Music Group LLC ....F 678 525-3982
Arlington (G-663)

Dixie Freight Solutions LP ....E 281 447-7500
Houston (G-9484)

Downey Publishing Inc ....E 817 416-6661
Southlake (G-19064)

East Dllas-Lakewood People Inc ....E 214 823-5885
Dallas (G-4294)

Entry Way Publishing ....F 972 517-6513
Plano (G-16864)

Express Inc ....A 972 233-2986
Dallas (G-4349)

Express Inc ....A 281 712-7187
Katy (G-13361)

Falcon Events LLC ....D 800 895-6934
Irving (G-13022)

Five Points Holdings LLC ....E 214 525-6700
Dallas (G-4367)

Four Point Publishing LLC ....E 281 228-6237
Houston (G-9846)

Franklin Covey Co ....G 713 527-9494
Houston (G-9855)

Gipson Group LLC ....G 512 931-2211
Georgetown (G-7654)

Glassview LLC ....E 646 844-4922
Fort Worth (G-6671)

Gulf Publishing Company ....E 713 529-4301
Houston (G-10067)

Gulf Publishing Company ....E 713 529-4301
Houston (G-10068)

Harper Dirctry Dist Group LLC ....F 940 808-0769
Denton (G-5372)

Hart Energy Publishing LLC ....D 713 993-9320
Houston *(G-10130)*

Hart Energy Publishing Lllp ....F 713 952-9500
Houston *(G-10131)*

Hart Energy Publishing Lllp ....D 713 993-9320
Houston *(G-10132)*

Hartman Newspapers LP ....E 281 232-3737
Rosenberg *(G-17587)*

Hill Country Directories Ltd ....F 512 864-2973
Georgetown *(G-7656)*

▲ Idea Incubator LP ....E 512 892-3022
Austin *(G-1218)*

Igahu Inc ....F 469 474-9490
Desoto *(G-5433)*

Iglehart Enterprises Inc ....G 512 282-2559
Austin *(G-1220)*

Ihs Global Inc ....B 713 840-8282
Houston *(G-10319)*

Incongruity LLC ....F 954 889-6854
Dallas *(G-4495)*

Independent Tele Dirctry Co ....F 972 722-4796
Rockwall *(G-17550)*

Industrial Info Resources Inc ....D 713 783-5147
Sugar Land *(G-19498)*

Interface Lgic Tech Dcmnttion ....F 713 446-3560
Pearland *(G-16570)*

Interline Travel & Tour Inc ....E 512 691-4500
Austin *(G-1235)*

International Assn Drlg Contrs ....E 713 292-1945
Houston *(G-10398)*

Jana Inc ....D 210 616-0083
Universal City *(G-20183)*

JDC Enterprises Inc ....E 972 550-1880
Irving *(G-13068)*

Ji Communications Inc ....D 512 346-6921
Austin *(G-1255)*

Katy Ind Publications & Prtg ....F 281 396-6250
Katy *(G-13414)*

Key Maps Incorporated ....E 713 522-7949
Houston *(G-10524)*

Lawe Industries LLC ....F 512 262-1933
Kyle *(G-13684)*

Legal Directories Pubg Co ....D 214 321-3238
Mesquite *(G-15058)*

Libredigital Inc ....F 512 334-5100
Austin *(G-1291)*

Mapsco Inc ....D 214 476-5480
Flower Mound *(G-6271)*

Marketmap Inc ....F 512 576-6403
Austin *(G-1327)*

Matutech Ltd Liability Company ....F 832 989-3208
Kingwood *(G-13649)*

Maverick Concepts LLC ....E 972 418-7189
Garland *(G-7546)*

McElvy Vasquez Inc ....F 713 686-8494
Houston *(G-10811)*

Milestone International Inc ....G 210 226-2122
San Antonio *(G-18306)*

Mirror Publishers Inc ....F 281 486-6558
Texas City *(G-19798)*

Mometrix Media LLC ....E 888 248-1219
Beaumont *(G-1931)*

New Lifestyles Inc ....E 214 824-0022
Dallas *(G-4729)*

Newsletter Company ....F 214 871-7997
Dallas *(G-4734)*

Noisy Trumpet LLC ....F 210 852-0505
San Antonio *(G-18349)*

One Book At A Time Pubg LLC ....F 972 392-2679
Addison *(G-152)*

Online Training Solutions Inc ....E 888 308-6874
Argyle *(G-602)*

▲ Perryman Group Inc ....E 254 751-9595
Waco *(G-20445)*

Platinum Press Inc ....D 469 733-1506
Fort Worth *(G-6909)*

Pre Management Inc ....G 512 891-0300
Austin *(G-1428)*

Press Masters Inc ....F 713 661-9100
Houston *(G-11409)*

Promotional Products Assn Intl ....D 972 252-0404
Irving *(G-13160)*

Pronto Publishings & Prtg Co ....F 210 658-6857
Converse *(G-3400)*

Publishing Concepts LP ....B 214 530-0335
Dallas *(G-4835)*

◆ Quickfilter Technologies Inc ....F 972 442-3964
Richardson *(G-17380)*

Rbc Music Company ....F 210 736-6902
San Antonio *(G-18412)*

Reality Publishing Co ....F 281 493-4105
Georgetown *(G-7673)*

Roger Hooper ....F 903 784-3328
Paris *(G-16368)*

Sandford Prepress Systems ....E 214 808-3070
Dallas *(G-4932)*

Schuhmacher Publishing Co Inc ....G 210 805-8006
San Antonio *(G-18460)*

Scott Publishing LLC ....F 817 632-8100
Fort Worth *(G-6981)*

Seawall Specialty Company Inc ....F 713 522-9064
Houston *(G-11808)*

Shopper ....G 940 872-6186
Bowie *(G-2201)*

Sips By LLC ....G 214 208-0184
Austin *(G-1507)*

▲ Somerset House Publishing Inc ....F 281 346-8900
Fulshear *(G-7330)*

Somerset House Publishing Inc ....E 713 932-6847
Houston *(G-11949)*

Space City Publishing ....G 281 480-3600
Houston *(G-11989)*

Specialty Research Associates ....F 817 441-6044
Aledo *(G-202)*

Stratfor Enterprises LLC ....D 512 744-4300
Austin *(G-1542)*

Streetloc Inc ....E 254 274-2500
Dallas *(G-5016)*

▲ Supermedia LLC ....E 972 453-7000
Dfw Airport *(G-5456)*

Swim Swam Partners LLC ....E 512 827-9040
Austin *(G-1553)*

▲ T-System Inc ....C 972 503-8899
Plano *(G-17019)*

Tandem Marketing Services Inc ....D 361 949-7703
Corpus Christi *(G-3635)*

Teleometrics International ....F 254 776-2060
Waco *(G-20464)*

Telephone Directory of Texas ....E 903 586-2987
Jacksonville *(G-13263)*

Texas Publishing Co ....E 361 991-1306
Corpus Christi *(G-3638)*

▲ Texstar International LLC ....F 817 740-9072
Haslet *(G-8225)*

The Texas A&M University Sys ....E 979 845-6601
College Station *(G-3207)*

Thryv Inc ....E 903 593-5400
Tyler *(G-20162)*

Thryv Inc ....F 281 312-3258
Kingwood *(G-13654)*

Thryv Inc ....C 972 453-7000
Dfw Airport *(G-5457)*

Total Spcalty Publications LLC ....F 813 405-2610
Riesel *(G-17470)*

Uglypress L L C ....F 806 322-1050
Amarillo *(G-516)*

University of TX Med Brnch Gal ....D 409 772-5900
Galveston *(G-7411)*

▲ Uno Network LLC ....F 844 885-5000
Houston *(G-12471)*

USA Printing Corporation ....F 281 498-4310
Houston *(G-12500)*

User Friendly Phone Book LLC ....E 281 465-5400
The Woodlands *(G-19933)*

Valley Media Inc ....E 956 546-5113
Brownsville *(G-2419)*

Vant Marketing Inc ....F 830 217-2523
New Braunfels *(G-15830)*

◆ Viatech Pubg Solutions Inc ....D 214 827-8151
Dallas *(G-5165)*

Voyager Learning Company ....E 214 932-9500
Dallas *(G-3858)*

Waco Publications Inc ....F 254 752-0334
Waco *(G-20476)*

Want ADS of San Angelo Inc ....F 325 944-7653
San Angelo *(G-17837)*

Weno Healthcare Inc ....E 210 912-8143
Austin *(G-1716)*

West Texas Want Ads Inc ....F 325 673-4521
Abilene *(G-94)*

Winifred S Hayes Incorporated ....E 215 855-0615
Dallas *(G-5197)*

Woodland Publishing Inc ....E 281 485-7501
Houston *(G-16611)*

World Wide Celebrity Mag LLP ....F 832 305-8716
Spring *(G-19263)*

X Press Bags Inc ....F 972 513-9899
Irving *(G-13210)*

Yoyo Management Inc ....G 512 447-1455
Austin *(G-1684)*

Yp LLC ....C 713 867-6500
Houston *(G-12719)*

Zeus Development Corp ....F 713 952-9500
Houston *(G-12728)*

Zor N Terprize ....F 832 304-0504
Houston *(G-12732)*

2752 Commercial Printing: Lithographic

123print Inc ....C 800 877-5147
Dallas *(G-3862)*

2d Inc ....F 281 893-3366
Houston *(G-8405)*

3d Print Bureau of Texas LLC ....G 713 357-4700
Houston *(G-8408)*

3f Investments Co ....F 713 541-2258
Houston *(G-8409)*

3jg Printing LLC ....F 214 553-8664
Garland *(G-7422)*

Abbott TI Investments LLC ....C 210 344-5200
San Antonio *(G-17854)*

ABC Printing Service ....F 254 559-3561
Breckenridge *(G-2219)*

Abco Inc ....D 214 428-8996
Dallas *(G-3878)*

Ables-Land Inc ....E 903 593-8407
Tyler *(G-20043)*

▲ AC Printing LLC ....E 817 267-8990
Euless *(G-6125)*

Accurate Die Cutting Inc ....E 972 562-7921
McKinney *(G-14922)*

▲ Adolphs Litho Services Inc ....F 972 225-5303
Hutchins *(G-12861)*

AG Development Inc ....F 817 472-7260
Arlington *(G-612)*

Alice Newspapers Inc ....E 361 664-6588
Alice *(G-203)*

All Color Press Texas Inc ....E 214 744-2258
Dallas *(G-3920)*

Alliance Press Leasing Inc ....E 713 957-3349
Houston *(G-8546)*

Alliance Printing LP ....E 713 957-3349
Houston *(G-8547)*

AlphaGraphics Willowbrook ....F 281 890-0200
Spring *(G-19099)*

Altlite LLC ....E 469 767-1959
Dallas *(G-3935)*

Altman & Nelson Prtg Co Inc ....F 361 575-3118
Victoria *(G-20238)*

Always Printing Inc ....G 512 250-5056
Austin *(G-1689)*

▲ AMA Printing / Finishing Inc ....E 254 776-8860
Waco *(G-20359)*

Amarillo Litho Inc ....F 806 372-2245
Amarillo *(G-395)*

▲ American Color Labs of Texas ....F 210 308-0222
San Antonio *(G-17903)*

American Printers Exchange Inc ....F 512 452-5058
Austin *(G-917)*

American Printing & Off Pdts ....F 254 771-2422
Temple *(G-19669)*

American Printing Industries ....G 830 624-9000
New Braunfels *(G-15773)*

▲ American Prtg & Promotions Inc ....E 713 645-1991
Houston *(G-8605)*

American Whl Thermographers ....F 713 896-9008
Cypress *(G-3773)*

American Whl Thermographers ....C 281 256-4100
Cypress *(G-3772)*

Amzg Products LLC ....F 713 628-5504
Houston *(G-8632)*

An Authorized Affiliate of PRI ....G 817 430-6202
Fort Worth *(G-6387)*

Anchor Graphics Inc ....E 972 422-4300
McKinney *(G-14923)*

Anmar Enterprises Inc ....F 915 772-7488
El Paso *(G-5644)*

ARC Document Solutions LLC ....B 713 988-9200
Houston *(G-8678)*

ARC Document Solutions LLC ....F 713 787-1244
Houston *(G-8679)*

▲ Arlington Prtg Plying Card LLC ....F 817 275-2731
Grand Prairie *(G-7836)*

Arrow Printing Inc ....E 432 335-3407
Odessa *(G-15919)*

Associated Creditors Inc ....F 210 341-5642
San Antonio *(G-17919)*

Associated Texas Newspapers ....B 830 426-3346
Hondo *(G-8353)*

Aus-Tex Duplicators Inc ....E 512 476-7581
Austin *(G-949)*

Company	Loc	Phone
Austin Texas Print Inc ....G		512 507-2684
Manor (G-14644)		
B & C Printing Inc ....F		940 766-0033
Wichita Falls (G-20741)		
B Impressed Inc ....E		210 524-9229
San Antonio (G-17931)		
Banc Professional Services ....F		972 734-1200
Glen Rose (G-7731)		
Bankers Products & Printing ....G		903 438-0500
Sulphur Springs (G-19580)		
◆ Barrport Properties Inc ....F		713 271-2253
Houston (G-8818)		
Bass Printing Inc ....F		817 293-4913
Fort Worth (G-6439)		
Bayside Printing Inc ....E		281 209-9500
Houston (G-8838)		
BCT International Inc ....E		972 401-9171
Dallas (G-4009)		
Bdm Group LLC ....F		214 412-2291
Grand Prairie (G-7843)		
Beck-Drennan Inc ....F		915 772-3800
El Paso (G-5660)		
Beeville Publishing Company ....E		361 358-2550
Beeville (G-1984)		
Bernadette Debrango ....F		806 342-0606
Amarillo (G-408)		
Best Press Inc ....D		972 930-1000
Addison (G-107)		
Blanks Printing & Imaging Inc ....D		214 741-3905
Dallas (G-4030)		
▲ Bmp Paper & Printing Inc ....E		713 228-9191
Houston (G-8928)		
Boss & Hughes LLC ....F		713 664-9829
Houston (G-8961)		
Brazos Offset Printers Inc ....F		806 828-5681
Slaton (G-18970)		
Brenholb Inc ....E		210 349-4024
San Antonio (G-17965)		
Brodnax Printing Company I LLC ....E		214 528-2622
Dallas (G-4058)		
Brumley Printing Inc ....F		817 336-5551
Fort Worth (G-6474)		
Brunswick Press Inc ....E		713 462-0600
Houston (G-9000)		
Burrell Printing Company Inc ....E		512 990-1188
Pflugerville (G-16662)		
Business EXT Bur Texas Inc ....E		713 528-5568
Houston (G-9021)		
Business Printing Inc ....F		214 445-5000
Carrollton (G-2706)		
C & B Printing Co ....F		806 374-6262
Amarillo (G-410)		
C & G Printing Company Inc ....E		817 738-8350
Fort Worth (G-6481)		
C & H Label Co Inc ....E		214 371-2355
Dallas (G-4071)		
Caddy Printing & Graphics ....F		972 991-1770
Dallas (G-4076)		
Capital Printing LLC ....D		512 442-1415
Austin (G-1027)		
Capital Spectrum Inc C		512 478-3448
Buda (G-2524)		
▲ Carta Mundi Inc ....D		214 330-7761
Dallas (G-4087)		
Cash Engraving Co ....F		817 831-8585
Fort Worth (G-6495)		
Cedrone OBrien Inc ....F		512 426-5200
Austin (G-1036)		
Cellisco Inc ....E		210 692-1927
San Antonio (G-17989)		
Central Tape & Label Co ....E		713 462-8585
Houston (G-9139)		
Central Texas Printing Inc ....E		254 754-4653
Waco (G-20381)		
Century Graphics & Sign Inc ....E		432 686-8244
Midland (G-15157)		
Cenveo Worldwide Limited C		210 923-7591
San Antonio (G-17994)		
Cenveo Worldwide Limited ....D		806 376-4347
Amarillo (G-414)		
CFC Print Solutions LLC ....F		972 890-9248
Grand Prairie (G-7852)		
Champions Printing & Pubg Inc ....E		281 583-7661
Houston (G-9160)		
Chandler Consultants Inc ....F		210 344-5200
San Antonio (G-17999)		
Chas P Young Company ....D		713 652-2100
Houston (G-9166)		
▲ Checks In Mail Inc ....B		830 609-5500
New Braunfels (G-15783)		
City of Corpus Christi C		361 695-7350
Corpus Christi (G-3499)		
Clarke Harland Corp ....D		210 694-1492
Dallas (G-4126)		
Clarke Harland Corp ....D		210 697-8888
Houston (G-9210)		
Classic Printing ....F		361 852-7261
Corpus Christi (G-3501)		
Clear Visions Inc ....D		210 496-6006
San Antonio (G-18012)		
Cloud Printing Co of Abilene ....E		325 676-9396
Abilene (G-32)		
Cnhi LLC ....E		806 273-5611
Borger (G-2169)		
Cockrell Printing Co ....D		817 336-0571
Fort Worth (G-6528)		
Color Contorl Network ....E		972 754-1912
Dallas (G-4143)		
Colvin Painovich LP ....F		512 459-4139
Austin (G-1057)		
Company Printing ....F		325 949-9941
San Angelo (G-17788)		
Complete Reprographics Inc ....F		915 779-5000
El Paso (G-5702)		
Concho Business Solutions Inc ....F		325 653-1697
San Angelo (G-17789)		
Conley Printing Co Inc ....F		325 675-5500
Abilene (G-35)		
◆ Consolidated Graphics Inc ....F		713 787-0977
Houston (G-9275)		
Cooksey Luther Printing Co ....F		817 332-2842
Fort Worth (G-6545)		
Copy Center LLC ....E		210 481-9305
San Antonio (G-18026)		
Copy Plus LLC ....F		956 668-7587
McAllen (G-14851)		
Copy Stop Print and Postal ....F		979 774-4111
Bryan (G-2466)		
Cord Communications Inc ....G		254 776-1822
Waco (G-20390)		
Corporate Bus Solutions Inc ....E		817 701-1390
Arlington (G-647)		
Corporate Vsual Cmmnctions Inc ....E		214 206-3763
Dallas (G-4172)		
Craftsman Printers Inc ....E		806 744-8429
Lubbock (G-14397)		
Cramer Computer Supplies Ltd ....F		806 371-7310
Amarillo (G-485)		
Creative Computing West Inc ....F		512 804-2299
Austin (G-1072)		
Csg Systems Inc C		817 230-2700
Fort Worth (G-6563)		
Csg Systems Inc ....D		512 949-2200
Austin (G-1076)		
Curry Printing Ltd ....E		817 540-5252
Euless (G-6139)		
D & D Twin Print Inc ....F		210 647-7576
San Antonio (G-18040)		
D & L Printing Inc ....F		512 863-8145
Georgetown (G-7646)		
D R & J Inc ....F		512 474-4331
Austin (G-1083)		
Daily Court Review Inc ....F		713 869-5434
Houston (G-9394)		
Darling Quick Print Inc ....F		915 858-5055
El Paso (G-5714)		
Data Print Ltd ....E		806 324-4350
Amarillo (G-420)		
Detail Products Inc ....E		713 722-7789
Clute (G-3152)		
Dfm Print Pak LLC ....F		817 385-0600
Grand Prairie (G-7864)		
▼ Digital Print Inc ....F		817 512-3153
Cresson (G-3708)		
Dimaco Ltd ....F		972 242-2427
Carrollton (G-2724)		
Disc Pro Graphics Inc ....D		281 999-2717
Houston (G-9477)		
Dla Document Services ....F		210 671-1407
San Antonio (G-18064)		
Document Solutions ....E		512 471-5464
Austin (G-1099)		
Dolphin Graphics Inc ....E		713 789-7474
Houston (G-9492)		
Downtown Color Express Inc ....F		214 630-5533
Dallas (G-4276)		
Duke Forms & Printing ....F		512 985-6587
Cedar Creek (G-2935)		
Dunphy Graphics Solutions Inc ....G		281 363-9261
The Woodlands (G-19854)		
Earth Color Houston Inc ....D		713 861-8158
Houston (G-9569)		
Eastland County Newspaper Inc ....F		254 629-1707
Eastland (G-5564)		
Easy Print Inc ....E		806 374-7711
Amarillo (G-421)		
Echo Commercial Printing Inc ....D		903 885-0861
Sulphur Springs (G-19585)		
Echo Publishing Company ....E		903 885-2030
Sulphur Springs (G-19586)		
Edwards Printing Service Inc ....E		972 387-3575
Dallas (G-4300)		
Egh Printing LLC ....F		972 788-4266
Carrollton (G-2728)		
Eight Eighty-Eight Inc ....F		972 404-0155
Addison (G-118)		
Einsteins Inc ....E		972 387-8485
Carrollton (G-2729)		
El Dorado Logistics LLC ....F		214 871-3555
Dallas (G-4304)		
El Paso Heat Transfer Inc ....F		915 779-6334
El Paso (G-5735)		
Ellis Co Newspapers ....F		972 875-3801
Ennis (G-6096)		
Emco Press Corporation ....E		713 956-6055
Houston (G-9610)		
Ennis Inc C		903 496-2244
Wolfe City (G-20906)		
Ennis Inc ....E		972 875-5873
Ennis (G-6098)		
Exalt Printing Solutions LLC ....E		972 245-3858
Carrollton (G-2734)		
Executive Press Inc ....F		214 217-7000
Richardson (G-17306)		
▲ Exhibitco Inc ....F		713 830-8989
Houston (G-9723)		
FBC Enterprises Inc ....E		817 740-1951
Fort Worth (G-6624)		
Fedex Office & Print Svcs Inc ....E		512 396-1559
San Marcos (G-18687)		
Fedex Office & Print Svcs Inc ....E		281 364-7898
The Woodlands (G-19864)		
Fedex Office & Print Svcs Inc ....F		281 395-0077
Katy (G-13403)		
Fedex Office & Print Svcs Inc ....E		713 977-2666
Houston (G-9773)		
Fedex Office & Print Svcs Inc ....E		512 339-1191
Austin (G-1149)		
Fedex Office & Print Svcs Inc ....F		409 895-4000
Beaumont (G-1892)		
Fedex Office & Print Svcs Inc ....E		512 331-0800
Austin (G-1148)		
Fedex Office & Print Svcs Inc ....E		210 821-6911
San Antonio (G-18107)		
Fedex Office & Print Svcs Inc ....E		713 521-9465
Houston (G-9772)		
Fgs - Dallas Inc ....E		972 375-0253
Grand Prairie (G-7871)		
Firmin Business Forms Inc ....F		254 776-5742
Waco (G-20402)		
First National Trading Co LLC ....G		713 771-3600
Houston (G-9791)		
Fiserv Solutions LLC C		281 242-8569
Stafford (G-19313)		
Forms & Printing Service Inc ....F		713 266-4201
Houston (G-9835)		
Fort Dearborn Company C		817 625-1116
Fort Worth (G-6641)		
Forward Times Publishing Co ....E		713 526-4727
Houston (G-9845)		
Foust Incorporated ....E		806 374-7005
Amarillo (G-424)		
Fox Marketing Corporation ....F		713 686-8300
Katy (G-13404)		
Fred Bennett Printing Company ....E		817 641-9861
Cleburne (G-3089)		
Gainesville Printing Co Inc ....E		940 665-5517
Gainesville (G-7344)		
Garner & Golding Corporation ....F		254 753-8061
Waco (G-20406)		
Gateway Printing & Off Sup Inc ....G		956 546-0632
Brownsville (G-2359)		
Gea Associates Inc ....G		903 295-2727
Longview (G-14239)		
General Labels & Printing LLC ....G		915 532-7131
El Paso (G-5781)		
Gincop Inc ....E		512 454-6874
Austin (G-1183)		
Gipson Group LLC ....G		512 931-2211
Georgetown (G-7654)		

Girard Investments Inc.....................G.. 972 423-0299	K T F Inc...G.. 713 932-6954	Mtc Printing Inc................................G.. 972 620-3212
Plano *(G-16880)*	Houston *(G-10497)*	Carrollton *(G-2783)*
▲ Grafikshop Corporation...................E.. 713 977-2555	Kalle Enterprises Inc.......................F.. 210 340-1841	Multicopy Printing Company............F.. 210 923-8373
Houston *(G-10012)*	San Antonio *(G-18216)*	San Antonio *(G-18326)*
◆ Graphic Image Inc.........................E.. 563 285-5214	Kelly Associates..............................F.. 214 357-8752	National Mail Advertising Inc...........C.. 713 869-8551
Flower Mound *(G-6267)*	Dallas *(G-4548)*	Spring *(G-19152)*
Graphtex Inc....................................F.. 979 968-6333	◆ Kelmscott Communications LLC.....D.. 713 787-0977	Nationwide Press LLC......................F.. 817 885-8855
La Grange *(G-13696)*	Houston *(G-10515)*	Richland Hills *(G-17444)*
Great Southwest Ventures LLC........F.. 817 306-9204	Kenner Co Inc..................................F.. 432 333-1921	Ncp Solutions LLC...........................F.. 210 694-1528
Fort Worth *(G-6674)*	Odessa *(G-16046)*	San Antonio *(G-18338)*
Greeneway Enterprises Inc...............F.. 903 843-2503	Kennys Kustom Kards Inc.................F.. 817 332-8639	New Horizon Publishers Inc..............E.. 956 399-2436
Gilmer *(G-7707)*	Haltom City *(G-8149)*	San Benito *(G-18661)*
Grunwald Printing Company..............B.. 361 882-5654	Kggt Management Corp.....................F.. 713 462-0900	Newman Printing Company Inc..........E.. 979 779-7700
Corpus Christi *(G-3538)*	Houston *(G-10528)*	Bryan *(G-2495)*
GSC Enterprises Inc.........................E.. 903 885-1283	Kng LLC...G.. 713 263-1900	Newspaper Holding Inc....................F.. 817 645-2441
Sulphur Springs *(G-19589)*	Houston *(G-10545)*	Cleburne *(G-3102)*
Guardian Southwest String Tag.........F.. 972 938-0123	Kpw Enterprises Inc.........................G.. 214 630-8088	Newspaper Holding Inc....................F.. 817 594-7440
Waxahachie *(G-20544)*	Dallas *(G-4567)*	Weatherford *(G-20607)*
Gulf Business Forms Systems...........F.. 210 265-1620	Kwik-Kopy Corporation.....................C.. 281 256-4100	Nieman Printing Inc..........................C.. 972 506-7400
San Antonio *(G-18156)*	Cypress *(G-3808)*	Dallas *(G-4739)*
Gulfstream Holdings Inc....................D.. 713 696-9996	L C Colormark..................................D.. 972 243-1919	Night Owls Print Shop LLC...............F.. 281 741-7032
Houston *(G-10073)*	Carrollton *(G-2773)*	Houston *(G-11054)*
H E B & Associates Inc.....................F.. 972 234-0347	Lagan Interests Inc...........................F.. 713 472-1100	Northern & Nye Printing Inc..............F.. 254 662-2292
Richardson *(G-17324)*	Pasadena *(G-16470)*	Waco *(G-20438)*
Hart Engineering Company................E.. 903 758-0166	Laser Image Inc...............................F.. 214 267-1313	▲ Nx Media Inc.................................F.. 713 270-1198
Longview *(G-14247)*	Dallas *(G-4582)*	Houston *(G-11104)*
Henderson Newspapers Inc..............E.. 903 657-2501	Laser Printing Inc.............................G.. 972 235-2488	Oak Cliff Office Sup Prtg Inc............E.. 214 943-7421
Henderson *(G-8265)*	Garland *(G-7536)*	Dallas *(G-4750)*
Herald Democrat...............................F.. 903 893-8181	Law Publications Inc........................F.. 800 527-0156	Odee Company.................................E.. 214 340-0415
Sherman *(G-18917)*	Carrollton *(G-2774)*	Dallas *(G-4754)*
Herff Jones LLC................................G.. 903 592-3800	Lebco Graphics Inc...........................E.. 830 755-8226	Office Printing & Supply Inc.............E.. 512 474-2036
Tyler *(G-20096)*	Boerne *(G-2126)*	Austin *(G-1377)*
Herring Printing Co...........................F.. 830 257-7242	Litho Press Inc.................................E.. 210 333-1711	OKelley Office Supply Inc.................F.. 325 673-6422
Kerrville *(G-13520)*	San Antonio *(G-18254)*	Abilene *(G-61)*
Hewell Enterprises Inc......................E.. 972 466-2442	Lithographics Inc..............................G.. 210 226-1722	Omega Printing LP............................G.. 972 256-1234
Carrollton *(G-2869)*	San Antonio *(G-18255)*	Irving *(G-13131)*
Hill Country Publishing Co................E.. 512 556-6262	Loftus & Woosley Inc........................F.. 214 631-1975	▲ ONeil Digital Solutions LLC..........B.. 972 881-1282
Lampasas *(G-13834)*	Dallas *(G-4601)*	Plano *(G-16954)*
Hill Print Solutions Ltd.....................F.. 214 826-0092	Lone Star Printing............................F.. 956 535-2194	Orora Visual TX LLC.........................D.. 972 289-0705
Dallas *(G-4458)*	Harlingen *(G-8194)*	Mesquite *(G-15065)*
Hillsboro Reporter Inc......................F.. 254 582-3431	Long Plan Printing Inc......................G.. 713 797-1125	Orora Visual TX LLC.........................G.. 972 289-0705
Hillsboro *(G-8328)*	Houston *(G-10684)*	Mesquite *(G-15066)*
Hov Services Inc..............................E.. 248 837-7100	Lopez Printing Incorporated..............F.. 210 732-3232	P3 Imaging Solutions LLC.................E.. 210 494-9998
Irving *(G-13059)*	San Antonio *(G-18265)*	San Antonio *(G-18360)*
Hoyt Deryl..F.. 325 372-3825	LSI Integrated Graphics LP...............C.. 713 744-4100	Pamela Printing Co...........................F.. 281 240-1313
San Saba *(G-18717)*	Houston *(G-10696)*	Sugar Land *(G-19523)*
Hudson Graphics Inc.........................E.. 903 758-1773	▲ M & M Designs Inc.......................G.. 936 295-2682	▲ Panini America Inc........................F.. 817 662-5300
Longview *(G-14248)*	Huntsville *(G-12817)*	Irving *(G-13139)*
Ideal Printers Inc..............................E.. 713 880-8800	M L Holdings Inc..............................F.. 817 732-1708	Papergraphics Ltd............................F.. 254 526-4303
Houston *(G-10314)*	Fort Worth *(G-6803)*	Temple *(G-19696)*
Imagery Marketing Design Inc...........F.. 817 576-3735	Mail & Parcels Plus Inc....................F.. 409 899-1771	Parks Printing Co.............................F.. 806 747-2881
Dallas *(G-4489)*	Beaumont *(G-1923)*	Lubbock *(G-14457)*
Imaging Products Corp......................F.. 214 631-8899	Mail Mart Inc....................................D.. 214 630-9643	Pccs Printing Solutions Inc..............E.. 210 340-1841
Dallas *(G-4491)*	Dallas *(G-4629)*	San Antonio *(G-18368)*
▲ Impact Printing & Graphics............F.. 214 904-0808	Mail Services Houston Inc.................D.. 713 594-3362	Peacock Press LLC...........................F.. 972 272-7764
Dallas *(G-4494)*	Houston *(G-10738)*	Garland *(G-7566)*
Impressive Image Works Inc.............E.. 903 597-4599	Marfield Inc......................................E.. 972 245-9122	Perfect Ink Inc.................................F.. 281 376-4781
Tyler *(G-20101)*	Carrollton *(G-2778)*	Spring *(G-19157)*
Indoormedia Inc................................C.. 281 206-2500	Masterpiece Litho Inc.......................F.. 713 869-9990	Performance Companies LP..............C.. 214 665-1000
Houston *(G-10344)*	Houston *(G-10789)*	Dallas *(G-4797)*
▲ Indoormedia Inc............................B.. 800 247-4793	MBK-Wi Inc......................................A.. 972 375-0253	Personalized Printing Inc.................F.. 903 886-7173
Houston *(G-10345)*	Grand Prairie *(G-7922)*	Commerce *(G-3245)*
Ink It Printing..................................F.. 972 428-9623	McCarthy Print Inc............................F.. 512 479-8938	Phase 1 Prototypes LLC...................F.. 972 406-9988
Crandall *(G-3696)*	Austin *(G-1332)*	Dallas *(G-4801)*
Ink Spot..F.. 817 831-4438	McCord Printing Inc..........................E.. 214 631-1809	Polk County Publishing Co...............E.. 936 327-4357
Fort Worth *(G-6720)*	Dallas *(G-4660)*	Livingston *(G-14160)*
International Aerial Mapping..............E.. 210 826-8681	Mds Printgraphics Inc.......................F.. 972 647-0043	Porfirio Diaz Exit LP.........................F.. 915 544-6688
San Antonio *(G-18192)*	Grand Prairie *(G-7923)*	El Paso *(G-5916)*
◆ Iq Enterprises Inc.........................E.. 866 789-0508	Meera Enterprises Inc.......................F.. 972 385-3900	Port Lavaca Wave.............................E.. 361 552-9788
Fort Worth *(G-6728)*	Addison *(G-148)*	Port Lavaca *(G-17154)*
Issgr Inc..E.. 713 869-7700	Mendes Printing Co Inc.....................F.. 956 722-2222	Portele Printing Company Inc...........F.. 936 441-3738
Houston *(G-10429)*	Laredo *(G-13911)*	Conroe *(G-3352)*
J M H Printing Company....................E.. 972 263-1226	Metro-Graphics Inc...........................E.. 214 638-6780	Positive Marketing (usa) Inc.............F.. 877 284-4488
Grand Prairie *(G-7899)*	Dallas *(G-4671)*	Dallas *(G-4813)*
J-Peam LLC......................................F.. 817 927-1819	Metroplex Graphics & Mktg Inc.........E.. 817 831-7215	Post Oak Graphics Inc......................F.. 713 850-3563
Fort Worth *(G-6733)*	Richland Hills *(G-17442)*	Houston *(G-11370)*
Jarvis Press Inc................................D.. 214 637-2340	Midtown Prtg & Graphics Inc............F.. 806 744-3382	Precision Printing & Off Sup.............F.. 936 825-2488
Dallas *(G-4526)*	Lubbock *(G-14447)*	Navasota *(G-15742)*
Jayroe Litho Inc...............................F.. 972 243-3835	Minuteman Press..............................F.. 817 864-3000	▲ Premier Printing & Ltr Svc Inc.......E.. 713 868-6300
Dallas *(G-4528)*	Fort Worth *(G-6843)*	Houston *(G-11404)*
JM Graphics LLC..............................F.. 817 460-7562	Mix Printing Company Inc.................E.. 972 248-9000	▲ Primary Color LLC........................E.. 214 630-8800
Arlington *(G-711)*	Carrollton *(G-2781)*	Dallas *(G-4823)*
Jpt Graphics Inc...............................G.. 972 785-1013	Modern Print Shop Inc......................G.. 713 861-7262	Print Group......................................F.. 817 847-7860
Irving *(G-13070)*	Houston *(G-10904)*	Fort Worth *(G-6916)*
Juan Garza......................................G.. 956 723-6687	Molloy Corporation...........................E.. 713 771-9485	Print Premium..................................E.. 972 292-7227
Laredo *(G-13900)*	Houston *(G-10907)*	Plano *(G-16977)*
K & J Businesses Inc........................F.. 254 628-9208	Morton Printers Inc..........................F.. 210 223-4258	Print Shop.......................................E.. 903 295-2727
Killeen *(G-13609)*	San Antonio *(G-18320)*	Marshall *(G-14799)*
K & T Printing Inc.............................E.. 281 988-8088	Ms Dallas Reprographics Inc............E.. 214 521-7000	Print Systems Inc.............................F.. 713 812-8126
Houston *(G-10494)*	Dallas *(G-4701)*	Houston *(G-11421)*

S
I
C

Print World Inc ....F 817 446-9555
   Fort Worth *(G-6917)*

Printcitycom ....F 214 728-1230
   Dallas *(G-4825)*

Printdallas Inc ....F 214 363-1101
   Dallas *(G-4826)*

Printedd Products & Svcs Ltd ....E 512 835-2253
   Austin *(G-1432)*

Printers Service Florida Inc ....F 817 477-1291
   Mansfield *(G-14704)*

▲ Printmailers Inc ....D 832 201-2000
   Houston *(G-11422)*

Printmpro Ltd ....E 512 821-9000
   Austin *(G-1433)*

Process Industry Practices ....G 512 232-3041
   Austin *(G-1434)*

Prompt Printers Inc ....F 210 223-9177
   San Antonio *(G-18399)*

Pronto Publishings & Prtg Co ....F 210 658-6857
   Converse *(G-3400)*

Qg Printing Corp ....F 936 634-3357
   Lufkin *(G-14547)*

Quad/Graphics Inc ....C 972 892-3803
   Dallas *(G-4841)*

Quadrangle Press Inc ....E 210 828-8191
   San Antonio *(G-18405)*

Quality Graphics & Forms Inc ....F 915 592-4500
   El Paso *(G-5922)*

Quick Tick International Inc ....E 832 249-6400
   Houston *(G-11511)*

Quik Print of Austin Inc ....D 512 467-9382
   Austin *(G-1444)*

Quinn Printing Co Inc ....F 972 788-4266
   Carrollton *(G-2802)*

R R Donnelley & Sons Company ......B 713 468-7175
   Houston *(G-11526)*

R R Donnelley & Sons Company ......D 972 353-6130
   Lewisville *(G-14086)*

R S Graphic Services Inc ....E 817 921-6266
   Fort Worth *(G-6932)*

Ramirez Everardo ....E 915 593-5349
   El Paso *(G-5926)*

Rapid Reprographics LP ....F 214 357-5444
   Coppell *(G-3437)*

◆ Rediform Inc ....E 972 393-8080
   Coppell *(G-3438)*

Regency Plz Prtg & Off Sup Inc ......F 214 939-3456
   Dallas *(G-4882)*

Register Tapes Unlimited LP ....C 281 206-2500
   Houston *(G-11586)*

Renaissance Printing ....E 972 234-0347
   Dallas *(G-4886)*

Resonant Tech Partners LLC ....F 210 477-3671
   San Antonio *(G-18422)*

Responsible Prtg & Signs LLC ....F 713 722-0100
   Houston *(G-11612)*

Reynolds Brothers Ltd ....E 432 682-7393
   Midland *(G-15383)*

Rfv Enterprises Inc ....F 281 842-1877
   La Porte *(G-13788)*

Richmond Printing LLC ....D 713 952-0800
   Houston *(G-11619)*

▲ Rigba International Inc ....F 915 239-1070
   El Paso *(G-5939)*

River Oaks Printing Co Inc ....F 817 738-5461
   River Oaks *(G-17479)*

Rley Enterprises Inc ....F 956 715-8228
   Edinburg *(G-5599)*

Rockdale Reporter Inc ....F 512 446-5838
   Rockdale *(G-17526)*

Royal Printing Group Inc ....F 972 241-5686
   Dallas *(G-4914)*

Royal Publishing Inc ....E 713 895-9727
   Houston *(G-11683)*

S P (texas) Inc ....G 713 666-5166
   Houston *(G-11712)*

Schulenburg Prtg Off Sups Inc ....E 979 743-4511
   Schulenburg *(G-18778)*

Sclm Enterprises Inc ....E 972 243-1688
   Dallas *(G-4942)*

Scott-Merriman Inc ....F 972 484-7113
   Dallas *(G-4944)*

Scripps Texas Newspapers LP ....C 325 653-1221
   San Angelo *(G-17826)*

Seebridge Media LLC ....C 832 201-2000
   Houston *(G-11812)*

Selectouch Corporation ....E 972 924-3289
   Anna *(G-585)*

Service Photo Copy Inc ....F 713 225-1988
   Houston *(G-11840)*

Shakun Solutions LLC ....F 936 756-3738
   Conroe *(G-3363)*

Shannon Dunn ....F 210 653-7222
   San Antonio *(G-18468)*

Si Printing LP ....F 817 375-9016
   Arlington *(G-781)*

Sides Printing Company Inc ....E 806 765-8168
   Lubbock *(G-14479)*

▲ Signature Press Inc ....E 713 956-8555
   Houston *(G-11894)*

Signazon Corporation ....F 214 296-0022
   Plano *(G-17006)*

Simon Printing Company ....E 713 666-1296
   Houston *(G-11902)*

Sir Speedy 4092 ....F 512 338-9818
   Austin *(G-1508)*

Slocum Printing Incorporated ....F 214 748-2238
   Wylie *(G-20950)*

Somani Texas Inc ....F 214 698-0556
   Dallas *(G-4980)*

Sorcerers Apprentice Inc ....G 210 377-1212
   San Antonio *(G-18485)*

Sorita Enterprises Inc ....F 817 860-2679
   Arlington *(G-783)*

Southern Newspapers Inc ....E 830 379-5402
   Seguin *(G-18864)*

Southwest Precision Prtrs LP ....D 713 777-3333
   Houston *(G-11983)*

Spartan Printing Inc ....E 817 640-6341
   Arlington *(G-784)*

Speed Printing Conroe Inc ....F 936 441-2248
   Conroe *(G-3366)*

Spinner Printing Co ....F 972 380-0789
   Carrollton *(G-2818)*

Spotted Dog Printing Inc ....F 972 234-3033
   Richardson *(G-17401)*

Spotted Dog Printing Inc ....F 972 234-4391
   Frisco *(G-7264)*

State House Printing Inc ....F 512 472-5331
   Austin *(G-1532)*

Stephenville Printing Company ....F 254 965-5012
   Stephenville *(G-19424)*

Steward Printing & Advg Inc ....F 214 348-1200
   Dallas *(G-5011)*

Store Front Printers Inc ....E 281 367-3373
   Spring *(G-19255)*

Supreme Printing Company ....F 214 742-2511
   Dallas *(G-5030)*

T S Moore Printing Co Inc ....G 956 687-6868
   Mission *(G-15565)*

Tcca Inc ....F 361 668-9636
   Alice *(G-239)*

Technology Media Group Inc ....E 469 463-7647
   Dallas *(G-5044)*

▲ Technology Media Group Inc ....D 800 777-9091
   Dallas *(G-5045)*

Tejas Vsual Communications Inc ....E 972 243-6612
   Dallas *(G-5078)*

Texas City Newspapers Inc ....A 409 945-3441
   Texas City *(G-19803)*

Texas Offset Printing LP ....E 214 628-7430
   Dallas *(G-5078)*

Thomas Graphics Inc ....D 512 719-3535
   Austin *(G-1576)*

Thomas Kurtz ....F 361 578-2594
   Victoria *(G-20310)*

Thomas Printworks ....F 832 201-2000
   Houston *(G-12274)*

Thomas Reprographics Inc ....F 210 829-7000
   San Antonio *(G-18548)*

Thompson Business Forms Inc ....E 210 734-5356
   San Antonio *(G-18549)*

Thompson Family Partnership ....F 972 238-7664
   Richardson *(G-17411)*

Tmf Graphics Inc ....F 817 483-0237
   Kennedale *(G-13505)*

TNT Printing ....G 281 449-9090
   Houston *(G-12315)*

Tops Printing Inc ....E 979 779-1234
   Bryan *(G-2512)*

Tovar Printing Inc ....F 915 584-5900
   El Paso *(G-6010)*

Town & Country Printing Inc ....F 713 973-6666
   Houston *(G-12362)*

▲ Tpi Mexico LLC ....E 915 881-5808
   El Paso *(G-6011)*

Transfer Graphics Inc ....F 940 566-2679
   Denton *(G-5407)*

Trend Offset Printing Svcs Inc ....C 972 243-3556
   Carrollton *(G-2840)*

Trew Investments Inc ....F 806 749-3200
   Lubbock *(G-14498)*

Triangle Blue Print Company ....F 409 835-6810
   Beaumont *(G-1962)*

Triangle Reproductions of San ....E 713 780-0236
   San Antonio *(G-18566)*

Tristar Web Graphics Inc ....C 713 691-0001
   Houston *(G-12379)*

Turner Capital Inc ....F 281 488-4900
   Houston *(G-12412)*

Two Talents Image Plus Prtg ....E 817 379-5926
   Fort Worth *(G-7086)*

Union Printers Inc ....F 713 526-6364
   Houston *(G-12436)*

United Group Printing ....F 972 428-3000
   Dallas *(G-5134)*

Universal Graphics Inc ....F 915 591-8943
   El Paso *(G-6020)*

Universal Pen & Print Inc ....F 210 656-4000
   San Antonio *(G-18579)*

University of Texas At Austin ....F 512 471-1865
   Austin *(G-1610)*

USA Printing Corporation ....F 281 498-4310
   Houston *(G-12500)*

Ussery Printing Company Inc ....D 972 438-8344
   Addison *(G-174)*

Vari Doc Management Group LLC ....E 214 528-9925
   Dallas *(G-5155)*

Vastav Inc ....E 972 466-2442
   Carrollton *(G-2894)*

Veco Printing Inc ....F 956 968-1589
   Port Isabel *(G-17140)*

Versa Printing Inc ....E 972 243-5353
   Dallas *(G-5163)*

Vincent Graphics & Supply Inc ....E 903 882-3123
   Tyler *(G-20176)*

W B Mason Co Inc ....F 888 926-2766
   Pflugerville *(G-16691)*

W B Mason Co Inc ....E 888 926-2766
   Irving *(G-13205)*

W B Mason Co Inc ....E 888 926-2766
   Houston *(G-12584)*

Watermark Graphics Inc ....F 361 576-6874
   Victoria *(G-20319)*

Watermark Group Inc ....E 210 599-0400
   San Antonio *(G-18611)*

Wcn Inc ....E 830 216-4519
   Floresville *(G-6258)*

Webb-Mason Inc ....E 214 205-1123
   Dallas *(G-5179)*

Webb-Mason Inc ....E 800 992-2665
   Fort Worth *(G-7132)*

Webbmason ....F 682 432-0548
   Fort Worth *(G-7133)*

West Texas Printing Company ....D 325 646-3598
   Brownwood *(G-2449)*

Westar Graphics Inc ....F 713 957-4575
   Houston *(G-12638)*

▲ Westcave Printing Corporation .....E 512 989-0006
   Austin *(G-1657)*

▲ Whitley Group LLC ....E 512 476-7101
   Austin *(G-1663)*

Wiley Holdings Group Inc ....F 214 443-0908
   Dallas *(G-5188)*

Wilkins & Associates Inc ....E 713 472-6585
   Pasadena *(G-16527)*

William G Burns ....F 972 233-4700
   Dallas *(G-5189)*

William Totah Printing LLC ....F 512 916-9780
   Austin *(G-1668)*

Williams Printing ....F 210 599-6204
   San Antonio *(G-18621)*

Wood Printing Company Inc ....F 214 421-7393
   Dallas *(G-5201)*

Worldwide Spanish Literature ....F 940 692-4933
   Wichita Falls *(G-20836)*

Wrights Printing & Mktg LLP ....F 281 367-6060
   The Woodlands *(G-19941)*

Younger Colorpress Inc ....F 817 923-1331
   Fort Worth *(G-7158)*

Zachry Associates Inc ....E 325 677-1342
   Abilene *(G-97)*

2754 Commercial Printing: Gravure

Anchor Graphics Inc ....E 972 422-4300
   McKinney *(G-14923)*

B2b Copies LLC ....G 512 402-9775
   Lakeway *(G-13815)*

◆ Clarke Harland Corp ....A 830 609-5500
   San Antonio *(G-18009)*

Cyclone Production Inc......................F...... 713 979-1101
Houston *(G-9384)*

D R & J Inc...F...... 512 474-4331
Austin *(G-1083)*

Dac Labels & Graphic Spc.................F...... 214 340-2055
Dallas *(G-4205)*

Election Systems & Sftwr LLC...........D...... 469 675-8990
Allen *(G-264)*

Embossed Graphics Inc.....................F...... 713 667-0034
Houston *(G-9608)*

Engraving and Printing Bureau..........E...... 817 847-3800
Fort Worth *(G-6615)*

Garner & Golding Corporation ....F...... 254 753-8061
Waco *(G-20406)*

▲ Gc Packaging LLC ....D...... 214 383-7700
Allen *(G-270)*

Genti Studios Inc ....E...... 214 951-9696
Dallas *(G-4402)*

Hill Print Solutions Ltd ....F...... 214 826-0092
Dallas *(G-4458)*

▲ Liberty Playing Cards LP ....F...... 214 252-8175
Grand Prairie *(G-7912)*

M Alvarez Enterprises Inc ....F...... 972 514-2255
Addison *(G-147)*

Mrs John L Strong & Co LLC..............F...... 212 838-3775
Houston *(G-10933)*

Orora Visual TX LLC..........................F...... 972 289-0705
Mesquite *(G-15066)*

Paco Label Systems Inc ....F...... 903 561-2125
Tyler *(G-20137)*

R R Donnelley & Sons Company..........E...... 713 957-8910
Houston *(G-11524)*

R R Donnelley & Sons Company..........E...... 713 354-1300
Houston *(G-11527)*

Reichert Corporation ....F...... 972 267-1300
Carrollton *(G-2805)*

Taylor Communications Inc ....D...... 800 755-6405
Brenham *(G-2275)*

Tcr Business Systems ....F...... 972 807-8000
Dallas *(G-5041)*

▲ Vericast Corp ....D...... 210 697-8888
San Antonio *(G-18591)*

Wood Printing Company Inc ....F...... 214 421-7393
Dallas *(G-5201)*

2759 Commercial Printing

1 To 1 Printers LLC ....G...... 281 821-4400
Houston *(G-8398)*

3dgence America Inc ....F...... 469 466-2950
Dallas *(G-3869)*

4 Over LLC ....F...... 801 263-2727
Arlington *(G-605)*

A & B Labels and Printing Inc ....F...... 915 774-0007
El Paso *(G-5632)*

A J L Advertising Specialties ....E...... 512 320-0070
Austin *(G-872)*

A-Z Graphics LLC ....F...... 210 495-3468
San Antonio *(G-17852)*

Abbott Label Inc ....D...... 866 228-0100
Dallas *(G-3877)*

ABC Imaging of Washington ....F...... 832 426-5815
Houston *(G-8445)*

ABC Printing Service ....F...... 254 559-3561
Breckenridge *(G-2219)*

Abilene Printing & Sty Co ....F...... 325 677-2673
Abilene *(G-6)*

Absolute Color Ltd............................F...... 713 996-0202
Houston *(G-8449)*

Accent Screen Printing Inc ....G...... 713 782-6683
Houston *(G-8454)*

Action Screen Graphics ....F...... 512 478-6248
Austin *(G-886)*

Action Sportswear Inc ....E...... 972 487-6960
Garland *(G-7427)*

Action Wear Plus Inc ....F...... 281 376-4300
Spring *(G-19098)*

Alecom Technologies Group Inc ....G...... 972 870-9400
Flower Mound *(G-6259)*

All Star Caps Inc ....F...... 210 509-9086
San Antonio *(G-17893)*

Aluma Graphics LP............................F...... 972 442-3299
Wylie *(G-20925)*

▲ Alvin J Bart & Sons Inc ....C...... 718 417-1300
Addison *(G-103)*

▲ Amdec Inc ....D...... 214 654-0560
Plano *(G-16784)*

▲ American Film & Printing Ltd..........D...... 817 783-7600
Alvarado *(G-323)*

American Screen Graphics & EMB ......F...... 281 354-2581
Houston *(G-8609)*

American Whl Thermographers ....C...... 281 256-4100
Cypress *(G-3772)*

Americom ....E...... 936 344-9052
New Waverly *(G-15852)*

Anderton Group II Ltd........................F...... 254 751-1012
Waco *(G-20361)*

Anderton Group Inc ....E...... 254 751-1012
Waco *(G-20362)*

ARC Document Solutions LLC............B...... 713 988-9200
Houston *(G-8678)*

ARC Document Solutions LLC............F...... 713 787-1244
Houston *(G-8679)*

Associated Label & Tape Co ....E...... 214 744-1662
Dallas *(G-3972)*

Athletic Decals Inc ....F...... 713 774-0663
Houston *(G-8734)*

▲ Aztec Custom Screenprinting ....F...... 512 744-0195
Austin *(G-971)*

B Impressed Inc ....E...... 210 524-9229
San Antonio *(G-17931)*

Banc Professional Services................F...... 972 734-1200
Glen Rose *(G-7731)*

Bankson Group Ltd ....F...... 210 699-3800
San Antonio *(G-17938)*

Banner Sign Graphics ....F...... 512 458-5348
Round Rock *(G-17626)*

Barron Manufacturing Inc ....F...... 214 747-2544
Dallas *(G-4007)*

Bauer Visual Graphics Inc ....F...... 713 473-5241
Pasadena *(G-16394)*

Beeville Publishing Company ....E...... 361 358-2550
Beeville *(G-1984)*

Bells Advertising Inc ....E...... 512 454-9663
Austin *(G-989)*

Bertrand Enterprises Inc ....F...... 409 833-0922
Beaumont *(G-1864)*

Best Letter Press Inc ....F...... 713 123-4567
Houston *(G-8863)*

Bisi Inc ....G...... 512 478-3334
Austin *(G-992)*

Blanks Printing & Imaging Inc ....D...... 214 741-3905
Dallas *(G-4030)*

Blumbergexcelsior Inc ....E...... 817 462-1530
Arlington *(G-632)*

Blunck Studios Inc ....G...... 806 358-7064
Amarillo *(G-482)*

Bobs Monogram Embroidery ....F...... 210 341-6700
San Antonio *(G-17959)*

Branded ....F...... 210 532-4212
San Antonio *(G-17964)*

Brenholb Inc ....F...... 210 349-4024
San Antonio *(G-17965)*

Brides & Belles of Tyler ....G...... 903 581-8211
Tyler *(G-20060)*

Bridwell Publishing Company ....F...... 940 683-4021
Bridgeport *(G-2291)*

Brooks Industrial Coatings Inc ....F...... 512 990-5333
Austin *(G-1012)*

Brunswick Press Inc ....E...... 713 462-0600
Houston *(G-9000)*

Burrell Printing Company Inc ....E...... 512 990-1188
Pflugerville *(G-16662)*

Business For American Minority ....F...... 806 786-5052
Lubbock *(G-14386)*

Business Investment & Dev Corp ....E...... 432 335-3410
Odessa *(G-15947)*

Business Printing Inc ....F...... 214 445-5000
Carrollton *(G-2706)*

Campus Design Incorporated.............F...... 806 744-9998
Lubbock *(G-14387)*

Carlton Industries LP ....E...... 979 242-5055
La Grange *(G-13693)*

Cattilac Style ....G...... 325 695-6263
Abilene *(G-30)*

▲ CC Creations Ltd ....C...... 979 693-9664
College Station *(G-3181)*

Cc3 ....F...... 817 230-2700
Fort Worth *(G-6498)*

Central Texas Printing Inc..................E...... 254 754-4653
Waco *(G-20381)*

Cenveo Worldwide Limited ....C...... 210 923-7591
San Antonio *(G-17994)*

Cenveo Worldwide Limited ....D...... 806 376-4347
Amarillo *(G-414)*

Clarke Harland Corp ....D...... 210 694-1492
Dallas *(G-4126)*

Clear Film Printing Inc ....F...... 972 962-4422
Kaufman *(G-13458)*

Clear Visions Inc ....D...... 210 496-6006
San Antonio *(G-18012)*

Cloud Printing Co of Abilene ....G...... 325 676-9396
Abilene *(G-32)*

Clown Co Inc ....F...... 972 288-6954
Mesquite *(G-15034)*

▲ Cme Printing Inc ....E...... 713 271-7700
Houston *(G-9218)*

Cnhi LLC ....E...... 940 665-5511
Gainesville *(G-7339)*

Co Co MO Joes ....F...... 409 212-9892
Beaumont *(G-1871)*

Colordynamics Inc ....B...... 972 390-6500
Allen *(G-259)*

Company Printing ....F...... 325 949-9941
San Angelo *(G-17788)*

Creative Signworks Inc ....F...... 850 785-8899
San Angelo *(G-17792)*

Curry Printing Ltd ....F...... 817 540-5252
Euless *(G-6139)*

Custom TS ....F...... 903 874-7626
Corsicana *(G-3668)*

Cynco Specialty Inc ....G...... 281 499-0519
Stafford *(G-19298)*

D Custom ....F...... 214 523-0300
Dallas *(G-4202)*

D R & J Inc..F...... 512 474-4331
Austin *(G-1083)*

Dac Labels & Graphic Spc ....F...... 214 340-2055
Dallas *(G-4205)*

Dahill Office Technology Corp............F...... 713 329-9909
Houston *(G-9392)*

◆ Dahill Office Technology Corp ....C...... 210 805-8200
San Antonio *(G-18041)*

Dallas Chinese News Inc ....F...... 972 680-9577
Richardson *(G-17297)*

Dallas Decal Inc................................F...... 972 772-4641
Rockwall *(G-17546)*

Dancar Investment Group Inc ....F...... 972 633-1200
Dallas *(G-4232)*

Daniel Ayala ....F...... 469 245-3181
Dallas *(G-4235)*

Danwal Inc ....F...... 903 581-0777
Tyler *(G-20074)*

Data Dallas Corporation ....E...... 214 662-5165
Dallas *(G-4241)*

Davids Apparel Inc ....E...... 915 590-3744
El Paso *(G-5715)*

Ddsep LLC ....D...... 972 931-8000
Carrollton *(G-2722)*

Deq Coatings Inc...............................F...... 713 645-1777
Houston *(G-9438)*

Digital Corp Companies Inc ....F...... 817 801-8000
Arlington *(G-662)*

▲ Dime EMB LLC ....E...... 888 739-0555
Dallas *(G-4260)*

Display Graphics Inc ....F...... 713 977-7888
Houston *(G-9480)*

▲ Diversco Inc ....D...... 972 478-6400
Carrollton *(G-2725)*

Diverse Educatn Resources LLC.........E...... 817 769-8968
Fort Worth *(G-6588)*

Diversified Printing Svcs Inc ....G...... 210 226-2888
San Antonio *(G-18062)*

Dlt Printing Inc ....F...... 281 880-8883
Houston *(G-9487)*

Dollar B R Sr Et Al A TX Ptnr.............D...... 940 665-6262
Gainesville *(G-7342)*

DOT It Rest Fulfillment LLC ....D...... 817 275-7714
Arlington *(G-665)*

Dps Teck LLC ....E...... 972 241-0339
Dallas *(G-4277)*

Dragonfly Garment Design Corp ....G...... 830 549-5113
Seguin *(G-18836)*

Drake Industries Inc..........................F...... 512 251-2231
Austin *(G-1100)*

E & L Graphics LLC ....F...... 915 591-8789
El Paso *(G-5728)*

Easy Print Inc ....F...... 806 374-7711
Amarillo *(G-421)*

Echo Commercial Printing Inc ....D...... 903 885-0861
Sulphur Springs *(G-19585)*

Embossed Graphics Inc ....F...... 713 667-0034
Houston *(G-9608)*

Emco Press Corporation ....E...... 713 956-6055
Houston *(G-9610)*

Ennis Inc ....A...... 972 775-9801
Midlothian *(G-15480)*

Excel Label LLC ....E...... 713 477-6995
Pasadena *(G-16435)*

F W Promo ....E...... 817 231-8040
Haltom City *(G-8140)*

Far East Printing ....F 281 495-6161
El Paso (G-5764)

Fedex Office & Print Svcs Inc ....F 972 570-5110
Irving (G-13024)

Fedex Office & Print Svcs Inc ....E 512 339-1191
Austin (G-1149)

Fedex Office & Print Svcs Inc ....F 915 592-1190
El Paso (G-5768)

Fedex Office & Print Svcs Inc ....E 956 682-4040
McAllen (G-14860)

Fedex Office & Print Svcs Inc ....F 409 895-4000
Beaumont (G-1892)

Fedex Office & Print Svcs Inc ....E 361 806-2220
Corpus Christi (G-3526)

Fedex Office & Print Svcs Inc ....F 713 956-2366
Houston (G-9774)

Fedex Office & Print Svcs Inc ....G 512 331-0800
Austin (G-1148)

Fedex Office & Print Svcs Inc ....E 210 821-6911
San Antonio (G-18107)

Fedex Office & Print Svcs Inc ....F 806 359-9684
Amarillo (G-488)

Fedex Office & Print Svcs Inc ....E 512 472-4448
Austin (G-1151)

Fedex Office & Print Svcs Inc ....F 210 521-8395
San Antonio (G-18108)

Fedex Office & Print Svcs Inc ....F 713 521-9465
Houston (G-9772)

Fedex Office & Print Svcs Inc ....E 254 776-7763
Waco (G-20401)

Fedex Office & Print Svcs Inc ....F 512 528-9690
Cedar Park (G-2969)

Firmin Printing & Off Eqp Co ....F 903 793-5566
Texarkana (G-19763)

Fiserv Solutions LLC ....C 281 242-8569
Stafford (G-19313)

For Heavens Sake ....F 409 898-3340
Beaumont (G-1896)

For Sale By Owner Magazine ....F 713 457-0181
Houston (G-9832)

Fort Dearborn Company ....C 817 625-1116
Fort Worth (G-6641)

Fortis Solutions Group LLC ....F 512 302-0204
Austin (G-1169)

Foust Incorporated ....E 806 374-7005
Amarillo (G-424)

G & A Label Inc ....E 915 544-1766
El Paso (G-5777)

G and G Investments Inc ....E 325 949-7864
San Angelo (G-17801)

G9graphix ....G 940 268-1411
Wichita Falls (G-20766)

Gainesville Printing Co Inc ....E 940 665-5517
Gainesville (G-7344)

Gatehouse Media LLC ....F 956 546-5113
Brownsville (G-2358)

Genuine Letterpress Inc ....E 214 748-8215
Frisco (G-7288)

Gib Lewis Properties Inc ....E 817 834-7334
Fort Worth (G-6669)

Gincop Inc ....E 512 454-6874
Austin (G-1183)

▲ Grafikshop Corporation ....E 713 977-2555
Houston (G-10012)

Groggy Dog Sprtswear Grphic Ds .....F 940 891-4022
Denton (G-5370)

Gulf Business Forms Inc ....D 512 353-8313
San Marcos (G-18691)

Gulf States Label Company LLC ....F 713 812-8390
Houston (G-10071)

Guru Garments ....G 832 674-0990
Houston (G-10076)

H & B Copies Inc ....E 979 694-2679
College Station (G-3185)

H & H Dinero Tree Inc ....F 915 591-6245
El Paso (G-5792)

Harvey Dupriest & Sons Inc ....D 214 337-4731
Dallas (G-4440)

Hewell Enterprises Inc ....E 972 466-2442
Carrollton (G-2869)

HF Guyton Inc ....E 713 869-6483
Houston (G-10167)

Hollis Baker Sign Co Inc ....F 512 835-5782
Austin (G-1207)

Hoyt Deryl ....F 325 372-3825
San Saba (G-18717)

◆ ID Technology LLC ....D 817 626-7779
Fort Worth (G-6713)

Image Imprinting Inc ....E 972 243-8125
Dallas (G-4487)

▲ Impresa Label Inc ....E 915 592-4500
El Paso (G-5810)

Industrial Tape & Label Corp ....F 713 748-3105
Houston (G-10354)

Infovine Inc ....E 713 223-9994
Houston (G-10360)

▲ Inkjet Partners Inc ....E 972 991-4577
Dallas (G-4500)

◆ Inovar Packaging Group LLC ....F 817 277-6666
Dallas (G-4504)

Instant Embroidery ....G 281 888-0485
Houston (G-10380)

Interpress Technologies Inc ....F 972 926-6768
Garland (G-7520)

Ireo Reproductions LLC ....E 214 337-4731
Dallas (G-4512)

Islamic Services Foundation ....D 972 414-5090
Richardson (G-17337)

J & J Nameplate and Label LLC ....F 972 939-1157
Carrollton (G-2873)

J D Documents Inc ....E 972 733-1080
Dallas (G-4518)

J PS Fund Wear ....F 806 794-5777
Lubbock (G-14428)

Jeb Sales Company Inc ....G 903 342-3112
Winnsboro (G-20898)

Jefferson At Montfort Limited ....E 972 789-3600
Dallas (G-4530)

Jj of Dallas Manufacturing Inc ....E 972 866-9866
Addison (G-141)

K & R Screen Graphics ....G 214 821-9562
Dallas (G-4541)

K & T Printing Inc ....E 281 988-8088
Houston (G-10494)

K W Brock Directories Inc ....F 806 687-6270
Lubbock (G-14432)

Katy Printers Inc ....G 281 391-7072
Katy (G-13367)

Kelly Associates ....F 214 357-8752
Dallas (G-4548)

Kenner Co Inc ....F 432 333-1921
Odessa (G-16046)

Kevin Hall ....F 972 771-4246
Rockwall (G-17551)

Killeen Blueprint Co ....E 254 634-2779
Killeen (G-13610)

Kpt Inc ....E 214 620-9700
Coppell (G-3427)

Kruckeberg Corporation ....G 806 352-9262
Amarillo (G-496)

La Luz Marketing Group Inc ....E 210 202-1800
San Antonio (G-18234)

▲ Landes Inc ....E 713 665-0655
Houston (G-10593)

Laser Image Inc ....E 214 267-1313
Dallas (G-4582)

Laser Prtrs & Mailing Svcs LLC ....F 210 590-6565
San Antonio (G-18237)

Lebco Graphics Inc ....E 830 755-8226
Boerne (G-2126)

Liberty Cards LP ....E 214 646-9923
Dallas (G-4594)

Lithographics Inc ....E 210 226-1722
San Antonio (G-18255)

Lobues Rubber Stamp Co ....F 713 652-0031
Houston (G-10661)

Local Phone Book ....F 409 386-2244
Silsbee (G-18953)

Logo Factory ....F 972 642-4222
Grand Prairie (G-7917)

▲ Lone Star Corrugated Cont Corp ....C 972 579-1551
Irving (G-13089)

▲ Lown Brothers Inc ....E 915 594-4499
El Paso (G-5848)

Lsc Communications Us LLC ....C 817 640-9987
Arlington (G-724)

LSI Integrated Graphics LP ....F 713 744-4100
Houston (G-10696)

▲ M & M Designs Inc ....E 936 295-2682
Huntsville (G-12817)

M Patel Enterprises Inc ....E 512 892-2721
Sunset Valley (G-19626)

▲ M W Periscope Inc ....E 972 247-4202
Dallas (G-4622)

M3 Partners LLC ....F 602 561-6464
Kingwood (G-13648)

Magnetic Ticket & Label Corp ....E 214 634-8600
Dallas (G-4626)

Marian Graphics Inc ....E 915 542-0033
El Paso (G-5865)

Maverick Business Forms Inc ....E 903 663-7503
Diana (G-5460)

▲ Mayer Enterprises Inc ....E 281 498-2600
Houston (G-10807)

Mc Creless Company ....F 432 332-1213
Odessa (G-16076)

McAllen Sports Inc ....E 956 687-5500
McAllen (G-14889)

McDowell Packg & Advg Co Inc ....D 469 246-2700
Plano (G-16923)

Men of Cloth LP ....F 281 464-3141
Houston (G-10827)

Merch Legacy ....F 817 682-6855
Fort Worth (G-6826)

Metro Label Corporation ....D 214 369-9377
Garland (G-7549)

Metro Mini Courses Inc ....E 214 826-2300
Dallas (G-4670)

Miller Imging Dgital Solutions ....F 512 381-5266
Austin (G-1344)

Molloy Corporation ....E 713 771-9485
Houston (G-10907)

Mooney Saenger Enterprises ....F 512 869-0979
Georgetown (G-7665)

Mountain Products LP ....D 713 895-1350
Houston (G-10927)

Multi Packaging Solutions Inc ....C 214 343-7600
Dallas (G-4704)

Murphy Connected Entps Inc ....E 512 821-0222
Austin (G-1357)

▼ Murray Label & Printing Ltd ....F 972 234-2220
Dallas (G-4709)

Ndsventures LP ....E 713 395-0461
Houston (G-11021)

New Century Enterprises Inc ....E 972 926-6062
Garland (G-7562)

News Printing Inc ....E 817 275-5601
Arlington (G-738)

Northern & Nye Printing Inc ....E 254 662-2292
Waco (G-20438)

Northstar Graphix Inc ....F 817 385-1902
Arlington (G-740)

Odee Company ....E 214 340-0415
Dallas (G-4754)

On Site Decals LLC ....F 281 994-9000
Stafford (G-19361)

Outerwear USA ....F 806 792-8891
Wolfforth (G-20909)

▲ Overwraps Packaging Inc ....D 214 634-0427
Dallas (G-4774)

▲ Pacifica T-Shirts Inc ....F 714 508-4848
Round Rock (G-17677)

Page/Ntrntnal Cmmnications LLC ....C 713 341-6619
Houston (G-11221)

Pan Ector Industries LLC ....F 940 566-1414
Denton (G-5389)

Paper Planet ....F 817 451-8898
Fort Worth (G-6893)

Paragon Packaging Inc ....E 817 477-5211
Mansfield (G-14701)

Parker Business Forms Inc ....E 409 842-5251
Beaumont (G-1938)

Payton Interests Inc ....F 512 244-3221
Round Rock (G-17678)

Pccs Printing Solutions Inc ....E 210 340-1841
San Antonio (G-18368)

Performance Companies LP ....C 214 665-1000
Dallas (G-4797)

▲ Pesa Labeling Systems Inc ....E 956 544-3323
Brownsville (G-2392)

Philbo Enterprises Inc ....E 214 747-7018
Dallas (G-4802)

Pinnacle Graphics Inc ....F 972 418-1202
Addison (G-155)

Pls Inc ....E 713 650-1212
Houston (G-11349)

▲ Pointsmith Pnt-F-Prchase MGT S ....C 281 599-5900
Katy (G-13432)

▲ Pony Xpress Printing LLC ....E 214 221-7669
Garland (G-7570)

▼ Pp Exit LLC ....E 817 701-3555
Arlington (G-757)

▲ Premier Printing & Ltr Svc Inc ....E 713 868-6300
Houston (G-11404)

Prestige Embossing Company Inc ....E 713 864-0578
Houston (G-11411)

Prince Manufacturing Corp ....E 915 217-2664
El Paso (G-5918)

Printdallas Inc ....F 214 363-1101
Dallas (G-4826)

▲ Printed Supplies Inc ....E 210 946-2977
San Antonio *(G-18396)*

▲ Printedd Products & Svcs Ltd ....D 972 660-3800
Grand Prairie *(G-7954)*

Printedd Products & Svcs Ltd ....E 512 835-2253
Austin *(G-1432)*

Printmpro Ltd ....E 512 821-9000
Austin *(G-1433)*

Qti Promotions and Apparel Inc ....E 254 756-4444
Waco *(G-20452)*

Qti-Powers Inc ....E 254 662-3076
Waco *(G-20453)*

Quad/Graphics Inc ....C 972 892-3803
Dallas *(G-4841)*

Quadrangle Press Inc ....E 210 828-8191
San Antonio *(G-18405)*

R R Donnelley & Sons Company ....F 972 459-1493
Lewisville *(G-14084)*

R R Donnelley & Sons Company ....C 936 564-4683
Nacogdoches *(G-15711)*

R R Donnelley & Sons Company ....D 979 836-4451
Brenham *(G-2272)*

R R Donnelley & Sons Company ....E 214 521-4767
Dallas *(G-4856)*

R R Donnelley & Sons Company ....E 713 630-1000
Houston *(G-11525)*

R R Donnelley & Sons Company ....E 972 459-1400
Lewisville *(G-14085)*

Raymer Enterprises Inc ....F 972 242-8863
Dallas *(G-4859)*

Real Estate Foreclosures ....F 210 733-4262
San Antonio *(G-18413)*

◆ Rediform Inc ....E 972 393-8080
Coppell *(G-3438)*

Redstone Impressions Inc ....E 817 921-6266
Fort Worth *(G-6950)*

Reliant Labels and Prtg Inc ....E 915 595-2999
El Paso *(G-5936)*

Renfrow & Co Inc ....E 361 884-5541
Corpus Christi *(G-3608)*

River Oaks Printing Co Inc ....F 817 738-5461
River Oaks *(G-17479)*

▲ Rivercity Sportswear LLC ....E 512 754-8039
San Marcos *(G-18707)*

Safe-T-Pet Inc ....F 903 569-0590
Mineola *(G-15511)*

◆ Safeguard Business Systems Inc ......C 800 523-2422
Dallas *(G-4926)*

San Bay Studio Inc ....F 940 387-4466
Denton *(G-5399)*

San Patricio Publishing Co Inc ....F 361 364-1270
Sinton *(G-18965)*

Sclm Enterprises Inc ....E 972 243-1688
Dallas *(G-4942)*

▲ Semasys Inc ....C 713 869-8331
Houston *(G-11825)*

Shadowgraph Inc ....F 281 208-1280
Missouri City *(G-15592)*

Sides Printing Company Inc ....F 806 765-8168
Lubbock *(G-14479)*

Six B Labels Corporation ....E 214 349-7824
Dallas *(G-4965)*

Slpc Inc ....E 281 398-6655
Katy *(G-13443)*

Soccer 4 All Inc ....F 281 376-7890
Spring *(G-19166)*

South Texas Bindery ....F 210 340-1110
San Antonio *(G-18486)*

Southern Newspapers Inc ....E 903 785-6900
Paris *(G-16370)*

Sports Magic Inc ....F 903 832-1975
Texarkana *(G-19774)*

Star Engraving Company Inc ....G 281 951-5808
Houston *(G-12044)*

▲ Stingray Worldwide LLC ....E 972 818-6025
Addison *(G-165)*

Sunline Product ....F 281 398-6655
Katy *(G-13447)*

Super Color Digital LLC ....F 702 242-6335
Farmers Branch *(G-6217)*

Super Imprint Solutions LLC ....G 877 570-5573
Houston *(G-12106)*

Superior Label Systems Inc ....F 214 330-7770
Dallas *(G-5026)*

Supermedia Services Inc ....F 972 453-7000
Dallas *(G-5027)*

Swift Screen Printing Inc ....F 972 494-1144
Garland *(G-7594)*

T Rich Inc ....G 214 748-8700
Dallas *(G-5033)*

T Shirts N Trends ....F 972 272-2581
Garland *(G-7595)*

Taconic Industries Corporation ....E 972 241-5200
Carrollton *(G-2823)*

Tatex Inc ....C 254 799-4911
Waco *(G-20463)*

Taylor Cmmnctons Scure Cstmer ......C 817 283-9500
Fort Worth *(G-7036)*

Taylor Communications Inc ....E 713 456-4089
Houston *(G-12166)*

Taylor Communications Inc ....E 214 275-3200
Mesquite *(G-15078)*

Taylor Publishing Company ....F 713 782-0700
Dallas *(G-12167)*

Tech Dogs LLC ....F 972 985-4730
Plano *(G-17023)*

▲ Technology Media Group Inc ....D 800 777-9091
Dallas *(G-5045)*

Tekna Impact ....F 956 213-8285
McAllen *(G-14910)*

Tension Envelope Corporation ....D 817 451-5811
Fort Worth *(G-7042)*

Texas 28 LLC ....F 806 644-9663
Spearman *(G-19088)*

Texas Mri LP ....C 940 549-5462
Graham *(G-7790)*

Texas Mri LP ....E 214 630-9625
Dallas *(G-5077)*

Texas Star Envelope Inc ....E 210 293-8820
San Antonio *(G-18543)*

Thomas Reprographics Inc ....F 281 875-2500
Houston *(G-12276)*

Thomas Reprographics Inc ....F 713 977-6363
Houston *(G-12275)*

Thomas Reprographics Inc ....D 210 829-7000
San Antonio *(G-18548)*

▲ Titan Custom Products Inc ....F 214 678-9105
Dallas *(G-5096)*

TNT Printing ....G 281 449-9090
Houston *(G-12315)*

Transfer Graphics Inc ....F 940 566-2679
Denton *(G-5407)*

Tre Stars Incorporated ....F 915 351-1433
El Paso *(G-6014)*

Tri-Win Outsourcing Inc ....E 214 826-2244
Dallas *(G-5110)*

Triangle Reproductions Inc ....E 713 780-0236
Houston *(G-12365)*

Triaz Digital Printing LLC ....F 512 491-7000
Austin *(G-1592)*

◆ Trust Printshop Inc ....F 817 453-3121
Fort Worth *(G-7082)*

Ttc Trammell Co Inc ....E 713 921-7121
Houston *(G-12399)*

TWC Print Shop ....F 512 927-0002
Austin *(G-1600)*

Twg Solutions LLC ....E 512 472-8972
Austin *(G-1601)*

Uniforms Inc ....F 214 630-0924
Dallas *(G-5132)*

Val and Val Inc ....E 361 852-8992
Corpus Christi *(G-3649)*

Velocity Promotions LLC ....G 800 523-8078
Houston *(G-12545)*

Versa Printing Inc ....E 972 243-5353
Dallas *(G-5163)*

Viatran Inc ....E 512 832-8400
Austin *(G-1632)*

Voyager Learning Company ....E 214 932-9500
Dallas *(G-3858)*

W & W Silkscreening Inc ....E 817 590-4479
Fort Worth *(G-7112)*

W Promotions ....E 254 753-3411
Waco *(G-20474)*

Wahoo Inc ....G 817 332-2310
Burleson *(G-2601)*

Watermark Group Inc ....F 210 599-0400
San Antonio *(G-18611)*

Westgate Graphics ....F 713 688-1292
Houston *(G-12645)*

Weyerhaeuser Company ....D 972 929-8581
Irving *(G-13207)*

Wholesale Envelope Inc ....E 806 762-2255
Lubbock *(G-14512)*

Wilmot Printing Company Inc ....E 915 843-6424
El Paso *(G-6039)*

Wood Printing Company Inc ....E 214 421-7393
Dallas *(G-5201)*

Zubie Wear ....E 210 590-8892
Universal City *(G-20186)*

2761 Manifold Business Forms

Blumbergexcelsior Inc ....E 817 462-1530
Arlington *(G-632)*

Cash Engraving Co ....F 817 831-8585
Fort Worth *(G-6495)*

Data Print Ltd ....E 806 324-4350
Amarillo *(G-420)*

Ennis Inc ....A 972 775-9801
Midlothian *(G-15480)*

Gulf Business Forms Inc ....D 512 353-8313
San Marcos *(G-18691)*

◆ Impreso Inc ....D 972 462-0100
Coppell *(G-3421)*

Impressive Image Works Inc ....E 903 597-4599
Tyler *(G-20101)*

▲ Label Products Inc ....E 713 869-2959
Houston *(G-10584)*

Printegra Corp ....E 800 972-1175
Arlington *(G-759)*

Quality Graphics & Forms Inc ....F 915 592-4500
El Paso *(G-5922)*

R R Donnelley & Sons Company ....C 936 564-4683
Nacogdoches *(G-15711)*

R R Donnelley & Sons Company ....D 972 353-6130
Lewisville *(G-14086)*

◆ Rediform Inc ....E 972 393-8080
Coppell *(G-3438)*

Renfrow & Co Inc ....E 361 884-5541
Corpus Christi *(G-3608)*

Royal Business Forms Inc ....E 817 640-5253
Arlington *(G-774)*

Taylor Communications Inc ....E 972 581-7711
Dallas *(G-5038)*

◆ Tst/Impreso Inc ....E 972 462-0100
Coppell *(G-3451)*

Weyerhaeuser Company ....D 972 929-8581
Irving *(G-13207)*

Wood Printing Company Inc ....E 214 421-7393
Dallas *(G-5201)*

▲ Wrs Group Ltd ....E 254 776-6461
Waco *(G-20481)*

2771 Greeting Card Publishing

Quad/Graphics Inc ....C 972 892-3803
Dallas *(G-4841)*

2782 Blankbooks & Looseleaf Binders

Abco Inc ....D 214 428-8996
Dallas *(G-3878)*

▲ AMA Printing / Finishing Inc ....E 254 776-8860
Waco *(G-20359)*

B and D Binder and Index Inc ....E 817 261-8227
Arlington *(G-627)*

▲ Checks In Mail Inc ....B 830 609-5500
New Braunfels *(G-15783)*

◆ Clarke Harland Corp ....A 830 609-5500
San Antonio *(G-18009)*

Clarke Harland Corp ....A 817 329-7113
Grapevine *(G-8022)*

Clarke Harland Corp ....D 210 694-1492
Dallas *(G-4126)*

Clarke Harland Corp ....D 210 697-8888
Houston *(G-9210)*

▲ Dallas Lghthouse For Blind Inc ....C 214 821-2375
Dallas *(G-4217)*

Data Print Ltd ....E 806 324-4350
Amarillo *(G-420)*

Design Packaging Group Ltd ....F 254 840-2500
Mc Gregor *(G-14820)*

Firmin Business Forms Inc ....F 254 776-5742
Waco *(G-20402)*

Impressive Image Works Inc ....E 903 597-4599
Tyler *(G-20101)*

JPS Alliance Inc ....E 817 534-0044
Fort Worth *(G-6746)*

▲ Panini America Inc ....D 817 662-5300
Irving *(G-13139)*

Printegra Corp ....E 800 972-1175
Arlington *(G-759)*

◆ Samsill Corporation ....C 817 536-1906
Fort Worth *(G-6972)*

▲ South Txas Lghthouse For Blind ......C 361 883-6553
Corpus Christi *(G-3627)*

Space Age Lmnating Bindery Inc ....F 713 868-1471
Houston *(G-11987)*

Thompson Business Forms Inc ....E 210 734-5356
San Antonio *(G-18549)*

▲ Travis Assn For The Blind ....C 512 442-2329
Austin *(G-1590)*

▲ Vericast Corp ....D 210 697-8888
San Antonio (G-18591)
▲ VIP Samples Incorporated ....C 972 647-8888
Grand Prairie (G-7991)
Westgate Graphics ....F 713 688-1292
Houston (G-12645)

2789 Bookbinding

Alliance Press Leasing Inc ....E 713 957-3349
Houston (G-8546)
ARC Document Solutions LLC ....B 713 988-9200
Houston (G-8678)
ARC Document Solutions LLC ....F 713 787-1244
Houston (G-8679)
Beeville Publishing Company ....E 361 358-2550
Beeville (G-1984)
Bookbinding & Laminating Spc ....F 806 785-1126
Lubbock (G-14378)
Brenholb Inc ....E 210 349-4024
San Antonio (G-17965)
Brunswick Press Inc ....E 713 462-0600
Houston (G-9000)
Business Printing Inc ....F 214 445-5000
Carrollton (G-2706)
C & G Printing Company Inc ....E 817 738-8350
Fort Worth (G-6481)
Capital Printing LLC ....D 512 442-1415
Austin (G-1027)
Central Texas Printing Inc ....E 254 754-4653
Waco (G-20381)
Cenveo Worldwide Limited ....C 210 923-7591
San Antonio (G-17994)
Cenveo Worldwide Limited ....D 806 376-4347
Amarillo (G-414)
Clear Visions Inc ....D 210 496-6006
San Antonio (G-18012)
Cloud Printing Co of Abilene ....G 325 676-9396
Abilene (G-32)
Cockrell Printing Co ....D 817 336-0571
Fort Worth (G-6528)
Company Printing ....F 325 949-9941
San Angelo (G-17788)
Curry Printing Ltd ....E 817 540-5252
Euless (G-6139)
Easy Print Inc ....E 806 374-7711
Amarillo (G-421)
Fedex Office & Print Svcs Inc ....E 210 821-6911
San Antonio (G-18107)
Fedex Office & Print Svcs Inc ....E 713 977-2666
Houston (G-9773)
Fedex Office & Print Svcs Inc ....E 512 476-3242
Austin (G-1150)
Fedex Office & Print Svcs Inc ....F 806 359-9684
Amarillo (G-488)
Fedex Office & Print Svcs Inc ....F 281 463-8433
Houston (G-9775)
Fedex Office & Print Svcs Inc ....F 713 521-9465
Houston (G-9772)
Fedex Office & Print Svcs Inc ....E 254 776-7763
Waco (G-20401)
Fedex Office & Print Svcs Inc ....E 512 452-3600
Austin (G-1152)
Fedex Office & Print Svcs Inc ....E 817 543-0833
Arlington (G-678)
Finishing & Mailing Center LLC ....E 214 747-6244
Dallas (G-4362)
Gainesville Printing Co Inc ....E 940 665-5517
Gainesville (G-7344)
Girard Investments Inc ....G 972 423-0299
Plano (G-16880)
▲ Grafikshop Corporation ....E 713 977-2555
Houston (G-10012)
◆ Graphic Image Inc ....E 563 285-5214
Flower Mound (G-6267)
H and H Bindery Services Inc ....G 713 641-1831
Houston (G-10082)
Hewell Enterprises Inc ....E 972 466-2442
Carrollton (G-2869)
J M H Printing Company ....E 972 263-1226
Grand Prairie (G-7899)
Jbd Bindery Inc ....F 713 457-4606
Houston (G-10458)
K & T Printing Inc ....E 281 988-8088
Houston (G-10494)
Kenner Co Inc ....F 432 333-1921
Odessa (G-16046)
L C Colormark ....D 972 243-1919
Carrollton (G-2773)
Le Boufs Bindery Inc ....E 281 485-0332
Pearland (G-16576)

Lebco Graphics Inc ....E 830 755-8226
Boerne (G-2126)
Lithographics Inc ....G 210 226-1722
San Antonio (G-18255)
Marathon Bindery Services Inc ....E 713 690-6040
Houston (G-10752)
Odee Company ....E 214 340-0415
Dallas (G-4754)
Paper Network Inc ....E 972 239-6567
Dallas (G-4786)
▲ Premier Printing & Ltr Svc Inc ....E 713 868-6300
Houston (G-11404)
Quadrangle Press Inc ....E 210 828-8191
San Antonio (G-18405)
Quality Hand Bindery Inc ....F 281 445-8682
Houston (G-11494)
Rapid Reprographics LP ....E 214 357-5444
Coppell (G-3437)
▲ Rasch Graphic Services Corp ....E 713 785-5750
Houston (G-11550)
Reynolds Brothers Ltd ....E 432 682-7393
Midland (G-15383)
S P (texas) Inc ....E 713 666-5166
Houston (G-11712)
▲ Seidls Bindery Inc ....E 713 681-3815
Houston (G-11814)
Simon Printing Company ....E 713 666-1296
Houston (G-11902)
Spartan Printing Inc ....E 817 640-6341
Arlington (G-784)
Specialty Bindery Service Inc ....F 713 869-0594
Houston (G-11998)
Thomas Reprographics Inc ....D 210 829-7000
San Antonio (G-18548)
◆ Three Chiefs & No Indians LLC ....C 909 465-6314
Grand Prairie (G-7983)
TNT Printing ....G 281 449-9090
Houston (G-12315)
Transfer Graphics Inc ....E 940 566-2679
Denton (G-5407)

2791 Typesetting

Alliance Press Leasing Inc ....E 713 957-3349
Houston (G-8546)
ARC Document Solutions LLC ....B 713 988-9200
Houston (G-8678)
ARC Document Solutions LLC ....F 713 787-1244
Houston (G-8679)
Bayside Printing Inc ....E 281 209-9500
Houston (G-8838)
Beeville Publishing Company ....E 361 358-2550
Beeville (G-1984)
Blanks Printing & Imaging Inc ....D 214 741-3905
Dallas (G-4030)
Brenholb Inc ....E 210 349-4024
San Antonio (G-17965)
Brunswick Press Inc ....E 713 462-0600
Houston (G-9000)
Burrell Printing Company Inc ....E 512 990-1188
Pflugerville (G-16662)
Business Printing Inc ....F 214 445-5000
Carrollton (G-2706)
Cellisco Inc ....E 210 692-1927
San Antonio (G-17989)
Central Texas Printing Inc ....E 254 754-4653
Waco (G-20381)
Cenveo Worldwide Limited ....C 210 923-7591
San Antonio (G-17994)
Cenveo Worldwide Limited ....D 806 376-4347
Amarillo (G-414)
Champions Printing & Pubg Inc ....E 281 583-7661
Houston (G-9160)
Clear Visions Inc ....D 210 496-6006
San Antonio (G-18012)
Cloud Printing Co of Abilene ....G 325 676-9396
Abilene (G-32)
Cockrell Printing Co ....D 817 336-0571
Fort Worth (G-6528)
Consumer Guide Inc ....F 713 417-6152
Houston (G-9280)
Digital I M ....F 281 855-4933
Houston (G-9472)
Einsteins Inc ....F 972 387-8485
Carrollton (G-2729)
Fayette County Record Inc ....G 979 968-3155
La Grange (G-13695)
Fedex Office & Print Svcs Inc ....F 713 521-9465
Houston (G-9772)
Fedex Office & Print Svcs Inc ....E 254 776-7763
Waco (G-20401)

Gainesville Printing Co Inc ....E 940 665-5517
Gainesville (G-7344)
Girard Investments Inc ....G 972 423-0299
Plano (G-16880)
▲ Grafikshop Corporation ....E 713 977-2555
Houston (G-10012)
◆ Graphic Image Inc ....E 563 285-5214
Flower Mound (G-6267)
Hearst Corporation ....C 432 682-5311
Midland (G-15244)
Henderson Newspapers Inc ....E 903 657-2501
Henderson (G-8265)
Hewell Enterprises Inc ....E 972 466-2442
Carrollton (G-2869)
Hudson Graphics Inc ....E 903 758-1773
Longview (G-14248)
▲ Image Type Corporation ....F 214 956-9050
Dallas (G-4488)
J M H Printing Company ....E 972 263-1226
Grand Prairie (G-7899)
Jefferson At Montfort Limited ....E 972 789-3600
Dallas (G-4530)
L C Colormark ....D 972 243-1919
Carrollton (G-2773)
Lebco Graphics Inc ....E 830 755-8226
Boerne (G-2126)
Lithographics Inc ....G 210 226-1722
San Antonio (G-18255)
Molloy Corporation ....E 713 771-9485
Houston (G-10907)
Nieman Printing Inc ....C 972 506-7400
Dallas (G-4739)
Quadrangle Press Inc ....E 210 828-8191
San Antonio (G-18405)
R S Graphic Services Inc ....E 817 921-6266
Fort Worth (G-6932)
Rapid Reprographics LP ....F 214 357-5444
Coppell (G-3437)
Reynolds Brothers Ltd ....E 432 682-7393
Midland (G-15383)
S P (texas) Inc ....G 713 666-5166
Houston (G-11712)
Sandford Prepress Systems ....E 214 808-3070
Dallas (G-4932)
Southwest Precision Prtrs LP ....D 713 777-3333
Houston (G-11983)
Spartan Printing Inc ....E 817 640-6341
Arlington (G-784)
Stratasys Direct Inc ....F 512 821-1112
Austin (G-1541)
Thomas Graphics Inc ....D 512 719-3535
Austin (G-1576)
TNT Printing ....G 281 449-9090
Houston (G-12315)
Type Excellence Inc ....F 830 833-9005
Coupland (G-3693)
▲ Universe Tchncal Trnsltion Inc ....E 713 827-8800
Houston (G-12466)
Waterfront Publishing Inc ....F 281 334-2202
Kemah (G-13482)
West Texas Printing Company ....D 325 646-3598
Brownwood (G-2449)
William G Burns ....F 972 233-4700
Dallas (G-5189)

2796 Platemaking & Related Svcs

Aluma Graphics LP ....E 972 442-3299
Wylie (G-20925)
Blanks Printing & Imaging Inc ....D 214 741-3905
Dallas (G-4030)
Blumbergexcelsior Inc ....E 817 462-1530
Arlington (G-632)
Business Printing Inc ....E 214 445-5000
Carrollton (G-2706)
Cash Engraving Co ....F 817 831-8585
Fort Worth (G-6495)
Cooksey Luther Printing Co ....F 817 332-2842
Fort Worth (G-6545)
Corpus Christi Stamp Works Inc ....E 361 884-4801
Corpus Christi (G-3509)
Engraving and Printing Bureau ....E 817 847-3800
Fort Worth (G-6615)
J & J Nameplate and Label LLC ....G 972 939-1157
Carrollton (G-2873)
Kelly Associates ....F 214 357-8752
Dallas (G-4548)
License Plates of Texas LLC ....F 512 583-8585
Austin (G-1292)
Nieman Printing Inc ....C 972 506-7400
Dallas (G-4739)

One Stop Printing Inc ....F 817 338-1962
Fort Worth **(G-6885)**

Quad/Graphics Inc ....C 972 892-3803
Dallas **(G-4841)**

R S Graphic Services Inc ....E 817 921-6266
Fort Worth **(G-6932)**

Roy Johnson Incorporated ....E 817 468-2939
Arlington **(G-773)**

Sandford Prepress Systems ....E 214 808-3070
Dallas **(G-4932)**

Southern Graphic Systems LLC ....E 214 565-9000
Richardson **(G-17400)**

Thomas Graphics Inc ....D 512 719-3535
Austin **(G-1576)**

Timesaver Templates Inc ....F 972 620-2197
Dallas **(G-5095)**

USA Printing Corporation ....F 281 498-4310
Houston **(G-12500)**

28 CHEMICALS AND ALLIED PRODUCTS

2812 Alkalies & Chlorine

Buckeye International Inc ....F 281 873-4200
Houston **(G-9007)**

Dow Chemical Company ....E 979 238-2011
Freeport **(G-7196)**

FMC Corporation ....D 281 591-4470
Houston **(G-9819)**

FMC Corporation ....F 936 559-0031
Nacogdoches **(G-15697)**

▼ Genesis Alkali LLC ....D 713 860-2500
Houston **(G-9930)**

◆ Occidental Chemical Corp ....B 972 404-3800
Dallas **(G-4751)**

Occidental Chemical Corp ....E 512 476-2245
Austin **(G-1375)**

Occidental Chemical Corp ....F 361 776-6000
Gregory **(G-8103)**

Occidental Chemical Corp ....C 800 699-5123
Addison **(G-151)**

Occidental Petroleum Corp ....G 325 574-8567
Ira **(G-12913)**

Occidental Petroleum Corp ....E 713 640-7500
Houston **(G-11117)**

Solvay Chemicals Inc ....D 713 307-3800
La Porte **(G-13789)**

◆ Solvay Fluorides Llc ....D 713 525-6700
Houston **(G-11946)**

Solvay USA Inc ....D 940 552-9911
Vernon **(G-20230)**

◆ Tricon Energy Inc ....D 713 963-0066
Houston **(G-12369)**

◆ Westlake Vinyls Company LP ....C 713 960-9111
Houston **(G-12655)**

2813 Industrial Gases

Acacia Energy Inc ....E 877 997-2946
Houston **(G-8452)**

◆ Air Liquide Advanced Mtls Inc ....E 713 624-8000
Houston **(G-8509)**

Air Liquide America Corp ....F 512 748-5943
Manor **(G-14642)**

Air Liquide America LP ....C 713 896-2100
Houston **(G-8510)**

Air Liquide America LP ....F 281 474-5800
Pasadena **(G-16380)**

Air Liquide America LP ....B 713 438-6000
Pasadena **(G-16381)**

Air Liquide America LP ....F 281 474-8490
La Porte **(G-13717)**

Air Liquide America LP ....E 361 299-2999
Corpus Christi **(G-3468)**

Air Liquide America LP ....D 281 291-5360
La Porte **(G-13718)**

Air Liquide America LP ....F 979 239-5250
Freeport **(G-7190)**

Air Liquide America LP ....F 903 237-1740
Longview **(G-14188)**

Air Liquide America LP ....F 409 720-4200
Port Neches **(G-17157)**

▲ Air Liquide Electronics US LP ....A 972 301-5200
Dallas **(G-3905)**

Air Liquide Electronics US LP ....C 972 994-2403
Dallas **(G-3906)**

Air Liquide Large Inds US LP ....E 903 237-1739
Longview **(G-14189)**

▲ Air Liquide Large Inds US LP ....B 713 624-8000
Houston **(G-8511)**

Air Liquide USA LLC ....A 713 402-2221
Houston **(G-8512)**

▲ Air Lqide Advanced Tech US LLC ....B 713 624-8000
Houston **(G-8513)**

◆ Air Lqide Amer Spclty Gses LLC ....E 800 217-2688
Houston **(G-8514)**

Air Lqide Hydrgen Enrgy US LLC ....E 346 971-3051
Houston **(G-8515)**

Airgas Inc ....E 281 893-9353
Houston **(G-8516)**

Airgas Usa LLC ....D 972 994-2400
Dallas **(G-3912)**

Airgas Usa LLC ....E 281 474-8400
La Porte **(G-13719)**

Airgas Usa LLC ....F 361 533-0758
Corpus Christi **(G-3469)**

Airgas Usa LLC ....E 281 474-8300
Pasadena **(G-16382)**

Airgas Usa LLC ....E 972 660-0500
Grand Prairie **(G-7825)**

Albemarle Corporation ....A 713 740-1000
Pasadena **(G-16386)**

▲ Alig LLC ....D 212 626-4936
Houston **(G-8538)**

American A Lquide Holdings Inc ....E 713 624-8000
Houston **(G-8581)**

◆ American Air Liquide Inc ....F 877 855-9533
Houston **(G-8582)**

Atlantic Richfield Company ....E 806 592-4900
Denver City **(G-5415)**

Dcp Midstream LLC ....F 325 392-1000
Ozona **(G-16280)**

Dow Chemical Company ....E 979 238-2011
Freeport **(G-7196)**

Duke Energy Natural Gas Corp ....E 361 579-4600
Hallettsville **(G-8121)**

E I Du Pont De Nemours & Co ....E 361 776-1872
Ingleside **(G-12895)**

Generon Igs Inc ....E 713 937-5200
Houston **(G-9928)**

Linde Gas North America LLC ....F 866 543-3427
Houston **(G-10645)**

Linde Gas North America LLC ....F 210 287-9788
San Antonio **(G-18252)**

Linde Gas North America LLC ....F 903 939-0613
Tyler **(G-20114)**

Linde Gas North America LLC ....F 254 718-5124
Temple **(G-19684)**

Linde Gas North America LLC ....D 713 767-4100
La Porte **(G-13768)**

Linde Inc ....E 281 478-1500
Deer Park **(G-5282)**

Linde Inc ....E 325 643-5813
Brownwood **(G-2437)**

Linde Inc ....E 972 271-1531
Garland **(G-7537)**

Linde Inc ....G 210 489-5800
San Antonio **(G-18253)**

Linde Inc ....F 409 963-0141
Groves **(G-8109)**

Linde Inc ....E 281 471-4585
La Porte **(G-13769)**

Linde Inc ....E 409 943-9280
Texas City **(G-19796)**

Linde Inc ....E 281 203-3600
Spring **(G-19227)**

Linde Inc ....E 409 835-3939
Beaumont **(G-1919)**

Linde Inc ....E 979 774-0638
Bryan **(G-2490)**

Matheson Tri-Gas Inc ....G 361 887-0011
Corpus Christi **(G-3575)**

Matheson Tri-Gas Inc ....E 972 432-8800
Dallas **(G-4651)**

Matheson Tri-Gas Inc ....F 713 869-7351
Houston **(G-10793)**

Matheson Tri-Gas Inc ....G 281 474-1291
Pasadena **(G-16481)**

Matheson Tri-Gas Inc ....C 972 560-5700
Irving **(G-13096)**

Matheson Tri-Gas Inc ....E 512 385-0611
Austin **(G-1330)**

Matheson Tri-Gas Inc ....F 281 498-2310
Stafford **(G-19352)**

Matheson Tri-Gas Inc ....F 210 225-3151
San Antonio **(G-18283)**

Matheson Tri-Gas Inc ....E 281 471-2544
Houston **(G-10794)**

Matheson Tri-Gas Inc ....F 817 354-9536
Dallas **(G-4652)**

Matheson Tri-Gas Inc ....F 817 551-0550
Fort Worth **(G-6817)**

▼ McGuffy Energy Services LP ....D 281 255-6955
Cypress **(G-3809)**

Messer LLC ....E 713 767-4155
La Porte **(G-13776)**

Messer LLC ....E 281 837-0184
Baytown **(G-1829)**

Messer LLC ....E 903 626-4877
Jewett **(G-13307)**

Monument Chemicals Inc ....F 281 452-5951
Houston **(G-10918)**

New Altrnative Green Enrgy Inc ....F 972 523-9970
Kaufman **(G-13462)**

Nitrogen Services LLC ....C 925 336-1560
Midland **(G-15320)**

Nuco2 Supply LLC ....E 817 676-7580
Amarillo **(G-503)**

Oilfield Services & Tech LLC ....E 432 614-0076
Odessa **(G-16100)**

Parker Petroleum Pros Inc ....F 903 360-5450
Grand Saline **(G-7998)**

Praxair Inc ....E 936 295-3912
Huntsville **(G-12823)**

Praxair Inc Freeport Psa ....G 281 203-3682
Freeport **(G-7207)**

Texas Gas Utilities LLC ....F 281 252-6700
Magnolia **(G-14628)**

▲ Western Intl Gas Cylinders Inc ....C 979 865-5991
Bellville **(G-2015)**

Ws Group Inc ....G 214 337-4761
Dallas **(G-5204)**

2816 Inorganic Pigments

A1 Chrome Shop Inc ....F 713 885-1727
Houston **(G-8432)**

Acme Brick Company ....D 817 332-4101
El Paso **(G-5636)**

▲ Adtec Colorant Corporation ....F 817 633-3004
Arlington **(G-610)**

American Roller Company LLC ....F 262 878-2445
Houston **(G-8607)**

Contran Corporation ....E 972 233-1700
Dallas **(G-4161)**

▲ Gulf Reduction Corporation ....E 713 926-1705
Houston **(G-10069)**

▲ Huntsman Corporation ....E 281 719-6000
The Woodlands **(G-19877)**

◆ Huntsman International LLC ....D 281 719-6000
The Woodlands **(G-19878)**

Kronos International Inc ....F 972 233-1700
Dallas **(G-4568)**

Kronos Worldwide Inc ....D 972 233-1700
Dallas **(G-4569)**

Kronos Worldwide Inc ....E 609 860-6200
Dallas **(G-4570)**

Lonza Inc ....D 281 291-2300
Pasadena **(G-16475)**

Teknor Color Company ....D 903 586-0583
Jacksonville **(G-13262)**

▲ Tor Minerals International Inc ....D 361 883-5591
Corpus Christi **(G-3642)**

◆ Valhi Inc ....E 972 233-1700
Dallas **(G-5151)**

Venator Americas LLC ....F 281 719-6000
The Woodlands **(G-19936)**

◆ Venator Americas LLC ....D 281 465-6700
The Woodlands **(G-19935)**

Venator Materials LLC ....A 281 465-6700
The Woodlands **(G-19937)**

Zochem LLC ....E 615 446-8791
Houston **(G-12731)**

2819 Indl Inorganic Chemicals, NEC

▲ A E Santos & Co ....E 956 723-8359
Laredo **(G-13852)**

▲ Access Chemicals & Svcs LLC ....F 713 270-7215
Houston **(G-8457)**

Aceschem Inc ....F 817 863-6948
Frisco **(G-7265)**

▲ Air Liquide Electronics US LP ....A 972 301-5200
Dallas **(G-3905)**

Albemarle Corporation ....F 713 740-1866
Pasadena **(G-16384)**

Albemarle Corporation ....E 281 480-4747
Houston **(G-8530)**

Albemarle Corporation ....B 281 474-2864
Pasadena **(G-16385)**

Albemarle Corporation ....E 281 480-4747
Houston **(G-8529)**

SIC

Company		Phone
Albemarle Corporation A		713 740-1000
Pasadena (G-16386)		
Algae Production Systems F		832 515-9670
Houston (G-8537)		
▲ Altivia Chemicals LLC E		713 658-9000
Houston (G-8570)		
▲ Altivia Corporation F		713 658-9000
Houston (G-8571)		
◆ Altivia Specialty Chem LLC D		713 658-9000
Houston (G-8572)		
Ambar Inc C		281 873-7600
Houston (G-8576)		
▲ Aqua/Process Inc E		713 910-2977
Houston (G-8672)		
Arkema Inc D		409 838-3981
Beaumont (G-1854)		
Arkema Inc C		713 751-7340
Pasadena (G-16389)		
Arkema Inc D		713 455-1211
Houston (G-8698)		
Arkema Inc D		281 328-3561
Crosby (G-3725)		
Arrow-Magnolia Intl Inc E		972 247-7111
Dallas (G-3967)		
◆ Artlux Inc F		214 716-1990
Dallas (G-3968)		
Asarco LLC A		806 468-4000
Amarillo (G-401)		
◆ Athlon Solutions LLC F		713 457-2400
Pasadena (G-16391)		
Atlantic Dwntwn Dllas Vntr LLC E		469 399-1049
Dallas (G-3980)		
Auc Management LLC F		713 983-3255
Houston (G-8748)		
Austin White Lime Company F		512 255-3646
Austin (G-966)		
▲ Avastar Brands LLC E		512 804-9337
Austin (G-968)		
◆ Baikowski Malakoff Inc F		903 489-1910
Malakoff (G-14634)		
Baker Petrolite LLC D		281 474-5166
Pasadena (G-16392)		
BASF Corporation C		800 794-1019
Houston (G-8821)		
Basin Water Inc F		877 312-8950
Kingwood (G-13640)		
▲ BBC Biochemical Corporation C		360 542-8400
McKinney (G-14925)		
▲ Biotics Research Corporation D		281 344-0909
Rosenberg (G-17577)		
◆ Blue Line Corporation E		210 225-0400
San Antonio (G-17958)		
Brenntag Pacific Inc F		281 474-5400
Pasadena (G-16399)		
◆ Brookshire Chemical Svcs LLC E		281 371-2600
Brookshire (G-2311)		
◆ Cabot Norit Americas Inc C		903 938-9211
Marshall (G-14765)		
Cabot Norit Americas Inc C		800 641-9245
Marshall (G-14766)		
Cadre Material Products LLC D		301 682-0600
Katy (G-13354)		
Cadre Material Products LLC C		325 400-2793
Voca (G-20344)		
Carbide Grinding Inc F		713 944-0015
Houston (G-9090)		
Carbide Specialists Inc F		281 354-5585
Porter (G-17172)		
Carbonfree Chemicals Spe I LLC G		210 476-5906
San Antonio (G-17983)		
Carbonfree Chemicals Spe I LLC E		210 476-5906
San Antonio (G-17984)		
Celanese Americas LLC E		361 584-6000
Bishop (G-2105)		
Celanese Americas LLC E		979 241-4000
Bay City (G-1770)		
◆ Celanese Americas LLC F		972 443-4000
Irving (G-12963)		
◆ Celanese Corporation B		972 443-4000
Irving (G-12964)		
◆ Celanese Eva Performance F		972 443-4000
Irving (G-12965)		
◆ Celanese International Corp A		972 443-4000
Irving (G-12966)		
▼ Celanese US Holdings LLC A		972 443-4000
Dallas (G-4094)		
Championx LLC D		432 363-9105
Odessa (G-15959)		
Chemical Exchange Inds Inc E		713 455-1206
Galena Park (G-7378)		
▼ Chemicals Incorporated D		281 576-5000
Baytown (G-1813)		
◆ Chemquest Chemicals LLC E		281 291-9966
Pasadena (G-16407)		
Chemtrade Chemicals US LLC F		361 368-2200
Odem (G-15894)		
Chemtrade Refinery Svcs Inc E		409 835-6641
Beaumont (G-1869)		
Chemtrade Solutions LLC E		972 775-2307
Midlothian (G-15476)		
Clariant Corporation B		832 753-3042
Pasadena (G-16410)		
◆ Cls Indstrial Purification LLC E		281 538-4669
League City (G-13953)		
◆ CNA Holdings LLC E		972 443-4000
Irving (G-12976)		
Continental Carbon Company F		281 647-3728
Houston (G-9284)		
Continental Carbon Company E		806 935-4174
Sunray (G-19616)		
Ctci Americas Inc E		281 870-9998
Houston (G-9354)		
Diamond Shamrock Ref & Mktg Co B		361 786-2536
Three Rivers (G-19944)		
▲ Diapac LLC E		713 715-6300
Houston (G-9460)		
◆ Dixie Chemical Company Inc E		281 474-3271
Pasadena (G-16418)		
Dow Chemical Company D		281 474-4495
La Porte (G-13732)		
Dow Chemical Company E		979 238-2011
Freeport (G-7196)		
Dow Chemical Company B		281 228-2800
Deer Park (G-5268)		
Dow Chemical Company D		713 767-1615
Deer Park (G-5269)		
Dow Chemical Company D		409 948-5886
Texas City (G-19788)		
Dow Chemical Company E		281 228-3060
Deer Park (G-5270)		
Dow Chemical Company E		713 246-0369
La Porte (G-13733)		
Dow Chemical Company G		713 826-5234
Houston (G-9506)		
Dow Chemical Company D		713 751-7285
Pasadena (G-16420)		
Dow Chemical Company D		409 722-3451
Beaumont (G-1884)		
Dpc Enterprises LP E		713 863-1947
Houston (G-9511)		
Dupont Specialty Pdts USA LLC E		281 474-8614
Pasadena (G-16421)		
Dx Holding Company Inc E		713 863-1947
Houston (G-9540)		
Dx Service Company Inc E		281 457-4888
Houston (G-9542)		
Dynalloy Industries Inc E		936 825-2532
Navasota (G-15729)		
Dynalloy Industries Inc E		936 825-2532
Navasota (G-15730)		
E I Du Pont De Nemours & Co B		409 883-8411
Orange (G-16241)		
E I Du Pont De Nemours & Co E		281 470-2371
La Porte (G-13734)		
▼ Eastman Chemical Texas Cy Inc E		409 942-3307
Texas City (G-19791)		
Eco Services Operations Corp F		844 812-1812
The Woodlands (G-19860)		
Eco Services Operations Corp C		713 924-1401
Houston (G-9576)		
Eco Services Operations LLC B		800 642-4200
Spring (G-19210)		
El Dorado Chemical Company C		254 445-2720
Dublin (G-5516)		
◆ Enviro-Tech Specialties Inc F		281 476-9803
Channelview (G-3019)		
▲ Eurecat U S Incorporated F		281 218-0669
Houston (G-9710)		
Eurecat U S Incorporated F		281 842-6700
Pasadena (G-16433)		
Fino Oilfield Services Corp E		361 394-7700
Freer (G-7224)		
◆ Finoric LLC D		855 346-6742
Beasley (G-1840)		
Freeport Minerals Corporation C		915 778-9881
El Paso (G-5774)		
Frontier Chemical LLC F		325 672-0072
Abilene (G-42)		
Fujifilm Ultra Pure Sltons Inc E		972 245-3797
Carrollton (G-2742)		
Global Chemliquidations LLC E		832 539-3969
Houston (G-9968)		
◆ Haldor Topsoe Inc C		281 228-5000
Houston (G-10094)		
Haldor Topsoe Inc C		281 228-5000
Pasadena (G-16452)		
Huntsman International LLC E		713 924-6400
Houston (G-10287)		
Hyett Mfg & Instr Co Inc F		409 735-5383
Bridge City (G-2285)		
Icl Specialty Products Inc E		281 471-4700
La Porte (G-13747)		
Imerys Perlite Usa Inc F		281 471-3122
La Porte (G-13749)		
◆ Ineos Calabrian Corporation F		281 348-2303
Kingwood (G-13645)		
Ineos Calabrian Corporation E		409 727-1471
Port Neches (G-17166)		
Inhance Technologies LLC E		713 678-7352
Houston (G-10365)		
International Sulphur Inc E		903 577-5500
Mount Pleasant (G-15652)		
JM Huber Corporation D		830 693-3575
Marble Falls (G-14746)		
◆ K & K Chemical Company Inc E		972 635-2482
Royse City (G-17721)		
Kem-Tron Technologies Inc E		281 261-5778
Stafford (G-19339)		
Klean Corp International E		361 578-1524
Victoria (G-20281)		
Kuraray America Inc E		281 471-2771
La Porte (G-13765)		
Lanxess Corporation E		281 383-7761
Baytown (G-1795)		
◆ Liquid Minerals Group Ltd E		936 291-2424
Huntsville (G-12816)		
Lonza Inc D		281 291-2300
Pasadena (G-16475)		
Lubchem Inc F		281 350-9600
Spring (G-19143)		
M N Gumbert Corporation E		214 340-8383
Dallas (G-4621)		
Martin Midstream Partners LP E		281 471-2211
La Porte (G-13774)		
Martin Resource MGT Corp F		432 381-0271
Odessa (G-16072)		
Martinek Grain & Bins Inc F		972 382-8500
Celina (G-2992)		
◆ Merichem Company C		713 428-5000
Houston (G-10833)		
Mfg Chemical LLC E		281 291-2300
Pasadena (G-16483)		
Mineral Resource Tech Inc F		281 362-1060
Houston (G-10886)		
N L Industries Inc E		972 233-1700
Dallas (G-4711)		
▲ Napco Chemical Company Inc E		281 651-6800
Spring (G-19151)		
▼ Nashtec LLC E		361 777-2280
Gregory (G-8102)		
Nch Corporation C		972 438-0551
Irving (G-13116)		
Nerium Biotechnology Inc F		210 822-7908
San Antonio (G-18342)		
▲ Noah Technologies Corp Texas D		210 691-2000
San Antonio (G-18347)		
Occidental Petroleum Corp G		325 574-8567
Ira (G-12913)		
Occidental Petroleum Corp E		713 640-7500
Houston (G-11117)		
◆ OXY Vinyls LP F		877 699-8465
Dallas (G-4775)		
Peak Nanosystems LLC E		469 464-4504
Coppell (G-3434)		
Pencco Inc E		979 885-0005
Sealy (G-18814)		
Pergan D		903 938-5141
Marshall (G-14797)		
Peroxychem LLC D		281 474-4171
Pasadena (G-16495)		
Phillip Townsend Assoc Inc E		281 873-8733
Houston (G-11323)		
Phyton Biotech LLC E		817 900-4050
Fort Worth (G-6906)		
Pilot Chemical Company Ohio E		936 291-2424
Huntsville (G-12822)		
▲ Precision Additives Inc E		713 896-0606
Houston (G-11386)		
◆ Prince Energy LLC E		713 955-5398
Houston (G-11418)		

Questspecialty Corporation...................D 713 896-8188
  Brenham *(G-2271)*

RB Processing LLc.............................G 281 992-3500
  Houston *(G-11556)*

Reagent Chemical & RES Inc ....F 713 626-1843
  Houston *(G-11561)*

Reagent Chemical & RES Inc ....E 409 962-1116
  Vidor *(G-20331)*

Reagent Chemical & RES Inc ....E 281 862-9464
  Houston *(G-11562)*

Reagent Chemical & RES Inc ....F 432 458-3403
  Stanton *(G-19404)*

Reagent Chemical & RES Inc ....F 409 899-3400
  Beaumont *(G-1946)*

Redox Chemicals LLC ....F 972 923-7734
  Waxahachie *(G-20555)*

◆ Rohm and Haas Texas Inc ....C 281 476-8304
  Deer Park *(G-5291)*

Royal Chemical Company Ltd ....F 214 358-1861
  Dallas *(G-4913)*

S F Sulphur Company ....F 979 233-3555
  Freeport *(G-7208)*

Sasol Chemicals (usa) LLC ....C 713 428-5400
  Houston *(G-11755)*

Sasol Chemicals (usa) LLC ....G 409 296-9091
  Winnie *(G-20890)*

◆ Scotch Corporation ....E 214 943-4605
  Dallas *(G-4943)*

Select Industries Inc ....E 940 855-0461
  Wichita Falls *(G-20807)*

◆ Shell Catalysts & Tech LP ....D 713 241-3000
  Houston *(G-11857)*

◆ Sherwin Alumina Company LLC ....A 361 777-2200
  Gregory *(G-8105)*

Smolecule Inc ....F 512 262-9938
  Houston *(G-11925)*

◆ Solvay America Inc ....E 713 525-4000
  Houston *(G-11944)*

◆ Solvay Chemicals Inc ....C 713 525-6800
  Houston *(G-11945)*

◆ Solvay Fluorides Llc ....D 713 525-6700
  Houston *(G-11946)*

Solvay Info Svcs Nafta LLC ....D 713 525-6000
  Houston *(G-11947)*

Solvay North America LLC ....B 713 525-6000
  Houston *(G-11948)*

Solvay Spclty Polymers USA LLC ....E 770 772-8200
  Borger *(G-2186)*

Solvay USA Inc ....E 281 984-3030
  Pasadena *(G-16508)*

Solvay USA Inc ....D 940 552-9911
  Vernon *(G-20230)*

Solvay USA Inc ....G 281 882-4700
  The Woodlands *(G-19921)*

SOS Environmental Inc ....F 281 723-8282
  Spring *(G-19251)*

Southern Ionics Incorporated ....E 281 474-4826
  Pasadena *(G-16509)*

▲ Syntech Chemicals Inc ....E 713 433-5818
  Houston *(G-12136)*

Syzygy Plasmonics Inc ....F 806 470-5779
  Houston *(G-12141)*

Tbc-Brinadd LLC ....F 281 438-2565
  Houston *(G-8393)*

Terra Biochem LLC ....F 409 489-1700
  Jasper *(G-13280)*

Tetra Technologies Inc ....C 281 367-1983
  The Woodlands *(G-19928)*

Texas Brine Company LLC ....F 281 385-6048
  Mont Belvieu *(G-15619)*

Texas Materials Group Inc ....D 214 372-7700
  Dallas *(G-5076)*

Texas Sodium Bentonite Inc ....G 325 885-2339
  Comanche *(G-3236)*

Texas United Corporation ....E 713 877-1793
  Houston *(G-12258)*

◆ Texmark Chemicals Inc ....E 713 455-1206
  Galena Park *(G-7383)*

▲ Tor Minerals International Inc ....D 361 883-5591
  Corpus Christi *(G-2249)*

Total Ptrchemicals Ref USA Inc ....G 281 452-8577
  Channelview *(G-3043)*

Tri Element Incorporated ....F 361 664-5000
  Alice *(G-242)*

U S Silica Company ....F 806 470-2035
  Lamesa *(G-13831)*

▲ Unicat Catalyst Tech LLC ....F 281 331-2231
  Alvin *(G-384)*

▼ Univation Technologies LLC..............C 713 892-3650
  Houston *(G-12460)*

UOP LLC ....E 832 551-9638
  Houston *(G-12472)*

US Silica Holdings Inc ....F 281 258-2170
  Houston *(G-12490)*

◆ USS Holdings Inc ....F 301 682-0600
  Katy *(G-13383)*

Venator Chemicals LLC ....F 979 233-8183
  Freeport *(G-7218)*

Veolia North America Reg Serv ....E 915 782-5550
  El Paso *(G-6026)*

Whm Custom Services Inc ....D 254 854-2111
  Grandview *(G-8003)*

Wilson Systems Inc ....F 432 684-5567
  Midland *(G-15470)*

2821 Plastics, Mtrls & Nonvulcanizable Elastomers

◆ A & C Plastic Products Inc................E 713 645-4915
  Houston *(G-8423)*

▲ Advanced Laser Materials LLC ....F 254 773-3080
  Temple *(G-19667)*

◆ Albemarle Catalysts Company LP .....B 281 474-2864
  Pasadena *(G-16383)*

Albemarle Corporation ....E 281 480-4747
  Houston *(G-8529)*

Albemarle Corporation ....A 713 740-1000
  Pasadena *(G-16386)*

Alloy Polymers Texas LP ....E 936 544-4043
  Latexo *(G-13941)*

American Excelsior Company ....E 817 385-4300
  Arlington *(G-616)*

American Industrial Polymers ....E 979 542-3654
  Giddings *(G-7691)*

American Thermoplastics Corp ....D 713 671-6900
  Houston *(G-8611)*

American Thermowell Inc ....F 409 246-1111
  Kountze *(G-13668)*

◆ Americas Styrenics LLC ....D 832 616-7800
  The Woodlands *(G-19826)*

Ameron International Corp ....C 940 569-1471
  Burkburnett *(G-2563)*

◆ Ascend Performance Mtls Inc ....F 713 315-5700
  Houston *(G-8713)*

◆ Ascend Prfmce Mtls Hldings Inc........F 713 315-5700
  Houston *(G-8714)*

Ascend Prfmce Mtls Oprtons LLC.........B 281 228-4000
  Alvin *(G-352)*

◆ Ascend Prfmce Mtls Oprtons LLC ......E 713 315-5700
  Houston *(G-8715)*

Asia Chemical Corporation Inc ....F 713 673-4100
  Houston *(G-8721)*

◆ Avangard Innovative LP ....E 281 582-0700
  Houston *(G-8755)*

Axiomagnets LLC ....F 956 283-5920
  McAllen *(G-14840)*

Bamberger Polymers Inc ....F 281 481-9100
  Houston *(G-8811)*

Bamberger Polymers Corp ....F 281 481-9100
  Houston *(G-8812)*

▼ Basell USA Inc.................................F 682 518-0687
  Mansfield *(G-14657)*

◆ Birch Plastics Inc ....E 713 433-1898
  Houston *(G-8891)*

Braskem America Inc ....C 713 255-4747
  Houston *(G-8976)*

Braskem America Inc ....G 215 841-3100
  Port Lavaca *(G-17142)*

Braskem America Inc ....F 979 705-2532
  Freeport *(G-7193)*

Bravo Concealment LLC ....F 956 783-7682
  Alamo *(G-177)*

◆ Brisco Plastics and Chem LLC ....F 713 395-7081
  Houston *(G-8985)*

Britec Solutions Inc ....G 903 707-7471
  Tyler *(G-20061)*

◆ Bruegmann Usa Inc ....E 713 742-0788
  Houston *(G-8997)*

C & P Plastics Inc ....E 979 251-7991
  Brenham *(G-2249)*

▼ C-Square Intl Trdg LLC ....F 817 633-9000
  Arlington *(G-635)*

▲ CAM Specialty Products Inc ....E 936 228-0824
  Houston *(G-9058)*

Cameron International Corp ....D 281 391-4600
  Katy *(G-13356)*

Carpenter Co ....E 214 330-0373
  Dallas *(G-4085)*

CCT Corporation ....F 713 223-2521
  Houston *(G-9111)*

◆ Celanese Americas LLC....................F 972 443-4000
  Irving *(G-12963)*

◆ Celanese Corporation ....B 972 443-4000
  Irving *(G-12964)*

Celanese Ltd ....E 713 456-1525
  Pasadena *(G-16402)*

Celanese Ltd ....E 281 474-0554
  Pasadena *(G-16403)*

▼ Celanese US Holdings LLC ....A 972 443-4000
  Dallas *(G-4094)*

▲ Chemtrusion Inc ....D 713 675-1616
  Houston *(G-9173)*

Chevron Oronite Company LLC ....E 713 432-2500
  Houston *(G-9180)*

◆ Chevron Phillips Chem Co LLC ....A 832 813-4100
  The Woodlands *(G-19843)*

Chevron Phillips Chem Co LP ....A 281 421-6500
  Baytown *(G-1814)*

Chevron Phillips Chem Co LP ....E 972 599-6600
  Plano *(G-16822)*

Chevron Phillips Chem Co LP ....C 409 882-6000
  Orange *(G-16234)*

Chevron Phillips Chem Co LP ....E 713 475-3666
  Pasadena *(G-16408)*

Chevron Phillips Chem Co LP ....D 832 813-4100
  The Woodlands *(G-19844)*

Chevron Phillips Chem Co LP ....D 325 646-6561
  Brownwood *(G-2427)*

Chevron Phillips Chem Co LP ....C 409 882-6262
  Orange *(G-16235)*

Chevron Phillips Chem Co LP ....C 281 359-6500
  Humble *(G-12757)*

Chevron Phillips Chem Co LP ....E 806 275-5500
  Borger *(G-2168)*

Chevron Phillips Chem Co LP ....B 409 985-0700
  Port Arthur *(G-17104)*

Chevron Phillips Chem Co LP ....E 936 539-3154
  Conroe *(G-3275)*

Chevron Phillips Chem Co LP ....E 979 798-3950
  Brazoria *(G-2218)*

◆ Cipherwaste Polymers LP ....G 281 946-8090
  Houston *(G-9193)*

◆ CNA Holdings LLC ....E 972 443-4000
  Irving *(G-12976)*

Composites One Llc ....E 817 595-4991
  Fort Worth *(G-6537)*

Cook Compression ....E 713 433-2002
  Houston *(G-9301)*

Covestro LLC ....E 281 350-9000
  Spring *(G-19108)*

Covestro LLC ....E 281 383-6000
  Baytown *(G-1782)*

▲ Cryogenic Plastics Inc......................E 512 295-2683
  Kyle *(G-13681)*

Cytec Engineered Materials Inc ....C 903 457-8500
  Greenville *(G-8068)*

Dallas Plastics LLC ....F 903 291-0960
  Longview *(G-14221)*

Dallas Plastics LLC ....E 972 289-5500
  Mesquite *(G-15037)*

▲ Demilec International Inc ....E 817 640-4900
  Arlington *(G-660)*

◆ Dianal America Inc ....E 713 758-8100
  Pasadena *(G-16416)*

Dow Chemical Company ....D 713 667-5133
  Bellaire *(G-1994)*

Dow Chemical Company ....D 281 474-4495
  La Porte *(G-13732)*

Dow Chemical Company ....B 281 228-2800
  Deer Park *(G-5268)*

Dow Chemical Company ....D 713 767-1615
  Deer Park *(G-5269)*

Dow Chemical Company ....E 979 238-2011
  Freeport *(G-7196)*

◆ Drilling Specialties Co LLC ....F 800 423-3985
  The Woodlands *(G-19853)*

E I Du Pont De Nemours & Co ....C 409 883-8411
  Orange *(G-16239)*

E I Du Pont De Nemours & Co ....B 361 572-1330
  Victoria *(G-20260)*

Eastman Chemical Company................A 409 942-3532
  Texas City *(G-19790)*

Eastman Chemical Company................C 903 237-6755
  Longview *(G-14231)*

Eastman Chemical Company................E 423 229-2000
  Longview *(G-14230)*

Eastman Chemical Texas Cy Inc ....C 409 945-4431
  Texas City *(G-19792)*

▼ Eastman Chemical Texas Cy Inc ....E 409 942-3307
  Texas City *(G-19791)*

SIC

Eastman Performance Films LLC	E	817 445-1102	
Euless (G-6142)			
▼ Effectus Corporation	F	713 446-5275	
Pearland (G-16558)			
Epsilyte LLC	C	815 224-1525	
The Woodlands (G-19862)			
Equistar Chemicals LP	A	713 209-7000	
La Porte (G-13736)			
Equistar Chemicals LP	E	281 862-4000	
Channelview (G-3020)			
Evonik Corporation	C	713 477-6841	
Pasadena (G-16434)			
◆ Express Freight Systems Inc	F	713 861-1888	
Houston (G-9731)			
Exxonmobil Chemical Company	B	409 860-1300	
Beaumont (G-1891)			
Exxonmobil Chemical Company	A	281 834-5200	
Baytown (G-1817)			
◆ Exxonmobil Chemical Company	B	800 243-9966	
Spring (G-19116)			
Exxonmobil Research & Engrg Co	E	815 521-7411	
Spring (G-19118)			
Foam Supplies Inc	E	972 436-7008	
Lewisville (G-14050)			
Formosa Industries Corporation	E	361 987-7000	
Point Comfort (G-17083)			
▲ Formosa Plastics Corp America	D	361 987-7000	
Point Comfort (G-17084)			
◆ Formosa Plastics Corp Texas	B	361 987-7000	
Point Comfort (G-17085)			
▲ Formosa Utility Venture Ltd	A	361 987-7000	
Point Comfort (G-17086)			
Friedson Hill Inc	F	817 294-3309	
Fort Worth (G-6649)			
Friedson Hill Inc	F	817 244-6500	
Benbrook (G-2039)			
▲ Gem-Tech Inc	E	817 329-3586	
Grapevine (G-8040)			
▼ General Plas & Composites LP	C	713 644-1449	
Houston (G-9927)			
Genpak LLC	C	903 297-4445	
Longview (G-14241)			
Georgia-Pacific LLC	D	936 634-3308	
Lufkin (G-14529)			
Georgia-Pacific LLC	B	866 924-1397	
El Paso (G-5784)			
Greene Tweed & Co Inc	B	281 821-8337	
Houston (G-10033)			
Greene Tweed & Co LLC	E	281 765-4500	
Houston (G-10034)			
▲ Griffith Polymers Inc	E	503 612-0999	
Arlington (G-693)			
▲ Harvest Incorporated	E	254 933-1000	
Belton (G-2024)			
▲ Hexcel Reinforcements Corp	D	830 379-1580	
Seguin (G-18843)			
Hexion Inc	D	281 727-3163	
Deer Park (G-5279)			
Hexpol Compounding LLC	D	817 483-9797	
Kennedale (G-13498)			
Hickory Springs Mfg Co	F	817 831-1785	
Fort Worth (G-6695)			
Honeywell International Inc	A	281 890-0088	
Cypress (G-3801)			
◆ Huntsman Advnced Mtls Amrcas L	F	281 719-6000	
The Woodlands (G-19876)			
▲ Huntsman Bldg Slutions USA LLC	D	817 640-4900	
Arlington (G-701)			
Huntsman Chemical	G	936 539-1961	
Conroe (G-3308)			
Huntsman Corporation	C	409 722-8381	
Port Neches (G-17163)			
▲ Huntsman Corporation	E	281 719-6000	
The Woodlands (G-19877)			
◆ Huntsman International LLC	D	281 719-6000	
The Woodlands (G-19878)			
Huntsman Intl Trdg Corp	E	281 719-7400	
The Woodlands (G-19879)			
◆ Huntsman Intl Trdg Corp	E	281 719-6000	
The Woodlands (G-19880)			
Huntsman Petrochemical LLC	C	936 756-3381	
Conroe (G-3309)			
Huntsman Petrochemical LLC	A	409 722-8381	
Port Neches (G-17164)			
Huntsman Petrochemical LLC	C	409 724-4474	
Port Neches (G-17165)			
Husa Accurate Mch Works Inc	F	713 691-0685	
Houston (G-10289)			
▲ Idea Planet LP	E	972 380-9867	
Dallas (G-3844)			

▲ Ifs Coatings Inc	E	940 668-1062	
Gainesville (G-7345)			
Igi The Intl Group Inc	E	281 573-9280	
Baytown (G-1792)			
Incounters Inc	E	325 675-5909	
Abilene (G-51)			
Independent Plastic Inc	F	713 329-9955	
Houston (G-10341)			
Ineos	F	979 415-8500	
Freeport (G-7199)			
Ineos LLC	C	361 552-8205	
Port Lavaca (G-17147)			
Ineos Americas LLC	D	713 920-4300	
Pasadena (G-16457)			
Ineos Americas LLC	B	361 552-8244	
Port Lavaca (G-17148)			
Ineos Americas LLC	E	713 307-3000	
La Porte (G-13751)			
Ineos Americas LLC	E	713 767-5714	
La Porte (G-13752)			
Ineos Americas LLC	E	409 985-0863	
Port Arthur (G-17113)			
Ineos New Planet Bioenergy LLC	D	630 857-7143	
League City (G-13961)			
▲ Ineos Nitriles USA LLC	E	281 535-6600	
League City (G-13962)			
Ineos Styrolution America LLC	F	281 474-1000	
Pasadena (G-16458)			
Ineos Styrolution America LLC	E	281 474-1009	
League City (G-13964)			
◆ Ineos USA LLC	C	281 535-6600	
League City (G-13965)			
Ineos USA LLC	E	281 535-6600	
League City (G-13966)			
◆ Ingenia Polymers Inc	D	281 862-2111	
Houston (G-10362)			
◆ Interactive Life Forms LLC	D	888 804-4453	
Austin (G-1234)			
Invista Capital Management LLC	A	409 886-5080	
West Orange (G-20695)			
Invista Capital Management LLC	E	409 886-6982	
Orange (G-16249)			
Invista Capital Management LLC	E	281 470-3434	
La Porte (G-13757)			
Invista Capital Management LLC	A	409 886-9373	
Orange (G-16250)			
J-M Manufacturing Company Inc	D	979 532-5640	
Wharton (G-20700)			
Johnnies Plastics Inc	E	210 533-8463	
San Antonio (G-18205)			
◆ K-Bin Inc	E	979 233-6610	
Freeport (G-7202)			
◆ Kaneka North America LLC	C	281 474-7084	
Pasadena (G-16468)			
Kraton Corporation	C	281 504-4700	
Houston (G-10563)			
Kraton Polymers LLC	F	832 204-5400	
Houston (G-10564)			
◆ Kraton Polymers LLC	E	281 504-4700	
Houston (G-10565)			
◆ Kraton Polymers US LLC	D	281 504-4700	
Houston (G-10566)			
Kraton Polymers US LLC	D	281 668-3163	
Houston (G-10567)			
◆ Kuraray America Inc	E	800 423-9762	
Houston (G-10571)			
Lavaca Pipe Line Company	E	361 987-8900	
Point Comfort (G-17088)			
Lifoam Industries LLC	D	972 937-6512	
Waxahachie (G-20551)			
Lonza Inc	D	281 291-2300	
Pasadena (G-16475)			
Luc Urethanes Inc	F	936 539-2170	
Conroe (G-3326)			
Lucite International Inc	C	409 729-1300	
Nederland (G-15755)			
Lyondell Chemical Company	D	979 245-1225	
Bay City (G-1774)			
Lyondellbasell Industries Inc	F	713 209-1248	
La Porte (G-19813)			
▲ Lyondllbasell Industries Inc	D	713 309-7200	
Houston (G-10709)			
◆ Lyondllbsell Advnced Plymers I	D	713 309-7200	
Houston (G-10710)			
Lyondllbsell Advnced Plymers I	C	832 663-3104	
Spring (G-19229)			
Lyondllbsell Advnced Plymers I	E	281 867-3000	
La Porte (G-13772)			
M-Master LLC	F	915 242-2315	
El Paso (G-5855)			

▲ Manner Polymers Inc	E	972 542-6789	
McKinney (G-14956)			
Marine Rubber Inc	F	281 446-4132	
Humble (G-12787)			
Material Difference Tech LLC	F	713 640-2040	
Houston (G-10792)			
Medical Components of America	G	830 237-6405	
Seguin (G-18851)			
◆ Metton America Inc	E	281 479-8078	
La Porte (G-13777)			
Multi Plastics	F	972 402-9100	
Dallas (G-4706)			
Nan Ya Plastics Corp America	B	979 532-5494	
Wharton (G-20702)			
▲ Nan Ya Plastics Corp America	C	281 727-7300	
Wharton (G-20703)			
▲ Napco Bag & Film Gp LLC	E	972 245-8190	
Carrollton (G-2880)			
Neutrex Inc	F	281 807-9449	
Houston (G-11033)			
Nialti Manufacturing LLC	F	281 894-4995	
Houston (G-11051)			
◆ Noltex LLC	D	281 842-5000	
La Porte (G-13779)			
Nova Chemicals Inc	D	281 474-1000	
Pasadena (G-16491)			
▲ Octal Inc	F	972 985-4370	
Plano (G-16952)			
One Source Mfg Tech LLC	D	512 259-3272	
Leander (G-13996)			
◆ OXY Vinyls LP	F	877 699-8465	
Dallas (G-4775)			
OXY Vinyls LP	E	281 476-2927	
La Porte (G-13781)			
OXY Vinyls LP	F	281 884-4000	
Pasadena (G-16492)			
OXY Vinyls LP	D	281 476-2640	
Deer Park (G-5289)			
◆ Oxymar Inc	C	361 776-6321	
Ingleside (G-12899)			
Pactiv LLC	E	903 654-4745	
Corsicana (G-3683)			
◆ Phillips Smika Plyprpylene LLC	C	832 813-4100	
The Woodlands (G-19902)			
◆ Phoenix Plastics LP	F	936 760-2311	
Conroe (G-3349)			
▲ Plaskolite Texas LLC	D	903 962-7573	
Grand Saline (G-7999)			
◆ Plastic Specialties Inc	E	512 835-5873	
Austin (G-1420)			
Poly-America LP	D	281 385-3700	
Mont Belvieu (G-15620)			
Poly-Flex Construction Inc	F	972 647-4374	
Grand Prairie (G-7950)			
Polynt Composites USA Inc	F	903 938-9571	
Marshall (G-14798)			
Polynt Composites USA Inc	E	713 799-1800	
Houston (G-11360)			
Polynt Composites USA Inc	D	972 875-8634	
Ennis (G-6115)			
Polyone Corporation	C	281 474-2831	
Seabrook (G-18790)			
Polyone Corporation	C	281 474-2831	
Seabrook (G-18789)			
Pore Technology Inc	E	903 601-4466	
Jefferson (G-13286)			
Ppe LLC	F	979 353-7300	
Brenham (G-2270)			
▲ Precision Specialties Company	E	800 527-3295	
Sherman (G-18927)			
Quality Fiberglass Inc	F	817 473-3563	
Mansfield (G-14706)			
Ravago Americas LLC	F	817 635-4770	
Arlington (G-768)			
▼ Reef Industries Inc	E	713 507-4200	
Houston (G-11577)			
Reichhold Industries Inc	F	713 453-5431	
Houston (G-11587)			
Ruth Vending Inc	F	972 905-3523	
The Colony (G-19813)			
Saint-Gobain Prfmce Plas Corp	D	903 572-3475	
Mount Pleasant (G-15663)			
Sani-Safe Products Inc	E	210 646-6706	
San Antonio (G-18452)			
Scicron Technologies LLC	E	806 372-8300	
Amarillo (G-462)			
◆ Shell Oil Company	A	713 241-6161	
Houston (G-11860)			
Sheperd Maury	E	713 921-3456	
Houston (G-11865)			

◆ Shintech Incorporated ....F 713 965-0713
Houston *(G-11869)*

Shintech Incorporated ....C 979 233-7861
Freeport *(G-7210)*

Solvay USA Inc ....C 325 515-7609
Snyder *(G-19009)*

Solvay USA Inc ....D 940 552-9911
Vernon *(G-20230)*

Spartech Polycom (texas) Inc ....E 817 640-5600
Arlington *(G-785)*

Starrfoam Manufacturing Inc ....E 915 886-4636
Anthony *(G-590)*

Styrochem Canada ....F 817 847-8254
Saginaw *(G-17757)*

Supplyone Tucson Inc ....G 915 860-9911
El Paso *(G-5988)*

Tarquin Polymers & Colors Inc ....G 281 240-0202
Sugar Land *(G-19561)*

▲ Team Promark LLC ....E 303 926-1328
Fort Worth *(G-7039)*

Tecpac Plastics & Seals LLC ....F 281 547-0620
Tomball *(G-20013)*

▲ Tefco II Lc ....F 281 398-9684
Houston *(G-12183)*

Tekni-Plex Inc ....C 214 337-4711
Dallas *(G-5048)*

Teknor Color Company ....D 903 586-0583
Jacksonville *(G-13262)*

Tex-Co Resin Distribution Inc ....F 972 722-8603
Rockwall *(G-17568)*

Texas Materials Group Inc ....D 214 372-7700
Dallas *(G-5076)*

Total E&P RES & Tech USA LLC ....E 713 647-3000
Houston *(G-12329)*

Total Ptrchemicals Ref USA Inc ....E 409 291-7296
Beaumont *(G-1961)*

Total Ptrchemicals Ref USA Inc ....B 409 963-6837
Port Arthur *(G-17129)*

Total Ptrchemicals Ref USA Inc ....G 281 452-8577
Channelview *(G-3043)*

Total Ptrchemicals Ref USA Inc ....C 281 542-9542
La Porte *(G-13797)*

Total Ptrchemicals SEC USA Inc ....E 713 483-5000
Houston *(G-12333)*

Total Ptrchmcals USA Fundation ....F 713 483-5000
La Porte *(G-13798)*

Tpe Solutions Inc ....F 978 425-3033
Arlington *(G-801)*

◆ Tribute Energy Inc ....F 281 768-5300
Houston *(G-12367)*

◆ Tricon Energy Inc ....D 713 963-0066
Houston *(G-12369)*

Trs Distribution LLC ....F 281 372-8479
Stafford *(G-19389)*

◆ Tsi Products Inc ....E 817 649-2626
Arlington *(G-806)*

◆ Tsrc Specialty Materials LLC ....G 281 754-5800
Houston *(G-12398)*

◆ Ttwf LP ....A 713 960-9111
Houston *(G-12400)*

Union Carbide Corporation ....B 281 966-2727
Houston *(G-12434)*

Union Carbide Corporation ....D 361 553-2000
Seadrift *(G-18797)*

United Film Solutions Inc ....F 713 715-4197
Houston *(G-12447)*

Univar Solutions USA Inc ....E 281 297-0678
Spring *(G-19261)*

Valor Plastics LLC ....E 512 663-2489
Burnet *(G-2618)*

Velas Builders LLC ....F 956 464-7827
Donna *(G-5495)*

▲ Vertec Polymers Inc ....F 866 283-7832
Houston *(G-12555)*

Western Wire Works Inc ....F 817 654-3373
Fort Worth *(G-7141)*

Westlake Chemical Corporation ....B 903 242-7513
Longview *(G-14336)*

Westlake Chemical Corporation ....B 713 960-9111
Houston *(G-12646)*

Westlake Chemical Opco LP ....E 713 960-9111
Houston *(G-12647)*

Westlake Longview Corpora ....F 903 242-7500
Longview *(G-14337)*

◆ Westlake Longview Corporation ....C 713 960-9111
Houston *(G-12649)*

Westlake Monomers Corp ....F 270 395-4151
Houston *(G-12650)*

Westlake Vinyls Inc ....F 800 321-8550
Houston *(G-12654)*

◆ Westlake Vinyls Company LP ....C 713 960-9111
Houston *(G-12655)*

Wilsonart Intl Holdings Inc ....E 254 207-7000
Temple *(G-19715)*

Wilsonart Intl Holdings LLC ....E 254 207-6000
Temple *(G-19717)*

Wilsonart Intl Holdings LLC ....E 254 207-7000
Temple *(G-19718)*

Wilsonart Jordan Holdings Inc ....F 512 302-6500
Austin *(G-1670)*

Wilsonart LLC ....E 254 742-2451
Temple *(G-19720)*

Wilsonart LLC ....E 254 207-0207
Temple *(G-19722)*

Wilsonart LLC ....F 713 576-5500
Houston *(G-12676)*

Woodbridge Sales & Engrg Inc ....C 915 751-1000
El Paso *(G-6040)*

Worldwide Sorbent Products Inc ....E 409 983-7800
Beaumont *(G-1970)*

Worldwide Stffing Slutions LLC ....F 210 293-3600
San Antonio *(G-18625)*

2822 Synthetic Rubber (Vulcanizable Elastomers)

Arlanxeo USA LLC ....B 409 883-9990
Orange *(G-16232)*

Cosmec Inc ....E 903 677-2871
Athens *(G-825)*

Covestro LLC ....E 281 350-9000
Spring *(G-19108)*

Covestro LLC ....B 281 383-6000
Baytown *(G-1782)*

Dow Chemical Company ....D 409 722-3451
Beaumont *(G-1884)*

E I Du Pont De Nemours & Co ....D 361 572-1330
Victoria *(G-20259)*

E R Carpenter LP ....C 281 474-7257
Pasadena *(G-16422)*

◆ Equistar Chemicals LP ....A 713 309-7200
Houston *(G-9689)*

G V C Holdings Inc ....B 409 722-8321
Port Neches *(G-17161)*

General Polymer Services LLC ....E 281 424-4673
Baytown *(G-1818)*

General Polymer Services LLC ....D 281 424-4673
Baytown *(G-1819)*

Green Links ....F 713 205-6629
Houston *(G-10029)*

Habitek International Inc ....F 512 347-8800
Austin *(G-1196)*

Hexpol Compounding LLC ....D 817 483-9797
Kennedale *(G-13498)*

▲ Indevco Plas - Longview LLC ....F 903 291-1115
Longview *(G-14250)*

Jamak Fabrication-Tex Ltd ....F 817 594-8771
Weatherford *(G-20598)*

Jenkem Technology USA Inc ....F 972 673-0603
Plano *(G-16899)*

Kraton Corporation ....C 281 504-4700
Houston *(G-10563)*

◆ Lcy Elastomers LP ....D 281 424-6100
Baytown *(G-1826)*

Lion Elastomers Orange LLC ....C 409 924-4500
Orange *(G-1672)*

Longwood Elastomers Inc ....C 979 830-1111
Brenham *(G-2261)*

Lyondell Chemical Company ....D 361 242-8000
Corpus Christi *(G-3565)*

▲ McV Sales Co L L C ....F 713 785-0088
Houston *(G-10812)*

Molding Acquisition Corp ....E 209 723-5000
Fort Worth *(G-6846)*

Monument Chemical LLC ....E 281 474-5550
Pasadena *(G-16486)*

Nucera Solutions LLC ....E 281 275-7473
Sugar Land *(G-19520)*

▲ Nukote Coating Systems Intl ....E 832 770-7100
Houston *(G-11098)*

Polyspec (tx) LLC ....F 281 397-0033
Houston *(G-11361)*

Roy Johnson Incorporated ....E 817 468-2939
Arlington *(G-773)*

Univar Solutions USA Inc ....E 281 297-0678
Spring *(G-19261)*

Utex Industries Inc ....B 979 725-8503
Weimar *(G-20651)*

▲ Vertec Polymers Inc ....F 866 283-7832
Houston *(G-12555)*

◆ Westlake Olefins Corporation ....E 713 960-9111
Houston *(G-12651)*

▲ Whitefield Plastics Corp ....E 281 214-8510
Houston *(G-12664)*

Wichita Falls Mfg Inc ....E 940 322-4491
Wichita Falls *(G-20831)*

2823 Cellulosic Man-Made Fibers

◆ CNA Holdings LLC ....E 972 443-4000
Irving *(G-12976)*

Eastman Chemical Company ....E 423 229-2000
Longview *(G-14230)*

James Hardie Building Pdts Inc ....C 817 556-7000
Cleburne *(G-3097)*

Tascon Inc ....E 713 937-0900
Houston *(G-12163)*

2824 Synthetic Organic Fibers, Exc Cellulosic

America Plastics LLC ....C 972 245-4525
Carrollton *(G-2697)*

Carpenter Co ....D 254 778-0131
Temple *(G-19674)*

◆ Celanese Americas LLC ....F 972 443-4000
Irving *(G-12963)*

Celanese Ltd ....E 281 474-0554
Pasadena *(G-16403)*

Dal-Tile Corporation ....F 817 831-6935
Haltom City *(G-8136)*

E I Du Pont De Nemours & Co ....A 409 886-6442
Orange *(G-16240)*

Fiberio Technology Corporation ....E 956 207-5448
McAllen *(G-14861)*

◆ Future Pipe Industries Inc ....C 281 847-2987
Houston *(G-9879)*

Greene Tweed & Co LLC ....E 281 765-4500
Houston *(G-10034)*

Honeywell International Inc ....E 281 890-0088
Cypress *(G-3801)*

Invista Capital Management LLC ....A 361 572-1111
Victoria *(G-20274)*

J P C Plastics Inc ....F 325 672-2895
Abilene *(G-53)*

◆ Monument Chemical Houston LLC ....C 281 452-5951
Houston *(G-10916)*

Monument Chemical Houston LLC ....F 832 376-2201
Houston *(G-10917)*

2833 Medicinal Chemicals & Botanical Prdts

Aloe Vera of America Inc ....C 956 585-9704
Alton *(G-321)*

Ashley Industries LLC ....G 864 834-1167
Round Rock *(G-17623)*

Bluebonnet Nutraceutical Ltd ....E 281 340-0322
Sugar Land *(G-19451)*

Bluebonnet Nutrition Corp ....D 281 240-3332
Sugar Land *(G-19452)*

Darling Ingredients Inc ....D 313 928-7400
Irving *(G-12993)*

▲ Diamond Green Diesel LLC (jv) ....E 210 345-2009
San Antonio *(G-18055)*

Drucker Labs LP ....E 972 881-2344
Plano *(G-16852)*

▲ E I Products Inc ....F 512 357-2776
Austin *(G-1106)*

Fluoromed Products LP ....F 512 255-6877
Round Rock *(G-17658)*

GL Brands Inc ....F 888 811-4367
Fort Worth *(G-6670)*

Kbs Research LLC ....E 214 984-3724
Dallas *(G-4546)*

Mannatech Incorporated ....C 972 471-7400
Flower Mound *(G-6270)*

Mother Earth Labs Inc ....G 210 695-3535
San Antonio *(G-18321)*

Mothers Journey Inc ....F 877 279-7975
Frisco *(G-7261)*

Nutrition Supply Corp ....F 936 334-0514
Liberty *(G-14124)*

Peroxychem LLC ....D 281 474-4171
Pasadena *(G-16495)*

◆ Prosupps USA LLC ....D 214 310-1188
Frisco *(G-7308)*

Sigma-Genosys of Texas LLC ....C 281 363-3693
Spring *(G-19250)*

▲ Spfm LP ....D 210 805-8931
San Antonio *(G-18491)*

Titan Environmental USA LLC ....E 713 849-1311
Houston *(G-12297)*

▲ Vollara LLC ....E 800 989-2299
Dallas (G-5169)

2834 Pharmaceuticals

Abeona Therapeutics Inc ....F 214 784-7177
Dallas (G-3879)

Acelity LP Inc ....E 210 524-9000
San Antonio (G-17859)

Actitech LP ....D 903 893-2551
Sherman (G-18904)

Aegle Nutrition LLC ....E 972 446-9600
Carrollton (G-2692)

Aeglea Biotherapeutics Inc ....E 512 942-2935
Austin (G-896)

Aesthetic Medical Educators ....F 512 301-2125
Austin (G-899)

Akhu Therapeutics Inc ....G 979 820-2740
College Station (G-3173)

▲ Alcon Laboratories Inc ....A 817 293-0450
Fort Worth (G-6363)

▲ Alcon Laboratories Holdg Corp ....A 817 293-0450
Fort Worth (G-6365)

Alcon Manufacturing Ltd ....E 713 668-9100
Houston (G-8531)

Alcon Research LLC ....C 817 551-4555
Fort Worth (G-6366)

Alcon Vision LLC ....E 713 668-9100
Houston (G-8532)

Alk-Abello Inc ....D 512 251-0037
Round Rock (G-17621)

Allergan Inc ....G 512 527-6649
Austin (G-909)

Allergan Sales LLC ....D 254 666-3331
Waco (G-20358)

Allied Bioscience Inc ....E 214 432-5580
Plano (G-16783)

Aloe Laboratories Inc ....D 956 428-8416
Harlingen (G-8178)

Ampac Fine Chemicals Texas LLC ....E 281 842-1459
La Porte (G-13723)

Anthera Pharmaceuticals Inc ....E 510 856-5600
Houston (G-8649)

Aravas Inc ....F 512 614-1848
Austin (G-928)

Aravive Inc ....F 936 355-1910
Houston (G-8674)

Aravive Biologics Inc ....F 936 355-1910
Houston (G-8675)

Armaceutica Inc ....F 949 677-6001
El Paso (G-5652)

▼ Banyan International Corp ....E 888 782-8548
Abilene (G-15)

BASF Corporation ....C 800 794-1019
Houston (G-8821)

Bayer Healthcare LLC ....E 972 377-1950
Plano (G-16800)

Bellicum Pharmaceuticals Inc ....D 832 384-1100
Houston (G-8853)

Bettera Brands LLC ....F 800 344-6225
Plano (G-16802)

Bio-Path Holdings Inc ....F 832 742-1357
Bellaire (G-1990)

Biomed Laboratories LLC ....E 972 707-1210
Dallas (G-4026)

Bioniche Animal Health USA Inc ....F 706 549-4503
Fort Worth (G-6452)

Bionumerik Pharmaceuticals Inc ......D 210 614-1701
San Antonio (G-17954)

Biotics Building Partnership ....D 281 344-0909
Rosenberg (G-17576)

Biotool LLC ....F 713 732-2181
Houston (G-8887)

Bluebonnet Nutrition Corp ....D 281 240-3332
Sugar Land (G-19452)

▲ Boccard Life Sciences Inc ....E 281 269-6020
Houston (G-8933)

Bristol-Myers Squibb Company ....D 210 826-2999
San Antonio (G-17967)

Bristol-Myers Squibb Company ....E 214 381-5050
Dallas (G-4056)

Bristol-Myers Squibb Company ....E 212 546-4000
Houston (G-8986)

Capellon Phrmctcals Ltd Partnr ....E 817 595-5820
Fort Worth (G-6492)

Capital Returns Inc ....D 414 466-2418
Fort Worth (G-6493)

Carefusion 213 LLC ....B 915 231-5000
El Paso (G-5683)

Cassava Sciences Inc ....G 512 501-2444
Austin (G-1031)

Celltex Therapeutics Corp ....E 713 590-1000
Houston (G-9119)

Central Admxture Phrm Svcs Inc ......E 713 748-2200
Houston (G-9137)

Central Admxture Phrm Svcs Inc ......F 972 242-2788
Carrollton (G-2713)

▼ Chemicals Incorporated ....D 281 576-5000
Baytown (G-1813)

Cina Pharmaceutical Inc ....G 281 602-3491
Houston (G-9191)

Dermatlgical Assn of Texas LLP ....F 281 333-3376
Webster (G-20637)

Dfb Pharmaceuticals LLC ....E 817 900-4050
Fort Worth (G-6584)

Dna Stat LLC ....F 469 500-1137
Princeton (G-17208)

Dpt Laboratories Ltd ....A 210 531-7100
San Antonio (G-18066)

Dpt Laboratories Ltd ....B 210 396-6252
San Antonio (G-18067)

▲ Dpt Laboratories Ltd ....C 866 225-5378
San Antonio (G-18068)

Dpt Laboratories Ltd ....E 210 476-8100
San Antonio (G-18069)

Dpt Laboratories Ltd ....A 210 531-7100
San Antonio (G-18070)

Drucker Labs LP ....E 972 881-2344
Plano (G-16852)

DSM Nutritional Products LLC ....F 979 373-5010
Freeport (G-7197)

El Dorado Pharmacy LLC ....G 214 329-4580
Richardson (G-17304)

▲ Eltamd Inc ....D 972 385-2900
Addison (G-119)

▲ Empower Clinic Services LLC ....C 832 678-4417
Houston (G-9621)

Eosera Inc ....F 844 732-7929
Fort Worth (G-6617)

Essa Pharmaceuticals ....E 832 831-5958
Houston (G-9700)

Evestra Inc ....F 210 673-3300
Schertz (G-18749)

Executive Enterprises LLC ....E 346 224-2125
Dallas (G-4346)

Falcon Pharmaceuticals Ltd ....A 800 343-2133
Fort Worth (G-6623)

Formation Biologics Corp ....F 713 357-1062
Austin (G-1166)

G & S Enterprises Incorporated ....E 281 530-3077
Houston (G-9884)

◆ Galderma Laboratories LP ....C 817 961-5000
Fort Worth (G-6660)

Galderma Laboratories LP ....E 817 961-5000
Fort Worth (G-6659)

Galderma Research & Dev Inc ....E 817 961-5000
Fort Worth (G-6661)

Glaxosmithkline LLC ....E 830 481-8939
New Braunfels (G-15796)

Glaxosmithkline LLC ....E 210 627-0572
San Antonio (G-18143)

Glaxosmithkline LLC ....E 469 547-1722
Richardson (G-17321)

Gtcr Golder Rauner LLC ....F 972 670-7975
Carrollton (G-2749)

Hemotek LLC ....F 972 312-1609
Plano (G-16885)

Human Power of N Company ....G 855 636-4040
Austin (G-1214)

◆ Humco Holding Group Inc ....C 903 831-7808
Texarkana (G-19766)

Ibio Inc ....F 979 446-0027
Bryan (G-2479)

Icu Medical Inc ....D 512 255-2000
Austin (G-1217)

Immunogenesis Inc ....F 713 276-7600
Houston (G-10331)

Inner Health Group Inc ....E 210 661-8311
San Antonio (G-18187)

Introgen Therapeutics Inc ....D 512 708-9310
Austin (G-1240)

Iq Life Sciences Corporation ....F 281 444-6454
Houston (G-10417)

Iq Scientific Corporation ....F 281 444-6454
Houston (G-10418)

ISO-Tex Diagnostics Inc ....F 281 482-1231
Friendswood (G-7246)

Lumos Pharma Sub Inc ....E 512 215-2630
Austin (G-1310)

Mallinckrodt LLC ....E 915 298-6010
El Paso (G-5862)

Merck & Co Inc ....E 908 740-4000
Fort Worth (G-6828)

Minae Products Inc ....F 830 620-1303
New Braunfels (G-15813)

◆ Mission Pharmacal Company ....D 210 696-8400
San Antonio (G-18312)

Mission Pharmacal Company ....C 210 696-8400
Boerne (G-2129)

Mission Pharmacal Company ....E 210 696-8400
San Antonio (G-18313)

Molecular Biologicals LLC ....E 281 998-1227
Pasadena (G-16485)

Molecular Templates Inc ....E 512 869-1555
Austin (G-1705)

Moleculin Biotech Inc ....F 713 300-5160
Houston (G-10906)

Mylan Bertek Pharmaceuticals ....E 281 240-1000
Sugar Land (G-19508)

Mylan Institutional Inc ....D 281 240-1000
Sugar Land (G-19509)

Mystic Pharmaceuticals Inc ....E 512 918-2900
Cedar Park (G-2979)

Nationwide Pharmaceutical LLC ....F 800 697-3329
San Antonio (G-18336)

▲ Naturich Cosmetique Labs Inc ......E 972 926-9200
Garland (G-7559)

Neora LLC ....F 855 463-7486
Dallas (G-4721)

Neos Therapeutics Inc ....E 972 408-1300
Grand Prairie (G-7931)

Neos Therapeutics LP ....D 972 408-1300
Grand Prairie (G-7932)

Newgen Biotech Usa Inc ....F 972 241-1438
Farmers Branch (G-6209)

Novartis Pharmaceuticals Corp ....F 817 293-0450
Fort Worth (G-6871)

Novartis Services Inc ....E 817 293-0450
Fort Worth (G-6872)

Nutrex America Inc ....E 714 943-9119
Katy (G-13373)

O D C L Inc ....E 956 565-3131
Mercedes (G-15009)

▲ Ocusoft Inc ....D 281 342-3350
Rosenberg (G-17592)

▲ OHM Pharma Inc ....E 940 325-4797
Mineral Wells (G-15535)

Op2 Labs LLC ....F 888 448-8468
Euless (G-6151)

Orano Med LLC ....G 301 841-1673
Plano (G-16958)

Pfizer Inc ....G 817 293-8887
Fort Worth (G-6905)

Pfizer Inc ....C 212 733-2323
Roanoke (G-17493)

Pfizer Inc ....D 817 491-8400
Roanoke (G-17494)

Pharmscript LLC ....E 281 492-7220
Houston (G-11320)

Physicians Wellness Group Inc ....E 817 703-2102
Irving (G-13143)

▼ Plus Therapeutics Inc ....E 737 255-7194
Austin (G-1423)

▲ Polymed Therapeutics Inc ....F 713 777-7088
Houston (G-11357)

Premark Health Science Inc ....E 972 894-0020
Irving (G-13155)

Prescrption Dspensing Labs Inc ....F 512 219-0724
Cedar Park (G-2983)

▲ Progressive Laboratories Inc ....D 972 518-9660
Irving (G-13157)

Quality Bioresources Inc ....E 830 372-4797
Seguin (G-18858)

Quva Pharma Inc ....D 888 339-0874
Sugar Land (G-19532)

Quva Pharma Inc ....E 201 306-4412
Temple (G-19700)

▲ Remington Health Products LLC .....F 817 847-0606
Fort Worth (G-6954)

S/T Health Group Consulting ....F 281 491-5555
Houston (G-11714)

Sanara Medtech Inc ....F 817 529-2300
Fort Worth (G-6973)

Sanofi-Aventis US LLC ....C 800 981-2491
College Station (G-3201)

Savara Inc ....E 512 614-1848
Austin (G-1488)

▼ Scp International Inc ....E 817 326-0257
Cleveland (G-3135)

Shattuck Labs Inc ....E 919 864-2700
Austin (G-1497)

Shield Bearer Inc ....G....... 817 868-1400
Bedford *(G-1979)*

Sovereign Pharmaceuticals LLC ....C 817 284-0429
Fort Worth *(G-7007)*

▲ Spfm LP ....D....... 210 805-8931
San Antonio *(G-18491)*

St Jude Medical LLC ....E 512 732-7400
Austin *(G-1530)*

Stem Cell Innovations Inc ....E 281 679-7000
Houston *(G-12057)*

Stratgic Ltigation Partners LP ....C 713 995-8225
Katy *(G-13445)*

Streamline Polymers LLC ....E 832 376-4500
Houston *(G-12077)*

Superlife Products Inc ....F 281 298-5550
Spring *(G-19257)*

Swiss-American Cdmo LLC ....C 214 239-2280
Carrollton *(G-2822)*

Taysha Gene Therapies Inc ....E 214 612-0000
Dallas *(G-5040)*

Tex ISO Inc ....F 281 482-1231
Friendswood *(G-7250)*

Third Coast Rx Inc ....F 361 749-6337
Corpus Christi *(G-3639)*

Topway Global Inc ....E 713 784-1808
Houston *(G-12322)*

▲ United Laboratories Mfg LLC ....C 972 490-3300
Carrollton *(G-2843)*

Uniwell Laboratories LLC ....E 817 510-1850
Fort Worth *(G-7094)*

▲ USA Millennium LP ....F 409 840-6801
Beaumont *(G-1966)*

◆ Vetoquinol USA Inc ....E 817 529-7500
Fort Worth *(G-7098)*

◆ Virbac Corporation ....C 800 338-3659
Westlake *(G-20697)*

West-Ward Pharmaceutical Corp ....F 800 631-2174
Dallas *(G-5180)*

▲ Woodfield Pharmaceutical LLC ....D 281 530-3077
Houston *(G-12689)*

Zoetis Inc ....E 817 293-8887
Irving *(G-13212)*

2835 Diagnostic Substances

Allied McRobial Investigations ....E 713 941-9200
South Houston *(G-19037)*

▲ Ambion Inc ....C 512 651-0200
Austin *(G-911)*

Aspira Womens Health Inc ....E 512 519-0400
Austin *(G-940)*

Asuragen Inc ....D 512 681-5200
Austin *(G-942)*

Bio-RAD Laboratories Inc ....D 972 596-6165
Plano *(G-16805)*

Castle Biosciences Inc ....D 866 788-9007
Friendswood *(G-7242)*

Dicqie M Fuller Looney ....F 713 266-2117
Houston *(G-9465)*

Exact Diagnostics LLC ....E 817 989-9262
Fort Worth *(G-6620)*

Fujirebio Diagnostics Inc ....E 830 372-1391
Seguin *(G-18837)*

Helena Laboratories Corp ....B 409 842-3714
Beaumont *(G-1902)*

Microbes Inc ....E 281 367-7500
The Woodlands *(G-19894)*

Pattern Bioscience Inc ....E 512 905-9527
Austin *(G-1400)*

PETnet Houston LLC ....F 713 791-1734
Houston *(G-11298)*

Quality Bioresources Inc ....E 830 372-4797
Seguin *(G-18858)*

Separation Technology Inc ....F 830 249-0772
Boerne *(G-2136)*

◆ Stanbio Laboratory LP ....D 830 824-0772
Boerne *(G-2137)*

Steeplechase Diagnostic Center ....E 281 955-0440
Houston *(G-12055)*

Vax-Immune LLC ....F 832 423-0055
Houston *(G-12540)*

2836 Biological Prdts, Exc Diagnostic Substances

Aeglea Development Company Inc ....F 512 942-2935
Austin *(G-897)*

▲ Ambion Inc ....C 512 651-0200
Austin *(G-911)*

American Animal Health Inc ....F 817 293-6363
Grand Prairie *(G-7828)*

American Animal Health Inc ....F 972 641-5420
Grand Prairie *(G-7829)*

Assure Labs Inc ....D 713 561-5529
Houston *(G-8728)*

Astrotech Corporation ....G 512 485-9530
Webster *(G-20633)*

Bellicum Pharmaceuticals Inc ....D 832 384-1100
Houston *(G-8853)*

Bpl Plasma Inc ....C 512 582-7525
Austin *(G-1004)*

Caliber Biotherapeutics LLC ....E 979 314-7740
Bryan *(G-2465)*

Cone Bioproducts Seguin LLC ....F 830 379-0197
Seguin *(G-18832)*

Csl Plasma Inc ....E 972 329-0186
Dallas *(G-4188)*

DCI Biologicals Austin II LLC ....F 512 865-4200
Austin *(G-4190)*

Digital Forge Media LLC ....F 432 559-6068
Odessa *(G-15977)*

Dnatrix Inc ....F 832 930-2401
Houston *(G-9489)*

DSM Nutritional Products LLC ....F 979 373-5010
Freeport *(G-7197)*

Ecm Biosurgery Inc ....F 281 229-0348
Houston *(G-9574)*

Fujifilm Diosynth Biotechnolog ....F 979 431-3500
College Station *(G-3183)*

Futursarch Trials Neurology LP ....F 512 380-9925
Austin *(G-1175)*

Immunotek Bio Centers LLC ....E 432 307-6774
Odessa *(G-16029)*

Immunotek Bio Centers LLC ....E 806 310-2859
Amarillo *(G-438)*

Immunotek Bio Centers LLC ....E 214 453-2748
Dallas *(G-4492)*

Immunotek Bio Centers LLC ....E 404 345-3570
Dallas *(G-4493)*

Immunotek Bio Centers LLC ....E 404 345-3570
Bedford *(G-1975)*

Imunize El Paso ....F 915 857-2474
El Paso *(G-5811)*

International Lab Sup Ltd ....E 281 298-9410
Spring *(G-19218)*

Matica Biotechnology Inc ....F 979 321-7500
College Station *(G-3192)*

Micro-Tes Inc ....F 210 558-4757
San Antonio *(G-18300)*

Peloton Therapeutics Inc ....D 972 629-4100
Dallas *(G-4795)*

Players Media Group Inc ....F 509 254-4949
Dallas *(G-4810)*

Qualtex Laboratories ....E 210 736-8952
San Antonio *(G-18406)*

▲ Santa Cruz Biotechnology Inc ....C 214 902-3900
Dallas *(G-4933)*

Sigma-Genosys of Texas LLC ....C 281 363-3693
Spring *(G-19250)*

SKW Alliance Med LLC ....G 972 358-5171
Carrollton *(G-2888)*

Vax-Immune LLC ....F 832 423-0055
Houston *(G-12540)*

◆ Vetoquinol USA Inc ....E 817 529-7500
Fort Worth *(G-7098)*

Wondercide LLC ....F 877 896-7426
Austin *(G-1676)*

2841 Soap & Detergents

4e Brands Northamerica LLC ....A 210 819-7385
San Antonio *(G-17845)*

Acme Soap Inc ....F 210 731-9800
San Antonio *(G-17862)*

Akzo Nobel Inc ....E 817 625-1500
Fort Worth *(G-6360)*

▼ Ankem of Texas Inc ....E 903 802-7133
Farmers Branch *(G-6186)*

Anko Products Company of Texas ....F 972 227-4466
Lancaster *(G-13837)*

Buckeye International Inc ....F 281 873-4200
Houston *(G-9007)*

Chemstation International Inc ....F 281 457-2020
Houston *(G-9171)*

Ecolab Inc ....F 281 908-4877
Houston *(G-9578)*

Ecolab Inc ....E 817 916-9600
Haltom City *(G-8138)*

Ecolab Inc ....D 972 840-3994
Garland *(G-7483)*

Ecolab Inc ....D 800 325-1671
Houston *(G-9579)*

▲ Hall Tree Antiques Inc ....D 325 944-4794
San Angelo *(G-17803)*

Henkel Consumer Goods Inc ....C 832 261-2000
Houston *(G-10155)*

Montgomery Mfg Co LLC ....F 817 478-3221
Kennedale *(G-13500)*

▲ North American Research Corp ....F 972 492-1800
Lewisville *(G-14074)*

▲ Ocusoft Inc ....D 281 342-3350
Rosenberg *(G-17592)*

Omega Chemical Products Inc ....E 219 208-0500
Weatherford *(G-20608)*

Pro Star Industries Inc ....E 979 779-9399
Bryan *(G-2499)*

▲ Pure & Gentle Inc ....E 830 379-1937
Seguin *(G-18857)*

Royal Chemical Company Ltd ....F 214 358-1861
Dallas *(G-4913)*

Sorb All Company ....F 713 223-4575
Houston *(G-11955)*

▲ Spfm LP ....D 210 805-8931
San Antonio *(G-18491)*

Startkleen Legacy LLC ....F 903 207-1079
Gunter *(G-8117)*

◆ Stinger Chemical LLC ....D 713 227-1340
Houston *(G-12067)*

Sun Products Corporation ....E 281 474-9855
Pasadena *(G-16515)*

Thomason Family Corporation ....F 713 223-4575
Houston *(G-12277)*

Trans-Mate LLC ....F 800 867-9274
Dallas *(G-5105)*

Two Old Goats LLC ....F 817 520-4230
Haltom City *(G-8159)*

Unifirst Corporation ....E 979 774-0577
College Station *(G-3208)*

2842 Spec Cleaning, Polishing & Sanitation Preparations

▲ ABc Compounding Co Texas Inc ......C 972 988-9200
Grand Prairie *(G-7818)*

Akzo Nobel Inc ....E 817 625-1500
Fort Worth *(G-6360)*

Allied Assets Corporation ....E 713 413-9700
Houston *(G-8548)*

Ambassador Facility Svcs LLC ....F 210 849-7677
Cibolo *(G-3061)*

Amrep Inc ....D 972 227-3304
Desoto *(G-5428)*

▼ Ankem of Texas Inc ....E 903 802-7133
Farmers Branch *(G-6186)*

Arden Companies Inc ....C 806 335-1147
Amarillo *(G-400)*

Ashmore & Ashmore Properties ....D 214 327-9228
Dallas *(G-3970)*

◆ Auto Wax Company Inc ....E 214 631-4000
Dallas *(G-3988)*

▲ B C Williams Industries Inc ....F 214 352-4255
Dallas *(G-3996)*

Beacon Lighthouse Inc ....D 940 767-0888
Wichita Falls *(G-20743)*

Beta Technology Inc ....E 281 647-9700
Houston *(G-8865)*

Buckeye International Inc ....E 512 870-8555
Austin *(G-1014)*

Buckeye International Inc ....F 281 873-4200
Houston *(G-9007)*

Care Laboratories Inc ....E 281 835-9600
Missouri City *(G-15577)*

Chemax Corporation ....E 409 866-4232
Beaumont *(G-1868)*

City of Pasadena ....E 713 475-7884
Pasadena *(G-16409)*

Cliff Dunta Bros Inc ....F 940 325-4855
Mineral Wells *(G-15523)*

Clorox Manufacturing Company ....D 713 674-5042
Houston *(G-9216)*

▼ Cobb Carpet Supply Co ....F 214 634-2622
Dallas *(G-4133)*

Color Fast Industries Inc ....E 817 546-4910
Alvarado *(G-327)*

Commercial Bev Concepts LLC ....E 713 554-4569
Houston *(G-9249)*

Crain Chemical Company Inc ....E 214 358-3301
Dallas *(G-4180)*

Disingerm Inc ....F 214 482-9135
Ennis *(G-6093)*

E-Mist Innovations Inc ....F 844 563-6478
Fort Worth *(G-6601)*

East Texas Municpl Utility Dst ....F 903 877-3644
Tyler (G-20080)
Ecoclean Supply & Services LLC ....F 800 245-9896
Southlake (G-19065)
Ecolab Inc ....E 800 532-7732
Grapevine (G-8030)
Ecolab Inc ....D 972 840-3994
Garland (G-7483)
Envirocleanse LLC ....E 713 840-0404
Katy (G-13400)
Envirocon Technologies Inc ....E 512 382-9842
Austin (G-1127)
G G A Inc ....F 254 732-1701
Waco (G-20405)
Houston Kik Inc ....C 713 747-8710
Houston (G-10236)
Industrial Chem Tex Inc ....G 903 759-2642
Longview (G-14251)
Jimmy Smart ....E 432 381-5450
Odessa (G-16039)
Josan Corporation ....F 281 261-4747
Stafford (G-19337)
Juniper Specialty Products LLC ....F 346 310-6241
Pasadena (G-16466)
◆ K & K Chemical Company Inc ....E 972 635-2482
Royse City (G-17721)
K2 Industrial Services Inc ....F 850 477-6437
La Porte (G-13760)
Kiwo Holdings Inc ....E 281 474-9777
Seabrook (G-18787)
Lighthuse For The Blind Huston ....E 713 284-8420
Houston (G-10640)
Mbs Medical Technologies Inc ....E 888 482-4201
El Paso (G-5871)
McDonald Lighting & Maint Sup ....G 903 297-8181
Longview (G-14275)
Montoya Building Services Inc ....E 713 367-0231
Houston (G-10915)
◆ NCH Corporation ....A 972 438-0211
Irving (G-13114)
Nch Corporation ....E 972 438-0024
Irving (G-13117)
NCH Corporation ....G 800 336-0450
Irving (G-13118)
NCH Corporation ....F 972 438-0211
Irving (G-13119)
NCH Corporation ....F 972 438-0211
Irving (G-13120)
NCH Corporation ....A 972 438-0381
Irving (G-13115)
Nch Corporation ....C 972 438-0551
Irving (G-13116)
Nexnol LLC ....F 833 463-9665
Brownsville (G-2387)
▲ Norwex Usa Inc ....C 214 614-6707
Coppell (G-3433)
Ntw Services Inc ....G 210 885-8637
San Antonio (G-18352)
Nuvinair LLC ....E 844 984-6247
Plano (G-16950)
Omega Chemical Products Inc ....E 219 208-0500
Weatherford (G-20608)
Pro Star Industries Inc ....E 979 779-9399
Bryan (G-2499)
Pro-Chem of Dfw Inc ....F 817 695-1660
Arlington (G-761)
Purocol LLC ....F 310 926-9007
Garland (G-7573)
Questspecialty Corporation ....D 713 896-8188
Brenham (G-2271)
R J C Enterprises Inc ....E 806 793-8238
Lubbock (G-14469)
▼ Romix Chemicals Inc ....E 817 685-0006
Euless (G-6156)
Sanitizenow Inc ....E 602 699-3150
Houston (G-11748)
Sanotech 360 LLC ....F 817 697-7116
Fort Worth (G-6974)
Scentsible LLC ....D 972 818-8200
Addison (G-161)
◆ Stinger Chemical LLC ....D 713 227-1340
Houston (G-12067)
Taf Incorporated ....E 713 896-4040
Houston (G-12147)
Tc Sanitizer Co LLC ....D 832 296-4561
Houston (G-12169)
◆ Texas Nova-Chem Corporation ....F 972 771-1161
Rockwall (G-17569)
▲ Therm Processes Inc ....F 214 942-3131
Dallas (G-5083)
Thomason Family Corporation ....F 713 223-4575
Houston (G-12277)
Titan Chemical Corporation ....F 713 747-3134
Houston (G-12296)
◆ Trecora Chemical Inc ....D 281 474-7500
Pasadena (G-16519)
▲ USa Screen Printing Chem Inc ....E 281 474-9777
Seabrook (G-18793)
Viarden Lab LLC ....F 956 294-0260
Mission (G-15573)
Virus Light Rx LLC ....F 817 917-2800
Fort Worth (G-7106)
Well Body Purify LLC ....F 443 847-6501
Seabrook (G-18794)
◆ Whitmore Manufacturing Company ..F 972 771-1000
Rockwall (G-17571)

2843 Surface Active & Finishing Agents, Sulfonated Oils

BASF Corporation ....C 800 794-1019
Houston (G-8821)
◆ Chemguard Inc ....F 817 473-9964
Mansfield (G-14662)
Corchem Manufacturing Inc ....F 432 332-1335
Odessa (G-15968)
Monument Chemical LLC ....E 281 474-5550
Pasadena (G-16486)
Sentinel Midstream LLC ....F 214 712-2141
Richardson (G-17397)

2844 Perfumes, Cosmetics & Toilet Preparations

Aloe Queen Inc ....E 956 631-8869
McAllen (G-14834)
◆ Aloe Vera of America Inc ....D 214 355-5400
Dallas (G-3929)
Aloe Vera of America Inc ....C 956 585-9704
Alton (G-321)
Aloecorp Inc ....E 956 223-6931
Mercedes (G-15001)
Aroma Alternatives Ltd Co ....F 512 535-3646
Austin (G-934)
▲ Atlantis Laboratories Inc ....F 936 760-1255
Conroe (G-3258)
▲ Bayport Laboratories LLC ....E 832 230-0480
Houston (G-8837)
▲ Beauty Elite Group Inc ....E 800 619-1333
Houston (G-8847)
▲ Beauty Mfg Solutions Corp ....C 972 241-9665
Coppell (G-3410)
Black Star Styles LLC ....C 832 207-4563
Killeen (G-13606)
Carbon and Clay Company ....E 844 624-4263
New Braunfels (G-15777)
Casey Products LLC ....E 903 927-3500
Marshall (G-14770)
Chateau Noblesse Inc ....D 972 365-7017
Carrollton (G-2859)
Colgate-Palmolive Company ....B 903 832-8615
Texarkana (G-19760)
▲ Cosmetic Laboratories Inc ....E 972 986-9098
Irving (G-12981)
▲ Dhaliwal Laboratories LLC ....C 214 446-5862
Dallas (G-4256)
▲ Eltamd Inc ....D 972 385-2900
Addison (G-119)
Eoh Industries Inc ....D 817 468-3181
Arlington (G-671)
◆ Farouk Systems Inc ....B 281 876-2000
Houston (G-9765)
Farouk Systems Inc ....F 281 443-0715
Houston (G-9766)
◆ Fruit of Earth Inc ....E 817 510-1600
Grand Prairie (G-7880)
Gdmi Inc ....D 972 494-7477
Garland (G-7498)
▲ Goodier Cosmetics LLC ....C 214 630-1803
Irving (G-13041)
◆ Humco Holding Group Inc ....C 903 831-7808
Texarkana (G-19766)
Inner Health Group Inc ....E 210 661-8311
San Antonio (G-18187)
▲ Jack Black LLC ....D 469 341-2700
Coppell (G-3423)
Jahkur International LLC ....E 832 431-3232
Houston (G-10450)
Kale Naturals LLC ....F 214 402-6040
Dallas (G-4543)
◆ La Tee Da LLC ....E 903 927-3500
Marshall (G-14785)
▲ Macadamia Beauty LLC ....E 800 807-3950
Plano (G-16915)
Maison De Navar ....G 512 266-6100
Austin (G-1319)
▼ Naterra International Inc ....D 972 616-6100
Coppell (G-3429)
Natural Cosmeceuticals of Amer ....F 832 771-0882
Houston (G-11006)
Natural Technology Inc ....E 972 551-2563
Terrell (G-19743)
▲ Naturich Cosmetique Labs Inc ....E 972 926-9200
Garland (G-7559)
Neora LLC ....F 855 463-7486
Dallas (G-4721)
◆ O D C L Inc ....F 940 566-9914
Denton (G-5385)
O D C L Inc ....E 956 565-3131
Mercedes (G-15009)
▲ Ocusoft Inc ....D 281 342-3350
Rosenberg (G-17592)
Phlur Inc ....F 888 771-9434
Austin (G-1415)
Premark Health Science Inc ....E 972 894-0020
Irving (G-13155)
▲ Quatrefoil Partners LLC ....F 214 631-7117
Dallas (G-4848)
R&D Futures LLC ....E 214 473-9955
Plano (G-16983)
◆ Revision LLC ....E 972 756-1026
Irving (G-13165)
Scent Shop Inc ....E 972 271-4661
Garland (G-7585)
Scentsible LLC ....D 972 818-8200
Addison (G-161)
▲ Scruples Prof Salon Pdts Inc ....E 952 469-4646
Houston (G-11793)
▲ Shany Enterprises Inc ....E 713 772-1345
Stafford (G-19377)
Source Vital LLC ....F 713 622-2190
Houston (G-11958)
Southern Fields Aloe Inc ....F 956 565-5102
Mercedes (G-15010)
▲ Spfm LP ....D 210 805-8931
San Antonio (G-18491)
Sports Solutions Inc ....F 214 351-2834
Dallas (G-4999)
Swiss-American Cdmo LLC ....C 214 239-2280
Carrollton (G-2822)
T L R Group ....E 361 500-4136
Corpus Christi (G-3634)
Two Old Goats LLC ....G 817 520-4230
Haltom City (G-8159)
Txsyn Int LLC ....E 210 884-3895
San Antonio (G-18574)
▲ United Laboratories Mfg LLC ....C 972 490-3300
Carrollton (G-2843)
Venus Spa ....E 214 469-1615
Lewisville (G-14105)
Warren Laboraties LLC ....F 254 580-9990
Abbott (G-1)
Worth Beauty LLC ....F 713 660-0025
Houston (G-12697)

2851 Paints, Varnishes, Lacquers, Enamels

Adams Manufacturing Co ....F 806 744-0839
Lubbock (G-14358)
Akzo Nobel Coatings Inc ....F 713 684-1324
Houston (G-8520)
Akzo Nobel Coatings Inc ....F 817 232-9745
Fort Worth (G-6359)
Akzo Nobel Inc ....E 512 244-9038
Round Rock (G-17620)
Akzo Nobel Inc ....E 210 520-6566
San Antonio (G-17879)
▼ American Coatings LP ....E 281 351-1776
Tomball (G-19957)
American Indus Mfrs Bldg Mate ....C 214 254-4720
Plano (G-16787)
American Roller Company LLC ....F 262 878-2445
Houston (G-8607)
▲ Anc Ion Coating Inc ....F 281 207-0300
Houston (G-8638)
▲ Axalt Powde Coati Syste Usa I ....C 800 247-3886
Houston (G-8756)
◆ Axalta Pwdr Cating Systems Inc ....C 832 955-0201
Houston (G-8757)
Barten Industrial Coatings LLC ....F 979 732-8441
Columbus (G-3230)

Behr Process Corporation ....D..... 817 837-2600
Roanoke *(G-17483)*

Benjamin Moore & Co ....D..... 972 285-6346
Mesquite *(G-15031)*

Carboline Company ....E..... 800 848-4645
Dallas *(G-4082)*

Carchalk Inc ....F..... 210 667-3890
Seguin *(G-18828)*

◆ Carlisle Ctngs Wtrproofing Inc........D..... 972 442-6545
Wylie *(G-20929)*

CC Coating & Machine Inc ....E..... 361 884-9753
Corpus Christi *(G-3497)*

▲ Century Indus Coatings Inc ....E..... 903 586-9197
Jacksonville *(G-13233)*

▼ Ceram-Kote Coatings Inc ....E..... 432 263-8497
Big Spring *(G-2074)*

Chem-Coat Industries Inc ....F..... 972 485-8648
Dallas *(G-4108)*

▼ Coastline Indus Coatings Inc..........E..... 281 499-0633
Stafford *(G-19297)*

Complementary Coatings Corp ....E..... 210 651-6996
Schertz *(G-18748)*

Compliant Paint Booths LLC ....F..... 800 609-6408
Terrell *(G-19731)*

Corchem Manufacturing Inc ....F..... 432 332-1335
Odessa *(G-15968)*

▼ Corev America Inc ....E..... 713 849-3671
Houston *(G-9319)*

Corrpro Companies Inc ....C..... 713 460-6000
Houston *(G-9325)*

Creative Coatings Inc ....F..... 903 984-8454
Kilgore *(G-13541)*

Custom Pipe Coating Inc ....F..... 713 675-2324
Houston *(G-9373)*

Dap Products Inc ....D..... 214 349-9951
Dallas *(G-4237)*

Dow Chemical Company ....E..... 713 246-0369
La Porte *(G-13733)*

Dow Chemical Company ....E..... 979 238-2011
Freeport *(G-7196)*

Ennis-Flint Inc ....F..... 817 706-3777
Ennis *(G-6099)*

Entail Engine LLC ....G..... 956 467-5198
Brownsville *(G-2354)*

▼ Envirokind Inc ....F..... 713 434-9900
Houston *(G-9668)*

F & L Coatings and Con LLC ....F..... 281 316-2203
League City *(G-13956)*

▲ Fusion Operations LP ....D..... 713 691-6547
Houston *(G-9878)*

Gardner-Gibson Incorporated ....F..... 832 288-4111
Houston *(G-9899)*

Gemini Coatings Inc ....F..... 405 262-5710
Dallas *(G-4397)*

Gillespie Coatings Oper LLC ....E..... 903 753-0393
Longview *(G-14242)*

Groco Paint Mfg Co Inc ....E..... 972 286-7890
Dallas *(G-4417)*

Gulfstream Aerospace Corp ....A..... 214 902-7520
Dallas *(G-4423)*

◆ Hempel (usa) Inc ....D..... 936 523-6000
Conroe *(G-3302)*

Hempel (usa) Inc ....C..... 214 353-1600
Dallas *(G-4448)*

Henry Company ....E..... 972 272-5488
Garland *(G-7510)*

Hillburn Defense Systems Inc ....G..... 512 636-8498
Wimberley *(G-20882)*

Hvac Corrosion Tech LLC ....F..... 214 790-9609
Dallas *(G-4476)*

▲ Ifs Coatings Inc ....F..... 940 668-1062
Gainesville *(G-7345)*

Illinois Tool Works Inc ....F..... 314 733-1110
Houston *(G-10326)*

Inhance Technologies LLC ....E..... 713 678-7352
Houston *(G-10365)*

Intercoastal Paint Co Inc ....F..... 281 448-5258
Houston *(G-10392)*

◆ International Paint LLC ....B..... 713 682-1711
Houston *(G-10403)*

International Paint LLC ....F..... 817 834-0141
Fort Worth *(G-6724)*

International Paint LLC ....C..... 713 684-1500
Houston *(G-10404)*

▼ Invisishield LLC ....F..... 713 539-6700
Houston *(G-10411)*

Isomeric Industries Inc ....E..... 832 491-8106
The Woodlands *(G-19886)*

Isothrmal Prtctive Catings Inc ....F..... 281 485-4440
Pearland *(G-16572)*

Kelly-Moore Paint Company Inc ....F..... 800 772-7408
Hurst *(G-12848)*

Kelly-Moore Paint Company Inc ....F..... 817 268-1511
Hurst *(G-12847)*

◆ Lapolla Industries LLC ....E..... 281 219-4100
Houston *(G-10599)*

Lbs Enterprises LLC ....F..... 903 845-6436
Gladewater *(G-7725)*

Lonza Inc ....D..... 281 291-2300
Pasadena *(G-16475)*

LSI Integrated Graphics LP ....C..... 713 744-4100
Houston *(G-10696)*

◆ Mascorp Ltd ....E..... 713 465-0304
Houston *(G-10783)*

◆ Metal Coatings Corp ....D..... 713 977-0123
Houston *(G-10844)*

Metroplex Roof and Fence Inc ....F..... 469 417-8003
Corinth *(G-3458)*

▲ Nukote Coating Systems Intl ....E..... 832 770-7100
Houston *(G-11098)*

Picco Coatings Co ....E..... 281 447-8877
Waller *(G-20506)*

Pitzer Family Ltd Partnership ....E..... 214 398-1491
Dallas *(G-4807)*

Polyglass Coatings Limited LLC ....E..... 832 736-9243
Pearland *(G-16594)*

Polynt Composites USA Inc ....E..... 713 799-1800
Houston *(G-11360)*

Powder Coaters of Texas Inc ....G..... 979 387-2049
Beasley *(G-1844)*

PPG Industries Inc ....E..... 940 665-9590
Gainesville *(G-7358)*

PPG Industries Inc ....E..... 806 467-9707
Amarillo *(G-509)*

PPG Industries Inc ....E..... 979 693-7097
College Station *(G-3197)*

PPG Industries Inc ....E..... 936 441-1533
Conroe *(G-3353)*

PPG Industries Inc ....E..... 361 225-2250
Corpus Christi *(G-3595)*

PPG Industries Inc ....E..... 214 902-8922
Dallas *(G-4815)*

PPG Industries Inc ....E..... 713 683-8025
Houston *(G-11381)*

PPG Industries Inc ....E..... 806 794-0180
Lubbock *(G-14464)*

PPG Industries Inc ....E..... 214 544-0700
McKinney *(G-14965)*

PPG Industries Inc ....E..... 713 576-8418
Houston *(G-11382)*

PPG Industries Inc ....E..... 512 288-5505
Austin *(G-1426)*

PPG Industries Inc ....E..... 281 487-6416
Pasadena *(G-16497)*

PPG Industries Inc ....E..... 512 218-9551
Round Rock *(G-17680)*

PPG Industries Inc ....E..... 210 656-5541
Universal City *(G-20184)*

PPG Industries Inc ....E..... 281 265-5333
Sugar Land *(G-19528)*

PPG Industries Inc ....E..... 281 357-0455
Tomball *(G-20000)*

PPG Industries Inc ....E..... 281 890-4481
Houston *(G-11383)*

PPG Industries Inc ....E..... 817 613-1860
Weatherford *(G-20611)*

PPG Industries Inc ....E..... 972 517-2226
Plano *(G-16975)*

PPG Industries Inc ....E..... 940 322-5201
Wichita Falls *(G-20797)*

PPG Industries Inc ....E..... 956 791-1191
Laredo *(G-13922)*

PPG Industries Inc ....E..... 281 842-9518
La Porte *(G-13784)*

Quality Precision Coatings LLC ....G..... 713 631-8141
Houston *(G-11498)*

Ready Seal Inc ....E..... 817 594-8198
Weatherford *(G-20615)*

Reichhold Industries Inc ....F..... 713 453-5431
Houston *(G-11587)*

Rexcel Coatings Corporation ....F..... 915 581-2797
El Paso *(G-5938)*

Robroy Industries Inc ....C..... 412 828-2100
Gilmer *(G-7712)*

Rok Protective Systems Inc ....G..... 713 467-6999
Houston *(G-11658)*

Skudo USA Distribution LLC ....F..... 972 993-0777
Dallas *(G-4968)*

◆ Southwestern Petroleum Corp.........E..... 817 348-7233
Fort Worth *(G-7006)*

Spectrum Semiconductor Tech Lc......F..... 972 562-2552
McKinney *(G-14977)*

Standard Paints Inc ....F..... 817 477-5060
Mansfield *(G-14720)*

TCI Coatings Inc ....F..... 806 762-0871
Lubbock *(G-14491)*

Teknor Color Company ....D..... 903 586-0583
Jacksonville *(G-13262)*

Texas Finishing Company ....E..... 972 416-2961
Carrollton *(G-2830)*

▲ Triarch Industries Inc ....E..... 713 690-9977
Houston *(G-12366)*

▲ Trinkote Indus Finishes Inc ....E..... 817 396-4747
Cresson *(G-3715)*

True Value Company LLC ....C..... 903 872-8365
Corsicana *(G-3688)*

US Bioservices ....C..... 214 572-8300
Frisco *(G-7321)*

Verdia Inc ....F..... 713 999-5090
Conroe *(G-3383)*

Vitro Architectural Glass ....F..... 940 851-4374
Wichita Falls *(G-20824)*

◆ Whitmore Manufacturing Company...F..... 972 771-1000
Rockwall *(G-17571)*

2861 Gum & Wood Chemicals

Cedar Fiber Company Inc ....E..... 325 446-2571
Junction *(G-13337)*

Clorox Sales Company ....F..... 972 915-0430
Irving *(G-12973)*

▼ Eastman Chemical Texas Cy Inc .....E..... 409 942-3307
Texas City *(G-19791)*

Hexion Inc ....E..... 936 829-5566
Diboll *(G-5467)*

Holdingcross ....F..... 214 705-6502
Frisco *(G-7291)*

Impact Composite Tech Ltd ....E..... 806 385-1015
Littlefield *(G-14146)*

Oci Methanol Marketing LLC ....E..... 409 723-1900
Houston *(G-11130)*

Oci Partners LP ....E..... 409 723-1900
Nederland *(G-15757)*

▲ Texarome Inc ....E..... 830 232-6079
Leakey *(G-13983)*

2865 Cyclic-Crudes, Intermediates, Dyes & Org Pigments

Akzo Nobel Inc ....E..... 713 433-7289
Houston *(G-8370)*

◆ Americas Styrenics LLC ....D..... 832 616-7800
The Woodlands *(G-19826)*

Baker Hughes A GE Company LLC ......B..... 713 625-4200
Houston *(G-8801)*

Baker Petrolite ....E..... 903 389-2903
Fairfield *(G-6169)*

Braskem America Inc ....C..... 713 255-4747
Houston *(G-8976)*

Braskem America Inc ....G..... 215 841-3100
Port Lavaca *(G-17142)*

Braskem America Inc ....F..... 979 705-2532
Freeport *(G-7193)*

Celanese Ltd ....E..... 281 474-0554
Pasadena *(G-16403)*

E I Du Pont De Nemours & Co ....C..... 409 883-8411
Orange *(G-16239)*

Eastman Chemical Company ....E..... 423 229-2000
Longview *(G-14230)*

▼ Eastman Chemical Texas Cy Inc .....E..... 409 942-3307
Texas City *(G-19791)*

Evonik Corporation ....C..... 713 477-6841
Pasadena *(G-16434)*

▲ Huntsman Corporation ....E..... 281 719-6000
The Woodlands *(G-19877)*

◆ Huntsman International LLC ....D..... 281 719-6000
The Woodlands *(G-19878)*

◆ Ineos Americas LLC ....C..... 251 535-6600
League City *(G-13960)*

Jeg Holdings LLC ....C..... 972 532-6419
Addison *(G-140)*

Kuraray America Inc ....E..... 281 471-2771
La Porte *(G-13765)*

Lonza Inc ....D..... 281 291-2300
Pasadena *(G-16475)*

◆ M-I LLC ....B..... 281 561-1300
Houston *(G-10725)*

▲ Noah Technologies Corp Texas........D..... 210 691-2000
San Antonio *(G-18347)*

Saturn Polymers Inc ....G..... 936 334-0675
Liberty *(G-14125)*

Si Group Inc.	C	979 238-8000
Freeport (G-7211)		
Sierra Dust Control LLC	F	903 836-4642
Tatum (G-19645)		
Sierra Dust Control LLC	F	903 836-4642
Harwood (G-8212)		
Solvay USA Inc	D	940 552-9911
Vernon (G-20230)		
Solvay USA Inc	C	325 515-7609
Snyder (G-19009)		
◆ Ttwf LP	A	713 960-9111
Houston (G-12400)		
◆ US Petrochemicals Inc	F	713 871-1951
Houston (G-12487)		
Venator Materials LLC	A	281 465-6700
The Woodlands (G-19937)		

2869 Industrial Organic Chemicals, NEC

A-1 Fuel Stop Inc	G	713 674-3683
Houston (G-8431)		
AA Scientific Inc	F	979 696-8080
College Station (G-3171)		
▲ Access Chemicals & Svcs LLC	F	713 270-7215
Houston (G-8457)		
Ace Cmpltion Enhncment Svcs LP	C	432 653-0732
Odessa (G-15900)		
Ace Cmpltion Enhncment Svcs LP	E	432 703-7169
Odessa (G-15901)		
Acentum Inc	F	713 668-8742
Houston (G-8467)		
Action Fuels LP	F	210 651-9308
San Antonio (G-18634)		
Akzo Nobel Inc	E	281 584-0093
Houston (G-8521)		
Albemarle Corporation	A	713 740-1000
Pasadena (G-16386)		
Altivia Specialty Chem LLC	C	713 658-9000
La Porte (G-13720)		
▲ American Acryl LP	D	281 909-2600
Pasadena (G-16387)		
American Acryl Na LLC	D	281 909-2600
Pasadena (G-16388)		
▼ Ampco Services LLC	B	281 872-8324
Houston (G-8627)		
▲ Aqua/Process Inc	E	713 910-2977
Houston (G-8672)		
Arkema Inc	D	713 455-1211
Houston (G-8698)		
Arkema Inc	D	409 838-3981
Beaumont (G-1854)		
Ashland LLC	C	973 628-3245
Port Neches (G-17158)		
◆ Baker Petrolite LLC	B	281 276-5400
Sugar Land (G-19448)		
Bam Denton MGT Ventures LLC	E	940 898-1200
Dallas (G-4002)		
BASF Corporation	C	800 794-1019
Houston (G-8821)		
BASF Corporation	F	409 960-5000
Port Arthur (G-17101)		
BASF Corporation	D	713 383-4500
Houston (G-8822)		
BASF Corporation	F	973 245-6000
Carrollton (G-2702)		
BASF Corporation	D	409 981-5000
Beaumont (G-1858)		
BASF Corporation	E	281 884-4400
Pasadena (G-16393)		
Baze Chemical Inc	E	903 723-3146
Palestine (G-16296)		
▲ BBC Biochemical Corporation	C	360 542-8400
McKinney (G-14925)		
Beacon Energy (texas) Corp	F	817 558-9255
Cleburne (G-3081)		
Black Diamond Structures LLC	F	512 900-3822
Austin (G-858)		
Bobs Fuels Inc	G	325 646-7571
Brownwood (G-2426)		
Braskem America Inc	C	713 255-4747
Houston (G-8976)		
Braskem America Inc	G	215 841-3100
Port Lavaca (G-17142)		
Braskem America Inc	F	979 705-2532
Freeport (G-7193)		
C & W Fuels Inc	F	830 426-4301
Hondo (G-8354)		
◆ Celanese Corporation	B	972 443-4000
Irving (G-12964)		
◆ Celanese International Corp	A	972 443-4000
Irving (G-12966)		

Celanese Ltd	E	281 474-0554
Pasadena (G-16403)		
▲ Centauri Technologies LP	E	281 474-4675
Pasadena (G-16404)		
▲ Cerilliant Corporation	D	512 238-9974
Round Rock (G-17632)		
Chemicals Incorporated	E	979 244-0100
Bay City (G-1771)		
▼ Chemicals Incorporated	D	281 576-5000
Baytown (G-1813)		
◆ Chevron Marine Products LLC	E	832 854-2767
Houston (G-9179)		
◆ Chryso Inc	E	972 772-6010
Rockwall (G-17542)		
Clear Diamond Inc	F	325 597-9240
Brady (G-2212)		
Defense Logistics Agency	E	210 925-4455
San Antonio (G-18047)		
Dicqie M Fuller Looney	E	713 266-2117
Houston (G-9465)		
Dieselgreen Fuels LLC	E	512 247-3835
Austin (G-1090)		
◆ Dixie Chemical Company Inc	E	281 474-3271
Pasadena (G-16418)		
Dow Chemical Company	C	281 452-5951
Houston (G-9505)		
Dow Chemical Company	D	409 722-3451
Beaumont (G-1884)		
Dpc Enterprises LP	E	713 863-1947
Houston (G-9511)		
Dx Holding Company Inc	E	713 863-1947
Houston (G-9540)		
E I Du Pont De Nemours & Co	E	361 776-1872
Ingleside (G-12895)		
◆ E R Carpenter LP	C	804 359-0800
Temple (G-19680)		
Eastman Chemical Company	E	423 229-2000
Longview (G-14230)		
▼ Eastman Chemical Texas Cy Inc	E	409 942-3307
Texas City (G-19791)		
◆ Economy Mud Products Company	D	800 231-2066
Houston (G-9580)		
Endicott Biofuels II LLC	E	281 598-2180
Houston (G-9628)		
Energy Transfer Fuel LP	F	903 931-1922
Jacksonville (G-13237)		
Energy Transfer LP	F	682 518-7583
Mansfield (G-14669)		
Equistar Chemicals LP	G	361 572-2547
Victoria (G-20261)		
Equistar Chemicals LP	E	281 862-4000
Channelview (G-3020)		
Equistar Chemicals LP	E	281 474-4040
Pasadena (G-16430)		
◆ Equistar Chemicals LP	A	713 309-7200
Houston (G-9689)		
Ethyl Corporation	D	713 740-8300
Pasadena (G-16431)		
Evolution Fuels Inc	E	214 389-9800
Dallas (G-4338)		
Evonik Corporation	C	713 477-6841
Pasadena (G-16434)		
Flint Hills Resources LP	D	903 239-5200
Longview (G-14235)		
▲ Flotek Industries Inc	E	713 849-9911
Houston (G-9806)		
Foremark Performance Chem Inc	E	281 867-1330
League City (G-13957)		
Foremark Performance Chem Inc	E	281 867-1330
La Porte (G-13737)		
Fueland Inc	G	972 899-3727
Jacksonville (G-13239)		
Green Plains Hereford LLC	D	806 258-7800
Hereford (G-8289)		
Greenamerica Biofuels LLC	E	865 474-4086
Houston (G-10032)		
Gt Products Inc	E	817 481-7113
Grapevine (G-8042)		
Hampshire Chemical Corp	D	281 479-9525
Deer Park (G-5278)		
Hereford Biofuels LP	D	972 980-7159
Dallas (G-4452)		
Heseyeon LLC	E	214 483-3800
Carrollton (G-2868)		
Hexion Inc	E	936 829-5566
Diboll (G-5467)		
Hexion Inc	F	956 565-6301
Mercedes (G-15005)		
Hexion Inc	E	281 325-3368
Stafford (G-19325)		

▲ Huntsman Corporation	E	281 719-6000
The Woodlands (G-19877)		
Huntsman International LLC	E	713 924-6400
Houston (G-10287)		
◆ Huntsman International LLC	D	281 719-6000
The Woodlands (G-19878)		
Ict Holdings LLC	E	713 652-6600
Littlefield (G-14145)		
◆ Ineos Americas LLC	C	251 535-6600
League City (G-13960)		
Ineos Calabrian Corporation	E	409 727-1471
Port Neches (G-17166)		
Ineos Nitriles USA LLC	C	361 552-8200
Port Lavaca (G-17149)		
Ineos Oligomers USA LLC	E	281 581-3203
Alvin (G-366)		
Integrity Bio-Chemicals LLC	E	408 396-7797
Cresson (G-3709)		
Interntnal Flvors Frgrnces Inc	D	496 557-7001
Carrollton (G-2770)		
Jahkur International LLC	E	832 431-3232
Houston (G-10450)		
Kior Inc	E	281 694-8700
Pasadena (G-16469)		
◆ Kmg-Bernuth Inc	F	817 761-6100
Fort Worth (G-6767)		
Ktx Properties Inc	E	281 328-3501
Houston (G-10570)		
Kuraray America Inc	E	281 471-2771
La Porte (G-13765)		
Lanxess Corporation	E	281 383-7761
Baytown (G-1795)		
Lyondell Chemical Company	F	281 597-8935
Houston (G-10704)		
Lyondell Chemical Company	D	361 242-8000
Corpus Christi (G-3565)		
Lyondell Chemical Company	E	281 474-4191
Pasadena (G-16477)		
Lyondell Chemical Company	D	979 245-1225
Bay City (G-1774)		
Lyondell Chemical Company	D	361 572-2500
Victoria (G-20284)		
Lyondell Chemical Company	E	281 291-1488
Houston (G-10706)		
Lyondell Chemical Company	F	281 385-7010
Mont Belvieu (G-15622)		
Lyondell Chemical Company	D	972 512-3171
Carrollton (G-2879)		
Lyondell Chemical Company	F	281 862-4000
Channelview (G-3030)		
◆ Lyondell Chemical Company	D	713 309-7200
Houston (G-10705)		
▼ Lyondellbasell Acetyls LLC	F	713 309-7200
Houston (G-10708)		
◆ M-I LLC	B	281 561-1300
Houston (G-10725)		
Master Builders LLC	C	972 228-7400
Lancaster (G-13847)		
▲ Merisol LP	E	713 428-5652
Houston (G-10836)		
Momentum Chemical LLC	G	713 266-1042
Houston (G-10908)		
Monument Chemical LLC	E	281 474-5550
Pasadena (G-16486)		
Monument Chemical Houston LLC	F	832 376-2201
Houston (G-10917)		
◆ Monument Chemical Houston LLC	C	281 452-5951
Houston (G-10916)		
Neom LLC	F	210 372-3475
Boerne (G-2130)		
▲ Nissan Chemical Houston Corp	F	281 291-0200
Pasadena (G-16489)		
Occidental Chemical Holdg Corp	E	972 404-3800
Dallas (G-4753)		
Occidental Petroleum Corp	G	325 574-8567
Ira (G-12913)		
Occidental Petroleum Corp	E	713 640-7500
Houston (G-11117)		
▲ Oci Beaumont LLC	C	409 723-1900
Nederland (G-15756)		
Odysseus Holdings LLC	F	281 769-2399
Houston (G-11136)		
Oiltek Systems LLC	E	325 200-0423
Colorado City (G-3225)		
Olin Blue Cubellc	F	979 201-1789
Freeport (G-7206)		
Oq Chemicals Corporation	C	972 481-2771
Bay City (G-1776)		
◆ Oq Chemicals Corporation	E	713 830-3135
Houston (G-11187)		

Originclear Inc ....F 323 939-6645
McKinney (G-14960)

Panda Ethanol Inc ....F 972 361-1200
Dallas (G-4783)

Pandemx LLC ....E 432 638-3055
Midland (G-15335)

Pergan ....D 903 938-5141
Marshall (G-14797)

◆ Phillips 66 ....C 281 293-6600
Houston (G-11324)

Phoenix Services LLC ....F 713 952-5533
Houston (G-11329)

▲ Phyto-Source LP ....E 281 474-7500
Pasadena (G-16496)

Pier 19 Marine Field ....E 409 763-5423
Galveston (G-7405)

Pilot Thomas Logistics LLC .....E 432 741-1514
Midland (G-15352)

Plainview Bioenergy LLC ....E 806 296-8000
Plainview (G-16761)

Planet Resource Recovery Inc ...E 281 996-5315
Pearland (G-16592)

Proman Usa Inc ....F 713 943-2200
Houston (G-11444)

Proman USA (pampa) LLC ....F 713 943-2200
Houston (G-11445)

Pure Biofuels Corp ....E 281 540-9317
Houston (G-11473)

▲ Rbf Port Neches LLC ....E 713 386-2600
Houston (G-11557)

Regional Acid Production LP .....D 281 381-7866
Stafford (G-19368)

Renewable Biofuels Inc ....E 713 386-2600
Houston (G-11599)

Rio Valley Biofuel Transport .....E 915 791-8720
El Paso (G-5940)

◆ Rohm and Haas Texas Inc ....C 281 476-8304
Deer Park (G-5291)

Royal Chemical Company Ltd ...F 214 358-1861
Dallas (G-4913)

◆ Sachem Inc ....E 512 421-4900
Austin (G-1479)

Sachem Inc ....D 512 421-4946
Austin (G-1480)

Sachem Inc ....D 817 202-3200
Cleburne (G-3108)

Sasol Chemicals (usa) LLC ......C 713 428-5652
Houston (G-11754)

Sasol Chemicals (usa) LLC ......C 713 428-5400
Houston (G-11755)

◆ Sasol Chemicals (usa) LLC ...D 281 588-3000
Houston (G-11756)

Sasol Chemicals (usa) LLC ......G 409 296-9091
Winnie (G-20890)

◆ Sasol Chemicals North Amer LLC ...F 281 588-3000
Houston (G-11757)

▲ Sea Lion Inc ....D 409 948-4351
Texas City (G-19801)

Serafy Laboratories Ltd ....E 956 546-5313
Brownsville (G-2405)

◆ Shell Catalysts & Tech LP .....D 713 241-3000
Houston (G-11857)

◆ Shell Chemical LP ....E 855 697-4355
Houston (G-11858)

◆ Shell Oil Company ....A 713 241-6161
Houston (G-11860)

Si Group Inc ....C 979 238-8000
Freeport (G-7211)

Sierra Dust Control LLC ....F 903 836-4642
Tatum (G-19645)

Sierra Dust Control LLC ....F 903 836-4642
Harwood (G-8212)

Silver Star I Pwr Partners LLC ...E 713 354-2168
Houston (G-11898)

Smithfield Bioenergy LLC ....E 817 558-9255
Cleburne (G-3109)

◆ Solvay Fluorides Llc ....D 713 525-6700
Houston (G-11946)

Solvay USA Inc ....C 325 515-7609
Snyder (G-19009)

Solvay USA Inc ....D 940 552-9911
Vernon (G-20230)

Spectrum Quality Standards .....F 281 578-7575
Houston (G-12009)

Ssi Maxim Company Inc ....G 903 984-5600
Kilgore (G-13593)

▼ Sunrise Chemical LLC ....D 713 754-1000
Pasadena (G-16516)

▲ Syntech Chemicals Inc ....E 713 433-5818
Houston (G-12136)

◆ T & R Chemicals Inc ....E 915 851-2761
Clint (G-3148)

▲ Texas Ingredient Corporation ...D 817 645-1328
Cleburne (G-3113)

◆ Texas Petrochemicals LP ....E 713 477-9211
Houston (G-12243)

Texas Petrochemicals LP ....C 409 724-4857
Port Neches (G-17169)

Texas Petrochemicals LP ....D 713 627-7474
Houston (G-12244)

◆ Total Ptrchemicals Ref USA Inc ...B 713 483-5000
Houston (G-12332)

Total Ptrchemicals Ref USA Inc ...G 281 452-8577
Channelview (G-3043)

Total Ptrchemicals Ref USA Inc ...B 409 963-6800
Port Arthur (G-17130)

Transcendia Inc ....E 800 659-4254
Carrollton (G-2838)

◆ Trecora Chemical Inc ....D 281 474-7500
Pasadena (G-16519)

◆ Tricon Energy Inc ....D 713 963-0066
Houston (G-12369)

◆ Ttwf LP ....A 713 960-9111
Houston (G-12400)

Ultra Chem Ltd ....F 713 641-1444
Houston (G-12429)

Union Carbide Corporation ......D 361 553-2000
Seadrift (G-18797)

Union Carbide Corporation ......D 713 849-7000
Houston (G-12435)

Union Carbide Corporation ......B 281 966-2727
Houston (G-12434)

Univar Solutions USA Inc ....E 281 297-0678
Spring (G-19261)

▲ Vencorex Us Inc ....E 979 233-7871
Freeport (G-7219)

Vencorex Us Inc ....E 979 233-7871
Freeport (G-7220)

▲ Vrc Technologies Inc ....F 325 643-8038
Brownwood (G-2447)

We Hereford LLC ....E 806 360-7400
Hereford (G-8297)

Westlake Chemical Partners LP ...F 713 585-2900
Houston (G-12648)

◆ Westlake Olefins Corporation ...E 713 960-9111
Houston (G-12651)

◆ Westlake Polymers LLC ....C 713 960-9111
Houston (G-12652)

◆ Westlake Vinyls Company LP ...C 713 960-9111
Houston (G-12655)

White Energy Holding Co LLC ...F 972 715-6490
Frisco (G-7326)

▲ Wpt LLC ....E 713 960-9111
Houston (G-12698)

2873 Nitrogenous Fertilizers

Advanced McRbial Solutions LLC ...F 800 787-3724
Plano (G-16774)

Agrium US Inc ....D 806 274-5204
Borger (G-2161)

▼ American Plant Food Corp .....D 713 675-2231
Galena Park (G-7376)

Brenntag Pacific Inc ....F 281 474-5400
Pasadena (G-16399)

Cvr Energy Inc ....D 281 207-3200
Sugar Land (G-19472)

Cvr Partners LP ....C 281 207-3200
Sugar Land (G-19473)

▲ El Dorado Nitrogen LP ....F 281 383-1807
Baytown (G-1786)

Green Industries Inc ....G 972 483-6408
Italy (G-13213)

Hope Agri Products of Texas .....E 903 732-3361
Powderly (G-17199)

Hyponex Corporation ....E 936 291-6386
Huntsville (G-12814)

Ineos Nitriles USA LLC ....C 361 552-8200
Port Lavaca (G-17149)

Ineos Olgmers Chclat Bayou LLC ...F 281 535-6738
League City (G-13963)

JR Simplot Company ....E 361 987-2682
Point Comfort (G-17087)

JR Simplot Company ....D 979 826-8063
Hempstead (G-8253)

Nitro-Phos Inc ....E 713 228-1868
Houston (G-11060)

Occidental Chemical Holdg Corp ...E 972 404-3800
Dallas (G-4753)

Oci Partners LP ....F 409 723-1900
Nederland (G-15757)

Poole Chemical Co Inc ....F 806 647-2121
Dimmitt (G-5485)

Scotts Miracle-Gro Company .....E 281 821-1022
Houston (G-11792)

Scotts Miracle-Gro Company .....E 830 591-0299
Uvalde (G-20195)

Texas Landfill Management LLC ...E 210 651-6115
San Antonio (G-18537)

2874 Phosphatic Fertilizers

Abilene AG Service & Sup Inc ...D 325 677-4371
Abilene (G-4)

▼ Ball Dpf LLC ....E 888 839-8722
Sherman (G-18907)

Itafos Services LLC ....B 713 242-8446
Houston (G-10430)

JR Simplot Company ....E 361 987-2682
Point Comfort (G-17087)

JR Simplot Company ....D 979 826-8063
Hempstead (G-8253)

Martin Resource MGT Corp ....F 432 381-0271
Odessa (G-16072)

Nitro-Phos Inc ....E 713 228-1868
Houston (G-11060)

Occidental Chemical Corp ....F 214 421-7607
Dallas (G-4752)

Occidental Chemical Corp ....C 800 699-5123
Addison (G-151)

Occidental Chemical Corp ....F 361 242-8000
Corpus Christi (G-3582)

Occidental Chemical Holdg Corp ...E 972 404-3800
Dallas (G-4753)

▼ PCI Nitrogen LLC ....D 713 920-5300
Pasadena (G-16493)

Poole Chemical Co Inc ....F 806 647-2121
Dimmitt (G-5485)

2875 Fertilizers, Mixing Only

Agrium US Inc ....D 806 274-5204
Borger (G-2161)

American Plant Food Corp ....F 817 624-7132
Fort Worth (G-6383)

Back To Nature Inc ....E 806 745-3559
Slaton (G-18969)

Bonus Crop Fertilizer Inc ....E 903 455-9439
Greenville (G-8065)

Compostology LLC ....F 318 787-7442
Waco (G-20389)

Dairymans Choice Organics Inc ...F 817 641-2015
Godley (G-7734)

Diamond Shamrock Ref & Mktg Co ...B 361 786-2536
Three Rivers (G-19944)

East Side Compost Pedallers .....F 512 436-3884
Austin (G-1111)

◆ Easy Gardener Products Inc ...D 254 753-5353
Waco (G-20394)

El Dorado Chemical Company ....C 254 445-2720
Dublin (G-5516)

Employee Owned Nursery Entps ...F 512 276-1211
Elgin (G-6054)

▼ Greensmiths Inc ....G 972 242-5310
Carrollton (G-2748)

Hope Agri Products Inc ....F 214 371-7120
Dallas (G-4466)

Jh Biotech Inc ....E 830 557-4220
Mc Queeney (G-14829)

JMJ Organics Ltd ....F 281 798-3056
Crosby (G-3735)

Kbg Management Company LP ...G 806 627-4276
Tulia (G-20035)

Letco Group LLC ....D 713 466-7360
Houston (G-10626)

▲ Letco Group LLC ....D 972 506-8575
Dallas (G-4592)

Letco Group LLC ....E 972 869-4332
Dallas (G-4593)

Letco Group LLC ....D 281 431-3400
Rosharon (G-17607)

Letco Group LLC ....F 972 274-2835
Lancaster (G-13844)

Letco Group LLC ....E 409 584-2155
Pineland (G-16740)

Letco Group LLC ....E 281 342-6113
Richmond (G-17461)

Letco Group LLC ....F 281 537-2377
Houston (G-10627)

Natures Way Resources Inc ....F 936 273-1200
Conroe (G-3341)

Nelson Facilities Inc ....F 979 865-8596
Bellville (G-2011)

S
I
C

Poole Chemical Co Inc ....D 806 362-4261
Texline (G-19808)

Ramrod Enterprises LLC ....E 936 756-4846
Conroe (G-3356)

Rhizogen LLC ....F 281 367-7500
The Woodlands (G-19910)

Scarab International Lllp ....E 806 883-7621
White Deer (G-20711)

▲ Sinochem American Holdings ....E 713 263-8880
Houston (G-11905)

Soil Mender Products L P ....E 806 627-4276
Tulia (G-20038)

Soil Mender Products L P ....E 806 627-4276
Tulia (G-20039)

South Plains Compost Inc ....E 806 745-3559
Slaton (G-18974)

Sun Gro Horticulture Dist Inc ....E 903 938-7348
Marshall (G-14804)

Texas Landfill Management LLC ....E 210 651-6115
San Antonio (G-18537)

◆ United Amercn Acquisition Corp .....E 859 987-5389
Waco (G-20470)

Wholearth Organic Composting ....F 210 621-2411
Elmendorf (G-6078)

Wilbur-Ellis Company LLC ....F 830 663-3644
Devine (G-5451)

Wilbur-Ellis Company LLC ....F 979 279-3486
Hearne (G-8233)

Wilbur-Ellis Company LLC ....F 956 748-2382
Rio Hondo (G-17476)

2879 Pesticides & Agricultural Chemicals, NEC

▲ Agpro Systems Inc ....F 903 636-5545
Big Sandy (G-2064)

Akzo Nobel Inc ....E 817 625-1500
Fort Worth (G-6360)

American Plant Food Corp ....F 817 624-7132
Fort Worth (G-6383)

BASF Corporation ....D 409 981-5000
Beaumont (G-1858)

BASF Corporation ....C 800 794-1019
Houston (G-8821)

Bayer Cropscience LP ....D 806 741-2010
Lubbock (G-14367)

Bayer Cropscience LP ....E 806 765-8846
Lubbock (G-14368)

Cedarcide Industries Inc ....F 281 367-5075
Lewisville (G-14034)

▼ Celanese US Holdings LLC ....A 972 443-4000
Dallas (G-4094)

Chemours Company Fc LLC ....F 281 471-2771
La Porte (G-13728)

◆ Control Solutions Inc ....E 281 892-2500
Pasadena (G-16413)

Disingerm Inc ....F 214 482-9135
Ennis (G-6093)

E I Du Pont De Nemours & Co ....A 409 886-6442
Orange (G-16240)

E I Du Pont De Nemours & Co ....B 281 471-2771
Missouri City (G-15580)

E I Du Pont De Nemours & Co ....G 713 413-0000
Houston (G-9553)

◆ Easy Gardener Products Inc ....D 254 753-5353
Waco (G-20394)

▲ Ecofusion Inc ....G 972 403-7449
Plano (G-16855)

▼ Energetic Solutions LLC ....F 512 382-6864
Austin (G-860)

Gb Biosciences LLC ....F 713 453-7281
Houston (G-9908)

Global Chemliquidations LLC ....E 832 539-3969
Houston (G-9968)

Helena Agri-Enterprises LLC ....G 806 365-4433
Hartley (G-8211)

▼ Humatech Inc ....F 832 321-3098
Houston (G-10278)

▼ Innova Supply Inc ....E 713 473-3345
Pasadena (G-16459)

Insect Control Solutions Inc ....F 832 299-2400
Spring (G-19134)

JR Simplot Company ....E 361 987-2682
Point Comfort (G-17087)

JR Simplot Company ....D 979 826-8063
Hempstead (G-8253)

Kuraray America Inc ....E 281 471-2771
La Porte (G-13765)

Monsanto Company ....E 806 935-5623
Dumas (G-5525)

Moreman Community Gin Assn ....E 361 552-9407
Port Lavaca (G-17152)

Occidental Chemical Holdg Corp ....E 972 404-3800
Dallas (G-4753)

Ramsey Properties LP ....E 409 985-4200
Port Arthur (G-17122)

Rchemco Inc ....F 817 791-7304
Dallas (G-4864)

Schirm USA Inc ....E 972 878-4400
Ennis (G-6117)

Solugen Inc ....D 713 380-2134
Houston (G-11943)

Ssi Maxim Company Inc ....G 903 984-5600
Kilgore (G-13593)

◆ Stoller International Inc ....E 713 461-1493
Houston (G-12069)

◆ Vic West Importers Ltd Co ....F 888 698-6463
Austin (G-1633)

Village Farms LP ....C 432 426-2301
Fort Davis (G-6320)

▲ Westrade Usa Inc ....F 713 785-0053
Houston (G-12656)

◆ Zxp Technologies LLC ....B 281 426-8800
Highlands (G-8317)

2891 Adhesives & Sealants

▲ Adco Inc ....E 972 484-6177
Dallas (G-3887)

▲ Akfix USA Inc ....D 972 276-9600
Garland (G-7431)

American Indus Mfrs Bldg Mate ....C 214 254-4720
Plano (G-16787)

Armor Plate Inc ....E 281 487-2023
Pasadena (G-16390)

Aviation Products Inc ....F 817 457-2040
Fort Worth (G-6413)

◆ Bestolife Corporation ....E 972 865-8961
Irving (G-12947)

Bo-GE Assembly Inc ....E 281 462-0073
Crosby (G-3727)

Centennial Moisture Ctrl Inc ....D 214 350-7689
Irving (G-12967)

◆ Championx LLC ....A 281 632-6500
Sugar Land (G-19455)

▼ Corev America Inc ....E 713 849-3671
Houston (G-9319)

Dap Products Inc ....D 214 349-9951
Dallas (G-4237)

Denovus LLC ....E 214 789-5725
Ennis (G-6092)

E J Reynolds Company Inc ....E 281 331-4556
Alvin (G-361)

▲ Edge Adhesives Inc ....D 817 232-2026
Fort Worth (G-6604)

Furmanite America Inc ....E 713 844-7656
Houston (G-9876)

Gardner-Gibson Mfg Inc ....E 713 637-4791
Houston (G-9900)

Gardner-Gibson Mfg Inc ....F 972 878-1602
Ennis (G-6103)

Gulf States Asphalt Company LP ....D 713 941-4410
South Houston (G-19042)

HB Fuller Cnstr Pdts Inc ....E 713 926-3125
Houston (G-10139)

HB Fuller Company ....F 972 728-0707
Mesquite (G-15050)

Hexpol Compounding LLC ....D 817 483-9797
Kennedale (G-13498)

His Company Inc ....F 713 934-1600
Houston (G-10187)

Holdtite USA Inc ....F 817 441-1723
Fort Worth (G-6702)

Igi The Intl Group Inc ....E 281 573-9280
Baytown (G-1792)

Illinois Tool Works Inc ....D 281 580-1589
Houston (G-10324)

Indumar Products Inc ....E 713 977-4100
Houston (G-10346)

◆ ITW Plymers Salants N Amer Inc ......C 972 438-9111
Irving (G-13067)

◆ Lapolla Industries LLC ....E 281 219-4100
Houston (G-10599)

Laticrete International Inc ....E 972 641-3266
Grand Prairie (G-7909)

Mapei Corporation ....D 972 271-9500
Garland (G-7542)

▲ Mar-Tek Industries Inc ....E 214 350-9401
Forney (G-6313)

▲ Multi-Seal Corporation ....F 281 591-0111
Spring (G-19235)

◆ Nov MSI Pipe Prtction Tech Inc ....E 281 890-4595
Houston (G-11086)

▲ Orrex Plastics Company LLC ....E 432 332-1229
Odessa (G-16104)

Parker-Hannifin Corporation ....C 936 560-8900
Nacogdoches (G-15708)

PRC - Desoto International Inc ....E 817 640-1067
Grand Prairie (G-7953)

▲ PRC-Desoto International Inc ....D 972 540-0360
McKinney (G-14966)

▲ Precision Additives Inc ....E 713 896-0606
Houston (G-11386)

Precision Polymer Engrg Ltd ....F 713 482-0123
Houston (G-11394)

Pro Line Products Inc ....F 972 488-4200
Dallas (G-4830)

Protective Industries Inc ....E 281 399-2600
New Caney (G-15848)

QEP Co Inc ....E 817 477-1183
Mansfield (G-14705)

◆ Rectorseal LLC ....D 713 263-8001
Houston (G-11565)

◆ Rex-Hide Incorporated ....F 903 593-7387
Tyler (G-20146)

Rocka Solutions Inc ....F 514 602-9449
El Paso (G-5943)

◆ Royal White Cement Inc ....E 713 676-0000
Houston (G-11685)

Sealant Solution Inc ....F 214 886-6688
Flower Mound (G-6280)

◆ Silco Inc ....G 713 785-6272
Houston (G-11895)

◆ South Coast Products LP ....E 713 434-2141
Houston (G-11962)

Specilty Adhesives Coating Inc ....F 972 641-7600
Grand Prairie (G-7975)

Vertrauen Chemie Solutions Inc ....E 469 283-0789
McKinney (G-14986)

W R Grace & Co-Conn ....E 713 675-6445
Houston (G-12587)

Westech Seal Inc ....F 432 367-1188
Odessa (G-16211)

Wil-Cor Inc ....F 281 487-6547
Pasadena (G-16526)

Wilsonart LLC ....F 214 634-2310
Dallas (G-5192)

2892 Explosives

Austin Powder Company ....E 817 371-6147
Covington (G-3694)

Austin Powder Company ....E 940 644-5771
Chico (G-3050)

Austin Powder Company ....G 512 863-3676
Georgetown (G-7638)

Austin Powder Company ....F 940 382-4111
Denton (G-5352)

▲ Austin Star Detonator Company ....E 956 831-7751
Brownsville (G-2337)

El Dorado Chemical Company ....C 254 445-2720
Dublin (G-5516)

Expal USA Inc ....E 903 472-4970
Irving (G-13020)

◆ Geodynamics Inc ....C 817 341-5300
Millsáp (G-15502)

Halliburton Company ....F 817 783-5111
Alvarado (G-333)

Harrison Jet Guns II LP ....D 817 478-9216
Kennedale (G-13497)

La Blanc Bob ....E 972 492-1898
Carrollton (G-2876)

◆ Maxam North America Inc ....F 801 233-6000
Irving (G-13097)

◆ Owen Oil Tools LP ....C 817 551-0540
Godley (G-7738)

2893 Printing Ink

Alx Imaging LLC ....E 210 651-5000
Seguin (G-18824)

▲ Electroninks Incorporated ....E 512 766-7555
Austin (G-1119)

Flint Group US LLC ....E 214 638-6700
Dallas (G-4370)

▼ Impression Inks Ltd ....E 817 590-9711
Fort Worth (G-6717)

◆ Inkjet Inc ....D 936 856-6600
Willis (G-20848)

Inkjet Inc ....E 936 856-6600
Willis (G-20849)

INX International Ink Co ....E 817 375-0075
Arlington (G-707)

▲ MPS Group ....F 210 344-0332
San Antonio *(G-18322)*

Ncc Nano LLC ....E 512 491-9500
Austin *(G-1362)*

Sun Chemical Corporation ....E 972 647-1641
Grand Prairie *(G-7977)*

Sun Chemical Corporation ....D 972 270-6735
Dallas *(G-5022)*

▲ Top Level Printing Ink Inc ....F 214 267-9010
Dallas *(G-5101)*

Toyo Ink America LLC ....E 979 778-1538
Bryan *(G-2513)*

Wikoff Color Corporation ....F 972 647-1371
Grand Prairie *(G-7994)*

2895 Carbon Black

Cabot Corporation ....C 806 661-3100
Pampa *(G-16317)*

◆ Continental Carbon Company ....D 281 647-3700
Houston *(G-9283)*

Engineered Carbons Inc ....D 806 274-6347
Borger *(G-2178)*

▲ Federal Reserve Bank Dallas .....A 214 922-6000
Dallas *(G-4358)*

G V C Holdings Inc ....B 409 722-8321
Port Neches *(G-17161)*

◆ Orion Engineered Carbons LLC ...D 832 445-3300
Kingwood *(G-13651)*

Orion Engineered Carbons LLC ...D 409 883-9966
Orange *(G-16256)*

Orion Engineered Carbons LLC ...D 806 274-6347
Borger *(G-2181)*

Thermal Specialties Texas LLC ...G 918 836-4800
Fort Worth *(G-7055)*

◆ Tokai Carbon CB Ltd ....E 817 390-8600
Fort Worth *(G-7065)*

Tokai Carbon CB Ltd ....D 432 263-7389
Big Spring *(G-2100)*

Tokai Carbon CB Ltd ....C 806 274-7213
Borger *(G-2188)*

Venator Americas LLC ....F 281 719-6000
The Woodlands *(G-19936)*

2899 Chemical Preparations, NEC

Accurate Cargo Treatment ....F 281 685-8573
Pasadena *(G-16376)*

Advanced Rupture Disk Tech Inc ..G 281 591-6700
Katy *(G-13388)*

Afton Chemical Corporation ....F 281 475-1040
Spring *(G-19193)*

Agribiofuels LLC ....F 936 257-0826
Dayton *(G-5220)*

Akzo Nobel Inc ....E 713 433-7289
Houston *(G-8370)*

Albemarle Corporation ....B 281 474-2864
Pasadena *(G-16385)*

Alcor Inc ....F 210 349-6491
San Antonio *(G-17890)*

◆ Allchem Services Incorporated ...E 713 796-8000
Houston *(G-8542)*

Allied Bioscience Inc ....E 214 432-5580
Plano *(G-16783)*

Alpha Labs Inc ....F 806 744-1960
Lubbock *(G-14359)*

Alpha Lubricants LLC ....F 214 971-1170
Sealy *(G-18804)*

American Polymers Corp ....F 817 684-7335
Bedford *(G-1973)*

Aqua Solutions Inc ....E 800 256-2586
Deer Park *(G-5261)*

Arkema Inc ....D 409 838-3981
Beaumont *(G-1854)*

Ashburn Industries ....F 832 399-1000
Houston *(G-8718)*

▲ Ask Industries Inc ....F 432 686-2520
Fort Worth *(G-6403)*

Athlon Solutions LLC ....C 713 457-2400
Houston *(G-8735)*

◆ Baker Hghes Olfld Oprtions LLC ..F 713 879-1000
Houston *(G-8796)*

Baker Hughes A GE Company LLC ..B 713 625-4200
Houston *(G-8801)*

◆ Baker Petrolite LLC ....B 281 276-5400
Sugar Land *(G-19448)*

Baker Petrolite LLC ....B 713 599-7400
Houston *(G-8809)*

Baker Petrolite LLC ....D 281 474-5166
Pasadena *(G-16392)*

▲ Banner Technology Inc ....F 713 675-3100
Houston *(G-8815)*

BASF Corporation ....C 800 794-1019
Houston *(G-8821)*

Bb Chemicals Inc ....E 432 381-2595
Odessa *(G-15929)*

Benchmark Research & Tech Inc ...C 432 697-8171
Midland *(G-15138)*

Big Lake Fuels LLC ....E 713 943-2200
Houston *(G-8882)*

Bio-RAD Laboratories Inc ....D 972 596-6165
Plano *(G-16805)*

Biosuite LLC ....F 713 849-5319
Sugar Land *(G-19450)*

▲ Blentech Corporation ....E 713 673-3436
Houston *(G-8914)*

Border Manufacturer Contrs LLC ...E 956 982-0910
Brownsville *(G-2338)*

Buckeye International Inc ....F 281 873-4200
Houston *(G-9007)*

▼ C Treat Offshore Watermakers ...E 281 367-2800
The Woodlands *(G-19837)*

Calhoun Chemical LLC ....E 713 254-8974
Port Lavaca *(G-17143)*

◆ Carlisle Ctngs Wtrproofing Inc ...D 972 442-6545
Wylie *(G-20929)*

Carols Mch & Fabrication Inc ......E 713 921-7266
Wharton *(G-20698)*

▲ Carpenter Chemical Co Inc ....E 281 474-5111
Pasadena *(G-16401)*

Cedar Fiber Company Inc ....E 325 446-2571
Junction *(G-13337)*

CEo Performance Chem LLC ....E 281 457-2020
Houston *(G-9143)*

◆ Championx LLC ....A 281 632-6500
Sugar Land *(G-19455)*

Chemax Corporation ....E 409 866-4232
Beaumont *(G-1868)*

▼ Chemicals Incorporated ....D 281 576-5000
Baytown *(G-1813)*

◆ Chemquest Chemicals LLC ....E 281 291-9966
Pasadena *(G-16407)*

Chemstation International Inc ......F 281 457-2020
Houston *(G-9171)*

▲ Chemsystems Inc ....F 713 329-9066
Houston *(G-9172)*

Chemtrade Sulfate Chem Inc ....E 416 496-4176
Celina *(G-2991)*

Chemtreat Inc ....F 409 724-1111
Nederland *(G-15748)*

Chevron Phillips Chem Co LP ......A 281 421-6500
Baytown *(G-1814)*

CK Kustoms Iron Works Inc ....F 281 850-6118
Rockport *(G-17529)*

◆ CMC Materials Inc ....D 817 761-6100
Fort Worth *(G-6524)*

Compass Services Inc ....E 713 937-9538
Houston *(G-9258)*

◆ Concrete Producers Solutions ....F 281 398-6244
Pearland *(G-16549)*

▼ Corev America Inc ....E 713 849-3671
Houston *(G-9319)*

Corrpro Companies Inc ....C 713 460-6000
Houston *(G-9325)*

Custom Building Products Inc ......D 972 641-6996
Grand Prairie *(G-7860)*

Cytec Industries Inc ....D 281 296-1622
Spring *(G-19206)*

Cytec Industries Inc ....A 903 454-2004
Greenville *(G-8069)*

David Bacon Incorporated ....F 512 321-2323
Bastrop *(G-1754)*

David Keels ....E 409 316-9265
Hitchcock *(G-8336)*

◆ Denso North America USA Inc ....E 281 821-3355
Houston *(G-9437)*

Diamond Shamrock Ref & Mktg Co ..B 361 786-2536
Three Rivers *(G-19944)*

◆ Dipper Inc ....G 281 585-8400
Alvin *(G-359)*

Dome Petrochemical Lc ....F 713 540-9075
Baytown *(G-1784)*

▲ Dorf Ketal Chemicals LLC ....E 713 343-2377
Houston *(G-9499)*

Dow Chemical Company ....E 979 238-2011
Freeport *(G-7196)*

Dow Chemical Company ....D 409 722-3451
Beaumont *(G-1884)*

Drink A Pak Inc ....F 325 690-1550
Abilene *(G-38)*

E Z Cleaning Solutions ....F 214 841-9626
Dallas *(G-4286)*

◆ Economy Mud Products Company ...D 800 231-2066
Houston *(G-9580)*

Electroniks Writeables Inc ....F 512 766-7555
Austin *(G-1120)*

Equistar Chemicals LP ....E 281 862-4000
Channelview *(G-3020)*

Equistar Chemicals LP ....E 281 474-4040
Pasadena *(G-16430)*

◆ ESAB Group Inc ....C 800 372-2123
Denton *(G-5365)*

Ethyl Corporation ....D 713 740-8300
Pasadena *(G-16431)*

Evonik Corporation ....C 713 477-6841
Pasadena *(G-16434)*

Fgl Group LLC ....F 817 481-7857
Grapevine *(G-8034)*

Fithen Properties ....F 806 762-1121
Lubbock *(G-14410)*

Flame Seal Products Inc ....F 713 668-4291
Houston *(G-8380)*

Flamestop Inc ....E 817 306-1222
Fort Worth *(G-6636)*

Flare Well Testers Inc ....E 281 741-9335
Houston *(G-9797)*

Flares & Stacks Inc ....E 281 356-1408
Conroe *(G-3297)*

Flomin Inc ....F 281 573-6401
Baytown *(G-1787)*

▲ Flotek Industries Inc ....E 713 849-9911
Houston *(G-9806)*

Fqe Chemicals Inc ....F 281 476-9249
Deer Park *(G-5275)*

◆ Fritz Industries Inc ....B 972 285-5471
Mesquite *(G-15042)*

Fritz Industries Inc ....C 214 244-7822
Greenville *(G-8075)*

Fritz Industries Inc ....E 972 288-5425
Mesquite *(G-15043)*

Gardner-Gibson Incorporated ......F 832 288-4111
Houston *(G-8899)*

Garratt-Callahan Company ....G 972 661-5006
Dallas *(G-4391)*

Gc3 Specialty Chemicals Inc ....F 713 802-1761
Houston *(G-9909)*

Genesis Cstm Chem Blending LLC ...F 469 309-2790
Ennis *(G-6104)*

▲ Global Business & Commerce Inc ..F 214 449-0566
Dallas *(G-3843)*

Global Cathodic Protection Inc .....F 713 784-9588
Houston *(G-9967)*

Global Wstewater Solutions Inc ....G 832 286-4600
Houston *(G-9981)*

Globe Chemical LLC ....F 432 684-4939
Odessa *(G-16015)*

Gps International LLC ....F 832 319-1730
The Woodlands *(G-19870)*

▲ Grayden Cedarworks Inc ....E 325 446-3366
Junction *(G-13339)*

Green Stream Solutions LLC ....D 832 404-2436
Houston *(G-10030)*

Haas Group International LLC ....E 512 519-3989
Austin *(G-1195)*

Hampshire Chemical Corp ....D 281 479-9525
Deer Park *(G-5278)*

▼ Haverhill Chemicals LLC ....C 281 885-8900
Houston *(G-10137)*

Herbal Essentials LLC ....F 832 439-3114
Fresno *(G-7239)*

Hercules LLC ....E 409 866-4778
Beaumont *(G-1903)*

Hexion Inc ....E 936 829-5566
Diboll *(G-5467)*

Honeywell International Inc ....D 409 886-7445
Orange *(G-16246)*

Honeywell International Inc ....F 979 778-4477
Bryan *(G-2478)*

Houston Medical Tstg Svcs Inc .....E 713 665-4687
Houston *(G-10237)*

◆ Humco Holding Group Inc ....C 903 831-7808
Texarkana *(G-19766)*

Huntsman International LLC ....E 713 924-6400
Houston *(G-10287)*

Huss Services Inc ....F 817 819-4138
Jourdanton *(G-13332)*

Hydrite Chemical Co ....D 806 368-5660
Lubbock *(G-14423)*

▲ Ifs Coatings Inc ....E 940 668-1062
Gainesville *(G-7345)*

Immatics Us Inc ....E 346 204-5400
Houston *(G-10330)*

▲ Independence Oilfield Chem LLC.....E 713 936-4340
The Woodlands *(G-19882)*

Independence Oilfield Chem LLC.....G....... 210 888-0300
Pleasanton *(G-17069)*

Indorama Ventures Oxides LLC.....A....... 346 365-6056
The Woodlands *(G-19883)*

Ineos Nitriles USA LLC.....C....... 361 552-8200
Port Lavaca *(G-17149)*

Inkjet Inc.....E....... 936 856-6600
Willis *(G-20849)*

▲ Integrity Delaware LLC.....E....... 361 595-5561
Kingsville *(G-13630)*

Jentek Water Treatment Inc.....F....... 214 349-7111
Dallas *(G-4531)*

◆ Jx Nippon Chemical Texas Inc.....D....... 713 754-1000
Pasadena *(G-16467)*

Katoen Ntie Specialty Chem Inc.....E....... 281 941-1001
La Porte *(G-13762)*

Katoen Ntie Specialty Chem Inc.....F....... 281 470-5423
La Porte *(G-13763)*

▼ Kcc Corrosion Control Co Ltd.....F....... 281 550-1199
Houston *(G-10504)*

Kiwo Holdings Inc.....E....... 281 474-9777
Seabrook *(G-18787)*

◆ Kmg Electronic Chemicals Inc.....E....... 817 761-6100
Fort Worth *(G-6766)*

Kronos Worldwide Inc.....E....... 609 860-6200
Dallas *(G-4570)*

Laticrete International Inc.....E....... 972 641-3266
Grand Prairie *(G-7909)*

Liberty Tower & Flare Inc.....F....... 281 339-1410
Bacliff *(G-1734)*

Linde Gas North America LLC.....D....... 713 767-4100
La Porte *(G-13768)*

Loco Solutions LLC.....D....... 817 437-6438
Amarillo *(G-498)*

Lubrizol Corporation.....E....... 281 479-2851
Pasadena *(G-16476)*

M & G Chemicals.....F....... 361 500-4747
Houston *(G-10711)*

◆ Macdermid Canning Ltd.....E....... 713 472-5081
Pasadena *(G-16478)*

▲ Magic In Sky LLC.....E....... 210 267-5371
Boerne *(G-2128)*

Marubeni America Corporation.....E....... 713 871-5700
Houston *(G-10780)*

Mesa Processing Inc.....F....... 817 626-0319
Fort Worth *(G-6829)*

Metalloid Corporation.....F....... 800 686-3201
Jacksonville *(G-13250)*

Miracon Technologies LLC.....F....... 972 387-3099
Richardson *(G-17358)*

▲ Mountain Pure TX LLC.....E....... 903 723-1362
Palestine *(G-16304)*

Nalco Company LLC.....G....... 210 493-0379
San Antonio *(G-18330)*

◆ NCH Corporation.....A....... 972 438-0211
Irving *(G-13114)*

NCH Corporation.....A....... 972 438-0381
Irving *(G-13115)*

Newpark Indus Blnding Sltons L.....E....... 713 898-3829
The Woodlands *(G-19895)*

Ng Operations LLC.....F....... 972 660-7140
Grand Prairie *(G-7935)*

▲ Noah Technologies Corp Texas.....D....... 210 691-2000
San Antonio *(G-18347)*

North Houston Alcohol DRG Tstg.....E....... 713 816-4990
Houston *(G-11074)*

Nuclear Sources and Svcs Inc.....E....... 713 641-0391
Houston *(G-11096)*

◆ Oiltanking Texas City LP.....F....... 409 797-1710
Texas City *(G-19799)*

Oq Chemicals Bishop LLC.....E....... 361 584-6920
Bishop *(G-2108)*

Oq Chemicals Holding Corp.....G....... 972 481-2700
Dallas *(G-4765)*

OXY Vinyls LP.....F....... 281 476-8000
La Porte *(G-13782)*

◆ OXY Vinyls LP.....F....... 877 699-8465
Dallas *(G-4775)*

Pacific Sensor LLC.....F....... 972 242-5750
Carrollton *(G-2788)*

◆ Pan Asian Chemicals Inc.....F....... 713 621-1888
Houston *(G-11227)*

Panda-Brandywine L P.....E....... 972 980-7159
Dallas *(G-4785)*

Pencco Inc.....F....... 979 885-0005
Sealy *(G-18814)*

Pilot Thomas Logistics LLC.....C....... 817 877-8300
Fort Worth *(G-6908)*

◆ Power Service Products Inc.....E....... 817 599-9486
Weatherford *(G-20610)*

Precision Pack.....F....... 214 553-8044
Dallas *(G-4820)*

Quantum Ink Company.....F....... 713 688-2288
Houston *(G-11506)*

R & F Industries Inc.....F....... 830 875-6927
Luling *(G-14564)*

◆ Ramsey Properties LP.....C....... 281 328-3501
Crosby *(G-7741)*

◆ Reagens Usa Inc.....E....... 281 291-8484
Pasadena *(G-16501)*

◆ Revere Smelting & Ref Corp.....C....... 214 631-6070
Dallas *(G-4893)*

Riteks Inc.....E....... 972 529-1118
McKinney *(G-14972)*

▲ Rock Fin Countertops Inc.....E....... 713 460-4441
Houston *(G-11649)*

◆ Rohm and Haas Texas Inc.....C....... 281 476-8304
Deer Park *(G-5291)*

Royal Oak Enterprises LLC.....D....... 903 455-5803
Greenville *(G-8090)*

RPS Environmental Solutions LP.....E....... 972 247-1556
Dallas *(G-4915)*

Sachem Inc.....D....... 817 202-3200
Cleburne *(G-3108)*

Scale Free Company Inc.....F....... 281 873-5555
Houston *(G-11764)*

◆ Scotch Corporation.....E....... 214 943-4605
Dallas *(G-4943)*

Seapac Inc.....D....... 281 383-2400
Baytown *(G-1801)*

Sekisui Spcialty Chem Amer LLC.....F....... 713 456-1525
Pasadena *(G-16504)*

◆ Sekisui Spcialty Chem Amer LLC.....E....... 972 277-2900
Dallas *(G-4947)*

Shoreline Inc.....E....... 361 643-3135
Portland *(G-17187)*

Solenis LLC.....E....... 713 991-3722
Houston *(G-11938)*

Solenis LLC.....E....... 713 738-6815
Houston *(G-11939)*

Solnexus Chemical LLC.....E....... 432 689-6180
Midland *(G-15415)*

Solution Integrated Chem LLC.....F....... 361 584-5000
Bishop *(G-2109)*

Solvay USA Inc.....C....... 325 515-7609
Snyder *(G-19009)*

◆ Solvchem Inc.....E....... 281 485-5377
Pearland *(G-16600)*

◆ South Coast Terminals LP.....D....... 713 672-2401
Houston *(G-11963)*

▼ Strata Control Services Inc.....E....... 337 785-0000
Spring *(G-19256)*

Suez Wts Usa Inc.....E....... 409 866-4756
Beaumont *(G-1955)*

Sun Chemical Corporation.....E....... 972 647-1641
Grand Prairie *(G-7977)*

▲ Syntech Chemicals Inc.....E....... 713 433-5818
Houston *(G-12136)*

▼ Tackaberry Dooley Systems.....E....... 281 479-9700
Deer Park *(G-5299)*

Talke Usa Inc.....E....... 832 260-8325
Mont Belvieu *(G-15621)*

Technology Fleet Products Inc.....F....... 713 907-8394
Houston *(G-12177)*

Texas Brine Company LLC.....E....... 713 877-2700
Houston *(G-12223)*

Texas Materials Group Inc.....D....... 214 372-7700
Dallas *(G-5076)*

Texas SEC & Surveillance Inc.....E....... 512 693-4003
Round Rock *(G-17693)*

Texas United Corporation.....E....... 713 877-1793
Houston *(G-12258)*

◆ Third Coast Packaging Inc.....E....... 281 412-0275
Pearland *(G-16604)*

◆ Thrillworks Inc.....E....... 916 663-1749
Athens *(G-840)*

▼ Tm Chemicals Ltd Partnership.....C....... 281 930-2525
Deer Park *(G-5300)*

Tokai Carbon CB Ltd.....D....... 432 263-7389
Big Spring *(G-2100)*

◆ Total Ptrchemicals Ref USA Inc.....B....... 713 483-5000
Houston *(G-12332)*

Total Ptrchemicals Ref USA Inc.....C....... 281 542-9542
La Porte *(G-13797)*

Total Ptrchemicals Ref USA Inc.....B....... 409 963-6800
Port Arthur *(G-17130)*

◆ Trecora Chemical Inc.....D....... 281 474-7500
Pasadena *(G-16519)*

◆ Tricon Energy Inc.....D....... 713 963-0066
Houston *(G-12369)*

Tricon Energy Ltd.....D....... 713 963-0066
Houston *(G-12370)*

Trothyhide LLC.....F....... 817 455-1118
Fort Worth *(G-7080)*

True Grit Works.....F....... 978 604-4915
Ravenna *(G-17234)*

Turf Technologies LLC.....E....... 419 422-4356
Dallas *(G-5122)*

U S Foam Inc.....F....... 903 753-3901
Longview *(G-14327)*

U S Machine Shop Inc.....F....... 940 495-3964
Electra *(G-6050)*

U S Weatherford L P.....E....... 432 332-4798
Odessa *(G-16187)*

◆ United Salt Baytown LLC.....E....... 713 877-2600
Houston *(G-12453)*

United Salt Baytown LLC.....E....... 936 372-3931
Hockley *(G-8350)*

United Salt Carlsbad LLC.....D....... 713 877-2600
Houston *(G-12454)*

United Salt Corporation.....F....... 713 877-2600
Houston *(G-12455)*

United Salt Saltville LLC.....E....... 713 877-2600
Houston *(G-12456)*

United Worth Hydrochem Corp.....F....... 682 518-6200
Venus *(G-20224)*

USA Petrovalve Inc.....F....... 713 466-9881
Houston *(G-12498)*

▲ USa Screen Printing Chem Inc.....E....... 281 474-9777
Seabrook *(G-18793)*

Valero Refining-Texas LP.....C....... 281 470-4900
La Porte *(G-13799)*

◆ Valhi Inc.....E....... 972 233-1700
Dallas *(G-5151)*

Vitalpure Labs LLC.....E....... 573 469-1302
Junction *(G-13340)*

Wages White Lion Invstmnts LLC.....F....... 214 880-6440
Richardson *(G-17425)*

Wesco Chemicals Inc.....F....... 972 938-0913
Waxahachie *(G-20568)*

Whitecap Wastewater Treatment.....F....... 361 826-4142
Corpus Christi *(G-3656)*

Yci Methanol One LLC.....D....... 832 924-1998
Houston *(G-12714)*

Zxp Technologies LLC.....C....... 281 426-8800
Highlands *(G-8316)*

29 PETROLEUM REFINING AND RELATED INDUSTRIES

2911 Petroleum Refining

3 Diamond Services LLC.....F....... 361 442-6949
Ingleside *(G-12891)*

Absolute Fuels LLC.....E....... 806 712-0330
Lubbock *(G-14357)*

◆ Air Lqide Amer Spclty Gses LLC.....E....... 800 217-2688
Houston *(G-8514)*

Alon Usa LP.....B....... 432 263-7661
Big Spring *(G-2069)*

Alon USA Partners LP.....A....... 972 367-3600
Dallas *(G-3930)*

American Liberty Oil Co LP.....F....... 972 932-2266
Kaufman *(G-13457)*

Anadarko E&P Onshore LLC.....F....... 832 636-1000
The Woodlands *(G-19828)*

◆ Andeavor LLC.....C....... 210 626-6000
San Antonio *(G-17907)*

Antelope Refining LLC.....E....... 713 860-2746
Houston *(G-8648)*

Arcooil Corp.....E....... 940 549-4444
Graham *(G-7776)*

Armstead Oil.....E....... 713 454-3866
Houston *(G-8699)*

Belvan Partners LP.....F....... 432 682-4349
Midland *(G-15137)*

Black Eagle Inc.....E....... 214 871-3555
Dallas *(G-4027)*

Blades Group LLC.....F....... 830 278-1211
Uvalde *(G-20188)*

BP Corporation North Amer Inc.....A....... 281 366-3988
Houston *(G-8966)*

◆ BP Corporation North Amer Inc.....A....... 281 366-2000
Houston *(G-8965)*

BP Corporation North Amer Inc.....A....... 281 366-2000
Houston *(G-8967)*

Buckley Oil Company.....E....... 214 421-4147
Midlothian *(G-15475)*

Calumet Branded Products LLC	D	281 354-8600	
Porter (G-17171)			
Calumet Karns City Ref LLC	D	281 337-1534	
Dickinson (G-5471)			
Cameron Solutions Inc	F	325 573-8521	
Snyder (G-18985)			
Catalyst Partners Inc	G	940 644-5625	
Chico (G-3052)			
▼ Chemex Modular LLC	D	801 565-8099	
New Waverly (G-15856)			
▼ Chemtec Energy Services LLC	E	936 856-1704	
Willis (G-20844)			
▲ Chevron Phillips Chem Co LP	A	832 813-4100	
The Woodlands (G-19845)			
Chevron USA Inc	C	925 842-1000	
Houston (G-9181)			
Citgo Holding Terminals LLC	B	832 486-4000	
Houston (G-9200)			
Citgo Petroleum Corporation	F	832 486-5900	
Sugar Land (G-19458)			
◆ Citgo Petroleum Corporation	A	832 486-4000	
Houston (G-9201)			
Coastal Caverns Inc	G	409 833-5504	
Beaumont (G-1872)			
▲ Coffeyville Resources LLC	D	281 207-3200	
Sugar Land (G-19462)			
Coffeyville Resources LLC	F	281 207-7711	
Sugar Land (G-19463)			
Coffeyvlle Rsrces Ref Mktg LLC	E	281 207-3200	
Sugar Land (G-19465)			
◆ Conocophillips Company	A	281 293-1000	
Houston (G-9273)			
Conocophillips Company	E	325 835-4451	
Mertzon (G-15020)			
▲ Conocophillips Holding Company	D	281 293-1000	
Houston (G-9274)			
Cowboy Containments Inc	F	361 576-9550	
Victoria (G-20255)			
▲ Crystaphase Products Inc	E	281 874-2110	
Houston (G-9352)			
Cvr Energy Inc	D	281 207-3200	
Sugar Land (G-19472)			
Cvr Refining LP	F	281 207-3200	
Sugar Land (G-19474)			
Cvr Refining Holdings LLC	B	281 207-3200	
Sugar Land (G-19475)			
Dcg Partnership I Limited	E	281 648-1894	
Pearland (G-16553)			
Dcp Midstream LLC	D	432 827-1945	
Goldsmith (G-7741)			
Delek Renewables LLC	E	817 558-9255	
Cleburne (G-3088)			
Delek US Holdings Inc	D	432 684-4210	
Midland (G-15190)			
Diamond Shamrock Ref & Mktg Co	B	361 786-2536	
Three Rivers (G-19944)			
Diamond Shamrock Ref & Mktg Co	A	210 345-2000	
San Antonio (G-18057)			
Dstj Corporation	F	936 447-1174	
Montgomery (G-15632)			
▲ Dysol Inc	E	817 335-1826	
Rhome (G-17255)			
Eagle Hydrocarbons LLC	E	713 300-3245	
Houston (G-9558)			
◆ El Paso Cgp Company LLC	E	713 420-2600	
Houston (G-9585)			
Emgs Americas Inc	E	281 920-5601	
Houston (G-9615)			
Enterprise Products Oper LLC	B	281 385-4200	
Mont Belvieu (G-15617)			
Enterprise Products Oper LLC	D	832 501-4000	
Mont Belvieu (G-15618)			
Ep Energy Resale Company LLC	F	713 997-1000	
Houston (G-9677)			
◆ Equilon Enterprises LLC	E	713 767-5337	
Houston (G-9685)			
Ergon Inc	F	972 875-1122	
Ennis (G-6100)			
▼ Exxon Mobil Corporation	B	972 940-6000	
Irving (G-13021)			
Exxon Mobil Corporation		713 656-3636	
Houston (G-9739)			
▲ Exxonmobil Pipeline Company	C	713 656-3636	
Spring (G-19117)			
◆ Exxonmobil Sales and Sup LLC		800 243-9966	
Spring (G-19119)			
Fabrication & Cnstr Svcs LP		936 257-0466	
Dayton (G-5226)			
Flint Hills Resources LP	C	361 889-7282	
Corpus Christi (G-3529)			
Flint Hills Resources LP	E	281 363-7200	
The Woodlands (G-19865)			
Flint Hills Resources LP	B	432 640-8933	
Odessa (G-16004)			
Flint Hills Resources LP	E	361 241-4811	
Corpus Christi (G-3530)			
Flint Hills Resources LP	C	361 241-4811	
Corpus Christi (G-3531)			
▲ Flint Hlls Rsrces Hston Chem L	D	713 740-3900	
Houston (G-9803)			
Formosa Hydrocarbons Co Inc	E	361 987-8900	
Point Comfort (G-17082)			
▲ Frontier Oil Corporation	F	214 871-3555	
Dallas (G-4383)			
Frontier Petroleum Resources	E	832 242-1510	
Houston (G-9869)			
Gardner Denver Inc	G	817 248-4510	
Fort Worth (G-6662)			
Giant Industries Inc	A	915 775-3300	
El Paso (G-5786)			
Global Alternative Fuels LLC	E	915 791-8720	
El Paso (G-5787)			
Grizzly Operating LLC	E	903 876-2227	
Poynor (G-17201)			
Gron Fuels LLC	B	813 220-3331	
Houston (G-10049)			
▲ Hermes Consolidated LLC	F	303 894-9966	
Houston (G-10160)			
Hh Oil Tools Inc	F	281 550-0633	
Houston (G-10169)			
Hollyfrontier Corporation	B	214 871-3555	
Dallas (G-4462)			
▼ Hollyfrontier Ref & Mktg LLC	C	214 871-3555	
Dallas (G-4463)			
Hunt Petroleum Corporation	C	214 880-8400	
Fort Worth (G-6710)			
Innospec Inc	F	832 748-0284	
Spring (G-19217)			
◆ Intergulf Corporation	D	281 474-4210	
La Porte (G-13754)			
Intertek USA Inc	E	361 289-7474	
Corpus Christi (G-3556)			
Iwc Oil & Refinery LLC	E	210 900-9928	
San Antonio (G-18196)			
J L Davis Company	E	432 399-4575	
Coahoma (G-3165)			
Jag Energy Company	E	832 997-0575	
Houston (G-10449)			
◆ Jx Nippon Chemical Texas Inc	D	713 754-1000	
Pasadena (G-16467)			
Keane Group Holdings LLC	A	281 716-9152	
Houston (G-10511)			
Koch Industries Inc	F	806 347-2645	
Matador (G-14816)			
Koch Supply & Trading LP	E	713 544-4123	
Houston (G-10555)			
Lacy Operations Ltd	E	903 693-3501	
Beckville (G-1971)			
Lazarus Energy LLC	G	830 582-3202	
Houston (G-10610)			
Lazarus Energy Holdings LLC	F	713 850-0500	
Houston (G-10611)			
Lima Refining Company	F	409 839-3500	
Beaumont (G-1918)			
Lima Refining Company	F	409 985-1000	
Port Arthur (G-17116)			
◆ Lyondell Chemical Company	D	713 309-7200	
Houston (G-10705)			
▲ Lyondell-Citgo Refining LLC	F	713 321-4111	
Houston (G-10707)			
◆ Macdermid Canning Ltd	E	713 472-5081	
Pasadena (G-16478)			
Madmackenzie Solutions LLC	E	281 615-8102	
Missouri City (G-15584)			
Marathon Oil Company	E	713 296-4336	
Houston (G-10755)			
◆ Marathon Oil Company	A	713 629-6600	
Houston (G-10754)			
◆ Marathon Oil Corporation	A	713 629-6600	
Houston (G-10756)			
◆ Martin Resource Mgt Corp	C	903 983-6200	
Kilgore (G-13570)			
Morgan Kinder Treating LP	D	713 369-8515	
Houston (G-10921)			
Murphy USA Inc	F	512 332-0622	
Bastrop (G-1760)			
Nexlube Operating LLC	F	972 590-9908	
Addison (G-150)			
Novvi LLC	F	281 488-0833	
Deer Park (G-5287)			
Oilfield Anchor Company Inc	D	903 723-2833	
Palestine (G-16306)			
Osaka Gas USA Corporation	F	713 354-9100	
Houston (G-11196)			
◆ Oxbow Calcining LLC	E	281 907-9425	
Spring (G-19238)			
Pacific Refining Company	E	713 877-6929	
Houston (G-11219)			
▲ Par Hawaii Refining LLC	C	281 899-4800	
Houston (G-11234)			
Par Pacific Holdings Inc	D	281 899-4800	
Houston (G-11235)			
Paramount Petroleum Corp	E	800 882-6541	
Channelview (G-3031)			
◆ Pasadena Refining System Inc	C	713 920-1874	
Houston (G-11255)			
◆ Pdvsa Services Inc	D	281 531-0004	
Houston (G-11266)			
▲ Pelican Refining Company LLC	G	713 877-7777	
Houston (G-11273)			
Petra Oil Company Inc	F	888 738-7261	
Cypress (G-3812)			
◆ Phillips 66	C	281 293-6600	
Houston (G-11324)			
Phillips 66 Carrier LLC	E	855 283-9237	
Houston (G-11325)			
▲ Polymer Dynamics Inc	F	281 894-6382	
Houston (G-11358)			
▲ Premcor Refining Group Inc	G	210 345-2000	
San Antonio (G-18388)			
Premier Pressure Pumping LLC	F	903 981-0081	
Kilgore (G-13583)			
Pride Refining Inc	B	325 677-5444	
Abilene (G-66)			
▲ Qri International LLC	F	713 485-8800	
Houston (G-11487)			
Quaker State Investment Corp	F	713 546-4000	
Houston (G-11491)			
Quantum Reservoir Impact LLC	E	713 485-8800	
Houston (G-11508)			
Rancho Lpg Holdings LLC	E	713 993-5331	
Houston (G-11539)			
Raven Butene-1 LLC	E	251 414-6955	
Baytown (G-1833)			
Reatta Energy Inc	F	432 682-7495	
Midland (G-15378)			
Rio Valley Biofuels LLC	F	915 791-8720	
El Paso (G-5941)			
San Antonio Refinery LLC	E	512 350-7898	
San Antonio (G-18447)			
San Antonio Refinery LLC	E	210 918-7436	
San Antonio (G-18448)			
Sandifers LP Gas & Svc Co Inc	F	409 963-1269	
Port Arthur (G-17124)			
Shell Oil Company	C	713 332-7606	
Houston (G-11862)			
Shell Oil Company	D	713 246-6462	
Deer Park (G-5296)			
Shell Oil Company	F	713 546-4000	
Houston (G-11863)			
Shell Oil Company	E	713 721-6282	
Houston (G-11864)			
◆ Shell Oil Company	A	713 241-6161	
Houston (G-11860)			
◆ South Hampton Resources Inc	E	409 385-1400	
Silsbee (G-18956)			
Southcross Ala Pipeline LLC	E	214 979-3700	
Dallas (G-4981)			
Southtex Treaters Inc	D	432 563-2766	
Odessa (G-16158)			
Southwest Impreglon R Inc	E	281 441-2000	
Humble (G-12798)			
Strathmore Products Inc	E	281 269-9658	
Rockwall (G-17567)			
▲ Tesoro Refining & Mktg Co LLC	C	210 828-8484	
San Antonio (G-18530)			
Texas Oil & Chemical Co II Inc	D	409 385-1400	
Silsbee (G-18957)			
◆ Tiger Offshore Rentals LLC	D	409 951-4048	
Beaumont (G-1959)			
Total Ptrchemicals Ref USA Inc	C	281 476-3700	
Deer Park (G-5301)			
Total Ptrchemicals Ref USA Inc	E	409 963-6800	
Port Arthur (G-17130)			
◆ Total Ptrchemicals Ref USA Inc	B	713 483-5000	
Houston (G-12332)			
Trecora Resources	E	281 980-5522	
Sugar Land (G-19568)			
Tri Resources Inc	E	940 644-2233	
Chico (G-3054)			

S I C

▼ Trican Well Service LP ....A 281 716-9152
Houston *(G-12368)*
Ultramar Inc ....A 210 345-2000
San Antonio *(G-18576)*
United Energy Group LLC ....D 281 839-0080
Baytown *(G-1838)*
Univar Solutions USA Inc ....E 281 297-0678
Spring *(G-19261)*
UOP LLC ....E 832 551-9638
Houston *(G-12472)*
Upham Oil & Gas Company LP ....E 940 325-4491
Mineral Wells *(G-15544)*
◆ US Petrochemicals Inc ....F 713 871-1951
Houston *(G-12487)*
▲ Valero Energy Corporation ....A 210 345-2000
San Antonio *(G-18583)*
Valero Energy Corporation ....E 903 567-6001
Canton *(G-2661)*
Valero Energy Corporation ....E 903 765-2900
Alba *(G-183)*
Valero Energy Corporation ....F 325 347-6561
Rocksprings *(G-17533)*
Valero Energy Corporation ....B 806 935-1307
Sunray *(G-19623)*
Valero Energy Corporation ....F 936 594-6233
Riverside *(G-17481)*
Valero Marketing and Supply Co ....C 877 882-5376
Amarillo *(G-517)*
▲ Valero Ref Company-California ....C 210 345-2000
San Antonio *(G-18584)*
◆ Valero Ref Company-New Jersey ....B 210 345-2000
San Antonio *(G-18585)*
Valero Refining Company ....D 210 345-2000
San Antonio *(G-18586)*
Valero Refining-Texas LP ....B 713 923-6641
Houston *(G-12519)*
Valero Refining-Texas LP ....B 409 945-4451
Texas City *(G-19806)*
Valero Refining-Texas LP ....C 281 470-4900
La Porte *(G-13799)*
◆ Valero Refining-Texas LP ....B 210 345-2000
San Antonio *(G-18587)*
Valero Renewable Fuels Co LLC ....D 210 345-2000
San Antonio *(G-18588)*
◆ Valero Rfining-New Orleans LLC ....C 210 345-2000
San Antonio *(G-18589)*
Valero Services Inc ....A 210 345-2000
San Antonio *(G-18590)*
Vertex Energy Inc ....E 866 660-8156
Houston *(G-12556)*
Virgin Fields LLC ....E 972 322-7902
Frisco *(G-7323)*
◆ Vp Racing Fuels Inc ....D 210 635-7744
San Antonio *(G-18600)*
Western Gas Resources Inc ....E 432 395-2448
Fort Stockton *(G-6331)*
Western Refining Inc ....B 915 775-3300
El Paso *(G-6033)*
Western Refining Company LP ....F 915 775-3246
El Paso *(G-6034)*
Western Refining Company LP ....F 915 534-1400
El Paso *(G-6035)*
▼ WRB Refining LP ....F 281 293-6600
Houston *(G-12699)*
Wynnewood Energy Company LLC ....B 281 207-3200
Sugar Land *(G-19574)*
▲ Wynnewood Refining Company LLC ....D
281 207-3444
Sugar Land *(G-19575)*

2951 Paving Mixtures & Blocks

Alamo Concrete Tile Inc ....E 210 534-8821
San Antonio *(G-17883)*
American Indus Mfrs Bldg Mate ....C 214 254-4720
Plano *(G-16787)*
Ark-La-Tex Custom Coatings ....F 903 845-6436
Gladewater *(G-7717)*
Asphalt Inc LLC ....E 512 428-5739
Austin *(G-939)*
Big Creek Sand and Gravel Inc ....E 806 273-7501
Borger *(G-2164)*
Bryan & Bryan Asp Rd Oil Co ....E 903 657-2391
Henderson *(G-8259)*
Btb Refining LLC ....F 561 347-5500
Corpus Christi *(G-3490)*
▲ Builders Post-Tension Inc ....E 281 873-9500
Houston *(G-9014)*
▲ Capitol Aggregates Inc ....C 210 871-6100
San Antonio *(G-17981)*
Caprock Materials LLC ....F 806 778-0343
Lubbock *(G-14390)*
Cemex El Paso Inc ....C 915 565-4681
El Paso *(G-5691)*
Century Asphalt Ltd ....F 512 285-4499
Elgin *(G-6053)*
Century Asphalt Ltd ....F 281 421-2621
Baytown *(G-1811)*
Cleveland Asphalt Products Inc ....E 936 628-6200
Shepherd *(G-18900)*
Coffeyville Resources Trml LLC ....F 281 207-3200
Sugar Land *(G-19464)*
Colorado Materials Ltd ....F 512 353-7757
New Braunfels *(G-15784)*
Crafco Texas Inc ....F 210 496-2070
San Antonio *(G-18029)*
Crh Americas Materials Inc ....C 409 866-1444
Beaumont *(G-1878)*
Csa Materials Inc ....D 325 655-4511
San Angelo *(G-17793)*
▼ David L Jennings ....D 281 778-3223
Missouri City *(G-15579)*
Dlc Construction Inc ....F 915 771-7580
El Paso *(G-5722)*
▲ Dmg Equipment Company LLC ....C 936 756-6960
Conroe *(G-3295)*
Frontera Materials Inc ....D 956 316-8952
Elsa *(G-6079)*
G & S Asphalt Inc ....F 281 499-1551
Stafford *(G-19320)*
Gem Asset Acquisition LLC ....E 214 333-4343
Dallas *(G-4396)*
Guerro Ready Mix ....E 281 342-4022
Rosenberg *(G-17583)*
Gulf States Asphalt Company LP ....D 713 941-4410
South Houston *(G-19042)*
Gulf States Materials Inc ....E 281 470-8645
La Porte *(G-13742)*
Hanson Aggregates LLC ....D 210 658-7461
New Braunfels *(G-15801)*
Hanson Aggregates LLC ....C 469 417-1200
Irving *(G-13049)*
Henry Company ....E 972 272-5488
Garland *(G-7510)*
▲ Hunter Industries Ltd ....B 512 353-7757
San Marcos *(G-18695)*
J Lee Milligan Inc ....C 806 373-5352
Amarillo *(G-441)*
Legacy Vulcan LLC ....E 325 646-8526
Brownwood *(G-2435)*
Legacy Vulcan LLC ....E 325 529-3785
Abilene *(G-58)*
Libcon Inc ....D 956 724-6459
Laredo *(G-13907)*
Longview Asphalt Inc ....F 903 758-0065
Longview *(G-14266)*
Longview Asphalt Inc ....G 903 758-4428
Longview *(G-14267)*
▲ Martin Mrtta Mtls Suthwest LLC ....B 210 208-4400
San Antonio *(G-18280)*
Midwest Asphalt Corporation ....F 940 668-1480
Gainesville *(G-7348)*
Moore Asphalt Co Inc ....E 903 561-1321
Tyler *(G-20131)*
◆ Omega Paving Contractor Inc ....F 915 595-1280
El Paso *(G-5901)*
Owens Corning Sales LLC ....C 972 438-1050
Irving *(G-13138)*
Owens Corning Sales LLC ....D 713 672-8338
Houston *(G-11208)*
Pavement Tool Mfg Inc ....F 903 734-7531
Big Sandy *(G-2066)*
Pro Pavers Houston LLC ....E 281 665-4718
Katy *(G-13433)*
Quality Hot Mix Inc ....F 979 543-6464
El Campo *(G-5627)*
Ram-Bro Contracting Inc ....E 361 387-2795
Robstown *(G-17515)*
Tarmac Materials LLC ....F 281 342-9314
Richmond *(G-17466)*
▲ Texas Crushed Stone Company ....C 512 255-4405
Georgetown *(G-7684)*
Thompson Jr Inc ....E 940 665-2533
Gainesville *(G-7372)*
Trinity Asphalt Inc ....E 903 657-2391
Henderson *(G-8275)*
US Lbm Holdings LLC ....C 713 650-6200
Houston *(G-12485)*
US Polyco Inc ....F 972 875-9300
Ennis *(G-6122)*
Valley Caliche Products Inc ....D 956 581-2751
Mission *(G-15571)*
Vantacore Partners LLC ....F 215 751-1403
Houston *(G-12530)*
Vulcan Materials Company ....F 210 349-3311
San Antonio *(G-18603)*
Vulcan Materials Company ....F 210 494-9555
San Antonio *(G-18604)*
Word Constructors LLC ....F 830 693-2933
Marble Falls *(G-14752)*
Zack Burkett Co ....E 940 322-2101
Wichita Falls *(G-20838)*

2952 Asphalt Felts & Coatings

ABG Contracting Group LLC ....E 281 431-7223
Pearland *(G-16536)*
American Indus Mfrs Bldg Mate ....C 214 254-4720
Plano *(G-16787)*
Argio Roofing & Cnstr Llc ....F 956 434-6411
Rio Hondo *(G-17475)*
Ark-La-Tex Custom Coatings ....F 903 845-6436
Gladewater *(G-7717)*
▼ Asphalt Products Inc ....F 956 423-8315
Harlingen *(G-8181)*
Certainteed LLC ....D 972 875-9661
Ennis *(G-6090)*
Coatings Group Inc ....C 817 633-7383
Grand Prairie *(G-7857)*
Elk Corporation of Texas ....C 972 875-9611
Ennis *(G-6095)*
▼ Elk Corporation of Texas ....D 972 851-0500
Dallas *(G-4312)*
◆ Elkcorp ....E 972 851-0500
Dallas *(G-4313)*
Everest Coatings Inc ....F 281 350-9800
Spring *(G-19114)*
▲ Extruded Ennis Products ....F 972 875-1770
Ennis *(G-6101)*
F3 Foam LLC ....G 936 661-3172
Montgomery *(G-15633)*
Gardner-Gibson Incorporated ....F 832 288-4111
Houston *(G-9899)*
Gardner-Gibson Mfg Inc ....F 972 878-1602
Ennis *(G-6103)*
Hco Holding I Corporation ....F 214 764-3021
Garland *(G-7508)*
Henry Company ....E 972 272-5488
Garland *(G-7510)*
▲ JW Industries Ltd ....F 972 291-7474
Cedar Hill *(G-2947)*
◆ Lapolla Industries LLC ....E 281 219-4100
Houston *(G-10599)*
Market Makers Inc ....F 281 893-9261
Houston *(G-10769)*
Owens Corning Sales LLC ....D 713 672-8338
Houston *(G-11208)*
Owens Corning Sales LLC ....C 972 438-1050
Irving *(G-13138)*
Palacio Ivis ....F 214 402-6856
Dallas *(G-4777)*
Professional Coating Tech Inc ....F 972 291-7474
Cedar Hill *(G-2952)*
Quikrete ....G 210 208-1511
San Antonio *(G-18644)*
◆ Siplast Inc ....E 469 995-2200
Irving *(G-13181)*
Standard Industries Inc ....C 972 851-0460
Dallas *(G-5004)*
Thermo Mfg Systems LLC ....F 903 881-8771
Lindale *(G-14136)*

2992 Lubricating Oils & Greases

Ashburn Industries ....E 832 399-1000
Houston *(G-8718)*
◆ Championx LLC ....A 281 632-6500
Sugar Land *(G-19455)*
Chemax Corporation ....E 409 866-4232
Beaumont *(G-1868)*
◆ Chevron Marine Products LLC ....D 832 854-2767
Houston *(G-9179)*
Darling Ingredients Inc ....E 713 224-0438
Houston *(G-9404)*
◆ Delta Companies Group ....E 281 479-7288
Deer Park *(G-5267)*
Diamond Shamrock Ref & Mktg Co ....B 361 786-2536
Three Rivers *(G-19944)*
Enventives LLC ....E 612 930-1977
Seagraves *(G-18803)*
◆ Equilon Enterprises LLC ....B 713 767-5337
Houston *(G-9685)*

Ethyl Corporation.................................D 713 740-8300
Pasadena (G-16431)

Flex Tank Systems LLC.......................E 281 862-2900
Channelview (G-3022)

Globalpetrochem LLC..........................F 832 788-3952
Houston (G-9983)

▼ HI Tech Oil Blends Inc ....F 972 231-5464
Allen (G-274)

Hydrotex Holdings Inc ....D 972 389-8500
Dallas (G-4477)

Hydrotex Partners................................E 972 389-8500
Farmers Branch (G-6203)

◆ Intergulf Corporation ....D 281 474-4210
La Porte (G-13754)

James Walker Oil & Gas Co ....E 281 875-0002
Conroe (G-3313)

Kluber Lubrication N Amer LP ....D 903 534-8021
Tyler (G-20109)

Kluber Lubrication NA LP ....G 903 534-8021
Tyler (G-20110)

Lubchem Inc ....F 281 350-9600
Spring (G-19143)

◆ Macdermid Canning Ltd ....E 713 472-5081
Pasadena (G-16478)

◆ Pennzoil-Quaker State Company ....A 800 237-8645
Houston (G-11284)

Ramses Lubr Repackaging LLC............F 972 672-8717
Grand Prairie (G-7962)

◆ Ramsey Properties LP ....C 281 328-3501
Crosby (G-3741)

◆ Rectorseal LLC..................................D 713 263-8001
Houston (G-11565)

Shell Rapid Lube Lonestar Auto ....F 254 953-4360
Harker Heights (G-8173)

◆ South Coast Products LP ....E 713 434-2141
Houston (G-11962)

◆ South Coast Terminals LP..................D 713 672-2401
Houston (G-11963)

South Coast Terminals LP.....................E 281 842-1286
La Porte (G-13790)

◆ Southwestern Petroleum Corp............E 817 348-7233
Fort Worth (G-7006)

◆ Stinger Chemical LLC.........................D 713 227-1340
Houston (G-12067)

Sun Coast Resources Inc......................C 713 844-9600
Houston (G-12097)

Texas Oil Group Ltd Co ....F 281 645-9398
San Antonio (G-18540)

Texas Refinery Corp ....F 682 518-1405
Mansfield (G-14722)

◆ Total Specialties Usa Inc ....E 713 969-4651
Houston (G-12334)

◆ Vexa Pak LLC ....F 713 671-1100
Houston (G-12559)

Western Marketing Inc ....G 817 232-8626
Saginaw (G-17759)

◆ Whitmore Manufacturing Company......F 972 771-1000
Rockwall (G-17571)

Wtg Fuels Inc ....F 432 837-2518
Alpine (G-313)

◆ Zxp Technologies LLC ....B 281 426-8800
Highlands (G-8317)

2999 Products Of Petroleum & Coal, NEC

▼ Certispec Services Inc.......................F 409 945-3338
Texas City (G-19786)

Juniper Specialty Products LLC............F 346 310-6241
Pasadena (G-16466)

Master Flo ....F 713 690-2789
Houston (G-10787)

◆ Rain Cii Carbon LLC ....E 281 318-2400
Kingwood (G-13652)

Trans-Mate LLC....................................E 800 867-9274
Dallas (G-5105)

◆ Trecora Chemical Inc ....D 281 474-7500
Pasadena (G-16519)

Trecora Resources................................E 281 980-5522
Sugar Land (G-19568)

30 RUBBER AND MISCELLANEOUS PLASTICS PRODUCTS

3011 Tires & Inner Tubes

American Tire Distributors Inc ....F 281 872-0397
Houston (G-8612)

American Tire Distributors Inc ....F 704 992-2000
Austin (G-918)

Austin Rubber Company LLC.................G 512 904-0152
Austin (G-959)

Carlstar Group LLC...............................C 972 606-2126
Grand Prairie (G-7851)

▲ En Plast Technology LLC....................F 832 730-4606
Houston (G-9622)

Goodyear Tire & Rubber Company.........A 361 289-8251
Corpus Christi (G-3537)

J Morco Incorporated ....E 817 596-3989
Weatherford (G-20597)

▲ Lone Star Wheel Components ....D 903 654-1132
Corsicana (G-3676)

Michelin North America Inc...................B 864 458-5000
El Paso (G-5877)

▲ Multi-Seal Corporation ....F 281 591-0111
Spring (G-19235)

Nbr Wheels and Tires LLC ....E 855 575-3879
Irving (G-13113)

▲ Roadrunner Rubber Corp...................F 713 697-0633
Houston (G-11641)

Sanchez Tire Shop 5.............................F 956 423-0047
Harlingen (G-8200)

T & W Tire LLC.....................................G 940 683-3558
Bridgeport (G-2302)

Titan International Inc ....C 956 541-7500
Brownsville (G-2413)

Tjp Enterprises LLC..............................E 817 779-4360
Fort Worth (G-7064)

▲ Trans-Texas Tire LLC........................E 903 572-0267
Mount Pleasant (G-15664)

3021 Rubber & Plastic Footwear

◆ Bio World Merchandising Inc ....C 972 488-0655
Irving (G-12948)

Fossil Partners LP................................G 972 437-0452
Richardson (G-17315)

◆ Handgards LLC..................................C 915 779-6606
El Paso (G-5794)

Nike Inc ....E 956 565-2446
Mercedes (G-15008)

Nike Inc ....E 972 980-1946
Dallas (G-4740)

Vans Inc ....F 713 436-7925
Pearland (G-16609)

3052 Rubber & Plastic Hose & Belting

All-State Industries Inc ....E 972 434-4222
Lewisville (G-14020)

▲ D E Shipp Belting Company ....F 254 776-0493
Waco (G-20392)

Eastex Rubber & Gasket Co ....F 409 727-6800
Nederland (G-15752)

Flexaust Inc ....C 915 872-3100
El Paso (G-5770)

▲ Flexmaster USA Inc ....D 713 462-7694
Houston (G-9801)

G T Southwest Hose Inc ....F 214 689-4673
Dallas (G-4388)

Gates E&S North America Inc................D 361 887-9807
Corpus Christi (G-3533)

◆ Ghx Industrial LLC ....E 713 341-3407
Houston (G-9950)

Ghx Industrial LLC ....F 713 939-7423
Houston (G-9951)

Ghx Industrial LLC ....E 713 222-2231
Houston (G-9952)

Hasse Enterprises Inc ....E 512 835-7697
Austin (G-1199)

Parts Suppliers Inc ....F 830 773-5069
Eagle Pass (G-5552)

▲ Purvis Industries LLC........................D 214 358-5500
Dallas (G-4837)

Reliable Hose Solutions LLC.................F 713 983-9090
Houston (G-11590)

Republic Tube LLC................................C 832 672-6000
Houston (G-11603)

Swan Products LLC...............................C 254 772-6979
Waco (G-20461)

3053 Gaskets, Packing & Sealing Devices

▲ A-1 Gasket & Industrial Supply..........F 432 332-1444
Odessa (G-15897)

▲ Ace Rubber Products Inc ....F 817 572-1011
Kennedale (G-13496)

All-State Industries Inc ....E 972 434-4222
Lewisville (G-14020)

▲ American Gasket Mfg Co Inc ....E 214 388-0603
Dallas (G-3941)

American Industrial Polymers ....E 979 542-3654
Giddings (G-7691)

Anchor Texacone LLC...........................E 972 288-4404
Mesquite (G-15026)

Applied Consultants Inc........................E 903 643-0956
Longview (G-14196)

▲ Applied Rubber Technology Inc ....D 936 760-4100
Conroe (G-3257)

▲ Beaumont Bolt & Gasket Inc ....E 409 838-6304
Beaumont (G-1859)

▲ Buffalo Seal and Gasket Co ....E 713 694-9003
Houston (G-9011)

C T Gasket & Polymer Co Inc ....E 713 856-8667
Houston (G-9034)

▲ CDI Energy Products Inc ....B 281 446-6662
Humble (G-12753)

Champion Group Inc ....E 713 644-2181
Houston (G-9157)

Champion Sales & Manufacturing.........E 281 356-6162
Magnolia (G-14595)

▲ Conroe Plastics Molding Inc ....D 936 539-2005
Conroe (G-3283)

◆ Corpus Chrsti Gsket Fstner Inc ....C 361 884-6366
Corpus Christi (G-3510)

Creative Molded Packaging LLC............E 915 881-8401
El Paso (G-5705)

Dan-Loc Group LLC ....D 713 356-3500
Houston (G-9399)

◆ Dan-Loc, LLC.....................................F 713 356-3500
Houston (G-9400)

E G C Corporation.................................B 281 774-6100
Humble (G-12764)

▲ Eagle Gasket and Packing Co ....E 713 290-8811
Tomball (G-19975)

▲ Eagleburgmann Industries LP ....E 713 939-9515
Houston (G-9567)

Eagleburgmann Industries LP ....E 979 265-2320
Clute (G-3153)

Eastex Rubber & Gasket Co ....F 409 727-6800
Nederland (G-15752)

Enpro Industries Inc ....D 281 207-4600
Stafford (G-19312)

Enpro Industries Inc ....E 713 983-4222
Houston (G-9650)

Enpro Industries Inc ....E 713 983-4200
Houston (G-9651)

Federal-Mogul Powertrain LLC..............B 915 860-2300
El Paso (G-5767)

Ferpa Precision Machine Inc ....E 281 874-9747
Houston (G-9777)

Fgi Acquisition Corp..............................E 281 604-2400
Houston (G-9782)

Flange Protection & Gaskets ....F 281 991-4550
Pasadena (G-16437)

Flexitallic Group Inc ....E 281 604-2400
Deer Park (G-5274)

▼ Flexitallic Group Inc ....E 281 604-2525
Houston (G-9799)

Flexitallic Investments Inc ....E 281 604-2525
Houston (G-9800)

▲ Fluid Sealing Products Inc ....D 713 910-1028
Houston (G-9816)

Garlock Sealing Tech LLC......................C 281 840-4853
Houston (G-9901)

Gasket Service Inc ....F 432 332-0853
Odessa (G-16011)

◆ Ghx Industrial LLC ....E 713 341-3407
Houston (G-9950)

Ghx Industrial LLC ....F 713 939-7423
Houston (G-9951)

Ghx Industrial LLC ....E 713 222-2231
Houston (G-9952)

Ghx Industrial LLC ....F 409 832-3461
Beaumont (G-1898)

Greene Tweed & Co Inc ....B 281 821-8337
Houston (G-10033)

Greenpacks USA ....F 888 498-7774
Dallas (G-4415)

Gs Liquid Technologies LLC ....F 817 556-6262
Cleburne (G-3093)

Gund Company Inc ....E 972 389-0615
Euless (G-6147)

H K Specialties Co Inc ....F 713 466-1567
Houston (G-10084)

▲ Han-Boone International Inc ....F 817 838-5196
Fort Worth (G-6686)

◆ Hi-Tech Champion Manufacturing ......E 713 644-2181
Houston (G-10172)

▲ Houston Mfg Specialty Co Inc ....E 281 888-4635
Houston (G-10239)

Houston Thermoseal Inc ....F 713 997-8111
Houston (G-8385)

▲ Humble Industries Inc ....F 281 987-9175
Humble (G-12778)

Employee Codes: A=Over 500 employees, B=251-500
C=101-250, D=51-100, E=20-50, F=10-19, G=9

2021 Harris Texas
Manufacturers Directory

969

SIC

▲ Indian Industries LP ....F 817 265-6731
Arlington *(G-704)*

◆ Jaeger Products Inc 817 695-5680
Arlington *(G-710)*

Jamak Fabrication-Tex Ltd ....F 817 594-8771
Weatherford *(G-20598)*

James L Rembert Jr Inc ....F 281 240-7070
Sugar Land *(G-19500)*

Jim Ray Company Inc ....F 713 941-2275
South Houston *(G-19048)*

John Crane Inc ....D 281 474-1700
Pasadena *(G-16464)*

Jones Holt Enterprises Inc ....E 210 657-5917
San Antonio *(G-18207)*

Justiss Oil Company Inc ....D 903 859-2111
Arp *(G-812)*

◆ Kalsi Engineering Incorporated ....E 281 240-6500
Sugar Land *(G-19501)*

◆ Lamons Gasket Company ....B 713 222-0284
Houston *(G-10589)*

◆ Leader Gasket Technologies Inc....D 281 542-0600
La Porte *(G-13766)*

Leader Gasket Technologies Inc ....F 361 289-1614
Corpus Christi *(G-3563)*

▲ LGS Technologies LP ....E 972 224-9201
Lancaster *(G-13845)*

Lone Star Gasket and Sup Inc ....F 432 333-1615
Odessa *(G-16064)*

Longwood Elastomers Inc ....C 979 830-1111
Brenham *(G-2261)*

▲ M & P Sealing Co ....F 409 745-2002
Orange *(G-16253)*

▲ Mariposa Corporation ....E 713 222-0220
Houston *(G-10768)*

McGaskets & Ptfe Spc Inc ....F 713 847-6700
Humble *(G-12788)*

Midwest Industrial Rubber Inc ....F 972 988-6700
Grand Prairie *(G-7928)*

Miller Machine & Welding LLC ....E 254 582-2185
Whitney *(G-20731)*

Oil States International Inc ....D 713 652-0582
Houston *(G-11161)*

P I Components Corp ....D 979 830-5400
Brenham *(G-2267)*

Panhandle Packing & Gasket Inc ....E 806 763-2801
Lubbock *(G-14456)*

Pelican Tank Parts Inc ....F 713 862-5557
Houston *(G-11274)*

◆ Pelican Worldwide Incorporated....E 713 862-5557
Houston *(G-11275)*

▲ Pipeline Seal & Insulator Inc ....D 713 747-6948
Houston *(G-11336)*

Refrigration Gaskets Texas Inc ....F 713 880-8066
Houston *(G-11582)*

▲ Rsi Inc ....E 512 268-7500
Kyle *(G-13686)*

▲ Seal-Jet of Texas Inc ....E 713 983-7233
Houston *(G-11804)*

Sealing Technology Inc ....E 281 330-6363
Houston *(G-11805)*

SKF USA Inc ....D 281 506-3250
Houston *(G-11913)*

T F E Company Inc ....E 979 836-6111
Brenham *(G-2274)*

Tape Innovations LLC ....E 817 568-1212
Fort Worth *(G-7034)*

Temperatsure LLC ....E 502 715-2819
Carrollton *(G-2827)*

Tenneco Inc ....A 915 832-4661
El Paso *(G-5997)*

Tex Cnp/Seal Inc ....E 214 688-7770
Dallas *(G-5051)*

▲ Texas Gasket and Packing Co ....F 713 674-7531
Houston *(G-12232)*

Texas Precision Polymers Inc ....G 936 588-4333
Conroe *(G-3371)*

Texas Seal Supply Co Inc ....F 817 640-1193
Arlington *(G-794)*

▲ TXG Industries Inc ....E 713 222-0220
Houston *(G-12417)*

▲ Utex Industries Inc ....D 713 467-1000
Houston *(G-12505)*

Utex Industries Inc ....B 979 725-8503
Weimar *(G-20651)*

Utex Industries Inc ....G 713 559-0203
Venus *(G-20225)*

Utex Industries Inc ....E 432 333-4151
Odessa *(G-16192)*

Utex Industries Inc ....D 936 760-4100
Conroe *(G-3381)*

Utex Industries Inc ....C 832 358-0350
Houston *(G-12506)*

Vanco Ring Gsket Spclty Corp I ....F 281 499-1543
Stafford *(G-19394)*

▼ Western Rubber and Mfg Co ....E 936 588-3033
Conroe *(G-3385)*

◆ Wolar Industrial Inc ....D 713 926-2440
Houston *(G-12680)*

3061 Molded, Extruded & Lathe-Cut Rubber Mechanical Goods

▲ Ace Rubber Products Inc ....F 817 572-1011
Kennedale *(G-13496)*

Advanced Mat Systems LLC ....G 281 839-4258
Alvin *(G-349)*

Akwel Cadillac Usa Inc ....F 956 718-8387
Laredo *(G-13856)*

Akwel Cadillac Usa Inc ....F 956 717-4147
Laredo *(G-13857)*

Anchor Texacone LLC ....E 972 288-4404
Mesquite *(G-15026)*

Blue Medical Services Inc ....E 954 417-5442
Cypress *(G-3781)*

Bulk Liquid Storage Systems LP ....E 817 473-0083
Mansfield *(G-14658)*

▲ Elastotech Southwest Inc ....E 936 545-8550
Crockett *(G-3718)*

◆ Ghx Industrial LLC ....E 713 341-3407
Houston *(G-9950)*

Ghx Industrial LLC ....E 713 939-7423
Houston *(G-9951)*

Ghx Industrial LLC ....E 713 222-2231
Houston *(G-9952)*

◆ Gren Industries Inc ....E 972 881-2606
Plano *(G-16881)*

Henniges Auto Mexico SA De Cv ....E 956 794-3606
Laredo *(G-13891)*

Houston Specialties Products ....F 936 931-5256
Houston *(G-10253)*

▲ Indian Rubber Company Inc ....E 817 265-6732
Arlington *(G-705)*

Jamak Fabrication-Tex Ltd ....F 817 594-8771
Weatherford *(G-20598)*

▲ Jmk International Inc ....E 817 737-3703
Weatherford *(G-20599)*

▲ M P Industries Inc ....E 903 561-4232
Tyler *(G-20118)*

Midwest Industrial Rubber Inc ....F 972 988-6700
Grand Prairie *(G-7928)*

Oil States Industries Inc ....F 713 510-2200
Houston *(G-11155)*

Oil States Industries Inc ....C 713 445-2200
Houston *(G-11157)*

◆ Oil States Industries Inc ....C 817 548-4200
Arlington *(G-743)*

Oil States Industries Inc ....C 713 445-2200
Houston *(G-11160)*

Oil States International Inc ....D 713 652-0582
Houston *(G-11161)*

P I Components Corp ....D 979 830-5400
Brenham *(G-2267)*

Parker-Hannifin Corporation ....C 936 560-8900
Nacogdoches *(G-15708)*

◆ Rex-Hide Incorporated ....F 903 593-7387
Tyler *(G-20146)*

Rex-Hide Industries Inc ....D 903 593-7387
Tyler *(G-20147)*

▲ Utex Industries Inc ....D 713 467-1000
Houston *(G-12505)*

Utex Industries Inc ....B 979 725-8503
Weimar *(G-20651)*

Utex Industries Inc ....D 936 760-4100
Conroe *(G-3381)*

▼ Western Rubber and Mfg Co ....E 936 588-3033
Conroe *(G-3385)*

Zeon Chemicals LP ....E 281 474-9693
Pasadena *(G-16529)*

▼ Zeon Chemicals Texas Inc ....E 502 775-2000
Pasadena *(G-16530)*

3069 Fabricated Rubber Prdts, NEC

Accurate Elastomer Pdts Inc ....D 512 285-4585
Bastrop *(G-1748)*

Ace Carton & Tape of Laredo ....F 956 727-1600
Laredo *(G-13854)*

▲ Ace Rubber Products Inc ....F 817 572-1011
Kennedale *(G-13496)*

Advanced Materials Group Inc ....D 469 246-4100
Garland *(G-7428)*

Advanced Rubber Molding Inc ....E 972 647-4040
Grand Prairie *(G-7823)*

Airmec Inc ....E 972 438-4015
Irving *(G-12926)*

▲ All Mark Impressions Ltd ....F 817 834-0080
Fort Worth *(G-6370)*

All-State Belting LLC ....F 713 433-1272
Houston *(G-8371)*

Aqseptence Group Inc ....C 651 636-3900
Houston *(G-8671)*

Baari Inc ....F 214 566-5165
Plano *(G-16797)*

Biogenix LLC ....E 888 418-7172
Houston *(G-8886)*

▲ Classic Balloon Corporation ....E 972 242-2711
Dallas *(G-4127)*

▲ Component Manufacturing Corp ....E 800 275-3011
Conroe *(G-3280)*

Continental American Corp ....E 214 630-3121
Dallas *(G-4157)*

◆ Core International LLC ....F 281 880-0200
Houston *(G-9314)*

Dacon Industries Co ....E 903 589-7456
Jacksonville *(G-13235)*

DMD Products LLC ....E 281 778-2051
Rosharon *(G-17604)*

Dyna-Mix Inc ....F 903 593-7387
Tyler *(G-20078)*

▲ Eagle Molded Products ....F 281 894-4995
Houston *(G-9559)*

▲ Elder Rubber Incorporated ....E 214 426-2890
Irving *(G-13013)*

◆ Elgi Rubber Company LLC ....E 830 875-5539
Luling *(G-14561)*

▲ En Plast Technology LLC ....F 832 730-4606
Houston *(G-9622)*

Eutsler Technical Products Inc ....D 713 686-8209
Houston *(G-9713)*

▲ EZ Flex LLC ....E 817 632-4800
Fort Worth *(G-6621)*

Fiberspar Corporation ....D 713 849-2609
Houston *(G-9783)*

Firestone Polymers LLC ....C 409 924-4500
Orange *(G-16242)*

▲ Funsource Partners ....E 713 864-3412
Houston *(G-9875)*

G V C Holdings Inc ....B 409 722-8321
Port Neches *(G-17161)*

▲ Gayla Industries Inc ....D 713 681-2411
Houston *(G-9907)*

GP Rubber LP ....E 817 838-8222
Haltom City *(G-8143)*

Hickory Springs Mfg Co ....F 817 831-1785
Fort Worth *(G-6695)*

▲ Indian Rubber Company Inc ....E 817 265-6732
Arlington *(G-705)*

Jet Rubber Inc ....E 713 673-5202
Houston *(G-10470)*

Keyston Bros ....F 713 692-2132
Houston *(G-10526)*

▲ Kgp Group Inc ....E 817 354-0766
Fort Worth *(G-6760)*

Kirkland Sales Inc ....E 972 864-1424
Garland *(G-7533)*

◆ Lapolla Industries LLC ....E 281 219-4100
Houston *(G-10599)*

M Tripple Oil Tool Inc ....E 432 337-1452
Odessa *(G-16067)*

Marian Fort Worth Inc ....E 817 332-6151
Fort Worth *(G-6811)*

Market Makers Inc ....F 281 893-9261
Houston *(G-10769)*

Metso Minerals Industries Inc ....E 210 491-9521
San Antonio *(G-18295)*

▲ Mosites Rubber Company Inc ....E 817 335-3451
Fort Worth *(G-6854)*

◆ National Hose Aquisition Corp ....D 713 920-2030
Pasadena *(G-16487)*

Neb Products LLC ....G 281 528-9428
Spring *(G-19154)*

Next Gen Compounding LLC ....E 972 602-9717
Grand Prairie *(G-7934)*

▲ Nipples Elbows & Couplings Inc ....E 281 405-8240
Houston *(G-11059)*

Ogburn Truck Parts LP ....F 281 331-0005
Alvin *(G-375)*

Oil States Industries Inc ....E 512 556-5471
Lampasas *(G-13835)*

Old Nocona Boot Factory LLC ....F 682 237-7644
Roanoke *(G-17491)*

Paco Label Systems Inc ....F 903 561-2125
Tyler *(G-20137)*
Pamco Ltd ....E 713 621-0002
Houston *(G-11226)*
Parco Double-E LLC ....D 214 631-2290
Dallas *(G-4788)*
Parker-Hannifin Corporation ....C 936 560-8900
Nacogdoches *(G-15708)*
Performance Elastomers Inc ....G 817 293-7503
Fort Worth *(G-6903)*
Pheasant Rubber Company Inc ....F 432 367-5137
Odessa *(G-16122)*
▲ Prestige Ameritech Ltd ....B 817 427-2700
North Richland Hills *(G-15879)*
Pugh Acquisition Company ....E 361 884-9351
Corpus Christi *(G-3600)*
R-Interests LLC ....F 940 759-4181
Muenster *(G-15672)*
▲ Ranco Industries Inc ....E 713 228-5543
Houston *(G-11540)*
Ranco Rhino Mats & Matting ....F 713 228-5543
Houston *(G-11541)*
Republic Tube LLC ....C 832 672-6000
Houston *(G-11603)*
◆ Rex-Hide Incorporated ....F 903 593-7387
Tyler *(G-20146)*
Roy Johnson Incorporated ....E 817 468-2939
Arlington *(G-773)*
Rumber Materials Incorporated ....G 940 759-4181
Muenster *(G-15673)*
◆ S & B Technical Products Inc ....D 800 432-8213
Fort Worth *(G-6970)*
Spirit Industries Inc ....E 936 597-5144
Montgomery *(G-15641)*
State Rbr Envmtl Solutions LLC ....E 806 592-3803
Denver City *(G-5424)*
Supreme Manufacturing Company ....F 281 447-3153
Houston *(G-12123)*
SW Foam LLC ....E 915 751-1000
El Paso *(G-5989)*
▲ Tacki Mac Grips ....G 281 358-6738
Humble *(G-12800)*
Texas Medplast LLC ....F 832 288-2106
Houston *(G-12240)*
▲ Titan Bop Rubber Products Inc ....E 713 895-9230
Houston *(G-12295)*
US Machinery Parts Sales Inc ....E 972 551-3551
Mesquite *(G-15084)*
Valley Roller Company Inc ....F 817 453-8950
Mansfield *(G-14726)*
▲ Wesmar Corporation ....E 915 599-1572
El Paso *(G-6029)*
▼ Western Falcon LLC ....E 832 391-9461
Houston *(G-12643)*
Woodbridge Sales & Engrg Inc ....C 915 751-1000
El Paso *(G-6040)*

3081 Plastic Unsupported Sheet & Film

3M Company ....A 325 643-9798
Brownwood *(G-2423)*
Aerowindtech Inc ....F 817 438-4777
Mansfield *(G-14652)*
Akrotex Films Inc ....E 409 886-0632
Orange *(G-16229)*
▼ Akrotex Films Inc ....E 409 886-0111
Orange *(G-16230)*
Akrotex Films Inc ....E 409 886-0063
West Orange *(G-20692)*
◆ Amtopp Corporation ....B 361 874-3000
Lolita *(G-14173)*
Berry Global Films LLC ....C 972 576-8193
Waxahachie *(G-20529)*
◆ C E Shepherd Company LP ....D 713 924-4300
Houston *(G-9028)*
Cooper Supply Inc ....E 817 222-9055
Fort Worth *(G-6548)*
Curbell Plastics Inc ....E 214 239-3870
Arlington *(G-654)*
▼ Fresh-Pak Corp ....C 713 690-8742
Houston *(G-9866)*
◆ GSE Environmental Inc ....D 281 443-8564
Houston *(G-10053)*
▼ GSE Holding Inc ....C 281 443-8564
Houston *(G-10054)*
GSE International Inc ....F 281 443-8564
Houston *(G-10055)*
◆ Handgards LLC ....C 915 779-6606
El Paso *(G-5794)*
Hercules Films LLC ....G 920 284-0796
Sugar Land *(G-19491)*
Hercules Films LLC ....F 920 284-0796
Sugar Land *(G-19492)*
▲ Huntsman Corporation ....E 281 719-6000
The Woodlands *(G-19877)*
◆ Huntsman International LLC ....D 281 719-6000
The Woodlands *(G-19878)*
Illinois Tool Works Inc ....D 713 996-4200
Houston *(G-10325)*
◆ Innovative Gas Systems Inc ....D 713 937-5200
Houston *(G-10370)*
▲ Integrted Bagging Systems Corp ....F 361 874-3000
Lolita *(G-14175)*
Inteplast Group Corporation ....D 361 874-3000
Lolita *(G-14176)*
◆ Kaneka North America LLC ....C 281 474-7084
Pasadena *(G-16468)*
▲ Komplete Group Inc ....D 214 252-8100
Grand Prairie *(G-7907)*
◆ Kuraray America Inc ....E 800 423-9762
Houston *(G-10571)*
◆ Marco Dsplay Specialists GP Lc ....C 817 244-8300
Fort Worth *(G-6810)*
Marian Fort Worth Inc ....E 817 332-6151
Fort Worth *(G-6811)*
Nan Ya Plastics Corp USA ....C 979 532-5494
Wharton *(G-20704)*
Orbis Rpm LLC ....F 940 387-6711
Denton *(G-5386)*
Plastiform Inc ....F 972 579-8803
Irving *(G-13150)*
◆ Poly-America LP ....A 972 337-7100
Grand Prairie *(G-7948)*
Poly-America LP ....C 972 337-7107
Grand Prairie *(G-7949)*
◆ Polytex Fibers Corp ....C 713 690-9055
Houston *(G-11362)*
Printpack Inc ....C 409 883-9325
Orange *(G-16257)*
Printpack Inc ....E 972 641-4421
Grand Prairie *(G-7956)*
▼ Reef Industries Inc ....E 713 507-4200
Houston *(G-11577)*
Reef Industries Inc ....D 713 507-4329
Houston *(G-11578)*
▲ Republic Plastics Ltd ....E 830 557-5574
Mc Queeney *(G-14830)*
Revolution Plastics LLC ....C 903 984-8596
Kilgore *(G-13586)*
Rodeo Plastic Bag & Film LLC ....D 972 216-3331
Mesquite *(G-15075)*
◆ Samsill Corporation ....C 817 536-1906
Fort Worth *(G-6972)*
Select Plastics LLC ....E 817 595-3804
Fort Worth *(G-6982)*
Selectouch Corporation ....E 972 924-3289
Anna *(G-585)*
◆ Solmax Geosynthetics LLC ....B 281 443-8564
Houston *(G-11941)*
Sonoco Products Company ....D 254 666-4777
Waco *(G-20458)*
◆ Super Sack Bag Inc ....F 214 340-7060
Dallas *(G-5024)*
Supplynet Inc ....E 484 582-1004
Dallas *(G-5028)*
Supplynet Inc ....D 214 637-0160
Dallas *(G-5029)*
Transcendia Inc ....E 800 659-4254
Carrollton *(G-2838)*
Tru-Vision Plastics Inc ....F 979 836-1091
Brenham *(G-2276)*
V-Kool Inc ....G 713 856-8333
Houston *(G-12512)*
▲ Winzen Film Inc ....E 214 340-7060
Dallas *(G-5198)*

3082 Plastic Unsupported Profile Shapes

Borger Oil Chemical Indus Plas ....F 806 273-9518
Borger *(G-2165)*
Bryan Container Company Inc ....G 979 822-7998
Bryan *(G-2463)*
Dlhbowles Inc ....D 956 986-6000
Brownsville *(G-2350)*
Gray Sales Inc ....G 361 527-4460
Hebbronville *(G-8234)*
Hancor Inc ....E 361 293-6313
Yoakum *(G-20967)*
Medical Extrusion Tech Inc ....E 951 698-4346
Lewisville *(G-14063)*
Polytex Fibers International ....B 713 690-9055
Houston *(G-11363)*
▲ S H Leggitt Company ....C 956 504-6440
San Marcos *(G-18708)*
SMI-Carr Inc ....F 325 677-0491
Abilene *(G-80)*

3083 Plastic Laminated Plate & Sheet

Advanced Drainage Systems Inc ....D 972 878-9600
Ennis *(G-6087)*
◆ Atco Rubber Products Inc ....A 817 595-2894
Fort Worth *(G-6406)*
Avey Plastics ....F 512 784-7047
San Marcos *(G-18678)*
Composite Lining Systems LP ....C 432 617-0242
Midland *(G-15174)*
Consolidated Armor Pdts LLC ....E 214 382-4100
Addison *(G-113)*
Coverlay Manufacturing Inc ....E 325 659-4697
San Angelo *(G-17791)*
◆ Delfingen Us-Texas LP ....E 915 858-5577
El Paso *(G-5717)*
Federal-Mogul Powertrain LLC ....B 915 860-2300
El Paso *(G-5767)*
Hull Supply Company Inc ....E 512 385-1262
Austin *(G-1213)*
◆ ITW Minigrip Inc ....C 830 372-4400
Seguin *(G-18845)*
Johnnies Plastics Inc ....E 210 533-8463
San Antonio *(G-18205)*
Lamrite ....F 512 385-4455
Austin *(G-1281)*
Medical Plastics Laboratory ....B 254 865-7221
Gatesville *(G-7619)*
Millennium Plastics Tech LLC ....E 915 834-2700
El Paso *(G-5878)*
▲ Panel Specialists Inc ....D 254 774-9800
Temple *(G-19695)*
Plastic Specialties & Tech Inc ....D 254 772-6979
Waco *(G-20447)*
Port City Inc ....E 713 673-7272
Houston *(G-11365)*
Precision Sheet Metal Shop Inc ....D 972 771-1423
Rockwall *(G-17561)*
Proske Plastic Products Inc ....E 713 926-9941
Houston *(G-11461)*
Prototype Machine Co ....E 512 282-1590
Manchaca *(G-14641)*
▼ Reef Industries Inc ....E 713 507-4200
Houston *(G-11577)*
Reef Industries Inc ....D 713 507-4329
Houston *(G-11578)*
Reef Industries Inc ....D 956 399-1352
San Benito *(G-18663)*
▼ Research Advanced Methods Inds ....E 254 442-1008
Cisco *(G-3068)*
▲ S G & P Incorporated ....F 979 233-7491
Freeport *(G-7209)*
Skylights Over Texas LLC ....F 210 402-0500
San Antonio *(G-18478)*
Southanchor Manufacturing LLC ....E 915 590-6718
El Paso *(G-5970)*
▼ Technology Container Corp ....E 972 228-1617
Desoto *(G-5444)*
▲ Texas Nameplate Company Inc ....D 214 428-8341
Lancaster *(G-13849)*
Therm-All Inc ....F 214 630-4800
Dallas *(G-5084)*
Timesaver Templates Inc ....F 972 620-2197
Dallas *(G-5095)*

3084 Plastic Pipe

Advanced Drainage Systems Inc ....D 972 878-9600
Ennis *(G-6087)*
Atco Rubber Products Inc ....E 713 674-6665
Houston *(G-8732)*
◆ Atco Rubber Products Inc ....A 817 595-2894
Fort Worth *(G-6406)*
Blue Diamond Industries LLC ....E 859 224-0415
Aubrey *(G-847)*
Border Tm Industries Inc ....C 915 779-6431
El Paso *(G-5671)*
Cantex Inc ....F 817 215-7000
Mineral Wells *(G-15520)*
Cantex Inc ....B 940 325-3344
Mineral Wells *(G-15521)*
◆ Cantex Inc ....D 817 215-7000
Fort Worth *(G-6491)*
◆ Centron International Inc ....C 940 328-1032
Mineral Wells *(G-15522)*
Certainteed Corporation ....D 800 233-8990
Waco *(G-20382)*

S I C

Charlotte Pipe and Foundry Co ....E 254 697-6556
Cameron *(G-2641)*

▲ Chevron Phillips Chem Co LP ....A 832 813-4100
The Woodlands *(G-19845)*

Co-Ex Pipe Co ....E 432 263-0206
Big Spring *(G-2077)*

Cresline Plastic Pipe Co Inc ....E 903 872-7418
Corsicana *(G-3667)*

Diamond Plastics Corporation ....D 806 763-8021
Lubbock *(G-14405)*

◆ Exquip USA Llc ....F 936 372-3002
Hockley *(G-8343)*

◆ Fiber Glass Systems LP ....D 210 477-7500
San Antonio *(G-18112)*

◆ Fiberspar Corporation ....F 713 849-2609
Houston *(G-9784)*

◆ Future Pipe Industries Inc ....C 281 847-2987
Houston *(G-9879)*

G B Manufacturing Inc ....E 713 681-5837
Houston *(G-9885)*

Hancor Inc ....E 361 293-6313
Yoakum *(G-20967)*

▲ Hobas Pipe Usa Inc ....C 281 821-2200
Houston *(G-10190)*

◆ Industrial Pipe Fittings LLC ....F 800 241-4175
Stafford *(G-19328)*

J P C Plastics Inc ....F 325 672-2895
Abilene *(G-53)*

N A Petroflex Ltd ....E 800 433-5711
Gainesville *(G-7350)*

◆ North American Pipe Corp ....C 855 624-7473
Houston *(G-11073)*

North American Pipe Corp ....D 940 855-4100
Wichita Falls *(G-20787)*

▲ Nupi Americas Inc ....F 281 590-4471
Houston *(G-11099)*

▲ Plastic Tubing Inds Texas Inc ......F 979 921-9990
Hempstead *(G-8255)*

Polyflow LLC ....E 432 686-2001
Midland *(G-15361)*

Polyone Corporation ....C 281 474-2831
Seabrook *(G-18789)*

Pw Eagle Inc ....E 979 532-5640
Wharton *(G-20705)*

Western AG Sales Co Inc ....E 806 293-2517
Plainview *(G-16767)*

▲ Westlake Pvc Corporation ....C 713 960-9111
Houston *(G-12653)*

WL Plastics Corporation ....E 325 574-6100
Snyder *(G-19014)*

Wl Plastics Corporation ....D 940 872-8300
Bowie *(G-2202)*

3085 Plastic Bottles

Bkh Enterprises LLC ....D 979 743-6577
Schulenburg *(G-18772)*

▲ Cal Sierra International LLC ....F 832 615-6002
Houston *(G-9047)*

CKS Packaging Inc ....C 817 924-2205
Fort Worth *(G-6521)*

CKS Packaging Inc ....E 214 358-2441
Dallas *(G-4125)*

Graham Packaging Company LP ....C 713 869-5471
Houston *(G-10013)*

Houston Kik Inc ....C 713 747-8710
Houston *(G-10236)*

Paragon Packaging Inc ....E 817 477-5211
Mansfield *(G-14701)*

Plastcos Arco Iris of San Antn ....E 210 308-6500
San Antonio *(G-18381)*

Plastic Industries Inc ....D 817 477-5211
Mansfield *(G-14703)*

Plastipak Packaging Inc ....C 972 276-8660
Garland *(G-7568)*

Polymers Sales & Logistics LLC ....F 281 874-8072
Houston *(G-11359)*

Ringwood Containers LP ....E 817 625-7214
Fort Worth *(G-6960)*

Thomas Plastics Inc ....D 817 654-3238
Fort Worth *(G-7057)*

▲ Western Container Corporation ......B 346 309-3238
Sugar Land *(G-19572)*

Western Container Corporation ....C 432 263-8361
Big Spring *(G-2103)*

Western Container Corporation ....C 713 691-0730
Houston *(G-12642)*

3086 Plastic Foam Prdts

Acme Brick Company ....D 817 332-4101
El Paso *(G-5636)*

American Excelsior Company ....E 817 385-4300
Arlington *(G-616)*

Atlas Roofing Corporation ....C 903 645-3988
Daingerfield *(G-3830)*

Atlas Roofing Corporation ....E 936 829-5279
Diboll *(G-5461)*

▲ Bags Elite Inc ....E 972 279-7798
Mesquite *(G-15029)*

▲ Blacksheep Inc ....B 903 592-3853
Tyler *(G-20059)*

◆ Blakeman Industries Inc ....E 817 267-4444
Euless *(G-6133)*

Carlisle Construction Mtls LLC ....E 214 515-5200
Terrell *(G-19730)*

Carpenter Co ....D 254 778-0131
Temple *(G-19674)*

Carpenter Co ....E 214 330-0373
Dallas *(G-4085)*

Champion Pallet & Packaging ....E 972 551-2474
Irving *(G-12968)*

▲ Cnc Plastics ....C 979 884-0608
Giddings *(G-7693)*

◆ Concote Corporation ....C 214 956-0077
Coppell *(G-3412)*

Concote Corporation ....F 903 581-0697
Tyler *(G-20070)*

Cryovac LLC ....F 940 851-6060
Wichita Falls *(G-20758)*

◆ Diab Holdings Inc ....E 972 228-7600
Desoto *(G-5429)*

Dolco Packaging Corp ....C 214 337-4711
Dallas *(G-4271)*

E R Carpenter LP ....C 281 474-7257
Pasadena *(G-16422)*

E R Carpenter LP ....E 804 359-0800
Dallas *(G-4284)*

◆ E R Carpenter LP ....E 804 359-0800
Temple *(G-19680)*

Epe Industries Usa Inc ....E 800 315-0336
Houston *(G-9679)*

F3 Foam LLC ....G 936 661-3172
Montgomery *(G-15633)*

Fairbanks Packaging LLC ....G 817 849-1366
Grand Prairie *(G-7869)*

Fgl Group LLC ....E 817 478-3221
Garland *(G-7489)*

Foam Fabricators Inc ....F 817 379-6520
Keller *(G-13467)*

Foam Pak US LP ....D 832 212-8896
Houston *(G-9829)*

Foam Supplies Inc ....E 972 436-7008
Lewisville *(G-14050)*

◆ Foampack US ....E 281 565-9619
Stafford *(G-19314)*

▲ Fresno Manfacturing LLC ....D 281 437-6000
Fresno *(G-7237)*

Future Foam Inc ....C 214 350-6611
Dallas *(G-4386)*

Future Foam Inc ....E 214 905-6043
Dallas *(G-4387)*

Great Lakes Textiles Inc ....F 713 670-9700
Houston *(G-10027)*

▲ Greif Flexibles USA Inc ....E 713 461-0840
Houston *(G-10040)*

Guardian Packaging Inds LP ....E 214 349-1500
Garland *(G-7507)*

Harris Packaging Corporation ....D 817 429-6262
Haltom City *(G-8148)*

◆ Heubach Corporation ....E 214 291-0238
Garland *(G-7511)*

◆ Houston Foam Plastics Inc ....C 713 224-3484
Houston *(G-10234)*

Houston R-Co Incorporated ....E 281 987-9909
Houston *(G-10248)*

Huntington Foam LLC ....E 512 581-7500
Bastrop *(G-1758)*

Igloo Products Corp ....B 713 461-5955
Katy *(G-13364)*

◆ Igloo Products Corp ....A 281 394-6800
Katy *(G-13365)*

Industrial Insul & Shtmtl Inc ....E 432 332-8203
Odessa *(G-16030)*

Innocor Foam Tech - Acp Inc ....F 972 563-1559
Terrell *(G-19738)*

▲ Innocor Form Tech Brenham LLC ....F 732 945-6222
Brenham *(G-2258)*

◆ Inovar Packaging Group LLC ....F 817 277-6666
Dallas *(G-4504)*

Johnson County Foam Inc ....E 817 477-5061
Mansfield *(G-14684)*

Jones Holt Enterprises Inc ....E 210 657-5917
San Antonio *(G-18207)*

L B Foster Company ....E 832 934-3107
Magnolia *(G-14613)*

Lifoam Industries LLC ....D 972 937-6512
Waxahachie *(G-20551)*

Nppi Intermediate Inc ....E 512 476-7100
Austin *(G-1371)*

Orange County Industrial Inc ....G 409 697-3559
Orange *(G-16255)*

▲ P Diamond Enterprises Inc ....F 325 643-5629
Brownwood *(G-2441)*

Pactiv LLC ....E 903 654-4745
Corsicana *(G-3683)*

Pactiv LLC ....G 254 770-4100
Temple *(G-19693)*

Pbp Inc ....E 832 902-2231
Baytown *(G-1799)*

▲ Pipeline Seal & Insulator Inc ....D 713 747-6948
Houston *(G-11336)*

Pmc Inc ....C 817 695-5680
Arlington *(G-754)*

Polly Knapp Pig Inc ....E 713 222-0146
Houston *(G-11355)*

Port City Inc ....E 713 673-7272
Houston *(G-11365)*

Quality Cases & Containers LLC ....F 972 690-9911
Richardson *(G-17379)*

▼ Reef Industries Inc ....E 713 507-4200
Houston *(G-11577)*

Reef Industries Inc ....D 713 507-4329
Houston *(G-11578)*

▲ Republic Plastics Ltd ....E 830 557-5574
Mc Queeney *(G-14830)*

◆ Rilco Manufacturing Co Inc ....C 713 466-4777
Houston *(G-11624)*

Rivercity Waterjet Inc ....F 210 590-0300
San Antonio *(G-18428)*

Rohart Company ....E 713 695-5333
Houston *(G-11657)*

Sealed Air Corporation ....D 940 851-6060
Wichita Falls *(G-20806)*

Sealed Air Corporation ....D 817 540-2020
Grand Prairie *(G-7972)*

Sealed Air Corporation ....D 940 592-2111
Iowa Park *(G-12910)*

SES Foam LLC ....E 713 239-0252
Spring *(G-19165)*

Sika Corporation ....C 972 387-4500
Dallas *(G-4963)*

Southwestern Foam Tech Inc ....F 254 939-6379
Belton *(G-2028)*

◆ Tasus Texas Corporation ....C 512 869-7766
Georgetown *(G-7683)*

▲ Texas Foam Inc ....E 512 581-7500
Bastrop *(G-1763)*

Thermafoam Operating LLC ....E 254 582-2730
Hillsboro *(G-8331)*

◆ TRC Recreation LP ....E 940 322-4463
Wichita Falls *(G-20820)*

Tuffys AC & Htg Svc Inc ....F 817 596-0150
Weatherford *(G-20627)*

Ufp Technologies Inc ....E 915 598-7377
El Paso *(G-6018)*

Western Industries Corporation ....D 214 503-8322
Carrollton *(G-2848)*

Western Industries Corporation ....E 512 837-0240
Austin *(G-1658)*

Whitehorse Manufacturing Co ....F 512 376-2112
Kyle *(G-13688)*

Williams Products Inc ....F 214 630-3131
Arlington *(G-809)*

▲ Wna Cups Illustrated Inc ....C 972 224-8407
Lancaster *(G-13850)*

◆ Yeti Coolers LLC ....C 512 394-9384
Austin *(G-1680)*

Yeti Holdings Inc ....E 512 394-8220
Austin *(G-1681)*

Z Fab USA Inc ....F 817 380-1156
Fort Worth *(G-7159)*

3087 Custom Compounding Of Purchased Plastic Resins

Adaptive 3d Technologies LLC ....E 469 573-0024
Plano *(G-16770)*

▲ Chemtrusion Inc ....D 713 675-1616
Houston *(G-9173)*

E R Carpenter LP ....C 281 474-7257
Pasadena *(G-16422)*

Hexpol Compounding LLC.................D....... 817 483-9797
Kennedale (G-13498)

Marble Masters of Texas Inc............E....... 830 303-7744
New Braunfels (G-15811)

Miller Waste Mills Inc......................D....... 817 293-6163
Fort Worth (G-6842)

▲ Orrex Plastics Company LLC.........E....... 432 332-1229
Odessa (G-16104)

Polyone Corporation.......................C....... 281 474-2831
Seabrook (G-18789)

Purchasing Dept.............................F....... 956 318-2626
Edinburg (G-5598)

Ticona Polymers Inc.......................C....... 972 443-4000
Dallas (G-5091)

3088 Plastic Plumbing Fixtures

▲ American Acrylic Injection Inc.......E....... 972 784-7759
Farmersville (G-6221)

Aquatic Co......................................F....... 817 801-8300
Arlington (G-621)

Aquatic Co......................................C....... 972 227-6692
Lancaster (G-13838)

Aries Acrylic Mfg Inc.......................F....... 972 771-6286
Rockwall (G-17538)

Border States Industries Inc............E....... 432 332-0591
Odessa (G-15940)

Border States Industries Inc............F....... 432 520-0230
Midland (G-15147)

Border States Industries Inc............F....... 325 698-4595
Abilene (G-23)

Border States Industries Inc............F....... 512 458-6313
Austin (G-1001)

Border States Industries Inc............F....... 325 655-9163
San Angelo (G-17785)

Border States Industries Inc............F....... 806 457-4100
Amarillo (G-409)

Border States Industries Inc............F....... 806 765-5741
Lubbock (G-14379)

Border States Industries Inc............F....... 956 831-3441
Brownsville (G-2339)

Border States Industries Inc............F....... 575 434-2022
El Paso (G-5670)

◆ Clarke Products Inc......................C....... 972 660-1992
Colleyville (G-3212)

Dal-Tex Specialty & Mfg Co.............F....... 903 883-3689
Greenville (G-8070)

◆ Eljer Industries Inc......................E....... 972 560-2000
Dallas (G-4311)

Ganten Group LLC...........................F....... 214 530-5483
Richardson (G-17320)

Hoskin & Muir Inc...........................F....... 817 640-7220
Arlington (G-700)

Killeen Marble.................................E....... 254 699-3408
Killeen (G-13612)

▲ Kinro Composties..........................C....... 800 262-8827
Waxahachie (G-20548)

▲ L F Manufacturing Inc..................D....... 979 542-8027
Giddings (G-7699)

Mansfield Plumbing Pdts LLC...........D....... 903 657-1436
Henderson (G-8267)

▲ Niagara Conservation Corp...........E....... 817 391-0800
Flower Mound (G-6275)

▲ Palmer of Texas Tanks Inc...........D....... 432 523-5904
Andrews (G-556)

Perfect Surface of Austin.................F....... 512 339-9937
Austin (G-1411)

Prolux LLC......................................F....... 801 955-7070
Grand Prairie (G-7957)

Proske Plastic Products Inc.............E....... 713 926-9941
Houston (G-11461)

Ralph Cordova Company..................E....... 972 771-7281
Royse City (G-17725)

RC Christopher Industries Inc..........E....... 972 875-6555
Ennis (G-6116)

Sunbelt Hot Tubs LLC.....................C....... 281 575-9814
Houston (G-12098)

Sustain Ability Solutions Inc............F....... 888 657-7582
Flower Mound (G-6285)

Swc Industries Inc..........................D....... 903 657-1436
Henderson (G-8274)

▲ Tex-Lam Manufacturing Inc..........E....... 713 695-5975
Houston (G-12216)

▲ TW Tanks and Construction Co.....F....... 361 358-8869
Beeville (G-1989)

Venetian Marble Co Lubbock Inc......F....... 806 763-5777
Lubbock (G-14506)

▲ W & W Fiberglass Tank Company....D....... 806 669-1128
Pampa (G-16344)

3089 Plastic Prdts

▲ 3d Plastics LLC............................D....... 903 844-9333
Gladewater (G-7716)

▲ 3p Performance Plastics Pdts.........F....... 281 537-8816
Houston (G-8410)

A & M Composites Corporation.........E....... 432 267-6525
Big Spring (G-2068)

A & M Plastics Inc..........................G....... 713 941-1033
South Houston (G-19036)

▼ A B C Plastic Molding Inc.............E....... 713 692-9122
Houston (G-8424)

▼ Accredo Packaging Inc.................D....... 713 580-4800
Sugar Land (G-19436)

Acrylic Source................................E....... 800 275-0316
Arlington (G-609)

▲ Advance Fiberglass LLC................F....... 956 544-1000
Brownsville (G-2335)

Advanced Drainage Systems Inc.......F....... 361 293-6313
Yoakum (G-20958)

Advanced Pedestals Ltd...................D....... 940 668-7283
Gainesville (G-7333)

Aer Manufacturing LP......................F....... 972 392-4130
Addison (G-101)

Aerostar International Inc.................E....... 903 885-0728
Sulphur Springs (G-19578)

Airborn Interconnect Inc..................E....... 903 629-7821
Winnsboro (G-20895)

▲ Aire Plastics Inc..........................F....... 830 779-2289
La Vernia (G-13800)

All Plastic LLC................................D....... 830 896-6464
Kerrville (G-13517)

▲ All-Plastics LLC............................D....... 972 239-2686
Addison (G-102)

▲ Allflex Usa Inc.............................D....... 972 456-3686
Dallas (G-3924)

▲ Alpha Plastics Inc........................E....... 281 564-8838
Sugar Land (G-19441)

Altium Packaging............................E....... 281 391-4244
Katy (G-13349)

Altium Packaging............................E....... 817 491-9229
Fort Worth (G-6375)

Altium Packaging............................G....... 214 333-4179
Dallas (G-3934)

Altium Packaging............................E....... 903 870-7080
Sherman (G-18905)

Altium Packaging LP........................D....... 678 742-4600
Houston (G-8569)

Amcor Rigid Packaging Usa LLC........D....... 817 267-5917
Fort Worth (G-6377)

America Plastics LLC.......................C....... 972 245-4525
Carrollton (G-2697)

▲ America Samkwang Inc.................E....... 956 686-0221
McAllen (G-14838)

American Tietek LLC........................E....... 903 503-5538
Marshall (G-14760)

Amphion Inc....................................E....... 210 771-8116
San Antonio (G-17906)

▲ Apex Plastics & Tooling Inc...........E....... 972 205-9000
Garland (G-7438)

Arlon Inc..E....... 210 798-1900
San Antonio (G-17914)

Atlantis Plastic Company.................F....... 713 643-8387
Houston (G-8742)

Atrium Extrusion Systems Inc...........A....... 903 455-8560
Greenville (G-8062)

▲ Atrium Windows and Doors Inc.....D....... 214 583-1840
Dallas (G-3983)

▲ Atron Group LLC..........................E....... 214 292-9840
Dallas (G-3984)

Axion Strl Innovations LLC...............D....... 254 420-2078
Waco (G-20365)

Bace Manufacturing Inc...................C....... 713 329-8954
Houston (G-8786)

Bace Manufacturing Inc...................C....... 713 466-5563
Houston (G-8787)

Baileys Premier Services LLC...........F....... 817 292-2423
Fort Worth (G-6419)

▲ Ballqube Lc.................................E....... 903 863-5572
Cushing (G-3767)

Basler Plastics LLC.........................G....... 512 392-2800
San Marcos (G-18679)

Bayland Inc.....................................F....... 281 489-1930
Manvel (G-14732)

Bee Jay Molding Inc........................F....... 830 249-2425
Boerne (G-2114)

Bee Jay Molding Inc........................E....... 281 487-0377
Pasadena (G-16397)

Belco Manufacturing Co Inc.............C....... 254 933-9000
Belton (G-2019)

Bentley Consultants Co Inc..............F....... 972 289-2750
Mesquite (G-15032)

Berry Global Inc..............................C....... 409 794-1011
Beaumont (G-1863)

Berry Global Inc..............................C....... 361 575-9565
Victoria (G-20246)

Berry Global Films LLC....................C....... 972 576-8193
Waxahachie (G-20529)

BG Absolute....................................F....... 409 724-0300
Nederland (G-15746)

▲ Blackwell Plastics LP....................E....... 713 643-6577
Houston (G-8912)

Blossom Machine & Mfg Inc.............E....... 903 982-5500
Blossom (G-2112)

Brazosport Plastics Inc....................G....... 979 849-5422
Angleton (G-566)

Brown Precision Inc.........................G....... 530 384-2506
Cameron (G-2639)

C & G Plastics Inc...........................F....... 972 254-2541
Irving (G-12955)

◆ C E Shepherd Company LP............D....... 713 924-4300
Houston (G-9028)

Cadillac Fabrication........................F....... 713 910-2200
Houston (G-9045)

◆ Cantex Inc...................................F....... 817 215-7000
Fort Worth (G-6491)

Capco Plastics Inc..........................F....... 915 772-1395
El Paso (G-5679)

▲ Caprock Manufacturing Inc...........E....... 806 745-6454
Lubbock (G-14389)

Capsonic Group LLC........................E....... 915 872-3539
El Paso (G-5681)

Caraustar Industries Inc..................E....... 903 793-6231
Texarkana (G-19758)

▲ Carbon Silica Partners LP..............D....... 361 572-4040
Victoria (G-20251)

Carthage Cup Co.............................G....... 903 693-7151
Carthage (G-2902)

Cascade Engineering Inc..................B....... 817 490-6300
Fort Worth (G-6494)

Caterpillar Work Tools Inc................D....... 254 297-2321
Waco (G-20378)

◆ Centron International Inc..............C....... 940 328-1032
Mineral Wells (G-15522)

Charlotte Pipe and Foundry Co.........E....... 254 697-6556
Cameron (G-2641)

Chem-Pruf Door Co Ltd....................D....... 956 544-1000
Brownsville (G-2346)

▲ Chemplast Inc.............................E....... 281 208-2585
Stafford (G-19294)

▲ Chevron Phillips Chem Co LP.........A....... 832 813-4100
The Woodlands (G-19845)

CKS Packaging Inc..........................C....... 817 924-2205
Fort Worth (G-6521)

CKS Packaging Inc..........................E....... 214 358-2441
Dallas (G-4125)

Clarion Tech Lonestar Inc................D....... 972 278-9700
Garland (G-7457)

▲ Cni...F....... 830 765-7484
Del Rio (G-5312)

Coastal Plastic Molding Inc..............F....... 281 331-7909
Alvin (G-356)

Complete Plastic Fabricators............F....... 713 674-7686
Houston (G-9259)

Consolidated Armor Pdts LLC...........E....... 214 382-4100
Addison (G-113)

Consolidated Containment LLC.........E....... 409 781-4254
Beaumont (G-1876)

Contemporary Design Plastics...........E....... 817 640-7539
Arlington (G-646)

Cool Cruisers of Texas.....................F....... 972 772-5517
Rockwall (G-17545)

▲ Core Pacific Inc...........................F....... 800 860-1637
Houston (G-9318)

Covalnce Spcalty Adhesives LLC.......E....... 713 676-0085
Houston (G-9331)

Coverlay Manufacturing Inc..............E....... 325 659-4697
San Angelo (G-17791)

CPI Products LLC.............................E....... 877 756-2388
Burnet (G-2605)

Creative MENus&folders LLC............F....... 254 653-2775
Olden (G-16219)

Cs Manufacturing Inc......................G....... 281 442-3400
Houston (G-9353)

CT Greggs and Sons LLC..................E....... 972 333-1960
Flower Mound (G-6264)

Curtis Technical Service Inc.............F....... 979 388-0007
Clute (G-3151)

D & L Tooling and Plastics Inc..........E....... 903 586-9894
Jacksonville (G-13234)

D/Fw Plastics Inc	F	817 439-3600	
Saginaw *(G-17745)*			
Dallas Rosti Inc	F	972 554-1597	
Irving *(G-12990)*			
Dalworth Technologies Inc	G	817 297-7976	
Crowley *(G-3754)*			
David Keels	E	409 316-9265	
Hitchcock *(G-8336)*			
◆ Daxwell LLC	E	281 669-0622	
Houston *(G-9411)*			
▲ Dcm Manufacturing Inc	E	817 428-3636	
Grand Prairie *(G-7862)*			
Dcu Inc	F	972 816-6667	
Wylie *(G-20932)*			
◆ Delfingen Us-Texas LP	E	915 858-5577	
El Paso *(G-5717)*			
Dement Plastics LLC	E	903 586-9894	
Jacksonville *(G-13236)*			
Denton Door Company Inc	F	940 891-0600	
Denton *(G-5358)*			
Detroit Forming Inc	F	903 832-4653	
Nash *(G-15721)*			
◆ Dexas International Ltd	D	469 635-8100	
Coppell *(G-3415)*			
Diamond Plastics Corporation	D	806 763-8021	
Lubbock *(G-14405)*			
Dlhbowles Inc	D	956 986-6000	
Brownsville *(G-2350)*			
E & T Plastic Mfg Co Inc	F	214 622-6263	
Dallas *(G-4283)*			
E G C Corporation	B	281 774-6100	
Humble *(G-12764)*			
Edwards Sptic Grease Trck Svcs	F	903 643-7585	
Kilgore *(G-13549)*			
Emu Plastics Tex Limited Inc	E	956 618-5200	
McAllen *(G-14859)*			
▲ Enduro Composites Inc	D	713 358-4000	
Houston *(G-9630)*			
Ensinger Special Polymers Inc	E	281 580-3600	
Houston *(G-9659)*			
Entegris Inc	B	940 393-4232	
Decatur *(G-5246)*			
▲ Epak International Inc	A	512 231-8083	
Austin *(G-1128)*			
Epsilon Industries Inc	F	469 573-9566	
Garland *(G-7488)*			
▲ Exel Bobbins & Plas Components	E	956 832-0807	
Brownsville *(G-2355)*			
▲ F & F Composite Group Inc	E	817 379-4411	
Fort Worth *(G-6622)*			
◆ Fiber Glass Systems LP	D	210 477-7500	
San Antonio *(G-18112)*			
Fibergrate Composite	D	254 977-1302	
Stephenville *(G-19411)*			
Fibergrate Composite	D	254 965-3148	
Greenville *(G-8072)*			
Fibergrate Composite	C	254 965-3148	
Stephenville *(G-19412)*			
◆ Fibergrate Composite	E	972 250-1633	
Dallas *(G-4360)*			
Fireplace Installers Inc	D	713 937-4575	
Houston *(G-9789)*			
▲ Fischbach Texas LP	F	469 533-5500	
Dallas *(G-4365)*			
◆ Fittings Inc	D	817 332-3300	
Fort Worth *(G-6634)*			
▼ Formtex Plastics Corporation	E	713 493-6628	
Houston *(G-9836)*			
Fox Valley Molding Inc	E	956 428-2506	
Harlingen *(G-8189)*			
Franks Manufacturing Co	F	210 492-3222	
San Antonio *(G-18125)*			
▼ Freeman David Products Inc	E	866 310-2556	
Burnet *(G-2608)*			
◆ Future Pipe Industries Inc	C	281 847-2987	
Houston *(G-9879)*			
Futurefab Inc	F	972 423-6606	
Plano *(G-16876)*			
▼ Fwave LLC	F	817 754-9021	
Burleson *(G-2579)*			
G Kustoms Auto Customizing LLC	F	682 703-1583	
Fort Worth *(G-6658)*			
Gabhen Inc	F	512 832-7902	
Austin *(G-1177)*			
Gajeske Inc	F	972 314-8100	
Grand Prairie *(G-7881)*			
▲ Gamma2 LLC	E	760 734-4003	
Arlington *(G-685)*			
Gate-Mold Inc	F	512 255-3470	
Round Rock *(G-17659)*			
Gemini Incorporated	F	507 263-3957	
Hidalgo *(G-8308)*			
◆ General Technologies Inc	E	281 240-0550	
Stafford *(G-19321)*			
Genpak LLC	C	903 297-4445	
Longview *(G-14241)*			
Genpak LLC	C	903 693-7151	
Carthage *(G-2908)*			
Genpak Southwest LP	C	903 693-7151	
Carthage *(G-2909)*			
Georg Fischer Central Plas LLC	C	972 641-2080	
Dallas *(G-4403)*			
Geotex Inc	E	817 656-9797	
Fort Worth *(G-6666)*			
GL Automotive LLC	C	925 360-3937	
San Antonio *(G-18141)*			
▲ Globe Industries Inc	E	281 440-3999	
Houston *(G-9985)*			
Graham Packaging Company LP	C	713 869-5471	
Houston *(G-10013)*			
Grande Garbage Collectn Co LLC	F	956 487-4234	
Rio Grande City *(G-17472)*			
Gs Liquid Technologies LLC	F	817 556-6262	
Cleburne *(G-3093)*			
▼ Gudgel & Sons Inc	E	903 989-2232	
Trenton *(G-20016)*			
▲ Gw Plastics San Antonio Inc	C	210 225-1516	
San Antonio *(G-18157)*			
Hagans Plastics Co Inc	F	972 790-9001	
Grand Prairie *(G-7885)*			
◆ Handgards LLC	C	915 779-6606	
El Paso *(G-5794)*			
▼ Hayes Holdings Inc	E	281 565-8111	
Sugar Land *(G-19490)*			
Helmy Associates & Co Inc	E	210 681-0101	
San Antonio *(G-18164)*			
Hightower Company	F	972 874-2419	
Houston *(G-10178)*			
▲ Higuchi Manufacturing Amer LLC	C	210 633-2877	
San Antonio *(G-18167)*			
Hill Plastics Inc	F	972 436-9717	
Lewisville *(G-14052)*			
Hoffman Company	E	361 882-9281	
Corpus Christi *(G-3549)*			
◆ Hood Flexible Packaging Corp	D	903 593-1793	
Tyler *(G-20100)*			
◆ Hoover Group Inc	C	800 844-8683	
Houston *(G-10204)*			
◆ Hoover Mtls Hdlg Group Inc	D	800 844-8683	
Houston *(G-10205)*			
▲ Houston Mfg Specialty Co Inc	E	281 888-4635	
Houston *(G-10239)*			
▲ Houston Shutters LLC	B	713 723-7100	
Houston *(G-10251)*			
▲ IDM Group LLC	F	972 578-1010	
Plano *(G-16889)*			
Illinois Tool Works Inc	D	713 797-2181	
Houston *(G-10323)*			
Illinois Tool Works Inc	B	956 215-2000	
Pharr *(G-16700)*			
Illinois Tool Works Inc	F	714 870-8661	
Fort Worth *(G-6716)*			
Impact Composite Tech Ltd	E	806 385-1015	
Littlefield *(G-14146)*			
Industrial Models Inc	C	940 665-7841	
Gainesville *(G-7346)*			
◆ Industrial Molding Corporation	D	806 474-1047	
Lubbock *(G-14426)*			
Industrial Thermoform Inc	C	972 299-5391	
Cedar Hill *(G-2945)*			
▲ Inhance Technologies LLC	E	800 929-1743	
Houston *(G-10364)*			
Integrted Mlding Solutions Inc	C	281 587-9761	
Houston *(G-10390)*			
▲ Intrepid Industries Inc	G	281 479-8301	
La Porte *(G-13756)*			
Iris Usa Inc	E	972 329-0400	
Mesquite *(G-15053)*			
ITW Blding Cmponents Group Inc	E	972 660-4422	
Grand Prairie *(G-7897)*			
◆ ITW Minigrip Inc	C	830 372-4400	
Seguin *(G-18845)*			
▲ J V Plastics Inc	E	972 606-0500	
Grand Prairie *(G-7900)*			
Jacksonville Tool & Die Inc	F	903 586-6030	
Jacksonville *(G-13245)*			
Jacqueline Thompson	E	210 269-1548	
Round Rock *(G-17663)*			
Jamestown Plastics Inc	E	956 831-8800	
Brownsville *(G-2368)*			
Jdp Manufacturing Inc	E	817 529-4009	
Fort Worth *(G-6737)*			
JRS Company Inc	D	626 967-2432	
Hutto *(G-12881)*			
K & L Precision Plastics Inc	F	972 234-4231	
Richardson *(G-17338)*			
◆ Kaston Fixs & Design Group LLC	E	972 243-5334	
Dallas *(G-4544)*			
Ken Ross Inc	F	972 442-3523	
Wylie *(G-20939)*			
Kerick Industries	F	214 432-2446	
Dallas *(G-4552)*			
▲ Kings Eco Plastics LLC	D	956 631-1115	
McAllen *(G-14883)*			
Knickerbocker Partition Corp	F	972 438-5330	
Irving *(G-13078)*			
Kps Global LLC	C	817 281-5121	
Fort Worth *(G-6770)*			
▲ L F Manufacturing Inc	D	979 542-8027	
Giddings *(G-7699)*			
◆ Laird Plastics Inc	B	469 299-7000	
Irving *(G-13082)*			
Leatherwood Plastics	F	972 221-7656	
Lewisville *(G-14060)*			
▲ Lee Linco Plastics Inc	E	281 487-0377	
Pasadena *(G-16471)*			
Leelinco Plastics Inc	F	281 487-0377	
Pasadena *(G-16472)*			
Lomont Molding LLC	E	512 763-3600	
Georgetown *(G-7660)*			
Lone Star Molding Inc	F	936 539-0008	
Conroe *(G-3324)*			
▲ Lonestar Badge & Sign Inc	E	512 357-2261	
Martindale *(G-14810)*			
Lorentson Mfg Co Southwest Inc	E	956 399-8902	
San Benito *(G-18660)*			
Louis Barriga	E	817 923-7370	
Fort Worth *(G-6801)*			
▲ Lsp Products Group Inc	D	775 884-4242	
Irving *(G-13091)*			
Lucite International Inc	C	409 729-1300	
Nederland *(G-15755)*			
M & G Resins Usa LLC	E	281 873-5780	
Houston *(G-10712)*			
M & G Resins Usa LLC	F	304 576-2041	
Corpus Christi *(G-3566)*			
M and N Plastics Inc	F	915 877-1900	
El Paso *(G-5852)*			
◆ Marco Dsplay Specialists GP Lc	C	817 244-8300	
Fort Worth *(G-6810)*			
▲ Marian Mexico Inc	E	915 591-8558	
El Paso *(G-5866)*			
Mauser Usa LLC	D	936 273-1279	
Conroe *(G-3328)*			
Mauser Usa LLC	C	713 670-2332	
Houston *(G-10799)*			
Maxwell Manufacturing Inc	E	512 357-2772	
Maxwell *(G-14818)*			
McElroy Plastics Inc	E	903 842-2180	
Troup *(G-20025)*			
Medco Manufacturing LLC	G	281 379-3100	
Spring *(G-19145)*			
Medical Components of America	G	830 237-6405	
Seguin *(G-18851)*			
▲ Medplast Group Inc	E	480 553-6400	
Houston *(G-10821)*			
Melet Plastics Usa Inc	F	210 822-0460	
San Antonio *(G-18291)*			
Metro Custom Plastics Inc	E	817 640-5646	
Arlington *(G-731)*			
Metro Gate & Mfg Co Inc	E	903 785-8911	
Paris *(G-16365)*			
Micro Mold Plastics Inc	E	817 536-0930	
Fort Worth *(G-6837)*			
Micro Mold Plastics Usa Inc	E	817 536-0930	
Fort Worth *(G-6838)*			
Mighty Molding & Mfg	F	254 629-2525	
Eastland *(G-5567)*			
Mike Strand	F	940 482-3426	
Krum *(G-13675)*			
Mitchell Machine & Fabricating	F	903 880-0249	
Mabank *(G-14579)*			
Molded Fiber Glass Companies	D	940 668-0302	
Gainesville *(G-7349)*			
▲ Momentum Plastics LLC	C	713 678-7741	
Houston *(G-10909)*			
Moore Fabrication Inc	E	713 643-7477	
Houston *(G-10919)*			
MPA International LP	C	915 474-7832	
El Paso *(G-5887)*			

Multi Packg Solutions Intl Ltd.............E....... 214 634-2131
  Dallas *(G-4705)*

Mvp Plastics Sa LLC.............F....... 440 834-1790
  McAllen *(G-14893)*

Myco Plastics Inc.............E....... 903 586-0551
  Jacksonville *(G-13252)*

N A Petroflex Ltd.............D....... 940 668-7283
  Gainesville *(G-7351)*

Nan Ya Plastics Corp USA.............D....... 713 674-7822
  Houston *(G-10962)*

National Plastic Molders Inc.............F....... 281 346-1942
  Richmond *(G-17463)*

Nationwide Tank & Pipe LLC.............E....... 830 387-4027
  New Braunfels *(G-15815)*

▲ Neon Electric Corporation.............D....... 281 987-1144
  Houston *(G-11023)*

New Teraco Inc.............E....... 800 687-3999
  Midland *(G-15316)*

North America Packaging Corp.............C....... 979 779-5900
  Bryan *(G-2496)*

▲ North Texas Plastics Inc.............E....... 940 458-7954
  Sanger *(G-18728)*

▲ Ntl-Brands Ltd.............D....... 214 631-0307
  Dallas *(G-4746)*

▼ Numo Manufacturing Inc.............C....... 800 253-0434
  Kaufman *(G-13463)*

Occidental Chemical Holdg Corp.............E....... 972 404-3800
  Dallas *(G-4753)*

One Source Recycling Inc.............D....... 512 549-2812
  Austin *(G-1386)*

P-Mcom Incorporated.............E....... 866 310-2556
  Fort Worth *(G-6888)*

Paragon Packaging Inc.............E....... 817 477-5211
  Mansfield *(G-14701)*

Paragon Rio Grande LLC.............F....... 956 831-8249
  Brownsville *(G-2391)*

Paso Del Norte Hardware LLC.............F....... 915 591-6200
  El Paso *(G-5904)*

Pat Garcia.............F....... 254 559-2815
  Breckenridge *(G-2232)*

Peacock Plastics Company.............F....... 903 586-2531
  Jacksonville *(G-13256)*

Peak Nanosystems LLC.............E....... 469 464-4504
  Coppell *(G-3434)*

Performance Gear Hdqtr LLC.............E....... 281 402-6816
  Cypress *(G-3811)*

Pfi Molding Inc.............F....... 713 946-3300
  Houston *(G-11314)*

Pi Holdings Inc.............D....... 903 586-2408
  Jacksonville *(G-13257)*

Plas Mac Inc.............F....... 806 447-0065
  Wellington *(G-20656)*

▲ Plastech Corporation.............E....... 972 490-1155
  Addison *(G-156)*

Plasti Fab Inc.............E....... 817 485-0156
  Richland Hills *(G-17445)*

Plastic Forming Inc.............E....... 817 284-7878
  Richland Hills *(G-17446)*

Plastic Molded Products Inc.............E....... 254 840-3721
  Mc Gregor *(G-14821)*

▼ Plastic Molding Technology Inc.............C....... 915 593-6922
  El Paso *(G-5911)*

Plastic Vacuum Forming Inc.............E....... 210 344-8531
  San Antonio *(G-18382)*

Plastiform Inc.............F....... 972 241-2593
  Irving *(G-13149)*

Plastix Plus LLC.............E....... 281 469-3451
  Houston *(G-11346)*

▲ Plastronics Interconnections.............F....... 972 258-2580
  Irving *(G-13152)*

Plastronics Interconnections.............E....... 972 255-1964
  Irving *(G-13153)*

▲ Poly Sac Inc.............F....... 713 978-7888
  Houston *(G-11356)*

Poly U Molding & Mfg LP.............F....... 817 701-0779
  Arlington *(G-755)*

Polymer Products LP.............F....... 972 647-1000
  Arlington *(G-756)*

Polymerica Ltd.............C....... 915 845-6288
  El Paso *(G-5915)*

▲ Polyweld USA Inc.............E....... 281 821-4156
  Houston *(G-11364)*

Ponderosa Precision Plas Inc.............E....... 281 471-3221
  La Porte *(G-13783)*

Port Plastics Inc.............F....... 817 834-7678
  Fort Worth *(G-6911)*

Portage Plastics Corporation.............F....... 956 504-6102
  Brownsville *(G-2395)*

◆ Powerseal Pipeline Pdts Corp.............D....... 940 767-5566
  Wichita Falls *(G-20796)*

Precision Fluorocarbon Inc.............E....... 281 351-4070
  Tomball *(G-20001)*

Precision Formed Plastics Inc.............E....... 972 579-8803
  Irving *(G-13154)*

Preferred Plastics Inc.............F....... 361 594-3535
  Shiner *(G-18948)*

▲ Premier Plastics Dallas Inc.............D....... 972 554-1597
  Irving *(G-13156)*

◆ Prime Products Inc.............D....... 979 743-6555
  Schulenburg *(G-18777)*

Prism Industries LLC.............E....... 956 425-3300
  Harlingen *(G-8198)*

Prototype Machine Co.............E....... 512 282-1590
  Manchaca *(G-14641)*

Put-In-Cups LLC.............F....... 800 506-7891
  Corpus Christi *(G-3601)*

▲ Qfc Plastics Inc.............C....... 817 375-5774
  Arlington *(G-764)*

Qt Industries LLC.............F....... 972 221-0537
  Dallas *(G-4840)*

R & E Tooling & Plastics Inc.............E....... 817 834-2858
  Fort Worth *(G-6930)*

R Slater Enterprises LLC.............F....... 832 456-4900
  Houston *(G-11528)*

Ranger Plastic Extrusions Inc.............F....... 817 640-6067
  Arlington *(G-767)*

Ravago Mfg Americas LLC.............F....... 281 443-6220
  Houston *(G-11553)*

Reama Inc.............F....... 409 744-9222
  Galveston *(G-7407)*

Reed Fiberglass Inc.............F....... 432 332-8265
  Odessa *(G-16135)*

Reed Prototype and Model Inc.............E....... 512 457-0560
  Lockhart *(G-14172)*

▼ Reef Industries Inc.............E....... 713 507-4200
  Houston *(G-11577)*

Reef Industries Inc.............D....... 713 507-4329
  Houston *(G-11578)*

Regal Plastic Supply Co Inc.............F....... 210 599-8291
  San Antonio *(G-18419)*

Regal Plastic Supply Co Inc.............F....... 512 836-3629
  Austin *(G-1457)*

Regency Plastics - Ubly Inc.............D....... 915 860-1997
  El Paso *(G-5935)*

Rehrig Pacific Company.............D....... 214 631-7943
  Dallas *(G-4885)*

▲ Reliant Worldwide Plastics LLC.............E....... 214 382-9672
  Gainesville *(G-7361)*

Reno Machine Works LLC.............F....... 903 224-6275
  Reno *(G-17252)*

▼ Research Advanced Methods Inds.............E....... 254 442-1008
  Cisco *(G-3068)*

Rim Manufacturing LLC.............E....... 817 599-6521
  Weatherford *(G-20617)*

▼ Rio Plastics Inc.............E....... 956 831-2715
  Brownsville *(G-2401)*

RMC Plastics Inc.............F....... 713 722-9322
  Houston *(G-11635)*

Rodeo Plastic Bag & Film LLC.............D....... 972 216-3331
  Mesquite *(G-15075)*

Ropak Southwest Inc.............C....... 817 473-0259
  Mansfield *(G-14714)*

Royal Case Company Inc.............G....... 903 328-3371
  Sherman *(G-18931)*

Royal Technologies Corporation.............C....... 956 424-9388
  Mission *(G-15563)*

▲ Royberg Inc.............E....... 210 525-0094
  San Antonio *(G-18435)*

▲ Schlemmer Usa Inc.............D....... 210 491-4800
  San Antonio *(G-18457)*

Select Plastics LLC.............E....... 817 595-3804
  Fort Worth *(G-6982)*

▲ Semasys Inc.............C....... 713 869-8331
  Houston *(G-11825)*

◆ Senox Corporation.............E....... 512 251-3333
  Austin *(G-1492)*

Sherman Roto Tank LLC.............E....... 281 648-0909
  Pearland *(G-16599)*

▲ Shieldcoat Technologies Inc.............E....... 936 633-6387
  Lufkin *(G-14551)*

▲ Sigmapro Engineering & Mfg LLC.............F....... 682 888-1234
  Fort Worth *(G-6986)*

▲ Signature Cards LP.............D....... 972 783-7600
  Richardson *(G-17398)*

▲ Silgan Plastics of Texas.............F....... 713 242-0923
  Houston *(G-11896)*

Simplified Strl Thrmforming Inc.............G....... 903 887-8546
  Mabank *(G-14581)*

Smart Pipe Company Inc.............F....... 281 945-5700
  Houston *(G-11919)*

Solid Distribution LLC.............G....... 915 235-4357
  El Paso *(G-5967)*

Southern Manufacturing Co LLC.............E....... 409 962-4501
  Groves *(G-8110)*

▲ Southern Plastics Inc.............C....... 903 984-6229
  Kilgore *(G-13591)*

▲ Southwest Quality Molding LP.............E....... 281 643-4500
  Manvel *(G-14738)*

Spears Manufacturing Co.............E....... 469 528-3000
  Flower Mound *(G-6282)*

Spears Manufacturing Co.............F....... 817 293-0292
  Fort Worth *(G-7008)*

Spirit Industries Inc.............E....... 936 597-5144
  Montgomery *(G-15641)*

Star Delta Motor Controls Inc.............E....... 210 479-3550
  San Antonio *(G-18497)*

Sunbelt Plastics Incorporated.............E....... 972 335-4100
  Frisco *(G-7316)*

Talbot Group Inc.............F....... 866 866-5020
  Hurst *(G-12860)*

Tallyho Plastics Inc.............D....... 903 586-2263
  Jacksonville *(G-13261)*

Tasus Corporation.............D....... 512 869-7766
  Georgetown *(G-7682)*

◆ Tasus Texas Corporation.............F....... 512 869-7766
  Georgetown *(G-7683)*

Tdi LLC.............E....... 972 877-5780
  Flower Mound *(G-6286)*

Te Connectivity Corporation.............E....... 469 568-0657
  Carrollton *(G-2826)*

▲ Team Promark LLC.............E....... 303 926-1328
  Fort Worth *(G-7039)*

Tech Tool Plastics Inc.............E....... 817 246-4694
  Fort Worth *(G-7040)*

Technimark Reynosa LLC.............F....... 336 498-4171
  Pharr *(G-16712)*

▼ Teebaud Co LLC.............F....... 713 682-5161
  Houston *(G-12182)*

Tekni-Plex Inc.............C....... 214 337-4711
  Dallas *(G-5048)*

▲ Temple Tag II Ltd.............D....... 254 982-4212
  Temple *(G-19710)*

Texas Injection Molding LLC.............D....... 281 489-4292
  Houston *(G-12237)*

Texstars LLC.............C....... 972 647-1366
  Arlington *(G-796)*

Thermo Plastics Corporation.............E....... 817 281-9010
  Fort Worth *(G-7056)*

Thermo-Mold Inc.............F....... 713 944-6336
  Houston *(G-12271)*

▲ Thermo-Serv Inc.............C....... 214 631-0307
  Dallas *(G-5085)*

Think Plastics LLC.............F....... 713 771-7700
  Sugar Land *(G-19565)*

▲ Thomas M Niland Company.............E....... 915 779-1405
  El Paso *(G-6002)*

Tietek Global LLC.............E....... 281 444-3494
  Marshall *(G-14805)*

Tiger Ridge Manufacturing Inc.............E....... 903 364-1810
  Whitewright *(G-20729)*

Toter LLC.............F....... 830 775-3411
  Del Rio *(G-5326)*

Trident Laboratories Inc.............E....... 972 226-4986
  Mesquite *(G-15081)*

Trix & Kix Dannys.............F....... 281 353-6618
  Spring *(G-19182)*

◆ Tsi Products Inc.............E....... 817 649-2626
  Arlington *(G-806)*

Tyco International MGT Co LLC.............E....... 361 575-9565
  Victoria *(G-20312)*

◆ TYG Products LP.............D....... 972 542-1828
  McKinney *(G-14984)*

United Commodities LLC.............F....... 956 621-1798
  Brownsville *(G-2418)*

United Plastics Group Inc.............E....... 713 466-5563
  Houston *(G-12451)*

Upg Company LLC.............C....... 713 466-5563
  Houston *(G-12474)*

US Farathane Holdings Corp.............C....... 734 656-9000
  Austin *(G-1616)*

◆ Veka South Inc.............E....... 972 551-2030
  Terrell *(G-19755)*

◆ Vista Cntrs & Closures LLC.............F....... 713 609-9250
  Houston *(G-12573)*

▲ W & W Fiberglass Tank Company.............D....... 806 669-1128
  Pampa *(G-16344)*

Waco Composites.............G....... 866 688-3088
  Waco *(G-20475)*

▲ Waddington N Amer - Houston.............D....... 713 686-6700
  Houston *(G-12592)*

S I C

◆ Welbilt Walk-Ins LP ....C 817 281-5121
Fort Worth *(G-7134)*

▲ Wesmar Corporation ....E 915 599-1572
El Paso *(G-6029)*

West Texas Drum Company Ltd II ....E 281 383-1901
Baytown *(G-1805)*

WFC Company Inc ....E 903 586-0476
Jacksonville *(G-13267)*

▲ Windsor Mold USA Inc ....F 956 787-8737
Pharr *(G-16716)*

▲ Wna Cups Illustrated Inc ....C 972 224-8407
Lancaster *(G-13850)*

Wylie & Son Inc ....D 806 667-3566
Petersburg *(G-16652)*

Wylie & Son Inc ....F 325 695-0000
Abilene *(G-95)*

Xerxes Corporation ....E 830 372-0090
Seguin *(G-18875)*

31 LEATHER AND LEATHER PRODUCTS

3111 Leather Tanning & Finishing

▲ AA&e Leathercraft LLC ....G 361 293-6366
Yoakum *(G-20957)*

▼ Custom Skin Co Inc ....F 325 655-9585
San Angelo *(G-17794)*

Damuth Taxidermy Inc ....F 325 597-0001
Brady *(G-2213)*

Doiy LLC ....F 469 513-4159
Dallas *(G-4270)*

▲ Gulf Coast Bag Inc ....F 281 556-8500
Houston *(G-10057)*

Justin Brands Inc ....A 915 778-8311
El Paso *(G-5824)*

▲ Magna Leather Corp ....F 915 772-0004
El Paso *(G-5858)*

Quality Fur Dressing ....F 281 292-2617
Spring *(G-19246)*

Tasman Industries Inc ....E 806 372-3850
Amarillo *(G-512)*

◆ Texpac Hide & Skin Ltd ....D 817 626-6586
Fort Worth *(G-7052)*

▲ Tony Lama Company Inc ....A 915 778-8311
El Paso *(G-6007)*

3131 Boot & Shoe Cut Stock & Findings

Counter Club Inc ....G 817 573-5040
Granbury *(G-7795)*

Honcho Boots LLC ....F 915 855-9300
El Paso *(G-5796)*

San Antonio Shoe Inc ....F 210 223-0166
San Antonio *(G-18449)*

San Antonio Shoe Inc ....A 830 768-7200
Del Rio *(G-5323)*

▲ Texas Leather Trim Inc ....E 817 535-5883
Fort Worth *(G-7049)*

3143 Men's Footwear, Exc Athletic

Anderson Bean Boot Co Inc ....E 956 565-2618
Mercedes *(G-15002)*

Anderson Bean Boot Co Inc ....F 956 565-2618
Mercedes *(G-15003)*

▲ Cowtown Boot Company ....D 915 593-2929
El Paso *(G-5704)*

Falconhead Boots Belts Buckles ......F 915 544-2727
El Paso *(G-5762)*

Franklin-Leddy Corporation ....D 817 624-3149
Fort Worth *(G-6648)*

Franklin-Leddy Corporation ....E 325 653-3397
San Angelo *(G-17800)*

Holicks Manufacturing Co LLC ....F 979 846-6721
Bryan *(G-2477)*

Honcho Boots LLC ....F 915 855-9300
El Paso *(G-5796)*

Justin Brands Inc ....B 940 226-1706
Childress *(G-3055)*

◆ Justin Brands Inc ....C 817 332-4385
Fort Worth *(G-6748)*

Justin Brands Inc ....A 915 778-8311
El Paso *(G-5824)*

Justin Industries Inc ....B 817 332-4385
Fort Worth *(G-6749)*

Kenneth Cole Productions Inc ....C 956 825-7116
Mercedes *(G-15007)*

Lagarto Inc ....E 915 598-2668
El Paso *(G-5837)*

Lucchese Inc ....B 915 778-8585
El Paso *(G-5849)*

Lucchese Inc ....B 915 778-8585
El Paso *(G-5850)*

San Antonio Shoe Inc ....A 830 768-7200
Del Rio *(G-5323)*

Stallion Boot Co Inc ....E 915 532-6268
El Paso *(G-5974)*

▲ Tony Lama Company Inc ....A 915 778-8311
El Paso *(G-6007)*

Western Leather Goods Inc ....D 800 717-1853
Mercedes *(G-15011)*

Western Leather Goods Inc ....F 956 565-2618
Mercedes *(G-15012)*

▲ Westmoor Corp ....E 817 625-2841
Fort Worth *(G-7142)*

3144 Women's Footwear, Exc Athletic

Anderson Bean Boot Co Inc ....F 956 565-2618
Mercedes *(G-15003)*

▲ Cowtown Boot Company ....D 915 593-2929
El Paso *(G-5704)*

Franklin-Leddy Corporation ....E 325 653-3397
San Angelo *(G-17800)*

◆ Justin Brands Inc ....C 817 332-4385
Fort Worth *(G-6748)*

Justin Brands Inc ....A 915 778-8311
El Paso *(G-5824)*

Lucchese Inc ....B 915 778-8585
El Paso *(G-5849)*

▲ Lucchese Inc ....B 915 778-8585
El Paso *(G-5850)*

San Antonio Shoe Inc ....G 210 921-8274
San Antonio *(G-18450)*

San Antonio Shoe Inc ....A 830 768-7200
Del Rio *(G-5323)*

Stallion Boot Co Inc ....E 915 532-6268
El Paso *(G-5974)*

▲ Tefkab Footwear LLC ....F 281 988-0977
Houston *(G-12184)*

▲ Tony Lama Company Inc ....A 915 778-8311
El Paso *(G-6007)*

3149 Footwear, NEC

Fossil Partners LP ....G 972 437-0452
Richardson *(G-17315)*

◆ Justin Brands Inc ....C 817 332-4385
Fort Worth *(G-6748)*

3151 Leather Gloves & Mittens

▲ Guard-Line Inc ....C 903 796-4111
Atlanta *(G-843)*

Guard-Line Inc ....D 903 796-4111
Atlanta *(G-844)*

▲ Innovative Gloves & Safety LLC ......F 281 582-0700
Houston *(G-10371)*

▲ Ringers Technology Group Inc ......F 281 953-5300
Houston *(G-11625)*

3161 Luggage

◆ Bio World Merchandising Inc ....C 972 488-0655
Irving *(G-12948)*

▲ Blacksheep Inc ....B 903 592-3853
Tyler *(G-20059)*

▲ Custom Direct Inc ....F 201 934-4229
Plano *(G-16834)*

◆ Eagle Creek Inc ....D 760 431-6400
Uvalde *(G-20189)*

Esip Group LLC ....F 281 965-4942
Richmond *(G-17455)*

▲ Jon Hart Design Co ....E 210 226-8544
San Antonio *(G-18206)*

▲ Marc Johnsonusa Inc ....F 713 780-8486
Houston *(G-10762)*

Richard Eric LLC ....F 214 477-5230
Plano *(G-16994)*

▲ Royal Case Company Inc ....C 903 868-0288
Sherman *(G-18930)*

3171 Handbags & Purses

▲ Custom Direct Inc ....F 201 934-4229
Plano *(G-16834)*

▲ Double J Saddlery Inc ....D 361 293-6364
Yoakum *(G-20964)*

▲ Jon Hart Design Co ....E 210 226-8544
San Antonio *(G-18206)*

Vera Bradley Inc ....D 713 647-0323
Houston *(G-12549)*

3172 Personal Leather Goods

◆ 3-D Belt Company LP ....E 979 743-4567
Schulenburg *(G-18770)*

▲ Barrington Group Ltd Inc ....F 214 528-6990
Dallas *(G-4006)*

Brushy Creek Belt & Buckle Co ....F 361 293-2345
Yoakum *(G-20960)*

Franklin-Leddy Corporation ....E 325 653-3397
San Angelo *(G-17800)*

Justin Brands Inc ....A 915 778-8311
El Paso *(G-5824)*

Longhorn Leather Co ....E 903 454-4866
Greenville *(G-8083)*

R E M Industries Inc ....F 915 544-2233
El Paso *(G-5924)*

▲ R K Texas Leather Mfg Inc ....G 903 378-2100
Honey Grove *(G-8358)*

▲ Royal Case Company Inc ....C 903 868-0288
Sherman *(G-18930)*

Royal Case Company Inc ....E 903 364-5231
Whitewright *(G-20728)*

◆ Samsill Corporation ....C 817 536-1906
Fort Worth *(G-6972)*

San Antonio Shoe Inc ....A 830 768-7200
Del Rio *(G-5323)*

▼ Simco Longhorn Leather ....D 972 542-8700
McKinney *(G-14974)*

Stallion Boot Co Inc ....E 915 532-6268
El Paso *(G-5974)*

▲ Tony Lama Company Inc ....A 915 778-8311
El Paso *(G-6007)*

▲ Travis Assn For The Blind ....C 512 442-2329
Austin *(G-1590)*

3199 Leather Goods, NEC

▲ Beck Cowboy Boots Inc ....G 806 373-1600
Amarillo *(G-402)*

Big Bend Saddlery Inc ....F 432 837-5551
Alpine *(G-311)*

▲ Builders Post-Tension Inc ....E 281 873-9500
Houston *(G-9014)*

Calvin Allen Saddlery ....F 817 598-0505
Weatherford *(G-20581)*

▲ Circle Y Saddles Inc ....F 361 293-3501
Yoakum *(G-20961)*

▲ Double J Saddlery Inc ....D 361 293-6364
Yoakum *(G-20964)*

Europa Designs ....F 972 792-0997
Dallas *(G-4336)*

Franklin-Leddy Corporation ....E 325 653-3397
San Angelo *(G-17800)*

Franklin-Leddy Corporation ....D 817 624-3149
Fort Worth *(G-6648)*

JK Manufacturing Inc ....F 956 723-6893
Laredo *(G-13899)*

Joyson Sfety Systems Acqstion ......E 210 250-5000
San Antonio *(G-18210)*

King Ranch Holdings Inc ....E 832 681-5700
Houston *(G-10535)*

R E M Industries Inc ....F 915 544-2233
El Paso *(G-5924)*

Rocking T Saddlery ....F 903 455-6629
Greenville *(G-8089)*

▼ Simco Longhorn Leather ....D 972 542-8700
McKinney *(G-14974)*

Tex Tan Western Co Yoakum Inc ......F 361 293-2314
Yoakum *(G-20973)*

◆ Texpac Hide & Skin Ltd ....D 817 626-6586
Fort Worth *(G-7052)*

▲ Tucker Saddlery Inc ....E 361 293-3501
Yoakum *(G-20974)*

32 STONE, CLAY, GLASS, AND CONCRETE PRODUCTS

3211 Flat Glass

A & B Glass LLC ....F 432 517-4565
Big Spring *(G-2067)*

Advanced Window and Glass Mfg ......G 210 735-9959
San Antonio *(G-17870)*

Ballistics Systems Inc ....F 713 939-1160
Hockley *(G-8341)*

Berger Iron Works Inc ....E 713 869-7386
Houston *(G-8860)*

Cardinal Glass Industries Inc ....D 972 937-4969
Waxahachie *(G-20533)*

Cardinal Glass Industries Inc ....C 972 937-1708
Waxahachie *(G-20534)*

Consolidated Armor Pdts LLC .... E 214 382-4100
Addison *(G-113)*

▲ Cristacurva LLC .... G 713 353-5800
Houston *(G-9345)*

Dryco Skylights Inc .... G 817 477-3441
Mansfield *(G-14667)*

▲ Fluenta Inc .... F 832 456-2021
Houston *(G-9815)*

Guardian Industries LLC .... B 903 872-4871
Corsicana *(G-3673)*

Hartung Glass Industries Inc .... G 972 629-6890
Farmers Branch *(G-6201)*

Hou-Tex Newnom Inc .... D 713 777-0748
Houston *(G-10215)*

Jpon Glass Company Inc .... E 214 349-1400
Garland *(G-7528)*

Kats Glass LLC .... E 281 592-5211
Cleveland *(G-3131)*

▲ Kinro Composties .... C 800 262-8827
Waxahachie *(G-20548)*

Kovach Enclosure Systems LLC .... D 480 926-9292
Spring *(G-19225)*

Kovach Enclosure Systems LLC .... D 480 926-9292
Austin *(G-1273)*

Kovach Enclosure Systems LLC .... D 480 926-9292
Farmers Branch *(G-6205)*

▲ Lumina Global Inc .... F 713 783-7056
Houston *(G-10702)*

▲ Sky Glass Inc .... F 972 807-9616
Dallas *(G-4969)*

Skylights Over Texas LLC .... F 210 402-0500
San Antonio *(G-18478)*

Texstars LLC .... C 972 647-1366
Arlington *(G-796)*

Trulite GL Alum Solutions LLC .... E 210 653-7790
San Antonio *(G-18570)*

Trulite GL Alum Solutions LLC .... C 800 395-4224
Houston *(G-12385)*

USA Securglass Corporation .... E 214 907-9445
Addison *(G-173)*

Wilson Steel Services LLC .... F 903 275-2995
Brownsboro *(G-2333)*

3221 Glass Containers

Jarden LLC .... C 903 455-0691
Greenville *(G-8078)*

Owens-Brockway Glass Cont Inc .... E 956 717-4200
Laredo *(G-13917)*

Owens-Brockway Glass Cont Inc .... E 956 717-4200
Plano *(G-16961)*

3229 Pressed & Blown Glassware, NEC

Acme Brick Company .... D 817 332-4101
El Paso *(G-5636)*

Builders Depot Direct LLC .... F 832 384-7272
Houston *(G-9012)*

▲ Corning Optical Communications ...... E 817 431-7120
Fort Worth *(G-6550)*

Creekside Mirror and Glass LLC .... F 972 617-9805
Waxahachie *(G-20539)*

Crystal Images Inc .... F 972 438-2337
Irving *(G-12985)*

Displays & Optical Tech .... E 512 246-6400
Georgetown *(G-7648)*

◆ Fiber Glass Systems LP .... D 210 477-7500
San Antonio *(G-18112)*

Fiberglass Creations Inc .... E 903 657-6616
Henderson *(G-8262)*

Glass Samuels Company LLC .... D 210 227-2481
San Antonio *(G-18142)*

◆ Glass Wholesalers Ltd .... F 713 353-5800
Houston *(G-9961)*

Greenstar North Amer Holdings .... A 713 965-0005
Houston *(G-10036)*

Guadalupe Valley Ventures LP .... E 830 885-4411
New Braunfels *(G-15799)*

Haleaux Inc .... F 214 742-2795
Dallas *(G-4428)*

Innovative Building Products .... E 940 387-0408
Millsap *(G-15503)*

▲ John Roberts Enterprises Inc .... F 512 252-0174
Pflugerville *(G-16678)*

Kamal Incorporated .... D 210 695-2678
Helotes *(G-8241)*

McBroom Industries .... F 817 645-2248
Cleburne *(G-3101)*

Opteconn LP .... C 972 331-4627
Plano *(G-16955)*

Optical Cabling Systems LC .... E 972 331-4627
Plano *(G-16957)*

Potters Industries LLC .... E 325 752-6711
Brownwood *(G-2442)*

Ramin Corporation .... F 281 356-5178
Magnolia *(G-14623)*

Satco Products Inc .... C 972 247-2437
Dallas *(G-4936)*

Sawyer Oilfield Products LLC .... E 254 644-7261
Brownwood *(G-2443)*

▲ Sensortran Inc .... E 281 876-2323
Austin *(G-1493)*

WT Fiber Link LLC .... D 432 758-2700
Seminole *(G-18888)*

3231 Glass Prdts Made Of Purchased Glass

A & B Glass LLC .... F 432 517-4565
Big Spring *(G-2067)*

Alpha Door and Rail Inc .... F 817 358-8687
Aurora *(G-853)*

American Building Supply Inc .... D 469 322-8100
Coppell *(G-3408)*

Architectural Stained Glass .... F 432 426-3311
Fort Davis *(G-6318)*

▲ Arrowall Company .... D 713 462-1751
San Antonio *(G-18639)*

Ballistic GL Armor Sltions LLC .... F 214 382-4100
Addison *(G-105)*

Bielas Glass & Aluminum Pdts .... E 210 333-8040
San Antonio *(G-17952)*

Builders Frstsrc-Txas Group LP .... B 817 640-1234
Arlington *(G-634)*

Cardinal Glass Industries Inc .... D 972 937-4969
Waxahachie *(G-20533)*

Cardinal Glass Industries Inc .... C 972 937-1708
Waxahachie *(G-20534)*

▲ Cavallini Co Inc .... F 210 733-8161
San Antonio *(G-17988)*

◆ Christmas By Krebs Corporation ...... F 972 929-2880
Irving *(G-12970)*

El Habr Corporation .... F 817 731-4660
Fort Worth *(G-6608)*

Fiberglass Creations Inc .... E 903 657-6616
Henderson *(G-8262)*

Gardner Glass Products Inc .... D 936 291-7271
Huntsville *(G-12814)*

Glass Beveling Company Inc .... E 713 466-5262
Houston *(G-9960)*

Glass Samuels Company LLC .... D 210 227-2481
San Antonio *(G-18142)*

▲ Glasscraft Door Mfg Corp .... C 713 690-8282
Houston *(G-9962)*

Guardian Industries LLC .... B 903 872-4871
Corsicana *(G-3673)*

Kamal Incorporated .... D 210 695-2678
Helotes *(G-8241)*

Lone Star Glass Inc .... F 713 661-0091
Houston *(G-10677)*

▲ Longhorn Glass Mfg LP .... C 713 679-7500
Houston *(G-10685)*

Main Glass & Mirror Co .... F 210 637-1011
Schertz *(G-18752)*

Morenos Auto Glass Inc .... F 361 855-1471
Corpus Christi *(G-3579)*

Offenhauser Company .... D 713 928-2981
Houston *(G-11140)*

Oldcastle Building Envelope .... E 972 647-4028
Grand Prairie *(G-7940)*

▲ Oldcastle Buildingenvelope Inc ...... F 800 392-9815
Houston *(G-11168)*

◆ Oldcastle Buildingenvelope Inc ...... F 214 273-3400
Dallas *(G-4759)*

Oldcastle Buildingenvelope Inc .... D 713 827-1965
Houston *(G-11169)*

Overhead Door Corporation .... B 361 884-6640
Corpus Christi *(G-3586)*

Potters Industries LLC .... D 903 785-1633
Paris *(G-16366)*

Potters Industries LLC .... E 325 752-6711
Brownwood *(G-2442)*

▲ RE Watson & Associates Inc .... E 817 478-4401
Kennedale *(G-13501)*

▲ S G & P Incorporated .... F 979 233-7491
Freeport *(G-7209)*

Star Glass and Metal Svcs LLC .... F 770 490-9055
Dallas *(G-5008)*

▲ Swarco-Reflex LLC .... E 254 562-9879
Mexia *(G-15092)*

Swarco-Reflex LLC .... E 254 562-9879
Mexia *(G-15093)*

▲ Texas Lamp Manufacturers Inc .... E 972 564-5267
Forney *(G-6315)*

Tideline Designs Inc .... F 214 275-3958
Arlington *(G-799)*

Trulite GL Alum Solutions LLC .... E 210 653-7790
San Antonio *(G-18570)*

Vitro Flat Glass LLC .... B 940 855-3804
Wichita Falls *(G-20825)*

▲ Weissker Mfg Ltd Lblty Co .... F 903 538-2271
Palestine *(G-16309)*

Western Glass LLC .... F 512 820-2475
Georgetown *(G-7688)*

3241 Cement, Hydraulic

Ahi Supply Inc .... D 281 331-0088
Alvin *(G-350)*

▲ Alamo Cement Company .... C 210 208-1880
San Antonio *(G-18635)*

▼ Ardex Engineered Cements Inc .... D 817 435-5020
Mansfield *(G-14656)*

Ash Grove Cement Company .... E 713 674-4100
Houston *(G-8717)*

Buzzi Unicem USA Inc .... E 214 638-8391
Dallas *(G-4069)*

▲ Capitol Aggregates Inc .... C 210 871-6100
San Antonio *(G-17981)*

Cemex Inc .... C 830 625-7338
New Braunfels *(G-15778)*

◆ Cemex Cement Inc .... B 713 650-6200
Houston *(G-9121)*

Cemex Construction Mtls S LLC .... F 936 372-0493
Hockley *(G-8342)*

Cemex Construction Mtls S LLC .... E
Houston *(G-9126)*

Cemex Construction Mtls S LLC .... C 281 651-6426
Spring *(G-19104)*

Custom Building Products Inc .... D 972 641-6996
Grand Prairie *(G-7860)*

Eagle Materials Inc .... C 214 432-2000
Dallas *(G-4292)*

Florencio Villanueva .... C 210 534-4879
San Antonio *(G-18117)*

▲ Giant Cement Company .... F 843 851-9898
Houston *(G-9953)*

▲ Giant Cement Holding Inc .... F 571 302-7150
Houston *(G-9954)*

Hanson Aggregates LLC .... F 210 658-3533
New Braunfels *(G-15802)*

Holcim Inc .... G 713 672-4316
Houston *(G-10193)*

Holcim (us) Inc .... F 214 596-9760
Addison *(G-134)*

Houston Cement Company LP .... F 713 754-8000
Houston *(G-10224)*

James Hardie Building Pdts Inc .... C 972 923-9300
Waxahachie *(G-20547)*

Knife River Corporation .... D 979 361-2900
Bryan *(G-2488)*

▲ Lehigh Cement Company LLC .... C 877 534-4442
Irving *(G-13085)*

Lone Star Industries Inc .... F 512 917-8394
Austin *(G-1299)*

Old Castle Apg West .... D 844 576-1364
Grapevine *(G-8048)*

Quikrete Companies LLC .... D 817 783-3010
Alvarado *(G-339)*

Quikrete Companies LLC .... E 979 732-8210
Columbus *(G-3232)*

River Cement Sales Company .... F 325 288-4224
Maryneal *(G-14811)*

Saudi Basic Industries Corp .... F 713 532-4999
Houston *(G-11758)*

Southdown Inc .... B 713 650-6200
Houston *(G-11971)*

Texas Industries Inc .... E 817 838-4212
Fort Worth *(G-7048)*

▲ Texas Industries Inc .... C 972 647-6700
Dallas *(G-5062)*

Texas Industries Inc .... E 936 564-8301
Nacogdoches *(G-15716)*

Texas Industries Inc .... E 903 843-2327
Gilmer *(G-7715)*

Texas Industries Inc .... C 512 396-4244
New Braunfels *(G-15827)*

Texas Industries Inc .... E 972 775-3449
Midlothian *(G-15495)*

Texas Lehigh Cement Company LP ..... D 512 434-9330
Wimberley *(G-20884)*

Texas Lehigh Cement Company LP ..... C 512 295-6111
Buda *(G-2540)*

▲ Texas Lehigh Cement Company LP .. C 512 295-6111
Buda *(G-2541)*

◆ Zachry Consolidated LLC..................A...... 210 588-5000
San Antonio *(G-18630)*

Zachry Construction & Mtls Inc..........D...... 210 479-1027
San Antonio *(G-18631)*

3251 Brick & Structural Clay Tile

Acme Brick Company......................D...... 817 332-4101
El Paso *(G-5636)*

Acme Brick Company......................D...... 325 949-7685
San Angelo *(G-17770)*

Acme Brick Company......................D...... 254 662-9846
Waco *(G-20354)*

▲ Acme Brick Company....................C...... 817 332-4101
Fort Worth *(G-6343)*

Acme Brick Company......................D...... 512 281-5744
Elgin *(G-6052)*

Clay DHanis Products Inc...............E...... 830 363-7636
D Hanis *(G-3828)*

Faber Cnk......................................F...... 832 831-7222
Houston *(G-9748)*

▲ Justin Industries Inc..................D...... 817 332-4101
Fort Worth *(G-6750)*

Justin Industries Inc....................D...... 979 885-4124
Sealy *(G-18811)*

Meridian Brick LLC.........................E...... 903 675-2256
Athens *(G-833)*

Meridian Brick LLC.........................F...... 281 442-8400
Houston *(G-10835)*

Meridian Brick LLC.........................E...... 830 980-7071
Schertz *(G-18756)*

Meridian Brick LLC.........................D...... 940 325-9466
Mineral Wells *(G-15532)*

Meridian Brick LLC.........................F...... 972 245-1542
Carrollton *(G-2779)*

Mission Clay Products LLC.............F...... 830 393-2568
Floresville *(G-6248)*

Quikrete Companies LLC.................E...... 979 732-8210
Columbus *(G-3232)*

Texas Industries Inc.......................C...... 512 396-4244
New Braunfels *(G-15827)*

3253 Ceramic Tile

Alamo Concrete Tile Inc.................E...... 210 534-8821
San Antonio *(G-17883)*

American Marazzi Tile Inc..............G...... 972 232-3800
Fort Worth *(G-6381)*

Architerra Inc...............................F...... 512 441-8062
Austin *(G-930)*

Arizona Tile LLC...........................E...... 713 292-1001
Houston *(G-8696)*

C&D Allbritton Holdings Inc...........E...... 833 227-2243
Salado *(G-17764)*

Creative Tile Inc............................G...... 214 827-0552
Dallas *(G-4182)*

Dal-Tile Corporation.......................F...... 972 578-1600
Plano *(G-16836)*

▲ Diamond Living LLC...................F...... 281 766-1600
Magnolia *(G-14600)*

▲ Exacta Packaging Designs Inc....D...... 972 323-1063
Carrollton *(G-2733)*

Gilsa North America LLC.................F...... 956 223-2900
San Juan *(G-18674)*

◆ Graniti Vicentia LLC..................E...... 713 869-0800
Houston *(G-10015)*

IB Supply LLC...............................F...... 469 709-9650
Carrollton *(G-2870)*

◆ Interceramic Inc.......................B...... 214 503-5501
Carrollton *(G-2871)*

Lone Star Ceramics Company.........E...... 972 247-3111
Dallas *(G-4603)*

Marks Floor Design Inc.................F...... 713 974-2300
Houston *(G-10770)*

Patara Stone Inc............................E...... 713 681-2301
Houston *(G-11257)*

Roca USA Inc................................F...... 713 983-8008
Houston *(G-11648)*

Runnels Carpet and Tile Inc...........F...... 903 392-8026
Henderson *(G-8272)*

◆ Styleaccess LLC.......................D...... 972 392-3800
Carrollton *(G-2821)*

Tbk Materials LLC.........................E...... 214 239-4916
Plano *(G-17021)*

◆ United Lynn-Con Corporation.......F...... 972 223-2540
Desoto *(G-5446)*

3255 Clay Refractories

Allied Mineral Products Inc.............G...... 956 831-2022
Brownsville *(G-2336)*

Custom Building Products Inc.........D...... 972 641-6996
Grand Prairie *(G-7860)*

Harbisonwalker Intl Inc...................E...... 713 635-3200
Houston *(G-10123)*

Ifs Industries Inc..........................E...... 972 864-2202
Garland *(G-7517)*

Quikrete Companies LLC.................E...... 979 732-8210
Columbus *(G-3232)*

▲ Robert J Jenkins Co...................E...... 281 332-3566
Webster *(G-20643)*

Team Cooperheat-Mqs Inc.............E...... 713 673-3660
Houston *(G-12171)*

Texas Technical Ceramics Inc.........E...... 936 856-2903
Willis *(G-20866)*

Wesco Refractories Inc.................F...... 682 518-5035
Mansfield *(G-14729)*

3259 Structural Clay Prdts, NEC

Architerra Inc...............................F...... 512 441-8062
Austin *(G-930)*

Kenmark Architectural Pdts Inc.......F...... 800 788-8263
Dallas *(G-4550)*

Mission Clay Products LLC.............F...... 830 393-2568
Floresville *(G-6248)*

3261 China Plumbing Fixtures & Fittings

Arrow Marble LLC..........................D...... 832 467-4345
Houston *(G-8705)*

As America Inc..............................F...... 214 530-9831
Hutchins *(G-12862)*

Border States Industries Inc..........E...... 432 332-0591
Odessa *(G-15940)*

Border States Industries Inc..........F...... 432 520-0230
Midland *(G-15147)*

Border States Industries Inc..........F...... 325 698-4595
Abilene *(G-23)*

Border States Industries Inc..........F...... 512 458-6313
Austin *(G-1001)*

Border States Industries Inc..........F...... 325 655-9163
San Angelo *(G-17785)*

Border States Industries Inc..........F...... 806 457-4100
Amarillo *(G-409)*

Border States Industries Inc..........F...... 806 765-5741
Lubbock *(G-14379)*

Border States Industries Inc..........F...... 956 831-3441
Brownsville *(G-2339)*

Border States Industries Inc..........F...... 575 434-2022
El Paso *(G-5670)*

◆ Eljer Industries Inc.....................E...... 972 560-2000
Dallas *(G-4311)*

3262 China, Table & Kitchen Articles

▲ En Plast Technology LLC.............F...... 832 730-4606
Houston *(G-9622)*

3264 Porcelain Electrical Splys

Commscope Technologies LLC.........A...... 214 634-8502
Dallas *(G-4149)*

Coorstek Inc.................................F...... 432 381-0052
Odessa *(G-15967)*

◆ Ppc Usa Inc..............................E...... 281 257-8222
Houston *(G-11380)*

Sword Company..............................E...... 903 561-1921
Tyler *(G-20159)*

Texas Technical Ceramics Inc.........E...... 936 856-2903
Willis *(G-20866)*

3269 Pottery Prdts, NEC

Doiy LLC......................................F...... 469 513-4159
Dallas *(G-4270)*

Harris Potteries LP........................D...... 903 938-8884
Marshall *(G-14781)*

◆ Marshall Pottery Inc...................C...... 903 938-9201
Marshall *(G-14791)*

3271 Concrete Block & Brick

Acme Brick Company......................E...... 214 637-2720
Dallas *(G-3883)*

Acme Brick Company......................E...... 512 255-2573
Elgin *(G-6051)*

Acme Brick Company......................E...... 512 281-5744
Elgin *(G-6052)*

Ahi Supply Inc..............................E...... 281 331-0088
Alvin *(G-350)*

Alamo Concrete Products Ltd.........E...... 210 208-1580
San Antonio *(G-18636)*

Alamo Concrete Tile Inc.................E...... 210 534-8821
San Antonio *(G-17883)*

Arcosa Inc....................................C...... 972 942-6500
Dallas *(G-3958)*

Big D Concrete Inc.........................E...... 972 737-7976
Dallas *(G-4023)*

Brick Dudes LLC............................F...... 214 592-7904
Allen *(G-258)*

Camp Logan Cement Works Inc.......E...... 713 869-3385
Houston *(G-9080)*

Casting Designs Inc.......................C...... 817 551-7373
Fort Worth *(G-6496)*

◆ Cemex Inc.................................B...... 713 650-6200
Houston *(G-9120)*

Cemex Construction Mtls S LLC.......A...... 713 650-6200
Houston *(G-9128)*

Del Norte Masonry Products Inc.......E...... 915 584-4453
El Paso *(G-5716)*

Dfw Infrastructure Inc...................F...... 888 739-9070
Alvarado *(G-328)*

Featherlite Building Pdts Corp.........B...... 512 472-2424
Austin *(G-1147)*

Featherlite Corp............................E...... 409 727-8800
Port Neches *(G-17160)*

Headwaters Cnstr Mtls LLC.............E...... 903 729-2217
Palestine *(G-16299)*

Headwaters Cnstr Mtls LLC.............C...... 713 393-3300
Alleyton *(G-308)*

Headwaters Incorporated................F...... 713 393-3328
Alleyton *(G-309)*

Houston Products Proc Inc..............G...... 281 487-0766
Channelview *(G-3026)*

Innovative Block S Texas Ltd...........F...... 956 682-3181
McAllen *(G-14873)*

▲ Innovative Block S Texas Ltd.......G...... 956 797-4200
La Feria *(G-13691)*

J & G Concrete LP........................E...... 972 937-9200
Waxahachie *(G-20546)*

▲ Justin Industries Inc.................D...... 817 332-4101
Fort Worth *(G-6750)*

Lonestar Landscape Dfw LLC...........F...... 817 863-5609
Forest Hill *(G-6298)*

Mar-Con Services LLC....................D...... 713 473-1800
Pasadena *(G-16480)*

Mason Fencing and Cnstr LLC..........E...... 432 272-8347
Odessa *(G-16073)*

Meridian Brick LLC.........................E...... 830 980-7071
Schertz *(G-18756)*

Meridian Brick LLC.........................D...... 940 325-9466
Mineral Wells *(G-15532)*

Metro Cutting and Sealing Inc.........E...... 972 434-8722
Lewisville *(G-14066)*

▲ Napco Precast LLC....................C...... 210 424-4371
San Antonio *(G-18332)*

▲ Oldcastle Apg Texas Inc............E...... 817 545-8325
Grapevine *(G-8049)*

Oldcastle GL Engnered Pdts Inc.......C...... 972 563-2627
Terrell *(G-19747)*

Pavestone LLC..............................E...... 512 558-7283
San Marcos *(G-18703)*

▲ PC Calendar 2010 LLC...............E...... 214 491-5103
Dallas *(G-4791)*

PSI Concrete Construction LLC.........E...... 210 204-1529
San Antonio *(G-18400)*

▲ RMC Usa Inc............................F...... 713 650-6200
Houston *(G-11637)*

Southwest Concrete Products Co......C...... 888 464-9341
Columbus *(G-3233)*

Southwest Maintenance LLC.............F...... 254 662-3966
Robinson *(G-17502)*

Tex-Art Stone Inc.........................F...... 817 481-9602
Keller *(G-13470)*

Texas Building Products Inc............E...... 254 672-5262
Strawn *(G-19433)*

Texas Industries Inc......................E...... 972 775-3449
Midlothian *(G-15495)*

Texas Industries Inc......................E...... 903 873-2849
Wills Point *(G-20878)*

Texas Industries Inc......................F...... 903 758-7351
Longview *(G-14316)*

Texas Industries Inc......................F...... 903 454-2029
Greenville *(G-8094)*

Texas Industries Inc......................D...... 817 838-4212
Fort Worth *(G-7048)*

Trevway Inc...................................F...... 832 687-6269
Katy *(G-13380)*

Trnlwb LLC....................................C...... 800 581-3117
Arlington *(G-805)*

Turner Company LLC......................E...... 817 638-9053
Rhome *(G-17261)*

▲ Txi Operations LP........................C...... 972 647-6700
Dallas *(G-5125)*

3272 Concrete Prdts

37 Building Products Ltd ....C 817 341-3130
Weatherford *(G-20571)*
4693057371 ....F 469 305-7371
Frisco *(G-7255)*
A & W Industries Inc ....E 817 481-3577
Grapevine *(G-8010)*
Acme Brick Company ....E 512 255-2573
Elgin *(G-6051)*
Advanced Cast Stone Inc ....C 817 572-0018
Fort Worth *(G-6347)*
Aj Commercial Services Inc ....G 361 336-2113
Corpus Christi *(G-3470)*
Al Tex Concrete Products Inc ....F 830 964-5150
Canyon Lake *(G-2677)*
Alamo Concrete Products Ltd ....E 956 423-6388
Harlingen *(G-8175)*
Alamo Concrete Products Ltd ....E 210 208-1500
San Antonio *(G-17881)*
Alamo Concrete Products Ltd ....E 956 423-6380
Harlingen *(G-8176)*
Alamo Concrete Products Co ....E 210 208-1500
San Antonio *(G-18637)*
Alamo Concrete Products Co ....F 281 443-2644
Houston *(G-8522)*
Alamo Concrete Tile Inc ....E 210 534-8821
San Antonio *(G-17883)*
American Cast-Stone Inc ....E 817 695-1800
Arlington *(G-615)*
American Maatco Ltd ....E 817 284-7222
Richland Hills *(G-17435)*
▼ American Masonry Supply Inc ....C 817 695-1800
Arlington *(G-617)*
◆ Ameron International Corp ....E 713 375-3700
Houston *(G-8623)*
Antiquestone Inc ....F 512 355-2722
Bertram *(G-2051)*
Argos USA LLC ....D 972 299-5274
Cedar Hill *(G-2936)*
Ark-Concrete Specialties Inc ....E 713 692-6736
Houston *(G-8697)*
Arlington Cast Stone Inc ....F 817 284-5933
Hurst *(G-12834)*
Atlas Sand Company LLC ....E 432 276-3990
Austin *(G-946)*
Beltran Precast Inc ....F 915 599-8777
El Paso *(G-5661)*
Bexar Concrete Works I Ltd ....C 210 497-3773
San Antonio *(G-17950)*
Buchanan Septic Tanks Inc ....F 512 793-3100
Buchanan Dam *(G-2517)*
Buena Vista Burial Park Inc ....F 956 542-5271
Brownsville *(G-2342)*
Builders Depot Direct LLC ....F 832 384-7272
Houston *(G-9012)*
Camp Logan Cement Works Inc ....E 713 869-3385
Houston *(G-9080)*
Cast Fireplaces ....F 713 937-1080
Houston *(G-9095)*
Cates Caststone Co Inc ....F 903 839-0309
Tyler *(G-20064)*
◆ Cemex Inc ....B 713 650-6200
Houston *(G-9120)*
Cemex Construction Mtls S LLC ....A 713 650-6200
Houston *(G-9128)*
Cemex Materials LLC ....E 979 885-7403
Sealy *(G-18807)*
Century Concrete Partners Inc ....G 281 585-5742
Rosharon *(G-17601)*
CFS Forming Structure Company ....D 210 698-9252
San Antonio *(G-17996)*
Charles Barton ....E 512 759-1231
Hutto *(G-12877)*
Charlottes Concrete Inc ....E 210 648-4774
San Antonio *(G-18001)*
Coast Precast LLC ....F 936 890-5500
Conroe *(G-3278)*
Comal Concrete Products Inc ....F 830 606-4732
New Braunfels *(G-15786)*
Composite Access Products LP ....F 956 765-2907
McAllen *(G-14850)*
Concrete ASAP LLC ....F 713 222-6216
Houston *(G-9268)*
▲ Continental Stone LLC ....E 713 462-5700
Houston *(G-9289)*
Coreslab Structures Texas Inc ....C 512 250-0755
Cedar Park *(G-2964)*
Creative Stone Inc ....E 512 303-7866
Bastrop *(G-1752)*
▲ Crown Building Products LLC ....E 214 636-5163
Mansfield *(G-14664)*
Custom Crete Inc ....F 713 937-3966
Houston *(G-9369)*
Custom Iron Works ....G 806 745-2757
Lubbock *(G-14399)*
Dallas Cast Stone II Corp ....E 940 382-6922
Dallas *(G-4213)*
▼ David L Jennings ....D 281 778-3223
Missouri City *(G-15579)*
Del Norte Masonry Products Inc ....E 915 584-4453
El Paso *(G-5716)*
Delzotto Products Minn Inc ....E 903 981-0400
Gladewater *(G-7720)*
Delzotto Products Texas Inc ....E 903 981-0400
Gladewater *(G-7721)*
Diversitech Corporation ....D 678 542-3600
Columbus *(G-3231)*
Dn Tanks Inc ....E 972 823-3300
Grand Prairie *(G-7865)*
Dumpzit LLC ....F 817 238-6563
Fort Worth *(G-6596)*
East Texas Precast Company ....C 281 463-0654
Hempstead *(G-8252)*
▲ Enterprise Concrete Pdts LLC ....D 214 631-7006
Dallas *(G-4326)*
Enterprise Prcast Con Txas LLC ....E 903 875-1077
Corsicana *(G-3671)*
▲ Erect-A-Line Inc ....F 214 630-1154
Dallas *(G-4330)*
Espinoza Cast Stone Inc ....F 214 396-5280
Waxahachie *(G-20542)*
Excalibur LLC ....G 214 632-0161
The Colony *(G-19810)*
Featherlite Corporation ....C 817 332-4101
Fort Worth *(G-6625)*
Fencecrete America Inc ....C 281 438-1444
Houston *(G-9776)*
Fencecrete America Inc ....C 210 492-7911
San Antonio *(G-18109)*
First Texas Precast Inc ....E 214 350-5612
Dallas *(G-4364)*
▲ Flexicore of Texas Inc ....C 281 437-5700
Houston *(G-8381)*
Form and Fiber Inc ....F 888 314-8852
Gun Barrel City *(G-8114)*
Forterra Inc ....A 469 458-7973
Irving *(G-13032)*
Forterra Pipe & Precast LLC ....E 806 765-6721
Lubbock *(G-14412)*
◆ Forterra Pipe & Precast LLC ....D 469 458-7973
Irving *(G-13033)*
Forterra Pipe & Precast LLC ....E 972 262-3600
Cedar Hill *(G-2941)*
Forterra Pipe & Precast LLC ....E 512 385-3950
Austin *(G-1168)*
Forterra Pipe & Precast LLC ....E 361 767-1060
Robstown *(G-17511)*
Forterra Pipe & Precast LLC ....C 972 263-2181
Grand Prairie *(G-7877)*
Forterra Pipe & Precast LLC ....B 972 262-1571
Grand Prairie *(G-7878)*
Forterra US Holdings LLC ....E 469 284-8678
Irving *(G-13034)*
◆ Fountain People Inc ....D 512 392-1155
San Marcos *(G-18688)*
Gate Precast Company ....E 281 485-3273
Pearland *(G-16564)*
Gate Precast Company ....C 254 582-7200
Hillsboro *(G-8325)*
Genesis Granite Inc ....F 940 692-0611
Wichita Falls *(G-20767)*
Gfrc 360 LLC ....E 972 494-9000
Garland *(G-7503)*
▲ Gifford Monument Works Inc ....F 972 544-6305
Wylie *(G-20936)*
Hanson Aggregates LLC ....F 972 556-0735
Dallas *(G-4433)*
Hanson Lehigh Inc ....E 281 616-0700
Houston *(G-10120)*
◆ Hanson Lehigh Inc ....B 972 653-5500
Irving *(G-13052)*
Hauck Enterprises Ltd ....E 409 727-2227
Port Neches *(G-17162)*
Headwaters Incorporated ....F 830 562-3239
Tarpley *(G-19643)*
Heldenfels Enterprises Inc ....C 512 396-2376
San Marcos *(G-18694)*
Hexa Containment LLC ....E 281 884-8026
La Porte *(G-13743)*
Hill Country Site Supply LLC ....G 512 608-0069
Lakeway *(G-13816)*
Hoesman Industries Inc ....E 512 247-4173
Del Valle *(G-5331)*
Holcim (us) Inc ....F 214 596-9760
Addison *(G-134)*
Hydro Conduit of Texas LP ....E 817 491-4321
Northlake *(G-15887)*
Hydro Conduit of Texas LP ....E 832 590-5400
Houston *(G-10304)*
Hydro Conduit of Texas LP ....E 979 885-7403
Sealy *(G-18808)*
Hydro Conduit of Texas LP ....E 979 885-7403
Sealy *(G-18809)*
Hydro Conduit of Texas LP ....E 832 590-5400
Houston *(G-10305)*
Hydro Conduit of Texas LP ....E 832 590-5300
Houston *(G-10303)*
James Hardie Building Pdts Inc ....C 817 556-7000
Cleburne *(G-3097)*
JD Abrams LP ....E 512 243-1090
Austin *(G-1253)*
JD Abrams LP ....E 512 322-4000
Austin *(G-1252)*
L & R Pre-Cast Con Works Inc ....E 956 583-6293
Mission *(G-15558)*
Lattimore Materials Corp ....D 972 569-4622
McKinney *(G-14951)*
Lavender Enterprises Inc ....E 214 631-8080
Dallas *(G-4585)*
Littlefield Brothers Con Cnstr ....E 281 399-1488
Conroe *(G-3322)*
Locke Investments LLC ....D 832 804-7062
Houston *(G-10662)*
Lone Star Stone Texas Inc ....E 254 694-6613
Whitney *(G-20730)*
Lonestar Prestress Mfg Inc ....E 713 896-0994
Bellville *(G-2010)*
Lowe Precast Inc ....E 254 776-9690
Waco *(G-20428)*
Lyons Manufacturing Inc ....E 214 381-8100
Dallas *(G-4615)*
Manco Structures Ltd ....D 210 690-1705
Schertz *(G-18753)*
Manufactured Concrete Ltd ....C 210 690-1705
Schertz *(G-18754)*
Materials Products Inc ....F 512 821-3303
Austin *(G-1329)*
Murphy Wall Products Intl Inc ....E 713 694-8365
Houston *(G-10943)*
▲ Napco Precast LLC ....C 210 424-4371
San Antonio *(G-18332)*
New England Lead Burning Inc ....F 713 675-3266
Houston *(G-11034)*
Niblett Enterprises Inc ....D 940 383-2887
Gainesville *(G-7353)*
Noel Duque ....E 281 447-5789
Houston *(G-11065)*
North American Precast Company ....C 210 509-9100
San Antonio *(G-18350)*
North Texas Coring Inc ....F 817 279-8930
Granbury *(G-7802)*
Oldcastle Infrastructure Inc ....E 281 841-9187
Houston *(G-11170)*
Oldcastle Infrastructure Inc ....D 817 477-2914
Mansfield *(G-14698)*
Oldcastle Infrastructure Inc ....E 210 922-7306
San Antonio *(G-18354)*
Oldcastle Infrastructure Inc ....E 713 991-2400
Brookshire *(G-2321)*
P & L Cast Stone Inc ....F 817 430-8114
Roanoke *(G-17492)*
Pavestone LLC ....E 281 769-5098
Katy *(G-13376)*
Pavestone LLC ....D 817 481-5802
Grapevine *(G-8051)*
Pavestone LLC ....E 512 558-7283
San Marcos *(G-18703)*
Pb Materials Holdings Inc ....E 432 563-8036
Odessa *(G-16106)*
◆ Precision-Hayes Intl Inc ....C 972 287-2390
Seagoville *(G-18802)*
Premier Concrete Products Inc ....F 713 641-2727
Houston *(G-11399)*
Pristine Cast Stone Inc ....F 972 772-9490
Rockwall *(G-17562)*
PSI Concrete Construction LLC ....F 210 204-1529
San Antonio *(G-18400)*
Pyramid Stone Co Inc ....F 210 533-3511
San Antonio *(G-18402)*

SIC

Quanex Building Products Corp ....E 731 961-4600
Houston *(G-11504)*

Quanex Screens LLC ....D 713 961-4600
Houston *(G-11505)*

Quikrete Companies LLC ....D 936 587-4450
Raywood *(G-17235)*

Quikrete Companies LLC ....E 979 732-8210
Columbus *(G-3232)*

Quikrete Companies LLC ....E 325 672-4634
Abilene *(G-68)*

Quikrete Companies LLC ....E 432 694-5432
Midland *(G-15374)*

Randolph D & L Company LLC ....F 903 886-3055
Commerce *(G-3246)*

Ranger Coml Con Contrs LLC ....F 210 831-7052
Bulverde *(G-2558)*

Ranger Ready Mix LLC ....E 512 363-7630
Georgetown *(G-7672)*

Rcss ....D 210 661-8474
Converse *(G-3401)*

◆ Ready Cable of Houston Inc ....D 713 856-5132
Houston *(G-11560)*

Reinforced Earth Company ....D 254 836-1847
Waco *(G-20454)*

Rio Valley Pipe LLC ....E 956 580-3466
Palmview *(G-16312)*

Rio Valley Pipe LLC ....E 956 519-4960
Penitas *(G-16630)*

▲ RMC Usa Inc ....F 713 650-6200
Houston *(G-11637)*

Rocla Concrete Tie Inc ....E 806 383-7071
Amarillo *(G-459)*

Royal Metal Bldg Components ....E 956 399-2271
San Benito *(G-18665)*

▲ S C S C Inc ....E 214 398-1199
Dallas *(G-4922)*

Sepsa Precast Solutions Corp ....F 832 291-8930
Katy *(G-13440)*

Siteworks Incorporated ....E 281 931-1000
Houston *(G-11909)*

South Houston Concrete Pipe Co ....E 713 946-2831
Houston *(G-11965)*

▲ Speed-Fab-Crete Corp Intl ....C 817 572-0351
Kennedale *(G-13503)*

Stone Cast Inc ....F 713 683-6780
Houston *(G-12071)*

Stromberg Architectural Produc ....D 903 454-0904
Greenville *(G-8092)*

◆ Stromberg Archtctral Pdts Stha ....E 903 454-8682
Greenville *(G-8093)*

Suncoast Post-Tension Ltd ....E 512 259-7908
Leander *(G-13998)*

Superior Cladding Products LLC ....E 281 405-9400
Houston *(G-12110)*

Superior Con Fence Texas Inc ....E 817 558-6658
Cleburne *(G-3110)*

Superior Con Fence Texas Inc ....F 817 277-9255
Euless *(G-6160)*

Surface Burial Vault Monument ....F 361 275-3213
Cuero *(G-3766)*

Tex-Art Stone Inc ....F 817 481-9602
Keller *(G-13470)*

Texas Carved Stone LP ....F 254 793-2384
Florence *(G-6245)*

▲ Texas Cement Products Inc ....E 713 682-8411
Houston *(G-12225)*

Texas Concrete Chemical Inc ....E 936 638-4273
Groveton *(G-8113)*

Texas Concrete Partners LP ....C 361 573-9145
Victoria *(G-20308)*

Texas Concrete Partners LP ....D 254 822-1351
Elm Mott *(G-6065)*

Texas Eifs LLC ....F 210 472-2935
San Antonio *(G-18536)*

Texas Stone Designs Inc ....E 817 265-4011
Arlington *(G-795)*

Tpg Pressure Inc ....D 972 262-3600
Grand Prairie *(G-7985)*

Transit Ready Mix LLC ....F 956 584-0039
Mission *(G-15568)*

Trinity Stairs Inc ....E 972 335-0700
Frisco *(G-7320)*

▲ Txi Operations LP ....C 972 647-6700
Dallas *(G-5125)*

Tyler Products Sales Inc ....E 903 593-8633
Tyler *(G-20172)*

United Commercial Cast Stone ....F 940 668-8133
Gainesville *(G-7374)*

▼ US Concrete Inc ....E 817 835-4105
Euless *(G-6166)*

Vault 55 ....F 512 482-8810
Austin *(G-1625)*

Vison Tech Products LLC ....F 832 850-6085
Houston *(G-12572)*

Vulcan Materials Company ....F 210 349-3311
San Antonio *(G-18603)*

Vulcan Materials Company ....F 210 494-9555
San Antonio *(G-18604)*

W R Meadows Inc ....E 817 834-1969
Fort Worth *(G-7113)*

Wallace Monument Company ....F 806 874-2442
Clarendon *(G-3071)*

Wallis Concrete LLC ....F 979 478-6734
Wallis *(G-20510)*

Wareing Athon & Co ....B 713 222-8804
Houston *(G-12599)*

Western Precast Concrete Inc ....D 915 859-9362
El Paso *(G-6032)*

Western Ready Mix LLC ....F 830 433-1963
Seguin *(G-18873)*

Wilbert Burial Vault Corp ....F 817 481-3577
Grapevine *(G-8060)*

Wilbert Funeral Services Inc ....F 972 291-7854
Cedar Hill *(G-2956)*

Wilbert Funeral Services Inc ....F 806 762-1162
Lubbock *(G-14513)*

Wilbert Funeral Services Inc ....F 210 922-2122
San Antonio *(G-18619)*

Wilbert Funeral Services Inc ....F 972 875-9605
Ennis *(G-6123)*

Wise Products Co Inc ....F 903 378-2233
Honey Grove *(G-8359)*

▲ Xella Aircrete North Amer Inc ....F 229 896-1593
San Antonio *(G-18626)*

3273 Ready-Mixed Concrete

849 Red Baron Supply Co LLC ....E 903 882-1700
Lindale *(G-14132)*

Affordable Asphalt Paving Inc ....F 903 596-7003
Tyler *(G-20044)*

Alamo Concrete Products Ltd ....F 512 444-2464
Austin *(G-904)*

Alamo Concrete Products Ltd ....F 210 208-1880
San Antonio *(G-17882)*

Alamo Concrete Products Ltd ....F 361 578-9678
Victoria *(G-20237)*

Alamo Concrete Products Ltd ....F 830 773-6334
Eagle Pass *(G-5547)*

Alamo Concrete Products Ltd ....F 361 552-9525
Port Lavaca *(G-17141)*

Alamo Concrete Products Ltd ....D 512 444-2464
Austin *(G-905)*

Alamo Concrete Products Ltd ....F 210 208-1580
San Antonio *(G-18636)*

Alamo Concrete Products Ltd ....F 979 245-8365
Bay City *(G-1767)*

Alamo Concrete Products Ltd ....F 979 345-4631
West Columbia *(G-20673)*

Alamo Concrete Products Ltd ....F 979 849-6378
West Columbia *(G-20674)*

Alamo Concrete Products Ltd ....E 210 208-1500
San Antonio *(G-17881)*

Alamo Concrete Products Ltd ....E 361 289-9200
Corpus Christi *(G-3471)*

Alamo Concrete Products Ltd ....F 361 572-0231
Victoria *(G-20236)*

Alamo Concrete Products L ....G 361 592-5114
Kingsville *(G-13623)*

Alamo Lumber Company ....F 361 275-2321
Cuero *(G-3758)*

Alamo Ready Mix LLC ....E 713 330-3000
Houston *(G-8523)*

Alleyton Resource Company LLC ....E 281 238-1010
Columbus *(G-3228)*

Alpha Ready Mix LLC ....F 512 846-2221
Hutto *(G-12875)*

◆ Ameron International Corp ....E 713 375-3700
Houston *(G-8623)*

Ant Enterprises Incorporated ....D 281 456-7446
Baytown *(G-1778)*

Arcosa Aggregates Inc ....E 254 662-1025
Waco *(G-20364)*

Arcosa Aggregates Inc ....F 972 287-4343
Seagoville *(G-18798)*

Arcosa Aggregates Inc ....F 254 982-4158
Rogers *(G-17573)*

Arcosa Lw Ky LLC ....F 214 631-4420
Dallas *(G-3960)*

Argos USA LLC ....D 713 664-4527
Jersey Village *(G-13291)*

Argos USA LLC ....D 817 551-0931
Fort Worth *(G-6400)*

Argos USA LLC ....D 817 468-1333
Arlington *(G-623)*

Argos USA LLC ....F 281 391-4554
Katy *(G-13350)*

Argos USA LLC ....F 713 273-2700
Sugar Land *(G-19446)*

Argos USA LLC ....F 972 621-0999
Irving *(G-12932)*

Argos USA LLC ....F 972 436-3026
Lewisville *(G-14023)*

Argos USA LLC ....G 713 692-4408
Houston *(G-8689)*

Argos USA LLC ....D 817 329-8550
Grapevine *(G-8012)*

Argos USA LLC ....D 972 256-6571
Irving *(G-12933)*

Argos USA LLC ....F 972 285-8823
Mesquite *(G-15027)*

Argos USA LLC ....F 713 273-2800
Houston *(G-8690)*

Argos USA LLC ....E 972 556-0735
Dallas *(G-3965)*

Art Mix LLC ....G 713 552-9028
Houston *(G-8708)*

Austin Ready-Mix LLC ....F 512 386-7187
Austin *(G-958)*

B & B Ready Mix Inc ....F 972 287-9998
Seagoville *(G-18799)*

B Mayfield McCraw ....D 903 664-2332
Telephone *(G-19665)*

Bell Concrete Products Co ....F 903 885-3126
Sulphur Springs *(G-19581)*

Bodin Concrete LP ....E 972 463-7348
Rowlett *(G-17702)*

Borger Redi-Mix Con Co Inc ....E 806 273-2874
Borger *(G-2166)*

Boyd Ready Mix Inc ....E 979 778-5199
Bryan *(G-2458)*

Breckenridge Ready Mix Inc ....F 254 559-3775
Breckenridge *(G-2226)*

Brenham Ready Mix Inc ....F 979 830-1989
Brenham *(G-2246)*

Brm Concrete ....F 346 570-2975
Houston *(G-8987)*

Brookhollow Rental Co Inc ....F 214 631-6883
Dallas *(G-4059)*

Budget Ready Mix ....F 281 452-5233
Channelview *(G-3014)*

Budget Ready Mix LLC ....E 281 452-5233
Houston *(G-9010)*

Bullet Concrete Materials Inc ....F 281 367-9747
Conroe *(G-3267)*

Burnco Texas LLC ....E 940 242-3100
Irving *(G-12954)*

Cajun Ready Mix Ltd ....E 936 597-8455
Montgomery *(G-15627)*

Campbell Concrete & Mtls LP ....F 281 277-0022
Sugar Land *(G-19453)*

Campbell Concrete & Mtls LP ....F 713 734-6600
Houston *(G-9081)*

Campbell Concrete & Mtls LP ....F 281 424-5650
Baytown *(G-1810)*

▲ Campbell Concrete & Mtls LP ....E 281 592-5201
Houston *(G-9082)*

Campbell Concrete & Mtls LP ....G 713 783-4761
Houston *(G-9083)*

Campbell Concrete & Mtls LP ....F 281 391-4700
Katy *(G-13391)*

Campbell Concrete & Mtls LP ....F 281 356-5444
Magnolia *(G-14593)*

Campbell Concrete & Mtls LP ....F 281 491-7376
Richmond *(G-17451)*

Canadian Redi-Mix Inc ....F 806 323-5379
Canadian *(G-2647)*

Cementos Ready Mix ....G 432 385-7477
Odessa *(G-15956)*

Cemex Inc ....F 713 332-4070
Jersey Village *(G-13295)*

Cemex Inc ....D 830 625-7338
New Braunfels *(G-15778)*

◆ Cemex Inc ....B 713 650-6200
Houston *(G-9120)*

Cemex Cement Inc ....D 432 385-2800
Odessa *(G-15957)*

◆ Cemex Cement Inc ....B 713 650-6200
Houston *(G-9121)*

▲ Cemex Construction Mtls LP ....F 713 650-6200
Houston *(G-9122)*

Cemex Construction Mtls S LLC	F	956 386-1452	Edinburg (G-5581)

Cemex Construction Mtls S LLC ....F 956 386-1452
   Edinburg (G-5581)
Cemex Construction Mtls S LLC ....E 915 855-9658
   El Paso (G-5689)
Cemex Construction Mtls S LLC ....F 281 457-0031
   Channelview (G-3015)
Cemex Construction Mtls S LLC ....E 713 650-6200
   Houston (G-9123)
Cemex Construction Mtls S LLC ....E 915 565-4681
   El Paso (G-5690)
Cemex Construction Mtls S LLC ....E 713 967-5416
   Houston (G-9124)
Cemex Construction Mtls S LLC ....E 956 943-2472
   Port Isabel (G-17136)
Cemex Construction Mtls S LLC ....E 281 260-9651
   Houston (G-9125)
Cemex Construction Mtls S LLC ....E 501 350-2696
   Levelland (G-14005)
Cemex Construction Mtls S LLC ....E 210 250-4100
   New Braunfels (G-15780)
Cemex Construction Mtls S LLC ....E 281 391-2655
   Katy (G-13357)
Cemex Construction Mtls S LLC ....F 512 247-3400
   Del Valle (G-5329)
Cemex Construction Mtls S LLC ....E 281 444-8306
   Houston (G-9127)
Cemex Construction Mtls S LLC ....G 713 767-7983
   Houston (G-9129)
Cemex Construction Mtls S LLC ....A 713 650-6200
   Houston (G-9128)
Cemex El Paso Inc ....C 915 565-4681
   El Paso (G-5691)
Cemex International Trdg LLC ....E 713 650-6200
   Houston (G-9130)
Cemex Materials LLC ....E 713 650-6200
   Houston (G-9131)
Cemex Materials LLC ....E 210 677-8191
   Castroville (G-2926)
Cemex Materials LLC ....E 210 677-8191
   San Antonio (G-17991)
Cemex Materials LLC ....D 832 590-5400
   Houston (G-9132)
Cemex Materials LLC ....E 940 665-8355
   Gainesville (G-7337)
Cemex Southeast LLC ....C 713 722-5818
   Houston (G-9133)
Cemex Trading LLC ....F 713 650-6200
   Houston (G-9134)
Cemex USA Inc ....C 432 385-2892
   Odessa (G-15958)
Centex Materials LLC ....E 512 251-5106
   Austin (G-1038)
Centex Materials LLC ....E 512 444-9591
   Austin (G-1039)
▲ Centex Materials LLC ....F 512 460-3003
   Austin (G-1040)
Centex Materials LLC ....E 512 295-4801
   Buda (G-2525)
Central Ready Mix Concrete Co ....E 956 383-2261
   San Juan (G-18672)
Central Ready Mix Concrete Co ....E 956 541-6082
   San Benito (G-18655)
Charleys Concrete Co Ltd ....E 817 431-2016
   Euless (G-6135)
Charleys Concrete Co Ltd ....E 817 431-3515
   Fort Worth (G-6510)
Charleys Concrete Co Ltd ....E 972 734-6300
   Princeton (G-17205)
Charleys Concrete Co Ltd ....E 817 568-2400
   Crowley (G-3753)
Childs Ready-Mix Concrete Co ....F 254 968-4755
   Stephenville (G-19408)
Childs Ready-Mix Concrete Co ....F 817 594-3832
   Willow Park (G-20872)
◆ Chryso Inc ....E 972 772-6010
   Rockwall (G-17542)
City Concrete Inc ....F 817 636-2690
   Rhome (G-17253)
City Ready Mix Inc ....E 956 722-6315
   Laredo (G-13874)
Coastal Crushed Concrete LLC ....E 713 941-3232
   Houston (G-9224)
Coastal Ready Mix Inc ....E 409 287-3307
   Nederland (G-15749)
Concho Concrete Company Inc ....E 325 653-3354
   San Angelo (G-17790)
Concrete Mobility LLC ....F 325 728-5858
   Colorado City (G-3223)
◆ Conroe Concrete Ltd ....D 936 539-1761
   Conroe (G-3281)

Continntal Con Mxer Sltons LLC ....E 859 234-1100
   Austin (G-1062)
Contractors Supplies Inc ....E 936 634-3341
   Lufkin (G-14523)
Contractors Supplies Inc ....E 903 753-5766
   Longview (G-14213)
Contractors Supplies Inc ....E 903 597-1308
   Tyler (G-20072)
Contractors Supplies Inc ....F 903 670-1085
   Athens (G-824)
Cooper Concrete Co ....E 972 276-1167
   Garland (G-7463)
Cowboys Ready Mix LLC ....E 281 972-7000
   Wallisville (G-20511)
Cowtown Redi Mix Inc ....F 817 759-1919
   Fort Worth (G-6552)
Coyote Ready Mix LLC ....F 832 432-2025
   Magnolia (G-14598)
Crh Americas Materials Inc ....C 409 866-1444
   Beaumont (G-1878)
◆ Custom Crete Inc ....C 972 243-4466
   Dallas (G-4195)
Custom Crete Inc ....E 512 443-5787
   Austin (G-1079)
Custom Crete Inc ....F 713 937-3966
   Houston (G-9369)
Ddm Materials Inc ....F 970 726-1122
   Valley View (G-20202)
Dorsett Bros Concrete Sup Inc ....E 281 487-0264
   Pasadena (G-16419)
Eagle Materials Inc ....C 214 432-2000
   Dallas (G-4292)
El Paso Star Ready-Mix ....E 915 860-8555
   El Paso (G-5742)
Erasmo Lopez Jr ....E 956 487-3366
   Rio Grande City (G-17471)
Far South Mining LLC ....G 210 688-2607
   San Antonio (G-18104)
Farris Concrete Company ....D 972 838-2217
   Melissa (G-14997)
Few Ready Mix Corp ....D 936 560-5675
   Nacogdoches (G-15696)
◆ Fritz-Pak Corporation ....F 214 221-9494
   Mesquite (G-15044)
G E Huebner Concrete Inc ....F 979 865-2274
   Bellville (G-2009)
Gcc Rio Grande Inc ....F 915 544-1750
   El Paso (G-5779)
Granchelli Construction LLC ....F 956 928-1122
   McAllen (G-14867)
Great Southern Ready Mix LLC ....E 281 689-9339
   New Caney (G-15841)
Gulf Coast Con & Shell Inc ....D 281 238-8883
   Manvel (G-14734)
Halls Lumber Inc ....F 806 285-2393
   Olton (G-16226)
Hanson Aggregates LLC ....E 806 372-8114
   Amarillo (G-432)
Hanson Aggregates LLC ....F 972 875-9590
   Ennis (G-6107)
Hanson Aggregates LLC ....F 254 622-3239
   Clifton (G-3144)
Hanson Aggregates LLC ....E 713 692-4408
   Houston (G-10118)
Hanson Aggregates LLC ....E 713 937-7405
   Houston (G-10119)
Hanson Aggregates LLC ....F 281 238-4759
   Richmond (G-17456)
Hanson Aggregates LLC ....C 469 417-1200
   Irving (G-13049)
Hanson Aggregates LLC ....F 972 644-6415
   Richardson (G-17326)
Hanson Aggregates LLC ....F 972 263-2181
   Grand Prairie (G-7887)
Hanson Aggregates LLC ....F 281 367-4557
   Conroe (G-3301)
Hanson Aggregates LLC ....F 972 256-6571
   Irving (G-13050)
Hanson Aggregates LLC ....F 972 556-0735
   Dallas (G-4433)
Hanson Aggregates LLC ....F 903 794-6161
   Texarkana (G-19764)
▲ Hanson Aggregates New York LLC ..E 972 621-0345
   Irving (G-13051)
Hanson Concrete Balch Springs ....F 972 289-0601
   Mesquite (G-15048)
Hanson Lehigh Inc ....G 281 491-7376
   Dallas (G-4434)
◆ Hanson Lehigh Inc ....B 972 653-5500
   Irving (G-13052)

Hanson Lehigh Inc ....E 281 616-0700
   Houston (G-10120)
Heath Transit Mix Concrete Co ....F 432 283-2127
   Van Horn (G-20214)
High Plains Concrete Company ....F 806 293-8313
   Plainview (G-16757)
Highland Concrete Co ....F 432 561-5858
   Midland (G-15246)
Houston Cnty Ready-Mix Con Co ....F 936 544-7200
   Crockett (G-3720)
Houston Ready Mix LLC ....F 832 532-7408
   Sugar Land (G-19494)
Houtex Ready Mix ....E 713 987-0303
   Houston (G-10267)
Hueco Quarry Inc ....F 915 859-5767
   El Paso (G-5806)
Hunter Construction Inc ....D 806 244-5331
   Dalhart (G-3835)
Image Concrete Inc ....E 817 430-0339
   Dallas (G-4486)
Ingram Concrete LLC ....E 325 677-2001
   Abilene (G-52)
Ingram Readymix Inc ....E 830 379-2765
   Seguin (G-18844)
Ingram Readymix Inc ....E 361 533-2225
   Corpus Christi (G-3553)
Ingram Readymix Inc ....E 210 633-9161
   San Antonio (G-18183)
Ingram Readymix Inc ....E 830 606-9619
   New Braunfels (G-15805)
Ingram Readymix Inc ....E 361 552-6071
   Port Lavaca (G-17150)
Ingram Readymix Inc ....E 210 798-2676
   San Antonio (G-18184)
Ingram Readymix Inc ....E 830 672-6420
   Gonzales (G-7757)
Ingram Readymix Inc ....E 361 575-6358
   Victoria (G-20273)
Ingram Readymix Inc ....E 830 693-4396
   Marble Falls (G-14745)
Ingram Readymix Inc ....E 830 896-4525
   Kerrville (G-13521)
Ingram Readymix Inc ....E 210 659-4468
   Converse (G-3397)
Ingram Readymix Inc ....E 830 569-2187
   Pleasanton (G-17070)
Ingram Readymix Inc ....E 956 722-8736
   Laredo (G-13896)
Ingram Readymix Inc ....E 210 492-8851
   San Antonio (G-18185)
Ingram Readymix Inc ....E 830 249-3506
   Boerne (G-2122)
Ingram Readymix Inc ....D 361 888-9281
   Corpus Christi (G-3554)
Ingram Readymix Inc ....E 512 396-3136
   San Marcos (G-18696)
Ingram Readymix Inc ....F 830 997-6506
   Fredericksburg (G-7183)
Ingram Readymix Inc ....E 361 516-1756
   Kingsville (G-13629)
Ingram Readymix Inc ....F 830 334-3622
   Pearsall (G-16613)
Ingram Readymix Inc ....E 210 622-5621
   San Antonio (G-18186)
J-III Concrete Co ....F 956 787-5518
   Pharr (G-16702)
J-III Concrete Co ....E 956 968-1371
   Weslaco (G-20661)
J-III Concrete Co ....G 361 396-1951
   Alice (G-217)
Jimmie Hahn Partnership Ltd ....E 979 836-3664
   Brenham (G-2259)
Jobe Materials LP ....B 915 298-9900
   El Paso (G-5821)
Johnson County Redi-Mix Ltd ....F 817 556-9214
   Cleburne (G-3099)
K C Crushed Concrete Inc ....E 281 219-0820
   Houston (G-10495)
Killeen Ready Mix Ltd ....E 254 634-4514
   Killeen (G-13613)
Knife River Corp - South ....F 979 361-2900
   College Station (G-3191)
Knife River Corporation ....D 979 779-1112
   Bryan (G-2487)
Knife River Corporation ....D 409 842-2100
   Beaumont (G-1915)
Knife River Corporation ....D 979 361-2900
   Bryan (G-2488)
Kosmos Cement Company Inc ....F 713 722-1788
   Houston (G-10561)

Koy Concrete Ltd	E	281 391-2178	
Katy (G-13421)			
La Grange Con & Aggregates	F	979 836-3664	
Brenham (G-2260)			
Laredo Ready Mix Ltd	D	956 723-7429	
Laredo (G-13906)			
Lattimore Materials Company LP	E	817 491-2400	
Roanoke (G-17487)			
▲ Lattimore Materials Corp	C	972 221-4646	
Addison (G-143)			
Lattimore Materials Corp	E	972 423-8359	
Plano (G-16907)			
Lattimore Materials Corp	D	972 569-4622	
McKinney (G-14951)			
Lattimore Materials Corp	E	972 346-3002	
Prosper (G-17214)			
Lattimore Materials Corp	F	903 868-9585	
Sherman (G-18920)			
Lauren Concrete Inc	D	512 389-2113	
Austin (G-1283)			
Lauren Concrete Inc	E	512 233-1348	
Round Rock (G-17667)			
Lauren Concrete LP	F	512 389-2113	
Round Rock (G-17668)			
Legacy Vulcan LLC	F	830 693-2756	
Marble Falls (G-14747)			
Legacy Vulcan LLC	F	254 629-2850	
Eastland (G-5566)			
Legacy Vulcan LLC	F	817 594-4524	
Millsap (G-15504)			
Legacy Vulcan LLC	E	325 676-0001	
Abilene (G-57)			
Legacy Vulcan LLC	E	210 349-3311	
San Antonio (G-18242)			
Legacy Vulcan LLC	F	830 934-2625	
Knippa (G-13661)			
Legacy Vulcan LLC	E	956 831-8888	
Brownsville (G-2376)			
Legacy Vulcan LLC	D	210 492-1053	
San Antonio (G-18243)			
Lehigh Cement Company LLC	D	254 776-7162	
Waco (G-20425)			
Lehigh Cement Company LLC	D	254 772-9350	
Waco (G-20426)			
▲ Lehigh Cement Company LLC	C	877 534-4442	
Irving (G-13085)			
Lehigh Hanson Inc	D	713 466-6306	
Houston (G-10622)			
Liberty Materials Inc	E	281 572-4003	
Conroe (G-3320)			
Lilly Construction Inc	E	325 392-2669	
Ozona (G-16285)			
Liquid-Stone Concrete	E	817 295-5151	
Burleson (G-2587)			
Live Oak Materials Inc	E	361 775-0065	
Ingleside (G-12896)			
Lmp Readymix LLC	F	903 572-2500	
Mount Pleasant (G-15653)			
Lone Star Ready-Mix LP	F	512 260-0300	
Leander (G-13994)			
Lone Star Ready-Mix LP	E	512 260-3629	
Austin (G-1300)			
Magic Valley Concrete LLC	E	956 432-0600	
Palmview (G-16311)			
Mainland Concrete Inc	E	281 337-7400	
Texas City (G-19797)			
Martin Marietta Materials Inc	E	830 741-8227	
Hondo (G-8355)			
Martin Marietta Materials Inc	E	409 835-4933	
Beaumont (G-1926)			
Martin Marietta Materials Inc	F	972 647-4985	
Midlothian (G-15484)			
▲ Martin Mrtta Mtls Suthwest LLC	B	210 208-4400	
San Antonio (G-18280)			
Mesquite Concrete Inc	F	830 216-1530	
Falls City (G-6183)			
Metro Ready Mix Ltd Company	F	713 991-6466	
Houston (G-10856)			
Mid-County Ready Mix	E	830 876-3800	
Carrizo Springs (G-2686)			
Miniconcrete Materials Inc	F	915 852-4468	
El Paso (G-5880)			
Modern Concrete & Mtls LLC	F	409 840-2080	
Beaumont (G-1929)			
Montana Nelson Ready Mix LLC	G	936 328-5688	
Livingston (G-14159)			
Mullen-Telles Inc	D	915 859-5767	
El Paso (G-5891)			
Murphy & Murphy Inc	F	940 325-2666	
Mineral Wells (G-15533)			
Navasota Concrete Inc	F	936 825-8106	
Navasota (G-15741)			
Nelson Bros Ready Mix Ltd	D	972 436-6558	
Lewisville (G-14073)			
New Boston Concrete Inc	F	903 628-3556	
New Boston (G-15767)			
Newhrm LP	E	713 978-7474	
Houston (G-11041)			
Nortex Redimix LLC	F	214 681-5200	
Farmers Branch (G-6210)			
Nortex Redimix LLC	E	214 681-5200	
Aubrey (G-851)			
OK Concrete Company	E	940 723-4324	
Wichita Falls (G-20790)			
OK Concrete Company	F	940 552-5162	
Vernon (G-20228)			
Old Castle Apg Texas Inc	E	512 864-9601	
Georgetown (G-7669)			
Otis T Dickerson	F	713 988-2533	
Pearland (G-16585)			
Pampa Concrete Co Inc	E	806 669-3111	
Pampa (G-16331)			
Pb Materials Holdings Inc	E	806 745-5332	
Lubbock (G-14459)			
Pb Materials Holdings Inc	D	432 208-2761	
Kermit (G-13513)			
Porter Ready-Mix Inc	E	281 354-5181	
Porter (G-17181)			
Porter Ready-Mix Inc	E	281 443-6363	
Houston (G-11367)			
Powerhouse Ready-Mix LLC	F	832 620-1922	
Rosenberg (G-17594)			
Precision Ready Mix Ltd	F	210 872-6053	
San Antonio (G-18387)			
Quality Readymix Ltd LLP	F	361 289-2515	
Corpus Christi (G-3603)			
Redi-Mix LLC	E	210 651-4141	
Garden Ridge (G-7419)			
Redi-Mix LLC	D	817 835-4105	
Euless (G-6153)			
Redi-Mix LP	E	972 335-2060	
Frisco (G-7263)			
Redi-Mix LP	E	817 561-9785	
Kennedale (G-13502)			
Redi-Mix LP	F	972 242-4550	
Carrollton (G-2885)			
Redi-Mix LP	F	817 485-4850	
Euless (G-6154)			
Richmond Materials Inc	E	281 238-5488	
Richmond (G-17465)			
River City Ready Mix Inc	F	210 520-1941	
San Antonio (G-18427)			
▲ RMC Usa Inc	F	713 650-6200	
Houston (G-11637)			
Roger D Stevens Contractor	F	830 796-3714	
Bandera (G-1744)			
Sandy Hill Redi-Mix Con Co	F	940 627-8769	
Decatur (G-5253)			
Sealy Concrete Inc	E	281 391-3435	
Sealy (G-18818)			
Solid Rock Ready Mix Inc	F	281 931-3003	
Houston (G-11940)			
South Texas Concrete	D	956 381-9886	
Edinburg (G-5602)			
South Texas Concrete	F	956 464-4440	
Donna (G-5491)			
South Texas Concrete	E	956 485-2301	
Sullivan City (G-19577)			
Southdown Inc	B	713 650-6200	
Houston (G-11971)			
St Ready Mix LLC	E	830 480-0933	
Jourdanton (G-13334)			
Strickland Bridge Inc	E	940 864-2677	
Haskell (G-8214)			
Strong Ready Mix Ltd	F	325 260-6935	
Abilene (G-84)			
Sweetwater Ready-Mix Con Co	F	325 236-6200	
Sweetwater (G-19638)			
Tarrant Concrete Co Inc	D	817 926-6660	
Fort Worth (G-7035)			
Texas Aggregates LP	E	512 303-4215	
Bastrop (G-1762)			
Texas Concrete Enterprise LLC	F	713 227-1122	
Houston (G-12226)			
Texas Concrete Entp Rdymx Inc	E	713 227-1122	
Houston (G-12227)			
Texas Industries Inc	E	972 775-3449	
Midlothian (G-15495)			
Texas Industries Inc	C	940 683-4277	
Bridgeport (G-2303)			
Texas Industries Inc	E	903 873-2849	
Wills Point (G-20878)			
Texas Industries Inc	D	972 556-0751	
Dallas (G-5063)			
Texas Industries Inc	F	903 758-7351	
Longview (G-14316)			
Texas Industries Inc	F	903 454-2029	
Greenville (G-8094)			
Texas Industries Inc	E	512 276-7990	
Manor (G-14650)			
Texas Industries Inc	D	817 838-4212	
Fort Worth (G-7048)			
▲ Texas Industries Inc	C	972 647-6700	
Dallas (G-5062)			
Texcon Ready Mix Inc	D	281 572-1712	
Porter (G-17183)			
Thomas Redi-Mix Company Inc	E	806 381-8485	
Amarillo (G-467)			
Top Cat Ready Mix LLC	D	972 486-3162	
Dallas (G-5100)			
Torres Brothers	F	713 732-4237	
Houston (G-12324)			
Treffinger Inc	E	972 286-8852	
Dallas (G-5106)			
Triple C Concrete Lubbock Ltd	E	806 762-3227	
Lubbock (G-14499)			
Triple S Ready Mix LLC	E	830 769-2629	
Jourdanton (G-13335)			
Troy Vines Incorporated	F	432 682-7031	
Midland (G-15447)			
True Grit Redi Mix Ltd	E	817 439-5914	
Fort Worth (G-7081)			
Txi Operations LP	C	936 295-7672	
Huntsville (G-12826)			
▲ Txi Operations LP	C	972 647-6700	
Dallas (G-5125)			
▼ US Concrete Inc	E	817 835-4105	
Euless (G-6166)			
US Concrete Inc	E	806 373-4951	
Amarillo (G-472)			
Uvalde Concrete Inc	E	830 278-9200	
Uvalde (G-20198)			
Vulcan Construction Mtls LLC	F	210 492-1053	
San Antonio (G-18602)			
Vulcan Construction Mtls LLC	E	254 629-2850	
Eastland (G-5570)			
Vulcan Materials Company	F	713 631-7200	
Houston (G-12583)			
Vulcan Materials Company	F	409 833-4177	
Beaumont (G-1967)			
Vulcan Materials Company	F	972 335-0008	
Frisco (G-7325)			
Vulcan Materials Company	F	325 529-3785	
Abilene (G-91)			
Vulcan Materials Company	F	210 695-3081	
Helotes (G-8244)			
Vulcan Materials Company	F	210 349-3311	
San Antonio (G-18603)			
Vulcan Materials Company	F	210 494-9555	
San Antonio (G-18604)			
W P Murphy Inc	E	210 658-4947	
Schertz (G-18769)			
Wise Ready Mix Concrete	E	940 683-5260	
Bridgeport (G-2305)			
Yarrington Road Materials LP	F	512 306-7800	
Austin (G-1678)			

3274 Lime

Austin White Lime Company	F	512 255-3646	
Austin (G-966)			
Chemical Lime-Southwest LLC	F	281 431-0575	
Rosharon (G-17602)			
Chemical Lime-Southwest LLC	E	512 756-8668	
Burnet (G-2604)			
Chemical Lime-Southwest LLC	E	281 471-4500	
La Porte (G-13727)			
Chemical Lime-Southwest LLC	E	817 268-1188	
Hurst (G-12842)			
Chemical Lime-Southwest LLC	C	254 675-8668	
Clifton (G-3142)			
▲ Kdm Holding Inc	D	817 732-8164	
Fort Worth (G-6752)			
Lhoist North America Inc	D	830 625-2327	
New Braunfels (G-15809)			
Lhoist North America Inc	E	214 544-1717	
McKinney (G-14954)			
▲ Lhoist North America Ala LLC	D	817 732-8164	
Fort Worth (G-6785)			
Lhoist North America Ala LLC	E	817 268-1187	
Hurst (G-12849)			

Lhoist North America MO Inc ....D 817 732-8164
  Fort Worth *(G-6786)*
Lhoist North America Texas Ltd ....E 830 625-2327
  New Braunfels *(G-15810)*
Lhoist North America Texas Ltd ....E 512 756-8668
  Burnet *(G-2611)*
Lhoist North America Texas Ltd ....E 817 732-8164
  Hurst *(G-12850)*
▲ Lime Holding Inc ....C 817 732-8164
  Fort Worth *(G-6790)*
▲ Martin Mrtta Mtls Suthwest LLC ......B 210 208-4400
  San Antonio *(G-18280)*
Texas Lime Company ....D 817 641-4433
  Cleburne *(G-3114)*
United States Lime & Mnrl Inc ....E 972 991-8400
  Dallas *(G-5138)*

3275 Gypsum Prdts

▲ American Gypsum Company ....C 214 530-5500
  Dallas *(G-3943)*
Caraustar Industries Inc ....E 903 793-6231
  Texarkana *(G-19758)*
Casting Designs Inc ....E 817 551-7373
  Fort Worth *(G-6496)*
Eagle Materials Inc ....C 214 432-2000
  Dallas *(G-4292)*
Enviro-San Corporation ....F 281 373-4200
  Cypress *(G-3788)*
Georgia-Pacific Bldg Pdts LLC ....F 830 557-5802
  Mc Queeney *(G-14828)*
Georgia-Pacific Bldg Pdts LLC ....F 830 997-4341
  Fredericksburg *(G-7181)*
Georgia-Pacific LLC ....C 940 663-6111
  Quanah *(G-17217)*
Georgia-Pacific LLC ....C 936 829-5511
  Diboll *(G-5466)*
Georgia-Pacific LLC ....B 866 924-1397
  El Paso *(G-5784)*
Lsf8 Gypsum Holdings LP ....A 703 480-3800
  Dallas *(G-4609)*
Murphy Wall Products Intl Inc ....E 713 694-8365
  Houston *(G-10943)*
Ng Operations LLC ....D 325 735-2221
  Rotan *(G-17618)*
Ng Operations LLC ....E 817 645-3435
  Cleburne *(G-3104)*
Ng Operations LLC ....F 972 660-7140
  Grand Prairie *(G-7935)*
Ng Operations LLC ....D 830 864-4100
  Harper *(G-8210)*
Unifix Inc ....E 817 645-3435
  Cleburne *(G-3116)*
United States Gypsum Company ....C 713 308-5400
  Galena Park *(G-7385)*
United States Gypsum Company ....E 214 424-2500
  Dallas *(G-5137)*

3281 Cut Stone Prdts

77 Stone ....F 915 590-0770
  El Paso *(G-5631)*
▲ A J Brauer Stone ....D 512 746-5792
  Jarrell *(G-13268)*
▲ Aguado Stone Incorporated ....D 512 746-5094
  Georgetown *(G-7632)*
◆ Allied Stone Inc ....D 214 838-2225
  Dallas *(G-3927)*
American Marble Mosaic Company ....E 713 747-7634
  Houston *(G-8600)*
Arnold Stone Inc ....F 972 248-1953
  Lewisville *(G-14024)*
Artistic Counters Inc ....C 210 651-3281
  Garden Ridge *(G-7418)*
Ashcraft-Southern Marble Co ....E 903 581-5501
  Tyler *(G-20049)*
Aspen Marble Inc ....F 817 478-5140
  Fort Worth *(G-6404)*
Bedrock Manufacturing Co LP ....E 214 247-2453
  Dallas *(G-4013)*
Bolfing Brothers Marble Inc ....E 281 351-7195
  Cypress *(G-3782)*
Bonanza Industries Inc ....D 713 466-7900
  Houston *(G-8948)*
Builders Depot Direct LLC ....F 832 384-7272
  Houston *(G-9012)*
Capitol Aggregates Inc ....C 210 871-7228
  San Antonio *(G-17982)*
Choice Fabricated Stone LLC ....E 817 222-2201
  Fort Worth *(G-6515)*
Churchill Manufacturing Inc ....F 903 660-4585
  Hallsville *(G-8128)*

▼ Colorado Stone Pdts Texas Inc ....D 972 434-2515
  Carrollton *(G-2716)*
Continental Cut Stone Inc ....E 254 793-2329
  Florence *(G-6238)*
▲ Craig Baker Marble Co Inc ....D 281 492-2365
  Barker *(G-1745)*
Custom Crete Inc ....F 713 937-3966
  Houston *(G-9369)*
Dallas Cast Stone II Corp ....E 940 382-6922
  Dallas *(G-4213)*
Dallas Marble Company Inc ....D 972 291-9145
  Midlothian *(G-15478)*
Decorum Tile & Stone Inc ....F 512 344-9235
  Austin *(G-1087)*
▲ Delta Granite and Marble Inc ....E 210 829-7171
  San Antonio *(G-18050)*
▲ Designer Stone Center Inc ....E 713 862-0120
  Houston *(G-9443)*
Dimension In Stone & Glass ....F 214 651-7230
  Alba *(G-182)*
Dura-Mar Venus Inc ....D 972 223-8008
  Desoto *(G-5430)*
Dutch Marble Creations ....F 956 399-6767
  San Benito *(G-18656)*
Elm Mott Marble Co ....E 254 829-1552
  Elm Mott *(G-6064)*
Featherlite Building Pdts Corp ....B 512 472-2424
  Austin *(G-1147)*
Fort Worth Crushed Stone LLC ....E 817 596-5512
  Weatherford *(G-20593)*
◆ Gemstar Stoneworks Inc ....E 281 257-6500
  Spring *(G-19124)*
GMI Stone LLC ....F 469 360-8847
  Dallas *(G-4411)*
Gold Star Marble Corporation ....E 512 251-9279
  Austin *(G-1186)*
▲ Golden Stones LP ....E 713 934-7887
  Houston *(G-9994)*
▲ Import Mdsg Concepts GP LLC ....F 214 572-2000
  Addison *(G-136)*
Incounters Inc ....E 325 675-5909
  Abilene *(G-51)*
Irving Counter Inc ....E 972 438-4343
  Irving *(G-13066)*
J & J Stone Company ....E 512 869-3527
  Jarrell *(G-13271)*
Justin Industries Inc ....D 512 258-1474
  Cedar Park *(G-2975)*
K & K Langham Ltd ....D 512 835-5100
  Austin *(G-1263)*
Kamal Incorporated ....D 210 695-2678
  Helotes *(G-8241)*
Killeen Marble ....E 254 699-3408
  Killeen *(G-13612)*
Lavender Enterprises Inc ....E 214 631-8080
  Dallas *(G-4585)*
Lithic Industries Inc ....F 254 793-3791
  Florence *(G-6240)*
Marble & Granite Resources ....F 713 957-2646
  Houston *(G-10759)*
Marble Gallery Inc ....F 903 759-4726
  Longview *(G-14274)*
Marble Masters of Texas Inc ....E 830 303-7744
  New Braunfels *(G-15811)*
Mezger Enterprises Ltd ....D 254 547-8207
  Lueders *(G-14518)*
Mj Stone LLC ....F 832 887-3575
  Houston *(G-10894)*
National Stone Ltd ....E 214 651-7667
  Grand Prairie *(G-7930)*
National Stone Inc ....F 214 651-7667
  Irving *(G-13112)*
▲ Natural Stone Inc ....F 713 678-4407
  Houston *(G-11011)*
Northside Cultured Marble Inc ....G 281 429-5288
  Conroe *(G-3343)*
Ortega Bath Environments Inc ....E 806 763-5777
  Lubbock *(G-14454)*
Panel Specialists Inc ....E 254 774-9197
  Temple *(G-19694)*
Permian Limestone ....E 254 547-8207
  Kempner *(G-13487)*
Pks Designs Inc ....F 817 429-5174
  Alvarado *(G-337)*
▲ Qts LLC ....E 713 462-7072
  Houston *(G-11489)*
Quarries Direct International ....E 602 269-7900
  Dallas *(G-4847)*
▲ Quarries Direct Intl LLC ....E 713 808-9849
  Houston *(G-11509)*

Ralph Cordova Company ....E 972 771-7281
  Royse City *(G-17725)*
Rawlins Monument Inc ....F 817 594-2726
  Weatherford *(G-20614)*
▲ Real Granite Inc ....E 210 732-8350
  San Antonio *(G-18414)*
Red Dog Track Inc ....E 254 672-5261
  Strawn *(G-19432)*
Regal Marble Co ....F 361 572-8498
  Victoria *(G-20300)*
Royal Baths Manufacturing Co ....B 281 442-3400
  Houston *(G-11682)*
Royal Baths Mfg Co Ltd ....E 512 707-0094
  Buda *(G-2535)*
▲ S C S C Inc ....E 214 398-1199
  Dallas *(G-4922)*
Sawyer Technical Materials LLC ....D 936 756-8886
  Conroe *(G-3361)*
▲ Sigma MBL Granite-Houston Inc ....E 713 290-8530
  Houston *(G-11886)*
Siri Granite Inc ....F 832 203-8322
  Houston *(G-11907)*
Siteworks Incorporated ....E 281 931-1000
  Houston *(G-11909)*
▲ Southwest Marble & Granite Inc ....G 512 918-0135
  Austin *(G-1712)*
Stone Masters ....F 915 216-1702
  El Paso *(G-5982)*
Stone Production Inc ....E 512 990-9800
  Austin *(G-1539)*
Stone Systems Centl Texas LLC ....E 512 295-2950
  Austin *(G-1540)*
Stonemode Granite LLC ....E 214 484-8820
  Dallas *(G-5012)*
Stonexpressions LLC ....G 214 366-2216
  Dallas *(G-5013)*
Target Stone LLC ....E 832 827-8663
  Houston *(G-12161)*
Tex-Art Stone Inc ....E 817 481-9602
  Keller *(G-13470)*
▼ Texas Archtctral Aggregate Inc ....E 325 372-5105
  San Saba *(G-18719)*
Texas Home & Projects LLC ....G 956 546-8400
  Brownsville *(G-2410)*
▲ Texas Industries Inc ....C 972 647-6700
  Dallas *(G-5062)*
◆ Thorntree LP ....E 713 690-8200
  Houston *(G-12280)*
Unlimited Stone LLC ....F 903 297-0829
  Longview *(G-14328)*
US Lbm Holdings LLC ....C 713 650-6200
  Houston *(G-12485)*
Venetian Marble Co Lubbock Inc ....E 806 763-5777
  Lubbock *(G-14506)*
Venus Marble Co Inc ....D 972 223-8008
  Desoto *(G-5447)*
Wallace Monument Company ....F 806 874-2442
  Clarendon *(G-3071)*
West Coast Group Inc ....F 281 447-2020
  Houston *(G-12635)*
West U Marble LLC ....E 713 433-4424
  Houston *(G-12636)*
West University Marble Co ....F 713 433-2240
  Houston *(G-8396)*
Zodiac Stone LLC ....F 972 243-2112
  Dallas *(G-5212)*

3291 Abrasive Prdts

Asset Guard Products Inc ....E 940 627-1400
  Decatur *(G-5242)*
Box Gang Manufacturing LLC ....E 713 742-5555
  Houston *(G-8963)*
Carbo Ceramics Inc ....B 281 921-6400
  Houston *(G-9091)*
▼ Cerametals Carbide LLC ....E 713 937-3801
  Houston *(G-9144)*
Custom Abrasives LLC ....F 281 286-7200
  Houston *(G-9362)*
Dunn Enterprises Inc ....E 713 869-4841
  Porter *(G-17174)*
Dynalloy Industries Inc ....E 936 825-2532
  Navasota *(G-15729)*
Dynalloy Industries Inc ....E 936 825-2532
  Navasota *(G-15730)*
Dynalloy Industries Inc ....F 713 856-9377
  Houston *(G-9545)*
Gulf States Abrasive Mfg ....D 713 869-4841
  Porter *(G-17177)*
▲ Hartwell Industries Inc ....E 713 771-4311
  Houston *(G-10134)*

▲ Hudson Abrasive Company ....F 713 977-0037
Houston *(G-10276)*

KB Structures Inc ....F 713 875-1024
Wallisville *(G-20512)*

M & M Coastal Mfg Inc ....D 713 472-0700
Houston *(G-10714)*

Made In America Mfg LLC ....G 512 435-9952
Austin *(G-1316)*

Oldcastle Apg Texas Inc ....F 972 335-4122
Frisco *(G-7302)*

◆ Opti-Blast Inc ....F 903 589-0452
Jacksonville *(G-13254)*

▲ Saige Usa Inc ....F 281 980-8393
Sugar Land *(G-19540)*

Saint-Gobain Abrasives Inc ....C 956 541-5285
Brownsville *(G-2404)*

Saint-Gobain Abrasives Inc ....F 956 519-5047
Mcallen *(G-14904)*

Saint-Gobain Abrasives Inc ....A 254 918-2307
Stephenville *(G-19421)*

Samuel Son & Co (usa) Inc ....D 713 462-5000
Houston *(G-11740)*

▲ Scot Hone Corporation ....D 903 639-2551
Lone Star *(G-14184)*

▲ Syntex Super Materials Inc ....E 281 821-9495
Houston *(G-12137)*

UM Abrasives Inc ....F 817 572-1344
Kennedale *(G-13506)*

US Minerals Inc ....F 409 740-3355
Galveston *(G-7412)*

3292 Asbestos products

▲ Builders Post-Tension Inc ....E 281 873-9500
Houston *(G-9014)*

Certainteed LLC ....D 214 630-7377
Dallas *(G-4103)*

▲ Chevron Phillips Chem Co LP ....A 832 813-4100
The Woodlands *(G-19845)*

MCR Oil Tools LLC ....E 817 704-6677
Arlington *(G-730)*

3295 Minerals & Earths: Ground Or Treated

▼ Advance Technology Products ......F 713 450-5990
Houston *(G-8484)*

Arcosa Lw Hpb LLC ....E 214 631-4420
Dallas *(G-3959)*

Arcosa Materials Inc ....B 817 635-8500
Arlington *(G-622)*

◆ Bentonite Performance Mnrl LLC ....F 281 871-7900
Houston *(G-8858)*

Excalibar Minerals LLC ....E 281 864-9550
Channelview *(G-3021)*

Fjcj LLC ....F 409 740-3355
Galveston *(G-7396)*

Imerys Talc America Inc ....D 281 272-7200
Houston *(G-10329)*

John Crane Inc ....F 979 239-1201
Freeport *(G-7200)*

M-I LLC ....E 409 763-2249
Galveston *(G-7403)*

New England Lead Burning Inc ....F 713 675-3266
Houston *(G-11034)*

◆ Prince Minerals LLC ....D 646 747-4222
Houston *(G-11419)*

Sidco Minerals Inc ....F 903 838-4493
Texarkana *(G-19772)*

Tms International LLC ....F 409 768-1241
Beaumont *(G-1960)*

◆ Tribute Energy Inc ....F 281 768-5300
Houston *(G-12367)*

U S Silica Company ....E 254 375-2225
Kosse *(G-13667)*

United Minerals and Prpts Inc ....E 713 881-9466
Houston *(G-12449)*

Uranium Resources Inc ....F 972 219-3330
Lewisville *(G-14102)*

3296 Mineral Wool

Aagape First Investments LLC ....E 903 675-7876
Athens *(G-818)*

American Rockwool Mfg LLC ....E 214 882-1343
Plano *(G-16788)*

Bay Energy Blanket Inc ....F 512 353-4064
San Marcos *(G-18680)*

Distribution International Inc ....E 214 637-0151
Dallas *(G-4263)*

Glt Fabricators Inc ....E 713 670-9700
La Porte *(G-13739)*

Gulfstream Aerospace Corp ....A 214 902-7520
Dallas *(G-4423)*

Industrial Insul & Shtmtl Inc ....E 432 332-8203
Odessa *(G-16030)*

Jayvic Inc ....F 806 374-9402
Amarillo *(G-442)*

Johns Manville Corporation ....B 817 645-9101
Cleburne *(G-3098)*

Owens Corning ....F 940 723-5998
Wichita Falls *(G-20791)*

Owens Corning Sales LLC ....B 972 937-1340
Waxahachie *(G-20554)*

Owens Corning Sales LLC ....B 806 622-1582
Amarillo *(G-504)*

Owens Corning Sales LLC ....D 903 538-2271
Palestine *(G-16307)*

▼ Pamrod Products Company ....E 830 372-1500
Seguin *(G-18854)*

Pittsburgh Corning LLC ....F 281 437-6000
Fresno *(G-7240)*

Protective Concepts Inc ....F 832 843-7619
Cypress *(G-3816)*

Seguins Budget Auto Inc ....F 830 372-1790
Seguin *(G-18863)*

SMC Industries Inc ....G 281 860-9950
Houston *(G-11920)*

▲ Sudaglass Fiber Technology ....D 281 496-5427
Houston *(G-12090)*

◆ Superior Energies Inc ....F 409 962-8549
Groves *(G-8111)*

United Insul Sls Fbrcation Inc ....F 409 727-3191
Port Arthur *(G-17131)*

United States Mineral Pdts Co ....D 713 462-1709
Houston *(G-12457)*

US Silica Holdings Inc ....F 281 258-2170
Houston *(G-12490)*

3297 Nonclay Refractories

Able Supply Co ....F 713 926-9623
Houston *(G-8448)*

Allied Mineral Products Inc ....G 956 831-2022
Brownsville *(G-2336)*

Asi Industrial Services LLC ....F 713 378-9200
Houston *(G-8720)*

▲ Delta Refractories Inc ....E 281 944-9644
Katy *(G-13394)*

Hanson Lehigh Inc ....E 281 616-0700
Houston *(G-10120)*

◆ Hanson Lehigh Inc ....B 972 653-5500
Irving *(G-13052)*

▲ J T Thorpe Company ....C 713 644-1247
Houston *(G-10444)*

Select Sands America Corp ....E 501 276-5928
Houston *(G-11823)*

▲ Southwest Refractory Texas LP ....E 979 285-7219
Alvin *(G-380)*

Vesuvius U S A Corporation ....D 903 597-7237
Tyler *(G-20175)*

Vesuvius U S A Corporation ....C 903 597-7237
Hillsboro *(G-8332)*

Wesco Refractories Inc ....F 682 518-5035
Mansfield *(G-14729)*

3299 Nonmetallic Mineral Prdts, NEC

Addax Minerals LLC ....F 214 445-6000
Dallas *(G-3888)*

Allied Imaging Group LLC ....E 713 812-8100
Houston *(G-8549)*

California Stucco ....G 210 838-7433
San Antonio *(G-17976)*

◆ Carbo Ceramics Inc ....G 281 921-6400
Irving *(G-12960)*

Carbo Ceramics Inc ....G 972 401-0090
Irving *(G-12961)*

Casci Ornamental Plaster Inc ....F 214 421-3390
Dallas *(G-4088)*

Ceradyne Inc ....F 281 773-4135
Humble *(G-12755)*

Creations Unlimted Inc ....E 281 821-1382
Houston *(G-9339)*

Emerald Masonry & Stucco ....G 281 356-9400
Magnolia *(G-14604)*

Hmj Plastering LLC ....F 713 941-2807
Pasadena *(G-16454)*

Kenneth Wyatt Galleries ....F 806 995-2239
Tulia *(G-20036)*

Master Wall Inc ....F 979 885-6905
Sealy *(G-18812)*

Natural Graphics Inc ....E 713 661-5075
Houston *(G-11009)*

Premier Antique Stucco LLC ....E 210 602-8054
San Antonio *(G-18389)*

Rydar Inc ....E 979 877-0703
Sealy *(G-18817)*

Scan-Pac Mfg Inc ....E 281 356-1640
Magnolia *(G-14626)*

▲ Texas Industries Inc ....C 972 647-6700
Dallas *(G-5062)*

Texas Technical Ceramics Inc ....E 936 856-2903
Willis *(G-20866)*

Texas United Corporation ....E 713 877-1793
Houston *(G-12258)*

Unifrax I LLC ....E 281 251-5595
Carrollton *(G-2842)*

Western Stucco Product ....F 915 858-3494
El Paso *(G-6036)*

33 PRIMARY METAL INDUSTRIES

3312 Blast Furnaces, Coke Ovens, Steel & Rolling Mills

AAA Flame Cut Steel Inc ....F 713 868-2337
Houston *(G-8435)*

Aap Metals LLC ....F 800 231-8890
Houston *(G-8439)*

ABB Installation Products Inc ....C 713 466-6761
Houston *(G-8444)*

Abbco Display Company ....G 214 319-8148
Dallas *(G-3876)*

Abrasive Blast Systems LLC ....E 972 205-9309
Garland *(G-7426)*

Abrasive Contour Tech LLC ....F 281 288-8800
Spring *(G-19097)*

Accurate Flamecutting Stl LLC ....E 281 987-9100
Houston *(G-8462)*

Alco Machine Tool & Steel Inc ....F 915 779-7013
El Paso *(G-5640)*

Amarillo Waterblasters Inc ....F 806 352-2765
Amarillo *(G-479)*

American Railcar Inds Inc ....C 903 759-3946
Longview *(G-14195)*

Arrow Steel Processors Inc ....F 713 670-0160
Houston *(G-8707)*

Atlas Iron & Scrap Metal Co ....E 972 225-4221
Dallas *(G-3981)*

Atlas Metal Works Inc ....F 214 741-4788
Dallas *(G-3982)*

Automotive Rentals Inc ....E 817 624-3650
Fort Worth *(G-6411)*

Axis Pipe and Tube Inc ....E 979 703-6847
Bryan *(G-2455)*

Axis Pipe and Tube LLC ....C 281 494-0900
Houston *(G-8761)*

Azz Glvnzing - San Antonio LLC ....F 210 661-8574
San Antonio *(G-17927)*

Azz Inc ....E 817 297-4361
Crowley *(G-3751)*

◆ Azz Inc ....D 817 810-0095
Fort Worth *(G-6414)*

Basden Steel and Erection Inc ....E 817 295-6100
Burleson *(G-2569)*

▲ Brazos Pipe Stl Fbricators Inc .....E 979 233-7895
Freeport *(G-7194)*

C D Steel & Service Inc ....G 713 957-3604
Houston *(G-9027)*

◆ C M C Steel Fabricators Inc ....A 830 372-8200
Seguin *(G-18827)*

Carols Mch & Fabrication Inc ....E 713 921-7266
Wharton *(G-20698)*

Carports Childers & Structures ....F 713 460-2181
Houston *(G-9094)*

CB&i LLC ....C 713 649-4277
Houston *(G-9106)*

CB&i LLC ....C 713 375-8000
Houston *(G-9107)*

CB&i LLC ....C 713 485-1000
Houston *(G-9108)*

CB&i LLC ....E 281 456-5700
Houston *(G-9105)*

CB&i LLC ....C 409 980-5500
Beaumont *(G-1867)*

CC Coating & Machine Inc ....E 361 884-9753
Corpus Christi *(G-3497)*

CMC Steel Us LLC ....F 214 689-4300
Irving *(G-12975)*

Commercial Metals Company ....B 214 689-4300
Irving *(G-12977)*

Commercial Metals Company ....F 512 246-1424
Round Rock *(G-17634)*

Commercial Metals Company ....E 972 838-9050
Melissa *(G-14995)*

Commercial Metals Company	F	956 702-4434	Pharr (G-16696)
Commercial Metals Company	F	830 372-8200	Seguin (G-18831)
Commercial Metals Company	F	512 282-8820	Buda (G-2526)
Commercial Metals Company	D	409 842-3316	Beaumont (G-1875)
Conner Steel Products Inc	B	325 655-8225	Houston (G-9271)
Custom Flame Cutting Inc	F	281 342-3250	Rosenberg (G-17579)
Cws Road Plate LLC	D	713 242-7711	Houston (G-9380)
Cyclone Steel Services LLC	E	713 635-5555	Houston (G-9385)
▲ Deacero Usa Inc	C	713 697-1500	Houston (G-9418)
Delta Steel Inc	E	918 437-7501	Fort Worth (G-6583)
Dennis Steel Inc	D	512 259-4001	Leander (G-13987)
Desoto Environmental MGT	C	972 458-0028	Dallas (G-4249)
Express Fabricators LLC	F	972 734-3855	Farmersville (G-6222)
▼ Fabenco Inc	E	713 686-6620	Houston (G-9747)
Friedman Industries Inc	F	903 639-2511	Lone Star (G-14182)
◆ G2 Automated Technologies LLC	E	972 479-0699	Dallas (G-4390)
▲ General Dynamics Ordnance	F	972 276-5131	Garland (G-7500)
Gerdau Ameristeel Corp	G	972 779-7010	Midlothian (G-15481)
◆ Gerdau Ameristeel Us Inc	A	972 775-8241	Midlothian (G-15482)
Gerdau Ameristeel US Inc	A	972 775-8241	Midlothian (G-15483)
Gordons Specialties Inc	E	972 225-1660	Hutchins (G-12866)
Grant & Gerhardt Machine & Mfg	F	713 946-4664	Houston (G-10016)
◆ Grant Prideco Inc	E	936 825-7070	Navasota (G-15737)
GTC Technology LLC	E	817 685-9125	Irving (G-13045)
▲ Gulf Copper & Mfg Corp	F	409 989-0300	Port Arthur (G-17111)
◆ Harris Rebar	E	936 258-8221	Dayton (G-5228)
Hearne Steel Company	D	979 279-3464	Hearne (G-8232)
Imperial Group Mfg Inc	C	940 627-1700	Decatur (G-5247)
▲ Independent Pipe Services LLC	E	281 436-0380	Houston (G-10340)
Industrial Insptn Innovation	F	281 636-7215	La Porte (G-13750)
Integrated Pipe & Supply LLC	F	409 834-6123	Village Mills (G-20337)
Interstate Fittings Inc	D	214 637-6720	Dallas (G-4508)
◆ Intsel Steel Distributors LLC	C	713 937-9500	Houston (G-10410)
Ipsco Koppel Tubulars LLC	E	281 383-2603	Baytown (G-1822)
Jarco Steel Inc	D	713 644-4900	Houston (G-10456)
◆ Joy Glbal Lngview Oprtions LLC	A	903 237-7000	Longview (G-14257)
◆ Jsw Steel (usa) Inc	A	281 383-2525	Baytown (G-1794)
K-T Galvanizing Co Inc	E	817 477-4434	Venus (G-20220)
Kdr Supply Inc	F	936 334-1353	Liberty (G-14120)
Kloeckner Metals Corporation	D	713 633-7400	Houston (G-10540)
L B Foster Company	E	832 934-3107	Magnolia (G-14613)
Lnc Fabrication LLC	F	409 769-0403	Vidor (G-20329)
◆ Lone Star Technologies Inc	D	972 770-6401	Dallas (G-4604)
Mac Fabricators	G	979 265-0235	Clute (G-3156)
Manufctred Component Parts Ltd	E	713 880-0590	Houston (G-10749)

Maverick Stainless LLC	E	214 884-2700	Dallas (G-4653)
Mayhan Fabricators Inc	E	903 734-4198	Gilmer (G-7709)
Metalloy Inc	F	800 828-0500	Houston (G-10850)
Mica Steelworks Inc	E	817 529-5000	Fort Worth (G-6836)
Mica Steelworks Inc	C	817 581-9500	Haltom City (G-8154)
Mica Steelworks Inc	C	972 287-5410	Kaufman (G-13460)
Mica Steelworks Inc	E	817 267-9699	Euless (G-6149)
Mineraltech Gulf Coast Abr LLC	E	832 838-8623	Highlands (G-8313)
▲ Narstco Inc	D	972 775-5560	Midlothian (G-15487)
North Amrcn Glvnzing Ctngs Inc	A	817 810-0095	Fort Worth (G-6867)
Northwest Pipe Company	D	817 847-1402	Saginaw (G-17753)
Nucor Corporation	B	903 626-4461	Jewett (G-13308)
Nucor Corporation	C	972 524-5407	Terrell (G-19745)
Nucor Corporation	F	214 340-1883	Dallas (G-4747)
▼ Nucor Steel Longview LLC	D	800 256-5757	Longview (G-14286)
Oil Tech Services Inc	F	281 456-9023	Houston (G-11162)
▼ Oil Tech Services Inc	F	713 789-5144	Houston (G-11163)
Omnimax International Inc	E	817 481-3521	Fort Worth (G-6882)
Optimus Steel LLC	B	800 303-9543	The Woodlands (G-19820)
▲ Overlay Product Systems Inc	D	281 552-3500	Houston (G-11206)
Parker-Hannifin Corporation	E	817 232-1040	Saginaw (G-17754)
Pennar Global Inc	F	281 362-2707	The Woodlands (G-19900)
Phillips Iron Works Inc	E	337 364-2337	Houston (G-11327)
Precision Turning	G	817 472-7999	Arlington (G-758)
Presidio Custom Metal Works	F	512 284-8549	Round Rock (G-17682)
Prestige Kitchen Inc	F	972 366-3322	Venus (G-20221)
Procon Construction Co Inc	F	281 375-6829	Brookshire (G-2323)
Quality Lnings Fabrication Inc	E	713 863-7013	Houston (G-11495)
R2r and D LLC	D	432 264-7500	Big Spring (G-2094)
Renfro Street Holdings Ltd	E	817 295-6100	Burleson (G-2596)
Rio Grande Steel Ltd	E	956 361-4443	San Benito (G-18664)
Roy Johnson Incorporated	E	817 468-2939	Arlington (G-773)
Russell Mfg & Fabg Inc	E	281 590-8185	Houston (G-11699)
Sabre Alloys LP	F	281 405-8580	Houston (G-11721)
SAE Towers Ltd	F	281 763-2282	Houston (G-11722)
Seadrift Coke LP	C	361 552-8887	Port Lavaca (G-17155)
Selkirk Corporation	B	972 943-6100	Richardson (G-17395)
Shaw Fabricators Inc	D	713 991-5313	Houston (G-11850)
▲ Sigma Tube & Bar LLC	E	281 369-5525	Houston (G-11887)
▲ Southeast Texas Industries Inc	B	409 994-3570	Buna (G-2562)
Southeast Texas Industries Inc	C	409 792-0084	Bridge City (G-2286)
Spur Industrial LLC	E	817 293-1515	Cresson (G-3713)
◆ Ssab Texas Inc	C	713 341-7700	Houston (G-12031)
◆ Standard Forged Products LLC	E	214 631-4420	Dallas (G-5003)
Structural & Stl Pdts Mfg Ltd	D	817 869-2301	Fort Worth (G-7021)

▼ Structural Metals Inc	A	830 372-8200	Seguin (G-18866)
Tejas Alloys LLC	E	830 303-4422	Seguin (G-18867)
Tenaris Rods (usa) Inc	E	713 767-4400	Houston (G-12201)
Texas Industries Inc	E	972 263-5077	Dallas (G-5064)
Texas Industries Inc	D	817 838-4212	Fort Worth (G-7048)
Texas Iron & Steel LLC	F	903 758-9498	Longview (G-14317)
Texas Pipe Works Inc	C	936 825-0652	Navasota (G-15744)
Trans-Tex Fabricating Co Inc	E	210 924-4431	San Antonio (G-18562)
United Casing Incorporated	E	432 682-0110	Midland (G-15455)
United States Steel Corp	D	903 656-6521	Lone Star (G-14185)
▼ Vinton Steel LLC	E	915 886-2000	Vinton (G-20342)
▲ W Silver Inc	C	915 886-3553	Vinton (G-20343)
▲ Wheels America Alloy Wheel	E	214 330-9866	Dallas (G-5185)
▲ White Star Steel Inc	D	713 675-6501	Houston (G-12663)

3313 Electrometallurgical Prdts

Alloy Carbide Company	E	713 923-2700	Houston (G-8556)
Elah Holdings Inc	F	805 435-1255	Dallas (G-4307)

3315 Steel Wire Drawing & Nails & Spikes

A P Manufacturing Incorporated	E	432 638-4708	Midland (G-15101)
Aquacut Inc	E	972 247-6288	Grand Prairie (G-7832)
Bullgang Tools LLC	G	979 203-9009	Brenham (G-2248)
Buzz Services LLC	E	817 263-9788	Fort Worth (G-6480)
Classic Fence	F	806 517-0708	Amarillo (G-483)
Cox Industries Inc	E	972 288-7555	Mesquite (G-15036)
▲ Derbec Enterprises Ltd	E	713 533-9059	Houston (G-9439)
Fusion Services Inc	E	512 444-4283	Austin (G-1173)
Geo Space LP	F	713 939-7093	Houston (G-9933)
◆ Granite Security Products Inc	E	817 483-0910	Mansfield (G-14677)
Hearne Steel Company	D	979 279-3464	Hearne (G-8232)
◆ Houston Wire Works Inc	F	713 946-2920	Houston (G-10265)
Jayco Steel Services Inc	E	281 399-0189	New Caney (G-15842)
Keystone Consolidated Inds	D	903 893-0191	Sherman (G-18919)
Kta Services	F	832 368-0138	San Antonio (G-18229)
Ldia Holdings LLC	E	512 247-3700	Austin (G-1284)
Lee Specialties	F	281 519-1719	Houston (G-10617)
◆ Lichtgitter Usa Inc	D	844 548-7911	Houston (G-10635)
Linden Steel LP	E	972 285-0200	Forney (G-6312)
M A R X Steel LLC	E	281 679-9700	Houston (G-10718)
▲ Master-Halco Inc	D	972 714-7300	Dallas (G-4645)
Master-Halco Inc	E	817 378-8086	Fort Worth (G-6815)
Master-Halco Inc	F	214 275-3100	Dallas (G-4646)
Master-Halco Inc	E	214 391-3190	Dallas (G-4647)
Metro Gate & Mfg Co Inc	E	903 785-8911	Paris (G-16365)
Nitro Fiber LLC	F	888 906-4202	Plano (G-16945)
Ntx Gates & Fences Inc	E	817 740-9449	Fort Worth (G-6874)

Optical Cabling Systems LC ....E 972 331-4627
Plano *(G-16957)*

Peninsula Steel Inc ....E 956 795-1966
Laredo *(G-13919)*

PMC Acquisition Company Inc ....C 915 225-8758
El Paso *(G-5913)*

Progressive Steel & Wire LLC ....F 972 999-8778
Irving *(G-13158)*

QMF Steel Inc ....E 903 455-3618
Campbell *(G-2646)*

R-Tex Services LLC ....D 817 774-3333
Joshua *(G-13324)*

◆ Ranger Steel Supply LP ....E 713 633-1306
Houston *(G-11547)*

S Y G Corporation ....D 361 884-4927
Corpus Christi *(G-3613)*

Sumitomo Elc Wirg Systems Inc ....C 915 845-7700
El Paso *(G-5986)*

Suncoast Post-Tension Ltd ....C 972 287-0307
Irving *(G-13190)*

◆ Suncoast Post-Tension Ltd ....C 281 445-8886
Houston *(G-12100)*

Suncoast Post-Tension Ltd ....C 281 445-8886
Houston *(G-12101)*

Superior Essex Intl LP ....E 325 646-8591
Brownwood *(G-2446)*

Tach Services Inc ....E 254 547-7121
Copperas Cove *(G-3456)*

Telespace LLC ....G 210 489-6600
San Antonio *(G-18527)*

Textray & Strut Ltd ....E 713 864-2551
Houston *(G-12265)*

Therm-O-Link Inc ....D 915 860-9933
El Paso *(G-6001)*

Tubal Cain Industries Inc ....F 281 789-7087
Magnolia *(G-14633)*

Universal Wire Works Inc ....F 713 649-3828
Houston *(G-12465)*

Vestal Steel Specialties Inc ....E 210 651-4333
Schertz *(G-18768)*

Vrt Investments Inc ....E 972 226-1981
Forney *(G-6316)*

3316 Cold Rolled Steel Sheet, Strip & Bars

C M C Steel Fabricators Inc ....D 214 631-6699
Dallas *(G-4073)*

Confederate Steel Corporation ....F 713 643-8526
Houston *(G-9269)*

Friedman Industries Inc ....D 903 758-3431
Longview *(G-14237)*

GTC Technology LLC ....E 817 685-9125
Irving *(G-13045)*

Kloeckner Metals Corporation ....D 713 633-7400
Houston *(G-10540)*

Landreth Fastner Corporation ....F 281 414-3103
Houston *(G-10594)*

Mayhan Fabricators Inc ....E 903 734-4198
Gilmer *(G-7709)*

Nucor Corporation ....C 972 524-5407
Terrell *(G-19745)*

Promicom Inc ....G 832 544-0855
The Woodlands *(G-19906)*

◆ Richardson Trident Company LLC ...D 972 231-5176
Richardson *(G-17390)*

Suncoast Post-Tension Ltd ....C 972 287-0307
Irving *(G-13190)*

◆ Suncoast Post-Tension Ltd ....C 281 445-8886
Houston *(G-12100)*

Suncoast Post-Tension Ltd ....C 281 445-8886
Houston *(G-12101)*

▼ Vinton Steel LLC ....B 915 886-2000
Vinton *(G-20342)*

▲ White Star Steel Inc ....D 713 675-6501
Houston *(G-12663)*

3317 Steel Pipe & Tubes

ABB Installation Products Inc ....C 713 466-6761
Houston *(G-8444)*

▲ American Materials Tech I LLC ....F 281 345-0169
Houston *(G-8602)*

▲ Ameritex Pipe & Products LLC ....D 830 372-2300
Seguin *(G-18825)*

Ameron International Corp ....G 940 569-1471
Houston *(G-8622)*

◆ Ameron International Corp ....E 713 375-3700
Houston *(G-8623)*

▲ Axxairusa Inc ....G 281 968-7138
Alvin *(G-353)*

B&L Pipeco Services Inc ....F 281 955-3500
Houston *(G-8780)*

Baker & Company Cnstr LLC ....E 903 561-1763
Tyler *(G-20056)*

▲ Bendco Inc ....E 713 473-1557
Pasadena *(G-16398)*

Boardwalk Midstream LLC ....F 888 315-5005
Houston *(G-8931)*

Boomerang Tube LLC ....B 713 289-5555
Liberty *(G-14116)*

Boomerang Tube LLC ....C 713 231-2929
Houston *(G-8952)*

▲ Borusan Mannesmann Pipe US Inc...C 832 399-6000
Houston *(G-8960)*

▲ Brazos Pipe Stl Fbricators Inc ....E 979 233-7895
Freeport *(G-7194)*

Cab Incorporated ....E 936 569-9430
Nacogdoches *(G-15687)*

Centric Pipe LLC ....E 214 526-4423
Dallas *(G-4101)*

▼ Clock Spring Company Inc ....D 281 590-8491
Houston *(G-9215)*

Coil Solutions Inc ....E 361 444-0058
Alice *(G-206)*

Corrpro Companies Inc ....C 713 460-6000
Houston *(G-9325)*

Custom Fab Inc ....F 210 923-3376
San Antonio *(G-18037)*

Energy Technology Manufa ....F 281 862-2829
Houston *(G-9637)*

Friedman Industries Inc ....D 903 758-3431
Longview *(G-14237)*

◆ Global Tubing LLC ....C 713 265-5000
Dayton *(G-5227)*

Gulf States Tube LLC ....E 281 375-5113
Brookshire *(G-2317)*

Instrument Products Inc ....F 281 491-0237
Stafford *(G-19329)*

Integrated Pipe & Supply LLC ....F 409 834-6123
Village Mills *(G-20337)*

▲ Ipsco Tubulars (ky) Inc ....C 859 292-6000
Houston *(G-10415)*

▲ Ipsco Tubulars Inc ....E 281 949-1023
Houston *(G-10416)*

J Simmons Group Inc ....B 713 675-5100
Houston *(G-10443)*

◆ Jindal Saw Usa LLC ....E 281 573-3002
Baytown *(G-1793)*

◆ Jsw Steel (usa) Inc ....A 281 383-2525
Baytown *(G-1794)*

Kdr Supply Inc ....F 936 334-1353
Liberty *(G-14120)*

Labarge Coating LLC ....D 713 378-7225
Channelview *(G-3028)*

Legacy Tubular LLC ....E 281 363-1900
Magnolia *(G-14614)*

Ljt Texas LLC ....D 254 771-2253
Temple *(G-19685)*

Lock Joint Tube LLC ....C 254 771-2253
Temple *(G-19686)*

◆ Lone Star Technologies Inc ....D 972 770-6401
Dallas *(G-4604)*

Longhorn Tube LP ....F 972 556-0234
Dallas *(G-4605)*

Lqc Pipe & Tube Ltd Partnr ....E 832 559-7676
Houston *(G-10692)*

▲ Mapa Manufacturing LLC ....G 903 897-2371
Naples *(G-15719)*

◆ Maverick Tube Corporation ....B 713 767-4400
Houston *(G-10802)*

Maverick Tube Corporation ....B 936 539-2136
Conroe *(G-3329)*

Mecor Usa Inc ....F 713 817-0683
Spring *(G-19231)*

Merchants Moving and Stor Inc ....D 361 293-7202
Yoakum *(G-20970)*

Northwest Pipe Company ....E 817 847-1402
Saginaw *(G-17752)*

Ntx Gates & Fences Inc ....E 817 740-9449
Fort Worth *(G-6874)*

▲ Omk Tube Inc ....E 281 609-8150
Houston *(G-11175)*

Omk Tube Inc ....C 281 609-8970
Houston *(G-11176)*

PCC Klad LLC ....E 713 433-5151
Pearland *(G-16588)*

Permian Enterprises Ltd ....E 432 332-0903
Odessa *(G-16116)*

Peyton Salas & Mendoza LLC ....E 512 784-5875
Houston *(G-11313)*

◆ Priefert Mfg Co Inc ....A 903 572-1741
Mount Pleasant *(G-15660)*

Promicom Inc ....G 832 544-0855
The Woodlands *(G-19906)*

▲ Pyramid Tubular Products LLC ....E 281 405-8090
Spring *(G-19245)*

QMF Steel Inc ....E 903 455-3618
Campbell *(G-2646)*

RSD Supply Inc ....E 713 983-6363
Houston *(G-11691)*

▼ S & T International Inc ....E 409 745-4990
Orange *(G-16259)*

◆ Salzgtter Mnnsmann Stnless Tbe ....D 713 466-7278
Houston *(G-11735)*

◆ Sivco Inc ....E 713 466-1100
Houston *(G-11910)*

▲ Southern Tube LLC ....E 713 231-2929
Houston *(G-11979)*

Splendora Pipe Services LLC ....D 281 432-1400
Cleveland *(G-3136)*

▲ Team Alloys LLC ....E 713 360-1060
Houston *(G-12170)*

Teda Tpco America Corporation ....E 361 826-2610
Gregory *(G-8106)*

Tejas Casing Ltd ....D 281 215-1500
Houston *(G-12187)*

Tejas Tubular Products Inc ....C 254 965-5162
Stephenville *(G-19426)*

◆ Tejas Tubular Products Inc ....B 281 822-3400
Houston *(G-12188)*

◆ Tenaris Coiled Tubes LLC ....C 281 458-2883
Houston *(G-12198)*

Tenaris Global Svcs USA Corp ....F 936 525-3101
Houston *(G-12199)*

◆ Tenaris Global Svcs USA Corp ....D 713 767-4400
Houston *(G-12200)*

◆ Tex-Tube Company ....C 713 686-4351
Houston *(G-12217)*

◆ Thermacor Process Inc ....D 817 847-7300
Fort Worth *(G-7054)*

◆ Tmk North America Inc ....F 281 949-1023
Houston *(G-12309)*

◆ Vallourec Drlg Pdts USA Inc ....B 713 844-3700
Houston *(G-12522)*

▲ Vallourec Tube-Alloy LLC ....C 713 462-7613
Houston *(G-12523)*

◆ Vallourec USA Corporation ....E 713 479-3200
Houston *(G-12524)*

▲ Vulcan Finned Tubes LP ....E 281 255-4775
Tomball *(G-20015)*

Welding Outlets Inc ....D 281 590-0190
Houston *(G-12630)*

Z-Modular Killeen LLC ....D 254 833-6645
Killeen *(G-13619)*

3321 Gray Iron Foundries

◆ Alamo Iron Works Inc ....B 210 223-6161
San Antonio *(G-17885)*

▼ Conine Manufacturing Company ....G 903 894-6150
Flint *(G-6236)*

▲ Ebaa Iron Inc ....B 254 629-1737
Eastland *(G-5565)*

Ebaa Iron Inc ....E 325 762-3084
Albany *(G-187)*

Ej Usa Inc ....F 210 946-3224
San Antonio *(G-18085)*

▲ Facilities Rehab Inc ....F 512 352-6035
Taylor *(G-19655)*

Flowserve Corporation ....B 972 443-6500
Irving *(G-13027)*

Flowserve Corporation ....F 800 446-0401
Irving *(G-13028)*

Frazier & Frazier Inds Inc ....B 254 786-2293
Coolidge *(G-3407)*

◆ Gas Equipment Company Inc ....C 972 241-2333
Dallas *(G-4393)*

Grandor Corporation ....C 903 872-6571
Corsicana *(G-3672)*

Harris Industries Incorporated ....D 903 759-4485
Dallas *(G-4437)*

J B Smith Mfg Co LLC ....D 713 928-5711
Houston *(G-10435)*

Jdh Pacific Inc ....E 562 926-8088
Lubbock *(G-14429)*

◆ Key 3 Casting LLC ....D 817 332-9500
Fort Worth *(G-6757)*

L B Foster Company ....E 832 934-3107
Magnolia *(G-14613)*

◆ Lufkin Gears LLC ....F 936 634-2211
Lufkin *(G-14539)*

Lufkin Industries LLC ....F 281 495-1100
Missouri City *(G-15583)*

McKinley Iron Works Inc ....E 817 335-1268
Fort Worth *(G-6822)*

◆ McWane Inc ....C 800 527-8478
Tyler *(G-20123)*

McWane Inc ....A 903 882-5511
Tyler *(G-20124)*

Meador Products Inc ....D 940 767-8541
Wichita Falls *(G-20782)*

▲ Merla LLC ....E 281 931-6900
Magnolia *(G-14618)*

Metso Minerals Industries Inc ....E 210 491-9521
San Antonio *(G-18295)*

▲ Newage Casting LP ....E 281 565-0928
Sugar Land *(G-19512)*

Oil City Iron Works Inc ....C 903 872-6571
Corsicana *(G-3681)*

Prestige Tank & Pump Svcs Inc ....E 512 698-9645
Austin *(G-1431)*

▲ Standard Industrial Pdts Co ....E 281 280-0147
Webster *(G-20647)*

Star Pipe Usa LLC ....D 620 251-5700
Houston *(G-12047)*

Stuart Pressure Control ....F 713 678-0154
The Woodlands *(G-19925)*

Texaloy Foundry Company ....E 830 393-6679
Floresville *(G-6252)*

Waterfleet LLC ....E 855 744-5222
San Antonio *(G-18610)*

3322 Malleable Iron Foundries

Industrial Castings Co Inc ....F 713 747-5336
Houston *(G-10347)*

Mid-South Metals LLC ....E 817 838-8000
Fort Worth *(G-6839)*

Standard Alloys Incorporated ....D 409 983-3201
Port Arthur *(G-17125)*

3324 Steel Investment Foundries

▲ Consolidated Casting LLC ....C 972 225-7305
Hutchins *(G-12865)*

▼ Dal-Air Tool Co Inc ....E 903 598-2226
Point *(G-17079)*

▲ DSA Operating Company LLC ....E 210 734-5121
San Antonio *(G-18072)*

Houston Texcast Inc ....E 713 697-8006
Houston *(G-10255)*

Howmet Castings & Services Inc ....B 940 855-8100
Wichita Falls *(G-20771)*

Lone Star Cast Mch Partners LP ....F 903 986-8300
Kilgore *(G-13563)*

National Oilwell Varco Inc ....A 830 693-5312
Marble Falls *(G-14748)*

Netfires LLC ....F 972 603-2702
Grand Prairie *(G-7933)*

Sure Cast Inc ....D 512 756-6500
Burnet *(G-2615)*

◆ Texas Precision Metalcraft Inc ....E 281 240-9191
Sugar Land *(G-19563)*

3325 Steel Foundries, NEC

Ahmsa International Inc ....E 210 341-3777
San Antonio *(G-17875)*

◆ Alamo Iron Works Inc ....B 210 223-6161
San Antonio *(G-17885)*

American Railcar Inds Inc ....C 903 759-3946
Longview *(G-14195)*

▲ American Spincast Inc ....D 254 939-0292
Belton *(G-2018)*

Centrifugal Castings Inc ....E 254 773-9068
Temple *(G-19675)*

◆ Chicago Bridge & Iron Co Del ....C 832 513-1000
Houston *(G-9183)*

▲ Delta Centrifugal LLC ....C 254 773-9055
Temple *(G-19679)*

Fasteel LLC ....G 210 661-2603
San Antonio *(G-18106)*

Gerdau Ameristeel US Inc ....E 972 782-7902
Farmersville *(G-6223)*

Lone Star Cast Mch Partners LP ....F 903 986-8300
Kilgore *(G-13563)*

Penatek Foundry & Machining ....E 432 368-0888
Odessa *(G-16110)*

Pumpworks Castings LLC ....F 936 634-4206
Lufkin *(G-14546)*

Qualico Steel Company Inc ....D 972 775-1400
Midlothian *(G-15492)*

ROC Industries Inc ....E 713 468-7743
Houston *(G-11647)*

Service Metal Products Company ....E 281 499-3020
Houston *(G-11839)*

▲ Sfi-Gray Steel LLC ....A 713 864-6450
Houston *(G-11842)*

Shumate Energy Tech LLC ....E 936 539-9533
Conroe *(G-3364)*

Star Pipe Usa LLC ....D 620 251-5700
Houston *(G-12047)*

United States Steel Corp ....D 903 656-6521
Lone Star *(G-14185)*

◆ Wolar Industrial Inc ....D 713 926-2440
Houston *(G-12680)*

3331 Primary Smelting & Refining Of Copper

Aleris Ohio Management Inc ....F 972 815-0800
Irving *(G-12927)*

Asarco LLC ....A 806 468-4000
Amarillo *(G-401)*

Deepwater Mfg USA Inc ....E 713 983-7117
Houston *(G-9425)*

Freeport Minerals Corporation ....C 915 778-9881
El Paso *(G-5774)*

Mac Fabricators ....G 979 265-0235
Clute *(G-3156)*

▲ Reaper Miniatures Inc ....E 940 484-6464
Denton *(G-5397)*

3334 Primary Production Of Aluminum

Aastek Electronics Corp ....F 903 953-0888
Emory *(G-6081)*

Howmet Aerospace Inc ....B 866 385-2137
The Woodlands *(G-19874)*

Kaiser Aluminum Fab Pdts LLC ....C 903 868-1556
Sherman *(G-18918)*

◆ Pigs Unlimited Intl Inc ....E 281 351-2749
Tomball *(G-19998)*

Quality Cast Metals Inc ....E 817 921-3595
Fort Worth *(G-6927)*

TPI ....E 972 276-2901
Garland *(G-7604)*

3339 Primary Nonferrous Metals, NEC

Amorphous Materials Inc ....G 972 494-5624
Garland *(G-7436)*

Asarco LLC ....A 806 468-4000
Amarillo *(G-401)*

Central Jewelry & Refining ....F 214 350-4653
Dallas *(G-4099)*

Dillon Gage Refining Inc ....E 972 484-3377
Dallas *(G-4259)*

Eco-Bat America LLC ....C 214 631-6070
Dallas *(G-4299)*

Elemetal LLC ....G 214 956-7600
Dallas *(G-4309)*

▲ Hi-Tech Prcous Mtls Rfnery LLC ....E 972 239-0597
Dallas *(G-4456)*

Monitor Canopies Inc ....F 903 893-6336
Sherman *(G-18923)*

Shaneda Machine Inc ....E 432 333-7083
Odessa *(G-16152)*

Total Alloy Foundry Inc ....F 806 259-2255
Memphis *(G-14999)*

3341 Secondary Smelting & Refining Of Nonferrous Metals

Alpha Omega Recycling Inc ....F 903 297-7272
Longview *(G-14192)*

Asarco LLC ....A 806 468-4000
Amarillo *(G-401)*

Ashley Salvage Company ....E 210 922-7631
San Antonio *(G-17916)*

Atlas Iron & Scrap Metal Co ....E 972 225-4221
Dallas *(G-3981)*

Commercial Metals Company ....D 713 226-0100
Houston *(G-9251)*

Commercial Metals Company ....E 979 265-4642
Clute *(G-3150)*

Commercial Metals Company ....E 817 429-4005
Fort Worth *(G-6531)*

Commercial Metals Company ....D 361 884-4071
Corpus Christi *(G-3505)*

Commercial Metals Company ....E 469 729-0180
Dallas *(G-4147)*

Commercial Metals Company ....C 214 565-0668
Dallas *(G-4134)*

Ebt Newco LLC ....F 972 996-0458
Dallas *(G-4298)*

▲ EC Wrecking & Salvage Corp ....F 915 855-7999
El Paso *(G-5734)*

▲ Ecs Refining Texas LLC ....E 972 524-1075
Terrell *(G-19732)*

Elah Holdings Inc ....F 805 435-1255
Dallas *(G-4307)*

Elemetal LLC ....G 214 956-7600
Dallas *(G-4309)*

Elg Metals Inc ....E 281 457-2100
Houston *(G-9600)*

Exide Technologies ....C 972 335-2121
Frisco *(G-7284)*

Fulton Supply and Recycl Inc ....E 940 382-3611
Denton *(G-5367)*

◆ Galvotec Alloys Inc ....C 956 630-3500
McAllen *(G-14863)*

▲ Garland Steel Inc ....E 972 494-6000
Garland *(G-7495)*

Gateway Metal Recycling Inc ....E 956 723-0409
Laredo *(G-13889)*

▲ Gulf Reduction Corporation ....C 713 926-1705
Houston *(G-10069)*

Interntnal Shpbreaking Ltd LLC ....C 956 831-4112
Brownsville *(G-2364)*

▼ J L Proler Iron and Steel Co ....E 713 675-3191
Houston *(G-10441)*

Jrn Management LP ....D 210 222-9511
San Antonio *(G-18211)*

Kaiser Aluminum Fab Pdts LLC ....C 903 868-1556
Sherman *(G-18918)*

Lee Quigley Company ....F 512 762-4046
Austin *(G-1286)*

◆ Lopez Scrap Metal Inc ....G 915 859-0770
El Paso *(G-5847)*

Newell Ltd ....E 210 222-9511
San Antonio *(G-18343)*

Pine Street Salvage Co ....C 325 677-8831
Abilene *(G-65)*

▲ Quemetco Metals Limited Inc ....F 214 631-6070
Dallas *(G-4849)*

◆ Quexco Incorporated ....E 214 688-4000
Dallas *(G-4851)*

◆ Revere Smelting & Ref Corp ....E 214 631-6070
Dallas *(G-4893)*

▲ Sarbali Alloys LLC ....E 281 384-3500
Houston *(G-11752)*

◆ Techemet LP ....D 281 991-8300
Pasadena *(G-16518)*

Tyler Iron & Metal Ltd ....E 903 592-8144
Tyler *(G-20170)*

◆ US Zinc Corporation ....C 713 926-1705
Houston *(G-12493)*

◆ W Silver Recycling Inc ....D 915 532-5643
El Paso *(G-6027)*

3351 Rolling, Drawing & Extruding Of Copper

◆ Bae Systems Resolution Inc ....E 713 868-7700
Houston *(G-8789)*

▼ Copper Craft Inc ....E 817 490-9622
Fort Worth *(G-6549)*

International Wire Group Inc ....D 915 877-5500
El Paso *(G-5816)*

McClinton Energy Group L L C ....C 432 563-5500
Midland *(G-15296)*

McClinton Energy Group L L C ....C 432 563-5500
Odessa *(G-16077)*

Multalloy LLC ....E 713 943-3544
Pearland *(G-16583)*

Optical Cable Corporation ....E 972 509-1500
Plano *(G-16956)*

Quality Copper & Alloys LLC ....F 346 223-1032
Houston *(G-11493)*

Southwire Company LLC ....F 940 328-1047
Mineral Wells *(G-15542)*

3353 Aluminum Sheet, Plate & Foil

Aluminum Tank & Tank ACC Inc ....F 817 378-8455
Fort Worth *(G-6376)*

▲ Baker Metal Products Inc ....C 972 241-3553
Dallas *(G-3999)*

◆ Circuit Breaker Sales LLC ....C 940 665-4444
Gainesville *(G-7338)*

Columbia Alum Processors Co JV ....E 972 771-7150
Rockwall *(G-17543)*

Coretech Industries LLC ....F 440 949-9592
Dallas *(G-4168)*

Cubeco Inc ....E 713 671-2466
Houston *(G-9356)*

Howmet Aerospace Inc ....F 940 243-4491
Denton *(G-5374)*

Howmet Aerospace Inc ....B 903 832-8471
Texarkana *(G-19765)*

Howmet Aerospace Inc ....C 214 631-0200
Dallas *(G-4469)*

SIC

Howmet Aerospace Inc ....C 972 416-6500
Carrollton *(G-2762)*

Howmet Globl Fastening Systems ....C 830 774-7156
Del Rio *(G-5317)*

JRS Company Inc ....D 626 967-2432
Hutto *(G-12881)*

Meister Industries Inc ....E 432 366-2875
Odessa *(G-16078)*

Oil States International Inc ....D 713 652-0582
Houston *(G-11161)*

Peyton Salas & Mendoza LLC ....E 512 784-5875
Houston *(G-11313)*

QMF Steel Inc ....E 903 455-3618
Campbell *(G-2646)*

Quanex Building Products Corp ....E 731 961-4600
Houston *(G-11504)*

▲ RDS Metal LP ....E 817 539-7400
Mansfield *(G-14708)*

▲ Team Pride Extrusions Inc ....E 940 562-2205
Megargel *(G-14994)*

3354 Aluminum Extruded Prdts

Affinity Chemical LLC ....F 214 696-1037
Dallas *(G-3901)*

▲ American Extrusion Company ....F 713 869-9551
Houston *(G-8596)*

▲ Atrium Windows and Doors Inc ......D 214 583-1840
Dallas *(G-3983)*

Bielas Glass & Aluminum Pdts ....E 210 333-8040
San Antonio *(G-17952)*

◆ Brandon Industries Inc ....E 972 542-3000
McKinney *(G-14929)*

◆ C E Shepherd Company LP ....D 713 924-4300
Houston *(G-9028)*

Columbia Alum Processors Co JV ....E 972 771-7150
Rockwall *(G-17543)*

Crh Americas Inc ....E 903 765-2212
Alba *(G-181)*

Crown Cork & Seal Usa Inc ....C 281 240-4838
Sugar Land *(G-14469)*

Crown Cork & Seal Usa Inc ....C 936 539-5401
Conroe *(G-3287)*

Diamond Plastics Corporation ....D 806 763-8021
Lubbock *(G-14405)*

Everlite Inc ....E 903 297-3444
Longview *(G-14232)*

Hudson & Hudson Neon Inc ....E 281 720-0100
Houston *(G-10275)*

Innovative Building Products ....E 940 387-0408
Millsap *(G-15503)*

International Aluminum Corp ....C 972 937-7032
Waxahachie *(G-20545)*

Justiss Oil Company Inc ....D 903 859-2111
Arp *(G-812)*

Kaiser Aluminum Fab Pdts LLC ....C 903 868-1556
Sherman *(G-18918)*

North American Pipe Corp ....D 940 855-4100
Wichita Falls *(G-20787)*

Oldcastle Buildingenvelope Inc ....A 972 551-6100
Terrell *(G-19746)*

Omnimax International Inc ....E 817 473-1541
Mansfield *(G-14699)*

PSI Industries Inc ....E 940 564-3563
Olney *(G-16224)*

Quality Cast Metals Inc ....E 817 921-3595
Fort Worth *(G-6927)*

R C Technical Welding & Fabr ....E 281 933-6004
Stafford *(G-19367)*

Sigmatron International Inc ....F 830 775-5524
Del Rio *(G-5324)*

Texas Aluminum Industries Inc ....B 713 941-7186
Houston *(G-12220)*

Tower Extrusions Ltd ....B 972 442-3535
Wylie *(G-20952)*

▲ Tower Extrusions Ltd ....C 940 564-5681
Olney *(G-16225)*

Tower Extrusions Ltd ....C 972 442-7200
Wylie *(G-20953)*

TPI ....E 972 276-2901
Garland *(G-7604)*

William L Bonnell Company Inc ....B 409 543-0600
El Campo *(G-5629)*

3355 Aluminum Rolling & Drawing, NEC

Alcoa USA Corp ....C 512 446-8681
Rockdale *(G-17524)*

Champlain Cable Texas Corp ....F 915 860-0010
El Paso *(G-5695)*

Custom Extrusions Holdings LLC ....F 972 442-7200
Wylie *(G-20931)*

General Cable Corporation ....E 903 938-8151
Marshall *(G-14780)*

Lonestar Aluminum Spc LLC ....E 281 617-7177
Houston *(G-10682)*

Mark House of Hot Rods Inc ....E 817 466-9942
Mansfield *(G-14687)*

Quality Cast Metals Inc ....E 817 921-3595
Fort Worth *(G-6927)*

Southwire Company LLC ....F 940 328-1047
Mineral Wells *(G-15542)*

Total Rod Concepts Inc ....F 432 689-0300
Midland *(G-15441)*

▼ Ultraflote LLC ....E 713 461-2100
Houston *(G-12430)*

Xterra Industries LLC ....E 281 998-0442
Pasadena *(G-16528)*

3356 Rolling, Drawing-Extruding Of Nonferrous Metals

Asarco LLC ....A 806 468-4000
Amarillo *(G-401)*

Bhc Industries of Texas Inc ....F 817 556-2306
Alvarado *(G-325)*

Elemetal LLC ....G 214 956-7600
Dallas *(G-4309)*

▲ Etkon USA Inc ....G 817 701-1181
Arlington *(G-673)*

Hutcheson Fabricating & Wldg ....F 713 224-9703
Houston *(G-10290)*

Interstate Fittings Inc ....D 214 637-6720
Dallas *(G-4508)*

▲ Jamestown North America LLC ....F 713 672-6655
Houston *(G-10452)*

Lemetrix Solutions LLC ....E 281 381-0714
Pearland *(G-16578)*

Metal & Materials Proc LLC ....G 713 664-0050
Houston *(G-10843)*

Metalloy Inc ....F 800 828-0500
Houston *(G-10850)*

▼ MMS Traders LLC ....F 832 433-7948
Houston *(G-10897)*

◆ National Specialty Alloys Inc ....E 281 345-2115
Houston *(G-11002)*

New England Lead Burning Inc ....F 713 675-3266
Houston *(G-11034)*

Nickel Rock LLC ....F 512 395-7416
San Marcos *(G-18701)*

▲ Overlay Product Systems Inc ....D 281 552-3500
Houston *(G-11206)*

◆ Prince Minerals LLC ....D 646 747-4222
Houston *(G-11419)*

Rmi Titanium Company LLC ....F 713 466-8222
Houston *(G-11639)*

▲ Rti Extrusions Inc ....E 713 641-6010
Houston *(G-11692)*

◆ Salzgtter Mnnsmann Stnless Tbe ....D 713 466-7278
Houston *(G-11735)*

Southern Stud Weld Inc ....F 972 790-3339
Irving *(G-13185)*

▲ Spf Corporation of America ....F 713 983-9373
Houston *(G-12014)*

Thermo Plastics Corporation ....E 817 281-9010
Fort Worth *(G-7056)*

Titanium Emergency Group LLP ....G 940 613-2653
Wichita Falls *(G-20818)*

Titanium Metals Corporation ....D 972 233-1700
Dallas *(G-5097)*

US Zinc North America Inc ....C 713 926-1705
Houston *(G-12494)*

US Zinc North America Inc ....D 713 926-1705
Houston *(G-12495)*

◆ US Zinc North America Inc ....F 713 926-1705
Houston *(G-12496)*

3357 Nonferrous Wire Drawing

A & B Auto Electric Inc ....F 713 928-3219
Houston *(G-8422)*

◆ Applied Optical Systems Inc ....D 972 509-1500
Plano *(G-16791)*

B Comm Constructors LLC ....E 210 257-0102
San Antonio *(G-17929)*

Btp Manufacturing Inc ....E 214 467-0094
Dallas *(G-4064)*

Channl-Track Tube-Way Inds Inc ....E 713 864-2551
Houston *(G-9162)*

▲ Custom Cmpt Cables Amer Inc ....F 972 638-9309
Plano *(G-16833)*

Data Connection Inc ....F 972 231-2185
Dallas *(G-4240)*

Encore Wire Corporation ....B 972 562-9473
McKinney *(G-14940)*

Encore Wire Corporation ....C 972 562-9473
McKinney *(G-14941)*

Essex Group Inc ....F 915 772-6041
El Paso *(G-5759)*

▲ Fiber Systems Intl Inc ....C 214 547-2400
Allen *(G-267)*

◆ Galaxy Electronics Company ....F 972 234-0065
Richardson *(G-17319)*

General Cable Corporation ....E 903 938-8151
Marshall *(G-14780)*

Geo Space LP ....F 713 939-7093
Houston *(G-9933)*

Global Teknicians Inc ....E 407 504-9087
Houston *(G-9978)*

Incab America LLC ....E 833 344-6222
Arlington *(G-702)*

Jacqueline Construction Inc ....F 469 258-4402
Garland *(G-7525)*

Keystone Consolidated Inds ....D 903 893-0191
Sherman *(G-18919)*

▲ Megladon Mfg Group Ltd ....E 512 491-0006
Austin *(G-1336)*

New Concept Services Inc ....F 903 342-5523
Winnsboro *(G-20900)*

Optical Cable Corporation ....E 972 509-1500
Plano *(G-16956)*

Prysmian Cbles Systems USA LLC ....F 281 209-1070
Houston *(G-11468)*

Sanwa Electronics USA Corp ....G 972 503-3031
Plano *(G-17001)*

Scott Fennell Inc ....E 817 822-1283
Iola *(G-12900)*

Southwire Company LLC ....F 940 328-1047
Mineral Wells *(G-15542)*

▲ Steward Enterprises Inc ....C 432 687-2553
Midland *(G-15420)*

Superior Essex Intl LP ....E 325 646-8591
Brownwood *(G-2446)*

Therm-O-Link Inc ....D 915 860-9933
El Paso *(G-6001)*

Trans Cable International Inc ....E 903 449-4622
Bonham *(G-2156)*

◆ Umbilicals International Inc ....D 281 275-6600
Stafford *(G-19392)*

◆ United Copper Industries LLC ....B 940 243-8200
Denton *(G-5408)*

Xact Technologies USA Corp ....F 403 862-3383
Houston *(G-12704)*

3363 Aluminum Die Castings

Brown Die Casting & Mfg Inc ....E 972 636-9575
Royse City *(G-17716)*

Coastal Foundry Company ....E 713 695-4008
Houston *(G-9226)*

Kruger Aluminum & Brass Fndry ....F 940 767-0432
Wichita Falls *(G-20777)*

Quality Cast Metals Inc ....E 817 921-3595
Fort Worth *(G-6927)*

Shamrock Industries Ltd ....E 817 336-1413
Fort Worth *(G-6984)*

Superior Die Cast LLC ....E 903 586-0637
Jacksonville *(G-13260)*

Texas Die Casting LLC ....C 903 845-2224
Gladewater *(G-7727)*

3364 Nonferrous Die Castings, Exc Aluminum

Anadite Cal Restoration Tr ....F 817 282-9171
Hurst *(G-12833)*

Coastal Foundry Company ....E 713 695-4008
Houston *(G-9226)*

Fisher Controls Intl LLC ....B 972 542-5512
McKinney *(G-14943)*

Fore Machine LLC ....D 817 834-6251
Haltom City *(G-8141)*

Gaus Anodes International LLC ....E 832 243-0700
Houston *(G-9906)*

Kruger Aluminum & Brass Fndry ....F 940 767-0432
Wichita Falls *(G-20777)*

Quality Cast Metals Inc ....E 817 921-3595
Fort Worth *(G-6927)*

Resource Oilfield Pdts Co Inc ....F 281 442-8600
Houston *(G-11610)*

Superior Die Cast LLC ....E 903 586-0637
Jacksonville *(G-13260)*

Valley Die Castings Inc ....F 956 630-0268
McAllen *(G-14913)*

Wichita Falls Mfg Inc ....E 940 322-4491
Wichita Falls *(G-20831)*

3365 Aluminum Foundries

A&B Foundry LLC ....F 972 247-3579
Dallas *(G-3872)*

Airfoil Impellers Corporation ....E 979 822-6418
Bryan *(G-2452)*

▼ Alloy Casting Co Inc ....E 800 527-1318
Mesquite *(G-15025)*

Anadite Cal Restoration Tr ....F 817 282-9171
Hurst *(G-12833)*

Anodico Corporation ....F 713 690-6100
Houston *(G-8647)*

Arsham Metal Industries Inc ....E 713 896-8585
Jersey Village *(G-13292)*

Be-Technologies Ltd ....F 972 242-1853
Carrollton *(G-2704)*

Blaylock Industries Inc ....E 817 831-0170
Fort Worth *(G-6456)*

▼ Cole Industries Inc ....F 972 271-0280
Garland *(G-7460)*

Cytec Engineered Materials Inc .....C 903 457-8500
Greenville *(G-8068)*

◆ Denison Industries Inc ....C 903 786-4444
Denison *(G-5340)*

◆ Galvotec Alloys Inc ....C 956 630-3500
McAllen *(G-14863)*

Gamma Aerospace LLC ....C 817 477-2193
Mansfield *(G-14675)*

Gaus Anodes International LLC ....E 832 243-0700
Houston *(G-9906)*

Harlow Arostructures Texas LLC ....D 817 583-8820
Mansfield *(G-14679)*

Honeycomb One LLP ....D 817 649-7056
Arlington *(G-697)*

◆ Kessler Industries Inc ....E 915 591-8161
El Paso *(G-5828)*

◆ Key 3 Casting LLC ....D 817 332-9500
Fort Worth *(G-6757)*

Longview Brass & Aluminum Co ....F 903 758-8171
Longview *(G-14268)*

M G Products Company ....E 915 541-8950
El Paso *(G-5853)*

▲ Mayday Manufacturing Co ....C 940 898-8301
Denton *(G-5381)*

Samuel Son & Co (usa) Inc ....D 972 438-3949
Irving *(G-13171)*

Skyway Aviation Group LLC ....D 830 278-4481
San Antonio *(G-18479)*

Superior Die Cast LLC ....C 903 586-0637
Jacksonville *(G-13260)*

Texas Aluminum Foundry Inc ....E 817 834-5568
Fort Worth *(G-7045)*

Winklman Wnkleman Partners LLC .....E 817 831-0170
Fort Worth *(G-7150)*

YKK AP America Inc ....E 972 245-9551
Coppell *(G-3454)*

3366 Copper Foundries

A&B Foundry LLC ....F 972 247-3579
Dallas *(G-3872)*

American Bronze Alum Cast Corp .....E 713 222-0236
Houston *(G-8591)*

Baart Industrial Group ....F 713 690-1690
Houston *(G-8783)*

Baumann Propellers LLC ....F 713 714-5573
Houston *(G-8831)*

C & L Aluminum Foundry Inc ....F 817 923-0533
Fort Worth *(G-6483)*

▲ Claytex Trophies Inc ....C 940 538-6521
Henrietta *(G-8279)*

Deep In Heart Art Foundry ....E 512 321-7868
Bastrop *(G-1755)*

Demco Manufacturing Inc ....E 936 829-4771
Diboll *(G-5462)*

Esna LLC ....B 817 281-8816
North Richland Hills *(G-15877)*

Hoka Hey Inc ....F 254 445-2017
Stephenville *(G-19416)*

J DS Machine Shop ....F 903 532-6240
Howe *(G-12734)*

▲ Jc/Fz Holdings Inc ....E 713 948-6000
Houston *(G-10459)*

Longview Brass & Aluminum Co ....F 903 758-8171
Longview *(G-14268)*

M G Products Company ....E 915 541-8950
El Paso *(G-5853)*

▲ Mayday Manufacturing Co ....C 940 898-8301
Denton *(G-5381)*

O & D Manufacturing Inc ....D 903 295-2057
White Oak *(G-20718)*

Odessa JPK Investments Ltd ....E 432 368-0888
Odessa *(G-16096)*

Permocast Corporation ....E 254 778-5216
Temple *(G-19699)*

Schaefer Art Bronze LP ....F 817 460-1102
Arlington *(G-779)*

▲ Solidiform Inc ....E 817 831-2626
Fort Worth *(G-7000)*

Texas Metal Casting Co ....E 936 639-1131
Lufkin *(G-14555)*

Wearalloy Inc ....E 979 543-1133
Houston *(G-12610)*

3369 Nonferrous Foundries: Castings, NEC

American Railcar Inds Inc ....C 903 759-3946
Longview *(G-14195)*

Anodico Corporation ....F 713 690-6100
Houston *(G-8647)*

Centrifugal Castings Inc ....E 254 773-9068
Temple *(G-19675)*

Clear Lk Program Solutions LLC ....F 713 784-0111
Webster *(G-20636)*

◆ Coastal Casting Service ....D 713 223-4439
Houston *(G-9223)*

Coastal Foundry Company ....E 713 695-4008
Houston *(G-9226)*

▲ Consolidated Casting LLC ....C 972 225-7305
Hutchins *(G-12865)*

D C G Machine Inc ....E 903 297-2053
White Oak *(G-20713)*

▲ Delta Centrifugal LLC ....C 254 773-9055
Temple *(G-19679)*

◆ Galvotec Alloys Inc ....C 956 630-3500
McAllen *(G-14863)*

Globalfoundries US Inc ....C 512 457-3407
Austin *(G-1184)*

Kgp Group Inc ....F 817 349-3135
Fort Worth *(G-6759)*

Superior Die Cast LLC ....C 903 586-0637
Jacksonville *(G-13260)*

V-S Precision Usa LLC ....B 915 590-2707
El Paso *(G-6022)*

3398 Metal Heat Treating

Ameritek Heat Treating and F ....C 281 480-5637
La Porte *(G-13722)*

Analytic Stress Relieving Inc ....E 361 883-0315
Corpus Christi *(G-3473)*

Analytic Stress Relieving Inc ....D 281 471-9600
La Porte *(G-13724)*

▲ Backer Marathon Inc ....E 830 775-1417
Del Rio *(G-5307)*

Bodycote K-Tech Inc ....F 281 227-8222
Houston *(G-8937)*

Bodycote K-Tech Inc ....F 214 904-2420
Dallas *(G-4037)*

Bodycote Thermal Proc Inc ....E 214 904-2420
Dallas *(G-4038)*

Bodycote Thermal Proc Inc ....E 713 225-6050
Houston *(G-8938)*

Bodycote Thermal Proc Inc ....E 817 265-5878
Arlington *(G-633)*

◆ Bodycote Usa Inc ....D 214 904-2420
Dallas *(G-4039)*

Bwt LLC ....E 281 442-6694
Houston *(G-9024)*

Chromalloy Gas Turbine LLC ....F 972 241-2501
Dallas *(G-4114)*

Curtiss-Wright Surfc Tech LLC ....F 972 641-8011
Grand Prairie *(G-7859)*

Eckel Heat Treating Co ....D 432 362-4336
Odessa *(G-15984)*

◆ Eckel Manufacturing Co Inc ....E 432 362-4336
Odessa *(G-15985)*

◆ Ellwood Texas Forge LP ....C 713 434-5100
Houston *(G-9605)*

Gamma Engineering Inc ....C 817 477-2193
Mansfield *(G-14676)*

Gemstar Inc ....E 432 362-2315
Odessa *(G-16013)*

Gill Metallurgical Inc ....F 281 593-0807
Cleveland *(G-3127)*

Houston Thermal Processing LLC ....F 281 590-9600
Houston *(G-10256)*

Industrial Thermal Svcs LLC ....E 409 886-9700
Orange *(G-16247)*

Lark Industries Incorporated ....E 713 937-9089
Houston *(G-10601)*

▲ Lone Star Heat Treating Corp ....D 713 672-6616
Houston *(G-10678)*

Lst Heat Treating LLC ....G 903 757-2115
Longview *(G-14272)*

Mannings USA Inc ....E 281 443-7474
Pasadena *(G-16479)*

Metal Improvement Company LLC ....E 972 660-3692
Grand Prairie *(G-7926)*

Metal Improvement Company LLC ....F 713 691-0257
Houston *(G-10846)*

Modern Heat Treat Inc ....D 817 616-0333
Richland Hills *(G-17443)*

National Heat Treat LLC ....E 281 809-9840
Houston *(G-10969)*

National Oilwell Varco Inc ....C 936 825-7070
Navasota *(G-15739)*

Nci Group Inc ....E 713 921-7997
Houston *(G-11018)*

▲ Omk Tube Inc ....E 281 609-8150
Houston *(G-11175)*

Osr Services LP ....E 281 422-7206
Baytown *(G-1830)*

Republic Heat Treat Inc ....F 713 692-3308
Houston *(G-11601)*

Rhr Acquisition Co LLC ....F 713 699-3892
Houston *(G-11615)*

Rhr Acquisition Co LLC ....F 936 856-6607
Conroe *(G-3357)*

Southwest Indus Surfaces Inc ....E 972 641-4393
Grand Prairie *(G-7974)*

Southwest Metal Treating Corp ....E 817 551-1004
Fort Worth *(G-7003)*

Specialty Heat Treat Inc ....E 713 937-3101
Houston *(G-11999)*

Superior Shot Peening Inc ....E 281 432-0900
Cleveland *(G-3138)*

Swht LLC ....E 281 442-6694
Houston *(G-12132)*

Team Cooperheat-Mqs Inc ....E 713 673-3660
Houston *(G-12171)*

Texas Heat Treating Inc ....E 512 255-5884
Round Rock *(G-17692)*

◆ Texas Steel Conversion Inc ....C 713 733-6013
Houston *(G-12252)*

Texas Stress Inc ....E 281 930-0897
La Porte *(G-13795)*

3399 Primary Metal Prdts, NEC

Advanced Aero Coatings LLC ....F 817 280-0467
Hurst *(G-12831)*

◆ Baikowski Malakoff Inc ....F 903 489-1910
Malakoff *(G-14634)*

CMC Steel Us LLC ....F 214 689-4300
Irving *(G-12975)*

Diversified Pure Chem LLC ....F 817 677-9418
Rhome *(G-17254)*

Elijah Tooling Inc ....F 940 591-1340
Denton *(G-5363)*

Express Fabrication ....G 469 628-3960
Princeton *(G-17209)*

Fabhar Manufacturing LLC ....E 214 802-9400
Princeton *(G-17210)*

Halo Coatings ....F 817 443-3710
Fort Worth *(G-6684)*

Huck International Inc ....B 254 751-5283
Waco *(G-20417)*

◆ Laguna Tubular Products Corp ....D 832 734-0044
Houston *(G-10586)*

Ncc Nano LLC ....E 512 491-9500
Austin *(G-1362)*

New Crosslink LP ....F 972 484-3322
Dallas *(G-4722)*

Pattonair Usa Inc ....F 817 284-4449
Fort Worth *(G-6897)*

Powder Coaters of Texas Inc ....F 979 387-2049
Beasley *(G-1844)*

Powder Metallurgy Company Inc ....E 972 436-3502
Lewisville *(G-14082)*

▲ RDS Metal LP ....F 817 539-7400
Mansfield *(G-14708)*

▲ Rodens All Star Mch & Mfg Inc ....E 817 927-2825
Millsap *(G-15505)*

▲ Sigma Fasteners Inc ....D 281 214-8800
Houston *(G-11885)*

Stelco Industries Inc ....F 972 923-3603
Waxahachie *(G-20563)*

▲ Sunbelt Stud Welding Inc ....F 713 939-8903
Houston *(G-12099)*

SIC

34 FABRICATED METAL PRODUCTS, EXCEPT MACHINERY AND TRANSPORTATION EQUIPMENT

3411 Metal Cans

Ball Corporation ....C...... 817 551-3100
Fort Worth *(G-6424)*
Ball Metal Beverage Cont Corp ....C...... 936 760-2255
Conroe *(G-3261)*
Ball Metal Beverage Cont Corp ....C...... 817 551-3100
Fort Worth *(G-6425)*
Bway ....F...... 979 779-5900
Bryan *(G-2464)*
Crown Cork & Seal Usa Inc ....C...... 281 240-4838
Sugar Land *(G-19469)*
Crown Cork & Seal Usa Inc ....C...... 936 539-5401
Conroe *(G-3287)*
◆ Hoover Group Inc ....E...... 800 844-8683
Houston *(G-10204)*
Kegspeed LLC ....F...... 267 714-8854
Austin *(G-1266)*
Mauser Packaging Solutions ....F...... 817 473-0259
Mansfield *(G-14692)*
Palladium Exchange LLC ....F...... 214 421-8600
Dallas *(G-4778)*
Reynolds Metals Company LLC ....A...... 361 777-2200
Gregory *(G-8104)*
Weldforce Fabricators LLC ....E...... 713 270-7733
Houston *(G-8395)*

3412 Metal Barrels, Drums, Kegs & Pails

Climate Control Containers ....F...... 409 963-2137
Port Arthur *(G-17105)*
Dallas Steel Drums Inc ....E...... 214 638-7027
Dallas *(G-4226)*
◆ Hoover Group Inc ....E...... 800 844-8683
Houston *(G-10204)*
Keal Cases Incorporated ....E...... 512 244-9100
Round Rock *(G-17665)*
Mauser Usa LLC ....C...... 713 670-2332
Houston *(G-10799)*
Mobile Mini Inc ....D...... 480 894-6311
Houston *(G-10900)*
Modern AG Products LLC ....E...... 281 470-1903
La Porte *(G-13778)*
Schmidt Manufacturing Inc ....F...... 281 431-0581
Bellaire *(G-2002)*
▲ Self Industries ....E...... 713 672-2559
Houston *(G-11824)*
Thomas Steel Drums Inc ....E...... 817 838-6891
Fort Worth *(G-7058)*
Westrock Cp LLC ....D...... 281 830-0131
Houston *(G-12657)*
Weyerhaeuser Company ....C...... 972 641-3891
Grand Prairie *(G-7992)*

3421 Cutlery

Angel Sword Corp ....E...... 512 847-9679
Driftwood *(G-5498)*
▼ Ddr Manufacturing Inc ....G...... 469 728-7242
Forney *(G-6307)*
◆ Dexas International Ltd ....D...... 469 635-8100
Coppell *(G-3415)*
Knives of Alaska Inc ....E...... 903 786-7366
Denison *(G-5341)*
Overtime LLC ....E...... 409 833-3300
Beaumont *(G-1937)*
Sir Hc20 Inc ....F...... 817 228-9449
Fort Worth *(G-6990)*

3423 Hand & Edge Tools

3M Company ....B...... 512 984-1800
Austin *(G-869)*
Bwi Companies Inc ....D...... 979 743-4581
Schulenburg *(G-18773)*
Bwi Companies Inc ....D...... 972 242-4755
Carrollton *(G-2708)*
▲ Component Manufacturing Corp ....E...... 800 275-3011
Conroe *(G-3280)*
▲ DK Drill I LP ....E...... 817 539-2500
Mansfield *(G-14665)*
◆ Equalizer Industries Inc ....E...... 512 388-7715
Round Rock *(G-17656)*
Ferreira Holding Group LLC ....E...... 214 293-9233
Dallas *(G-4359)*
Geotex Inc ....E...... 817 656-9797
Fort Worth *(G-6666)*

H & T Auger Company ....E...... 432 362-4471
Odessa *(G-16022)*
Holmes Auto Supply Inc ....F...... 432 689-8008
Midland *(G-15248)*
J S Technology Inc ....D...... 469 326-5900
Garland *(G-7523)*
▲ Kgp Group Inc ....E...... 817 354-0766
Fort Worth *(G-6760)*
Lineage LLC ....E...... 806 688-7384
Pampa *(G-16327)*
Northrop Grumman Systems Corp ....A...... 972 946-9000
Dallas *(G-4743)*
Pelletizer Knives Inc ....F...... 281 859-4492
Houston *(G-11276)*
Pineforest Jewelry Inc ....F...... 713 451-1321
Houston *(G-11333)*
Pro-Steel Inc ....E...... 817 572-4959
Fort Worth *(G-6919)*
Rosewood Prvate Invstments Inc ....F...... 214 849-9000
Dallas *(G-4911)*
Southanchor Manufacturing LLC ....E...... 915 590-6718
El Paso *(G-5970)*
Standard Motor Products Inc ....C...... 972 316-8100
Lewisville *(G-14094)*
Stanley Black & Decker Inc ....F...... 972 247-1367
Dallas *(G-5006)*
Stanley Industrial & Auto LLC ....B...... 972 247-1367
Dallas *(G-5007)*
▲ Sumner Manufacturing Co LLC ....C...... 281 999-6900
Houston *(G-12096)*
Taylor Design Group Inc ....F...... 972 243-7943
Carrollton *(G-2825)*
▲ Texas Tempered Glass Inc ....E...... 713 697-2828
Houston *(G-12256)*
Trans Tool LLC ....E...... 210 225-6745
San Antonio *(G-18560)*
◆ United Amercn Acquisition Corp .....E...... 859 987-5389
Waco *(G-20470)*
Wildcat Manufacturing Inc ....E...... 806 327-5602
Tahoka *(G-19642)*
Xg Ventures LLC ....E...... 936 744-1800
Trinity *(G-20020)*

3425 Hand Saws & Saw Blades

Clover Group Inc ....E...... 915 590-2525
El Paso *(G-5698)*
Cutting Solutions Inc ....E...... 214 637-4849
Dallas *(G-4198)*
Falcon-Auger Inc ....F...... 713 690-2761
Houston *(G-9758)*

3429 Hardware, NEC

▲ ABC Exclusive Inc ....D...... 972 485-8182
Garland *(G-7425)*
▲ Accu-Lock Inc ....E...... 866 222-8562
Grandview *(G-8001)*
Adell Corporation ....E...... 972 226-4600
Mesquite *(G-15024)*
Allen and Allen LLC ....D...... 210 733-9191
San Antonio *(G-17894)*
◆ American Block Company ....C...... 800 572-9087
Houston *(G-8588)*
Antx Inc ....F...... 512 255-2800
Cedar Park *(G-2960)*
Architectural Products Co Inc ....E...... 915 584-9424
El Paso *(G-5649)*
ASAP Glass & Door LLC ....F...... 214 770-8266
Denton *(G-5351)*
▲ Bags Elite Inc ....E...... 972 279-7798
Mesquite *(G-15029)*
Berridge Manufacturing Company ....E...... 830 401-5200
Seguin *(G-18826)*
▲ Blacksheep Inc ....B...... 903 592-3853
Tyler *(G-20059)*
◆ Block Division Inc ....F...... 940 723-7308
Wichita Falls *(G-20746)*
◆ C E Shepherd Company LP ....D...... 713 924-4300
Houston *(G-9028)*
Carroll Systems LP ....E...... 512 927-1200
Austin *(G-1030)*
Cki Locker LLC ....E...... 817 329-1600
Dfw Airport *(G-5452)*
Cord Keeper LLC ....F...... 361 992-1122
Corpus Christi *(G-3507)*
Corrections Products Co Ltd ....E...... 210 829-7951
San Antonio *(G-18027)*
DC Controls Inc ....F...... 361 906-0123
Lewisville *(G-14043)*
Delta Rigging & Tools Inc ....D...... 877 889-8833
Hurst *(G-12844)*

Door Controls Usa Inc ....C...... 903 833-5815
Ben Wheeler *(G-2033)*
Esna LLC ....B...... 817 281-8816
North Richland Hills *(G-15877)*
Fabrication Specialty Inc ....F...... 214 742-3571
Granbury *(G-7797)*
◆ Fairfield Industries Inc ....C...... 281 275-7500
Houston *(G-9752)*
▲ Firstex Industries Inc ....F...... 972 602-1478
Grand Prairie *(G-7872)*
Glass Magic Inc ....F...... 806 535-4724
Lubbock *(G-14416)*
◆ Golden Blount Inc ....E...... 972 250-3113
Addison *(G-131)*
Guardian Compliance ....A...... 713 641-2020
Deer Park *(G-5277)*
▲ Hollywood Ovrhd Door of Dallas .....E...... 214 348-7240
Dallas *(G-4464)*
▲ I & I Design Inc ....F...... 713 667-6800
Houston *(G-10308)*
Indian Aerospace Inc ....E...... 817 265-5137
Arlington *(G-703)*
Indumar Products Inc ....F...... 713 977-4100
Houston *(G-10346)*
Inman & Company Inc ....F...... 713 224-4740
Houston *(G-10367)*
Innovative Hinge Products ....E...... 817 598-4846
Weatherford *(G-20596)*
Jcm Industries Inc ....C...... 903 832-2581
Nash *(G-15722)*
Kaba Ilco Corp ....B...... 972 668-7996
Frisco *(G-7294)*
Keymex LLC ....F...... 210 300-7056
San Antonio *(G-18224)*
Keystone Consolidated Inds ....D...... 903 893-0191
Sherman *(G-18919)*
▲ Lebus International Inc ....D...... 903 758-5521
Longview *(G-14263)*
Lee Products Inc ....F...... 817 641-9893
Cleburne *(G-3100)*
LFC Industries Inc ....D...... 817 640-1322
Arlington *(G-721)*
Lock Dock Inc ....F...... 903 759-1288
Longview *(G-14265)*
Maintenance Builders Sup Ltd ....E...... 713 462-8213
Houston *(G-10741)*
Marsol Technologies Inc ....F...... 346 701-8268
Houston *(G-10774)*
Maxistrut of Texas Inc ....E...... 713 880-4228
Houston *(G-10805)*
National Crane Cmplnce Inspcto ....E...... 888 720-6224
Manvel *(G-14735)*
NCH Corporation ....A...... 972 438-0381
Irving *(G-13115)*
◆ NCH Corporation ....A...... 972 438-0211
Irving *(G-13114)*
Pattonair Usa Inc ....E...... 817 284-4449
Fort Worth *(G-6897)*
Piping Accessories Inc ....E...... 409 842-5000
Beaumont *(G-1942)*
Pro-Steel Inc ....E...... 817 572-4959
Fort Worth *(G-6919)*
◆ Progressive Incorporated ....B...... 817 465-3221
Arlington *(G-762)*
▲ Pt Hardware Inc ....E...... 214 744-4491
Dallas *(G-4834)*
Ra-Lock Security Solutions Inc ....E...... 972 775-6301
Midlothian *(G-15493)*
Rf Manufacturing LLC ....E...... 817 479-1950
Haltom City *(G-8157)*
◆ Rolland Safe & Lock Co LLC ....D...... 972 243-3711
Dallas *(G-4909)*
▲ S C S C Inc ....E...... 214 398-1199
Dallas *(G-4922)*
Sanitz Enterprises Inc ....F...... 719 439-2183
Willow City *(G-20871)*
Scan-Pac Mfg Inc ....E...... 281 356-1640
Magnolia *(G-14626)*
Sey Tec Inc ....E...... 817 595-1949
North Richland Hills *(G-15880)*
Sle Electronics-Usa Inc ....E...... 915 594-4998
El Paso *(G-5963)*
◆ Southern Flger Dtntion Eqp LLC .....C...... 210 533-1231
San Antonio *(G-18487)*
Southern Foodservice MGT Inc ....B...... 903 463-1313
Denison *(G-5346)*
SPEP Acquisition Corp ....F...... 310 608-0693
Lancaster *(G-13848)*
◆ Taprite Inc ....E...... 210 523-0800
San Antonio *(G-18522)*

▲ Texas Starwares Inc .... F 972 641-2100
   Grand Prairie (G-7981)

Titus Group Inc .... E 469 289-1773
   Dallas (G-5098)

Toyotetsu Texas Inc .... D 210 231-5515
   San Antonio (G-18557)

Trane Technologies Company LLC .... E 903 730-4000
   Tyler (G-20163)

Triple C Hardware & Lumber Inc .... E 325 392-4123
   Ozona (G-16289)

US Home Systems Inc .... E 214 488-6300
   Irving (G-13204)

◆ Valhi Inc .... E 972 233-1700
   Dallas (G-5151)

Vision Systems Intl LLC .... E 817 234-6600
   Fort Worth (G-7107)

Wallace-Thompson Company .... F 903 683-2223
   Rusk (G-17733)

Waste Repurposing Intl Inc .... E 760 525-7180
   Austin (G-1647)

Worldwide Locking Systems Inc .... F 972 775-6320
   Midlothian (G-15496)

▲ Worldwide Wndows Tratments LLC .E 718 893-9370
   Dallas (G-5203)

Zimco Marine LLC .... F 956 831-7828
   Brownsville (G-2422)

3431 Enameled Iron & Metal Sanitary Ware

▲ American Acrylic Injection Inc .... E 972 784-7759
   Farmersville (G-6221)

▲ Arrow Mirror & Glass Inc .... C 832 467-4345
   Houston (G-8706)

◆ Eljer Industries Inc .... E 972 560-2000
   Dallas (G-4311)

Griffin Products Inc .... E 903 873-6388
   Wills Point (G-20875)

Kohler Co .... D 920 457-4441
   Grand Prairie (G-7906)

Kohler Co .... A 325 643-2661
   Brownwood (G-2433)

Mansfield Plumbing Pdts LLC .... D 903 657-1436
   Henderson (G-8267)

Ptp Incorporated .... F 281 342-8775
   Rosenberg (G-17595)

Sage International Inc .... D 972 623-2004
   Grand Prairie (G-7971)

Space Enterprises LLC .... F 800 559-2923
   San Antonio (G-18490)

Space Enterprises LLC .... E 281 846-9613
   The Woodlands (G-19923)

▲ Ssi Interests LP .... G 713 221-3488
   Houston (G-12032)

Zurn Industries LLC .... E 972 277-0900
   Carrollton (G-2852)

3432 Plumbing Fixture Fittings & Trim, Brass

As America Inc .... F 214 530-9831
   Hutchins (G-12862)

Brasscraft Manufacturing Co .... D 248 305-6000
   Lancaster (G-13841)

C Pearson Plumbing Inc .... F 817 488-0490
   Grapevine (G-8018)

▲ Chevron Phillips Chem Co LP .... A 832 813-4100
   The Woodlands (G-19845)

▲ Clarke Products Inc .... F 972 660-1992
   Waco (G-20383)

▲ Component Manufacturing Corp .... E 800 275-3011
   Conroe (G-3280)

Dal-Tex Specialty & Mfg Co .... F 903 883-3689
   Greenville (G-8070)

◆ Eljer Industries Inc .... E 972 560-2000
   Dallas (G-4311)

Fisher Controls Intl LLC .... B 972 542-5512
   McKinney (G-14943)

◆ Flowtronex Psi LLC .... C 469 221-1200
   Dallas (G-4372)

▲ Isenberg Bath Corporation .... F 888 342-2284
   Dallas (G-4513)

John W Gasparini Inc .... D 972 466-4104
   Carrollton (G-2874)

Kerr Feed & Grain Company .... F 940 538-4354
   Henrietta (G-8281)

Kohler Co .... B 325 643-2661
   Brownwood (G-2432)

National Well Supplies Co Inc .... F 713 467-0462
   Houston (G-11005)

National Wholesale Supply Inc .... F 469 517-0600
   Waxahachie (G-20553)

◆ NCH Corporation .... A 972 438-0211
   Irving (G-13114)

NCH Corporation .... A 972 438-0381
   Irving (G-13115)

Nibco Inc .... B 936 564-8321
   Nacogdoches (G-15706)

Northwest Pipe Company .... D 817 847-1402
   Saginaw (G-17753)

◆ Powerseal Pipeline Pdts Corp .... D 940 767-5566
   Wichita Falls (G-20796)

Royal Baths Manufacturing Co .... B 281 442-3400
   Houston (G-11682)

3433 Heating Eqpt

A O Smith Corporation .... E 915 400-2800
   El Paso (G-5634)

Abutec LLC .... D 512 836-9473
   Austin (G-881)

American Steam Inc .... E 972 442-4499
   Wylie (G-20926)

CCI Thermal Tech Texas Inc .... F 855 219-2101
   Houston (G-9109)

▼ Cisco Boiler Service Co Inc .... E 713 928-5700
   Houston (G-9196)

Enginered Packaged Systems Inc .... E 409 866-5213
   Beaumont (G-1887)

▲ Epcon Industrial Systems LP .... D 936 273-1774
   Shenandoah (G-18896)

Exotherm Corporation .... F 713 981-9100
   Houston (G-9726)

Exyte Americas Holding Inc .... E 972 535-7300
   Plano (G-16868)

Fives N Amercn Combustn Inc .... E 281 488-2667
   Houston (G-9795)

Flares & Stacks Inc .... F 281 356-1408
   Conroe (G-3297)

Fuzzys Indus Mint Mnfacture LP .... D 806 273-2818
   Borger (G-2179)

Gaumer Company Inc .... C 713 460-5200
   Houston (G-9905)

◆ Golden Blount Inc .... E 972 250-3113
   Addison (G-131)

◆ Hart Heat Transfer Pdts Inc .... D 713 675-9848
   Houston (G-10133)

▲ Hght Inc .... G 281 446-1155
   Humble (G-12776)

Houston Global Heat Transf LLC .... D 281 446-1155
   Humble (G-12777)

Huber Construction Company Inc .... E 713 926-9623
   Houston (G-10274)

Louisiana Wild LLC .... G 512 799-2537
   Austin (G-1304)

▲ Mortex Products Inc .... B 817 624-0820
   Fort Worth (G-6853)

Neu Plumbing Inc .... D 940 580-2200
   Pilot Point (G-16726)

Qtran Corp .... F 817 870-1855
   Fort Worth (G-6926)

Reatta Energy Inc .... F 432 682-7495
   Midland (G-15378)

Rm Manifold Group Inc .... F 817 897-5330
   Fort Worth (G-6961)

Selkirk Corporation .... B 972 943-6100
   Richardson (G-17395)

Skyven Technologies Inc .... E 972 861-0893
   Richardson (G-17399)

Texas Responsible Energy & .... F 903 266-9103
   Tyler (G-20161)

▲ Tisdale AC & Htg Co .... F 936 856-1500
   Conroe (G-3372)

Universal Solar Technology Inc .... F 832 764-8260
   Houston (G-12464)

Welch Hvac Incorporated .... F 214 222-8600
   Lewisville (G-14112)

3441 Fabricated Structural Steel

1st Source Restaurant Svcs Inc .... F 214 551-5338
   Lewisville (G-14019)

3d Steel Building Systems LLC .... E 325 365-5494
   Ballinger (G-1739)

5 Fab Energy Inc .... G 832 596-7140
   Cypress (G-3769)

5 Star Fabrications Inc .... F 512 267-0470
   Jonestown (G-13314)

A & S Fabrication Inc .... F 817 626-7720
   Fort Worth (G-6335)

A Better Fabrication LLC .... E 817 629-8908
   Weatherford (G-20572)

A Fab Industries LLC .... F 817 337-4776
   Keller (G-13466)

A&T Steel Fabricators Inc .... E 281 351-7650
   Tomball (G-19953)

Able Industrial LLC .... D 281 946-2200
   Deer Park (G-5260)

▲ Accelerated Process Systems .... C 713 937-6838
   Houston (G-8453)

▲ Accura Systems Inc .... C 972 226-0195
   Mesquite (G-15023)

Ace Fabricators Inc .... D 281 442-0992
   Houston (G-8466)

Acute Technological Svcs Inc .... D 713 983-9353
   Houston (G-8473)

Advanced Archtectural Mtls Inc .... F 713 983-9979
   Houston (G-8485)

Advanced Diversified Svcs Inc .... E 817 377-2718
   Benbrook (G-2036)

Advanced Machining & Tool Inc .... D 972 228-1987
   Lancaster (G-13836)

Advanced Sheet Metal LLC .... E 254 772-0134
   Waco (G-20355)

Advantage Steel Service Inc .... E 817 589-0088
   Fort Worth (G-6349)

AES Industries Inc .... E 817 341-7250
   Weatherford (G-20574)

Ahi Supply Inc .... D 281 331-0088
   Alvin (G-350)

Airtech Spray Systems Inc .... E 713 681-0013
   Houston (G-8518)

Akidco Inc .... F 214 905-6064
   Dallas (G-3915)

AI3 Incorporated .... E 512 746-4200
   Jarrell (G-13269)

◆ Alamo Iron Works Inc .... B 210 223-6161
   San Antonio (G-17885)

Alamo Structural Steel LLC .... F 254 799-2471
   Waco (G-20357)

Albas Custom Iron Inc .... F 281 401-9797
   Houston (G-8528)

Alecom Metal Works Inc .... E 972 438-1032
   Dallas (G-3918)

Alexs Air Conditioning Inc .... E 409 935-2496
   La Marque (G-13705)

▲ Allied Precision Fabg Inc .... E 713 757-9810
   Caldwell (G-2625)

Alnc Inc .... D 325 658-3612
   San Angelo (G-17774)

Alpha Fabricators Inc .... E 713 694-1392
   New Caney (G-15834)

Aluminum Techniques Inc .... F 281 499-9026
   Stafford (G-19285)

Amco Steel Fabrication LLC .... F 210 488-9023
   Elmendorf (G-6066)

American Block Company .... D 281 820-5332
   Houston (G-8587)

◆ American Block Company .... C 800 572-9087
   Houston (G-8588)

American Block Company .... D 281 820-5332
   Houston (G-8589)

American Steel & Alum Co Inc .... D 972 264-1533
   Grand Prairie (G-7830)

Americase Fbrication Cnstr LLC .... F 972 910-2296
   Ennis (G-6088)

Ameritex Machine and Fab LLC .... E 936 228-5070
   Willis (G-20842)

▼ Anchor Machine Works Inc .... F 713 988-0400
   Houston (G-8640)

Angelina Steel Inc .... F 936 634-6649
   Lufkin (G-14520)

Apache Fabricators LLC .... E 832 804-6236
   Houston (G-8655)

Apache Steel Works LLC .... E 832 473-4525
   Houston (G-8661)

APS Industrial Services Inc .... E 817 385-5500
   Arlington (G-619)

▲ ARC Designs Inc .... E 281 940-0430
   Houston (G-8677)

Architectural Products Co Inc .... E 915 584-9424
   El Paso (G-5649)

Arcosa Wind Towers Inc .... G 817 378-3700
   Fort Worth (G-6398)

Area Iron & Steel Works Inc .... F 915 833-9494
   El Paso (G-5650)

Armor Industrial Fabricators .... E 281 573-2777
   Baytown (G-1779)

Associated Stl Fabricators Inc .... F 281 516-0909
   Tomball (G-19961)

Atascosa Steel Industries Inc .... F 830 276-4322
   Poteet (G-17193)

Atkore International Group Inc .... D 708 339-1610
   Houston (G-8736)

Audio and Prfmce Solutions LLC .... E 210 549-4242
   San Antonio (G-17922)

Austin Western Railroad LLC ....E ...... 512 388-6350 Austin (G-965)	C M C Steel Fabricators Inc ....D ...... 512 282-8820 Buda (G-2522)	Cor-Tex Steel ....F ...... 903 872-3991 Corsicana (G-3662)
B & B Pipe & Industrial Tools ....F ...... 832 581-3179 Houston (G-8374)	C M C Steel Fabricators Inc ....D ...... 254 799-2471 Waco (G-20373)	Creative Alloy Products Co ....E ...... 936 894-2060 Plantersville (G-17058)
Baker Steel Company Inc ....E ...... 713 479-9399 Katy (G-13351)	C M C Steel Fabricators Inc ....D ...... 713 225-4446 Houston (G-9032)	Crist Industries Inc ....D ...... 817 847-8500 Fort Worth (G-6561)
Baldwin Metals Company Inc ....E ...... 214 637-1030 Dallas (G-4000)	C M C Steel Fabricators Inc ....D ...... 877 297-9111 Houston (G-9033)	Croft Construction Co Inc ....E ...... 936 258-7902 Dayton (G-5225)
Bar H Welding LLC ....G ...... 903 806-3110 Longview (G-14200)	◆ C M C Steel Fabricators Inc ....A ...... 830 372-8200 Seguin (G-18827)	CT & S Inc ....E ...... 972 438-9796 Irving (G-12986)
Barker & Bratton Steel Inc ....E ...... 972 556-1951 Dallas (G-4005)	C M C Steel Fabricators Inc ....D ...... 214 631-6699 Dallas (G-4073)	Cubeco Inc ....E ...... 713 671-2466 Houston (G-9356)
Barr Fabrication LLC ....E ...... 325 643-2277 Brownwood (G-2425)	C M C Steel Fabricators Inc ....D ...... 361 575-4561 Victoria (G-20250)	Custom Air Products & Svcs Inc ....D ...... 713 434-1192 Houston (G-9364)
Basden Steel and Erection Inc ....E ...... 817 295-6100 Burleson (G-2569)	C M C Steel Fabricators Inc ....E ...... 817 838-6811 Fort Worth (G-6484)	▲ Custom Air Products & Svcs Inc ....D ...... 281 802-7419 Houston (G-9365)
Basden Steel Corporation ....D ...... 817 295-6100 Burleson (G-2570)	C S Aguirre Sons Inc ....F ...... 432 381-5221 Odessa (G-15951)	Custom Fabricators & RPS Inc ....F ...... 979 775-4297 Bryan (G-2468)
Batterson Iron Works L L P ....D ...... 713 688-5433 Houston (G-8828)	C T & S Metal Fabricators Inc ....E ...... 972 554-9629 Irving (G-12957)	▼ Cyber Manufacturing LLC ....F ...... 713 946-4903 Houston (G-9381)
Bawco Fabricators Inc ....E ...... 281 449-0171 Houston (G-8832)	C W Precision Fabrication Wldg ....F ...... 281 820-4224 Houston (G-9036)	D & D Fabrication & Erection ....E ...... 817 237-3306 Fort Worth (G-6568)
Bawco Inc ....F ...... 281 485-3337 Pearland (G-16541)	C&A Machine and Repair Svc Inc ....E ...... 713 937-3426 Houston (G-9037)	D & L Quality Painting Inc ....E ...... 281 458-3588 Houston (G-9387)
Bayside Industrial Inc ....E ...... 832 632-2815 League City (G-13948)	C&F Fabrication Indus Svcs LLC ....F ...... 409 994-2135 Buna (G-2561)	Dallas Fabrication Inc ....E ...... 972 245-8771 Carrollton (G-2864)
Beall Construction Company Inc ....D ...... 325 677-2112 Abilene (G-16)	Cameo Fabricators Inc ....E ...... 281 449-6207 Houston (G-9060)	Dallas Metal Fabricators Inc ....F ...... 214 421-7417 Dallas (G-4220)
▲ Beck Steel Inc ....C ...... 806 762-3255 Lubbock (G-14369)	Carbery Fabricators Company ....F ...... 432 337-5015 Odessa (G-15955)	Daniel Steel Industries Inc ....E ...... 214 235-4509 Mesquite (G-15038)
Bellows Systems Inc ....F ...... 281 721-2947 Houston (G-8854)	Cast Sheet Metal LLC ....E ...... 956 580-9960 Alton (G-322)	Davis Iron Works Inc ....D ...... 254 666-1000 Hewitt (G-8299)
Beltran Brothers Fabrication ....E ...... 281 987-2331 Houston (G-8855)	Cen-Tex Marine Fabricators ....E ...... 512 237-2496 Smithville (G-18976)	▲ Delta Fabrication and Mch Inc ....D ...... 903 645-3994 Daingerfield (G-3831)
Benchmark Metal Service Inc ....E ...... 940 479-9134 Ponder (G-17094)	Centennial Steel Inc ....E ...... 972 412-5144 Rowlett (G-17703)	Dennis Steel Inc ....D ...... 512 259-4001 Leander (G-13987)
Bend-It Inc ....F ...... 713 991-0745 Houston (G-8856)	Central Texas Ex Metalwork LLC ....E ...... 210 337-2260 San Antonio (G-17992)	Diamante Enterprises Inc ....F ...... 210 655-9061 San Antonio (G-18054)
Benningfeld Stl Fbrication LLC ....F ...... 832 831-3691 Houston (G-8857)	Cerda Industries Inc ....C ...... 713 242-7700 Houston (G-9145)	Dietrich Industries Inc ....E ...... 281 383-1617 Baytown (G-1783)
Bentintoshape LLC ....F ...... 214 228-2985 Dallas (G-4018)	Certi-Fab Industries Inc ....F ...... 281 328-7244 Crosby (G-3728)	Diversified Plant Svcs L L C ....D ...... 979 848-8900 Angleton (G-570)
Best Strl Fabricators Inc ....F ...... 361 265-0550 Corpus Christi (G-3486)	Certified Pipe Svc Houston Inc ....E ...... 281 457-2454 Baytown (G-1812)	Diversified Steel ....E ...... 281 213-3340 Cypress (G-3786)
▼ Big 4 Steel Services LP ....E ...... 281 353-5333 Spring (G-19103)	Cessac Welding Service Inc ....F ...... 979 828-9067 Franklin (G-7164)	◆ Drilling Structures Intl Inc ....D ...... 281 880-8833 Houston (G-9530)
Big M Constructors Inc ....E ...... 281 469-9770 Houston (G-8883)	Channel Sheet Metal Inc ....F ...... 713 473-2878 Pasadena (G-16405)	Dynamic Crane Svc Fbrction Inc ....E ...... 713 849-1341 Houston (G-9547)
Big State Fabrication Inc ....E ...... 281 572-1375 New Caney (G-15835)	Chaparral Wldg Fabrication Inc ....E ...... 972 243-7747 Dallas (G-4104)	Dynamic Industries Inc ....F ...... 361 775-1500 Ingleside (G-12894)
Blastroom Eqp & Cnstr Inc ....E ...... 903 845-2083 Gladewater (G-7719)	Cherokee Steel Fabricators Inc ....E ...... 903 759-3844 White Oak (G-20712)	E-Z Line Pipe Support Co LLC ....E ...... 713 675-6693 Manvel (G-14733)
Bludau Fabrication Inc ....E ...... 361 798-4339 Hallettsville (G-8119)	Cherry Construction Systems ....E ...... 903 675-5901 Athens (G-822)	Eagle Fabricators Inc ....D ...... 281 442-8787 Houston (G-9556)
Bratton Interim Inc ....D ...... 972 556-1951 Dallas (G-4046)	Chisum Site & Steel Inc ....E ...... 903 783-0058 Paris (G-16360)	Eagle Metal Products LLC ....E ...... 903 887-3581 Mabank (G-14576)
Bratton Steel LP ....E ...... 972 556-1951 Dallas (G-4047)	Cls Metal Fabrication LLC ....F ...... 817 994-0891 Forest Hill (G-6295)	Eddie Richardson ....F ...... 972 878-6181 Ennis (G-6094)
▲ Brazos Pipe Stl Fbricators Inc ....E ...... 979 233-7895 Freeport (G-7194)	CMC Steel Us LLC ....F ...... 214 689-4300 Irving (G-12975)	◆ Efficient-Tec Intl LLC ....E ...... 214 221-9405 Dallas (G-4302)
Brock Services LLC ....C ...... 281 807-8200 Houston (G-8991)	Cnh Group Incorporated ....F ...... 832 453-9977 Houston (G-9219)	Efi Panels LLC ....F ...... 615 301-0745 Orchard (G-16273)
Broome Welding Co ....E ...... 409 744-0407 Galveston (G-7390)	Coast To Coast Tower Svc Inc ....F ...... 972 923-9504 Waxahachie (G-20537)	El Campo Sheet Metal LLC ....F ...... 979 543-5751 El Campo (G-5617)
Brush Mechanical Inc ....F ...... 713 937-9027 Jersey Village (G-13294)	▲ Cody Builders Supply Inc ....E ...... 512 339-9834 Austin (G-1055)	El Paso Machine & Steel Inc ....E ...... 915 533-7483 El Paso (G-5737)
Bulldog Ironworks LLC ....F ...... 972 935-0575 Waxahachie (G-20531)	Coldstream Energy Holdings LLC ....E ...... 940 682-4772 Millsap (G-15501)	Eldred Sheet Metal Works LP ....E ...... 713 227-3251 Houston (G-9588)
Bulldog Steel Products Inc ....E ...... 325 893-5806 Clyde (G-3162)	Coleman Machine & Welding Svc ....F ...... 325 625-5186 Coleman (G-3169)	Elite Metal Fabricators Inc ....F ...... 817 489-2599 Newark (G-15862)
Bullgang Tools LLC ....G ...... 979 203-9009 Brenham (G-2248)	Commercial Metals Company ....D ...... 713 690-0347 Houston (G-9252)	Endeavour Machine and Fab Inc ....F ...... 361 551-2077 Port Lavaca (G-17146)
Bulloch Fabricating Inc ....D ...... 972 221-6277 Lewisville (G-14031)	Commercial Metals Company ....C ...... 972 938-9500 Waxahachie (G-20538)	Entech Technology Inc ....E ...... 972 542-0210 Dallas (G-4325)
Butler Weldments Corporation ....D ...... 254 697-6416 Cameron (G-2640)	Commercial Metals Company ....B ...... 214 689-4300 Irving (G-12977)	Entex Fabrication Inc ....E ...... 940 592-2173 Iowa Park (G-12904)
Buzzard Industries Inc ....F ...... 936 264-1010 Conroe (G-3268)	Complete Mfg Svcs Inc ....E ...... 281 252-3111 Magnolia (G-14597)	Ernmex Interntational Inc ....E ...... 281 458-0152 Houston (G-9693)
▲ Bwfs Industries LLC ....D ...... 281 590-9391 Houston (G-9023)	Complete Sys Fabrication LLC ....E ...... 817 682-0729 Springtown (G-19272)	Essner Manufacturing LP ....D ...... 817 551-5511 Fort Worth (G-6618)
Bwj Metalworks LLC ....D ...... 325 672-4909 Abilene (G-26)	Conreco Inc ....G ...... 361 851-0352 Corpus Christi (G-3506)	Est of James T Jones ....E ...... 254 799-4515 Waco (G-20398)
C & C Metals Inc ....E ...... 936 760-5640 Conroe (G-3270)	▼ Conservatek Industries Inc ....D ...... 713 290-9944 Conroe (G-3284)	Excel Stamping & Mfg Inc ....E ...... 281 304-0771 Cypress (G-3789)
C & F Steel Company Inc ....E ...... 254 386-8847 Hamilton (G-8165)	Contract Fabricating Svcs LLC ....E ...... 281 501-8664 Houston (G-9292)	Express Fabricators LLC ....F ...... 972 734-3855 Farmersville (G-6222)
C M C Steel Fabricators Inc ....D ...... 972 938-9500 Waxahachie (G-20532)	Contractors Metal Works Inc ....F ...... 713 856-6600 Houston (G-9293)	Extreme Fab Inc ....D ...... 713 637-0001 Houston (G-9738)
C M C Steel Fabricators Inc ....D ...... 713 799-1150 Houston (G-9031)	Cooper B-Line Inc ....C ...... 903 813-1746 Sherman (G-18913)	F & R Machine Services Inc ....F ...... 214 631-4946 Dallas (G-4350)

Fab Services Ltd ....E 936 931-1004
  Waller *(G-20497)*

Fab Tex Oilfield Services Inc ....D 432 339-1011
  Odessa *(G-15998)*

▲ Fabco LLC ....D 713 633-6500
  Houston *(G-9745)*

Fabcorp Inc ....E 713 466-3962
  Houston *(G-9746)*

▲ Fabricating Specialties Ltd ....C 281 405-2010
  Houston *(G-9749)*

Fabrication Unlimited Inc ....E 713 433-6401
  Houston *(G-9750)*

Falcon Steel Fabricator Inc ....E 281 227-2766
  Houston *(G-9757)*

Fine Line Met Fabricators Inc ....E 972 524-6248
  Terrell *(G-19734)*

Fischbeck Welding Inc ....F 830 625-3249
  New Braunfels *(G-15792)*

Fluxmetals LLC ....E 832 948-4307
  Houston *(G-9818)*

▼ Ford Steel LLC ....D 281 354-3011
  Porter *(G-17176)*

Four-Star Fabrication Inc ....G 214 748-3494
  Dallas *(G-4373)*

◆ Freeport Welding and Fabg Inc ....C 979 233-0121
  Freeport *(G-7198)*

▲ Fwt LLC ....C 817 255-2965
  Fort Worth *(G-6657)*

G & H Diversified Mfg LP ....D 713 856-1600
  Houston *(G-9883)*

G Fabricating LLC ....E 281 421-3100
  Crosby *(G-3731)*

GA Steel LLC ....F 281 741-7284
  Houston *(G-9888)*

Gadutex Inc ....F 713 413-0006
  Houston *(G-8382)*

Gadutex Inc ....E 713 413-0006
  Houston *(G-9889)*

Gadutex Inc ....F 713 413-0006
  Houston *(G-9890)*

Gallop Contracting Group Inc ....E 281 449-1051
  Houston *(G-9894)*

Gavin Steel Fabricating Inc ....E 210 695-9672
  Helotes *(G-8237)*

General Metal Fabricating Inc ....F 713 641-5509
  Houston *(G-9924)*

◆ Global Fabrication Svcs Inc ....C 281 367-9333
  Houston *(G-9973)*

Gms Steel Manufacture LLC ....G 817 270-0447
  Azle *(G-1724)*

Gonzalez Mechanical Contr LLC ....G 915 345-1282
  El Paso *(G-5788)*

Gordons Specialties Inc ....E 972 225-1660
  Hutchins *(G-12866)*

Graywolf Industrial Inc ....E 281 441-5400
  Humble *(G-12771)*

Greenwood Manufacturing Inc ....F 281 862-9001
  Houston *(G-10038)*

Griffin Products Inc ....E 903 873-6388
  Wills Point *(G-20875)*

Grimes Industrial Inc ....E 713 921-0000
  Tomball *(G-19980)*

Grogan-Hazel Steel Inc ....E 713 466-7501
  Houston *(G-10048)*

▲ Gs-Hydro US Inc ....E 281 209-1000
  Houston *(G-10052)*

Gst Manufacturing Ltd ....E 817 520-2320
  Haltom City *(G-8147)*

▲ Guardiar USA LLC ....D 972 878-7000
  Ennis *(G-6106)*

◆ Gulf Coast Alloy Welding Inc ....E 281 821-0543
  Humble *(G-12772)*

Gulf Coast Fabricators Inc ....F 409 727-2372
  Port Arthur *(G-17109)*

Gulf Coast Fabricators Inc ....E 409 866-6721
  Beaumont *(G-1900)*

Gulf Coast Steel Inc ....E 281 768-8392
  Houston *(G-10063)*

Gulf Coast Welding LLC ....E 713 460-3700
  Houston *(G-10064)*

▲ Gulf Copper & Mfg Corp ....F 409 989-0300
  Port Arthur *(G-17111)*

▲ Gulf Island Fabrication Inc ....B 713 714-6100
  Houston *(G-10065)*

▲ Gulfex Holdings ....D 713 946-6614
  South Houston *(G-19043)*

H & S Metals Inc ....E 281 421-9488
  Baytown *(G-1821)*

Halo Fbrication Metalworks LLC ....E 972 587-0788
  Terrell *(G-19736)*

Hamar Industries Inc ....E 817 756-8990
  Fort Worth *(G-6685)*

Hefco Enterprises Inc ....E 281 431-1571
  Fresno *(G-7238)*

Hemco Industries Inc ....E 713 681-2426
  Houston *(G-10152)*

Henderson Fabrication Inc ....E 979 245-5350
  Bay City *(G-1773)*

▼ Hendrix Spclty Fabrication Inc ....E 713 466-6888
  Houston *(G-10154)*

Heritage Stl Erction Fbrcation ....F 817 790-5170
  Alvarado *(G-334)*

Herndon Fabrication Works ....F 713 941-3785
  South Houston *(G-19045)*

Hill Country Steel LP ....E 210 667-9737
  Converse *(G-3396)*

▼ Hirschfeld Holdings LP ....A 325 486-4201
  San Angelo *(G-17805)*

Hirschfeld of Nevada Inc ....B 325 486-4201
  San Angelo *(G-17806)*

Holloway Welding & Piping Co ....F 972 562-5033
  Allen *(G-276)*

Hollywood Steel Inc ....E 713 686-4325
  Houston *(G-10196)*

Hose Master Inc ....E 713 926-2288
  Houston *(G-10211)*

Houston Fab Truck Rigging RPS ....E 713 455-6161
  Houston *(G-10233)*

Houston Wifi C/Hston Cnstr Svc ....F 832 444-8300
  Spring *(G-19131)*

Hrk Enterprises Inc ....F 817 654-2008
  Fort Worth *(G-6706)*

Hvac Mechanical Svcs of Texas ....B 713 266-3900
  Houston *(G-10292)*

Hydradyne Hydraulics Inc ....E 713 937-8111
  Houston *(G-10294)*

Hydraulic Fabrication Svcs Inc ....E 832 844-3724
  Houston *(G-10297)*

Illinois Tool Works Inc ....E 800 231-1024
  Houston *(G-10327)*

Imperial Group Mfg Inc ....C 940 627-1700
  Decatur *(G-5247)*

Industrial Pro Fab LLC ....G 713 205-7245
  Katy *(G-13409)*

Insight Equity A P X L P ....F 817 488-7775
  Southlake *(G-19075)*

Insight Equity LP ....F 817 488-7775
  Southlake *(G-19076)*

▲ Insulation Investors Inc ....C 713 691-3661
  Houston *(G-10382)*

▼ Interstate Treating Inc ....D 432 362-9291
  Odessa *(G-16034)*

Inwesco Incorporated ....F 817 538-0387
  Fort Worth *(G-6727)*

Irwin Steel LLC ....C 817 636-2508
  Justin *(G-13344)*

Ism Industries Inc ....D 409 769-7841
  Vidor *(G-20327)*

J & N Welding and Fabricators ....E 956 585-3992
  Penitas *(G-16629)*

J & S Contractors Inc ....F 979 647-0040
  Sweeny *(G-19628)*

J 2 Fabrications LLC ....E 281 989-2984
  Magnolia *(G-14611)*

J E F Fabrication Inc ....E 281 367-2032
  Spring *(G-19223)*

J M Davidson Inc ....C 361 883-0983
  Aransas Pass *(G-592)*

J S McKinney Inc ....F 979 849-7283
  Angleton *(G-574)*

J W Hall Enterprises Inc ....F 409 925-7712
  Alvin *(G-368)*

J&A Fabrication ....F 903 981-0136
  Longview *(G-14254)*

◆ Jackrabbit Steel Products Inc ....E 281 550-4551
  Houston *(G-10446)*

Jackup Structures Alliance Inc ....G 713 910-7556
  Houston *(G-10447)*

▲ James Barker III ....F 936 298-2851
  Cleveland *(G-3130)*

Jayco Steel Services Inc ....E 281 399-0189
  New Caney *(G-15842)*

Jbc Steel Products LLC ....E 214 340-1510
  Dallas *(G-4529)*

JD Pro-Service LLC ....F 936 264-4003
  Conroe *(G-3314)*

▼ Jedco Building Systems Inc ....E 281 591-2860
  Houston *(G-10462)*

Jestex 2 LLC ....E 713 921-7187
  Houston *(G-10467)*

Jjm Oil & Gas Inc ....F 832 740-4606
  Houston *(G-10475)*

Joe Bush & Associates Inc ....F 512 238-0450
  Round Rock *(G-17664)*

Johnston Products Dallas Inc ....E 469 272-7212
  Cedar Hill *(G-2946)*

Joint Holdings/Basic Met Inds ....E 713 937-7474
  Houston *(G-10484)*

Jordans Manufacturing Company ....F 817 656-1033
  Fort Worth *(G-6745)*

Junction Industries LLC ....E 817 607-8873
  Fort Worth *(G-6747)*

Justiss Oil Company Inc ....D 903 859-2111
  Arp *(G-812)*

◆ JV Industrial Companies Ltd ....D 713 568-2600
  San Antonio *(G-18213)*

Katy Steel Co Incorporated ....E 281 391-7047
  Katy *(G-13368)*

◆ Kellogg Brown & Root Intl Inc ....F 713 753-2000
  Houston *(G-10512)*

▲ Kennedy Fabricating Inc ....C 281 399-3008
  Splendora *(G-19096)*

Kensing Iron Works Inc ....F 830 625-2815
  New Braunfels *(G-15808)*

Kikers Machine Works Inc ....F 432 381-8142
  Odessa *(G-16052)*

King Fabrication LLC ....D 281 209-0811
  Houston *(G-10533)*

Koenig Welding Service Inc ....E 979 532-4161
  Wharton *(G-20701)*

Kpr & Rsw Investments Inc ....F 281 499-2910
  Stafford *(G-19342)*

L & M Shtmtl & Stl Fabricators ....E 210 433-7131
  San Antonio *(G-18231)*

L B Foster Company ....E 254 296-6100
  Hillsboro *(G-8329)*

L B Foster Company ....E 832 934-3107
  Magnolia *(G-14613)*

Labelleco Fab LLC ....D 409 225-5499
  Beaumont *(G-1916)*

Lacy Construction Services LLC ....F 903 498-0683
  Kemp *(G-13485)*

Lake Road Welding Co ....E 940 692-4988
  Wichita Falls *(G-20778)*

Landmark Fabrication LP ....E 817 230-8857
  Decatur *(G-5248)*

Larwel Industries Inc ....E 817 491-1200
  Roanoke *(G-17486)*

Lauren Engineers & Constrs Inc ....E 469 417-7600
  Irving *(G-13083)*

Liberty Fluid Power Inc ....E 972 623-0927
  Grand Prairie *(G-7911)*

Longhorn Fabrication Inc ....D 972 225-6800
  Terrell *(G-19739)*

▲ Longview Fab & Machine Inc ....E 903 238-8300
  Longview *(G-14269)*

▼ Longview Mechanical Contrs Inc ....E 903 759-1331
  Longview *(G-14270)*

M & H Metal Specialities Inc ....F 972 296-9057
  Dallas *(G-4616)*

M&M Prcsion Mtal Fbrcation Inc ....F 940 726-3379
  Valley View *(G-20204)*

Mac Fabricators ....G 979 265-0235
  Clute *(G-3156)*

Mach International Inc ....E 713 695-6000
  Houston *(G-10731)*

Madewell LLC ....E 713 674-1050
  Houston *(G-10732)*

Maggie Chacon ....E 915 857-3100
  El Paso *(G-5857)*

Magni-Fab Southwest Co ....E 903 532-5533
  Howe *(G-12736)*

Makers Company Inc ....E 817 834-5538
  Fort Worth *(G-6807)*

Manufctred Component Parts Ltd ....E 713 880-0590
  Houston *(G-10749)*

Markle Mfg Co San Antonio Inc ....D 210 655-7130
  San Antonio *(G-18277)*

Master Fabricators ....F 832 294-8103
  Houston *(G-10786)*

Material Handling Concepts ....F 512 836-6598
  Austin *(G-1328)*

Mayhan Fabricators Inc ....E 903 734-4198
  Gilmer *(G-7709)*

Mc Welding & Fabrication Inc ....F 361 289-9605
  Corpus Christi *(G-3576)*

McBermett Milner LLC ....E 325 643-2277
  Brownwood *(G-2440)*

Medcalf Fabrication Inc ....E 281 893-0775
  Houston *(G-10817)*

Mercer Metals LP ....E.... 214 905-9915
Grand Prairie *(G-7925)*
Metal Spinners Inc ....E.... 817 847-0086
Saginaw *(G-17750)*
Metal Transformation & Design ....F.... 915 235-4645
El Paso *(G-5873)*
Metcon Inc ....G.... 817 281-1620
Fort Worth *(G-6830)*
Metfab Inc ....E.... 713 472-3900
Houston *(G-10853)*
Microteq Engineering Inc ....F.... 210 736-2611
San Antonio *(G-18303)*
▲ Mil Ltd ....C.... 713 691-5200
Houston *(G-10879)*
◆ Milestone Metals Inc ....D.... 281 448-9151
Houston *(G-10881)*
Miscellaneous Specialties Inc ....F.... 281 351-1177
Tomball *(G-19988)*
Mitchell Manufacturing Inc ....E.... 281 351-9641
Tomball *(G-19989)*
Mk Specialty Metal Fabricators ....E.... 972 225-6562
Hutchins *(G-12869)*
Mmw Fab Ltd ....D.... 817 589-0881
Hurst *(G-12852)*
▲ Mobil Steel International Inc ....E.... 713 991-0450
Houston *(G-10899)*
Modern AG Products LLC ....E.... 281 470-1903
La Porte *(G-13778)*
▲ Modern Group Ltd ....D.... 800 231-8198
Beaumont *(G-1930)*
Morrison Products Inc ....D.... 972 279-4000
Mesquite *(G-15063)*
◆ MPW Corporation ....F.... 713 640-2700
Houston *(G-10931)*
Mueller Construction Company ....E.... 903 868-3585
Sherman *(G-18924)*
Murray Building & Crane Inds ....D.... 713 464-6506
Houston *(G-10944)*
N-Fab Inc ....F.... 281 880-6322
Houston *(G-10949)*
Nci Building Systems LP ....D.... 806 747-4291
Lubbock *(G-14450)*
New Mllennium Bldg Systems LLC ....C.... 915 298-5050
El Paso *(G-5894)*
Nichols Enterprises Inc ....F.... 979 543-4833
El Campo *(G-5625)*
North American Steel Corp ....E.... 817 332-7069
Fort Worth *(G-6866)*
◆ North Shore Supply Company Inc ....C.... 713 453-3533
Houston *(G-11076)*
NRG Manufacturing Inc ....D.... 281 320-2525
Tomball *(G-19993)*
NRG Manufacturing Inc ....F.... 281 320-2525
Waller *(G-20505)*
▼ Nucon Steel Commercial Corp ....F.... 940 891-3050
Denton *(G-5384)*
Nucor Corporation ....C.... 936 687-4665
Grapeland *(G-8007)*
Oakwood Steel Fabrication Inc ....F.... 903 545-2266
Oakwood *(G-15893)*
Ober & Sons Inc ....F.... 281 879-6760
Houston *(G-11112)*
Omnimax International Inc ....E.... 817 481-3521
Fort Worth *(G-6882)*
Orizon Industries Inc ....C.... 281 375-7700
Brookshire *(G-2322)*
P & K Services LLC ....E.... 361 299-1800
Corpus Christi *(G-3587)*
Palmer Steel Supplies Inc ....C.... 956 686-6575
McAllen *(G-14898)*
Parker-Hannifin Corporation ....E.... 817 232-1040
Saginaw *(G-17754)*
Parkline Inc ....D.... 409 935-1037
La Marque *(G-13713)*
Parks Metal Fabricators Inc ....F.... 903 838-0535
Wake Village *(G-20487)*
Partner Metalfab LP ....F.... 409 933-0026
La Marque *(G-13714)*
Partners Metalfab LP ....E.... 713 672-6888
Houston *(G-11250)*
Patriot Erectors LLC ....C.... 512 858-9100
Dripping Springs *(G-5511)*
Patriot Parent LLC ....B.... 512 858-9100
Dripping Springs *(G-5512)*
Patriot Trinity LLC ....E.... 936 594-5948
Trinity *(G-20019)*
Peterson Beckner Inds Inc ....F.... 281 872-1806
Houston *(G-11296)*
Phoenix Metalworks LP ....F.... 979 992-3909
Cat Spring *(G-2932)*
Pinchback Industrial Inc ....E.... 409 860-1964
Beaumont *(G-1941)*
Piping Accessories Inc ....E.... 409 842-5000
Beaumont *(G-1942)*
◆ Piping Technology & Pdts Inc ....A.... 800 787-5914
Houston *(G-11338)*
Plant Fabricators Inc ....E.... 830 393-3064
Floresville *(G-6249)*
Plate Cut Inc ....F.... 713 802-1291
Houston *(G-11347)*
Polytrnix McHning Fbrction LLC ....F.... 972 436-0422
Richardson *(G-17374)*
◆ Power Seal ....D.... 940 767-5566
Wichita Falls *(G-20795)*
▲ Precise Steel Inc ....E.... 713 673-6300
Houston *(G-11385)*
▲ Precision Components ....F.... 888 554-4999
Houston *(G-11387)*
Precision M/C Products Inc ....F.... 972 429-6200
Wylie *(G-20944)*
Premium Weld Services Inc ....F.... 940 329-0222
Santo *(G-18738)*
▲ Prism Resources Inc ....E.... 713 947-2800
Houston *(G-11423)*
Process Manufacturing Corp ....D.... 713 426-1403
Houston *(G-11431)*
Professional Projects Inc ....D.... 281 351-6315
Cypress *(G-3814)*
Property Works Central Texas ....F.... 512 940-9353
Manchaca *(G-14640)*
Prostar Manufacturing Inc ....F.... 281 910-0110
Pasadena *(G-16499)*
▲ Purvis Industries LLC ....D.... 214 358-5500
Dallas *(G-4837)*
PWC Industries Inc ....E.... 361 289-0557
Corpus Christi *(G-3602)*
Qualico Steel Company Inc ....D.... 972 775-1400
Midlothian *(G-15492)*
Quality Lnings Fabrication Inc ....E.... 713 863-7013
Houston *(G-11495)*
▲ Quietaire Corporation ....F.... 713 228-9421
Houston *(G-11513)*
R & N Manufacturing Ltd ....D.... 713 466-6252
Cypress *(G-3817)*
R & S Steel Fabricating Co ....F.... 713 675-9007
Houston *(G-11521)*
R Lute S Inc ....F.... 281 595-3777
Rosharon *(G-17610)*
R Neal John & Associates Inc ....E.... 214 340-1464
Dallas *(G-4855)*
R R Ramsower Inc ....E.... 979 849-6441
Angleton *(G-576)*
R2 Fabrication Inc ....E.... 817 230-2015
Fort Worth *(G-6935)*
Randco Industries Inc ....E.... 432 520-0820
Midland *(G-15377)*
Rast Iron Work Company Inc ....E.... 210 659-6704
San Antonio *(G-18409)*
Ratec Inc ....F.... 903 687-3811
Waskom *(G-20520)*
Ratliff Industries Inc ....E.... 409 755-1830
Lumberton *(G-14569)*
Rays Welding Shop Inc ....F.... 972 775-2822
Midlothian *(G-15494)*
RE Campbell Company Ltd ....E.... 713 957-8721
Houston *(G-11558)*
Reactive & Alloy Mtls Inds Inc ....F.... 979 885-2244
Sealy *(G-18816)*
Reama Inc ....F.... 409 744-9222
Galveston *(G-7407)*
▲ Rebar Supply Company Ltd ....E.... 713 937-8999
Houston *(G-11564)*
Red Steel Company ....E.... 972 243-4242
Dallas *(G-4871)*
REE Holding Inc ....E.... 409 840-5650
Beaumont *(G-1947)*
Reliable Design Services LP ....F.... 972 584-0551
Quinlan *(G-17226)*
Renfrow Metalsmiths LLC ....G.... 832 724-8517
Houston *(G-11600)*
▲ RH Tamlyn & Sons ....E.... 281 499-9604
Stafford *(G-19370)*
Rice Metal Fabricators Inc ....F.... 713 462-1978
Houston *(G-11618)*
Rilco Manufacturing Co Inc ....D.... 713 466-4777
Katy *(G-13437)*
Rising S Company LLC ....E.... 214 455-0560
Murchison *(G-15682)*
Rising S Company LLC ....F.... 903 469-4452
Canton *(G-2659)*
◆ RJ Global Wika LP ....E.... 281 897-9222
Houston *(G-11633)*
Rln Consulting Enterprises LLC ....F.... 713 515-3638
Springtown *(G-19275)*
▲ Rose Machine & Fab Inc ....F.... 713 670-9007
Houston *(G-11663)*
Royce Tower Service Inc ....F.... 409 684-1913
Port Bolivar *(G-17134)*
Rus Industrial LLC ....C.... 281 864-9070
Channelview *(G-3033)*
▲ Rwn Contractors LLC ....D.... 817 523-7900
Springtown *(G-19276)*
S C S Technologies LLC ....E.... 432 264-6500
Big Spring *(G-2097)*
S F L Inc ....E.... 936 856-1433
Willis *(G-20863)*
▼ Sabre Industries Inc ....B.... 817 852-1700
Alvarado *(G-343)*
Sabre Industries Inc ....F.... 817 852-1950
Alvarado *(G-344)*
Sac Manufacturing Inc ....F.... 903 643-9100
Longview *(G-14301)*
San-Co Steel Ltd ....C.... 956 464-7766
Donna *(G-5490)*
Sanco Metal Fabricators LLC ....F.... 806 745-9674
Lubbock *(G-14477)*
Saulsbury Industries Inc ....E.... 903 392-2248
Henderson *(G-8273)*
▲ Sbi Industrial LLC ....E.... 972 284-1250
Canton *(G-2660)*
▲ Scott Manufacturing Inc ....C.... 806 747-3395
Wolfforth *(G-20912)*
Sefton Steel LP ....D.... 281 449-8677
Houston *(G-11813)*
▲ Seismic Products Inc ....E.... 903 675-8571
Athens *(G-839)*
Septh Group LLC ....E.... 713 988-4200
Houston *(G-11832)*
Serpa Fabrication Inc ....F.... 361 883-2266
Corpus Christi *(G-3621)*
Sharp-Bilt LLC ....F.... 409 886-0066
Orange *(G-16262)*
Shioleno Industries Inc ....F.... 817 465-9361
Arlington *(G-780)*
▲ Signal Metal Industries Inc ....C.... 972 438-1022
Irving *(G-13179)*
Sikes Fabricating Co Inc ....F.... 409 941-0727
Texas City *(G-19802)*
▲ SMI Manufacturing Inc ....D.... 281 449-0345
Houston *(G-11921)*
South Texas Steel Svc Co LLC ....F.... 713 699-2500
Houston *(G-11968)*
Southeast Texas Industries Inc ....C.... 409 783-0009
Vidor *(G-20332)*
Southeast Texas Industries Inc ....E.... 409 722-7351
Beaumont *(G-1951)*
Southeast Texas Industries Inc ....C.... 409 792-0084
Bridge City *(G-2286)*
Southern Frac LLC ....C.... 877 576-0821
Waxahachie *(G-20560)*
▲ Spf Corporation of America ....F.... 713 983-9373
Houston *(G-12014)*
Spitzer Industries Inc ....E.... 713 230-4200
Houston *(G-12017)*
Spitzer Industries Inc ....E.... 713 466-1518
Houston *(G-12018)*
▲ Spitzer Industries Inc ....B.... 832 783-7000
Houston *(G-12019)*
Spitzer Industries Inc ....E.... 713 856-9208
Houston *(G-12020)*
Stainless Steel Products Inc ....G.... 361 884-1281
Corpus Christi *(G-3628)*
Stainless Stl Cstm Fbrctors In ....E.... 713 433-0495
Houston *(G-12038)*
Stainless Stl Fabricators Ltd ....E.... 903 595-6625
Tyler *(G-20157)*
Staley Steel Inc ....E.... 940 686-6000
Pilot Point *(G-16729)*
Starks Welding & Mfg Svcs Inc ....E.... 512 863-2424
Georgetown *(G-7681)*
Steel Building Supply Inc ....E.... 936 598-6373
Center *(G-3009)*
Steel Designs Inc ....E.... 713 937-3006
Houston *(G-12053)*
Steel Effects LLC ....F.... 713 729-1100
Houston *(G-12054)*
Steelfab Texas Inc ....E.... 972 562-7720
McKinney *(G-14979)*
◆ Steelhead Inc ....E.... 210 628-1066
San Antonio *(G-18498)*

Steffani Metals Inc F 713 896-9160
Houston *(G-12056)*
Sterling Group LP E 713 877-8257
Houston *(G-12060)*
Steven-Sharon Corporation D 409 744-4538
Galveston *(G-7409)*
Stis Inc B 409 697-3350
Bridge City *(G-2287)*
Structural Fabrications Inc E 903 868-2979
Sherman *(G-18934)*
▼ **Structural Metals Inc** A 830 372-8200
Seguin *(G-18866)*
Sturm Welding Inc F 940 686-2492
Pilot Point *(G-16730)*
Sulta Manufacturing Company E 903 885-2139
Sulphur Springs *(G-19599)*
Summit Metals Corporation E 940 433-8788
Rhome *(G-17260)*
Summit Seals Inc F 409 769-8151
Vidor *(G-20335)*
Summit Steel Fabricators Inc D 713 451-6960
Houston *(G-12095)*
Suncoast Post-Tension Ltd E 512 259-7908
Leander *(G-13998)*
Superior Grating Inc F 713 686-9475
Houston *(G-12115)*
▼ **Sweco Fab Inc** B 713 731-0030
Houston *(G-12130)*
T & B Construction Svcs LLC D 936 824-3914
Lufkin *(G-14553)*
T O F Enterprises Inc F 281 328-2553
Crosby *(G-3744)*
Tank and Vessel Builders LP E 325 854-8450
Baird *(G-1736)*
Tankheads Inc G 817 636-2085
Haslet *(G-8224)*
Tcw Investments Inc F 409 796-1883
Beaumont *(G-1956)*
Team Fabricators LLC D 409 962-0266
Port Arthur *(G-17128)*
Techmar Industries LLC F 832 246-6200
Spring *(G-19175)*
Teco Metal Products LLC E 214 221-5020
Dallas *(G-5046)*
Tex Cnp/Seal Inc E 214 688-7770
Dallas *(G-5051)*
Texas Steel Fabricators Inc F 936 372-1616
Waller *(G-20508)*
Texas Toolmakers Inc E 210 494-3651
San Antonio *(G-18544)*
Texas Vessels Fabrication LLC E 903 541-4883
Jacksonville *(G-13264)*
Texcraft Inc F 806 744-6651
Lubbock *(G-14494)*
Texweld & Fabrication Inc G 903 586-1775
Jacksonville *(G-13265)*
TH Precision LLC E 830 549-5864
Seguin *(G-18868)*
Thornton Steel Holdings Inc D 817 926-3324
Fort Worth *(G-7059)*
Thorpe Plant Services Inc E 713 644-1247
Houston *(G-12281)*
Thybar Corporation E 972 416-6220
Dallas *(G-5090)*
◆ **Thyssenkrupp Arprt Systems Inc** C 817 834-6984
Fort Worth *(G-7061)*
Tippen Steel Services Inc E 940 433-3132
Boyd *(G-2208)*
Tips Iron & Steel Co Inc E 512 478-8511
Austin *(G-1581)*
Tlr Energy Services Inc F 940 969-2400
Paradise *(G-16355)*
Tns Industries Inc E 713 690-4000
Houston *(G-12313)*
Total Steel Fabrication LLC E 972 846-4703
Ennis *(G-6120)*
Trace Metal Industries Inc E 817 921-6251
Fort Worth *(G-7070)*
▲ **Tradco Inc** F 713 333-9300
Houston *(G-12339)*
Trailers By Southern LLC E 469 517-0410
Joshua *(G-13327)*
Trans-Tex Fabricating Co Inc E 210 633-0100
Elmendorf *(G-6072)*
Tres Palacios Marine LP E 361 972-3097
Palacios *(G-16293)*
Tri-Construction Co Inc C 979 233-7211
Freeport *(G-7217)*
Trinity Industrial Svcs LLC B 409 722-6700
Beaumont *(G-1964)*
▼ **Trinity Industries Inc** B 214 631-4420
Dallas *(G-5112)*
Trinity Specialty Products Inc G 210 304-2100
San Antonio *(G-18568)*
Triofab Inc F 713 417-1205
Houston *(G-12377)*
Truform Metalservice Inc D 512 258-1675
Austin *(G-1715)*
Trupply LLC F 281 516-8100
Houston *(G-12386)*
▲ **Tsgc Inc** C 361 289-0901
Corpus Christi *(G-3644)*
Turboweld D 713 896-6467
Houston *(G-12411)*
Turn-Tech Inc E 281 356-1290
Pinehurst *(G-16737)*
TX Tinman Enterprises LLC F 817 288-6116
Fort Worth *(G-7087)*
United Marine Enterprise Inc D 409 833-0303
Beaumont *(G-1965)*
United Metal Services Inc F 817 932-3330
Rhome *(G-17263)*
▲ **Universal Ornaments Inc** D 713 699-1500
Houston *(G-12462)*
Urbanovsky Advanced Cnstr LLC D 817 556-3288
Cleburne *(G-3117)*
Uribe Steel F 281 452-5696
Houston *(G-12479)*
US Bellows Inc B 713 731-0030
Houston *(G-12481)*
USA Frametek LLC E 512 515-6500
Liberty Hill *(G-14130)*
Valley Welding Service E 956 585-1043
Palmview *(G-16313)*
Valmont Industries Inc C 979 836-9395
Brenham *(G-2277)*
Valmont Industries Inc D 979 277-3359
Brenham *(G-2278)*
Valmont Industries Inc D 979 865-9137
Bellville *(G-2013)*
Valmont Newmark Inc E 979 865-9137
Bellville *(G-2014)*
Veriovox Corporation E 713 409-7216
Katy *(G-13384)*
Vessel Technology F 903 643-9111
Longview *(G-14329)*
Vestal Steel Specialties Inc E 210 651-4333
Schertz *(G-18768)*
Vickery Street Fabricators Inc E 713 695-9195
Houston *(G-12564)*
▼ **Vince Hagan Company** F 214 330-4601
Sunnyvale *(G-19615)*
Vulcraft Carrier Corporation E 936 687-4665
Grapeland *(G-8008)*
W&W-Afco Steel LLC D 325 676-1422
Abilene *(G-92)*
W&W-Afco Steel LLC C 806 765-5781
Lubbock *(G-14508)*
Wabb Industries Inc E 903 427-3980
Clarksville *(G-3078)*
Walkup Company D 713 675-6383
Houston *(G-12595)*
Walston Ventures LLC F 409 796-1883
Beaumont *(G-1968)*
Watkins Metal Fabrication Inc E 940 325-6008
Mineral Wells *(G-15546)*
Wells/Mccoy Steel Services Inc E 469 742-0888
McKinney *(G-14990)*
West Texas Steel and Sup Inc E 325 651-7322
San Angelo *(G-17838)*
WHW Properties Inc E 903 572-4161
Mount Pleasant *(G-15665)*
Wichita Metal Products Inc E 940 322-9611
Wichita Falls *(G-20833)*
Wilborn Steel Company E 210 532-6852
San Antonio *(G-18620)*
Wilbur L Anderson Inc E 325 658-6539
San Angelo *(G-17841)*
Wills Pro Custom Mfg Inc F 817 534-6009
Fort Worth *(G-7149)*
Wilson Metal Fabricators Inc E 972 227-0200
Dallas *(G-5191)*
Wilson Steel Services LLC F 903 275-2995
Brownsboro *(G-2333)*
▲ **Wind Clean Corp** E 325 625-1899
Grandview *(G-8004)*
Wldg Wilkerson & Fabrication F 817 528-1032
Overton *(G-16277)*
◆ **Woven Metal Products Inc** E 281 331-4466
Alvin *(G-386)*
Wyatt Resources Inc D 281 346-6100
Fulshear *(G-7332)*
Xtreme Strctres Fbrication LLC E 903 438-1100
Sulphur Springs *(G-19605)*
Zachry Holdings Inc A 210 588-5000
San Antonio *(G-18632)*
Zinsmeyer Mech & Wldg Ltd E 830 985-3498
Castroville *(G-2929)*

3442 Metal Doors, Sash, Frames, Molding & Trim

A & E Venetian Blind Company F 940 767-1449
Wichita Falls *(G-20735)*
▲ **Accura Systems Inc** C 972 226-0195
Mesquite *(G-15023)*
Ace Automatics Inc F 903 852-3004
Ben Wheeler *(G-2030)*
Airtite Products Llc F 325 672-5774
Abilene *(G-11)*
Alenco Holding Corporation B 979 779-1051
Bryan *(G-2453)*
▲ **All Seasons Commercial Div Inc** E 979 823-6557
Bryan *(G-2454)*
Allen and Allen LLC F 210 733-9191
San Antonio *(G-17895)*
Allmetal Inc E 972 245-9264
Carrollton *(G-2855)*
▼ **American Door Products Inc** D 713 681-8047
Houston *(G-8594)*
American Shredder Entps LLC F 817 378-8511
Fort Worth *(G-6385)*
Apco Building Specialties Inc E 915 581-6005
El Paso *(G-5645)*
Aramco Home Improvement LLC E 409 762-9652
Galveston *(G-7387)*
Arch Aluminum and GL Co Texas F 972 647-9230
Grand Prairie *(G-7834)*
Architectural Products Co Inc E 915 584-9424
El Paso *(G-5649)*
Assa Abloy Door Group LLC F 713 466-6790
Houston *(G-8724)*
Assa Abloy Entrance Systems US F 713 934-9095
Houston *(G-8725)*
▲ **Atrium Windows and Doors Inc** D 214 583-1840
Dallas *(G-3983)*
B & B Windows Inc F 817 237-2212
Fort Worth *(G-6417)*
Bielas Glass & Aluminum Pdts E 210 333-8040
San Antonio *(G-17952)*
Bochelle Inc F 972 837-1080
McKinney *(G-14928)*
Brothers Wholesale LLC G 903 587-2900
Leonard *(G-14001)*
Cerda-Fied Specialists Inc F 281 392-8063
Brookshire *(G-2313)*
Chem-Pruf Door Co Ltd D 956 544-1000
Brownsville *(G-2346)*
◆ **Classic Industries LP** E 972 564-2192
Forney *(G-6305)*
Cold King Inc F 210 227-0264
San Antonio *(G-18017)*
▲ **Columbia Coml Bldg Pdts Acqsti** D 800 668-1645
Rockwall *(G-17544)*
Cook & Boardman Group LLC E 214 630-3965
Dallas *(G-4165)*
Country Glass & Mirror Inc E 972 216-9100
Mesquite *(G-15035)*
Custom Manufacturing Company E 214 428-5173
Dallas *(G-4196)*
Don Young Company Incorporated D 214 630-0934
Dallas *(G-4272)*
Frameworks Manufacturing LLC E 713 692-5222
Houston *(G-9853)*
General Aluminum Co Texas LP C 972 242-5271
Flower Mound *(G-6266)*
Glass Samuels Company LLC D 210 227-2481
San Antonio *(G-18142)*
Grenier Service Company Llc E 512 335-7441
Cedar Park *(G-2972)*
Highlite Inc F 214 741-4116
Mesquite *(G-15051)*
▲ **Hoelscher Weatherstrip Mfg Inc** D 713 869-6466
Tomball *(G-19982)*
▲ **Hollywood Ovrhd Door of Dallas** E 214 348-7240
Dallas *(G-4464)*
Hrh Door Corp F 281 821-8572
Houston *(G-10273)*
Hufcor Inc F 972 850-2200
Dallas *(G-4470)*

SIC

International Steel Frmng LLC..............F 817 591-0507
Richland Hills (G-17438)

Janus International Group LLC............E 713 463-4427
Houston (G-10453)

Jeld-Wen Inc................................C 903 885-0660
Sulphur Springs (G-19590)

Kawneer Company Inc ....E 972 829-7160
Coppell (G-3425)

Kawneer Company Inc ....E 972 438-1212
Irving (G-13073)

Kinro Texas Ltd Partnership...............B 817 483-7791
Arlington (G-712)

Lobato Studio LLC..........................F 512 483-1327
Austin (G-1297)

Macgmc LLC.................................F 214 774-4455
Plano (G-16916)

Masonite International Corp ....D 972 686-5500
Dallas (G-4643)

Modern AG Products LLC ....E 281 470-1903
La Porte (G-13778)

Nci Group Inc................................E 281 302-1900
Houston (G-11017)

Next Century Screens Inc ....F 972 496-4981
Garland (G-7563)

Oldcastle Buildingenvelope Inc..........A 972 551-6100
Terrell (G-19746)

Olney Door & Screen Co ....E 940 564-3543
Olney (G-16222)

Olney Sales Inc.............................E 940 564-3592
Olney (G-16223)

◆ Overhead Door Corporation ....C 469 549-7100
Lewisville (G-14080)

Overhead Door Corporation ....B 361 884-6640
Corpus Christi (G-3586)

Overhead Door Corporation ....D 214 630-4669
Dallas (G-4773)

Pearland Industries Inc ....D 713 434-9898
Houston (G-8391)

Plantation Shutter..........................F 214 341-3677
Dallas (G-4809)

▲ Premex Door Supply Inc ....F 214 341-2212
Garland (G-7572)

Ram Indstries Acquisitions LLC.........D 281 495-9056
Houston (G-11535)

Rehme Custom Doors & Ltg Inc.........E 512 916-0511
Spicewood (G-19093)

Ritescreen Company LLC.................C 903 482-9200
Van Alstyne (G-20212)

Rushman Draperies Inc ....E 214 943-1000
Plano (G-16999)

Safe-T-Pet Inc...............................F 903 569-0590
Mineola (G-15511)

◆ Sanwa Usa Inc ....E 972 503-3031
Plano (G-17002)

▲ Sky Glass Inc..............................F 972 807-9616
Dallas (G-4969)

Solara Ironworks LLC......................E 214 744-9900
Dallas (G-4975)

Southern Shutters Inc ....F 512 272-9711
Manor (G-14649)

▲ Steves & Sons Inc ....B 210 921-1400
San Antonio (G-18505)

Trident Laboratories Inc...................E 972 226-4986
Mesquite (G-15081)

▲ Window Outfitters LP ....E 469 619-0892
Dallas (G-5193)

3443 Fabricated Plate Work

2011 Angelina Mfg LLC....................D 936 632-8330
Lufkin (G-14519)

A M Fabrication Inc.........................E 817 345-7600
Fort Worth (G-6337)

▲ A&A Machine & Fabrication LLC ....D 409 938-4274
La Marque (G-13704)

▲ AB Bellco Corporation....................E 713 781-6447
Houston (G-8440)

▲ Accelerated Process Systems ....C 713 937-6838
Houston (G-8453)

▲ Accura Systems Inc ....C 972 226-0195
Mesquite (G-15023)

Aggregate Plant Products Co ....D 210 333-1111
San Antonio (G-17874)

Alareal Corporation.........................G 915 858-4097
El Paso (G-5639)

Alfa Laval Inc................................F 713 329-1270
Houston (G-8535)

Alfa Laval Inc................................F 804 236-3106
Rockwall (G-17536)

▲ Amec Foster Wheeler USA Corp.....E 713 929-5000
Houston (G-8578)

◆ American Alloy Steel Inc................C 713 462-8081
Houston (G-8584)

Applied Cryo Technologies Inc ....D 281 888-3884
Houston (G-8666)

ARC Marine LLC............................G 713 489-7719
Dickinson (G-5469)

Architectural Products Co Inc ....E 915 584-9424
El Paso (G-5649)

▼ Arcosa Tank LLC..........................E 214 631-4420
Dallas (G-3962)

◆ Atco Rubber Products Inc ....A 817 595-2894
Fort Worth (G-6406)

Atco Rubber Products Inc..................E 713 674-6665
Houston (G-8732)

Austex Dumpsters LLC ....E 512 292-3867
Austin (G-950)

Azz Inc.......................................E 972 840-0934
Garland (G-7446)

▼ Ba-Ker Tank Head Company Inc......E 817 232-8030
Fort Worth (G-6418)

Baldwin Metals Company Inc ....E 214 637-1030
Dallas (G-4000)

Bayside Industrial Inc......................E 832 632-2815
League City (G-13948)

Beaumont Machine Works Inc ....D 409 838-0261
Lumberton (G-14566)

Bell Intercoolers LLC.......................F 830 438-6150
Spring Branch (G-19268)

▲ Bendco Inc.................................E 713 473-1557
Pasadena (G-16398)

Bendel Tank Heat Exchnger Corp ....E 832 436-4626
The Woodlands (G-19835)

Bgi Contractors Inc.........................C 409 833-0303
Port Arthur (G-17102)

Bise Welding & Fabricating Inc ....D 713 681-0958
Houston (G-8892)

Boatman Industries Inc ....E 713 641-6006
Houston (G-8932)

Brandon Wldg & Fabrication Inc ....E 361 242-3344
Corpus Christi (G-3488)

▲ Brazos Pipe Stl Fbricators Inc ....E 979 233-7895
Freeport (G-7194)

Bryan Container Company Inc ....E 979 822-7998
Bryan (G-2463)

Buffalo Tank Company Inc ....G 903 322-4153
Buffalo (G-2543)

Bulldog Steel Products Inc ....E 325 893-5806
Clyde (G-3162)

Butler Weldments Corporation............D 254 697-6416
Cameron (G-2640)

Carbery Fabricators Company ....F 432 337-5015
Odessa (G-15955)

Caterpillar Inc...............................D 210 637-3700
San Antonio (G-17987)

CB&i LLC....................................E 832 513-1848
Houston (G-9104)

CB&i LLC....................................E 281 456-5700
Houston (G-9105)

CB&i LLC....................................C 713 649-4277
Houston (G-9106)

CB&i LLC....................................E 713 375-8000
Houston (G-9107)

CB&i LLC....................................C 713 485-1000
Houston (G-9108)

CB&i LLC....................................C 409 980-5500
Beaumont (G-1867)

Cen-Tex Tanks LLC........................D 936 590-4441
Center (G-2995)

Challenger Process Systems Co ....C 903 839-7291
Troup (G-20024)

▲ Charles W Weaver Mfg Co Inc ....B 972 539-1537
Flower Mound (G-6263)

Chart Inc....................................E 713 413-3000
Houston (G-9165)

Chart Industries Inc ....C 281 364-8700
The Woodlands (G-19841)

Chem Fabrication LLC.....................D 979 265-6600
Clute (G-3149)

Cherokee Indus Fabricators Ltd ....F 936 634-2108
Lufkin (G-14522)

▲ Chromium Corporation ....F 972 851-0500
Dallas (G-4115)

Chutehelp Inc...............................E 855 248-8343
Carbon (G-2682)

▼ Cisco Boiler Service Co Inc ....E 713 928-5700
Houston (G-9196)

Cohn & Gregory Supply LLC ....F 817 624-1141
Fort Worth (G-6529)

Commercial Forms Inc ....E 903 675-2511
Athens (G-823)

Conner Steel Products Inc ....B 325 655-8225
Houston (G-9271)

Consolidated Fabricators Inc ....G 214 376-4389
Dallas (G-4156)

▼ Contain Water Systems Inc ....E 512 770-9080
Dripping Springs (G-5502)

◆ Containment Solutions Inc ....E 936 756-7731
Conroe (G-3286)

Contech Engnered Solutions LLC........F 979 743-4123
Schulenburg (G-18774)

Contech Engnered Solutions LLC........F 903 885-0673
Sulphur Springs (G-19584)

Cooper B-Line Inc..........................C 903 813-1746
Sherman (G-18913)

Cox Tank Construction Co Inc ....E 361 528-3524
Taft (G-19640)

▲ Crall Products Inc ....E 806 665-8446
Pampa (G-16320)

Croft Construction Co Inc ....F 936 258-7902
Dayton (G-5225)

Custom Manufacturing Company ....E 214 428-5173
Dallas (G-4196)

Danhard Inc.................................F 214 328-8541
Dallas (G-4233)

Delzotto Products Minn Inc ....E 903 981-0400
Gladewater (G-7720)

Dlh Wendland LLC.........................E 325 655-6778
San Angelo (G-17795)

Doosan Mecatec America Co Ltd ....F 713 961-4646
Houston (G-9498)

▼ Dragon Products LLC....................C 409 833-2665
Beaumont (G-1886)

Dyna Therm Corporation ....F 832 616-3094
The Woodlands (G-19856)

Eads Cooling Solutions LLC ....F 713 780-1551
Houston (G-9555)

Eagle Metal Products LLC.................E 903 887-3581
Mabank (G-14576)

East Texas Radiator Inc ....E 903 753-7286
Longview (G-14228)

◆ Ecodyne Heat Exchanger LLC ....D 713 675-3511
Houston (G-9577)

EICA Industries Inc ....G 817 847-0917
Fort Worth (G-6607)

▲ Electro-Mechanical Inds Inc............E 281 894-1600
Houston (G-9592)

Entex Fabrication Inc.......................E 940 592-2173
Iowa Park (G-12904)

Entrans International LLC ....E 281 459-5350
Houston (G-9665)

▲ Epcon Industrial Systems LP ....D 936 273-1774
Shenandoah (G-18896)

Evco Fabrication Inc........................E 432 561-8561
Midland (G-15224)

Fabcorp Inc.................................E 713 466-3962
Houston (G-9746)

Fabricating Solutions ....F 409 735-7141
Bridge City (G-2283)

Fabrication Unlimited Inc ....E 713 433-6401
Houston (G-9750)

◆ Fisher Industries Inc ....F 713 937-6838
Hockley (G-8344)

Fluxmetals LLC.............................D 832 948-4307
Houston (G-9818)

◆ Forged Components Inc ....C 281 441-4088
Humble (G-12767)

▲ Fort Worth F and D Head Co ....D 817 236-8773
Fort Worth (G-6642)

Fox Tank Company.........................F 830 792-0770
Kerrville (G-13519)

◆ FR Global Trading Co Inc ....E 214 281-8668
Dallas (G-4376)

◆ Freeport Welding and Fabg Inc ....C 979 233-0121
Freeport (G-7198)

G Fabricating LLC..........................E 281 421-3100
Crosby (G-3731)

Generon Igs Inc.............................E 713 937-5200
Houston (G-9928)

George Bros Fabrication Co Inc ....F 432 563-3390
Odessa (G-16014)

▼ GTM Manufacturing LLC ....E 806 373-9473
Amarillo (G-431)

▲ Hahn & Clay Ltd ....C 713 672-1671
Houston (G-10089)

▼ Hamilton Form Co Ltd ....D 817 590-2111
Richland Hills (G-17437)

▲ Harbison-Fischer Inc ....B 817 297-2211
Crowley (G-3755)

◆ Harris Manufacturing Company ....E 972 262-3524
Mansfield (G-14680)

Harrison Fabricators Inc	F	214 374-1684	McGill Maintenance Partnr Ltd	C	979 233-5438
Dallas (G-4438)			Freeport (G-7203)		
◆ Hart Heat Transfer Pdts Inc	D	713 675-9848	Metalforms Ltd	D	409 842-1626
Houston (G-10133)			Beaumont (G-1928)		
Haydon Corporation	F	972 641-6400	Modern Welding Co of Texas	E	817 636-2215
Grand Prairie (G-7888)			Rhome (G-17259)		
Hep Mechanical Services LLC	F	903 278-6826	Modern Welding Co Texas Inc	E	713 675-4211
Queen City (G-17221)			Houston (G-10905)		
Herring Enterprises Inc	F	713 862-3614	▲ Monolithic Constructors Inc	E	972 483-7423
Houston (G-10162)			Italy (G-13214)		
▼ Herring Tank Company Inc	E	817 377-1851	National Oilwell Varco Inc	F	817 985-5000
Benbrook (G-2041)			Fort Worth (G-6861)		
◆ Hexa Containment LLC	E	713 360-9221	Nci Group Inc	B	713 466-7788
Nederland (G-15754)			Houston (G-11019)		
High-Tech Fabrication Inc	E	281 351-0882	◆ Norris Cylinder Company	C	903 757-7633
Tomball (G-19981)			Longview (G-14285)		
◆ Hmt LLC	E	281 681-7000	▲ North Txas Prssure Vessels Inc	E	940 327-0800
Shenandoah (G-18897)			Mineral Wells (G-15534)		
Holloway Company Inc	E	817 232-8663	Northast Txas McHning Wldg Hrd	F	903 427-2277
Saginaw (G-17746)			Clarksville (G-3076)		
Holloway Company Inc	E	713 453-4691	NSM Industries Inc	E	713 697-2091
Houston (G-10195)			Houston (G-11095)		
◆ Hoover Group Inc	E	800 844-8683	O & I Fabrication Incorporated	E	281 617-7732
Houston (G-10204)			Houston (G-11105)		
Hou Fab & Maintenance Inc	G	713 672-1993	▲ Ohmstede Industrial Svcs Inc	A	409 840-6644
Crosby (G-3733)			League City (G-13971)		
Howmet Aerospace Inc	E	775 343-4010	Ohmstede Ltd	C	281 471-4140
Elmendorf (G-6070)			La Porte (G-13780)		
◆ Hudson Products Corporation	E	281 396-8195	Ohmstede Ltd	F	281 867-3260
Beasley (G-1841)			Deer Park (G-5288)		
◆ Hudson Products Holdings Inc	E	281 396-8100	Ohmstede Ltd	D	361 289-1701
Beasley (G-1842)			Corpus Christi (G-3584)		
Huffman Company Ltd	F	432 332-5723	Ohmstede Ltd	F	409 840-6644
Odessa (G-16028)			League City (G-13972)		
Hughes Tank Company Inc	F	972 366-8684	◆ Ohmstede Ltd	B	409 833-6375
Venus (G-20218)			Beaumont (G-1935)		
Ig Holdings LP	F	940 565-8505	▲ Olaer Usa Inc	F	713 937-8900
Denton (G-5375)			Houston (G-11167)		
Imperial Group Mfg Inc	C	940 627-1700	Old Df Inc	E	281 590-5467
Decatur (G-5247)			Tomball (G-19994)		
Industrial Alloy Fbrcation Inc	F	409 600-8222	Old Dt Holdings	C	432 267-7141
Beaumont (G-1906)			Big Spring (G-2090)		
Insight Equity A P X L P	F	817 488-7775	▲ Palmer of Texas Tanks Inc	D	432 523-5904
Southlake (G-19075)			Andrews (G-556)		
Insight Equity LP	F	817 488-7775	Pangea Enterprises Inc	E	956 542-9494
Southlake (G-19076)			Houston (G-11232)		
Ios Inspection	E	432 684-6440	Paragon Fabricators Inc	E	409 935-6602
Midland (G-15255)			La Marque (G-13712)		
Iron Ram Services LLC	F	361 241-2346	Parker-Hannifin Corporation	E	817 232-1040
Corpus Christi (G-3557)			Saginaw (G-17754)		
◆ J D Fields & Company Inc	E	281 558-7199	▲ Pasadena Tank Corporation	C	281 457-3996
Houston (G-10437)			Baytown (G-1798)		
J S McKinney Inc	D	979 849-7283	Pat Tank Inc	D	409 982-7319
Angleton (G-574)			Port Arthur (G-17121)		
Joe White Tank Company Inc	F	817 624-1141	Permian Tank & Mfg Inc	D	432 550-7317
Fort Worth (G-6744)			Odessa (G-16118)		
Justiss Oil Company Inc	D	903 859-2111	Permian Tank & Mfg Inc	D	432 580-1050
Arp (G-812)			Odessa (G-16119)		
▲ Keppel Amfels Inc	A	956 838-3110	Permian Tank & Mfg Inc	D	903 984-2516
Brownsville (G-2374)			Kilgore (G-13581)		
▼ Klein Products of Texas Inc	E	903 589-4546	Peyton Salas & Mendoza LLC	E	512 784-5875
Jacksonville (G-13247)			Houston (G-11313)		
Kmi Fabricators Inc	E	940 325-7841	Pitts Oilfield Pdts & Svcs LLC	E	325 340-4401
Mineral Wells (G-15531)			San Angelo (G-17821)		
▲ Koch Heat Transfer Company LP	E	713 466-3535	Plant Fabricators Inc	E	830 393-3064
Houston (G-10552)			Floresville (G-6249)		
Koch-Glitsch LP	E	281 445-7026	Plant Process Equipment Inc	E	281 332-2589
Houston (G-10556)			League City (G-13975)		
Koch-Glitsch LP	D	214 583-3000	Portersville Sales & Testing	E	806 373-6811
Dallas (G-4564)			Amarillo (G-507)		
Kohlhaas Corporation	E	915 778-5357	Prentex Alloy Fabricators Inc	E	214 748-7837
El Paso (G-5831)			Dallas (G-4822)		
Kurosky & Co Pntg Contrs Inc	E	817 834-7179	Pressure Products Inc	F	817 249-1338
Fort Worth (G-6776)			Fort Worth (G-6915)		
▲ Lebus International Inc	D	903 758-5521	Proco Inc	E	361 516-1112
Longview (G-14263)			Kingsville (G-13634)		
Lektrotech Inc	F	972 225-2356	Professional Projects Inc	D	281 351-6315
Greenville (G-8082)			Cypress (G-3814)		
Lely Tank Waste Solutions LLC	F	800 367-5359	Proske Plastic Products Inc	E	713 926-9941
Troy (G-20029)			Houston (G-11461)		
▲ Lide Industries LLC	C	254 562-0233	Prostar Manufacturing Inc	F	281 910-0110
Odessa (G-16063)			Pasadena (G-16499)		
Lopez Tank Lining LLC	F	936 257-9779	QMF Steel Inc	E	903 455-3618
Dayton (G-5233)			Campbell (G-2646)		
Marine Services LLC	E	713 923-6688	R & N Manufacturing Ltd	D	713 466-6252
Houston (G-10765)			Cypress (G-3817)		
◆ Maxco LLC	D	832 554-0980	▲ R & R Heat Exchangers Inc	E	281 951-0003
Houston (G-10804)			Houston (G-11520)		
McDermott International Inc	B	281 588-6600	R & R Oilfield Services Inc	D	361 289-5892
Houston (G-10810)			Corpus Christi (G-3604)		
R C Technical Welding & Fabr	E	281 933-6004			
Stafford (G-19367)					
Rack Industries LLC	D	432 687-1868			
Odessa (G-16131)					
Rack Technology Inc	E	817 468-2233			
Arlington (G-766)					
Rapid Turn Laser & Machine Ltd	F	281 447-5000			
Houston (G-11549)					
RE Campbell Company Ltd	E	713 957-8721			
Houston (G-11558)					
Refined Industrial Supply Inc	E	409 789-1794			
League City (G-13978)					
Refrigrtion Vssels Systems Cor	D	979 778-0095			
Bryan (G-2500)					
Rentech Boiler Services Inc	C	325 672-2900			
Abilene (G-70)					
Rmf Manufacturing LLC	E	713 910-9777			
Houston (G-11638)					
◆ Robbins & Myers Inc	F	936 890-1064			
Willis (G-20861)					
S A Fabtecmex C V	B	956 504-0707			
Brownsville (G-2403)					
▲ S C S C Inc	E	214 398-1199			
Dallas (G-4922)					
Same Day Dumpster Rental LLC	F	866 223-6227			
Katy (G-13379)					
Sanco Metal Fabricators LLC	F	806 745-9674			
Lubbock (G-14477)					
Sani-Weld Inc	E	281 442-0667			
Houston (G-11747)					
Sartartia Fabrication Inc	E	281 240-1222			
Sugar Land (G-19541)					
Sas Global Corporation	D	903 643-9111			
Longview (G-14302)					
Saulsbury Industries Inc	A	972 884-6000			
Dallas (G-4938)					
Schmidt Manufacturing Inc	F	281 431-0581			
Bellaire (G-2002)					
▲ Scott Manufacturing Inc	C	806 747-3395			
Wolfforth (G-20912)					
Seguins Budget Auto Inc	F	830 372-1790			
Seguin (G-18863)					
Sepra-Chem Corporation	F	478 788-9789			
Tyler (G-20151)					
▲ Sierra Industries Ltd	D	210 805-3188			
San Antonio (G-18472)					
Sikes Fabricating Co Inc	F	409 941-0727			
Texas City (G-19802)					
◆ Sivalls Inc	D	432 337-3571			
Odessa (G-16153)					
Sivalls Inc	E	325 643-3621			
Brownwood (G-2445)					
Smith Tank & Equipment Company	E	903 597-5541			
Tyler (G-20153)					
▲ Southeast Texas Industries Inc	B	409 994-3570			
Buna (G-2562)					
Southern Heat Exchanger Corp	E	281 668-4619			
Houston (G-11974)					
Stephens Pneumatics Inc	E	817 636-9004			
Haslet (G-8223)					
Strike LLC	A	361 939-0800			
Corpus Christi (G-3631)					
Sulta Manufacturing Company	E	903 885-2139			
Sulphur Springs (G-19599)					
▼ Sweco Fab Inc	B	713 731-0030			
Houston (G-12130)					
T&B Boiler Inc	F	972 576-1920			
Red Oak (G-17236)					
Tank Wind-Down Corp	F	936 539-1747			
Conroe (G-3369)					
Tapcoenpro International Inc	C	281 247-8100			
Channelview (G-3041)					
◆ Taprite Inc	E	210 523-0800			
San Antonio (G-18522)					
Techmar Industries LLC	F	832 246-6200			
Spring (G-19175)					
Techniek LLC	E	832 618-7085			
Houston (G-12174)					
Tejas Boiler Services Inc	E	713 631-8200			
Houston (G-12186)					
Texas Aluminum Industries Inc	B	713 941-7186			
Houston (G-12220)					
▲ Texas Hydraulics Inc	A	254 778-4701			
Temple (G-19712)					
Texas Integrity Waste	F	940 479-0189			
Ponder (G-17096)					
Texas Pipe Fabricators Inc	E	361 882-5541			
Corpus Christi (G-3637)					
Texas Precision Plating Inc	E	972 494-1547			
Garland (G-7599)					

S
I
C

Employee Codes: A=Over 500 employees, B=251-500
C=101-250, D=51-100, E=20-50, F=10-19, G=9   2021 Harris Texas
Manufacturers Directory   997

Texas Vessels Fabrication LLC ....E 903 541-4883
  Jacksonville *(G-13264)*

Thrailkill All Metals Fabg Inc ....D 972 747-1230
  Allen *(G-302)*

Tiger Industries Inc ....E 713 896-9300
  Houston *(G-12290)*

Titanium Fabrication Corp ....F 832 375-1800
  Houston *(G-12300)*

Tonatco Cryogenic Services ....F 281 651-0305
  Spring *(G-19179)*

TPI ....E 972 276-2901
  Garland *(G-7604)*

Trans-TEC Machine Ltd ....E 713 643-9114
  Houston *(G-12345)*

Transition Superior Systems Lc ....F 325 690-0248
  Merkel *(G-15018)*

◆ Tranter Inc ....C 940 723-7125
  Wichita Falls *(G-20819)*

Tray-Tec Inc ....E 281 441-7314
  Humble *(G-12805)*

Trinity Industries Inc ....D 817 665-1499
  Fort Worth *(G-7075)*

▼ Trinity Industries Inc ....B 214 631-4420
  Dallas *(G-5112)*

▼ Triple S Manufacturing Company ....F 817 281-0602
  Fort Worth *(G-7079)*

▼ Tryer Process Equipment Ltd ....E 940 432-0130
  Wichita Falls *(G-20822)*

▲ UNI-Form Components Co ....D 281 456-9724
  Houston *(G-12433)*

United Marine Enterprise Inc ....D 409 833-0303
  Beaumont *(G-1965)*

US Fabrication East Texas Inc ....F 903 531-0000
  Tyler *(G-20173)*

V-S Precision Usa LLC ....B 915 590-2707
  El Paso *(G-6022)*

Viceroy Inc ....E 713 475-4518
  Pasadena *(G-16524)*

▼ Vince Hagan Company ....F 214 330-4601
  Sunnyvale *(G-19615)*

W W Metal Products Inc ....E 903 838-4329
  Texarkana *(G-19783)*

Wagner Plate Works LLC ....E 713 462-1946
  Houston *(G-12593)*

Walkup Company ....D 713 675-6383
  Houston *(G-12595)*

Wastequip Manufacturing Co LLC ....F 214 905-9101
  Dallas *(G-5174)*

Watco Tanks Inc ....E 830 947-0101
  Floresville *(G-6257)*

Westfield Engrg & Svcs Inc ....E 281 438-2047
  Houston *(G-8397)*

Wichita Tank Mfg Inc ....D 940 692-5791
  Wichita Falls *(G-20834)*

Willborn Bros Co LLC ....E 806 372-4311
  Amarillo *(G-475)*

William Grant Tank Vessel Inc ....F 903 657-6100
  Henderson *(G-8278)*

Williams & Davis Boilers Inc ....E 972 225-2356
  Hutchins *(G-12873)*

Windlass Metalworks LLC ....F 713 849-9292
  Houston *(G-12677)*

▼ Winston/Royal Guard Corp ....E 903 757-7341
  White Oak *(G-20722)*

◆ Woven Metal Products Inc ....E 281 331-4466
  Alvin *(G-386)*

Xg Ventures LLC ....E 936 744-1800
  Trinity *(G-20020)*

Youngs Tank Incorporated ....E 800 345-7952
  Boyd *(G-2210)*

3444 Sheet Metal Work

10-4 Tubular Inc ....E 281 436-0380
  Houston *(G-8399)*

6-K Inc ....F 979 830-0251
  Brenham *(G-2242)*

A & B Sheet Metal Inc ....G 512 365-7870
  Taylor *(G-19646)*

A & E Venetian Blind Company ....F 940 767-1449
  Wichita Falls *(G-20735)*

A Zahner Company ....F 469 348-2000
  Grand Prairie *(G-7817)*

A-1 Sheet Metal and AC Inc ....E 409 833-4715
  Beaumont *(G-1846)*

A-1 Smf LLC ....E 512 288-9900
  Austin *(G-874)*

ABG Contracting Group LLC ....E 281 431-7223
  Pearland *(G-16536)*

Abilene Sheet Metal Inc ....F 325 677-2654
  Abilene *(G-7)*

Absolute Metal Products LLC ....F 713 340-5990
  Houston *(G-8451)*

▲ AC Metals LLC ....E 214 630-5554
  Dallas *(G-3880)*

Accurate Air Solutions LLC ....E 325 672-2966
  Abilene *(G-9)*

Accurate Metal Stamping LLC ....E 817 284-9444
  Richland Hills *(G-17434)*

ACS Manufacturing Inc ....E 903 462-2001
  Denison *(G-5334)*

Admp LLC ....F 832 519-9746
  Houston *(G-8480)*

Advanced Sheet Metal LLC ....E 254 772-0134
  Waco *(G-20355)*

Advisory Cons Stl Erection Mfg ....E 817 924-1991
  Fort Worth *(G-6350)*

AES Industries Inc ....E 817 341-7250
  Weatherford *(G-20574)*

Air Duct Systems Mfg Co ....E 832 519-9746
  Houston *(G-8506)*

All-Rite Sheet Metal Inc ....E 713 680-0515
  Houston *(G-8541)*

▲ Allied Alumina Group Inc ....C 361 777-2400
  Gregory *(G-8098)*

Allied Precision Fabg Inc ....E 713 757-9810
  Caldwell *(G-2625)*

Allmetal Inc ....E 972 245-9264
  Carrollton *(G-2855)*

Alloy Cnc LLC ....F 936 449-4001
  Montgomery *(G-15626)*

◆ American Block Company ....C 800 572-9087
  Houston *(G-8588)*

American Duct Systems Inc ....E 972 494-7300
  Garland *(G-7433)*

American Fence and Sup Co Inc ....F 512 930-4000
  Georgetown *(G-7634)*

American Petroleum Welding Inc ....E 806 747-7272
  Lubbock *(G-14361)*

American Sheet Metal Inc ....F 281 999-5210
  Houston *(G-8610)*

▲ Amtex Prcision Fabrication Inc ....F 281 489-7042
  Manvel *(G-14731)*

Appleton Grp LLC ....C 281 774-3700
  Houston *(G-8665)*

Architectural Products Co Inc ....E 915 584-9424
  El Paso *(G-5649)*

Argenbrght Nat Shtmtl Wrks Inc ....E 214 357-9161
  Dallas *(G-3964)*

▼ Arrow Fabricated Tubing Ltd ....C 972 276-3010
  Garland *(G-7442)*

Astro Sheet Metal Co Inc ....E 972 438-1110
  Grand Prairie *(G-7837)*

◆ Atco Rubber Products Inc ....A 817 595-2894
  Fort Worth *(G-6406)*

Atco Rubber Products Inc ....E 713 674-6665
  Houston *(G-8732)*

Athens Steel Building Corp ....E 903 675-5733
  Athens *(G-820)*

▲ Atlas Building Systems Inc ....F 903 597-4211
  Tyler *(G-20052)*

Atlas Metal Works Inc ....F 214 741-4788
  Dallas *(G-3982)*

▲ Atron Group LLC ....D 214 292-9840
  Dallas *(G-3984)*

◆ Awntech Corporation ....E 817 354-9600
  Euless *(G-6132)*

Azteca Fabrication ....E 432 943-8888
  Monahans *(G-15599)*

Azz Enclosure Systems ....C 832 295-1200
  Houston *(G-8768)*

B & S Premium Sheet Metal Inc ....E 214 388-4724
  Dallas *(G-3995)*

B G Metals Inc ....E 210 648-5071
  San Antonio *(G-17930)*

◆ B W Sinclair Inc ....D 940 766-2556
  Wichita Falls *(G-20742)*

Baldwin Metals Company Inc ....E 214 637-1030
  Dallas *(G-4000)*

Bates AC & Svc Co Inc ....E 713 869-5521
  Houston *(G-8824)*

BD Hildebrandt Entps Inc ....F 936 825-0500
  Navasota *(G-15725)*

Beach Sheet Metal Company Inc ....E 972 226-4440
  Mesquite *(G-15030)*

Beaumont Metal Industries Inc ....E 409 833-1777
  Beaumont *(G-1861)*

Bemis Sheet Metal Inc ....E 281 427-1538
  Baytown *(G-1809)*

Berridge Manufacturing Company ....D 972 506-8496
  Dallas *(G-4020)*

Berridge Manufacturing Company ....E 830 401-5200
  Seguin *(G-18826)*

Berridge Manufacturing Company ....F 713 223-4971
  Houston *(G-8861)*

▼ Berridge Manufacturing Company ...E 210 650-7056
  San Antonio *(G-17949)*

Best Fender Products Inc ....D 903 577-0510
  Mount Pleasant *(G-15646)*

Bgrs Inc ....F 281 890-6862
  Houston *(G-8871)*

Binco Contracting Services ....F 281 356-3144
  Magnolia *(G-14591)*

Birdview Skylights ....F 817 439-9266
  Fort Worth *(G-6453)*

Bise Welding & Fabricating Inc ....D 713 681-0958
  Houston *(G-8892)*

Bison Profab Inc ....E 281 356-0026
  Magnolia *(G-14592)*

Blackburn Machine & Fab LLC ....E 713 644-2386
  Houston *(G-8910)*

Blumenthal Inc ....E 713 228-6432
  Houston *(G-8923)*

Boro Park Marketing and Mfg Co ....E 281 890-3848
  Houston *(G-8959)*

◆ Brandon Industries Inc ....E 972 542-3000
  McKinney *(G-14929)*

Bryne Sheet Metal Inc ....D 281 354-1100
  Humble *(G-12749)*

Buferd Company Inc ....D 972 272-9502
  Garland *(G-7451)*

▲ Builders Best Inc ....D 903 586-8283
  Jacksonville *(G-13230)*

Burgess Specialty Fabg Inc ....E 713 462-0293
  Houston *(G-9018)*

Burke & Company Inc ....F 210 271-0008
  Elmendorf *(G-6067)*

Butler Weldments Corporation ....D 254 697-6416
  Cameron *(G-2640)*

Byrne Metals Corp ....E 281 354-1100
  Humble *(G-12750)*

C H Industries Inc ....G 512 278-1100
  Manor *(G-14647)*

C H Industries Inc ....B 972 416-1304
  Carrollton *(G-2710)*

▲ C H Industries Inc ....D 972 416-1304
  Carrollton *(G-2709)*

C K Kelley & Sons Inc ....E 713 778-9232
  Houston *(G-9030)*

C M C Steel Fabricators Inc ....D 713 225-4446
  Houston *(G-9032)*

Cains Welding Service Inc ....E 281 303-9517
  Mont Belvieu *(G-15616)*

California Expanded Met Pdts ....F 817 568-1525
  Fort Worth *(G-6488)*

Canopy Solutions LLC ....E 713 510-3800
  Dickinson *(G-5472)*

Capitol Food & Beverage Inc ....F 972 660-4450
  Grand Prairie *(G-7850)*

Carbery Fabricators Company ....F 432 337-5015
  Odessa *(G-15955)*

Cardinal Tool Co ....F 972 564-2314
  Forney *(G-6304)*

Carey Sheet Metal Shop Inc ....E 956 423-1394
  Harlingen *(G-8184)*

Carports Childers & Structures ....F 713 460-2181
  Houston *(G-9094)*

Casteel Mfg Inc ....F 210 923-4558
  San Antonio *(G-17986)*

Caterpillar Inc ....D 210 637-3700
  San Antonio *(G-17987)*

Ccpjv Inc ....E 713 690-1622
  Houston *(G-9110)*

Central Txas Met Roofg Sup Inc ....F 512 452-1515
  Austin *(G-1041)*

CFS Forming Structure Company ....D 210 698-9252
  San Antonio *(G-17996)*

Chatsworth Products Inc ....C 512 863-7800
  Georgetown *(G-7644)*

Cherokee Indus Fabricators Ltd ....F 936 634-2108
  Lufkin *(G-14522)*

Cherry Construction Systems ....E 903 675-5901
  Athens *(G-822)*

Classic Stainless Inc ....E 214 467-8700
  Dallas *(G-4129)*

Cleburne Metal Works LLC ....E 817 237-5060
  Fort Worth *(G-6523)*

Cody Company Inc ....E 210 651-5305
  San Antonio *(G-18640)*

▲ Cody Company LLC ....D 972 875-5884
  Ennis *(G-6091)*

Company	Code	Phone	Location
Col-Met Gp LLC	E	972 494-3900	Garland (G-7459)
Collier Metal Specialties Ltd	F	972 494-3900	Garland (G-7461)
Commercial Forms Inc	E	903 675-2511	Athens (G-823)
◆ Composite Cooling Solutions LP	D	817 246-8700	Fort Worth (G-6536)
Composite Panl Tchnlgy-Suth In	E	972 720-0477	Addison (G-112)
Con-Tex Builders Inc	E	281 847-3336	Houston (G-9266)
Contech Engnered Solutions LLC	E	940 888-3671	Seymour (G-18889)
Cooper Sheet Metal Inc	E	817 232-4250	Fort Worth (G-6547)
▼ Copper Craft Inc	E	817 490-9622	Fort Worth (G-6549)
Corsicana Sheet Metal Co Inc	F	903 872-8434	Corsicana (G-3666)
Crystal Distribution Inc	E	763 391-7790	Irving (G-12984)
Cubeco Inc	E	713 671-2466	Houston (G-9356)
Custom AC & Shtmtl	F	713 868-5557	Houston (G-9363)
Custom Bilt Holdings LLC	F	214 699-4876	Irving (G-12987)
Custom Delis Equipment Co Inc	E	817 831-7080	Fort Worth (G-6567)
Custom Precision Shtmtl Inc	E	713 856-9997	Houston (G-9374)
D & R Specialties Inc	E	936 873-2947	Navasota (G-15728)
Dallas Texas Tool and Die Inc	F	214 634-7175	Dallas (G-4227)
Darville Co	F	432 580-9675	Odessa (G-15974)
▲ Data Matique Properties LP	C	972 272-3446	Garland (G-7476)
Delta Studweld Inc	F	409 755-0720	Lumberton (G-14567)
Dickey-Webb Inc	F	281 933-5400	Stafford (G-19304)
Die & Tool Service Inc	F	281 498-3317	Sugar Land (G-19479)
Diversified Metal Works Inc	F	409 769-1146	Vidor (G-20326)
Dlt Manufacturing Inc	D	214 330-8334	Dallas (G-4266)
Dralco Systems LLC	D	817 599-7335	Weatherford (G-20588)
Dusold Designs Inc	F	972 221-1455	Lewisville (G-14045)
Edge Fabrication Inc	E	972 714-3893	Irving (G-13009)
Efi Panel Systems LLC	D	281 533-9100	Orchard (G-16272)
▼ Ekj Enterprises LP	C	972 772-1919	Rockwall (G-17547)
Eldred Sheet Metal Works LP	E	713 227-3251	Houston (G-9588)
Electronic Visions Systems	E	512 989-3000	Pflugerville (G-16669)
Enerflex Inc	C	801 292-0493	Houston (G-9632)
Entex Fabrication Inc	E	940 592-2173	Iowa Park (G-12904)
▲ Epcon Industrial Systems LP	D	936 273-1774	Shenandoah (G-18896)
Esquire Tooling & Mfg Inc	E	903 886-4779	Commerce (G-3243)
Essner Manufacturing LP	D	817 551-5511	Fort Worth (G-6618)
◆ Ets-Lindgren Inc	C	512 531-6400	Cedar Park (G-2968)
Eureka Sheet Metal Inc	F	210 735-4426	San Antonio (G-18098)
Everest Systems LLC	E	800 575-8966	Houston (G-9716)
Evs Texas Inc	D	512 989-3000	Pflugerville (G-16671)
Fabcorp Inc	E	713 466-3962	Houston (G-9746)
Fabhar Manufacturing LLC	E	214 802-9400	Princeton (G-17210)
First Quality Fabricating Inc	F	214 748-0071	Dallas (G-4363)
Fisher Select Products Inc	E	972 484-1188	Carrollton (G-2738)
Flamco of Texas Inc	F	254 799-4936	Waco (G-20403)
Fleming & Son Corporation	E	972 263-1713	Grand Prairie (G-7873)
▲ Flexmaster USA Inc	D	713 462-7694	Houston (G-9801)
▲ Fong Kai Usa Inc	E	972 644-1584	Carrollton (G-2740)
Fuqua Enterprises Inc	G	817 641-1074	Cleburne (G-3090)
G Fabricating LLC	E	281 421-3100	Crosby (G-3731)
G N P Inc Sheet Metal	E	972 564-0450	Forney (G-6308)
G W Vines Company Inc	E	214 742-8371	Dallas (G-4389)
Gamma Engineering Inc	C	817 477-2193	Mansfield (G-14676)
Garrison Metal Products Inc	E	903 938-1319	Marshall (G-14779)
Georgia-Pacific LLC	C	936 829-5511	Diboll (G-5466)
Givco Inc	G	830 624-8598	New Braunfels (G-15795)
Graco Interests Inc	B	713 978-7000	Houston (G-10010)
Graco Mechanical Inc	D	713 978-7000	Houston (G-10011)
Gst Manufacturing Ltd	C	817 335-1401	Haltom City (G-8146)
▲ Gtech Precision Inds USA Ltd	F	817 539-8014	Mansfield (G-14678)
◆ Gulf Copper Ship Repair Inc	D	361 883-1040	Corpus Christi (G-3540)
Guzman Mfg Inc	F	972 475-3003	Rowlett (G-17706)
H & S Metals Inc	F	281 421-9488	Baytown (G-1821)
▲ Hahn & Clay Ltd	C	713 672-1671	Houston (G-10089)
Haydon Corporation	F	972 641-6400	Grand Prairie (G-7888)
Heat Air Products Company	E	817 222-9567	Fort Worth (G-6694)
Heat Shield Inc	F	903 845-4066	Gladewater (G-7722)
Hightower Metal Works Inc	F	713 937-7181	Houston (G-10179)
Hill Country Insulation	G	512 515-7707	Pflúgerville (G-16675)
Holly Fabrication Inc	E	972 233-5362	Addison (G-135)
Holmes Construction Co LP	D	806 376-8629	Amarillo (G-435)
▲ Hou-Stone Inc	D	713 827-8700	Houston (G-10214)
Houston Tsm Inc	E	713 691-5271	Houston (G-10260)
▲ Humanetics II Ltd	C	972 416-1304	Carrollton (G-2763)
Humanetics II Ltd	D	956 994-9200	McAllen (G-14868)
Hvac Mechanical Svcs of Texas	B	713 266-3900	Houston (G-10292)
Ikg Usa LLC	D	281 452-6637	Houston (G-10320)
Imfab Inc	E	903 577-0510	Mount Pleasant (G-15651)
Industrial Insul & Shtmtl Inc	E	432 332-8203	Odessa (G-16030)
Integrated Metal Products Inc	E	512 259-4143	Leander (G-13993)
▼ Interstate Treating Inc	D	432 362-9291	Odessa (G-16034)
▲ Intrapack Industries Inc	E	214 348-7105	Dallas (G-4510)
◆ Intsel Steel Distributors LLC	C	713 937-9500	Houston (G-10410)
Irving Tool & Mfg Co Inc	D	972 926-4000	Garland (G-7521)
J & A Manufacturing Inc	D	972 494-5552	Garland (G-7522)
J & L Sheet Metal Co Inc	E	713 864-7714	Houston (G-10433)
J B Edwards Company	G	281 429-7143	Conroe (G-3312)
J K Welding Service LLC	E	281 550-1008	Cypress (G-3803)
▲ J M Fabrication Company LLC	F	817 652-0526	Arlington (G-709)
Jayco Steel Services Inc	E	281 399-0189	New Caney (G-15842)
Jimco Sales & Mfg Inc	E	817 924-6173	Fort Worth (G-6742)
Johnston Products Dallas Inc	E	469 272-7212	Cedar Hill (G-2946)
Karel Manufacturing Inc	D	210 651-6643	Selma (G-18876)
Kayco Spray Booths Inc	F	830 779-2051	La Vernia (G-13802)
Kieschnick Industries Inc	E	409 833-5611	Beaumont (G-1914)
Kikers Machine Works Inc	F	432 381-8142	Odessa (G-16052)
Kinlau Sheet Metal Works Inc	F	940 552-5311	Vernon (G-20227)
Knottsmith Construction Co Inc	E	214 499-5667	Dallas (G-4563)
Kuest Corporation	E	210 655-1220	San Antonio (G-18230)
L R West Manufacturing Co	F	281 485-6057	Pearland (G-16575)
Lane Supply Inc	D	817 261-9116	Arlington (G-717)
Ledsome Machine & Welding Co	F	325 646-4691	Brownwood (G-2434)
Lewis & Lambert LLLP	C	817 834-7146	Haltom City (G-8150)
▼ Longview Mechanical Contrs Inc	E	903 759-1331	Longview (G-14270)
Lubbock Skylight Manufacturing	F	806 744-2300	Lubbock (G-14442)
◆ M&M Manufacturing Inc	C	817 336-2311	Fort Worth (G-6804)
M&M Manufacturing Inc	C	972 485-1504	Garland (G-7540)
M&M Manufacturing Inc	E	817 334-0034	Fort Worth (G-6805)
M&M Manufacturing Inc	E	713 460-1677	Houston (G-10722)
M3 Distribution Inc	F	281 357-0604	Tomball (G-19986)
Mabco Equipment Ltd	E	817 599-7335	Weatherford (G-20602)
Mac Fabricators	G	979 265-0235	Clute (G-3156)
Magni- Power Company	C	903 532-5533	Howe (G-12735)
March Resources Co	E	281 931-3986	Houston (G-10763)
Mason Road Sheet Metal Inc	D	713 466-5054	Houston (G-10784)
Mc Daniel Metals Inc	C	281 987-8400	Houston (G-10809)
Mc Hone Metal Fabricators Inc	F	972 524-7775	Terrell (G-19741)
McGill Airflow LLC	E	254 580-1680	Hillsboro (G-8330)
Mechanical Sheet Metal Inc	E	972 524-6200	Terrell (G-19742)
Mel Northey Co Inc	F	281 445-3485	Houston (G-10825)
Met International Trdg Co Inc	D	281 445-5005	Houston (G-10841)
Metal Sales Manufacturing Corp	E	254 791-6650	Temple (G-19689)
Metal Specialties Inc	E	432 332-8762	Odessa (G-16081)
Metal Zinc LLC	G	832 252-9116	Humble (G-12789)
Metal Zinc LLC	F	281 449-2787	Houston (G-10848)
▼ Metallic Products Corporation	D	713 856-9696	Houston (G-10849)
Metroplex Sheet Metal Inc	E	972 276-6736	Garland (G-7550)
Micro Metl Corporation	D	903 248-4800	Longview (G-14276)
Miller Machine & Welding LLC	E	254 582-2185	Whitney (G-20731)
Milltech Manufacturing Company	D	972 276-1786	Garland (G-7554)
Mitchell Machine & Fabricating	F	903 880-0249	Mabank (G-14579)
Mobile Mini Inc	D	480 894-6311	Houston (G-10900)
Modern Fabricating Inc	F	800 543-1581	San Antonio (G-18315)
Moffitt West LLC	F	903 463-5700	Denison (G-5342)

S I C

Morgan Roofing	E	409 762-8068
Galveston (G-7404)		
Morrison Products Inc	D	972 279-4000
Mesquite (G-15063)		
Motor Controls Inc	B	972 247-4440
Dallas (G-4691)		
Mueller Supply Company Inc	F	361 580-1427
Victoria (G-20286)		
Mueller Supply Company Inc	E	915 886-3383
Anthony (G-588)		
Multi-Metal & Mfg Co Inc	D	972 771-1376
Rockwall (G-17556)		
▲ Nailor Industries Texas Inc	C	281 590-1172
Houston (G-10961)		
Native American Industries Inc	F	817 731-6786
Fort Worth (G-6863)		
Nci Group Inc	C	817 481-2501
Southlake (G-19080)		
Nci Group Inc	E	806 747-4291
Lubbock (G-14451)		
Nci Group Inc	B	713 466-7788
Houston (G-11019)		
Nci Group Inc	E	281 897-7788
Houston (G-11015)		
Nema Enclosure Mfg Corp	D	713 921-2233
Houston (G-11022)		
New England Lead Burning Inc	F	713 675-3266
Houston (G-11034)		
▲ Nicholson Metal Fabricators	E	214 920-3654
Dallas (G-4738)		
▲ Nipples Elbows & Couplings Inc	E	281 405-8240
Houston (G-11059)		
Northast Txas McHning Wldg Hrd	F	903 427-2277
Clarksville (G-3076)		
Northwest Metal and Steel Inc	G	281 444-5269
Houston (G-11082)		
Nova Construction Co Inc	E	972 869-3041
Carrollton (G-2785)		
Nucor Corporation	G	281 251-8857
Spring (G-19156)		
Nucor Corporation	C	936 687-4665
Grapeland (G-8007)		
Nut Place Inc	E	713 462-3147
Houston (G-11100)		
Oaks Precision Fabricating Inc	E	713 937-9190
Houston (G-11107)		
Odyssey Precision Fabricating	E	713 849-3043
Houston (G-11137)		
Offenhauser Company	D	713 928-2981
Houston (G-11140)		
Omnimax Holdings Inc	E	469 366-3208
Fort Worth (G-6881)		
Omnimax International Inc	A	469 366-3200
Fort Worth (G-6883)		
Omnimax International Inc	F	972 522-0148
Grand Prairie (G-7941)		
Omnimax International Inc	E	817 481-3521
Fort Worth (G-6884)		
Omnimax International Inc	E	817 481-3521
Fort Worth (G-6882)		
P & W Quality Machines Inc	E	972 299-0500
Cedar Hill (G-2949)		
P M P E Ltd	D	830 303-0056
Seguin (G-18852)		
▼ Paradigm Metals Incorporated	E	512 255-2622
Pflugerville (G-16683)		
Parker-Hannifin Corporation	E	817 232-1040
Saginaw (G-17754)		
Parkline Inc	D	409 935-5743
Hitchcock (G-8339)		
Parkline Inc	D	409 935-1037
La Marque (G-13713)		
Parsleys Shtmtl & Roofg Co	E	806 669-6461
Pampa (G-16333)		
▲ PCI Industries Inc	C	817 509-2300
Fort Worth (G-6898)		
Petersen Aluminum Corporation	E	903 581-6228
Tyler (G-20140)		
Phillips Fabrication Inc	E	432 264-6600
Big Spring (G-2093)		
Phoenix Mfg Inc	F	214 544-7507
Allen (G-293)		
▲ Pi-Co Prcision Fabrication Inc	E	512 759-1026
Hutto (G-12883)		
Pick Instrument Products Co	E	713 672-1686
Galena Park (G-7381)		
Pine Street Salvage Co	F	806 372-5678
Amarillo (G-454)		
Pittsburg Steel LLC	E	903 855-7515
Pittsburg (G-16750)		

Pivot Corporation	D	972 475-4747
Rowlett (G-17710)		
Plasteco Inc	D	713 673-7710
Houston (G-11345)		
Polk Mechanical Company LLC	C	972 339-1200
Grand Prairie (G-7947)		
Precision M/C Mfg Inc	F	972 429-6200
Wylie (G-20943)		
Precision Sheet Metal Shop Inc	D	972 771-1423
Rockwall (G-17561)		
Preferred Stampings of Texas	E	512 255-7803
Round Rock (G-17681)		
Presidio Custom Metal Works	F	512 284-8549
Round Rock (G-17682)		
◆ Priefert Mfg Co Inc	A	903 572-1741
Mount Pleasant (G-15660)		
Proco Inc	F	361 516-1112
Kingsville (G-13634)		
▼ Quality Fabrication Design LP	D	972 304-3266
Coppell (G-3436)		
Quality Industries Inc	E	615 708-4980
Denton (G-5395)		
◆ Quietflex Manufacturing Co LP	B	877 694-3669
Houston (G-11514)		
R & R Design Inc	F	972 524-1789
Terrell (G-19748)		
▲ R F Higginbotham Inc	E	512 836-8985
Austin (G-1447)		
R Guerra Construction Inc	F	956 854-4038
Weslaco (G-20667)		
R-D Sheet Metal Inc	F	817 332-2177
Fort Worth (G-6933)		
R-O Mfg Co	F	817 293-6150
Fort Worth (G-6934)		
◆ Raider Manufacturing Ltd	D	806 762-3227
Lubbock (G-14470)		
Raytheon Company	A	972 205-4277
Dallas (G-4860)		
RE Campbell Company Ltd	E	713 957-8721
Houston (G-11558)		
Reama Inc	F	409 744-9222
Galveston (G-7407)		
REE Holding Inc	E	409 840-5650
Beaumont (G-1947)		
◆ Regal Research and Mfg Co LLC	C	972 494-0359
Plano (G-16990)		
Reliance Steel & Aluminum Co	E	972 276-2676
Garland (G-7577)		
Renovated Homes Inc	F	214 678-9114
Dallas (G-4888)		
▲ RH Tamlyn & Sons	E	281 499-9604
Stafford (G-19370)		
RH Tamlyn & Sons LP	F	214 348-9676
Dallas (G-4895)		
Rheaco Inc	D	972 264-4748
Grand Prairie (G-7965)		
Rmf Manufacturing LLC	E	713 910-9777
Houston (G-11638)		
Robinson Aerospace Inc	E	817 253-0639
Dallas (G-4906)		
Robroy Industries-Texas LLC	D	903 843-5591
Gilmer (G-7713)		
Rooftop Systems Inc	D	972 247-7447
Carrollton (G-2809)		
▲ RPR Products Inc	D	713 697-7003
Houston (G-11689)		
S & H Shtmtl & Fabg Co Inc	E	713 926-8805
Houston (G-11706)		
Sage International Inc	D	972 623-2004
Grand Prairie (G-7971)		
Samuel Jackson Mfg Co	F	806 795-5218
Lubbock (G-14476)		
San-Co Steel Ltd	C	956 464-7766
Donna (G-5490)		
Seabreeze Culvert Inc	F	409 296-4098
Stowell (G-19431)		
Sechrist-Hall Company	F	361 884-5264
Corpus Christi (G-3620)		
Selkirk Corporation	B	972 943-6100
Richardson (G-17395)		
Shade Structures Inc	G	214 905-9500
Dallas (G-4951)		
Sheet Metal Air Plus Co LLC	E	915 566-8131
El Paso (G-5958)		
Sign & Awning Services Inc	E	817 926-7270
Fort Worth (G-6987)		
Simpson Strong-Tie Company Inc	C	972 542-0326
McKinney (G-14975)		
Sn & Db Holdings Inc	E	713 645-3370
Houston (G-11927)		

Snapp Tool & Die Inc	E	915 821-2046
El Paso (G-5964)		
Solar Accessories Corporation	F	972 524-2099
Terrell (G-19750)		
Southeast Texas Industries Inc	C	409 792-0084
Bridge City (G-2286)		
Southeastern Metals Mfg Co Inc	D	210 651-6331
San Antonio (G-18645)		
Southern Strtch Frming Fbrctio	E	940 591-0410
Denton (G-5400)		
▼ Special Products & Mfg Inc	D	972 771-8851
Rockwall (G-17566)		
Spectra Metal Sales Inc	D	972 556-2564
Farmers Branch (G-6216)		
Splendora Pipe Services LLC	D	281 432-1400
Cleveland (G-3136)		
Spring Branch Shtmtl Co Inc	B	281 469-8855
Houston (G-12026)		
Stainless Mfg & Seals Svc	G	806 795-8932
Lubbock (G-14486)		
Stainless Steel Concepts LLC	F	214 630-4430
Dallas (G-5001)		
Steel Designs Inc	E	713 937-3006
Houston (G-12053)		
Steeltron Metal Works	F	210 774-4127
San Antonio (G-18499)		
Sterling Group LP	E	713 877-8257
Houston (G-12060)		
Stuarts Sheet Metal Inc	E	512 491-0112
Austin (G-1543)		
Suburban Sheet Metal Ltd	E	817 478-0801
Kennedale (G-13504)		
▼ Sweco Fab Inc	B	713 731-0030
Houston (G-12130)		
Sweetwater Machine and Welding	E	325 235-2922
Sweetwater (G-19637)		
T W Havens Metals Inc	F	817 834-2621
Fort Worth (G-7028)		
◆ Taprite Inc	E	210 523-0800
San Antonio (G-18522)		
Taylor Metal Works & Pipe Co	E	409 736-3555
Port Arthur (G-17127)		
Telkin Sheetmetal Inc	E	713 691-3707
Houston (G-12192)		
Tex Cnp/Seal Inc	E	214 688-7770
Dallas (G-5051)		
Texas Aluminum Industries Inc	B	713 941-7186
Houston (G-12220)		
Texas Profab Corporation	E	972 241-5050
Carrollton (G-2831)		
Texas Roof Management Inc	C	972 272-7663
Richardson (G-17409)		
Texas Sheet Metal Works	G	806 765-8404
Lubbock (G-14493)		
Texas Toolmakers Inc	E	210 494-3651
San Antonio (G-18544)		
Theriot Inc	E	979 233-6391
Freeport (G-7215)		
Thrailkill All Metals Fabg Inc	D	972 747-1230
Allen (G-302)		
Thur-Co Inc	F	956 982-4424
Brownsville (G-2412)		
Thybar Corporation	E	972 416-6220
Dallas (G-5090)		
Tietjen Inc	E	979 249-3888
La Grange (G-13703)		
Tip Top Sheet Metal Inc	E	281 931-7823
Houston (G-12294)		
Titanium Fabrication Corp	F	832 375-1800
Houston (G-12300)		
Tmp Truck & Trailer LP	E	432 686-2500
Midland (G-15438)		
Tomball Sheet Metal LP	E	281 356-1200
Magnolia (G-14631)		
Torans Precision Fabricating	G	281 371-2352
Katy (G-13451)		
Total Metal Products Inc	D	214 330-7453
Dallas (G-5102)		
Tri-Construction Co Inc	C	979 233-7211
Freeport (G-7217)		
Tricor Industrial Inc	E	936 273-2661
Conroe (G-3373)		
▼ Trinity Industries Inc	B	214 631-4420
Dallas (G-5112)		
Triple C Industries Inc	E	936 931-1171
Hockley (G-8349)		
Trotti Service Company Inc	F	281 894-5095
Houston (G-12383)		
Tubal Cain Industries Inc	D	409 786-1783
Vidor (G-20336)		

TW Stamping & Tool Inc ....E....... 903 877-2353
Tyler (G-20166)

Two Hills Studio Inc ....E....... 512 707-7571
Austin (G-1602)

United Parcel Service Inc ....F....... 817 490-7300
Fort Worth (G-7093)

Urban Sheet Metal Inc ....E....... 713 522-6441
Houston (G-12478)

USA Machine Inc ....E....... 972 636-7400
Royse City (G-17727)

Ventilation Service Inc ....E....... 713 683-1003
Houston (G-12548)

▼ Vince Hagan Company ....F....... 214 330-4601
Sunnyvale (G-19615)

Vista Machining Company LLC ....E....... 817 710-2987
Fort Worth (G-7108)

Vlj Inc ....F....... 972 442-4673
Wylie (G-20955)

Vogler Sheet Metal Company ....E....... 713 861-1154
Spring (G-19186)

Wagner Plate Works LLC ....E....... 713 462-1946
Houston (G-12593)

Ward Vessel and Exchanger Corp ....E....... 713 413-8416
Houston (G-8394)

▲ Weldfit Corporation ....C....... 713 460-3700
Houston (G-12628)

Weldforce Fabricators LLC ....E....... 713 270-7733
Houston (G-8395)

Western Sheet Metal Inc ....E....... 804 732-0230
Irving (G-13206)

Westside Welding Inc ....E....... 915 877-5345
Canutillo (G-2668)

Whitaker Metal Deck Sales ....F....... 972 938-1445
Waxahachie (G-20570)

Wilson Culverts Inc ....F....... 903 764-5605
Elkhart (G-6061)

Windlass Metalworks LLC ....F....... 713 849-9292
Houston (G-12677)

◆ Woven Metal Products Inc ....E....... 281 331-4466
Alvin (G-386)

3446 Architectural & Ornamental Metal Work

A 1 Distributors Sign Supply ....D....... 432 682-0083
Midland (G-15100)

A M Fabrication Inc ....E....... 817 345-7600
Fort Worth (G-6337)

A Zahner Company ....F....... 469 348-2000
Grand Prairie (G-7817)

A&S Interests Inc ....E....... 713 695-0000
Houston (G-8430)

Aaron Architectural Iron LLC ....E....... 817 731-9281
Fort Worth (G-6339)

Albas Custom Iron Inc ....F....... 281 401-9797
Houston (G-8528)

Allied Fence Co of Dallas ....F....... 903 892-9640
Dallas (G-3926)

Allmetal Inc ....E....... 972 245-9264
Carrollton (G-2855)

Amarillo Sperior Ironworks Inc ....G....... 806 331-9353
Amarillo (G-398)

Anchor Industrial Services LLC ....D....... 281 385-0607
Houston (G-8639)

Architectural Metal Crafts ....F....... 281 449-1881
Houston (G-8684)

Arrowhead Stairs and Trim ....F....... 972 484-0406
Farmers Branch (G-6188)

Artistic Iron & Forge ....F....... 281 807-3440
Cypress (G-3776)

B&B Ornamental Iron Company ....E....... 214 350-0639
Dallas (G-3997)

Baker & Company Cnstr LLC ....E....... 903 561-1763
Tyler (G-20056)

Bandana Installation LP ....F....... 903 764-2933
Elkhart (G-6058)

Berger Iron Works Inc ....E....... 713 869-7386
Houston (G-8860)

▼ Berridge Manufacturing Company ....E....... 210 650-7056
San Antonio (G-17949)

Binford Fence Supply Ltd ....F....... 972 286-2881
Balch Springs (G-1737)

Branch Ironworks LLC ....F....... 817 783-5183
Alvarado (G-326)

Broome Welding Co ....F....... 409 744-0407
Galveston (G-7390)

Builders Equipment & Tool Co ....D....... 713 869-3491
Houston (G-9013)

California Expanded Met Pdts ....D....... 817 568-1525
Fort Worth (G-6487)

Camp Logan Cement Works Inc ....E....... 713 869-3385
Houston (G-9080)

Cerda-Fied Specialists Inc ....F....... 281 392-8063
Brookshire (G-2313)

CK Kustoms Iron Works Inc ....F....... 281 850-6118
Rockport (G-17529)

Colonial Art Inc ....F....... 713 697-8407
Houston (G-9245)

Columns Inc ....F....... 281 485-3254
Pearland (G-16547)

Construction Specialties Inc ....F....... 830 774-0151
Del Rio (G-5314)

Country Glass & Mirror Inc ....E....... 972 216-9100
Mesquite (G-15035)

Creative Casting Inc ....F....... 903 463-6160
Denison (G-5339)

Cubeco Inc ....E....... 713 671-2466
Houston (G-9356)

Custom Iron Works ....G....... 806 745-2757
Lubbock (G-14399)

Custom Manufacturing Company ....E....... 214 428-5173
Dallas (G-4196)

Custom SEC Fence Ir Works LLC ....F....... 281 219-1400
Houston (G-9375)

De Walch Enterprise Inc ....D....... 713 861-8993
Houston (G-9417)

Demco Manufacturing Inc ....E....... 936 829-4771
Diboll (G-5462)

Eagle Metal Products LLC ....E....... 903 887-3581
Mabank (G-14576)

East Txas Archtctral Shtmtal L ....F....... 903 569-6909
Mineola (G-15507)

Elegante Iron Inc ....F....... 214 342-8987
Farmers Branch (G-6195)

◆ Eljer Industries Inc ....E....... 972 560-2000
Dallas (G-4311)

▲ Envirnmntal Sgnage Sltions Inc ....E....... 972 915-3800
Irving (G-13015)

Fehrs Industrial Mfg LLC ....D....... 432 758-0068
Seminole (G-18883)

First Texas Precast Inc ....E....... 214 350-5612
Dallas (G-4364)

Fortitude Specialty Mfg LLC ....D....... 713 465-3370
Houston (G-9839)

▲ Fortress Iron LP ....D....... 972 231-4001
Garland (G-7491)

Fusion Services Inc ....E....... 512 444-4283
Austin (G-1173)

G N P Inc Sheet Metal ....E....... 972 564-0450
Forney (G-6308)

General Garage Door Service ....F....... 956 782-7373
Mission (G-15555)

▲ Georgejean Inc ....G....... 214 748-6644
Dallas (G-4404)

Harsco Corporation ....D....... 713 378-3944
Channelview (G-3024)

Harsco Corporation ....D....... 281 452-6637
Houston (G-10129)

Harsco Corporation ....E....... 713 378-3900
Spring (G-19128)

Hart & Cooley Inc ....B....... 915 852-9111
Horizon City (G-8365)

Hayes Company LLC ....C....... 972 288-9755
Mesquite (G-15049)

Hemco Industries Inc ....E....... 713 681-2426
Houston (G-10152)

Hill Country Land Improvement ....E....... 512 766-8122
Wimberley (G-20881)

Hoffa Inc ....F....... 713 460-9000
Houston (G-10192)

Hutto Holding Group Inc ....D....... 512 832-8746
Hutto (G-12879)

International Steel Frmng LLC ....F....... 817 591-0507
Richland Hills (G-17438)

J C Ornamental Ironworks Inc ....F....... 972 442-6293
Wylie (G-20938)

J-N Fence Co Inc ....E....... 972 226-7205
Mesquite (G-15054)

▲ Jwtmbg Enterprise LLC ....F....... 817 230-2513
Southlake (G-19078)

Kawneer Company Inc ....E....... 972 438-1212
Irving (G-13073)

Kawneer Company Inc ....E....... 713 896-8906
Houston (G-10503)

Kentex Fabrications ....F....... 325 214-0025
Coleman (G-3170)

Kikers Machine Works Inc ....F....... 432 381-8142
Odessa (G-16052)

Lacy Construction Services LLC ....F....... 903 498-0663
Kemp (G-13485)

Lane Supply Inc ....D....... 817 261-9116
Arlington (G-717)

▲ Master-Halco Inc ....D....... 972 714-7300
Dallas (G-4645)

Materials Products Inc ....F....... 512 821-3303
Austin (G-1329)

Mathis Iron Works Inc ....F....... 713 991-5846
Houston (G-10796)

McFadden & Associates Inc ....E....... 972 680-8333
Richardson (G-17353)

McNichols Company ....E....... 877 884-4653
Garland (G-7548)

Merchants Moving & Storage Inc ....E....... 361 293-7202
Yoakum (G-20969)

▼ Metallic Products Corporation ....D....... 713 856-9696
Houston (G-10849)

Meyer-Smith Inc ....F....... 713 862-7339
Houston (G-10862)

Miscellaneous Steel Inds Inc ....E....... 512 268-2831
Kyle (G-13685)

Modern Iron Works Inc ....E....... 915 778-6469
El Paso (G-5881)

Nci Group Inc ....E....... 281 897-7788
Houston (G-11015)

◆ Nci Group Inc ....B....... 281 897-7788
Houston (G-11016)

Neu Security Services LLC ....D....... 512 469-9980
Austin (G-1364)

Northeast Gate Co Inc ....F....... 903 739-8778
Sumner (G-19608)

Ntx Gates & Fences Inc ....E....... 817 740-9449
Fort Worth (G-6874)

Offenhauser Company ....D....... 713 928-2981
Houston (G-11140)

One Ten Welding Inc ....G....... 903 561-8549
Whitehouse (G-20726)

Patina Metals Inc ....E....... 713 462-6117
Houston (G-11259)

Pettigrews Custom Iron & Mtls ....F....... 214 637-1494
Dallas (G-4800)

Pool Custom Iron Works Inc ....F....... 936 756-4292
Conroe (G-3351)

Premier Entry Systems LLC ....F....... 817 422-5908
Fort Worth (G-6913)

Presidio Custom Metal Works ....F....... 512 284-8549
Round Rock (G-17682)

◆ Priefert Mfg Co Inc ....A....... 903 572-1741
Mount Pleasant (G-15660)

Pysz Enterprises Inc ....F....... 972 964-3980
Plano (G-16981)

Quality Access Control Systems ....F....... 830 981-5400
Boerne (G-2133)

Quality Ironworks Inc ....E....... 214 688-0180
Dallas (G-4844)

Quality Lnings Fabrication Inc ....E....... 713 863-7013
Houston (G-11495)

RE Campbell Company Ltd ....E....... 713 957-8721
Houston (G-11558)

Richard-Marcus Inc ....E....... 972 484-0406
Dallas (G-4898)

Rodgers Ornamental Iron Inc ....F....... 817 535-2127
Fort Worth (G-6963)

Rwc Material LLC ....F....... 210 219-2987
Fowlerton (G-7162)

S F L Inc ....E....... 936 856-1433
Willis (G-20863)

SA Quality Fence Ltd ....E....... 210 545-6767
San Antonio (G-18440)

▲ Sentech Archtctral Systems LLC ....E....... 512 266-7045
Austin (G-1494)

Septh Group LLC ....E....... 713 988-4200
Houston (G-11832)

Sorensen Industries Inc ....E....... 940 365-9999
Crossroads (G-3750)

South Texas Moulding Inc ....F....... 956 831-0340
Brownsville (G-2406)

Southern Archtctral Systems In ....E....... 713 462-6379
Houston (G-11972)

Southwest Fenter Inc ....F....... 817 577-3837
Haltom City (G-8158)

Srg Ventures LLC ....E....... 281 214-8560
Houston (G-12030)

▼ Stairways Inc ....E....... 713 680-3110
Houston (G-12039)

Stan Thompson Investments ....E....... 713 910-2320
Pasadena (G-16511)

▲ Stay-Tuff Fence Mfg Inc ....E....... 830 608-9302
New Braunfels (G-15826)

Steel Designs Inc ....E....... 713 937-3006
Houston (G-12053)

Steel Specialties Inc ....E....... 915 590-2337
El Paso (G-5976)

Summit Steel Fabricators Inc ....D 713 451-6960
Houston (G-12095)

Sunterra International LLC.................D 210 501-9510
San Antonio (G-18513)

Superior Grating Inc ....F 713 686-9475
Houston (G-12115)

Symonds Flags & Poles Inc ....E 214 596-1900
Fort Worth (G-7026)

T G & P Inc ....F 979 778-8255
Bryan (G-2509)

Tebo Concre Fence LLC.....................F 512 219-1018
Florence (G-6244)

Texarkan Fence ....F 870 779-0660
Nash (G-15724)

Texas Best Panels Inc ....E 512 752-3777
Lometa (G-14178)

Texas Iron & Steel LLC.....................F 903 758-9498
Longview (G-14317)

▲ Texas Stairs and Rails Inc ....E 281 987-2115
Houston (G-12251)

Texas Stone Designs Inc ....E 817 265-4011
Arlington (G-795)

Tietjen Inc ....E 979 249-3888
La Grange (G-13703)

Trinity Stairs Inc ....E 972 335-0700
Frisco (G-7320)

Triple - C Fence Llc ....E 817 439-9500
Haslet (G-8226)

▲ TS Distributors Inc ....D 832 467-5400
Houston (G-12394)

Walls Across Texas I Ltd ....E 210 826-4123
San Antonio (G-18608)

▲ Watkins Ornamental Iron Inc ....F 972 931-5350
Carrollton (G-2847)

William L Bonnell Company Inc ....B 409 543-0600
El Campo (G-5629)

◆ Woven Metal Products Inc.............E 281 331-4466
Alvin (G-386)

Yellow Rose Stl Fbricators Inc...........E 713 862-7339
Houston (G-12715)

3448 Prefabricated Metal Buildings & Cmp-nts

Abac LLC ....F 940 479-9163
Ponder (G-17092)

Alvarez & Marsal Inc ....C 212 759-4433
Houston (G-8575)

American Carports Inc ....E 866 730-9865
Joshua (G-13316)

American Steel Carports Inc ....E 866 471-8761
Joshua (G-13317)

Apache Construction Inc ....F 903 839-2242
Whitehouse (G-20725)

Athens Steel Building Corp ....E 903 675-5733
Athens (G-820)

▲ Atlas Building Systems Inc ....F 903 597-4211
Tyler (G-20052)

Atlas Building Systems Inc................E 903 865-1153
Wills Point (G-20873)

Atomic Container Homes Inc ....E 915 433-4817
El Paso (G-5653)

Bathsystem America LLC ....E 713 382-8585
Houston (G-8825)

BD Hildebrandt Entps Inc ....F 936 825-0500
Navasota (G-15725)

Berridge Manufacturing Company ......E 830 401-5200
Seguin (G-18826)

Berrys Tin Shop Inc ....F 903 586-3552
Jacksonville (G-13229)

◆ Bluff Holdings Inc ....D 817 293-3018
Fort Worth (G-6460)

▲ Bluff Manufacturing Inc ....D 817 293-3018
Fort Worth (G-6461)

Braden and Prewitt Inc ....F 713 699-2262
Houston (G-8974)

Capco Steel Inc ....C 210 493-9992
San Antonio (G-17979)

Carolina Carports Inc ....E 800 670-4262
Emory (G-6082)

Carports Childers & Structures ....F 713 460-2181
Houston (G-9094)

Cato Construction Company ....E 979 830-1398
Brenham (G-2250)

Central States Mfg Inc ....E 469 272-0041
Cedar Hill (G-2938)

Chism Company.................................F 210 824-6315
San Antonio (G-18004)

Cornerstone Bldg Brands Inc ....C 281 897-7788
Houston (G-9320)

Cornerstone Bldg Brands Inc ....G 281 897-7726
Houston (G-9321)

Cornerstone Bldg Brands Inc ....G 713 466-0712
Houston (G-9322)

Cotton Construction Inc ....F 936 931-2510
Waller (G-20496)

Cozart Mtal Bldngs Systems Inc ....G 817 237-2282
Fort Worth (G-6555)

D & R Custom Wldg & Cnstr Inc........E 830 997-1058
Fredericksburg (G-7175)

Diamond Door Products Ltd ....E 979 826-0238
Hempstead (G-8251)

Doyles Construction & Mfg Inc..........F 940 549-5517
Graham (G-7780)

FE Sawyer Bldg Systems Inc.............E 903 531-0182
Tyler (G-20087)

Fehrs Industrial Mfg LLC...................D 432 758-0068
Seminole (G-18883)

Floyd Tate A.....................................F 409 745-3256
Orange (G-16243)

General Shlters of Bvlle Texas ....E 936 598-3389
Center (G-2998)

▲ Geometrica Inc ....F 832 220-1200
Cypress (G-3795)

Ghm Corp ....C 972 840-1200
Dallas (G-4406)

▲ Green-Span Profiles LP ....F 281 807-7400
Waller (G-20503)

Guard-All Bldg Sltions Mfg LLC ....F 877 397-1594
Dallas (G-4420)

Hawk Portable Buildings Inc ....E 325 893-5120
Clyde (G-3163)

Horizon Structural Systems Inc..........B 830 629-8000
New Braunfels (G-15803)

Indicom Buildings Inc........................B 817 447-1213
Burleson (G-2582)

Industrial Cmponents Texas LLC........F 936 755-5697
Houston (G-10348)

Infinity Carports Inc ....G 903 765-2057
Edgewood (G-5572)

J B R Enterprises Inc........................G 972 542-3939
McKinney (G-14947)

▼ Jedco Building Systems Inc ....E 281 591-2860
Houston (G-10462)

Ktec Cleanroom Systems Inc ....E 512 388-2396
Georgetown (G-7659)

Lakeside Trailer Sales ....F 936 564-6252
Nacogdoches (G-15701)

Lane Supply Inc ....D 817 261-9116
Arlington (G-717)

Light Gauge Solutions Inc ....F 682 564-0378
Arlington (G-722)

Lubbock Gas & Building Inc ....E 806 745-9695
Lubbock (G-14441)

M&I Electric LLC ....C 409 838-0441
Beaumont (G-1922)

McElroy Metal Mill Inc.......................B 214 703-3113
Garland (G-7547)

McElroy Metal Mill Inc.......................F 972 226-7075
Mesquite (G-15062)

Metal Construction Mtls Inc ....F 281 550-8383
Houston (G-10845)

◆ Metl-Span LLC ....B 972 221-6656
Lewisville (G-14065)

Mg Building Materials Ltd ....F 210 798-0650
San Antonio (G-18297)

▲ Minearc Systems America LLC........F 214 337-5100
Dallas (G-4678)

Mobile Mini Inc ....E 817 439-2288
Rhome (G-17258)

Mobile Mini Inc ....F 512 251-2461
Austin (G-1347)

Modular Concepts Inc ....F 817 945-1667
Fort Worth (G-6845)

Morgan Buildings & Spas Inc ....F 972 864-7300
Richardson (G-17360)

▲ Mueller Supply Company Inc ....C 325 365-3555
Ballinger (G-1741)

Mueller Supply Company Inc ....D 936 344-9057
Willis (G-20855)

Mueller Supply Company Inc ....D 512 308-9173
Bastrop (G-1759)

Mueller Supply Company Inc ....D 325 690-7700
Abilene (G-60)

Mueller Supply Company Inc ....E 972 932-3208
Kaufman (G-13461)

Mueller Supply Company Inc ....G 409 886-2233
Orange (G-16254)

Mueller Supply Company Inc ....F 254 742-2754
Temple (G-19692)

Mueller Supply Company Inc..............F 903 892-6222
Sherman (G-18925)

Nci Group Inc ....C 817 481-2501
Southlake (G-19080)

Nci Group Inc ....E 281 897-7788
Houston (G-11015)

◆ Nci Group Inc ....B 281 897-7788
Houston (G-11016)

Nci Group Inc ....D 972 221-6656
Lewisville (G-14072)

Nci Group Inc ....E 806 747-4291
Lubbock (G-14451)

Nci Group Inc ....E 972 299-5556
Midlothian (G-15488)

Nci Group Inc ....D 817 488-8511
Irving (G-13121)

Nci Group Inc ....B 713 466-7788
Houston (G-11019)

Northast Txas McHning Wldg Hrd ......F 903 427-2277
Clarksville (G-3076)

Nucor Bldg Systems Sls Corp ....C 972 524-5407
Terrell (G-19744)

Oldcastle Buildingenvelope Inc ....A 972 551-6100
Terrell (G-19746)

Omnimax International Inc ....E 817 481-3521
Fort Worth (G-6882)

Palomar Modular Buildings LLC ....C 469 727-0727
Desoto (G-5438)

Parkline Inc ....D 409 935-5743
Hitchcock (G-8339)

Parkline Inc ....D 409 935-1037
La Marque (G-13713)

Peterson Construction ....F 254 227-0738
Axtell (G-1718)

Powell Electrical Systems Inc.............E 281 452-4885
Houston (G-11374)

Prengler Ltd ....F 972 965-5188
Sherman (G-18928)

▲ Protect Controls Inc ....C 713 691-5183
Conroe (G-3355)

R Slater Enterprises LLC...................F 832 456-4900
Houston (G-11528)

Ramtech Building Systems Inc ....E 817 473-9376
Mansfield (G-14707)

Rhodes Building Systems Inc ....E 979 596-1451
Somerville (G-19023)

Richard Phillips Inc...........................E 972 264-5315
Grand Prairie (G-7966)

▼ Rigid Global Buildings LLC ....B 281 443-9065
Houston (G-11621)

▼ Robertson-Ceco II Corporation ......C 281 897-7788
Houston (G-11644)

Rounhouse Corporation.....................F 281 593-1118
Cleveland (G-3134)

Schulte Building Systems Inc.............D 281 304-6111
Hockley (G-8348)

Shaun K Boyer ....F 281 442-3800
Houston (G-11848)

Smpl Inc ....E 402 525-5078
Austin (G-1513)

Southwest Metal Systems LLC ....E 903 569-8811
Mineola (G-15513)

Standard Structures Inc ....D 432 580-5353
Odessa (G-16164)

Steel Building Supply Inc ....F 936 598-6373
Center (G-3009)

Supaks Inc ....G 979 968-5654
La Grange (G-13701)

Techmar Industries LLC ....F 832 246-6200
Spring (G-19175)

Texas Aluminum Industries Inc ....B 713 941-7186
Houston (G-12220)

Tyler Building Systems LP ....E 903 561-3000
Tyler (G-20167)

Unique Stainless Designs LLC............F 972 254-8424
Grand Prairie (G-7990)

◆ United Structures America Inc ....B 281 442-8247
Houston (G-12458)

United Structures America Inc ....C 281 442-8247
Houston (G-12459)

USA Eagle Carports Inc.....................F 817 788-5395
Haltom City (G-8161)

USA Frametek LLC ....E 512 515-6500
Liberty Hill (G-14130)

Whirlwind Holding Company Inc ....B 713 946-7140
Houston (G-12660)

◆ Whirlwind Steel Buildings Inc ....B 713 946-7140
Houston (G-12661)

Wingate Partners V LP......................F 214 720-1313
Dallas (G-5196)

Xg Ventures LLC ....E 936 744-1800
Trinity *(G-20020)*

3449 Misc Structural Metal Work

A Sklar Company Inc ....E 361 573-5775
Victoria *(G-20233)*

Adobe Fab Consultants Inc ....E 936 447-6400
Conroe *(G-3253)*

Advanced Waterjet Cutting Inc ....D 214 358-2194
Dallas *(G-3891)*

▲ Baker Metal Products Inc ....C 972 241-3553
Dallas *(G-3999)*

Baseline Mfg Partners LP ....F 936 344-2858
New Waverly *(G-15855)*

Bionic Welder LLC ....E 817 579-5080
Granbury *(G-7793)*

▲ Brougher Inc ....D 713 869-7577
Houston *(G-8996)*

C M C Steel Fabricators Inc ....E 817 838-6811
Fort Worth *(G-6484)*

CK &B Machine Shop ....G 281 485-5760
Pearland *(G-16544)*

Crh Americas Inc ....E 903 765-2212
Alba *(G-181)*

Daniel Steel Industries Inc ....E 214 235-4509
Mesquite *(G-15038)*

Delzotto Products Minn Inc ....E 903 981-0400
Gladewater *(G-7720)*

Delzotto Products Texas Inc ....E 903 981-0400
Gladewater *(G-7721)*

Ecological Services Intl Inc ....D 956 233-4609
Los Fresnos *(G-14346)*

Effective Metal Services LLC ....F 832 962-8626
Houston *(G-9584)*

▲ Efi Inc ....E 940 380-8000
Denton *(G-5362)*

El Campo Sheet Metal LLC ....F 979 543-5751
El Campo *(G-5617)*

El Paso Machine & Steel Inc ....E 915 533-7483
El Paso *(G-5737)*

Fabhar Manufacturing LLC ....E 214 802-9400
Princeton *(G-17210)*

Fortitude Specialty Mfg LLC ....D 713 465-3370
Houston *(G-9839)*

G Fabricating LLC ....E 281 421-3100
Crosby *(G-3731)*

Graywolf Industrial Inc ....E 281 441-5400
Humble *(G-12771)*

Haydon Corporation ....F 972 641-6400
Grand Prairie *(G-7888)*

Hogan Steel Erectors Inc ....D 409 883-8208
West Orange *(G-20694)*

Ironforce Supply LLC ....F 713 681-5600
Houston *(G-10421)*

◆ Isotherm Inc ....E 817 472-9922
Arlington *(G-708)*

Joists of Texas Inc ....E 713 466-1212
Jersey Village *(G-13301)*

Katy Steel Co Incorporated ....E 281 391-7047
Katy *(G-13368)*

▲ Keppel Amfels Inc ....A 956 838-3110
Brownsville *(G-2374)*

Lane Supply Inc ....D 817 261-9116
Arlington *(G-717)*

Meridian Construction Services ....F 830 305-5700
Kingsbury *(G-13620)*

Modern Machine Shop Inc ....D 956 722-4656
Laredo *(G-13913)*

▲ National Frame Rail Inc ....E 940 482-9494
Sanger *(G-18727)*

◆ National Hose Aquisition Corp ....D 713 920-2030
Pasadena *(G-16487)*

NRG Manufacturing Inc ....D 281 320-2525
Tomball *(G-19993)*

NRG Manufacturing Inc ....F 281 320-2525
Waller *(G-20505)*

Nucor Corporation ....G 281 251-8857
Spring *(G-19156)*

Omp Specialties Inc ....E 903 874-0045
Corsicana *(G-3682)*

Pid Group Inc ....D 936 699-4743
Lufkin *(G-14544)*

Pixels & Powertools LLC ....F 844 458-1847
Austin *(G-1419)*

Polytrnix McHning Fbrction LLC ....F 972 436-0422
Richardson *(G-17374)*

Presidio Custom Metal Works ....F 512 284-8549
Round Rock *(G-17682)*

◆ Priefert Mfg Co Inc ....A 903 572-1741
Mount Pleasant *(G-15660)*

R Lutes Inc ....E 281 595-3777
Rosharon *(G-17611)*

◆ Raider Manufacturing Ltd ....D 806 762-3227
Lubbock *(G-14470)*

Renfrow Metalsmiths LLC ....G 832 724-8517
Houston *(G-11600)*

Rik-Mar Fabricators Inc ....E 979 779-1616
Bryan *(G-2501)*

◆ Rodrill Inc ....E 210 667-2130
Converse *(G-3402)*

Shape Corp ....D 616 846-8700
Garland *(G-7588)*

Slz Rebar LLC ....F 832 427-5860
Cypress *(G-3820)*

Son-Lan Industries Inc ....G 972 937-8162
Waxahachie *(G-20558)*

Southern State Steel Co ....E 409 866-1409
Beaumont *(G-1953)*

Spartan Reinforcing LLC ....E 832 271-1721
Houston *(G-11994)*

Spartan Reinforcing LLC ....E 915 269-5222
Buda *(G-2538)*

Steelway International LLC ....E 972 563-2000
Terrell *(G-19752)*

◆ Suncoast Post-Tension Ltd ....C 281 445-8886
Houston *(G-12100)*

Tritan Productz Ltd ....G 940 224-1575
Wichita Falls *(G-20821)*

Tubal Cain Industries Inc ....D 409 786-1783
Vidor *(G-20336)*

◆ Tubular Resource Inc ....F 281 240-3343
Sugar Land *(G-19569)*

Turrubiartes Benedicto ....G 832 675-1569
Houston *(G-12413)*

US Bellows Inc ....B 713 731-0030
Houston *(G-12481)*

▼ Vinton Steel LLC ....B 915 886-2000
Vinton *(G-20342)*

Willbanks Metals Inc ....E 817 625-6161
Fort Worth *(G-7146)*

◆ Willbanks Metals Inc ....C 817 625-6161
Fort Worth *(G-7147)*

Wilson Steel Services LLC ....F 903 275-2995
Brownsboro *(G-2333)*

Worldfab Inc ....F 281 446-9777
Humble *(G-12807)*

3451 Screw Machine Prdts

▲ Automatic Products Corp ....C 972 272-6422
Garland *(G-7444)*

Bonney Forge Corporation ....D 713 695-3633
Houston *(G-8950)*

Chevas Company LLC ....F 713 225-6595
Houston *(G-9176)*

Cox Manufacturing Company ....F 210 657-7731
San Antonio *(G-18028)*

D & R Precision Manufacturing ....F 956 386-0685
Edinburg *(G-5584)*

Fabrication Specialty Inc ....F 214 742-3571
Cranbury *(G-7797)*

▲ J M Fabrication Company LLC ....F 817 652-0526
Arlington *(G-709)*

Kaspar Machine LLC ....E 254 836-1564
Waco *(G-20422)*

Lewis Engineering Company ....E 903 938-6754
Marshall *(G-14787)*

Macro Tex Machine Works LLC ....F 281 540-2141
Humble *(G-12786)*

Nytex Automatic Products Inc ....E 830 997-8986
Bulverde *(G-2557)*

▼ P T Products & Services Inc ....E 512 251-3592
Pflugerville *(G-16682)*

◆ Pgi International Ltd ....B 713 466-0056
Houston *(G-11316)*

Production Machine & Tool LP ....E 940 767-9400
Wichita Falls *(G-20798)*

Pyle Machine Company Inc ....E 817 485-6011
Fort Worth *(G-6924)*

▲ Quantex Instrument Company ....E 936 544-5732
Crockett *(G-3723)*

R D Screw Machine Products Inc ....F 210 337-8942
San Antonio *(G-18408)*

RDS Products Inc ....F 817 656-8277
Fort Worth *(G-6945)*

Rothe Enterprises Inc ....F 210 310-0447
San Antonio *(G-18432)*

▲ S H Leggitt Company ....C 956 504-6440
San Marcos *(G-18708)*

Tecnotrat Metal Processing LLC ....F 281 894-9189
Houston *(G-12180)*

3452 Bolts, Nuts, Screws, Rivets & Washers

Aab Mfg Holdings LP ....E 281 438-1599
Houston *(G-8438)*

▲ Alcoa Lake Charles Carbn Plant ......C 845 334-7203
Rockdale *(G-17523)*

▲ All-Pro Threaded Products ....F 817 467-5700
Arlington *(G-614)*

All-Spec Sales Inc ....F 972 641-4053
Grand Prairie *(G-7827)*

▲ Beaumont Bolt & Gasket Inc ....E 409 838-6304
Beaumont *(G-1859)*

C M C Steel Fabricators Inc ....D 713 225-4446
Houston *(G-9032)*

Caterpillar Inc ....E 830 401-5600
Seguin *(G-18829)*

Caterpillar Inc ....D 210 637-3700
San Antonio *(G-17987)*

Colgan-Wilson Metals LLC ....F 409 882-9296
Beaumont *(G-1873)*

◆ Corpus Chrsti Gsket Fstner Inc ....C 361 884-6366
Corpus Christi *(G-3510)*

◆ Dale Company Inc ....F 713 928-3437
Houston *(G-9398)*

Dan-Loc Group LLC ....D 713 356-3500
Houston *(G-9399)*

◆ Dan-Loc, LLC ....D 713 356-3500
Houston *(G-9400)*

Eagle Metal Products LLC ....E 903 887-3581
Mabank *(G-14576)*

▲ Efi Inc ....E 940 380-8000
Denton *(G-5362)*

Fabrication Specialty Inc ....E 214 742-3571
Granbury *(G-7797)*

Fastserv Supply Inc ....E 800 527-4126
Plano *(G-16870)*

▲ Fluid Sealing Products Inc ....D 713 910-1028
Houston *(G-9816)*

Frontier Bolt Company Texas ....F 817 477-5319
Mansfield *(G-14674)*

Hillman Group Inc ....D 903 592-2826
Tyler *(G-20099)*

Indian Aerospace Inc ....F 817 265-5137
Arlington *(G-703)*

Ingram Industries Inc ....E 903 848-8411
Canton *(G-2657)*

K-T Bolt Mfg Co ....E 281 391-2196
Katy *(G-13412)*

Landreth Fastner Corporation ....F 281 414-3103
Houston *(G-10594)*

LFC Industries Inc ....D 817 640-1322
Arlington *(G-721)*

Lgc US Asset Holdings LLC ....F 713 222-0284
Houston *(G-10631)*

Lgc US Holdings LLC ....C 713 222-0284
Houston *(G-10632)*

▲ Lok-Mor Inc ....E 817 477-0232
Mansfield *(G-14685)*

◆ Lone Star Fasteners LLC ....C 281 353-1191
Spring *(G-19142)*

Mack Larry ....F 979 778-8088
Bryan *(G-2492)*

Macro Tex Machine Works LLC ....F 281 540-2141
Humble *(G-12786)*

Maintenance Tool & Supply Co ....F 361 888-8801
Corpus Christi *(G-3571)*

▲ Mayday Manufacturing Co ....C 940 898-8301
Denton *(G-5381)*

Mw Industries Inc ....E 281 233-0448
Houston *(G-10945)*

North Amrcn Sling Slutions LLC ....F 817 984-8000
Fort Worth *(G-6868)*

▲ Northwest Fastener and Sup Inc ......E 281 921-7880
Houston *(G-11080)*

Novaria Group LLC ....E 817 381-3810
Fort Worth *(G-6870)*

Pattonair Usa Inc ....E 817 284-4449
Fort Worth *(G-6897)*

Pin Oak Caregivers LLC ....F 713 301-3481
Houston *(G-11332)*

Robert L Rowan & Associates ....F 713 681-5811
Houston *(G-11643)*

Shamrock Precision Usa LLC ....E 972 241-4226
Farmers Branch *(G-6213)*

▲ South Texas Bolt & Fitting Inc ....E 713 673-5376
Houston *(G-11966)*

Spring Bolt and Nut Mfg Ltd ....E 281 448-4440
Houston *(G-12025)*

SPS Technologies LLC ....A 817 467-0031
Arlington *(G-786)*

Steelfast Inc ....F 972 243-5312
Dallas *(G-5009)*

Texas Bolt & Nut Company Ltd ....E 713 869-7111
Houston *(G-12222)*

▲ Tnn Manufacturing Company Inc ....D 713 849-0062
Houston *(G-12311)*

Tubal Cain Industries Inc ....D 409 786-1783
Vidor *(G-20336)*

US Bolt Manufacturing Inc ....D 713 726-1000
Houston *(G-12482)*

▲ Winzer Corporation ....C 214 341-2122
Plano *(G-17051)*

Worldwide Manufacturing Inc ....E 713 645-6552
Houston *(G-12693)*

Zero Products Inc ....E 713 675-0123
Houston *(G-12726)*

3462 Iron & Steel Forgings

AGH Industries Inc ....E 817 284-1742
Euless *(G-6129)*

▲ Amarillo Gear Company LLC ....C 806 622-1273
Amarillo *(G-478)*

Ameribolt Inc ....E 713 580-4997
Houston *(G-8579)*

▲ Ameriforge Corporation ....F 713 393-4200
Houston *(G-8615)*

◆ Ameriforge Group Inc ....E 713 393-4200
Houston *(G-8616)*

Ameriforge Group Inc ....E 409 283-8138
Woodville *(G-20914)*

◆ Andrews Safety Anchors Inc ....F 432 524-6659
Andrews *(G-535)*

B&B Roadway SEC Solutions LLC ....F 972 385-7899
Mckinney *(G-14924)*

Beta Arkansas LLC ....F 972 490-2340
Dallas *(G-4022)*

Better Burglar Bars Inc ....E 713 699-9543
Houston *(G-8867)*

Boltex Manufacturing Co LP ....D 713 451-2180
Houston *(G-8947)*

Bonney Forge Corporation ....D 713 695-3633
Houston *(G-8950)*

▲ Brougher Inc ....D 713 869-7577
Houston *(G-8996)*

▲ C-B-Gear & Machine Inc ....E 281 449-0777
Houston *(G-9040)*

Cab Incorporated ....E 936 569-9430
Nacogdoches *(G-15687)*

Cerda-Fied Specialists Inc ....F 281 392-8063
Brookshire *(G-2313)*

Chem Fabrication LLC ....D 979 265-6600
Clute *(G-3149)*

◆ Chicago Bridge & Iron Co Del ....C 832 513-1000
Houston *(G-9183)*

CK Kustoms Iron Works Inc ....F 281 850-6118
Rockport *(G-17529)*

Crosby Group LLC ....B 918 834-4611
Longview *(G-14216)*

Crow Precision Components LLC ....D 817 536-2861
Fort Worth *(G-6562)*

Dan-Loc Group LLC ....D 713 356-3500
Houston *(G-9399)*

◆ Dan-Loc, LLC ....C 713 356-3500
Houston *(G-9400)*

▲ Delta Flange & Mfg Inc ....F 713 686-9702
Houston *(G-9431)*

▲ Ellwood Advnced Components LLC C 336 969-4000
Navasota *(G-15732)*

◆ Ellwood Texas Forge LP ....C 713 434-5100
Houston *(G-9605)*

◆ Ellwood Txas Frge Navasota LLC ....B 936 825-7531
Navasota *(G-15733)*

Evans Sons Prtble Rock Crshing ....F 830 214-3629
Euless *(G-6144)*

Flange Protection & Gaskets ....F 281 991-4550
Pasadena *(G-16437)*

Flanges Inc ....F 713 673-4117
Kingwood *(G-13643)*

◆ Forged Components Inc ....C 281 441-4088
Humble *(G-12767)*

Forged Components Inc ....D 936 825-7518
Navasota *(G-15735)*

Forged Components Inc ....E 409 246-2427
Kountze *(G-13670)*

Forged Products Inc ....D 713 462-3416
Houston *(G-9833)*

Franklin Machine & Gear Corp ....F 281 441-3177
Humble *(G-12768)*

▲ Futaba Industrial Texas Corp ....C 210 927-2288
San Antonio *(G-18132)*

◆ Galperti Inc ....C 713 433-0700
Houston *(G-9895)*

General Electric Company ....D 412 469-6080
Southlake *(G-19071)*

GK Steel Fabrication LLC ....F 972 291-5514
Duncanville *(G-5531)*

Gulf Manufacturing Inc ....E 281 446-0093
Humble *(G-12773)*

Gulfco Forge Company LLC ....C 409 842-1311
Houston *(G-10072)*

Houston Gear USA Inc ....E 281 495-8274
Stafford *(G-19326)*

▲ Liberty Forge Inc ....D 936 336-5785
Liberty *(G-14121)*

◆ Lufkin Gears LLC ....B 936 634-2211
Lufkin *(G-14539)*

Lufkin Industries LLC ....E 281 495-1100
Missouri City *(G-15583)*

◆ Maddox Metal Works Inc ....D 214 333-2311
Dallas *(G-4625)*

Martin Sprocket & Gear Inc ....E 325 677-3591
Abilene *(G-59)*

Martin Sprocket & Gear Inc ....E 214 428-2191
Dallas *(G-4641)*

Matek Performance Inc ....E 817 626-9006
Fort Worth *(G-6816)*

Modern Forge Texas LLC ....E 817 268-0781
Hurst *(G-12853)*

Morsco Supply LLC ....F 903 234-2183
Longview *(G-14282)*

▲ Moventas Gears Inc ....E 503 247-6107
Spring *(G-19234)*

National Flange & Fitting Co ....E 713 688-2515
Houston *(G-10968)*

National Foundry & Mfg Co ....E 432 558-3444
Crane *(G-3700)*

National Oilwell Varco Inc ....C 936 825-7070
Navasota *(G-15739)*

O E M Industries Inc ....E 214 330-7271
Dallas *(G-4748)*

Orbix Corporation ....E 254 675-8651
Clifton *(G-3145)*

▲ Oteco Inc ....C 713 695-3693
Houston *(G-11200)*

Oteco Inc ....D 713 695-3693
Houston *(G-11201)*

▲ Parish International Inc ....E 281 463-9233
Hempstead *(G-8254)*

▼ Ram-Gear Manufacturing Inc ....F 361 668-0235
Alice *(G-231)*

▲ Samco Sales Inc ....F 713 733-5700
Houston *(G-11738)*

Skipper Industries Inc ....E 254 897-1292
Glen Rose *(G-7533)*

▲ Standard Industrial Pdts Co ....E 281 280-0147
Webster *(G-20647)*

▼ Structural Metals Inc ....A 830 372-8200
Seguin *(G-18866)*

Sure Trac Inc ....E 254 666-6732
Hewitt *(G-8301)*

◆ Taper-Lok Corporation ....F 713 467-3333
Houston *(G-12158)*

Texas Steel Tech LLC ....F 817 894-7041
Weatherford *(G-20626)*

Timken Gears & Services Inc ....E 713 224-4900
Houston *(G-12292)*

Trinity Forge Inc ....C 817 473-1515
Mansfield *(G-14723)*

TX Tinman Enterprises LLC ....F 817 288-6116
Fort Worth *(G-7087)*

◆ Voestalpine Texas LLC ....E 361 704-9000
Portland *(G-17188)*

▲ W Silver Inc ....C 915 886-3553
Vinton *(G-20343)*

▲ Western Forge & Flange Co Inc ....E 800 352-6433
Cleveland *(G-3141)*

Windstrom Industries & Assoc ....E 214 298-6342
Dallas *(G-5194)*

3463 Nonferrous Forgings

AGH Industries Inc ....E 817 284-1742
Euless *(G-6129)*

Chem Fabrication LLC ....D 979 265-6600
Clute *(G-3149)*

◆ Coastal Flange Inc ....E 713 937-3333
Jersey Village *(G-13296)*

▼ Copper Craft Inc ....E 817 490-9622
Fort Worth *(G-6549)*

◆ Ellwood Texas Forge LP ....C 713 434-5100
Houston *(G-9605)*

▲ Federal Flange Inc ....D 713 681-0606
Houston *(G-9768)*

Federal Flange Inc ....C 713 681-0606
Houston *(G-9769)*

◆ Federal Flange & Fitting Co ....D 713 681-0606
Houston *(G-9770)*

▼ Flexitallic Group Inc ....E 281 604-2525
Houston *(G-9799)*

Flowserve Corporation ....E 832 375-0807
Houston *(G-9813)*

Flowserve Corporation ....B 972 443-6500
Irving *(G-13027)*

Flowserve Corporation ....F 800 446-0401
Irving *(G-13028)*

▲ GE Oil Gas Cmprssion Systems L ....B 713 354-1900
Houston *(G-9916)*

General Dynamics Ordnance ....B 972 276-5131
Garland *(G-7499)*

▲ M&P Flange Pipe Protection Inc ....F 713 463-6339
Houston *(G-10723)*

◆ Maass Flanges Corporation ....E 713 329-5500
Houston *(G-10729)*

National Flange & Fitting Co ....E 713 688-2515
Houston *(G-10968)*

▼ Non-Frrous Extrsion Scrap Mtls ....D 713 869-9551
Houston *(G-11067)*

O & D Manufacturing Inc ....D 903 295-2057
White Oak *(G-20718)*

Pump Arts Inc ....E 713 946-0500
Houston *(G-11472)*

Wilson Supply Corporate Office ....F 713 237-3309
Houston *(G-12675)*

3465 Automotive Stampings

▲ ABC Exclusive Inc ....D 972 485-8182
Garland *(G-7425)*

Anderton Castings LLC ....B 254 938-2541
Troy *(G-20027)*

Batterson Truck Equipment LLC ....F 281 598-6588
Houston *(G-8829)*

Caldwell Upfitters LLC ....F 832 203-5658
Houston *(G-9049)*

Caldwell Upfitters LLC ....E 254 773-1959
Temple *(G-19672)*

CW Sehorn Enterprises Ltd ....E 713 895-8834
Houston *(G-9379)*

HP Car Accessories & Atv Sales ....E 903 675-0032
Athens *(G-828)*

Illinois Tool Works Inc ....B 956 215-2000
Pharr *(G-16700)*

International Assembly Inc ....E 956 525-4533
Brownsville *(G-2362)*

Kirchhoff Auto Dallas Inc ....C 214 553-0208
Garland *(G-7531)*

Kirchhoff Auto Dallas Inc ....C 214 553-0208
Garland *(G-7532)*

▲ Mahle Systema De Filtracion D ....G 956 753-9100
Laredo *(G-13909)*

Nuco Tool Inc ....E 956 383-6620
McAllen *(G-14895)*

Richard H Smith LLC ....E 817 267-6750
Euless *(G-6155)*

▼ Stemco Products Inc ....F 903 758-9981
Longview *(G-14312)*

Takumi Stamping Inc ....E 210 380-1087
San Antonio *(G-18519)*

Toyoda Gosei ....F 210 628-1337
San Antonio *(G-18555)*

Toyotetsu Texas Inc ....D 210 231-5515
San Antonio *(G-18557)*

◆ TYG Products LP ....D 972 542-1828
McKinney *(G-14984)*

3466 Crowns & Closures

Modco Industries Inc ....E 936 539-9222
Conroe *(G-3331)*

Screen Play Promotions Inc ....G 817 788-8608
Hurst *(G-12858)*

▲ Self Industries ....E 713 672-2559
Houston *(G-11824)*

3469 Metal Stampings, NEC

14703 Partners Industries LLC ....F 281 847-0788
Houston *(G-8402)*

A & I Industries Inc ....F 915 633-8444
El Paso *(G-5633)*

◆ Aap Metals LLC ....E 214 357-6161
Dallas *(G-3875)*

Airfoil Impellers Corporation ....E 979 822-6418
Bryan *(G-2452)*

Alco Machine Tool & Steel Inc ....F 915 779-7013
El Paso (G-5640)

Alfred Kager ....E 830 997-9391
Fredericksburg (G-7169)

Allied Tools of Texas Corp ....G 713 943-8500
Houston (G-8554)

Atlantic Durant Technology Inc ....E 956 440-8005
Harlingen (G-8182)

Auto License ....E 956 318-2158
Edinburg (G-5576)

Axxion Group Corporation ....D 915 225-8888
El Paso (G-5656)

▲ Baumann Springs Texas Ltd ....E 972 641-7272
Grand Prairie (G-7840)

▲ Baumann Springs Usa Inc ....D 972 641-7272
Grand Prairie (G-7841)

Baumann Springs Usa Inc ....F 972 641-7272
Fort Worth (G-6440)

▲ Baumann Sprng Txas Hldings LLC ..E 972 641-7272
Grand Prairie (G-7842)

▲ Bettcher Manufacturing LLC ....D 956 618-5805
McAllen (G-14842)

Bettcher Manufacturing LLC ....D 956 519-0468
McAllen (G-14843)

Brandt Precision Machining ....E 512 339-7251
Austin (G-1005)

Buferd Company Inc ....D 972 272-9502
Garland (G-7451)

▲ C H Industries Inc ....D 972 416-1304
Carrollton (G-2709)

Cambrian Industries Inc ....E 915 771-6100
El Paso (G-5677)

Camtech Precision Mfg Inc ....E 404 444-9646
Euless (G-6134)

Cannon Cnon Indus McHining Inc ......G 972 293-6278
Lone Oak (G-14179)

CC Coating & Machine Inc ....E 361 884-9753
Corpus Christi (G-3497)

▲ Coiling Technologies Inc ....D 713 849-4000
Houston (G-9241)

Command Manufacturing LLC ....E 512 927-0033
Austin (G-1058)

Commercial Kitchens Inc ....D 281 442-8001
Houston (G-9250)

Custom Kitchen Eqp Co Inc ....E 281 446-8187
Humble (G-12762)

D & D Tooling and Mfg Inc ....E 915 590-2655
El Paso (G-5710)

◆ Delta Electronics (usa) Inc ....C 469 330-9100
Plano (G-16837)

Diamond Manufacturing Company ......D 972 291-8800
Cedar Hill (G-2939)

DNB Stainless Concepts LLC ....F 940 479-0079
Justin (G-13341)

Eagle Metal Products LLC ....E 903 887-3581
Mabank (G-14576)

El Paso Tool & Die Co Inc ....E 915 591-0346
El Paso (G-5744)

Emf Company Inc ....D 214 350-6848
Dallas (G-4319)

Essner Manufacturing LP ....D 817 551-5511
Fort Worth (G-6618)

◆ Ets-Lindgren Inc ....C 512 531-6400
Cedar Park (G-2968)

Excel Stamping & Mfg Inc ....E 281 304-0771
Cypress (G-3789)

Exper-Tech Products Company ....F 936 825-3573
Navasota (G-15734)

Fleming & Son Corporation ....E 972 263-1713
Grand Prairie (G-7873)

G & H Diversified Mfg LP ....D 713 856-1600
Houston (G-9883)

Gamma Engineering Inc ....C 817 477-2193
Mansfield (G-14676)

General Motors LLC ....D 817 652-2200
Arlington (G-690)

Glenn Metalcraft Texas LLC ....F 817 838-9000
Fort Worth (G-6672)

▲ Gobar Systems Inc ....F 956 377-4836
Brownsville (G-2360)

Griffiths Corporation ....D 817 488-6547
Grapevine (G-8041)

Hansen Manufacturing Inc ....E 713 682-1075
Houston (G-10117)

Industrial Tool & Die Co Inc ....E 281 859-4499
Houston (G-10355)

Industrial Tool & Die Co Inc ....F 956 440-9960
Harlingen (G-8190)

Itd Precision ....E 956 440-9960
Harlingen (G-8191)

▲ Jayco Manufacturing LLC ....D 972 623-2004
Grand Prairie (G-7901)

JLK Industries Inc ....E 713 462-7761
Houston (G-10476)

Kitchen Equipment Fabg Co ....D 713 747-3611
Houston (G-10538)

Langley Manufacturing Inc ....F 936 569-8824
Nacogdoches (G-15702)

Larsen Manufacturing LLC ....D 915 790-0762
El Paso (G-5840)

▼ Leeco Precision Spring Mfg Co ......F 713 692-6281
Houston (G-10618)

▲ Lsg Sky Chefs N Amer Sltons In ......B 972 793-9517
Irving (G-13090)

◆ M & R USA ....F 281 497-8973
Houston (G-10717)

M J Celco Inc ....D 915 594-1777
El Paso (G-5854)

Manufctring Oprations MGT Intl ....F 682 521-5800
Hurst (G-12851)

▲ Maudlin Assets Management Inc ......E 281 334-7566
Kemah (G-13477)

McAllen Metal Stamping Inc ....F 956 682-3438
McAllen (G-14888)

Metals Incorporated ....F 713 923-9491
Houston (G-10852)

Midland Stamping and Fabg Corp ......F 830 422-2052
Del Rio (G-5320)

Moffitt West LLC ....D 972 298-0531
Duncanville (G-5535)

Motor City Tool & Die Corp ....F 512 251-7700
Pflugerville (G-16681)

MPA International LP ....C 915 474-7832
El Paso (G-5887)

Mpl Industries Inc ....F 214 253-2332
Dallas (G-4696)

▲ National Manufacturing LLC ....F 281 856-7693
Houston (G-10970)

Native American Industries Inc ....F 817 731-6786
Fort Worth (G-6863)

◆ New Process Steel LP ....D 713 686-9631
Houston (G-11035)

Newcomb Spring Corp ....E 972 241-6781
Dallas (G-4732)

P Rockin Enterprises Inc ....G 915 886-4912
Anthony (G-589)

Plantex Machine LLC ....G 936 894-0226
Plantersville (G-17060)

▲ Pmr Global Inc ....E 817 484-1100
Burleson (G-2593)

Precision Alloys Corporation ....E 800 321-0759
Dallas (G-4818)

Preferred Stampings of Texas ....E 512 255-7803
Round Rock (G-17681)

▲ Quantex Instrument Company ....E 936 544-5732
Crockett (G-3723)

R-5 Metal Fabricators Inc ....F 903 873-2633
Wills Point (G-20877)

Raytheon Company ....A 972 205-4277
Dallas (G-4860)

Richard H Smith LLC ....E 817 267-6750
Euless (G-6155)

Rittal Corp ....F 937 399-0500
Houston (G-11626)

Safe-T-Pet Inc ....F 903 569-0590
Mineola (G-15511)

Sage International Inc ....D 972 623-2004
Grand Prairie (G-7971)

Spring Engineers Houston Ltd ....E 713 690-9488
Houston (G-12027)

Stainless Stl Cstm Fbrctors In ....E 713 433-0495
Houston (G-12038)

▲ Star Manufacturing Ltd ....E 830 401-5951
Seguin (G-18865)

Stewart Efi LLC ....E 915 775-2558
El Paso (G-5978)

▲ Stewart Efi Finishing LLC ....F 915 775-2558
El Paso (G-5979)

▲ Takumi Stamping Inc ....B 210 924-3110
San Antonio (G-18520)

Taylor Press Products Company ....E 512 746-5556
Jarrell (G-13274)

Toolco Precision Machine Inc ....F 713 433-3700
Houston (G-12318)

Toro Company ....C 915 231-7200
El Paso (G-6008)

Transportation Texas Dept ....F 940 937-2571
Childress (G-3056)

TW Stamping & Tool Inc ....E 903 877-2353
Tyler (G-20166)

Universal Metal Products Inc ....F 956 283-7200
Pharr (G-16713)

Wipco Acquisition LLC ....F 936 327-8250
Livingston (G-14164)

▲ Wood Gallery Inc ....F 972 869-9161
Dallas (G-5200)

3471 Electroplating, Plating, Polishing, Anodizing & Coloring

3-D Honing Inc ....G 281 391-8989
Katy (G-13386)

3c Metal USA Inc ....F 713 808-9651
Houston (G-8407)

AAA Blast-Cote Inc ....E 281 482-1236
Friendswood (G-7241)

Accurate Precision Plating LLC ....E 281 598-8835
Houston (G-8463)

Acme Holdings Inc ....E 210 798-3460
San Antonio (G-17861)

Advanced Aero Coatings LLC ....F 940 367-5963
Ponder (G-17093)

Aef Plating LLC ....E 956 994-1991
McAllen (G-14832)

Aero-Tech Metal Finishing Inc ....E 210 522-0802
San Antonio (G-17872)

Aft Industries Inc ....E 469 865-2800
Mansfield (G-14653)

Aft Industries Inc ....E 972 988-1999
Mansfield (G-14654)

Ai Lonestar LLC ....F 512 990-3999
Pflugerville (G-16656)

Airline Plating Inc ....F 713 692-6369
Houston (G-8517)

Alamo Plating Inc ....E 210 658-4024
Converse (G-3387)

Alamo Plating & Met Finshg Ltd ....E 210 658-4024
Converse (G-3388)

Alkote Inc ....E 713 695-3609
Houston (G-8539)

Als Associates ....E 817 921-2679
Fort Worth (G-6373)

American Plating Co Texas Ltd ....E 281 452-4241
Houston (G-8604)

Anadite Cal Restoration Tr ....F 817 282-9171
Hurst (G-12833)

Anodics Inc ....F 817 281-2743
Fort Worth (G-6389)

Apci Inc ....E 817 927-5362
Fort Worth (G-6391)

Arrow Construction Co Inc ....E 325 573-3571
Snyder (G-18982)

Artistic Plating Inc ....F 713 864-1352
Houston (G-8711)

Azz Inc ....E 972 840-0934
Garland (G-7446)

B & C Coating Inc ....F 281 351-4773
Tomball (G-19962)

B Finishing Co Inc ....F 512 759-2100
Hutto (G-12876)

Bhc Industries of Texas Inc ....F 817 556-2306
Alvarado (G-325)

Billmark Company ....F 817 834-2481
Fort Worth (G-6451)

Brock Enterprises LLC ....E 409 729-6353
Nederland (G-15747)

Brooks Industrial Coatings Inc ....F 512 990-5333
Austin (G-1012)

Commercial Mfg Co Inc ....F 903 794-1321
Texarkana (G-19761)

Concote Corporation ....F 903 581-0697
Tyler (G-20070)

◆ Concote Corporation ....C 214 956-0077
Coppell (G-3412)

Consolidated Metal Tech Inc ....D 512 255-9296
Round Rock (G-17637)

Cor-Pro Systems Inc ....E 713 896-1091
Houston (G-9312)

Courter-Hall Company ....F 972 276-8531
Garland (G-7468)

Cy-Fair Coatings Inc ....E 281 351-7427
Cypress (G-3784)

Cynco Specialty Inc ....G 281 499-0519
Stafford (G-19298)

Daggett Street Properties ....F 817 332-5604
Fort Worth (G-6572)

Dean-Chem Inc ....E 713 644-3882
Houston (G-9419)

Dels Plating Industries Corp ....F 713 785-4955
Houston (G-9428)

SIC

Delstar Metal Finishing Inc ....E 713 849-2090
Houston *(G-9429)*

▲ Dixie Electro Plating Company ....E 713 224-1826
Houston *(G-9483)*

Dura-Tech Processes Inc ....F 817 473-7888
Mansfield *(G-14668)*

East Texas Plating Inc ....F 903 935-7000
Marshall *(G-14775)*

Electro-Coatings Texas Inc ....E 210 798-3460
Houston *(G-9591)*

Elkcorp ....E 936 633-6387
Lufkin *(G-14526)*

◆ Elkcorp ....E 972 851-0500
Dallas *(G-4313)*

F & W Industries Inc ....F 432 563-8895
Odessa *(G-15997)*

▲ Fin-Tech Inc ....E 713 680-3777
Houston *(G-9787)*

Finley Investments Inc ....E 713 686-4629
Houston *(G-9788)*

General Magnaplate Corporation ....D 817 640-1761
Arlington *(G-687)*

Genes Paul Enterprises Inc ....E 817 558-7868
Cleburne *(G-3091)*

Gleco Plating Inc ....D 972 475-4300
Rowlett *(G-17705)*

▲ H & M Plating Company Inc ....D 713 643-6516
Houston *(G-10080)*

Hall Plating Co................................F 830 620-7825
New Braunfels *(G-15800)*

Har-Conn Chrome Company..............E 817 626-5437
Fort Worth *(G-6689)*

Harrison Electropolishing LP ....F 832 467-3100
Houston *(G-10126)*

Hi-Tech Metals Inc ....D 940 243-0516
Denton *(G-5373)*

▲ Houston Mfg Specialty Co Inc ....E 281 888-4635
Houston *(G-10239)*

Houston Plating & Coatings LLC ....D 713 946-8920
South Houston *(G-19046)*

Houston Plating & Coatings LLC ....C 713 946-8920
South Houston *(G-19047)*

Hwm Hurst Inc.................................E 817 268-6111
Hurst *(G-12845)*

ICP Industries LLC ....F 210 226-1261
San Antonio *(G-18178)*

◆ Integrted Crrsion Cmpanies Inc ....E 713 789-9181
Houston *(G-10389)*

J & S Plating and Repair Inc ....F 972 784-8718
Farmersville *(G-6224)*

J E Titus Company ....F 713 991-1100
Houston *(G-10439)*

Jdh Iron Designs LLC.......................F 254 486-9150
Valley Mills *(G-20201)*

Knight Industrial Services Inc ....C 281 421-5049
Baytown *(G-1825)*

Lone Star Corrosion Svcs Inc.............D 281 955-1313
Houston *(G-10675)*

M & K Plating Inc.............................E 817 332-6021
Fort Worth *(G-6802)*

Mam LLC ....F 512 407-9940
Austin *(G-1320)*

Mirror Acquisitions LLC ....F 713 686-4435
Houston *(G-10889)*

Morrell Plating Co Inc ....E 214 357-9850
Dallas *(G-4689)*

MSA Industries Inc...........................F 432 337-6062
Odessa *(G-16084)*

New Tk Coatings LLC........................E 713 666-1375
Houston *(G-11037)*

Noles Davis Plating Co ....G 214 358-1731
Dallas *(G-4741)*

North Shore Supply Company Inc.......D 713 400-3320
Houston *(G-11077)*

Outdoor Furn Refinishing Inc ....D 713 741-9779
Houston *(G-11202)*

Outdoor Furniture Refinishing ....F 713 741-9779
Houston *(G-11203)*

P & M Blasting & Coating Inc ....F 713 896-4691
Houston *(G-11212)*

Panasonic Corp North America...........A 956 984-3432
Mcallen *(G-14899)*

Precise Hard Chrome ....F 254 756-6879
Waco *(G-20449)*

Quality Bumper Service Dallas............E 214 824-7300
Dallas *(G-4843)*

▲ Reinfro LLC...................................D 956 838-9814
Brownsville *(G-2398)*

Result Enterprises Inc ....D 713 666-0550
Houston *(G-11614)*

Riley Industrial Services Inc ....E 432 332-9630
Odessa *(G-16141)*

▲ Rister Crnkshaft Spcialist Ltd ....F 361 289-0588
Corpus Christi *(G-3610)*

Ronald Noles ....F 281 489-7727
Manvel *(G-14737)*

Rubens Electroplating Inc..................F 915 779-3796
El Paso *(G-5948)*

▲ S + S Industries Inc ....D 713 643-8888
Houston *(G-11709)*

▲ Schumacher Company Inc ....F 713 923-5548
Houston *(G-11783)*

Schumacher International Inc.............F 713 923-5548
Houston *(G-11784)*

Sentinel Plating Inc..........................F 972 276-2780
Garland *(G-7587)*

Sifco Applied Srfc Cncepts LLC ....F 281 444-6500
Houston *(G-11882)*

Signature Plating Ltd ....E 210 380-0020
Cibolo *(G-3065)*

Southwestern Plating Company ....F 713 223-1331
Houston *(G-11986)*

Specialty Metal Finishing Inc.............F 713 528-5428
Houston *(G-12000)*

Stuart-Dean Co Inc ....F 972 513-9781
Irving *(G-13189)*

Surface Techniques Inc ....F 713 932-8050
Houston *(G-12124)*

▲ T G Industries Inc.........................F 281 356-2001
Pinehurst *(G-16735)*

Tecplate LP ....F 972 487-0636
Garland *(G-7596)*

Tenth Street Industries LP ....F 972 578-5155
Plano *(G-17024)*

Texas Hydraulics Inc ....E 254 756-6879
Waco *(G-20466)*

◆ Texas Metal Industries Inc ....E 972 288-2333
Mesquite *(G-15080)*

Texas Mpp LP ....E 903 874-5781
Corsicana *(G-3685)*

Texas Precision Plating Inc ....F 972 494-1547
Garland *(G-7599)*

Tlmi Corporation ....F 512 833-7075
Austin *(G-1582)*

Trevinos Painting Inc ....F 956 571-3999
Edinburg *(G-604)*

Trinity Powder Coating ....F 214 703-3609
Garland *(G-7605)*

U S Plating LLP ....F 972 871-2800
Irving *(G-13201)*

Valence Surface Tech LLC ....F 855 370-5920
The Woodlands *(G-19934)*

Vanguard Metal Technologies ....F 713 641-1859
Houston *(G-12529)*

W & S Precision Finishing Co ....F 214 339-7181
Dallas *(G-5170)*

Weatherford Artificia..........................F 918 224-7428
Kingwood *(G-13660)*

West Ltd ....F 409 794-9090
Beaumont *(G-1969)*

Western Grinding Co Inc ....F 214 631-3090
Dallas *(G-5182)*

William L Bonnell Company Inc ....B 409 543-0600
El Campo *(G-5629)*

3479 Coating & Engraving, NEC

3M Company.....................................F 979 848-8489
Angleton *(G-564)*

3p Industries LLC.............................G 903 877-3960
Tyler *(G-20042)*

A&A Coating Inc ....F 903 656-2581
Lone Star *(G-14181)*

A-1 Powder Coat Paint Inc ....F 972 494-6861
Garland *(G-7424)*

AAA Blast-Cote Inc ....E 281 482-1236
Friendswood *(G-7241)*

Accurate Inc ....C 979 921-7777
Brookshire *(G-2309)*

◆ Accurate Inc ....D 512 352-5278
Taylor *(G-19647)*

Alkote Inc ....E 713 695-3609
Houston *(G-8539)*

Alliance Coatings LLC ....F 817 834-8817
Fort Worth *(G-6372)*

Aluminum Mint Systems Txas Inc........C 713 522-8925
Houston *(G-8574)*

American Powder Coating Corp ....F 817 446-9400
Fort Worth *(G-6384)*

American Roller Company LLC............F 262 878-2445
Houston *(G-8607)*

American Roller Company LLC ....E 713 466-0550
Houston *(G-8608)*

APAC International Inc ....F 940 696-2525
Wichita Falls *(G-20738)*

◆ Apache Global Painting Inc ....C 713 450-9307
Houston *(G-8658)*

Armadillo Blast Coat Inc ....E 281 485-2743
Pearland *(G-16539)*

Aztec Mnfcturing-Waskom Partnr ....E 903 687-3943
Waskom *(G-20514)*

Azz Inc..E 832 467-3772
Houston *(G-8771)*

Azz Inc..F 281 458-1550
Houston *(G-8769)*

Azz Incorporated ....D 817 268-2414
Hurst *(G-12836)*

Bdm Metal Coaters LLC ....D 713 400-2300
Houston *(G-8844)*

▼ Berridge Manufacturing Company ....E 210 650-7056
San Antonio *(G-17949)*

Berridge Manufacturing Company ....F 713 223-4971
Houston *(G-8861)*

◆ Bredero Shaw LLC ....E 281 886-2350
Houston *(G-8982)*

◆ C E Shepherd Company LP ....D 713 924-4300
Houston *(G-9028)*

C&F Fabrication Indus Svcs LLC ....E 409 994-2135
Buna *(G-2561)*

▼ Ceram-Kote Coatings Inc ....E 432 263-8497
Big Spring *(G-2074)*

Cincinnati Thermal Spray Inc ....F 281 431-1629
Rosharon *(G-17603)*

Coating Industries Inc ....E 713 937-8581
Houston *(G-9230)*

Cobra Coating ....F 432 332-0272
Odessa *(G-15963)*

▲ Coiling Technologies Inc.................D 713 849-4000
Houston *(G-9241)*

Contract Powder Coating Inc ....F 972 494-4444
Garland *(G-7462)*

▼ Corev America Inc.........................E 713 849-3671
Houston *(G-9319)*

Corrosion Prtction Prcsses of ....F 713 869-9454
Houston *(G-9324)*

Cox Industries Inc ....E 972 288-7555
Mesquite *(G-15036)*

Crosslink McKnney Pwdr Cting L ....F 972 542-5441
McKinney *(G-14933)*

Crosslink Pwdr Cting Astin Ltd ....G 512 989-6458
Pflugerville *(G-16664)*

Cy-Fair Coatings Inc ....F 281 351-7427
Cypress *(G-3784)*

Daggett Street Properties..................F 817 332-5604
Fort Worth *(G-6572)*

Dean-Chem Inc ....F 713 644-3882
Houston *(G-9419)*

Deq Coatings Inc ....F 713 645-1777
Houston *(G-9438)*

Dobbs Coating Systems Inc ....F 817 341-1777
Weatherford *(G-20587)*

E-Coating Inc ....F 936 715-0700
Nacogdoches *(G-15695)*

Egm Cleaning & Remodeling ....G 210 666-0234
San Antonio *(G-18084)*

El Paso Pwdr Cting Hydrgrphics ....F 915 313-9333
El Paso *(G-5739)*

El Paso Tool & Die Co Inc ....E 915 591-0346
El Paso *(G-5744)*

Electro-Coatings of Iowa Inc..............G 800 806-6059
San Antonio *(G-18086)*

Elite Coating Services ....F 469 431-3353
Alvarado *(G-329)*

F & W Industries Inc ....F 432 563-8895
Odessa *(G-15997)*

Ford Contract Services Inc ....E 713 862-2960
Livingston *(G-14154)*

▲ Fusion Operations LP ....D 713 691-6547
Houston *(G-9878)*

G&C Coatings & Industrial Serv ....G 832 916-6070
Houston *(G-9887)*

Gartner Coatings Inc ....E 281 997-3500
Pearland *(G-16563)*

General Magnaplate Corporation ....D 817 640-1761
Arlington *(G-687)*

General Magnaplate Texas Inc............E 817 649-8989
Arlington *(G-688)*

General Magnaplate Wisconsin ....F 800 441-6173
Arlington *(G-689)*

▲ Gfk Interests Ltd ....D 713 225-0010
Houston *(G-9947)*

Grothe Industrial Coating LLC.............F 281 354-1574
Crosby (G-3732)

Gulf Coast Powdr Gelworks Inc ....E 409 962-1211
Port Arthur (G-17110)

◆ Gull Industries Inc ....E 713 224-2430
Houston (G-10074)

◆ Harris Manufacturing Company ....E 972 262-3524
Mansfield (G-14680)

High Plins Cntrs MGT Group Inc ....E 806 935-5858
Dumas (G-5522)

Houston Powder Coaters LLC ....E 281 676-3888
Houston (G-10245)

Houston Unlimited Metal Proc ....E 979 836-7568
Chappell Hill (G-3046)

Hwm Hurst Inc ....E 817 268-6111
Hurst (G-12845)

Impreglon Surface Tech Inc ....E 713 466-9655
Houston (G-10335)

Industrial Chemicals Corp ....F 940 383-0035
Denton (G-5377)

International Paint LLC ....C 713 684-1500
Houston (G-10404)

Interntnal Glvnzers Partnr Ltd ....E 409 842-0216
Beaumont (G-1910)

Interntnal Glvnzers Partnr Ltd ....E 817 810-0095
Fort Worth (G-6726)

Jar-Tex Industries Inc ....E 817 332-9922
Fort Worth (G-6735)

JRS Company Inc ....D 626 967-2432
Hutto (G-12881)

K-T Galvanizing Co Inc ....E 281 391-9201
Katy (G-13413)

K-T Galvanizing Co Inc ....E 817 477-4434
Venus (G-20220)

Keith Darwin Raines ....F 713 477-8534
Deer Park (G-5281)

Labarge Coating LLC ....D 713 378-7225
Channelview (G-3028)

Labarge Coating LLC ....E 281 457-0200
Channelview (G-3029)

Land Industrial Trial Sevices ....E 281 385-2504
Old River Winfree (G-16218)

LB Foster Ball Winch Inc ....D 936 228-0077
Willis (G-20853)

Lehmberg Enterprises Inc ....F 210 924-6811
San Antonio (G-18244)

Lifelast Inc ....G 512 628-2112
Pflugerville (G-16679)

▼ Liquidmtal Ctngs Solutions LLC ......F 281 359-1283
Spring (G-19141)

Longhorn Powder Coating I ....G 817 759-2224
Haltom City (G-8152)

Marking Systems Inc ....D 972 475-0770
Garland (G-7543)

Meister Industries Inc ....E 432 366-2875
Odessa (G-16078)

Meister Industries Inc ....E 432 425-0293
Odessa (G-16079)

◆ Metal Coatings Corp ....D 713 977-0123
Houston (G-10844)

Metal Processing Intl LP ....E 956 205-0083
Mission (G-15560)

Metalplate Galvanizing LP ....E 713 672-9480
Houston (G-10851)

Metokote Corporation ....E 210 628-1955
San Antonio (G-18294)

Modine Jacksonville Inc ....E 903 589-0009
Jacksonville (G-13251)

Nano Coat LP ....F 281 217-5265
San Antonio (G-18331)

National Oilwell Varco Inc ....E 281 456-8551
Houston (G-10991)

Nci Group Inc ....E 713 921-7997
Houston (G-11018)

ND Industries Inc ....D 817 633-2788
Arlington (G-737)

Nipco Inc ....F 432 362-1936
Odessa (G-16093)

◆ Nov Tuboscope ....F 713 799-5100
Houston (G-11087)

Orbit Industries Inc ....F 806 744-8300
Lubbock (G-14453)

P & M Blasting & Coating Inc ....F 713 896-4691
Houston (G-11212)

Paul Krivoy ....E 361 854-7911
Corpus Christi (G-3589)

◆ Polibrid Coatings Inc ....F 956 831-7818
Brownsville (G-2394)

▲ Polymer Dynamics Inc ....F 281 894-6382
Houston (G-11358)

Powder Finishes Inc ....E 254 968-5601
Stephenville (G-19419)

Praxair Surface Tech Inc ....E 713 849-9474
Houston (G-11384)

Precision Coatings ....F 432 362-7696
Odessa (G-16124)

Prince Manufacturing Corp ....C 915 217-2664
El Paso (G-5918)

Pro-Kleen Inc ....E 713 855-2760
Houston (G-11427)

Prodigy Painting ....E 817 277-2468
Pantego (G-16351)

Protective Powder Coatings LLC ....F 361 854-7911
Corpus Christi (G-3598)

▲ Quality Powder Coating Inc ....G 972 466-0655
Carrollton (G-2801)

▲ Quality Product Finishing Inc ....E 281 469-6970
Houston (G-11499)

Recon Coating Solutions LLC ....F 979 277-8455
Alvord (G-390)

Royalty Metal Finishing Inc ....E 281 208-4455
Houston (G-11686)

Schumacher International Inc ....F 713 923-5548
Houston (G-11784)

Shawcor Pipe Protection LLC ....F 281 485-8321
Pearland (G-16598)

Shawcor Pipe Protection LLC ....E 281 940-0700
Houston (G-11851)

Shawcor Pipe Protection LLC ....F 713 378-7200
Channelview (G-3036)

◆ Shawcor Pipe Protection LLC ....D 281 886-2350
Houston (G-11852)

Son-Lan Industries Inc ....E 972 937-8162
Waxahachie (G-20558)

▼ Southwest Galvanizing Inc ....C 800 799-8413
Houston (G-11980)

Southwest Impreglon R Inc ....E 281 441-2000
Humble (G-12798)

Southwest Spray Inc ....E 972 875-5665
Ennis (G-6118)

Spraymetal Inc ....F 713 923-2000
Houston (G-12023)

Stampcoat Inc ....E 915 591-0346
El Paso (G-5975)

Superior Shot Peening Inc ....E 281 432-0900
Cleveland (G-3138)

▲ Superior Shot Peening Inc ....D 281 449-6559
Houston (G-12119)

▲ T G Industries Inc ....F 281 356-2001
Pinehurst (G-16735)

Taconic Industries Corporation ....E 972 241-5200
Carrollton (G-2823)

▲ Ternium Usa Inc ....C 318 698-7500
Houston (G-12208)

Texas Custom Coaters Inc ....F 936 825-7211
Navasota (G-15743)

Texas Finishing Company ....E 972 416-2961
Houston (G-2830)

Texas Intrnal Pipe Coating LLC ....F 936 348-2508
Madisonville (G-14590)

▲ Texas Nameplate Company Inc ....D 214 428-8341
Lancaster (G-13849)

▲ Texas Powder Coating Inc ....G 713 690-6226
Houston (G-12246)

Texas Refinery Corp ....F 682 518-1405
Mansfield (G-14722)

▲ Thermal Designs Inc ....E 713 433-6003
Houston (G-12269)

Three D Finishing Inc ....F 972 475-2726
Rowlett (G-17713)

Tim Yockey ....F 281 252-6175
Magnolia (G-14630)

Trinity Coatings LLC ....F 281 845-0022
Rosharon (G-17615)

Ttc Trammell Co Inc ....E 713 921-7121
Houston (G-12399)

▲ United Galvanizing Inc ....C 713 466-4161
Houston (G-12448)

US Galvanizing LLC ....B 817 268-6111
Dallas (G-5147)

US Galvanizing LP ....E 817 572-2280
Kennedale (G-13507)

Varco LP ....E 432 367-9726
Odessa (G-16198)

Varco LP ....E 432 337-1570
Odessa (G-16199)

◆ Varco LP ....C 713 799-5272
Houston (G-12534)

W & W Silkscreening Inc ....E 817 590-4479
Fort Worth (G-7112)

Womble Company Inc ....B 713 636-8700
Houston (G-12681)

XCEL Metal Finishing Inc ....F 972 772-4440
Rockwall (G-17572)

3482 Small Arms Ammunition

◆ Aerostar Global Logistics LLC ....E 630 458-8844
Irving (G-12925)

Expansion Industries LLC ....E 888 707-9343
Carrollton (G-2735)

True Velocity Ammunition LLC ....D 972 487-6500
Garland (G-7606)

Wrights Ammunitions LLC ....D 972 257-1111
Irving (G-13209)

3483 Ammunition, Large

Expal USA Inc ....E 903 472-4970
Irving (G-13020)

3484 Small Arms

Advanced Weapons and Armor Inc ......E 830 459-5263
Kerrville (G-13516)

Airtronic Usa LLC ....E 830 980-9788
Spring Branch (G-19265)

Bayou Arms Inc ....E 281 475-4470
Spring (G-19102)

Brace Steel Components LLC ....F 972 272-2016
Garland (G-7450)

Brown Precision Inc ....G 530 384-2506
Cameron (G-2639)

Cactus Weapons Systems Inc ....F 210 858-6703
Del Rio (G-5310)

Chip McCormick Custom LLC ....E 830 798-2863
Bogata (G-2145)

▼ Ddr Manufacturing Inc ....G 469 728-7242
Forney (G-6307)

Dreadnaught Industries ....G 210 601-8149
Von Ormy (G-20347)

Dregon LLC ....F 910 670-8211
El Paso (G-5724)

▲ F-1 Firearms LLC ....E 832 299-6100
Spring (G-19120)

High Standard Manufacturing Co ....F 713 462-4200
Houston (G-10175)

Liberty A&A ....F 213 221-8110
San Antonio (G-18251)

▼ P T Products & Services Inc ....E 512 251-3592
Pflugerville (G-16682)

PLbennett Entp & Inv Fund A ....G 903 405-1940
Trenton (G-20018)

Psd3 Enterprises LLC ....F 830 995-3894
Comfort (G-3240)

Staccato 2011 LLC ....D 512 819-0656
Georgetown (G-7680)

Stillers Prcision Firearms LLC ....F 972 429-5000
Garland (G-7592)

White Wing Weaponry LLC ....F 940 382-0830
Carrollton (G-2897)

3489 Ordnance & Access, NEC

Lewis Engineering Company ....E 903 938-6754
Marshall (G-14787)

Lockheed Martin Corporation ....A 972 603-1000
Grand Prairie (G-7914)

Lonestar Couplings Inc ....F 713 690-1873
Houston (G-10683)

3491 Industrial Valves

▲ AAA Products International Inc ....F 214 357-3851
Dallas (G-3873)

◆ Accumulators Inc ....E 713 465-0202
Houston (G-8460)

Aeon Process Equipment ....D 972 690-8200
Plano (G-16776)

▲ American Valve Hydrant Mfg Co ....F 409 832-7721
Beaumont (G-1852)

American Valve Hydrant Mfg Co ....C 409 832-7721
Beaumont (G-1853)

Apergy Artfl Lift Intl LLC ....D 713 466-3552
Houston (G-8662)

◆ Array Holdings Inc ....E 281 260-8366
Houston (G-8704)

Automatic Switch Company ....A 281 829-2900
Houston (G-8753)

Barkley Holdings LLC ....F 832 413-4400
Kingwood (G-13639)

Bexxt Inc ....F 832 209-7970
Cypress (G-3778)

Employee Codes: A=Over 500 employees, B=251-500
C=101-250, D=51-100, E=20-50, F=10-19, G=9
     2021 Harris Texas
Manufacturers Directory
     1007

S
I
C

◆ Bray International Inc ....C 281 894-7979
Houston *(G-8979)*

Broen Inc ....E 713 300-0480
Conroe *(G-3265)*

▲ Btic America Corporation ....F 713 779-8882
Houston *(G-9003)*

C&C Industries Inc ....F 832 631-2687
Houston *(G-9038)*

▲ Calvary Valve Inc ....F 903 729-0485
Palestine *(G-16297)*

Cameron International Corp ....D 281 582-9500
Houston *(G-9064)*

◆ Cameron International Corp ....E 713 939-2282
Houston *(G-9072)*

Cameron International Corp ....C 713 354-1900
Houston *(G-9068)*

Cfg Industries LLC ....G 281 259-7244
Magnolia *(G-14594)*

▲ Chromatic Industries Inc ....E 936 539-5770
Conroe *(G-3276)*

◆ Circor Energy Products LLC ....C 713 400-2200
Houston *(G-9194)*

Collins Instrument Company ....E 979 849-8266
Angleton *(G-569)*

Control Components Inc ....F 832 467-7200
Houston *(G-9294)*

▲ Cooper Valves LLC ....E 832 409-6050
Pasadena *(G-16414)*

Curtiss-Wright Corporation ....E 713 581-3400
Houston *(G-9361)*

◆ Daniel Measurement & Ctrl LLC ..B 713 827-5033
Houston *(G-9402)*

Doosan Hf Controls Corporation ...E 469 568-6500
Carrollton *(G-2726)*

Downstream Aggregator LLC ....F 281 247-8118
Channelview *(G-3017)*

▲ Drake Controls LLC ....F 713 996-0190
Houston *(G-9515)*

◆ Dresser LLC ....C 262 549-2626
Houston *(G-9517)*

Dresser LLC ....E 361 881-8182
Corpus Christi *(G-3517)*

Dresser LLC ....D 281 884-1000
Deer Park *(G-5271)*

Dresser LLC ....F 979 265-1309
Richwood *(G-17468)*

▲ DSA Operating Company LLC .....E 210 734-5121
San Antonio *(G-18072)*

Emerson Atmtn Sltons Fnal Ctrl ....D 832 261-2400
Pasadena *(G-16424)*

Emerson Atmtn Sltons Fnal Ctrl ....C 956 430-2500
Harlingen *(G-8187)*

◆ Emerson Atmtn Sltons Fnal Ctrl ..B 713 986-4665
Houston *(G-9612)*

Emerson Automation Solutions .....D 832 261-2400
Pasadena *(G-16425)*

Emerson Automation Solutions .....E 281 274-4400
Stafford *(G-19309)*

Emerson Automation Solutions .....G 512 835-2190
Round Rock *(G-17653)*

Emerson Automation Solutions .....B 281 274-4400
Stafford *(G-19310)*

▲ Energy Valve & Supply Co LLC ...F 713 675-7525
Houston *(G-9638)*

◆ Eproduction Solutions LLC ....B 281 348-1000
Kingwood *(G-13641)*

◆ Everest Valve Company Inc ....E 713 923-8696
Houston *(G-9717)*

▲ Fabco Products Inc ....E 903 769-3707
Hawkins *(G-8229)*

Fisher Controls Intl LLC ....B 972 542-5512
McKinney *(G-14943)*

▲ Flotek Industries Inc ....E 713 849-9911
Houston *(G-9806)*

Flowserve Corporation ....C 903 439-3324
Sulphur Springs *(G-19587)*

Flowserve Corporation ....D 713 374-7100
Pasadena *(G-16438)*

Flowserve Corporation ....B 972 443-6500
Irving *(G-13027)*

Flowserve Corporation ....F 800 446-0401
Irving *(G-13028)*

Flowserve Corporation ....E 832 375-0807
Houston *(G-9813)*

▲ Flowserve US Inc ....D 972 443-6500
Irving *(G-13030)*

◆ GE Oil & Gas Pressure Ctrl LP ...D 281 398-8901
Houston *(G-9915)*

Gordon Martin Inc ....F 281 424-1301
Baytown *(G-1820)*

◆ Groth Corporation ....D 913 952-8114
Stafford *(G-19324)*

H & S Valve ....E 432 362-0486
Odessa *(G-16021)*

Hoerbiger Service Inc ....E 281 442-2497
Houston *(G-10191)*

◆ Ies International Energy Svcs ......D 713 928-5311
Houston *(G-10317)*

◆ Jetstream of Houston LLP ....D 832 590-1300
Houston *(G-10471)*

JI Bryan Eqp & Lease Svcs Inc .....E 806 435-4511
Perryton *(G-16638)*

Keiser Manufacturing Inc ....G 830 303-3397
Seguin *(G-18846)*

Kf Valves LLC ....E 713 400-2200
Houston *(G-10527)*

▲ Ladish Valve Company LLC ....E 281 880-8560
Houston *(G-10585)*

▲ M & J Valve Company ....C 281 469-0550
Houston *(G-10713)*

Marathon Special Services Inc ......F 713 784-4918
Houston *(G-10757)*

Master Valve USA Inc ....F 832 838-4999
Katy *(G-13424)*

McC Holdings Inc ....D 936 588-5301
Montgomery *(G-15636)*

◆ McC Holdings Inc ....D 936 271-6500
The Woodlands *(G-19893)*

McWane Inc ....B 800 527-8478
Tyler *(G-20122)*

Microstaq Inc ....E 512 628-2890
Austin *(G-1341)*

Movement Industries Corp ....F 713 849-1300
Houston *(G-10928)*

▲ MSP Drilex Inc ....E 281 377-4393
Tomball *(G-19990)*

National Oilwell Varco LP ....D 806 274-5293
Borger *(G-2180)*

National Wholesale Supply Inc ......E 972 331-7770
Dallas *(G-4716)*

▲ Neway Valve Usa LP ....E 281 969-5500
Stafford *(G-19357)*

Nibco Inc ....B 936 564-8321
Nacogdoches *(G-15706)*

Nigen International LLC ....E 713 956-8022
Houston *(G-11053)*

NSM Inc ....F 281 880-8188
Missouri City *(G-15586)*

Oil States International Inc ....D 713 652-0582
Houston *(G-11161)*

Omc Americas Inc ....E 713 893-7413
Houston *(G-11173)*

▲ Onesubsea LLC ....A 713 939-2282
Houston *(G-11182)*

▲ Pacific Valves ....D 562 426-2531
Spring *(G-19239)*

Pathway Control Products Inc ....F 281 354-3699
New Caney *(G-15845)*

◆ Pbv-Usa Inc ....D 800 231-3530
Stafford *(G-19363)*

▲ Pentair Valves & Controls LLC .....B 713 986-4665
Houston *(G-11286)*

Petnair Valves & Controls ....E 713 986-8468
Houston *(G-11297)*

Pietro Fiorenpini ....F 832 299-6075
Spring *(G-19240)*

Proserv Operations Inc ....B 713 468-8778
Houston *(G-11458)*

Rays Flow Control LLC ....F 832 827-3427
Houston *(G-11554)*

◆ Robbins Myers Enrgy Systems LP ..B 936 890-1064
Willis *(G-20862)*

Roda Deaco Valve Inc ....E 780 465-4429
Houston *(G-11654)*

Rotork Controls Inc ....F 713 353-7887
Houston *(G-11673)*

▲ S H Leggitt Company ....E 956 504-6440
San Marcos *(G-18708)*

Samco Enterprises Inc ....E 281 443-6505
Houston *(G-11737)*

▲ Samson Controls Inc ....E 281 383-3677
Baytown *(G-1800)*

◆ Seaboard International Inc ....D 713 644-3535
Houston *(G-11798)*

▲ Severe Service Valve Inc ....D 832 390-2380
Houston *(G-11841)*

◆ Silverwell Technology Inc ....F 281 389-3020
Houston *(G-11900)*

Sooner Pipe LLC ....E 281 328-4877
Crosby *(G-3743)*

◆ Specialty Valve Group LLC ....E 281 385-8200
Houston *(G-12003)*

Sturrock & Robson USA Svcs Inc ...F 281 907-8928
Flower Mound *(G-6284)*

▲ T-3 Energy Services Inc ....F 713 944-5950
Houston *(G-12143)*

▲ Tapcoenpro LLC ....D 281 247-8100
Channelview *(G-3040)*

Tapcoenpro International Inc ....C 281 247-8100
Channelview *(G-3041)*

Tfw Industrial Sup Cnc Mch LLC ....F 817 898-9140
Dallas *(G-5081)*

▲ Tyco Engineered Pdts & Svcs ......D 609 720-4200
Houston *(G-12418)*

Tyco International MGT Co LLC ......F 713 644-8872
Houston *(G-12419)*

US VT ....E 713 856-9171
Houston *(G-12491)*

Valve Index International Inc ....G 281 712-8246
Missouri City *(G-15598)*

▲ Valves and Control Systems Inc ...F 713 378-0311
South Houston *(G-19054)*

▲ Victaulic-Bermad LLC ....E 713 856-1700
Houston *(G-12565)*

Vogt Valves Inc ....D 346 304-2566
Stafford *(G-19396)*

Watts Water Technologies Inc ....D 713 943-0688
Houston *(G-12606)*

Wnco Valve International Inc ....F 432 362-2136
Odessa *(G-16213)*

▲ Womack Machine Supply Co ....D 800 569-9800
Farmers Branch *(G-6219)*

◆ Xomox Corporation ....C 936 271-6500
The Woodlands *(G-19942)*

3492 Fluid Power Valves & Hose Fittings

▲ AAA Products International Inc .....F 214 357-3851
Dallas *(G-3873)*

Apergy Artfl Lift Intl LLC ....D 713 466-3552
Houston *(G-8662)*

▲ Camozzi Pneumatics Inc ....E 972 548-8885
McKinney *(G-14931)*

▼ D/A Mfg Co Inc ....E 806 995-2316
Tulia *(G-20034)*

Dar International Inc ....F 972 402-0493
Irving *(G-12991)*

Delafield Corporation ....F 903 887-2860
Mabank *(G-14575)*

Direct Prchase Qick Cplngs Inc .....E 281 388-0253
Alvin *(G-360)*

DSM Fluid Power Inc ....E 512 243-1986
Austin *(G-1104)*

◆ Fittings Inc ....D 817 332-3300
Fort Worth *(G-6634)*

▲ Fluid Sealing Products Inc ....D 713 910-1028
Houston *(G-9816)*

◆ George Myer Company Inc ....F 713 928-2606
Houston *(G-9941)*

Ghx Industrial LLC ....E 409 832-3461
Beaumont *(G-1898)*

Globe Products Company Inc ....D 972 875-1660
Ennis *(G-6105)*

Hydraquip Custom Systems Inc .....F 281 822-5000
Houston *(G-10296)*

Hydraulics Inc ....F 817 923-1965
Fort Worth *(G-6711)*

▲ Lastrad LLC ....G 713 589-9477
Houston *(G-10607)*

Mid-West Hose & Specialty ....F 713 472-2900
Pasadena *(G-16484)*

Mid-West Hose & Specialty ....F 214 638-3210
Carrollton *(G-2780)*

▲ Pantex Ennerflo Systems Inc ....E 832 861-7700
Houston *(G-8390)*

Proserv Operations Inc ....B 832 467-3110
Houston *(G-11457)*

Scada Products LLC ....E 888 649-4283
Fort Worth *(G-6975)*

Schlumberger International ....A 713 747-4000
Houston *(G-11766)*

▲ Seal-Jet of Texas Inc ....E 713 983-7233
Houston *(G-11804)*

Shf Inc ....C 832 456-2000
Pasadena *(G-16506)*

Subsea Hydraulic Leads LLC ....G 832 327-4853
Houston *(G-12088)*

▲ Tubular Instrumentat ....C 832 467-3110
Houston *(G-12402)*

Vaughan Investments Inc ....F 956 686-3725
McAllen *(G-14916)*

Warrior G Industries ....F 409 594-5258
Woodville *(G-20919)*

◆ Welker Inc ....D 281 491-2331
Sugar Land *(G-19571)*

▲ Zimmermann & Jansen Inc ....D 281 446-8000
Houston *(G-12730)*

3493 Steel Springs, Except Wire

▲ Baumann Springs Texas Ltd ....E 972 641-7272
Grand Prairie *(G-7840)*

▲ Baumann Springs Usa Inc ....E 972 641-7272
Grand Prairie *(G-7841)*

▲ Coiling Technologies Inc ....D 713 849-4000
Houston *(G-9241)*

Diamond Wire Spring Company ....E 903 581-2358
Tyler *(G-20076)*

Draco Spring Manufacturing Co ....D 713 645-4973
Houston *(G-9512)*

Draco Spring Manufacturing Co ....D 713 645-4973
Houston *(G-9513)*

Heitman Company Inc ....F 713 675-9001
Houston *(G-10148)*

▼ Leeco Precision Spring Mfg Co ....F 713 692-6281
Houston *(G-10618)*

Matthew Warren Inc ....D 800 364-0391
Houston *(G-10797)*

Newcomb Spring Corp ....E 972 241-6781
Dallas *(G-4732)*

Rays Chmpn Spring & Mtr Svc ....E 817 921-3600
Fort Worth *(G-6943)*

Suhm Spring Works Inc ....F 214 330-9111
Dallas *(G-5020)*

Suhm Spring Works Inc ....C 713 224-9293
Houston *(G-12091)*

Turner Manufacturing Co Inc ....F 254 840-2601
Mc Gregor *(G-14826)*

3494 Valves & Pipe Fittings, NEC

▲ AAA Products International Inc ....F 214 357-3851
Dallas *(G-3873)*

Allbright & Associates Inc ....F 432 366-8897
Odessa *(G-15909)*

Ameriforge Group Inc ....E 409 283-8138
Woodville *(G-20914)*

Apergy Artfl Lift Intl LLC ....D 713 466-3552
Houston *(G-8662)*

◆ Azz Inc ....D 817 810-0095
Fort Worth *(G-6414)*

Bay Advanced Technologies LLC ......E 512 929-5400
Austin *(G-979)*

▲ Best Pump and Flow LP ....E 713 690-4511
Fort Worth *(G-6448)*

Boltex Manufacturing Co LP ....D 713 451-2180
Houston *(G-8947)*

Bonney Forge Corporation ....D 713 695-3633
Houston *(G-8950)*

▲ Bonney Forge Texas LP ....E 713 695-3633
Houston *(G-8951)*

Borusan Mannesmann Pipe US Inc ....E 832 399-6000
Baytown *(G-1780)*

Cameo Fabricators Inc ....E 281 449-6207
Houston *(G-9060)*

Cameron International Corp ....D 713 946-2122
Houston *(G-9061)*

▲ Camozzi Pneumatics Inc ....E 972 548-8885
McKinney *(G-14931)*

Cgp Manufacturing Inc ....E 713 641-5544
Houston *(G-9152)*

◆ Coastal Flange Inc ....E 713 937-3333
Jersey Village *(G-13296)*

Consumer Energy Alliance ....F 713 337-8800
Houston *(G-9279)*

▼ Cse W-Industries Inc ....C 713 466-9463
Jersey Village *(G-13297)*

▼ D/A Mfg Co Inc ....E 806 995-2316
Tulia *(G-20034)*

Daniel Industries Inc ....D 713 467-6000
Houston *(G-9401)*

Dlugosch III LLC ....C 361 564-9504
Yorktown *(G-20977)*

Dlugosch III LLC ....F 361 275-9282
Cuero *(G-3759)*

◆ Dresser LLC ....C 262 549-2626
Houston *(G-9517)*

◆ Dynamic Products Inc ....D 281 457-3500
Houston *(G-9550)*

Emergent Machine Svcs Ltd Co ....F 903 876-3679
Frankston *(G-7165)*

◆ Emerson Atmtn Sltons Fnal Ctrl ....B 713 986-4665
Houston *(G-9612)*

Emerson Automation Solutions ....G 512 835-2190
Round Rock *(G-17653)*

Enercon Steam Solutions LLC ....F 214 292-3485
Dallas *(G-4322)*

▲ Federal Flange Inc ....D 713 681-0606
Houston *(G-9768)*

Federal Flange Inc ....C 713 681-0606
Houston *(G-9769)*

Fishing Tool/Crystin Inc ....E 432 366-6504
Odessa *(G-16002)*

▲ Flow-Tek Inc ....D 832 912-2300
Houston *(G-9809)*

Flowserve Corporation ....E 832 375-0807
Houston *(G-9813)*

Flowserve Corporation ....D 972 443-6500
Irving *(G-13027)*

Flowserve Corporation ....F 800 446-0401
Irving *(G-13028)*

◆ Forged Components Inc ....C 281 441-4088
Humble *(G-12767)*

◆ Fujikoki America Inc ....C 214 333-4266
Dallas *(G-4384)*

◆ Future Pipe Industries Inc ....C 281 847-2987
Houston *(G-9879)*

▲ Grayloc Products LLC ....E 713 466-8853
Houston *(G-10021)*

▲ Gs-Hydro US Inc ....E 281 209-1000
Houston *(G-10052)*

▲ Gulf Coast Oil & Gas Inds LLC ....D 713 236-1158
Houston *(G-10061)*

H and L Crimp Inc ....F 325 672-9282
Abilene *(G-45)*

H Lorimer Corporation ....E 903 643-3239
Longview *(G-14245)*

Houston Roll Pipe LLC ....E 713 686-8970
Houston *(G-10249)*

Jcm Industries Inc ....C 903 832-2581
Nash *(G-15722)*

◆ Joy Pipe Usa LP ....F 830 249-7400
Boerne *(G-2125)*

▲ Ladish Valve Company LLC ....D 281 880-8560
Houston *(G-10585)*

▲ Lastrad LLC ....G 713 589-9477
Houston *(G-10607)*

M Fab & Machine ....F 936 264-2388
Conroe *(G-3327)*

Modco Industries Inc ....E 936 539-9222
Conroe *(G-3331)*

Motion Reps Inc ....E 940 565-9411
Denton *(G-5383)*

Mueller Co LLC ....E 956 621-3086
Brownsville *(G-2384)*

National Flange & Fitting Co ....E 713 688-2515
Houston *(G-10968)*

◆ Newco Valves LLC ....D 281 325-0041
Stafford *(G-19359)*

Nibco Inc ....E 574 295-3000
McAllen *(G-14894)*

Nibco Inc ....B 936 564-8321
Nacogdoches *(G-15706)*

▲ Nipples Elbows & Couplings Inc ....E 281 405-8240
Houston *(G-11059)*

Ohmstede Ltd ....E 281 471-4140
La Porte *(G-13780)*

Overhead Door Corporation ....B 361 884-6640
Corpus Christi *(G-3586)*

◆ Pgi International Ltd ....B 713 466-0056
Houston *(G-11316)*

Pipe Pros LLC ....E 432 699-4245
Midland *(G-15358)*

Pipe Pros LLC ....D 903 981-7801
Kilgore *(G-13582)*

Piping Accessories Inc ....E 409 842-5000
Beaumont *(G-1942)*

▲ Piping Technology & Pdts Inc ....F 713 731-0030
Houston *(G-11337)*

◆ Piping Technology & Pdts Inc ....A 800 787-5914
Houston *(G-11338)*

Pj Piping Inc ....F 713 730-3457
Houston *(G-11341)*

▲ Progressive Sales Inc ....E 432 333-6631
Odessa *(G-16127)*

Puffer-Sweiven Holdings Inc ....E 281 470-2000
La Porte *(G-13785)*

▲ Romar/Mec LLC ....F 281 440-1725
Houston *(G-11660)*

Senior Operations LLC ....C 830 629-8080
New Braunfels *(G-15821)*

Senior Operations LLC ....C 830 629-8080
New Braunfels *(G-15822)*

◆ Serampore Inds Private Ltd Inc ....E 713 923-6111
Houston *(G-11833)*

Shf Inc ....C 832 456-2000
Pasadena *(G-16506)*

◆ Sivco Inc ....E 713 466-1100
Houston *(G-11910)*

▼ Sweco Fab Inc ....B 713 731-0030
Houston *(G-12130)*

Ta Chen International Inc ....E 713 672-0177
Houston *(G-12145)*

Tapcoenpro International Inc ....E 281 247-8100
Channelview *(G-3041)*

Tenaris Coiled Tubes LLC ....F 713 460-1500
Houston *(G-12197)*

Texas Pneumatic Systems Inc ....D 817 794-0068
Pantego *(G-16353)*

Texas Pneumatic Systems Inc ....F 817 794-0068
Arlington *(G-792)*

▲ Tmco Inc ....D 713 465-3255
Houston *(G-12308)*

▲ Townsend International Inc ....F 432 381-8750
Odessa *(G-16181)*

United Oilfield Supply LLC ....F 713 489-2000
Houston *(G-12450)*

Universal Outlets Inc ....F 903 983-3261
Kilgore *(G-13600)*

US Bellows Inc ....B 713 731-0030
Houston *(G-12481)*

US Hose Corp ....E 281 458-0400
Houston *(G-12483)*

V I J Corporation ....E 817 838-2020
Fort Worth *(G-7096)*

▲ Valco Instruments Company ....B 713 688-9345
Houston *(G-12517)*

VCM Industries Inc ....D 713 462-7444
Houston *(G-12541)*

Vector Group Inc ....F 713 979-4444
Houston *(G-12542)*

Watts Water Technologies Inc ....D 713 943-0688
Houston *(G-12606)*

Westbrook Sales & Distrg Corp ....C 713 675-6438
Houston *(G-12639)*

▲ Western Valve Inc ....F 806 373-6811
Amarillo *(G-523)*

Western Valve Inc ....F 806 373-6811
Amarillo *(G-524)*

◆ Xomox Corporation ....C 936 271-6500
The Woodlands *(G-19942)*

▲ Zimmermann & Jansen Inc ....D 281 446-8000
Houston *(G-12730)*

3495 Wire Springs

▲ Baumann Springs Texas Ltd ....E 972 641-7272
Grand Prairie *(G-7840)*

▲ Baumann Springs Usa Inc ....E 972 641-7272
Grand Prairie *(G-7841)*

▲ Baumann Sprng Txas Hldings LLC ...E 972 641-7272
Grand Prairie *(G-7842)*

CB Solutions LP ....F 512 267-9596
Lago Vista *(G-13804)*

▲ Coiling Technologies Inc ....D 713 849-4000
Houston *(G-9241)*

Draco Spring Manufacturing Co ....D 713 645-4973
Houston *(G-9512)*

Draco Spring Manufacturing Co ....D 713 645-4973
Houston *(G-9513)*

Exper-Tech Products Company ....F 936 825-3573
Navasota *(G-15734)*

Gifford Spring Co Inc ....F 972 272-5645
Garland *(G-7504)*

Gulf Coast Spring Co Inc ....F 713 461-5092
Houston *(G-10062)*

Hickory Springs Mfg Co ....F 817 831-1785
Fort Worth *(G-6695)*

Katy Spring & Mfg Inc ....E 281 391-1888
Katy *(G-13416)*

▲ Kern-Liebers Texas Inc ....E 956 781-6563
Pharr *(G-16704)*

▼ Leeco Precision Spring Mfg Co ....F 713 692-6281
Houston *(G-10618)*

Leggett & Platt Incorporated ....B 972 875-8401
Ennis *(G-6109)*

Lone Star Indus Corp Texas ....E 915 779-7255
El Paso *(G-5846)*

Newcomb Spring Corp ....E 972 241-6781
Dallas *(G-4732)*

Spring Engineers Houston Ltd ....E 713 690-9488
Houston *(G-12027)*

Suhm Spring Works Inc ....C 713 224-9293
Houston *(G-12091)*

SIC

3496 Misc Fabricated Wire Prdts

Aceros Turia Inc ....E 832 791-5479
The Woodlands *(G-19819)*

◆ **ACS Industries LP** ....D 713 434-0934
Houston *(G-8369)*

All-State Belting LLC ....F 713 433-1272
Houston *(G-8371)*

◆ **American Block Company** ....C 800 572-9087
Houston *(G-8588)*

◆ **Amistco Separation Pdts Inc** ....D 281 331-5956
Houston *(G-8373)*

▼ **Azz - Texas Welded Wire LLC** ...E 817 282-4560
Hurst *(G-12835)*

▲ **Baumann Springs Texas Ltd** .....E 972 641-7272
Grand Prairie *(G-7840)*

▲ **Baumann Springs Usa Inc** ....D 972 641-7272
Grand Prairie *(G-7841)*

▲ **Baumann Sprng Txas Hldings LLC** ..E 972 641-7272
Grand Prairie *(G-7842)*

Blp Settlement Company ....F 713 674-2266
Beaumont *(G-1866)*

Blp Settlement Company ....E 432 332-0381
Odessa *(G-15939)*

◆ **Blp Settlement Company** ....D 713 674-2266
Houston *(G-8916)*

BMC West LLC ....D 325 698-4465
Abilene *(G-18)*

Brec Inc ....F 979 823-4466
Bryan *(G-2460)*

Bridon-American Corporation ......E 713 921-4101
Houston *(G-8984)*

◆ **Bright Coop Inc** ....C 936 564-8378
Nacogdoches *(G-15686)*

◆ **Burly Corp** ....E 817 295-1128
Burleson *(G-2573)*

Buzz Services LLC ....E 817 263-9788
Fort Worth *(G-6480)*

C M C Steel Fabricators Inc ....D 512 282-8820
Buda *(G-2522)*

▲ **Cesar-Scott Inc** ....F 915 543-3212
El Paso *(G-5694)*

Conveyor Aggregate Pdts Corp ....E 214 358-5588
Dallas *(G-4164)*

◆ **CPI Wirecloth & Screens Inc** ......D 281 485-2300
Pearland *(G-16550)*

Custom Safety Products Inc ....F 281 482-8668
Friendswood *(G-7244)*

De La Garza Fence Company ......E 210 674-8302
San Antonio *(G-18044)*

▲ **Dekoron Wire and Cable LLC** ....D 903 572-0657
Mount Pleasant *(G-15650)*

Delta Rigging & Tools Inc ....D 877 889-8833
Hurst *(G-12844)*

◆ **Delta Rigging & Tools Inc** ....C 713 512-1700
Houston *(G-9433)*

◆ **Delta Screen & Filtration LLC** ....D 713 856-0300
Houston *(G-9434)*

▲ **Display Source Alliance LLC** .....C 972 288-7471
Garland *(G-7479)*

Display Surce Design Fctry Ltd ...C 972 288-7471
Mesquite *(G-15039)*

▲ **Dorstener Wire Tech Inc** ....F 281 651-6226
Spring *(G-19111)*

◆ **Eljer Industries Inc** ....E 972 560-2000
Dallas *(G-4311)*

Exper-Tech Products Company ....F 936 825-3573
Navasota *(G-15734)*

▲ **Falcon Fine Wire Wire Pdts Inc** ..D 214 771-3441
Rockwall *(G-17548)*

Hearne Steel Company ....D 979 279-3464
Hearne *(G-8232)*

Hohmann & Barnard Inc ....E 817 625-9781
Fort Worth *(G-6701)*

◆ **Hoover Group Inc** ....E 800 844-8683
Houston *(G-10204)*

▲ **Houston Post Tension Inc** ....D 713 937-6990
Houston *(G-10244)*

◆ **Houston Wire Works Inc** ....F 713 946-2920
Houston *(G-10265)*

Huckaby Enterprises Inc ....F 817 732-5541
Fort Worth *(G-6707)*

Hunter Inc ....E 713 473-9333
Pasadena *(G-16456)*

HWC Wire & Cable Company ......C 713 453-8518
Houston *(G-10293)*

Installer Pro Inc ....E 713 854-3656
Houston *(G-10379)*

Insteel Wire Products Company ...D 936 258-7625
Dayton *(G-5230)*

IPC Fabricators LLC ....D 409 935-8800
Santa Fe *(G-18735)*

▲ **Kaspar Wire Works Inc** ....E 361 594-3327
Shiner *(G-18943)*

Kaspar Wire Works Inc ....A 361 594-3327
Shiner *(G-18944)*

▲ **Keats Southwest Inc** ....E 915 599-2950
El Paso *(G-5827)*

Kennedy Wire Rope & Sling Co ...F 210 527-0555
San Antonio *(G-18223)*

Kennedy Wire Rope & Sling Co ...E 800 392-5510
Houston *(G-10517)*

▲ **Kennedy Wire Rope & Sling Co** ...D 361 289-1444
Corpus Christi *(G-3560)*

Keystone Consolidated Inds ....D 903 893-0191
Sherman *(G-18919)*

▲ **Kirby Midco Inc** ....F 214 688-0444
Dallas *(G-4558)*

Land & Sea Industries LLC ....F 832 622-4216
Spring *(G-19140)*

▲ **Laserweld Inc** ....E 713 333-0804
Katy *(G-13422)*

▲ **Lebus International Inc** ....D 903 758-5521
Longview *(G-14263)*

▼ **Leeco Precision Spring Mfg Co** ...F 713 692-6281
Houston *(G-10618)*

Lift-All Company Inc ....E 281 445-2256
Houston *(G-10638)*

Lone Star Rigging LP ....F 409 842-2263
Beaumont *(G-1920)*

▲ **Master-Halco Inc** ....D 972 714-7300
Dallas *(G-4645)*

McNichols Company ....E 877 884-4653
Garland *(G-7548)*

Merchants Metals Inc ....E 817 293-9641
Fort Worth *(G-6827)*

Merrick Engineering Inc ....C 254 741-6330
Waco *(G-20436)*

Mettle Filtration Products LLC ....E 713 609-9370
Houston *(G-10858)*

▼ **Millsap Waterproofing Inc** ....D 713 956-6677
Houston *(G-10883)*

▲ **Mueller Supply Company Inc** ......C 325 365-3555
Ballinger *(G-1741)*

National Oilwell Varco Inc ....E 936 441-0006
Conroe *(G-3338)*

▼ **National Strand Products LP** ......D 713 455-2888
Houston *(G-11003)*

Newcomb Spring Corp ....E 972 241-6781
Dallas *(G-4732)*

▲ **Pan American Wire Inc** ....F 817 332-6486
Fort Worth *(G-6891)*

Parker Systems Inc ....F 800 262-4891
Houston *(G-11245)*

Pipers Welding Service Inc ....F 940 682-4663
Weatherford *(G-20609)*

▲ **Progressive Sales Inc** ....E 432 333-6631
Odessa *(G-16127)*

◆ **Quality Mat Company** ....C 409 898-1170
Beaumont *(G-1944)*

▲ **Renfro Industries Inc** ....D 972 563-4295
Terrell *(G-19749)*

▲ **Rowe Equipment Inc** ....F 281 255-0555
Hockley *(G-8347)*

▲ **Russell Industries Inc** ....F 713 692-7225
Houston *(G-11698)*

Sorensen Industries Inc ....E 940 365-9999
Crossroads *(G-3750)*

Southern Spring Manufacturing ...F 713 692-7191
Houston *(G-11977)*

◆ **Suncoast Post-Tension Ltd** ....C 281 445-8886
Houston *(G-12100)*

T&V Optimum LLC ....E 512 398-5271
Austin *(G-1554)*

Towsley and Bailey Inc ....G 972 563-5400
Terrell *(G-19753)*

▲ **Trinity Sling Authority Inc** ....F 817 589-2404
Arlington *(G-803)*

Unified Screening & Crushing - ....F 210 946-6900
Schertz *(G-18767)*

Universal Display & Fixs Co ....B 972 221-5157
Lewisville *(G-14100)*

Universal Display and Fix Co ......C 972 221-5157
Flower Mound *(G-6291)*

◆ **US Rubber Corporation** ....E 936 756-1977
Conroe *(G-3380)*

▲ **Verope USA Inc** ....F 832 831-0132
Houston *(G-12553)*

Western Wire Works Inc ....F 817 654-3373
Fort Worth *(G-7141)*

Wire Mesh Sales LLC ....E 706 922-5179
The Woodlands *(G-19821)*

▲ **Wire Sales Inc** ....E 903 892-9473
Sherman *(G-18938)*

Wmc Steel LLC ....E 706 922-5179
Conroe *(G-3386)*

Work Services Corporation ....D 940 766-3207
Wichita Falls *(G-20835)*

▲ **Zimair LP** ....D 817 624-7245
Fort Worth *(G-7160)*

3498 Fabricated Pipe & Pipe Fittings

▲ **AAA Technology and Spc Co Inc** ...E 713 849-3366
Houston *(G-8436)*

Advanced Industries Inc ....E 972 366-9000
Venus *(G-20217)*

▼ **Advanced Piping Products Inc** ....F 713 956-2922
Houston *(G-8490)*

Advanced Welding Services Inc ....F 713 933-2626
Houston *(G-8493)*

▼ **Aluminum Metal Products Inc** ....F 806 745-6026
Lubbock *(G-14360)*

Ameri-Fab LLC ....D 817 458-4262
Weatherford *(G-20575)*

Ameron International Corp ....C 940 569-1471
Burkburnett *(G-2563)*

Anvil International LLC ....E 800 451-4414
Irving *(G-12931)*

APAC International Inc ....D 940 696-2525
Wichita Falls *(G-20738)*

Apex Coil LLC ....E 903 843-4534
Gilmer *(G-7705)*

Asi Piping LLC ....E 409 786-1080
Vidor *(G-20324)*

▲ **Atlas Tubular LLC** ....D 361 387-7505
Robstown *(G-17503)*

Azz Inc ....E 713 225-9340
Crowley *(G-3752)*

Benchmark Manufacturing Inc .....E 903 882-4311
Lindale *(G-14133)*

Berry Gp Inc ....A 361 693-2100
Corpus Christi *(G-3484)*

◆ **Berry Holdings LP** ....A 361 693-2100
Corpus Christi *(G-3485)*

◆ **Boccard Pipe Fabricators Inc** .....B 713 643-0681
Houston *(G-8934)*

Bonney Forge Corporation ....D 713 695-3633
Houston *(G-8950)*

▲ **Builders Best Inc** ....D 903 586-8283
Jacksonville *(G-13230)*

C M C Steel Fabricators Inc ....C 361 575-4561
Victoria *(G-20250)*

Cameo Fabricators Inc ....E 281 449-6207
Houston *(G-9060)*

Carbery Fabricators Company .....F 432 337-5015
Odessa *(G-15955)*

Castronics Inc ....C 308 235-4881
Houston *(G-9098)*

CCB Fabricators Inc ....E 361 387-7900
Robstown *(G-17504)*

Charbonneau Industries Inc ....F 770 664-4319
Houston *(G-9163)*

Chatsworth Products Inc ....C 512 863-7800
Georgetown *(G-7644)*

Chem Fabrication LLC ....D 979 265-6600
Clute *(G-3149)*

▲ **Crown To Ground Supply Inc** .....F 936 588-7457
Magnolia *(G-14599)*

Custom Piping Systems LLC ....E 210 867-6356
San Antonio *(G-18038)*

D&R Pipe Fab Plus Inc ....F 281 375-2401
Brookshire *(G-2315)*

◆ **Daniel Measurement & Ctrl LLC** ...B 713 827-5033
Houston *(G-9402)*

Diamond Fab ....F 936 441-9353
Conroe *(G-3293)*

Diversified Plant Svcs L L C ....D 979 848-8900
Angleton *(G-570)*

◆ **Dynamic Products Inc** ....D 281 457-3500
Houston *(G-9550)*

Echo Maintenance LLC ....C 409 724-0456
Port Arthur *(G-17106)*

Epic Distribution LLC ....F 346 308-6038
Houston *(G-9680)*

◆ **Forged Components Inc** ....C 281 441-4088
Humble *(G-12767)*

Friedman Industries Inc ....D 903 639-2511
Lone Star *(G-14182)*

◆ **Future Pipe Industries Inc** ....C 281 847-2987
Houston *(G-9879)*

G Fabricating LLC ....E 281 421-3100
Crosby (G-3731)

Glt Fabricators Inc ....E 713 670-9700
La Porte (G-13739)

◆ Groth Corporation ....D 913 952-8114
Stafford (G-19324)

Gulf Coast Fabricators Inc ....E 409 866-6721
Beaumont (G-1900)

▲ Gulf Copper & Mfg Corp ....F 409 989-0300
Port Arthur (G-17111)

Haydon Corporation ....F 972 641-6400
Grand Prairie (G-7888)

Houston Elbow & Nipple Co Inc ....F 713 225-2257
Houston (G-10231)

▲ Houston Pipe Benders LLC ....E 281 449-8241
Houston (G-10243)

Houston Roll Pipe LLC ....E 713 686-8970
Houston (G-10249)

Hunting Energy Services Inc ....D 281 821-5577
Houston (G-10281)

▲ Ipsco Tubulars Inc ....D 281 949-1023
Houston (G-10416)

Isco Industries Inc ....E 817 477-2900
Mansfield (G-14683)

▲ ITEX Piping Products LLC ....E 832 604-7900
Houston (G-10431)

◆ J D Rush Corporation ....F 281 558-8004
Houston (G-10438)

J S McKinney Inc ....D 979 849-7283
Angleton (G-574)

Jake Harris & Sons Inc ....F 281 471-0214
La Porte (G-13758)

Jcm Industries Inc ....C 903 832-2581
Nash (G-15722)

▲ Johnson County Pipe Inc ....D 817 783-3444
Alvarado (G-336)

JR Manufacturing LP ....E 713 462-5900
Houston (G-10487)

L B Pipe & Coupling Pdts LLC ....E 832 934-1850
Katy (G-13370)

Labarge Coating LLC ....D 713 378-7225
Channelview (G-3028)

Lincoln Manufacturing Inc ....D 281 357-1541
Magnolia (G-14616)

Lonestar Pipe Fabrication Inc ....E 817 439-5575
Saginaw (G-17749)

M4 Products LLC ....F 972 481-9300
Dallas (G-4623)

Mclp Industrial Entps Corp ....F 832 767-4006
Pearland (G-16581)

Metro-Tex Fabricators Inc ....E 713 473-3900
Houston (G-10857)

Mfs Piping and Indus Svcs LLC ......E 979 472-7658
Sealy (G-18813)

Morsco Supply LLC ....F 903 234-2183
Longview (G-14282)

National Oilwell Varco Inc ....C 936 825-7070
Navasota (G-15739)

▲ Nichirin-Flex USA Inc ....B 915 859-1199
El Paso (G-5896)

▲ Nipples Elbows & Couplings Inc ..E 281 405-8240
Houston (G-11059)

North American Pipe Corp ....D 940 855-4100
Wichita Falls (G-20787)

Northwest Pipe Company ....D 817 847-1402
Saginaw (G-17753)

Ofs International LLC ....B 281 452-3036
Houston (G-11148)

Oil School Services LLC ....G 903 657-7600
Henderson (G-8268)

Peyton Salas & Mendoza LLC ....E 512 784-5875
Houston (G-11313)

▲ Pipeline Seal & Insulator Inc ......D 713 747-6948
Houston (G-11336)

Piping Accessories Inc ....E 409 842-5000
Beaumont (G-1942)

Polk Mechanical Company LLC ....C 972 339-1200
Grand Prairie (G-7947)

◆ Powerseal Pipeline Pdts Corp .....D 940 767-5566
Wichita Falls (G-20796)

Pressure Point Service ....F 713 641-2325
Houston (G-11410)

Primera Fabrication Inc ....F 956 367-8690
Harlingen (G-8197)

Prostar Manufacturing Inc ....F 281 910-0110
Pasadena (G-16499)

Prototype Machine Co ....F 512 282-1590
Manchaca (G-14641)

R & R Oilfield Services Inc ....D 361 289-5892
Corpus Christi (G-3604)

RE Pipe Inc ....D 713 634-0439
Houston (G-11559)

Reconditioned Couplings Inc ....F 832 878-6255
Highlands (G-8314)

Refined Industrial Supply Inc ....E 409 789-1794
League City (G-13978)

◆ Rotary Drilling Tools USA LLC .....E 979 387-3223
Houston (G-11669)

Royco Industries Inc ....G 713 413-9191
Houston (G-11687)

▲ Rti Energy Systems Inc ....E 281 379-4289
Spring (G-19163)

Sentry Supply Inc ....F 409 840-4800
Beaumont (G-1948)

Shaw Acquisition Holdings LLC ......A 337 562-3471
Houston (G-11849)

Shaw Fabricators Inc ....D 713 991-5313
Houston (G-11850)

Southeast Texas Industries Inc .....C 409 792-0084
Bridge City (G-2286)

Southwest Nipple Company Inc ......F 210 333-3720
San Antonio (G-18488)

◆ Star Pipe LLC ....D 281 558-3000
Houston (G-12045)

◆ Star Pipe Products Ltd ....C 281 558-3000
Houston (G-12046)

Star Pipe Usa LLC ....D 620 251-5700
Houston (G-12047)

Storage & Processors Inc ....D 832 360-2800
Houston (G-12072)

Team Fabricators LLC ....D 409 962-0266
Port Arthur (G-17128)

◆ Technip S&W International Inc ....E 281 870-1111
Houston (G-12175)

◆ Tejas Tubular Products Inc ....B 281 822-3400
Houston (G-12188)

▲ Texas Pipe Works Inc ....G 936 825-6571
Longview (G-14318)

Texas Pmw Inc ....D 713 679-7900
Houston (G-12245)

Texas Steel Conversion Inc ....C 832 230-8228
Houston (G-12253)

Texas Steel Conversion Inc ....E 281 452-2260
Houston (G-12254)

Texas Steel Conversion Inc ....E 281 459-2905
Houston (G-12255)

◆ Thermacor Process Inc ....D 817 847-7300
Fort Worth (G-7054)

Titanium Fabrication Corp ....F 832 375-1800
Houston (G-12300)

Tpg Pressure Inc ....C 972 262-3600
Grand Prairie (G-7984)

Trey Industries Inc ....C 409 948-8891
Texas City (G-19804)

▼ Tube Products Inc ....F 817 489-2264
Aurora (G-855)

▼ Tubular Prfrting Mfr of Conroe ...E 936 441-8660
Conroe (G-3374)

Tubular Solutions Inc ....F 713 391-8005
Houston (G-12406)

Turner Industries Group LLC ....A 903 782-9379
Paris (G-16372)

TW Stamping & Tool Inc ....E 903 877-2353
Tyler (G-20166)

Tyco Simplexgrinnell ....B 903 759-4417
Houston (G-12420)

U S Weatherford L P ....C 281 348-1090
Kingwood (G-13656)

U S Weatherford L P ....F 817 249-7200
Benbrook (G-2047)

▲ Unisert Multi Wall Systems Inc ...E 936 441-7722
Conroe (G-3378)

Universal Outlets Inc ....F 903 983-3261
Kilgore (G-13600)

US Bellows Inc ....B 713 731-0030
Houston (G-12481)

US Composite Pipe Inc ....E 817 783-3444
Alvarado (G-348)

US Pipe Fabrication ....F 817 232-5858
San Antonio (G-18581)

Valley Farm Service Inc ....F 806 364-6900
Hereford (G-8296)

◆ Vam Usa LLC ....C 281 821-5510
Houston (G-12525)

▲ Vinson Process Controls Co LP ...D 972 459-8200
Lewisville (G-14106)

▼ Wachs Subsea LLC ....E 713 983-0784
Houston (G-12591)

Weatherford International LLC ....E 210 621-2156
Elmendorf (G-6075)

Welding Outlets Inc ....D 281 590-0190
Houston (G-12630)

3499 Fabricated Metal Prdts, NEC

Acero Fab Inc ....F 956 584-1166
Mission (G-15548)

Advanced Industrial Metal Fabr ....F 940 964-2691
Forestburg (G-6299)

▲ Advantage Interests Inc ....D 713 983-7253
Houston (G-8494)

Airline Mortuary Associates ....G 281 540-4141
Humble (G-12744)

Amphion Inc ....F 210 771-8116
San Antonio (G-17906)

▲ Applied Services Corporation .....F 972 432-6509
Dallas (G-3954)

Aquamarine Power Usa LLC ....F 972 606-2912
Grand Prairie (G-7833)

▲ Arne Distributors Inc ....F 713 869-8321
Houston (G-8700)

Assa Abloy Door Group LLC ....F 713 466-6790
Houston (G-8724)

B G Metals Inc ....E 210 648-5071
San Antonio (G-17930)

B&B Roadway SEC Solutions LLC ...F 972 385-7899
Mckinney (G-14924)

▲ Bandy Incorporated ....F 972 276-6516
Garland (G-7448)

BCAD Zion Corporation ....D 210 657-9090
New Braunfels (G-15775)

Benchmark Completions LLC ....E 281 537-8483
Spring (G-19200)

Beyond Creations LLC ....F 956 972-1903
McAllen (G-14844)

Bhl International Inc ....E 281 449-5762
Houston (G-8874)

Brownsville Sheet Metal Works .....E 956 546-4517
Brownsville (G-2340)

Bubbaco ....F 972 768-0282
Terrell (G-19729)

Buyers Barricades Inc ....F 817 535-3939
Grapevine (G-8016)

C Bar Contractors I Ltd ....F 409 925-5757
Hitchcock (G-8334)

Cerda-Fied Specialists Inc ....F 281 392-8063
Brookshire (G-2313)

▲ Charles W Weaver Mfg Co Inc ....B 972 539-1537
Flower Mound (G-6263)

Classic Picture Company Inc ....F 972 225-7590
Hutchins (G-12864)

▲ Claytex Trophies Inc ....C 940 538-6521
Henrietta (G-8279)

Complete Tchncal Rprsnttion In .....E 972 621-1111
Carrollton (G-2718)

Cowtown Traffic Control Inc ....G 817 924-4524
Fort Worth (G-6553)

▲ Dallas Lite and Barricade Inc .....E 214 748-5791
Dallas (G-4218)

◆ Daniel Measurement & Ctrl LLC ...B 713 827-5033
Houston (G-9402)

▲ Defiant Safe Co Inc ....E 972 243-3711
Dallas (G-4248)

Demco Manufacturing Inc ....E 936 829-4771
Diboll (G-5462)

Doiy LLC ....F 469 513-4159
Dallas (G-4270)

Double Barrel Fabrication Inc ....F 512 496-7448
San Angelo (G-17796)

Dyna Group International Inc ....D 830 620-4400
New Braunfels (G-15788)

East Creek Corporation ....E 903 527-5190
Caddo Mills (G-2623)

Emissions & Silencer Tech Inc ....F 281 259-9979
Pinehurst (G-16734)

◆ Ferrell-Ross Roll Mfg Inc ....D 806 364-9051
Hereford (G-8288)

Fleming & Son Corporation ....E 972 263-1713
Grand Prairie (G-7873)

Form and Fiber Inc ....F 888 314-8852
Gun Barrel City (G-8114)

Fullers Alamo Safe & Lock ....G 210 344-4523
San Antonio (G-18130)

◆ G2 Automated Technologies LLC ...F 972 479-0699
Dallas (G-4390)

▲ Gibraltar Global LLC ....F 512 715-9650
Marble Falls (G-14743)

◆ Great American Products Ltd ......C 830 620-4400
New Braunfels (G-15797)

Heitman Company Inc ....F 713 675-9001
Houston (G-10148)

S I C

Highway Barricades & Svcs LLC......D......361 883-6300
　Corpus Christi (G-3548)

▲ Hollon Safe Company LLC......F......888 455-2337
　Corpus Christi (G-3550)

Indo-Mim Inc......C......609 580-9745
　San Antonio (G-18181)

Innovative Machine & Laser LLC......E......214 330-1141
　Dallas (G-4502)

Isaiah 49 16 Inc......F......713 896-1765
　Houston (G-10424)

ITW Bldng Cmponents Group Inc......E......972 660-4422
　Grand Prairie (G-7897)

Jerryco Mch & Boiler Works LP......D......713 224-7900
　Houston (G-10466)

Karlee Integration Facility......E......972 543-3175
　Garland (G-7530)

Larson-Juhl US LLC......E......713 895-0296
　Houston (G-10602)

Lewis Engineering Company......E......903 938-6754
　Marshall (G-14787)

Mabco Equipment Ltd......E......817 599-7335
　Weatherford (G-20602)

Material Control Inc......D......817 695-1400
　Arlington (G-729)

Montes Machine Works LLC......F......346 320-4960
　South Houston (G-19051)

Nailhead Spur Company Inc......F......512 588-6112
　Burnet (G-2613)

P W Platforms Inc......F......713 731-7155
　Houston (G-11214)

Portable Pipe Hangers Inc......E......713 672-5088
　Houston (G-11366)

Ra-Lock Security Solutions Inc......E......972 775-6301
　Midlothian (G-15493)

Reel-Logix LLC......E......713 369-3139
　Houston (G-11581)

Rising S Company LLC......E......214 455-0560
　Murchison (G-15682)

SA Quality Fence Ltd......D......210 545-6767
　San Antonio (G-18440)

Scientific Machine & Wldg Inc......E......512 926-8400
　Austin (G-1490)

Seabreeze Culvert......F......409 296-4675
　Winnie (G-20891)

Spraying Systems Co......E......903 535-5036
　Tyler (G-20155)

◆ Taprite Inc......E......210 523-0800
　San Antonio (G-18522)

Team Fabricators LLC......D......409 962-0266
　Port Arthur (G-17128)

Theriot Inc......E......979 233-6391
　Freeport (G-7215)

▲ Tidel Engineering LP......C......972 484-3358
　Carrollton (G-2834)

Trade-Mark Industrial LLC......D......519 650-7444
　San Antonio (G-18558)

Tropar Manufacturing Co Inc......F......972 875-5831
　Ennis (G-6121)

▲ Tsgc Inc......C......361 289-0901
　Corpus Christi (G-3644)

Two Hills Studio Inc......E......512 707-7571
　Austin (G-1602)

Unlimited Stone LLC......E......903 297-0829
　Longview (G-14328)

Vixen Creations Inc......G......512 928-4933
　Austin (G-1642)

Werner Co......E......915 851-4933
　Socorro (G-19020)

Win-Holt Equipment Corp......C......972 641-4658
　Grand Prairie (G-7995)

35 INDUSTRIAL AND COMMERCIAL MACHINERY AND COMPUTER EQUIPMENT

3511 Steam, Gas & Hydraulic Turbines & Engines

A&C Green Energy Inc......G......972 516-0692
　Garland (G-7423)

ABB Enterprise Software Inc......F......281 930-8383
　Deer Park (G-5259)

Airway Services Inc......C......325 617-5813
　San Angelo (G-17772)

Babcock & Wilcox Company......F......281 405-6800
　Houston (G-8784)

▲ Btec Turbines LP......D......281 864-9122
　Houston (G-9002)

Cameron International Corp......C......713 354-1900
　Houston (G-9068)

Caterpillar Inc......A......309 675-1000
　Waco (G-20377)

Continental Turbine Services......F......281 541-6060
　Houston (G-9290)

Cor Thermotics LLC......F......832 308-5151
　Houston (G-9311)

▲ Dewind Co......E......469 420-9886
　Irving (G-12997)

▲ Dresser-Rand Group Inc......C......713 354-6100
　Houston (G-9522)

Dresser-Rand LLC......F......713 467-2221
　Houston (G-9523)

Eaton Corporation......F......956 283-1468
　McAllen (G-14854)

Eaton Corporation......F......956 843-3450
　Hidalgo (G-8306)

Endiprev USA Inc......E......214 897-5740
　Flower Mound (G-6265)

Ethos Energy LP......C......713 336-1300
　Houston (G-9704)

Ethosenergy (usa) LLC......E......713 812-2300
　Houston (G-9705)

Ethosenergy Field Services LLC......F......713 849-8835
　Houston (G-9706)

▲ Ethosenergy Light Turbines LLC......D......713 849-8800
　Houston (G-9707)

Ethosenergy Tc Inc......E......713 336-1300
　Houston (G-9708)

GE Energy Manufacturing Inc......D......281 864-2669
　Houston (G-9914)

◆ GE Packaged Power LLC......C......713 803-0900
　Houston (G-9917)

▼ GE Packaged Power LP......E......281 452-3610
　Houston (G-9918)

General Electric Company......D......214 902-6600
　Dallas (G-4399)

General Electric Company......B......713 803-0437
　Houston (G-9923)

General Electric Company......B......281 812-0634
　Humble (G-12769)

General Electric Company......G......325 794-5100
　Abilene (G-43)

General Electric Company......E......281 921-2850
　Houston (G-9922)

HMC Capital Inc......G......936 441-2666
　The Woodlands (G-19872)

◆ Houston Grinding & Mfg Co......D......713 869-3573
　Houston (G-10235)

Hpi LLC......F......713 457-7500
　Houston (G-10272)

◆ Hydraulic Systems Inc......E......832 791-5000
　The Woodlands (G-19881)

Immi Turbines Inc......F......936 788-2229
　Conroe (G-3310)

Jvm Mechanical Inc......E......713 910-3839
　Houston (G-10492)

Katch Filters LLC......E......713 425-7400
　Houston (G-10501)

▲ Kawasaki Gas Turbines-Americas......F......281 970-3255
　Houston (G-10502)

Mitsubshi Hvy Inds Cmprsr Intl......C......713 652-0300
　Houston (G-10892)

Nexgen - Advnced Fuel Systems......E......281 789-2000
　Houston (G-11046)

▼ Oliver Equipment Company LLC......E......713 856-9206
　Houston (G-11171)

Pal-Con LLC......E......254 968-3335
　Stephenville (G-19418)

▲ Pantex Ennerflo Systems Inc......E......832 861-7700
　Houston (G-8390)

◆ Power Process Developments Inc......F......713 926-5840
　Houston (G-11378)

◆ Preco Turbine Comprsr Svcs Inc......C......281 821-9620
　Houston (G-11397)

Revak Keene Turbomachinery LP......D......281 427-8800
　La Porte (G-13787)

Riva Services LLC......D......713 675-2525
　Houston (G-11627)

Roma Steam Bath Inc......E......281 578-9945
　Houston (G-11659)

◆ Rwg (repair Overhauls USA Inc......D......713 538-9700
　Houston (G-11704)

Safran Power Units Dallas Inc......F......972 606-7681
　Grand Prairie (G-7970)

Siemens Energy Inc......E......281 328-3777
　Houston (G-11878)

Siemens Energy Inc......F......972 929-5044
　Irving (G-13177)

Solar Turbines Incorporated......B......972 228-5500
　Desoto (G-5442)

Solar Turbines Incorporated......B......903 880-1461
　Mabank (G-14582)

Solar Turbines Incorporated......B......713 895-2300
　Houston (G-11935)

Solar Turbines Incorporated......B......281 860-6703
　Channelview (G-3038)

Solar Turbines Incorporated......D......800 851-6594
　Midland (G-15414)

Solar Turbines Incorporated......F......903 880-1200
　Mabank (G-14583)

◆ Tesco Corporation (us)......D......713 359-7000
　Houston (G-12212)

◆ Transcanada Turbines Inc......E......281 880-2900
　Houston (G-12347)

▲ Turbine Resources Inc......E......817 540-0249
　Euless (G-6163)

Wind Energy Turbine Services......D......325 235-1555
　Sweetwater (G-19639)

3519 Internal Combustion Engines, NEC

◆ American Air Liquide Inc......E......877 855-9533
　Houston (G-8582)

Atlas Radiator Inc......E......361 882-5661
　Corpus Christi (G-3477)

Cameron International Corp......C......713 354-1900
　Houston (G-9068)

Caterpillar Inc......A......309 675-1000
　Waco (G-20377)

Clearvlue Combustn Systems Inc......F......281 261-9543
　Missouri City (G-15578)

Cummins - Allison Corp......F......972 661-5390
　Dallas (G-4192)

Cummins Diesel Fuel Inc......C......915 858-7310
　El Paso (G-5706)

Cummins Inc......F......915 858-7310
　El Paso (G-5708)

Cummins Inc......E......915 791-6600
　El Paso (G-5707)

Cummins Jrez Emission Solution......D......844 401-0221
　El Paso (G-5709)

Cummins Southern Plains LLC......E......806 373-3793
　Amarillo (G-419)

Cummins Southern Plains LLC......E......817 624-2107
　Fort Worth (G-6566)

Cummins Southern Plains LLC......F......432 332-9121
　Odessa (G-15973)

Cummins Southern Plains LLC......E......512 389-2276
　Austin (G-1077)

◆ Cummins Southern Plains LLC......D......817 640-6801
　Arlington (G-653)

Cummins Southern Plains LLC......C......713 679-2220
　Houston (G-9358)

Enduro Products Inc......E......817 704-7346
　Arlington (G-670)

Engine Service Inc......E......713 473-4167
　South Houston (G-19038)

Fairbanks Morse LLC......E......713 896-9455
　Houston (G-9751)

Harbor Engine & Grinding Inc......F......361 882-1571
　Corpus Christi (G-3545)

John H Sorola Inc......F......210 224-8597
　San Antonio (G-18204)

Man Energy Solutions USA Inc......F......713 780-4200
　Brookshire (G-2320)

◆ Natural Gas Vehicles Texas Inc......F......214 630-1000
　Dallas (G-4717)

Nickens Brothers Racing Engs......F......936 441-1131
　Conroe (G-3342)

Pratt Whtney Line Mint Svcs In......G......972 894-0139
　Dallas (G-4817)

Quaint Slutions Trdg Ltd Lblty......F......832 758-3074
　Rosenberg (G-17597)

▲ Quality Trbchrgr Cmpnents LLC......E......713 849-4200
　Houston (G-11502)

Stewart Stevenson Pwr Pdts LLC......C......504 347-4326
　Houston (G-12064)

Texas Environmental Tech LLC......G......817 534-4275
　Fort Worth (G-7047)

◆ Tom Daenen Inc......E......409 978-2132
　Hitchcock (G-8340)

◆ Winnsboro Spclty Prts Intl Inc......E......903 342-3551
　Winnsboro (G-20902)

3523 Farm Machinery & Eqpt

▼ Aermotor Company......E......325 651-4951
　San Angelo (G-17771)

◆ Agpro Inc......E......903 785-5531
　Reno (G-17251)

▲ Alamo Group (tx) Inc...............B...... 800 882-5762
Seguin (G-18822)

Alamo Sales Corp...............D...... 800 882-5762
Seguin (G-18823)

All Seasons Feeders Inc...............E...... 210 648-0979
San Antonio (G-17892)

▼ Aluminum Metal Products Inc...............F...... 806 745-6026
Lubbock (G-14360)

Alvarez & Marsal Inc...............C...... 212 759-4433
Houston (G-8575)

American West Windmill Co...............F...... 806 373-0478
Amarillo (G-399)

Aspire Food Group Usa Inc...............E...... 512 645-0700
Austin (G-941)

Atlas Metal Works Inc...............F...... 214 741-4788
Dallas (G-3982)

▲ Belltec Industries Inc...............F...... 254 939-9404
Belton (G-2020)

Big Country Livestock Eqp...............E...... 254 643-1119
Rising Star (G-17478)

▲ Bigham Brothers Inc...............D...... 806 745-0384
Lubbock (G-14373)

Bowie Industries Incorporated...............E...... 940 872-1106
Bowie (G-2192)

Boyd AG LLC...............F...... 512 863-2589
Georgetown (G-7642)

Boyd Industries Inc...............E...... 940 433-2315
Boyd (G-2203)

Brec Inc...............F...... 979 823-4466
Bryan (G-2460)

Brookside Equipment Sales Inc...............F...... 281 391-2165
Katy (G-13353)

C Diamond F Inc...............E...... 903 842-3107
Troup (G-20022)

Compliant Power Systems LLC...............F...... 903 427-0071
Clarksville (G-3072)

▲ Consolidated Cotton Gin Co...............D...... 806 745-1191
Lubbock (G-14396)

County Barn Precinct 4...............F...... 936 258-5202
Dayton (G-5224)

▼ Dalhart R & R Mch Works Inc...............E...... 806 244-5686
Dalhart (G-3834)

▲ Dasilveira Southwest Inc...............E...... 936 349-1900
Madisonville (G-14586)

▲ Delta Technology Corporation...............E...... 713 464-7407
Houston (G-9436)

▼ Denny Kincer Inc...............E...... 806 762-1069
Lubbock (G-14401)

Dugan Trailer...............F...... 254 729-3253
Groesbeck (G-8107)

▲ Eieio Inc...............E...... 512 342-8044
Pflugerville (G-16668)

◆ Flowtronex Psi LLC...............C...... 469 221-1200
Dallas (G-4372)

Foster Farm & Equipment Supply...............F...... 281 256-6900
Hockley (G-8345)

Gicon Pumps & Equipment Ltd...............G...... 806 373-0478
Amarillo (G-428)

H & H Landscape Services LLC...............F...... 832 831-9133
Hockley (G-8346)

Harris Fabrication LLC...............F...... 361 547-6910
Mathis (G-14817)

Hayes & Stolz Indus Mfg Co LLC...............E...... 817 926-3391
Burleson (G-2581)

▲ Hcr Electronics Inc...............E...... 512 756-8164
Burnet (G-2610)

Heritage Equipment Company Inc...............D...... 806 745-4451
Wolfforth (G-20908)

J&J Weaver Co...............E...... 254 756-2139
Waco (G-20419)

◆ K and M Manufacturing Co Inc...............E...... 512 352-2588
Taylor (G-19659)

Knox Jr Leighton...............E...... 806 327-5420
Tahoka (G-19641)

Lee Products Inc...............F...... 817 641-9893
Cleburne (G-3100)

▲ Leeagra Inc...............E...... 800 825-3446
Lubbock (G-14435)

Lone Star Livestock Eqp Co Inc...............F...... 281 399-3550
New Caney (G-15844)

▲ Manitou North America Inc...............D...... 254 799-0232
Waco (G-20429)

Module Truck Systems Inc...............E...... 806 783-0777
Lubbock (G-14448)

Montoya Building Services Inc...............E...... 713 367-0231
Houston (G-10915)

Olton Welding & Machine Inc...............F...... 806 285-3006
Olton (G-16227)

Pearsons Inc...............E...... 308 645-2231
Vernon (G-20229)

Pelican Industrial Inc...............E...... 832 678-4808
Houston (G-11272)

Perryton Feeders LLC...............E...... 806 435-5466
Perryton (G-16644)

◆ Pierce Arrow Inc...............F...... 940 538-5643
Henrietta (G-8282)

▲ Pierce Corporation...............E...... 541 998-0300
San Antonio (G-18375)

◆ Pilot Plastics LLC...............G...... 800 918-6765
Fort Worth (G-6907)

◆ Priefert Mfg Co Inc...............A...... 903 572-1741
Mount Pleasant (G-15660)

Pyranha Inc...............F...... 832 467-3840
Houston (G-11480)

◆ Raider Manufacturing Ltd...............D...... 806 762-3227
Lubbock (G-14470)

Ranews Texas Incorporated...............E...... 770 229-5090
Seguin (G-18859)

▲ Riley-Built Inc...............G...... 806 798-9684
Lubbock (G-14472)

▼ Roadclipper Enterprises Inc...............D...... 903 572-2834
Mount Pleasant (G-15662)

▲ Roll-A-Cone Mfg Distrg Co Ltd...............E...... 806 668-4722
Tulia (G-20037)

Sam Stevens Inc...............E...... 806 872-8365
Lamesa (G-13829)

Schwarze Industries Inc...............F...... 830 379-1480
Seguin (G-18862)

Southern Nut N Tree Equipment...............E...... 325 938-5460
Goldthwaite (G-7745)

Steel Metal Dairy Inc...............E...... 903 866-2536
Como (G-3250)

◆ Sweeney Enterprises Inc...............G...... 830 537-4631
Boerne (G-2138)

T & S Manufacturing Inc...............F...... 940 342-2005
Jermyn (G-13290)

Techsys Chassis Inc...............E...... 903 395-4155
Paris (G-16371)

◆ Telsco Industries Inc...............G...... 972 278-6131
Garland (G-7597)

Texas High Roller Inc...............E...... 979 778-7460
Bryan (G-2511)

Texas Incinerator Co Inc...............F...... 432 687-5045
Midland (G-15436)

Texas Industrial Remcor Inc...............F...... 254 982-4236
Little River Academy (G-14143)

Toro Company...............C...... 915 231-7200
El Paso (G-6008)

Toro Company...............D...... 325 673-8762
Abilene (G-89)

Travis Scott...............F...... 254 829-0651
Ross (G-17617)

▲ Trench-Tech Ltd...............F...... 817 491-0621
Roanoke (G-17496)

Triangle Resources Inc...............E...... 409 861-2267
Beaumont (G-1963)

Valley Farm Service Inc...............F...... 806 364-6900
Hereford (G-8296)

W & R Industrial Services Inc...............F...... 806 637-8204
Brownfield (G-2332)

West Texas Lee Co Inc...............E...... 800 825-3346
Lubbock (G-14510)

Wildcat Manufacturing Inc...............E...... 806 327-5602
Tahoka (G-19642)

William L Bonnell Company Inc...............B...... 409 543-0600
El Campo (G-5629)

Wylie & Son Inc...............D...... 806 667-3566
Petersburg (G-16652)

Wylie & Son Inc...............F...... 325 695-0000
Abilene (G-95)

3524 Garden, Lawn Tractors & Eqpt

American Maintenance Sups LLC...............F...... 281 304-8369
Cypress (G-3771)

Gorman Outdoor Inc...............F...... 806 832-0159
Shallowater (G-18890)

▲ Manitou North America Inc...............D...... 254 799-0232
Waco (G-20429)

Miller Power Equipment Co LLC...............G...... 903 592-7201
Tyler (G-20130)

▼ Mistaway Systems Inc...............E...... 713 468-6464
Houston (G-10890)

Pro-Steel Inc...............E...... 817 572-4959
Fort Worth (G-6919)

Six & Mango Equipment LLP...............E...... 972 335-2731
Frisco (G-7312)

Toro Company...............D...... 325 673-8762
Abilene (G-89)

Wheel-A-Rama Inc...............G...... 325 655-7373
San Angelo (G-17840)

3531 Construction Machinery & Eqpt

3ps Inc...............D...... 512 610-5200
Cedar Park (G-2958)

A Trace Matic Corporation...............E...... 713 538-1370
Houston (G-8428)

Altec Industries Inc...............F...... 713 336-6230
Houston (G-8568)

Altec Industries Inc...............F...... 972 937-8284
Waxahachie (G-20526)

▼ Amber/Booth Inc...............D...... 713 466-0003
Houston (G-8577)

◆ Ammann America Inc...............D...... 253 266-4023
Houston (G-8625)

Apergy Artfl Lift Intl LLC...............F...... 281 602-2176
Spring (G-19196)

Associated Supply Company Inc...............E...... 512 272-8922
Manor (G-14643)

Baldwin Metals Company Inc...............E...... 214 637-1030
Dallas (G-4000)

▲ Belltec Industries Inc...............F...... 254 939-9404
Belton (G-2020)

Cameron International Corp...............A...... 601 629-3300
Houston (G-9066)

Carey Crutcher Inc...............E...... 281 346-0045
Fulshear (G-7328)

Caterpillar Global Min Eqp LLC...............D...... 903 786-2981
Denison (G-5336)

Caterpillar Inc...............B...... 713 895-2316
Houston (G-9100)

Caterpillar Inc...............B...... 254 752-3456
Waco (G-20376)

Caterpillar Inc...............E...... 361 580-5600
Victoria (G-20252)

Caterpillar Inc...............E...... 713 895-2300
Houston (G-9101)

Caterpillar Inc...............A...... 309 675-1000
Waco (G-20377)

▲ Caterpllar Globl Min Mxico LLC...............F...... 224 551-4000
Del Rio (G-5311)

Cherry Construction Systems...............E...... 903 675-5901
Athens (G-822)

Christian Fort Bend Academy...............E...... 281 980-3724
Sugar Land (G-19456)

Clarendon Mfg & Distrg Co Inc...............F...... 806 874-3584
Clarendon (G-3070)

▲ Coastal Hydraulic Cranes Inc...............F...... 281 448-8998
Spring (G-19106)

Conner Machine and Welding Inc...............C...... 806 274-2281
Borger (G-2171)

Construction Eqp Mfg Co Inc...............E...... 940 257-6215
Olney (G-16220)

▲ CRC-Evans Intl Holdings Inc...............E...... 832 249-3100
Houston (G-9336)

▲ CRC-Evans Pipeline Intl Inc...............C...... 800 664-9224
Houston (G-9337)

Crocker Crane Rentals LP...............E...... 512 258-1323
Leander (G-13985)

◆ D and H Equipment Ltd...............E...... 830 833-5366
Blanco (G-2110)

▲ Dallas Lite and Barricade Inc...............E...... 214 748-5791
Dallas (G-4218)

Dealers Truck Equipment Co Inc...............F...... 512 312-2100
Buda (G-2527)

Deep Down Inc...............D...... 281 517-5000
Houston (G-9420)

▲ Domatex Inc...............D...... 281 219-1800
Houston (G-9493)

◆ Dynacon Inc...............F...... 979 823-2690
Bryan (G-2470)

Elizondo Enterprises Inc...............G...... 956 831-7174
Brownsville (G-2353)

Epcs Environmental LLC...............F...... 817 975-5790
Arlington (G-672)

Essentium Inc...............E...... 210 616-1931
Pflugerville (G-16670)

◆ Excel Machinery Ltd...............F...... 806 335-1553
Amarillo (G-486)

Faber Cnk...............F...... 832 831-7222
Houston (G-9748)

Famco Logistics Inc...............F...... 915 307-2536
El Paso (G-5763)

▲ Favelle Favco Cranes Usa Inc...............D...... 956 428-7488
Harlingen (G-8188)

Fenton Environmental Tech Inc...............F...... 800 521-1708
Brownwood (G-2428)

Fordyce Ltd...............F...... 956 581-0672
Palmview (G-16310)

Forestry Supply Service Inc...............F...... 936 632-3394
Lufkin (G-14528)

S
I
C

Forestry Supply Service Inc ....F 409 384-3213	Psp Industries Inc ....F 210 651-9595	Bersal Energy LLC ....F 956 270-1155
Jasper *(G-13276)*	Schertz *(G-18760)*	McAllen *(G-14841)*
Frontier Tubular Solutions LLC ....E 903 236-2100	▲ Ram Winch and Hoist Ltd ....E 281 999-8665	◆ Cameron Rig Solutions LLC ....D 832 782-6500
Marshall *(G-14778)*	Houston *(G-11536)*	Houston *(G-9076)*
Gcc Permian LLC ....D 432 385-2800	Raybar Services LLC ....F 409 698-2548	Caprock Oil Tools Inc ....E 281 485-4777
Odessa *(G-16012)*	Brookeland *(G-2308)*	Pearland *(G-16542)*
Global Crane Sales ....F 832 364-8301	Reeves Roofing Equipment Co ....E 210 695-3567	Caterpillar Global Min Eqp LLC ....D 903 786-2981
Houston *(G-9970)*	Weatherford *(G-20616)*	Denison *(G-5336)*
Goodcrane Corporation ....D 713 434-3322	◆ Reliance Industries Inc ....E 281 499-9926	▲ Command Tubular Products LLC ....B 281 572-3900
Houston *(G-9997)*	Missouri City *(G-15587)*	New Caney *(G-15836)*
H D Industries Inc ....E 903 586-6126	Reynolds Scrapers LLC ....E 830 303-0794	◆ Current Power Solutions Inc ....D 281 943-7700
Jacksonville *(G-13242)*	Seguin *(G-18861)*	Houston *(G-9359)*
▲ Halfen Usa Inc ....E 210 945-1399	▼ River City Manufacturing Inc ....F 512 335-5194	Db Bits LLC ....G 936 539-4948
Converse *(G-3394)*	Bertram *(G-2053)*	Conroe *(G-3289)*
Hanson Aggregates LLC ....E 979 758-3662	▲ Rki Inc ....B 713 688-4414	Derrick Corporation ....E 281 590-3003
Garwood *(G-7614)*	Houston *(G-11634)*	Houston *(G-9440)*
◆ Hensley Industries Inc ....B 972 241-2321	Roadway Specialties Inc ....D 512 280-6666	◆ DK Drill I Management Co LLC ....E 817 539-2500
Dallas *(G-4450)*	Austin *(G-866)*	Mansfield *(G-14666)*
High Roller Sand Operating LLC ....F 936 632-6033	◆ Rowan Companies LLC ....C 713 621-7800	Drilformance LLC ....E 832 772-7808
Lufkin *(G-14530)*	Houston *(G-11676)*	Houston *(G-9528)*
Hoerbiger Service Inc ....D 281 474-4458	Schwarze Industries Inc ....F 830 379-1480	Drilformance LLC ....F 832 704-2025
La Porte *(G-13745)*	Seguin *(G-18862)*	Midland *(G-15197)*
◆ Holt Texas Ltd ....B 210 648-1111	Scott Newland Office ....F 903 758-1500	▼ Drilling Supply and Mfg Inc ....E 512 243-1986
San Antonio *(G-18171)*	Longview *(G-14307)*	Austin *(G-1102)*
▲ Houston Vibrator Ltd ....F 713 939-0404	◆ Seatrax Inc ....B 713 896-6500	▲ DSA Operating Company LLC ....E 210 734-5121
Houston *(G-10261)*	Houston *(G-11806)*	San Antonio *(G-18072)*
Houston Vibrator MGT Inc ....F 713 939-0404	Seatrax Inc ....F 713 896-6500	Elmer Christy ....G 972 436-0273
Houston *(G-10262)*	Houston *(G-11807)*	Lewisville *(G-14048)*
Howard Keith Melton ....F 972 222-1900	SMI-Carr Inc ....F 325 677-0491	Epiroc North America Corp ....A 972 496-7353
Mesquite *(G-15052)*	Abilene *(G-80)*	Garland *(G-7487)*
Humdinger Equipment Ltd ....E 806 771-9944	Souther Equipment Sales Inc ....F 972 296-5231	▲ Galleon Mining Tools Inc ....F 432 563-1867
Lubbock *(G-14420)*	Dallas *(G-4985)*	Midland *(G-15234)*
Imogene Wagner Company Inc ....E 210 669-8927	◆ Sparrows Offshore LLC ....E 832 467-7300	H & T Auger Company ....E 432 362-4471
San Antonio *(G-18179)*	Houston *(G-11993)*	Odessa *(G-16022)*
James Manufacturing Inc ....E 903 872-2346	Spartan Structures LLC ....E 936 591-9280	▲ Hacker International LLC ....F 903 657-3546
Corsicana *(G-3675)*	Center *(G-3008)*	Henderson *(G-8264)*
◆ Joy Glbal Lngview Oprtions LLC .....A 903 237-7000	Stewart Stevenson Pwr Pdts LLC ....E 361 299-6839	Ios Inspection ....E 432 684-6440
Longview *(G-14257)*	Corpus Christi *(G-3629)*	Midland *(G-15255)*
Kalco Machine & Mfg Co ....D 940 761-1060	Stewart Stevenson Pwr Pdts LLC ....E 915 790-1848	◆ Joy Glbal Lngview Oprtions LLC .....A 903 237-7000
Wichita Falls *(G-20775)*	El Paso *(G-5980)*	Longview *(G-14261)*
Ken Garner Mfg - Vto Inc ....F 361 485-0541	Strong Industries Inc ....E 281 448-9315	Kay Rock Bit Company ....F 512 478-2900
Victoria *(G-20280)*	Houston *(G-12081)*	Austin *(G-1265)*
King Terrain Corporation ....C 830 379-1480	Sturgeon Services Texas Inc ....F 661 322-4408	Komatsu Mining Corp ....E 903 983-7744
Seguin *(G-18847)*	Midland *(G-15421)*	Kilgore *(G-13562)*
Kirk Construction Inc ....F 281 392-4063	▲ Technical Services Intl ....E 972 285-7400	Komatsu Mining Corp ....E 903 237-7000
Katy *(G-13369)*	Mesquite *(G-15079)*	Longview *(G-14261)*
▼ Klein Products of Texas Inc ....E 903 589-4546	Tecnon Supply LLC ....E 281 888-9045	Longwood Elastomers Inc ....C 979 830-1111
Jacksonville *(G-13247)*	Houston *(G-12179)*	Brenham *(G-2261)*
◆ Kobelco Construction McHy USA .....E 281 684-8761	Terex Corporation ....D 903 786-2981	▲ M C R Oil Tools LLC ....F 817 701-5100
Katy *(G-13419)*	Denison *(G-5347)*	Arlington *(G-726)*
◆ Letourneau Tech Amer Inc ....D 903 237-7000	Texas High Roller Inc ....E 979 778-7460	Metso Minerals Industries Inc ....E 210 491-9521
Longview *(G-14264)*	Bryan *(G-2511)*	San Antonio *(G-18295)*
Lewis-Quinn Cnstr Svcs Inc ....E 936 321-8111	Texas Machinery Co ....F 972 792-0166	▲ Midland Wellhead Inc ....E 432 682-0856
Conroe *(G-3319)*	Wills Point *(G-20879)*	Midland *(G-15303)*
Longhorn Mulching Inc ....E 936 699-1160	Thompson Jr Inc ....E 940 665-2533	◆ Mud Technology Intl Inc ....E 903 675-3240
Lufkin *(G-14533)*	Gainesville *(G-7372)*	Athens *(G-834)*
▼ Longview Mechanical Contrs Inc .....E 903 759-1331	◆ Thrustmaster of Texas Inc ....B 713 937-6295	New Railhead Manufacturing LLC ......F 817 594-6663
Longview *(G-14270)*	Houston *(G-12284)*	Weatherford *(G-20606)*
▲ M G Bryan Equipment Co LP ....F 972 623-4300	Trane Technologies Company LLC ......E 903 730-4000	Optiblend Industries Inc ....E 281 584-0047
Grand Prairie *(G-7919)*	Tyler *(G-20163)*	Katy *(G-13431)*
Marshall-Gruber Company LLC ....F 682 518-7400	▼ Trinity Industries Inc ....B 214 631-4420	Pileworks LLC ....E 936 372-9760
Mansfield *(G-14688)*	Dallas *(G-5112)*	Magnolia *(G-14620)*
▼ Masterpiece Machine and Mfg Co ....D 713 952-4102	Tropiscapes Inc ....E 281 371-2955	Psp Industries Inc ....F 210 651-9595
Stafford *(G-19351)*	Katy *(G-13452)*	Schertz *(G-18760)*
Material Handling Concepts ....F 512 836-6598	Vermeer Equipment Texas LLC ....F 512 244-0505	Sandvik Mining & Cnstr USA LLC ....D 817 453-2800
Austin *(G-1328)*	Round Rock *(G-17697)*	Mansfield *(G-14715)*
McNeilus Truck and Mfg Inc ....E 972 225-2313	Versalift Southwest LLC ....D 254 399-2100	◆ Smith International Inc ....A 281 443-3370
Hutchins *(G-12868)*	Waco *(G-20473)*	Houston *(G-11923)*
▲ MDU Cnstruction Svcs Group Inc .....E 817 447-8085	▼ Vince Hagan Company ....F 214 330-4601	Strong Industries Inc ....E 281 448-9315
Burleson *(G-2590)*	Sunnyvale *(G-19615)*	Houston *(G-12081)*
▲ Megapower Inc ....G 832 415-6995	W R Grace & Co-Conn ....E 713 223-8353	Terex Corporation ....D 903 786-2981
Houston *(G-10822)*	Houston *(G-12586)*	Denison *(G-5347)*
Offshore Wind Power Systems of ....F 682 367-0652	Waukesha-Pearce Industries Inc ....E 512 989-4900	TMC Foundation Inc ....F 214 212-4645
Grapevine *(G-8047)*	Pflugerville *(G-16692)*	McKinney *(G-14983)*
Oft Enterprises Inc ....E 713 787-5373	Western Refining Company LP ....F 915 775-3246	Vulcan Industrial Holdings LLC ....F 715 294-3200
Bellaire *(G-2000)*	El Paso *(G-6034)*	Houston *(G-12582)*
Ortiz Inc ....E 713 688-0374	Wright Landscaping & Cnst LLC ....E 254 213-3912	▲ Womack Machine Supply Co ....D 800 569-9800
Houston *(G-11195)*	Killeen *(G-13618)*	Farmers Branch *(G-6219)*
Pave/Lock/Plus LLC ....F 281 239-3033	Xit Sand and Gravel LLC ....G 806 249-8743	
Rosenberg *(G-17593)*	Dalhart *(G-3836)*	
Pavestone LLC ....E 281 769-5098		**3533 Oil Field Machinery & Eqpt**
Katy *(G-13376)*	**3532 Mining Machinery & Eqpt**	
◆ Pierce Arrow Inc ....F 940 538-5643		A R Machining Inc ....E 512 846-1789
Henrietta *(G-8282)*	◆ Aqua Drill International LLC ....D 281 337-0900	Hutto *(G-12874)*
Precision Wire Products LLC ....F 214 436-4923	Dickinson *(G-5468)*	◆ A Varco Shaffer Co ....D 713 937-5500
Frisco *(G-7307)*	Arcosa Lw Hpb LLC ....B 214 631-4420	Houston *(G-8429)*
Proserv Crane & Equipment Inc ....D 972 438-5100	Dallas *(G-3959)*	A&W Energy Inc ....F 817 704-7346
Irving *(G-13161)*	Arcosa Materials Inc ....B 817 635-8500	Fort Worth *(G-6338)*
▲ Protech Diamond Usa Inc ....F 972 602-0080	Arlington *(G-622)*	A9 Manufacturing Inc ....G 832 554-2464
Grand Prairie *(G-7959)*	Austin North Taxi Service ....F 512 704-9999	Houston *(G-8434)*
	Austin *(G-957)*	▲ AAA Products International Inc ....F 214 357-3851
		Dallas *(G-3873)*

▲ Abco Products Inc ....E 713 871-8020
  Houston *(G-8447)*
Absolute Fabrication LLC ....E 832 226-3345
  Houston *(G-8450)*
Adroit Fabrication Inc ....F 432 288-0656
  Midland *(G-15105)*
Advance Fabrication Svcs LLC ....E 432 561-8776
  Odessa *(G-15903)*
Advance Fbrction Msurement LLC ..E 713 468-9581
  Houston *(G-8482)*
Advanced Indicators and Mfg..........F 713 932-6464
  Houston *(G-8488)*
Air Liquide America LP ....F 409 720-4200
  Port Neches *(G-17157)*
▲ Aker Solutions Inc ....C 713 685-5700
  Houston *(G-8519)*
Allendale Machine Co Inc ....F 713 477-8776
  Houston *(G-8543)*
Allendale Machine Co Inc ....F 713 477-8776
  Houston *(G-8544)*
Allied Equipment Inc ....D 432 367-6000
  Odessa *(G-15912)*
Allied Prod Solutions GP LLC ....C 405 224-5779
  Houston *(G-8552)*
Ameri-Fab LLC ....D 817 458-4262
  Weatherford *(G-20575)*
◆ American Block Company ....C 800 572-9087
  Houston *(G-8588)*
American Jereh Intl Corp ....E 432 288-2431
  Houston *(G-8599)*
Amerus Oilfield Solutions LLC ....F 432 559-0843
  Midland *(G-15114)*
◆ Andrews Safety Anchors Inc ....F 432 524-6659
  Andrews *(G-535)*
Apergy Artfl Lift Intl LLC ....D 713 466-3552
  Houston *(G-8662)*
◆ Apergy Artfl Lift Intl LLC ....E 281 403-5742
  Spring *(G-19195)*
Athena Oilfield Services LLC ....F 713 426-1969
  Houston *(G-8733)*
Atlantic Maritime Services LLC ....F 713 621-7800
  Houston *(G-8739)*
Axon Ep Inc ....E 281 855-3200
  Houston *(G-8762)*
▲ Axon Pressure Products Inc ....D 281 855-3200
  Houston *(G-8763)*
Axon Pressure Products Inc ....F 713 478-8007
  Houston *(G-8764)*
Baker Hghes Olfld Oprtions LLC......C 800 441-0535
  Yorktown *(G-20976)*
Baker Hughes A GE Company LLC .....B 713 625-4200
  Houston *(G-8801)*
Baker Hughes Company ....C 713 439-8600
  Houston *(G-8802)*
◆ Baker Hughes Holdings LLC ....C 713 439-8600
  Houston *(G-8806)*
Baker Hughes Holdings LLC ....D 281 231-1000
  Houston *(G-8807)*
Baker Hughes Incorporated............D 817 838-0583
  Fort Worth *(G-6422)*
Baker Hughes Incorporated............D 956 781-9133
  Pharr *(G-16694)*
Baker Hughes Incorporated............D 432 264-9007
  Big Spring *(G-2071)*
Baker Petrolite...............................E 903 389-2903
  Fairfield *(G-6169)*
Bar Yam Engineering Inc ....G 281 999-8664
  Houston *(G-8816)*
BC Oilfield Services Inc ....F 361 573-6354
  Victoria *(G-20245)*
Bellville Tube Company ....E 281 467-7177
  Bellville *(G-2008)*
Bersal Energy LLC ....F 956 270-1155
  McAllen *(G-14841)*
▲ Bestway Oilfield Inc ....E 281 452-2525
  Channelview *(G-3013)*
Beta Arkansas LLC ....F 972 490-2340
  Dallas *(G-4022)*
Beta Engineering Inc ....F 817 265-3367
  Arlington *(G-631)*
Big Bee Drilling Inc ....D 432 333-2932
  Odessa *(G-15933)*
Big Red Engineering LLC ....F 817 539-9560
  Fort Worth *(G-6450)*
Bill West Properties Inc ....E 713 726-0151
  Houston *(G-8885)*
Bkg Machine & Fabrication Inc.........F 361 575-9592
  Victoria *(G-20247)*
Black Horse LLC ....F 281 598-8100
  Houston *(G-8904)*

◆ BOP Products LLC ....F 281 955-6321
  Houston *(G-8957)*
Bronco Manufacturing LLC..............E 918 446-7196
  Houston *(G-8993)*
Brumley Manufacturing Inc.............D 979 826-4222
  Hempstead *(G-8250)*
C & J Equipment Mfg Corp ....E 830 569-1968
  Pleasanton *(G-17063)*
Cactus Inc ....E 713 626-8800
  Houston *(G-9043)*
Calvary Steel Mfg LLC ....F 936 494-5775
  Conroe *(G-3272)*
CAM-Tech Products Inc ....F 281 548-0188
  Humble *(G-12751)*
Cameron International Corp ....E 713 571-3100
  Waller *(G-20495)*
Cameron International Corp ....D 432 362-2511
  Odessa *(G-15953)*
Cameron International Corp ....D 713 849-7789
  Houston *(G-9062)*
Cameron International Corp ....F 713 939-2211
  Houston *(G-9063)*
Cameron International Corp ....E 281 716-1000
  Houston *(G-9065)*
Cameron International Corp ....B 281 901-3100
  Houston *(G-9073)*
Cameron International Corp ....D 281 582-9500
  Houston *(G-9064)*
Cameron International Corp ....A 601 629-3300
  Houston *(G-9066)*
◆ Cameron International Corp ....E 713 939-2282
  Houston *(G-9072)*
Cameron International Corp ....C 713 354-1900
  Houston *(G-9068)*
Cameron Solutions Inc ....D 713 849-6556
  Houston *(G-9078)*
◆ Cameron Solutions Inc ....C 713 849-7500
  Houston *(G-9079)*
Cameron Solutions Inc ....E 713 896-3600
  Houston *(G-9077)*
Catec Americas Inc ....F 281 398-8806
  Houston *(G-9099)*
Cee-San Mch & Fabrication Co........F 713 466-4586
  Houston *(G-9118)*
◆ Challenger Eqp & TI Co Inc ....E 281 351-4247
  Tomball *(G-19970)*
Challenger Process Systems Co.......C 903 839-7291
  Troup *(G-20024)*
▲ Chammas Cutters Inc ....G 713 856-8777
  Houston *(G-9155)*
Championx Corporation ....C 281 403-5772
  The Woodlands *(G-19840)*
Charger Services LLC ....E 432 218-7674
  Midland *(G-15158)*
▼ Chemtec Energy Services LLC ......E 936 856-1704
  Willis *(G-20844)*
Chief Oilfield Tech LLC....................F 432 614-4481
  Midland *(G-15164)*
▲ Church Energy Services Ltd ....E 281 931-1400
  Houston *(G-9187)*
Citation 2002 Inv Ltd Partnr ....F 281 891-1000
  Houston *(G-9198)*
Clean Energy Tech Assn Inc ....E 903 389-4136
  Fairfield *(G-6171)*
Coil Solutions Inc...........................E 361 444-0058
  Alice *(G-206)*
Conslidated Rigworks LP ....E 817 446-5272
  Fort Worth *(G-6543)*
Consolidated Pressure Ctrl LLC........D 281 893-5900
  Conroe *(G-3285)*
Consolidated Rig Works LP ....E 817 446-5272
  Fort Worth *(G-6544)*
Continental Laboratories Inc ....E 713 460-0780
  Houston *(G-9285)*
◆ Control Flow Inc ....C 281 890-8300
  Houston *(G-9295)*
Craig Godwin Inc ....E 936 344-6548
  New Waverly *(G-15859)*
Crosby Group LLC ....B 918 834-4611
  Longview *(G-14216)*
Csi Compressco LP ....B 281 367-1983
  The Woodlands *(G-19850)*
CTW Brake Rims Inc ....F 806 665-0289
  Pampa *(G-6321)*
Custom Components Incorporated.....F 281 485-2200
  Pearland *(G-16551)*
D C G Machine Inc ....E 903 297-2053
  White Oak *(G-20713)*
▼ Davis-Lynch LLC ....D 281 485-8301
  Pearland *(G-16552)*

Deep Down Inc ....D 281 517-5000
  Houston *(G-9420)*
Derrick Corporation ....E 281 590-3003
  Houston *(G-9440)*
▲ Detail Design Inc ....E 281 890-4715
  Houston *(G-9444)*
Dimensional Cnc LLC ....E 713 329-9711
  Houston *(G-9474)*
Diversified Industrial Svc Co ....E 806 274-2214
  Borger *(G-2174)*
Djmw Investments LLC ....E 281 821-0010
  Houston *(G-9486)*
DK Oil Field Services LLC ....F 830 857-6339
  San Marcos *(G-18684)*
Dow Machinery Corporation ....E 832 467-0600
  Houston *(G-9507)*
Dragon Esp Ltd ....F 409 833-2665
  Beaumont *(G-1885)*
Dreco Inc ....B 281 452-7900
  Houston *(G-9516)*
◆ Dril-Quip Inc ....A 713 939-7711
  Houston *(G-9525)*
Dril-Quip Inc ....E 713 939-7711
  Houston *(G-9526)*
Drillform Drilling Eqp Inc ....E 281 948-9122
  Odessa *(G-15980)*
◆ Drilling & Prod Resources LLC .....F 713 996-7600
  Houston *(G-9529)*
Dudley J Perio Inc ....E 512 295-4234
  Buda *(G-2528)*
◆ Duoline Technologies LLC ....E 903 734-1371
  Gilmer *(G-7706)*
Duron Systems Inc ....C 281 469-0040
  Houston *(G-9539)*
Dw Energy Group.............................E 214 758-0880
  Irving *(G-13004)*
Dx Oilfield Products LLC ....E 713 863-1947
  Houston *(G-9541)*
◆ Dyna Drill Technologies LLC ....C 281 227-1250
  Katy *(G-13398)*
Eagle Manufacturing & Svc Ltd ....E 432 561-7000
  Odessa *(G-15983)*
Eagle Pco LLC ....F 432 400-2771
  Midland *(G-15202)*
Eagle Pco LLC ....F 361 756-0666
  Pleasanton *(G-17065)*
Eagle Pco LLC ....F 817 678-8998
  Navasota *(G-15731)*
Eagle Pipe LLC ....F 713 464-7473
  Houston *(G-9560)*
Eagle Rock Manufacturing LLC.........F 432 682-3030
  Midland *(G-15203)*
◆ Eckel Manufacturing Co Inc ....D 432 362-4336
  Odessa *(G-15985)*
▲ Ecofusion Inc ....G 972 403-7449
  Plano *(G-16855)*
▲ Electro-Mechanical Inds Inc ....E 281 894-1600
  Houston *(G-9592)*
Electronic Data Devices Co ....E 432 366-8699
  Odessa *(G-15987)*
◆ Elgin Sprtion Sltons Indstrals ....D 281 261-5778
  Stafford *(G-19308)*
◆ Elmar Services Inc ....D 713 983-9281
  Houston *(G-9606)*
Eml Manufacturing Llc ....E 281 880-7517
  Houston *(G-9617)*
Endurance Lift Solutions LLC ....C 903 595-8600
  Fort Worth *(G-6611)*
Enerflow Industries Inc ....D 918 355-6300
  Anderson *(G-529)*
Engineered Cstm Solutions LLC ....F 832 598-2083
  Houston *(G-9646)*
Envirocal Inc..................................F 832 296-4205
  Houston *(G-9667)*
Ernmex Interntational Inc................E 281 458-0152
  Houston *(G-9693)*
Excell 7 Machine Shop Inc ....F 281 416-0001
  Houston *(G-8379)*
◆ Expro Americas LLC ....E 713 463-9776
  Houston *(G-9734)*
EZ Pipe Paddler Padding Mch ....E 432 333-9587
  Odessa *(G-15996)*
Faith Manufacturing Co Inc.............E 281 441-9595
  Humble *(G-12766)*
Falconview Energy Products LLC.......F 832 665-2850
  Houston *(G-9759)*
▼ Fd-Thru Power Systems Cnnctors ..E 281 476-9100
  Deer Park *(G-5273)*
◆ Ferrell-Ross Roll Mfg Inc ....D 806 364-9051
  Hereford *(G-8288)*

SIC

Fifo Technologies Inc	F	817 991-1388
Fort Worth (G-6630)		
Fishing Tool/Crystin Inc	E	432 366-6504
Odessa (G-16002)		
▼ Flexitallic Group Inc	E	281 604-2525
Houston (G-9799)		
Flotek Industries Inc	F	325 347-0005
Mason (G-14814)		
▲ Flotek Industries Inc	E	713 849-9911
Houston (G-9806)		
▲ Flow Process Technologies Inc	F	281 351-9427
Cypress (G-3790)		
Flowco Prod Solutions LLC	E	830 779-2163
La Vernia (G-13801)		
Flowco Prod Solutions LLC	E	281 528-6298
Houston (G-9810)		
Flowco Prod Solutions LLC	E	281 528-6298
Houston (G-9811)		
FMC Technologies Inc	F	254 968-2181
Stephenville (G-19413)		
◆ FMC Technologies Inc	E	281 591-4000
Houston (G-9820)		
FMC Technologies Inc	F	281 591-4000
Kilgore (G-13554)		
FMC Technologies Inc	F	281 260-2190
Houston (G-9821)		
FMC Technologies Inc	E	254 968-2181
Stephenville (G-19414)		
FMC Technologies Inc	F	432 561-8063
Odessa (G-16006)		
FMC Technologies Inc	F	432 563-0335
Odessa (G-16007)		
FMC Technologies Inc	F	281 821-2355
Houston (G-9822)		
FMC Technologies Inc	E	214 363-8000
Addison (G-124)		
FMC Technologies Inc	E	361 668-0886
Alice (G-214)		
FMC Technologies Inc	E	817 887-8063
Fort Worth (G-6639)		
FMC Technologies Inc	E	361 290-9795
San Antonio (G-18119)		
FMC Technologies Inc	E	281 591-4000
Houston (G-9824)		
FMC Technologies Inc	G	281 569-6194
Houston (G-9825)		
FMC Technologies Inc	F	254 968-2181
Stephenville (G-19415)		
FMC Technologies Inc	F	281 260-2121
Houston (G-9826)		
FMC Technologies Inc	E	817 599-3337
Weatherford (G-20592)		
FMC Technologies Inc	F	281 405-7927
Houston (G-9827)		
Fogle Manufacturing Svcs LP	D	281 495-1828
Stafford (G-19315)		
Force Pressure Control LLC	C	361 210-9650
Marion (G-14756)		
Forum Energy Technologies Inc	C	940 612-5890
Houston (G-9841)		
Forum Energy Technologies Inc	D	713 329-8730
Houston (G-9842)		
Forum Energy Technologies Inc	D	361 664-6024
Robstown (G-17512)		
◆ Forum Energy Technologies Inc	C	281 949-2500
Houston (G-9843)		
Frank White	E	713 937-3800
Houston (G-9854)		
Freer Iron Works Inc	E	361 394-7273
Freer (G-7225)		
◆ FSI Holdings LLC	E	832 467-9898
Houston (G-9872)		
Full Circle Enterprises Inc	E	936 441-0101
Spring (G-19212)		
Fullco Machine Works	F	432 563-3443
Odessa (G-16009)		
◆ Fwm Tubular & Equipment Corp	E	281 806-7918
Cleveland (G-3126)		
◆ G B Industry Co LP	F	281 996-0020
Pearland (G-16562)		
Gardner Denver Inc	E	817 248-4500
Benbrook (G-2040)		
Gardner Denver Inc	D	832 421-5469
Pasadena (G-16446)		
Garzo Inc	E	936 931-5631
Waller (G-20499)		
Gaumer Company Inc	C	713 460-5200
Houston (G-9905)		
Gemstar Inc	E	432 362-2315
Odessa (G-16013)		

◆ Geodynamics Inc	C	817 341-5300
Millsap (G-15502)		
Gjr Meyer Service Inc	E	361 289-2130
Corpus Christi (G-3535)		
Globaltech Subsea Inc	F	713 504-0331
South Houston (G-19040)		
Gmu Downhole Tool Corporation	G	361 573-5100
Victoria (G-20268)		
◆ Grant Prideco Inc	D	281 878-8000
Houston (G-10017)		
Grant Prideco LP		281 878-8000
Houston (G-10018)		
Green Equipment Co Inc	F	817 589-2704
Fort Worth (G-6676)		
◆ Gulf Coast Downhole Tech LLC	F	713 667-4238
Houston (G-10059)		
▲ Gulf Coast Oil & Gas Inds LLC	D	713 236-1158
Houston (G-10061)		
H & T Auger Company	E	432 362-4471
Odessa (G-16022)		
H C Howell Company	F	432 368-0835
Odessa (G-16023)		
H D H Instruments Corp	C	281 375-6835
Pattison (G-16532)		
Halliburton Company	C	817 783-5111
Alvarado (G-333)		
▲ Harbison-Fischer Inc	B	817 297-2211
Crowley (G-3755)		
Harbison-Fischer Inc	F	432 580-3592
Odessa (G-16026)		
Harrison Mullane Inc	C	281 449-4846
Houston (G-10128)		
Hartmanns Inc	F	325 695-7641
Abilene (G-46)		
Hdi Instruments LLC	E	713 688-8555
Houston (G-10142)		
Heartland Enterprises Ltd	E	830 997-9434
Fredericksburg (G-7182)		
▲ Heshka Oil LLC	G	936 760-3453
Conroe (G-3303)		
HMC Instrmentation Contrls LLC	C	832 252-9280
Cypress (G-3799)		
▲ HMC Instrument & Mch Works Ltd	E	713 468-1426
Houston (G-10189)		
◆ Honghua America LLC	E	832 448-8100
Houston (G-10203)		
▲ Hunt Engine Incorporated	D	713 721-9400
Houston (G-10279)		
Hunting Specialty Supply LP	E	281 970-8444
Cypress (G-3802)		
Hunting Titan Inc	D	972 493-2580
Milford (G-15500)		
▲ Hutchison Hayes Separation Inc	C	713 455-9600
Houston (G-10287)		
◆ Hydralift Amclyde Inc	D	713 375-3700
Houston (G-10295)		
◆ Hydraulic Pwr Technology-Texas	E	512 295-4234
Buda (G-2530)		
◆ Hydril Company	A	713 670-3500
Houston (G-10298)		
Hydril Company LP		281 449-2000
Houston (G-10299)		
◆ Hydril USA Distribution LLC	B	281 449-2000
Houston (G-10300)		
Hydril USA Distribution LLC		832 295-5557
Houston (G-10301)		
Hydril USA Distribution LLC	D	713 670-3500
Houston (G-10302)		
Ict Energy Solutions LLC	E	432 203-0576
Midland (G-15250)		
Industrial Cmmssning Cons Intl	F	833 873-4224
La Marque (G-13708)		
Industrial Olfld Mar Cmpnnts I	F	713 266-1900
Tomball (G-19985)		
Innova Intgrated Solutions Inc	F	713 937-9999
Houston (G-10369)		
Integrated Drive Systems L L C	E	713 462-1400
Houston (G-10384)		
International Chemical Technol	F	432 339-9361
Odessa (G-16031)		
Interstate Gas Treating Inc	E	432 362-9291
Odessa (G-16032)		
Interstate Treating Inc	E	432 362-9291
Odessa (G-16033)		
Istick Capital Management LLC	E	214 231-4000
Dallas (G-4514)		
J&F Machine Shop Inc	E	713 466-1760
Houston (G-10445)		
▲ J-Hobbs Machine Corporation	E	432 563-1526
Odessa (G-16036)		

J-W Energy Company	D	972 233-8191
Addison (G-137)		
◆ Joy Glbal Lngview Oprtions LLC	A	903 237-7000
Longview (G-14257)		
Jt Oilfiled Manufacturing Co	F	713 947-7006
Houston (G-10489)		
Jt Oilfiled Manufacturing Co	E	713 947-7006
Friendswood (G-7247)		
JW Williams Inc	F	307 237-8345
Odessa (G-16043)		
Karis Resources LLC	E	903 595-0900
Tyler (G-20106)		
▲ Kelley Instrument Machine Inc	E	903 832-3332
Texarkana (G-19767)		
Keppel Letourneau Usa Inc	E	281 677-4482
Houston (G-10518)		
Kestran Inc	E	281 276-2700
Stafford (G-19340)		
Keystone Synergy LLC	D	817 636-3300
Rhome (G-17256)		
Kirks Machine Works	G	432 368-5333
Odessa (G-16053)		
Kw International LLC	C	713 468-9581
Houston (G-10572)		
L J Machine Works Inc	E	713 928-5786
Houston (G-10573)		
▲ Lamot Corporation	D	816 792-1500
Stafford (G-19344)		
Lancaster Flow Automation LLC	F	832 237-9444
Houston (G-10591)		
Larkin Products Inc	E	972 937-3640
Waxahachie (G-20549)		
Legacy Automtn Pwr Design Inc	F	281 888-5402
Houston (G-10620)		
▲ Liberty Lift Solutions LLC	E	713 575-2300
Houston (G-10633)		
Lincoln Manufacturing Inc	C	713 514-0059
Houston (G-10644)		
◆ Lincoln Manufacturing Inc	B	281 252-9494
Magnolia (G-14615)		
Loadcraft Industries Ltd	C	325 646-7581
Brownwood (G-2438)		
▼ Loadcraft Industries Ltd		325 597-2911
Brady (G-2214)		
Lonestar Couplings Inc	F	713 690-1873
Houston (G-10683)		
Longwood Elastomers Inc	C	979 830-1111
Brenham (G-2261)		
Louis Hill Kennon Inc	E	713 926-2623
Houston (G-10689)		
Ls Energy Fabrication LLC	D	281 573-9500
Baytown (G-1796)		
Ls Energy Fabrication LLC	D	281 573-9500
Houston (G-8387)		
Lubri Tech Products	E	214 870-4070
Midland (G-15288)		
Lueras Welding Service Inc	E	361 668-4572
Alice (G-225)		
M B & G Oilfld Fabrication Inc	F	903 593-0400
Tyler (G-20116)		
▲ M C R Oil Tools LLC	F	817 701-5100
Arlington (G-726)		
▲ M P Industries Inc	E	903 561-4232
Tyler (G-20118)		
Markco Machine Works Inc	E	432 362-8921
Odessa (G-16070)		
◆ Martin-Decker Totco Inc	B	512 340-5000
Cedar Park (G-2978)		
McKay Equipment Co	E	432 381-5510
Krum (G-13674)		
MCR Oil Tools LLC	E	817 704-6677
Arlington (G-730)		
Melco Blowout Preventer Spc	G	432 362-0491
Odessa (G-16080)		
Merritt Prfrred Components Inc	D	903 983-1592
Kilgore (G-13574)		
▲ Midland Wellhead Inc	E	432 682-0856
Midland (G-15303)		
Mitchell Manufacturing Inc	E	281 351-9641
Tomball (G-19989)		
Monmouth Real Estate Inv Corp	C	281 784-4360
Houston (G-10911)		
◆ Nabors Industries Inc	C	281 874-0035
Houston (G-10953)		
◆ Natco Group Inc	F	713 849-7500
Houston (G-10964)		
▲ National Oilwell Dht LP	D	713 346-7500
Houston (G-10971)		
National Oilwell Varco Inc	E	830 693-5312
Marble Falls (G-14748)		

National Oilwell Varco Inc .... F 817 985-5000
Fort Worth *(G-6861)*

National Oilwell Varco Inc .... E 281 351-2222
Tomball *(G-19991)*

National Oilwell Varco Inc .... E 713 935-8170
Houston *(G-10975)*

National Oilwell Varco Inc .... F 903 984-2553
Kilgore *(G-13577)*

National Oilwell Varco Inc .... E 713 634-3327
Houston *(G-10978)*

National Oilwell Varco Inc .... E 832 424-6000
Houston *(G-10980)*

National Oilwell Varco Inc .... E 210 572-4012
San Antonio *(G-18333)*

National Oilwell Varco Inc .... E 713 237-3766
Sugar Land *(G-19510)*

National Oilwell Varco Inc .... E 432 563-1173
Odessa *(G-16091)*

National Oilwell Varco Inc .... E 713 237-9793
Houston *(G-10981)*

National Oilwell Varco Inc .... E 281 820-5400
Houston *(G-10982)*

National Oilwell Varco Inc .... F 281 854-0537
Houston *(G-10983)*

National Oilwell Varco Inc .... D 512 340-5000
Cedar Park *(G-2980)*

National Oilwell Varco Inc .... E 936 856-9180
Conroe *(G-3334)*

National Oilwell Varco Inc .... E 281 943-5948
Houston *(G-10984)*

National Oilwell Varco Inc .... D 713 849-8011
Houston *(G-10986)*

National Oilwell Varco Inc .... D 281 599-4700
Houston *(G-10987)*

National Oilwell Varco Inc .... C 936 777-6100
Conroe *(G-3336)*

National Oilwell Varco Inc .... E 281 878-8000
Houston *(G-10992)*

National Oilwell Varco Inc .... C 713 468-7328
Houston *(G-10993)*

National Oilwell Varco Inc .... C 936 873-2600
Anderson *(G-530)*

National Oilwell Varco Inc .... E 832 575-2000
Conroe *(G-3337)*

National Oilwell Varco Inc .... E 432 683-6696
Midland *(G-15310)*

National Oilwell Varco Inc .... F 432 381-4111
Odessa *(G-16090)*

National Oilwell Varco Inc .... E 281 854-0300
Houston *(G-10976)*

National Oilwell Varco Inc .... F 713 395-5000
Houston *(G-10990)*

◆ National Oilwell Varco Inc .... A 713 346-7500
Houston *(G-10988)*

National Oilwell Varco Inc .... E 361 576-3161
Victoria *(G-20287)*

National Oilwell Varco LP .... D 936 825-2211
Navasota *(G-15740)*

National Oilwell Varco LP .... F 817 203-8302
Willis *(G-20856)*

National Oilwell Varco LP .... D 281 586-2046
Houston *(G-10995)*

National Oilwell Varco LP .... E 713 346-7500
Houston *(G-10996)*

National Oilwell Varco LP .... D 713 375-3700
Houston *(G-10997)*

National Oilwell Varco LP .... D 281 599-4700
Houston *(G-10998)*

National Oilwell Varco LP .... F 713 849-6121
Houston *(G-10999)*

◆ National Oilwell Varco LP .... B 713 375-3700
Houston *(G-11000)*

National Oilwell Varco LP .... B 936 756-4800
Conroe *(G-3340)*

National Oilwell Varco LP .... D 806 274-5293
Borger *(G-2180)*

New Railhead Manufacturing LLC .... F 817 594-6663
Weatherford *(G-20606)*

▼ New Tech Systems Inc .... E 817 779-6262
Mansfield *(G-14697)*

Nk Energy LLC .... F 832 857-8228
Kingwood *(G-13650)*

Now Inc .... E 281 823-4700
Houston *(G-11091)*

Nu Energy Services LP .... F 817 832-0724
Aledo *(G-200)*

Nustar Gp LLC .... A 210 370-2000
San Antonio *(G-18353)*

O & C Equipment Inc .... F 281 232-4686
Rosenberg *(G-17591)*

Oceaneering Reflange .... E 713 682-5105
Houston *(G-11129)*

Octg Material Hdlg Systems Inc .... F 432 687-5420
Midland *(G-15325)*

Odessa Separator Inc .... E 432 580-7111
Odessa *(G-16097)*

◆ ODrill/Mcm Inc .... E 832 782-6300
Houston *(G-11132)*

OEM Components Inc .... D 281 449-6258
Houston *(G-11138)*

▼ Ofi Testing Equipment Inc .... D 713 880-9885
Houston *(G-11145)*

Ofs International LLC .... B 281 452-3036
Houston *(G-11148)*

Oil Country Manufacturing Inc .... E 432 563-8014
Odessa *(G-16099)*

Oil States Energy Services LLC .... F 361 384-0041
Orange Grove *(G-16269)*

Oil States Energy Services LLC .... F 903 986-3791
Kilgore *(G-13580)*

▲ Oil States Energy Services LLC .... E 713 425-2400
Houston *(G-11154)*

Oil States Energy Services LLC .... E 432 563-1304
Midland *(G-15326)*

Oil States Energy Services LLC .... E 903 526-4777
Tyler *(G-20135)*

Oil States Industries Inc .... C 713 445-2200
Houston *(G-11160)*

Oil States Industries Inc .... C 713 445-2200
Houston *(G-11157)*

◆ Oil States Industries Inc .... C 817 548-4200
Arlington *(G-743)*

Oilfield Services & Tech LLC .... E 432 614-0076
Odessa *(G-16100)*

▲ Onesubsea LLC .... A 713 939-2282
Houston *(G-11182)*

Orbix Corporation .... E 254 675-8651
Clifton *(G-3145)*

Osies Inc .... E 713 849-5131
Houston *(G-11197)*

Oso Perforating LLC .... F 972 754-7773
Irving *(G-13135)*

◆ Owen Oil Tools LP .... C 817 551-0540
Godley *(G-7738)*

Pan American Industries Inc .... G 281 572-4842
Porter *(G-17180)*

Parco Double-E LLC .... D 214 631-2290
Dallas *(G-4788)*

Patterson Well Service Co LLC .... F 361 575-9600
Victoria *(G-20292)*

Pbp Fabrication Inc .... E 432 381-5542
Odessa *(G-16107)*

Pd Supply Inc .... E 713 435-6100
Houston *(G-11264)*

Pelican Energy Partners LP .... D 713 559-7110
Houston *(G-11271)*

Perales Group Ventures Inc .... F 830 780-3336
Karnes City *(G-13346)*

Permian Basin Instruments Inc .... E 432 687-4445
Denton *(G-5392)*

◆ Petroleum Products & Svcs Inc .... F 281 448-1000
Tomball *(G-19997)*

▲ Petron Industries Inc .... D 713 693-8700
Houston *(G-11310)*

▲ Petronash Americas LLC .... E 281 566-6600
Sugar Land *(G-19526)*

▲ Petrotrim Services LLC .... E 281 821-2111
Humble *(G-12793)*

Powell Manufacturing Company .... E 972 278-9507
Garland *(G-7571)*

Precision Energy Services Inc .... D 281 892-0600
Houston *(G-11392)*

◆ Precision Energy Services Inc .... C 713 693-4000
Houston *(G-11393)*

▲ Preferred Pump & Equipment LP .... E 817 536-9800
Fort Worth *(G-6912)*

▲ Premium Valve Services LLC .... E 281 457-2565
Houston *(G-11406)*

▲ Probe Technology Services Inc .... E 817 568-8528
Fort Worth *(G-6920)*

Procegas LLC .... E 832 652-2129
Houston *(G-11430)*

Propell American LLC .... D 817 573-3550
Granbury *(G-7806)*

Protek Specialty Company .... F 713 667-6691
Houston *(G-11464)*

▲ Prucka-Laney Inc .... F 432 687-0799
Midland *(G-15370)*

Psp Industries Inc .... F 210 651-9595
Schertz *(G-18760)*

▼ Quali-Tex Ball & Seat Co .... E 432 332-3755
Odessa *(G-16128)*

Quality Manufacturing Inc .... F 940 592-5790
Iowa Park *(G-12908)*

R & D Advantage Inc .... D 713 836-4000
Houston *(G-11519)*

R3 Energy Services LLC .... F 432 335-7800
Odessa *(G-16130)*

Rae Energy Solutions Inc .... G 281 440-3434
Houston *(G-11533)*

▲ Ram International Inc .... F 361 688-1966
Corpus Christi *(G-3605)*

Rama Fabrication Inc .... E 432 362-9291
Odessa *(G-16132)*

Ranger Energy Services Inc .... E 830 569-1940
Pleasanton *(G-17072)*

Razor Specialties LLC .... G 888 578-9656
San Antonio *(G-18411)*

▲ Reactive Downhole Tls USA Inc .... E 281 821-6566
Humble *(G-12796)*

Red Rock Oilfield Service LLC .... F 325 933-0224
Colorado City *(G-3226)*

Reef Services LLC .... E 325 573-1133
Snyder *(G-19003)*

Reef Services LLC .... E 432 560-5600
Houston *(G-11579)*

Reel Power Oil & Gas Inc .... E 713 937-4494
Houston *(G-11580)*

Remlap Manufacturing Inc .... F 713 462-3199
Houston *(G-11595)*

Reynolds Lift Technologies LLC .... F 866 629-6298
Missouri City *(G-15589)*

▼ Rig Works Inc .... F 432 366-4501
Odessa *(G-16140)*

◆ Robbins & Myers Inc .... E 936 890-1064
Willis *(G-20861)*

◆ Robbins Myers Enrgy Systems LP ... B 936 890-1064
Willis *(G-20862)*

Robinson Drilling Texas Ltd .... E 432 267-5277
Big Spring *(G-2096)*

Rockwell Precision Inc .... F 281 890-9331
Houston *(G-11653)*

Rotary Components Intl Inc .... F 281 590-6484
Houston *(G-11668)*

◆ Rotary Drilling Tools USA LLC .... E 979 387-3223
Houston *(G-11669)*

◆ Rowan Companies LLC .... C 713 621-7800
Houston *(G-11676)*

Rt Precision Machinery LP .... E 281 354-0910
Kingwood *(G-13653)*

◆ Rti Energy Systems Inc .... E 281 379-4289
Spring *(G-19163)*

◆ Rush Sales Company .... C 432 337-2397
Odessa *(G-16145)*

▲ Russell Oilfield Equipment Co .... F 281 540-8982
Humble *(G-12797)*

S Q I Inc .... F 432 366-9264
Odessa *(G-16148)*

▲ Safoco Inc .... E 713 956-5936
Houston *(G-11728)*

Schlumberger International .... A 713 747-4000
Houston *(G-11766)*

Schlumberger Norge As .... E 281 227-9854
Houston *(G-11769)*

Schlumberger Technology Corp .... E 713 747-1040
Houston *(G-11780)*

Schlumberger Technology Corp .... E 281 285-8500
Houston *(G-11780)*

◆ Schlumberger Technology Corp .... A 281 285-8500
Sugar Land *(G-19542)*

Schlumberger Technology Corp .... C 281 285-8500
Sugar Land *(G-19549)*

▲ Scorpion Oiltools Inc .... E 281 999-2222
Houston *(G-11789)*

▲ Seaboard Holdings Inc .... E 713 644-3535
Houston *(G-11797)*

◆ Seaboard International Inc .... E 713 644-3535
Houston *(G-11798)*

Sensia LLC .... E 866 773-6742
Houston *(G-11831)*

▲ Serimax North America LLC .... D 832 230-2700
Houston *(G-11836)*

◆ Serva Corporation .... F 940 761-3361
Wichita Falls *(G-20808)*

◆ Sharewell LP .... E 281 288-2560
Houston *(G-11845)*

Shell Machine Works Inc .... F 361 883-7073
Corpus Christi *(G-3622)*

Sivalls Inc .... E 325 643-3621
Brownwood *(G-2445)*

▲ SMI Manufacturing Inc................D....... 281 449-0345
  Houston *(G-11921)*

◆ Smith International Inc................A....... 281 443-3370
  Houston *(G-11923)*

Snelson Oilfield Ltg Co Inc............E....... 817 926-0571
  Fort Worth *(G-6998)*

◆ Sofec Inc...............................D....... 713 510-6600
  Houston *(G-11931)*

Sonic Surveys Ltd.......................F....... 281 385-6500
  Baytown *(G-1802)*

▲ Southern Tube LLC....................E....... 713 231-2929
  Houston *(G-11979)*

▼ Specialty Devices Incorporated.......F....... 972 429-7240
  Wylie *(G-20951)*

Spectra Engineering Inc.................E....... 432 367-8413
  Odessa *(G-16160)*

Spectrum Batteries Inc..................E....... 281 533-9735
  Fulshear *(G-7331)*

Speedorange Inc.........................F....... 281 448-5900
  Pasadena *(G-16510)*

◆ SPM Flow Control Inc.................C....... 817 246-2461
  Fort Worth *(G-7013)*

SPM Flow Control Inc....................C....... 903 984-8153
  Kilgore *(G-13592)*

SPM Flow Control Inc....................C....... 432 580-3887
  Odessa *(G-16162)*

SPM Flow Control Inc....................C....... 817 246-2461
  Deer Park *(G-5297)*

SPM Flow Control Inc....................C....... 281 820-7807
  Houston *(G-12021)*

SRI Energy Inc..........................F....... 832 742-7500
  Sugar Land *(G-19558)*

Standard Machine Works Inc.............F....... 713 673-1111
  Pasadena *(G-16512)*

Starjb..................................F....... 713 408-8327
  Houston *(G-12048)*

Steeltex Fabricators LLC...............E....... 817 225-0973
  Venus *(G-20223)*

Step Energy Svcs Holdings Ltd..........F....... 918 423-4300
  San Antonio *(G-18501)*

◆ Stewart & Stevenson LLC..............D....... 713 751-2700
  Houston *(G-12062)*

◆ Stewart Stevenson Pwr Pdts LLC.......C....... 713 751-2600
  Houston *(G-12065)*

Stream-Flo USA LLC......................E....... 903 753-6785
  Longview *(G-14313)*

Stream-Flo USA LLC......................E....... 361 362-2600
  Beeville *(G-1988)*

Stream-Flo USA LLC......................F....... 903 983-2992
  Kilgore *(G-13595)*

▲ Stream-Flo USA LLC...................D....... 903 912-1022
  Houston *(G-12076)*

Streamline Supply Inc...................F....... 713 914-0330
  Houston *(G-12078)*

Strongfab Solutions Inc.................E....... 713 856-6511
  Houston *(G-12082)*

▲ Stuckey Terry & Associates...........E....... 281 590-8628
  Houston *(G-12083)*

Subsea Services Intl Inc................D....... 281 578-6523
  Katy *(G-13446)*

◆ Summit Casing Services LLC...........F....... 877 860-0969
  Fort Worth *(G-7022)*

Summit Energy Equipment................F....... 903 951-1217
  Sulphur Springs *(G-19600)*

Superior Energy Services Inc...........E....... 713 654-2200
  Houston *(G-12112)*

Supply Chain Solutions Ltd.............F....... 281 288-0658
  Spring *(G-19169)*

▲ Surf Subsea Inc......................E....... 281 305-4411
  Montgomery *(G-15643)*

Surveys & Analysis Inc..................E....... 508 842-4011
  Houston *(G-12127)*

▲ Swm International Inc.................D....... 806 665-8747
  Pampa *(G-16340)*

Synergy Industries LP...................D....... 817 295-1161
  Burleson *(G-2597)*

Syrgis Holdings Inc.....................G....... 361 438-1139
  Kerrville *(G-13527)*

◆ Tam International Inc.................C....... 713 462-7617
  Houston *(G-12155)*

Tam International Inc....................F....... 713 462-7617
  Houston *(G-12156)*

▲ Tams Industries LLC..................D....... 281 370-3087
  Spring *(G-19174)*

Taylors Oilfield Mfg Inc................E....... 281 442-4084
  Houston *(G-12168)*

▲ Tcm Investments Inc..................E....... 432 366-5433
  Odessa *(G-16173)*

▲ TE&s Limited.........................D....... 817 573-3550
  Granbury *(G-7811)*

▼ Team Oil Tools LLC...................E....... 918 461-8104
  Houston *(G-12172)*

▲ Tesco Corporation....................C....... 713 359-7000
  Houston *(G-12211)*

▲ Tesco Corporation (us)...............D....... 713 359-7000
  Houston *(G-12212)*

Tex Webb LLC............................F....... 214 770-7073
  Dallas *(G-5052)*

Texas Couplings.........................F....... 281 350-2494
  Spring *(G-19177)*

Texas Fabco Solutions Inc...............F....... 979 255-3530
  Round Mountain *(G-17619)*

◆ Texas First Indus Corp Inc...........E....... 281 934-1190
  Brookshire *(G-2327)*

Texokan Operating Inc...................F....... 214 484-2322
  Dallas *(G-5080)*

◆ Tiw Corporation......................C....... 713 939-7711
  Houston *(G-12303)*

Tiw International Inc....................F....... 713 729-2110
  Houston *(G-12304)*

TMC Foundation Inc......................C....... 214 212-4645
  McKinney *(G-14983)*

Tommy Chappell LLC......................F....... 432 967-2469
  Odessa *(G-16180)*

▼ Top-Co Cementing Products Inc........C....... 832 300-3660
  Houston *(G-12321)*

Tops Well Services LLC..................D....... 979 627-7434
  Sealy *(G-18820)*

Total Oilfield Eqp & Sup LLC............E....... 361 442-2922
  Robstown *(G-17518)*

▲ Townsend International Inc...........E....... 432 381-8750
  Odessa *(G-16181)*

◆ Trelleborg Offshore Us Inc...........B....... 281 774-2600
  Houston *(G-12360)*

▲ Tri-Max Corporation..................E....... 713 937-8808
  Houston *(G-12363)*

▲ Triangle Pump Components Inc.........F....... 817 202-8530
  Cleburne *(G-3115)*

▲ Tribocor Technologies Inc............E....... 281 277-7200
  Stafford *(G-19388)*

Trx Industries Inc......................F....... 254 694-6256
  Whitney *(G-20733)*

▼ Tryer Process Equipment Ltd..........E....... 940 432-0130
  Wichita Falls *(G-20822)*

▲ TSC Offshore Corporation.............A....... 832 456-3900
  Houston *(G-12396)*

TSC Offshore Corporation................F....... 832 456-3900
  Houston *(G-12397)*

Tubular Repair LLC......................E....... 979 387-3223
  Houston *(G-12403)*

▼ Turbo Drill Industries Inc...........D....... 936 756-3210
  Conroe *(G-3375)*

Turn-Tex Machine & Tool Inc.............F....... 903 759-0989
  Longview *(G-14325)*

▲ TW Tanks and Construction Co.........F....... 361 358-8869
  Beeville *(G-1989)*

U S Weatherford L P.....................E....... 281 443-5627
  Houston *(G-12423)*

U S Weatherford L P.....................E....... 432 561-8892
  Midland *(G-15452)*

U S Weatherford L P.....................E....... 817 293-5192
  Fort Worth *(G-7091)*

U S Weatherford L P.....................E....... 361 668-8362
  Elmendorf *(G-6073)*

U S Weatherford L P.....................C....... 281 348-1090
  Kingwood *(G-13656)*

U S Weatherford L P.....................E....... 817 249-7200
  Benbrook *(G-2047)*

▲ Ulterra Drilling Tech LP.............E....... 817 293-7555
  Fort Worth *(G-7092)*

▼ United Service Alliance Inc..........E....... 409 935-9500
  Texas City *(G-19805)*

Universal Well Svc Holdings.............C....... 325 573-6209
  Snyder *(G-19013)*

▼ USA Petroleum Equipment Sup Co.......F....... 281 893-2471
  Houston *(G-12497)*

V & V Industries Inc....................F....... 713 224-1751
  Houston *(G-12509)*

Valiant Artfl Lift Sltions LLC..........F....... 432 253-2233
  Midland *(G-15460)*

▲ Vallourec Tube-Alloy LLC.............C....... 713 462-7613
  Houston *(G-12523)*

◆ Varco Shaffer Inc....................A....... 713 937-5000
  Houston *(G-12536)*

Vetco Gray LLC..........................A....... 281 445-8968
  Houston *(G-12557)*

◆ Vetco Gray LLC.......................E....... 281 448-4410
  Houston *(G-12558)*

Vfuels LLC..............................F....... 713 456-3443
  Houston *(G-12561)*

Victor Nicolle Inc......................F....... 713 896-4911
  Houston *(G-12566)*

▲ Vinson Process Controls Co LP........D....... 972 459-8200
  Lewisville *(G-14106)*

Vita International Inc..................E....... 281 591-1300
  Houston *(G-12575)*

Voyager Energy Services LLC............F....... 830 583-9590
  Kenedy *(G-13493)*

Warfab Oilfield Services Inc...........E....... 903 295-1011
  Longview *(G-14331)*

▲ Watson Grinding and Mfg Co...........D....... 713 466-3053
  Houston *(G-12605)*

▼ Wayne Wilk...........................E....... 570 326-1164
  Houston *(G-12608)*

Weatherford International LLC...........E....... 361 815-2104
  Alice *(G-246)*

Weatherford International LLC...........E....... 210 621-2156
  Elmendorf *(G-6075)*

Weatherford International Inc...........E....... 361 693-6800
  Corpus Christi *(G-3653)*

◆ Welker Inc...........................D....... 281 491-2331
  Sugar Land *(G-19571)*

Wellflex Enrgy Prtners Fort Wr.........E....... 817 730-5111
  Rhome *(G-17264)*

Westfield Engrg & Svcs Inc.............E....... 281 438-2047
  Houston *(G-8397)*

Wildkat Precision LLC...................F....... 936 890-9572
  Willis *(G-20869)*

Wilson International Inc................E....... 281 823-4700
  Houston *(G-12673)*

Windy Cove Energy LLC...................E....... 281 402-1880
  Houston *(G-12678)*

Wipco Acquisition LLC...................F....... 936 327-8250
  Livingston *(G-14164)*

Worldwide Dpwter Solutions LLC.........E....... 281 238-6000
  Richmond *(G-17467)*

◆ Worldwide Oilfield Machine Inc.......C....... 713 729-9200
  Houston *(G-12694)*

Worldwide Oilfield Machine Inc.........D....... 713 721-5200
  Houston *(G-12695)*

Worldwide Oilfield Machine Inc.........E....... 713 937-0795
  Houston *(G-12696)*

Wwl Industries Inc......................E....... 432 362-0326
  Odessa *(G-16215)*

3534 Elevators & Moving Stairways

▲ Alimak Group USA Inc.................D....... 713 640-8500
  Webster *(G-20632)*

Austin Elevator Company LLC............F....... 512 376-2107
  Kyle *(G-13678)*

Century Elevators Inc...................F....... 281 667-3000
  Webster *(G-20635)*

▲ Eklunds Inc..........................E....... 817 949-2030
  Southlake *(G-19067)*

Hemco Industries Inc....................E....... 713 681-2426
  Houston *(G-10152)*

Kone Inc................................C....... 469 854-8861
  Allen *(G-283)*

National Elevator Company Inc..........E....... 925 484-5050
  Flower Mound *(G-6273)*

◆ OFlaherty Holdings Inc...............B....... 254 399-2100
  Waco *(G-20439)*

Otis Elevator Company...................F....... 214 741-6207
  Dallas *(G-4772)*

Tower Elevator Systems Inc.............F....... 512 266-6200
  Round Rock *(G-17696)*

3535 Conveyors & Eqpt

Action Rigging and Pump Svc LP.........F....... 512 670-9567
  Austin *(G-885)*

▲ Alimak Group USA Inc.................D....... 713 640-8500
  Webster *(G-20632)*

All-State Belting LLC...................F....... 713 433-1272
  Houston *(G-8371)*

Ammeraal Beltech Inc....................F....... 972 647-8996
  Grand Prairie *(G-7831)*

◆ Apergy Artfl Lift Intl LLC...........E....... 281 403-5742
  Spring *(G-19195)*

◆ B W Sinclair Inc.....................E....... 940 766-2556
  Wichita Falls *(G-20742)*

Bowlin Engineering Co...................F....... 817 232-2020
  Saginaw *(G-17740)*

Cnc Fabrication and Maint..............F....... 817 295-9055
  Burleson *(G-2575)*

▲ Communications Conveyor Co Inc.......E....... 940 498-1850
  Lake Dallas *(G-13810)*

Conveyor Aggregate Pdts Corp...........F....... 713 856-5600
  Houston *(G-9299)*

Coperion Corporation....................F....... 281 449-9944
  Houston *(G-9309)*

Cugar Machine Inc ....F 817 927-0411
   Fort Worth (G-6565)
◆ Dallas A C Horn & Company Inc ....D 214 630-3311
   Dallas (G-4210)
Dover Equipment Inc ....E 713 690-5200
   Houston (G-9504)
Eckels - Bilt Inc ....F 817 246-4555
   Fort Worth (G-6603)
Edelhoff Technologies USA LLC ....F 713 947-6469
   Houston (G-9582)
Esco Group LLC ....E 903 984-3726
   Kilgore (G-13551)
Frazier & Son LP ....F 936 494-4040
   Conroe (G-3298)
◆ Glidepath LLC ....D 972 641-4200
   Arlington (G-692)
HI Industries Inc ....D 979 836-2661
   Brenham (G-2257)
Hou Fab & Maintenance Inc ....G 713 672-1993
   Crosby (G-3733)
Industrial Cnvyor Fbrction Ltd ....F 817 439-0735
   Fort Worth (G-6718)
Innovtive Cnveyor Concepts Inc ....F 972 323-0797
   Grand Prairie (G-7893)
Intelligrated Systems Inc ....B 972 899-9636
   Coppell (G-3422)
ISC Manufacturing LLC ....E 817 641-0691
   Burleson (G-2583)
J & J Manufacturing Company ....D 409 835-1330
   Beaumont (G-1912)
J Morco Incorporated ....E 817 596-3989
   Weatherford (G-20597)
▼ JVI Vibratory Equipment Inc ....F 832 467-3720
   Houston (G-10491)
▼ Kws Manufacturing Company Ltd .....C 817 295-2247
   Burleson (G-2586)
▲ Laserweld Inc ....E 713 333-0804
   Katy (G-13422)
Lee Contracting Inc ....E 281 456-9023
   Houston (G-10616)
M2I Systems LLC ....F 214 412-1400
   Grand Prairie (G-7920)
Martin Sprocket & Gear Inc ....D 817 473-1520
   Mansfield (G-14689)
Martin Sprocket & Gear Inc ....C 817 258-3000
   Fort Worth (G-6813)
Metroplex Conveyor & Svcs LLC ....F 972 584-0551
   Quinlan (G-17224)
Metso Minerals Industries Inc ....E 210 491-9521
   San Antonio (G-18295)
◆ Meyer Industries Inc ....D 210 736-1811
   San Antonio (G-18296)
Midwest Industrial Rubber Inc ....F 972 988-6700
   Grand Prairie (G-7928)
Midwest Machine LLC ....D 806 355-9400
   Amarillo (G-501)
Mueller Construction Company ....E 903 868-3585
   Sherman (G-18924)
Multitech Group Inc ....F 817 496-5500
   Arlington (G-734)
Newton Conveyors Inc ....F 817 558-1722
   Cleburne (G-3103)
Package Conveyer Co Inc ....E 817 332-7195
   Fort Worth (G-6889)
Plant Fabricators Inc ....E 830 393-3064
   Floresville (G-6249)
Ranger Conveying & Supply Co ....D 713 671-0004
   Houston (G-11544)
◆ Redcastle Manufacturing LLC ....F 817 350-6300
   Mansfield (G-14709)
Schenck Process LLC ....D 816 891-9300
   Houston (G-11765)
Siemens Industry Inc ....D 972 947-7100
   Dfw Airport (G-5454)
Siemens Logistics LLC ....A 972 947-7100
   Dfw Airport (G-5455)
Souther Equipment Sales Inc ....F 972 296-5231
   Dallas (G-4985)
Systems Automated Controls Inc ....E 818 898-1900
   Denton (G-5402)
▲ Systems Integration Inc ....E 817 468-1494
   Arlington (G-790)
▲ Transnorm System Inc ....D 972 606-0303
   Arlington (G-802)
Triple/S Dynamics Inc ....E 214 828-8600
   Dallas (G-5117)
▼ Unified Supply & Services Co ....F 972 355-8299
   Rhome (G-17262)

3536 Hoists, Cranes & Monorails

Ace Engineering Ltd ....C 817 237-7700
   Fort Worth (G-6341)
Ace Industries Inc ....D 281 443-6690
   Cleveland (G-3118)
▲ Ace Trucks Ltd ....D 817 237-7700
   Fort Worth (G-6342)
▲ Caplingers Crane & Eqp Svc Inc ......E 817 685-0710
   Hurst (G-12841)
Columbus McKinnon Corporation ....C 210 924-3700
   San Antonio (G-18018)
Columbus McKinnon Corporation ....E 281 443-6690
   Cleveland (G-3124)
Crane Equipment & Service Inc ....E 817 740-7911
   Fort Worth (G-6557)
Deshazo LLC ....D 281 227-6200
   Houston (G-9442)
Emerald Pt Marina Partners Ltd ....C 512 266-1535
   Austin (G-1123)
▲ Favelle Favco Cranes Usa Inc ....D 956 428-7488
   Harlingen (G-8188)
Fehrs Industrial Mfg LLC ....D 432 758-0068
   Seminole (G-18883)
General Crane Service Inc ....E 713 649-4088
   Houston (G-9921)
▲ Gh Cranes & Components USA Inc ....E 972 563-8333
   Terrell (G-19735)
Gulf Special Services Inc ....E 956 541-1445
   Brownsville (G-2361)
H & T Auger Company ....E 432 362-4471
   Odessa (G-16022)
Hight Marine Products Inc ....G 817 431-4569
   Fort Worth (G-6698)
Hiroko International Inc ....E 210 590-4411
   San Antonio (G-18168)
◆ Hydralift Amclyde Inc ....D 713 375-3700
   Houston (G-10295)
Integrated McHy Solutions LLC ....D 877 693-7467
   Azle (G-1725)
▲ Kobelco Cranes North Amer Inc ....F 713 856-5755
   Katy (G-13420)
Konecranes Inc ....G 361 289-9400
   Corpus Christi (G-3561)
Konecranes Inc ....E 281 631-0300
   Houston (G-10558)
Konecranes Inc ....D 800 486-7278
   Houston (G-10559)
Lift Moore Inc ....E 713 688-5533
   Houston (G-10637)
Liftex Corporation ....E 713 863-0900
   Houston (G-10639)
◆ Manitex Inc ....C 512 942-3000
   Georgetown (G-7662)
Morris Material Handling Inc ....C 281 445-2225
   Houston (G-10923)
National Oilwell Varco Inc ....E 361 576-3161
   Victoria (G-20287)
▲ Product Handling Design Inc ....F 972 231-4628
   Haslet (G-8222)
Proserv Crane & Equipment Inc ....D 972 438-5100
   Irving (G-13161)
▼ Proserv Crane & Equipment Inc ....D 281 405-9048
   Houston (G-11455)
Scan-Pac Mfg Inc ....E 281 356-1640
   Magnolia (G-14626)
◆ Seatrax Inc ....B 713 896-6500
   Houston (G-11806)
Seatrax Inc ....E 713 896-6500
   Houston (G-11807)
Turn-Tech Inc ....E 281 356-1290
   Pinehurst (G-16737)

3537 Indl Trucks, Tractors, Trailers & Stackers

428transporters LLC ....F 214 212-8648
   Desoto (G-5427)
◆ 4front Engneered Solutions Inc ....C 972 466-0707
   Carrollton (G-2690)
◆ Abasco LLC ....E 281 446-1500
   Humble (G-12742)
Ace Welding and Trailer Co ....E 210 667-1171
   San Antonio (G-17858)
All Forkliftscom Inc ....F 972 506-9108
   Dallas (G-3921)
Alltrans Port Trucking Inc ....E 713 673-3844
   Houston (G-8559)
▲ Ansung-Usa LLC ....F 469 877-5242
   Dallas (G-3949)
Azt Wood LLC ....F 409 283-5355
   Woodville (G-20915)

Balong Trucking LLC ....F 408 471-1383
   Richardson (G-17277)
Batteries Concord ....F 281 931-4488
   Houston (G-8827)
Bean In Motion Logistics LLC ....F 682 465-9083
   Fort Worth (G-6441)
▲ Blaze Equipment LLC ....E 817 439-0453
   Lake Worth (G-13812)
Boldwall LLC ....F 312 898-9460
   Houston (G-8946)
Buck Dandy Co ....F 903 784-6362
   Sumner (G-19606)
◆ Capacity of Texas Inc ....C 903 759-0610
   Longview (G-14207)
Channl-Track Tube-Way Inds Inc ....F 361 798-4979
   Hallettsville (G-8120)
Coker Enterprises ....F 903 533-8894
   Tyler (G-20069)
Craneworks Inc ....E 281 219-7779
   Houston (G-9334)
Crown Equipment Corporation ....D 281 985-0300
   Houston (G-9348)
Crown Equipment Corporation ....E 210 930-9360
   San Antonio (G-18031)
Crown Equipment Corporation ....C 972 988-9000
   Arlington (G-651)
Dcf Investments LLC ....F 281 744-7445
   Livingston (G-14152)
Diversified Bus Consulting LLC ....F 713 677-9282
   Houston (G-9481)
▲ Enviroflex Design & Mfg ....F 281 356-6700
   Magnolia (G-14605)
First Class Freightage LLC ....F 469 486-4695
   Little Elm (G-14139)
Flagship Transport LP ....G 713 253-7785
   Brenham (G-2254)
Fleetpride Inc ....F 361 883-4358
   Corpus Christi (G-3528)
Forklifts USA Inc ....F 956 568-9797
   Laredo (G-13887)
G & H Truck Equipment Inc ....F 817 467-9883
   Arlington (G-684)
Galvan National Carriers LLC ....F 956 346-7095
   San Benito (G-18657)
General Aviation Inds Inc ....E 817 598-4848
   Weatherford (G-20595)
Global 360 Bgs Inc ....E 210 826-5501
   San Antonio (G-18145)
Goldline International Inc ....E 713 475-0631
   Pasadena (G-16449)
▲ GP Terminals LLC ....F 713 209-7780
   Galena Park (G-7380)
Heil Trailer International LLC ....C 254 865-7235
   Gatesville (G-7618)
◆ Indepndent Rugh Trrain Ctr LLC ....C 210 599-6541
   Cibolo (G-3063)
Industrotech Inc ....F 817 847-1358
   Fort Worth (G-6719)
J&A Trucking Co ....F 713 854-0226
   Willis (G-20851)
James Manufacturing Inc ....E 903 872-2346
   Corsicana (G-3675)
John Bean Technologies Corp ....C 713 875-3735
   Houston (G-10480)
K W D Manufacturing Inc ....E 210 924-5999
   San Antonio (G-18214)
Kalamar Industries USA Inc ....D 903 759-5490
   White Oak (G-20716)
Kentucky Freight Systems Inc ....F 972 475-6567
   Rowlett (G-17708)
▲ Kjd Enterprises ....F 325 641-0420
   Brownwood (G-2431)
L L T Inc ....F 830 914-3800
   Odessa (G-16059)
Level Up Transportation LLC ....F 214 210-0701
   Lewisville (G-14061)
▼ LLT Inc ....F 830 995-3465
   Comfort (G-3239)
◆ Manitex Inc ....C 512 942-3000
   Georgetown (G-7662)
▲ Manitou North America Inc ....D 254 799-0232
   Waco (G-20429)
Mate Inc ....E 281 855-0045
   Houston (G-10790)
Miller Equipment Co ....F 469 366-4227
   Garland (G-7553)
◆ Mitsubshi Ctrpllar Frklift AME ....A 713 365-1000
   Houston (G-10891)
Morgan Truck Body LLC ....D 903 872-7445
   Corsicana (G-3679)

S
I
C

Nacco Industries Inc ....E 440 449-9600
Plano (G-16938)

Oft Enterprises Inc ....E 713 787-5373
Bellaire (G-2000)

On-Site Bennett Services LLC ....D 855 239-2505
Longview (G-14287)

◆ Overhead Door Corporation ....E 469 549-7100
Lewisville (G-14080)

Overland Tank Inc ....E 325 673-7132
Odessa (G-16105)

P W Platforms Inc ....F 713 731-7155
Houston (G-11214)

Paccar Inc ....C 940 566-7329
Corinth (G-3459)

Portersville Sales & Testing ....E 806 373-6811
Amarillo (G-507)

Proco Inc ....E 361 516-1112
Kingsville (G-13634)

▲ Progressive Sales Inc ....E 432 333-6631
Odessa (G-16127)

Prolift Equipment Inc ....F 214 682-3327
Duncanville (G-5538)

Provident Rmnfcturing Svcs Inc ....E 940 239-7775
Denton (G-5394)

▼ Ranger Lift Trucks LLC ....F 281 424-2111
Baytown (G-1832)

Rich Transport LLC ....C 214 819-3082
Dallas (G-4896)

Rockwall Chrysler Dodge ....F 469 698-2100
Rockwall (G-17563)

◆ Sanwa Usa Inc ....E 972 503-3031
Plano (G-17002)

Smarttruck Undertray Systems ....F 864 990-0781
Fort Worth (G-6993)

SPX Dock Products Inc ....G 972 466-0707
Carrollton (G-2819)

Ssi Lift USA Ltd ....E 432 488-6427
Midland (G-15417)

▼ Stewart Stevenson Capitl Corp ....D 713 868-7700
Houston (G-12063)

▲ Sumner Manufacturing Co LLC ....C 281 999-6900
Houston (G-12096)

Sunbelt Design & Dev Inc ....D 210 227-9162
San Antonio (G-18511)

Supreme Corporation of Texas ....C 817 641-8002
Cleburne (G-3112)

Texas Hydraulic & Eqp Co Inc ....F 214 748-7551
Hutchins (G-12872)

Texas Kenworth Co ....D 432 381-3300
Odessa (G-16175)

Western Hauler Enterprises ....F 817 332-1121
Fort Worth (G-7139)

Win-Holt Equipment Corp ....C 972 641-4658
Grand Prairie (G-7995)

Windlass Metalworks LLC ....F 713 849-9292
Houston (G-12677)

3541 Machine Tools: Cutting

Absolute Machine & Tooling LLC ....F 512 259-7676
Leander (G-13984)

▲ American National Carbide Co ....D 281 351-7165
Tomball (G-19958)

◆ Applied Maintenance Spc Inc ....F 409 994-5849
Buna (G-2559)

▲ B H M Pipe & Supply Inc ....E 281 328-5552
Crosby (G-3726)

Babin Machine Works Inc ....F 409 892-1231
Beaumont (G-1857)

Baldwin Metals Company Inc ....E 214 637-1030
Dallas (G-4000)

◆ Bauer Manufacturing LLC ....D 936 539-5030
Conroe (G-3262)

Caldwell Machine and Gear Inc ....F 903 572-1660
Mount Pleasant (G-15648)

Cambrian Management Ltd ....F 432 620-9181
Midland (G-15156)

Camcara Inc ....G 800 532-0383
Grand Prairie (G-7849)

Cameron International Corp ....A 601 629-3300
Houston (G-9066)

Carbide Grinding Inc ....F 713 944-0015
Houston (G-9090)

Chevas Company LLC ....F 713 225-6595
Houston (G-9176)

Ckb Machining LLC ....F 281 485-5760
Pearland (G-16545)

Cowan Coolant MGT Svcs LLC ....F 214 686-1010
Richardson (G-17293)

▲ CRC-Evans Pipeline Intl Inc ....C 800 664-9224
Houston (G-9337)

Cynco Specialty Inc ....G 281 499-0519
Stafford (G-19298)

▲ Data Matique Properties LP ....C 972 272-3446
Garland (G-7476)

◆ Doosan Turbomachinery Svcs Inc .....D 713 364-7500
La Porte (G-13731)

Downhole Drilling Dynamics LLC ....F 936 344-9329
New Waverly (G-15860)

Downhole Threading Svcs Inc ....E 281 462-9800
Crosby (G-3730)

Dynamic Precision Mfg LLC ....E 713 466-4545
Houston (G-9549)

Envirotech Pumpsystems Inc ....G 832 200-6220
Deer Park (G-5272)

◆ Epiroc Drilling Solutions LLC ....A 972 496-7400
Garland (G-7486)

Epiroc Drilling Solutions LLC ....D 214 547-7800
Allen (G-265)

◆ Forrest Mfg Co ....F 713 864-2545
Houston (G-9837)

▲ Fusion Operations LP ....F 713 691-6547
Houston (G-9878)

Gerber Technology Inc ....C 972 238-7211
Dallas (G-4405)

Ggctr Inc ....G 832 456-4585
Pasadena (G-16448)

Hawk Installation & Cnstr Inc ....F 903 665-8080
Jefferson (G-13284)

Hemaq America LLC ....D 877 700-5060
Helotes (G-8238)

▲ Highwood Machine Tool LLC ....F 254 412-0512
Waco (G-20411)

Holland and Associates LLC ....F 806 892-3504
Idalou (G-12889)

Industrial Castings Co Inc ....E 713 747-5336
Houston (G-10434)

Industrial Mill Maint Sup Inc ....E 800 537-1218
Wake Village (G-20486)

J & R Grinding LLC ....F 281 272-2344
Houston (G-10434)

Jcv Manufacturing Corporation ....F 281 201-4853
Houston (G-10460)

Jet Machine Works Inc ....F 281 449-0046
Houston (G-10469)

John Crane Inc ....F 979 239-1201
Freeport (G-7200)

Kimbell Gin Machinery Company ....D 806 763-6645
Lubbock (G-14433)

▲ Koch Machine Tool Company ....F 281 720-8500
Houston (G-10553)

Lake Road Welding Co ....E 940 692-4988
Wichita Falls (G-20778)

Landers Machine Co ....E 817 834-6383
Fort Worth (G-6779)

Ltn Industries Inc ....E 713 849-1300
Houston (G-10698)

M S I Corporation ....E 512 243-9000
Austin (G-1315)

Made In America Mfg LLC ....E 512 435-9952
Austin (G-1316)

Marshall Prcsion Machining Inc ....F 940 320-4240
Sanger (G-18726)

Master Machine Inc ....E 713 690-3480
Houston (G-10788)

Maverick Tube Corporation ....C 713 937-1800
Houston (G-10803)

Michael Ray ....G 832 567-2507
Houston (G-10865)

Mitchell Manufacturing Inc ....E 281 351-9641
Tomball (G-19989)

N & N Services LLC ....F 281 741-9714
Pearland (G-16584)

◆ National Hose Aquisition Corp ....D 713 920-2030
Pasadena (G-16487)

National Oilwell Varco Inc ....D 409 842-2114
Beaumont (G-1933)

Norse Cutng & Abandonment Inc .....E 832 327-3640
Houston (G-11070)

Ohmstede Ltd ....C 281 471-4140
La Porte (G-13780)

Oliver Machinery Inc ....F 903 489-2250
Malakoff (G-14636)

▲ OSG Usa Inc ....E 800 837-2223
Irving (G-13134)

◆ Pgi International Ltd ....B 713 466-0056
Houston (G-11316)

Polytrnix McHning Fbrction LLC ....F 972 436-0422
Richardson (G-17374)

Reliable Bus Resources LLC ....E 281 469-6400
Houston (G-11588)

▼ River City Manufacturing Inc ....F 512 335-5194
Bertram (G-2053)

Rogers Manufacturing Inc ....G 940 325-7806
Mineral Wells (G-15540)

▲ Royberg Inc ....E 210 525-0094
San Antonio (G-18435)

Southwest Metrics Inc ....E 817 581-4474
Fort Worth (G-7005)

Storm Vulcan Inc ....F 214 637-1430
Dallas (G-5014)

Superior Threaded Products LP ....E 281 459-3131
Houston (G-12120)

Superior Weighting Pdts LLC ....F 361 880-7160
Corpus Christi (G-3633)

Teledrill Inc ....F 281 550-0434
Katy (G-13448)

Texas High Roller Inc ....E 979 778-7460
Bryan (G-2511)

Thi Acquisition Inc ....C 281 485-8339
Pearland (G-16603)

▲ Tool-Flo Manufacturing Inc ....C 713 941-1080
Houston (G-12317)

Tri Tool Inc ....D 281 499-1188
Stafford (G-19387)

Two Elk Investments LLC ....F 972 465-3608
Irving (G-13200)

◆ Victor Equipment Company ....A 940 566-2000
Denton (G-5409)

Victor Technologies Group Inc ....E 940 566-2000
Denton (G-5410)

▲ Victor Technologies Intl Inc ....D 940 381-1353
Denton (G-5411)

Wells Manufacturing LLC ....E 713 690-4204
Houston (G-12632)

Wilson Supply Corporate Office ....F 713 237-3309
Houston (G-12675)

Wtb LLC ....E 432 366-1026
Odessa (G-16214)

3542 Machine Tools: Forming

Atlantic Durant Technology Inc ....E 956 440-8005
Harlingen (G-8182)

B&P Littleford LLC ....F 713 433-3304
Houston (G-8781)

Bridgestone Hosepower LLC ....E 432 367-4673
Odessa (G-15944)

▲ Chemplast Inc ....E 281 208-2585
Stafford (G-19294)

Ckb Machining LLC ....F 281 485-5760
Pearland (G-16545)

Concept Laser Inc ....E 817 328-6500
Grapevine (G-8023)

Formers By Ernie Inc ....F 713 991-3455
Houston (G-9834)

Galam Metals LLC ....F 713 934-8528
Houston (G-9893)

▲ George A Sturdevant Inc ....F 281 449-6466
New Caney (G-15840)

Imfab Inc ....E 903 577-0510
Mount Pleasant (G-15651)

▲ Mic Group LLC ....F 979 277-7806
Brenham (G-2263)

Mp Precision Services Inc ....F 915 599-9188
El Paso (G-5886)

Novaria Group LLC ....E 817 381-3810
Fort Worth (G-6870)

Rogers Manufacturing Inc ....G 940 325-7806
Mineral Wells (G-15540)

S&S Industries Inc ....C 972 438-7150
Irving (G-13168)

▲ Texas Extrusion Service Inc ....F 281 350-2288
Spring (G-19178)

Varco Shaffer Inc ....E 713 672-1711
Houston (G-12535)

3543 Industrial Patterns

Aqseptence Group Inc ....C 651 636-3900
Houston (G-8671)

Kruger Aluminum & Brass Fndry ....F 940 767-0432
Wichita Falls (G-20777)

Superior Pattern Works Inc ....F 281 442-1422
Spring (G-19168)

▲ Tri-Sen Systems Corporation ....E 832 632-1211
Webster (G-20648)

3544 Dies, Tools, Jigs, Fixtures & Indl Molds

Absolute Machine & Tooling LLC ....F 512 259-7676
Leander (G-13984)

▲ Advanced Integration Tech Inc ....C 972 423-8354
Plano (G-16772)

Advanced Integration Tech LP ....D .. 972 423-8354
Plano (G-16773)
Airborn Interconnect Inc ....E .. 903 629-7821
Winnsboro (G-20895)
▲ Al Knoch Interiors Inc ....D .. 915 886-5800
Canutillo (G-2662)
Alart Tool & Die Corp ....F .. 713 691-0434
Houston (G-8527)
▲ American Acrylic Injection Inc ....E .. 972 784-7759
Farmersville (G-6221)
▲ Apex Plastics & Tooling Inc ....E .. 972 205-9000
Garland (G-7438)
Arnim Tool Inc ....F .. 972 247-0802
Dallas (G-3966)
Atlantic Durant Technology Inc ....E .. 956 440-8005
Harlingen (G-8182)
Avey Plastics ....F .. 512 784-7047
San Marcos (G-18678)
◆ Balloffet Die Corporation Inc ....F .. 915 592-5252
El Paso (G-5658)
Batchelor Steel Rule Dies Inc ....F .. 972 263-2263
Grand Prairie (G-7839)
Bee Jay Molding Inc ....E .. 281 487-0377
Pasadena (G-16397)
▲ Bitech Tool & Die Inc ....E .. 915 757-8001
El Paso (G-5663)
▲ Blackwell Plastics LP ....E .. 713 643-6577
Houston (G-8912)
◆ Bowers Equipment Company Inc .....F .. 281 458-8891
Houston (G-8962)
Campbell Grinding & Machine ....F .. 972 221-2211
Lewisville (G-14032)
Crux Manufacturing Inc ....E .. 512 619-6170
Pflugerville (G-16665)
Danrick Industries Inc ....F .. 915 599-2988
El Paso (G-5713)
Decatur Machine Services Inc ....F .. 940 627-1062
Decatur (G-5244)
Deka Texas Inc ....E .. 214 618-1176
Frisco (G-7280)
Delcas Industries LLC ....G .. 956 831-3311
Brownsville (G-2348)
Densonone LLC ....E .. 972 494-1911
Garland (G-7478)
Detail Mold & Mfg LLC ....F .. 512 255-0525
Georgetown (G-7647)
Die & Tool Service Inc ....F .. 281 498-3317
Sugar Land (G-19479)
▲ Dieco Inc ....E .. 817 822-4292
Arlington (G-661)
▲ Dynamic Tool Company Inc ....D .. 915 598-2330
El Paso (G-5726)
Ennis Inc ....B .. 210 271-7971
San Antonio (G-18091)
▲ Exacta Packaging Designs Inc ....D .. 972 323-1063
Carrollton (G-2733)
Exco Extrusion Dies Texas Inc ....F .. 972 442-3131
Wylie (G-20935)
Exxene Corporation ....E .. 361 991-8391
Corpus Christi (G-3525)
F M Eagle Tool Co Inc ....F .. 915 590-6377
El Paso (G-5761)
Fort Worth Forging Die LP ....F .. 817 529-9990
Fort Worth (G-6644)
Fyco Tool & Die Inc ....F .. 281 304-4480
Cypress (G-3793)
G & H Diversified Mfg LP ....D .. 713 856-1600
Houston (G-9883)
Gate-Mold Inc ....F .. 512 255-3470
Round Rock (G-17659)
▼ Gemco of Port Lavaca Inc ....E .. 361 570-6611
Victoria (G-20266)
▲ Genesis Tool Inc ....E .. 915 781-1000
El Paso (G-5782)
Gme Inc ....E .. 903 586-7581
Jacksonville (G-13240)
Great Southwest Tool Co ....E .. 915 594-7804
El Paso (G-5789)
Gustavs Tool & Die Inc ....F .. 830 379-3551
Seguin (G-18840)
Halsey Manufacturing ....G .. 940 566-3306
Denton (G-5371)
Hansen Manufacturing Inc ....E .. 713 682-1075
Houston (G-10117)
Harrison Mullane Inc ....C .. 281 449-4846
Houston (G-10128)
Jacksonville Tool & Die Inc ....F .. 903 586-6030
Jacksonville (G-13245)
Jorge Trevino ....F .. 956 376-7114
Weslaco (G-20662)

Kiger Bros Mch Tl & Die Works ....E .. 281 447-1315
Houston (G-10532)
Lark Industrial LLC ....F .. 915 500-4347
El Paso (G-5839)
Lorentson Manufacturing Co ....E .. 956 399-8902
San Benito (G-18659)
M3 Tooling LLC ....E .. 210 946-4264
San Antonio (G-18270)
Marshall-Gruber Company LLC ....F .. 682 518-7400
Mansfield (G-14688)
▲ Mexican Technologies Co Inc ....F .. 915 595-2285
El Paso (G-5875)
Mitchell Machine & Fabricating ....F .. 903 880-0249
Mabank (G-14579)
Motor City Tool & Die Corp ....F .. 512 251-7700
Pflugerville (G-16681)
Mw Industries Inc ....E .. 281 233-0448
Houston (G-10945)
Norlus Group Inc ....F .. 915 590-2041
El Paso (G-5899)
▲ North Texas Plastics Inc ....E .. 940 458-7954
Sanger (G-18728)
One Source Mfg Tech LLC ....D .. 512 259-3272
Leander (G-13996)
Paragon Rio Grande LLC ....F .. 956 831-8249
Brownsville (G-2391)
Petrochem Energy LLC ....F .. 713 234-7814
Sugar Land (G-19525)
Pfi Molding Inc ....F .. 713 946-3300
Houston (G-11314)
Pheasant Rubber Company Inc ....F .. 432 367-5137
Odessa (G-16122)
▲ PI Tape Texas LLC ....F .. 903 266-9204
Tyler (G-20142)
▲ Quantex Instrument Company ....E .. 936 544-5732
Crockett (G-3723)
R & E Tooling & Plastics Inc ....F .. 817 834-2858
Fort Worth (G-6930)
Radke Machine & Tool Inc ....E .. 254 576-2513
Hubbard (G-12737)
Rct Global Inc ....F .. 915 595-8750
El Paso (G-5929)
▼ Research Advanced Methods Inds ...E .. 254 442-1008
Cisco (G-3068)
▲ Royberg Inc ....E .. 210 525-0094
San Antonio (G-18435)
Saucedas Prcision Grinding Inc ....E .. 956 399-1572
San Benito (G-18667)
Schaefer Mold Inc ....F .. 817 534-7461
Fort Worth (G-6976)
Schmidt Tool & Mfg Co ....F .. 936 856-5897
Willis (G-20864)
Snapp Tool & Die Inc ....E .. 915 821-2046
El Paso (G-5964)
Snelick Quality Tool Inc ....E .. 972 221-0537
Dallas (G-4973)
Team Manufacturing Inc ....F .. 903 583-7722
Bonham (G-2155)
Texas Toolmakers Inc ....E .. 210 494-3651
San Antonio (G-18544)
Titan Tool & Die Company ....F .. 713 849-4300
Houston (G-12299)
Tool and Die By H&H Inc ....E .. 713 943-0545
Houston (G-12316)
Tooling Designs Inc ....F .. 281 354-0421
Porter (G-17184)
USA Machine Inc ....F .. 972 636-7400
Royse City (G-17727)
Wichita Falls Mfg Inc ....F .. 940 322-4491
Wichita Falls (G-20831)

3545 Machine Tool Access

AGM Tools Inc ....F .. 832 499-6090
Houston (G-8503)
Alloy Carbide Company ....E .. 713 923-2700
Houston (G-8556)
Alyta International Corp ....F .. 972 978-1980
Allen (G-249)
◆ Amera-Seiki Corporation ....F .. 832 234-5960
Conroe (G-3255)
American Completion Tools Inc ....F .. 281 894-5213
Houston (G-8592)
▲ American National Carbide Co ....D .. 281 351-7165
Tomball (G-19958)
Baker Hghes Olfld Oprtions LLC ....B .. 281 363-6000
The Woodlands (G-19833)
Bastrop Scale Company Inc ....F .. 512 321-3443
Bastrop (G-1749)
Berlin Packaging LLC ....F .. 214 339-0054
Dallas (G-4019)

Btm Services LLC ....E .. 281 773-6060
Houston (G-9004)
Campbell Grinding & Machine ....F .. 972 221-2211
Lewisville (G-14032)
Carbide Grinding Inc ....F .. 713 944-0015
Houston (G-9090)
Carboline Prmium Cutng Tls Inc ....F .. 281 485-5505
Rosharon (G-17600)
Caterpillar Inc ....D .. 210 637-3700
San Antonio (G-17987)
▼ Computerized Cutters Inc ....E .. 972 422-6900
Plano (G-16829)
Corpro Inc ....E .. 432 563-0775
Midland (G-15180)
Crown Cork & Seal Usa Inc ....C .. 936 539-5401
Conroe (G-3287)
Cutting Solutions Inc ....E .. 214 637-4849
Dallas (G-4198)
D C Lites Inc ....F .. 972 556-0260
Dallas (G-4200)
D C Lites Company ....F .. 972 556-0260
Dallas (G-4201)
Daco Abrasives ....E .. 713 923-4664
Houston (G-9390)
Demarco Machine Ltd ....D .. 832 230-0850
Houston (G-8377)
Doggett Heavy McHy Svcs LLC ....F .. 361 289-0727
Corpus Christi (G-3515)
Ellis Tool & Machine Inc ....E .. 903 546-6540
Tom Bean (G-19951)
▲ Epiroc Drilling Tools LLC ....C .. 844 437-4762
Grand Prairie (G-7866)
Evo IDT LLC ....E .. 817 637-0149
Mansfield (G-14671)
Gauging Systems Inc ....E .. 281 980-3999
Sugar Land (G-19484)
Gds Realty LLC ....F .. 713 623-1449
Houston (G-9911)
Gunook Products Inc ....E .. 817 536-0136
Fort Worth (G-6682)
H & T Auger Company ....E .. 432 362-4471
Odessa (G-16022)
Handwheels Inc ....E .. 281 998-0560
Pasadena (G-16453)
▲ Higuchi Manufacturing Amer LLC ....C .. 210 633-2877
San Antonio (G-18167)
Industrial Diamond Products Co ....F .. 713 991-1600
Houston (G-10350)
Innosol Inc ....E .. 281 859-4428
Houston (G-10368)
▲ Inrock Drilling Systems Inc ....E .. 713 690-5600
Houston (G-10376)
▲ J M Fabrication Company LLC ....F .. 817 652-0526
Arlington (G-709)
Kalco Machine & Mfg Co ....D .. 940 761-1060
Wichita Falls (G-20775)
Lee Contracting Inc ....F .. 281 456-9023
Houston (G-10616)
Lewis & Lambert LLLP ....C .. 817 834-7146
Haltom City (G-8150)
Liberty Plant Maintenance Inc ....F .. 281 923-5307
Liberty (G-14122)
▼ M & F Gauge & Specialty Co Inc .....E .. 325 643-2655
Brownwood (G-2439)
Maintenance Tool & Supply Co ....F .. 361 888-8801
Corpus Christi (G-3571)
Master Precision Machining LLC ....F .. 915 877-0776
El Paso (G-5869)
Metro Mfg Support Svcs Inc ....E .. 817 330-3430
Fort Worth (G-6831)
▲ Midland Wellhead Inc ....E .. 432 682-0856
Midland (G-15303)
Milltech Manufacturing Company ....D .. 972 276-1786
Garland (G-7554)
Mitchell Machine & Fabricating ....F .. 903 880-0249
Mabank (G-14579)
Mitchell Manufacturing Inc ....E .. 281 351-9641
Tomball (G-19989)
◆ Multicam Inc ....C .. 972 929-4070
Dallas (G-4707)
Murphy Fw ....D .. 281 633-4500
Rosenberg (G-17590)
National Diamond Lab Texas Inc ....F .. 214 638-1435
Dallas (G-4714)
National Oilwell Varco Inc ....C .. 936 444-4000
Conroe (G-3335)
▲ Pollok Inc ....A .. 915 592-5700
El Paso (G-5914)
▲ Qfc Industries Inc ....F .. 817 640-2151
Arlington (G-763)

SIC

Qti Apparel & Promotions LLC ....E 254 662-3076
Waco *(G-20451)*

R & I Enterprises Inc ....F 956 544-7948
Brownsville *(G-2396)*

Remtex Inc ....F 903 758-0461
Longview *(G-14295)*

Retco Tool Company Inc ....E 214 358-5039
Dallas *(G-4892)*

▼ RSC Acquisitions ....D 713 222-2251
Houston *(G-11690)*

S Q I Inc ....F 432 366-9264
Odessa *(G-16148)*

Saucedas Prcision Grinding Inc ....E 956 399-1572
San Benito *(G-18667)*

SC Manufacturing Texas LLC ....E 817 556-3689
Joshua *(G-13326)*

Ss Machine LP ....E 281 970-8444
Cypress *(G-3822)*

▲ T & S Machines and Tools Inc ....F 940 668-1002
Gainesville *(G-7371)*

Thompson Scale Company ....E 713 932-9071
Houston *(G-12279)*

▲ Tool-Flo Manufacturing Inc ....C 713 941-1080
Houston *(G-12317)*

◆ Union Tech Co LLC ....E 281 583-7601
Houston *(G-12439)*

▲ Vanguard Machinery Intl LLC ....F 713 462-5800
Houston *(G-12528)*

▲ Varel Energy Solutions ....F 972 242-1160
Houston *(G-12537)*

Varel International Ind LLC ....F 713 304-5813
Corpus Christi *(G-3651)*

Varel International Ind LLC ....F 432 550-4816
Odessa *(G-16200)*

◆ Varel International Ind LLC ....D 281 272-6000
Houston *(G-12538)*

Varel Mining and Indus LLC ....F 469 476-4870
Carrollton *(G-2844)*

Vlj Inc ....F 972 442-4673
Wylie *(G-20955)*

Zyvex Corporation ....A 972 235-7881
Richardson *(G-17432)*

Zyvex Instruments LLC ....E 972 792-1625
Richardson *(G-17433)*

3546 Power Hand Tools

Bhl International Inc ....E 281 449-5762
Houston *(G-8874)*

Black & Decker Corporation ....E 713 466-1194
Houston *(G-8899)*

Black & Decker Corporation ....F 972 446-2996
Carrollton *(G-2705)*

▲ Church Hill Drilling Tools US ....F 281 893-0233
Houston *(G-9188)*

◆ Dyna Drill Technologies LLC ....C 281 227-1250
Katy *(G-13398)*

Express Drilling Fluids LLC ....E 361 289-1631
Corpus Christi *(G-3524)*

◆ Fastorq Bolting Systems Inc ....F 281 449-6466
New Caney *(G-15839)*

Henderson Drilling Pdts Inc ....F 281 661-3627
Humble *(G-12775)*

◆ Hilti of America Inc ....E 800 879-8000
Plano *(G-16886)*

Iae International Inc ....E 281 685-3091
Houston *(G-10311)*

Keith Properties Inc ....F 254 883-2531
Marlin *(G-14759)*

▲ Keppel Amfels Inc ....A 956 838-3110
Brownsville *(G-2374)*

National Oilwell Varco Inc ....C 936 444-4000
Conroe *(G-3335)*

Newsco Intl Enrgy Svcs USA Inc ....E 832 924-4020
Houston *(G-11042)*

Radius Hdd Direct LLC ....E 800 892-9114
Weatherford *(G-20613)*

Sharewell Hdd LLC ....E 281 288-2560
Houston *(G-11846)*

Straight Line Sawing & Sealing ....F 972 590-8922
Grand Prairie *(G-7976)*

Taylors Oilfield Mfg Inc ....E 281 442-4084
Houston *(G-12168)*

Trane Technologies Company LLC ....E 903 730-4000
Tyler *(G-20163)*

◆ Union Tech Co LLC ....E 281 583-7601
Houston *(G-12439)*

Valley Outdoor Power Eqp Inc ....F 956 787-0469
Pharr *(G-16715)*

Wheel-A-Rama Inc ....G 325 655-7373
San Angelo *(G-17840)*

3547 Rolling Mill Machinery & Eqpt

Andrews Pump & Supply Inc ....E 432 523-2166
Andrews *(G-534)*

Atkore Plastic Pipe Corp ....D 817 594-8791
Weatherford *(G-20576)*

Aztec Mnfcturing-Waskom Partnr ....E 903 687-3943
Waskom *(G-20514)*

Azz Inc ....E 817 297-4361
Crowley *(G-3751)*

B & H Enterprises ....E 817 558-2667
Cleburne *(G-3080)*

Bise Welding & Fabricating Inc ....D 713 681-0958
Houston *(G-8892)*

Coperion Corporation ....F 281 449-9944
Houston *(G-9309)*

J & J Manufacturing Company ....D 409 835-1330
Beaumont *(G-1912)*

K-T Galvanizing Co Inc ....E 817 477-4434
Venus *(G-20220)*

R D Moxie LLc ....G 210 633-2300
San Antonio *(G-18407)*

◆ Seah Steel USA LLC ....D 832 734-0044
Houston *(G-11802)*

Taurex Drill Bits LLC ....E 432 684-4711
Midland *(G-15431)*

Top Threading Services Inc ....E 281 426-8461
Crosby *(G-3745)*

3548 Welding Apparatus

▲ Allied Wear Systems LLC ....F 972 248-8838
Dallas *(G-3837)*

Bar H Welding LLC ....G 903 806-3110
Longview *(G-14200)*

◆ Bowers Equipment Company Inc ....F 281 458-8891
Houston *(G-8962)*

▲ Dyna Torque Technologies Inc ....F 713 937-6699
Houston *(G-9543)*

◆ ESAB Group Inc ....C 800 372-2123
Denton *(G-5365)*

Felux Metal Works & Supply LP ....G 830 484-3436
Poth *(G-17195)*

Hangar Welding & Fabrication ....F 915 857-2899
El Paso *(G-5795)*

▲ Higuchi Manufacturing Amer LLC ....C 210 633-2877
San Antonio *(G-18167)*

Ken Garner Mfg - Vto Inc ....F 361 485-0541
Victoria *(G-20280)*

Magnetrode Corporation ....E 903 795-3378
Jacksonville *(G-13249)*

◆ NCH Corporation ....A 972 438-0211
Irving *(G-13114)*

Peerless Mfg Co ....F 940 566-9029
Denton *(G-5390)*

▲ Petrohab Llc ....E 281 407-3800
Houston *(G-11302)*

Praxair Surface Tech Inc ....E 713 849-9474
Houston *(G-11384)*

RW Cox Inc ....E 903 739-8088
Paris *(G-16369)*

▲ Stanco Manufacturing Inc ....D 903 796-7936
Atlanta *(G-845)*

Tpws Inc ....F 713 291-5518
Magnolia *(G-14632)*

Tri Tool Inc ....D 281 499-1188
Stafford *(G-19387)*

Trident Process Systems LLC ....F 940 372-1535
Gainesville *(G-7373)*

Tsi Flow Products Inc ....F 903 984-2870
Kilgore *(G-13597)*

U S Alloy Co ....E 877 711-9274
Stafford *(G-19391)*

◆ Victor Equipment Company ....A 940 566-2000
Denton *(G-5409)*

Victor Technologies Group Inc ....E 940 566-2000
Denton *(G-5410)*

▲ Victor Technologies Intl Inc ....D 940 381-1353
Denton *(G-5411)*

3549 Metalworking Machinery, NEC

▲ B-W Grinding Service Inc ....D 713 641-0888
Houston *(G-8782)*

Bc Wind-Down Inc ....E 512 799-2075
Austin *(G-982)*

Be-Technologies Ltd ....F 972 242-1853
Carrollton *(G-2704)*

▼ Bk Corrosion LLC ....E 713 225-6661
Houston *(G-8897)*

Bright Machines Inc ....B 512 750-5266
Austin *(G-1009)*

Cactus Varied Industries LLC ....B 806 335-9470
Amarillo *(G-411)*

CER Tek Inc ....F 915 772-8290
El Paso *(G-5693)*

Cook Cmprssn-Parland Operation ....E 713 433-2002
Houston *(G-9300)*

◆ Granutch-Sturn Systems Corp AM ....D 972 790-7800
Grand Prairie *(G-7884)*

Hero Assemblers LP ....E 210 628-4800
San Antonio *(G-18165)*

Industrial Coils LLC ....F 956 664-9496
McAllen *(G-14871)*

International Commodities ....F 281 331-1252
Alvin *(G-367)*

▲ J-Mac Tool Inc ....E 817 237-6309
Fort Worth *(G-6732)*

James Manufacturing Inc ....E 903 872-2346
Corsicana *(G-3675)*

K & H Fabricators Inc ....E 512 237-5020
Smithville *(G-18977)*

Komax Corporation ....E 915 591-4551
El Paso *(G-5832)*

M N Gumbert Corporation ....E 214 340-8383
Dallas *(G-4621)*

M2 Global Technology Ltd ....F 210 561-4800
San Antonio *(G-18269)*

Makerarm Inc ....E 512 553-8033
Round Rock *(G-17670)*

Mercer Metals LP ....E 214 905-9915
Grand Prairie *(G-7925)*

▲ Offshore Kinematics Inc ....E 713 934-7300
Houston *(G-11142)*

▼ Powertech Components Inc ....F 210 521-0799
San Antonio *(G-18385)*

Premier Coil Solutions Inc ....E 713 677-0209
Waller *(G-20507)*

▲ Quiet Logistics Inc ....E 860 841-3892
Dallas *(G-4852)*

Rk Ranco Industries LLC ....F 903 831-5992
Nash *(G-15723)*

Sharp Iron Group LLC ....D 940 766-4545
Wichita Falls *(G-20810)*

Sons Design & Mfg Inc ....G 817 595-9800
Hurst *(G-12859)*

South Coast Manufacturing LLC ....E 713 670-0900
Galena Park *(G-7382)*

Specialized Manufacturing Ltd ....E 713 864-2551
Houston *(G-11997)*

Ta Fabrication LLC ....F 330 301-6800
Euless *(G-6161)*

Tamra Group Inc ....E 817 453-3370
Mansfield *(G-14721)*

Tendenci Inc ....E 281 497-6567
Houston *(G-12203)*

Triple/S Dynamics Inc ....E 214 828-8600
Dallas *(G-5117)*

3552 Textile Machinery

1 To 1 Printers LLC ....G 281 821-4400
Houston *(G-8398)*

▲ ABM International Inc ....D 936 441-4401
Montgomery *(G-15624)*

Beaver Graphix LLC ....F 325 227-3014
San Angelo *(G-17780)*

Gerber Technology Inc ....C 972 238-7211
Dallas *(G-4405)*

Kimbell Gin Machinery Company ....D 806 763-6645
Lubbock *(G-14433)*

Martex Fiber Southern Corp ....E 956 831-7707
Brownsville *(G-2381)*

Netfires LLC ....F 972 603-2702
Grand Prairie *(G-7933)*

▲ Ramann Enterprises Inc ....E 817 560-4222
Fort Worth *(G-6938)*

Stitch Gallery Inc ....F 512 550-6172
Lakeway *(G-13820)*

▲ Xact Xpressions Inc ....E 972 242-6332
Dallas *(G-5205)*

3553 Woodworking Machinery

B & B Stake Co ....G 936 327-2161
Livingston *(G-14150)*

Lindsay Forest Products Inc ....F 903 693-7526
Carthage *(G-2913)*

SC Industrial Resource Group ....E 972 272-4521
Garland *(G-7584)*

Universal Well Service LLC ....E 432 272-6686
Odessa *(G-16190)*

Vacuumpodscom Inc ....F 972 986-8876
Cedar Hill *(G-2954)*

3554 Paper Inds Machinery

Mayhan Fabricators Inc ....E 903 734-4198
Gilmer *(G-7709)*

Sendero Industries LLC ....E 713 868-6960
Houston *(G-11828)*

Southanchor Manufacturing LLC ......E 915 590-6718
El Paso *(G-5970)*

Texarkana Machine Inc ....F 903 831-4355
Texarkana *(G-19779)*

▼ **Unique Products Mfg LLC** ....E 915 590-2444
El Paso *(G-6019)*

3555 Printing Trades Machinery & Eqpt

Berry Machine Shop ....E 817 572-0948
Burleson *(G-2571)*

▲ **Citronix Inc** ....E 817 633-3200
Arlington *(G-643)*

Cyclone Production Inc ....F 713 979-1101
Houston *(G-9384)*

◆ **Digitech Solutions Group LLC** ....D 210 545-6000
San Antonio *(G-18060)*

Docresources LLC ....F 832 802-6008
Crosby *(G-3729)*

▲ **Epic Products Intl Corp** ....D 817 640-3037
Cedar Hill *(G-2940)*

Gandy Engineering LLC ....F 210 338-8303
San Antonio *(G-18135)*

▲ **Kgp Group Inc** ....E 817 354-0766
Fort Worth *(G-6760)*

Laser Care Inc ....F 817 640-6665
Arlington *(G-719)*

Laser Drum Products Inc ....F 713 263-9050
Houston *(G-10603)*

Mark/Trece Inc ....E 210 281-8348
San Antonio *(G-18276)*

▲ **Printing Research Corporation** ....D 214 353-9000
Dallas *(G-4827)*

Quality Roller Supply Inc ....F 817 783-5100
Alvarado *(G-338)*

Southern Graphic Systems LLC ....E 214 565-9000
Richardson *(G-17400)*

▲ **Stevens Technology LLC** ....E 817 831-3500
Fort Worth *(G-7019)*

▲ **Tresu Royse Inc** ....E 214 631-2844
Grapevine *(G-8058)*

▲ **USa Screen Printing Chem Inc** ....E 281 474-9777
Seabrook *(G-18793)*

3556 Food Prdts Machinery

Astro Foods International Corp ....F 214 349-7840
Dallas *(G-3977)*

▲ **Automated Food Systems Inc** ....F 469 517-0470
Waxahachie *(G-20528)*

Bakers Pride Oven Co Inc ....F 800 431-2745
Allen *(G-256)*

Bakery Equipment & Svc Co Inc ....E 210 734-5124
San Antonio *(G-17937)*

▲ **Boccard Life Sciences Inc** ....E 281 269-6020
Houston *(G-8933)*

◆ **Calan Group Inc** ....C 972 422-5808
Plano *(G-16817)*

Casteel Mfg Inc ....E 210 923-4558
San Antonio *(G-17986)*

▲ **Centrifuge Repair & Engrg LP** ....F 281 471-3767
La Porte *(G-13726)*

Champion Food Service 2 Inc ....F 210 736-2190
Von Ormy *(G-20346)*

Cnc Fabrication and Maint ....F 817 295-9055
Burleson *(G-2575)*

Commercial Kitchens Inc ....D 281 442-8001
Houston *(G-9250)*

Cugar Machine Inc ....F 817 927-0411
Fort Worth *(G-6565)*

Custom Delis Equipment Co Inc ....E 817 831-7080
Fort Worth *(G-6567)*

◆ **Dallas A C Horn & Company Inc** ......D 214 630-3311
Dallas *(G-4210)*

▼ **Denny Kincer Inc** ....E 806 762-1069
Lubbock *(G-14401)*

Double Jj Corporation ....E 214 353-0230
Dallas *(G-4274)*

East Texas Smoker Company ....G 903 245-0039
Tyler *(G-20081)*

EMI Industries LLC ....F 817 987-1516
Arlington *(G-669)*

◆ **Ferrell-Ross Roll Mfg Inc** ....D 806 364-9051
Hereford *(G-8288)*

Filtration Automation Inc ....E 817 999-8190
Alvarado *(G-332)*

FMC Technologies Inc ....F 281 591-4106
Houston *(G-9823)*

Freeman Brothers Inc ....F 806 883-7831
White Deer *(G-20709)*

Genemco Inc ....E 979 268-7447
Hearne *(G-8231)*

◆ **H & K International Inc** ....C 214 818-3500
Mesquite *(G-15047)*

Hilltop Texas Inc ....E 214 430-1311
Allen *(G-275)*

Insight Equity A P X L P ....F 817 488-7775
Southlake *(G-19075)*

Insight Equity LP ....F 817 488-7775
Southlake *(G-19076)*

▲ **Invision Automated Systems Inc** ......F 713 461-6642
Katy *(G-13410)*

John Bean Technologies Corp ....G 936 441-2077
Conroe *(G-3315)*

John Bean Technologies Corp ....C 713 875-3735
Houston *(G-10480)*

John Bean Technologies Corp ....F 915 859-3776
El Paso *(G-5822)*

Keiser Manufacturing Inc ....G 830 303-3397
Seguin *(G-18846)*

L S W Mfg Inc ....F 817 232-4482
Saginaw *(G-17747)*

Labeling Equipment Specialists ....F 903 734-5873
Gilmer *(G-7708)*

Landers Machine Co ....E 817 834-6383
Fort Worth *(G-6779)*

Logan Farms Inc ....E 713 781-3773
Richmond *(G-17462)*

▲ **M W Waldrop Co** ....E 713 337-5600
Houston *(G-10720)*

◆ **Maddox Metal Works Inc** ....D 214 333-2311
Dallas *(G-4625)*

◆ **Materials Transportation Co** ....C 800 433-3110
Temple *(G-19688)*

◆ **Meyer Industries Inc** ....D 210 736-1811
San Antonio *(G-18296)*

▲ **Project Services Group Inc** ....D 972 812-7370
Irving *(G-13159)*

Quality Custom Fabricators ....D 817 649-8020
Grand Prairie *(G-7960)*

▼ **Quality Fabrication Design LP** ....D 972 304-3266
Coppell *(G-3436)*

▼ **Roto-Flex Oven Co** ....F 210 222-2278
San Antonio *(G-18434)*

Rotom Inc ....E 806 293-7331
Plainview *(G-16762)*

Saginaw Machine Company ....F 817 232-4482
Saginaw *(G-17756)*

Sani-Weld Inc ....E 281 442-0667
Houston *(G-11747)*

▲ **Satake USA Inc** ....D 281 276-3600
Stafford *(G-19374)*

◆ **Sort-Rite International Inc** ....E 956 423-2427
Harlingen *(G-8202)*

SPX Flow Technology Usa Inc ....E 281 897-2964
Houston *(G-12028)*

◆ **Super Sack Bag Inc** ....F 214 340-7060
Dallas *(G-5024)*

▼ **Tables Manufacturing Inc** ....B 972 932-4148
Kaufman *(G-13464)*

Tejas Industries Inc ....E 806 293-4431
Plainview *(G-16763)*

Tetra Pak Global Information ....G 940 565-8800
Denton *(G-5403)*

Texas Tripe Inc ....F 903 674-8042
Detroit *(G-5448)*

▲ **Thunderbird Food Machinery** ....E 214 331-3000
Dallas *(G-5089)*

Tri-Pak Machinery Inc ....E 956 423-5140
Harlingen *(G-8207)*

Win-Holt Equipment Corp ....C 972 641-4658
Grand Prairie *(G-7995)*

3559 Special Ind Machinery, NEC

A&W Productions Inc ....D 940 458-4190
Sanger *(G-18723)*

Apache Refinery Svcs Intl LLC ....D 936 890-8586
Willis *(G-20843)*

◆ **Apergy Artfl Lift Intl LLC** ....E 281 403-5742
Spring *(G-19195)*

Applied Cryo Technologies Inc ....D 281 888-3884
Houston *(G-8666)*

APS Plastics LP ....F 281 290-9950
Tomball *(G-19959)*

Arlington Brick and Supply Inc ....F 817 460-5511
Arlington *(G-624)*

Associated Time Instrs Co Inc ....E 214 637-2763
Dallas *(G-3975)*

▲ **B Plan Inc** ....F 210 256-1700
San Antonio *(G-17933)*

B&P Littleford LLC ....F 713 433-3304
Houston *(G-8781)*

Bd Energy Systems LLC ....E 281 407-9812
Houston *(G-8843)*

C2 International USA LLC ....F 405 473-7144
Grapevine *(G-8019)*

Campbell-Randall Machinery Co ....F 936 539-1400
Conroe *(G-3273)*

▲ **Canon Nanotechnologies Inc** ....D 512 339-7760
Austin *(G-1024)*

Capital Asset Exch & Trdg LLC ....F 650 326-3313
Austin *(G-1025)*

▲ **Cash Processing Solutions Inc** ....B 972 582-1100
Irving *(G-12962)*

◆ **Championx LLC** ....A 281 632-6500
Sugar Land *(G-19455)*

Chart Industries Inc ....E 281 364-8700
The Woodlands *(G-19841)*

▼ **Chemtec Energy Services LLC** ....E 936 856-1704
Willis *(G-20844)*

Christnes Con Swing Saling LLC ....F 214 212-4808
Colleyville *(G-3211)*

Classic Auto Air Mfg LP ....F 817 442-4822
Coppell *(G-3411)*

Cleanplanet Chemical Inc ....E 855 256-7568
Austin *(G-1052)*

Colt Services LP ....F 361 299-2284
Corpus Christi *(G-3504)*

Conecraft Incorporated ....D 817 922-9200
Fort Worth *(G-6540)*

▲ **Consolidated Cotton Gin Co** ....D 806 745-1191
Lubbock *(G-14396)*

Coperion Corporation ....F 281 449-9944
Houston *(G-9309)*

Corona Designs Inc ....E 972 272-0471
Garland *(G-7464)*

Cosine Additive Inc ....F 832 519-8441
Houston *(G-9329)*

◆ **Cryognic Vssel Altrnatives Inc** ....A 713 357-9714
Houston *(G-9350)*

Dallas Metal Service ....F 972 481-1700
Dallas *(G-4221)*

▲ **Deltatech Controls Inc** ....F 956 755-9634
Brownsville *(G-2349)*

▲ **Dynocom Industries Inc** ....E 817 284-8844
Fort Worth *(G-6600)*

Electronic Drilling Control ....D 972 257-0322
Irving *(G-13014)*

Evergreen Solutions Inc ....E 512 389-0625
Austin *(G-11141)*

◆ **Excel Machinery Ltd** ....F 806 335-1553
Amarillo *(G-486)*

Expal USA Inc ....E 903 472-4970
Irving *(G-13020)*

F & F Industries Inc ....E 800 523-8473
Alvarado *(G-331)*

Fas Holdings Group LLC ....E 214 343-5300
Dallas *(G-4353)*

Federal-Mogul Powertrain LLC ....F 915 860-2300
El Paso *(G-5766)*

◆ **Fives Cryo Inc** ....E 281 820-6990
Houston *(G-9794)*

Ford Gin Service Inc ....E 806 745-3433
Lubbock *(G-14411)*

Ftg Aerospace Inc ....D 817 332-3806
Fort Worth *(G-6650)*

Gardner Denver Inc ....D 832 421-5469
Pasadena *(G-16446)*

GL Automation Inc ....F 214 503-9888
Dallas *(G-4407)*

Global Vapor Control Inc ....E 713 463-9200
Houston *(G-9979)*

▲ **Globe Industries Inc** ....E 281 440-3999
Houston *(G-9985)*

Guiverman Industries LLC ....E 866 235-8057
Plano *(G-16882)*

▼ **Hamilton Form Co Ltd** ....D 817 590-2111
Richland Hills *(G-17437)*

Hayes & Stolz Indus Mfg Co LLC ....E 817 926-3391
Burleson *(G-2581)*

I T Remarketing Inc ....E 713 263-8800
Houston *(G-10309)*

Industrial Cmmssning Cons Intl ....F 833 873-4224
La Marque *(G-13708)*

JAS Marketing Inc ....F 281 879-1844
Channelview *(G-3027)*

◆ Jim Coleman Company ....E 713 683-9878
　Houston **(G-10474)**

Kimbell Gin Machinery Company ....D 806 763-6645
　Lubbock **(G-14433)**

Koch Industries Inc ....F 806 347-2645
　Matador **(G-14816)**

Leading Testing Labs LLC ....E 281 600-8227
　Brookshire **(G-2318)**

Listo Inc ....E 469 544-4555
　Dallas **(G-4597)**

Lone Star Cryogenics Inc ....F 979 234-5001
　Eagle Lake **(G-5541)**

Lummus Corporation ....G 806 745-1191
　Lubbock **(G-14443)**

Makerarm Inc ....F 512 553-8033
　Round Rock **(G-17670)**

Mallorys Western & Leather Sup ....F 817 558-0804
　Joshua **(G-13322)**

◆ Materials Transportation Co ....C 800 433-3110
　Temple **(G-19688)**

▲ Megapower Inc ....G 832 415-6995
　Houston **(G-10822)**

Merichem Company ....E 713 428-5201
　Houston **(G-10834)**

Millennium Recycling LLP ....G 817 624-4307
　Fort Worth **(G-6840)**

Multiple Systems Inc ....E 806 373-7073
　Amarillo **(G-449)**

Multiple Systems Inc ....E 806 373-7073
　Amarillo **(G-450)**

▲ Naegles Industrial Lea McHy Co ......F 361 293-7015
　Yoakum **(G-20972)**

▲ Norriseal-Wellmark Inc ....C 713 466-3552
　Houston **(G-11069)**

Parking Sense Usa Inc ....F 830 428-0299
　Boerne **(G-2131)**

Pegicorn Enterprises LLC ....F 512 821-3300
　Austin **(G-1406)**

Penatek LLC ....E 432 368-0888
　Odessa **(G-16109)**

Photronics Inc ....C 469 675-8520
　Allen **(G-294)**

Plastronics Co ....E 972 986-0474
　Irving **(G-13151)**

Plus One Robotics Inc ....F 937 287-5060
　San Antonio **(G-18383)**

Prime Momento LLC ....F 832 643-4605
　Sugar Land **(G-19529)**

Psp Industries Inc ....F 210 651-9595
　Schertz **(G-18760)**

R C Technical Welding & Fabr ....E 281 933-6004
　Stafford **(G-19367)**

Rack Technology Inc ....E 817 468-2233
　Arlington **(G-766)**

◆ Raider Manufacturing Ltd ....D 806 762-3227
　Lubbock **(G-14470)**

Reactor Services International ....F 281 824-0841
　Alvin **(G-378)**

Safety-Kleen Systems Inc ....F 254 772-4419
　Waco **(G-20456)**

◆ Safety-Kleen Systems Inc ....B 800 669-5740
　Richardson **(G-17392)**

Samuel Jackson Incorporated ....E 806 795-5218
　Lubbock **(G-14475)**

Samuel Jackson Mfg Co ....F 806 795-5218
　Lubbock **(G-14476)**

Season Group Usa LLC ....E 210 522-1116
　San Antonio **(G-18461)**

Spectrum Semiconductor Tech Lc ....F 972 562-2552
　McKinney **(G-14977)**

SPX Flow Technology Usa Inc ....E 281 897-2964
　Houston **(G-12028)**

◆ Stanmar Manufacturing Inc ....F 936 967-3040
　Livingston **(G-14162)**

▲ T & S Machines and Tools Inc ....F 940 668-1002
　Gainesville **(G-7371)**

Taylor-Wharton America Inc ....D 281 738-2863
　Baytown **(G-1803)**

Tel Mnfacturing Engrg Amer Inc ....C 972 643-2000
　Allen **(G-301)**

Temple Precision Enterpise Inc ....F 409 283-8163
　Woodville **(G-20918)**

▲ Texas Extrusion Service Inc ....F 281 350-2288
　Spring **(G-19178)**

Tiger Tower Services LLC ....E 281 951-2500
　La Porte **(G-13796)**

Tokyo Electron America Inc ....B 512 424-1000
　Austin **(G-1583)**

Tokyo Electron America Inc ....F 512 424-1000
　Austin **(G-1584)**

Toppan Photomasks Inc ....E 972 398-0411
　Plano **(G-17034)**

▲ Toppan Photomasks Inc ....B 512 310-6500
　Round Rock **(G-17695)**

▲ Tote Systems International LP ....E 817 447-9110
　Fort Worth **(G-7068)**

Tristar Group Inc ....E 972 392-2848
　Dallas **(G-5118)**

Unconvntonal Gas Solutions LLC ....F 346 353-1048
　Houston **(G-12431)**

◆ US Rubber Corporation ....E 936 756-1977
　Conroe **(G-3380)**

V Gas LLC ....E 713 896-8531
　Houston **(G-12510)**

Vally Park USA Corp ....F 956 994-0000
　Mission **(G-15572)**

▲ Vanguard Pharmaceutical McHy ....E 281 528-8885
　Spring **(G-19185)**

Vector Systems Inc ....D 214 544-9500
　McKinney **(G-14985)**

Wolters Holdings Inc ....G 972 272-4600
　Garland **(G-7610)**

Worth Eqp Parts & Svc Co Inc ....E 817 473-7266
　Mansfield **(G-14730)**

3561 Pumps & Pumping Eqpt

Accelerated Prod Svcs Inc ....E 432 334-8580
　Odessa **(G-15898)**

Accelerated Pump ....F 432 582-2335
　Odessa **(G-15899)**

◆ Afton Pumps Inc ....D 713 923-9731
　Houston **(G-8500)**

Aggietech Energy Services LLC ....C 432 682-3131
　Midland **(G-15108)**

▲ American Acrylic Injection Inc ......E 972 784-7759
　Farmersville **(G-6221)**

American Petroleum Welding Inc ....E 806 747-7272
　Lubbock **(G-14361)**

Andrews Pump & Supply Inc ....F 432 523-2166
　Andrews **(G-534)**

Andrews Pump & Supply Inc ....F 806 592-4567
　Denver City **(G-5414)**

◆ Apergy Artfl Lift Intl LLC ....E 281 403-5742
　Spring **(G-19195)**

Baker Hughes A GE Company LLC ....B 713 625-4200
　Houston **(G-8801)**

Baker Hughes Company ....F 713 439-8600
　Houston **(G-8802)**

◆ Baker Hughes Holdings LLC ....C 713 439-8600
　Houston **(G-8806)**

Bayou City Pump Works LP ....F 713 472-7722
　Pasadena **(G-16396)**

Becker Industries Inc ....F 281 590-4900
　Houston **(G-8848)**

Borets US Inc ....E 713 980-4530
　Houston **(G-8958)**

Bowie Industries Incorporated ....E 940 872-1106
　Bowie **(G-2192)**

Cryognic Inds Svc Cmpanies LLC ....F 281 590-4800
　Houston **(G-9349)**

◆ CS&p Technologies LP ....D 713 467-0869
　Cypress **(G-3783)**

▲ Curflo Inc ....F 281 479-5000
　Deer Park **(G-5266)**

▲ Deran Inc ....F 806 746-6926
　Lubbock **(G-14402)**

Diversified Industrial Svc Co ....E 806 274-2214
　Borger **(G-2174)**

Dobbs Corporation ....F 806 655-7791
　Canyon **(G-2670)**

◆ Don-Nan Pump and Supply Co Inc ...C 432 682-7742
　Midland **(G-15194)**

◆ Dresser LLC ....C 262 549-2626
　Houston **(G-9517)**

Ellis Manufacturing Co Inc ....E 432 561-8819
　Midland **(G-15209)**

Endurance Lift Solutions LLC ....C 903 595-8600
　Fort Worth **(G-6611)**

Energy Devices of Texas Inc ....E 903 963-7906
　Van **(G-20207)**

Engineered Pump Services Inc ....E 713 472-7722
　Pasadena **(G-16428)**

Flowserve Corporation ....B 972 443-6500
　Irving **(G-13027)**

Flowserve Corporation ....F 800 446-0401
　Irving **(G-13028)**

Flowserve Corporation ....E 832 375-0807
　Houston **(G-9813)**

Flowserve Corporation ....E 409 727-1476
　Port Arthur **(G-17108)**

Flowserve Corporation ....E 713 863-9180
　Houston **(G-9814)**

Flowserve Corporation ....F 409 842-5594
　Beaumont **(G-1895)**

Flowserve Corporation ....F 412 787-8803
　Pasadena **(G-16439)**

Flowserve Corporation ....E 281 241-3500
　Pasadena **(G-16440)**

Flowserve International Inc ....F 972 443-6500
　Irving **(G-13029)**

▲ Flowserve US Inc ....D 972 443-6500
　Irving **(G-13030)**

Flowserve US Inc ....F 979 549-0029
　Pasadena **(G-16441)**

Flowserve US Inc ....G 502 267-2205
　Pasadena **(G-16442)**

◆ Flowtronex Psi LLC ....E 469 221-1200
　Dallas **(G-4372)**

Fluxmetals LLC ....D 832 948-4307
　Houston **(G-9818)**

Franks Machine Shop LLP ....G 806 747-4854
　Lubbock **(G-14413)**

Fts International Mfg LLC ....G 682 647-3300
　Fort Worth **(G-6653)**

Fts International Services LLC ....F 210 308-3400
　San Antonio **(G-18129)**

Fts International Services LLC ....F 817 334-0002
　Fort Worth **(G-6654)**

◆ Fts International Services LLC ....C 817 862-2000
　Fort Worth **(G-6655)**

Gardner Denver Inc ....E 817 248-4500
　Benbrook **(G-2040)**

◆ Gardner Dnver Wtr Jtting Syste ....C 281 448-5800
　Houston **(G-9898)**

▼ Gator Pump Inc ....G 325 643-3502
　Brownwood **(G-2429)**

Ggctr Inc ....E 832 456-4585
　Pasadena **(G-16448)**

◆ Gilkes Inc ....E 832 932-5282
　Kemah **(G-13475)**

▲ Global Oilfield Services Inc ....E 713 977-5900
　Sugar Land **(G-19488)**

▲ Griffin Dewatering LLC ....E 713 676-8000
　Houston **(G-10044)**

▲ Griffin Pump & Equipment Inc ....E 866 770-8100
　Houston **(G-10045)**

◆ Grundfos CBS Inc ....C 281 994-2700
　Brookshire **(G-2316)**

H Lorimer Corporation ....E 903 643-3239
　Longview **(G-14245)**

Hammonds Technical Svcs Inc ....E 281 999-2900
　Houston **(G-10115)**

◆ Houston Grinding & Mfg Co ....D 713 869-3573
　Houston **(G-10235)**

▲ Hyseco Inc ....E 713 991-4240
　Houston **(G-10307)**

◆ Integrated Flow Solutions LLC ....D 903 595-6511
　Tyler **(G-20102)**

▲ ITT Bornemann Usa Inc ....F 832 320-2500
　Stafford **(G-19334)**

ITT LLC ....D 469 221-1200
　Dallas **(G-4515)**

Jash Usa Inc ....F 281 962-6369
　Houston **(G-10457)**

K&B Machine ....B 281 456-0293
　Houston **(G-10498)**

▲ Kemlon Products & Dev Co ....B 281 997-3300
　Pearland **(G-16573)**

Kenergy Oilfield Solutions LLC ....F 979 574-6356
　New Braunfels **(G-15807)**

◆ Kmt Aqua-Dyne Inc ....E 713 864-6929
　Houston **(G-10544)**

Longwood Elastomers Inc ....C 979 830-1111
　Brenham **(G-2261)**

◆ Lufkin Gears LLC ....B 936 634-2211
　Lufkin **(G-14539)**

Lufkin Industries LLC ....E 281 495-1100
　Missouri City **(G-15583)**

▲ M G Bryan Equipment Co LP ....F 972 623-4300
　Grand Prairie **(G-7919)**

Marine Services LLC ....E 713 923-6688
　Houston **(G-10765)**

Merrimac Manufacturing Inc ....E 936 894-3900
　Plantersville **(G-17059)**

Metso Minerals Industries Inc ....E 210 491-9521
　San Antonio **(G-18295)**

Motor Controls Inc ....B 972 247-4440
　Dallas **(G-4691)**

Movement Industries Corp ....F 713 849-1300
　Houston **(G-10928)**

Murphy Fw ....D 281 633-4500
  Rosenberg *(G-17590)*

▲ Nikkiso Pumps America Inc ....E 281 310-6747
  Houston *(G-11055)*

▲ O F M Pump Inc ....E 432 381-7390
  Odessa *(G-16094)*

Oil States Industries Inc ....C 713 445-2200
  Houston *(G-11157)*

◆ Oil States Industries Inc ....C 817 548-4200
  Arlington *(G-743)*

Oil States International Inc ....D 713 652-0582
  Houston *(G-11161)*

▲ Oilwell Hydraulics Inc ....F 432 334-8580
  Odessa *(G-16101)*

▼ Oliver Equipment Company LLC .....E 713 856-9206
  Houston *(G-11171)*

▲ Oteco Inc ....C 713 695-3693
  Houston *(G-11200)*

Oteco Inc ....D 713 695-3693
  Houston *(G-11201)*

Pcs Ferguson Inc ....E 432 334-8580
  Odessa *(G-16108)*

◆ Pierce Arrow Inc ....F 940 538-5643
  Henrietta *(G-8282)*

Predominant Pumps & Automation ....F 281 987-0204
  Houston *(G-11398)*

▲ Pristech Products Inc ....E 210 520-8051
  San Antonio *(G-18398)*

Protek Specialty Company ....F 713 667-6691
  Houston *(G-11464)*

Prototype Machine Co ....E 512 282-1590
  Manchaca *(G-14641)*

Pump Arts Inc ....E 713 946-0500
  Houston *(G-11472)*

Pumps Plus Pump & Valve Repair ....F 903 987-9232
  Kilgore *(G-13585)*

▲ Reliable Pump Consultants Inc ....E 713 640-2718
  Houston *(G-11591)*

Robbco Pumps Inc ....F 806 892-2290
  Idalou *(G-12890)*

▲ Rotor-Tech Inc ....F 713 984-8900
  Houston *(G-11672)*

◆ S & N Pump Company ....E 281 445-2243
  Houston *(G-11707)*

Sanbar Balls & Seats Inc ....F 432 332-3755
  Odessa *(G-16149)*

Schlumberger International ....A 713 747-4000
  Houston *(G-11766)*

Sigma Drilling Tech LLC ....F 281 656-9298
  Katy *(G-13442)*

Solamotor of Texas ....F 432 426-3246
  Fort Davis *(G-6319)*

Spartan Pumps Inc ....G 713 858-9887
  Odessa *(G-16159)*

Ssi Lift USA Ltd ....E 432 488-6427
  Midland *(G-15417)*

Standard Indus Mfg Prtners LLC ....F 682 500-1718
  Cresson *(G-3714)*

Standard Indus Mfg Prtners LLC ....G 817 598-1500
  Weatherford *(G-20622)*

Standard Indus Mfg Prtners LLC ....F 940 580-3512
  Gainesville *(G-7369)*

Stealth Pump & Supply LLC ....E 432 385-7770
  Odessa *(G-16166)*

◆ Sulzer Pumps Houston Inc ....C 281 934-6014
  Brookshire *(G-2325)*

Sulzer USA Inc ....E 832 886-2300
  Houston *(G-12092)*

Super Heaters LLC ....F 713 952-5533
  Houston *(G-12105)*

Swaby Manufacturing Company ....F 281 479-7500
  Deer Park *(G-5298)*

▲ Tcm Investments Inc ....C 432 366-5433
  Odessa *(G-16173)*

Teikoku USA Inc ....E 713 983-9901
  Houston *(G-12185)*

Texco Trim Inc ....D 713 861-1892
  Houston *(G-12259)*

Tommy Chappell LLC ....F 432 967-2469
  Odessa *(G-16180)*

Trane Technologies Company LLC ....E 903 730-4000
  Tyler *(G-20163)*

▲ Triangle Pump Components Inc ....F 817 202-8530
  Cleburne *(G-3115)*

◆ TSC Manufacturing and Sup LLC ....E 832 456-3900
  Houston *(G-12395)*

◆ Unitra Inc ....E 281 240-1500
  Stafford *(G-19393)*

▲ Vere Technology LLC ....E 832 532-6745
  Houston *(G-12551)*

Vertical Trbine Spcialists Inc ....D 806 743-5555
  Lubbock *(G-14507)*

Weatherford Artificia ....E 432 561-5505
  Midland *(G-15466)*

Weatherford Artificia ....F 817 624-7810
  Fort Worth *(G-7128)*

◆ Weatherford Artificia ....C 713 836-4000
  Houston *(G-12611)*

Weatherford Artificia ....E 903 935-2416
  Marshall *(G-14807)*

Westech Seal Inc ....F 432 367-1188
  Odessa *(G-16211)*

▼ White Star Pump Company LLC ....F 281 357-4999
  Waller *(G-20509)*

3562 Ball & Roller Bearings

Gulf Coast Bearing & Seal Inc ....F 832 399-4227
  Houston *(G-10058)*

Magnus Mobility Systems Inc ....F 800 527-5142
  Dallas *(G-4627)*

▲ P&H Sales Ltd ....E 817 468-3850
  Arlington *(G-745)*

Roll Master Corp ....D 817 292-4319
  Fort Worth *(G-6965)*

Westech Seal Inc ....F 432 367-1188
  Odessa *(G-16211)*

3563 Air & Gas Compressors

Air Power Sales & Service LLC ....E 903 236-0500
  Longview *(G-14190)*

Air-Serv Group LLC ....E 651 454-0465
  Dallas *(G-3908)*

Alegacy Equipment LLC ....E 832 916-3700
  Waller *(G-20490)*

Angelo Bolt and Indus Sup Inc ....E 325 655-0075
  San Angelo *(G-17776)*

Ares Robotics LLC ....E 713 320-4690
  Houston *(G-8688)*

Atlas Copco Compressors LLC ....F 281 453-6800
  Houston *(G-8743)*

Atlas Copco Compressors LLC ....E 281 453-6800
  Houston *(G-8744)*

Atlas Copco Compressors LLC ....B 281 453-6800
  McAllen *(G-14839)*

Atlas Copco Rental LLC ....E 800 736-8267
  Deer Park *(G-5262)*

▲ Atron Group LLC ....D 214 292-9840
  Dallas *(G-3984)*

Baker Hughes Energy Svcs LLC ....D 713 439-8600
  Houston *(G-8803)*

Cameron International Corp ....D 281 582-9500
  Houston *(G-9064)*

◆ Cameron International Corp ....E 713 939-2282
  Houston *(G-9072)*

Cameron International Corp ....E 713 571-3100
  Waller *(G-20495)*

Cameron International Corp ....C 713 354-1900
  Houston *(G-9068)*

Cameron International Corp ....E 806 665-1647
  Pampa *(G-16318)*

Com-Pac Systems Inc ....F 432 332-4515
  Odessa *(G-15964)*

▲ Compositech Products Mfg Inc ....E 281 648-3557
  Pearland *(G-16548)*

Compressor Designs Inc ....F 432 425-0044
  Odessa *(G-15965)*

Compressor Elements Service ....F 432 943-6701
  Monahans *(G-15602)*

Cook Compression ....F 432 367-7786
  Odessa *(G-15966)*

Csi Compressco Sub Inc ....E 361 576-6827
  Victoria *(G-20256)*

Csi Compressco Sub Inc ....A 432 563-1170
  Midland *(G-15185)*

Diversified Industrial Svc Co ....E 806 274-2214
  Borger *(G-2174)*

Dresser-Rand Company ....D 713 346-2257
  Houston *(G-9519)*

Dresser-Rand Company ....F 713 354-6100
  Houston *(G-9520)*

Dresser-Rand Company ....D 713 468-4210
  Houston *(G-9521)*

▲ Dresser-Rand Group Inc ....C 713 354-6100
  Houston *(G-9522)*

Dresser-Rand LLC ....F 713 467-2221
  Houston *(G-9523)*

▲ Dresser-Rand LLC ....A 713 354-6100
  Houston *(G-9524)*

Enerflex Energy Systems Inc ....F 806 826-0126
  Wheeler *(G-20708)*

◆ Enerflex Energy Systems Inc ....B 281 345-9300
  Houston *(G-9631)*

Enerflex Energy Systems Inc ....D 281 758-4900
  Cypress *(G-3787)*

Fcx Performance Inc ....E 214 320-3604
  Dallas *(G-4357)*

Fluxmetals LLC ....D 832 948-4307
  Houston *(G-9818)*

Gardner Denver Inc ....D 832 421-5469
  Pasadena *(G-16446)*

Gardner Denver Inc ....E 432 366-5433
  Odessa *(G-16010)*

Global Compressor LP ....E 713 983-8773
  Houston *(G-9969)*

Heartland Enterprises Ltd ....E 830 997-9434
  Fredericksburg *(G-7182)*

Hicor Technologies Inc ....E 281 727-0250
  Houston *(G-10174)*

Houston Compression & Svcs LLC ......F 713 550-1556
  Houston *(G-10226)*

Imperial Pumps Co ....F 806 791-5242
  Lubbock *(G-14425)*

J-W Power Company ....C 972 233-8191
  Addison *(G-139)*

Knox Jr Leighton ....E 806 327-5420
  Tahoka *(G-19641)*

Kobelco Compressors Amer Inc ....C 713 470-1290
  La Porte *(G-13764)*

Lely Tank Waste Solutions LLC ....F 800 367-5359
  Troy *(G-20029)*

Lone Star Compressor Corp ....E 713 947-9975
  Friendswood *(G-7249)*

Natural Gas Services Group Inc ....C 432 262-2700
  Midland *(G-15311)*

Neuman & Esser Investments Inc ....E 281 497-5113
  Katy *(G-13427)*

◆ Neuman & Esser Usa Inc ....E 281 497-5113
  Katy *(G-13428)*

▲ Onesubsea LLC ....A 713 939-2282
  Houston *(G-11182)*

▲ Packaging Service Co Inc ....C 281 485-1458
  Pearland *(G-16586)*

Petro Chem Industries Inc ....E 713 645-5024
  Houston *(G-11300)*

Productioneered Products Co ....E 281 364-1086
  Spring *(G-19244)*

Red River Compression LLC ....F 832 831-0532
  Houston *(G-11568)*

◆ Sanden International USA Inc ....A 972 442-8400
  Wylie *(G-20948)*

Sanotech 360 LLC ....F 817 697-7116
  Fort Worth *(G-6974)*

▲ SEC Energy Products & Svcs LP ....E 281 890-9977
  Houston *(G-11811)*

Sunbelt Vacuum Services Inc ....E 972 449-3830
  Dallas *(G-5023)*

▲ Texas Turbine Inc ....E 817 444-5528
  Azle *(G-1730)*

Trane Technologies Company LLC ....E 903 730-4000
  Tyler *(G-20163)*

Trillium US Inc ....D 512 441-6893
  Austin *(G-1593)*

Unconvntonal Gas Solutions LLC ....F 346 353-1048
  Houston *(G-12431)*

United Industries Inc ....E 432 362-2361
  Odessa *(G-16189)*

V&L Industrail Services Inc ....F 409 724-3336
  Nederland *(G-15761)*

Wcsa Inc ....F 806 383-1060
  Amarillo *(G-473)*

▲ Werther International Inc ....F 800 655-4781
  Houston *(G-12634)*

3564 Blowers & Fans

▲ 3nine USA Inc ....F 512 667-6146
  San Marcos *(G-18676)*

◆ Aerus LLC ....E 214 378-4000
  Dallas *(G-3897)*

▲ Air Filters Inc ....E 713 896-8901
  Houston *(G-8507)*

▲ Air Liquide Electronics US LP ....A 972 301-5200
  Dallas *(G-3905)*

Air Oasis LLC ....E 806 373-7788
  Amarillo *(G-477)*

Air Quality Systems LLC ....F 214 495-9991
  Allen *(G-248)*

Air Relief Technologies Inc ....E 817 261-3791
  Fort Worth *(G-6357)*

Airbox LLC ....G 512 968-5496
  Austin *(G-901)*

SIC

Airflow Systems Inc ....D 800 818-6185
Dallas (G-3911)

Airfoil Impellers Corporation ....E 979 822-6418
Bryan (G-2452)

▲ American Green Technology Inc ....E 269 340-9975
Houston (G-8598)

▲ Atlantic Blowers LLC ....F 214 233-0280
Dallas (G-3979)

▲ Attic Breeze LLC ....E 254 865-9999
Gatesville (G-7617)

Beakley Enterprises Inc ....E 817 783-5000
Alvarado (G-324)

Bill West Properties Inc ....E 713 726-0151
Houston (G-8885)

Braided Green Brokerage LLC ....F 480 729-5506
Murphy (G-15683)

◆ Bullen Pump Inc ....E 281 274-1800
Houston (G-9017)

Carols Lighting and Fan Sp Inc .....F 281 292-1661
Conroe (G-3274)

Carrier Corporation ....C 903 510-7300
Tyler (G-20063)

Ceco Environmental Corp ....C 214 357-6181
Dallas (G-4092)

Christopher RAD Nader ....F 512 442-5326
Cedar Park (G-2963)

Clean Air Consultants Inc ....D 972 278-2664
Garland (G-7458)

Columbus Industries Inc ....C 915 843-2274
El Paso (G-5700)

Commscope Technologies LLC ....A 214 634-8502
Dallas (G-4149)

Compressor Designs Inc ....F 432 425-0044
Odessa (G-15965)

▲ Custom Air Products & Svcs Inc ..D 281 802-7419
Houston (G-9365)

▲ Dust Free LP ....E 972 635-9565
Royse City (G-17719)

Eastern Star Group LLC ....F 972 729-9955
Allen (G-263)

Emerson Climate Tech Inc ....C 817 277-7764
Arlington (G-668)

Filter Maintenance Company Inc .....E 713 432-7969
Houston (G-9786)

Filter-All Inc ....E 281 356-1257
Magnolia (G-14606)

Gardner Denver Inc ....B 432 366-5433
Odessa (G-16010)

Gardner Denver Inc ....F 281 873-1200
Houston (G-9897)

▼ Glasfloss Industries Inc ....C 740 687-1100
Desoto (G-5432)

▲ Goodman Global Holdings Inc .....F 713 861-2500
Waller (G-20500)

◆ Hanwha Pwr Systems Amricas Inc ..F 281 599-3377
Houston (G-10121)

◆ Houston Service Industries Inc ....E 713 947-1623
Houston (G-10250)

Jf Filtration Inc ....F 214 634-2200
Dallas (G-4534)

Jf Filtration Inc ....F 210 946-1688
San Antonio (G-18201)

Jf Filtration Inc ....F 956 412-3234
Harlingen (G-8192)

Joe Tipton Inc ....F 972 271-6666
Garland (G-7527)

Lasko Products LLC ....B 817 625-6381
Fort Worth (G-6780)

Lifetime Filter Inc ....B 281 391-8060
Katy (G-13423)

▼ Magnetic Technology Inc ....E 214 544-2700
McKinney (G-14955)

Metroplex Products Inc ....F 817 923-8241
Fort Worth (G-6832)

Morrison Products Inc ....D 972 279-4000
Mesquite (G-15063)

▼ Oliver Equipment Company LLC ...E 713 856-9206
Houston (G-11171)

Pollution System Solutions Inc ......F 713 574-6661
Spring (G-19241)

▲ Polsys Services Inc ....F 713 999-1100
The Woodlands (G-19903)

Psp Industries Inc ....E 210 651-9595
Schertz (G-18760)

Quietaire Cooling Inc ....E 713 228-9421
Houston (G-11512)

▲ Quietaire Corporation ....F 713 228-9421
Houston (G-11513)

▲ Radiant Indus Solutions Inc ....F 713 972-0196
Houston (G-11531)

Regal Beloit America Inc ....C 417 847-4775
Eagle Pass (G-5555)

▲ Republic Sales & Manufacturing ..E 214 631-8070
Dallas (G-4890)

Robinson Fans Inc ....E 325 437-3267
Abilene (G-74)

Sabio Environmental LLC ....E 512 869-0544
Round Rock (G-17689)

Selkirk Corporation ....B 972 943-6100
Richardson (G-17395)

Sepra-Chem Corporation ....E 478 788-9789
Tyler (G-20151)

Skyven Technologies Inc ....E 972 861-0893
Richardson (G-17399)

Smith Fans Inc ....F 806 872-8465
Lamesa (G-13830)

Technos Inc ....E 210 651-9393
Schertz (G-18764)

Thermtech Inc ....E 281 359-7555
Humble (G-12804)

Tiernan Aeration Inc ....E 806 372-4051
Amarillo (G-468)

Toro Company ....C 915 231-7200
El Paso (G-6008)

Unisorb Corporation ....F 713 943-3753
South Houston (G-19053)

◆ Ventamatic Ltd ....C 940 325-7887
Mineral Wells (G-15545)

Viron International Corp ....D 254 773-9292
Temple (G-19714)

▼ Winston/Royal Guard Corp ....E 903 757-7341
White Oak (G-20722)

3565 Packaging Machinery

Accutek Inc ....E 972 915-6888
Irving (G-12922)

Allpac Inc ....E 214 630-8804
Prosper (G-17212)

B T S Precision Machine ....G 903 498-7501
Scurry (G-18782)

Cowgirl Brands LLC ....F 512 466-3816
Kyle (G-13680)

Deka Texas Inc ....E 214 618-1176
Frisco (G-7280)

Faro Services Inc ....F 214 631-1888
Dallas (G-4352)

Foam Supplies Inc ....E 972 436-7008
Lewisville (G-14050)

Formers International Inc ....E 281 833-3310
Pasadena (G-16443)

Formers International Inc ....E 281 998-9570
Pasadena (G-16444)

◆ General Packaging Equipment Co ...E 713 686-4331
Houston (G-9926)

Gs Liquid Technologies LLC ....F 817 556-6262
Cleburne (G-3093)

Huhtamaki Inc ....B 903 427-5711
Clarksville (G-3073)

Ibac Interests LP ....F 281 681-0122
Oak Ridge North (G-15889)

◆ ID Technology LLC ....D 817 626-7779
Fort Worth (G-6713)

J & J Manufacturing Company ....D 409 835-1330
Beaumont (G-1912)

▲ Keaco Enterprises Inc ....F 210 651-6688
Schertz (G-18751)

Ls Packaging Design Inc ....E 713 645-9177
Houston (G-10694)

▲ M W Waldrop Co ....E 713 337-5600
Houston (G-10720)

Motor Controls Inc ....B 972 247-4440
Dallas (G-4691)

Nut Place Inc ....E 713 462-3147
Houston (G-11100)

◆ OMI Crane Systems Inc ....E 972 636-8000
Fate (G-6228)

Precision Business Mchs Inc ....F 972 224-9119
Desoto (G-5440)

Signode Industrial Group LLC ....E 409 745-2600
Orange (G-16263)

Superior Label Systems Inc ....E 214 330-7770
Dallas (G-5026)

◆ Tetra Pak Inc ....C 940 565-8800
Denton (G-5404)

Vistech Mfg Solutions LLC ....E 210 225-9900
San Antonio (G-18597)

Zynex Inc ....G 972 221-5050
Lewisville (G-14113)

3566 Speed Changers, Drives & Gears

▲ Amarillo Gear Company LLC ....C 806 622-1273
Amarillo (G-478)

▲ Appliance Controls Texas Corp ....E 214 501-3880
Garland (G-7439)

▲ Coyote Electronics Inc ....F 817 485-3336
Azle (G-1722)

▲ Deran Inc ....E 806 746-6926
Lubbock (G-14402)

▲ Deran Gear Inc ....D 806 746-6926
Lubbock (G-14403)

Fitz Torque Convertors Inc ....E 432 362-3261
Odessa (G-16003)

▼ Johnson Gear Inc ....F 806 749-6400
Lubbock (G-14431)

Kuzzy Industrial Supplier ....F 915 881-4105
El Paso (G-5833)

Martin Sprocket & Gear Inc ....D 817 473-1520
Mansfield (G-14689)

Martin Sprocket & Gear Inc ....F 817 258-3000
Houston (G-10778)

Martin Sprocket & Gear Inc ....D 903 427-2217
Clarksville (G-3075)

Martin Sprocket & Gear Inc ....D 325 677-3591
Abilene (G-59)

Martin Sprocket & Gear Inc ....F 817 258-3000
Fort Worth (G-6813)

Martin Sprocket & Gear Inc ....D 214 428-2191
Dallas (G-4641)

Metro Sprocket & Gear Inc ....F 972 723-3240
Midlothian (G-15485)

▲ Omni Usa Inc ....F 713 635-6331
Houston (G-11179)

▲ Polyspede Electronics Corp ....E 214 363-7245
Dallas (G-4811)

▼ Ram-Gear Manufacturing Inc ....F 361 668-0235
Alice (G-231)

Rave Gear LLC ....D 830 421-3295
Seguin (G-18860)

Sew-Eurodrive Inc ....C 214 330-4824
Desoto (G-5441)

3567 Indl Process Furnaces & Ovens

Air Performance Service Inc ....E 972 387-3334
Dallas (G-3907)

Ajax Tocco Magnethermic Corp ......F 903 297-2526
Longview (G-14191)

Carrier Corporation ....C 903 510-7300
Tyler (G-20063)

Clean Energy Tech Assn Inc ....E 903 389-4136
Fairfield (G-6171)

E-Z Heat Corporation ....F 830 693-4005
Horseshoe Bay (G-8367)

Energy Services Group Amer Inc ....F 281 452-5335
Channelview (G-3018)

▲ Epcon Industrial Systems LP ....D 936 273-1774
Shenandoah (G-18896)

Estovel Inc ....G 512 345-6997
Austin (G-1139)

Exotherm Corporation ....F 713 981-9100
Houston (G-9726)

Furnace Systems Inc ....F 972 423-7800
Plano (G-16875)

Haydon Corporation ....F 972 641-6400
Grand Prairie (G-7888)

Hou Fab & Maintenance Inc ....G 713 672-1993
Crosby (G-3733)

▲ Incinerator International Inc ....F 713 227-1466
Houston (G-10336)

Jerryco Mch & Boiler Works LP ......D 713 224-7900
Houston (G-10466)

Mayhan Fabricators Inc ....E 903 734-4198
Gilmer (G-7709)

Ncc Nano LLC ....E 512 491-9500
Austin (G-1362)

Osr Services LP ....E 281 422-7206
Baytown (G-1830)

◆ Paragon Industries LP ....D 972 288-7557
Mesquite (G-15067)

▲ Paragon Industries Inc ....D 972 288-7557
Mesquite (G-15068)

Pollution System Solutions Inc ......F 713 574-6661
Spring (G-19241)

Rae Energy Solutions Inc ....G 281 440-3434
Houston (G-11533)

Rik-Mar Fabricators Inc ....F 979 779-1616
Bryan (G-2501)

◆ Steelman Industries Inc ....E 903 984-3061
Kilgore (G-13594)

Team Cooperheat-Mqs Inc ....E 713 673-3660
  Houston *(G-12171)*

Texas Incinerator Co Inc ....F 432 687-5045
  Midland *(G-15436)*

3568 Mechanical Power Transmission Eqpt, NEC

▲ American Mast Inc ....E 713 643-4321
  Houston *(G-8601)*

▲ Ameridrives International LLC ....E 512 353-4000
  San Marcos *(G-18677)*

Arcosa Inc ....C 972 942-6500
  Dallas *(G-3958)*

Baart Industrial Group ....F 713 690-1690
  Houston *(G-8783)*

Balcones Technologies LLC ....F 512 699-5828
  Georgetown *(G-7639)*

▲ Best Pump and Flow LP ....E 713 690-4511
  Fort Worth *(G-6448)*

Bk Power Systems LLC ....F 713 225-6661
  Houston *(G-8898)*

Clutchco International Inc ....E 281 446-1297
  Humble *(G-12758)*

Clutchco USA ....F 936 588-3501
  Humble *(G-12759)*

Cosmec Inc ....E 903 677-2871
  Athens *(G-825)*

◆ GE Energy Manufacturing Inc ....D 713 803-0900
  Houston *(G-9913)*

GE Energy Manufacturing Inc ....D 281 864-2669
  Houston *(G-9914)*

Global Pwr Technical Svcs Inc ....E 214 574-2700
  Irving *(G-13039)*

Gpeg LLC ....E 214 574-2700
  Irving *(G-13042)*

▲ Jc/Fz Holdings Inc ....E 713 948-6000
  Houston *(G-10459)*

Jyoti International Inc ....C 936 523-4700
  Conroe *(G-3316)*

▲ Lastrad LLC ....G 713 589-9477
  Houston *(G-10607)*

Lonestar Couplings Inc ....E 713 690-1873
  Houston *(G-10683)*

Martin Sprocket & Gear Inc ....F 817 258-3000
  Houston *(G-10778)*

Martin Sprocket & Gear Inc ....D 903 427-2217
  Clarksville *(G-3075)*

Martin Sprocket & Gear Inc ....D 325 677-3591
  Abilene *(G-59)*

Martin Sprocket & Gear Inc ....D 214 428-2191
  Dallas *(G-4641)*

▲ Mayday Manufacturing Co ....C 940 898-8301
  Denton *(G-5381)*

Metro Sprocket & Gear Inc ....F 972 723-3240
  Midlothian *(G-15485)*

National Oilwell Varco Inc ....C 936 825-7070
  Navasota *(G-15739)*

Odessa Babbitt Bearing Company ....E 432 366-2836
  Odessa *(G-16095)*

▲ Purvis Industries LLC ....D 214 358-5500
  Dallas *(G-4837)*

ROC Industries Inc ....E 713 468-7743
  Houston *(G-11647)*

Scan-Pac Mfg Inc ....E 281 356-1640
  Magnolia *(G-14626)*

Standard Motor Products Inc ....C 972 316-8100
  Lewisville *(G-14094)*

Tb Woods Incorporated ....E 512 352-4000
  San Marcos *(G-18712)*

Tb Woods Incorporated ....F 512 353-4000
  San Marcos *(G-18713)*

Texas Precision Mfg Inc ....E 806 741-1166
  Lubbock *(G-14492)*

United Industries Inc ....E 432 362-2361
  Odessa *(G-16189)*

US Bellows Inc ....B 713 731-0030
  Houston *(G-12481)*

▲ Warner Electric LLC ....D 940 767-2000
  Wichita Falls *(G-20827)*

Williams Indus Svcs Group Inc ....C 281 884-8364
  Deer Park *(G-5303)*

▲ Wpt Power Corporation ....E 940 761-1971
  Wichita Falls *(G-20837)*

3569 Indl Machinery & Eqpt, NEC

A&K Industrial Repair LLC ....E 281 470-8848
  Deer Park *(G-5258)*

▲ AB Bellco Corporation ....E 713 781-6447
  Houston *(G-8440)*

ABC Fire Systems LLC ....G 830 625-3473
  New Braunfels *(G-15771)*

▲ Ag-Meier Industries LLC ....E 254 939-3731
  Belton *(G-2016)*

All American Filters Inc ....F 281 421-1909
  Baytown *(G-1807)*

Andritz Separation Inc ....F 903 856-0445
  Pittsburg *(G-16743)*

▲ ARC Specialties Inc ....E 713 631-7575
  Houston *(G-8680)*

Asher Enterprises Inc ....E 281 446-8131
  Humble *(G-12747)*

Baker Hghes Olfld Oprtions LLC ....C 800 441-0535
  Yorktown *(G-20976)*

Brooks Industrial Coatings Inc ....F 512 990-5333
  Austin *(G-1012)*

▲ Butterworth Inc ....F 281 821-7300
  Houston *(G-9022)*

◆ Cameron Solutions Inc ....C 713 849-7500
  Houston *(G-9079)*

CCI Thermal Tech Texas Inc ....F 855 219-2101
  Houston *(G-9109)*

Centex Mechatronics LLC ....F 830 387-4131
  New Braunfels *(G-15781)*

Champion Process Inc ....E 281 953-9000
  Houston *(G-9159)*

Chart Industries Inc ....C 281 364-8700
  The Woodlands *(G-19841)*

◆ Chemguard Inc ....F 817 473-9964
  Mansfield *(G-14662)*

Chief Fire Systems Inc ....D 281 252-5800
  Magnolia *(G-14596)*

Compressor Products Intl LLC ....D 713 462-1061
  Houston *(G-9261)*

▲ Crall Products Inc ....E 806 665-8446
  Pampa *(G-16320)*

Csw Industrials Inc ....E 214 884-3777
  Dallas *(G-4189)*

Csw Industrials Holdings Inc ....F 214 884-3777
  Dallas *(G-4190)*

▼ Dalhart R & R Mch Works Inc ....E 806 244-5686
  Dalhart *(G-3834)*

◆ Delta Screen & Filtration LLC ....D 713 856-0300
  Houston *(G-9434)*

Dfs Fire Systems LLC ....F 214 628-4061
  Richardson *(G-17301)*

Diversified Materials Inc ....E 361 993-4600
  Corpus Christi *(G-3514)*

◆ Eden Equipment Company Inc ....F 909 629-2217
  Austin *(G-1113)*

Emergency Vehicles Texas Inc ....F 817 281-4172
  Haltom City *(G-8139)*

◆ Ets-Lindgren Inc ....C 512 531-6400
  Cedar Park *(G-2968)*

◆ Exterran Energy Solutions LP ....C 281 836-7000
  Houston *(G-9736)*

Far East Energy (bermuda) Ltd ....F 832 598-0470
  Houston *(G-9761)*

Filtration Group LLC ....E 815 726-4600
  Dallas *(G-4361)*

Filtration Products LLC ....E 210 805-0200
  San Antonio *(G-18114)*

Fire Systems of Texas LLC ....E 956 391-1191
  McAllen *(G-14862)*

Flameout LLC ....E 713 984-8310
  Houston *(G-9796)*

Forterra Inc ....A 469 458-7973
  Irving *(G-13032)*

Frontier Fire Systems Inc ....E 214 343-9500
  Dallas *(G-4382)*

Gardner Denver Inc ....D 832 421-5469
  Pasadena *(G-16446)*

Generon Igs Inc ....E 713 937-5200
  Houston *(G-9928)*

◆ Generon Igs Inc ....D 713 937-5200
  Houston *(G-9929)*

Gep Haynesville LLC ....E 281 363-9161
  The Woodlands *(G-19867)*

Hammonds Technical Svcs Inc ....E 281 999-2900
  Houston *(G-10115)*

◆ Houston Grinding & Mfg Co ....D 713 869-3573
  Houston *(G-10235)*

Hurst Hydraulics Inc ....F 713 863-0340
  Houston *(G-10288)*

Idis America Co Ltd ....F 866 986-1312
  Coppell *(G-3420)*

Instruments Tech McHy Inc ....E 210 651-9066
  Schertz *(G-18750)*

Johnson Filtration Pdts Inc ....E 806 371-8033
  Amarillo *(G-444)*

K C Fab Inc ....E 713 921-5333
  Houston *(G-10496)*

K C Fab Inc ....F 806 372-9281
  Amarillo *(G-495)*

Katch Filters LLC ....G 713 425-7400
  Houston *(G-10501)*

Kirby - Smith Machinery Inc ....E 817 378-0600
  Fort Worth *(G-6763)*

Kirby - Smith Machinery Inc ....F 806 373-1229
  Amarillo *(G-445)*

Knight Corporation ....E 281 933-5363
  Houston *(G-10546)*

Linde Inc ....E 281 203-3600
  Spring *(G-19227)*

Lone Star Cast Mch Partners LP ....F 903 986-8300
  Kilgore *(G-13563)*

▼ Lubrication Systems Texas LLC ....D 713 464-6266
  Houston *(G-8388)*

▲ Magnum Fabrications Inc ....E 409 963-0161
  Port Arthur *(G-17117)*

▼ Mmlj Inc ....F 713 869-2227
  Houston *(G-10896)*

Morales Machine Sp & Trnsp LLC ....F 956 722-4485
  Laredo *(G-13915)*

Nexus Alarm & Suppression Inc ....E 877 828-1200
  Dallas *(G-4737)*

◆ Nitrocision LLC ....E 210 254-4100
  San Antonio *(G-18346)*

▲ Olaer Usa Inc ....E 713 937-8900
  Houston *(G-11167)*

◆ Peerless Mfg Co ....D 214 357-6181
  Dallas *(G-4794)*

▲ Planeview-Wmi LLC ....F 936 588-8988
  Conroe *(G-3350)*

Porous Metal Filters Inc ....F 866 288-2522
  Spring *(G-19160)*

▲ Purolator Efp LLC ....D 713 977-0610
  Houston *(G-11474)*

R & I Enterprises Inc ....F 956 544-7948
  Brownsville *(G-2396)*

Radix Us LLC ....E 832 377-9601
  Houston *(G-11532)*

▲ Reliable Pump Consultants Inc ....E 713 640-2718
  Houston *(G-11591)*

Robogistics LLC ....F 409 234-1033
  Houston *(G-11646)*

Romeo Engineering Incorporated ....E 817 656-0048
  Fort Worth *(G-6966)*

▲ Seltek International Inc ....E 915 772-8444
  El Paso *(G-5955)*

Sentrimax Centrifuges USA Inc ....F 817 453-8112
  Mansfield *(G-14718)*

Sepra-Chem Corporation ....F 478 788-9789
  Tyler *(G-20151)*

Siemens Industry Inc ....F 713 671-9510
  Houston *(G-11879)*

Sparkler Group Inc ....E 936 756-4471
  Conroe *(G-3365)*

Spec Americas LLC ....E 281 812-7732
  Houston *(G-11996)*

Strongarm Industries Inc ....F 409 835-1330
  Vidor *(G-20334)*

Sulphur River Gathering LP ....F 806 663-7700
  Pampa *(G-16339)*

◆ Sulzer Turbo Svcs Houston Inc ....B 713 567-2700
  La Porte *(G-13792)*

▼ T & S Randall and Sons LP ....G 713 466-6951
  Tomball *(G-20012)*

▲ Texas Turbine Inc ....E 817 444-5528
  Azle *(G-1730)*

TF Hudgins Holdings Inc ....C 713 682-3651
  Houston *(G-12266)*

◆ Thyssenkrupp Arprt Systems Inc ....C 817 834-6984
  Fort Worth *(G-7061)*

Tqi LLC ....E 830 401-4400
  Seguin *(G-18869)*

Turbomasters Inc ....F 210 690-1958
  San Antonio *(G-18572)*

▲ Tyco Fire Products LP ....A 806 472-2400
  Lubbock *(G-14502)*

Tyco Fire Products LP ....A 806 472-2400
  Lubbock *(G-14503)*

Unconvntonal Gas Solutions LLC ....F 346 353-1048
  Houston *(G-12431)*

Valtrek Group LLC ....F 915 201-7559
  El Paso *(G-6025)*

Vaquero Midstream LLC ....E 214 855-5546
  Dallas *(G-5154)*

▲ Wellstream Inc ....G 281 249-0900
  Houston *(G-12633)*

▼ Winston/Royal Guard Corp ....E 903 757-7341
  White Oak *(G-20722)*
World Wide Filtration Inc ....F 281 421-7676
  Baytown *(G-1839)*

3571 Electronic Computers

Acer America Corporation ....C 254 298-4000
  Temple *(G-19666)*
Boomi Inc ....E 800 289-3355
  Round Rock *(G-17628)*
▲ Convey Computer Corporation ......E 214 576-9630
  Dallas *(G-4163)*
▲ Corvalent Corporation ....E 512 456-2400
  Cedar Park *(G-2965)*
Cray Inc ....E 512 651-7020
  Austin *(G-1071)*
Crescent Systems Inc....................E 972 437-0400
  Richardson *(G-17294)*
Daniel Industries Inc ....E 713 467-6000
  Houston *(G-9401)*
◆ Daniel Measurement & Ctrl LLC....B 713 827-5033
  Houston *(G-9402)*
Dell America Latina Corp ....F 512 799-1022
  Round Rock *(G-17641)*
Dell Inc ....G 817 408-5725
  Arlington *(G-658)*
Dell Inc ....C 512 324-0137
  Round Rock *(G-17643)*
◆ Dell Inc ....A 800 289-3355
  Round Rock *(G-17642)*
▲ Dell Marketing LP ....C 512 513-9022
  Round Rock *(G-17644)*
◆ Dell Products LP ....A 866 413-3355
  Round Rock *(G-17645)*
Dell Technologies Inc ....C 800 289-3355
  Round Rock *(G-17646)*
Dell USA LP ....F 512 728-3366
  Austin *(G-1088)*
Dell USA LP ....D 512 725-1829
  Round Rock *(G-17647)*
Denali Intermediate Inc..................A 713 627-0933
  Round Rock *(G-17648)*
Enterprise Svcs Ltin Amer Corp.....E 703 245-9675
  Houston *(G-9664)*
Focus Wireless Inc ....F 586 907-5323
  Richardson *(G-17310)*
▲ Foxconn Assembly LLC ....D 281 668-1668
  Houston *(G-9848)*
◆ Foxconn Corporation ....E 281 668-1668
  Houston *(G-9849)*
Futuremedia Group Inc ....E 972 770-0000
  Carrollton *(G-2743)*
Gazoo Inc ....F 979 220-7753
  Bryan *(G-2475)*
General Dynmics Mssion Systems ..C 210 524-8200
  San Antonio *(G-18137)*
▲ Gtech Precision Inds USA Ltd ....F 817 539-8014
  Mansfield *(G-14678)*
Hewlett-Packard Company ....D 979 691-4540
  College Station *(G-3186)*
Hp Inc ....E 970 898-0000
  Houston *(G-10271)*
Hp Inc ....A 541 360-4763
  Spring *(G-19132)*
Hp Inc ....B 972 604-3355
  Plano *(G-16887)*
Iberon LLC ....F 877 559-2140
  Houston *(G-10312)*
Jack Saunders ....F 713 806-7997
  Baytown *(G-1823)*
Keil Software Inc ....F 972 312-1107
  Plano *(G-16901)*
▲ Laversab Inc ....E 281 325-8300
  Sugar Land *(G-19503)*
Link World Trade Inc......................C 972 713-8000
  Addison *(G-145)*
Linux Tech Inc ....F 972 907-0871
  Dallas *(G-4596)*
Micro-Smart Systems Inc ....F 713 433-2277
  Houston *(G-8389)*
▲ Mingtel Inc ....F 972 378-5559
  Plano *(G-16929)*
Nvent Thermal LLC ....B 800 545-6258
  Houston *(G-11102)*
Oracle Corporation ....A 737 867-1000
  Austin *(G-1391)*
PC Cable Connexion Inc ....F 281 338-5400
  League City *(G-13974)*
Rfmicron Inc ....E 512 535-4647
  Austin *(G-1465)*

▲ Rsi Inc ....E 512 268-7500
  Kyle *(G-13686)*
Salient Global Technologies ....D 925 526-1234
  Dallas *(G-4928)*
Simply Nuc Inc ....E 512 766-0402
  Round Rock *(G-17690)*
▲ Skiva Technologies Inc ....E 214 441-3517
  Dallas *(G-4967)*
Systel Inc ....E 281 207-7619
  Sugar Land *(G-19560)*
Touchmate Inc ....E 512 949-3330
  Austin *(G-1587)*
Tri-Cor Industries Inc ....E 210 979-0552
  San Antonio *(G-18565)*
▲ Winsystems Inc ....E 817 274-7553
  Grand Prairie *(G-7996)*
Xplore Technologies Corp ....F 512 637-1100
  Austin *(G-1677)*

3572 Computer Storage Devices

Bogey Free LLC ....F 972 272-6631
  Plano *(G-16809)*
▲ Cd3 Inc ....E 512 252-2592
  Austin *(G-1034)*
◆ Dell Inc ....A 800 289-3355
  Round Rock *(G-17642)*
Denali Intermediate Inc..................A 713 627-0933
  Round Rock *(G-17648)*
◆ Dinamica Inc ....E 281 564-5100
  Houston *(G-9476)*
EMC Corporation ....F 512 343-3332
  Austin *(G-1122)*
EMC Corporation ....C 972 892-7700
  Dallas *(G-4317)*
EMC Corporation ....E 713 621-9800
  Houston *(G-9609)*
Filecontrol Partners Ltd ....F 713 355-1111
  Houston *(G-9785)*
Hendricks BTS Corporation ....F 713 516-8716
  Pearland *(G-16568)*
Hewlett Packard Enterprise Co........C 650 687-5817
  Houston *(G-10166)*
▲ Keyscan Inc ....F 201 918-2396
  Odessa *(G-16051)*
Mangstor Inc ....F 512 779-6999
  Austin *(G-1322)*
Mangstor LLC ....F 512 879-9241
  Austin *(G-1323)*
N L Industries Inc ....E 972 233-1700
  Dallas *(G-4711)*
New ERA Solutions Intl LLC ....E 972 360-6112
  Frisco *(G-7262)*
Onyx Venture Group LLC ....F 281 395-4791
  Katy *(G-13375)*
Proactive Technologies Inc ....F 972 416-6298
  Carrollton *(G-2798)*
Quantum Corporation ....C 210 622-9235
  Atascosa *(G-817)*
Synaptic Cloud LLC ....E 972 591-0151
  McKinney *(G-14981)*
◆ Toshiba International Corp ....A 800 231-1412
  Houston *(G-12327)*
Vce Company LLC ....C 972 656-5300
  Richardson *(G-17418)*
Verge Labs Inc ....F 512 707-0001
  Austin *(G-1630)*
Viewcastcom Inc ....F 972 488-7200
  Grapevine *(G-8059)*

3575 Computer Terminals

American Fincl Mktg Group Inc........F 866 679-9241
  League City *(G-13945)*
Behemoth Corporation ....E 281 332-4798
  League City *(G-13949)*
◆ Dell Inc ....A 800 289-3355
  Round Rock *(G-17642)*
Englobal Corporation ....C 409 840-2100
  Beaumont *(G-1888)*
▲ Gtech Precision Inds USA Ltd ....F 817 539-8014
  Mansfield *(G-14678)*
Hewlett-Packard Dev Co LP ....F 281 370-0670
  Spring *(G-19129)*
IDEA Corporation ....F 915 845-6606
  El Paso *(G-5809)*
▲ Ikey Ltd ....E 512 837-0283
  Austin *(G-1223)*
▲ Key Ovation LLC ....F 512 259-5688
  Cedar Park *(G-2976)*
▲ Keyscan Inc ....F 201 918-2396
  Odessa *(G-16051)*

Ktech Products LLC ....E 972 333-7092
  Colleyville *(G-3218)*
NCR Corporation ....F 210 366-2959
  San Antonio *(G-18339)*
NCR Solutions Llc ....F 405 413-8278
  Little Elm *(G-14140)*
Photonic Inc ....E 956 722-3326
  Laredo *(G-13921)*
▲ Rose Electronics ....C 281 933-7673
  Houston *(G-11662)*
Singer Data Products Inc ....E 915 594-7650
  El Paso *(G-5962)*
▲ Telco Intercontinental Corp ....E 281 500-8270
  Houston *(G-12190)*
▲ Verity Instruments Inc ....D 972 446-9990
  Carrollton *(G-2896)*

3577 Computer Peripheral Eqpt, NEC

Access Imaging Solutions LLC ....F 210 590-8338
  San Antonio *(G-17857)*
Acer America Corporation ....C 214 383-3194
  Allen *(G-247)*
▲ Advanced Tracking Tech Inc ....E 800 279-0035
  Houston *(G-8492)*
Agent Systems Inc ....G 972 774-0400
  Dallas *(G-3902)*
Alecom Technologies Group Inc ......G 972 870-9400
  Flower Mound *(G-6259)*
▲ American Micro Systems Ltd ....E 817 571-9015
  Euless *(G-6130)*
▲ Augmentix Corporation ....D 512 334-0111
  Austin *(G-948)*
Automation Solutions LP ....F 281 286-6017
  Houston *(G-8754)*
Bauer Visual Graphics Inc ....F 713 473-5241
  Pasadena *(G-16394)*
Black Box Corporation ....F 713 307-4000
  Houston *(G-8900)*
Bowens Reed and Calloway Inc ....F 214 389-0002
  Dallas *(G-4045)*
Brady Corporation ....G 214 275-9595
  Mesquite *(G-15033)*
Bt5 Technologies LLC ....F 832 727-5214
  Houston *(G-9001)*
▲ Calrock Music ....D 432 213-8822
  Houston *(G-9054)*
Cisco Systems Inc ....A 210 357-2500
  San Antonio *(G-18008)*
Cisco Systems Inc ....C 469 255-0000
  Richardson *(G-17287)*
Cisco Systems Inc ....A 512 378-1112
  Austin *(G-1051)*
Cisco Systems Inc ....D 469 420-4700
  Irving *(G-12971)*
Cisco Systems Inc ....A 800 553-6387
  Lubbock *(G-14393)*
Cisco Systems Inc ....A 972 393-0874
  Houston *(G-9197)*
Cisco Systems Inc ....A 817 490-6062
  Roanoke *(G-17484)*
▲ Codesource LP ....F 940 891-1281
  Denton *(G-5355)*
▲ Corvalent Corporation ....E 512 456-2400
  Cedar Park *(G-2965)*
Creative Type ....E 214 420-1980
  Dallas *(G-4183)*
Crossroads Systems (texas)............C 512 349-0300
  Austin *(G-1074)*
Cypress Technologies LP ....E 512 267-9973
  Leander *(G-13986)*
Data Connection Inc ....F 972 231-2185
  Dallas *(G-4240)*
▲ Datatronic Control Corporation ......E 972 475-7879
  Rowlett *(G-17704)*
◆ Dell Inc ....A 800 289-3355
  Round Rock *(G-17642)*
Dell Technologies Inc ....C 800 289-3355
  Round Rock *(G-17646)*
Delta Group Electronics Inc.............D 972 606-2102
  Grand Prairie *(G-7863)*
Denali Intermediate Inc..................A 713 627-0933
  Round Rock *(G-17648)*
Digital Speech Systems Inc ....E 972 235-2999
  Allen *(G-262)*
Dynatouch Corporation ....E 210 828-8343
  San Antonio *(G-18076)*
E J Ward Inc ....E 210 824-7383
  San Antonio *(G-18078)*
▲ E Major Tech LLC ....F 972 385-6466
  Farmers Branch *(G-6194)*

▲ Enseo LLC ....E 972 234-2513
Plano *(G-16862)*

Epicor Software Corporation ....D 949 585-4000
Austin *(G-1131)*

Evans - Hamilton Inc ....E 281 448-6188
Houston *(G-9715)*

Fotown Productions ....F 225 773-1894
Cypress *(G-3791)*

Hp Inc ....B 512 432-8000
Austin *(G-1698)*

Intel Corporation ....D 281 370-9355
Spring *(G-19135)*

Intel Corporation ....D 512 362-1000
Austin *(G-1232)*

Intel Corporation ....F 972 987-2377
Plano *(G-16893)*

Intel Corporation ....F 281 251-7649
Houston *(G-10391)*

▲ Interphase Corporation ....D 214 654-5000
Carrollton *(G-2872)*

Intrusion Inc ....E 972 234-6400
Richardson *(G-17336)*

▲ Keyscan Inc ....F 201 918-2396
Odessa *(G-16051)*

Lap King LLC ....F 512 415-3034
Austin *(G-1282)*

Laser Pros International Corp ....E 715 369-5995
Marshall *(G-14786)*

Lexmark International Inc ....E 214 257-0001
Irving *(G-13086)*

Mesa Technologies LLC ....E 713 895-7000
Houston *(G-10838)*

Microsoft Corporation ....D 210 346-2500
San Antonio *(G-18302)*

Montano Investments Inc ....E 956 630-1877
McAllen *(G-14892)*

Motion Computing Inc ....C 512 637-1100
Austin *(G-1353)*

Motorola Solutions Inc ....E 915 872-1229
El Paso *(G-5884)*

Mtwd Holdings Inc ....F 972 346-2242
Frisco *(G-7300)*

▲ National Instruments Corp ....A 512 683-0100
Austin *(G-1360)*

Nationwide Press LLC ....F 817 885-8855
Richland Hills *(G-17444)*

Ncs Pearson Inc ....D 432 685-0033
Midland *(G-15314)*

Ncs Pearson Inc ....E 210 339-5000
San Antonio *(G-18340)*

New ERA Solutions Intl LLC ....E 972 360-6112
Frisco *(G-7262)*

▲ Newline Interactive Inc ....F 972 468-9728
Plano *(G-16944)*

Nextus Inc ....E 512 288-9080
Georgetown *(G-7667)*

◆ Omni Data Systems Ltd LLP ....F 281 469-4365
Houston *(G-11177)*

Omnidata Services Group LLC ....F 281 469-4365
Houston *(G-11180)*

Pason Systems USA Corp ....D 713 693-8700
Houston *(G-11256)*

Photonic Inc ....F 956 722-3326
Laredo *(G-13921)*

Ringdale Inc ....F 512 288-9080
Georgetown *(G-7675)*

▲ Rose Electronics ....C 281 933-7673
Houston *(G-11662)*

Salient Systems Corporation ....E 512 617-4800
Austin *(G-1484)*

◆ Samsill Corporation ....C 817 536-1906
Fort Worth *(G-6972)*

Scantron Corporation ....F 770 593-5050
San Antonio *(G-18455)*

Sigma Industrial Automtn Inc ....F 210 659-5000
Schertz *(G-18762)*

Sigmatron International Inc ....F 830 775-5524
Del Rio *(G-5324)*

Singer Data Products Inc ....E 915 594-7650
El Paso *(G-5962)*

▲ South Txas Lghthouse For Blind .....C 361 883-6553
Corpus Christi *(G-3627)*

Southeast Prtr Connection LLC ....E 256 880-9991
Plano *(G-17010)*

Systel Inc ....F 281 207-7619
Sugar Land *(G-19560)*

Techworks Inc ....F 512 349-1300
Austin *(G-1558)*

Telxon Corporation ....C 713 868-5511
Houston *(G-12195)*

◆ Texas Digital Systems Inc ....D 979 693-0933
College Station *(G-3204)*

◆ Touch International Inc ....D 512 832-8292
Austin *(G-1586)*

◆ Tpv International (usa) Inc ....F 512 241-1508
Austin *(G-1588)*

Tri-Cor Industries Inc ....D 210 979-0552
San Antonio *(G-18565)*

Unicom Engineering Inc ....D 972 673-1345
Plano *(G-17041)*

Uptime Devices Inc ....F 512 328-1800
Austin *(G-1615)*

Venture Research Inc ....E 469 246-4000
Plano *(G-17044)*

Viewcastcom Inc ....E 972 488-7200
Grapevine *(G-8059)*

Warren Watts Technology LLC ....F 817 924-1370
Fort Worth *(G-7127)*

▲ Wincor Nixdorf Inc ....D 512 676-5000
Austin *(G-1672)*

▼ Yokogawa Corporation America .....E 281 340-3800
Sugar Land *(G-19576)*

Zebra Technologies Corporation ....B 512 716-3088
Round Rock *(G-17700)*

Zebra Technologies Corporation ....B 956 630-0315
McAllen *(G-14920)*

Zebra Technologies Corporation ....B 956 571-3770
McAllen *(G-14921)*

3578 Calculating & Accounting Eqpt

Access Atm Inc ....F 713 463-9033
Houston *(G-8456)*

Advanced Ret MGT Systems Inc ....E 303 738-1800
Houston *(G-8491)*

American Pos Alliance LLC ....F 817 350-4714
Grapevine *(G-8011)*

Cannedy Contemporary Svcs Inc ......E 940 322-3856
Wichita Falls *(G-20749)*

Cummins - Allison Corp ....F 972 661-5390
Dallas *(G-4192)*

Diebold Nixdorf Incorporated ....F 210 242-6100
San Antonio *(G-18058)*

◆ Elias & Associates LLC ....E 956 244-6552
Harlingen *(G-8186)*

Ganart Technologies Inc ....E 972 512-6933
Carrollton *(G-2744)*

NCR Corporation ....E 210 366-2959
San Antonio *(G-18339)*

NCR Solutions Llc ....F 405 413-8278
Little Elm *(G-14140)*

One Source SEC & Sound Inc ....E 713 934-7400
Humble *(G-12791)*

▲ Renfro Industries Inc ....D 972 563-4295
Terrell *(G-19749)*

▲ Revolution Retail Systems LLC ....G 469 317-2910
Carrollton *(G-2806)*

▲ Texas Instruments Incorporated ......A 972 995-3773
Dallas *(G-5067)*

Texas Instruments Incorporated ....E 214 567-2075
Richardson *(G-17408)*

Touchpay Holdings LP ....E 972 215-0133
Irving *(G-13196)*

University Houston - System ....C 713 741-2447
Houston *(G-12467)*

Wincor Nixdorf Inc ....G 512 252-5622
Manor *(G-14651)*

3579 Office Machines, NEC

Associated Time Instrs Co Inc ....F 713 263-1366
Houston *(G-8726)*

Associated Time Instrs Co Inc ....E 214 637-2763
Dallas *(G-3975)*

Cummins - Allison Corp ....F 972 661-5390
Dallas *(G-4192)*

Dominion Voting Systems Inc ....F 214 907-3010
McKinney *(G-14937)*

Mail Contractors America Inc ....F 214 742-6103
Dallas *(G-4628)*

▲ National Presort LP ....D 214 634-2288
Fort Worth *(G-6862)*

▲ Parts Krafters Co ....F 515 981-4749
Dallas *(G-4789)*

Pitney Bowes Inc ....E 512 823-0833
Austin *(G-1418)*

▲ Premier Election Solutions Inc ....E 469 675-8990
Allen *(G-296)*

Straight Line Sawing & Sealing ....F 972 590-8922
Grand Prairie *(G-7976)*

Super Strong Products Inc ....F 972 342-6921
Grand Prairie *(G-7978)*

3581 Automatic Vending Machines

Cactus Coin ....F 817 640-1791
Arlington *(G-637)*

Cki Locker LLC ....F 817 329-1600
Dfw Airport *(G-5452)*

Karatech Cnc Machining LLC ....F 281 337-1208
Dickinson *(G-5476)*

Karatech Machining LLC ....F 281 337-1208
Dickinson *(G-5477)*

Kaspar Wire Works Inc ....A 361 594-3327
Shiner *(G-18944)*

Mechanism Exchange & Repr Inc ......E 361 293-6452
Yoakum *(G-20968)*

◆ Sandenvendo America Inc ....B 800 344-7216
Dallas *(G-4931)*

3582 Commercial Laundry, Dry Clean & Pressing Mchs

Brim Laundry Machinery Co Inc ....E 214 630-4517
Hutchins *(G-12863)*

C R D N N Dallas Restoration ....E 214 698-0059
Dallas *(G-4074)*

Iowa Techniques Inc ....F 512 846-2403
Hutto *(G-12880)*

My Sons Laundry LLC ....F 214 634-2080
Dallas *(G-4710)*

▲ North Txas Hlth Care Ldry Coop ......B 469 916-1150
Grand Prairie *(G-7938)*

Popes Cleaners LLC ....E 210 923-7785
San Antonio *(G-18384)*

3585 Air Conditioning & Heating Eqpt

1st Source Restaurant Svcs Inc ....F 214 551-5338
Lewisville *(G-14019)*

A-1 Smf LLC ....E 512 288-9900
Austin *(G-874)*

▲ ACC-Kp LLC ....F 972 407-1234
Addison *(G-98)*

Afb Manufacturing LLC ....D 410 581-0300
Garland *(G-7429)*

Air Distribution Tech Inc ....F 972 943-6100
Plano *(G-16779)*

Air Flow Products LP ....F 713 305-0258
Houston *(G-8508)*

◆ Air System Components Inc ....C 972 212-4888
Plano *(G-16780)*

Air System Components Inc ....B 915 852-1358
Horizon City *(G-8362)*

Air System Components Inc ....B 972 212-4700
Plano *(G-16781)*

Air System Components Inc ....B 972 680-9128
Richardson *(G-17268)*

Air System Components Inc ....B 972 212-4800
Plano *(G-16782)*

All State Fire Eqp Texas Inc ....F 972 412-0770
Wylie *(G-20924)*

American Air Services LLC ....F 832 715-8025
Houston *(G-8583)*

▲ American Cooling Tech Inc ....F 717 767-2775
Haslet *(G-8215)*

American Envircon Inc ....G 214 634-1744
Dallas *(G-3940)*

▲ Annex Manufacturing LLC ....E 817 293-8762
Lewisville *(G-14021)*

Apex Coil LLC ....E 903 843-4534
Gilmer *(G-7705)*

▲ Arctic Star Rfrgn Mfg Co ....E 817 274-1396
Pantego *(G-16350)*

▲ Aspen Manufacturing LLC ....C 281 441-6500
Humble *(G-12748)*

◆ Atco Rubber Products Inc ....A 817 595-2894
Fort Worth *(G-6406)*

Atco Rubber Products Inc ....E 713 674-6665
Houston *(G-8732)*

Atlantic Food Bars Inc ....D 888 632-5765
Garland *(G-7443)*

◆ Auto Air Export Inc ....D 972 812-7000
Irving *(G-12935)*

Bebco Envmtl Contrls Corp ....E 844 397-4822
La Marque *(G-13707)*

Bergstrom Climate Systems LLC ....E 210 507-5670
San Antonio *(G-17948)*

Bois DArc International Trade ....E 903 758-2647
Longview *(G-14203)*

Broad-Ocean Motor Houston LLC ....E 713 353-0100
Waller *(G-20494)*

Bus Air LLC ....E 817 636-2308
Haslet *(G-8217)*

C K Higgs	E	713 666-5739	
Bellaire (G-1992)			
Canales Sheetmetal & Welding	F	512 556-8613	
Lampasas (G-13832)			
Capitol Food & Beverage Inc	F	972 660-4450	
Grand Prairie (G-7850)			
Carrier Corporation	C	903 510-7300	
Tyler (G-20063)			
Carrier Corporation	E	210 495-2600	
San Antonio (G-17985)			
Century Arconditioning Sup L P	F	281 446-7820	
Humble (G-12754)			
Ces Industrial LLC	F	281 615-5621	
Stafford (G-19293)			
Champion Cooler Corporation	C	903 465-3294	
Denison (G-5337)			
Champion Cooler Corporation	D	903 463-1408	
Denison (G-5338)			
Cimarron Energy Holding Co LLC	E	432 563-9700	
Odessa (G-15961)			
Coburn Supply Company Inc	C	409 838-6363	
Houston (G-9233)			
Colair Inc	F	956 631-9889	
Mission (G-15550)			
▲ Cold Air Products Inc	E	817 531-2665	
Fort Worth (G-6530)			
Coldvault LLC	G	903 657-2377	
Henderson (G-8261)			
▲ Combined Rfrgn Resources Inc	E	281 540-7552	
Humble (G-12761)			
Component Parts Machine Co Inc	E	817 834-4771	
Fort Worth (G-6534)			
Compressors Unlimited Intl LLC	F	972 286-2264	
Dallas (G-4152)			
Contract Manufacturers Inc	E	903 597-8297	
Tyler (G-20071)			
Custom Controls Company	E	713 666-3258	
Houston (G-9368)			
▼ CW Davis Enterprises Inc	E	972 723-1247	
Midlothian (G-15477)			
Daikin Manufacturing Co LP	F	972 245-1510	
Houston (G-9393)			
Danhard Inc	F	214 328-8541	
Dallas (G-4233)			
Delta Industries Inc	D	214 941-3135	
Denton (G-5357)			
▲ Delta Tee International Inc	E	817 466-9991	
Arlington (G-659)			
DFW Comfort Experts Inc	F	817 633-2665	
North Richland Hills (G-15876)			
◆ Diversity Industries Inc	E	713 667-9595	
Stafford (G-19306)			
E I Du Pont De Nemours & Co	E	361 776-1872	
Ingleside (G-12895)			
E Tamez Coml Rfrgn & AC Inc	G	210 884-5059	
San Antonio (G-18079)			
E3rivers LLC	E	817 247-5828	
Decatur (G-5245)			
East Texas Radiator Inc	C	903 753-7286	
Longview (G-14228)			
East Texas Radiator Inc	F	903 759-3877	
Longview (G-14229)			
Emerson Climate Tech Inc	C	817 277-7764	
Arlington (G-668)			
Enerflex Energy Systems Inc	F	806 826-0126	
Wheeler (G-20708)			
◆ Enerflex Energy Systems Inc	B	281 345-9300	
Houston (G-9631)			
Enerflex Energy Systems Inc	D	281 758-4900	
Cypress (G-3787)			
Enerflex Inc	C	801 292-0493	
Houston (G-9632)			
Enginered Packaged Systems Inc	E	409 866-5213	
Beaumont (G-1887)			
Fiberglass Specialties Inc	D	903 657-6522	
Henderson (G-8263)			
◆ Folas Inc	E	830 625-1613	
New Braunfels (G-15793)			
◆ Fujikoki America Inc	C	214 333-4266	
Dallas (G-4384)			
▲ Goodman Global Holdings Inc	F	713 861-2500	
Waller (G-20500)			
Goodman Manufacturing Co LP	B	713 263-5556	
Houston (G-9998)			
◆ Goodman Manufacturing Co LP	C	713 861-2500	
Waller (G-20502)			
Goodman Manufacturing Co LP	F	713 263-5416	
Houston (G-9999)			
Goodman Manufacturing Co LP	F	936 372-5224	
Waller (G-20501)			
▲ Great American Coil LLC	D	903 297-4700	
White Oak (G-20714)			
▲ Gujarat Flrchmcals Amricas LLC	F	512 446-7700	
Irving (G-13046)			
◆ Hart Heat Transfer Pdts Inc	D	713 675-9848	
Houston (G-10133)			
Heat Air Products Company	E	817 222-9567	
Fort Worth (G-6694)			
Henderson Controls Inc	E	512 398-5700	
Buda (G-2529)			
▲ Hodyon LP	E	512 225-0165	
Cedar Park (G-2974)			
Hoshizaki America Inc	E	817 540-4665	
Fort Worth (G-6704)			
Hussmann Corporation	D	972 956-9045	
Coppell (G-3419)			
Hvac Manufacturing Inc	F	408 254-5420	
Athens (G-829)			
Hvac Mechanical Svcs of Texas	B	713 266-3900	
Houston (G-10292)			
Idq Acquisition Corp	E	214 778-4600	
Garland (G-7516)			
Jmn Energy Experts	E	817 703-9539	
Fort Worth (G-6743)			
John Bean Technologies Corp	E	713 875-3735	
Houston (G-10480)			
Kairak Inc	C	800 825-8220	
Fort Worth (G-6751)			
▲ Keeprite Refrigeration Inc	D	903 643-2261	
Longview (G-14260)			
Kegspeed LLC	F	267 714-8854	
Austin (G-1266)			
Koch Filter Corporation	E	502 634-4796	
Houston (G-10551)			
Kold Pack Incorporated	F	800 824-2661	
Fort Worth (G-6769)			
Kps Global LLC	E	817 339-2100	
Fort Worth (G-6771)			
Kps Global LLC	C	817 281-5121	
Fort Worth (G-6770)			
◆ Lancer Corporation	B	210 310-7250	
San Antonio (G-18236)			
Lennox Industries Inc	C	806 412-4160	
Lubbock (G-14436)			
Lennox International Inc	A	210 646-2399	
San Antonio (G-18246)			
▲ Lennox International Inc	E	972 497-5000	
Richardson (G-17343)			
▼ Loop Tech International Ltd	E	936 295-7038	
Willis (G-20854)			
Maddox Enterprises Inc	E	903 592-6531	
Tyler (G-20119)			
▼ Marc Climatic Controls Inc	F	713 464-8587	
Houston (G-10761)			
Marrone & Co LLC	E	281 227-8400	
Houston (G-10772)			
Marvin Dace Company	F	281 482-1450	
Alvin (G-373)			
▼ Matthiesen Equipment Co	F	210 333-1510	
San Antonio (G-18284)			
Maverick Enterprises	F	281 444-5010	
Houston (G-10800)			
MB Dustless Air Filter Co LLC	F	210 653-6901	
Houston (G-10808)			
Mechanical Technical Svcs LP	E	512 929-7090	
Round Rock (G-17671)			
▲ Mestex Ltd	E	214 638-6010	
Dallas (G-4668)			
Morrison Products Inc	D	972 279-4000	
Mesquite (G-15063)			
▲ Mortex Products Inc	B	817 624-0820	
Fort Worth (G-6853)			
Munters Corporation	D	210 651-5018	
Selma (G-18878)			
▲ Nance International Inc	D	409 838-6127	
Beaumont (G-1932)			
National Wholesale Supply Inc	E	972 331-7770	
Dallas (G-4716)			
Neu Plumbing Inc	D	940 580-2200	
Pilot Point (G-16726)			
▲ Nichirin-Flex USA Inc	B	915 859-1199	
El Paso (G-5896)			
Noren Products Inc	E	650 322-9500	
Taylor (G-19661)			
Ota Compression LLC	F	972 831-1300	
Irving (G-13136)			
Ota Compression LLC	F	817 326-8250	
Granbury (G-7803)			
◆ Packless Metal Hose Inc	D	254 666-7700	
Waco (G-20443)			
Pedraza Hvac Inc	F	281 970-4834	
Houston (G-11269)			
▲ Phoenix Mobile Air Inc	F	972 418-6444	
Carrollton (G-2791)			
◆ Portacool LLC	B	936 598-5651	
Center (G-3005)			
Portacool LLC	F	936 598-6353	
Center (G-3006)			
Refrigeration Design Inc	E	972 937-3240	
Waxahachie (G-20556)			
Refrigrtion Vssels Systems Cor	D	979 778-0095	
Bryan (G-2500)			
Rex Mechanical Inc	E	979 793-3340	
Needville (G-15763)			
S & M Aire LLC	F	915 921-9677	
El Paso (G-5951)			
◆ Sanden International USA Inc	A	972 442-8400	
Wylie (G-20948)			
Selkirk Corporation	B	972 943-6100	
Richardson (G-17395)			
▼ Skl Prime Services LLC	D	469 733-1540	
Arlington (G-782)			
▲ Snoke Special Products Co Inc	F	903 586-3618	
Jacksonville (G-13258)			
Standex International Corp	E	972 908-6100	
Allen (G-300)			
Suncoast A/C & Rfrgn Inc	F	956 428-1190	
Harlingen (G-8204)			
Synergy Environmental Svcs LLC	E	972 513-1118	
Arlington (G-789)			
Taprite-Fassco Mfg Inc	F	830 914-2539	
Marion (G-14758)			
Taylor Coml Foodservice Inc	B	972 937-1820	
Waxahachie (G-20564)			
Tex Cnp/Seal Inc	E	214 688-7770	
Dallas (G-5051)			
Texas Air Products Ltd	E	210 495-8100	
San Antonio (G-18532)			
Texas Furnace LLC	F	713 466-1504	
Houston (G-12231)			
▲ Thermal Edge Inc	E	972 580-0200	
Irving (G-13193)			
Thermal Solutions Texas LLC	F	281 351-4328	
Tomball (G-20014)			
▲ Tigerflow Systems LLC	D	214 337-8780	
Dallas (G-5093)			
▲ Tisdale AC & Htg Co	F	936 856-1500	
Conroe (G-3372)			
Trane Company	E	956 968-6425	
Weslaco (G-20669)			
Trane Company	E	915 593-3484	
El Paso (G-6012)			
Trane US Inc	F	239 277-7400	
Carrollton (G-2836)			
Trane US Inc	E	903 581-3200	
Tyler (G-20164)			
Trane US Inc	D	903 316-8033	
Tyler (G-20165)			
Trane US Inc	D	972 892-3900	
Dallas (G-5104)			
Trane US Inc	D	832 747-2000	
Houston (G-12342)			
Trane US Inc	D	713 266-3900	
Houston (G-12343)			
Trane US Inc	E	817 838-1310	
Fort Worth (G-7071)			
Trane US Inc	D	210 657-0901	
San Antonio (G-18559)			
Trane US Inc	B	469 758-3128	
Carrollton (G-2837)			
Trane US Inc	E	915 593-3484	
El Paso (G-6013)			
Trane US Inc	C	254 299-6300	
Mc Gregor (G-14825)			
▲ Traulsen & Co Inc	B	817 625-9671	
Fort Worth (G-7072)			
▲ Tresu Royse Inc	E	214 631-2844	
Grapevine (G-8058)			
▲ Tripac International Inc	E	817 534-9278	
Fort Worth (G-7078)			
◆ Turbine Air Systems Ltd	C	713 877-8700	
Houston (G-12408)			
▼ United Electric Company LP	C	940 397-2100	
Wichita Falls (G-20823)			
Valeo North America Inc	E	972 574-1900	
Dallas (G-5150)			
▲ Vintage Air Inc	D	210 296-2302	
San Antonio (G-18648)			
Vogt Ice LLC	E	940 387-4301	
Lewisville (G-14109)			

◆ Welbilt Walk-Ins LP ....C 817 281-5121
Fort Worth **(G-7134)**

Welch Hvac Incorporated ....F 214 222-8600
Lewisville **(G-14112)**

Winsupply San Antonio ....F 210 481-8123
San Antonio **(G-18623)**

3586 Measuring & Dispensing Pumps

▲ Bear Pump & Equipment Inc ......F 281 200-1000
Houston **(G-8846)**

Cft Dispensers Inc ....G 512 942-8300
Georgetown **(G-7643)**

Cowboy Pumps ....E 361 221-9786
Kingsville **(G-13625)**

Dualco Inc ....E 713 644-1164
Houston **(G-9536)**

◆ Fittings Inc ....D 817 332-3300
Fort Worth **(G-6634)**

Foam Supplies Inc ....F 972 436-7008
Lewisville **(G-14050)**

Predominant Pumps & Automation ......F 281 987-0204
Houston **(G-11398)**

Schlumberger Technology Corp ....C 281 285-8500
Houston **(G-11780)**

◆ Schlumberger Technology Corp ......A 281 285-8500
Sugar Land **(G-19542)**

Schlumberger Technology Corp ....C 281 285-8500
Sugar Land **(G-19549)**

▲ Tecalemit Inc ....D 281 446-7300
Humble **(G-12801)**

Triton Products LLC ....F 940 455-2800
Argyle **(G-604)**

Wayne Fueling Systems LLC ....F 512 388-8446
Austin **(G-1651)**

3589 Service Ind Machines, NEC

◆ A O Smith Wtr Trtmnt N Amer ....D 817 536-5250
Haltom City **(G-8131)**

▼ Advance Tabco Inc ....F 972 932-4148
Kaufman **(G-13456)**

▼ Advance Technology Products ....F 713 450-5990
Houston **(G-8484)**

◆ Advanced Cntinment Systems Inc ...C 713 987-0336
Houston **(G-8486)**

Advanced MBL Fltrtion Svcs LLC ......F 800 484-4590
Fort Worth **(G-6348)**

Alfa Laval US Holding Inc ....C 281 449-0322
Houston **(G-8536)**

Apollo Separation Tech USA Inc ......E 281 233-9600
Houston **(G-8664)**

▲ APS Pressure Systems LLC ....E 281 290-9950
Tomball **(G-19960)**

Aquaneers Corp ....E 956 727-1250
Laredo **(G-13862)**

◆ Aquapharm Pchem LLC ....F 346 237-4300
Latexo **(G-13942)**

Ark-La-Tex Shredding Co Inc ....F 903 877-3734
Tyler **(G-20048)**

Artesia Ecoscience LLC ....F 281 978-2521
Houston **(G-8710)**

Auto-Chlor Services LLC ....E 817 525-1021
Arlington **(G-626)**

B & M Oilfield Services LLC ....F 979 241-2051
Falls City **(G-6182)**

Baswood Inc ....E 888 560-5517
Allen **(G-257)**

Bexter Enterprises LLC ....E 972 647-4700
Grand Prairie **(G-7846)**

▼ Bingham Manufacturing Inc ....G 360 863-1170
Terrell **(G-19728)**

Biocope Inc ....F 806 655-2933
Canyon **(G-2669)**

Bosque Disposal Systems LLC ....D 254 435-2260
Fort Worth **(G-6462)**

Bosque Systems LLC ....D 817 289-9900
Fort Worth **(G-6463)**

▼ Chem-Aqua Inc ....E 972 438-0232
Irving **(G-12969)**

Cite Corporation ....F 817 477-1549
Mansfield **(G-14663)**

City of Bandera ....G 830 796-3401
Bandera **(G-1743)**

City of Colony The ....F 972 625-4471
Lewisville **(G-14037)**

City of Jefferson ....F 903 665-2832
Jefferson **(G-13283)**

City of Sherman ....E 903 892-7258
Sherman **(G-18909)**

◆ Colemn-Hnna Crwash Systems LLC E 713 683-9878
Houston **(G-9244)**

Cor Thermotics LLC ....F 832 308-5151
Houston **(G-9311)**

Corporate Records Management ....G 214 333-3453
Dallas **(G-4171)**

Cummings Inv Bankers Inc ....F 281 416-3007
Houston **(G-8376)**

Custom-Built Equipment Co Inc ......F 713 222-0342
Houston **(G-9377)**

◆ Dallas A C Horn & Company Inc ...D 214 630-3311
Dallas **(G-4210)**

De Nora Water Technologies LLC .....D 281 240-6770
Sugar Land **(G-19477)**

▲ Ecowater Industries LLC ....F 214 878-6527
Port Arthur **(G-17107)**

El Paso Water Indus Svcs Inc ....F 915 849-0401
El Paso **(G-5746)**

▲ Enviroflex Design & Mfg ....F 281 356-6700
Magnolia **(G-14605)**

Excell Technologies Intl Corp ....D 281 240-6770
Sugar Land **(G-19482)**

◆ Exterran Energy Solutions LP ....C 281 836-7000
Houston **(G-9736)**

▲ Falcon Prosolutions Inc ....D 210 547-2741
San Antonio **(G-18103)**

Filtration Automation Inc ....E 817 999-8190
Alvarado **(G-332)**

Flo Pura Corp ....E 281 320-9547
Spring **(G-19122)**

Gardner Denver Inc ....E 832 421-5469
Pasadena **(G-16446)**

Global Water Group Inc ....E 214 678-9866
Dallas **(G-4410)**

Gracon Construction Inc ....D 972 222-8533
Mesquite **(G-15046)**

◆ Granutch-Sturn Systems Corp AM ...D 972 790-7800
Grand Prairie **(G-7884)**

▲ Grayloc Products LLC ....E 713 466-8853
Houston **(G-10021)**

Guiverman Industries LLC ....E 866 235-8057
Plano **(G-16882)**

◆ H & K International Inc ....C 214 818-3500
Mesquite **(G-15047)**

H & L Fabrication Inc ....E 512 894-0918
Dripping Springs **(G-5506)**

Hobart Sales and Service Inc ....E 210 829-5663
San Antonio **(G-18169)**

Huffman & Huffman Inc ....G 972 434-3640
Lewisville **(G-14055)**

Inframark LLC ....F 281 579-4500
Forney **(G-6309)**

▼ Its Engineered Systems Inc ....D 281 371-8026
Katy **(G-13411)**

Janis Litchfield ....F 325 625-1001
Austin **(G-1251)**

◆ Jetstream of Houston LLP ....D 832 590-1300
Houston **(G-10471)**

JR Sheldon & Company Inc ....F 940 368-5793
Pottsboro **(G-17197)**

Keizer Technologies Americas ....F 817 685-7090
Euless **(G-6148)**

Liberto Management Co Inc ....E 210 226-4167
San Antonio **(G-18250)**

M3p Water Services LLC ....G 432 570-7500
Midland **(G-15290)**

Manning Pool Service Inc ....E 713 812-9098
Houston **(G-10745)**

Meco Inc ....E 281 276-7600
Sugar Land **(G-19507)**

Metal Kitchen Fabricators Inc ....F 713 683-8375
Houston **(G-10847)**

MI T Fine Car Wash Inc ....E 972 422-0707
Plano **(G-16926)**

Nap Industries LLC ....F 940 668-8111
Gainesville **(G-7352)**

National Wholesale Supply Inc ....E 972 331-7770
Dallas **(G-4716)**

▲ Omni Water Solutions Inc ....E 512 275-0804
Austin **(G-1381)**

Originclear Inc ....F 323 939-6645
McKinney **(G-14960)**

◆ Overhead Door Corporation ....C 469 549-7100
Lewisville **(G-14080)**

Pentair Rsdntial Fltration LLC ....F 936 525-2310
Conroe **(G-3347)**

Precision Water Tech Inc ....F 972 488-6755
Carrollton **(G-2793)**

▼ Procam Controls Inc ....E 972 422-1212
Plano **(G-16960)**

Process Engineered Eqp Co ....F 361 289-8891
Corpus Christi **(G-3597)**

Professional Fabrication Inc ....E 936 321-7070
Magnolia **(G-14622)**

▲ Project Services Group Inc ....D 972 812-7370
Irving **(G-13159)**

◆ Regency Wraps Inc ....E 214 357-0099
Dallas **(G-4883)**

▲ Renfro Industries Inc ....D 972 563-4295
Terrell **(G-19749)**

Restaurant Depot LLC ....E 512 454-5600
Austin **(G-1461)**

Rio Resources LLC ....E 830 438-4841
New Braunfels **(G-15820)**

◆ Riverside Engineering Inc ....F 210 227-9090
San Antonio **(G-18429)**

RSI Partners LLC ....D 817 640-5415
Arlington **(G-777)**

See You At The Top Inc ....E 210 556-5452
San Antonio **(G-18464)**

Smart Control Systems LLC ....E 210 224-4906
San Antonio **(G-18480)**

▲ Solofill LLC ....F 832 675-9862
Houston **(G-11942)**

◆ Steelhead Inc ....E 210 628-1066
San Antonio **(G-18498)**

Sterno Group LLC ....C 903 223-3400
Texarkana **(G-19775)**

Suez Wts Services Usa Inc ....E 214 339-2135
Dallas **(G-5018)**

T-Tex Equipment LP ....F 713 991-7070
Houston **(G-12144)**

Tacony Corporation ....D 817 551-0700
Fort Worth **(G-7030)**

Tank Town LLC ....E 512 894-0861
Austin **(G-1555)**

Temple Water Treatment ....F 254 939-2161
Temple **(G-19711)**

Tex Tech Environmental Inc ....E 817 295-3701
Burleson **(G-2598)**

Texas Air & Water LLC ....F 361 814-3131
Corpus Christi **(G-3636)**

▲ Texas Underground Inc ....D 281 485-9900
Pearland **(G-16602)**

Trans Tool LLC ....F 210 225-6745
San Antonio **(G-18560)**

Tri Element Incorporated ....F 361 664-5000
Alice **(G-242)**

Tri Star Metals Inc ....F 940 433-2173
Boyd **(G-2209)**

Triple/S Dynamics Inc ....E 214 828-8600
Dallas **(G-5116)**

Turbochef Technologies Inc ....E 214 379-6000
Carrollton **(G-2892)**

◆ Turbochef Technologies Inc ....E 214 379-6000
Carrollton **(G-2893)**

Twin Distributing Inc ....E 903 463-1194
Denison **(G-5349)**

Ultrafryer Systems Inc ....E 210 731-5000
San Antonio **(G-18575)**

◆ Unitra Inc ....E 281 240-1500
Stafford **(G-19393)**

Vizza Wash Services LLC ....E 512 246-8822
Round Rock **(G-17698)**

▼ Water Energy Technologies ....F 713 464-7117
Houston **(G-12601)**

Water Standard MGT US Inc ....E 713 400-4777
Houston **(G-12602)**

Water Std Spration Systems LLC ......F 713 433-7441
Houston **(G-12603)**

Watts Wtr Qulty Cond Pdts Inc ....D 210 677-0618
San Antonio **(G-18612)**

Wesco Chemicals Inc ....F 972 938-0913
Waxahachie **(G-20568)**

▲ Wheco Electric Inc ....F 817 244-6660
Lakeside **(G-13813)**

Wilson Environmental MGT Inc ....F 713 984-0800
Houston **(G-12672)**

Xedia Process Solutions LLC ....E 832 356-8347
Houston **(G-12706)**

3592 Carburetors, Pistons, Rings & Valves

3-C Valve & Equipment LP ....F 281 361-3283
Corpus Christi **(G-3462)**

◆ Atec Inc ....C 281 276-2700
Stafford **(G-19289)**

Borger Oil Chemical Indus Plas ....F 806 273-9518
Borger **(G-2165)**

Bray International Inc ....E 281 517-5400
Houston **(G-8978)**

Broen Inc ....E 713 300-0480
Conroe **(G-3265)**

Chromatic Industries LLC ....F 936 539-5770
Conroe *(G-3277)*

Delta Valves and Controls LLC ....F 713 205-1904
Pasadena *(G-16415)*

Greg-Co Piston Rings Inc ....E 817 831-0253
Fort Worth *(G-6679)*

Gvcc Inc ....G 281 416-4772
Pasadena *(G-16451)*

H Lorimer Corporation ....E 903 643-3239
Longview *(G-14245)*

Jaks Machine Inc ....F 361 575-2312
Victoria *(G-20276)*

▲ Ladish Valve Company LLC ....D 281 880-8560
Houston *(G-10585)*

Movement Industries Corp ....F 713 849-1300
Houston *(G-10928)*

Newco Valves LLC ....F 832 944-5930
Stafford *(G-19358)*

Nueces Valve Solutions LLC ....F 361 248-1700
Corpus Christi *(G-3581)*

Safety Seal Piston Ring Co ....E 903 938-9241
Marshall *(G-14802)*

Safety Seal Piston Ring Co ....E 817 283-1574
Hurst *(G-12856)*

Shf Inc ....C 832 456-2000
Pasadena *(G-16506)*

Specialty Comprsr & Eng Co Inc ....E 806 274-7135
Borger *(G-2187)*

▲ Tecnoval LLC ....F 956 782-1111
Mission *(G-15566)*

Tenneco Inc ....A 915 832-4661
El Paso *(G-5997)*

▲ Tiger Valve Houston Co LLC ....F 281 227-9911
Houston *(G-12291)*

Wesco Valve & Manufacturing Co ....E 903 938-9241
Marshall *(G-14808)*

3593 Fluid Power Cylinders & Actuators

Automation Technology Inc ....E 713 934-0171
Cypress *(G-3777)*

▲ Camozzi Pneumatics Inc ....E 972 548-8885
McKinney *(G-14931)*

◆ Dresser LLC ....C 262 549-2626
Houston *(G-9517)*

Emerson Process Management ....C 281 477-4100
Jersey Village *(G-13299)*

George Hall ....E 972 266-2700
Grand Prairie *(G-7882)*

▲ Hannon Hydraulics Inc ....D 972 438-2870
Irving *(G-13048)*

Hannon Hydraulics Inc ....E 713 849-4445
Houston *(G-10116)*

▲ Hot Hydraulics Inc ....E 713 722-7200
Houston *(G-10212)*

▲ Hyseco Inc ....E 713 991-4240
Houston *(G-10307)*

▲ Manitou North America Inc ....D 254 799-0232
Waco *(G-20429)*

Noremac Gas LLC ....F 281 248-6423
Katy *(G-13429)*

▲ Pantex Ennerflo Systems Inc ....E 832 861-7700
Houston *(G-8390)*

Pennar Global Inc ....F 281 362-2707
The Woodlands *(G-19900)*

▲ Qtrco Inc ....F 281 516-0277
Tomball *(G-20003)*

▲ Sfp Hydraulics Inc ....G 281 347-8080
Katy *(G-13441)*

▲ Temple Machine Shop Inc ....D 254 774-8099
Temple *(G-19709)*

▲ Texas Hydraulics Inc ....A 254 778-4701
Temple *(G-19712)*

▲ West Craft Manufacturing Inc ....D 936 858-4426
Alto *(G-319)*

◆ Xomox Corporation ....C 936 271-6500
The Woodlands *(G-19942)*

3594 Fluid Power Pumps & Motors

Airdraulics ....G 432 381-7867
Odessa *(G-15906)*

▲ American Acrylic Injection Inc ....E 972 784-7759
Farmersville *(G-6221)*

Bayou City Pump Works LP ....F 713 472-7722
Pasadena *(G-16396)*

▼ Cse W-Industries Inc ....C 713 466-9463
Jersey Village *(G-13297)*

◆ Diamond Hydraulics Inc ....E 409 440-8032
Hitchcock *(G-8337)*

◆ Dresser LLC ....C 262 549-2626
Houston *(G-9517)*

◆ Electronic Power Design Inc ....D 713 923-1191
Houston *(G-9596)*

Emerson Process Management ....C 281 477-4100
Jersey Village *(G-13299)*

Fisher Energy Partners LLC ....E 713 937-6838
Houston *(G-9792)*

Flint Energy Services Inc ....C 361 449-2405
George West *(G-7624)*

▲ Hannon Hydraulics Inc ....D 972 438-2870
Irving *(G-13048)*

Hannon Hydraulics Inc ....E 713 849-4445
Houston *(G-10116)*

Hartfiel Automation Inc ....F 972 633-0000
Plano *(G-16884)*

▲ Hot Hydraulics Inc ....E 713 722-7200
Houston *(G-10212)*

▲ Hyvair Corporation ....F 281 259-7768
Magnolia *(G-14608)*

Intertech Fluid Power Inc ....G 817 329-9733
Grapevine *(G-8044)*

ITT LLC ....E 281 504-6300
Stafford *(G-19335)*

Mjs Manufacturing Inc ....F 832 446-6440
Houston *(G-10895)*

◆ National Oilwell Varco Inc ....D 713 346-7500
Houston *(G-10988)*

National Oilwell Varco Inc ....F 817 985-5000
Fort Worth *(G-6861)*

Parker-Hannifin Corporation ....D 817 625-5081
Fort Worth *(G-6895)*

Pump Arts Inc ....E 713 946-0500
Houston *(G-11472)*

◆ Rda Corporation ....E 281 474-2881
Celina *(G-2993)*

Rolltex Inc ....G 432 570-7576
Midland *(G-15388)*

▼ Stationary Power Systems Inc ....F 877 924-4949
Arlington *(G-788)*

▲ Tcm Investments Inc ....E 432 366-5433
Odessa *(G-16173)*

Teikoku USA Inc ....E 713 983-9901
Houston *(G-12185)*

Texas Precision Mfg Inc ....F 806 741-1166
Lubbock *(G-14492)*

◆ Toshiba International Corp ....A 800 231-1412
Houston *(G-12327)*

▲ Womack Machine Supply Co ....D 800 569-9800
Farmers Branch *(G-6219)*

3596 Scales & Balances, Exc Laboratory

Keith Weighing Systems LLC ....F 806 655-3033
Canyon *(G-2672)*

Load Systems International ....D 281 664-1330
Houston *(G-10660)*

◆ Martin-Decker Totco Inc ....B 512 340-5000
Cedar Park *(G-2978)*

Mettler-Toledo LLC ....F 972 727-8669
Allen *(G-285)*

▲ Tru-Test Inc ....E 940 327-8020
Mineral Wells *(G-15543)*

3599 Machinery & Eqpt, Indl & Commercial, NEC

10-4 Tubular Inc ....E 281 436-0380
Houston *(G-8399)*

14703 Partners Industries LLC ....F 281 847-0788
Houston *(G-8402)*

2 K Machine Works Inc ....G 713 467-6921
Houston *(G-8403)*

365 Machine Inc ....F 281 378-7811
Tomball *(G-19952)*

820 Hydraulics LLC ....F 713 863-0340
Houston *(G-8416)*

▲ A & E Machine Shop Inc ....E 903 656-3485
Lone Star *(G-14180)*

A & M Machine & Wldg Works Inc ....G 281 421-1281
Baytown *(G-1806)*

A E Machine Works Inc ....E 281 970-2020
Cypress *(G-3770)*

A G H Machine Inc ....E 281 372-1200
Houston *(G-8426)*

▲ A&A Machine & Fabrication LLC ......D 409 938-4274
La Marque *(G-13704)*

Abcd Precision Inc ....E 832 230-5729
Houston *(G-8446)*

Absolute Machine & Tooling LLC ....F 512 259-7676
Leander *(G-13984)*

Accmach Inc ....E 979 774-0062
College Station *(G-3172)*

▲ Accuracy Products Inc ....F 940 325-0714
Mineral Wells *(G-15517)*

Accuturn Manufacturing Inc ....F 281 449-9000
Houston *(G-8464)*

Ace Machine & Fabrication Inc ....G 956 727-4223
Laredo *(G-13855)*

Ace Machining Technologies ....F 254 632-4250
Hillsboro *(G-8320)*

Action Rigging and Pump Svc LP ....F 512 670-9567
Austin *(G-885)*

Advance Tool & Die Inc ....E 817 923-8787
Fort Worth *(G-6346)*

▲ Advanced Precision Services LP ....F 281 290-9950
Tomball *(G-19954)*

Aero Cnc Inc ....F 817 295-0184
Burleson *(G-2565)*

Aerodynmic Prcsion McHning Inc ....F 713 856-9990
Houston *(G-8498)*

Affiliated Energy Products Inc ....E 940 592-4169
Iowa Park *(G-12902)*

Aggietech Energy Services LLC ....E 806 229-6129
Sundown *(G-19610)*

Airgas Usa LLC ....F 512 835-0202
Austin *(G-902)*

Alamo Industrial Group Inc ....B 210 223-6161
San Antonio *(G-17884)*

◆ Alamo Iron Works Inc ....B 210 223-6161
San Antonio *(G-17885)*

Alart Tool & Die Corp ....F 713 691-0434
Houston *(G-8527)*

Alexander Manufacturing Co ....F 972 641-7355
Cross Plains *(G-3746)*

Alexander Tank Co ....F 830 875-2759
Luling *(G-14558)*

Alexanders Mch Maint Svc Inc ....E 817 625-4175
Fort Worth *(G-6369)*

▲ All-Pro Threaded Products ....F 817 467-5700
Arlington *(G-614)*

Allbright & Associates Inc ....E 432 366-8897
Odessa *(G-15909)*

Alleys Industrial Service Inc ....E 432 362-0200
Odessa *(G-15910)*

Allied Threaded Mtls & McHy Co ....G 713 464-3594
Houston *(G-8553)*

Allied Tools of Texas Corp ....G 713 943-8500
Houston *(G-8554)*

▲ Allied Wear Systems LLC ....F 972 248-8838
Dallas *(G-3837)*

Alloy Carbide Company ....E 713 923-2700
Houston *(G-8556)*

Alloy Cnc LLC ....F 936 449-4001
Montgomery *(G-15626)*

Altech Machine Shop Inc ....G 817 718-8824
Springtown *(G-19271)*

Alternative Cutting Methods ....F 817 927-3332
Fort Worth *(G-6374)*

Always Integrity Machining LLC ....F 512 670-1010
Round Rock *(G-17622)*

Amaida Machine Shop LLC ....G 956 287-8824
Edinburg *(G-5574)*

America Industrial Pdts LLC ....F 832 974-4153
Houston *(G-8580)*

◆ American Block Company ....C 800 572-9087
Houston *(G-8588)*

◆ American Completion Tools Inc ....E 817 790-6608
Burleson *(G-2567)*

American Engine & Grinding Co ....F 713 224-5326
Houston *(G-8595)*

American Industrial Machine ....F 432 366-3516
Odessa *(G-15913)*

▲ Amfan Corporation ....E 214 638-2451
Dallas *(G-3947)*

▲ Ammr Services Inc ....F 281 449-7162
Houston *(G-8626)*

▼ Anchor Machine Works Inc ....F 713 988-0400
Houston *(G-8640)*

API Precision Machining Inc ....F 214 748-4994
Dallas *(G-3951)*

Applegate Edm Inc ....E 972 488-8997
Farmers Branch *(G-6187)*

Arbor Resources LLC ....G 936 632-9914
Pollok *(G-17091)*

Arlington Machine & Hydraulics ....E 972 988-6644
Grand Prairie *(G-7835)*

Artech Manufacturing Inc ....F 512 863-9050
Georgetown *(G-7635)*

ASAP Machine Inc ....E 281 448-4800
Houston *(G-8712)*

Astro Machine & Tool Works LLC ....F 903 595-6655
Tyler *(G-20050)*

Astro Mechanics Inc .... F .... 512 246-9200 Round Rock *(G-17624)*	Burgess Specialty Fabg Inc .... D .... 713 462-0293 Houston *(G-9018)*	Coastal Mechanics Tl & Mch Inc .... E .... 281 987-2530 Houston *(G-9228)*
◆ Atec Inc .... C .... 281 276-2700 Stafford *(G-19289)*	Burrows R & H Machine LLC .... E .... 903 753-1550 Longview *(G-14205)*	Coleman Machine & Welding Svc .... F .... 325 625-5186 Coleman *(G-3169)*
Atec Resources Inc .... E .... 281 276-2700 Stafford *(G-19290)*	Butler Weldments Corporation .... D .... 254 697-6416 Cameron *(G-2640)*	Collins Instrument Company .... E .... 979 849-8266 Angleton *(G-569)*
▲ Athena Manufacturing LP .... D .... 512 928-2693 Austin *(G-944)*	Byford Machine-Tool Inc .... E .... 254 932-6111 Valley Mills *(G-20200)*	Commiatos Mch & Repr Svc Inc .... G .... 903 694-9378 Carthage *(G-2904)*
Atlas Automatics Inc .... G .... 281 337-1128 Dickinson *(G-5470)*	C & R Machine Inc .... F .... 903 795-3378 Jacksonville *(G-13231)*	Component Parts Machine Co Inc .... E .... 817 834-4771 Fort Worth *(G-6534)*
Atlas Machine and Wldg Svc Inc ...... E .... 817 558-7778 Joshua *(G-13318)*	C D & N Manufacturing Inc .... D .... 281 438-2499 Missouri City *(G-15576)*	Component Parts Machine Co Inc .... F .... 817 834-4771 Fort Worth *(G-6535)*
Austin County Machine Shop Inc ...... G .... 979 885-3716 Sealy *(G-18805)*	C H I Alpha Whitestone Inc .... F .... 432 367-0006 Odessa *(G-15949)*	▼ Computerized Cutters Inc .... E .... 972 422-6900 Plano *(G-16829)*
Austin Dynamics Inc .... E .... 512 267-3117 Cedar Park *(G-2961)*	C Wrights Machine Tool Inc .... F .... 903 777-2344 Diana *(G-5459)*	Conroe Machine LLC .... D .... 936 494-2566 Conroe *(G-3282)*
Austin Waterjet Inc .... F .... 512 243-9000 Austin *(G-964)*	C&A Machine and Repair Svc Inc ...... E .... 713 937-3426 Houston *(G-9037)*	▲ Constntin Precision Instrs Inc .... E .... 713 461-9090 Katy *(G-13358)*
▲ Automatic Products Corp .... C .... 972 272-6422 Garland *(G-7444)*	C&M Machining LP .... E .... 936 825-8139 Navasota *(G-15727)*	▲ Continental Nh3 Pdts Co Inc .... D .... 214 741-6083 Dallas *(G-4160)*
B & J Machine Works Inc .... F .... 936 348-6371 Madisonville *(G-14584)*	▲ C-B-Gear & Machine Inc .... E .... 281 449-0777 Houston *(G-9040)*	Cordova Corporation .... F .... 817 484-1100 Burleson *(G-2577)*
B & R Productions Inc .... F .... 936 291-7827 New Waverly *(G-15854)*	Caldwell Manufacturing Inc .... E .... 512 398-4549 Lockhart *(G-14165)*	Cr Machine .... F .... 281 354-4755 Porter *(G-17173)*
B B T Industrial Engine Svc .... F .... 210 661-6703 San Antonio *(G-17928)*	Camden Machine & Tool Inc .... E .... 817 838-6731 Fort Worth *(G-6490)*	Craig Godwin Inc .... F .... 936 344-6548 New Waverly *(G-15858)*
B E R Precision Inc .... E .... 281 659-0100 Cleveland *(G-3119)*	Cameron Machine Shop .... E .... 972 235-8876 Richardson *(G-17283)*	Craig Instruments Inc .... E .... 713 690-6904 Houston *(G-9333)*
B M Higginbthams Mch Works Inc ...... E .... 713 941-1854 Houston *(G-8778)*	Campbell Grinding & Machine .... F .... 972 221-2211 Lewisville *(G-14032)*	Crumplers Mch & Wldg Svc Inc .... E .... 409 886-7934 Bridge City *(G-2282)*
▲ B-W Grinding Service Inc .... D .... 713 641-0888 Houston *(G-8782)*	Camtron Incorporated .... E .... 972 994-0000 Plano *(G-16818)*	Cryer Limited Partnership .... E .... 512 267-4944 Lago Vista *(G-13805)*
Babeco Inc .... E .... 512 352-5355 Taylor *(G-19648)*	Carbide Technologies Inc .... F .... 713 475-0444 Pasadena *(G-16400)*	Cryotech Precision Machine LLC .... E .... 713 690-2796 Houston *(G-9351)*
Babin Machine Works Inc .... F .... 409 892-1231 Beaumont *(G-1857)*	Carl R McEver .... F .... 903 842-2555 Troup *(G-20023)*	▲ Csjb Holdings Inc .... D .... 806 749-4300 Lubbock *(G-14398)*
Bamsch Enterprises Intl Ltd .... E .... 281 448-5925 Houston *(G-8813)*	Carols Mch & Fabrication Inc .... E .... 713 921-7266 Wharton *(G-20698)*	Custom Air Products & Svcs Inc .... D .... 713 434-1192 Houston *(G-9364)*
Banister Tool Incorporated .... E .... 512 258-8351 Pflugerville *(G-16661)*	Carpenter Welding & Machine .... F .... 254 796-2114 Hico *(G-8302)*	▲ Custom Air Products & Svcs Inc ..... D .... 281 802-7419 Houston *(G-9365)*
Barmalco Inc .... F .... 281 933-9128 Houston *(G-8817)*	Castronics Inc .... C .... 308 235-4881 Houston *(G-9098)*	Custom Cmpnents Assemblies Inc ..... E .... 713 937-6225 Houston *(G-9367)*
Bayport Machine Inc .... F .... 281 471-6223 Galveston *(G-7388)*	Caterpillar Inc .... D .... 210 637-3700 San Antonio *(G-17987)*	Custom Threading Inc .... E .... 713 645-8422 Houston *(G-9376)*
Beaumont Machine Works Inc .... D .... 409 838-0261 Lumberton *(G-14566)*	▲ Cates Machine Shop Inc .... F .... 903 592-2015 Tyler *(G-20065)*	Cutting Edge Onsite McHning LL .... F .... 832 663-6120 Onalaska *(G-16228)*
Bellows Systems Inc .... F .... 281 721-2947 Houston *(G-8854)*	Cazad Industries Inc .... F .... 972 635-2100 Royse City *(G-17718)*	Cutting Source Precision Inc .... F .... 281 859-2900 Houston *(G-9378)*
Benchmark Completions LLC .... E .... 281 537-8483 Spring *(G-19200)*	CCT Plastics Inc .... E .... 817 410-1222 Grapevine *(G-8020)*	◆ D & J Technologies Inc .... E .... 817 536-0718 Fort Worth *(G-6570)*
Berry Machine Shop .... E .... 817 572-0948 Burleson *(G-2571)*	CCT Precision Machining LLC .... E .... 817 410-1222 Grapevine *(G-8021)*	D & R Specialties Inc .... E .... 936 873-2947 Navasota *(G-15728)*
Best Quality Machining Inc .... F .... 512 864-1667 Georgetown *(G-7641)*	Cdr Machine & Fabricating Inc .... F .... 972 272-9145 Garland *(G-7454)*	D & S Machine Works Inc .... E .... 713 686-4222 Houston *(G-9388)*
Bexxt Inc .... F .... 832 209-7970 Cypress *(G-3778)*	Cecil Machine Shop Inc .... F .... 940 322-4072 Wichita Falls *(G-20751)*	D C G Machine Inc .... F .... 903 297-2053 White Oak *(G-20713)*
Bgs Industries Inc .... E .... 281 970-4118 Houston *(G-8872)*	Cee-San Mch & Fabrication Co .... F .... 713 466-4586 Houston *(G-9118)*	Dadeks Machine Works Corp .... F .... 281 447-4723 Houston *(G-9391)*
Bhi LLC .... F .... 713 644-2431 Houston *(G-8873)*	Cega Inc .... F .... 915 633-1660 El Paso *(G-5687)*	Dallas Texas Tool and Die Inc .... F .... 214 634-7175 Dallas *(G-4227)*
Bkg Machine & Fabrication Inc .... F .... 361 575-9592 Victoria *(G-20247)*	Cega Inc .... F .... 915 257-1898 El Paso *(G-5688)*	David W Arnold .... F .... 713 227-7869 Houston *(G-9408)*
Blackburn Machine & Fab LLC .... E .... 713 644-2386 Houston *(G-8910)*	▲ Centerline Manufacturing Ltd .... D .... 713 329-9070 Houston *(G-9136)*	Davis Machine & Mfg Co .... E .... 817 684-8703 Euless *(G-6140)*
Blade Lab Inc .... F .... 817 491-6755 Haslet *(G-8216)*	Centex Machine and Welding Inc ...... E .... 512 255-1477 Round Rock *(G-17630)*	Daytech Instruments Inc .... F .... 713 856-6555 Houston *(G-9412)*
Blaines Motor Supply Inc .... D .... 214 426-4400 Dallas *(G-4029)*	Central Dynamic Mfg Inc .... E .... 817 473-3899 Mansfield *(G-14660)*	Db Precision Co .... F .... 713 681-6400 Houston *(G-9414)*
Blossom Machine & Mfg Inc .... E .... 903 982-5500 Blossom *(G-2112)*	Centrex International LLC .... E .... 281 370-0720 Spring *(G-19105)*	DDI Machine Inc .... E .... 281 353-3721 Spring *(G-19109)*
Blue Chip Manufacturing Inc .... F .... 713 683-1555 Houston *(G-8918)*	Century Instr & Mch Co Inc .... E .... 281 587-5333 Houston *(G-9141)*	Ddi Machine Inc .... F .... 281 353-5108 Spring *(G-19110)*
Boatman Industries Inc .... E .... 713 641-6006 Houston *(G-8932)*	Challenge Mch & Fabrication .... E .... 281 441-3115 Humble *(G-12756)*	De Young Machine Works Inc .... E .... 832 328-1500 Stafford *(G-19300)*
Brady Machine Inc .... G .... 817 309-3302 Joshua *(G-13319)*	Chevas Company LLC .... F .... 713 225-6595 Houston *(G-9176)*	Decatur Machine Services Inc .... E .... 940 627-1062 Decatur *(G-5244)*
Brandt Precision Machining .... F .... 512 339-7251 Austin *(G-1005)*	Clark Machine Inc .... E .... 281 303-8698 Baytown *(G-1781)*	Deephole Solutions Inc .... F .... 713 896-1121 Houston *(G-9423)*
Brazos Valley Drivelines Inc .... F .... 979 775-3535 Bryan *(G-2459)*	Clarks Precision Machine & Tl .... E .... 817 444-2533 Azle *(G-1721)*	Delray Machine LLC .... F .... 830 693-5110 Marble Falls *(G-14742)*
Breaux Machine Works LP .... D .... 281 351-4042 Tomball *(G-19968)*	Clay Precision Ltd .... E .... 903 891-9022 Sherman *(G-18910)*	▲ Delta Fabrication and Mch Inc .... D .... 903 645-3994 Daingerfield *(G-3831)*
Breckenridge Auto & Engine Sup ...... F .... 254 559-8241 Breckenridge *(G-2224)*	Co Waggoner Inc .... F .... 972 641-8888 Grand Prairie *(G-7856)*	Demco Manufacturing Inc .... E .... 936 829-4771 Diboll *(G-5463)*
▲ Bronco Manufacturing Inc .... D .... 972 924-4576 Anna *(G-583)*	Coastal Bend Tooling & Automtn .... F .... 361 883-0376 Corpus Christi *(G-3502)*	▲ Deran Inc .... E .... 806 746-6926 Lubbock *(G-14402)*
Broome Welding Co .... E .... 409 744-0407 Galveston *(G-7390)*	◆ Coastal Casting Service .... D .... 713 223-4439 Houston *(G-9223)*	Desert Fbrction Millwright Svc .... G .... 915 821-3172 El Paso *(G-5720)*
BS Fab & Mechanical Inc .... E .... 817 373-2879 Rio Vista *(G-17477)*	Coastal Machine & Mech LLC .... E .... 979 849-9323 Angleton *(G-567)*	Deterling Company Inc .... E .... 832 399-9393 Houston *(G-8378)*

Devries Instruments Inc ... F ... 281 506-9100
Houston (G-9447)

Deyoung Machine Works Inc ... F ... 832 328-1500
Stafford (G-19303)

Diamond-Usa Prcsn-Mchining Ltd ... E ... 281 596-9300
Houston (G-9459)

Disco Machine Liberal Company ... E ... 806 274-2214
Borger (G-2173)

Diversified Industrial Svc Co ... E ... 806 274-2214
Borger (G-2175)

Diversified Industrial Svc Co ... E ... 806 274-2214
Borger (G-2174)

Diversified Machining Inc ... F ... 512 355-3270
Bertram (G-2052)

Dns Tool Cutter Grinding LLC ... F ... 972 484-7491
Dallas (G-4268)

Dominion Machining & Mfg Inc ... F ... 281 477-7355
Houston (G-9495)

◆ Don-Nan Pump and Supply Co Inc ... C ... 432 682-7742
Midland (G-15194)

▲ Dons Grinding Lapping Svc Inc ... E ... 713 643-7928
Houston (G-9496)

▼ Drawworks LP ... F ... 512 610-5200
Boling (G-2147)

▲ Drilex Corporation ... E ... 281 821-3360
Houston (G-9527)

Drw Precision Inc ... F ... 281 356-4900
Magnolia (G-14602)

Dtm Precision Machining Inc ... F ... 281 564-7997
Sugar Land (G-19480)

Duel Products Inc ... F ... 972 429-5607
Wylie (G-20934)

Duffin Engine Service ... F ... 210 341-8183
San Antonio (G-18073)

Duramast Industries Inc ... E ... 936 395-0334
Bedias (G-1981)

▲ Dynamic Attractions Inc ... F ... 817 652-1212
Arlington (G-667)

Dynamic Precision Mch Tls Inc ... E ... 713 466-4545
Houston (G-9548)

▲ Dynamic Tool Company Inc ... D ... 915 598-2330
El Paso (G-5726)

East Texas Machine Works Inc ... D ... 903 759-9796
Longview (G-14227)

Ed Prince Enterprises Inc ... F ... 806 274-7178
Borger (G-2177)

EDS Precision Mfg LLC ... D ... 713 956-1112
Houston (G-9583)

Efco Machine Shop LLC ... F ... 254 778-7394
Pendleton (G-16628)

Egs Production Machining Inc ... E ... 972 438-2251
Irving (G-13012)

Ehmer Production Machining Co ... F ... 972 422-2882
Plano (G-16859)

El Campo Machine & Repair Inc ... E ... 979 543-9663
El Campo (G-5615)

Ellis Tool & Machine Inc ... E ... 903 546-6540
Tom Bean (G-19951)

ELM Machine Inc ... F ... 936 377-5001
Oakhurst (G-15891)

Engelbrecht Manufacturing Inc ... F ... 281 341-5110
Rosenberg (G-17581)

Eurotech Industries Inc ... F ... 713 937-1730
Houston (G-9712)

EW & WG LP ... F ... 512 528-8771
Leander (G-13989)

Excel Pump & Machine Inc ... F ... 361 387-4508
Robstown (G-17510)

Excell Machine Co Inc ... E ... 817 473-6121
Mansfield (G-14672)

Expert Tool & Machine Inc ... F ... 972 241-5353
Dallas (G-4348)

Ez-Router Inc ... E ... 903 569-3190
Mineola (G-15508)

F & R Machine Services Inc ... F ... 214 631-4946
Dallas (G-4350)

Fabricon Inc ... E ... 214 630-5998
Duncanville (G-5530)

Famco ... F ... 713 433-2723
Houston (G-9760)

Farrow Machine & Mfg Co Inc ... E ... 817 633-4686
Arlington (G-676)

Finley Investments Inc ... E ... 713 686-4629
Houston (G-9788)

◆ Fisher Industries Inc ... F ... 713 937-6838
Hockley (G-8344)

Fjw Machine Inc ... F ... 936 931-5507
Waller (G-20498)

Fluxmetals LLC ... D ... 832 948-4307
Houston (G-9818)

Four Pnts Pltnum Invstmnts LLC ... F ... 512 588-7916
Pflugerville (G-16673)

Four-Star Fabricators & Svc Co ... E ... 903 965-4309
Bells (G-2006)

Franklin Machine & Gear Corp ... F ... 281 441-3177
Humble (G-12768)

Freer Iron Works Inc ... E ... 361 394-7273
Freer (G-7225)

FTC Industries Inc ... E ... 817 431-1511
Arlington (G-682)

Fullers Machining Center Inc ... F ... 713 943-0228
South Houston (G-19039)

G & C Mold Company ... F ... 915 590-6670
El Paso (G-5778)

G & G Machine & Maintenance ... E ... 713 673-4235
Kingwood (G-13644)

G A Jo Inc ... G ... 940 767-2340
Wichita Falls (G-20765)

Gary L Noble Inc ... G ... 409 886-0552
Orange (G-16244)

Gates Mch & Fabrication Inc ... E ... 210 651-6567
San Antonio (G-18642)

Gear Drive Service Pump Div ... F ... 806 948-5366
Sunray (G-19618)

Genes Machine Inc ... D ... 361 573-7146
Victoria (G-20267)

George Hall ... E ... 972 266-2700
Grand Prairie (G-7882)

Ggctr Inc ... E ... 832 456-4585
Pasadena (G-16448)

Ghx Industrial LLC ... E ... 409 832-3461
Beaumont (G-1898)

▲ Gibbons Inc ... F ... 940 872-2452
Bowie (G-2196)

Gil-Mar & Associates Inc ... E ... 972 926-9100
Garland (G-7505)

Gme Inc ... E ... 903 586-7581
Jacksonville (G-13240)

Goliath Manufacturing Inc ... E ... 713 641-6979
Houston (G-9996)

Goza Products Inc ... E ... 972 494-5956
Garland (G-7506)

Great Southwest Tool Co ... E ... 915 594-7804
El Paso (G-5789)

Green Machine & Tool Inc ... F ... 713 943-0402
South Houston (G-19041)

Greens Specialty Services ... F ... 817 924-4323
Fort Worth (G-6677)

Gretna Machine Shop Inc ... E ... 713 690-7328
Houston (G-10041)

Gulf Coast Modification LP ... D ... 713 896-3000
Houston (G-10060)

Gulf Coast Repair & Mch Sp Inc ... E ... 361 289-1273
Corpus Christi (G-3539)

▲ Gulf Copper & Mfg Corp ... F ... 409 989-0300
Port Arthur (G-17111)

Gurecky Manufacturing Svc Inc ... E ... 281 342-5926
Rosenberg (G-17584)

H & H Machine Service LLC ... F ... 979 836-2599
Brenham (G-2256)

H & H Water Well Service Inc ... G ... 806 659-5577
Spearman (G-19086)

H & R Mfg and Supply Inc ... E ... 936 856-5529
Willis (G-20847)

H & S Enterprises ... F ... 281 955-1652
Houston (G-10081)

H & W Manufacturing Co Ltd ... E ... 281 353-9079
Spring (G-19127)

H Lorimer Corporation ... E ... 903 643-3239
Longview (G-14245)

Hager Machine and Tool Inc ... E ... 281 872-6393
Houston (G-10088)

▲ Hahn & Clay Ltd ... C ... 713 672-1671
Houston (G-10089)

▲ Hamilton Machine & Mfg Inc ... E ... 432 362-8030
Odessa (G-16025)

Hanna-Wichita Tool Supply Co ... F ... 940 766-3151
Wichita Falls (G-20770)

Hardy Machine & Design Inc ... D ... 713 690-3335
Houston (G-10125)

Harris Industries Incorporated ... D ... 903 759-4485
Dallas (G-4437)

Harrison Mullane Inc ... C ... 281 449-4846
Houston (G-10128)

Heavy Equipment Maintenance Co ... E ... 903 984-9076
Kilgore (G-13557)

Hi-Tech Products Inc ... F ... 512 450-1465
Round Rock (G-17662)

High Plains Drilling Company ... F ... 806 935-2132
Dumas (G-5521)

High Tech Machine II Co LLC ... E ... 832 467-2806
Houston (G-10176)

Hole Specialists Inc ... E ... 281 290-7770
Tomball (G-19983)

Horizon Tech Industries Inc ... E ... 817 536-2263
Fort Worth (G-6703)

Houston Dynamic Service Inc ... E ... 713 636-5587
Houston (G-10230)

◆ Houston Grinding & Mfg Co ... D ... 713 869-3573
Houston (G-10235)

Houston Jvic Operations ... G ... 281 476-5775
La Porte (G-13746)

Houston Mfg & Fabg Co ... G ... 713 688-8383
Houston (G-10238)

▼ Houston North Machine Inc ... F ... 281 351-8108
Tomball (G-19984)

Hub Machine & Tool Inc ... E ... 940 549-0155
Graham (G-7784)

Huffco Industries Inc ... F ... 713 827-1248
Houston (G-10277)

▲ Humanetics II Ltd ... C ... 972 416-1304
Carrollton (G-2763)

Humanetics II Ltd ... D ... 956 994-9200
McAllen (G-14868)

Hunt & Hunt Ltd ... C ... 713 413-2500
Houston (G-8386)

Husa Accurate Mch Works Inc ... F ... 713 691-0685
Houston (G-10289)

Hvac Mechanical Svcs of Texas ... B ... 713 266-3900
Houston (G-10292)

I & R Machining Inc ... F ... 512 281-2251
Elgin (G-6055)

I Corp Inc ... F ... 409 981-9090
Beaumont (G-1905)

Industrial Machine Repair Inc ... F ... 713 937-7995
Jersey Village (G-13300)

Industrial Tool & Die Co Inc ... E ... 281 859-4499
Houston (G-10355)

Industrial Tool & Die Co Inc ... F ... 956 440-9960
Harlingen (G-8190)

Inland Machine ... F ... 281 497-8871
Houston (G-10366)

Inouii Alloy Fabrication Inc ... F ... 713 894-6662
Bacliff (G-1733)

Instruments Tech McHy Inc ... E ... 210 651-9066
Schertz (G-18750)

Integrated Production Svcs Inc ... E ... 281 774-6700
Houston (G-10385)

Integrated Production Systems ... F ... 817 385-0700
Arlington (G-706)

Integrity Precision Mch LLC ... E ... 832 859-4116
Houston (G-10388)

International Machine Shop ... G ... 956 838-1234
Brownsville (G-2363)

Irving Tool & Mfg Co Inc ... D ... 972 926-4000
Garland (G-7521)

ISO Machine Inc ... F ... 281 568-1700
Stafford (G-19333)

J & A Manufacturing Inc ... D ... 972 494-5552
Garland (G-7522)

J & J Machining Inc ... F ... 713 644-7916
Houston (G-10432)

J & S Rides Inc ... E ... 806 293-1353
Plainview (G-16759)

J L Rushing Inc ... E ... 903 759-6000
White Oak (G-20715)

J W Hall Enterprises Inc ... F ... 409 925-7712
Alvin (G-368)

J W Hall Ltd Liability Co ... F ... 281 337-6311
Alvin (G-369)

Jack Phipps ... F ... 972 278-3186
Dallas (G-4520)

Jadcap Machine Works Inc ... F ... 210 932-1019
San Antonio (G-18198)

James D Atkins ... F ... 979 209-2121
Bryan (G-2481)

Jayna Inc ... E ... 972 417-8922
Carrollton (G-2771)

Jerryco Mch & Boiler Works LP ... D ... 713 224-7900
Houston (G-10466)

Jesta Machine ... F ... 903 721-9168
Jacksonville (G-13246)

Jet Machine Works Inc ... E ... 281 449-0046
Houston (G-10469)

Jewell Hudgens Inc ... E ... 936 634-3731
Lufkin (G-14531)

Jims Machine Service Inc ... F ... 432 758-2611
Seminole (G-18885)

Jnb Machine Shop Inc ... F ... 832 237-5000
Houston (G-10477)

Jobe Systems Inc .....E ..... 713 344-1292 Houston (G-10479)	▲ Longview Fab & Machine Inc .....E ..... 903 238-8300 Longview (G-14269)	Metal Detail Inc .....F ..... 214 330-7757 Dallas (G-4669)
Joel G Gibbs Inc .....F ..... 281 595-3330 Rosharon (G-17606)	Lowrance Machine Shop Inc .....E ..... 281 449-6524 Houston (G-10691)	Meticulous Machining Inc .....E ..... 512 756-7471 Burnet (G-2612)
Joes Industrial Mch Sp Inc .....F ..... 210 359-7500 San Antonio (G-18202)	Lsmw Lone Star Machine Works .....E ..... 844 837-4200 Mabank (G-14578)	MI Inc .....E ..... 512 244-3676 Round Rock (G-17672)
Johnson Machine & Tool Inc .....G ..... 972 843-5065 Nevada (G-15765)	▼ M & F Gauge & Specialty Co Inc .....E ..... 325 643-2655 Brownwood (G-2439)	Mic Group LLC .....D ..... 979 277-7800 Brenham (G-2264)
Johnson Tool Company Inc .....E ..... 432 267-7612 Big Spring (G-2084)	M & M Metals Inc .....D ..... 210 341-1313 San Antonio (G-18268)	Mic-All Machining Inc .....F ..... 979 830-8558 Burton (G-2619)
Juggernaut Machinery LLC .....F ..... 210 399-3374 Jourdanton (G-13333)	M & R Machine Works Inc .....G ..... 713 462-0746 Houston (G-10716)	Micro Precision of Texas Inc .....F ..... 713 462-7599 Houston (G-10867)
JV Industrial Companies Ltd .....E ..... 979 373-0376 Freeport (G-7201)	M C(red)gibbins Inc .....E ..... 940 872-1681 Bowie (G-2197)	Microspace Instruments Inc .....F ..... 214 388-0461 Dallas (G-4676)
JV Industrial Companies Ltd .....D ..... 361 884-4022 Corpus Christi (G-3559)	M Fab & Machine .....F ..... 936 264-2388 Conroe (G-3327)	Midco Machine .....F ..... 432 563-2010 Odessa (G-16082)
K & K Machine Shop Inc .....F ..... 713 947-1705 Houston (G-10493)	M G Engineering LLC .....F ..... 626 913-1562 Lindale (G-14135)	▲ Midland Wellhead Inc .....F ..... 432 682-0856 Midland (G-15303)
K S W Corp .....F ..... 214 350-1943 Dallas (G-4542)	M Hastey Construction Co Inc .....E ..... 806 296-7444 Plainview (G-16760)	Midway Machine & Instr Co Inc .....E ..... 713 947-1312 South Houston (G-19050)
K-6 Machine Inc .....F ..... 254 386-3491 Hamilton (G-8166)	M&H Machining Inc .....F ..... 512 930-9059 Georgetown (G-7661)	Midway Machine & Wldg Sp Inc .....F ..... 817 447-0985 Burleson (G-2591)
K-6 Machine Inc .....G ..... 254 386-3491 Hamilton (G-8167)	M&M Machine Shop LLC .....F ..... 832 934-1542 Magnolia (G-14617)	Midwest Machine LLC .....E ..... 806 355-9400 Amarillo (G-501)
K-Line Machine Ltd .....G ..... 254 857-4848 Lorena (G-14342)	Mac Machine and Gear Corp .....F ..... 972 790-7800 Grand Prairie (G-7921)	Mikel Machine Inc .....E ..... 281 354-2750 Porter (G-17179)
Kam-Fab LLC .....F ..... 512 332-2252 Red Rock (G-17238)	Mach Industrial Group LP .....D ..... 713 695-6000 Houston (G-10730)	Mikes Machine Works Inc .....G ..... 979 233-1257 Freeport (G-7205)
Karltex Machine Inc .....F ..... 409 883-5889 Orange (G-16251)	Machine Tech Services Inc .....G ..... 432 385-0891 Odessa (G-16068)	Mills Machine Shop .....G ..... 940 479-2194 Ponder (G-17095)
Kaspar Die & Tool Inc .....F ..... 361 594-3327 Shiner (G-18941)	Machine Tech Services Inc .....F ..... 325 573-1741 Snyder (G-18993)	Milltech Manufacturing Company .....D ..... 972 276-1786 Garland (G-7554)
Keca Metal Products Inc .....F ..... 713 249-3392 Spring (G-19139)	Machining Solutions LLC .....F ..... 940 761-3030 Wichita Falls (G-20781)	Mitchell Manufacturing Inc .....E ..... 281 351-9641 Tomball (G-19989)
Keddie Enterprises Inc .....G ..... 214 337-5387 Dallas (G-4547)	Mack Larry .....F ..... 979 778-8088 Bryan (G-2492)	Modern Machine Shop Inc .....D ..... 956 722-4656 Laredo (G-13913)
Keith & Company Inc .....F ..... 972 285-3588 Mesquite (G-15056)	Macro Tex Machine Works LLC .....F ..... 281 540-2141 Humble (G-12786)	Mohawk Machine & Welding Inc .....E ..... 936 372-5103 Waller (G-20504)
Kennedy Machine & Mfg Inc .....E ..... 972 241-7610 Haslet (G-8219)	Magee Machine and Mfg Inc .....F ..... 972 285-2554 Mesquite (G-15060)	▲ Montgomery Machine Company Inc D ..... 713 453-6381 Houston (G-10914)
Kenney Industries Inc .....D ..... 214 421-4175 Dallas (G-4551)	Magnetic Instruments Corp .....C ..... 800 836-6696 Brenham (G-2262)	Moores Machine Shop .....F ..... 281 489-2925 Pearland (G-16582)
Kestran Inc .....E ..... 281 276-2700 Stafford (G-19340)	Magnum Machine and Mfg Co .....F ..... 903 935-5300 Marshall (G-14788)	▼ Morgan Performance .....E ..... 281 370-2465 Spring (G-19148)
Kevin Goss .....E ..... 281 812-1600 Humble (G-12782)	◆ Maintech International LLC .....E ..... 361 265-9901 Corpus Christi (G-3570)	Moseley Machine Company Inc .....F ..... 713 228-1382 Houston (G-10925)
Kiger Bros Mch Tl & Die Works .....E ..... 281 447-1315 Houston (G-10532)	Malone Industrial Machine LLC .....E ..... 713 477-7737 Deer Park (G-5283)	Motion Gear Works LLC .....F ..... 713 585-5245 Stafford (G-19355)
Kikers Machine Works Inc .....F ..... 432 381-8142 Odessa (G-16052)	Malor Manufacturing Inc .....E ..... 817 926-0278 Fort Worth (G-6808)	Motor City Tool & Die Corp .....F ..... 512 251-7700 Pflugerville (G-16681)
Knighten Machine and Svc Inc .....E ..... 877 457-7204 Odessa (G-16055)	Manda Machine Company .....E ..... 214 352-5946 Dallas (G-4630)	Movement Industries Corp .....F ..... 713 849-1300 Houston (G-10928)
◆ Knust-Godwin LLC .....D ..... 713 785-1060 Katy (G-13418)	Manderscheid Inc .....F ..... 972 424-8701 Plano (G-16918)	Moventas Gears Inc .....F ..... 432 517-4518 Big Spring (G-2088)
Koenig Welding Service Inc .....E ..... 979 532-4161 Wharton (G-20701)	Manufacturing Solutions Inc .....F ..... 409 842-4404 Beaumont (G-1925)	◆ Mpck Machining Inc .....F ..... 254 938-7555 Troy (G-20031)
L & J Technology Inc .....F ..... 281 354-4800 Porter (G-17178)	▲ Marberry Machine Inc .....D ..... 713 466-9666 Houston (G-10758)	Mpl Industries Inc .....G ..... 972 233-0757 Dallas (G-4697)
L C Burkett Drilling .....F ..... 806 948-4252 Sunray (G-19620)	▲ Marks Machine Co Inc .....D ..... 979 543-9204 El Campo (G-5621)	Mueller Manufacturing Inc .....E ..... 979 265-8303 Richwood (G-17469)
L L Machine Works Inc .....F ..... 713 466-7100 Houston (G-10575)	Martels Machine Shop .....G ..... 432 333-4556 Odessa (G-16071)	Mullins Machine & Mfg Co .....F ..... 713 672-0451 Houston (G-10936)
La Machine & Engineering Inc .....F ..... 903 764-5634 Elkhart (G-6060)	Master Machine Inc .....F ..... 713 690-3480 Houston (G-10788)	Multi-Machining Co Inc .....E ..... 972 429-6111 Wylie (G-20941)
Landreth Prcsion Machining Inc .....F ..... 713 944-7464 Houston (G-10595)	Maverick Precision Mfg Ltd .....F ..... 713 433-3756 Houston (G-10801)	Multiple Systems Inc .....E ..... 806 373-7073 Amarillo (G-449)
Langham Creek Mch Works Inc .....D ..... 281 550-9587 Houston (G-10597)	Maxie Hodges .....G ..... 432 333-4556 Odessa (G-16074)	Multiple Systems Inc .....E ..... 806 373-7073 Amarillo (G-450)
Larry Grimes Interest Inc .....F ..... 281 331-3273 Alvin (G-371)	Mayors Machine Works Inc .....E ..... 281 242-0636 Sugar Land (G-19506)	▲ Musshorn Enterprises Inc .....C ..... 915 772-9007 El Paso (G-5892)
Ledsome Machine & Welding Co .....F ..... 325 646-4691 Brownwood (G-2434)	Mc Manus Instrument Co Inc .....F ..... 409 834-2419 Village Mills (G-20338)	National Machine & Workholding .....F ..... 281 489-0490 Manvel (G-14736)
Lfm Industries Inc .....E ..... 713 928-5281 Houston (G-10629)	▼ McDonald Extrusion Tooling .....F ..... 817 594-1290 Weatherford (G-20604)	▲ National Manufacturing LLC .....F ..... 281 856-7693 Houston (G-10970)
Liberty Fluid Power Inc .....E ..... 972 623-0927 Grand Prairie (G-7911)	McGill Maintenance Partnr Ltd .....C ..... 979 233-5438 Freeport (G-7203)	Nelson Oil Field Eqp & Sup .....F ..... 361 375-2105 Pettus (G-16653)
Liberty Precision Company LLC .....D ..... 281 861-5530 Houston (G-10634)	McLeod Machine Works Inc .....F ..... 409 835-3429 Beaumont (G-1927)	New Braunfels Machine Inc .....E ..... 830 226-7179 New Braunfels (G-15817)
Lilly Machinery Inc .....E ..... 903 561-6733 Tyler (G-20113)	McQueary Industries Inc .....F ..... 817 335-1988 Fort Worth (G-6823)	Nexgen - Advnced Fuel Systems .....E ..... 281 789-2000 Houston (G-11046)
Lindsay Forest Products Inc .....F ..... 903 693-7526 Carthage (G-2913)	Md3 Industries Ltd .....F ..... 682 831-1414 Fort Worth (G-6824)	Nimco Instruments .....G ..... 713 723-5063 Houston (G-11057)
▲ Lloyd Company .....E ..... 281 590-8023 Houston (G-10657)	Mechanical Repair & Engrg LP .....E ..... 281 471-7811 La Porte (G-13775)	Noormac LLC .....F ..... 303 261-2818 El Paso (G-5898)
Lodor Enterprises Inc .....D ..... 214 651-1977 Dallas (G-4600)	▲ Mercury Tool and Machine Inc .....D ..... 254 752-1639 Waco (G-20435)	Northast Txas McHning Wldg Hrd .....F ..... 903 427-2277 Clarksville (G-3076)
Logik Precision Inc .....E ..... 713 939-0061 Houston (G-10673)	Merritt Prfrred Components Inc .....D ..... 903 983-1592 Kilgore (G-13574)	Northwest Machining Svcs LLC .....F ..... 281 894-5388 Houston (G-11081)
Lone Star Machine and Tool Co .....F ..... 806 622-5106 Amarillo (G-499)	Meta-Tech Industries Inc .....F ..... 713 467-6544 Houston (G-10842)	◆ Numerical Precision Inc .....D ..... 281 328-7343 Crosby (G-3739)

Omni Precision Inc ....F 713 688-3131	Progressive Machine Works Ltd ....E 281 209-9990	▲ RMC Reliable Machinists Corp ....E 281 444-2181
Houston (G-11178)	Houston (G-11443)	Houston (G-11636)
One Source Mfg Tech LLC ....D 512 259-3272	Prototype Machine Co ....E 512 282-1590	Rockmm Manufacturing Inc ....G 346 888-6188
Leander (G-13996)	Manchaca (G-14641)	Pearland (G-16595)
▲ Oteco Inc ....C 713 695-3693	Public Steel Inc ....E 806 376-8221	Rom Industrial Inc ....F 915 875-1186
Houston (G-11200)	Amarillo (G-457)	El Paso (G-5945)
Owens Mach & Manufacturing ....F 325 672-4161	Pump Arts Inc ....E 713 946-0500	Romco Manufacturing Inc ....F 281 479-9600
Abilene (G-62)	Houston (G-11472)	Deer Park (G-5292)
Owens Machine and Tool Company ....E 972 219-2354	Pv American Inc ....F 713 270-7772	Romco Manufacturing Inc ....E 281 479-9600
Lewisville (G-14081)	Houston (G-11481)	Deer Park (G-5293)
P & N Machine Company Inc ....D 281 469-9140	Pyle Machine Company Inc ....F 817 485-6011	Romtex Enterprises Inc ....D 281 494-0373
Houston (G-11213)	Fort Worth (G-6924)	Sugar Land (G-19537)
P & W Quality Machines Inc ....E 972 299-0500	Q M Company Inc ....F 713 673-1917	Ronald L Jordan Company ....E 281 485-6626
Cedar Hill (G-2949)	Houston (G-11481)	Pearland (G-16597)
P M W Ventures Inc ....F 940 855-6100	QMF Steel Inc ....E 903 455-3618	Ronco Machine and Mfg Inc ....F 713 697-8717
Wichita Falls (G-20792)	Campbell (G-2646)	Houston (G-11661)
▼ P T Products & Services Inc ....E 512 251-3592	QSD Manufacturing Inc ....F 713 957-0599	Rotom Inc ....E 806 293-7331
Pflugerville (G-16682)	Houston (G-11488)	Plainview (G-16762)
Padgett Machine Tools Co Inc ....E 254 865-9771	▼ Quality Machine Shop LLC ....E 979 885-6932	Roy B Wheeler Company Inc ....E 713 692-9729
Gatesville (G-7622)	Sealy (G-18815)	Houston (G-11681)
Pampa Machine & Supply Inc ....F 806 665-0013	Quality Manufacturing Inc ....F 940 592-5790	Rp Machine Shop ....F 713 939-7522
Pampa (G-16332)	Iowa Park (G-12908)	Houston (G-11688)
Panhandle Packing & Gasket Inc ....E 806 763-2801	◆ Quality Tubing Inc ....C 281 456-0751	RPM Services Inc ....D 281 595-3165
Lubbock (G-14456)	Houston (G-11503)	Rosharon (G-17612)
Panyanouvong Jose & Le Malysa ....F 310 279-7065	▲ Quantex Instrument Company ....E 936 544-5732	RWG Incorporated ....F 972 461-1920
Fort Worth (G-6892)	Crockett (G-3723)	Wylie (G-20946)
▼ Paradigm Metals Incorporated ....E 512 255-2622	▲ Quell Petroleum Services Inc ....E 432 943-8400	▲ Ryan Manufacturing Company Inc ..F 817 613-1890
Pflugerville (G-16683)	Monahans (G-15612)	Weatherford (G-20618)
Parland Inc ....F 903 843-3467	Questech Services Corporation ....E 972 278-8006	S & S McHining Fabrication Inc ....E 254 729-3685
Gilmer (G-7710)	Garland (G-7575)	Groesbeck (G-8108)
Pastusek Industries Inc ....E 972 291-0511	◆ Quietflex Manufacturing Co LP ....B 877 694-3669	S + S Instruments Inc ....F 281 463-1600
Fort Worth (G-6896)	Houston (G-11514)	Cypress (G-3818)
Patco Machine & Fab Inc ....E 281 443-2837	R & C Machine LLC ....E 254 694-9278	S K Industries Inc ....G 713 462-6997
Houston (G-11258)	Whitney (G-20732)	Houston (G-11710)
Payton Machine & Supply Inc ....E 806 274-5221	R & R Sheet Metal and Mch Sp ....F 806 274-2361	Salter Precision Machining ....F 281 391-4118
Borger (G-2182)	Borger (G-2183)	Katy (G-13438)
PDQ Machine Shop Inc ....E 832 327-4455	R C Schmidt & Son Inc ....F 713 673-5911	▲ Saturn Machine Inc ....D 281 391-7800
Houston (G-11265)	Houston (G-11522)	Brookshire (G-2324)
Peerless Mfg Co ....E 940 566-9029	◆ R J Machine Company Inc ....F 830 693-7493	Saturn Manufacturing Corp ....E 817 267-3961
Denton (G-5390)	Marble Falls (G-14750)	Hurst (G-12857)
Penta Industries Inc ....F 512 834-2421	R W Machine Inc ....E 281 784-1600	Saulsbury Industries Inc ....E 903 392-2248
Pflugerville (G-16684)	Houston (G-11529)	Henderson (G-8273)
▲ Petroluem Machinery Inc ....G 713 697-4999	R-5 Metal Fabricators Inc ....F 903 873-2633	Savage Prcsion Fabrication Inc ....F 972 429-0993
Houston (G-11309)	Wills Point (G-20877)	Wylie (G-20949)
Peyton Salas & Mendoza LLC ....E 512 784-5875	Radford Manufacturing Inc ....F 817 536-7706	Saxon Engineering Inc ....E 713 466-7500
Houston (G-11313)	Fort Worth (G-6936)	Houston (G-11761)
Phoenix Mfg Inc ....F 214 544-7507	Radke Machine & Tool Inc ....F 254 576-2513	Sbi Precision Components LLC ....G 713 715-6111
Allen (G-293)	Hubbard (G-12737)	Cypress (G-3819)
Pick Instrument Products Co ....E 713 672-1686	Rapid Hose ....F 713 468-4673	Schmidt Tool & Mfg Co ....E 936 856-5897
Galena Park (G-7381)	Houston (G-11548)	Willis (G-20864)
Piq Machine LLC ....F 281 354-9873	Rayson Company ....E 713 680-0540	Scientific Machine & Wldg Inc ....E 512 926-8400
New Caney (G-15846)	Houston (G-11555)	Austin (G-1490)
Platron Manufacturing and Pltg ....E 512 989-1362	RB Machine Works Inc ....E 281 446-1414	Sealy Precision Machining Inc ....F 979 885-7380
Pflugerville (G-16685)	Humble (G-12795)	Sealy (G-18819)
PMI Pump Parts LLC ....F 817 441-7787	Reactive Metals Corp ....F 979 849-7197	Senior Operations LLC ....C 830 629-8080
Aledo (G-201)	Angleton (G-577)	New Braunfels (G-15821)
Polk Mechanical Company LLC ....C 972 339-1200	Reama Inc ....E 409 744-9222	◆ Serampore Inds Private Ltd Inc .....E 713 923-6111
Grand Prairie (G-7947)	Galveston (G-7407)	Houston (G-11833)
Polyfab Inc ....G 361 594-3535	Redding Machine Shop Inc ....E 940 691-5218	Shaneda Machine Inc ....E 432 333-7083
Shiner (G-18947)	Wichita Falls (G-20802)	Odessa (G-16152)
Power Repair Service Inc ....D 361 289-1471	REE Holding Inc ....E 409 840-5650	Sharp-Bilt LLC ....F 409 886-0066
Corpus Christi (G-3594)	Beaumont (G-1947)	Orange (G-16262)
Praxis Fabrication Inc ....F 806 883-7621	Reef Process Systems LLC ....F 972 874-9300	Shell Machine Works Inc ....E 361 883-7073
White Deer (G-20710)	Flower Mound (G-6278)	Corpus Christi (G-3622)
Precise Machine & Fabrications ....F 936 298-2851	Ref Machining Ltd Partnr LLP ....F 512 251-9954	Sherman Machine Inc ....E 903 892-2889
Cleveland (G-3133)	Pflugerville (G-16686)	Sherman (G-18932)
Precision Custom Machining Inc ....F 713 462-8622	▲ Reliable Edm Ltd ....E 713 692-5454	Sienko Precision Inc ....E 713 462-7482
Houston (G-11388)	Houston (G-11589)	Houston (G-11880)
Precision Def Components LLC ....F 870 949-8590	Reliable Manufacturing Inc ....E 512 255-6572	Sikes Machine Shop Inc ....G 806 828-6568
Texarkana (G-19771)	Round Rock (G-17684)	Slaton (G-18973)
Precision Machine ....F 903 675-2300	◆ Reliance Industries Inc ....E 281 499-9926	▲ Silva Technologies Inc ....E 713 869-3631
Galveston (G-7406)	Missouri City (G-15587)	Houston (G-11897)
Premier Machining Services ....F 281 558-3242	Reno Machine Works LLC ....F 903 224-6275	Silver Creek Machine Ltd ....F 817 238-0131
Houston (G-11401)	Reno (G-17252)	Azle (G-1729)
Pro Machine LP ....D 713 466-3210	◆ Resource Metals Company ....E 281 442-8600	SKW Manufacturing LLC ....E 806 763-8118
Houston (G-11425)	Houston (G-11609)	Lubbock (G-14482)
Pro-Grind Inc ....E 713 645-2966	Rfr Vertex LLC ....F 713 851-2060	Snoe Inc Machining & Welding ....E 979 567-0808
Houston (G-11426)	Willis (G-20859)	Caldwell (G-2636)
Production Machine & Tool LP ....E 940 767-9400	Rheaco Inc ....D 972 264-4748	Sond Industries LLC ....F 281 372-8220
Wichita Falls (G-20798)	Grand Prairie (G-7965)	Houston (G-11951)
Production Manufacturing Inc ....F 915 629-9668	Rhino Machine Shop Inc ....G 281 290-7858	South Bay Solutions Inc ....E 936 494-0180
El Paso (G-5919)	Tomball (G-20006)	The Woodlands (G-19922)
Production Mch & TI MGT LLC ....D 940 767-9400	Richard H Smith LLC ....F 817 267-6750	South Coast Grinding Co LLC ....F 713 649-0001
Wichita Falls (G-20799)	Euless (G-6155)	Houston (G-11961)
Professional Machine Works ....F 713 645-7562	Richs Machinery Company Inc ....F 903 758-0531	South Texas Machine Shop Inc ....F 361 664-8902
Houston (G-11438)	Longview (G-14298)	Alice (G-236)
Professional Rebuild & Optimal ....E 806 358-3636	Riggs Machine and Welding Inc ....F 254 965-3910	South Texas Precision Inc ....F 713 939-0101
Amarillo (G-456)	Stephenville (G-19420)	Houston (G-11967)
Professnal Rbild Optmal Svc LL ....E 806 749-7761	Riverside Machine Shop Inc ....F 409 246-1600	Southwest Formseal Inc ....E 832 399-3900
Lubbock (G-14465)	Kountze (G-13672)	Houston (G-8392)

Southwest Industrial Svcs Inc..............E....... 817 332-6481
Fort Worth *(G-7002)*
▼ **Southwest Machine & Mfg Co Inc**....E....... 972 254-2014
Irving *(G-13186)*
Southwest Machine Works Inc...............F....... 713 433-6824
Houston *(G-11981)*
Southwest Manufacturing Corp.............G....... 214 638-0323
Dallas *(G-4991)*
◆ **Southwest Metrics Inc**.........................F....... 817 281-7697
Fort Worth *(G-7004)*
Southwest Metrics Inc............................E....... 817 581-4474
Fort Worth *(G-7005)*
Southwest Oilfield Pdts Inc....................G....... 254 559-8667
Breckenridge *(G-2238)*
Southwestern Paint Panels LLC.............F....... 281 442-0000
Houston *(G-11985)*
Southwire Company LLC........................F....... 940 328-1047
Mineral Wells *(G-15542)*
Space City Machine & Tool Co...............F....... 713 939-0011
Houston *(G-11988)*
Spaeth Machine Shop Inc......................E....... 972 438-3804
Irving *(G-13187)*
▲ **Sparkman Industries Inc**....................D....... 361 573-0001
Victoria *(G-20304)*
Specialty Comprsr & Eng Co Inc...........E....... 806 274-7135
Borger *(G-2187)*
◆ **SPM Flow Control Inc**........................C....... 817 246-2461
Fort Worth *(G-7013)*
▲ **Spm Technology Inc**............................E....... 512 931-0201
Georgetown *(G-7679)*
Spur Machine Works Inc.........................F....... 903 597-8757
Tyler *(G-20156)*
Square One Machine Inc........................F....... 254 968-5600
Stephenville *(G-19423)*
Standard Alloys Incorporated................G....... 409 769-7850
Vidor *(G-20333)*
Standard Alloys Incorporated................D....... 409 983-3201
Port Arthur *(G-17125)*
Starke Machine Co..................................D....... 817 625-6821
Fort Worth *(G-7017)*
▲ **Sterling Fabrication Tech**....................F....... 713 591-9004
Dallas *(G-5010)*
Stone Machinery Movers Inc..................E....... 936 446-2805
Conroe *(G-3368)*
Stuart Hose & Pipe Ltd...........................E....... 214 631-6682
Dallas *(G-5017)*
Sun Machine Ltd......................................E....... 832 448-1201
Jersey Village *(G-13305)*
Sunbelt Machine Works Corp.................E....... 281 499-0051
Stafford *(G-19380)*
Sundown Cnc Inc....................................G....... 281 342-8314
Needville *(G-15764)*
Superior McHning Fbrcation Inc............C....... 940 759-5066
Muenster *(G-15674)*
Sweetwater Machine and Welding.........E....... 325 235-2922
Sweetwater *(G-19637)*
Syneo LLC...G....... 979 849-8700
Angleton *(G-579)*
T and S Machine Company.....................E....... 936 264-1030
Cut and Shoot *(G-3768)*
T Squared Mfg Inc..................................E....... 254 732-9039
Waco *(G-20462)*
T W Havens Metals Inc...........................F....... 817 834-2621
Fort Worth *(G-7028)*
Tabco Machines Inc................................E....... 806 749-5649
Lubbock *(G-14490)*
Tapcoenpro International Inc.................C....... 281 247-8100
Channelview *(G-3041)*
Taylor Iron-Machine Works....................F....... 512 365-3646
Taylor *(G-19663)*
Techmar Industries LLC.........................F....... 832 246-6200
Spring *(G-19175)*
Tejas Precision Metalfabricatn...............D....... 210 648-1555
San Antonio *(G-18524)*
▲ **Temple Machine Shop Inc**....................D....... 254 774-8099
Temple *(G-19709)*
Texarkana Machine Inc...........................F....... 903 831-4355
Texarkana *(G-19779)*
Texas Agri Machine & Indus Mfg............E....... 806 296-5765
Plainview *(G-16764)*
Texas Automation Products Inc..............F....... 972 289-0300
Hutchins *(G-12871)*
Texas Enterprise Mfg & Mch...................F....... 281 342-0027
Wharton *(G-20707)*
▲ **Texas Honing Inc**..................................E....... 281 485-8339
Pearland *(G-16601)*
Texas Honing Inc......................................D....... 713 673-1111
Houston *(G-12234)*
Texas Honing Inc......................................E....... 281 953-5900
Houston *(G-12235)*
Texas Hydraulics Inc...............................E....... 254 756-6879
Waco *(G-20466)*
Texas Precision Mfg Inc..........................E....... 806 741-1166
Lubbock *(G-14492)*
▲ **Texas Shapes Inc**...................................E....... 713 641-1000
Houston *(G-12249)*
Texas Toolmakers Inc..............................E....... 210 494-3651
San Antonio *(G-18544)*
Texpert Machine Co Inc...........................F....... 713 263-7000
Houston *(G-12262)*
Textool Company......................................E....... 713 923-5595
Houston *(G-12264)*
Tiger Ridge Manufacturing Inc.................E....... 903 364-1810
Whitewright *(G-20729)*
▼ **Timkensteel Material Svcs LLC**............C....... 281 449-0319
Houston *(G-12293)*
▲ **Tj Machine & Tool Ltd**..........................D....... 817 444-5540
Azle *(G-1731)*
Tnn Machining Company LLC...................E....... 713 849-0062
Houston *(G-12310)*
▲ **Tnn Manufacturing Company Inc**.........D....... 713 849-0062
Houston *(G-12311)*
Tnn New World..D....... 281 598-6680
Houston *(G-12312)*
TNT Machine..F....... 713 722-0622
Houston *(G-12314)*
Toolex Inc...E....... 713 644-8071
Houston *(G-12319)*
Total Machining Solutions LLC.................G....... 281 355-7700
Spring *(G-19181)*
Trans-TEC Machine Ltd.............................E....... 713 643-9114
Houston *(G-12345)*
Traw Machine Works LLC...........................E....... 281 893-1710
Cypress *(G-3823)*
Triple/S Dynamics Inc................................E....... 214 828-8600
Dallas *(G-5116)*
Triple/S Dynamics Inc................................E....... 214 828-8600
Dallas *(G-5117)*
Turbine Component Repair Inc.................F....... 713 895-9551
Houston *(G-12409)*
Turbine Supply Company...........................F....... 806 763-5901
Lubbock *(G-14500)*
Turbo Machine Technology Inc.................F....... 281 443-4646
Houston *(G-12410)*
Turn-Tech Inc..E....... 281 356-1290
Pinehurst *(G-16737)*
Turnamatic Machine Inc.............................D....... 972 235-1923
Richardson *(G-17416)*
▲ **TW Tanks and Construction Co**..............F....... 361 358-8869
Beeville *(G-1989)*
U S Machine Shop Inc.................................F....... 940 495-3964
Electra *(G-6050)*
◆ **Union Tech Co LLC**...................................E....... 281 583-7601
Houston *(G-12439)*
Unique Machine Shop Inc...........................E....... 254 456-2972
Oglesby *(G-16216)*
Unisorb Corporation....................................F....... 713 943-3753
South Houston *(G-19053)*
United Machining Services Inc...................F....... 936 760-1153
Conroe *(G-3379)*
▼ **United Service Alliance Inc**....................E....... 409 935-9500
Texas City *(G-19805)*
Universal Machining Inds Inc.....................D....... 940 759-2430
Muenster *(G-15675)*
Upstart Acquisitions Corp...........................F....... 281 469-0815
Houston *(G-12476)*
USA Machine Inc...E....... 972 636-7400
Royse City *(G-17727)*
USA Precision LLC..E....... 281 458-7304
Houston *(G-12499)*
V&G Dynamic Machine LLC..........................F....... 830 693-4743
Marble Falls *(G-14751)*
V-Teq Manufacturing Inc..............................F....... 713 466-0660
Houston *(G-12513)*
Varco Shaffer Inc...E....... 713 672-1711
Houston *(G-12535)*
Vaughan Investments Inc.............................E....... 956 546-5175
Brownsville *(G-2420)*
VCM Industries Inc..D....... 713 462-7444
Houston *(G-12541)*
Vinh Ho Machine Shop Inc...........................F....... 713 896-7828
Houston *(G-12569)*
▲ **Vu Enterprise Inc**..E....... 713 944-0384
South Houston *(G-19055)*
W P C Services L L C.......................................F....... 903 686-0597
Longview *(G-14330)*
W W Metal Products Inc.................................E....... 903 838-4329
Texarkana *(G-19783)*
Walker Industrial Machining..........................F....... 713 434-5000
Houston *(G-12594)*
Wapco Inc...F....... 936 539-6272
Conroe *(G-3384)*
Waples Holdings Inc..E....... 817 568-1600
Fort Worth *(G-7125)*
▲ **Watson Grinding and Mfg Co**......................D....... 713 466-3053
Houston *(G-12605)*
Wcsc LLC...F....... 915 774-0348
El Paso *(G-6028)*
Webb Technology Inc.......................................F....... 214 348-8678
Dallas *(G-5178)*
Welasco Inc...F....... 903 784-5562
Paris *(G-16374)*
▲ **Weldfit Corporation**.......................................C....... 713 460-3700
Houston *(G-12628)*
Wells Manufacturing LLC.................................E....... 713 690-4204
Houston *(G-12632)*
Wesco Industries Inc..E....... 817 551-7063
Fort Worth *(G-7137)*
West Machine & Tool Inc...................................F....... 903 758-5401
Longview *(G-14335)*
Western Grinding Co Inc...................................F....... 214 631-3090
Dallas *(G-5182)*
◆ **Whip Industries Inc**..D....... 817 289-1404
Fort Worth *(G-7145)*
Whitehawk Machine & Tools Inc.......................G....... 903 450-1060
Greenville *(G-8097)*
Williams Fire Hazard Ctrl Inc............................E....... 409 745-3232
Port Arthur *(G-17133)*
Wilson Precision Mch Works LP.......................F....... 832 721-9918
Houston *(G-12674)*
Winco Machine & Repair Inc.............................F....... 903 844-2200
Gladewater *(G-7730)*
Woodlawn Manufacturing Ltd...........................C....... 903 938-1882
Marshall *(G-14809)*
Woods Tool and Machine Co Inc.......................F....... 817 275-4541
Arlington *(G-810)*
Woolley Fishing Tool Inc....................................E....... 903 984-3553
Kilgore *(G-13603)*
Woolley Tool Inc..F....... 903 984-3553
Kilgore *(G-13604)*
Xtreme High Prfmce Catings Inc........................E....... 281 695-8880
Houston *(G-12711)*
Zamorano Enterprises Inc...................................G....... 210 924-2320
San Antonio *(G-18633)*

SIC

36 ELECTRONIC AND OTHER ELECTRICAL EQUIPMENT AND COMPONENTS, EXCEPT COMPUTER

3612 Power, Distribution & Specialty Transformers

ABB Enterprise Software Inc.............................E....... 903 237-1030
Longview *(G-14187)*
Active Power Inc..D....... 512 836-6464
Austin *(G-887)*
Advanced Control Systems LLC........................E....... 832 529-2234
Houston *(G-8487)*
Ajax Tocco Magnethermic Corp..........................F....... 903 297-2526
Longview *(G-14191)*
Alamo Transformer Supply Co............................E....... 713 991-6060
Houston *(G-8526)*
◆ **Amran Inc**...C....... 281 243-2200
Sugar Land *(G-19443)*
Arcosa Inc...C....... 972 942-6500
Dallas *(G-3958)*
BP Wind Energy North Amer Inc........................D....... 713 354-2100
Houston *(G-8971)*
◆ **Circuit Breaker Sales LLC**.................................C....... 940 665-4444
Gainesville *(G-7338)*
Cooper Power Systems LLC................................C....... 936 569-9422
Nacogdoches *(G-15692)*
◆ **Cordyne Inc**...D....... 713 460-5151
Houston *(G-9313)*
▲ **Electromagnetic Industries LLC**.......................E....... 281 422-5225
Baytown *(G-1816)*
Fisher Controls Intl LLC.......................................B....... 972 542-5512
McKinney *(G-14943)*
Gibraltar Trading Inc..F....... 281 777-6786
Houston *(G-9956)*
Global Technical Solutions USA...........................F....... 832 410-4488
Spring *(G-19126)*
Greenville Transformer Co...................................E....... 903 455-1610
Greenville *(G-8076)*
▲ **Gtech Precision Inds USA Ltd**...........................F....... 817 539-8014
Mansfield *(G-14678)*
High Voltage Power Systems Inc..........................C....... 972 733-1700
Carrollton *(G-2756)*

Houston Transformer Co Ltd ....D 713 977-6009
Houston (G-10258)

Houtex Hi-Temp Transformer LLC.......E 713 271-8993
Houston (G-10266)

Hydradyne LLC ....F 210 661-4378
San Antonio (G-18177)

Intermatic Incorporated ....F 915 858-9204
El Paso (G-5813)

JCB Inc...F 254 687-2200
Itasca (G-13215)

Jefferson Electric Inc......................F 956 542-5491
Brownsville (G-2369)

◆ M&I Electric Industries Inc ....D 832 241-6330
Houston (G-10721)

Mag Flux Corporation ....E 972 272-8576
Garland (G-7541)

▼ Magnetic Technology Inc ....E 214 544-2700
McKinney (G-14955)

Mars Transformers LLC ....E 281 648-1600
Houston (G-10773)

Maviro Inc ....D 713 485-5193
Deer Park (G-5285)

Maxi Volt Corporation Inc...............F 806 371-0722
Amarillo (G-500)

Micropac Industries Inc ....F 972 272-3571
Garland (G-7551)

Nova Magnetics Inc ....D 972 272-8287
Garland (G-7564)

Ohmite Holding LLC ....F 956 542-0276
Brownsville (G-2388)

▲ Oilfield-Electric-Marine Inc ....F 713 680-9659
Houston (G-11165)

▲ Operating Technical Elec ....E 817 288-2600
Fort Worth (G-6886)

Panda-Brandywine L P ....E 972 980-7159
Dallas (G-4785)

Philips North America LLC ....E 915 298-4111
El Paso (G-5910)

▼ Powell Industries Inc ....B 713 944-6900
Houston (G-11376)

Puffer-Sweiven Holdings Inc ....E 281 470-2000
La Porte (G-13785)

Resa Power LLC ....F 832 900-8340
Houston (G-11604)

Robertshaw Controls Company ....F 956 724-4400
Laredo (G-13926)

Schneider Electric Usa Inc ....C 972 236-0300
Coppell (G-3444)

Sigma Electronics Inc ....E 800 874-7121
Houston (G-11884)

Solomon Transformers LLC..............D 512 763-3306
Georgetown (G-7677)

Sunbelt Transformer Ltd ....G 713 481-5500
Temple (G-19704)

◆ Sunbelt Transformer Ltd ....E 800 433-3128
Temple (G-19705)

Texas Electric Coops Inc ....E 512 454-0311
Austin (G-1567)

◆ Thermon Inc ....C 512 396-5801
San Marcos (G-18715)

▲ Tru-Test Inc ....E 940 327-8020
Mineral Wells (G-15543)

Upely Traders ....E 832 998-8432
Dallas (G-5143)

▲ Utility Agency & Import Inc ....F 817 477-9888
Mansfield (G-14725)

◆ Vantran Industries Inc ....E 254 772-9740
Waco (G-20471)

Wattstock LLC ....F 713 248-4148
Dallas (G-5175)

Younicos Inc ....C 512 268-8191
Austin (G-1683)

3613 Switchgear & Switchboard Apparatus

ABB Enterprise Software Inc ....E 903 237-1030
Longview (G-14187)

Accurate Control Company LLC ....E 713 699-3799
Houston (G-8461)

Advanced Elec & Mtr Contrls............E 972 253-7783
Irving (G-12924)

Amerimex Power Systems Inc ....F 832 678-3520
Houston (G-8619)

Aphthoria Solutions Inc ....D 214 821-8607
Dallas (G-3950)

▲ Atron Group LLC ....D 214 292-9840
Dallas (G-3984)

◆ Azz Inc ....D 817 810-0095
Fort Worth (G-6414)

▲ Beeco Motors & Controls Inc.........E 832 320-3100
Houston (G-8851)

BI Technology Inc ....E 832 698-8000
Tomball (G-19967)

Cates Control Systems Inc ....D 972 665-3200
Plano (G-16821)

◆ Circuit Breaker Sales LLC ....C 940 665-4444
Gainesville (G-7338)

Conloop Inc ....D 940 322-2206
Wichita Falls (G-20756)

▲ Control Panels USA Inc ....E 512 852-8280
Austin (G-1063)

Coordnated Designs Contrls Inc ......F 713 921-0220
Houston (G-9308)

◆ Cordyne Inc ....F 713 460-5151
Houston (G-9313)

◆ Coyote Electronics Inc ....F 817 485-3336
Azle (G-1722)

Crown Texas Inc ....D 972 905-4680
Garland (G-7471)

▼ Cse W-Industries Inc ....E 713 466-9463
Jersey Village (G-13297)

Custom Controls Company ....E 713 666-3258
Houston (G-9368)

Dial Electrical of Houston ....G 713 691-4666
Houston (G-9450)

Eaton Corporation ....F 915 772-6198
El Paso (G-5732)

Eaton Corporation ....E 713 849-1600
Houston (G-9572)

Elah Holdings Inc ....F 805 435-1255
Dallas (G-4307)

Electrical Contrls Houston Inc.........F 281 501-0729
New Caney (G-15838)

◆ Electronic Power Design Inc ....D 713 923-1191
Houston (G-9596)

Electrotechnics Corporation............F 903 938-1901
Marshall (G-14776)

◆ Ema Electromechanics Inc ....C 325 235-8000
Sweetwater (G-19629)

First Texas Products Corp ....F 915 633-8354
El Paso (G-5769)

▲ Forney Corporation ....E 972 458-6100
Addison (G-126)

▲ GE Zenith Controls Inc ....B 800 637-1738
Plano (G-16878)

Gil Automations LLC ....F 713 904-4600
Houston (G-9957)

Gonzales Elec Systems LLC..............E 409 860-3802
Beaumont (G-1899)

H Lorimer Corporation ....F 903 643-3239
Longview (G-14245)

▲ Hunting Innova Inc ....B 281 653-5500
Houston (G-10284)

Interconnect Wiring LLP ....C 817 377-9473
Fort Worth (G-6723)

Kelleys Controls Incorporated..........F 432 362-7998
Odessa (G-16045)

Lft Panels Inc ....E 713 984-9878
Houston (G-10630)

Littelfuse Inc ....D 830 513-8775
Eagle Pass (G-5549)

Logic Control LLC ....E 281 362-9600
Conroe (G-3323)

Lower Colorado River Authority.........A 512 473-3200
Austin (G-1305)

LSI Integrated Graphics LP ....C 713 744-4100
Houston (G-10696)

▲ Luminator Technology Group LLC...C 972 424-6511
Plano (G-16913)

M&I Electric LLC ....C 409 838-0441
Beaumont (G-1922)

◆ M&I Electric Industries Inc ....D 832 241-6330
Houston (G-10721)

Maverick Technical Systems Inc ......G 903 845-5574
Gladewater (G-7726)

Maxi Volt Corporation Inc ....F 806 371-0722
Amarillo (G-500)

Mico Group Ltd ....F 713 460-3172
Grapeland (G-8006)

Molex LLC ....D 915 591-5600
El Paso (G-5882)

Murphy Fw ....D 281 633-4500
Rosenberg (G-17590)

National Swtchgear Systems Inc ......F 972 420-0149
Lewisville (G-14071)

▼ Panelmatic Texas Inc ....E 281 890-1678
Houston (G-11231)

Parkline Inc ....E 409 935-1037
La Marque (G-13713)

Parkline Inc ....D 409 935-5743
Hitchcock (G-8339)

Philips North America LLC ....F 956 541-1224
Brownsville (G-2393)

▼ Powell Industries Inc ....B 713 944-6900
Houston (G-11376)

Quality Lnings Fabrication Inc ....E 713 863-7013
Houston (G-11495)

Rail Products Intl Inc ....D 956 541-1759
Brownsville (G-2397)

Ran Technologies Inc ....E 281 530-3248
Houston (G-11538)

Rnb Controls Inc ....E 325 388-6023
Kingsland (G-13622)

▲ Roxar Inc ....E 281 879-2600
Houston (G-11680)

Ruby Automation LLC ....E 972 881-9663
Plano (G-16997)

Schneider Electric Usa Inc ....C 972 323-1111
Carrollton (G-2814)

Schneider Electric Usa Inc ....B 877 248-3781
Laredo (G-13931)

Schneider Electric Usa Inc ....C 361 887-5055
Corpus Christi (G-3617)

Schneider Electric Usa Inc ....C 972 236-0300
Coppell (G-3444)

Sdrg Controls Inc ....F 713 242-0822
Houston (G-11794)

Shermco System Integration LLC .....C 940 322-2206
Wichita Falls (G-20811)

Siemens Industry Inc ....C 915 790-0219
El Paso (G-5960)

Siemens Industry Inc ....E 817 633-4430
Grand Prairie (G-7973)

Skledar-Greene LLC ....F 817 454-4214
Krum (G-13676)

Ss Electric Inc ....E 915 217-2200
El Paso (G-5973)

Sunrgy LLC ....E 832 786-5051
Stafford (G-19381)

▲ Texas Instruments Incorporated....A 972 995-3773
Dallas (G-5067)

Texas Instruments Incorporated ......E 214 567-2075
Richardson (G-17408)

▲ Texas Meter and Device Co LLC....D 254 732-1305
Waco (G-20467)

◆ Toshiba International Corp ....A 800 231-1412
Houston (G-12327)

▲ Unitron LP ....D 214 221-9094
Dallas (G-5139)

▲ Utility Agency & Import Inc ....F 817 477-9888
Mansfield (G-14725)

Vector Systems Inc ....D 214 544-9500
McKinney (G-14985)

Vertiv Corporation ....B 956 683-2948
McAllen (G-14917)

▲ Volta LLC ....C 832 369-2420
Houston (G-12581)

Webb Technology Inc ....E 214 348-8678
Dallas (G-5178)

▲ Williamsrdm Inc ....D 817 872-1500
Fort Worth (G-7148)

3621 Motors & Generators

A & A Genpro Inc ....E 713 830-3280
Houston (G-8419)

A O Smith Corporation ....C 915 859-1071
El Paso (G-5635)

A O Smith Corporation ....E 915 400-2800
El Paso (G-5634)

▲ Abaco Drilling Tech LLC ....C 281 869-0700
Houston (G-8441)

ACS Manufacturing Inc ....E 903 462-2001
Denison (G-5334)

▲ Air Starter Components Inc ....E 281 261-7939
Stafford (G-19282)

Arcosa Wind Towers Inc ....G 817 378-3700
Fort Worth (G-6398)

Auto Electric Systems Inc................E 972 241-2077
Plano (G-16796)

B J Electric Motor Service................F 432 570-4100
Midland (G-15127)

Baseline Energy Services LP ....F 432 248-9112
Midland (G-15133)

Baseline Energy Services LP ....E 817 889-0056
Fort Worth (G-6428)

Benchmark Manufacturing Inc ....E 903 882-4311
Lindale (G-14133)

▲ Breco International LLC ....F 713 641-6073
Houston (G-8981)

Broadwind Hvy Fabrications Inc ......F 325 437-5950
Abilene (G-25)

Cedar Creek II ....E 713 354-2100
  Houston (G-9115)
Competitive Energy - Texas LP ....G 713 957-9948
  Sugar Land (G-19466)
Compliant Power Systems LLC ....F 903 427-0071
  Clarksville (G-3072)
Comprssion/Generation Svcs LLC ....D 281 209-3616
  Houston (G-9262)
Consultingpoint Inc ....E 956 986-2727
  Brownsville (G-2347)
▲ Controlled Systems Sales Co ....E 972 234-6767
  Richardson (G-17291)
◆ Cordyne Inc ....D 713 460-5151
  Houston (G-9313)
Dayton-Phoenix Group Inc ....F 281 372-0685
  Houston (G-9413)
◆ Delta Electronics (usa) Inc ....C 469 330-9100
  Plano (G-16837)
◆ Diesel Engine and Parts Co LLC .....E 713 675-6100
  Houston (G-9466)
◆ Electronic Power Design Inc ....D 713 923-1191
  Houston (G-9596)
▲ Epd International Ltd ....D 713 923-1191
  Houston (G-9678)
Evans Enterprises Inc ....D 325 235-1776
  Abilene (G-40)
Evolve Holdings Inc ....E 832 375-0099
  Houston (G-9720)
▲ Fisher-Rosemount Systems Inc ....A 512 835-2190
  Round Rock (G-17657)
Flowserve Corporation ....B 972 443-6500
  Irving (G-13027)
Flowserve Corporation ....F 800 446-0401
  Irving (G-13028)
G B Coil Inc ....E 903 212-2645
  Longview (G-14238)
◆ GE Energy Manufacturing Inc ....D 713 803-0900
  Houston (G-9913)
GE Energy Manufacturing Inc ....D 281 864-2669
  Houston (G-9914)
Gestamp Wind Energy N Amer Inc ......F 713 263-8166
  Houston (G-9946)
Haastech Inc ....F 214 688-0280
  Dallas (G-4426)
Ideal Power Inc ....F 512 264-1542
  Austin (G-1219)
Indelect Corporation ....D 903 656-2518
  Lone Star (G-14183)
Industrial Control Inc ....F 713 464-8005
  Houston (G-10349)
▲ Inverter Designs Inc ....F 972 227-9085
  Lancaster (G-13843)
Just Energy (us) Corp ....B 713 850-6784
  Houston (G-10490)
▲ Lennox International Inc ....C 972 497-5000
  Richardson (G-17343)
Loftin Equipment Company ....E 281 310-6858
  Houston (G-10669)
▲ Luminant Generation Co LLC ....D 214 812-4600
  Irving (G-13092)
▲ Luminator Holding LP ....C 972 424-6511
  Plano (G-16911)
Lynn Electric Motor Co Inc ....F 940 657-3511
  Knox City (G-13664)
M-Trigen Inc ....E 713 469-5735
  Houston (G-10726)
▼ Magnetic Technology Inc ....E 214 544-2700
  McKinney (G-14955)
◆ Man Energy Solutions USA Inc ....F 713 780-4200
  Brookshire (G-2319)
Marine Services LLC ....E 713 923-6688
  Houston (G-10765)
Monico Monitoring Inc ....F 281 350-8751
  Spring (G-19147)
▲ Motor Trike Inc ....C 903 842-3094
  Troup (G-20026)
Mtc America Enterprises Inc ....F 972 926-0600
  Garland (G-7556)
▲ Musshorn Enterprises Inc ....C 915 772-9007
  El Paso (G-19282)
◆ National Electric Coil Co LP ....E 956 541-1759
  Brownsville (G-2385)
New Core Inc ....F 956 421-2446
  Harlingen (G-8196)
One Wind Services (us) Inc ....F 902 482-8687
  San Benito (G-18662)
Precision Power Associates ....F 972 234-6165
  Richardson (G-17375)
Regal Beloit America Inc ....C 715 284-9801
  Eagle Pass (G-5554)

Regal Beloit Corporation ....C 830 774-2677
  Del Rio (G-5322)
Regal Beloit Corporation ....E 412 968-0100
  El Paso (G-5934)
▲ RTC Manufacturing Inc ....F 817 860-1217
  Arlington (G-778)
SAI Power Systems Inc ....F 281 516-3130
  Tomball (G-20007)
Seldon Energy Partners LLC ....F 503 807-4300
  Houston (G-11820)
Siemens Industry Inc ....C 915 790-0219
  El Paso (G-5960)
▲ Solarcraft Inc ....E 281 340-1224
  Sugar Land (G-19557)
◆ Sun-Star Electric Inc ....D 806 793-2812
  Lubbock (G-14488)
Sunpower Corporation ....D 512 294-3859
  Austin (G-1545)
Toshiba International Corp ....G 713 466-0277
  Houston (G-12326)
◆ Toshiba International Corp ....A 800 231-1412
  Houston (G-12327)
Toshiba International Corp ....G 713 466-0277
  Houston (G-12328)
Trader Sam LLC ....F 214 537-0885
  Plano (G-17038)
Trulite Inc ....F 713 432-7238
  Houston (G-12384)
Txu Energy Services Co LLC ....C 903 389-6074
  Fairfield (G-6180)
▲ Tyco Engineered Pdts & Svcs ....D 609 720-4200
  Houston (G-12418)
▲ Unitron LP ....D 214 221-9094
  Dallas (G-5139)
Valeo North America Inc ....A 915 774-9340
  El Paso (G-6023)
Valeo North America Inc ....A 915 779-1625
  El Paso (G-6024)
◆ Waukesha-Pearce Industries LLC .....B 713 723-1050
  Houston (G-12607)
Wilderado Wind LLC ....F 806 267-0746
  Vega (G-20216)
Wise County Power Company LLC 940 374-9925
  Poolville (G-17099)

3624 Carbon & Graphite Prdts

Cabot Corporation ....C 806 661-3100
  Pampa (G-16317)
Carbon Carbn Advanced Tech Inc ....E 817 985-2500
  Arlington (G-639)
◆ Carbonyx Inc ....E 972 943-3355
  Plano (G-16820)
◆ Continental Carbon Company ....D 281 647-3700
  Houston (G-9283)
E Z Filter Base Manufacturing ....F 972 272-5800
  Garland (G-7482)
Infrared Thermal Imaging Inc ....F 361 779-1197
  Kingsville (G-13628)
Poco Graphite Holdings LLC ....B 940 627-2121
  Decatur (G-5251)
ROC Industries Inc ....E 713 468-7743
  Houston (G-11647)
Toray Composite Mtls Amer Inc ....F 972 899-2930
  Lewisville (G-14098)
▼ Winston/Royal Guard Corp ....E 903 757-7341
  White Oak (G-20722)

3625 Relays & Indl Controls

A & B Auto Electric Inc ....F 713 928-3219
  Houston (G-8422)
Accurate Control Company LLC ....E 713 699-3799
  Houston (G-8461)
Ace Controls LLC ....F 713 589-5494
  Humble (G-12743)
Advanced Control Systems LLC ....E 832 529-2234
  Houston (G-8487)
Advanced Elec & Mtr Contrls ....E 972 253-7783
  Irving (G-12924)
▲ Air Starter Components Inc ....E 281 261-7939
  Stafford (G-19282)
▲ Amerimex Motor & Controls LLC .....D 713 225-4300
  Houston (G-8618)
Ameripower LLC ....F 281 240-0405
  Sugar Land (G-19442)
Antx Inc ....E 512 255-2800
  Cedar Park (G-2960)
Apergy Artfl Lift Intl LLC ....D 713 466-3552
  Houston (G-9408)
Aphthoria Solutions Inc ....D 214 821-8607
  Dallas (G-3950)

▲ Appliance Controls Texas Corp ....E 214 501-3880
  Garland (G-7439)
Aqua Electric Inc ....F 972 243-2162
  Dallas (G-3956)
Avo Multi-AMP Corporation ....F 800 325-4574
  Dallas (G-3992)
B I Products LLC ....D 972 359-4000
  Allen (G-255)
Bk/Ja Holdings Inc ....E 281 879-9903
  Stafford (G-19291)
BI Technology Inc ....E 832 698-8000
  Tomball (G-19967)
▲ C-B-Gear & Machine Inc ....E 281 449-0777
  Houston (G-9040)
Capable Controls Inc ....E 915 594-7659
  El Paso (G-5678)
Capsonic Automotive Inc ....E 915 872-3585
  El Paso (G-5680)
Carling Technologies Inc ....E 956 546-5564
  Brownsville (G-2344)
Clairex Technologies Inc ....E 972 265-4905
  Plano (G-16825)
Conloop Inc ....E 940 322-2206
  Wichita Falls (G-20756)
Contrinex Inc ....E 574 340-7089
  Coppell (G-3413)
Control Alternative Solutions ....F 512 858-9603
  Dripping Springs (G-5503)
▲ Controlled Systems Sales Co ....E 972 234-6767
  Richardson (G-17291)
▲ Copperlogic Inc ....E 713 933-0999
  Houston (G-9310)
▼ Cse W-Industries Inc ....C 713 466-9463
  Jersey Village (G-13297)
Dallas Decal Inc ....E 972 772-4641
  Rockwall (G-17546)
DK Controls LLC ....E 972 580-9300
  Irving (G-13000)
Dresser LLC ....D 832 590-2306
  Houston (G-9518)
Eaton Corporation ....B 915 779-4524
  El Paso (G-5730)
Eaton Corporation ....B 262 765-9764
  El Paso (G-5731)
Eaton Corporation ....C 915 881-0259
  El Paso (G-5733)
Edwin Jones Company Inc ....G 214 361-4000
  Dallas (G-4301)
Electro-Quip Service Inc ....D 281 456-8600
  Houston (G-9593)
Electrolab Inc ....E 210 824-5364
  Boerne (G-2118)
◆ Electronic Power Design Inc ....D 713 923-1191
  Houston (G-9596)
Electronic Technical Svcs Corp ....E 281 446-4414
  Humble (G-12765)
Elliott Control Company Ltd ....F 713 589-3102
  Willis (G-20846)
Elliott Electric Supply Inc ....E 512 246-8001
  Round Rock (G-17652)
◆ Emerson Atmtn Sltons Fnal Ctrl ......B 713 986-4665
  Houston (G-9612)
Emerson Automation Solutions ....G 512 835-2190
  Round Rock (G-17653)
Evans Enterprises Inc ....D 325 235-1776
  Abilene (G-40)
Fisher Controls Intl LLC ....B 972 542-5512
  McKinney (G-14943)
▲ Fisher-Rosemount Systems Inc ....A 512 835-2190
  Round Rock (G-17657)
Glo-Jo Electrical Products Inc ....E 210 673-3583
  San Antonio (G-18144)
Hubbell Industrial Contrls Inc ....D 281 391-6800
  Katy (G-13407)
Industrial Accessories Inc ....F 956 728-7524
  Laredo (G-13895)
Industrial Olfld Mar Cmpnnts I ....F 713 266-1900
  Tomball (G-19985)
ITT LLC ....E 281 367-2800
  The Woodlands (G-19887)
Kelleys Controls Incorporated ....F 432 362-7998
  Odessa (G-16045)
L V Controls Inc ....F 713 691-4666
  Houston (G-10576)
Littelfuse Inc ....D 830 513-8775
  Eagle Pass (G-5549)
Longview Distribution I LLC ....E 832 467-4600
  Houston (G-10686)
◆ M&I Electric Industries Inc ....D 832 241-6330
  Houston (G-10721)

Markload Systems Inc ....F 281 485-8600
Pearland (G-16580)

Maverick Technical Systems Inc ....G... 903 845-5574
Gladewater (G-7726)

Maxitrol Company ....E 817 479-8505
Richland Hills (G-17441)

▲ McAps Inc ....F 713 941-1300
South Houston (G-19049)

Moore Control Systems Inc ....D 281 392-7747
Katy (G-13372)

Motor Controls Inc ....B 972 247-4440
Dallas (G-4691)

Mtc America Enterprises Inc ....F 972 926-0600
Garland (G-7556)

Northwest Independent Schl Dst ....C 817 698-7300
Fort Worth (G-6869)

NS Controls Inc ....E 713 465-7591
Houston (G-11094)

▲ Nuco Controls LLC ....F 940 257-7092
Wichita Falls (G-20789)

Ohmite Holding LLC ....F 956 542-0276
Brownsville (G-2388)

Omron Electronics LLC ....D 713 849-1900
Houston (G-11181)

Overhead Door Corporation ....B 361 884-6640
Corpus Christi (G-3586)

▲ Pegasus Automation Inc ....F 972 390-9548
Allen (G-290)

◆ Powell Electrical Systems Inc ....A 713 944-6900
Houston (G-11372)

Powell Electrical Systems Inc ....A 713 790-1700
Houston (G-11373)

Powell Electrical Systems Inc ....A 713 944-6900
Houston (G-11375)

▼ Powell Industries Inc ....B 713 944-6900
Houston (G-11376)

Process Automation Design Inc ....E 817 283-1500
Hurst (G-12855)

Ringdale Inc ....F 512 288-9080
Georgetown (G-7675)

▲ Robinson Engineering Co Inc ....E 972 272-2001
Garland (G-7580)

Rockwell Automation Inc ....F 713 353-2400
Houston (G-11652)

Rockwell Automation Inc ....D 972 417-5400
Lewisville (G-14090)

Rotork Controls Inc ....F 713 983-7381
Houston (G-11674)

Schenck Process LLC ....D 816 891-9300
Houston (G-11765)

Schlumberger Rig Tech Inc ....D 713 849-1700
Houston (G-11771)

Schmidt Manufacturing Inc ....F 281 431-0581
Bellaire (G-2002)

Schneider Electric Usa Inc ....C 972 236-0300
Coppell (G-3444)

Selectouch Corporation ....E 972 924-3289
Anna (G-585)

Shermco System Integration LLC ....C 940 322-2206
Wichita Falls (G-20811)

Siemens Industry Inc ....E 817 633-4430
Grand Prairie (G-7973)

Siemens Industry Inc ....B 972 947-7000
Dallas (G-4959)

Singer Data Products Inc ....E 915 594-7650
El Paso (G-5962)

Southern Transformers ....F 713 923-1191
Houston (G-11978)

Sprecher & Schuh Inc ....E 281 442-9000
Houston (G-12024)

Ss Electric Inc ....F 915 217-2200
El Paso (G-5973)

Stoneridge Inc ....B 915 778-1331
El Paso (G-5983)

Superior Controls Inc ....G 432 332-4051
Odessa (G-16170)

Tcw Investments Inc ....F 409 796-1883
Beaumont (G-1956)

Tech Power International Co ....D 281 494-4242
Stafford (G-19382)

Texan Electric Co Inc ....D 713 645-6560
Houston (G-12219)

Thompson Scale Company ....E 713 932-9071
Houston (G-12279)

Thunderco Inc ....G 713 681-4686
Houston (G-12286)

Total Grow Holdings LLC ....F 281 585-9500
Alvin (G-382)

▲ Tyco Engineered Pdts & Svcs ....D 609 720-4200
Houston (G-12418)

Ultramation Inc ....G 254 772-4860
Waco (G-20469)

Vanzandt Controls ....G 806 655-9367
Canyon (G-2676)

Vector Systems Inc ....D 214 544-9500
McKinney (G-14985)

▲ Vibration Management Corp ....E 713 983-8462
Houston (G-12563)

▲ Warner Electric LLC ....D 940 767-2000
Wichita Falls (G-12606)

Watts Water Technologies Inc ....F 713 943-0688
Houston (G-12606)

▼ Wesco Acquisition Partners Inc ....E 713 688-5551
Galena Park (G-7386)

Wgi Innovations Ltd ....E 469 733-1868
Grand Prairie (G-7993)

Williams Machine Inc ....F 713 462-2229
Cypress (G-3827)

3629 Electrical Indl Apparatus, NEC

▲ Analytical Sensors Instrs LLC ....D 281 565-8818
Houston (G-8636)

Bitcoin Crypto Crrncy Exch Cor ....F 713 465-1001
Houston (G-8895)

Blast Envmtl & Indus Svcs ....E 281 557-1000
League City (G-13950)

Cooper Crouse-Hinds Mtl Inc ....C 281 571-8065
Houston (G-9306)

◆ Cordyne Inc ....D 713 460-5151
Houston (G-9313)

◆ Delta Electronics (usa) Inc ....F 469 330-9100
Plano (G-16837)

Englobal Constant Power Inc ....C 713 880-6200
Houston (G-9647)

Exide Technologies LLC ....E 281 443-0382
Houston (G-9724)

Exide Technologies LLC ....F 972 633-6900
Irving (G-13018)

Exide Technologies LLC ....F 210 662-8999
San Antonio (G-18099)

Exide Technologies LLC ....F 972 870-0337
Irving (G-13019)

Exide Technologies LLC ....F 678 566-9000
The Woodlands (G-19863)

Freedom Power Systems Inc ....F 512 259-0941
Cedar Park (G-2971)

G C International Inc ....B 972 422-2395
Plano (G-16877)

Lufkins Six B Construction ....F 936 632-3470
Lufkin (G-14543)

M&I Electric LLC ....C 409 838-0441
Beaumont (G-1922)

Powersecure Inc ....E 203 683-6222
Frisco (G-7306)

Schmidt Manufacturing Inc ....F 281 431-0581
Bellaire (G-2002)

Seaport Steel Fab Inc ....F 361 884-1670
Corpus Christi (G-3618)

T L Tedford Enterprises Inc ....F 817 808-8052
Aurora (G-854)

Universal Rectifiers Inc ....E 281 342-8471
Rosenberg (G-17598)

Varo LLC ....B 972 840-5506
Garland (G-7607)

3631 Household Cooking Eqpt

Brand Commercial Services Inc ....E 844 232-7263
Lewisville (G-14029)

▲ Burkhead Manufacturing Company .E 713 227-5248
Houston (G-9019)

Burris Custom Smokers & Grills ....F 806 893-3360
Abernathy (G-2)

Circle J Fabrication Inc ....E 817 367-3877
Fort Worth (G-6519)

Klose Cnstr & Fabrication ....F 713 686-8720
Houston (G-10541)

Marsha Kitchens ....F 830 278-7262
Uvalde (G-20191)

Sunbeam Products Inc ....F 830 774-4517
Del Rio (G-5325)

TPC Acquisition Partners LP ....F 281 356-2168
Pinehurst (G-16736)

▲ Trampolines Usa Inc ....F 409 745-3139
Orange (G-16267)

Turbochef Technologies Inc ....E 214 379-6000
Carrollton (G-2892)

◆ Turbochef Technologies Inc ....E 214 379-6000
Carrollton (G-2893)

3632 Household Refrigerators & Freezers

Arctic Cooler-Freezer Repr Inc ....F 817 492-0200
Fort Worth (G-6399)

Brand Commercial Services Inc ....E 844 232-7263
Lewisville (G-14029)

Chill King ....E 512 303-1529
Bastrop (G-1750)

Cold King Inc ....F 210 227-0264
San Antonio (G-18017)

Coldvault LLC ....G 903 657-2377
Henderson (G-8261)

3633 Household Laundry Eqpt

North Shore Express Clean ....F 832 418-0535
Houston (G-11075)

3634 Electric Household Appliances

Aerus Holdings LLC ....F 214 378-4000
Dallas (G-3896)

Airbox LLC ....G 512 968-5496
Austin (G-901)

▲ American Permanent Ware Co ....C 972 908-6100
Allen (G-250)

Backer Ehp Inc ....F 615 556-7501
Laredo (G-13865)

Body Brother Inc ....F 713 487-8227
Houston (G-8935)

▲ Burkhead Manufacturing Company .E 713 227-5248
Houston (G-9019)

CPM Acquisition Corp ....F 972 243-8070
Carrollton (G-2719)

Entrematic Loading Dock Pdts ....E 972 466-0707
Carrollton (G-2732)

Haydon Corporation ....F 972 641-6400
Grand Prairie (G-7888)

Hydrocut Inc ....F 979 849-5422
Angleton (G-573)

Lady Hlth Ftness- Rockwall Inc ....F 972 906-0400
Carrollton (G-2877)

Lasko Products LLC ....B 817 625-6381
Fort Worth (G-6780)

Munters Corporation ....D 210 651-5018
Selma (G-18879)

Regal Ware Inc ....E 817 652-8151
Fort Worth (G-6952)

Requejo Construction Svcs LLC ....F 210 459-5161
San Antonio (G-18420)

S N D Manufacturing Ltd ....D 214 340-1592
Dallas (G-4923)

▲ Starion USA Inc ....E 956 283-1289
Mission (G-15564)

▲ Titan Chair LLC ....E 888 848-2630
Carrollton (G-2835)

TSA Griddle Systems Inc ....F 972 243-8070
Carrollton (G-2841)

Vent-A-Hood Ltd ....C 888 557-8368
Richardson (G-17419)

▲ Vollara LLC ....E 800 989-2299
Dallas (G-5169)

3635 Household Vacuum Cleaners

◆ Aerus LLC ....E 214 378-4000
Dallas (G-3897)

Bissell Inc ....E 956 631-5077
Mcallen (G-14845)

Flexaust Inc ....C 915 872-3100
El Paso (G-5770)

Flightsafety International Inc ....C 817 571-5925
Fort Worth (G-6638)

Scott Fetzer Company ....C 713 996-7331
Houston (G-11791)

Scott Fetzer Company ....C 432 523-5511
Andrews (G-558)

3639 Household Appliances, NEC

A O Smith Corporation ....E 915 400-2800
El Paso (G-5634)

Automated Ceiling Registers ....F 972 509-2400
Richardson (G-17274)

▲ Handcrafted Metal Inc ....F 512 386-5433
Converse (G-3395)

▲ Southwest Cutters LLC ....D 915 858-2200
El Paso (G-5971)

Standard Waste Services LLC ....F 210 619-7962
San Antonio (G-18496)

Thorne Electric Company ....F 210 590-1226
San Antonio (G-18551)

3641 Electric Lamps

Calyx Cultivation Tech Corp ....F 281 227-2208
Houston *(G-9055)*

Efficiency Aggregators LLC ....F 832 862-1103
Richmond *(G-17453)*

Elumenus Lighting Corp Inc ....F 214 392-2898
Plano *(G-16860)*

Fanlight Corporation Inc ....F 909 930-6868
Dallas *(G-4351)*

▲ Fleco Industries LLC ....C 972 247-3171
Carrollton *(G-2739)*

General Electric Company ....F 972 444-2000
Irving *(G-13037)*

Halco Lighting Tech LLC ....E 713 644-6073
Houston *(G-10090)*

▲ Iglo LLC ....F 214 893-8703
Fort Worth *(G-6715)*

▼ Light Emtting Dds-Nlimited LLC ....F 512 267-7315
Lago Vista *(G-13806)*

▲ Old World Design LLC ....F 214 741-6858
Dallas *(G-4758)*

Pruf Energy Solutions LLC ....F 254 870-0400
Waco *(G-20450)*

Satco Products Inc ....C 972 247-2437
Dallas *(G-4936)*

Sterling Group LP ....E 713 877-8257
Houston *(G-12060)*

▲ Texas Lamp Manufacturers Inc ....E 972 564-5267
Forney *(G-6315)*

▲ Upright Lighting LLC ....F 408 472-6379
Allen *(G-305)*

3643 Current-Carrying Wiring Devices

3h Manufacturing Inc ....E 281 342-1478
Richmond *(G-17449)*

▲ Advanced Lightning Tech Ltd ....D 940 455-7300
Argyle *(G-599)*

AF Technologies Inc ....C 817 649-2500
Arlington *(G-611)*

B I Products LLC ....D 972 359-4000
Allen *(G-255)*

Baker Hghes Olfld Oprtions LLC ....C 800 441-0535
Yorktown *(G-20976)*

Bk/Ja Holdings Inc ....E 281 879-9903
Stafford *(G-19291)*

BMC Industry LLC ....F 903 796-5330
Queen City *(G-17219)*

Cemtechnologies Inc ....F 972 238-3630
Richardson *(G-17285)*

Channl-Track Tube-Way Inds Inc ....E 713 864-2551
Houston *(G-9162)*

Cinch Connectors Inc ....B 956 686-1151
McAllen *(G-14847)*

Coleman Cable LLC ....C 915 858-7475
El Paso *(G-5699)*

Cotton Utility Constructors ....F 281 659-5707
Shepherd *(G-18901)*

Electronics & Metals Inds Inc ....E 512 267-0113
Leander *(G-13988)*

Electrotechnics Corporation ....E 903 938-1901
Marshall *(G-14776)*

◆ Galaxy Electronics Company ....F 972 234-0065
Richardson *(G-17319)*

▲ Hubbell Building Automtn Inc ....E 512 450-1100
Austin *(G-1212)*

◆ Ies Holdings Inc ....D 713 860-1500
Houston *(G-10316)*

Illinois Tool Works Inc ....F 314 733-1110
Houston *(G-10326)*

◆ Jdr Cable Systems Inc ....E 832 220-4690
Houston *(G-10461)*

▲ Kemlon Products & Dev Co ....B 281 997-3300
Pearland *(G-16573)*

Lightning Bolt & Supply Inc ....F 713 920-2525
Pasadena *(G-16473)*

Lone Star Indus Corp Texas ....E 915 779-7255
El Paso *(G-5846)*

▲ Luminator Holding LP ....C 972 424-6511
Plano *(G-16911)*

▲ Luminator Technology Group LLC ....C 972 424-6511
Plano *(G-16913)*

Massey Holding & Consultants ....E 817 477-3176
Mansfield *(G-14690)*

Molex LLC ....D 915 591-5600
El Paso *(G-5882)*

▲ Nicor Inc ....F 707 484-0835
Dripping Springs *(G-5510)*

◆ Optek Technology Inc ....D 972 323-2200
Carrollton *(G-2786)*

Plastronics Co ....E 972 986-0474
Irving *(G-13151)*

▲ Plastronics Interconnections ....F 972 258-2580
Irving *(G-13152)*

▼ Powell Industries Inc ....B 713 944-6900
Houston *(G-11376)*

Pro Connect Technology LLC ....F 972 543-2603
Plano *(G-16978)*

Prosource Industries Inc ....E 972 660-1400
Grand Prairie *(G-7958)*

Reliable Manufacturing Inc ....E 512 255-6572
Round Rock *(G-17684)*

Rhimco Industries Inc ....E 817 477-3176
Mansfield *(G-14711)*

▲ Rsi Inc ....E 512 268-7500
Kyle *(G-13686)*

Safran Usa Inc ....E 469 941-8150
Dallas *(G-13169)*

Selectouch Corporation ....F 972 924-3289
Anna *(G-585)*

▲ Svtronics Inc ....C 214 440-1234
Plano *(G-17017)*

Techline Sports Lighting LLC ....E 512 977-8880
Austin *(G-1557)*

Teradyne Inc ....D 972 231-5384
Plano *(G-17025)*

Teradyne Inc ....D 512 891-9600
Austin *(G-1563)*

◆ Thermon Inc ....C 512 396-5801
San Marcos *(G-18715)*

◆ Thermon Industries Inc ....B 512 396-5801
San Marcos *(G-18716)*

Tricon International Ltd ....E 713 963-0066
Houston *(G-12371)*

▲ Tyrex Group Ltd ....F 512 623-4694
Austin *(G-1603)*

◆ Umbilicals International Inc ....D 281 275-6600
Stafford *(G-19392)*

▼ Wesco Acquisition Partners Inc ....E 713 688-5551
Galena Park *(G-7386)*

3644 Noncurrent-Carrying Wiring Devices

Appleton Grp LLC ....C 281 774-3700
Houston *(G-8665)*

▲ Bartec US Corporation ....F 281 214-8542
Houston *(G-8819)*

Chemfoundry Inc ....F 725 218-1955
Tyler *(G-20066)*

▲ Chm Industries Inc ....F 682 286-0046
Saginaw *(G-17742)*

Cooper B-Line Inc ....C 903 813-1746
Sherman *(G-18913)*

Fielder Electric Supply Co Inc ....E 281 485-6599
Pearland *(G-16560)*

Galyean Investments LLC ....F 806 368-5430
Lubbock *(G-14414)*

Glt Fabricators Inc ....E 713 670-9700
La Porte *(G-13739)*

Gund Company Inc ....E 972 389-0615
Euless *(G-6147)*

▲ Nipples Elbows & Couplings Inc ....E 281 405-8240
Houston *(G-11059)*

R & B Electronics Inc ....E 906 632-1542
Grand Prairie *(G-7961)*

Regal Beloit America Inc ....F 956 213-0503
McAllen *(G-14900)*

Robroy Industries Inc ....C 412 828-2100
Gilmer *(G-7712)*

S & H Shtmtl & Fabg Co Inc ....E 713 926-8805
Houston *(G-11706)*

T G M Inc ....F 972 761-9101
Richardson *(G-17404)*

▲ Tyrex Group Ltd ....F 512 623-4694
Austin *(G-1603)*

3645 Residential Lighting Fixtures

▲ 2v Led LLC ....D 325 227-4577
San Angelo *(G-17767)*

Abbys Thres No Pl Like HM Fur ....F 817 244-3371
Fort Worth *(G-6340)*

▲ AC Electronics ....F 817 701-1400
Arlington *(G-606)*

Blako ....F 972 898-7772
Royse City *(G-17715)*

◆ Brandon Industries Inc ....E 972 542-3000
McKinney *(G-14929)*

Cooper Lighting LLC ....D 972 929-9400
Irving *(G-12980)*

▲ Creative Industries LLC ....F 830 249-1200
Boerne *(G-2117)*

Creative Nightscapes ....F 817 581-6936
Fort Worth *(G-6558)*

Crow Chandeliers Inc ....E 214 744-5488
Dallas *(G-4186)*

◆ DA Schoggin Inc ....D 214 350-0591
Dallas *(G-4204)*

DA Schoggin Inc ....E 817 641-6800
Cleburne *(G-3086)*

Dolan Northwest LLC ....E 972 559-6900
Frisco *(G-7257)*

Fleco Industries LLC ....D 214 369-1101
Dallas *(G-4368)*

▲ Fleco Industries LLC ....C 972 247-3171
Carrollton *(G-2739)*

Gill Assoc Prprty MGT Systems ....G 832 644-9751
Humble *(G-12770)*

Haleaux Inc ....F 214 742-2795
Dallas *(G-4428)*

▲ Iglo LLC ....F 214 893-8703
Fort Worth *(G-6715)*

Illuminate Vintage LLC ....G 903 948-1161
Houston *(G-10328)*

Intermatic Incorporated ....F 915 858-9204
El Paso *(G-5813)*

Jaguar Designs Inc ....E 214 634-7733
Dallas *(G-4522)*

▲ Melissa Lighting Inc ....E 214 388-7487
Dallas *(G-4665)*

▲ Pauluhn Electric Mfg LLP ....C 281 485-4311
Pearland *(G-16587)*

Principal Lighting Group LLC ....D 325 227-4577
San Angelo *(G-17824)*

Rulon Elc Illuminations Co Inc ....E 713 863-1133
Houston *(G-11697)*

Scout Goods & Design LLC ....F 512 865-8775
Spicewood *(G-19094)*

Solara Ironworks LLC ....E 214 744-9900
Dallas *(G-4975)*

◆ Solavanti Trading LLC ....E 214 221-9405
Dallas *(G-4976)*

▲ TMI LLC ....F 469 231-6918
The Colony *(G-19816)*

◆ Trade Source International ....G 972 393-3800
Coppell *(G-3450)*

Tritex Grass LLC ....E 817 573-6676
Granbury *(G-7814)*

◆ Visual Comfort of America LLC ....D 713 686-5999
Houston *(G-12574)*

▲ Wingate Partners LP ....F 214 720-1313
Dallas *(G-5195)*

Yankon Lighting Inc ....F 469 248-0749
McKinney *(G-14992)*

3646 Commercial, Indl & Institutional Lighting Fixtures

Acuity Brands Lighting Inc ....C 972 456-1451
Dallas *(G-3885)*

Aquila Environmental LLC ....G 817 953-3171
Fort Worth *(G-6397)*

ASG Energy LLC ....E 210 610-0036
San Antonio *(G-17915)*

Azz Inc ....E 713 943-0340
Houston *(G-8770)*

Blako ....F 972 898-7772
Royse City *(G-17715)*

◆ Brandon Industries Inc ....E 972 542-3000
McKinney *(G-14929)*

▲ Constellation Lighting Ltd ....G 832 717-5750
Houston *(G-9277)*

Cooper Lighting LLC ....D 972 929-9400
Irving *(G-12980)*

◆ DA Schoggin Inc ....D 214 350-0591
Dallas *(G-4204)*

DA Schoggin Inc ....E 817 641-6800
Cleburne *(G-3086)*

▲ Divine Ltg & Fabrication LLC ....E 936 494-3900
Conroe *(G-3294)*

Efficiency Aggregators LLC ....E 832 862-1103
Richmond *(G-17453)*

Encapsulite International Inc ....F 281 239-0225
Rosenberg *(G-17580)*

Energy Retrofitters Inc ....F 817 319-2796
Fort Worth *(G-6614)*

Fenner Technologies Inc ....C 972 264-0368
Grand Prairie *(G-7870)*

▲ Festoni Inc ....F 713 830-1077
Houston *(G-9781)*

Employee Codes: A=Over 500 employees, B=251-500
C=101-250, D=51-100, E=20-50, F=10-19, G=9   2021 Harris Texas
Manufacturers Directory   1041

▲ Fleco Industries LLC ....C 972 247-3171
　Carrollton *(G-2739)*

Fleco Industries LLC ....D 214 369-1101
　Dallas *(G-4368)*

◆ Fluence Bioengineering Inc ....D 512 212-4544
　Austin *(G-1163)*

▲ Iglo LLC ....F 214 893-8703
　Fort Worth *(G-6715)*

▲ Illumitex Inc ....D 512 279-5020
　Austin *(G-1224)*

Jaguar Designs Inc ....E 214 634-7733
　Dallas *(G-4522)*

Koncept Systems LLC ....E 800 773-4910
　Houston *(G-10557)*

▲ Lighting & Power Tech LLC ....F 877 666-5267
　Plano *(G-16909)*

Lights Fantastic Pro ....G 469 568-1111
　Lewisville *(G-14062)*

Luminated Living LLC ....F 512 523-5550
　Austin *(G-864)*

▲ Luminator Holding LP ....C 972 424-6511
　Plano *(G-16911)*

▲ Luminator Technology Group LLC ...C 972 424-6511
　Plano *(G-16913)*

Lunar Lighting Solutions LLC ....G 866 434-0732
　Austin *(G-1312)*

M & M Lighting LP ....D 713 667-5611
　Houston *(G-10715)*

▲ Melissa Lighting Inc ....E 214 388-7487
　Dallas *(G-4665)*

Michael R Atteberry ....F 214 222-3064
　Lewisville *(G-14067)*

◆ Neutex Advnced Enrgy Group Inc ...E 281 227-2208
　Houston *(G-11031)*

Neutex Advnced Enrgy Group Inc ...E 281 227-2208
　Houston *(G-11032)*

▲ Pauluhn Electric Mfg LLP ....C 281 485-4311
　Pearland *(G-16587)*

Philips North America LLC ....C 800 526-2731
　Carrollton *(G-2881)*

Retro Ltg & Conservation Lc ....E 281 302-6431
　Sugar Land *(G-19534)*

Robogistics LLC ....E 713 364-4430
　Port Arthur *(G-17123)*

Rulon Elc Illuminations Co Inc ....E 713 863-1133
　Houston *(G-11697)*

Shine Lighting Group Usa Inc ....E 973 865-5893
　Dallas *(G-4956)*

Signify North America Corp ....F 800 235-2314
　San Marcos *(G-18711)*

Signify North America Corp ....C 214 647-7880
　Dallas *(G-4961)*

Snelson Oilfield Ltg Co Inc ....E 817 926-0571
　Fort Worth *(G-6998)*

Snowball Lighting Inc ....F 915 227-7210
　El Paso *(G-5965)*

Solara Ironworks LLC ....E 214 744-9900
　Dallas *(G-4975)*

Texas Lightsmith Inc ....F 512 264-2266
　Austin *(G-1568)*

Texas Solar Resources Inc ....F 281 846-4968
　League City *(G-13981)*

Ultravision International ....E 214 260-4500
　Dallas *(G-5131)*

▲ US Led Ltd ....E 713 972-9191
　Houston *(G-12486)*

USA Promlite Technology Inc ....F 832 868-8866
　Houston *(G-12501)*

Vari-Lite LLC ....C 214 647-7880
　Dallas *(G-5156)*

▲ Xtralight Manufacturing Ltd ....D 713 943-9927
　Houston *(G-12709)*

3647 Vehicular Lighting Eqpt

▲ Feniex Industries Inc ....E 800 615-8350
　Austin *(G-1154)*

Fenner Technologies Inc ....C 972 264-0368
　Grand Prairie *(G-7870)*

Hamar Industries Inc ....E 817 756-8990
　Fort Worth *(G-6685)*

▲ Luminator Holding LP ....C 972 424-6511
　Plano *(G-16911)*

▲ Luminator Technology Group LLC ...C 972 424-6511
　Plano *(G-16913)*

Marelli Automotive Ltg USA LLC ....F 915 872-1104
　El Paso *(G-5864)*

Parrot Inc ....E 512 514-6840
　Austin *(G-1397)*

▲ Pauluhn Electric Mfg LLP ....C 281 485-4311
　Pearland *(G-16587)*

Tenneco Inc ....A 915 832-4661
　El Paso *(G-5997)*

3648 Lighting Eqpt, NEC

◆ Allan Banks ....F 936 337-4020
　Willis *(G-20841)*

B&B Roadway SEC Solutions LLC ....F 972 385-7899
　Mckinney *(G-14924)*

Clearpath Engineering Inc ....E 832 856-9040
　Katy *(G-13392)*

Control Products Corporation ....C 972 264-0368
　Grand Prairie *(G-7858)*

Cooper Lighting LLC ....F 770 486-4800
　Houston *(G-9307)*

▲ CPM Inc ....F 214 349-6886
　Garland *(G-7470)*

◆ DA Schoggin Inc ....D 214 350-0591
　Dallas *(G-4204)*

DA Schoggin Inc ....E 817 641-6800
　Cleburne *(G-3086)*

▲ Dallas Christie Lites Inc ....E 214 637-3535
　Dallas *(G-4214)*

◆ Drw Holdings ....F 949 581-9398
　Cedar Park *(G-2966)*

Genlyte Thomas Group LLC ....G 512 392-5821
　San Marcos *(G-18689)*

◆ Good Sportsman Marketing LLC ....E 877 269-8490
　Irving *(G-13040)*

▲ High End Systems Inc ....E 512 836-2242
　Austin *(G-1203)*

Hill & Smith Inc ....E 972 278-0553
　Garland *(G-7513)*

▲ Hubbell Building Automtn Inc ....C 512 450-1100
　Austin *(G-1212)*

Imperial Outdoor Power Eqp ....F 832 939-9838
　Sugar Land *(G-19495)*

Jaguar Designs Inc ....E 214 634-7733
　Dallas *(G-4522)*

Koncept Systems LLC ....E 800 773-4910
　Houston *(G-10557)*

▲ Kw Industries Inc ....C 281 240-0909
　Sugar Land *(G-19502)*

▲ Ledi2 Inc ....F 713 636-9152
　Houston *(G-10615)*

Lighting Etc Inc ....F 281 992-8308
　Pearland *(G-16579)*

▲ Luminator Holding LP ....C 972 424-6511
　Plano *(G-16911)*

▲ Lure Capital Corporation ....E 713 729-2424
　Houston *(G-10703)*

Marlin Environmental Products ....F 214 493-9128
　Richardson *(G-17351)*

▼ Maverick Poles & Structure LLC ....G 817 441-9688
　Benbrook *(G-2043)*

Mel Northey Co Inc ....F 281 445-3485
　Houston *(G-10825)*

Mercron Inc ....F 972 690-6565
　Irving *(G-13106)*

Modern Lantern ....F 214 507-8608
　Fort Worth *(G-6844)*

Nemesis Uvc LLC ....E 972 423-0075
　Garland *(G-7561)*

Party Props Inc ....E 713 868-5433
　Houston *(G-11253)*

Pool & Electrical Products Inc ....F 512 707-0109
　Austin *(G-1424)*

Premier Lighting Entps LLC ....F 855 426-4544
　Carrollton *(G-2794)*

Production Warehousing Inc ....D 915 779-1405
　El Paso *(G-5920)*

▲ Quality Lighting ....G 512 799-2341
　San Marcos *(G-18705)*

Rulon Elc Illuminations Co Inc ....E 713 863-1133
　Houston *(G-11697)*

Solais Lighting LLC ....E 469 294-1516
　Frisco *(G-7313)*

◆ Specialty Tower Lighting Ltd ....F 713 722-8123
　Houston *(G-12002)*

▲ Speedtech Lights Inc ....E 800 757-2581
　Buda *(G-2539)*

Sterling Group LP ....E 713 877-8257
　Houston *(G-12060)*

▲ Thomas M Niland Company ....F 915 779-1405
　El Paso *(G-6002)*

Tomcat Global Corporation ....D 432 694-7070
　Midland *(G-15439)*

◆ Twr Lighting Inc ....D 713 973-6905
　Houston *(G-12416)*

▲ Valen Light LLC ....E 512 222-5550
　Austin *(G-1621)*

Worksite Lighting LLC ....E 225 313-3711
　Haltom City *(G-8163)*

▲ Xtralight Manufacturing Ltd ....D 713 943-9927
　Houston *(G-12709)*

Yes Lighting LLC ....G 972 807-9197
　Dallas *(G-5207)*

3651 Household Audio & Video Eqpt

51 Home Technologies LLC ....F 713 589-5747
　Fresno *(G-7236)*

Alliance Entertainment LLC ....E 806 381-3945
　Amarillo *(G-392)*

Ce Labs LLC ....E 469 429-9200
　Garland *(G-7455)*

Chimera Lab Ltd ....F 214 428-3901
　Kemp *(G-13483)*

Commscope Technologies LLC ....A 214 634-8502
　Dallas *(G-4149)*

Conference Technologies Inc ....C 512 584-8275
　Austin *(G-1061)*

▲ Crossfire Inc ....E 972 570-0800
　Irving *(G-12983)*

Custom Electronics Inc ....F 512 454-8824
　Pflugerville *(G-16667)*

Diem Digital Interiors LLC ....F 972 899-1189
　Carrollton *(G-2723)*

Dm Home Entertainment LLC ....G 972 992-3155
　Carrollton *(G-2866)*

Dynamic Intgrtons Ctrl Systems ....F 512 716-0817
　Round Rock *(G-17650)*

Freeman Expositions LLC ....F 214 623-1300
　Dallas *(G-4378)*

▲ General Wreless Operations Inc ...C 800 843-7422
　Fort Worth *(G-6664)*

Heart of Texas Music Inc ....F 254 778-7422
　Temple *(G-19681)*

▲ Irex Group Ltd ....E 512 835-1200
　Austin *(G-1243)*

Jim Melhart Piano and Organ Co .....E 956 682-6147
　McAllen *(G-14879)*

Koncept Systems LLC ....E 800 773-4910
　Houston *(G-10557)*

Ksh Enterprises Inc ....F 817 313-0926
　Haslet *(G-8220)*

Iesco Distributing Inc ....F 972 446-1605
　Carrollton *(G-2776)*

Lg Electronics Alabama Inc ....A 956 784-6500
　Mission *(G-15559)*

▲ Mega Systems Inc ....E 210 684-2600
　Helotes *(G-8242)*

Mitek Corporation ....D 972 875-8413
　Ennis *(G-6110)*

Panasonic Corp North America ....A 956 984-3432
　Mcallen *(G-14899)*

▲ Peag LLC ....E 858 683-3634
　Dallas *(G-3850)*

▲ Primo Microphones Inc ....D 972 548-9807
　McKinney *(G-14967)*

▲ Qpower Incorporated ....E 713 266-5295
　Houston *(G-11486)*

◆ Radixon Inc ....E 855 723-4966
　Dallas *(G-4858)*

Rupert Neve Designs LLC ....F 512 847-3013
　Wimberley *(G-20883)*

Satellink Inc ....E 972 487-1434
　Garland *(G-7581)*

▲ Shure Electronics ....E 915 782-2800
　El Paso *(G-5959)*

Smbg Corsicana LLC ....F 254 262-4400
　Corsicana *(G-3684)*

◆ Sound Bridge Acoustic Labs Inc .....E 972 937-2030
　Waxahachie *(G-20559)*

▲ Speakermax Inc ....F 281 880-9922
　Houston *(G-11995)*

Technicolor Usa Inc ....C 915 872-8001
　El Paso *(G-5996)*

Technicolor Usa Inc ....C 915 841-7233
　Socorro *(G-19019)*

◆ Videotex Systems Inc ....F 214 349-6399
　Dallas *(G-5166)*

3652 Phonograph Records & Magnetic Tape

▲ Adams Evidence Grade Tech Inc .....F 830 966-4210
　Utopia *(G-20187)*

▲ AMA Printing / Finishing Inc ....E 254 776-8860
　Waco *(G-20359)*

Asinni 2000 Records Inc ....E 281 564-4111
　Houston *(G-8722)*

Austin Dvd Inc ....F 512 246-8759
　Round Rock *(G-17625)*

Broadcast Your Vision LLC ....F 972 984-0303
  Rockwall (G-17541)

▲ Casscom Media LP ....F 903 455-2555
  Greenville (G-8066)

Creative Sound Productions ....F 713 777-9975
  Houston (G-9340)

Hacienda Rec Recording Studio ....F 361 882-7066
  Corpus Christi (G-3543)

Joey Records Inc ....E 210 432-7893
  San Antonio (G-18203)

Jones Tape Duplicating Inc ....G 281 351-8109
  Cypress (G-3805)

Kadence Collective LLC ....F 888 901-5343
  San Antonio (G-18215)

Molecula Corp ....G 512 649-9113
  Austin (G-1350)

Nicole Dionne ....F 310 699-7556
  Austin (G-1366)

Quadrabyte LLC ....F 469 619-0749
  Austin (G-1441)

Tailwind Business Ventures LLC ....C 210 268-2717
  Cedar Park (G-2986)

Thug City Records ....F 832 264-4892
  Houston (G-12285)

Udundi LLC ....F 917 727-4220
  Austin (G-1604)

3661 Telephone & Telegraph Apparatus

3M Company......................................E 512 984-2708
  Austin (G-871)

▲ ABB Power Electronics Inc ....C 972 244-9288
  Plano (G-16768)

▲ Aei Communications Corp ....E 650 552-9416
  Carrollton (G-2693)

Affiliated Communications ....E 972 423-4222
  Plano (G-16777)

Affirmed Ntwrks Cmmnctons Tech ....E 469 461-3101
  Richardson (G-17267)

AT&T Inc ....A 210 821-4105
  Dallas (G-3978)

▼ Aviat US Inc ....B 408 941-7100
  Austin (G-969)

BBS Telecom LC ....G 512 328-9500
  Austin (G-981)

▲ Cellteks Inc ....F 830 249-8999
  Boerne (G-2116)

Colo4 LLC ....F 214 630-3100
  Dallas (G-4141)

Commscope Technologies LLC ....C 214 267-5900
  Richardson (G-17289)

Commscope Technologies LLC ....A 214 634-8502
  Dallas (G-4149)

Contel Federal Systems Inc ....A 972 718-5600
  Irving (G-12978)

Cooper Consulting Company ....E 512 527-1000
  Austin (G-1065)

Cuda Express II Inc ....E 806 433-1896
  Bushland (G-2621)

Cytracom LLC ....F 877 411-2987
  Allen (G-261)

Digital Speech Systems Inc ....E 972 235-2999
  Allen (G-262)

▲ Dynamic Voice Data Inc ....F 800 838-5070
  Stafford (G-19307)

◆ Dzs Inc ....C 469 327-1531
  Plano (G-16854)

Enterprise ESP Svc Prvider LLC ....F 469 619-3114
  Plano (G-16863)

Ericsson Smart Factory Inc ....D 469 266-3776
  Lewisville (G-14049)

▲ Estech Systems Inc ....C 972 422-9700
  Plano (G-16866)

Executive Voice Mail Systems ....F 817 329-9788
  Grapevine (G-8033)

▲ Fujitsu Ntwrk Cmmnications Inc ....A 972 479-6000
  Richardson (G-17318)

▲ Gtech Precision Inds USA Ltd ....F 817 539-8014
  Mansfield (G-14678)

Hold Phone LLC ....F 281 304-4777
  Cypress (G-3800)

Intervoice Inc ....E 972 454-8000
  Dallas (G-3845)

Intervoice LLC ....D 972 454-8000
  Dallas (G-3846)

▲ Krown Manufacturing Inc ....F 817 738-2485
  Fort Worth (G-6774)

Micheal J Arnold & Co ....F 979 742-3030
  Damon (G-5213)

Mitel Networks Inc ....E 469 365-3000
  Plano (G-16931)

Motive Wireless Ltd Lblty Co ....F 214 500-9242
  Spring (G-19149)

Motorola Solutions Inc ....E 512 895-2000
  Austin (G-1355)

Neosen Energy LLC ....F 972 422-0722
  Plano (G-16941)

◆ Optek Technology Inc ....D 972 323-2200
  Carrollton (G-2786)

Polycom Inc ....F 512 372-7000
  Austin (G-1709)

▲ Primo Microphones Inc ....D 972 548-9807
  McKinney (G-14967)

◆ Roi Telephony LLC ....F 214 364-2425
  Addison (G-160)

Sagem Communications USA LLC ......E 972 386-4641
  Dallas (G-4927)

Siemens Industry Inc ....G 512 339-6991
  Austin (G-1499)

Soloprotect Us LLC ....D 866 632-6577
  Coppell (G-3446)

Superior Essex Intl LP ....E 325 646-8591
  Brownwood (G-2446)

Telecom Management Corp ....F 281 404-5610
  Spring (G-19176)

Telecom Site Solutions LLC ....F 888 779-9069
  Dallas (G-5049)

Telecore Inc ....E 972 238-9000
  Richardson (G-17405)

Teleprime Advanced Communicati .....G 512 271-9503
  Austin (G-1561)

▲ Tellabs Inc ....E 800 690-2324
  Carrollton (G-2890)

Tko Telesystems LLC ....F 972 484-4900
  Dallas (G-5099)

TPI ....E 972 276-2901
  Garland (G-7604)

Vtech Communications Inc ....E 210 244-0600
  San Antonio (G-18601)

Vysk Communications Inc ....E 210 832-8322
  San Antonio (G-18606)

White Rock Networks Inc A De ....C 972 543-6900
  Richardson (G-17427)

Xtera Inc ....E 972 649-5000
  Allen (G-307)

Zti Merger Subsidiary III Inc ....F 510 777-7000
  Plano (G-17057)

3663 Radio & T V Communications, Systs & Eqpt, Broadcast/Studio

AC Global Systems Inc.......................G 214 497-0280
  Arlington (G-607)

Addvantage Tech Group Inc ....E 918 251-9121
  Carrollton (G-2853)

AGS Technology Inc ....E 817 490-0086
  Fort Worth (G-6356)

Alert Technologies Inc ....E 281 326-9900
  Houston (G-8534)

Alpha Satcom Inc ....F 903 238-8888
  Longview (G-14193)

Andrew & Associates ....D 713 471-0922
  Houston (G-8642)

▲ Antenna Products Corporation........D 940 325-3301
  Mineral Wells (G-15518)

Applied Systems Engrg Inc ....D 817 249-4180
  Benbrook (G-2037)

Arygin Corporation ....F 940 597-8275
  Denton (G-5350)

AT&T Inc ....A 210 821-4105
  Dallas (G-3978)

▼ Aviat US Inc ....B 408 941-7100
  Austin (G-969)

Awesome Paging Inc ....G 361 576-2255
  Victoria (G-20240)

Bock Technologies Inc ....E 972 869-2625
  Dallas (G-4036)

Boeing Company ....A 281 244-4000
  Houston (G-8942)

Broadcast Technical Svcs Inc ....F 832 467-0002
  Houston (G-8988)

Commscope Inc North Carolina ....C 214 583-6750
  Dallas (G-4148)

Commscope Technologies LLC ....F 972 243-0965
  Carrollton (G-2717)

Commscope Technologies LLC ....E 817 864-4100
  Euless (G-6138)

Commscope Technologies LLC ....A 214 634-8502
  Dallas (G-4149)

Commscope Technologies LLC ....E 956 205-6000
  Mission (G-15551)

Commscope Technologies LLC ....C 214 267-5900
  Richardson (G-17289)

Connectivity Solutions Mfg Inc ....C 972 792-3000
  Richardson (G-17290)

▲ Continental Electronics Corp ....D 214 381-7161
  Dallas (G-4159)

CPI Satcom & Antenna Tech Inc ....B 903 984-0555
  Kilgore (G-13539)

CPI Satcom & Antenna Tech Inc ....C 972 852-5300
  Plano (G-16830)

CPI Satcom & Antenna Tech Inc ....D 903 984-0555
  Kilgore (G-13540)

CPI Satcom & Antenna Tech Inc ....D 254 765-3304
  Wortham (G-20922)

Crown Castle Intl Corp ....F 713 570-3000
  Houston (G-9346)

◆ Curtis Mathes Inc ....F 888 725-0309
  Frisco (G-7277)

▲ Cve Technology Group Inc ....A 972 424-6606
  Plano (G-16835)

D C A E Inc ....E 972 278-0202
  Garland (G-7472)

Dbspectra Inc ....E 469 322-0080
  Lewisville (G-14041)

▼ Dbspectra Inc ....D 469 322-0080
  Lewisville (G-14042)

EF Johnson Company ....C 972 819-0700
  Irving (G-13010)

Ef Johnson Technologies Inc ....E 972 819-0700
  Irving (G-13011)

Espy Corporation ....E 512 261-1016
  Austin (G-861)

Ewing Electronics Inc ....E 469 519-2900
  Allen (G-266)

Falcon Events LLC.............................D 800 895-6934
  Irving (G-13022)

Forum Communications Systems ....F 972 619-8603
  Richardson (G-17311)

Front End Services ....E 214 672-0600
  Grand Prairie (G-7879)

▲ Fujitsu Ntwrk Cmmnications Inc ....A 972 479-6000
  Richardson (G-17318)

General Dynamics Mission ....E 254 532-2927
  Fort Hood (G-6323)

Golden Crescent Communications .....F 361 578-4091
  Victoria (G-20269)

◆ Good Sportsman Marketing LLC .....E 877 269-8490
  Irving (G-13040)

Hispanic Fmly Chrstn Ntwrk Inc ....F 214 331-2800
  Dallas (G-4460)

▲ Huawei Device USA Inc ....C 214 919-6688
  Plano (G-16888)

Imagine Communications Corp ....D 469 803-4900
  Frisco (G-7292)

Interco Products ....F 972 613-6749
  Garland (G-7519)

Isp Supplies LLC ....E 855 947-7776
  College Station (G-3187)

Kathrein Broadcast Usa Inc ....E 541 879-2300
  Frisco (G-7295)

◆ Kathrein Holding Usa Inc ....D 541 779-6500
  Richardson (G-17339)

Kegspeed LLC ....F 267 714-8854
  Austin (G-1266)

Kingston I-Tek Solutions LLC ....F 281 656-4900
  Houston (G-10536)

Kmt Wireless LLC ....B 817 591-4600
  Grapevine (G-8045)

◆ Kodiak Networks Inc ....F 972 665-0200
  Plano (G-16903)

▲ L3 Mobile-Vision Inc ....D 973 263-1090
  Houston (G-10578)

L3 Technologies Inc ....A 817 619-4756
  Arlington (G-713)

L3 Technologies Inc ....C 972 722-7927
  Rockwall (G-17553)

L3 Technologies Inc ....B 817 619-2000
  Arlington (G-714)

L3 Technologies Inc ....A 817 619-2000
  Arlington (G-715)

L3harris Technologies Inc ....A 903 457-7461
  Greenville (G-8081)

Lasso Technologies LLC ....F 866 392-0923
  Dallas (G-4583)

Ldia Holdings LLC ....E 512 247-3700
  Austin (G-1284)

Lockheed Martin Corporation ....D 817 777-2000
  Benbrook (G-2042)

Lockheed Martin Corporation ....B 817 777-2000
  Fort Worth (G-6798)

SIC

Logitech Inc ....D 512 347-9300
Austin *(G-1298)*

Logitek Electronic Systems ....F 713 664-4470
Houston *(G-10674)*

◆ Long Range Systems LLC ....E 214 553-5308
Richardson *(G-17349)*

Luminator Technology Group Inc ....B 972 516-3154
Plano *(G-16912)*

▲ Luminator Technology Group LLC ..C 972 424-6511
Plano *(G-16913)*

M2 Global Technology Ltd ....F 210 561-4800
San Antonio *(G-18269)*

Mace Security Intl Inc ....E 800 627-6734
Dallas *(G-4624)*

Marlink Inc ....F 713 910-3352
Houston *(G-10771)*

▲ Marvel Communications Company ..E 817 568-0177
Fort Worth *(G-6814)*

Micropac Industries Inc ....D 972 272-3571
Garland *(G-7551)*

◆ Microwave Networks Inc ....E 281 263-6500
Stafford *(G-19353)*

Mk Systems USA Inc ....E 469 626-9523
Frisco *(G-7298)*

Motorola Solutions Inc ....F 713 783-6400
Houston *(G-10926)*

Motorola Solutions Inc ....C 512 422-9028
Austin *(G-1354)*

Motorola Solutions Inc ....D 972 277-4600
Dallas *(G-4692)*

Motorola Solutions Inc ....E 972 587-5360
Dallas *(G-4693)*

Motorola Solutions Inc ....E 512 821-1560
Austin *(G-1356)*

Motorola Solutions Inc ....C 817 245-6000
Fort Worth *(G-6856)*

▲ National Electronic Devices ....F 936 273-4111
Conroe *(G-3333)*

Nec America Inc ....E 214 262-2387
Dfw Airport *(G-5453)*

Nec Corporation of America ....E 214 262-2387
Dallas *(G-4719)*

Nokia Inc ....C 214 496-0329
Irving *(G-13125)*

▲ Nokia Slutions Networks US LLC ....B 972 374-3000
Coppell *(G-3432)*

On-Board Communications Inc ....E 214 346-0300
Dallas *(G-4762)*

Orbis International Tech Inc ....E 972 929-5705
Carrollton *(G-2787)*

Palm Inc ....C 713 410-1331
Rosharon *(G-17609)*

Parsec Technologies Inc ....F 972 804-4600
Plano *(G-16966)*

Phazr Inc ....B 972 693-7829
Allen *(G-292)*

▲ Philips Consumer Electronic Co ....A 915 298-4111
El Paso *(G-5909)*

Prism Microwave Inc ....D 972 745-7222
Coppell *(G-3435)*

Qar Industries Inc ....F 940 325-3301
Mineral Wells *(G-15538)*

Qualcomm Technologies Inc ....C 512 623-3700
Austin *(G-1442)*

Radiation Sys Prec Cntrls ....A 972 907-9599
Richardson *(G-17381)*

Rcl Technologies Inc ....G 214 870-3703
Irving *(G-13163)*

▼ Rf Code Inc ....E 512 439-2200
Austin *(G-1464)*

▲ Rf Monolithics Inc ....E 972 233-2903
Carrollton *(G-2886)*

Riso Inc ....F 800 942-7476
Carrollton *(G-2808)*

Rockwell Collins Inc ....A 972 705-3156
Richardson *(G-17391)*

◆ Rolltchs Spcialty Vehicles LLC ......E 210 651-5700
Schertz *(G-18761)*

Ruckus Wireless Inc ....E 972 546-1700
Plano *(G-16998)*

Sat Radio Communications Ltd ....F 361 853-9943
Corpus Christi *(G-3615)*

Sat-Lite Technologies Ltd ....F 903 295-3400
White Oak *(G-20719)*

Satellink Inc ....E 972 487-1434
Garland *(G-7581)*

Scott Studios Corporation ....E 972 620-2211
Coppell *(G-3445)*

Sigmatron International Inc ....F 830 775-5524
Del Rio *(G-5324)*

Soloprotect Us LLC ....D 866 632-6577
Coppell *(G-3446)*

Southern Avionics Co ....E 409 842-1717
Beaumont *(G-1952)*

Speedcast Americas Inc ....F 281 340-2057
Houston *(G-12010)*

Synergy Telecom Service Co Inc ....F 210 599-7743
San Antonio *(G-18517)*

Tait Radio Communications ....E 281 944-3539
Houston *(G-12148)*

Teleprime Advanced Communicati ....G 512 271-9503
Austin *(G-1561)*

Uhu Technologies LLC ....F 972 523-2701
Richardson *(G-17417)*

Veripos (us) Inc ....F 281 966-7600
Houston *(G-12552)*

Waveware Technologies Inc ....E 972 479-1702
Garland *(G-7609)*

West-Com Nrse Call Systems Inc ....F 713 731-2500
Houston *(G-12637)*

▲ X-Analog Communications Inc ....E 409 925-4702
Alvin *(G-387)*

Xplore Technologies Corp ....F 512 637-1100
Austin *(G-1677)*

3669 Communications Eqpt, NEC

3M Company ....A 325 643-9798
Brownwood *(G-2423)*

Ademco Inc ....E 972 402-8612
Farmers Branch *(G-6184)*

Ademco Inc ....F 713 861-9418
Houston *(G-8479)*

Ademco Inc ....C 915 872-5542
El Paso *(G-5637)*

Ademco Inc ....D 915 875-0091
El Paso *(G-5638)*

Allestec Corporation ....E 281 359-1519
Kingwood *(G-13637)*

American Signal Corporation ....E 414 358-8000
Garland *(G-7435)*

Aviation Dvcs Elctrnic Cmpnnts ....E 817 738-9161
Fort Worth *(G-6412)*

Backwoods Communications LLC ....F 361 652-6900
Victoria *(G-20241)*

BI Technology Inc ....E 832 698-8000
Tomball *(G-19967)*

Brk Brands Inc ....F 915 860-3500
El Paso *(G-5673)*

Buyers Barricades Houston LLC ....E 817 535-3939
Grapevine *(G-8017)*

CF Industries Inc ....E 214 460-2804
Lewisville *(G-14035)*

City of Arlington ....A 817 459-5700
Arlington *(G-644)*

City of Irving ....E 972 721-2646
Irving *(G-12972)*

▲ Communications Conveyor Co Inc ...E 940 498-1850
Lake Dallas *(G-13810)*

Computerized Traffic Inc ....C 281 252-0505
Montgomery *(G-15629)*

Cubic Its Inc ....C 281 240-7233
Sugar Land *(G-19471)*

Cyber Dynamics Corporation ....F 818 706-3580
Round Rock *(G-17640)*

D&G Energy Corporation ....F 956 686-6040
McAllen *(G-14852)*

▲ Dallas Lite and Barricade Inc ....E 214 748-5791
Dallas *(G-4218)*

Fc Traffic Control Inc ....F 806 570-5633
Amarillo *(G-423)*

Henke Enterprises Inc ....F 936 291-2026
Huntsville *(G-12813)*

Hitech Fire Detection Corp ....E 281 475-7289
Spring *(G-19130)*

Impact Fire Services LLC ....E 254 857-4990
Lorena *(G-14341)*

Impact Fire Services LLC ....E 512 243-7788
Austin *(G-1225)*

▲ Impact Recovery Systems Inc ....E 210 736-4477
San Antonio *(G-18180)*

Integrated Roadway Svcs Inc ....E 214 352-1937
Dallas *(G-4505)*

Keylessco LLC ....F 972 331-2773
Irving *(G-13074)*

L3 Technologies Inc ....A 817 619-2000
Arlington *(G-715)*

L3 Technologies Inc ....E 972 722-7927
Rockwall *(G-17553)*

Ldia Holdings LLC ....E 512 247-3700
Austin *(G-1284)*

Medc International ....D 713 937-9772
Houston *(G-10816)*

Metro Fire Apprtus Specialists ....G 817 467-0911
Mansfield *(G-14695)*

Mobotrex Inc ....C 512 521-3060
Austin *(G-1348)*

National Circuit Assembly Inc ....D 972 278-2009
Garland *(G-7557)*

Noral Holding Company ....E 972 392-7780
Dallas *(G-4742)*

Open Options LLC ....E 972 818-7001
Addison *(G-153)*

Paradigm Traffic Systems Inc ....F 817 831-9406
Arlington *(G-748)*

Pathmark Traffic Equipment LLC ....E 512 392-2090
San Marcos *(G-18702)*

Peek Traffic Corporation ....C 281 453-0200
Houston *(G-11270)*

Securetech Systems Inc ....F 817 869-0569
Irving *(G-13174)*

Short-Line Corporation ....F 210 492-6088
San Antonio *(G-18470)*

Siemens Industry Inc ....B 972 947-7000
Dallas *(G-4959)*

Signal Group Inc ....F 281 453-0200
Houston *(G-11891)*

Simplex Time Recorder LLC ....D 210 402-6311
San Antonio *(G-18476)*

Southwest Signal Supply Inc ....F 713 946-7162
South Houston *(G-19052)*

Statewide Traffic Signal Co ....E 713 680-2875
Houston *(G-12052)*

System Sensor ....G 915 778-1301
El Paso *(G-5990)*

Talla-Com Tllhssee Cmmnctons I ....F 817 234-6726
Fort Worth *(G-7031)*

Tallahassee Technologies Inc ....D 817 234-6726
Fort Water *(G-7032)*

Tango Networks Inc ....E 469 920-2100
Frisco *(G-7318)*

▲ Tellabs Enterprise Inc ....D 972 588-7951
Carrollton *(G-2891)*

Texas Barricade Service ....F 915 355-6653
Canutillo *(G-2665)*

Third Coast Services LLC ....D 832 934-0240
Magnolia *(G-14629)*

Toon LLC ....F 817 609-0672
Fort Worth *(G-7066)*

Trafco Industries Inc ....G 979 234-5713
Eagle Lake *(G-5544)*

▲ Traffic Supply Inc ....F 979 234-5509
Eagle Lake *(G-5545)*

Tyco International MGT Co LLC ....F 713 644-8872
Houston *(G-12419)*

▲ Tyrex Group Ltd ....F 512 623-4694
Austin *(G-1603)*

Warren Watts Technology LLC ....F 817 924-1370
Fort Worth *(G-7127)*

Williamson Conference Center ....E 512 341-7000
Round Rock *(G-17699)*

Wilson Electronics LLC ....C 800 204-4104
Richardson *(G-17428)*

Ww Electronics Solutions LLC ....F 214 396-6636
Quinlan *(G-17227)*

Xarmr Corporation ....G 972 385-7899
McKinney *(G-14991)*

3671 Radio & T V Receiving Electron Tubes

◆ Jordan Technologies LLC ....D 502 267-8344
Austin *(G-1261)*

Ludlum Measurements Inc ....D 325 235-1418
Sweetwater *(G-19634)*

Patriot Premium Threading Serv ....D 432 250-6001
Midland *(G-15339)*

Stellar Micro Devices Inc ....F 512 997-7781
Austin *(G-1535)*

Suntronic Inc ....E 281 879-9562
Houston *(G-12104)*

3672 Printed Circuit Boards

Alltek Circuits Incorporated ....G 949 250-4499
Garland *(G-7432)*

▲ Alpha Circuits Incorporated ....D 281 980-2800
Stafford *(G-19283)*

▲ Am-Mex Products Inc ....E 956 631-7916
McAllen *(G-14836)*

▲ AMS Acquisition Corp ....E 512 491-7411
Austin *(G-921)*

Arctos Assembly Group Ltd ....F 512 682-4801
Austin *(G-931)*

▲ Austin Mfg Svcs I Inc ....D 512 491-7411
Austin *(G-956)*

Basler Electric Company ....E 512 352-3154
Taylor *(G-19649)*

Benchmark Electronics Inc ....C 979 849-6550
Angleton *(G-565)*

◆ Bencor LLC ....E 979 830-5252
Brenham *(G-2243)*

Best Circuit Boards Inc ....D 214 291-1427
Wylie *(G-20927)*

Boardwalk Technology LLC ....E 512 258-2303
Austin *(G-1000)*

Border Assembly Inc ....E 915 592-1172
El Paso *(G-5667)*

▲ Broach Bilt Manufacturing Inc .....E 972 529-9100
McKinney *(G-14930)*

Bsu Inc ....E 607 272-8100
Austin *(G-1013)*

Btp Manufacturing Inc ....E 214 467-0094
Dallas *(G-4064)*

Canyon Manufacturing Svcs Inc ....E 281 876-7105
Houston *(G-9086)*

Cemtechnologies Inc ....F 972 238-3630
Richardson *(G-17285)*

Circuit Services Inc ....F 713 465-4216
Houston *(G-9195)*

Concurrent Mfg Solutions LLC ....E 512 310-9139
Round Rock *(G-17635)*

▲ Corvalent Corporation ....E 512 456-2400
Cedar Park *(G-2965)*

▲ Creation Technologies Kentucky ....B 859 253-3066
Plano *(G-16831)*

Delta Group Electronics Inc ....D 972 606-2102
Grand Prairie *(G-7863)*

Delta V Instruments Inc ....F 972 644-6501
Richardson *(G-17299)*

Denmark Manufacturing Inc ....F 281 494-1527
Stafford *(G-19301)*

Dynalyst Corporation ....E 512 365-1203
Taylor *(G-19653)*

Dynalyst Manufacturing Corp ....E 281 293-7980
Houston *(G-9546)*

Dynalyst Manufacturing Corp ....E 512 365-1230
Taylor *(G-19654)*

▲ Eagle Circuits Inc ....E 214 349-0288
Dallas *(G-4290)*

Electro Plate Circuitry Inc ....D 972 466-0818
Carrollton *(G-2730)*

Electronic Services Unlimited ....F 713 683-0601
Houston *(G-9597)*

Electronics & Metals Inds Inc ....E 512 267-0113
Leander *(G-13988)*

Electroninks Writeables Inc ....F 512 766-7555
Austin *(G-1120)*

Ember Industries Inc ....E 512 396-1911
San Marcos *(G-18686)*

Emsolutions LLC ....E 214 575-5327
Dallas *(G-4321)*

▲ Enhanced Production Tech Inc ....G 512 759-2009
Hutto *(G-12878)*

Epic Technologies LLC ....C 915 791-5326
El Paso *(G-5757)*

Epic Technologies LLC ....D 915 229-6805
El Paso *(G-5758)*

Flagship Manufacturing Corp ....F 512 382-6410
Austin *(G-1157)*

Flextronics America LLC ....B 408 576-7000
Laredo *(G-13885)*

Flextronics America LLC ....A 512 425-4129
Austin *(G-1158)*

Flextronics America LLC ....E 408 576-7990
Laredo *(G-13886)*

Flextronics America LLC ....F 512 425-6180
Pflugerville *(G-16672)*

Flextronics America LLC ....F 512 698-1407
Austin *(G-1159)*

Flextronics Intl PA Inc ....E 512 425-4100
Austin *(G-1160)*

Flextronics Intl USA Inc ....A 512 425-4100
Austin *(G-1161)*

Flextronics Intl USA Inc ....B 817 837-5098
Plano *(G-16871)*

Flextronics Intl USA Inc ....A 512 740-1904
Austin *(G-1162)*

GI Circuits Inc ....E 281 495-2100
Stafford *(G-19322)*

GI Electrotech Inc ....E 832 886-4997
Stafford *(G-19323)*

Housetech Inc ....E 281 879-0484
Houston *(G-10217)*

▲ Hunting Innova Inc ....B 281 653-5500
Houston *(G-10284)*

▲ Ibe Smt Equipment Inc ....F 281 259-9660
Magnolia *(G-14609)*

Iondesign Inc ....F 512 260-5778
Jonestown *(G-13315)*

Jabil Inc ....B 727 577-9749
Laredo *(G-13898)*

JVB Electronics Inc ....E 972 877-8085
Irving *(G-13071)*

Kodiak Assembly Solutions LLC ....E 512 275-1700
Austin *(G-1271)*

◆ Krypton Solutions LLC ....C 972 424-3880
Plano *(G-16904)*

Leemah Corporation ....C 214 570-7170
Richardson *(G-17342)*

Libra Industries LLC ....D 972 664-0900
Richardson *(G-17344)*

▲ Lwo Acquisitions Company LLC .....D 972 573-1140
Irving *(G-13093)*

Micross Components-Tx LLC ....E 512 833-5868
Round Rock *(G-17673)*

Milspec Works LLC ....E 281 530-7002
Houston *(G-10885)*

Morgan Newton Company LP ....D 972 212-8080
Plano *(G-16933)*

National Circuit Assembly Inc ....D 972 278-2009
Garland *(G-7557)*

▲ Netvia Group LLC ....D 972 573-1400
Irving *(G-13122)*

Niltronix Circuits Inc ....F 713 465-4216
Houston *(G-11056)*

Npi Technologies Inc ....F 972 968-0400
Richardson *(G-17366)*

Npi Technologies 2 Inc ....F 281 265-2815
Sugar Land *(G-19519)*

Pen Tech Assembly LLC ....E 512 275-0590
Austin *(G-1407)*

Plano Acquisition LLC ....C 214 343-0131
Plano *(G-16972)*

PM Assembly LLC ....F 972 814-3727
Farmersville *(G-6225)*

▲ Precise Connections Inc ....E 972 298-1040
Duncanville *(G-5537)*

▲ Precision Technology Inc ....C 214 343-0131
Plano *(G-16976)*

▲ Primary Sourcing Corp ....D 713 952-5405
Houston *(G-11412)*

Protoline Inc ....F 281 561-0802
Houston *(G-11465)*

Q C Graphics Inc ....F 972 931-4100
Richardson *(G-17377)*

Reycomp Inc ....F 972 606-4600
Grand Prairie *(G-7964)*

Roca Precision Mfg Inc ....F 281 240-2020
Stafford *(G-19371)*

◆ Saberex Group Ltd ....E 512 623-4694
Austin *(G-1478)*

Sanmina Corporation ....E 408 964-3500
Laredo *(G-13927)*

Sanmina Corporation ....C 408 964-3500
Laredo *(G-13928)*

Sanmina Corporation ....E 512 997-1100
Austin *(G-1485)*

Sanmina Corporation ....B 972 512-3333
Carrollton *(G-2812)*

Sanmina Corporation ....C 210 623-5081
Von Ormy *(G-20349)*

Sanmina Corporation ....D 956 523-6800
Laredo *(G-13929)*

Sgm Corporation ....E 281 313-6111
Stafford *(G-19376)*

Siemens Industry Inc ....E 817 633-4430
Grand Prairie *(G-7973)*

Sigmatron International Inc ....F 830 775-5524
Del Rio *(G-5324)*

Silicon Hills Design Inc ....E 512 836-1088
Austin *(G-1504)*

▲ Svtronics Inc ....C 214 440-1234
Plano *(G-17017)*

Talla-Com Tllhssee Cmmnctons I ....F 817 234-6726
Fort Worth *(G-7031)*

◆ Test Spectrum Inc ....F 512 472-6750
Austin *(G-1564)*

Texas Circuitry Inc ....E 972 278-3838
Garland *(G-7598)*

Trylene Inc ....E 281 980-0400
Houston *(G-12392)*

▲ Tyrex Group Ltd ....F 512 623-4694
Austin *(G-1603)*

▲ Variosystems Inc ....C 817 416-7535
Southlake *(G-19083)*

▲ Virtex Assembly Services Inc ....D 512 835-6772
Austin *(G-1635)*

Virtex Enterprises LP ....E 512 835-6772
Austin *(G-1636)*

Zentech Dallas LLC ....E 972 907-2727
Richardson *(G-17431)*

3674 Semiconductors

Advanced Micro Devices Inc ....B 512 602-1000
Austin *(G-891)*

Advanced Micro Devices Inc ....C 512 602-1000
Austin *(G-892)*

Advanced Micro Devices Inc ....F 512 602-5204
Austin *(G-893)*

▲ Advanced Rfurbishment Tech LLC ..E 512 377-1016
Austin *(G-894)*

Alereon Inc ....D 512 345-4200
Austin *(G-906)*

Ambiq Micro Inc ....E 512 879-2850
Austin *(G-913)*

American Innovations Ltd ....C 512 249-3400
Austin *(G-916)*

Amkor Technology Inc ....D 512 953-0701
Austin *(G-919)*

▲ AMS Sensors USA Inc ....D 469 298-4252
Plano *(G-16789)*

Analog Devices Inc ....C 512 427-1000
Austin *(G-922)*

▲ Analytical Sensors Instrs LLC ....D 281 565-8818
Houston *(G-8636)*

Applied Materials Inc ....E 512 272-7075
Austin *(G-924)*

Applied Materials Inc ....D 469 340-7810
Richardson *(G-17271)*

Applied Materials Inc ....E 512 845-1126
Austin *(G-1690)*

Applied Materials Inc ....A 512 272-1000
Austin *(G-925)*

▲ Applied Optoelectronics Inc ....C 281 295-1800
Sugar Land *(G-19445)*

Aramark Services Inc ....C 512 602-1000
Austin *(G-927)*

Arm Inc ....F 408 576-1500
Austin *(G-932)*

Arm Inc ....D 512 327-9249
Austin *(G-933)*

◆ Atmi Materials Ltd ....E 512 715-5343
Burnet *(G-2602)*

Audex Inc ....F 903 757-4083
Hallsville *(G-8126)*

◆ Austin Samsung Semicdtr LLC ....A 512 672-1000
Austin *(G-960)*

▲ Austin Semiconductor Inc ....C 512 339-1188
Austin *(G-962)*

▲ Avant Technology Inc ....D 512 651-5300
Pflugerville *(G-16660)*

Black Sand Technologies Inc ....F 512 329-9400
Austin *(G-994)*

Ca Inc ....F 402 494-2411
Arlington *(G-636)*

Calxeda Inc ....D 512 582-5100
Austin *(G-1020)*

▲ Canon Nanotechnologies Inc ....D 512 339-7760
Austin *(G-1024)*

Cbg Corporation ....E 512 491-7541
Austin *(G-1033)*

Centaur Technology Inc ....D 512 418-5700
Austin *(G-1037)*

CER Tek Inc ....F 915 772-8290
El Paso *(G-5693)*

▲ Cirrus Logic Inc ....B 512 851-4000
Austin *(G-1050)*

Clairex Technologies Inc ....F 972 265-4905
Plano *(G-16825)*

Coherent Logix Incorporated ....E 512 382-8961
West Lake Hills *(G-20679)*

Connexa Energy LLC ....E 830 995-3600
Comfort *(G-3238)*

Consistent Reasoning Inc ....E 512 382-8940
West Lake Hills *(G-20680)*

Continental Auto Systems Inc ....A 830 372-7000
Seguin *(G-18833)*

Contrinex Inc ....F 574 340-7089
Coppell *(G-3413)*

Convergent Performance LLC ....G 713 398-8496
Houston *(G-9296)*

Cooper B-Line Inc ....E 713 678-4460
Houston *(G-9303)*

S I C

Criteria Labs Inc .... E 512 637-4500
Austin *(G-1073)*

◆ Curtis Mathes Inc .... F 888 725-0309
Frisco *(G-7277)*

Cypress Semiconductor Corp .... F 512 934-6699
Austin *(G-1082)*

▲ Datatronic Control Corporation ..... E 972 475-7879
Rowlett *(G-17704)*

◆ Dean Technology Inc .... F 972 248-7691
Addison *(G-115)*

▲ Diodes Fabtech Inc .... C 816 251-8800
Plano *(G-16844)*

Diodes Incorporated .... E 972 987-3900
Plano *(G-16845)*

▲ Diodes Incorporated .... C 972 987-3900
Plano *(G-16846)*

Drs Ntwork Imaging Systems LLC ..... C 214 996-2837
Dallas *(G-4279)*

Efficiency Aggregators LLC .... F 832 862-1103
Richmond *(G-17453)*

Energy Xtreme LLC .... F 512 617-7902
Austin *(G-1126)*

▲ Entech Solar Inc .... F 817 421-4658
Grapevine *(G-8031)*

Entegris Inc .... F 512 715-5344
Burnet *(G-2607)*

Entegris Prof Solutions Inc .... E 512 244-5200
Round Rock *(G-17655)*

Fairchild Semiconductor Corp .... E 972 910-8000
Richardson *(G-17308)*

Fas Technologies LLC .... E 214 343-5300
Dallas *(G-4354)*

Finisar Corporation .... C 214 509-2700
Allen *(G-268)*

▲ Fleco Industries LLC .... C 972 247-3171
Carrollton *(G-2739)*

Freescale Smcdtr Hldings V Inc ...... F 512 895-2000
Austin *(G-1171)*

Futurefab Inc .... F 972 423-6606
Plano *(G-16876)*

General Led Opco LLC .... F 210 360-1444
San Antonio *(G-18138)*

Global Nucleonics LLC .... F 281 578-7900
Houston *(G-9975)*

Globitech Incorporated .... C 903 957-1999
Sherman *(G-18916)*

Headway Research Inc .... F 972 272-5431
Garland *(G-7509)*

Hg Solutions Inc .... F 972 205-0888
Garland *(G-7512)*

High Tech Services Inc .... F 972 231-8037
Richardson *(G-17328)*

Ic Enable LLC .... E 214 575-9400
Richardson *(G-17330)*

Ichor Systems Inc .... D 512 246-9092
Austin *(G-1216)*

Innosync Inc .... E 972 644-7962
Dallas *(G-4501)*

▲ Intelligent Epitaxy Tech Inc ...... D 972 234-0068
Richardson *(G-17334)*

Interfet Corporation .... F 972 238-9700
Richardson *(G-17335)*

▼ Interntonal Resistive Texas LP ..... C 361 992-7900
Corpus Christi *(G-3555)*

▲ Jtm Technologies Inc .... F 972 635-6900
Royse City *(G-17720)*

KLA Corporation .... E 512 231-4200
Austin *(G-1270)*

▲ Kobi Electric LLC .... F 817 297-3200
Fort Worth *(G-6768)*

Legerity Holdings Inc .... C 512 228-5400
Austin *(G-1288)*

Leidos Inc .... E 210 731-1438
San Antonio *(G-18245)*

LSI Corporation .... E 817 430-5808
Roanoke *(G-17489)*

◆ Ltd Material LLC .... E 512 933-9292
Austin *(G-1306)*

Ludlum Measurements Inc .... D 325 235-1418
Sweetwater *(G-19634)*

M C Systems Inc .... F 972 247-6785
Dallas *(G-4620)*

Mactronix Inc .... E 972 690-0028
Richardson *(G-17350)*

Mardel Souza Inc .... E 956 459-3504
Weslaco *(G-20664)*

Maxim Integrated Products Inc .... A 210 522-7000
San Antonio *(G-18285)*

Maxim Integrated Products Inc .... A 214 458-0357
Irving *(G-13098)*

Maxim Integrated Products Inc .... A 972 371-4000
Dallas *(G-4654)*

Maxim Integrated Products Inc .... F 512 249-0307
Austin *(G-1703)*

MEI Micro Inc .... E 972 690-9494
Addison *(G-149)*

Memphis Electronic Inc .... G 713 600-6080
Houston *(G-10826)*

Mhc Semiconductor Processing .... F 512 331-6632
Austin *(G-1337)*

Micrel LLC .... C 972 235-9166
Richardson *(G-17357)*

Microchip Technology Inc .... G 512 334-1931
Austin *(G-1338)*

Micron Semiconductor Pdts Inc ...... D 512 248-8283
Austin *(G-1339)*

Micron Semiconductor Pdts Inc ...... D 281 970-3202
Tomball *(G-19987)*

Micron Technology Inc .... C 972 521-5200
Allen *(G-286)*

Micron Technology Texas Llc .... D 972 521-5200
Allen *(G-287)*

Micron Vision Corporation .... F 281 546-9632
Plano *(G-16927)*

Micropac Industries Inc .... D 972 272-3571
Garland *(G-7552)*

Micropac Industries Inc .... D 972 272-3571
Garland *(G-7551)*

Micropower Global Corporation .... D 512 245-8976
San Marcos *(G-18699)*

Microsemi Semiconductor (us) .... D 512 228-5400
Austin *(G-1340)*

▲ Microtune Inc .... F 972 673-1600
Plano *(G-16928)*

▲ Mission Solar Energy LLC .... D 210 531-8600
San Antonio *(G-18314)*

Modus Test LLC .... F 972 914-7866
Richardson *(G-17359)*

Muto Technology Inc .... E 512 251-2211
Austin *(G-1358)*

Neteffect Inc .... E 512 302-0002
Austin *(G-1363)*

Netrake Corporation .... E 214 291-1000
Plano *(G-16943)*

Nextech Solutions Inc .... E 214 343-5300
Dallas *(G-4736)*

North Texas Epitaxy LLC .... E 972 747-8603
Allen *(G-289)*

Nortonlifelock Inc .... D 210 403-7800
San Antonio *(G-18351)*

Nortonlifelock Inc .... D 650 527-8000
Houston *(G-11083)*

Nvidia Corporation .... F 408 486-2000
Richardson *(G-17367)*

Nvidia Corporation .... F 512 401-4762
Austin *(G-1707)*

Nxp Usa Inc .... A 512 933-6000
Austin *(G-1373)*

▲ Nxp Usa Inc .... A 512 933-8214
Austin *(G-1374)*

Nxp Usa Inc .... A 512 996-4000
Austin *(G-1708)*

One Semiconductor LLC .... F 512 785-4456
Austin *(G-1385)*

◆ Optek Technology Inc .... D 972 323-2200
Carrollton *(G-2786)*

Oracle Corporation .... A 737 867-1000
Austin *(G-1391)*

Painted Rock LLC .... E 512 832-5057
Cedar Park *(G-2981)*

Photodigm Inc .... E 972 235-7584
Richardson *(G-17373)*

Polaris Led Inc .... F 832 582-6263
Houston *(G-11354)*

Pricevision Inc .... E 972 770-0000
Carrollton *(G-2796)*

Progressive Mfg Tech Inc .... F 512 380-1991
Austin *(G-1435)*

Proportional Technologies Inc .... E 713 747-7324
Houston *(G-11450)*

Qorvo Inc .... F 336 678-5099
Farmers Branch *(G-6211)*

▲ Qorvo Texas LLC .... F 972 994-8200
Richardson *(G-17378)*

Quantum Materials Corp .... G 512 245-6646
San Marcos *(G-18706)*

Reedholm Instruments Co .... E 512 869-1935
Georgetown *(G-7674)*

Renesas Electronics Amer Inc .... E 408 432-8888
West Lake Hills *(G-20687)*

Resonant Inc .... D 805 308-9803
Austin *(G-1460)*

Retronix Global Inc .... C 512 808-5659
Austin *(G-1463)*

Santos CMI Inc (usa) .... F 713 273-4140
Houston *(G-11749)*

▲ Schunk Xycarb Technology Inc ..... E 512 863-0033
Georgetown *(G-7676)*

Science Applications Intl Corp .... F 469 557-8249
Carrollton *(G-2815)*

Semes America Inc .... G 512 251-3188
Pflugerville *(G-16687)*

◆ Semiconductor Support Svcs Co .... E 512 267-7087
Austin *(G-1491)*

Semiconductor Technology Inc .... F 512 468-8687
Lago Vista *(G-13808)*

Semtech Corporation .... E 972 231-1606
Richardson *(G-17396)*

Sigmasense .... E 844 248-9081
West Lake Hills *(G-20688)*

Silicon Laboratories Inc .... B 512 416-8500
Austin *(G-1505)*

Silicon Space Technology Corp ...... F 512 347-1814
Austin *(G-1506)*

Skorpios Technologies Inc .... C 512 356-2000
Austin *(G-1509)*

Solaro Energy Inc .... F 575 838-3813
Nacogdoches *(G-15713)*

Spansion LLC .... C 512 934-6427
Austin *(G-1523)*

Srj Holdings LLC .... E 972 747-8613
Allen *(G-299)*

Stmicrlctrnics N Amer Hldg Inc ...... E 972 466-6000
Carrollton *(G-2820)*

Sunpower Corporation .... F 512 735-0119
Austin *(G-1546)*

Sunrgy LLC .... F 832 786-5051
Stafford *(G-19381)*

Superconductor Tech Inc .... E 512 650-7775
Austin *(G-1549)*

Syndiant Inc .... E 972 248-3331
Dallas *(G-3852)*

Tallannquest LLC .... G 972 423-8455
Plano *(G-17020)*

◆ Tekmos Inc .... G 512 342-9871
Austin *(G-1559)*

Tempo Semiconductor Inc .... F 512 827-3440
Austin *(G-1562)*

Teradyne Inc .... D 972 231-5384
Plano *(G-17025)*

Texas Instrs Philippines LLC .... F 972 995-3773
Dallas *(G-5065)*

Texas Instruments Incorporated ...... D 972 995-2011
Dallas *(G-5066)*

▲ Texas Instruments Incorporated ..... A 972 995-3773
Dallas *(G-5067)*

Texas Instruments Incorporated ...... E 512 434-1560
West Lake Hills *(G-20690)*

Texas Instruments Incorporated ...... B 214 480-4691
Plano *(G-17029)*

Texas Instruments Incorporated ...... D 214 479-3773
Dallas *(G-5068)*

Texas Instruments Incorporated ...... B 214 966-9759
Double Oak *(G-5497)*

Texas Instruments Incorporated ...... D 214 567-5185
Dallas *(G-5069)*

Texas Instruments Incorporated ...... B 972 995-2011
Dallas *(G-5070)*

Texas Instruments Incorporated ...... F 832 939-2000
Sugar Land *(G-19562)*

Texas Instruments Incorporated ...... E 972 995-2011
Stafford *(G-19386)*

Texas Instruments Incorporated ...... C 972 644-5580
Dallas *(G-5071)*

Texas Instruments Incorporated ...... E 817 401-5563
Dallas *(G-5072)*

Texas Instruments Incorporated ...... E 972 995-2011
Plano *(G-17030)*

Texas Instruments Incorporated ...... E 214 567-2075
Richardson *(G-17408)*

Texas Instruments Incorporated ...... E 214 567-9863
Plano *(G-17031)*

Texas Instruments Incorporated ...... B 972 995-2011
Dallas *(G-5073)*

▲ Tokyo Electron US Holdings Inc .... B 512 424-1000
Austin *(G-1585)*

Tower Semicdtr San Antonio Inc ..... B 210 522-7000
San Antonio *(G-18554)*

◆ Tpg Capital Management LP .... B 817 871-4000
Fort Worth *(G-7069)*

Tronics Mems Inc ....D 469 872-0300
  Addison (G-171)
Trustkey Solutions Inc ....F 214 865-9354
  Richardson (G-17415)
Uhnder Inc ....E 512 722-6353
  Austin (G-1605)
Ultra Clean Technology Systems ....C 512 252-6100
  Austin (G-1606)
Viavi Solutions Inc ....F 972 907-8882
  Richardson (G-17422)
Vlsip Technologies Inc ....D 972 437-5506
  Richardson (G-17424)
Wintegra Inc ....C 512 345-3808
  Austin (G-1674)
▲ X-Fab Texas Inc ....B 806 747-4400
  Lubbock (G-14515)
▲ XI Technology LLC ....F 972 369-1359
  Wylie (G-20956)
Yerico Manufacturing Inc ....E 512 285-3444
  Elgin (G-6057)

3675 Electronic Capacitors

Centennial Radiator Inc ....E 214 634-8262
  Dallas (G-4096)
Integer Holdings Corporation ....D 214 618-5243
  Plano (G-16892)
Kemet Electronics Corporation ....F 956 548-7200
  Brownsville (G-2373)
Panasonic Corp North America ....A 956 984-3432
  Mcallen (G-14899)
◆ Steelman Industries Inc ....E 903 984-3061
  Kilgore (G-13594)
▲ Venkel Ltd ....E 512 794-0081
  Austin (G-1629)

3676 Electronic Resistors

▲ AB Interconnect Inc ....C 919 934-5181
  Corpus Christi (G-3463)
▼ Interntonal Resistive Texas LP ....C 361 992-7900
  Corpus Christi (G-3555)
Questech Services Corporation ....E 972 278-8006
  Garland (G-7575)
Sensata Technologies Inc ....F 817 608-2289
  Fort Worth (G-6983)
▲ Venkel Ltd ....E 512 794-0081
  Austin (G-1629)

3677 Electronic Coils & Transformers

▲ Abracon LLC ....F 512 371-6159
  Spicewood (G-19090)
Amkin Technologies LLC ....F 281 755-2046
  Cypress (G-3774)
B I Products LLC ....D 972 359-4000
  Allen (G-255)
Benchmark Manufacturing Inc ....E 903 882-4311
  Lindale (G-14133)
Blue Box Air LLC ....D 424 241-3060
  Dallas (G-4031)
Cooper Power Systems LLC ....C 936 569-9422
  Nacogdoches (G-15692)
◆ Ets-Lindgren Inc ....C 512 531-6400
  Cedar Park (G-2968)
Filtration Automation Inc ....E 817 999-8190
  Alvarado (G-332)
Gs Liquid Technologies LLC ....F 817 556-6262
  Cleburne (G-3093)
▲ Hipro Technologies Inc ....E 512 833-6600
  Austin (G-1205)
Houston Transformer Co Ltd ....D 713 977-6009
  Houston (G-10258)
Ipdisplays LLC ....F 214 453-3570
  Allen (G-278)
▼ Jonell Filtration Products Inc ....D 254 559-7591
  Breckenridge (G-2230)
Leightner Electronics Inc ....F 972 542-0176
  McKinney (G-14952)
Mag Flux Corporation ....E 972 272-8576
  Garland (G-7541)
▼ Magnetic Technology Inc ....E 214 544-2700
  McKinney (G-14955)
◆ Martin-Decker Totco Inc ....B 512 340-5000
  Cedar Park (G-2978)
Nova Magnetics Inc ....D 972 272-8287
  Garland (G-7564)
▲ Polara Engineering Inc ....D 951 547-5500
  Greenville (G-8086)
Sigma Electronics Inc ....E 800 874-7121
  Houston (G-11884)
Specialty Coils LLC ....E 903 212-2645
  Longview (G-14310)

Tecal Manufacturing LLC ....F 915 593-1413
  El Paso (G-5995)
Texas Electric Coops Inc ....D 512 868-8610
  Georgetown (G-7685)
Transcend Solutions Llc ....F 936 689-5618
  Houston (G-12350)
Universal Transformer Company ....F 972 784-7700
  Farmersville (G-6226)
Ups Inc ....E 713 222-7300
  Houston (G-12475)

3678 Electronic Connectors

ADI Electronics Inc ....F 214 818-4720
  Dallas (G-3889)
Airborn Interconnect Inc ....B 512 863-5585
  Georgetown (G-7633)
Amphenol Corporation ....B 214 547-2400
  Allen (G-251)
Capital City Appliance LLC ....F 512 491-7600
  Austin (G-1026)
Cinch Connectors Inc ....B 956 686-1151
  McAllen (G-14847)
▲ Fastener Specialty Inc ....F 972 988-0064
  North Richland Hills (G-15878)
▼ Fd-Thru Power Systems Cnnctors .....E 281 476-9100
  Deer Park (G-5273)
Kemp-Meek Manufacturing Inc ....F 903 569-9700
  Mineola (G-15509)
▲ Lwo Acquisitions Company LLC ....D 972 573-1140
  Irving (G-13093)
Molex LLC ....F 512 345-1092
  Austin (G-1351)
Simpson Strong-Tie Company Inc ....E 972 542-0326
  McKinney (G-14975)
Solution Tech Harn Group LLC ....E 214 221-0323
  Dallas (G-4978)
Te Connectivity Corporation ....D 610 893-9800
  El Paso (G-5993)
Teledyne Instruments Inc ....C 713 666-2561
  Houston (G-12191)
Welding Outlets Inc ....D 281 590-0190
  Houston (G-12630)

3679 Electronic Components, NEC

▲ AB Interconnect Inc ....C 919 934-5181
  Corpus Christi (G-3463)
▲ Abracon LLC ....F 512 371-6159
  Spicewood (G-19090)
Aees Inc ....D 210 491-2600
  San Antonio (G-17871)
Airborn Interconnect Inc ....B 512 863-5585
  Georgetown (G-7633)
▲ Alphabet McD Division ....E 915 593-2011
  El Paso (G-5642)
Amtech Manufacturing Inc ....E 817 563-1251
  Fort Worth (G-6386)
Apx Plastics Inc ....E 817 275-3883
  Arlington (G-620)
◆ ASC Signal Corporation ....E 214 291-7654
  Plano (G-16795)
▲ Atron Group LLC ....D 214 292-9840
  Dallas (G-3984)
▲ Austin American Tech Corp ....E 512 756-4150
  Burnet (G-2603)
▲ Bench Tree Group LLC ....E 512 869-6900
  Georgetown (G-7640)
▲ Benning Power Electronics Inc ....D 214 553-1444
  Richardson (G-17279)
Biztel LP ....F 713 600-2600
  Houston (G-8896)
Bk/Ja Holdings Inc ....E 281 879-9903
  Stafford (G-19291)
Border Assembly Inc ....E 915 592-1172
  El Paso (G-5667)
Btu Research LLC ....F 713 542-6228
  Houston (G-9005)
▲ Carter Glassblowing Inc ....F 940 440-3090
  Crossroads (G-3747)
Cathodic Rectifiers Inc ....F 903 759-6813
  Longview (G-14209)
Chiphong Inc ....F 512 933-9292
  Austin (G-1048)
Circuit Systems Company Inc ....E 817 861-6575
  Arlington (G-642)
Clairex Technologies Inc ....F 972 265-4905
  Plano (G-16825)
Cloud Ninjas LLC ....F 832 478-9158
  Houston (G-9217)
Co-Operative Inds Def LLC ....D 817 740-4700
  Fort Worth (G-6525)

Compass Electronics Group LLC ....D 915 594-0500
  El Paso (G-5701)
Concurrent Mfg Solutions LLC ....E 512 310-9139
  Round Rock (G-17635)
◆ Cordyne Inc ....D 713 460-5151
  Houston (G-9313)
▲ Creation Technologies Kentucky ....B 859 253-3066
  Plano (G-16831)
Ct-Technology Inc ....G 469 531-9472
  Carrollton (G-2862)
Dedicated Controls LLC ....F 972 632-8716
  Princeton (G-17207)
Delta Electronics (usa) Inc ....E 469 330-9100
  Richardson (G-17298)
◆ Delta Electronics (usa) Inc ....E 469 330-9100
  Plano (G-16837)
Delta Group Electronics Inc ....D 972 606-2102
  Grand Prairie (G-7863)
Dfm Technology Pvt USA Inc ....F 713 547-0114
  Houston (G-9449)
E-M Design Time Inc ....F 972 279-4720
  Dallas (G-4287)
▲ Elcom Inc ....F 915 298-2000
  El Paso (G-5749)
Electrical Components Intl Inc ....D 915 217-2700
  El Paso (G-5750)
Electronic Assembly Svcs Inc ....F 713 686-4390
  Houston (G-9594)
Electrotechnics Corporation ....E 903 938-1901
  Marshall (G-14776)
Engineering Spectrum Inc ....F 210 697-8828
  San Antonio (G-18090)
Futaba Corporation of America ....F 915 771-7858
  El Paso (G-5776)
▲ General Assembly Corporation ....F 915 701-0605
  El Paso (G-5780)
General Datatech LP ....E 214 857-6194
  Dallas (G-4398)
▲ Gilmore-Global Instrs Co Inc ....F 713 946-9133
  Houston (G-9958)
GNC Cable Technologies Inc ....F 832 876-1780
  Cypress (G-3797)
◆ Hayakawa Electronics Amer Inc ....F 972 457-0064
  Irving (G-13054)
High Point Design LLC ....F 972 753-2622
  Irving (G-13056)
Hvm Technology Inc ....E 830 626-5552
  New Braunfels (G-15804)
Indus Instruments ....F 281 286-1130
  Webster (G-20639)
Infratech Inc ....E 214 503-1087
  Dallas (G-4497)
Innowave Rf LLC ....F 737 200-7090
  Leander (G-13992)
▲ Intrapack Corporation ....E 214 348-7105
  Dallas (G-4509)
▲ J M Fabrication Company LLC ....F 817 652-0526
  Arlington (G-709)
Jar Industries LLC ....E 281 484-1777
  Houston (G-10455)
L3 Technologies Inc ....B 972 840-5600
  Garland (G-7535)
L3 Technologies Inc ....B 972 840-5600
  Dallas (G-4574)
L3 Technologies Inc ....A 817 619-2000
  Arlington (G-715)
▲ Lachmann Vllneva Hldngs GP LLC ..F 915 594-0500
  El Paso (G-5836)
Lee Tech LLC ....F 409 925-0553
  Santa Fe (G-18736)
Leidos Inc ....E 210 731-1438
  San Antonio (G-18245)
Leonard Elc Pdts Co Texas Inc ....F 956 350-5650
  Brownsville (G-2377)
Lucere LLc ....E 281 240-7355
  Missouri City (G-15582)
▲ Lwo Acquisitions Company LLC ....D 972 573-1140
  Irving (G-13093)
M3 Distribution Inc ....F 281 357-0604
  Tomball (G-19986)
Mach Speed Holdings LLC ....D 214 978-3800
  Plano (G-16917)
Mdi Security LLC ....F 210 477-5400
  San Antonio (G-18286)
▲ Modern Tektronix Assembly ....E 817 868-7173
  Euless (G-6150)
Mssl Wiring System Inc ....E 830 776-9221
  El Paso (G-5890)
Mtx Electronics Inc ....F 956 781-3476
  Pharr (G-16708)

SIC

▲ Newline Interactive Inc ....F 972 468-9728
Plano (G-16944)

Nextus Inc ....E 512 288-9080
Georgetown (G-7667)

Orbis International Tech Inc ....E 972 929-5705
Carrollton (G-2787)

◆ Orbital Systems LLC ....E 972 915-3669
Irving (G-13133)

Parsec Technologies Inc ....F 972 804-4600
Plano (G-16966)

▲ Petron Industries Inc ....D 713 693-8700
Houston (G-11310)

Pinner Wire & Cable Inc ....D 972 494-3333
Garland (G-7567)

▲ Polara Engineering Inc ....D 951 547-5500
Greenville (G-8086)

Polara Enterprises LLC ....F 903 366-0300
Greenville (G-8087)

Reedholm Instruments Co ....E 512 869-1935
Georgetown (G-7674)

◆ Regal Research and Mfg Co LLC ......C 972 494-0359
Plano (G-16990)

Rpmtronics Incorporated ....A 972 865-1330
Carrollton (G-2810)

Satpro Network Inc ....E 972 675-8475
Garland (G-7582)

Schneider Electric It USA Inc ....E 888 994-8867
Houston (G-11782)

▲ Season Group Usa LLC ....D 210 522-1116
San Antonio (G-18462)

Solution Tech Harn Group LLC .....E 214 221-0323
Dallas (G-4978)

Source Operations Group LLC .....E 888 557-7079
Houston (G-11957)

Southwest Quartz Ltd Co ....F 512 863-8415
Georgetown (G-7678)

Stoneridge Inc ....B 915 778-1331
El Paso (G-5983)

▲ Stoneridge Electronics Inc ....A 915 621-6111
El Paso (G-5984)

Tech Power International Co ....D 281 494-4242
Stafford (G-19382)

Texas Mri LP ....C 940 549-5462
Graham (G-7790)

◆ Texas Photonics Inc ....G 972 412-7111
Rowlett (G-17712)

Toppan Photomasks Inc ....C 512 310-6000
Round Rock (G-17694)

Trylene Inc ....E 281 980-0400
Houston (G-12392)

▲ Unitron LP ....D 214 221-9094
Dallas (G-5139)

Votronics Inc ....F 972 509-8494
Plano (G-17049)

Wigwag LLC ....F 512 814-6459
Austin (G-1665)

▲ Williamsrdm Inc ....D 817 872-1500
Fort Worth (G-7148)

Wolfson Microelectronics Inc ....B 408 329-9800
Austin (G-1675)

Yazaki North America Inc ....F 618 512-8723
El Paso (G-6041)

3691 Storage Batteries

Battery Solutions Inc ....F 806 771-3777
Lubbock (G-14366)

▲ Continental Battery Company .....D 214 631-5701
Dallas (G-4158)

▲ Eestor Inc ....G 512 259-7601
Cedar Park (G-2967)

Enersys ....F 972 245-6601
Carrollton (G-2731)

▲ Ereplacements LLC ....F 214 935-3591
Grapevine (G-8032)

Exide Technologies LLC ....F 972 633-6900
Irving (G-13018)

Exide Technologies LLC ....F 678 566-9000
The Woodlands (G-19863)

Ideal Power Inc ....F 512 264-1542
Austin (G-1219)

Integer Holdings Corporation ....D 214 618-5243
Plano (G-16892)

Otw-Ep Inc ....G 915 858-0448
Socorro (G-19017)

Panasonic Corp North America .....D 956 984-3700
Frisco (G-7305)

▲ Southwest Elctronic Enrgy Corp .....D 281 240-4000
Missouri City (G-15595)

Spectrum Brands Inc ....D 214 778-4600
Garland (G-7589)

Triathlon Btry Solutions Inc ....E 469 301-2128
Lewisville (G-14099)

Vitzrocellusa Inc ....F 832 850-7095
Houston (G-12577)

Zeta Energy LLC ....F 732 581-0838
Houston (G-12727)

3692 Primary Batteries: Dry & Wet

◆ CSB Energy Tech Americas Ltd ......E 817 244-7777
Haltom City (G-8135)

Grace IV Albert Thomas ....F 940 500-4323
Wichita Falls (G-20768)

Integer Holdings Corporation ....D 214 618-5243
Plano (G-16892)

OReilly Automotive Stores Inc ....F 936 856-2409
Willis (G-20857)

Panasonic Corp North America .....D 956 984-3700
Frisco (G-7305)

▲ Southwest Elctronic Enrgy Corp .....D 281 240-4000
Missouri City (G-15595)

Spectrum Batteries Inc ....E 281 533-9735
Fulshear (G-7331)

3694 Electrical Eqpt For Internal Combustion Engines

▲ 1a Smart Start LLC ....F 972 621-0252
Grapevine (G-8009)

A & B Auto Electric Inc ....F 713 928-3219
Houston (G-8422)

Alterstart Systems Inc ....G 214 330-2277
Dallas (G-3933)

Android Industries LLC ....D 972 343-3300
Arlington (G-618)

Batteries Concord ....F 281 931-4488
Houston (G-8827)

Borgwarner Pds Anderson LLC .....D 765 778-6499
Laredo (G-13870)

▲ C C Battery Company Inc ....E 361 882-5561
Corpus Christi (G-3492)

Channl-Track Tube-Way Inds Inc .....E 713 864-2551
Houston (G-9162)

Compliant Power Systems LLC .....C 903 427-0071
Clarksville (G-3072)

◆ Delta Electronics (usa) Inc ....C 469 330-9100
Plano (G-16837)

Elamex Usa Corp ....A 915 298-3061
El Paso (G-5748)

▲ Elcom Inc ....F 915 298-2000
El Paso (G-5749)

Englobal Constant Power Inc ....C 713 880-6200
Houston (G-9647)

▲ Fedex Sup Chain Lgstics Elec I .....A 817 491-7700
Fort Worth (G-6626)

▲ Harrison Hydra-Gen Ltd ....E 281 807-4420
Houston (G-10127)

Ignition Systems & Contrls Inc .....E 432 697-6472
Midland (G-15251)

Interconnect Wiring LLP ....C 817 377-9473
Fort Worth (G-6723)

◆ Interstate Batteries Inc ....C 972 991-1444
Dallas (G-4507)

Littelfuse Inc ....D 830 513-8775
Eagle Pass (G-5549)

◆ Manning Navcomp Inc ....F 877 680-1188
Austin (G-1324)

Msdp Group LLC ....F 915 857-5200
El Paso (G-5889)

Mtx Electronics Inc ....F 956 781-3476
Pharr (G-16708)

▲ Pearland Alternator Inc ....E 281 485-8871
Pearland (G-16589)

Penntex Industries Inc ....F 817 589-7501
Fort Worth (G-6900)

Perfect Performance Pdts LLC .....E 817 244-6898
Fort Worth (G-6902)

PHD Energy Inc ....E 800 318-3639
Round Rock (G-17679)

Sam and Sab Inc ....E 713 983-7500
Houston (G-11736)

Solrac Corporation ....B 915 772-3073
El Paso (G-5969)

Standard Motor Products Inc ....E 972 316-8100
Lewisville (G-14093)

Stealth Power LLC ....F 512 306-0088
Austin (G-1534)

Stitt Spark Plug Company Inc ....E 936 441-7796
Conroe (G-3367)

Sumitomo Elc Wirg Systems Inc .....E 210 507-3395
San Antonio (G-18510)

Teledyne Instruments Inc ....C 713 666-2561
Houston (G-12191)

Upex Auto Supply ....F 214 741-2400
Dallas (G-5144)

◆ USA Harness Inc ....D 903 342-3767
Winnsboro (G-20901)

Yazaki North America Inc ....F 618 512-8723
El Paso (G-6041)

3695 Recording Media

Arcube Multimedia Inc ....F 972 267-1800
Richardson (G-17273)

Arcube Optical Mfg LLC ....E 972 267-1800
Plano (G-16792)

At-Integration Inc ....G 512 819-4629
Georgetown (G-7637)

▲ Calrock Music ....D 432 213-8822
Houston (G-9054)

Conetic Software Systems Inc ....E 210 222-9621
San Antonio (G-18023)

▲ Dobbs-Stanford Corporation .....E 214 350-4222
Dallas (G-4269)

Ipcelerate Inc ....F 972 512-7100
Plano (G-16895)

◆ Jelec Inc ....E 713 977-6500
Houston (G-10464)

Simdesk Technologies Inc ....E 713 244-0850
Houston (G-11901)

Smart Imaging Technologies Co .....E 713 589-3500
Houston (G-11918)

Sony Electronics Inc ....C 858 942-2400
Laredo (G-13934)

Stark Holdings Inc ....F 512 329-8109
Austin (G-1531)

Tekvox Inc ....F 512 808-0845
West Lake Hills (G-20689)

Trusource Labs LLC ....E 512 487-7103
Austin (G-1598)

▼ Watchguard Inc ....B 972 423-9777
Allen (G-306)

3699 Electrical Machinery, Eqpt & Splys, NEC

A3im Inc ....F 713 378-7600
Houston (G-8433)

Absolute Cmmnctons Ntwrk Slton .....E 361 888-6776
Corpus Christi (G-3464)

Accent Door Co Inc ....E 913 780-5800
San Antonio (G-17856)

Active Power Inc ....D 512 836-6464
Austin (G-887)

AF Technologies Inc ....C 817 649-2500
Arlington (G-611)

▲ Agilemesh Inc ....F 972 231-2122
Plano (G-16778)

▲ Amgis LLC ....F 832 775-1319
Houston (G-8624)

Andrews Fabrication Inc ....G 281 372-0440
Houston (G-8643)

Appleton Grp LLC ....C 281 774-3700
Houston (G-8665)

◆ Applied Concepts Inc ....C 972 398-3750
Richardson (G-17270)

▲ Applied Optoelectronics Inc .....C 281 295-1800
Sugar Land (G-19445)

▲ Arbin Corporation ....E 979 690-2751
College Station (G-3174)

Assa Abloy Entrance Systems US .....F 713 934-9095
Houston (G-8725)

Atkore Plastic Pipe Corp ....D 817 594-8791
Weatherford (G-20577)

Axent Manufacturing Inc ....E 972 437-3737
Richardson (G-17276)

◆ Azz Inc ....B 817 810-0095
Fort Worth (G-6414)

Azz Inc ....E 281 458-1550
Houston (G-8769)

Azz Inc ....E 817 297-4361
Crowley (G-3751)

Azz Inc ....E 817 284-0119
Fort Worth (G-6415)

Azz Inc ....E 409 842-0216
Beaumont (G-1856)

Azz Inc ....E 713 225-9340
Crowley (G-3752)

Azz Incorporated ....E 817 810-0095
Fort Worth (G-6416)

Branson Ultrasonics Corp ....E 956 729-1550
Laredo (G-13871)

Bsco Inc ....F 817 568-0390
Fort Worth (G-6475)

CF Industries Inc	E	214 460-2804	Lewisville (G-14035)
◆ Champion Industrial Sales Co	G	713 921-7183	Houston (G-9158)
Cnc Precision Manufacturing	E	972 241-4226	Dallas (G-4131)
Compuink	F	281 705-0758	Houston (G-9264)
▲ Compx International Inc	D	972 448-1400	Dallas (G-4154)
Connexa Energy LLC	E	830 995-3600	Comfort (G-3238)
Cooper B-Line Inc	C	903 813-1746	Sherman (G-18913)
Cooper Crouse-Hinds LLC	E	806 358-4585	Amarillo (G-484)
Cooper Crouse-Hinds LLC	F	832 390-3858	Houston (G-9305)
◆ Cordyne Inc	D	713 460-5151	Houston (G-9313)
Craft Wireline Services Inc	F	432 943-5150	Monahans (G-15603)
Crawford Electric Sup Co Inc	E	512 593-4000	Round Rock (G-17638)
▲ CRC-Evans Pipeline Intl Inc	C	800 664-9224	Houston (G-9337)
▲ Crown To Ground Supply Inc	F	936 588-7457	Magnolia (G-14599)
Csi Techs Inc	D	210 875-7978	San Antonio (G-18033)
D Square Inc	F	915 834-6400	El Paso (G-5711)
Dallas Sight and Sound Inc	E	972 392-3202	Dallas (G-4225)
Designed Security Inc	E	512 321-4426	Bastrop (G-1756)
▲ Detex Corporation	D	800 729-3839	New Braunfels (G-15787)
▼ Digiop Technologies Ltd	E	713 333-4900	Houston (G-9470)
Dolan Northwest LLC	E	972 559-6900	Frisco (G-7257)
Door Control Services	F	210 732-1214	Ben Wheeler (G-2032)
▲ Dunan Microstaq Inc	F	512 628-2890	Austin (G-1105)
▲ Easy Protect Inc	E	469 916-1099	Dallas (G-4297)
Eaton Corporation	E	713 849-1600	Houston (G-9572)
Eisenbeck Corporation	F	972 526-5235	Garland (G-7485)
Electric Pwr Systems Intl Inc	E	972 907-3783	Richardson (G-17305)
▲ Electro Technical Inds Inc	D	713 691-5182	Houston (G-9590)
Electronic Drilling Control	D	972 257-0322	Irving (G-13014)
Elite Entrances LLC	E	832 922-7444	Magnolia (G-14603)
Elliott Electric Supply Inc	E	210 646-6950	San Antonio (G-18088)
Emf Company Inc	D	214 350-6848	Dallas (G-4319)
Enterprise SEC Sltons Txas Inc	E	940 320-3778	Justin (G-13343)
Enviro Cams LLC	E	430 255-7006	Kemp (G-13484)
Evco Partners LP	E	409 766-1900	Texas City (G-19793)
Fielder Electric Supply Co Inc	E	281 485-6599	Pearland (G-16560)
Fritel & Associates LLC	E	254 757-1177	Waco (G-20404)
▲ Frl Inc	A	915 633-8354	El Paso (G-5775)
Glo-Jo Electrical Products Inc	E	210 673-3583	San Antonio (G-18144)
Highrise Systems Inc	E	817 927-8711	Fort Worth (G-6697)
Hiller Measurements Inc	C	512 394-8356	Austin (G-863)
Hlcl Capital Corporation	E	972 660-4096	Grand Prairie (G-7892)
Hrh Door Corp	F	915 590-8997	El Paso (G-5805)
Hunnicutt Digital Electronics	E	817 336-5449	Fort Worth (G-6709)
Imfab Inc	E	903 577-0510	Mount Pleasant (G-15651)

Impact Fire Services LLC	D	713 263-7535	Houston (G-10332)
Innovative Idm LLC	E	281 880-2105	Houston (G-10372)
Innovative Idm LLC	E	214 574-9500	Lewisville (G-14056)
Intelligent Surveillance Corp	E	979 323-6900	Forney (G-6310)
Interconnect Wiring LLP	C	817 377-9473	Fort Worth (G-6723)
Kline Technical Consulting LLC	E	505 310-2679	Richmond (G-17460)
L3 Technologies Inc	C	361 516-8396	Kingsville (G-13632)
L3 Technologies Inc	A	817 619-4756	Arlington (G-713)
L3 Technologies Inc	A	903 457-4100	Greenville (G-8080)
L3harris Technologies Inc	A	903 457-7461	Greenville (G-8081)
Laselec Inc	F	817 460-7830	Grand Prairie (G-7908)
▲ Laser Masters Inc	E	832 467-4100	Houston (G-10604)
◆ Laser Shot Inc	D	281 240-1122	Stafford (G-19346)
Link World Trade Inc	C	972 713-8000	Addison (G-145)
Lithotripters Inc	D	888 252-6575	Austin (G-1702)
▲ Lojack Corporation	D	781 302-4200	Richardson (G-17347)
Lone Star Instrmnttion Elc Cor	D	432 368-7827	Odessa (G-16065)
Lone Star INStrmnttn&elctrc	E	817 458-9347	Weatherford (G-20600)
Materia Inc	F	936 295-4040	Huntsville (G-12818)
Maxistrut of Texas Inc	E	713 880-4228	Houston (G-10805)
Mercer Controls Inc	F	361 782-7168	Edna (G-5609)
Mid-Coast Electric Supply Inc	E	830 333-7030	Uvalde (G-20193)
Msf Electric Inc	D	210 781-4112	San Antonio (G-18323)
Msf Electric Inc	E	214 377-8710	Dallas (G-4702)
N L Industries Inc	E	972 233-1700	Dallas (G-4711)
National Swtchgear Systems Inc	E	972 420-0149	Lewisville (G-14071)
Northeast Gate Co Inc	F	903 739-8778	Sumner (G-19608)
Nubocam LLC	E	512 473-0500	West Lake Hills (G-20686)
▲ Ote International Holdings LLC	F	888 666-9361	Athens (G-837)
◆ Overhead Door Corporation	C	469 549-7100	Lewisville (G-14080)
Overhead Door Corporation	B	361 884-6640	Corpus Christi (G-3586)
Pcs Telecom Inc	F	281 469-3367	Pasadena (G-16494)
Powell Electrical Systems Inc	E	713 599-0324	Houston (G-11371)
Power Temp Systems Inc	F	281 617-7889	Houston (G-11379)
Precision M/C Products Inc	F	972 429-6200	Wylie (G-20944)
Pts - Power Temp Systems Inc	F	337 806-9779	Houston (G-11471)
▼ Quinstar Corporation	F	512 326-1011	Austin (G-1445)
R & R Oilfield Services Inc	D	361 289-5892	Corpus Christi (G-3604)
▲ Razberi Technologies Inc	E	469 828-3380	Farmers Branch (G-6212)
Red River Compression Svcs LLC	E	832 831-0532	Houston (G-11569)
Resa Power LLC	E	832 900-8340	Houston (G-11604)
Resideo Technologies Inc	F	512 726-3500	Austin (G-1459)
Rf Identity LLC	F	512 689-1586	Cedar Park (G-2984)
Richmonds American Svc Ctr Inc	F	972 681-2222	McKinney (G-14971)
Risk Management Armored SEC	F	817 932-5923	Alvarado (G-340)

Rivercity Waterjet Inc	F	210 590-0300	San Antonio (G-18428)
Saber Security Systems Inc	F	512 341-8700	Round Rock (G-17688)
Santanna Natural Gas Corp	E	512 346-2500	Austin (G-1710)
Sanwa Electronics USA Corp	G	972 503-3031	Plano (G-17001)
◆ Sanwa Usa Inc	F	972 503-3031	Plano (G-17002)
Satco South 1 LLC	F	361 961-1181	Corpus Christi (G-3616)
Sc-Integrity Inc	E	214 612-7000	Richardson (G-17393)
Schneder Elc Bldngs Amrcas Inc	C	859 243-8254	Laredo (G-13930)
Schneider Electric	F	915 834-6451	El Paso (G-5953)
Schneider Electric	F	956 205-7533	McAllen (G-14905)
Schneider Electric Usa Inc	E	512 295-8060	Buda (G-2537)
▲ Seaboard Controls LLC	E	281 328-8620	Crosby (G-3742)
Secure Control Systems Inc	F	210 530-5245	San Antonio (G-18463)
Simtek Inc	F	817 283-1801	Euless (G-6159)
Specialty Electrical LLC	F	817 355-5315	Fort Worth (G-7009)
Spectrum Technologies USA Inc	F	817 232-2373	Fort Worth (G-7011)
Spike Electric and Contrls LLC	F	832 243-5372	Houston (G-12015)
Spiral X LLC	F	855 346-8823	Garland (G-7590)
Strattec Security Corporation	E	915 790-5400	El Paso (G-5985)
Summit Electric Supply Co Inc	F	325 691-9600	Abilene (G-85)
Sunetics Intl Mktg Group LLC	F	888 266-2232	Plano (G-17014)
◆ Supercircuits Inc	D	877 995-2288	Austin (G-1548)
▲ Svtronics Inc	C	214 440-1234	Plano (G-17017)
▲ Synergy Catalyst LLC	F	248 786-7145	Coppell (G-3449)
▲ T S K Innovations Company	E	915 581-9718	El Paso (G-5991)
T S K Innovations Company	F	915 581-9718	El Paso (G-5992)
Tape Innovations LLC	F	817 568-1212	Fort Worth (G-7034)
Tendenci Inc	E	281 497-6567	Houston (G-12203)
Terra Metrics Ltd	F	432 337-3412	Odessa (G-16174)
Thiel Co	F	817 310-3110	Grapevine (G-8057)
Universal Tech	F	832 584-9460	Floresville (G-6256)
Uptime Solutions Inc	F	214 497-9635	McKinney (G-14993)
Vbi Group LLC	F	817 533-3180	Arlington (G-808)
Veracity USA Incoporated	F	972 786-6771	Dallas (G-5158)
▲ Virtex Assembly Services Inc	D	512 835-6772	Austin (G-1635)
Vistech Corporation	F	972 231-1746	Richardson (G-17423)
WD Norton Inc	F	903 758-0301	Longview (G-14332)
Wesco International Inc	F	432 699-2680	Midland (G-15469)
Yotta Solar Inc	F	512 856-7788	Austin (G-1682)

37 TRANSPORTATION EQUIPMENT

3711 Motor Vehicles & Car Bodies

9650 Nf Ltd	F	281 486-4604	Houston (G-8418)
A J Foyt Enterprises Inc	D	936 372-3698	Waller (G-20489)
▲ ABC Exclusive Inc	D	972 485-8182	Garland (G-7425)
American Honda Motor Co Inc	C	972 929-5444	Irving (G-12930)

SIC

◆ Bae Systems Resolution Inc ....E 713 868-7700
Houston **(G-8789)**

◆ Beck Manufacturing Intl Inc ....D 210 246-7510
Converse **(G-3389)**

Big Shot LLC ....E 504 877-2335
Lancaster **(G-13840)**

Brandfx LLC ....E 817 431-1131
Fort Worth **(G-6468)**

Browns Welding & Manufacturing ....F 830 625-8712
New Braunfels **(G-15776)**

Cgt US Limited ....C 830 627-4800
New Braunfels **(G-15782)**

City of McKinney ....D 972 547-7657
Mc Kinney **(G-14827)**

Conslidated Rigworks LP ....E 817 446-5272
Fort Worth **(G-6543)**

Cool City Inc ....F 940 682-1122
Weatherford **(G-20583)**

Cunningham Automotive Inc ....F 972 900-0405
Lewisville **(G-14039)**

Dunn Automotive Systems LLC ....A 956 283-5544
Fredericksburg **(G-7176)**

East Lake Bucahanan ....F 512 756-4566
Burnet **(G-2606)**

Fabco Industries Inc ....F 432 367-4988
Odessa **(G-15999)**

Fleetpride Inc ....E 800 549-7278
Grapevine **(G-8036)**

▲ Foretravel Inc ....B 936 564-8367
Nacogdoches **(G-15698)**

Frazer Ltd ....C 713 772-5511
Houston **(G-9858)**

General Body Manufacturing Co ....D 713 692-5177
Houston **(G-9920)**

General Motors LLC ....A 512 470-4730
Austin **(G-1181)**

Greg Corkran Enterprises Inc ....E 409 720-9199
Nederland **(G-15753)**

Harwood Industries Inc ....F 903 566-6001
Tyler **(G-20094)**

Hfj Group LLC ....E 833 777-3473
Houston **(G-10168)**

Hub Intrntnal Trnsp Insur Svcs ....F 800 369-9010
San Antonio **(G-18174)**

Lasmer Industries Inc ....F 830 895-4400
Kerrville **(G-13522)**

Lcw Automotive Corp ....E 210 732-5466
San Antonio **(G-18239)**

Lexus Group Inc ....F 682 323-5942
Arlington **(G-720)**

Lippert Components Inc ....D 972 232-3119
Waxahachie **(G-20552)**

Lockheed Martin Corporation ....E 915 852-1100
El Paso **(G-5845)**

Lufkin Industries LLC ....B 936 634-2211
Lufkin **(G-14541)**

Mission Wrecker Service S A ....E 210 341-0333
Converse **(G-3398)**

Nathan Faulk ....F 432 634-9223
Arlington **(G-736)**

Navistar Inc ....E 972 377-1217
Plano **(G-16940)**

Navistar International Corp ....D 972 487-6509
Garland **(G-7560)**

Norwood Equipment Houston Inc ....F 713 670-1320
Houston **(G-11084)**

Paccar Inc ....C 940 566-7100
Denton **(G-5387)**

Paccar Inc ....C 940 591-4000
Denton **(G-5388)**

Paccar Inc ....B 940 566-7752
Corinth **(G-3460)**

◆ Pierce Arrow Inc ....F 940 538-5643
Henrietta **(G-8282)**

Pohaku Classic - Oklahoma LLC ....E 972 840-8660
Garland **(G-7569)**

Pursuit Safety Inc ....F 972 772-4747
Royse City **(G-17724)**

◆ Rescue Rescue LLC ....F 210 648-2722
San Antonio **(G-18421)**

SC Autosports LLC ....F 972 271-0888
Garland **(G-7583)**

Sister2sster Dstiny Trnspt LLC ....F 346 337-6637
Houston **(G-11908)**

Southwest Prof Vehicles ....F 214 371-3474
Dallas **(G-4992)**

▲ Sst Truck Company LLC ....B 972 487-2900
Garland **(G-7591)**

▼ Stewart Stevenson Capitl Corp ....D 713 868-7700
Houston **(G-12063)**

Sub Assembly Group ....F 214 420-8367
Garland **(G-7593)**

▼ Taotao Usa Inc ....F 214 635-3980
Carrollton **(G-2824)**

▼ Texas Armoring Corporation ....F 210 333-0211
San Antonio **(G-18533)**

Thomas Bus Gulf Coast GP Inc ....E 713 580-8600
Houston **(G-12273)**

◆ Toyoda Gsei Brwnsvlle Txas LLC ....F 956 290-8802
Los Indios **(G-14350)**

◆ Toyota Motor North America Inc ....E 469 292-4000
Plano **(G-17036)**

Tymco International Inc ....C 254 799-5546
Waco **(G-20468)**

Versalift East LLC ....C 254 399-2100
Waco **(G-20472)**

Vutex Inc ....C 210 476-1700
San Antonio **(G-18605)**

3713 Truck & Bus Bodies

146 Business Park Inc ....E 281 260-0617
Houston **(G-8401)**

A G Van & Truck Eqp Inc ....E 214 638-8805
Dallas **(G-3870)**

AA Truck Sleeper LLC ....F 817 834-4781
Kennedale **(G-13495)**

Ace Welding and Trailer Co ....E 210 667-1171
San Antonio **(G-17858)**

Ameritrail Inc ....E 281 375-5458
Bellville **(G-2007)**

Automotive Rentals Inc ....E 817 624-3650
Fort Worth **(G-6411)**

Axton LLC ....F 210 637-7400
San Antonio **(G-17925)**

◆ Bae Systems Resolution Inc ....E 713 868-7700
Houston **(G-8789)**

▲ Bridgeport Truck Mfg Inc ....D 254 559-2533
Breckenridge **(G-2227)**

Comprobe Inc ....F 817 293-7333
Fort Worth **(G-6538)**

Crosby Group LLC ....B 918 834-4611
Longview **(G-14216)**

Cruising Kitchens LLC ....E 210 920-2658
San Antonio **(G-18032)**

◆ Dallas Towing and Autonet Inc ....E 972 219-8484
Lewisville **(G-14040)**

Deerskin Mfg Inc ....E 817 220-5535
Springtown **(G-19273)**

Energy Fabrication Inc ....E 432 362-0591
Odessa **(G-15990)**

Everlite Inc ....E 903 297-3444
Longview **(G-14232)**

Fabco Industries Inc ....F 432 367-4988
Odessa **(G-15999)**

General Body Manufacturing Co ....D 713 692-5177
Houston **(G-9920)**

Greg Corkran Enterprises Inc ....E 409 720-9199
Nederland **(G-15753)**

Houston Fab Truck Rigging RPS ....E 713 455-6161
Houston **(G-10233)**

Imperial Group Mfg Inc ....C 940 627-1700
Decatur **(G-5247)**

Industrial Models Inc ....C 940 665-7841
Gainesville **(G-7346)**

◆ J L Roberts Industries Inc ....F 817 831-0676
Fort Worth **(G-6730)**

Jac Enterprises Inc ....F 936 348-3934
Madisonville **(G-14588)**

Kings Truck Beds Inc ....F 940 433-2360
Boyd **(G-2205)**

Leach Trailers LLP ....E 254 687-2616
Itasca **(G-13216)**

Lecolift Inc ....F 713 676-1514
Houston **(G-10613)**

Liddell Industries Inc ....F 325 646-7581
Brownwood **(G-2436)**

Lone Star Body Systems LLC ....F 254 472-0852
Mexia **(G-15090)**

Lufkin Industries LLC ....B 936 634-2211
Lufkin **(G-14541)**

Marmon Highway Tech LLC ....E 214 631-8810
Dallas **(G-4636)**

Mateco Truck Equipment Co ....C 713 692-3888
Houston **(G-10791)**

McNeilus Truck and Mfg Inc ....E 972 225-2313
Hutchins **(G-12868)**

◆ Mobile Specialty Vehicles Inc ....F 409 383-0521
Newton **(G-15864)**

Module Truck Systems Inc ....E 806 783-0777
Lubbock **(G-14448)**

Morgan Truck Body LLC ....D 903 872-7445
Corsicana **(G-3679)**

Navistar Inc ....E 972 377-1217
Plano **(G-16940)**

▲ Norstar Industries LLC ....E 903 784-8900
Brookston **(G-2328)**

Norwood Equipment Houston Inc ....F 713 670-1320
Houston **(G-11084)**

Olivo Enterprises Inc ....D 713 694-3077
Houston **(G-11172)**

▼ Pak-Mor Ltd ....B 830 303-6238
Seguin **(G-18853)**

Proform Group Inc ....E 214 206-4100
Mesquite **(G-15072)**

Progressive Resources Inc ....G 915 778-9548
El Paso **(G-5921)**

▲ Rki Inc ....B 713 688-4414
Houston **(G-11634)**

Rudinger Enterprises Inc ....F 713 939-1234
Houston **(G-11694)**

Rudinger Enterprises Inc ....E 281 356-6219
Houston **(G-11695)**

Saf-Holland Inc ....C 972 442-3556
Wylie **(G-20947)**

▼ Snf Inc ....D 817 402-8040
Fort Worth **(G-6999)**

▲ Sst Truck Company LLC ....B 972 487-2900
Garland **(G-7591)**

▲ Supreme Corporation of Texas ....C 817 641-6282
Cleburne **(G-3111)**

Supreme Corporation of Texas ....C 817 641-8002
Cleburne **(G-3112)**

Synergy Industries LP ....D 817 295-1161
Burleson **(G-2597)**

Temple Freightliner LP ....E 254 770-1422
Temple **(G-19707)**

Texan Waste Equipment Inc ....F 210 224-5800
San Antonio **(G-18531)**

Texas Kenworth Co ....G 940 767-0001
Wichita Falls **(G-20816)**

Tietjen Inc ....E 979 249-3888
La Grange **(G-13703)**

◆ Toyota Mtr Engrg Mfg N Amer In ....C 469 292-1074
Plano **(G-17037)**

Weldon Manufacturing Inc ....F 817 834-2229
Fort Worth **(G-7135)**

Westex Welding Company ....F 254 826-5343
West **(G-20672)**

Youghall Enterprises Inc ....E 325 356-2233
Comanche **(G-3237)**

3714 Motor Vehicle Parts & Access

Adell Corporation ....E 972 226-4600
Mesquite **(G-15024)**

Adient US LLC ....E 210 271-2428
San Antonio **(G-17866)**

Aer Manufacturing Inc ....B 972 417-2582
Schertz **(G-18743)**

Aer Manufacturing Inc ....B 972 418-6499
Carrollton **(G-2694)**

▲ Al Knoch Interiors Inc ....D 915 886-5800
Canutillo **(G-2113)**

Albany Engnered Composites Inc ....D 830 249-4400
Boerne **(G-2113)**

All Star Wheel Repair LLC ....E 972 564-1610
Forney **(G-6302)**

Allen Prfmce Resources Inc ....F 817 270-0102
Azle **(G-1719)**

Alps Electric North Amer Inc ....D 956 217-6500
Mcallen **(G-14835)**

▲ Am-Mex Products Inc ....E 956 631-7916
McAllen **(G-14836)**

▲ American Friction Inc ....F 713 818-5919
Humble **(G-12745)**

Aptiv Services Us LLC ....B 956 366-4600
Los Indios **(G-14349)**

Aptiv Services Us LLC ....C 915 783-4201
Laredo **(G-13859)**

Aptiv Services Us LLC ....E 915 783-4200
El Paso **(G-5646)**

Aptiv Services Us LLC ....C 956 693-3300
Laredo **(G-13860)**

Aptiv Services Us LLC ....E 915 783-4769
El Paso **(G-5647)**

Aptiv Services Us LLC ....F 956 237-9066
Laredo **(G-13861)**

Aptiv Services Us LLC ....E 915 783-4787
El Paso **(G-5648)**

▲ ARA Automotive Systems Inc ....E 214 537-1659
Garland **(G-7440)**

◆ Atco Products Inc ....C 972 842-8178
Ferris (G-6230)
Austin Brake & Clutch Supply ....F 512 836-0482
Austin (G-951)
Auto Kabel North America Inc ....E 915 217-2253
El Paso (G-5654)
▲ Auto Kabel North America Inc ....F 915 217-2253
El Paso (G-5655)
▲ Autoelectric of America Inc ....F 210 402-6003
San Antonio (G-17924)
Aw Texas Inc ....C 210 381-0117
Marion (G-14755)
▲ Behr Service America ....F 817 624-7273
Fort Worth (G-6442)
Bell Experimental Group Inc ....G 830 438-2890
Spring Branch (G-19267)
▲ Bendco Inc ....E 713 473-1557
Pasadena (G-16398)
Beta Engineering Inc ....F 817 265-3367
Arlington (G-631)
Borets US Inc ....E 713 980-4530
Houston (G-8958)
Borgwarner Pds Anderson LLC ....D 765 778-6499
Laredo (G-13870)
Borgwarner Transm Systems LLC ....F 915 217-9268
El Paso (G-5672)
▲ Bracket Systems Inc ....E 817 232-8199
Fort Worth (G-6465)
Brenham Auto Ltd ....F 979 836-4524
Brenham (G-2245)
Bumper Manufacturing Co Inc ....E 817 831-4401
Fort Worth (G-6477)
▲ C C Battery Company Inc ....E 361 882-5561
Corpus Christi (G-3492)
Cadillac Products Inc ....F 248 813-8200
Schertz (G-18747)
Cameron International Corp ....E 806 665-1647
Pampa (G-16318)
Cannon Engineering Inc ....F 818 508-0123
Austin (G-1023)
▼ Chalks Truck Parts Inc ....E 713 672-6344
Houston (G-9153)
Chalks Truck Parts Inc ....F 713 672-6344
Houston (G-9154)
◆ Championx LLC ....A 281 632-6500
Sugar Land (G-19455)
Chromalloy Component Svcs Inc ....C 210 331-2300
San Antonio (G-18005)
Cleanfuel Holdings Inc ....E 512 864-0300
Mason (G-14812)
Component Parts Machine Co Inc ....E 817 834-4771
Fort Worth (G-6534)
▲ Compx International Inc ....D 972 448-1400
Dallas (G-4154)
Continental Auto Systems Inc ....B 847 862-0366
Laredo (G-13875)
Continental Auto Systems Inc ....A 830 372-7000
Seguin (G-18833)
Cooper-Standard Automotive Inc ....F 956 717-3835
Laredo (G-13876)
Covercraft Industries Inc ....D 940 763-2535
Wichita Falls (G-20757)
Cummins Inc ....G 615 986-2596
Arlington (G-652)
Cummins Southern Plains LLC ....E 800 286-6467
Dallas (G-4193)
Cummins Southern Plains LLC ....E 210 655-5420
San Antonio (G-18035)
Cylinder Heads International ....E 972 264-3449
Grand Prairie (G-7861)
▼ D & D Performance Enterprises ....E 817 834-8961
Fort Worth (G-6569)
◆ Dallas Towing and Autonet Inc ....E 972 219-8484
Lewisville (G-14040)
▲ Dallas Westport Inc ....C 214 231-1450
Dallas (G-4230)
Dana Global Products Inc ....G 915 860-7204
El Paso (G-5712)
Dealers Truck Equipment Co Inc ....F 903 758-4451
Longview (G-14223)
Delphi Powertrain Systems LLC ....F 915 783-4733
El Paso (G-5718)
Delphi Powertrain Systems LLC ....E 915 783-4769
El Paso (G-5719)
Dfw Camper Corral Inc ....F 972 241-6443
Dallas (G-4255)
Dlhbowles Inc ....F 410 800-6548
Laredo (G-13881)
▲ Don Hardy Race Cars Inc ....F 806 983-3774
Floydada (G-6292)
Dus Operating Inc ....B 956 371-3057
Brownsville (G-2351)
E & E Engine Machine and Parts ....G 210 225-1141
San Antonio (G-18077)
Eaton Corporation ....B 972 541-0461
Irving (G-13005)
Econtrols LLC ....B 210 495-9772
San Antonio (G-18081)
▲ Econtrols Group Inc ....E 210 495-9772
San Antonio (G-18082)
Emissions Technology Inc ....F 713 691-1211
Houston (G-9616)
EMLS Incorporated ....C 940 566-9500
Denton (G-5364)
Enduro Products Inc ....E 817 704-7346
Arlington (G-670)
Faurecia Exhaust Systems Inc ....C 812 314-5995
Arlington (G-677)
▲ Fedex Sup Chain Lgstics Elec I ....A 817 491-7700
Fort Worth (G-6626)
Fisher & Company Incorporated ....E 586 746-1961
Brownsville (G-2357)
Flex-N-Gate Texas LLC ....E 817 652-3400
Grand Prairie (G-7874)
▲ Flex-N-Gate Texas LLC ....E 817 652-3400
Grand Prairie (G-7875)
Forbes Rbuilt Automitive Parts ....F 817 332-7643
Fort Worth (G-6640)
Forma Automotive LLC ....F 210 212-4400
San Antonio (G-18122)
Forma Automotive LLC ....F 210 888-0410
San Antonio (G-18123)
Frankenstein Racing Heads LLC ....E 817 556-2434
Weatherford (G-20594)
General Motors LLC ....A 817 652-2182
Arlington (G-691)
◆ Gentherm (texas) Inc ....D 830 774-3512
Del Rio (G-5315)
◆ Go Industries Inc ....E 972 783-7444
Richardson (G-17323)
Grooms & Grooms Inc ....G 806 358-8119
Amarillo (G-490)
◆ Hart Heat Transfer Pdts Inc ....D 713 675-9848
Houston (G-10133)
Harwood Industries Inc ....E 903 566-6001
Tyler (G-20094)
Hilite Industries Auto LP ....D 972 242-2116
Carrollton (G-2757)
Hilite Industries Inc ....E 972 242-2116
Dallas (G-4457)
Hilite International Inc ....B 972 242-2116
Carrollton (G-2758)
▲ Hilite International Inc ....F 972 242-2116
Carrollton (G-2759)
Honeywell International Inc ....A 281 890-0088
Cypress (G-3801)
Horizon Global Americas Inc ....F 915 545-2720
El Paso (G-5804)
Hunton Group Inc ....F 806 788-1100
Houston (G-10286)
Imperial Group Mfg Inc ....C 940 627-1700
Decatur (G-5247)
Insight Equity A P X L P ....F 817 488-7775
Southlake (G-19075)
Insight Equity LP ....E 817 488-7775
Southlake (G-19076)
Inteva Products LLC ....B 248 655-8777
Brownsville (G-2365)
J&J Weaver Co ....E 254 756-2139
Waco (G-20419)
Johnson Controls Inc ....C 956 782-3000
Mcallen (G-14881)
K & N Engineering Inc ....E 951 826-0000
Grand Prairie (G-7904)
Kaspar Ranch Hand Eqp LLC ....C 361 594-4608
Shiner (G-18942)
Kautex Inc ....E 210 229-2300
San Antonio (G-18218)
Keiser Manufacturing Inc ....G 830 303-3397
Seguin (G-18846)
▲ Kongsberg Pwr Prod Systems I ....C 936 856-2971
Willis (G-20852)
L & L Products Inc ....F 972 475-5202
Rowlett (G-17709)
Lay Cooley RE Holdings 1 LLC ....E 972 721-4500
Irving (G-13084)
Lear Corporation ....B 915 791-5400
El Paso (G-5841)
Lear Corporation ....B 915 307-9237
El Paso (G-5842)
Lear Corporation ....B 915 787-5012
El Paso (G-5843)
Lear Corporation ....B 817 419-3000
Grand Prairie (G-7910)
Lear Siegler Logistics Intl ....F 210 490-0267
San Antonio (G-18240)
Lear Trim LP ....E 915 849-5660
El Paso (G-5844)
M P N Inc ....F 972 227-1210
Lancaster (G-13846)
Mahle Behr Mfg MGT Inc ....F 915 783-4213
El Paso (G-5860)
Mahle Behr Mfg MGT Inc ....F 248 735-3623
El Paso (G-5861)
Mahle Behr Mfg MGT Inc ....F 248 735-3623
Laredo (G-13908)
▲ Mahle Behr Service America LLC ....E 817 624-7273
Fort Worth (G-6806)
▲ Maremont Exhaust Products Inc ....C 865 458-4681
Schulenburg (G-18776)
Marmon Highway Tech LLC ....E 214 631-8810
Dallas (G-4636)
Mast Motorsports LLC ....E 936 560-2218
Nacogdoches (G-15703)
Matek Performance Inc ....E 817 626-9006
Fort Worth (G-6816)
McMt LLC ....F 903 592-9663
Tyler (G-20121)
Metalsa Light Truck Inc ....F 210 242-3403
San Antonio (G-18293)
▲ Michex International Inc ....F 281 397-7770
Houston (G-10866)
Modern Welding Co Texas Inc ....E 713 675-4211
Houston (G-10905)
▲ Mw Supply Inc ....D 254 897-4590
Glen Rose (G-7732)
▲ Nat G CNG Solutions LLC ....F 281 954-4600
Houston (G-10963)
Nat G CNG Solutions LLC ....F 512 998-9316
Converse (G-3399)
New Concept Services Inc ....F 903 342-5523
Winnsboro (G-20900)
▲ Nichirin-Flex USA Inc ....B 915 859-1199
El Paso (G-5896)
▲ Nitrous Express Inc ....F 940 767-7694
Wichita Falls (G-20786)
▲ North American Atk Corporation ....D 972 647-1400
Grand Prairie (G-7936)
Northeast Texas Hydraulics ....F 903 582-2692
Sulphur Springs (G-19593)
▲ Northwest Drive Train Inc ....F 713 937-8499
Jersey Village (G-13302)
▲ P&H Sales Ltd ....E 817 468-3850
Arlington (G-745)
▲ Pearland Alternator Inc ....E 281 485-8871
Pearland (G-16589)
◆ PEC Manufacturing ....F 830 693-7879
Marble Falls (G-14749)
Phillips Iron Works Inc ....E 337 364-2337
Houston (G-11327)
◆ Pierce Arrow Inc ....F 940 538-5643
Henrietta (G-8282)
Polar Corporation ....D 972 635-2464
Royse City (G-17722)
▲ Pollok Inc ....A 915 592-5700
El Paso (G-5914)
Pressure Systems International ....D 210 222-1926
San Antonio (G-18394)
◆ Quality Trailer Products LP ....D 817 444-4518
Azle (G-1728)
Regis Manufacturing Company ....F 214 421-5171
Dallas (G-4884)
▼ Reher-Morrison Racing Engines ....E 817 467-7171
Arlington (G-770)
▲ Reyes Automotive Group LLC ....C 210 228-2500
San Antonio (G-18423)
Reyes Automotive Group II LLC ....C 210 228-2500
San Antonio (G-18424)
▲ Road Kare International LP ....E 972 647-8300
Grand Prairie (G-7967)
Robert Bosch Auto Steering LLC ....E 956 857-4436
Laredo (G-13924)
Robert Bosch LLC ....F 956 753-6082
Laredo (G-13925)
Rough Country Accessories ....F 325 365-5258
Ballinger (G-1742)
Saf-Holland Inc ....C 972 442-3556
Wylie (G-20947)
◆ Sanden International USA Inc ....A 972 442-8400
Wylie (G-20948)

S I C

▲ Santech Industries LLC ....E 817 589-1212
Irving (G-13172)

Schrader Electronics Limited ....B ... 817 608-2289
Fort Worth (G-6979)

Service Electric Supply Inc ....F ... 972 620-2821
Dallas (G-4949)

Skledar-Greene LLC ....F 817 454-4214
Krum (G-13676)

Solrac Corporation ....B ... 915 772-3073
El Paso (G-5969)

Solution Tech Harn Group LLC ....E ... 214 221-0323
Dallas (G-4978)

▲ Standard Industrial Pdts Co ....E ... 281 280-0147
Webster (G-20647)

Standard Motor Products Inc ....C ... 972 316-8100
Lewisville (G-14094)

Standard Motor Products Inc ....C ... 972 316-8100
Lewisville (G-14095)

▼ Stemco Products Inc ....F 903 758-9981
Longview (G-14312)

Stoneridge Inc ....B ... 915 778-1331
El Paso (G-5983)

▲ Stoneridge Electronics Inc ....A ... 915 621-6111
El Paso (G-5984)

Strong Concrete Services Inc ....E ... 281 847-9304
Houston (G-12080)

Strong Industries Inc ....E ... 281 448-9315
Houston (G-12081)

Sumitomo Elc Wirg Systems Inc ....F ... 915 859-0555
El Paso (G-5987)

Sunshine Machine Inc ....F ... 281 445-0326
Houston (G-12103)

Superior Cooling Services Inc ....E ... 214 637-2162
Dallas (G-5025)

Techsys Chassis Inc ....E ... 903 395-4155
Paris (G-16371)

Tenneco Automotive Oper Co Inc ....E ... 210 304-9390
San Antonio (G-18528)

Tenneco Automotive Oper Co Inc ....C ... 979 691-7732
College Station (G-3203)

Tenneco Inc ....A ... 915 832-4661
El Paso (G-5997)

Texas Saddlebags Inc ....D ... 817 649-2626
Arlington (G-793)

Texas Spa Covers Inc ....G ... 512 756-2043
Burnet (G-2616)

TI Group Auto Systems LLC ....E ... 956 686-5400
McAllen (G-14912)

Tianhai Electric N Amer Inc ....E ... 915 881-9740
El Paso (G-6004)

Tietjen Inc ....E ... 979 249-3888
La Grange (G-13703)

Top Quality Spindles LLC ....F ... 972 937-2126
Waxahachie (G-20566)

Torqon Inc ....F ... 956 546-3239
Brownsville (G-2414)

▲ Toyoda Gosei Texas LLC ....C ... 210 302-4600
San Antonio (G-18556)

Toyota Motor North America Inc ....E ... 859 746-4351
Plano (G-17035)

Toyotetsu Texas Inc ....D ... 210 231-5515
San Antonio (G-18557)

▲ Trans-Texas Tire LLC ....E ... 903 572-0267
Mount Pleasant (G-15664)

Trey Industry SW ....E ... 915 591-5100
El Paso (G-6015)

◆ Trico Technologies Corporation ....C ... 956 544-2722
Brownsville (G-2416)

Truckpro LLC ....F ... 512 836-0482
Austin (G-1597)

◆ TYG Products LP ....D ... 972 542-1828
McKinney (G-14984)

United States Steel Corp ....D ... 903 656-6521
Lone Star (G-14185)

Veeder-Root Fuelquest LLC ....F ... 713 222-5700
Houston (G-12544)

▲ Victory Climate Systems LLC ....C ... 817 293-3331
Fort Worth (G-7105)

▲ Vintage Air Inc ....D ... 210 296-2302
San Antonio (G-18648)

Vitesco Technologies Usa LLC ....A ... 830 379-8850
Seguin (G-18872)

Warner Electric LLC ....D ... 940 723-3400
Wichita Falls (G-20828)

▼ Watson & Chalin Holding Corp ....E ... 972 547-6020
McKinney (G-14988)

▲ Watson & Chalin Mfg Inc ....D ... 972 547-6020
McKinney (G-14989)

Wells Vehicle Electronics LP ....C ... 956 630-4310
McAllen (G-14918)

Westport Innovations (us) ....F ... 214 231-1450
Dallas (G-5183)

Xerxes Corporation ....E ... 830 372-0090
Seguin (G-18875)

Xtreme Force Inc ....F ... 281 397-0073
Houston (G-12710)

Youngs Tank Incorporated ....E ... 800 345-7952
Boyd (G-2210)

ZF Elec Sys Plsnt Praire LLC ....F ... 915 790-5000
El Paso (G-6042)

ZF Passive Safety Systems US ....E ... 956 566-7680
Pharr (G-16717)

ZF Passive Safety US Inc ....E ... 956 632-8100
Pharr (G-16718)

ZF Passive Safety US Inc ....B ... 734 582-1139
El Paso (G-6043)

ZF TRW Auto Holdings Corp ....D ... 956 632-8100
Pharr (G-16719)

3715 Truck Trailers

1-Fast Rspnse Rntals Oil Feld ....D ... 210 437-2473
San Antonio (G-17844)

81 Trucking Services LLC ....F ... 713 259-1076
Houston (G-8415)

American Trailer Works Inc ....F ... 817 328-3686
Southlake (G-19058)

Beall Construction Company Inc ....D ... 325 677-2112
Abilene (G-16)

Blue Horse Express LLC ....E ... 832 966-1053
Cypress (G-3780)

Brazos Trailer Mfg LLC ....E ... 903 873-8130
Wills Point (G-20874)

◆ Bright Coop Inc ....C ... 936 564-8378
Nacogdoches (G-15686)

Buck Dandy Co ....E ... 903 784-6362
Sumner (G-19606)

C & S Trucking ....F ... 817 517-9172
Cleburne (G-3082)

Centerline Trailers Inc ....F ... 817 477-5533
Mansfield (G-14659)

Chase Transportation LLC ....E ... 915 307-5488
Horizon City (G-8363)

Compass Conversions LLC ....E ... 254 771-9909
Temple (G-19677)

Energy Fabrication Inc ....E ... 432 362-0591
Odessa (G-15990)

Everlite Inc ....E ... 903 297-3444
Longview (G-14232)

Factory Motorhomes Inc ....F ... 214 830-2910
Terrell (G-19733)

Fort Worth Fabrication Inc ....F ... 817 625-2321
Fort Worth (G-6643)

General Body Manufacturing Co ....D ... 713 692-5177
Houston (G-9920)

Great Dane LLC ....E ... 713 675-6577
Houston (G-10025)

Great Dane LLC ....F ... 214 637-2425
Dallas (G-4414)

Heil Trailer International LLC ....C ... 254 865-7235
Gatesville (G-7618)

HP Car Accessories & Atv Sales ....F ... 903 675-0032
Athens (G-828)

Imperial Group Mfg Inc ....A ... 940 565-8505
Denton (G-5376)

Imperial Group Mfg Inc ....D ... 940 627-1700
Decatur (G-5247)

International Flatbed Svcs Inc ....F ... 915 858-1200
El Paso (G-5814)

Iron Ram Services LLC ....E ... 361 241-2346
Corpus Christi (G-3557)

Jac Enterprises Inc ....F ... 936 348-3997
Madisonville (G-14587)

◆ Ledwell & Son Enterprises Inc ....C ... 903 838-6531
Texarkana (G-19768)

Lee Dill Inc ....D ... 325 677-0474
Abilene (G-56)

Lufkin Industries LLC ....B ... 936 634-2211
Lufkin (G-14541)

Mac Trailer Texas Inc ....D ... 330 956-0171
Rhome (G-17257)

▲ Magnum Custom Trlr Mfg Co Inc ....D ... 512 258-4101
Austin (G-1318)

Magnum Custom Trlr Mfg Co Inc ....F ... 512 258-4101
San Antonio (G-18271)

Maposa Tinashe ....F ... 512 704-4601
Leander (G-13995)

Mate Inc ....E ... 281 855-0045
Houston (G-10790)

Odom Trailer Mfg Co Inc ....F ... 936 756-3910
Conroe (G-3345)

Opulent Transport LLC ....E ... 713 551-1445
Houston (G-11186)

Performax Custom Trailers ....F ... 972 442-3527
Wylie (G-20942)

Portersville Sales & Testing ....E ... 806 373-6811
Amarillo (G-507)

◆ Pt Trucks Inc ....E ... 713 338-1375
Houston (G-11470)

Pull Rite Trailers LLC ....F ... 903 502-5000
Murchison (G-15681)

Randy Myers Enterprises Inc ....E ... 903 897-0681
Naples (G-15720)

Rising S Company LLC ....E ... 214 455-0560
Murchison (G-15682)

Spotted Lakes LLC ....C ... 817 441-9900
Weatherford (G-20621)

Techsys Chassis Inc ....E ... 903 395-4155
Paris (G-16371)

Texas Kenworth Co ....G ... 940 767-0001
Wichita Falls (G-20816)

▲ Texas Underground Inc ....D ... 281 485-9900
Pearland (G-16602)

Trailers By Southern LLC ....E ... 469 517-0410
Joshua (G-13327)

Travis Body and Trailer Inc ....D ... 713 466-5888
Houston (G-12356)

Tsi Flow Products Inc ....F ... 903 984-2870
Kilgore (G-13597)

USI Integrated Trnsp LLC ....E ... 956 781-6606
Pharr (G-16714)

Van Nu Technology Inc ....D ... 817 276-3300
Mansfield (G-14727)

Wabash National Trlr Ctrs Inc ....F ... 972 923-2200
Waxahachie (G-20567)

Wellco Holdings Inc ....D ... 254 772-1740
Waco (G-20477)

Wes-Tex Manufacturing Inc ....F ... 806 749-3795
Lubbock (G-14509)

Western Sls Tstg Amarillo Inc ....E ... 806 373-6811
Amarillo (G-522)

3716 Motor Homes

Coachworks LLC ....E ... 830 510-4224
Pipe Creek (G-16741)

Factory Motorhomes Inc ....F ... 214 830-2910
Terrell (G-19733)

▲ Foretravel Inc ....B ... 936 564-8367
Nacogdoches (G-15698)

3721 Aircraft

Ace Aeronautics LLC ....F ... 972 641-0835
Grand Prairie (G-7821)

Aero Brigham LLC ....F ... 940 626-4849
Decatur (G-5240)

Aerostar International Inc ....E ... 903 885-0728
Sulphur Springs (G-19578)

◆ Airbus Helicopters Inc ....B ... 972 641-0000
Grand Prairie (G-7824)

AVX Aircraft Company ....E ... 817 731-8003
Benbrook (G-2038)

B R L Consultants Inc ....F ... 210 341-3442
San Antonio (G-17934)

Be-Technologies Ltd ....F ... 972 242-1853
Carrollton (G-2704)

Bell Textron Inc ....C ... 817 280-2011
Fort Worth (G-6445)

Bell Textron Inc ....F ... 817 280-1587
Hurst (G-12837)

◆ Bell Textron Inc ....A ... 817 280-2011
Fort Worth (G-6444)

Bell Textron Services Inc ....F ... 817 280-2011
Fort Worth (G-6446)

Boeing Arospc Operations Inc ....A ... 210 932-6990
San Antonio (G-17960)

Boeing Company ....A ... 281 226-4000
Houston (G-8939)

Boeing Company ....A ... 281 226-4057
Houston (G-8940)

Boeing Company ....A ... 210 677-0900
San Antonio (G-17961)

Boeing Company ....B ... 972 491-5442
Plano (G-16808)

Boeing Company ....A ... 936 756-0505
Conroe (G-3263)

Boeing Company ....B ... 713 658-0831
Houston (G-8941)

Boeing Company ....A ... 915 834-1000
El Paso (G-5665)

Boeing Company ....A ... 972 344-7249
Richardson (G-17280)

Boeing Company ....B 281 244-3056
  Houston *(G-8943)*
Boeing Company ....D 281 226-4000
  Houston *(G-8944)*
Boeing Company ....F 325 696-5771
  Abilene *(G-21)*
◆ Bombardier Aerospace Corp ....F 972 960-3810
  Dallas *(G-4040)*
Bombardier Services Corp ....D 214 331-9400
  Dallas *(G-4041)*
Broadwing Aviation LLC ....E 817 332-0011
  Fort Worth *(G-6472)*
Carter Aerospace Dev LLC ....F 940 691-0819
  Wichita Falls *(G-20750)*
Cockrell Resources Inc ....E 713 454-1400
  Houston *(G-9236)*
Dean Baldwin Pntg Ltd Partnr ....E 210 293-3528
  San Antonio *(G-18045)*
▲ Draken International LLC ....E 863 289-0849
  Fort Worth *(G-6593)*
▲ Evans Composites Inc ....E 817 477-9014
  Mansfield *(G-14670)*
Gulfstream Aerospace Corp ....A 912 965-3000
  Dallas *(G-4422)*
Gulfstream Aerospace Corp ....A 972 899-1625
  Coppell *(G-3418)*
Gulfstream Aerospace Corp ....A 214 902-7520
  Dallas *(G-4423)*
Gulfstream Aerospace Corp GA ....A 214 350-4177
  Dallas *(G-4424)*
H6 Aircraft LLC ....F 830 741-3836
  D Hanis *(G-3829)*
Harris Composites Inc ....E 817 279-9546
  Granbury *(G-7799)*
Interntnal Arospc Coatings Inc ....F 806 335-2616
  Amarillo *(G-440)*
Jaffe Group Ltd ....E 830 598-2413
  Horseshoe Bay *(G-8368)*
Learjet Inc ....A 972 720-2400
  Richardson *(G-17341)*
▲ Legend Aircraft Mfg LP ....E 903 885-7000
  Sulphur Springs *(G-19591)*
Lockheed Martin Corporation ....C 956 425-4447
  Harlingen *(G-8193)*
Lockheed Martin Corporation ....A 972 603-1000
  Grand Prairie *(G-7914)*
Lockheed Martin Corporation ....E 915 852-1100
  El Paso *(G-5845)*
Lockheed Martin Corporation ....D 817 777-2000
  Benbrook *(G-2042)*
Lockheed Martin Corporation ....B 817 777-2000
  Fort Worth *(G-6798)*
M1 Support Services LP ....D 940 323-1119
  Denton *(G-5379)*
Martin Uav LLC ....E 972 381-2750
  Plano *(G-16919)*
Mooney Aerospace Group Ltd ....E 830 896-6000
  Kerrville *(G-13524)*
Mooney Airplane Company Inc ....B 830 896-6000
  Kerrville *(G-13525)*
Olaeris Inc ....F 877 750-5500
  Burleson *(G-2592)*
R & B Electronics Inc ....E 906 632-1542
  Grand Prairie *(G-7961)*
Rf Manufacturing LLC ....E 817 479-1950
  Haltom City *(G-8157)*
Sabre Sentinel Intl LLC ....E 972 529-6570
  McKinney *(G-14973)*
Schweizer Rsg LLC ....F 817 405-2100
  Fort Worth *(G-6980)*
▲ Seven Q Seven Ltd ....E 210 930-4040
  San Antonio *(G-18467)*
▲ Sierra Industries Ltd ....D 210 805-3188
  San Antonio *(G-18472)*
Skyway Group Inc ....F 830 278-4481
  Uvalde *(G-20196)*
Taylor - Deal Aviation LLC ....D 972 220-0943
  Irving *(G-13191)*
Textron Inc ....D 210 229-2303
  San Antonio *(G-18546)*
▲ Triumph Aerostructures LLC ....A 972 515-8276
  Red Oak *(G-17237)*
Valkyrie Systems Aerospace Inc ....F 888 426-2113
  Dallas *(G-3857)*
Vanguard Defense Inds LLC ....F 281 298-6672
  Spring *(G-19184)*
Velocity Aerospace Group Inc ....E 214 988-9898
  Frisco *(G-7322)*
Vertex Aerospace LLC ....F 210 652-4541
  Randolph *(G-17230)*

Vertex Aerospace LLC ....E 210 652-6717
  Universal City *(G-20185)*
W T Porter Corp ....G 713 946-4174
  South Houston *(G-19056)*

3724 Aircraft Engines & Engine Parts

Addison Jet Maintenance Inc ....F 972 559-1000
  Addison *(G-99)*
Aero Capital Solutions Inc ....E 737 717-0624
  Austin *(G-898)*
Aeromax Industries Inc ....F 818 701-9500
  Fort Worth *(G-6352)*
▲ Aircraft Engine & Accessory Co ....F 972 243-7404
  Dallas *(G-3910)*
Aviation Products Inc ....E 817 457-2040
  Fort Worth *(G-6413)*
BP Aero Engine Services LLC ....E 972 252-2800
  Irving *(G-12951)*
Broadwing Aviation LLC ....E 817 332-0011
  Fort Worth *(G-6472)*
▲ Chromalloy Component Svcs Inc ...E 210 331-2300
  San Antonio *(G-18006)*
Chromalloy Gas Turbine LLC ....F 972 241-2501
  Dallas *(G-4114)*
D & D Machinery and Sales Inc ....F 830 438-2309
  San Antonio *(G-18039)*
Dallas Airmotive Inc ....B 214 956-2505
  Dallas *(G-4211)*
Fore Machine LLC ....D 817 834-6251
  Haltom City *(G-8141)*
▲ GE Engine Svcs - McAllen L P ....A 956 971-5200
  McAllen *(G-14864)*
General Electric Company ....G 325 794-5100
  Abilene *(G-43)*
Honeywell Enraf Americas Inc ....F 281 885-7979
  Houston *(G-10199)*
Honeywell International Inc ....B 713 780-6500
  Houston *(G-10200)*
Honeywell International Inc ....B 972 792-1800
  Richardson *(G-17329)*
Honeywell International Inc ....A 361 937-1082
  Corpus Christi *(G-3551)*
Honeywell International Inc ....A 817 215-9800
  Mansfield *(G-14682)*
Honeywell International Inc ....D 480 353-4053
  El Paso *(G-5797)*
Honeywell International Inc ....E 979 491-2802
  Old Ocean *(G-16217)*
Honeywell International Inc ....C 480 592-2047
  El Paso *(G-5798)*
Honeywell International Inc ....E 915 778-7401
  El Paso *(G-5799)*
Honeywell International Inc ....A 281 890-0088
  Cypress *(G-3801)*
Honeywell International Inc ....E 915 544-6634
  El Paso *(G-5800)*
Honeywell International Inc ....F 480 592-2052
  El Paso *(G-5801)*
Honeywell International Inc ....E 480 592-7380
  El Paso *(G-5802)*
Honeywell International Inc ....D 972 896-0004
  Dallas *(G-4465)*
Honeywell International Inc ....A 717 771-8100
  El Paso *(G-5803)*
Honeywell International Inc ....E 281 444-2282
  Houston *(G-10202)*
Honeywell International Inc ....C 512 301-8414
  Austin *(G-1208)*
Honeywell International Inc ....E 409 833-4601
  Beaumont *(G-1904)*
International Airmotive Holdg ....F 214 956-3000
  Grapevine *(G-8043)*
Jet Learning Laboratory Inc ....E 713 524-6284
  Houston *(G-10468)*
L3 Technologies Inc ....C 512 251-3441
  Austin *(G-1279)*
Lobo Ventures Ltd ....E 210 525-9595
  San Antonio *(G-18256)*
M W Butler Company ....F 817 572-3306
  Burleson *(G-2589)*
Mooney Airplane Company Inc ....B 830 896-6000
  Kerrville *(G-13525)*
Mt Texas LLC ....E 210 599-0060
  San Antonio *(G-18324)*
Page Chester Ltd ....C 817 624-4001
  Fort Worth *(G-6890)*
▲ Pantex Ennerflo Systems Inc ....E 832 861-7700
  Houston *(G-8390)*
Polytrnix McHning Fbrction LLC ....F 972 436-0422
  Richardson *(G-17374)*

Pratt & Whitney Eng Svcs Inc ....B 972 343-1300
  Grand Prairie *(G-7952)*
Prime Turbines LLC ....E 972 406-2100
  Carrollton *(G-2797)*
Qsfirst Inc ....F 210 362-1983
  San Antonio *(G-18403)*
Quality Honeycomb LP ....E 817 640-1190
  Arlington *(G-765)*
Ranger Air Aviation LLC ....F 972 245-6699
  Lewisville *(G-14087)*
Raytheon Technologies Corp ....B 210 680-0283
  San Antonio *(G-18410)*
Raytheon Technologies Corp ....C 940 761-9200
  Wichita Falls *(G-20801)*
Safran Helicopter Engines USA ....E 972 606-7600
  Grand Prairie *(G-7969)*
Safran Usa Inc ....E 469 941-8150
  Irving *(G-13170)*
▲ Seven Q Seven Ltd ....E 210 930-4040
  San Antonio *(G-18467)*
▲ Sierra Industries Ltd ....D 210 805-3188
  San Antonio *(G-18472)*
Sunbelt Design & Dev Inc ....D 210 227-9162
  San Antonio *(G-18511)*
▲ Superior Air Parts Inc ....E 800 420-4727
  Coppell *(G-3447)*
Techmar Industries LLC ....F 832 246-6200
  Spring *(G-19175)*
Texas Almet LP ....D 817 649-7056
  Arlington *(G-791)*
Triumph Accssory Svcs - Grnd P ....D 972 623-9300
  Grand Prairie *(G-7986)*
Triumph Group Inc ....E 817 804-9400
  Arlington *(G-804)*
Tru ....E 254 831-6002
  Belton *(G-2029)*
Vanguard Defense Inds LLC ....F 281 298-6672
  Spring *(G-19184)*
▲ Wood Group Power Gp LLC ....E 281 828-3500
  Houston *(G-12686)*

3728 Aircraft Parts & Eqpt, NEC

▲ ACC-Kp LLC ....D 972 407-1234
  Addison *(G-98)*
Acerts Inc ....F 866 938-5599
  Southlake *(G-19057)*
Advanced Integration Tech GP ....E 972 522-6363
  Grand Prairie *(G-7822)*
▲ Advanced Integration Tech Inc ......C 972 423-8354
  Plano *(G-16772)*
Advanced Integration Tech LP ....D 972 423-8354
  Plano *(G-16773)*
Advanced Integration Tech LP ....E 210 762-3777
  San Antonio *(G-17868)*
Advanced Integration Tech SA ....A 210 762-3777
  San Antonio *(G-17869)*
Advantage Aviation Tech ....E 972 647-7300
  Dallas *(G-3892)*
Advantage Aviation Tech II LLC ....E 972 647-7300
  Dallas *(G-3893)*
Aereos Inc ....D 817 267-1371
  Euless *(G-6126)*
Aero Components LLC ....D 817 834-6251
  Fort Worth *(G-6351)*
Aero Composites Structures Inc ....F 972 694-5330
  Carrollton *(G-2695)*
Aero Dynamix Inc ....D 817 571-0729
  Euless *(G-6127)*
◆ Aerospace & Coml Tech Inc ....E 817 560-6600
  Fort Worth *(G-6353)*
Aerospace Fasteners Inc ....E 903 723-0693
  Palestine *(G-16295)*
Aerospace Products SE Inc ....F 210 924-2907
  San Antonio *(G-17873)*
Aerotech Engineering Inc ....E 817 267-1371
  Euless *(G-6128)*
Aeroxchange Ltd ....E 972 556-8500
  Farmers Branch *(G-6185)*
AGH Industries Inc ....E 817 284-1742
  Euless *(G-6129)*
◆ Air Power Inc ....E 817 557-5855
  Arlington *(G-613)*
Airco Industries, Inc. ....D 817 332-3806
  Fort Worth *(G-6358)*
▲ Aircraft Engine & Accessory Co .....F 972 243-7404
  Dallas *(G-3910)*
Aircraft On Ground LLC ....E 214 350-5334
  San Antonio *(G-17877)*
▲ Aircraft Technologies Inc ....E 210 590-6858
  San Antonio *(G-17878)*

S
I
C

Airtech Supply Inc ....E 501 525-7707
North Richland Hills (G-15873)

Albany Engnered Composites Inc........D 830 249-4400
Boerne (G-2113)

Alcocer LLC ....D 210 930-4580
San Antonio (G-17889)

Alcor Inc ....F 210 349-6491
San Antonio (G-17890)

American Armtive Cmponents Inc ....E 281 442-7791
Houston (G-8585)

Applied Avionics Inc ....D 817 451-1141
Fort Worth (G-6392)

Arlington Intl AVI Pdts LLC ....E 817 465-9880
Arlington (G-625)

Aviation Dvces Elctrnic Cmpnnts ....E 817 738-9161
Fort Worth (G-6412)

Bae Systems Inc ....D 512 276-3100
Austin (G-972)

Be-Technologies Ltd ....F 972 242-1853
Carrollton (G-2704)

Bell Boeing Joint Project Off ....E 301 866-6835
Amarillo (G-403)

Bell Helicopter Textron Inc ....F 806 341-3400
Amarillo (G-404)

Bell Helicopter Textron Inc ....F 817 280-4700
Amarillo (G-405)

Bell Textron Inc ....E 817 837-4700
Fort Worth (G-6443)

Bell Textron Inc ....F 817 280-1587
Hurst (G-12837)

Bell Textron Inc ....C 817 280-2011
Austin (G-987)

Bell Textron Inc ....D 817 280-2011
Grand Prairie (G-7845)

◆ Bell Textron Inc ....A 817 280-2011
Fort Worth (G-6444)

Bell Textron Inc ....E 817 280-2011
Hurst (G-12838)

Bell Textron Inc ....C 806 341-3400
Amarillo (G-406)

Bell Textron Inc ....D 817 280-2011
Hurst (G-12839)

Bell Textron Inc ....C 806 341-3400
Amarillo (G-407)

Bell Textron Services Inc ....F 817 280-2011
Fort Worth (G-6446)

Benz Companies Ltd ....F 817 280-0000
Fort Worth (G-6447)

Berry Machine Shop ....E 817 572-0948
Burleson (G-2571)

Beta Engineering Inc ....F 817 265-3367
Arlington (G-631)

Blackhawk Modifications Inc ....E 254 755-6711
Waco (G-20369)

Blackland Aerospace LP ....C 972 980-5970
Dallas (G-4028)

◆ BP Aerospace LLC ....D 972 252-2800
Irving (G-12952)

Broadwing Aviation LLC ....E 817 332-0011
Fort Worth (G-6472)

C & F Tool & Die Co LLC ....E 210 522-9310
San Antonio (G-17975)

Calcomp Inc ....E 817 862-9311
Fort Worth (G-6486)

Calkins Aero Service Inc ....F 281 579-6674
Houston (G-9050)

Can-AM Aero Support LLC ....D 281 810-4400
Houston (G-9084)

▲ Century Components Corporation ....F 817 831-8301
Fort Worth (G-6505)

▼ Coastal Mechanics Company Inc .....C 713 784-0111
Houston (G-9227)

▲ Composite Technology Inc ....E 972 456-6900
Dallas (G-4151)

Comsovereign Holding Corp ....E 469 930-2661
Dallas (G-4155)

Contract Fabrication ....E 972 736-2260
Princeton (G-17206)

Crown Aerospace Inc ....F 281 351-7068
Tomball (G-19972)

Cw Aerotech Services ....F 817 595-1949
North Richland Hills (G-15875)

Decatur Machine Services Inc ....E 940 627-1062
Decatur (G-5244)

Direct International ....G 817 284-7722
Fort Worth (G-6587)

◆ DK Drill I Management Co LLC ....E 817 539-2500
Mansfield (G-14666)

Enflite LLC ....D 512 868-3399
Georgetown (G-7650)

Esna LLC ....B 817 281-8816
North Richland Hills (G-15877)

Essner Precision Mfg LLC ....E 817 529-2580
Fort Worth (G-6619)

Euless Aero Components LLC ....D 817 267-1371
Euless (G-6143)

Fore Machine LLC ....F 817 834-6251
Haltom City (G-8141)

Ftg Aerospace Inc ....D 818 577-6126
Haltom City (G-8141)

▲ Gas Turbine Engines Inc ....F 281 824-9200
Alvin (G-363)

▲ Gdc Technics LLC ....C 210 496-5614
Fort Worth (G-6663)

General Aviation Inds Inc ....E 817 598-4848
Weatherford (G-20595)

Genesys Aerosystems Group Inc ....C 800 872-7832
Mineral Wells (G-15526)

GI Legacy LLC ....F 817 222-1414
Fort Worth (G-6668)

Goodrich Corporation ....C 512 754-3658
San Marcos (G-18690)

Goodrich Corporation ....F 214 689-9588
Dallas (G-4413)

Goodrich Corporation ....C 682 730-4270
Haltom City (G-8142)

Greenpoint Precision Mch Inc ....E 940 382-3933
Denton (G-5369)

▲ Greiner Aerospace Inc ....B 817 686-3100
Fort Worth (G-6680)

Gulfstream Aerospace Corp ....A 214 902-7520
Dallas (G-4423)

▲ H T A Aerostructures Inc ....C 512 754-3600
San Marcos (G-18692)

Halsey Manufacturing ....G 940 566-3306
Denton (G-5371)

Heartland Enterprises Ltd ....E 830 997-9434
Fredericksburg (G-7182)

Heldoorn Manufacturing Inc ....F 817 275-0835
Arlington (G-696)

Higher Planes Inc ....G 936 494-1717
Conroe (G-3304)

Honeywell International Inc ....A 281 890-0088
Cypress (G-3801)

Institute Flght Oprtons Dsptch ....G 817 967-4424
Irving (G-13064)

Intech Aerospace LLC ....E 281 810-4400
Houston (G-10383)

Jeff Bonner R & D Inc ....C 210 590-3133
San Antonio (G-18199)

Jose Alfonsin ....F 210 717-2306
San Antonio (G-18208)

K W D Manufacturing Inc ....E 210 924-5999
San Antonio (G-18214)

Kaspar Machine LLC ....E 254 836-1564
Waco (G-20422)

Kepler Aerospace Ltd ....E 855 553-7537
Midland (G-15267)

Kepler Spacecore Inc ....E 855 553-7537
Midland (G-15268)

L3 Technologies Inc ....C 512 251-3441
Austin (G-1279)

L3harris Technologies Inc ....A 254 799-5533
Waco (G-20424)

Labinal Salisbury LLC ....A 410 548-7800
Denton (G-5378)

Legacy Aeronautics Inc ....E 855 622-8600
Carrollton (G-2775)

Lockheed Martin Corporation ....F 915 852-1100
El Paso (G-5845)

Lockheed Martin Corporation ....D 817 777-2000
Benbrook (G-2042)

Lockheed Martin Corporation ....B 817 777-2000
Fort Worth (G-6798)

▲ Lone Star Aviation Corporation ....F 682 518-8882
Mansfield (G-14686)

M1 Support Services LP ....D 940 323-1119
Denton (G-5379)

◆ Maddox Metal Works Inc ....D 214 333-2311
Dallas (G-4625)

Marathonnorco Aerospace Inc ....C 254 776-0650
Waco (G-20430)

▲ Mayday Manufacturing Co ....C 940 898-8301
Denton (G-5381)

Merritt Prfrred Components Inc ....D 903 983-1592
Kilgore (G-13574)

Mooney Aerospace Group Ltd ....E 830 896-6000
Kerrville (G-13524)

Novaria Group LLC ....E 817 381-3810
Fort Worth (G-6870)

Ogf LLC ....F 817 484-4004
Fort Worth (G-6876)

Pae Avation Technical Svcs LLC ....F 940 257-2836
Sheppard Afb (G-18902)

Panasonic Avionics Corporation ....F 346 242-1599
Houston (G-11229)

▲ Pcx Aerostructures Tx LP ....E 817 583-8820
Mansfield (G-14702)

Precision Def Components LLC ....F 870 949-8590
Texarkana (G-19771)

Precision Helicopter Svcs Inc ....E 210 525-9595
San Antonio (G-18386)

◆ Progressive Incorporated ....B 817 465-3221
Arlington (G-762)

R & B Electronics Inc ....E 906 632-1542
Grand Prairie (G-7961)

Rave Gear LLC ....D 830 421-3295
Seguin (G-18860)

REB Technologies Inc ....E 817 285-7740
Bedford (G-1978)

▲ Recaro Arcft Sting Amricas LLC ......C 817 490-9160
Fort Worth (G-6946)

Rf Manufacturing LLC ....E 817 479-1950
Haltom City (G-8157)

Rkr Technologies Ltd ....D 817 640-5340
Arlington (G-771)

Rsg Aerodesign LLC ....D 817 625-9000
Fort Worth (G-6969)

Rsg Products Inc ....E 817 624-6600
Saginaw (G-17755)

▼ RSI Visual Systems Inc ....D 817 510-0350
Coppell (G-3442)

S & S Machine Inc ....D 972 438-6282
Irving (G-13167)

◆ S-TEC Corporation ....C 800 872-7832
Mineral Wells (G-15541)

Safran Elec & Pwr USA LLC ....A 940 272-5700
Denton (G-5398)

▲ Safran Elec Def Avnics USA LLC .....C 972 314-3600
Grand Prairie (G-7968)

◆ Safran Seats USA LLC ....A 940 668-4825
Gainesville (G-7362)

▲ Sierra Industries Ltd ....D 210 805-3188
San Antonio (G-18472)

▲ Sky TEC Ltd ....F 817 573-2250
Granbury (G-7810)

Smartdrone Corporation ....F 443 655-5556
Tyler (G-20152)

Spirit Aerosystems Inc ....D 316 523-4221
San Antonio (G-18492)

▲ Starr Aircraft Products Inc ....C 903 893-1106
Sherman (G-18933)

▲ Sumitomo Precision Usa Inc ....G 972 228-9300
Desoto (G-5443)

Sunbelt Design Holdings LLC ....E 210 227-9162
San Antonio (G-18512)

T-B & S Mfg Co ....F 817 281-9315
Fort Worth (G-7029)

Texas Aeroplastics ....F 817 430-3651
Boyd (G-2207)

Texas Almet LP ....D 817 649-7056
Arlington (G-791)

Texas Aviation Tech LLC ....F 210 680-8181
San Antonio (G-18534)

▲ Texas Starwares Inc ....F 972 641-2100
Grand Prairie (G-7981)

Texstars LLC ....C 972 647-1366
Arlington (G-796)

Textool Company ....F 713 923-5595
Houston (G-12264)

Triton Consolidated Inc ....F 972 362-1711
Duncanville (G-5539)

Triumph Accssory Svcs - Grnd P ....D 972 623-9300
Grand Prairie (G-7986)

Triumph Aerostructures LLC ....C 972 595-9900
Grand Prairie (G-7987)

▲ Triumph Aerostructures LLC ....A 972 515-8276
Red Oak (G-17237)

Triumph Group Inc ....F 610 251-1000
Dallas (G-5120)

Triumph Group Inc ....E 817 804-9400
Arlington (G-804)

Tulsa Arspc Cmpnent Ovrhaul RE ....G 940 479-2000
Ponder (G-17097)

Turbine Aircraft Marketing Inc ....F 972 248-3108
Addison (G-172)

Turbine Tool Corporation ....G 512 385-5311
Del Valle (G-5333)

Turbo Mach R & D II Inc ....F 210 340-4773
San Antonio (G-18571)

US Dept of the Air Force ....B 210 925-4401
San Antonio (G-18580)

V I J Corporation ....E 817 838-2020
Fort Worth (G-7096)

Vanguard Defense Inds LLC ....F 281 298-6672
Spring (G-19184)

VSE Corporation ....D 903 831-0192
New Boston (G-15769)

Weatherford Aerospace Inc ....C 817 598-0044
Weatherford (G-20630)

Weatherford Aerospace Inc ....D 817 594-5464
Weatherford (G-20631)

▲ Wesco Aircraft Hardware Corp ....B 661 775-7200
Fort Worth (G-7136)

Wilder Systems LLC ....F 713 825-7348
Austin (G-1666)

▲ Williamsrdm Inc ....D 817 872-1500
Fort Worth (G-7148)

▲ Zodiac Seats California LLC ....C 909 652-9700
Gainesville (G-7375)

3731 Shipbuilding & Repairing

Aethon I LP ....E 214 750-1522
Dallas (G-3900)

American Fincl Mktg Group Inc ....F 866 679-9241
League City (G-13945)

Amphion Inc ....F 210 771-8116
San Antonio (G-17906)

Arcosa Inc ....C 972 942-6500
Dallas (G-3958)

▲ Arcosa Marine Products Inc ....C 214 631-4420
Dallas (G-3961)

Atlantia Offshore Limited ....D 281 899-4300
Houston (G-8737)

Bb Chemicals Inc ....E 432 381-2595
Odessa (G-15929)

◆ Beacon Maritime Inc ....A 409 670-1060
West Orange (G-20693)

Bersal Energy LLC ....F 956 270-1155
McAllen (G-14841)

Best Drilling Services (bds) ....E 713 864-3900
Houston (G-8862)

Bgi Enterprise Inc ....E 409 833-0303
Beaumont (G-1865)

Big Shot LLC ....E 504 877-2335
Lancaster (G-13840)

Black Star Energy Services LLC ....E 432 272-3395
Odessa (G-15936)

Bludworth Marine LLC ....G 713 644-1595
Galveston (G-7389)

Burton Shipyard Inc ....E 409 735-2491
Bridge City (G-2281)

Conglobal Industries LLC ....E 713 675-7587
Galena Park (G-7379)

◆ Conrad Orange Shipyard Inc ....C 409 670-4900
Orange (G-16236)

CPI Satcom & Antenna Tech Inc ....D 254 765-3304
Wortham (G-20922)

Crumplers Shipbuilding Co Inc ....E 409 886-7934
Orange (G-16237)

David Keels ....E 409 316-9265
Hitchcock (G-8336)

Gates Fuel Services LLC ....E 409 925-8897
Santa Fe (G-18734)

Glendale Boat Works Inc ....F 281 452-7146
Channelview (G-3023)

Griffin Barge Line LLC ....E 713 560-6874
Houston (G-10043)

▲ Gulf Copper & Mfg Corp ....F 409 989-0300
Port Arthur (G-17111)

Gulf Copper & Mfg Corp ....C 409 982-6122
Port Arthur (G-17112)

◆ Gulf Copper Ship Repair Inc ....D 361 883-1040
Corpus Christi (G-3540)

H & S Fabricators Inc ....E 361 884-1212
Corpus Christi (G-3542)

Hasco Marine ....F 281 452-5017
Channelview (G-3025)

International Coating Services ....E 936 344-9494
Willis (G-20850)

▲ Intership Services Inc ....E 713 645-2666
Houston (G-10407)

▲ John Bludworth Shipyard LLC ....D 361 887-7981
Corpus Christi (G-3558)

▲ Keppel Amfels Inc ....A 956 838-3110
Brownsville (G-2374)

Keppel Offshore & Mar USA Inc ....E 713 600-8371
Houston (G-10519)

L&R Midland Inc ....E 713 680-0909
Houston (G-10577)

Long & Long Pier Drilling Co ....F 972 422-4084
Plano (G-16910)

Lynchburg Shipyard Inc ....E 281 426-2474
Baytown (G-1827)

▲ Main Marine Repair Inc ....E 713 645-3553
Houston (G-10740)

Mblh Marine LLC ....D 409 962-1302
Port Arthur (G-17118)

Modec International Inc ....B 281 529-8100
Houston (G-10902)

◆ MPW Corporation ....F 713 640-2700
Houston (G-10931)

Ocean Ship Holding Inc ....E 281 579-3700
Houston (G-11121)

Ocean Shipholdings Inc ....E 281 579-3700
Houston (G-11122)

Ocean Ships Inc ....E 281 579-3700
Houston (G-11123)

◆ Oceaneering International Inc ....C 713 329-4500
Houston (G-11124)

Oceaneering International Inc ....F 713 329-4318
Houston (G-11126)

Offshore Express Inc ....D 985 868-1438
Houston (G-11141)

Offshore Oil Services Inc ....E 979 265-3300
Clute (G-3157)

Offshore Service Vessels LLC ....G 832 251-6665
Houston (G-11143)

▲ Offshore Spclty Fbricators LLC ......C 985 868-1438
Houston (G-11144)

Oil States Industries Inc ....E 817 468-1400
Arlington (G-742)

Pangea Enterprises Inc ....E 956 542-9494
Houston (G-11232)

PCI Manufacturing LLC ....E 903 885-6772
Sulphur Springs (G-19596)

◆ Perry Slingsby Systems Inc ....E 561 743-7000
Houston (G-11294)

San Jac Marine LLC ....C 281 862-9764
Channelview (G-3035)

Smith-Hamm Inc ....D 409 740-3314
Galveston (G-7408)

▼ Sneed Shipbuilding Inc ....E 281 862-2266
Channelview (G-3037)

Southern Gulf Solutions LLC ....F 979 299-8808
Clute (G-3159)

Sterling Shipyard LP ....E 409 727-2009
Port Neches (G-17168)

▲ Stx Service Americas LLC ....F 713 637-4030
Houston (G-12084)

◆ Subsea 7 (us) LLC ....C 713 430-1100
Houston (G-12086)

Tarsco Construction Corp ....C 515 225-3003
Spring (G-19258)

Texas Marine Shipyard LLC ....F 409 457-6260
Dickinson (G-5478)

Texgulmarco Co Inc ....E 956 943-2673
Port Isabel (G-17139)

▼ Trinity Industries Inc ....B 214 631-4420
Dallas (G-5112)

Tyson Globl Trnspt & Cnstr LLC ....E 470 481-6161
Cypress (G-3824)

United Marine Enterprise Inc ....D 409 833-0303
Beaumont (G-1965)

Vls Recovery Services LLC ....D 409 962-8800
Port Arthur (G-17132)

◆ Wartsila North America Inc ....C 281 233-6200
Houston (G-12600)

West Gulf Marine Ltd ....D 409 744-0492
Galveston (G-7413)

Western Towing Company ....E 713 435-1800
Channelview (G-3044)

3732 Boat Building & Repairing

American Airboat Corporation ....E 409 883-7725
Orange (G-16231)

Austin Boats & Motors Inc ....F 512 263-1266
Lakeway (G-13814)

Burton Shipyard Inc ....E 409 735-2491
Bridge City (G-2281)

Crumplers Shipbuilding Co Inc ....E 409 886-7934
Orange (G-16237)

Dargel Boats Inc ....E 956 464-2263
Donna (G-5488)

David Keels ....E 409 316-9265
Hitchcock (G-8336)

Es Custom Boats LLC ....F 832 864-2331
Kemah (G-13473)

Forterra Pipe & Precast LLC ....D 713 466-6324
Houston (G-9838)

Four Brothers Boat Works Inc ....F 409 229-4302
Galveston (G-7397)

Gpd Marine Inc ....F 512 266-1834
Austin (G-1191)

▲ Gulf Copper & Mfg Corp ....F 409 989-0300
Port Arthur (G-17111)

Hards Marine Service Ltd ....D 281 452-0848
Hull (G-12741)

◆ Hart Heat Transfer Pdts Inc ....D 713 675-9848
Houston (G-10133)

Inland Boat Works Inc ....F 409 988-0005
Orange (G-16248)

JC Custom Boats Inc ....F 361 785-6035
Seadrift (G-18796)

Josephine Tug Inc ....F 409 744-1222
Galveston (G-7402)

Land & Sea Services 1 Inc ....G 409 935-9466
La Marque (G-13711)

Legend Marine Mangement LLC ....E 870 481-6750
Streetman (G-19435)

Mile 533 Marine Ways Inc ....F 361 758-5379
Aransas Pass (G-594)

North Shore Boat Works Inc ....F 361 776-2525
Ingleside (G-12897)

Pond King Inc ....F 940 668-2573
Gainesville (G-7357)

Pro Line Newwater Inc ....F 210 648-2206
Elmendorf (G-6071)

R & R Design Inc ....F 972 524-1789
Terrell (G-19748)

Seabrook Marina Inc ....F 281 694-0001
Seabrook (G-18791)

Shallow Sport of Texas Inc ....F 956 233-9489
Los Fresnos (G-14348)

Shoreline Services Inc ....F 936 856-4880
Willis (G-20865)

Simmons Custom Boats LLC ....F 832 864-2331
Freeport (G-7212)

▼ Skeeter Products Inc ....B 903 984-0541
Kilgore (G-13590)

Texas Marine Holdings Ltd ....E 817 589-7547
Fort Worth (G-7050)

◆ Tige Boats Inc ....C 325 676-7777
Abilene (G-87)

Transport Boats ....F 361 972-6629
Palacios (G-16292)

Wallace Marine of Texas Inc ....E 940 458-7343
Sanger (G-18732)

3743 Railroad Eqpt

750 Logistics LLC ....E 214 433-2615
Houston (G-8414)

American Railcar Inds Inc ....D 903 759-4406
Longview (G-14194)

American Railcar Inds Inc ....E 281 471-1930
La Porte (G-13721)

American Railcar Inds Inc ....D 936 365-2679
Goodrich (G-7768)

Automotive Rentals Inc ....E 817 624-3650
Fort Worth (G-6411)

Channl-Track Tube-Way Inds Inc ....F 361 798-4979
Hallettsville (G-8120)

Ctc Inc ....E 817 886-8210
Fort Worth (G-6564)

Eagle Railcar Services LP ....F 254 631-0168
Eastland (G-5563)

Fryoux Tankerman Svc of Texas ....E 281 842-9400
La Porte (G-13738)

Gunderson Rail Services LLC ....B 817 556-9191
Cleburne (G-3094)

New York Air Brake LLC ....F 972 893-2400
Irving (G-13123)

Progress Rail Services Corp ....G 817 693-2550
Fort Worth (G-6921)

Progress Rail Services Corp ....D 806 335-3900
Amarillo (G-510)

▲ Quality Trbchrger Cmpnents LLC .....E 713 849-4200
Houston (G-11502)

Salco Products Inc ....E 630 783-2570
Houston (G-11733)

Specialty Locomotive Services ....F 281 425-9850
Baytown (G-1836)

▼ Trinity Industries Inc ....B 214 631-4420
Dallas (G-5112)

Trinity Industries Inc ....D 817 665-1499
Fort Worth (G-7075)

Trinity Industries Intl ....A 214 589-8967
Dallas (G-5113)

Trinity Parts & Components LLC ....F 817 378-2003
Fort Worth (G-7076)

Trinity Rail Group LLC ....F 214 631-4420
Dallas (G-5114)

Union Tank Car Company ....C 281 592-6424
Cleveland (G-3140)

Union Tank Car Company ....B 281 456-9381
Houston (G-12437)

Union Tank Car Company ....E 713 926-6980
Galena Park (G-7384)

Union Tank Car Company ....C 281 847-8200
Houston (G-12438)

Wabtec Corporation ....D 713 222-0792
Houston (G-12590)

3751 Motorcycles, Bicycles & Parts

Amarillo Mop & Broom Co Inc ....E 806 372-8596
Amarillo (G-396)

▲ Bell Sports Corp ....E 469 417-6600
Irving (G-12946)

D & S Cycle of Arlington Inc ....F 817 465-5454
Arlington (G-657)

D&D Retail LP ....E 830 379-7340
Seguin (G-18835)

▲ Fallbrook Technologies Inc ....E 512 714-1964
Leander (G-13990)

▲ Motor Trike Inc ....C 903 842-3094
Troup (G-20026)

Texas Precision Mfg Inc ....E 806 741-1166
Lubbock (G-14492)

3761 Guided Missiles & Space Vehicles

A R Machining Inc ....E 512 846-1789
Hutto (G-12874)

Aerostar International Inc ....E 903 885-0728
Sulphur Springs (G-19578)

Axiom Space Inc ....E 346 293-7045
Houston (G-8759)

Blue Origin Texas LLC ....E 253 437-9300
Van Horn (G-20213)

Boeing Company ....A 281 244-4000
Houston (G-8942)

Cinch Connectors Inc ....B 956 686-1151
McAllen (G-14847)

Firefly Aerospace Inc ....C 512 277-6959
Cedar Park (G-2970)

Japan Arospc Exploration Agcy ....F 281 333-5999
Houston (G-10454)

Lockheed Martin Corporation ....D 210 729-8600
San Antonio (G-18259)

Lockheed Martin Corporation ....E 915 852-1100
El Paso (G-5845)

Lockheed Martin Corporation ....D 817 777-2000
Benbrook (G-2042)

Lockheed Martin Corporation ....B 817 777-2000
Fort Worth (G-6798)

Lockheed Martin Corporation ....C 956 425-4447
Harlingen (G-8193)

Nanoracks LLC ....D 832 632-7754
Webster (G-20641)

National Aeronautics ....E 915 782-5250
El Paso (G-5893)

Space Exploration Tech Corp ....C 310 363-6000
Mc Gregor (G-14823)

Space Exploration Tech Corp ....A 310 363-6000
Houston (G-11990)

Spacex Rocket Dev Test Fcilty ....F 254 840-5771
Mc Gregor (G-14824)

United Launch Alliance LLC ....D 956 425-4447
Harlingen (G-8208)

Vivace International Corp ....E 504 613-4329
San Antonio (G-18598)

3764 Guided Missile/Space Vehicle Propulsion Units & parts

Lockheed Martin Corporation ....D 817 777-2000
Benbrook (G-2042)

Lockheed Martin Corporation ....B 817 777-2000
Fort Worth (G-6798)

Sunbelt Design & Dev Inc ....D 210 227-9162
San Antonio (G-18511)

3769 Guided Missile/Space Vehicle Parts & Eqpt, NEC

Albany Engnered Composites Inc ....D 830 249-4400
Boerne (G-2113)

Boeing Company ....A 281 244-4000
Houston (G-8942)

Fabrication & Mfg Aliance LLC ....D 210 648-3131
San Antonio (G-18102)

General Dynamics Ordnance ....B 972 276-5131
Garland (G-7499)

Heads Up Technologies Inc ....E 972 980-4890
Carrollton (G-2755)

Heartland Enterprises Ltd ....E 830 997-9434
Fredericksburg (G-7182)

▲ J M Fabrication Company LLC ....F 817 652-0526
Arlington (G-709)

L3 Technologies Inc ....A 817 619-2000
Arlington (G-715)

Lockheed Martin Corporation ....A 972 603-1000
Grand Prairie (G-7914)

Lockheed Martin Corporation ....C 956 425-4447
Harlingen (G-8193)

▲ Mayday Manufacturing Co ....C 940 898-8301
Denton (G-5381)

Merritt Prfrred Components Inc ....D 903 983-1592
Kilgore (G-13574)

Rothe Joint Venture Lp ....D 281 483-3852
Houston (G-11670)

▼ Top-Co Cementing Products Inc ....C 832 300-3660
Houston (G-12321)

▲ Triumph Aerostructures LLC ....A 972 515-8276
Red Oak (G-17237)

Xtenti LLC ....G 818 434-5239
Dallas (G-3861)

3792 Travel Trailers & Campers

American Trailer World Corp ....E 855 289-0001
Richardson (G-17269)

▼ Casita Enterprises Inc ....D 903 326-4717
Rice (G-17265)

◆ Direct Trailer LP ....E 281 713-8925
Humble (G-12763)

Houston Trailer Inc ....E 281 459-5350
Houston (G-10257)

Michael Roy ....F 903 784-6362
Sumner (G-19607)

▲ Progressive Sales Inc ....E 432 333-6631
Odessa (G-16127)

Superior Trailer Sales Co ....E 713 674-2676
Houston (G-12121)

Wccog Corp ....F 903 667-0264
De Kalb (G-5237)

▲ Yj USA Corp ....F 877 927-8777
Addison (G-175)

3795 Tanks & Tank Components

▼ Ba-Ker Tank Head Company Inc ......E 817 232-8030
Fort Worth (G-6418)

Critical Solutions Intl Inc ....E 800 843-0000
Plano (G-16832)

Eleet Cryogenics Inc ....E 936 856-6549
Willis (G-20845)

Fabrication Specialty Inc ....F 214 742-3571
Granbury (G-7797)

General Dynmics Land Systems I ....E 586 825-7242
Fort Hood (G-6324)

▲ Lide Industries LLC ....C 254 562-0233
Odessa (G-16063)

Lide Industries LLC ....F 254 562-0233
Troy (G-20030)

Mtc America Enterprises Inc ....F 972 926-0600
Garland (G-7556)

Nordic Tankers ....F 281 538-3250
League City (G-13969)

Power Pipe and Tank LLC ....E 417 447-4508
Amarillo (G-508)

▲ Specialty Tank Services Ltd ....F 281 470-4880
La Porte (G-13791)

Team Fabricators LLC ....D 409 962-0266
Port Arthur (G-17128)

▲ Texas Liner Service LLC ....F 281 445-5050
Houston (G-12238)

Utlx Manufacturing LLC ....A 281 847-8200
Houston (G-12507)

3799 Transportation Eqpt, NEC

A Plus Three Trucking LLC ....F 210 852-9339
San Antonio (G-17847)

Big Shot LLC ....E 504 877-2335
Lancaster (G-13840)

Brazos Trailer Mfg LLC ....F 903 873-8130
Wills Point (G-20874)

Clegg Industries Inc ....E 361 578-0291
Victoria (G-20253)

Cnm Horizon Investments LLC ....E 713 333-3400
Galveston (G-7393)

Coastline Trailer Mfg Inc ....F 361 785-4073
Seadrift (G-18795)

▲ Dexter Brahma LLC ....F 817 284-5141
Azle (G-1723)

◆ Dfr Acquisition Corporation ....E 480 834-4392
Fort Worth (G-6585)

▲ Domatex Inc ....D 281 219-1800
Houston (G-9493)

Gewi North America LLC ....E 713 446-6902
Sugar Land (G-19486)

Horizon Global Americas Inc ....F 915 545-2720
El Paso (G-5804)

Horse Creek Mfg & Fabrication ....E 903 572-4211
Cookville (G-3404)

Island Carriages ....F 409 765-6951
Galveston (G-7401)

Jennings Trailers Inc ....E 903 473-4562
Emory (G-6084)

Jro LLC ....F 903 472-0924
Marshall (G-14784)

Kwest Rv LLC ....E 512 294-2634
Austin (G-1276)

▲ Norstar Industries LLC ....E 903 784-8900
Brookston (G-2328)

Ocean Freedom Shipping Inc ....E 281 579-3700
Houston (G-11120)

▲ Odes Industries LLC ....E 866 572-8420
Fort Worth (G-6875)

▲ Outlaw Conversions Inc ....C 254 968-5733
Stephenville (G-19417)

▲ Performance Metal Works Inc ....D 903 967-2622
Quitman (G-17228)

Quality Trailer Products LP ....E 903 572-7932
Mount Pleasant (G-15661)

Real Energy Solutions Inc ....F 713 864-9076
Houston (G-11563)

Regency Conversions Inc ....D 800 839-7551
Fort Worth (G-6953)

▼ Rolligon Nov LP ....C 936 873-2600
Anderson (G-531)

Rs Logistics LLC ....F 318 347-5915
Arlington (G-776)

Rv Station Ltd ....E 979 778-8000
College Station (G-3200)

Select Power Sport Inc ....F 936 967-2332
Livingston (G-14161)

Sherrod Rv Center Inc ....F 409 385-5689
Silsbee (G-18955)

Supreme Corporation of Texas ....C 817 641-8002
Cleburne (G-3112)

▲ Taxa Inc ....F 713 861-2540
Houston (G-12165)

Tims South Texas LLC ....F 830 278-3368
Uvalde (G-20197)

Tims South Texas LLC ....F 830 468-3860
Asherton (G-814)

Up 1 Trucking LLC ....F 833 398-7825
Dallas (G-5141)

Uv Country Inc ....E 713 649-0556
Alvin (G-385)

Worth Trailer Parts Inc ....F 817 496-7841
Fort Worth (G-7151)

38 MEASURING, ANALYZING AND CONTROLLING INSTRUMENTS; PHOTOGRAPHIC, MEDICAL AN

3812 Search, Detection, Navigation & Guidance Systs & Instrs

Affects Sat Corporation ....D 713 897-9935
Garland (G-7430)

Ahlers Aerospace Inc ....E 817 553-2155
Hurst (G-12832)

Allosense Inc ....G 830 900-3080
San Antonio (G-17898)

▲ Analytical Sensors Instrs LLC ....D 281 565-8818
Houston (G-8636)

◆ Applied Concepts Inc ....C 972 398-3750
Richardson (G-17270)

Astro Technology Inc ....F 281 464-0100
Houston (G-8731)

Bae Systems Info & Elec Sys ....D 972 994-4176
Dallas (G-3838)

Bae Systems Info & Elec Sys ....A 512 276-3100
Austin (G-973)

Bae Systems Land Armaments LP ....D 408 504-1877
Temple (G-19670)

Brains4drones LLC ....F 972 974-3476
Plano (G-16810)

Castlberry Instrs Avionics LLC	E	512 251-5322	Pflugerville (G-16663)
Chromalloy Gas Turbine LLC	F	972 241-2501	Dallas (G-4114)
Cobham Advnced Elctrnic Sltons	E	972 437-1049	Richardson (G-17288)
Comprobe Inc	E	817 293-7333	Fort Worth (G-6538)
Currentech	F	214 693-6751	Arlington (G-655)
Defense Logistics Agency	B	214 670-9259	Dallas (G-4247)
Drone Labs LLC	F	214 538-1467	Katy (G-13397)
Drs Ntwork Imaging Systems LLC	C	877 377-4783	Dallas (G-4280)
Drs Training Ctrl Systems LLC	C	214 381-7161	Dallas (G-4281)
◆ Efw Inc	A	817 916-1359	Fort Worth (G-6606)
Espy Corporation	E	512 261-1016	Austin (G-861)
Fci Environmental Inc	E	702 262-3953	Dallas (G-4356)
▲ Fieldtech Avionics Instrs Inc	E	817 740-7110	Fort Worth (G-6629)
▲ Forney Corporation	E	972 458-6100	Addison (G-126)
▼ Foxtronics Inc	F	214 358-4425	Dallas (G-4375)
Freeflight Acquisition Corp	E	254 662-7050	Robinson (G-17500)
Freeflight Acquisition Corp	F	254 662-0000	Irving (G-13035)
◆ Garrett Electronics Inc	C	972 494-6151	Garland (G-7497)
GE Flight Efficiency Svcs Inc	E	512 270-2701	Austin (G-1179)
Genesys Aerosystems Group Inc	C	800 872-7832	Mineral Wells (G-15526)
Geometris LP	F	281 856-9600	Houston (G-9938)
GKN Aerospace Inc	F	972 432-1900	Irving (G-13038)
Gvi Security Solutions Inc	D	972 236-6235	Carrollton (G-2867)
▲ Heath Consultants Incorporated	C	713 844-1300	Houston (G-10146)
Honeywell International Inc	E	832 252-3500	Houston (G-10201)
Honeywell International Inc	D	409 886-7445	Orange (G-16246)
Honeywell International Inc	A	281 890-0088	Cypress (G-3801)
▲ Hydroscience Technologies Inc	E	940 325-8221	Mineral Wells (G-15529)
Industrial Safety Tech LLC	A	713 559-9200	The Woodlands (G-19884)
Innovative Signal Analysis Inc	D	972 231-5702	Richardson (G-17333)
◆ Instrument Tech Corp	F	972 458-8785	Carrollton (G-2765)
Integrity Defense LLC	F	832 282-0993	Houston (G-10386)
Jaunt Air Mobility LLC	F	817 692-3030	Southlake (G-19077)
L 3 Cmncations Intgrtd Systms	C	903 455-3450	Rockwall (G-17552)
L3 Technologies Inc	C	972 722-7927	Rockwall (G-17553)
L3 Technologies Inc	A	903 457-4100	Greenville (G-8080)
L3 Technologies Inc	A	817 619-2000	Arlington (G-715)
L3harris Technologies Inc	D	972 550-2300	Irving (G-13080)
L3harris Technologies Inc	A	972 772-7501	Rockwall (G-17554)
L3harris Technologies Inc	A	903 457-7461	Greenville (G-8081)
Lockheed Martin	D	281 283-4400	Houston (G-10663)
Lockheed Martin Corporation	A	972 603-1000	Grand Prairie (G-7914)
Lockheed Martin Corporation	B	210 736-6461	San Antonio (G-18257)
Lockheed Martin Corporation	D	817 763-3035	Fort Worth (G-6792)
Lockheed Martin Corporation	A	281 283-4400	Houston (G-10664)

Lockheed Martin Corporation	B	281 335-2318	Friendswood (G-7248)
Lockheed Martin Corporation	B	817 655-8672	Richland Hills (G-17440)
Lockheed Martin Corporation	B	817 763-2663	Colleyville (G-3219)
Lockheed Martin Corporation	B	281 218-3000	Houston (G-10665)
Lockheed Martin Corporation	A	817 935-1363	Fort Worth (G-6793)
Lockheed Martin Corporation	B	210 581-6100	San Antonio (G-18258)
Lockheed Martin Corporation	B	281 853-3000	Houston (G-10666)
Lockheed Martin Corporation	B	817 495-0200	Fort Worth (G-6794)
Lockheed Martin Corporation	B	817 777-2000	Fort Worth (G-6795)
Lockheed Martin Corporation	E	210 445-5628	San Antonio (G-18260)
Lockheed Martin Corporation	B	817 777-2000	Fort Worth (G-6796)
Lockheed Martin Corporation	B	334 347-4472	Killeen (G-13615)
Lockheed Martin Corporation	E	254 285-5503	Fort Hood (G-6325)
Lockheed Martin Corporation	F	915 568-6264	Fort Bliss (G-6317)
Lockheed Martin Corporation	B	817 763-4246	Keller (G-13468)
Lockheed Martin Corporation	E	817 777-0786	Fort Worth (G-6797)
Lockheed Martin Corporation	D	432 358-4474	Marfa (G-14753)
Lockheed Martin Corporation	C	281 218-6021	Houston (G-10667)
Lockheed Martin Corporation	A	972 603-1000	Grand Prairie (G-7915)
Lockheed Martin Corporation	B	817 777-4242	Azle (G-1726)
Lockheed Martin Corporation	D	210 581-6100	San Antonio (G-18261)
Lockheed Martin Corporation	D	936 633-4800	Lufkin (G-14532)
Lockheed Martin Corporation	D	817 777-2000	Benbrook (G-2042)
Lockheed Martin Corporation	B	817 777-2000	Fort Worth (G-6798)
Lockheed Martin Corporation	E	915 852-1100	El Paso (G-5845)
Lockheed Martin Space Company	A	281 283-4650	Houston (G-10668)
Marathonnorco Aerospace Inc	C	254 315-7524	Waco (G-20431)
Marathonnorco Aerospace Inc	D	254 772-7358	Waco (G-20432)
Mc Manus Instrument Co Inc	F	409 834-2419	Village Mills (G-20338)
Milvian Solutions LLC	F	915 219-5260	El Paso (G-5879)
Mo2 Inc	F	214 575-7600	Dallas (G-4682)
Mtc America Enterprises Inc	F	972 926-0600	Garland (G-7556)
Mustang Technology Group LP	C	972 747-0707	Plano (G-16937)
Nautical Control Solutions LP	E	281 209-3480	Spring (G-19153)
Northrop Grumman Corporation	B	214 524-0102	Irving (G-13126)
Northrop Grumman Systems Corp	C	512 804-2153	Austin (G-1370)
Northrop Grumman Systems Corp	E	469 524-0109	Irving (G-13127)
Northrup Grmman Technical Svcs	F	405 736-8207	Irving (G-13128)
Novaria Group LLC	E	817 381-3810	Fort Worth (G-6870)
◆ Optek Technology Inc	D	972 323-2200	Carrollton (G-2786)
Orbital Sciences Corporation	B	281 218-6140	Houston (G-11192)
▼ P T Products & Services Inc	E	512 251-3592	Pflugerville (G-16682)
▲ Paradigm SRP LLC	F	877 677-9899	Houston (G-11239)
◆ Pharos Marine Autmtc Pwr Inc	E	713 228-5208	Houston (G-11321)
Pipeline Inspection Company	E	713 681-5837	Houston (G-11335)

◆ Progressive Incorporated	B	817 465-3221	Arlington (G-762)
◆ Pronav Inc	D	361 727-3300	Rockport (G-17532)
R2sonic LLC	F	512 891-0000	Austin (G-1449)
▲ Ranger Security Detectors Inc	E	915 590-4441	El Paso (G-5927)
Raytheon Company	E	972 952-4195	Carrollton (G-2884)
Raytheon Company	C	781 522-3000	Plano (G-16984)
Raytheon Company	C	972 231-4931	Richardson (G-17382)
Raytheon Company	C	972 494-2073	Garland (G-7576)
Raytheon Company	C	972 205-8846	Plano (G-16985)
Raytheon Company	A	972 205-4277	Dallas (G-4860)
Raytheon Company	B	972 344-2591	Plano (G-16986)
Raytheon Company	C	972 344-3000	Dallas (G-4861)
Raytheon Company	C	915 771-5466	Richardson (G-17383)
Raytheon Company	C	817 735-1251	Fort Worth (G-6944)
Raytheon Company	B	719 638-2756	Richardson (G-17384)
Raytheon Company	C	972 344-9133	Dallas (G-4862)
Raytheon Company	E	361 348-2712	Premont (G-17204)
Raytheon Company	C	972 952-2007	McKinney (G-14968)
Raytheon Company	B	915 779-7666	El Paso (G-5928)
Raytheon Company	C	972 272-0515	Richardson (G-17385)
Raytheon Company	B	781 522-3000	Plano (G-16987)
Raytheon Company	B	703 525-1550	Arlington (G-769)
Raytheon Company	C	972 344-8000	Richardson (G-17386)
Raytheon Company	D	972 952-2007	McKinney (G-14969)
Raytheon Company	E	877 291-9990	Plano (G-16988)
Raytheon Company	C	972 952-4067	McKinney (G-14970)
Rdrtec Incorporated	E	214 353-8755	Dallas (G-4866)
Reliance Coated Fabrics Inc	E	817 453-8829	Mansfield (G-14710)
Rockwell Collins Inc	C	325 695-0308	Abilene (G-75)
Rockwell Collins Inc	A	972 705-3156	Richardson (G-17391)
Rothe Joint Venture Lp	D	281 483-3852	Houston (G-11670)
Rothe Joint Venture Lp	G	210 648-3131	San Antonio (G-18433)
◆ S-TEC Corporation	C	800 872-7832	Mineral Wells (G-15541)
Sabre Sentinel Intl LLC	E	972 529-6570	McKinney (G-14973)
Sermatech Dynamic	E	713 849-9474	Houston (G-11838)
Sgt LLC	D	281 751-1071	Webster (G-20645)
Sierra Nevada Corporation	E	775 331-0222	Plano (G-17005)
Sierra Nevada Corporation	B	210 523-6500	San Antonio (G-18473)
Sikorsky Aircraft Corporation	C	817 377-7500	Fort Worth (G-6988)
Simtek Inc	D	817 283-1801	Euless (G-6159)
Skygrid LLC	F	844 205-7173	Austin (G-1510)
Southern Avionics Co	E	409 842-1717	Beaumont (G-1952)
Thomas Instrument Incorporated	E	830 331-1325	Boerne (G-2141)
◆ Tideland Signal Corporation	D	713 681-6101	Houston (G-12289)
Tracy and Associates	F	817 559-9274	Granbury (G-7813)

▲ Triumph Aerostructures LLC ....A 972 515-8276
Red Oak *(G-17237)*

Triumph Group Inc ....E 817 804-9400
Arlington *(G-804)*

Valkyrie Systems Aerospace Inc ....F....... 888 426-2113
Dallas *(G-3857)*

Vanguard Defense Inds LLC ....F 281 298-6672
Spring *(G-19184)*

Varo LLC ....B 972 840-5506
Garland *(G-7607)*

Vectornav Technologies LLC ....F....... 512 772-3615
Dallas *(G-5157)*

Wave Quantum Def & Tech LLC ....F....... 512 505-2339
Austin *(G-1650)*

Whrzt Inc ....F....... 888 507-9985
Carrollton *(G-2849)*

◆ Williamsrdm Inc ....D 817 872-1500
Fort Worth *(G-7148)*

3821 Laboratory Apparatus & Furniture

3024 East Seminary Group LLC ....F....... 817 534-6755
Forest Hill *(G-6294)*

▲ AB Bellco Corporation ....E 713 781-6447
Houston *(G-8440)*

Becton Dickinson and Company..........F 210 526-5000
San Antonio *(G-17943)*

Bnx Converting LLC ....F....... 713 936-2726
Houston *(G-8930)*

▲ Chemyx Inc ....E 281 277-5499
Stafford *(G-19295)*

Consci Ltd ....F....... 713 920-1696
Pasadena *(G-16412)*

Custom Solutions Group LLC ....F....... 281 507-9569
Katy *(G-13393)*

◆ Ets-Lindgren Inc ....C 512 531-6400
Cedar Park *(G-2968)*

Helena Laboratories Corp ....B 409 842-3714
Beaumont *(G-1902)*

Interav Inc ....F....... 210 344-2785
San Antonio *(G-18191)*

Lumadyne LLC ....G....... 281 220-2409
Alvin *(G-372)*

Nexeon Medsystems Inc ....D 844 919-9990
Dallas *(G-4735)*

▼ Onepointe Solutions LLC ....D 866 222-7494
Elgin *(G-6056)*

▲ Paragon Furniture Inc ....D 817 633-3242
Arlington *(G-749)*

Separation Technology Inc ....F....... 830 249-0772
Boerne *(G-2136)*

Sleep Disorder Centers LLC ....F....... 972 390-2014
McKinney *(G-14976)*

Spectrum Lifesciences LLC ....E 214 492-0506
Irving *(G-13188)*

Sterigenics US LLC ....E 817 293-0999
Fort Worth *(G-7018)*

Tech-Lab Industries Inc ....F....... 972 660-1111
Grand Prairie *(G-7980)*

Tel Mnfacturing Engrg Amer Inc ....C 972 643-2000
Allen *(G-301)*

Texas Medplast LLC ....E 832 288-2106
Houston *(G-12240)*

Texas Metal Equipment Co Ltd...........E 713 466-8722
Houston *(G-12241)*

Texas Metal Equipment Co Ltd...........E 214 446-7200
Irving *(G-13192)*

3822 Automatic Temperature Controls

A-Action Aire Inc ....F....... 210 648-3801
San Antonio *(G-17850)*

Absolute Acstic Noise Ctrl LLC ....F....... 817 594-4446
Weatherford *(G-20573)*

Ademco Inc..................................E 972 402-8612
Farmers Branch *(G-6184)*

Ademco Inc..................................F....... 713 861-9418
Houston *(G-8479)*

Ademco Inc..................................C 915 872-5542
El Paso *(G-5637)*

Ademco Inc..................................D 915 875-0091
El Paso *(G-5638)*

Altech Controls Corporation.............F....... 281 207-2775
Missouri City *(G-15575)*

Apergy Artfl Lift Intl LLC ....D 713 466-3552
Houston *(G-8662)*

APS Building Services Inc ....D 713 979-0720
Houston *(G-8670)*

Aqua Electric Inc ....F....... 972 243-2162
Dallas *(G-3956)*

Aqua Quality Water Systems ....G....... 210 493-4545
San Antonio *(G-17911)*

Ash Automated Ctrl Systems LLC ....F 281 346-1400
Fulshear *(G-7327)*

◆ Burly Corp ....E 817 295-1128
Burleson *(G-2573)*

C3 Environmental Spc LP ....E 210 653-7801
Schertz *(G-18746)*

City of Houston ....C 713 221-0404
Houston *(G-9203)*

Clarios ....F 361 289-9675
Corpus Christi *(G-3500)*

Climatic Systems Inc ....F 972 206-2590
Grand Prairie *(G-7853)*

Concord Mechanical Inc..................E 817 319-5575
Boyd *(G-2204)*

▲ Controlled Systems Sales Co ....E 972 234-6767
Richardson *(G-17291)*

Convergentz Bldg Systems LLC ....E 713 266-3900
Houston *(G-9297)*

Crisp Air ....E 903 530-4385
Winona *(G-20903)*

Digital Air Control Inc ....E 713 975-8160
Houston *(G-9471)*

Divcon Ems Austin LLC ....E 214 821-6958
Farmers Branch *(G-6193)*

Eml Manufacturing Llc ....E 281 880-7517
Houston *(G-9617)*

Environmental Fuel Systems ....F 800 375-7747
Boerne *(G-2119)*

Evolve Holdings Inc ....E 832 375-0099
Houston *(G-9720)*

▲ Forney Corporation ....E 972 458-6100
Addison *(G-126)*

George Wood and Company Inc ....F 713 672-7270
Houston *(G-9943)*

Incenergy LLC ....F 512 327-2020
Austin *(G-1226)*

Jefferson Gulf Coast Energy ....E 281 677-4900
Houston *(G-10463)*

Jessco Solutions LLC ....E 325 227-4196
San Angelo *(G-17811)*

Johnson Controls Be Operation ....A 956 782-3000
McAllen *(G-14880)*

Johnson Controls Inc ....E 281 633-5700
Richmond *(G-17457)*

Johnson Controls Inc ....E 512 973-3555
Austin *(G-1259)*

Ldia Holdings LLC ....E 512 247-3700
Austin *(G-1284)*

Logical Control Services LLP ....E 972 820-0100
Carrollton *(G-2878)*

Lower Colorado River Authority..........F 512 473-3270
Buchanan Dam *(G-2518)*

Maddox Enterprises Inc ....E 903 592-6531
Tyler *(G-20119)*

Maxitrol Company ....E 817 479-8505
Richland Hills *(G-17441)*

Midwest Energy Emissions Corp ....F 614 505-6115
Corsicana *(G-3678)*

Miller Mechanical Group ....F 361 594-8080
Shiner *(G-18945)*

Momentum Prssure Ctrl Rntl LLC ....D 903 643-3700
Longview *(G-14281)*

▲ Nailor Industries Texas Inc ....C 281 590-1172
Houston *(G-10961)*

Parkline Inc ....F 409 935-5743
Hitchcock *(G-8339)*

◆ Peerless Mfg Co ....D 214 357-6181
Dallas *(G-4794)*

Qa Support LP ....E 281 307-1000
La Porte *(G-13786)*

◆ Rampak Group Inc ....F 713 678-8898
Houston *(G-11537)*

Repco Replacement Parts Inc ....E 817 293-3639
Fort Worth *(G-6956)*

RMS Solutions Group LLC ....F 469 964-7127
Point *(G-17080)*

Robertshaw Controls Company ....C 956 831-9000
Brownsville *(G-2402)*

▲ Robinson Engineering Co Inc ....E 972 272-2001
Garland *(G-7580)*

Ruskin Company ....E 972 247-7448
Carrollton *(G-2811)*

Sabine River Authority Texas ....F 409 746-2192
Orange *(G-16261)*

▼ Schneder Elc Bldngs Amrcas Inc.....B 972 323-1111
Carrollton *(G-2813)*

▲ Schneider Elc Systems USA Inc........D 713 329-1600
Houston *(G-11781)*

Siemens Industry Inc ....D 956 797-5075
La Feria *(G-13692)*

Siemens Industry Inc......................B 972 947-7000
Dallas *(G-4959)*

Siemens Industry Inc......................C 972 550-8488
Irving *(G-13178)*

Standard Renewable Energy LP ....D 281 763-2020
Houston *(G-12043)*

Super-Tech Hvac LLC ....F 361 394-5549
Freer *(G-7234)*

Texas Ine Inc ....D 281 601-4884
Houston *(G-12236)*

▲ Texas Instruments Incorporated......A 972 995-3773
Dallas *(G-5067)*

Texas Instruments Incorporated ....E 214 567-2075
Richardson *(G-17408)*

Ultimate Control Solutions Inc ....F 972 383-9414
Dallas *(G-5129)*

Weimar Industries Inc ....G....... 979 725-8503
Weimar *(G-20652)*

Whitewater Resources LLC ....F 210 290-9005
San Antonio *(G-18618)*

Xencom Energy Management LLC ......F 469 429-1111
Plano *(G-17054)*

3823 Indl Instruments For Meas, Display & Control

AA Flood Masters LLC ....E 409 796-2620
Beaumont *(G-1847)*

ABB Inc ....D 713 587-8000
Houston *(G-8443)*

◆ Agar Corporation Inc ....D 832 476-5100
Houston *(G-8501)*

Alpa Precision LLP ....D 713 680-8556
Houston *(G-8560)*

Alpa Precision Mch Works Inc ....E 713 680-8556
Houston *(G-8561)*

Alpha Tech International Inc ....A 281 240-8989
Stafford *(G-19284)*

Amacs Process Tower Internals ....F 713 434-0934
Houston *(G-8372)*

Ameri Source Manufacturing Inc.........F 903 677-7734
Ben Wheeler *(G-2031)*

American Steam Inc.......................E 972 442-4499
Wylie *(G-20926)*

Analytical Instruments Corp ....F 713 460-5757
Conroe *(G-3256)*

▲ Analytical Sensors Instrs LLC ....D 281 565-8818
Houston *(G-8636)*

Analytical Systems Keco LLC ....F 281 255-6537
Houston *(G-8637)*

▲ Anova Industrials ....E 281 494-8896
Stafford *(G-19286)*

Appleton Grp LLC ....D 254 968-6071
Stephenville *(G-19406)*

Appleton Grp LLC ....F 214 349-2310
Dallas *(G-3953)*

▼ Aquasol Controllers Inc ....E 713 683-6406
Houston *(G-8673)*

B I Products LLC ....D 972 359-4000
Allen *(G-255)*

Barton Sprngs E Aquifer Cnsrvt..........F 512 282-8441
Austin *(G-975)*

▲ Bettis Corporation ....C 281 879-2300
Jersey Village *(G-13293)*

BI Technology Inc ....E 832 698-8000
Tomball *(G-19967)*

Chen Grner Stvens Prtners LLC ....F 512 302-4333
Austin *(G-1046)*

Chevas Company LLC ....E 713 225-6595
Houston *(G-9176)*

Coastal Flow Measurement Inc ....D 713 477-1956
Houston *(G-9225)*

Compass Instruments LLC ....E 832 698-2047
Tomball *(G-19971)*

Concept Controls Inc ....F 281 476-4400
La Porte *(G-13730)*

Contrinex Inc ....F 574 340-7089
Coppell *(G-3413)*

Control Products Corporation ....C 972 264-0368
Grand Prairie *(G-7858)*

◆ Cosa Xentaur Corporation ....E 713 947-9591
Houston *(G-9327)*

Cosa Xentaur Corporation ....E 631 345-3434
Houston *(G-9328)*

Daniel Industries Inc ....E 713 467-6000
Houston *(G-9401)*

◆ Daniel Measurement & Ctrl LLC........B 713 827-5033
Houston *(G-9402)*

Dcl America Inc ....F 281 651-5900
Conroe *(G-3290)*

Delta Controls Company Inc	F	281 469-4891
Cypress (G-3785)		
Digital Speech Systems Inc	E	972 235-2999
Allen (G-262)		
Double Mountain Inc	E	940 988-4491
Aspermont (G-815)		
Electrolab Inc	E	210 824-5364
Boerne (G-2118)		
Electronic Data Devices Co	E	432 366-8699
Odessa (G-15987)		
Emerson Electric Co	E	956 994-1427
McAllen (G-14857)		
Emerson Electric Co	E	956 702-2389
San Juan (G-18673)		
Emerson Electric Co	G	713 447-2839
Houston (G-9613)		
Emerson Electric Co	E	281 488-0788
Pearland (G-16559)		
Emerson Electric Co	E	314 553-3695
El Paso (G-5751)		
Emerson Electric Co	F	915 400-3888
El Paso (G-5752)		
Emerson Electric Co	F	956 683-0694
McAllen (G-14858)		
▲ Emerson Prcess MGT Rgltor Tech	E	972 548-3585
McKinney (G-14939)		
Emerson Prcess MGT Vlve Atmtn	D	832 261-2400
Pasadena (G-16426)		
Emerson Process Management	E	281 879-2300
Houston (G-9614)		
Emerson Process MGT Lllp	C	512 835-2190
Round Rock (G-17654)		
Emicon Corporation	F	915 857-5128
El Paso (G-5753)		
Emicon Corporation	F	915 593-6422
El Paso (G-5754)		
Endress + Hauser Inc	C	281 867-3400
La Porte (G-13735)		
Endress + Hauser Inc	F	713 300-6200
Houston (G-9629)		
Fci Environmental Inc	E	702 262-3953
Dallas (G-4356)		
First Time Right	E	832 264-5057
Kyle (G-13682)		
Fisher Controls Intl LLC	B	903 868-3200
Sherman (G-18914)		
Fisher-Rosemount Systems Inc	B	512 418-7400
The Hills (G-19818)		
Flozone Measurement Ltd	E	432 488-2799
Odessa (G-16005)		
Flozone Measurement Ltd	E	432 488-2799
Odem (G-15896)		
▲ Forney Corporation	E	972 458-6100
Addison (G-126)		
G2 Restoration LLC	E	469 296-4275
McKinney (G-14945)		
▲ Gagemaker LP	E	713 472-7360
Pasadena (G-16445)		
Gauging Systems Inc	E	281 980-3999
Sugar Land (G-19484)		
◆ Gayesco-Wika Usa LP	C	713 941-8540
Pasadena (G-16447)		
GK Techstar LLC	E	361 289-6825
Corpus Christi (G-3536)		
GK Techstar LLC	D	281 884-8257
Deer Park (G-5276)		
Glex Inc	E	713 849-4985
Houston (G-9965)		
Grace Instrument Company	E	713 783-1560
Houston (G-10009)		
Greenslade & Company Inc	F	817 870-8888
Fort Worth (G-6678)		
Hdi Instruments LLC	E	713 688-8555
Houston (G-10142)		
Hitachi America Ltd	D	972 488-3824
Carrollton (G-2761)		
◆ Hoffland Environmental Inc	E	936 856-4515
Conroe (G-3306)		
Hoffman Controls Corp	E	972 243-7425
Dallas (G-4461)		
Honeywell International Inc	E	832 252-3500
Houston (G-10201)		
Hpi LLC	E	713 457-7500
Houston (G-10272)		
Instrument & Valve Services Co	D	281 998-6600
Pasadena (G-16462)		
Instrument & Valve Services Co	E	281 884-8639
Pasadena (G-16463)		
Instrument & Valve Services Co	F	713 827-4395
Houston (G-10381)		

Instrument & Valve Services Co	F	409 840-8400
Beaumont (G-1908)		
Instrument & Valve Services Co	F	903 753-9922
Longview (G-14252)		
Integrated Flow Systems LLC	D	512 671-5002
Pflugerville (G-16676)		
Intercorr International Inc	E	281 444-2282
Houston (G-10393)		
▼ Intrinsic Safety Eqp Texas Inc	D	281 488-0788
Pearland (G-16571)		
J & J Manufacturing Company	D	409 835-1330
Beaumont (G-1912)		
Kam Controls Inc	E	713 784-0000
Houston (G-10500)		
Ludlum Measurements Inc	B	325 235-5494
Sweetwater (G-19633)		
◆ Martin-Decker Totco Inc	B	512 340-5000
Cedar Park (G-2978)		
Measurementation	E	979 373-9991
Freeport (G-7204)		
Mensor LP	D	512 396-4200
San Marcos (G-18698)		
Mercer Controls Inc	E	361 782-7168
Edna (G-5609)		
▲ Merla LLC	E	281 931-6900
Magnolia (G-14618)		
Metrix Instrument Co LP	E	281 940-1802
Houston (G-10854)		
Metrix PMC/Beta	E	713 461-2131
Houston (G-10855)		
Micro-Design Inc	G	972 488-8725
Dallas (G-4675)		
Micropac Industries Inc	D	972 272-3571
Garland (G-7551)		
Mo2 Inc	F	214 575-7600
Dallas (G-4682)		
Moore Control Systems Inc	D	281 392-7747
Katy (G-13372)		
Mueller Co LLC	C	956 621-3086
Brownsville (G-2384)		
Murphy Fw	D	281 633-4500
Rosenberg (G-17590)		
▲ Newline Interactive Inc	F	972 468-9728
Plano (G-16944)		
Norak Inc	E	281 585-4091
Alvin (G-374)		
Noshok Inc	F	281 897-6115
Houston (G-11085)		
NS Controls Inc	E	713 465-7591
Houston (G-11094)		
▲ Omni Flow Computers Inc	F	281 240-6161
Sugar Land (G-19522)		
▲ Orbital Gas Systems N Amer Inc	E	832 467-1420
Houston (G-11191)		
Parker-Hannifin Corporation	E	409 924-0300
Houston (G-11246)		
◆ Pecofacet (us) Inc	B	940 325-2575
Mineral Wells (G-15536)		
◆ Peerless Mfg Co	D	214 357-6181
Dallas (G-4794)		
▲ Petron Industries Inc	D	713 693-8700
Houston (G-11310)		
PMG Digital Inc	F	806 747-7446
Lubbock (G-14463)		
▲ Pollok Inc	A	915 592-5700
El Paso (G-5914)		
▼ Powell Industries Inc	B	713 944-6900
Houston (G-11376)		
Precision Flow Inc	F	432 332-0266
Odessa (G-16125)		
▲ Process Level Technology Ltd	F	281 332-6241
League City (G-13977)		
Professionalized Pdts & Svcs	E	281 933-9427
Houston (G-11440)		
◆ Puffer-Sweiven LP Inc	E	281 240-2000
Stafford (G-19364)		
R & R Oilfield Services Inc	E	361 289-5892
Corpus Christi (G-3604)		
R D McMillan Company Inc	E	512 863-0231
Georgetown (G-7671)		
◆ Rampak Group Inc	F	713 678-8898
Houston (G-11537)		
Rheonics Inc	E	713 364-5427
Sugar Land (G-19535)		
◆ Robbins & Myers Inc	E	936 890-1064
Willis (G-20861)		
Robertshaw Controls Company	C	956 831-9000
Brownsville (G-2402)		
▲ Rochester Gauges LLC	C	972 280-8478
Dallas (G-4907)		

Rosemount Inc	E	713 396-8700
Houston (G-11664)		
Rosemount Inc	E	281 240-2000
Stafford (G-11665)		
▲ Rosemunt Tank Gging N Amer Inc	E	281 988-4000
Houston (G-11665)		
Rus Industrial LLC	E	281 864-9070
Channelview (G-3033)		
S & A Systems Inc	F	972 722-1009
Rockwall (G-17564)		
San Antnio Lghthouse For Blind	E	210 533-5195
San Antonio (G-18444)		
Scada Products LLC	E	888 649-4283
Fort Worth (G-6975)		
Schenck Process LLC	D	816 891-9300
Houston (G-11765)		
Schlumberger Limited	E	713 513-2000
Houston (G-11767)		
Schneider Electric Systems USA	D	281 709-1200
Webster (G-20644)		
Schneider Electric Usa Inc	C	972 236-0300
Coppell (G-3444)		
Semicon Phtmtrlogy Sltions LLC	E	214 957-0295
Garland (G-7586)		
Softech Controls Inc	E	713 553-0365
Cypress (G-3821)		
Sor Inc	E	281 272-5333
Houston (G-11954)		
◆ Specialty Process Eqp Corp	D	281 812-7732
Humble (G-12799)		
Supreme Electrical Svcs Inc	D	713 676-2588
Houston (G-12122)		
▲ Tecalemit Inc	E	281 446-7300
Humble (G-12801)		
Technical Automtn Svcs Co Ltd	D	281 474-3232
Seabrook (G-18792)		
Tegron Holding LLC	E	903 759-1088
Longview (G-14314)		
Temperture Measurement Systems	E	800 967-6498
Malakoff (G-14637)		
TF Hudgins Holdings Inc	C	713 682-3651
Houston (G-12266)		
Therm-O-Disc Incorporated	B	915 860-9167
El Paso (G-6000)		
Thermo Finnigan LLC	D	512 251-1400
Austin (G-1572)		
Thermo Process Instruments LP	F	713 272-0404
Sugar Land (G-19564)		
Tolteq Group LLC	D	512 331-4241
Cedar Park (G-2988)		
Triseal Inc	E	713 589-5380
Kemah (G-13480)		
▲ Umc Energy Solutions Inc	E	432 524-2456
Joshua (G-13328)		
▲ Uson Lp	E	281 671-2000
Houston (G-12504)		
▲ Valco Instruments Company	B	713 688-9345
Houston (G-12517)		
Valco Instruments Company	F	713 688-9345
Houston (G-12518)		
Varo LLC	B	972 840-5506
Garland (G-7607)		
Vector Systems Inc	D	214 544-9500
McKinney (G-14985)		
Ventil USA Inc	F	281 280-0141
Houston (G-12547)		
W A Neel Co Inc	F	903 503-5834
Scottsville (G-18781)		
W-Industries of Louisiana	F	281 921-3067
Houston (G-12589)		
W-Industries of Louisiana	C	713 466-9463
Jersey Village (G-13306)		
Walton Process Tech Inc	E	682 518-9002
Mansfield (G-14728)		
◆ Welker Inc	D	281 491-2331
Sugar Land (G-19571)		
Wellsite Automation	F	432 218-9361
Midland (G-15468)		
▼ Wesco Acquisition Partners Inc	E	713 688-5551
Galena Park (G-7386)		
▼ Wfms Inc	E	281 491-2445
Sugar Land (G-19573)		
Wika Instrument LP	D	713 475-0022
Deer Park (G-5302)		
Winters Instruments Inc	F	281 880-8607
Houston (G-12679)		
Xentaur Corporation	E	631 345-3434
Houston (G-12707)		
Yokogawa Corporation America	E	936 653-2120
Coldspring (G-3168)		

3824 Fluid Meters & Counters

American Innovations Ltd ....E 512 249-3400
Austin *(G-916)*

◆ Applied Concepts Inc ....C 972 398-3750
Richardson *(G-17270)*

▲ Capstone Metering LLC ....E 214 469-1065
Plano *(G-16819)*

Daniel Industries Inc ....E 713 467-6000
Houston *(G-9401)*

◆ Daniel Measurement & Ctrl LLC .....B 713 827-5033
Houston *(G-9402)*

Dobie Supply LLC ....G 512 437-6499
Austin *(G-1098)*

Electronic Data Devices Co ....E 432 366-8699
Odessa *(G-15987)*

▲ Fluenta Inc ....F 832 456-2021
Houston *(G-9815)*

Hamar Industries Inc ....E 817 756-8990
Fort Worth *(G-6685)*

▲ Kelley Instrument Machine Inc ....E 903 832-3332
Texarkana *(G-19767)*

Kemp-Meek Manufacturing Inc ......F 903 569-9700
Mineola *(G-15509)*

Ludlum Measurements Inc ....B 325 235-5494
Sweetwater *(G-19633)*

◆ Master Meter Inc ....C 817 842-8000
Mansfield *(G-14691)*

Orbital Energy Group Inc ....E 832 467-1420
Houston *(G-11190)*

R & R Oilfield Services Inc ....D 361 289-5892
Corpus Christi *(G-3604)*

▲ Rg-5 Company LP ....F 903 753-3456
Longview *(G-14296)*

▲ Roxar Inc ....E 281 879-2600
Houston *(G-11680)*

S & A Systems Inc ....F 972 722-1009
Rockwall *(G-17564)*

Schlumberger Limited ....E 713 513-2000
Houston *(G-11767)*

Schlumberger Technology Corp ......C 281 285-8500
Sugar Land *(G-19549)*

◆ Schlumberger Technology Corp ....A 281 285-8500
Sugar Land *(G-19542)*

Thermo Finnigan LLC ....D 512 251-1400
Austin *(G-1572)*

Welbor Technology Inc ....F 713 980-2345
Houston *(G-12627)*

3825 Instrs For Measuring & Testing Electricity

1-Stop Enterprises LLC ....E 678 485-9873
Little Elm *(G-14138)*

3M Company ....B 512 984-1800
Austin *(G-869)*

American Innovations Ltd ....E 512 249-3400
Austin *(G-916)*

▼ Amptec Research Corporation ....F 512 858-4045
Austin *(G-856)*

▲ Arbin Corporation ....E 979 690-2751
College Station *(G-3174)*

◆ Arbin Instruments LLC ....E 979 690-2751
College Station *(G-3176)*

◆ Arias Logistics Inc ....E 915 872-0034
El Paso *(G-5651)*

▼ Avo Multi-AMP Corporation ....C 214 330-3201
Dallas *(G-3991)*

Avo USA Inc ....C 214 333-3201
Dallas *(G-3993)*

Bpm Microsystems Inc ....D 713 688-4600
Houston *(G-8972)*

Butler & Land Inc ....E 214 343-8800
Dallas *(G-4068)*

Circuit Check Inc ....F 972 480-0044
Richardson *(G-17286)*

Compass Metering Solutions ....E 972 834-5479
Greenville *(G-8067)*

▲ Computer Service Technology ....E 972 241-2662
Dallas *(G-4153)*

Dcg Partnership I Limited ....E 281 648-1894
Pearland *(G-16553)*

Delta V Instruments Inc ....F 972 644-6501
Richardson *(G-17299)*

Distributed Pwr Solutions LLC ....E 877 291-3354
Pearland *(G-16556)*

◆ Dresser LLC ....C 262 549-2626
Houston *(G-9517)*

Dresser Inc ....E 361 881-8182
Corpus Christi *(G-3517)*

◆ Electronic Power Design Inc ....D 713 923-1191
Houston *(G-9596)*

Engie Retail LLC ....E 713 636-1127
Houston *(G-9645)*

Envirosense LLC ....E 281 828-8989
Houston *(G-9669)*

Everything Energy LLC ....E 713 537-3000
Houston *(G-9718)*

Exfo America Inc ....E 972 761-9271
Richardson *(G-17307)*

George W Cox & Sons Inc ....E 210 661-8661
San Antonio *(G-18139)*

Gunvision Systems LLC ....E 512 858-4045
Austin *(G-862)*

Hdi Instruments LLC ....E 713 688-8555
Houston *(G-10142)*

▲ Hid Global Corporation ....C 800 237-7769
Austin *(G-1202)*

◆ Hilti of America Inc ....E 800 879-8000
Plano *(G-16886)*

Horiba Instruments Inc ....E 408 730-4772
Austin *(G-1209)*

Hunnicutt Digital Electronics ....F 817 336-5449
Fort Worth *(G-6709)*

M & M Meter Service Inc ....F 432 756-2801
Stanton *(G-19403)*

◆ M&I Electric Industries Inc ....D 832 241-6330
Houston *(G-10721)*

Mactronix Inc ....E 972 690-0028
Richardson *(G-17350)*

Maxmile Technologies LLC ....F 512 961-1187
Austin *(G-1331)*

Metrix Instrument Co LP ....D 281 940-1802
Houston *(G-10854)*

Micropac Industries Inc ....E 972 272-3571
Garland *(G-7551)*

Mitchell Machine & Fabricating ....F 903 880-0249
Mabank *(G-14579)*

National Oilwell Varco Inc ....C 936 444-4000
Conroe *(G-3335)*

Neosem Technology Inc ....F 512 257-5000
Austin *(G-1706)*

Newtek Partners Lp ....D 210 370-8000
San Antonio *(G-18345)*

▲ Oilfield-Electric-Marine Inc ....F 713 680-9659
Houston *(G-11165)*

◆ Optek Technology Inc ....D 972 323-2200
Carrollton *(G-2786)*

Phase Dynamics Inc ....E 972 680-1550
Richardson *(G-17372)*

Pico Sales and Dist LLC ....F 800 591-2796
Tyler *(G-20143)*

Pipeline Inspection Company ....E 713 681-5837
Houston *(G-11335)*

▲ Plastronics Interconnections ....F 972 258-2580
Irving *(G-13152)*

Psde LLC ....F 972 429-7160
Wylie *(G-20945)*

Reedholm Instruments Co ....E 512 869-1935
Georgetown *(G-7674)*

Reliable Manufacturing Inc ....E 512 255-6572
Round Rock *(G-17684)*

Rf Saw Inc ....F 469 227-0322
Fredericksburg *(G-7188)*

Rohde & Schwarz Usa Inc ....E 469 713-5300
Coppell *(G-3441)*

Schlumberger Limited ....E 713 513-2000
Houston *(G-11767)*

◆ Schlumberger Technology Corp ....A 281 285-8500
Sugar Land *(G-19542)*

Schlumberger Technology Corp ......C 281 285-8500
Sugar Land *(G-19549)*

Schweitzer Engrg Labs Inc ....E 509 334-8154
Houston *(G-11785)*

▼ Scientific Test Inc ....F 972 479-1300
Richardson *(G-17394)*

Sigma Electronics Inc ....E 800 874-7121
Houston *(G-11884)*

Softest Designs Corporation ....E 210 697-8828
San Antonio *(G-18481)*

Southern Transformers ....F 713 923-1191
Houston *(G-11978)*

▲ Spectra Test Solutions LLC ....E 214 349-0288
Dallas *(G-4995)*

▲ Tdk Rf Solutions Inc ....E 512 258-9478
Cedar Park *(G-2987)*

Tektronix Inc ....F 713 691-3658
Houston *(G-12189)*

Tektronix Inc ....E 512 926-7625
Austin *(G-1560)*

Teradyne Inc ....D 512 891-9600
Austin *(G-1563)*

Testequity LLC ....D 972 247-2470
Carrollton *(G-2829)*

Testforce Usa Inc ....F 925 281-3501
Addison *(G-168)*

Testronics Consolidated Inc ....E 972 542-3111
Richardson *(G-17406)*

▲ Texas Meter and Device Co LLC ...D 254 732-1305
Waco *(G-20467)*

Thermo Elctron Process Systems .....D 713 272-0404
Houston *(G-17406)*

Thermo Finnigan LLC ....D 512 251-1400
Austin *(G-1572)*

Tokyo Seimitsu Co Ltd ....F 214 459-1688
Richardson *(G-17412)*

Transdata Inc ....E 972 418-7717
Carrollton *(G-2839)*

Ultratest International Inc ....E 214 340-5252
Dallas *(G-5130)*

▲ Uson Lp ....E 281 671-2000
Houston *(G-12504)*

Van London Company Inc ....E 713 772-6641
Houston *(G-12527)*

Venable Corporation ....F 512 949-3144
Austin *(G-1627)*

▲ Verity Instruments Inc ....F 972 446-9990
Carrollton *(G-2896)*

Wabtec Mfg Solutions LLC ....F 814 449-9619
Fort Worth *(G-7114)*

Web Technology Inc ....E 214 343-9238
Dallas *(G-5177)*

Wenzel Associates Inc ....D 512 835-2038
Austin *(G-1655)*

▼ Yokogawa Corporation America .....E 281 340-3800
Sugar Land *(G-19576)*

3826 Analytical Instruments

A-Vox Systems Inc ....F 210 695-8242
San Antonio *(G-17851)*

Advanced Imaging Services ....F 210 680-4749
San Antonio *(G-17867)*

Alert Technologies Inc ....E 281 326-9900
Houston *(G-8534)*

Alpha Masurement Solutions LLC .....C 832 456-4100
Houston *(G-8563)*

Altus Health System ....F 409 554-0131
Beaumont *(G-1850)*

Ambion Diagnostics Inc ....C 512 651-0200
Austin *(G-912)*

Analytcal Applied Slutions LLC ....F 281 255-6537
Houston *(G-8635)*

▲ Analytical Sensors Instrs LLC ......D 281 565-8818
Houston *(G-8636)*

Applied Rigaku Tech Inc ....E 512 225-1796
Austin *(G-1691)*

ARC Pressure Data Inc ....F 432 563-2371
Aubrey *(G-846)*

Astrotech Corporation ....G 512 485-9530
Webster *(G-20633)*

Beckman Coulter Inc ....D 714 961-6558
College Station *(G-3177)*

Becton Dickinson and Company ....F 210 526-5000
San Antonio *(G-17943)*

Bruker Optics Inc ....F 978 439-9899
Conroe *(G-3266)*

Daniel Industries Inc ....E 713 467-6000
Houston *(G-9401)*

Detectachem Inc ....E 855 573-3537
Stafford *(G-19302)*

E-Spectrum Technologies Inc ....F 210 696-8848
San Antonio *(G-18080)*

▼ Expotech USA Inc ....E 281 879-8998
Houston *(G-9728)*

Fci Environmental Inc ....E 702 262-3953
Dallas *(G-4356)*

Fei Efa Inc ....F 972 792-1644
Richardson *(G-17309)*

First Capital Intl Inc ....G 713 629-4866
Houston *(G-9790)*

◆ Geospace Technologies Corp ....A 713 986-4444
Houston *(G-9945)*

Geotherm Usa LLC ....F 281 985-9344
Cypress *(G-3796)*

Gray Green Biomedical Svcs LLC .....G 832 288-5958
Pearland *(G-16566)*

Green Ocean Sciences Inc ....E 512 200-4505
Austin *(G-1192)*

▲ Gulf Coast Envmtl Systems LLC ....E 832 476-9024
Conroe *(G-3299)*

▲ Heath Consultants Incorporated ...C 713 844-1300
Houston *(G-10146)*

▲ Helena Laboratories Corp ....B 409 842-3714
  Beaumont *(G-1901)*

Helena Laboratories Corp ....B 409 842-3714
  Beaumont *(G-1902)*

Hempstead Halide Inc ....F 409 572-2505
  Galveston *(G-7400)*

Horiba Instruments Inc ....D 949 250-4811
  Pasadena *(G-16455)*

Iris Biotech LLC ....E 512 219-8020
  Austin *(G-1244)*

▲ Isgas Incorporated ....G 713 645-5886
  Houston *(G-10425)*

Ixrf Inc ....F 512 386-6100
  Austin *(G-1246)*

Ixrf Systems Inc ....F 512 386-6100
  Austin *(G-1247)*

Joe Ross ....F 903 450-9960
  Greenville *(G-8079)*

Kap Technologies Inc ....F 972 359-7060
  Plano *(G-16900)*

Key Scientific Products ....E 512 846-1440
  Hutto *(G-12882)*

Kin-Tek Analytical Inc ....G 409 938-3627
  La Marque *(G-13709)*

Kin-Tek Laboratories Inc ....F 409 938-3627
  La Marque *(G-13710)*

Life Technologies Corporation ....F 512 721-4857
  Austin *(G-1293)*

Ludlum Measurements Inc ....B 325 235-5494
  Sweetwater *(G-19633)*

Mo2 Inc ....F 214 575-7600
  Dallas *(G-4682)*

National Energetics Inc ....F 512 382-1894
  Round Rock *(G-17674)*

Ol Corporation ....C 979 690-1711
  College Station *(G-3196)*

Pearland Mri and Imaging Ctr ....F 281 412-3916
  Pearland *(G-16591)*

▲ Petroleum Analyzer Company LP ......D 281 940-1803
  Houston *(G-11304)*

▲ Raman Systems Inc ....E 512 673-7364
  Austin *(G-1451)*

▲ Rigaku Americas Corporation ....F 281 362-2300
  The Woodlands *(G-19911)*

◆ S&M International Co Inc ....F 281 749-8289
  Katy *(G-13378)*

Servomex Company ....F 281 295-5800
  Sugar Land *(G-19555)*

Shimadzu Scientific Instrs Inc ....F 713 467-1151
  Houston *(G-11868)*

Southern Methodist University ....F 214 768-2756
  Dallas *(G-4988)*

Spectra Dynamics Corporation ....F 512 255-2233
  Liberty Hill *(G-14129)*

Spectrasensors Inc ....F 713 466-3172
  Houston *(G-12007)*

Techcomp (usa) Inc ....F 512 215-8335
  Austin *(G-1556)*

Tecmag Inc ....F 713 667-8747
  Houston *(G-12178)*

Test Incorporated ....F 713 983-2800
  Houston *(G-12213)*

Testamerica Air Emission Corp ....F 800 394-1194
  Carrollton *(G-2828)*

Texas Best Proteins LP ....E 940 769-2028
  Santo *(G-18739)*

Texas Instruments Incorporated ....B 972 995-2011
  Dallas *(G-5073)*

Thermo Fisher Scientific Inc ....D 512 251-1525
  Austin *(G-1573)*

Thermo Fisher Scientific Inc ....F 972 437-3327
  Richardson *(G-17410)*

▲ Trajan Scientific Americas Inc ....F 512 837-7190
  Pflugerville *(G-16689)*

▲ Valco Instruments Company ....B 713 688-9345
  Houston *(G-12517)*

▲ Van London Company ....F 713 772-6641
  Houston *(G-12526)*

Yokogawa Leisure Analysis Div ....F 281 488-0409
  Houston *(G-12718)*

3827 Optical Instruments

▲ America Ilsin Tech LLC ....F 972 556-0916
  Carrollton *(G-2696)*

▲ American Electro Optics LLC ....F 817 546-0993
  Fort Worth *(G-6380)*

Amorphous Materials Inc ....G 972 494-5624
  Garland *(G-7436)*

▲ Applied Optoelectronics Inc ....C 281 295-1800
  Sugar Land *(G-19445)*

Archer Optx Inc ....E 972 722-1064
  Rockwall *(G-17537)*

Carl Zeiss Vision Inc ....F 972 906-9663
  Lewisville *(G-14033)*

◆ Ci Systems Inc ....F 805 520-2233
  Carrollton *(G-2715)*

◆ Dac Vision Incorporated ....D 972 677-2700
  Garland *(G-7474)*

Digital Video Camera Co ....F 512 301-9564
  Austin *(G-1094)*

Displays & Optical Tech ....F 512 246-6400
  Georgetown *(G-7648)*

Egma LLC ....F 972 488-3462
  Dallas *(G-4303)*

▲ Elbit Systems of America LLC ....E 817 234-6600
  Fort Worth *(G-6609)*

Eyemasters 13 Inc ....F 254 751-0010
  Waco *(G-20400)*

Helena Laboratories Corp ....B 409 842-3714
  Beaumont *(G-1902)*

I O U Enterprises Inc ....F 956 631-3366
  McAllen *(G-14870)*

▲ National Optcl & Scientfic Ins ....E 210 590-9010
  Schertz *(G-18757)*

Nivisys LLC ....G 915 633-8354
  El Paso *(G-5897)*

Omega Optics Inc ....F 512 996-8833
  Austin *(G-1378)*

Optex Systems Inc ....E 972 629-1701
  Dallas *(G-4764)*

Optex Systems Inc ....D 972 764-5700
  Richardson *(G-17368)*

Optex Systems Holdings Inc ....D 972 764-5700
  Richardson *(G-17369)*

Optical Filter Source LLC ....F 512 248-0605
  Round Rock *(G-17676)*

Origin Instruments Corp ....F 972 606-8740
  Grand Prairie *(G-7942)*

Peak Nanosystems LLC ....E 469 464-4504
  Coppell *(G-3434)*

▲ Petroleum Geo-Services Inc ....C 281 509-8000
  Houston *(G-11307)*

Pgs Finance Inc ....A 281 509-8000
  Houston *(G-11318)*

Ross Optical Industries Inc ....F 915 595-5417
  El Paso *(G-5946)*

▲ Schneider Optical Machines Inc ....F 972 247-4000
  Frisco *(G-7311)*

▼ Summit Night Vision Group Inc ....F 972 992-0046
  Plano *(G-17013)*

▲ Tyrex Group Ltd ....F 512 623-4694
  Austin *(G-1603)*

Vision Centers PA ....E 512 258-2020
  Austin *(G-1638)*

3829 Measuring & Controlling Devices, NEC

3M Company ....B 512 984-2370
  Austin *(G-870)*

Accent Environmental Services ....F 936 853-2264
  Pollok *(G-17090)*

Advanced Energy Industries Inc ....C 512 339-7100
  Austin *(G-889)*

Advanced Geosciences Inc ....E 512 335-3338
  Austin *(G-890)*

Allestec Corporation ....F 281 359-1519
  Kingwood *(G-13637)*

Alpha Tech International Inc ....A 281 240-8989
  Stafford *(G-19284)*

Ameri Source Manufacturing Inc ....F 903 677-7734
  Ben Wheeler *(G-2031)*

AMI Investments LLC ....E 972 717-5555
  Carrollton *(G-2698)*

Angus Measurement Services LP ....F 432 332-7200
  Odessa *(G-15915)*

▼ Anue Systems Inc ....D 512 600-5400
  Austin *(G-923)*

▲ Arbin Corporation ....E 979 690-2751
  College Station *(G-3174)*

Arbin Instruments Inc ....E 979 690-2751
  College Station *(G-3175)*

◆ Atec Inc ....C 281 276-2700
  Stafford *(G-19289)*

▲ Automatic Products Corp ....C 972 272-6422
  Garland *(G-7444)*

Axcelis Technologies Inc ....B 214 377-7298
  Richardson *(G-17275)*

◆ Bae Systems Resolution Inc ....E 713 868-7700
  Houston *(G-8789)*

Bobcat Contracting LLC ....E 432 332-1141
  Midland *(G-15145)*

Brk Brands Inc ....F 915 860-3500
  El Paso *(G-5673)*

Centrax International Corp ....E 281 465-0781
  Spring *(G-19203)*

Chca Bayshore LP ....G 713 359-2000
  Pasadena *(G-16406)*

Climax Portable Mch Tls Inc ....F 800 333-8311
  Deer Park *(G-5265)*

Coastal Flow Measurement Inc ....D 713 477-1956
  Houston *(G-9225)*

D and C Storm Solutions ....F 281 557-3450
  League City *(G-13954)*

▼ Daily Instruments Corporation ....E 713 780-8600
  Houston *(G-9395)*

Daniel Industries Inc ....E 713 467-6000
  Houston *(G-9401)*

Design Flex LLC ....E 940 825-6629
  Nocona *(G-15868)*

Dfw Instrument LLC ....F 214 217-7600
  Addison *(G-116)*

Draeger Safety Diagnostics Inc ....E 972 929-1100
  Irving *(G-13003)*

▲ Dsx Access Systems Inc ....E 214 553-6140
  Dallas *(G-4282)*

Dunns Valve Testers Inc ....E 281 350-4767
  Spring *(G-19207)*

Echometer Company ....E 940 767-4334
  Wichita Falls *(G-20763)*

Eligibility Trckng Calculators ....E 210 323-7846
  San Antonio *(G-18087)*

Ellis Tool & Machine Inc ....E 903 546-6540
  Tom Bean *(G-19951)*

ESP Enterprises Inc ....D 281 444-2377
  Houston *(G-9697)*

Exer-Tech Inc ....F 281 493-2220
  Katy *(G-13402)*

▲ Exile Technologies Corporation ....F 713 343-5662
  Houston *(G-9725)*

◆ Fairfield Industries Inc ....E 281 275-7500
  Houston *(G-9752)*

Fci Environmental Inc ....E 702 262-3953
  Dallas *(G-4356)*

Fenner & Associates Inc ....F 281 970-9977
  College Station *(G-3182)*

Freedom Communication Tech Inc ....E 844 903-7333
  Kilgore *(G-13555)*

G4 Spatial Technologies LLC ....E 512 447-9879
  Austin *(G-1176)*

▲ Gagemaker LP ....E 713 472-7360
  Pasadena *(G-16445)*

◆ Gardner Dnver Wtr Jtting Syste ....C 281 448-5800
  Houston *(G-9898)*

Geophysical Technology Inc ....F 281 222-3078
  Bellaire *(G-1996)*

◆ Geospace Technologies Corp ....A 713 986-4444
  Houston *(G-9945)*

Global Nucleonics LLC ....E 281 578-7900
  Houston *(G-9975)*

Global Vacuum Systems Inc ....F 800 843-0866
  Navasota *(G-15736)*

Gtl Supply Solutions LLC ....E 214 644-2402
  Allen *(G-271)*

Heitman Laboratories Inc ....F 972 982-2224
  Allen *(G-273)*

▲ Higuchi International Corp ....E 210 633-2877
  Elmendorf *(G-6069)*

▲ Higuchi Manufacturing Amer LLC ....C 210 633-2877
  San Antonio *(G-18167)*

Hilflo LLC ....F 936 756-2020
  Conroe *(G-3305)*

Horiba Instruments Inc ....E 408 730-4772
  Austin *(G-1209)*

Industrial Safety Tech LLC ....A 713 559-9200
  The Woodlands *(G-19884)*

◆ Inova Geophysical Inc ....E 281 568-2000
  Sugar Land *(G-19499)*

◆ Ion Geophysical Corporation ....C 281 933-3339
  Houston *(G-10413)*

Ion Science Inc ....F 877 864-7710
  Stafford *(G-19332)*

Kimray Inc ....F 936 441-2468
  Conroe *(G-3317)*

Kwivik Inc ....F 469 424-3144
  McKinney *(G-14949)*

▲ Laversab Inc ....E 281 325-8300
  Sugar Land *(G-19503)*

Ludlum Measurements Inc ....B 325 235-5494
  Sweetwater *(G-19633)*

Ludlum Measurements Inc ....D 325 235-1418
  Sweetwater *(G-19634)*

Ludlum Measurements Inc	D	325 235-4276
Sweetwater *(G-19635)*		
Macaulay Controls Company	F	281 282-0100
Webster *(G-20640)*		
Madden Systems Inc	F	432 332-0255
Odessa *(G-16069)*		
Magnetic Field Effects LLC	F	713 856-8111
Houston *(G-10735)*		
Management Services Intl	F	713 333-0200
Houston *(G-10744)*		
▲ Marlin Controls Inc	F	214 553-5700
Dallas *(G-4635)*		
Measurement Technologies Ltd	G	817 571-9981
Colleyville *(G-3220)*		
Medical Components of America	G	830 237-6405
Seguin *(G-18851)*		
Metrix Instrument Co LP	D	281 940-1802
Houston *(G-10854)*		
Metrix PMC/Beta	E	713 461-2131
Houston *(G-10855)*		
Mo2 Inc	F	214 575-7600
Dallas *(G-4682)*		
MPA International LP	C	915 474-7832
El Paso *(G-5887)*		
Murphy Fw	D	281 633-4500
Rosenberg *(G-17590)*		
Myramid Analytical Inc	F	512 288-5093
Austin *(G-865)*		
▲ National Manufacturing LLC	F	281 856-7693
Houston *(G-10970)*		
Omron Management Ctr Amer Inc	E	489 724-2899
Dallas *(G-4761)*		
On-X Life Technologies Inc	D	512 832-8548
Austin *(G-1384)*		
◆ Orbital Systems LLC	E	972 915-3669
Irving *(G-13133)*		
Otis Instruments Inc	E	432 563-0007
Midland *(G-15332)*		
Pem-Tech Inc	G	281 494-2079
Sugar Land *(G-19524)*		
Plotter Depot Corporation	F	469 608-9747
Rockwall *(G-17559)*		
◆ Provibtech Inc	E	713 830-7601
Houston *(G-11466)*		
◆ Quest-TEC Solutions Inc	E	281 240-0440
Houston *(G-11510)*		
◆ Rampak Group Inc	F	713 678-8898
Houston *(G-11537)*		
Redline Instruments Inc	F	979 776-7200
College Station *(G-3199)*		
Reedholm Instruments Co	E	512 869-1935
Georgetown *(G-7674)*		
Robert U Neese	F	281 342-2884
Boerne *(G-2134)*		
RSD Security Scanners LLC	E	915 590-4441
El Paso *(G-5947)*		
Sabio Environmental LLC	E	512 869-0544
Round Rock *(G-17689)*		
Safeplex Systems Inc	F	832 582-7029
Houston *(G-11724)*		
Sensatronics LLC	F	800 633-1033
Austin *(G-1711)*		
◆ Sercel Inc	B	281 492-6688
Houston *(G-11834)*		
◆ Sharewell LP	E	281 288-2560
Houston *(G-11845)*		
◆ Shockwatch Inc	E	214 630-9625
Dallas *(G-4957)*		
Sims Aviation Inc	F	972 733-3828
Addison *(G-163)*		
▲ Sonardyne Inc	F	281 890-2120
Houston *(G-11950)*		
▲ Sonatest Inc	G	210 697-0335
San Antonio *(G-18483)*		
Sor Inc	F	409 842-3334
Houston *(G-11953)*		
Standards Testing Labs Inc	D	325 651-4946
San Angelo *(G-17828)*		
STI Vibration Monitoring Inc	F	281 334-0766
League City *(G-13979)*		
Stress Engineering Svcs Inc	E	713 466-1527
Houston *(G-12079)*		
Sunbelt Design & Dev Inc	D	210 227-9162
San Antonio *(G-18511)*		
▲ Tdk Rf Solutions Inc	E	512 258-9478
Cedar Park *(G-2987)*		
Technical Automtn Svcs Co Ltd	D	281 474-3232
Seabrook *(G-18792)*		
▲ Teledyne Detcon Inc	C	281 367-4100
The Woodlands *(G-19926)*		

Teledyne Instruments Inc	C	713 666-2561
Houston *(G-12191)*		
Teledyne Real Time Systems Inc	E	830 990-2340
Fredericksburg *(G-7189)*		
Temperture Measurement Systems	E	800 967-6498
Malakoff *(G-14637)*		
Teradyne Inc	D	972 231-5384
Plano *(G-17025)*		
Texas Electronics Inc	F	214 327-2566
Dallas *(G-5058)*		
◆ Texas Sampling Inc	E	361 575-8087
Victoria *(G-20309)*		
Thermo Finnigan LLC	E	512 251-1400
Austin *(G-1572)*		
Thermo Sensors Corporation	F	972 494-1566
Garland *(G-7601)*		
Thermocontrol Inc	E	713 780-8600
Houston *(G-12272)*		
True Shot LLC	F	972 505-0433
Odessa *(G-16183)*		
United Elec Instrmentation Ltd	D	979 265-1256
Clute *(G-3161)*		
▲ Uson Lp	E	281 671-2000
Houston *(G-12504)*		
◆ Welker Inc	E	281 491-2331
Sugar Land *(G-19571)*		
▲ Williamsrdm Inc	D	817 872-1500
Fort Worth *(G-7148)*		
▲ Wireless Seismic Inc	E	832 532-5080
Stafford *(G-19399)*		

3841 Surgical & Medical Instrs & Apparatus

3M Company	E	915 860-5408
Socorro *(G-19016)*		
A-Vox Systems Inc	F	210 695-8242
San Antonio *(G-17851)*		
Accumed Biotech LLC	F	315 790-0466
Houston *(G-8459)*		
Acelity LP Inc	E	210 524-9000
San Antonio *(G-17859)*		
▲ Alcon Laboratories Inc	A	817 293-0450
Fort Worth *(G-6363)*		
▲ Alcon Laboratories Holdg Corp	A	817 293-0450
Fort Worth *(G-6365)*		
Alcon Research LLC	C	817 551-4555
Fort Worth *(G-6366)*		
Alcon Surgical LLC	A	817 293-0450
Fort Worth *(G-6367)*		
Alcon Vision LLC	D	817 293-0450
Fort Worth *(G-6368)*		
Alcon Vision LLC	E	713 668-9100
Houston *(G-8532)*		
Argon Medical Devices Inc	B	903 675-9321
Athens *(G-819)*		
◆ Argon Medical Devices Inc	B	903 675-9321
Frisco *(G-7266)*		
Armamentarium Inc	G	281 528-5700
Spring *(G-19101)*		
Arthrocare Corporation	C	512 391-3900
Austin *(G-937)*		
Astura Medical	F	760 814-8047
Irving *(G-12934)*		
Asuragen Inc	D	512 681-5200
Austin *(G-942)*		
▲ Atrion Corporation	E	972 390-9800
Allen *(G-253)*		
▲ Attentus Medical Sales Inc	G	281 776-5188
Spring *(G-19199)*		
B Braun Medical Inc	A	972 245-2243
Carrollton *(G-2700)*		
▼ Banyan International Corp	E	888 782-8548
Abilene *(G-15)*		
Baxter Healthcare Corporation	A	903 586-6502
Jacksonville *(G-13228)*		
Bay Area Anesthesia Associates	F	361 857-8588
Corpus Christi *(G-3482)*		
Becton Dickinson and Company	B	713 839-0753
Houston *(G-8849)*		
Becton Dickinson and Company	F	210 526-5000
San Antonio *(G-17943)*		
◆ Berchtold Corporation	C	843 569-6100
Flower Mound *(G-6260)*		
Biomerics LLC	B	903 677-9166
Athens *(G-821)*		
Bioniche Animal Health USA Inc	A	706 549-4503
Fort Worth *(G-6452)*		
Blackstone Medical Inc	D	214 937-2000
Lewisville *(G-14028)*		
Blue Medical Services Inc	E	954 417-5442
Cypress *(G-3781)*		

Breg Inc	F	972 647-0884
Grand Prairie *(G-7848)*		
Byrne Medical Inc	C	936 539-0391
Conroe *(G-3269)*		
C R Bard Inc	B	915 781-2489
El Paso *(G-5676)*		
C R Bard Inc	A	956 205-7100
Pharr *(G-16695)*		
Cardioquip LLC	E	979 691-0202
College Station *(G-3180)*		
Carefusion 213 LLC	B	915 231-5000
El Paso *(G-5683)*		
▲ CBI Laboratories Inc	D	972 241-7546
Fort Worth *(G-6497)*		
Cellright Technologies LLC	E	210 659-9353
Universal City *(G-20181)*		
◆ Celonova Biosciences Inc	C	210 489-4000
San Antonio *(G-17990)*		
Cen-Tex Machining Inc	D	512 255-1477
Round Rock *(G-17629)*		
Compass Orthopedic Tech & Pdts	F	713 995-7010
Houston *(G-9257)*		
Covidien LP	B	903 886-3153
Commerce *(G-3242)*		
Crest Orthopedic Implants LLC	E	254 931-6996
Georgetown *(G-7645)*		
Ctl Medical Corporation	F	214 545-5830
Addison *(G-114)*		
Cumberland Additive Inc	F	512 990-9100
Pflugerville *(G-16666)*		
◆ D4d Technologies LLC	C	972 534-3101
Richardson *(G-17296)*		
Dermatech International Inc	E	210 558-1387
Helotes *(G-8236)*		
Diversified Diagnostic Pdts	F	281 955-5323
Houston *(G-9482)*		
Dlk Medical Technologies Inc	E	214 613-5682
Dallas *(G-4265)*		
Dreamwrks Ansthesia Assoc Pllc	F	936 639-3036
Lufkin *(G-14525)*		
Eclipse Medcorp LLC	D	800 759-6876
Lewisville *(G-14047)*		
Egret Medical Products Inc	F	214 291-0238
Garland *(G-7484)*		
Eli-Shir Ltd	G	281 464-9616
Houston *(G-9601)*		
Eminent Spine LLC	E	512 868-5980
Georgetown *(G-7649)*		
▲ Epimed International Inc	E	972 373-9090
Farmers Branch *(G-6196)*		
Everly Well Inc	E	512 309-5588
Austin *(G-1143)*		
Evolution Spine LLC	F	214 228-6252
Dallas *(G-4339)*		
▲ Eyesys Vision Inc	G	281 885-3800
Houston *(G-9741)*		
Fairmont Diagnstc Cntr & Open	E	713 946-1500
Pasadena *(G-16436)*		
Falcon Pharmaceuticals Ltd	A	800 343-2133
Fort Worth *(G-6623)*		
Footprint Medical Inc	E	210 226-2600
San Antonio *(G-18120)*		
Galt Medical Corp	E	972 271-5177
Garland *(G-7492)*		
▲ Genesis Biosystems Inc	E	972 315-7888
Lewisville *(G-14051)*		
Genomics Usa Inc	F	847 359-1032
Round Rock *(G-17660)*		
Guidant Sales LLC	D	713 218-4069
Houston *(G-10056)*		
Healthpoint Ltd	C	817 900-4000
Fort Worth *(G-6692)*		
Healthtech Solutions Inc	F	763 559-7082
Austin *(G-1694)*		
▲ Helena Laboratories Corp	B	409 842-3714
Beaumont *(G-1901)*		
Helena Laboratories Corp	B	409 842-3714
Beaumont *(G-1902)*		
▲ HMC Instrument & Mch Works Ltd	E	713 468-1426
Houston *(G-10189)*		
Hypertec Inc	F	940 564-5600
Olney *(G-16221)*		
Imex Veterinary Inc	F	903 295-2196
Longview *(G-14249)*		
Infused Medical Technology Inc	F	214 330-4000
Dallas *(G-4498)*		
Inogen Inc	A	972 616-5500
Plano *(G-16891)*		
Instrument Specialists Inc	F	830 249-9535
Boerne *(G-2123)*		

Insurgical Inc....F....512 318-2980
Austin (G-1230)
▲ International Biophysics Corp....E....512 326-3244
Austin (G-1237)
Itec Manufacturing LLC....F....903 365-6390
Winnsboro (G-20897)
Kdl Medical Inc....F....972 783-7005
Richardson (G-17340)
Kyocera Medical Tech Inc....D....909 557-2360
Austin (G-1278)
Lake Region Medical Inc....C....978 570-6900
El Paso (G-5838)
LDR Holding Corporation....E....512 344-3333
Austin (G-1285)
▲ Life-Tech Inc....D....281 491-6600
Houston (G-10636)
Lone Star Medical Products Inc....E....281 340-6000
Stafford (G-19348)
Luminex Corporation....F....512 219-8020
Austin (G-1308)
Luminex Corporation....C....512 219-8020
Austin (G-1309)
Mc Manus Instrument Co Inc....F....409 834-2419
Village Mills (G-20338)
Medex South....E....713 838-1989
Houston (G-10818)
▲ Mediana Technologies Corp....E....425 406-2262
San Antonio (G-18289)
Medical Device Tech Inc....E....800 338-0440
Athens (G-831)
Medinc of Texas LP....D....713 979-4364
Houston (G-10820)
Medivators Inc....C....936 539-0391
Conroe (G-3330)
Medline Industries Inc....C....281 574-6200
Katy (G-13371)
Medtronic Minimed Inc....A....830 438-0383
Bulverde (G-2556)
Medtronic PS Medical Inc....C....817 788-6400
Haltom City (G-8153)
Medtronic Usa Inc....E....210 395-5769
San Antonio (G-18290)
Merc Medical Supply Co Inc....F....713 270-4936
Houston (G-10831)
Merit Medical Systems Inc....C....832 463-5100
Houston (G-10837)
Metric Medical Devices Inc....G....830 535-6300
Helotes (G-8243)
Micro Engineering Inc....F....936 291-6891
Huntsville (G-12819)
Micromed Technology Inc....E....713 838-9210
Houston (G-10868)
Microtek Medical Inc....E....903 597-2568
Tyler (G-20128)
Millar Inc....D....832 667-7000
Houston (G-10882)
Mli Supply Inc....F....713 266-1400
Stafford (G-19354)
Mobile Surgical Tech Inc....F....972 735-8003
Dallas (G-3849)
NA Acquisition Company....C....817 231-1300
Fort Worth (G-6859)
Neuro Resource Group Intl Inc....E....972 665-1810
Richardson (G-17365)
▲ Novosci Corp....E....281 363-4949
Conroe (G-3344)
▲ Nurse Assist LLC....C....800 649-6800
Haltom City (G-8155)
Nuvectra Corporation....D....214 474-3103
Plano (G-16949)
Origen Biomedical Inc....E....512 474-7278
Austin (G-1393)
Orthofix Inc....C....214 937-2000
Lewisville (G-14076)
Orthofix Inc....C....214 937-2000
Lewisville (G-14077)
▲ Orthofix Inc....C....214 937-2000
Lewisville (G-14078)
Orthofix Medical Inc....F....214 937-2000
Lewisville (G-14079)
Osseus Fusion Systems LLC....F....888 330-5960
Dallas (G-4770)
Osteogenics Biomedical Inc....F....806 796-1923
Lubbock (G-14455)
Osteomed LLC....C....972 677-4600
Addison (G-154)
◆ Pan-America Hyperbarics Inc....F....972 423-0377
Plano (G-16964)
Power Plastic Inc....F....713 957-3695
Houston (G-11377)
Procyrion Inc....F....713 579-9224
Houston (G-11435)
Prytime Medical Devices Inc....F....210 340-0116
Boerne (G-2132)
Quality Bioresources Inc....E....830 372-4797
Seguin (G-18858)
▲ Quest Medical Inc....C....800 627-0226
Allen (G-297)
◆ Rampak Group Inc....F....713 678-8898
Houston (G-11537)
▲ Refocus Group Inc....F....214 368-0200
Dallas (G-4880)
◆ Retractable Technologies Inc....C....972 294-1010
Little Elm (G-14141)
▼ Rockwell Medical Tech Inc....E....972 874-2130
Grapevine (G-8052)
Rush Eye Associates Pllc....E....806 353-0125
Amarillo (G-460)
▲ Seisa Medical Inc....E....915 774-4321
El Paso (G-5954)
Semmt Inc....G....713 966-5829
Houston (G-11826)
Seno Medical Instruments Inc....E....210 615-6501
San Antonio (G-18466)
Siteselect Inc....E....956 207-5587
McAllen (G-14906)
Skeletal Kinetics LLC....E....408 366-5000
Addison (G-164)
Smith & Nephew Wound MGT....C....800 876-1261
Fort Worth (G-6995)
Spectral Md Inc....F....972 499-4934
Dallas (G-4996)
Spectrum Lifesciences LLC....E....214 492-0506
Irving (G-13188)
Spinesmith Holdings LLC....E....512 637-2073
Austin (G-1527)
Stand By Systems Inc....D....214 346-2980
Dallas (G-5002)
▲ Stealth Products LLC....D....512 715-9995
Burnet (G-2614)
▲ Stryker Communications Inc....C....972 410-7000
Flower Mound (G-6283)
Stryker Corporation....C....214 461-4663
Addison (G-166)
▲ Systagenix Wound MGT US Inc....D....617 774-5500
San Antonio (G-18518)
Technical Innovations LLC....E....979 849-8700
Angleton (G-580)
Teresa A McVicker Pc....G....254 526-2823
Killeen (G-13617)
Texas Medical Technology LLC....F....832 512-7727
Houston (G-12239)
▲ Tracey Technologies Corp....G....281 445-1666
Houston (G-12338)
Transplant Technology Inc....E....210 696-7616
San Antonio (G-18563)
Tri Star Metals Inc....E....940 433-2173
Boyd (G-2209)
Trilliant Surgical LLC....G....800 495-2919
Houston (G-12373)
Trimira LLC....F....713 984-8994
Houston (G-12374)
Vax-Immune LLC....F....832 423-0055
Houston (G-12540)
Viant Medical Inc....F....830 792-1156
Kerrville (G-13528)
Viant San Antonio Inc....C....210 684-7553
San Antonio (G-18592)
Vitaltech Affiliates LLC....E....214 886-5249
Plano (G-17047)
▼ Wenzel Spine Inc....F....512 469-0600
Austin (G-1656)
Winfield Laboratories Inc....E....972 234-0940
Richardson (G-17430)
Zimmer....A....800 613-6131
Austin (G-1717)

3842 Orthopedic, Prosthetic & Surgical Appliances/Splys

A Speclzed Apprach To Prsthtic....F....832 813-5278
Spring (G-19190)
▲ ABM International Inc....D....936 441-4401
Montgomery (G-15624)
Acuity Surgical Devices LLC....F....214 862-5017
Dallas (G-3886)
▲ Adaptive Switch Laboratories....F....440 329-6276
Spicewood (G-19091)
Advanced Arm Dynamics....G....214 260-3197
Irving (G-12923)
Advanced Biomechanics....E....956 971-8200
Schertz (G-18742)
Advanced Limb & Brace....F....806 351-1775
Amarillo (G-391)
Advanced Orthotics Prosthetics....F....956 971-8200
Edinburg (G-5573)
Alafair Biosciences Inc....F....512 739-9510
Austin (G-903)
▲ Alex Orthopedic Inc....E....972 641-9680
Grand Prairie (G-7826)
Allen Orthotics & Prosthetics....F....432 683-3788
Midland (G-15112)
Allsport Dynamics Inc....F....936 569-1003
Nacogdoches (G-15684)
Argon Medical Devices Inc....B....903 675-9321
Athens (G-819)
◆ Argon Medical Devices Inc....B....903 675-9321
Frisco (G-7266)
▼ Armortex Inc....E....800 880-8306
Schertz (G-18744)
◆ Avcor Health Care Products Inc....E....817 551-0595
Grand Prairie (G-7838)
B C O Black Cane Original....G....832 883-5774
Houston (G-8774)
Baker O & P Enterprises Inc....F....817 332-7313
Fort Worth (G-6423)
▲ Bartec US Corporation....F....281 214-8542
Houston (G-8819)
Becton Dickinson and Company....F....210 526-5000
San Antonio (G-17943)
▲ Blacksheep Inc....B....903 592-3853
Tyler (G-20059)
Blackstone Medical Inc....D....214 937-2000
Lewisville (G-14028)
Bnx Converting LLC....F....713 936-2726
Houston (G-8930)
▲ Border Opprtnity Sver Systems....E....830 775-1225
Del Rio (G-5308)
Bound Tree Medical LLC....E....469 771-4010
Flower Mound (G-6261)
▲ Brazos Oaks Ltd....E....254 399-0505
Waco (G-20370)
BSN Medical Inc....E....956 926-4400
Hidalgo (G-8304)
Cardinal Health Inc....D....915 781-7465
El Paso (G-5682)
Cardinal Health 200 LLC....C....903 586-6502
Jacksonville (G-13232)
Cen-Tex Machining Inc....D....512 255-1477
Round Rock (G-17629)
Certoplast North America Inc....E....832 384-1244
Houston (G-9146)
Cryo Zone LLC....F....972 523-6060
Dallas (G-4187)
Dibellos Dynamic Orthotics....E....713 747-4171
Houston (G-9462)
Djo Global Inc....F....512 832-9500
Austin (G-1097)
◆ Djo Global Inc....A....800 321-9549
Lewisville (G-14044)
Dynatec Scientific Labs....E....915 849-1322
El Paso (G-5727)
El Paso Prosthetic Center LLC....E....915 234-2408
El Paso (G-5738)
▲ Encore Medical LP....A....512 832-9500
Austin (G-1125)
ESP Safety Inc....E....972 310-0754
Houston (G-9698)
Ethicon Inc....C....325 482-5200
San Angelo (G-17797)
Eugene B Smith & Co Inc....E....409 763-6401
Pasadena (G-16432)
▲ Freedom Wheels Inc....F....713 864-1460
Houston (G-9860)
Guard-Line Inc....D....903 796-4111
Atlanta (G-844)
▲ Guard-Line Inc....C....903 796-4111
Atlanta (G-843)
Gwm Products LLC....E....855 872-2013
Irving (G-13047)
Gwm Products LLC....F....855 872-2013
Allen (G-272)
Hanger Inc....E....817 923-2101
Fort Worth (G-6687)
Hanger Inc....C....512 777-3800
Austin (G-1197)
Hanger Prosthetics & Orthotics....E....817 923-2101
Fort Worth (G-6688)
◆ Hearing Lab Technology LLC....D....469 586-0448
Fort Worth (G-6693)

S I C

◆ Heubach Corporation.................E 214 291-0238
Garland *(G-7511)*

Howmedica Osteonics Corp ....G....... 512 491-0222
Austin *(G-1211)*

Ilc Dover LP ....E 281 333-8751
Houston *(G-10321)*

Integhrty Whlchair Van Svc LLC.......F .. 972 224-7017
Desoto *(G-5434)*

◆ International Biomedical Ltd ....D....... 512 873-0033
Austin *(G-1236)*

Isavela Enterprises Inc ....D....... 800 918-8242
McAllen *(G-14875)*

Isomedix Operations Inc ....E 915 855-2001
El Paso *(G-5819)*

▲ Jenessco Industries Inc ....E 281 498-8833
Houston *(G-10465)*

Joshuas Respiratory Care Inc ....F .. 469 916-9354
Dallas *(G-4539)*

▲ Kci Usa Inc ....C 800 275-4524
San Antonio *(G-18220)*

Kimberly-Clark Worldwide Inc ....F .. 972 281-1200
Irving *(G-13076)*

▲ Kinetic Concepts Inc ....B 800 531-5346
San Antonio *(G-18225)*

◆ KVP International Inc ....E 626 633-0077
McKinney *(G-14948)*

Letourneau Lflike Orthtics Prs ....F .. 409 832-5005
Beaumont *(G-1917)*

Lima Usa Inc ....E 817 385-0777
Arlington *(G-723)*

Lubbock Artfl Limb & Brace Ltd ......F .. 806 799-1518
Lubbock *(G-14440)*

▲ Maple Industries LLC ....F .. 972 745-2283
Irving *(G-13094)*

Medhab LLC ....E 817 233-5271
Mansfield *(G-14694)*

◆ Medical Concepts Dev Inc ....D....... 651 735-0498
El Paso *(G-5872)*

Medical Device Tech Inc ....E 800 338-0440
Athens *(G-831)*

▲ Medical Technology Inc ....C 972 647-0884
Grand Prairie *(G-7924)*

Medical Z ....F 210 681-7912
Houston *(G-10819)*

Medline Industries Inc ....C 281 574-6200
Katy *(G-13371)*

Medtex Converters Inc ....F .. 903 670-3270
Athens *(G-832)*

▲ Mentor Texas LP ....B 972 252-6060
Irving *(G-13105)*

MESA Orthopedic Supplies ....E 210 699-6911
San Antonio *(G-18292)*

Monogram Orthopaedics Inc ....F .. 512 399-2656
Austin *(G-1352)*

Muilenburg Prosthetics Inc ....F .. 713 524-3949
Houston *(G-10935)*

▲ Nearly ME Technologies LLC ....E 254 662-1752
Waco *(G-20437)*

◆ New Options Inc ....D....... 214 638-6422
Farmers Branch *(G-6208)*

Oceaneering International Inc ....B 281 228-5300
Houston *(G-11128)*

Orthofix Inc ....C 214 937-2000
Lewisville *(G-14076)*

Orthorx Inc ....F 214 501-0180
Plano *(G-16959)*

Osteocentric Technologies Inc ....F .. 800 969-0639
Austin *(G-1394)*

Pall Corporation ....A 713 896-9995
Jersey Village *(G-13304)*

▲ Petrohab Llc ....E 281 407-3800
Houston *(G-11302)*

Pivot Corporation ....D....... 972 475-4747
Rowlett *(G-17710)*

Precision Prosthetic Inc ....F .. 915 544-2961
El Paso *(G-5917)*

Prescotts Limbs & Braces ....E 210 224-0726
San Antonio *(G-18393)*

Quality Mattress Company Inc ....F .. 713 433-9155
Houston *(G-11497)*

◆ Rehab Plus Thrapeutic Pdts Inc ...F .. 806 791-2288
Wolfforth *(G-20911)*

Reynolds Consumer Products LLC ...E 254 770-4100
Temple *(G-19701)*

Royal Baths Manufacturing Co.........B 281 442-3400
Houston *(G-11682)*

Royal Baths Mfg Co Ltd ....E 817 589-7300
Richland Hills *(G-17447)*

Safety N95 LLC...........................F 281 624-1812
Houston *(G-11726)*

Safety Wear Ltd ....F 832 243-0100
Houston *(G-11727)*

▲ Seaflex Inc ....D....... 281 448-8821
Houston *(G-11800)*

Sheepskin Ranch Inc ....F 817 738-2485
Fort Worth *(G-6985)*

Smith & Nephew Inc ....F 512 358-5975
Austin *(G-1512)*

Smith & Nephew Inc ....B 817 900-4000
Fort Worth *(G-6994)*

Sola Prosthetics Inc ....F 972 492-7652
Carrollton *(G-2889)*

Spectrum Lifesciences LLC............E 214 492-0506
Irving *(G-13188)*

▲ Stanco Manufacturing Inc ....D....... 903 796-7936
Atlanta *(G-845)*

Starkey Laboratories Inc ....B 956 541-1917
Brownsville *(G-2408)*

Sten Corporation ....F 903 586-0914
Jacksonville *(G-13259)*

Texas Medical Industries Inc ....E 972 636-9556
Royse City *(G-17726)*

Texas Orthopaedic PDT Svcs LLC ...F .. 972 772-8776
Rockwall *(G-17570)*

Total Orthtic Prsthtic Sltions ....G....... 915 541-8677
El Paso *(G-6009)*

◆ Tri-Tex Enterprises Inc ....E 214 744-1246
Dallas *(G-5109)*

Trilliant Surgical LLC ....G....... 800 495-2919
Houston *(G-12373)*

Valley Orthopedic Inc ....E 512 771-1970
Austin *(G-1622)*

Valley Orthpd & Prosthetics ....G....... 956 686-0032
McAllen *(G-14915)*

Veterans Mfg LLC ....G....... 713 854-9261
Katy *(G-13454)*

Violet Care LLC ....F 210 482-0237
San Antonio *(G-18593)*

Weathrford Artfl Lift Systems ....F 281 630-5919
Houston *(G-12623)*

Wheel Rack ....F 210 342-0333
San Antonio *(G-18616)*

Xenex Disinfection Svcs Inc ....C 800 553-0069
San Antonio *(G-18627)*

Zimmer ....A 800 613-6131
Austin *(G-1717)*

3843 Dental Eqpt & Splys

Align Technology Inc ....F 408 470-1311
El Paso *(G-5641)*

◆ Beyond International Inc ....E 281 277-4352
Sugar Land *(G-19449)*

Certified Technical Profession ....G....... 757 831-9235
Canyon Lake *(G-2678)*

Clearcorrect Operating LLC............C 888 331-3323
Round Rock *(G-17633)*

Dentsply International Inc ....D....... 800 877-0020
San Antonio *(G-18051)*

Forward Science Holding Inc ....F 855 696-7254
Stafford *(G-19318)*

Forward Science Tech LLC ....F 855 696-7254
Stafford *(G-19319)*

Fuji Ceramics Inc ....E 972 722-1130
Rockwall *(G-17549)*

Gel Investments ....F 214 699-6996
Cedar Hill *(G-2942)*

International Tool & Mfg Co ....F 800 753-1004
Carrollton *(G-2769)*

Kerr Corporation ....C 800 355-5063
Coppell *(G-3426)*

◆ Kuraray America Inc ....E 800 423-9762
Houston *(G-10571)*

National Dentex Corporation ....F 903 597-3198
Tyler *(G-20132)*

Orthodontic Technologies Inc ....E 800 522-4636
Houston *(G-11194)*

▲ Ramon Guardiola ....F 956 330-8026
Mission *(G-15562)*

Scott Mc Gaha ....F 817 540-2309
Euless *(G-6157)*

Seretti Dental Lab Inc ....F 512 452-8989
Austin *(G-1495)*

Sybron Dental Specialties Inc..........A 469 635-6100
Coppell *(G-3448)*

Westbrook & Associates Inc ....F 972 840-0858
Richardson *(G-17426)*

Whitehill Manufacturing Inc ....F 281 240-2003
Stafford *(G-19398)*

3844 X-ray Apparatus & Tubes

Diversified Diagnostic Pdts ....F 281 955-5323
Houston *(G-9482)*

Protom International Inc ....D....... 972 410-3551
Flower Mound *(G-6277)*

▲ Rigaku Americas Corporation ....F 281 362-2300
The Woodlands *(G-19911)*

▲ S & S X-Ray Products Inc ....D....... 281 815-1300
Houston *(G-11708)*

3845 Electromedical & Electrotherapeutic Apparatus

Actium Biosystems.......................F 832 379-4222
Houston *(G-8471)*

Advanced Nrmdltion Systems Inc......B 972 309-8000
Plano *(G-16775)*

Alcon Laboratories Inc ....C 817 293-7276
Fort Worth *(G-6364)*

Apollo Endosurgery Inc ....E 512 279-5100
West Lake Hills *(G-20677)*

Argon Medical Devices Inc ....B 903 675-9321
Athens *(G-819)*

◆ Argon Medical Devices Inc ....B 903 675-9321
Frisco *(G-7266)*

Astanza Holdings LLC ....B 800 364-9010
Dallas *(G-3976)*

Avazzia Inc ....F 214 575-2820
Dallas *(G-3990)*

Bio-Signal Technologies LLC............G....... 214 405-0524
McKinney *(G-14926)*

Broadband Technology Corp ....E 806 698-0396
Lubbock *(G-14383)*

Ccmm Inc ....F 936 827-7930
Mission *(G-15549)*

Eclipse Medcorp LLC ....D....... 800 759-6876
Lewisville *(G-14047)*

▲ Electromedical Pdts Intl Inc ....E 940 328-0788
Mineral Wells *(G-15525)*

Endocare Inc ....E 512 328-2892
Austin *(G-1692)*

Global Cardiac Monitors LLC ....F 281 788-7269
Houston *(G-9966)*

Gulf Coast II Lithotripsy LP ....B 866 598-2734
Austin *(G-1693)*

Healthtech Solutions Inc ....F 763 559-7082
Austin *(G-1694)*

Healthtrnics MBL Solutions LLC.......D....... 866 598-2734
Austin *(G-1695)*

▲ Healthtronics Inc ....F 512 328-2892
Austin *(G-1696)*

▲ Hmt High Medical Tech USA Inc ...E 512 721-4700
West Lake Hills *(G-20682)*

▲ Ht Intermediate Company LLC ......G....... 512 328-2892
Austin *(G-1699)*

Laser Scientific LLC ....F 512 733-8709
Round Rock *(G-17666)*

Laser Ventures Inc ....F 770 516-4600
Austin *(G-1701)*

▲ Livanova Usa Inc ....B 281 228-7200
Houston *(G-10655)*

▲ Mediana Technologies Corp ....E 425 406-2262
San Antonio *(G-18289)*

Medstone International Inc ....E 512 328-2892
Austin *(G-1704)*

Microtransponder ....F 214 280-9677
Austin *(G-1342)*

▲ National Mri Shielding Inc ....F 855 996-9820
Desoto *(G-5436)*

Natus Medical Incorporated...........E 650 802-0400
Flower Mound *(G-6274)*

Omni Surgical LP ....F 512 327-6400
Austin *(G-1380)*

Orthofix Inc ....C 214 937-2000
Lewisville *(G-14077)*

▲ Quest Medical Inc ....C 800 627-0226
Allen *(G-297)*

Radiology Associates N Texas ....E 817 321-0300
Fort Worth *(G-6937)*

Respiratory Technology Corp ....F 858 673-3700
Houston *(G-11611)*

Right Pathways LLC ....D....... 817 522-3600
Coppell *(G-3439)*

Rio Grande Imaging Center Inc ....F .. 956 668-6900
McAllen *(G-14901)*

Sunetics Intl Mktg Group LLC ....F .. 888 266-2232
Plano *(G-17014)*

Volcano Corporation.......................F 210 582-5820
San Antonio *(G-18599)*

3851 Ophthalmic Goods

Alcon Vision LLC ....A 713 668-9100
  Houston *(G-8533)*
Alcon Vision LLC ....D 817 293-0450
  Fort Worth *(G-6368)*
▲ **Ciba Vision Corporation** ....A 817 551-6881
  Fort Worth *(G-6517)*
Ciba Vision Inc ....A 847 294-3000
  Fort Worth *(G-6518)*
Cooper Optical Co Inc ....F 903 753-7606
  Longview *(G-14214)*
◆ **Dac Vision Incorporated** ....D 972 677-2700
  Garland *(G-7474)*
Eoa Holding Co Inc ....F 214 496-4000
  Dallas *(G-4328)*
Essilor Laboratories Amer Inc ....E 713 663-3000
  Houston *(G-9702)*
◆ **Essilor Laboratories Amer Inc** ....B 972 241-4141
  Dallas *(G-4332)*
Essilor of America Inc ....E 214 496-4000
  Dallas *(G-4333)*
▲ **Essilor of America Inc** ....B 214 496-4000
  Dallas *(G-4334)*
Essilor of America Inc ....E 214 496-4235
  Dallas *(G-4335)*
▲ **Hoya Lens of America Inc** ....D 972 221-4141
  Lewisville *(G-14053)*
Hoya Optical Labs America Inc ....E 972 221-4141
  Lewisville *(G-14054)*
Luxottica of America Inc ....E 512 450-1234
  Austin *(G-1313)*
Med Logics Inc ....G 949 582-3891
  Athens *(G-830)*
Metro Optics of Austin Inc ....E 512 251-2386
  Pflugerville *(G-16680)*
Omega Optical Co LP ....F 972 241-4141
  Dallas *(G-4760)*
Ragsdale Vision Ctr ....F 940 387-9595
  Denton *(G-5396)*
Safety Rx Services & Sup Corp ....E 281 487-0505
  Pasadena *(G-16502)*
South Texas Eye Cons Pllc ....E 361 992-9400
  Corpus Christi *(G-3623)*
Tru-Form Optics Inc ....E 817 267-9261
  Bedford *(G-1980)*
▲ **Visionworks of America Inc** ....A 800 669-1183
  San Antonio *(G-18596)*
Williams Optometrist ....F 281 332-6021
  League City *(G-13982)*

3861 Photographic Eqpt & Splys

Alpha Laser Recharge Inc ....F 713 861-2425
  Houston *(G-8562)*
Associated Pro Inc ....A 214 902-8211
  Dallas *(G-3974)*
Brazen Animation LLC ....F 214 880-0101
  Richardson *(G-17281)*
▲ **CPM Inc** ....F 214 349-6886
  Garland *(G-7470)*
Dahill Office Technology Corp ....E 713 329-9909
  Houston *(G-9392)*
◆ **Dahill Office Technology Corp** ....C 210 805-8200
  San Antonio *(G-18041)*
Docresources LLC ....F 832 802-6008
  Crosby *(G-3729)*
Eastman Kodak Company ....D 214 585-4955
  McKinney *(G-14938)*
Eastman Kodak Company ....D 972 241-1611
  Dallas *(G-4295)*
◆ **Eastman Park Micrographics Inc** .....E 214 580-8390
  Dallas *(G-4296)*
Fedex Office & Print Svcs Inc ....E 512 472-4448
  Austin *(G-1151)*
Fujifilm North America Corp ....D 972 242-0662
  Carrollton *(G-2741)*
High Plins Cntrs MGT Group Inc ....E 806 935-5858
  Dumas *(G-5522)*
▲ **Horizon Worldwide Corporation** ......D 713 647-7400
  Houston *(G-10208)*
Illinois Tool Works Inc ....F 713 944-3200
  La Porte *(G-13748)*
Infrared Cameras Inc ....F 409 861-0788
  Beaumont *(G-1907)*
Inview Technology Corporation ....F 512 243-8751
  Austin *(G-1241)*
Jeh-Eas Inc ....G 210 490-9156
  San Antonio *(G-18200)*
▼ **Keynote Technologies LLC** ....F 877 528-4747
  Allen *(G-282)*

Missionary Tech Team ....F 903 757-4530
  Longview *(G-14277)*
Osv Investment LLC ....E 512 301-2848
  Dallas *(G-4771)*
Photronics Texas Allen Inc ....C 972 889-6275
  Allen *(G-295)*
Precision Dcment Solutions Inc ....E 866 916-1177
  Carrollton *(G-2792)*
Quality Business Solutions ....E 972 285-2000
  Mesquite *(G-15074)*
Redrock Microsystems LLC ....E 817 490-1326
  Roanoke *(G-17495)*
Rosco Laboratories Inc ....F 512 388-5299
  Round Rock *(G-17685)*
Skycam LLC ....F 817 984-6840
  Fort Worth *(G-6992)*
Varieon Inc ....F 469 916-1099
  Lewisville *(G-14104)*

3873 Watch & Clock Devices & Parts

▲ **Adao Global LLC** ....F 512 431-7743
  Georgetown *(G-7631)*
▲ **Egana of Switzerland (america)** ......F 972 839-2808
  Frisco *(G-7258)*
◆ **Fossil Group Inc** ....B 972 234-2525
  Richardson *(G-17312)*
H P Creations ....E 817 749-4367
  Southlake *(G-19073)*
◆ **Skagen Designs Ltd** ....D 775 336-5667
  Dallas *(G-4966)*

39 MISCELLANEOUS MANUFACTURING INDUSTRIES

3911 Jewelry: Precious Metal

AAC Group Holding Corp ....F 512 444-0571
  Austin *(G-875)*
▲ **American Achievement Corp** ....E 512 444-0571
  Dallas *(G-3937)*
Balfour Scholastic School Sup ....F 903 455-4556
  Greenville *(G-8063)*
Ben Adams Precious Jewels ....E 210 826-6535
  San Antonio *(G-17945)*
Bravelets LLC ....F 800 780-9227
  Houston *(G-8977)*
◆ **Cfj Manufacturing LP** ....D 817 625-9559
  Fort Worth *(G-6506)*
Cfj Manufacturing LP ....D 817 232-9251
  Saginaw *(G-17741)*
▲ **Chapal/Zenray Inc** ....D 214 638-0402
  Carrollton *(G-2714)*
Commemorative Brands Inc ....E 800 225-3687
  Dallas *(G-4145)*
Grissoms Fine Jewelry ....G 817 244-9754
  Fort Worth *(G-6681)*
H P Creations ....E 817 749-4367
  Southlake *(G-19073)*
Holland Jewelry Inc ....F 325 655-3135
  San Angelo *(G-17807)*
Houston Numismatic Exchange ....F 713 528-2135
  Houston *(G-10241)*
I W Marks Jewelers LP ....F 713 668-5000
  Houston *(G-10310)*
J Brandt Recognition Ltd ....F 817 877-0513
  Fort Worth *(G-6729)*
James Avery Craftsman Inc ....F 956 509-2912
  Brownsville *(G-2367)*
Jeep Collins Jewelry Maker ....D 830 997-3135
  Fredericksburg *(G-7184)*
Joann Baik ....F 281 469-1000
  Houston *(G-10478)*
Jonsil Manufacturing Corp ....F 915 544-4244
  El Paso *(G-5823)*
Lilyrain Jewelry LLC ....F 713 467-5459
  Houston *(G-10641)*
▲ **M A E W Inc** ....F 956 627-3554
  McAllen *(G-14886)*
Main Jewell LLC ....G 713 623-0499
  Houston *(G-10739)*
Milke Manufacturing Jewelers ....G 972 296-4319
  Duncanville *(G-5534)*
New World Jewelry Inc ....F 972 243-2931
  Dallas *(G-4731)*
◆ **Pampillonia Designs II Inc** ....D 214 503-7272
  Richardson *(G-17370)*
Phoeben Inc ....F 832 486-9500
  Houston *(G-11328)*
Precision Set Incorporated ....F 972 385-6732
  Dallas *(G-4821)*

▲ **Premier Manufacturing LP** ....E 972 355-3285
  Flower Mound *(G-6276)*
Robinson Pipe & Supply Inc ....E 713 672-4152
  Houston *(G-11645)*
Roots Rocks Inc ....F 512 346-1780
  Austin *(G-1473)*
Serious Cigars Llc ....G 281 397-9800
  Houston *(G-11837)*
Sevendipity Jewelry Mfg LLC ....G 915 594-8500
  El Paso *(G-5956)*
Shaudra Company Inc ....G 915 544-4244
  El Paso *(G-5957)*
Sonias Accessories ....G 832 443-7586
  Katy *(G-13444)*
Southern Jwly Mfg Houston Co ....E 713 460-5533
  Houston *(G-11975)*
T J Manufacturing Co ....F 806 348-7546
  Roaring Springs *(G-17497)*
▲ **Time Delay Corporation** ....E 214 369-4063
  Dallas *(G-5094)*
▲ **Worldwide J R Wood LLC** ....E 512 858-2556
  Austin *(G-867)*

3914 Silverware, Plated & Stainless Steel Ware

▲ **American Permanent Ware Co** ....C 972 908-6100
  Allen *(G-250)*
Integrated Flow Systems LLC ....D 512 671-5002
  Pflugerville *(G-16676)*
▲ **Mass Transfer Limited** ....F 281 991-8866
  Deer Park *(G-5284)*
Shaudra Company Inc ....G 915 544-4244
  El Paso *(G-5957)*
Texas Trophies Inc ....F 210 674-6099
  San Antonio *(G-18545)*
Venus Fabrication Inc ....F 972 366-3565
  Venus *(G-20226)*

3915 Jewelers Findings & Lapidary Work

Carriage Casting Inc ....G 915 760-6800
  El Paso *(G-5685)*
Diamond Ethanol LLC ....F 806 897-0911
  Levelland *(G-14006)*
Fossil Partners LP ....F 972 234-2525
  Richardson *(G-17313)*
J Keiths Jewelry Inc ....F 806 791-0092
  Lubbock *(G-14427)*
James Avery Craftsman Inc ....F 512 541-3823
  Austin *(G-1250)*
Southwest Diamond Cutters Inc ....G 972 387-1078
  Dallas *(G-4989)*
▲ **Time Delay Corporation** ....E 214 369-4063
  Dallas *(G-5094)*

3931 Musical Instruments

▲ **Dbz Guitars LLC** ....F 713 934-0110
  Houston *(G-9415)*
▲ **DK Drill I LP** ....E 817 539-2500
  Mansfield *(G-14665)*
▲ **Jarvis Industries Inc** ....G 281 370-5455
  Spring *(G-19136)*
Lisle Violin Shop ....F 281 487-7303
  Pasadena *(G-16474)*
Portsmouth Trading Co Inc ....G 713 957-0470
  Houston *(G-11368)*
Precision Pearl Inlay Inc ....F 512 442-4941
  Austin *(G-1430)*
Redman Pipe Organs LLC ....F 817 332-2953
  Fort Worth *(G-6949)*
Victorious Music Co ....F 713 450-3306
  Houston *(G-12567)*

3942 Dolls & Stuffed Toys

Ashley Industries LLC ....G 864 834-1167
  Round Rock *(G-17623)*
Beecon Learning LLC ....F 877 923-3266
  Dallas *(G-4014)*
▲ **Idea Planet LP** ....E 972 380-9867
  Dallas *(G-3844)*

3944 Games, Toys & Children's Vehicles

Ariel Kennard ....F 832 997-4537
  Houston *(G-8693)*
Bank of New York Mellon Corp ....F 214 239-6420
  Dallas *(G-4004)*
Beecon Learning LLC ....F 877 923-3266
  Dallas *(G-4014)*

Bigtrak Technologies LLC .... G 361 944-3982
Corpus Christi *(G-3487)*

Blue Goji LLC .... E 512 270-4747
Austin *(G-997)*

Brock Enterprises Inc .... F 281 870-8200
Houston *(G-8990)*

▲ Casino Supply Company .... F 972 241-4833
Dallas *(G-4090)*

▲ Everi Games Holding Inc .... D 512 334-7500
West Lake Hills *(G-20681)*

Gayla Industries Inc .... E 979 335-7503
East Bernard *(G-5558)*

▲ Gayla Industries Inc .... D 713 681-2411
Houston *(G-9907)*

Graphtec Inc .... E 713 690-9999
Houston *(G-10019)*

Jasmine Lewis .... F 325 200-5769
Humble *(G-12781)*

▲ Jax Ltd Inc .... D 763 449-9699
Plano *(G-16897)*

▲ Lc Sciences .... F 713 664-7087
Houston *(G-10612)*

LLC Battle Beaver .... D 888 390-4363
Richardson *(G-17346)*

Maks Family Fun & Events LLC ...... E 254 518-0005
Copperas Cove *(G-3455)*

Mattel Inc .... G 817 302-3300
Fort Worth *(G-6819)*

Mattel Inc .... F 310 252-2000
Laredo *(G-13910)*

Mobile Toys Inc .... F 979 268-6066
College Station *(G-3193)*

▲ Pressman Toy Corporation .... E 732 562-1590
Richardson *(G-17376)*

Randolph Products Inc .... F 713 468-6070
Richmond *(G-17464)*

▲ Ruby Red Paint Inc .... F 972 221-8665
Flower Mound *(G-6279)*

Safe-T-Pet Inc .... F 903 569-0590
Mineola *(G-15511)*

▲ Soft Air Usa Inc .... F 817 717-4300
Grapevine *(G-8054)*

▲ Steve Jackson Games Inc .... E 512 447-7866
Austin *(G-1536)*

3949 Sporting & Athletic Goods, NEC

◆ Act Global Sports Tech Inc .... E 512 733-5300
Austin *(G-884)*

Adventure Plygrund Systems Inc ..... F 713 935-9684
Houston *(G-8496)*

▲ American Acrylic Injection Inc ..... E 972 784-7759
Farmersville *(G-6221)*

▲ Animal Paintball LLC .... G 956 753-8272
Laredo *(G-13858)*

Aries Acrylic Mfg Inc .... F 972 771-6286
Rockwall *(G-17538)*

ARX Fit .... F 512 633-3768
Austin *(G-938)*

▲ Athletic Bag Company LP .... E 903 520-3343
Tyler *(G-20051)*

Athletic Hlmet Rcndtioning LLC ...... E 936 858-9990
Alto *(G-314)*

Ballqube Inc .... F 800 543-1470
Dallas *(G-4001)*

Bell Sports Inc .... E 972 343-1000
Grand Prairie *(G-7844)*

▲ Bell Sports Corp .... E 469 417-6600
Irving *(G-12946)*

Bella Design Group LLC .... F 972 304-4100
Arlington *(G-630)*

Best American Mfg Corp .... F 972 475-0092
Rowlett *(G-17701)*

▲ Blacksheep Inc .... B 903 592-3853
Tyler *(G-20059)*

Bt5 Technologies LLC .... F 832 727-5214
Houston *(G-9001)*

Callaway Golf Ball Oprtons Inc .... D 844 534-6426
Fort Worth *(G-6489)*

◆ Clarke Products Inc .... C 972 660-1992
Colleyville *(G-3212)*

▲ Cobra Manufacturing Co Inc .... F 918 366-7622
Euless *(G-6137)*

Cortwear Sports AP & Eqp LLC ...... F 361 728-1868
Kingsville *(G-13624)*

▲ Covers Etc Inc .... E 817 467-5030
Arlington *(G-649)*

Cs Platinum Sports LLC .... F 936 559-1883
Nacogdoches *(G-15693)*

Dacos Bowling International .... E 972 394-6507
Carrollton *(G-2863)*

◆ Dollamur LP .... D 817 534-3344
Fort Worth *(G-6589)*

▲ Douglas Pads & Sports Inc .... E 713 697-9787
Houston *(G-9503)*

Ecological Services Intl Inc .... D 956 233-4609
Los Fresnos *(G-14346)*

Emergent Manufacturing Systems ... F 903 876-3679
Frankston *(G-7166)*

◆ Flowtronex Psi LLC .... C 469 221-1200
Dallas *(G-4372)*

Fort Hood Sportsmens Center .... F 254 532-4552
Fort Hood *(G-6322)*

Fungoman LLC .... F 318 775-0000
Dallas *(G-4385)*

Gamebreaker Inc .... F 818 224-7424
San Antonio *(G-18134)*

▲ Global Manufacturing LLC .... F 210 598-4100
San Antonio *(G-18147)*

◆ Golf Time LLC .... E 214 366-1595
Carrollton *(G-2746)*

◆ Granite Security Products Inc ...... F 817 483-0910
Mansfield *(G-14677)*

Index Skateboarding .... F 817 887-9779
Hurst *(G-12846)*

Jobran Unlimited LLC .... F 956 541-1309
Brownsville *(G-2371)*

▲ Kdr Outdoor & Leisure Pdts Inc ...... F 281 259-8033
Magnolia *(G-14612)*

▲ Kelye B Stites Inc .... F 817 284-3499
Richland Hills *(G-17439)*

Kent Sporting Goods Co Inc .... C 903 592-3853
Tyler *(G-20108)*

▲ Knight Manufacturing Co Inc .... D 903 561-0522
Tyler *(G-20111)*

Knox Jr Leighton .... E 806 327-5420
Tahoka *(G-19641)*

Lisco LLP .... F 806 762-5126
Lubbock *(G-14437)*

Liscosports LLC .... F 806 762-5126
Lubbock *(G-14438)*

Magnum Feeders Inc .... F 281 261-0803
Rosharon *(G-17608)*

Mansfield Plumbing Pdts LLC .... D 903 657-1436
Henderson *(G-8267)*

MB Ranch King Blinds LLC .... F 817 558-7320
Joshua *(G-13323)*

◆ Multisports Inc .... F 713 460-8188
Houston *(G-10939)*

◆ Nash Manufacturing Inc .... D 817 926-5223
Fort Worth *(G-6860)*

◆ North American Trade Corp .... F 936 588-1010
Montgomery *(G-15637)*

Owen-Bunnell Inc .... F 972 578-9100
Plano *(G-16960)*

Perma Pom Partnership Ltd .... F 979 532-3106
Lane City *(G-13851)*

Playground Constructors Inc .... F 915 585-6336
El Paso *(G-5912)*

▼ Playgrund Shade Structures Inc ...... G 512 642-6124
Hutto *(G-12884)*

Playwood Outdoor Fun .... E 512 250-8819
Austin *(G-1421)*

Precision Tackle Inc .... F 936 597-6145
Montgomery *(G-15639)*

Presidential Billiards LP .... F 281 572-4733
New Caney *(G-15847)*

Progressive Coml Aquatics Inc .... D 281 982-0212
Houston *(G-11442)*

▲ Promaxima Manufacturing Ltd ..... D 800 231-6652
Houston *(G-11446)*

◆ Quantum Fitness Corporation ...... D 281 495-3003
Sugar Land *(G-19531)*

Quest and Sons Inc .... E 806 744-2351
Lubbock *(G-14468)*

Reagent Chemical & RES Inc .... F 713 626-1843
Houston *(G-11561)*

Reagent Chemical & RES Inc .... E 409 962-1116
Vidor *(G-20331)*

Reagent Chemical & RES Inc .... E 281 862-9464
Houston *(G-11562)*

Reagent Chemical & RES Inc .... E 432 458-3403
Stanton *(G-19404)*

Retail Concepts Inc .... E 512 467-2782
Austin *(G-1462)*

▼ Rio Plastics Inc .... E 956 831-2715
Brownsville *(G-2401)*

Rk Global Inc .... F 972 339-8016
Coppell *(G-3440)*

Rocket Distribution LLC .... F 817 688-9454
Lewisville *(G-14089)*

Rocksolid LLC .... F 855 282-8880
Frisco *(G-7309)*

Royal Baths Manufacturing Co .... B 281 442-3400
Houston *(G-11682)*

Safespace Concepts Inc .... F 713 956-0820
Houston *(G-11725)*

◆ Sellmark Corporation .... D 817 225-0310
Mansfield *(G-14717)*

Simpson Helmets Inc .... C 830 625-1774
New Braunfels *(G-15823)*

South Texas Sports Academy .... F 361 992-3364
Corpus Christi *(G-3626)*

▲ T Hangers Inc .... F 830 741-8383
Hondo *(G-8356)*

T L W Archery Inc .... G 830 227-5171
Canyon Lake *(G-2680)*

Taiga Coolers LLC .... G 214 762-3648
Mesquite *(G-15077)*

Tenth Frame Inc .... E 979 743-6585
Schulenburg *(G-18780)*

Texas Firecrckrs Fstptch Softb .... F 713 818-4661
Conroe *(G-3370)*

◆ Tko Sports Group USA Limited ..... E 713 895-9270
Houston *(G-12305)*

Top Golf USA Inc .... C 214 494-6310
The Colony *(G-19817)*

Topgolf International Inc .... F 832 200-0106
Spring *(G-19180)*

Track What Matters LLC .... F 817 430-9201
Bartonville *(G-1747)*

Trampoline USA Inc .... F 800 872-6765
Orange *(G-16266)*

▲ Truglo Inc .... D 972 774-0300
Richardson *(G-17414)*

Ultimate Trining Munitions Inc .... F 908 392-5390
Brownsville *(G-2417)*

Unlimited Supply Inc .... E 936 890-8997
Willis *(G-20868)*

◆ USA Sports Inc .... D 713 957-2882
Houston *(G-12502)*

◆ Ust-Mamiya Inc .... E 817 267-2219
Fort Worth *(G-7095)*

▲ Vibra-Whirl Sports Ltd .... D 806 537-3526
Panhandle *(G-16348)*

▲ Walter Solomon .... F 903 938-2096
Marshall *(G-14806)*

Western Bowl .... E 806 359-5211
Amarillo *(G-521)*

Wheels and Fitness In Motion .... F 210 828-4542
San Antonio *(G-18617)*

Yeti Holdings Inc .... E 512 394-8220
Austin *(G-1681)*

▲ Yj USA Corp .... F 877 927-8777
Addison *(G-175)*

3951 Pens & Mechanical Pencils

▲ Barrington Group Ltd Inc .... F 214 528-6990
Dallas *(G-4006)*

▲ Dallas Lghthouse For Blind Inc ... C 214 821-2375
Dallas *(G-4217)*

Glass Chalk .... G 830 379-1814
Seguin *(G-18838)*

San Antnio Lghthouse For Blind ...... C 210 533-5195
San Antonio *(G-18444)*

▲ West Txas Lighthouse For Blind ... D 325 653-4231
San Angelo *(G-17839)*

3952 Lead Pencils, Crayons & Artist's Mtrls

Pearland Arts League .... F 713 304-0672
Pearland *(G-16590)*

Sun Chemical Corporation .... E 972 647-1641
Grand Prairie *(G-7977)*

3953 Marking Devices

American Assn Notaries Inc .... F 713 644-2299
Houston *(G-8586)*

Budget Signs Ltd .... E 210 349-7446
San Antonio *(G-17971)*

Corpus Christi Stamp Works Inc ...... E 361 884-4801
Corpus Christi *(G-3509)*

Foust Incorporated .... E 806 374-7005
Amarillo *(G-424)*

Gemini Incorporated .... D 512 352-5207
Taylor *(G-19656)*

◆ ID Technology LLC .... D 817 626-7779
Fort Worth *(G-6713)*

Lobues Rubber Stamp Co .... F 713 652-0031
Houston *(G-10661)*

Mail & Parcels Plus Inc .... F 409 899-1771
Beaumont *(G-1923)*

Material Control Inc ....D...... 817 695-1400
Arlington (G-729)

Pavement Tool Mfg Inc ....F...... 903 734-7531
Big Sandy (G-2066)

R-J Typesetters Inc ....G...... 915 562-4461
El Paso (G-5925)

Stamp Shop Inc ....E...... 210 824-7373
San Antonio (G-18495)

Thiink Biig Tax Service Inc ....F...... 832 606-3380
Katy (G-13450)

Timesaver Templates Inc ....F...... 972 620-2197
Dallas (G-5095)

3955 Carbon Paper & Inked Ribbons

Advanced Materials Group Inc ....D...... 469 246-4100
Garland (G-7428)

Alpha Laser Recharge Inc ....F...... 713 861-2425
Houston (G-8562)

Ecmm Services Inc ....G...... 909 979-4526
Houston (G-9575)

Fine Line Ribbon Inc ....E...... 972 875-8681
Ennis (G-6102)

Kaufman Independent School Dst ....E...... 972 932-6940
Kaufman (G-13459)

3961 Costume Jewelry & Novelties

Adele Charles Corp............................G...... 972 740-1028
Plano (G-16771)

Creative Casting Inc ....F...... 903 463-6160
Denison (G-5339)

Dyna Group International Inc.............D...... 830 620-4400
New Braunfels (G-15788)

Julie Keck ....F...... 210 435-3535
San Antonio (G-18212)

▲ Premier Manufacturing LP ....E...... 972 355-3285
Flower Mound (G-6276)

South By Midwest Ret Partners.........F...... 281 465-8480
Spring (G-19252)

◆ Treska Inc ....E...... 682 647-0352
Fort Worth (G-7074)

Wireless Maniac.................................E...... 817 209-9524
Dallas (G-5199)

▲ Worldwide J R Wood LLC ....E...... 512 858-2556
Austin (G-867)

Wristbands With A Message Inc ....F...... 281 494-2424
Stafford (G-19400)

▲ Z Fabulous Inc ....E...... 972 385-0202
Plano (G-17056)

3965 Fasteners, Buttons, Needles & Pins

Bobby Pins LLC ....F...... 920 267-6388
Dallas (G-4035)

◆ Corpus Chrsti Gsket Fstner Inc ....C...... 361 884-6366
Corpus Christi (G-3510)

Creative Casting Inc ....F...... 903 463-6160
Denison (G-5339)

Cyclone Bolt Incorporated ....E...... 281 372-6050
Houston (G-9382)

▼ Flexitallic Group Inc ....E...... 281 604-2525
Houston (G-9799)

▲ Fluid Sealing Products Inc ....D...... 713 910-1028
Houston (G-9816)

Globe Products Company Inc ....E...... 972 875-1660
Ennis (G-6105)

Houston Precision Fas I LP ....D...... 713 462-2227
Houston (G-10246)

▲ South Texas Bolt & Fitting Inc ....E...... 713 673-5376
Houston (G-11966)

Tfp Corporation ....E...... 281 598-2330
Houston (G-12267)

▲ Utility Composites Inc ....F...... 512 846-4027
Hutto (G-12887)

3991 Brooms & Brushes

All Washed Up Inc..............................F...... 512 288-5522
Austin (G-908)

◆ Birdwell Cleaning Products Inc ....D...... 800 722-8006
Burleson (G-2572)

Bluebonnet Industrial Brush Co.........F...... 713 923-2855
Houston (G-8922)

Bz & Sons Sweeping & Wshg Inc.......G...... 903 732-9882
Powderly (G-17198)

Eagle Brush & Chemical Inc ....F...... 972 484-0391
Dallas (G-4289)

Harman Property Services LLC ....F...... 469 446-2909
Dallas (G-4436)

▲ Magnolia Brush Mfrs Inc ....D...... 903 427-2261
Clarksville (G-3074)

▼ Mobile Products Inc..........................E...... 800 323-0135
Longview (G-14278)

Quickie Manufacturing Corp...............D...... 915 859-2522
El Paso (G-5923)

San Antonio Broom Factory Inc ....E...... 210 226-9762
San Antonio (G-18446)

True Value Company LLC ....C...... 903 872-8365
Corsicana (G-3688)

3993 Signs & Advertising Displays

21c Sign Company..............................F...... 915 775-8514
El Paso (G-5630)

▲ 4d Signworx LLC...............................E...... 713 984-2010
Houston (G-8412)

A 1 Distributors Sign Supply ....D...... 432 682-0083
Midland (G-15100)

A Sign of Quality LLC ....F...... 972 722-4147
Royse City (G-17714)

A&B Foundry LLC ....F...... 972 247-3579
Dallas (G-3872)

A-1 Siign Engravers Inc......................F...... 432 682-3492
Midland (G-15102)

A-Ero TEC Graphics Inc ....F...... 972 289-9854
Mesquite (G-15022)

AAA Electrical Signs ....F...... 956 464-3221
Donna (G-5486)

Abney Group Inc ....E...... 512 832-0000
Austin (G-877)

Accent Graphics Inc ....E...... 972 399-0333
Grand Prairie (G-7820)

Accent Sign & Awning Co LLC ....F...... 713 780-1151
Houston (G-8455)

Acm Hub LLC ....F...... 210 248-9631
San Antonio (G-17860)

Acme Sign & Plastics Co ....F...... 325 677-9469
Abilene (G-10)

▲ Acp International Inc..........................D...... 817 640-0992
Arlington (G-608)

Action Sportswear Inc ....E...... 972 487-6960
Garland (G-7427)

Ad Display Sign Systems Inc ....E...... 281 392-8325
Katy (G-13348)

Adcorp Sign Systems LLC..................F...... 936 321-4888
Conroe (G-3252)

ADS Custom Signs Inc ....E...... 713 943-0895
Pasadena (G-16378)

▲ Airbrush Images Inc..........................E...... 936 523-1000
Conroe (G-3254)

Airmark Industries Inc ....E...... 325 641-1999
Brownwood (G-2424)

Alamo Outdoor Structures Inc............F...... 210 651-0425
San Antonio (G-18638)

Allied Advertising Agency Inc ....E...... 210 732-7874
San Antonio (G-17897)

Ally Wholesale Signs LLC...................F...... 830 438-2500
Bulverde (G-2553)

Ally Wholesale Signs LLC...................F...... 830 438-2500
Bulverde (G-2554)

Aluma Graphics LP ....E...... 972 442-3299
Wylie (G-20925)

▲ American Prtg & Promotions Inc.......E...... 713 645-1991
Houston (G-8605)

Andax Corp...F...... 972 392-3999
Addison (G-104)

Apache Sign & Service Inc.................F...... 713 462-3220
Houston (G-8660)

Architectural Graphic Products..........G...... 713 683-8942
Houston (G-8683)

Arns Holdings Ltd ....D...... 713 863-0600
Houston (G-8701)

Artografx Inc ....E...... 214 349-1075
Dallas (G-3969)

Ashter Construction LLC ....E...... 832 786-0053
Waller (G-20493)

Atlas Sign Services Inc ....F...... 713 699-1121
Houston (G-8746)

Austin Archtctral Graphics Inc ....E...... 512 473-2075
Creedmoor (G-3705)

Austin Screen Printing Inc ....E...... 512 454-6249
Austin (G-961)

Badmoon Enterprises LLC..................F...... 817 548-0561
Arlington (G-629)

Baker Macy Edward ....F...... 817 572-7346
Fort Worth (G-6420)

Bankson Group Ltd ....E...... 210 699-3800
San Antonio (G-17938)

Banner Sign Graphics ....F...... 512 458-5348
Round Rock (G-17626)

Bauer Visual Graphics Inc ....F...... 713 473-5241
Pasadena (G-16394)

Beaed LP..D...... 281 331-2035
Alvin (G-354)

Beaed LP..E...... 281 968-7249
Alvin (G-355)

Beehive Specialty Co..........................F...... 512 912-7940
Austin (G-985)

Big Star Branding Inc ....E...... 210 590-2662
San Antonio (G-17953)

Blind Dog Productions Ltd ....E...... 254 778-0722
Temple (G-19671)

◆ Bob Hughes Displays LLC ....F...... 713 468-7726
Marble Falls (G-14739)

Brick Stone Graphics By Gartex ....F...... 214 343-0573
Dallas (G-4049)

Brite Lite Sign Service Inc ....E...... 713 849-5545
Conroe (G-3264)

Brooks & Brooks Services Inc............G...... 817 560-9965
Weatherford (G-20579)

▼ Build A Sign LLC...............................C...... 512 374-9850
Austin (G-1015)

Build A Sign LLC ....F...... 512 339-4447
Austin (G-1016)

C & M Graphics & Signs ....F...... 956 421-2114
Harlingen (G-8183)

Caasco Signs Inc ....G...... 281 332-1502
League City (G-13951)

Carlton Industries LP.........................E...... 979 242-5055
La Grange (G-13693)

Casteel & Associates Inc ....F...... 214 352-7446
Dallas (G-4091)

Century Graphics & Sign Inc ....E...... 432 686-8244
Midland (G-15157)

◆ Cfj Manufacturing LP ....D...... 817 625-9559
Fort Worth (G-6506)

Cfj Manufacturing LP ....D...... 817 232-9251
Saginaw (G-17741)

Chandler Signs LLC............................D...... 760 734-1708
Fort Worth (G-6508)

Chandler Signs LLC............................C...... 214 902-2000
Fort Worth (G-6509)

Chandler Signs LLC............................F...... 210 349-3804
San Antonio (G-18000)

Chandler Signs LLC............................D...... 361 643-4115
Portland (G-17185)

Chism Company ....F...... 210 824-6315
San Antonio (G-18004)

City Sign Services Inc ....E...... 214 826-4475
Dallas (G-4124)

Cjhorak Enterprises Inc......................G...... 817 260-0700
Southlake (G-19059)

Clark Fire Equipment Inc ....F...... 713 453-3778
Houston (G-9209)

▲ Claytex Trophies Inc.........................C...... 940 538-6521
Henrietta (G-8279)

Cnd Signs LLC ....E...... 512 394-5421
Cedar Creek (G-2934)

Coast Graphics & Signs Inc ....E...... 281 499-9721
Stafford (G-19296)

Cohn Signs ....G...... 210 626-2157
San Antonio (G-18016)

Comet Signs LLC ....C...... 210 341-7244
San Antonio (G-18021)

Comet Signs LLC ....E...... 281 492-6581
Houston (G-9247)

Contractors Service Ltd ....F...... 325 692-4317
Abilene (G-36)

Crabtree Barricade Systems Inc.........E...... 409 842-2073
Beaumont (G-1877)

▲ Craftmark Products Inc ....E...... 817 457-8753
Fort Worth (G-6556)

Craftsman Printers Inc ....F...... 806 744-8429
Lubbock (G-14397)

Creative Signworks Inc ....E...... 850 785-8899
San Angelo (G-17792)

Custom Sign Creations LLC ....E...... 512 374-9300
Austin (G-1080)

D & R Signs LLC.................................F...... 281 988-9995
Stafford (G-19299)

D-Signs Inc ....E...... 214 327-2373
Garland (G-7473)

▲ Datatronic Control Corporation.........E...... 972 475-7879
Rowlett (G-17704)

▲ Day Night Signs Inc ....E...... 254 965-9000
Stephenville (G-19409)

Dbt Inc ....F...... 409 892-2300
Beaumont (G-1880)

Derse Inc ....D...... 972 393-9046
Coppell (G-3414)

Design Center Signs Inc.....................F...... 903 561-4995
Tyler (G-20075)

Company	Grade	Phone
Digimagination LLC	F	281 445-6671
Houston (G-9469)		
Digital Banner Plus LLC	G	210 647-3124
San Antonio (G-18059)		
Digital Copy LLC	E	214 740-2480
Dallas (G-4258)		
Dinaco Inc	E	281 848-3600
Houston (G-9475)		
Display Graphics Inc	F	713 977-7888
Houston (G-9480)		
▲ Display Products Inc	D	972 406-1221
Dallas (G-4262)		
Display Surce Design Fctry Ltd	C	972 288-7471
Mesquite (G-15039)		
Distinctive Graphics Inc	F	817 329-0411
Southlake (G-19062)		
Double S Signs LLC	F	903 838-8999
Texarkana (G-19762)		
Dragonfly Garment Design Corp	G	830 549-5113
Seguin (G-18836)		
▲ Drake Alliance Corporation	D	713 869-9121
Houston (G-9514)		
Dukes Outdoor Advertising	F	432 447-2251
Pecos (G-16620)		
Dyna Group International Inc	D	830 620-4400
New Braunfels (G-15788)		
Dynamic Signs Systems Mktg LLC	F	281 255-0420
Tomball (G-19974)		
Eagle Eye Signs LP	F	972 466-2100
Carrollton (G-2727)		
Eagle Traffic Signs Safety LLC	G	713 987-9178
Houston (G-9566)		
El Paso Heat Transfer Inc	F	915 779-6334
El Paso (G-5735)		
El Paso Reprographics LLC	F	915 532-6255
El Paso (G-5740)		
Electrical Sign Displays Inc	F	713 644-8081
Houston (G-9589)		
Emma Grace Sign Co	F	713 864-4644
Houston (G-9618)		
Ep Big Media Inc	F	915 585-0444
El Paso (G-5756)		
Esbee Signs Inc	F	281 550-4577
Houston (G-9695)		
Ezzi Signs Inc	E	713 232-0771
Houston (G-9742)		
Farrz Inc	F	936 539-3278
Conroe (G-3296)		
Fastsigns	G	915 229-8000
El Paso (G-5765)		
Fastsigns International Inc	D	888 285-5935
Carrollton (G-2736)		
Fastsigns Nat Advg Council Inc	E	214 346-5600
Carrollton (G-2737)		
Federal Heath Sign Company LLC	E	903 589-2100
Jacksonville (G-13238)		
◆ Federal Heath Sign Company LLC	D	817 685-9075
Euless (G-6146)		
Fedex Office & Print Svcs Inc	G	512 331-0800
Austin (G-1148)		
Fedex Office & Print Svcs Inc	E	817 543-0833
Arlington (G-678)		
Fedex Office & Print Svcs Inc	F	210 521-8395
San Antonio (G-18108)		
Fource Communications Limited	F	214 630-2125
Dallas (G-4374)		
Foust Incorporated	E	806 374-7005
Amarillo (G-424)		
Fusion Led Inc	F	281 990-6011
Houston (G-9877)		
Garrison Bros Signs Inc	F	806 744-1161
Lubbock (G-14415)		
Gem Sign Service Inc	F	830 609-1052
New Braunfels (G-15794)		
Global Signs Inc	F	817 834-1123
Forest Hill (G-6296)		
Goodman Fine Art Inc	F	210 733-0190
San Antonio (G-18151)		
Graphtec Inc	E	713 690-9999
Houston (G-10019)		
Greshare Enterprises Inc	F	512 869-7446
Georgetown (G-7655)		
Gulf Coast Sign Inc	E	956 399-0755
San Benito (G-18658)		
H & H Sign Co Inc	E	254 752-1801
Waco (G-20409)		
Halo Branded Solutions Inc	E	972 536-4069
Dallas (G-4432)		
Hardman Signs LP	D	713 957-2324
Houston (G-10124)		
Harris Cabinet & Wdwkg Inc	G	817 561-2959
Fort Worth (G-6690)		
Harvey Dupriest & Sons Inc	D	214 337-4731
Dallas (G-4440)		
Hi-Plains Canvas Products Inc	E	806 352-5345
Amarillo (G-492)		
◆ Hightech Grafix Inc	G	817 616-3204
Fort Worth (G-6699)		
Hines Chaunte	F	469 583-0985
Farmers Branch (G-6202)		
Hoarel Sign Co	F	806 373-2175
Amarillo (G-434)		
Houston Sign & Service Inc	F	281 442-0175
Houston (G-10252)		
Hughes Manufacturing Inc	F	979 542-0333
Giddings (G-7696)		
Humble Texas Signs LLC	F	281 812-2100
Humble (G-12779)		
Huntington Sky Production Ltd	F	956 618-1800
McAllen (G-14869)		
Iconic Sign Group LLC	F	361 883-7446
Corpus Christi (G-3552)		
Ideal Signs	F	512 930-7446
Georgetown (G-7657)		
Identity Solutions Inc	F	972 926-0929
Garland (G-7515)		
Image Display Systems Inc	F	281 395-9100
Katy (G-13408)		
▲ Impact Recovery Systems Inc	E	210 736-4477
San Antonio (G-18180)		
Industrial Neon Sign Corp	F	713 748-6600
Houston (G-10352)		
▲ Inkjet Partners Inc	F	972 991-4577
Dallas (G-4500)		
▲ Insignia Marketing Inc	F	281 465-0040
Magnolia (G-14610)		
Intex United Inc	F	281 568-4000
Houston (G-10409)		
Ion Art Inc	F	512 326-9333
Austin (G-1242)		
Ixtapa Inc	E	956 782-9601
Pharr (G-16701)		
Jackie Todaro	F	281 354-2581
Kingwood (G-13646)		
Jackson Promotions Inc	F	281 474-1313
Seabrook (G-18786)		
Jackson Sign and Lighting Inc	G	254 751-0390
Woodway (G-20921)		
Janus Signs	F	972 420-8770
Lewisville (G-14059)		
Janus Signs Inc	F	214 503-1333
Dallas (G-4525)		
JDC Enterprises Inc	E	972 550-1880
Irving (G-13068)		
JDM Designs Inc	E	281 356-6131
Stagecoach (G-19401)		
Jim Dandy Boxes Inc	F	817 608-9180
Grand Prairie (G-7903)		
Jim McNabb Inc	F	512 365-2010
Taylor (G-19658)		
▲ JIT Manufacturing Inc	F	903 887-0226
Mabank (G-14577)		
Jones Holt Enterprises Inc	E	210 657-5917
San Antonio (G-18207)		
KB & KB Enterprises Inc	F	979 764-7446
College Station (G-3189)		
Keller Advg & Media Svcs	E	210 695-8767
San Antonio (G-18222)		
Kmp Graphics Inc	F	817 295-5350
Burleson (G-2585)		
Kuster Sign LLC	G	972 991-5841
Addison (G-142)		
▲ Landes Inc	E	713 665-0655
Houston (G-10593)		
Lassiter Industries Inc	E	281 781-8708
Houston (G-10606)		
▲ Led OEM Partners LLC	E	832 769-0593
Houston (G-10614)		
Legacy National Signs	F	972 790-8900
Dallas (G-4589)		
Leons Signs Inc	E	903 597-7731
Tyler (G-20112)		
Lewis Sign Builders Inc	F	512 312-4555
Buda (G-2532)		
Liberty Signs Inc	F	512 255-3887
Round Rock (G-17669)		
▲ Lone Star Corrugated Cont Corp	F	972 579-1551
Irving (G-13089)		
Lone Star Faces Inc	E	713 706-3223
Houston (G-10676)		
Lone Star Signs of West Texas	E	432 683-0016
Midland (G-15285)		
Lonestar Logos MGT Co LLC	E	512 462-1310
West Lake Hills (G-20684)		
◆ Lorente International LLC	E	877 281-6469
Farmers Branch (G-6206)		
▲ Lown Brothers Inc	F	915 594-4499
El Paso (G-5848)		
▲ Lozz Quatezz LLC	F	956 687-7446
Pharr (G-16706)		
LSI Integrated Graphics LP	C	713 744-4100
Houston (G-10696)		
Luma Vue Inc	E	214 842-8347
Frisco (G-7260)		
▲ Luminator Technology Group LLC	C	972 424-6511
Plano (G-16913)		
M2w Inc	D	972 407-1332
Mesquite (G-15059)		
M3 Image LLC	F	915 845-7676
El Paso (G-5856)		
Main Street Installers LLC	F	817 459-2001
Arlington (G-727)		
Makitso USA LLC	F	281 495-1300
Stafford (G-19350)		
◆ Marco Display Specialists LP	B	817 244-8300
Fort Worth (G-6809)		
◆ Marco Dsplay Specialists GP Lc	C	817 244-8300
Fort Worth (G-6810)		
Martin Inc	E	972 247-7160
Dallas (G-4639)		
Masterco Inc	G	214 381-5690
Dallas (G-4648)		
Media Displays Inc	F	210 495-6338
San Antonio (G-18288)		
Mercury Signs and Display Ltd	E	713 462-1068
Houston (G-10832)		
Michael Egan Allen		956 702-0692
Pharr (G-16707)		
Mighty Works Signage LLC	G	713 305-8355
Houston (G-10877)		
Millennium Signs America LLC	B	903 944-7981
Tyler (G-20129)		
Mlc Signs LP	F	972 420-8770
Lewisville (G-14069)		
Mr Sign Inc	G	214 526-7446
Dallas (G-4699)		
Multi-Quest Inc	F	972 235-2356
Richardson (G-17361)		
N & P Sign System Inc	F	281 444-9535
Houston (G-10947)		
◆ National Banner Company Inc	C	972 241-2131
Dallas (G-4712)		
National Banner Company Inc	D	972 241-2131
Dallas (G-4713)		
National Banner Company Inc	E	903 378-2761
Honey Grove (G-8357)		
National Signs LLC	E	832 433-4957
Houston (G-11001)		
Nationwide Applications LLC	E	210 651-0202
Schertz (G-18758)		
Natural Graphics Inc	E	713 661-5075
Houston (G-11009)		
▲ Neon Electric Corporation	D	281 987-1144
Houston (G-11023)		
Neon Signs and Designs Inc	F	903 463-7446
Denison (G-5343)		
New Teraco Inc	E	800 687-3999
Midland (G-15316)		
Northwest Advantage Inc	F	713 622-4888
Tomball (G-19992)		
NW Sign Industries Inc	D	972 602-9434
Grand Prairie (G-7939)		
OConn LLC	F	956 630-6116
McAllen (G-14896)		
Odee Company	E	214 340-0415
Dallas (G-4754)		
One Focus Inc	F	817 750-7667
Haslet (G-8221)		
Outdoor Lighting Services LP	C	713 690-6301
Houston (G-11204)		
Outfront Media LLC	D	713 868-2284
Houston (G-11205)		
Outstnding Grphic Slutions Inc	G	972 255-2022
Irving (G-13137)		
Paladin Signs and Graphics Inc	F	817 744-7361
Benbrook (G-2044)		
Paul Smoke	F	281 422-4228
Baytown (G-1831)		
Pb Unlimited LLC	F	817 831-4336
Haltom City (G-8156)		

Pdn Ssl LLC ....E 915 629-9100	**Southwestern Nameplate Mfg Co** ......F 972 924-3289	**Zspace LLC** ....F 713 662-3123
El Paso *(G-5906)*	Anna *(G-586)*	Houston *(G-12733)*
Permian Sign Co Inc ....F 432 563-3072	**Sparkle Lighting Services** ....E 713 856-8500	
Midland *(G-15346)*	Houston *(G-11992)*	### 3995 Burial Caskets
Prince Signs LLC ....F 281 345-4488	▲ **Spectrum Corporation** ....D 713 944-6200	**Esser Casket Co LLC** ....E 713 225-5548
Houston *(G-11420)*	Houston *(G-12008)*	Houston *(G-9701)*
Printdallas Inc ....E 214 363-1101	**SSC Signs & Lighting LLC** ....E 972 219-2495	**Freeman Metal Products Inc** ....E 877 278-2275
Dallas *(G-4826)*	Lewisville *(G-14092)*	Greenville *(G-8074)*
Proworx Inc ....E 713 666-3131	**Stamp Shop Inc** ....F 210 824-7373	**Wise Products Co Inc** ....F 903 378-2233
Houston *(G-11467)*	San Antonio *(G-18495)*	Honey Grove *(G-8359)*
Qti Promotions and Apparel Inc ......E 254 756-4444	**Starlite Sign LP** ....D 817 430-8359	**York Group Inc** ....F 412 995-1600
Waco *(G-20452)*	Denton *(G-5401)*	Katy *(G-13385)*
Quality Signs Inc ....E 713 671-9222	**State Sign Corporation** ....D 713 943-1831	
Houston *(G-11500)*	Houston *(G-12051)*	### 3996 Linoleum & Hard Surface Floor Coverings, NEC
R W Gonzalez Office Pdts Inc ....F 512 300-2300	**STI Graphics Inc** ....E 281 351-2776	
Austin *(G-1448)*	Tomball *(G-20011)*	**Colorstone Mfg** ....F 713 690-3100
Reagan Outdoor Advertising ....E 512 926-7740	**Stokes Sign Company Inc** ....F 512 263-7446	Houston *(G-9246)*
Austin *(G-1454)*	Lakeway *(G-13821)*	**Ipr Industrial LLC** ....E 281 362-1131
Recs Signs LLC ....G 832 226-8000	▲ **Store Dcor Inc - Rtailgraphics** ......D 972 475-4404	The Woodlands *(G-19885)*
Katy *(G-13435)*	Rowlett *(G-17711)*	**Lets Gel Inc** ....F 512 628-1709
Refuge Industries LLC ....F 512 961-4907	**Summit Sportswear Inc** ....G 281 335-5370	Waco *(G-20427)*
Austin *(G-1456)*	League City *(G-13980)*	▲ **Redco Distribution LLC** ....E 832 320-4950
Richards Signs & Cranes Inc ....F 940 325-6585	**Superior Signs** ....F 210 646-7799	Houston *(G-11573)*
Mineral Wells *(G-15539)*	San Antonio *(G-18514)*	◆ **Signature Systems Group LLC** ......E 972 684-5736
▲ **Right Signs Inc** ....F 281 429-3683	**Synergy Signs & Services LLC** ....E 817 745-2330	Flower Mound *(G-6281)*
Porter *(G-17182)*	Fort Worth *(G-7027)*	**Tarkett Inc** ....F 800 366-2689
Rmg Networks Holding Corp ....E 800 827-9666	**Tc Signs Inc** ....F 972 492-2801	Houston *(G-12162)*
Addison *(G-159)*	Lewisville *(G-14097)*	▲ **Unilin North America LLC** ....D 214 398-1411
Robert Leshea Inc ....F 803 407-9284	▲ **Technographix LLC** ....C 817 336-5671	Dallas *(G-5133)*
Katy *(G-13377)*	Fort Worth *(G-7041)*	
Ron T Felt ....F 512 258-5523	**Tejas Signs Wetz** ....F 830 609-6246	### 3999 Manufacturing Industries, NEC
Austin *(G-1471)*	San Antonio *(G-18646)*	
Ron T Felt ....F 512 335-7446	**Tesoro Corp** ....E 956 682-7831	**1954 Manufacturing Inc** ....F 760 524-1378
Austin *(G-1472)*	Donna *(G-5494)*	Graham *(G-7774)*
Ruben Reyes ....F 214 331-4307	**Texas 28 LLC** ....F 806 644-9663	**AAA Pipe Cleaning Corporation** ......E 281 476-5200
Dallas *(G-4918)*	Spearman *(G-19088)*	La Porte *(G-13715)*
Scanlin Sign Service Inc ....E 281 561-9924	**Texas and Oklahoma Elc Svc LLC** ......E 972 222-2229	◆ **Act Global Sports Tech Inc** ....E 512 733-5300
Stafford *(G-19375)*	Dallas *(G-5054)*	Austin *(G-884)*
Sel Corporate Enterprises Inc ....G 214 348-8784	**Texas Marking Products Inc** ....F 281 364-7100	▲ **Act Global Tech Industries** ....F 210 651-2543
Dallas *(G-4948)*	The Woodlands *(G-19929)*	San Antonio *(G-17864)*
Selectouch Corporation ....E 972 924-3289	▲ **Texas Nameplate Company Inc** ......D 214 428-8341	**Advanced Aero Coatings LLC** ....F 940 367-5963
Anna *(G-585)*	Lancaster *(G-13849)*	Ponder *(G-17093)*
▲ **Semasys Inc** ....C 713 869-8331	**Texas Neon Advertising Company** ......F 210 734-6694	**Advanced Telesensors Inc** ....F 888 292-2208
Houston *(G-11825)*	San Antonio *(G-18538)*	Austin *(G-895)*
Sign City Inc ....G 281 338-1203	**Texas Republic Signs LLC** ....E 832 727-5415	▲ **Advantage Supplies Inc** ....F 972 250-1339
Webster *(G-20646)*	Houston *(G-12247)*	Carrollton *(G-2854)*
Sign Erection Ltd ....E 817 267-1554	**Theag North Arlington LLC** ....F 817 261-3027	**Aequs Oil and Gas LLC** ....F 832 616-3110
Euless *(G-6158)*	Arlington *(G-797)*	Paris *(G-16357)*
Sign Factory Inc ....E 713 849-4575	◆ **Tpg Capital Management LP** ....B 817 871-4000	**Al Root Company** ....F 210 223-2948
Houston *(G-11889)*	Fort Worth *(G-7069)*	San Antonio *(G-17876)*
Sign International Inc ....F 409 832-0117	**Transfer Graphics Inc** ....F 940 566-2679	**Aloterra Energy LLC** ....F 713 412-5311
Beaumont *(G-1949)*	Denton *(G-5407)*	The Woodlands *(G-19823)*
Sign Pro of Lubbock Ltd ....F 806 798-7446	**Turner Sign Systems Inc** ....F 817 222-0033	**American Kart Mfg LLC** ....F 979 505-5076
Wolfforth *(G-20913)*	Grand Prairie *(G-7988)*	Schulenburg *(G-18771)*
Sign Shop ....G 325 641-2424	**Ultimate Decals Inc** ....F 936 539-5719	**American Vapor Company LLC** ....F 512 596-1892
Brownwood *(G-2444)*	Conroe *(G-3376)*	Pflugerville *(G-16657)*
Sign Technologies Inc ....F 903 838-8999	**Universal Display & Fixs Co** ....B 972 221-5157	**Aquajet Manufacturing** ....E 832 484-9244
Texarkana *(G-19773)*	Lewisville *(G-14100)*	Cypress *(G-3775)*
Sign Wave Corporation ....G 214 890-4444	◆ **Universal Display and Fix Co** ......C 972 434-8067	**Arden Companies Inc** ....C 806 335-1147
Dallas *(G-4960)*	Lewisville *(G-14101)*	Amarillo *(G-400)*
Signad Inc ....F 713 861-6013	**Universal Display and Fix Co** ....C 972 221-5157	▲ **Arne Distributors Inc** ....F 713 869-8321
Houston *(G-11890)*	Flower Mound *(G-6291)*	Houston *(G-8700)*
Signazon Corporation ....E 214 296-0022	**US Signs Inc** ....F 713 977-7900	**Asteria Learning Inc** ....E 210 960-3855
Plano *(G-17006)*	Houston *(G-12489)*	Spring Branch *(G-19266)*
Signit Inc ....E 817 589-9988	**Vixxo Corporation** ....C 713 977-7900	◆ **Atlas Match LLC** ....E 817 267-1500
Richland Hills *(G-17448)*	Houston *(G-12578)*	Euless *(G-6131)*
Signs & Graphics Plus LLC ....F 915 590-7446	**Vmc Signs Inc** ....F 361 575-0548	**Austin Industries Inc** ....E 512 288-1831
El Paso *(G-5961)*	Victoria *(G-20317)*	Austin *(G-857)*
▲ **Signs Manufacturing Corp** ....E 214 339-2227	**Voip Tel LP** ....F 512 543-9556	**Autistic Treatment Ctr** ....E 972 644-2076
Dallas *(G-4962)*	Austin *(G-1644)*	Dallas *(G-3987)*
Signs Now Corporation ....F 972 398-8648	**Walton Signage Ltd** ....C 210 886-0644	▲ **Auto Fit Inc** ....F 713 696-9000
Plano *(G-17007)*	San Antonio *(G-18609)*	Houston *(G-8752)*
Signs On Go ....F 806 722-7446	**Wellborn Sign Inc** ....F 806 331-3563	▲ **Ayc Group LLC** ....F 214 838-2630
Lubbock *(G-14480)*	Amarillo *(G-474)*	Garland *(G-7445)*
Signs Universe ....G 972 880-2884	**Wetz Sign & Lighting Service** ....F 830 609-6246	**Azan Industries Inc** ....F 832 310-4459
Carrollton *(G-2887)*	San Antonio *(G-18649)*	Richmond *(G-17450)*
Signs West Inc ....F 512 282-5001	**Willow Creek Signs Inc** ....E 817 847-0571	**B&B Custom Fabrication LLC** ....E 214 773-9240
Austin *(G-1502)*	Haslet *(G-8227)*	Grand Saline *(G-7997)*
Signtex Imaging Inc ....E 281 351-2776	**Willow Creek Signs Inc** ....E 817 847-0571	▲ **Barcana Inc** ....F 800 638-4533
Tomball *(G-20008)*	Saginaw *(G-17760)*	Irving *(G-12943)*
▲ **Signtex Outdoor Inc** ....F 281 351-8023	▲ **Worlds of Wow LLC** ....F 817 380-4215	**Bartos Industries Ltd** ....F 800 858-8497
Tomball *(G-20009)*	Denton *(G-5413)*	Richland Hills *(G-17436)*
Smurfit Kappa North Amer LLC ....E 713 869-5900	**Wraps Gorilla** ....F 817 652-2882	▼ **Beaed LP** ....D 281 331-2035
Houston *(G-11926)*	Arlington *(G-811)*	Alvin *(G-354)*
Son and Daughters Inc ....F 956 423-2689	▲ **Wrs Group Ltd** ....F 254 776-6461	**Beako Manufacturing Co LLC** ....F 903 796-5330
Harlingen *(G-8201)*	Waco *(G-20481)*	Queen City *(G-17218)*
South Texas Neon Signs Co ....G 956 723-4665	**Wwwhoustonsignmakercom** ....F 281 990-7446	**Bhc Industries of Texas Inc** ....F 817 556-2306
Laredo *(G-13935)*	Houston *(G-12703)*	Alvarado *(G-325)*
Southwest Sign Group Inc ....D 210 648-3221	**Xgrafx LLC** ....F 210 681-7177	**Big City Manufacturing Inc** ....F 713 649-7769
San Antonio *(G-18489)*	San Antonio *(G-18628)*	Houston *(G-8881)*

▼ Bio-Derm Laboratories Inc..............E.......903 753-6744
Longview (G-14202)

Bless-Scent Candle Company LLC.....F.......832 431-9923
Cypress (G-3779)

Bluestone Industries LLC..............E.......469 916-8090
McKinney (G-14927)

Bmv Media LLC.............................E.......915 216-3554
El Paso (G-5664)

Bobby Pins LLC............................F.......920 267-6388
Dallas (G-4035)

Boulware & Anson Family Ltd..........G.......210 822-9245
San Antonio (G-17963)

Brk Brands Inc............................F.......915 860-3500
El Paso (G-5673)

Buddys Grass Farm Inc..................F.......936 258-7954
Dayton (G-5222)

C&S Lease Service LC....................E.......903 988-8642
Kilgore (G-13534)

Calyan Wax Company LLC...............F.......817 455-0895
Arlington (G-638)

Candle Cottage............................G.......409 720-7087
Orange (G-16233)

Carlisle Systems Inc.....................G.......713 703-9256
Stafford (G-19292)

Cbd Farmhouse.............................F.......214 971-6688
Farmers Branch (G-6191)

▲ Chassis Liner............................F.......817 284-2545
Euless (G-6136)

Chem Eleven Products Inc..............E.......512 278-8800
Austin (G-1045)

▲ Chris Christensen Systems Inc......E.......903 389-7949
Fairfield (G-6170)

▲ Circle E Candles Inc..................F.......830 990-4478
Fredericksburg (G-7173)

Classic Protection Systems............E.......713 468-3573
Houston (G-9212)

Cooper Crouse Hinds LLC................E.......713 280-3400
Houston (G-9304)

Cree Visual Marketing Company........E.......214 905-8485
Carrollton (G-2720)

Crowned Plus Enterprises LLC.........F.......469 585-9658
Forney (G-6306)

Cypress Industries Oilfield SE........F.......281 482-3464
Friendswood (G-7245)

D & W Nameplate Service Inc...........F.......713 681-6616
Houston (G-9389)

Dallas Coffee Exchange.................F.......214 507-5903
Irving (G-12989)

▲ Dallas Market Center Co Ltd.........C.......214 655-6100
Dallas (G-4219)

Danielle Howard..........................F.......469 554-6772
Dallas (G-4236)

Daphany Broussard........................F.......832 229-0999
Houston (G-9403)

Dcp Operating Company LP..............C.......361 584-8509
Bishop (G-2107)

DDB Candles Inc..........................F.......817 927-3377
Fort Worth (G-6579)

◆ Deansteel Manufacturing Co.........C.......210 226-8271
San Antonio (G-18046)

Distribuidora Comercial LLC..........F.......830 438-3877
Spring Branch (G-19269)

Dmi International Inc...................F.......936 591-8006
Center (G-2997)

Drsk Limited Partnership..............F.......972 644-1490
Richardson (G-17302)

▲ Duna USA Inc...........................E.......281 383-3862
Baytown (G-1785)

▲ Eakin Industries LLC.................G.......281 620-8625
Porter (G-17175)

◆ Enerflex Services Inc...............E.......281 345-9300
Houston (G-9633)

Enviromental Industries LP............F.......972 390-9899
Dallas (G-4327)

▲ Es Group of Texas Inc...............F.......281 796-6214
Kingwood (G-13642)

Everi Games Inc..........................E.......512 439-3100
Austin (G-1142)

Fassco Manufacturing Inc..............D.......210 523-0800
San Antonio (G-18105)

Flexcon Industrial LLC.................E.......210 798-1900
San Antonio (G-18116)

▲ Flip Manufacturing...................G.......903 454-1538
Greenville (G-8073)

◆ Fosters Point Inc....................E.......281 353-6696
Tomball (G-19979)

▲ Frog Street Press LLC................F.......817 251-0510
Southlake (G-19069)

From Here Inc............................F.......805 368-3363
Addison (G-128)

Gaines Group LLC.........................D.......713 467-4774
Houston (G-9891)

◆ Gemmy Industries Corporation.......C.......972 538-4200
Coppell (G-3417)

Global Co Pak LLC........................E.......817 449-3115
Fort Worth (G-6673)

Global Operations Texas LP............F.......915 595-2250
San Antonio (G-18148)

Glycol Technologies LLC................F.......281 779-4753
Houston (G-9986)

Golf Greens Texascom....................F.......806 559-7048
Lubbock (G-14417)

Goodman Manufacturing Co LP..........F.......936 372-5224
Waller (G-20501)

GSW Manufacturing Inc...................F.......956 223-2644
Pharr (G-16699)

Gt Silicones Inc........................E.......610 252-5800
Farmers Branch (G-6198)

▼ Gtx Technologies LLC.................F.......806 367-7074
Amarillo (G-491)

Gulf Copper & Mfg Corp..................F.......409 941-6200
Galveston (G-7399)

H Rosen Usa LLC..........................B.......281 442-8282
Houston (G-10085)

Hadlock & Fox Mfg Co L L C.............F.......830 778-6017
Del Rio (G-5316)

Haleaux Inc..............................F.......214 742-2795
Dallas (G-4428)

▲ Hall Tree Antiques Inc...............D.......325 944-4794
San Angelo (G-17803)

Hammer Industriess LLC..................F.......281 763-2189
Houston (G-10114)

Hangar R LLC.............................F.......469 865-2110
Grand Prairie (G-7886)

Hhbodu LLC...............................F.......210 464-2669
Grand Prairie (G-7891)

Hickham Industries......................F.......713 567-2700
La Porte (G-13744)

Holicks Manufacturing Co LLC.........F.......979 846-6721
Bryan (G-2477)

◆ Home Fragrance Holdings Inc........B.......718 641-3759
Houston (G-10197)

Hooks Industeial Service Ctr.........F.......361 299-6112
Conroe (G-3307)

◆ Howco Metals Management LLC........C.......281 649-8800
Houston (G-10268)

◆ Ineos USA LLC.........................C.......281 535-6600
League City (G-13965)

Insight Equity Holdings LLC..........C.......512 372-9063
Austin (G-1229)

▲ Insignia Marketing Inc..............F.......281 465-0040
Magnolia (G-14610)

Intelligen..............................F.......940 692-3334
Wichita Falls (G-20772)

▲ Isomeric Industries Inc.............E.......678 713-4275
Spring (G-19222)

Jayden Inc...............................E.......214 389-7300
Dallas (G-4527)

▲ Kdh Companies Inc....................F.......281 583-8861
Houston (G-10506)

▲ Kelye B Stites Inc...................F.......817 284-3499
Richland Hills (G-17439)

Kerr Feed & Grain Company.............F.......940 538-4354
Henrietta (G-8281)

Kit Professionals Inc..................F.......713 783-8700
Houston (G-10537)

Kotara Mfg Inc..........................G.......830 745-9007
Stockdale (G-19429)

Kyle Bunting Holdings Inc.............F.......512 264-1148
Austin (G-1277)

Lacore Labs Inc.........................F.......469 995-7791
Mckinney (G-14950)

▲ Lash Mfg & Dev Group LLC............F.......956 465-0330
Brownsville (G-2375)

Lawe Industries LLC.....................E.......210 833-9497
San Antonio (G-18238)

Lazel Inc................................E.......214 932-9500
Dallas (G-3847)

▲ Light House Candles LLC.............F.......713 467-4774
Sugar Land (G-11593)

▼ Loadcraft Industries Ltd............F.......325 597-1930
Brady (G-2215)

▲ Lonestar Badge & Sign Inc...........F.......512 357-2261
Martindale (G-14810)

Losoya Industries LLC...................F.......210 559-6066
Boerne (G-2127)

LSI Industries..........................G.......513 793-3200
Houston (G-10695)

▲ Luraco Inc............................E.......817 633-1080
Arlington (G-725)

M & F Wholesale Floral Sups...........F.......915 542-1238
El Paso (G-5851)

M&R Manufacturing LLC....................E.......281 590-7200
Houston (G-10724)

Marking Services Inc....................E.......817 419-0061
Arlington (G-728)

Mash Group Holdings LLC.................E.......314 638-4200
Frisco (G-7297)

McKee True Value Hdwr & Lbr...........E.......903 874-6581
Corsicana (G-3677)

Merit Sales Inc.........................D.......512 863-8541
Georgetown (G-7664)

Michaels Companies Inc..................D.......972 409-1300
Irving (G-13108)

Mid South Manufacturing LLC...........D.......903 759-5490
White Oak (G-20717)

Mohf Manufacturing Inc..................F.......346 317-3618
Spring (G-19233)

Morgan Building & Spa Mfg Corp.......D.......254 629-1599
Eastland (G-5568)

▲ Mortex Products Inc..................B.......817 624-0820
Fort Worth (G-6853)

Mr Maiz-Ito-Inc.........................F.......915 873-9270
El Paso (G-5888)

Mustang Group Ltd.......................F.......830 968-0291
Eagle Pass (G-5550)

Mykytyn Enterprise Inc..................F.......281 866-9263
Houston (G-10946)

Nail Therapie Htx.......................F.......832 703-4386
Houston (G-10960)

▲ Natures Finest LLC...................E.......972 673-1526
Plano (G-16939)

Navarrete Industries LLC...............F.......432 332-0272
Odessa (G-16092)

Noahmaya Candle Co......................F.......210 341-7373
San Antonio (G-18348)

Noble Gent LLC..........................F.......214 516-8609
Desoto (G-5437)

◆ Noltex LLC............................D.......281 842-5000
La Porte (G-13779)

▲ OEM Outsourcing LLC..................E.......972 742-7950
McKinney (G-14959)

Open Road Mobility LLC..................F.......806 866-0275
Lubbock (G-14452)

P I Components Corp.....................D.......979 830-5400
Brenham (G-2267)

Pacific Resources Intl LLC............B.......214 504-3853
McKinney (G-14962)

Page Eagle Industries Inc.............F.......409 960-4310
Port Arthur (G-17120)

PCI Manufacturing LLC...................E.......903 439-1080
Sulphur Springs (G-19595)

Peerless Mfg Co Inc.....................F.......972 559-6380
Denton (G-5391)

Permian Basin Eqp & Sup LLC...........E.......432 563-1044
Odessa (G-16113)

◆ Petmate Holdings Co..................A.......817 467-5116
Arlington (G-753)

Pmq Alternatives Inc....................G.......713 690-7672
Houston (G-11353)

Polk Mechanical Company LLC...........C.......972 339-1200
Grand Prairie (G-7947)

◆ Prism Enterprises....................F.......210 520-8051
San Antonio (G-18397)

Promaxima Mfg LLP Prom..................F.......713 667-9606
Houston (G-11447)

Prostar Manufacturing Inc.............F.......936 585-0737
Pasadena (G-16500)

Ptp Incorporated........................F.......281 342-8775
Rosenberg (G-17595)

▲ Qt Dog LLC............................F.......214 333-4477
Dallas (G-4839)

Ravago Mfg Americas LLC................F.......281 443-6220
Houston (G-11553)

Reed Candle Company.....................C.......210 737-7156
San Antonio (G-18417)

Refrigeration Design Inc..............E.......972 937-3240
Waxahachie (G-20556)

Reliance Prcision Mfg Partners.......F.......281 894-0044
Houston (G-11593)

Rival Prcsion Mnfctrng RPM LLC.......F.......817 487-9694
Alvarado (G-341)

Rodbouban Corporation...................E.......972 841-8989
Houston (G-11655)

▲ S 5 Manufacturing LLC................G.......940 592-2100
Iowa Park (G-12909)

Santre Export USA LLC...................F.......811 053-1165
Hidalgo (G-8309)

Scentchips Inc..........................G.......210 341-7373
San Antonio (G-18456)

◆ Schusters of Texas Inc ....F 325 648-2267
   Goldthwaite *(G-7744)*
Serenity Candles ....F 281 565-0130
   Sugar Land *(G-19554)*
Shermco Industries Inc ....G 512 267-2324
   Cedar Park *(G-2985)*
Siemens Industry Inc ....E 512 837-8300
   Austin *(G-1500)*
Soho ....F 713 526-3755
   Houston *(G-11932)*
Solera Co ....F 915 637-6471
   El Paso *(G-5966)*
▲ **South Txas Lghthouse For Blind** .....C 361 883-6553
   Corpus Christi *(G-3627)*
▲ **Southwest Cutters LLC** ....D 915 858-2200
   El Paso *(G-5971)*
Sports Solutions Inc ....F 214 351-2834
   Dallas *(G-4999)*
▲ **St Jude Candle Company LP** ....D 281 768-7800
   Houston *(G-12033)*
Starmark Solutions LLC ....E 877 823-7847
   Hutto *(G-12885)*
▲ **Starrfoam Manufacturing Inc** ......E 817 654-4688
   Arlington *(G-787)*
Stoller Group Inc ....F 713 461-1493
   Houston *(G-12068)*
Supply Solutions Inc ....D 214 766-6866
   Plano *(G-17015)*
▲ **Tag Waterblock LLC** ....E 281 862-0300
   Channelview *(G-3039)*
Taylor Made Bit Co LLC ....F 432 362-4471
   Odessa *(G-16172)*
Tdindustries Ltd ....F 972 888-9500
   Dallas *(G-5042)*
▲ **Technical Composite Corp** ....E 210 832-0200
   San Antonio *(G-18523)*
◆ **Tex-Tube Company** ....C 713 686-4351
   Houston *(G-12217)*
Texas Almet LP ....D 817 649-7056
   Arlington *(G-791)*
▲ **Texas Lamp Manufacturers Inc** .....E 972 564-5267
   Forney *(G-6315)*
▲ **Texas Scenic Company Inc** ....D 210 684-0091
   San Antonio *(G-18542)*
Texas Scientific Products ....F 972 757-2304
   Argyle *(G-603)*
Tgc Industries ....E 903 464-9908
   Denison *(G-5348)*
Theatrical Warehouse Inc ....E 214 634-2965
   Dallas *(G-5082)*
Thyssenkrupp Elevator Corp ....E 817 922-9590
   Fort Worth *(G-7062)*
Thyssenkrupp Elevator Corp ....F 512 486-1000
   Austin *(G-1578)*
Tmd Manufacturing Inc ....F 903 919-0600
   Sulphur Springs *(G-19603)*
Tommy Lewis Industries ....E 806 291-4433
   Plainview *(G-16766)*
Tooling Technologies Mfg LLC .....F 713 722-8501
   Houston *(G-12320)*
Top Shelf Industries Oper Ltd ......F 806 995-2224
   Tulia *(G-20040)*
Townsend Oilfield Services LP .....F 361 449-1444
   George West *(G-7630)*
Traxis Manufacturing LLC ....F 512 383-0089
   Austin *(G-1591)*
▲ **Trimmings Inc** ....C 903 872-1556
   Corsicana *(G-3687)*
Trinity Industries 068 ....F 903 295-0356
   Longview *(G-14321)*
Trinity Industries Plant 181 ....F 214 631-4420
   Longview *(G-14322)*
Trix & Kix Dannys ....F 281 353-6618
   Spring *(G-19182)*
◆ **Troy Helen Texas Corporation** ......D 915 225-8000
   El Paso *(G-6017)*
Twin Eagle Sand Logistics LLC .....E 713 341-7300
   Houston *(G-12414)*
Tyco International MGT Co LLC .....F 713 644-8872
   Houston *(G-12419)*
▲ **Tyler Candle Company LLC** ....F 903 877-2298
   Tyler *(G-20168)*
▲ **Usm Inc** ....D 281 619-0144
   Houston *(G-12503)*
Uvc Manufacturing Group LLC .....G 281 969-6059
   Spring *(G-19183)*
Valor Containments LLC ....F 432 202-4220
   Midland *(G-15461)*
Valtek Industries Inc ....F 432 339-8481
   Odessa *(G-16194)*

Vector Industrial Group LLC ....F 281 967-1093
   Kemah *(G-13481)*
Vee Interests LLC ....F 832 864-2001
   Pasadena *(G-16523)*
Venus Beauty Inc ....F 301 503-4052
   Garland *(G-7608)*
Victaulic Company ....F 281 494-5000
   Stafford *(G-19395)*
Weatherford Well Screen Techno ....F 281 670-0005
   Houston *(G-12622)*
Westlake Enes Scence Tech Assn ..G 512 751-5049
   Austin *(G-1659)*
Wmk LLC ....F 817 429-1273
   Haltom City *(G-8162)*
World Research Company Inc ....F 903 581-3720
   Tyler *(G-20177)*
Wrs Group Ltd ....D 254 776-6461
   Waco *(G-20480)*
▲ **Wrs Group Ltd** ....F 254 776-6461
   Waco *(G-20481)*
Ww Electronics Solutions LLC ....F 214 396-6636
   Quinlan *(G-17227)*
▲ **Xtreme Lashes LLC** ....E 281 907-0689
   Spring *(G-19189)*

73 BUSINESS SERVICES

7372 Prepackaged Software

1 Starview Solutions LP ....F 512 366-3939
   Austin *(G-868)*
2da Analytics Incorporated ....F 832 472-2093
   Houston *(G-8406)*
3core Software Corporation ....F 281 440-3000
   Katy *(G-13387)*
3s Business Corporation ....D 281 823-9222
   Houston *(G-8411)*
Abacus Computer Co Inc ....F 713 467-2136
   Houston *(G-8442)*
Absolute Software Inc ....E 512 600-7455
   Austin *(G-880)*
Abuyo Inc ....E 855 850-3850
   Austin *(G-882)*
Accept Software Corporation ....E 512 201-8222
   Austin *(G-883)*
Aci Worldwide Corp ....F 361 579-4800
   Victoria *(G-20234)*
Action1 Corporation ....F 346 444-8530
   Houston *(G-8470)*
▲ **Active Network LLC** ....A 888 543-7223
   Dallas *(G-3884)*
Acumen Pm LLC ....E 512 291-6259
   Austin *(G-888)*
Ad Valorem Records Inc ....E 713 523-1623
   Houston *(G-8474)*
Adobe Inc ....E 469 955-9500
   Dallas *(G-3890)*
Advent Global Solutions Inc ....F 281 970-3000
   Houston *(G-8495)*
Aibuy Inc ....E 972 616-6400
   Dallas *(G-3903)*
Aim Solutions Inc ....F 214 373-6084
   Dallas *(G-3904)*
▼ **Alphatrust Corporation** ....G 214 234-9200
   Dallas *(G-3931)*
Ambernet Technologies Inc ....F 972 707-4000
   Dallas *(G-3936)*
▲ **American Micro Systems Ltd** ....E 817 571-9015
   Euless *(G-6130)*
Anderson Merchandisers LLC ....C 972 987-5516
   Plano *(G-16790)*
Anderson Software LLC ....F 936 569-0447
   Kerrville *(G-13518)*
Annapurna Solutions LLC ....F 916 905-3144
   Houston *(G-8646)*
Apex Custom Software Inc ....G 214 725-9792
   The Colony *(G-19809)*
Apex Software Solutions Inc ....E 210 699-6666
   San Antonio *(G-17909)*
Applied Geophysical Services ....F 832 327-3408
   Houston *(G-8668)*
Applied Software Tech Inc ....E 210 732-9212
   San Antonio *(G-17910)*
Applied Training Resources Inc .....E 281 370-9540
   Spring *(G-19100)*
Appy Health Inc ....F 844 764-2779
   Dallas *(G-3955)*
Aprima Medical Software Inc ....E 214 466-8000
   Richardson *(G-17272)*
Aquilan Technologies Inc ....F 512 751-4226
   Austin *(G-926)*

Argus Software Inc ....D 713 621-4343
   Houston *(G-8692)*
Arrow Electronics Inc ....G 303 824-4000
   Plano *(G-16793)*
▲ **Artemis Intl Solutions Corp** ....D 512 201-8222
   Austin *(G-936)*
Ascent Business Systems Inc ....F 281 497-8882
   Houston *(G-8716)*
Asna Inc ....E 210 408-0212
   San Antonio *(G-17917)*
Aspyr Media Inc ....F 512 708-8100
   West Lake Hills *(G-20678)*
Associated Telephone ....F 512 288-6215
   Kyle *(G-13677)*
Assurance Systems Inc ....F 770 242-6832
   Carrollton *(G-2858)*
Asure Software Inc ....F 512 437-2700
   Austin *(G-943)*
Audiotel Corporation ....D 972/359-5500
   Allen *(G-254)*
Automatize Logistics LLC ....F 817 221-8106
   Grapevine *(G-8013)*
Autopoint Inc ....F 888 335-5762
   Roanoke *(G-17482)*
Autostar Solutions Inc ....F 817 377-2995
   Irving *(G-12936)*
Avatar Systems Inc ....E 972 720-1800
   Frisco *(G-7267)*
Avatar Systems Inc ....F 972 334-0162
   Frisco *(G-7268)*
Avolin LLC ....C 512 524-6149
   Austin *(G-970)*
B&B Worldwide Technology ....F 713 471-2387
   Cibolo *(G-3062)*
Base Base Corporation ....F 832 236-9801
   Houston *(G-8820)*
Basis Technologies Inc ....E 888 623-0220
   Addison *(G-106)*
Baxter Planning Systems Inc ....E 512 323-5959
   Austin *(G-977)*
Baxter Plg Systems Opco LLC ....D 512 323-5959
   Austin *(G-978)*
Baytek International Inc ....E 281 218-8880
   Houston *(G-8839)*
Baytek International Inc ....F 361 887-8988
   Corpus Christi *(G-3483)*
▲ **Bazaarvoice Inc** ....C 512 551-6000
   Austin *(G-980)*
Bc Connect LLC ....C 800 347-0855
   Carrollton *(G-2703)*
Bcs Systems Inc ....F 713 978-6511
   Houston *(G-8842)*
Beicip Inc ....F 281 293-8550
   Houston *(G-8852)*
Bell and Howell LLC ....C 972 753-0711
   Irving *(G-12945)*
Bi Solutions Inc ....E 469 287-5784
   Plano *(G-16803)*
Bigcommerce Inc ....C 512 865-4500
   Austin *(G-990)*
Biractual LLC ....F 713 623-5099
   Houston *(G-8888)*
Birch Grove Software Inc ....D 888 907-0301
   Austin *(G-991)*
Bizness Apps Inc ....F 415 655-9496
   Austin *(G-993)*
Blackbaud Inc ....F 512 652-7969
   Austin *(G-995)*
Bloomfire Inc ....E 512 485-0910
   Austin *(G-996)*
Blue Moon Software ....F 512 322-0460
   Austin *(G-998)*
BMC Software Inc ....E 512 343-1961
   Austin *(G-999)*
▲ **BMC Software Inc** ....A 713 918-8800
   Houston *(G-8924)*
BMC Software Inc ....F 972 484-1200
   Dallas *(G-4034)*
BMC Software Inc ....E 214 442-0397
   Plano *(G-16807)*
BMC Software Federal LLC ....F 713 918-8800
   Houston *(G-8925)*
Bms Solutions Usa Inc ....D 713 954-4970
   Houston *(G-8929)*
Bookstore Manager Software ....E 325 673-2826
   Abilene *(G-22)*
Borland Software Corporation ....E 512 340-2200
   Austin *(G-1002)*
Boxer Parent Company Inc ....E 713 918-8800
   Houston *(G-8964)*

Bradmark Technologies Inc ....E 713 621-2808	Condusiv Technologies Corp ....E 818 252-5538	E-Ceptionist Inc ....E 713 520-6688
Houston *(G-8975)*	Austin *(G-1060)*	Houston *(G-9554)*
Bresa Tech LLC ....E 866 728-2889	Connectione LLC ....E 512 310-1000	E-Mds Inc ....C 512 257-5200
Plano *(G-16811)*	Round Rock *(G-17636)*	Austin *(G-1107)*
Brit Systems LLC ....F 214 630-0636	Controlr Software Inc ....F 214 909-8676	E2open LLC ....D 866 432-6736
Dallas *(G-4057)*	Dallas *(G-4162)*	Austin *(G-1108)*
Broadaxis Inc ....F 469 688-2272	Convergepoint Inc ....F 347 948-4258	E2open LLC ....D 925 460-1700
Plano *(G-16814)*	Houston *(G-9298)*	Austin *(G-1109)*
Broadleaf Commerce LLC ....E 800 282-7443	Convio Inc ....C 512 652-2600	Ebizsoft Inc ....E 954 272-0500
Plano *(G-16815)*	Austin *(G-1064)*	Austin *(G-1112)*
Broadleaf Commerce LLC ....E 800 282-7443	Cooper Consulting Company ....E 512 527-1000	Eci Software Solutions Inc ....C 703 737-6620
Austin *(G-1011)*	Austin *(G-1065)*	Fort Worth *(G-6602)*
Bvsn LLC ....D 512 524-6149	Coretrac Inc ....E 512 236-9120	Eclectic Innvtive Slutions LLC ....F 737 999-1907
Austin *(G-1017)*	Austin *(G-1066)*	Dripping Springs *(G-5505)*
Bynari Inc ....F 214 350-5772	Cornerstone Atomtn Systems LLC ....D 972 346-2242	Economic Trnsfrmtion Tech Corp ....F 253 332-7362
Dallas *(G-4070)*	Frisco *(G-7275)*	Frisco *(G-7281)*
C&C Software ....E 714 635-3603	Corona Labs Inc ....F 312 953-7586	Edge Software Inc ....E 512 345-7793
Irving *(G-12958)*	Austin *(G-1067)*	Austin *(G-1114)*
Ca Inc ....B 972 577-3223	Correlog Inc ....F 239 514-3331	Edgenuity Inc ....C 512 478-9600
Plano *(G-16816)*	Houston *(G-9323)*	Austin *(G-1115)*
Cadence Design Systems Inc ....D 512 349-1100	Covey Software Systems Inc ....F 972 353-8716	Edshah Capital ....F 469 770-3740
Austin *(G-1019)*	Irving *(G-12982)*	Plano *(G-16857)*
Calix Inc ....G 707 766-3000	Cpfd LLC ....F 713 429-1252	Education Advanced Inc ....G 903 858-4497
Richardson *(G-17282)*	Houston *(G-9332)*	Tyler *(G-20083)*
Calytera Us Inc ....D 512 623-9786	Crayon Software Experts LLC ....E 469 329-0290	Eduphoria Incorporated ....E 972 535-5570
Austin *(G-1021)*	Dallas *(G-4181)*	Plano *(G-16858)*
Camber Def SEC Systems Sltons ....E 210 279-3608	Creative Education Inst Inc ....D 254 751-1188	Eduspark Inc ....F 512 535-6139
San Antonio *(G-17977)*	Waco *(G-20391)*	Austin *(G-1116)*
Cambium Learning Group Inc ....D 214 932-9500	Crocodile Digital Corporation ....F 713 382-1891	Eixsys LLC ....G 512 666-3574
Dallas *(G-3839)*	Galveston *(G-7395)*	Austin *(G-1117)*
Candeo Interactive LLC ....F 214 394-8499	Crossvale Inc ....B 972 714-4782	Election Systems & Sftwr LLC ....D 469 675-8990
Forney *(G-6303)*	Dallas *(G-4185)*	Allen *(G-264)*
Capitalsoft Inc ....F 972 220-1560	Cstorepro Technologies Inc ....E 866 265-5826	Electronic Med Resources LL C ....E 832 456-2600
Richardson *(G-17284)*	Sugar Land *(G-19470)*	Houston *(G-9595)*
Cardinal Automation Inc ....F 214 233-3773	Cubelogic LLC ....E 832 498-6374	Embarcadero Technologies Inc ....C 512 226-8080
Dallas *(G-4083)*	Austin *(G-9357)*	Austin *(G-1121)*
Cardinal Software Inc ....F 512 275-0072	Cubix Software Ltd Inc ....F 903 297-7771	EMC Corporation ....C 972 892-7700
Austin *(G-1028)*	Longview *(G-14217)*	Dallas *(G-4317)*
Carreker Corporation ....C 800 486-1981	Cybernance Corporation ....F 512 850-5909	Emergency Technologies Inc ....E 919 676-6200
Dallas *(G-4086)*	Austin *(G-1081)*	Austin *(G-1124)*
Cdb Software Inc ....F 713 588-1778	Cypress Telecommunications ....E 281 449-4000	Energy Exchange 3 LP ....F 972 668-6601
Houston *(G-9112)*	Spring *(G-19205)*	Frisco *(G-7282)*
CDM Software Solutions Inc ....E 972 469-3082	Daegis Inc ....E 214 584-6400	Epicor Software Corporation ....D 512 328-2300
Frisco *(G-7272)*	Irving *(G-12988)*	Austin *(G-1130)*
Cev Multimedia Ltd ....E 806 745-8820	Dairy LLC ....F 214 442-5928	Epicor Software Corporation ....D 800 776-7438
Lubbock *(G-14391)*	Frisco *(G-7278)*	Plano *(G-16865)*
Cfa Services ....F 210 758-5721	Dartican LLC ....F 281 645-6370	Epicor Software Corporation ....C 512 328-2300
San Antonio *(G-17995)*	Pinehurst *(G-16733)*	Austin *(G-1132)*
Cgi Technologies Solutions Inc ....B 866 344-3221	Data Voice International Inc ....F 972 390-8808	EPM Live Inc ....C 425 452-1111
Houston *(G-9150)*	McKinney *(G-14934)*	Austin *(G-1133)*
Checkfree Corporation ....D 281 333-9800	Datagration Solutions Inc ....E 713 568-4580	Eship Global Inc ....F 972 518-1775
Houston *(G-9167)*	Houston *(G-9405)*	Dallas *(G-3842)*
Chequedcom Inc ....E 888 412-0699	DBA Software Inc ....F 512 342-1769	Esi Technologies LLC ....G 512 633-2897
Dallas *(G-4110)*	Austin *(G-1085)*	Austin *(G-1138)*
Chiron Health Holdings LLC ....F 319 400-3772	DC Cadd Company ....E 210 732-9212	Esw Holdings Inc ....F 512 524-6149
Austin *(G-1049)*	San Antonio *(G-18043)*	Austin *(G-1140)*
Chuck Atkinson Inc ....F 817 560-8139	Deligent LLC ....E 972 550-6111	Ethosiq LLC ....F 281 616-5711
Fort Worth *(G-6516)*	Irving *(G-12995)*	Houston *(G-9709)*
Cimarron Software Services Inc ....E 281 226-5100	◆ Dell Inc ....A 800 289-3355	Ets Zone ....F 713 559-1400
Houston *(G-9190)*	Round Rock *(G-17642)*	Spring *(G-19211)*
Cisco Systems Inc ....A 512 378-1112	Dell Software Inc ....E 469 221-4335	Everest Global Inc ....F 972 980-0013
Austin *(G-1051)*	Grapevine *(G-8029)*	Dallas *(G-4337)*
Cistera Networks Inc ....F 972 381-4699	Dell Technologies Inc ....C 800 289-3355	Evoleap LLC ....F 832 371-6677
Plano *(G-16823)*	Round Rock *(G-17646)*	Houston *(G-9719)*
Cityon Systems Inc ....F 972 519-1673	Denali Intermediate Inc ....A 713 627-0933	Excel Media LLC ....F 409 832-5770
Plano *(G-16824)*	Round Rock *(G-17648)*	Beaumont *(G-1890)*
Client Connect LLC ....E 214 295-4940	Detechtion USA Inc ....E 713 357-4775	Excelente Inc ....E 855 209-1970
Plano *(G-16826)*	Houston *(G-9445)*	Plano *(G-16867)*
Cloud Logix LLC ....E 682 310-0665	Digerati Dist & Mktg LLC ....E 512 569-1772	Excelergy Corp ....F 214 953-9373
Irving *(G-12974)*	Austin *(G-1092)*	Dallas *(G-4340)*
Coastal Resources Group LLC ....F 281 549-4132	Dilogr LLC ....F 800 455-9632	Exceleron Software LLC ....F 972 852-2700
Kemah *(G-13471)*	Austin *(G-1095)*	Dallas *(G-4341)*
Cobalt Group Inc ....E 206 269-6363	Distribution Management Co Inc ....F 817 421-3311	Exela Technologies Inc ....D 844 935-2832
Austin *(G-1054)*	Southlake *(G-19063)*	Irving *(G-13017)*
Coda Global LLC ....E 844 366-8250	Diyatech Corp ....E 214 769-6933	Exigo Office Inc ....F 214 367-9999
Southlake *(G-19060)*	Dallas *(G-4264)*	Dallas *(G-4347)*
Codekko Inc ....E 214 919-0565	Docs On Demand Inc ....E 713 980-9500	Exit Plan LLC ....E 213 444-6106
Plano *(G-16827)*	Houston *(G-9490)*	Austin *(G-1145)*
Cognite Inc ....F 512 593-7120	Dronesense Inc ....F 512 582-0444	Express Info Systems Inc ....F 210 614-9410
Houston *(G-9239)*	Austin *(G-1103)*	San Antonio *(G-18100)*
Common Source LP ....F 281 443-7575	Droplets Inc ....E 214 969-9970	Falconstor Software Inc ....E 631 777-5188
Houston *(G-9253)*	Plano *(G-16851)*	Austin *(G-1146)*
Complete Intelligence Tech Inc ....F 281 710-9131	DSI Solutions LLC ....F 817 633-1772	Fellowship Technologies LP ....D 469 442-0100
The Woodlands *(G-19847)*	Arlington *(G-666)*	Irving *(G-13025)*
Compu-Data International LLC ....E 281 292-1333	Dwell App LLC ....F 214 417-9424	Fifth Rock Software Inc ....E 281 265-0944
Houston *(G-9263)*	Plano *(G-16853)*	Sugar Land *(G-19483)*
Computer Labs Inc ....E 915 775-1839	Dynatron Software Inc ....F 972 488-0393	Figtree Technologies Inc ....G 469 361-6643
El Paso *(G-5703)*	Richardson *(G-17303)*	McKinney *(G-14942)*
Concur Technologies Inc ....F 972 612-7121	Dyopath LLC ....D 855 749-6758	Filecontrol Partners Ltd ....F 713 355-1111
Allen *(G-260)*	Houston *(G-9551)*	Houston *(G-9785)*

Filestack	F	210 364-1833	
San Antonio *(G-18113)*			
Filetrail Inc	E	408 289-1300	
Austin *(G-1155)*			
Financial Industry Com	D	972 458-8583	
Addison *(G-123)*			
Fishbowl Games LLC	F	469 449-3275	
Dallas *(G-4366)*			
Flightaware LLC	D	713 877-9010	
Houston *(G-9802)*			
Flow-Cal Inc	E	832 240-4800	
Houston *(G-9808)*			
Flutura Business Solutions LLC	F	832 265-9172	
Houston *(G-9817)*			
Fooder LLC	F	832 953-8944	
Spring *(G-19123)*			
Forcepoint LLC	E	858 320-8000	
Austin *(G-1164)*			
Forproject Technology Inc	F	214 550-8156	
Irving *(G-13031)*			
Four Cornerstone Solutions LLC	E	817 377-1144	
Fort Worth *(G-6646)*			
Four Rivers Sftwr Systems Inc	E	412 256-9020	
Austin *(G-1170)*			
Frh Consumer Services Inc	G	512 657-8945	
Austin *(G-1172)*			
Gearbox Publishing LLC	D	972 312-8202	
Frisco *(G-7287)*			
Gem-Cap Inc	E	512 219-7610	
Austin *(G-1180)*			
Genesis Entitai LLC	E	904 803-2457	
The Colony *(G-19811)*			
Genmz LP	F	214 683-6635	
Dallas *(G-4401)*			
Gensym Corporation	D	512 377-9700	
Austin *(G-1182)*			
Geomechanics International Inc	F	713 599-0373	
Houston *(G-9937)*			
Ghg Corp	B	281 461-6533	
Webster *(G-20638)*			
Gibraltar Monex Centurion Svc		800 409-2674	
Houston *(G-9955)*			
Girl Talk Boutique & Spa LLC	F	956 225-7898	
Pharr *(G-16698)*			
Global Shop Solutions Inc	D	281 681-1959	
The Woodlands *(G-19868)*			
Globalscape Inc	D	210 308-8267	
San Antonio *(G-18150)*			
Globeranger Corporation	F	972 744-9977	
Richardson *(G-17322)*			
Goengineer Inc	F	713 735-3295	
Houston *(G-9990)*			
Greenbasket Inc	E	212 203-3302	
Frisco *(G-7259)*			
Gresham Enterprise Storage Inc	E	512 250-0916	
Austin *(G-1194)*			
Greyheller LLC	D	925 415-5050	
Dallas *(G-4416)*			
Happy Shopper Inc	F	281 751-7138	
Houston *(G-10122)*			
Harris N Computer Corporation	F	903 535-8222	
Tyler *(G-20093)*			
◆ Harte Hanks Inc	E	512 343-1100	
Austin *(G-1198)*			
Hbs Systems Inc	D	972 234-4444	
Richardson *(G-17327)*			
Health Management Systems Inc	C	214 453-3000	
Irving *(G-13055)*			
Health Management Systems Inc	E	512 407-9680	
Austin *(G-1200)*			
Healthcare Pymnt Spcalists LLC	E	800 784-2175	
Fort Worth *(G-6691)*			
Healthmark Medical Group LLC	F	800 659-4035	
Dallas *(G-4445)*			
Hewlett Packard Enterprise Co	C	650 687-5817	
Houston *(G-10166)*			
High Point Design LLC	F	972 753-2622	
Irving *(G-13056)*			
Hill Cntry Bb Ch Drpping Sprng	F	512 843-0035	
Dripping Springs *(G-5507)*			
Hotschedulescom Inc	E	512 904-4299	
Austin *(G-1210)*			
Hp Inc	A	541 360-4763	
Spring *(G-19132)*			
Human Resource Micro Systems	F	415 362-8400	
Irving *(G-13060)*			
Hyper9 Inc	E	800 748-0685	
Austin *(G-1215)*			
Hyphen Solutions LLC	D	972 728-8100	
Dallas *(G-4480)*			
I Net Software Technologies	E	972 401-0100	
Irving *(G-13062)*			
I2 Technologies Inc	E	469 357-1000	
Dallas *(G-4482)*			
IBM Global Systems Inc	F	972 468-1944	
Irving *(G-13063)*			
Idera Inc	D	713 523-4433	
Houston *(G-10315)*			
Igt Global Solutions Corp	E	512 908-4310	
Austin *(G-1221)*			
Imagination Station Inc	E	214 237-9300	
Dallas *(G-4490)*			
Immediatek Inc	E	888 661-6565	
Bedford *(G-1974)*			
Impac Systems Engineering LLP	F	713 784-3500	
Temple *(G-19682)*			
Inclusive Products Inc	F	281 650-7057	
Houston *(G-10337)*			
Info-Power International Inc	G	972 424-4447	
Plano *(G-16890)*			
Infocyte Inc	E	844 463-6298	
Austin *(G-1228)*			
Infor (us) LLC	C	800 915-3243	
Dallas *(G-4496)*			
Information Store Inc	F	713 787-6798	
Houston *(G-10358)*			
Infosys Limited	D	214 306-2100	
Richardson *(G-17332)*			
Infosys Limited	F	281 454-0300	
Houston *(G-10359)*			
Inherent Software LLC	F	817 379-0328	
Wylie *(G-20937)*			
Innovative Sftwr Solutions Inc	F	830 265-6835	
San Antonio *(G-18188)*			
Inspired Elearning LLC	D	210 579-0224	
San Antonio *(G-18189)*			
Integrated MGT Concepts Inc	E	805 778-1629	
Austin *(G-1231)*			
Integrated Tax Solutions LLC	F	855 792-6657	
San Antonio *(G-18190)*			
Intellicentrics Inc	E	214 222-7484	
Flower Mound *(G-6268)*			
Interact Inc	E	512 501-2680	
Austin *(G-1233)*			
Intesolv Inc	E	512 681-7272	
Austin *(G-1239)*			
Intuit Inc	E	214 387-2000	
Plano *(G-16894)*			
Inventory Services Network	E	972 660-7365	
Livingston *(G-14157)*			
Involta LLC	F	817 937-8943	
Dallas *(G-4511)*			
Ioffice LP	E	713 526-1029	
Houston *(G-10412)*			
◆ Ion Geophysical Corporation	C	281 933-3339	
Houston *(G-10413)*			
Ion Geophysical Corporation	D	281 552-3000	
Stafford *(G-19331)*			
Iron Sky	F	281 468-8255	
Houston *(G-10420)*			
Itron Networked Solutions Inc	F	210 762-4400	
San Antonio *(G-18195)*			
J Paul Horst & Associates	F	713 460-9386	
Houston *(G-10442)*			
Jarvantech Inc	F	832 742-7220	
The Woodlands *(G-19888)*			
Jcjh LLC	F	830 331-2240	
Boerne *(G-2124)*			
Jeeves Information Systems Inc	F	512 333-4418	
Austin *(G-1254)*			
Jeh-Eas Inc	G	210 490-9156	
San Antonio *(G-18200)*			
Jericho Systems Corporation	E	972 231-2000	
Dallas *(G-4533)*			
Jive Software Inc	D	877 495-3700	
Austin *(G-1256)*			
John Galt Development Inc	F	312 701-9026	
Dallas *(G-4536)*			
Jollyrhino Inc	F	909 732-8507	
Austin *(G-1260)*			
Jones Lang Lasalle Ip Inc	E	214 777-5100	
Dallas *(G-4538)*			
Journeyedcom Inc	D	800 876-3507	
Allen *(G-280)*			
JR Peterson Inc	E	210 695-4455	
Helotes *(G-8239)*			
Jr3 Websmart LLC	E	254 759-1902	
Waco *(G-20421)*			
Kainexus Inc	F	512 522-3940	
Irving *(G-13072)*			
Kamico Instructional Media Inc	E	254 947-7283	
Salado *(G-17765)*			
Keen Solutions Group Inc		903 253-0476	
Tyler *(G-20107)*			
Kerio Technologies Inc	C	408 496-4500	
Austin *(G-1267)*			
Kev Group Inc		866 891-9138	
Fort Worth *(G-6756)*			
Keytrak Inc	D	979 595-2600	
College Station *(G-3190)*			
Khoros LLC	B	415 757-3100	
Austin *(G-1268)*			
Kibo Software Inc	D	707 780-1600	
Dallas *(G-4555)*			
Kicstand Inc	F	210 324-0421	
Houston *(G-10531)*			
Kidasa Software Inc	F	512 368-2326	
Austin *(G-1269)*			
Kingsisle Entertainment Inc	E	972 265-1900	
Plano *(G-16902)*			
Kloudnation LLC	E	214 682-8692	
Frisco *(G-7296)*			
Kontract Sftwr Solutions LLC	E	281 994-6104	
Houston *(G-10560)*			
Kony Inc	C	512 792-2900	
Austin *(G-1272)*			
Kudzookinect Inc	E	512 363-0704	
Austin *(G-1274)*			
Lacerte Software Corporation	C	214 387-2000	
Plano *(G-16906)*			
Lansa Inc	C	630 874-7042	
Houston *(G-10598)*			
Learnsap A Texas Ltd Lblty Co	E	832 419-7371	
Pearland *(G-16577)*			
Lendflow Inc	F	512 265-1261	
Kingwood *(G-13647)*			
Levelfieldcom Inc	F	512 401-9200	
Austin *(G-1290)*			
Lightside Games Inc	G	650 814-0293	
West Lake Hills *(G-20683)*			
Liquid Litigation MGT Inc	E	210 757-4881	
Austin *(G-1294)*			
Liquid Motors Inc	E	214 393-2323	
Richardson *(G-17345)*			
Lisam America Inc	E	979 307-7384	
Bryan *(G-2491)*			
▲ LMS Acquisitions LLC	F	512 371-7028	
Austin *(G-1296)*			
Lookout Services Inc	F	713 668-6200	
Stafford *(G-19349)*			
Lyris Technologies Inc	E	510 844-1600	
Austin *(G-1314)*			
M-Files Inc	B	972 516-4210	
Plano *(G-16914)*			
Magdata Inc	C	425 372-2699	
Austin *(G-1317)*			
Management Controls Inc	C	281 590-5881	
Houston *(G-10743)*			
Mapspeople Inc	E	512 368-0038	
Austin *(G-1325)*			
Marine Computation Svcs Kenny	D	281 646-4155	
Houston *(G-10764)*			
Mavenir Prvate Holdings II Ltd	A	469 916-4393	
Richardson *(G-17352)*			
McAfee LLC	A	972 963-7000	
Plano *(G-16921)*			
McAfee Public Sector LLC	E	972 963-7000	
Plano *(G-16922)*			
◆ McKesson Corporation	A	972 446-4800	
Irving *(G-13102)*			
Medapoint Inc	G	512 659-1117	
Austin *(G-1333)*			
Medassets Inc	A	972 813-7500	
Austin *(G-1333)*			
Medcognition Inc	F	210 960-0930	
San Antonio *(G-18287)*			
Medeanalytics Inc	C	469 476-5423	
Richardson *(G-17355)*			
Medhost Inc	C	972 560-3100	
Plano *(G-16925)*			
Medical Present Value Inc	E	512 795-0015	
Austin *(G-1334)*			
Medical Web Experts LLC	E	619 819-8610	
Dallas *(G-4663)*			
Medici Technologies LLC	F	800 768-8131	
Austin *(G-1335)*			
Medifacts Inc	E	817 571-8181	
Colleyville *(G-3221)*			
Medimobile Inc	F	512 686-0817	
Georgetown *(G-7663)*			

Metapath Software Intl	F	972 907-3600	
Richardson *(G-17356)*			
Microsoft Corporation	C	210 402-0577	
San Antonio *(G-18301)*			
Microsoft Corporation	C	469 775-0000	
Irving *(G-13109)*			
Microsoft Corporation	D	469 775-0000	
Irving *(G-13110)*			
Microsoft Corporation	D	832 252-4300	
Houston *(G-10870)*			
Microsoft Corporation	E	972 345-3610	
Irving *(G-13111)*			
Mindpower International Inc	F	469 287-2735	
Lewisville *(G-14068)*			
Mlc Cad Systems LLC	F	512 288-8511	
Austin *(G-1346)*			
Moneyonmobile Inc	B	214 758-8600	
Dallas *(G-4685)*			
Monolith Tech Holdings LLC	E	972 532-7387	
Frisco *(G-7299)*			
Motor Crier Sfety Slutions Inc	F	956 726-3377	
Laredo *(G-13916)*			
Mtwd Holdings Inc	E	972 346-2242	
Frisco *(G-7300)*			
Muroc Systems Inc	F	214 295-9442	
Dallas *(G-4708)*			
Myedu Corporation	E	512 469-9777	
Austin *(G-1359)*			
National Instruments Corp	B	214 227-4788	
Garland *(G-7558)*			
▲ National Instruments Corp	A	512 683-0100	
Austin *(G-1360)*			
Navitaire	E	512 617-2121	
Austin *(G-1361)*			
Ncs Pearson Inc	D	210 339-5000	
San Antonio *(G-18340)*			
Neofirma Inc	F	214 233-7111	
Richardson *(G-17362)*			
Neon Systems Inc	D	281 276-5900	
Sugar Land *(G-19511)*			
Nerve Software LLC	G	972 231-4775	
Richardson *(G-17363)*			
Netiq Corporation	D	713 548-1700	
Houston *(G-11028)*			
Netscout Systems Texas LLC	B	469 330-4000	
Allen *(G-288)*			
Netwatch Solutions Inc	F	214 446-8486	
Richardson *(G-17364)*			
Network Info Systems Inc	E	713 255-4800	
Houston *(G-11030)*			
Newtek Inc	E	210 370-8000	
San Antonio *(G-18344)*			
Newtek Partners Lp	D	210 370-8000	
San Antonio *(G-18345)*			
Nextgenauto LLC	F	888 481-9756	
Irving *(G-13124)*			
Nobix Inc	E	925 659-3500	
McKinney *(G-14958)*			
Northrop Grumman Systems Corp	D	512 374-4100	
Austin *(G-1369)*			
Ntt Data Inc	C	800 745-3263	
Plano *(G-16948)*			
Nuview Systems Inc	D	978 296-6600	
Austin *(G-1372)*			
O9 Solutions Inc	E	214 838-3125	
Dallas *(G-4749)*			
Occupational Marketing Inc	G	281 492-8250	
Houston *(G-11119)*			
Oceanus Automotive LLC	E	512 551-9726	
Austin *(G-1376)*			
Omnibase Services of Texas	F	512 346-6511	
Austin *(G-1382)*			
Online Training Solutions Inc	E	888 308-6874	
Argyle *(G-602)*			
Openconnect Systems Inc	E	972 484-5200	
Dallas *(G-4763)*			
Optimum Consultancy Svcs LLC	F	713 505-0300	
Houston *(G-11185)*			
Optimum Path Systems Inc	F	813 990-8204	
Hurst *(G-12854)*			
Oracle America Inc	F	650 506-7000	
San Antonio *(G-18356)*			
Oracle America Inc	E	512 401-1000	
Austin *(G-1389)*			
Oracle America Inc	C	972 980-7799	
Dallas *(G-4766)*			
Oracle America Inc	G	972 580-0629	
Irving *(G-13132)*			
Oracle America Inc	D	214 494-4527	
Frisco *(G-7303)*			

Oracle Corporation	B	817 422-5231	
Keller *(G-13469)*			
Oracle Corporation	B	512 372-8207	
Austin *(G-1390)*			
Oracle Corporation	B	972 652-8000	
Frisco *(G-7304)*			
Oracle Corporation	F	512 832-1599	
Austin *(G-1392)*			
Oracle Corporation	F	713 595-7656	
Houston *(G-11188)*			
Oracle Corporation	A	737 867-1000	
Austin *(G-1391)*			
Oracle Glass LLC	F	713 462-4759	
Houston *(G-11189)*			
Oracle Systems Corporation	B	713 658-6925	
Lewisville *(G-14075)*			
Ordermygear LLC	F	214 945-4000	
Dallas *(G-4767)*			
Orion Communications Inc	E	214 361-1203	
Dallas *(G-4768)*			
Osisoft LLC	E	281 920-6170	
Houston *(G-11198)*			
Overnite Software Inc	E	979 319-8371	
Angleton *(G-575)*			
P2 Energy Solutions Inc	E	713 787-6300	
Houston *(G-11215)*			
P2es Holdings LLC	D	713 481-2000	
Houston *(G-11216)*			
P2es Holdings LLC	D	210 402-5900	
San Antonio *(G-18359)*			
Paradigm Ses LLC	F	713 402-6140	
Houston *(G-11238)*			
Parlevel Systems Inc	E	210 200-8873	
San Antonio *(G-18367)*			
Pas Group LLC	D	281 286-6565	
Houston *(G-11254)*			
Passare Inc	E	325 695-3412	
Abilene *(G-63)*			
Patient Conversation Media Inc	E	512 522-0966	
Austin *(G-1399)*			
PC Legal Tools Inc	E	415 808-8800	
Austin *(G-1402)*			
Peek Traffic Corporation	C	281 453-0200	
Houston *(G-11270)*			
Peopleadmin Inc	E	877 637-5800	
Austin *(G-1408)*			
Perception Software Inc	F	512 593-6996	
Austin *(G-1409)*			
Percomonline Incorporated	F	325 480-2617	
Abilene *(G-64)*			
Perfomix LLC	D	713 893-8310	
Bellaire *(G-2001)*			
Periscope Intermediate Corp	D	512 717-0684	
Austin *(G-1412)*			
Peritus Inc	C	817 726-4626	
Irving *(G-13141)*			
Pestroutes Opco LLC	D	404 800-7378	
McKinney *(G-14963)*			
Petrasoft Counsulting	F	832 448-5600	
Houston *(G-11299)*			
Phaseware Inc	F	214 432-9043	
McKinney *(G-14964)*			
Photonic Inc	F	956 722-3326	
Laredo *(G-13921)*			
Phunware Inc	D	512 693-4199	
Austin *(G-1416)*			
Pivot3 Inc	E	281 516-6000	
Spring *(G-19158)*			
Pixel and Texel LLC	F	214 240-0013	
Dallas *(G-4808)*			
Playnet Inc	E	817 358-7580	
Bedford *(G-1977)*			
Plugged In LLC	F	512 380-0900	
Austin *(G-1422)*			
Plus One Robotics Inc	F	937 287-5060	
San Antonio *(G-18383)*			
Pointwise Inc	F	817 377-2807	
Fort Worth *(G-6910)*			
Practice Interactive Inc	F	844 413-2602	
Austin *(G-1427)*			
Premier Digital Design LLC	G	210 774-5456	
San Antonio *(G-18390)*			
▲ Presidio Ntwrked Sltons Group	B	469 549-3800	
Lewisville *(G-14083)*			
Privacy Inc	E	214 760-8700	
Dallas *(G-4829)*			
Pro-Tem LLC	F	281 334-5547	
League City *(G-13976)*			
▲ Procera Networks Inc	E	510 230-2777	
Plano *(G-16980)*			

Prodektive Specialty Svcs LLC	E	713 425-3075	
Houston *(G-11436)*			
Profitable Decisions Inc	F	281 972-3030	
Houston *(G-11441)*			
Pros Inc	A	713 335-5151	
Houston *(G-11452)*			
Pros Holdings Inc	C	713 335-5151	
Houston *(G-11453)*			
Pushnami LLC	F	512 961-7042	
Austin *(G-1438)*			
Pwr Technologies LLC	F	469 609-3537	
Mesquite *(G-15073)*			
Q2 Holdings Inc	E	512 275-0072	
Austin *(G-1439)*			
Qnet Inc	D	214 341-7638	
Dallas *(G-4838)*			
Quacito LLC	F	210 695-0795	
San Antonio *(G-18404)*			
Quest Software Inc	E	949 754-8000	
Dallas *(G-4850)*			
Quick Intrnet Sftwr Sltons Inc	F	979 846-3008	
College Station *(G-3198)*			
▼ Quinstar Corporation	F	512 326-1011	
Austin *(G-1445)*			
Qvinci Software	F	512 637-7337	
Austin *(G-1446)*			
R T L X LLC	E	214 778-6400	
Plano *(G-16982)*			
Rational Systems LLC	F	832 476-8468	
Houston *(G-11552)*			
Realpage Inc	A	972 820-3000	
Richardson *(G-17387)*			
Red Book Connect LLC	B	877 741-9610	
Austin *(G-1455)*			
Redhouse Virtual Education LLC	F	210 872-4989	
Dallas *(G-4878)*			
Renaissance Cmpt Group Not Inc	F	713 256-6067	
Houston *(G-11597)*			
Republic Title of Texas Inc	C	972 578-8611	
Plano *(G-16991)*			
Revenue Technology Svcs Corp	E	972 573-1600	
Plano *(G-16992)*			
Revitalu International LLC	F	469 270-5533	
Plano *(G-16993)*			
▼ Rignet Inc	C	281 674-0100	
Houston *(G-11622)*			
Rlra Inc	F	817 783-3335	
Alvarado *(G-342)*			
Rmg Enterprise Solutions Inc	E	877 796-6634	
Dallas *(G-4904)*			
Rmg Networks Holding Corp	E	800 827-9666	
Addison *(G-159)*			
ROC Software LP	E	512 336-4200	
Austin *(G-1468)*			
Rogii Inc	E	346 714-8694	
Houston *(G-11656)*			
Royal Technocrats Inc	E	713 776-8300	
Houston *(G-11684)*			
▲ Rubicon Communications LLC	E	512 646-4100	
Austin *(G-1476)*			
Rubrix LLC	E	512 581-5513	
San Antonio *(G-18437)*			
Rush Apparel LLC	F	713 208-5194	
Magnolia *(G-14625)*			
Saddle Creek Corp	F	817 306-2000	
Fort Worth *(G-6971)*			
Safertek Software LLC	E	972 331-2984	
Coppell *(G-3443)*			
Sage Software Inc	C	512 331-0723	
Austin *(G-1481)*			
Sagl Enterprises Inc	E	281 496-3737	
Houston *(G-11729)*			
Sailpoint Tech Holdings Inc	A	512 346-2000	
Austin *(G-1482)*			
Sailpoint Technologies Inc	C	512 346-2000	
Austin *(G-1483)*			
Samsung SDS Globl Scl Amer Inc	E	201 263-3000	
Plano *(G-17000)*			
Sapling Systems Inc	E	512 323-6565	
Austin *(G-1486)*			
Sas Institute Inc	D	512 258-5171	
Austin *(G-1487)*			
Scalable Software Inc	F	512 501-2828	
Austin *(G-1489)*			
Scott Traffic LLC	F	972 937-6040	
Waxahachie *(G-20557)*			
Sencha Inc	D	713 523-4433	
Houston *(G-11827)*			
Seremedi Inc	G	832 671-8622	
Houston *(G-11835)*			

Sevco Security Inc ...... F ...... 512 413-2211 Austin *(G-1496)*	**SW Health Care Solutions LLC** ...... F ...... 832 578-6694 Houston *(G-12128)*	**Ultimate Kronos Group** ...... F ...... 469 221-1823 Irving *(G-13202)*
Shadowsoft Inc ...... E ...... 972 841-2469 Irving *(G-13176)*	**Swye360 Learning Inc** ...... F ...... 214 263-2932 Frisco *(G-7317)*	**Ultimate Kronos Group** ...... E ...... 469 221-1800 Irving *(G-13203)*
Sharco Technologies Inc ...... F ...... 512 258-0573 Pflugerville *(G-16688)*	▲ **Synergen Health LLC** ...... F ...... 214 643-6002 Dallas *(G-5032)*	**Unique System LLC** ...... F ...... 713 937-6193 Houston *(G-12440)*
Shi International Corp ...... F ...... 732 764-8888 Dallas *(G-4954)*	▲ **System Development Inc** ...... E ...... 713 266-5667 Houston *(G-12139)*	**Upay Inc** ...... F ...... 972 888-6052 Dallas *(G-5142)*
Shi/Government Solutions Inc ...... E ...... 512 634-8100 Austin *(G-1498)*	**Systum Inc** ...... F ...... 406 600-3684 Plano *(G-17018)*	**Upland Software Inc** ...... C ...... 833 875-2631 Austin *(G-1611)*
Shiftsmart Inc ...... F ...... 817 271-3604 Dallas *(G-4955)*	▲ **T-System Inc** ...... C ...... 972 503-8899 Plano *(G-17019)*	**Upland Software I Inc** ...... D ...... 617 494-5515 Austin *(G-1612)*
Shipcom Wireless Inc ...... D ...... 281 558-5252 Houston *(G-11870)*	**Taxsation Inc** ...... F ...... 888 829-1120 Dallas *(G-5037)*	**Uplogix Inc** ...... E ...... 512 857-7000 Austin *(G-1613)*
Siemens Industry Software Inc ...... C ...... 972 987-3000 Plano *(G-17003)*	**Tbx Employee Benefits LLC** ...... E ...... 972 248-9030 Plano *(G-17022)*	**Utax Software LLC** ...... G ...... 844 440-8829 El Paso *(G-6021)*
Siemens Industry Software Inc ...... E ...... 972 391-2476 Plano *(G-17004)*	◆ **Test Spectrum Inc** ...... F ...... 512 472-6750 Austin *(G-1564)*	▲ **Vapor Io Inc** ...... E ...... 512 600-1123 Austin *(G-1623)*
Sigga USA LLC ...... F ...... 855 744-4287 Sugar Land *(G-19556)*	**Texas Logic Inc** ...... F ...... 956 682-3466 McAllen *(G-14911)*	**Vedero Software Inc** ...... E ...... 972 309-9870 Carrollton *(G-2895)*
Signacert Inc ...... F ...... 512 577-4894 Austin *(G-1501)*	**Texas Source Group Inc** ...... F ...... 713 464-9702 Houston *(G-12250)*	**Veeder-Root Fuelquest LLC** ...... F ...... 713 222-5700 Houston *(G-12544)*
Simplelegal Inc ...... F ...... 415 763-5366 Houston *(G-11903)*	**Thinkgeo LLC** ...... F ...... 785 727-4133 Frisco *(G-7319)*	**Vercom Software Inc** ...... E ...... 972 661-9336 Dallas *(G-5161)*
Sk Global Software LLC ...... F ...... 301 963-7300 Houston *(G-11912)*	**Thinksmart LLC** ...... F ...... 888 489-4284 Austin *(G-1574)*	**Verge Ventures LLC** ...... F ...... 972 200-1707 Richardson *(G-17420)*
Smart City Locating Inc ...... E ...... 214 586-0519 Dallas *(G-4971)*	▼ **Thinkwell Corporation** ...... F ...... 888 416-8880 Austin *(G-1575)*	**Versata Inc** ...... D ...... 512 524-6149 Austin *(G-1631)*
Smart Imaging Technologies Co ...... E ...... 713 589-3500 Houston *(G-11918)*	**Thomson Reuters Corporation** ...... D ...... 972 250-7000 Carrollton *(G-2832)*	**Vertical Computer Systems Inc** ...... F ...... 972 437-5200 Richardson *(G-17421)*
Smart Packager Inc ...... E ...... 713 316-4903 Austin *(G-1511)*	**Thru Inc** ...... D ...... 214 496-0100 Irving *(G-13194)*	**Viewcastcom Inc** ...... E ...... 972 488-7200 Grapevine *(G-8059)*
Smartdraw Software LLC ...... E ...... 858 225-3300 The Woodlands *(G-19919)*	**Thru Holding Company LLC** ...... F ...... 214 496-0100 Irving *(G-13195)*	**Visionael Corporation** ...... F ...... 650 963-0960 Austin *(G-1639)*
Smpl Inc ...... E ...... 402 525-5078 Austin *(G-1513)*	**Thryv Holdings Inc** ...... A ...... 972 453-7000 Dfw Airport *(G-5458)*	**Visionmonitor Software LLC** ...... F ...... 713 935-0500 Houston *(G-12571)*
Soff Corporation ...... F ...... 469 467-9700 Plano *(G-17008)*	**Thursby Software Systems LLC** ...... E ...... 817 478-5070 Arlington *(G-798)*	**Visual Bi Solutions Inc** ...... E ...... 972 232-2233 Plano *(G-17046)*
Soff Corporation ...... F ...... 469 467-9700 Plano *(G-17009)*	**Tibco Software Inc** ...... E ...... 713 344-2045 Houston *(G-12287)*	**Visual Click Software Inc** ...... E ...... 512 231-9990 Austin *(G-1640)*
Softest Designs Corporation ...... E ...... 210 697-8828 San Antonio *(G-18481)*	**Tillman Learning LLC** ...... F ...... 866 540-9677 Plano *(G-17033)*	**Visualml Operations LLC** ...... G ...... 855 847-8256 Liberty Hill *(G-14131)*
Software Construction Co Inc ...... F ...... 214 495-7387 Allen *(G-298)*	**Timeclock Plus LLC** ...... D ...... 325 223-9300 San Angelo *(G-17834)*	**Volusion LLC** ...... F ...... 800 646-3517 Austin *(G-1645)*
Software Development Tech ...... E ...... 650 906-6135 Trophy Club *(G-20021)*	**Tips Incorporated** ...... F ...... 512 863-3653 Georgetown *(G-7686)*	**VSI Solutions Inc** ...... F ...... 855 712-7677 McKinney *(G-14987)*
Software Global Ltd ...... F ...... 832 274-0478 Austin *(G-1516)*	**Tom Lanham Software** ...... G ...... 254 773-2513 Temple *(G-19713)*	**Wargaming America Inc** ...... E ...... 510 962-6747 Austin *(G-1646)*
Solarwinds Corporation ...... F ...... 512 682-9300 Austin *(G-1517)*	**Tops Software Corporation** ...... E ...... 972 739-8677 Allen *(G-303)*	**Waterfall International Inc** ...... E ...... 844 627-2438 Austin *(G-1648)*
Solarwinds Holdings Inc ...... F ...... 512 682-9300 Austin *(G-1518)*	**Touchshare Inc** ...... F ...... 626 639-5460 Houston *(G-12335)*	**Websense LLC** ...... B ...... 858 320-8000 Austin *(G-1653)*
Solarwinds North America Inc ...... C ...... 512 682-9300 Austin *(G-1519)*	**Toutatis Aztec Solutions** ...... D ...... 972 484-3060 Dallas *(G-5103)*	**Webvent Inc** ...... F ...... 617 418-4126 Lewisville *(G-14111)*
Solarwinds Worldwide LLC ...... E ...... 512 682-9300 Austin *(G-1520)*	**Tpg Software Inc** ...... E ...... 713 974-1375 Houston *(G-12337)*	**Wellsmith Inc** ...... F ...... 866 266-7793 Austin *(G-1654)*
Solid Integrations LLC ...... E ...... 915 235-4357 El Paso *(G-5968)*	**Tradesorg LLC** ...... E ...... 512 729-3544 Austin *(G-1589)*	**Western Atlas Intl Inc** ...... B ...... 713 972-4000 Houston *(G-12641)*
Solovis Inc ...... F ...... 678 234-4583 Irving *(G-13183)*	**Transmedia Dynamics Inc** ...... E ...... 512 971-2313 Kyle *(G-13687)*	**Wheel Innovationz Inc** ...... F ...... 408 390-2871 Austin *(G-1660)*
▲ **Solutions In Software Inc** ...... E ...... 214 221-9995 Dallas *(G-4979)*	**Travis Software Inc** ...... F ...... 281 496-3737 Houston *(G-12358)*	**White Cloud Security Inc** ...... F ...... 512 887-8783 Cedar Park *(G-2990)*
Sourceday Inc ...... E ...... 512 361-7029 Austin *(G-1521)*	**Travistin Inc** ...... F ...... 512 275-4812 Lago Vista *(G-13809)*	**Whole Tomato Software Inc** ...... C ...... 512 226-8080 Austin *(G-1664)*
Southwest Data Systems Inc ...... F ...... 817 370-9966 Fort Worth *(G-7001)*	**Trax Holdings Inc** ...... F ...... 855 999-7828 Flower Mound *(G-6290)*	**Win-911 Software** ...... E ...... 512 326-1011 Austin *(G-1671)*
Specter Instruments Inc ...... F ...... 512 326-1011 Austin *(G-1524)*	**Traxsales LLC** ...... E ...... 713 466-7177 Houston *(G-12359)*	**Window On Wallstreet Inc** ...... E ...... 972 727-3626 Richardson *(G-17429)*
Spiceworks Inc ...... B ...... 512 346-7743 Austin *(G-1525)*	▲ **Trend Micro Incorporated** ...... C ...... 408 257-1500 Irving *(G-13199)*	**Wizetrade Group** ...... C ...... 407 206-6500 Plano *(G-17053)*
Spigit Inc ...... D ...... 855 774-4480 Austin *(G-1526)*	**Trifectix Inc** ...... E ...... 512 580-2809 Georgetown *(G-7687)*	**Workiva Inc** ...... B ...... 817 308-1153 Irving *(G-13208)*
Splunk Inc ...... F ...... 972 244-8806 Plano *(G-17011)*	**Trinity Millennium Group Inc** ...... C ...... 210 615-1606 San Antonio *(G-18567)*	**Yadblue LLC** ...... F ...... 214 542-6140 Southlake *(G-19084)*
St George Software L L C ...... E ...... 512 442-6794 Austin *(G-1529)*	**Triple Aim Ventures LLC** ...... E ...... 210 417-4170 San Antonio *(G-18569)*	**Yash & Lujan Consulting Inc** ...... B ...... 800 519-5221 Austin *(G-1679)*
Stark Holdings Inc ...... E ...... 512 329-8109 Austin *(G-1531)*	**Triseum LLC** ...... F ...... 979 773-8909 Bryan *(G-2514)*	**Yellow Folder LLC** ...... E ...... 214 431-3600 Carrollton *(G-2851)*
▼ **Statacorp LLC** ...... C ...... 979 696-4600 College Station *(G-3202)*	**Tritech Software Development** ...... E ...... 972 680-2223 Allen *(G-304)*	**Yoolotto LLC** ...... E ...... 469 383-6488 Dallas *(G-5208)*
Stone Bond Technologies ...... F ...... 713 622-8798 Houston *(G-12070)*	**Troux Technologies Inc** ...... D ...... 512 346-8600 Austin *(G-1596)*	**Ziften Technologies Inc** ...... E ...... 512 298-5501 Austin *(G-1686)*
Stone Cliff Technology LLC ...... F ...... 512 640-0650 Austin *(G-1538)*	**Tyler Technologies Inc** ...... C ...... 972 713-3700 Plano *(G-17039)*	**Zix Corporation** ...... D ...... 214 370-2000 Dallas *(G-5210)*
Superior Information Systems ...... F ...... 713 524-8998 Houston *(G-12116)*	**Tyler Technologies Inc** ...... E ...... 903 753-4292 Longview *(G-14326)*	**Zixcorp Systems Inc** ...... E ...... 214 370-2000 Dallas *(G-5211)*
Superior It Solutions LLC ...... F ...... 713 501-1260 Houston *(G-12117)*	**Tyler Technologies Inc** ...... D ...... 972 713-3770 Plano *(G-17040)*	
Surgical Notes Inc ...... E ...... 214 821-3850 Dallas *(G-5031)*	**Tyler Technologies Inc** ...... C ...... 806 797-0761 Lubbock *(G-14504)*	

S I C

76 MISCELLANEOUS REPAIR SERVICES

7692 Welding Repair

A & A Welding Inc	F	817 910-9700	Granbury (G-7791)
A & D Cstm Wldg & Fabrication	F	210 310-7610	San Antonio (G-17846)
A & M Machine & Wldg Works Inc	G	281 421-1281	Baytown (G-1806)
A & W Welding Inc	G	281 499-4332	Stafford (G-19279)
A&K Industrial Repair LLC	E	281 470-8848	Deer Park (G-5258)
Accuweld Inc	E	281 442-5900	Houston (G-8465)
Ace Welding and Trailer Co	E	210 667-1171	San Antonio (G-17858)
Advanced Metal Fusion Inc	F	512 422-0888	Cedar Park (G-2959)
Advanced Welding Services Inc	F	713 933-2626	Houston (G-8493)
Advanced Welding Solutions LLC	E	713 473-0099	League City (G-13944)
Aggietech Energy Services LLC	E	806 229-6129	Sundown (G-19610)
Alamo Welding & Boiler Work	F	210 227-6502	San Antonio (G-17888)
Alexanders Mch Maint Svc Inc	E	817 625-4175	Fort Worth (G-6369)
Allbright & Associates Inc	F	432 366-8897	Odessa (G-15909)
Als Inc	F	361 325-2154	Falfurrias (G-6181)
American Welding Services	E	409 440-8143	Hitchcock (G-8333)
American Wldg Fabrication Inc	F	210 661-4159	San Antonio (G-17905)
▼ Anchor Machine Works Inc	F	713 988-0400	Houston (G-8640)
Apache Instrumentations & Gas	E	432 336-7755	Fort Stockton (G-6327)
Aranda Ironworks Inc	F	956 722-5084	Laredo (G-13863)
ARC Rite Welding & Fabrication	F	830 774-6058	Del Rio (G-5305)
Asi Piping LLC	E	409 786-1080	Vidor (G-20324)
◆ Associated Welding Supply Inc	F	281 485-2755	Pearland (G-16540)
B & J Welding Supply Ltd	F	432 563-1277	Midland (G-15126)
Ballew Casting Repair Inc	F	361 882-9901	Corpus Christi (G-3481)
Bay Area Industrial Contrs LP	C	281 471-0400	La Porte (G-13725)
BCAD Zion Corporation	F	210 657-9090	New Braunfels (G-15775)
Berry Machine Shop	E	817 572-0948	Burleson (G-2571)
Big State Welding & Machine Lc	F	940 766-0191	Wichita Falls (G-20745)
Bill Gilmore Welding Inc	E	940 592-4945	Iowa Park (G-12903)
Bise Welding & Fabricating Inc	D	713 681-0958	Houston (G-8892)
Blackburn Machine & Fab LLC	E	713 644-2386	Houston (G-8910)
Blade Runner Turbomachinery SE	E	713 669-1155	Navasota (G-15726)
Brave Services Incorporated	E	432 355-4001	Andrews (G-541)
Browns Welding & Manufacturing	F	830 625-8712	New Braunfels (G-15776)
Burns Welding Works Inc	F	432 682-0495	Midland (G-15153)
Bwm Services LP	E	979 272-7708	Caldwell (G-2629)
C&C Welding	G	903 436-9150	Bells (G-2005)
C&J Cladding LLC	E	281 987-2383	Houston (G-9039)
Cains Welding Service Inc	E	281 303-9517	Mont Belvieu (G-15616)
CC Coating & Machine Inc	E	361 884-9753	Corpus Christi (G-3497)
Cessac Welding Service Inc	F	979 828-9067	Franklin (G-7164)
Chaparral Wldg Fabrication Inc	E	972 243-7747	Dallas (G-4104)
Chapman Dock Inc	E	325 388-6545	Kingsland (G-13621)
Cherokee Welding Inc	F	512 243-0002	Austin (G-1047)
Chris Burns Welding LLC	G	940 845-4945	Sunset (G-19624)
Chriss Welding & Fabricating	F	409 986-6094	Hitchcock (G-8335)
Circle M Welding & Svcs Inc	D	325 573-8005	Snyder (G-18987)
▲ City Machine & Welding Inc	E	806 358-7293	Amarillo (G-416)
Cns Tech Wldg & Fabrication Lc	E	281 239-2555	Humble (G-12760)
Coleman Machine & Welding Svc	F	325 625-5186	Coleman (G-3169)
Colliers Top of Texas Inc	E	806 363-2867	Hereford (G-8287)
Crisp Industries Inc	D	830 372-1110	Seguin (G-18834)
Crumplers Mch & Wldg Svc Inc	E	409 886-7934	Bridge City (G-2282)
Curtis Oilfield Services LLC	E	409 385-2937	Silsbee (G-18952)
▲ Custom Heliarc Inc	F	281 375-2075	Brookshire (G-2314)
D & R Specialties Inc	E	936 873-2947	Navasota (G-15728)
D&R Steel Works Inc	F	210 639-8314	Castroville (G-2927)
Daltons Welding Service Inc	F	940 682-7237	Weatherford (G-20586)
▲ Data Matique Properties LP	C	972 272-3446	Garland (G-7476)
Delray Machine LLC	F	830 693-5110	Marble Falls (G-14742)
Die & Tool Service Inc	F	281 498-3317	Sugar Land (G-19479)
Diversified Machining Inc	F	512 355-3270	Bertram (G-2052)
Duane Ollinger	E	806 935-6786	Dumas (G-5520)
E X P Fabrication LLC	E	940 453-3382	Justin (G-13342)
East Texas Machine Works Inc	D	903 759-9796	Longview (G-14227)
Ebling Welding LLC	G	830 905-7235	Canyon Lake (G-2679)
Edward Bloch Ltd	F	210 648-6011	San Antonio (G-18083)
El Paso Tool & Die Co Inc	E	915 591-0346	El Paso (G-5744)
Eldred Sheet Metal Works LP	E	713 227-3251	Houston (G-9588)
Elite Specialty Welding LLC	D	832 649-4251	Pasadena (G-16423)
Empire Wldg & Fabrication LLC	F	915 706-4070	El Paso (G-5755)
Energy Fabrication Inc	E	432 362-0591	Odessa (G-15990)
Ernies Welding Shop Inc	F	512 459-6346	Austin (G-1137)
F & R Machine Services Inc	F	214 631-4946	Dallas (G-4350)
Fab Tex Oilfield Services Inc	D	432 339-1011	Odessa (G-15998)
Fabricating Solutions	F	409 735-7141	Bridge City (G-2283)
Fife Services Inc	E	432 827-3601	Goldsmith (G-7742)
Forge Tech Inc	G	888 854-8414	Kemah (G-13474)
Franklin Welding Service Inc	C	361 592-1322	Kingsville (G-13627)
Freer Iron Works Inc	E	361 394-7273	Freer (G-7225)
G W Vines Company Inc	E	214 742-8371	Dallas (G-4389)
Genes Machine Inc	D	361 573-7146	Victoria (G-20267)
▲ Gibbons Inc	F	940 872-2452	Bowie (G-2196)
Global Welding Services Inc	D	713 991-3555	Houston (G-9980)
Grazco LLC	F	281 252-0151	Houston (G-10023)
Green Machine & Tool Inc	F	713 943-0402	South Houston (G-19041)
Gulf Copper & Mfg Corp	C	409 982-6122	Port Arthur (G-17112)
H M W Fabrications Inc	F	940 325-0300	Mineral Wells (G-15527)
H&A Machine & Welding LLC	F	832 857-8505	Houston (G-10086)
Harrison Fabricators Inc	F	214 374-1684	Dallas (G-4438)
Hefco Enterprises Inc	E	281 431-1571	Fresno (G-7238)
Herrin Welding Service Inc	F	903 984-7139	Kilgore (G-13558)
Houston Fab Truck Rigging RPS	E	713 455-6161	Houston (G-10233)
Houston Truck Tarps LLC	F	346 571-1832	Houston (G-10259)
Hub Machine & Tool Inc	E	940 549-0155	Graham (G-7784)
Industrial Pro Fab LLC	G	713 205-7245	Katy (G-13409)
Industrial Spclty Svcs USA LLC	F	713 987-9117	Deer Park (G-5280)
Industrial Welding Academy	F	713 944-0701	Houston (G-10356)
International Plant Svcs LLC	B	281 867-8400	La Porte (G-13755)
J & E Welding Inc	F	409 794-2311	Beaumont (G-1911)
J B R Enterprises Inc	G	972 542-3939	McKinney (G-14947)
J&J Welding & Awning	F	214 227-5606	Garland (G-7524)
Jac Enterprises Inc	F	936 348-3934	Madisonville (G-14588)
Jack Phipps	F	972 278-3186	Dallas (G-4520)
Jalem Welding Service LLC	F	956 467-2355	McAllen (G-14876)
James Puryear Weldng Fabrctn	F	325 672-2009	Abilene (G-54)
Jefes Welding Company	F	903 389-4036	Fairfield (G-6177)
Jerryco Mch & Boiler Works LP	D	713 224-7900	Houston (G-10466)
Johnson Tool Company Inc	E	432 267-7612	Big Spring (G-2084)
Johnston Products Dallas Inc	E	469 272-7212	Cedar Hill (G-2946)
Jones Manufacturing Inc	F	254 399-8940	Waco (G-20420)
Judys Iron & Metal Inc	E	409 681-0500	Vidor (G-20328)
JV Industrial Companies Ltd	F	903 579-8900	Tyler (G-20105)
JV Industrial Companies Ltd	F	281 417-7019	La Porte (G-13759)
◆ JV Industrial Companies Ltd	D	713 568-2600	San Antonio (G-18213)
Kennedy Machine & Mfg Inc	E	972 241-7610	Haslet (G-8219)
Kiger Bros Mch Tl & Die Works	E	281 447-1315	Houston (G-10532)
Knighten Machine and Svc Inc	E	877 457-7204	Odessa (G-16055)
▲ Kobelco Welding of America	G	281 240-5600	Stafford (G-19341)
Lake Road Welding Co	E	940 692-4988	Wichita Falls (G-20778)
Lake Services Inc	F	512 261-3625	Lakeway (G-13817)
Landry Corporation	F	281 449-1052	Houston (G-10596)
Laser Welding Solutions LLC	F	713 895-0800	Houston (G-10605)
▲ Laserweld Inc	E	713 333-0804	Katy (G-13422)
Ledsome Machine & Welding Co	F	325 646-4691	Brownwood (G-2434)
Lonestar Fencing and Wldg LLC	G	210 992-0441	San Antonio (G-18264)
Lons Welding	E	806 435-2278	Perryton (G-16639)
Luttrell Welding Services	E	940 433-3131	Boyd (G-2206)
Lwf Services LLC	F	432 425-9795	Odessa (G-16066)
M & S Mechanical Inc	E	318 755-2431	Pittsburg (G-16747)
M R Fabrication	G	940 427-4701	Alvord (G-388)

Magee Machine and Mfg Inc F 972 285-2554
Mesquite *(G-15060)*
Mainliners Welding Academy F 409 229-1632
La Porte *(G-13773)*
Manufctred Component Parts Ltd E 713 880-0590
Houston *(G-10749)*
Martels Machine Shop G 432 333-4556
Odessa *(G-16071)*
Maxie Hodges G 432 333-4556
Odessa *(G-16074)*
McDonald Welding Co F 325 573-5329
Snyder *(G-18994)*
McMahan Welding Service Ltd F 361 275-0111
Cuero *(G-3763)*
Mepco Enterprises Inc E 713 943-9240
Houston *(G-10830)*
Merritt Prfrred Components Inc D 903 983-1592
Kilgore *(G-13574)*
Midwest Fab & Construction Inc F 806 335-9126
Amarillo *(G-446)*
Midwest Machine LLC E 806 355-9400
Amarillo *(G-501)*
Miller Machine & Welding LLC E 254 582-2185
Whitney *(G-20731)*
Modisette Welding & Supply E 903 984-2502
Kilgore *(G-13575)*
▲ **Montgomery Machine Company Inc** D 713 453-6381
Houston *(G-10914)*
Mp Precision Services Inc F 915 599-9188
El Paso *(G-5886)*
N & N Services LLC F 281 741-9714
Pearland *(G-16584)*
Northast Txas McHning Wldg Hrd F 903 427-2277
Clarksville *(G-3076)*
Ober & Sons Inc F 281 879-6760
Houston *(G-11112)*
Omni Contracting F 972 890-4536
Midlothian *(G-15489)*
One Source Mfg Tech LLC D 512 259-3272
Leander *(G-13996)*
Pampa Machine & Supply Inc F 806 665-0013
Pampa *(G-16332)*
Panyanouvong Jose & Le Malysa F 310 279-7065
Fort Worth *(G-6892)*
Phillips Fabrication Inc E 432 264-6600
Big Spring *(G-2093)*
Pick Instrument Products Co E 713 672-1686
Galena Park *(G-7381)*
Platts Welding and Cnstr LLC F 972 333-5830
Denison *(G-5345)*
Precision Iron Fabrication LLC F 972 636-7581
Royse City *(G-17723)*
Precision M/C Products Inc F 972 429-6200
Wylie *(G-20944)*
▲ **Premium Welding Inc** F 713 957-2724
Houston *(G-11407)*
Premium Welding & Mfg Inc D 713 957-2724
Houston *(G-11408)*
Prime Downhole Mfg LLC E 832 957-3200
Houston *(G-11413)*
Professional Machine Works F 713 645-7562
Houston *(G-11438)*
Pwf Enterprises F 512 295-6412
Buda *(G-2534)*
R & N Manufacturing Ltd D 713 466-6252
Cypress *(G-3817)*
R & R Sheet Metal and Mch Sp F 806 274-2361
Borger *(G-2183)*
R C Technical Welding & Fabr E 281 933-6004
Stafford *(G-19367)*
R R Ramsower Inc E 979 849-6441
Angleton *(G-576)*
Radke Machine & Tool Inc E 254 576-2513
Hubbard *(G-12737)*
Randco Industries Inc E 432 520-0820
Midland *(G-15377)*
Ratec Inc F 903 687-3811
Waskom *(G-20520)*
RE Campbell Company Ltd E 713 957-8721
Houston *(G-11558)*
Reama Inc F 409 744-9222
Galveston *(G-7407)*
Redding Machine Shop Inc F 940 691-5218
Wichita Falls *(G-20802)*
Riggs Machine and Welding Inc F 254 965-3910
Stephenville *(G-19420)*
Road Runner Service Point E 713 675-5110
Houston *(G-11640)*
Robert Early Welding E 325 573-0029
Snyder *(G-19004)*
Robotic Welding Solutions LLC G 281 706-5967
Conroe *(G-3359)*
Ronald L Jordan Company E 281 485-6626
Pearland *(G-16597)*
Rosado Welding Inc F 469 730-2222
Dallas *(G-4910)*
Rotom Inc E 806 293-7331
Plainview *(G-16762)*
Rp Welding Inc F 940 315-1024
Crossroads *(G-3749)*
Rs Welding LLC F 940 488-4144
Pilot Point *(G-16728)*
RSI Inspection LLC E 325 673-9800
Abilene *(G-77)*
Rudd Welding Inc F 806 435-5501
Perryton *(G-16648)*
Santin Auto and Truck Repr Ctr E 210 648-4100
San Antonio *(G-18454)*
Saulsbury Industries Inc E 903 392-2248
Henderson *(G-8273)*
Sb Southern Welding LLC E 469 517-0410
Joshua *(G-13325)*
Scientific Machine & Wldg Inc E 512 926-8400
Austin *(G-1490)*
Second Gnration ARC Spark Wldg E 979 778-1999
Bryan *(G-2507)*
Septh Group LLC E 713 988-4200
Houston *(G-11832)*
Sharp Iron Group LLC E 940 855-2710
Wichita Falls *(G-20809)*
Sharp Iron Group LLC D 940 766-4545
Wichita Falls *(G-20810)*
Snoe Inc Machining & Welding E 979 567-0808
Caldwell *(G-2636)*
Solansky Welding and Pump Inc E 830 374-3318
Crystal City *(G-3757)*
Southern Welding LLC F 469 517-0410
Waxahachie *(G-20561)*
Spillar Welding Inc E 512 264-0351
Spicewood *(G-19095)*
Starks Welding & Mfg Svcs Inc E 512 863-2424
Georgetown *(G-7681)*
Sturm Welding Inc F 940 686-2492
Pilot Point *(G-16730)*
Sullivan Welding Inc F 512 259-3440
Leander *(G-13997)*
Sulzer Pump Services (us) Inc E 432 614-2574
Odessa *(G-16168)*
Superior Welding Inc E 432 523-2038
Andrews *(G-559)*
Sweetwater Machine and Welding E 325 235-2922
Sweetwater *(G-19637)*
T L Precision Welding Inc F 713 896-4500
Houston *(G-12142)*
T O F Enterprises Inc F 281 328-2553
Crosby *(G-3744)*
Taurus Industrial Group LLC E 713 554-0157
La Porte *(G-13793)*
Tcw Investments Inc F 409 796-1883
Beaumont *(G-1956)*
Temples Trailer Sales Inc F 903 885-7301
Sulphur Springs *(G-19602)*
Texas Stud Welding LLC G 210 300-2500
Somerset *(G-19021)*
Texweld & Fabrication Inc G 903 586-1775
Jacksonville *(G-13265)*
Thompson Welding G 432 381-1531
Odessa *(G-16178)*
Tietjen Inc E 979 249-3888
La Grange *(G-13703)*
Titanium Welding Services LLC F 281 380-7043
Houston *(G-12301)*
Tlr Welding & Fabricating Inc F 940 969-2400
Paradise *(G-16356)*
Tombstone Welding F 325 573-8446
Snyder *(G-19012)*
Top Deck Inc E 409 745-3955
Orange *(G-16265)*
Trevino Industries Inc F 281 489-1754
Pearland *(G-16605)*
Trevinos Welding F 806 250-3669
Friona *(G-7254)*
Tri-Construction Co Inc C 979 233-7211
Freeport *(G-7217)*
Trinity Casting Service Inc E 214 631-4248
Dallas *(G-5111)*
Trinity Services Group Inc C 903 277-7128
Texarkana *(G-19781)*
Triple C Industries Inc E 936 931-1171
Hockley *(G-8349)*
Triple S Welding Co F 210 464-2878
Lytle *(G-14574)*
▲ **TW Tanks and Construction Co** F 361 358-8869
Beeville *(G-1989)*
TX Tinman Enterprises LLC F 817 288-6116
Fort Worth *(G-7087)*
Txtb Tech Llc F 832 928-5740
Montgomery *(G-15644)*
UNI-Fab LLC F 936 344-2800
Willis *(G-20867)*
Universal Management Svcs LLC E 979 481-5711
Angleton *(G-581)*
Vales Welding Service F 936 336-5148
Liberty *(G-14126)*
Varco Shaffer Inc E 713 672-1711
Houston *(G-12535)*
Vinyard Water Service E 806 256-2766
Shamrock *(G-18893)*
Vmg Welding F 832 605-3933
Houston *(G-12579)*
Walsh Welding Inc F 325 387-2357
Sonora *(G-19032)*
Welasco Inc F 903 784-5562
Paris *(G-16374)*
Weld Revolution LLC F 832 585-1244
Spring *(G-19187)*
▲ **Weldfit Corporation** C 713 460-3700
Houston *(G-12628)*
Welding Material Sales Inc F 713 672-4166
Houston *(G-12629)*
Welding Works Intl Inc E 956 838-5636
Brownsville *(G-2421)*
Welfab Inc E 361 552-4033
Port Lavaca *(G-17156)*
West Machine & Tool Inc F 903 758-5401
Longview *(G-14335)*
Whm Custom Services Inc D 254 854-2111
Grandview *(G-8003)*
Williams Alloy & Welding G 713 896-9096
Houston *(G-12668)*
Winnie Wldg Works & Cnstr Inc E 409 296-2953
Winnie *(G-20894)*
Wldg Wilkerson & Fabrication F 817 528-1032
Overton *(G-16277)*
Wwl Industries Inc E 432 362-0326
Odessa *(G-16215)*
Zachry Holdings Inc A 210 588-5000
San Antonio *(G-18632)*

7694 Armature Rewinding Shops

A & R Enterprises Inc F 903 984-9057
Kilgore *(G-13530)*
▲ **Abaco Drilling Tech LLC** C 281 869-0700
Houston *(G-8441)*
▲ **Acg Quality Electric Inc** F 713 225-6531
Houston *(G-8468)*
Airgen Equipment LLC F 432 332-1870
Odessa *(G-15907)*
All American Pump & Mch Inc F 325 653-6597
San Angelo *(G-17773)*
Alliance Machine & Spc Inc F 432 367-9113
Odessa *(G-15911)*
Alsay Incorporated E 210 628-1090
San Antonio *(G-17900)*
Amarillo Elc Specialists Inc F 806 372-3798
Amarillo *(G-394)*
▲ **Amerimex Motor & Controls LLC** D 713 225-4300
Houston *(G-8618)*
Austin Armature Works LP E 512 312-0088
Buda *(G-2520)*
B J Electric Motor Service F 432 570-4100
Midland *(G-15127)*
Bayou Processing & Storage LP E 713 450-8401
Houston *(G-8836)*
Blade Runner Turbomachinery SE E 713 669-1155
Navasota *(G-15726)*
Border Industrial Motors Inc G 915 542-4266
El Paso *(G-5668)*
▲ **Bradleys Inc** D 361 643-0100
Gregory *(G-8099)*
Brandon & Clark Inc C 806 771-5600
Lubbock *(G-14380)*
Brandon & Clark Inc G 432 332-0163
Odessa *(G-15941)*
Brandon & Clark Inc E 806 771-5646
Lubbock *(G-14381)*
Brandon & Clark Inc E 817 838-5593
Fort Worth *(G-6469)*
Brandon & Clark Inc F 432 332-0163
Odessa *(G-15942)*

S I C

Brandon & Clark Inc ....F 806 364-5470
Hereford *(G-8284)*

Brenham Repair Center LLC ....F 979 277-9071
Brenham *(G-2247)*

Buna Electric Motor Svc Inc ....E 409 769-5402
Vidor *(G-20325)*

▲ C P E Inc ....F 972 313-1133
Irving *(G-12956)*

Cajun Electric Motors Inc..............F 972 227-9000
Ferris *(G-6231)*

Capital Dallas Elc Mtr Svc ....F 214 630-8487
Dallas *(G-4081)*

Cems Acquire Co LLC ....E 817 308-0165
Dallas *(G-4095)*

Chapman Electric Company ....F 214 824-8095
Dallas *(G-4105)*

Chester R Wright III ....F 832 693-8038
Friendswood *(G-7243)*

City of Marshall ....F 903 935-4500
Marshall *(G-14771)*

▲ Commercial Armature Works..........F 713 672-7873
Houston *(G-9248)*

Community Motors Inc ....F 281 354-8087
New Caney *(G-15837)*

Corpus Christi CD Electric LP ....F 361 888-4133
Corpus Christi *(G-3508)*

Cudd Pumping Services Inc ....B 432 580-3544
Odessa *(G-15972)*

Daily Electric Inc ....G 903 753-2732
Longview *(G-14220)*

Davenport Electric Motors LLC ....F 361 299-6440
Corpus Christi *(G-3511)*

Electrico Inc............................F 903 872-6567
Corsicana *(G-3670)*

Etheredge Elc Co Tyler Inc ....E 903 877-4774
Tyler *(G-20084)*

Evans Enterprises Inc ....F 254 772-4710
Waco *(G-20399)*

Evans Enterprises Inc ....F 940 723-7466
Wichita Falls *(G-20764)*

▲ Flanders Electric Ltd ....D 903 759-9439
Longview *(G-14234)*

G E Jones Electric Co Inc ....E 806 372-5505
Amarillo *(G-426)*

Gauntlett Inc............................G 806 293-9849
Plainview *(G-16754)*

General Electric Company ....D 214 902-6600
Dallas *(G-4400)*

General Electric Company ....D 412 469-6080
Southlake *(G-19071)*

▲ Globaltech Motor & Contrls Inc ......E 281 487-9300
Houston *(G-9984)*

▲ Grayson Armature Works Inc ....F 713 473-4404
Pasadena *(G-16450)*

Grayson Sulzer Inc ....E 409 882-9112
Orange *(G-16245)*

H L Hailey Enterprises Inc ....F 903 759-1881
Longview *(G-14244)*

Heights Armature Works Inc............F 713 937-7676
Houston *(G-10147)*

Hiroko International Inc ....F 210 590-4411
San Antonio *(G-18168)*

Hoffman Industrial Electric ....G 361 573-6365
Victoria *(G-20272)*

Houma Armture Wrks Houston LLC......E 713 748-0702
Houston *(G-8384)*

Indeco-Industrial Electric Co ....F 325 653-4255
San Angelo *(G-17809)*

Indelect Corporation ....E 903 656-2518
Lone Star *(G-14183)*

Industrial Spclty Svcs USA LLC ....F 713 987-9117
Deer Park *(G-5280)*

Integrated Power Services LLC ....E 281 471-4611
La Porte *(G-13753)*

Integrated Power Services LLC ....E 409 833-9477
Beaumont *(G-1909)*

Land Enterprises Inc ....F 713 924-5929
Houston *(G-10592)*

Lufkin Armature Works Inc ....F 936 632-6607
Lufkin *(G-14535)*

Lufkin Electric Co ....F 936 639-2377
Lufkin *(G-14538)*

Lynn Electric Motor Co Inc ....F 940 657-3511
Knox City *(G-13664)*

◆ M&I Electric Industries Inc ....D 832 241-6330
Houston *(G-10721)*

Martin Electric Co Inc ....E 979 543-6421
El Campo *(G-5622)*

Massengale Armature Works Inc........F 210 732-5168
San Antonio *(G-18282)*

◆ Megatron Inc ....E 281 558-0034
Houston *(G-10824)*

Mission Cycleplex LLC ....F 210 250-0057
San Antonio *(G-18310)*

Monahans Electric Inc ....E 432 943-3246
Monahans *(G-15609)*

▲ Morefield Development Inc ....E 713 869-2111
Houston *(G-10920)*

▲ Musshorn Enterprises Inc ....C 915 772-9007
El Paso *(G-5892)*

New Core Inc ....F 956 421-2446
Harlingen *(G-8196)*

Phase Electric Motors Inc ....F 972 291-9221
Cedar Hill *(G-2950)*

Rail Products Intl Inc ....D 956 541-1759
Brownsville *(G-2397)*

▲ Remsa Usa Inc ....F 915 855-8621
El Paso *(G-5937)*

Roundhouse Elc & Eqp Co Inc ....F 432 333-3923
Odessa *(G-16143)*

San Antonio Armature Works Inc........E 210 227-0291
San Antonio *(G-18445)*

Smith Pump Company Inc ....G 817 589-2060
Fort Worth *(G-6996)*

▲ Sulzer Electro-Mechanical Serv.......D 713 473-3231
Pasadena *(G-16513)*

Sulzer Electro-Mechanical Serv.........E 409 882-9112
Orange *(G-16264)*

◆ Sun-Star Electric Inc ....D 806 793-2812
Lubbock *(G-14488)*

Sytek Electric Corporaiton.............E 713 862-8813
Houston *(G-12140)*

Texas Electric Eqp Co Ltd ....E 281 479-6086
La Porte *(G-13794)*

Tolbert Electric Motor Company.........F 972 272-6541
Garland *(G-7603)*

Trinity Services Group Inc ....C 903 277-7128
Texarkana *(G-19781)*

Valley Armature & Elc Co Inc ....F 956 393-2233
Edinburg *(G-5605)*

▲ Warfield Electric Texas Inc ....F 214 637-1200
Carrollton *(G-2845)*

ALPHABETIC SECTION

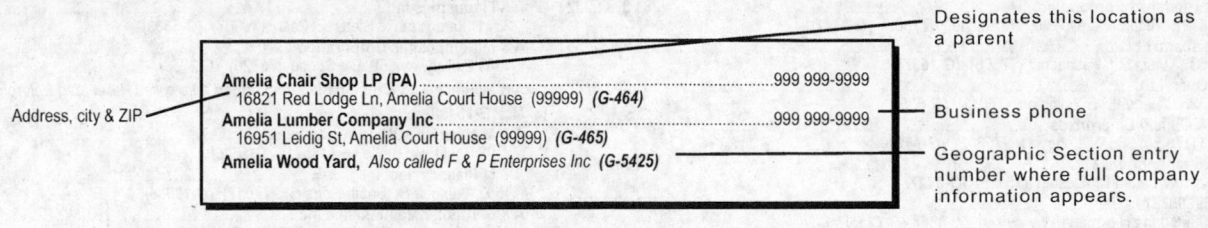

Designates this location as a parent

Address, city & ZIP

Amelia Chair Shop LP (PA) 999 999-9999
16821 Red Lodge Ln, Amelia Court House (99999) *(G-464)*
Amelia Lumber Company Inc 999 999-9999
16951 Leidig St, Amelia Court House (99999) *(G-465)*
Amelia Wood Yard, *Also called F & P Enterprises Inc (G-5425)*

Business phone

Geographic Section entry number where full company information appears.

See footnotes for symbols and codes identification.

* Companies listed alphabetically.

* Complete physical or mailing address.

---

1 Play Away LLC 972 532-6226
504 E Belt Line Rd Unit B Desoto (75115) *(G-5426)*
1 Quacito, San Antonio *Also called Quacito LLC (G-18404)*
1 Starview Solutions LP 512 366-3939
9433 Fm 2244 Rd Austin (78733) *(G-868)*
1 To 1 Printers LLC 281 821-4400
15031 Woodham Dr Ste 370 Houston (77073) *(G-8398)*
1-Fast Rspnse Rntals Oil Feld 210 437-2473
6825 Us Highway 87 E C San Antonio (78263) *(G-17844)*
1-Stop Enterprises LLC 678 485-9873
2640 Deer Hollow Dr Little Elm (75068) *(G-14138)*
10-4 Tubular Inc 281 436-0380
9025 Pineland Rd Houston (77044) *(G-8399)*
101 Products LLC 832 247-7979
2400 Central Pkwy Ste D Houston (77092) *(G-8400)*
12 Adaptive Marketing, Forney *Also called Candeo Interactive LLC (G-6303)*
123print Inc 800 877-5147
12750 Merit Dr Ste 900 Dallas (75251) *(G-3862)*
146 Business Park Inc 281 260-0617
13531 W Hardy Rd Houston (77060) *(G-8401)*
14703 Partners Industries LLC 281 847-0788
14703 W Hardy Rd Houston (77060) *(G-8402)*
1604 Plant, San Antonio *Also called Vulcan Materials Company (G-18604)*
1845 Oil Field Services, Weatherford *Also called Spotted Lakes LLC (G-20621)*
1851 Vineyards LLC 830 391-8510
4222 S State Highway 16 Fredericksburg (78624) *(G-7168)*
1954 Manufacturing Inc 760 524-1378
4688 State Highway 16 S Graham (76450) *(G-7774)*
1a Smart Start LLC (PA) **972 621-0252**
500 E Dallas Rd Ste 100 Grapevine (76051) *(G-8009)*
1st Original Texas Chili Inc 817 626-0983
3313 N Jones St Fort Worth (76106) *(G-6333)*
1st Source Restaurant Svcs Inc 214 551-5338
665 E Jones St Lewisville (75057) *(G-14019)*
2 K Machine Works Inc 713 467-6921
1716 Townhurst Dr Houston (77043) *(G-8403)*
20 Spc Inc 972 687-6700
14901 Quorum Dr Ste 425 Dallas (75254) *(G-3863)*
2011 Angelina Mfg LLC 936 632-8330
1916 Old Mill Rd Lufkin (75904) *(G-14519)*
2018 Kidwell LLC 214 824-9463
6324 Prospect Ave Dallas (75214) *(G-3864)*
212 Resources LLC 303 892-5616
450 Gears Rd Ste 212 Houston (77067) *(G-8404)*
21c Sign Company 915 775-8514
6999 Commerce Ave El Paso (79915) *(G-5630)*
21st Century Fox America Inc 214 981-0800
2626 Howell St Ste 960 Dallas (75204) *(G-3865)*
2d Inc 281 893-3366
15020 Mintz Ln Houston (77014) *(G-8405)*
2da Analytics Incorporated 832 472-2093
945 Mckinney St Houston (77002) *(G-8406)*
2logo Inc 214 350-2505
10859 Shady Trl Ste 102 Dallas (75220) *(G-3866)*
2nd Chance Pallets LLC 817 847-8005
213 E Mcleroy Blvd Saginaw (76179) *(G-17735)*
2v Led LLC 325 227-4577
3490 Venture Dr San Angelo (76905) *(G-17767)*
2w Services LLC 361 645-1010
145 N Jefferson St Goliad (77963) *(G-7746)*
3 Amorez LLC 432 269-4199
7000 S County Road 1165 Midland (79706) *(G-15099)*
3 Axis Technologies, Austin *Also called AMS Acquisition Corp (G-921)*
3 Diamond Services LLC 361 442-6949
1296 6th St Ingleside (78362) *(G-12891)*
3 L Designs Inc 214 920-9223
8821 Directors Row Dallas (75247) *(G-3867)*
3 Marthas, Dallas *Also called Quatrefoil Partners LLC (G-4848)*

3 Point Solutions, Cedar Park *Also called 3ps Inc (G-2958)*
3 Star Custom Cabinets Inc 940 686-2124
1297 N Saint James Rd Pilot Point (76258) *(G-16720)*
3-C Valve & Equipment LP (PA) 281 361-3283
1825 N Lexington Blvd Corpus Christi (78409) *(G-3462)*
3-D Belt Company LP 979 743-4567
1001 Huser Blvd Schulenburg (78956) *(G-18770)*
3-D Honing Inc 281 391-8989
1103 Glenwood Dr Katy (77493) *(G-13386)*
3-D Powder Coating, Rowlett *Also called Three D Finishing Inc (G-17713)*
3-T Exploration Inc 940 691-5091
3707 Maplewood Ave # 100 Wichita Falls (76308) *(G-20734)*
3024 East Seminary Group LLC 817 534-6755
3024 E Seminary Dr Forest Hill (76119) *(G-6294)*
31 Group LLC 972 810-1031
3021 Ridge Rd Ste 156 Rockwall (75032) *(G-17534)*
31 Operating LLC 972 810-1031
3021 Ridge Rd Ste 156 Rockwall (75032) *(G-17535)*
3144 Labs, Austin *Also called Green Ocean Sciences Inc (G-1192)*
34 Oaks Fine Cabinetry LLC 469 533-0730
2605 Rodney Ln Dallas (75229) *(G-3868)*
360 Press Solutions LLC 512 381-2360
2009 Windy Ter Cedar Park (78613) *(G-2957)*
360 West Magazine, Fort Worth *Also called Scott Publishing LLC (G-6981)*
365 Certified Logistics LLC 512 743-9304
819 Indian Run Dr Pflugerville (78660) *(G-16655)*
365 Machine Inc 281 378-7811
27830 Commercial Park Rd Tomball (77375) *(G-19952)*
37 Building Products Ltd 817 341-3130
3133 Ranger Hwy Weatherford (76088) *(G-20571)*
3c Metal USA Inc 713 808-9651
5100 Westheimer Rd # 595 Houston (77056) *(G-8407)*
3core Software Corporation (PA) **281 440-3000**
1840 Snake River Rd Ste E Katy (77449) *(G-13387)*
3d Plastics LLC 903 844-9333
1095 E Commerce Ave Gladewater (75647) *(G-7716)*
3d Print Bureau of Texas LLC 713 357-4700
3923 Artdale St Houston (77063) *(G-8408)*
3d Steel Building Systems LLC 325 365-5494
45 Pr 4592 Ballinger (76821) *(G-1739)*
3dgence America Inc 469 466-2950
1841 E Levee St Dallas (75207) *(G-3869)*
3di Sign & Design, Arlington *Also called Badmoon Enterprises LLC (G-629)*
3f Investments Co 713 541-2258
9000 Suthwest Fwy Ste 100 Houston (77074) *(G-8409)*
3h Manufacturing Inc 281 342-1478
1318 Newlin Dr Richmond (77406) *(G-17449)*
3jg Printing LLC 214 553-8664
614 N 1st St Garland (75040) *(G-7422)*
3M Company 325 643-9798
4501 Highway 377 S Brownwood (76801) *(G-2423)*
3M Company 979 848-8489
1508 E Cedar St Angleton (77515) *(G-564)*
3M Company 915 860-5408
11751 Alameda Ave Ste A Socorro (79927) *(G-19016)*
3M Company 512 984-1800
11705 Rsrch Blvd Bldg 137 Austin (78759) *(G-869)*
3M Company 512 984-2370
11705 Res Blvd Bldg 1 Austin (78759) *(G-870)*
3M Company 512 984-2708
11705 Research Blvd Austin (78759) *(G-871)*
3M Medical Solutions, San Antonio *Also called Kci Usa Inc (G-18220)*
3nine USA Inc 512 667-6146
4768 N State Highway 123 San Marcos (78666) *(G-18676)*
3p Industries LLC 903 877-3960
11942 Laney Rd Tyler (75708) *(G-20042)*
3p Performance Plastics Pdts 281 537-8816
12317 Cutten Rd Houston (77066) *(G-8410)*

3ps Inc 512 610-5200
1300 Arrow Point Dr Cedar Park (78613) *(G-2958)*

3s Business Corporation 281 823-9222
11271 Richmond Ave Ste H1 Houston (77082) *(G-8411)*

3s Team LLC 918 396-4155
5330 Vista Rd Pasadena (77505) *(G-16375)*

4 Over LLC 801 263-2727
3200 Avenue E E Arlington (76011) *(G-605)*

4-A Oilfield Enterprises 903 668-3815
11178 Fm 968 W Longview (75602) *(G-14186)*

428transporters LLC 214 212-8648
205 W Lanett Dr Desoto (75115) *(G-5427)*

4693057371 .... 469 305-7371
9300 John Hickman Pkwy Frisco (75035) *(G-7255)*

4d Signworx LLC 713 984-2010
2022 Pech Rd Houston (77055) *(G-8412)*

4e Brands Northamerica LLC 210 819-7385
17806 Ih 10 W Ste 300 San Antonio (78257) *(G-17845)*

4front Engneered Solutions Inc (HQ) **972 466-0707**
1612 Hutton Dr Ste 140 Carrollton (75006) *(G-2690)*

4l Oilfield Services LLC 830 879-5300
902 S Main St Cotulla (78014) *(G-3689)*

5 Elements Drilling LLC 281 203-0405
12650 Crossroads Park Dr Houston (77065) *(G-8413)*

5 Fab Energy Inc 832 596-7140
16703 Steinhagen Rd Cypress (77429) *(G-3769)*

5 Star Fabrications Inc 512 267-0470
18794 Fm 1431 Jonestown (78645) *(G-13314)*

5 Star Measurement, Weatherford *Also called Five Star Field Services LLC (G-20591)*

51 Home Technologies LLC 713 589-5747
2531 Harpers Creek Ct Fresno (77545) *(G-7236)*

5l Energy Services LLC 936 539-1232
5750 W Davis St Conroe (77304) *(G-3251)*

6-K Inc 979 830-0251
1802 Buchannan St Brenham (77833) *(G-2242)*

686 Inc 830 876-5541
1908 N 1st St Carrizo Springs (78834) *(G-2683)*

7 S Packing LLC 325 716-4047
1809 N Bell St San Angelo (76903) *(G-17768)*

7 Up Bottling Co, Waco *Also called American Bottling Company (G-20360)*

7 Up Bottling of Beaumont, Beaumont *Also called American Bottling Company (G-1851)*

72nd & Thornhill LLC 469 318-5087
306 Trenton Dr Wylie (75098) *(G-20923)*

750 Logistics LLC 214 433-2615
2207 Blodgett St Houston (77004) *(G-8414)*

77 Stone 915 590-0770
337 E Sunset Rd El Paso (79922) *(G-5631)*

7up/Rc/Big Red of Austin, Austin *Also called American Bottling Company (G-915)*

7up/Rc/Bigred of Harlingen, Harlingen *Also called American Bottling Company (G-8180)*

81 Trucking Services LLC 713 259-1076
11811 North Fwy Ste 500 Houston (77060) *(G-8415)*

820 Hydraulics LLC 713 863-0340
3714 Pinemont Dr Houston (77018) *(G-8416)*

8228 Corporation 713 465-1303
1141 A Half Brittmoore Rd Houston (77043) *(G-8417)*

849 Red Baron Supply Co LLC (PA) **903 882-1700**
2561 S Main St Bldg B Lindale (75771) *(G-14132)*

900 Global Manufacturing, San Antonio *Also called Global Manufacturing LLC (G-18147)*

9650 Nf Ltd 281 486-4604
11415 Gulf Fwy Houston (77034) *(G-8418)*

A & A Custom Engravers, El Paso *Also called Carrion Enterprises Inc (G-5686)*

A & A Genpro Inc 713 830-3280
2870 Gessner Rd Ste C14 Houston (77080) *(G-8419)*

A & A Pallet and Lumber Co 713 462-4575
10350 W Montgomery Rd Houston (77088) *(G-8420)*

A & A Pallet Co 713 480-9861
1028 Candlelight Ln Houston (77018) *(G-8421)*

A & A Welding Inc 817 910-9700
333 Liberty Rd Granbury (76049) *(G-7791)*

A & B Auto Electric Inc 713 928-3219
9225 Manchester St Houston (77012) *(G-8422)*

A & B Glass LLC 432 517-4565
1811 S Gregg St Big Spring (79720) *(G-2067)*

A & B Labels and Printing Inc 915 774-0007
7245 Copperqueen Dr El Paso (79915) *(G-5632)*

A & B Sheet Metal Inc 512 365-7870
4804 W 2nd St Taylor (76574) *(G-19646)*

A & C Cabinet Co 817 244-4303
5681 Kelly Rd Fort Worth (76126) *(G-6334)*

A & C Plastic Products Inc (PA) **713 645-4915**
6135 Northdale St Houston (77087) *(G-8423)*

A & D Cstm Wldg & Fabrication 210 310-7610
7316 Ne Loop 410 San Antonio (78219) *(G-17846)*

A & E - The Graphics Complex, Houston *Also called Thomas Reprographics Inc (G-12275)*

A & E Blind and Awning Co, Wichita Falls *Also called A & E Venetian Blind Company (G-20735)*

A & E Machine Shop Inc (PA) **903 656-3485**
920 E Industrial Blvd Lone Star (75668) *(G-14180)*

A & E Mill & Welding Supply, Lone Star *Also called A & E Machine Shop Inc (G-14180)*

A & E Venetian Blind Company 940 767-1449
3601 Sheridan Rd Wichita Falls (76302) *(G-20735)*

A & I Industries Inc 915 633-8444
337 N Zaragoza Rd Ste D El Paso (79907) *(G-5633)*

A & M Composites Corporation 432 267-6525
1409 E Highway 350 Big Spring (79720) *(G-2068)*

A & M Fence Sup & Installation, Midlothian *Also called Pallet King Enterprises Inc (G-15490)*

A & M Machine & Wldg Works Inc 281 421-1281
7108 East Fwy Baytown (77521) *(G-1806)*

A & M Plastics Inc 713 941-1033
1502 Alabama St South Houston (77587) *(G-19036)*

A & M Tubular Maintenance Inc 903 983-1007
1004 N Longview St Kilgore (75662) *(G-13529)*

A & R Energy Services Corp 254 732-7759
517 Jancy St Waco Waco (76706) *(G-20353)*

A & R Enterprises Inc (PA) **903 984-9057**
4302 State Highway 42 Kilgore (75662) *(G-13530)*

A & S Fabrication Inc 817 626-7720
1701 Brennan Ave Fort Worth (76106) *(G-6335)*

A & W Industries Inc 817 481-3577
827 Dawn Ln Grapevine (76051) *(G-8010)*

A & W Welding Inc 281 499-4332
1403 Moore Rd Stafford (77477) *(G-19279)*

A 1 Automatic Door Systems, Ben Wheeler *Also called Door Control Services (G-2032)*

A 1 Distributors Sign Supply 432 682-0083
1100 Garden City Hwy Midland (79701) *(G-15100)*

A 1 Signs, San Antonio *Also called Tejas Signs Wetz (G-18646)*

A 2nd To None, San Antonio *Also called Ntw Services Inc (G-18352)*

A A A Backhoe, Mesquite *Also called Howard Keith Melton (G-15052)*

A A A Super Strong Products, Grand Prairie *Also called Super Strong Products Inc (G-7978)*

A A T, Burnet *Also called Austin American Tech Corp (G-2603)*

A and M Services Inc 432 290-5536
3255 Se 2000 Andrews (79714) *(G-532)*

A and W Industry, Grapevine *Also called Wilbert Burial Vault Corp (G-8060)*

A B B Small Pwr Trnsfrmers Lqu, Longview *Also called ABB Enterprise Software Inc (G-14187)*

A B C Flag Acquisition Corp 817 335-2548
212 S Main St Fort Worth (76104) *(G-6336)*

A B C Flag Manufacturing, Fort Worth *Also called A B C Flag Acquisition Corp (G-6336)*

A B C Plastic Molding Inc 713 692-9122
501 E Parker Rd Houston (77076) *(G-8424)*

A Better Fabrication LLC 817 629-8908
220 Adams Dr Weatherford (76086) *(G-20572)*

A C F Tarp & Awning, Fort Worth *Also called Matson Inc (G-6818)*

A C N Millwork Corp 713 649-6015
5711 Ransom St Houston (77087) *(G-8425)*

A C T, Fort Worth *Also called Aerospace & Coml Tech Inc (G-6353)*

A D S Steel Services, Benbrook *Also called Advanced Diversified Svcs Inc (G-2036)*

A E & Sons LLC 281 898-4021
2211 Lost Bridge Ln Pearland (77584) *(G-16535)*

A E Machine Works Inc 281 970-2020
14602 Cypress N Huston Rd Cypress (77429) *(G-3770)*

A E Quest & Sons, Lubbock *Also called Quest and Sons Inc (G-14468)*

A E S Custom Wood Inc 972 262-0755
3118 E Main St Grand Prairie (75050) *(G-7816)*

A E Santos & Co 956 723-8359
1518 Sherman St Laredo (78040) *(G-13852)*

A F, Amarillo *Also called Affiliated Foods Inc (G-476)*

A F C Lease Service Inc 361 364-2547
1200 Railroad Ave Sinton (78387) *(G-18960)*

A F I, Farmersville *Also called Advanced Fixtures Inc (G-6220)*

A F S, Waxahachie *Also called Automated Food Systems Inc (G-20528)*

A Fab & Construction, Keller *Also called A Fab Industries LLC (G-13466)*

A Fab Industries LLC 817 337-4776
8330 B Old Denton Rd Keller (76244) *(G-13466)*

A Freedom Graphic Systems, Grand Prairie *Also called Fgs - Dallas Inc (G-7871)*

A G H Machine Inc 281 372-1200
13610 Reeveston Rd Houston (77039) *(G-8426)*

A G R, Fort Worth *Also called Matek Performance Inc (G-6816)*

A G Van & Truck Eqp Inc 214 638-8805
2323 N Support Rd Dallas (75261) *(G-3870)*

A G Welding, Houston *Also called Septh Group LLC (G-11832)*

A H Belo Corporation (PA) **214 977-8222**
1954 Commerce St Dallas (75201) *(G-3871)*

A H I, Alvin *Also called Ahi Supply Inc (G-350)*

A I, Venus *Also called Advanced Industries Inc (G-20217)*

A J Brauer Stone 512 746-5792
251 County Road 235 Jarrell (76537) *(G-13268)*

A J Foyt Enterprises Inc 936 372-3698
19480 Stokes Rd Waller (77484) *(G-20489)*

A J L Advertising Specialties 512 320-0070
2101 Airport Blvd Ste 100 Austin (78722) *(G-872)*

A L K, Round Rock *Also called Alk-Abello Inc (G-17621)*

A L T, Argyle *Also called Advanced Lightning Tech Ltd (G-599)*

2021 Harris Texas
Manufacturers Directory

(G-0000) Company's Geographic Section entry number

A Lakhany International Inc....................................713 266-8799
10190 Katy Fwy Ste 350 Houston (77043) *(G-8427)*

A Lyondell Chemical Company, Channelview *Also called Equistar Chemicals LP (G-3020)*

A M A, Humble *Also called Airline Mortuary Associates (G-12744)*

A M Fabrication Inc....................................817 345-7600
8932 South Fwy Fort Worth (76140) *(G-6337)*

A N C Iron Coating, Houston *Also called Anc Ion Coating Inc (G-8638)*

A O Smith Corporation....................................915 400-2800
1270 Don Haskins Dr Ste A El Paso (79936) *(G-5634)*

A O Smith Corporation....................................915 859-1071
1265 Peter Cooper Dr El Paso (79936) *(G-5635)*

A O Smith Wtr Trtmnt N Amer (HQ)..........................**817 536-5250**
6310 Midway Rd Haltom City (76117) *(G-8131)*

A P F, Galena Park *Also called American Plant Food Corp (G-7376)*

A P M, Addison *Also called All-Plastics LLC (G-102)*

A P Manufacturing Incorporated....................................432 638-4708
1 E Industrial Loop Midland (79701) *(G-15101)*

A Plus Three Trucking LLC....................................210 852-9339
5886 Dzvala Rd Ste 102-47 San Antonio (78249) *(G-17847)*

A R C O, Denver City *Also called Atlantic Richfield Company (G-5415)*

A R Machining Inc....................................512 846-1789
632 W Front St Hutto (78634) *(G-12874)*

A R T, Austin *Also called Applied Rigaku Tech Inc (G-1691)*

A S C, Plano *Also called Air System Components Inc (G-16780)*

A S E, Benbrook *Also called Applied Systems Engrg Inc (G-2037)*

A S I, Pasadena *Also called Adrian Scott Industries Inc (G-16377)*

A S I Piping, Vidor *Also called Asi Piping LLC (G-20324)*

A S P, Austin *Also called Austin Screen Printing Inc (G-961)*

A Sign of Quality LLC....................................972 722-4147
5707 State Highway 276 Royse City (75189) *(G-17714)*

A Sklar Company Inc....................................361 573-5775
5274 State Highway 185 Victoria (77905) *(G-20233)*

A Speclzed Apprach To Prsthtic....................................832 813-5278
500 Spring Hill Dr # 200 Spring (77386) *(G-19190)*

A T D Austin....................................512 288-6215
7225 W Highway 71 Ste A Austin (78735) *(G-873)*

A Touch of Vegas, Dallas *Also called Casino Supply Company (G-4090)*

A Trace Matic Corporation....................................713 538-1370
7210 Empire Central Dr Houston (77040) *(G-8428)*

A Varco Shaffer Co....................................713 937-5500
6390 N Eldridge Pkwy Houston (77041) *(G-8429)*

A Z Graphics.com, San Antonio *Also called A-Z Graphics LLC (G-17852)*

A Zahner Company....................................469 348-2000
2860 Alouette Dr Grand Prairie (75052) *(G-7817)*

A&A Coating Inc....................................903 656-2581
3679 Fm 250 Lone Star (75668) *(G-14181)*

A&A Concepts....................................210 435-1300
750 Merida St Ste 105 San Antonio (78207) *(G-17848)*

A&A Machine & Fabrication LLC (PA)..........................**409 938-4274**
3101 Texas Ave La Marque (77568) *(G-13704)*

A&B Foundry LLC....................................972 247-3579
11165 Denton Dr Dallas (75229) *(G-3872)*

A&C Green Energy Inc....................................972 516-0692
1839 Wall St Garland (75041) *(G-7423)*

A&C Plastics, Houston *Also called A & C Plastic Products Inc (G-8423)*

A&E Oilfield Services LLC....................................956 380-5098
3701 E Lincoln Ave Mission (78573) *(G-15547)*

A&K Industrial Repair LLC....................................281 470-8848
1250 Underwood Rd Deer Park (77536) *(G-5258)*

A&S Interests Inc....................................713 695-0000
8321 Bauman Rd Houston (77022) *(G-8430)*

A&S New Braunfels LLC....................................832 206-4202
275 Landa Ave San Antonio (78237) *(G-17849)*

A&T Steel Fabricators Inc....................................281 351-7650
14608 Union St Tomball (77377) *(G-19953)*

A&W Energy Inc....................................817 704-7346
1301 Forum Way S Fort Worth (76140) *(G-6338)*

A&W Productions Inc....................................940 458-4190
1002 Cowling Rd Sanger (76266) *(G-18723)*

A-1 Distributors, Midland *Also called A 1 Distributors Sign Supply (G-15100)*

A-1 Fuel Stop Inc....................................713 674-3683
9161 Wallisville Rd Houston (77029) *(G-8431)*

A-1 Gasket & Industrial Supply (PA)..........................**432 332-1444**
2022 W 2nd St Odessa (79763) *(G-15897)*

A-1 Lumber & Pallet Co, Houston *Also called Stephens A-1 Lbr & Pallet Inc (G-12058)*

A-1 Paper Tubes & Sales, Dallas *Also called Paper Tubes & Sales Co (G-4787)*

A-1 Powder Coat Paint Inc....................................972 494-6861
1410 N 1st St Garland (75040) *(G-7424)*

A-1 Printing, Richardson *Also called Dallas Chinese News Inc (G-17297)*

A-1 Public Scales, Houston *Also called George Wood and Company Inc (G-9943)*

A-1 Sand Company, San Antonio *Also called Espey Silica Sand Co Inc (G-18095)*

A-1 Servomotor Repair, Irving *Also called C P E Inc (G-12956)*

A-1 Sheet Metal and AC Inc....................................409 833-4715
2935 Milam St Beaumont (77701) *(G-1846)*

A-1 Signs and Tejas, San Antonio *Also called Wetz Sign & Lighting Service (G-18649)*

A-1 Siign Engravers Inc....................................432 682-3492
1200 Garden City Hwy Midland (79701) *(G-15102)*

A-1 Smf LLC....................................512 288-9900
9409 Highway 290 W Austin (78736) *(G-874)*

A-Action Aire Inc....................................210 648-3801
7625 Us Highway 87 E San Antonio (78263) *(G-17850)*

A-C Compressor, Houston *Also called Preco Turbine Comprsr Svcs Inc (G-11397)*

A-Ero TEC Graphics Inc....................................972 289-9854
12709 Eastgate Dr Mesquite (75181) *(G-15022)*

A-Rock Materials, Lubbock *Also called Associated Group Investment Co (G-14364)*

A-Vox Systems Inc....................................210 695-8242
12001 Network Blvd # 314 San Antonio (78249) *(G-17851)*

A-Z Graphics LLC....................................210 495-3468
11908 Radium St San Antonio (78216) *(G-17852)*

A.C.I. Metal Works, Houston *Also called Albas Custom Iron Inc (G-8528)*

A1 Chrome Shop Inc....................................713 885-1727
4520 N Mccarty St Houston (77013) *(G-8432)*

A1 Engravers, San Antonio *Also called Stamp Shop Inc (G-18495)*

A1 Pallet, Irving *Also called Dfw A-1 Pallet Inc (G-12998)*

A3im Inc....................................713 378-7600
8866 Gulf Fwy Ste 550 Houston (77017) *(G-8433)*

A9 Manufacturing Inc....................................832 554-2464
14401 Interdrive W Houston (77032) *(G-8434)*

AA Flood Masters LLC....................................409 796-2620
10655 Fm 365 Rd Beaumont (77705) *(G-1847)*

Aa Genpro Electric, Houston *Also called A & A Genpro Inc (G-8419)*

AA Scientific Inc....................................979 696-8080
2151 Harvey Mitchell Pkwy College Station (77840) *(G-3171)*

AA Truck Sleeper LLC....................................817 834-4781
705 W Kennedale Pkwy B Kennedale (76060) *(G-13495)*

AA&e Leathercraft LLC....................................361 293-6366
208 Industrial Loop Yoakum (77995) *(G-20957)*

AAA Blast-Cote Inc....................................281 482-1236
14302 Beamer Rd Friendswood (77546) *(G-7241)*

AAA Custom & Electrical Signs, Donna *Also called Tesoro Corp (G-5494)*

AAA Electrical Signs (PA)..........................**956 464-3221**
2407 E Business Hwy 8 Donna (78537) *(G-5486)*

AAA Flame Cut Steel Inc....................................713 868-2337
1015 Judiway St Houston (77018) *(G-8435)*

AAA Flexible Pipe, La Porte *Also called AAA Pipe Cleaning Corporation (G-13715)*

AAA Lock & Safe, Longview *Also called Lock Dock Inc (G-14265)*

AAA Pallet, Houston *Also called Saifee Corporation (G-11730)*

AAA Pipe Cleaning Corporation....................................281 476-5200
3900 Underwood Rd La Porte (77571) *(G-13715)*

AAA Products International Inc....................................214 357-3851
7114 Harry Hines Blvd Dallas (75235) *(G-3873)*

AAA Signs of Amarillo, Amarillo *Also called Hi-Plains Canvas Products Inc (G-492)*

AAA Technology and Spc Co Inc (PA)..........................**713 849-3366**
6219 Brittmoore Rd Houston (77041) *(G-8436)*

AAA Woodwork....................................713 935-0002
9817 Honeywell St Houston (77074) *(G-8437)*

Aab Mfg Holdings LP....................................281 438-1599
13913 Buxley St Houston (77045) *(G-8438)*

AAC, Dallas *Also called American Achievement Corp (G-3937)*

AAC Group Holding Corp (HQ)..........................**512 444-0571**
7211 Circle S Rd Austin (78745) *(G-875)*

AAe Manufacturing Co Inc....................................956 748-0033
28764 Fm 106 Rio Hondo (78583) *(G-17474)*

Aagape Drywall Systems, Athens *Also called Aagape First Investments LLC (G-818)*

Aagape First Investments LLC....................................903 675-7876
1322 S Palestine St Athens (75751) *(G-818)*

Aalfs Manufacturing Inc....................................972 991-3945
5440 Harvest Hill Rd # 182 Dallas (75230) *(G-3874)*

Aap Metals LLC....................................800 231-8890
8411 Irvington Blvd Houston (77022) *(G-8439)*

Aap Metals LLC....................................214 357-6161
811 Regal Row Dallas (75247) *(G-3875)*

Aaron Architectural Iron LLC....................................817 731-9281
107 W Barron Ave Fort Worth (76140) *(G-6339)*

Aaron Iron Parts, Fort Worth *Also called Aaron Architectural Iron LLC (G-6339)*

Aastek Electronics Corp....................................903 953-0888
212 Enterprise Rd Emory (75440) *(G-6081)*

AB Bellco Corporation....................................713 781-6447
6650 W Sam Houston Pkwy N Houston (77041) *(G-8440)*

AB Interconnect Inc....................................919 934-5181
4222 S Staples St Corpus Christi (78411) *(G-3463)*

AB Mauri Food Inc....................................903 454-3891
6311 Industrial Dr Greenville (75402) *(G-8061)*

Ab-Tex Beverage Ltd....................................830 775-1543
131 Foster Dr Del Rio (78840) *(G-5304)*

Ab-Tex Beverage Ltd....................................325 655-9588
1023 Foster St San Angelo (76903) *(G-17769)*

Ab-Tex Beverage Ltd (HQ)..........................**325 673-7171**
650 Colonial Dr Abilene (79603) *(G-3)*

Ab-Tex Beverage Ltd....................................956 722-9934
4700 Santa Maria Ave Laredo (78041) *(G-13853)*

Ab-Tex Beverage Ltd....................................940 322-5416
1100 7th St Wichita Falls (76301) *(G-20736)*

A
L
P
H
A
B
E
T
I
C

Abac LLC..940 479-9163
141 Seaborn Rd Ponder (76259) *(G-17092)*

Abaco Drilling Tech LLC (HQ)..........................**281 869-0700**
713 Northpark Central Dr # 400 Houston (77073) *(G-8441)*

Abaco Operating LLC..210 828-4567
1020 Ne Loop 410 San Antonio (78209) *(G-17853)*

Abacus Computer Co Inc......................................713 467-2136
11111 Katy Fwy Ste 725 Houston (77079) *(G-8442)*

Abasco LLC...281 446-1500
8561 E North Belt Humble (77396) *(G-12742)*

ABB Enterprise Software Inc................................281 930-8383
1109 Howard Dr Deer Park (77536) *(G-5259)*

ABB Enterprise Software Inc................................903 237-1030
300 W Cotton St Longview (75601) *(G-14187)*

ABB Inc..713 587-8000
3700 W Sam Houston Pkwy S # 600 Houston (77042) *(G-8443)*

ABB Installation Products Inc..............................713 466-6761
8700 Fairbanks N Houston Houston (77064) *(G-8444)*

ABB Power Electronics Inc (HQ)..........................**972 244-9288**
601 Shiloh Rd Plano (75074) *(G-16768)*

ABB Turbocharger Co, Deer Park *Also called ABB Enterprise Software Inc (G-5259)*

Abbco Display Company.......................................214 319-8148
13910 Distribution Way B Dallas (75234) *(G-3876)*

Abbott Label Inc (PA)...**866 228-0100**
11440 Hillguard Rd Dallas (75243) *(G-3877)*

Abbott TI Investments LLC...................................210 344-5200
2714 West Ave San Antonio (78201) *(G-17854)*

Abbys Thres No Pl Like HM Fur............................817 244-3371
855 Foch St Fort Worth (76107) *(G-6340)*

Abbys Thres No Pl Like HM Furn, Fort Worth *Also called Abbys Thres No Pl Like HM Fur (G-6340)*

ABc Compounding Co Texas Inc...........................972 988-9200
1102 E Avenue J Grand Prairie (75050) *(G-7818)*

ABC Exclusive Inc...972 485-8182
430 Forest Gate Dr Garland (75042) *(G-7425)*

ABC Fire Systems LLC..830 625-3473
166 Trade Center Dr New Braunfels (78130) *(G-15771)*

ABC Imaging of Washington.................................832 426-5815
4902 Richmond Ave Ste C Houston (77027) *(G-8445)*

ABC Ingredients Corp..972 602-2427
1179 109th St Grand Prairie (75050) *(G-7819)*

ABC Printing and Office Sups, Breckenridge *Also called ABC Printing Service (G-2219)*

ABC Printing Service...254 559-3561
139 E Walker St Breckenridge (76424) *(G-2219)*

Abcd Precision Inc..832 230-5729
7045 Satsuma Dr Houston (77041) *(G-8446)*

Abco Inc...214 428-8996
1621 Wall St Dallas (75215) *(G-3878)*

Abco Products Inc..713 871-8020
7108 W Little York Rd Houston (77040) *(G-8447)*

Abco Subsea, Houston *Also called Abco Products Inc (G-8447)*

Abeona Therapeutics Inc......................................214 784-7177
3333 Lee Pkwy Ste 600 Dallas (75219) *(G-3879)*

ABF Packing Inc...254 968-4919
8758 S Us Highway 377 Dublin (76446) *(G-5514)*

ABG Contracting Group LLC.................................281 431-7223
10223 Broadway St P351 Pearland (77584) *(G-16536)*

ABI Digital Solutions, Conroe *Also called Airbrush Images Inc (G-3254)*

Abiie LLC..512 514-6325
Plz 7000 7000 N Mop Austin (78731) *(G-876)*

Abilene AG Service & Sup Inc (PA).......................**325 677-4371**
303 S 14th St Abilene (79602) *(G-4)*

Abilene Heavy Industries, Abilene *Also called Broadwind Hvy Fabrications Inc (G-25)*

Abilene Ice Company, Abilene *Also called Hipple Ice Company (G-50)*

Abilene Lumber, Abilene *Also called BMC West LLC (G-18)*

Abilene Mill Work..325 677-8856
533 Plum St Abilene (79601) *(G-5)*

Abilene Printing & Sty Co.....................................325 677-2673
1274 N 2nd St Abilene (79601) *(G-6)*

Abilene Reporter-News, Abilene *Also called Scripps Texas Newspapers LP (G-79)*

Abilene Sheet Metal Inc.......................................325 677-2654
1025 Walnut St Abilene (79601) *(G-7)*

Abimar Foods Inc...325 691-5425
5425 N 1st St Abilene (79603) *(G-8)*

Able Industrial LLC..281 946-2200
1250 Clay Ct Ste 200 Deer Park (77536) *(G-5260)*

Able Refractory Products, Houston *Also called Able Supply Co (G-8448)*

Able Supply Co..713 926-9623
5220 Texas St Houston (77011) *(G-8448)*

Ables-Land Inc (PA)...**903 593-8407**
420-428 S Fannin Ave Tyler (75702) *(G-20043)*

ABM International Inc...936 441-4401
18473 Kinkaid Rd E Montgomery (77316) *(G-15624)*

Abney Group Inc..512 832-0000
1707 Hydro Dr Austin (78728) *(G-877)*

Abox Packaging, Forney *Also called Abox Paperboard Company (G-6301)*

Abox Paperboard Company (PA)..........................**972 932-9800**
12950 Fm 1641 Forney (75126) *(G-6301)*

Abracon LLC (PA)..**512 371-6159**
5101 Hidden Creek Ln Spicewood (78669) *(G-19090)*

Abrams & Company Publs Inc..............................800 227-9120
4503 E Rapid Springs Cv Austin (78746) *(G-878)*

Abrams Learning Trends, Austin *Also called Abrams & Company Publs Inc (G-878)*

Abrasive Blast Systems LLC.................................972 205-9309
250 S Shiloh Rd Garland (75042) *(G-7426)*

Abrasive Contour Tech LLC..................................281 288-8800
2731 Spring Stuebner Rd Spring (77389) *(G-19097)*

Abraxas Petroleum Corporation (PA)....................**210 490-4788**
18803 Meisner Dr San Antonio (78258) *(G-17855)*

Abraxas Petroleum Corporation............................325 573-6010
11141 Cr 2138 Ira (79527) *(G-12912)*

ABS Blast, Garland *Also called Abrasive Blast Systems LLC (G-7426)*

ABS Printing Services...806 747-3702
524 E 40th St Unit A Lubbock (79404) *(G-14356)*

Abshier Energy LLC..432 352-4338
301 Elvis Rd Bowie (76230) *(G-2189)*

Absolute Acstic Noise Ctrl LLC (PA)......................**817 594-4446**
3208 Fm 920 Weatherford (76088) *(G-20573)*

Absolute Cmmnctons Ntwrk Slton (PA)..................**361 888-6776**
2333 Pollex Ave Corpus Christi (78415) *(G-3464)*

Absolute Color Ltd...713 996-0202
11101 Ella Blvd Houston (77067) *(G-8449)*

Absolute Enrrgy Field Pdts Svcs, Houston *Also called Absolute Fabrication LLC (G-8450)*

Absolute Fabrication LLC (PA)..............................**832 226-3345**
7218 Clinton Dr Houston (77020) *(G-8450)*

Absolute Fuels LLC..806 712-0330
2517 74th St Lubbock (79423) *(G-14357)*

Absolute Machine & Tooling LLC..........................512 259-7676
16001 Rnald W Reagan Blvd Leander (78641) *(G-13984)*

Absolute Metal Products LLC................................713 340-5990
7208 Gessner Rd Houston (77040) *(G-8451)*

Absolute Multimedia Inc......................................512 892-8682
8868 Res Blvd Ste 108 Austin (78758) *(G-879)*

Absolute Noise Control, Weatherford *Also called Absolute Acstic Noise Ctrl LLC (G-20573)*

Absolute Roustabout Svc LLC...............................432 488-8788
6218 N C R 1150 Midland (79705) *(G-15103)*

Absolute Software Inc (HQ)................................**512 600-7455**
11401 Century Oaks Ter Austin (78758) *(G-880)*

Absolute Spa Cover and More, Burnet *Also called Texas Spa Covers Inc (G-2616)*

Absolutely World Class, Abilene *Also called Gooch Investments Inc (G-44)*

Abuata Enterprises Inc...281 969-7947
425 Summer Park Dr Stafford (77477) *(G-19280)*

Abutec LLC...512 836-9473
16310 Bratton Ln Ste 350 Austin (78728) *(G-881)*

Abuyo Inc..855 850-3850
611 S Congress Ave # 130 Austin (78704) *(G-882)*

AC Electronics..817 701-1400
3401 Avenue D Arlington (76011) *(G-606)*

AC Global Gps, Arlington *Also called AC Global Systems Inc (G-607)*

AC Global Systems Inc...214 497-0280
301 W Abram St Arlington (76010) *(G-607)*

AC Metals LLC...214 630-5554
256 Regal Row Dallas (75247) *(G-3880)*

AC Printing LLC..817 267-8990
3400 Raider Dr Ste 1 Euless (76040) *(G-6125)*

Acacia Energy Inc...877 997-2946
11011 Brooklet Dr Ste 220 Houston (77099) *(G-8452)*

Acacia Originals LLC..877 565-5995
17415 Louis Ln Porter (77365) *(G-17170)*

Academy Venetian Blinds Co Inc..........................361 852-6088
4303 S Padre Island Dr Corpus Christi (78411) *(G-3465)*

Acbc, Amarillo *Also called Amarillo Custom Box Co (G-393)*

ACC-Kp LLC..972 407-1234
4554 Claire Chennault St Addison (75001) *(G-98)*

Accelerate Resources Oper LLC...........................214 292-8960
5949 Sherry Ln Ste 1060 Dallas (75225) *(G-3881)*

Accelerated Process Systems...............................713 937-6838
7227 Wright Rd Houston (77041) *(G-8453)*

Accelerated Prod Svcs Inc....................................432 334-8580
1460 Windway Odessa (79763) *(G-15898)*

Accelerated Pump...432 582-2335
1460 W Interstate 20 Odessa (79763) *(G-15899)*

Accent Door Co Inc...913 780-5800
25010 Cloudy Crk San Antonio (78255) *(G-17856)*

Accent Environmental Services.............................936 853-2264
523 Fm 1819 Pollok (75969) *(G-17090)*

Accent Graphics Inc...972 399-0333
523 E Rock Island Rd Grand Prairie (75050) *(G-7820)*

Accent Mercantile Inc...817 579-6076
440 E Pearl St Granbury (76048) *(G-7792)*

Accent Ribbons, New Waverly *Also called Cheryl L McDaniel (G-15857)*

Accent Screen Printing Inc...................................713 782-6683
10400 Wstffice Dr Ste 110 Houston (77042) *(G-8454)*

Accent Sign & Awning Co LLC...............................713 780-1151
6015 Skyline Dr Houston (77057) *(G-8455)*

Accent Signs & Graphics, Houston *Also called Accent Sign & Awning Co LLC (G-8455)*

Accents and Accessories, El Paso *Also called Stella Hasegawa (G-5977)*

Accept Software Corporation 512 201-8222
401 Congress Ave Ste 2650 Austin (78701) ***(G-883)***

Access Atm Inc (PA) **713 463-9033**
10801 Hammerly Blvd # 238 Houston (77043) ***(G-8456)***

Access Chemicals & Svcs LLC 713 270-7215
7322 Southwest Fwy # 2000 Houston (77074) ***(G-8457)***

Access Drilling, San Marcos *Also called Sign Crafters Inc* ***(G-18710)***

Access Imaging Solutions LLC 210 590-8338
4224 Centergate St San Antonio (78217) ***(G-17857)***

Access Intelligence Events LLC 832 242-1969
11000 Richmond Ave # 690 Houston (77042) ***(G-8458)***

Accessesp LLC 713 589-2599
13215 N Promenade Blvd Stafford (77477) ***(G-19281)***

Accmach Inc 979 774-0062
4400 Pate Rd College Station (77845) ***(G-3172)***

Acco Feeds Division, Abilene *Also called Volume Feed & Seed Inc* ***(G-90)***

Accounts Payable Department, Dallas *Also called Hanson Lehigh Inc* ***(G-4434)***

Accredo Packaging Inc 713 580-4800
12682 Cardinal Mdw Sugar Land (77478) ***(G-19436)***

Accretech America, Richardson *Also called Tokyo Seimitsu Co Ltd* ***(G-17412)***

Accu-Lock Inc 866 222-8562
9901 S Interstate 35 W Grandview (76050) ***(G-8001)***

Accu-Print, San Antonio *Also called Cellisco Inc* ***(G-17989)***

Accuauto, Carrollton *Also called Assurance Systems Inc* ***(G-2858)***

Acculock, Grandview *Also called Accu-Lock Inc* ***(G-8001)***

Accumed Biotech LLC 315 790-0466
16727 Park Row Houston (77084) ***(G-8459)***

Accumulators Inc 713 465-0202
18435 Morton Rd Houston (77084) ***(G-8460)***

Accumulators.com, Houston *Also called Accumulators Inc* ***(G-8460)***

Accura Systems Inc 972 226-0195
326 Clay Rd Mesquite (75182) ***(G-15023)***

Accuracy Products Inc 940 325-0714
3800 N Highway 281 Mineral Wells (76067) ***(G-15517)***

Accurate Inc 979 921-7777
37233 Fm 529 Rd Brookshire (77423) ***(G-2309)***

Accurate Inc (PA) **512 352-5278**
207 Allison Taylor (76574) ***(G-19647)***

Accurate Air Solutions LLC 325 672-2966
6737 E I 20 Abilene Abilene (79601) ***(G-9)***

Accurate Cargo Treatment 281 685-8573
3139 Federal Rd Ste D Pasadena (77504) ***(G-16376)***

Accurate Coatings, Taylor *Also called Accurate Inc* ***(G-19647)***

Accurate Connections Inc 972 484-8500
1700 Capital Ave Ste 100 Plano (75074) ***(G-16769)***

Accurate Control Company LLC (PA) **713 699-3799**
6526 Petropark Dr Houston (77041) ***(G-8461)***

Accurate Die Cutting Inc (PA) **972 562-7921**
413 Interchange St McKinney (75071) ***(G-14922)***

Accurate Elastomer Pdts Inc (PA) **512 285-4585**
769 N State Highway 95 Bastrop (78602) ***(G-1748)***

Accurate Flame Cutting and Stl, Houston *Also called Accurate Flamecutting Stl LLC* ***(G-8462)***

Accurate Flamecutting Stl LLC 281 987-9100
842 Buschong St Houston (77039) ***(G-8462)***

Accurate Litho & Printing Co, San Antonio *Also called Lithographics Inc* ***(G-18255)***

Accurate Machine Shop, Rosharon *Also called Joel G Gibbs Inc* ***(G-17606)***

Accurate Machine Works, College Station *Also called Accmach Inc* ***(G-3172)***

Accurate Metal Stamping LLC 817 284-9444
7124 Belton St Richland Hills (76118) ***(G-17434)***

Accurate Pmpg Contractings Inc 254 562-9747
1824 Highway 84 W Mexia (76667) ***(G-15086)***

Accurate Precision Plating LLC 281 598-8835
1506 Lone Oak Rd Houston (77093) ***(G-8463)***

Accutek Inc 972 915-6888
8051 Jetstar Dr Ste 175 Irving (75063) ***(G-12922)***

Accuturn Manufacturing Inc 281 449-9000
845 Buschong St Houston (77039) ***(G-8464)***

Accuweld Inc 281 442-5900
845 Buschong St Houston (77039) ***(G-8465)***

Ace Aeronautics LLC 972 641-0835
2985 Red Hawk Dr Grand Prairie (75052) ***(G-7821)***

Ace Automatics Inc 903 852-3004
7439 Fm 314 Ben Wheeler (75754) ***(G-2030)***

Ace Carton & Tape of Laredo 956 727-1600
919 Santa Maria Ave Laredo (78040) ***(G-13854)***

Ace Cmpltion Enhncment Svcs LP 432 653-0732
1301 W 1st St Odessa (79763) ***(G-15900)***

Ace Cmpltion Enhncment Svcs LP 432 703-7169
250 Solo Rd Ste B Odessa (79762) ***(G-15901)***

Ace Controls LLC 713 589-5494
327 Derrick Dr Humble (77338) ***(G-12743)***

Ace Energy Solutions Inc 281 394-9989
24275 Katy Fwy Ste 325 Katy (77494) ***(G-13347)***

Ace Engineering Ltd 817 237-7700
10200 Jacksboro Hwy Fort Worth (76135) ***(G-6341)***

Ace Fabricators Inc 281 442-0992
7010 Furay Rd Houston (77016) ***(G-8466)***

Ace Hanger Strap Inc 214 742-8585
334 Rock Island St Dallas (75207) ***(G-3882)***

Ace Hardware, El Paso *Also called Paso Del Norte Hardware LLC* ***(G-5904)***

Ace Hardware, Marlin *Also called Keith Properties Inc* ***(G-14759)***

Ace Hardwood Flooring Inc 512 719-3555
4238 Bee Caves Rd West Lake Hills (78746) ***(G-20676)***

Ace Houston Warehouse, Houston *Also called A & B Auto Electric Inc* ***(G-8422)***

Ace Industries Inc 281 443-6690
1436 N Duck Creek Rd Cleveland (77328) ***(G-3118)***

Ace Machine & Fabrication Inc 956 727-4223
7226 Hwy 359 Laredo (78043) ***(G-13855)***

Ace Machine Works, Houston *Also called David W Arnold* ***(G-9408)***

Ace Machining Technologies 254 632-4250
110 Private Road 435 Hillsboro (76645) ***(G-8320)***

Ace Rubber Products Inc 817 572-1011
832 Valley Ln Kennedale (76060) ***(G-13496)***

Ace Sand and Gravel 432 290-1205
8818 N 1053 Fort Stockton (79735) ***(G-6326)***

Ace Trucks Ltd 817 237-7700
10200 Jacksboro Hwy Fort Worth (76135) ***(G-6342)***

Ace Welding and Trailer Co (PA) **210 667-1171**
9425 Saint Hedwig Rd San Antonio (78263) ***(G-17858)***

Acelity LP Inc (HQ) **210 524-9000**
12930 W Interstate 10 San Antonio (78249) ***(G-17859)***

Acentum Inc 713 668-8742
3752 Darcus St Houston (77005) ***(G-8467)***

Acer America Corporation 214 383-3194
900 Guardians Way Allen (75013) ***(G-247)***

Acer America Corporation 254 298-4000
1394 Eberhardt Rd Temple (76504) ***(G-19666)***

Acero Fab Inc 956 584-1166
12225 N Bryan Rd Mission (78573) ***(G-15548)***

Aceros Turia Inc (PA) **832 791-5479**
25219 Kuykendahl Rd # 290 The Woodlands (77375) ***(G-19819)***

Acerts Inc 866 938-5599
1801 Native Dancer Pl Southlake (76092) ***(G-19057)***

Aceschem Inc 817 863-6948
5454 Surrey Path Ste 205 Frisco (75034) ***(G-7265)***

Acg Materials, San Antonio *Also called Harrison Gypsum LLC* ***(G-18159)***

Acg Quality Electric Inc 713 225-6531
1004 Collingsworth St Houston (77009) ***(G-8468)***

Aci Worldwide Corp 361 579-4800
1501 E Mockingbird Ln Victoria (77904) ***(G-20234)***

Acid and Cementing Svcs Inc 903 729-2500
3212 W Oak St Palestine (75801) ***(G-16294)***

Acj Produce & Spices LLC 956 627-4246
4324 W Military Hwy McAllen (78503) ***(G-14831)***

Acm Hub LLC 210 248-9631
2643 Mossrock San Antonio (78230) ***(G-17860)***

Acme Brick Company 214 637-2720
3815 Singleton Blvd Dallas (75212) ***(G-3883)***

Acme Brick Company 817 332-4101
325 N Americas Ave El Paso (79907) ***(G-5636)***

Acme Brick Company 512 255-2573
1776 Old Mcdade Rd Elgin (78621) ***(G-6051)***

Acme Brick Company 325 949-7685
4012 Arden Rd San Angelo (76901) ***(G-17770)***

Acme Brick Company 254 662-9846
1620 W Loop 340 Waco (76712) ***(G-20354)***

Acme Brick Company (HQ) **817 332-4101**
3024 Acme Brick Plz Fort Worth (76109) ***(G-6343)***

Acme Brick Company 512 281-5744
1776 Old Mcdade Rd Elgin (78621) ***(G-6052)***

Acme Building Brands, Austin *Also called Featherlite Building Pdts Corp* ***(G-1147)***

Acme Building Brands, Elgin *Also called Acme Brick Company* ***(G-6052)***

Acme Energy Services Inc 432 561-5271
110 N Marienfeld St # 200 Midland (79701) ***(G-15104)***

Acme Holdings Inc (PA) **210 798-3460**
12015 Radium St San Antonio (78216) ***(G-17861)***

Acme Rental Center, Houston *Also called Lure Capital Corporation* ***(G-10703)***

Acme Sign & Plastics Co 325 677-9469
1225 Walnut St Abilene (79601) ***(G-10)***

Acme Skid, Silsbee *Also called Apache Products Inc* ***(G-18949)***

Acme Soap Inc 210 731-9800
4351 Director Dr San Antonio (78219) ***(G-17862)***

Acme Soap Company, San Antonio *Also called Acme Soap Inc* ***(G-17862)***

Acme Truck Line Inc 361 576-2934
6811 Us Highway 59 N Victoria (77905) ***(G-20235)***

Acock Consulting LLC 210 826-2553
8610 N New Braunfels Ave # 517 San Antonio (78217) ***(G-17863)***

Acp International Inc 817 640-0992
521 N Great Sw Pkwy Arlington (76011) ***(G-608)***

Acrylic Source 800 275-0316
401 Exchange Dr Arlington (76011) ***(G-609)***

Acrylink G, Pearland *Also called Isothrmal Prtctive Catings Inc* ***(G-16572)***

ACS Industries LP 713 434-0934
14211 Industry St Houston (77053) ***(G-8369)***

ACS Manufacturing Inc 903 462-2001
1601 Commerce Blvd Denison (75020) ***(G-5334)***

ACS Pump & Supply, Midland *Also called Endeavor Energy Resources LP* ***(G-15211)***
Acsem, Fort Worth *Also called Advisory Cons Stl Erection Mfg* ***(G-6350)***
Acsi, Houston *Also called Advanced Cntinment Systems Inc* ***(G-8486)***
Act Global Sports Tech Inc (HQ)......**512 733-5300**
4201 W Parmer Ln Ste B175 Austin (78727) ***(G-884)***
Act Global Tech Industries......210 651-2543
8666 Huebner Rd Ste 204 San Antonio (78240) ***(G-17864)***
Act-PSM, Dallas *Also called Renovated Homes Inc* ***(G-4888)***
Action Box Co Inc......713 869-7701
6207 N Houston Rosslyn Rd Houston (77091) ***(G-8469)***
Action Fuels LP......210 651-9308
23090 Fm 3009 San Antonio (78266) ***(G-18634)***
Action Rigging and Pump Svc LP......512 670-9567
13807 Dragline Dr Ste B Austin (78728) ***(G-885)***
Action Screen Graphics......512 478-6248
1406 Smith Rd Ste F Austin (78721) ***(G-886)***
Action Signs & Banner, Garland *Also called Action Sportswear Inc* ***(G-7427)***
Action Sportswear Inc......972 487-6960
1101 Main St Garland (75040) ***(G-7427)***
Action Trophies, Spring *Also called Action Wear Plus Inc* ***(G-19098)***
Action Trucking Co, Houston *Also called Hauling & Excavating Casco* ***(G-10136)***
Action Wear Plus Inc......281 376-4300
18610 Klein Church Rd Spring (77379) ***(G-19098)***
Action1 Corporation......346 444-8530
12333 Sowden Rd B36066 Houston (77080) ***(G-8470)***
Actitech LP......903 893-2551
301 W Fm 1417 Sherman (75092) ***(G-18904)***
Actium Biosystems......832 379-4222
11777 Katy Fwy Ste 120s Houston (77079) ***(G-8471)***
Active Network LLC (HQ)......**888 543-7223**
717 N Harwood St Ste 2500 Dallas (75201) ***(G-3884)***
Active Power Inc......512 836-6464
2128 W Braker Ln Ste Bk12 Austin (78758) ***(G-887)***
Activtrak, Austin *Also called Birch Grove Software Inc* ***(G-991)***
Actual Seo Media Inc......832 834-0661
1880 S Dairy Ashford Rd # 682 Houston (77077) ***(G-8472)***
Acuity Brands Lighting Inc......972 456-1451
2700 Easter Ave Ste 100 Dallas (75216) ***(G-3885)***
Acuity Surgical Devices LLC......214 862-5017
14215 Proton Rd Dallas (75244) ***(G-3886)***
Acumen Pm LLC......512 291-6259
7320 N Mo Pac Expy # 301 Austin (78731) ***(G-888)***
Acuren Inspection Inc......281 228-0000
101 Old Underwood Rd La Porte (77571) ***(G-13716)***
Acute Technological Svcs Inc......713 983-9353
11925 Brittmoore Park Dr Houston (77041) ***(G-8473)***
Ad Display Sign Systems Inc......281 392-8325
27255 Katy Fwy Katy (77494) ***(G-13348)***
Ad Pages, Plano *Also called Billmyr Enterprises Inc* ***(G-16804)***
Ad Sack Area Weekly Shopper, Corpus Christi *Also called Ad Sack Inc* ***(G-3466)***
Ad Sack Inc......361 854-0137
2660 S Padre Island Dr Corpus Christi (78415) ***(G-3466)***
Ad Valorem Records Inc......713 523-1623
12332 Cutten Rd Houston (77066) ***(G-8474)***
Ada Energy Services, Houston *Also called Air Drilling Associates Inc* ***(G-8505)***
Adam Nerren Ltd......936 422-4800
2612 Fm Rd 328 Huntington (75949) ***(G-12808)***
Adam's Extract & Spice, Gonzales *Also called Adams Flvors Fods Ingrdnts LLC* ***(G-7748)***
Adampac, Grand Prairie *Also called Komplete Group Inc* ***(G-7907)***
Adams Evidence Grade Tech Inc......830 966-4210
4123 N Little Creek Rd Utopia (78884) ***(G-20187)***
Adams Flvors Fods Ingrdnts LLC......830 672-1850
3217 Johnson Rd Gonzales (78629) ***(G-7748)***
Adams Manufacturing Co (PA)......**806 744-0839**
1416 N University Ave Lubbock (79415) ***(G-14358)***
Adams Moulding and Lumber Co, El Paso *Also called Nfs Inc* ***(G-5895)***
Adams Paint Company, Lubbock *Also called Adams Manufacturing Co* ***(G-14358)***
Adams Resources & Energy Inc (PA)......**713 881-3600**
17 S Briar Hollow Ln # 100 Houston (77027) ***(G-8475)***
Adams Resources Marketing Ltd (HQ)......**281 902-4100**
16800 Imperial Valley Dr # 2 Houston (77060) ***(G-8476)***
Adao Global LLC......512 431-7743
308 Goodnight Dr Georgetown (78628) ***(G-7631)***
Adaptive 3d Technologies LLC......469 573-0024
608 Development Dr # 200 Plano (75074) ***(G-16770)***
Adaptive Switch Laboratories......440 329-6276
125 Spur 191 Ste C Spicewood (78669) ***(G-19091)***
Adaptor Content, Corpus Christi *Also called Asiel Enterprises Inc* ***(G-3476)***
Adco Inc......972 484-6177
13911 Distribution Way Dallas (75234) ***(G-3887)***
Adcorp Sign Systems LLC......936 321-4888
10965 Highway 242 Conroe (77385) ***(G-3252)***
Addax Minerals LLC......214 445-6000
5950 Berkshire Ln # 1250 Dallas (75225) ***(G-3888)***
Addax Petro Cameroon Co LLC......713 245-1263
910 Louisiana St Houston (77002) ***(G-8477)***
Addison Collection LP......817 921-4450
2901 W Bolt St Fort Worth (76110) ***(G-6344)***
Addison Jet Maintenance Inc......972 559-1000
4553 Glenn Curtiss Dr Addison (75001) ***(G-99)***
Addison Oil LLC (PA)......**972 239-2400**
15851 Dallas Pkwy Ste 401 Addison (75001) ***(G-100)***
Addvantage Tech Group Inc (PA)......**918 251-9121**
1430 Bradley Ln Ste 196 Carrollton (75007) ***(G-2853)***
Adele Charles Corp......972 740-1028
2921 Falling Brook Dr Plano (75023) ***(G-16771)***
Adelita Tortilla Factory......210 733-5352
1130 Fresno San Antonio (78201) ***(G-17865)***
Adell Corporation......972 226-4600
200 Adell Blvd Mesquite (75182) ***(G-15024)***
Adem Ruman Inc......713 266-8584
3700 Crossview Dr A Houston (77063) ***(G-8478)***
Ademco Inc......972 402-8612
12880 Valley Branch Ln Farmers Branch (75234) ***(G-6184)***
Ademco Inc......713 861-9418
7425 Pinemont Dr Ste 100 Houston (77040) ***(G-8479)***
Ademco Inc......915 872-5542
12220 Rojas Dr Ste A El Paso (79936) ***(G-5637)***
Ademco Inc......915 875-0091
3950 Doniphan Dr Ste N&O El Paso (79922) ***(G-5638)***
Adexco Operating Company......817 332-3891
309 W 7th St Ste 400 Fort Worth (76102) ***(G-6345)***
ADI Electronics Inc......214 818-4720
3920 Bryan St Frnt Frnt Dallas (75204) ***(G-3889)***
ADI Global Distribution, Farmers Branch *Also called Ademco Inc* ***(G-6184)***
ADI Global Distribution, Houston *Also called Ademco Inc* ***(G-8479)***
ADI Global Distribution, El Paso *Also called Ademco Inc* ***(G-5638)***
Adient Clanton Inc......956 525-4515
4694 Coffeeport Rd Brownsville (78521) ***(G-2334)***
Adient US LLC......210 271-2428
1 Lone Star Pass Bldg 41 San Antonio (78264) ***(G-17866)***
ADM, Comanche *Also called Archer-Daniels-Midland Company* ***(G-3235)***
ADM, Hillsboro *Also called Collingwood Grain Inc* ***(G-8324)***
ADM, Saginaw *Also called Archer-Daniels-Midland Company* ***(G-17736)***
ADM, Hereford *Also called Archer-Daniels-Midland Company* ***(G-8283)***
ADM, Dallas *Also called Archer-Daniels-Midland Company* ***(G-3957)***
ADM, Slaton *Also called Archer-Daniels-Midland Company* ***(G-18968)***
ADM Milling Co......830 625-2301
398 E San Antonio St New Braunfels (78130) ***(G-15772)***
Admin - South Cement Const Pro, Houston *Also called Cemex Construction Mtls S LLC* ***(G-9123)***
Administration Office, Odessa *Also called Varco LP* ***(G-16197)***
Administrative Office, Midland *Also called Nabors Well Services Ltd* ***(G-15309)***
Admp LLC......832 519-9746
6401 Long Point Rd # 506 Houston (77055) ***(G-8480)***
Adobe Fab Consultants Inc......936 447-6400
7187 Old Highway 105 W Conroe (77304) ***(G-3253)***
Adobe Inc......469 955-9500
15950 Dallas Pkwy Ste 400 Dallas (75248) ***(G-3890)***
Adobe Oilfield Ltd......432 337-3731
705 W Hillmont Rd Odessa (79764) ***(G-15902)***
Adobe Oilfield Services, Odessa *Also called Adobe Oilfield Ltd* ***(G-15902)***
Adolphs Litho Services Inc......972 225-5303
1600 S Intrstate 45 Svc R Hutchins (75141) ***(G-12861)***
Adrian Scott Industries Inc......713 941-3300
306 1/2 Pampa St Pasadena (77504) ***(G-16377)***
Adroit Fabrication Inc......432 288-0656
3504 Princeton Ave Midland (79703) ***(G-15105)***
ADS Custom Signs Inc......713 943-0895
4402 Glen Avon Dr Pasadena (77505) ***(G-16378)***
ADS Manufacturing Co, Houston *Also called Air Duct Systems Mfg Co* ***(G-8506)***
Adtec Colorant Corporation......817 633-3004
514 N Great Sw Pkwy Arlington (76011) ***(G-610)***
Adtech, Harlingen *Also called Atlantic Durant Technology Inc* ***(G-8182)***
Advance Energy Partners Llc......832 672-4700
11490 Westheimer Rd # 950 Houston (77077) ***(G-8481)***
Advance Fabrication Svcs LLC (PA)......**432 561-8776**
4315 S County Road 1290 Odessa (79765) ***(G-15903)***
Advance Fbrction Msurement LLC......713 468-9581
1223 Brittmoore Rd Houston (77043) ***(G-8482)***
Advance Fiberglass LLC......956 544-1000
5224 Ruben Torres Sr Blvd Brownsville (78526) ***(G-2335)***
Advance Graphix, Lubbock *Also called Campus Design Incorporated* ***(G-14387)***
Advance Hydrocarbon Corp......979 778-8100
1559 Crosswind Dr Bryan (77808) ***(G-2451)***
Advance Hydrocarbon Corp......979 542-1520
1003 County Road 237 Giddings (78942) ***(G-7690)***
Advance Hydrocarbon Corp (HQ)......**979 690-2226**
10343 Sam Houston Park Dr # 325 Houston (77064) ***(G-8483)***
Advance Machining Tech., Austin *Also called Chiphong Inc* ***(G-1048)***
Advance Polybag (nevada) Inc......702 642-1110
12682 Cardinal Mdw Sugar Land (77478) ***(G-19437)***
Advance Polybag (texas) Inc (PA)......**713 580-4800**
12682 Cardinal Mdw Sugar Land (77478) ***(G-19438)***

Advance Polybag North East Inc (PA) 410 796-8551
  12682 Cardinal Mdw Sugar Land (77478) (G-19439)

Advance Tabco, Kaufman Also called Tables Manufacturing Inc (G-13464)

Advance Tabco Inc 972 932-4148
  2000 S Houston St Kaufman (75142) (G-13456)

Advance Technology Products 713 450-5990
  14123 Market Street Rd Houston (77015) (G-8484)

Advance Tool & Die Inc 817 923-8787
  3428 S Jones St Fort Worth (76110) (G-6346)

Advanced Aero Coatings LLC 940 367-5963
  3361 Amyx Hill Rd Ponder (76259) (G-17093)

Advanced Aero Coatings LLC (PA) 817 280-0467
  9004 Trinity Blvd Hurst (76053) (G-12831)

Advanced Architectural Stone, Fort Worth Also called Advanced Cast Stone Inc (G-6347)

Advanced Archtectural Mtls Inc 713 983-9979
  6100 Brittmoore Rd Ste S Houston (77041) (G-8485)

Advanced Arm Dynamics 214 260-3197
  3501 N Macarthur Blvd Irving (75062) (G-12923)

Advanced Beverages, Dallas Also called Marsmith Enterprises Inc (G-4638)

Advanced Biomechanics 956 971-8200
  4500 Cascade Dr Schertz (78154) (G-18742)

Advanced Cast Stone Inc 817 572-0018
  115 Lee St Fort Worth (76140) (G-6347)

Advanced Cementing Svcs Inc 979 921-0356
  40466 Fm 1488 Rd Hempstead (77445) (G-8248)

Advanced Cntinment Systems Inc 713 987-0336
  8720 Lambright Rd Houston (77075) (G-8486)

Advanced Control Systems LLC 832 529-2234
  4903 W Sam Houston Pkwy N B Houston (77041) (G-8487)

Advanced Corrosion Technology, Fort Worth Also called AGS Technology Inc (G-6356)

Advanced Data Spectrum, Allen Also called Software Construction Co Inc (G-298)

Advanced Diversified Svcs Inc 817 377-2718
  7461 W Vickery Blvd Benbrook (76116) (G-2036)

Advanced Drainage Systems Inc 972 878-9600
  210 Metro Park Blvd Ennis (75119) (G-6087)

Advanced Drainage Systems Inc 361 293-6313
  801 Hickey Rd Yoakum (77995) (G-20958)

Advanced Elec & Mtr Contrls 972 253-7783
  1801 Hurd Dr Irving (75038) (G-12924)

Advanced Energy Industries Inc 512 339-7100
  8601 Cross Park Dr # 100 Austin (78754) (G-889)

Advanced Fabric Tech LLC 281 872-7272
  2441 High Timbers Dr # 400 Spring (77380) (G-19191)

Advanced Fillers & Pigments, Orange Also called Orion Engineered Carbons LLC (G-16256)

Advanced Fillers & Pigments, Borger Also called Orion Engineered Carbons LLC (G-2181)

Advanced Film Division, Corpus Christi Also called Interntonal Resistive Texas LP (G-3555)

Advanced Fixtures Inc 972 784-8800
  2655 E Audie Murphy Pkwy Farmersville (75442) (G-6220)

Advanced Flow Products, Houston Also called Advanced Indicators and Mfg (G-8488)

Advanced Geophysical Tech Inc 281 888-6789
  14100 Southwest Fwy # 110 Sugar Land (77478) (G-19440)

Advanced Geosciences Inc 512 335-3338
  2121 Geoscience Dr Austin (78726) (G-890)

Advanced Hydrstatic Svcs L L C 940 337-7950
  5514 Northwest Fwy Wichita Falls (76305) (G-20737)

Advanced Imaging Services 210 680-4749
  5501 Grissom Rd Ste 101 San Antonio (78238) (G-17867)

Advanced Indicators and Mfg 713 932-6464
  1463 Brittmoore Rd Houston (77043) (G-8488)

Advanced Industrial Metal Fabr 940 964-2691
  1541 Merritt Rd Forestburg (76239) (G-6299)

Advanced Industries Inc 972 366-9000
  1014 S Fm 157 Venus (76084) (G-20217)

Advanced Integration Tech GP 972 522-6363
  901 Avenue S Grand Prairie (75050) (G-7822)

Advanced Integration Tech Inc 972 423-8354
  2805 E Plano Pkwy Ste 300 Plano (75074) (G-16772)

Advanced Integration Tech LP (PA) 972 423-8354
  2805 E Plano Pkwy Ste 300 Plano (75074) (G-16773)

Advanced Integration Tech LP 210 762-3777
  1900 1st Ave San Antonio (78216) (G-17868)

Advanced Integration Tech SA 210 762-3777
  1900 1st Ave San Antonio (78216) (G-17869)

Advanced Laser Materials LLC 254 773-3080
  3115 Lucius Mccelvey Dr Temple (76504) (G-19667)

Advanced Lightning Tech Ltd (PA) 940 455-7300
  122 Leesley Ln Argyle (76226) (G-599)

Advanced Limb & Brace 806 351-1775
  4 Medical Dr Ste B Amarillo (79106) (G-391)

Advanced Machine Maintenance, Houston Also called Ammr Services Inc (G-8626)

Advanced Machining & Tool Inc 972 228-1987
  1616 N Interstate 35 E Lancaster (75134) (G-13836)

Advanced Mat Systems LLC 281 839-4258
  1030 1/2 County Road 129 Alvin (77511) (G-349)

Advanced Materials Group Inc 469 246-4100
  2364 Merritt Dr Ste A Garland (75041) (G-7428)

Advanced MBL Fltrtion Svcs LLC 800 484-4590
  6300 Ridglea Plste 1011 Fort Worth (76116) (G-6348)

Advanced McRbial Solutions LLC 800 787-3724
  5601 Granite Pkwy Ste 740 Plano (75024) (G-16774)

Advanced Metal Fusion Inc 512 422-0888
  3507 Valley Pike Rd Cedar Park (78613) (G-2959)

Advanced Micro Devices Inc 512 602-1000
  5204 E Ben White Blvd Austin (78741) (G-891)

Advanced Micro Devices Inc 512 602-1000
  7171 Southwest Pkwy Austin (78735) (G-892)

Advanced Micro Devices Inc 512 602-5204
  5900 E Ben White Blvd Austin (78741) (G-893)

Advanced Nrmdltion Systems Inc (HQ) 972 309-8000
  6901 Preston Rd Plano (75024) (G-16775)

Advanced Ocean Shipping 281 300-0191
  323 S Cesar Chavez Blvd Houston (77011) (G-8489)

Advanced Orthotics Prosthetics 956 971-8200
  5428 S Jackson Rd Edinburg (78539) (G-5573)

Advanced Pedestals Ltd 940 668-7283
  2227 Foundry Rd Gainesville (76240) (G-7333)

Advanced Piping Products Inc 713 956-2922
  5611 Guhn Rd Ste A1 Houston (77040) (G-8490)

Advanced Precision Services LP 281 290-9950
  701 S Persimmon St Ste 50 Tomball (77375) (G-19954)

Advanced Pressure Systems, Tomball Also called APS Pressure Systems LLC (G-19960)

Advanced Ret MGT Systems Inc (PA) 303 738-1800
  2555 Westhollow Dr Houston (77082) (G-8491)

Advanced Rfurbishment Tech LLC 512 377-1016
  9208 Wtrford Cntre Blvd S Austin (78758) (G-894)

Advanced Rpture Disk Advnced R, Katy Also called Advanced Rupture Disk Tech Inc (G-13388)

Advanced Rubber Molding Inc 972 647-4040
  1202 E Avenue J Grand Prairie (75050) (G-7823)

Advanced Rupture Disk Tech Inc 281 591-6700
  1010 Avenue A Katy (77493) (G-13388)

Advanced Sheet Metal LLC 254 772-0134
  2901 E Industrial Blvd Waco (76705) (G-20355)

Advanced Starter Service, Dallas Also called Haastech Inc (G-4426)

Advanced Stimulation Tech Inc (PA) 432 617-3250
  2903 E Interstate 20 Midland (79706) (G-15106)

Advanced Telesensors Inc 888 292-2208
  6203 Sotol Cv Austin (78759) (G-895)

Advanced Tracking Tech Inc 800 279-0035
  6001 Savoy Dr Ste 301 Houston (77036) (G-8492)

Advanced Waterjet Cutting Inc 214 358-2194
  2825 Reward Ln Dallas (75220) (G-3891)

Advanced Weapons and Armor Inc 830 459-5263
  2220 Medina Hwy Kerrville (78028) (G-13516)

Advanced Welding Services Inc 713 933-2626
  9840 Windmill Park Ln Houston (77064) (G-8493)

Advanced Welding Solutions LLC 713 473-0099
  2600 S Shore Blvd Ste 300 League City (77573) (G-13944)

Advanced Window and Glass Mfg 210 735-9959
  1923 Capitol Ave San Antonio (78201) (G-17870)

Advanced Wire Cloth, Conroe Also called National Oilwell Varco Inc (G-3338)

Advantage Aviation Tech 972 647-7300
  201 Regal Row Dallas (75247) (G-3892)

Advantage Aviation Tech II LLC 972 647-7300
  201 Regal Row Dallas (75247) (G-3893)

Advantage Energy Solutions, Houston Also called Red River Compression Svcs LLC (G-11569)

Advantage Fire SEC Integration, Houston Also called Advantage Interests Inc (G-8494)

Advantage Interests Inc 713 983-7253
  7840 W Little York Rd Houston (77040) (G-8494)

Advantage Label Company, Dallas Also called Advantage Marking & Labeling (G-3894)

Advantage Machine & Mfg, Plano Also called Manderscheid Inc (G-16918)

Advantage Marking & Labeling 214 638-5225
  8727 Empress Row Dallas (75247) (G-3894)

Advantage Steel Service Inc 817 589-0088
  3700 Flory St Fort Worth (76180) (G-6349)

Advantage Supplies Inc 972 250-1339
  4257 Marsh Ridge Rd Carrollton (75010) (G-2854)

Advent Global Solutions Inc (PA) 281 970-3000
  12777 Jones Rd Ste 445 Houston (77070) (G-8495)

Adventure Explrtion Prtners LL 432 684-8006
  500 W Texas Ave Ste 600 Midland (79701) (G-15107)

Adventure Plygrund Systems Inc 713 935-9684
  10845 Church Ln Houston (77043) (G-8496)

Advertisers Dynmc Svcs Co Inc 972 392-9722
  1100 Valwood Pkwy Ste 118 Carrollton (75006) (G-2691)

Advisory Cons Stl Erection Mfg 817 924-1991
  3113 Saint Louis Ave Fort Worth (76110) (G-6350)

Advocate Publishing, Dallas Also called East Dllas-Lakewood People Inc (G-4294)

Aeamc, Irving Also called Advanced Elec & Mtr Contrls (G-12924)

AEC Boerne, Boerne Also called Albany Engnered Composites Inc (G-2113)

Aeco, Houston Also called Dynaenergetics Us Inc (G-9544)

Aees Inc 210 491-2600
  211 N Loop 1604 E Ste 290 San Antonio (78232) (G-17871)

Aef Plating LLC 956 994-1991
  4000 W Ursula Ave McAllen (78503) (G-14832)

A L P H A B E T I C

Aegis Chemical Solutions LLC (PA) 281 258-4095
4560 Kendrick Plaza Dr Houston (77032) (G-8497)

Aegis Oil Limited Ventures LLC (PA) 214 431-5201
100 Crescent Ct Ste 700 Dallas (75201) (G-3895)

Aegis Ventures, Dallas Also called Aegis Oil Limited Ventures LLC (G-3895)

Aegle Nutrition LLC 972 446-9600
1300 Hutton Dr Ste 110 Carrollton (75006) (G-2692)

Aeglea Biotherapeutic Holdings, Austin Also called Aeglea Development Company
Inc (G-897)

Aeglea Biotherapeutics Inc (PA) 512 942-2935
805 Las Cimas Pkwy # 100 Austin (78746) (G-896)

Aeglea Development Company Inc 512 942-2935
805 Las Cimas Pkwy # 100 Austin (78746) (G-897)

Aei Communications Corp 650 552-9416
3310 Keller Springs Rd # 160 Carrollton (75006) (G-2693)

Aeon Process Equipment 972 690-8200
811 E Plano Pkwy Ste 103 Plano (75074) (G-16776)

Aequs Oil and Gas LLC 832 616-3110
2220 W Park St Paris (75460) (G-16357)

Aer Manufacturing Inc 972 417-2582
5915 Corridor Pkwy Schertz (78154) (G-18743)

Aer Manufacturing Inc 972 418-6499
3420 Wiley Post Rd Carrollton (75006) (G-2694)

Aer Manufacturing LP 972 392-4130
4040 Lindbergh Dr Addison (75001) (G-101)

Aera Products, Austin Also called Advanced Energy Industries Inc (G-889)

Aereos Inc (PA) 817 267-1371
1100 S Pipeline Rd W Euless (76040) (G-6126)

Aermotor Company 325 651-4951
4277 Dan Hanks Ln San Angelo (76904) (G-17771)

Aero - Ft Worth, Fort Worth Also called Lockheed Martin Corporation (G-6797)

Aero Brigham LLC 940 626-4849
351 Airport Rd Bldg 500 Decatur (76234) (G-5240)

Aero Capital Solutions Inc 737 717-0624
3700 N Cpitl Of Txas Hwy Austin (78746) (G-898)

Aero Cnc Inc 817 295-0184
960 S Burleson Blvd Burleson (76028) (G-2565)

Aero Components LLC 817 834-6251
5124 Kaltenbrun Rd Fort Worth (76119) (G-6351)

Aero Composites Structures Inc 972 694-5330
1533 Crescent Dr Ste 102 Carrollton (75006) (G-2695)

Aero Dynamix Inc 817 571-0729
3227 W Euless Blvd Euless (76040) (G-6127)

Aero-Tech Metal Finishing Inc 210 522-0802
7927 Mainland Dr San Antonio (78250) (G-17872)

Aerodynmic Prcsion McHning Inc 713 856-9990
6627 Theall Rd Houston (77066) (G-8498)

Aeromax Industries Inc 818 701-9500
1310 Ranchers Legacy Trl Fort Worth (76126) (G-6352)

Aerospace & Coml Tech Inc 817 560-6600
970 Fm 2871 Fort Worth (76126) (G-6353)

Aerospace Fasteners Inc 903 723-0693
255 N Us Highway 287 Palestine (75803) (G-16295)

Aerospace Optics, Fort Worth Also called Applied Avionics Inc (G-6392)

Aerospace Products SE Inc 210 924-2907
913 Billy Mitchell Blvd San Antonio (78226) (G-17873)

Aerostar Global Logistics LLC 630 458-8844
9500 N Royal Ln Ste 170 Irving (75063) (G-12925)

Aerostar International Inc 903 885-0728
186 Heritage Ct Sulphur Springs (75482) (G-19578)

Aerotech Engineering Inc 817 267-1371
1100 S Pipeline Rd W Euless (76040) (G-6128)

Aerowindtech Inc 817 438-4777
2411 Fm 917 Ste 200 Mansfield (76063) (G-14652)

Aeroxchange Ltd 972 556-8500
1503 Lbj Fwy Ste 275 Farmers Branch (75234) (G-6185)

Aerus Holdings LLC (PA) 214 378-4000
14841 Dallas Pkwy Ste 500 Dallas (75254) (G-3896)

Aerus LLC (HQ) 214 378-4000
14841 Dallas Pkwy Ste 500 Dallas (75254) (G-3897)

AES, San Antonio Also called E-Spectrum Technologies Inc (G-18080)

AES Drilling Fluid, Houston Also called Champion Drilling Fluids Inc (G-9156)

AES Drilling Fluids LLC (HQ) 888 556-4533
11767 Katy Fwy Ste 230 Houston (77079) (G-8499)

AES Industries Inc 817 341-7250
1831 Barnett Dr Weatherford (76087) (G-20574)

Aesthetic Medical Educators 512 301-2125
7606 Hawkeye Dr Austin (78749) (G-899)

Aethon Energy Management LLC 214 750-3820
12377 Merit Dr Ste 1200 Dallas (75251) (G-3898)

Aethon Energy Operating LLC 214 750-3833
12377 Merit Dr Ste 1200 Dallas (75251) (G-3899)

Aethon I LP 214 750-1522
5910 N Central Expy Dallas (75206) (G-3900)

AF Global, Houston Also called Ameriforge Group Inc (G-8616)

AF Technologies Inc 817 649-2500
2801 E Randol Mill Rd Arlington (76011) (G-611)

Afam Capital Inc 512 354-7041
221 W 6th St 5 Austin (78701) (G-900)

Afb Manufacturing LLC 410 581-0300
2450 Merritt Dr Garland (75041) (G-7429)

Affects Sat Corporation 713 897-9935
7109 Christina Ln Garland (75043) (G-7430)

Affilate Amran Instr Trnsfrmer, Houston Also called Amgis LLC (G-8624)

Affiliated Communications 972 423-4222
800 Jupiter Rd Ste 200 Plano (75074) (G-16777)

Affiliated Energy Products Inc 940 592-4169
900 Nw 287 Access Rd Iowa Park (76367) (G-12902)

Affiliated Foods Inc (PA) 806 372-3851
1401 W Farmers Ave Amarillo (79118) (G-476)

Affinity Chemical LLC (PA) 214 696-1037
3016 Southwestern Blvd Dallas (75225) (G-3901)

Affirm Oilfield Services LLC 817 644-3360
3575 Lone Star Cir Ste 41 Fort Worth (76177) (G-6354)

Affirmed Ntwrks Cmmnctons Tech 469 461-3101
2280 Campbell Creek Blvd Richardson (75082) (G-17267)

Affordable Asphalt Paving Inc 903 596-7003
5696 County Road 1143 Tyler (75704) (G-20044)

Affordable Concrete, Tyler Also called Affordable Asphalt Paving Inc (G-20044)

Affordable Neighbor Homes, Stafford Also called A & W Welding Inc (G-19279)

Affordable Signs, Georgetown Also called Greshare Enterprises Inc (G-7655)

Afi Unlimited LLC 936 591-9300
114 Fm 417 W Shelbyville (75973) (G-18894)

Afm, Houston Also called Advance Fbrction Msurement LLC (G-8482)

Afmg Industrial Services, League City Also called American Fincl Mktg Group Inc (G-13945)

Afren Resources USA, Spring Also called Afren Usa Inc (G-19192)

Afren Usa Inc 281 363-8600
10001 Woodloch Forest Dr Spring (77380) (G-19192)

Afs, Odessa Also called Advance Fabrication Svcs LLC (G-15903)

Aft Industries Inc 469 865-2800
204 S 6th Ave Mansfield (76063) (G-14653)

Aft Industries Inc (PA) 972 988-1999
204 S 6th Ave Mansfield (76063) (G-14654)

Afton Chemical Corporation 281 475-1040
4526 Res Frest Dr Ste 375 Spring (77381) (G-19193)

Afton Pumps Inc 713 923-9731
7335 Avenue N Houston (77011) (G-8500)

AG Development Inc 817 472-7260
801 Avenue H E Ste 100 Arlington (76011) (G-612)

AG III Contractors LLC 956 456-0628
22414 W Us Highway 281 San Benito (78586) (G-18653)

AG Warehouse, Ennis Also called Schirm USA Inc (G-6117)

Ag-Jax Ltd 903 705-0625
6775 Old Jacksonville Hwy Tyler (75703) (G-20045)

Ag-Meier Industries LLC 254 939-3731
920 E 6th Ave Belton (76513) (G-2016)

Agalite - Dallas, Farmers Branch Also called Hartung Glass Industries Inc (G-6201)

Agar Corporation Inc (HQ) 832 476-5100
5150 Tacoma Dr Houston (77041) (G-8501)

Agave Midstream Company, Dallas Also called Lucid Energy Group LLC (G-4610)

Age Industries Ltd 254 939-5828
801 Industrial Park Rd Belton (76513) (G-2017)

Age Industries Ltd 956 399-8279
1701 Amistad Dr San Benito (78586) (G-18654)

Age Industries Ltd (PA) 817 477-5266
3601 County Road 316c Cleburne (76031) (G-3079)

Age Industries Ltd 210 659-1301
1204 Schneider Cibolo (78108) (G-3060)

Age Industries Ltd 713 460-3060
7001 Barney Rd Houston (77092) (G-8502)

Age Industries Ltd 915 852-9099
491 S Darrington Rd Horizon City (79928) (G-8361)

Agent Systems Inc 972 774-0400
13375 N Stemmons Fwy # 300 Dallas (75234) (G-3902)

Aggietech Energy Services LLC (PA) 432 682-3131
5101 W Interstate 20 Midland (79706) (G-15108)

Aggietech Energy Services LLC 806 229-6129
690 W Richardson Sundown (79372) (G-19610)

Aggietech Oil Ltd 432 682-3131
5101 W Interstate 20 Midland (79708) (G-15109)

Aggregate Plant Products Co (PA) 210 333-1111
7640 Us Highway 87 E San Antonio (78263) (G-17874)

AGH Industries Inc 817 284-1742
1103 Stanley Dr Euless (76040) (G-6129)

Agi, Austin Also called Advanced Geosciences Inc (G-890)

Agilemesh Inc 972 231-2122
1825 Summit Ave Ste 206 Plano (75074) (G-16778)

Agilight, San Antonio Also called General Led Opco LLC (G-18138)

AGM Tools Inc 832 499-6090
5074 Steadmont Dr Houston (77040) (G-8503)

Agp, Houston Also called Architectural Graphic Products (G-8683)

Agpro Inc 903 785-5531
859 Airport Rd Reno (75462) (G-17251)

Agpro Systems Inc (PA) 903 636-5545
242 Private Road 3341 Big Sandy (75755) (G-2064)

Agrana Fruit Us Inc 817 625-9053
2400 Northeast Pkwy Fort Worth (76106) (G-6355)

Agri Wood Products Inc...254 709-6584
8102 Knottingham Dr Waco (76712) *(G-20356)*

Agri-Tex Wood Shavings Co LLC....................................936 628-1950
200 Industrial Blvd Shepherd (77371) *(G-18899)*

Agribag Inc..713 847-8008
8830 Market St Houston (77029) *(G-8504)*

Agribiofuels LLC...936 257-0826
138 Seaberg Industrial Rd Dayton (77535) *(G-5220)*

Agricen, Plano *Also called Advanced McRbial Solutions LLC (G-16774)*

Agrifos LLC...713 920-5300
2001 Jackson Rd Pasadena (77506) *(G-16379)*

Agrium US Inc..806 274-5204
9201 Fm 1551 Borger (79007) *(G-2161)*

AGS, Houston *Also called Applied Geophysical Services (G-8668)*

AGS Technology Inc..817 490-0086
4800 Alliance Gateway Fwy # 130 Fort Worth (76177) *(G-6356)*

Aguado Stone Incorporated..512 746-5094
3601 County Road 239 Georgetown (78633) *(G-7632)*

Aguilar Oilfield Services..432 230-2548
4250 N Stockton Ave Odessa (79764) *(G-15904)*

Aha Process Inc (PA)..281 426-5300
421 Jones Rd Highlands (77562) *(G-8311)*

Ahc Western Hatters Ltd Lblty.....................................940 872-2404
3091 Highway 81 N Bowie (76230) *(G-2190)*

Ahi Supply Inc (PA)..281 331-0088
2800 N Gordon St Alvin (77511) *(G-350)*

Ahlers Aerospace Inc (PA)..817 553-2155
3621 Raider Dr Hurst (76053) *(G-12832)*

Ahmsa International Inc..210 341-3777
5150 N Loop 1604 W San Antonio (78249) *(G-17875)*

Ai Lonestar LLC..512 990-3999
1009 W Wells Branch Pkwy Pflugerville (78660) *(G-16656)*

Al Root Company..210 223-2948
918 S Laredo St San Antonio (78204) *(G-17876)*

Aiap, Arlington *Also called Arlington Intl AVI Pdts LLC (G-625)*

Aibuy Inc...972 616-6400
13455 Noel Rd Dallas (75240) *(G-3903)*

Aic, Conroe *Also called Analytical Instruments Corp (G-3256)*

Aim Building Materials, Plano *Also called American Indus Mfrs Bldg Mate (G-16787)*

Aim Directional Services LLC......................................432 934-0628
7606 W Highway 80 Midland (79706) *(G-15110)*

Aim Directional Services LLC (PA)..............................361 653-6500
500 N Water St Ste 400 Corpus Christi (78401) *(G-3467)*

Aim Media Texas LLC...432 337-4661
700 N Grant Ave Ste 800 Odessa (79761) *(G-15905)*

Aim Media Texas Operating LLC (PA)..........................956 683-4000
1400 E Nolana Ave McAllen (78504) *(G-14833)*

Aim Media Texas Operating LLC..................................956 430-6200
1310 S Commerce St Harlingen (78550) *(G-8174)*

Aim Oilfield Services...281 814-9787
2640 Broadway St Ste 106 Pearland (77581) *(G-16537)*

Aim Solar Screens Inc...281 997-1543
2641 Roy Rd Pearland (77581) *(G-16538)*

Aim Solutions Inc...214 373-6084
10440 N Cntl Expy Ste 240 Dallas (75231) *(G-3904)*

Aim World Services Inc...281 847-2000
9450 Grogans Mill Rd # 1 The Woodlands (77380) *(G-19822)*

AIN Khudairi Trdg & Contract, Houston *Also called Khudairi Group Incorporated (G-10530)*

Aint, Plano *Also called Advanced Integration Tech Inc (G-16772)*

Air Distribution Tech Inc (HQ).....................................972 943-6100
605 Shiloh Rd Plano (75074) *(G-16779)*

Air Drilling Associates Inc (PA)...................................832 957-6093
18155 Chisholm Trl Houston (77060) *(G-8505)*

Air Duct Systems Mfg Co..832 519-9746
6401 Long Point Rd # 506 Houston (77055) *(G-8506)*

Air Filters Inc...713 896-8901
8282 Warren Rd Houston (77040) *(G-8507)*

Air Flow Products LP...713 305-0258
5310 Glenmont Dr Ste C Houston (77081) *(G-8508)*

Air Liquide Advanced Mtls Inc (HQ)............................713 624-8000
9811 Katy Fwy Ste 100 Houston (77024) *(G-8509)*

Air Liquide America Corp..512 748-5943
12700 Beltex Rd Manor (78653) *(G-14642)*

Air Liquide America LP..713 896-2100
12800 W Little York Rd Houston (77041) *(G-8510)*

Air Liquide America LP..281 474-5800
9810 Bay Area Blvd Pasadena (77507) *(G-16380)*

Air Liquide America LP..713 438-6000
3011 Pasadena Fwy Ste 190 Pasadena (77503) *(G-16381)*

Air Liquide America LP..281 474-8490
11450 W Fairmont Pkwy La Porte (77571) *(G-13717)*

Air Liquide America LP..361 299-2999
5880 Up River Rd Corpus Christi (78407) *(G-3468)*

Air Liquide America LP..281 291-5360
11440 W Fairmont Pkwy La Porte (77571) *(G-13718)*

Air Liquide America LP..979 239-5250
1811 Fm 523 Rd Freeport (77541) *(G-7190)*

Air Liquide America LP..903 237-1740
5361 W Loop 281 S Longview (75603) *(G-14188)*

Air Liquide America LP..409 720-4200
2121 Park St Port Neches (77651) *(G-17157)*

Air Liquide Electronics US LP (HQ).............................972 301-5200
9101 Lyndon B Johnson Fwy # 800 Dallas (75243) *(G-3905)*

Air Liquide Electronics US LP......................................972 994-2403
13140 T I Blvd Dallas (75243) *(G-3906)*

Air Liquide Large Inds US LP......................................903 237-1739
5361 W Loop 281 S Longview (75603) *(G-14189)*

Air Liquide Large Inds US LP (HQ)..............................713 624-8000
9811 Katy Fwy Ste 100 Houston (77024) *(G-8511)*

Air Liquide USA LLC...713 402-2221
9811 Katy Fwy Ste 100 Houston (77024) *(G-8512)*

Air Lqide Advanced Tech US LLC (HQ).........................713 624-8000
9807 Katy Fwy Houston (77024) *(G-8513)*

Air Lqide Amer Spclty Gses LLC (HQ)..........................800 217-2688
2700 Post Oak Blvd Houston (77056) *(G-8514)*

Air Lqide Hydrgen Enrgy US LLC.................................346 971-3051
9811 Katy Fwy Ste 100 Houston (77024) *(G-8515)*

Air Mate Division, Richardson *Also called Selkirk Corporation (G-17395)*

Air Oasis LLC...806 373-7788
3401 Airway Blvd Amarillo (79118) *(G-477)*

Air Performance Service Inc (PA)................................972 387-3334
10510 Markison Rd Dallas (75238) *(G-3907)*

Air Power Inc...817 557-5855
4900 S Collins St Arlington (76018) *(G-613)*

Air Power Inc Engines, Arlington *Also called Air Power Inc (G-613)*

Air Power Sales & Service LLC....................................903 236-0500
823 W Marshall Ave Longview (75601) *(G-14190)*

Air Products, Pasadena *Also called Evonik Corporation (G-16434)*

Air Quality Systems LLC...214 495-9991
207 W Main St Ste 202 Allen (75013) *(G-248)*

Air Relief Technologies Inc (PA)..................................817 261-3791
5757 E Rosedale St Fort Worth (76112) *(G-6357)*

Air Starter Components Inc (PA)..................................281 261-7939
13935 Stafford Rd Stafford (77477) *(G-19282)*

Air System Components Inc (HQ)................................972 212-4888
605 Shiloh Rd Plano (75074) *(G-16780)*

Air System Components Inc..915 852-1358
12504 Weaver Rd Horizon City (79928) *(G-8362)*

Air System Components Inc..972 212-4700
605 Shiloh Rd Plano (75074) *(G-16781)*

Air System Components Inc..972 680-9128
1401 N Plano Rd Richardson (75081) *(G-17268)*

Air System Components Inc..972 212-4800
605 Shiloh Rd Plano (75074) *(G-16782)*

Air-Serv Group LLC (HQ)..651 454-0465
3201 W Royal Ln Ste 100 Dallas (75229) *(G-3908)*

Airborn Connectors, Winnsboro *Also called Airborn Interconnect Inc (G-20895)*

Airborn Georgetown, Georgetown *Also called Airborn Interconnect Inc (G-7633)*

Airborn Interconnect Inc..512 863-5585
3500 Airborn Cir Georgetown (78626) *(G-7633)*

Airborn Interconnect Inc..903 629-7821
Fm 312 S St Winnsboro (75494) *(G-20895)*

Airborne Life Support System, Austin *Also called International Biomedical Ltd (G-1236)*

Airbox LLC...512 968-5496
2213 Ranch Road 620 N # 10 Austin (78734) *(G-901)*

Airbrush Images Inc...936 523-1000
851 N Fm 3083 Rd E Conroe (77303) *(G-3254)*

Airbus Helicopters Inc (HQ).......................................972 641-0000
2701 N Forum Dr Grand Prairie (75052) *(G-7824)*

Airco Industries, Inc...817 332-3806
5600 Blue Mound Rd Fort Worth (76131) *(G-6358)*

Aircraft Composite Inc..214 638-0138
2777 Irving Blvd Ste 112 Dallas (75207) *(G-3909)*

Aircraft Engine & Accessory Co...................................972 243-7404
2275 Crown Rd Dallas (75229) *(G-3910)*

Aircraft On Ground Inc (PA)..214 350-5334
11502 Jnes Maltsberger Rd San Antonio (78216) *(G-17877)*

Aircraft Technologies Inc..210 590-6858
3650 Highpoint San Antonio (78217) *(G-17878)*

Airdraulics...432 381-7867
3351 Nw Loop 338 Odessa (79764) *(G-15906)*

Aire Plastics Inc...830 779-2289
132 Industrial Dr La Vernia (78121) *(G-13800)*

Airflow Systems Inc..800 818-6185
11221 Pagemill Rd Dallas (75243) *(G-3911)*

Airfoil Impellers Corporation.......................................979 822-6418
2010 Fountain Ave Bryan (77801) *(G-2452)*

Airgas Inc..281 893-9353
14833 Tomball Pkwy Houston (77086) *(G-8516)*

Airgas Usa LLC..972 994-2400
13140 T I Blvd Dallas (75243) *(G-3912)*

Airgas Usa LLC..281 474-8400
11426 W Fairmont Pkwy La Porte (77571) *(G-13719)*

Airgas Usa LLC..972 660-0500
801 W North Carrier Pkwy Grand Prairie (75050) *(G-7825)*

Airgas Usa LLC..281 474-8300
11400 Bay Area Blvd Pasadena (77507) *(G-16382)*

Airgas Usa LLC..361 533-0758
301 Hereford Rd Corpus Christi (78408) *(G-3469)*

A
L
P
H
A
B
E
T
I
C

Airgas Usa LLC..512 835-0202
11111 N Lamar Blvd Austin (78753) *(G-902)*

Airgen Equipment LLC......................................432 332-1870
3600 Kermit Hwy Odessa (79764) *(G-15907)*

Airline Mortuary Associates................................281 540-4141
1331 S Houston Ave Humble (77338) *(G-12744)*

Airline Plating Inc..713 692-6369
6901 Airline Dr Houston (77076) *(G-8517)*

Airmark Industries Inc......................................325 641-1999
5701 Highway 377 S Brownwood (76801) *(G-2424)*

Airmec Inc...972 438-4015
2102 Vanco Dr Irving (75061) *(G-12926)*

Airpax, Brownsville *Also called Philips North America LLC* *(G-2393)*

Airport Printing Service, El Paso *Also called Anmar Enterprises Inc* *(G-5644)*

Airtech Spray Systems Inc..................................713 681-0013
4303 Pinemont Dr Houston (77018) *(G-8518)*

Airtech Supply Inc...501 525-7707
6625 Iron Horse Blvd North Richland Hills (76180) *(G-15873)*

Airtight Mobile Gasket & Seals, Lubbock *Also called Stainless Mfg & Seals Svc* *(G-14486)*

Airtite Products Llc..325 672-5774
4008 S Treadaway Blvd Abilene (79602) *(G-11)*

Airtronic Usa LLC...830 980-9788
21155 State Highway 46 W Spring Branch (78070) *(G-19265)*

Airtrust Intl Systems Corp (PA)...........................**713 491-4455**
1201 N Logan St Ste 100 Texas City (77590) *(G-19785)*

Airway Services Inc..325 617-5813
5001 Christoval Rd San Angelo (76904) *(G-17772)*

Ait Aerospace Components Svcs, Grand Prairie *Also called Advanced Integration Tech GP* *(G-7822)*

Ait Aerospace Components Svcs, San Antonio *Also called Advanced Integration Tech SA* *(G-17869)*

Ait Aerospace Components Svcs, San Antonio *Also called Advanced Integration Tech LP* *(G-17868)*

Aix Energy Inc...214 292-3482
8401 N Central Expy # 840 Dallas (75225) *(G-3913)*

Aj Commercial Services Inc.................................361 336-2113
6429 Crosstown Expy Ste D Corpus Christi (78417) *(G-3470)*

Ajax Tocco Magnethermic Corp.............................903 297-2526
5807 W Marshall Ave Longview (75604) *(G-14191)*

Ajooo Inc..469 494-7317
13526 Vargon St Dallas (75243) *(G-3914)*

Ajr Media Group LLC......................................713 942-7676
25132 Oakhurst Dr Ste 201 Spring (77386) *(G-19194)*

AK, Fort Worth *Also called Ask Industries Inc* *(G-6403)*

Akcorp Inc (PA)...**409 833-8002**
1280 S 11th St Beaumont (77701) *(G-1848)*

Aker Solutions Inc (HQ)...................................**713 685-5700**
2103 Citywest Blvd # 800 Houston (77042) *(G-8519)*

Akfix USA Inc...972 276-9600
238 Lavon Dr Garland (75040) *(G-7431)*

Akhu Therapeutics Inc.....................................979 820-2740
2713 Horse Haven Ln College Station (77845) *(G-3173)*

Akidco Inc..214 905-6064
3420 Singleton Blvd Dallas (75212) *(G-3915)*

Akrotex Films Inc...409 886-0632
Fm 1006 Orange (77631) *(G-16229)*

Akrotex Films Inc (PA)....................................**409 886-0111**
1301 S Childers Rd Orange (77630) *(G-16230)*

Akrotex Films Inc...409 886-0063
1804 Austin St West Orange (77630) *(G-20692)*

Akwel Cadillac Usa Inc....................................956 718-8387
110 Consolidation Pt Laredo (78045) *(G-13856)*

Akwel Cadillac Usa Inc....................................956 717-4147
8511 Milo Rd Laredo (78045) *(G-13857)*

Akzo Coatings, Fort Worth *Also called Akzo Nobel Coatings Inc* *(G-6359)*

Akzo Nobel, Fort Worth *Also called International Paint LLC* *(G-6724)*

Akzo Nobel Coatings, Round Rock *Also called Akzo Nobel Inc* *(G-17620)*

Akzo Nobel Coatings Inc...................................713 684-1324
6001 Antoine Dr Houston (77091) *(G-8520)*

Akzo Nobel Coatings Inc...................................817 232-9745
3201 Ne Loop 820 Ste 200 Fort Worth (76137) *(G-6359)*

Akzo Nobel Inc..512 244-9038
401 Texas Ave Ste B Round Rock (78664) *(G-17620)*

Akzo Nobel Inc..713 433-7289
15200 Almeda Rd Houston (77053) *(G-8370)*

Akzo Nobel Inc..210 520-6566
4211 Blanco Rd San Antonio (78212) *(G-17879)*

Akzo Nobel Inc..817 625-1500
611 E Northside Dr Fort Worth (76164) *(G-6360)*

Akzo Nobel Inc..281 584-0093
14502 Richmond Ave Houston (77082) *(G-8521)*

Al Knoch Interiors Inc......................................915 886-5800
9010 N Desert Blvd Canutillo (79835) *(G-2662)*

Al Legacy Partners Inc.....................................972 296-9599
4501 Mountain Creek Pkwy Dallas (75236) *(G-3916)*

Al Rowan...903 963-7036
160 W Main St Van (75790) *(G-20205)*

Al Tex Concrete Products Inc...............................830 964-5150
1398 Fm 2673 Ste B Canyon Lake (78133) *(G-2677)*

Al's Millwork, Bacliff *Also called Hoffman Ventures Inc* *(G-1732)*

Al/Tex Homes Inc...817 847-1355
8701 Harmon Rd Fort Worth (76177) *(G-6361)*

Al3 Incorporated..512 746-4200
13685 N I 35 Jarrell (76537) *(G-13269)*

Alachisoft, Dallas *Also called Diyatech Corp* *(G-4264)*

Alafair Biosciences Inc....................................512 739-9510
6101 W Courtyard Dr 2-2 Austin (78730) *(G-903)*

Alamo 25, Cuero *Also called Alamo Lumber Company* *(G-3758)*

Alamo Cement Company (HQ).............................210 208-1880
6055 W Green Mountain Rd San Antonio (78266) *(G-18635)*

Alamo City Counter Tops Inc..............................210 732-4800
940 W Laurel San Antonio (78201) *(G-17880)*

Alamo Concrete Pavers, San Antonio *Also called Alamo Concrete Tile Inc* *(G-17883)*

Alamo Concrete Products Ltd.............................956 423-6388
2301 Industrial Crossway Harlingen (78550) *(G-8175)*

Alamo Concrete Products Ltd.............................512 444-2464
4200 Todd Ln Austin (78744) *(G-904)*

Alamo Concrete Products Ltd.............................210 208-1500
7003 Lesli Rd San Antonio (78254) *(G-17881)*

Alamo Concrete Products Ltd.............................210 208-1880
6977 Evens Grv San Antonio (78265) *(G-17882)*

Alamo Concrete Products Ltd.............................361 572-0231
10006 Holletsville Hwy Victoria (77904) *(G-20236)*

Alamo Concrete Products Ltd.............................361 578-9678
10006 Halletsville Hwy Victoria (77904) *(G-20237)*

Alamo Concrete Products Ltd.............................830 773-6334
Fm 1021 El Indio Hwy Eagle Pass (78852) *(G-5547)*

Alamo Concrete Products Ltd.............................361 552-9525
2049 W Main St Port Lavaca (77979) *(G-17141)*

Alamo Concrete Products Ltd (PA)........................**512 444-2464**
6055 W Green Mountain Rd Austin (78744) *(G-905)*

Alamo Concrete Products Ltd.............................210 208-1580
6981 E Evans Rd San Antonio (78266) *(G-18636)*

Alamo Concrete Products Ltd.............................956 423-6380
2301 Industrial Crossway Harlingen (78550) *(G-8176)*

Alamo Concrete Products Ltd.............................979 245-8365
Plant 76 End Of Clmbus Rd Bay City (77414) *(G-1767)*

Alamo Concrete Products Ltd.............................361 289-9200
6129 Agnes St Corpus Christi (78406) *(G-3471)*

Alamo Concrete Products Ltd.............................979 345-4631
County Rd 437 West Columbia (77486) *(G-20673)*

Alamo Concrete Products Ltd.............................979 849-6378
Hwy 35 E West Columbia (77486) *(G-20674)*

Alamo Concrete Products Co (PA).........................**210 208-1500**
6981 E Evans Rd San Antonio (78266) *(G-18637)*

Alamo Concrete Products Co...............................281 443-2644
18880 E Hardy Rd Houston (77073) *(G-8522)*

Alamo Concrete Products L, San Antonio *Also called Alamo Concrete Products Ltd* *(G-17881)*

Alamo Concrete Products L................................361 592-5114
801 N 6th St Kingsville (78363) *(G-13623)*

Alamo Concrete Tile Inc...................................210 534-8821
1008 Hoefgen Ave San Antonio (78210) *(G-17883)*

Alamo Distilling Company, San Antonio *Also called Alamo Premium Distillery Inc* *(G-17886)*

Alamo Group (tx) Inc......................................800 882-5762
1502 E Walnut St Seguin (78155) *(G-18822)*

Alamo Industrial Group Inc...............................210 223-6161
943 At And T Center Pkwy San Antonio (78219) *(G-17884)*

Alamo Iron Works Inc.....................................210 223-6161
943 At And T Center Pkwy San Antonio (78219) *(G-17885)*

Alamo Lumber Company...................................361 275-2321
704 N Esplanade St Cuero (77954) *(G-3758)*

Alamo North Texas RR, Dallas *Also called Martin Marietta Materials Inc* *(G-4640)*

Alamo Outdoor Structures Inc.............................210 651-0425
18860 Goll St San Antonio (78266) *(G-18638)*

Alamo Pallet Recyclers Inc.................................972 296-2090
5623 W Ledbetter Dr Dallas (75236) *(G-3917)*

Alamo Plating Inc...210 658-4024
9230 Converse Business Ln Converse (78109) *(G-3387)*

Alamo Plating & Met Finshg Ltd...........................210 658-4024
9230 Converse Ln Converse (78109) *(G-3388)*

Alamo Premium Distillery Inc.............................210 325-7853
2030 E Houston St San Antonio (78202) *(G-17886)*

Alamo Pressure Pumping LLC (PA).........................**432 695-6210**
11000 W County Rd Midland (79707) *(G-15111)*

Alamo Ready Mix Concrete, Port Lavaca *Also called Alamo Concrete Products Ltd* *(G-17141)*

Alamo Ready Mix Concrete, West Columbia *Also called Alamo Concrete Products Ltd* *(G-20674)*

Alamo Ready Mix LLC......................................713 330-3000
1818 Federal Rd Houston (77015) *(G-8523)*

Alamo Resources LLC......................................281 398-9500
820 Gessner Rd Ste 1650 Houston (77024) *(G-8524)*

Alamo Sales Corp..800 882-5762
1502 E Walnut St Seguin (78155) *(G-18823)*

Alamo Structural Steel LLC 254 799-2471
  2784 Old Dallas Rd Waco (76705) *(G-20357)*

Alamo Structural Steel Co, Waco *Also called Alamo Structural Steel LLC (G-20357)*

Alamo Tamale Company LP 713 228-6445
  809 Berry Rd Houston (77022) *(G-8525)*

Alamo Tees & Advertising, San Antonio *Also called Bankson Group Ltd (G-17938)*

Alamo Transformer Supply Co 713 991-6060
  10220 Mykawa Rd Houston (77048) *(G-8526)*

Alamo Waterproofing Svcs Inc 210 648-2100
  4600 Boldt Rd San Antonio (78222) *(G-17887)*

Alamo Welding & Boiler Work 210 227-6502
  816 N Flores St San Antonio (78212) *(G-17888)*

Alamo Wood, San Antonio *Also called Pallet Ops - San Antonio LLC (G-18364)*

Alan Charles Incorporated...817 922-9834
  3446 May St Fort Worth (76110) *(G-6362)*

Alareal Corporation 915 858-4097
  8417 Beverly Pl El Paso (79907) *(G-5639)*

Alart Tool & Die Corp 713 691-0434
  37 Berry Rd Houston (77022) *(G-8527)*

Albany Engnered Composites Inc 830 249-4400
  1281 N Main St Boerne (78006) *(G-2113)*

Albas Custom Iron Inc 281 401-9797
  7105 Fulton St Houston (77022) *(G-8528)*

Albemarle Catalysts Company LP 281 474-2864
  13000 Baypark Rd Pasadena (77507) *(G-16383)*

Albemarle Corporation 713 740-1866
  2500 N South St Pasadena (77503) *(G-16384)*

Albemarle Corporation 281 480-4747
  13100 Space Center Blvd # 400 Houston (77059) *(G-8529)*

Albemarle Corporation 281 480-4747
  2625 Bay Area Blvd # 250 Houston (77058) *(G-8530)*

Albemarle Corporation 281 474-2864
  13000 Baypark Rd Pasadena (77507) *(G-16385)*

Albemarle Corporation 713 740-1000
  2500 N South St Pasadena (77503) *(G-16386)*

Albermarle, Pasadena *Also called Albemarle Corporation (G-16386)*

Alco Machine Tool & Steel Inc 915 779-7013
  6805 Alameda Ave El Paso (79905) *(G-5640)*

Alcoa, Gregory *Also called Reynolds Metals Company LLC (G-8104)*

Alcoa Fastening Systems, Waco *Also called Huck International Inc (G-20417)*

Alcoa Howmet, Wichita Falls, Wichita Falls *Also called Howmet Castings & Services Inc (G-20771)*

Alcoa Lake Charles Carbn Plant 845 334-7203
  4069 Chrles Mrtn Hall Ss Rockdale (76567) *(G-17523)*

Alcoa USA Corp 512 446-8681
  3155 Charles Mrtn Hall Rd Rockdale (76567) *(G-17524)*

Alcoa World Alumina LLC 361 987-2631
  State Hwy 35 Point Comfort (77978) *(G-17081)*

Alcocer LLC 210 930-4580
  9521 Middlex Dr San Antonio (78217) *(G-17889)*

Alcomat, Columbus *Also called Alleyton Resource Company LLC (G-3228)*

Alcon, Fort Worth *Also called Ciba Vision Corporation (G-6517)*

Alcon Laboratories Inc (HQ) **817 293-0450**
  6201 South Fwy Fort Worth (76134) *(G-6363)*

Alcon Laboratories Inc 817 293-7276
  6201 South Fwy Fort Worth (76134) *(G-6364)*

Alcon Laboratories Holdg Corp (HQ) **817 293-0450**
  6201 South Fwy Fort Worth (76134) *(G-6365)*

Alcon Manufacturing Ltd 713 668-9100
  9965 Buffalo Speedway Houston (77054) *(G-8531)*

Alcon Research LLC (PA) **817 551-4555**
  6201 South Fwy Fort Worth (76134) *(G-6366)*

Alcon Surgical, Houston *Also called Alcon Vision LLC (G-8533)*

Alcon Surgical, Fort Worth *Also called Alcon Laboratories Inc (G-6364)*

Alcon Surgical Inc 817 293-0450
  6201 South Fwy Fort Worth (76134) *(G-6367)*

Alcon Vision LLC (HQ) **817 293-0450**
  6201 South Fwy Fort Worth (76134) *(G-6368)*

Alcon Vision LLC 713 668-9100
  2650 W Belford St Houston (77002) *(G-8532)*

Alcon Vision LLC 713 668-9100
  9965 Buffalo Speedway Houston (77054) *(G-8533)*

Alcor Aviation, San Antonio *Also called Alcor Inc (G-17890)*

Alcor Inc 210 349-6491
  300 Breesport St San Antonio (78216) *(G-17890)*

Aldersgate Enrichment Center 325 646-2566
  5001 Highway 84 E Early (76802) *(G-5556)*

Aldersgate Industries, Early *Also called Aldersgate Enrichment Center (G-5556)*

Alecom Metal Works Inc 972 438-1032
  2803 Chalk Hill Rd Dallas (75212) *(G-3918)*

Alecom Technologies Group Inc 972 870-9400
  1001 Spinks Rd Ste 230 Flower Mound (75028) *(G-6259)*

Alegacy Equipment LLC 832 916-3700
  1475 Alegacy Pl Waller (77484) *(G-20490)*

Alenco Holding Corporation (HQ) **979 779-1051**
  615 W Carson St Bryan (77801) *(G-2453)*

Alereon Inc 512 345-4200
  10800 Pecan Park Blvd # 100 Austin (78750) *(G-906)*

Aleris Ohio Management Inc 972 815-0800
  5525 N Macarthur Blvd Irving (75038) *(G-12927)*

Alert Control Technologies LLC 281 288-1321
  9421 Fm 2920 Rd Tomball (77375) *(G-19955)*

Alert Technologies Inc 281 326-9900
  16875 Diana Ln Houston (77058) *(G-8534)*

Alex Esolutions Inc 512 305-6500
  807 Las Cimas Pkwy # 300 Austin (78746) *(G-907)*

Alex Orthopedic Inc...972 641-9680
  510 Fountain Pkwy Grand Prairie (75050) *(G-7826)*

Alexander & Co 325 677-1309
  155 Pine St Abilene (79601) *(G-12)*

Alexander Group, San Antonio *Also called Alexander Production Company (G-17891)*

Alexander Machine & Maint Svc, Fort Worth *Also called Alexanders Mch Maint Svc Inc (G-6369)*

Alexander Manufacturing Co 972 641-7355
  11573 County Road 436 Cross Plains (76443) *(G-3746)*

Alexander Moulding Mill Co 254 386-3187
  Hwy 281 S Hamilton (76531) *(G-8164)*

Alexander Production Company 210 271-3691
  700 N Saint Marys St # 1200 San Antonio (78205) *(G-17891)*

Alexander Tank Co 830 875-2759
  2400 E Pierce St Luling (78648) *(G-14558)*

Alexander's Tractor Parts, Winnsboro *Also called Winnsboro Spclty Prts Intl Inc (G-20902)*

Alexanders Mch Maint Svc Inc 817 625-4175
  3700 N Commerce St Fort Worth (76106) *(G-6369)*

Alexs Air Conditioning Inc (PA) **409 935-2496**
  706 Bayou Rd La Marque (77568) *(G-13705)*

Alfa Laval Inc 713 329-1270
  10470 Deer Trail Dr Houston (77038) *(G-8535)*

Alfa Laval Inc 804 236-3106
  7132 Hunt Ln Rockwall (75087) *(G-17536)*

Alfa Laval Thermal, Houston *Also called Alfa Laval Inc (G-8535)*

Alfa Laval US Holding Inc 281 449-0322
  11600 E Hardy Rd Houston (77093) *(G-8536)*

Alfonso Hinostroza..956 781-1845
  1806 N Raul Longoria Rd San Juan (78589) *(G-18670)*

Alfred Kager 830 997-9391
  3168 N State Highway 16 Fredericksburg (78624) *(G-7169)*

Algae Production Systems 832 515-9670
  9337b Katy Fwy Ste 193 Houston (77024) *(G-8537)*

Algostim, Plano *Also called Nuvectra Corporation (G-16949)*

Alice Newspapers Inc...361 664-6588
  405 E Main St Alice (78332) *(G-203)*

Alice Southern Equipment, Laredo *Also called Select Energy Services LLC (G-13932)*

Alice Southern Equipment, Bryan *Also called Select Energy Services LLC (G-2508)*

Aliento Inc 214 302-6580
  110 N Main St Duncanville (75116) *(G-5527)*

Alig LLC (HQ) **212 626-4936**
  2700 Post Oak Blvd Houston (77056) *(G-8538)*

Align Technology Inc..408 470-1311
  10 Leigh Fisher Blvd El Paso (79906) *(G-5641)*

Alimak Group USA Inc (HQ) **713 640-8500**
  12552 Galveston Rd Webster (77598) *(G-20632)*

Alinet Oilfield Services Corp 903 984-2307
  2019 S Henderson Blvd A Kilgore (75662) *(G-13531)*

Alk-Abello Inc (HQ) **512 251-0037**
  1700 Royston Ln Round Rock (78664) *(G-17621)*

Alkote Inc 713 695-3609
  13 Farrell St Houston (77022) *(G-8539)*

Alkusari Texas Limestone Corp 512 339-2299
  4121 E State Highway 29 Bertram (78605) *(G-2050)*

All American Awnings Inc 214 388-5444
  4612 S Buckner Blvd Dallas (75227) *(G-3919)*

All American Filters Inc 281 421-1909
  5334 East Rd Baytown (77521) *(G-1807)*

All American Pump & Mch Inc 325 653-6597
  1310 N Bell St San Angelo (76903) *(G-17773)*

All American Tire Recyclers, Fort Worth *Also called Tjp Enterprises LLC (G-7064)*

All City Well Service 432 332-8863
  1410 W Interstate 20 Odessa (79763) *(G-15908)*

All Color Press Texas Inc 214 744-2258
  4818 Woodall St Dallas (75247) *(G-3920)*

All Forkliftscom Inc 972 506-9108
  1616 Tantor Rd Dallas (75229) *(G-3921)*

All Mark Impressions Ltd 817 834-0080
  823 N Riverside Dr Fort Worth (76111) *(G-6370)*

All Metal, Carrollton *Also called Allmetal Inc (G-2855)*

All Plastic LLC 830 896-6464
  200 Holdsworth Dr Kerrville (78028) *(G-13517)*

All Points Equipment Co LLC 337 369-6314
  9710 Telge Rd Houston (77095) *(G-8540)*

All Seasons, Bryan *Also called Alenco Holding Corporation (G-2453)*

All Seasons Commercial Div Inc 979 823-6557
  1293 N Hrvey Mitchell Pkwy Bryan (77803) *(G-2454)*

All Seasons Feeders Inc 210 648-0979
  8424 Us Highway 87 E San Antonio (78263) *(G-17892)*

All Star Caps Inc 210 509-9086
  7939 Mainland Dr San Antonio (78250) *(G-17893)*

All Star Corrugated (PA) 817 551-5580
1425 Forum Way S Fort Worth (76140) **(G-6371)**
All Star Corrugated 817 454-8640
208 Hiddenglen St Burleson (76028) **(G-2566)**
All Star Pallet, Dallas *Also called Pallet Advisor LLC* **(G-4780)**
All Star Wheel Repair LLC 972 564-1610
220 Industrial Dr Forney (75126) **(G-6302)**
All State Belting, Lewisville *Also called All-State Industries Inc* **(G-14020)**
All State Fire Eqp Texas Inc 972 412-0770
1307 Century Way Wylie (75098) **(G-20924)**
All Tech Services, Houston *Also called Oil Tech Services Inc* **(G-11162)**
All Transportation Services, Houston *Also called Alltrans Port Trucking Inc* **(G-8559)**
All Truss Building Systems Inc 817 247-7671
5930 Royal Ln Ste E Dallas (75230) **(G-3922)**
All Washed Up Inc 512 288-5522
15106 W Hwy 71 Austin (78738) **(G-908)**
All Wood Custom Cabinets Inc 940 686-2795
1217 N Highway 377 Pilot Point (76258) **(G-16721)**
All-Plastics LLC 972 239-2686
15700 Midway Rd Addison (75001) **(G-102)**
All-Pro Threaded Products 817 467-5700
191 Peyco Dr N Arlington (76001) **(G-614)**
All-Rite Sheet Metal Inc 713 680-0515
5718 Broom St Houston (77091) **(G-8541)**
All-Spec Sales Inc 972 641-4053
2125 109th St Grand Prairie (75050) **(G-7827)**
All-State Belting LLC 713 433-1272
3939 Anderson Rd Houston (77053) **(G-8371)**
All-State Industries Inc 972 434-4222
1400 Lakeway Dr Lewisville (75057) **(G-14020)**
Allamon Tool Company Inc 936 449-5433
18935 Freeport Dr Montgomery (77356) **(G-15625)**
Allan Banks 936 337-4020
14414 Lake Vista Ct Willis (77318) **(G-20841)**
Allan Knight & Associates Inc 214 741-2227
150 Turtle Creek Blvd # 101 Dallas (75207) **(G-3923)**
Allar Company 940 549-0077
735 Elm St Graham (76450) **(G-7775)**
Allbright & Associates Inc 432 366-8897
8011 Andrews Hwy Odessa (79765) **(G-15909)**
Allchem Services Incorporated 713 796-8000
9011 E Almeda St Houston (77054) **(G-8542)**
Allegiant Industrial LLC 409 782-7963
850 Pine St Beaumont (77701) **(G-1849)**
Allegra Marketing Print Mail, San Antonio *Also called Pccs Printing Solutions Inc* **(G-18368)**
Allegra Marketing-Print-Mail, San Antonio *Also called Kalle Enterprises Inc* **(G-18216)**
Allegra Print & Imaging, Houston *Also called 2d Inc* **(G-8405)**
Allegra Print & Imaging, Addison *Also called Eight Eighty-Eight Inc* **(G-118)**
Allen and Allen LLC (PA) **210 733-9191**
202 Culebra Rd San Antonio (78201) **(G-17894)**
Allen and Allen LLC 210 733-9191
701 San Fernando St San Antonio (78207) **(G-17895)**
Allen Calvin Sad & Wstn Wr, Weatherford *Also called Calvin Allen Saddlery* **(G-20581)**
Allen Distribution Center, Allen *Also called Epiroc Drilling Solutions LLC* **(G-265)**
Allen Orthotics & Prosthetics (PA) **432 683-3788**
2502 W Ohio Ave Midland (79701) **(G-15112)**
Allen Prfmce Resources Inc 817 270-0102
11468 S Fm 730 Azle (76020) **(G-1719)**
Allen Tharp LLC 210 878-0034
16109 University Oak San Antonio (78249) **(G-17896)**
Allendale Machine Co Inc (PA) **713 477-8776**
10014 Lucore St Houston (77017) **(G-8543)**
Allendale Machine Co Inc 713 477-8776
10017 Steelman St Houston (77017) **(G-8544)**
Allergan Inc 512 527-6649
12331 Riata Trace Pkwy Austin (78727) **(G-909)**
Allergan Sales LLC 254 666-3331
8301 Mars Dr Waco (76712) **(G-20358)**
Allestec Corporation 281 359-1519
810 Russell Palmer Rd B Kingwood (77339) **(G-13637)**
Alleys Industrial Service Inc 432 362-0200
6826 N County Rd W Odessa (79764) **(G-15910)**
Alleyton Resource Company LLC (HQ) **281 238-1010**
755 Fm 762 Columbus (78934) **(G-3228)**
Allflex Usa Inc (HQ) **972 456-3686**
2805 E 14th St Dallas (75261) **(G-3924)**
Alliance Carpet Cushion Co 903 886-4153
3100 Industrial Dr Commerce (75428) **(G-3241)**
Alliance Coatings LLC 817 834-8817
1001 N Blue Mound Rd Fort Worth (76131) **(G-6372)**
Alliance Energy Corporation 713 333-4000
3 Riverway Ste 825 Houston (77056) **(G-8545)**
Alliance Entertainment LLC 806 381-3945
6900 W I 40 Ste 200 Amarillo (79106) **(G-392)**
Alliance Field Services LLC 432 332-4308
12801 W County Road 91 Midland (79707) **(G-15113)**
Alliance Graphics & Printing, Houston *Also called Alliance Printing LP* **(G-8547)**
Alliance Laser Technologies, Arlington *Also called Laser Care Inc* **(G-719)**
Alliance Loose Leaf, Fort Worth *Also called JPS Alliance Inc* **(G-6746)**
Alliance Machine & Spc Inc 432 367-9113
8711 Andrews Hwy Odessa (79765) **(G-15911)**
Alliance Petroleum Interests 469 249-8985
17311 Dallas Pkwy Ste 200 Dallas (75248) **(G-3925)**
Alliance Press Leasing Inc 713 957-3349
5225 Hollister St Houston (77040) **(G-8546)**
Alliance Printing LP 713 957-3349
5225 Hollister St Houston (77040) **(G-8547)**
Allied Advertising Agency Inc 210 732-7874
1503 Stag Pt San Antonio (78248) **(G-17897)**
Allied Alumina Group Inc 361 777-2400
4633 Hwy 361 Gregory (78359) **(G-8098)**
Allied Assets Corporation 713 413-9700
2950 Mowery Rd Houston (77045) **(G-8548)**
Allied Bioscience Inc (PA) **214 432-5580**
7500 Dallas Pkwy Ste 800 Plano (75024) **(G-16783)**
Allied Design & Graphics, San Antonio *Also called Allied Advertising Agency Inc* **(G-17897)**
Allied Equipment Inc 432 367-6000
8000 Golder Ave Odessa (79764) **(G-15912)**
Allied Fence Co of Dallas (PA) **903 892-9640**
266 W Commerce St Dallas (75208) **(G-3926)**
Allied Gate Company, Dallas *Also called Allied Fence Co of Dallas* **(G-3926)**
Allied Imaging Group LLC 713 812-8100
2519 Fairway Park Dr # 310 Houston (77092) **(G-8549)**
Allied McRobial Investigations 713 941-9200
1309 Illinois St South Houston (77587) **(G-19037)**
Allied Mineral Products Inc 956 831-2022
3025 Mineral Loop Brownsville (78521) **(G-2336)**
Allied Natural Gas Corporation 713 658-1144
1001 Fannin St Ste 900 Houston (77002) **(G-8550)**
Allied Ofs LLC (PA) **832 482-3730**
11211 Fm 2920 Rd Tomball (77375) **(G-19956)**
Allied Oil Field Mch Pump LLC 806 894-7263
202 Hulon Moreland Rd Levelland (79336) **(G-14003)**
Allied Pallet & Eqp Co LLC 281 850-8090
16760 Beaumont Hwy Houston (77049) **(G-8551)**
Allied Powder Coating, Houston *Also called Outdoor Furn Refinishing Inc* **(G-11202)**
Allied Precision Fabg Inc 713 757-9810
1105 Foundation Dr Caldwell (77836) **(G-2625)**
Allied Prod Solutions GP LLC (PA) **405 224-5779**
10344 Sam Houston Park Dr # 300 Houston (77064) **(G-8552)**
Allied Stone Inc (HQ) **214 838-2225**
2405 Crown Rd Dallas (75229) **(G-3927)**
Allied Threaded Mtls & McHy Co 713 464-3594
8918 Spring Branch Dr A Houston (77080) **(G-8553)**
Allied Tools of Texas Corp 713 943-8500
5230 Galveston Rd Houston (77017) **(G-8554)**
Allied Truss LLC 903 586-1982
387 County Road 3216 Jacksonville (75766) **(G-13225)**
Allied Wear Systems LLC 972 248-8838
17810 Davenport Rd # 109 Dallas (75252) **(G-3837)**
Allied Welding Systems, Dallas *Also called Allied Wear Systems LLC* **(G-3837)**
Allied Well Service Inc 361 664-6122
2681 W Front St Alice (78332) **(G-204)**
Allied Wireline Services LLC (PA) **713 343-7280**
3200 Wilcrest Dr Ste 170 Houston (77042) **(G-8555)**
Allied-Hrizontal Wireline Svcs, Houston *Also called Allied Wireline Services LLC* **(G-8555)**
Allis Chalmers, Houston *Also called Knight Energy Services LLC* **(G-10548)**
Allmetal Inc 972 245-9264
1413 Bradley Ln Carrollton (75007) **(G-2855)**
Allosense Inc 830 900-3080
110 E Houston St Fl 7 San Antonio (78205) **(G-17898)**
Alloy Carbide Company (PA) **713 923-2700**
7827 Avenue H Houston (77012) **(G-8556)**
Alloy Carbide Company 713 923-2700
7820 Avenue I Houston (77012) **(G-8557)**
Alloy Casting Co Inc 800 527-1318
3900 S Peachtree Rd Mesquite (75180) **(G-15025)**
Alloy Cnc LLC 936 449-4001
18473 Kinkaid Rd E Montgomery (77316) **(G-15626)**
Alloy Polymers Texas LP 936 544-4043
Hwy 287 & Fm2160 # 2160 Latexo (75849) **(G-13941)**
Alloy Products Group, Houston *Also called Overlay Product Systems Inc* **(G-11206)**
Allpac Inc 214 630-8804
810 Buffalo Springs Dr Prosper (75078) **(G-17212)**
Allpoints Oilfield Svcs LLC 713 393-4200
945 Bunker Hill Rd # 500 Houston (77024) **(G-8558)**
Allred Construction Company 806 435-5817
302 Se 9th Ave Perryton (79070) **(G-16631)**
Allsport Dynamics Inc 936 569-1003
2724 Se Stallings Dr Nacogdoches (75961) **(G-15684)**
Allstar Door & Maintenance LP 817 748-0667
4205 Colleyville Blvd Colleyville (76034) **(G-3210)**
Allstates Coatings Company, Gladewater *Also called Lbs Enterprises LLC* **(G-7725)**
Allstream Envmtl Svcs LLC 713 408-7237
10004 Wurzbach Rd Pmb 273 San Antonio (78230) **(G-17899)**
Alltek Circuits Incorporated 949 250-4499
3524 Dividend Dr Garland (75042) **(G-7432)**

2021 Harris Texas Manufacturers Directory
(G-0000) Company's Geographic Section entry number
1090

Alltrans Port Trucking Inc.....713 673-3844
9640 Clinton Dr Houston (77029) ***(G-8559)***
Ally Wholesale Signs LLC.....830 438-2500
20540 Hwy 45 E Ste 115 St Bulverde (78163) ***(G-2553)***
Ally Wholesale Signs LLC (PA).....**830 438-2500**
300 Broyles Ln Bulverde (78163) ***(G-2554)***
Alm Media LLC.....214 744-9300
1999 Bryan St Dallas (75201) ***(G-3928)***
Almeda Cultured Marble, Houston *Also called West U Marble LLC* ***(G-12636)***
Alnc Inc.....325 658-3612
2152 Fm Hwy 2105 San Angelo (76902) ***(G-17774)***
Aloe Farms Inc (PA).....**956 425-1289**
3102 Wilson Rd Harlingen (78552) ***(G-8177)***
Aloe Laboratories Inc.....956 428-8416
5821 E Harrison Ave Harlingen (78550) ***(G-8178)***
Aloe Queen Inc.....956 631-8869
2601 Zinnia Ave McAllen (78504) ***(G-14834)***
Aloe Vera of America Inc (PA).....**214 355-5400**
13745 Jupiter Rd Dallas (75238) ***(G-3929)***
Aloe Vera of America Inc.....956 585-9704
1401 N Inspiration Blvd Alton (78573) ***(G-321)***
Aloecorp Inc.....956 223-6931
701 Vogel Dr Mercedes (78570) ***(G-15001)***
Alon Usa LP.....432 263-7661
200 Refinery Rd Big Spring (79720) ***(G-2069)***
Alon USA Partners LP.....972 367-3600
12700 Park Central Dr # 1600 Dallas (75251) ***(G-3930)***
Aloterra Energy LLC (PA).....**713 412-5311**
2002 Timberloch Pl # 420 The Woodlands (77380) ***(G-19823)***
Aloterra Packaging LLC (PA).....**440 689-0986**
2002 Timberloch Pl # 420 The Woodlands (77380) ***(G-19824)***
Alpa Precision LLP.....713 680-8556
1819 Antoine Dr Houston (77055) ***(G-8560)***
Alpa Precision Mch Works Inc.....713 680-8556
1819 Antoine Dr Houston (77055) ***(G-8561)***
Alpar Energy LP.....806 435-6566
320 Se 24th Ave Perryton (79070) ***(G-16632)***
Alpha Circuits Incorporated.....281 980-2800
4855 Alpine Dr Ste 100 Stafford (77477) ***(G-19283)***
Alpha Door and Rail Inc.....817 358-8687
110 Aurora Vista Trl Aurora (76078) ***(G-853)***
Alpha Fabricators Inc.....713 694-1392
18900 E Industrial Pkwy New Caney (77357) ***(G-15834)***
Alpha Foods Co.....936 372-5858
19802 G H Cir Waller (77484) ***(G-20491)***
Alpha Graphics 544, Fort Worth *Also called Great Southwest Ventures LLC* ***(G-6674)***
Alpha Labs Inc.....806 744-1960
101 Sherman Ave Lubbock (79415) ***(G-14359)***
Alpha Laser Recharge Inc.....713 861-2425
821 Hodgkins St Ste B Houston (77032) ***(G-8562)***
Alpha Lubricants LLC.....214 971-1170
415 Walker St Sealy (77474) ***(G-18804)***
Alpha Mar-Imw, Houston *Also called MPW Corporation* ***(G-10931)***
Alpha Masurement Solutions LLC (PA).....**832 456-4100**
10540 Rockley Rd Houston (77099) ***(G-8563)***
Alpha Omega Intruments, Houston *Also called Cosa Xentaur Corporation* ***(G-9327)***
Alpha Omega Recycling Inc.....903 297-7272
315 Whatley Rd Longview (75604) ***(G-14192)***
Alpha Plastics Inc.....281 564-8838
5819 Mogo Creek Ln Sugar Land (77479) ***(G-19441)***
Alpha Ready Mix LLC.....512 846-2221
212 Investment Loop Hutto (78634) ***(G-12875)***
Alpha Satcom Inc.....903 238-8888
1221 Judson Rd Ste 300 Longview (75601) ***(G-14193)***
Alpha Tech International Inc.....281 240-8989
12701 Executive Dr # 604 Stafford (77477) ***(G-19284)***
Alpha Waterjet Machining, Aurora *Also called Alpha Door and Rail Inc* ***(G-853)***
Alphabet McD Division.....915 593-2011
7 Zane Grey St Ste A El Paso (79906) ***(G-5642)***
AlphaGraphics, The Woodlands *Also called Dunphy Graphics Solutions Inc* ***(G-19854)***
AlphaGraphics, Arlington *Also called Sorita Enterprises Inc* ***(G-783)***
AlphaGraphics, Conroe *Also called Shakun Solutions LLC* ***(G-3363)***
AlphaGraphics, Dallas *Also called Somani Texas Inc* ***(G-4980)***
AlphaGraphics, Spring *Also called Perfect Ink Inc* ***(G-19157)***
AlphaGraphics, Carrollton *Also called Vastav Inc* ***(G-2894)***
AlphaGraphics, Dallas *Also called Printdallas Inc* ***(G-4826)***
AlphaGraphics, Dallas *Also called Imagery Marketing Design Inc* ***(G-4489)***
AlphaGraphics, Plano *Also called Girard Investments Inc* ***(G-16880)***
AlphaGraphics, Fort Worth *Also called M L Holdings Inc* ***(G-6803)***
AlphaGraphics, Austin *Also called Cedrone OBrien Inc* ***(G-1036)***
AlphaGraphics, Carrollton *Also called Hewell Enterprises Inc* ***(G-2869)***
AlphaGraphics, San Antonio *Also called Abbott Tl Investments LLC* ***(G-17854)***
AlphaGraphics 103, Richardson *Also called Spotted Dog Printing Inc* ***(G-17401)***
AlphaGraphics 391, Addison *Also called Meera Enterprises Inc* ***(G-148)***
AlphaGraphics Willowbrook.....281 890-0200
17126 Stuebner Airline Rd Spring (77379) ***(G-19099)***
Alphagrphics Bryan/College Stn, Bryan *Also called Tops Printing Inc* ***(G-2512)***

Alphatrust Corporation.....214 234-9200
8226 Douglas Ave Ste 625 Dallas (75225) ***(G-3931)***
Alpine Drinking Water, Richardson *Also called Summit Springs Bottled Water* ***(G-17403)***
Alps Electric North Amer Inc.....956 217-6500
7100 Intl Pkwy Ste 100 Mcallen (78503) ***(G-14835)***
Als Associates.....817 921-2679
2829 Bryan Ave Fort Worth (76104) ***(G-6373)***
Als Empirica, Houston *Also called Empirica LLC* ***(G-9620)***
Als Inc.....361 325-2154
3660 E Highway 285 Falfurrias (78355) ***(G-6181)***
Als Welding, Falfurrias *Also called Als Inc* ***(G-6181)***
Alsay Incorporated.....210 628-1090
3359 Se Loop 410 San Antonio (78222) ***(G-17900)***
Alta Marcellus Development LLC.....713 759-1155
500 Dallas St Ste 2930 Houston (77002) ***(G-8564)***
Alta Mesa Holdings LP (HQ).....**281 530-0991**
4119 Montrose Blvd # 230 Houston (77006) ***(G-8565)***
Alta Mesa Resources Inc (PA).....**214 647-7630**
2101 Cedar Springs Rd # 1100 Dallas (75201) ***(G-3932)***
Alta Operating, Houston *Also called Alta Resources LLC* ***(G-8566)***
Alta Resources, Houston *Also called Ard Operating LLC* ***(G-8687)***
Alta Resources LLC (PA).....**713 759-1155**
500 Dallas St Ste 2920 Houston (77002) ***(G-8566)***
Alta Resources Development LLC.....713 759-1155
1 Allen Ctr 500 Dllas S Houston (77002) ***(G-8567)***
Altair Company, The, Richardson *Also called Richardson Trident Company LLC* ***(G-17390)***
Altec Industries Inc.....713 336-6230
6902 E Orem Dr Houston (77075) ***(G-8568)***
Altec Industries Inc.....972 937-8284
1001 Solon Rd Waxahachie (75165) ***(G-20526)***
Alteca LLC.....956 423-1885
25691 Altas Palmas Rd Harlingen (78552) ***(G-8179)***
Altech Controls Corporation.....281 207-2775
13203 Stafford Rd Ste 500 Missouri City (77489) ***(G-15575)***
Altech Machine Shop Inc.....817 718-8824
396 Goshen Rd Springtown (76082) ***(G-19271)***
Alterman Energy Services Inc.....210 496-6888
14703 Jones Maltsberger San Antonio (78247) ***(G-17901)***
Alternative Business Services, Lubbock *Also called ABS Printing Services* ***(G-14356)***
Alternative Cutting Methods.....817 927-3332
120 E Felix St Ste 310 Fort Worth (76115) ***(G-6374)***
Alterstart Systems Inc.....214 330-2277
4919 W Davis St Dallas (75211) ***(G-3933)***
Altium Packaging.....281 391-4244
27807 Highway Blvd Katy (77494) ***(G-13349)***
Altium Packaging.....817 491-9229
5651 Alliance Gateway Fwy # 1 Fort Worth (76177) ***(G-6375)***
Altium Packaging.....214 333-4179
4525 Joseph Hardin Dr # 101 Dallas (75236) ***(G-3934)***
Altium Packaging.....903 870-7080
4201 S Us Highway 75 Sherman (75090) ***(G-18905)***
Altium Packaging LP.....678 742-4600
6831 Silsbee St Houston (77033) ***(G-8569)***
Altivia Chemicals LLC (PA).....**713 658-9000**
1100 La St Ste 4800 Houston (77002) ***(G-8570)***
Altivia Corporation (HQ).....**713 658-9000**
1100 La St Ste 4800 Houston (77002) ***(G-8571)***
Altivia Specialty Chem LLC (HQ).....**713 658-9000**
1100 La St Ste 4800 Houston (77002) ***(G-8572)***
Altivia Specialty Chem LLC.....713 658-9000
1901 W H St La Porte (77571) ***(G-13720)***
Altlite LLC.....469 767-1959
11520 N Cntl Expy Ste 154 Dallas (75243) ***(G-3935)***
Altman & Nelson Prtg Co Inc.....361 575-3118
2407 N Laurent St Victoria (77901) ***(G-20238)***
Altus Health System.....409 554-0131
390 N 11th St Beaumont (77702) ***(G-1850)***
Altus Intervention USA Inc (HQ).....**346 231-0060**
15150 Sommermeyer St Houston (77041) ***(G-8573)***
Aluf Plastics Texas Division, Sulphur Springs *Also called API Industries Inc* ***(G-19579)***
Aluma Graphics LP (PA).....**972 442-3299**
103 Security Ct Wylie (75098) ***(G-20925)***
Aluminum Metal Products Inc.....806 745-6026
6802 Martin L King Blvd Lubbock (79404) ***(G-14360)***
Aluminum Mint Systems Txas Inc.....713 522-8925
7777 Parnell St Houston (77021) ***(G-8574)***
Aluminum Tank & Tank ACC Inc.....817 378-8455
2702 N Nichols St Ste B Fort Worth (76106) ***(G-6376)***
Aluminum Techniques Inc.....281 499-9026
13302 Redfish Ln Stafford (77477) ***(G-19285)***
Alvarez & Marsal Inc.....212 759-4433
700 Louisiana St Ste 3300 Houston (77002) ***(G-8575)***
Alvin Emile Maxwell, Lancaster *Also called Big Shot LLC* ***(G-13840)***
Alvin J Bart & Sons Inc.....718 417-1300
4130 Lindbergh Dr Addison (75001) ***(G-103)***
Alvin Sun & Advertiser Inc.....281 331-4421
570 Dula St Alvin (77511) ***(G-351)***
Alvin Sun, The, Alvin *Also called Alvin Sun & Advertiser Inc* ***(G-351)***

ALPHABETIC

Always Integrity Machining LLC 512 670-1010
  16800 Radholme Ct Ste A Round Rock (78664) **(G-17622)**

Always Printing Inc 512 250-5056
  13200 Pond Springs Rd A101 Austin (78729) **(G-1689)**

Alx Imaging LLC 210 651-5000
  7000 Fm 466 Seguin (78155) **(G-18824)**

Aly Centrifuge Inc 972 382-4400
  5039 N Chadbourne St San Angelo (76903) **(G-17775)**

Alyta International Corp (PA) 972 978-1980
  1511 Bethlehem Rd Allen (75002) **(G-249)**

Am-Mex Products Inc (PA) 956 631-7916
  3801 W Military Hwy McAllen (78503) **(G-14836)**

AMA Printing / Finishing Inc (PA) 254 776-8860
  920 N Valley Mills Dr Waco (76710) **(G-20359)**

Amacs, Houston Also called Amistco Separation Pdts Inc **(G-8373)**

Amacs Process Tower Internals 713 434-0934
  14211 Industry St Houston (77053) **(G-8372)**

Amaida Machine Shop LLC 956 287-8824
  919 N 10th Ave Ste C Edinburg (78541) **(G-5574)**

Amarillo Custom Box Co (HQ) **806 371-9111**
  1501 S Johnson St Amarillo (79101) **(G-393)**

Amarillo Depot, Amarillo Also called Nuco2 Supply LLC **(G-503)**

Amarillo Elc Specialists Inc 806 372-3798
  2620 Tee Anchor Blvd Amarillo (79104) **(G-394)**

Amarillo Gear Company LLC (HQ) **806 622-1273**
  2401 W Sundown Ln Amarillo (79118) **(G-478)**

Amarillo Globe Times, Amarillo Also called Morris Communications Co LLC **(G-447)**

Amarillo Litho Inc 806 372-2245
  2400 Sw 7th Ave Amarillo (79106) **(G-395)**

Amarillo Mop & Broom Co Inc 806 372-8596
  1712 Se 27th Ave Amarillo (79103) **(G-396)**

Amarillo Plant, Amarillo Also called Asarco LLC **(G-401)**

Amarillo Plstic Fbricators Ltd 806 372-1207
  305 S Jefferson St Amarillo (79101) **(G-397)**

Amarillo Sperior Ironworks Inc 806 331-9353
  1203 Sw 5th Ave Amarillo (79101) **(G-398)**

Amarillo Transmission, Amarillo Also called Grooms & Grooms Inc **(G-490)**

Amarillo Waterblasters Inc 806 352-2765
  4614 Mccarty Blvd Amarillo (79110) **(G-479)**

Amazing Wristbands, Houston Also called Amzg Products LLC **(G-8632)**

Ambar Inc 281 873-7600
  16825 Northchase Dr # 16 Houston (77060) **(G-8576)**

Ambassador Facility Svcs LLC 210 849-7677
  220 Country Vale Cibolo (78108) **(G-3061)**

Amber/Booth Inc 713 466-0003
  11930 Brittmoore Park Dr Houston (77041) **(G-8577)**

Ambernet Technologies Inc 972 707-4000
  3010 Lbj Fwy Fl 1200 Dallas (75234) **(G-3936)**

Ambiente Home Decor, San Antonio Also called Space Enterprises LLC **(G-18490)**

Ambiente Opco LLC (PA) **512 835-2299**
  2314 Rutland Dr Ste 205 Austin (78758) **(G-910)**

Ambiente Wine, Austin Also called Ambiente Opco LLC **(G-910)**

Ambion Inc (HQ) **512 651-0200**
  2130 Woodward St Ste 200 Austin (78744) **(G-911)**

Ambion Austin Finished Gds DC, Austin Also called Ambion Inc **(G-911)**

Ambion Diagnostics Inc 512 651-0200
  2150 Woodward St Ste 100 Austin (78744) **(G-912)**

Ambiq Micro Inc 512 879-2850
  6500 Rver Pl Blvd Bldg 7 Austin (78730) **(G-913)**

AMC Publishing LLC 512 380-1611
  5114 Balcones Woods Dr Austin (78759) **(G-914)**

Amco Enterprises, Fort Worth Also called Southwest Metrics Inc **(G-7004)**

Amco Steel Fabrication LLC 210 488-9023
  8051 S Loop 1604 E Elmendorf (78112) **(G-6066)**

Amcor Rigid Packaging Usa LLC 817 267-5917
  4324 Fleetwood Rd Fort Worth (76155) **(G-6377)**

Amdec Inc 214 654-0560
  4512 Bentley Dr Plano (75093) **(G-16784)**

Amec Foster Wheeler USA Corp (HQ) **713 929-5000**
  17325 Park Row Houston (77084) **(G-8578)**

Amera-Seiki Corporation 832 234-5960
  4213 N Frazier St Ste B1 Conroe (77303) **(G-3255)**

Ameri Source Manufacturing Inc 903 677-7734
  17785 Fm 773 Ben Wheeler (75754) **(G-2031)**

Ameri-Fab LLC 817 458-4262
  6364 W Interstate 20 Weatherford (76088) **(G-20575)**

Ameri-Tech Dist Inc (PA) **915 772-9090**
  5201 El Paso Dr El Paso (79905) **(G-5643)**

Ameribolt Inc 713 580-4997
  9506 Bamboo Rd Houston (77041) **(G-8579)**

America Empack Inc (PA) **956 618-3922**
  6401 S 36th St Bldg H28 McAllen (78503) **(G-14837)**

America Ilsin Tech LLC 972 556-0916
  3330 Earhart Dr Ste 208 Carrollton (75006) **(G-2696)**

America Industrial Pdts LLC 832 974-4153
  3880 Grnhse Rd Ste 427 Houston (77084) **(G-8580)**

America Plastics LLC 972 245-4525
  1420 Vinylex Dr Carrollton (75006) **(G-2697)**

America Samkwang Inc (PA) **956 686-0221**
  6801 S 33rd St Ste M McAllen (78503) **(G-14838)**

America Screen Graphics, Kingwood Also called Jackie Todaro **(G-13646)**

American A Lquide Holdings Inc (HQ) **713 624-8000**
  2700 Post Oak Blvd Houston (77056) **(G-8581)**

American Achievement Corp (HQ) **512 444-0571**
  1550 W Mockingbird Ln Dallas (75235) **(G-3937)**

American Achvement Group Holdg, Austin Also called AAC Group Holding Corp **(G-875)**

American Acryl LP 281 909-2600
  4631 Old Highway 146 B Pasadena (77507) **(G-16387)**

American Acryl Na LLC 281 909-2600
  4631 Old Highway 146 B Pasadena (77507) **(G-16388)**

American Acrylic Injection Inc 972 784-7759
  419 Welch Dr Farmersville (75442) **(G-6221)**

American Air Liquide Inc 877 855-9533
  9811 Katy Fwy Ste 100 Houston (77024) **(G-8582)**

American Air Services LLC 832 715-8025
  10925 Grant Rd 435 Houston (77070) **(G-8583)**

American Airboat Corporation 409 883-7725
  108 Lutcher Dr Orange (77632) **(G-16231)**

American Alloy Steel Inc (PA) **713 462-8081**
  6230 N Houston Rosslyn Rd Houston (77091) **(G-8584)**

American Animal Health Inc (PA) **817 293-6363**
  2619 Skyway Dr Grand Prairie (75052) **(G-7828)**

American Animal Health Inc 972 641-5420
  2619 Skyway Dr Grand Prairie (75052) **(G-7829)**

American Armtive Cmponents Inc 281 442-7791
  1733 Lauder Rd Houston (77039) **(G-8585)**

American Assn Notaries Inc 713 644-2299
  8027 Gulf Fwy Houston (77017) **(G-8586)**

American Blanket, Mansfield Also called Printers Service Florida Inc **(G-14704)**

American Block Company 281 820-5332
  5900 Bingle Rd Houston (77092) **(G-8587)**

American Block Company (PA) **800 572-9087**
  6311 Breen Dr Houston (77086) **(G-8588)**

American Block Company 281 820-5332
  7903 Breen Dr Houston (77064) **(G-8589)**

American Block Mfg Co, Houston Also called American Block Company **(G-8588)**

American Bottling Company 956 423-2705
  915 N Ed Carey Dr Harlingen (78550) **(G-8180)**

American Bottling Company 210 662-4400
  4518 Seguin Rd San Antonio (78219) **(G-17902)**

American Bottling Company 512 385-4477
  2120 Grand Avenue Pkwy # 20 Austin (78728) **(G-915)**

American Bottling Company 972 579-1024
  2304 Century Center Blvd Irving (75062) **(G-12928)**

American Bottling Company 903 893-6536
  1915 Us Highway 82 E Sherman (75090) **(G-18906)**

American Bottling Company 254 412-1900
  100 Aviation Pkwy Waco (76705) **(G-20360)**

American Bottling Company 972 721-8197
  2304 Century Center Blvd Irving (75062) **(G-12929)**

American Bottling Company 214 330-0491
  4350 Mint Way Dallas (75237) **(G-3938)**

American Bottling Company 361 851-9977
  3127 Cabaniss Rd Corpus Christi (78415) **(G-3472)**

American Bottling Company 713 799-1024
  2400 Holly Hall St Houston (77054) **(G-8590)**

American Bottling Company 409 842-6061
  7410 Frint Dr Beaumont (77705) **(G-1851)**

American Bottling Company 903 874-5666
  2401 S Business 45 Corsicana (75110) **(G-3660)**

American Bottling Company (HQ) **972 673-7000**
  5301 Legacy Dr Plano (75024) **(G-16785)**

American Bronze Alum Cast Corp 713 222-0236
  2408 Everett St Houston (77009) **(G-8591)**

American Building Supply Inc 469 322-8100
  350 Northpoint Dr Coppell (75019) **(G-3408)**

American Canopies, Gladewater Also called Heat Shield Inc **(G-7722)**

American Canvas, Friona Also called Campbell Trailers & Leasing **(G-7251)**

American Canvas Products Inc (PA) **817 429-3108**
  1319 N Main St Fort Worth (76164) **(G-6378)**

American Carports Inc 866 730-9865
  457 N Brdwy St Joshua (76058) **(G-13316)**

American Carton Company Inc 817 473-2992
  607 S Wisteria St Mansfield (76063) **(G-14655)**

American Cast-Stone Inc 817 695-1800
  3500 Avenue E E Arlington (76011) **(G-615)**

American Classifieds, Waco Also called Waco Publications Inc **(G-20476)**

American Classifieds 806 376-8663
  15097 S Dowell Rd Amarillo (79119) **(G-480)**

American Classifieds (PA) **254 771-2777**
  2905 W Adams Ave Temple (76504) **(G-19668)**

American Cmnty Newspapers LLC 972 424-6565
  624 Krona Dr Ste 170 Plano (75074) **(G-16786)**

American Coatings LP 281 351-1776
  10625 Mahaffey Rd Tomball (77375) **(G-19957)**

American Color Labs of Texas 210 308-0222
  981 Isom Rd San Antonio (78216) **(G-17903)**

American Commodities Inc (PA) 817 740-8326
3701 N Grove St Fort Worth (76106) (G-6379)

American Completion Tools Inc 281 894-5213
1255 Grand Plaza Dr Houston (77067) (G-8592)

American Completion Tools Inc (HQ) 817 790-6608
3084 S Burleson Blvd Burleson (76028) (G-2567)

American Concrete Products, Dallas Also called Enterprise Concrete Pdts LLC (G-4326)

American Cooling Tech Inc 717 767-2775
6630 E State Highway 114 Haslet (76052) (G-8215)

American Darling Valve, Beaumont Also called American Valve Hydrant Mfg Co (G-1852)

American Dawn Inc 713 670-8505
8505 North Loop E Ste 103 Houston (77029) (G-8593)

American Dehydrated Foods Inc 903 838-0366
Lone Star Army Amntn Plnt Hooks (75561) (G-8360)

American Denimatrix, Littlefield Also called Denimatrix LLC (G-14144)

American Distributing, Dallas Also called Dallco Marketing Inc (G-4231)

American Door Products Inc (PA) 713 681-8047
7967 Blankenship Dr Houston (77055) (G-8594)

American Dream Vction Rv Rentl, Austin Also called Kwest Rv LLC (G-1276)

American Duct Systems Inc 972 494-7300
601 E Walnut Cir Garland (75040) (G-7433)

American Eagle Enteprise 972 494-3357
3114 Benton St Garland (75042) (G-7434)

American Egle Mailbox Mfr Corp 214 358-2873
2618 Manana Dr Dallas (75220) (G-3939)

American Electro Optics LLC 817 546-0993
210 Shelby Rd Fort Worth (76140) (G-6380)

American Embryo Systems, Grand Prairie Also called American Animal Health Inc (G-7828)

American Engine & Grinding Co 713 224-5326
100 N Jackson St Houston (77002) (G-8595)

American Envircon Inc (PA) 214 634-1744
8305 Sovereign Row Dallas (75247) (G-3940)

American Excelsior Company 817 385-4300
900 Avenue H E Arlington (76011) (G-616)

American Extrusion Company 713 869-9551
9210 Emmott Rd Houston (77040) (G-8596)

American Fastsigns, Carrollton Also called Fastsigns International Inc (G-2736)

American Fence and Sup Co Inc 512 930-4000
3501 N Interstate 35 Georgetown (78628) (G-7634)

American Film & Printing Ltd 817 783-7600
502 E Shelton St Alvarado (76009) (G-323)

American Fincl Mktg Group Inc 866 679-9241
2600 S Shore Blvd Ste 300 League City (77573) (G-13945)

American Fluorite Inc 281 363-9161
1425 Lake Front Cir # 200 The Woodlands (77380) (G-19825)

American Friction Inc 713 818-5919
2401 Wilson Rd Humble (77396) (G-12745)

American Gasket Mfg Co Inc 214 388-0603
3828 Samuell Blvd Dallas (75228) (G-3941)

American Gear, Houston Also called American Mast Inc (G-8601)

American Gilsonite Company 713 400-7600
16200 Park Row Ste 250 Houston (77084) (G-8597)

American Grand Stand Inc 214 638-7007
8604 Chancellor Row Dallas (75247) (G-3942)

American Grandstands, Dallas Also called American Grand Stand Inc (G-3942)

American Green Technology Inc 269 340-9975
1301 Mckinney St Ste 5100 Houston (77010) (G-8598)

American Gypsum Company (HQ) 214 530-5500
5960 Berkshire Ln Ste 800 Dallas (75225) (G-3943)

American Hat Company, Bowie Also called Ahc Western Hatters Ltd Lblty (G-2190)

American Homestar Corporation (PA) 281 334-9700
2450 S Shore Blvd Ste 300 League City (77573) (G-13946)

American Homestar Lancaster LP (HQ) 281 334-9700
2450 S Shore Blvd Ste 300 League City (77573) (G-13947)

American Honda Motor Co Inc 972 929-5444
4525 W Royal Ln Irving (75063) (G-12930)

American Indus Mfrs Bldg Mate 214 254-4720
6505 W Park Blvd Plano (75093) (G-16787)

American Industrial Machine 432 366-3516
3401 N County Rd W Odessa (79764) (G-15913)

American Industrial Polymers 979 542-3654
1233 N Orange St Giddings (78942) (G-7691)

American Innovations Ltd (PA) 512 249-3400
12211 Technology Blvd Austin (78727) (G-916)

American Jereh Intl Corp 432 288-2431
7501 Miller Rd Ste 2 Houston (77049) (G-8599)

American Kart Mfg LLC 979 505-5076
707 Demel Ave Schulenburg (78956) (G-18771)

American Lea Operations LLC 972 296-8016
4501 Mountain Creek Pkwy Dallas (75236) (G-3944)

American Legend Aircraft, Sulphur Springs Also called Legend Aircraft Mfg LP (G-19591)

American Liberty Oil Co LP (PA) 972 932-2266
3725 W Us Highway 175 Kaufman (75142) (G-13457)

American Maatco Ltd 817 284-7222
2499 Austin Rd Richland Hills (76118) (G-17435)

American Made Solar Wind Tech, Weslaco Also called Mardel Souza Inc (G-20664)

American Maintenance Sups LLC 281 304-8369
15922 Cyprs N Hstn Rd Cypress (77429) (G-3771)

American Management, El Paso Also called Fox John (G-5773)

American Marazzi Tile Inc 972 232-3800
6313 Airport Fwy Ste A Fort Worth (76117) (G-6381)

American Marble Mosaic Company 713 747-7634
6314 Saint Augustine St Houston (77021) (G-8600)

American Masonry Supply Inc 817 695-1800
3500 Avenue E E Arlington (76011) (G-617)

American Mast Inc (PA) 713 643-4321
5400 Cedar Crest St Houston (77087) (G-8601)

American Materials, Stafford Also called G & S Asphalt Inc (G-19320)

American Materials Tech I LLC 281 345-0169
15821 Fm 529 Rd Ste 282 Houston (77095) (G-8602)

American Micro Systems Ltd 817 571-9015
2190 Regal Pkwy Euless (76040) (G-6130)

American Microsystems, Euless Also called American Micro Systems Ltd (G-6130)

American National Carbide Co 281 351-7165
915 S Cherry St Tomball (77375) (G-19958)

American Natural Resources Co (HQ) 832 320-5000
717 Texas St Ste 2400 Houston (77002) (G-8603)

American Paint Horse Assn 817 834-2742
122 E Exchange Ave Fort Worth (76164) (G-6382)

American Patriot Sales & Svcs, Willow City Also called Sanitz Enterprises Inc (G-20871)

American Permanent Ware Co 972 908-6100
1307 N Watters Rd Ste 180 Allen (75013) (G-250)

American Petroleum Welding Inc 806 747-7272
4002 N Fm 2528 Lubbock (79416) (G-14361)

American Plant Food Corp (PA) 713 675-2231
903 Mayo Shell Rd Galena Park (77547) (G-7376)

American Plant Food Corp 817 624-7132
3800 Deen Rd Fort Worth (76106) (G-6383)

American Plating Co Texas Ltd 281 452-4241
2421 Wadsworth St Houston (77015) (G-8604)

American Pole and Timber, Houston Also called Building Products Plus LLC (G-9016)

American Polymers Corp 817 684-7335
2100 Reliance Pkwy Bedford (76021) (G-1973)

American Pos Alliance LLC 817 350-4714
715 N Dove Rd Grapevine (76051) (G-8011)

American Powder Coating Corp 817 446-9400
5950 Tension Dr Fort Worth (76112) (G-6384)

American Printers Exchange Inc 512 452-5058
1606 Headway Cir Ste 100 Austin (78754) (G-917)

American Printing & Off Pdts 254 771-2422
4106 Eagle Rd Temple (76502) (G-19669)

American Printing and Mailing, Austin Also called American Printers Exchange Inc (G-917)

American Printing Industries (PA) 830 624-9000
1788 S Business Ih 35 New Braunfels (78130) (G-15773)

American Prtg & Promotions Inc 713 645-1991
6100 Skyline Dr Ste M Houston (77057) (G-8605)

American Pumping & Trucking, Victoria Also called Sparkman Well Service Inc (G-20305)

American Quartz LLC 214 243-6676
11129 Zodiac Ln Ste 300 Dallas (75229) (G-3945)

American Rail Car Coatings, Goodrich Also called American Railcar Inds Inc (G-7768)

American Railcar Inds Inc 903 759-4406
300 Stevens St Longview (75604) (G-14194)

American Railcar Inds Inc 903 759-3946
600 Foundry Dr Longview (75604) (G-14195)

American Railcar Inds Inc 281 471-1930
222 N 16th St La Porte (77571) (G-13721)

American Railcar Inds Inc 936 365-2679
1718 State Hwy Loop 393 Goodrich (77335) (G-7768)

American Rice Inc (HQ) 281 272-8800
10700 North Fwy Ste 800 Houston (77037) (G-8606)

American Rice Inc 979 233-8248
505 Port Rd Freeport (77541) (G-7191)

American Right Way Associates, Fort Worth Also called Trwa Inc (G-7083)

American Rockwool Mfg LLC (PA) 214 882-1343
1316 Village Creek Dr # 600 Plano (75093) (G-16788)

American Roller Company LLC 262 878-2445
14100 Westfair East Dr Houston (77041) (G-8607)

American Roller Company LLC 713 466-0550
14100 Westfair East Dr Houston (77041) (G-8608)

American Safety Services Inc (PA) 432 552-7625
8715 Andrews Hwy Odessa (79765) (G-15914)

American Safety Training, Austin Also called Mancomm Inc (G-1321)

American Sales, Laredo Also called JK Manufacturing Inc (G-13899)

American Screen Graphics & EMB 281 354-2581
1701 Park St Ste 15 Houston (77019) (G-8609)

American Sheet Metal Inc 281 999-5210
1110 Blue Bell Rd Houston (77038) (G-8610)

American Shredder Entps LLC 817 378-8511
3800 N Commerce St Fort Worth (76106) (G-6385)

American Signal Company, San Antonio Also called Short-Line Corporation (G-18470)

American Signal Corporation 414 358-8000
3524 Dividend Dr Garland (75042) (G-7435)

American Spincast 254 939-0292
2505 Taylors Valley Rd Belton (76513) (G-2018)

American Steam Inc 972 442-4499
49 Steel Rd Wylie (75098) (G-20926)

American Steel & Alum Co Inc 972 264-1533
  3545 E Main St Grand Prairie (75050) **(G-7830)**

American Steel Carports Inc (PA).........................**866 471-8761**
  457 N Broadway St Joshua (76058) **(G-13317)**

American Thermoplastics Corp 713 671-6900
  1235 Kress St Houston (77020) **(G-8611)**

American Thermowell Inc 409 246-1111
  4861 Paula Rd Kountze (77625) **(G-13668)**

American Tietek LLC 903 503-5538
  429 S Memory Ln Marshall (75670) **(G-14760)**

American Tire Distributors Inc 281 872-0397
  860 Greens Pkwy Ste 100 Houston (77067) **(G-8612)**

American Tire Distributors Inc 704 992-2000
  810 W Howard Ln Austin (78753) **(G-918)**

American Trailer Works, Richardson *Also called American Trailer World Corp* **(G-17269)**

American Trailer Works Inc (HQ) **817 328-3686**
  180 State St Ste 230 Southlake (76092) **(G-19058)**

American Trailer World Corp (HQ) **855 289-0001**
  1701 N Plano Rd Bldg 9 Richardson (75081) **(G-17269)**

American Trphy Hnters Assn Inc 210 523-8500
  326 Sterling Browning Rd # 101 San Antonio (78232) **(G-17904)**

American Truss Systems Inc 281 442-4584
  1502 Strawn Rd Houston (77039) **(G-8613)**

American Turf & Carpet, Flower Mound *Also called Signature Systems Group LLC* **(G-6281)**

American Valve Hydrant Mfg Co (HQ) **409 832-7721**
  3525 Hollywood St Beaumont (77701) **(G-1852)**

American Valve Hydrant Mfg Co 409 832-7721
  3350 Hollywood St Beaumont (77701) **(G-1853)**

American Vapor Company LLC 512 596-1892
  13400 Immanuel Rd Ste 2 Pflugerville (78660) **(G-16657)**

American Welding Services 409 440-8143
  5923 Delany Rd Hitchcock (77563) **(G-8333)**

American West Windmill Co 806 373-0478
  1701 Se 3rd Ave Amarillo (79102) **(G-399)**

American Whl Thermographers (HQ) **281 256-4100**
  12715 Telge Rd Cypress (77429) **(G-3772)**

American Whl Thermographers 713 896-9008
  12715 Telge Rd Cypress (77429) **(G-3773)**

American Wholesale Lbr & Mfg 281 342-7020
  9100 Kneitz Rd Needville (77461) **(G-15762)**

American Wire and Insul Sups, Lubbock *Also called Brandon & Clark Inc* **(G-14380)**

American Wldg Fabrication Inc 210 661-4159
  2301 Ackerman Rd San Antonio (78219) **(G-17905)**

American Wood Fibers Inc 903 923-8700
  6203 Fm 1998 Marshall (75672) **(G-14761)**

American Woodmark Corporation 469 635-1960
  1350 Lakeshore Dr Ste 160 Coppell (75019) **(G-3409)**

American Zebra Line, The, Houston *Also called American Prtg & Promotions Inc* **(G-8605)**

Americana Cabinets LLC 281 973-8255
  5839 Bender Rd Humble (77396) **(G-12746)**

Americas Odl, Houston *Also called Odl Inc* **(G-11131)**

Americas Styrenics LLC (HQ) **832 616-7800**
  24 Waterway Ave Ste 1200 The Woodlands (77380) **(G-19826)**

Americase Ennis, Ennis *Also called Americase Fbrication Cnstr LLC* **(G-6088)**

Americase Fbrication Cnstr LLC 972 910-2296
  1001 S Kaufman St Ennis (75119) **(G-6088)**

Americo Energy Resources LLC 713 984-9700
  7575 San Felipe St 200a Houston (77063) **(G-8614)**

Americom 936 344-9052
  555 State Rt 150 New Waverly (77358) **(G-15852)**

Ameridrives International LLC 512 353-4000
  2000 Clovis Barker Rd San Marcos (78666) **(G-18677)**

Ameridrives Power Transmission, San Marcos *Also called Ameridrives International LLC* **(G-18677)**

Ameriforge Corporation (HQ) **713 393-4200**
  945 Bunker Hill Rd # 500 Houston (77024) **(G-8615)**

Ameriforge Group Inc (PA) **713 393-4200**
  945 Bunker Hill Rd # 500 Houston (77024) **(G-8616)**

Ameriforge Group Inc 409 283-8138
  Hwy 69 Woodville (75979) **(G-20914)**

Amerig Solutions LLC 713 960-6606
  4265 San Felipe St Houston (77027) **(G-8617)**

Amerimax Building Products, Fort Worth *Also called Omnimax Holdings Inc* **(G-6881)**

Amerimex Motor & Controls LLC (HQ) **713 225-4300**
  610 N Milby St Houston (77003) **(G-8618)**

Amerimex Power Systems Inc 832 678-3520
  11902 Rockville Dr Houston (77064) **(G-8619)**

Ameripack Foods LLC 903 639-4007
  601 Fm 161 S Hughes Springs (75656) **(G-12738)**

Ameripower LLC (PA) **281 240-0405**
  2808 Grants Lake Blvd Sugar Land (77479) **(G-19442)**

Ameripro Partnership LP (PA) **713 526-3936**
  6566 Mcgrew St Houston (77087) **(G-8620)**

Amerisource Companies LP 972 380-2000
  2828 Trade Ctr Ste 110 Carrollton (75007) **(G-2856)**

Ameritek Design Inc 281 442-7767
  14203 Luthe Rd Houston (77039) **(G-8621)**

Ameritek Heat Treating and F 281 480-5637
  420 S 16th St La Porte (77571) **(G-13722)**

Ameritex Machine and Fab LLC 936 228-5070
  13391 E Fm 1097 Rd Willis (77378) **(G-20842)**

Ameritex Petroleum LLC 972 528-6644
  13140 Coit Rd Ste 510 Dallas (75240) **(G-3946)**

Ameritex Pipe & Products LLC 830 372-2300
  3960 E Us Highway 90 Seguin (78155) **(G-18825)**

Ameritrail Inc (PA) **281 375-5458**
  1005 S Front St Bellville (77418) **(G-2007)**

Ameron International Corp 940 569-1471
  400 N Sam Houston Pkwy E Houston (77060) **(G-8622)**

Ameron International Corp 940 569-1471
  1004 Ameron Rd Burkburnett (76354) **(G-2563)**

Ameron International Corp (HQ) **713 375-3700**
  7909 Parkwood Circle Dr Houston (77036) **(G-8623)**

Amerus Oilfield Solutions LLC 432 559-0843
  2306 N Fm 1788 Midland (79707) **(G-15114)**

Amfan Corporation 214 638-2451
  3443 Morse Dr Dallas (75236) **(G-3947)**

Amgis LLC 832 775-1319
  10899 Kinghurst Dr # 220 Houston (77099) **(G-8624)**

AMI Investments LLC 972 717-5555
  2304 Tarpley Rd Ste 110 Carrollton (75006) **(G-2698)**

Amigos Canning, San Antonio *Also called Durrset Amigos Ltd* **(G-18074)**

Amistco Separation Pdts Inc 281 331-5956
  14211 Industry St Houston (77053) **(G-8373)**

Amkin Technologies LLC 281 755-2046
  12320 Barker Cypress Rd Cypress (77429) **(G-3774)**

Amko International, Houston *Also called Joann Baik* **(G-10478)**

Amkor Technology Inc 512 953-0701
  8140 N Mopac Expy Ste 150 Austin (78759) **(G-919)**

Ammann America Inc 253 266-4023
  1900 West Loop S Ste 1550 Houston (77027) **(G-8625)**

Ammeraal Beltech Inc 972 647-8996
  1014 Santerre St Grand Prairie (75050) **(G-7831)**

Ammonia Services, Italy *Also called Green Industries Inc* **(G-13213)**

Ammr Services Inc 281 449-7162
  14410 Luthe Rd Ste 106 Houston (77039) **(G-8626)**

Amorphous Materials Inc 972 494-5624
  3130 Benton St Garland (75042) **(G-7436)**

Ampac Fine Chemicals Texas LLC 281 842-1459
  914 S 16th St La Porte (77571) **(G-13723)**

Ampco Services LLC 281 872-8324
  16945 Northchase Dr # 1950 Houston (77060) **(G-8627)**

Ampersand Art Supply Inc 512 322-0278
  1235 S Loop 4 Ste 400 Buda (78610) **(G-2519)**

Amphenol Corporation 214 547-2400
  1300 Cntl Expy N Ste 100 Allen (75013) **(G-251)**

Amphenol Fiber Systems, Allen *Also called Amphenol Corporation* **(G-251)**

Amphenol Fiber Systems Intl, Allen *Also called Fiber Systems Intl Inc* **(G-267)**

Amphion Inc 210 771-8116
  999 E Basse Rd Ste 180 San Antonio (78209) **(G-17906)**

Amplify Acquisitionco Inc 713 490-8900
  500 Dallas St Ste 1700 Houston (77002) **(G-8628)**

Amplify Energy Corp (PA) **713 490-8900**
  500 Dallas St Ste 1700 Houston (77002) **(G-8629)**

Amplify Energy Holdings LLC (HQ) **713 490-8900**
  500 Dallas St Ste 1600 Houston (77002) **(G-8630)**

Amplify Snack Brands Inc (HQ) **512 600-9893**
  500 W 5th St Ste 1350 Austin (78701) **(G-920)**

Amptec Research Corporation 512 858-4045
  13231 Rooster Springs Rd Austin (78737) **(G-856)**

Amran Inc 281 243-2200
  12320 Cardinal Mdw # 100 Sugar Land (77478) **(G-19443)**

Amran Instrument Transformers, Sugar Land *Also called Amran Inc* **(G-19443)**

Amrep Inc 972 227-3304
  525 E Centre Park Blvd Desoto (75115) **(G-5428)**

AMS, Austin *Also called Austin Mfg Svcs I Inc* **(G-956)**

AMS Acquisition Corp (PA) **512 491-7411**
  4616 W Howard Ln 5-550 Austin (78728) **(G-921)**

AMS Sensors USA Inc (HQ) **469 298-4252**
  5556 Tennyson Pkwy Plano (75024) **(G-16789)**

Amsr, Houston *Also called Bitcoin Crypto Crrncy Exch Cor* **(G-8895)**

Amst, Houston *Also called Aluminum Mint Systems Txas Inc* **(G-8574)**

Amstock Supply, Belton *Also called American Spincast Inc* **(G-2018)**

Amsty, The Woodlands *Also called Americas Styrenics LLC* **(G-19826)**

Amtech Manufacturing Inc 817 563-1251
  5129 Vesta Farley Rd Fort Worth (76119) **(G-6386)**

Amtex Corp (HQ) **972 276-7626**
  832 E Walnut St Garland (75040) **(G-7437)**

Amtex Prcision Fabrication Inc 281 489-7042
  3920 Bahler Ave Manvel (77578) **(G-14731)**

Amtopp Corporation (HQ) **361 874-3000**
  101 Interplast Blvd Lolita (77971) **(G-14173)**

Amweld International LLC 888 775-2397
  13901 Midway Rd Dallas (75244) **(G-3948)**

Amy Food Inc 713 910-5860
  3324 S Richey St Houston (77017) **(G-8631)**

Amy's, Houston *Also called Amy Food Inc* **(G-8631)**

(G-0000) Company's Geographic Section entry number

Amzg Products LLC 713 628-5504
   4025 Willowbend Blvd Houston (77025) *(G-8632)*

An Authorized Affiliate of PRI 817 430-6202
   1712 Lacy Dr Fort Worth (76177) *(G-6387)*

Ana-Log Inc 903 597-6341
   11067 Hwy 848 Tyler (75707) *(G-20046)*

Anadarko Algeria Corporation 832 636-1000
   1201 Lake Robbins Dr The Woodlands (77380) *(G-19827)*

Anadarko E&P Onshore LLC (HQ) **832 636-1000**
   1201 Lake Robbins Dr The Woodlands (77380) *(G-19828)*

Anadarko Energy Services Co 832 636-1000
   1201 Lake Robbins Dr The Woodlands (77380) *(G-19829)*

Anadarko Holding Company (HQ) 832 636-7200
   17001 Northchase Dr Houston (77060) *(G-8633)*

Anadarko Petroleum Corporation 432 684-2800
   10 Desta Dr Ste 650e Midland (79705) *(G-15115)*

Anadarko Petroleum Corporation 903 389-3814
   921 S Hgwy 75 Buffalo (75831) *(G-2542)*

Anadarko Petroleum Corporation (HQ) **832 636-1000**
   1201 Lake Robbins Dr The Woodlands (77380) *(G-19830)*

Anadarko Petroleum Corporation 979 828-1668
   3436 Fm 2096 Franklin (77856) *(G-7163)*

Anadarko Petroleum Corporation 979 567-7013
   206 S Wright St Caldwell (77836) *(G-2626)*

Anadarko Petroleum Corporation 817 877-7449
   4200 N Main St Bldg 27n Fort Worth (76106) *(G-6388)*

Anadarko Petroleum Corporation 830 491-3300
   4674 Us Hwy 277 N Gate Carrizo Springs (78834) *(G-2684)*

Anadarko US Offshore Corp 832 636-1000
   1201 Lake Robbins Dr The Woodlands (77380) *(G-19831)*

Anadite Cal Restoration Tr (PA) **817 282-9171**
   711 W Hurst Blvd Hurst (76053) *(G-12833)*

Anadrill Directional Svcs Inc 281 745-6983
   11757 Katy Fwy Ste 1300 Houston (77079) *(G-8634)*

Analog Devices Inc 512 427-1000
   6500 River Place Blvd # 1 Austin (78730) *(G-922)*

Analytcal Applied Slutions LLC 281 255-6537
   9515 Windfern Rd Houston (77064) *(G-8635)*

Analytic Stress Relieving Inc 361 883-0315
   1302 Cathead Rd Corpus Christi (78409) *(G-3473)*

Analytic Stress Relieving Inc 281 471-9600
   125 N 17th St La Porte (77571) *(G-13724)*

Analytical Instruments Corp 713 460-5757
   12621 Highway 105 W # 205 Conroe (77304) *(G-3256)*

Analytical Sensors Instrs LLC (HQ) **281 565-8818**
   10540 Rockley Rd Ste 100 Houston (77099) *(G-8636)*

Analytical Systems Intl, Houston *Also called Analytcal Applied Slutions LLC (G-8635)*

Analytical Systems Keco LLC 281 255-6537
   9515 Windfern Rd Houston (77064) *(G-8637)*

Anc Ion Coating Inc 281 207-0300
   12823 Trinity St Houston (77036) *(G-8638)*

Anchor Graphics Inc 972 422-4300
   3943 E University Dr McKinney (75069) *(G-14923)*

Anchor Graphics Marketing, McKinney *Also called Anchor Graphics Inc (G-14923)*

Anchor Industrial, Fort Worth *Also called Junction Industries LLC (G-6747)*

Anchor Industrial Services LLC 281 385-0607
   2707 Wadsworth St Houston (77015) *(G-8639)*

Anchor Machine Works Inc 713 988-0400
   6211 Evergreen St Houston (77081) *(G-8640)*

Anchor Texacone LLC 972 288-4404
   4111 Forney Rd Mesquite (75149) *(G-15026)*

Anco, Irving *Also called Chem-Aqua Inc (G-12969)*

Andalucia Nuts, Plainview *Also called Great Host International Inc (G-16755)*

Andalucia Nuts, Houston *Also called Great Host International Inc (G-10026)*

Andax Corp 972 392-3999
   4213 Wiley Post Rd Addison (75001) *(G-104)*

Andeavor, El Paso *Also called Western Refining Inc (G-6033)*

Andeavor, El Paso *Also called Western Refining Company LP (G-6035)*

Andeavor LLC (HQ) **210 626-6000**
   19100 Ridgewood Pkwy San Antonio (78259) *(G-17907)*

Andeavor Rio Holdings LLC (HQ) **281 566-3000**
   2150 Town Square Pl # 700 Sugar Land (77479) *(G-19444)*

Anderson Bean Boot Co Inc 956 565-2618
   1750 E Expy 83 Mercedes (78570) *(G-15002)*

Anderson Bean Boot Co Inc (HQ) **956 565-2618**
   105 S Vermont Ave Mercedes (78570) *(G-15003)*

Anderson Bean Boot Company, Mercedes *Also called Western Leather Goods Inc (G-15011)*

Anderson Merchandisers LLC (HQ) **972 987-5516**
   5601 Gran Pkwy Ste 1400 Plano (75024) *(G-16790)*

Anderson Mud Logging Service 903 693-5817
   1401 Hills Lake Rd Carthage (75633) *(G-2898)*

Anderson Oil Ltd (PA) **713 652-5746**
   5005 Woodway Dr Ste 300 Houston (77056) *(G-8641)*

Anderson Perforating Ltd 830 569-1120
   101055 Ih 37 Pleasanton (78064) *(G-17061)*

Anderson Software LLC 936 569-0447
   1645 Harper Rd Kerrville (78028) *(G-13518)*

Andersons Inc 913 748-4401
   20615 Interstate 35 S Lytle (78052) *(G-14572)*

Andersons Lytle Grain, The, Lytle *Also called Andersons Inc (G-14572)*

Anderton Castings LLC 254 938-2541
   222 Lely Dr Troy (76579) *(G-20027)*

Anderton Group II Ltd (PA) **254 751-1012**
   700 W Loop 340 Waco (76712) *(G-20361)*

Anderton Group Inc (PA) **254 751-1012**
   700 W Loop 340 Waco (76712) *(G-20362)*

Andrew & Associates 713 471-0922
   5103 Heathercrest St Houston (77045) *(G-8642)*

Andrew Solutions, Mission *Also called Commscope Technologies LLC (G-15551)*

Andrews Anchors & Service, Andrews *Also called Superior Welding Inc (G-559)*

Andrews County News 432 523-2085
   210 E Broadway St Andrews (79714) *(G-533)*

Andrews Fabrication Inc 281 372-0440
   1528 Mooney Rd Houston (77093) *(G-8643)*

Andrews Pump & Supply Inc (PA) **432 523-2166**
   507 Nw Mustang Dr Andrews (79714) *(G-534)*

Andrews Pump & Supply Inc 806 592-4567
   1115 W Broadway St Denver City (79323) *(G-5414)*

Andrews Safety Anchors Inc 432 524-6659
   1200 Se Mustang Dr Andrews (79714) *(G-535)*

Andritz Separation Inc 903 856-0445
   110 Dickson St Pittsburg (75686) *(G-16743)*

Android Industries LLC 972 343-3300
   3408 E Randol Mill Rd Arlington (76011) *(G-618)*

Andy Garcia Foods, San Antonio *Also called Garcia Foods Inc (G-18136)*

Angel Sword Corp 512 847-9679
   350 Jennifer Ln Driftwood (78619) *(G-5498)*

Angelina Steel Inc 936 634-6649
   1702 N Raguet St Lufkin (75904) *(G-14520)*

Angelina Tank & Manufacturing, Lufkin *Also called 2011 Angelina Mfg LLC (G-14519)*

Angelo Bolt and Indus Sup Inc 325 655-0075
   808 Warehouse Rd San Angelo (76903) *(G-17776)*

Angelo Pellets Inc (PA) **325 655-5751**
   1111 N Bell St San Angelo (76903) *(G-17777)*

Angelo Pellets Feed Mill, San Angelo *Also called Angelo Pellets Inc (G-17777)*

Angiotech, Athens *Also called Medical Device Tech Inc (G-831)*

Angus Measurement Services LP (PA) **432 332-7200**
   3800 Nw Loop 338 Odessa (79764) *(G-15915)*

Anheuser-Busch LLC 713 670-1629
   775 Gellhorn Dr Houston (77029) *(G-8644)*

Anheuser-Busch LLC 713 675-2311
   8657 Market St Houston (77029) *(G-8645)*

Animal Customs, Laredo *Also called Animal Paintball LLC (G-13858)*

Animal Paintball LLC 956 753-8272
   5460 Springfield Ave # 106 Laredo (78041) *(G-13858)*

Animal Science Products Inc 936 560-0003
   3418 Rayburn Dr Nacogdoches (75961) *(G-15685)*

Animas Well Services, Houston *Also called Cogent Energy Services LLC (G-9238)*

Ankem Chemicals, Farmers Branch *Also called Ankem of Texas Inc (G-6186)*

Ankem of Texas Inc 903 802-7133
   3500 Garden Brook Dr Farmers Branch (75234) *(G-6186)*

Anko Products Company of Texas 972 227-4466
   146 Industrial St Lancaster (75134) *(G-13837)*

Anmar Enterprises Inc 915 772-7488
   7 Leigh Fisher Blvd El Paso (79906) *(G-5644)*

Annapurna Solutions LLC 916 905-3144
   5000 Gulf Fwy Houston (77023) *(G-8646)*

Annex Manufacturing LLC 817 293-8762
   1801 Waters Ridge Dr Lewisville (75057) *(G-14021)*

Anodico Corporation 713 690-6100
   5900 Frbanks N Houston Rd Houston (77040) *(G-8647)*

Anodics Inc 817 281-2743
   4105 Murray Ave Fort Worth (76117) *(G-6389)*

Anova Industrials 281 494-8896
   10905 Cash Rd Stafford (77477) *(G-19286)*

Ans-Plano-Manufacturing, Plano *Also called Advanced Nrmdltion Systems Inc (G-16775)*

Ansca Mobile, Austin *Also called Corona Labs Inc (G-1067)*

Ansung-Usa LLC 469 877-5242
   5200 E Grand Ave Ste 505 Dallas (75223) *(G-3949)*

Ant Enterprises Incorporated 281 456-7446
   8602 Tri City Beach Rd Baytown (77523) *(G-1778)*

Antares U S A, Spring *Also called Supply Chain Solutions Ltd (G-19169)*

Antelope Oil Tools & Mfg Co, Spring *Also called Benchmark Completions LLC (G-19200)*

Antelope Refining LLC 713 860-2746
   919 Milam St Ste 2100 Houston (77002) *(G-8648)*

Antenna Products Corporation 940 325-3301
   101 Se 25th Ave Mineral Wells (76067) *(G-15518)*

Anthera Pharmaceuticals Inc 510 856-5600
   700 Milam St Ste 1300 Houston (77002) *(G-8649)*

Anthony Machine, San Antonio *Also called DSA Operating Company LLC (G-18072)*

Antiquestone Inc 512 355-2722
   330 N Lampasas St Bertram (78605) *(G-2051)*

Anton Cabinetry, Pantego *Also called Southwest Cabinet Corporation (G-16352)*

Antx Inc 512 255-2800
   3005 Glacier Pass Cedar Park (78613) *(G-2960)*

Anue Systems Inc..512 600-5400
  8310 N Cptl Tx Hwy # 300 Austin (78731) *(G-923)*

Anvil International LLC.....................................800 451-4414
  1401 Valley View Ln # 150 Irving (75061) *(G-12931)*

Anything Goes Enterprises LLC........................210 608-1741
  1330 Pinnacle Fls San Antonio (78260) *(G-17908)*

Anzures Welding Roustabout A.........................432 385-4122
  5742 W Turner St Odessa (79763) *(G-15916)*

AOC, Allen *Also called Finisar Corporation (G-268)*

Aoi, Sugar Land *Also called Applied Optoelectronics Inc (G-19445)*

AP Fullerton, College Station *Also called Beckman Coulter Inc (G-3177)*

APAC, Dallas *Also called Texas Materials Group Inc (G-5076)*

APAC, Beaumont *Also called Crh Americas Materials Inc (G-1878)*

APAC International Inc.....................................940 696-2525
  6308 Seymour Hwy Wichita Falls (76310) *(G-20738)*

Apache Construction Inc.................................903 839-2242
  905 State Highway 110 N Whitehouse (75791) *(G-20725)*

Apache Corporation (PA)................................713 296-6000
  2000 Post Oak Blvd Ste 10 Houston (77056) *(G-8650)*

Apache Corporation..432 524-2277
  209 Nw 12th St Andrews (79714) *(G-536)*

Apache Corporation..713 296-6000
  303 Veterans Airpark Ln # 3000 Midland (79705) *(G-15116)*

Apache Corporation..325 835-2323
  301 Ranch Rd 2469 Mertzon (76941) *(G-15019)*

Apache Corporation..432 558-2065
  1 Mile N Of Crane Hwy 385 Crane (79731) *(G-3697)*

Apache Corporation..432 558-2572
  8602 Exxon Loop Crane (79731) *(G-3698)*

Apache Corporation..800 272-2434
  2000 Post Oak Blvd # 100 Houston (77056) *(G-8651)*

Apache Corporation..713 296-6000
  2000 Post Oak Blvd # 100 Houston (77056) *(G-8652)*

Apache Corporation..806 229-3010
  3749 Sagebrush Rd Sundown (79372) *(G-19611)*

Apache Corporation..806 755-2231
  1811 County Road 690 Welch (79377) *(G-20654)*

Apache Corporation..806 234-2058
  2811 N State Road 168 Lubbock (79407) *(G-14362)*

Apache Corporation..979 543-4391
  9625 Pierce Ranch Rd El Campo (77437) *(G-5610)*

Apache Crude Oil Marketing............................713 296-6000
  2000 Post Oak Blvd # 100 Houston (77056) *(G-8653)*

Apache Deepwater LLC....................................713 296-6000
  2000 Post Oak Blvd Ste 10 Houston (77056) *(G-8654)*

Apache Drilling, Houston *Also called Apache Corporation (G-8652)*

Apache Fabricators LLC...................................832 804-6236
  8101 E Houston Rd Houston (77028) *(G-8655)*

Apache Foundation..713 296-6000
  2000 Post Oak Blvd B100 Houston (77056) *(G-8656)*

Apache Gathering Company.............................713 296-6000
  2000 Post Oak Blvd # 100 Houston (77056) *(G-8657)*

Apache Global Painting Inc (PA).....................713 450-9307
  9011 Sheldon Rd Houston (77049) *(G-8658)*

Apache Industrial Painting, Houston *Also called Apache Global Painting Inc (G-8658)*

Apache Instrmntation Gen Cnstr, Fort Stockton *Also called Apache Instrumentations & Gas (G-6327)*

Apache Instrumentations & Gas (PA)...............432 336-7755
  4501 N State Highway 18 Fort Stockton (79735) *(G-6327)*

Apache International LLC.................................713 296-6000
  2000 Post Oak Blvd Ste 10 Houston (77056) *(G-8659)*

Apache Offshore, Houston *Also called Apache Corporation (G-8651)*

Apache Packers LLC..432 758-6202
  344 County Road 306 Seminole (79360) *(G-18880)*

Apache Products Inc.......................................409 385-7021
  1012 John Hare Rd Silsbee (77656) *(G-18949)*

Apache Refinery Svcs Intl LLC.........................936 890-8586
  10301 Farrell Rd Willis (77378) *(G-20843)*

Apache Rifleworks, Comfort *Also called Psd3 Enterprises LLC (G-3240)*

Apache Sign & Service Inc...............................713 462-3220
  4125 Hollister St Houston (77080) *(G-8660)*

Apache Steel Works LLC..................................832 473-4525
  7410 Apache St Houston (77028) *(G-8661)*

Apani Southwest, Abilene *Also called Drink A Pak Inc (G-38)*

Apani Southwest Inc.......................................325 690-1550
  5401 N 1st St Abilene (79603) *(G-13)*

Apartment Furnishings Co Inc..........................817 568-2002
  1200 W Risinger Rd Fort Worth (76134) *(G-6390)*

Apci Inc..817 927-5362
  3129 May St Fort Worth (76110) *(G-6391)*

Apco Building Specialties Inc..........................915 581-6005
  4737 Osborne Dr El Paso (79922) *(G-5645)*

Ape Piling Products, LLC, Magnolia *Also called Pileworks LLC (G-14620)*

Apergy, Odessa *Also called Pcs Ferguson Inc (G-16108)*

Apergy Artfl Lift Intl LLC.................................903 266-3552
  12424 Hwy 64 W Tyler (75704) *(G-20047)*

Apergy Artfl Lift Intl LLC (HQ).......................281 403-5742
  2445 Tech Frest Blvd Ste Spring (77381) *(G-19195)*

Apergy Artfl Lift Intl LLC.................................713 466-3552
  11122 W Little York Rd Houston (77041) *(G-8662)*

Apergy Artfl Lift Intl LLC.................................281 602-2176
  2445 Tech Forest Blvd Spring (77381) *(G-19196)*

Apex, Houston *Also called Atlas Ptro Explrtion Worldwide (G-8745)*

Apex Coil LLC..903 843-4534
  204 Dean St Gilmer (75644) *(G-7705)*

Apex Custom Software Inc...............................214 725-9792
  3512 Balbirnie Ct The Colony (75056) *(G-19809)*

Apex Intl Enrgy MGT LLC.................................832 770-6900
  1300 Post Oak Blvd Houston (77056) *(G-8663)*

Apex Plastics & Tooling Inc.............................972 205-9000
  3625 Miller Park Dr Ste A Garland (75042) *(G-7438)*

Apex Sign Group, San Antonio *Also called Southwest Sign Group Inc (G-18489)*

Apex Software Solutions Inc............................210 699-6666
  5139 Beckwith Blvd # 109 San Antonio (78249) *(G-17909)*

Apex/Fcc LLC..830 875-2429
  2200 E Pierce St Luling (78648) *(G-14559)*

Apha, Fort Worth *Also called American Paint Horse Assn (G-6382)*

Aphelion Checkfree, Houston *Also called Checkfree Corporation (G-9167)*

Aphthoria Solutions Inc...................................214 821-8607
  9125 Viscount Row Dallas (75247) *(G-3950)*

API, Sugar Land *Also called Accredo Packaging Inc (G-19436)*

API, Gainesville *Also called Advanced Pedestals Ltd (G-7333)*

API Industries Inc..845 365-2200
  1212 Elm St Sulphur Springs (75482) *(G-19579)*

API Precision Machining Inc............................214 748-4994
  617 W Commerce St Dallas (75208) *(G-3951)*

Apogee Semiconductor, Plano *Also called Tallannquest LLC (G-17020)*

Apollo Brands, Plano *Also called Mach Speed Holdings LLC (G-16917)*

Apollo Distributors, Houston *Also called Sbu Group LP (G-11763)*

Apollo Endosurgery Inc (PA)..........................512 279-5100
  1120 S Capital Of Texas H West Lake Hills (78746) *(G-20677)*

Apollo Perforators Inc....................................432 563-0891
  12801 W I 20 Odessa (79765) *(G-15917)*

Apollo Resources Intl Inc................................214 389-9800
  3001 Knox St Ste 403 Dallas (75205) *(G-3952)*

Apollo Separation Tech USA Inc.......................281 233-9600
  1111 Goodnight Trl Houston (77060) *(G-8664)*

Apolo Commercial LLC....................................956 688-8207
  899 S Castell Ave Ste 205 New Braunfels (78130) *(G-15774)*

Apparel Art, El Paso *Also called Lown Brothers Inc (G-5848)*

Apparel Group Ltd (HQ).................................214 469-3300
  883 Trinity Dr Lewisville (75056) *(G-14022)*

Appco, San Antonio *Also called Aggregate Plant Products Co (G-17874)*

Apple Contractors, Houston *Also called Robert K Dean (G-11642)*

Apple Corrugated Packaging Inc.......................214 331-9000
  1346 N Main St Duncanville (75116) *(G-5528)*

Applegate Edm Inc...972 488-8997
  2405 Squire Pl Farmers Branch (75234) *(G-6187)*

Appleton Grp LLC...254 968-6071
  2150 W South Loop Stephenville (76401) *(G-19406)*

Appleton Grp LLC...214 349-2310
  11404 Pagemill Rd Dallas (75243) *(G-3953)*

Appleton Grp LLC...281 774-3700
  13639 Aldine Westfield Rd Houston (77039) *(G-8665)*

Appliance Controls Texas Corp.........................214 501-3880
  2734 W Kingsley Rd Ste J2 Garland (75041) *(G-7439)*

Applied Avionics Inc (PA)..............................817 451-1141
  3201 Sandy Ln Fort Worth (76112) *(G-6392)*

Applied Concepts Inc......................................972 398-3750
  855 E Collins Blvd Richardson (75081) *(G-17270)*

Applied Consultants Inc (PA).........................903 643-0956
  2100 N Eastman Rd Longview (75601) *(G-14196)*

Applied Cryo Technologies Inc (PA)................281 888-3884
  7150 Almeda Genoa Rd Houston (77075) *(G-8666)*

Applied Drilling Tech Inc.................................281 925-7100
  1311 Brdfeld Blvd Ste 110 Houston (77084) *(G-8667)*

Applied Geophysical Services..........................832 327-3408
  11490 Westheimer Rd # 800 Houston (77077) *(G-8668)*

Applied Magnets, Dallas *Also called Applied Services Corporation (G-3954)*

Applied Maintenance Spc Inc...........................409 994-5849
  34369 Us Highway 96 S Buna (77612) *(G-2559)*

Applied Materials Inc......................................512 272-7075
  8505 Cross Park Dr # 300 Austin (78754) *(G-924)*

Applied Materials Inc......................................469 340-7810
  1717 Firman Dr Ste 150 Richardson (75081) *(G-17271)*

Applied Materials Inc......................................512 845-1126
  10000 Spectrum Dr Austin (78717) *(G-1690)*

Applied Materials Inc......................................512 272-1000
  9700 E Highway 290 Austin (78724) *(G-925)*

Applied Optical Systems Inc............................972 509-1500
  1700 Capital Ave Ste 150 Plano (75074) *(G-16791)*

Applied Optics Center, Dallas *Also called Optex Systems Inc (G-4764)*

Applied Optoelectronics Inc (PA)....................281 295-1800
  13139 Jess Pirtle Blvd Sugar Land (77478) *(G-19445)*

Applied Rigaku Tech Inc..................................512 225-1796
  9825 Spectrum Dr Bldg 4 Austin (78717) *(G-1691)*

Applied Rubber Technology Inc..............936 760-4100
116a Industrial Ct Conroe (77301) *(G-3257)*

Applied Services Corporation..............972 432-6509
7523 Midbury Dr Dallas (75230) *(G-3954)*

Applied Software Tech Inc..............210 732-9212
10010 San Pedro Ave San Antonio (78216) *(G-17910)*

Applied Systems Engrg Inc..............817 249-4180
7510 Benbrook Pkwy Benbrook (76126) *(G-2037)*

Applied Training Resources Inc..............281 370-9540
6405 Cypresswood Dr # 250 Spring (77379) *(G-19100)*

Applied US Energy Inc..............713 466-1538
8790 West Rd Ste 100 Houston (77064) *(G-8669)*

Applied US Energy Inc..............432 689-0102
2904 S County Road 1250 Midland (79706) *(G-15117)*

Approach Mdstream Holdings LLC..............817 989-9000
1 Ridgmar Ctr 6500 W Fwy Fort Worth (76116) *(G-6393)*

Approach Resources I LP..............817 989-9000
6500 West Fwy Ste 900 Fort Worth (76116) *(G-6394)*

Approach Resources Inc (PA)..............817 989-9000
6500 West Fwy Ste 900 Fort Worth (76116) *(G-6395)*

Approach Resources Inc..............325 392-8900
638 State Hwy 163 N Ozona (76943) *(G-16278)*

Approach Services LLC..............817 989-9000
6500 West Fwy Ste 800 Fort Worth (76116) *(G-6396)*

Appsian, Dallas *Also called Greyheller LLC (G-4416)*

Appy Health Inc..............844 764-2779
8204 Elmbrook Dr Ste 228 Dallas (75247) *(G-3955)*

Aprima Financial Services, Richardson *Also called Aprima Medical Software Inc (G-17272)*

Aprima Medical Software Inc (HQ)..............214 466-8000
1010 E Arapaho Rd Ste 100 Richardson (75081) *(G-17272)*

APS Building Services Inc..............713 979-0720
11050 W Little York Rd P Houston (77041) *(G-8670)*

APS Industrial Services Inc..............817 385-5500
3430 Dalworth St Arlington (76011) *(G-619)*

APS Plastics, Tomball *Also called Advanced Precision Services LP (G-19954)*

APS Plastics LP..............281 290-9950
701 Suth Persimmon Ste 85 Tomball (77375) *(G-19959)*

APS Pressure Systems LLC (HQ)..............281 290-9950
701 S Persimmon St Ste 85 Tomball (77375) *(G-19960)*

Apsco, Amarillo *Also called Gicon Pumps & Equipment Ltd (G-428)*

Aptiv Services Us LLC..............956 366-4600
601 Joaquin Cavazos Rd Los Indios (78567) *(G-14349)*

Aptiv Services Us LLC..............915 783-4201
301 Vallecillo Rd Laredo (78045) *(G-13859)*

Aptiv Services Us LLC..............915 783-4200
48 Walter Jones Blvd El Paso (79906) *(G-5646)*

Aptiv Services Us LLC..............956 693-3300
13701 Fm 1472 Laredo (78045) *(G-13860)*

Aptiv Services Us LLC..............915 783-4769
48 Walter Jones Blvd El Paso (79906) *(G-5647)*

Aptiv Services Us LLC..............956 237-9066
8410 W Bob Bullock Loop Laredo (78045) *(G-13861)*

Aptiv Services Us LLC..............915 783-4787
48 Walter Jones Blvd D El Paso (79906) *(G-5648)*

Apw/Wyott Foodservice Eqp Co, Allen *Also called American Permanent Ware Co (G-250)*

Apx Plastics Inc..............817 275-3883
621 109th St Arlington (76011) *(G-620)*

Aqseptence Group Inc..............651 636-3900
515 Post Oak Blvd Houston (77027) *(G-8671)*

Aqua Cut, Grand Prairie *Also called Aquacut Inc (G-7832)*

Aqua Drill International LLC (PA)..............281 337-0900
1300 Fm 646 Rd W Dickinson (77539) *(G-5468)*

Aqua Electric Inc..............972 243-2162
11252 Goodnight Ln # 900 Dallas (75229) *(G-3956)*

Aqua Quality Water Systems..............210 493-4545
12015 Starcrest Dr San Antonio (78247) *(G-17911)*

Aqua Services, San Antonio *Also called Dynamic Downhole Services LLC (G-18075)*

Aqua Solutions Inc (PA)..............800 256-2586
6913 Highway 225 Deer Park (77536) *(G-5261)*

Aqua Swim Spas, Brownsville *Also called Rio Plastics Inc (G-2401)*

Aqua Transfer & Enrgy Svcs LLC..............903 874-4946
309 N Beaton St Corsicana (75110) *(G-3661)*

Aqua-Tech Electric, Dallas *Also called Aqua Electric Inc (G-3956)*

Aqua/Process Inc..............713 910-2977
125 Southbelt Indus Dr Houston (77047) *(G-8672)*

Aquacut Inc..............972 247-6288
1249 Avenue R Grand Prairie (75050) *(G-7832)*

Aquajet Manufacturing..............832 484-9244
18635 Telge Rd Cypress (77429) *(G-3775)*

Aquamarine Power Usa LLC..............972 606-2912
2005 Westfield St Grand Prairie (75050) *(G-7833)*

Aquaneers Corp..............956 727-1250
1211 San Dario Ave # 464 Laredo (78040) *(G-13862)*

Aquapharm Pchem LLC (PA)..............346 237-4300
3985 Us Hwy 287 N Latexo (75849) *(G-13942)*

Aquasana, Inc., Haltom City *Also called A O Smith Wtr Trtmnt N Amer (G-8131)*

Aquasol Controllers Inc (PA)..............713 683-6406
1707 Townhurst Dr Houston (77043) *(G-8673)*

Aquatic Co..............817 801-8300
1521 N Cooper St Ste 500 Arlington (76011) *(G-621)*

Aquatic Co..............972 227-6692
151 Industrial St Lancaster (75134) *(G-13838)*

Aquila & Priscilla Tentmakers..............254 848-4432
398 Cherokee Trl Waco (76712) *(G-20363)*

Aquila Drilling Co LP..............940 761-3153
2525 Kell Blvd Ste 405 Wichita Falls (76308) *(G-20739)*

Aquila Environmental LLC..............817 953-3171
509 Pecan St Ste 200 Fort Worth (76102) *(G-6397)*

Aquilan Technologies Inc..............512 751-4226
901 S Mo Pac Expy Austin (78746) *(G-926)*

Ar-Case Inc..............210 735-5175
1007 W Ashby Pl San Antonio (78212) *(G-17912)*

ARA Automotive Systems Inc..............214 537-1659
3405 Express Dr Garland (75041) *(G-7440)*

Arabella's, McKinney *Also called David McNeff Inc (G-14935)*

Aramark Services Inc..............512 602-1000
7171 Southwest Pkwy Austin (78735) *(G-927)*

Aramco Home Improvement LLC..............409 762-9652
208 Coconut St Galveston (77554) *(G-7387)*

Aranda Ironworks Inc..............956 722-5084
6201 Mcpherson Rd Unit 2 Laredo (78041) *(G-13863)*

Aransas Fuel LLC..............361 992-5223
5858 S Padre Island Dr Corpus Christi (78412) *(G-3474)*

Aravas Inc (HQ)..............512 614-1848
6836 Bee Caves Rd Bldg 3s Austin (78746) *(G-928)*

Aravive Inc (PA)..............936 355-1910
3730 Kirby Dr Ste 1200 Houston (77098) *(G-8674)*

Aravive Biologics Inc..............936 355-1910
3730 Kirby Dr Ste 1200 Houston (77098) *(G-8675)*

Arbin Corporation..............979 690-2751
762 Peach Creek Cut Off College Station (77845) *(G-3174)*

Arbin Instruments, College Station *Also called Arbin Corporation (G-3174)*

Arbin Instruments Inc..............979 690-2751
762 Peach Creek Cut Off College Station (77845) *(G-3175)*

Arbin Instruments LLC..............979 690-2751
762 Peach Creek Cut Off College Station (77845) *(G-3176)*

Arbol Publishing LP..............512 476-8636
2519 E 5th Street Austin (78702) *(G-929)*

Arbor Christian Academy, Amarillo *Also called Trinity Fellowship (G-515)*

Arbor Metals, Dallas *Also called Aap Metals LLC (G-3875)*

Arbor Renewable Gas LLC..............281 849-9834
1800 Bering Dr Ste 510 Houston (77057) *(G-8676)*

Arbor Resources LLC..............936 632-9914
3921 W State Highway 7 Pollok (75969) *(G-17091)*

ARC Designs Inc..............281 940-0430
11957 Fm 529 Rd Houston (77041) *(G-8677)*

ARC Document Solutions LLC (HQ)..............713 988-9200
6300 Gulfton St Houston (77081) *(G-8678)*

ARC Document Solutions LLC..............713 787-1244
16840 Barker Springs Rd Houston (77084) *(G-8679)*

ARC Marine LLC..............713 489-7719
2921 Windy Hollow Ln Dickinson (77539) *(G-5469)*

ARC Pressure Data Inc (PA)..............432 563-2371
3718 Warschun Rd Aubrey (76227) *(G-846)*

ARC Rite Welding & Fabrication..............830 774-6058
5555 W Us Highway 90 Del Rio (78840) *(G-5305)*

ARC Specialties Inc..............713 631-7575
1730 Stebbins Dr Houston (77043) *(G-8680)*

Arcanum Consulting, Carrollton *Also called Arcanum Corp (G-2857)*

Arcanum Corp..............214 507-3433
2918 Panorama Dr Carrollton (75007) *(G-2857)*

Arch Aluminum and GL Co Texas (PA)..............972 647-9230
930 W N Carrier Pkwy Grand Prairie (75050) *(G-7834)*

Archer, Victoria *Also called Qes Pressure Control LLC (G-20297)*

Archer Optx Inc..............972 722-1064
1208 Sigma Ct Rockwall (75087) *(G-17537)*

Archer Prod Cmpletion Svcs LLC..............281 951-4038
911 Regional Park Dr Houston (77060) *(G-8681)*

Archer The Well Company, Houston *Also called Archer Well Company Inc (G-8682)*

Archer Well Company Inc (HQ)..............713 856-4222
5510 Clara Rd Houston (77041) *(G-8682)*

Archer-Daniels-Midland Company..............325 356-2511
508 Moorman Rd Comanche (76442) *(G-3235)*

Archer-Daniels-Midland Company..............817 917-2810
425 Fairmount St Saginaw (76179) *(G-17736)*

Archer-Daniels-Midland Company..............806 723-5117
2300 E 50th St Lubbock (79404) *(G-14363)*

Archer-Daniels-Midland Company..............806 364-4732
3746 S Progressive Rd Hereford (79045) *(G-8283)*

Archer-Daniels-Midland Company..............214 357-3331
9965 Monroe Dr Dallas (75220) *(G-3957)*

Archer-Daniels-Midland Company..............806 828-3948
7414 E County Road 7500 Slaton (79364) *(G-18968)*

Architctral Interiors By Salas..............210 733-1269
502 Riverside Dr San Antonio (78223) *(G-17913)*

Architechtual Design Mfg, Royse City *Also called Cameron Knight (G-17717)*

Architectural Bldg Components, Houston *Also called March Resources Co (G-10763)*

Architectural Caseworks of TX, San Antonio *Also called Ar-Case Inc (G-17912)*

Architectural Fabrication, Fort Worth *Also called Sign & Awning Services Inc (G-6987)*

Architectural Graphic Products 713 683-8942
10616 Hempstead Rd Ste E Houston (77092) *(G-8683)*

Architectural Metal Crafts 281 449-1881
14320 1/2 Luthe Rd Houston (77039) *(G-8684)*

Architectural Products Co Inc (PA) **915 584-9424**
4737 Osborne Dr El Paso (79922) *(G-5649)*

Architectural Stained Glass 432 426-3311
506 Limpia Canyon Trl Fort Davis (79734) *(G-6318)*

Architectural Wood Designs 972 935-0222
408 Higgins Rd Waxahachie (75167) *(G-20527)*

Architerra Inc 512 441-8062
1701 Evergreen Ave Unit 2 Austin (78704) *(G-930)*

Architerra Austin, Austin *Also called Architerra Inc (G-930)*

Archrock Inc (PA) **281 836-8000**
9807 Katy Fwy Ste 100 Houston (77024) *(G-8685)*

Archrock Inc 432 567-1050
9704 W Interstate 20 Midland (79706) *(G-15118)*

Archrock Inc 432 336-8632
3105 W 9th St Fort Stockton (79735) *(G-6328)*

Archrock Inc 361 572-9904
8193 Lone Tree Rd Victoria (77905) *(G-20239)*

Archrock Inc 903 389-5666
105 Bailiff Dr Fairfield (75840) *(G-6168)*

Archrock Inc 806 669-8900
305 S Price Rd Pampa (79065) *(G-16314)*

Arcooil Corp 940 549-4444
471 State Highway 67 Graham (76450) *(G-7776)*

Arcosa Inc (PA) **972 942-6500**
500 N Akard St Ste 400 Dallas (75201) *(G-3958)*

Arcosa Aggregates Inc (HQ) **972 544-5900**
401 N Interstate Hwy 45 Ferris (75125) *(G-6229)*

Arcosa Aggregates Inc 254 662-1025
544 Rosenfeld Rd Waco (76706) *(G-20364)*

Arcosa Aggregates Inc 972 287-4343
3829 Bilindsay Rd Seagoville (75159) *(G-18798)*

Arcosa Aggregates Inc 254 982-4158
5050 Reeds Lake Rd Rogers (76569) *(G-17573)*

Arcosa Lightweight, Dallas *Also called Arcosa Lw Hpb LLC (G-3959)*

Arcosa Lw Hpb LLC (HQ) **214 631-4420**
500 N Akard St Dallas (75201) *(G-3959)*

Arcosa Lw Ky LLC 214 631-4420
500 N Akard St Dallas (75201) *(G-3960)*

Arcosa Marine Products Inc (HQ) **214 631-4420**
500 N Akard St Dallas (75201) *(G-3961)*

Arcosa Materials Inc (HQ) **817 635-8500**
1112 E Cpeland Rd Ste 500 Arlington (76011) *(G-622)*

Arcosa Tank LLC 214 631-4420
500 N Akard St Dallas (75201) *(G-3962)*

Arcosa Wind Towers Inc 817 378-3700
1000 Ne 28th St R Fort Worth (76106) *(G-6398)*

Arcot Manufacturing, Houston *Also called Allied Assets Corporation (G-8548)*

Arcrite Welding and Truck Acce, Del Rio *Also called ARC Rite Welding & Fabrication (G-5305)*

Arctic Cooler-Freezer Repr Inc 817 492-0200
7331 John T White Rd Fort Worth (76120) *(G-6399)*

Arctic Pipe Inspection Houston, Houston *Also called Arctic Pipe Insptn Inc Texas (G-8686)*

Arctic Pipe Insptn Inc Texas 281 456-8300
9500 Sheldon Rd Houston (77049) *(G-8686)*

Arctic Star of Texas, Pantego *Also called Arctic Star Rfrgn Mfg Co (G-16350)*

Arctic Star Rfrgn Mfg Co 817 274-1396
3540 W Pioneer Pkwy Pantego (76013) *(G-16350)*

Arctic Warehouse Facility Repr, Fort Worth *Also called Arctic Cooler-Freezer Repr Inc (G-6399)*

Arctos Assembly Group Ltd 512 682-4801
12317 Technology Blvd Austin (78727) *(G-931)*

Arcturus Corporation 214 720-0075
2828 N Harwood St # 2000 Dallas (75201) *(G-3963)*

Arcube Multimedia Inc (PA) **972 267-1800**
959 E Collins Blvd # 123 Richardson (75081) *(G-17273)*

Arcube Optical Mfg LLC 972 267-1800
3817 Sandia Dr Plano (75023) *(G-16792)*

Ard Operating LLC (PA) **713 759-1155**
500 Dallas St Ste 2700 Houston (77002) *(G-8687)*

Arden Companies Inc 806 335-1147
10901 Airport Blvd Amarillo (79111) *(G-400)*

Ardent Mills LLC 512 789-5165
1100 S Main St Galena Park (77547) *(G-7377)*

Ardent Mills LLC 817 847-3400
401 E Industrial Ave Saginaw (76131) *(G-17737)*

Ardex Engineered Cements Inc 817 435-5020
201 Airport Dr Mansfield (76063) *(G-14656)*

Area Iron & Steel Works Inc 915 833-9494
4605 Osborne Dr El Paso (79922) *(G-5650)*

Area Wide Phonebook, San Angelo *Also called Associated Publishing Company (G-17779)*

Area-Wide Phone Book, Midland *Also called Associated Publishing Company (G-15121)*

Arena Brands Inc (HQ) **972 494-7133**
601 Marion Dr Garland (75042) *(G-7441)*

Arena Offshore LP 218 210-3138
2103 Res Frest Dr Ste 200 The Woodlands (77380) *(G-19832)*

Arepet Industries LLC 210 628-1622
3603 Speedway Run Von Ormy (78073) *(G-20345)*

Ares Robotics LLC 713 320-4690
4807 Cripple Creek Dr Houston (77017) *(G-8688)*

Argenbrght Nat Shtmtl Wrks Inc 214 357-9161
9121 King Arthur Dr Dallas (75247) *(G-3964)*

Argio Roofing & Cnstr Lllc (PA) **956 434-6411**
29729 Norman Rd Rio Hondo (78583) *(G-17475)*

Argon Medical Devices Inc 903 675-9321
1445 Flat Creek Rd Athens (75751) *(G-819)*

Argon Medical Devices Inc (HQ) **903 675-9321**
2600 Dallas Pkwy Ste 440 Frisco (75034) *(G-7266)*

Argos USA LLC 972 299-5274
2138 S Highway 67 Cedar Hill (75104) *(G-2936)*

Argos USA LLC 713 664-4527
16060 Dillard Dr Jersey Village (77040) *(G-13291)*

Argos USA LLC 817 551-0931
6100 Old Hemphill Rd Fort Worth (76134) *(G-6400)*

Argos USA LLC 817 468-1333
640 New York Ave Arlington (76010) *(G-623)*

Argos USA LLC 281 391-4554
28601 Highway Blvd Katy (77494) *(G-13350)*

Argos USA LLC 713 273-2700
620 Sartartia Rd Sugar Land (77479) *(G-19446)*

Argos USA LLC 972 621-0999
8500 Freport Pkwy Ste 200 Irving (75063) *(G-12932)*

Argos USA LLC 972 436-3026
1225 S Railroad St Lewisville (75057) *(G-14023)*

Argos USA LLC 713 692-4408
302 Bennington St Houston (77022) *(G-8689)*

Argos USA LLC 817 329-8550
1968 Brumlow Ave Grapevine (76092) *(G-8012)*

Argos USA LLC 972 256-6571
5150 Valley View Ln Irving (75038) *(G-12933)*

Argos USA LLC 972 285-8823
1719 W Scyene Rd Mesquite (75149) *(G-15027)*

Argos USA LLC 713 273-2800
10715 Highway 3 Houston (77034) *(G-8690)*

Argos USA LLC 972 556-0735
1946 California Xing Dallas (75220) *(G-3965)*

Arguijo Oilfield Services Inc 432 550-5650
2800 W 42nd St Odessa (79764) *(G-15918)*

Argus Media Inc (HQ) **713 968-0000**
2929 Allen Pkwy Ste 700 Houston (77019) *(G-8691)*

Argus Software Inc (HQ) **713 621-4343**
750 Town And Country Blvd # 800 Houston (77024) *(G-8692)*

ARI, Houston *Also called American Rice Inc (G-8606)*

Arias Logistics Inc (PA) **915 872-0034**
543 S Americas Ave Ste A1 El Paso (79907) *(G-5651)*

Ariel Kennard 832 997-4537
12639 Ashford Pine Dr Houston (77082) *(G-8693)*

Aries Acrylic Mfg Inc 972 771-6286
4176 E Interstate 30 Rockwall (75087) *(G-17538)*

Aries Building Systems LLC 254 938-0800
1919 Mueller Ln Troy (76579) *(G-20028)*

Aries Building Systems LLC (PA) **254 938-0800**
12621 Featherwood Dr # 300 Houston (77034) *(G-8694)*

Aries One LLC 832 564-3628
2416 W Main St Houston (77098) *(G-8695)*

Aries Spas, Rockwall *Also called Aries Acrylic Mfg Inc (G-17538)*

Aris Designs Inc 361 881-8131
4451 Baldwin Blvd Corpus Christi (78408) *(G-3475)*

Arismendy Josias 817 353-1244
340 Bellvue Ct Fort Worth (76134) *(G-6401)*

Arizona Tile LLC 713 292-1001
10811 S Westview Circle D Houston (77043) *(G-8696)*

Ark La Tex Surveying Co Inc 903 938-9939
305 W Rusk St Ste B Marshall (75670) *(G-14762)*

Ark, The, Houston *Also called Ark-Concrete Specialties Inc (G-8697)*

Ark-Concrete Specialties Inc 713 692-6736
713 Lehman St Houston (77018) *(G-8697)*

Ark-La-Tex Custom Coatings 903 845-6436
100 N Lee Dr Gladewater (75647) *(G-7717)*

Ark-La-Tex Shredding Co Inc 903 877-3734
12405 State Highway 155 N Tyler (75708) *(G-20048)*

Arkema Inc 713 455-1211
2231 Haden Rd Houston (77015) *(G-8698)*

Arkema Inc 281 328-3561
18000 Crosby Eastgate Rd Crosby (77532) *(G-3725)*

Arkema Inc 409 838-3981
2810 Gulf States Rd Beaumont (77701) *(G-1854)*

Arkema Inc 713 751-7340
9502b Bayport Blvd Pasadena (77507) *(G-16389)*

Arkhoma Transports Inc (PA) **806 435-2380**
102 S Juniper St Perryton (79070) *(G-16633)*

Arkoma Basin Resources Ltd (PA) 972 771-6000
  203 E Interstate 30 Rockwall (75087) *(G-17539)*

Arkoma Development, Rockwall *Also called Arkoma Basin Resources Ltd (G-17539)*

Arkos Field Services LP (HQ) 832 783-5400
  19750 Fm 362 Rd Ste 100 Waller (77484) *(G-20492)*

Arlanxeo USA LLC 409 883-9990
  4647 Fm 1006 Orange (77630) *(G-16232)*

Arlington Brick and Supply Inc 817 460-5511
  9 Nora Ct Arlington (76013) *(G-624)*

Arlington Cast Stone Inc 817 284-5933
  721 W Hurst Blvd Hurst (76053) *(G-12834)*

Arlington Intl AVI Pdts LLC 817 465-9880
  7321 Commercial Blvd E Arlington (76001) *(G-625)*

Arlington Machine & Hydraulics 972 988-6644
  2413 Arkansas Ln Grand Prairie (75052) *(G-7835)*

Arlington Police Department, Arlington *Also called City of Arlington (G-644)*

Arlington Prtg Plying Card LLC 817 275-2731
  202 N Great Sw Pkwy Grand Prairie (75050) *(G-7836)*

Arlon Inc 210 798-1900
  6110 Rittiman Rd San Antonio (78218) *(G-17914)*

Arm Inc 408 576-1500
  5707 Sw Pkwy Ste 1-100 Austin (78735) *(G-932)*

Arm Inc 512 327-9249
  Encino Trace 5707 Sw Park Austin (78735) *(G-933)*

Arm Systems, Houston *Also called Advanced Ret MGT Systems Inc (G-8491)*

Arm Trucking, Lubbock *Also called Pb Materials Holdings Inc (G-14459)*

Armaceutica Inc 949 677-6001
  1155 Galloway Dr El Paso (79902) *(G-5652)*

Armadillo Blast Coat Inc 281 485-2743
  1537 Stone Rd Pearland (77581) *(G-16539)*

Armamentarium Inc (PA) 281 528-5700
  22317 Gosling Rd Spring (77389) *(G-19101)*

Armando G Martinez (PA) 325 653-5640
  215 W Avenue N San Angelo (76903) *(G-17778)*

Armbrust Inc 512 807-0744
  3813a Helios Way 290 Pflugerville (78660) *(G-16658)*

Armoloy Co, Fort Worth *Also called Daggett Street Properties (G-6572)*

Armoloy Company of Fort Worth, Fort Worth *Also called Jar-Tex Industries Inc (G-6735)*

Armoloy of Texas, Houston *Also called Gull Industries Inc (G-10074)*

Armor Industrial Fabricators 281 573-2777
  11344 Interstate 10 E Baytown (77523) *(G-1779)*

Armor Petroleum Inc 940 692-5001
  4245 Kemp Blvd Ste 910 Wichita Falls (76308) *(G-20740)*

Armor Plate Inc 281 487-2023
  2823 Randolph Rd Pasadena (77503) *(G-16390)*

Armortex Inc 800 880-8306
  5926 Corridor Pkwy Schertz (78154) *(G-18744)*

Armstead Oil 713 454-3866
  7825 Creekbend Dr Houston (77071) *(G-8699)*

Arne Distributors Inc 713 869-8321
  2830 Hicks St Houston (77007) *(G-8700)*

Arne's Wholesale, Houston *Also called Arne Distributors Inc (G-8700)*

Arnim Tool Inc 972 247-0802
  2204 Joe Field Rd Dallas (75229) *(G-3966)*

Arnold Stone Inc (PA) 972 248-1953
  405 State Highway 121 Byp A250 Lewisville (75067) *(G-14024)*

Arns Holdings Ltd 713 863-0600
  2611 El Camino St Houston (77054) *(G-8701)*

Aroc Inc 832 538-0300
  1000 La St Ste 6700 Houston (77002) *(G-8702)*

Aroma Alternatives Ltd Co (PA) 512 535-3646
  11110 Metric Blvd Ste D Austin (78758) *(G-934)*

Arpco Valves & Controls LLC 903 834-7007
  120 Marvin A Smith Rd Kilgore (75662) *(G-13532)*

Array Coating Technology LLC 936 321-7000
  11987 Fm 529 Rd Houston (77041) *(G-8703)*

Array Holdings Inc (PA) 281 260-8366
  15900 Morales Rd Houston (77032) *(G-8704)*

Arrington Companies, Pampa *Also called William L Arrington (G-16345)*

Arrington Lbr & Pallet Co Inc 903 586-4070
  445 Country Rd 1538 Jacksonville (75766) *(G-13226)*

Arrington Lumber, Jacksonville *Also called Arrington Sawmill Inc (G-13227)*

Arrington Oil & Gas Oper LLC 432 682-6685
  500 W Wall St Ste 300 Midland (79701) *(G-15119)*

Arrington Sawmill Inc 903 586-4070
  Hwy 69 S Jacksonville (75766) *(G-13227)*

Arrow Construction Co Inc (PA) 325 573-3571
  2700 21st St Snyder (79549) *(G-18982)*

Arrow Crushed Stone Inc 817 423-1337
  4641 Ivanhoe Dr Fort Worth (76132) *(G-6402)*

Arrow Electronics Inc 303 824-4000
  1820 Preston Park Blvd # 2800 Plano (75093) *(G-16793)*

Arrow Fabricated Tubing Ltd (PA) 972 276-3010
  1010 E Walnut St Garland (75040) *(G-7442)*

Arrow Manufactured Products, Wichita Falls *Also called Machining Solutions LLC (G-20781)*

Arrow Marble LLC 832 467-4345
  12306 Shiloh Church Rd Houston (77066) *(G-8705)*

Arrow Mirror & Glass Inc (PA) 832 467-4345
  12306 Shiloh Church Rd Houston (77066) *(G-8706)*

Arrow Plating Co, Fort Worth *Also called Apci Inc (G-6391)*

Arrow Printing Inc 432 335-3407
  109 N Hancock Ave Odessa (79761) *(G-15919)*

Arrow S Ranch, Houston *Also called Djh Services LLC (G-9485)*

Arrow Steel Processors Inc 713 670-0160
  8710 Clinton Dr Houston (77029) *(G-8707)*

Arrow-Magnolia Intl Inc 972 247-7111
  2646 Rodney Ln Dallas (75229) *(G-3967)*

Arrowall Company (PA) 713 462-1751
  18985 Goll St San Antonio (78266) *(G-18639)*

Arrowhead Manufacturing, Fort Worth *Also called Southwest Metrics Inc (G-7005)*

Arrowhead Operating Inc 432 683-9700
  400 E Loop 250 N Ste 107 Midland (79705) *(G-15120)*

Arrowhead Sperior Woodcrafters, Dallas *Also called Richard-Marcus Inc (G-4898)*

Arrowhead Stairs and Trim 972 484-0406
  2115 Valley View Ln # 100 Farmers Branch (75234) *(G-6188)*

Arrowwood Cabinetry, San Antonio *Also called Maryfield Enterprises LP (G-18281)*

Arsham Aluminum Alloys, Jersey Village *Also called Arsham Metal Industries Inc (G-13292)*

Arsham Metal Industries Inc 713 896-8585
  11280 Charles Rd Jersey Village (77041) *(G-13292)*

Art Mix LLC 713 552-9028
  3701 W Alabama St Ste 250 Houston (77027) *(G-8708)*

Art Office Signs, Taylor *Also called Jim McNabb Inc (G-19658)*

Art Semi, Austin *Also called Advanced Rfurbishment Tech LLC (G-894)*

ART&quilt Magazine 713 975-7140
  9502 Meadowbriar Ln Houston (77063) *(G-8709)*

Arte Sano LLC 512 400-8743
  6110 Trade Center Dr Austin (78744) *(G-935)*

Artech Manufacturing Inc 512 863-9050
  1840 County Road 120 Georgetown (78626) *(G-7635)*

Artemis Intl Solutions Corp (HQ) 512 201-8222
  401 Congress Ave Ste 2650 Austin (78701) *(G-936)*

Artesia Ecoscience LLC 281 978-2521
  15 River Cir Houston (77063) *(G-8710)*

Arthrocare Corporation (HQ) 512 391-3900
  7000 W William Cannon Dr # 1 Austin (78735) *(G-937)*

Artificial Lift Company, Stafford *Also called Accessesp LLC (G-19281)*

Artisan Collection, Dallas *Also called Creative Tile Inc (G-4182)*

Artisans Cabinetry & Woodwork 512 626-7311
  2200 S Church St Ste 103 Georgetown (78626) *(G-7636)*

Artistic Counters Inc 210 651-3281
  18630 Goll St Garden Ridge (78266) *(G-7418)*

Artistic Iron & Forge 281 807-3440
  11834 Dula Ln Cypress (77429) *(G-3776)*

Artistic Plating Inc 713 864-1352
  1231 W 34th St Ste B Houston (77018) *(G-8711)*

Artlux Inc (PA) 214 716-1990
  10925 Alder Cir Dallas (75238) *(G-3968)*

Artografx Inc 214 349-1075
  2611 Andjon Dr Dallas (75220) *(G-3969)*

Artwin Graphics, Pasadena *Also called Wilkins & Associates Inc (G-16527)*

Aruba Petroleum Inc 940 466-9438
  15076 Fm 455 Decatur (76234) *(G-5241)*

Aruba Petroleum Inc (PA) 972 312-9366
  555 Republic Dr Ste 505 Plano (75074) *(G-16794)*

ARX Fit 512 633-3768
  9715a Burnet Rd Austin (78758) *(G-938)*

Arygin Corporation 940 597-8275
  4101 Mill Run Rd Denton (76208) *(G-5350)*

As America Inc 214 530-9831
  801 E Wintergreen Rd Hutchins (75141) *(G-12862)*

ASAP, Dallas *Also called Regency Plz Prtg & Off Sup Inc (G-4882)*

ASAP Glass & Door LLC 214 770-8266
  512 N Locust St Denton (76201) *(G-5351)*

ASAP Machine Inc 281 448-4800
  9026 Sweetwater Ln Houston (77037) *(G-8712)*

ASAP Precision Machine, Houston *Also called ASAP Machine Inc (G-8712)*

ASAP Printing, Arlington *Also called 4 Over LLC (G-605)*

ASAP Printing Solutions, McAllen *Also called OConn LLC (G-14896)*

Asaprosthetics, Spring *Also called A Speclzed Apprach To Prsthtic (G-19190)*

Asarco LLC 806 468-4000
  8 Miles Ne Cy On Hwy 136 Amarillo (79120) *(G-401)*

ASC Paving, Corpus Christi *Also called Aj Commercial Services Inc (G-3470)*

ASC Signal Corporation (HQ) 214 291-7654
  1120 Jupiter Rd Ste 102 Plano (75074) *(G-16795)*

Ascend Performance Mtls Inc (HQ) 713 315-5700
  1010 Travis St Ste 900 Houston (77002) *(G-8713)*

Ascend Prfmce Mtls Hldings Inc (HQ) 713 315-5700
  1010 Travis St Ste 900 Houston (77002) *(G-8714)*

Ascend Prfmce Mtls Oprtons Inc 281 228-4000
  Fm Rd 2917 Alvin (77512) *(G-352)*

Ascend Prfmce Mtls Oprtons LLC (HQ) 713 315-5700
  1010 Travis St Ste 900 Houston (77002) *(G-8715)*

Ascendant Tsg, Houston *Also called Texas Source Group Inc (G-12250)*

A
L
P
H
A
B
E
T
I
C

Ascent Business Systems Inc................................281 497-8882
1880 S Dairy Ashford Rd # 535 Houston (77077) *(G-8716)*

Ascot Enterprises Inc...254 582-1970
304 Coke Ave Hillsboro (76645) *(G-8321)*

Asdfg, Houston *Also called Kizer Energy Inc (G-10539)*

ASG Energy LLC..210 610-0036
11765 West Ave San Antonio (78216) *(G-17915)*

Ash Automated Ctrl Systems LLC.........................281 346-1400
32810 Rogers Rd Fulshear (77441) *(G-7327)*

Ash Grove Cement Company................................713 674-4100
9550 Clinton Dr Houston (77029) *(G-8717)*

Ashburn Industries..832 399-1000
7403 Wright Rd Houston (77041) *(G-8718)*

Ashcraft-Southern Marble Co...............................903 581-5501
13822 State Highway 155 S Tyler (75703) *(G-20049)*

Ashcraft/European Bakery, Stafford *Also called Ashcrft-Uropean Bky Ltd Partnr (G-19287)*

Ashcrft-Uropean Bky Ltd Partnr............................281 403-5040
220 Murphy Rd Stafford (77477) *(G-19287)*

Asher Enterprises Inc...281 446-8131
19703 Highway 59 N Humble (77338) *(G-12747)*

Asher Oil Field Specialty.....................................361 293-0562
1001 Us Highway 77a N Yoakum (77995) *(G-20959)*

Asher Plumbing Company, Humble *Also called Asher Enterprises Inc (G-12747)*

Asherton Store, Asherton *Also called Tims South Texas LLC (G-814)*

Ashland LLC..973 628-3245
1015 Main St Port Neches (77651) *(G-17158)*

Ashland Water Technologies, Houston *Also called Solenis LLC (G-11939)*

Ashley Donuts & Ice Cream Inc............................281 486-5644
2160 Bay Area Blvd Houston (77058) *(G-8719)*

Ashley Industries LLC..864 834-1167
2541 S Interstate 35 Round Rock (78664) *(G-17623)*

Ashley S Division, El Paso *Also called Teasdale Foods Inc (G-5994)*

Ashley Salvage Company.....................................210 922-7631
4918 Roosevelt Ave San Antonio (78214) *(G-17916)*

Ashley Worldwide Inc..956 383-0636
1500 S 25th Ave Edinburg (78542) *(G-5575)*

Ashley's Donuts, Houston *Also called Ashley Donuts & Ice Cream Inc (G-8719)*

Ashmore & Ashmore Properties............................214 327-9228
6865 Westlake Ave Dallas (75214) *(G-3970)*

Ashter Construction LLC.....................................832 786-0053
36417 Richard Frey Rd Waller (77484) *(G-20493)*

Asi Industrial Services LLC..................................713 378-9200
8412 Mosley Rd Houston (77075) *(G-8720)*

Asi Piping LLC..409 786-1080
3530 Lakeview Cutoff St Vidor (77662) *(G-20324)*

Asi Signage Innovations, Irving *Also called Envirmmntal Sgnage Sltions Inc (G-13015)*

Asi Standards, Oak Ridge North *Also called Sardisco Enterprises Inc (G-15890)*

Asia Chemical Corporation Inc.............................713 673-4100
1417 Kress St Houston (77020) *(G-8721)*

Asian2u.com, Willis *Also called Allan Banks (G-20841)*

Asics America Corporation...................................972 678-0200
820 W Stacy Rd Ste 218 Allen (75013) *(G-252)*

Asiel Enterprises Inc..361 765-6670
8306 Serenity Ct Corpus Christi (78414) *(G-3476)*

Asinni 2000 Records Inc......................................281 564-4111
14601 Bellaire Blvd 308-A Houston (77083) *(G-8722)*

Ask Industries Inc...432 686-2520
301 Commerce St Ste 1810 Fort Worth (76102) *(G-6403)*

Asmar Custom Cabinets Inc.................................972 241-7676
2643 Brenner Dr Dallas (75220) *(G-3971)*

Asmar Custom Furn & Cabinets, Dallas *Also called Asmar Custom Cabinets Inc (G-3971)*

Asmar Truck Equipment, El Paso *Also called Progressive Resources Inc (G-5921)*

Asna Inc...210 408-0212
1026 Central Pkwy S San Antonio (78232) *(G-17917)*

Asp Westward LP (PA).......................................**713 256-0953**
523 N Sam Houston Pkwy E Houston (77060) *(G-8723)*

Asp Westward LP..903 845-2235
211 N Main St Gladewater (75647) *(G-7718)*

Asp Westward LP..903 237-7700
320 E Methvin St Longview (75601) *(G-14197)*

Aspen Beverage Group, San Antonio *Also called Aspen Enterprises Ltd (G-17918)*

Aspen Enterprises Ltd..210 684-6363
7015 Fairgrounds Pkwy San Antonio (78238) *(G-17918)*

Aspen Manufacturing LLC....................................281 441-6500
373 Atascocita Rd Humble (77396) *(G-12748)*

Aspen Marble Inc..817 478-5140
5399 Oak St Fort Worth (76140) *(G-6404)*

Aspen Operating Company LLC.............................817 882-9063
6777 Camp Bowie Blvd # 600 Fort Worth (76116) *(G-6405)*

Asphalt Inc LLC..512 428-5739
11675 Jllyvlle Rd Ste 205 Austin (78759) *(G-939)*

Asphalt Products Inc..956 423-8315
5809 Progress Dr Harlingen (78550) *(G-8181)*

Asphwax Inc..281 568-8415
12972 Sugar Ridge Blvd Stafford (77477) *(G-19288)*

Aspira Womens Health Inc (PA)............................**512 519-0400**
12117 Bee Cves Rd Bldg 3 Austin (78738) *(G-940)*

Aspire Food Group Usa Inc..................................512 645-0700
6231 E Stassney Ln 12-105 Austin (78744) *(G-941)*

Aspyr Media Inc...512 708-8100
1250 S Cpitl Of Txas Hwy West Lake Hills (78746) *(G-20678)*

Assa Abloy Door Group LLC.................................713 466-6790
550 Greens Pkwy Ste 100 Houston (77067) *(G-8724)*

Assa Abloy Entrance Systems US..........................713 934-9095
9001 Jameel Rd Ste 190 Houston (77040) *(G-8725)*

Asset Guard Products Inc....................................940 627-1400
2242 E Highway 380 Decatur (76234) *(G-5242)*

Associated Canvas Pdts I Ltd...............................281 457-1480
16917 Market St Channelview (77530) *(G-3012)*

Associated Creditors Inc (PA)..............................**210 341-5642**
8938 Broadway San Antonio (78217) *(G-17919)*

Associated Group Investment Co...........................806 794-9507
12 Mile W Slide Rd Lubbock (79404) *(G-14364)*

Associated Label & Tape Co.................................214 744-1662
2009 Farrington St Dallas (75207) *(G-3972)*

Associated Locksmiths Amer Inc...........................214 819-9733
1408 N Riverfront Blvd # 30 Dallas (75207) *(G-3973)*

Associated Pro Inc..214 902-8211
3620 Pallos Verdas Dr Dallas (75229) *(G-3974)*

Associated Publishing Company............................325 949-1910
2825 Sherwood Way San Angelo (76901) *(G-17779)*

Associated Publishing Company............................432 687-1756
4519 N Garfield St Midland (79705) *(G-15121)*

Associated Stl Fabricators Inc..............................281 516-0909
25234 Fm 2978 Rd Tomball (77375) *(G-19961)*

Associated Supply Company Inc............................512 272-8922
12805 Us Highway 290 E Manor (78653) *(G-14643)*

Associated Telephone...512 288-6215
151 Kirkham Cir Unit B Kyle (78640) *(G-13677)*

Associated Texas Newspapers...............................830 426-3346
1601 Avenue K Hondo (78861) *(G-8353)*

Associated Time & Prkg Contrls, Houston *Also called Associated Time Instrs Co Inc (G-8726)*

Associated Time & Prkg Contrls, Dallas *Also called Associated Time Instrs Co Inc (G-3975)*

Associated Time Instrs Co Inc..............................713 263-1366
6699 Portwest Dr Ste 160 Houston (77024) *(G-8726)*

Associated Time Instrs Co Inc (PA)........................**214 637-2763**
9104 Diplomacy Row Dallas (75247) *(G-3975)*

Associated Truss & Lumber, Mesquite *Also called Associated Truss Company (G-15028)*

Associated Truss Company...................................972 226-1973
388 S Larkin Rd Mesquite (75182) *(G-15028)*

Associated Welding Supply Inc.............................281 485-2755
3002 S Main St Pearland (77581) *(G-16540)*

Assocted Bldrs Cntrs Grter Hst, Houston *Also called Assocted Bldrs Cntrs Grter Hst (G-8727)*

Assocted Bldrs Cntrs Grter Hst............................713 523-6222
4910 Dacoma St Houston (77092) *(G-8727)*

Assurance Systems Inc..770 242-6832
1415 Halsey Way Ste 314 Carrollton (75007) *(G-2858)*

Assure Labs Inc..713 561-5529
5250 Gulfton St Ste 2c Houston (77081) *(G-8728)*

AST Waterjet, Grand Prairie *Also called Camcara Inc (G-7849)*

Astanza Holdings LLC...800 364-9010
1810 S Akard St Ste 500 Dallas (75215) *(G-3976)*

Astanza Laser, Dallas *Also called Astanza Holdings LLC (G-3976)*

Asteria Learning Inc...210 960-3855
116 Kestrel Dr Spring Branch (78070) *(G-19266)*

Asti Manufacturing Corp Inc................................972 241-3055
13950 Senlac Dr Ste 300 Farmers Branch (75234) *(G-6189)*

Astrimar Consultants LLC....................................281 994-7816
1400 Brdfeld Blvd Ste 200 Houston (77084) *(G-8729)*

Astrimar Consultants LLC....................................281 994-7816
1400 Brdfeld Blvd Ste 200 Houston (77084) *(G-8730)*

Astro Foods International Corp..............................214 349-7840
10720 Miller Rd Ste 300 Dallas (75238) *(G-3977)*

Astro Machine & Tool Works LLC..........................903 595-6655
8044 County Road 313 E Tyler (75706) *(G-20050)*

Astro Mechanics Inc...512 246-9200
1411a Sam Bass Rd Round Rock (78681) *(G-17624)*

Astro Sheet Metal Co Inc....................................972 438-1110
1906 S Great Sw Pkwy Grand Prairie (75051) *(G-7837)*

Astro Technology Inc..281 464-0100
15255 Gulf Fwy Ste 116f Houston (77034) *(G-8731)*

Astrotech Corporation (PA)..................................**512 485-9530**
555 Forge River Rd # 100 Webster (77598) *(G-20633)*

Astura Medical..760 814-8047
4949 W Royal Ln Irving (75063) *(G-12934)*

Asuragen Inc..512 681-5200
2150 Woodward St Ste 100 Austin (78744) *(G-942)*

Asure Software Inc (PA)......................................**512 437-2700**
3700 N Capital Of Texas H Austin (78746) *(G-943)*

AT&T Inc (PA)..**210 821-4105**
208 S Akard St Dallas (75202) *(G-3978)*

At-Integration Inc...512 819-4629
204 S Interstate 35 # 105 Georgetown (78628) *(G-7637)*

Atascosa Steel Industries Inc 830 276-4322
1275 Schuettig Rd Poteet (78065) *(G-17193)*
Atco Products Inc 972 842-8178
601 S Interstate Hwy 45 Ferris (75125) *(G-6230)*
Atco Rubber Products Inc (HQ) **817 595-2894**
7101 Atco Dr Fort Worth (76118) *(G-6406)*
Atco Rubber Products Inc 713 674-6665
9222 Wood Forest Blvd Houston (77013) *(G-8732)*
Atco Strctres Lgistics USA Inc 208 242-3804
480 Wildwood Forest Dr Spring (77380) *(G-19197)*
Atco Strctres Lgistics USA Inc (HQ) **936 829-2325**
480 Wildwood Forest Dr Spring (77380) *(G-19198)*
Ate Group, Houston *Also called Dynalyst Manufacturing Corp (G-9546)*
Atec Inc (PA) **281 276-2700**
12600 Executive Dr Stafford (77477) *(G-19289)*
Atec Resources Inc 281 276-2700
12600 Executive Dr Stafford (77477) *(G-19290)*
Athena Manufacturing LP 512 928-2693
15900 Bratton Ln Austin (78728) *(G-944)*
Athena Oilfield Services LLC 713 426-1969
601 Sawyer St Ste 200 Houston (77007) *(G-8733)*
Athens Daily Review, Athens *Also called Newspaper Holding Inc (G-835)*
Athens Group Holdings LLC (PA) **512 345-0600**
3301 Northland Dr Ste 500 Austin (78731) *(G-945)*
Athens Steel Building Corp 903 675-5733
900 Ne Loop 7 Athens (75752) *(G-820)*
Athletic Bag Company LP (PA) **903 520-3343**
316 S Glenwood Blvd Tyler (75702) *(G-20051)*
Athletic Decals Inc 713 774-0663
8800 Bissonnet St Ste N Houston (77074) *(G-8734)*
Athletic Hlmet Rcndtioning LLC 936 858-9990
17548 Us Highway 69 S Alto (75925) *(G-314)*
Athletic Sewing Center Inc 210 681-9744
7210 Eckhert Rd San Antonio (78238) *(G-17920)*
Athlon Energy Inc 817 984-8200
420 Throckmorton St # 1200 Fort Worth (76102) *(G-6407)*
Athlon Solutions LLC (HQ) **713 457-2400**
5500 N Sam Houston Pkwy W # 800 Houston (77086) *(G-8735)*
Athlon Solutions LLC (HQ) **713 457-2400**
11200 Bay Area Blvd Pasadena (77507) *(G-16391)*
Athlon, A Halliburton Service, Houston *Also called Athlon Solutions LLC (G-8735)*
ATI, Houston *Also called Astro Technology Inc (G-8731)*
ATI Actuators, Cypress *Also called Automation Technology Inc (G-3777)*
Atk North America, Grand Prairie *Also called North American Atk Corporation (G-7936)*
Atk Oilfield Trnsp USA Inc 432 452-3550
7701 E Highway 191 # 932 Odessa (79762) *(G-15920)*
Atkore International Group Inc 708 339-1610
11539 N Huston Rosslyn Rd Houston (77088) *(G-8736)*
Atkore Plastic Pipe Corp (HQ) **817 594-8791**
1202 N Bowie Dr Weatherford (76086) *(G-20576)*
Atkore Plastic Pipe Corp 817 594-8791
1202 N Bowie Dr Weatherford (76086) *(G-20577)*
Atlantia Offshore Limited 281 899-4300
1255 Enclave Pkwy Ste 600 Houston (77077) *(G-8737)*
Atlantic Blowers LLC 214 233-0280
1134 Longpoint Ave Dallas (75247) *(G-3979)*
Atlantic Cof Indus Sltions LLC 713 228-9501
3900 Harrisburg Blvd Houston (77003) *(G-8738)*
Atlantic Coffee Solutions, Houston *Also called Atlantic Cof Indus Sltions LLC (G-8738)*
Atlantic Durant Technology Inc 956 440-8005
5801 Progress Dr Harlingen (78550) *(G-8182)*
Atlantic Dwntwn Dllas Vntr LLC 469 399-1049
4005 Gaston Ave Dallas (75246) *(G-3980)*
Atlantic Food Bars, Garland *Also called Afb Manufacturing LLC (G-7429)*
Atlantic Food Bars Inc 888 632-5765
2450 Merritt Dr Garland (75041) *(G-7443)*
Atlantic Maritime Services LLC 713 621-7800
2800 Post Oak Blvd Fl 54 Houston (77056) *(G-8739)*
Atlantic Operating Inc 432 683-3272
300 N Marienfeld St # 400 Midland (79701) *(G-15122)*
Atlantic Pacific Marine Corp 713 346-4300
2500 City W Blvd Ste 1850 Houston (77042) *(G-8740)*
Atlantic Richfield Company 806 592-4900
4 Miles North On Hwy 214 Denver City (79323) *(G-5415)*
Atlantica Management USA Inc 832 494-2200
515 Post Oak Blvd Ste 120 Houston (77027) *(G-8741)*
Atlantis Laboratories Inc 936 760-1255
1601 Airport Rd Conroe (77301) *(G-3258)*
Atlantis Plastic Company 713 643-8387
5705 Hogue St Houston (77087) *(G-8742)*
Atlas Automatics, Dickinson *Also called Karatech Cnc Machining LLC (G-5476)*
Atlas Automatics Inc 281 337-1128
4211 21st St Dickinson (77539) *(G-5470)*
Atlas Automatics Screw Mch Sp, Dickinson *Also called Atlas Automatics Inc (G-5470)*
Atlas Bradford Division, Houston *Also called Grant Prideco Inc (G-10017)*
Atlas Building Systems Inc (PA) **903 597-4211**
5511 State Highway 31 W Tyler (75709) *(G-20052)*
Atlas Building Systems Inc 903 865-1153
23370 Interstate 20 Wills Point (75169) *(G-20873)*
Atlas Copco Compressors LLC 281 453-6800
224 N Mccoll Rd McAllen (78501) *(G-14839)*
Atlas Copco Compressors LLC 281 453-6800
15045 Lee Rd Houston (77032) *(G-8743)*
Atlas Copco Compressors LLC 281 453-6800
6755a Willow Brook Park Houston (77066) *(G-8744)*
Atlas Copco Rental LLC (HQ) **800 736-8267**
2300 E 13th St Deer Park (77536) *(G-5262)*
Atlas Energy Group LLC (PA) **412 489-0006**
425 Houston St Ste 300 Fort Worth (76102) *(G-6408)*
Atlas Energy Products Div, Diboll *Also called Atlas Roofing Corporation (G-5461)*
Atlas Growth Partners Gp LLC 412 489-0006
425 Houston St Ste 300 Fort Worth (76102) *(G-6409)*
Atlas Iron & Scrap Metal Co 972 225-4221
9506 S Central Expy Dallas (75241) *(G-3981)*
Atlas Machine and Wldg Svc Inc 817 558-7778
860 S Broadway St Joshua (76058) *(G-13318)*
Atlas Match LLC (PA) **817 267-1500**
1301 Texas Star Pkwy Euless (76040) *(G-6131)*
Atlas Metal Works Inc 214 741-4788
818 Singleton Blvd Dallas (75212) *(G-3982)*
Atlas Oilfield Cnstr Co LLC (PA) **325 428-0552**
2 Village Dr Ste 207 Abilene (79606) *(G-14)*
Atlas Pallet, San Antonio *Also called Atlas Southwest Pallet Co Inc (G-17921)*
Atlas Ptro Explrtion Worldwide 281 579-5200
16600 Park Row Houston (77084) *(G-8745)*
Atlas Radiator Inc 361 882-5661
824 N Chaparral St Corpus Christi (78401) *(G-3477)*
Atlas Roofing Corporation 903 645-3988
1100 E Georgia Pacific Dr Daingerfield (75638) *(G-3830)*
Atlas Roofing Corporation 936 829-5279
101 W Borden St Diboll (75941) *(G-5461)*
Atlas Sand Company LLC (PA) **432 276-3990**
5918 W Courtyard Dr # 500 Austin (78730) *(G-946)*
Atlas Scrap Management, Dallas *Also called Atlas Iron & Scrap Metal Co (G-3981)*
Atlas Sign Co, Houston *Also called Atlas Sign Services Inc (G-8746)*
Atlas Sign Services Inc 713 699-1121
6411 Airline Dr Houston (77076) *(G-8746)*
Atlas Soundolier, Ennis *Also called Mitek Corporation (G-6110)*
Atlas Southwest Pallet Co Inc (PA) **210 532-5343**
51 Essex St San Antonio (78210) *(G-17921)*
Atlas Tubular LLC (PA) **361 387-7505**
1710 S Highway 77 Robstown (78380) *(G-17503)*
Atlas Well Service LLC 432 683-3835
2709 N Big Spring St Midland (79705) *(G-15123)*
Atlaswerks, Dallas *Also called Cardinal Automation Inc (G-4083)*
Atmi Materials Ltd (HQ) **512 715-5343**
706 Houston Clinton Dr Burnet (78611) *(G-2602)*
Atomic Container Homes Inc 915 433-4817
1575 E San Antonio Ave El Paso (79901) *(G-5653)*
Atr, Spring *Also called Applied Training Resources Inc (G-19100)*
Atrion Corporation (PA) **972 390-9800**
1 Allentown Pkwy Allen (75002) *(G-253)*
Atrium Extrusion Systems Inc 903 455-8560
1001 Ed Rutherford Dr Greenville (75402) *(G-8062)*
Atrium Windows and Doors Inc (HQ) **214 583-1840**
9001 Ambassador Row Dallas (75247) *(G-3983)*
Atron Cs, Dallas *Also called Atron Group LLC (G-3984)*
Atron Group LLC 214 292-9840
9125 Viscount Row Dallas (75247) *(G-3984)*
Atropos Exploration Company (PA) **214 691-2377**
8117 Preston Rd Ste 600 Dallas (75225) *(G-3985)*
Ats Drilling LP 817 498-0040
6559 Midway Rd Haltom City (76117) *(G-8132)*
Atsco, Houston *Also called Alamo Transformer Supply Co (G-8526)*
Attentus Medical Sales Inc 281 776-5188
10101 Woodloch Forest Dr Spring (77380) *(G-19199)*
Attic Breeze LLC 254 865-9999
1370 Fm 116 Gatesville (76528) *(G-7617)*
Attoyac Rock LLC 936 275-3636
1450 Eddings Ln San Augustine (75972) *(G-18650)*
Atwood Oceanics Management LLC 281 749-7800
5847 San Felipe St # 3300 Houston (77057) *(G-8747)*
Atx Oil and More LLC 512 660-0696
9311 N Fm 620 Rd Austin (78726) *(G-947)*
Auc Group, Houston *Also called Auc Management LLC (G-8748)*
Auc Management LLC 713 983-3255
1800 Augusta Dr Ste 108 Houston (77057) *(G-8748)*
Audex Inc (PA) **903 757-4083**
332 W Main St Hallsville (75650) *(G-8126)*
Audio and Prfmce Solutions LLC 210 549-4242
6324 Bandera Rd San Antonio (78238) *(G-17922)*
Audiotel Corporation 972 359-5500
1021 Central Expy S Allen (75013) *(G-254)*
Augmentix Corporation 512 334-0111
4030 W Braker Ln Ste 100 Austin (78759) *(G-948)*
Augusta Vin LLC 830 307-1007
140 Augusta Vin Ln Fredericksburg (78624) *(G-7170)*

A L P H A B E T I C

Aus-Mex Company Inc (PA)................................**432 561-8866**
7820 W Highway 80 Midland (79706) *(G-15124)*

Aus-Tex Duplicators Inc................................512 476-7581
2431 Forbes Dr Austin (78754) *(G-949)*

Aus-Tex Printing & Mailing, Austin *Also called Aus-Tex Duplicators Inc (G-949)*

Austex Dumpsters LLC................................512 292-3867
9608 Swansons Ranch Rd Austin (78748) *(G-950)*

Austin American Awnings, Austin *Also called Roche Rouge Company L L C (G-1469)*

Austin American Tech Corp................................512 756-4150
401 Industrial Blvd Burnet (78611) *(G-2603)*

Austin Archtctral Graphics Inc................................512 473-2075
11400 Old Lockhart Hwy Creedmoor (78610) *(G-3705)*

Austin Armature Works LP................................512 312-0088
496 Commercial Dr Buda (78610) *(G-2520)*

Austin Boats & Motors Inc................................512 263-1266
1208 Ranch Road 620 S Lakeway (78734) *(G-13814)*

Austin Boats and Motors, Lakeway *Also called Austin Boats & Motors Inc (G-13814)*

Austin Brake & Clutch Supply, Austin *Also called Truckpro LLC (G-1597)*

Austin Brake & Clutch Supply................................512 836-0482
8151 N Lamar Blvd Austin (78753) *(G-951)*

Austin Cabinets, Houston *Also called Austins Cabinets & Cnstr (G-8751)*

Austin Chronicle Corporation................................512 454-5766
4000 N Intrstate 35 Frnta Austin (78751) *(G-952)*

Austin Coca-Cola Bottling Co................................979 543-2522
1001 W Jackson St El Campo (77437) *(G-5611)*

Austin Coca-Cola Bottling Co................................512 832-2652
9600 Burnet Rd Austin (78758) *(G-953)*

Austin Coca-Cola Bottling Co................................713 799-7296
1700 Crosspoint Ave Houston (77054) *(G-8749)*

Austin Coca-Cola Bottling Co (PA)................................**210 225-2601**
1 Coca Cola Pl San Antonio (78219) *(G-17923)*

Austin Coca-Cola Bottling Co................................409 899-5080
11450 Eastex Fwy Beaumont (77708) *(G-1855)*

Austin Coca-Cola Bottling Co................................903 597-9325
3200 W Gentry Pkwy Tyler (75702) *(G-20053)*

Austin Coca-Cola Bottling Co................................817 232-8600
3400 Fossil Creek Blvd Fort Worth (76137) *(G-6410)*

Austin Coca-Cola Bottling Co................................713 805-9722
1722 Brittmoore Rd Houston (77043) *(G-8750)*

Austin Coca-Cola Bottling Co................................512 836-0870
2311 Denton Dr Austin (78758) *(G-954)*

Austin Counter Tops, Austin *Also called K & K Langham Ltd (G-1263)*

Austin County Machine Shop Inc................................979 885-3716
9364 Fm 1458 Rd Sealy (77474) *(G-18805)*

Austin Duraclean, Cedar Park *Also called Christopher RAD Nader (G-2963)*

Austin Dvd Inc................................512 246-8759
3800 Julianas Way Round Rock (78665) *(G-17625)*

Austin Dynamics Inc................................512 267-3117
3200 W Whitestone Blvd D Cedar Park (78613) *(G-2961)*

Austin Elevator Company LLC................................512 376-2107
336 Millennium Dr Kyle (78640) *(G-13678)*

Austin Fit Magazine LP................................512 407-8383
2499 S Cpitl Of Txas Hwy Austin (78746) *(G-955)*

Austin Industries Inc................................512 288-1831
8302 La Plata Loop Austin (78737) *(G-857)*

Austin Mfg Svcs I Inc................................512 491-7411
Na4616 W Howard Ln Bldg Na Austin (78728) *(G-956)*

Austin Monthly, Austin *Also called Open Sky Media Inc (G-1388)*

Austin North Taxi Service................................512 704-9999
3314 W Parmer Ln Austin (78727) *(G-957)*

Austin Pallet Company................................512 990-0090
1605 Century St Pflugerville (78660) *(G-16659)*

Austin Powder Company................................817 371-6147
2793 Fm 67 Covington (76636) *(G-3694)*

Austin Powder Company................................940 644-5771
306 County Road 1347 Chico (76431) *(G-3050)*

Austin Powder Company................................512 863-3676
8850 W Hwy 29 Georgetown (78626) *(G-7638)*

Austin Powder Company................................940 382-4111
19 Oak Forrest Cir Denton (76210) *(G-5352)*

Austin Pre-Stressed, Austin *Also called JD Abrams LP (G-1253)*

Austin Ready-Mix LLC................................512 386-7187
4005 Banister Ln Ste 225c Austin (78704) *(G-958)*

Austin Rubber Company LLC................................512 904-0152
506 W 14th St Ste C Austin (78701) *(G-959)*

Austin Samsung Semicdtr LLC................................512 672-1000
12100 Samsung Blvd Austin (78754) *(G-960)*

Austin Scientific, Austin *Also called Trillium US Inc (G-1593)*

Austin Screen Printing Inc................................512 454-6249
4204 Medical Pkwy Austin (78756) *(G-961)*

Austin Semiconductor Inc................................512 339-1188
8701 Crotx Pk Dr Ste 105 Austin (78754) *(G-962)*

Austin Star Detonator Company................................956 831-7751
901 Cantu Rd Brownsville (78521) *(G-2337)*

Austin Stone Works, Austin *Also called Stone Production Inc (G-1539)*

Austin Technical Branch, Austin *Also called Stark Holdings Inc (G-1531)*

Austin Texas Print Inc................................512 507-2684
12917 Snow Ln Manor (78653) *(G-14644)*

Austin Ventures LP (PA)................................**512 485-1900**
835 W 6th St Ste 1500 Austin (78703) *(G-963)*

Austin Waterjet Inc................................512 243-9000
8510 Lava Hill Rd Austin (78744) *(G-964)*

Austin Western Railroad LLC................................512 388-6350
14205 N Mo Pac Expy # 130 Austin (78728) *(G-965)*

Austin White Lime Company (PA)................................**512 255-3646**
14001 Mcneil Rd Austin (78728) *(G-966)*

Austin Window Fashion Inc (PA)................................**512 836-3388**
10321 Burnet Rd Ste A Austin (78758) *(G-967)*

Austins Cabinets & Cnstr................................281 987-3308
2622 Lakemont Dr Houston (77039) *(G-8751)*

Austinuts Wholesale Inc................................512 272-8007
12911 Beltex Rd Manor (78653) *(G-14645)*

Austral Integrated Services................................936 266-0945
8601 Fawn Trl Bldg 3 Conroe (77385) *(G-3259)*

Austron, Pflugerville *Also called Paradigm Metals Incorporated (G-16683)*

Authentic Gelato LLC (HQ)................................**214 654-9501**
1215 Viceroy Dr Dallas (75247) *(G-3986)*

Authentic Presence, Austin *Also called Curse of Good Taste Inc (G-1078)*

Authesism Treatment Center, Dallas *Also called Autistic Treatment Ctr (G-3987)*

Autistic Treatment Ctr................................972 644-2076
10503 Metric Dr Dallas (75243) *(G-3987)*

Auto Air Export Inc (PA)................................**972 812-7000**
1401 Valley View Ln # 100 Irving (75061) *(G-12935)*

Auto Dril Inc................................432 561-8455
915 E County Road 125 Midland (79706) *(G-15125)*

Auto Electric Systems Inc................................972 241-2077
2708 K Ave Ste B Plano (75074) *(G-16796)*

Auto Fire and Safety Cons................................832 585-0423
7398 Teaswood Dr Conroe (77304) *(G-3260)*

Auto Fit Inc (PA)................................**713 696-9000**
6969 North Fwy Houston (77076) *(G-8752)*

Auto Fit Company, Houston *Also called Auto Fit Inc (G-8752)*

Auto Kabel North America Inc................................915 217-2253
1320 Henry Brennan Dr El Paso (79936) *(G-5654)*

Auto Kabel North America Inc (HQ)................................**915 217-2253**
7362 Remcon Cir El Paso (79912) *(G-5655)*

Auto License................................956 318-2158
100 E Cano St Ste 102 Edinburg (78539) *(G-5576)*

Auto Wax Company Inc................................214 631-4000
1275 Round Table Dr Dallas (75247) *(G-3988)*

Auto-Chlor Services LLC................................817 525-1021
701 107th St Arlington (76011) *(G-626)*

Auto-Out, Fort Worth *Also called Warren Watts Technology LLC (G-7127)*

Autoelectric of America Inc (HQ)................................**210 402-6003**
12500 San Pedro Ave # 30 San Antonio (78216) *(G-17924)*

Automated Ceiling Registers................................972 509-2400
903 N Bowser Rd Ste 162 Richardson (75081) *(G-17274)*

Automated Food Systems Inc................................469 517-0470
1000 Lofland St Waxahachie (75165) *(G-20528)*

Automated Service Systems, Houston *Also called Ascent Business Systems Inc (G-8716)*

Automatic Products Corp................................972 272-6422
2735 Forest Ln Garland (75042) *(G-7444)*

Automatic Switch Company................................281 829-2900
16203 Park Row Houston (77084) *(G-8753)*

Automation Controls Direct, Lewisville *Also called Innovative Idm LLC (G-14056)*

Automation Solutions LP (PA)................................**281 286-6017**
16055 Space Center Blvd # 45 Houston (77062) *(G-8754)*

Automation Technology Inc (PA)................................**713 934-0171**
21225 Fm 529 Rd Cypress (77433) *(G-3777)*

Automatize Logistics LLC................................817 221-8106
1123 S Main St Grapevine (76051) *(G-8013)*

Automotive Rentals Inc................................817 624-3650
711 Airway Dr Fort Worth (76106) *(G-6411)*

Autopoint Inc (HQ)................................**888 335-5762**
1301 Solana Blvd Ste 2100 Roanoke (76262) *(G-17482)*

Autoseis Inc................................972 332-3388
17103 Preston Rd Ste 200 Dallas (75248) *(G-3989)*

Autosol, Austin *Also called Avastar Brands LLC (G-968)*

Autosol, Houston *Also called Automation Solutions LP (G-8754)*

Autostar Solutions Inc................................817 377-2995
7301 State Highway 161 # 400 Irving (75039) *(G-12936)*

Autotest, San Antonio *Also called George W Cox & Sons Inc (G-18139)*

Autumnwood Millworks LLC................................936 344-9784
6462 Fm 1374 Rd New Waverly (77358) *(G-15853)*

Avangard Innovative LP (PA)................................**281 582-0700**
11906 Brittmoore Park Dr A Houston (77041) *(G-8755)*

Avant Technology Inc (HQ)................................**512 651-5300**
828 New Meister Ln # 300 Pflugerville (78660) *(G-16660)*

Avastar Brands LLC................................512 804-9337
13219 N Highway 183 Ste I Austin (78750) *(G-968)*

Avatar Systems Inc (PA)................................**972 720-1800**
2801 Network Blvd Ste 210 Frisco (75034) *(G-7267)*

Avatar Systems Inc................................972 334-0162
2801 Network Blvd Ste 210 Frisco (75034) *(G-7268)*

Avazzia Inc................................214 575-2820
13140 Coit Rd Ste 515 Dallas (75240) *(G-3990)*

Avco, Houston *Also called Marygrove Awning LLC (G-10782)*

Avcor Health Care Products Inc.....................817 551-0595
  2750 113th St Ste 300 Grand Prairie (75050) **(G-7838)**

Avdec, Fort Worth *Also called Aviation Dvcs Elctrnic Cmpnnts* **(G-6412)**

Aventis Cropscience, Lubbock *Also called Bayer Cropscience LP* **(G-14368)**

Avery Dennison Corporation.....................972 919-6900
  2025 Mckenzie Dr Ste 100 Carrollton (75006) **(G-2699)**

Avey Plastics.....................512 784-7047
  251 Uhland Rd San Marcos (78666) **(G-18678)**

Aviat US Inc (HQ).....................**408 941-7100**
  200 Parker Dr Ste C100a Austin (78728) **(G-969)**

Aviation Dvcs Elctrnic Cmpnnts.....................817 738-9161
  3215 W Loop 820 S Fort Worth (76116) **(G-6412)**

Aviation Products Inc.....................817 457-2040
  5621 E Rosedale St Ste A Fort Worth (76112) **(G-6413)**

Avid Gofer Magazine, Irving *Also called Avid Media Venture Inc* **(G-12937)**

Avid Golfer Magazine, Irving *Also called Avid Media Ventures, Inc* **(G-12938)**

Avid Media Venture Inc.....................972 550-9000
  1825 W Walnut Hill Ln # 10 Irving (75038) **(G-12937)**

Avid Media Ventures Inc.....................972 550-9000
  1825 W Walnut Hill Ln # 10 Irving (75038) **(G-12938)**

Avila Stone LLC.....................956 453-4747
  501 South Ave Donna (78537) **(G-5487)**

Avk Construction Group Inc.....................972 255-9464
  2311 Texas Dr Ste 105 Irving (75062) **(G-12939)**

Avo Multi-AMP Corporation (HQ).....................**214 330-3201**
  4545 W Davis St Dallas (75211) **(G-3991)**

Avo Multi-AMP Corporation.....................800 325-4574
  4545 W Davis St Dallas (75211) **(G-3992)**

Avo USA Inc.....................214 333-3201
  4271 Bronze Way Dallas (75237) **(G-3993)**

Avolin LLC.....................512 524-6149
  401 Congress Ave Ste 2650 Austin (78701) **(G-970)**

Avomex Inc (HQ).....................**817 509-0626**
  300 Burlington Rd Saginaw (76179) **(G-17738)**

Avon Golf Grips, Humble *Also called Tacki Mac Grips* **(G-12800)**

Avr, Houston *Also called Ad Valorem Records Inc* **(G-8474)**

Avteq Inc.....................214 905-9001
  9003 Governors Row Dallas (75247) **(G-3994)**

AVX Aircraft Company.....................817 731-8003
  6310 Southwest Blvd # 106 Benbrook (76109) **(G-2038)**

AW Installers Inc.....................210 649-1618
  4514 Billy Sames Adkins (78101) **(G-176)**

Aw Texas Inc.....................210 381-0117
  565 Bolton Rd Marion (78124) **(G-14755)**

Awesome Paging Inc (PA).....................**361 576-2255**
  3902 Houston Hwy Victoria (77901) **(G-20240)**

Awntech Corporation.....................817 354-9600
  10950 S Pipeline Rd Euless (76040) **(G-6132)**

Aws, Houston *Also called Advanced Welding Services Inc* **(G-8493)**

Awt, Cypress *Also called American Whl Thermographers* **(G-3773)**

Axalt Powde Coati Syste Usa I (HQ).....................**800 247-3886**
  9800 Genard Rd Houston (77041) **(G-8756)**

Axalta Pwdr Cating Systems Inc.....................832 955-0201
  9800 Genard Rd Houston (77041) **(G-8757)**

Axcelis Technologies Inc.....................214 377-7298
  870 N Dorothy Dr Ste 710 Richardson (75081) **(G-17275)**

Axent Manufacturing Inc.....................972 437-3737
  1226 Exchange Dr Richardson (75081) **(G-17276)**

Axess North America Inc.....................281 994-0364
  15915 Katy Fwy Houston (77094) **(G-8758)**

Axiom Manufacturing, Richardson *Also called Axent Manufacturing Inc* **(G-17276)**

Axiom Space Inc.....................346 293-7045
  1290 Hercules Ave Ste 120 Houston (77058) **(G-8759)**

Axiom Technologies LLC.....................281 931-0907
  255 Pennbright Dr Ste 220 Houston (77090) **(G-8760)**

Axiomagnets LLC.....................956 283-5920
  817 Chicago Ave McAllen (78501) **(G-14840)**

Axion Strl Innovations LLC.....................254 420-2078
  501 Old Hewitt Rd Waco (76712) **(G-20365)**

Axis Energy Services LLC.....................903 643-3700
  199 Corporate Rd Longview (75603) **(G-14198)**

Axis Pipe and Tube Inc.....................979 703-6847
  1451 Louis Mikulin Rd Bryan (77807) **(G-2455)**

Axis Pipe and Tube LLC (PA).....................**281 494-0900**
  770 S Post Oak Ln Ste 200 Houston (77056) **(G-8761)**

Axis Well Services LLC (PA).....................**903 759-0082**
  851 W Harrison Rd Longview (75604) **(G-14199)**

Axis Well Services LLC.....................432 333-1111
  1390 W Interstate 20 Odessa (79763) **(G-15921)**

Axon Energy Products, Houston *Also called Axon Ep Inc* **(G-8762)**

Axon Energy Services, Houston *Also called Axon Pressure Products Inc* **(G-8763)**

Axon Ep Inc (HQ).....................**281 855-3200**
  12606 N Huston Rosslyn Rd Houston (77086) **(G-8762)**

Axon Pressure Products Inc (HQ).....................**281 855-3200**
  12606 N Huston Rosslyn Rd Houston (77086) **(G-8763)**

Axon Pressure Products Inc.....................713 478-8007
  12606 N Huston Rosslyn Rd Houston (77086) **(G-8764)**

Axon Well Intervention Pdts, Houston *Also called Axon Pressure Products Inc* **(G-8764)**

Axton Fleet Systems, San Antonio *Also called Axton LLC* **(G-17925)**

Axton LLC.....................210 637-7400
  4844 Whirlwind Dr San Antonio (78217) **(G-17925)**

Axxairusa Inc.....................281 968-7138
  2201 Highway 35 Byp N D Alvin (77511) **(G-353)**

Axxea Systems, Lewisville *Also called CF Industries Inc* **(G-14035)**

Axxion Group Corporation.....................915 225-8888
  4731 Ripley Dr Ste A El Paso (79922) **(G-5656)**

Axxis Drilling Inc.....................985 868-6969
  15015 Vickery Dr Houston (77032) **(G-8765)**

Axxon, Austin *Also called Rfmicron Inc* **(G-1465)**

Ayc Group LLC.....................214 838-2630
  1036 S Jupiter Rd Ste 200 Garland (75042) **(G-7445)**

AZ Pallet Exchange.....................713 332-6145
  13100 Northwest Fwy Houston (77040) **(G-8766)**

AZ Terminal, Crosby *Also called Sooner Pipe LLC* **(G-3743)**

Azan Industries Inc.....................832 310-4459
  24811 Montclair Creek Ct Richmond (77406) **(G-17450)**

Azar Distilling LLC (PA).....................**210 403-5142**
  222 Austin Hwy Ste 3 San Antonio (78209) **(G-17926)**

Azar Services LLC.....................956 717-0023
  201 W Hillside Rd Ste 23 Laredo (78041) **(G-13864)**

Azle News, Azle *Also called Azle Tri-County Advertiser* **(G-1720)**

Azle Tri-County Advertiser (PA).....................**817 270-3340**
  321 W Main St Azle (76020) **(G-1720)**

Azpen Innovation, Plano *Also called Mingtel Inc* **(G-16929)**

Azt Wood LLC.....................409 283-5355
  950 N Pine St Woodville (75979) **(G-20915)**

Aztec Custom Screenprinting (PA).....................**512 744-0195**
  2815 Manor Rd Austin (78722) **(G-971)**

Aztec Fr Apparel Inc.....................830 422-1775
  2144 Cienegas Rd Del Rio (78840) **(G-5306)**

Aztec Galvanizing Services, Crowley *Also called Azz Inc* **(G-3751)**

Aztec Galvanizing Services, Waskom *Also called Aztec Mnfcturing-Waskom Partnr* **(G-20514)**

Aztec Imports Inc.....................915 858-2287
  9701 Pan American Dr # 100 El Paso (79927) **(G-5657)**

Aztec Mnfcturing-Waskom Partnr.....................903 687-3943
  990 E Texas Ave Waskom (75692) **(G-20514)**

Aztec Systems, Dallas *Also called Toutatis Aztec Solutions* **(G-5103)**

Azteca Fabrication.....................432 943-8888
  201 N Industrial Rd Monahans (79756) **(G-15599)**

Azteca Milling LP.....................806 258-7704
  4819 Fm 809 Dawn (79025) **(G-5216)**

Azteca Milling LP (HQ).....................**956 383-4911**
  5601 Executive Dr Ste 650 Irving (75038) **(G-12940)**

Azteca Milling LP.....................972 232-5363
  1159 Cottonwood Ln # 130 Irving (75038) **(G-12941)**

Azteca Milling LP.....................806 291-5633
  1388 County Road U Plainview (79072) **(G-16751)**

Azteca Milling LP.....................956 383-4911
  501 W Chapin St Edinburg (78541) **(G-5577)**

Azteca Tortilla Factory.....................956 702-7395
  1800 N Raul Longoria Rd San Juan (78589) **(G-18671)**

Azure Midstream Company LLC (HQ).....................**281 680-4300**
  12121 Wickchester Ln # 750 Houston (77079) **(G-8767)**

Azz - Texas Welded Wire LLC.....................817 282-4560
  637 W Hurst Blvd Ste B Hurst (76053) **(G-12835)**

Azz Enclosure Systems.....................832 295-1200
  1318 Bammel Rd Houston (77073) **(G-8768)**

Azz Galvanizing, Fort Worth *Also called Interntnal Glvnzers Partnr Ltd* **(G-6726)**

Azz Galvanizing Services, Fort Worth *Also called North Amrcn Glvnzing Ctngs Inc* **(G-6867)**

Azz Galvanizing-Beaumont, Beaumont *Also called Interntnal Glvnzers Partnr Ltd* **(G-1910)**

Azz Glvnzing - San Antonio LLC.....................210 661-8574
  5731 Fm 1346 San Antonio (78220) **(G-17927)**

Azz Inc (PA).....................**817 810-0095**
  3100 W 7th St Ste 500 Fort Worth (76107) **(G-6414)**

Azz Inc.....................281 458-1550
  7407 C E King Pkwy Houston (77044) **(G-8769)**

Azz Inc.....................817 297-4361
  200 N Beverly St Crowley (76036) **(G-3751)**

Azz Inc.....................817 284-0119
  7410 Pebble Dr Fort Worth (76118) **(G-6415)**

Azz Inc.....................409 842-0216
  5885 Industrial Rd Beaumont (77705) **(G-1856)**

Azz Inc.....................972 840-0934
  2314 Executive Dr Garland (75041) **(G-7446)**

Azz Inc.....................713 943-0340
  8500 Hansen Rd Houston (77075) **(G-8770)**

Azz Inc.....................832 467-3772
  9103 Frbanks N Houston Rd Houston (77064) **(G-8771)**

Azz Inc.....................713 225-9340
  400 N Tarrant St Crowley (76036) **(G-3752)**

Azz Incorporated.....................817 810-0095
  3100 W 7th St Ste 500 Fort Worth (76107) **(G-6416)**

Azz Incorporated.....................817 268-2414
  625 W Hurst Blvd Hurst (76053) **(G-12836)**

Azz Pwdr Coating Pltg Garland, Garland *Also called Azz Inc* **(G-7446)**

Azz Rig-A-Lite Product, Houston *Also called Azz Inc* **(G-8770)**

B & B Box and Lumber Company 903 592-7369
2800 Sunnybrook Dr Tyler (75701) *(G-20054)*

B & B Pipe & Industrial Tools 832 581-3179
4433 South Dr Houston (77053) *(G-8374)*

B & B Ready Mix Inc 972 287-9998
4240 S Belt Line Rd Seagoville (75159) *(G-18799)*

B & B Roustabout Inc 806 872-7276
211 S Lynn Ave Lamesa (79331) *(G-13822)*

B & B Stake Co 936 327-2161
1907 S Houston Ave Livingston (77351) *(G-14150)*

B & B Technology, Cibolo *Also called B&B Worldwide Technology (G-3062)*

B & B Windows Inc 817 237-2212
7714 Camp Bowie West Blvd Fort Worth (76116) *(G-6417)*

B & C Coating Inc 281 351-4773
826 S Persimmon St Tomball (77375) *(G-19962)*

B & C Printing Inc 940 766-0033
600 Ohio Ave Wichita Falls (76301) *(G-20741)*

B & D Services Inc 979 733-9938
Hwy 90 Sheridan (77475) *(G-18903)*

B & E Roustabout Inc 432 393-5672
103 Aztec St Big Spring (79720) *(G-2070)*

B & G Electric, Pampa *Also called Larry & Matt Inc (G-16326)*

B & G Foods, Houston *Also called B&G Foods Inc (G-8779)*

B & G Inc 713 944-1200
11460 Gulf Fwy Houston (77034) *(G-8772)*

B & H Bag Company 713 641-0921
35270 Cooper Rd Brookshire (77423) *(G-2310)*

B & H Enterprises 817 558-2667
803 Rose Ave Cleburne (76033) *(G-3080)*

B & J Accessories Inc 972 494-6939
5068 Lakehill Blvd Frisco (75034) *(G-7269)*

B & J Machine Works Inc 936 348-6371
402 Industrial Park Ln Madisonville (77864) *(G-14584)*

B & J Vacuum Tank Service Inc 936 536-6148
Hwy 770 1 Mile S Daisetta (77533) *(G-3832)*

B & J Welding Supply Ltd 432 563-1277
8102 W I 20 Midland (79706) *(G-15126)*

B & M Machinery Company, El Paso *Also called Musshorn Enterprises Inc (G-5892)*

B & M Oilfield Services LLC 979 241-2051
11174 Us Highway 181 S Falls City (78113) *(G-6182)*

B & M Tool Co, Midland *Also called Midland Wellhead Inc (G-15303)*

B & R Productions Inc 936 291-7827
5909 Fm 1374 Rd New Waverly (77358) *(G-15854)*

B & R Sign Company, Houston *Also called Houston Sign & Service Inc (G-10252)*

B & S Hardware Inc (PA) **903 856-3552**
112 N Greer Blvd Pittsburg (75686) *(G-16744)*

B & S Premium Sheet Metal Inc 214 388-4724
7877 Carr St Dallas (75227) *(G-3995)*

B & S Services Inc 281 342-1052
11928 Fm 1301 Rd Boling (77420) *(G-2146)*

B & T Directional Drilling Inc 903 629-3406
4581 N Fm 2869 Winnsboro (75494) *(G-20896)*

B & W Cabinets & Millwork, North Richland Hills *Also called B & W Remodeling Inc (G-15874)*

B & W Remodeling Inc 817 485-0444
8200 Precinct Line Rd North Richland Hills (76182) *(G-15874)*

B and D Binder and Index Inc 817 261-8227
2621 S Cooper St Arlington (76015) *(G-627)*

B and D Index Inc 817 261-8227
2621 S Cooper St Arlington (76015) *(G-628)*

B and L Machine, Houston *Also called Silva Technologies Inc (G-11897)*

B B L Ltd 254 559-3355
300 N Breckenridge Ave Breckenridge (76424) *(G-2220)*

B B M, McKinney *Also called Broach Bilt Manufacturing Inc (G-14930)*

B B T Industrial Engine Svc 210 661-6703
5858 Bicentennial St San Antonio (78219) *(G-17928)*

B Bad Sports Inc 713 664-3838
5325 Glenmont Dr Ste E Houston (77081) *(G-8773)*

B Braun Medical Inc 972 245-2243
1601 Wallace Dr Ste 150 Carrollton (75006) *(G-2700)*

B C F Products, Greenville *Also called Bonus Crop Fertilizer Inc (G-8065)*

B C O Black Cane Original 832 883-5774
5720 Wayne St Houston (77026) *(G-8774)*

B C T, San Antonio *Also called B Impressed Inc (G-17931)*

B C Williams Industries Inc 214 352-4255
6000 Denton Dr Dallas (75235) *(G-3996)*

B Comm Constructors LLC (PA) **210 257-0102**
1010 Creekview San Antonio (78219) *(G-17929)*

B D Production Co Inc 361 888-4741
615 N Upr Brdway St # 1900 Corpus Christi (78401) *(G-3478)*

B D W Company, Odessa *Also called Wwl Industries Inc (G-16215)*

B E I, Mesquite *Also called Bags Elite Inc (G-15029)*

B E R Precision Inc 281 659-0100
1100 N Washington Ave Cleveland (77327) *(G-3119)*

B E T C O, Houston *Also called Builders Equipment & Tool Co (G-9013)*

B Finishing Co Inc 512 759-2100
208 Tradesmen Dr Hutto (78634) *(G-12876)*

B G Metals Inc 210 648-5071
8410 Us Highway 87 E San Antonio (78263) *(G-17930)*

B H M Pipe & Supply Inc 281 328-5552
11615 F M Road 2100 Crosby (77532) *(G-3726)*

B I Products LLC 972 359-4000
915 Enterprise Blvd Allen (75013) *(G-255)*

B Impressed Inc 210 524-9229
8610 Botts St San Antonio (78217) *(G-17931)*

B J Electric Motor Service 432 570-4100
2900 W Francis Ave Midland (79701) *(G-15127)*

B J Services Company USA 713 625-4200
17015 Aldine Westfield Rd Houston (77073) *(G-8775)*

B J Services Company USA 281 357-2700
11211 Fm 2920 Rd Tomball (77375) *(G-19963)*

B J Services Company USA 713 879-1727
17021 Aldine Westfield Rd Houston (77073) *(G-8776)*

B J Services Company USA 713 439-8600
2929 Allen Pkwy Ste 2100 Houston (77019) *(G-8777)*

B J'S Custom Cables, Cypress *Also called GNC Cable Technologies Inc (G-3797)*

B M Higginbthams Mch Works Inc 713 941-1854
8353 Mosley Rd Houston (77075) *(G-8778)*

B Martinez & Sons Company Inc 210 226-6772
623 S Leona St San Antonio (78207) *(G-17932)*

B Mayfield McCraw 903 664-2332
3765 County Road 2135 Telephone (75488) *(G-19665)*

B O S S Medical, Del Rio *Also called Border Opprtnity Sver Systems (G-5308)*

B P Amoco Business Services, Houston *Also called BP Corporation North Amer Inc (G-8965)*

B P I Texas, Houston *Also called Building Plastics Inc (G-9015)*

B P Upstream Technology, Div, Houston *Also called BP Energy Company (G-8968)*

B Plan Inc 210 256-1700
1802 Shipman Dr San Antonio (78219) *(G-17933)*

B R G, Dallas *Also called Jones Lang Lasalle Ip Inc (G-4538)*

B R L Consultants Inc 210 341-3442
219 W Rhapsody Dr San Antonio (78216) *(G-17934)*

B T S Precision Machine 903 498-7501
8615 County Road 4074 Scurry (75158) *(G-18782)*

B W, Cameron *Also called Butler Weldments Corporation (G-2640)*

B W Energy Consultants Inc 903 593-1173
516 S Spring Ave Tyler (75702) *(G-20055)*

B W I of Schulenburg, Schulenburg *Also called Bwi Companies Inc (G-18773)*

B W Sinclair Inc 940 766-2556
13923 Us Highway 287 N Wichita Falls (76310) *(G-20742)*

B&B Aggregates Inc 281 659-9004
3469 Fm 1010 Rd Cleveland (77327) *(G-3120)*

B&B Custom Fabrication LLC 214 773-9240
915 Vz County Road 1818 Grand Saline (75140) *(G-7997)*

B&B Ornamental Iron Company 214 350-0639
1760 W Northwest Hwy Dallas (75220) *(G-3997)*

B&B Roadway SEC Solutions LLC (PA) **972 385-7899**
5900 S Lk Frest Dr Ste 23 Mckinney (75070) *(G-14924)*

B&B Steel Products, Houston *Also called B & B Pipe & Industrial Tools (G-8374)*

B&B Worldwide Technology 713 471-2387
608 Hinge Fls Cibolo (78108) *(G-3062)*

B&C Metal Works, Houston *Also called Turrubiartes Benedicto (G-12413)*

B&C Texas Leasing LLC 432 362-0548
2902 S Bickley Ave Pecos (79772) *(G-16616)*

B&G Foods Inc 281 821-6680
14700 North Fwy Houston (77090) *(G-8779)*

B&L Pipeco Services Inc (HQ) **281 955-3500**
20465 Sh 249 Ste 200 Houston (77070) *(G-8780)*

B&M Machine Works, Houston *Also called B M Higginbthams Mch Works Inc (G-8778)*

B&P Littleford LLC 713 433-3304
13135 South Fwy Houston (77047) *(G-8781)*

B&R Leasing, Fort Worth *Also called D & D Performance Enterprises (G-6569)*

B-29 Investments LP 940 665-4373
201 W California St Gainesville (76240) *(G-7334)*

B-P Supply Inc 806 872-9169
1317 S Lynn Ave Lamesa (79331) *(G-13823)*

B-TEC, Houston *Also called Btec Turbines LP (G-9002)*

B-W Grinding Service Inc 713 641-0888
5807 Nunn St Houston (77087) *(G-8782)*

B2b Copies LLC 512 402-9775
1310 Ranch Road 620 S A5 Lakeway (78734) *(G-13815)*

Ba-Ker Tank Head Company Inc 817 232-8030
10405 North Fwy Fort Worth (76177) *(G-6418)*

Baari Inc 214 566-5165
7801 Alma Dr Ste 10516 Plano (75025) *(G-16797)*

Baart Industrial Group (PA) **713 690-1690**
4660 Pine Timbers St # 165 Houston (77041) *(G-8783)*

Babcock & Wilcox Company 281 405-6800
363 N Sam Houston Pkwy E # 600 Houston (77060) *(G-8784)*

Babeco Inc 512 352-5355
1101 Crlos Parker Blvd Nw Taylor (76574) *(G-19648)*

Babin Machine Works Inc 409 892-1231
2510 N 9th St Beaumont (77703) *(G-1857)*

BAC and Btic America, Houston *Also called Btic America Corporation (G-9003)*

BAC Products Inc 832 230-1463
10197 Windfern Rd Houston (77064) *(G-8785)*

Bace Manufacturing Inc 713 329-8954
7131 Perimeter Park Dr Houston (77041) *(G-8786)*

Bace Manufacturing Inc 713 466-5563
7131 Perimeter Park Dr Houston (77041) *(G-8787)*

Back To Nature Inc 806 745-3559
5407 E Highway 84 Slaton (79364) *(G-18969)*

Backer Ehp Inc 615 556-7501
13209 S Unitec Dr Laredo (78045) *(G-13865)*

Backer Marathon Inc 830 775-1417
808 Hackberry Ln Del Rio (78840) *(G-5307)*

Backwoods Communications LLC 361 652-6900
918 Conti Ln Victoria (77904) *(G-20241)*

Badger Bmb Services Inc 432 447-0498
1724 S Bickley Ave Pecos (79772) *(G-16617)*

Badger Midstream Energy LP 713 395-6111
919 Milam St Ste 2300 Houston (77002) *(G-8788)*

Badger Pressure Control LLC (PA) **903 687-4100**
1197 Magnolia Rd Ste B Waskom (75692) *(G-20515)*

Badj Inc 254 918-5397
139 Private Road 1705 Stephenville (76401) *(G-19407)*

Badmoon Enterprises LLC 817 548-0561
1133 W Main St Arlington (76013) *(G-629)*

Bae Systems Inc 512 276-3100
6500 Tracor Ln Austin (78725) *(G-972)*

Bae Systems Info & Elec Sys 972 994-4176
17111 Waterview Pkwy Dallas (75252) *(G-3838)*

Bae Systems Info & Elec Sys 512 276-3100
6500 Tracor Ln Austin (78725) *(G-973)*

Bae Systems Land Armaments LP 408 504-1877
3831 Lucius Mccelvey Dr Temple (76504) *(G-19670)*

Bae Systems Resolution Inc (HQ) **713 868-7700**
1000 La St Ste 4950 Houston (77002) *(G-8789)*

Bags Elite Inc 972 279-7798
3030 E Meadows Blvd Mesquite (75150) *(G-15029)*

Baikowski Malakoff Inc 903 489-1910
1631 W Royall Blvd Malakoff (75148) *(G-14634)*

Bailey & Harley Services LLC 409 994-5857
227 Business Hwy 96 S Buna (77612) *(G-2560)*

Baileys Premier Services LLC 817 292-2423
4200 S Hulen St Fort Worth (76109) *(G-6419)*

Baily International Inc 713 673-0080
5600 Harvey Wilson Dr Houston (77020) *(G-8790)*

Bainbridge Uinta LLC 214 580-2059
8150 N Central Expy # 650 Dallas (75206) *(G-3998)*

Bairds Mrs Bakeries Bus Tr 713 996-5000
6650 N Houston Rosslyn Rd Houston (77091) *(G-8791)*

Baker Macy Edward 817 572-7346
5213 Sun Valley Dr Fort Worth (76119) *(G-6420)*

Baker & Company Cnstr LLC 903 561-1763
4955 Profit Dr Tyler (75707) *(G-20056)*

Baker Atlas, Midland *Also called Baker Hghes Olfld Oprtions LLC (G-15129)*

Baker Atlas, Victoria *Also called Baker Hghes Olfld Oprtions LLC (G-20242)*

Baker Atlas, Victoria *Also called Baker Hughes A GE Company LLC (G-20243)*

Baker Atlas, Carrollton *Also called Baker Hghes Olfld Oprtions LLC (G-2701)*

Baker Atlas, Hempstead *Also called Baker Hughes A GE Company LLC (G-8249)*

Baker Hghes Olfld Oprtions Inc 806 665-5786
1043 N Price Rd Pampa (79065) *(G-16315)*

Baker Hghes Olfld Oprtions LLC 432 685-8900
6 Desta Dr Ste 5300 Midland (79705) *(G-15128)*

Baker Hghes Olfld Oprtions LLC 281 456-5300
9902 Sheldon Rd Houston (77049) *(G-8792)*

Baker Hghes Olfld Oprtions LLC 713 879-3760
1902 Cypress Station Dr B Houston (77090) *(G-8793)*

Baker Hghes Olfld Oprtions LLC 940 626-4169
11047 Fm 14 Tyler (75706) *(G-20057)*

Baker Hghes Olfld Oprtions LLC 713 923-9351
14990 Yorktown Plaza Dr Houston (77040) *(G-8794)*

Baker Hghes Olfld Oprtions LLC 432 694-7761
2001 Commerce Dr Midland (79703) *(G-15129)*

Baker Hghes Olfld Oprtions LLC 361 573-2493
4206 N Main St Victoria (77901) *(G-20242)*

Baker Hghes Olfld Oprtions LLC 432 694-9517
2105 Market St Midland (79703) *(G-15130)*

Baker Hghes Olfld Oprtions LLC 361 692-3000
6938 Fm 1784 Pleasanton (78064) *(G-17062)*

Baker Hghes Olfld Oprtions LLC 210 662-5650
4302 Profit St San Antonio (78219) *(G-17935)*

Baker Hghes Olfld Oprtions LLC 713 466-1322
9100 Emmott Rd Houston (77040) *(G-8795)*

Baker Hghes Olfld Oprtions LLC 281 363-6000
9110 Grogans Mill Rd The Woodlands (77380) *(G-19833)*

Baker Hghes Olfld Oprtions LLC (PA) **713 879-1000**
2001 Rankin Rd Houston (77073) *(G-8796)*

Baker Hghes Olfld Oprtions LLC 972 466-2673
1875 Monetary Ln Carrollton (75006) *(G-2701)*

Baker Hghes Olfld Oprtions LLC 432 563-1900
10912 W Highway 80 E Odessa (79765) *(G-15922)*

Baker Hghes Olfld Oprtions LLC 832 519-2000
4101 Oates Rd Houston (77013) *(G-8797)*

Baker Hghes Olfld Oprtions LLC 817 806-3200
309 W 7th St Ste 1520 Fort Worth (76102) *(G-6421)*

Baker Hghes Olfld Oprtions LLC 281 351-8131
11211 Fm 2920 Rd Tomball (77375) *(G-19964)*

Baker Hghes Olfld Oprtions LLC 800 441-0535
714 N Riedel St Yorktown (78164) *(G-20976)*

Baker Hghes Olfld Oprtions LLC 361 289-0373
322 Manning Rd Corpus Christi (78409) *(G-3479)*

Baker Hghes Prcess Ppline Svcs 832 519-2000
4101 Oates Rd Houston (77013) *(G-8798)*

Baker Hughes, Lufkin *Also called Lufkin Gears LLC (G-14539)*

Baker Hughes, Fairfield *Also called Baker Petrolite (G-6169)*

Baker Hughes, Decatur *Also called Baker Petrolite LLC (G-5243)*

Baker Hughes, Kilgore *Also called Baker Petrolite (G-13533)*

Baker Hughes 806 273-6531
Magic Plains Indus Park Borger (79007) *(G-2162)*

Baker Hughes 432 385-7861
311 Old Lubbock Snyder (79549) *(G-18983)*

Baker Hughes A GE Company LLC 281 351-8131
11211 Fm 2920 Rd Tomball (77375) *(G-19965)*

Baker Hughes A GE Company LLC 713 580-9700
2001 Rankin Rd Houston (77073) *(G-8799)*

Baker Hughes A GE Company LLC 361 883-1591
430 Navigation Blvd Corpus Christi (78408) *(G-3480)*

Baker Hughes A GE Company LLC 432 685-8900
6 Desta Dr Ste 5300 Midland (79705) *(G-15131)*

Baker Hughes A GE Company LLC 432 248-3000
6165 W Murphy St Odessa (79763) *(G-15923)*

Baker Hughes A GE Company LLC 713 625-4200
2001 Rankin Rd Houston (77073) *(G-8800)*

Baker Hughes A GE Company LLC 956 383-0142
Fm 1925 E St Edinburg (78539) *(G-5578)*

Baker Hughes A GE Company LLC 210 662-5200
11245 Old Corpus Christi San Antonio (78223) *(G-17936)*

Baker Hughes A GE Company LLC 936 336-7218
Hwy 146 N Liberty Liberty (77575) *(G-14114)*

Baker Hughes A GE Company LLC 903 690-0026
3115 Sw Loop Carthage (75633) *(G-2899)*

Baker Hughes A GE Company LLC 956 791-0466
402 Boomtown St Laredo (78043) *(G-13866)*

Baker Hughes A GE Company LLC 361 573-2493
4206 N Main St Victoria (77901) *(G-20243)*

Baker Hughes A GE Company LLC 972 550-3933
1333 Cooper Dr Ste 350 Irving (75061) *(G-12942)*

Baker Hughes A GE Company LLC 281 276-5400
12645 W Airport Blvd Sugar Land (77478) *(G-19447)*

Baker Hughes A GE Company LLC 432 681-8300
2105 Market St Midland (79703) *(G-15132)*

Baker Hughes A GE Company LLC 713 625-4200
15355 Vantage Pkwy W # 300 Houston (77032) *(G-8801)*

Baker Hughes A GE Company LLC 281 363-6000
9110 Grogans Mill Rd The Woodlands (77380) *(G-19834)*

Baker Hughes A GE Company LLC 979 826-3621
35372 Betka Rd Hempstead (77445) *(G-8249)*

Baker Hughes Company (PA) **713 439-8600**
17021 Aldine Westfield Rd Houston (77073) *(G-8802)*

Baker Hughes Drilling Fluids, Houston *Also called Baker Hghes Olfld Oprtions LLC (G-8792)*

Baker Hughes Energy Svcs LLC (HQ) **713 439-8600**
17021 Aldine Westfield Rd Houston (77073) *(G-8803)*

Baker Hughes Financing LLC (HQ) **713 439-8600**
2001 Rankin Rd Houston (77073) *(G-8804)*

Baker Hughes Forum SPD, San Antonio *Also called Baker Hghes Olfld Oprtions LLC (G-17935)*

Baker Hughes Holdings LLC 956 285-2002
5718 San Bernardo Ave Laredo (78041) *(G-13867)*

Baker Hughes Holdings LLC 325 853-2553
Hwy 277 Eldorado (76936) *(G-6044)*

Baker Hughes Holdings LLC 713 625-4200
17021 Aldine Westfield Rd Houston (77073) *(G-8805)*

Baker Hughes Holdings LLC (HQ) **713 439-8600**
17021 Aldine Westfield Rd Houston (77073) *(G-8806)*

Baker Hughes Holdings LLC 281 231-1000
7000 Hollister St Ste 300 Houston (77040) *(G-8807)*

Baker Hughes Holdings LLC 713 439-8600
1999 Rankin Rd Houston (77073) *(G-8808)*

Baker Hughes Holdings LLC 806 637-4745
702 S 14th St Brownfield (79316) *(G-2329)*

Baker Hughes Holdings LLC 817 426-7080
1980 Sw Wilshire Blvd Burleson (76028) *(G-2568)*

Baker Hughes Incorporated 817 838-0583
2426 Ne 35th St Fort Worth (76111) *(G-6422)*

Baker Hughes Incorporated 956 781-9133
5510 N Cage Blvd Pharr (78577) *(G-16694)*

Baker Hughes Incorporated 432 264-9007
3609 E Interstate 20 Big Spring (79720) *(G-2071)*

Baker Hughes Oilfld Operations, Burleson *Also called Baker Hughes Holdings LLC (G-2568)*

Baker Hughes Solutions, Pleasanton *Also called Baker Hghes Olfld Oprtions LLC (G-17062)*

Baker Hughes Solutions, Houston *Also called Baker Hghes Olfld Oprtions LLC (G-8796)*

Baker Hughs Inteq, Corpus Christi *Also called Baker Hghes Olfld Oprtions LLC (G-3479)*

Baker Metal Products Inc (PA) ... **972 241-3553**
11140 Zodiac Ln Dallas (75229) *(G-3999)*

Baker O & P Enterprises Inc (HQ) ... **817 332-7313**
810 Lipscomb St Ste A Fort Worth (76104) *(G-6423)*

Baker Oil Tool, Houston *Also called Baker Hghes Olfld Oprtions LLC (G-8793)*

Baker Oil Tools, Pampa *Also called Baker Hghes Olfld Oprtions Inc (G-16315)*

Baker Oil Tools, Odessa *Also called Baker Hghes Olfld Oprtions LLC (G-15922)*

Baker Oil Tools, Yorktown *Also called Baker Hghes Olfld Oprtions LLC (G-20976)*

Baker Operating Inc ... 432 367-5808
700 W 65th St Odessa (79764) *(G-15924)*

Baker Orthotics & Prosthetics, Fort Worth *Also called Baker O & P Enterprises Inc (G-6423)*

Baker Petrolite ... 903 389-2903
111 Bailiff Dr Fairfield (75840) *(G-6169)*

Baker Petrolite ... 432 498-9191
10520 W Interstate 20 Odessa (79765) *(G-15925)*

Baker Petrolite ... 903 984-0251
1100 Stone Rd Ste 107 Kilgore (75662) *(G-13533)*

Baker Petrolite LLC ... 940 658-3574
3009 State Highway 222 E Knox City (79529) *(G-13662)*

Baker Petrolite LLC ... 979 567-9859
Cty Rd 108 Hwy 21 W Caldwell (77836) *(G-2627)*

Baker Petrolite LLC (HQ) ... **281 276-5400**
12645 W Airport Blvd Sugar Land (77478) *(G-19448)*

Baker Petrolite LLC ... 940 626-4436
1404 S Fm 51 Decatur (76234) *(G-5243)*

Baker Petrolite LLC ... 281 474-5166
13200 Baypark Rd Pasadena (77507) *(G-16392)*

Baker Petrolite LLC ... 361 394-7544
Hwy 59 N Freer (78357) *(G-7222)*

Baker Petrolite LLC ... 409 935-2248
209 Fm 1765 Rd La Marque (77568) *(G-13706)*

Baker Petrolite LLC ... 806 229-8121
E Hwy 301 Sundown (79372) *(G-19612)*

Baker Petrolite LLC ... 713 599-7400
3900 Essex Ln Ste 1200 Houston (77027) *(G-8809)*

Baker Sign, Fort Worth *Also called Baker Macy Edward (G-6420)*

Baker Steel Company Inc (PA) ... **713 479-9399**
7600 Cherokee St Katy (77494) *(G-13351)*

Baker's Pride, Allen *Also called Bakers Pride Oven Co Inc (G-256)*

Bakers Pride Oven Co Inc ... 800 431-2745
1307 N Watters Rd Ste 180 Allen (75013) *(G-256)*

Bakery Equipment & Svc Co Inc ... 210 734-5124
200 Lombrano St San Antonio (78207) *(G-17937)*

Bakery Express Centl Texas LP ... 972 221-8394
1301a Ridgeview Ste 400 Lewisville (75057) *(G-14025)*

Bakeryworks LLC ... 972 250-1818
4436 Mcewen Rd Farmers Branch (75244) *(G-6190)*

Bakken Express LLC ... 281 359-8382
12 Shorelake Dr Kingwood (77339) *(G-13638)*

Balbia, Missouri City *Also called North Blue Oak Inc (G-15585)*

Balcones Distilling LLC (PA) ... **254 755-6003**
225 S 11th St Waco (76701) *(G-20366)*

Balcones Technologies LLC ... 512 699-5828
104 Alabaster Caverns Dr Georgetown (78628) *(G-7639)*

Balder USA, Houston *Also called Freedom Wheels Inc (G-9860)*

Balderas Welding Services LLC ... 432 661-3164
1403 N Washington Ave Odessa (79761) *(G-15926)*

Baldwin Metals Company Inc ... 214 637-1030
1901 W Commerce St Dallas (75208) *(G-4000)*

Balfour Scholastic School Sup ... 903 455-4556
2511 Ridgecrest Rd Greenville (75402) *(G-8063)*

Ball Corporation ... 817 551-3100
6600 Will Rogers Blvd Fort Worth (76140) *(G-6424)*

Ball Dpf LLC ... 888 839-8722
307 E Mulberry St Sherman (75090) *(G-18907)*

Ball Metal Beverage Cont Corp ... 936 760-2255
1001 N Fm 3083 Rd E Conroe (77303) *(G-3261)*

Ball Metal Beverage Cont Corp ... 817 551-3100
6600 Will Rogers Blvd Fort Worth (76140) *(G-6425)*

Ball Winch Pipeline Services, Willis *Also called LB Foster Ball Winch Inc (G-20853)*

Ballard Exploration Co Inc (PA) ... **713 651-0181**
1021 Manor St Ste 2310 Houston (77015) *(G-8810)*

Ballew Casting Repair Inc ... 361 882-9901
673 Omaha Dr Corpus Christi (78408) *(G-3481)*

Ballistic GL Armor Sltions LLC ... 214 382-4100
15504 Wright Brothers Dr Addison (75001) *(G-105)*

Ballistics Systems Inc ... 713 939-1160
26200 Lakeview Dr Hockley (77447) *(G-8341)*

Balloffet Die Corporation Inc ... 915 592-5252
11450 Rojas Dr Ste D17 El Paso (79936) *(G-5658)*

Ballqube Lc ... 903 863-5572
12146 County Road 4233 W Cushing (75760) *(G-3767)*

Ballqube Inc ... 800 543-1470
3317 Stanford Ave Dallas (75225) *(G-4001)*

Ballroom, Stafford *Also called Techniplex Conference Center (G-19383)*

Bally Plus, Garland *Also called Garland Ventures Ltd (G-7496)*

Bally United Produce Ltd ... 972 487-7788
429 Forest Gate Dr Garland (75042) *(G-7447)*

Balong Trucking LLC ... 408 471-1383
110 W Cityline Dr # 3072 Richardson (75082) *(G-17277)*

Balt Best Rite, Temple *Also called Mooreco Inc (G-19691)*

Bam Denton MGT Ventures LLC ... 940 898-1200
7515 Lemmon Ave Dallas (75209) *(G-4002)*

Bam Operating, Eastland *Also called CAM Services Inc (G-5561)*

Bamberger Polymers Inc ... 281 481-9100
12600 N Featherwood Dr # 300 Houston (77034) *(G-8811)*

Bamberger Polymers Corp ... 281 481-9100
11550 Fuqua St Ste 205 Houston (77034) *(G-8812)*

Bamsch Enterprises Intl Ltd ... 281 448-5925
7113 Chippewa Blvd Houston (77086) *(G-8813)*

Bana Inc (PA) ... **817 232-3750**
624 E Mcleroy Blvd Saginaw (76179) *(G-17739)*

Bana Box, Saginaw *Also called Bana Inc (G-17739)*

Banc Professional Services ... 972 734-1200
100 Progress St Glen Rose (76043) *(G-7731)*

Band Mans Co Southwest Inc (PA) ... **214 350-0631**
2845 Ladybird Ln Dallas (75220) *(G-4003)*

Bandana Installation LP ... 903 764-2933
215 N Us Highway 287 Elkhart (75839) *(G-6058)*

Bandera Rock and Road, Bandera *Also called Roger D Stevens Contractor (G-1744)*

Bandit Energy Services, New Braunfels *Also called Enersol Group Inc (G-15790)*

Bandy Incorporated ... 972 276-6516
201 S International Rd Garland (75042) *(G-7448)*

Banister Tool Incorporated ... 512 258-8351
3009 A W Grimes Blvd Pflugerville (78660) *(G-16661)*

Bank of New York Mellon Corp ... 214 239-6420
2001 Bryan St Fl 11 Dallas (75201) *(G-4004)*

Bank of NY M Trust Co N A, Dallas *Also called Bank of New York Mellon Corp (G-4004)*

Bankers Products & Printing ... 903 438-0500
216 Jackson St N Sulphur Springs (75482) *(G-19580)*

Bankpoint, McKinney *Also called VSI Solutions Inc (G-14987)*

Banks Group, The, Austin *Also called Banks Petroleum Inc (G-974)*

Banks Petroleum Inc ... 512 478-0059
1601 Rio Grande St # 331 Austin (78701) *(G-974)*

Bankson Group Ltd ... 210 699-3800
12814 Cogburn San Antonio (78249) *(G-17938)*

Banner Sign Graphics ... 512 458-5348
607 Buckskin Dr Round Rock (78681) *(G-17626)*

Banner Supply Inc ... 713 802-2225
4800 W 34th St Ste D1 Houston (77092) *(G-8814)*

Banner Technology Inc ... 713 675-3100
959 Pleasantville Dr Houston (77029) *(G-8815)*

Banyan Foods Company, Houston *Also called CGJ Enterprises Inc (G-9151)*

Banyan Industries Inc ... 817 413-7945
2701 Ludelle St Ste A Fort Worth (76105) *(G-6426)*

Banyan International Corp ... 888 782-8548
2118 E I 20 Abilene (79601) *(G-15)*

Baptist Book Store, Texarkana *Also called Baptist Sunday Schl Committee (G-19756)*

Baptist Sunday Schl Committee ... 903 792-2783
4605 N State Line Ave Texarkana (75503) *(G-19756)*

Bar H Welding Consult, Longview *Also called Bar H Welding LLC (G-14200)*

Bar H Welding LLC ... 903 806-3110
1381 E I 20 Access Rd Longview (75603) *(G-14200)*

Bar Yam Engineering Inc ... 281 999-8664
13911 Faber St Houston (77037) *(G-8816)*

Barbeque Wood Flavors, Ennis *Also called Bwf Enterprises Inc (G-6089)*

Barcana Inc (PA) ... **800 638-4533**
2301 Crown Ct Irving (75038) *(G-12943)*

Barco Industries ... 979 732-2086
3554 Fm 109 Columbus (78934) *(G-3229)*

Bard Oprtion Ctr Reynosa Plant, Pharr *Also called C R Bard Inc (G-16695)*

Bargain Book, Brownsville *Also called Valley Media Inc (G-2419)*

Bargainartusa.com, Houston *Also called Somerset House Publishing Inc (G-11949)*

Barite Logistics LLC ... 281 635-0584
2301 Pin Hook Ct Seabrook (77586) *(G-18784)*

Bariven, Houston *Also called Pdvsa Services Inc (G-11266)*

Bark To Basics LLC (PA) ... **913 825-1760**
600 Las Colinas Blvd E Irving (75039) *(G-12944)*

Barker & Bratton Steel Inc ... 972 556-1951
10733 Newkirk St Dallas (75220) *(G-4005)*

Barkley Holdings LLC ... 832 413-4400
5011 Walnut Hills Dr Kingwood (77345) *(G-13639)*

Barlite, San Antonio *Also called Alamo Concrete Products Ltd (G-18636)*

Barmac LLC ... 903 454-3166
8916 Wesley St Greenville (75402) *(G-8064)*

Barmalco Inc ... 281 933-9128
12943 Old Richmond Rd Houston (77099) *(G-8817)*

Barmalco Prcision Mch Tls Dies, Houston *Also called Barmalco Inc (G-8817)*

Barnes Barnett LLC ... 214 445-6800
5000 Legacy Dr Ste 300 Plano (75024) *(G-16798)*

Barnes Oil & Gas LLC (PA) ... **214 445-6800**
5000 Legacy Dr Ste 300 Plano (75024) *(G-16799)*

Barnett Gathering LLC (HQ) ... **817 870-2800**
810 Houston St Fort Worth (76102) *(G-6427)*

Barons Creek Vineyards LLC 830 304-3000
5963 E Us Highway 290 Fredericksburg (78624) *(G-7171)*

Barr Fabrication LLC 325 643-2277
4501 Danhil Dr Brownwood (76801) *(G-2425)*

Barrera Contractors Inc 432 639-2516
104 S Underwood St Iraan (79744) *(G-12916)*

Barrilleaux Inc 903 545-2280
1412 W Broad St Oakwood (75855) *(G-15892)*

Barrington Group Ltd Inc 214 528-6990
2300 N Haskell Ave Dallas (75204) *(G-4006)*

Barron Manufacturing Inc 214 747-2544
1195 Empire Central Dr Dallas (75247) *(G-4007)*

Barrport Properties Inc (HQ) **713 271-2253**
6131 Corporate Dr Houston (77036) *(G-8818)*

Bartec US Corporation 281 214-8542
650 Century Plaza Dr # 120 Houston (77073) *(G-8819)*

Barten Industrial Coatings LLC 979 732-8441
4176 Highway 71 Columbus (78934) *(G-3230)*

Barton and Company, Columbus *Also called Barco Industries* *(G-3229)*

Barton Publications Inc 512 262-1110
1717 N Burleson St Kyle (78640) *(G-13679)*

Barton Resources, Irving *Also called Southern Stud Weld Inc* *(G-13185)*

Barton Springs Mill Inc 512 554-5981
16604 Fitzhugh Rd B Dripping Springs (78620) *(G-5501)*

Barton Sprngs E Aquifer Cnsrvt 512 282-8441
1124 Regal Row Austin (78748) *(G-975)*

Barton Table LLC 512 791-2260
1626 Palma Plz Apt 6 Austin (78703) *(G-976)*

Bartos Industries Ltd 800 858-8497
2901 Wesley Way Richland Hills (76118) *(G-17436)*

Bartos Irrigation Equipment, Lubbock *Also called Aluminum Metal Products Inc* *(G-14360)*

Bartush-Schnitzius Foods Co 972 219-1270
1137 N Kealy Ave Lewisville (75057) *(G-14026)*

Basa Resources Inc 936 655-2477
6729 Fm 2781 Kennard (75847) *(G-13494)*

Basa Resources Inc 254 559-3366
566 Fm 2231e Breckenridge (76424) *(G-2221)*

Basa Resources Inc (PA) **214 580-5203**
14875 Landmark Blvd # 400 Dallas (75254) *(G-4008)*

Basden Steel and Erection Inc (HQ) **817 295-6100**
645 E Renfro St Ste C Burleson (76028) *(G-2569)*

Basden Steel Corporation 817 295-6100
645 E Renfro St Ste C Burleson (76028) *(G-2570)*

Base Base Corporation 832 236-9801
2746 Clay St Houston (77003) *(G-8820)*

Baseline Energy Services LP 432 248-9112
5001 W Wadley Ave Midland (79707) *(G-15133)*

Baseline Energy Services LP (PA) **817 889-0056**
201 N Foch St Fort Worth (76107) *(G-6428)*

Baseline Mfg Partners LP 936 344-2858
1070 Tafelski Rd New Waverly (77358) *(G-15855)*

Basell USA Inc 682 518-0687
100 S Mitchell Rd Mansfield (76063) *(G-14657)*

BASF Corporation 800 794-1019
3120 Hayes Rd Ste 200 Houston (77082) *(G-8821)*

BASF Corporation 409 960-5000
Gate 66 State Hwy 366 Port Arthur (77643) *(G-17101)*

BASF Corporation 713 383-4500
1703 Crosspoint Ave Houston (77054) *(G-8822)*

BASF Corporation 973 245-6000
1216 Trend Dr Carrollton (75006) *(G-2702)*

BASF Corporation 409 981-5000
14385 W Port Arthur Rd Beaumont (77705) *(G-1858)*

BASF Corporation 281 884-4400
4403 La Porte Rd Pasadena (77501) *(G-16393)*

Basic Babes, Pearland *Also called Chapman Shameka* *(G-16543)*

Basic Energy Services Inc 361 348-3320
1104 Fm 716 Premont (78375) *(G-17203)*

Basic Energy Services Inc (PA) **817 334-4100**
801 Cherry St Unit 2 Fort Worth (76102) *(G-6429)*

Basic Energy Services Inc 817 645-0853
801 Cherry St Unit 21 Fort Worth (76102) *(G-6430)*

Basic Energy Services Inc 918 225-1111
801 Cherry St Unit 21 Fort Worth (76102) *(G-6431)*

Basic Energy Services Inc 432 523-4251
510 Nw Mustang Dr Andrews (79714) *(G-537)*

Basic Energy Services Inc 432 445-2216
2307 S Bickley Ave Pecos (79772) *(G-16618)*

Basic Energy Services Inc 361 578-3503
1303 E Constitution St Victoria (77901) *(G-20244)*

Basic Energy Services Inc 432 620-5500
5805 E Highway 80 Midland (79706) *(G-15134)*

Basic Energy Services Inc 940 683-5484
2103 Hwy 114 Bridgeport (76426) *(G-2288)*

Basic Energy Services Inc 432 586-2586
312 E Hwy 302 Kermit (79745) *(G-13508)*

Basic Energy Services Inc 979 733-0488
183 Martin St El Campo (77437) *(G-5612)*

Basic Energy Services Inc 254 442-2200
801 Cherry St Unit 21 Fort Worth (76102) *(G-6432)*

Basic Energy Services Inc 903 295-0817
5209 Estes Pkwy Longview (75603) *(G-14201)*

Basic Energy Services Inc 903 895-4448
1995 State Highway 42 N Overton (75684) *(G-16275)*

Basic Energy Services Inc 325 884-5901
101 N Mississippi Ave Big Lake (76932) *(G-2054)*

Basic Energy Services Inc 432 267-8885
1203 Highway 176 Big Spring (79720) *(G-2072)*

Basic Energy Services Inc 936 248-2788
724 84 Hwy E Tenaha (75974) *(G-19723)*

Basic Energy Services Inc 325 762-2239
5690 E Us Highway 180 Albany (76430) *(G-184)*

Basic Energy Services Inc 432 620-0880
3503 S County Road 1210 Midland (79706) *(G-15135)*

Basic Energy Services Inc 325 573-8837
213 N College Ave Snyder (79549) *(G-18984)*

Basic Energy Services Inc 361 574-9512
16500 San Pedro Ave # 400 San Antonio (78232) *(G-17939)*

Basic Energy Services Inc 432 580-8821
2900 E Interstate 20 Odessa (79766) *(G-15927)*

Basic Energy Services LP 432 264-1212
2206 N Hwy 87 Big Spring (79720) *(G-2073)*

Basic Energy Services LP 432 530-0907
3301 N Fm 1936 Odessa (79764) *(G-15928)*

Basic Energy Services LP 432 758-9215
W Hwy 180 & Cr 209 Seminole (79360) *(G-18881)*

Basic Energy Services LP 903 657-8171
3139 County Road 205 N Henderson (75652) *(G-8257)*

Basic Energy Services LP 806 592-4287
2753 Chisholm Trl Denver City (79323) *(G-5416)*

Basic Energy Services LP (HQ) **817 334-4100**
801 Cherry St Unit 2 Fort Worth (76102) *(G-6433)*

Basic Energy Services LP 361 358-2505
4638 Fish Ln Beeville (78102) *(G-1982)*

Basic Energy Services LP 903 643-1140
801 Cherry St Unit 21 Fort Worth (76102) *(G-6434)*

Basic Energy Services LP 409 842-6262
1705 Highway 146 Dayton (77535) *(G-5221)*

Basic Esa Inc 817 334-4100
100 Birch St Knox City (79529) *(G-13663)*

Basic Marine Services Inc 817 334-4100
801 Cherry St Unit 2 Fort Worth (76102) *(G-6435)*

Basic Oil & Gas Well Services, Fort Worth *Also called Basic Energy Services LP* *(G-6433)*

Basileia Investments Inc 806 765-5791
2001 N Avenue P Lubbock (79403) *(G-14365)*

Basils Oilfield Service Inc 936 274-5575
F M 787 Saratoga (77585) *(G-18740)*

Basin Drilling LP 903 561-8211
1121 E Se Loop 323 # 218 Tyler (75701) *(G-20058)*

Basin Drilling 2, Tyler *Also called Basin Drilling LP* *(G-20058)*

Basin Oil & Gas LLC 817 820-8910
1320 S University Dr Fort Worth (76107) *(G-6436)*

Basin Pipeline LLC 817 460-7777
7950 John T White Rd Fort Worth (76120) *(G-6437)*

Basin Water Inc 877 312-8950
700 Rockmead Dr Ste 105 Kingwood (77339) *(G-13640)*

Basintek LLC, Houston *Also called Abaco Drilling Tech LLC* *(G-8441)*

Basis Technologies Inc 888 623-0220
16301 Quorum Dr Ste 100b Addison (75001) *(G-106)*

Basler Electric Circuits Div, Taylor *Also called Basler Electric Company* *(G-19649)*

Basler Electric Company 512 352-3154
204 Highland Dr Taylor (76574) *(G-19649)*

Basler Plastics LLC 512 392-2800
201 Center Point Rd San Marcos (78666) *(G-18679)*

Bass Bros Enterprises, Fort Worth *Also called Bass Enterprises Production Co* *(G-6438)*

Bass Energy Services LLC (PA) **903 687-1800**
1197 Magnolia Rd Ste B Waskom (75692) *(G-20516)*

Bass Enterprises Production Co (PA) **817 698-0200**
201 Main St Ste 2700 Fort Worth (76102) *(G-6438)*

Bass Enterprises Production Co 432 586-2563
7 Mile Rd Ne Kermit (79745) *(G-13509)*

Bass Printing Inc 817 293-4913
4620 S Edgewood Ter Fort Worth (76119) *(G-6439)*

Basset Wood Work, El Paso *Also called Bassett Woodworks* *(G-5659)*

Bassett Furniture Direct, San Antonio *Also called Bassett Furniture Inds Inc* *(G-17940)*

Bassett Furniture Inds Inc 210 641-0101
12720 W Ih 10 San Antonio (78230) *(G-17940)*

Bassett Woodworks 915 855-2144
11905 Golden Gate Rd El Paso (79936) *(G-5659)*

Bassler Energy Services Inc (PA) **979 535-4593**
8050 State Highway 21 E Caldwell (77836) *(G-2628)*

Bastion Technologies Inc (PA) **281 283-9330**
17625 El Cmino Real Ste 3 Houston (77058) *(G-8823)*

Bastrop Cnty Prcnct 2 Rd Brdge 512 360-4224
911 Se Mrtn Lther King Rd Smithville (78957) *(G-18975)*

Bastrop Scale Company Inc (PA) **512 321-3443**
192 Harmon Rd Bastrop (78602) *(G-1749)*

Baswood Inc (HQ) **888 560-5517**
825 Watters Creek Blvd # 200 Allen (75013) *(G-257)*

Batchelor Steel Rule Dies Inc....972 263-2263
2121 Galveston St Grand Prairie (75051) **(G-7839)**
Bates AC & Svc Co Inc....713 869-5521
620 Rankin Cir N Houston (77073) **(G-8824)**
Bates Embroidery & Digitizing, Dallas *Also called Band Mans Co Southwest Inc* **(G-4003)**
Bathcrest Prolux Mfg, Grand Prairie *Also called Prolux LLC* **(G-7957)**
Bathsystem America LLC....713 382-8585
5301 Polk St Bldg 20 Houston (77023) **(G-8825)**
Batson Lumber Company LLC....936 262-8000
25960 Hwy 770 S Batson (77519) **(G-1766)**
Battalion Oil Corporation (PA)....**832 538-0300**
1000 La St Ste 6700 Houston (77002) **(G-8826)**
Batten Flow Testing, Bryan *Also called Crab Ventures LLC* **(G-2467)**
Batteries Concord....281 931-4488
5875 W 34th St Houston (77092) **(G-8827)**
Batterson Iron Works L L P....713 688-5433
6800 Dixie Dr Houston (77087) **(G-8828)**
Batterson Truck Equipment LLC....281 598-6588
5430 Killough St Houston (77086) **(G-8829)**
Battery Solutions Inc....806 771-3777
2301 Avenue B Lubbock (79404) **(G-14366)**
Battle Beaver Customs, Richardson *Also called LLC Battle Beaver* **(G-17346)**
Battle Mountain Dominian Repub....713 655-1742
333 Clay St Fl 42 Houston (77002) **(G-8830)**
Bauer Manufacturing LLC....936 539-5030
100 N Fm 3083 Rd E Conroe (77303) **(G-3262)**
Bauer Visual Graphics Inc (PA)....**713 473-5241**
1600 Strawberry Rd Pasadena (77502) **(G-16394)**
Baulch's Sandpit, Hitchcock *Also called Johnny Baulch* **(G-8338)**
Baumann Propellers LLC....713 714-5573
2309 Ssgt Mcrio Grcia Dr Houston (77011) **(G-8831)**
Baumann Springs Texas Ltd....972 641-7272
3075 N Great Sw Pkwy 10 Grand Prairie (75050) **(G-7840)**
Baumann Springs Usa Inc (HQ)....**972 641-7272**
3075 N Great Sw Pkwy Grand Prairie (75050) **(G-7841)**
Baumann Springs Usa Inc....972 641-7272
14813 Trinity Blvd Fort Worth (76155) **(G-6440)**
Baumann Sprng Txas Hldings LLC....972 641-7272
3075 N Great Sw Pkwy Grand Prairie (75050) **(G-7842)**
Baw, Katy *Also called Brammers Athletic Wearhouse LP* **(G-13390)**
Baw Athletic Wear LP....281 391-3335
5040 Franz Rd Katy (77493) **(G-13389)**
Baw Enterprises, Katy *Also called Baw Athletic Wear LP* **(G-13389)**
Bawco Fabricators Inc....281 449-0171
1159 Aldine Bender Rd Houston (77032) **(G-8832)**
Bawco Inc....281 485-3337
3910 Fm 1128 Rd Pearland (77584) **(G-16541)**
Baxter Healthcare Corporation....903 586-6502
200 Mcknight St Jacksonville (75766) **(G-13228)**
Baxter Planning Systems Inc....512 323-5959
7801 N Capital Of Texas H Austin (78731) **(G-977)**
Baxter Plg Systems Opco LLC....512 323-5959
7801 N Capital Of Tx Ste Austin (78731) **(G-978)**
Bay Advanced Tech 0054, Austin *Also called Bay Advanced Technologies LLC* **(G-979)**
Bay Advanced Technologies LLC....512 929-5400
8200 Cross Park Dr Ste 2a Austin (78754) **(G-979)**
Bay Area Anesthesia Associates....361 857-8588
4444 Corona Dr Ste 232 Corpus Christi (78411) **(G-3482)**
Bay Area Deer Processing, Pasadena *Also called Bay Deer Processing Inc* **(G-16395)**
Bay Area Industrial Contrs LP....281 471-0400
1606 Sens Rd La Porte (77571) **(G-13725)**
Bay Area Printing, Houston *Also called Turner Capital Inc* **(G-12412)**
Bay Area/General Crane Svc Co, Houston *Also called General Crane Service Inc* **(G-9921)**
Bay City Tribune....979 245-2920
2901 Carey Smith Blvd Bay City (77414) **(G-1768)**
Bay Deer Processing Inc....713 472-6000
2243 Pasadena Blvd Pasadena (77502) **(G-16395)**
Bay Energy Blanket Inc....512 353-4064
111 E Mccarty Ln San Marcos (78666) **(G-18680)**
Bay Limited, Corpus Christi *Also called Berry Holdings LP* **(G-3485)**
Bay Pro Computers, Baytown *Also called Jack Saunders* **(G-1823)**
Bay Valley Foods LLC....210 436-5551
5342 Enrique M Barrera Pa San Antonio (78227) **(G-17941)**
Bay Valley Foods LLC....210 436-5551
5310 Old Highway 90 W San Antonio (78227) **(G-17942)**
Bayan Imports Inc....972 437-1122
750 S Sherman St Richardson (75081) **(G-17278)**
Bayer Cropscience LP....806 741-2010
3410 N Elm Ave Lubbock (79403) **(G-14367)**
Bayer Cropscience LP....806 765-8846
103 Erskine St Lubbock (79403) **(G-14368)**
Bayer Healthcare LLC....972 377-1950
5601 Granite Pkwy Ste 750 Plano (75024) **(G-16800)**
Bayland Inc....281 489-1930
7900 Bissell Rd Manvel (77578) **(G-14732)**
Bayou Arms Inc....281 475-4470
4401 Spring Cypress Rd Spring (77388) **(G-19102)**
Bayou Bouillon Operating LLC....346 802-3134
5120 Woodway Dr Ste 1014 Houston (77056) **(G-8833)**
Bayou City Lumber Company....713 991-2377
11106 Telephone Rd Houston (77075) **(G-8834)**
Bayou City Pump Works LP (PA)....**713 472-7722**
109 N Richey St Ste A Pasadena (77506) **(G-16396)**
Bayou Gasket & Hose Co, Beaumont *Also called Ghx Industrial LLC* **(G-1898)**
Bayou Imaging Products LLC....713 923-8300
829 S 75th St Houston (77023) **(G-8835)**
Bayou Processing & Storage LP....713 450-8401
13925 Industrial Rd Houston (77015) **(G-8836)**
Bayport Laboratories LLC (PA)....**832 230-0480**
15864 W Hardy Rd Ste 710 Houston (77060) **(G-8837)**
Bayport Machine Inc....281 471-6223
314 Barracuda Ave Galveston (77550) **(G-7388)**
Bayside Industrial Inc....832 632-2815
614 Clear Creek Ave League City (77573) **(G-13948)**
Bayside Printing Inc....281 209-9500
160 Lockhaven Dr Houston (77073) **(G-8838)**
Baystar Printing, Angleton *Also called College Port Enterprises Inc* **(G-568)**
Baytek International Inc....281 218-8880
16902 El Cam Houston (77058) **(G-8839)**
Baytek International Inc....361 887-8988
401 N Shoreline Blvd Corpus Christi (78401) **(G-3483)**
Baytex Energy (usa) Inc....713 402-1920
5444 Westheimr Rd # 1000 Houston (77056) **(G-8840)**
Baytown Sun, The, Baytown *Also called Southern Newspapers Inc* **(G-1835)**
Baytown Tech & Engg Complex, Baytown *Also called Exxonmobil Chemical Company* **(G-1817)**
Bazaarvoice Inc (HQ)....**512 551-6000**
10901 Stonelake Blvd Austin (78759) **(G-980)**
Baze Chemical Inc....903 723-3146
2187 E Fm 323 Palestine (75801) **(G-16296)**
Bb Chemicals Inc....432 381-2595
16107 W University Blvd Odessa (79764) **(G-15929)**
BBA&j&v Inc....469 998-0660
11625 Custer Rd 110-20 Frisco (75035) **(G-7256)**
Bbat, Midland *Also called Aggietech Oil Ltd* **(G-15109)**
Bbb Tank Services LLC....832 695-2132
162 Independence Pkwy N Baytown (77520) **(G-1808)**
BBC Biochemical Corporation....360 542-8400
2090 Commerce Dr McKinney (75069) **(G-14925)**
Bbi, Houston *Also called Better Bags Inc* **(G-8866)**
Bbq Pits By Klose, Houston *Also called Klose Cnstr & Fabrication* **(G-10541)**
BBS Telecom LC....512 328-9500
2499 S Cpitl Of Texas Hwy Austin (78746) **(G-981)**
Bc Connect LLC....800 347-0855
2340 E Trinity Mills Rd # 300 Carrollton (75006) **(G-2703)**
Bc Johnson Assoc LLC....281 489-4894
1080 Eldridge Pkwy # 1200 Houston (77077) **(G-8841)**
BC Oilfield Services Inc....361 573-6354
110 Moller Rd Victoria (77905) **(G-20245)**
Bc Operating Inc....432 684-9696
4000 N Big Spring St # 310 Midland (79705) **(G-15136)**
Bc Supply, Lubbock *Also called Raider Manufacturing Ltd* **(G-14470)**
Bc Wetlands Ltd....903 718-1530
226 Highland Terrace Cir Denison (75020) **(G-5335)**
Bc Wind-Down Inc....512 799-2075
11000 N Mopac Expy # 150 Austin (78759) **(G-982)**
BCAD Zion Corporation....210 657-9090
9425 Schoenthal Rd New Braunfels (78132) **(G-15775)**
Bcc, Lubbock *Also called Bioremediation Contrs Cons Inc* **(G-14374)**
Bcca LLC....361 547-3341
410 1st St Tynan (78391) **(G-20180)**
BCM & Associates Inc....432 580-7161
2638 S Fulton Ave Odessa (79766) **(G-15930)**
BCM & Associates Inc....432 580-7161
2674 W County Rd S Odessa (79766) **(G-15931)**
Bcs Eagle....979 776-4444
1729 Briarcrest Dr Bryan (77802) **(G-2456)**
Bcs Systems Inc....713 978-6511
10300 Town Park Dr Se1 Houston (77072) **(G-8842)**
BCT International Inc....972 401-9171
10580 Newkirk St Ste 110 Dallas (75220) **(G-4009)**
Bcw Food Products Inc....214 350-3320
6000 Denton Dr Dallas (75235) **(G-4010)**
Bd Energy Systems LLC (PA)....**281 407-9812**
1001 S Dar Ashford Ste 41 Houston (77077) **(G-8843)**
BD Hildebrandt Entps Inc....936 825-0500
12503 Highway 6 Navasota (77868) **(G-15725)**
Bd Medical Equipment & Sups, San Antonio *Also called Becton Dickinson and Company* **(G-17943)**
Bdm Coil Coaters, Houston *Also called Bdm Metal Coaters LLC* **(G-8844)**
Bdm Group LLC....214 412-2291
1017 Santerre St Grand Prairie (75050) **(G-7843)**
Bdm Metal Coaters LLC....713 400-2300
13855 Industrial Rd Houston (77015) **(G-8844)**

Be-Technologies Ltd 972 242-1853
1540 Selene Dr Ste 100 Carrollton (75006) *(G-2704)*
Beach Sheet Metal Company Inc 972 226-4440
353 Long Creek Rd Mesquite (75182) *(G-15030)*
Beaco Manufacturing, Queen City *Also called BMC Industry LLC (G-17219)*
Beacon Energy (texas) Corp 817 558-9255
3102 Windmill Rd Cleburne (76033) *(G-3081)*
Beacon Lighthouse Inc 940 767-0888
300 7th St Wichita Falls (76301) *(G-20743)*
Beacon Lighthouse For Blind, Wichita Falls *Also called Beacon Lighthouse Inc (G-20743)*
Beacon Maritime Inc (PA) **409 670-1060**
505 Highway 87 S West Orange (77630) *(G-20693)*
Beacon Offshore, West Orange *Also called Beacon Maritime Inc (G-20693)*
Beacon Offshore Enrgy Oper LLC 346 867-0509
333 Clay St Ste 4200 Houston (77002) *(G-8845)*
Beaed LP (PA) **281 331-2035**
1850 Highway 35 Byp N Alvin (77511) *(G-354)*
Beaed LP 281 968-7249
1900 Highway 35 Byp N Alvin (77511) *(G-355)*
Beagle Steam Service Inc 806 274-6892
400 Dallas St Borger (79007) *(G-2163)*
Beakley Enterprises Inc (PA) **817 783-5000**
6933 Shelmor Rd Alvarado (76009) *(G-324)*
Beako Manufacturing Co LLC 903 796-5330
304 Fm 74 Queen City (75572) *(G-17218)*
Beall Construction Company Inc 325 677-2112
2631 Fm 3034 Abilene (79601) *(G-16)*
Bean In Motion Logistics LLC 682 465-9083
8200 Willow Glen Ct Fort Worth (76134) *(G-6441)*
Bear Cotton, Waco *Also called Qti Promotions and Apparel Inc (G-20452)*
Bear Creek Smokehouse LLC 903 935-5217
10857 State Highway 154 Marshall (75670) *(G-14763)*
Bear Custom Moulding Inc 940 686-5547
1024 N Highway 377 Pilot Point (76258) *(G-16722)*
Bear Paw Custom Embroidery LLC 903 394-0722
3678 S County Road 481 Centerville (75833) *(G-3011)*
Bear Pump & Equipment Inc 281 200-1000
9616 Telge Rd Houston (77095) *(G-8846)*
Bearded Brothers LLC 940 367-8256
1321 Rutherford Ln # 170 Austin (78753) *(G-983)*
Bearings Plus, Houston *Also called Jc/Fz Holdings Inc (G-10459)*
Beaumont Bolt & Gasket Inc (HQ) **409 838-6304**
1060 Fannin St Beaumont (77701) *(G-1859)*
Beaumont Coca-Cola Bottling Co 409 899-5080
11450 Eastex Fwy Beaumont (77708) *(G-1860)*
Beaumont Machine Works Inc 409 838-0261
11357 Beasley Dr Lumberton (77657) *(G-14566)*
Beaumont Metal Industries Inc 409 833-1777
3115 Milam St Beaumont (77701) *(G-1861)*
Beaumont Plant, Beaumont *Also called Arkema Inc (G-1854)*
Beaumont Polyethylene Plant, Beaumont *Also called Exxonmobil Chemical Company (G-1891)*
Beaumont Rice Mills Inc 409 832-2521
1800 Pecos St Beaumont (77701) *(G-1862)*
Beauty Elite Group Inc 800 619-1333
20411 Imperial Valley Dr Houston (77073) *(G-8847)*
Beauty Mfg Solutions Corp 972 241-9665
1250 Freeport Pkwy Coppell (75019) *(G-3410)*
Beaver Graphix LLC 325 227-3014
4722 Karsten Creek Dr San Angelo (76904) *(G-17780)*
Beb Data, Houston *Also called Business EXT Bur Texas Inc (G-9021)*
Bebco Envmtl Contrls Corp 844 397-4822
4725 Lawndale St La Marque (77568) *(G-13707)*
Bebco Industries, Hitchcock *Also called Parkline Inc (G-8339)*
Bebco Industries, La Marque *Also called Parkline Inc (G-13713)*
Becerra Corp 512 787-2755
201 S Lbj Dr San Marcos (78666) *(G-18681)*
Beck Bros Inc 361 289-6082
2171 Ellis Rd Beeville (78102) *(G-1983)*
Beck Cowboy Boots Inc 806 373-1600
723 S Georgia St Amarillo (79106) *(G-402)*
Beck Industrial, Converse *Also called Beck Manufacturing Intl Inc (G-3389)*
Beck Manufacturing Intl Inc 210 246-7510
2510 Fm 1516 N Converse (78109) *(G-3389)*
Beck Steel Inc 806 762-3255
401 N Loop 289 Lubbock (79403) *(G-14369)*
Beck-Drennan Inc 915 772-3800
7741 Lockheed Dr El Paso (79925) *(G-5660)*
Becker Industries Inc 281 590-4900
2712 Frank Rd Houston (77032) *(G-8848)*
Beckett Collectibles Inc 855 777-2325
4635 Mcewen Rd Dallas (75244) *(G-4011)*
Beckett Media, Dallas *Also called Beckett Collectibles Inc (G-4011)*
Beckett Media LLC 972 991-6657
4635 Mcewen Rd Dallas (75244) *(G-4012)*
Beckman Coulter Inc 714 961-6558
1450 Texas Ave S College Station (77840) *(G-3177)*
Beckman Well Servicing Company 806 435-2543
1000 Ne 6th St Perryton (79070) *(G-16634)*
Becton Dickinson and Company 713 839-0753
6428 Community Dr Houston (77005) *(G-8849)*
Becton Dickinson and Company 210 526-5000
5859 Farinon Dr Ste 200 San Antonio (78249) *(G-17943)*
Bedrock Energy Partners, Houston *Also called Bedrock Production LLC (G-8850)*
Bedrock Manufacturing Co LP (PA) **214 247-2453**
301 N Crowdus St Ste 200 Dallas (75226) *(G-4013)*
Bedrock Production LLC 281 786-0220
820 Gessner Rd Ste 1100 Houston (77024) *(G-8850)*
Bee Builders Supply Inc (PA) **972 422-4960**
1300 Capital Ave Plano (75074) *(G-16801)*
Bee Delightful LLC 253 722-3018
2105 W 10th St Austin (78703) *(G-984)*
Bee Jay Molding Inc (PA) **830 249-2425**
39500 Interstate 10 W Boerne (78006) *(G-2114)*
Bee Jay Molding Inc 281 487-0377
1511 Genoa Red Bluff Rd Pasadena (77504) *(G-16397)*
Beeco Motors & Controls Inc 832 320-3100
5630 Guhn Rd Ste 110 Houston (77040) *(G-8851)*
Beecon Learning LLC 877 923-3266
2012 Farrington St Dallas (75207) *(G-4014)*
Beehive Specialty Co 512 912-7940
9101 Wall St Ste 1080 Austin (78754) *(G-985)*
Beer Dudes Canning Co LLC 972 342-4819
1210 Duncan St Bldg 6 Denton (76205) *(G-5353)*
Beer Dudes Mobile Canning, Denton *Also called Beer Dudes Canning Co LLC (G-5353)*
Beernet Communications 210 805-8006
909 Ne Loop 410 Ste 720 San Antonio (78209) *(G-17944)*
Beetnik Foods LLC 512 584-8228
2407 S Congress Ave E212 Austin (78704) *(G-986)*
Beeville Bee-Picayune, Beeville *Also called Beeville Publishing Company (G-1984)*
Beeville Publishing Company (PA) **361 358-2550**
111 N Washington St Beeville (78102) *(G-1984)*
BEg Liquid Mud Services Corp 979 542-7000
2502 E Austin St Giddings (78942) *(G-7692)*
Behavioral Science Res Press 972 243-8543
12803 Demetra Dr Ste 100 Dallas (75234) *(G-4015)*
Behemoth Corporation 281 332-4798
202 Reynolds Ave League City (77573) *(G-13949)*
Behr Process Corporation 817 837-2600
701 Gateway Pkwy Roanoke (76262) *(G-17483)*
Behr Service America 817 624-7273
5020 Augusta Dr Fort Worth (76106) *(G-6442)*
Behrends Feed & Fertilizer LLC 830 997-3410
3599 Ranch Road 1376 Fredericksburg (78624) *(G-7172)*
BEI Angleton, Angleton *Also called Benchmark Electronics Inc (G-565)*
Beicip Inc 281 293-8550
1880 S Dairy Ashford Rd # 630 Houston (77077) *(G-8852)*
Belarco Indus Clg Odessa LLC 432 381-0999
3511 W Arcadia St Odessa (79764) *(G-15932)*
Belco Manufacturing Co Inc 254 933-9000
2303 Taylors Valley Rd Belton (76513) *(G-2019)*
Bell and Howell LLC 972 753-0711
8080 Tristar Dr Ste 106 Irving (75063) *(G-12945)*
Bell Boeing Joint Project Off 301 866-6835
401 Tiltrotor Dr Amarillo (79111) *(G-403)*
Bell Concrete Products Co 903 885-3126
625 7th St Sulphur Springs (75482) *(G-19581)*
Bell Engineering Group, Spring Branch *Also called Bell Experimental Group Inc (G-19267)*
Bell Experimental Group Inc 830 438-2890
203 Kestrel Dr Spring Branch (78070) *(G-19267)*
Bell Helicopter Plant 2, Hurst *Also called Bell Textron Inc (G-12838)*
Bell Helicopter Plant 5, Grand Prairie *Also called Bell Textron Inc (G-7845)*
Bell Helicopter Services Inc., Fort Worth *Also called Bell Textron Services Inc (G-6446)*
Bell Helicopter Textron Inc 806 341-3400
401 Tiltrotor Dr Amarillo (79111) *(G-404)*
Bell Helicopter Textron Inc 817 280-4700
401 Tiltrotor Dr Amarillo (79111) *(G-405)*
Bell Helicptr Training Academy, Fort Worth *Also called Bell Textron Inc (G-6445)*
Bell Intercoolers LLC 830 438-6150
247 Kestrel Dr Spring Branch (78070) *(G-19268)*
Bell Mountain Vineyards Inc 830 685-3297
463 Bell Mountain Rd Willow City (78675) *(G-20870)*
Bell Processing Incorporated (PA) **940 322-8621**
1326 Burkburnett Rd Wichita Falls (76306) *(G-20744)*
Bell Publications, Hurst *Also called Bell Textron Inc (G-12839)*
Bell Sports Inc 972 343-1000
602 Fountain Pkwy Grand Prairie (75050) *(G-7844)*
Bell Sports Corp (HQ) **469 417-6600**
6333 N State Highway 161 # 300 Irving (75038) *(G-12946)*
Bell Textron Inc 817 837-4700
3255 Bell Flight Blvd Fort Worth (76118) *(G-6443)*
Bell Textron Inc 817 280-1587
3405 Lake Knoll Ct Hurst (76053) *(G-12837)*
Bell Textron Inc 817 280-2011
9801 Metric Blvd Bldg 10 Austin (78758) *(G-987)*

ALPHABETIC

Bell Textron Inc 817 280-2011
1700 N Hwy 360 Grand Prairie (75050) *(G-7845)*

Bell Textron Inc (HQ) **817 280-2011**
3255 Bell Flight Blvd Fort Worth (76118) *(G-6444)*

Bell Textron Inc 817 280-2011
3000 S Norwood Dr Hurst (76053) *(G-12838)*

Bell Textron Inc 806 341-3400
401 Tiltrotor Dr Amarillo (79111) *(G-406)*

Bell Textron Inc 817 280-2011
600 E Hurst Blvd Hurst (76053) *(G-12839)*

Bell Textron Inc 817 280-2011
13901 Aviator Way Fort Worth (76177) *(G-6445)*

Bell Textron Inc 806 341-3400
10901 Airport Blvd Bldg 9 Amarillo (79111) *(G-407)*

Bell Textron Services Inc (HQ) **817 280-2011**
3255 Bell Flight Blvd Fort Worth (76118) *(G-6446)*

Bell Wooden Products Inc 214 388-5421
4341 Cedar Lake Dr Dallas (75227) *(G-4016)*

Bella Design Group LLC 972 304-4100
709 109th St Arlington (76011) *(G-630)*

Bella Group, Arlington *Also called Bella Design Group LLC (G-630)*

Bellagio Menswear LLC 512 496-8322
12701 Hill Country Blvd Austin (78738) *(G-988)*

Bellicum Pharmaceuticals Inc (PA) **832 384-1100**
2710 Reed Rd Ste 160 Houston (77051) *(G-8853)*

Bellows Systems Inc 281 721-2947
11981 Fm 529 Rd Houston (77041) *(G-8854)*

Bells Advertising Inc (HQ) **512 454-9663**
109 Denson Dr Ste D Austin (78752) *(G-989)*

Bells Collegiate Products, Austin *Also called Bells Advertising Inc (G-989)*

Belltec Industries Inc 254 939-9404
2057 Commerce St Belton (76513) *(G-2020)*

Bellville Tube Company 281 467-7177
141 Miller Rd E Bellville (77418) *(G-2008)*

Belo Corp 979 776-4444
1729 Briarcrest Dr Bryan (77802) *(G-2457)*

Belton Journal, Belton *Also called Belton Newspaper Inc (G-2021)*

Belton Newspaper Inc 254 939-5754
210 N Penelope St Belton (76513) *(G-2021)*

Beltran Brothers Fabrication 281 987-2331
11826 Connor St Houston (77039) *(G-8855)*

Beltran Precast Inc 915 599-8777
860 Kastrin St El Paso (79907) *(G-5661)*

Belvan Partners LP (HQ) **432 682-4349**
211 N Colorado St Midland (79701) *(G-15137)*

Belvieu Enviromental Fuel, Mont Belvieu *Also called Enterprise Products Oper LLC (G-15617)*

Bemis Sheet Metal Inc 281 427-1538
1207 S Airhart Dr Baytown (77520) *(G-1809)*

Bems, Vidor *Also called Buna Electric Motor Svc Inc (G-20325)*

Ben Adams, San Antonio *Also called Ben Adams Precious Jewels (G-17945)*

Ben Adams Precious Jewels (PA) **210 826-6535**
255 E Basse Rd Ste 1018 San Antonio (78209) *(G-17945)*

Ben Dunn Corporation 210 614-0396
7272 Wurzbach Rd Ste 204 San Antonio (78240) *(G-17946)*

Benbella Books Inc 214 750-3600
10440 N Cntl Expy Ste 800 Dallas (75231) *(G-4017)*

Bench Tree Group LLC (PA) **512 869-6900**
4681 County Road 110 Georgetown (78626) *(G-7640)*

Benchmark Completions LLC (PA) **281 537-8483**
1400 Woodloch Forest Dr Spring (77380) *(G-19200)*

Benchmark Electronics Inc 979 849-6550
3000 Technology Rd Angleton (77515) *(G-565)*

Benchmark Manufacturing Inc 903 882-4311
211 S Industrial St Lindale (75771) *(G-14133)*

Benchmark Metal Service Inc 940 479-9134
155 Seaborn Rd Ponder (76259) *(G-17094)*

Benchmark Research & Tech Inc 432 697-8171
4113 W Industrial Ave Midland (79703) *(G-15138)*

Benchmark Signs, Weatherford *Also called Brooks & Brooks Services Inc (G-20579)*

Bencor LLC 979 830-5252
4629 Highway 290 W Brenham (77833) *(G-2243)*

Bend-It Inc 713 991-0745
6120 Nunn St Houston (77087) *(G-8856)*

Bendco Inc 713 473-1557
801 Houston Ave Pasadena (77502) *(G-16398)*

Bendco/Bending & Coiling Co, Pasadena *Also called Bendco Inc (G-16398)*

Bendel Tank Heat Exchnger Corp 832 436-4626
27 W Misty Morning Trce The Woodlands (77381) *(G-19835)*

Bendt Distilling LLC 214 814-0545
225 S Charles St Lewisville (75057) *(G-14027)*

Benedettini Cabinetry, Rosenberg *Also called Benedettini Cabinets LP (G-17575)*

Benedettini Cabinets LP 281 633-8200
533 Highway 36 N Rosenberg (77471) *(G-17575)*

Benedum Gas Plant, Midkiff *Also called Western Gas Resources Inc (G-15098)*

Benjamin Moore & Co 972 285-6346
700 W Kearney St Mesquite (75149) *(G-15031)*

Bennett Production Corp 940 872-1183
815 Highway 59 N Bowie (76230) *(G-2191)*

Bennetts Printing & Office Sup, Cleburne *Also called Fred Bennett Printing Company (G-3089)*

Benning Power Electronics Inc 214 553-1444
1220 Presidential Dr # 100 Richardson (75081) *(G-17279)*

Benningfeld Stl Fbrication LLC 832 831-3691
901 Marcella St Houston (77091) *(G-8857)*

Benson Box Inc 210 662-6383
5810 Business Park San Antonio (78218) *(G-17947)*

Bentintoshape LLC 214 228-2985
10590 King William Dr Dallas (75220) *(G-4018)*

Bentley Consultants Co Inc 972 289-2750
12717 Eastgate Dr Ste 4 Mesquite (75181) *(G-15032)*

Benton Oil Co 806 763-5302
3102 Clovis Rd Lubbock (79415) *(G-14370)*

Bentonite Performance Mnrl LLC (HQ) **281 871-7900**
3000 N Sam Houston Pkwy E Houston (77032) *(G-8858)*

Bentwood Companies Inc (PA) **972 227-6855**
2007 N Lncster Htchins Rd Lancaster (75134) *(G-13839)*

Bentwood Kitchens, Lancaster *Also called Bentwood Companies Inc (G-13839)*

Benz Airborne Systems, Fort Worth *Also called Benz Companies Ltd (G-6447)*

Benz Companies Ltd 817 280-0000
2400 Handley Ederville Rd Fort Worth (76118) *(G-6447)*

Bep Oilfield Ltd 281 873-9100
12941 North Fwy Ste 520 Houston (77060) *(G-8859)*

Ber Precission, Cleveland *Also called B E R Precision Inc (G-3119)*

Berchtold Corporation 843 569-6100
571 Silveron Flower Mound (75028) *(G-6260)*

Berger Iron Works Inc 713 869-7386
8107 W Little York Rd Houston (77040) *(G-8860)*

Bergman, William R, Midland *Also called CHI Energy Inc (G-15163)*

Bergstein Enterprises Ltd 806 741-1080
2310 Fordham St Lubbock (79415) *(G-14371)*

Bergstein Well Servicing LLC 806 741-1095
2416 Erskine St Lubbock (79415) *(G-14372)*

Bergstrom Climate Systems LLC 210 507-5670
202 Tayman St Ste 400b San Antonio (78226) *(G-17948)*

Berlin Packaging LLC 214 339-0054
3737 Rock Quarry Rd # 100 Dallas (75211) *(G-4019)*

Bernadette Debrango 806 342-0606
416 Sw 8th Ave Amarillo (79101) *(G-408)*

Bernie Star Newspaper 830 249-2441
941 N School St Boerne (78006) *(G-2115)*

Berridge Manufacturing Company 972 506-8496
2015 Cal Crossing Rd Dallas (75220) *(G-4020)*

Berridge Manufacturing Company (PA) **210 650-7056**
6515 Fratt Rd San Antonio (78218) *(G-17949)*

Berridge Manufacturing Company 713 223-4971
1720 Maury St Houston (77026) *(G-8861)*

Berridge Manufacturing Company 830 401-5200
2201 Rudeloff Rd Seguin (78155) *(G-18826)*

Berry Corporation (bry) (PA) **661 616-3900**
16000 Dallas Pkwy Ste 500 Dallas (75248) *(G-4021)*

Berry Global Inc 409 794-1011
10463 Highway 124 Beaumont (77705) *(G-1863)*

Berry Global Inc 361 575-9565
202 John Stockbauer Dr Victoria (77901) *(G-20246)*

Berry Global Films LLC 972 576-8193
6250 N I Hwy 35 E Waxahachie (75165) *(G-20529)*

Berry Gp Inc (PA) **361 693-2100**
1414 Corn Product Rd Corpus Christi (78409) *(G-3484)*

Berry Holdings LP (PA) **361 693-2100**
1414 Corn Product Rd Corpus Christi (78409) *(G-3485)*

Berry Machine Shop 817 572-0948
7782 Berry Rd Burleson (76028) *(G-2571)*

Berry Marketing Logistics, Abilene *Also called Bml Inc (G-19)*

Berry Pool, Brownsville *Also called Jobran Unlimited LLC (G-2371)*

Berry's Air Conditioning, Jacksonville *Also called Berrys Tin Shop Inc (G-13229)*

Berrys Tin Shop Inc 903 586-3552
300 E Tena St Jacksonville (75766) *(G-13229)*

Bersal Energy LLC 956 270-1155
4900 W Expressway 83 McAllen (78501) *(G-14841)*

Bertrand Enterprises Inc 409 833-0922
2400 Gulf St Beaumont (77703) *(G-1864)*

Besam Entrance Solutions, Houston *Also called Assa Abloy Entrance Systems US (G-8725)*

Besco Mfg, San Antonio *Also called Bakery Equipment & Svc Co Inc (G-17937)*

Best American Mfg Corp 972 475-0092
4821 Grisham Dr Rowlett (75088) *(G-17701)*

Best Circuit Boards Inc (HQ) **214 291-1427**
901 Hensley Ln Wylie (75098) *(G-20927)*

Best Drilling Services (bds) 713 864-3900
925 W 20th St Houston (77008) *(G-8862)*

Best Fender Products Inc (PA) **903 577-0510**
2364 Texas Highway 49 Mount Pleasant (75455) *(G-15646)*

Best Letter Press Inc 713 123-4567
5853 W 34th St Houston (77092) *(G-8863)*

Best Machining Services, Fort Worth *Also called Best Pump and Flow LP (G-6448)*

Best Made Designs LLC 432 943-9995
309 S Betty Ave Unit C Monahans (79756) *(G-15600)*

(G-0000) Company's Geographic Section entry number

Best Press Inc 972 930-1000
4201 Airborn Dr Addison (75001) *(G-107)*

Best Publications LLP 281 488-8300
1199 W Nasa Pkwy Webster (77598) *(G-20634)*

Best Pump and Flow LP 713 690-4511
1329 Markum Gate Way Fort Worth (76126) *(G-6448)*

Best Quality Machining Inc 512 864-1667
3205 Vortac Ln Georgetown (78628) *(G-7641)*

Best Software Non Profit, Austin *Also called Sage Software Inc (G-1481)*

Best Southwest Focus, Desoto *Also called Focus Newspapers of Dfw Inc (G-5431)*

Best Strl Fabricators Inc 361 265-0550
8631 Old Brownsville Rd Corpus Christi (78415) *(G-3486)*

Bestolife Corporation (HQ) 972 865-8961
2126 Vanco Dr Irving (75061) *(G-12947)*

Bestway Oilfield Inc (PA) 281 452-2525
16030 Market St Channelview (77530) *(G-3013)*

Bet Minerals, Houston *Also called Bentonite Performance Mnrl LLC (G-8858)*

Bet-Lar Services, Houston *Also called Upstart Acquisitions Corp (G-12476)*

Beta Arkansas LLC 972 490-2340
14185 Dallas Pkwy # 1020 Dallas (75254) *(G-4022)*

Beta Engineering Inc 817 265-3367
468 Dodson Lake Dr Arlington (76012) *(G-631)*

Beta Offshore, Houston *Also called Beta Operating Company LLC (G-8864)*

Beta Operating Company LLC (HQ) 562 628-8900
500 Dallas St Ste 1600 Houston (77002) *(G-8864)*

Beta Technology Inc 281 647-9700
16810 Barker Springs Rd Houston (77084) *(G-8865)*

Betban Investments LLC 254 776-2243
22003 Bush Dr Waco (76712) *(G-20367)*

Bettcher Manufacturing LLC (PA) 956 618-5805
6801 S 33rd St Ste 9 McAllen (78503) *(G-14842)*

Bettcher Manufacturing LLC 956 519-0468
5801 George Mcvay Dr McAllen (78503) *(G-14843)*

Bettcher Mfg & Met Stampg, McAllen *Also called Bettcher Manufacturing LLC (G-14842)*

Better Bags Inc 713 864-8200
6419 Toledo St Houston (77008) *(G-8866)*

Better Built Metal Buildings, Orange *Also called Floyd Tate A (G-16243)*

Better Burglar Bars Inc 713 699-9543
1910 Turner Dr Apt C Houston (77093) *(G-8867)*

Bettera Brands LLC (PA) 800 344-6225
5345 Towne Square Dr # 240 Plano (75024) *(G-16802)*

Bettis Boyle & Stovall Inc 940 549-0780
505 5th St Graham (76450) *(G-7777)*

Bettis Corporation 281 879-2300
19200 Northwest Fwy Jersey Village (77065) *(G-13293)*

Beumer Glidepath, Arlington *Also called Glidepath LLC (G-692)*

Beusa Energy LLC 281 296-1500
1780 Hughes Landing Blvd # 100 The Woodlands (77380) *(G-19836)*

Beusa Energy, Inc, The Woodlands *Also called Beusa Energy LLC (G-19836)*

Bexar Concrete Works I Ltd 210 497-3773
19440 Judson Rd San Antonio (78259) *(G-17950)*

Bexar Manufacturing & Trdg Co 210 977-9585
1990 Cupples Rd San Antonio (78226) *(G-17951)*

Bexar Steel Company, San Antonio *Also called Trans-Tex Fabricating Co Inc (G-18562)*

Bexter Enterprises LLC 972 647-4700
734 Greenview Dr Grand Prairie (75050) *(G-7846)*

Bexxt Inc 832 209-7970
21233 Fm 529 Rd Cypress (77433) *(G-3778)*

Beyond Creations LLC 956 972-1903
909 W Dove Ave McAllen (78504) *(G-14844)*

Beyond International Inc 281 277-4352
711 Julie Rivers Dr Sugar Land (77478) *(G-19449)*

Beyond Ordinary Services, Fort Worth *Also called Arismendy Josias (G-6401)*

Bfx Fire Apparatus, Fort Worth *Also called Snf Inc (G-6999)*

BG Absolute 409 724-0300
2920 N Twin City Hwy Nederland (77627) *(G-15746)*

Bg Brasilia LLC 713 599-4000
910 Louisiana St Houston (77002) *(G-8868)*

Bg Energy Merchants LLC 713 599-4000
811 Main St Ste 3400 Houston (77002) *(G-8869)*

Bg Group, Houston *Also called Bg Brasilia LLC (G-8868)*

Bg LNG Services LLC 713 599-4000
811 Main St Ste 2100 Houston (77002) *(G-8870)*

Bg LNG Trading, Houston *Also called Bg LNG Services LLC (G-8870)*

Bgem, Houston *Also called Bg Energy Merchants LLC (G-8869)*

Bgi Contractors Inc 409 833-0303
2410 Coke Dock Rd Port Arthur (77642) *(G-17102)*

Bgi Enterprise Inc (PA) 409 833-0303
1325 Spindletop Rd Beaumont (77705) *(G-1865)*

Bgrs Inc 281 890-6862
9318 Reid Lake Dr Houston (77064) *(G-8871)*

Bgs Industries Inc 281 970-4118
11155 Windfern Rd Houston (77064) *(G-8872)*

Bhc Industries of Texas Inc 817 556-2306
486 County Road St 318 Alvarado (76009) *(G-325)*

Bhi LLC 713 644-2431
11111 Forbes Rd Houston (77075) *(G-8873)*

Bhi International Inc 281 449-5762
5223 Hopper Rd Houston (77093) *(G-8874)*

BHP Billiton, Houston *Also called Broken Hill Propty USA Inc (G-8992)*

BHP Billiton Petro N Amer Inc (HQ) 713 961-8500
1500 Post Oak Blvd Houston (77056) *(G-8875)*

BHP Bllton Petro Deepwater Inc 713 961-8500
1500 Post Oak Blvd Houston (77056) *(G-8876)*

BHP Mineral Resources Inc 713 961-8500
1360 Post Oak Blvd # 150 Houston (77056) *(G-8877)*

BHP Minerals International LLC (HQ) 713 961-8500
1500 Post Oak Blvd Houston (77056) *(G-8878)*

Bi Solutions Inc 469 287-5784
5048 Tennyson Pkwy # 250 Plano (75024) *(G-16803)*

Bianco Brothers 817 922-0885
3008 Stuart Dr Fort Worth (76104) *(G-6449)*

Bianco Brothers Mfg Co, Fort Worth *Also called Bianco Brothers (G-6449)*

Bico Drilling Tools Inc (HQ) 832 598-9200
4667 Kennedy Commerce Dr Houston (77032) *(G-8879)*

Bielas Glass & Aluminum Pdts 210 333-8040
5585 Us Highway 87 E San Antonio (78222) *(G-17952)*

Big 4 Inc 409 787-2733
301 Worth St Hemphill (75948) *(G-8245)*

Big 4 Services, Hemphill *Also called Big 4 Inc (G-8245)*

Big 4 Steel Services LP 281 353-5333
27444 E Hardy Rd Spring (77373) *(G-19103)*

Big 6 Drilling Company 713 783-2300
7500 San Felipe St # 250 Houston (77063) *(G-8880)*

Big Bear Oil Company Inc (HQ) 915 775-1945
1025 Wall St El Paso (79915) *(G-5662)*

Big Bear-Aggietech, Midland *Also called Aggietech Energy Services LLC (G-15108)*

Big Bear-Aggietech, Sundown *Also called Aggietech Energy Services LLC (G-19610)*

Big Bee Drilling Inc 432 333-2932
1509 W 2nd St Odessa (79763) *(G-15933)*

Big Bend Saddlery Inc 432 837-5551
2701 E Highway 90 Alpine (79830) *(G-311)*

Big Buck Brewery & Steakhouse 972 691-5100
2501 Bass Pro Dr Ste 100 Grapevine (76051) *(G-8014)*

Big C Rentals LLC 432 266-8834
203 Se 1000 Andrews (79714) *(G-538)*

Big City Manufacturing Inc 713 649-7769
7561 Morley St Houston (77061) *(G-8881)*

Big Country Livestock Eqp 254 643-1119
804 W College St Rising Star (76471) *(G-17478)*

Big Creek Sand and Gravel Inc 806 273-7501
3300 S Cedar Borger (79007) *(G-2164)*

Big D Companies, Midland *Also called Big D Equipment Company Ltd (G-15139)*

Big D Concrete Inc 972 737-7976
10361 Bickham Rd Dallas (75220) *(G-4023)*

Big D Equipment Company Ltd 432 682-1664
4501 E Highway 80 Midland (79706) *(G-15139)*

Big D Ready Mix, Dallas *Also called Big D Concrete Inc (G-4023)*

Big Dog Drilling, Midland *Also called Acme Energy Services Inc (G-15104)*

Big E Drilling Co., Bellaire *Also called Eastham Drilling Inc (G-1995)*

Big E Services LLC 432 550-2443
6106 Cargo Rd Odessa (79762) *(G-15934)*

Big Lake Fluid Services, Big Lake *Also called Globe Well Service Inc (G-2057)*

Big Lake Fuels LLC 713 943-2200
600 Travis St Ste 3680 Houston (77002) *(G-8882)*

Big Lake Services Company LLC 432 686-0475
3709 S State Highway 349 Midland (79706) *(G-15140)*

Big M Constructors Inc 281 469-9770
10200 Windfern Rd Houston (77064) *(G-8883)*

Big Red, Austin *Also called North American Beverages Ltd (G-1368)*

Big Red Inc 713 791-9886
2400 Holly Hall St Houston (77054) *(G-8884)*

Big Red 7 Up Btlg Co S Texas, San Antonio *Also called American Bottling Company (G-17902)*

Big Red Engineering LLC (PA) 817 539-9560
6070 Copperfield Dr # 614 Fort Worth (76132) *(G-6450)*

Big Rock Energy Services Inc 432 235-8509
602 N Baird St Ste 204 Midland (79701) *(G-15141)*

Big Shot LLC 504 877-2335
202 W Park Place Dr # 202 Lancaster (75134) *(G-13840)*

Big Spring Cat Cnstr Inc 432 394-4161
600 Se Broadway Coahoma (79511) *(G-3164)*

Big Spring Herald, Big Spring *Also called Cnhi LLC (G-2076)*

Big Star Branding Inc 210 590-2662
4009 Naco Perrin Blvd San Antonio (78217) *(G-17953)*

Big Star LLC 325 617-5731
4774 N Chadbourne St San Angelo (76903) *(G-17781)*

Big Star Oil & Gas LLC 432 687-4900
5102 N County Road 1150 Midland (79705) *(G-15142)*

Big State Fabrication Inc 281 572-1375
19891 W Industrial Park New Caney (77357) *(G-15835)*

Big State Welding & Machine Lc 940 766-0191
3015 Old Jacksboro Hwy Wichita Falls (76302) *(G-20745)*

Big Tex Well Services LLC 817 599-6155
327 N Denton St Ste 100 Weatherford (76086) *(G-20578)*

Big Tom Construction Inc 903 752-1008
17636 Fm 2089 Overton (75684) *(G-16276)*

Bigcommerce Inc (HQ) **512 865-4500**
11305 Four Points Dr I Austin (78726) *(G-990)*

Bigham Brothers Inc 806 745-0384
705 E Slaton Rd Lubbock (79404) *(G-14373)*

Bigs Packaging and Lumber, Dallas *Also called Ufp Dallas LLC (G-5127)*

Bigtrak Technologies LLC 361 944-3982
5262 S Staples St Ste 300 Corpus Christi (78411) *(G-3487)*

Bil Mar Foods, Irving *Also called Hillshire Brands Company (G-13057)*

Bilingual Yellow Pages 214 823-4384
4310 N Central Expy Dallas (75206) *(G-4024)*

Bill Gilmore Welding Inc 940 592-4945
1150 Us 287 E Iowa Park (76367) *(G-12903)*

Bill Smalley Drilling & Trckg 325 762-3409
160 Fm 1084 Albany (76430) *(G-185)*

Bill West Properties Inc 713 726-0151
11800 Fairmont St Houston (77035) *(G-8885)*

Bill's Welding Service, Cleburne *Also called Lee Products Inc (G-3100)*

Billmark Company 817 834-2481
2232 Solona St Fort Worth (76117) *(G-6451)*

Billmyr Enterprises Inc 972 424-1980
1705 K Ave Ste A Plano (75074) *(G-16804)*

Billor Machine Tool Service, Irving *Also called Two Elk Investments LLC (G-13200)*

Billy Pugh Company, Corpus Christi *Also called Pugh Acquisition Company (G-3600)*

Billy R Coats Inc 432 523-3861
1805 Sw Mustang Dr Andrews (79714) *(G-539)*

Bimbo Bakeries Usa Inc 254 750-2500
225 S 17th St Waco (76701) *(G-20368)*

Bimbo Bakeries Usa Inc 903 785-6401
2020 19th St Nw Paris (75460) *(G-16358)*

Bin There Dump That, El Paso *Also called Alareal Corporation (G-5639)*

Binco Contracting Services 281 356-3144
17619 Winding Creek Ln Magnolia (77355) *(G-14591)*

Binford Fence Supply Ltd (PA) **972 286-2881**
2815 Hickory Tree Rd Balch Springs (75180) *(G-1737)*

Bingham Industries, Terrell *Also called Bingham Manufacturing Inc (G-19728)*

Bingham Manufacturing Inc 360 863-1170
2000 Airport Rd Terrell (75160) *(G-19728)*

Bingo Express, Lubbock *Also called Brown and Anthony Inc (G-14384)*

Bio Trust Nutrition LLC (PA) **800 766-5086**
4100 Spring Valley Rd # 32 Dallas (75244) *(G-4025)*

Bio World Merchandising Inc (PA) **972 488-0655**
1159 Cottonwood Ln Irving (75038) *(G-12948)*

Bio-Derm Laboratories Inc 903 753-6744
1600 Redmon Rd Longview (75602) *(G-14202)*

Bio-Path Holdings Inc 832 742-1357
4710 Bellaire Blvd # 210 Bellaire (77401) *(G-1990)*

Bio-RAD Laboratories Inc 972 596-6165
3201 Technology Dr Plano (75074) *(G-16805)*

Bio-Signal Technologies LLC 214 405-0524
5201 Collin Mckinney Pkwy McKinney (75070) *(G-14926)*

Biocope Inc 806 655-2933
23711 Hix Dr Canyon (79015) *(G-2669)*

Biogenix LLC 888 418-7172
2800 Post Oak Blvd Houston (77056) *(G-8886)*

Biomed Laboratories LLC 972 707-1210
8181 Eastpoint Dr Ste 500 Dallas (75227) *(G-4026)*

Biomerics LLC 903 677-9166
1605 Enterprise St Athens (75751) *(G-821)*

Bionic Welder LLC 817 579-5080
2080 Miller Ct Granbury (76049) *(G-7793)*

Bioniche Animal Health USA Inc (HQ) **706 549-4503**
4250 N Sylvania Ave Fort Worth (76137) *(G-6452)*

Bionumerik Pharmaceuticals Inc 210 614-1701
8023 Vantage Dr Ste L1 San Antonio (78230) *(G-17954)*

Biored, Stafford *Also called Forward Science Tech LLC (G-19319)*

Bioremediation Contrs Cons Inc 806 771-8033
3302 122nd St Lubbock (79423) *(G-14374)*

Biosuite LLC 713 849-5319
12625 W Airport Blvd Sugar Land (77478) *(G-19450)*

Biotics Building Partnership 281 344-0909
6801 Biotics Research Dr Rosenberg (77471) *(G-17576)*

Biotics Pharma, Rosenberg *Also called Biotics Research Corporation (G-17577)*

Biotics Research, Rosenberg *Also called Biotics Building Partnership (G-17576)*

Biotics Research Corporation (PA) **281 344-0909**
6801 Biotics Research Dr Rosenberg (77471) *(G-17577)*

Biotool LLC 713 732-2181
9330 Kirby Dr Ste 200 Houston (77054) *(G-8887)*

Biotrust Nutrition, Dallas *Also called Bio Trust Nutrition LLC (G-4025)*

Bioworld, Irving *Also called Bio World Merchandising Inc (G-12948)*

Biractual LLC 713 623-5099
10700 Richmond Ave # 310 Houston (77042) *(G-8888)*

Birch B LLC 646 942-8058
1223 Wynden Commons Ln Houston (77056) *(G-8889)*

Birch Grove Software Inc 888 907-0301
1301 S Mo Pac Expy Ste Ll Austin (78746) *(G-991)*

Birch Operations Inc (PA) **832 701-1776**
909 Fannin St Ste 1350 Houston (77010) *(G-8890)*

Birch Plastics Inc 713 433-1898
5957 South Loop E Houston (77033) *(G-8891)*

Bird Electron Beam, Dallas *Also called Bodycote Thermal Proc Inc (G-4038)*

Birdsong Corporation 254 734-2266
601 Mc Call St Gorman (76454) *(G-7771)*

Birdsong Corporation 806 637-7200
1564 C R 474 Brownfield (79316) *(G-2330)*

Birdview Skylights 817 439-9266
201 Longhorn Rd Fort Worth (76179) *(G-6453)*

Birdwell Cleaning Products Inc 800 722-8006
1075 Nw John Jones Dr Burleson (76028) *(G-2572)*

Bise Welding & Fabricating Inc 713 681-0958
1900 De Soto St Houston (77091) *(G-8892)*

Bishop Lifting, Odessa *Also called Blp Settlement Company (G-15939)*

Bisi Inc 512 478-3334
8708 S Congress Ave A180 Austin (78745) *(G-992)*

Bisn Oil Tools LLC (PA) **832 919-7500**
4514 Brittmoore Rd Houston (77041) *(G-8893)*

Bison Development Company 806 355-8253
5744 Canyon Dr Amarillo (79109) *(G-481)*

Bison Drlg & Field Svcs LLC 405 463-6912
12201 W County Road 122 Odessa (79765) *(G-15935)*

Bison Energy Partners Inc (PA) **281 873-9100**
13700 Veterans Mem Dr 4 Houston (77014) *(G-8894)*

Bison Profab Inc 281 356-0026
12519 Wanda Ln Magnolia (77354) *(G-14592)*

Bissell Inc 956 631-5077
5700 S Intl Pkwy Ste B Mcallen (78503) *(G-14845)*

Bissell Mc Allen, Mcallen *Also called Bissell Inc (G-14845)*

Bitcoin Crypto Crrncy Exch Cor 713 465-1001
19 Briar Hollow Ln # 125 Houston (77027) *(G-8895)*

Bitech Tool & Die Inc 915 757-8001
5240 Tetons Dr El Paso (79904) *(G-5663)*

Bizness Apps Inc 415 655-9496
401 Congress Ave Ste 2650 Austin (78701) *(G-993)*

Biztel LP 713 600-2600
1235 North Loop W Ste 400 Houston (77008) *(G-8896)*

BJ Hookers Distilleries LLC 713 249-2022
23 Chestnut Hill Ct Spring (77380) *(G-19201)*

BJ Services LLC (PA) **281 408-2361**
11211 Fm 2920 Rd Tomball (77375) *(G-19966)*

BJ Services 7833, Fort Worth *Also called Baker Hghes Olfld Oprtions LLC (G-6421)*

BJ Services Co, Tomball *Also called Baker Hughes A GE Company LLC (G-19965)*

BJ Unichem Chemical Services, Tomball *Also called Baker Hghes Olfld Oprtions LLC (G-19964)*

Bjhr Inc 409 735-5305
333 W Round Bunch Rd Bridge City (77611) *(G-2280)*

Bk Corrosion LLC 713 225-6661
4411 Navigation Blvd Houston (77011) *(G-8897)*

Bk Power Systems LLC 713 225-6661
601 Century Plaza Dr Houston (77073) *(G-8898)*

Bk/Ja Holdings Inc 281 879-9903
13715 N Promenade Blvd Stafford (77477) *(G-19291)*

Bkbl Holdings Ltd (PA) **214 436-4161**
2591 Dallas Pkwy Ste 201 Frisco (75034) *(G-7270)*

Bkg Machine & Fabrication Inc 361 575-9592
5509 State Highway 185 Victoria (77905) *(G-20247)*

Bkh Enterprises LLC 979 743-6577
633 Oakland Rd Schulenburg (78956) *(G-18772)*

Bl Technology Inc (PA) **832 698-8000**
1730 S Cherry St Tomball (77375) *(G-19967)*

Black & Decker Corporation 713 466-1194
10245 W Little York Rd # 300 Houston (77040) *(G-8899)*

Black & Decker Corporation 972 446-2996
1300 N Interstate 35 # 112 Carrollton (75006) *(G-2705)*

Black Box Corporation 713 307-4000
5959 Corp Dr Ste 250ll Houston (77036) *(G-8900)*

Black Diamond Energy Inc (PA) **307 684-2910**
26022 Sebey Ridge Ln Katy (77494) *(G-13352)*

Black Diamond Minerals LLC 720 341-2212
500 Dallas St Ste 1800 Houston (77002) *(G-8901)*

Black Diamond Structures LLC 512 900-3822
12310 Trail Dr Austin (78737) *(G-858)*

Black Eagle Inc 214 871-3555
100 Crescent Ct Ste 1600 Dallas (75201) *(G-4027)*

Black Elk Energy LLC (PA) **281 507-7652**
3100 S Gessner Rd Ste 215 Houston (77063) *(G-8902)*

Black Elk Energy Offshore Oper 832 973-4230
842 W Sam Houston Pkwy N # 500 Houston (77024) *(G-8903)*

Black Gold Oper & Cnstr Inc 903 766-3636
119 County Road 335 Waskom (75692) *(G-20517)*

Black Hawk Specialty, Port Arthur *Also called United Insul Sls Fbrcation Inc (G-17131)*

Black Horse LLC 281 598-8100
9950 W Gulf Bank Rd Houston (77040) *(G-8904)*

Black Horse Test Services 903 938-8554
11441 State Highway 43 S Marshall (75670) *(G-14764)*

Black Jack Boots, El Paso *Also called Lagarto Inc (G-5837)*

Black Lemon Media Inc 832 666-6600
3702 Cypress Creek Steo Houston (77068) *(G-8905)*

Black Mountain Sand LLC (PA) **817 698-9901**
420 Commerce St Ste 500 Fort Worth (76102) *(G-6454)*

Black Mtn Royalty I 2009 LP 888 698-9901
500 Main St Fort Worth (76102) *(G-6455)*

Black Rifle Coffee Company LLC 844 899-9330
355 Spencer Ln San Antonio (78201) *(G-17955)*

Black Sail Holdings Corp 281 315-4955
250 Ed English Dr Shenandoah (77385) *(G-18895)*

Black Sand Technologies Inc 512 329-9400
9600 N Mopac Expy Ste 900 Austin (78759) *(G-994)*

Black Sheep Oilfield Svcs LLC 940 644-1720
691 N Davis St Chico (76431) *(G-3051)*

Black Spur Quarry, Uvalde *Also called Martin Marietta Materials Inc (G-20192)*

Black Star Energy Services LLC (PA) **432 272-3395**
12502 W County Rd 100 Odessa (79765) *(G-15936)*

Black Star Styles LLC 832 207-4563
308 Estate Dr Killeen (76549) *(G-13606)*

Black Stone Energy Company LLC 713 658-0647
1001 Fannin St Ste 2020 Houston (77002) *(G-8906)*

Black Stone Holdings Partnr, Houston *Also called Black Stone Energy Company LLC (G-8906)*

Black Stone Minerals LP (PA) **713 445-3200**
1001 Fannin St Ste 2020 Houston (77002) *(G-8907)*

Black Stone Minerals Co LP (PA) **713 658-0647**
1001 Fannin St Ste 2020 Houston (77002) *(G-8908)*

Black Stone Ntral Rsources MGT 713 445-3241
1001 Fannin St Ste 2020 Houston (77002) *(G-8909)*

Black Widow Energy LLC 956 378-5363
4943 S Jackson Rd Ste 105 Edinburg (78539) *(G-5579)*

Blackbaud Inc 512 652-7969
11501 Domain Dr Ste 200 Austin (78758) *(G-995)*

Blackbrush Cnsld Holdings LLC 210 495-5577
18615 Tuscany Stone # 300 San Antonio (78258) *(G-17956)*

Blackbrush Oil & Gas LP (PA) **210 495-5577**
18615 Tuscany Stone # 300 San Antonio (78258) *(G-17957)*

Blackbrush Texstar, San Antonio *Also called Blackbrush Oil & Gas LP (G-17957)*

Blackburn Machine & Fab LLC 713 644-2386
7525 Wynlea St Houston (77061) *(G-8910)*

Blackgold Services Inc 936 336-9600
3608 E Highway 90 Liberty (77575) *(G-14115)*

Blackhawk Modifications Inc 254 755-6711
7601 Karl May Dr Waco (76708) *(G-20369)*

Blackland Aerospace LP 972 980-5970
13355 Noel Rd Ste 1805 Dallas (75240) *(G-4028)*

Blacklands Publications Inc (PA) **512 352-8535**
211 W 3rd St Taylor (76574) *(G-19650)*

Blacksheep, Tyler *Also called Kent Sporting Goods Co Inc (G-20108)*

Blacksheep Inc 903 592-3853
3220 W Gentry Pkwy Tyler (75702) *(G-20059)*

Blackstar Energy Services, Odessa *Also called Black Star Energy Services LLC (G-15936)*

Blackstar Envmtl Indus Svcs LL 713 280-0590
505 N Sam Houston Pkwy E Houston (77060) *(G-8911)*

Blackstone Medical Inc (PA) **214 937-2000**
3451 Plano Pkwy Lewisville (75056) *(G-14028)*

Blackwell Plastics LP 713 643-6577
5606 Cavanaugh St Houston (77021) *(G-8912)*

Bladc Energy Partners Ltd (PA) **972 712-8407**
2600 Network Blvd Ste 550 Frisco (75034) *(G-7271)*

Blade Lab Inc 817 491-6755
791 Westport Pkwy Haslet (76052) *(G-8216)*

Blade Runner Turbomachinery SE 713 669-1155
3552 County Road 325 Navasota (77868) *(G-15726)*

Blades Group LLC 830 278-1211
3 Fm 1403 Uvalde (78801) *(G-20188)*

Blaines Motor Supply Inc 214 426-4400
4700 Scyene Rd Dallas (75210) *(G-4029)*

Blakely Construction Co Inc 432 363-6650
2830 W I 20 Odessa (79763) *(G-15937)*

Blakely Oilfield Maint & Cnstr, Odessa *Also called Blakely Construction Co Inc (G-15937)*

Blakeman Industries Inc 817 267-4444
13108 Euless St Euless (76040) *(G-6133)*

Blako 972 898-7772
1103 Walnut St Royse City (75189) *(G-17715)*

Blanks Printing & Imaging Inc 214 741-3905
2343 N Beckley Ave Dallas (75208) *(G-4030)*

Blast Envmtl & Indus Svcs 281 557-1000
416 Highway 3 S League City (77573) *(G-13950)*

Blastroom Eqp & Cnstr Inc 903 845-2083
605 E Pacific Ave Gladewater (75647) *(G-7719)*

Blaxtone Energy LLC 432 250-9039
904 W 69th St Odessa (79764) *(G-15938)*

Blaylock Industries Inc 817 831-0170
5600 Midway Rd Fort Worth (76117) *(G-6456)*

Blaze Equipment LLC 817 439-0453
4200 White St Lake Worth (76135) *(G-13812)*

Blaze Sales and Service Inc 713 828-1685
7824 Scott St Houston (77051) *(G-8913)*

Blazing Needles LP 817 831-2668
401 N Beach St Fort Worth (76111) *(G-6457)*

Bledsoe Brace Systems, Grand Prairie *Also called Medical Technology Inc (G-7924)*

Blencor LLC 979 627-7801
2324 Fm 3013 Rd Sealy (77474) *(G-18806)*

Blentech Corporation 713 673-3436
1305 Rye St Houston (77029) *(G-8914)*

Bless Oilfield Services Inc (PA) **281 227-3300**
6301 Mount Houston Rd Houston (77050) *(G-8915)*

Bless-Scent Candle Company LLC 832 431-9923
8803 Clemens Dr Cypress (77433) *(G-3779)*

Blessings Womans Care, Gregory *Also called Teda Tpco America Corporation (G-8106)*

Blind Dog Productions Ltd 254 778-0722
2526 Charter Oak Dr # 100 Temple (76502) *(G-19671)*

Block Component Div, El Paso *Also called Solrac Corporation (G-5969)*

Block Division Inc 940 723-7308
618 Front St Wichita Falls (76301) *(G-20746)*

Bloomfire Inc 512 485-0910
1717 W 6th St Ste 100 Austin (78703) *(G-996)*

Blossom Machine & Mfg Inc 903 982-5500
121 E Front St Blossom (75416) *(G-2112)*

Blount Fine Foods, McKinney *Also called Food Source Inc (G-14944)*

Blowpro, Houston *Also called Beauty Elite Group Inc (G-8847)*

Blp Settlement Company (HQ) **713 674-2266**
125 Mccarty St Houston (77029) *(G-8916)*

Blp Settlement Company 713 674-2266
4175 W Cardinal Dr Beaumont (77705) *(G-1866)*

Blp Settlement Company 432 332-0381
3346 Kermit Hwy Odessa (79764) *(G-15939)*

Blsr Operating Ltd 281 369-2032
11160 Fm 521 Rd Sandy Point (77583) *(G-18722)*

Bludau Fabrication Inc 361 798-4339
431 County Rd 187 Hallettsville (77964) *(G-8119)*

Bludworth Marine LLC 713 644-1595
6200 Harborside Dr Galveston (77554) *(G-7389)*

Bludwrth Mar Galveston Shipyrd, Galveston *Also called Bludworth Marine LLC (G-7389)*

Blue Bell Creameries LP 806 749-9005
401 E Lehigh St Lubbock (79403) *(G-14375)*

Blue Bell Energy LLC 713 661-1040
8955 Katy Fwy Ste 310 Houston (77024) *(G-8917)*

Blue Box Air LLC 424 241-3060
3927 Main St Ste 130 Dallas (75226) *(G-4031)*

Blue Box Filtration, Dallas *Also called Blue Box Air LLC (G-4031)*

Blue Chip Manufacturing Inc 713 683-1555
2330 Wirtcrest Ln Houston (77055) *(G-8918)*

Blue Creek Foundry, Houston *Also called Wearalloy Inc (G-12610)*

BLUE CUBE OPERATIONS LLC 979 238-2011
2301 N Brazosport Blvd Freeport (77541) *(G-7192)*

Blue Diamond Industries LLC 859 224-0415
917 S Highway 377 Ste 240 Aubrey (76227) *(G-847)*

Blue Goji LLC 512 270-4747
4201 S Congress Ave # 32 Austin (78745) *(G-997)*

Blue Horse Express LLC 832 966-1053
15214 Flintridge Lake Ln Cypress (77429) *(G-3780)*

Blue Line Corporation (PA) **210 225-0400**
3443 E Commerce St San Antonio (78220) *(G-17958)*

Blue Line Drilling Co LLC 325 653-1891
2102 Pecos St Ste 9 San Angelo (76901) *(G-17782)*

Blue Medical Services Inc 954 417-5442
7522 Alpine Park Ln Cypress (77433) *(G-3781)*

Blue Moon Software 512 322-0460
500 W 16th St Ste 100 Austin (78701) *(G-998)*

Blue Mountain Midstream LLC (HQ) **281 377-8770**
717 Texas St Ste 2000 Houston (77002) *(G-8919)*

Blue Origin Texas LLC 253 437-9300
35961 State Hwy 54 Van Horn (79855) *(G-20213)*

Blue Ostrich Wineries LLC 940 995-3100
5611 Fm 2382 Saint Jo (76265) *(G-17762)*

Blue Quail Energy Services LLC (PA) **432 684-0999**
2261 Wolfcamp Cir Midland (79706) *(G-15143)*

Blue Racer Finance Corp 214 580-3700
5949 Sherry Ln Ste 1300 Dallas (75225) *(G-4032)*

Blue Ribbon Products Inc 214 647-1825
6 Austin Corners St Rockwall (75032) *(G-17540)*

Blue Ridge Mtn Resources Inc (HQ) **469 444-1647**
122 W John Carpenter Fwy # 300 Irving (75039) *(G-12949)*

Blue Star Ltd 281 893-6035
15603 Kuykendahl Rd # 219 Houston (77090) *(G-8920)*

Blue Streak LLC 940 440-2105
14565 Industrial Park Aubrey (76227) *(G-848)*

Blue Thumb Inc 713 523-6523
2414 Woodhead St Houston (77019) *(G-8921)*

Bluebonnet Bakery Inc 817 731-4233
4705 Camp Bowie Blvd Fort Worth (76107) *(G-6458)*

Bluebonnet Beer Company LLC 512 774-4258
1700 Bryant Dr Ste 107 Round Rock (78664) *(G-17627)*

Bluebonnet Industrial Brush Co 713 923-2855
8302 La Porte Rd Houston (77012) *(G-8922)*

**A
L
P
H
A
B
E
T
I
C**

Bluebonnet Nutraceutical Ltd 281 340-0322
  12915 Dairy Ashford Rd Sugar Land (77478) *(G-19451)*

Bluebonnet Nutrition, Sugar Land *Also called Bluebonnet Nutraceutical Ltd (G-19451)*

Bluebonnet Nutrition Corp 281 240-3332
  12915 Dairy Ashford Rd Sugar Land (77478) *(G-19452)*

Bluecrest Energy Inc (PA) **817 731-0066**
  1320 S University Dr # 825 Fort Worth (76107) *(G-6459)*

Bluejack Energy Solutions LLC 720 320-2709
  5851 Legacy Cir Ste 600 Plano (75024) *(G-16806)*

Blues Crawlers, The, Austin *Also called Yoyo Management Inc (G-1684)*

Bluescape Resources Co LLC 469 398-2202
  200 Crescent Ct Ste 1900 Dallas (75201) *(G-4033)*

Bluescape Resources Company, Dallas *Also called BRC Operating Company LLC (G-4048)*

Bluestone Industries LLC 469 916-8090
  3001 S Hardin Blvd # 110 McKinney (75070) *(G-14927)*

Bluff Creek Petroleum LLC 325 676-5557
  4625 N 1st St Abilene (79603) *(G-17)*

Bluff Holdings Inc 817 293-3018
  1400 Everman Pkwy Ste 156 Fort Worth (76140) *(G-6460)*

Bluff Manufacturing, Fort Worth *Also called Bluff Holdings Inc (G-6460)*

Bluff Manufacturing Inc (HQ) **817 293-3018**
  1400 Everman Pkwy Ste 130 Fort Worth (76140) *(G-6461)*

Bluhms, Cuero *Also called Larry McHorse Services LLC (G-3762)*

Blumbergexcelsior Inc 817 462-1530
  2300 Ashcroft Ln Apt 620 Arlington (76006) *(G-632)*

Blumenthal Inc 713 228-6432
  1710 Burnett St Houston (77026) *(G-8923)*

Blumenthal Sheet Metal Company, Houston *Also called Blumenthal Inc (G-8923)*

Blunck Studios Inc 806 358-7064
  3303 Wimberly Rd Amarillo (79109) *(G-482)*

BMC Industry LLC 903 796-5330
  304 Fm 74 Queen City (75572) *(G-17219)*

BMC Millwork 512 456-2000
  1920 E Whitestone Blvd Cedar Park (78613) *(G-2962)*

BMC Software Inc 512 343-1961
  10431 Morado Cir Ste 1 Austin (78759) *(G-999)*

BMC Software Inc (PA) **713 918-8800**
  2103 Citywest Blvd # 2100 Houston (77042) *(G-8924)*

BMC Software Inc 972 484-1200
  1501 Lbj Fwy Ste 450 Dallas (75234) *(G-4034)*

BMC Software Inc 214 442-0397
  5000 Headquarters Dr Plano (75024) *(G-16807)*

BMC Software Federal LLC 713 918-8800
  2103 Citywest Blvd # 2100 Houston (77042) *(G-8925)*

BMC Stock Holdings Inc 972 606-6200
  1001 E Avenue K Grand Prairie (75050) *(G-7847)*

BMC West LLC 806 747-1580
  801 E 40th St Lubbock (79404) *(G-14376)*

BMC West LLC 325 698-4465
  2025 Industrial Blvd Abilene (79602) *(G-18)*

BMC West LLC 817 952-3124
  104 E Hurst Blvd Hurst (76053) *(G-12840)*

BMC West Door Plant, Hurst *Also called BMC West LLC (G-12840)*

Bmf Oil & Gas Services Inc 832 443-2089
  9006 Fawnshadow Ct Houston (77064) *(G-8926)*

Bmi Inc (PA) **325 676-3355**
  4841 Hill St Abilene (79602) *(G-19)*

Bmicrude Inc 325 676-3355
  4841 Hill St Abilene (79602) *(G-20)*

Bmp & Associates Inc 713 779-8677
  1707 Hartwick Rd Houston (77093) *(G-8927)*

Bmp Paper & Printing Inc 713 228-9191
  4923 W 34th St Houston (77092) *(G-8928)*

Bms Solutions Usa Inc 713 954-4970
  10375 Richmond Ave # 290 Houston (77042) *(G-8929)*

Bmsc, Coppell *Also called Beauty Mfg Solutions Corp (G-3410)*

Bmv Media LLC 915 216-3554
  6209 Airport Rd El Paso (79925) *(G-5664)*

Bnx Converting LLC 713 936-2726
  16727 Park Row Houston (77084) *(G-8930)*

Bo-GE Assembly Inc 281 462-0073
  1123 Church St Crosby (77532) *(G-3727)*

Boa Studio LLC 210 314-4547
  117 Pecan Dr Schertz (78154) *(G-18745)*

Board of Gvrnors of Fdral Rsrv, Dallas *Also called Federal Reserve Bank Dallas (G-4358)*

Boardwalk Midstream LLC 888 315-5005
  9 Greenway Plz Ste 2800 Houston (77046) *(G-8931)*

Boardwalk Technology LLC 512 258-2303
  11100 Metric Blvd 200c Austin (78758) *(G-1000)*

Boatman Industries Inc 713 641-6006
  7355 Airport Blvd Houston (77061) *(G-8932)*

Boaz Energy II LLC 432 253-7074
  201 W Wall St Midland (79701) *(G-15144)*

Bob Davis Fences & Gates, Fort Worth *Also called Huckaby Enterprises Inc (G-6707)*

Bob Hughes Displays LLC 713 468-7726
  6617 Singleton Bend Rd Marble Falls (78654) *(G-14739)*

Bob Lilly Prof Promotions, Garland *Also called Bob Lillys Prof Mktg Group Inc (G-7449)*

Bob Lillys Prof Mktg Group Inc 214 231-2082
  4002 W Miller Rd Ste 140 Garland (75041) *(G-7449)*

Bob's Well Service, Albany *Also called Snyder Drilling Corp (G-194)*

Bobbitt Construction Inc 903 769-4513
  599 E Blackbourn St Hawkins (75765) *(G-8228)*

Bobby G Smith Do 817 481-9463
  416 E College St Grapevine (76051) *(G-8015)*

Bobby Pins LLC 920 267-6388
  2828 Hood St Apt 1408 Dallas (75219) *(G-4035)*

Bobcat Contracting LLC 432 332-1141
  3612 S County Road 1198 Midland (79706) *(G-15145)*

Bobcat Contracting LLC (PA) **254 582-0205**
  1721 Hcr 3106 Hillsboro (76645) *(G-8322)*

Bobs Fuels Inc 325 646-7571
  1107 W Commerce St Brownwood (76801) *(G-2426)*

Bobs Monogram Embroidery 210 341-6700
  10646 Gulfdale St Ste 3 San Antonio (78216) *(G-17959)*

Boc Gases, Baytown *Also called Messer LLC (G-1829)*

Boc Gases, Jewett *Also called Messer LLC (G-13307)*

Boccard Life Sciences Inc (HQ) **281 269-6020**
  2500 Galveston Rd Houston (77017) *(G-8933)*

Boccard Pipe Fabricators Inc 713 643-0681
  2500 Galveston Rd Houston (77017) *(G-8934)*

Boccard USA, Houston *Also called Boccard Pipe Fabricators Inc (G-8934)*

Bochelle Inc 972 837-1080
  855 E Cottage Hill Pkwy McKinney (75071) *(G-14928)*

Bock Technologies Inc 972 869-2625
  11496 Luna Rd Ste 1200 Dallas (75234) *(G-4036)*

Bodin Concrete Co, Rowlett *Also called Bodin Concrete LP (G-17702)*

Bodin Concrete LP (PA) **972 463-7348**
  4810 Boyd Blvd Rowlett (75088) *(G-17702)*

Body Brother Inc 713 487-8227
  10355 Harwin Dr Unit B Houston (77036) *(G-8935)*

Body Language Fashions Inc 713 974-0960
  9931 Harwin Dr Ste 152 Houston (77036) *(G-8936)*

Bodycote Houston Thermal Spray, Houston *Also called Bodycote K-Tech Inc (G-8937)*

Bodycote K-Tech Inc 281 227-8222
  5151 World Houston Pkwy # 150 Houston (77032) *(G-8937)*

Bodycote K-Tech Inc (HQ) **214 904-2420**
  12750 Merit Dr Ste 1400 Dallas (75251) *(G-4037)*

Bodycote Thermal Proc Inc (HQ) **214 904-2420**
  12750 Merit Dr Ste 1400 Dallas (75251) *(G-4038)*

Bodycote Thermal Proc Inc 713 225-6050
  1301 Hays St Houston (77009) *(G-8938)*

Bodycote Thermal Proc Inc 817 265-5878
  428 Dodson Lake Dr Arlington (76012) *(G-633)*

Bodycote Usa Inc (HQ) **214 904-2420**
  12750 Merit Dr Ste 1400 Dallas (75251) *(G-4039)*

Boeing Arospc Operations Inc 210 932-6990
  375 Airlift Dr Ste 2 San Antonio (78226) *(G-17960)*

Boeing Company 281 226-4000
  3700 Bay Area Blvd # 150 Houston (77058) *(G-8939)*

Boeing Company 281 226-4057
  5122 Huckleberry Cir Houston (77056) *(G-8940)*

Boeing Company 210 677-0900
  7323 W Hwy 90 Ste 500 San Antonio (78227) *(G-17961)*

Boeing Company 972 491-5442
  7221 Regency Ct Plano (75024) *(G-16808)*

Boeing Company 936 756-0505
  4724 S Parkway St Conroe (77303) *(G-3263)*

Boeing Company 713 658-0831
  1600 Smith St Houston (77002) *(G-8941)*

Boeing Company 281 244-4000
  3700 Bay Area Blvd Houston (77058) *(G-8942)*

Boeing Company 915 834-1000
  9566 Railroad Dr El Paso (79924) *(G-5665)*

Boeing Company 972 344-7249
  3373 Breckinridge Blvd Richardson (75082) *(G-17280)*

Boeing Company 281 244-3056
  3700 Bay Area Blvd Houston (77058) *(G-8943)*

Boeing Company 281 226-4000
  3700 Bay Area Blvd # 150 Houston (77058) *(G-8944)*

Boeing Company 325 696-5771
  426 3rd St Bldg 7008 Abilene (79607) *(G-21)*

BOF Services Inc (PA) **806 741-1080**
  2416 Erskine St Lubbock (79415) *(G-14377)*

BOF Services Inc 432 523-2110
  1300 S Us Highway 385 Andrews (79714) *(G-540)*

BOF Services Inc 325 653-1755
  2539 W Fm 2105 San Angelo (76901) *(G-17783)*

Bogey Free LLC 972 272-6631
  2805 E Plano Pkwy Ste 200 Plano (75074) *(G-16809)*

Boggs Enterprises Inc 903 572-8722
  1232 Dove Ave Mount Pleasant (75455) *(G-15647)*

Bohama, Cypress *Also called Kk Meier Co LLC (G-3807)*

Bois DArc International Trade 903 758-2647
  205 E Timpson St Longview (75602) *(G-14203)*

Bold Energy II LLC 432 686-1100
  600 N Marienfeld St # 1000 Midland (79701) *(G-15146)*

Bold Mfg & Supply, Austin *Also called Refuge Industries LLC (G-1456)*

Bold Production Services LLC....281 615-6799
10880 Alcott Dr Unit A Houston (77043) *(G-8945)*
Boldwall LLC....312 898-9460
17350 State Highway 249 # 2 Houston (77064) *(G-8946)*
Bolfing Brothers Marble Inc....281 351-7195
18407 Telge Rd Cypress (77429) *(G-3782)*
Bollman Industries Inc....325 655-0112
928 Hughes St San Angelo (76903) *(G-17784)*
Bolners Fiesta Products Inc (PA)....**210 734-6404**
426 Menchaca St San Antonio (78207) *(G-17962)*
Boltex Manufacturing Co LP....713 451-2180
13609 Industrial Rd Houston (77015) *(G-8947)*
Boltex Mfg Forge Plant, Houston *Also called Boltex Manufacturing Co LP (G-8947)*
Bolttech Mannings, Pasadena *Also called Mannings USA Inc (G-16479)*
Bombardier Aerospace Corp (HQ)....**972 960-3810**
7336 Aviation Pl Dallas (75235) *(G-4040)*
Bombardier Arospc - Dallas Mro, Dallas *Also called Bombardier Services Corp (G-4041)*
Bombardier Flexjet, Richardson *Also called Learjet Inc (G-17341)*
Bombardier Services Corp....214 331-9400
4039 Rock Quarry Rd # 600 Dallas (75211) *(G-4041)*
Bonanza Industries Inc....713 466-7900
7043 Satsuma Dr Ste C Houston (77041) *(G-8948)*
Bonanza Marble Company, Houston *Also called Bonanza Industries Inc (G-8948)*
Bond Clothier Inc....713 784-7121
9311 Summerbell Ln Houston (77074) *(G-8949)*
Bonded Abrasives, Brownsville *Also called Saint-Gobain Abrasives Inc (G-2404)*
Bone Bank Allografts, San Antonio *Also called Transplant Technology Inc (G-18563)*
Bonnell Campo, El Campo *Also called William L Bonnell Company Inc (G-5629)*
Bonney Forge Corporation....713 695-3633
4404 Haygood St Houston (77022) *(G-8950)*
Bonney Forge Texas LP (HQ)....**713 695-3633**
4404 Haygood St Houston (77022) *(G-8951)*
Bonsavor Foods, Frisco *Also called Epic Source Food Company LLC (G-7283)*
Bonus Crop Fertilizer Inc....903 455-9439
5903 Hwy 66 Greenville (75402) *(G-8065)*
Bookbinding & Laminating Spc....806 785-1126
6522 8th St Lubbock (79416) *(G-14378)*
Bookstore Manager Software....325 673-2826
201 Fannin St Abilene (79603) *(G-22)*
Boomerang Tube LLC....713 289-5555
1100 Fm 3361 Rd Liberty (77575) *(G-14116)*
Boomerang Tube LLC....713 231-2929
13500 Industrial Rd Houston (77015) *(G-8952)*
Boomi Inc....800 289-3355
1 Dell Way Ms Round Rock (78682) *(G-17628)*
Boone Industries....940 325-6215
155 Henderson Rd Mineral Wells (76067) *(G-15519)*
Boots & Coots LLC....281 931-8884
7908 N Sam Houston Pkwy W # 300 Houston (77064) *(G-8953)*
Boots & Coots LLC (HQ)....**281 871-2699**
3000 N Sam Houston Pkwy E Houston (77032) *(G-8954)*
Boots & Coots Services LLC (HQ)....**281 931-8884**
7908 N Sam Houston Pkwy W # 300 Houston (77064) *(G-8955)*
Boots & Coots Services Inc (HQ)....**281 931-8884**
7908 N Sam Houston Pkwy W # 300 Houston (77064) *(G-8956)*
BOP Products LLC (PA)....**281 955-6321**
9118 Sweetbrush Dr Houston (77064) *(G-8957)*
Bora Gear, Carrollton *Also called Diem Digital Interiors LLC (G-2723)*
Boral Bricks Studio, Houston *Also called Meridian Brick LLC (G-10835)*
Boral Building Products, Carrollton *Also called Meridian Brick LLC (G-2779)*
Borden Dairy, Dallas *Also called New Dairy Opco LLC (G-4725)*
Borden Dairy Company (HQ)....**855 311-1583**
8750 N Central Expy # 400 Dallas (75231) *(G-4042)*
Borden Transport Co Ohio LLC....214 459-1100
8750 N Central Expy # 400 Dallas (75231) *(G-4043)*
Border Apparel Laundry Ltd....915 772-7170
6969 Industrial Ave El Paso (79915) *(G-5666)*
Border Assembly Inc....915 592-1172
11394 James Watt Dr # 405 El Paso (79936) *(G-5667)*
Border Delivery, El Paso *Also called Border Assembly Inc (G-5667)*
Border Industrial Motors Inc....915 542-4266
9305 Lait Dr El Paso (79925) *(G-5668)*
Border Lease Services Inc....956 728-1959
3905 Rotary Dr Laredo (78043) *(G-13868)*
Border Manufacturer Contrs LLC....956 982-0910
3320 E 14th St Brownsville (78521) *(G-2338)*
Border Opprtnity Sver Systems....830 775-1225
594 Industrial Blvd Del Rio (78840) *(G-5308)*
Border Pallets Inc....915 852-3939
291 S Darrington Rd El Paso (79928) *(G-5669)*
Border States Industries Inc....432 332-0591
850 W University Blvd Odessa (79764) *(G-15940)*
Border States Industries Inc....432 520-0230
3303 W Illinois Ave Ste A Midland (79703) *(G-15147)*
Border States Industries Inc....325 698-4595
2250 Industrial Blvd Abilene (79602) *(G-23)*
Border States Industries Inc....512 458-6313
622 Morrow St Austin (78752) *(G-1001)*
Border States Industries Inc....325 655-9163
425 Mrtin Lther King Blvd San Angelo (76903) *(G-17785)*
Border States Industries Inc....806 457-4100
700 S Adams St Amarillo (79101) *(G-409)*
Border States Industries Inc....806 765-5741
520 E 50th St Lubbock (79404) *(G-14379)*
Border States Industries Inc....956 831-3441
2781 Robindale Rd Brownsville (78526) *(G-2339)*
Border States Industries Inc....575 434-2022
8101 Lockheed Dr El Paso (79925) *(G-5670)*
Border Swabbing Inc....361 575-7852
5903 Us Highway 59 N Victoria (77905) *(G-20248)*
Border Tm Industries Inc....915 779-6431
201b N Clark Dr El Paso (79905) *(G-5671)*
Border Well Services Inc....956 753-7540
7195 State Highway 359 Laredo (78043) *(G-13869)*
Borderfree, Fort Worth *Also called Sensata Technologies Inc (G-6983)*
Borets US Inc....254 559-5502
1586 Us Highway 180 E Breckenridge (76424) *(G-2222)*
Borets US Inc....432 697-1900
2222 Commerce Dr Midland (79703) *(G-15148)*
Borets US Inc....713 980-4530
10497 Town And Country Wa Houston (77024) *(G-8958)*
Borets Worldwide, Houston *Also called Borets US Inc (G-8958)*
Borger News Herald, Borger *Also called Cnhi LLC (G-2169)*
Borger Oil Chemical Indus Plas....806 273-9518
Airport Rd Borger (79007) *(G-2165)*
Borger Redi-Mix Con Co Inc....806 273-2874
529 N Florida St Borger (79007) *(G-2166)*
Borgwarner Pds Anderson LLC....765 778-6499
417 Union Pacific Blvd Laredo (78045) *(G-13870)*
Borgwarner Transm Systems LLC....915 217-9268
45 Butterfield Cir Ste D El Paso (79906) *(G-5672)*
Boriack Interiors Inc....214 376-1814
1230 E Ledbetter Dr Dallas (75216) *(G-4044)*
Borland Software Corporation (HQ)....**512 340-2200**
8310 N Cpitl Of Texas Hwy Austin (78731) *(G-1002)*
Boro Park Marketing and Mfg Co....281 890-3848
10435 Woodedge Dr Houston (77070) *(G-8959)*
Borusan Mannesmann Pipe US Inc (HQ)....**832 399-6000**
363 N Sam H Pkwy E Ste 63 Houston (77060) *(G-8960)*
Borusan Mannesmann Pipe US Inc....832 399-6000
4949 Borusan Rd Baytown (77523) *(G-1780)*
Bosque Disposal Systems LLC....254 435-2260
420 Throckmorton St # 640 Fort Worth (76102) *(G-6462)*
Bosque Systems LLC....817 289-9900
420 Throckmorton St # 640 Fort Worth (76102) *(G-6463)*
Boss & Hughes LLC....713 664-9829
10200 Hempstead Rd Ste 2g Houston (77092) *(G-8961)*
Boss Crane & Rigging, Longview *Also called On-Site Bennett Services LLC (G-14287)*
Boss Hog Energy Services, Houston *Also called Downhole Technology LLC (G-9509)*
Boss Oil Field Service Inc....361 574-7939
2307 Fm 2615 Victoria (77905) *(G-20249)*
Boss Tiedowns & Strapping, Alto *Also called Warner Bailey Inc (G-318)*
Bottom Line Fd Processors Inc....512 218-3500
200 Michael Angelo Way Austin (78728) *(G-1003)*
Boulware & Anson Family Ltd....210 822-9245
144 Park Hill Dr San Antonio (78212) *(G-17963)*
Bound Tree Medical LLC....469 771-4010
1420 Lkeside Pkwy Ste 105 Flower Mound (75028) *(G-6261)*
Boutte's Boudin, Lumberton *Also called Singleton ML Inc (G-14570)*
Bowden Saddle Tree Company Inc....915 877-3191
8227 Doniphan Dr Vinton (79821) *(G-20340)*
Bowens Reed and Calloway Inc....214 389-0002
4315 S Lancaster Rd Dallas (75216) *(G-4045)*
Bowers Equipment Company Inc....281 458-8891
10303 Pineland Rd Houston (77044) *(G-8962)*
Bowie Industries Incorporated....940 872-1106
1004 E Wise St Bowie (76230) *(G-2192)*
Bowie News Inc....940 872-2247
301 Sanders St Bowie (76230) *(G-2193)*
Bowlin Engineering Co....817 232-2020
600 Burlington Rd Saginaw (76179) *(G-17740)*
Bowmans Oilfield Service LLC....903 657-0698
608 E Main St Ste 102 Henderson (75652) *(G-8258)*
Bowtex Company, Houston *Also called R M S Inc (G-11523)*
Box Company The, El Paso *Also called Ics Enterprises Ltd (G-5807)*
Box Gang Manufacturing LLC....713 742-5555
16736 E Hardy Rd Houston (77032) *(G-8963)*
Boxer Parent Company Inc (PA)....**713 918-8800**
2103 Citywest Blvd Houston (77042) *(G-8964)*
Boxx Modular Inc (HQ)....**972 492-4040**
3475 High River Rd Fort Worth (76155) *(G-6464)*
Boy Scouts of America (PA)....**972 580-2000**
1325 W Walnut Hill Ln Irving (75038) *(G-12950)*
Boyd AG LLC....512 863-2589
3208 Sierra Dr Georgetown (78628) *(G-7642)*
Boyd Built Buildings, Boyd *Also called Boyd Industries Inc (G-2203)*

Boyd Industries Inc 940 433-2315
200 E Lawrence Boyd (76023) (G-2203)

Boyd Ready Mix Inc 979 778-5199
2853 N Hrvey Mtchell Pkwy Bryan (77807) (G-2458)

BP Aero Engine Services LLC 972 252-2800
5260 Valley View Ln Irving (75038) (G-12951)

BP Aerospace LLC 972 252-2800
4965 Hanson Dr Irving (75038) (G-12952)

BP America East Texas, Hallsville Also called BP America Production Company (G-8127)

BP America Production Company 903 927-8999
886 Finklea Rd Hallsville (75650) (G-8127)

BP America Production Company 806 935-8810
1330 Fm 2203 Dumas (79029) (G-5519)

BP Corporation North Amer Inc (HQ) 281 366-2000
501 Westlake Park Blvd Houston (77079) (G-8965)

BP Corporation North Amer Inc 281 366-3988
200 Westlake Park Blvd Houston (77079) (G-8966)

BP Corporation North Amer Inc 281 366-2000
201 Helios Way Houston (77079) (G-8967)

BP Energy Company, Houston Also called BP Corporation North Amer Inc (G-8967)

BP Energy Company (HQ) 281 366-2000
501 Westlake Park Blvd Houston (77079) (G-8968)

BP Exploration & Prod Inc 800 333-3991
501 Westlake Park Blvd Houston (77079) (G-8969)

BP International Ltd 281 366-2000
501 Westlake Park Blvd Houston (77079) (G-8970)

BP Surface Solutions LLC 325 387-3881
424 S Chadbourne St San Angelo (76903) (G-17786)

BP Wind Energy North Amer Inc (HQ) 713 354-2100
700 Louisiana St Fl 33 Houston (77002) (G-8971)

Bpi Equipment and Service, Longview Also called Buffco Production Inc (G-14204)

Bpl Plasma Inc (PA) 512 582-7525
2801 Via Fortuna Ste 400 Austin (78746) (G-1004)

Bpm Microsystems Inc 713 688-4600
15000 Northwest Fwy Houston (77040) (G-8972)

Bpz Energy, Houston Also called Bpz Resources Inc (G-8973)

Bpz Resources Inc 281 556-6200
10497 Town And Cntry Way Houston (77024) (G-8973)

Brace Manufacturing Company, Garland Also called Brace Steel Components LLC (G-7450)

Brace Steel Components LLC 972 272-2016
540 Easy St Garland (75042) (G-7450)

Bracket Systems Inc 817 232-8199
8781 Harmon Rd Fort Worth (76177) (G-6465)

Braden and Prewitt Inc 713 699-2262
2525 Vaughn St Houston (77093) (G-8974)

Braden Exploration LLC 817 717-7020
307 W 7th St Ste 1300 Fort Worth (76102) (G-6466)

Braden Exploration II LLC 817 717-7020
307 W 7th St Ste 1300 Fort Worth (76102) (G-6467)

Bradley Operating Company 806 665-7130
11805 W Mccullough St Pampa (79065) (G-16316)

Bradleys Inc 361 643-0100
600 E Hwy 35 Gregory (78359) (G-8099)

Bradmark Technologies Inc (PA) 713 621-2808
4265 San Felipe St # 700 Houston (77027) (G-8975)

Brady Corporation 214 275-9595
1801 Big Town Blvd # 100 Mesquite (75149) (G-15033)

Brady Machine Inc 817 309-3302
6125 Sky Rd Joshua (76058) (G-13319)

Brady Standard Herald Inc 325 597-2959
201 S Bridge St Brady (76825) (G-2211)

Braided Green Brokerage LLC 480 729-5506
709 Paint Creek Rd Murphy (75094) (G-15683)

Brains4drones LLC 972 974-3476
6524 Pheasant Run Rd Plano (75023) (G-16810)

Bralco Metals, Garland Also called Reliance Steel & Aluminum Co (G-7577)

Brammer Petroleum Inc 940 665-4807
6178 E Us Highway 82 Gainesville (76240) (G-7335)

Brammer Pipe & Steel, Gainesville Also called Brammer Pipe and Steel Inc (G-7336)

Brammer Pipe and Steel, Gainesville Also called Brammer Petroleum Inc (G-7335)

Brammer Pipe and Steel Inc (PA) 940 665-4807
6178 E Us Highway 82 Gainesville (76240) (G-7336)

Brammers Athletic Wearhouse LP 281 391-1441
5017 E 5th St Katy (77493) (G-13390)

Brance-Krachy, Houston Also called Integrted Crrsion Cmpanies Inc (G-10389)

Branch Ironworks LLC 817 783-5183
7733 E Fm 917 Alvarado (76009) (G-326)

Brand Commercial Services Inc 844 232-7263
414 E Church St Lewisville (75057) (G-14029)

Brand Fx Body Co, Fort Worth Also called Brandfx LLC (G-6468)

Branded 210 532-4212
1720 S Presa St San Antonio (78210) (G-17964)

Branded Tees, San Antonio Also called Branded (G-17964)

Brandfx LLC (PA) 817 431-1131
2800 Golden Triangle Blvd Fort Worth (76177) (G-6468)

Brandom Cabinets, Hillsboro Also called Brandom Holdings LLC (G-8323)

Brandom Holdings LLC 800 366-8001
404 Hawkins St Hillsboro (76645) (G-8323)

Brandon & Clark Inc (PA) 806 771-5600
3623 Interstate 27 Lubbock (79404) (G-14380)

Brandon & Clark Inc 432 332-0163
930 S County Rd W Odessa (79763) (G-15941)

Brandon & Clark Inc 806 771-5646
4605 Locust Ave Lubbock (79404) (G-14381)

Brandon & Clark Inc 817 838-5593
2475 E Long Ave Fort Worth (76106) (G-6469)

Brandon & Clark Inc 432 332-0163
930 S Country Rd W Odessa (79763) (G-15942)

Brandon & Clark Inc 806 364-5470
501 E 1st St Hereford (79045) (G-8284)

Brandon Industries Inc 972 542-3000
1601 Wilmeth Rd McKinney (75069) (G-14929)

Brandon Wldg & Fabrication Inc 361 242-3344
9002 Leopard St Corpus Christi (78409) (G-3488)

Brandt A Varco Company 940 683-6286
5764 Us Highway 380 Bridgeport (76426) (G-2289)

Brandt N O V, Conroe Also called National Oilwell Varco LP (G-3340)

Brandt Precision Machining 512 339-7251
11116 N Lamar Blvd Unit D Austin (78753) (G-1005)

Branson Ultrasonics Corp 956 729-1550
12013 Sara Rd Laredo (78045) (G-13871)

Brashear Custom Cabinets, Weatherford Also called Brycon Inc (G-20580)

Braskem America Inc 713 255-4747
5100 Westheimer Rd # 495 Houston (77056) (G-8976)

Braskem America Inc 215 841-3100
7501 State Hwy 185 N Port Lavaca (77979) (G-17142)

Braskem America Inc 979 705-2532
2301 N Brazosport Blvd Freeport (77541) (G-7193)

Brass Craft Thomasville, Lancaster Also called Brasscraft Manufacturing Co (G-13841)

Brasscraft Manufacturing Co 248 305-6000
555 S Lncster Hutchins Rd Lancaster (75146) (G-13841)

Bratton Interim Inc (PA) 972 556-1951
10733 Newkirk St Dallas (75220) (G-4046)

Bratton Steel LP 972 556-1951
10733 Newkirk St Dallas (75220) (G-4047)

Brave Services Incorporated 432 355-4001
109 Sw Mustang Dr Andrews (79714) (G-541)

Bravelets LLC 800 780-9227
337 Garden Oaks Blvd Houston (77018) (G-8977)

Bravo Concealment LLC 956 783-7682
1012 N Alamo Rd Alamo (78516) (G-177)

Bray Controls USA, Houston Also called Bray International Inc (G-8979)

Bray International Inc 281 517-5400
13788 West Rd Ste 200 Houston (77041) (G-8978)

Bray International Inc (PA) 281 894-7979
13333 Westland East Blvd Houston (77041) (G-8979)

Bray Sales-Texas, Houston Also called Bray International Inc (G-8978)

Brayton Operating Corp 361 884-8741
606 N Carancahua St # 615 Corpus Christi (78401) (G-3489)

Brazco Development Inc (PA) 432 684-8031
414 W Texas Ave Ste 304 Midland (79701) (G-15149)

Brazen Animation LLC 214 880-0101
1210 E Campbell Rd # 110 Richardson (75081) (G-17281)

Brazoria County News (PA) 979 345-3127
113 E Bernard St West Columbia (77486) (G-20675)

Brazos Delaware Gas LLC 817 332-6800
3017 W 7th St Ste 300 Fort Worth (76107) (G-6470)

Brazos Forest Products LP 512 443-0777
600 Industrial Blvd Austin (78745) (G-1006)

Brazos Mdstream Hldings II LLC 817 332-6800
777 Main St Ste 3700 Fort Worth (76102) (G-6471)

Brazos Midstream, Fort Worth Also called Brazos Delaware Gas LLC (G-6470)

Brazos Oaks Ltd 254 399-0505
6408 Gholson Rd Waco (76705) (G-20370)

Brazos Offset Printers Inc 806 828-5681
9th & Industrial St Slaton (79364) (G-18970)

Brazos Pipe Stl Fbricators Inc 979 233-7895
3135 E Highway 332 Freeport (77541) (G-7194)

Brazos Running Company LLC 979 485-9830
1667 Texas Ave S College Station (77840) (G-3178)

Brazos Trailer Mfg LLC (PA) 903 873-8130
22488 I 20 Svc Rd Wlls Pt Wills Point (75169) (G-20874)

Brazos Valley Brewing Co LLC 979 353-5361
206 S Jackson St Brenham (77833) (G-2244)

Brazos Valley Drivelines Inc 979 775-3535
840 N Hrvey Mitchell Pkwy Bryan (77807) (G-2459)

Brazos Walking Sticks 254 799-7119
6408 Gholson Rd Waco (76705) (G-20371)

Brazosport Facts, Clute Also called Southern Newspapers Inc (G-3160)

Brazosport Plastics Inc 979 849-5422
2015 County Road 220 Angleton (77515) (G-566)

BRC Operating Company LLC 214 855-2260
200 Crescent Ct Ste 1900 Dallas (75201) (G-4048)

Break-Thru Products, Lancaster Also called Anko Products Company of Texas (G-13837)

Breakwater Energy Partners LLC (PA) 281 648-1268
8 Greenway Plz Ste 1005 Houston (77046) (G-8980)

Breaux Machine Works LP 281 351-4042
13842 Hirschfield Rd Tomball (77377) *(G-19968)*

Brec Inc 979 823-4466
400 Stone City Dr Bryan (77803) *(G-2460)*

Breck Operating Corp (HQ) **254 559-3355**
300 N Breckenridge Ave Breckenridge (76424) *(G-2223)*

Breckenridge American, Breckenridge Also called Lake County Newspaper *(G-2231)*

Breckenridge Auto & Engine Sup (PA) **254 559-8241**
1811 W Walker St Breckenridge (76424) *(G-2224)*

Breckenridge Exploration Co 254 559-7566
2301 E Us Highway 180 Breckenridge (76424) *(G-2225)*

Breckenridge Ready Mix Inc 254 559-3775
508 E Lindsey St Breckenridge (76424) *(G-2226)*

Breco, Gladewater Also called Blastroom Eqp & Cnstr Inc *(G-7719)*

Breco International LLC (HQ) **713 641-6073**
6830 La Paseo St Houston (77087) *(G-8981)*

Breco Trucking Inc 903 870-0396
620 E Pecan St Sherman (75090) *(G-18908)*

Breco Wood Products, Sherman Also called Breco Trucking Inc *(G-18908)*

Bredero Shaw LLC (HQ) **281 886-2350**
3838 N S Houston Pkwy E Houston (77032) *(G-8982)*

Breedlove Foods Inc 806 741-0404
1818 N Mlk Blvd Lubbock (79403) *(G-14382)*

Breg Inc 972 647-0884
2601 Pinewood Dr Grand Prairie (75051) *(G-7848)*

Brenham Auto Ltd 979 836-4524
1102 S Austin St Brenham (77833) *(G-2245)*

Brenham Ready Mix Inc 979 830-1989
2200 Highway 290 E Brenham (77833) *(G-2246)*

Brenham Repair Center LLC 979 277-9071
1404 W Main St Brenham (77833) *(G-2247)*

Brenholb Inc 210 349-4024
1234 Triplett St San Antonio (78216) *(G-17965)*

Brenner Printing & Mailing, San Antonio Also called Brenholb Inc *(G-17965)*

Brenntag Pacific Inc 281 474-5400
5100 Underwood Rd Pasadena (77507) *(G-16399)*

Brentex Division, Brenham Also called Mount Vernon Mills Inc *(G-2265)*

Bresa Tech LLC 866 728-2889
6860 Dallas Pkwy Ste 200 Plano (75024) *(G-16811)*

Bresatech, Plano Also called Bresa Tech LLC *(G-16811)*

Bret Broussard Inc 210 224-6220
4985 Eisenhauer Rd # 103 San Antonio (78218) *(G-17966)*

Bri Consulting Group Inc 713 468-6813
1616 S Voss Rd Ste 845 Houston (77057) *(G-8983)*

Briannas Salad Dressings, Brenham Also called Del Sol Food Company Inc *(G-2251)*

Bric Mc Mann Industries Inc 830 775-9153
505 E 8th St Del Rio (78840) *(G-5309)*

Brick Dudes LLC 214 592-7904
2347 Timberlake Cir Allen (75013) *(G-258)*

Brick Stone Graphics By Gartex 214 343-0573
10310 Plano Rd Ste B Dallas (75238) *(G-4049)*

Brides & Belles of Tyler 903 581-8211
109 E 7th St Tyler (75701) *(G-20060)*

Bridgeline Holdings LP (HQ) **713 432-6000**
4800 Fournace Pl Bellaire (77401) *(G-1991)*

Bridgeport Brewing Company, San Antonio Also called Comeback Brewing Inc *(G-18019)*

Bridgeport Index, Bridgeport Also called Bridwell Publishing Company *(G-2291)*

Bridgeport Refuse Trucks, Breckenridge Also called Bridgeport Truck Mfg Inc *(G-2227)*

Bridgeport Tank Trucks LLC (HQ) **940 683-9440**
601 Us Highway 380 Bridgeport (76426) *(G-2290)*

Bridgeport Truck Mfg Inc 254 559-2533
1000 Industrial Pkwy Breckenridge (76424) *(G-2227)*

Bridges Equipment, Cresson Also called Bridges Holdings Inc *(G-3706)*

Bridges Equipment Ltd (PA) **432 333-9741**
2122 Maurice Rd Odessa (79763) *(G-15943)*

Bridges Holdings Inc 817 396-4340
14400 Cleburne Hwy Cresson (76035) *(G-3706)*

Bridgestone Hosepower LLC 432 367-4673
3511 Mankins Ave Odessa (79764) *(G-15944)*

Bridgford Food Proc Texas LP 214 428-1535
1601 S Good Latimer Dallas (75226) *(G-4050)*

Bridgford Foods, Dallas Also called Bridgford Marketing Company *(G-4054)*

Bridgford Foods, Dallas Also called Bridgford Industries Inc *(G-4053)*

Bridgford Foods Corporation 214 428-1535
1707 S Good Latimer Expy Dallas (75226) *(G-4051)*

Bridgford Foods Corporation 214 631-7970
9001 Chancellor Row Dallas (75247) *(G-4052)*

Bridgford Frozen Rite Foods, Dallas Also called Bridgford Foods Corporation *(G-4051)*

Bridgford Industries Inc (PA) **214 428-1535**
1601 S Good Latimer Expy Dallas (75226) *(G-4053)*

Bridgford Marketing Company 214 428-1535
1707 S Good Latimer Expy Dallas (75226) *(G-4054)*

Bridon-American Corporation 713 921-4101
1110 Lockwood Dr Houston (77020) *(G-8984)*

Bridwell Oil Management LLC 325 672-1512
1801 Henson St Abilene (79603) *(G-24)*

Bridwell Oil Management LLC (PA) **940 723-4351**
810 8th St Wichita Falls (76301) *(G-20747)*

Bridwell Publishing Company 940 683-4021
916 Halsell St Bridgeport (76426) *(G-2291)*

Brigadier Oil & Gas LLC (PA) **469 209-0760**
5800 Granite Pkwy Ste 820 Plano (75024) *(G-16812)*

Brigadier Operating LLC 469 209-0760
5800 Granite Pkwy Ste 860 Plano (75024) *(G-16813)*

Briggo, Austin Also called Bc Wind-Down Inc *(G-982)*

Briggs News Alliance LLC 432 943-4313
107 W 2nd St Monahans (79756) *(G-15601)*

Brigham Minerals Inc 512 220-6350
5914 W Courtyard Dr # 100 Austin (78730) *(G-1007)*

Bright Coop Inc (PA) **936 564-8378**
803 W Seale St Nacogdoches (75964) *(G-15686)*

Bright Industries LLC (PA) **972 410-6500**
4400 State Highway 121 # 90 Lewisville (75056) *(G-14030)*

Bright Initiatives LLC 512 466-4734
11308 Pickard Ln Austin (78748) *(G-1008)*

Bright Machines Inc 512 750-5266
12455 Res Blvd D Dock Austin (78759) *(G-1009)*

Brighter Horizons Academy, Richardson Also called Islamic Services Foundation *(G-17337)*

Brightleaf Group Inc 512 795-8900
7000 N Mo Pac Expy Ste 20 Austin (78731) *(G-1010)*

Brill Inc 214 343-4816
10741 Miller Rd Dallas (75238) *(G-4055)*

Brim Laundry Machinery Co Inc 214 630-4517
302 Nichols Dr Hutchins (75141) *(G-12863)*

Brinkerhoff Inspection Inc (PA) **432 924-2915**
707 Tradewinds Blvd Ste A Midland (79706) *(G-15150)*

Brinkerhoff Inspection Inc 432 770-4626
2509 N County Road 1287 Midland (79707) *(G-15151)*

Brisco Plastics and Chem LLC 713 395-7081
16225 Park Ten Pl Ste 500 Houston (77084) *(G-8985)*

Bristlecone Ventures 2 LLC 512 231-9603
7717 Gilbert Rd Manor (78653) *(G-14646)*

Bristol-Myers Squibb Company 210 826-2999
723 Larkwood Dr San Antonio (78209) *(G-17967)*

Bristol-Myers Squibb Company 212 546-4000
1034 Hercules Ave Houston (77058) *(G-8986)*

Bristol-Myers Squibb Company 214 381-5050
8901 Forney Rd Dallas (75227) *(G-4056)*

Brit Systems LLC 214 630-0636
13737 Noel Rd Ste 100 Dallas (75240) *(G-4057)*

Brite Lite Sign Service Inc 713 849-5545
2603 Sand Shore Dr Conroe (77304) *(G-3264)*

Britec Solutions Inc 903 707-7471
3709 Westway St 1-A Tyler (75703) *(G-20061)*

Britt Construction Company, Lamesa Also called Britt Dirt Contracting Inc *(G-13824)*

Britt Dirt Contracting Inc (PA) **806 872-5194**
1900 Seminole Rd Lamesa (79331) *(G-13824)*

Brittany Energy LLC 210 785-2893
4040 Brdy Ste 305 San Antonio (78209) *(G-17968)*

Brk Brands Inc 915 860-3500
1301 Joe Battle Blvd El Paso (79936) *(G-5673)*

Brm Concrete 346 570-2975
1731 Peach Leaf St Houston (77039) *(G-8987)*

Broach Bilt Manufacturing Inc 972 529-9100
2140 Redbud Blvd Ste A McKinney (75069) *(G-14930)*

Broad-Ocean Motor Houston LLC 713 353-0100
18140 Kickapoo Rd Waller (77484) *(G-20494)*

Broadaxis Inc 469 688-2272
1400 Preston Rd Ste 400 Plano (75093) *(G-16814)*

Broadband Technology Corp (PA) **806 698-0396**
4414 82nd St Unit 212 Lubbock (79424) *(G-14383)*

Broadcast Technical Svcs Inc 832 467-0002
7219 Gessner Rd Houston (77040) *(G-8988)*

Broadcast Your Vision LLC 972 984-0303
2931 Ridge Rd Ste 101-120 Rockwall (75032) *(G-17541)*

Broadleaf Commerce LLC (PA) **800 282-7443**
5550 Granite Pkwy Ste 155 Plano (75024) *(G-16815)*

Broadleaf Commerce LLC 800 282-7443
807 Brazos St Ste 401 Austin (78701) *(G-1011)*

Broadspectrum Downstream Servi 713 964-2800
1330 Post Oak Blvd # 1250 Houston (77056) *(G-8989)*

Broadwind Hvy Fabrications Inc 325 437-5950
1126 N Arnold Blvd Abilene (79603) *(G-25)*

Broadwing Aviation LLC 817 332-0011
5300 W Vickery Blvd Fort Worth (76107) *(G-6472)*

Brock Enterprises Inc 281 870-8200
10343 Sam Houston Park Dr # 200 Houston (77064) *(G-8990)*

Brock Enterprises LLC 409 729-6353
4835 Bourque Rd Nederland (77627) *(G-15747)*

Brock Services LLC (HQ) **281 807-8200**
10343 Sam Houston Park Dr # 200 Houston (77064) *(G-8991)*

Brock Specialty Services, Houston Also called Brock Enterprises Inc *(G-8990)*

Brocks Logging Inc 281 593-1531
3469 Fm 1010 Rd Cleveland (77327) *(G-3121)*

Brodnax Printing Company I LLC 214 528-2622
737 Regal Row Dallas (75247) *(G-4058)*

Broen Inc 713 300-0480
27657 Commerce Oaks Dr Conroe (77385) *(G-3265)*

Broken Duckfeet Cafe, George West *Also called Joe Garcia* ***(G-7626)***
Broken Hill Propty USA Inc (HQ)......**713 961-8500**
1360 Post Oak Blvd Ste 15 Houston (77056) ***(G-8992)***
Bronco Manufacturing LLC......918 446-7196
12502 Mosielee St Houston (77086) ***(G-8993)***
Bronco Manufacturing Inc......972 924-4576
500 W White St Anna (75409) ***(G-583)***
Broncs Inc......432 614-8305
4200 N Sierra Ave Odessa (79764) ***(G-15945)***
Bronx Industries Inc......713 467-6155
8566 Katy Fwy Ste 128 Houston (77024) ***(G-8994)***
Brook Sara Enterprises Inc (PA)......**713 522-9999**
3600 Kirby Dr Ste D Houston (77098) ***(G-8995)***
Brookhollow Concrete, Dallas *Also called Brookhollow Rental Co Inc* ***(G-4059)***
Brookhollow Rental Co Inc (PA)......**214 631-6883**
8200 Harry Hines Blvd Dallas (75235) ***(G-4059)***
Brooks & Brooks Services Inc......817 560-9965
1826 Barnett Dr Weatherford (76087) ***(G-20579)***
Brooks Industrial Coatings Inc......512 990-5333
1902 Bench Mark Dr Austin (78728) ***(G-1012)***
Brooks Instrument, Allen *Also called B I Products LLC* ***(G-255)***
Brookshire Chemical Svcs LLC......281 371-2600
30653 Fm 529 Rd Brookshire (77423) ***(G-2311)***
Brookside Equipment Sales Inc......281 391-2165
28715 Katy Brookshire Rd Katy (77494) ***(G-13353)***
Broome Welding & Machine Co., Galveston *Also called Broome Welding Co* ***(G-7390)***
Broome Welding Co......409 744-0407
7909 Bayside Ave Galveston (77554) ***(G-7390)***
Brother's Trucking, El Campo *Also called Brothers Well Service Ltd* ***(G-5613)***
Brothers Well Service Ltd (PA)......**979 543-6851**
County Rd 453 El Campo (77437) ***(G-5613)***
Brothers Wholesale LLC......903 587-2900
601 S Cedar St Leonard (75452) ***(G-14001)***
Brougher Inc......713 869-7577
8881 Hempstead Rd Houston (77008) ***(G-8996)***
Broussard Group, San Antonio *Also called Bret Broussard Inc* ***(G-17966)***
Brown and Anthony Inc......806 762-1975
3601 N Loop 289 Unit 1 Lubbock (79415) ***(G-14384)***
Brown Die Casting & Mfg Inc......972 636-9575
1209 Industrial Park Dr Royse City (75189) ***(G-17716)***
Brown Fndation Repr Consulting, Dallas *Also called Brown Fndtion Repr In Cnslting* ***(G-4060)***
Brown Fndtion Repr In Cnslting......972 271-2621
1619 Bluebank Rd Dallas (75229) ***(G-4060)***
Brown Oil & Gas Co Inc......254 562-2818
901 S Belknap St Mexia (76667) ***(G-15087)***
Brown Precision Inc......530 384-2506
1484 County Road 241a Cameron (76520) ***(G-2639)***
Browning Offshore Inc......214 739-3481
12377 Merit Dr Ste 450 Dallas (75251) ***(G-4061)***
Browning Oil Company Inc (PA)......**214 739-3481**
12377 Merit Dr Ste 450 Dallas (75251) ***(G-4062)***
Brownlow Gifts, Fort Worth *Also called Brownlow Publishing Company* ***(G-6473)***
Brownlow Publishing Company......817 831-3831
6309 Airport Fwy Fort Worth (76117) ***(G-6473)***
Browns Welding & Manufacturing......830 625-8712
6701 Fm 1101 New Braunfels (78130) ***(G-15776)***
Brownsville Millwork, Brownsville *Also called Brownsvlle Architectural Mllwk* ***(G-2341)***
Brownsville Sheet Metal Works......956 546-4517
1954 S Price Rd Brownsville (78521) ***(G-2340)***
Brownsville Yard, Brownsville *Also called Legacy Vulcan LLC* ***(G-2376)***
Brownsvlle Architectural Mllwk......956 592-5423
4764 Martinal Rd Brownsville (78526) ***(G-2341)***
Bruce A Wilbanks Company Inc......432 682-7582
505 N Big Spring St # 500 Midland (79701) ***(G-15152)***
Bruce Foods Corporation......915 821-2500
8000 Ashley Rd El Paso (79934) ***(G-5674)***
Bruce Kennedy Sand & Gravel Co (PA)......**903 838-3377**
1201 S Robison Rd Texarkana (75501) ***(G-19757)***
Brucemark Petroleum Inc (PA)......**630 339-5490**
14275 Midway Rd Ste 220 Addison (75001) ***(G-108)***
Bruegmann Usa Inc......713 742-0788
589 Garden Oaks Blvd Houston (77018) ***(G-8997)***
Bruin E&P Operating LLC......713 456-3000
602 Sawyer St Ste 710 Houston (77007) ***(G-8998)***
Bruin E&P Partners LLC (PA)......**713 456-3000**
602 Sawyer St Ste 710 Houston (77007) ***(G-8999)***
Bruker Optics Inc......978 439-9899
3750 Fm 1488 Rd Ste 104 Conroe (77384) ***(G-3266)***
Brumley Manufacturing Inc......979 826-4222
22840 Mack Washington Ln Hempstead (77445) ***(G-8250)***
Brumley Printing Inc......817 336-5551
820 N Main St Fort Worth (76164) ***(G-6474)***
Brumley, LLC, Hempstead *Also called Brumley Manufacturing Inc* ***(G-8250)***
Brunswick Press Inc......713 462-0600
9430 Baythorne Dr Houston (77041) ***(G-9000)***
Brunton International Inc......214 638-4600
3310 Quebec St Dallas (75247) ***(G-4063)***
Brush Mechanical Inc......713 937-9027
11811 Charles Rd Jersey Village (77041) ***(G-13294)***
Brushy Creek Belt & Buckle Co......361 293-2345
204 Industrial Loop Yoakum (77995) ***(G-20960)***
Brushy Resources Inc (HQ)......**210 999-5400**
300 E Sonterra Blvd # 122 San Antonio (78258) ***(G-17969)***
Bryan & Bryan Asp Rd Oil Co......903 657-2391
8621 Fm 2276 N Henderson (75652) ***(G-8259)***
Bryan Baking Inc (HQ)......**979 778-6600**
600 Phil Gramm Blvd Bryan (77807) ***(G-2461)***
Bryan Baking Company LLC......979 778-6600
600 Phil Gramm Blvd Bryan (77807) ***(G-2462)***
Bryan College Station Eagle, Bryan *Also called Bcs Eagle* ***(G-2456)***
Bryan Container Company Inc......979 822-7998
1121 Turkey Creek Rd Bryan (77801) ***(G-2463)***
Bryan Enterprise, Fort Worth *Also called Cowtown Western Belt Inc* ***(G-6554)***
Bryan Research Equipment Co., Bryan *Also called Brec Inc* ***(G-2460)***
Bryant Grain Co......817 441-9782
300 N Front St Aledo (76008) ***(G-196)***
Bryant Industrial Services LLC......956 838-5120
125 Taylor Ave Port Isabel (78578) ***(G-17135)***
Bryant Manufacturing, Port Isabel *Also called Bryant Industrial Services LLC* ***(G-17135)***
Brycon Inc......817 444-2724
400 Mary Dr Weatherford (76085) ***(G-20580)***
Bryne Sheet Metal Inc......281 354-1100
848 S Houston Ave Humble (77338) ***(G-12749)***
BS Fab & Mechanical Inc......817 373-2879
981 N Highway 174 Rio Vista (76093) ***(G-17477)***
Bscene Magazine, Tyler *Also called H3 Media LLC* ***(G-20092)***
Bsco Inc......817 568-0390
2934 Se Loop 820 Fort Worth (76140) ***(G-6475)***
Bsg Pipeline, Fort Worth *Also called Four Sevens Operating Co Ltd* ***(G-6647)***
BSI, Houston *Also called Bellows Systems Inc* ***(G-8854)***
BSI, Fort Worth *Also called Bracket Systems Inc* ***(G-6465)***
BSN Medical Inc......956 926-4400
400 Olmos Hidalgo (78557) ***(G-8304)***
Bsu Inc......607 272-8100
1611 Hdway Cir Bldg 1ste Austin (78754) ***(G-1013)***
Bt5 Technologies LLC......832 727-5214
433 North Loop W Houston (77008) ***(G-9001)***
Btb Refining LLC (PA)......**561 347-5500**
6600 Up River Rd Corpus Christi (78409) ***(G-3490)***
Btec Turbines LP......281 864-9122
6755 Willow Brook Park Houston (77066) ***(G-9002)***
Btic America Corporation (PA)......**713 779-8882**
6600 Sands Point Dr # 121 Houston (77074) ***(G-9003)***
Btm Services LLC......281 773-6060
4637 Orange Grove Dr Houston (77039) ***(G-9004)***
Btp Manufacturing Inc......214 467-0094
5535 Red Bird Center Dr Dallas (75237) ***(G-4064)***
Btt, Bridgeport *Also called Bridgeport Tank Trucks LLC* ***(G-2290)***
Btu Research LLC......713 542-6228
3030 Post Oak Blvd Unit 6 Houston (77056) ***(G-9005)***
Bu Growers Ltd......979 245-2043
1800 Avenue E Bay City (77414) ***(G-1769)***
Bubbaco......972 768-0282
2031 Dogpatch Dr Terrell (75161) ***(G-19729)***
Buchanan Septic Tanks Inc......512 793-3100
15648 E State Highway 29 Buchanan Dam (78609) ***(G-2517)***
Buck Dandy Co......903 784-6362
12900 Farm Road 79 Sumner (75486) ***(G-19606)***
Buck Production......940 567-3005
3691 Mountain Home Rd Jacksboro (76458) ***(G-13217)***
Buck's Awning, Forest Hill *Also called Inpro Fabrication Ltd* ***(G-6297)***
Buckeye Cleaning Center, Houston *Also called Buckeye International Inc* ***(G-9007)***
Buckeye Corrugated Inc......713 869-9121
1401 Greengrass Dr Houston (77008) ***(G-9006)***
Buckeye International Inc......512 870-8555
720 Bastrop Hwy S Austin (78741) ***(G-1014)***
Buckeye International Inc......281 873-4200
16420 W Hardy Rd Ste 150 Houston (77060) ***(G-9007)***
Buckhead Meat of San Antonio (HQ)......**210 337-1011**
4241 Director Dr San Antonio (78219) ***(G-17970)***
Buckhead Meats Houston, Houston *Also called Buckhead Mt Safood Houston Inc* ***(G-9009)***
Buckhead Midstream LLC......832 752-4526
109 N Post Oak Ln Ste 520 Houston (77024) ***(G-9008)***
Buckhead Mt Safood Houston Inc (HQ)......**281 405-3201**
10310 Grens Crossing Blvd Houston (77038) ***(G-9009)***
Buckley Oil Company (PA)......**214 421-4147**
2900 Kemp Ranch Xing Midlothian (76065) ***(G-15475)***
Bud's Custom EMB & Screen Prtg, San Antonio *Also called Kingdom Captain of Texas LLC* ***(G-18226)***
Buda Woodworks LLC......512 312-0550
2041 Fm 2001 Buda (78610) ***(G-2521)***
Buddys Grass Farm Inc......936 258-7954
11574 Fm 686 Dayton (77535) ***(G-5222)***
Buddys Natural Chickens Inc......830 672-6262
2430 Church St Gonzales (78629) ***(G-7749)***

Buddys Natural Chickens Inc 830 305-0553
  2548 Church St Gonzales (78629) (G-7750)

Budget Box Company, Dallas Also called D & S Container Inc (G-4199)

Budget Ready Mix 281 452-5233
  14915 Market St Channelview (77530) (G-3014)

Budget Ready Mix LLC 281 452-5233
  14915 Market Street Rd Houston (77015) (G-9010)

Budget Signs Ltd 210 349-7446
  2801 West Ave San Antonio (78201) (G-17971)

Buena Vista Burial Park Inc 956 542-5271
  5 Mcdavitt Blvd Brownsville (78521) (G-2342)

Buferd Company Inc 972 272-9502
  210 E Buckingham Rd Garland (75040) (G-7451)

Buffalo Creek Millwork Inc 972 938-2392
  509 N Interstate Hwy 35 E Waxahachie (75165) (G-20530)

Buffalo Seal and Gasket Co 713 694-9003
  3780 Yale St Houston (77018) (G-9011)

Buffalo Tank Company Inc 903 322-4153
  219 Donie Rd Buffalo (75831) (G-2543)

Buffco Production Inc 903 988-8199
  5006 State Highway 31 N Longview (75603) (G-14204)

Build A Sign LLC (HQ) 512 374-9850
  11525 Stonehollow Dr A100 Austin (78758) (G-1015)

Build A Sign LLC 512 339-4447
  11550 Stonehollow Dr # 140 Austin (78758) (G-1016)

Buildasign.com, Austin Also called Build A Sign LLC (G-1015)

Builders Best Inc (PA) 903 586-8283
  201 Broiles St Jacksonville (75766) (G-13230)

Builders Depot Direct LLC 832 384-7272
  7830 Westglen Dr Houston (77063) (G-9012)

Builders Direct Depot, Houston Also called Builders Depot Direct LLC (G-9012)

Builders Equipment & Tool Co (HQ) 713 869-3491
  1617 Enid St Houston (77009) (G-9013)

Builders Exchange of Texas (PA) 210 564-6900
  4047 Naco Perrin Blvd # 100 San Antonio (78217) (G-17972)

Builders Firstsource Inc 956 755-0301
  302 N Mile 2 1/2 East Rd Mercedes (78570) (G-15004)

Builders Firstsource Inc 972 621-2233
  8701 Sterling St Ste 180 Irving (75063) (G-12953)

Builders Firstsource Inc 817 625-1200
  500 Terminal Rd Fort Worth (76106) (G-6476)

Builders Firstsource - SE Grp (HQ) 214 880-3500
  2001 Bryan St Ste 1600 Dallas (75201) (G-4065)

Builders Firstsource (PA) 214 880-3500
  2001 Bryan St Ste 1600 Dallas (75201) (G-4066)

Builders Firstsource-Ohio Vall (HQ) 214 880-3500
  2001 Bryan St Ste 1600 Dallas (75201) (G-4067)

Builders Frstsrc-Txas Group LP 817 640-1234
  3403 E Abram St Arlington (76010) (G-634)

Builders Post-Tension Inc (PA) 281 873-9500
  403 Richey Rd Houston (77090) (G-9014)

Building Plastics Inc 713 896-9001
  10375 Tanner Rd Houston (77041) (G-9015)

Building Products Plus LLC 713 946-7939
  12317 Almeda Rd Houston (77045) (G-9016)

Building Services Dept, Houston Also called City of Houston (G-9203)

Builtrite Reel & Lumber, Houston Also called Hoyafam Holdings Ltd (G-10270)

Bulk Liquid Storage Systems LP 817 473-0083
  950 S 6th Ave Mansfield (76063) (G-14658)

Bulk Material Equipment, Houston Also called Windlass Metalworks LLC (G-12677)

Bulldog Ironworks LLC 972 935-0575
  2561 S Highway 77 Waxahachie (75165) (G-20531)

Bulldog Steel Products Inc (PA) 325 893-5806
  1217 S Access Rd Clyde (79510) (G-3162)

Bulldog Wireline Inc 936 399-3999
  18462 Highway 21 W North Zulch (77872) (G-15884)

Bulldog Wireline Inc (PA) 979 260-9034
  13757 S Dowling Rd College Station (77845) (G-3179)

Bullen Pump Inc 281 274-1800
  12305 Kurland Dr Houston (77034) (G-9017)

Bullet Concrete Materials Inc 281 367-9747
  9393 Broadway Ave Conroe (77385) (G-3267)

Bullet Production Services LLC 361 504-4200
  4250 Ih 69 Access Rd Corpus Christi (78410) (G-3491)

Bullgang Tools LLC 979 203-9009
  2450 Highway 290 E Brenham (77833) (G-2248)

Bulloch Fabricating Inc 972 221-6277
  450 E Purnell Rd Lewisville (75057) (G-14031)

Bullzeye Oilfield Service LLC 325 665-0220
  581 County Road 307 Tye (79563) (G-20041)

Bumper Manufacturing Co Inc 817 831-4401
  2500 Minnis Dr Fort Worth (76117) (G-6477)

Buna Electric Motor Svc Inc 409 769-5402
  465 S Main St Vidor (77662) (G-20325)

Bunge Milling Southwest Inc 806 799-3755
  4401 82nd St Unit 1150 Lubbock (79424) (G-14385)

Bunge Milling Southwest Inc (HQ) 800 852-8291
  1972 County Road 1068 Muleshoe (79347) (G-15676)

Bunge Oils Inc 817 568-4900
  6700 Snowden Rd Fort Worth (76140) (G-6478)

Burgess Specialty Fabg Inc 713 462-0293
  8222 Fawndale Ln Houston (77040) (G-9018)

Burgoon Company, Texas City Also called Evco Partners LP (G-19793)

Burk Royalty Co Ltd (PA) 940 397-8600
  4245 Kemp Blvd Ste 600 Wichita Falls (76308) (G-20748)

Burke & Company Inc 210 271-0008
  13105 Donop Rd Elmendorf (78112) (G-6067)

Burke Texgals LLC 210 344-9463
  16630 San Pedro Ave San Antonio (78232) (G-17973)

Burkhead Manufacturing Company 713 227-5248
  1620 Maury St Houston (77026) (G-9019)

Burleson Feed Mill, Burleson Also called R J Smelley Company Inc (G-2595)

Burlington Resources LLC (HQ) 281 293-1000
  600 N Dairy Ashford Rd Houston (77079) (G-9020)

Burly Corp (PA) 817 295-1128
  754 N Burleson Blvd Burleson (76028) (G-2573)

Burnco Texas LLC 940 242-3100
  8505 Freport Pkwy Ste 150 Irving (75063) (G-12954)

Burnett Oil Co Inc (PA) 817 332-5108
  801 Cherry St Unit 9 Fort Worth (76102) (G-6479)

Burns Tool Co, Hutchins Also called Texas Automation Products Inc (G-12871)

Burns Welding Works Inc 432 682-0495
  804 Collins Ave Midland (79701) (G-15153)

Burns Wlliam G Mktg Cmmnctions, Dallas Also called William G Burns (G-5189)

Burnsco Blowt Prvntr RPR & Srv 432 367-5329
  3401 N County Rd W Odessa (79764) (G-15946)

Burrell Printing Company Inc 512 990-1188
  901 Fm 685 Pflugerville (78660) (G-16662)

Burrell-Leder Beltech, Grand Prairie Also called Ammeraal Beltech Inc (G-7831)

Burris Custom Smokers & Grills 806 893-3360
  1480 County Road 315 Abernathy (79311) (G-2)

Burrows R & H Machine LLC 903 753-1550
  2694 S Access Rd Longview (75602) (G-14205)

Burton, McAllen Also called Vaughan Investments Inc (G-14916)

Burton Co, Brownsville Also called Vaughan Investments Inc (G-2420)

Burton Oil Svc Operations LLC 713 805-2934
  102 N College Ave # 1036 Tyler (75702) (G-20062)

Burton Shipyard Inc 409 735-2491
  E Roundbunch Rd Bridge City (77611) (G-2281)

Bus Air LLC 817 636-2308
  6630 E State Highway 114 Haslet (76052) (G-8217)

Bush and Associates, Round Rock Also called Joe Bush & Associates Inc (G-17664)

Business, Fort Worth Also called Cc3 (G-6498)

Business Air Management, Dallas Also called Bam Denton MGT Ventures LLC (G-4002)

Business EXT Bur Texas Inc 713 528-5568
  4802 Travis St Houston (77002) (G-9021)

Business For American Minority 806 786-5052
  5808 78th St Lubbock (79424) (G-14386)

Business Investment & Dev Corp 432 335-3410
  312 E 2nd St Odessa (79761) (G-15947)

Business Jrnl Publications Inc 210 341-3202
  200 E Grayson St Ste 110 San Antonio (78215) (G-17974)

Business Print Center Inc 505 864-3553
  10313 Vigilante Trl Converse (78109) (G-3390)

Business Printing Inc (PA) 214 445-5000
  3209 Commander Dr Carrollton (75006) (G-2706)

Business Printing Service, Carrollton Also called Business Printing Inc (G-2706)

Business Supply Center, Hillsboro Also called Hill County Press Inc (G-8327)

Busters Well Service Inc (PA) 432 586-2533
  1600 Monahans Hwy Kermit (79745) (G-13510)

Bustin Industrial Products, Glen Rose Also called Mw Supply Inc (G-7732)

Butchers Welding & Fabg Svc, Houston Also called Bwfs Industries LLC (G-9023)

Butchs Oilfield Services Inc 956 381-8409
  12404 Vicksburg Dr Edinburg (78542) (G-5580)

Butchs Rat Hole Anchr Svc Inc (PA) 806 894-6294
  700 Austin St Levelland (79336) (G-14004)

Butler & Land Inc (PA) 214 343-8800
  10823 Sanden Dr Dallas (75238) (G-4068)

Butler Weldments Corporation 254 697-6416
  1200 Industrial Blvd Cameron (76520) (G-2640)

Butter Krust Thrift Shop, San Antonio Also called Flowers Bkg Co San Antonio LLC (G-18118)

Butterfly Effect Hair, Houston Also called Daphany Broussard (G-9403)

Butterworth Inc 281 821-7300
  16737 W Hardy Rd Houston (77060) (G-9022)

Buyers Barricades Inc (PA) 817 535-3939
  1024 Texan Trl Grapevine (76051) (G-8016)

Buyers Barricades Houston LLC 817 535-3939
  1024 Texan Trl Grapevine (76051) (G-8017)

Buzz Custom Fence, Fort Worth Also called Buzz Services LLC (G-6480)

Buzz Print, Dallas Also called Imaging Products Corp (G-4491)

Buzz Services LLC (PA) 817 263-9788
  5104 W Vickery Blvd Fort Worth (76107) (G-6480)

Buzzard Industries Inc 936 264-1010
  12826 Highway 105 E Conroe (77306) (G-3268)

Buzzballz LLC 972 242-3777
  2114 Mcdaniel Dr Carrollton (75006) (G-2707)

Buzzi Unicem USA Inc....................................214 638-8391
  1801 Lone Star Dr Dallas (75212) *(G-4069)*

Bvsn LLC (HQ)...**512 524-6149**
  401 Congress Ave Ste 2650 Austin (78701) *(G-1017)*

Bw Fabricators, Wichita Falls *Also called Sharp Iron Group LLC (G-20810)*

Bway..979 779-5900
  1591 N Hrvey Mtchell Pkwy Bryan (77803) *(G-2464)*

Bwf Enterprises Inc (PA).............................**972 875-8391**
  141 Lyons Rd Ennis (75119) *(G-6089)*

Bwfs Industries LLC...................................281 590-9391
  5637 Etheline Dr Houston (77039) *(G-9023)*

Bwi Companies Inc....................................972 242-4755
  1418 Upfield Dr Carrollton (75006) *(G-2708)*

Bwi Companies Inc....................................979 743-4581
  100 N Main St Schulenburg (78956) *(G-18773)*

Bwi of Dallas/Fort Worth, Carrollton *Also called Bwi Companies Inc (G-2708)*

Bwj Metalworks LLC...................................325 672-4909
  3125 E Us Highway 80 Abilene (79601) *(G-26)*

Bwm Services LP.......................................979 272-7708
  4007 State Highway 21 E Caldwell (77836) *(G-2629)*

Bws Construction LLC................................254 562-6820
  1310 E Milam St Mexia (76667) *(G-15088)*

Bwt LLC..281 442-6694
  1733 Lauder Rd Houston (77039) *(G-9024)*

Byford Machine-Tool Inc.............................254 932-6111
  2038 State Hwy 6 N Valley Mills (76689) *(G-20200)*

Bynari Inc...214 350-5772
  2639 Electronic Ln # 110 Dallas (75220) *(G-4070)*

Byrd Oilfield Services LLC..........................432 385-7635
  4320 Johnson Rd Odessa (79764) *(G-15948)*

Byrd Oilfield Services LLC (PA)...................**325 690-0053**
  4725 Loop 322 Abilene (79602) *(G-27)*

Byrne Medical, Conroe *Also called Medivators Inc (G-3330)*

Byrne Medical Inc.....................................936 539-0391
  3150 Pollok Dr Conroe (77303) *(G-3269)*

Byrne Metals Corp.....................................281 354-1100
  848 S Houston Ave Humble (77338) *(G-12750)*

Bz & Sons Sweeping & Wshg Inc.................903 732-9882
  5400 Us Highway 271 N Powderly (75473) *(G-17198)*

C & A Contractors Inc (PA).........................**817 441-4178**
  1217 Gerry Dr Aledo (76008) *(G-197)*

C & B Marketing, Amarillo *Also called C & B Printing Co (G-410)*

C & B Printing Co......................................806 374-6262
  2400 Sw 6th Ave Amarillo (79106) *(G-410)*

C & C Coating Inc.....................................432 682-7201
  225 S 12th St Waco (76701) *(G-20372)*

C & C Logging..903 895-4738
  4105 Rusk County Rd New London (75682) *(G-15849)*

C & C Metals Inc.......................................936 760-5640
  1402 E Davis St Conroe (77301) *(G-3270)*

C & C Oil Field, New London *Also called C & C Logging (G-15849)*

C & C Western Wear Inc.............................903 753-8991
  1700 N Eastman Rd Ste 101 Longview (75601) *(G-14206)*

C & C Wood Company Inc...........................361 865-3444
  4710 Jeddo Rd Waelder (78959) *(G-20482)*

C & F Steel Company Inc............................254 386-8847
  91 State Hwy 36 W Hamilton (76531) *(G-8165)*

C & F Tool & Die Co LLC............................210 522-9310
  7202 Eckhert Rd Ste 6 San Antonio (78238) *(G-17975)*

C & G Plastics Inc......................................972 254-2541
  1716 Parkside Ave Irving (75061) *(G-12955)*

C & G Printing Company Inc........................817 738-8350
  6237 Genoa Rd Fort Worth (76116) *(G-6481)*

C & H Hardwoods Inc.................................817 561-7711
  320 Thomas Pl Fort Worth (76140) *(G-6482)*

C & H Label Co Inc....................................214 371-2355
  6928 S R L Thornton Fwy Dallas (75232) *(G-4071)*

C & J, Houston *Also called C&J Cladding LLC (G-9039)*

C & J Equipment Mfg Corp..........................830 569-1968
  233 Corgey Rd Pleasanton (78064) *(G-17063)*

C & K Management Co Inc (PA)....................**713 774-7429**
  6545 Bissonnet St Houston (77074) *(G-9025)*

C & L Aluminum Foundry Inc......................817 923-0533
  3024 S Main St Fort Worth (76110) *(G-6483)*

C & L Millwork Inc.....................................817 605-0002
  4237 Janada St Haltom City (76117) *(G-8133)*

C & L Printing, Carrollton *Also called Advertisers Dynmc Svcs Co Inc (G-2691)*

C & M Graphics & Signs..............................956 421-2114
  1149 S Commerce St Harlingen (78550) *(G-8183)*

C & M Manufacturing, Waxahachie *Also called Cmcabco LLC (G-20536)*

C & P Plastics Inc......................................979 251-7991
  8005 Highway 36 N Brenham (77833) *(G-2249)*

C & R Bindery Inc......................................214 688-5258
  2935 Irving Blvd Ste 201 Dallas (75247) *(G-4072)*

C & R Machine, Jacksonville *Also called Magnetrode Corporation (G-13249)*

C & R Machine Inc.....................................903 795-3378
  2907 Fm 1910 W Jacksonville (75766) *(G-13231)*

C & S Cnstr Backhoe Svcs, Kountze *Also called Griffith Oil Field Services (G-13671)*

C & S Media Inc...972 442-5515
  110 N Ballard Ave Wylie (75098) *(G-20928)*

C & S Trucking...817 517-9172
  5154 N Fm 199 Cleburne (76033) *(G-3082)*

C & W Fuels Inc (PA)..................................**830 426-4301**
  670 Fm 462 N Hondo (78861) *(G-8354)*

C & W Manufacturing & Sales Co, Alvarado *Also called Beakley Enterprises Inc (G-324)*

C A A S C O Mfg & Installation, League City *Also called Caasco Signs Inc (G-13951)*

C A P S, Houston *Also called Central Admxture Phrm Svcs Inc (G-9137)*

C A P S, Carrollton *Also called Central Admxture Phrm Svcs Inc (G-2713)*

C Automation Inc (PA)................................**832 467-4644**
  10535 Fisher Rd Houston (77041) *(G-9026)*

C B G, Austin *Also called Cbg Corporation (G-1033)*

C B M B I, Barker *Also called Craig Baker Marble Co Inc (G-1745)*

C Bar Contractors I Ltd..............................409 925-5757
  5757 Ghinaudo Rd Hitchcock (77563) *(G-8334)*

C C Battery Company Inc............................361 882-5561
  3513 Agnes St Corpus Christi (78405) *(G-3492)*

C C C, Houston *Also called Coastal Crushed Concrete LLC (G-9224)*

C C E, Hurst *Also called Caplingers Crane & Eqp Svc Inc (G-12841)*

C C I, Fort Worth *Also called The Cumming Company Inc (G-7053)*

C C I Valve, Houston *Also called Control Components Inc (G-9294)*

C C P, Houston *Also called Polynt Composites USA Inc (G-11360)*

C C P I, Houston *Also called Corrugated Concepts Packg Inc (G-9326)*

C Cushions Inc...361 729-1244
  206 Highway 35 S Rockport (78382) *(G-17527)*

C D & N Manufacturing Inc.........................281 438-2499
  1011 Buffalo Run Missouri City (77489) *(G-15576)*

C D C, Lewisville *Also called E A Sween Company (G-14046)*

C D Steel & Service Inc..............................713 957-3604
  6318 Deihl Rd Houston (77092) *(G-9027)*

C Diamond F Inc......................................903 842-3107
  938 S Railroad St Troup (75789) *(G-20022)*

C E C, Dallas *Also called Continental Electronics Corp (G-4159)*

C E Shepherd Company LP (PA)...................**713 924-4300**
  2221 Canada Dry St Houston (77023) *(G-9028)*

C G G, Houston *Also called Cgg Services (us) Inc (G-9149)*

C G S, Houston *Also called Comprssion/Generation Svcs LLC (G-9262)*

C H Guenther & Son, San Antonio *Also called CH Guenther & Son LLC (G-17997)*

C H I Alpha Whitestone Inc.........................432 367-0006
  600 E Yukon Rd Odessa (79762) *(G-15949)*

C H Industries Inc (HQ).............................**972 416-1304**
  1700 Columbian Club Dr Carrollton (75006) *(G-2709)*

C H Industries Inc....................................512 278-1100
  12918 Beltex Rd Manor (78653) *(G-14647)*

C H Industries Inc....................................972 416-1304
  1700 Columbian Club Dr Carrollton (75006) *(G-2710)*

C H V Corporation.....................................713 526-1347
  1111 W Drew St Houston (77006) *(G-9029)*

C Hinton Enterprises Inc............................432 339-0411
  7111 Andrews Hwy Odessa (79765) *(G-15950)*

C Hinton Entps Fshng Rentl Tl, Odessa *Also called C Hinton Enterprises Inc (G-15950)*

C K, San Antonio *Also called Cruising Kitchens LLC (G-18032)*

C K Higgs..713 666-5739
  5007 Elm St Bellaire (77401) *(G-1992)*

C K Kelley & Sons Inc................................713 778-9232
  10651 Harwin Dr Ste 700 Houston (77036) *(G-9030)*

C K Nickels, Muleshoe *Also called Triple Nickel Inc (G-15679)*

C K S Regal Plastics, Dallas *Also called CKS Packaging Inc (G-4125)*

C L T, San Antonio *Also called Viant San Antonio Inc (G-18592)*

C M C Construction Services, Melissa *Also called Commercial Metals Company (G-14995)*

C M C Steel Fabricators Inc (HQ)..................**830 372-8200**
  1 Steel Mill Dr Seguin (78155) *(G-18827)*

C M C Steel Fabricators Inc.........................214 631-6699
  2323 Irving Blvd Dallas (75207) *(G-4073)*

C M C Steel Fabricators Inc.........................972 938-9500
  4100 N I Hwy 35 E Waxahachie (75165) *(G-20532)*

C M C Steel Fabricators Inc.........................713 799-1150
  777 N Eldridge Pkwy # 500 Houston (77079) *(G-9031)*

C M C Steel Fabricators Inc.........................361 575-4561
  255 Skytop Rd Victoria (77905) *(G-20250)*

C M C Steel Fabricators Inc.........................817 838-6811
  2400 Ne 36th St Fort Worth (76111) *(G-6484)*

C M C Steel Fabricators Inc.........................512 282-8820
  Exit 221 At I 35 N Buda (78610) *(G-2522)*

C M C Steel Fabricators Inc.........................254 799-2471
  2784 Old Dallas Rd Waco (76705) *(G-20373)*

C M C Steel Fabricators Inc.........................713 225-4446
  235 Portwall St Houston (77029) *(G-9032)*

C M C Steel Fabricators Inc.........................877 297-9111
  15990 N Barkers Landing R Houston (77079) *(G-9033)*

C M I Brokerage, Houston *Also called Central Management Inc (G-9138)*

C M T, Round Rock *Also called Consolidated Metal Tech Inc (G-17637)*

C M Trautschold Millwork Co.......................254 752-6547
  1500 Franklin Ave Waco (76701) *(G-20374)*

C N A Inc 915 533-2425
2217 E Mills Ave El Paso (79901) *(G-5675)*

C P Bailey Cnstr Co Inc 936 348-3627
1618 Highway 75 N Madisonville (77864) *(G-14585)*

C P E Inc 972 313-1133
3330 Stovall St Irving (75061) *(G-12956)*

C Pearson Plumbing Inc 817 488-0490
910 S Pine St Grapevine (76051) *(G-8018)*

C R Bard, El Paso *Also called C R Bard Inc (G-5676)*

C R Bard Inc 915 781-2489
6930 Market Ave El Paso (79915) *(G-5676)*

C R Bard Inc 956 205-7100
201 W Anaya Rd Pharr (78577) *(G-16695)*

C R D N N Dallas Restoration 214 698-0059
4830 Lakawana St Dallas (75247) *(G-4074)*

C S & P Cryogenics, Cypress *Also called CS&p Technologies LP (G-3783)*

C S Aguirre Sons Inc 432 381-5221
6829 W 16th St Odessa (79763) *(G-15951)*

C T & S Metal Fabricators Inc 972 554-9629
1513 Maryland Dr Irving (75061) *(G-12957)*

C T C, Leander *Also called Cypress Technologies LP (G-13986)*

C T G, Houston *Also called C T Gasket & Polymer Co Inc (G-9034)*

C T Gasket & Polymer Co Inc 713 856-8667
12308 Cutten Rd Houston (77066) *(G-9034)*

C T I, Dallas *Also called Composite Technology Inc (G-4151)*

C T R, Carrollton *Also called Complete Tchncal Rprsnttion In (G-2718)*

C Treat Offshore Watermakers 281 367-2800
309 Briar Rock Rd The Woodlands (77380) *(G-19837)*

C Villanueva Company LLc 281 974-2361
2909 Hillcroft St Ste 255 Houston (77057) *(G-9035)*

C W Precision Fabrication Wldg 281 820-4224
13118 Sundale Rd Houston (77038) *(G-9036)*

C Wrights Machine Tool Inc 903 777-2344
12293 Fm 2879 Diana (75640) *(G-5459)*

C X I, Galena Park *Also called Chemical Exchange Inds Inc (G-7378)*

C&A Machine and Repair Svc Inc 713 937-3426
6227 Nyoka St Houston (77041) *(G-9037)*

C&C Industries Inc 832 631-2687
10350 Clay Rd Ste 150 Houston (77041) *(G-9038)*

C&C Software (PA) **714 635-3603**
703 N Irving Heights Dr Irving (75061) *(G-12958)*

C&C Welding 903 436-9150
302 Sunshine Trl Bells (75414) *(G-2005)*

C&D Allbritton Holdings Inc (PA) **833 227-2243**
14019 Blackberry Rd Salado (76571) *(G-17764)*

C&D Bobcat and Backhoe LLC 512 358-0163
15121 Spillman Ranch Loop Austin (78738) *(G-1018)*

C&F Fabrication Indus Svcs LLC 409 994-2135
537 County Road 737 Buna (77612) *(G-2561)*

C&J Cladding LLC 281 987-2383
6611 Willow Brook Park Houston (77066) *(G-9039)*

C&J Specialty Rental Tools, Houston *Also called Nextier Cmpltion Solutions Inc (G-11048)*

C&J Well Services Inc 817 573-3550
4801 Glen Rose Hwy Granbury (76048) *(G-7794)*

C&M Machining LP 936 825-8139
5898 Fm 3455 Rd Navasota (77868) *(G-15727)*

C&S Lease Service LC (PA) **903 988-8642**
1873 Fm 1252 E Kilgore (75662) *(G-13534)*

C'Treat, The Woodlands *Also called C Treat Offshore Watermakers (G-19837)*

C-B-Gear & Machine Inc 281 449-0777
4232 Mooney Rd Houston (77093) *(G-9040)*

C-Cat, Arlington *Also called Carbon Carbn Advanced Tech Inc (G-639)*

C-D Electric Motor Sales & Svc, Corpus Christi *Also called Corpus Christi CD Electric LP (G-3508)*

C-L & Associates Inc 903 831-4311
616 S Wake Village Rd Wake Village (75501) *(G-20485)*

C-Square Intl Trdg LLC (PA) **817 633-9000**
3703 Avenue E E Arlington (76011) *(G-635)*

C-Stripe, Beaumont *Also called Crabtree Barricade Systems Inc (G-1877)*

C-Trec, Houston *Also called Network Info Systems Inc (G-11030)*

C.I. Actuation, Houston *Also called Charbonneau Industries Inc (G-9163)*

C.T. and S. Metalworks, Inc., Irving *Also called C T & S Metal Fabricators Inc (G-12957)*

C2 International USA LLC 405 473-7144
801 Hanover Dr Ste 500 Grapevine (76051) *(G-8019)*

C2 Pipeline Services LLC 713 253-6980
16525 Old Houston Rd Conroe (77302) *(G-3271)*

C3 Environmental Spc LP 210 653-7801
130 Nell Deane Blvd Schertz (78154) *(G-18746)*

Ca Inc 402 494-2411
624 Six Flags Dr Ste 250 Arlington (76011) *(G-636)*

Ca Inc 972 577-3223
5465 Legacy Dr Ste 700 Plano (75024) *(G-16816)*

Caasco Signs Inc 281 332-1502
1340 Highway 3 S Ste Ab League City (77573) *(G-13951)*

Cab Flange Manufacturing, Nacogdoches *Also called Cab Incorporated (G-15687)*

Cab Incorporated 936 569-9430
2306 Rayburn Dr Nacogdoches (75961) *(G-15687)*

Caballo Loco Marketing, Midland *Also called Caballo Loco Midstream LLC (G-15154)*

Caballo Loco Midstream LLC 432 262-1011
400 E Loop 250 N Ste 113 Midland (79705) *(G-15154)*

Cabfixco Inc 214 389-1520
10350 Brockwood Rd Dallas (75238) *(G-4075)*

Cabinet Concepts, Stephenville *Also called Badj Inc (G-19407)*

Cabinet Creation Inc 830 709-4116
14421 Main St Lytle (78052) *(G-14573)*

Cabinet Shoppe, The, Canyon *Also called Keeling Homes Inc (G-2671)*

Cabinet Specialists, Waxahachie *Also called West-Reeves, Ltd. (G-20569)*

Cabinets By Michael Inc 817 485-1962
4301 Murray Ave Fort Worth (76117) *(G-6485)*

Cabinets Deluxe By Dale Inc (PA) **512 259-2531**
3232 Brazos River Rd Freeport (77541) *(G-7195)*

Cabinettech Inc 325 670-0414
3557 E Us Highway 80 Abilene (79601) *(G-28)*

Cablecam Systems, Fort Worth *Also called Skycam LLC (G-6992)*

Cabot Corporation 806 661-3100
3 Miles W On Hwy 60 Pampa (79065) *(G-16317)*

Cabot Norit Americas Inc (HQ) **903 938-9211**
3200 University Ave Marshall (75670) *(G-14765)*

Cabot Norit Americas Inc 800 641-9245
3200 University Ave Marshall (75670) *(G-14766)*

Cabot Oil & Gas Corporation (PA) **281 589-4600**
840 Gessner Rd Ste 1400 Houston (77024) *(G-9041)*

Caco Manufacturing Corporation (PA) **713 644-0170**
5816 Heiser St Houston (77087) *(G-9042)*

Cactus Inc (PA) **713 626-8800**
920 Mmrial Cy Way Ste 300 Houston (77024) *(G-9043)*

Cactus Coin 817 640-1791
1112 111th St Arlington (76011) *(G-637)*

Cactus Cyn Quarries of Texas 830 693-4331
7232 County Road 120 Marble Falls (78654) *(G-14740)*

Cactus Express LP 936 632-3031
3860 E State Highway 103 Lufkin (75901) *(G-14521)*

Cactus Fuel, Midland *Also called Pilot Thomas Logistics LLC (G-15352)*

Cactus Ropes Inc 830 569-8744
5116 E State Highway 97 Pleasanton (78064) *(G-17064)*

Cactus Varied Industries LLC 806 335-9470
2005 Ave B Hngr 7000 Amarillo (79107) *(G-411)*

Cactus Weapons Systems Inc 210 858-6703
109 Pierce St Del Rio (78840) *(G-5310)*

Cactus Wellhead LLC (HQ) **713 626-8800**
920 Mmrial Cy Way Ste 300 Houston (77024) *(G-9044)*

Caddo Creek Resources Co LLC 903 927-1130
3900 Fm 1186 Marshall (75672) *(G-14767)*

Caddo Packing Co Inc 903 935-2211
609 S Washington Ave Marshall (75670) *(G-14768)*

Caddy Printing & Graphics 972 991-1770
13701 Neutron Rd Dallas (75244) *(G-4076)*

Caddy Quick Print, Dallas *Also called Caddy Printing & Graphics (G-4076)*

Cadena Services LLC 956 727-9391
405 Martens Rd Laredo (78041) *(G-13872)*

Cadence Design Systems Inc 512 349-1100
12515 Res Blvd Ste 7-250 Austin (78759) *(G-1019)*

Cadillac Fabrication 713 910-2200
8980 Scranton St Houston (77075) *(G-9045)*

Cadillac Products Inc 248 813-8200
6389 Fm 3009 Ste B203 Schertz (78154) *(G-18747)*

Cadillac Products Auto Co, Schertz *Also called Cadillac Products Inc (G-18747)*

Cadre Material Products LLC 301 682-0600
24275 Katy Fwy Ste 100 Katy (77494) *(G-13354)*

Cadre Material Products LLC 325 400-2793
153 County Rd 220 Voca (76887) *(G-20344)*

Cadre Timber Products Inc 409 246-3573
4527 Highway 327 Kountze (77625) *(G-13669)*

Cae Online, Austin *Also called Capital Asset Exch & Trdg LLC (G-1025)*

Caelus Energy Alaska LLC (PA) **214 368-6050**
8401 N Central Expy # 400 Dallas (75225) *(G-4077)*

Cagle Fishing & Rental Tls Inc (PA) **432 381-3061**
5221 W 42nd St Odessa (79764) *(G-15952)*

Cailip Gas Marketing LLC 281 833-4217
1980 Post Oak Blvd # 2000 Houston (77056) *(G-9046)*

Caiman Energy LLC (PA) **214 580-3700**
5949 Sherry Ln Ste 1300 Dallas (75225) *(G-4078)*

Cain Food Industries Inc 214 630-4511
8401 Sovereign Row Dallas (75247) *(G-4079)*

Cains Welding Service Inc 281 303-9517
9533 N Highway 146 Mont Belvieu (77523) *(G-15616)*

Caisson Fabrication Co, Houston *Also called Cnh Group Incorporated (G-9219)*

Cajun Electric Motors Inc 972 227-9000
205 N Main St Ferris (75125) *(G-6231)*

Cajun Ready Mix Ltd 936 597-8455
204 Kings Ln Montgomery (77356) *(G-15627)*

Cake Craft Factory LLC 469 782-2500
2001 Platinum St Garland (75042) *(G-7452)*

Cal Sierra International LLC 832 615-6002
6333 Rothway St Houston (77040) *(G-9047)*

Cal-Maine Farms, Waelder *Also called Cal-Maine Foods Inc (G-20483)*

Cal-Maine Foods Inc..830 540-4105
1680 County Road 431 Waelder (78959) *(G-20483)*

Cal-Tex Lumber Company Inc................................936 564-6426
2912 Rayburn Dr Nacogdoches (75961) *(G-15688)*

Calan Group Inc...972 422-5808
808 Stewart Dr Plano (75074) *(G-16817)*

Calcasieu Lumber Company, Austin *Also called Stock Building Sup Texas LLC (G-1537)*

Calco Bean Sprouts Distributor, Houston *Also called Houston Calco Inc (G-10221)*

Calco Equipment and Supply, Houston *Also called Transcontinental Energy Corp (G-12351)*

Calco Taiwan Marketing Service...........................713 247-9918
3988 Clay St Houston (77023) *(G-9048)*

Calcomp Inc...817 862-9311
1001 Le Loop 820 Ste 425 Fort Worth (76131) *(G-6486)*

Calcon Analytical, Austin *Also called Myramid Analytical Inc (G-865)*

Caldwell Machine and Gear Inc..............................903 572-1660
2370 Farm Road 127 Mount Pleasant (75455) *(G-15648)*

Caldwell Manufacturing Inc....................................512 398-4549
1309 Industrial Blvd Lockhart (78644) *(G-14165)*

Caldwell Upfitters LLC...832 203-5658
4909 Fulton St Houston (77009) *(G-9049)*

Caldwell Upfitters LLC (PA)...................................**254 773-1959**
4715 S General Bruce Dr Temple (76502) *(G-19672)*

Calfrac Well Services Corp.....................................210 268-0800
11226 Interstate 10 E Converse (78109) *(G-3391)*

Calhoun Chemical LLC..713 254-8974
11674 State Highway 185 N Port Lavaca (77979) *(G-17143)*

Caliber Biotherapeutics LLC..................................979 314-7740
8800 Hlth Scence Ctr Pkwy Bryan (77807) *(G-2465)*

California Expanded Met Pdts.................................817 568-1525
8600 Will Rogers Blvd Fort Worth (76140) *(G-6487)*

California Expanded Met Pdts.................................817 568-1525
8600 Ill Rogers Fort Worth (76140) *(G-6488)*

California Expanded Metals Co, Fort Worth *Also called California Expanded Met Pdts (G-6487)*

California Sample Services, Grand Prairie *Also called Three Chiefs & No Indians LLC (G-7983)*

California Stucco..210 838-7433
2438 Wayne Dr San Antonio (78222) *(G-17976)*

Calix Inc...707 766-3000
2350 Campbell Crk Ste 100 Richardson (75082) *(G-17282)*

Calkins Aero Service Inc..281 579-6674
18000 Groschke Rd Ste 3e Houston (77084) *(G-9050)*

Callaway Golf Ball Oprtons Inc...............................844 534-6426
9200 Oak Grove Rd Fort Worth (76140) *(G-6489)*

Caller-Times Publishing Co....................................361 883-1111
820 N Lower Broadway St Corpus Christi (78401) *(G-3493)*

Callon Petroleum Company, Houston *Also called Callon Petroleum Operating Co (G-9053)*

Callon Petroleum Company.....................................432 218-2800
6 Desta Dr Ste 4000 Midland (79705) *(G-15155)*

Callon Petroleum Company (PA).............................**281 589-5200**
2000 W Houston Pkwy S # 2000 Houston (77042) *(G-9051)*

Callon Petroleum Company.....................................713 328-1000
500 Dallas St Ste 2300 Houston (77002) *(G-9052)*

Callon Petroleum Operating Co (HQ)......................**601 442-1601**
2000 W Houston Pkwy S # 2000 Houston (77042) *(G-9053)*

Calrock Music...432 213-8822
1321 Upland Dr Houston (77043) *(G-9054)*

Calrock Records, Houston *Also called Calrock Music (G-9054)*

Calumet Branded Products LLC..............................281 354-8600
1 Royal Purple Ln Porter (77365) *(G-17171)*

Calumet Karns City Ref LLC...................................281 337-1534
4401 Park Ave Dickinson (77539) *(G-5471)*

Calvary Steel Mfg LLC...936 494-5775
2418 N Frazier St Ste 108 Conroe (77303) *(G-3272)*

Calvary Valve Inc...903 729-0485
220 Threll St Palestine (75803) *(G-16297)*

Calvin Allen Saddlery...817 598-0505
3830 E I 20 Exit 415 Weatherford (76087) *(G-20581)*

Calxeda Inc...512 582-5100
7000 N Mo Pac Expy # 250 Austin (78731) *(G-1020)*

Calyan Wax Company LLC......................................817 455-0895
7901 Valcasi Dr Ste 300 Arlington (76001) *(G-638)*

Calytera Us Inc...512 623-9786
804 Las Cimas Pkwy # 100 Austin (78746) *(G-1021)*

Calyx Cultivation Tech Corp (PA)...........................**281 227-2208**
14340 Torrey Chase Blvd Houston (77014) *(G-9055)*

Calyx Energy LLC...918 949-4224
4544 Post Ok Pl Dr Ste 37 Houston (77027) *(G-9056)*

CAM Field Solutions LLC.......................................832 533-2706
1700 Katy Fwy Houston (77094) *(G-9057)*

CAM Services Inc...254 629-8561
Airport Rd Eastland (76448) *(G-5561)*

CAM Specialty Products Inc...................................936 228-0824
10810 Katy Fwy Ste 100 Houston (77043) *(G-9058)*

CAM-Tech Products Inc..281 548-0188
1811 Humble Place Dr Humble (77338) *(G-12751)*

Camac International Corp (PA)................................**713 965-5100**
1330 Post Oak Blvd Ste 22 Houston (77056) *(G-9059)*

Camber Def SEC Systems Sltons (HQ)...................210 279-3608
70 Ne Loop 410 Ste 400 San Antonio (78216) *(G-17977)*

Cambium Learning Group Inc (HQ).........................214 932-9500
17855 Dallas Pkwy Ste 400 Dallas (75287) *(G-3839)*

Cambium Learning Inc (HQ)....................................214 932-9500
17855 Dallas Pkwy Ste 400 Dallas (75287) *(G-3840)*

Cambrian Industries Inc...915 771-6100
8900 Viscount Blvd El Paso (79925) *(G-5677)*

Cambrian Management Ltd (PA)..............................**432 620-9181**
415 W Wall St Ste 900 Midland (79701) *(G-15156)*

Camcara Inc...800 532-0383
1000 Avenue N Grand Prairie (75050) *(G-7849)*

Camden Machine & Tool Inc...................................817 838-6731
4900 Northeast Pkwy Fort Worth (76106) *(G-6490)*

Cameo Fabricators Inc...281 449-6207
13835 Chrisman Rd Houston (77039) *(G-9060)*

Cameron A Schlumberger Company, Houston *Also called Cameron International Corp (G-9065)*

Cameron Drilling Systems, Houston *Also called Cameron International Corp (G-9063)*

Cameron Energy Services, Houston *Also called Cameron International Corp (G-9068)*

Cameron International Corp.....................................713 571-3100
20110 Gh Cir Waller (77484) *(G-20495)*

Cameron International Corp.....................................713 946-2122
8820 Meldrum Ln Houston (77075) *(G-9061)*

Cameron International Corp.....................................432 362-2511
8927 Andrews Hwy Odessa (79765) *(G-15953)*

Cameron International Corp.....................................361 289-1455
6441 Interstate 37 Corpus Christi (78409) *(G-3494)*

Cameron International Corp.....................................713 849-7789
11210 Equity Dr Houston (77041) *(G-9062)*

Cameron International Corp.....................................713 939-2211
4601 Westway Park Blvd Houston (77041) *(G-9063)*

Cameron International Corp.....................................281 582-9500
3600 Briarpark Dr Houston (77042) *(G-9064)*

Cameron International Corp.....................................281 716-1000
4800 W Greens Rd Ste 400 Houston (77066) *(G-9065)*

Cameron International Corp.....................................601 629-3300
6500 Brittmoore Rd Houston (77041) *(G-9066)*

Cameron International Corp.....................................713 939-2211
4646 W Sam Houston Pkwy N Houston (77041) *(G-9067)*

Cameron International Corp.....................................713 354-1900
16250 Port Nw Ste 100 Houston (77041) *(G-9068)*

Cameron International Corp.....................................806 665-1647
423 S Gray St Pampa (79065) *(G-16318)*

Cameron International Corp.....................................281 391-4600
29501 Katy Fwy Katy (77494) *(G-13355)*

Cameron International Corp.....................................713 946-2122
8820 Meldrum Ln Houston (77075) *(G-9069)*

Cameron International Corp.....................................713 939-2650
4646 W Sam Houston Pkwy N Houston (77041) *(G-9070)*

Cameron International Corp.....................................713 849-7500
4901 W Sam Houston Pkwy N Houston (77041) *(G-9071)*

Cameron International Corp.....................................281 391-4600
29501 Katy Fwy Katy (77494) *(G-13356)*

Cameron International Corp (HQ)............................**713 939-2282**
4646 W Sam Houston Pkwy N Houston (77041) *(G-9072)*

Cameron International Corp.....................................281 901-3100
4646 W Sam Houston Pkwy N Houston (77041) *(G-9073)*

Cameron International Holding (HQ)........................**713 513-3300**
4646 W Sam Houston Pkwy N Houston (77041) *(G-9074)*

Cameron Knight..972 636-7172
9494 State Highway 276 Royse City (75189) *(G-17717)*

Cameron LNG Holdings LLC...................................832 783-5500
2925 Briarpark Dr # 1000 Houston (77042) *(G-9075)*

Cameron Machine Shop..972 235-8876
404 N Bowser Rd Richardson (75081) *(G-17283)*

Cameron Process Systems, Houston *Also called Cameron International Corp (G-9071)*

Cameron Process Valves, Houston *Also called Cameron International Corp (G-9061)*

Cameron Rig Solutions LLC (HQ)...........................**832 782-6500**
6500 Brittmoore Rd Houston (77041) *(G-9076)*

Cameron Rig Solutions, Inc., Houston *Also called Cameron Rig Solutions LLC (G-9076)*

Cameron Solutions Inc..713 896-3600
4901 W Sam Houston Pkwy N Houston (77041) *(G-9077)*

Cameron Solutions Inc..713 849-6556
10810 Train Ct Houston (77041) *(G-9078)*

Cameron Solutions Inc..325 573-8521
720 N Fm 1611 Snyder (79549) *(G-18985)*

Cameron Solutions Inc (HQ)...................................**713 849-7500**
3600 Briarpark Dr Houston (77042) *(G-9079)*

Cameron's Valves & Measurement, Houston *Also called Cameron International Corp (G-9069)*

Camin Cargo Control Inc...409 729-3399
1550 Industrial Park Dr Port Arthur (77640) *(G-17103)*

Camin Cargo Control Inc...361 884-3922
218 Centaurus St Corpus Christi (78405) *(G-3495)*

Camino Agave Inc (PA)...**830 393-1051**
314 Us Highway 181 N Floresville (78114) *(G-6246)*

Camino Agave Inc...956 765-4635
N Hwy 83 Zapata (78076) *(G-20979)*

Camino Real Community Mhmr Ctr 830 276-8578
510 Ave Poteet Poteet (78065) *(G-17194)*

Camozzi Pneumatics Inc 972 548-8885
2160 Redbud Blvd Ste 101 McKinney (75069) *(G-14931)*

Camp Logan Cement Works Inc 713 869-3385
1212 Asbury St Houston (77007) *(G-9080)*

Campbell Bosworth Machinery Co, Yoakum *Also called Naegles Industrial Lea McHy Co (G-20972)*

Campbell Concrete & Mtls LP 281 277-0022
14011 Fm 1464 Rd Sugar Land (77498) *(G-19453)*

Campbell Concrete & Mtls LP 713 734-6600
3935 Schurmier Rd Houston (77047) *(G-9081)*

Campbell Concrete & Mtls LP 281 424-5650
4704 W Cedar Bayou Lynchb Baytown (77521) *(G-1810)*

Campbell Concrete & Mtls LP (HQ) 281 592-5201
16155 Park Row Ste 120 Houston (77084) *(G-9082)*

Campbell Concrete & Mtls LP 713 783-4761
9500 Harwin Dr Houston (77036) *(G-9083)*

Campbell Concrete & Mtls LP 281 391-4700
24610 Franz Rd Katy (77493) *(G-13391)*

Campbell Concrete & Mtls LP 281 356-5444
19503 Fm 1488 Rd Magnolia (77355) *(G-14593)*

Campbell Concrete & Mtls LP 281 491-7376
10621 Sm 1464 Richmond (77469) *(G-17451)*

Campbell Contrete & Materials, Houston *Also called Campbell Concrete & Mtls LP (G-9081)*

Campbell Grinding & Machine 972 221-2211
582 Benjamins Way Lewisville (75057) *(G-14032)*

Campbell Millwork LLC 210 349-9294
207 E Nakoma St San Antonio (78216) *(G-17978)*

Campbell Soup Company 903 784-3341
500 Nw Loop 286 Paris (75460) *(G-16359)*

Campbell Testing Company, Odessa *Also called Rapid Service Inc (G-16133)*

Campbell Trailers & Leasing 806 250-3611
1106 W 11th St Friona (79035) *(G-7251)*

Campbell-Randall Machinery Co 936 539-1400
405 Fm 3083 Rd Conroe (77301) *(G-3273)*

Campus Design Incorporated 806 744-9998
520 23rd St Lubbock (79404) *(G-14387)*

Campus Impressions, Houston *Also called Taylor Publishing Company (G-12167)*

Camtech Precision Mfg Inc 404 444-9646
1400 Westpark Way Euless (76040) *(G-6134)*

Camterra Rsources Partners Ltd (PA) 903 938-9949
2615 E End Blvd S Marshall (75672) *(G-14769)*

Camtron Incorporated 972 994-0000
3101 Summit Ave Ste 300 Plano (75074) *(G-16818)*

Can-AM Aero Support LLC 281 810-4400
4750 World Hstn Pkwy Houston (77032) *(G-9084)*

Canada Blower, Dallas *Also called Atlantic Blowers LLC (G-3979)*

Canadian Locker, Dfw Airport *Also called Cki Locker LLC (G-5452)*

Canadian Redi-Mix Inc 806 323-5379
11130 Us Highway 60 Canadian (79014) *(G-2647)*

Canales Sheetmetal & Welding 512 556-8613
1306 E Ave Lampasas (76550) *(G-13832)*

Canary LLC 432 563-1970
2401 S Market St Odessa (79766) *(G-15954)*

Cancom Services, Houston *Also called Spartan Reinforcing LLC (G-11994)*

Canden Resources Ltd 403 473-8786
101 6th Avenue Sw Austin (73301) *(G-1022)*

Candeo Interactive LLC 214 394-8499
408 S Center St Forney (75126) *(G-6303)*

Candle Cottage 409 720-7087
3644 W Roundbunch Rd Orange (77630) *(G-16233)*

Candy Kings Inc 409 762-6100
2323 Strand St Galveston (77550) *(G-7391)*

Caney Creek Moulding Inc 936 560-1331
12072 Fm 343 Nacogdoches (75964) *(G-15689)*

Cannedy Contemporary Svcs Inc 940 322-3856
1912 Kemp Blvd Wichita Falls (76309) *(G-20749)*

Cannon Cnon Indus McHining Inc 972 293-6278
203 Norton St Lone Oak (75453) *(G-14179)*

Cannon Engineering Inc 818 508-0123
1611 Linscomb Ave Austin (78704) *(G-1023)*

Canon Nanotechnologies Inc 512 339-7760
1807 W Braker Ln Bldg C30 Austin (78758) *(G-1024)*

Canon Safety Services Ltd (PA) 903 984-5928
1800 Cox Dr Kilgore (75662) *(G-13535)*

Canon Safety/ Rhi Group, Kilgore *Also called Canon Safety Services Ltd (G-13535)*

Canopy Solutions LLC 713 510-3800
2260 Dickinson Ave Ste L Dickinson (77539) *(G-5472)*

Canrig Drilling Technology, Magnolia *Also called Nabors Drilling Tech USA Inc (G-14619)*

Canrig Drilling Technology Ltd 281 443-1414
19510 Oil Center Blvd Houston (77073) *(G-9085)*

Canteen Spirits, Austin *Also called Spirited Cocktails Corporation (G-1528)*

Cantera Energy LLC (PA) 832 246-6100
10001 Woodloch Forest Dr # 400 The Woodlands (77380) *(G-19838)*

Cantera Operating LLC 832 246-6100
10001 Woodloch Forest Dr # 400 The Woodlands (77380) *(G-19839)*

Cantex Inc 817 215-7000
2407 Martin L King Blvd Mineral Wells (76067) *(G-15520)*

Cantex Inc 940 325-3344
2101 Se 1st St Mineral Wells (76067) *(G-15521)*

Cantex Inc (HQ) 817 215-7000
301 Commerce St Ste 2700 Fort Worth (76102) *(G-6491)*

Cantrell International Div, Dallas *Also called Dallas A C Horn & Company Inc (G-4210)*

Cantwell Mattress Company (PA) 361 883-8525
4634 Baldwin Blvd Corpus Christi (78408) *(G-3496)*

Cantwell Sleep Stores, Corpus Christi *Also called Cantwell Mattress Company (G-3496)*

Canvas USA Inc 361 729-0638
1010 Hwy 35 S Rockport (78382) *(G-17528)*

Canvas USA Manufacturing, Rockport *Also called Canvas USA Inc (G-17528)*

Canyon Manufacturing Svcs Inc 281 876-7105
523 Rankin Cir N Houston (77073) *(G-9086)*

Canyon Midstream Partners LLC (PA) 713 655-9500
1331 Lamar St Ste 1675 Houston (77010) *(G-9087)*

Canyon Offshore Inc (HQ) 713 856-6010
5212 Brittmoore Rd Houston (77041) *(G-9088)*

Cap, Houston *Also called Conveyor Aggregate Pdts Corp (G-9299)*

Cap Architectural Products, Addison *Also called Consolidated Armor Pdts LLC (G-113)*

Cap Rock Winery Inc 806 863-2704
408 E Woodrow Rd Lubbock (79423) *(G-14388)*

Cap Software, Fort Worth *Also called Chuck Atkinson Inc (G-6516)*

Capa, Palmview *Also called Rio Valley Pipe LLC (G-16312)*

Capable Controls Inc 915 594-7659
3800 Buckner St El Paso (79925) *(G-5678)*

Capacity of Texas Inc 903 759-0610
401 Capacity Dr Longview (75604) *(G-14207)*

Capco, Rockwall *Also called Columbia Alum Processors Co JV (G-17543)*

Capco General Contracting, San Antonio *Also called Capco Steel Inc (G-17979)*

Capco Plastics Inc 915 772-1395
9231 Billy The Kid St El Paso (79907) *(G-5679)*

Capco Steel Inc 210 493-9992
9828 Lorene Ln San Antonio (78216) *(G-17979)*

Capco West, El Paso *Also called Capco Plastics Inc (G-5679)*

Capellon Phrmctcals Ltd Partnr 817 595-5820
7509 Flagstone St Fort Worth (76118) *(G-6492)*

Capistran Tortilla Factory 956 541-3053
1305 Lincoln St Brownsville (78521) *(G-2343)*

Capistran Tortillas Bar-B-Que, Brownsville *Also called Capistran Tortilla Factory (G-2343)*

Capital Asset Exch & Trdg LLC (PA) 650 326-3313
401 Congress Ave Austin (78701) *(G-1025)*

Capital City Appliance LLC 512 491-7600
2209b Rutland Dr 100 Austin (78758) *(G-1026)*

Capital City Container Corp 512 312-1222
150 Precision Buda (78610) *(G-2523)*

Capital City Processors LLC 405 232-5511
2621 State St Dallas (75204) *(G-4080)*

Capital Dallas Elc Mtr Svc 214 630-8487
9109 Sovereign Row Dallas (75247) *(G-4081)*

Capital Hardwoods & Mllwk LLC 210 657-1200
15421 Capital Prt San Antonio (78249) *(G-17980)*

Capital Mechanical, Dallas *Also called Capital Dallas Elc Mtr Svc (G-4081)*

Capital Printing LLC 512 442-1415
4001 Caven Rd Austin (78744) *(G-1027)*

Capital Returns Inc 414 466-2418
4332 Empire Rd Fort Worth (76155) *(G-6493)*

Capital Spectrum Inc 512 478-3448
502 S Loop 4 Buda (78610) *(G-2524)*

Capital Well Service LLC 830 767-2036
1437 E St Jourdanton (78026) *(G-13329)*

Capitalsoft Inc 972 220-1560
1702 N Collins Blvd # 21 Richardson (75080) *(G-17284)*

Capitol Aggregates Inc (HQ) 210 871-6100
2330 N Loop 1604 W San Antonio (78248) *(G-17981)*

Capitol Aggregates Inc 432 447-9667
7001 Hwy 17 S Pecos (79772) *(G-16619)*

Capitol Aggregates Inc 830 693-3533
719 County Rd 121 Marble Falls (78654) *(G-14741)*

Capitol Aggregates Inc 210 871-7228
11551 Nacogdoches Rd San Antonio (78217) *(G-17982)*

Capitol Cement Division, San Antonio *Also called Capitol Aggregates Inc (G-17981)*

Capitol Company, Austin *Also called R F Higginbotham Inc (G-1447)*

Capitol Food & Beverage Inc 972 660-4450
2430 January Ln Grand Prairie (75050) *(G-7850)*

Capitol Manufacturing, Grand Prairie *Also called Capitol Food & Beverage Inc (G-7850)*

Capitol Seating Company 254 939-1853
209 E Grove Rd Belton (76513) *(G-2022)*

Caplingers Crane & Eqp Svc Inc 817 685-0710
10741 Tube Dr Hurst (76053) *(G-12841)*

Capps Construction and Gas Co 903 693-2580
1108 N Saint Mary St Carthage (75633) *(G-2900)*

Capps Construction Co, Carthage *Also called Capps Construction and Gas Co (G-2900)*

Caprock Manufacturing Inc 806 745-6454
616 E Slaton Rd Lubbock (79404) *(G-14389)*

Caprock Materials LLC 806 778-0343
1924 Marshall St Bldg 200 Lubbock (79415) *(G-14390)*

Caprock Oil Tools Inc 281 485-4777
3446 S Main St Pearland (77581) *(G-16542)*

A L P H A B E T I C

Caprock Permian Processing LLC..............................832 914-1679
5810 Wilson Rd Ste 100 Humble (77396) *(G-12752)*

Capsonic Automotive Inc...915 872-3585
7 Zane Grey St Ste B El Paso (79906) *(G-5680)*

Capsonic Group LLC...915 872-3539
7 Zane Grey St El Paso (79906) *(G-5681)*

Capstone Metering LLC...214 469-1065
1600 Capital Ave Ste 200 Plano (75074) *(G-16819)*

Capt Nemos Steak Submarines.................................972 438-7777
1426 N Irving Heights Dr Irving (75061) *(G-12959)*

Car-Ber Testing Services, Deer Park Also called Carber Holdings Inc *(G-5263)*

Car-Ber Testing Services, Houston Also called Carber Holdings Inc *(G-9089)*

Car-Tex Transport & Vacuum Svc..............................903 693-6271
County Rd 301 Carthage (75633) *(G-2901)*

Caraustar Industrial and Con..................................409 898-6600
932 John Hare Rd Silsbee (77656) *(G-18950)*

Caraustar Industries Inc...903 793-6231
112 S Lelia Ave Texarkana (75501) *(G-19758)*

Caraustar Industries Inc...903 799-5100
902 S William St Atlanta (75551) *(G-841)*

Carber Holdings Inc...281 837-8003
5110 Railroad St Deer Park (77536) *(G-5263)*

Carber Holdings Inc (PA)..**713 797-2859**
12600 N Featherwood Dr # 450 Houston (77034) *(G-9089)*

Carbery Fabricators Company..................................432 337-5015
9214 Cromwell Ter Odessa (79764) *(G-15955)*

Carbide Fabricators, Houston Also called Gulf Coast Oil & Gas Inds LLC *(G-10061)*

Carbide Grinding Inc..713 944-0015
9317 Gamebird Ln Houston (77034) *(G-9090)*

Carbide Specialists Inc...281 354-5585
21782 E Wallis Dr Porter (77365) *(G-17172)*

Carbide Technologies Inc..713 475-0444
524 Vermillion Dr Pasadena (77506) *(G-16400)*

Carbo Ceramics Inc (PA)..**281 921-6400**
6565 N Macarthur Blvd # 1050 Irving (75039) *(G-12960)*

Carbo Ceramics Inc...972 401-0090
6565 N Macarthur Blvd # 1 Irving (75039) *(G-12961)*

Carbo Ceramics Inc (PA)..**281 921-6400**
575 N Dairy Ashford Rd # 300 Houston (77079) *(G-9091)*

Carboline Company..800 848-4645
8888 Governors Row Dallas (75247) *(G-4082)*

Carboline Prmium Cutng Tls Inc...............................281 485-5505
1914 County Road 894 Rosharon (77583) *(G-17600)*

Carbon and Clay Company......................................844 624-4263
1965 Post Rd Ste 600 New Braunfels (78130) *(G-15777)*

Carbon Carbn Advanced Tech Inc.............................817 985-2500
4704 Eden Rd Arlington (76001) *(G-639)*

Carbon Silica Partners LP.......................................361 572-4040
1036 Industrial Park Dr Victoria (77905) *(G-20251)*

Carbonfree Chemicals Spe I LLC (PA).......................**210 476-5906**
11839 Nacogdoches Rd San Antonio (78217) *(G-17983)*

Carbonfree Chemicals Spe I LLC..............................210 476-5906
11503 Bulverde Rd San Antonio (78217) *(G-17984)*

Carbonyx Carbon Technologies, Plano Also called Carbonyx Inc *(G-16820)*

Carbonyx Inc (PA)...**972 943-3355**
5513 Roberts Dr Plano (75093) *(G-16820)*

Carchalk Inc..210 667-3890
5075 N State Highway 123 Seguin (78155) *(G-18828)*

Cardet Wholesale Inc...713 266-9834
30602 Goya Rd Brookshire (77423) *(G-2312)*

Cardinal Automation Inc..214 233-3773
11036 Aladdin Dr Dallas (75229) *(G-4083)*

Cardinal Glass Industries Inc...................................972 937-4969
201 Cardinal Rd Waxahachie (75165) *(G-20533)*

Cardinal Glass Industries Inc...................................972 937-1708
203 Cardinal Rd Waxahachie (75165) *(G-20534)*

Cardinal Health Inc...915 781-7465
1 Butterfield Trail Blvd El Paso (79906) *(G-5682)*

Cardinal Health 200 LLC...903 586-6502
200 Mcknight St Jacksonville (75766) *(G-13232)*

Cardinal Ig, Waxahachie Also called Cardinal Glass Industries Inc *(G-20533)*

Cardinal Midstream II LLC.......................................214 468-0700
8150 N Cntrl Expy # 1725 Dallas (75206) *(G-4084)*

Cardinal Showers, Arlington Also called Hoskin & Muir Inc *(G-700)*

Cardinal Software Inc (HQ)......................................**512 275-0072**
6850 Austin Center Blvd Austin (78731) *(G-1028)*

Cardinal Tool Co...972 564-2314
2 Mustang Cir Forney (75126) *(G-6304)*

Cardioquip LLC..979 691-0202
8422 Calibration Ct College Station (77845) *(G-3180)*

Care Converge, Houston Also called Convergepoint Inc *(G-9298)*

Care Laboratories Inc..281 835-9600
12706 Settemont Rd Missouri City (77489) *(G-15577)*

Care Products Inc...956 383-6049
6 N 12th St McAllen (78501) *(G-14846)*

Career Concepts Inc..972 276-9332
210 Bronze St Garland (75042) *(G-7453)*

Career Uniforms, Houston Also called Radia Enterprises Inc *(G-11530)*

Carefusion 213 LLC...915 231-5000
1550 Northwestern Dr El Paso (79912) *(G-5683)*

Carey Crutcher Inc..281 346-0045
7330 Fm 359 Rd S Fulshear (77441) *(G-7328)*

Carey Sheet Metal Shop Inc....................................956 423-1394
14392 W Expressway 83 Harlingen (78552) *(G-8184)*

Cargill Incorporated..806 364-3891
3537 S Progressive Rd Hereford (79045) *(G-8285)*

Cargill Incorporated..254 799-6211
2510 E Lake Shore Dr Waco (76705) *(G-20375)*

Cargill Incorporated..325 672-3271
1025 China St Abilene (79602) *(G-29)*

Cargill Incorporated..254 774-9022
251 Berger Rd Temple (76501) *(G-19673)*

Cargill Meat Solutions Corp....................................806 295-8393
4 Miles W Hgwy60 Ste 60 Friona (79035) *(G-7252)*

Cargill Meat Solutions Corp....................................806 293-5181
2226 F M 3183 Plainview (79072) *(G-16752)*

Cargill Meat Solutions Corp....................................806 295-8243
1530 W Us Highway 60 Friona (79035) *(G-7253)*

Cargo Crating Company Ltd.....................................713 699-0172
15370 Vantage Pkwy W Houston (77032) *(G-9092)*

Cargo Forwarding International, Houston Also called Cargo Crating Company Ltd *(G-9092)*

Cargo Systems Inc..512 837-1300
2120 Denton Dr Ste 108 Austin (78758) *(G-1029)*

Caribbean Marine, Dallas Also called Garvon Inc *(G-4392)*

Carl Kisabeth Co Inc (PA).......................................**817 281-7560**
5320 Glenview Dr Haltom City (76117) *(G-8134)*

Carl R McEver...903 842-2555
8198 Fm 2064 N Troup (75789) *(G-20023)*

Carl Zeiss Vision Inc..972 906-9663
440 E Vista Ridge Mall Dr Lewisville (75067) *(G-14033)*

Carling Technologies Inc...956 546-5564
3734 International Blvd Brownsville (78521) *(G-2344)*

Carlisle Construction Mtls LLC.................................214 515-5200
10 Rexel Ct Terrell (75160) *(G-19730)*

Carlisle Ctngs Wtrproofing Inc (HQ).........................**972 442-6545**
900 Hensley Ln Wylie (75098) *(G-20929)*

Carlisle Systems Inc...713 703-9256
12814 Murphy Rd Stafford (77477) *(G-19292)*

Carlstar Group LLC...972 606-2126
1504 W North Carrier Pkwy Grand Prairie (75050) *(G-7851)*

Carlton Foods Corp (HQ)..**830 625-7583**
2030 North Loop W Ste 100 Houston (77018) *(G-9093)*

Carlton Industries LP...979 242-5055
4225 W State Highway 71 La Grange (78945) *(G-13693)*

Carlton Mfg Inc..903 537-4591
I-30 S Service Rd Mount Vernon (75457) *(G-15666)*

Carlton Mfg Associates, Mount Vernon Also called Carlton Mfg Inc *(G-15666)*

Carmies Kitchen Inc..972 442-1337
210 Windco Cir Wylie (75098) *(G-20930)*

Carnicria Y Tortilleria El Sol....................................915 877-5553
6215 Upper Valley Rd M El Paso (79932) *(G-5684)*

Carol Turner Collection, San Angelo Also called Zrc Ltd *(G-17843)*

Carolina Carports Inc...800 670-4262
3740 Fm 2324 Emory (75440) *(G-6082)*

Carols Crister, Rosenberg Also called Hartman Newspapers LP *(G-17586)*

Carols Lighting and Fan Sp Inc.................................281 292-1661
27132 Interstate 45 N Conroe (77385) *(G-3274)*

Carols Mch & Fabrication Inc...................................713 921-7266
841 Fm 102 Rd Wharton (77488) *(G-20698)*

Carpenter Chemical Co Inc......................................281 474-5111
11002 Choate Rd Pasadena (77507) *(G-16401)*

Carpenter Co...254 778-0131
2611 N General Bruce Dr Temple (76501) *(G-19674)*

Carpenter Co...512 365-5833
302 Highland Dr Taylor (76574) *(G-19651)*

Carpenter Co...214 330-0373
4443 Bronze Way Dallas (75236) *(G-4085)*

Carpenter Co Morning Glory Div, Taylor Also called Carpenter Co *(G-19651)*

Carpenter Co., Pasadena Also called E R Carpenter LP *(G-16422)*

Carpenter Welding & Machine..................................254 796-2114
Hwy 281 N Hico (76457) *(G-8302)*

Carpet One, Houston Also called Venetian Blind Flr Cvg Sp Ltd *(G-12546)*

Carports Childers & Structures................................713 460-2181
11711 Brittmoore Park Dr Houston (77041) *(G-9094)*

Carreker Corporation (HQ)......................................**800 486-1981**
4055 Valley View Ln # 800 Dallas (75244) *(G-4086)*

Carriage Casting Inc..915 760-6800
1206 Mcrae Blvd A El Paso (79925) *(G-5685)*

Carrier Corporation...903 510-7300
1700 E Duncan St Tyler (75702) *(G-20063)*

Carrier Corporation...210 495-2600
12029 Starcrest Dr San Antonio (78247) *(G-17985)*

Carrion Enterprises Inc..915 593-1338
7230 Gateway Blvd E Ste C El Paso (79915) *(G-5686)*

Carrizo Well Service LLC...325 574-6291
1105 Old Lubbock Hwy Snyder (79549) *(G-18986)*

Carrizo Wood Products Inc 936 569-0582
  8807 Fm 2259 Nacogdoches (75961) *(G-15690)*
Carroll Systems LP 512 927-1200
  4603 Commercial Park Dr Austin (78724) *(G-1030)*
Carruth Nursery Irrigation 903 236-7555
  137 Gilmer Rd Longview (75604) *(G-14208)*
Carta Mundi Inc (HQ) **214 330-7761**
  5101 Highland Place Dr Dallas (75236) *(G-4087)*
Carter Aerospace Dev LLC 940 691-0819
  2730 Commerce St Ste 500 Wichita Falls (76301) *(G-20750)*
Carter Glassblowing Inc 940 440-3090
  5751 Fm 424 Crossroads (76227) *(G-3747)*
Carter Lee Properties LLC 713 385-8092
  5560 Fm 1640 Rd Richmond (77406) *(G-17452)*
Carter's Pharmacy, Corpus Christi *Also called Third Coast Rx Inc (G-3639)*
Carthage Cup Co 903 693-7151
  505 E Cotton St Carthage (75633) *(G-2902)*
Carthage Hardwoods LLC 903 693-9300
  1314 Hills Lake Rd Carthage (75633) *(G-2903)*
Cartoon Mascots, Edinburg *Also called Claudia Rodriguez (G-5583)*
Casa Rica LP 806 296-7582
  105 N Interstate 27 Plainview (79072) *(G-16753)*
Casa Rica Foods, Plainview *Also called Casa Rica LP (G-16753)*
Cascade Engineering Inc 817 490-6300
  5400 Alliance Gateway Fwy Fort Worth (76177) *(G-6494)*
Casci Ornamental Plaster Inc 214 421-3390
  2615 S Good Latimer Expy Dallas (75215) *(G-4088)*
Case Hafer Inc 281 341-5070
  1018 Mulcahy St Rosenberg (77471) *(G-17578)*
Case Hill Group Inc 903 657-7000
  700 Kilgore Dr Henderson (75652) *(G-8260)*
Casero's and Associates, Dallas *Also called Caseros Imports Inc (G-4089)*
Caseros Imports Inc 972 247-1991
  4343 Sigma Rd Ste 300 Dallas (75244) *(G-4089)*
Casey Products LLC 903 927-3500
  1070 Pumpkin Center Rd Marshall (75672) *(G-14770)*
Cash Engraving Co 817 831-8585
  1403 Oak Knoll Dr Fort Worth (76117) *(G-6495)*
Cash Processing Solutions Inc 972 582-1100
  6401 Commerce Dr Irving (75063) *(G-12962)*
Casi, Frisco *Also called Cornerstone Atomtn Systems LLC (G-7275)*
Casino Supply Company 972 241-4833
  2416 Walnut Ridge St Dallas (75229) *(G-4090)*
Casita Enterprises Inc 903 326-4717
  5029 Se Mckinney St # 1 Rice (75155) *(G-17265)*
Cassava Sciences Inc 512 501-2444
  7801 N Cpitl Of Txas Hwy Austin (78731) *(G-1031)*
Casscom Media LP 903 455-2555
  6000 Industrial Dr Greenville (75402) *(G-8066)*
Cast Fireplaces (PA) **713 937-1080**
  10425 Tanner Rd Houston (77041) *(G-9095)*
Cast Limestone Products Texas, Hutto *Also called Charles Barton (G-12877)*
Cast Sheet Metal LLC 956 580-9960
  715 N Bryan Blvd Alton (78573) *(G-322)*
Cast Stone Commercial Services, Dallas *Also called S C S C Inc (G-4922)*
Casteel & Associates Inc 214 352-7446
  11106 Morrison Ln Dallas (75229) *(G-4091)*
Casteel Mfg Inc 210 923-4558
  3747 Pitluk Ave San Antonio (78211) *(G-17986)*
Casteel Sign, Dallas *Also called Casteel & Associates Inc (G-4091)*
Castell LP 972 938-2739
  200 Butcher Rd Waxahachie (75165) *(G-20535)*
Castex Energy Inc 281 447-8601
  333 Clay St Ste 2000 Houston (77002) *(G-9096)*
Castia, Rice *Also called Casita Enterprises Inc (G-17265)*
Casting Designs Inc 817 551-7373
  9320 Crowley Rd Fort Worth (76134) *(G-6496)*
Castlberry Instrs Avionics LLC 512 251-5322
  13405 Immanuel Rd Ste 1a Pflugerville (78660) *(G-16663)*
Castle Biosciences Inc 866 788-9007
  820 S Friendswood Dr # 20 Friendswood (77546) *(G-7242)*
Castro Cheese Company Inc 713 460-0329
  4006 Campbell Rd Houston (77080) *(G-9097)*
Castronics Inc 308 235-4881
  7814 Miller Road 3 Houston (77049) *(G-9098)*
Catalyst Oilfld Svcs 2016 LLC (HQ) **432 563-0727**
  11999 E Us Highway 158 Gardendale (79758) *(G-7420)*
Catalyst Partners Inc 940 644-5625
  146 Prvate Rd 1738 Unit 2 Chico (76431) *(G-3052)*
Catalyst Partners Oil Field, Chico *Also called Catalyst Partners Inc (G-3052)*
Catec Americas Inc 281 398-8806
  1400 Brdfeld Blvd Ste 200 Houston (77084) *(G-9099)*
Caterpillar Global Min Eqp LLC 903 786-2981
  3501 N Fm Highway 1417 Denison (75020) *(G-5336)*
Caterpillar Inc 713 895-2316
  13105 Nw Fwy Ste 1010 Houston (77040) *(G-9100)*
Caterpillar Inc 254 752-3456
  2100 Orchard Ln Unit C Waco (76705) *(G-20376)*

Caterpillar Inc 361 580-5600
  7300 Lone Tree Rd Victoria (77905) *(G-20252)*
Caterpillar Inc 830 401-5600
  1720 W Kingsbury St Seguin (78155) *(G-18829)*
Caterpillar Inc 713 895-2300
  10203 Sam Houston Park Dr Houston (77064) *(G-9101)*
Caterpillar Inc 210 637-3700
  4633 Perrin Crk San Antonio (78217) *(G-17987)*
Caterpillar Inc 309 675-1000
  2901 Gateway Blvd Waco (76712) *(G-20377)*
Caterpillar Work Tools Inc 254 297-2321
  2000 Texas Central Pkwy Waco (76712) *(G-20378)*
Caterpillar Globl Min Mxico LLC (HQ) **224 551-4000**
  557 Finegan Rd 10 Del Rio (78840) *(G-5311)*
Cates Caststone Co Inc 903 839-0309
  3901 S Southwest Loop 323 Tyler (75701) *(G-20064)*
Cates Control Systems Inc 972 665-3200
  4001 E Plano Pkwy Ste 500 Plano (75074) *(G-16821)*
Cates Machine Shop Inc 903 592-2015
  12198 State Highway 64 W Tyler (75704) *(G-20065)*
Cathedral Energy Services Inc (PA) **303 825-1001**
  6622 Willow Brook Park Houston (77066) *(G-9102)*
Cathodic Rectifiers Inc 903 759-6813
  802 Fisher Rd Longview (75604) *(G-14209)*
Cato Construction Company 979 830-1398
  1906 Longwood Dr Brenham (77833) *(G-2250)*
Catocon Inc 903 348-3350
  739 County Road 1183 Sulphur Springs (75482) *(G-19582)*
Catspring Yaupon, Cat Spring *Also called Holly Yaupon Tea LLC (G-2930)*
Cattilac Style 325 695-6263
  2317 S Danville Dr Abilene (79605) *(G-30)*
Cavalier Casting, Driftwood *Also called Angel Sword Corp (G-5498)*
Cavallini Co Inc 210 733-8161
  4719 Blanco Rd San Antonio (78212) *(G-17988)*
Cavern Solutions Inc 713 393-7733
  2515 Texas St Houston (77003) *(G-9103)*
Caviness Beef Packers Ltd 806 372-5781
  4206 E Amarillo Blvd Amarillo (79107) *(G-412)*
Caviness Beef Packers Ltd 806 372-5781
  4206 E Amarillo Blvd Amarillo (79107) *(G-413)*
Caviness Packing Company Inc 806 357-2443
  3255 Hwy 60 Hereford (79045) *(G-8286)*
Caza Oil & Gas Inc (PA) **281 363-4442**
  200 Valley Wood Dr B200 Spring (77380) *(G-19202)*
Caza Petroleum, Spring *Also called Caza Oil & Gas Inc (G-19202)*
Cazad Industries Inc 972 635-2100
  160 County Road 979 Royse City (75189) *(G-17718)*
CB Solutions LP 512 267-9596
  21508 Lake Park Dr Lago Vista (78645) *(G-13804)*
CB&i Beaumont, Beaumont *Also called CB&i LLC (G-1867)*
CB&i LLC 832 513-1848
  3600 W Sam Houston Pkwy S Houston (77042) *(G-9104)*
CB&i LLC 281 456-5700
  9803 Sheldon Rd Houston (77049) *(G-9105)*
CB&i LLC 409 980-5500
  Edison Plaza 350 Pine St Beaumont (77701) *(G-1867)*
CB&i LLC 713 649-4277
  7330 Neuhaus St Houston (77061) *(G-9106)*
CB&i LLC 713 375-8000
  3600 W Sam Houston Pkwy S Houston (77042) *(G-9107)*
CB&i LLC 713 485-1000
  5850 Rogerdale Rd Ste 150 Houston (77072) *(G-9108)*
Cbd Farmhouse 214 971-6688
  4360 Spring Valley Rd Farmers Branch (75244) *(G-6191)*
Cbg Corporation 512 491-7541
  2601 Mchale Ct Ste 45 Austin (78758) *(G-1032)*
Cbg Corporation 512 491-7541
  4616 W Howard Ln Ste 900 Austin (78728) *(G-1033)*
CBI Laboratories Inc 972 241-7546
  4201 Diplomacy Rd Fort Worth (76155) *(G-6497)*
CC Coating & Machine Inc 361 884-9753
  658 Omaha Dr Corpus Christi (78408) *(G-3497)*
CC Creations Ltd (PA) **979 693-9664**
  114 Holleman Dr College Station (77840) *(G-3181)*
CC West, Austin *Also called Creative Computing West Inc (G-1072)*
Cc3 .... 817 230-2700
  5600 Stratum Dr Fort Worth (76137) *(G-6498)*
CCB Fabricators Inc 361 387-7900
  4515 Us Highway 77 Robstown (78380) *(G-17504)*
CCI, Richardson *Also called Circuit Check Inc (G-17286)*
CCI Group, Longview *Also called Colony Cabinets Inc (G-14211)*
CCI Publishing, Waco *Also called Cord Communications Inc (G-20390)*
CCI Thermal Tech Texas Inc 855 219-2101
  15550 Vickery Dr Ste 100 Houston (77032) *(G-9109)*
CCI-Triad, Austin *Also called Epicor Software Corporation (G-1130)*
Ccisd Print Shop, Corpus Christi *Also called City of Corpus Christi (G-3499)*
Ccmm Inc 936 827-7930
  107 Rio Grande Dr Mission (78572) *(G-15549)*

(PA)=Parent Co (HQ)=Headquarters (DH)=Div Headquarters

Ccpjv Inc..713 690-1622
7229 Fairview St Houston (77041) *(G-9110)*

CCS Cupcake Heaven....................................817 732-2993
1420 Heidi Ct Fort Worth (76108) *(G-6499)*

Ccsolutions, Fort Worth *Also called Composite Cooling Solutions LP (G-6536)*

Ccswb, Dallas *Also called Coca-Cola Southwest Bevs LLC (G-4138)*

CCT Corporation...713 223-2521
300 N Palmer St Houston (77003) *(G-9111)*

CCT Plastics Inc..817 410-1222
804 Port America Pl Ste B Grapevine (76051) *(G-8020)*

CCT Precision Machining LLC.........................817 410-1222
804 Port America Pl Grapevine (76051) *(G-8021)*

Cd3 Inc...512 252-2592
15505 Long Vista Dr Ste 2 Austin (78728) *(G-1034)*

Cdb Software Inc (PA).............................**713 588-1778**
10011 Meadowglen Ln # 110 Houston (77042) *(G-9112)*

Cdc, Corpus Christi *Also called Coastal Drilling Company L L C (G-3503)*

CDI, Fort Worth *Also called Casting Designs Inc (G-6496)*

CDI Energy Products Inc................................281 446-6662
8103 Rankin Rd Humble (77396) *(G-12753)*

CDI Products, Tomball *Also called Challenger Drilling Inc (G-19969)*

CDI Vessel Holdings LLC...............................713 361-2600
2500 Citywest Blvd # 2200 Houston (77042) *(G-9113)*

CDK Perforating..817 945-1051
8101 Boat Club Rd Ste 330 Fort Worth (76179) *(G-6500)*

CDK Perforating Inc (HQ)...........................**817 945-1051**
6500 West Fwy Ste 600 Fort Worth (76116) *(G-6501)*

CDK Perforating Holdings Inc.........................817 945-1051
6500 West Fwy Ste 600 Fort Worth (76116) *(G-6502)*

CDM Resource Management LLC (HQ)...........**281 376-2980**
20405 State Hwy Houston (77070) *(G-9114)*

CDM Software Solutions Inc...........................972 469-3082
2591 Dallas Pkwy Ste 300 Frisco (75034) *(G-7272)*

Cdr Machine & Fabricating Inc.......................972 272-9145
209 S Kirby St Ste 312 Garland (75042) *(G-7454)*

Cdw Consultant Group LLC............................361 237-9339
624 Traylor Rd Bloomington (77951) *(G-2111)*

Cdw Consulting, Bloomington *Also called Cdw Consultant Group LLC (G-2111)*

Ce Labs LLC...469 429-9200
3209 Wood Dr Garland (75041) *(G-7455)*

Ce Soir Lingerie Co Inc..................................512 953-4500
12317 Tech Blvd Ste 300 Austin (78727) *(G-1035)*

Cec Corrosion Services LLC............................361 883-6930
3388 County Rd 48 Corpus Christi (78403) *(G-3498)*

Cece's Veggie Co., Austin *Also called Veggie Noodle Co LLC (G-1626)*

Cecil Machine Shop Inc..................................940 322-4072
526 Front St Wichita Falls (76301) *(G-20751)*

Cecil Phillips Lumber Mill...............................903 684-3516
Fm Rd 1326 De Kalb (75559) *(G-5236)*

Ceco Environmental Corp (PA).....................**214 357-6181**
14651 Dallas Pkwy Ste 50 Dallas (75254) *(G-4092)*

Ceda International Inc (HQ).........................**281 478-2600**
2600 S Shore Blvd Ste 300 League City (77573) *(G-13952)*

Cedar Creek II..713 354-2100
700 Louisiana St Fl 33 Houston (77002) *(G-9115)*

Cedar Fiber Company Inc................................325 446-2571
Fm 2169 Junction (76849) *(G-13337)*

Cedar Fiber Company Inc................................325 446-2571
644 Industrial Dr Junction (76849) *(G-13338)*

Cedar Mill Co Inc...713 984-2600
2121 Brittmoore Rd # 200 Houston (77043) *(G-9116)*

Cedar Supply Inc (PA)..............................**972 242-6561**
1200 Denton Dr Carrollton (75006) *(G-2711)*

Cedarcide Industries Inc.................................281 367-5075
1025 N Mill St Ste D Lewisville (75057) *(G-14034)*

Cedra Pharmacy Houston LLC........................713 621-0621
1607 S Post Oak Ln Houston (77056) *(G-9117)*

Cedrone OBrien Inc.......................................512 426-5200
2227 W Braker Ln Austin (78758) *(G-1036)*

Cee-San Mch & Fabrication Co........................713 466-4586
5609 Clara Rd Houston (77041) *(G-9118)*

Cega Inc..915 633-1660
11501 Rojas Dr Ste F El Paso (79936) *(G-5687)*

Cega Inc..915 257-1898
1220 Barranca Dr Ste 3 El Paso (79935) *(G-5688)*

Celanese Acetate LLC...................................972 443-4000
1601 Lyndon B Johnson Fwy Dallas (75234) *(G-4093)*

Celanese Americas LLC.................................361 584-6000
Us Hwy 77 Bishop (78343) *(G-2105)*

Celanese Americas LLC.................................979 241-4000
2001 Fm 3057 Bay City (77414) *(G-1770)*

Celanese Americas LLC (HQ)......................**972 443-4000**
222 Colinas Blvd W # 900 Irving (75039) *(G-12963)*

Celanese Corporation (PA).........................**972 443-4000**
222 Las Colinas Blvd W Irving (75039) *(G-12964)*

Celanese Eva Performance.............................972 443-4000
222 Las Colinas Blvd W Irving (75039) *(G-12965)*

Celanese International Corp............................972 443-4000
222 Las Colinas Blvd W Irving (75039) *(G-12966)*

Celanese Ltd...713 456-1525
1423 Hwy 225 Pasadena (77506) *(G-16402)*

Celanese Ltd...281 474-0554
9502 Bayport Blvd Pasadena (77507) *(G-16403)*

Celanese US Holdings LLC..............................972 443-4000
1601 Lyndon B Johnson Fwy Dallas (75234) *(G-4094)*

Celco Industries, El Paso *Also called M J Celco Inc (G-5854)*

Celebrity Group Magazine..............................956 579-2020
2353 Old Port Isabel Rd Brownsville (78521) *(G-2345)*

Celero Energy (PA)...................................**817 708-3800**
301 Commerce St Ste 2001 Fort Worth (76102) *(G-6503)*

Celero Energy II LP......................................817 708-3800
301 Commerce St Ste 2001 Fort Worth (76102) *(G-6504)*

Celeste Stein Designs Inc...............................409 763-1009
7801 Bayside Ave Galveston (77554) *(G-7392)*

Celling Biosciences, Austin *Also called Spinesmith Holdings LLC (G-1527)*

Cellisco Inc (PA)......................................**210 692-1927**
3503 Crosspoint San Antonio (78217) *(G-17989)*

Cellright Technologies LLC.............................210 659-9353
1808 Universal City Blvd Universal City (78148) *(G-20181)*

Cellteks Inc..830 249-8999
113 Parkway Boerne (78006) *(G-2116)*

Celltex Therapeutics Corp (PA)...................**713 590-1000**
2401 Ftn View Dr Ste 416 Houston (77057) *(G-9119)*

Celonova Biosciences Inc (PA).....................**210 489-4000**
8023 Vantage Dr Ste 1400 San Antonio (78230) *(G-17990)*

Cem - Balcones Plant, New Braunfels *Also called Cemex Construction Mtls S LLC (G-15780)*

Cem - De Zavala Terminal, Channelview *Also called Cemex Construction Mtls S LLC (G-3015)*

Cem - Houston Terminal, Houston *Also called Cemex Construction Mtls S LLC (G-9124)*

Cem - Lubbock Terminal, Levelland *Also called Cemex Construction Mtls S LLC (G-14005)*

Cemco, Olney *Also called Construction Eqp Mfg Co Inc (G-16220)*

Cementos Ready Mix.....................................432 385-7477
11041 W 42nd St Odessa (79764) *(G-15956)*

Cemex Inc..713 332-4070
16100 Dillard Dr Jersey Village (77040) *(G-13295)*

Cemex Inc..830 625-7338
2580 Wald Rd New Braunfels (78132) *(G-15778)*

Cemex Inc (HQ).......................................**713 650-6200**
10100 Katy Fwy Ste 300 Houston (77043) *(G-9120)*

Cemex Cement Inc.......................................432 385-2800
104 W Interstate 20 Odessa (79761) *(G-15957)*

Cemex Cement Inc (HQ)............................**713 650-6200**
10100 Katy Fwy Ste 300 Houston (77043) *(G-9121)*

Cemex Construction Mtls LP (PA)................**713 650-6200**
929 Gessner Rd Ste 1900 Houston (77024) *(G-9122)*

Cemex Construction Mtls S LLC......................956 386-1452
3710 S Expy 281 Edinburg (78542) *(G-5581)*

Cemex Construction Mtls S LLC......................915 855-9658
2050 Cherrington St El Paso (79928) *(G-5689)*

Cemex Construction Mtls S LLC......................281 457-0031
16530 De Zavalla Rd Channelview (77530) *(G-3015)*

Cemex Construction Mtls S LLC......................830 608-3556
2682 Wald Rd New Braunfels (78132) *(G-15779)*

Cemex Construction Mtls S LLC......................713 650-6200
929 Gessner Rd Ste 1900 Houston (77024) *(G-9123)*

Cemex Construction Mtls S LLC......................915 565-4681
1 Mckelligon Canyon Rd El Paso (79930) *(G-5690)*

Cemex Construction Mtls S LLC......................936 372-0493
17919 Kermier Rd Hockley (77447) *(G-8342)*

Cemex Construction Mtls S LLC......................713 967-5416
6203 Industrial Way Houston (77011) *(G-9124)*

Cemex Construction Mtls S LLC......................956 943-2472
1250 Port Rd Port Isabel (78578) *(G-17136)*

Cemex Construction Mtls S LLC......................281 260-9651
12132 Mosielee St Houston (77086) *(G-9125)*

Cemex Construction Mtls S LLC......................501 350-2696
117 Commerce St Levelland (79336) *(G-14005)*

Cemex Construction Mtls S LLC.......................................
202 Holmes Rd Houston (77045) *(G-9126)*

Cemex Construction Mtls S LLC......................210 250-4100
2580 Wald Rd New Braunfels (78132) *(G-15780)*

Cemex Construction Mtls S LLC......................281 391-2655
27734 Katy Brookshire Rd Katy (77494) *(G-13357)*

Cemex Construction Mtls S LLC......................512 247-3400
3901 Norwood Ln Del Valle (78617) *(G-5329)*

Cemex Construction Mtls S LLC......................281 444-8306
11331 Cutten Rd Houston (77066) *(G-9127)*

Cemex Construction Mtls S LLC......................281 651-6426
1115 W Riley Fuzzel Rd Spring (77373) *(G-19104)*

Cemex Construction Mtls S LLC......................713 650-6200
920 Mmrial Cy Way Ste 100 Houston (77024) *(G-9128)*

Cemex Construction Mtls S LLC......................713 767-7983
5303 Navigation Blvd Houston (77011) *(G-9129)*

Cemex El Paso Inc (HQ)............................**915 565-4681**
1 Mckelligon Canyon Rd El Paso (79930) *(G-5691)*

Cemex El Paso Inc.......................................915 564-8400
6101 Stan Roberts Sr Ave El Paso (79934) *(G-5692)*

Cemex International Trdg LLC 713 650-6200
10100 Katy Fwy Ste 3000 Houston (77043) *(G-9130)*

Cemex Materials LLC 979 885-7403
2735 Highway 36 Sealy (77474) *(G-18807)*

Cemex Materials LLC 713 650-6200
929 Gessner Rd Ste 1900 Houston (77024) *(G-9131)*

Cemex Materials LLC 210 677-8191
6145 Mechler Ln N Castroville (78009) *(G-2926)*

Cemex Materials LLC 210 677-8191
6145 Mechler Rd San Antonio (78252) *(G-17991)*

Cemex Materials LLC 832 590-5400
6560 Langfield Rd Bldg 3 Houston (77092) *(G-9132)*

Cemex Materials LLC 940 665-8355
1310 N Clements St Gainesville (76240) *(G-7337)*

Cemex Southeast LLC (HQ) **713 722-5818**
840 Gessner Rd Ste 1400 Houston (77024) *(G-9133)*

Cemex Trading LLC (HQ) **713 650-6200**
920 Mmrial Cy Way Ste 100 Houston (77024) *(G-9134)*

Cemex USA, New Braunfels Also called Cemex Inc *(G-15778)*

Cemex USA Inc 432 385-2892
16501 W Murphy St Odessa (79763) *(G-15958)*

Cems Acquire Co LLC 817 308-0165
811 N Bishop Ave Apt 2 Dallas (75208) *(G-4095)*

Cemtechnologies Inc (PA) **972 238-3630**
1360 Presidential Dr # 140 Richardson (75081) *(G-17285)*

Cen-Tex Machining Inc 512 255-1477
1513 Sam Bass Rd Round Rock (78681) *(G-17629)*

Cen-Tex Marine Fabricators (PA) **512 237-2496**
1100 Ne 1st St Smithville (78957) *(G-18976)*

Cen-Tex Tanks LLC 936 590-4441
946 Loop 500 Center (75935) *(G-2995)*

Cenikor Foundation 817 921-2771
6801 Paces Trl Apt 321 Arlington (76017) *(G-640)*

Censored Soles 832 443-4365
10222 Royal Oaks Dr Houston (77016) *(G-9135)*

Centaur Technology Inc 512 418-5700
9111 Jollyville Rd # 206 Austin (78759) *(G-1037)*

Centauri Technologies LP 281 474-4675
5200 Underwood Rd Pasadena (77507) *(G-16404)*

Centennial Moisture Ctrl Inc (PA) **214 350-7689**
1780 Hurd Dr Irving (75038) *(G-12967)*

Centennial Radiator Inc (PA) **214 634-8262**
447 W Mockingbird Ln Dallas (75247) *(G-4096)*

Centennial Radiator Service, Dallas Also called Centennial Radiator Inc *(G-4096)*

Centennial Resource Dev Inc 281 302-5048
2245 Texas Dr Ste 490 Sugar Land (77479) *(G-19454)*

Centennial Steel Inc (PA) **972 412-5144**
5304 Dexham Rd Rowlett (75088) *(G-17703)*

Center Fixtures 936 598-2247
1010 Logansport St Center (75935) *(G-2996)*

Center Line Machine, Odessa Also called C H I Alpha Whitestone Inc *(G-15949)*

Center-Line Curtains Inc 972 299-5902
1213 S Cedar Hill Rd Cedar Hill (75104) *(G-2937)*

Centerline Manufacturing Ltd 713 329-9070
5711 Campbell Rd Houston (77041) *(G-9136)*

Centerline Trailers Inc 817 477-5533
1301 E Dallas St Mansfield (76063) *(G-14659)*

Centerpoint Productions Inc 214 905-0000
1232 Crowley Dr Carrollton (75006) *(G-2712)*

Centex Corporation (HQ) **214 981-5000**
2728 N Harwood St Dallas (75201) *(G-4097)*

Centex Machine and Welding Inc 512 255-1477
1513 Sam Bass Rd Round Rock (78681) *(G-17630)*

Centex Manufacturing Co 254 752-2531
3718 Franklin Ave Waco (76710) *(G-20379)*

Centex Materials LLC 512 251-5106
16438 N Ih 35 Austin (78728) *(G-1038)*

Centex Materials LLC 512 444-9591
817 E Saint Elmo Rd Austin (78745) *(G-1039)*

Centex Materials LLC (HQ) **512 460-3003**
3019 Alvin Devane Blvd # 100 Austin (78741) *(G-1040)*

Centex Materials LLC 512 295-4801
1100 Hwy 2770 Buda (78610) *(G-2525)*

Centex Meat Company LP 512 352-6357
2211 W 2nd St Taylor (76574) *(G-19652)*

Centex Mechatronics LLC 830 387-4131
1484 Churchill Dr New Braunfels (78130) *(G-15781)*

Centex Supply, Madisonville Also called C P Bailey Cnstr Co Inc *(G-14585)*

Central Admxture Phrm Svcs Inc 713 748-2200
1000 S Loop W Ste 115 Houston (77054) *(G-9137)*

Central Admxture Phrm Svcs Inc 972 242-2788
1601 Wallace Dr Ste 130 Carrollton (75006) *(G-2713)*

Central Dynamic Mfg Inc 817 473-3899
300 Industrial Blvd Mansfield (76063) *(G-14660)*

Central Hardwoods Inc (PA) **972 241-3571**
1959 W Northwest Hwy Dallas (75220) *(G-4098)*

Central Jewelry & Refining (PA) **214 350-4653**
2650 Andjon Dr Dallas (75220) *(G-4099)*

Central Management Inc (PA) **713 961-9777**
820 Gessner Rd Ste 1525 Houston (77024) *(G-9138)*

Central Marble, Alba Also called Dimension In Stone & Glass *(G-182)*

Central Millwork LLC 925 963-5448
Blystone Ln Dallas (75220) *(G-4100)*

Central Pallets No 2 .... 956 726-4023
7910 Mines Rd Laredo (78045) *(G-13873)*

Central Plastics, Houston Also called Express Freight Systems Inc *(G-9731)*

Central Ready Mix Concrete Co (PA) **956 383-2261**
304 W Railroad St San Juan (78589) *(G-18672)*

Central Ready Mix Concrete Co 956 541-6082
2101 Utex Dr San Benito (78586) *(G-18655)*

Central Renovation Solutions 469 567-2400
3146 Springfield Ave Lancaster (75134) *(G-13842)*

Central States Mfg Inc 469 272-0041
660 Grigsby Way Cedar Hill (75104) *(G-2938)*

Central Tape & Label Co 713 462-8585
5525 Bingle Rd Houston (77092) *(G-9139)*

Central Texas Corrugated Inc 254 776-6902
7200 Mars Dr Waco (76712) *(G-20380)*

Central Texas Ex Metalwork LLC 210 337-2260
304 El Paso St San Antonio (78207) *(G-17992)*

Central Texas Oilfield Sup Co 254 562-5522
Rr 4 Box 406 Mexia (76667) *(G-15089)*

Central Texas Oilfield Svcs, Mexia Also called Central Texas Oilfield Sup Co *(G-15089)*

Central Texas Printing Inc 254 754-4653
1522 Washington Ave Waco (76701) *(G-20381)*

Central Txas Met Roofg Sup Inc (PA) **512 452-1515**
830 Sagebrush Dr Austin (78758) *(G-1041)*

Centramatic, Alvarado Also called F & F Industries Inc *(G-331)*

Centrax International Corp (PA) **281 465-0781**
8505 Tech Frest Pl Ste 70 Spring (77381) *(G-19203)*

Centrex International LLC 281 370-0720
18334 Stuebner Airline Rd Spring (77379) *(G-19105)*

Centric Pipe LLC 214 526-4423
14850 Montfort Dr Ste 100 Dallas (75254) *(G-4101)*

Centrifugal Castings Inc 254 773-9068
3320 Parkway Dr Temple (76504) *(G-19675)*

Centrifuge Repair & Engrg LP 281 471-3767
302 N 16th St La Porte (77571) *(G-13726)*

Centron International Inc 940 328-1032
600 Fm 1195 Mineral Wells (76067) *(G-15522)*

Centurion Pallet Service 210 823-3530
402 Tidewind St San Antonio (78221) *(G-17993)*

Centurion Pipeline LP (HQ) **713 215-7000**
5 Greenway Plz Ste 110 Houston (77046) *(G-9140)*

Century 21 Cabinet Refacing, Lewisville Also called US Remodelers Inc *(G-14103)*

Century Arconditioning Sup L P 281 446-7820
1919 Humble Place Dr Humble (77338) *(G-12754)*

Century Asphalt Ltd 512 285-4499
1858 Old Mcdade Rd Elgin (78621) *(G-6053)*

Century Asphalt Ltd 281 421-2621
4008 N Highway 146 Baytown (77520) *(G-1811)*

Century Components Corporation 817 831-8301
5524 Midway Rd Ste 1 Fort Worth (76117) *(G-6505)*

Century Concrete Partners Inc 281 585-5742
8726 E Fm 1462 Rd Rosharon (77583) *(G-17601)*

Century Elevators Inc 281 667-3000
12130 Galveston Rd Bldg 5 Webster (77598) *(G-20635)*

Century Graphics & Sign Inc 432 686-8244
501 W Indl Ave Midland (79701) *(G-15157)*

Century Indus Coatings Inc 903 586-9197
37094 Us Highway 69 N Jacksonville (75766) *(G-13233)*

Century Instr & Mch Co Inc 281 587-5333
3601 Bacor Rd Houston (77084) *(G-9141)*

Century Label, Round Rock Also called Century Tape & Label LLC *(G-17631)*

Century Millwork LLC 281 821-0191
18927 Aldine Westfield Rd Houston (77073) *(G-9142)*

Century Tape & Label LLC 972 576-0826
21 Cypress Blvd Ste 1120 Round Rock (78665) *(G-17631)*

Century Wheel & Rim, Azle Also called Quality Trailer Products LP *(G-1728)*

Cenveo Worldwide Limited 972 729-5700
14001 Inwood Rd Dallas (75244) *(G-4102)*

Cenveo Worldwide Limited 210 923-7591
5101 S Zarzamora St San Antonio (78211) *(G-17994)*

Cenveo Worldwide Limited 806 376-4347
109 S Fillmore St Amarillo (79101) *(G-414)*

CEo Performance Chem LLC 281 457-2020
2701 Appelt Dr Houston (77015) *(G-9143)*

CER Tek Inc 915 772-8290
5740 Cleveland Ave El Paso (79925) *(G-5693)*

Ceradyne Inc 281 773-4135
2838 N Strathford Ln Humble (77345) *(G-12755)*

Ceralox Division, Houston Also called Sasol Chemicals (usa) LLC *(G-11756)*

Ceram-Kote Coatings Inc 432 263-8497
1800 Industrial Park Big Spring (79720) *(G-2074)*

Cerametals Carbide LLC 713 937-3801
7425 Carbide Cir Houston (77040) *(G-9144)*

Cerda Industries, Houston Also called Cws Road Plate LLC *(G-9380)*

Cerda Industries Inc 713 242-7700
7600 S Santa Fe Dr B-W Houston (77061) *(G-9145)*

A L P H A B E T I C

C

Cerda-Fied Specialists Inc 281 392-8063
707 Bains St Brookshire (77423) *(G-2313)*

Cerilliant Corporation 512 238-9974
811 Paloma Dr Ste A Round Rock (78665) *(G-17632)*

Certainteed Corporation 800 233-8990
501 Hewitt Dr Waco (76712) *(G-20382)*

Certainteed Corporation 940 723-5998
211 Randy Dr Wichita Falls (76306) *(G-20752)*

Certainteed LLC 972 875-9661
2901 N Kaufman St Ennis (75119) *(G-6090)*

Certainteed LLC 214 630-7377
3000 W Commerce St Dallas (75212) *(G-4103)*

Certi-Fab Industries Inc 281 328-7244
25150 Crosby Fwy Crosby (77532) *(G-3728)*

Certi-Fab Steel Fabricators, Crosby Also called Certi-Fab Industries Inc *(G-3728)*

Certified Laboratories, Irving Also called NCH Corporation *(G-13119)*

Certified Pipe Svc Houston Inc 281 457-2454
6225 Fm 1942 Rd Baytown (77521) *(G-1812)*

Certified Technical Profession 757 831-9235
14613 Fm 306 Canyon Lake (78133) *(G-2678)*

Certispec Services Inc 409 945-3338
1448 Texas Ave Texas City (77590) *(G-19786)*

Certoplast North America Inc 832 384-1244
1900 West Loop S Houston (77027) *(G-9146)*

Ces Industrial LLC 281 615-5621
13802 Murphy Rd Stafford (77477) *(G-19293)*

Cesar-Scott Inc (PA) **915 543-3212**
1731 Myrtle Ave El Paso (79901) *(G-5694)*

Cessac Welding Service Inc (PA) **979 828-9067**
13345 E Us Highway 79 Franklin (77856) *(G-7164)*

Cetco Energy Services Co LLC 281 578-8911
16350 Park Ten Pl Ste 217 Houston (77084) *(G-9147)*

Cetx Energy Agency, Sugar Land Also called Competitive Energy - Texas LP *(G-19466)*

Cev Multimedia Ltd 806 745-8820
1020 Se Loop 289 Lubbock (79404) *(G-14391)*

CF Industries Inc 214 460-2804
1620 E State Highway 121 A100 Lewisville (75056) *(G-14035)*

Cfa Services 210 758-5721
3300 Nacogdoches Rd # 216 San Antonio (78217) *(G-17995)*

CFC Print Solutions LLC 972 890-9248
2800 112th St Ste 300 Grand Prairie (75050) *(G-7852)*

Cfd, Princeton Also called Contract Fabrication *(G-17206)*

Cfg Industries LLC 281 259-7244
22535 Magnolia Hills Dr Magnolia (77354) *(G-14594)*

Cfj Manufacturing LP (PA) **817 625-9559**
701 Eight Twenty Blvd # 145 Fort Worth (76106) *(G-6506)*

Cfj Manufacturing LP 817 232-9251
708 S Saginaw Blvd Saginaw (76179) *(G-17741)*

CFS Brands LLC (PA) **972 466-1030**
3304 Druid Way Flower Mound (75028) *(G-6262)*

CFS Forming Structure Company 210 698-9252
21120 Milsa Dr San Antonio (78256) *(G-17996)*

Cft Dispensers Inc 512 942-8300
116 Halmar Cv Georgetown (78628) *(G-7643)*

Cgg Marine (us) Inc 713 369-5600
6100 Hillcroft St Ste 100 Houston (77081) *(G-9148)*

Cgg Services (us) Inc (HQ) **832 351-8300**
10300 Town Park Dr Houston (77072) *(G-9149)*

Cgi Commercial Accounts, Grand Prairie Also called Coatings Group Inc *(G-7857)*

Cgi Technologies Solutions Inc 866 344-3221
3700 W Sam Houston Pkwy S Houston (77042) *(G-9150)*

CGJ Enterprises Inc 281 575-8801
10940 S Wilcrest Dr Houston (77099) *(G-9151)*

Cgp Manufacturing Inc 713 641-5544
8363 Market St Houston (77029) *(G-9152)*

Cgt US Limited 830 627-4800
695 Holcan Dr New Braunfels (78130) *(G-15782)*

CH Guenther & Son LLC 972 298-4281
627 Big Stone Gap Rd Duncanville (75137) *(G-5529)*

CH Guenther & Son LLC (PA) **210 227-1401**
2201 Broadway St San Antonio (78215) *(G-17997)*

Chachos Lease Service Inc 361 661-1143
4933 S Us Highway 281 Alice (78332) *(G-205)*

Chalk Mountain Svcs Texas LLC (PA) **817 473-1931**
990 N Walnut Creek Dr # 1001 Mansfield (76063) *(G-14661)*

Chalks Truck Parts Inc (PA) **713 672-6344**
818 Mc Carty Dr Houston (77029) *(G-9153)*

Chalks Truck Parts Inc 713 672-6344
8025 Market St Houston (77029) *(G-9154)*

Challenge Mch & Fabrication 281 441-3115
6460 Aldine Bender Rd Humble (77396) *(G-12756)*

Challenger Drilling Inc 281 290-8335
14102 Pine Meadow Ln Tomball (77377) *(G-19969)*

Challenger Eqp & Tl Co Inc 281 351-4247
12814 Old Boudreaux Ln Tomball (77375) *(G-19970)*

Challenger Process Systems Co 903 839-7291
21249 State Highway 110 S Troup (75789) *(G-20024)*

Challenger Services Inc 361 874-4433
2169 County Road 429 Lolita (77971) *(G-14174)*

Chameleon Cold Brew LLC 512 323-0345
6205 Burnet Rd Austin (78757) *(G-1042)*

Chammas Cutters Inc 713 856-8777
11320 Fm 529 Rd Ste I Houston (77041) *(G-9155)*

Champion Cooler Corporation 903 465-3294
2011 Macgregor Dr Denison (75020) *(G-5337)*

Champion Cooler Corporation 903 463-1408
3328 Interurban Rd Denison (75021) *(G-5338)*

Champion Custom Cabinets Inc 817 834-8552
875 Haltom Rd Fort Worth (76117) *(G-6507)*

Champion Drilling Fluids Inc 580 225-3450
11767 Katy Fwy Ste 230 Houston (77079) *(G-9156)*

Champion Food Service 2 Inc 210 736-2190
15326 Watson Rd Von Ormy (78073) *(G-20346)*

Champion Group Inc (PA) **713 644-2181**
5565 Maudlin St Houston (77087) *(G-9157)*

Champion Group Inc 210 490-1482
4416 Lockhill Selma Rd San Antonio (78249) *(G-17998)*

Champion HI Tech, Allen Also called HI Tech Oil Blends Inc *(G-274)*

Champion Industrial Sales Co (PA) **713 921-7183**
6420 Navigation Blvd Houston (77011) *(G-9158)*

Champion Oilfield Services LLC 512 327-3300
401 Congress Ave Fl 33 Austin (78701) *(G-1043)*

Champion Pallet & Packaging 972 551-2474
1126 Hidden Rdg Apt 2145 Irving (75038) *(G-12968)*

Champion Process Inc 281 953-9000
5171 Ashley Ct Houston (77041) *(G-9159)*

Champion Sales & Manufacturing 281 356-6162
32510 Decker Prairie Rd Magnolia (77355) *(G-14595)*

Champion Steel Processing, Denison Also called Champion Cooler Corporation *(G-5337)*

Champions Printing & Pubg Inc 281 583-7661
6608 Fm 1960 Rd W Ste G Houston (77069) *(G-9160)*

Championx Corporation (PA) **281 403-5772**
2445 Tech Frest Blvd Bldg The Woodlands (77381) *(G-19840)*

Championx LLC (HQ) **281 632-6500**
11177 S Stadium Dr Sugar Land (77478) *(G-19455)*

Championx LLC 432 363-9105
115 Proctor Ave Odessa (79762) *(G-15959)*

Champlain Cable Texas Corp 915 860-0010
9560 Plaza Cir El Paso (79927) *(G-5695)*

Champwear, Houston Also called Men of Cloth LP *(G-10827)*

Chana Enterprises, Carrollton Also called Chapal/Zenray Inc *(G-2714)*

Chandler Consultants Inc 210 344-5200
2714 West Ave San Antonio (78201) *(G-17999)*

Chandler Mfg LLC 940 763-1528
2701 Business Hwy 287j E Wichita Falls (76305) *(G-20753)*

Chandler Signs LLC 760 734-1708
14201 Sovereign Rd 101 Fort Worth (76155) *(G-6508)*

Chandler Signs LLC (PA) **214 902-2000**
14201 Sovereign Rd 101 Fort Worth (76155) *(G-6509)*

Chandler Signs LLC 210 349-3804
17319 San Pedro Ave # 200 San Antonio (78232) *(G-18000)*

Chandler Signs LLC 361 643-4115
206 Doral Dr Portland (78374) *(G-17185)*

Channel Brfinery Terminals LLC 713 965-4150
13605 Industrial Rd Houston (77015) *(G-9161)*

Channel Sheet Metal Inc 713 473-2878
1908 Magnolia Dr Pasadena (77503) *(G-16405)*

Channel Shipyard, Baytown Also called Lynchburg Shipyard Inc *(G-1827)*

Channel-Track Tubeway, Houston Also called Channl-Track Tube-Way Inds Inc *(G-9162)*

Channl-Track Tube-Way Inds Inc (PA) **713 864-2551**
1209 W 17th St Houston (77008) *(G-9162)*

Channl-Track Tube-Way Inds Inc 361 798-4979
1411 Us Highway 90a W Hallettsville (77964) *(G-8120)*

Chapal/Zenray Inc (PA) **214 638-0402**
2452 Lacy Ln Ste 116 Carrollton (75006) *(G-2714)*

Chaparral Energy LLC 806 435-7533
12650 Fm 1267 Perryton (79070) *(G-16635)*

Chaparral Wldg Fabrication Inc 972 243-7747
2453 Merrell Rd Dallas (75229) *(G-4104)*

Chapas Oilfield Services LLC 956 847-6460
811 Zapata Ave Zapata (78076) *(G-20980)*

Chapman Shameka 281 507-8790
2017 Mountain Creek St Pearland (77584) *(G-16543)*

Chapman Dock Inc 325 388-6545
2247 W Ranch Road 1431 Kingsland (78639) *(G-13621)*

Chapman Electric Company 214 824-8095
3131 S Haskell Ave Dallas (75223) *(G-4105)*

Chapman's, Kingsland Also called Chapman Dock Inc *(G-13621)*

Chaps, Richardson Also called Fossil Partners LP *(G-17314)*

Charbonneau Industries Inc (PA) **770 664-4319**
1619 E Richey Rd Houston (77073) *(G-9163)*

Charger Services LLC 432 218-7674
23 W Industrial Loop Midland (79701) *(G-15158)*

Charles Barton 512 759-1231
105 Green Pasture Hutto (78634) *(G-12877)*

Charles De Vuae Inc 713 789-8485
6100 Richmond Ave Ste 216 Houston (77057) *(G-9164)*

Charles Howard Construction 325 387-3093
  601 W 8th St Sonora (76950) *(G-19024)*

Charles W Weaver Mfg Co Inc 972 539-1537
  3101 Justin Rd Flower Mound (75028) *(G-6263)*

Charleys Concrete Co Ltd 817 431-2016
  Fm 1171 & I 35w Euless (76039) *(G-6135)*

Charleys Concrete Co Ltd (PA) **817 431-3515**
  11801 Katy Rd Fort Worth (76244) *(G-6510)*

Charleys Concrete Co Ltd 972 734-6300
  1134 Fm 982 Princeton (75407) *(G-17205)*

Charleys Concrete Co Ltd 817 568-2400
  10016 E Crowley Rd Crowley (76036) *(G-3753)*

Charlotte Pipe and Foundry Co 254 697-6556
  2700 N Blake Ave Cameron (76520) *(G-2641)*

Charlotte Plastic S/W, Cameron *Also called Charlotte Pipe and Foundry Co (G-2641)*

Charlottes Concrete Inc 210 648-4774
  4950 Lane Dr San Antonio (78263) *(G-18001)*

Charro Operating LLC 361 643-5577
  321 5th St Portland (78374) *(G-17186)*

Chart Dist & Stor Group, Houston *Also called Chart Inc (G-9165)*

Chart Inc 713 413-3000
  55 Southbelt Indus Dr Houston (77047) *(G-9165)*

Chart Industries Inc 281 364-8700
  8665 New Trils Dr Ste 100 The Woodlands (77381) *(G-19841)*

Charta Group Inc 310 327-0244
  301 W Howard Ln Ste 300 Austin (78753) *(G-1044)*

Charts Ltd 432 697-7801
  2031 Trade Dr Midland (79706) *(G-15159)*

Chartwell Global Sourcing, Lubbock *Also called Southwest Textiles Inc (G-14485)*

Chas P Young Company 713 652-2100
  1645 W Sam Houston Pkwy N Houston (77043) *(G-9166)*

Chase Elastomers, Kennedale *Also called Hexpol Compounding LLC (G-13498)*

Chase Medical, Richardson *Also called Kdl Medical Inc (G-17340)*

Chase Pecan LP 706 556-6216
  201 Main St Ste 1801 Fort Worth (76102) *(G-6511)*

Chase Transportation LLC 915 307-5488
  16005 Darley Dr Horizon City (79928) *(G-8363)*

Chassis Liner 817 284-2545
  11500 S Pipeline Rd Euless (76040) *(G-6136)*

Chateau Noblesse Inc 972 365-7017
  4228 N Josey Ln 112 Carrollton (75010) *(G-2859)*

Chatsworth Products Inc 512 863-7800
  3004 S Austin Ave Georgetown (78626) *(G-7644)*

Chca Bayshore LP 713 359-2000
  4000 Spencer Hwy Pasadena (77504) *(G-16406)*

Checkfree Corporation 281 333-9800
  1100 Nasa Pkwy Ste 606 Houston (77058) *(G-9167)*

Checks In Mail Inc 830 609-5500
  2435 Goodwin Ln New Braunfels (78135) *(G-15783)*

Cheerleader & Danzteam, Plano *Also called Nsg Corporation (G-16947)*

Cheerleading Company Inc 800 411-4105
  11350 Hillguard Rd Dallas (75243) *(G-4106)*

Cheers Health Inc 518 379-6133
  1334 Brittmoore Rd # 1003 Houston (77043) *(G-9168)*

Cheesecake Royale Bakery, Dallas *Also called Cheesecake Royale Inc (G-4107)*

Cheesecake Royale Inc (PA) **214 328-9102**
  9016 Garland Rd Dallas (75218) *(G-4107)*

Cheesemakers Inc 281 593-1319
  2266 S Walker Rd Cleveland (77328) *(G-3122)*

Chef Units LLC (PA) **713 589-2613**
  2501 Karbach St Ste C Houston (77092) *(G-9169)*

Chem Eleven Products Inc 512 278-8800
  6300 Bridge Point Pkwy Austin (78730) *(G-1045)*

Chem Fabrication LLC 979 265-6600
  911 Highway 288 S B Clute (77531) *(G-3149)*

Chem Organics, Houston *Also called Banner Technology Inc (G-8815)*

Chem Rock Technologies LLC 432 940-2299
  2404 E County Road 123 Midland (79706) *(G-15160)*

Chem-Aqua Inc (HQ) **972 438-0232**
  2727 Chemsearch Blvd Irving (75062) *(G-12969)*

Chem-Coat Industries Inc 972 485-8648
  729 3rd Ave Dallas (75226) *(G-4108)*

Chem-Pruf Door Co Ltd 956 544-1000
  5224 Ruben Torres Sr Blvd Brownsville (78526) *(G-2346)*

Chem-Tech, Shamrock *Also called Lubrication Technologies Inc (G-18892)*

Chemax Corporation 409 866-4232
  12175 Highway 90 Beaumont (77713) *(G-1868)*

Chemex Global Inc 346 388-6100
  24 Waterway Ave Ste 900 The Woodlands (77380) *(G-19842)*

Chemex Modular LLC 801 565-8099
  2722 Interstate Hwy 45 S New Waverly (77358) *(G-15856)*

Chemfoundry Inc 725 218-1955
  4845 Cantina Dr Tyler (75708) *(G-20066)*

Chemguard Inc (HQ) **817 473-9964**
  204 S 6th Ave Mansfield (76063) *(G-14662)*

Chemical Blending Facility, Odessa *Also called Ace Cmpltion Enhncment Svcs LP (G-15900)*

Chemical Data LLC 713 683-3900
  3355 W Alabama St Ste 700 Houston (77098) *(G-9170)*

Chemical Exchange Inds Inc (PA) 713 455-1206
  900 Clinton Dr Galena Park (77547) *(G-7378)*

Chemical Lime-Southwest LLC 254 675-8668
  2861 Fm 2602 Clifton (76634) *(G-3142)*

Chemical Lime-Southwest LLC 281 431-0575
  5710 County Road 48 Rosharon (77583) *(G-17602)*

Chemical Lime-Southwest LLC 512 756-8668
  7829 S Us Highway 281 Burnet (78611) *(G-2604)*

Chemical Lime-Southwest LLC 281 471-4500
  801 N 16th St La Porte (77571) *(G-13727)*

Chemical Lime-Southwest LLC 817 268-1188
  3110 S Precinct Line Rd Hurst (76053) *(G-12842)*

Chemical Plant, Pasadena *Also called Southern Ionics Incorporated (G-16509)*

Chemical Service Company 432 523-5290
  401 Ne 3100 Andrews (79714) *(G-542)*

Chemical Tracers Inc 936 564-1866
  2097 County Road 256 Nacogdoches (75965) *(G-15691)*

Chemicals Incorporated 979 244-0100
  8055 State Highway 60 S Bay City (77414) *(G-1771)*

Chemicals Incorporated (PA) **281 576-5000**
  12321 Hatcherville Rd Baytown (77521) *(G-1813)*

Chemlime, Rosharon *Also called Chemical Lime-Southwest LLC (G-17602)*

Chemours Company Fc LLC 281 471-2771
  12501 Strang Rd La Porte (77571) *(G-13728)*

Chemplast Inc 281 208-2585
  1002 Fm 2234 Rd Ste A Stafford (77477) *(G-19294)*

Chemplex Solvay Group, Snyder *Also called Solvay USA Inc (G-19009)*

Chemquest Chemicals LLC 281 291-9966
  9730 Bay Area Blvd Pasadena (77507) *(G-16407)*

Chemsearch Division, Irving *Also called NCH Corporation (G-13114)*

Chemsearch Fe, Irving *Also called NCH Corporation (G-13120)*

Chemstation International Inc 281 457-2020
  2701 Appelt Dr Houston (77015) *(G-9171)*

Chemstation Texas Gulf Coast, Houston *Also called CEo Performance Chem LLC (G-9143)*

Chemsystems Inc 713 329-9066
  10101 Genard Rd Houston (77041) *(G-9172)*

Chemtec Energy Services LLC 936 856-1704
  11745 Cude Cemetery Rd Willis (77318) *(G-20844)*

Chemtops, Elgin *Also called Onepointe Solutions LLC (G-6056)*

Chemtrade Chemicals US LLC 361 368-2200
  5302 County Road 2047 Odem (78370) *(G-15894)*

Chemtrade Refinery Svcs Inc 409 835-6641
  1400 Olin Rd Beaumont (77705) *(G-1869)*

Chemtrade Solutions LLC 972 775-2307
  500 N 9th St Midlothian (76065) *(G-15476)*

Chemtrade Sulfate Chem Inc (HQ) **416 496-4176**
  Business Hwy 289 N Celina (75009) *(G-2991)*

Chemtreat Inc 409 724-1111
  4200 N Twin City Hwy Nederland (77627) *(G-15748)*

Chemtrusion Inc (PA) **713 675-1616**
  7115 Clinton Dr Houston (77020) *(G-9173)*

Chemyx Inc 281 277-5499
  10905 Cash Rd Stafford (77477) *(G-19295)*

Chen Grner Stvens Prtners LLC 512 302-4333
  2113 Wlls Br Pkwy Ste 440 Austin (78728) *(G-1046)*

Cheniere Cch Holdco II LLC (HQ) **713 375-5000**
  700 Milam St Ste 1900 Houston (77002) *(G-9174)*

Cheniere Energy Inc (PA) **713 375-5000**
  700 Milam St Ste 1900 Houston (77002) *(G-9175)*

Chep (usa) Inc 214 688-4108
  2805 Mican Dr Dallas (75212) *(G-4109)*

Chep (usa) Inc 806 577-4447
  7507 Spur 331 Lubbock (79404) *(G-14392)*

Chep (usa) Inc 806 553-5655
  13001 Ne 29th Ave Amarillo (79111) *(G-415)*

Chep (usa) Inc 210 662-7733
  5250 Tacco San Antonio (78244) *(G-18002)*

Chequedcom Inc 888 412-0699
  13355 Noel Rd Ste 1500 Dallas (75240) *(G-4110)*

Cherokee Horn Production LP 619 435-8950
  5950 Berkshire Ln # 1250 Dallas (75225) *(G-4111)*

Cherokee Indus Fabricators Ltd 936 634-2108
  5499 E State Highway 103 Lufkin (75901) *(G-14522)*

Cherokee Steel Fabricators Inc 903 759-3844
  2001 Cherokee Trce White Oak (75693) *(G-20712)*

Cherokee Welding Inc (PA) **512 243-0002**
  6312 Us Highway 183 S Austin (78744) *(G-1047)*

Cherry Construction Systems 903 675-5901
  11293 State Highway 19 N Athens (75752) *(G-822)*

Cherry De Mexico, El Paso *Also called ZF Elec Sys Plsnt Praire LLC (G-6042)*

Cheryl L McDaniel 281 814-0533
  76 Ranch Rd New Waverly (77358) *(G-15857)*

Chesapeake Energy Corporation 817 502-5000
  100 Energy Way Fort Worth (76102) *(G-6512)*

Chesapeake Operating LLC 806 273-5820
  303 Industrial Blvd Borger (79007) *(G-2167)*

Chester R Wright III 832 693-8038
  3104 Tyler Ct Friendswood (77546) *(G-7243)*

Chevas Company LLC 713 225-6595
  1927 Edmundson St Houston (77003) (G-9176)

Chevron Corporation 907 276-7600
  1400 Smith St Ste 3600 Houston (77002) (G-9177)

Chevron Corporation 903 963-8631
  108 Vz County Rd Ste 1417 Van (75790) (G-20206)

Chevron Corporation 713 754-3998
  1600 Smith St Ste 3895 Houston (77002) (G-9178)

Chevron Corporation 432 523-7950
  21 M Sw Of Andrews Andrews (79714) (G-543)

Chevron Marine Products LLC (HQ) 832 854-2767
  1500 Louisiana St Houston (77002) (G-9179)

Chevron Midcontinent LP (HQ) 432 498-8600
  500 W Illinois Ave # 100 Midland (79701) (G-15161)

Chevron Oronite Company LLC 713 432-2500
  4800 Fournace Place Bella Houston (77001) (G-9180)

Chevron Phillips Chem Co LLC (PA) 832 813-4100
  10001 Six Pines Dr The Woodlands (77380) (G-19843)

Chevron Phillips Chem Co LP 281 421-6500
  9500 I 10 East Exit 796 Baytown (77521) (G-1814)

Chevron Phillips Chem Co LP 972 599-6600
  5085 W Park Blvd Ste 500 Plano (75093) (G-16822)

Chevron Phillips Chem Co LP 409 882-6000
  5309 Fm 1006 Orange (77630) (G-16234)

Chevron Phillips Chem Co LP 713 475-3666
  1400 Jefferson Pasadena (77506) (G-16408)

Chevron Phillips Chem Co LP 832 813-4100
  10001 Six Pines Dr The Woodlands (77380) (G-19844)

Chevron Phillips Chem Co LP 325 646-6561
  1400 Drisco Dr Brownwood (76801) (G-2427)

Chevron Phillips Chem Co LP 409 882-6262
  5309 Farm Mkt Rd Ste 106 Orange (77631) (G-16235)

Chevron Phillips Chem Co LP 281 359-6500
  1862 Kingwood Dr Humble (77339) (G-12757)

Chevron Phillips Chem Co LP (HQ) 832 813-4100
  10001 Six Pines Dr The Woodlands (77380) (G-19845)

Chevron Phillips Chem Co LP 806 275-5500
  Spur 119 N Borger (79007) (G-2168)

Chevron Phillips Chem Co LP 409 985-0700
  2001 Gulfway Dr Port Arthur (77640) (G-17104)

Chevron Phillips Chem Co LP 936 539-3154
  5450 Jefferson Chem Rd Conroe (77301) (G-3275)

Chevron Phillips Chem Co LP 979 798-3950
  2611 County Road 314 Brazoria (77422) (G-2218)

Chevron USA Inc 432 687-7100
  6301 Deauville Midland (79706) (G-15162)

Chevron USA Inc 925 842-1000
  1301 Mckinney St Ste 900 Houston (77010) (G-9181)

Cheyenne Services Inc 713 937-7733
  12206 Fm 529 Rd Houston (77041) (G-9182)

CHI Energy Inc 432 685-5001
  212 N Main St Ste 200 Midland (79701) (G-15163)

Chicago Bridge & Iron Co Del (HQ) 832 513-1000
  915 N Eldridge Pkwy Houston (77079) (G-9183)

Chicago Bridge & Iron Company, Houston Also called CB&i LLC (G-9107)

Chicago Flameproof WD Spc Corp 817 534-9800
  4215 Chickasaw Ave Fort Worth (76119) (G-6513)

Chico, Bridgeport Also called Vulcan Materials Company (G-2304)

Chico Building System, Houston Also called Cornerstone Bldg Brands Inc (G-9322)

Chico Stone Inc 972 276-2284
  4217 N Garland Ave Garland (75040) (G-7456)

Chief Adhesive, Forest Hill Also called 3024 East Seminary Group LLC (G-6294)

Chief Fabrication, Mount Pleasant Also called WHW Properties Inc (G-15665)

Chief Fire Systems Inc 281 252-5800
  32628 Decker Prairie Rd Magnolia (77355) (G-14596)

Chief Oil & Gas LLC (PA) 214 265-9590
  8111 Westchester Dr # 600 Dallas (75225) (G-4112)

Chief Oilfield Tech LLC 432 614-4481
  2309 Garden City Hwy Midland (79701) (G-15164)

Chief Operating, Dallas Also called Chief Oil & Gas LLC (G-4112)

Childbirth Graphics, Waco Also called Wrs Group Ltd (G-20481)

Childress Furniture & Fabr Inc 214 565-0900
  15201 Midway Rd Addison (75001) (G-109)

Childs Ready-Mix Concrete Co 254 968-4755
  1375 N Bates St Stephenville (76401) (G-19408)

Childs Ready-Mix Concrete Co 817 594-3832
  6222 E Interstate 20 Willow Park (76008) (G-20872)

Childs Ready-Mix Concrete Co 817 477-5151
  4989 N Fm 199 Cleburne (76033) (G-3083)

Chill King 512 303-1529
  115 Modock Dr Bastrop (78602) (G-1750)

Chimera Lab Ltd 214 428-3901
  9461 E Highway 175 Kemp (75143) (G-13483)

Chip McCormick Custom LLC 830 798-2863
  150 County Road 4603 Bogata (75417) (G-2145)

Chiphong Inc 512 933-9292
  8115 Altoga Dr Austin (78724) (G-1048)

Chippenhook Corporation (HQ) 800 527-5866
  1955 Lakeway Dr Ste 210 Lewisville (75057) (G-14036)

Chippenhook Services, Lewisville Also called Chippenhook Corporation (G-14036)

Chips Custom Cabinets, Arlington Also called Hornbeek Enterprises Inc (G-699)

Chiron Health, Austin Also called Medici Technologies LLC (G-1335)

Chiron Health Holdings LLC 319 400-3772
  2350 Wilson St Austin (78704) (G-1049)

Chiron Holdings Inc (HQ) 210 524-9000
  12930 W Interstate 10 San Antonio (78249) (G-18003)

Chisholm Energy Operating LLC 817 953-6063
  801 Cherry St Ste 1200 Fort Worth (76102) (G-6514)

Chisholm Trail Oilfield Svc 979 567-4943
  545 State Highway 36 S Caldwell (77836) (G-2630)

Chism Company (PA) 210 824-6315
  8310 Broadway San Antonio (78209) (G-18004)

Chisum Site & Steel Inc 903 783-0058
  121 County Road 11400 Paris (75462) (G-16360)

Chm Industries Inc 682 286-0046
  700 E Mcleroy Blvd Ste A Saginaw (76179) (G-17742)

Chm Sports Lighting, Saginaw Also called Chm Industries Inc (G-17742)

Choat Enterprises Inc 432 367-8459
  3300 Sherbrook Rd Odessa (79762) (G-15960)

Choate Co Inc 432 687-5977
  4902 N Midkiff Rd Midland (79705) (G-15165)

Choctaw II Oil & Gas Ltd (PA) 713 632-0222
  815 Walker St Ste 1040 Houston (77002) (G-9184)

Choctaw Lease Service LLC 361 449-3506
  2272 Hwy 59 George West (78022) (G-7623)

Choice Cap Inc (PA) 832 251-9551
  8000 Harwin Dr Ste 165 Houston (77036) (G-9185)

Choice Exploration Inc 817 633-7777
  2221 Avenue J Arlington (76006) (G-641)

Choice Fabricated Stone LLC 817 222-2201
  6308 Eden Dr Fort Worth (76117) (G-6515)

Choiers Company 817 312-1364
  2716 Fox Glenn Ct Hurst (76054) (G-12843)

Cholla Petroleum Inc (HQ) 214 692-7052
  6688 N Central Expy # 1610 Dallas (75206) (G-4113)

Chorizo De San Manuel Guer 956 383-8751
  36080 N Hwy 281 Edinburg (78542) (G-5582)

Chris Burns Welding LLC 940 845-4945
  264 Sunset School Rd Sunset (76270) (G-19624)

Chris Christensen Systems Inc 903 389-7949
  325 Industrial Park Dr Fairfield (75840) (G-6170)

Chriss Welding & Fabricating 409 986-6094
  5930 Delany Rd Hitchcock (77563) (G-8335)

Chriss Welding & Sign Erection, Hitchcock Also called Chriss Welding & Fabricating (G-8335)

Christeros Services LLC 325 884-1100
  108 N Ohio Ave Big Lake (76932) (G-2055)

Christian Fort Bend Academy 281 980-3724
  12919 1/2 Dar Ashford Rd Sugar Land (77478) (G-19456)

Christmas By Krebs Corporation (PA) 972 929-2880
  8324 Sterling St Irving (75063) (G-12970)

Christnes Con Swing Saling LLC 214 212-4808
  2916 Meadowview Dr Colleyville (76034) (G-3211)

Christopher RAD Nader 512 442-5326
  1511 Dandridge Dr Cedar Park (78613) (G-2963)

Chroma Energy Inc (PA) 281 340-6100
  13135 Dairy Ashford Rd # 290 Sugar Land (77478) (G-19457)

Chromalloy Component Svcs Inc 210 331-2300
  303 Industrial Park Rd San Antonio (78226) (G-18005)

Chromalloy Component Svcs Inc (HQ) 210 331-2300
  303 Industrial Park Rd San Antonio (78226) (G-18006)

Chromalloy Gas Turbine LLC 972 241-2501
  14042 Distribution Way Dallas (75234) (G-4114)

Chromatic Industries Inc 936 539-5770
  15b S Trade Center Pkwy Conroe (77385) (G-3276)

Chromatic Industries LLC (HQ) 936 539-5770
  15b S Trade Center Pkwy Conroe (77385) (G-3277)

Chrome Stop, The, Houston Also called A1 Chrome Shop Inc (G-8432)

Chromium Corporation (HQ) 972 851-0500
  14911 Quorum Dr Ste 600 Dallas (75254) (G-4115)

Chryso Inc 972 772-6010
  1611 State Highway 276 Rockwall (75032) (G-17542)

Chuck Atkinson Inc 817 560-8139
  7250 W Vickery Blvd Fort Worth (76116) (G-6516)

Chung's Gourmet Foods, Houston Also called Chungs Products LP (G-9186)

Chungs Products LP 713 741-2118
  777 Post Oak Blvd Ste 250 Houston (77056) (G-9186)

Church Energy Services Ltd 281 931-1400
  2810 Washington Dr Houston (77038) (G-9187)

Church Hill Drilling Tools US 281 893-0233
  5440 Guhn Rd Houston (77040) (G-9188)

Churchill Manufacturing Inc 903 660-4585
  13062 I H 20 N Service Rd Hallsville (75650) (G-8128)

Churro Factory LLC 214 566-5894
  2156 W Northwest Hwy # 302 Dallas (75220) (G-4116)

Chutehelp Inc 855 248-8343
  500 S Main St Carbon (76435) (G-2682)

Ci Systems Inc 805 520-2233
1500 N Interstate 35 # 116 Carrollton (75006) *(G-2715)*

Ciba Vision Corporation 817 551-6881
6201 South Fwy Fort Worth (76134) *(G-6517)*

Ciba Vision Inc 847 294-3000
6201 South Fwy Fort Worth (76134) *(G-6518)*

CIC Construction Inc 979 648-2968
38337 Us Hwy 59 Louise (77455) *(G-14351)*

Cierra Tank Services LLC 713 568-4028
4322 South Dr Houston (77053) *(G-8375)*

Cimarex Energy Co 432 571-7800
600 N Marienfeld St # 600 Midland (79701) *(G-15166)*

Cimarex Energy Co 432 634-1674
S Interstate 10 Unit Pump Iraan (79744) *(G-12917)*

Cimarron Energy Holding Co LLC 701 352-9620
11025 Equity Dr Ste 200 Houston (77041) *(G-9189)*

Cimarron Energy Holding Co LLC 432 563-9700
2600 W 81st St Odessa (79764) *(G-15961)*

Cimarron Software Services Inc (PA) 281 226-5100
18050 Saturn Ln Ste 280 Houston (77058) *(G-9190)*

Cimbar Performance Mineral, Houston *Also called United Minerals and Prpts Inc* *(G-12449)*

Cina Pharmaceutical Inc 281 602-3491
21602 E Hardy Rd Houston (77073) *(G-9191)*

Cinch Connectors Inc 956 686-1151
6900 S Bentsen Rd McAllen (78503) *(G-14847)*

Cincinnati Thermal Spray Inc 281 431-1629
4011 Chance Ln Rosharon (77583) *(G-17603)*

Cinco Energy MGT Group LLC (PA) 713 463-6009
1616 S Voss Rd Ste 100 Houston (77057) *(G-9192)*

Cinco Energy Services, Houston *Also called Cinco Energy MGT Group LLC* *(G-9192)*

Cinco Natural Resources Corp 214 520-7727
2626 Howell St Ste 800 Dallas (75204) *(G-4117)*

Cinco Oil & Gas LLC 214 520-7727
2626 Howell St Ste 800 Dallas (75204) *(G-4118)*

Cinco Resources, Dallas *Also called Cinco Natural Resources Corp* *(G-4117)*

Cinco Resources Inc (HQ) 214 520-7727
2626 Howell St Ste 800 Dallas (75204) *(G-4119)*

Cinnamon Creek Wild Game Proc, Roanoke *Also called M & M Italian Style Foods Inc* *(G-17490)*

Cipherwaste Polymers LP 281 946-8090
1130 Enclave Pkwy Houston (77077) *(G-9193)*

Circle 8 Crane Services LLC (PA) 361 933-0696
3174 County Road 48 Robstown (78380) *(G-17505)*

Circle 8 Crane Services LLC 432 332-6900
2989 S County Rd W Odessa (79766) *(G-15962)*

Circle 8 Crane Services LLC 361 442-0306
4646 Daniel Dr Robstown (78380) *(G-17506)*

Circle 8 Fluid Services, Odessa *Also called Circle 8 Crane Services LLC* *(G-15962)*

Circle A Xpress Inc 956 547-9393
27283 S Altas Palmas Rd Harlingen (78552) *(G-8185)*

Circle B Ready-Mix, Round Rock *Also called Lauren Concrete LP* *(G-17668)*

Circle c Millwork Inc 210 649-1228
9254 Us Highway 87 E San Antonio (78263) *(G-18007)*

Circle D Specialties, Houston *Also called CW Sehorn Enterprises Ltd* *(G-9379)*

Circle E Candles Inc 830 990-4478
4181 E Us Highway 290 Fredericksburg (78624) *(G-7173)*

Circle J Fabrication Inc 817 367-3877
8020 White Settlement Rd Fort Worth (76108) *(G-6519)*

Circle M Welding & Svcs Inc 325 573-8005
7393 W Us Highway 180 Snyder (79549) *(G-18987)*

Circle R Embroidery Co Inc 214 741-1555
4901 Woodall St Dallas (75247) *(G-4120)*

Circle T Western Wear Ltd (PA) 214 808-1100
5349 Drane Dr Dallas (75209) *(G-4121)*

Circle U Foods Inc 817 626-6918
751 Eight Twenty Blvd # 101 Fort Worth (76106) *(G-6520)*

Circle Y Saddles Inc 361 293-3501
1708 N South St Yoakum (77995) *(G-20961)*

Circon Environmental, La Porte *Also called Intergulf Corporation* *(G-13754)*

Circor Energy Products LLC (HQ) 713 400-2200
11331 Tanner Rd Houston (77041) *(G-9194)*

Circor Energy Products, Inc., Houston *Also called Circor Energy Products LLC* *(G-9194)*

Circuit Breaker Sales LLC (HQ) 940 665-4444
1315 Columbine Dr Gainesville (76240) *(G-7338)*

Circuit Breaker Sales Co Inc, Gainesville *Also called Circuit Breaker Sales LLC* *(G-7338)*

Circuit Check Inc 972 480-0044
681 N Plano Rd Ste 101 Richardson (75081) *(G-17286)*

Circuit Services Inc 713 465-4216
1765 Upland Dr Houston (77043) *(G-9195)*

Circuit Systems Company Inc 817 861-6575
5301 W Pioneer Pkwy Arlington (76013) *(G-642)*

Circuitronics, Irving *Also called Lwo Acquisitions Company LLC* *(G-13093)*

Cirrus Logic Inc (PA) 512 851-4000
800 W 6th St Austin (78701) *(G-1050)*

Cisco, Houston *Also called Champion Industrial Sales Co* *(G-9158)*

Cisco Boiler Service Co Inc 713 928-5700
2403 Appelt Dr Houston (77015) *(G-9196)*

Cisco Press, Cisco *Also called Eastland County Newspaper Inc* *(G-3066)*

Cisco Systems Inc 210 357-2500
18615 Tuscany Stone # 250 San Antonio (78258) *(G-18008)*

Cisco Systems Inc 469 255-0000
2300 E President Georger Richardson (75082) *(G-17287)*

Cisco Systems Inc 512 378-1112
12515 Res Blvd Bldg 3 Austin (78759) *(G-1051)*

Cisco Systems Inc 469 420-4700
7301 State Highway 161 # 200 Irving (75039) *(G-12971)*

Cisco Systems Inc 800 553-6387
1208 14th St Bsmt Lubbock (79401) *(G-14393)*

Cisco Systems Inc 972 393-0874
10650 Okanella St Houston (77041) *(G-9197)*

Cisco Systems Inc 817 490-6062
724 Henrietta Creek Rd Roanoke (76262) *(G-17484)*

Cistera Networks Inc (PA) 972 381-4699
5045 Lorimar Dr Ste 180 Plano (75093) *(G-16823)*

Citation 2002 Inv Ltd Partnr 281 891-1000
14077 Cutten Rd Houston (77069) *(G-9198)*

Citation Oil & Gas, Houston *Also called Citation 2002 Inv Ltd Partnr* *(G-9198)*

Citation Oil & Gas Corp 432 262-7600
2609 S County Road 1242 Midland (79706) *(G-15167)*

Citation Oil & Gas Corp (PA) 281 891-1000
14077 Cutten Rd Houston (77069) *(G-9199)*

Citation Oil & Gas Corp 956 248-5741
7766 Citation Cnty Rd Lyford (78569) *(G-14571)*

Cite Corporation (PA) 817 477-1549
710 S 5th Ave Mansfield (76063) *(G-14663)*

Citgo Holding Terminals LLC 832 486-4000
1293 Eldridge Pkwy Houston (77077) *(G-9200)*

Citgo Petroleum Corporation 832 486-5900
220 Terminal Ln Sugar Land (77498) *(G-19458)*

Citgo Petroleum Corporation (HQ) 832 486-4000
1293 Eldridge Pkwy Houston (77077) *(G-9201)*

Citrolim Inc 281 453-5150
14405 Walters Rd Ste 600 Houston (77014) *(G-9202)*

Citronix Inc 817 633-3200
2241 S Watson Rd Ste 111 Arlington (76010) *(G-643)*

City Colour, Dallas *Also called Genti Studios Inc* *(G-4402)*

City Concrete Inc 817 636-2690
90776 E Hwy 114 Rhome (76078) *(G-17253)*

City Glass, Cleveland *Also called Kats Glass LLC* *(G-3131)*

City Hatz/City Flagz 214 376-2589
6708 Sweet Sue Ln Dallas (75241) *(G-4122)*

City Iron & Metal Co, Wichita Falls *Also called Bell Processing Incorporated* *(G-20744)*

City Machine & Welding Inc 806 358-7293
9701 Business I 40 W 40 I Amarillo (79124) *(G-416)*

City Mattress Co, Fort Worth *Also called Royal Sleep Products Ltd* *(G-6967)*

City Newspapers Management LLC 214 739-2244
750 N Saint Paul St # 2100 Dallas (75201) *(G-4123)*

City of Arlington 817 459-5700
620 W Division St Arlington (76011) *(G-644)*

City of Bandera 830 796-3401
548 State Highway 16 S Bandera (78003) *(G-1743)*

City of Colony The 972 625-4471
4180 Main St Lewisville (75056) *(G-14037)*

City of Corpus Christi 361 695-7350
801 Leopard St Corpus Christi (78401) *(G-3499)*

City of Houston 713 221-0404
900 Bagby St Fl 2 Houston (77002) *(G-9203)*

City of Irving 972 721-2646
825 W Irving Blvd Irving (75060) *(G-12972)*

City of Jefferson 903 665-2832
1401 N Line St Jefferson (75657) *(G-13283)*

City of Marshall 903 935-4500
1600 Starr St Marshall (75670) *(G-14771)*

City of McKinney 972 547-7657
301 N Mcdonald St Mc Kinney (75069) *(G-14827)*

City of Pasadena 713 475-7884
120 N Pasadena Blvd Pasadena (77506) *(G-16409)*

City of Sherman 903 892-7258
243 La Cima Rd Sherman (75092) *(G-18909)*

City Ready Mix Inc 956 722-6315
1810 Main Ave Laredo (78040) *(G-13874)*

City Sign Services Inc 214 826-4475
3914 Elm St Dallas (75226) *(G-4124)*

City Tortilla Factory Inc 361 776-3578
2715 Main St Ingleside (78362) *(G-12892)*

Cityon Systems Inc 972 519-1673
4120 W Spring Creek Pkwy Plano (75024) *(G-16824)*

Cjhorak Enterprises Inc 817 260-0700
2838 Market Loop Ste 104 Southlake (76092) *(G-19059)*

Cjr Contractors Inc 806 592-2232
401 W Broadway St Denver City (79323) *(G-5417)*

CK &B Machine Shop 281 485-5760
2413 Roy Rd Pearland (77581) *(G-16544)*

CK Kustoms Iron Works Inc 281 850-6118
2102 Picton Ln Rockport (78382) *(G-17529)*

Ckb Machining LLC 281 485-5760
6953 Brookside Rd Pearland (77581) *(G-16545)*

Cki Locker LLC........817 329-1600
2701 Regent Blvd Ste 200 Dfw Airport (75261) ***(G-5452)***
Ckl Distilling LLC........512 963-2373
211 Darden Hill Rd A200 Driftwood (78619) ***(G-5499)***
CKS Packaging Inc........817 924-2205
109 E Felix St S Fort Worth (76115) ***(G-6521)***
CKS Packaging Inc........214 358-2441
2818 Merrell Rd Dallas (75229) ***(G-4125)***
CL&f Offshore LLC (HQ)........**281 873-9378**
16945 Northchase Dr # 15 Houston (77060) ***(G-9204)***
CL&f Operating LLC (PA)........**281 873-9378**
16945 Northchase Dr # 15 Houston (77060) ***(G-9205)***
CL&f Resources LP (PA)........**281 873-9378**
16945 Nrthchase D Ste 150 Houston (77060) ***(G-9206)***
Clairex Semiconductor, Plano *Also called Clairex Technologies Inc* ***(G-16825)***
Clairex Technologies Inc........972 265-4905
1000 Jupiter Rd Ste 100 Plano (75074) ***(G-16825)***
Clajon Holding Corp........432 682-6324
6 Desta Dr Ste 3000 Midland (79705) ***(G-15168)***
Clanton's Quality Awning, Dallas *Also called All American Awnings Inc* ***(G-3919)***
Clarendon Mfg & Distrg Co Inc........806 874-3584
200 W 1st St Clarendon (79226) ***(G-3070)***
Clariant Corporation........832 753-3042
9502 Bayport Blvd Pasadena (77507) ***(G-16410)***
Clariant Corporation........281 465-9100
2645 Technology Frst The Woodlands (77381) ***(G-19846)***
Clarion Events Inc........713 963-6220
1700 West Loop S Ste 1000 Houston (77027) ***(G-9207)***
Clarion Tech Lonestar Inc........972 278-9700
2405 S Shiloh Rd Garland (75041) ***(G-7457)***
Clarios........254 774-9287
18 S Main St Temple (76501) ***(G-19676)***
Clarios........817 733-4326
2500 Lou Menk Dr Fort Worth (76131) ***(G-6522)***
Clarios........281 518-8053
20555 State Highway 249 Houston (77070) ***(G-9208)***
Clarios........361 289-9675
2209 N Padre Island Dr Corpus Christi (78408) ***(G-3500)***
Clark Fire Equipment Inc........713 453-3778
1838 Federal Rd Houston (77015) ***(G-9209)***
Clark Machine Inc........281 303-8698
6650 W Bay Rd Baytown (77523) ***(G-1781)***
Clark Pillow Company........409 842-5767
6281 Industrial Rd Beaumont (77705) ***(G-1870)***
Clarke Harland Corp (HQ)........**830 609-5500**
15955 La Cantera Pkwy San Antonio (78256) ***(G-18009)***
Clarke Harland Corp........817 329-7113
4055 Corporate Dr Ste 100 Grapevine (76051) ***(G-8022)***
Clarke Harland Corp........210 694-1492
10575 Vista Park Rd Dallas (75238) ***(G-4126)***
Clarke Harland Corp........210 697-8888
1713 Townhurst Dr Houston (77043) ***(G-9210)***
Clarke Products Inc........972 660-1992
820 Central Dr Colleyville (76034) ***(G-3212)***
Clarke Products Inc........972 660-1992
2100 Orchard Ln Unit B Waco (76705) ***(G-20383)***
Clarks Hardwood Lumber Co LP........713 862-6628
700 E 5 And A Half St Houston (77007) ***(G-9211)***
Clarks Precision Machine & Tl, Azle *Also called Clarks Precision Machine & Tl* ***(G-1721)***
Clarks Precision Machine & Tl........817 444-2533
636 Profit St Azle (76020) ***(G-1721)***
Classic Auto Air Mfg LP........817 442-4822
910 Freeport Pkwy Ste 100 Coppell (75019) ***(G-3411)***
Classic Balloon Corporation........972 242-2711
2200 Ross Ave Ste 3300 Dallas (75201) ***(G-4127)***
Classic Caps & Embroidery, Dallas *Also called Circle R Embroidery Co Inc* ***(G-4120)***
Classic Corrugated Inc........940 381-0137
1725 Cooper Creek Rd Denton (76208) ***(G-5354)***
Classic Doors Systems Co........214 678-9555
151 Regal Row Ste 220 Dallas (75247) ***(G-4128)***
Classic Fence........806 517-0708
15005 Mescalero Trl Amarillo (79118) ***(G-483)***
Classic Foods LP........817 332-1071
3165 S Burleson Blvd Burleson (76028) ***(G-2574)***
Classic Galleries, Hutchins *Also called Classic Picture Company Inc* ***(G-12864)***
Classic Industries LP........972 564-2192
13020 Fm 1641 Forney (75126) ***(G-6305)***
Classic Millwork and Products........915 833-9922
275 Rio West Dr El Paso (79932) ***(G-5696)***
Classic Picture Company Inc........972 225-7590
1601 S Main St Hutchins (75141) ***(G-12864)***
Classic Printing........361 852-7261
4639 Corona Dr Ste 101 Corpus Christi (78411) ***(G-3501)***
Classic Protection Systems........713 468-3573
1648 W Sam Houston Pkwy N Houston (77043) ***(G-9212)***
Classic Stainless Inc........214 467-8700
4031 Bronze Way Dallas (75237) ***(G-4129)***
Claudes Sauces Inc........915 858-4299
935 Loma Verde Dr El Paso (79936) ***(G-5697)***
Claudia Rodriguez........956 381-0845
1815 Nora Dr Edinburg (78539) ***(G-5583)***
Claussen Inc........512 556-2180
1303 Mclean St Lampasas (76550) ***(G-13833)***
Clay Cooley Chrysler, Irving *Also called Lay Cooley RE Holdings 1 LLC* ***(G-13084)***
Clay DHanis Products Inc........830 363-7636
Old Eagle Pass Rd D Hanis (78850) ***(G-3828)***
Clay Magic, Dallas *Also called Auto Wax Company Inc* ***(G-3988)***
Clay Precision Ltd........903 891-9022
1102 Fm 1417 Ne Sherman (75090) ***(G-18910)***
Claytex Trophies Inc (PA)........**940 538-6521**
Highway 287 W Henrietta (76365) ***(G-8279)***
Clayton Homes Inc........254 666-9570
9000 Chapel Rd Waco (76712) ***(G-20384)***
Clayton Homes Inc........210 946-2222
13700 Judson Rd Ofc San Antonio (78233) ***(G-18010)***
Clayton Homes Inc........254 772-1808
7001 Imperial Dr Waco (76712) ***(G-20385)***
Clayton Homes Inc........210 677-6100
1824 Sw Loop 410 San Antonio (78227) ***(G-18011)***
Clayton W Williams Jr, Midland *Also called Nbl Permian LLC* ***(G-15312)***
Clayton Williams Energy, Midland *Also called Clajon Holding Corp* ***(G-15168)***
Clayton, Dubilier & Rice, Houston *Also called Sterling Group LP* ***(G-12060)***
Clean Air Consultants Inc........972 278-2664
2525 National Dr Garland (75041) ***(G-7458)***
Clean Combustion Inc........832 333-7800
14210 Highway 146 Dayton (77535) ***(G-5223)***
Clean Energy Tech Assn Inc........903 389-4136
123 E Commerce St Fairfield (75840) ***(G-6171)***
Clean Fueling Technologies, Georgetown *Also called Cft Dispensers Inc* ***(G-7643)***
Clean Harbors San Leon Inc (PA)........**281 339-1352**
2700 Avenue S Dickinson (77539) ***(G-5473)***
Clean Hrbors Explrtion Svcs In........281 478-2600
802 Seaco Ct Deer Park (77536) ***(G-5264)***
Cleanfuel Holdings Inc........512 864-0300
824 Wheeler St Mason (76856) ***(G-14812)***
Cleanfuel USA, Mason *Also called Cleanfuel Holdings Inc* ***(G-14812)***
Cleanplanet Chemical Inc........855 256-7568
6207 Fm 2244 Rd Ste 165 Austin (78746) ***(G-1052)***
Cleanquip, Houston *Also called Mmlj Inc* ***(G-10896)***
Cleanroom Certification Cnstr, Greenville *Also called Joe Ross* ***(G-8079)***
Clear Diamond Inc........325 597-9240
807 San Angelo Hwy Brady (76825) ***(G-2212)***
Clear Film Printing Inc........972 962-4422
3000 E Us Highway 175 Kaufman (75142) ***(G-13458)***
Clear Fork Incorporated........325 677-1309
155 Pine St Abilene (79601) ***(G-31)***
Clear Lake Plant, Pasadena *Also called Arkema Inc* ***(G-16389)***
Clear Lk Program Solutions LLC........713 784-0111
18422 Highway 3 Webster (77598) ***(G-20636)***
Clear View Unlimited LLC........409 782-3594
3417 Old Spurger Hwy Silsbee (77656) ***(G-18951)***
Clear Visions Inc (HQ)........**210 496-6006**
121 Interpark Blvd # 801 San Antonio (78216) ***(G-18012)***
Clear Water Resources, San Marcos *Also called Cwr Management LLC* ***(G-18683)***
Clearcorrect Operating LLC........888 331-3323
21 Cypress Blvd Ste 1010 Round Rock (78665) ***(G-17633)***
Clearfork Petroleum Inc........806 763-5625
519 Main St Lubbock (79401) ***(G-14394)***
Clearly Petroleum Opco LLC........281 781-0412
5825 N Houston Pkwy Ste 5 Houston (77086) ***(G-9213)***
Clearmediaone Inc (PA)........**713 622-9393**
19 Briar Hollow Ln # 235 Houston (77027) ***(G-9214)***
Clearpath Engineering Inc........832 856-9040
20456 Wstfeld Commerce Dr Katy (77449) ***(G-13392)***
Clearvlue Combustn Systems Inc........281 261-9543
4402 Ringrose Dr Missouri City (77459) ***(G-15578)***
Clearwater Engineer Chemistry, Latexo *Also called Aquapharm Pchem LLC* ***(G-13942)***
Cleburne Metal Works LLC........817 237-5060
6432 Nine Mile Bridge Rd Fort Worth (76135) ***(G-6523)***
Cleburne Sheet Metal, Fort Worth *Also called Cleburne Metal Works LLC* ***(G-6523)***
Cleburne Times Review, Cleburne *Also called Newspaper Holding Inc* ***(G-3102)***
Cleereco Services Inc........325 658-6533
14 E Beauregard Ave San Angelo (76903) ***(G-17787)***
Clegg Industries Inc........361 578-0291
16400 Nw Zac Lentz Pkwy Victoria (77905) ***(G-20253)***
Clemens Sheet Metal Works, Haltom City *Also called Gst Manufacturing Ltd* ***(G-8147)***
Clements Fluids Buffalo Ltd........903 581-5110
701 Old Bllard Rd Pmb 20 Tyler (75703) ***(G-20067)***
Clements Fluids Henderson Ltd........903 581-5110
5201 S Broadway Ave # 212 Tyler (75703) ***(G-20068)***
Clements Nut Co Inc........972 436-4596
614 E Main St Lewisville (75057) ***(G-14038)***
Clementson Inc (HQ)........**956 631-9121**
3721 N Mccoll Rd McAllen (78501) ***(G-14848)***
Cleveland Asphalt Products Inc........936 628-6200
Hwy 59 N Shepherd (77371) ***(G-18900)***

Client Connect LLC (PA) 214 295-4940
5700 Granite Pkwy Ste 200 Plano (75024) (G-16826)

Cliff Dunta Bros Inc 940 325-4855
2301 Sw 4th Ave Mineral Wells (76067) (G-15523)

Clifton Moulding Corp 877 882-1803
100 S Avenue B Clifton (76634) (G-3143)

Clifton Record, Clifton Also called Progrssive Mdia Communications (G-3146)

Clifton Upholstery Co Inc 254 753-0211
416 Mary Ave Waco (76701) (G-20386)

Climate Control Containers 409 963-2137
6648 Gulfway Dr Port Arthur (77642) (G-17105)

Climatic Systems Inc 972 206-2590
2337 W Warrior Trl Grand Prairie (75052) (G-7853)

Climax Investors LLC 832 582-9622
7272 Marvin D Love Fwy # 518 Dallas (75237) (G-4130)

Climax Portable Mch Tls Inc 800 333-8311
7003 Highway 225 Ste B Deer Park (77536) (G-5265)

Cline Construction and Paving, Big Spring Also called Cline Construction Inc (G-2075)

Cline Construction Inc 432 267-6006
1807 N Fm 700 Big Spring (79720) (G-2075)

Clint & Sons Processing, White Deer Also called Freeman Brothers Inc (G-20709)

Clock Spring Company Inc (PA) 281 590-8491
621 Lockhaven Dr Houston (77073) (G-9215)

Clorox Manufacturing Company 713 674-5042
5822 Armour Dr Houston (77020) (G-9216)

Clorox Sales Company 972 915-0430
8500 Freport Pkwy Ste 275 Irving (75063) (G-12973)

Cloud Logix LLC 682 310-0665
8432 Sterling St Ste 200 Irving (75063) (G-12974)

Cloud Ninjas LLC 832 478-9158
10757 Cutten Rd Bldg 5 Houston (77066) (G-9217)

Cloud Printing Co of Abilene 325 676-9396
858 N 1st St Abilene (79601) (G-32)

Clover Group Inc 915 590-2525
2914 Alameda Ave El Paso (79905) (G-5698)

Clown Co Inc 972 288-6954
706 E Kearney St Mesquite (75149) (G-15034)

Cls Indstrial Purification LLC (PA) 281 538-4669
2551 S Shore Blvd Ste C League City (77573) (G-13953)

Cls Metal Fabrication LLC 817 994-0891
2915 Horton Rd Forest Hill (76119) (G-6295)

Clutchco International Inc (PA) 281 446-1297
319 Derrick Dr Humble (77338) (G-12758)

Clutchco USA 936 588-3501
319 Derrick Dr Humble (77338) (G-12759)

Clw Inc (PA) 281 592-4691
10001 Fm 2025 Rd Cleveland (77328) (G-3123)

Clyde Union, Houston Also called S & N Pump Company (G-11707)

CMC, Irving Also called Commercial Metals Company (G-12977)

CMC Alamo Steel, Waco Also called C M C Steel Fabricators Inc (G-20373)

CMC Alamo Steel, Houston Also called C M C Steel Fabricators Inc (G-9033)

CMC Construction Services, Dallas Also called C M C Steel Fabricators Inc (G-4073)

CMC Construction Services, Waxahachie Also called C M C Steel Fabricators Inc (G-20532)

CMC Construction Services, Fort Worth Also called C M C Steel Fabricators Inc (G-6484)

CMC Materials Inc (HQ) 817 761-6100
300 Throckmorton St Fort Worth (76102) (G-6524)

CMC Metals Recycling, Seguin Also called Commercial Metals Company (G-18831)

CMC Products, Bogata Also called Chip McCormick Custom LLC (G-2145)

CMC Rbar San Antnio E Location, Seguin Also called C M C Steel Fabricators Inc (G-18827)

CMC Recycling, Houston Also called Commercial Metals Company (G-9251)

CMC Recycling, Beaumont Also called Commercial Metals Company (G-1875)

CMC Recycling, Clute Also called Commercial Metals Company (G-3150)

CMC Recycling, Corpus Christi Also called Commercial Metals Company (G-3505)

CMC Recycling, Dallas Also called Commercial Metals Company (G-4147)

CMC Recycling & Express Retail, Fort Worth Also called Commercial Metals Company (G-6531)

CMC Steel Texas, Seguin Also called Structural Metals Inc (G-18866)

CMC Steel Us LLC (HQ) 214 689-4300
6565 N Macarthur Blvd # 8 Irving (75039) (G-12975)

CMC Sterling Steel, Houston Also called Commercial Metals Company (G-9252)

CMC Texas Cold Finished Steel, Houston Also called C M C Steel Fabricators Inc (G-9032)

Cmcabco LLC (PA) 972 617-8605
3637 N Highway 77 Waxahachie (75165) (G-20536)

Cmcs Group LLC 972 647-6260
2457 Nw Dallas St Grand Prairie (75050) (G-7854)

Cmd, Clarendon Also called Clarendon Mfg & Distrg Co Inc (G-3070)

Cme Printing Inc 713 271-7700
8181 Commerce Park Dr # 708 Houston (77036) (G-9218)

CMF, Wharton Also called Carols Mch & Fabrication Inc (G-20698)

CMH Manufacturing Inc 903 439-0242
2600 Main St Sulphur Springs (75482) (G-19583)

CMH Manufacturing Inc 254 666-3534
9000 Van American Dr Waco (76712) (G-20387)

CMH Manufacturing Inc 800 445-3516
333 Austin Dr Bonham (75418) (G-2152)

Cml Exploration LLC 325 573-0750
1105 Old Lubbock Hwy Snyder (79549) (G-18988)

Cml Exploration LLC (PA) 512 328-8085
Barton Oaks Plz 1 Ste 430 Austin (78746) (G-1053)

CMOS X-RAY DBA ENVISION CMOSXRAY, La Porte Also called Illinois Tool Works Inc (G-13748)

Cmp Express LLC 469 348-2272
901 Avenue M Grand Prairie (75050) (G-7855)

CNA Holdings LLC (HQ) 972 443-4000
222 Las Colinas Blvd W Irving (75039) (G-12976)

CNA Insurance, El Paso Also called C N A Inc (G-5675)

Cnc Fabrication and Maint 817 295-9055
2171 E Renfro St Burleson (76028) (G-2575)

Cnc Manufacturing, Missouri City Also called C D & N Manufacturing Inc (G-15576)

Cnc Plastics 979 884-0608
4031 County Road 117 B Giddings (78942) (G-7693)

Cnc Precision Manufacturing 972 241-4226
14850 Venture Dr Dallas (75234) (G-4131)

Cnd Signs LLC 512 394-5421
5213 Tucker Hill Ln Cedar Creek (78612) (G-2934)

Cnh Group Incorporated 832 453-9977
12227 Fm 529 Rd Houston (77041) (G-9219)

Cnhi LLC 806 273-5611
207 S Main St Borger (79007) (G-2169)

Cnhi LLC 432 263-7331
710 Scurry St Big Spring (79720) (G-2076)

Cnhi LLC 940 665-5511
306 E California St Gainesville (76240) (G-7339)

Cni 830 765-7484
865 Industrial Blvd Del Rio (78840) (G-5312)

CNJ, Big Lake Also called Nabors Well Services Co (G-2059)

Cnm Horizon Investments LLC 713 333-3400
8126 Broadway St Galveston (77554) (G-7393)

Cnooc Energy Holdings USA Inc 713 380-4800
945 Bunker Hill Rd # 1000 Houston (77024) (G-9220)

Cnooc Marketing USA Inc 713 380-4800
945 Bunker Hill Rd # 1000 Houston (77024) (G-9221)

Cnooc Petroleum Offshr USA Inc 972 450-4600
12790 Merit Dr Ste 800 Dallas (75251) (G-4132)

Cnpc USA Corporation (HQ) 713 465-7382
2901 Wilcrest Dr Fl 3 Houston (77042) (G-9222)

Cns Tech Wldg & Fabrication Lc 281 239-2555
1881 Treble Dr Humble (77338) (G-12760)

Co Co MO Joes 409 212-9892
2024 Calder St Beaumont (77701) (G-1871)

Co Waggoner Inc 972 641-8888
2100 S Great Southwest Pk Grand Prairie (75051) (G-7856)

Co-Ex Pipe Co 432 263-0206
714 Anna St Big Spring (79720) (G-2077)

Co-Operative Inds Arospc & Def, Fort Worth Also called Co-Operative Inds Def LLC (G-6525)

Co-Operative Inds Def LLC 817 740-4700
1401 S Cherry Ln Fort Worth (76108) (G-6525)

Coachworks LLC 830 510-4224
10498 State Highway 16 S Pipe Creek (78063) (G-16741)

Coast Graphics & Signs Inc 281 499-9721
12999 Murphy Rd Ste E1 Stafford (77477) (G-19296)

Coast Precast LLC 936 890-5500
11261 Meador Rd Conroe (77303) (G-3278)

Coast To Coast Minerals LLC 210 781-8505
5169 Randolph Blvd Bldg 1 San Antonio (78233) (G-18013)

Coast To Coast Tower Svc Inc 972 923-9504
753 Arrowhead Rd Waxahachie (75167) (G-20537)

Coastal Bend Tooling & Automtn 361 883-0376
510 S Staples St Corpus Christi (78401) (G-3502)

Coastal Casting Service (PA) 713 223-4439
2903 Gano St Houston (77009) (G-9223)

Coastal Caverns Inc 409 833-5504
6045 Highland Ave Beaumont (77705) (G-1872)

Coastal Crushed Concrete LLC (PA) 713 941-3232
9026 Lambright Rd Houston (77075) (G-9224)

Coastal Drilling Company L L C 361 852-6195
311 Saratoga Blvd Corpus Christi (78417) (G-3503)

Coastal Flange Inc 713 937-3333
11906 Fm 529 Rd Jersey Village (77041) (G-13296)

Coastal Flow Measurement Inc (HQ) 713 477-1956
2525 Bay Area Blvd # 500 Houston (77058) (G-9225)

Coastal Foundry Company 713 695-4008
506 Rosamond St Houston (77076) (G-9226)

Coastal Gulf & Intl Inc 713 740-9800
1604 Shaver St Pasadena (77502) (G-16411)

Coastal Hydraulic Cranes Inc 281 448-8998
9723 Sotherloch Lake Dr Spring (77379) (G-19106)

Coastal Machine & Mech LLC 979 849-9323
14004 S Highway 288b Angleton (77515) (G-567)

Coastal Mechanics Company Inc 713 784-0111
7660 Woodway Dr Ste 510 Houston (77063) (G-9227)

Coastal Mechanics TI & Mch Inc 281 987-2530
14375 Luthe Rd Houston (77039) (G-9228)

ALPHABETIC

Coastal Plains Exploration LLC 361 553-9000
323 Alcoa Dr Port Lavaca (77979) *(G-17144)*
Coastal Plastic Molding Inc 281 331-7909
735 County Road 281 Alvin (77511) *(G-356)*
Coastal Plating Company, Corpus Christi *Also called Rister Crnkshaft Spcialist Ltd* *(G-3610)*
Coastal Production Services, Rockport *Also called Promar LP* *(G-17531)*
Coastal Ready Mix Inc 409 287-3307
6363 N Twin Cy Hwy Unit 1 Nederland (77627) *(G-15749)*
Coastal Resources Group LLC 281 549-4132
2105 Anders Ln Ste D Kemah (77565) *(G-13471)*
Coastal Wireline Services Inc 281 485-6548
3909 Halik St Pearland (77581) *(G-16546)*
Coastels, Houston *Also called Mexssub International Inc* *(G-10861)*
Coastline Indus Coatings Inc 281 499-0633
3401 5th St Stafford (77477) *(G-19297)*
Coastline Petroleum LLC 281 844-4272
5601 Irvington Blvd Houston (77009) *(G-9229)*
Coastline Trailer Mfg Inc 361 785-4073
306 S Main St Seadrift (77983) *(G-18795)*
Coated Abrasive Division, Stephenville *Also called Saint-Gobain Abrasives Inc* *(G-19421)*
Coates Energy Trust 210 820-0113
7373 Broadway Ste 406 San Antonio (78209) *(G-18014)*
Coating Applicators, Houston *Also called Impreglon Surface Tech Inc* *(G-10335)*
Coating Industries Inc 713 937-8581
6414 Thomas Rd Houston (77041) *(G-9230)*
Coatings Group Inc (PA) **817 633-7383**
616 E Avenue J Grand Prairie (75050) *(G-7857)*
Coats Construction Company, Andrews *Also called Billy R Coats Inc* *(G-539)*
Cobalt Group Inc 206 269-6363
7004 Bee Caves Rd Ste 100 Austin (78746) *(G-1054)*
Cobalt International Energy LP (HQ) **713 452-2322**
920 Mmrial Cy Way Ste 100 Houston (77024) *(G-9231)*
Cobalt International Enrgy Inc (PA) **713 579-9100**
920 Mmrial Cy Way Ste 100 Houston (77024) *(G-9232)*
Cobb Carpet Supply Co (PA) **214 634-2622**
1314 Viceroy Dr Dallas (75247) *(G-4133)*
Cobham Advnced Elctrnic Sltons 972 437-1049
405 Interntl Pkwy Ste 20 Richardson (75081) *(G-17288)*
Cobra Coating 432 332-0272
2300 E Murphy St Odessa (79761) *(G-15963)*
Cobra Manufacturing Co Inc 918 366-7622
1001 Pamela Dr Euless (76040) *(G-6137)*
Cobra Oil & Gas Corporation (PA) **940 723-4331**
2201 Kell Blvd Wichita Falls (76308) *(G-20754)*
Coburn Supply Company Inc 409 838-6363
5910 Gardendale Dr Houston (77092) *(G-9233)*
Coca Cola Btlg Co of Southwest 210 229-0555
1 Coca Cola Pl San Antonio (78219) *(G-18015)*
Coca Cola Btlg of Shreveport (HQ) 214 902-2600
14185 Dallas Pkwy # 1400 Dallas (75254) *(G-4134)*
Coca Cola Btlg of Shreveport 956 632-3773
2400 W Expressway 83 McAllen (78501) *(G-14849)*
Coca-Cola, Houston *Also called Odwalla Inc* *(G-11134)*
Coca-Cola, Dallas *Also called Coca Cola Btlg of Shreveport* *(G-4134)*
Coca-Cola, Nacogdoches *Also called Nacogdoches Coca Cola Btlg Co* *(G-15704)*
Coca-Cola, Lufkin *Also called Lufkin Coca Cola Bottling Co* *(G-14536)*
Coca-Cola, San Antonio *Also called Coca Cola Btlg Co of Southwest* *(G-18015)*
Coca-Cola, McAllen *Also called Coca Cola Btlg of Shreveport* *(G-14849)*
Coca-Cola Bottling Co 830 775-8561
1310 E 1st St Del Rio (78840) *(G-5313)*
Coca-Cola Company 281 302-4317
2105 Town Square Pl # 400 Sugar Land (77479) *(G-19459)*
Coca-Cola Company 817 847-3000
3400 Fossil Creek Blvd Fort Worth (76137) *(G-6526)*
Coca-Cola Company 713 799-7332
9300 Center Point Dr Houston (77054) *(G-9234)*
Coca-Cola Company 214 351-4797
6445 Lemmon Ave Dallas (75209) *(G-4135)*
Coca-Cola Company 254 666-5500
8400 Imperial Dr Waco (76712) *(G-20388)*
Coca-Cola Enterprises 817 232-8600
3400 Fossil Creek Blvd Fort Worth (76137) *(G-6527)*
Coca-Cola Enterprises Bottling 214 253-5747
14185 Dallas Pkwy # 1400 Dallas (75254) *(G-4136)*
Coca-Cola Refreshments USA Inc 903 893-0194
1820 N Frisco Rd Sherman (75090) *(G-18911)*
Coca-Cola Refreshments USA Inc 800 438-2653
2150 Town Square Pl # 400 Sugar Land (77479) *(G-19460)*
Coca-Cola Refreshments USA Inc 214 253-5600
13727 Noel Rd Ste 900 Dallas (75240) *(G-4137)*
Coca-Cola Refreshments USA Inc 281 452-7635
15221 Market St Channelview (77530) *(G-3016)*
Coca-Cola Refreshments USA Inc 325 672-3232
2074 N 1st St Abilene (79603) *(G-33)*
Coca-Cola Refreshments USA Inc 903 276-1295
1930 New Boston Rd Texarkana (75501) *(G-19759)*
Coca-Cola Refreshments USA Inc 806 324-5300
8700 Centerport Blvd Amarillo (79108) *(G-417)*

Coca-Cola Refreshments USA Inc 806 472-3200
6101 Avenue A Lubbock (79404) *(G-14395)*
Coca-Cola Refreshments USA Inc 325 437-5000
1849 Albany Hwy Abilene (79603) *(G-34)*
Coca-Cola Refreshments USA Inc 940 720-3907
1512 Lamar St Wichita Falls (76301) *(G-20755)*
Coca-Cola Southwest Bevs LLC (HQ) **214 902-2600**
14185 Dallas Pkwy # 1300 Dallas (75254) *(G-4138)*
Coca-Cola Southwest Bevs LLC 214 388-6000
8161 Moberly Ln Dallas (75227) *(G-4139)*
Cockrell Enovation, Fort Worth *Also called Cockrell Printing Co* *(G-6528)*
Cockrell Foundation, Houston *Also called Cockrell Oil Corporation* *(G-9235)*
Cockrell Oil Corporation 713 209-7300
1600 Smith St Ste 4600 Houston (77002) *(G-9235)*
Cockrell Printing Co (PA) **817 336-0571**
218 W Broadway Ave Fort Worth (76104) *(G-6528)*
Cockrell Resources Inc 713 454-1400
8620 W Monroe Rd Ste 200 Houston (77061) *(G-9236)*
Cocomo Joe's, Beaumont *Also called Co Co MO Joes* *(G-1871)*
Coda Global LLC 844 366-8250
550 Reserve St Ste 190 Southlake (76092) *(G-19060)*
Codekko Inc 214 919-0565
1820 Preston Park Blvd Plano (75093) *(G-16827)*
Codesource LP 940 891-1281
4115 Mesa Dr Denton (76207) *(G-5355)*
Cody Builders Supply Inc 512 339-9834
12002 N Lamar Blvd Austin (78753) *(G-1055)*
Cody Company Inc 210 651-5305
7951 E Evans Rd San Antonio (78266) *(G-18640)*
Cody Company LLC (HQ) **972 875-5884**
4200 N Interstate Hwy 45 Ennis (75119) *(G-6091)*
Coen Furniture Inc 281 983-0100
10506 Kinghurst Dr Houston (77099) *(G-9237)*
Cofco Americas Resources Corp 832 944-6359
16190 City Walk Ste 200 Sugar Land (77479) *(G-19461)*
Coffee Legends, Pflugerville *Also called Eieio Inc* *(G-16668)*
Coffee Traders Inc 512 476-2279
1400 E 4th St Austin (78702) *(G-1056)*
Coffeyville Resources LLC (HQ) **281 207-3200**
2277 Plaza Dr Ste 500 Sugar Land (77479) *(G-19462)*
Coffeyville Resources LLC 281 207-7711
2277 Plaza Dr Ste 500 Sugar Land (77479) *(G-19463)*
Coffeyville Resources Nitrogen, Sugar Land *Also called Coffeyville Resources LLC* *(G-19463)*
Coffeyville Resources Trml LLC 281 207-3200
2277 Plaza Dr Ste 500 Sugar Land (77479) *(G-19464)*
Coffeyvlle Rsrces Ref Mktg LLC (HQ) **281 207-3200**
2277 Plaza Dr Ste 500 Sugar Land (77479) *(G-19465)*
Cog Operating, Midland *Also called Devon Permian Corporation* *(G-15191)*
Cog Operating LLC (HQ) **432 685-0727**
600 W Illinois Ave Midland (79701) *(G-15169)*
Cogent Energy Services LLC 713 554-1200
919 Milam St Ste 2480 Houston (77002) *(G-9238)*
Cogent Midstream Westex LLC 469 290-4100
2305 Cedar Springs Rd # 100 Dallas (75201) *(G-4140)*
Cognite Inc 512 593-7120
1000 N Post Oak Rd Ste 22 Houston (77055) *(G-9239)*
Coherent Logix Incorporated 512 382-8961
1120 S Capital Of Texas H West Lake Hills (78746) *(G-20679)*
Cohn & Gregory Supply LLC 817 624-1141
2710 N Nichols St Fort Worth (76106) *(G-6529)*
Cohn Signs 210 626-2157
21713 Us Highway 281 S San Antonio (78264) *(G-18016)*
Cohort Energy Company, Addison *Also called J-W Operating Company* *(G-138)*
Cohort Energy Company 972 233-8191
15508 Wright Brothers Dr Addison (75001) *(G-110)*
Coi Graphics, Irving *Also called Smurfit Kappa North Amer LLC* *(G-13182)*
Coil Solutions Inc 361 444-0058
1465 S Flournoy Rd Alice (78332) *(G-206)*
Coil Tubing Partners LLC 432 201-4111
8411 W I 20 Frontage Rd Midland (79706) *(G-15170)*
Coil Tubing Services, Angleton *Also called Schlumberger Technology Corp* *(G-578)*
Coil Tubing Technology Inc (PA) **281 651-0200**
3002 Farrell Rd Houston (77073) *(G-9240)*
Coiling Technologies Inc (PA) **713 849-4000**
7777 Wright Rd Houston (77041) *(G-9241)*
Coker Enterprises 903 533-8894
7106 Us Highway 271 Tyler (75708) *(G-20069)*
Cokers Doors & Mouldings Inc 409 727-4600
4116 N Twin City Hwy Nederland (77627) *(G-15750)*
Cokinos Oil Company 713 974-0101
5718 Westheimer Rd # 900 Houston (77057) *(G-9242)*
Col Met Spray Booth, Rockwall *Also called Ekj Enterprises LP* *(G-17547)*
Col-Met, Garland *Also called Collier Metal Specialties Ltd* *(G-7461)*
Col-Met Gp LLC 972 494-3900
3333 Miller Park S Garland (75042) *(G-7459)*
Colaco Consultants Inc 281 370-2948
8523 Delachase Cir Spring (77379) *(G-19107)*

2021 Harris Texas
Manufacturers Directory

(G-0000) Company's Geographic Section entry number

Colair Inc (PA) 956 631-9889
  1221 E Interstate 2 A Mission (78572) *(G-15550)*

Cold Air Products Inc 817 531-2665
  1201 Forum Way S Fort Worth (76140) *(G-6530)*

Cold King Inc 210 227-0264
  309 S Salado St San Antonio (78207) *(G-18017)*

Cold Shot Chillers, Houston *Also called Marrone & Co Inc (G-10772)*

Coldstream Energy Holdings LLC 940 682-4772
  464 Cool Jct Millsap (76066) *(G-15501)*

Coldvault LLC (PA) 903 657-2377
  100 Millard Dr Henderson (75652) *(G-8261)*

Cole & Ashcroft LP 713 937-8657
  5631 Brystone Dr Houston (77041) *(G-9243)*

Cole Industries Inc 972 271-0280
  2644 National Pl Garland (75041) *(G-7460)*

Coleman Cable LLC 915 858-7475
  7811 Hoover Ave El Paso (79912) *(G-5699)*

Coleman Machine & Welding Svc 325 625-5186
  800 W 24th St Coleman (76834) *(G-3169)*

Coleman Wood Products Inc 940 440-2300
  5650 Us Highway 377 S Aubrey (76227) *(G-849)*

Colemn-Hnna Crwash Systems LLC 713 683-9878
  5842 W 34th St Houston (77092) *(G-9244)*

Colgan-Wilson Metals LLC 409 882-9296
  3165 Milam St Beaumont (77701) *(G-1873)*

Colgate Energy LLC 432 695-4222
  300 N Marienfeld St # 1000 Midland (79701) *(G-15171)*

Colgate Energy Partners LLC 432 695-4222
  300 N Marienfeld St # 1000 Midland (79701) *(G-15172)*

Colgate-Palmolive Company 903 832-8615
  303 Falvey Ave Texarkana (75501) *(G-19760)*

Colgin Companies, The, Dallas *Also called Richard E Colgin I Ltd (G-4897)*

Collado-Ryerson, Brownsville *Also called S A Fabtecmex C V (G-2403)*

Collections Fine Jewelry, Fort Worth *Also called Cfj Manufacturing LP (G-6506)*

Collections Fine Jewelry, Saginaw *Also called Cfj Manufacturing LP (G-17741)*

College Port Enterprises Inc (PA) 979 848-3070
  200 S Velasco St Angleton (77515) *(G-568)*

Collier Metal Specialties Ltd 972 494-3900
  3333 Miller Park S Garland (75042) *(G-7461)*

Colliers Top of Texas Inc 806 363-2867
  715 E New York St Hereford (79045) *(G-8287)*

Collin County Coml Record, Dallas *Also called Daily Commercial Record Inc (G-4206)*

Collingwood Grain Inc 254 582-5344
  221 Chestnut St Hillsboro (76645) *(G-8324)*

Collins Concrete, Dallas *Also called Treffinger Inc (G-5106)*

Collins Gold Label Inc 972 960-7346
  4115 Lindbergh Dr Addison (75001) *(G-111)*

Collins Instrument Company 979 849-8266
  1520 Gifford Ln Angleton (77515) *(G-569)*

Collins Roustabout & Well Svc 325 754-4237
  7726 State Highway 153 Winters (79567) *(G-20904)*

Collins Surveying and Mapping 903 234-8051
  910a Judson Rd Longview (75601) *(G-14210)*

Colo4 LLC 214 630-3100
  3004 Irving Blvd Dallas (75247) *(G-4141)*

Coloc Manufacturing, Canton *Also called Ingram Industries Inc (G-2657)*

Colonel Kababz, Garland *Also called Kaiser Foodline LLC (G-7529)*

Colonial Art Inc 713 697-8407
  5701 Cochran St Houston (77009) *(G-9245)*

Colonial Truss Co LLC 469 320-1000
  2825 Storey Ln Dallas (75220) *(G-4142)*

Colony Cabinets Inc 903 753-2488
  900 Estes Dr Longview (75602) *(G-14211)*

Color Contorl Network 972 754-1912
  1908 Royal Ln Dallas (75229) *(G-4143)*

Color Fast Industries Inc 817 546-4910
  912 W Highway 67 Alvarado (76009) *(G-327)*

Colorado Cnty Sand Grav L L C 979 543-3791
  Hwy 71 N One Mile El Campo (77437) *(G-5614)*

Colorado County Rice Mill Inc 979 234-5554
  1006 Mccormick Rd Eagle Lake (77434) *(G-5540)*

Colorado Materials, San Marcos *Also called Hunter Industries Ltd (G-18695)*

Colorado Materials Ltd (PA) 512 353-7757
  4501 Hunter Rd New Braunfels (78132) *(G-15784)*

Colorado Materials Ltd 512 396-1555
  5080 Fm 2439 New Braunfels (78132) *(G-15785)*

Colorado Stone Pdts Texas Inc 972 434-2515
  2025 Country Club Dr Carrollton (75006) *(G-2716)*

Colordynamics Inc 972 390-6500
  200 E Bethany Dr Allen (75002) *(G-259)*

Colorfast, Alvarado *Also called Color Fast Industries Inc (G-327)*

Colorite Plastics, Waco *Also called Plastic Specialties & Tech Inc (G-20447)*

Colormark Printing, Carrollton *Also called L C Colormark (G-2773)*

Colorstone Mfg 713 690-3100
  9707 Clay Rd Houston (77080) *(G-9246)*

Colt Services LP 361 299-2284
  4822 Leopard St Corpus Christi (78408) *(G-3504)*

Colt Services LP (PA) 281 471-9099
  626 N 16th St La Porte (77571) *(G-13729)*

Colt Services LP 409 842-6929
  6029 Industrial Rd Beaumont (77705) *(G-1874)*

Columbia Alum Processors Co JV 972 771-7150
  1450 E Washington St Rockwall (75087) *(G-17543)*

Columbia Coml Bldg Pdts Acqsti 800 668-1645
  1200 E Washington St Rockwall (75087) *(G-17544)*

Columbia Commercial Bldg Pdts, Rockwall *Also called Columbia Coml Bldg Pdts Acqsti (G-17544)*

Columbia Packing Co Inc (PA) 214 946-8171
  2807 E 11th St Dallas (75203) *(G-4144)*

Columbus Industries Inc 915 843-2274
  32 Spur Dr Ste A El Paso (79906) *(G-5700)*

Columbus Industry of Texas, El Paso *Also called Columbus Industries Inc (G-5700)*

Columbus McKinnon Corporation 210 924-3700
  2546 Boardwalk St San Antonio (78217) *(G-18018)*

Columbus McKinnon Corporation 281 443-6690
  1436 N Duck Creek Rd Cleveland (77328) *(G-3124)*

Columns Inc 281 485-3254
  1011 N Main St Pearland (77581) *(G-16547)*

Colvin Painovich LP 512 459-4139
  8905 Mccann Dr Austin (78757) *(G-1057)*

Colvin Timber Company LC 936 563-4404
  1714 Nettles Cemetery Rd Livingston (77351) *(G-14151)*

Com-Pac Systems Inc 432 332-4515
  2412 S Market St Odessa (79766) *(G-15964)*

Comac Fixtures Inc 806 376-4511
  205 S Philadelphia St Amarillo (79104) *(G-418)*

Comac Well Service Inc 806 274-2259
  1100 Industrial Blvd Borger (79007) *(G-2170)*

Comaco, San Antonio *Also called Cox Manufacturing Company (G-18028)*

Comal Concrete Products Inc 830 606-4732
  4222 Fm 482 New Braunfels (78132) *(G-15786)*

Comanche Moon Publishing LLC 325 572-3339
  3002 Fm 89 Buffalo Gap (79508) *(G-2550)*

Combined Rfrgn Resources Inc 281 540-7552
  1118 1st St E Humble (77338) *(G-12761)*

Comco Systems, Lake Dallas *Also called Communications Conveyor Co Inc (G-13810)*

Comeback Brewing Inc (HQ) 210 490-9128
  14800 San Pedro Ave San Antonio (78232) *(G-18019)*

Comeback Brewing II Inc (PA) 210 490-9128
  14800 San Pedro Ave Fl 3 San Antonio (78232) *(G-18020)*

Comet Cleaners, Mineral Wells *Also called Cliff Dunta Bros Inc (G-15523)*

Comet Cleaners and Laundry, Lubbock *Also called R J C Enterprises Inc (G-14469)*

Comet Signs LLC (PA) 210 341-7244
  5003 Stout Dr San Antonio (78219) *(G-18021)*

Comet Signs LLC 281 492-6581
  7630 Hansen Rd Houston (77061) *(G-9247)*

Comfy Choice LLC 972 302-8094
  5725 Hathaway Pkwy # 9409 Plano (75024) *(G-16828)*

Command Manufacturing LLC 512 927-0033
  8116 Ferguson Cut Off Austin (78724) *(G-1058)*

Command Packaging LLC 903 984-8596
  2500 N Longview St Kilgore (75662) *(G-13536)*

Command Tubular Products LLC 281 572-3900
  18911 W Industrial Pkwy New Caney (77357) *(G-15836)*

Commemorative Brands Inc 800 225-3687
  1550 W Mockingbird Ln Dallas (75235) *(G-4145)*

Commerce Grinding Co., Dallas *Also called Lodor Enterprises Inc (G-4600)*

Commerce Journal, Commerce *Also called Newspaper Holding Inc (G-3244)*

Commercial Armature Works 713 672-7873
  10029 Market St Houston (77029) *(G-9248)*

Commercial Bev Concepts LLC 713 554-4569
  2408 Karbach St Houston (77092) *(G-9249)*

Commercial Chemical, Houston *Also called Aquasol Controllers Inc (G-8673)*

Commercial Chemical Products, Houston *Also called Taf Incorporated (G-12147)*

Commercial Diesl Parts Svc Ltd 830 372-1594
  1900 E Us Highway 90 Seguin (78155) *(G-18830)*

Commercial Eqp Specialist, Friendswood *Also called Chester R Wright III (G-7243)*

Commercial Forms Inc 903 675-2511
  11293 State Highway 19 N Athens (75752) *(G-823)*

Commercial Indus Fcilities Div, El Paso *Also called Eaton Corporation (G-5732)*

Commercial Kitchens Inc 281 442-8001
  2320 Peyton Rd Houston (77032) *(G-9250)*

Commercial Machining, Dallas *Also called Kenney Industries Inc (G-4551)*

Commercial Metal Forming, Saginaw *Also called Parker-Hannifin Corporation (G-17754)*

Commercial Metals Company 713 226-0100
  2015 Quitman St Houston (77026) *(G-9251)*

Commercial Metals Company (PA) 214 689-4300
  6565 N Macarthur Blvd # 800 Irving (75039) *(G-12977)*

Commercial Metals Company 512 246-1424
  16709 Central Commerce Dr Round Rock (78664) *(G-17634)*

Commercial Metals Company 409 842-3316
  5250 College St Beaumont (77707) *(G-1875)*

Commercial Metals Company 214 565-0668
  2215 S Good Latimer Expy Dallas (75226) *(G-4146)*

Commercial Metals Company 979 265-4642
215 Mockingbird Ln Clute (77531) *(G-3150)*

Commercial Metals Company 817 429-4005
4500 Old Decatur Rd Fort Worth (76106) *(G-6531)*

Commercial Metals Company 361 884-4071
4614 Agnes St Corpus Christi (78405) *(G-3505)*

Commercial Metals Company 713 690-0347
2001 Brittmoore Rd Houston (77043) *(G-9252)*

Commercial Metals Company 972 838-9050
2202 Mckinney St Melissa (75454) *(G-14995)*

Commercial Metals Company 956 702-4434
Hwy 281 And East Owassa Pharr (78577) *(G-16696)*

Commercial Metals Company 469 729-0180
1839 W Commerce St Dallas (75208) *(G-4147)*

Commercial Metals Company 830 372-8200
100 Steel Mill Dr Seguin (78155) *(G-18831)*

Commercial Metals Company 972 938-9500
4100 N I 35 Waxahachie (75165) *(G-20538)*

Commercial Metals Company 512 282-8820
14501 S Ih 35 Buda (78610) *(G-2526)*

Commercial Mfg Co Inc 903 794-1321
1713 W 24th St Texarkana (75501) *(G-19761)*

Commercial Millwork, Grand Prairie Also called Cmcs Group LLC *(G-7854)*

Commercial Printing, Austin Also called Triaz Digital Printing LLC *(G-1592)*

Commiatos Mch & Repr Svc Inc 903 694-9378
1141 Ne Loop Carthage (75633) *(G-2904)*

Commissary Express Inc 903 357-5670
609 E Pecan St Sherman (75090) *(G-18912)*

Common Source LP 281 443-7575
14500 North Fwy Houston (77090) *(G-9253)*

Commonwealth Urology 281 372-1112
4720 Aldine Mail Rte Houston (77039) *(G-9254)*

Commscope, Richardson Also called Connectivity Solutions Mfg Inc *(G-17290)*

Commscope Inc North Carolina 214 583-6750
8635 N Stemmons Fwy Dallas (75247) *(G-4148)*

Commscope Technologies LLC 972 243-0965
2430 Lacy Ln Carrollton (75006) *(G-2717)*

Commscope Technologies LLC 214 267-5900
2601 Telecom Pkwy Richardson (75082) *(G-17289)*

Commscope Technologies LLC 817 864-4100
11312 S Pipeline Rd Euless (76040) *(G-6138)*

Commscope Technologies LLC 214 634-8502
8635 N Stemmons Fwy Dallas (75247) *(G-4149)*

Commscope Technologies LLC 956 205-6000
4101 E Military Hwy Ste A Mission (78572) *(G-15551)*

Communication Specialists, Buda Also called Capital Spectrum Inc *(G-2524)*

Communications Conveyor Co Inc 940 498-1850
306 W Overly Dr Lake Dallas (75065) *(G-13810)*

Communikay Graphics, Alvin Also called Beaed LP *(G-354)*

Communikay Graphics, Alvin Also called Beaed LP *(G-355)*

Community Chemical, Willis Also called Inkjet Inc *(G-20848)*

Community Impact Newspaper, Pflugerville Also called JG Media Inc *(G-16677)*

Community Motors Inc 281 354-8087
22159 Kent Dr New Caney (77357) *(G-15837)*

Community News, Weatherford Also called Community Ventures Inc *(G-20582)*

Community Newspapers Holdings 512 392-6143
1910 S Interstate 35 San Marcos (78666) *(G-18682)*

Community Ventures Inc 817 441-7661
5190 E I 20 Svc Rd S Weatherford (76087) *(G-20582)*

Company Printing 325 949-9941
3419 Knickerbocker Rd San Angelo (76904) *(G-17788)*

Compaq, Houston Also called Enterprise Svcs Ltin Amer Corp *(G-9664)*

Compass Alpha LLC 512 557-9138
1701 Dirs Blvd Ste 110 Austin (78744) *(G-1059)*

Compass Cementing Services, Fort Worth Also called Compass Well Services LLC *(G-6532)*

Compass Conversions LLC 254 771-9909
1822 Industrial Blvd Temple (76504) *(G-19677)*

Compass Drctional Guidance Inc 281 442-7484
14230 Interdrive E Houston (77032) *(G-9255)*

Compass Drctional Guidance Inc 281 442-7484
14427 Interdrive W Houston (77032) *(G-9256)*

Compass Electronics Group LLC 915 594-0500
45 Butterfield Cir Ste C El Paso (79906) *(G-5701)*

Compass Instruments LLC 832 698-2047
321 S Persimmon St Tomball (77375) *(G-19971)*

Compass Metering Solutions 972 834-5479
5217 County Road 2208 Greenville (75402) *(G-8067)*

Compass Orthopedic Tech & Pdts 713 995-7010
6776 Suthwest Fwy Ste 160 Houston (77074) *(G-9257)*

Compass Services Inc 713 937-9538
11620 Brittmoore Park Dr # 200 Houston (77041) *(G-9258)*

Compass Well Services LLC 325 387-2940
1930 Highway 277 S Sonora (76950) *(G-19025)*

Compass Well Services LLC (PA) **817 244-2555**
4100 Intl Plz Ste 500 Fort Worth (76109) *(G-6532)*

Compass Well Services LLC 432 561-5970
10013 W County Road 157 Midland (79706) *(G-15173)*

Competitive Energy - Texas LP 713 957-9948
1 Sugar Creek Center Blvd # 700 Sugar Land (77478) *(G-19466)*

Complementary Coatings Corp 210 651-6996
7451 Fm 3009 Schertz (78154) *(G-18748)*

Complete Curb Products, Houston Also called Ccpjv Inc *(G-9110)*

Complete Energy Services Inc 940 668-5186
3333 Ih 35 N Bldg F Gainesville (76240) *(G-7340)*

Complete Energy Services Inc 940 665-4373
201 W California St Gainesville (76240) *(G-7341)*

Complete Enrgy Svcs Well Svcs, Gainesville Also called Superior Energy Services Inc *(G-7370)*

Complete Intelligence Tech Inc 281 710-9131
8111 Ashlane Way Ste 211 The Woodlands (77382) *(G-19847)*

Complete Mfg Svcs Inc 281 252-3111
33525 Dobbin Huffsmith Rd Magnolia (77354) *(G-14597)*

Complete Pipe Services LLC 903 988-1124
5678 Fm 1249 E Kilgore (75662) *(G-13537)*

Complete Plastic Fabricators 713 674-7686
8533 Market St Houston (77029) *(G-9259)*

Complete Production Svcs Inc (HQ) **281 372-2300**
1001 Louisiana St Houston (77002) *(G-9260)*

Complete Reprographics Inc 915 779-5000
6122 Trowbridge Dr El Paso (79905) *(G-5702)*

Complete Restaurant Svcs Inc 214 350-1110
2668 Myrtle Springs Ave Dallas (75220) *(G-4150)*

Complete Solids Control LLC 817 372-2702
944 Hemlock Trl Fort Worth (76131) *(G-6533)*

Complete Sys Fabrication LLC 817 682-0729
4948 E Highway 199 Springtown (76082) *(G-19272)*

Complete Tchncal Rprsnttion In 972 621-1111
1705 John Connally Dr Carrollton (75006) *(G-2718)*

Complete Woodworks Inc 830 992-3163
895 Teague Ln Fredericksburg (78624) *(G-7174)*

Completion Services, Odessa Also called Superior Energy Services LLC *(G-16171)*

Completion Technologies Inc 936 760-2734
1925 Longmire Rd Ste 2 Conroe (77304) *(G-3279)*

Compliance Group Inc 936 447-6100
14884 Highway 105 W # 100 Montgomery (77356) *(G-15628)*

Compliant Paint Booths LLC 800 609-6408
6 Skyline Dr Terrell (75160) *(G-19731)*

Compliant Power Systems LLC 903 427-0071
1801 Industrial Way Clarksville (75426) *(G-3072)*

Component Manufacturing Corp 800 275-3011
3565 S Loop 336 E Conroe (77301) *(G-3280)*

Component Parts Machine Co Inc (PA) **817 834-4771**
3100 Chesser Boyer Rd Fort Worth (76111) *(G-6534)*

Component Parts Machine Co Inc 817 834-4771
4100 Hahn Blvd Fort Worth (76117) *(G-6535)*

Component Structures Inc (HQ) **940 566-1166**
2400 Worthington Dr Denton (76207) *(G-5356)*

Composite Access Products LP 956 765-2907
5216 N 26th St McAllen (78504) *(G-14850)*

Composite Cooling Solutions LP 817 246-8700
4150 Intl Plz Ste 500 Fort Worth (76109) *(G-6536)*

Composite Lining Systems LP 432 617-0242
7812 W Highway 80 Midland (79706) *(G-15174)*

Composite Panl Tchnlgy-Suth In 972 720-0477
4125 Billy Mitchell Dr # 100 Addison (75001) *(G-112)*

Composite Technology Inc (HQ) **972 456-6900**
1727 S Main St Dallas (75261) *(G-4151)*

Compositech Products Mfg Inc 281 648-3557
4531 S Main St Pearland (77581) *(G-16548)*

Composites One Llc 817 595-4991
905 Railhead Dr Fort Worth (76177) *(G-6537)*

Compostology LLC 318 787-7442
747 Fort Graham Rd Waco (76705) *(G-20389)*

Compound Security Specialists, Austin Also called Fusion Services Inc *(G-1173)*

Compression Coat, Pearland Also called Shawcor Pipe Protection LLC *(G-16598)*

Compressor Designs Inc 432 425-0044
12201 W County Road 128 Odessa (79765) *(G-15965)*

Compressor Elements Service 432 943-6701
2306 S Stockton Ave Monahans (79756) *(G-15602)*

Compressor Products Intl LLC 713 462-1061
14028 Aston St Houston (77040) *(G-9261)*

Compressors Unlimited Intl LLC 972 286-2264
2531 S Belt Line Rd Dallas (75253) *(G-4152)*

Comprobe Inc 817 293-7333
9632 Crowley Rd Fort Worth (76134) *(G-6538)*

Comprssion Contrls Rentals LLC 903 643-7970
5797 Fm 2011 Longview (75603) *(G-14212)*

Comprssion/Generation Svcs LLC (PA) **281 209-3616**
15502 Stone Gables Ln Houston (77044) *(G-9262)*

Compu-Data International LLC 281 292-1333
14610 Falling Creek Dr Houston (77068) *(G-9263)*

Compuink 281 705-0758
10007 Lynette Falls Dr Houston (77095) *(G-9264)*

Compulogic Design Co, Brownsville Also called R & I Enterprises Inc *(G-2396)*

Computer Comforts Inc 281 535-2288
367 Columbia Mem Pkwy Kemah (77565) *(G-13472)*

Computer Concepts P, Coppell *Also called Scott Studios Corporation* *(G-3445)*
Computer Labs Inc 915 775-1839
  3 Buttrfeld Trail Blvd St El Paso (79906) *(G-5703)*
Computer Rggdztion Integration, Kyle *Also called Rsi Inc* *(G-13686)*
Computer Service Technology 972 241-2662
  2336 Lufield Dr Dallas (75229) *(G-4153)*
Computer Software, Dallas *Also called Pixel and Texel LLC* *(G-4808)*
Computerized Cutters Inc 972 422-6900
  2900 Guilder Dr Plano (75074) *(G-16829)*
Computerized Millwork Svcs Inc 281 575-1699
  10855 Seaboard Loop Houston (77099) *(G-9265)*
Computerized Traffic Inc 281 252-0505
  2220 Fm 1486 Rd Montgomery (77316) *(G-15629)*
Compx International Inc (HQ) **972 448-1400**
  5430 Lyndon B Johnson Fwy Dallas (75240) *(G-4154)*
Comsovereign Holding Corp (PA) **469 930-2661**
  5000 Quorum Dr Ste 400 Dallas (75254) *(G-4155)*
Comstock Oil & Gas Llc (HQ) **972 668-8800**
  5300 Twn Cntry Blvd Frisco (75034) *(G-7273)*
Comstock Oil & Gas, LP, Frisco *Also called Comstock Oil & Gas Llc* *(G-7273)*
Comstock Resources Inc (PA) **972 668-8800**
  5300 Twn Cntry Blvd # 500 Frisco (75034) *(G-7274)*
Con Global, Galena Park *Also called Conglobal Industries LLC* *(G-7379)*
Con-Tex Builders Inc 281 847-3336
  820 Turney Dr Houston (77038) *(G-9266)*
Con-Tex Roofing, Houston *Also called Con-Tex Builders Inc* *(G-9266)*
Con-Trac Packaging, Irving *Also called Premark Health Science Inc* *(G-13155)*
Conagra Brands Inc 817 210-1600
  4701 Gold Spike Dr Fort Worth (76106) *(G-6539)*
Concept Cellular International, Boerne *Also called Cellteks Inc* *(G-2116)*
Concept Controls Inc 281 476-4400
  1318 Underwood Rd Ste 110 La Porte (77571) *(G-13730)*
Concept Laser Inc 817 328-6500
  1000 Texan Trl Ste 150 Grapevine (76051) *(G-8023)*
Concepts In Cabinetry, Saint Hedwig *Also called Zamo Inc* *(G-17761)*
Concho Bike Shop, San Angelo *Also called Wheel-A-Rama Inc* *(G-17840)*
Concho Business Solutions Inc 325 653-1697
  3302 Foster St San Angelo (76903) *(G-17789)*
Concho Concrete Company Inc 325 653-3354
  1040 Foster St San Angelo (76903) *(G-17790)*
Concho Oil & Gas LLC 432 683-7443
  600 W III Ave Midland Midland (79701) *(G-15175)*
Concho Oilfield Services LLC 325 762-3300
  9555 S Us Highway 283 Albany (76430) *(G-186)*
Concho Resources Inc 713 739-7561
  1001 Fannin St Houston (77002) *(G-9267)*
Concho Resources Inc 432 221-0400
  550 W Texas Ave Ste 945 Midland (79701) *(G-15176)*
Concho Resources Inc (PA) **432 683-7443**
  600 W Illinois Ave Midland (79701) *(G-15177)*
Concho Services LLC 325 869-5242
  814 W Broadway St Eden (76837) *(G-5571)*
Concierge Renovation Company 940 458-3075
  1850 N Stemmons St Sanger (76266) *(G-18724)*
Conclusive Strategies, Austin *Also called Marketmap Inc* *(G-1327)*
Concord Mechanical Inc 817 319-5575
  1715 County Road 4757 Boyd (76023) *(G-2204)*
Concord Oil Co 210 224-4455
  100 W Houston St Ste 1500 San Antonio (78205) *(G-18022)*
Concote Corporation (PA) **214 956-0077**
  600 Freeport Pkwy Ste 150 Coppell (75019) *(G-3412)*
Concote Corporation 903 581-0697
  2340 E Erwin St Tyler (75702) *(G-20070)*
Concrete ASAP LLC 713 222-6216
  2918 Elysian St Houston (77009) *(G-9268)*
Concrete Mobility LLC 325 728-5858
  373 Concrete Mobility Way Colorado City (79512) *(G-3223)*
Concrete Producers Solutions 281 398-6244
  11807 Sea Shadow Bnd Pearland (77584) *(G-16549)*
Concretex, Florence *Also called Tebo Concre Fence LLC* *(G-6244)*
Concur Technologies Inc 972 612-7121
  700 Central Expy S # 230 Allen (75013) *(G-260)*
Concurrent Mfg Solutions LLC 512 310-9139
  800 Paloma Dr Ste 240 Round Rock (78665) *(G-17635)*
Condusiv Technologies Corp (PA) **818 252-5538**
  3600 Kellywood Dr Austin (78739) *(G-1060)*
Cone Bioproducts Seguin LLC (PA) **830 379-0197**
  1012 N Austin St Seguin (78155) *(G-18832)*
Conecraft Incorporated 817 922-9200
  3209 S Grove St Fort Worth (76110) *(G-6540)*
Conetic Software Systems Inc 210 222-9621
  10860 Gulfdale St San Antonio (78216) *(G-18023)*
Confab Oilfield Contractors 817 992-6563
  4014 Windmill Rd Burleson (76097) *(G-2576)*
Confederate Steel Corporation 713 643-8526
  4507 Cypress Pond Ct Houston (77059) *(G-9269)*
Conference Technologies Inc 512 584-8275
  11525 Stonehollow Dr Austin (78758) *(G-1061)*

Conglobal Industries LLC 713 675-7587
  500 Mayo Shell Rd Galena Park (77547) *(G-7379)*
Conine Manufacturing Company 903 894-6150
  10891 Fm 346 W Flint (75762) *(G-6236)*
Conley Printing Co Inc 325 675-5500
  2401 Industrial Blvd Abilene (79605) *(G-35)*
Conloop Inc (PA) **940 322-2206**
  1411 Twin Oaks St Wichita Falls (76302) *(G-20756)*
Connectione LLC 512 310-1000
  2550 N Mays St Ste B Round Rock (78665) *(G-17636)*
Connectivity Solutions Mfg Inc 972 792-3000
  2601 Telecom Pkwy Richardson (75082) *(G-17290)*
Conner Distributors, Alamo *Also called Conner Industries Inc* *(G-178)*
Conner Industries, Borger *Also called Conner Machine and Welding Inc* *(G-2171)*
Conner Industries Inc 817 439-3555
  1951 Keller Hicks Rd Fort Worth (76177) *(G-6541)*
Conner Industries Inc 713 944-6766
  5707 Mitchelldale St Houston (77092) *(G-9270)*
Conner Industries Inc 956 781-0215
  700 N Tower Rd Alamo (78516) *(G-178)*
Conner Machine and Welding Inc 806 274-2281
  118 Bunton St Borger (79007) *(G-2171)*
Conner Steel Products Inc 325 655-8225
  9224 Beechnut St Houston (77036) *(G-9271)*
Connexa Energy LLC 830 995-3600
  147 Us Highway 87 Comfort (78013) *(G-3238)*
Connor Media Group LLC 817 336-8300
  101 Summit Ave Ste 803 Fort Worth (76102) *(G-6542)*
Connor Sports Flooring LLC 817 944-0269
  1160 Highland Oaks Dr Southlake (76092) *(G-19061)*
Conoco Natural Gas & Gas Lqds, Mertzon *Also called Conocophillips Company* *(G-15020)*
Conocophillips (PA) **281 293-1000**
  925 N Eldridge Pkwy Houston (77079) *(G-9272)*
Conocophillips Company (HQ) **281 293-1000**
  925 N Eldridge Pkwy Houston (77079) *(G-9273)*
Conocophillips Company 325 835-4451
  7 Miles S W Of Mertzon Mertzon (76941) *(G-15020)*
Conocophillips Holding Company (HQ) **281 293-1000**
  600 N Dairy Ashford Rd Houston (77079) *(G-9274)*
Conrad Orange Shipyard Inc 409 670-4900
  710 Market St Orange (77630) *(G-16236)*
Conreco Inc 361 851-0352
  414 Saratoga Blvd Corpus Christi (78417) *(G-3506)*
Conroe Concrete Ltd 936 539-1761
  1701 Royal College Hl Rd Conroe (77304) *(G-3281)*
Conroe Machine LLC 936 494-2566
  701 Conroe Park North Dr Conroe (77303) *(G-3282)*
Conroe Plastics Molding Inc 936 539-2005
  1700 Orval Rd Conroe (77301) *(G-3283)*
Consci Ltd 713 920-1696
  1416 Southmore Ave Pasadena (77502) *(G-16412)*
Conservatek Industries Inc 713 290-9944
  498 N Loop 336 E Conroe (77301) *(G-3284)*
Consistent Reasoning Inc 512 382-8940
  1120 S Cptl Of Tx 3 200 West Lake Hills (78746) *(G-20680)*
Conslidated Rigworks LP 817 446-5272
  6000 E Berry St Fort Worth (76119) *(G-6543)*
Consolidated Armor Pdts LLC (PA) **214 382-4100**
  15504 Wright Brothers Dr Addison (75001) *(G-113)*
Consolidated Casting LLC 972 225-7305
  1501 S I 45 Svc Rd Hutchins (75141) *(G-12865)*
Consolidated Containment LLC 409 781-4254
  5450 Avenue A Beaumont (77705) *(G-1876)*
Consolidated Cotton Gin Co 806 745-1191
  8606 Highway 87 Lubbock (79423) *(G-14396)*
Consolidated Crate, Bullard *Also called Consolidated Wood Products Inc* *(G-2551)*
Consolidated Fabricators Inc 214 376-4389
  5480 La Sierra Dr Dallas (75231) *(G-4156)*
Consolidated Graphics Inc (HQ) **713 787-0977**
  5858 Westheimer Rd # 200 Houston (77057) *(G-9275)*
Consolidated Metal Tech Inc 512 255-9296
  800 N Georgetown St Round Rock (78664) *(G-17637)*
Consolidated Mills Inc 713 896-4196
  7190 Brittmoore Rd # 150 Houston (77041) *(G-9276)*
Consolidated Pressure Ctrl LLC 281 893-5900
  27264 Oakridge Park Dr Conroe (77385) *(G-3285)*
Consolidated Rig Works LP 817 446-5272
  6000 E Berry St Fort Worth (76119) *(G-6544)*
Consolidated Sciences, Pasadena *Also called Consci Ltd* *(G-16412)*
Consolidated Wellsite Svcs LLC 903 983-9811
  104 Metrotex Dr Haslet (76052) *(G-8218)*
Consolidated Wood Products Inc 903 894-7745
  1940 County Road 3703 Bullard (75757) *(G-2551)*
Constance & Company, Houston *Also called Teebaud Co LLC* *(G-12182)*
Constellation Lighting Ltd 832 717-5750
  21175 State Highway 249 Houston (77070) *(G-9277)*
Constntin Precision Instrs Inc 713 461-9090
  7633 Cherokee St Katy (77494) *(G-13358)*
Construct Capital LLC (PA) **214 637-1444**
  2821 E Randol Mill Rd Arlington (76011) *(G-645)*

A
L
P
H
A
B
E
T
I
C

Construct Capital LLC 713 322-6714
10912 Metronome Dr Houston (77043) **(G-9278)**

Construct Capital LLC 210 654-4400
12050 Crwnpint Dr Ste 160 San Antonio (78233) **(G-18024)**

Construction Contractors, Austin Also called Gobbato Builders LLC **(G-1185)**

Construction Eqp Mfg Co Inc 940 257-6215
782 Highway 251 S Olney (76374) **(G-16220)**

Construction Specialties Inc 830 774-0151
107 Industrial Blvd Del Rio (78840) **(G-5314)**

Consultingpoint Inc 956 986-2727
301 Mexico Blvd Ste 700 Brownsville (78520) **(G-2347)**

Consumer Energy Alliance 713 337-8800
2211 Norfolk St Ste 610 Houston (77098) **(G-9279)**

Consumer Guide Inc 713 417-6152
9894 Bissonnet St Ste 900 Houston (77036) **(G-9280)**

Contain Water Systems Inc 512 770-9080
252 Frog Pond Ln Unit C Dripping Springs (78620) **(G-5502)**

Containment Solutions Inc (HQ) **936 756-7731**
500 Conroe Park West Dr Conroe (77303) **(G-3286)**

Contanda LLC (PA) **832 699-4001**
1111 Bagby St Ste 1800 Houston (77002) **(G-9281)**

Contango Oil & Gas Company (PA) **713 236-7400**
717 Texas St Ste 2900 Houston (77002) **(G-9282)**

Contech Engnered Solutions LLC 940 888-3871
1100 N Main St Seymour (76380) **(G-18889)**

Contech Engnered Solutions LLC 979 743-4123
232 Oakland Rd Schulenburg (78956) **(G-18774)**

Contech Engnered Solutions LLC 903 885-0673
1009 Como St S Sulphur Springs (75482) **(G-19584)**

Contel Federal Systems Inc 972 718-5600
600 Hidden Rdg Irving (75038) **(G-12978)**

Contemporary Design Plastics 817 640-7539
412 113th St Arlington (76011) **(G-646)**

Context Home and Garden, Stafford Also called SAM&m Group LLC **(G-19373)**

Conti Systems, Flower Mound Also called Alecom Technologies Group Inc **(G-6259)**

Continental American Corp 214 630-3121
4025 Singleton Blvd Dallas (75212) **(G-4157)**

Continental Auto Systems Inc 830 372-7000
3740 N Austin St Seguin (78155) **(G-18833)**

Continental Auto Systems Inc 847 862-0366
11302c Eastpoint Dr Laredo (78045) **(G-13875)**

Continental Battery Company (PA) **214 631-5701**
4919 Woodall St Dallas (75247) **(G-4158)**

Continental Capstone, Lueders Also called Continental Quarries **(G-14517)**

Continental Carbon Company (HQ) **281 647-3700**
16850 Park Row Houston (77084) **(G-9283)**

Continental Carbon Company 281 647-3728
10655 Richmond Ave # 100 Houston (77042) **(G-9284)**

Continental Carbon Company 806 935-4174
11702 Carbon Black Rd Sunray (79086) **(G-19616)**

Continental Cut Stone Inc 254 793-2329
460 County Road 219 Florence (76527) **(G-6238)**

Continental Electronics Corp (HQ) **214 381-7161**
4212 S Buckner Blvd Dallas (75227) **(G-4159)**

Continental Guadalajara, Laredo Also called Continental Auto Systems Inc **(G-13875)**

Continental Laboratories Inc 713 460-0780
6600 Frbanks N Houston Rd Houston (77040) **(G-9285)**

Continental Land & Fur Co Inc 281 873-9378
16945 Northchase Dr # 1500 Houston (77060) **(G-9286)**

Continental Manufacturing, Dallas Also called Continental Nh3 Pdts Co Inc **(G-4160)**

Continental Nh3 Pdts Co Inc 214 741-6083
130 Yorktown St Dallas (75208) **(G-4160)**

Continental Operating Co 713 209-1110
9805 Katy Fwy Ste 500 Houston (77024) **(G-9287)**

Continental Poly Inc 281 277-6550
767 Industrial Blvd Sugar Land (77478) **(G-19467)**

Continental Poly Bags, Sugar Land Also called Continental Poly Inc **(G-19467)**

Continental Prod Svcs Inc 281 431-0502
5124 Polk St Houston (77023) **(G-9288)**

Continental Quarries 325 228-4180
2699 Fm 142 Lueders (79533) **(G-14517)**

Continental Stone LLC (PA) **713 462-5700**
8758 Clay Rd Ste 400 Houston (77080) **(G-9289)**

Continental Turbine Services 281 541-6060
430 E Helms Rd Ste D2 Houston (77037) **(G-9290)**

Continntal Con Mxer Sltons LLC 859 234-1100
105 Riley Rd Austin (78746) **(G-1062)**

Continntal Silverline Pdts LLC 713 222-7394
710 N Drennan St Houston (77003) **(G-9291)**

Contract Fabricating Svcs LLC 281 501-8664
801 E Whitney St Houston (77022) **(G-9292)**

Contract Fabrication 972 736-2260
5427 Fm 546 Princeton (75407) **(G-17206)**

Contract Manufacturers Inc 903 597-8297
729 N Fleishel Ave Tyler (75702) **(G-20071)**

Contract Powder Coating Inc 972 494-4444
549 N 5th St Garland (75040) **(G-7462)**

Contractors Metal Works Inc 713 856-6600
8707 Frbanks N Houston Rd Houston (77064) **(G-9293)**

Contractors Service Ltd (PA) 325 692-4317
967 S 25th St Abilene (79602) **(G-36)**

Contractors Supplies Inc (PA) **936 634-3341**
304 Webber St Lufkin (75904) **(G-14523)**

Contractors Supplies Inc 903 753-5766
417 Calvin Blvd Longview (75602) **(G-14213)**

Contractors Supplies Inc 903 597-1308
1601 John Carney Dr Tyler (75701) **(G-20072)**

Contractors Supplies Inc 903 670-1085
1400 N Palestine St Athens (75751) **(G-824)**

Contran Corporation (PA) **972 233-1700**
5430 Lyndon B Johnson Fwy Dallas (75240) **(G-4161)**

Contrinex Inc 574 340-7089
480 Wrangler Dr Ste 100 Coppell (75019) **(G-3413)**

Control Alternative Solutions 512 858-9603
1001 Barton Creek Dr Dripping Springs (78620) **(G-5503)**

Control Components Inc 832 467-7200
4525 Kennedy Commerce Dr Houston (77032) **(G-9294)**

Control Concepts and Tech, Jersey Village Also called W-Industries of Louisiana **(G-13306)**

Control Flow Inc (PA) **281 890-8300**
9201 Frbanks N Houston Rd Houston (77064) **(G-9295)**

Control Panels USA Inc 512 852-8280
16310 Bratton Ln Ste 100 Austin (78728) **(G-1063)**

Control Products Corporation (PA) **972 264-0368**
1513 W Jefferson St Grand Prairie (75051) **(G-7858)**

Control Solutions Inc (HQ) **281 892-2500**
5903 Genoa Red Bluff Rd Pasadena (77507) **(G-16413)**

Controlled Systems Sales Co 972 234-6767
1758 Firman Dr 200 Richardson (75081) **(G-17291)**

Controlr Software Inc 214 909-8676
3309 Elm St Ste 3w1 Dallas (75226) **(G-4162)**

Convergent Performance LLC 713 398-8496
13719 Chelwood Pl Houston (77069) **(G-9296)**

Convergentz Bldg Systems LLC 713 266-3900
10555 Westpark Dr Houston (77042) **(G-9297)**

Convergepoint Inc 347 948-4258
1011 Highway 6 S Ste 105 Houston (77077) **(G-9298)**

Convermex USA Corp 210 319-2972
4400 Tejasco Ste 120 San Antonio (78218) **(G-18025)**

Conversation Pieces Inc 409 762-2799
1428 Ball St Galveston (77550) **(G-7394)**

Converting Division, Dallas Also called Pratt Industries Inc **(G-4816)**

Converting Division, Schertz Also called Pratt Industries Inc **(G-18759)**

Convey Computer Corporation 214 576-9630
5542 Merrimac Ave Dallas (75206) **(G-4163)**

Conveying Pwr Transm Solutions, Itasca Also called JCB Inc **(G-13215)**

Conveying Techniques, Houston Also called Lee Contracting Inc **(G-10616)**

Conveyor Aggregate Pdts Corp 713 856-5600
5131 Steadmont Dr Houston (77040) **(G-9299)**

Conveyor Aggregate Pdts Corp (HQ) **214 358-5588**
10500 N Stemmons Fwy Dallas (75220) **(G-4164)**

Conveyor Division, Mansfield Also called Martin Sprocket & Gear Inc **(G-14689)**

Convio Inc (HQ) **512 652-2600**
11501 Domain Dr Ste 200 Austin (78758) **(G-1064)**

Convoy Servicing Co 214 638-3050
101 Decker Ct Ste 100 Irving (75062) **(G-12979)**

Cook & Boardman Group LLC 214 630-3965
11240 Gemini Ln Dallas (75229) **(G-4165)**

Cook Cmprssn-Parland Operation 713 433-2002
11951 Spectrum Blvd Houston (77047) **(G-9300)**

Cook Composites, Marshall Also called Polynt Composites USA Inc **(G-14798)**

Cook Compression 432 367-7786
2605 W 42nd St Odessa (79764) **(G-15966)**

Cook Compression (HQ) **713 433-2002**
11951 Spectrum Blvd Houston (77047) **(G-9301)**

Cook Portable Warehouse, Bastrop Also called Cook Sales Inc **(G-1751)**

Cook Sales Inc 512 321-2888
1398 State Highway 95 Bastrop (78602) **(G-1751)**

Cooke County Crushed Stone 940 759-4104
8416 W Highway 82 Muenster (76252) **(G-15668)**

Cookies-N-Milk Inc 214 491-6370
181 Industrial Blvd McKinney (75069) **(G-14932)**

Cooksey Luther Printing Co 817 332-2842
1920 Wenneca Ave Fort Worth (76102) **(G-6545)**

Cool Attic, Mineral Wells Also called Ventamatic Ltd **(G-15545)**

Cool City Inc 940 682-1122
10655 Mineral Wells Hwy Weatherford (76088) **(G-20583)**

Cool City Motor Company, Weatherford Also called Cool City Inc **(G-20583)**

Cool Cruisers of Texas 972 772-5517
512 Willow Springs Dr Rockwall (75032) **(G-17545)**

Cool-A-Zone, Houston Also called Air Flow Products LP **(G-8508)**

Coole School Inc 713 552-1600
1213 West Loop N Ste 100 Houston (77055) **(G-9302)**

Cooper B-Line Inc 713 678-4460
7106 Cavalcade St Houston (77028) **(G-9303)**

Cooper B-Line Inc 903 813-1746
4901 Marshall St Sherman (75090) **(G-18913)**

Cooper Compression, Odessa Also called Cameron International Corp **(G-15953)**

Cooper Concrete Co 972 276-1167
1100 N 5th St Garland (75040) (G-7463)

Cooper Consulting Company 512 527-1000
1705 Crossing Pl Apt 101a Austin (78741) (G-1065)

Cooper Crouse Hinds LLC 713 280-3400
3413 N Sam Houston Pkwy W # 212 Houston (77086) (G-9304)

Cooper Crouse Hinds Pauluhn, Houston Also called Cooper Crouse-Hinds LLC (G-9305)

Cooper Crouse-Hinds LLC 806 358-4585
1901 W Farmers Ave Amarillo (79118) (G-484)

Cooper Crouse-Hinds LLC 832 390-3858
3530 S Sam Houston Pkwy E Houston (77047) (G-9305)

Cooper Crouse-Hinds Mtl Inc 281 571-8065
3413 N Sam Houston Pkwy W # 212 Houston (77086) (G-9306)

Cooper Energy Services Div, Waller Also called Cameron International Corp (G-20495)

Cooper Lighting LLC 972 929-9400
9500 N Royal Ln Ste 140 Irving (75063) (G-12980)

Cooper Lighting LLC 770 486-4800
600 Travis St Ste 5600 Houston (77002) (G-9307)

Cooper Oil Company Inc 817 332-7755
777 Main St Ste 800 Fort Worth (76102) (G-6546)

Cooper Operating, Fort Worth Also called Cooper Oil Company Inc (G-6546)

Cooper Optical Co Inc (PA) 903 753-7606
306 W Whaley St Longview (75601) (G-14214)

Cooper Power Systems LLC 936 569-9422
2315 Se Stallings Dr Nacogdoches (75961) (G-15692)

Cooper Sheet Metal Inc 817 232-4250
10056 Hicks Field Rd Fort Worth (76179) (G-6547)

Cooper Supply Inc 817 222-9055
2524 Minnis Dr Fort Worth (76117) (G-6548)

Cooper Valves LLC (HQ) 832 409-6050
818 E Sam Houston Pkwy S Pasadena (77503) (G-16414)

Cooper-Standard Automotive Inc 956 717-3835
1001 Carriers Dr Laredo (78045) (G-13876)

Cooperative Industries, Fort Worth Also called Page Chester Ltd (G-6890)

Coordnated Designs Contrls Inc 713 921-0220
601 Mcfarland St Ste 1 Houston (77011) (G-9308)

Coorstek Inc 432 381-0052
3565 W 16th St Odessa (79763) (G-15967)

Coorstek Odessa, Odessa Also called Coorstek Inc (G-15967)

Copan Corporation 806 665-1267
101 Doyle St Pampa (79065) (G-16319)

Copano Company (PA) 361 578-6271
1 Oconnor Plz Ste 1100 Victoria (77901) (G-20254)

Copano Company 361 526-2115
431 T C Oil Rd Refugio (78377) (G-17239)

Copano Field Svcs Agua Dulce, Alice Also called Copano/Operations Inc (G-207)

Copano/Operations Inc 361 668-8580
3943 N Hwy281 Alice (78332) (G-207)

Coperion Corporation 281 449-9944
5825 N Sam Houston Pkwy W # 250 Houston (77086) (G-9309)

Coppell Woodworks Inc (PA) 940 482-8900
633 W Belt Line Rd Richardson (75080) (G-17292)

Copper Craft Inc 817 490-9622
300 Railhead Rd Fort Worth (76106) (G-6549)

Copperbeck Energy Partners LLC (PA) 214 238-4881
750 N Saint Paul St # 1320 Dallas (75201) (G-4166)

Copperlogic Inc (HQ) 713 933-0999
4140 World Houston Pkwy Houston (77032) (G-9310)

Copy Center LLC 210 481-9305
20330 Huebner Rd Ste 104 San Antonio (78258) (G-18026)

Copy Corner, College Station Also called H & B Copies Inc (G-3185)

Copy Plus LLC 956 668-7587
4500 N 10th St Ste 240 McAllen (78504) (G-14851)

Copy Stop Print and Postal 979 774-4111
2290 Boonville Rd Ste 800 Bryan (77808) (G-2466)

Cor Thermotics LLC 832 308-5151
15995 N Barkers Lndg Houston (77079) (G-9311)

Cor-Pro Systems Inc 713 896-1091
10555 W Little York Rd Houston (77041) (G-9312)

Cor-Tex Steel 903 872-3991
3701 S Business 45 Corsicana (75109) (G-3662)

Corchem Manufacturing Inc 432 332-1335
1227 S Murphy St Odessa (79766) (G-15968)

Cord Communications Inc 254 776-1822
4901 Bosque Blvd Fl 2 Waco (76710) (G-20390)

Cord Keeper LLC 361 992-1122
5801 S Staples St Ste D Corpus Christi (78413) (G-3507)

Cordova Corporation 817 484-1100
4290 E Fm 1187 Burleson (76028) (G-2577)

Cordyne Inc (PA) 713 460-5151
9820 Drysdale Ln Houston (77041) (G-9313)

Cordyne Electrical Mfg & Dist, Houston Also called Cordyne Inc (G-9313)

Core International LLC (HQ) 281 880-0200
10540 Bissonnet St # 100 Houston (77099) (G-9314)

Core Lab, Houston Also called Protechnics (G-11462)

Core Laboratories (texas) LLC 713 328-2673
6316 Windfern Rd Houston (77040) (G-9315)

Core Laboratories Holding Inc 713 328-2673
6316 Windfern Rd Houston (77040) (G-9316)

Core Laboratories LP 432 687-5797
705 W Wadley Ave Ste 250 Midland (79705) (G-15178)

Core Laboratories LP 903 984-4223
2505 State Hwy Kilgore (75662) (G-13538)

Core Laboratories LP (HQ) 713 328-2673
6316 Windfern Rd Houston (77040) (G-9317)

Core Pacific Inc. 800 860-1637
4000 Leeland St Houston (77023) (G-9318)

Core Rubber Resources, Houston Also called Core International LLC (G-9314)

Corelite Inc 214 905-4359
5101 Norwood Rd Dallas (75247) (G-4167)

Coreslab Structures Texas Inc (HQ) 512 250-0755
15916 Anderson Mill Rd Cedar Park (78613) (G-2964)

Coretech Industries Inc 440 949-9592
8300 S Central Expy Dallas (75241) (G-4168)

Coretrac Inc 512 236-9120
6101 W Courtyard Dr 2-100 Austin (78730) (G-1066)

Corev America Inc (PA) 713 849-3671
11620 Brittmoore Park Dr Houston (77041) (G-9319)

Coria Pharmaceuticals, Fort Worth Also called Healthpoint Ltd (G-6692)

Cornerstone Apparel Inc 903 939-0188
4601 S Broadway Ave C08 Tyler (75703) (G-20073)

Cornerstone Atomtn Systems LLC 972 346-2242
10601 Clarence Dr Ste 100 Frisco (75033) (G-7275)

Cornerstone Bldg Brands Inc 281 897-7788
10943 Sam Houston Pkwy W Houston (77064) (G-9320)

Cornerstone Bldg Brands Inc 281 897-7726
10943 N Sam Huston Pkwy W Houston (77064) (G-9321)

Cornerstone Bldg Brands Inc 713 466-0712
7301 Fairview St Houston (77041) (G-9322)

Cornerstone Commercial Svcs, Dallas Also called Willbnks Fncl Cnsltng Group L (G-3860)

Cornerstone Energy Services, Panhandle Also called Cornerstone Synergy LLC (G-16347)

Cornerstone Infield Services, Channelview Also called Rus Industrial LLC (G-3033)

Cornerstone Synergy LLC 806 679-9178
1150 Us Hwy 60 Panhandle Panhandle (79068) (G-16347)

Cornerstone Valve, Missouri City Also called NSM Inc (G-15586)

Corning, Hidalgo Also called Eaton Corporation (G-8306)

Corning Optical Communications 817 431-7120
5940 Optical Way Fort Worth (76244) (G-6550)

Corona Designs Inc 972 272-0471
828 E Walnut St Garland (75040) (G-7464)

Corona Labs Inc 312 953-7586
720 Brazos St Ste 1100 Austin (78701) (G-1067)

Coronado Midstream LLC (HQ) 432 684-3870
300 N Mrnfield St Ste 120 Midland (79701) (G-15179)

Coronado Paint Products, Schertz Also called Complementary Coatings Corp (G-18748)

Coronado Resources GP LLC 214 651-6245
3811 Trtl Crk Blvd Dallas (75219) (G-4169)

Coronet Enterprises Inc 214 630-1116
3220 Quebec St Dallas (75247) (G-4170)

Corporate Bus Solutions Inc 817 701-1390
401 Exchange Dr Arlington (76011) (G-647)

Corporate Records Management 214 333-3453
3141 Hansboro Ave Dallas (75233) (G-4171)

Corporate Texas Co LLC 940 549-1400
901 4th St Graham (76450) (G-7778)

Corporate Vsual Cmmnctions Inc 214 206-3763
9011 John W Carpenter Fwy Dallas (75247) (G-4172)

Corpro Inc 432 563 0775
2003 Commerce Dr Midland (79703) (G-15180)

Corpus Christi Caller Times, Corpus Christi Also called Caller-Times Publishing Co (G-3493)

Corpus Christi Caller Times, Corpus Christi Also called EW Scripps Company (G-3522)

Corpus Christi CD Electric LP (PA) 361 888-4133
617 High Starr Dr Corpus Christi (78408) (G-3508)

Corpus Christi Facility, Houston Also called M & G Chemicals (G-10711)

Corpus Christi Pipeline GP LLC 713 375-5000
554 Hwy 35 Gregory (78359) (G-8100)

Corpus Christi Readymix, Corpus Christi Also called Highway Barricades & Svcs LLC (G-3548)

Corpus Christi Stamp Works Inc 361 884-4801
502 S Staples St Corpus Christi (78401) (G-3509)

Corpus Chrsti Gsket Fstner Inc 361 884-6366
341 Westchester Dr Corpus Christi (78408) (G-3510)

Corr-Wood Mfg Inc 817 467-5525
1912 Peyco Dr S Arlington (76001) (G-648)

Corradi USA Inc 972 466-0721
1433 W Frankford Rd # 100 Carrollton (75007) (G-2860)

Corrections Products Co Ltd 210 829-7951
5802 Rocky Pt San Antonio (78249) (G-18027)

Correlog Inc 239 514-3331
2103 Citywest Blvd # 2100 Houston (77042) (G-9323)

Corrigan Osb LLC (HQ) 318 448-0405
1923 Us Highway 287 W Corrigan (75939) (G-3659)

Corrosion Ltd 432 561-8504
4321 S County Road 1290 Odessa (79765) (G-15969)

Corrosion Products Services, Deer Park Also called Keith Darwin Raines (G-5281)

Corrosion Prtction Prcsses of 713 869-9454
340 W 26th St Houston (77008) (G-9324)

Corrotec, Dallas *Also called Hvac Corrosion Tech LLC* *(G-4476)*

Corrpro Companies Inc 713 460-6000
7000 Hollister St Bldg B Houston (77040) *(G-9325)*

Corrugated Concepts Packg Inc 713 462-5600
5050 Campbell Rd Ste C Houston (77041) *(G-9326)*

Corrugated Container Div, Fort Worth *Also called Westrock Cp LLC* *(G-7144)*

Corrugated Services Garland 972 494-4059
726 E Walnut St Garland (75040) *(G-7465)*

Corsicana Air Conditioning, Corsicana *Also called Corsicana Sheet Metal Co Inc* *(G-3666)*

Corsicana Bedding LLC 903 872-2591
2700 E Hwy 31 Corsicana (75109) *(G-3663)*

Corsicana Bedding LLC (PA) 800 323-4349
1420 W Mockingbird Ln Dallas (75247) *(G-4173)*

Corsicana Bedding LLC 903 257-3360
2700 E State Highway 31 Corsicana (75109) *(G-3664)*

Corsicana Box Company Inc 903 874-5615
1000 Ferguson St Corsicana (75110) *(G-3665)*

Corsicana Dr Pepper Btlg Co, Corsicana *Also called American Bottling Company* *(G-3660)*

Corsicana Mattress Company, Dallas *Also called Corsicana Bedding LLC* *(G-4173)*

Corsicana Mattress Company, Corsicana *Also called Corsicana Bedding LLC* *(G-3664)*

Corsicana Sheet Metal Co Inc 903 872-8434
625 W 2nd Ave Corsicana (75110) *(G-3666)*

Cortez Resources LLC 214 628-9155
3131 Mckinney Ave Ste 430 Dallas (75204) *(G-4174)*

Cortwear Sports AP & Eqp LLC 361 728-1868
1015 S 6th St Kingsville (78363) *(G-13624)*

Corvalent Corporation 512 456-2400
1101 Arrwpint Dr Bldg 501 Cedar Park (78613) *(G-2965)*

Cosa Xentaur Corporation (PA) 713 947-9591
4140 World Houston Pkwy # 180 Houston (77032) *(G-9327)*

Cosa Xentaur Corporation 631 345-3434
4140 World Hstn Pkwy # 180 Houston (77032) *(G-9328)*

Cosi Energy Services LLC 956 765-6729
3050 S Us Highway 83 Zapata (78076) *(G-20981)*

Cosine Additive Inc 832 519-8441
8181 W Hardy Rd Houston (77022) *(G-9329)*

Cosmax Nbt Usa Inc 469 661-9700
3350 Marquis Dr Garland (75042) *(G-7466)*

Cosmax Nbt USA Inc 469 298-2222
3366 Miller Park S Garland (75042) *(G-7467)*

Cosmec Inc 903 677-2871
1501 Rocky Ridge Rd Athens (75751) *(G-825)*

Cosmetic Laboratories Inc 972 986-9098
3131 Premier Dr Irving (75063) *(G-12981)*

Costello Doab Enterprises LLC 512 364-1708
411 W Saint Elmo Rd # 22 Austin (78745) *(G-1068)*

Cothran AG Services LLC 254 625-1715
402 Fm 1451 Teague (75860) *(G-19664)*

Cotton Construction Inc 936 931-2510
30505 Betka Rd Waller (77484) *(G-20496)*

Cotton Utility Constructors 281 659-5707
5101 Fm 2666 Rd Shepherd (77371) *(G-18901)*

Cottons Inspection Service Inc 432 366-2631
102 E Yukon Rd Odessa (79765) *(G-15970)*

Cougar Cleaning Equipment, Odessa *Also called Jimmy Smart* *(G-16039)*

Cougar Pallet Inc 281 442-1177
13417 Aldine Westfield Rd Houston (77039) *(G-9330)*

Counter Club Inc (PA) 817 573-5040
701 N Houston St Granbury (76048) *(G-7795)*

Counter Crast, Houston *Also called Kitchen Equipment Fabg Co* *(G-10538)*

Country Cottage Florist, Mount Pleasant *Also called Boggs Enterprises Inc* *(G-15647)*

Country Fresh LLC (HQ) 616 243-0173
2711 N Haskell Ave # 3400 Dallas (75204) *(G-4175)*

Country Fresh Meats, Plainview *Also called Cargill Meat Solutions Corp* *(G-16752)*

Country Fresh Wesley, Dallas *Also called Country Fresh LLC* *(G-4175)*

Country Glass & Mirror Inc 972 216-9100
1250 Us Highway 80 E Mesquite (75149) *(G-15035)*

County Barn Precinct 4 ....936 258-5202
1034 County Road 605 Dayton (77535) *(G-5224)*

Courson Oil & Gas Inc 806 435-2910
1800 S Main St Perryton (79070) *(G-16636)*

Courter-Hall Company 972 276-8531
1910 N 1st St Garland (75040) *(G-7468)*

Couture American Lifestyle 972 487-1641
3620 Marquis Dr Garland (75042) *(G-7469)*

Covalence Adhesives, Houston *Also called Covalnce Spcalty Adhesives LLC* *(G-9331)*

Covalnce Spcalty Adhesives LLC 713 676-0085
13835 Beaumont Hwy Houston (77049) *(G-9331)*

Covercraft Industries Inc 940 763-2535
2720 Market St Wichita Falls (76301) *(G-20757)*

Coverlay Manufacturing Inc 325 659-4697
4017 N Us Highway 67 San Angelo (76905) *(G-17791)*

Covers Etc Inc 817 467-5030
925 W Harris Rd Arlington (76001) *(G-649)*

Covestro LLC 281 350-9000
2400 Spring Stuebner Rd Spring (77389) *(G-19108)*

Covestro LLC 281 383-6000
8500 W Bay Rd Baytown (77523) *(G-1782)*

Covey Park Energy Holdings LLC 214 548-6000
8401 N Central Expy # 700 Dallas (75225) *(G-4176)*

Covey Park II LLC (PA) 214 548-6000
5300 Twn Cntry Blvd # 500 Frisco (75034) *(G-7276)*

Covey Software Systems Inc 972 353-8716
1825 W Walnut Hill Ln # 12 Irving (75038) *(G-12982)*

Covia Holdings Corporation 281 298-8088
2829 Tech Frest Blvd Ste The Woodlands (77381) *(G-19848)*

Covia Holdings Corporation 254 897-4408
1788 County Road 308 Cleburne (76033) *(G-3084)*

Covidien LP 903 886-3153
400 Maple St Commerce (75428) *(G-3242)*

Cow Girls & Lace, Dripping Springs *Also called Le Ragge Ruggs Inc* *(G-5508)*

Cowan Coolant MGT Svcs LLC 214 686-1010
903 N Bowser Rd Ste 330 Richardson (75081) *(G-17293)*

Cowan Costumes Inc 817 641-3126
108 S Caddo St Cleburne (76031) *(G-3085)*

Cowboy Containments Inc 361 576-9550
3802 E Rio Grande St Victoria (77901) *(G-20255)*

Cowboy Publishing Group 817 737-6397
2112 Montgomery St Fort Worth (76107) *(G-6551)*

Cowboy Pumps 361 221-9786
129 W Huisache Ave Kingsville (78363) *(G-13625)*

Cowboys Ready Mix LLC 281 972-7000
24015 Interstate 10 Wallisville (77597) *(G-20511)*

Cowboys Resources Corp (PA) 432 686-7797
415 W Wall St Ste 1800 Midland (79701) *(G-15181)*

Cowgirl Brands LLC 512 466-3816
23703 Int State Hwy35 Ste Kyle (78640) *(G-13680)*

Cowtown Boot Company (PA) 915 593-2929
11401 Gateway Blvd W El Paso (79936) *(G-5704)*

Cowtown Redi Mix Inc 817 759-1919
3401 Bethlehem St Fort Worth (76111) *(G-6552)*

Cowtown Traffic Control Inc (PA) 817 924-4524
112 W Jessamine St Fort Worth (76110) *(G-6553)*

Cowtown Western Belt Inc 817 625-4411
5608 Scoggins St Fort Worth (76114) *(G-6554)*

Cox Fence Fittings, Mesquite *Also called Cox Industries Inc* *(G-15036)*

Cox Industries Inc 972 288-7555
11324 Russell St Mesquite (75180) *(G-15036)*

Cox Manufacturing Company 210 657-7731
5500 N Loop 1604 E San Antonio (78247) *(G-18028)*

Cox North Carolina Publication, Marshall *Also called Marshall News Messenger Inc* *(G-14790)*

Cox Oil LLC (PA) 214 420-7710
4514 Cole Ave Ste 1175 Dallas (75205) *(G-4177)*

Cox Operating LLC (HQ) 504 267-9138
4514 Cole Ave Ste 1175 Dallas (75205) *(G-4178)*

Cox Tank Construction Co Inc 361 528-3524
Us Hwy 181 Taft (78390) *(G-19640)*

Cox Texas Newspapers LP 512 445-3500
305 S Congress Ave Austin (78704) *(G-1069)*

Cox Texas Newspapers LP 903 237-7777
320 E Methvin St Longview (75601) *(G-14215)*

Cox Texas Newspapers LP (HQ) 512 445-3500
305 S Congress Ave Austin (78704) *(G-1070)*

Coyote Designs, Stephenville *Also called Stephenville Printing Company* *(G-19425)*

Coyote Electronics Inc 817 485-3336
525 Logan Dr Azle (76020) *(G-1722)*

Coyote Ready Mix LLC 832 432-2025
25277 Fm 1488 Rd Magnolia (77355) *(G-14598)*

Coyote Roustabout LLC 325 455-0090
13000 Fm 707 Hawley (79525) *(G-8230)*

Cozart Mtal Bldngs Systems Inc 817 237-2282
6428 Nine Mile Bridge Rd Fort Worth (76135) *(G-6555)*

Cpchem, The Woodlands *Also called Chevron Phillips Chem Co LP* *(G-19845)*

Cpchem, Port Arthur *Also called Chevron Phillips Chem Co LP* *(G-17104)*

Cpfd LLC 713 429-1252
1255 Enclave Pkwy Ste E Houston (77077) *(G-9332)*

Cpfd Software, Houston *Also called Cpfd LLC* *(G-9332)*

CPI, Georgetown *Also called Chatsworth Products Inc* *(G-7644)*

CPI - Marine, Kyle *Also called Cryogenic Plastics Inc* *(G-13681)*

CPI Communications, Wylie *Also called Psde LLC* *(G-20945)*

CPI Importers Inc 214 353-0328
2324 Shorecrest Dr Dallas (75235) *(G-4179)*

CPI Products LLC 877 756-2388
307 Industrial Blvd Burnet (78611) *(G-2605)*

CPI Products Intl Inc 512 868-0346
4100 Fm 1105 Walburg (78673) *(G-20488)*

CPI Satcom & Antenna Tech Inc 254 765-3304
1004 N Mrtn Lther King Av Wortham (76693) *(G-20922)*

CPI Satcom & Antenna Tech Inc 903 984-0555
2600 N Longview St Kilgore (75662) *(G-13539)*

CPI Satcom & Antenna Tech Inc 972 852-5300
1000 Klein Rd Plano (75074) *(G-16830)*

CPI Satcom & Antenna Tech Inc 903 984-0555
2600 N Longview St Kilgore (75662) *(G-13540)*

CPI Wirecloth & Screens Inc (PA) 281 485-2300
2425 Roy Rd Pearland (77581) *(G-16550)*

CPM Acquisition Corp 972 243-8070
2009 Mckenzie Dr Ste 116 Carrollton (75006) *(G-2719)*

CPM Inc 214 349-6886
2447 Merritt Dr Garland (75041) *(G-7470)*

CPS Houston, Baytown *Also called Certified Pipe Svc Houston Inc (G-1812)*

Cpsi, Houston *Also called Current Power Solutions Inc (G-9359)*

CPT International (usa) LLC 713 747-4773
12950 Executive Dr Sugar Land (77478) *(G-19468)*

Cpy, Houston *Also called Chas P Young Company (G-9166)*

Cr Machine 281 354-4755
23411 Albert Dr Porter (77365) *(G-17173)*

Crab Ventures LLC 979 571-0258
6328 Fm 1179 Bryan (77808) *(G-2467)*

Crabtree Barricade Systems Inc 409 842-2073
7375 Frint Dr Beaumont (77705) *(G-1877)*

Crafco Texas Inc 210 496-2070
102 Limestone Creek Rd San Antonio (78232) *(G-18029)*

Craft Wireline Services Inc 432 943-5150
4400 S Loop 464 Rd Monahans (79756) *(G-15603)*

Craftmark Idntfication Systems, Fort Worth *Also called Craftmark Products Inc (G-6556)*

Craftmark Products Inc 817 457-8753
3212 S Cravens Rd Fort Worth (76119) *(G-6556)*

Craftmasters Countertops, Houston *Also called Bmp & Associates Inc (G-8927)*

Craftsman Awards, Houston *Also called Glass Wholesalers Ltd (G-9961)*

Craftsman Printers Inc 806 744-8429
535 32nd St Lubbock (79404) *(G-14397)*

Craig Baker Marble Co Inc 281 492-2365
1918 Baker Rd Barker (77413) *(G-1745)*

Craig Godwin Inc (PA) **936 344-6548**
9353 State Highway 75 S New Waverly (77358) *(G-15858)*

Craig Godwin Inc 936 344-6548
220a Longstreet Rd New Waverly (77358) *(G-15859)*

Craig Instruments Inc 713 690-6904
6333 Guhn Rd Houston (77040) *(G-9333)*

Crain Chemical Company Inc 214 358-3301
2624 Andjon Dr Dallas (75220) *(G-4180)*

Crain M-M Sales, Dallas *Also called Southwest Prof Vehicles (G-4992)*

Crall Products Inc 806 665-8446
2930 Hwy 152 W Pampa (79065) *(G-16320)*

Cramer Computer Supplies Ltd 806 371-7310
3221 Church St Amarillo (79109) *(G-485)*

Crane Co, Spring *Also called Pacific Valves (G-19239)*

Crane Energy Flow Solutions, The Woodlands *Also called McC Holdings Inc (G-19893)*

Crane Equipment & Service Inc 817 740-7911
2426 Gravel Dr Fort Worth (76118) *(G-6557)*

Crane Pro Parts, Houston *Also called Konecranes Inc (G-10559)*

Crane Pro Services, Houston *Also called Konecranes Inc (G-10558)*

Crane Valve North America, Montgomery *Also called McC Holdings Inc (G-15636)*

Craneworks Inc (PA) **281 219-7779**
7795 Little York Rd Houston (77016) *(G-9334)*

Crawford Electric Sup Co Inc 512 593-4000
2251 Picadilly Dr Round Rock (78664) *(G-17638)*

Crawford Energy Inc 713 626-2637
770 S Post Oak Ln Ste 520 Houston (77056) *(G-9335)*

Crawford Industrial Svcs LLC 409 925-9580
3811 1/2 Fm 646 Rd N Santa Fe (77510) *(G-18733)*

Cray Inc 512 651-7020
6011 W Courtyard Dr # 200 Austin (78730) *(G-1071)*

Crayon Software Experts LLC (HQ) **469 329-0290**
12221 Merit Dr Ste 800 Dallas (75251) *(G-4181)*

CRC-Evans Intl Holdings Inc (HQ) **832 249-3100**
7011 High Life Dr Houston (77066) *(G-9336)*

CRC-Evans Pipeline Intl, Houston *Also called CRC-Evans Intl Holdings Inc (G-9336)*

CRC-Evans Pipeline Intl Inc (HQ) **800 664-9224**
7011 High Life Dr Houston (77066) *(G-9337)*

Crc/Mastercraft Inc 281 897-8880
11350 Fm 1960 Rd W Houston (77065) *(G-9338)*

Cre, La Porte *Also called Centrifuge Repair & Engrg LP (G-13726)*

Creation Tchnologies-Lexington, Plano *Also called Creation Technologies Kentucky (G-16831)*

Creation Technologies Kentucky 859 253-3066
1001 Klein Rd Ste 100 Plano (75074) *(G-16831)*

Creations Unlimted Inc 281 821-1382
18927 Aldine Westfield Rd Houston (77073) *(G-9339)*

Creative Alloy Products Co 936 894-2060
17151 Highway 105 E Plantersville (77363) *(G-17058)*

Creative Casting Inc 903 463-6160
1827 S Armstrong Ave # 102 Denison (75020) *(G-5339)*

Creative Coatings Inc (PA) **903 984-8454**
428 N Longview St Kilgore (75662) *(G-13541)*

Creative Communications, Waco *Also called AMA Printing / Finishing Inc (G-20359)*

Creative Computing West Inc 512 804-2299
3636 Dime Cir Ste 301 Austin (78744) *(G-1072)*

Creative Custom Cabinets Inc 512 821-0300
1500 W Industrial Blvd Round Rock (78681) *(G-17639)*

Creative Education Inst Inc 254 751-1188
4567 Lake Shore Dr Waco (76710) *(G-20391)*

Creative Handworks Inc 214 682-2090
2400 E Randol Mill Rd Arlington (76011) *(G-650)*

Creative Industries LLC 830 249-1200
140 Old San Antonio Rd Boerne (78006) *(G-2117)*

Creative MENus&folders LLC 254 653-2775
409 Old Hwy 80 Olden (76466) *(G-16219)*

Creative Molded Packaging LLC 915 881-8401
6980 Market Ave El Paso (79915) *(G-5705)*

Creative Nightscapes 817 581-6936
5755 Carlisle Ct Ste 300 Fort Worth (76180) *(G-6558)*

Creative Signworks Inc 850 785-8899
6861 S Us Highway 277 San Angelo (76904) *(G-17792)*

Creative Sound Productions 713 777-9975
8383 Commerce Park Dr # 604 Houston (77036) *(G-9340)*

Creative Spclty Fd Sltions LLC 713 864-7777
3713 Jensen Dr Houston (77026) *(G-9341)*

Creative Stitches Inc 817 284-0061
578 N Beach St Fort Worth (76111) *(G-6559)*

Creative Stone Inc 512 303-7866
140 Watterson Rd Bastrop (78602) *(G-1752)*

Creative Tile Inc (PA) **214 827-0552**
2906 N Fitzhugh Ave Dallas (75204) *(G-4182)*

Creative Type 214 420-1980
1350 Mnscture Ring Ste 11 Dallas (75207) *(G-4183)*

Creative Wood Concepts Inc 972 539-2555
1959 W Northwest Hwy Dallas (75220) *(G-4184)*

Cree Visual Marketing Company 214 905-8485
1200 Crowley Dr Carrollton (75006) *(G-2720)*

Creek's Welding, Sonora *Also called Luther M Creek (G-19027)*

Creekside Mirror & Glass, Waxahachie *Also called Creekside Mirror and Glass LLC (G-20539)*

Creekside Mirror and Glass LLC 972 617-9805
3811 S Us Highway 287 Waxahachie (75165) *(G-20539)*

Creme Lure, Tyler *Also called Knight Manufacturing Co Inc (G-20111)*

Crescent Directional Drlg LP (PA) **281 668-9500**
2040 Aldine Western Rd Houston (77038) *(G-9342)*

Crescent Reel Manufacturing Co 713 695-4587
201 Burbank St Houston (77076) *(G-9343)*

Crescent Systems Inc 972 437-0400
1155 E Collins Blvd # 10 Richardson (75081) *(G-17294)*

Cresline Plastic Pipe Co Inc 903 872-7418
3801 E State Highway 31 Corsicana (75109) *(G-3667)*

Crest Orthopedic Implants LLC 254 931-6996
7200 N Intrstate 35 Bldg Georgetown (78626) *(G-7645)*

Crest Pumping Technologies LLC (HQ) **817 484-5100**
6500 West Fwy Ste 601 Fort Worth (76116) *(G-6560)*

Cretic Energy Corp 713 922-3784
11633 Grandview Dr Montgomery (77356) *(G-15630)*

Crh Americas Inc 903 765-2212
650 W Greenville St 69n Alba (75410) *(G-181)*

Crh Americas Materials Inc 409 866-1444
12907 Highway 90 Beaumont (77713) *(G-1878)*

Crick Tool, Ben Wheeler *Also called Ameri Source Manufacturing Inc (G-2031)*

Cricket Trailer, Houston *Also called Taxa Inc (G-12165)*

Crimson Exploration Inc (HQ) **713 236-7400**
717 Texas St Ste 2900 Houston (77002) *(G-9344)*

Crimstone AAA Operating Co LP 210 662-9400
5891 Fm 1346 San Antonio (78220) *(G-18030)*

Crisp Air 903 530-4385
10330 County Road 3168 Winona (75792) *(G-20903)*

Crisp Industries Inc 830 372-1110
4547 W Interstate 10 Seguin (78155) *(G-18834)*

Crist Industries Inc 817 847-8500
9965 Saginaw Blvd Fort Worth (76179) *(G-6561)*

Cristacurva LLC 713 353-5800
13105 Nw Fwy Ste 800 Houston (77040) *(G-9345)*

Criteria Labs Inc (PA) **512 637-4500**
706 Brentwood St Austin (78752) *(G-1073)*

Critical Solutions Intl Inc 800 843-0000
821 Jupiter Rd Ste 406 Plano (75074) *(G-16832)*

Crocker Crane Rentals LP 512 258-1323
8600 Fm 2243 Leander (78641) *(G-13985)*

Crockett County Mining, Odessa *Also called Permian Basin Materials LLC (G-16114)*

Crockett Sand and Gravel Inc 936 545-1021
9812 State Highway 7 W Crockett (75835) *(G-3716)*

Crocodile Digital Corporation 713 382-1891
305 21st St Ste 243 Galveston (77550) *(G-7395)*

Croft Construction Co Inc 936 258-7902
4866 Fm 1008 Dayton (77535) *(G-5225)*

Crosby Group LLC 918 834-4611
2414 Crosby Way Longview (75602) *(G-14216)*

Cross Link Powder Coating, Pflugerville *Also called Crosslink Pwdr Cting Astin Ltd (G-16664)*

Crossfire Inc 972 570-0800
3247 Story Rd W Irving (75038) *(G-12983)*

Crossfire LLC 970 884-4869
1800 Hughes Landing Blvd The Woodlands (77380) *(G-19849)*

Crossfire Car Audio, Irving *Also called Crossfire Inc (G-12983)*

A
L
P
H
A
B
E
T
I
C

Crosslink McKnney Pwdr Cting L..............972 542-5441
2787 County Road 407 # 1 McKinney (75071) *(G-14933)*

Crosslink Pwdr Cting Astin Ltd..............512 989-6458
2310 Patterson Indus Dr Pflugerville (78660) *(G-16664)*

Crossroads Systems (texas)..............512 349-0300
11000 N Mopac Expy # 100 Austin (78759) *(G-1074)*

Crossroads Tanks, Jourdanton *Also called Huss Services Inc (G-13332)*

Crossroads Winery..............817 421-2999
415 S Main St Grapevine (76051) *(G-8024)*

Crossvale Inc (PA)..............**972 714-4782**
4201 Spring Valley Rd # 306 Dallas (75244) *(G-4185)*

Crow Chandelier Service, Dallas *Also called Crow Chandeliers Inc (G-4186)*

Crow Chandeliers Inc..............214 744-5488
1333 Slocum St Dallas (75207) *(G-4186)*

Crow Precision Components LLC..............817 536-2861
200 Luxton St Fort Worth (76104) *(G-6562)*

Crowder Construction Co Inc..............254 629-1688
318 N Seaman St Eastland (76448) *(G-5562)*

Crowder Services Inc..............325 853-2852
306 S Us Highway 277 Eldorado (76936) *(G-6045)*

Crowfut Honey Company, Austin *Also called Good Flow Honey & Juice Co (G-1188)*

Crown Aerospace Inc..............281 351-7068
611 S Persimmon St Tomball (77375) *(G-19972)*

Crown Beverage Packaging, Conroe *Also called Crown Cork & Seal Usa Inc (G-3287)*

Crown Building Products LLC..............214 636-5163
2155 Fm 1187 Mansfield (76063) *(G-14664)*

Crown Castle Intl Corp (PA)..............**713 570-3000**
1220 Augusta Dr Ste 600 Houston (77057) *(G-9346)*

Crown Cork & Seal Usa Inc..............281 240-4838
12910 Jess Pirtle Blvd Sugar Land (77478) *(G-19469)*

Crown Cork & Seal Usa Inc..............936 539-5401
2501 N Frazier St Conroe (77303) *(G-3287)*

Crown Energy Technologies Inc (HQ)..............**403 215-5300**
1617 E Richey Rd Houston (77073) *(G-9347)*

Crown Equipment Corporation..............281 985-0300
1650 N Sam Houston Pkwy E Houston (77032) *(G-9348)*

Crown Equipment Corporation..............210 930-9360
4400 Ne Loop 410 Ste 140 San Antonio (78218) *(G-18031)*

Crown Equipment Corporation..............972 988-9000
4000 Scientific Dr Arlington (76014) *(G-651)*

Crown Exploration Ltd..............972 395-1133
4024 Nazarene Dr Ste A Carrollton (75010) *(G-2861)*

Crown Lift Trucks, Houston *Also called Crown Equipment Corporation (G-9348)*

Crown Lift Trucks, San Antonio *Also called Crown Equipment Corporation (G-18031)*

Crown Lift Trucks, Arlington *Also called Crown Equipment Corporation (G-651)*

Crown Oil Partners LP..............432 683-2950
303 Veterans Airpark Ln # 6101 Midland (79705) *(G-15182)*

Crown Supply, Borger *Also called Ed Prince Enterprises Inc (G-2177)*

Crown Texas Inc..............972 905-4680
2350 Crist Rd Ste 1300 Garland (75040) *(G-7471)*

Crown To Ground Supply Inc..............936 588-7457
6315b Fm 1488 Rd Ste 148 Magnolia (77354) *(G-14599)*

Crown Trophy, Hurst *Also called Screen Play Promotions Inc (G-12858)*

Crowned Plus Enterprises LLC..............469 585-9658
1812 Chadwick Ln Forney (75126) *(G-6306)*

Crownquest, Midland *Also called Crownrock LP (G-15184)*

Crownquest Operating LLC..............432 818-0300
18 Desta Dr Midland (79705) *(G-15183)*

Crownrock LP..............432 818-0300
500 W Texas Ave Ste 500 # 500 Midland (79701) *(G-15184)*

Crudechem Technology LLC (PA)..............**832 206-0790**
1998 Fm 362 Rd Pattison (77423) *(G-16531)*

Cruising Kitchens LLC..............210 920-2658
14732 Bulverde Rd San Antonio (78247) *(G-18032)*

Crumplers Mch & Wldg Svc Inc..............409 886-7934
335 Bland Dr Bridge City (77611) *(G-2282)*

Crumplers Shipbuilding Co Inc..............409 886-7934
1799 S Childers Rd Orange (77630) *(G-16237)*

Crusader Energy Group LLC..............512 328-2953
807 Las Cimas Pkwy # 350 Austin (78746) *(G-1075)*

Crushing Tigers, Austin *Also called Costello Doab Enterprises LLC (G-1068)*

Crux Manufacturing LLC..............512 619-6170
1421 W Wlls Br Pkwy Ste 3 Pflugerville (78660) *(G-16665)*

Cryer Limited Partnership (PA)..............**512 267-4944**
20202 Alfalfa Dr Lago Vista (78645) *(G-13805)*

Cryo Zone LLC..............972 523-6060
3326 Courtyard Pl Dallas (75234) *(G-4187)*

Cryogenic Plastics Inc..............512 295-2683
1098 Windy Hill Rd Kyle (78640) *(G-13681)*

Cryognic Inds Svc Cmpanies LLC..............281 590-4800
14014 Interdrive E Houston (77032) *(G-9349)*

Cryognic Vssel Altrnatives Inc..............713 357-9714
952 Echo Ln Ste 250 Houston (77024) *(G-9350)*

Cryotech Precision Machine LLC..............713 690-2796
10029 Tanner Rd Houston (77041) *(G-9351)*

Cryovac LLC..............940 851-6060
3800 Central Fwy Wichita Falls (76306) *(G-20758)*

Crystal Distribution Inc..............763 391-7790
6701 N Belt Line Rd Irving (75063) *(G-12984)*

Crystal Feed Mills Inc..............903 488-3261
700 W Main St Como (75431) *(G-3247)*

Crystal Images Inc..............972 438-2337
1915 Peters Rd Ste 313 Irving (75061) *(G-12985)*

Crystaphase Products Inc (PA)..............**281 874-2110**
16945 North Fwy Ste 1610 Houston (77090) *(G-9352)*

Cs Manufacturing Inc..............281 442-3400
14635 Chrisman Rd Houston (77039) *(G-9353)*

Cs Platinum Sports LLC..............936 559-1883
916 Ruby St Nacogdoches (75961) *(G-15693)*

Cs Well Service LLC..............325 242-2438
2313 N State Highway 208 Colorado City (79512) *(G-3224)*

CS&p Technologies LP (PA)..............**713 467-0869**
18119 Telge Rd Cypress (77429) *(G-3783)*

Csa Materials Inc..............325 655-4511
3001 Foster St San Angelo (76903) *(G-17793)*

CSB Energy Tech Americas Ltd..............817 244-7777
4008 Clay Ave Ste 210 Haltom City (76117) *(G-8135)*

Cse W-Industries Inc (HQ)..............**713 466-9463**
11500 Charles Rd Jersey Village (77041) *(G-13297)*

Csg Industries, Houston *Also called Premier Concrete Products Inc (G-11399)*

Csg Systems Inc..............817 230-2700
5600 Stratum Dr Fort Worth (76137) *(G-6563)*

Csg Systems Inc..............512 949-2200
15404 Long Vista Dr Austin (78728) *(G-1076)*

Csi, Porter *Also called Carbide Specialists Inc (G-17172)*

Csi, Kilgore *Also called Southern Plastics Inc (G-13591)*

Csi Compressco LP (PA)..............**281 367-1983**
24955 Interstate 45 The Woodlands (77380) *(G-19850)*

Csi Compressco Sub Inc..............432 563-1170
3809 S Fm 1788 Midland (79706) *(G-15185)*

Csi Compressco Sub Inc..............361 576-6827
11503 Us Highway 59 N Victoria (77905) *(G-20256)*

Csi Security, San Antonio *Also called Csi Techs Inc (G-18033)*

Csi Techs Inc..............210 875-7978
1247 Range Fld San Antonio (78245) *(G-18033)*

Csjb Holdings Inc..............806 749-4300
521 Ne Loop 289 Lubbock (79403) *(G-14398)*

Csl Plasma Inc..............972 329-0186
10121 Lake June Rd 503 Dallas (75217) *(G-4188)*

CST Covers, Conroe *Also called Tank Wind-Down Corp (G-3369)*

CST Covers, Conroe *Also called Conservatek Industries Inc (G-3284)*

Cstorepro Technologies Inc..............866 265-5826
77 Sugar Creek Center Blv Sugar Land (77478) *(G-19470)*

Csw Industrials Inc (PA)..............**214 884-3777**
5420 Lyndon B Johnson Fwy Dallas (75240) *(G-4189)*

Csw Industrials Holdings Inc..............214 884-3777
5420 Lyndon B Johnson Fwy Dallas (75240) *(G-4190)*

CT & S Inc..............972 438-9796
1513 Maryland Dr Irving (75061) *(G-12986)*

CT & S Meta Works, Irving *Also called CT & S Inc (G-12986)*

CT Greggs and Sons LLC (PA)..............**972 333-1960**
1400 Harvest Glen Dr Flower Mound (75028) *(G-6264)*

Ct-Technology Inc (PA)..............**469 531-9472**
1448 Halsey Way Ste 112 Carrollton (75007) *(G-2862)*

Ctc, Waco *Also called Central Texas Corrugated Inc (G-20380)*

Ctc Inc..............817 886-8210
9601 Camp Bowie West Blvd Fort Worth (76116) *(G-6564)*

Ctci Americas Inc..............281 870-9998
11490 Westheimer Rd # 200 Houston (77077) *(G-9354)*

CTI Arlington LLC..............817 869-1090
504 Sansom Blvd Saginaw (76179) *(G-17743)*

CTI Foods, Saginaw *Also called CTI Arlington LLC (G-17743)*

CTI Saginaw I LLC..............817 869-1090
504 Sansom Blvd Saginaw (76179) *(G-17744)*

Ctj Energy Solutions, Fort Worth *Also called A M Fabrication Inc (G-6337)*

Ctl Medical Corporation..............214 545-5830
4550 Excel Pkwy Ste 300 Addison (75001) *(G-114)*

CTS, Clute *Also called Curtis Technical Service Inc (G-3151)*

CTT, Houston *Also called Coil Tubing Technology Inc (G-9240)*

CTW Brake Rims Inc..............806 665-0289
Pampa Industrial Park E Pampa (79065) *(G-16321)*

Cuatro Cinco Enterprises LLC..............713 647-2846
3715 Jensen Dr Houston (77026) *(G-9355)*

Cube Solutions LLC (PA)..............**972 783-4880**
7331 Maplecrest Dr Dallas (75254) *(G-4191)*

Cubeco Inc..............713 671-2466
1415 Harris St Houston (77020) *(G-9356)*

Cubelogic LLC..............832 498-6374
4004 Rice Blvd Houston (77005) *(G-9357)*

Cubelogic Software, Houston *Also called Cubelogic LLC (G-9357)*

Cubic Its Inc (HQ)..............**281 240-7233**
522 Gillingham Blvd Sugar Land (77478) *(G-19471)*

Cubie Co, San Antonio *Also called Universal Pen & Print Inc (G-18579)*

Cubix Software Ltd Inc..............903 297-7771
306 Bridgers Hill Rd Longview (75604) *(G-14217)*

Cuda Express II Inc..............806 433-1896
5255 Adkisson Rd Bushland (79012) *(G-2621)*

2021 Harris Texas
Manufacturers Directory

(G-0000) Company's Geographic Section entry number

Cudd Energy Service, Robstown *Also called Cudd Pressure Control Inc (G-17507)*

Cudd Energy Services, Odessa *Also called Cudd Pumping Services Inc (G-15972)*

Cudd Energy Services, The Woodlands *Also called Cudd Pumping Services Inc (G-19851)*

Cudd Pressure Control Inc 361 387-8521
1420 Highway 44 Robstown (78380) *(G-17507)*

Cudd Pressure Control Inc 432 580-3544
1300 S John Ben Sheppard Odessa (79766) *(G-15971)*

Cudd Pressure Control Inc 903 988-2161
2600 N Hwy 135 Kilgore (75662) *(G-13542)*

Cudd Pumping Services, Odessa *Also called Cudd Pressure Control Inc (G-15971)*

Cudd Pumping Services, Kilgore *Also called Cudd Pressure Control Inc (G-13542)*

Cudd Pumping Services Inc 432 580-3544
1300 S John Ben Sheppard Odessa (79766) *(G-15972)*

Cudd Pumping Services Inc 210 310-1330
5251 Tacco San Antonio (78244) *(G-18034)*

Cudd Pumping Services Inc (HQ) **832 295-5555**
2828 Tech Forest Blvd The Woodlands (77381) *(G-19851)*

Cudd Well Control 713 849-2769
2828 Tech Forest Blvd Spring (77381) *(G-19204)*

Cude Energy Services, Conroe *Also called Cude Oilfield Contractors Inc (G-3288)*

Cude Oilfield Contractors Inc 281 298-0600
100 Interstate 45 N # 400 Conroe (77301) *(G-3288)*

Cugar Machine Inc 817 927-0411
3579 Mccart Ave Fort Worth (76110) *(G-6565)*

Culligan Southeast Texas Water 409 838-6261
850 Mcfaddin St Beaumont (77701) *(G-1879)*

Cumberland Additive Inc 512 990-9100
1007 S Hthrwld Blvd Pflugerville (78660) *(G-16666)*

Cummings Inv Bankers Inc 281 416-3007
4202 Bluebonnet Dr Houston (77053) *(G-8376)*

Cummins - Allison Corp 972 661-5390
13721 Gamma Rd Dallas (75244) *(G-4192)*

Cummins Diesel Fuel Inc 915 858-7310
9615 Plaza Cir Ste 100 El Paso (79927) *(G-5706)*

Cummins Engine Company, Arlington *Also called Cummins Inc (G-652)*

Cummins Inc 915 791-6600
14333 Gateway Blvd W El Paso (79928) *(G-5707)*

Cummins Inc 915 858-7310
9615 Plaza Cir Ste 100 El Paso (79927) *(G-5708)*

Cummins Inc (PA) **615 986-2596**
600 N Watson Rd Arlington (76011) *(G-652)*

Cummins Jrez Emission Solution 844 401-0221
9615 Plaza Cir Ste 100 El Paso (79927) *(G-5709)*

Cummins Southern Plains LLC 806 373-3793
5224 I 40 E Amarillo (79103) *(G-419)*

Cummins Southern Plains LLC 817 624-2107
3250 North Fwy Fort Worth (76111) *(G-6566)*

Cummins Southern Plains LLC 432 332-9121
1210 S Grandview Ave Odessa (79761) *(G-15973)*

Cummins Southern Plains LLC 210 655-5420
6226 N Pan Am Expy San Antonio (78218) *(G-18035)*

Cummins Southern Plains LLC 512 389-2276
1700 Smith Rd Austin (78721) *(G-1077)*

Cummins Southern Plains LLC 800 286-6467
4895 Mountain Creek Pkwy Dallas (75236) *(G-4193)*

Cummins Southern Plains LLC (HQ) **817 640-6801**
600 N Watson Rd Arlington (76011) *(G-653)*

Cummins Southern Plains LLC 713 679-2220
7045 North Loop E 610 Houston (77028) *(G-9358)*

Cummins-Allison, Dallas *Also called Cummins - Allison Corp (G-4192)*

Cunningham Automotive Inc 972 900-0405
1079 W Round Grove Rd Lewisville (75067) *(G-14039)*

Curbco, Houston *Also called Spring Branch Shtmtl Co Inc (G-12026)*

Curbell Plastics Inc 214 239-3870
2001 Timberlake Dr Arlington (76010) *(G-654)*

Curflo Inc 281 479-5000
1113 Howard Dr Deer Park (77536) *(G-5266)*

Current Power Solutions Inc 281 943-7700
5050 W Greens Rd Houston (77066) *(G-9359)*

Currentech 214 693-6751
1810 Lakeside Dr Arlington (76013) *(G-655)*

Currid & Company 713 893-8401
11152 Westheimer Rd # 883 Houston (77042) *(G-9360)*

Curry Printing Ltd 817 540-5252
1109 Pamela Dr Euless (76040) *(G-6139)*

Curse of Good Taste Inc 512 327-9660
3016 Guadalupe St Ste 200 Austin (78705) *(G-1078)*

Curtis Mathes Inc (PA) **888 725-0309**
6201 Tech Dr Ste 106 Frisco (75033) *(G-7277)*

Curtis Mathes International, Frisco *Also called Curtis Mathes Inc (G-7277)*

Curtis Oilfield Services LLC 409 385-2937
4779 Highway 96 Byp Silsbee (77656) *(G-18952)*

Curtis Technical Service Inc 979 388-0007
920 S Shanks St Clute (77531) *(G-3151)*

Curtis Welding Service, Silsbee *Also called Curtis Oilfield Services LLC (G-18952)*

Curtiss-Wright Corporation 713 581-3400
13805 Industrial Rd Houston (77015) *(G-9361)*

Curtiss-Wright Surfc Tech LLC 972 641-8011
1450 Avenue S Grand Prairie (75050) *(G-7859)*

Custom Abrasives LLC (PA) **281 286-7200**
2525 Bay Area Blvd # 290 Houston (77058) *(G-9362)*

Custom AC & Shtmtl 713 868-5557
1729 Stebbins Dr 100 Houston (77043) *(G-9363)*

Custom Air Products & Svcs Inc 713 434-1192
16635 Buffalo Speedway Houston (77047) *(G-9364)*

Custom Air Products & Svcs Inc (PA) **281 802-7419**
35 Southbelt Indus Dr Houston (77047) *(G-9365)*

Custom Bilt Holdings LLC (PA) **214 699-4876**
3001 Skyway Cir N Ste 160 Irving (75038) *(G-12987)*

Custom Bilt Metals, Irving *Also called Custom Bilt Holdings LLC (G-12987)*

Custom Blast Services, Nederland *Also called Brock Enterprises LLC (G-15747)*

Custom Box Solutions LLC 888 376-8061
10685 Hazelhurst Dr Ste B Houston (77043) *(G-9366)*

Custom Building Products 972 641-6996
1795 109th St Grand Prairie (75050) *(G-7860)*

Custom Cabinet Doors Inc 940 686-2808
924 N Industrial Blvd Pilot Point (76258) *(G-16723)*

Custom Chenille Embroidery Inc 214 343-0888
11330 Hillguard Rd Dallas (75243) *(G-4194)*

Custom Cmpnents Assemblies Inc 713 937-6225
3347 Frick Rd Houston (77086) *(G-9367)*

Custom Cmpt Cables Amer Inc 972 638-9309
1600 10th St Ste A Plano (75074) *(G-16833)*

Custom Components Incorporated 281 485-2200
3446 S Main St Pearland (77581) *(G-16551)*

Custom Controls Company 713 666-3258
5712 Yale St Houston (77076) *(G-9368)*

Custom Crates & Pallets Ltd 915 886-4985
1501 Westway Blvd Canutillo (79835) *(G-2663)*

Custom Creations Furniture, Houston *Also called Delatorre Inc (G-9426)*

Custom Crete Inc (HQ) **972 243-4466**
2624 Joe Field Rd Dallas (75229) *(G-4195)*

Custom Crete Inc 512 443-5787
4433 Terry O Ln Austin (78745) *(G-1079)*

Custom Crete Inc 713 937-3966
4523 Brittmoore Rd Houston (77041) *(G-9369)*

Custom Crushed Stone Inc 210 688-3413
8845 Leslie Rd San Antonio (78254) *(G-18036)*

Custom Delis Equipment Co Inc 817 831-7080
153 N Riverside Dr Fort Worth (76111) *(G-6567)*

Custom Direct Inc 201 934-4229
5048 Tennyson Pkwy # 250 Plano (75024) *(G-16834)*

Custom Direct International, Plano *Also called Custom Direct Inc (G-16834)*

Custom Door Company Inc 940 686-4500
10279 Fm 455 E Bldg 5 Pilot Point (76258) *(G-16724)*

Custom Drapery Blinds & Carpet, Houston *Also called Custom Drapery Company Inc (G-9370)*

Custom Drapery Company Inc 713 225-9221
3402 E T C Jester Blvd Houston (77018) *(G-9370)*

Custom Duct, Houston *Also called Custom AC & Shtmtl (G-9363)*

Custom Electronics Inc 512 454-8824
102 W Pecan St Pflugerville (78660) *(G-16667)*

Custom Equipment Fabricators, Anthony *Also called P Rockin Enterprises Inc (G-589)*

Custom Extrusions Holdings LLC (PA) **972 442-7200**
1405 Martinez Ln Wylie (75098) *(G-20931)*

Custom Fab Inc 210 923-3376
7030 Old Seal Rd San Antonio (78252) *(G-18037)*

Custom Fabricators & RPS Inc 979 775-4297
1379 N Hrvey Mtchell Pkwy Bryan (77803) *(G-2468)*

Custom Filter Supply Inc 713 947-8147
8581 Mosley Rd 17 Houston (77075) *(G-9371)*

Custom Flame Cutting Inc 281 342-3250
1313 Daily Rd Rosenberg (77471) *(G-17579)*

Custom Floors Unlimited Inc 713 861-4139
12405 Sowden Rd Houston (77080) *(G-9372)*

CUSTOM GRAPHIC SERVICES, Fort Worth *Also called FBC Enterprises Inc (G-6624)*

Custom Heliarc Inc 281 375-2075
34430 Sunset Ln Brookshire (77423) *(G-2314)*

Custom Home Builder, Sugar Land *Also called Design Woodworks (G-19478)*

Custom Imprint Wearables, College Station *Also called CC Creations Ltd (G-3181)*

Custom Iron Works 806 745-2757
12701 Highway 87 Lubbock (79423) *(G-14399)*

Custom Kitchen Eqp Co Inc 281 446-8187
2601 Wilson Rd Humble (77396) *(G-12762)*

Custom Label Converter, Carrollton *Also called Diversco Inc (G-2725)*

Custom Manufacturing Company 214 428-5173
5501 S Lamar St Dallas (75215) *(G-4196)*

Custom Photo Manufacturing, Garland *Also called CPM Inc (G-7470)*

Custom Pipe Coating Inc 713 675-2324
7177 Cavalcade St Houston (77028) *(G-9373)*

Custom Piping Systems LLC 210 867-6356
4230 Milling Rd San Antonio (78219) *(G-18038)*

Custom Ppr Tube Southwest Inc 817 385-5367
925 111th St Arlington (76011) *(G-656)*

Custom Precision Shtmtl Inc 713 856-9997
8913 Elsie Ln Houston (77064) *(G-9374)*

ALPHABETIC

Custom Rods & Draperies...972 889-0580
1225 N Plano Rd Richardson (75081) ***(G-17295)***
Custom Safety Products Inc...281 482-8668
1030 County Rd 129 Friendswood (77546) ***(G-7244)***
Custom SEC Fence Ir Works LLC...281 219-1400
13824 E Hardy Rd Houston (77039) ***(G-9375)***
Custom Shutters Inc...903 488-3224
811 W Main St Como (75431) ***(G-3248)***
Custom Sign Creations LLC...512 374-9300
1130 Rutherford Ln # 180 Austin (78753) ***(G-1080)***
Custom Skin Co Inc...325 655-9585
2800 N Bell St San Angelo (76903) ***(G-17794)***
Custom Solutions Group LLC (PA)...**281 507-9569**
1419 Avenue A Katy (77493) ***(G-13393)***
Custom Stone Supply, Dallas *Also called Custom Crete Inc* ***(G-4195)***
Custom Stone Supply, Frisco *Also called Oldcastle Apg Texas Inc* ***(G-7302)***
Custom Threading Inc...713 645-8422
5835 Cheswood St Houston (77087) ***(G-9376)***
Custom TS...903 874-7626
1712 W 2nd Ave Corsicana (75110) ***(G-3668)***
Custom Vinyl Division, Waco *Also called Patrick Industries Inc* ***(G-20444)***
Custom Window Treatment, Robinson *Also called Plumlee Place LLC* ***(G-17501)***
Custom Wood Designs & Mfg, Stagecoach *Also called JDM Designs Inc* ***(G-19401)***
Custom Wood Workers, Dallas *Also called John D Blankenship* ***(G-4535)***
Custom Work Room Services...214 631-2795
1307 Medical District Dr Dallas (75207) ***(G-4197)***
Custom-Built Equipment Co Inc...713 222-0342
1400 Rothwell St Houston (77002) ***(G-9377)***
Custom-Crete, Garden Ridge *Also called Redi-Mix LLC* ***(G-7419)***
Customer Care Division, Plano *Also called Bayer Healthcare LLC* ***(G-16800)***
Customer Service & Support Co, Fort Hood *Also called General Dynmics Land Systems I* ***(G-6324)***
Cutten Road Rm Dual, Houston *Also called Cemex Construction Mtls S LLC* ***(G-9127)***
Cutting Edge Onsite McHning LL...832 663-6120
359 N Fm 356 Onalaska (77360) ***(G-16228)***
Cutting Solutions Inc...214 637-4849
4647 Leston St Ste 603 Dallas (75247) ***(G-4198)***
Cutting Source Precision Inc...281 859-2900
7951 Fairview St Houston (77041) ***(G-9378)***
Cuvee Coffee LLC...512 264-1479
22601 Hwy 71 W Spicewood (78669) ***(G-19092)***
Cve Technology Group Inc...972 424-6606
3000 E Plano Pkwy Plano (75074) ***(G-16835)***
CVI, Palestine *Also called Calvary Valve Inc* ***(G-16297)***
Cvr Energy Inc (PA)...**281 207-3200**
2277 Plaza Dr Ste 500 Sugar Land (77479) ***(G-19472)***
Cvr Partners LP (HQ)...**281 207-3200**
2277 Plaza Dr Ste 500 Sugar Land (77479) ***(G-19473)***
Cvr Refining LP (HQ)...**281 207-3200**
2277 Plaza Dr Ste 500 Sugar Land (77479) ***(G-19474)***
Cvr Refining Holdings LLC (HQ)...**281 207-3200**
2277 Plaza Dr Ste 500 Sugar Land (77479) ***(G-19475)***
Cw Aerotech Services (PA)...**817 595-1949**
8825 Bud Jenson Dr North Richland Hills (76180) ***(G-15875)***
CW Davis Enterprises Inc (PA)...**972 723-1247**
5130 Edgefield Ln Midlothian (76065) ***(G-15477)***
CW Ford Rentals LP (PA)...**903 935-7608**
1603 N Longview St Kilgore (75662) ***(G-13543)***
Cw Resources Inc...903 759-8822
811 Gilmer Rd Longview (75604) ***(G-14218)***
CW Sehorn Enterprises Ltd...713 895-8834
14105 Packard St Houston (77040) ***(G-9379)***
Cwr Management LLC...512 212-9737
101 Uhland Rd Ste 212 San Marcos (78666) ***(G-18683)***
Cws, Franklin *Also called Cessac Welding Service Inc* ***(G-7164)***
Cws Road Plate LLC...713 242-7711
8411 Villa Dr Houston (77061) ***(G-9380)***
Cy-Fair Coatings Inc...281 351-7427
18115 Telge Rd 1 Cypress (77429) ***(G-3784)***
Cyanco International LLC...832 590-3641
2245 Texas Dr Ste 500 Sugar Land (77479) ***(G-19476)***
Cyber Dynamics Corporation...818 706-3580
3926 Harvey Penick Dr Round Rock (78664) ***(G-17640)***
Cyber Manufacturing LLC...713 946-4903
10060 W Gulf Bank Rd Houston (77040) ***(G-9381)***
Cyber Shield, Lufkin *Also called Elkcorp* ***(G-14526)***
Cybernance Corporation...512 850-5909
5805 Davenport Divide Rd Austin (78738) ***(G-1081)***
Cybershield of Texas, Lufkin *Also called Shieldcoat Technologies Inc* ***(G-14551)***
Cyclone Bolt Incorporated...281 372-6050
5258 N Sam Houston Pkwy E Houston (77032) ***(G-9382)***
Cyclone Bolt and Gasket, Houston *Also called Cyclone Bolt Incorporated* ***(G-9382)***
Cyclone Construction LLC...512 288-0430
12117 W Highway 290 Apt 3 Austin (78737) ***(G-859)***
Cyclone Cotton Candy LLC...281 748-9163
142 Knobcrest Dr Houston (77060) ***(G-9383)***
Cyclone Production Inc...713 979-1101
6102 Brittmoore Rd Ste C Houston (77041) ***(G-9384)***
Cyclone Services LLC...817 594-5571
220 Overton Ridge Cir Weatherford (76088) ***(G-20584)***
Cyclone Steel Services LLC...713 635-5555
4950 W Greens Rd Houston (77066) ***(G-9385)***
Cylinder Heads International...972 264-3449
3900 E Jefferson St Grand Prairie (75051) ***(G-7861)***
Cynacon, Rosenberg *Also called Ocusoft Inc* ***(G-17592)***
Cynco Specialty Inc...281 499-0519
226 Brand Ln Stafford (77477) ***(G-19298)***
Cynergy, Grapevine *Also called Kmt Wireless LLC* ***(G-8045)***
Cypress Industries Oilfield SE...281 482-3464
1302 Buttonwood Dr Friendswood (77546) ***(G-7245)***
Cypress Lumber Company Inc...903 572-6561
4191 S Us Highway 271 Mount Pleasant (75455) ***(G-15649)***
Cypress River Logging Corp...903 236-7696
4015 Valley Ranch Rd Longview (75602) ***(G-14219)***
Cypress Semiconductor Corp...512 934-6699
5204 E Ben White Blvd Austin (78741) ***(G-1082)***
Cypress Technologies LP (PA)...**512 267-9973**
17301 Fm 1431 Leander (78641) ***(G-13986)***
Cypress Telecommunications...281 449-4000
1511 Sungail Dr Spring (77386) ***(G-19205)***
Cytec Aerospace Materials, Greenville *Also called Cytec Industries Inc* ***(G-8069)***
Cytec Engineered Materials Inc...903 457-8500
4300 Jackson St Greenville (75402) ***(G-8068)***
Cytec Industries Inc...281 296-1622
25227 Grogans Mill Rd # 125 Spring (77380) ***(G-19206)***
Cytec Industries Inc...903 454-2004
4300 Jackson St Greenville (75402) ***(G-8069)***
Cytel, Spring *Also called Cypress Telecommunications* ***(G-19205)***
Cytracom LLC...877 411-2987
450 Century Pkwy Ste 100 Allen (75013) ***(G-261)***
D & A Welding & Fabrication Co, Hitchcock *Also called David Keels* ***(G-8336)***
D & D Drapery Company...713 522-1643
5000 San Jacinto St Houston (77004) ***(G-9386)***
D & D Fabrication & Erection...817 237-3306
4200 White St Fort Worth (76135) ***(G-6568)***
D & D Machinery and Sales Inc...830 438-2309
2420 Wr Larson Rd San Antonio (78261) ***(G-18039)***
D & D Performance Enterprises...817 834-8961
2923 Edith Ln Fort Worth (76117) ***(G-6569)***
D & D Swabbing LLC...903 729-7922
3471 E Us Highway 84 Palestine (75801) ***(G-16298)***
D & D Tooling and Mfg Inc...915 590-2655
1330 Pullman Dr El Paso (79936) ***(G-5710)***
D & D Twin Print Inc...210 647-7576
6387 Babcock Rd San Antonio (78240) ***(G-18040)***
D & H Quality Cabinets...903 882-0274
18558 Us Highway 69 N Lindale (75771) ***(G-14134)***
D & J Technologies Inc...817 536-0718
2010 Mrtin Lther King Fwy Fort Worth (76104) ***(G-6570)***
D & L Printing Inc...512 863-8145
552 Stadium Dr Georgetown (78626) ***(G-7646)***
D & L Quality Painting Inc...281 458-3588
12212 Green River Dr Houston (77044) ***(G-9387)***
D & L Timber Inc...936 422-3153
403 Martin Cochran Rd Huntington (75949) ***(G-12809)***
D & L Tooling and Plastics Inc...903 586-9894
950 Se Loop 456 Jacksonville (75766) ***(G-13234)***
D & L Well Service Inc...432 336-8101
4451 N State Highway 18 Fort Stockton (79735) ***(G-6329)***
D & R Casing Services Inc...432 263-8900
1317 E 11th Pl Big Spring (79720) ***(G-2078)***
D & R Custom Wldg & Cnstr Inc...830 997-1058
3494 Ranch Road 1631 Fredericksburg (78624) ***(G-7175)***
D & R Precision Manufacturing...956 386-0685
1810 S Expressway 281 Edinburg (78542) ***(G-5584)***
D & R Signs LLC (PA)...**281 988-9995**
12999 Murphy Rd Ste J1 Stafford (77477) ***(G-19299)***
D & R Specialties Inc...936 873-2947
7400 Fm 1774 Rd Navasota (77868) ***(G-15728)***
D & S Container Inc...214 637-7957
3304 Halifax St Dallas (75247) ***(G-4199)***
D & S Cycle of Arlington Inc...817 465-5454
3636 S Cooper St Arlington (76015) ***(G-657)***
D & S Drilling Ltd...806 794-8866
8008 Slide Rd Ste 29 Lubbock (79424) ***(G-14400)***
D & S Machine Works Inc...713 686-4222
4136 Pinemont Dr Houston (77018) ***(G-9388)***
D & S Tool, Dallas *Also called Dns Tool Cutter Grinding LLC* ***(G-4268)***
D & V Day Investments Corp...409 943-4265
501 6th St N Texas City (77590) ***(G-19787)***
D & W Nameplate Service Inc...713 681-6616
5200 Mitchelldale St E19 Houston (77092) ***(G-9389)***
D and C Storm Solutions...281 557-3450
1401 W Leag Cy Pkwy Ste 1 League City (77573) ***(G-13954)***
D and H Equipment Ltd...830 833-5366
1564 S Loop 163 Blanco (78606) ***(G-2110)***
D C A E Inc (PA)...**972 278-0202**
2162 S Jupiter Rd Garland (75041) ***(G-7472)***

D C G Machine Inc..903 297-2053
 1001 Cherokee Trce White Oak (75693) *(G-20713)*
D C Lites Inc...972 556-0260
 10740 Goodnight Ln Dallas (75220) *(G-4200)*
D C Lites Company..972 556-0260
 10740 Goodnight Ln Dallas (75220) *(G-4201)*
D C Organics, Godley *Also called Dairymans Choice Organics Inc (G-7734)*
D Courtney Construction Inc.................................903 694-2911
 1300 Ne Loop Carthage Carthage (75633) *(G-2905)*
D Custom..214 523-0300
 750 N Saint Paul St # 2100 Dallas (75201) *(G-4202)*
D E Shipp Belting Company....................................254 776-0493
 123 S Industrial Dr Waco (76710) *(G-20392)*
D F I, Conroe *Also called DFI Piling Inc (G-3291)*
D F I Form-Fit, Nash *Also called Detroit Forming Inc (G-15721)*
D F W Elite News...214 372-6500
 5258 County Road 3110 Campbell (75422) *(G-2645)*
D J Young Publishing...361 238-4188
 2181 Capeheart St Ingleside (78362) *(G-12893)*
D M Glover Incorporated...325 392-2561
 2973 Inter State 10 E Ozona (76943) *(G-16279)*
D Magazine Partners LP...214 939-3636
 750 N Saint Paul St # 2100 Dallas (75201) *(G-4203)*
D P S, Plano *Also called Dr Pepper Snpple Group Emplyee (G-16849)*
D R & J Inc...512 474-4331
 1209 E Cesar Chavez St Austin (78702) *(G-1083)*
D S D Services Inc...361 594-4114
 723 N Avenue E Shiner (77984) *(G-18939)*
D Square Inc..915 834-6400
 1601 Northwestern Dr # 100 El Paso (79912) *(G-5711)*
D W R Strl Con Reinforcing, Houston *Also called Deacero Usa Inc (G-9418)*
D X Distributors, Houston *Also called Dx Service Company Inc (G-9542)*
D&D Pallets Inc...817 625-7966
 3251 Weber St Fort Worth (76106) *(G-6571)*
D&D Retail LP...830 379-7340
 516 Intrstate 10 Frntage Seguin (78155) *(G-18835)*
D&G Energy Corporation (PA)................................956 686-6040
 10225 N Bentsen Rd McAllen (78504) *(G-14852)*
D&R Pipe Fab Plus Inc..281 375-2401
 520 Purdy St Brookshire (77423) *(G-2315)*
D&R Steel Works Inc..210 639-8314
 252 County Road 485 Castroville (78009) *(G-2927)*
D&S, Houston *Also called D & S Machine Works Inc (G-9388)*
D'Hanis Brick & Tile Co, D Hanis *Also called Clay DHanis Products Inc (G-3828)*
D-J's Well Svc Roustabout Off, Borger *Also called D-Js Well Svc Roustabout Inc (G-2172)*
D-Js Well Svc Roustabout Inc...............................806 273-2667
 1621 N Main St Borger (79007) *(G-2172)*
D-Signs Inc...214 327-2373
 2602 National Pl Garland (75041) *(G-7473)*
D/A Mfg Co Inc..806 995-2316
 7574 Highway 86 Tulia (79088) *(G-20034)*
D/Fw Plastics Inc..817 439-3600
 901 E Industrial Ave Saginaw (76131) *(G-17745)*
D4d Technologies LLC...972 534-3101
 2920 Telecom Pkwy Ste 100 Richardson (75082) *(G-17296)*
DA Schoggin Inc (PA)..214 350-0591
 2707 Satsuma Dr Dallas (75229) *(G-4204)*
DA Schoggin Inc...817 641-6800
 1701 Hal Ave Cleburne (76031) *(G-3086)*
Dac, Houston *Also called Digital Air Control Inc (G-9471)*
Dac Labels & Graphic Spc.....................................214 340-2055
 10491 Brockwood Rd Dallas (75238) *(G-4205)*
Dac Vision Incorporated (HQ)................................972 677-2700
 3630 W Miller Rd Ste 350 Garland (75041) *(G-7474)*
Dace Manufacturing, Alvin *Also called Marvin Dace Company (G-373)*
Daco Abrasives...713 923-4664
 7030 Avenue C Houston (77011) *(G-9390)*
Dacon Industries Co..903 589-7456
 119 Progress St Jacksonville (75766) *(G-13235)*
Dacos Bowling International (PA)...........................972 394-6507
 3618 Canyon Oaks Dr Carrollton (75007) *(G-2863)*
Dadeks Machine Works Corp..................................281 447-4723
 150 Raymac St Houston (77037) *(G-9391)*
Daeco Ltd..361 526-7017
 703 W Commons St Refugio (78377) *(G-17240)*
Daegis Inc (HQ)..214 584-6400
 600 Las Colinas Blvd E # 1500 Irving (75039) *(G-12988)*
Daggett Street Properties......................................817 332-5604
 204 E Daggett Ave Fort Worth (76104) *(G-6572)*
Dahill Industries, San Antonio *Also called Global Operations Texas LP (G-18148)*
Dahill Office Technology Corp................................713 329-9909
 2100 West Loop S Ste 1300 Houston (77027) *(G-9392)*
Dahill Office Technology Corp (HQ).......................210 805-8200
 8200 W Interstate 10 # 4 San Antonio (78230) *(G-18041)*
Daikin Manufacturing Co LP..................................972 245-1510
 5151 San Felipe St # 500 Houston (77056) *(G-9393)*
Daily Commercial Record Inc.................................214 741-6366
 706 Main St Bsmt Dallas (75202) *(G-4206)*

Daily Court Review Inc...713 869-5434
 8 Greenway Plz Ste 101 Houston (77046) *(G-9394)*
Daily DOT LLC...512 420-9403
 3112 Windsor Rd Ste A391 Austin (78703) *(G-1084)*
Daily Electric Inc...903 753-2732
 700 S Eastman Rd Longview (75602) *(G-14220)*
Daily Electric Motor, Longview *Also called Daily Electric Inc (G-14220)*
Daily Instruments Corporation (PA).......................**713 780-8600**
 5700 Hartsdale Dr Houston (77036) *(G-9395)*
Daily Offrngs Cof Roastery LLC.............................805 423-7410
 1106 Preston Trl Wolfforth (79382) *(G-20907)*
Daily Sentinel..936 631-2607
 4920 Colonial Dr Nacogdoches (75965) *(G-15694)*
Daily Texan Publications, Austin *Also called University of Texas At Austin (G-1610)*
Daily Thermetrics, Houston *Also called Daily Instruments Corporation (G-9395)*
Daily Tribune, Bay City *Also called Bay City Tribune (G-1768)*
Dairy Farmers America Inc.....................................979 743-4161
 801 James Ave Schulenburg (78956) *(G-18775)*
Dairy Farmers America Inc.....................................817 410-4500
 3500 William D Tate Ave # 100 Grapevine (76051) *(G-8025)*
Dairy LLC (HQ)..**214 442-5928**
 3801 Parkwood Blvd # 300 Frisco (75034) *(G-7278)*
Dairy Manufacturers Inc (PA)................................**972 347-2878**
 601 N Coleman St Prosper (75078) *(G-17213)*
Dairy Queen..281 481-8505
 12930 Scarsdale Blvd Houston (77089) *(G-9396)*
Dairy.com, Frisco *Also called Dairy LLC (G-7278)*
Dairymans Choice Organics Inc.............................817 641-2015
 3101 Fm 2331 Godley (76044) *(G-7734)*
Daisy Brand LLC (PA)...**972 726-0800**
 12750 Merit Dr Ste 600 Dallas (75251) *(G-4207)*
Daisy Brand LLC..972 271-7314
 3636 Leon Rd Garland (75041) *(G-7475)*
Dakota Cabinets Inc...281 741-7695
 13519 Sundale Rd Houston (77038) *(G-9397)*
Dal-Air Investment Castings, Point *Also called Dal-Air Tool Co Inc (G-17079)*
Dal-Air Tool Co Inc..903 598-2226
 Hwy 69 Nw Ste 591indus Point (75472) *(G-17079)*
Dal-Tex Specialty & Mfg Co...................................903 883-3689
 174 County Road 3318 Greenville (75402) *(G-8070)*
Dal-Tile Corporation...817 831-6935
 6323 Airport Fwy Ste A Haltom City (76117) *(G-8136)*
Dal-Tile Corporation...972 578-1600
 1300 E Plano Pkwy Ste A Plano (75074) *(G-16836)*
Dalco Athletic Lettering Inc...................................903 201-6244
 2030 Haggar St Corsicana (75110) *(G-3669)*
Dale Company Inc..713 928-3437
 6216 Navigation Blvd Houston (77011) *(G-9398)*
Dale Nichols Marble Inc...817 341-8970
 2927 Greenlee Park Weatherford (76088) *(G-20585)*
Dale Operating Company..214 979-9010
 2100 Ross Ave Ste 1870 Dallas (75201) *(G-4208)*
Dalence Operating Company, Kingwood *Also called Valence Midstream Ltd (G-13658)*
Dalhart Daily Texan, Dalhart *Also called Dalhart Publishing Co (G-3833)*
Dalhart Publishing Co..806 244-4511
 410 Denrock Ave Dalhart (79022) *(G-3833)*
Dalhart R & R Mch Works Inc.................................806 244-5686
 1006 Liberal St Dalhart (79022) *(G-3834)*
Dalla Compress Ener Solutio LL............................214 265-0400
 8150 N Central Expy Dallas (75206) *(G-4209)*
Dallas A C Horn & Company Inc.............................214 630-3311
 1269 Majesty Dr Dallas (75247) *(G-4210)*
Dallas Airmotive Inc...214 956-2505
 6114 Forest Park Rd Dallas (75235) *(G-4211)*
Dallas Baked Snacks, Dallas *Also called Frito-Lay North America Inc (G-4381)*
Dallas Bakery, Frisco *Also called Dallas Gourmet Bakery Inc (G-7279)*
Dallas Bias Fabrics Inc (PA)..................................**214 824-2036**
 1401 N Carroll Ave Dallas (75204) *(G-4212)*
Dallas Business Journal, Houston *Also called Houston Business Journals Inc (G-10219)*
Dallas Cast Stone II Corp.......................................940 382-6922
 4107 Hancock St Dallas (75210) *(G-4213)*
Dallas Child Magazine, Addison *Also called Lauren Publications Inc (G-144)*
Dallas Chinese News Inc..972 680-9577
 200 S Interurban St Richardson (75081) *(G-17297)*
Dallas Christie Lites Inc...214 637-3535
 12121 N Stemmons Fwy # 100 Dallas (75234) *(G-4214)*
Dallas Coffee Exchange...214 507-5903
 3201 N Britain Rd Irving (75062) *(G-12989)*
Dallas Decal Inc...972 772-4641
 2317 Woodmont Cir Rockwall (75032) *(G-17546)*
Dallas Directional Drlg Inc.....................................214 254-6985
 6212 Lovett Ave Dallas (75227) *(G-4215)*
Dallas Fabrication Inc..972 245-8771
 1520 Halsey Way Carrollton (75007) *(G-2864)*
Dallas Flag & Flagpole Co Lc (PA).........................**972 607-0958**
 2300 Valley View Ln # 109 Dallas (75234) *(G-4216)*
Dallas Fort Wrth Fyrestone LLC.............................817 429-0999
 5955 Eden Dr Fort Worth (76117) *(G-6573)*

Dallas Gourmet Bakery Inc (PA)................................972 247-9835
  3766 Summit Ct Frisco (75034) *(G-7279)*

Dallas Label and Packaging Inc................................972 487-6064
  14832 Venture Dr Farmers Branch (75234) *(G-6192)*

Dallas Lghthouse For Blind Inc................................214 821-2375
  4306 Capitol Ave Dallas (75204) *(G-4217)*

Dallas Lite and Barricade Inc (PA)............................214 748-5791
  1607 Fort Worth Ave Dallas (75208) *(G-4218)*

Dallas Marble Company Inc....................................972 291-9145
  1014 Lake Grove Loop Midlothian (76065) *(G-15478)*

Dallas Marble Installation, Midlothian *Also called Dallas Marble Company Inc* *(G-15478)*

Dallas Market Center Co Ltd (PA)..............................214 655-6100
  2100 N Stemmons Fwy # 1000 Dallas (75207) *(G-4219)*

Dallas Metal Fabricators Inc...................................214 421-7417
  2817 Logan St Dallas (75215) *(G-4220)*

Dallas Metal Service...972 481-1700
  13346 Bee St Ste 102 Dallas (75234) *(G-4221)*

Dallas Metal Services, Dallas *Also called Dallas Metal Service* *(G-4221)*

Dallas Morning News, Dallas *Also called Dmn Inc* *(G-4267)*

Dallas Observer LP...214 757-9000
  2030 Main St Ste 410 Dallas (75201) *(G-4222)*

Dallas Oil..214 638-9055
  3018 Ruder St Dallas (75212) *(G-4223)*

Dallas Oil Service, Dallas *Also called Dallas Oil* *(G-4223)*

Dallas Plastics LLC...903 291-0960
  900 Jordan Valley Rd Longview (75604) *(G-14221)*

Dallas Plastics LLC (PA)......................................972 289-5500
  924 Dalworth Dr Mesquite (75149) *(G-15037)*

Dallas Production Inc...940 328-1241
  300 Travis St Mineral Wells (76067) *(G-15524)*

Dallas Production Inc (PA)....................................214 369-9266
  4600 Greenville Ave # 300 Dallas (75206) *(G-4224)*

Dallas R&D Center, Richardson *Also called Affirmed Ntwrks Cmmnctons Tech* *(G-17267)*

Dallas Rosti Inc...972 554-1597
  2109 Vanco Dr Irving (75061) *(G-12990)*

Dallas Sight and Sound Inc...................................972 392-3202
  14354 Proton Rd Dallas (75244) *(G-4225)*

Dallas Steel Drums Inc.......................................214 638-7027
  2214 Singleton Blvd Dallas (75212) *(G-4226)*

Dallas Texas Tool and Die Inc................................214 634-7175
  2925 Mican Dr Dallas (75212) *(G-4227)*

Dallas Tortilla & Tamale Fctry, Dallas *Also called Dallas Tortillas Inc* *(G-4228)*

Dallas Tortillas Inc (PA).....................................214 943-7681
  309 N Marsalis Ave Dallas (75203) *(G-4228)*

Dallas Towing and Autonet Inc (PA)...........................972 219-8484
  1605 Lakeway Dr Lewisville (75057) *(G-14040)*

Dallas USA Foods Inc...214 905-1511
  1880 Lone Star Dr Dallas (75212) *(G-4229)*

Dallas Voice, Dallas *Also called Voice Publishing Co Inc* *(G-5168)*

Dallas Westport Inc..214 231-1450
  2180 French Settlement Rd Dallas (75212) *(G-4230)*

Dallco Marketing Inc...214 217-7800
  11333 Pagemill Rd Dallas (75243) *(G-4231)*

Dalpack..972 446-8101
  4400 Glenview Dr Haltom City (76117) *(G-8137)*

Daltons Best Maid Products Inc...............................800 447-3581
  1401 S Riverside Dr Fort Worth (76104) *(G-6574)*

Daltons Welding Service Inc...................................940 682-7237
  467 Rawhide Trl Weatherford (76088) *(G-20586)*

Dalworth Molds & Tools, Crowley *Also called Dalworth Technologies Inc* *(G-3754)*

Dalworth Technologies Inc....................................817 297-7976
  1065 Floyd Hampton Rd Crowley (76036) *(G-3754)*

Damuth Taxidermy Inc..325 597-0001
  2300 S Bridge St Brady (76825) *(G-2213)*

Dan A. Hughes Company, Beeville *Also called Hughes Dan A Company Lp* *(G-1985)*

Dan Blocker Petroleum Cons...................................903 234-2093
  2704 E Marshall Ave Longview (75601) *(G-14222)*

Dan-Loc Drennan, Houston *Also called Dan-Loc Group LLC* *(G-9399)*

Dan-Loc Group, Houston *Also called Dan-Loc, LLC* *(G-9400)*

Dan-Loc Group LLC (PA)......................................713 356-3500
  725 N Drennan St Houston (77003) *(G-9399)*

Dan-Loc, LLC (PA)...713 356-3500
  725 N Drennan St Houston (77003) *(G-9400)*

Dana Global Products Inc......................................915 860-7204
  12150 Rojas Dr Ste A El Paso (79936) *(G-5712)*

Dancar Investment Group Inc..................................972 633-1200
  10551 Miller Rd Ste 100 Dallas (75238) *(G-4232)*

Dancar Printing Group, Dallas *Also called Dancar Investment Group Inc* *(G-4232)*

Dandi Co, Sumner *Also called Michael Roy* *(G-19607)*

Danhard Inc (PA)..214 328-8541
  3839 Dilido Rd Dallas (75228) *(G-4233)*

Danhil Containers II Ltd (HQ)................................254 773-0704
  3715 Lucius Mccelvey Dr Temple (76504) *(G-19678)*

Danick Resources..214 827-2222
  5005 Lyndon B Johnson Fwy # 1250 Dallas (75244) *(G-4234)*

Daniel Ayala...469 245-3181
  8414 Endicott Ln Dallas (75227) *(G-4235)*

Daniel H Braman Jr Estate....................................361 578-6271
  1 Oconnor Plz Ste 1100 Victoria (77901) *(G-20257)*

Daniel Industries Inc (HQ)...................................713 467-6000
  11100 Brittmoore Park Dr Houston (77041) *(G-9401)*

Daniel Level Gages, Houston *Also called Quest-TEC Solutions Inc* *(G-11510)*

Daniel Measurement & Ctrl Inc, Houston *Also called Daniel Measurement & Ctrl LLC* *(G-9402)*

Daniel Measurement & Ctrl LLC (HQ)..........................713 827-5033
  5650 Brittmoore Rd Houston (77041) *(G-9402)*

Daniel Mike Construction Inc.................................903 389-2595
  366 West St 27 Fairfield (75840) *(G-6172)*

Daniel Steel Industries Inc...................................214 235-4509
  4640 N Belt Line Rd Mesquite (75182) *(G-15038)*

Danielle Howard...469 554-6772
  5210 Bexar St Apt 204 Dallas (75215) *(G-4236)*

Daniels Terry Cstm Trim Mllwk................................817 295-6750
  2026 Haltom Rd Fort Worth (76117) *(G-6575)*

Dankworth Packing Co Inc.....................................325 365-3552
  1609 Eubank Ave Ballinger (76821) *(G-1740)*

Dannon Yogurt, Fort Worth *Also called Danone Us LLC* *(G-6577)*

Danone Us LLC..817 336-2320
  1313 Samuels Ave Fort Worth (76102) *(G-6576)*

Danone Us LLC..817 332-1264
  1300 W Peter Smith St Fort Worth (76104) *(G-6577)*

Danos LLC..985 219-3313
  1501 W Francis Ave Midland (79701) *(G-15186)*

Danrick Industries Inc.......................................915 599-2988
  850 Kastrin St El Paso (79907) *(G-5713)*

Danwal Inc...903 581-0777
  12404 State Highway 155 S Tyler (75703) *(G-20074)*

Dap Products Inc..214 349-9951
  13555 Jupiter Rd Dallas (75238) *(G-4237)*

Dapco Services Inc..281 482-1479
  18854 Avitts Acres Alvin (77511) *(G-357)*

Daphany Broussard...832 229-0999
  17522 Stonebelt Dr Houston (77073) *(G-9403)*

Dar International Inc...972 402-0493
  2200 Creekside Cir S Irving (75063) *(G-12991)*

Darby Equipment Company, Marshall *Also called Martex Well Services LLP* *(G-14792)*

Darco Activated Carbon, Marshall *Also called Cabot Norit Americas Inc* *(G-14766)*

Dargel Boats Inc..956 464-2263
  4110 N Fm 493 Donna (78537) *(G-5488)*

Darling Global Holdings Inc., Irving *Also called Darling Ingredients Inc* *(G-12994)*

Darling Ingredients Inc (PA).................................972 717-0300
  5601 N Macarthur Blvd Irving (75038) *(G-12992)*

Darling Ingredients Inc......................................313 928-7400
  251 O Connor Ridge Blvd Irving (75038) *(G-12993)*

Darling Ingredients Inc......................................512 303-2571
  264 Fm 2336 Bastrop (78602) *(G-1753)*

Darling Ingredients Inc......................................979 778-0298
  601 Liberty Dr Bryan (77807) *(G-2469)*

Darling Ingredients Inc......................................972 717-0300
  5601 N Macarthur Blvd Irving (75038) *(G-12994)*

Darling Ingredients Inc......................................713 224-0438
  3701 Schalker Dr Houston (77026) *(G-9404)*

Darling Ingredients Inc......................................214 948-7501
  1240 Sargent Rd Dallas (75203) *(G-4238)*

Darling International, Bastrop *Also called Darling Ingredients Inc* *(G-1753)*

Darling Quick Print Inc......................................915 858-5055
  12130 Freight Ln El Paso (79936) *(G-5714)*

Dartican LLC..281 645-6370
  37707 Millers Pass Pinehurst (77362) *(G-16733)*

Darville Co...432 580-9675
  311 W 42nd St Odessa (79764) *(G-15974)*

Daryan Design Inc...214 905-6022
  3145 Halifax St Dallas (75247) *(G-4239)*

Daryan Displays, Dallas *Also called Daryan Design Inc* *(G-4239)*

Das Brot Inc..972 243-8443
  2441 Midway Rd Carrollton (75006) *(G-2721)*

Dasilveira Southwest Inc.....................................936 349-1900
  712 Industrial Blvd Madisonville (77864) *(G-14586)*

Data Center Systems, Dallas *Also called Kevin M Ehringer Entps Inc* *(G-4553)*

Data Connection Inc...972 231-2185
  11420 Chairman Dr Dallas (75243) *(G-4240)*

Data Dallas Corporation......................................214 662-5165
  1111 W Mockingbird Ln # 300 Dallas (75247) *(G-4241)*

Data Flow, Amarillo *Also called Cramer Computer Supplies Ltd* *(G-485)*

Data Matique Properties LP...................................972 272-3446
  2110 Sherwin St Garland (75041) *(G-7476)*

Data Print Ltd..806 324-4350
  509 S Johnson St Amarillo (79101) *(G-420)*

Data Voice International Inc...................................972 390-8808
  2200 Bush Dr McKinney (75070) *(G-14934)*

Datadirect Technologies, Sugar Land *Also called Neon Systems Inc* *(G-19511)*

Datagration Solutions Inc.....................................713 568-4580
  5555 San Felipe St # 2100 Houston (77056) *(G-9405)*

Dataseismic Corporation......................................713 650-3200
  1001 Texas St Ste 1020 Houston (77002) *(G-9406)*

Dataseismic Geophysical Svcs, Houston *Also called Dataseismic Corporation* **(G-9406)**
Datatronic Control Corporation 972 475-7879
  5130 Dexham Rd Rowlett (75088) **(G-17704)**
Datavoice International, McKinney *Also called Data Voice International Inc* **(G-14934)**
Davenport Electric Motors LLC 361 299-6440
  421 Junior Beck Dr Ste B Corpus Christi (78405) **(G-3511)**
Daves Tubing Testing &HOt Oil 432 263-1747
  5901 N Service Rd Big Spring (79720) **(G-2079)**
David 713 357-6393
  9950 Westpark Dr Houston (77063) **(G-9407)**
David Bacon Incorporated 512 321-2323
  445 Fm 20 Bastrop (78602) **(G-1754)**
David Hatton Logging Inc 409 656-8535
  601 County Road 4390 Hillister (77624) **(G-8318)**
David Keels 409 316-9265
  7610 Fm 2004 Rd Hitchcock (77563) **(G-8336)**
David L Jennings 281 778-3223
  9603 Pennington Ln Missouri City (77459) **(G-15579)**
David Lee Roberson 210 662-8215
  5935 Encanto Point Dr San Antonio (78244) **(G-18042)**
David McNeff Inc 972 562-0607
  114 E Louisiana St Frnt McKinney (75069) **(G-14935)**
David Pond Well Service Inc 806 435-2384
  606 S Juniper St Perryton (79070) **(G-16637)**
David R Rogers Cnstr Inc 940 549-6374
  2811 State Highway 16 S Graham (76450) **(G-7779)**
David W Arnold 713 227-7869
  2001 Lyons Ave Houston (77020) **(G-9408)**
Davids Apparel Inc 915 590-3744
  9901 Carnegie Ave El Paso (79925) **(G-5715)**
Davis Applicators LLC 830 857-3222
  18 Park Place Dr Gonzales (78629) **(G-7751)**
Davis Brothers Pubg Co Ltd 254 754-5636
  4500 Speight Ave Waco (76711) **(G-20393)**
Davis Chemical Services LLC 903 938-3800
  281 Gateway Park Dr Marshall (75672) **(G-14772)**
Davis Coiled Tubing Svcs LLC (PA) **903 927-5555**
  6310 Elysian Fields Rd Marshall (75671) **(G-14773)**
Davis Energy Services LLC 903 935-9269
  6310 Elysian Fields Rd Marshall (75671) **(G-14774)**
Davis Iron Works Inc 254 666-1000
  224 N Hewitt Dr Hewitt (76643) **(G-8299)**
Davis Machine & Mfg Co 817 684-8703
  1503 Royal Pkwy Euless (76040) **(G-6140)**
Davis Offshore LP 713 933-0064
  1360 Post Oak Blvd # 2400 Houston (77056) **(G-9409)**
Davis Steel Services, Hewitt *Also called Davis Iron Works Inc* **(G-8299)**
Davis, J L Company, Midland *Also called James Lee Davis* **(G-15258)**
Davis-Lynch LLC (HQ) **281 485-8301**
  2005 Garden Rd Pearland (77581) **(G-16552)**
Davoil Inc (PA) **817 737-6678**
  6300 Ridglea Pl Ste 1208 Fort Worth (76116) **(G-6578)**
Dawn Food Products Inc 972 485-8004
  3353 Miller Park S # 100 Garland (75042) **(G-7477)**
Dawson Geophysical Company 713 917-6772
  10333 Richmond Ave # 800 Houston (77042) **(G-9410)**
Dawson Geophysical Company (PA) **432 684-3000**
  508 W Wall St Ste 800 Midland (79701) **(G-15187)**
Daxwell LLC (PA) **281 669-0622**
  2825 Wilcrest Dr Ste 500 Houston (77042) **(G-9411)**
Day Breakers, San Angelo *Also called Toastmasters International* **(G-17835)**
Day Night Signs Inc 254 965-9000
  1715 N Graham St Stephenville (76401) **(G-19409)**
Day Ranch & Cattle, Brownwood *Also called Kjd Enterprises* **(G-2431)**
Daycor Enterprises Inc 972 838-2700
  2702 Mckinney St Melissa (75454) **(G-14996)**
Daytech Instruments Inc 713 856-6555
  6102 Brittmoore Rd Ste G Houston (77041) **(G-9412)**
Dayton-Phoenix Group Inc 281 372-0685
  3340b Greens Rd Houston (77032) **(G-9413)**
Db Bits LLC 936 539-4948
  12072 Fm 3083 Rd Conroe (77301) **(G-3289)**
Db Precision Co 713 681-6400
  6207 W Little York Rd Houston (77091) **(G-9414)**
Db Texas Holdings, Inc., Sherman *Also called Herald Democrat* **(G-18917)**
DBA Software Inc 512 342-1769
  9111 Jollyville Rd # 204 Austin (78759) **(G-1085)**
Dbljs7 Inc (PA) **440 746-1200**
  106 Mason Ct Horseshoe Bay (78657) **(G-8366)**
Dbs Group Inc 817 453-8386
  242 Churchill Loop Grapevine (76051) **(G-8026)**
Dbspectra Inc 469 322-0080
  1590 E Business Hwy 121 Lewisville (75056) **(G-14041)**
Dbspectra Inc 469 322-0080
  1590 E Hwy 121 Bus Bldg A Lewisville (75056) **(G-14042)**
Dbt Inc (PA) **409 892-2300**
  4108 Dowlen Rd Beaumont (77706) **(G-1880)**
Dbz Guitars LLC 713 934-0110
  8637 Windfern Rd Houston (77064) **(G-9415)**

DC Cadd Company (PA) **210 732-9212**
  10010 San Pedro Ave San Antonio (78216) **(G-18043)**
DC Controls Inc 361 906-0123
  335 Mcdonnell St Lewisville (75057) **(G-14043)**
Dcaf Inc 956 286-9177
  401 Mayfair Dr Laredo (78045) **(G-13877)**
Dcf Investments LLC 281 744-7445
  3601 Us Highway 190 W Livingston (77351) **(G-14152)**
Dcg Partnership I Limited (PA) **281 648-1894**
  4170a S Main St Pearland (77581) **(G-16553)**
DCI Biologicals Austin II LLC 512 865-4200
  1807 W Slaughter Ln # 4 Austin (78748) **(G-1086)**
Dcl America Inc 281 651-5900
  27603 Commerce Oaks Dr Conroe (77385) **(G-3290)**
Dcm Manufacturing Inc 817 428-3636
  2800 112th St Ste 200 Grand Prairie (75050) **(G-7862)**
Dcp Midstream LLC 432 343-7112
  2821 Waha Rd Coyanosa (79730) **(G-3695)**
Dcp Midstream LLC 361 584-8500
  7202 County Road 16 Bishop (78343) **(G-2106)**
Dcp Midstream LLC 325 392-1000
  594 S State Hwy 163 Ozona (76943) **(G-16280)**
Dcp Midstream LLC 806 228-6241
  11300 Fm 281 Spearman (79081) **(G-19085)**
Dcp Midstream LLC 432 827-1945
  Highway 158 Goldsmith (79741) **(G-7741)**
Dcp Midstream LLC 432 693-2204
  1788 Pegasus Fld Midkiff (79755) **(G-15095)**
Dcp NGL Services LP (HQ) **713 735-3600**
  5718 Westheimer Rd # 2000 Houston (77057) **(G-9416)**
Dcp Operating Company LP 361 584-8509
  7202 County Road 16 Bishop (78343) **(G-2107)**
Dcu Inc 972 816-6667
  2774 Capital Street Wylie Wylie (75098) **(G-20932)**
Dd Fluids LLC (PA) **361 985-2600**
  2699 Highway 44 Robstown (78380) **(G-17508)**
DDB Candles Inc (PA) **817 927-3377**
  2612 W Waggoman St Fort Worth (76110) **(G-6579)**
Ddi, Houston *Also called Detail Design Inc* **(G-9444)**
DDI Machine Inc 281 353-3721
  21422 Holzwarth Rd Spring (77388) **(G-19109)**
Ddi Machine Inc 281 353-5108
  1806 Fm 2920 Rd Spring (77388) **(G-19110)**
Ddm Materials Inc 970 726-1122
  807 N Frontage Rd Valley View (76272) **(G-20202)**
Ddr Manufacturing Inc 469 728-7242
  12034 S Profit Row Forney (75126) **(G-6307)**
Ddsep LLC 972 931-8000
  3305 Wiley Post Rd Carrollton (75006) **(G-2722)**
De La Garza Fence Company 210 674-8302
  6475 Enrique M Barrera Pa San Antonio (78227) **(G-18044)**
De La Rue Cash Systems, Irving *Also called Cash Processing Solutions Inc* **(G-12962)**
De Laune Drilling Service Ltd 361 664-0106
  200 Hub Alice (78332) **(G-208)**
De Maiz Tortilleria L L C 956 702-8855
  700 W Sioux Rd Pharr (78577) **(G-16697)**
De Nora Water Technologies LLC 281 240-6770
  1110 Industrial Blvd Sugar Land (77478) **(G-19477)**
De Walch Enterprise Inc 713 861-8993
  6850 Wynnwood Ln Houston (77008) **(G-9417)**
De Young Machine Works Inc 832 328-1500
  12999 Murphy Rd Ste G1 Stafford (77477) **(G-19300)**
Deacero Usa Inc (HQ) **713 697-1500**
  8411 Irvington Blvd Houston (77022) **(G-9418)**
Dealers Truck Equipment Co Inc 903 758-4451
  1231 W Marshall Ave Longview (75604) **(G-14223)**
Dealers Truck Equipment Co Inc 512 312-2100
  16201 S Ih 35 Buda (78610) **(G-2527)**
Dean Baldwin Pntg Ltd Partnr 210 293-3528
  9800 John Saunders San Antonio (78216) **(G-18045)**
Dean Chem Co, Houston *Also called Dean-Chem Inc* **(G-9419)**
Dean Due Logging Inc 936 642-2782
  1180 Rainey Ave Groveton (75845) **(G-8112)**
Dean Foods Company 214 944-4960
  1114 N Lancaster Fort Worth (76102) **(G-6580)**
Dean Foods Company 817 684-3600
  14760 Trinity Blvd Fort Worth (76155) **(G-6581)**
Dean Foods Company (PA) **214 303-3400**
  2711 N Haskell Ave # 340 Dallas (75204) **(G-4242)**
Dean Holding Company (HQ) **214 303-3400**
  2711 N Haskell Ave # 340 Dallas (75204) **(G-4243)**
Dean Intllctual Prprty Svcs II 214 303-3400
  2515 Mckinney Ave Dallas (75201) **(G-4244)**
Dean Technology Inc (PA) **972 248-7691**
  4117 Billy Mitchell Dr Addison (75001) **(G-115)**
Dean-Chem Inc 713 644-3882
  5616 Corl St Houston (77087) **(G-9419)**
Deansteel Manufacturing Co 210 226-8271
  931 S Flores St San Antonio (78204) **(G-18046)**

Debes Ice Company 409 835-4431
3750 Milam St Beaumont (77701) ***(G-1881)***
Decatur Machine Services Inc 940 627-1062
3720 Us Highway 380 Decatur (76234) ***(G-5244)***
Decorum Architectural Stone, Austin *Also called Decorum Tile & Stone Inc* ***(G-1087)***
Decorum Tile & Stone Inc 512 344-9235
4308 Terry O Ln Austin (78745) ***(G-1087)***
Dedicated Controls LLC 972 632-8716
9603 Private Road 5196 Princeton (75407) ***(G-17207)***
Dee Foundries, Houston *Also called American Bronze Alum Cast Corp* ***(G-8591)***
Deejay's Candles By Diane, Fort Worth *Also called DDB Candles Inc* ***(G-6579)***
Deen Drilling Company 940 574-2561
501 E South St Archer City (76351) ***(G-595)***
Deen Meats and Cooked Foods, Fort Worth *Also called Deen Wholesale Meat Co* ***(G-6582)***
Deen Wholesale Meat Co 817 335-2257
813 E Northside Dr Fort Worth (76102) ***(G-6582)***
DEEP DOWN, Houston *Also called Deep Down Inc* ***(G-9420)***
Deep Down Inc (PA) **281 517-5000**
18511 Beaumont Hwy Houston (77049) ***(G-9420)***
Deep Ellum Brewing Company LLC 214 888-3322
2823 Saint Louis St Dallas (75226) ***(G-4245)***
Deep Gulf Energy II LLC 281 596-0933
15011 Katy Fwy Ste 800 Houston (77094) ***(G-9421)***
Deep Gulf Energy LP 281 596-0933
15011 Katy Fwy Ste 800 Houston (77094) ***(G-9422)***
Deep Imaging Technologies Inc 281 290-0492
990 Village Square Dr A Tomball (77375) ***(G-19973)***
Deep In Heart Art Foundry 512 321-7868
405 S Jackson St Bastrop (78602) ***(G-1755)***
Deep South Barrels LLC 713 340-3103
2849 Miller Ranch Rd # 549 Pearland (77584) ***(G-16554)***
Deep Vellum Publishing Inc 972 638-7741
3000 Commerce St Dallas (75226) ***(G-4246)***
Deep Well Services, Midland *Also called Sun Energy Services LLC* ***(G-15424)***
Deep Well Tubular Service Inc 432 699-6675
6604 W Highway 80 Midland (79706) ***(G-15188)***
Deephole Solutions Inc 713 896-1121
9802 Windmill Park Ln Houston (77064) ***(G-9423)***
Deepsea Technologies Inc 713 849-5555
7807 Fairview St Houston (77041) ***(G-9424)***
Deepwater Mfg USA Inc 713 983-7117
13813 Fm 529 Rd Houston (77041) ***(G-9425)***
Deepwater Subsea LLC 832 356-6781
410 W Grand Pkwy S # 100 Katy (77494) ***(G-13359)***
Deepwell Energy Services LLC 337 780-8297
1245 W Cardinal Dr Beaumont (77705) ***(G-1882)***
Deepwell Energy Services LLC 817 796-9970
1065 Texan Trl Ste 300 Grapevine (76051) ***(G-8027)***
Deer Park Cnstr Assoc Inc 281 839-0020
5300 Barkaloo Rd Baytown (77521) ***(G-1815)***
Deerborne Energy Company 281 485-8705
2640 Broadway St Ste 102 Pearland (77581) ***(G-16555)***
Deerskin Mfg Inc 817 220-5535
4078 W Highway 199 Springtown (76082) ***(G-19273)***
Defense Contracting, Dallas *Also called Defense Logistics Agency* ***(G-4247)***
Defense Logistics Agency 214 670-9259
600 N Pearl St Dallas (75201) ***(G-4247)***
Defense Logistics Agency 210 925-4455
1014 Zbilly Mitchell Blvd # 1621 San Antonio (78226) ***(G-18047)***
Defense Solutions Group Inc 800 382-7571
6100 Conveyor Dr Cleburne (76031) ***(G-3087)***
Defiant Safe Co Inc 972 243-3711
3140 Towerwood Dr Dallas (75234) ***(G-4248)***
Deka Texas Inc 214 618-1176
8000 Dallas Pkwy Frisco (75034) ***(G-7280)***
Dekoron Wire and Cable LLC 903 572-0657
1300 Industrial Rd Mount Pleasant (75455) ***(G-15650)***
Dekron Wiring Cable, Mount Pleasant *Also called Saint-Gobain Prfmce Plas Corp* ***(G-15663)***
Del Monte Foods Inc 830 374-3451
2205 Old Uvalde Hwy Crystal City (78839) ***(G-3756)***
Del Norte Masonry Products Inc 915 584-4453
4560 Ripley Dr El Paso (79922) ***(G-5716)***
Del Rio Sun, Del Rio *Also called Val Verde Publishing LLC* ***(G-5328)***
Del Sol Food Company Inc 979 836-5978
3015 S Blue Bell Rd Brenham (77833) ***(G-2251)***
Del Valle Paper Company, Donna *Also called Sunshine Paper Corp* ***(G-5493)***
Del's Plating Works, Houston *Also called Dels Plating Industries Corp* ***(G-9428)***
Del-Dixi, Fort Worth *Also called Daltons Best Maid Products Inc* ***(G-6574)***
Delafield Corporation 903 887-2860
1103 N 3rd St Mabank (75147) ***(G-14575)***
Delaney Vineyards Inc (PA) **817 421-0950**
2000 Champagne Blvd Grapevine (76051) ***(G-8028)***
Delatorre Inc 713 522-5833
1200 Missouri St Houston (77006) ***(G-9426)***
Delaware Champion Group, San Antonio *Also called Champion Group Inc* ***(G-17998)***
Delaware River Swd LLC 432 683-7443
400 N Marienfeld St Ste 2 Midland (79701) ***(G-15189)***
Delcas Industries LLC 956 831-3311
4630 Mar St Brownsville (78521) ***(G-2348)***
Delek Renewables LLC 817 558-9255
3102 Windmill Rd Cleburne (76033) ***(G-3088)***
Delek US Holdings Inc 432 684-4210
306 W Wall St Midland (79701) ***(G-15190)***
Delfingen Us-Texas LP (HQ) **915 858-5577**
12270 Rojas Dr Ste 300 El Paso (79936) ***(G-5717)***
Deligent LLC 972 550-6111
1231 Greenway Dr Ste 270 Irving (75038) ***(G-12995)***
Dell America Latina Corp (HQ) **512 799-1022**
1 Dell Way Round Rock (78682) ***(G-17641)***
Dell Boomi, Round Rock *Also called Boomi Inc* ***(G-17628)***
Dell Computer, Round Rock *Also called Dell Inc* ***(G-17642)***
Dell Computer, Round Rock *Also called Dell Inc* ***(G-17643)***
Dell Inc (HQ) **800 289-3355**
1 Dell Way Round Rock (78682) ***(G-17642)***
Dell Inc 817 408-5725
3811 S Cooper St Ste 2056 Arlington (76015) ***(G-658)***
Dell Inc 512 324-0137
501 Dell Center Blvd # 2 Round Rock (78664) ***(G-17643)***
Dell Marketing LP (HQ) **512 513-9022**
1 Dell Way Round Rock (78682) ***(G-17644)***
Dell Products LP 866 413-3355
1 Dell Way Round Rock (78682) ***(G-17645)***
Dell Software Inc 469 221-4335
2417 Bonham Trl Grapevine (76051) ***(G-8029)***
Dell Technologies Inc (PA) **800 289-3355**
1 Dell Way Round Rock (78682) ***(G-17646)***
Dell USA LP 512 728-3366
2214 W Braker Ln Ste D Austin (78758) ***(G-1088)***
Dell USA LP (HQ) **512 725-1829**
401 Dell Way Round Rock (78664) ***(G-17647)***
Delmar Systems Inc 832 252-7100
900 Town And Country Ln # 400 Houston (77024) ***(G-9427)***
Delphi, Los Indios *Also called Aptiv Services Us LLC* ***(G-14349)***
Delphi, El Paso *Also called Aptiv Services Us LLC* ***(G-5646)***
Delphi Energy, El Paso *Also called Aptiv Services Us LLC* ***(G-5648)***
Delphi Powertrain Systems LLC 915 783-4733
48 Walter Jones Blvd El Paso (79906) ***(G-5718)***
Delphi Powertrain Systems LLC 915 783-4769
48 Walter Jones Blvd El Paso (79906) ***(G-5719)***
Delphi Thermal Systems, Laredo *Also called Aptiv Services Us LLC* ***(G-13861)***
Delray Machine LLC 830 693-5110
2407 Commerce St Marble Falls (78654) ***(G-14742)***
Delray Machine Works, Marble Falls *Also called Delray Machine LLC* ***(G-14742)***
Delray Oil Inc (PA) **210 824-7214**
900 Ne Loop 410 Ste A107 San Antonio (78209) ***(G-18048)***
Delrio Tortilla Factory (PA) **210 922-4810**
1402 Gillette Blvd San Antonio (78224) ***(G-18049)***
Dels Plating Industries Corp 713 785-4955
8736 Schumacher Ln Houston (77063) ***(G-9428)***
Delstar Metal Finishing Inc 713 849-2090
11501 Brittmoore Park Dr Houston (77041) ***(G-9429)***
Delta and Pine Land Company 806 839-2491
1596 I H 27 87 Hale Center (79041) ***(G-8118)***
Delta Centrifugal LLC 254 773-9055
3402 Center St Temple (76504) ***(G-19679)***
Delta Communications & Elec, Garland *Also called D C A E Inc* ***(G-7472)***
Delta Companies Group 281 479-7288
334 Tidal Rd Deer Park (77536) ***(G-5267)***
Delta Composites LLC 281 907-0619
1617 Peach Leaf St Houston (77039) ***(G-9430)***
Delta Controls Company Inc 281 469-4891
18410 E Paloma Dr Cypress (77433) ***(G-3785)***
Delta Deluxe, L.L.C., Deer Park *Also called Delta Companies Group* ***(G-5267)***
Delta Doors, Houston *Also called Delta Millwork* ***(G-9432)***
Delta Electronics (usa) Inc (HQ) **469 330-9100**
2925 E Plano Pkwy Plano (75074) ***(G-16837)***
Delta Electronics (usa) Inc 469 330-9100
1249 Commerce Dr Richardson (75081) ***(G-17298)***
Delta Fabrication and Mch Inc (PA) **903 645-3994**
1379 County Road 2110 Daingerfield (75638) ***(G-3831)***
Delta Flange & Mfg Inc 713 686-9702
3807 Pinemont Dr Houston (77018) ***(G-9431)***
Delta Granite and Marble Inc 210 829-7171
2011 Sable Ln San Antonio (78217) ***(G-18050)***
Delta Group Electronics Inc 972 606-2102
2920 N State Highway 360 # 100 Grand Prairie (75050) ***(G-7863)***
Delta Industries Inc 214 941-3135
9129 Perimeter St Denton (76207) ***(G-5357)***
Delta Marine Technologies 936 582-7237
550 Club Dr Ste 345 Montgomery (77316) ***(G-15631)***
Delta Millwork 713 849-2281
5210 Ashley Ct Houston (77041) ***(G-9432)***
Delta Oil & Gas Ltd (PA) **254 559-9841**
1851 E Us Highway 180 # 1 Breckenridge (76424) ***(G-2228)***
Delta Paper Stock Corp 713 666-1440
4814 Linden St Bellaire (77401) ***(G-1993)***

Delta Precision Products, Wichita Falls *Also called G A Jo Inc* ***(G-20765)***
Delta Refractories Inc....281 944-9644
21557 Provincial Blvd A Katy (77450) ***(G-13394)***
Delta Rigging & Tools Inc....877 889-8833
1149 W Hurst Blvd Hurst (76053) ***(G-12844)***
Delta Rigging & Tools Inc (HQ)....**713 512-1700**
125 Mccarty St Houston (77029) ***(G-9433)***
Delta Screen & Filtration LLC....713 856-0300
6649 N Eldridge Pkwy Houston (77041) ***(G-9434)***
Delta Seaboard LLC (PA)....**713 782-1468**
1212 W Sam Houston Pkwy N Houston (77043) ***(G-9435)***
Delta Steel Inc....918 437-7501
9217 South Fwy Fort Worth (76140) ***(G-6583)***
Delta Studweld Inc....409 755-0720
618 S Village Creek Pkwy Lumberton (77657) ***(G-14567)***
Delta Subsea, Montgomery *Also called Delta Marine Technologies* ***(G-15631)***
Delta Technology Corporation....713 464-7407
1602 Townhurst Dr Houston (77043) ***(G-9436)***
Delta Tee International Inc....817 466-9991
1000 Commercial Blvd S # 100 Arlington (76001) ***(G-659)***
Delta V Instruments Inc....972 644-6501
1870 Firman Dr Richardson (75081) ***(G-17299)***
Delta Valves and Controls LLC....713 205-1904
2843 Westside Dr Ste 17 Pasadena (77502) ***(G-16415)***
Deltatech Controls Inc....956 755-9634
594 S Vermillion Ave Brownsville (78521) ***(G-2349)***
Deluxe Honeydrop, Houston *Also called Birch B LLC* ***(G-8889)***
Delzotto Products Minn Inc....903 981-0400
5701 Highway 135 Gladewater (75647) ***(G-7720)***
Delzotto Products Texas Inc....903 981-0400
5701 State Highway 135 Gladewater (75647) ***(G-7721)***
Demarco Machine Ltd....832 230-0850
6750 Mchard Rd Houston (77053) ***(G-8377)***
Demco Manufacturing Inc....936 829-4771
1121 N Temple Dr Diboll (75941) ***(G-5462)***
Demco Manufacturing Inc....936 829-4771
1121 N Temple Dr Diboll (75941) ***(G-5463)***
Dement Plastics LLC....903 586-9894
1065 County Road 1407 Jacksonville (75766) ***(G-13236)***
Demilec International Inc....817 640-4900
3315 E Division St Arlington (76011) ***(G-660)***
Denali Intermediate Inc (HQ)....**713 627-0933**
1 Dell Way Round Rock (78682) ***(G-17648)***
Denbury Inc (PA)....**972 673-2000**
5851 Legacy Cir Ste 600 Plano (75024) ***(G-16838)***
Denbury Management, Alvin *Also called Denbury Onshore LLC* ***(G-358)***
Denbury Marine LLC....972 673-2000
5320 Legacy Dr Plano (75024) ***(G-16839)***
Denbury Onshore LLC....409 729-0211
4512 Hodgson Rd Nederland (77627) ***(G-15751)***
Denbury Onshore LLC (HQ)....**972 673-2000**
5320 Legacy Dr Plano (75024) ***(G-16840)***
Denbury Onshore LLC....281 482-7581
19315 N Highway 35 Alvin (77511) ***(G-358)***
Denbury Operating Company....972 673-2000
5320 Legacy Dr Plano (75024) ***(G-16841)***
Denbury Pipeline Holdings LLC....972 673-2000
5320 Legacy Dr Plano (75024) ***(G-16842)***
Denbury Resources Inc....972 378-4776
5100 Tennyson Pkwy Plano (75024) ***(G-16843)***
Denimatrix LLC....806 385-6401
1926 Fm 54 Littlefield (79339) ***(G-14144)***
Denison Industries Inc....903 786-4444
22 Fielder Dr Denison (75020) ***(G-5340)***
Denmark Manufacturing Inc....281 494-1527
10700 Corp Dr Ste 110 Stafford (77477) ***(G-19301)***
Dennis Energy Services Inc....956 712-1114
E Hwy 359 Laredo (78044) ***(G-13878)***
Dennis Steel Inc....512 259-4001
1105 Leander Dr Leander (78641) ***(G-13987)***
Dennis W Oates Logging LLC....936 526-2700
308 Thompson St Diboll (75941) ***(G-5464)***
Denny Kincer Inc....806 762-1069
4101 87th St Lubbock (79423) ***(G-14401)***
Denovus LLC....214 789-5725
4101 S Hwy 45 Ennis (75119) ***(G-6092)***
Denso North America USA Inc....281 821-3355
9710 Telge Rd Houston (77095) ***(G-9437)***
Densonone LLC....972 494-1911
714 Shepherd Dr Garland (75042) ***(G-7478)***
Denton Custom Window, Krum *Also called Mike Strand* ***(G-13675)***
Denton Door Company Inc....940 891-0600
2690 Old Alton Rd Denton (76210) ***(G-5358)***
Denton Publishing Company (HQ)....**940 387-3811**
314 E Hickory St Denton (76201) ***(G-5359)***
Denton Record-Chronicle, Denton *Also called Denton Publishing Company* ***(G-5359)***
Dentsply International Inc....800 877-0020
6415 Badcok Rd San Antonio (78269) ***(G-18051)***
Depco, Houston *Also called Diesel Engine and Parts Co LLC* ***(G-9466)***
Deq Coatings Inc....713 645-1777
8532 South Loop E Houston (77017) ***(G-9438)***
Deran Inc (PA)....**806 746-6926**
9405 N County Road 2000 Lubbock (79415) ***(G-14402)***
Deran Gear Inc....806 746-6926
9405 N County Road 2000 Lubbock (79415) ***(G-14403)***
Derbec Enterprises Ltd....713 533-9059
10800 Northwest Fwy Houston (77092) ***(G-9439)***
Dermatech International Inc....210 558-1387
11844 Bandera Rd Ste 105 Helotes (78023) ***(G-8236)***
Dermatlgical Assn of Texas LLP (PA)....**281 333-3376**
451 N Texas Ave Webster (77598) ***(G-20637)***
Deroma USA, Marshall *Also called Marshall Pottery Inc* ***(G-14791)***
Derrick Corporation....281 590-3003
15630 Export Plaza Dr Houston (77032) ***(G-9440)***
Derrick Equipment Company, Houston *Also called Derrick Corporation* ***(G-9440)***
Derse Inc....972 393-9046
586 S Royal Ln Coppell (75019) ***(G-3414)***
Desert Door, Driftwood *Also called Ckl Distilling LLC* ***(G-5499)***
Desert Fbrction Millwright Svc....915 821-3172
10342 Grouse Rd El Paso (79924) ***(G-5720)***
Desert Ndt LLC....325 864-6547
6849 E Hwy 80 Abilene (79601) ***(G-37)***
Desert Ndt LLC....580 225-2108
5875 N Sam Houston Pkwy W # 200 Houston (77086) ***(G-9441)***
Desert Rock Co....915 859-5969
8500 Plant Rd El Paso (79907) ***(G-5721)***
Deshazo LLC....281 227-6200
14223 Interdrive E Houston (77032) ***(G-9442)***
Deshazo Crane, Houston *Also called Deshazo LLC* ***(G-9442)***
Design Center Signs Inc....903 561-4995
2971 Elkton Trl Tyler (75703) ***(G-20075)***
Design Electric, Houston *Also called Outdoor Lighting Services LP* ***(G-11204)***
Design Flex LLC....940 825-6629
1108 E Highway 82 Nocona (76255) ***(G-15868)***
Design Packaging Group Ltd....254 840-2500
103 N Garfield St Mc Gregor (76657) ***(G-14820)***
Design Power International, Hitchcock *Also called Tom Daenen Inc* ***(G-8340)***
Design Ventures, Baytown *Also called Paul Smoke* ***(G-1831)***
Design Woodworks....713 478-7397
2603 Hodges Bend Cir Sugar Land (77479) ***(G-19478)***
Designed Security Inc....512 321-4426
1402 Hawthorne St Bastrop (78602) ***(G-1756)***
Designer Graphics, Tyler *Also called Danwal Inc* ***(G-20074)***
Designer Stone Center Inc....713 862-0120
11811 Brittmoore Park Dr Houston (77041) ***(G-9443)***
Designers Furniture Mfg, Houston *Also called Regency Purchasing Inc* ***(G-11585)***
Designs In Machine Embroidery, Dallas *Also called Dime EMB LLC* ***(G-4260)***
Designs On Garments, San Marcos *Also called Rivercity Sportswear LLC* ***(G-18707)***
Desoto Environmental MGT....972 458-0028
5430 Lyndon B Johnson Fwy # 800 Dallas (75240) ***(G-4249)***
Dessert Dreams Inc....972 313-2138
409 N Briery Rd Irving (75061) ***(G-12996)***
Dessert Gallery, The, Houston *Also called Brook Sara Enterprises Inc* ***(G-8995)***
Detail Design Inc....281 890-4715
12125 Ann Ln Houston (77064) ***(G-9444)***
Detail Mold & Mfg LLC....512 255-0525
14773 Ranch Road 2338 Georgetown (78633) ***(G-7647)***
Detail Products Inc....713 722-7789
1604 Old Angleton Rd Clute (77531) ***(G-3152)***
Detechtion USA Inc....713 357-4775
8 Greenway Plz Ste 1300 Houston (77046) ***(G-9445)***
Detectachem Inc....855 573-3537
4100 Greenbriar Dr # 180 Stafford (77477) ***(G-19302)***
Detering Company of Houston LP....713 869-3761
6800 Helmers St Houston (77022) ***(G-9446)***
Detering Company, The, Houston *Also called Detering Company of Houston LP* ***(G-9446)***
Deterling Company Inc....832 399-9393
4323 South Dr Houston (77053) ***(G-8378)***
Detex Corporation (PA)....**800 729-3839**
302 Detex Dr New Braunfels (78130) ***(G-15787)***
Detroit Forming Inc....903 832-4653
697 N Pecan St Nash (75569) ***(G-15721)***
Detsco Inc....713 999-5260
7230 Senate Ave Jersey Village (77040) ***(G-13298)***
Devon Energy Corporation....903 693-7196
611 S Shelby St Carthage (75633) ***(G-2906)***
Devon Energy Corporation....817 396-4000
9500 Glasscock Dr Cresson (76035) ***(G-3707)***
Devon Energy Corporation....806 229-6300
2560 Farm Rd Ste 301 Whiteface (79379) ***(G-20724)***
Devon Permian Corporation....432 685-0727
600 W Illinois Ave Midland (79701) ***(G-15191)***
Devonian Dirt Works LLC....432 253-7777
11611 W County Road 122 Odessa (79765) ***(G-15975)***
Devos Custom Woodworking....512 894-0464
1451 W Highway 290 Dripping Springs (78620) ***(G-5504)***

ALPHABETIC

Devries Instruments Inc 281 506-9100
5510 Brystone Dr Houston (77041) ***(G-9447)***
Dewayne Rogers Logging Inc 936 831-2060
3451 Bwo Rd Apple Springs (75926) ***(G-591)***
Dewbre Petroleum Corporation 361 888-7978
802 N Carancahua St # 1800 Corpus Christi (78401) ***(G-3512)***
Dewind Co (HQ) **469 420-9886**
2201 W Royal Ln Ste 200 Irving (75063) ***(G-12997)***
Dexas International Ltd 469 635-8100
585 S Royal Ln Ste 200 Coppell (75019) ***(G-3415)***
Dexco Polymers L.P., Houston *Also called Tsrc Specialty Materials LLC* ***(G-12398)***
Dexter Brahma LLC 817 284-5141
604 W Main St Azle (76020) ***(G-1723)***
Dexyp, Dfw Airport *Also called Thryv Inc* ***(G-5457)***
Deyoung Machine Works Inc 832 328-1500
12999 Murphy Rd Bldg G Stafford (77477) ***(G-19303)***
Dfa Dairy Brands Distrg N LLC 214 303-3400
2711 N Haskell Ave # 340 Dallas (75204) ***(G-4250)***
Dfa Dairy Brands Distrg S LLC 214 303-3400
2711 N Haskell Ave # 340 Dallas (75204) ***(G-4251)***
Dfa Dairy Brands Distrg W LLC 214 303-3400
2711 N Haskell Ave # 340 Dallas (75204) ***(G-4252)***
Dfa Dairy Brands Fluid LLC 210 732-1111
1314 Fredericksburg Rd San Antonio (78201) ***(G-18052)***
Dfa Dairy Brands Fluid LLC 361 854-4561
5330 Ayers St Corpus Christi (78415) ***(G-3513)***
Dfa Dairy Brands Fluid LLC 956 722-1718
8119 San Dario Ave Laredo (78045) ***(G-13879)***
Dfa Dairy Brands Fluid LLC 512 755-6015
1819 Rutland Dr Austin (78758) ***(G-1089)***
Dfa Dairy Brands Fluid LLC 806 765-8833
201 University Ave Lubbock (79415) ***(G-14404)***
Dfa Dairy Brands Fluid LLC 972 542-9391
1220 N Tennessee St McKinney (75069) ***(G-14936)***
Dfa Dairy Brands Fluid LLC 713 223-5296
3417 Leeland St Houston (77003) ***(G-9448)***
Dfa Dairy Brands Fluid LLC 956 686-0511
525 Beaumont Ave McAllen (78501) ***(G-14853)***
Dfa Dairy Brands Fluid LLC 903 758-8211
405 Ambassador Row Longview (75604) ***(G-14224)***
Dfa Dairy Brands Ice Cream LLC 214 905-5003
400 N Grove Rd Richardson (75081) ***(G-17300)***
Dfa Dairy Brands Ip LLC 214 303-3400
2711 N Haskell Ave # 340 Dallas (75204) ***(G-4253)***
Dfa Dairy Brands Trnsp LLC (HQ) **214 303-3400**
2711 N Haskell Ave # 340 Dallas (75204) ***(G-4254)***
Dfb Pharmaceuticals LLC (PA) **817 900-4050**
3909 Hulen St Fort Worth (76107) ***(G-6584)***
DFI Piling Inc 877 334-7453
610 Aurora Business Pk Dr Conroe (77301) ***(G-3291)***
Dfm Print Pak LLC 817 385-0600
1350 Avenue S Ste 23 Grand Prairie (75050) ***(G-7864)***
Dfm Technology Pvt USA Inc 713 547-0114
3119 Canal St Houston (77003) ***(G-9449)***
Dfr Acquisition Corporation 480 834-4392
4900 Alliance Gateway Fwy Fort Worth (76177) ***(G-6585)***
Dfs Fire Systems LLC 214 628-4061
885 E Collins Blvd # 104 Richardson (75081) ***(G-17301)***
Dfs Worldwide, Houston *Also called Dixie Freight Solutions LP* ***(G-9484)***
Dfw A-1 Pallet Inc 972 401-3502
3000 E Grauwyler Rd Irving (75061) ***(G-12998)***
Dfw Camper Corral Inc 972 241-6443
11600 N Stemmons Fwy Dallas (75229) ***(G-4255)***
DFW Comfort Experts Inc 817 633-2665
5750 Rufe Snow Dr Ste 120 North Richland Hills (76180) ***(G-15876)***
Dfw Hightech Signs, Dallas *Also called Sel Corporate Enterprises Inc* ***(G-4948)***
Dfw Infrastructure Inc 888 739-9070
809 Fm 2738 Alvarado (76009) ***(G-328)***
Dfw Instrument LLC 214 217-7600
4570 Westgrove Dr Ste 270 Addison (75001) ***(G-116)***
Dfw Instruments, Addison *Also called Dfw Instrument LLC* ***(G-116)***
Dfw Oilfield Services Inc 972 893-8025
8432 Sterling St Ste 101 Irving (75063) ***(G-12999)***
Dfw Rotec, Saginaw *Also called D/Fw Plastics Inc* ***(G-17745)***
Dge, Houston *Also called Deep Gulf Energy LP* ***(G-9422)***
Dgg Group LLC 512 398-4523
1403 E Mlk Jr Indus Blvd Lockhart (78644) ***(G-14166)***
DH Braman III 361 578-6271
201 E Santa Rosa St Victoria (77901) ***(G-20258)***
Dhaliwal Laboratories LLC (PA) **214 446-5862**
11910 Shiloh Rd Ste 130 Dallas (75228) ***(G-4256)***
Dhaliwal Labs, Dallas *Also called Dhaliwal Laboratories LLC* ***(G-4256)***
Dhw Well Service Inc (PA) **830 876-9615**
255 Loop 517 Carrizo Springs (78834) ***(G-2685)***
Diab Holdings Inc (HQ) **972 228-7600**
315 Seahawk Dr Desoto (75115) ***(G-5429)***
Diageo North America Inc 972 716-7700
5080 Spectrum Dr 1200e Addison (75001) ***(G-117)***
Dial Electrical Controls, Houston *Also called Dial Electrical of Houston* ***(G-9450)***
Dial Electrical of Houston 713 691-4666
60 Rittenhouse St Houston (77076) ***(G-9450)***
Dial-A-Pick Co 210 736-1901
1207 Fulton Ave San Antonio (78201) ***(G-18053)***
Dialog Wireline Services L L C (PA) **903 988-2311**
3100 Maverick Dr Kilgore (75662) ***(G-13544)***
Dialog Wireline Services L L C 936 264-3847
13040 Highway 105 E Conroe (77306) ***(G-3292)***
Diamante Construction & Design 361 449-7072
909 Queens Ct Laredo (78045) ***(G-13880)***
Diamante Enterprises Inc 210 655-9061
4427 Centergate St San Antonio (78217) ***(G-18054)***
Diamond C Trailer Mfg, Mount Pleasant *Also called Roadclipper Enterprises Inc* ***(G-15662)***
Diamond D Slickline Svc Co Inc 325 573-0220
2006 N Us Highway 84 Snyder (79549) ***(G-18989)***
Diamond Door Products Ltd (PA) **979 826-0238**
52294 Highway 290 Hempstead (77445) ***(G-8251)***
Diamond Ethanol LLC (HQ) **806 897-0911**
103 S Fm 2646 Levelland (79336) ***(G-14006)***
Diamond Fab 936 441-9353
1150 Beach Airport Rd Conroe (77301) ***(G-3293)***
Diamond Fiberglass, Victoria *Also called Carbon Silica Partners LP* ***(G-20251)***
Diamond Green Diesel LLC (jv) (PA) **210 345-2009**
1 Valero Way San Antonio (78249) ***(G-18055)***
Diamond Hydraulics Inc 409 440-8032
6776 Fm 2004 Rd Hitchcock (77563) ***(G-8337)***
Diamond Living LLC 281 766-1600
33031 Tamina Rd Magnolia (77354) ***(G-14600)***
Diamond M Drlg Exploration Co 210 310-3135
8620 N New San Antonio (78217) ***(G-18056)***
Diamond Manufacturing Company 972 291-8800
1548 Edgefield Way Cedar Hill (75104) ***(G-2939)***
Diamond Metal Products, San Antonio *Also called Diamante Enterprises Inc* ***(G-18054)***
Diamond Mfg Co Southwest, Cedar Hill *Also called Diamond Manufacturing Company* ***(G-2939)***
Diamond Modern Furniture LLC 877 349-5003
9524 Westheimer Rd Houston (77063) ***(G-9451)***
Diamond Offshore Company (HQ) **281 492-5300**
15415 Katy Fwy Ste 100 Houston (77094) ***(G-9452)***
Diamond Offshore Drilling Inc (HQ) **281 492-5300**
15415 Katy Fwy Ste 100 Houston (77094) ***(G-9453)***
Diamond Offshore Drlg Svcs Inc 281 492-5300
15415 Katy Fwy Ste 400 Houston (77094) ***(G-9454)***
Diamond Offshore Finance Co (HQ) **281 492-5300**
15415 Katy Fwy Ste 100 Barker (77413) ***(G-1746)***
Diamond Offshore General Co 281 492-5300
15415 Katy Fwy Ste 100 Houston (77094) ***(G-9455)***
Diamond Offshore Management Co 281 492-5300
15415 Katy Fwy Ste 100 Houston (77094) ***(G-9456)***
Diamond Offshore Nthrlands B U 281 492-5300
15415 Katy Fwy Ofc Houston (77094) ***(G-9457)***
Diamond P Lease & Well Svc Inc 979 567-1919
400 S Banks St Caldwell (77836) ***(G-2631)***
Diamond P Lease & Well Svc Inc (PA) **979 884-6111**
7981 Fm 141 Dime Box (77853) ***(G-5484)***
Diamond Plastics Corporation 806 763-8021
2323 Marshall St Lubbock (79415) ***(G-14405)***
Diamond Refractory Svcs LLC 713 378-9200
8412 Mosley Rd Houston (77075) ***(G-9458)***
Diamond Shamrock Ref & Mktg Co 361 786-2536
301 Leeroy St Three Rivers (78071) ***(G-19944)***
Diamond Shamrock Ref & Mktg Co (HQ) **210 345-2000**
6000 N Loop 1604 W San Antonio (78249) ***(G-18057)***
Diamond Specialty Services, Ingleside *Also called 3 Diamond Services LLC* ***(G-12891)***
Diamond Tank Rental Inc 432 337-0011
2655 S County Rd W Odessa (79766) ***(G-15976)***
Diamond USA Precision, Houston *Also called Diamond-Usa Prcsn-Mchining Ltd* ***(G-9459)***
Diamond Wire Spring Company 903 581-2358
4501 Candy Ln Tyler (75701) ***(G-20076)***
Diamond-Usa Prcsn-Mchining Ltd 281 596-9300
4004 Westhollow Pkwy Houston (77082) ***(G-9459)***
DIAMONDBACK, Midland *Also called Viper Energy Partners LP* ***(G-15462)***
Diamondback E&P LLC (HQ) **866 531-3667**
500 W Texas Ave Ste 1200 Midland (79701) ***(G-15192)***
Diamondback Energy Inc (PA) **432 221-7400**
500 W Texas Ave Ste 1200 Midland (79701) ***(G-15193)***
Diamonds 88, Somerville *Also called Rhodes Building Systems Inc* ***(G-19023)***
Dianal America Inc 713 758-8100
9675 Bayport Blvd Pasadena (77507) ***(G-16416)***
Diapac LLC 713 715-6300
283 Lockhaven Dr Ste 300 Houston (77073) ***(G-9460)***
Diaper Sports Group LLC 214 871-5131
6565 Hillcrest Ave # 100 Dallas (75205) ***(G-4257)***
Dibella Baking Company LLC 281 987-8985
14212 Interdrive W Houston (77032) ***(G-9461)***
Dibellos Dynamic Orthotics (HQ) **713 747-4171**
11155 Main St Houston (77025) ***(G-9462)***
Dickey Manufacturing, Stafford *Also called Dickey-Webb Inc* ***(G-19304)***

Dickey-Webb Inc 281 933-5400
　12999 Murphy Rd Bldg G Stafford (77477) (G-19304)

Dickies, Fort Worth Also called Vf Outdoor LLC (G-7099)

Dickies, Fort Worth Also called Vf Outdoor LLC (G-7100)

Dickies, Fort Worth Also called Vf Outdoor LLC (G-7101)

Dickson Furniture Industries, Houston Also called Dickson Furniture Mfrs LLC (G-9463)

Dickson Furniture Mfrs LLC (PA) 713 747-0341
　6900 Overmyer Dr Houston (77008) (G-9463)

Dickson Furniture Mfrs LLC 281 299-6197
　1502 Greengrass Dr Houston (77008) (G-9464)

Dicqie M Fuller Looney 713 266-2117
　2900 Wilcrest Dr Ste 220 Houston (77042) (G-9465)

Die & Tool Service Inc 281 498-3317
　9431 Gaines Rd Sugar Land (77498) (G-19479)

Diebold Nixdorf Incorporated 210 242-6100
　3453 N Ih 35 Ste 300 San Antonio (78219) (G-18058)

Dieco Inc (PA) 817 822-4292
　3321 Dalworth St Ste B Arlington (76011) (G-661)

Diem Digital Interiors LLC 972 899-1189
　2420 Tarpley Rd Ste 210 Carrollton (75006) (G-2723)

Diesel, Richardson Also called Fossil Partners LP (G-17316)

Diesel Displays & Interior LLC 800 747-4417
　2941 Commodore Dr Carrollton (75007) (G-2865)

Diesel Engine and Parts Co LLC 713 675-6100
　8123 Hillsboro St Houston (77029) (G-9466)

Dieselgreen Fuels LLC 512 247-3835
　2823 E M L Kng Jr Blvd Austin (78702) (G-1090)

Dietrich Industries Inc 281 383-1617
　4200 Cedar Blvd Baytown (77523) (G-1783)

Dietz Memorial Company Inc 512 451-1983
　4522 Burnet Rd Austin (78756) (G-1091)

Dietzgen Corporation 713 937-1632
　15080 Sommermeyer St # 100 Houston (77041) (G-9467)

Digco Utility Construction LP 281 833-2000
　8706 E Hardy Rd Houston (77093) (G-9468)

Digerati Dist & Mktg LLC 512 569-1772
　2000 Kinney Ave Austin (78704) (G-1092)

Digimagination LLC 281 445-6671
　10115 Sweetwater Ln Houston (77037) (G-9469)

Digiop Technologies Ltd 713 333-4900
　5902 Sovereign Dr Houston (77036) (G-9470)

Digital, Carrollton Also called Ddsep LLC (G-2722)

Digital Air Control Inc (PA) 713 975-8160
　11251 Northwest Fwy # 200 Houston (77092) (G-9471)

Digital Alliance Media Inc 512 238-3014
　1000 Heritage Center Cir Round Rock (78664) (G-17649)

Digital Banner Plus LLC 210 647-3124
　7107 Eckhert Rd Ste 1a San Antonio (78238) (G-18059)

Digital Communication Svcs Inc 682 478-2134
　1021 S Handley Dr Fort Worth (76112) (G-6586)

Digital Copy LLC 214 740-2480
　500 N Akard St Ste 250 Dallas (75201) (G-4258)

Digital Corp Companies Inc 817 801-8000
　801 Station Dr Ste 109 Arlington (76015) (G-662)

Digital Forge Media LLC 432 559-6068
　11339 W University Blvd Odessa (79764) (G-15977)

Digital I M 281 855-4933
　6615 Stonechase Houston (77084) (G-9472)

Digital Marketer Labs LLC 512 892-3022
　4330 Gaines Ranch Loop Austin (78735) (G-1093)

Digital Office Systems, McAllen Also called Montano Investments Inc (G-14892)

Digital Print Inc 817 512-3153
　217 Performance Ln # 102 Cresson (76035) (G-3708)

Digital Speech Systems Inc 972 235-2999
　901 Kilgore Ct Allen (75013) (G-262)

Digital Video Camera Co 512 301-9564
　4120 Freidrich Ln Ste 500 Austin (78744) (G-1094)

Digitcom, Fort Worth Also called Digital Communication Svcs Inc (G-6586)

Digitech Solutions Group LLC 210 545-6000
　2121 Mannix Dr San Antonio (78217) (G-18060)

Dillard Kay R & Estate AR D 940 716-5100
　2201 Kell Blvd Wichita Falls (76308) (G-20759)

Dillon Gage Refining Inc 972 484-3377
　11231 Gemini Ln Dallas (75229) (G-4259)

Dilly Letter Jackets 713 334-3232
　1221 Lumpkin Rd Houston (77043) (G-9473)

Dilogr LLC 800 455-9632
　43 Rainey St Apt 3201 Austin (78701) (G-1095)

Dimaco Ltd 972 242-2427
　1100 Valwood Pkwy Ste 104 Carrollton (75006) (G-2724)

Dime EMB LLC (PA) 888 739-0555
　10495 Olympic Dr Ste 100 Dallas (75220) (G-4260)

Dimension In Stone & Glass 214 651-7230
　205 N Hopkins St Alba (75410) (G-182)

Dimension Millworks Inc 210 281-0356
　702 San Fernando St San Antonio (78207) (G-18061)

Dimensional Cnc LLC 713 329-9711
　6920 San Antonio St Houston (77040) (G-9474)

Dimmitt Sulfur Products, Dimmitt Also called Poole Chemical Co Inc (G-5485)

Dinaco Inc (PA) 281 848-3600
　11275 S Sm Hustn Pwyw 3 Houston (77031) (G-9475)

Dinamica Inc 281 564-5100
　10808 Fallstone Rd # 350 Houston (77099) (G-9476)

Diodes Fabtech Inc 816 251-8800
　4949 Hedgcoxe Rd Ste 100 Plano (75024) (G-16844)

Diodes Incorporated 972 987-3900
　4949 Hedgcoxe Rd Plano (75024) (G-16845)

Diodes Incorporated (PA) 972 987-3900
　4949 Hedgcoxe Rd Ste 200 Plano (75024) (G-16846)

Dionysus Group LLLP 512 572-7000
　8711 W Fm 487 Florence (76527) (G-6239)

Dipper Inc 281 585-8400
　1107 W Highway 6 Alvin (77511) (G-359)

Direct Animal Products, Boyd Also called Tri Star Metals Inc (G-2209)

Direct International 817 284-7722
　2309 E Loop 820 N Fort Worth (76118) (G-6587)

Direct Prchase Qick Cplngs Inc 281 388-0253
　860 Fm 517 Rd Alvin (77511) (G-360)

Direct Trailer LP 281 713-8925
　20550 Townsen Blvd # 1001 Humble (77338) (G-12763)

Direct Trailer & Equipment Co, Humble Also called Direct Trailer LP (G-12763)

Directional Drilling, Midland Also called Scientific Drilling Intl Inc (G-15399)

Directional Prj Support Inc 281 259-7819
　33311 Lois Ln Magnolia (77354) (G-14601)

Directors Assistant LLC 972 816-5553
　2115 Irving Blvd Dallas (75207) (G-4261)

Dirnett Inc 361 375-2194
　Hwy 181 Tuleta (78162) (G-20033)

Dirt Road Music Group LLC 678 525-3982
　2608 Southern Hills Blvd Arlington (76006) (G-663)

Disc Pro Graphics Inc 281 999-2717
　339 Greens Landing Dr Houston (77038) (G-9477)

Disco, Borger Also called Diversified Industrial Svc Co (G-2175)

Disco Compressor, Borger Also called Diversified Industrial Svc Co (G-2174)

Disco Machine Liberal Company (PA) 806 274-2214
　103 Texas St Borger (79007) (G-2173)

Discount Telephone, Corpus Christi Also called Absolute Cmmnctons Ntwrk Slton (G-3464)

Discovery Acquisition Svcs LLC 281 371-2700
　4141 Katy Hockley Rd Katy (77493) (G-13395)

Discovery Green Conservancy 713 400-7336
　1500 Mckinney St Houston (77010) (G-9478)

Discovery Green Conservancy 713 529-5534
　1500 Mckinney St Houston (77010) (G-9479)

Dishaka LLC 713 988-2900
　13843 Stafford Rd Stafford (77477) (G-19305)

Dishaka U S A, Stafford Also called Dishaka LLC (G-19305)

Disingerm Inc 214 482-9135
　1200 Nesuda Rd Ste B Ennis (75119) (G-6093)

Display and Exibit Store, The, Fort Worth Also called Walls & Forms Inc (G-7117)

Display Graphics Inc 713 977-7888
　9227 Alberene Dr Houston (77074) (G-9480)

Display Products Inc 972 406-1221
　800 Fabric Xpress Way Dallas (75234) (G-4262)

Display Source Alliance LLC (HQ) 972 288-7471
　4010 Dist Dr Ste 200 Garland (75041) (G-7479)

Display Surce Design Fctry Ltd (PA) 972 288-7471
　1371 S Town East Blvd Mesquite (75149) (G-15039)

Displays & Optical Tech 512 246-6400
　110 Market St Georgetown (78626) (G-7648)

Displays By Martin Paul, Denton Also called Martin Paul Inc (G-5380)

Displays By Martin Paul Inc 940 458-7976
　9307 Interstate 35 Denton (76207) (G-5360)

Distinctive Doors Inc 972 487-6680
　933 Hensley Ln Wylie (75098) (G-20933)

Distinctive Graphics Inc 817 329-0411
　2840 Market Loop Southlake (76092) (G-19062)

Distinctive Inds Texas Inc (PA) 512 491-3500
　4516 Seton Center Pkwy # 13 Austin (78759) (G-1096)

Distribuidora Comercial LLC 830 438-3877
　5140 Us Highway 281 N Spring Branch (78070) (G-19269)

Distributed Pwr Solutions LLC 877 291-3354
　4300 Rice Drier Rd Pearland (77581) (G-16556)

Distribution Center, Brownsville Also called Starkey Laboratories Inc (G-2408)

Distribution Center 1, Sulphur Springs Also called Saputo Dairy Foods Usa LLC (G-19598)

Distribution International Inc 214 637-0151
　2322 French Settlement Rd # 300 Dallas (75212) (G-4263)

Distribution Management Co Inc 817 421-3311
　1121 S Carroll Ave # 120 Southlake (76092) (G-19063)

Distrilens, Dallas Also called Essilor Laboratories Amer Inc (G-4332)

Ditta Meat Company 281 487-2010
　4924 Oak Ave Pasadena (77503) (G-16417)

Ditta Meat Foodservice Co, Pasadena Also called Ditta Meat Company (G-16417)

Divcon Controls, Farmers Branch Also called Divcon Ems Austin LLC (G-6193)

Divcon Ems Austin LLC 214 821-6958
　1801 Royal Ln Ste 100 Farmers Branch (75229) (G-6193)

Diversco Inc 972 478-6400
　1100 Venture Ct Ste 100 Carrollton (75006) (G-2725)

**A
L
P
H
A
B
E
T
I
C**

Diverse Educatn Resources LLC 817 769-8968
2951 Northern Cross Blvd Fort Worth (76137) *(G-6588)*

Diverse Energy Systems, Houston *Also called Cimarron Energy Holding Co LLC (G-9189)*

Diverse Energy Systems, Odessa *Also called Cimarron Energy Holding Co LLC (G-15961)*

Diverse Minerals, San Antonio *Also called Coast To Coast Minerals LLC (G-18013)*

Diversfied Lbling Slutions Inc 817 471-1310
900 N Great Sw Pkwy Arlington (76011) *(G-664)*

Diversified Bus Consulting LLC 713 677-9282
10311 Urban Oak Trl Houston (77044) *(G-9481)*

Diversified Diagnostic Pdts, Houston *Also called Diversified Diagnostic Pdts (G-9482)*

Diversified Diagnostic Pdts 281 955-5323
11603 Windfern Rd Houston (77064) *(G-9482)*

Diversified Industrial Svc Co (PA) **806 274-2214**
1400 N Main St Borger (79007) *(G-2174)*

Diversified Industrial Svc Co 806 274-2214
1400 N Main St Borger (79007) *(G-2175)*

Diversified Machining Inc 512 355-3270
3703 E State Highway 29 Bertram (78605) *(G-2052)*

Diversified Materials Inc 361 993-4600
857 Cantwell Ln Corpus Christi (78408) *(G-3514)*

Diversified Metal Works Inc 409 769-1146
4810 Evangeline Dr Vidor (77662) *(G-20326)*

Diversified Plant Svcs L L C 979 848-8900
14004 S Highway 288b Angleton (77515) *(G-570)*

Diversified Printing Svcs Inc 210 226-2888
1927 W Commerce St San Antonio (78207) *(G-18062)*

Diversified Product Dev, Waco *Also called Fritel & Associates LLC (G-20404)*

Diversified Pure Chem LLC (HQ) **817 677-9418**
11050 S Us Highway 287 Rhome (76078) *(G-17254)*

Diversified Steel 281 213-3340
15922 Stenbury Ct Cypress (77429) *(G-3786)*

Diversitech Corporation 678 542-3600
Fm 949 At Interstate 10 Columbus (78934) *(G-3231)*

Diversity Industries Inc 713 667-9595
10404 Mula Rd Stafford (77477) *(G-19306)*

Diversity Petroleum LP 972 772-6025
3819 Towne Crossing Blvd Mesquite (75150) *(G-15040)*

Divine Lighting and Mfg, Conroe *Also called Divine Ltg & Fabrication LLC (G-3294)*

Divine Ltg & Fabrication LLC 936 494-3900
3704 Hilltop Dr Ste 200 Conroe (77303) *(G-3294)*

Divison Alamo Industrial Group, San Antonio *Also called Ace Welding and Trailer Co (G-17858)*

Dixie Chemical Company Inc (PA) **281 474-3271**
10601 Bay Area Blvd Pasadena (77507) *(G-16418)*

Dixie Electro Plating Company 713 224-1826
3001 Engelke St Houston (77003) *(G-9483)*

Dixie Flag and Banner Company 210 227-5039
1930 N Interstate 35 San Antonio (78208) *(G-18063)*

Dixie Freight Solutions LP 281 447-7500
15600 W Hardy Rd Houston (77060) *(G-9484)*

Dixie Manufacturing Company, San Antonio *Also called Dixie Flag and Banner Company (G-18063)*

Dixie Reel & Box Co, Irving *Also called Lone Star Container Sales Corp (G-13088)*

Dixon Farms, Tyler *Also called Southern Utilities Company (G-20154)*

Dixon Services Inc 903 579-9300
12559 County Road 192 Tyler (75703) *(G-20077)*

Diyatech Corp 214 769-6933
12005 Ford Rd Ste 520 Dallas (75234) *(G-4264)*

Djh Services LLC (PA) **713 228-5911**
712 Main St Ste 1900 Houston (77002) *(G-9485)*

Djh Services LLC 325 392-3671
Hwy 163 N Ozona (76943) *(G-16281)*

Djmw Investments LLC 281 821-0010
19255 Aldine Westfield Rd Houston (77073) *(G-9486)*

Djo Global Inc 512 832-9500
9800 Metric Blvd Austin (78758) *(G-1097)*

Djo Global Inc (HQ) **800 321-9549**
2900 Lake Vista Dr Lewisville (75067) *(G-14044)*

Djo Surgical, Austin *Also called Encore Medical LP (G-1125)*

DK Controls LLC 972 580-9300
3680 W Royal Ln Ste 175 Irving (75063) *(G-13000)*

DK Drill I LP (HQ) **817 539-2500**
820 S 6th Ave Mansfield (76063) *(G-14665)*

DK Drill I Management Co LLC (PA) **817 539-2500**
820 S 6th Ave Mansfield (76063) *(G-14666)*

DK Oil Field Services LLC 830 857-6339
101 Uhland Rd Ste 205 San Marcos (78666) *(G-18684)*

Dla Document Services 210 671-1407
1531 Connally St # 6629 San Antonio (78236) *(G-18064)*

Dlc Construction Inc 915 771-7580
8411 Lockheed Dr Ste 3 El Paso (79925) *(G-5722)*

Dlh Wendland LLC 325 655-6778
601 W 11th St San Angelo (76903) *(G-17795)*

Dlhbowles Inc 956 986-6000
3301 Nafta Pkwy Ste A Brownsville (78526) *(G-2350)*

Dlhbowles Inc 410 800-6548
12114 J E F Dr Ste A Laredo (78045) *(G-13881)*

Dlk Medical Technologies Inc 214 613-5682
5440 Red Bird Center Dr Dallas (75237) *(G-4265)*

Dlt Envelopes, Houston *Also called Dlt Printing Inc (G-9487)*

Dlt Manufacturing Inc 214 330-8334
4081 Shilling Way Dallas (75237) *(G-4266)*

Dlt Printing Inc 281 880-8883
6618 Gant Rd Houston (77066) *(G-9487)*

Dlugosch III LLC (PA) **361 564-9504**
507 E Main St Yorktown (78164) *(G-20977)*

Dlugosch III LLC 361 275-9282
101 W Heaton St Cuero (77954) *(G-3759)*

Dm, Prosper *Also called Dairy Manufacturers Inc (G-17213)*

Dm Home Entertainment LLC 972 992-3155
4300 Marsh Ridge Rd # 112 Carrollton (75010) *(G-2866)*

DMd Custom Crates & Bxs Inc 915 849-1744
12570 Weaver Rd Horizon City (79928) *(G-8364)*

DMD Products LLC 281 778-2051
9973 Fm 521 Rd Rosharon (77583) *(G-17604)*

Dmg Equipment Company LLC (PA) **936 756-6960**
1575 Fm 1485 Rd Conroe (77301) *(G-3295)*

Dmi International Inc 936 591-8006
2055 Loop 500 E Center (75935) *(G-2997)*

Dmn Inc 214 745-8383
613 W State St Garland (75040) *(G-7480)*

Dmn Inc (HQ) **214 977-8222**
1954 Commerce St Dallas (75201) *(G-4267)*

Dmn Inc 214 977-6931
3900 W Plano Pkwy Plano (75075) *(G-16847)*

Dmv Wicks Inc 713 520-0340
2015 S Shepherd Dr Houston (77019) *(G-9488)*

Dn Tanks Inc 972 823-3300
410 E Trinity Blvd Grand Prairie (75050) *(G-7865)*

Dna Stat LLC 469 500-1137
4388 County Road 444 Princeton (75407) *(G-17208)*

Dnatrix Inc 832 930-2401
2450 Holcombe Blvd Ste X2 Houston (77021) *(G-9489)*

DNB Stainless Concepts LLC 940 479-0079
9535 Swafford Rd Ste 100 Justin (76247) *(G-13341)*

Dnp Industrial, Alvin *Also called Direct Prchase Qick Cplngs Inc (G-360)*

Dns Tool Cutter Grinding LLC 972 484-7491
12029 Denton Dr Dallas (75234) *(G-4268)*

Dnv GL Noble Denton Usa LLC 281 396-1000
1400 Ravello Rd Katy (77449) *(G-13396)*

Do It Best, Plano *Also called Foxworth-Galbraith Lumber Co (G-16872)*

Do It Best, Ozona *Also called Triple C Hardware & Lumber Inc (G-16289)*

Dobbs Coating Systems Inc (PA) **817 341-1777**
1888 Mineral Wells Hwy Weatherford (76088) *(G-20587)*

Dobbs Corporation 806 655-7791
100 Highway 60 Canyon (79015) *(G-2670)*

Dobbs-Stanford Corporation 214 350-4222
2715 Electronic Ln Dallas (75220) *(G-4269)*

Dobie Supply LLC (PA) **512 437-6499**
3809 S 2nd St Ste D200 Austin (78704) *(G-1098)*

Docresources LLC 832 802-6008
5010 Fm 2100 Rd Ste 107 Crosby (77532) *(G-3729)*

Docs On Demand Inc 713 980-9500
1500 Citywest Blvd # 700 Houston (77042) *(G-9490)*

Document Solutions 512 471-5464
2706 Montopolis Dr Austin (78741) *(G-1099)*

Dof Subsea Usa Inc 713 896-2500
5365 W Sam Houston Pkwy N # 400 Houston (77041) *(G-9491)*

Doggett Heavy McHy Svcs LLC 361 289-0727
134 N Padre Island Dr Corpus Christi (78406) *(G-3515)*

Doguets Rice Milling Company 409 866-2297
795 S Major Dr Beaumont (77707) *(G-1883)*

Doiy LLC 469 513-4159
325 N Saint Paul St # 3100 Dallas (75201) *(G-4270)*

Dolan Northwest LLC 972 559-6900
4855 Ohio Dr Frisco (75035) *(G-7257)*

Dolco Packaging Corp 214 337-4711
4700 S Westmoreland Rd Dallas (75237) *(G-4271)*

Dollamur LP (PA) **817 534-3344**
1734 E El Paso St Ste 110 Fort Worth (76102) *(G-6589)*

Dollamur Sport Surfaces, Fort Worth *Also called Dollamur LP (G-6589)*

Dollar B R Sr Et Al A TX Ptnr 940 665-6262
1908 N Weaver St Gainesville (76240) *(G-7342)*

Dollar Enterprise, Gainesville *Also called Dollar B R Sr Et Al A TX Ptnr (G-7342)*

Dollar Saver, Midland *Also called Hearst Corporation (G-15244)*

Dolphin Geophysical, Houston *Also called Shearwater Geoservices Inc (G-11855)*

Dolphin Graphics Inc 713 789-7474
5601 Bintliff Dr Ste 530 Houston (77036) *(G-9492)*

Domar Leasing, Midland *Also called Doyle Hartman Oil Producer (G-15196)*

Domatex Inc 281 219-1800
842 Buschong St Houston (77039) *(G-9493)*

Dome Energy Inc (HQ) **281 558-8585**
6363 Woodway Dr Ste 715 Houston (77057) *(G-9494)*

Dome Petrochemical Lc 713 540-9075
6655 W Bay Rd Baytown (77523) *(G-1784)*

Dominion Building Products, Houston *Also called Assa Abloy Door Group LLC (G-8724)*

(G-0000) Company's Geographic Section entry number

Dominion Machining & Mfg Inc 281 477-7355
9140 Meadow Vista Blvd Houston (77064) (G-9495)

Dominion Voting Systems Inc 214 907-3010
2010 Redbud Blvd Ste 110 McKinney (75069) (G-14937)

Domtar Industries LLC 972 929-3565
8800 Sterling St Irving (75063) (G-13001)

Domtar Paper Company LLC 972 929-8581
8800 Sterling St Irving (75063) (G-13002)

Don Brock Distributor Inc 361 592-5126
400 General Cavazos Blvd Kingsville (78363) (G-13626)

Don H Wilson Inc 903 478-3860
3499 Fm 2022 Elkhart (75839) (G-6059)

Don Hardy Race Cars Inc 806 983-3774
202 W Missouri St Floydada (79235) (G-6292)

Don Lane Logging Inc 409 584-2288
Hwy 83 Pineland (75968) (G-16738)

Don Spencer Co 817 389-4413
12656 Fm 2331 Godley (76044) (G-7735)

Don Young Company Incorporated (PA) 214 630-0934
8181 Ambassador Row Dallas (75247) (G-4272)

Don-Nan Machine & Mfg, Midland Also called Don-Nan Pump and Supply Co Inc (G-15194)

Don-Nan Pump and Supply Co Inc (PA) 432 682-7742
3427 E Garden Cy Hwy 158 Midland (79706) (G-15194)

Don-Nan Pump and Supply Co Inc 432 530-1925
8350 W 42nd St Odessa (79764) (G-15978)

Donnelley Financial, Dallas Also called R R Donnelley & Sons Company (G-4856)

Donovan White Cabinets Inc 903 569-5611
1348 Bromberg St Mineola (75773) (G-15506)

Dons Grinding Lapping Svc Inc 713 643-7928
8700 Tweed Dr Houston (77061) (G-9496)

Door Center 713 932-9343
1843 Bingle Rd Houston (77055) (G-9497)

Door Control Services 210 732-1214
321 Vz County Road 4500 Ben Wheeler (75754) (G-2032)

Door Controls Usa Inc 903 833-5815
321 Vz County Road 4500 Ben Wheeler (75754) (G-2033)

Door Masters Woodworks, Houston Also called Door Center (G-9497)

Door Sa-Lutions Inc 915 781-0664
6840 Industrial Ave El Paso (79915) (G-5723)

Doors and Bldg Component Dbci, Houston Also called Nci Group Inc (G-11017)

Doosan Hf Controls Corporation 469 568-6500
1624 W Crosby Rd Ste 124 Carrollton (75006) (G-2726)

Doosan Mecatec America Co Ltd 713 961-4646
4900 Woodway Dr Ste 725 Houston (77056) (G-9498)

Doosan Turbomachinery Svcs Inc 713 364-7500
12000 N P St La Porte (77571) (G-13731)

Dorado Construction Group, San Angelo Also called BP Surface Solutions LLC (G-17786)

Dorado Oil Company (PA) 361 241-3200
9101 Up River Rd Corpus Christi (78409) (G-3516)

Dorchester Minerals LP (PA) 214 559-0300
3838 Oak Lawn Ave Ste 300 Dallas (75219) (G-4273)

Dorf Ketal Chemicals LLC 713 343-2377
11200 Westheimer Rd # 400 Houston (77042) (G-9499)

Doris Usa Inc 713 973-2520
840 Gessner Rd Ste 400 Houston (77024) (G-9500)

Dormae Products Inc 512 398-2650
1300 Blackjack St Lockhart (78644) (G-14167)

Dorsal Services Inc (PA) 361 394-6300
6052 E Highway 44 Alice (78332) (G-209)

Dorsett Bros Concrete Sup Inc (PA) 281 487-0264
3210 Lilac St Pasadena (77505) (G-16419)

Dorstener Wire Tech Inc (HQ) 281 651-6226
19994 Hickory Twig Way Spring (77388) (G-19111)

Dos Carolinas Inc 210 222-9117
2400 S Flores St San Antonio (78204) (G-18065)

Dossey Oilfield Services LLC 325 928-0001
2450 Fm 1235 Merkel (79536) (G-15014)

DOT It Rest Fulfillment LLC 817 275-7714
2001 E Randol Mill Rd Arlington (76011) (G-665)

DOT Metals Products, San Antonio Also called Southeastern Metals Mfg Co Inc (G-18645)

DOT-It Restaurant Fulfillment, Dallas Also called Inovar Packaging Group LLC (G-4504)

Double B Foods Inc 254 435-6187
109 E Morgan Meridian (76665) (G-15013)

Double Barrel Downhole Tech 281 495-1200
10511 Fallstone Rd Houston (77099) (G-9501)

Double Barrel Fabrication Inc 512 496-7448
4605 Krupala Rd San Angelo (76905) (G-17796)

Double C Canvas & Repairs Inc 972 723-8000
4551 Old Highway 67 N Midlothian (76065) (G-15479)

Double D Ranchwear Inc 361 293-9239
120 W Grand Ave Yoakum (77995) (G-20962)

Double D Ranchwear Inc (PA) 361 293-2394
122 W Grand Ave Yoakum (77995) (G-20963)

Double D Tongs Inc 432 381-0602
7507 Andrews Hwy Odessa (79765) (G-15979)

Double Eagle Energy Oper LLC 817 928-3260
3724 Hulen St Fort Worth (76107) (G-6590)

Double Eagle Lone Star LLC 817 928-3260
3724 Hulen St Fort Worth (76107) (G-6591)

Double J Saddlery Inc 361 293-6364
2243 Us Highway 77a S Yoakum (77995) (G-20964)

Double Jj Corporation (PA) 214 353-0230
2604 Freewood Dr Dallas (75220) (G-4274)

Double K Drilling LLC 940 567-2855
518 Us Highway 281 N Jacksboro (76458) (G-13218)

Double K Well Service LP 940 567-2855
518 Us Highway 281 N Jacksboro (76458) (G-13219)

Double L Leather LLC 888 643-5117
2321 N Masch Branch Rd # 329 Denton (76207) (G-5361)

Double Mountain Inc 940 988-4491
305 E Swenson Ave Aspermont (79502) (G-815)

Double O Field Services 361 364-2673
2000 S San Patricio St Sinton (78387) (G-18961)

Double R Brand Foods LLC (PA) 713 868-0030
6633 Portwest Dr Ste 110 Houston (77024) (G-9502)

Double R Brand Mfg LLC 979 289-3421
11700 Highway 290 W Brenham (77833) (G-2252)

Double R Brnd Prmium Fd Pdts L 713 868-0030
800 Ellen Trout Dr Lufkin (75904) (G-14524)

Double R Construction Inc 903 452-7890
6202 State Highway 42 N Kilgore (75662) (G-13545)

Double S Signs LLC 903 838-8999
3502 New Boston Rd Texarkana (75501) (G-19762)

Double T Oilfield Service LLC 325 315-2370
4707 E County Road 133 Midland (79706) (G-15195)

Double T Ranch, Dallas Also called Thompson & Thompson (G-5086)

Double T Ranch, Ozona Also called Thompson & Thompson (G-16287)

Double-E, Inc., Dallas Also called Parco Double-E LLC (G-4788)

Douglas Pads & Sports Inc 713 697-9787
12325 Cutten Rd Houston (77066) (G-9503)

Douglassville Timber Co 903 796-7691
307 N Louise St Ste B Atlanta (75551) (G-842)

Dover Equipment Inc (PA) 713 690-5200
5829 W S Houston Pky N407 Houston (77041) (G-9504)

Dovetail Custom Wood & Metal, Del Valle Also called Dovetail Custom Woodworks Inc (G-5330)

Dovetail Custom Woodworks Inc 512 501-6717
5235 Hwy 71 E Bldg A Del Valle (78617) (G-5330)

DOW CHEMICAL, Houston Also called Union Carbide Corporation (G-12434)

Dow Chemical Company 281 474-4495
13300 Bay Area Blvd La Porte (77571) (G-13732)

Dow Chemical Company 979 238-2011
2301 N Brazosport Blvd Freeport (77541) (G-7196)

Dow Chemical Company 713 667-5133
4709 Laurel St Bellaire (77401) (G-1994)

Dow Chemical Company 281 228-2800
4460 Highway 225 Deer Park (77536) (G-5268)

Dow Chemical Company 713 767-1615
1800 Tidal Rd Deer Park (77536) (G-5269)

Dow Chemical Company 281 452-5951
16717 Jacintoport Blvd Houston (77015) (G-9505)

Dow Chemical Company 409 948-5886
3301 5th Ave S Texas City (77590) (G-19788)

Dow Chemical Company 281 228-3060
1900 Tidal Rd Deer Park (77536) (G-5270)

Dow Chemical Company 713 246-0369
550 Independence Pkwy S La Porte (77571) (G-13733)

Dow Chemical Company 713 826-5234
1254 Enclave Pkwy Houston (77077) (G-9506)

Dow Chemical Company 409 722-3451
Hwy 347 Beaumont (77705) (G-1884)

Dow Chemical Company 713 751-7285
9502b Bayport Blvd Pasadena (77507) (G-16420)

Dow Jones & Company Inc 214 951-7251
3333 Lee Pkwy Ste 600 Dallas (75219) (G-4275)

Dow Machinery Corporation 832 467-0600
12530 Taylor Rd Houston (77041) (G-9507)

Dowell Schlumberger, Sugar Land Also called Schlumberger Technology Corp (G-19548)

Dowell Schlumberger, Alice Also called Schlumberger Technology Corp (G-234)

Dowell Schlumberger, Longview Also called Schlumberger Technology Corp (G-14305)

Dowell Schlumberger, Midland Also called Schlumberger Technology Corp (G-15398)

Dowell Schlumberger, Sugar Land Also called Schlumberger Technology Corp (G-19552)

Dowell Schlumberger, Sugar Land Also called Schlumberger Technology Corp (G-19553)

Downey Publishing Inc (PA) 817 416-6661
2545 E Southlake Blvd Southlake (76092) (G-19064)

Downhole Drilling Dynamics LLC (PA) 936 344-9329
220 Longstreet Rd New Waverly (77358) (G-15860)

Downhole Energy LLC 469 250-7179
310 E Interstate 30 Garland (75043) (G-7481)

Downhole Innovations LLC 936 537-4640
6807 Willow Brook Park Houston (77066) (G-9508)

Downhole Technology LLC 281 820-2545
12450 Cutten Rd Houston (77066) (G-9509)

Downhole Threading Svcs Inc 281 462-9800
2935 Highway 90 Crosby (77532) (G-3730)

Downhole Well Solutions LLC 832 761-5111
18300 Strack Dr Ste 900 Spring (77379) (G-19112)

A
L
P
H
A
B
E
T
I
C

Downing Well Service Inc 830 665-4923
207 State Highway 132 N C Devine (78016) *(G-5449)*

Downstream Aggregator LLC (HQ) **281 247-8118**
16315 Market St Channelview (77530) *(G-3017)*

Downtown Color Express Inc 214 630-5533
2707 N Stemmons Fwy Dallas (75207) *(G-4276)*

Downunder Gosolutions Amer LLC 832 582-3221
16200 Park Row Ste 100 Houston (77084) *(G-9510)*

Doyle & Hamilton Inc 817 882-8080
2927 Morton St Fort Worth (76107) *(G-6592)*

Doyle Hartman Oil Producer 432 684-4011
500 N Main St Midland (79701) *(G-15196)*

Doyles Construction & Mfg Inc 940 549-5517
624 6th St Graham (76450) *(G-7780)*

Dozier Cabinet Works Inc 940 566-5315
2742 Milam Rd E Sanger (76266) *(G-18725)*

Dpc Enterprises LP 713 863-1947
300 Jackson Hill St Houston (77007) *(G-9511)*

Dpr, Houston *Also called Drilling & Prod Resources LLC (G-9529)*

Dps Holdings Inc 972 673-7000
5301 Legacy Dr Plano (75024) *(G-16848)*

Dps Teck LLC 972 241-0339
11937 Denton Dr Ste 102 Dallas (75234) *(G-4277)*

Dpt Laboratories Ltd 210 531-7100
8045 Lindbergh Lndg San Antonio (78235) *(G-18066)*

Dpt Laboratories Ltd 210 396-6252
4040 Broadway Ste 401 San Antonio (78209) *(G-18067)*

Dpt Laboratories Ltd (PA) **866 225-5378**
318 Mccullough Ave San Antonio (78215) *(G-18068)*

Dpt Laboratories Ltd 210 476-8100
307 E Josephine St San Antonio (78215) *(G-18069)*

Dpt Laboratories Ltd 210 531-7100
3300 Research Plz San Antonio (78235) *(G-18070)*

Dr Pepper, Mason *Also called Mason Bottling Company (G-14815)*

Dr Pepper, Irving *Also called American Bottling Company (G-12928)*

Dr Pepper Bottling Co In Texas, Sherman *Also called American Bottling Company (G-18906)*

Dr Pepper Snapple Group, Plano *Also called American Bottling Company (G-16785)*

Dr Pepper Snpple Group Emplyee 972 673-7000
5301 Legacy Dr Plano (75024) *(G-16849)*

Dr Pepper/Seven Up Inc (HQ) **972 673-7000**
5301 Legacy Dr Fl 1 Plano (75024) *(G-16850)*

Dr Pepper/Seven Up Inc 979 532-8801
505 Rugeley Ln Wharton (77488) *(G-20699)*

Dr Ppper Btlg Wichita FLS Inc 940 322-5416
1100 7th St Wichita Falls (76301) *(G-20760)*

Dr Welding & Construction, Fredericksburg *Also called D & R Custom Wldg & Cnstr Inc (G-7175)*

Draco Spring Manufacturing Co (PA) **713 645-4973**
7042 Long Dr Houston (77087) *(G-9512)*

Draco Spring Manufacturing Co 713 645-4973
7143 Edna St Houston (77087) *(G-9513)*

Draco Technologies LLC 432 213-5626
711 Colgate Ave Big Spring (79720) *(G-2080)*

Draeger Safety Diagnostics Inc (HQ) **972 929-1100**
4040 W Royal Ln Ste 136 Irving (75063) *(G-13003)*

Drafft Root Beer Inc 214 638-8442
3138 Quebec St Ste 106 Dallas (75247) *(G-4278)*

Drag N Fly Trucking 903 987-0027
434 Copperhead Trl Kilgore (75662) *(G-13546)*

Dragon Esp Ltd (PA) **409 833-2665**
1655 Louisiana St Beaumont (77701) *(G-1885)*

Dragon Industries & Products, La Porte *Also called Modern AG Products LLC (G-13778)*

Dragon Products LLC (HQ) **409 833-2665**
1655 Louisiana St Beaumont (77701) *(G-1886)*

Dragonfire Racing, Fort Worth *Also called Dfr Acquisition Corporation (G-6585)*

Dragonfly Garment Design Corp 830 549-5113
217 S River St Ste 202 Seguin (78155) *(G-18836)*

Draka USA Distributions, Houston *Also called Prysmian Cbles Systems USA LLC (G-11468)*

Drake Alliance Corporation (HQ) **713 869-9121**
10343 Ella Blvd Houston (77038) *(G-9514)*

Drake Company, The, Houston *Also called Drake Alliance Corporation (G-9514)*

Drake Controls LLC 713 996-0190
8731 Fallbrook Dr Houston (77064) *(G-9515)*

Drake Industries Inc 512 251-2231
1916 Hydro Dr Austin (78728) *(G-1100)*

Draken International LLC (PA) **863 289-0849**
9800 Hillwood Pkwy # 100 Fort Worth (76177) *(G-6593)*

Dralco Systems LLC (PA) **817 599-7335**
1219 Fort Worth Hwy Weatherford (76086) *(G-20588)*

Drapery Man Corporation 210 733-5444
2911 Dason Ledge San Antonio (78258) *(G-18071)*

Drawworks LP 512 610-5200
10555 Fm 1301 Rd Boling (77420) *(G-2147)*

Drc Media LLC 817 336-8300
101 Summit Ave Ste 803 Fort Worth (76102) *(G-6594)*

Dreadnaught Industries 210 601-8149
1648 Palo Alto Dr Von Ormy (78073) *(G-20347)*

Dreamwrks Ansthesia Assoc Pllc 936 639-3036
505 S John Redditt Dr Lufkin (75904) *(G-14525)*

Dreco Inc 281 452-7900
16730 Jacintoport Blvd Houston (77015) *(G-9516)*

Dreco Channelview, Houston *Also called Dreco Inc (G-9516)*

Dregon LLC 910 670-8211
5108 Bragg Ave El Paso (79904) *(G-5724)*

Dresser LLC (HQ) **262 549-2626**
4425 Westway Park Blvd Houston (77041) *(G-9517)*

Dresser LLC 361 881-8182
1257 Southern Minerals Rd Corpus Christi (78409) *(G-3517)*

Dresser LLC 281 884-1000
1250 Hall Ct Deer Park (77536) *(G-5271)*

Dresser LLC 979 265-1309
2024 Brazosport Blvd N Richwood (77531) *(G-17468)*

Dresser LLC 832 590-2306
16240 Port Nw Ste 100 Houston (77041) *(G-9518)*

Dresser Flow Control, Corpus Christi *Also called Dresser LLC (G-3517)*

Dresser Measurement & Control, Richwood *Also called Dresser LLC (G-17468)*

Dresser Natural Gas Solutions, Houston *Also called Natural Gas Sltions N Amer LLC (G-11008)*

Dresser-Masoneilan Ctrl Valves, Deer Park *Also called Dresser LLC (G-5271)*

Dresser-Rand Company, Houston *Also called Dresser-Rand Group Inc (G-9522)*

Dresser-Rand Company 713 346-2257
1415 Lumpkin Rd Houston (77043) *(G-9519)*

Dresser-Rand Company 713 354-6100
1210 W Sam Houston Pkwy N Houston (77043) *(G-9520)*

Dresser-Rand Company 713 468-4210
1200 W Sam Houston Pkwy N Houston (77043) *(G-9521)*

Dresser-Rand Control Systems, Houston *Also called Dresser-Rand LLC (G-9523)*

Dresser-Rand Group Inc (HQ) **713 354-6100**
15375 Memorial Dr Ste 600 Houston (77079) *(G-9522)*

Dresser-Rand LLC 713 467-2221
1202 W Sam Houston Pkwy N Houston (77043) *(G-9523)*

Dresser-Rand LLC (HQ) **713 354-6100**
1200 W Sam Houston Pkwy N Houston (77043) *(G-9524)*

Driftwood Estate Winery LLC 512 692-6229
4001 Elder Hill Rd Driftwood (78619) *(G-5500)*

Driftwood Vineyard, Driftwood *Also called Driftwood Estate Winery LLC (G-5500)*

Dril-Quip Inc (PA) **713 939-7711**
6401 N Eldridge Pkwy Houston (77041) *(G-9525)*

Dril-Quip Inc 713 939-7711
13550 Hempstead Rd Houston (77040) *(G-9526)*

Drilex Corporation 281 821-3360
16311 Aldine Westfield Rd Houston (77032) *(G-9527)*

Drilformance LLC (PA) **832 772-7808**
15815 Waverly Dr Houston (77032) *(G-9528)*

Drilformance LLC 832 704-2025
5400 N Big Spring St Midland (79705) *(G-15197)*

Drill King International, Mansfield *Also called DK Drill I LP (G-14665)*

Drill-Master International, Mansfield *Also called Sandvik Mining & Cnstr USA LLC (G-14715)*

Drillbit Industries, Houston *Also called Tri-Max Corporation (G-12363)*

Drillchem Drlg Solutions LLC 281 713-8941
8701 New Trls Dr Ste 100 The Woodlands (77381) *(G-19852)*

Drillform Drilling Eqp Inc 281 948-9122
12120 W County Road 100 Odessa (79765) *(G-15980)*

Drilling & Prod Resources LLC 713 996-7600
9455 Baythorne Dr Houston (77041) *(G-9529)*

Drilling & Production Systems, Katy *Also called Cameron International Corp (G-13355)*

Drilling Info Inc (PA) **512 477-9200**
2901 Via Fortuna Ste 200 Austin (78746) *(G-1101)*

Drilling Spc Animal Plants, Conroe *Also called Chevron Phillips Chem Co LP (G-3275)*

Drilling Specialties Co LLC 800 423-3985
10001 Six Pines Dr The Woodlands (77380) *(G-19853)*

Drilling Specialties Company, The Woodlands *Also called Drilling Specialties Co LLC (G-19853)*

Drilling Structures Intl Inc 281 880-8833
2431 Kelly Ln Houston (77066) *(G-9530)*

Drilling Supply and Mfg Inc 512 243-1986
7301 Hwy 183 S Austin (78744) *(G-1102)*

Drilltec, Houston *Also called Dtc P&T Liquidating Co (G-9534)*

Drilltec Technologies Inc 713 895-9852
10875 Kempwood Dr Ste 2 Houston (77043) *(G-9531)*

Drilltools 903 986-3745
4001 Enterprise St Kilgore (75662) *(G-13547)*

Drink A Pak Inc 325 690-1550
5401 N 1st St Abilene (79603) *(G-38)*

Drive Shafts By Cannon, Austin *Also called Cannon Engineering Inc (G-1023)*

Driver License Office, Childress *Also called Transportation Texas Dept (G-3056)*

Drivetanks.com, Houston *Also called Paradigm SRP LLC (G-11239)*

Drone Detector, Katy *Also called Drone Labs LLC (G-13397)*

Drone Labs LLC 214 538-1467
2507 Blue Reef Dr Katy (77449) *(G-13397)*

Dronesense Inc 512 582-0444
2600 Via Fortuna Ste 340 Austin (78746) *(G-1103)*

Droplets Inc 214 969-9970
555 Republic Dr Ste 311 Plano (75074) *(G-16851)*

Droubis Bakery & Deli Inc (PA) **713 988-5897**
7333 Hillcroft St Houston (77081) *(G-9532)*

Drover Energy Services LLC 903 986-8911
2505 N Longview St Kilgore (75662) *(G-13548)*

Drs Infrared Technology, Dallas *Also called Drs Ntwork Imaging Systems LLC (G-4280)*

Drs Ntwork Imaging Systems LLC 214 996-2837
13544 N Central Expy Dallas (75243) *(G-4279)*

Drs Ntwork Imaging Systems LLC 877 377-4783
13532 N Central Expy Dallas (75243) *(G-4280)*

Drs Training Ctrl Systems LLC 214 381-7161
4212 S Buckner Blvd Dallas (75227) *(G-4281)*

Drsk Limited Partnership 972 644-1490
113 E Polk St Richardson (75081) *(G-17302)*

Drucker Labs LP 972 881-2344
1600 Capital Ave Ste 100 Plano (75074) *(G-16852)*

Drug Prevention Resources Inc 972 518-1821
201 Ferris Ave Ste G Waxahachie (75165) *(G-20540)*

Drum Equipment Inc 936 336-9256
311 River Bend Rd Liberty (77575) *(G-14117)*

Drw Holdings 949 581-9398
1809 Hur Industrial Blvd Cedar Park (78613) *(G-2966)*

Drw Precision Inc 281 356-4900
13113 Noack Rd Magnolia (77355) *(G-14602)*

Dryco Skylights Inc 817 477-3441
11800 E Farm Rd 917 Mansfield (76063) *(G-14667)*

Ds Oilfield Construction LLC 361 396-0089
186 Fm 2507 Alice (78332) *(G-210)*

Ds Services of America Inc 281 391-3770
27815 Highway Blvd Katy (77494) *(G-13360)*

Ds Services of America Inc 713 947-1900
8206 1/2 Mosley Rd Houston (77075) *(G-9533)*

Ds2, Sheppard Afb *Also called Pae Avation Technical Svcs LLC (G-18902)*

DSA Operating Company LLC 210 734-5121
1235 W Laurel San Antonio (78201) *(G-18072)*

Dsgi, Cleburne *Also called Defense Solutions Group Inc (G-3087)*

DSI, Bastrop *Also called Designed Security Inc (G-1756)*

DSI Solutions LLC 817 633-1772
701 Highlander Blvd # 250 Arlington (76015) *(G-666)*

Dsl Forming Collars, Houston *Also called Ls Packaging Design Inc (G-10694)*

DSM Fluid Power Inc 512 243-1986
7301 Us Highway 183 S Austin (78744) *(G-1104)*

DSM Mayhew, Austin *Also called Drilling Supply and Mfg Inc (G-1102)*

DSM Nutritional Products LLC 979 373-5010
1000 County Road 227 A Freeport (77541) *(G-7197)*

Dstj Corporation 936 447-1174
13948 Parrish Trl Montgomery (77316) *(G-15632)*

Dsx Access Systems Inc 214 553-6140
10731 Rockwall Rd Dallas (75238) *(G-4282)*

Dtac, Midlothian *Also called CW Davis Enterprises Inc (G-15477)*

Dtc P&T Liquidating Co (PA) 713 996-8802
10875 Kempwood Dr Ste 2 Houston (77043) *(G-9534)*

DTE Gas Resources LLC 817 302-4600
301 Commerce St Ste 1800 Fort Worth (76102) *(G-6595)*

Dtm Precision Machining Inc 281 564-7997
15117 Aurora St Sugar Land (77498) *(G-19480)*

Dtn LLC 713 430-7100
2925 Briarpark Dr Ste 710 Houston (77042) *(G-9535)*

DTR, Odessa *Also called Diamond Tank Rental Inc (G-15976)*

Dualco Inc 713 644-1164
8404 Braniff St Houston (77061) *(G-9536)*

Duane Ollinger (PA) 806 935-6786
1 Mile West On 87 Dumas (79029) *(G-5520)*

Dubai Petroleum Company 281 293-1000
600 N Dairy Ashford Rd Houston (77079) *(G-9537)*

Dublin Bottling Works Inc 254 445-3939
221 S Patrick St Dublin (76446) *(G-5515)*

Dublin Dr Pepper, Dublin *Also called Dublin Bottling Works Inc (G-5515)*

Dudley J Perio Inc 512 295-4234
18109 Foust Dr Buda (78610) *(G-2528)*

Duel Products Inc 972 429-5607
702 Cooper Dr Wylie (75098) *(G-20934)*

Duffco Oil Tools Inc 325 672-2446
810 Anson Ave Abilene (79601) *(G-39)*

Duffens Optical, Houston *Also called Essilor Laboratories Amer Inc (G-9702)*

Duffin Engine Service 210 341-8183
1227 Hallmark Dr San Antonio (78216) *(G-18073)*

Dugan Trailer 254 729-3253
1326 Highway 164 W Groesbeck (76642) *(G-8107)*

Dugga Boys Inc 361 364-4311
1010 Sodville St Sinton (78387) *(G-18962)*

Duke Energy Natural Gas Corp 361 579-4600
404 Private Road 1045 Hallettsville (77964) *(G-8121)*

Duke Forms & Printing 512 985-6587
417 Colorado Dr Cedar Creek (78612) *(G-2935)*

Dukes Outdoor Advertising 432 447-2251
181 S Frontage Rd Pecos (79772) *(G-16620)*

Dumpzit LLC 817 238-6563
10021 Jacksboro Hwy Fort Worth (76135) *(G-6596)*

Duna USA Inc (HQ) 281 383-3862
4210 Fm 1405 Rd Baytown (77523) *(G-1785)*

Dunagin Transport Company (PA) 325 928-5253
10179 S Access Rd I 20 20 I Merkel (79536) *(G-15015)*

Dunagin Transport Company 325 928-5253
1215 S Broadway St Aspermont (79502) *(G-816)*

Dunan Microstaq Inc 512 628-2890
4120 Freidrich Ln Ste 225 Austin (78744) *(G-1105)*

Duncan Drilling Company 432 263-7721
402 E Fm 700 Rd 700th Big Spring (79720) *(G-2081)*

Dunlaps Custom Cabinets Inc 254 829-2279
6448 Old Dallas Rd Elm Mott (76640) *(G-6063)*

Dunn Automotive Systems LLC 956 283-5544
165 S Oak Trl Fredericksburg (78624) *(G-7176)*

Dunn Bros Coffee, Houston *Also called Grand Coffees of Texas LLC (G-10014)*

Dunn Enterprises Inc (PA) 713 869-4841
23438 Dunn Ln Porter (77365) *(G-17174)*

Dunn Pallet Co 409 722-2933
516 Orchard Ave Port Neches (77651) *(G-17159)*

Dunn Services Inc 361 275-3952
9827 Us Highway 183 S Cuero (77954) *(G-3760)*

Dunn Welding Equipment, Porter *Also called Gulf States Abrasive Mfg (G-17177)*

Dunns Valve Testers Inc 281 350-4767
1827 Riley Fuzzel Rd # 2 Spring (77386) *(G-19207)*

Dunphy Graphics Solutions Inc 281 363-9261
2319 Timberloch Pl Ste A The Woodlands (77380) *(G-19854)*

Duoline Technologies LLC (HQ) 903 734-1371
250 W Bluebird Rd Gilmer (75645) *(G-7706)*

Duphil Inc (PA) 409 883-8550
6608 Interstate 10 W Orange (77632) *(G-16238)*

Dupont, Ingleside *Also called E I Du Pont De Nemours & Co (G-12895)*

Dupont, Orange *Also called E I Du Pont De Nemours & Co (G-16241)*

Dupont, La Porte *Also called E I Du Pont De Nemours & Co (G-13734)*

Dupont Coating Solutions, Houston *Also called Axalt Powde Coati Syste Usa I (G-8756)*

Dupont High Performance Mtl, Pasadena *Also called Dupont Specialty Pdts USA LLC (G-16421)*

Dupont Packg & Indus Polymers, Orange *Also called E I Du Pont De Nemours & Co (G-16239)*

Dupont Specialty Pdts USA LLC 281 474-8614
9701 Bayport Blvd Pasadena (77507) *(G-16421)*

Dupont Victoria Plant, Victoria *Also called E I Du Pont De Nemours & Co (G-20259)*

Dupr Energy Services LLC (PA) 713 231-9000
510 Bering Dr Ste 455 Houston (77057) *(G-9538)*

Dupriest Company The, Dallas *Also called Ireo Reproductions LLC (G-4512)*

Dura, Brownsville *Also called Dus Operating Inc (G-2351)*

Dura-Mar Venus Inc (PA) 972 223-8008
1101 S Hampton Rd Desoto (75115) *(G-5430)*

Dura-Tech Processes Inc 817 473-7888
1204 Antler Dr Mansfield (76063) *(G-14668)*

Durabox Corrugated Pdts Inc 915 440-4409
9155 Billy The Kid St El Paso (79907) *(G-5725)*

Duramast Industries Inc 936 395-0334
9756 Fm 1696 Rd Bedias (77831) *(G-1981)*

Durango Midstream LLC (HQ) 346 351-2787
10077 Grogans Mill Rd # 300 Spring (77380) *(G-19208)*

Durham Inc 432 684-5557
505 N Big Spring St # 403 Midland (79701) *(G-15198)*

Duro Bag Manufacturing Company 956 843-6607
410 N 4th St Hidalgo (78557) *(G-8305)*

Duro Metals, Dallas *Also called Leggett & Platt Incorporated (G-4590)*

Duron Systems Inc 281 469-0040
9110 Taub Rd Houston (77064) *(G-9539)*

Durrset Amigos Ltd (PA) 210 798-5360
4669 W Us Highway 90 San Antonio (78237) *(G-18074)*

Dus Operating Inc 956 371-3057
3201 Nafta Pkwy Brownsville (78526) *(G-2351)*

Dusold Designs Inc 972 221-1455
1491 N Kealy Ave Ste 29 Lewisville (75057) *(G-14045)*

Dust Free LP 972 635-9565
1112 Industrial Dr Royse City (75189) *(G-17719)*

Dutch Marble Creations 956 399-6767
901 S Williams Rd San Benito (78586) *(G-18656)*

Dutchmans Market Inc 830 997-5693
1609 E Main St Fredericksburg (78624) *(G-7177)*

Duval Well Service Inc 361 394-7079
Us Hwy 59 Ne Freer (78357) *(G-7223)*

DVC Company, Austin *Also called Digital Video Camera Co (G-1094)*

Dve Management Inc 214 957-1095
2824 Terrell Rd Ste 406 Greenville (75402) *(G-8071)*

Dw Energy Group 214 758-0880
104 Decker Ct Ste 300 Irving (75062) *(G-13004)*

Dwell App LLC 214 417-9424
3333 Premier Dr Plano (75023) *(G-16853)*

Dwo Enterprises, Diboll *Also called Dennis W Oates Logging LLC (G-5464)*

Dx Holding Company Inc (PA) 713 863-1947
300 Jackson Hill St Houston (77007) *(G-9540)*

Dx Oilfield Products LLC 713 863-1947
300 Jackson Hill St Houston (77007) *(G-9541)*

Dx Service Company Inc 281 457-4888
1919 Jacintoport Blvd Houston (77015) *(G-9542)*

Dycem Corporation 832 447-1420
  1725 Hughes Landing Blvd # 865 The Woodlands (77380) *(G-19855)*

Dyna Drill Technologies LLC (HQ) **281 227-1250**
  23400 Colonial Pkwy Katy (77493) *(G-13398)*

Dyna Group International Inc (PA) **830 620-4400**
  1661 S Seguin Ave New Braunfels (78130) *(G-15788)*

Dyna Therm Corporation 832 616-3094
  10077 Grogans Mill Rd # 300 The Woodlands (77380) *(G-19856)*

Dyna Torque Technologies Inc 713 937-6699
  11050 W Little York Rd F Houston (77041) *(G-9543)*

Dyna-Chem, Dallas *Also called Cobb Carpet Supply Co* *(G-4133)*

Dyna-Drill, Katy *Also called Dyna Drill Technologies LLC* *(G-13398)*

Dyna-Mix Inc 903 593-7387
  705 S Lyons Ave Ste A Tyler (75702) *(G-20078)*

Dyna-Mix Texas, Tyler *Also called Dyna-Mix Inc* *(G-20078)*

Dynacon Inc 979 823-2690
  831 Industrial Blvd Bryan (77803) *(G-2470)*

Dynaenergetics Us Inc (HQ) **512 327-2043**
  2050 W Sam Houston Pkwy S # 1750 Houston (77042) *(G-9544)*

Dynalloy Industries Inc (PA) **936 825-2532**
  25880 State Highway 6 S Navasota (77868) *(G-15729)*

Dynalloy Industries Inc 936 825-2532
  25 880 Hwy 6 S Navasota (77868) *(G-15730)*

Dynalloy Industries Inc 713 856-9377
  6103 Brittmoore Rd Houston (77041) *(G-9545)*

Dynalyst Corporation 512 365-1203
  1008 Crlos Parker Blvd Sw Taylor (76574) *(G-19653)*

Dynalyst Manufacturing Corp (PA) **281 293-7980**
  738 Highway 6 S Ste 230 Houston (77079) *(G-9546)*

Dynalyst Manufacturing Corp 512 365-1230
  1008 Crlos Parker Blvd Sw Taylor (76574) *(G-19654)*

Dynamax, Houston *Also called Dinamica Inc* *(G-9476)*

Dynamic Attractions Inc (PA) **817 652-1212**
  1601 E Lamar Blvd Ste 214 Arlington (76011) *(G-667)*

Dynamic Color Graphics, Arlington *Also called DOT It Rest Fulfillment LLC* *(G-665)*

Dynamic Crane Svc Fbrction Inc 713 849-1341
  5512 Clara Rd Houston (77041) *(G-9547)*

Dynamic Downhole Services LLC 210 881-9002
  4714 College Park San Antonio (78249) *(G-18075)*

Dynamic Drilling Fluids, Robstown *Also called Dd Fluids LLC* *(G-17508)*

Dynamic Fishing & Rentals LLC 432 684-3898
  3400 N County Road 1148 Midland (79705) *(G-15199)*

Dynamic Inc (PA) **817 838-1800**
  2801 Glenda St Fort Worth (76117) *(G-6597)*

Dynamic Industries Inc 361 775-1500
  1074 Fm 2725 Ingleside (78362) *(G-12894)*

Dynamic Intgrtons Ctrl Systems 512 716-0817
  475 Round Rock West Dr Round Rock (78681) *(G-17650)*

Dynamic Lifting Solutions, Houston *Also called Dynamic Crane Svc Fbrction Inc* *(G-9547)*

Dynamic Orthotics Prosthetics, Houston *Also called Dibellos Dynamic Orthotics* *(G-9462)*

Dynamic Precision Mch Tls Inc 713 466-4545
  5852 Thomas Rd Houston (77041) *(G-9548)*

Dynamic Precision Mfg LLC 713 466-4545
  5852 Thomas Rd Houston (77041) *(G-9549)*

Dynamic Production (HQ) **817 838-1800**
  5070 Mark Iv Pkwy Fort Worth (76106) *(G-6598)*

Dynamic Products Inc 281 457-3500
  16520 Peninsula St Houston (77015) *(G-9550)*

Dynamic Rubber Div, Athens *Also called Cosmec Inc* *(G-825)*

Dynamic Signs Systems Mktg LLC 281 255-0420
  24501 Hufsmth Kohrvll 4 Tomball (77375) *(G-19974)*

Dynamic Tool Company Inc 915 598-2330
  1421 Vanderbilt Dr El Paso (79935) *(G-5726)*

Dynamic Voice Data Inc 800 838-5070
  4403 Greenbriar Dr Stafford (77477) *(G-19307)*

Dynamo Paintball Company, Plano *Also called Baari Inc* *(G-16797)*

Dynasty Consolidated Inds Inc 214 630-3132
  4250 Cambridge Rd Fort Worth (76155) *(G-6599)*

Dynasty Wireline Services LLC 432 363-3100
  6800 W Highway 80 Midland (79706) *(G-15200)*

Dynatec Scientific Labs 915 849-1322
  11940 Golden Gate Rd El Paso (79936) *(G-5727)*

Dynatouch Corporation 210 828-8343
  9901 Broadway Ste 115 San Antonio (78217) *(G-18076)*

Dynatron Software Inc 972 488-0393
  2703 Telecom Pkwy Ste 140 Richardson (75082) *(G-17303)*

Dyne Oil & Gas Inc 806 274-2952
  116 W 7th St Borger (79007) *(G-2176)*

Dynegy, Chico *Also called Tri Resources Inc* *(G-3054)*

Dynegy, Midland *Also called Tri Resources Inc* *(G-15445)*

Dynegy, Gladewater *Also called Tri Resources Inc* *(G-7729)*

Dynegy, Mont Belvieu *Also called Tri Resources Inc* *(G-15623)*

Dynegy, Canadian *Also called Tri Resources Inc* *(G-2655)*

Dynegy, Breckenridge *Also called Tri Resources Inc* *(G-2240)*

Dynegy, Waskom *Also called Tri Resources Inc* *(G-20523)*

Dynegy, Breckenridge *Also called Tri Resources Inc* *(G-2241)*

Dynocom Industries Inc 817 284-8844
  2447 Riverbend West Dr Fort Worth (76118) *(G-6600)*

Dyopath LLC (PA) **855 749-6758**
  13430 Nw Fwy Ste 1000 Houston (77040) *(G-9551)*

Dysol Inc 817 335-1826
  5475 E State Hwy 114 Rhome (76078) *(G-17255)*

Dzignpak, Carrollton *Also called Hager Containers L P* *(G-2750)*

Dziuk Meat Market Inc 830 538-3082
  608 Us Highway 90 W Castroville (78009) *(G-2928)*

Dzs Inc (HQ) **469 327-1531**
  5700 Tennyson Pkwy # 400 Plano (75024) *(G-16854)*

E & A Materials Inc 940 692-3290
  6007 Seymour Hwy Wichita Falls (76310) *(G-20761)*

E & A Ventures LLC 903 297-0829
  114 Stevens St Longview (75604) *(G-14225)*

E & E Engine Machine and Parts 210 225-1141
  1602 S Flores St San Antonio (78204) *(G-18077)*

E & E Polaris Services Inc 281 367-6000
  2700 Res Frest Dr Ste 100 Spring (77381) *(G-19209)*

E & H, Houston *Also called E and H Originals In Wood Inc* *(G-9552)*

E & H Drilling Co 940 549-0370
  New Castle Hwy Graham (76450) *(G-7781)*

E & I Contractors, Dallas *Also called Palacio Ivis* *(G-4777)*

E & L Graphics LLC 915 591-8789
  1144 Vista De Oro Dr A El Paso (79935) *(G-5728)*

E & T Plastic Mfg Co Inc 214 622-6263
  1174 Security Dr Dallas (75247) *(G-4283)*

E A C, Navasota *Also called Ellwood Advnced Components LLC* *(G-15732)*

E A Sween Company 972 219-0566
  1301 Ridgeview Ste 100 Lewisville (75057) *(G-14046)*

E and H Originals In Wood Inc 832 203-7629
  10902 Kingspoint Rd Houston (77075) *(G-9552)*

E B R Energy LP 281 265-6500
  245 Commerce Green Blvd # 165 Sugar Land (77478) *(G-19481)*

E Barr Feeds Inc 830 672-6515
  212 Saint Louis St Gonzales (78629) *(G-7752)*

E C I, El Paso *Also called Electrical Components Intl Inc* *(G-5750)*

E C S, Houston *Also called Engineered Cstm Solutions LLC* *(G-9646)*

E G C Corporation 281 774-6100
  8103 Lancoln Rd Humble (77396) *(G-12764)*

E I Du Pont De Nemours & Co 409 883-8411
  2739 Fm 1006 Orange (77630) *(G-16239)*

E I Du Pont De Nemours & Co 409 886-6442
  3055 Fm 1006 Orange (77630) *(G-16240)*

E I Du Pont De Nemours & Co 281 471-2771
  4107 Lake Ct Missouri City (77459) *(G-15580)*

E I Du Pont De Nemours & Co 361 572-1330
  2697 Old Bloomington Rd N Victoria (77905) *(G-20259)*

E I Du Pont De Nemours & Co 361 776-1872
  4127 Hwy 361 Ingleside (78362) *(G-12895)*

E I Du Pont De Nemours & Co 409 883-8411
  2739 Fm 1006 Orange (77630) *(G-16241)*

E I Du Pont De Nemours & Co 281 470-2371
  11621 Strang Rd La Porte (77571) *(G-13734)*

E I Du Pont De Nemours & Co 361 572-1330
  2695 Old Bloomington Rd N Victoria (77905) *(G-20260)*

E I Du Pont De Nemours & Co 713 413-0000
  12701 Almeda Rd Houston (77045) *(G-9553)*

E I Products Inc 512 357-2776
  3000 S Interstate 35 # 375 Austin (78704) *(G-1106)*

E J Reynolds Company Inc 281 331-4556
  4252 Fm 528 Rd Alvin (77511) *(G-361)*

E J Ward Inc (PA) **210 824-7383**
  8620 N New Braunfels Ave # 200 San Antonio (78217) *(G-18078)*

E L F, Odessa *Also called E L Farmer & Company* *(G-15981)*

E L Farmer & Company (PA) **432 366-2010**
  3800 E 42nd St Ste 417 Odessa (79762) *(G-15981)*

E M I, Leander *Also called Electronics & Metals Inds Inc* *(G-13988)*

E M I, Houston *Also called Electro-Mechanical Inds Inc* *(G-9592)*

E Major Tech LLC 972 385-6466
  13620 Omega Rd Farmers Branch (75244) *(G-6194)*

E P M, Dallas *Also called Eastman Park Micrographics Inc* *(G-4296)*

E P S, Pasadena *Also called Engineered Pump Services Inc* *(G-16428)*

E P T, Hutto *Also called Enhanced Production Tech Inc* *(G-12878)*

E R Carpenter LP 281 474-7257
  11002 Choate Rd Pasadena (77507) *(G-16422)*

E R Carpenter LP 804 359-0800
  4443 Bronze Way Dallas (75236) *(G-4284)*

E R Carpenter LP (PA) **804 359-0800**
  2611 N General Bruce Dr Temple (76501) *(G-19680)*

E R T, Houston *Also called Talos Ert LLC* *(G-12152)*

E S D Sign Services, Houston *Also called Electrical Sign Displays Inc* *(G-9589)*

E S I, San Antonio *Also called Engineering Spectrum Inc* *(G-18090)*

E S I, Plano *Also called Estech Systems Inc* *(G-16866)*

E S Tooling Co, Pasadena *Also called Gagemaker LP* *(G-16445)*

E Seis, Houston *Also called Eseis Inc* *(G-9696)*

E T Associates, Longview *Also called Jason Jones* *(G-14256)*

E T C, Tyler *Also called East Texas Containers Inc (G-20079)*

E T C Company 210 403-6402
8111 Westchester Dr # 600 Dallas (75225) *(G-4285)*

E Tamez Coml Rfrgn & AC Inc 210 884-5059
2403 N Zarzamora St San Antonio (78201) *(G-18079)*

E X P Fabrication LLC 940 453-3382
9435 Swafford Rd Justin (76247) *(G-13342)*

E Z Cleaning Solutions 214 841-9626
2603 N Carroll Ave Dallas (75204) *(G-4286)*

E Z Filter Base Manufacturing 972 272-5800
406 S Barnes Dr Garland (75042) *(G-7482)*

E Z Roustabout 432 556-8419
1400 S Fairgrounds Rd Midland (79701) *(G-15201)*

E&P Services Group, Kilgore *Also called Riddles Dehi & Chem Svc Co LLC (G-13587)*

E&R Vacuum Truck Services LLC 956 618-9590
8 And A Half Ware Rd Edinburg (78539) *(G-5585)*

E-Ceptionist Inc 713 520-6688
405 Main St Ste 800 Houston (77002) *(G-9554)*

E-Coating Inc 936 715-0700
1413 S University Dr Nacogdoches (75961) *(G-15695)*

E-M Design Time Inc 972 279-4720
3915 Fairlakes Dr Dallas (75228) *(G-4287)*

E-Mds Inc (PA) 512 257-5200
10901 Stonelake Blvd Austin (78759) *(G-1107)*

E-Mist, Fort Worth *Also called Sanotech 360 LLC (G-6974)*

E-Mist Innovations Inc 844 563-6478
3013 Joyce Dr Fort Worth (76116) *(G-6601)*

E-Spectrum Technologies Inc (PA) 210 696-8848
12725 Spectrum Dr San Antonio (78249) *(G-18080)*

E-Z Heat Corporation 830 693-4005
7375 A Highway 281 S Horseshoe Bay (78657) *(G-8367)*

E-Z Line Pipe Support Co LLC 713 675-6693
21340 Highway 6 Manvel (77578) *(G-14733)*

E2 Energy Services LLC 214 365-3200
8150 N Central Expy Dallas (75206) *(G-4288)*

E2open LLC (PA) 866 432-6736
9600 Great Hills Trl 300e Austin (78759) *(G-1108)*

E2open LLC 925 460-1700
9600 Great Hills Trl 300e Austin (78759) *(G-1109)*

E3rivers LLC 817 247-5828
4163 S Fm 730 Decatur (76234) *(G-5245)*

E4d Technologies, Richardson *Also called D4d Technologies LLC (G-17296)*

E9 Treatments, Boerne *Also called Electrolab Inc (G-2118)*

Ea Services Inc (PA) 866 711-1001
2800 Broadway St Ste C Pearland (77581) *(G-16557)*

Eads Cooling Solutions LLC 713 780-1551
3914 Fairhill Dr Ste 200 Houston (77063) *(G-9555)*

Eagle Automation, Fort Worth *Also called Scada Products LLC (G-6975)*

Eagle Brush & Chemical Inc 972 484-0391
11242 Indian Trl Dallas (75229) *(G-4289)*

Eagle Burgmann Industries, Houston *Also called Eagleburgmann Industries LP (G-9567)*

Eagle Burgmann Industries, Clute *Also called Eagleburgmann Industries LP (G-3153)*

Eagle Circuits Inc 214 349-0288
10820 Sanden Dr Dallas (75238) *(G-4290)*

Eagle Completion Usa Ltd 432 561-7000
13600 W I 20 E Odessa (79765) *(G-15982)*

Eagle Creek Inc (HQ) 760 431-6400
510 Crystal City Hwy # 5 Uvalde (78801) *(G-20189)*

Eagle Creek Travel Gear, Uvalde *Also called Eagle Creek Inc (G-20189)*

Eagle Energy Acquisitions, Houston *Also called Eagle Hydrocarbons LLC (G-9558)*

Eagle Eye Signs LP 972 466-2100
13375 N Stmmons Fwy Ste 4 Carrollton (75006) *(G-2727)*

Eagle Fabricators Inc (PA) 281 442-8787
5522 Shirley Ln Houston Houston (77032) *(G-9556)*

Eagle Family Foods Group LLC 915 584-7189
255 Montoya Rd El Paso (79932) *(G-5729)*

Eagle Ford Gathering System, San Antonio *Also called Texas Pipeline Webb (G-18541)*

Eagle Ford Reclamation Co LLC 361 786-3960
119 N Hwy 281a 281 A Three Rivers (78071) *(G-19945)*

Eagle Gas & Oil Co Inc 214 369-1545
5950 Berkshire Ln # 1100 Dallas (75225) *(G-4291)*

Eagle Gasket and Packing Co 713 290-8811
1110 Ulrich Rd Tomball (77375) *(G-19975)*

Eagle Gaskets, Tomball *Also called Eagle Gasket and Packing Co (G-19975)*

Eagle Geophysical Inc (PA) 713 881-2800
520 Post Oak Blvd Ste 320 Houston (77027) *(G-9557)*

Eagle Hydrocarbons LLC 713 300-3245
11750 Katy Fwy Ste 830 Houston (77079) *(G-9558)*

Eagle Manufacturing & Svc Ltd 432 561-7000
13600 W Interstate 20 Odessa (79765) *(G-15983)*

Eagle Materials Inc (PA) 214 432-2000
5960 Berkshire Ln Ste 900 Dallas (75225) *(G-4292)*

Eagle Metal Products LLC (PA) 903 887-3581
802 N 3rd St Mabank (75147) *(G-14576)*

Eagle Molded Products 281 894-4995
12018 Palmerton Dr Ste A Houston (77064) *(G-9559)*

Eagle Oil & Gas Co (HQ) 940 723-7322
2525 Kell Blvd Ste 510 Wichita Falls (76308) *(G-20762)*

Eagle Oilfield Welding 830 965-4255
17544 S Interstate Hwy 35 Dilley (78017) *(G-5480)*

Eagle Pco LLC 432 400-2771
3109 W County Rd 1108 Midland (79706) *(G-15202)*

Eagle Pco LLC 361 756-0666
1189 County Road 429 Pleasanton (78064) *(G-17065)*

Eagle Pco LLC (PA) 817 678-8998
5808 Fm 3455 Rd Navasota (77868) *(G-15731)*

Eagle Pipe LLC 713 464-7473
9525 Katy Fwy Ste 306 Houston (77024) *(G-9560)*

Eagle Pressure Control, Navasota *Also called Eagle Pco LLC (G-15731)*

Eagle Print, San Antonio *Also called Associated Creditors Inc (G-17919)*

Eagle Printing Company 979 776-4444
1729 Briarcrest Dr Bryan (77802) *(G-2471)*

Eagle Railcar Services LP (PA) 254 631-0168
9701 E I 20 Eastland (76448) *(G-5563)*

Eagle Rock Energy, Canadian *Also called Eagle Rock Field Services LP (G-2648)*

Eagle Rock Energy, Houston *Also called Eagle Rock Pipeline LP (G-9565)*

Eagle Rock Energy G&P LLC 281 408-1200
1415 La St Ste 2700 Houston (77002) *(G-9561)*

Eagle Rock Energy Partners LP (HQ) 281 408-1200
5847 San Felipe St # 3000 Houston (77057) *(G-9562)*

Eagle Rock Field Services LP 806 323-5381
9898 County Rd 3 Canadian (79014) *(G-2648)*

Eagle Rock Field Services LP (HQ) 281 408-1200
1415 La St Ste 2700 Houston (77002) *(G-9563)*

Eagle Rock Manufacturing LLC 432 682-3030
1113 Dayton Rd Midland (79706) *(G-15203)*

Eagle Rock Operating LP (HQ) 281 408-1200
1415 La St Ste 2700 Houston (77002) *(G-9564)*

Eagle Rock Pipeline LP 281 408-1200
5847 San Felipe St # 3000 Houston (77057) *(G-9565)*

Eagle Specialty Brush, Dallas *Also called Eagle Brush & Chemical Inc (G-4289)*

Eagle Tool Company, El Paso *Also called F M Eagle Tool Co Inc (G-5761)*

Eagle Traffic Signs Safety LLC 713 987-9178
10800 Telephone Rd Houston (77075) *(G-9566)*

Eagle Vly Enrgy Partners LLC 512 413-7140
13413 Galleria Cir # 100 Austin (78738) *(G-1110)*

Eagleburgmann Industries LP (HQ) 713 939-9515
10035 Brookriver Dr Houston (77040) *(G-9567)*

Eagleburgmann Industries LP 979 265-2320
228 W Plantation Dr Clute (77531) *(G-3153)*

Eagleclaw Midstream Svcs LLC 432 789-1333
414 W Texas Ave Ste 315 Midland (79701) *(G-15204)*

Eaglehawk Field Services LLC 832 204-2700
1000 La St Ste 5600 Houston (77002) *(G-9568)*

Eagleridge Energy LLC 214 295-6704
3300 Oak Lawn Ave Ste 500 Dallas (75219) *(G-4293)*

Eagleridge Operating, Dallas *Also called Eagleridge Energy LLC (G-4293)*

Eagles Nest Cathedral, Dallas *Also called W V Grant Intl Ministries (G-5171)*

Eakin Industries LLC 281 620-8625
24632 Hosford Meadows Dr Porter (77365) *(G-17175)*

Earls Apparel Inc 936 544-5521
908 S 4th St Crockett (75835) *(G-3717)*

Earth Color Houston Inc 713 861-8158
7021 Portwest Dr Ste 190 Houston (77024) *(G-9569)*

Earth Haulers Inc 817 540-2777
11500 Mosier Valley Rd Euless (76040) *(G-6141)*

Earthstone, Houston *Also called Continental Stone LLC (G-9289)*

Earthstone Energy Inc (PA) 281 298-4246
1400 Woodloch Forest Dr # 300 The Woodlands (77380) *(G-19857)*

Earthstone Energy Holdings LLC (HQ) 281 298-4246
1400 Woodloch Forest Dr # 300 The Woodlands (77380) *(G-19858)*

Earthstone Operating LLC 281 298-4246
1400 Woodloch Forest Dr The Woodlands (77380) *(G-19859)*

Eason Properties I LLC 409 945-4416
915 6th Ave N Texas City (77590) *(G-19789)*

East Bernard Milling Co LLC 979 335-7554
854 Wallace St East Bernard (77435) *(G-5557)*

East Creek Corporation 903 527-5190
4894 Interstate 30 W Caddo Mills (75135) *(G-2623)*

East Dllas-Lakewood People Inc 214 823-5885
6301 Gaston Ave Ste 820 Dallas (75214) *(G-4294)*

East Fieldmore Gas Plant, Coahoma *Also called J L Davis Company (G-3165)*

East Lake Bucahanan 512 756-4566
101 County Road 128 Burnet (78611) *(G-2606)*

East Side Compost Pedallers 512 436-3884
1000 Brazos St Ste C Austin (78701) *(G-1111)*

East Texas Acoustical Inc 903 663-3820
7793 Us Highway 259 Longview (75605) *(G-14226)*

East Texas Containers Inc 903 595-6444
10235 County Road 489 Tyler (75706) *(G-20079)*

East Texas Machine Works Inc 903 759-9796
2808 W Marshall Ave Longview (75604) *(G-14227)*

East Texas Municpl Utility Dst 903 877-3644
12162 State Highway 155 N Tyler (75708) *(G-20080)*

East Texas Oilfield Services, New London *Also called Etos Inc (G-15850)*

East Texas Paint & Coating, Kilgore *Also called Creative Coatings Inc (G-13541)*

East Texas Pipe Service Inc 903 639-2541
Fm Rd 161 S Hughes Springs (75656) ***(G-12739)***
East Texas Plating Inc 903 935-7000
1707 Commerce St Marshall (75672) ***(G-14775)***
East Texas Precast Company 281 463-0654
44855 Old Houston Hwy Hempstead (77445) ***(G-8252)***
East Texas Radiator Inc (PA) **903 753-7286**
703 W Cotton St Longview (75604) ***(G-14228)***
East Texas Radiator Inc 903 759-3877
100 Coolant Ln Longview (75604) ***(G-14229)***
East Texas Smoker Company 903 245-0039
10228 County Road 290 Tyler (75707) ***(G-20081)***
East Texas Truss LLC 409 283-3728
532 Fm 1013 Rd Hillister (77624) ***(G-8319)***
East Txas Archtctral Shtmtal L 903 569-6909
1450 Bromberg St Mineola (75773) ***(G-15507)***
East Txas Lighthouse For Blind 903 595-3444
500 N Bois D Arc Ave Tyler (75702) ***(G-20082)***
Eastern Oil Well Service, Carrizo Springs *Also called Prime Operating Company* ***(G-2687)***
Eastern Oil Well Service Corp (HQ) **203 358-5700**
9821 Katy Fwy Ste 1050 Houston (77024) ***(G-9570)***
Eastern Star Group LLC 972 729-9955
1512 Harvest Run Dr Allen (75002) ***(G-263)***
Eastex Crude Company (PA) **903 856-2401**
10907 State Highway 11 W Leesburg (75451) ***(G-13999)***
Eastex Crude Trucking LLC 800 443-8580
10851 State Highway 11 W Leesburg (75451) ***(G-14000)***
Eastex Farms 903 683-5726
1975 County Road 1605 Rusk (75785) ***(G-17730)***
Eastex Rubber & Gasket Co 409 727-6800
2633 Highway 69 N Nederland (77627) ***(G-15752)***
Eastham Drilling Inc 713 661-6890
4710 Bellaire Blvd # 350 Bellaire (77401) ***(G-1995)***
Eastland County Newspaper Inc (PA) **254 629-1707**
215 S Seaman St Eastland (76448) ***(G-5564)***
Eastland County Newspaper Inc 254 442-2000
700 Conrad Hilton Blvd Cisco (76437) ***(G-3066)***
Eastland Oil Co (PA) **432 683-6293**
415 W Wall St Ste 1415 Midland (79701) ***(G-15205)***
Eastland Resources, Midland *Also called Eastland Oil Co* ***(G-15205)***
Eastlander Designs, Eastland *Also called Tri-Tex Enterprises Inc* ***(G-5569)***
Eastman Chemical Company 409 942-3532
201 Bay St S Texas City (77590) ***(G-19790)***
Eastman Chemical Company 423 229-2000
300 Kodak Blvd Longview (75602) ***(G-14230)***
Eastman Chemical Company 903 237-6755
2290 Callahan Rd Longview (75602) ***(G-14231)***
Eastman Chemical Texas Cy Inc (HQ) **409 942-3307**
201 Bay St S Texas City (77590) ***(G-19791)***
Eastman Chemical Texas Cy Inc 409 945-4431
201 Bay St S Texas City (77590) ***(G-19792)***
Eastman Kodak Company 214 585-4955
87 Stone Hinge Dr McKinney (75069) ***(G-14938)***
Eastman Kodak Company 972 241-1611
3400 Carlisle St Dallas (75204) ***(G-4295)***
Eastman Park Micrographics Inc (PA) **214 580-8390**
6300 Cedar Springs Rd Dallas (75235) ***(G-4296)***
Eastman Performance Films LLC 817 445-1102
1385 Westpark Way Euless (76040) ***(G-6142)***
Easton Energy LLC 214 712-2141
15375 Memorial Dr Houston (77079) ***(G-9571)***
Easy Comm & Alarm, Lewisville *Also called Varieon Inc* ***(G-14104)***
Easy Gardener, Waco *Also called United Amercn Acquisition Corp* ***(G-20470)***
Easy Gardener Products Inc (PA) **254 753-5353**
400 Austin Ave Ste 1101 Waco (76701) ***(G-20394)***
Easy Print Inc (PA) **806 374-7711**
501 S Jackson St Amarillo (79101) ***(G-421)***
Easy Protect Inc 469 916-1099
2035 Royal Ln Ste 290 Dallas (75229) ***(G-4297)***
Easy Way Leisure Corporation 956 831-6442
2705 Quality Ln Ste B Brownsville (78526) ***(G-2352)***
Eaton Cooper Crouse-Hinds, Amarillo *Also called Cooper Crouse-Hinds LLC* ***(G-484)***
Eaton Corporation 956 283-1468
5800 S 42nd St Ste G McAllen (78503) ***(G-14854)***
Eaton Corporation 915 779-4524
6 Founders Blvd El Paso (79906) ***(G-5730)***
Eaton Corporation 713 849-1600
14825 Nw Fwy Ste 100 Houston (77040) ***(G-9572)***
Eaton Corporation 956 843-3450
300 E Olmos Dr Ste B Hidalgo (78557) ***(G-8306)***
Eaton Corporation 262 765-9764
7800 Trade Center Ave El Paso (79912) ***(G-5731)***
Eaton Corporation 915 772-6198
60 A Basset Ctr El Paso (79925) ***(G-5732)***
Eaton Corporation 915 881-0259
45 Butterfield Cir Ste C El Paso (79906) ***(G-5733)***
Eaton Corporation 972 541-0461
4545 Fuller Dr Irving (75038) ***(G-13005)***
Eaton Electrical, El Paso *Also called Eaton Corporation* ***(G-5733)***
Ebaa Iron Inc (PA) **254 629-1737**
County Rd 442 Fm 570 S 1 Eastland (76448) ***(G-5565)***
Ebaa Iron Inc 325 762-3084
5 Miles S Hwy 6 Albany (76430) ***(G-187)***
Ebizsoft Inc 954 272-0500
2028 E Ben White Blvd Austin (78741) ***(G-1112)***
Ebling Welding LLC 830 905-7235
621 Ridgehaven St Canyon Lake (78133) ***(G-2679)***
Ebrofrost North America Inc 281 727-8139
2777 Allen Pkwy Ste 1600 Houston (77019) ***(G-9573)***
Ebt Newco LLC 972 996-0458
2777 N Stemmons Fwy # 18 Dallas (75207) ***(G-4298)***
EC Wrecking & Salvage Corp 915 855-7999
1931 Texas Ave El Paso (79901) ***(G-5734)***
Ecd Acquisitions Inc (PA) **254 776-2360**
701 Texas Central Pkwy Waco (76712) ***(G-20395)***
Ecdg, Houston *Also called Ellwood Texas Forge LP* ***(G-9605)***
Echo Commercial Printing Inc 903 885-0861
401 Church St Sulphur Springs (75482) ***(G-19585)***
Echo Maintenance LLC 409 724-0456
6711 N Twin City Hwy Port Arthur (77642) ***(G-17106)***
Echo Publishing Company (PA) **903 885-2030**
401 Church St Ste B Sulphur Springs (75482) ***(G-19586)***
Echometer Company 940 767-4334
5001 Ditto Ln Wichita Falls (76302) ***(G-20763)***
Eci Software Solutions Inc (HQ) **703 737-6620**
4400 Alliance Gateway Fwy # 154 Fort Worth (76177) ***(G-6602)***
Eci2, Fort Worth *Also called Eci Software Solutions Inc* ***(G-6602)***
Eckel Heat Treating Co 432 362-4336
8035 N County Rd W Odessa (79764) ***(G-15984)***
Eckel International, Odessa *Also called Eckel Manufacturing Co Inc* ***(G-15985)***
Eckel Manufacturing Co Inc (PA) **432 362-4336**
8035 N County Rd W Odessa (79764) ***(G-15985)***
Eckel Manufacturing Company, Odessa *Also called Eckel Heat Treating Co* ***(G-15984)***
Eckels - Bilt Inc 817 246-4555
7700 Harwell St Fort Worth (76108) ***(G-6603)***
Eckels-Bilt, Fort Worth *Also called Eckels - Bilt Inc* ***(G-6603)***
Eclectic Innvtive Slutions LLC 737 999-1907
102 Old Fitzhugh Rd Ste 3 Dripping Springs (78620) ***(G-5505)***
Eclipse Medcorp LLC 800 759-6876
5916 Stone Creek Dr Ste 1 Lewisville (75056) ***(G-14047)***
Eclipse Resources Holdings LP 814 308-9754
122 W John Carpenter Fwy # 300 Irving (75039) ***(G-13006)***
Eclipse Resources I LP (HQ) **814 308-9754**
122 W John Carpenter Fwy # 300 Irving (75039) ***(G-13007)***
Eclipse Resources-Pa LP 814 409-7006
122 W John Carpenter Fwy # 300 Irving (75039) ***(G-13008)***
Ecm Biosurgery Inc 281 229-0348
4235 Oberlin St Houston (77005) ***(G-9574)***
Ecmm Services Inc 909 979-4526
10305 Round Up Ln Ste 400 Houston (77064) ***(G-9575)***
Eco Plus, Plano *Also called Fastserv Supply Inc* ***(G-16870)***
Eco Services Operations Corp 844 812-1812
2002 Timberloch Pl The Woodlands (77380) ***(G-19860)***
Eco Services Operations Corp 713 924-1401
8615 Manchester St Houston (77012) ***(G-9576)***
Eco Services Operations LLC 800 642-4200
2002 Timberloch Pl # 300 Spring (77380) ***(G-19210)***
Eco Werks, Port Arthur *Also called Ecowater Industries LLC* ***(G-17107)***
Eco-Bat America LLC (HQ) **214 631-6070**
2777 N Stemmons Fwy # 185 Dallas (75207) ***(G-4299)***
Eco-Stim Energy Solutions, Katy *Also called Ecostim Inc* ***(G-13399)***
Ecoclean Supply & Services LLC 800 245-9896
950 E State Highway 114 # 1 Southlake (76092) ***(G-19065)***
Ecodyne Heat Exchanger LLC (HQ) **713 675-3511**
4847 Homestead Rd Ste 416 Houston (77028) ***(G-9577)***
Ecofusion Inc 972 403-7449
6600 Chase Oaks Blvd Plano (75023) ***(G-16855)***
Ecolab, Tyler *Also called Microtek Medical Inc* ***(G-20128)***
Ecolab Inc 281 908-4877
8150 Westpark Dr Houston (77063) ***(G-9578)***
Ecolab Inc 800 532-7732
4050 Corporate Dr Grapevine (76051) ***(G-8030)***
Ecolab Inc 817 916-9600
2121 Solona St Haltom City (76117) ***(G-8138)***
Ecolab Inc 972 840-3994
2305 Sherwin St Garland (75041) ***(G-7483)***
Ecolab Inc 800 325-1671
20465 State Highway 249 # 200 Houston (77070) ***(G-9579)***
Ecological Services Intl Inc 956 233-4609
41786 Fm 510 Los Fresnos (78566) ***(G-14346)***
Ecoloop Energy Inc 972 885-5130
500 N Cent Expy Ste 266 Plano (75074) ***(G-16856)***
Econo-Print, Longview *Also called Gea Associates Inc* ***(G-14239)***
Economic Trnsfrmtion Tech Corp 253 332-7362
1 Cowboys Way Ste 575 Frisco (75034) ***(G-7281)***
Economy Metal Works, Houston *Also called Sn & Db Holdings Inc* ***(G-11927)***
Economy Metal Works, Houston *Also called Fortitude Specialty Mfg LLC* ***(G-9839)***

Economy Mills Ltd 806 765-5547
  5828 Fm 41 Lubbock (79424) *(G-14406)*

Economy Mud Products Company (PA) 800 231-2066
  435 E Anderson Rd Houston (77047) *(G-9580)*

Economy Polymers & Chemical, Houston *Also called Economy Mud Products Company* *(G-9580)*

Econtrols LLC (HQ) 210 495-9772
  5757 Farinon Dr San Antonio (78249) *(G-18081)*

Econtrols Group Inc (PA) 210 495-9772
  5757 Farinon Dr San Antonio (78249) *(G-18082)*

Ecopetrol America Inc 713 634-3800
  2800 Post Oak Blvd Houston (77056) *(G-9581)*

Ecostim Inc 281 531-7200
  1773 Westborough Dr 110 Katy (77449) *(G-13399)*

Ecostream LLC 832 429-5317
  2140 E Southlake Blvd L203 Southlake (76092) *(G-19066)*

Ecowater Industries LLC 214 878-6527
  6200 Procter St Ext Port Arthur (77642) *(G-17107)*

Ecs Refining Texas LLC 972 524-1075
  106 Tejas Dr Terrell (75160) *(G-19732)*

Ed Prince Enterprises Inc 806 274-7178
  515 E 10th St Borger (79007) *(G-2177)*

Eda Label Products, Dallas *Also called Daniel Ayala* *(G-4235)*

Edc, Irving *Also called Electronic Drilling Control* *(G-13014)*

Edd's & Towing, Fort Worth *Also called Hight Marine Products Inc* *(G-6698)*

Eddie Richardson 972 878-6181
  751 Cody Rd Ennis (75119) *(G-6094)*

Eddy Packing Co Inc (PA) 361 580-3800
  404 Airport Rd Yoakum (77995) *(G-20965)*

Edelhoff Technologies USA LLC 713 947-6469
  9361 Winkler Dr Ste A Houston (77017) *(G-9582)*

Edelhoff U.S.a, Houston *Also called Edelhoff Technologies USA LLC* *(G-9582)*

Eden Equipment Company Inc (PA) 909 629-2217
  6231 E Stassney Ln 12-100 Austin (78744) *(G-1113)*

Edf Trading North America LLC 830 351-5075
  930 E Pierce St Luling (78648) *(G-14560)*

Edge Adhesives Inc (PA) 817 232-2026
  5117 Northeast Pkwy Fort Worth (76106) *(G-6604)*

Edge Fabrication Inc 972 714-3893
  1800 Hurd Dr Irving (75038) *(G-13009)*

Edge Integrity Services LLC 817 585-1007
  5225 El Campo Ave Fort Worth (76107) *(G-6605)*

Edge Software Inc 512 345-7793
  15101 Kevin Ln Austin (78734) *(G-1114)*

Edge Specialty Services Inc 361 668-3343
  3784 W Highway 44 Alice (78332) *(G-211)*

Edgenuity Inc 512 478-9600
  11501 Domain Dr Ste 160 Austin (78758) *(G-1115)*

Edi Oilfield Pumps and Sups, Van *Also called Energy Devices of Texas Inc* *(G-20207)*

Edi Weyerhaeuser McAllen 956 682-9406
  200 N 26th St McAllen (78501) *(G-14855)*

Edible Arrngements - Grapevine, Fort Worth *Also called Jensar Corporation* *(G-6738)*

Edinburg Rm, Edinburg *Also called Cemex Construction Mtls S LLC* *(G-5581)*

Edison Chouest Offshore, Houston *Also called Offshore Service Vessels LLC* *(G-11143)*

EDM, Magnolia *Also called Enviroflex Design & Mfg* *(G-14605)*

Edmar Company LLC 432 686-8888
  3000 N Grfield St Ste 108 Midland (79705) *(G-15206)*

Edmonds Pubg & Media Group LLC 214 460-7560
  3101 Woodland Heights Cir Colleyville (76034) *(G-3213)*

Edna Harold Publishing, Edna *Also called Jackson County Herald Tribune* *(G-5607)*

EDS Precision Mfg LLC 713 956-1112
  6061 Thomas Rd Houston (77041) *(G-9583)*

Edshah Capital 469 770-3740
  500 N Central Expy Plano (75074) *(G-16857)*

Education Advanced Inc (PA) 903 858-4497
  2702 E 5th St Ste 372 Tyler (75701) *(G-20083)*

Eduphoria Incorporated 972 535-5570
  1700 Alma Dr Ste 410 Plano (75075) *(G-16858)*

Eduspark Inc 512 535-6139
  2028 E Ben White Blvd Austin (78741) *(G-1116)*

Edward Bloch Ltd 210 648-6011
  2751 S Foster Rd San Antonio (78220) *(G-18083)*

Edwards Michael Custom 210 651-3800
  18975 Marbach Ln Ste 900 San Antonio (78266) *(G-18641)*

Edwards Printing Service Inc 972 387-3575
  13643 Beta Rd Dallas (75244) *(G-4300)*

Edwards Sptic Grease Trck Svcs 903 643-7585
  2821 State Highway 42 N Kilgore (75662) *(G-13549)*

Edwin Jones Company Inc (PA) 214 361-4000
  6445 Prestonshire Ln Dallas (75225) *(G-4301)*

Eeac, McAllen *Also called M A E W Inc* *(G-14886)*

Eestor Inc 512 259-7601
  715 Discovery Blvd # 107 Cedar Park (78613) *(G-2967)*

EF Johnson Company (PA) 972 819-0700
  1440 Corporate Dr Irving (75038) *(G-13010)*

Ef Johnson Technologies Inc (HQ) 972 819-0700
  1440 Corporate Dr Irving (75038) *(G-13011)*

Efco Machine Shop LLC 254 778-7394
  9740 Spur Rd 1237 Pendleton (76564) *(G-16628)*

Effective Metal Services LLC 832 962-8626
  14173 Nw Fwy 147 Houston (77040) *(G-9584)*

Effectus Corporation (PA) 713 446-5275
  10223 Broadway St P358 Pearland (77584) *(G-16558)*

Efficiency Aggregators LLC (PA) 832 862-1103
  1207 Fm 359 Rd Richmond (77406) *(G-17453)*

Efficient-Tec Intl LLC 214 221-9405
  9659 Wendell Rd Dallas (75243) *(G-4302)*

Efi Inc (PA) 940 380-8000
  2200 Worthington Dr Denton (76207) *(G-5362)*

Efi Panel Systems LLC 281 533-9100
  9631 Hwy 36 W Orchard (77464) *(G-16272)*

Efi Panels, Orchard *Also called Efi Panel Systems LLC* *(G-16272)*

Efi Panels LLC 615 301-0745
  9631 Hwy 36 Orchard (77464) *(G-16273)*

Efsi, Houston *Also called Energy Facility Services Inc* *(G-9634)*

Efw Inc (HQ) 817 916-1359
  4700 Marine Creek Pkwy Fort Worth (76179) *(G-6606)*

Egana of Switzerland (america) 972 839-2808
  10810 Spring Lake Rd Frisco (75035) *(G-7258)*

Eganagoldpfeil USA, Frisco *Also called Egana of Switzerland (america)* *(G-7258)*

Egc Corp Careers, Humble *Also called E G C Corporation* *(G-12764)*

Eggemeyer Land Clearing LLC 210 366-4100
  333 N Solms Rd New Braunfels (78132) *(G-15789)*

Egh Printing LLC 972 788-4266
  2001 Midway Rd Ste 128 Carrollton (75006) *(G-2728)*

EGI Resources Inc 432 687-6560
  223 W Wall St Ste 900 Midland (79701) *(G-15207)*

Egm Cleaning & Remodeling 210 666-0234
  10470 Culebra Rd San Antonio (78251) *(G-18084)*

Egma LLC 972 488-3462
  11234 Goodnight Ln Dallas (75229) *(G-4303)*

Egress Technology, Austin *Also called E I Products Inc* *(G-1106)*

Egret Medical Products Inc 214 291-0238
  2713 Industrial Ln Garland (75041) *(G-7484)*

Egs Production Machining Inc 972 438-2251
  2332 E Grauwyler Rd Irving (75061) *(G-13012)*

Ehmer Production Machining Co 972 422-2882
  1135 E Plano Pkwy Ste 3 Plano (75074) *(G-16859)*

EICA Industries Inc 817 847-0917
  1700 E Hicks Field Rd Fort Worth (76179) *(G-6607)*

Eica Tankheads, Fort Worth *Also called EICA Industries Inc* *(G-6607)*

Eieio Inc 512 342-8044
  3813 Helios Way Ste 200 Pflugerville (78660) *(G-16668)*

Eight Eighty-Eight Inc 972 404-0155
  14131 Midway Rd Ste 119 Addison (75001) *(G-118)*

Einsteins Inc 972 387-8485
  1800 Surveyor Blvd Carrollton (75006) *(G-2729)*

Eisen Gustav Tool & Die Works, Seguin *Also called Gustavs Tool & Die Inc* *(G-18840)*

Eisenbeck Corp SEC Fire Div, Garland *Also called Eisenbeck Corporation* *(G-7485)*

Eisenbeck Corporation 972 526-5235
  3814 Marquis Dr Ste 103 Garland (75042) *(G-7485)*

Eixsys LLC 512 666-3574
  501 W Powell Ln Ste 219 Austin (78753) *(G-1117)*

Ej Usa Inc 210 946-3224
  12019 Nacogdoches Rd B San Antonio (78217) *(G-18085)*

Ejr Consulting Services Inc 432 634-2905
  5601 Ponderosa Dr Odessa (79762) *(G-15986)*

Ekf Life Sciences, Boerne *Also called Stanbio Laboratory LP* *(G-2137)*

Ekj Enterprises LP 972 772-1919
  2975 Discovery Blvd Rockwall (75032) *(G-17547)*

Eklunds Inc (PA) 817 949-2030
  2860 Market Loop Ste 200 Southlake (76092) *(G-19067)*

El Campo Leader News, El Campo *Also called El Campo Newspapers Inc* *(G-5616)*

El Campo Machine & Repair Inc (PA) 979 543-9663
  Highway 71 El Campo (77437) *(G-5615)*

El Campo Newspapers Inc 979 543-3363
  203 E Jackson St El Campo (77437) *(G-5616)*

El Campo Sheet Metal LLC 979 543-5751
  28385 Us 59 Hwy El Campo (77437) *(G-5617)*

El Chilito Foods Inc 512 391-0550
  2209 Manor Rd Austin (78722) *(G-1118)*

El Diario De Elpaso, El Paso *Also called Paso Del Norte Publishing Inc* *(G-5905)*

El Dorado Chemical Company 254 445-2720
  300 E Oneil St Dublin (76446) *(G-5516)*

El Dorado Logistics LLC 214 871-3555
  2828 N Harwood St Dallas (75201) *(G-4304)*

El Dorado Nitrogen LP 281 383-1807
  8490 W Bay Rd Baytown (77523) *(G-1786)*

El Dorado Pharmacy LLC 214 329-4580
  1300 E Arapaho Rd Ste 210 Richardson (75081) *(G-17304)*

El Extra Newspaper, Dallas *Also called El Extra Spnish Lngage Newsppr* *(G-4305)*

El Extra Spnish Lngage Newsppr 214 309-0990
  1214 Gardenview Dr Dallas (75217) *(G-4305)*

El Habr Corporation 817 731-4660
  4115 W Vickery Blvd Fort Worth (76107) *(G-6608)*

El Heraldo News Incorporated 214 827-9700
4532 Columbia Ave Dallas (75226) **(G-4306)**

El Hispano Newspaper, Dallas *Also called Marcos N Suarez* **(G-4634)**

El Manana Inc 956 712-1122
6010 Mcpherson Rd Ste 300 Laredo (78041) **(G-13882)**

El Milagro of Texas Inc 512 477-6476
400 Barnes Dr San Marcos (78666) **(G-18685)**

El Mundo Newspaper, Austin *Also called Arbol Publishing LP* **(G-929)**

El Paso, El Paso *Also called Investor Publications Inc* **(G-5817)**

El Paso Cgp Company LLC (HQ) **713 420-2600**
1001 Louisiana St Houston (77002) **(G-9585)**

El Paso CNG Company LLC (HQ) **713 420-2600**
9 Greenway Plz Houston (77046) **(G-9586)**

El Paso Distribution Center, El Paso *Also called Te Connectivity Corporation* **(G-5993)**

El Paso Field Services LP 361 552-9601
1234 Rosenbaum Rd Port Lavaca (77979) **(G-17145)**

El Paso Field Services LP 210 621-2031
20733 Lamm Rd Elmendorf (78112) **(G-6068)**

El Paso Heat Transfer Inc 915 779-6334
5400 Suncrest Dr Ste C6 El Paso (79912) **(G-5735)**

El Paso Lighthouse For Blind 915 532-4495
205 Tobin Pl El Paso (79905) **(G-5736)**

El Paso Machine & Steel Inc 915 533-7483
1600 E 4th Ave El Paso (79901) **(G-5737)**

El Paso Mail and Print Service, El Paso *Also called E & L Graphics LLC* **(G-5728)**

El Paso Prosthetic Center LLC 915 234-2408
1800 N Mesa St Ste 100 El Paso (79902) **(G-5738)**

El Paso Pwdr Cting Hydrgrphics 915 313-9333
5559 El Paso Dr El Paso (79905) **(G-5739)**

El Paso Regional Admin Office, El Paso *Also called Cemex Construction Mtls S LLC* **(G-5690)**

El Paso Reprographics LLC 915 532-6255
109 Argonaut Dr El Paso (79912) **(G-5740)**

El Paso Saddleblanket Co LP 915 544-1000
6935 Commerce Ave El Paso (79915) **(G-5741)**

El Paso Saddlery, El Paso *Also called R E M Industries Inc* **(G-5924)**

El Paso Star Ready-Mix 915 860-8555
117 S Moon Rd El Paso (79927) **(G-5742)**

El Paso Tce, Socorro *Also called Technicolor Usa Inc* **(G-19019)**

El Paso Times Charitable Corp (HQ) **915 546-6100**
500 W Overland Ave # 150 El Paso (79901) **(G-5743)**

El Paso Tool & Die Co Inc 915 591-0346
10859 Pellicano Dr El Paso (79935) **(G-5744)**

El Paso Truss Inc 915 751-0025
9931 Railroad Dr El Paso (79924) **(G-5745)**

El Paso Water Indus Svcs Inc 915 849-0401
4500 Turf Rd El Paso (79938) **(G-5746)**

El Paso Wood Products Inc 915 545-2974
1025 Myrtle Ave El Paso (79901) **(G-5747)**

El Periodico U S A Inc 956 631-5628
801 E Fir Ave McAllen (78501) **(G-14856)**

El Rancho Food Service, San Antonio *Also called Marbros L L C* **(G-18275)**

El Tejano Hispanic Community 361 884-2238
2505 Sarita St Corpus Christi (78405) **(G-3518)**

El Venado Foods 713 692-0688
3919 Eastex Fwy Houston (77026) **(G-9587)**

Elah Holdings Inc (PA) **805 435-1255**
8214 Westchester Dr # 950 Dallas (75225) **(G-4307)**

Elamex Usa Corp 915 298-3061
1800 Northwestern Dr El Paso (79912) **(G-5748)**

Eland Energy Inc (PA) **214 368-6100**
16400 Dallas Pkwy Ste 100 Dallas (75248) **(G-4308)**

Elastotech Southwest Inc 936 545-8550
1700 Sw Loop 304 Crockett (75835) **(G-3718)**

Elbit Systems, Fort Worth *Also called Tallahassee Technologies Inc* **(G-7032)**

Elbit Systems of America LLC (HQ) **817 234-6600**
4700 Marine Creek Pkwy Fort Worth (76179) **(G-6609)**

Elcom Inc (HQ) **915 298-2000**
20 Butterfield Trail Blvd El Paso (79906) **(G-5749)**

Eld Operations LLC 630 338-5425
4529 E State Rt 302 Kermit (79745) **(G-13511)**

Elder Rubber Incorporated 214 426-2890
2102 Vanco Dr Irving (75061) **(G-13013)**

Eldred Sheet Metal Works LP 713 227-3251
3119 Chapman St Houston (77009) **(G-9588)**

Election Systems & Sftwr LLC 469 675-8990
1253 Allen Station Pkwy Allen (75002) **(G-264)**

Electric Pwr Systems Intl Inc 972 907-3783
783 N Grove Rd Ste 101 Richardson (75081) **(G-17305)**

Electric Submersible Pump Inc 325 573-8101
2507 25th St Snyder (79549) **(G-18990)**

Electric Supply Source, El Paso *Also called Ss Electric Inc* **(G-5973)**

Electrical Automation Controls, Conroe *Also called Logic Control LLC* **(G-3323)**

Electrical Components Intl Inc 915 217-2700
12415 Rojas Dr El Paso (79928) **(G-5750)**

Electrical Contrls Houston Inc 281 501-0729
21061 Gene Campbell Blvd New Caney (77357) **(G-15838)**

Electrical Maintenance & Cnstr, Midland *Also called Endeavor Energy Resources LP* **(G-15214)**

Electrical Productions Div, Gilmer *Also called Robroy Industries Inc* **(G-7712)**

Electrical Sign Displays Inc 713 644-8081
6537 Rupley Cir Houston (77087) **(G-9589)**

Electrico Inc 903 872-6567
2500 S Business 45 Corsicana (75110) **(G-3670)**

Electro Plate Circuitry Inc (PA) **972 466-0818**
1430 Century Dr Carrollton (75006) **(G-2730)**

Electro Tech Industries, Houston *Also called Electro Technical Inds Inc* **(G-9590)**

Electro Technical Inds Inc 713 691-5182
303 Little York Rd Houston (77076) **(G-9590)**

Electro-Coatings of Iowa Inc 800 806-6059
12015 Radium St San Antonio (78216) **(G-18086)**

Electro-Coatings Texas Inc 210 798-3460
216 Baywood St Houston (77011) **(G-9591)**

Electro-Mechanical Inds Inc 281 894-1600
11230 Neeshaw Dr Houston (77065) **(G-9592)**

Electro-Quip Service Inc 281 456-8600
8145 Miller Road 2 Houston (77049) **(G-9593)**

Electrolab Inc 210 824-5364
159 Enterprise Pkwy Boerne (78006) **(G-2118)**

Electromagnetic Industries LLC 281 422-5225
1507 Beaumont Rd Baytown (77520) **(G-1816)**

Electromedical Pdts Intl Inc (PA) **940 328-0788**
2201 Garrett Morris Pkwy Mineral Wells (76067) **(G-15525)**

Electronic Assembly Svcs Inc 713 686-4390
4501 S Pinemont Dr # 108 Houston (77041) **(G-9594)**

Electronic Data Devices Co (PA) **432 366-8699**
840 Oxford Dr Odessa (79764) **(G-15987)**

Electronic Drilling Control 972 257-0322
3110 Story Rd W Irving (75038) **(G-13014)**

Electronic Med Resources LL C 832 456-2600
333 N Sam Houston Pkwy E Houston (77060) **(G-9595)**

Electronic Power Design Inc 713 923-1191
15200 North Fwy Houston (77090) **(G-9596)**

Electronic Services Unlimited 713 683-0601
1906 Johanna Dr Ste A Houston (77055) **(G-9597)**

Electronic Technical Svcs Corp 281 446-4414
2616 Wilson Rd Humble (77396) **(G-12765)**

Electronic Visions Systems 512 989-3000
400 S Heatherwilde Blvd Pflugerville (78660) **(G-16669)**

Electronics & Metals Inds Inc 512 267-0113
17414 Fm 1431 Leander (78641) **(G-13988)**

Electronics & Safety, El Paso *Also called Aptiv Services Us LLC* **(G-5647)**

Electronics Division, Beaumont *Also called Helena Laboratories Corp* **(G-1902)**

Electroninks Incorporated 512 766-7555
7901 E Riverside Dr # 150 Austin (78744) **(G-1119)**

Electroninks Writeables Inc 512 766-7555
7901 E Riverside Dr # 150 Austin (78744) **(G-1120)**

Electroplating of El Paso, El Paso *Also called Rubens Electroplating Inc* **(G-5948)**

Electrostatic Misting, Fort Worth *Also called E-Mist Innovations Inc* **(G-6601)**

Electrotechnics Corporation 903 938-1901
1310 Commerce St Marshall (75672) **(G-14776)**

Eleet Cryogenics Inc 936 856-6549
17301 E Fm 1097 Rd Willis (77378) **(G-20845)**

Elegante Iron Inc 214 342-8987
13619 Inwood Rd Ste 360 Farmers Branch (75244) **(G-6195)**

Element Dallas Downtown East, Dallas *Also called Atlantic Dwntwn Dllas Vntr LLC* **(G-3980)**

Element Markets LLC (HQ) **281 207-7200**
3200 Southwest Fwy # 1310 Houston (77027) **(G-9598)**

Elemetal LLC (PA) **214 956-7600**
15850 Dallas Pkwy Dallas (75248) **(G-4309)**

Elevate Midstream Partners LLC 214 215-9298
1415 La St Ste 3400 Houston (77002) **(G-9599)**

Elevated Techology, Houston *Also called Superior It Solutions LLC* **(G-12117)**

Elevation Resources LLC 432 686-7500
200 N Loraine St Ste 1010 Midland (79701) **(G-15208)**

Elg Metals Inc 281 457-2100
15135 Jacintoport Blvd Houston (77015) **(G-9600)**

Elgi Rubber Company LLC 830 875-5539
600 N Magnolia Ave Luling (78648) **(G-14561)**

Elgie Company Inc 214 691-6216
4600 Greenville Ave # 200 Dallas (75206) **(G-4310)**

Elgin Sprtion Sltons Indstrals (HQ) **281 261-5778**
10050 Cash Rd Stafford (77477) **(G-19308)**

Eli-Shir Ltd 281 464-9616
11550 Fuqua St Ste 250 Houston (77034) **(G-9601)**

Elias & Associates LLC 956 244-6552
1327 E Washington Ave # 138 Harlingen (78550) **(G-8186)**

Eligibility Trckng Calculators 210 323-7846
14607 San Pedro Ave # 250 San Antonio (78232) **(G-18087)**

Elijah Tooling Inc (PA) **940 591-1340**
1025 Shady Oaks Dr # 103 Denton (76205) **(G-5363)**

Elite Cabinets & Closets 903 737-0848
133 Pine Bluff St Paris (75460) **(G-16361)**

Elite Coating Services 469 431-3353
10616 County Road 604 Alvarado (76009) **(G-329)**

Elite Entrances LLC.....832 922-7444
30225 Tudor Way Ste B Magnolia (77355) *(G-14603)*
Elite Industrial Services, Pasadena *Also called Elite Specialty Welding LLC (G-16423)*
Elite Manufacturing, Denton *Also called EMLS Incorporated (G-5364)*
Elite Metal Fabricators Inc.....817 489-2599
907 Georgetta Ln Newark (76071) *(G-15862)*
Elite Oilfield Services, Perryton *Also called OMI Oilfield Investments LLC (G-16643)*
Elite Publications Inc.....713 263-9476
4520 W 34th St Ste E Houston (77092) *(G-9602)*
Elite Specialty Welding LLC.....832 649-4251
1411 Preston Ave Pasadena (77503) *(G-16423)*
Elite Staircases LLC.....512 466-6590
836 Centerra Hills Cir Round Rock (78665) *(G-17651)*
Elite Upstream LLC.....832 674-3050
16610 Crystal View Cir Houston (77095) *(G-9603)*
Elite Wellsite Services LLC.....940 393-2116
1804 Overland Dr Bridgeport (76426) *(G-2292)*
Elizondo Crane Service, Brownsville *Also called Elizondo Enterprises Inc (G-2353)*
Elizondo Enterprises Inc.....956 831-7174
4699 Ruben Torres Sr Blvd Brownsville (78526) *(G-2353)*
Eljen Technology, Sweetwater *Also called Ludlum Measurements Inc (G-19635)*
Eljer Industries Inc (HQ).....**972 560-2000**
14801 Quorum Dr Fl 3 Dallas (75254) *(G-4311)*
Eljer Plumbing Ware, Dallas *Also called Eljer Industries Inc (G-4311)*
Elk Corporation of Texas.....972 875-9611
202 Cedar Rd Ennis (75119) *(G-6095)*
Elk Corporation of Texas (HQ).....**972 851-0500**
14911 Quorum Dr Ste 600 Dallas (75254) *(G-4312)*
Elkcorp (HQ).....**972 851-0500**
14911 Quorum Dr Ste 600 Dallas (75254) *(G-4313)*
Elkcorp.....936 633-6387
308 Ellen Trout Dr Lufkin (75904) *(G-14526)*
Ellard John.....214 352-5946
2683 Myrtle Springs Ave Dallas (75220) *(G-4314)*
Ellinger Materials LLC.....281 227-6233
14508 Chrisman Rd Ste 200 Houston (77039) *(G-9604)*
Elliot Electric 29, Round Rock *Also called Elliott Electric Supply Inc (G-17652)*
Elliott Control Company Ltd.....713 589-3102
13344 N Highway 75 Willis (77378) *(G-20846)*
Elliott Electric Supply Inc.....512 246-8001
445 Texas Ave Round Rock (78664) *(G-17652)*
Elliott Electric Supply Inc.....210 646-6950
4306 Naco Patx Ste 101 San Antonio (78217) *(G-18088)*
Elliott's Agri-Service, Pineland *Also called Letco Group LLC (G-16740)*
Ellis Co Newspapers.....972 875-3801
213 N Dallas St Ennis (75119) *(G-6096)*
Ellis County Chronicle.....972 937-3310
200 W Marvin Ave Waxahachie (75165) *(G-20541)*
Ellis County Newspapers Inc.....972 872-9113
213 N Dallas St Ennis (75119) *(G-6097)*
Ellis Manufacturing Co Inc (PA).....**432 561-8819**
8101 W Industrial Ave Midland (79706) *(G-15209)*
Ellis Pumps and Tools, Midland *Also called Ellis Manufacturing Co Inc (G-15209)*
Ellis Tool & Machine Inc.....903 546-6540
310 Luby Dr Tom Bean (75090) *(G-19951)*
Ellison Insulation, Aspermont *Also called Double Mountain Inc (G-815)*
Ellwood Advnced Components LLC.....336 969-4000
10908 County Road 419 Navasota (77868) *(G-15732)*
Ellwood Texas Forge LP.....713 434-5100
12500 Amelia Dr Houston (77045) *(G-9605)*
Ellwood Txas Frge Navasota LLC.....936 825-7531
10908 County Road 419 Navasota (77868) *(G-15733)*
ELM Machine Inc.....936 377-5001
50 Elm St Oakhurst (77359) *(G-15891)*
Elm Mott Marble Co.....254 829-1552
1064 N Mclennan Dr # 104 Elm Mott (76640) *(G-6064)*
Elm Ridge Exploration Co LLC.....972 889-2100
12225 Grnvlle Ave Ste 950 Dallas (75243) *(G-4315)*
Elm Ridge Resources Inc (PA).....**972 889-2100**
12225 Grnvlle Ave Ste 950 Dallas (75243) *(G-4316)*
Elmar Services Inc.....713 983-9281
11993 Fm 529 Rd Houston (77041) *(G-9606)*
Elmer Christy.....972 436-0273
4000 Ace Ln Trlr 432 Lewisville (75067) *(G-14048)*
Elmer Lewis Enterprises, Olton *Also called Olton Welding & Machine Inc (G-16227)*
Eltamd Inc (PA).....**972 385-2900**
15601 Dallas Pkwy # 1000 Addison (75001) *(G-119)*
Eltec, Marshall *Also called Electrotechnics Corporation (G-14776)*
Elumenus Lighting Corp Inc.....214 392-2898
555 Republic Dr Ste 200 Plano (75074) *(G-16860)*
Ema Electromechanics Inc.....325 235-8000
16 Industrial St Sweetwater (79556) *(G-19629)*
Emas AMC, Houston *Also called Emas Chiyoda Subsea Inc (G-9607)*
Emas Chiyoda Subsea Inc (HQ).....**832 487-7300**
17220 Katy Fwy Ste 100 Houston (77094) *(G-9607)*
Emax, La Grange *Also called Supaks Inc (G-13701)*
Embarcadero Technologies Inc (HQ).....**512 226-8080**
10801 N Mopac Expy 1-100 Austin (78759) *(G-1121)*
Ember Industries Inc.....512 396-1911
321 Carlson Cir San Marcos (78666) *(G-18686)*
Embossed Graphics Inc.....713 667-0034
5325 Glenmont Dr Ste D Houston (77081) *(G-9608)*
Embroidery Concepts.....210 684-8362
5419 Bandera Rd Ste 701 San Antonio (78238) *(G-18089)*
Embroidery Graphix, Dallas *Also called Uniforms Inc (G-5132)*
EMC Corporation.....512 343-3332
11044 Res Blvd Ste B500 Austin (78759) *(G-1122)*
EMC Corporation.....972 892-7700
14755 Preston Rd Ste 200 Dallas (75254) *(G-4317)*
EMC Corporation.....713 621-9800
1 Riverway Ste 1700 Houston (77056) *(G-9609)*
EMC Dell, Richardson *Also called Vce Company LLC (G-17418)*
Emco Envelopes, Houston *Also called Emco Press Corporation (G-9610)*
Emco Press Corporation.....713 956-6055
4935 Milwee St Houston (77092) *(G-9610)*
Emerald Gathering & Trnsp LLC.....713 621-2242
9801 Westheimer Rd # 1060 Houston (77042) *(G-9611)*
Emerald Luxury Coaches, Stephenville *Also called Outlaw Conversions Inc (G-19417)*
Emerald Masonry & Stucco.....281 356-9400
28075 Fm 2978 Rd Ste A Magnolia (77354) *(G-14604)*
Emerald Pt Marina Partners Ltd.....512 266-1535
5973 Hiline Rd Austin (78734) *(G-1123)*
Emerge Energy Services LP (PA).....**817 618-4020**
6500 West Fwy Ste 800 Fort Worth (76116) *(G-6610)*
Emergency Ice Inc (PA).....**972 988-0577**
8700 Diplomacy Row Dallas (75247) *(G-4318)*
Emergency Technologies Inc.....919 676-6200
9020 N Capital Of Texas H Austin (78759) *(G-1124)*
Emergency Vehicles Texas Inc.....817 281-4172
6000 Huddleston St Haltom City (76137) *(G-8139)*
Emergent Machine Svcs Ltd Co.....903 876-3679
23628 County Road 4117 Frankston (75763) *(G-7165)*
Emergent Manufacturing Systems.....903 876-3679
23628 County Road 4117 Frankston (75763) *(G-7166)*
Emerson, Beaumont *Also called Instrument & Valve Services Co (G-1908)*
Emerson Atmtn Sltons Fnal Ctrl.....832 261-2400
4607 New West Rd Pasadena (77507) *(G-16424)*
Emerson Atmtn Sltons Fnal Ctrl.....956 430-2500
5801 E Harrison Ave Harlingen (78550) *(G-8187)*
Emerson Atmtn Sltons Fnal Ctrl (HQ).....**713 986-4665**
10707 Clay Rd Houston (77041) *(G-9612)*
Emerson Automation Solutions, Pasadena *Also called Emerson Prcess MGT Vlve Atmtn (G-16426)*
Emerson Automation Solutions.....832 261-2400
4607 New West Rd Pasadena (77507) *(G-16425)*
Emerson Automation Solutions.....281 274-4400
3950 Greenbriar Dr Stafford (77477) *(G-19309)*
Emerson Automation Solutions.....512 835-2190
1100 W Louis Henna Blvd Round Rock (78681) *(G-17653)*
Emerson Automation Solutions.....281 274-4400
3950 Greenbriar Dr Stafford (77477) *(G-19310)*
Emerson Climate Tech Inc.....817 277-7764
3100 W Arkansas Ln # 102 Arlington (76016) *(G-668)*
Emerson Climate Technologies, El Paso *Also called Emerson Electric Co (G-5752)*
Emerson Electric Co.....956 994-1427
6100 S International Pkwy McAllen (78503) *(G-14857)*
Emerson Electric Co.....956 702-2389
2216 Olmo St San Juan (78589) *(G-18673)*
Emerson Electric Co.....713 447-2839
10241 W Little York Rd Houston (77040) *(G-9613)*
Emerson Electric Co.....281 488-0788
3902 Magnolia Pkwy Pearland (77584) *(G-16559)*
Emerson Electric Co.....314 553-3695
1281 Joe Battle Blvd B El Paso (79936) *(G-5751)*
Emerson Electric Co.....915 400-3888
1281 Joe Battle Blvd B El Paso (79936) *(G-5752)*
Emerson Electric Co.....956 683-0694
5109 Tanya Ave Ste 300 McAllen (78503) *(G-14858)*
Emerson Prcess MGT Rgltor Tech (HQ).....**972 548-3585**
3200 Emerson Way McKinney (75069) *(G-14939)*
Emerson Prcess MGT Vlve Atmtn.....832 261-2400
4607 New West Rd Pasadena (77507) *(G-16426)*
Emerson Process Management, Houston *Also called Rosemunt Tank Gging N Amer Inc (G-11665)*
Emerson Process Management.....281 879-2300
6005 Rogerdale Rd Houston (77072) *(G-9614)*
Emerson Process Management.....281 477-4100
19200 Northwest Fwy Jersey Village (77065) *(G-13299)*
Emerson Process MGT Lllp (HQ).....**512 835-2190**
1100 W Louis Henna Blvd Round Rock (78681) *(G-17654)*
Emf Company Inc.....214 350-6848
106 Regal Row Dallas (75247) *(G-4319)*
Emgs Americas Inc (HQ).....**281 920-5601**
16285 Park Ten Pl Ste 410 Houston (77084) *(G-9615)*
EMI Industries LLC.....817 987-1516
1110 Eden Rd Arlington (76001) *(G-669)*

Emicon Corporation (PA)....................**915 857-5128**
12285 Pellicano Dr Ste A5 El Paso (79936) ***(G-5753)***
Emicon Corporation....................915 593-6422
1147 Larry Mahan Dr Ste E El Paso (79925) ***(G-5754)***
Emily Armenta Designs, Houston *Also called Phoeben Inc* ***(G-11328)***
Eminent Spine LLC....................512 868-5980
7200 N Interstate 35 # 1 Georgetown (78626) ***(G-7649)***
Emissions & Silencer Tech Inc....................281 259-9979
531 Goodson Loop Pinehurst (77362) ***(G-16734)***
Emissions Technology Inc....................713 691-1211
360 Garden Oaks Blvd Houston (77018) ***(G-9616)***
Emk3, Frisco *Also called Energy Exchange 3 LP* ***(G-7282)***
Eml Manufacturing Llc....................281 880-7517
14315 Beacons Trace Ct Houston (77069) ***(G-9617)***
EMLS Incorporated....................940 566-9500
3650 Shelby Ln Denton (76207) ***(G-5364)***
Emma Grace Sign Co....................713 864-4644
5660 Allen St Houston (77007) ***(G-9618)***
Empire Baking Company L P (PA)....................**972 851-5677**
6440 N Central Expy # 508 Dallas (75206) ***(G-4320)***
Empire Electric Inc....................713 688-0151
944 Fisher St Houston (77018) ***(G-9619)***
Empire Precision Machining, Fort Worth *Also called Md3 Industries Ltd* ***(G-6824)***
Empire Tubing Tongs Inc....................432 366-7702
4801 N County Rd W Odessa (79764) ***(G-15988)***
Empire Wireline LLC....................985 264-7746
400 Hobbs Rd Ste 201 League City (77573) ***(G-13955)***
Empire Wldg & Fabrication LLC....................915 706-4070
2211 E Missouri Ave # 221 El Paso (79903) ***(G-5755)***
Empirica LLC....................713 466-7400
6360 W Sam Houston Pkwy N # 100 Houston (77041) ***(G-9620)***
Employee Owned Nursery Entps....................512 276-1211
2040 Fm 969 Elgin (78621) ***(G-6054)***
Empower Clinic Services LLC....................832 678-4417
5980 W Sam Houston Pkwy N S Houston (77041) ***(G-9621)***
Empower Pharmacy, Houston *Also called Empower Clinic Services LLC* ***(G-9621)***
Ems Usa Inc (HQ)....................**713 595-7600**
5391 Bay Oaks Dr Pasadena (77505) ***(G-16427)***
Emsolutions LLC....................214 575-5327
10810 Alder Cir Dallas (75238) ***(G-4321)***
Emu Plastics Tex Limited Inc....................956 618-5200
6100 S 35th St McAllen (78503) ***(G-14859)***
En Plast Technology LLC....................832 730-4606
17510 Carlsway Houston (77073) ***(G-9622)***
En-Fab Inc (PA)....................**713 225-4913**
3905 Jensen Dr Houston (77026) ***(G-9623)***
Enbridge Pipelines, Pampa *Also called Midcoast Energy LLC* ***(G-16329)***
Enbridge Pipelines, Houston *Also called Midcoast Energy LLC* ***(G-10871)***
Encapsulite International Inc....................281 239-0225
1220 Bamore Rd Rosenberg (77471) ***(G-17580)***
Enceptia, San Antonio *Also called DC Cadd Company* ***(G-18043)***
Encino Energy LLC (PA)....................**281 254-7070**
5847 San Felipe St # 300 Houston (77057) ***(G-9624)***
Encompass Group LLC....................972 732-7694
16415 Addison Rd Ste 660 Addison (75001) ***(G-120)***
Encompass Medical, Addison *Also called Encompass Group LLC* ***(G-120)***
Encore Bits, Houston *Also called Tercel Oilfield Pdts USA LLC* ***(G-12207)***
Encore Cabinets Ltd....................979 968-9482
1000 E Eblin St La Grange (78945) ***(G-13694)***
Encore Medical LP....................512 832-9500
9800 Metric Blvd Austin (78758) ***(G-1125)***
Encore Wellhead Systems LLC (PA)....................**832 742-1350**
3403 Marquart St Houston (77027) ***(G-9625)***
Encore Wellhead Systems LLC....................832 742-1325
28024 N Highway 288b C Angleton (77515) ***(G-571)***
Encore Wellhead Systems LLC....................903 983-4481
2850 State Highway 42 Kilgore (75662) ***(G-13550)***
Encore Wire Corporation (PA)....................**972 562-9473**
1329 Millwood Rd McKinney (75069) ***(G-14940)***
Encore Wire Corporation....................972 562-9473
1410 Millwood Rd McKinney (75069) ***(G-14941)***
Endeavor Energy Resources, Midland *Also called McMillan Welding* ***(G-15297)***
Endeavor Energy Resources LP (PA)....................**432 687-1575**
110 N Marienfeld St # 200 Midland (79701) ***(G-15210)***
Endeavor Energy Resources LP....................432 221-9300
110 N Mrianefield Ste 200 Midland (79706) ***(G-15211)***
Endeavor Energy Resources LP....................432 683-4292
3000 Fm 715 Midland (79706) ***(G-15212)***
Endeavor Energy Resources LP....................432 687-1575
414 W Texas Ave Ste 316 Midland (79701) ***(G-15213)***
Endeavor Energy Resources LP....................432 563-5000
6501 S Fm 1788 Midland (79706) ***(G-15214)***
Endeavor Natural Gas LLC....................713 658-8555
1201 La St Ste 3350 Houston (77002) ***(G-9626)***
Endeavour International Corp (PA)....................**713 307-8700**
811 Main St Ste 2100 Houston (77002) ***(G-9627)***
Endeavour Machine and Fab Inc....................361 551-2077
2512 Fm 3084 Port Lavaca (77979) ***(G-17146)***

Endicott Biofuels II LLC (PA)....................**281 598-2180**
305 Wells Fargo Dr Ste A8 Houston (77090) ***(G-9628)***
Endiprev USA Inc....................214 897-5740
1045 Cross Timbers Rd Flower Mound (75028) ***(G-6265)***
Endocare Inc (HQ)....................**512 328-2892**
9825 Spectrum Dr Bldg 2 Austin (78717) ***(G-1692)***
Endress + Hauser Inc....................281 867-3400
10057 Porter Rd La Porte (77571) ***(G-13735)***
Endress + Hauser Inc....................713 300-6200
4333 W Sam Houston Pkwy N # 190 Houston (77043) ***(G-9629)***
Endtime Inc....................972 422-0857
2701 E President George B Plano (75074) ***(G-16861)***
Endurance Lift Solutions LLC....................903 595-8600
420 Throckmorton St # 740 Fort Worth (76102) ***(G-6611)***
Endurance Lift Solutions LLC (PA)....................**281 269-6880**
114 E Foreline St Gainesville (76240) ***(G-7343)***
Endurance Resources LLC....................214 996-0900
15455 Dallas Pkwy # 1050 Addison (75001) ***(G-121)***
Endurance Roustabout....................432 697-1300
2618 Franklin Ave Midland (79701) ***(G-15215)***
Endurance Sands, Houston *Also called Hermitage Operating LLC* ***(G-10161)***
Enduro Composites Inc (PA)....................**713 358-4000**
16602 Central Green Blvd Houston (77032) ***(G-9630)***
Enduro Products Inc....................817 704-7346
728 111th St Arlington (76011) ***(G-670)***
Enduro Resource Partners LLC (HQ)....................**817 744-8200**
777 Main St Ste 800 Fort Worth (76102) ***(G-6612)***
Enercon Steam Solutions LLC....................214 292-3485
8401 N Central Expy # 840 Dallas (75225) ***(G-4322)***
Enercorp Engnred Solutions LLC (HQ)....................**832 791-1276**
25700 I 45 N Ste 110 The Woodlands (77386) ***(G-19861)***
Enercorp Sand Solutions, LLC, The Woodlands *Also called Enercorp Engnred Solutions LLC* ***(G-19861)***
Enerflex Energy Systems Inc....................806 826-0126
120 W Texas Ave Wheeler (79096) ***(G-20708)***
Enerflex Energy Systems Inc (HQ)....................**281 345-9300**
10815 Telge Rd Houston (77095) ***(G-9631)***
Enerflex Energy Systems Inc....................281 758-4900
12015 Barker Cypress Rd Cypress (77433) ***(G-3787)***
Enerflex Inc (HQ)....................**801 292-0493**
10815 Telge Rd Houston (77095) ***(G-9632)***
Enerflex Services Inc....................281 345-9300
711 Louisiana St Fl 17 Houston (77002) ***(G-9633)***
Enerflow Industries Inc....................918 355-6300
6740 Highway 30 Anderson (77830) ***(G-529)***
Energen Corporation (HQ)....................**205 326-2700**
500 W Texas Ave Ste 500 # 500 Midland (79701) ***(G-15216)***
Energen Resources Corporation....................432 687-1155
3300 N A St Ste 10 Midland (79705) ***(G-15217)***
Energen Resources Corporation....................205 326-2700
500 W Texas Ave Ste 500 # 500 Midland (79701) ***(G-15218)***
Energes Odessa, Odessa *Also called Energes Services LLC* ***(G-15989)***
Energes Oilfield Solutions LLC....................830 769-1484
1438 E St Jourdanton (78026) ***(G-13330)***
Energes Services LLC....................432 307-0650
2161 W Interstate 20 Svcr Odessa (79766) ***(G-15989)***
Energetic Solutions LLC....................512 382-6864
11101 W Highway 290 Austin (78737) ***(G-860)***
Energy Devices of Texas Inc (PA)....................**903 963-7906**
303 Park Row St Van (75790) ***(G-20207)***
Energy Exchange 3 LP....................972 668-6601
1415 Legacy Dr Ste 220 Frisco (75034) ***(G-7282)***
Energy Explration Partners Inc....................817 789-6712
420 Throckmorton St # 120 Fort Worth (76102) ***(G-6613)***
Energy Fabrication Inc....................432 362-0591
3750 Kermit Hwy Odessa (79764) ***(G-15990)***
Energy Facility Services Inc....................281 286-8500
15255 Gulf Fwy Ste 140d Houston (77034) ***(G-9634)***
Energy Fishing & Rental Svc....................361 668-8000
2101 Energy Ave Alice (78332) ***(G-212)***
Energy Fishing Rentl Svcs Inc....................713 433-5506
6925 Burkett St Houston (77021) ***(G-9635)***
Energy Management Co Texas, Dallas *Also called Energy Management Company* ***(G-4323)***
Energy Management Company (PA)....................**972 885-6799**
5910 N Central Expy # 1300 Dallas (75206) ***(G-4323)***
Energy Manufacturing Gov Contg, Lubbock *Also called Broadband Technology Corp* ***(G-14383)***
Energy Operators Inc....................281 351-1780
1431 Graham Dr Ste 203 Tomball (77375) ***(G-19976)***
Energy Precision Tstg Lab LLC (PA)....................**806 665-0750**
905 S Polk St Amarillo (79101) ***(G-422)***
Energy Reserves Group LLC....................713 659-7800
333 Clay St Ste 4400 Houston (77002) ***(G-9636)***
Energy Retrofitters Inc....................817 319-2796
4090 H C Meacham Blvd Fort Worth (76135) ***(G-6614)***
Energy Services Group Amer Inc....................281 452-5335
15019 N Brentwood St Channelview (77530) ***(G-3018)***
Energy Solutions Inc....................281 257-2994
17210 Leeside Dr Tomball (77377) ***(G-19977)***

Energy Specialties Intl, Houston *Also called Global Wstewater Solutions Inc* ***(G-9981)***
Energy Technology Manufa.......281 862-2829
15438 Miller 1 Rd Lot B Lot B 1st Houston (77049) ***(G-9637)***
Energy Transfer Company, Houston *Also called Etc Intrastate Procurement LLC* ***(G-9703)***
Energy Transfer Fuel LP.......903 931-1922
1044 N Jackson St Jacksonville (75766) ***(G-13237)***
Energy Transfer LP.......682 518-7583
2001 Stephens Ave Mansfield (76063) ***(G-14669)***
Energy Valve & Supply Co LLC.......713 675-7525
8207 North Loop E Ste 400 Houston (77029) ***(G-9638)***
Energy Xtreme LLC.......512 617-7902
2215 Westlake Dr Fl 2 Austin (78746) ***(G-1126)***
Energy Xxi, Houston *Also called Exploitation Company LLP* ***(G-9727)***
Energy Xxi Gom LLC.......713 659-2100
1021 Main St Ste 2626 Houston (77002) ***(G-9639)***
Energy Xxi Gulf Coast Inc (HQ).......**713 351-3000**
1021 Main St Ste 2626 Houston (77002) ***(G-9640)***
Energy Xxi Ltd.......713 351-3000
1021 Main St Ste 2626 Houston (77002) ***(G-9641)***
Energy Xxi USA Inc.......713 351-3000
1021 Main St Ste 2626 Houston (77002) ***(G-9642)***
Enerquest Resources LLC.......432 685-3116
18 Desta Dr Midland (79705) ***(G-15219)***
Enersol Group Inc.......830 387-4011
1015 W San Antonio St New Braunfels (78130) ***(G-15790)***
Enersys.......972 245-6601
1600 Wallace Dr Ste 120 Carrollton (75006) ***(G-2731)***
Enersys Corporation.......281 598-7100
12875 Capricorn St Stafford (77477) ***(G-19311)***
Enertech Industries Inc.......432 550-0543
321 Georgia St Odessa (79764) ***(G-15991)***
Enervest Ltd (PA).......**713 659-3500**
1001 Fannin St Ste 800 Houston (77002) ***(G-9643)***
Enervest Operating LLC.......979 542-2054
1055 County Road 237 Giddings (78942) ***(G-7694)***
Enervest Operating LLC.......940 683-1966
306 Us Highway 380 Bridgeport (76426) ***(G-2293)***
Enervest Operating LLC (HQ).......**713 659-3500**
1001 Fannin St Ste 800 Houston (77002) ***(G-9644)***
Enflite LLC.......512 868-3399
105 W Cooperative Way Georgetown (78626) ***(G-7650)***
Engelbrecht Manufacturing Inc.......281 341-5110
708 Damascus St Rosenberg (77471) ***(G-17581)***
Engenuity, Conroe *Also called Hilflo LLC* ***(G-3305)***
Engie Retail LLC.......713 636-1127
11807 Westheimer Rd # 550 Houston (77077) ***(G-9645)***
Engine & Compressor ACC, Waller *Also called Garzo Inc* ***(G-20499)***
Engine Service Inc.......713 473-4167
531 Georgia St South Houston (77587) ***(G-19038)***
Engineer Composite System, Belton *Also called Jones-Bell LLC* ***(G-2026)***
Engineered Carbons Inc.......806 274-6347
Fm 1559 Borger (79007) ***(G-2178)***
Engineered Cstm Solutions LLC.......832 598-2083
13720 Fm 529 Rd Ste 200 Houston (77041) ***(G-9646)***
Engineered Fluids, Tyler *Also called Chemfoundry Inc* ***(G-20066)***
Engineered Polymer Systems Div, Nacogdoches *Also called Parker-Hannifin Corporation* ***(G-15708)***
Engineered Pump Services Inc.......713 472-7722
109 N Richey St Ste A Pasadena (77506) ***(G-16428)***
Engineered Spring Products, Houston *Also called Matthew Warren Inc* ***(G-10797)***
Engineering Spectrum Inc.......210 697-8828
5807 Sebastian Pl Ste 13 San Antonio (78249) ***(G-18090)***
Enginered Packaged Systems Inc.......409 866-5213
6280 Westwood Blvd Beaumont (77707) ***(G-1887)***
Englander Dzignpak, Waco *Also called Ecd Acquisitions Inc* ***(G-20395)***
Englander-Sonntag, Carrollton *Also called Packaging Corporation America* ***(G-2789)***
Englobal Constant Power Inc.......713 880-6200
1400 N Sam Houston Pkwy E S Houston (77032) ***(G-9647)***
Englobal Corporation.......409 840-2100
3105 Executive Blvd Beaumont (77705) ***(G-1888)***
Engrave It Houston, Houston *Also called Isaiah 49 16 Inc* ***(G-10424)***
Engraving and Printing Bureau.......817 847-3800
9000 Blue Mound Rd Fort Worth (76131) ***(G-6615)***
Enhanced Production Tech Inc.......512 759-2009
402 Tradesmens Park Dr Hutto (78634) ***(G-12878)***
Eni Petroleum US LLC.......713 393-6100
1201 La St Ste 3500 Houston (77002) ***(G-9648)***
Eni USA Inc.......713 393-6100
1200 Smith St Ste 1700 Houston (77002) ***(G-9649)***
Enlink Midstream Inc (HQ).......**214 953-9500**
2501 Cedar Springs Rd # 600 Dallas (75201) ***(G-4324)***
Enlink Midstream Partners LP.......817 599-3492
410 Pearson Ranch Rd Weatherford (76087) ***(G-20589)***
Enlink N Texas Gathering LP.......432 221-9757
5023 Princeton Ave Ste 2 Midland (79703) ***(G-15220)***
Ennis Inc (PA).......**972 775-9801**
2441 Presidential Pkwy Midlothian (76065) ***(G-15480)***
Ennis Inc.......210 271-7971
3463 E Commerce St San Antonio (78220) ***(G-18091)***
Ennis Inc.......903 496-2244
118 E Main St Wolfe City (75496) ***(G-20906)***
Ennis Inc.......972 875-5873
114 Ne Main St Ennis (75119) ***(G-6098)***
Ennis Daily News, Ennis *Also called Ellis Co Newspapers* ***(G-6096)***
Ennis Daily News, The, Ennis *Also called Ellis County Newspapers Inc* ***(G-6097)***
Ennis Tag & Label, Wolfe City *Also called Ennis Inc* ***(G-20906)***
Ennis-Flint Inc.......817 706-3777
2802 Spur 469 Ennis (75119) ***(G-6099)***
Enpro Industries Inc.......281 207-4600
4410 Greenbriar Dr Stafford (77477) ***(G-19312)***
Enpro Industries Inc.......713 983-4222
6455 Clara Rd Ste 300 Houston (77041) ***(G-9650)***
Enpro Industries Inc.......713 983-4200
10633 W Little York Rd # 300 Houston (77041) ***(G-9651)***
Enrud Resources Inc (PA).......**713 943-1600**
1006 Vista Rd Pasadena (77504) ***(G-16429)***
Ensco International Inc (HQ).......**800 423-8006**
5847 San Felipe St # 330 Houston (77057) ***(G-9652)***
Ensemble Theatre.......713 520-0055
3535 Main St Houston (77002) ***(G-9653)***
Enseo LLC.......972 234-2513
2201 10th St Plano (75074) ***(G-16862)***
Enserco Midstream LLC.......713 341-7378
8847 W Sam Houston Pkwy N Houston (77040) ***(G-9654)***
Ensign, Houston *Also called Ofs Global Inc* ***(G-11147)***
Ensign Intl Enrgy Svcs Inc.......281 872-7770
450 Gears Rd Ste 777 Houston (77067) ***(G-9655)***
Ensign Management LLC.......281 403-6304
5875 N Sam Houston Pkwy W Houston (77086) ***(G-9656)***
Ensign United States Drlg Inc (HQ).......**303 292-1206**
15015 Vickery Dr Houston (77032) ***(G-9657)***
Ensign US Southern Drlg LLC.......303 292-1206
15015 Vickery Dr Houston (77032) ***(G-9658)***
Ensinger Special Polymers Inc.......281 580-3600
12331 Cutten Rd Houston (77066) ***(G-9659)***
Ensosoft LLC.......713 360-4841
16307 S Temple Dr Houston (77095) ***(G-9660)***
Entail Engine LLC.......956 467-5198
1445 E Madison St Ste 177 Brownsville (78520) ***(G-2354)***
Entech Solar Inc (PA).......**817 421-4658**
641 Industrial Blvd Grapevine (76051) ***(G-8031)***
Entech Technology Inc.......972 542-0210
16326 Sunset Valley Dr Dallas (75248) ***(G-4325)***
Entegris Inc.......940 393-4232
300 Old Greenwood Rd Decatur (76234) ***(G-5246)***
Entegris Inc.......512 715-5344
706 Houston Clinton Dr Burnet (78611) ***(G-2607)***
Entegris Prof Solutions Inc.......512 244-5200
700 Jeffrey Way Ste 400 Round Rock (78665) ***(G-17655)***
Enterprise, Livingston *Also called Polk County Publishing Co* ***(G-14160)***
Enterprise Concrete Pdts LLC.......214 631-7006
4040 Singleton Blvd Dallas (75212) ***(G-4326)***
Enterprise ESP Svc Prvider LLC.......469 619-3114
840 F Ave Ste 105 Plano (75074) ***(G-16863)***
Enterprise Gas Processing LLC.......713 381-4068
2727 North Loop W Ste 700 Houston (77008) ***(G-9661)***
Enterprise Hydrocarbons LP.......713 381-6500
1100 La St Fl 10 Flr 10 San Antonio (78209) ***(G-18092)***
Enterprise Offshore Drlg LLC.......832 399-6500
11700 Katy Fwy Ste 550 Houston (77079) ***(G-9662)***
Enterprise Pipe & Steel, Mount Enterprise *Also called Spivey Stake & Supply Inc* ***(G-15645)***
Enterprise Prcast Con Txas LLC.......903 875-1077
800 N Interstate 45 Corsicana (75110) ***(G-3671)***
Enterprise Products Company (HQ).......**713 381-6500**
1100 Louisiana St Houston (77002) ***(G-9663)***
Enterprise Products Company.......432 221-7700
4500 E Highway 80 Midland (79706) ***(G-15221)***
Enterprise Products Company.......432 686-5421
1031 Andrews Hwy Midland (79701) ***(G-15222)***
Enterprise Products Oper LLC.......281 385-4200
10207 Fm Rd 1942 Mont Belvieu (77580) ***(G-15617)***
Enterprise Products Oper LLC.......832 501-4000
10910 Evil Dr Mont Belvieu (77580) ***(G-15618)***
Enterprise SEC Sltons Txas Inc.......940 320-3778
316 E 5th St Justin (76247) ***(G-13343)***
Enterprise Svcs Ltin Amer Corp (HQ).......**703 245-9675**
20555 State Highway 249 Houston (77070) ***(G-9664)***
Entertainment Networks, Dallas *Also called Edwin Jones Company Inc* ***(G-4301)***
Entertainment Technology, Carrollton *Also called Philips North America LLC* ***(G-2881)***
Entex Fabrication Inc.......940 592-2173
1010 Texowa Rd Iowa Park (76367) ***(G-12904)***
Enthusiastic Sales LLC.......832 698-1608
9421 Fm 2920 Rd Bldg 10a Tomball (77375) ***(G-19978)***
Entrans International LLC.......281 459-5350
7600 E Sam Houston Pkwy N Houston (77049) ***(G-9665)***

A L P H A B E T I C

Entrec Corporation...432 301-2794
  4003 Scr 1294 Odessa (79765) *(G-15992)*

Entrematic Loading Dock Pdts...............................972 466-0707
  1612 Hutton Dr Ste 140 Carrollton (75006) *(G-2732)*

Entry Way Publishing..972 517-6513
  6205 Oregon Ct Plano (75023) *(G-16864)*

Envasco, Houston *Also called Energy Valve & Supply Co LLC (G-9638)*

Enven Energy Ventures LLC................................713 335-7000
  609 Main St Ste 3200 Houston (77002) *(G-9666)*

Enventives LLC..612 930-1977
  2945 Old Seagraves Rd Seagraves (79359) *(G-18803)*

Enverus, Austin *Also called Drilling Info Inc (G-1101)*

Envirnmntal Sgnage Sltions Inc............................972 915-3800
  8181 Jetstar Dr Ste 110 Irving (75063) *(G-13015)*

Enviro Cams LLC...430 255-7006
  201 N Elm St Kemp (75143) *(G-13484)*

Enviro Solutions, Nederland *Also called Petrofuels Quality Mktg LP (G-15759)*

Enviro-San Corporation...281 373-4200
  16522 Cypress Rosehill Rd Cypress (77429) *(G-3788)*

Enviro-Tech Specialties Inc.................................281 476-9803
  121 Dell Dale St Channelview (77530) *(G-3019)*

Envirocal Inc...832 296-4205
  4006 Windsong Trl Houston (77084) *(G-9667)*

Envirocleanse LLC...713 840-0404
  22762 Westheimer Pkwy Katy (77450) *(G-13400)*

Envirocon Technologies Inc................................512 382-9842
  3601 S Congress Ave G600 Austin (78704) *(G-1127)*

Enviroflex Design & Mfg..281 356-6700
  29639 Fm 2978 Rd Magnolia (77354) *(G-14605)*

Envirokind Inc...713 434-9900
  75 Southbelt Indus Dr Houston (77047) *(G-9668)*

Enviromatic Systems, Grand Prairie *Also called Climatic Systems Inc (G-7853)*

Enviromental Industries LP....................................972 390-9899
  8801 Governors Row Dallas (75247) *(G-4327)*

Environment, Houston *Also called Coen Furniture Inc (G-9237)*

Environmental Floors Inc.....................................713 956-5526
  505 Martin Creek Ln Georgetown (78633) *(G-7651)*

Environmental Fuel Systems.................................800 375-7747
  213 Commerce Ave Boerne (78006) *(G-2119)*

Envirosense LLC (PA)...281 828-8989
  18527 Berry Leaf Ct Houston (77084) *(G-9669)*

Envirotainer Inc (HQ)...972 831-3800
  222 Las Colinas Blvd W Irving (75039) *(G-13016)*

Envirotech Drilling Services..................................832 493-8063
  4214 Creekmont Dr Houston (77091) *(G-9670)*

Envirotech Pumpsystems Inc..............................832 200-6220
  920 Seaco Ave Deer Park (77536) *(G-5272)*

Envision Dallas, Dallas *Also called Dallas Lghthouse For Blind Inc (G-4217)*

Eoa Holding Co Inc...214 496-4000
  13555 N Stemmons Fwy Dallas (75234) *(G-4328)*

Eog Resources Inc...830 879-4614
  402 N Main St Cotulla (78014) *(G-3690)*

Eog Resources Inc...361 866-4300
  539 N Carancahua St # 900 Corpus Christi (78401) *(G-3519)*

Eog Resources Inc...979 245-2201
  3211 Avenue F Bay City (77414) *(G-1772)*

Eog Resources Inc...210 403-7700
  19100 Ridgewood Pkwy # 2 San Antonio (78259) *(G-18093)*

Eog Resources Inc...432 586-9141
  107 E Winkler St Kermit (79745) *(G-13512)*

Eog Resources Inc...432 686-3600
  5509 Champions Dr Midland (79706) *(G-15223)*

Eog Resources Inc...817 339-9380
  421 W 3rd St Ste 300 Fort Worth (76102) *(G-6616)*

Eog Resources Inc (PA)..713 651-7000
  1111 Bagby Sky Lbby 2 Houston (77002) *(G-9671)*

Eog Resources Inc...940 567-9777
  954 S Main St Jacksboro (76458) *(G-13220)*

Eog Resources Inc...325 392-3782
  Hwy 163 S Ozona (76943) *(G-16282)*

Eog Resources Inc...940 696-6000
  2100 Briar Creek Rd Bowie (76230) *(G-2194)*

Eog Resources Inc...817 212-3100
  4449 S Interstate 35 W Alvarado (76009) *(G-330)*

Eog Resources Inc...817 598-8300
  395 Jones Rd Weatherford (76088) *(G-20590)*

Eog Resources Investments Inc............................713 651-6914
  333 Clay St Ste 4200 Houston (77002) *(G-9672)*

Eoh Industries Inc...817 468-3181
  1901 Southeast Pkwy Arlington (76018) *(G-671)*

Eos North America, Temple *Also called Advanced Laser Materials LLC (G-19667)*

Eos Well Service Inc..281 914-2191
  1860 Fm 359 Rd 328 Richmond (77406) *(G-17454)*

Eosera Inc...844 732-7929
  5000 South Fwy Fort Worth (76115) *(G-6617)*

Ep Big Media Inc..915 585-0444
  5710 Doniphan Dr El Paso (79932) *(G-5756)*

Ep Energy Corporation (PA)...................................713 997-1000
  601 Travis St Ste 1400 Houston (77002) *(G-9673)*

Ep Energy E&P Company LP (HQ)..........................713 997-1200
  601 Travis St Ste 1400 Houston (77002) *(G-9674)*

Ep Energy LLC (HQ)..713 997-1200
  601 Travis St Ste 1400 Houston (77002) *(G-9675)*

Ep Energy Management LLC (HQ)..........................713 997-1000
  601 Travis St Ste 1400 Houston (77002) *(G-9676)*

Ep Energy Resale Company LLC (HQ).....................713 997-1000
  601 Travis St Ste 1400 Houston (77002) *(G-9677)*

Epak International Inc..512 231-8083
  4926 Spicewood Springs Rd # 200 Austin (78759) *(G-1128)*

Epcon Industrial Systems LP...............................936 273-1774
  17777 Interstate 45 S Shenandoah (77385) *(G-18896)*

Epcs Environmental LLC..817 975-5790
  5409 S Collins St Ste 111 Arlington (76018) *(G-672)*

Epd, Houston *Also called Electronic Power Design Inc (G-9596)*

Epd Inc...979 239-1917
  1407 E Cedar St Angleton (77515) *(G-572)*

Epd International Ltd...713 923-1191
  15200 North Fwy Houston (77090) *(G-9678)*

Epe Industries Usa Inc..800 315-0336
  6615 Roxburgh Dr Ste 200 Houston (77041) *(G-9679)*

Epe USA, Houston *Also called Epe Industries Usa Inc (G-9679)*

Epi, San Antonio *Also called Glo-Jo Electrical Products Inc (G-18144)*

Epic Bottling LLC...512 947-8608
  204 Airline Dr Ste 700 Coppell (75019) *(G-3416)*

Epic De Juarez SA De RI De Cv, El Paso *Also called Epic Technologies LLC (G-5757)*

Epic Distribution LLC...346 308-6038
  9260 Bryant St Houston (77075) *(G-9680)*

Epic Energy Resources Inc...................................281 419-3742
  10330 Lake Rd Ste D Houston (77070) *(G-9681)*

Epic Energy Services LLC....................................361 222-1226
  6397 Highway 77 Odem (78370) *(G-15895)*

Epic Products Intl Corp...817 640-3037
  902 Kck Way Cedar Hill (75104) *(G-2940)*

Epic Provisions LLC (HQ).....................................512 944-8502
  1902 S Congress Ave D Austin (78704) *(G-1129)*

Epic Source Food Company LLC...........................214 407-7154
  7158 Main St Frisco (75033) *(G-7283)*

Epic Technologies LLC...915 791-5326
  995 Loma Verde Dr El Paso (79936) *(G-5757)*

Epic Technologies LLC...915 229-6805
  9600 Joe Rodriguez Ste 4 El Paso (79927) *(G-5758)*

Epic Y-Grade Marketing LP...................................210 920-2285
  18615 Tuscany Stone # 30 San Antonio (78258) *(G-18094)*

Epica Applied Technologies LLC............................281 367-1983
  2290 Fm 1516 N Unit 1 Converse (78109) *(G-3392)*

Epica Applied Technologies LLC............................210 310-7710
  2290 Fm 1516 N Unit 1 Converse (78109) *(G-3393)*

Epicor Software Corporation.................................512 328-2300
  804 Las Cimas Pkwy # 200 Austin (78746) *(G-1130)*

Epicor Software Corporation.................................949 585-4000
  804 Las Cimas Pkwy # 200 Austin (78746) *(G-1131)*

Epicor Software Corporation.................................800 776-7438
  2400 Dallas Pkwy Plano (75093) *(G-16865)*

Epicor Software Corporation (PA)..........................512 328-2300
  804 Las Cimas Pkwy # 200 Austin (78746) *(G-1132)*

Epii, Mineral Wells *Also called Electromedical Pdts Intl Inc (G-15525)*

Epimed International Inc (PA)...............................972 373-9090
  13958 Diplomat Dr Farmers Branch (75234) *(G-6196)*

Epiroc Drilling Solutions LLC (HQ).........................972 496-7400
  2100 N 1st St Garland (75040) *(G-7486)*

Epiroc Drilling Solutions LLC................................214 547-7800
  815 Enterprise Blvd Allen (75013) *(G-265)*

Epiroc Drilling Tools LLC (HQ)................................844 437-4762
  1600 S Great Sw Pkwy Grand Prairie (75051) *(G-7866)*

Epiroc North America Corp....................................972 496-7353
  2100 N 1st St Garland (75040) *(G-7487)*

Epitek Silicon, Allen *Also called Srj Holdings LLC (G-299)*

Epl Oil & Gas Inc..713 228-0711
  919 Milam St Ste 1650 Houston (77002) *(G-9682)*

EPM Live Inc..425 452-1111
  401 Congress Ave Ste 1850 Austin (78701) *(G-1133)*

Epoch Mdia Group Suthern Texas, Houston *Also called Epochtimes Public Media Inc (G-9683)*

Epochtimes Public Media Inc..............................713 790-0815
  7001 Corporate Dr Ste 206 Houston (77036) *(G-9683)*

Eproduction Solutions LLC..................................281 348-1000
  22001 Northpark Dr Kingwood (77339) *(G-13641)*

Eps, Beaumont *Also called Engineered Packaged Systems Inc (G-1887)*

Epsilon Energy Usa Inc..281 670-0002
  16945 Northchase Dr # 1610 Houston (77060) *(G-9684)*

Epsilon Industries Inc..469 573-9566
  3538 Dividend Dr Garland (75042) *(G-7488)*

Epsilyte LLC...815 224-1525
  1330 Lake Robbins Dr # 310 The Woodlands (77380) *(G-19862)*

Equalizer Industries Inc.......................................512 388-7715
  2611 Oakmont Dr Round Rock (78665) *(G-17656)*

Equibrand Products Group LP (HQ).......................817 573-1884
  3500 W Us Highway 377 Granbury (76048) *(G-7796)*

(G-0000) Company's Geographic Section entry number

Equilon Enterprises LLC (HQ)........................713 767-5337
  910 Louisiana St Ste 2 Houston (77002) *(G-9685)*

Equinor Energy LP..512 427-3300
  6300 Bridge Point Pkwy # 2 Austin (78730) *(G-1134)*

Equinor Exploration Company (HQ)...............512 427-3300
  6300 Bridge Point Pkwy Austin (78730) *(G-1135)*

Equinor Gulf of Mexico LLC (HQ).................713 918-8200
  2107 Citywest Blvd # 100 Houston (77042) *(G-9686)*

Equinor US Operations LLC (HQ).................713 918-8200
  2107 Citywest Blvd # 100 Houston (77042) *(G-9687)*

Equinor USA E&P Inc (HQ)..........................713 918-8200
  2107 Citywest Blvd # 100 Houston (77042) *(G-9688)*

Equinor USA Properties Inc (HQ)................713 918-8200
  6300 Bridge Point Pkwy Austin (78730) *(G-1136)*

Equipment Storage Service Inc (HQ).............214 374-3995
  3839 E Overton Rd Dallas (75216) *(G-4329)*

Equistar Chemicals LP..................................361 572-2547
  2695 Old Bloomington Rd N Victoria (77905) *(G-20261)*

Equistar Chemicals LP..................................281 862-4000
  2502 Sheldon Rd Channelview (77530) *(G-3020)*

Equistar Chemicals LP..................................281 474-4040
  5761 Underwood Rd Pasadena (77507) *(G-16430)*

Equistar Chemicals LP..................................713 209-7000
  1515 Miller Cut Off Rd La Porte (77571) *(G-13736)*

Equistar Chemicals LP (HQ)..........................713 309-7200
  1221 Mckinney St Ste 300 Houston (77010) *(G-9689)*

Er Carpenter, Dallas *Also called Carpenter Co (G-4085)*

Erasmo Lopez Jr...956 487-3366
  600 N West St Rio Grande City (78582) *(G-17471)*

Erath Publishers Inc....................................254 965-3124
  702 E South Loop Stephenville (76401) *(G-19410)*

Erect-A-Line Inc..214 630-1154
  3912 W Illinois Ave Dallas (75211) *(G-4330)*

Ereplacements LLC (PA)...............................214 935-3591
  600 E Dallas Rd Ste 200 Grapevine (76051) *(G-8032)*

Erg Resources LLC......................................713 812-1800
  333 Clay St Ste 4400 Houston (77002) *(G-9690)*

Ergomart, Dallas *Also called Ergotect Corporation (G-4331)*

Ergon Inc...972 875-1122
  203 Cedar Rd Ennis (75119) *(G-6100)*

Ergotect Corporation....................................214 747-3746
  5200 E Grand Ave Ste 500 Dallas (75223) *(G-4331)*

Erhc Energy Inc (PA)....................................713 626-4700
  5444 Westheimr Rd # 1440 Houston (77056) *(G-9691)*

Eric Industries Inc......................................972 248-8009
  5934 Tree Shadow Trl Dallas (75252) *(G-3841)*

Ericsson Smart Factory Inc..........................469 266-3776
  2601 S Valley Pkwy Lewisville (75067) *(G-14049)*

Eriksen Marine, Austin *Also called Gpd Marine Inc (G-1191)*

Erin Energy Corporation...............................713 797-2940
  1330 Post Oak Blvd # 2250 Houston (77056) *(G-9692)*

Erna Frac Sand LC......................................325 265-4400
  224 Evans Ln Mason (76856) *(G-14813)*

Ernie's Fiesta Graphics, Brownsville *Also called Fiesta Graphics (G-2356)*

Ernies Welding Shop Inc..............................512 459-6346
  6511 Burnet Ln Austin (78757) *(G-1137)*

Ernmex Interntational Inc.............................281 458-0152
  12543 Unison Rd Houston (77044) *(G-9693)*

Erskine Energy LLC.....................................281 225-7223
  11700 Katy Fwy Ste 1200 Houston (77079) *(G-9694)*

Erskine Energy Prod Companies, Houston *Also called Erskine Energy LLC (G-9694)*

Erwin Containers Inc...................................817 295-5256
  535 Memorial Plz Burleson (76028) *(G-2578)*

Es Custom Boats LLC...................................832 864-2331
  2332 Anders Ln Kemah (77565) *(G-13473)*

Es Group of Texas Inc.................................281 796-6214
  3903 Shady Terrace Dr Kingwood (77345) *(G-13642)*

Es Windpower, Kingwood *Also called Es Group of Texas Inc (G-13642)*

ESAB Group Inc (HQ)...................................800 372-2123
  2800 Airport Rd Denton (76207) *(G-5365)*

ESAB Welding & Cutting Pdts, Denton *Also called ESAB Group Inc (G-5365)*

Esbee Sign Sysyems, Houston *Also called Esbee Signs Inc (G-9695)*

Esbee Signs Inc..281 550-4577
  5322 Addicks Satsuma Rd B Houston (77084) *(G-9695)*

Esco Group LLC...903 984-3726
  2103 State Highway 31 E Kilgore (75662) *(G-13551)*

Esco Industries Inc.....................................254 296-0500
  4901 Steinbeck Bend Dr Waco (76708) *(G-20396)*

Esco Laminating Texas Inc...........................254 296-0500
  4901 Steinbeck Bend Dr Waco (76708) *(G-20397)*

Escondido Resources II MGT LLC (PA)............713 662-0332
  2002 W Grand Pkwy N # 205 Katy (77449) *(G-13401)*

Eseis Inc..281 531-1447
  12012 Wickchester Ln # 60 Houston (77079) *(G-9696)*

Esenjay Exploration Inc (PA)........................361 883-7464
  500 N Water St Ste 1100 Corpus Christi (78401) *(G-3520)*

Esenjay Petroleum Corporation.....................361 883-7464
  500 N Water St Ste 1100 Corpus Christi (78401) *(G-3521)*

Eship Global Inc..972 518-1775
  18111 Preston Rd Ste 650 Dallas (75252) *(G-3842)*

Esi Technologies LLC...................................512 633-2897
  6705 Lakewood Point Cv Austin (78750) *(G-1138)*

Esigns, Houston *Also called Digimagination LLC (G-9469)*

Esip Group LLC...281 965-4942
  19221 Beechnut St Apt 332 Richmond (77407) *(G-17455)*

Esna LLC (HQ)...817 281-8816
  6625 Iron Horse Blvd North Richland Hills (76180) *(G-15877)*

ESP Enterprises Inc....................................281 444-2377
  13161 Misty Willow Dr Houston (77070) *(G-9697)*

ESP Safety Inc..972 310-0754
  4001 W Sam Houston Pkwy N # 150 Houston (77043) *(G-9698)*

ESP Services, Houston *Also called ESP Enterprises Inc (G-9697)*

Espada Oilfield Services LLC........................361 894-1810
  1501 E Mockingbird Ln # 211 Victoria (77904) *(G-20262)*

Espey Silica Sand Co Inc.............................210 626-2800
  27265 Us Highway 281 S San Antonio (78264) *(G-18095)*

Espinoza Cast Stone Inc...............................214 396-5280
  4743 N Intrstate Hwy 35 E Waxahachie (75165) *(G-20542)*

Espinoza Services Inc (PA)...........................806 592-8463
  2887 Dulin Dr Denver City (79323) *(G-5418)*

Espinoza Stone Inc......................................830 629-2530
  8200 N Interstate 35 New Braunfels (78130) *(G-15791)*

Espitias Cabinet & Door Makers.....................713 329-9515
  8529 Rannie Rd Houston (77080) *(G-9699)*

Espy Corporation...512 261-1016
  13033 Trautwein Rd Austin (78737) *(G-861)*

Esquire Tooling & Mfg Inc.............................903 886-4779
  111 State Highway 224 Commerce (75428) *(G-3243)*

Essa Pharmaceuticals..................................832 831-5958
  2130 W Holcombe Blvd # 900 Houston (77030) *(G-9700)*

Essence Bottling Co Texas Inc.......................806 993-1391
  2401 Ne Loop 289 Lubbock (79403) *(G-14407)*

Essential Safety Ppe LLC.............................844 372-3377
  22936 Kuykendahl Rd Spring (77389) *(G-19113)*

Essentium Inc (PA).......................................210 616-1931
  19025 N Hthrwld Blvd Pflugerville (78660) *(G-16670)*

Essentium Materials, Pflugerville *Also called Essentium Inc (G-16670)*

Esser Casket Co LLC...................................713 225-5548
  7100 Cavalcade St Houston (77028) *(G-9701)*

Esser Caskets, Houston *Also called Esser Casket Co LLC (G-9701)*

Essex Group Inc..915 772-6041
  24 Spur Dr Ste A El Paso (79906) *(G-5759)*

Essex Group Industrial Pdts, El Paso *Also called Essex Group Inc (G-5759)*

Essilor Laboratories Amer Inc.......................713 663-3000
  3625 Willowbend Blvd # 110 Houston (77054) *(G-9702)*

Essilor Laboratories Amer Inc (HQ)...............972 241-4141
  13515 N Stemmons Fwy Dallas (75234) *(G-4332)*

Essilor Labs of America, Dallas *Also called Eoa Holding Co Inc (G-4328)*

Essilor of America Inc.................................214 496-4000
  13515 N Stemmons Fwy Dallas (75234) *(G-4333)*

Essilor of America Inc (HQ)..........................214 496-4000
  13555 N Stemmons Fwy Dallas (75234) *(G-4334)*

Essilor of America Inc.................................214 496-4235
  13455 Branch View Ln Dallas (75234) *(G-4335)*

Esskay Manufacturing Co..............................210 222-9585
  122 Stribling San Antonio (78204) *(G-18096)*

Essner Manufacturing LP..............................817 551-5511
  6651 Will Rogers Blvd B Fort Worth (76140) *(G-6618)*

Essner Precision Mfg LLC.............................817 529-2580
  6651 Will Rogers Blvd B Fort Worth (76140) *(G-6619)*

Esst, Justin *Also called Enterprise SEC Sltons Txas Inc (G-13343)*

Est of James T Jones...................................254 799-4515
  117 Virginia Rd Waco (76705) *(G-20398)*

Estech Systems Inc.....................................972 422-9700
  3701 E Plano Pkwy Ste 100 Plano (75074) *(G-16866)*

Estill Inc..806 789-1548
  4704 88th St Lubbock (79424) *(G-14408)*

Estis Compression LLC.................................318 397-5557
  2019 State Highway 135 N Kilgore (75662) *(G-13552)*

Estovel Inc..512 345-6997
  6203 Shadow Mountain Cv Austin (78731) *(G-1139)*

Esw Holdings Inc (HQ)..................................512 524-6149
  401 Congress Ave Ste 2650 Austin (78701) *(G-1140)*

Etc Intrastate Procurement LLC.....................713 989-2688
  1300 Main St Houston (77002) *(G-9703)*

Etech Envmtl Safety Solutions (PA)...............432 563-2200
  13000 W County Road 100 Odessa (79765) *(G-15993)*

Etech-Web, Round Rock *Also called Micross Components-Tx LLC (G-17673)*

Etheredge Elc Co Tyler Inc...........................903 877-4774
  11698 Fm 3270 Tyler (75708) *(G-20084)*

Ethicon Inc...325 482-5200
  3348 Pulliam St San Angelo (76905) *(G-17797)*

Ethos Energy LP..713 336-1300
  2800 North Loop W # 1100 Houston (77092) *(G-9704)*

Ethosenergy (usa) LLC (HQ).........................713 812-2300
  2800 North Loop W Houston (77092) *(G-9705)*

Ethosenergy Field Services LLC 713 849-8835
  6225 W Sam Houston Pkwy N A Houston (77041) *(G-9706)*
Ethosenergy Light Turbines LLC (HQ) **713 849-8800**
  6225 W Sam Houston Pkwy N Houston (77041) *(G-9707)*
Ethosenergy Tc Inc 713 336-1300
  3100 S Sam Houston Pkwy E Houston (77047) *(G-9708)*
Ethosiq LLC 281 616-5711
  17121 W Rd Ste 201 Huston Houston (77095) *(G-9709)*
Ethyl, Spring Also called Afton Chemical Corporation *(G-19193)*
Ethyl Corporation 713 740-8300
  1000 N South St Pasadena (77503) *(G-16431)*
Eti, Austin Also called Emergency Technologies Inc *(G-1124)*
Etkon USA Inc 817 701-1181
  916 113th St Ste A Arlington (76011) *(G-673)*
Etos Inc 903 895-2220
  595 N Main Hwy New London (75682) *(G-15850)*
Ets Lindgren, Cedar Park Also called Ets-Lindgren Inc *(G-2968)*
Ets Oilfield Services LP (PA) **361 767-4200**
  15406 Northwest Blvd Robstown (78380) *(G-17509)*
Ets Zone 713 559-1400
  2170 Buckthorne Pl # 250 Spring (77380) *(G-19211)*
Ets-Lindgren Inc (HQ) **512 531-6400**
  1301 Arrow Point Dr Cedar Park (78613) *(G-2968)*
Etsco, Humble Also called Electronic Technical Svcs Corp *(G-12765)*
Ett, Frisco Also called Economic Trnsfrmtion Tech Corp *(G-7281)*
Euclid Media Group LLC 210 227-0044
  915 Dallas St San Antonio (78215) *(G-18097)*
Eugene B Smith & Co Inc 409 763-6401
  404 N Witter St Pasadena (77506) *(G-16432)*
Euless Aero Components, Euless Also called Aereos Inc *(G-6126)*
Euless Aero Components LLC 817 267-1371
  1100 S Pipeline Rd W Euless (76040) *(G-6143)*
Eurecat U S Incorporated (HQ) **281 218-0669**
  1331 Gemini St Ste 310 Houston (77058) *(G-9710)*
Eurecat U S Incorporated 281 842-6700
  13100 Baypark Rd Pasadena (77507) *(G-16433)*
Eureka Midstream LLC 832 203-4544
  1111 La St Ste 4520 Houston (77002) *(G-9711)*
Eureka Sheet Metal Inc 210 735-4426
  550 Delgado St San Antonio (78207) *(G-18098)*
Eureka Water Probes, Austin Also called Chen Grner Stvens Prtners LLC *(G-1046)*
Euro Tex, Freeport Also called Cabinets Deluxe By Dale Inc *(G-7195)*
Europa Designs 972 792-0997
  13720 Neutron Rd Dallas (75244) *(G-4336)*
Europa Sports Products Inc 214 388-7444
  1851 Big Town Blvd # 500 Mesquite (75149) *(G-15041)*
Eurotech Industries Inc 713 937-1730
  11701 Brittmoore Park Dr Houston (77041) *(G-9712)*
Eutsler Technical Products Inc 713 686-8209
  3718 Creekmont Dr Houston (77091) *(G-9713)*
Ev Energy Partners LP (PA) **713 659-3500**
  1001 Fannin St Ste 800 Houston (77002) *(G-9714)*
Evadale Paperboard Mill, Evadale Also called Westrock Mwv LLC *(G-6167)*
Evans - Hamilton Inc (PA) **281 448-6188**
  411 N Sam Houston Pkwy E Houston (77060) *(G-9715)*
Evans Cabinet and Door Ltd (PA) **979 836-6934**
  308 W First St Brenham (77833) *(G-2253)*
Evans Composites Inc 817 477-9014
  300 S Wisteria St Mansfield (76063) *(G-14670)*
Evans Electric, Waco Also called Evans Enterprises Inc *(G-20399)*
Evans Electric, Wichita Falls Also called Evans Enterprises Inc *(G-20764)*
Evans Enterprises Inc 254 772-4710
  201 S Industrial Dr Waco (76710) *(G-20399)*
Evans Enterprises Inc 940 723-7466
  2707 Central Fwy E Wichita Falls (76302) *(G-20764)*
Evans Enterprises Inc 325 235-1776
  1650 Vision Dr Ste 100 Abilene (79602) *(G-40)*
Evans Foods Inc 817 640-5626
  615 N Great Sw Pkwy Arlington (76011) *(G-674)*
Evans Sons Prtble Rock Crshing 830 214-3629
  2100 Heritage Ave # 5202 Euless (76039) *(G-6144)*
Evco Fabrication Inc 432 561-8561
  10925 W County Rd 125 Midland (79711) *(G-15224)*
Evco Partners LP 409 766-1900
  2701 Palmer Hwy Ste B Texas City (77590) *(G-19793)*
Everest Coatings Inc 281 350-9800
  2400 Spring Stuebner Rd Spring (77389) *(G-19114)*
Everest Global Inc 972 980-0013
  13455 Noel Rd Ste 2100 Dallas (75240) *(G-4337)*
Everest Systems LLC (PA) **800 575-8966**
  16601 Central Green Blvd # 100 Houston (77032) *(G-9716)*
Everest Valve Company Inc 713 923-8696
  6612 Avenue U Houston (77011) *(G-9717)*
Everett LLC 432 381-5700
  2970 N Eastview Ave Odessa (79764) *(G-15994)*
Evergreen Solutions Inc 512 389-0625
  3500 Dime Cir 109 Austin (78744) *(G-1141)*
Everhardt Antennas, Fort Worth Also called Marvel Communications Company *(G-6814)*

Everi Games Holding Inc (HQ) 512 334-7500
  206 Wild Basin Rd Bldg B West Lake Hills (78746) *(G-20681)*
Everi Games Inc 512 439-3100
  4616 W Howard Ln Ste 500 Austin (78728) *(G-1142)*
Everise Px, Austin Also called Trusource Labs LLC *(G-1598)*
Everlite Inc (PA) **903 297-3444**
  607 Fisher Rd Longview (75604) *(G-14232)*
Everly Well Inc 512 309-5588
  823 Congress Ave Ste 1200 Austin (78701) *(G-1143)*
Evers and Sons Inc 979 596-2139
  12905 State Highway 36 S Caldwell (77836) *(G-2632)*
Everything Energy LLC 713 537-3000
  1201 Fannin St Houston (77002) *(G-9718)*
Everywell, Austin Also called Everly Well Inc *(G-1143)*
Evestra Inc (PA) **210 673-3300**
  6410 Tri County Pkwy Schertz (78154) *(G-18749)*
Evo IDT LLC 817 637-0149
  820 S 6th Ave Mansfield (76063) *(G-14671)*
Evo Integrated Drilling Tech, Mansfield Also called Evo IDT LLC *(G-14671)*
Evodesk, Round Rock Also called Next Technologies Inc *(G-17675)*
Evoleap LLC 832 371-6677
  10333 Richmond Ave # 450 Houston (77042) *(G-9719)*
Evolution Fuels Inc 214 389-9800
  3001 Knox St Ste 403 Dallas (75205) *(G-4338)*
Evolution Spine LLC 214 228-6252
  4225 Office Pkwy Dallas (75204) *(G-4339)*
Evolve Holdings Inc (PA) **832 375-0099**
  10555 Cossey Rd Houston (77070) *(G-9720)*
Evonik Corporation 713 477-6841
  1423 Pasadena Fwy Pasadena (77506) *(G-16434)*
Evosite LLC 713 365-3900
  7240 Brittmoore Rd # 100 Houston (77041) *(G-9721)*
Evs Texas Inc 512 989-3000
  400 S Heatherwilde Blvd Pflugerville (78660) *(G-16671)*
EW & WG LP 512 528-8771
  995 N Bagdad Rd Leander (78641) *(G-13989)*
EW Scripps Company 325 659-8200
  34 W Harris Ave San Angelo (76903) *(G-17798)*
EW Scripps Company 361 886-3652
  820 N Lower Broadway St Corpus Christi (78401) *(G-3522)*
Ewb International Inc 972 764-5252
  16220 Midway Rd Addison (75001) *(G-122)*
Ewd Solutions, Carrollton Also called Testequity LLC *(G-2829)*
Ewing Electronics Inc 469 519-2900
  1022 S Grnvlle Ave Ste 30 Allen (75002) *(G-266)*
Ewing Engineered Solutions, Allen Also called Ewing Electronics Inc *(G-266)*
Ewm Enterprises, Austin Also called Boardwalk Technology LLC *(G-1000)*
Exact Diagnostics LLC 817 989-9262
  3400 Camp Bowie Blvd Fort Worth (76107) *(G-6620)*
Exacta Packaging Designs Inc 972 323-1063
  1223 Crowley Dr Carrollton (75006) *(G-2733)*
Exalt Printing Solutions LLC 972 245-3858
  1628 W Crosby Rd Ste 104 Carrollton (75006) *(G-2734)*
Examiner Corporation 409 833-1755
  795 Willow St Beaumont (77701) *(G-1889)*
Examiner Newspaper Group Inc 713 526-3617
  4635 Suthwest Fwy Ste 320 Houston (77027) *(G-9722)*
Examiner Newspaper, The, Beaumont Also called Examiner Corporation *(G-1889)*
Excalibar Minerals LLC 281 864-9550
  2400 Appelt Channelview (77530) *(G-3021)*
Excalibar Minerals LLC 361 883-5227
  4138 Joe Fulton Intl Tc Corpus Christi (78402) *(G-3523)*
Excalibur Comics, San Antonio Also called Ben Dunn Corporation *(G-17946)*
Excalibur Computer Systems, Houston Also called P2 Energy Solutions Inc *(G-11215)*
Excalibur LLC 214 632-0161
  5532 Big River Dr The Colony (75056) *(G-19810)*
Exceed Drilling Tech LLC (PA) **512 656-9669**
  3112 Windsor Rd Ste 519 Austin (78703) *(G-1144)*
Excel Garment Mfg Ltd 915 544-5006
  3517 Frutas Ave El Paso (79905) *(G-5760)*
Excel Label LLC (PA)................................**713 477-6995**
  909 Shaver St Pasadena (77506) *(G-16435)*
Excel Linen Company, Houston Also called A Lakhany International Inc *(G-8427)*
Excel Machinery Ltd (PA) **806 335-1553**
  12100 E Interstate 40 Amarillo (79118) *(G-486)*
Excel Manufacturing, El Paso Also called Excel Garment Mfg Ltd *(G-5760)*
Excel Media LLC 409 832-5770
  80 Interstate 10 N # 209 Beaumont (77702) *(G-1890)*
Excel Media Kxxf Radio, Beaumont Also called Excel Media LLC *(G-1890)*
Excel Production Co 806 665-0366
  1050 N Price Rd Pampa (79065) *(G-16322)*
Excel Pump & Machine Inc 361 387-4508
  1450 Highway 44 Robstown (78380) *(G-17510)*
Excel Stamping & Mfg Inc 281 304-0771
  20101 Schiel Rd Cypress (77433) *(G-3789)*
Excel Steel, Dallas Also called B&B Ornamental Iron Company *(G-3997)*
Excelente Inc.......................................855 209-1970
  2701 W 15th St 513 Plano (75075) *(G-16867)*

Excelergy Corp 214 953-9373
3102 Maple Ave Ste 450 Dallas (75201) *(G-4340)*

Exceleron Software LLC 972 852-2700
8144 Walnut Hill Ln # 905 Dallas (75231) *(G-4341)*

Excell 7 Machine Shop Inc 281 416-0001
4206 Bluebonnet Dr Houston (77053) *(G-8379)*

Excell Machine Co Inc 817 473-6121
602 S 4th Ave Mansfield (76063) *(G-14672)*

Excell Technologies Intl Corp 281 240-6770
1110 Industrial Blvd Sugar Land (77478) *(G-19482)*

Exceltec, Sugar Land Also called Excell Technologies Intl Corp *(G-19482)*

Exceptional Signs, Farmers Branch Also called Hines Chaunte *(G-6202)*

Exclusive Oriental Rugs Inc 214 747-5557
2050 N Stemmons Fwy # 111 Dallas (75207) *(G-4342)*

Exco Extrusion Dies Texas Inc 972 442-3131
911 Hensley Ln Wylie (75098) *(G-20935)*

Exco Holdings Inc 214 368-2084
12377 Merit Dr Ste 1700 Dallas (75251) *(G-4343)*

Exco Operating Company LP (HQ) **214 368-2084**
12377 Merit Dr Ste 1700 Dallas (75251) *(G-4344)*

Exco Resources Inc (PA) **214 368-2084**
12377 Merit Dr Ste 1700 Dallas (75251) *(G-4345)*

Executive Enterprises LLC (PA) **346 224-2125**
8360 Lbj Fwy Ste 215 Dallas (75243) *(G-4346)*

Executive Press Inc 214 217-7000
1400 Presidential Dr # 110 Richardson (75081) *(G-17306)*

Executive Voice Mail Systems 817 329-9788
226 N Dove Rd Grapevine (76051) *(G-8033)*

Exel Bobbins & Plas Components 956 832-0807
3301 Nafta Pkwy Ste C Brownsville (78526) *(G-2355)*

Exel N Amercn Logistics Inc 972 647-1101
802 W North Carrier Pkwy Grand Prairie (75050) *(G-7867)*

Exela Technologies Inc (PA) **844 935-2832**
2701 E Grauwyler Rd Irving (75061) *(G-13017)*

Exer-Tech Inc 281 493-2220
1227 Price Plz Katy (77449) *(G-13402)*

Exfo America Inc (HQ) **972 761-9271**
3400 Waterview Pkwy # 100 Richardson (75080) *(G-17307)*

Exhibitco Inc (PA) **713 830-8989**
1421 Preston St Houston (77002) *(G-9723)*

Exide Batteries, Houston Also called Exide Technologies LLC *(G-9724)*

Exide Technologies 972 335-2121
7471 5th St Frisco (75034) *(G-7284)*

Exide Technologies LLC 678 566-9000
22 Windledge Pl The Woodlands (77381) *(G-19863)*

Exide Technologies LLC 281 443-0382
14820 North Fwy Houston (77090) *(G-9724)*

Exide Technologies LLC 972 633-6900
9500 N Royal Ln Ste 150 Irving (75063) *(G-13018)*

Exide Technologies LLC 210 662-8999
8569 Ne Loop 410 Ste 150 San Antonio (78219) *(G-18099)*

Exide Technologies LLC 972 870-0337
8181 Jetstar Dr Ste 120 Irving (75063) *(G-13019)*

Exigo Office Inc (PA) **214 367-9999**
1600 Viceroy Dr Ste 125 Dallas (75235) *(G-4347)*

Exile Technologies Corporation (HQ) **713 343-5662**
7007 Pinemont Dr Houston (77040) *(G-9725)*

Exit Plan LLC 213 444-6106
1102 Kinney Ave Austin (78704) *(G-1145)*

Exl Petroleum LP 432 686-8080
6 Desta Dr Ste 2800 Midland (79705) *(G-15225)*

Exl Petroleum Management LLC (PA) **432 686-8080**
6 Desta Dr Ste 2800 Midland (79705) *(G-15226)*

Exl Petroleum Operating Inc 432 686-8080
6 Desta Dr Ste 2800 Midland (79705) *(G-15227)*

Exotherm Corporation 713 981-9100
888 Wilcrest Dr Houston (77042) *(G-9726)*

Exp Controls, New Caney Also called Electrical Contrls Houston Inc *(G-15838)*

Expal USA Inc (HQ) **903 472-4970**
433 Las Colinas Blvd E # 900 Irving (75039) *(G-13020)*

Expansion Arms and Ammunition, Carrollton Also called Expansion Industries LLC *(G-2735)*

Expansion Industries LLC 888 707-9343
2410 Luna Rd Ste 130 Carrollton (75006) *(G-2735)*

Expedite Commerce, Plano Also called Client Connect LLC *(G-16826)*

Exper-Tech Products Company 936 825-3573
124 N La Salle St Navasota (77868) *(G-15734)*

Expert Tool & Machine Inc 972 241-5353
2433 Arbuckle Ct Dallas (75229) *(G-4348)*

Exploitation Company LLP 713 351-3000
1021 Main St Ste 2626 Houston (77002) *(G-9727)*

Exploration Center Building 806 353-9123
5402 Meadowgreen Dr Amarillo (79110) *(G-487)*

Expo Group, Houston Also called Expro Americas LLC *(G-9734)*

Expotech USA Inc 281 879-8998
10700 Rockley Rd Houston (77099) *(G-9728)*

Express Inc 972 233-2986
13350 Dallas Pkwy # 2300 Dallas (75240) *(G-4349)*

Express Inc 281 712-7187
5000 Katy Mills Cir # 736 Katy (77494) *(G-13361)*

Express Commercial Services, Dallas Also called Harman Property Services LLC *(G-4436)*

Express Contracting, San Antonio Also called Central Texas Ex Metalwork LLC *(G-17992)*

Express Custom USB, Houston Also called Super Imprint Solutions LLC *(G-12106)*

Express Drilling Fluids LLC 361 289-1631
5412 Leopard St Corpus Christi (78408) *(G-3524)*

Express Energy Services GP LLC 713 625-7400
9800 Richmond Ave Ste 700 Houston (77042) *(G-9729)*

Express Energy Svcs Oper LP 325 659-4412
1182 Gas Plant Rd San Angelo (76904) *(G-17799)*

Express Energy Svcs Oper LP 432 530-1111
2258 N Mercury Ave Odessa (79763) *(G-15995)*

Express Energy Svcs Oper LP (PA) **713 625-7400**
9800 Richmond Ave Ste 500 Houston (77042) *(G-9730)*

Express Energy Svcs Oper LP 979 589-2255
9637 E State Highway 21 Bryan (77808) *(G-2472)*

Express Energy Svcs Oper LP 713 625-7403
8520 N Moorefield Rd Mission (78574) *(G-15552)*

Express Energy Svcs Oper LP 830 569-8606
716 Eagle Ford Dr Pleasanton (78064) *(G-17066)*

Express Energy Svcs Oper LP 940 592-4391
426 Rifle Range Rd Iowa Park (76367) *(G-12905)*

Express Fabrication 469 628-3960
3033 County Road 743 Princeton (75407) *(G-17209)*

Express Fabricators LLC 972 734-3855
708 State Highway 78 S Farmersville (75442) *(G-6222)*

Express Freight Systems Inc 713 861-1888
1215 Seamist Dr Houston (77008) *(G-9731)*

Express Info Systems Inc (PA) **210 614-9410**
4115 Medical Dr Ste 604 San Antonio (78229) *(G-18100)*

Express Plastic Corporation 713 664-9588
11500 Main St Ste 144 Houston (77025) *(G-9732)*

Express Scale Svc, Canyon Also called Keith Weighing Systems LLC *(G-2672)*

Express Signs Plus, Haslet Also called One Focus Inc *(G-8221)*

Expro Americas LLC 903 753-2003
5396 Se Loop 281 Longview (75602) *(G-14233)*

Expro Americas LLC 281 977-2600
10815 Huffmeister Rd Houston (77065) *(G-9733)*

Expro Americas LLC (HQ) **713 463-9776**
1311 Brdfeld Blvd Ste 400 Houston (77084) *(G-9734)*

Exquip USA Llc (PA) **936 372-3002**
31975 Joseph Rd Hockley (77447) *(G-8343)*

Exquisita Tortillas Inc (PA) **956 383-6712**
700 W Chapin St Edinburg (78541) *(G-5586)*

Exquisita Tortillas Inc 956 383-3011
320 N 12th Ave Edinburg (78541) *(G-5587)*

Extech Consulting LLC 940 613-6461
115 N Main St Henrietta (76365) *(G-8280)*

Exterran Corporation (PA) **281 836-7000**
11000 Equity Dr Ste 100 Houston (77041) *(G-9735)*

Exterran Energy, Houston Also called Exterran Trinidad LLC *(G-9737)*

Exterran Energy Solutions LP (HQ) **281 836-7000**
11000 Equity Dr Houston (77041) *(G-9736)*

Exterran Trinidad LLC (HQ) **281 921-9337**
12001 N Huston Rosslyn Rd Houston (77086) *(G-9737)*

Extreme Engineering, Athens Also called Thrillworks Inc *(G-840)*

Extreme Fab Inc 713 637-0001
12889 Market Street Rd Houston (77015) *(G-9738)*

Extreme Well Testing LLC 956 969-4452
2401 E Expressway 83 Weslaco (78599) *(G-20659)*

Extruded Ennis Products 972 875-1770
4200 Knighthurst St Ennis (75119) *(G-6101)*

Exxene Corporation 361 991-8391
5939 Holly Rd Corpus Christi (78412) *(G-3525)*

Exxon Mobil Corporation (PA) **972 940-6000**
5959 Las Colinas Blvd Irving (75039) *(G-13021)*

Exxon Mobil Corporation 713 656-3636
800 Bell St Houston (77002) *(G-9739)*

Exxon Mobil Fuels Marketing Co (HQ) **703 846-3000**
22777 Sprngwoods Vlg Pkwy Spring (77389) *(G-19115)*

Exxon Trading Interamerica, Spring Also called Exxonmobil Sales and Sup LLC *(G-19119)*

Exxonmobil, Irving Also called Exxon Mobil Corporation *(G-13021)*

Exxonmobil Abu Dhabi Gas Ventr, Houston Also called Exxonmobil Development Company *(G-9740)*

Exxonmobil Chemical Company 409 860-1300
11440 Highway 90 Beaumont (77713) *(G-1891)*

Exxonmobil Chemical Company 281 834-5200
5200 Bayway Dr Baytown (77520) *(G-1817)*

Exxonmobil Chemical Company (HQ) **800 243-9966**
22777 Sprngwoods Vlg Pkwy Spring (77389) *(G-19116)*

Exxonmobil Development Company 713 656-3636
12450 Greenspoint Dr # 1000 Houston (77060) *(G-9740)*

Exxonmobil Lubr & Petro Spc, Spring Also called Exxonmobil Chemical Company *(G-19116)*

Exxonmobil Pipeline Company (HQ) **713 656-3636**
22777 Sprngwoods Vlg Pkwy Spring (77389) *(G-19117)*

Exxonmobil Research & Engrg Co 815 521-7411
22777 Sprngwoods Vlg Pkwy Spring (77389) *(G-19118)*

Exxonmobil Sales and Sup LLC (HQ) **800 243-9966**
22777 Sprngwoods Vlg Pkwy Spring (77389) *(G-19119)*

A
L
P
H
A
B
E
T
I
C

Exyte Americas Holding Inc (HQ)................972 535-7300
  1001 Klein Rd Ste 400 Plano (75074) *(G-16868)*

Eye On Security Systems, Bridge City Also called Hbreaux Companies Inc *(G-2284)*

Eyecare Optical, Corpus Christi Also called South Texas Eye Cons Pllc *(G-3623)*

Eyemasters 13 Inc.................................254 751-0010
  6001 W Waco Dr Ste 612 Waco (76710) *(G-20400)*

Eyesys Vision Inc.................................281 885-3800
  16720 Hedgecroft Dr # 208 Houston (77060) *(G-9741)*

EZ Flex LLC...817 632-4800
  1701 Pharr St Fort Worth (76102) *(G-6621)*

EZ Flex Sport Mats, Fort Worth Also called EZ Flex LLC *(G-6621)*

EZ Pipe Paddler Padding Mch................432 333-9587
  3276 N County Rd W Odessa (79766) *(G-15996)*

EZ Pipeline, Odessa Also called EZ Pipe Paddler Padding Mch *(G-15996)*

Ez-Router Inc......................................903 569-3190
  140 County Road 2840 Mineola (75773) *(G-15508)*

Ezell-Key Feed & Seed, Snyder Also called Ezell-Key Grain Company Inc *(G-18991)*

Ezell-Key Grain Company Inc (PA)...........325 573-9373
  3101 Us Hwy 84 Snyder (79550) *(G-18991)*

Eznectar LLC......................................210 732-6400
  246 Early Trl San Antonio (78228) *(G-18101)*

Ezzi Signs Inc....................................713 232-0771
  16611 W Little York Rd Houston (77084) *(G-9742)*

F & F Composite Group Inc....................817 379-4411
  5800 Egg Farm Rd Ste 260 Fort Worth (76244) *(G-6622)*

F & F Industries Inc.............................800 523-8473
  5345 S Interstate 35 W Alvarado (76009) *(G-331)*

F & F Metal Products, Greenville Also called Freeman Metal Products Inc *(G-8074)*

F & H Ribbon Company Inc.....................817 283-5891
  3010 S Pipeline Rd Euless (76040) *(G-6145)*

F & L Coatings and Con LLC...................281 316-2203
  1902 E Independence Ave League City (77573) *(G-13956)*

F & R Machine Services Inc....................214 631-4946
  7217 Harry Hines Blvd Dallas (75235) *(G-4350)*

F & W Disposal, Big Lake Also called Fisher Lease Service Inc *(G-2056)*

F & W Industries Inc.............................432 563-8895
  6698 Andrews Hwy Odessa (79762) *(G-15997)*

F A I, Houston Also called Falcon-Auger Inc *(G-9758)*

F and B Holdings LLC............................956 424-7775
  9625 N Moorefield Rd Mission (78574) *(G-15553)*

F C Designs Inc..................................713 462-1442
  11440 Brittmoore Park Dr Houston (77041) *(G-9743)*

F F Foster & Associates Inc....................713 266-2883
  675 Bering Dr Ste 800 Houston (77057) *(G-9744)*

F M Eagle Tool Co Inc...........................915 590-6377
  8810 Yermoland Dr El Paso (79907) *(G-5761)*

F W Promo...817 231-8040
  5941 Posey Ln Haltom City (76117) *(G-8140)*

F&G Cranes, Terrell Also called Gh Cranes & Components USA Inc *(G-19735)*

F-1 Firearms LLC.................................832 299-6100
  5045 Fm 2920 Rd Spring (77388) *(G-19120)*

F. W. Gartner Therman Spraying, Houston Also called Gfk Interests Ltd *(G-9947)*

F/K/A Nextlock, El Paso Also called Strattec Security Corporation *(G-5985)*

F3 Foam LLC..936 661-3172
  3450 Spring Branch Rd Montgomery (77316) *(G-15633)*

Fab Services Ltd.................................936 931-1004
  2405 Washington St Waller (77484) *(G-20497)*

Fab Tech, Plano Also called Diodes Fabtech Inc *(G-16844)*

Fab Tex Oilfield Services Inc..................432 339-1011
  2228 Steven Rd Odessa (79764) *(G-15998)*

Fab-Tex Fixture & Mfg Co.......................972 660-6304
  2353 Nw Dallas St Grand Prairie (75050) *(G-7868)*

Fabco Industries Inc............................432 367-4988
  8406 Sprague Rd Odessa (79764) *(G-15999)*

Fabco LLC (PA)....................................713 633-6500
  13835 Beaumont Hwy Houston (77049) *(G-9745)*

Fabco Products Inc.............................903 769-3707
  2521 S Fm 2869 Hawkins (75765) *(G-8229)*

Fabcorp Inc (PA)..................................713 466-3962
  6951 W Little York Rd Houston (77040) *(G-9746)*

Fabenco Inc..713 686-6620
  2002 Karbach St Houston (77092) *(G-9747)*

Faber Cnk..832 831-7222
  6500 Long Point Rd # 304 Houston (77055) *(G-9748)*

Fabhar Manufacturing LLC.....................214 802-9400
  524 E Hazelwood St Princeton (75407) *(G-17210)*

Fabhar Metal Works, Princeton Also called Fabhar Manufacturing LLC *(G-17210)*

Fabricas Elena, Del Rio Also called Construction Specialties Inc *(G-5314)*

Fabricating Solutions...........................409 735-7141
  745 Jones St Bridge City (77611) *(G-2283)*

Fabricating Specialties Ltd....................281 405-2010
  11505 Todd St Houston (77055) *(G-9749)*

Fabrication & Cnstr Svcs LP...................936 257-0466
  4665 Fm 1960 Dayton (77535) *(G-5226)*

Fabrication & Mfg Aliance LLC.................210 648-3131
  4614 Sinclair Rd San Antonio (78222) *(G-18102)*

Fabrication Specialty Inc.......................214 742-3571
  6530 Smoky Hill Ct Granbury (76049) *(G-7797)*

Fabrication Unlimited Inc.......................713 433-6401
  5410 Trafalgar Dr Houston (77045) *(G-9750)*

Fabrications, Fort Worth Also called T W Havens Metals Inc *(G-7028)*

Fabricon Inc..214 630-5998
  1146 Explorer St Duncanville (75137) *(G-5530)*

Fabuluex, Dallas Also called Danielle Howard *(G-4236)*

Facilities Rehab Inc.............................512 352-6035
  716 N Main St Ste.3 Taylor (76574) *(G-19655)*

Factory Motorhomes Inc.......................214 830-2910
  11394 County Road 2312 Terrell (75160) *(G-19733)*

Factory Outlet Tooling, McKinney Also called Bluestone Industries LLC *(G-14927)*

Facts..979 237-0100
  720 S Main St Clute (77531) *(G-3154)*

Faifer Arlin D Woodmill Co......................830 216-4189
  6850 Us Highway 181 N Floresville (78114) *(G-6247)*

Fair-West Trailers, Hallettsville Also called Channl-Track Tube-Way Inds Inc *(G-8120)*

Fairbanks Morse LLC............................713 896-9455
  12253 Fm 529 Rd Houston (77041) *(G-9751)*

Fairbanks Packaging LLC.......................817 849-1366
  608 E Avenue K Grand Prairie (75050) *(G-7869)*

Fairchild Semiconductor Corp..................972 910-8000
  2400 Lkeside Blvd Ste 700 Richardson (75082) *(G-17308)*

Fairfield Industries Inc (HQ)...................281 275-7500
  9811 Katy Fwy Houston (77024) *(G-9752)*

Fairfieldnodal, Houston Also called Fairfield Industries Inc *(G-9752)*

Fairmont Diagnstc Cntr & Open.................713 946-1500
  3692 E Sam Houston Pkwy S Pasadena (77505) *(G-16436)*

Fairmont Minerals, Galveston Also called Fjcj LLC *(G-7396)*

Fairway Rsrces Prtners III LLC.................817 416-1946
  538 Silicon Dr Ste 101 Southlake (76092) *(G-19068)*

Fairways Exploration Prod LLC.................713 622-3492
  1800 Bering Dr Ste 935 Houston (77057) *(G-9753)*

Fairways Offshore Expl..........................713 622-3492
  20445 State Highway 249 # 280 Houston (77070) *(G-9754)*

Fairways Resources, Houston Also called Fairways Exploration Prod LLC *(G-9753)*

Faith Drilling LLC.................................432 758-6352
  191 Us Highway 180 E Seminole (79360) *(G-18882)*

Faith Manufacturing Co Inc....................281 441-9595
  406 Atascocita Rd Humble (77396) *(G-12766)*

Falchion Publications LLC.......................214 244-9645
  3635 Navarro Way Frisco (75034) *(G-7285)*

Falcon Bay Energy L L C.........................432 682-7424
  200 N Loraine St Ste 1550 Midland (79701) *(G-15228)*

Falcon Events LLC................................800 895-6934
  3001 Gateway Dr Ste 130 Irving (75063) *(G-13022)*

Falcon Fast Print, Houston Also called Grafikshop Corporation *(G-10012)*

Falcon Fine Wire Wire Pdts Inc.................214 771-3441
  2401 Discovery Blvd Rockwall (75032) *(G-17548)*

Falcon Pharmaceuticals Ltd....................800 343-2133
  6201 South Fwy Fort Worth (76134) *(G-6623)*

Falcon Prosolutions Inc........................210 547-2741
  16026 University Oak San Antonio (78249) *(G-18103)*

Falcon Seaboard Holdings LLC (PA)...........713 622-0055
  3 Homewood Row Ln Houston (77056) *(G-9755)*

Falcon Seaboard Oil & Gas LLC................713 622-0055
  1224 N Post Oak Rd Ste 10 Houston (77055) *(G-9756)*

Falcon Steel Fabricator Inc....................281 227-2766
  13411 Reeveston Rd Houston (77039) *(G-9757)*

Falcon Structures, Manor Also called Bristlecone Ventures 2 LLC *(G-14646)*

Falcon Technologies, Decatur Also called Asset Guard Products Inc *(G-5242)*

Falcon Wood Products 2 Ltd.....................936 295-9381
  7031 State Highway 75 S Huntsville (77340) *(G-12811)*

Falcon-Auger Inc (PA)...........................713 690-2761
  4802 Blalock Rd Houston (77041) *(G-9758)*

Falconhead Boots Belts Buckles...............915 544-2727
  421 S Cotton St El Paso (79901) *(G-5762)*

Falconstor Software Inc (PA)...................631 777-5188
  701 Brazos St Ste 400 Austin (78701) *(G-1146)*

Falconview Energy Products LLC...............832 665-2850
  6834 Bourgeois Rd Houston (77066) *(G-9759)*

Fallbrook Technologies Inc (PA)...............512 714-1964
  1501 Leander Dr Leander (78641) *(G-13990)*

Famco...713 433-2723
  14823 Hooper Rd Houston (77047) *(G-9760)*

Famco Logistics Inc.............................915 307-2536
  11710 Gateway Blvd E El Paso (79927) *(G-5763)*

Famco Machine Shop, Houston Also called Famco *(G-9760)*

Fanlight Corporation Inc........................909 930-6868
  11011 Regency Crest Dr # 800 Dallas (75238) *(G-4351)*

Fann Instrument Company, Houston Also called Halliburton Energy Svcs Inc *(G-10110)*

Fann Instrument Company, Houston Also called Halliburton Company *(G-10105)*

Fannin County Leader LLC.......................903 583-3280
  224 N Main Bonham Bonham (75418) *(G-2153)*

Far East Energy (bermuda) Ltd.................832 598-0470
  333 N Sam Houston Pkwy E Houston (77060) *(G-9761)*

Far East Energy Corporation (PA)..............832 598-0470
  333 N Sam Houston Pkwy E # 230 Houston (77060) *(G-9762)*

Far East Printing.............281 495-6161
3608 Prairie Rose St El Paso (79936) *(G-5764)*

Far South Mining LLC.............210 688-2607
8845 Leslie Rd San Antonio (78254) *(G-18104)*

Farm & Ranch Construction LLC.............254 364-2226
14641 Highway 6 Iredell (76649) *(G-12921)*

Farm Ctch Ctfish Prcessors Inc.............903 639-2394
1221 601 Hwy 161 S Hughes Springs (75656) *(G-12740)*

Farmer Bros Co (PA).............**682 549-6767**
1912 Farmer Brothers Dr Northlake (76262) *(G-15885)*

Farmer Bros Co.............682 549-6600
1912 Farmer Brothers Dr Northlake (76262) *(G-15886)*

Farmer Bros Co.............817 640-8111
744 Avenue H E Arlington (76011) *(G-675)*

Farmer Bros Co.............713 864-1487
6300 W By Northwest Blvd # 400 Houston (77040) *(G-9763)*

Farmer Brothers, Northlake *Also called Farmer Bros Co (G-15885)*

Farmers Brothers Coffee, Northlake *Also called Farmer Bros Co (G-15886)*

Farmers Brothers Coffee, Arlington *Also called Farmer Bros Co (G-675)*

Farmers Brothers Coffee, Houston *Also called Farmer Bros Co (G-9763)*

Farmers Oil Co.............281 874-2101
211 Highland Cross Dr Houston (77073) *(G-9764)*

Faro Services Inc.............214 631-1888
3701 La Reunion Pkwy Dallas (75212) *(G-4352)*

Farouk Systems Inc (PA).............**281 876-2000**
250 Pennbright Dr Houston (77090) *(G-9765)*

Farouk Systems Inc.............281 443-0715
20805 Fernbush Dr Houston (77073) *(G-9766)*

Farris Concrete Company.............972 838-2217
2425 Throckmorton Rd Melissa (75454) *(G-14997)*

Farrow Machine & Mfg Co Inc.............817 633-4686
1030 Commercial Blvd N Arlington (76001) *(G-676)*

Farrz Inc.............936 539-3278
206b S Loop 336 W Conroe (77304) *(G-3296)*

Fas Holdings Group LLC.............214 343-5300
10480 Markison Rd Dallas (75238) *(G-4353)*

Fas Technologies LLC.............214 343-5300
10480 Markison Rd Dallas (75238) *(G-4354)*

Fasco, Eagle Pass *Also called Regal Beloit America Inc (G-5555)*

Fasco Eldon Rbc, Eagle Pass *Also called Regal Beloit America Inc (G-5554)*

Fashion Forms, Austin *Also called Ce Soir Lingerie Co Inc (G-1035)*

Fashion Works Inc.............972 596-5815
4609 Saxon Dr Plano (75093) *(G-16869)*

Fashionit, Dallas *Also called I&G Designs and Logistics LLC (G-4481)*

Fassco Manufacturing Inc.............210 523-0800
3248 Northwestern San Antonio (78238) *(G-18105)*

Fast Back Rope Mfg.............817 279-1851
3721 Tin Top Hwy Granbury (76048) *(G-7798)*

Fast Printing, El Paso *Also called R-J Typesetters Inc (G-5925)*

Fast Response Transportation, San Antonio *Also called 1-Fast Rspnse Rntals Oil Feld (G-17844)*

Fast Signs Oaklawn, Dallas *Also called Mr Sign Inc (G-4699)*

Fasteel LLC.............210 661-2603
4900 Center Park Blvd San Antonio (78218) *(G-18106)*

Fastener Specialty Inc.............972 988-0064
6625 Iron Horse Blvd North Richland Hills (76180) *(G-15878)*

Fasterra Group LP.............940 240-5800
200 Highland Cir Argyle (76226) *(G-600)*

Fastorq, New Caney *Also called George A Sturdevant Inc (G-15840)*

Fastorq Bolting Systems Inc.............281 449-6466
18914 E Industrial Pkwy New Caney (77357) *(G-15839)*

Fastphalt, Cedar Hill *Also called Professional Coating Tech Inc (G-2952)*

Fastserv Supply Inc (PA).............**800 527-4126**
4060 E Plano Pkwy Plano (75074) *(G-16870)*

Fastsigns, Austin *Also called Ron T Felt (G-1471)*

Fastsigns, McAllen *Also called Huntington Sky Production Ltd (G-14869)*

Fastsigns, Lewisville *Also called Mlc Signs LP (G-14069)*

Fastsigns, Austin *Also called Ron T Felt (G-1472)*

Fastsigns, Lewisville *Also called Janus Signs (G-14059)*

Fastsigns, Arlington *Also called Theag North Arlington LLC (G-797)*

Fastsigns, Richland Hills *Also called Signit Inc (G-17448)*

Fastsigns, Dallas *Also called Janus Signs Inc (G-4525)*

Fastsigns, College Station *Also called KB & KB Enterprises Inc (G-3189)*

Fastsigns, Irving *Also called Outstnding Grphic Slutions Inc (G-13137)*

Fastsigns, Beaumont *Also called Dbt Inc (G-1880)*

Fastsigns.............915 229-8000
1355 George Dieter Dr # 103 El Paso (79936) *(G-5765)*

Fastsigns Conroe, Conroe *Also called Farrz Inc (G-3296)*

Fastsigns International Inc (PA).............**888 285-5935**
2542 Highlander Way Carrollton (75006) *(G-2736)*

Fastsigns Nat Advg Council Inc.............214 346-5600
2542 Highlander Way Carrollton (75006) *(G-2737)*

Faubion Associates Inc.............214 565-1000
1000 Forest Ave Dallas (75215) *(G-4355)*

Faulconer Energy Joint Ventr S.............903 581-4382
1001 E Se Loop 323 # 160 Tyler (75701) *(G-20085)*

Faulconer Resources Corp.............903 581-4382
1001 E Se Loop 323 # 160 Tyler (75701) *(G-20086)*

Faurecia Exhaust Systems Inc.............812 314-5995
2100 Design Rd Ste 110 Arlington (76014) *(G-677)*

Favelle Favco Cranes Usa Inc.............956 428-7488
26360 Fm 106 Harlingen (78550) *(G-8188)*

Fay-J Packaging Division, Wake Village *Also called C-L & Associates Inc (G-20485)*

Fayette County Record Inc.............979 968-3155
127 S Washington St La Grange (78945) *(G-13695)*

Fayetteville-Floyd Gas Company (PA).............**432 682-6685**
500 W Wall St Ste 300 Midland (79701) *(G-15229)*

FB, Irving *Also called Figueroa Brothers Inc (G-13026)*

FBC Enterprises Inc.............817 740-1951
5110 Rondo Dr Fort Worth (76106) *(G-6624)*

FC Dsigns Qulty WD Work Corp.............713 462-1442
12218 Jones Rd Ste D117 Houston (77070) *(G-9767)*

Fc Traffic Control Inc.............806 570-5633
1100 S Fillmore St 105a Amarillo (79101) *(G-423)*

FCD Division, Irving *Also called Flowserve US Inc (G-13030)*

Fci Environmental Inc.............702 262-3953
13111 N Cntl Expy Ste 440 Dallas (75243) *(G-4356)*

Fcx Performance Inc.............214 320-3604
9010 John W Carpenter Fwy Dallas (75247) *(G-4357)*

Fd-Thru Power Systems Cnnctors.............281 476-9100
212 Deerwood Glen Dr Deer Park (77536) *(G-5273)*

FDL Operating LLC.............469 453-7346
5221 N O Connor Blvd # 1100 Irving (75039) *(G-13023)*

FE Hill Co LLP.............903 389-3616
300 S Keechi St Fairfield (75840) *(G-6173)*

FE Sawyer Bldg Systems Inc.............903 531-0182
12562 State Highway 64 W Tyler (75704) *(G-20087)*

Featherlite Building Pdts Corp.............512 472-2424
2824 Real St Austin (78722) *(G-1147)*

Featherlite Building Products, Elgin *Also called Acme Brick Company (G-6051)*

Featherlite Corp.............409 727-8800
1600 Main St Port Neches (77651) *(G-17160)*

Featherlite Corporation (HQ).............**817 332-4101**
3024 Acme Brick Plz Fort Worth (76109) *(G-6625)*

Federal Connects, Houston *Also called Federal Flange & Fitting Co (G-9770)*

Federal Flange Inc (PA).............**713 681-0606**
4014 Pinemont Dr Houston (77018) *(G-9768)*

Federal Flange Inc.............713 681-0606
3945 Creekmont Dr Houston (77091) *(G-9769)*

Federal Flange & Fitting Co.............713 681-0606
4014 Pinemont Dr Houston (77018) *(G-9770)*

Federal Heath Sign Company LLC.............903 589-2100
1500 N Bolton St Jacksonville (75766) *(G-13238)*

Federal Heath Sign Company LLC (HQ).............**817 685-9075**
2300 St Hwy 121 Euless (76039) *(G-6146)*

Federal Prison Industries.............972 287-4040
2113 N Highway 175 Seagoville (75159) *(G-18800)*

Federal Prison Industries.............432 466-2300
1900 Simler Ave Big Spring (79720) *(G-2082)*

Federal Prison Industries.............512 321-3903
1341 State Highway 95 Bastrop (78602) *(G-1757)*

Federal Reserve Bank Dallas (HQ).............**214 922-6000**
2200 N Pearl St Dallas (75201) *(G-4358)*

Federal Royalty Partners Ltd.............713 529-3729
2001 Kirby Dr Ste 1210 Houston (77019) *(G-9771)*

Federal-Mogul Powertrain LLC.............915 860-2300
1273 Joe Battle Blvd A El Paso (79936) *(G-5766)*

Federal-Mogul Powertrain LLC.............915 860-2300
1277 Joe Battle Blvd El Paso (79936) *(G-5767)*

Federos, Frisco *Also called Monolith Tech Holdings LLC (G-7299)*

Fedex Office & Print Svcs Inc.............972 570-5110
3201 W Arprt Fwy Ste 100 Irving (75062) *(G-13024)*

Fedex Office & Print Svcs Inc.............512 331-0800
13729 N Hwy 183 Ste 820 Austin (78750) *(G-1148)*

Fedex Office & Print Svcs Inc.............210 821-6911
4418 Broadway San Antonio (78209) *(G-18107)*

Fedex Office & Print Svcs Inc.............713 521-9465
2455 Rice Blvd Houston (77005) *(G-9772)*

Fedex Office & Print Svcs Inc.............713 977-2666
12121 Westheimer Rd # 201 Houston (77077) *(G-9773)*

Fedex Office & Print Svcs Inc.............512 396-1559
303 N Edward Gary St San Marcos (78666) *(G-18687)*

Fedex Office & Print Svcs Inc.............512 339-1191
9222 Burnet Rd Ste 101 Austin (78758) *(G-1149)*

Fedex Office & Print Svcs Inc.............915 592-1190
1410 N Lee Trevino Dr El Paso (79936) *(G-5768)*

Fedex Office & Print Svcs Inc.............512 476-3242
2711 Guadalupe St Austin (78705) *(G-1150)*

Fedex Office & Print Svcs Inc.............806 359-9684
3801 Olsen Blvd Unit 2 Amarillo (79109) *(G-488)*

Fedex Office & Print Svcs Inc.............512 472-4448
327 Congress Ave Ste 100 Austin (78701) *(G-1151)*

Fedex Office & Print Svcs Inc.............956 682-4040
2812 N 10th St McAllen (78501) *(G-14860)*

Fedex Office & Print Svcs Inc.............254 776-7763
1821 S Valley Mills Dr # 140 Waco (76711) *(G-20401)*

Fedex Office & Print Svcs Inc.................................281 364-7898
479 Sawdust Rd The Woodlands (77380) *(G-19864)*

Fedex Office & Print Svcs Inc.................................512 452-3600
6406 N Ih 35 Ste 1210 Austin (78752) *(G-1152)*

Fedex Office & Print Svcs Inc.................................817 543-0833
1400 E Copeland Rd Arlington (76011) *(G-678)*

Fedex Office & Print Svcs Inc.................................409 895-4000
5775 Eastex Fwy Beaumont (77706) *(G-1892)*

Fedex Office & Print Svcs Inc.................................361 806-2220
3850 S Padre Island Dr Corpus Christi (78415) *(G-3526)*

Fedex Office & Print Svcs Inc.................................210 521-8395
5755 Nw Loop 410 Ste 101 San Antonio (78238) *(G-18108)*

Fedex Office & Print Svcs Inc.................................713 956-2366
10670 Northwest Fwy Houston (77092) *(G-9774)*

Fedex Office & Print Svcs Inc.................................512 528-9690
1335 E Whitestone Blvd # 300 Cedar Park (78613) *(G-2969)*

Fedex Office & Print Svcs Inc.................................281 395-0077
430 S Mason Rd Ste 108 Katy (77450) *(G-13403)*

Fedex Office & Print Svcs Inc.................................281 463-8433
7700 Highway 6 N Ste 103 Houston (77095) *(G-9775)*

Fedex Office Print & Ship Ctr, San Marcos *Also called Fedex Office & Print Svcs Inc (G-18687)*

Fedex Sup Chain Lgstics Elec I.................................817 491-7700
13500 Independence Pkwy Fort Worth (76177) *(G-6626)*

Feeders Supply.................................806 889-3391
15902 County Road 2170 Lubbock (79423) *(G-14409)*

Feedmill, Gonzales *Also called Holmes Foods Inc (G-7755)*

Fehrs Industrial Mfg LLC.................................432 758-0068
373 County Road 307 Seminole (79360) *(G-18883)*

Fei Efa Inc.................................972 792-1644
1321 N Plano Rd Richardson (75081) *(G-17309)*

Feinkind Inc.................................914 591-5868
1000 E 5th St Apt 656 Austin (78702) *(G-1153)*

Feldlo, Brownsville *Also called International Machine Shop (G-2363)*

Felipe & Felipe Imports, Laredo *Also called Felipe Arreazola (G-13883)*

Felipe Arreazola.................................956 334-3136
3218 Diaz St Laredo (78043) *(G-13883)*

Fellfab Corporation.................................817 595-7408
2680 Gravel Dr Bldg 5 Fort Worth (76118) *(G-6627)*

Fellowship Technologies LP.................................469 442-0100
6363 N State Highway 161 Irving (75038) *(G-13025)*

Felux Metal Works & Supply LP.................................830 484-3436
Hwy 181 Poth (78147) *(G-17195)*

Fencecrete America Inc (PA).................................**210 492-7911**
15089 Tradesman San Antonio (78249) *(G-18109)*

Fencecrete America Inc.................................281 438-1444
15100 West Rd Houston (77095) *(G-9776)*

Feniex Industries Inc.................................800 615-8350
6320 E Stassney Ln Bldg 1 Austin (78744) *(G-1154)*

Fenner & Associates Inc.................................281 970-9977
5257 Vintage Oaks Dr College Station (77845) *(G-3182)*

Fenner Advanced Sealing Tech, Humble *Also called CDI Energy Products Inc (G-12753)*

Fenner Technologies Inc.................................972 264-0368
1513 W Jefferson St Grand Prairie (75051) *(G-7870)*

Fenton Environmental Tech Inc.................................800 521-1708
4306 Highway 377 S Brownwood (76801) *(G-2428)*

Fermin Aguilar Welding Svcs, Odessa *Also called Aguilar Oilfield Services (G-15904)*

Ferpa Precision Machine Inc.................................281 874-9747
1402 Hugh Rd Houston (77067) *(G-9777)*

Ferreira Holding Group LLC.................................214 293-9233
9319 L B Jhnson Ste 208-A Johnson Dallas (75243) *(G-4359)*

Ferrell-Ross Roll Mfg Inc.................................806 364-9051
3690 Fm 2856 Hereford (79045) *(G-8288)*

Ferus LP.................................832 709-0750
20445 State Highway 249 # 250 Houston (77070) *(G-9778)*

Fervid Group LLC.................................713 364-3378
11222 Richmond Ave # 120 Houston (77082) *(G-9779)*

Ferza Company LLC.................................956 686-7100
1314 E Ramon Ayala Dr 4 Hidalgo (78557) *(G-8307)*

Fesco Ltd.................................361 575-7533
4906 Houston Hwy Victoria (77901) *(G-20263)*

Fesco Ltd.................................956 724-7501
4801 Fesco Laredo (78043) *(G-13884)*

Fesco Ltd.................................361 882-4124
627 Omaha Dr Corpus Christi (78408) *(G-3527)*

Fesco Ltd.................................361 661-1538
1400 E Main St Alice (78332) *(G-213)*

Fesco Ltd.................................936 632-7036
3702 Ellen Trout Dr Lufkin (75904) *(G-14527)*

Fesco Ltd.................................361 661-7000
10919 Us Highway 60 Canadian (79014) *(G-2649)*

Fesco Ltd.................................903 984-4814
206 Beall St Kilgore (75662) *(G-13553)*

Fesco Ltd.................................979 543-9451
310 N Wharton St El Campo (77437) *(G-5618)*

Fesco Ltd.................................325 392-3773
105 Medical Dr Ozona (76943) *(G-16283)*

Fesco Ltd.................................979 775-1825
450 Stone City Dr Bryan (77803) *(G-2473)*

Fesco Ltd.................................409 842-3000
2205 W Florida St Beaumont (77705) *(G-1893)*

Fesco Ltd.................................956 383-8378
4501 W University Dr Edinburg (78539) *(G-5588)*

Fesco Ltd.................................432 332-3211
2600 S Einstein Ave Odessa (79766) *(G-16000)*

Fesco Ltd.................................361 526-4644
207 E Plasuela St Refugio (78377) *(G-17241)*

Festive Tents LP.................................713 468-3687
3302 Chartreuse Way Houston (77082) *(G-9780)*

Festoni Inc.................................713 830-1077
1291 N Post Oak Rd # 100 Houston (77055) *(G-9781)*

Few Ready Mix Corp.................................936 560-5675
1423 Bennett Clark Rd Nacogdoches (75961) *(G-15696)*

Fgf LLC (HQ).................................**210 475-9981**
122 Stribling San Antonio (78204) *(G-18110)*

Fgf LLC.................................210 475-9981
9910 Teal Ave San Antonio (78224) *(G-18111)*

Fgf Texas, San Antonio *Also called Fgf LLC (G-18110)*

Fgi Acquisition Corp (HQ).................................**281 604-2400**
4150 N Sam Houston Pkwy E Houston (77032) *(G-9782)*

Fgl Group LLC.................................817 481-7857
1901 N Port Ct Grapevine (76051) *(G-8034)*

Fgl Group LLC.................................817 478-3221
2900 W Kingsley Rd Garland (75041) *(G-7489)*

Fgs - Dallas Inc.................................972 375-0253
1040 S State Highway 161 # 105 Grand Prairie (75051) *(G-7871)*

Fib-R-Dor Division, Brownsville *Also called Advance Fiberglass LLC (G-2335)*

Fiber Glass Systems, Houston *Also called Fiberspar Corporation (G-9784)*

Fiber Glass Systems LP (HQ).................................**210 477-7500**
2425 Sw 36th St San Antonio (78237) *(G-18112)*

Fiber Systems Intl Inc (HQ).................................**214 547-2400**
1300 Central Expy N # 100 Allen (75013) *(G-267)*

Fiberco Inc (PA).................................**682 647-1332**
1300 Eden Dr Fort Worth (76117) *(G-6628)*

Fiberglass Creations Inc.................................903 657-6616
1601 Hamlett St Henderson (75652) *(G-8262)*

Fiberglass Specialties Inc.................................903 657-6522
500 Austin Ave Henderson (75652) *(G-8263)*

Fibergrate Composite.................................254 977-1302
840 Airport Rd Stephenville (76401) *(G-19411)*

Fibergrate Composite.................................254 965-3148
900 Fm 205 Greenville (75401) *(G-8072)*

Fibergrate Composite.................................254 965-3148
900 Fm 205 Stephenville (76401) *(G-19412)*

Fibergrate Composite (HQ).................................**972 250-1633**
5151 Belt Line Rd Ste 700 Dallas (75254) *(G-4360)*

Fiberio Technology Corporation.................................956 207-5448
4409 Wanda Ave Ste B McAllen (78503) *(G-14861)*

Fiberspar Corporation.................................713 849-2609
W12239 Fm 529 Houston (77041) *(G-9783)*

Fiberspar Corporation (HQ).................................**713 849-2609**
12239 Fm 529 Rd Houston (77041) *(G-9784)*

Fics, Addison *Also called Financial Industry Com (G-123)*

Fieldco Energy Services Inc.................................903 693-5900
101 Timberlane Dr Carthage (75633) *(G-2907)*

Fielder Electric Supply Co Inc.................................281 485-6599
2900 Manvel Rd Pearland (77584) *(G-16560)*

Fieldtech Avionics Instrs Inc (PA).................................**817 740-7110**
4151 N Main St Fort Worth (76106) *(G-6629)*

Fiesta Auto Salvage, El Paso *Also called EC Wrecking & Salvage Corp (G-5734)*

Fiesta Graphics.................................956 546-1722
205 Paredes Line Rd Brownsville (78521) *(G-2356)*

Fiesta Tortilla Factory, Austin *Also called Ixpalia Inc (G-1245)*

Fife Services Inc.................................432 827-3601
616 Odessa St Goldsmith (79741) *(G-7742)*

Fife, J M Welding, Goldsmith *Also called Fife Services Inc (G-7742)*

Fifo Technologies Inc.................................817 991-1388
8949 First Hills Dr Fort Worth (76101) *(G-6630)*

Fifth Rock Software Inc.................................281 265-0944
3707 Adonia Pl Sugar Land (77479) *(G-19483)*

Figtree Technologies Inc.................................469 361-6643
430 S Hwy 5 McKinney (75069) *(G-14942)*

Figueroa Brothers Inc.................................214 351-9060
1740 Hurd Dr Irving (75038) *(G-13026)*

Filecontrol Partners Ltd (PA).................................**713 355-1111**
1300 Texas St Houston (77002) *(G-9785)*

Filestack.................................210 364-1833
118 Broadway St Ste 627 San Antonio (78205) *(G-18113)*

Filetrail Inc.................................408 289-1300
2505 E 6th St Ste D Austin (78702) *(G-1155)*

Film Technology, Houston *Also called Sheperd Maury (G-11865)*

Filter 1 Clean Air Consultants, Garland *Also called Clean Air Consultants Inc (G-7458)*

Filter Maintenance Company Inc (PA).................................**713 432-7969**
8278 Warren Rd Houston (77040) *(G-9786)*

Filter Warehouse, Houston *Also called Filter Maintenance Company Inc (G-9786)*

Filter-All Inc.................................281 356-1257
6907 Fm 1488 Rd Magnolia (77354) *(G-14606)*

Filters Express, Plano *Also called Procam Controls Inc (G-16979)*

Filtration Automation Inc 817 999-8190
4541 J D Mouser Pkwy Alvarado (76009) *(G-332)*

Filtration Group LLC 815 726-4600
11500 Hillguard Rd Dallas (75243) *(G-4361)*

Filtration Products LLC 210 805-0200
1218 N Hackberry St San Antonio (78202) *(G-18114)*

Fim Cranes, Seminole *Also called Fehrs Industrial Mfg LLC (G-18883)*

Fin-Tech Inc 713 680-3777
5225 Milwee St Houston (77092) *(G-9787)*

Finalrod, Big Spring *Also called R2r and D LLC (G-2094)*

Financial Industry Com 972 458-8583
14285 Midway Rd Ste 200 Addison (75001) *(G-123)*

Finck Cigar Co 210 226-4191
12923 Jnes Maltsberger Rd San Antonio (78247) *(G-18115)*

Fine Line Met Fabricators Inc 972 524-6248
3975 Tem Tex Blvd Terrell (75160) *(G-19734)*

Fine Line Metalfab, Terrell *Also called Fine Line Met Fabricators Inc (G-19734)*

Fine Line Ribbon Company, Ennis *Also called Fine Line Ribbon Inc (G-6102)*

Fine Line Ribbon Inc 972 875-8681
2405 N Preston St Ennis (75119) *(G-6102)*

Fineline Packaging, Dallas *Also called Classic Balloon Corporation (G-4127)*

Fineline Production, Euless *Also called Richard H Smith LLC (G-6155)*

Fineline Sportswear Inc 512 832-1441
8407 N Lamar Blvd A Austin (78753) *(G-1156)*

Fini Enterprises, Inc., Celina *Also called Chemtrade Sulfate Chem Inc (G-2991)*

Finial Company, The, Dallas *Also called Fleuron Enterprises Inc (G-4369)*

Finisar Corporation 214 509-2700
600 Millenium Dr Allen (75013) *(G-268)*

Finishing & Mailing Center LLC 214 747-6244
2151 W Commerce St Dallas (75212) *(G-4362)*

Finley, Dallas *Also called Moll McNeill Inc (G-4684)*

Finley Co 830 816-2107
306 Wollschlaeger Dr Boerne (78006) *(G-2120)*

Finley Investments Inc 713 686-4629
11510 Kilburn Rd Houston (77055) *(G-9788)*

Finley Production Company, Fort Worth *Also called Finley Resources Inc (G-6631)*

Finley Resources Inc 817 336-1924
1308 Lake St Ste 200 Fort Worth (76102) *(G-6631)*

Fino Oilfield Services Corp 361 394-7700
5109 Highway 44 Freer (78357) *(G-7224)*

Finoric LLC 855 346-6742
8115 Loop 540 Beasley (77417) *(G-1840)*

Fire Equipment Service Co., Dallas *Also called Texas Flameproofing Inc (G-5061)*

Fire Systems of Texas LLC 956 391-1191
11500 N 10th St McAllen (78504) *(G-14862)*

Firefly Aerospace Inc (HQ) 512 277-6959
1320 Arrow Point Dr # 109 Cedar Park (78613) *(G-2970)*

Fireplace Installers Inc 713 937-4575
6742 N Eldridge Pkwy Houston (77041) *(G-9789)*

Firestick Productions 817 360-7740
420 Lillard Rd Ste 101 Arlington (76012) *(G-679)*

Firestone Polymers LLC 409 924-4500
5713 Farm Rd 1006 Orange (77630) *(G-16242)*

Firestone Robertson Distlg LLC 817 840-9140
2601 Whiskey Ranch Rd Fort Worth (76119) *(G-6632)*

Firmin Business Forms Inc 254 776-5742
202 Deb Ave Waco (76712) *(G-20402)*

Firmin Printing & Off Eqp Co (PA) 903 793-5566
2217 N State Line Ave Texarkana (75501) *(G-19763)*

Firmin's Office City, Texarkana *Also called Firmin Printing & Off Eqp Co (G-19763)*

First Capital Intl Inc (PA) 713 629-4866
5120 Woodway Dr Ste 9004 Houston (77056) *(G-9790)*

First Choice Pallets, Dallas *Also called Alamo Pallet Recyclers Inc (G-3917)*

First Class Freightage LLC 469 486-4695
1408 Villa Paloma Blvd Little Elm (75068) *(G-14139)*

First Energy Services Company 817 334-4100
801 Cherry St Unit 2 Fort Worth (76102) *(G-6633)*

First Food Company, Dallas *Also called John Hogan Interests Inc (G-4537)*

First Monday Directory, Wills Point *Also called Van Zandt Newspapers LLC (G-20880)*

First National Trading Co LLC 713 771-3600
2117 Chenevert St Houston (77003) *(G-9791)*

First Place Foods LLC 972 272-1111
515 Mills Rd Garland (75040) *(G-7490)*

First Place Screen Prtg & Pdts, Dallas *Also called Raymer Enterprises Inc (G-4859)*

First Position Publications, San Antonio *Also called Real Estate Foreclosures (G-18413)*

First Quality Fabricating Inc 214 748-0071
1529 N Edgefield Ave Dallas (75208) *(G-4363)*

First Texas Concrete Repair, Dallas *Also called First Texas Precast Inc (G-4364)*

First Texas Precast Inc 214 350-5612
6839 Harry Hines Blvd Dallas (75235) *(G-4364)*

First Texas Products Corp (PA) 915 633-8354
1120 Alza Dr El Paso (79907) *(G-5769)*

First Time Right 832 264-5057
1000 Desert Rose Cv Kyle (78640) *(G-13682)*

Firstex Industries Inc 972 602-1478
111 Ne 11th St Grand Prairie (75050) *(G-7872)*

Fischbach Texas LP 469 533-5500
1901 Hutton Ct Ste 100 Dallas (75234) *(G-4365)*

Fischbeck Welding Inc 830 625-3249
537 Kohlenberg Rd New Braunfels (78130) *(G-15792)*

Fiserv Solutions LLC 281 242-8569
13100 N Promenade Blvd Stafford (77477) *(G-19313)*

Fishbowl Games LLC 469 449-3275
2707 N Fitzhugh Ave # 1122 Dallas (75204) *(G-4366)*

Fisher & Company Incorporated 586 746-1961
2045 Les Mauldin Rd 3f Brownsville (78521) *(G-2357)*

Fisher Construction 432 332-7532
2463 W Catlin St Odessa (79766) *(G-16001)*

Fisher Controls Intl LLC 972 542-5512
310 E University Dr McKinney (75069) *(G-14943)*

Fisher Controls Intl LLC 903 868-3200
4725 S Us Highway 75 Sherman (75090) *(G-18914)*

Fisher Dynamics, Brownsville *Also called Fisher & Company Incorporated (G-2357)*

Fisher Energy Partners LLC 713 937-6838
7227 Wright Rd Houston (77041) *(G-9792)*

Fisher Ham and Meat Co 281 376-1644
5023 Spring Cypress Rd Spring (77379) *(G-19121)*

Fisher Industries Inc 713 937-6838
26091 Pine Shadows Dr Hockley (77447) *(G-8344)*

Fisher Lease Service Inc (PA) 325 884-2701
303 N State Highway 137 Big Lake (76932) *(G-2056)*

Fisher Research Laboratory, El Paso *Also called Frl Inc (G-5775)*

Fisher Select Products Inc 972 484-1188
3201 Skylane Dr Ste 110 Carrollton (75006) *(G-2738)*

Fisher-Rosemount Systems Inc 512 418-7400
6 Cloverbrook Ct The Hills (78738) *(G-19818)*

Fisher-Rosemount Systems Inc (HQ) 512 835-2190
1100 W Louis Henna Blvd Round Rock (78681) *(G-17657)*

Fisherpump, Hockley *Also called Fisher Industries Inc (G-8344)*

Fishing Tool Repair and Mfg, Odessa *Also called Fishing Tool/Crystin Inc (G-16002)*

Fishing Tool/Crystin Inc 432 366-6504
8001 Golder Ave Odessa (79764) *(G-16002)*

Fisk/MEI Inspection Svcs Inc (PA) 281 436-5500
2 Northpoint Dr Ste 700 Houston (77060) *(G-9793)*

Fithen Properties 806 762-1121
1703 E 50th St Lubbock (79404) *(G-14410)*

Fitness In Motion South Texas, San Antonio *Also called Wheels and Fitness In Motion (G-18617)*

Fittings Inc 817 332-3300
3300 Fisher Ave Fort Worth (76111) *(G-6634)*

Fitz Aerospace, LLC, North Richland Hills *Also called Esna LLC (G-15877)*

Fitz Torque Converter, Odessa *Also called Fitz Torque Convertors Inc (G-16003)*

Fitz Torque Convertors Inc 432 362-3261
2616 Cessna Ave Odessa (79764) *(G-16003)*

Five - Jab Inc 281 356-7767
16202 Butera Rd Magnolia (77355) *(G-14607)*

Five Points Holdings LLC 214 525-6700
1919 Mckinney Ave Ste 100 Dallas (75201) *(G-4367)*

Five Star Consolidated Co Ltd (PA) 806 592-3113
Plains Hwy Denver City (79323) *(G-5419)*

Five Star Construction, O Brien *Also called Five Star Roustabouts LLC (G-15888)*

Five Star Custom Foods Ltd (HQ) 682 647-2700
3709 E 1st St Fort Worth (76111) *(G-6635)*

Five Star Field Services LLC 817 594-9799
217 W Intersta Weatherford (76087) *(G-20591)*

Five Star Roustabouts LLC 940 657-4778
1925 County Road 196 O Brien (79539) *(G-15888)*

Fivepayne LLC (PA) 817 310-0147
818 S Main St Ste 200 Grapevine (76051) *(G-8035)*

Fivepayne LLC 817 310-0907
7400 Rendon Bloodworth Rd Mansfield (76063) *(G-14673)*

Fives Cryo Inc 281 820-6990
17314 State Highway 249 # 108 Houston (77064) *(G-9794)*

Fives N Amercn Combustn Inc 281 488-2667
11507 Orchard Mountain Dr Houston (77059) *(G-9795)*

Fivestones Energy LLC 432 618-9929
5211 Preston Dr Midland (79707) *(G-15230)*

Fixture Exchange Corporation 817 429-2496
1720 Summit Dr Joshua (76058) *(G-13320)*

Fjcj LLC 409 740-3355
5712 Harborside Dr Galveston (77554) *(G-7396)*

Fjw Machine Inc 936 931-5507
43313 Old Houston Hwy Waller (77484) *(G-20498)*

Fki USA, Carrollton *Also called Fong Kai Usa Inc (G-2740)*

Fla Safety & Prod Svcs Inc 830 570-7286
11404 W Fm 140 Charlotte (78011) *(G-3047)*

Flag Systems, Dallas *Also called Dallas Flag & Flagpole Co Lc (G-4216)*

Flagship Carrier., Brenham *Also called Flagship Transport LP (G-2254)*

Flagship Manufacturing Corp 512 382-6410
2101 Donley Dr Austin (78758) *(G-1157)*

Flagship Transport LP 713 253-7785
6500 Earlywine Rd Brenham (77833) *(G-2254)*

Flamco of Texas Inc 254 799-4936
2525 Gholson Rd Waco (76704) *(G-20403)*

A **L** **P** **H** **A** **B** **E** **T** **I** **C**

Flame Retardant Clothes, Pasadena *Also called Newinn Inc* ***(G-16488)***
Flame Seal Products Inc.....713 668-4291
15200 West Dr Houston (77053) ***(G-8380)***
Flameout LLC.....713 984-8310
1701 Brittmoore Rd Houston (77043) ***(G-9796)***
Flamestop Inc.....817 306-1222
924 S Blue Mound Rd Fort Worth (76131) ***(G-6636)***
Flanders Electric Ltd.....903 759-9439
901 W Harrison Rd Longview (75604) ***(G-14234)***
Flange Protection & Gaskets.....281 991-4550
2535 Preston Ave Pasadena (77503) ***(G-16437)***
Flanges Inc.....713 673-4117
3306 Spring Manor Dr Kingwood (77345) ***(G-13643)***
Flare Well Testers Inc (PA).....**281 741-9335**
16000 Barkers Point Ln # 150 Houston (77079) ***(G-9797)***
Flares & Stacks Inc.....281 356-1408
12697 Johnson Rd Conroe (77302) ***(G-3297)***
Flat Creek Resources LLC.....817 310-8570
777 Main St Ste 3600 Fort Worth (76102) ***(G-6637)***
Flatrock Compression Ltd (PA).....**281 517-3680**
17350 State Hwy Ste 249 Houston (77064) ***(G-9798)***
Fleaux Services Louisiana LLC.....432 694-0004
2161 Commerce Dr Midland (79703) ***(G-15231)***
Fleco Industries LLC (HQ).....**972 247-3171**
2055 Luna Rd Ste 142 Carrollton (75006) ***(G-2739)***
Fleco Industries LLC.....214 369-1101
4637 Greenville Ave Dallas (75206) ***(G-4368)***
Fleet Body Equipment, Fort Worth *Also called Automotive Rentals Inc* ***(G-6411)***
Fleet Trax, Flower Mound *Also called Trax Holdings Inc* ***(G-6290)***
Fleetfilter, Brenham *Also called Brenham Auto Ltd* ***(G-2245)***
Fleetpride Inc.....361 883-4358
424 S Port Ave Corpus Christi (78405) ***(G-3528)***
Fleetpride Inc.....800 549-7278
4050 Corporate Dr Ste 400 Grapevine (76051) ***(G-8036)***
Fleetwatch, Rockwall *Also called S & A Systems Inc* ***(G-17564)***
Fleishmanns Yeast, Greenville *Also called AB Mauri Food Inc* ***(G-8061)***
Fleming & Son Corporation.....972 263-1713
1950 E Main St Grand Prairie (75050) ***(G-7873)***
Fleshlight, Austin *Also called Interactive Life Forms LLC* ***(G-1234)***
Fleuron Enterprises Inc.....214 678-0805
4030 La Reunion Pkwy # 10 Dallas (75212) ***(G-4369)***
Flex Tank Systems LLC.....281 862-2900
16514 De Zavalla Rd Channelview (77530) ***(G-3022)***
Flex-N-Gate Texas LLC.....817 652-3400
823-841 Heinz Way Grand Prairie (75051) ***(G-7874)***
Flex-N-Gate Texas LLC (HQ).....**817 652-3400**
2150 Bardin Rd Grand Prairie (75052) ***(G-7875)***
Flexaust Inc.....915 872-3100
12134 Esther Lama Dr # 300 El Paso (79936) ***(G-5770)***
Flexcon Industrial LLC.....210 798-1900
6110 Rittiman Rd San Antonio (78218) ***(G-18116)***
Flexelement, Houston *Also called Jvm Mechanical Inc* ***(G-10492)***
Flexhaust Appliance Div, El Paso *Also called Flexaust Inc* ***(G-5770)***
Flexible Packing Group, Orange *Also called Printpack Inc* ***(G-16257)***
Flexicore of Texas Inc.....281 437-5700
8634 Mchard Rd Houston (77053) ***(G-8381)***
Flexitallic, Houston *Also called Fgi Acquisition Corp* ***(G-9782)***
Flexitallic Group Inc.....281 604-2400
6915 Highway 225 Deer Park (77536) ***(G-5274)***
Flexitallic Group Inc (HQ).....**281 604-2525**
201 Kngwood Med Dr Ste B2 Houston (77067) ***(G-9799)***
Flexitallic Investments Inc (HQ).....**281 604-2525**
4660 N Sam Houston Pkwy E Houston (77032) ***(G-9800)***
Flexmaster USA Inc.....713 462-7694
5235 Ted St Houston (77040) ***(G-9801)***
Flextronics America LLC.....408 576-7000
8311 Killam Indus Blvd Laredo (78045) ***(G-13885)***
Flextronics America LLC.....512 425-4129
12455 Research Blvd Austin (78759) ***(G-1158)***
Flextronics America LLC.....408 576-7990
5802 Bob Bullock Loop Laredo (78041) ***(G-13886)***
Flextronics America LLC.....512 425-6180
900 New Meister Ln Pflugerville (78660) ***(G-16672)***
Flextronics America LLC.....512 698-1407
9500 Metric Blvd Austin (78758) ***(G-1159)***
Flextronics Intl PA Inc.....512 425-4100
12455 Research Blvd Austin (78759) ***(G-1160)***
Flextronics Intl USA Inc.....512 425-4100
12455 Research Blvd Austin (78759) ***(G-1161)***
Flextronics Intl USA Inc.....817 837-5098
600 Shiloh Rd Plano (75074) ***(G-16871)***
Flextronics Intl USA Inc.....512 740-1904
9500 Metric Blvd Austin (78758) ***(G-1162)***
Flextronics Logistics USA, Pflugerville *Also called Flextronics America LLC* ***(G-16672)***
Flightaware LLC (PA).....**713 877-9010**
11 Greenway Plz Ste 2900 Houston (77046) ***(G-9802)***
Flightsafety International Inc.....817 571-5925
4660 Diplomacy Rd Fort Worth (76155) ***(G-6638)***
Flint Energy Services Inc.....956 585-9779
11916 W Mile 7 Rd Mission (78573) ***(G-15554)***
Flint Energy Services Inc.....903 389-8716
341 Hwy 45 Fairfield (75840) ***(G-6174)***
Flint Energy Services Inc.....830 569-8453
756 Eagle Ford Dr Pleasanton (78064) ***(G-17067)***
Flint Energy Services Inc.....361 449-2405
3425 Highway 281 George West (78022) ***(G-7624)***
Flint Energy Services Inc.....940 683-4181
756 Eagle Ford Dr Pleasanton (78064) ***(G-17068)***
Flint Group Print Media N Amer, Dallas *Also called Flint Group US LLC* ***(G-4370)***
Flint Group US LLC.....214 638-6700
11625 Columbia Center Dr # 300 Dallas (75229) ***(G-4370)***
Flint Hills Resources LP.....361 889-7282
1700 Nueces Bay Blvd Corpus Christi (78407) ***(G-3529)***
Flint Hills Resources LP.....281 363-7200
1330 Lake Robbins Dr # 400 The Woodlands (77380) ***(G-19865)***
Flint Hills Resources LP.....903 239-5200
118 Huntsman Way Longview (75602) ***(G-14235)***
Flint Hills Resources LP.....432 640-8933
2495 S Grandview Ave Odessa (79766) ***(G-16004)***
Flint Hills Resources LP.....361 241-4811
2825 Suntide Rd Corpus Christi (78409) ***(G-3530)***
Flint Hills Resources LP.....361 241-4811
8606 Ih 37 Corpus Christi (78409) ***(G-3531)***
Flint Hlls Rsrces Hston Chem L.....713 740-3900
9822 La Porte Fwy Houston (77017) ***(G-9803)***
Flintlock, Houston *Also called Home Fragrance Holdings Inc* ***(G-10197)***
Flip Manufacturing.....903 454-1538
4410 Ed Rutherford Rd Greenville (75402) ***(G-8073)***
Flo Pura Corp.....281 320-9547
6717 Klein Cemetary Rd G Spring (77379) ***(G-19122)***
Flo Trend Systems Inc.....713 699-0152
1400 Kowis St Houston (77093) ***(G-9804)***
Flocap Injection Services LLC.....432 614-1609
11002 W County Road 77 Midland (79707) ***(G-15232)***
Flomin Inc.....281 573-6401
7500 Fm 1405 Rd Baytown (77523) ***(G-1787)***
Flora International, Houston *Also called Cole & Ashcroft LP* ***(G-9243)***
Florencio Villanueva.....210 534-4879
233 E Malone Ave San Antonio (78214) ***(G-18117)***
Flores Pallets LLC.....713 645-1022
6101 Dixie Dr Houston (77087) ***(G-9805)***
Flotek Industries Inc.....325 347-0005
1402 Ft Mckavitt Mason (76856) ***(G-14814)***
Flotek Industries Inc (PA).....**713 849-9911**
8846 N Sam Houston Pkwy W # 150 Houston (77064) ***(G-9806)***
Flotek Pump Services, Houston *Also called USA Petrovalve Inc* ***(G-12498)***
Flour Milling Division, Saginaw *Also called Ardent Mills LLC* ***(G-17737)***
Flow Control Division Cameron.....713 513-3300
6213 W Sam Houston Pkwy N Houston (77041) ***(G-9807)***
Flow Process Technologies Inc.....281 351-9427
17818 Grant Rd Cypress (77429) ***(G-3790)***
Flow Software, Southlake *Also called Distribution Management Co Inc* ***(G-19063)***
Flow-Cal Inc.....832 240-4800
2525 Bay Area Blvd # 500 Houston (77058) ***(G-9808)***
Flow-Tek Inc.....832 912-2300
8323 N Eldridge Pkwy 100b Houston (77041) ***(G-9809)***
Flow-Zone LLC (HQ).....**281 997-8899**
3504 Dwayne Rd Rosharon (77583) ***(G-17605)***
Flowback Champion Services LLC.....832 731-5783
3305 Beacon View Ct Pearland (77584) ***(G-16561)***
Flowback Green Services LLC.....409 217-1482
3005 Silver St Beaumont (77703) ***(G-1894)***
Flowco Prod Solutions LLC.....830 779-2163
109 S Parkway Dr La Vernia (78121) ***(G-13801)***
Flowco Prod Solutions LLC (PA).....**281 528-6298**
20405 State Highway 249 # 600 Houston (77070) ***(G-9810)***
Flowco Prod Solutions LLC.....281 528-6298
6825 Theall Rd Houston (77066) ***(G-9811)***
Flowers Bakeries LLC.....915 533-8434
301 Dallas St El Paso (79901) ***(G-5771)***
Flowers Bakeries LLC.....361 814-0558
3717 Saratoga Blvd Corpus Christi (78415) ***(G-3532)***
Flowers Bakery, Tyler *Also called Flowers Baking Co Tyler LLC* ***(G-20088)***
Flowers Bakery, Houston *Also called Flowers Baking Co Houston LLC* ***(G-9812)***
Flowers Baking Co Denton LLC.....214 343-6796
10879 Bekay St Dallas (75238) ***(G-4371)***
Flowers Baking Co Denton LLC.....972 263-3363
180 W Pioneer Grand Prairie (75051) ***(G-7876)***
Flowers Baking Co Denton LLC (HQ).....**940 383-5280**
4210 Edwards Rd Denton (76208) ***(G-5366)***
Flowers Baking Co El Paso LLC (HQ).....**915 533-8434**
301 Dallas St El Paso (79901) ***(G-5772)***
Flowers Baking Co Houston LLC (HQ).....**713 869-5701**
3000 Washington Ave Houston (77007) ***(G-9812)***
Flowers Baking Co Tyler LLC (HQ).....**903 595-2421**
1200 W Erwin St Tyler (75702) ***(G-20088)***

Flowers Baking Co Tyler LLC 903 758-2369
403 Ambassador Row Longview (75604) *(G-14236)*

Flowers Baking Co Tyler LLC 903 677-2455
1601 Rocky Ridge Rd Athens (75751) *(G-826)*

Flowers Baking Company El Paso, El Paso *Also called Flowers Bakeries LLC* *(G-5771)*

Flowers Bkg Co San Antonio LLC (HQ) **210 661-2361**
6000 Ne Loop 410 San Antonio (78218) *(G-18118)*

Flowers Ranch, Alice *Also called W L Flowers Mch Wldg Co Inc* *(G-244)*

Flowserve Corporation (PA) **972 443-6500**
5215 N Ocnnor Blvd Ste 23 Connor Irving (75039) *(G-13027)*

Flowserve Corporation 800 446-0401
4343 W Royal Ln Ste 106 Irving (75063) *(G-13028)*

Flowserve Corporation 832 375-0807
6840 Wynnwood Ln Houston (77008) *(G-9813)*

Flowserve Corporation 409 727-1476
2220 Highway 365 Port Arthur (77640) *(G-17108)*

Flowserve Corporation 903 439-3324
1511 Jefferson St E Sulphur Springs (75482) *(G-19587)*

Flowserve Corporation 713 374-7100
4001 Flowserve Way Pasadena (77503) *(G-16438)*

Flowserve Corporation 713 863-9180
3993 W Sam Houston Pkwy N # 100 Houston (77043) *(G-9814)*

Flowserve Corporation 409 842-5594
2920 W Cardinal Dr Beaumont (77705) *(G-1895)*

Flowserve Corporation 412 787-8803
4001 Emerald Field Dr Pasadena (77503) *(G-16439)*

Flowserve Corporation 281 241-3500
4015 Lowserve Way Pasadena (77503) *(G-16440)*

Flowserve International Inc (HQ) **972 443-6500**
5215 N O Connor Blvd # 2300 Irving (75039) *(G-13029)*

Flowserve US Inc (HQ) **972 443-6500**
5215 N Oconnor Blvd Ste Connor Irving (75039) *(G-13030)*

Flowserve US Inc 979 549-0029
4001 Flowserve Way 100 Pasadena (77503) *(G-16441)*

Flowserve US Inc 502 267-2205
4001 Flowserve Way 300 Pasadena (77503) *(G-16442)*

Flowtronex Psi LLC (HQ) **469 221-1200**
10661 Newkirk St Dallas (75220) *(G-4372)*

Floyd Tate A 409 745-3256
10383 Highway 12 Ste 116 Orange (77632) *(G-16243)*

Floyd County Hesperian-Beacon 888 400-1083
201 W California St Ste A Floydada (79235) *(G-6293)*

Flozone Measurement Ltd (PA) **432 488-2799**
3981 S County Road 1297 Odessa (79765) *(G-16005)*

Flozone Measurement Ltd 432 488-2799
6091 Highway 77 Odem (78370) *(G-15896)*

Flr Oilfield Services LLC 432 693-2245
1010 W Us Highway 67 Rankin (79778) *(G-17232)*

Fluence Bioengineering Inc 512 212-4544
4129 Coml Ctr Dr Ste 450 Austin (78744) *(G-1163)*

Fluenta Inc (PA) **832 456-2021**
1155 Dairy Ashford Rd # 211 Houston (77079) *(G-9815)*

Fluid Containment Acquisition, Conroe *Also called Containment Solutions Inc* *(G-3286)*

Fluid Disposal Specialties Inc 903 927-2050
8000 Us Highway 59 S Marshall (75672) *(G-14777)*

Fluid Sealing Products Inc 713 910-1028
155 Southbelt Indus Dr Houston (77047) *(G-9816)*

Fluid Service Technologies, Houston *Also called Ashburn Industries* *(G-8718)*

Fluid Systems, Houston *Also called FSI Holdings LLC* *(G-9872)*

Fluids Clements Management LLC 903 581-5110
4710 Kinsey Dr Ste 200 Tyler (75703) *(G-20089)*

Fluoromed Products LP 512 255-6877
2350 Double Creek Dr Round Rock (78664) *(G-17658)*

Flurry and Son Logging Contr 409 384-5441
706 Maol Rd Jasper (75951) *(G-13275)*

Flutura Business Solutions LLC 832 265-9172
5858 Westheimer Rd # 405 Houston (77057) *(G-9817)*

Fluxmetals LLC 832 948-4307
650 N Sam Houston Pkwy E Houston (77060) *(G-9818)*

Flying A Pumping Services LLC 325 794-1667
9555 S Us Highway 283 Albany (76430) *(G-188)*

Flying Circle Bag Co 830 249-2480
10045 Johns Rd Boerne (78006) *(G-2121)*

Flying Circle Bags, Boerne *Also called Flying Circle Bag Co* *(G-2121)*

Flying Penguin Ice, Bryan *Also called Heath Inc* *(G-2476)*

FMC Corporation 281 591-4470
1777 Gears Rd Houston (77067) *(G-9819)*

FMC Corporation 936 559-0031
3226 N University Dr # 100 Nacogdoches (75965) *(G-15697)*

FMC Subsea Systems, Stephenville *Also called FMC Technologies Inc* *(G-19413)*

FMC Technologies Inc 254 968-2181
2825 W Washington St Stephenville (76401) *(G-19413)*

FMC Technologies Inc (HQ) **281 591-4000**
11740 Katy Fwy Enrgy Twr Houston (77079) *(G-9820)*

FMC Technologies Inc 281 591-4000
640 Four S Indus Blvd Kilgore (75662) *(G-13554)*

FMC Technologies Inc 281 260-2190
1803 Gears Rd Houston (77067) *(G-9821)*

FMC Technologies Inc 254 968-2181
2825 W Washington St Stephenville (76401) *(G-19414)*

FMC Technologies Inc 432 561-8063
12620 W County Road 133 Odessa (79765) *(G-16006)*

FMC Technologies Inc 432 563-0335
3500 N County Rd W Odessa (79764) *(G-16007)*

FMC Technologies Inc 281 821-2355
16700 E Hardy Rd Houston (77032) *(G-9822)*

FMC Technologies Inc 214 363-8000
15851 Dallas Pkwy # 1103 Addison (75001) *(G-124)*

FMC Technologies Inc 281 591-4106
11220 Tc Gester Houston (77067) *(G-9823)*

FMC Technologies Inc 361 668-0886
1266 N Hwy 281 Byp Alice (78332) *(G-214)*

FMC Technologies Inc 817 887-8063
777 Main St Ste 600 Fort Worth (76102) *(G-6639)*

FMC Technologies Inc 361 290-9795
8620 N New Braunfels Ave San Antonio (78217) *(G-18119)*

FMC Technologies Inc 281 591-4000
1777 Gears Rd Houston (77067) *(G-9824)*

FMC Technologies Inc 281 569-6194
13460 Lockwood Rd S01 Houston (77044) *(G-9825)*

FMC Technologies Inc 254 968-2181
2830 W Frey St Stephenville (76401) *(G-19415)*

FMC Technologies Inc 281 260-2121
500 N Sam Houston Pkwy E Houston (77060) *(G-9826)*

FMC Technologies Inc 817 599-3337
1822 Ranger Hwy Weatherford (76088) *(G-20592)*

FMC Technologies Inc 281 405-7927
16736 E Hardy Rd Houston (77032) *(G-9827)*

FMC Technologies Offshore LLC 713 341-7742
2000 W Sam Houston Pkwy S Houston (77042) *(G-9828)*

Foam Fabricators Inc 817 379-6520
900 Keller Pkwy Ste 101 Keller (76248) *(G-13467)*

Foam Pak US LP 832 212-8896
1103 S Dr Houston (77099) *(G-9829)*

Foam Supplies Inc 972 436-7008
590 Benjamins Way Lewisville (75057) *(G-14050)*

Foampack US 281 565-9619
13630 Dublin Ct Stafford (77477) *(G-19314)*

Focus Exploration LLC 713 435-0021
10333 Richmond Ave # 750 Houston (77042) *(G-9830)*

Focus Newspapers of Dfw Inc 972 223-9175
1337 Marilyn Ave Desoto (75115) *(G-5431)*

Focus Wireless Inc 586 907-5323
709 N Glenville Dr # 500 Richardson (75081) *(G-17310)*

Fogle Manufacturing Svcs LP 281 495-1828
10101 Mula Rd Stafford (77477) *(G-19315)*

Folas Inc 830 625-1613
1150 Schwab Rd New Braunfels (78132) *(G-15793)*

Fong Kai Usa Inc (HQ) **972 644-1584**
2525 Carter Dr Carrollton (75006) *(G-2740)*

Food Group Ventures LLC 936 327-4443
202 N Washington Ave # 100 Livingston (77351) *(G-14153)*

Food Source Inc (HQ) **972 548-9001**
2200 Redbud Blvd McKinney (75069) *(G-14944)*

Fooder LLC 832 953-8944
20311 Sienna Pines Ct Spring (77379) *(G-19123)*

Foot Prints, Katy *Also called Framework Offshore LLC* *(G-13405)*

Foothills Resources Inc (PA) **713 621-9408**
2450 Fondren Rd Ste 200 Houston (77063) *(G-9831)*

Footprint Medical Inc 210 226-2600
12727 Cimarron Path San Antonio (78249) *(G-18120)*

For Heavens Sake 409 898-3340
4190 Calder Ave Beaumont (77706) *(G-1896)*

For Sale By Owner Magazine 713 457-0181
10560 Northwest Fwy Houston (77092) *(G-9832)*

Forbes Energy Services Ltd (PA) **361 664-0549**
3000 S Business Hwy 281 Alice (78332) *(G-215)*

Forbes Rbuilt Automitive Parts 817 332-7643
2712 White Settlement Rd Fort Worth (76107) *(G-6640)*

Forbius, Austin *Also called Formation Biologics Corp* *(G-1166)*

Force Pressure Control LLC 361 210-9650
11895 W Interstate 10 Marion (78124) *(G-14756)*

Forcepoint LLC (PA) **858 320-8000**
10900 A Stnlake Blvd Quar Austin (78759) *(G-1164)*

Ford Contract Services Inc 713 862-2960
335 Old Highway 35 N Livingston (77351) *(G-14154)*

Ford Gin Service Inc 806 745-3433
904 Private Road 7150 Lubbock (79423) *(G-14411)*

Ford Steel LLC 281 354-3011
24800 Ford Rd Porter (77365) *(G-17176)*

Fordyce Ltd 956 581-0672
3601 N Abram Rd Palmview (78572) *(G-16310)*

Fordyce Holdings Inc 361 573-4309
210 W Juan Linn St Victoria (77901) *(G-20264)*

Fore Machine LLC 817 834-6251
5933 Eden Dr Haltom City (76117) *(G-8141)*

Foreclosure Listing Service 972 250-0993
4851 Keller Springs Rd # 219 Addison (75001) *(G-125)*

A
L
P
H
A
B
E
T
I
C

Foremark Performance Chem Inc (PA)............281 867-1330
2450 S Shore Blvd Ste 402 League City (77573) *(G-13957)*

Foremark Performance Chem Inc............281 867-1330
12511 Strang Rd La Porte (77571) *(G-13737)*

Forest Health Bariatric Center, La Porte *Also called Bay Area Industrial Contrs LP (G-13725)*

Forest Nix Industries Inc............936 254-2441
14732 State Highway 87 N Timpson (75975) *(G-19948)*

Forest Ogletree Products Inc............936 327-2424
1410 Noblitt St Livingston (77351) *(G-14155)*

Forestry Supply Service Inc............936 632-3394
3853 S Us Highway 69 Lufkin (75901) *(G-14528)*

Forestry Supply Service Inc (PA)............409 384-3213
104 N Manuel St Jasper (75951) *(G-13276)*

Foretravel Inc (PA)............936 564-8367
1221 Nw Stallings Dr Nacogdoches (75964) *(G-15698)*

Foretravel Motorcoach, Nacogdoches *Also called Foretravel Inc (G-15698)*

Forever Aloe Plantations, Dallas *Also called Aloe Vera of America Inc (G-3929)*

Forge Energy LLC............210 478-5950
15727 Anthem Pkwy Ste 501 San Antonio (78249) *(G-18121)*

Forge Tech Inc............888 854-8414
900 Anders Ln Ste 15 Kemah (77565) *(G-13474)*

Forge USA, Houston *Also called Brougher Inc (G-8996)*

Forged Components Inc (PA)............281 441-4088
14527 Smith Rd Humble (77396) *(G-12767)*

Forged Components Inc............936 825-7518
9533 Fm 379 Navasota (77868) *(G-15735)*

Forged Components Inc............409 246-2427
1299 Highway 69 S Kountze (77625) *(G-13670)*

Forged Products Inc............713 462-3416
6505 N Houston Rosslyn Rd Houston (77091) *(G-9833)*

Forklifts USA Inc............956 568-9797
8116 San Gabriel Dr Laredo (78045) *(G-13887)*

Form and Fiber Inc............888 314-8852
538 Welch Ln Gun Barrel City (75156) *(G-8114)*

Forma Automotive LLC............210 212-4400
1 Lone Star Pass Ste 1105 San Antonio (78264) *(G-18122)*

Forma Automotive LLC (PA)............210 888-0410
45 Ne Loop 410 Ste 902 San Antonio (78216) *(G-18123)*

Formals, Dallas *Also called S N D Manufacturing Ltd (G-4923)*

Formaspace LP............512 279-2576
1100 E Howard Ln Ste 400 Austin (78753) *(G-1165)*

Formation Biologics Corp (HQ)............713 357-1062
701 Brazos St Ste 930 Austin (78701) *(G-1166)*

Formers By Ernie Inc............713 991-3455
7905 Almeda Genoa Rd A Houston (77075) *(G-9834)*

Formers International Inc (PA)............281 833-3310
3333 Watters Rd Pasadena (77504) *(G-16443)*

Formers International Inc............281 998-9570
3533 Preston Ave Pasadena (77505) *(G-16444)*

Formosa Hydrocarbons Co Inc............361 987-8900
103 Fannin Rd Point Comfort (77978) *(G-17082)*

Formosa Industries Corporation............361 987-7000
201 Formosa Dr Point Comfort (77978) *(G-17083)*

Formosa Plastics Corp America............361 987-7000
201 Formosa Dr Point Comfort (77978) *(G-17084)*

Formosa Plastics Corp Texas (HQ)............361 987-7000
201 Formosa Dr Point Comfort (77978) *(G-17085)*

Formosa Utility Venture Ltd............361 987-7000
301 Formosa Dr Point Comfort (77978) *(G-17086)*

Forms & Printing Service Inc............713 266-4201
3737 Westcenter Dr Houston (77042) *(G-9835)*

Formtex Plastics Corporation............713 493-6628
6817 Wynnwood Ln Houston (77008) *(G-9836)*

Formulary Productions LLC............901 767-3000
301 Cedar Hurst Ln Austin (78734) *(G-1167)*

Formulife Inc............214 221-4911
1253 Andrews Pkwy Allen (75002) *(G-269)*

Forney Corporation (HQ)............972 458-6100
16479 Dallas Pkwy Ste 600 Addison (75001) *(G-126)*

Forney International, Addison *Also called Forney Corporation (G-126)*

Forproject Technology Inc............214 550-8156
4020 N Macarthur Blvd # 1 Irving (75038) *(G-13031)*

Forrest Hodges Operations............936 867-4910
10922 State Highway 21 Alto (75925) *(G-315)*

Forrest Mfg Co............713 864-2545
2825 W 11th St Houston (77008) *(G-9837)*

Fort Bend Business Journal............281 690-4200
4655 Techniplex Dr # 300 Stafford (77477) *(G-19316)*

Fort Bend County Road & Bridge, Sugar Land *Also called Christian Fort Bend Academy (G-19456)*

Fort Bend Herald, Rosenberg *Also called Hartman Newspapers LP (G-17587)*

Fort Bend Publishing Group............281 240-2445
10707 Corp Dr Ste 170 Stafford (77477) *(G-19317)*

Fort Bend South West Star, Stafford *Also called Fort Bend Business Journal (G-19316)*

Fort Dearborn Company............817 625-1116
4601 Pylon St Fort Worth (76106) *(G-6641)*

Fort Hood Herald, Killeen *Also called Frank Mayborn Enterprises Inc (G-13608)*

Fort Hood Sportsmens Center............254 532-4552
Bldg 1937 Fort Hood (76544) *(G-6322)*

Fort Worth Business Press, Fort Worth *Also called Drc Media LLC (G-6594)*

Fort Worth Commercial Recorder, Fort Worth *Also called Recorder Publishing Co Inc (G-6947)*

Fort Worth Crushed Stone LLC............817 596-5512
4313 Bethel Rd Weatherford (76087) *(G-20593)*

Fort Worth Division, Fort Worth *Also called Brandon & Clark Inc (G-6469)*

Fort Worth F and D Head Co............817 236-8773
3040 Peden Rd Fort Worth (76179) *(G-6642)*

Fort Worth F&D Head Company, Fort Worth *Also called Fort Worth F and D Head Co (G-6642)*

Fort Worth Fabrication Inc............817 625-2321
5316 Blue Mound Rd Fort Worth (76106) *(G-6643)*

Fort Worth Facility, Fort Worth *Also called Engraving and Printing Bureau (G-6615)*

Fort Worth Forging Die LP............817 529-9990
2579 Berner St Fort Worth (76111) *(G-6644)*

Fort Worth Gasket & Supply, Fort Worth *Also called Han-Boone International Inc (G-6686)*

Fort Worth II Distribution Ctr, Fort Worth *Also called Vf Outdoor LLC (G-7102)*

Fort Worth Plastics, Fort Worth *Also called Altium Packaging (G-6375)*

Fort Worth Star Telegram, Fort Worth *Also called Star-Telegram Operating Ltd (G-7016)*

Fortay Inc............806 948-4166
7525 Fm 119 Sunray (79086) *(G-19617)*

Forterra Inc (HQ)............469 458-7973
511 E John Carpenter Fwy # 6 Irving (75062) *(G-13032)*

Forterra Pipe & Precast LLC............806 765-6721
1624 Marshall St Lubbock (79403) *(G-14412)*

Forterra Pipe & Precast LLC (HQ)............469 458-7973
511 E John Carpenter Fwy Irving (75062) *(G-13033)*

Forterra Pipe & Precast LLC............972 262-3600
2138 S Highway 67 Cedar Hill (75104) *(G-2941)*

Forterra Pipe & Precast LLC............512 385-3950
801 Airport Blvd Austin (78702) *(G-1168)*

Forterra Pipe & Precast LLC............361 767-1060
1610 S Highway 77 Robstown (78380) *(G-17511)*

Forterra Pipe & Precast LLC............972 263-2181
1000 Macarthur Blvd Grand Prairie (75050) *(G-7877)*

Forterra Pipe & Precast LLC............713 466-6324
11201 Fm 529 Rd Houston (77041) *(G-9838)*

Forterra Pipe & Precast LLC............972 262-1571
1004 Macarthur Blvd Grand Prairie (75050) *(G-7878)*

Forterra Pressure Pipe, Grand Prairie *Also called Forterra Pipe & Precast LLC (G-7878)*

Forterra US Holdings LLC (PA)............469 284-8678
511 E John Carpenter Fwy Irving (75062) *(G-13034)*

Fortis Foods International LP............214 472-6400
2591 Dallas Pkwy Ste 103 Frisco (75034) *(G-7286)*

Fortis Solutions Group LLC............512 302-0204
1610a Dungan Ln Austin (78754) *(G-1169)*

Fortitude Specialty Mfg LLC............713 465-3370
8400 Villa Dr Houston (77061) *(G-9839)*

Fortress Company, The, Garland *Also called Fortress Iron LP (G-7491)*

Fortress Iron LP............972 231-4001
1720 N 1st St Garland (75040) *(G-7491)*

Fortson Oil Company............817 335-5641
306 W 7th St Ste 901 Fort Worth (76102) *(G-6645)*

Fortune One Foods Inc............713 426-1133
935 W 18th St Houston (77008) *(G-9840)*

Forum Communications Intl, Richardson *Also called Forum Communications Systems (G-17311)*

Forum Communications Systems............972 619-8603
1223 N Glenville Dr Richardson (75081) *(G-17311)*

Forum Energy Technologies Inc............432 550-9000
2495 S Grandview Ave Odessa (79766) *(G-16008)*

Forum Energy Technologies Inc............940 612-5890
10344 Sam Houston Park Dr # 300 Houston (77064) *(G-9841)*

Forum Energy Technologies Inc............713 329-8730
10344 Sam Houston Park Dr # 300 Houston (77064) *(G-9842)*

Forum Energy Technologies Inc............361 664-6024
4802 County Road 69 Robstown (78380) *(G-17512)*

Forum Energy Technologies Inc (PA)............281 949-2500
10344 Sam Houston Park Dr # 300 Houston (77064) *(G-9843)*

Forum Energy Technologies Inc............817 602-1174
6335 Fm 1830 Argyle (76226) *(G-601)*

Forum Flow Equipment Mfg, Robstown *Also called Forum Energy Technologies Inc (G-17512)*

Forum Industries Inc............210 225-9600
1400 Currency St San Antonio (78219) *(G-18124)*

Forum Oilfield Technologies, Odessa *Also called Forum Energy Technologies Inc (G-16008)*

Forum Production Equipment, Houston *Also called Forum Energy Technologies Inc (G-9841)*

Forum Us Inc (HQ)............713 351-7900
10344 Sam Houston Park Dr # 300 Houston (77064) *(G-9844)*

Forum-Direct, San Antonio *Also called Forum Industries Inc (G-18124)*

Forum-Valve Solutions, Houston *Also called Forum Us Inc (G-9844)*

Forward Science Holding Inc............855 696-7254
10401 Greenbough Dr 100 Stafford (77477) *(G-19318)*

Forward Science Tech LLC (PA)............855 696-7254
10401 Greenbough Dr 100 Stafford (77477) *(G-19319)*

Forward Times Publishing Co............713 526-4727
4411 Almeda Rd Houston (77004) *(G-9845)*

Fossil Group Inc (PA) **972 234-2525**
  901 S Central Expy Richardson (75080) *(G-17312)*
Fossil Partners LP 972 234-2525
  901 S Central Expy Richardson (75080) *(G-17313)*
Fossil Partners LP 972 234-2525
  901 S Central Expy Richardson (75080) *(G-17314)*
Fossil Partners LP 972 437-0452
  2280 N Greenville Ave Richardson (75082) *(G-17315)*
Fossil Partners LP 469 587-2627
  2880 Greenville Richardson (75080) *(G-17316)*
Fossil Partners LP (HQ) 972 234-2525
  901 S Central Expy Richardson (75080) *(G-17317)*
Fossil Retrodome, Richardson *Also called Fossil Partners LP (G-17317)*
Foster Farm & Equipment Supply 281 256-6900
  33402 Highway 290 Hockley (77447) *(G-8345)*
Foster Geotechnical, Hillsboro *Also called L B Foster Company (G-8329)*
Foster Testing Co Inc (PA) **806 435-6876**
  376 S 2 Fm Farnsworth (79033) *(G-6227)*
Fosters Point Inc (PA) 281 353-6696
  23810 Fm 2978 Rd Tomball (77375) *(G-19979)*
Fosters Work & Play, Livingston *Also called Dcf Investments LLC (G-14152)*
Fotown Diaster Solutions, Cypress *Also called Fotown Productions (G-3791)*
Fotown Productions 225 773-1894
  19034 Greenview Glen Dr Cypress (77433) *(G-3791)*
Foundation Energy MGT LLC (PA) **972 707-2500**
  5057 Keller Springs Rd # 650 Addison (75001) *(G-127)*
Founders Oil & Gas Oper LLC 817 390-1800
  1341 Horton Cir Arlington (76011) *(G-680)*
Fountain People Inc 512 392-1155
  4600 N State Highway 123 San Marcos (78666) *(G-18688)*
Fountain Valley Foods Inc 281 592-0610
  304 W Mill St Livingston (77351) *(G-14156)*
Four Brothers Boat Works Inc 409 229-4302
  7500 Harborside Dr Galveston (77554) *(G-7397)*
Four Cornerstone Solutions LLC 817 377-1144
  316 Bailey Ave Fort Worth (76107) *(G-6646)*
Four K Services Inc 806 323-8560
  1821 Willard St Canadian (79014) *(G-2650)*
Four Pnts Pltnum Invstmnts LLC 512 588-7916
  2219 Patterson Indus Dr Pflugerville (78660) *(G-16673)*
Four Pnts Pltnum Machining Mfg, Pflugerville *Also called Four Pnts Pltnum Invstmnts LLC (G-16673)*
Four Point Publishing LLC 281 228-6237
  1440 S Creek Dr Houston (77084) *(G-9846)*
Four Rivers Sftwr Systems Inc 412 256-9020
  11500 Alterra Pkwy # 110 Austin (78758) *(G-1170)*
Four Sevens Operating Co Ltd 817 870-9088
  306 W 7th St Ste 1045 Fort Worth (76102) *(G-6647)*
Four Star Construction, Dumas *Also called Duane Ollinger (G-5520)*
Four Way Pallet Co 713 675-7788
  7911 Richards St Houston (77029) *(G-9847)*
Four-Star Fabrication Inc 214 748-3494
  2041 W Commerce St Dallas (75208) *(G-4373)*
Four-Star Fabricators & Svc Co 903 965-4309
  1140 N Pecan St Bells (75414) *(G-2006)*
Fource Communications Limited 214 630-2125
  1351 Regal Row Dallas (75247) *(G-4374)*
Foust Incorporated (PA) **806 374-7005**
  1500 S Polk St Amarillo (79101) *(G-424)*
Fowler Post Co Inc 903 966-2417
  309 Farm Road 2118 Bagwell (75412) *(G-1735)*
Fowlerton Energy Services LLC 830 570-4507
  Sherman Ave 110 Fowlerton (78021) *(G-7161)*
Fox John 915 755-0080
  4741 Maxwell Ave Apt 13 El Paso (79904) *(G-5773)*
Fox Marketing Corporation (PA) **713 686-8300**
  21601 Park Row Dr Katy (77449) *(G-13404)*
Fox Nde (PA) 325 690-1633
  1102 Energy Dr Abilene (79602) *(G-41)*
Fox Tank Company (PA) **830 792-0770**
  117 Airport Commerce Pkwy Kerrville (78028) *(G-13519)*
Fox Valley Molding Inc 956 428-2506
  5506 E Grimes St Harlingen (78550) *(G-8189)*
Foxconn Assembly LLC 281 668-1668
  8801 Fallbrook Dr Houston (77064) *(G-9848)*
Foxconn Corporation (HQ) **281 668-1668**
  8801 Fallbrook Dr Houston (77064) *(G-9849)*
Foxmark, Katy *Also called Fox Marketing Corporation (G-13404)*
Foxtronics Inc 214 358-4425
  3448 W Mockingbird Ln Dallas (75235) *(G-4375)*
Foxworth-Galbraith Lumber Co (PA) **972 665-2400**
  4965 Preston Park Blvd # 400 Plano (75093) *(G-16872)*
Foxxe Energy Services LLC 713 960-0381
  2121 Sage Rd Ste 370 Houston (77056) *(G-9850)*
Foxy Propaganda, Kennedale *Also called Tmf Graphics Inc (G-13505)*
Fqe Chemicals Inc 281 476-9249
  4820 Railroad St Deer Park (77536) *(G-5275)*
FR Global Trading Co Inc 214 281-8668
  11311 Harry Hines Blvd Dallas (75229) *(G-4376)*

Fr Hruska Store 979 378-2333
  109 W State Highway 71 Ellinger (78938) *(G-6062)*
Frac Fuel Solutions LLC 713 907-4371
  17811 Fairhaven Sunset Ct Cypress (77433) *(G-3792)*
Frac Sand Services LLC 713 668-6766
  5419 Ariel St Houston (77096) *(G-9851)*
Frac Tank Supply Company, Midland *Also called Prucka-Laney Inc (G-15370)*
Framecrafters Inc 713 973-1333
  1410 Campbell Rd Houston (77055) *(G-9852)*
Framework Offshore LLC 281 610-1078
  20127 Chateau Bend Dr Katy (77450) *(G-13405)*
Frameworks Manufacturing LLC 713 692-5222
  1910 Cypress Station Dr # 100 Houston (77090) *(G-9853)*
Frank Mayborn Enterprises Inc 254 501-7499
  1809 Florence Rd Killeen (76541) *(G-13607)*
Frank Mayborn Enterprises Inc 254 634-6666
  1809 Florence Rd Killeen (76541) *(G-13608)*
Frank W Murphy, Rosenberg *Also called Murphy Fw (G-17590)*
Frank White 713 937-3800
  6927 Brittmoore Rd Houston (77041) *(G-9854)*
Frankenstein Engine Dynamics, Weatherford *Also called Frankenstein Racing Heads LLC (G-20594)*
Frankenstein Racing Heads LLC 817 556-2434
  2410 Ranger Hwy Weatherford (76088) *(G-20594)*
Frankie VS Kitchen LLC 214 303-9910
  2101 Cedar Springs Rd # 1220 Dallas (75201) *(G-4377)*
Franklin Covey Co 713 527-9494
  2611 S Shepherd Dr # 140 Houston (77098) *(G-9855)*
Franklin Howard Intl LLC 281 815-1527
  777 S Post Oak Ln 1700 Houston (77056) *(G-9856)*
Franklin Industrial Minerals, Crawford *Also called Lhoist North America Tenn Inc (G-3704)*
Franklin Machine & Gear Corp 281 441-3177
  5903 Frost St Humble (77396) *(G-12768)*
Franklin Quest Store, Houston *Also called Franklin Covey Co (G-9855)*
Franklin Welding Service Inc 361 592-1322
  1710 Young Dr Kingsville (78363) *(G-13627)*
Franklin's Printing, Waco *Also called Northern & Nye Printing Inc (G-20438)*
Franklin-Leddy Corporation 325 653-3397
  2200 W Beauregard Ave San Angelo (76901) *(G-17800)*
Franklin-Leddy Corporation (PA) **817 624-3149**
  2455 N Main St Fort Worth (76164) *(G-6648)*
Franks International, Houston *Also called Franks International LLC (G-9857)*
Franks International LLC 281 331-1501
  3735 E Hwy 6 Alvin (77511) *(G-362)*
Franks International LLC (HQ) **281 966-7300**
  10260 Westheimer Rd Houston (77042) *(G-9857)*
Franks International LLC 979 778-8700
  4100 Carrabba Rd Bryan (77808) *(G-2474)*
Franks Machine Shop LLP 806 747-4854
  4302 Adrian St Lubbock (79415) *(G-14413)*
Franks Manufacturing Co 210 492-3222
  1336 W Blanco Rd San Antonio (78232) *(G-18125)*
Fraser Mining & Industrial Sup, Mansfield *Also called Isco Industries Inc (G-14683)*
Frazer Ltd 713 772-5511
  7219 Rampart St Houston (77081) *(G-9858)*
Frazerbilt, Houston *Also called Frazer Ltd (G-9858)*
Frazier & Frazier Inds Inc 254 786-2293
  817 S 1st St Coolidge (76635) *(G-3407)*
Frazier & Son LP 936 494-4040
  101 Longview St Conroe (77301) *(G-3298)*
Fred Bennett Printing Company (PA) **817 641-9861**
  300 E Chambers St Cleburne (76031) *(G-3089)*
Fred Brown Methanol Inc 806 665-0034
  101 Naida St Pampa (79065) *(G-16323)*
Fred Clark Felt Co Beaumont (PA) **409 842-5080**
  6305 Industrial Rd Beaumont (77705) *(G-1897)*
Freddys Frz Cstard Stakburgers 210 521-5400
  5415 W Loop 1604 N San Antonio (78253) *(G-18126)*
Freddys Well Service Inc 361 578-4559
  Old Goliad Rd Victoria (77902) *(G-20265)*
Fredercksburg Stndrd-Rdio Post, Fredericksburg *Also called Fredericksburg Publishing Co (G-7179)*
Fredericksburg Brewing Company 830 997-1646
  245 E Main St Fredericksburg (78624) *(G-7178)*
Fredericksburg Publishing Co 830 997-2155
  712 W Main St Fredericksburg (78624) *(G-7179)*
Freecom, Big Spring *Also called Ceram-Kote Coatings Inc (G-2074)*
Freedom Architectural Millwork 281 592-5377
  12380 Fm 1725 Rd Cleveland (77328) *(G-3125)*
Freedom Communication Tech Inc 844 903-7333
  2002 Synergy Blvd Ste 200 Kilgore (75662) *(G-13555)*
Freedom Graphic Systems, Grand Prairie *Also called MBK-Wi Inc (G-7922)*
Freedom Leaf, Fort Worth *Also called GL Brands Inc (G-6670)*
Freedom Oil & Gas Inc (HQ) **832 783-5700**
  1010 Nantucket Dr Unit E Houston (77057) *(G-9859)*
Freedom Power Systems Inc 512 259-0941
  1620 La Jaita Dr Ste 100 Cedar Park (78613) *(G-2971)*

A
L
P
H
A
B
E
T
I
C

Freedom Wheels Inc (PA) 713 864-1460
580 T C Jester Blvd Houston (77007) *(G-9860)*
Freeflight Acquisition Corp 254 662-7050
7333 Interstate 35 S Robinson (76706) *(G-17500)*
Freeflight Acquisition Corp (PA) 254 662-0000
8080 Tristar Dr Ste 100 Irving (75063) *(G-13035)*
Freeflight Systems, Robinson *Also called Freeflight Acquisition Corp (G-17500)*
Freeflight Systems, Irving *Also called Freeflight Acquisition Corp (G-13035)*
Freeman & Curiel Engineers LLP 713 895-8668
13101 Nw Fwy Ste 320 Houston (77040) *(G-9861)*
Freeman Brothers Inc 806 883-7831
115 W 3rd St White Deer (79097) *(G-20709)*
Freeman David Products Inc 866 310-2556
3303 Ranch Rd 620 N Burnet (78611) *(G-2608)*
Freeman Ep, Burnet *Also called CPI Products LLC (G-2605)*
Freeman Expositions LLC 214 623-1300
3801 Adler Dr Ste 150 Dallas (75211) *(G-4378)*
Freeman Metal Products Inc 877 278-2275
4410 Ed Rutherford Rd Greenville (75402) *(G-8074)*
Freeport Minerals Corporation 915 778-9881
897 Hawkins Blvd El Paso (79915) *(G-5774)*
Freeport Welding and Fabg Inc (PA) 979 233-0121
200 Navigation Blvd Freeport (77541) *(G-7198)*
Freeport-Mcmoran Oil & Gas LLC (HQ) 713 579-6000
700 Milam St Ste 3100 Houston (77002) *(G-9862)*
Freer Iron Works Inc 361 394-7273
202 N Norton St Freer (78357) *(G-7225)*
Freescale Smcdtr Hldings V Inc (HQ) 512 895-2000
6501 W William Cannon Dr Austin (78735) *(G-1171)*
Freeze Technology Intl (HQ) 806 371-8854
500 S Taylor St Unit 1010 Amarillo (79101) *(G-425)*
Freight Mate, San Antonio *Also called Benson Box Inc (G-17947)*
Frenchys Sausage Co Inc 713 862-2299
4220 Pine Mt Houston (77018) *(G-9863)*
Fresh Brew Group Usa LP 281 847-2222
11600 Big John St Houston (77038) *(G-9864)*
Fresh From Texas, San Antonio *Also called Malim Inc (G-18272)*
Fresh Meadows Industries Inc 713 464-9554
8570 Katy Fwy Ste 119 Houston (77024) *(G-9865)*
Fresh-Pak Corp 713 690-8742
16240 Port Nw Ste 200 Houston (77041) *(G-9866)*
Fresherized Foods, Saginaw *Also called Avomex Inc (G-17738)*
Fresno Manfacturing LLC 281 437-6000
810 Fm 521 Rd Fresno (77545) *(G-7237)*
Fresno Manufacturing, Fresno *Also called Pittsburgh Corning LLC (G-7240)*
Freudenberg Oil & Gas LLC (HQ) 281 233-1400
10035 Brookriver Dr # 400 Houston (77040) *(G-9867)*
Freudenberg Oil & Gas Tech, Houston *Also called Vector Group Inc (G-12542)*
Frh Consumer Services Inc 512 657-8945
7801 N Capital Of Texas H Austin (78731) *(G-1172)*
Friedel Drilling Co 361 293-5545
555 City Of Hochheim Rd Yoakum (77995) *(G-20966)*
Friedman Industries Inc (PA) 903 758-3431
1121 Judson Rd Ste 124 Longview (75601) *(G-14237)*
Friedman Industries Inc 903 639-2511
3681 Fm 250 Rd 250th Lone Star (75668) *(G-14182)*
Friedson Hill Inc (PA) 817 294-3309
6804 Trinity Landing Dr N Fort Worth (76132) *(G-6649)*
Friedson Hill Inc 817 244-6500
8155 Camp Bowie West Blvd A Benbrook (76116) *(G-2039)*
Friendly Car Care, Austin *Also called Pegicorn Enterprises LLC (G-1406)*
Friendswood Reporter News, Pearland *Also called Woodland Publishing Inc (G-16611)*
Friona Division Beef Plant, Friona *Also called Cargill Meat Solutions Corp (G-7252)*
Frisco Style Magazine, Frisco *Also called Style Publishing Group LLC (G-7315)*
Fritel & Associates LLC 254 757-1177
1001 Webster Ave Waco (76706) *(G-20404)*
Frito-Lay Inc (HQ) 972 334-7000
7701 Legacy Dr Plano (75024) *(G-16873)*
Frito-Lay North America Inc 972 579-2543
701 N Wildwood Dr Irving (75061) *(G-13036)*
Frito-Lay North America Inc 210 662-2100
4855 Greatland San Antonio (78218) *(G-18127)*
Frito-Lay North America Inc 817 649-3266
948 Avenue H E Arlington (76011) *(G-681)*
Frito-Lay North America Inc 214 631-8485
1141 Regal Row Dallas (75247) *(G-4379)*
Frito-Lay North America Inc 214 944-5238
3420 Duncanville Rd Dallas (75236) *(G-4380)*
Frito-Lay North America Inc 214 331-7000
3548 Duncanville Rd Dallas (75236) *(G-4381)*
Frito-Lay North America Inc (HQ) 972 334-7000
7701 Legacy Dr Plano (75024) *(G-16874)*
Frito-Lay North America Inc 903 868-2657
4809 Marshall St Sherman (75090) *(G-18915)*
Fritz Industries Inc (PA) 972 285-5471
500 N Sam Houston Rd Mesquite (75149) *(G-15042)*
Fritz Industries Inc 214 244-7822
6902 Hwy 66 Greenville (75402) *(G-8075)*
Fritz Industries Inc 972 288-5425
2950 Executive Blvd Mesquite (75149) *(G-15043)*
Fritz-Pak Corporation 214 221-9494
4821 Eastover Cir Mesquite (75149) *(G-15044)*
Frl Inc 915 633-8354
1120 Alza Dr El Paso (79907) *(G-5775)*
Frog Street Press LLC 817 251-0510
530 S Nolen Dr Southlake (76092) *(G-19069)*
From Here Inc 805 368-3363
4901 Keller Springs Rd 106a Addison (75001) *(G-128)*
Front End Services 214 672-0600
1100 Fountain Pkwy Grand Prairie (75050) *(G-7879)*
Frontera Materials Inc 956 316-8952
22630 N Fm 88 Elsa (78543) *(G-6079)*
Frontera Resources Corporation (PA) 713 585-3200
3040 Post Oak Blvd # 1100 Houston (77056) *(G-9868)*
Frontier Bolt Company Texas (PA) 817 477-5319
555 Airport Dr Mansfield (76063) *(G-14674)*
Frontier Chemical LLC 325 672-0072
7551 Us Highway 277 S Abilene (79606) *(G-42)*
Frontier Fire Systems Inc 214 343-9500
9671 Wendell Rd Dallas (75243) *(G-4382)*
Frontier Oil Corporation (HQ) 214 871-3555
2828 N Harwood St # 1300 Dallas (75201) *(G-4383)*
Frontier Petroleum Resources 832 242-1510
6200 Savoy Dr Ste 650 Houston (77036) *(G-9869)*
Frontier Services Inc 361 668-1188
2404 N Us Highway 281 Alice (78332) *(G-216)*
Frontier Services Inc (PA) 210 520-1118
21222 Gathering Oak # 102 San Antonio (78260) *(G-18128)*
Frontier Tubular Solutions LLC 903 236-2100
11441 State Highway 43 S Marshall (75670) *(G-14778)*
Frontline Energy Inc 713 228-3577
1716 Lubbock St Houston (77007) *(G-9870)*
Frontline Geoservices Ltd 281 371-2800
4141 Katy Hockley Rd Katy (77493) *(G-13406)*
Frost Crushed Stone Co Inc 254 587-2472
Fm 1771 & County Rd 248 Kosse (76653) *(G-13666)*
Frostwood Energy LLC 713 623-7133
8558 Katy Fwy Ste 320 Houston (77024) *(G-9871)*
Fruit of Earth Inc (PA) 817 510-1600
3325 W Trinity Blvd Grand Prairie (75050) *(G-7880)*
Fryoux Tankerman Svc of Texas 281 842-9400
915 S 8th St La Porte (77571) *(G-13738)*
Fs Solutions, Houston *Also called Jetstream of Houston LLP (G-10471)*
FSI, Houston *Also called Fabricating Specialties Ltd (G-9749)*
FSI Apparel Inc 562 906-3000
1080 S Kimball Ave # 130 Southlake (76092) *(G-19070)*
FSI Holdings LLC (PA) 832 467-9898
18720 Intrcntnntal Crssin Houston (77073) *(G-9872)*
FSI Nutritional Products, Carrollton *Also called Aegle Nutrition LLC (G-2692)*
Ft Worth Lite & Barricade, Dallas *Also called Dallas Lite and Barricade Inc (G-4218)*
Ft. Davis Division, Fort Davis *Also called Village Farms LP (G-6320)*
FTC Industries Inc 817 431-1511
728 111th St Arlington (76011) *(G-682)*
Ftg Aerospace Inc 817 332-3806
4084 Sandshell Dr Fort Worth (76137) *(G-6650)*
Ftg Aerospace Inc 818 577-6126
4084 Sandshell Dr Fort Worth (76137) *(G-6651)*
Fto Services, Houston *Also called FMC Technologies Offshore LLC (G-9828)*
Ftr Equipment, Lufkin *Also called Forestry Supply Service Inc (G-14528)*
Ftr Equipment, Jasper *Also called Forestry Supply Service Inc (G-13276)*
Fts International Inc 903 590-2440
19081 State Highway 155 S Flint (75762) *(G-6237)*
Fts International Inc (PA) 817 862-2000
777 Main St Ste 2900 Fort Worth (76102) *(G-6652)*
Fts International Mfg LLC 682 647-3300
4700 S Edgewood Ter Fort Worth (76119) *(G-6653)*
Fts International Services LLC 210 308-3400
70 Ne Loop 410 San Antonio (78216) *(G-18129)*
Fts International Services LLC 817 334-0002
777 Main St Ste 1600 Fort Worth (76102) *(G-6654)*
Fts International Services LLC (HQ) 817 862-2000
777 Main St Ste 2900 Fort Worth (76102) *(G-6655)*
Fts International Services LLC 817 862-2000
119 Nu Energy Rd Aledo (76008) *(G-198)*
Fts International Services LLC 817 862-2000
777 Main St Ste 3000 Fort Worth (76102) *(G-6656)*
Fueland Inc 972 899-3727
1623 S Jackson St Jacksonville (75766) *(G-13239)*
Fueltrax, Spring *Also called Nautical Control Solutions LP (G-19153)*
Fugro-Geoteam, Inc., Houston *Also called Cgg Marine (us) Inc (G-9148)*
Fuji Ceramics Inc (PA) 972 722-1130
2686 S Goliad St Rockwall (75032) *(G-17549)*
Fuji Ceramics Dental Lab, Rockwall *Also called Fuji Ceramics Inc (G-17549)*
Fuji Photo U S A, Carrollton *Also called Fujifilm North America Corp (G-2741)*
Fuji Semiconductor, Carrollton *Also called High Voltage Power Systems Inc (G-2756)*

Fujifilm Diosynth Biotechnolog ... 979 431-3500
3939 Biomedical Way College Station (77845) *(G-3183)*
Fujifilm North America Corp ... 972 242-0662
1628 W Crosby Rd Ste 100 Carrollton (75006) *(G-2741)*
Fujifilm Ultra Pure Sltons Inc ... 972 245-3797
1200 W Jackson Rd Carrollton (75006) *(G-2742)*
Fujikoki America Inc (HQ) ... **214 333-4266**
4040 Bronze Way Dallas (75237) *(G-4384)*
Fujirebio Diagnostics Inc ... 830 372-1391
940 Crossroads Blvd Seguin (78155) *(G-18837)*
Fujitsu Ntwrk Cmmnications Inc (HQ) ... **972 479-6000**
2801 Telecom Pkwy Richardson (75082) *(G-17318)*
Ful-Vue Display Systems, Lewisville *Also called Universal Display & Fixs Co (G-14100)*
Fulfer Vanek Well Servicing Co ... 940 438-2276
5941 Pace Rd Iowa Park (76367) *(G-12906)*
Fulfillment Resource, Addison *Also called M Alvarez Enterprises Inc (G-147)*
Fulkrum Tchnical Resources Inc ... 713 485-4519
1415 North Loop W Ste 800 Houston (77008) *(G-9873)*
Full Circle Enterprises Inc (PA) ... **936 441-0101**
3 Gabled Pines Pl Spring (77382) *(G-19212)*
Full of Grace Divine Design, Plano *Also called Adele Charles Corp (G-16771)*
Fullco General Machine Works, Odessa *Also called Fullco Machine Works (G-16009)*
Fullco Machine Works ... 432 563-3443
12915 W County Road 122 Odessa (79765) *(G-16009)*
Fuller Production Inc ... 432 683-5661
1010 W Wall St Midland (79701) *(G-15233)*
Fuller-Phnix Architectual Pdts, Houston *Also called Braden and Prewitt Inc (G-8974)*
Fullers Alamo Safe & Lock ... 210 344-4523
3723 West Ave San Antonio (78213) *(G-18130)*
Fullers Machining Center Inc ... 713 943-0228
701 Dumont St South Houston (77587) *(G-19039)*
Fulton Supply and Recycl Inc (PA) ... **940 382-3611**
1404 Fort Worth Dr Denton (76205) *(G-5367)*
Fultons Metal and Hardware, Denton *Also called Fulton Supply and Recycl Inc (G-5367)*
Fun Da Mentals For Contruction, Houston *Also called Fun Da Mentals For Educatn LLC (G-9874)*
Fun Da Mentals For Educatn LLC ... 832 368-3345
5330 Griggs Rd Ste F104 Houston (77021) *(G-9874)*
Funeral Home, Rusk *Also called Wallace-Thompson Company (G-17733)*
Fungoman LLC ... 318 775-0000
10840 Switzer Ave Ste 102 Dallas (75238) *(G-4385)*
Funsource Partners ... 713 864-3412
3244 Locke Ln Houston (77019) *(G-9875)*
Funtastic, Houston *Also called Funsource Partners (G-9875)*
Fuqua Enterprises Inc ... 817 641-1074
205 E Vaughn Rd Cleburne (76031) *(G-3090)*
Furmanite America Inc ... 713 844-7656
6330 Dixie Dr Houston (77087) *(G-9876)*
Furnace Systems Inc ... 972 423-7800
1209 Ave N Ste 15 Plano (75074) *(G-16875)*
Furniture By Thurston ... 210 227-4747
2 Winnco Dr San Antonio (78218) *(G-18131)*
Furniture Land, Weatherford *Also called Moein Inc (G-20605)*
Fury Offroad Tires, Irving *Also called Nbr Wheels and Tires LLC (G-13113)*
Fusion Led Inc ... 281 990-6011
1924 Rankin Rd Ste 300 Houston (77073) *(G-9877)*
Fusion Operations LP ... 713 691-6547
6911 Fulton St Houston (77022) *(G-9878)*
Fusion Services Inc ... 512 444-4283
440 Industrial Blvd Austin (78745) *(G-1173)*
Futaba Corporation of America ... 915 771-7858
26 Walter Jones Blvd B El Paso (79906) *(G-5776)*
Futaba Industrial Texas Corp ... 210 927-2288
1 Lone Star Pass Bldg 34 San Antonio (78264) *(G-18132)*
Future Foam Inc ... 214 350-6611
10726 Doric St Dallas (75220) *(G-4386)*
Future Foam Inc ... 214 905-6043
8611 Ambassador Row Dallas (75247) *(G-4387)*
Future Horizons Inc ... 817 277-0727
107 W Randol Mill Rd # 100 Arlington (76011) *(G-683)*
Future Mart, New Braunfels *Also called Minae Products Inc (G-15813)*
Future Pipe Industries Inc (HQ) ... **281 847-2987**
11811 Proctor St Houston (77038) *(G-9879)*
Future Proof Brands LLC ... 512 790-9967
1023 Springdale Rd Ste 1j Austin (78721) *(G-1174)*
Futurefab Inc ... 972 423-6606
1209 Ave N Ste 12 Plano (75074) *(G-16876)*
Futuremedia Group Inc ... 972 770-0000
2120 Hutton Dr Ste 800 Carrollton (75006) *(G-2743)*
Futursarch Trials Neurology LP ... 512 380-9925
5508 Parkcrest Dr Ste 300 Austin (78731) *(G-1175)*
Fuzzy's Radiator, Borger *Also called Fuzzys Indus Mint Mnfacture LP (G-2179)*
Fuzzys Indus Mint Mnfacture LP (PA) ... **806 273-2818**
204 W 1st St Borger (79007) *(G-2179)*
Fwave LLC ... 817 754-9021
921 S Burleson Blvd Burleson (76028) *(G-2579)*
Fwm Tubular & Equipment Corp ... 281 806-7918
10111 Fostoria Rd Cleveland (77328) *(G-3126)*
Fwt LLC (HQ) ... **817 255-2965**
5750 E Interstate 20 Fort Worth (76119) *(G-6657)*
Fxm International LLC ... 832 886-0003
800 Town And Country Blvd # 300 Houston (77024) *(G-9880)*
Fyco Tool & Die Inc ... 281 304-4480
20101 Schiel Rd Cypress (77433) *(G-3793)*
G & A Label Inc ... 915 544-1766
1601 Wyoming Ave El Paso (79902) *(G-5777)*
G & A Pallet LLC ... 713 670-8118
8827 Clinton Dr Houston (77029) *(G-9881)*
G & A Pallet Co ... 713 670-8118
8827 Clinton Dr Houston (77029) *(G-9882)*
G & C Mold Company ... 915 590-6670
11430 Cedar Oak Dr El Paso (79936) *(G-5778)*
G & F Oil Field Services, Laredo *Also called Dcaf Inc (G-13877)*
G & G Logging LLC ... 936 269-9086
209 County Road 3274 Joaquin (75954) *(G-13310)*
G & G Machine & Maintenance (PA) ... **713 673-4235**
5110 Timber Shade Dr Kingwood (77345) *(G-13644)*
G & H Diversified Mfg LP (PA) ... **713 856-1600**
11660 Brittmoore Park Dr Houston (77041) *(G-9883)*
G & H Truck Equipment Inc ... 817 467-9883
1015 Commercial Blvd S Arlington (76001) *(G-684)*
G & L Tool, Snyder *Also called Basic Energy Services Inc (G-18984)*
G & M Welding, Galveston *Also called Reama Inc (G-7407)*
G & S Asphalt Inc ... 281 499-1551
10126 Cash Rd Stafford (77477) *(G-19320)*
G & S Custom Draperies, Houston *Also called Fresh Meadows Industries Inc (G-9865)*
G & S Enterprises Incorporated ... 281 530-3077
10863 Rockley Rd Houston (77099) *(G-9884)*
G & S Lumber Co Inc ... 936 564-7676
291 S Us Highway 59 Nacogdoches (75964) *(G-15699)*
G & W Trucking Inc ... 325 573-6338
2111 Avenue Z Snyder (79549) *(G-18992)*
G A Jo Inc ... 940 767-2340
363 Us Highway 281 Wichita Falls (76310) *(G-20765)*
G and G Investments Inc ... 325 949-7864
2027 Industrial Ave San Angelo (76904) *(G-17801)*
G B Coil Inc ... 903 212-2645
5902 Old Highway 80 Longview (75604) *(G-14238)*
G B I, Pearland *Also called G B Industry Co LP (G-16562)*
G B Industry Co LP (PA) ... **281 996-0020**
2019 County Road 124 Pearland (77581) *(G-16562)*
G B Manufacturing Inc ... 713 681-5837
1919 Antoine Dr Houston (77055) *(G-9885)*
G C 3, Houston *Also called Gc3 Specialty Chemicals Inc (G-9909)*
G C International Inc ... 972 422-2395
1301 Precision Dr Plano (75074) *(G-16877)*
G D Edgar Lumber Co Inc ... 409 787-2452
379 Sawmill Dr Hemphill (75948) *(G-8246)*
G E Huebner Concrete Inc ... 979 865-2274
217 S Mathews St Bellville (77418) *(G-2009)*
G E Jones Electric Co Inc ... 806 372-5505
200 N Polk St 16 Amarillo (79107) *(G-426)*
G E Oil Technology Inc ... 713 774-0340
6407b Hillcroft St Ste B Houston (77081) *(G-9886)*
G Fabricating LLC ... 281 421-3100
4101 Barbers Hill Rd Crosby (77532) *(G-3731)*
G G A Inc ... 254 732-1701
6802 Broad Ave Waco (76712) *(G-20405)*
G G A Pest Management Services, Waco *Also called G G A Inc (G-20405)*
G H X Indl, Houston *Also called Ghx Industrial LLC (G-9950)*
G H X West, Houston *Also called Ghx Industrial LLC (G-9951)*
G Kustoms Auto Customizing LLC ... 682 703-1583
1929 Golden Heights Rd Fort Worth (76177) *(G-6658)*
G L A, Dallas *Also called GL Automation Inc (G-4407)*
G M I, Houston *Also called Geomechanics International Inc (G-9937)*
G M I, Humble *Also called Gulf Manufacturing Inc (G-12773)*
G N P Inc Sheet Metal, Forney *Also called G N P Inc Sheet Metal (G-6308)*
G N P Inc Sheet Metal ... 972 564-0450
202 Fm 1641 Forney (75126) *(G-6308)*
G S L, Houston *Also called G & S Enterprises Incorporated (G-9884)*
G S M, Amarillo *Also called Grace Shursen Moore Assoc Inc (G-429)*
G S Petroleum Inc ... 936 336-4114
4408 N Main St Liberty (77575) *(G-14118)*
G T Enterprises, Alvin *Also called Gas Turbine Engines Inc (G-363)*
G T Products, Grapevine *Also called Gem-Tech Inc (G-8040)*
G T Southwest Hose Inc ... 214 689-4673
644 W Mockingbird Ln Dallas (75247) *(G-4388)*
G Tacos Inc ... 806 371-0411
1100 Ross St Amarillo (79102) *(G-427)*
G V C Holdings Inc ... 409 722-8321
1215 Main St Port Neches (77651) *(G-17161)*
G W Vines Company Inc ... 214 742-8371
3839 Singleton Blvd Dallas (75212) *(G-4389)*
G&C Coatings & Industrial Serv ... 832 916-6070
7450 Miller Road 2 Houston (77049) *(G-9887)*

ALPHABETIC

G&S Suzuki, Wichita Falls *Also called Grace IV Albert Thomas* **(G-20768)**
G-Con LLC 214 220-4303
6161 Imperial Loop College Station (77845) **(G-3184)**
G-III Apparel Group Ltd 281 256-3661
29300 Highway 290 Ste 946 Cypress (77433) **(G-3794)**
G2 Automated Technologies LLC 972 479-0699
10500 Metric Dr Ste 122 Dallas (75243) **(G-4390)**
G2 Restoration LLC 469 296-4275
2241 Redbud Blvd McKinney (75069) **(G-14945)**
G4 Spatial Technologies LLC (HQ) 512 447-9879
4111 Todd Ln Austin (78744) **(G-1176)**
G9graphix 940 268-1411
4517 Southwest Pkwy Wichita Falls (76308) **(G-20766)**
GA Steel LLC 281 741-7284
11117 N Huston Rosslyn Rd Houston (77088) **(G-9888)**
Gabhen Inc 512 832-7902
9200 Waterfrd Ctr Blvd Austin (78758) **(G-1177)**
Gaby's Shoppe, Dallas *Also called Georgejean Inc* **(G-4404)**
Gadutex Inc (PA) 713 413-0006
5710 Arthington St Houston (77053) **(G-8382)**
Gadutex Inc 713 413-0006
14023 S Post Oak Rd Ste B Houston (77045) **(G-9889)**
Gadutex Inc 713 413-0006
3930 Fuqua St Houston (77047) **(G-9890)**
GAF Materials, Dallas *Also called Standard Industries Inc* **(G-5004)**
GAF Materials, Dallas *Also called Elkcorp* **(G-4313)**
Gaffey Crane Div, Cleveland *Also called Ace Industries Inc* **(G-3118)**
Gaffey Cranes & Hoists, Fort Worth *Also called Crane Equipment & Service Inc* **(G-6557)**
Gagemaker LP 713 472-7360
712 Southmore Ave Pasadena (77502) **(G-16445)**
Gaines Group LLC (PA) 713 467-4774
2901 W Sam Houston Pkwy N A100 Houston (77043) **(G-9891)**
Gainesville Daily Register, Gainesville *Also called Cnhi LLC* **(G-7339)**
Gainesville Printing Co Inc 940 665-5517
200 Denison St Gainesville (76240) **(G-7344)**
Gaither Petroleum Corporation 281 579-5200
16600 Park Row Houston (77084) **(G-9892)**
Gaitz Memorials, Houston *Also called 4d Signworx LLC* **(G-8412)**
Gajeske Inc 972 314-8100
1314 W Oakdale Rd Grand Prairie (75050) **(G-7881)**
Galam Metals LLC 713 934-8528
13240 Hempstead Rd Houston (77040) **(G-9893)**
Galaxy Electronics Company 972 234-0065
201 E Arapaho Rd Richardson (75081) **(G-17319)**
Galaxy Fiber Optics and Elec, Richardson *Also called Galaxy Electronics Company* **(G-17319)**
Galaxy Stones, Houston *Also called West Coast Group Inc* **(G-12635)**
Galderma Laboratories LP 817 961-5000
2929 Texas Longhorn Way Fort Worth (76177) **(G-6659)**
Galderma Laboratories LP (HQ) 817 961-5000
14501 North Fwy Fort Worth (76177) **(G-6660)**
Galderma Research & Dev Inc 817 961-5000
14501 North Fwy Fort Worth (76177) **(G-6661)**
Galderma USA, Fort Worth *Also called Galderma Laboratories LP* **(G-6659)**
Gall Art Novelties LLC 956 290-3124
2019 Jefferson St Laredo (78040) **(G-13888)**
Galleon Mining Tools Inc 432 563-1867
11316 County Rd 128 W Midland (79711) **(G-15234)**
Galleon Turbeco, Midland *Also called Galleon Mining Tools Inc* **(G-15234)**
Gallery Designs, Forney *Also called Texas Lamp Manufacturers Inc* **(G-6315)**
Gallery One Point LLC 512 428-5710
401 W Pecan St Ste E Pflugerville (78660) **(G-16674)**
Gallop Contracting Group Inc 281 449-1051
1602 Mooney Rd Houston (77093) **(G-9894)**
Galperti Inc 713 433-0700
160 Southbelt Indus Dr Houston (77047) **(G-9895)**
Galt Medical Corp (HQ) 972 271-5177
2220 Merritt Dr Garland (75041) **(G-7492)**
Galt Wine Cellars, Bellaire *Also called C K Higgs* **(G-1992)**
Galvan National Carriers LLC 956 346-7095
34005 La Brecha Dr San Benito (78586) **(G-18657)**
Galveston Bay Gathering LLC 281 408-1200
1415 La St Ste 2700 Houston (77060) **(G-9896)**
Galveston Brace & Limb, San Antonio *Also called Prescotts Limbs & Braces* **(G-18393)**
Galveston County Daily News, Galveston *Also called Galveston Newspapers Inc* **(G-7398)**
Galveston Newspapers Inc (HQ) 409 683-5200
8522 Teichman Rd Galveston (77554) **(G-7398)**
Galvotec Alloys Inc (PA) 956 630-3500
6712 S 36th St McAllen (78503) **(G-14863)**
Galyean Insulating, Lubbock *Also called Galyean Investments LLC* **(G-14414)**
Galyean Investments LLC 806 368-5430
1101 E Slaton Rd Lubbock (79404) **(G-14414)**
Gambrinus Company (PA) 210 483-5100
14800 San Pedro Ave # 310 San Antonio (78232) **(G-18133)**
Gambrinus Company 361 594-3383
603 E Brewery St Shiner (77984) **(G-18940)**

Game Day Sports Apparel LLC 214 499-0028
2140 Hall Johnson Rd # 1 Grapevine (76051) **(G-8037)**
Gamebreaker 818 224-7424
4404 N Interstate 35 San Antonio (78218) **(G-18134)**
Gamestop Corp (PA) 817 424-2000
625 Westport Pkwy Grapevine (76051) **(G-8038)**
Gamestop Holdings Corp 817 424-2159
625 Westport Pkwy Grapevine (76051) **(G-8039)**
Gametime, Richland Hills *Also called Kelye B Stites Inc* **(G-17439)**
Gamma Aerospace LLC (PA) 817 477-2193
601 Airport Dr Mansfield (76063) **(G-14675)**
Gamma Engineering Inc 817 477-2193
601 Airport Dr Mansfield (76063) **(G-14676)**
Gamma2 LLC (HQ) 760 734-4003
2300 E Randol Mill Rd Arlington (76011) **(G-685)**
Ganart Technologies Inc 972 512-6933
1700 Columbian Club Dr Carrollton (75006) **(G-2744)**
Gandy Digital, San Antonio *Also called Gandy Engineering LLC* **(G-18135)**
Gandy Engineering LLC 210 338-8303
5750 Northwest Pkwy # 850 San Antonio (78249) **(G-18135)**
Gandy Ink, San Angelo *Also called G and G Investments Inc* **(G-17801)**
Ganten Group LLC 214 530-5483
1730 N Greenville Ave Richardson (75081) **(G-17320)**
Gapms, Humble *Also called Gill Assoc Prprty MGT Systems* **(G-12770)**
Garcia Foods, San Antonio *Also called Papa Grande Gourmet Foods LLC* **(G-18366)**
Garcia Foods Inc 210 349-6262
1802 Jackson Keller Rd San Antonio (78213) **(G-18136)**
Garcias Well Servicing Inc 432 527-3748
203 Ashby Ave Wink (79789) **(G-20887)**
Garden State Salsa Inc 512 242-4534
828 W 6th St Austin (78703) **(G-1178)**
Gardner Denver Inc 817 248-4500
441 Winscott Rd Benbrook (76126) **(G-2040)**
Gardner Denver Inc 832 421-5469
407 Eagle Ave Pasadena (77506) **(G-16446)**
Gardner Denver Inc 432 366-5433
8620 E Highway 191 Odessa (79765) **(G-16010)**
Gardner Denver Inc 281 873-1200
785 Greens Pkwy Ste 225 Houston (77067) **(G-9897)**
Gardner Denver Inc 817 248-4510
2600 Sylvania Cross Dr Fort Worth (76137) **(G-6662)**
Gardner Denver Pumps, Houston *Also called Gardner Denver Inc* **(G-9897)**
Gardner Dnver Wtr Jtting Syste 281 448-5800
785 Greens Pkwy Ste 225 Houston (77067) **(G-9898)**
Gardner Glass Products Inc 936 291-7271
7553 Highway 75 S Huntsville (77340) **(G-12812)**
Gardner Pumps, Lubbock *Also called Imperial Pumps Co* **(G-14425)**
Gardner-Gibson Incorporated 832 288-4111
6733 Silsbee St Houston (77033) **(G-9899)**
Gardner-Gibson Mfg Inc 713 637-4791
919 Crosstimbers St Houston (77022) **(G-9900)**
Gardner-Gibson Mfg Inc 972 878-1602
2801 N Old Hwy 75 Ennis (75119) **(G-6103)**
Garfam Industries, Houston *Also called 14703 Partners Industries LLC* **(G-8402)**
Garland Drapery Inc 972 276-5297
1918 Copper St Garland (75042) **(G-7493)**
Garland Independent School Dst 972 494-8580
414 Stadium Dr Garland (75040) **(G-7494)**
Garland Service Company, Garland *Also called Densonone LLC* **(G-7478)**
Garland Steel Inc (PA) 972 494-6000
312 S International Rd Garland (75042) **(G-7495)**
Garland Ventures Ltd 972 485-8878
115 S Intl Rd Ste A Garland (75042) **(G-7496)**
Garlock Metallic Gasket Div, Houston *Also called Garlock Sealing Tech LLC* **(G-9901)**
Garlock Sealing Tech LLC 281 840-4853
250 Portwall St Ste 300 Houston (77029) **(G-9901)**
Garnea Llc 512 398-4523
1403 Mlk Jr Indus Blvd E Lockhart (78644) **(G-14168)**
Garner & Golding Corporation 254 753-8061
500 S 26th St Waco (76706) **(G-20406)**
Garratt-Callahan Company 972 661-5006
13721 Welch Rd Dallas (75244) **(G-4391)**
Garrett Electronics Inc 972 494-6151
1881 W State St Garland (75042) **(G-7497)**
Garrett Metal Detectors, Garland *Also called Garrett Electronics Inc* **(G-7497)**
Garrison, San Antonio *Also called Texas Nom Limited Partnership* **(G-18539)**
Garrison Bros Signs Inc 806 744-1161
2523 E 50th St Lubbock (79404) **(G-14415)**
Garrison Contractors Inc (PA) 432 639-2811
205 W 6th St Iraan (79744) **(G-12918)**
Garrison Metal Products Inc (PA) 903 938-1319
2902 W Pinecrest Dr Marshall (75670) **(G-14779)**
Gartner Coatings Inc 281 997-3500
2433 Reid Blvd Pearland (77581) **(G-16563)**
Garvon Inc (HQ) 214 691-0711
12015 Shiloh Rd Ste 120 Dallas (75228) **(G-4392)**
Garwood Sand & Gravel, Garwood *Also called Marietta Martin Materials Inc* **(G-7615)**

Gary L Noble Inc....409 886-0552
17439 Highway 62 S Orange (77630) ***(G-16244)***
Gary Sanvig....903 885-7956
1317 Jefferson St E Sulphur Springs (75482) ***(G-19588)***
Garzo Inc....936 931-5631
42146 Hwy 290 Business Waller (77484) ***(G-20499)***
Gas Acquisition & Supply Inc....940 872-1183
815 Highway 59 N Bowie (76230) ***(G-2195)***
Gas Equipment Company Inc (HQ)....**972 241-2333**
11616 Harry Hines Blvd Dallas (75229) ***(G-4393)***
Gas Sensing Technology Corp (PA)....**307 742-6340**
1415 N Loop W Messanine A Houston (77008) ***(G-9902)***
Gas System, Pollok *Also called Accent Environmental Services* ***(G-17090)***
Gas Turbine Engines Inc (PA)....**281 824-9200**
1001 Highway 35 Byp N Alvin (77511) ***(G-363)***
Gas Ventures Ltd Liability Co....307 864-3754
6363 Woodway Dr Ste 1025 Houston (77057) ***(G-9903)***
Gasket Service Inc....432 332-0853
2120 Kermit Hwy Odessa (79761) ***(G-16011)***
Gastar Exploration Inc (PA)....**713 739-1800**
1331 Lamar St Ste 650 Houston (77010) ***(G-9904)***
Gate Precast Company....281 485-3273
3201 Veterans Dr Pearland (77584) ***(G-16564)***
Gate Precast Company....254 582-7200
1220 N Highway 77 Hillsboro (76645) ***(G-8325)***
Gate-Mold Inc....512 255-3470
1413 Sam Bass Rd Round Rock (78681) ***(G-17659)***
Gatehouse Media LLC....956 546-5113
2494 Central Blvd Ste A Brownsville (78520) ***(G-2358)***
Gates E&S North America Inc (HQ)....**361 887-9807**
134 44th St Bldg 7 Corpus Christi (78405) ***(G-3533)***
Gates Fuel Services LLC....409 925-8897
3813 Fm 646 Rd N Santa Fe (77510) ***(G-18734)***
Gates Mch & Fabrication Inc....210 651-6567
8025 Jethro Ln San Antonio (78266) ***(G-18642)***
Gates Molder Products Company, Brenham *Also called Longwood Elastomers Inc* ***(G-2261)***
Gatesville Messenger, The, Gatesville *Also called Messenger Publishing Co Inc* ***(G-7620)***
Gateway Concrete, Irving *Also called Burnco Texas LLC* ***(G-12954)***
Gateway Metal Recycling Inc....956 723-0409
13491 S Unitec Dr Laredo (78045) ***(G-13889)***
Gateway Printing & Off Sup Inc....956 546-0632
1460 N Expressway 77 Brownsville (78521) ***(G-2359)***
Gator Pump Inc....325 643-3502
302 Corrigan Ave Brownwood (76801) ***(G-2429)***
Gatsby Mens Ware, Austin *Also called Bellagio Menswear LLC* ***(G-988)***
Gauging Systems Inc....281 980-3999
910 Industrial Blvd Ste A Sugar Land (77478) ***(G-19484)***
Gaumer Company Inc....713 460-5200
13616 Hempstead Rd Houston (77040) ***(G-9905)***
Gaumer Process, Houston *Also called Gaumer Company Inc* ***(G-9905)***
Gauntlett Inc....806 293-9849
2109 S Date St Plainview (79072) ***(G-16754)***
Gaus Anodes International LLC....832 243-0700
6425 Cunningham Rd Houston (77041) ***(G-9906)***
Gavin Steel Fabricating Inc....210 695-9672
18593 Bandera Rd Helotes (78023) ***(G-8237)***
Gavson Inc....214 341-0440
9880 Chartwell Dr Dallas (75243) ***(G-4394)***
Gavson Salon Classics, Dallas *Also called Gavson Inc* ***(G-4394)***
Gavstar Services....817 657-4020
8160lla Frontera Arlington (76002) ***(G-686)***
Gay Engineering & Sales Co., Pasadena *Also called Gayesco-Wika Usa LP* ***(G-16447)***
Gayesco-Wika Usa LP (PA)....**713 941-8540**
229 Beltway Green Blvd Pasadena (77503) ***(G-16447)***
Gayla Industries Inc (PA)....**713 681-2411**
6401 Antoine Dr Houston (77091) ***(G-9907)***
Gayla Industries Inc....979 335-7503
770 Leverage East Bernard (77435) ***(G-5558)***
Gayla International, Houston *Also called Gayla Industries Inc* ***(G-9907)***
Gaylord Boxes USA, Houston *Also called Packaging One Inc* ***(G-11220)***
Gazoo Inc....979 220-7753
120 N Main St Bryan (77803) ***(G-2475)***
Gb Biosciences LLC....713 453-7281
2239 Haden Rd Houston (77015) ***(G-9908)***
Gc Packaging LLC (PA)....**214 383-7700**
204 E Bethany Dr Allen (75002) ***(G-270)***
Gc3 Specialty Chemicals Inc....713 802-1761
733 Heights Blvd Houston (77007) ***(G-9909)***
Gca Products Inc....972 506-3196
10671 N Stemmons Fwy Dallas (75220) ***(G-4395)***
Gcc Permian LLC....432 385-2800
16501 W Murphy St Odessa (79763) ***(G-16012)***
Gcc Rio Grande Inc....915 544-1750
2825 W Paisano Dr El Paso (79922) ***(G-5779)***
Gcdt, Houston *Also called Gulf Coast Downhole Tech LLC* ***(G-10059)***
Gces, Conroe *Also called Gulf Coast Envmtl Systems LLC* ***(G-3299)***
Gcv Enterprise LLC....830 644-2710
10587 E Us Highway 290 Fredericksburg (78624) ***(G-7180)***
Gd Satcom-Cpg, Kilgore *Also called CPI Satcom & Antenna Tech Inc* ***(G-13540)***
Gdc Technics LLC (PA)....**210 496-5614**
2060 Eagle Pkwy Fort Worth (76177) ***(G-6663)***
Gdmi Inc....972 494-7477
2763 Marquis Dr Garland (75042) ***(G-7498)***
Gds International LLC....713 623-1449
9841 Windml Lks Blvd Houston (77075) ***(G-9910)***
Gds Realty LLC....713 623-1449
9841 Windmill Park Ln Houston (77064) ***(G-9911)***
Gdsware....832 350-1166
15603 Kuykendahl Rd # 114 Houston (77090) ***(G-9912)***
GE Aero Energy Products, Houston *Also called GE Energy Manufacturing Inc* ***(G-9913)***
GE Energy, Houston *Also called GE Packaged Power LP* ***(G-9918)***
GE Energy Manufacturing Inc (HQ)....**713 803-0900**
1333 West Loop S Ste 700 Houston (77027) ***(G-9913)***
GE Energy Manufacturing Inc....281 864-2669
16415 Jacintoport Blvd Houston (77015) ***(G-9914)***
GE Engine Svcs - McAllen L P....956 971-5200
6200 S 42nd St McAllen (78503) ***(G-14864)***
GE Flight Efficiency Svcs Inc....512 270-2701
400 W 15th St Ste 1000 Austin (78701) ***(G-1179)***
GE Mobile Water, Dallas *Also called Suez Wts Services Usa Inc* ***(G-5018)***
GE Oil & Gas, Houston *Also called Vetco Gray LLC* ***(G-12557)***
GE Oil & Gas, Houston *Also called Vetco Gray LLC* ***(G-12558)***
GE Oil & Gas Logging Svcs Inc....361 299-9457
4910 Leopard St Ste 400 Corpus Christi (78408) ***(G-3534)***
GE Oil & Gas Logging Svcs Inc....281 992-9676
3446 S Main St Pearland (77581) ***(G-16565)***
GE Oil & Gas Logging Svcs Inc (HQ)....**281 579-9879**
13000 Executive Dr Sugar Land (77478) ***(G-19485)***
GE Oil & Gas Pressure Ctrl LP (HQ)....**281 398-8901**
4424 W Sam Houston Pkwy N S Houston (77041) ***(G-9915)***
GE Oil & Gas Pressure Ctrl LP....432 686-0720
306 W Wall St Ste 1414 Midland (79701) ***(G-15235)***
GE Oil Gas Cmprssion Systems L (PA)....**713 354-1900**
16250 Port Nw Houston (77041) ***(G-9916)***
GE Packaged Power LLC (HQ)....**713 803-0900**
1330 West Loop S Ste 1000 Houston (77027) ***(G-9917)***
GE Packaged Power LP (HQ)....**281 452-3610**
16415 Jacintoport Blvd Houston (77015) ***(G-9918)***
GE Zenith Controls Inc (HQ)....**800 637-1738**
601 Shiloh Rd Plano (75074) ***(G-16878)***
Gea Associates Inc....903 295-2727
705 Plum Creek Rd Longview (75605) ***(G-14239)***
Gear Drive Service Pump Div....806 948-5366
100 Highway Ave 281w Sunray (79086) ***(G-19618)***
Gearbox Publishing LLC....972 312-8202
5757 Main St Ste 500 Frisco (75034) ***(G-7287)***
Gearench, Clifton *Also called Orbix Corporation* ***(G-3145)***
Gel Investments....214 699-6996
2135 Becky Ln Cedar Hill (75104) ***(G-2942)***
Gel Pro, Austin *Also called Lets Gel Inc* ***(G-1289)***
Gel Technologies Corp....432 683-1881
24 Smith Rd Ste 200 Midland (79705) ***(G-15236)***
Gelu Italian Ice LLC....970 986-9535
9809 Rowlett Rd Ste G Houston (77075) ***(G-9919)***
Gem Asset Acquisition LLC....214 333-4343
3111 W Saner Ave Dallas (75233) ***(G-4396)***
Gem Food Services Corp....281 232-8013
4310 Avenue H Ste 66 Rosenberg (77471) ***(G-17582)***
Gem Services LLP....210 863-2020
1201 S 1st St McAllen (78501) ***(G-14865)***
Gem Sign Service Inc....830 609-1052
1631 Whispering Woods Trl New Braunfels (78132) ***(G-15794)***
Gem-Cap Inc....512 219-7610
12007 Res Blvd Ste 103 Austin (78759) ***(G-1180)***
Gem-Tech Inc (PA)....**817 329-3586**
501 Industrial Blvd Grapevine (76051) ***(G-8040)***
Gemco Manufacturing, Wylie *Also called RWG Incorporated* ***(G-20946)***
Gemco of Port Lavaca Inc....361 570-6611
6611 Lone Tree Rd Victoria (77905) ***(G-20266)***
Gemco Plltizing Dies Machining, Victoria *Also called Gemco of Port Lavaca Inc* ***(G-20266)***
Gemini Incorporated....507 263-3957
600 E Produce Rd Hidalgo (78557) ***(G-8308)***
Gemini Incorporated....512 352-5207
102 Wagner Way Taylor (76574) ***(G-19656)***
Gemini Coatings Inc....405 262-5710
7230 C F Hawn Fwy Dallas (75217) ***(G-4397)***
Gemini Contracting, Houston *Also called Holloway Company Inc* ***(G-10195)***
Gemmy Industries Corporation (PA)....**972 538-4200**
117 Wrangler Dr Ste 100 Coppell (75019) ***(G-3417)***
Gemseal Pvements Pdts - Dallas, Dallas *Also called Gem Asset Acquisition LLC* ***(G-4396)***
Gemstar Inc....432 362-2315
6501 Trunk St Odessa (79762) ***(G-16013)***
Gemstar Group USA, Spring *Also called Gemstar Stoneworks Inc* ***(G-19124)***
Gemstar Stoneworks Inc....281 257-6500
17819 Theiss Mail Rt Rd Spring (77379) ***(G-19124)***
Genco Atc, Fort Worth *Also called Fedex Sup Chain Lgstics Elec I* ***(G-6626)***

Genco Energy Services Inc (PA) 956 380-3710
  1701 W State Highway 107 McAllen (78504) (G-14866)
Gene Powell Investments Inc 903 234-1155
  1523 Colony Cir Longview (75604) (G-14240)
Gene's Paul MBL Wshsand Blast, Cleburne Also called Genes Paul Enterprises Inc (G-3091)
Genemco Inc 979 268-7447
  3385 S San Gabriel St Hearne (77859) (G-8231)
General Aluminum Co Texas LP (HQ) 972 242-5271
  1900 Lakeside Pkwy Flower Mound (75028) (G-6266)
General Assembly Corporation (HQ) 915 701-0605
  7101 N Mesa St Ste 544 El Paso (79912) (G-5780)
General Aviation Inds Inc 817 598-4848
  415 Jones Rd Weatherford (76088) (G-20595)
General Body Manufacturing Co (PA) 713 692-5177
  7110 Jensen Dr Houston (77093) (G-9920)
General Cable Corporation 903 938-8151
  9975 Us Highway 80 W Marshall (75670) (G-14780)
General Chemical, Midlothian Also called Chemtrade Solutions LLC (G-15476)
General Cntr For Ptro UST/AST, Jersey Village Also called Detsco Inc (G-13298)
General Crane Service Inc (PA) 713 649-4088
  4206 Weslow St Houston (77087) (G-9921)
General Datatech LP 214 857-6194
  1212 Medical District Dr Dallas (75207) (G-4398)
General Dynamics Mission 254 532-2927
  Terminal Ave Bldg 3820 Fort Hood (76544) (G-6323)
General Dynamics Ordnance 972 276-5131
  1200 N Glenbrook Dr Garland (75040) (G-7499)
General Dynamics Ordnance 972 276-5131
  1201 N 5th St Garland (75040) (G-7500)
General Dynmics Land Systems I 586 825-7242
  Logistics Ln Bldg 88037 Fort Hood (76544) (G-6324)
General Dynmics Mssion Systems 210 524-8200
  389 E Ramsey Rd San Antonio (78216) (G-18137)
General Electric Company 412 469-6080
  914 Independence Pkwy Southlake (76092) (G-19071)
General Electric Company 214 902-6600
  3202 Manor Way Dallas (75235) (G-4399)
General Electric Company 325 794-5100
  162 Caddo Dr Ste 100 Abilene (79602) (G-43)
General Electric Company 214 902-6600
  3020 Manor Dallas (75235) (G-4400)
General Electric Company 281 921-2850
  11330 Clay Rd Houston (77041) (G-9922)
General Electric Company 713 803-0437
  2707 North Loop W Ste 9 Houston (77008) (G-9923)
General Electric Company 281 812-0634
  18710 Atscocita Forest Dr Humble (77346) (G-12769)
General Electric Company 972 444-2000
  6051 N State Highway 161 Irving (75038) (G-13037)
General Garage Door Service 956 782-7373
  7216 W Interstate 2 Mission (78572) (G-15555)
General Labels & Printing LLC 915 532-7131
  2000 E Mills Ave El Paso (79901) (G-5781)
General Led Opco LLC (PA) 210 360-1444
  1074 Arion Cir Ste 116 San Antonio (78216) (G-18138)
General Magnaplate Corporation (PA) 817 640-1761
  801 Avenue G Arlington (76011) (G-687)
General Magnaplate Texas Inc 817 649-8989
  801 Avenue G Arlington (76011) (G-688)
General Magnaplate Wisconsin 800 441-6173
  801 Avenue G Arlington (76011) (G-689)
General Metal Fabricating Inc 713 641-5509
  6495 Dixie Dr Houston (77087) (G-9924)
General Mills Inc 817 490-6940
  4901 Henrietta Creek Rd Roanoke (76262) (G-17485)
General Mills Inc 972 892-4100
  15305 Dallas Pkwy Ste 710 Addison (75001) (G-129)
General Mills Inc 281 890-0784
  7525 Fm 1960 Rd W Houston (77070) (G-9925)
General Motors LLC 817 652-2200
  2525 E Abram St Arlington (76010) (G-690)
General Motors LLC 512 470-4730
  13201 Mccallen Pass Austin (78753) (G-1181)
General Motors LLC 817 652-2182
  2919 E Division St Arlington (76011) (G-691)
General Packaging Equipment Co 713 686-4331
  6048 Westview Dr Houston (77055) (G-9926)
General Plas & Composites LP 713 644-1449
  6910 E Orem Dr Houston (77075) (G-9927)
General Polymer Services LLC (PA) 281 424-4673
  4724 Decker Dr Baytown (77520) (G-1818)
General Polymer Services LLC 281 424-4673
  5110 Decker Dr Baytown (77520) (G-1819)
General Ptnr Wnstn Lnd & Cattl, Lufkin Also called Winston Land & Cattle Co Inc (G-14557)
General Shlters of Bvlle Texas 936 598-3389
  1639 State Highway 87 N Center (75935) (G-2998)
General Technologies Inc (PA) 281 240-0550
  13022 Trinity Dr Stafford (77477) (G-19321)
General Truck Body, Houston Also called General Body Manufacturing Co (G-9920)

General Wreless Operations Inc (HQ) 800 843-7422
  801 Ne 38th St Fort Worth (76106) (G-6664)
Generon Igs Inc 713 937-5200
  16250 Tomball Pkwy Houston (77086) (G-9928)
Generon Igs Inc (HQ) 713 937-5200
  16250 State Highway 249 Houston (77086) (G-9929)
Genes Machine Inc 361 573-7146
  235 Leeper Ln Victoria (77904) (G-20267)
Genes Paul Enterprises Inc 817 558-7868
  301 N Pendell Ave Cleburne (76033) (G-3091)
Genesis Alkali LLC (HQ) 713 860-2500
  919 Milam St Ste 2100 Houston (77002) (G-9930)
Genesis Biosystems Inc 972 315-7888
  1500 Eagle Ct Lewisville (75057) (G-14051)
Genesis Crude Oil LP (HQ) 713 860-2500
  919 Milam St Ste 2100 Houston (77002) (G-9931)
Genesis Cstm Chem Blending LLC 469 309-2790
  2708 Ne Main St Ennis (75119) (G-6104)
Genesis Entitai LLC 904 803-2457
  303 5733 Sh 121 Ste 210 The Colony (75056) (G-19811)
Genesis Granite Inc 940 692-0611
  7635 Seymour Hwy Ste B Wichita Falls (76310) (G-20767)
Genesis Millwork LLC (PA) 469 402-3940
  920 Profit Dr Garland (75040) (G-7501)
Genesis Tool Inc 915 781-1000
  111 S Concepcion St El Paso (79905) (G-5782)
Genesys Aerosystems, Mineral Wells Also called S-TEC Corporation (G-15541)
Genesys Aerosystems Group Inc (HQ) 800 872-7832
  1 S Tec Way Mineral Wells (76067) (G-15526)
Genisys Group, Dallas Also called Carreker Corporation (G-4086)
Genlyte Thomas Group LLC 512 392-5821
  1611 Clovis R Barker Rd San Marcos (78666) (G-18689)
Genmz LP 214 683-6635
  2101 Cedar Springs Rd # 1875 Dallas (75201) (G-4401)
Genomics Usa Inc (PA) 847 359-1032
  2018 Westvalley Pl Round Rock (78665) (G-17660)
Genpak LLC 903 297-4445
  1101 W Harrison Rd Longview (75604) (G-14241)
Genpak LLC 903 693-7151
  505 E Cotton St Carthage (75633) (G-2908)
Genpak Southwest LP 903 693-7151
  505 E Cotton St Carthage (75633) (G-2909)
Gensym Corporation (HQ) 512 377-9700
  401 Congress Ave Ste 2600 Austin (78701) (G-1182)
Gentherm (texas) Inc (HQ) 830 774-3512
  2121b Frontera Rd Del Rio (78840) (G-5315)
Genti Studios Inc (PA) 214 951-9696
  1825 W Mockingbird Ln Dallas (75235) (G-4402)
Genuine Letterpress Inc 214 748-8215
  40 Clear Pond Dr Frisco (75034) (G-7288)
Geo Halcon Holdings LLC 832 538-0300
  1000 La St Ste 6700 Houston (77002) (G-9932)
Geo Mesa Analysis LLC 443 637-2436
  4287 Belt Line Rd Pmb 155 Addison (75001) (G-130)
Geo Southern Energy, The Woodlands Also called American Fluorite Inc (G-19825)
Geo Space LP 713 939-7093
  7334 Gessner Rd Houston (77040) (G-9933)
Geo Space Offshore, Houston Also called Geo Space LP (G-9933)
Geocables Systems, Stafford Also called Umbilicals International Inc (G-19392)
Geodynamics Inc (HQ) 817 341-5300
  10400 W Interstate 20 Millsap (76066) (G-15502)
Geoforce Inc (PA) 972 546-3878
  5830 Gran Pkwy Ste 1200 Plano (75024) (G-16879)
Geokinetics Acquisition Co (HQ) 281 509-8000
  15150 Memorial Dr # 1009 Houston (77079) (G-9934)
Geokinetics Inc (HQ) 713 850-7600
  1500 Citywest Blvd # 800 Houston (77042) (G-9935)
Geolog Americas Inc 281 984-7078
  10402 Valley Forge Dr Houston (77042) (G-9936)
Geomechanics International Inc (HQ) 713 599-0373
  5444 Westheimer Rd Houston (77056) (G-9937)
Geometrica Inc (PA) 832 220-1200
  12300 Dundee Ct Ste 200 Cypress (77429) (G-3795)
Geometrics, Houston Also called Geometris LP (G-9938)
Geometris LP 281 856-9600
  16125 Timber Creek Place Houston (77084) (G-9938)
Geonix Operating LP (PA) 903 983-3249
  2008 N Longview St Kilgore (75662) (G-13556)
Geophyscal Explrtion Technolgy 713 979-9900
  3000 Wilcrest Dr Ste 155 Houston (77042) (G-9939)
Geophysical Technology Inc 281 222-3078
  800 Mulberry Ln Bellaire (77401) (G-1996)
Geoquest, Houston Also called Schlumberger Technology Corp (G-11774)
Georesources Inc (HQ) 832 538-0300
  1000 La St Ste 6700 Houston (77002) (G-9940)
Georg Fischer Central Plas LLC 972 641-2080
  4949 Joseph Hardin Dr Dallas (75236) (G-4403)
George A Sturdevant Inc 281 449-6466
  18914 E Industrial Pkwy New Caney (77357) (G-15840)

George Bartee Cnstr Co Inc 936 687-4811
  13363 U S Hwy 287 N Grapeland (75844) *(G-8005)*

George Bros Fabrication Co Inc 432 563-3390
  4023 S County Road 1282 Odessa (79765) *(G-16014)*

George Hall 972 266-2700
  2226 E Main St Grand Prairie (75050) *(G-7882)*

George Howard, Pflugerville Also called P T Products & Services Inc *(G-16682)*

George Myer Company Inc 713 928-2606
  2619 Lidstone St Houston (77023) *(G-9941)*

George R Brown Partnership (PA) **713 652-4901**
  1001 Fannin St Ste 4700 Houston (77002) *(G-9942)*

George W Cox & Sons Inc 210 661-8661
  5347 Dietrich Rd San Antonio (78219) *(G-18139)*

George Wood and Company Inc 713 672-7270
  773 Mccarty St Houston (77029) *(G-9943)*

Georgejean Inc 214 748-6644
  1311 Dragon St Dallas (75207) *(G-4404)*

Georgetown Shirt Co, Georgetown Also called Mooney Saenger Enterprises *(G-7665)*

Georgetown Winery LLC (PA) **512 869-8600**
  715 S Main St Georgetown (78626) *(G-7652)*

Georgetown Woodworks LLC 512 868-9048
  500 Wildflower Ln Georgetown (78626) *(G-7653)*

Georgia Pacific, Camden Also called Georgia-Pacific WD Pdts S LLC *(G-2638)*

Georgia Sandwich Company Inc 770 426-5678
  276 Pine Dr Southlake (76092) *(G-19072)*

Georgia Tre Magazine LLC (PA) **770 755-5420**
  3202 N Shiloh Rd Garland (75044) *(G-7502)*

Georgia-Pacific Bldg Pdts LLC 830 997-4341
  1650 Gypsum Mine Rd Fredericksburg (78624) *(G-7181)*

Georgia-Pacific Bldg Pdts LLC 830 557-5802
  Fm 78 Cypress Ridge Rd Mc Queeney (78123) *(G-14828)*

Georgia-Pacific LLC 940 663-6111
  5 Miles W Of Quanah On Us Quanah (79252) *(G-17217)*

Georgia-Pacific LLC 817 625-9091
  4747 Mark Iv Pkwy Fort Worth (76106) *(G-6665)*

Georgia-Pacific LLC 434 283-6202
  Plant 1610 El Paso (79998) *(G-5783)*

Georgia-Pacific LLC 936 634-3308
  1429 E Lufkin Ave Lufkin (75901) *(G-14529)*

Georgia-Pacific LLC 800 231-6060
  303 S Temple Dr Diboll (75941) *(G-5465)*

Georgia-Pacific LLC 409 584-4227
  105 Yellow Pine Hwy Pineland (75968) *(G-16739)*

Georgia-Pacific LLC 936 829-5511
  600 A St Diboll (75941) *(G-5466)*

Georgia-Pacific LLC 972 937-8804
  5800 N Intrstate Hwy 35 E Waxahachie (75165) *(G-20543)*

Georgia-Pacific LLC 866 924-1397
  6 Founders Blvd El Paso (79906) *(G-5784)*

Georgia-Pacific LLC 940 205-9558
  1725 Cooper Creek Rd Denton (76208) *(G-5368)*

Georgia-Pacific WD Pdts S LLC 936 398-2511
  20000125 E Fm 942 Sm 62 Camden (75934) *(G-2638)*

Geoservices Incorporated 281 443-3370
  3600 Briarpark Dr Houston (77042) *(G-9944)*

Geosite Inc 325 655-4356
  5956 Side View Rd San Angelo (76901) *(G-17802)*

Geosouthern Energy Corporation (PA) **281 363-9161**
  1425 Lake Front Cir # 200 The Woodlands (77380) *(G-19866)*

Geosouthern Energy Corporation 979 836-5203
  5416 Highway 290 W Brenham (77833) *(G-2255)*

Geospace Technologies Corp (PA) **713 986-4444**
  7007 Pinemont Dr Houston (77040) *(G-9945)*

Geotex Inc 817 656-9797
  6700 Davis Blvd Ste A Fort Worth (76182) *(G-6666)*

Geotherm Usa LLC 281 985-9344
  21239 Fm 529 Rd Ste F Cypress (77433) *(G-3796)*

Gep Haynesville LLC 281 363-9161
  1425 Lake Front Cir The Woodlands (77380) *(G-19867)*

Gerber Manufacturing Company, Edinburg Also called Ashley Worldwide Inc *(G-5575)*

Gerber Technology Inc 972 238-7211
  12225 Grnvlle Ave Ste 900 Dallas (75243) *(G-4405)*

Gerdau Ameristeel Corp 972 779-7010
  300 Ward Rd Midlothian (76065) *(G-15481)*

Gerdau Ameristeel Us Inc 972 775-8241
  300 Ward Rd Midlothian (76065) *(G-15482)*

Gerdau Ameristeel US Inc 972 782-7902
  2411 E Audie Murphy Pkwy Farmersville (75442) *(G-6223)*

Gerdau Ameristeel US Inc 972 775-8241
  300 Ward Rd Midlothian (76065) *(G-15483)*

Gerdau Midlothian, Midlothian Also called Gerdau Ameristeel Corp *(G-15481)*

Geronimo Alloys, Seguin Also called Tejas Alloys LLC *(G-18867)*

Gestamp Wind Energy N Amer Inc 713 263-8166
  5120 Woodway Dr Ste 9004 Houston (77056) *(G-9946)*

Get Low Transportation, Arlington Also called Nathan Faulk *(G-736)*

Get Rx'd, Houston Also called Multisports Inc *(G-10939)*

Getech, Houston Also called Geophyscal Explrtion Technolgy *(G-9939)*

Gewi North America LLC (PA) 713 446-6902
  19901 Southwest Fwy Sugar Land (77479) *(G-19486)*

Gfk Interests Ltd 713 225-0010
  25 Southbelt Indus Dr Houston (77047) *(G-9947)*

Gfl Americas, LLC, Irving Also called Gujarat Flrchmcals Amricas LLC *(G-13046)*

Gfrc 360 LLC 972 494-9000
  118 N Shiloh Rd Garland (75042) *(G-7503)*

Gfrc Cladding, Garland Also called Gfrc 360 LLC *(G-7503)*

Ggc USS Holdings LLC 800 345-6170
  24275 Katy Fwy Ste 100 Katy (77494) *(G-13362)*

Ggctr Inc 832 456-4585
  5213 Spencer Hwy Pasadena (77505) *(G-16448)*

Ggm Exploration Inc (PA) **817 338-1137**
  420 Throckmorton St # 200 Fort Worth (76102) *(G-6667)*

Ggs Wiping Products LLC 713 672-7200
  13327 Wallisville Rd Houston (77049) *(G-9948)*

Gh Cranes & Components USA Inc 972 563-8333
  14891 Hwy 205 Terrell (75160) *(G-19735)*

Gh Dairy 915 790-2609
  9747 Pan American Dr El Paso (79927) *(G-5785)*

Gh Dairy El Paso, El Paso Also called Gh Dairy *(G-5785)*

Ghashim Capital Ventures Corp 713 266-1888
  11321 Richmond Ave M10 Houston (77082) *(G-9949)*

Ghg Corp 281 461-6533
  960 Clear Lake City Blvd Webster (77598) *(G-20638)*

Ghm Corp (PA) **972 840-1200**
  12700 Hillcrest Rd Ste C Dallas (75230) *(G-4406)*

Ghx Houston, Houston Also called Ghx Industrial LLC *(G-9952)*

Ghx Industrial LLC (HQ) **713 341-3407**
  13311 Lockwood Rd Houston (77044) *(G-9950)*

Ghx Industrial LLC 713 939-7423
  6507 W Little York Rd Houston (77040) *(G-9951)*

Ghx Industrial LLC 713 222-2231
  13311 Lockwood Rd Houston (77044) *(G-9952)*

Ghx Industrial LLC 409 832-3461
  3155 W Cardinal Dr Beaumont (77705) *(G-1898)*

GI Circuits, Stafford Also called GI Electrotech Inc *(G-19323)*

GI Circuits Inc 281 495-2100
  12701 Royal Dr Stafford (77477) *(G-19322)*

GI Electrotech Inc 832 886-4997
  12701 Royal Dr Stafford (77477) *(G-19323)*

GI Legacy LLC 817 222-1414
  2521 E Loop 820 N Fort Worth (76118) *(G-6668)*

Giant Cement Company (HQ) **843 851-9898**
  396 W Greens Rd Ste 300 Houston (77067) *(G-9953)*

Giant Cement Holding Inc (HQ) **571 302-7150**
  396 W Greens Rd Ste 300 Houston (77067) *(G-9954)*

Giant Industries Inc 915 775-3300
  6500 Trowbridge Dr El Paso (79905) *(G-5786)*

Gib Lewis Properties Inc 817 834-7334
  2300 Race St Fort Worth (76111) *(G-6669)*

Gibbons Inc 940 872-2452
  1007 E Wise St Bowie (76230) *(G-2196)*

Gibraltar Global LLC 512 715-9650
  4303 W Innovation Loop Marble Falls (78654) *(G-14743)*

Gibraltar Monex Centurion Svc 800 409-2674
  5100 Westheimer Rd # 200 Houston (77056) *(G-9955)*

Gibraltar Trading Inc 281 777-6786
  6885 Harwin Dr Ste K Houston (77036) *(G-9956)*

Gicon Pumps & Equipment Ltd 806 373-0478
  1701 Se 3rd Ave Amarillo (79102) *(G-428)*

Giddings Volunteer Fire Dept 979 492-1156
  151 W Independence St Giddings (78942) *(G-7695)*

Gifford Monument Works Inc (PA) **972 544-6305**
  77 Paul Wilson Rd Wylie (75098) *(G-20936)*

Gifford Spring Co Inc 972 272-5645
  219 Gold St Garland (75042) *(G-7504)*

Gifford-Hill Concrete Products, Cedar Hill Also called Argos USA LLC *(G-2936)*

Gil Automations LLC 713 904-4600
  16840 Barker Springs Rd # 306 Houston (77084) *(G-9957)*

Gil-Mar & Associates Inc 972 926-9100
  2418 Executive Dr Garland (75041) *(G-7505)*

Giles Efton 210 662-2800
  8523 Ne Loop 410 San Antonio (78219) *(G-18140)*

Gilkes Inc 832 932-5282
  471 Columbia Mem Pkwy Kemah (77565) *(G-13475)*

Gill Assoc Prprty MGT Systems 832 644-9751
  1212 1st St E Ste C Humble (77338) *(G-12770)*

Gill Metallurgical Inc 281 593-0807
  691 County Road 2201 Cleveland (77327) *(G-3127)*

Gill Services, Houston Also called National Oilwell Varco Inc *(G-10982)*

Gillespie Coatings Oper LLC 903 753-0393
  211 Gum Springs Rd Longview (75602) *(G-14242)*

Gilmer Mirror, The, Gilmer Also called Greeneway Enterprises Inc *(G-7707)*

Gilmore-Global Instrs Co Inc 713 946-9133
  9195 Winkler Dr Ste D Houston (77017) *(G-9958)*

Gilsa North America LLC 956 223-2900
  801 E Expy 83 San Juan (78589) *(G-18674)*

Gilson/Stanley-Ameripro, Houston Also called Ameripro Partnership LP *(G-8620)*

Gincop Inc (HQ) **512 454-6874**
  8410 Tuscany Way Ste B Austin (78754) *(G-1183)*

ALPHABETIC

Ginny's Printing, Austin *Also called Gincop Inc* *(G-1183)*
Gip II Blue Holding Partnr LP................................713 496-4200
  1501 Mckinney St Houston (77010) *(G-9959)*
Gipson Group LLC..512 931-2211
  1904 S Austin Ave Georgetown (78626) *(G-7654)*
Girard Investments Inc (PA)...........................**972 423-0299**
  601 W Plano Pkwy Ste 127 Plano (75075) *(G-16880)*
Girl Talk Boutique & Spa LLC...........................956 225-7898
  807 S Jackson Rd Ste 3 Pharr (78577) *(G-16698)*
Gis Oilfield Contractors, Pearsall *Also called Grand Isle Shipyard Inc* *(G-16612)*
Gisler Brothers Logging Co...............................830 239-4651
  106 E Main St Runge (78151) *(G-17729)*
Givco Inc..830 624-8598
  22133 Old Nacogdoches Rd New Braunfels (78132) *(G-15795)*
Gjr Meyer Service Inc.....................................361 289-2130
  6733 Leopard St Corpus Christi (78409) *(G-3535)*
GK Steel Fabrication LLC.................................972 291-5514
  906 Mercury Ave Duncanville (75137) *(G-5531)*
GK Techstar LLC...361 289-6825
  5541 Bear Ln Corpus Christi (78405) *(G-3536)*
GK Techstar LLC (PA)....................................**281 884-8257**
  802 W 13th St Deer Park (77536) *(G-5276)*
GKN Aerospace Inc (HQ)................................**972 432-1900**
  6031 Connection Dr # 600 Irving (75039) *(G-13038)*
GL Automation Inc...214 503-9888
  10710 Sandhill Rd Dallas (75238) *(G-4407)*
GL Automotive LLC..925 360-3937
  13602 Applewhite Rd San Antonio (78224) *(G-18141)*
GL Brands Inc (PA)..**888 811-4367**
  3101 W 6th St Fort Worth (76147) *(G-6670)*
Gladewater Mirror, Gladewater *Also called Asp Westward LP* *(G-7718)*
Gladu Southwest, Dallas *Also called Cutting Solutions Inc* *(G-4198)*
Glasfloss Industries Inc (PA)............................**740 687-1100**
  420 E Danieldale Rd Desoto (75115) *(G-5432)*
Glass Beveling Company Inc (PA).......................713 466-5262
  5214 Brittmoore Rd Houston (77041) *(G-9960)*
Glass Chalk...830 379-1814
  5075 N State Highway 123 Seguin (78155) *(G-18838)*
Glass Magic Inc (PA)......................................**806 535-4724**
  4302 W Loop 289 Unit B Lubbock (79407) *(G-14416)*
Glass Mountain Pipeline LLC............................214 880-6000
  2626 Cole Ave Ste 900 Dallas (75204) *(G-4408)*
Glass Samuels Company LLC (PA).....................**210 227-2481**
  3011 Ne Loop 410 Ste 120 San Antonio (78218) *(G-18142)*
Glass Wholesalers Ltd (PA).............................**713 353-5800**
  13105 Nw Fwy Ste 800 Houston (77040) *(G-9961)*
Glasscraft Door Mfg Corp................................713 690-8282
  2002 Brittmoore Rd Houston (77043) *(G-9962)*
Glassview LLC (PA).......................................**646 844-4922**
  813 May St Ste 3 Fort Worth (76104) *(G-6671)*
Glaxosmithkline LLC.......................................830 481-8939
  2239 S Abbey Loop New Braunfels (78130) *(G-15796)*
Glaxosmithkline LLC.......................................210 627-0572
  12522 Wandering Trl San Antonio (78249) *(G-18143)*
Glaxosmithkline LLC.......................................469 547-1722
  2425 N Central Expy # 470 Richardson (75080) *(G-17321)*
Glazers Wholesale Distributors, Farmers Branch *Also called Southern Glazers Wine and Sp* *(G-6215)*
Gleco Plating Inc..972 475-4300
  2220 Grisham Dr Rowlett (75088) *(G-17705)*
Glen Kammerman Enterprises Inc.......................713 666-0602
  9415 W Bellfort Ave Houston (77031) *(G-9963)*
Glen Oaks Industries Inc (PA)...........................**214 631-1340**
  1201 Elm St Ste 2500 Dallas (75270) *(G-4409)*
Glen Rose Petroleum Corp (PA).........................832 437-0701
  1210 W Clay St Ste 5 Houston (77019) *(G-9964)*
Glendale Boat Works Inc.................................281 452-7146
  18300 Market St Channelview (77530) *(G-3023)*
Glenmount Global Solutions, Longview *Also called Tegron Holding LLC* *(G-14314)*
Glenn Metalcraft Texas LLC.............................817 838-9000
  2101 Franklin Dr Fort Worth (76106) *(G-6672)*
Glens Packing Company Inc...............................361 798-2601
  200 E 1st St Hallettsville (77964) *(G-8122)*
Glenwood Blind & Awning Co Inc........................903 597-2088
  3025 Spur 124 Tyler (75707) *(G-20090)*
Glex Inc..713 849-4985
  12900 Fm 529 Rd Houston (77041) *(G-9965)*
Glidepath LLC..972 641-4200
  2241 S Watson Rd Ste 151 Arlington (76010) *(G-692)*
Glo-Jo Electrical Products Inc...........................210 673-3583
  10000 W Commerce St San Antonio (78227) *(G-18144)*
Global 360 Bgs Inc..210 826-5501
  10537 Gulfdale St San Antonio (78216) *(G-18145)*
Global Alternative Fuels LLC............................915 791-8720
  3500 Doniphan Dr El Paso (79922) *(G-5787)*
Global Am-Tx, Inc...281 331-0200
  210 S Hood St Alvin (77511) *(G-364)*
Global Animal Products Inc...............................806 622-9600
  3701 Airway Blvd Amarillo (79118) *(G-489)*

Global Business & Commerce Inc........................214 449-0566
  18208 Preston Rd Dallas (75252) *(G-3843)*
Global Business Services, Houston *Also called Baker Hughes Holdings LLC* *(G-8805)*
Global Cardiac Monitors LLC............................281 788-7269
  2002 Norfolk St Apt B Houston (77098) *(G-9966)*
Global Casework Mfg Inc.................................281 494-6181
  910 Industrial Blvd Ste D Sugar Land (77478) *(G-19487)*
Global Cathodic Protection Inc..........................713 784-9588
  9300 Lawndale St Ste A Houston (77012) *(G-9967)*
Global Chemliquidations LLC............................832 539-3969
  198 Hirsch Rd Houston (77020) *(G-9968)*
Global Co Pak LLC..817 449-3115
  2600 Ne Loop 820 130 Fort Worth (76106) *(G-6673)*
Global Compressor LP....................................713 983-8773
  13415 Emmett Rd Houston (77041) *(G-9969)*
Global Crane Sales..832 364-8301
  14702 Jersey Shore Dr Houston (77047) *(G-9970)*
Global Data Solutions, Houston *Also called Oceaneering International Inc* *(G-11126)*
Global Dispense...210 310-2337
  6203 Krempen Ave 102 San Antonio (78233) *(G-18146)*
Global Drilling Support, Houston *Also called Gds Realty LLC* *(G-9911)*
Global Drilling Support, Houston *Also called Gds International LLC* *(G-9910)*
Global Empire Incorporated..............................713 503-5545
  4023 Westhollow Pkwy Houston (77082) *(G-9971)*
Global Enterprises, El Paso *Also called Polymerica Ltd* *(G-5915)*
Global Entp Worldwide LLC..............................713 260-9687
  10777 Westheimer Rd # 1100 Houston (77042) *(G-9972)*
Global Fabrication Svcs Inc..............................281 367-9333
  14460 Wagg Way Rd Houston (77041) *(G-9973)*
Global Fbrgls Sltons Texas LLC.........................425 483-1303
  13 Industrial St Sweetwater (79556) *(G-19630)*
Global Industries Inc......................................972 236-1366
  2025 W Belt Line Rd # 100 Carrollton (75006) *(G-2745)*
Global Innovation, Wylie *Also called Best Circuit Boards Inc* *(G-20927)*
Global Manufacturing LLC...............................210 598-4100
  1303 Rilling Rd San Antonio (78214) *(G-18147)*
Global Marine Inc (HQ)...................................**713 232-7500**
  4 Greenway Plz Ste 100 Houston (77046) *(G-9974)*
Global Nucleonics LLC....................................281 578-7900
  16203 Park Row Ste 110 Houston (77084) *(G-9975)*
Global Oilfield Services Inc (HQ).......................**713 977-5900**
  2150 Town Square Pl # 410 Sugar Land (77479) *(G-19488)*
Global Operations Texas LP..............................915 595-2250
  8200 W Interstate 10 # 400 San Antonio (78230) *(G-18148)*
Global Plus Trading Co LLC..............................210 807-0190
  7100 San Pedro Ave # 310 San Antonio (78216) *(G-18149)*
Global Pwr Technical Svcs Inc...........................214 574-2700
  400 Las Colinas Blvd E Irving (75039) *(G-13039)*
Global Remote Technologies LLC (HQ)...............**888 381-3222**
  21617 Rhodes Rd Spring (77388) *(G-19125)*
Global Santa Fe Drilling Co (HQ)........................**281 925-6821**
  4 Greenway Plz Ste 100 Houston (77046) *(G-9976)*
Global Santa Fe Inc.......................................281 925-6000
  4 Greenway Plz Ste 100 Houston (77046) *(G-9977)*
Global Shop Solutions Inc (PA).........................**281 681-1959**
  975 Evergreen Cir The Woodlands (77380) *(G-19868)*
Global Signs Inc...817 834-1123
  5105 E California Pkwy Forest Hill (76119) *(G-6296)*
Global Stl & Flamecutting Svcs, Houston *Also called Global Fabrication Svcs Inc* *(G-9973)*
Global Technical Solutions USA..........................832 410-4488
  6114 Windrose Hollow Ln Spring (77379) *(G-19126)*
Global Teknicians Inc.....................................407 504-9087
  2016 Main St Ste 101 Houston (77002) *(G-9978)*
Global Tubing LLC (HQ)..................................**713 265-5000**
  501 County Road 493 Dayton (77535) *(G-5227)*
Global Vacuum Systems Inc.............................800 843-0866
  15431 Highway 6 Navasota (77868) *(G-15736)*
Global Vapor Control Inc.................................713 463-9200
  12600 N Featherwood Dr # 330 Houston (77034) *(G-9979)*
Global Water Group Inc...................................214 678-9866
  8601 Sovereign Row Dallas (75247) *(G-4410)*
Global Water Home Systems, Dallas *Also called Global Water Group Inc* *(G-4410)*
Global Welding Services Inc.............................713 991-3555
  7931 Hall Rd Houston (77075) *(G-9980)*
Global Wstewater Solutions Inc.........................832 286-4600
  6766 Bourgeois Rd Houston (77066) *(G-9981)*
Globalfoundries US Inc...................................512 457-3407
  5113 Sw Pkwy Austin (78735) *(G-1184)*
Globalogix Inc...817 441-5570
  701 Bear Cat Rd Unit B Aledo (76008) *(G-199)*
Globalogix Inc (PA).......................................**713 987-7630**
  7840 N Sam Houston Pkwy W # 300 Houston (77064) *(G-9982)*
Globalpetrochem LLC.....................................832 788-3952
  10301 Northwest Fwy # 312 Houston (77092) *(G-9983)*
Globalscape Inc (HQ).....................................**210 308-8267**
  4500 Lockhill Selma Rd San Antonio (78249) *(G-18150)*
Globaltech Motor & Contrls Inc..........................281 487-9300
  525 Mccarty St Houston (77029) *(G-9984)*

Globaltech Subsea Inc 713 504-0331
1016 Indiana St South Houston (77587) *(G-19040)*
Globe Chemical LLC 432 684-4939
13316 W County Road 100 Odessa (79765) *(G-16015)*
Globe Industries Inc 281 440-3999
3303 Cypress Creek Pkwy # 250 Houston (77068) *(G-9985)*
Globe Products Company Inc 972 875-1660
1490 Jack Mckay Blvd Ennis (75119) *(G-6105)*
Globe Well Service Inc 325 884-3091
159 Santa Rita Rd Big Lake (76932) *(G-2057)*
Globeranger Corporation 972 744-9977
1130 E Arapaho Rd Ste 450 Richardson (75081) *(G-17322)*
Globex America, Dallas *Also called CPI Importers Inc (G-4179)*
Globitech Incorporated 903 957-1999
200 W Fm 1417 Sherman (75092) *(G-18916)*
Glori Energy Inc 713 237-8880
4315 South Dr Houston (77053) *(G-8383)*
Glover Inc 325 392-2561
2973 Hwy 10 E Ozona (76943) *(G-16284)*
Glover Company, Ozona *Also called Glover Inc (G-16284)*
Glover Company, The, Ozona *Also called D M Glover Incorporated (G-16279)*
Glt Fabricators Inc 713 670-9700
2902 E 13th St Ste 200 La Porte (77571) *(G-13739)*
Glt Products, Houston *Also called Great Lakes Textiles Inc (G-10027)*
Glycol Technologies LLC 281 779-4753
1502 Augusta Dr Ste 120 Houston (77057) *(G-9986)*
GM Oilfield & Trckg Svcs LLC 432 934-6525
4514 E Cnty Rd 133 Mdland Midland (79706) *(G-15237)*
GM Pipeline, Dallas *Also called Glass Mountain Pipeline LLC (G-4408)*
GM Trucking, Midland *Also called GM Oilfield & Trckg Svcs LLC (G-15237)*
Gma Garnet (usa) Corp (HQ) **832 243-9300**
1780 Hughes Landing Blvd # 725 The Woodlands (77380) *(G-19869)*
Gmco, Houston *Also called George Myer Company Inc (G-9941)*
Gme Inc 903 586-7581
515 Se Loop 456 Jacksonville (75766) *(G-13240)*
GMI Stone LLC 469 360-8847
10574 King William Dr Dallas (75220) *(G-4411)*
Gmp Energy LLC 713 963-4600
1700 Post Oak Blvd Houston (77056) *(G-9987)*
Gms Steel Manufacture LLC 817 270-0447
230 S Cardinal Rd Azle (76020) *(G-1724)*
Gmt Exploration Co Texas LLC 713 334-6001
10260 Westheimer Rd # 460 Houston (77042) *(G-9988)*
Gmu Downhole Tool Corporation 361 573-5100
1602 La Valliere St Victoria (77901) *(G-20268)*
Gmyp Manufacturing LLC 682 313-3023
4260 Spring Valley Rd Farmers Branch (75244) *(G-6197)*
GNB Industrial Power, Irving *Also called Exide Technologies LLC (G-13018)*
GNC Cable Technologies Inc 832 876-1780
18222 Alemarble Oak St Cypress (77429) *(G-3797)*
Go Industries Inc (PA) **972 783-7444**
420 N Grove Rd Richardson (75081) *(G-17323)*
Gobar Systems Inc 956 377-4836
3320 E 14th St Brownsville (78521) *(G-2360)*
Gobbato Builders LLC 737 843-4327
11601 Anderson Mill Rd Austin (78750) *(G-1185)*
Gods Word In Time Inc 713 466-6799
9777 W Gulf Bank Rd # 300 Houston (77040) *(G-9989)*
Godwin & Son Sign Co, Harlingen *Also called Son and Daughters Inc (G-8201)*
Goelzer Industries Inc 214 524-6700
201 E Trinity Blvd Grand Prairie (75050) *(G-7883)*
Goengineer Inc 713 735-3295
13105 Nw Fwy Ste 700 Houston (77040) *(G-9990)*
Gold Bond Building Pdts LLC 830 864-4100
5124 Gypsum Mine Rd Harper (78631) *(G-8209)*
Gold Star Cabinets, Austin *Also called Gold Star Marble Corporation (G-1186)*
Gold Star Construction, Houston *Also called Ortiz Inc (G-11195)*
Gold Star Marble Corporation 512 251-9279
16240 N Interstate 35 Austin (78728) *(G-1186)*
Gold Taste Foods Inc 713 378-0198
10765 Kingspoint Rd Houston (77075) *(G-9991)*
Golden Blount Inc (PA) **972 250-3113**
4301 Westgrove Dr Addison (75001) *(G-131)*
Golden Crescent Communications 361 578-4091
103 John Stockbauer Dr Victoria (77901) *(G-20269)*
Golden Crescent Construction, Victoria *Also called A Sklar Company Inc (G-20233)*
Golden Duck Inc 713 222-9262
2619 Texas St Houston (77003) *(G-9992)*
Golden Gulf Coast Directory, Austin *Also called A T D Austin (G-873)*
Golden Mattress Co, Dallas *Also called Golden Pedic Inc (G-4412)*
Golden Needle, Fort Worth *Also called Blazing Needles LP (G-6457)*
Golden Oil Company 713 626-1110
2000 Bering Dr Ste 255 Houston (77057) *(G-9993)*
Golden Oolong Tea, Houston *Also called Kmr Group LLC (G-10543)*
Golden Peanut Company LLC 254 893-2034
1401 Highway 1496 De Leon (76444) *(G-5238)*
Golden Pedic Inc 214 630-5588
1240 Titan Dr Dallas (75247) *(G-4412)*
Golden Spread, Amarillo *Also called US Concrete Inc (G-472)*
Golden Stones LP 713 934-7887
7902 Hillmont St Houston (77040) *(G-9994)*
Goldline International Inc 713 475-0631
110 N Shaver St Pasadena (77506) *(G-16449)*
Goldston Oil Corporation 713 355-3408
1819 Saint James Pl Houston (77056) *(G-9995)*
Goldtouch, Cedar Park *Also called Key Ovation LLC (G-2976)*
Golf Greens Texascom 806 559-7048
5107 150th St Lubbock (79424) *(G-14417)*
Golf Time LLC 214 366-1595
2221 Luna Rd Carrollton (75006) *(G-2746)*
Goliad Brewing Company Inc 936 441-6100
252 Metting Rd Goliad (77963) *(G-7747)*
Goliath Manufacturing Inc 713 641-6979
13942 Chrisman Rd Houston (77039) *(G-9996)*
Gomez Plant, Fort Stockton *Also called Western Gas Resources Inc (G-6332)*
Gomo, Austin *Also called Exit Plan LLC (G-1145)*
Gonco Oilfield Services LLC 432 208-2389
2817 John Ben Shpperd Pkw Odessa (79762) *(G-16016)*
Gonzales Elec Systems LLC 409 860-3802
4950 Washington Blvd Beaumont (77707) *(G-1899)*
Gonzales Inquirer, Gonzales *Also called Guadalupe Valley Publishing Co (G-7754)*
Gonzalez Mechanical Contr LLC (PA) **915 345-1282**
7201 Stiles Dr El Paso (79915) *(G-5788)*
Gonzalez Solutions For Bus, Austin *Also called R W Gonzalez Office Pdts Inc (G-1448)*
Gooch Investments Inc 325 677-5904
1250 Canterbury Dr Abilene (79602) *(G-44)*
Good Fat Co Ltd 512 300-8391
8641 Old Bee Caves Rd Austin (78735) *(G-1187)*
Good Flow Honey & Juice Co 512 472-6714
6001 Techni Center Dr # 3 Austin (78721) *(G-1188)*
Good Flow Juice Company LLC 512 472-6714
6001 Tehnictr Dr 3 Austin (78721) *(G-1189)*
Good Seed, Austin *Also called Super Seed Foods LLC (G-1547)*
Good Sportsman Marketing LLC (PA) **877 269-8490**
5250 Frye Rd Irving (75061) *(G-13040)*
Goodart Candy Inc 806 747-2600
335 E 40th St Lubbock (79404) *(G-14418)*
Goodcrane Corporation 713 434-3322
12221 Almeda Rd Houston (77045) *(G-9997)*
Goodier Cosmetics LLC 214 630-1803
5930 Campus Circle Dr W Irving (75063) *(G-13041)*
Goodman A Cndtioners Coolg Htg, Waller *Also called Goodman Manufacturing Co LP (G-20502)*
Goodman Fine Art Inc 210 733-0190
4226 Blanco Rd San Antonio (78212) *(G-18151)*
Goodman Global Holdings Inc (HQ) **713 861-2500**
19001 Kermier Rd Waller (77484) *(G-20500)*
Goodman Manufacturing Co LP 936 372-5224
19001 Kermier Rd Waller (77484) *(G-20501)*
Goodman Manufacturing Co LP 713 263-5556
2727 W 18th St Apt 250 Houston (77008) *(G-9998)*
Goodman Manufacturing Co LP (HQ) **713 861-2500**
19001 Kermier Rd Waller (77484) *(G-20502)*
Goodman Manufacturing Co LP 713 263-5416
6751 N Eldridge Pkwy Houston (77041) *(G-9999)*
Goodrich Corporation 512 754-3658
2005 Technology Way San Marcos (78666) *(G-18690)*
Goodrich Corporation 214 689-9588
9151 King Arthur Dr Dallas (75247) *(G-4413)*
Goodrich Corporation 682 730-4270
4630 N Beach St Ste 104 Haltom City (76137) *(G-8142)*
Goodrich Drillers LLC 713 659-3680
1001 Fannin St Ste 4670 Houston (77002) *(G-10000)*
Goodrich Petroleum Co La LLC 713 780-9494
801 Louisiana St Ste 700 Houston (77002) *(G-10001)*
Goodrich Petroleum Company LLC 713 780-9494
801 Louisiana St Ste 700 Houston (77002) *(G-10002)*
Goodrich Petroleum Corporation (PA) **713 780-9494**
801 Louisiana St Ste 700 Houston (77002) *(G-10003)*
Goodrich Wheel and Brake Svcs, Dallas *Also called Goodrich Corporation (G-4413)*
Goodyear Tire & Rubber Company 361 289-8251
1134 S Navigation Blvd Corpus Christi (78405) *(G-3537)*
Gooeys 832 788-9644
15407 Hickory Dale St Cypress (77429) *(G-3798)*
Gordon Martin Inc 281 424-1301
5810 Wade Rd Baytown (77521) *(G-1820)*
Gordons Specialties Inc 972 225-1660
720 W Wintergreen Rd Hutchins (75141) *(G-12866)*
Gordy Gas Corporation 979 922-1313
100 Waugh Dr Ste 400 Houston (77007) *(G-10004)*
Gordy Oil Company 713 951-0100
100 Waugh Dr Ste 400 Houston (77007) *(G-10005)*
Gore Completions, Fort Worth *Also called Gdc Technics LLC (G-6663)*
Gorman Mat Specialists, Houston *Also called Gormans Uniform Rental Inc (G-10006)*
Gorman Milling Co Inc (PA) **254 734-2252**
502 E Lubbock St Gorman (76454) *(G-7772)*

ALPHABETIC

Gorman Outdoor Inc 806 832-0159
7212 N Fm 179 Shallowater (79363) *(G-18890)*

Gormans Uniform Rental Inc 713 467-5424
9021 Katy Fwy Houston (77024) *(G-10006)*

Gourmet Cuisine Inc 972 289-7441
214 S Town East Blvd Mesquite (75149) *(G-15045)*

Gourmet Grdns Spclty Foods Inc 903 284-6215
300 E Tena St Jacksonville (75766) *(G-13241)*

Gourmet Table Skirts & Linens, Houston *Also called Glen Kammerman Enterprises Inc (G-9963)*

Gowell International LLC 713 909-2555
10642 W Little York Rd Houston (77041) *(G-10007)*

Goya Foods of Texas, Brookshire *Also called Cardet Wholesale Inc (G-2312)*

Goza Products Inc 972 494-5956
405 S Kirby St Garland (75042) *(G-7506)*

GP II Energy Inc 432 684-4748
303 Veterans Airpark Ln # 4113 Midland (79705) *(G-15238)*

GP Rubber LP 817 838-8222
2211 Moneda St Haltom City (76117) *(G-8143)*

GP Terminals LLC 713 209-7780
1606 Clinton Dr Galena Park (77547) *(G-7380)*

GP Tm Acquisition LLC (PA) 512 320-6900
816 Congress Ave Ste 1700 Austin (78701) *(G-1190)*

GP&c, Houston *Also called General Plas & Composites LP (G-9927)*

Gpd Marine Inc 512 266-1834
5975 Hiline Rd Austin (78734) *(G-1191)*

Gpeg LLC 214 574-2700
400 Las Colinas Blvd E Irving (75039) *(G-13042)*

Gps International LLC (PA) 832 319-1730
4200 Res Frest Dr Ste 110 The Woodlands (77381) *(G-19870)*

Gps-Global Pallets Svcs LLC 281 862-9244
7215 Miller Road 2 Houston (77049) *(G-10008)*

Gr Energy Services MGT LP 281 201-6812
2150 Town Square Pl # 410 Sugar Land (77479) *(G-19489)*

Grace Instrument Company 713 783-1560
10770 Moss Ridge Rd Houston (77043) *(G-10009)*

Grace IV Albert Thomas 940 500-4323
1001 Scott Ave Wichita Falls (76301) *(G-20768)*

Grace Shursen Moore Assoc Inc 806 358-6894
221 Grace Ln Amarillo (79124) *(G-429)*

Graco Fishing & Rental Tls Inc (PA) 214 618-3930
5300 Town And Cntry Blvd Frisco (75034) *(G-7289)*

Graco Fishing & Rental Tls Inc 432 943-5019
3601 S I 20 Service Rd Monahans (79756) *(G-15604)*

Graco Interests Inc (PA) 713 978-7000
5910 Schumacher Ln Houston (77057) *(G-10010)*

Graco Mechanical Inc 713 978-7000
5910 Schumacher Ln Houston (77057) *(G-10011)*

Graco Oilfield Services, Frisco *Also called Graco Fishing & Rental Tls Inc (G-7289)*

Graco Oilfield Services, Monahans *Also called Graco Fishing & Rental Tls Inc (G-15604)*

Gracon Construction Inc 972 222-8533
4343 Lasater Rd Mesquite (75181) *(G-15046)*

Gracy Cabinets 972 843-3123
10963 State Highway 205 Lavon (75166) *(G-13943)*

Grader Corpus Christi Tele, Corpus Christi *Also called Texas Publishing Co (G-3638)*

Grafikshop Corporation 713 977-2555
5906 Star Ln Houston (77057) *(G-10012)*

Graham Custom Cabinets LLC 940 549-4311
Hc 60 Box 260 Graham (76450) *(G-7782)*

Graham Embroidery Co Inc 254 772-7020
300 S Valley Mills Dr Waco (76710) *(G-20407)*

Graham Packaging Company LP 713 869-5471
3833 W 11th St Houston (77055) *(G-10013)*

Granberry Gray Wireline, Cresson *Also called Qes Wireline LLC (G-3712)*

Granchelli Construction LLC 956 928-1122
2001 Industrial Dr McAllen (78504) *(G-14867)*

Grand Coffees of Texas LLC 281 530-8321
6915 La Granada Dr Houston (77083) *(G-10014)*

Grand Energy Inc (PA) 972 788-2080
15303 Dallas Pkwy # 1010 Addison (75001) *(G-132)*

Grand Financial, Addison *Also called Grand Operating Inc (G-133)*

Grand Isle Shipyard Inc 432 362-0019
325 Solo Rd Odessa (79762) *(G-16017)*

Grand Isle Shipyard Inc 830 334-2665
3300 Bus Interstate 35 E Pearsall (78061) *(G-16612)*

Grand Operating Inc 972 788-2080
15303 Dallas Pkwy # 1010 Addison (75001) *(G-133)*

Grand Signs, Austin *Also called Voip Tel LP (G-1644)*

Grande Garbage Collectn Co LLC (PA) 956 487-4234
505 E Main St Rio Grande City (78582) *(G-17472)*

Grandor Corporation (PA) 903 872-6571
814 S Main St Corsicana (75110) *(G-3672)*

Granite Operating Company 806 323-9118
8450 E Crescent Pkwy St Canadian (79014) *(G-2651)*

Granite Publications LLC (PA) 512 352-8285
211 W 3rd St Taylor (76574) *(G-19657)*

Granite Security Products Inc 817 483-0910
99 Regency Pkwy Ste 207 Mansfield (76063) *(G-14677)*

Graniti Vicentia LLC (PA) 713 869-0800
1075 W Sam Houston Pkwy N # 214 Houston (77043) *(G-10015)*

Grant & Gerhardt Machine & Mfg 713 946-4664
3631 Deal St Houston (77025) *(G-10016)*

Grant Prideco Inc (HQ) 281 878-8000
10100 Houston Oaks Dr Houston (77064) *(G-10017)*

Grant Prideco LP 281 878-8000
400 N Sam Houston Pkwy E # 900 Houston (77060) *(G-10018)*

Grant Prideco Inc 936 825-7070
9475 Fm 1227 Rd Navasota (77868) *(G-15737)*

Grant, Thomas Jr., Midlothian *Also called Omni Contracting (G-15489)*

Granutch-Sturn Systems Corp AM (PA) 972 790-7800
201 E Shady Grove Rd Grand Prairie (75050) *(G-7884)*

Granville R Damron Trucking (PA) 806 842-3519
8602 Fm 400 Slaton (79364) *(G-18971)*

Granville R Damron Trucking 806 842-3519
8602 Hwy 400 Slaton (79364) *(G-18972)*

Grape Creek Vineyard, Fredericksburg *Also called Gcv Enterprise LLC (G-7180)*

Grape Vine, The, New Braunfels *Also called Patrick S Molak Corp (G-15818)*

Graphic Converting Ltd 972 554-8000
1210 Champion Cir Ste 100 Carrollton (75006) *(G-2747)*

Graphic Image Inc 563 285-5214
601 Silveron Ste 200 Flower Mound (75028) *(G-6267)*

Graphic Packaging Intl LLC 903 796-7101
9978 Fm 3129 Queen City (75572) *(G-17220)*

Graphic Technologies, Fort Worth *Also called C & G Printing Company Inc (G-6481)*

Graphtec Inc 713 690-9999
6209 Windfern Rd Houston (77040) *(G-10019)*

Graphtex Inc 979 968-6333
155 W Travis St La Grange (78945) *(G-13696)*

Gravity Midstream LLC 832 426-3302
1990 Post Oak Blvd # 2400 Houston (77056) *(G-10020)*

Gravity Oilfield Services Inc (PA) 432 218-7888
3300 N A St Bldg 4-100 Midland (79705) *(G-15239)*

Gravity Oilfield Services LLC 830 203-5210
1915 E Sarah Dewitt Dr Gonzales (78629) *(G-7753)*

Gravity Oilfield Services LLC 806 894-3151
1700 10th St Levelland (79336) *(G-14007)*

Gravity Oilfield Services LLC 817 558-9194
1717 Hal Ave Cleburne (76031) *(G-3092)*

Gravity Oilfield Services LLC (HQ) 432 218-7889
3300 N A St Bldg 4-100 Midland (79705) *(G-15240)*

Gravity Services Group, Boerne *Also called Robert U Neese (G-2134)*

Gray Energy Services LLC 806 894-6008
1912 West Ave Levelland (79336) *(G-14008)*

Gray Green Biomedical Svcs LLC 832 288-5958
2911 Broadway St Ste 309 Pearland (77581) *(G-16566)*

Gray Sales Inc 361 527-4460
57 E State Highway 359 Hebbronville (78361) *(G-8234)*

Gray Wireline Services 361 526-4729
711 E Empresario St Refugio (78377) *(G-17242)*

Grayden Cedarworks Inc 325 446-3366
8782 Ranch Rd 2169 Jct Junction (76849) *(G-13339)*

Grayloc Products LLC (HQ) 713 466-8853
9342 Telge Rd Houston (77095) *(G-10021)*

Grayson Armature, Orange *Also called Grayson Sulzer Inc (G-16245)*

Grayson Armature Works Inc 713 473-4404
315 Curtis Ave Pasadena (77502) *(G-16450)*

Grayson Mill Energy LLC 832 271-8050
1160 Dar Ashford Ste 140 Houston (77079) *(G-10022)*

Grayson Sulzer Inc 409 882-9112
3904 Tulane Rd Orange (77630) *(G-16245)*

Graywolf Industrial Inc (HQ) 281 441-5400
14500 Smith Rd Humble (77396) *(G-12771)*

Grazco LLC (PA) 281 252-0151
10002 Sweetwater Ln Houston (77037) *(G-10023)*

Great American Coil LLC 903 297-4700
1704 Cherokee Trce White Oak (75693) *(G-20714)*

Great American Marketing Co 713 682-6471
1224 N Post Oak Rd 160b Houston (77055) *(G-10024)*

Great American Products Ltd 830 620-4400
1661 S Seguin Ave New Braunfels (78130) *(G-15797)*

Great Basin Petroleum Svcs LP 432 561-9702
4909 S County Road 1303 Odessa (79765) *(G-16018)*

Great Dane LLC 713 675-6577
10030 Wallisville Rd Houston (77013) *(G-10025)*

Great Dane LLC 214 637-2425
4115 Port Blvd Dallas (75241) *(G-4414)*

Great Dane Trailers, Houston *Also called Great Dane LLC (G-10025)*

Great Dane Trailers, Dallas *Also called Great Dane LLC (G-4414)*

Great Host International Inc 806 296-5455
5205 N Interstate 27 Plainview (79072) *(G-16755)*

Great Host International Inc (PA) 713 977-9090
3505 Bering Dr Houston (77057) *(G-10026)*

Great Lakes Textiles Inc 713 670-9700
2902 E 13th St Ste 200 Houston (77029) *(G-10027)*

Great Rug Company (PA) 713 789-3666
3001 Fondren Rd Ste L Houston (77063) *(G-10028)*

(G-0000) Company's Geographic Section entry number

Great Southern Ready Mix LLC...281 689-9339
20333 Us Highway 59 New Caney (77357) *(G-15841)*
Great Southwest Tool Co...915 594-7804
1220 Barranca Dr Ste 1c El Paso (79935) *(G-5789)*
Great Southwest Ventures LLC...817 306-9204
4296 Western Center Blvd Fort Worth (76137) *(G-6674)*
Great Texas Compression LLC...210 569-6742
18615 Tuscany Stone # 39 San Antonio (78258) *(G-18152)*
Great White Pressure Control, Longview *Also called Qes Pressure Control LLC (G-14291)*
Greater Dallas Mfg Intl, Garland *Also called Gdmi Inc (G-7498)*
Greater Dallas Press, Garland *Also called New Century Enterprises Inc (G-7562)*
Greater Houston Office Pdts, League City *Also called Office Furn Cmpanies Texas LLC (G-13970)*
Greater Southwest Art Center...915 566-2410
3101 E Yandell Dr El Paso (79903) *(G-5790)*
Green & Hansen LLC...210 289-2482
3276 County Road 303 Jourdanton (78026) *(G-13331)*
Green Bay Packaging Inc...817 551-1934
7901 South Fwy Fort Worth (76134) *(G-6675)*
Green Bay Packaging Inc...915 822-9700
10515 Railroad Dr El Paso (79924) *(G-5791)*
Green Energy Oilfield Svcs LLC...210 904-3400
335 Industrial Dr Fairfield (75840) *(G-6175)*
Green Equipment Co Inc...817 589-2704
2563 Gravel Dr Fort Worth (76118) *(G-6676)*
Green Industries Inc...972 483-6408
1874 S Hwy 77 Italy (76651) *(G-13213)*
Green It Connection, Dallas *Also called Data Connection Inc (G-4240)*
Green Links...713 205-6629
1624 Van Buren St Houston (77006) *(G-10029)*
Green Machine & Tool Inc...713 943-0402
1007 Pennsylvania St South Houston (77587) *(G-19041)*
Green Ocean Sciences Inc...512 200-4505
3636 Dime Cir Ste A Austin (78744) *(G-1192)*
Green Plains Hereford LLC...806 258-7800
4300 County Road 6 Hereford (79045) *(G-8289)*
Green Specialty, Fort Worth *Also called Greens Specialty Services (G-6677)*
Green Stream Solutions LLC...832 404-2436
7941 Katy Fwy Ste 153 Houston (77024) *(G-10030)*
Green Vly Oil Svcs Free Zone...936 242-0603
5821 Southwest Fwy Houston (77057) *(G-10031)*
Green Wood Milling LLC...210 544-5777
3510 Barrington St San Antonio (78217) *(G-18153)*
Green-Span Profiles LP...281 807-7400
21200 Fm 362 Rd Waller (77484) *(G-20503)*
Greenamerica Biofuels LLC...865 474-4086
20 Greenway Plz Ste 310 Houston (77046) *(G-10032)*
Greenbasket Inc...212 203-3302
14679 Maroon Bells Ln Frisco (75035) *(G-7259)*
Greenberg Smoked Turkeys Inc...903 595-0725
221 Mcmurrey Dr Tyler (75702) *(G-20091)*
Greene Tweed & Co Inc...281 821-8337
1930 Rankin Rd Ste 100 Houston (77073) *(G-10033)*
Greene Tweed & Co LLC...281 765-4500
1930 Rankin Rd Houston (77073) *(G-10034)*
Greene Tweed Fluid Group, Houston *Also called Greene Tweed & Co Inc (G-10033)*
Greenes Energy Group LLC (PA)...**337 232-1830**
11757 Katy Fwy Ste 700 Houston (77079) *(G-10035)*
Greeneway Enterprises Inc...903 843-2503
214 E Marshall St Gilmer (75644) *(G-7707)*
Greenhaw Cabinets Inc...325 646-8319
2815 Stephen F Austin Dr Brownwood (76801) *(G-2430)*
Greenhead Industries Inc...936 867-4801
Hwy 69 N Wells (75976) *(G-20657)*
Greenleaf Book Group LLC...512 891-6100
4005 Banister Ln Ste B Austin (78704) *(G-1193)*
Greenleaf Enterprises, Austin *Also called Greenleaf Book Group LLC (G-1193)*
Greenpacks USA...888 498-7774
3331 Towerwood Dr Ste 304 Dallas (75234) *(G-4415)*
Greenpoint Precision Mch Inc...940 382-3933
3561 Shelby Ln Denton (76207) *(G-5369)*
Greens Specialty Services...817 924-4323
301 W Morningside Dr Fort Worth (76110) *(G-6677)*
Greensheet, Houston *Also called Helen Gordon Interests Ltd (G-10149)*
Greenslade & Company Inc...817 870-8888
2234 Wenneca Ave Fort Worth (76102) *(G-6678)*
Greensmiths Inc...972 242-5310
1419 Upfield Dr Carrollton (75006) *(G-2748)*
Greenstar North Amer Holdings...713 965-0005
3411 Richmond Ave Ste 700 Houston (77046) *(G-10036)*
Greentree Packaging and Lumber, Grapevine *Also called Fivepayne LLC (G-8035)*
Greenville Transformer Co...903 455-1610
1807 Church St Greenville (75401) *(G-8076)*
Greenway Textile Products, Houston *Also called Advanced Ocean Shipping (G-8489)*
Greenwell Energy Solutions LLC (PA)...**713 993-7772**
2000 Edwards St Unit B Houston (77007) *(G-10037)*
Greenwell Energy Solutions LLC...432 381-2595
16107 W University Blvd Odessa (79764) *(G-16019)*
Greenwood Manufacturing Inc...281 862-9001
7450 Miller Road 2 Houston (77049) *(G-10038)*
Greer Industries, LLC, Fort Worth *Also called GI Legacy LLC (G-6668)*
Greg Corkran Enterprises Inc...409 720-9199
2274 Highway 69 N Nederland (77627) *(G-15753)*
Greg-Co Piston Rings Inc...817 831-0253
4407 Ne 28th St Fort Worth (76117) *(G-6679)*
Gregg Indus Insulators Inc (HQ)...**903 757-5754**
201 Estes Dr Longview (75602) *(G-14243)*
Gregory Pile Driving, Stephenville *Also called Shinn and Gregory Inc (G-19422)*
Greif Inc...281 573-6380
233 Delta Pkwy Baytown (77523) *(G-1788)*
Greif Inc...281 470-4469
10700 Strang Rd La Porte (77571) *(G-13740)*
Greif Inc...817 834-6333
3800 N Beach St Haltom City (76137) *(G-8144)*
Greif Inc...281 470-4400
10850 Strang Rd La Porte (77571) *(G-13741)*
Greif Inc...346 263-2639
616b Logistics Dr Baytown (77523) *(G-1789)*
Greif Inc...817 222-0413
3800 N Beach St Haltom City (76137) *(G-8145)*
Greif Inc...713 462-0073
9280 Baythorne Dr Houston (77041) *(G-10039)*
Greif Flexible Products & Svcs, Houston *Also called Greif Flexibles USA Inc (G-10040)*
Greif Flexibles USA Inc...713 461-0840
7111 Perimeter Park Dr # 300 Houston (77041) *(G-10040)*
Greiner Aerospace Inc...817 686-3100
7621 Pebble Dr Fort Worth (76118) *(G-6680)*
Gren Industries Inc...972 881-2606
740 Ave F Ste 300 Plano (75074) *(G-16881)*
Grenadier Energy Partners LLC...281 907-4120
24 Waterway Ave Ste 875 Spring (77380) *(G-19213)*
Grenadier Enrgy Prtners II LLC...281 907-4120
24 Waterway Ave Ste 875 The Woodlands (77380) *(G-19871)*
Grenier Service Company Llc...512 335-7441
1408 N Bell Blvd Cedar Park (78613) *(G-2972)*
Gresham Enterprise Storage Inc...512 250-0916
10205 Brimfield Dr Austin (78726) *(G-1194)*
Greshare Enterprises Inc...512 869-7446
4185 E University Ave A Georgetown (78626) *(G-7655)*
Gretna Machine Shop Inc...713 690-7328
3450 Lang Rd Houston (77092) *(G-10041)*
Greyheller LLC...925 415-5050
8111 Lyndon B Johnson Fwy Dallas (75251) *(G-4416)*
Grierson Springs Midstream LLC...713 655-9500
1331 Lamar St Ste 1675 Houston (77010) *(G-10042)*
Griffin Barge Line LLC...713 560-6874
4265 San Felipe St Houston (77027) *(G-10043)*
Griffin Dewatering, Houston *Also called Griffin Pump & Equipment Inc (G-10045)*
Griffin Dewatering LLC (HQ)...**713 676-8000**
5306 Clinton Dr Houston (77020) *(G-10044)*
Griffin Logging Co, Nacogdoches *Also called Rhonda Griffin (G-15712)*
Griffin Products Inc...903 873-6388
303 Bluebird Pkwy Wills Point (75169) *(G-20875)*
Griffin Pump & Equipment Inc (HQ)...**866 770-8100**
5306 Clinton Dr Houston (77020) *(G-10045)*
Griffith Land Services Inc...713 465-3273
11060 Timberline Rd Houston (77043) *(G-10046)*
Griffith Oil Field Services...409 246-8530
3747 Fm 1293 Rd Kountze (77625) *(G-13671)*
Griffith Polymers Inc...503 612-0999
432 W Fork Dr Ste A Arlington (76012) *(G-693)*
Griffiths Corporation...817 488-6547
650 Industrial Blvd Grapevine (76051) *(G-8041)*
Grimes Industrial Inc...713 921-0000
929 E Main St Tomball (77375) *(G-19980)*
Grissom & Friends, Fort Worth *Also called Grissoms Fine Jewelry (G-6681)*
Grissoms Fine Jewelry...817 244-9754
9524 Camp Bowie West Blvd B Fort Worth (76116) *(G-6681)*
Grizzly Energy LLC (PA)...**832 327-2255**
5847 San Felipe St # 3000 Houston (77057) *(G-10047)*
Grizzly Operating LLC...903 876-2227
1133 Fm 315 S Poynor (75782) *(G-17201)*
Groco Paint Mfg Co Inc...972 286-7890
10818 C F Hawn Fwy Dallas (75217) *(G-4417)*
Grogan-Hazel Steel Inc...713 466-7501
10547 Fisher Rd Houston (77041) *(G-10048)*
Groggy Dog Sprtswear Grphic Ds (PA)...**940 891-4022**
4017 Mesa Dr Denton (76207) *(G-5370)*
Gron Fuels LLC...813 220-3331
109 N Post Oak Ln Ste 440 Houston (77024) *(G-10049)*
Grooms & Grooms Inc...806 358-8119
4410 Canyon Dr Amarillo (79109) *(G-490)*
Groth Corporation...913 952-8114
13650 N Promenade Blvd Stafford (77477) *(G-19324)*
Grothe Industrial Coating LLC...281 354-1574
20115 Fm 2100 Rd Crosby (77532) *(G-3732)*
Groundzeroprecision Com, Trenton *Also called PLbennett Entp & Inv Fund A (G-20018)*

Groves Pallet Company, Port Neches *Also called Dunn Pallet Co* *(G-17159)*

Growth Holdings LLC 972 241-9535
2861 Merrell Rd Dallas (75229) *(G-4418)*

Grt, Spring *Also called Global Remote Technologies LLC* *(G-19125)*

Gruma Corporation 972 232-5000
5601 Executive Dr Irving (75038) *(G-13043)*

Gruma Corporation (HQ)..**972 232-5000**
5601 Executive Dr Ste 800 Irving (75038) *(G-13044)*

Gruma Corporation 972 709-1217
4000 Dan Morton Dr # 100 Dallas (75236) *(G-4419)*

Gruma Corporation 956 380-4090
501 W Chapin St Edinburg (78541) *(G-5589)*

Gruma Corporation 210 304-6700
4340 Dividend San Antonio (78219) *(G-18154)*

Gruma Corporation 832 441-5982
12600 Wallisville Rd Houston (77013) *(G-10050)*

Grundfos CBS Inc (HQ)...**281 994-2700**
902 Koomey Rd Brookshire (77423) *(G-2316)*

Grunwald Printing Company 361 882-5654
1418 Morgan Ave Corpus Christi (78404) *(G-3538)*

Gryphon Oilfield Solutions LLC (PA).............................**281 738-3110**
11300 Windfern Rd Houston (77064) *(G-10051)*

Gryphon Production Co LLC 806 688-9697
216 S Price Rd Pampa (79065) *(G-16324)*

Gs Liquid Technologies LLC 817 556-6262
601 W Industrial Blvd A Cleburne (76033) *(G-3093)*

Gs-Hydro US Inc 281 209-1000
16405 A Ctr Blvd Ste 400 Houston (77032) *(G-10052)*

Gsa, Grapevine *Also called Game Day Sports Apparel LLC* *(G-8037)*

GSC Chipotle Texas Ltd 915 769-0097
101 Port Of Entry Rd Fort Hancock (79839) *(G-6321)*

GSC Enterprises Inc 903 885-1283
1301 Main St Sulphur Springs (75482) *(G-19589)*

GSE Environmental, Houston *Also called GSE Holding Inc* *(G-10054)*

GSE Environmental Inc (HQ)......................................**281 443-8564**
19103 Gundle Rd Houston (77073) *(G-10053)*

GSE Holding Inc (HQ)..**281 443-8564**
19103 Gundle Rd Houston (77073) *(G-10054)*

GSE International Inc (HQ).......................................**281 443-8564**
19103 Gundle Rd Houston (77073) *(G-10055)*

Gsi Highway Products, Hutchins *Also called Gordons Specialties Inc* *(G-12866)*

GSM - Walker Products, Fort Worth *Also called Hearing Lab Technology LLC* *(G-6693)*

GSM Enterprises Inc (PA)..**806 358-6894**
221 Grace Ln Amarillo (79124) *(G-430)*

GSM Outdoors, Irving *Also called Good Sportsman Marketing LLC* *(G-13040)*

Gst Manufacturing Ltd 817 335-1401
4201 Janada St Haltom City (76117) *(G-8146)*

Gst Manufacturing Ltd (PA)......................................**817 520-2320**
4201 Janada St Haltom City (76117) *(G-8147)*

GSW Manufacturing Inc 956 223-2644
500 Capote Central Ave # 400 Pharr (78577) *(G-16699)*

Gt Oilfield Repair Inc 361 782-7300
802 W Main St Edna (77957) *(G-5606)*

Gt Products Inc 817 481-7113
501 Industrial Blvd Grapevine (76051) *(G-8042)*

Gt Silicones Inc 610 252-5800
13700 Diplomat Dr Farmers Branch (75234) *(G-6198)*

GTC Technology LLC 817 685-9125
8505 Freport Pkwy Ste 210 Irving (75063) *(G-13045)*

Gtcr Golder Rauner LLC 972 670-7975
3414 Midcourt Rd Ste 100 Carrollton (75006) *(G-2749)*

GTE Directories Distribution, Dallas *Also called Supermedia Services Inc* *(G-5027)*

Gtech Precision Inds USA Ltd 817 539-8014
900 N Walnut Creek Dr # 1001 Mansfield (76063) *(G-14678)*

Gti, Stafford *Also called General Technologies Inc* *(G-19321)*

Gtl Supply Solutions LLC 214 644-2402
101 N Greenville Ave C Allen (75002) *(G-271)*

GTM Manufacturing LLC 806 373-9473
2100 Spruce St Amarillo (79103) *(G-431)*

Gtx Technologies LLC 806 367-7074
13636 S Fm 1541 Amarillo (79118) *(G-491)*

Gtz Services LLC 956 750-6147
202 Carla St Zapata (78076) *(G-20982)*

Guadalupe Brewing Company LLC 512 878-9214
1586 Wald Rd New Braunfels (78132) *(G-15798)*

Guadalupe Valley Publishing Co 830 672-2861
622 Saint Paul St Gonzales (78629) *(G-7754)*

Guadalupe Valley Ventures LP 830 885-4411
36101 Fm 3159 New Braunfels (78132) *(G-15799)*

Guar Resources LLC 806 637-4662
807 N 5th St Brownfield (79316) *(G-2331)*

Guard-All Bldg Sltions Mfg LLC 877 397-1594
1011 Regal Row Dallas (75247) *(G-4420)*

Guard-Line Inc 903 796-4111
1001 Progress Dr Atlanta (75551) *(G-843)*

Guard-Line Inc 903 796-4111
1001 Progress Dr Atlanta (75551) *(G-844)*

Guardian Compliance 713 641-2020
5110 Railroad St Deer Park (77536) *(G-5277)*

Guardian Industries LLC...903 872-4871
3801 S Hwy 287 Corsicana (75109) *(G-3673)*

Guardian Insptn Tbular MGT LLC..................................403 233-7561
2712 E Interstate 20 Midland (79706) *(G-15241)*

Guardian Packaging Inds LP......................................214 349-1500
3615 Security St Garland (75042) *(G-7507)*

Guardian Southwest String Tag..................................972 938-0123
300 N Rogers St Waxahachie (75165) *(G-20544)*

Guardian Tag & Label, Waxahachie *Also called Guardian Southwest String Tag* *(G-20544)*

Guardian Wellhead Protection....................................432 368-5449
6907 E Commerce St Odessa (79762) *(G-16020)*

Guardiar USA LLC (HQ)...**972 878-7000**
3309 Sw Interstate 45 Ennis (75119) *(G-6106)*

Gudgel & Sons Inc...903 989-2232
300 S Us Highway 69 Trenton (75490) *(G-20016)*

Guenther Family LP..210 829-1800
153 Treeline Park Ste 300 San Antonio (78209) *(G-18155)*

Guerra's Grocery & Meat Market, Edinburg *Also called Chorizo De San Manuel Guer* *(G-5582)*

Guerro Ready Mix..281 342-4022
770 Walsh Rd Rosenberg (77471) *(G-17583)*

Guess Inc...915 877-1948
7051 S Desert Blvd A177 Canutillo (79835) *(G-2664)*

Guess Factory, Canutillo *Also called Guess Inc* *(G-2664)*

Guest Solutions, Dallas *Also called Sports Solutions Inc* *(G-4999)*

Guidant Sales LLC...713 218-4069
8934 Kirby Dr Houston (77054) *(G-10056)*

Guidant/C P I, Houston *Also called Guidant Sales LLC* *(G-10056)*

Guiverman Industries LLC (PA)...................................**866 235-8057**
5851 Legacy Cir Ste 600 Plano (75024) *(G-16882)*

Gujarat Flrchmcals Amricas LLC..................................512 446-7700
1212 Corporate Dr Ste 540 Irving (75038) *(G-13046)*

Gulf, Houston *Also called A-1 Fuel Stop Inc* *(G-8431)*

Gulf Business Forms Inc...512 353-8313
2460 S Ih 35 San Marcos (78666) *(G-18691)*

Gulf Business Forms Systems.....................................210 265-1620
434 W Nakoma St San Antonio (78216) *(G-18156)*

Gulf Caost Stabilized Mtls, Houston *Also called Campbell Concrete & Mtls LP* *(G-9082)*

Gulf Cast Drywall Pnt Svcs Cnt, Houston *Also called Houston R-Co Incorporated* *(G-10248)*

Gulf Coast Alloy Welding Inc....................................281 821-0543
4403 Theiss Rd Humble (77338) *(G-12772)*

Gulf Coast Automotive, Port Arthur *Also called Gulf Coast Powdr Gelworks Inc* *(G-17110)*

Gulf Coast Bag Inc (PA)...**281 556-8500**
4422 W 12th St Houston (77055) *(G-10057)*

Gulf Coast Bag & Bagging Co, Houston *Also called Gulf Coast Bag Inc* *(G-10057)*

Gulf Coast Bearing & Seal Inc...................................832 399-4227
8730 Meldrum Ln Houston (77075) *(G-10058)*

Gulf Coast Cabinet Doors LLC....................................979 265-1519
220 Highway 332 Clute (77531) *(G-3155)*

Gulf Coast Casing Inc...361 575-5488
833 Lower Mission Vly Rd Victoria (77905) *(G-20270)*

Gulf Coast Con & Shell Inc......................................281 238-8883
4401 County Road 58 Manvel (77578) *(G-14734)*

Gulf Coast Control Valves, Pasadena *Also called Gvcc Inc* *(G-16451)*

Gulf Coast Downhole Tech LLC....................................713 667-4238
1610 Greens Rd Ste 300 Houston (77032) *(G-10059)*

Gulf Coast Envmtl Systems LLC...................................832 476-9024
1689 Hawthorne Dr Conroe (77301) *(G-3299)*

Gulf Coast Fabricators Inc (PA).................................**409 727-2372**
6711 N Twin City Hwy Port Arthur (77642) *(G-17109)*

Gulf Coast Fabricators Inc......................................409 866-6721
9695 Walden Rd Beaumont (77707) *(G-1900)*

Gulf Coast Ignition & Controls, Houston *Also called Longview Distribution I LLC* *(G-10686)*

Gulf Coast II Lithotripsy LP....................................866 598-2734
9825 Spectrum Dr Bldg 3 Austin (78717) *(G-1693)*

Gulf Coast Limestone Inc (PA)...................................**281 474-4124**
1402 3rd St Seabrook (77586) *(G-18785)*

Gulf Coast Machine Shop, Corpus Christi *Also called Gulf Coast Repair & Mch Sp Inc* *(G-3539)*

Gulf Coast Modification LP......................................713 896-3000
22806 Nw Lake Dr Houston (77095) *(G-10060)*

Gulf Coast Oil & Gas Inds LLC...................................713 236-1158
1204 Hays St Houston (77009) *(G-10061)*

Gulf Coast Powdr Gelworks Inc...................................409 962-1211
4141 32nd St Port Arthur (77642) *(G-17110)*

Gulf Coast Repair & Mch Sp Inc..................................361 289-1273
6802 Leopard St Corpus Christi (78409) *(G-3539)*

Gulf Coast Sign Inc...956 399-0755
951 Falcon Blvd San Benito (78586) *(G-18658)*

Gulf Coast Spring Co Inc..713 461-5092
9125 Spring Branch Dr Houston (77080) *(G-10062)*

Gulf Coast Stabilized Mtls, Richmond *Also called Campbell Concrete & Mtls LP* *(G-17451)*

Gulf Coast Steel Inc..281 768-8392
403 S Loop W Houston (77054) *(G-10063)*

Gulf Coast Tool & Rental, Pasadena *Also called Ggctr Inc* *(G-16448)*

Gulf Coast Tribune, West Columbia *Also called Brazoria County News* *(G-20675)*

Gulf Coast Welding, Houston *Also called Weldfit Corporation* *(G-12628)*

Gulf Coast Welding LLC 713 460-3700
  4133 Southerland Rd Houston (77092) *(G-10064)*

Gulf Coast Well Analysis, Pearland *Also called Coastal Wireline Services Inc* *(G-16546)*

Gulf Coast Western LLC (PA) **972 284-0600**
  14160 Dallas Pkwy Dallas (75254) *(G-4421)*

Gulf Copper & Mfg Corp (PA) **409 989-0300**
  5700 Procter Ext Port Arthur (77642) *(G-17111)*

Gulf Copper & Mfg Corp 409 982-6122
  2020 Gulfway Dr Port Arthur (77640) *(G-17112)*

Gulf Copper & Mfg Corp 409 941-6200
  2920 Todd Rd Galveston (77554) *(G-7399)*

Gulf Copper Drydock & Rig Repr, Galveston *Also called Gulf Copper & Mfg Corp* *(G-7399)*

Gulf Copper Ship Repair Inc 361 883-1040
  4385 Joe Fulton Intl Tc Corpus Christi (78402) *(G-3540)*

Gulf Island Fabrication Inc (PA) **713 714-6100**
  16225 Park Ten Pl Ste 300 Houston (77084) *(G-10065)*

Gulf Manufacturing Inc (PA) **281 446-0093**
  1221 Indiana St Humble (77396) *(G-12773)*

Gulf Pacific Ingredients LLC, Houston *Also called Southwest Spice Company LLC* *(G-11984)*

Gulf Pacific Rice Co Inc 713 464-0606
  12010 Taylor Rd Houston (77041) *(G-10066)*

Gulf Plains Plant, Bishop *Also called Dcp Midstream LLC* *(G-2106)*

Gulf Publishing Company (PA) **713 529-4301**
  2 Greenway Plz Ste 1020 Houston (77046) *(G-10067)*

Gulf Publishing Company 713 529-4301
  3 Greenwood St 1020 Houston (77011) *(G-10068)*

Gulf Reduction Corporation 713 926-1705
  6020 Esperson St Houston (77011) *(G-10069)*

Gulf Rice Milling Inc 713 464-0606
  12010 Taylor Rd Houston (77041) *(G-10070)*

Gulf Runner Yatchs, Alvin *Also called J W Hall Ltd Liability Co* *(G-369)*

Gulf Special Services Inc 956 541-1445
  7770 Padre Island Hwy Brownsville (78521) *(G-2361)*

Gulf States Abrasive Mfg 713 869-4841
  23438 Dunn Ln Porter (77365) *(G-17177)*

Gulf States Abrasives, Porter *Also called Dunn Enterprises Inc* *(G-17174)*

Gulf States Asphalt Company LP (PA) **713 941-4410**
  300 Christi Pl South Houston (77587) *(G-19042)*

Gulf States Label Company LLC 713 812-8390
  4537 Brittmoore Rd Houston (77041) *(G-10071)*

Gulf States Materials Inc 281 470-8645
  555 Sens Rd La Porte (77571) *(G-13742)*

Gulf States Tube LLC 281 375-5113
  34066 Sunset Ln Brookshire (77423) *(G-2317)*

Gulfco Forge Company LLC 409 842-1311
  12500 Amelia Dr Houston (77045) *(G-10072)*

Gulfex Holdings 713 946-6614
  401 State St South Houston (77587) *(G-19043)*

Gulfstream Aerospace Corp 912 965-3000
  8555 Lemmon Ave Dallas (75209) *(G-4422)*

Gulfstream Aerospace Corp 972 899-1625
  812 Kilbridge Ln Coppell (75019) *(G-3418)*

Gulfstream Aerospace Corp 214 902-7520
  7350 Cedar Springs Rd Dallas (75235) *(G-4423)*

Gulfstream Aerospace Corp GA 214 350-4177
  7440 Aviation Pl Dallas (75235) *(G-4424)*

Gulfstream Holdings Inc 713 696-9996
  331 Garden Oaks Blvd Houston (77018) *(G-10073)*

Gull Industries Inc (PA) **713 224-2430**
  3233 Gano St Houston (77009) *(G-10074)*

Gunckel Archtectural Millworks 830 303-0688
  404 W Kingsbury St Seguin (78155) *(G-18839)*

Gund Company Inc 972 389-0615
  3010 S Pipeline Rd Euless (76040) *(G-6147)*

Gunderson Rail Services LLC 817 556-9191
  101 Park St Cleburne (76031) *(G-3094)*

Gunn Oil Company 940 723-5585
  811 6th St Ste 100 Wichita Falls (76301) *(G-20769)*

Gunness Udv, Addison *Also called Diageo North America Inc* *(G-117)*

Gunns Restoration 281 645-2260
  2423 Greens Rd Houston (77032) *(G-10075)*

Gunook Products Inc 817 536-0136
  2401 Ludelle St Fort Worth (76105) *(G-6682)*

Gunter Lumber & Mill, Gunter *Also called Gunter Lumber Company Inc* *(G-8115)*

Gunter Lumber Company Inc 903 433-1303
  520 N Preston Rd Gunter (75058) *(G-8115)*

Gunvision Systems LLC 512 858-4045
  14101 W Hwy 290 Ste 2000a Austin (78737) *(G-862)*

Gurecky Manufacturing Svc Inc 281 342-5926
  2420 3rd St Rosenberg (77471) *(G-17584)*

Guru Garments 832 674-0990
  2411 Karbach St Ste 4 Houston (77092) *(G-10076)*

Gus Specialty Advertising, Denison *Also called Neon Signs and Designs Inc* *(G-5343)*

Gustavs Tool & Die Inc 830 379-3551
  1503 N Austin St Seguin (78155) *(G-18840)*

Gutor North America, Houston *Also called Schneider Electric It USA Inc* *(G-11782)*

Guzman Mfg Inc 972 475-3003
  4206 Industrial St Rowlett (75088) *(G-17706)*

Gvcc Inc 281 416-4772
  3923 Mickey Gilley Blvd B Pasadena (77505) *(G-16451)*

Gvi Security Solutions Inc 972 236-6235
  2801 Trade Ctr Ste 120 Carrollton (75007) *(G-2867)*

Gvs, Navasota *Also called Global Vacuum Systems Inc* *(G-15736)*

Gw Marine (usa) LLC 281 809-6213
  430 Highway 6 S Ste 212 Houston (77079) *(G-10077)*

Gw Plastics San Antonio Inc 210 225-1516
  901 Paulsun St San Antonio (78219) *(G-18157)*

Gwm Products LLC 855 872-2013
  8925 Sterling St Ste 100 Irving (75063) *(G-13047)*

Gwm Products LLC 855 872-2013
  825 Watters Creek Blvd # 250 Allen (75013) *(G-272)*

Gyrodata Incorporated 432 561-8458
  10504 W County Road 72 Midland (79707) *(G-15242)*

Gyrodata Incorporated (PA) **713 461-3146**
  23000 Nw Lake Dr Houston (77095) *(G-10078)*

Gyrodata Incorporated 361 289-1031
  1805 N Lexington Blvd Corpus Christi (78409) *(G-3541)*

Gz Manufacturing, Rowlett *Also called Guzman Mfg Inc* *(G-17706)*

H & B Copies Inc 979 694-2679
  2307 Texas Ave S Ste B College Station (77840) *(G-3185)*

H & B Packing Co Inc 254 752-2506
  702 Forrest St Waco (76704) *(G-20408)*

H & H Dinero Tree Inc 915 591-6245
  9431 Carnegie Ave El Paso (79925) *(G-5792)*

H & H Landscape Services LLC 832 831-9133
  35514 Old Highway 290 Hockley (77447) *(G-8346)*

H & H Machine Service LLC 979 836-2599
  1503 Industrial Blvd Brenham (77833) *(G-2256)*

H & H Mailing Services, El Paso *Also called H & H Dinero Tree Inc* *(G-5792)*

H & H Sign Co Inc (PA) **254 752-1801**
  2611 S Univ Parks Dr Waco (76706) *(G-20409)*

H & H T-Shirt Printing Inc 254 628-1453
  5696 Fm 439 Belton (76513) *(G-2023)*

H & H Water Well Service Inc 806 659-5577
  Gruver Hwy W Spearman (79081) *(G-19086)*

H & K International Inc (HQ) **214 818-3500**
  2200 Skyline Dr Mesquite (75149) *(G-15047)*

H & K Vacuum Trucks, Sinton *Also called Dugga Boys Inc* *(G-18962)*

H & K Well Service LLC 361 394-7165
  2762 Cr 409 Freer (78357) *(G-7226)*

H & L Fabrication Inc 512 894-0918
  2025 Harmon Hills Rd Dripping Springs (78620) *(G-5506)*

H & M Baking LLC 713 568-5674
  9330 W Arprt Blvd Ste 100 Houston (77031) *(G-10079)*

H & M Dirt Contractors Inc 806 495-3293
  805 E Main St Post (79356) *(G-17190)*

H & M Plating Company Inc 713 643-6516
  6804 La Paseo St Houston (77087) *(G-10080)*

H & P Drilling, Seguin *Also called Helmerich & Payne Intl Drlg Co* *(G-18842)*

H & R Black Mfg Co LLC 806 364-2040
  210 Ross Ave Hereford (79045) *(G-8290)*

H & R Mfg and Supply Inc 936 856-5529
  12400 Rose Rd Willis (77378) *(G-20847)*

H & S Enterprises 281 955-1652
  10523 Mills Cove St Houston (77070) *(G-10081)*

H & S Fabricators Inc 361 884-1212
  1133 E Port Ave Corpus Christi (78401) *(G-3542)*

H & S Metals Inc 281 421-9488
  820 Sharon Ln Baytown (77521) *(G-1821)*

H & S Valve (PA) **432 362-0486**
  6704 N County Rd W Odessa (79764) *(G-16021)*

H & T Auger Company (PA) **432 362-4471**
  4519 Brazos Ave Odessa (79764) *(G-16022)*

H & W Manufacturing Co Ltd 281 353-9079
  2731 Spring Stuebner Rd H Spring (77389) *(G-19127)*

H and H Bindery Services Inc 713 641-1831
  6504 Mcgrew St Houston (77087) *(G-10082)*

H and L Crimp Inc 325 672-9282
  8001 Us Highway 277 Abilene (79601) *(G-45)*

H B A, Austin *Also called Hubbell Building Automtn Inc* *(G-1212)*

H C Howell Company 432 368-0835
  901 W 59th St Odessa (79764) *(G-16023)*

H C L, Odessa *Also called H C Howell Company* *(G-16023)*

H C T, Houston *Also called Health Care Temporaries Inc* *(G-10143)*

H D H Instruments Corp 281 375-6835
  3166 Hwy 359 N Pattison (77466) *(G-16532)*

H D Industries Inc 903 586-6126
  Highway 79 S Jacksonville (75766) *(G-13242)*

H E & D Operating Inc 713 650-8008
  1415 La St Ste 2150 Houston (77002) *(G-10083)*

H E B & Associates Inc 972 234-0347
  1215 Commerce Dr Richardson (75081) *(G-17324)*

H E B Printing, Richardson *Also called H E B & Associates Inc* *(G-17324)*

H E Butt Grocery Company 956 702-2289
  1211 W Frontage Rd Alamo (78516) *(G-179)*

H G Nichols Construction Co 903 876-2527
  16760 Hwy 175 E Poynor (75782) *(G-17202)*

H G P Industries, Houston *Also called Oldcastle Buildingenvelope Inc* ***(G-11169)***

H J G Trucking Inc (PA) **817 834-7181**
701 Denair St Fort Worth (76111) ***(G-6683)***

H J Gruy and Associates Inc (PA) **713 739-1000**
6575 West Loop S Ste 550 Bellaire (77401) ***(G-1997)***

H K Specialties Co Inc 713 466-1567
4711 Steffani Ln Houston (77041) ***(G-10084)***

H L Brown Jr 432 683-5216
300 W La Ave Ste 100 Midland (79701) ***(G-15243)***

H L Hailey Enterprises Inc 903 759-1881
3020 W Loop 281 Longview (75604) ***(G-14244)***

H Lorimer Corporation 903 643-3239
2401 Highway 322 Longview (75603) ***(G-14245)***

H M S, Houston *Also called Houston Mfg Specialty Co Inc* ***(G-10239)***

H M W Fabrications Inc 940 325-0300
539 Taylor Rd Mineral Wells (76067) ***(G-15527)***

H P Creations 817 749-4367
2525 E Southlake Blvd Southlake (76092) ***(G-19073)***

H Power I LLC 214 978-8943
1900 N Akard St Dallas (75201) ***(G-4425)***

H R Stasney & Sons Ltd 325 762-3311
441 S 2nd St Albany (76430) ***(G-189)***

H Rosen Usa LLC 281 442-8282
14120 Interdrive E Houston (77032) ***(G-10085)***

H S I, Houston *Also called Houston Service Industries Inc* ***(G-10250)***

H T A Aerostructures Inc 512 754-3600
2005 Technology Way San Marcos (78666) ***(G-18692)***

H W D Casings Inc 210 661-6161
5010 Interstate 10 E San Antonio (78219) ***(G-18158)***

H&A Machine & Welding LLC 832 857-8505
11666 Gulf Pointe Dr Houston (77089) ***(G-10086)***

H&S Manufacturing Co, Rowlett *Also called Pivot Corporation* ***(G-17710)***

H-E-B Food Store 421, Alamo *Also called H E Butt Grocery Company* ***(G-179)***

H2eco Bulk LLC 713 812-8400
16310 Aldine Westfield Rd Houston (77032) ***(G-10087)***

H2o Greenworks LLC 817 884-7788
405 Lemon Dr Arlington (76018) ***(G-694)***

H3 Media LLC 903 581-4237
3650 Old Bullard Rd # 110 Tyler (75701) ***(G-20092)***

H6 Aircraft LLC 830 741-3836
732 County Road 312 D Hanis (78850) ***(G-3829)***

Haas Group International LLC 512 519-3989
10801 N Mopac Expy 3-150 Austin (78759) ***(G-1195)***

Haastech Inc 214 688-0280
2711 Irving Blvd Dallas (75207) ***(G-4426)***

Habitek International Inc 512 347-8800
8121 Fm 2244 Rd Ste 100 Austin (78746) ***(G-1196)***

Hacienda Rec Recording Studio 361 882-7066
1236 S Staples St Corpus Christi (78404) ***(G-3543)***

Hacker Brothers Well Service 940 759-4196
Hwy 373 Muenster (76252) ***(G-15669)***

Hacker International LLC 903 657-3546
1601 N Frisco St Henderson (75652) ***(G-8264)***

Hadlock & Fox Mfg Co L L C 830 778-6017
594 Industrial Blvd Del Rio (78840) ***(G-5316)***

Hagans Plastics Co Inc 972 790-9001
121 W Rock Island Rd Grand Prairie (75050) ***(G-7885)***

Hager Containers L P 972 417-7660
1015 Hayden Dr Carrollton (75006) ***(G-2750)***

Hager Machine and Tool Inc 281 872-6393
1303 Hugh Rd Houston (77067) ***(G-10088)***

Haggar Clothing Co, Dallas *Also called Haggar Womens Wear Ltd* ***(G-4427)***

Haggar Clothing Co (HQ) **214 352-8481**
1507 Lyndon B Johnson Fwy # 100 Farmers Branch (75234) ***(G-6199)***

Haggar Clothing Co 214 352-8481
5885 Gulf Fwy Ste 715 Texas City (77591) ***(G-19794)***

Haggar Clothing Company, Farmers Branch *Also called Haggar Corp* ***(G-6200)***

Haggar Corp (HQ) **214 352-8481**
1507 Lyndon B Johnson Fwy # 100 Farmers Branch (75234) ***(G-6200)***

Haggar Womens Wear Ltd 214 637-5300
1507 Lyndon B Johnson Fwy Dallas (75234) ***(G-4427)***

Hahn & Clay Ltd 713 672-1671
5100 Clinton Dr Houston (77020) ***(G-10089)***

Hajost Pecan Farm, Clint *Also called Ramirez Pecan Farm LLC* ***(G-3147)***

Halbert Mill Company Texas Inc (PA) **903 683-2788**
3939 Fm 347 N Jacksonville (75766) ***(G-13243)***

Halco Lighting Tech LLC 713 644-6073
6323 Brookhill Dr Houston (77087) ***(G-10090)***

Halcon Gulf States LLC 832 538-0300
1000 Louisiana St # 6700 Houston (77002) ***(G-10091)***

Halcon Holdings Inc (HQ) **832 538-0300**
1000 La St Ste 6700 Houston (77002) ***(G-10092)***

Halcon Operating Co Inc 832 538-0300
1000 La St Ste 6700 Houston (77002) ***(G-10093)***

Haldor Topsoe Inc (HQ) **281 228-5000**
17629 El Cmino Real Ste 3 Houston (77058) ***(G-10094)***

Haldor Topsoe Inc 281 228-5000
10010 Bayport Blvd Pasadena (77507) ***(G-16452)***

Haleaux Inc 214 742-2795
2025 Irving Blvd Ste 108 Dallas (75207) ***(G-4428)***

Half Price Bks Rec Mgzines Inc 512 244-0203
1601 S I H 35 Round Rock (78664) ***(G-17661)***

Half Price Bks Rec Mgzines Inc 512 805-7503
900 Bugg Ln Ste 301124 San Marcos (78666) ***(G-18693)***

Half Price Bks Rec Mgzines Inc 281 540-3950
9743 Fm 1960 Bypass Rd W Humble (77338) ***(G-12774)***

Half Price Bks Rec Mgzines Inc 713 340-0094
2556 Smith Ranch Rd Pearland (77584) ***(G-16567)***

Half Price Bks Rec Mgzines Inc 817 295-8560
12616 South Fwy Ste 134 Burleson (76028) ***(G-2580)***

Halfen Usa Inc (HQ) **210 945-1399**
402 Gibbs Sprawl Rd Converse (78109) ***(G-3394)***

Halff Tritex LLC 214 217-6500
1201 N Bowser Rd Richardson (75081) ***(G-17325)***

Halgo, Plano *Also called Aeon Process Equipment* ***(G-16776)***

Hall Plating Co (PA) **830 620-7825**
915 Gruene River Dr New Braunfels (78132) ***(G-15800)***

Hall Tree Antiques Inc 325 944-4794
5213 Green Valley Trl San Angelo (76904) ***(G-17803)***

Hall-Houston Exploration LP 713 333-0975
4605 Post Oak Place Dr # 100 Houston (77027) ***(G-10095)***

Hall-Houston Exploration II LP 713 333-0930
4605 Post Oak Place Dr # 100 Houston (77027) ***(G-10096)***

Halliburton Company 361 527-2780
833 County Road 4614 Dilley (78017) ***(G-5481)***

Halliburton Company 281 297-1200
445 Woodline Dr Spring (77386) ***(G-19214)***

Halliburton Company 972 418-3221
3220 Keller Springs Rd # 128 Carrollton (75006) ***(G-2751)***

Halliburton Company 281 575-5000
555 N Carancahua St # 775 Corpus Christi (78401) ***(G-3544)***

Halliburton Company 281 575-3000
10200 Bellaire Blvd Houston (77072) ***(G-10097)***

Halliburton Company 281 871-6875
15081 Milner Rd Houston (77032) ***(G-10098)***

Halliburton Company 281 871-2908
15081 1/2 Milner Rd Gate3 Houston (77032) ***(G-10099)***

Halliburton Company 281 297-1200
14524 Hthrow Forrest Pkwy Houston (77032) ***(G-10100)***

Halliburton Company 972 418-3000
2601 E Belt Line Rd Carrollton (75006) ***(G-2752)***

Halliburton Company 281 871-4000
3000 N Sam Houston Pkwy E Houston (77032) ***(G-10101)***

Halliburton Company 713 455-9547
13609 Industrial Rd Houston (77015) ***(G-10102)***

Halliburton Company 936 442-4700
16548 Donwick Dr Conroe (77385) ***(G-3300)***

Halliburton Company 903 981-7032
212 Industrial Dr Longview (75602) ***(G-14246)***

Halliburton Company 210 621-1800
101 Holt Rd Victoria (77905) ***(G-20271)***

Halliburton Company 713 839-2000
2101 City West Blvd Houston (77042) ***(G-10103)***

Halliburton Company 281 986-4400
3950 Interwood S Pkwy Houston (77032) ***(G-10104)***

Halliburton Company 903 389-9275
114 W Us Highway 84 Fairfield (75840) ***(G-6176)***

Halliburton Company 281 871-4482
15112 Morales Rd Fl 4 Houston (77032) ***(G-10105)***

Halliburton Company 281 871-4000
3000 N Sam Houston Pkwy E Houston (77032) ***(G-10106)***

Halliburton Company 817 783-5111
8432 S I 35 W S Alvarado (76009) ***(G-333)***

Halliburton Company (PA) **281 871-2699**
3000 N Sam Houston Pkwy E Houston (77032) ***(G-10107)***

Halliburton Company 432 571-8600
6155 W Murphy St Odessa (79763) ***(G-16024)***

Halliburton Company 713 455-9547
4000 Cedar Blvd Baytown (77523) ***(G-1790)***

Halliburton Delaware Inc (HQ) **713 759-2600**
3000 Houston Ave Houston (77009) ***(G-10108)***

Halliburton Energy Services, Corpus Christi *Also called Halliburton Company* ***(G-3544)***

Halliburton Energy Services, Houston *Also called Halliburton Company* ***(G-10101)***

Halliburton Energy Services, Conroe *Also called Halliburton Company* ***(G-3300)***

Halliburton Energy Svcs Inc (HQ) **281 871-4000**
3000 N Sam Houston Pkwy E Houston (77032) ***(G-10109)***

Halliburton Energy Svcs Inc 281 871-4482
14851 Milner Rd Gate5a Houston (77032) ***(G-10110)***

Halliburton International Inc 214 759-2600
500 N Akard St Ste 3600 Dallas (75201) ***(G-4429)***

Halliburton Technology Center, Houston *Also called Halliburton Company* ***(G-10099)***

Halls Lumber Inc 806 285-2393
108 Ave E Olton (79064) ***(G-16226)***

Hallwood Energy, Dallas *Also called Hallwood Petroleum LLC* ***(G-4431)***

Hallwood Group Incorporated (HQ) **214 528-5588**
10440 N Cntl Expy Ste 240 Dallas (75231) ***(G-4430)***

Hallwood Petroleum LLC 214 528-5588
10440 N Cntl Expy Ste 240 Dallas (75231) ***(G-4431)***

Halo Branded Solutions Inc..972 536-4069
  12801 N Stemmons Fwy # 8 Dallas (75234) *(G-4432)*

Halo Coatings..817 443-3710
  5221 Pyramid Blvd Fort Worth (76126) *(G-6684)*

Halo Fbrication Metalworks LLC........................972 587-0788
  203 Metro Dr Terrell (75160) *(G-19736)*

Halres LLC..832 538-0300
  1000 La St Ste 6700 Houston (77002) *(G-10111)*

Halsey Manufacturing..940 566-3306
  209 N Mayhill Rd Denton (76208) *(G-5371)*

Halsey Mfg, Denton *Also called Halsey Manufacturing (G-5371)*

Haltermann Solutions, Houston *Also called Monument Chemical Houston LLC (G-10916)*

Hamar Industries Inc..817 756-8990
  5216 David Strickland Rd Fort Worth (76119) *(G-6685)*

Hamer Enterprises, McAllen *Also called Texas Logic Inc (G-14911)*

Hamill Resources Inc..281 556-9581
  1160 Dairy Ashford Rd # 250 Houston (77079) *(G-10112)*

Hamill, Claud B Estate, Houston *Also called Hamill Resources Inc (G-10112)*

Hamiltn-Steele Outdoor Accents, Houston *Also called Derbec Enterprises Ltd (G-9439)*

Hamilton Form Co Ltd..817 590-2111
  7009 Midway Rd Richland Hills (76118) *(G-17437)*

Hamilton Machine & Mfg Inc..............................432 362-8030
  2120 W 44th St Odessa (79764) *(G-16025)*

Hamilton Oilfield Services Inc............................325 944-2540
  3150 Executive Dr San Angelo (76904) *(G-17804)*

Hamilton Ranch, Carrizo Springs *Also called 686 Inc (G-2683)*

Hamilton Shirt Interests Ltd............................713 780-8222
  5700 Richmond Ave Houston (77057) *(G-10113)*

Hamilton Shirts, Houston *Also called Hamilton Shirt Interests Ltd (G-10113)*

Hamlin Pet Worx LLC..855 430-9888
  701 E Lake Dr Hamlin (79520) *(G-8170)*

Hamm Well Service Co..940 549-4769
  652 State Highway 67 Graham (76450) *(G-7783)*

Hammer Construction Inc..................................940 683-3131
  3232 S Hwy 101 Bridgeport (76426) *(G-2294)*

Hammer Industriess LLC....................................281 763-2189
  21430 Springbridge Dr Houston (77073) *(G-10114)*

Hammon's Janitorial, Pampa *Also called Melvin Hammon (G-16328)*

Hammonds Technical Svcs Inc..........................281 999-2900
  6807 W Little York Rd Houston (77040) *(G-10115)*

Hampshire Chemical Corp..................................281 479-9525
  739 Battleground Rd Deer Park (77536) *(G-5278)*

Han-Boone International Inc..............................817 838-5196
  2200 Gravel Dr Fort Worth (76118) *(G-6686)*

Han-D-Pac Products Inc....................................915 595-2212
  9420 Carnegie Ave El Paso (79925) *(G-5793)*

Hancock Industries, Cedar Park *Also called Hodyon LP (G-2974)*

Hancor, Yoakum *Also called Advanced Drainage Systems Inc (G-20958)*

Hancor Inc..361 293-6313
  801 Hickey Rd Yoakum (77995) *(G-20967)*

Handcrafted Metal Inc..512 386-5433
  310 Avenue E St Converse (78109) *(G-3395)*

Handgards LLC (HQ)..**915 779-6606**
  901 Hawkins Blvd El Paso (79915) *(G-5794)*

Handwheels Inc..281 998-0560
  6933 Olson Ln Pasadena (77505) *(G-16453)*

Hanesbrands Inc..254 582-7541
  104 I 35 Hwy Se Ste 138b Hillsboro (76645) *(G-8326)*

Hangar 6, D Hanis *Also called H6 Aircraft LLC (G-3829)*

Hangar R LLC..469 865-2110
  2550 N Great Sw Pkwy Grand Prairie (75050) *(G-7886)*

Hangar Welding & Fabrication............................915 857-2899
  15501 Peggy Hopkins El Paso (79938) *(G-5795)*

Hanger Inc (PA)..**512 777-3800**
  10910 Domain Dr Ste 300 Austin (78758) *(G-1197)*

Hanger Inc..817 923-2101
  1401 W Magnolia Ave Fort Worth (76104) *(G-6687)*

Hanger Prosthetics & Orthotics........................817 923-2101
  1401 W Magnolia Ave Fort Worth (76104) *(G-6688)*

Hanita Tek Window Films, Carrollton *Also called Hanitatek LLC (G-2753)*

Hanitatek LLC..214 351-5818
  2025 Mckenzie Dr Ste 100 Carrollton (75006) *(G-2753)*

Hanley Wood Exhibition Div, Irving *Also called Hw Holdco LLC (G-13061)*

Hanna, Houston *Also called Jim Coleman Company (G-10474)*

Hanna-Wichita Tool Supply Co..........................940 766-3151
  104 Oak St Wichita Falls (76301) *(G-20770)*

Hannon Hydraulics Inc (PA)..............................**972 438-2870**
  625 N Loop 12 Irving (75061) *(G-13048)*

Hannon Hydraulics Inc......................................713 849-4445
  11550 Brittmoore Park Dr Houston (77041) *(G-10116)*

Hannon Offshore Drilling Eqp, Irving *Also called Hannon Hydraulics Inc (G-13048)*

Hansen Manufacturing Inc................................713 682-1075
  4807 Ramus St Houston (77092) *(G-10117)*

Hansen Metal Processing, Houston *Also called Hansen Manufacturing Inc (G-10117)*

Hanson Aggregates Bristol, Ennis *Also called Hanson Aggregates LLC (G-6107)*

Hanson Aggregates LLC......................................940 683-4294
  Chico Hwy 101 Bridgeport (76426) *(G-2295)*

Hanson Aggregates LLC......................................806 372-8114
  2001 W Amarillo Blvd Amarillo (79107) *(G-432)*

Hanson Aggregates LLC......................................972 875-9590
  7000 E Highway 34 Ennis (75119) *(G-6107)*

Hanson Aggregates LLC......................................254 622-3239
  856 Sm 2114 Clifton (76634) *(G-3144)*

Hanson Aggregates LLC......................................713 692-4408
  302 Bennington St A Houston (77022) *(G-10118)*

Hanson Aggregates LLC......................................903 794-6161
  2515 W 7th St Texarkana (75501) *(G-19764)*

Hanson Aggregates LLC......................................713 937-7405
  7641 Wright Rd Houston (77041) *(G-10119)*

Hanson Aggregates LLC......................................281 238-4759
  19707 Fm 1093 Rd Richmond (77407) *(G-17456)*

Hanson Aggregates LLC (HQ)............................**469 417-1200**
  8505 Freport Pkwy Ste 500 Irving (75063) *(G-13049)*

Hanson Aggregates LLC......................................972 556-0735
  1946 California Xing Dallas (75220) *(G-4433)*

Hanson Aggregates LLC......................................972 644-6415
  1250 Digital Dr Richardson (75081) *(G-17326)*

Hanson Aggregates LLC......................................972 263-2181
  1000 Macarthur Blvd Grand Prairie (75050) *(G-7887)*

Hanson Aggregates LLC......................................210 658-7461
  21303 Fm 2252 New Braunfels (78132) *(G-15801)*

Hanson Aggregates LLC......................................281 367-4557
  12541 Sleepy Hollow Rd Conroe (77385) *(G-3301)*

Hanson Aggregates LLC......................................972 256-6571
  5150 Valley View Ln Irving (75038) *(G-13050)*

Hanson Aggregates LLC......................................512 756-8255
  4901 S Us Highway 281 Burnet (78611) *(G-2609)*

Hanson Aggregates LLC......................................210 658-3533
  Corner Of Fm 2252 New Braunfels (78132) *(G-15802)*

Hanson Aggregates LLC......................................979 758-3662
  County Road 111 Garwood (77442) *(G-7614)*

Hanson Aggregates New York LLC (HQ)............**972 621-0345**
  8505 Freport Pkwy Ste 500 Irving (75063) *(G-13051)*

Hanson and Pipe Precast, Robstown *Also called Forterra Pipe & Precast LLC (G-17511)*

Hanson Concrete Balch Springs........................972 289-0601
  13950 Lake June Rd Mesquite (75180) *(G-15048)*

Hanson Concrete Truck Maint, Dallas *Also called Hanson Aggregates LLC (G-4433)*

Hanson Lehigh Inc..281 491-7376
  10620 Coldine Rd Dallas (75265) *(G-4434)*

Hanson Lehigh Inc..972 653-3735
  7510 Highway 180 E Mineral Wells (76067) *(G-15528)*

Hanson Lehigh Inc..281 616-0700
  16155 Park Row Houston (77084) *(G-10120)*

Hanson Lehigh Inc (HQ)......................................**972 653-5500**
  300 E John Carpenter Fwy Irving (75062) *(G-13052)*

Hanwha Pwr Systems Amricas Inc....................281 599-3377
  11700 Katy Fwy Houston (77079) *(G-10121)*

Hapco, Fort Worth *Also called Heat Air Products Company (G-6694)*

Happy Shopper Inc..281 751-7138
  13700 Veterans Memorial D Houston (77014) *(G-10122)*

Happymecom..972 503-4803
  6010 W Spring Creek Pkwy Plano (75024) *(G-16883)*

Har-Conn Chrome Co of Texas, Fort Worth *Also called Har-Conn Chrome Company (G-6689)*

Har-Conn Chrome Company................................817 626-5437
  5000 Augusta Dr Fort Worth (76106) *(G-6689)*

Harbison-Fischer Inc (HQ)..................................**817 297-2211**
  901 N Crowley Rd Crowley (76036) *(G-3755)*

Harbison-Fischer Inc..432 580-3592
  1311 E Pool Rd Odessa (79766) *(G-16026)*

Harbison-Fischer Manufacturing, Crowley *Also called Harbison-Fischer Inc (G-3755)*

Harbison-Fischer Sales Co, Odessa *Also called Harbison-Fischer Inc (G-16026)*

Harbisonwalker Intl Inc......................................713 635-3200
  4845 Homestead Rd Ste 500 Houston (77028) *(G-10123)*

Harbor Engine & Grinding Inc............................361 882-1571
  2845 Agnes St Corpus Christi (78405) *(G-3545)*

Harborlite, La Porte *Also called Imerys Perlite Usa Inc (G-13749)*

Harcourt Achieve, Inc, Austin *Also called Hmh Supplemental Publishers (G-1206)*

Hard Band Industries Inc....................................432 563-3752
  12200 W County Road 129 Odessa (79765) *(G-16027)*

Hard Rock Crushing..806 383-1721
  2300 E Hastings Ave Amarillo (79108) *(G-433)*

Harding Energy Partners LLC............................214 723-5112
  13465 Midway Rd Ste 400 Dallas (75244) *(G-4435)*

Hardman Signs LP (PA)......................................**713 957-2324**
  9980 Bammel N Houston Rd Houston (77086) *(G-10124)*

Hards Marine Service, Hull *Also called Hards Marine Service Ltd (G-12741)*

Hards Marine Service Ltd..................................281 452-0848
  266 County Road 2075 Hull (77564) *(G-12741)*

Hardwood Bargains, Austin *Also called Rbt Industries LLC (G-1453)*

Hardwood Products & Doors Inc........................512 259-3094
  9430 Eastranch Rd 2243 Leander (78641) *(G-13991)*

Hardy Don Fuel Effcent Eng Svc, Floydada *Also called Don Hardy Race Cars Inc (G-6292)*

Hardy Machine & Design Inc............................713 690-3335
  5737 Windfern Rd Houston (77041) *(G-10125)*

A L P H A B E T I C

Harlow Arostructures Texas LLC 817 583-8820
800 S 6th Ave Mansfield (76063) *(G-14679)*

Harman Property Services LLC 469 446-2909
9538 Mossridge Cir Dallas (75238) *(G-4436)*

Harper Dirctry Dist Group LLC 940 808-0769
2925 Country Club Rd # 103 Denton (76210) *(G-5372)*

Harper's Bluebonnet Bakery, Fort Worth *Also called Bluebonnet Bakery Inc (G-6458)*

Harris Cabinet & Wdwkg Inc 817 561-2959
5090 Dick Price Rd Fort Worth (76140) *(G-6690)*

Harris Composites Inc 817 279-9546
600 Holmes Dr Granbury (76048) *(G-7799)*

Harris Fabrication LLC 361 547-6910
525 N State Highway 359 Mathis (78368) *(G-14817)*

Harris Industries Incorporated 903 759-4485
13355 Noel Rd Dallas (75240) *(G-4437)*

Harris Manufacturing Company 972 262-3524
625 S Wisteria St Ste 101 Mansfield (76063) *(G-14680)*

Harris Manufacturing Esop Co, Mansfield *Also called Harris Manufacturing Company (G-14680)*

Harris N Computer Corporation 903 535-8222
3800 Paluxy Dr Ste 540 Tyler (75703) *(G-20093)*

Harris Packaging Corporation (PA) **817 429-6262**
1600 Carson St Haltom City (76117) *(G-8148)*

Harris Potteries LP 903 938-8884
333 Marshall St Marshall (75670) *(G-14781)*

Harris Rebar (HQ) **936 258-8221**
9500 Hwy 90 W At Frost Rd Dayton (77535) *(G-5228)*

Harrison Electropolishing LP 832 467-3100
13002 Brittmoore Park Dr Houston (77041) *(G-10126)*

Harrison Fabricators Inc 214 374-1684
3402 E Illinois Ave Dallas (75216) *(G-4438)*

Harrison Gypsum LLC 210 225-9502
302 Casa Blanca San Antonio (78215) *(G-18159)*

Harrison Hydra-Gen Ltd 281 807-4420
14233 W Road Houston Houston (77041) *(G-10127)*

Harrison Jet Guns II LP 817 478-9216
6915 Hudson Village Crk Kennedale (76060) *(G-13497)*

Harrison Mullane Inc 281 449-4846
10938 Lucerne St Houston (77016) *(G-10128)*

Harsco Corporation 713 378-3944
1514 Sheldon Rd Channelview (77530) *(G-3024)*

Harsco Corporation 281 452-6637
15635 Jacintoport Blvd # 203 Houston (77015) *(G-10129)*

Harsco Corporation 713 378-3900
1514 S Sheldon Rd Spring (77373) *(G-19128)*

Harsco Ikg Industries, Channelview *Also called Harsco Corporation (G-3024)*

Hart & Cooley Inc 915 852-9111
12504 Weaver Rd Horizon City (79928) *(G-8365)*

Hart Energy Publishing LLC (PA) **713 993-9320**
1616 S Voss Rd Ste 1000 Houston (77057) *(G-10130)*

Hart Energy Publishing Lllp 713 952-9500
2424 Wilcrest Dr Ste 100 Houston (77042) *(G-10131)*

Hart Energy Publishing Lllp 713 993-9320
4545 Postoak Pl Houston (77027) *(G-10132)*

Hart Engineering Company 903 758-0166
109 W Hoyt Dr Longview (75601) *(G-14247)*

Hart Heat Transfer Pdts Inc 713 675-9848
8226 Kerr St Houston (77029) *(G-10133)*

Hart Publication, Houston *Also called Leopard Media LLC (G-10625)*

Hart Radiators, Houston *Also called Hart Heat Transfer Pdts Inc (G-10133)*

Hartco, Dallas *Also called Mail Contractors America Inc (G-4628)*

Harte Hanks Inc (PA) **512 343-1100**
2800 Wells Branch Pkwy Austin (78728) *(G-1198)*

Hartfiel Automation Inc 972 633-0000
2600 Tech Dr Ste 300 Plano (75074) *(G-16884)*

Hartman Newspapers LP (PA) **281 342-8691**
1914 4th St Rosenberg (77471) *(G-17585)*

Hartman Newspapers LP 361 729-9900
1002 E Wharf St Rockport (78382) *(G-17530)*

Hartman Newspapers LP 972 563-6476
150 9th St Terrell (75160) *(G-19737)*

Hartman Newspapers LP 936 336-3611
1939 Trinity St Ste A Liberty (77575) *(G-14119)*

Hartman Newspapers LP 281 342-7304
1902 4th St Rosenberg (77471) *(G-17586)*

Hartman Newspapers LP 281 232-3737
1902 4th St Rosenberg (77471) *(G-17587)*

Hartmanns Inc 325 695-7641
1221 Fulwiler Rd Abilene (79603) *(G-46)*

Hartsfield & Pierce Cabinet Co 972 288-5487
200 Sewell Ct Irving (75038) *(G-13053)*

Hartsfield Cabinet, Irving *Also called Hartsfield & Pierce Cabinet Co (G-13053)*

Hartung Glass Industries Inc 972 629-6890
12900 Nicholson Rd Farmers Branch (75234) *(G-6201)*

Hartwell Industries Inc 713 771-4311
8930 Bissonnet St Houston (77074) *(G-10134)*

Harvest House Farms 830 868-7253
506 N Nugent Ave Johnson City (78636) *(G-13312)*

Harvest Incorporated (HQ) **254 933-1000**
815 Kirkley Blvd Belton (76513) *(G-2024)*

Harvest Natural Resources Inc 281 899-5700
8117 Preston Rd Ste 300 Dallas (75225) *(G-4439)*

Harvest Pipeline Company 830 334-3280
1111 Travis St Houston (77002) *(G-10135)*

Harvey Dayco, Dallas *Also called Halo Branded Solutions Inc (G-4432)*

Harvey Dupriest & Sons Inc 214 337-4731
633 Sunnyside Ave Dallas (75211) *(G-4440)*

Harwood Industries Inc 903 566-6001
17833 State Highway 31 E Tyler (75705) *(G-20094)*

Hasco Marine 281 452-5017
906 Elsbeth St Channelview (77530) *(G-3025)*

Hass Tcm, Austin *Also called Haas Group International LLC (G-1195)*

Hasse Enterprises Inc 512 835-7697
10201b Mckalla Pl Unit D Austin (78758) *(G-1199)*

Hauck Enterprises Ltd (PA) **409 727-2227**
342 Twin City Hwy Port Neches (77651) *(G-17162)*

Hauling & Excavating Casco 713 433-6209
1306 E Anderson Rd Houston (77047) *(G-10136)*

Haverhill Chemicals LLC 281 885-8900
16800 Imperial Valley Dr # 499 Houston (77060) *(G-10137)*

Hawk Installation & Cnstr Inc 903 665-8080
555 Fm 728 Jefferson (75657) *(G-13284)*

Hawk Portable Buildings Inc (PA) **325 893-5120**
1825 S Access Rd Clyde (79510) *(G-3163)*

Hawkins Lease Service Inc (PA) **281 331-2739**
3205 Fm 2403 Rd Alvin (77511) *(G-365)*

Hawkins Rmote Snsing Explrtion 210 829-5330
8531 N New Braunfels Ave # 201 San Antonio (78217) *(G-18160)*

Hawkwood Energy East Texas LLC 303 823-4175
1999 Bryan St Ste 900 Dallas (75201) *(G-4441)*

Hay King, Taylor *Also called K and M Manufacturing Co Inc (G-19659)*

Hayakawa Electronics Amer Inc 972 457-0064
1425 Greenway Dr Ste 140 Irving (75038) *(G-13054)*

Haydon Corporation 972 641-6400
1139 W N Carrier Pkwy Grand Prairie (75050) *(G-7888)*

Hayes & Stolz Indus Mfg Co LLC 817 926-3391
6500 Cirrus Dr Burleson (76028) *(G-2581)*

Hayes Building Service Inc 940 484-7775
1011 E Oak Shores Dr Crossroads (76227) *(G-3748)*

Hayes Carpentry L L C 713 944-2608
1404 Illinois St South Houston (77587) *(G-19044)*

Hayes Company, South Houston *Also called Hayes Carpentry L L C (G-19044)*

Hayes Company LLC 972 288-9755
1201 Chase Rd Mesquite (75149) *(G-15049)*

Hayes Farm 817 477-1661
7580 Bennett Lawson Rd Mansfield (76063) *(G-14681)*

Hayes Holdings Inc 281 565-8111
14030 Florence Rd Ste E Sugar Land (77498) *(G-19490)*

Hayes Retail Services, Mesquite *Also called Hayes Company LLC (G-15049)*

Hayes Software Systems, Austin *Also called Gem-Cap Inc (G-1180)*

Hayhurst Bros Drilling Co 325 340-1865
12906 County Road 218 Abilene (79602) *(G-47)*

Haynes International Inc 713 937-7597
12241 Fm 529 Rd Houston (77041) *(G-10138)*

Hazelett Drilling and Sup Corp 512 398-6682
915 Old Mcmahan Rd Lockhart (78644) *(G-14169)*

HB Fuller Cnstr Pdts Inc 713 926-3125
6107 Industrial Way Houston (77011) *(G-10139)*

HB Fuller Company 972 728-0707
3500 Executive Blvd Mesquite (75149) *(G-15050)*

Hb2 Energy Inc (PA) **713 377-9860**
2777 Allen Pkwy Ste 600 Houston (77019) *(G-10140)*

Hbreaux Companies Inc 409 792-9212
3165 Texas Ave Bridge City (77611) *(G-2284)*

Hbs Systems Inc 972 234-4444
3400 Waterview Pkwy # 200 Richardson (75080) *(G-17327)*

Hc Interiors Inc 214 350-0468
1000 W Crosby Rd Ste 100 Carrollton (75006) *(G-2754)*

HCA Hston Healthcare Southeast, Pasadena *Also called Chca Bayshore LP (G-16406)*

Hcf Group, Corpus Christi *Also called Colt Services LP (G-3504)*

Hco Holding I Corporation 214 764-3021
3810 Miller Park Dr Garland (75042) *(G-7508)*

Hcr Electronics Inc 512 756-8164
2708 S Water St Burnet (78611) *(G-2610)*

Hdd Rotary Sales LLC 936 446-1200
1221 Mckinney St Ste 2850 Houston (77010) *(G-10141)*

Hde, Fort Worth *Also called Hunnicutt Digital Electronics (G-6709)*

Hdi Instruments LLC (PA) **713 688-8555**
7240 Brittmoore Rd # 119 Houston (77041) *(G-10142)*

Hds, Houston *Also called Houston Dynamic Service Inc (G-10230)*

Headcovers Unlimited Inc 281 334-4287
214 S Iowa Ave League City (77573) *(G-13958)*

Headcovers.com, League City *Also called Headcovers Unlimited Inc (G-13958)*

Headington Companies, Dallas *Also called Headington Oil Limited 1993 LP (G-4443)*

Headington Energy Partners, Corpus Christi *Also called Headington Oil Limited 1993 LP (G-3546)*

2021 Harris Texas
Manufacturers Directory

(G-0000) Company's Geographic Section entry number

Headington Energy Partners LLC 214 307-5400
1700 Redbud Blvd Ste 400 McKinney (75069) *(G-14946)*
Headington Oil, Dallas *Also called Headingtron Oil LP (G-4444)*
Headington Oil Company 214 696-0606
2711 N Haskell Ave # 2800 Dallas (75204) *(G-4442)*
Headington Oil Limited 1993 LP (PA) **214 696-0606**
2711 N Haskell Ave # 2800 Dallas (75204) *(G-4443)*
Headington Oil Limited 1993 LP 361 885-0110
500 N Shoreline Blvd # 902 Corpus Christi (78401) *(G-3546)*
Headingtron Oil LP 214 696-0606
2711 N Haskell Ave # 2800 Dallas (75204) *(G-4444)*
Headquarters, Fort Worth *Also called Lhoist North America MO Inc (G-6786)*
Heads Up Technologies Inc 972 980-4890
2033 Chenault Dr Ste 100 Carrollton (75006) *(G-2755)*
Headwaters Cnstr Mtls LLC (HQ) **903 729-2217**
2500 W Reagan St Palestine (75801) *(G-16299)*
Headwaters Cnstr Mtls LLC 713 393-3300
2088 Fm 949 Alleyton (78935) *(G-308)*
Headwaters Construction Mtls, Columbus *Also called Southwest Concrete Products Co (G-3233)*
Headwaters Incorporated 713 393-3328
2088 Fm 949 Alleyton (78935) *(G-309)*
Headwaters Incorporated 830 562-3239
5555 Fellowship Ln Spg Spring Tarpley (78883) *(G-19643)*
Headway Research Inc 972 272-5431
3637 Marquis Dr Ste 102 Garland (75042) *(G-7509)*
Health Care Temporaries Inc 713 631-7106
8926 Sherbourne St Ste D Houston (77016) *(G-10143)*
Health Management Systems Inc (HQ) **214 453-3000**
5615 High Point Dr # 100 Irving (75038) *(G-13055)*
Health Management Systems Inc 512 407-9680
505 E Huntland Dr Ste 380 Austin (78752) *(G-1200)*
Healthcare Pymnt Spcalists LLC 800 784-2175
100 Lexington St Ste 300 Fort Worth (76102) *(G-6691)*
Healthmark Group, Dallas *Also called Healthmark Medical Group LLC (G-4445)*
Healthmark Medical Group LLC 800 659-4035
325 N Saint Paul St # 1650 Dallas (75201) *(G-4445)*
Healthpoint Ltd 817 900-4000
5600 Clearfork Main St Fort Worth (76109) *(G-6692)*
Healthtech Solutions Inc 763 559-7082
9825 Spectrum Dr Bldg 3 Austin (78717) *(G-1694)*
Healthtrnics MBL Solutions LLC 866 598-2734
9825 Spectrum Dr Bldg 3 Austin (78717) *(G-1695)*
Healthtronics, West Lake Hills *Also called Hmt High Medical Tech USA Inc (G-20682)*
Healthtronics Inc (HQ) **512 328-2892**
9825 Spectrum Dr Bldg 3 Austin (78717) *(G-1696)*
Healthtronics Service Ctr LLC 512 328-2892
9825 Spectrum Dr Bldg 3 Austin (78717) *(G-1697)*
Hearing Lab Technology LLC (PA) **469 586-0448**
14301 F A A Blvd Fort Worth (76155) *(G-6693)*
Hearne Steel Company 979 279-3464
1011 Vaughn Ln Hearne (77859) *(G-8232)*
Hearne Steel Company, Inc., Hearne *Also called Hearne Steel Company (G-8232)*
Hearst Corporation 210 271-2700
420 Broadway St San Antonio (78205) *(G-18161)*
Hearst Corporation 956 728-2500
111 Esperanza Dr Laredo (78041) *(G-13890)*
Hearst Corporation 432 682-5311
201 E Illinois Ave Midland (79701) *(G-15244)*
Hearst Corporation 409 384-3441
702 S Wheeler St Jasper (75951) *(G-13277)*
Hearst Corporation 210 250-3000
301 Avenue E San Antonio (78205) *(G-18162)*
Hearst Newspapers LLC (PA) **713 220-7171**
4747 Southwest Fwy Houston (77027) *(G-10144)*
Hearst Newspapers LLC 713 220-7171
4747 Southwest Fwy Houston (77027) *(G-10145)*
Hearstcorporation 806 296-1300
820 Broadway St Plainview (79072) *(G-16756)*
Heart Land Petroleum Corp 325 437-8430
1213 E South 11th St A Abilene (79602) *(G-48)*
Heart Land Trucking, Abilene *Also called Heart Land Petroleum Corp (G-48)*
Heart of Texas Biscuits Inc 254 753-0046
204 Deb Ave Waco (76712) *(G-20410)*
Heart of Texas Music Inc (PA) **254 778-7422**
808 S 31st St Temple (76504) *(G-19681)*
Heart of Texas Music Temple, Temple *Also called Heart of Texas Music Inc (G-19681)*
Heart of Texas Perfect Surface, Austin *Also called Perfect Surface of Austin (G-1411)*
Heartland Enterprises Ltd 830 997-9434
1039 Kerr Rd Fredericksburg (78624) *(G-7182)*
Heartland Furniture Inc 817 483-6161
7900 Valcasi Dr Arlington (76001) *(G-695)*
Heat Air Products Company 817 222-9567
3024 N Sylvania Ave Fort Worth (76111) *(G-6694)*
Heat Shield Inc 903 845-4066
1710 N Main St Gladewater (75647) *(G-7722)*
Heath Inc 979 822-6924
422 Dellwood St Bryan (77801) *(G-2476)*
Heath Auto Supply, Van Horn *Also called Heath Transit Mix Concrete Co (G-20214)*
Heath Consultants Incorporated (PA) **713 844-1300**
9030 W Monroe Rd Houston (77061) *(G-10146)*
Heath Transit Mix Concrete Co (PA) **432 283-2127**
401 W Broadway St Van Horn (79855) *(G-20214)*
Heavy Equipment Maintenance Co (PA) **903 984-9076**
418 Hwy 42 West Access Rd Kilgore (75662) *(G-13557)*
Heb Plus 210 673-4900
8219 Marbach Rd San Antonio (78227) *(G-18163)*
Hefco Enterprises Inc 281 431-1571
3523 Fm 521 Rd Fresno (77545) *(G-7238)*
Heights Armature Works Inc 713 937-7676
12250 Taylor Rd Houston (77041) *(G-10147)*
Heil Trailer International LLC 254 865-7235
1505 W Main St Gatesville (76528) *(G-7618)*
Heines Custom Draperies Inc 281 391-3103
27223 Highway Blvd Katy (77494) *(G-13363)*
Heitman Company Inc 713 675-9001
1422 Mccarty St Houston (77029) *(G-10148)*
Heitman Laboratories Inc 972 982-2224
4711 Sycamore Ln Allen (75002) *(G-273)*
Heldenfels Enterprises Inc (PA) **512 396-2376**
5700 S Ih 35 San Marcos (78666) *(G-18694)*
Heldoorn Manufacturing Inc 817 275-0835
419 W Fork Dr Arlington (76012) *(G-696)*
Helen Gordon Interests Ltd (PA) **713 371-3500**
2020 North Loop W Ste 220 Houston (77018) *(G-10149)*
Helen Gordon Interests Ltd 214 853-6088
7929 Brookriver Dr # 350 Dallas (75247) *(G-4446)*
Helen's Heart and Vienna Prom, Dallas *Also called Helens Heart LLC (G-4447)*
Helena & Harry The IV, Dallas *Also called Ingamia Inc (G-4499)*
Helena Agri-Enterprises LLC 806 365-4433
410 4th St Hartley (79044) *(G-8211)*
Helena Laboratories Corp (PA) **409 842-3714**
1530 Lindbergh Dr Beaumont (77707) *(G-1901)*
Helena Laboratories Corp 409 842-3714
3795 Washington Blvd Beaumont (77705) *(G-1902)*
Helens Heart LLC 972 247-1414
13628 Beta Rd Ste A Dallas (75244) *(G-4447)*
Helix Enrgy Slutions Group Inc (PA) **281 618-0400**
3505 W Sam Houston Pkwy N S Houston (77043) *(G-10150)*
Helmerich & Payne Inc 830 379-5858
567 E Ih 10 Seguin (78155) *(G-18841)*
Helmerich & Payne Intl Drlg Co 361 664-0114
4074 N State Highway 123 Seguin (78155) *(G-18842)*
Helmerich & Payne Intl Drlg Co 832 782-6800
2930 W Sam Houston Pkwy N # 250 Houston (77043) *(G-10151)*
Helmy Associates & Co Inc 210 681-0101
7334 Caribou San Antonio (78238) *(G-18164)*
Hemaq America LLC 877 700-5060
342 Santa Domingo Helotes (78023) *(G-8238)*
Hemco, Kilgore *Also called Heavy Equipment Maintenance Co (G-13557)*
Hemco, Dallas *Also called Hunt Exploration Mining Co (G-4473)*
Hemco Industries Inc 713 681-2426
9318 Reid Lake Dr Houston (77064) *(G-10152)*
Hemotek LLC 972 312-1609
701 E Plano Pkwy Ste 500 Plano (75074) *(G-16885)*
Hempel (usa) Inc (HQ) **936 523-6000**
600 Conroe Park North Dr Conroe (77303) *(G-3302)*
Hempel (usa) Inc 214 353-1600
2728 Empire Central Dallas (75235) *(G-4448)*
Hempstead Halide Inc 409 572-2505
305 21st St Ste 228 Galveston (77550) *(G-7400)*
Henco, Houston *Also called Houston Elbow & Nipple Co Inc (G-10231)*
Hendee Enterprises Inc 713 796-2322
9350 S Point Dr Houston (77054) *(G-10153)*
Henderson Controls Inc 512 398-5700
900 W Goforth Rd Buda (78610) *(G-2529)*
Henderson Daily News, Henderson *Also called Henderson Newspapers Inc (G-8265)*
Henderson Drilling Pdts Inc 281 661-3627
6750 Bender Rd Humble (77396) *(G-12775)*
Henderson Fabrication Inc 979 245-5350
3107 Nichols Ave Bay City (77414) *(G-1773)*
Henderson Newspapers Inc 903 657-2501
1711 Us Highway 79 S Henderson (75654) *(G-8265)*
Hendricks BTS Corporation 713 516-8716
2700 Cullen Blvd 1946 Pearland (77584) *(G-16568)*
Hendrix Spclty Fabrication Inc 713 466-6888
9840 Windmill Park Ln Houston (77064) *(G-10154)*
Hengst Printing & Supplies, La Grange *Also called Graphtex Inc (G-13696)*
Henke Enterprises Inc 936 291-2026
1792 Highway 30 E Huntsville (77320) *(G-12813)*
Henkel Consumer Goods Inc 832 261-2000
1110 Nasa Pkwy Ste 470 Houston (77058) *(G-10155)*
Henniges Auto Mexico SA De Cv 956 794-3606
13209 S Unitec Dr Laredo (78045) *(G-13891)*
Henry Company 972 272-5488
3802 Miller Park Dr Garland (75042) *(G-7510)*
Henry Oil LC 214 696-5150
8117 Preston Rd Ste 300 Dallas (75225) *(G-4449)*

ALPHABETIC

Henry Resources LLC 432 694-3000
   3525 Andrews Hwy Midland (79703) *(G-15245)*

Hensley Attachments, Dallas *Also called Hensley Industries Inc* *(G-4450)*

Hensley Industries Inc (HQ) **972 241-2321**
   2108 Joe Field Rd Dallas (75229) *(G-4450)*

Hep El Dorado LLC 214 871-3555
   2828 N Harwood St # 1300 Dallas (75201) *(G-4451)*

Hep Mechanical Services LLC 903 278-6826
   295 County Road 3552 Queen City (75572) *(G-17221)*

Hep Services LLC 210 278-1563
   9805 Katy Fwy Ste 900 Houston (77024) *(G-10156)*

Herald Banner, Greenville *Also called Newspaper Holding Inc* *(G-8085)*

Herald Democrat (HQ) **903 893-8181**
   603 S Sam Rayburn Fwy Sherman (75090) *(G-18917)*

Herald of Truth Ministries 325 698-4370
   3444 N 1st St Ste 400 Abilene (79603) *(G-49)*

Herald Publishing Co, Houston *Also called Jewish Herald Voice Inc* *(G-10472)*

Herald Truth Rdo & TV Programs, Abilene *Also called Herald of Truth Ministries* *(G-49)*

Herald Zeitung, New Braunfels *Also called Southern Newspapers Inc* *(G-15825)*

Herb Hilltop Farm & Restaurant 832 397-4020
   235 Chain O Lakes Resort Cleveland (77327) *(G-3128)*

Herbal Essentials LLC 832 439-3114
   3435 Dartmouth Field Ln Fresno (77545) *(G-7239)*

Hercules Drilling Company LLC 713 350-5100
   9 Greenway Plz Ste 2200 Houston (77046) *(G-10157)*

Hercules Films LLC (PA) **920 284-0796**
   12600 Cardinal Mdw Sugar Land (77478) *(G-19491)*

Hercules Films LLC 920 284-0796
   12510 Cardinal Mdw Sugar Land (77478) *(G-19492)*

Hercules International Drlg, Houston *Also called Hercules Drilling Company LLC* *(G-10157)*

Hercules LLC 409 866-4778
   10658 Highway 90 Beaumont (77713) *(G-1903)*

Hercules Offshore Inc (PA) **713 350-5100**
   9 Greenway Plz Ste 2300 Houston (77046) *(G-10158)*

Herd Producing Co Inc 903 509-3456
   3901 Manhatton Dr Tyler (75701) *(G-20095)*

Hereford Biofuels LP 972 980-7159
   4100 Spring Valley Rd Dallas (75244) *(G-4452)*

Hereford Brand Inc 806 364-2030
   506 S 25 Mile Ave Hereford (79045) *(G-8291)*

Hereford Brand, The, Hereford *Also called Hereford Brand Inc* *(G-8291)*

Hereford Division, Hereford *Also called Brandon & Clark Inc* *(G-8284)*

Herff Jones LLC 903 592-3800
   107 W 6th St Tyler (75701) *(G-20096)*

Heritage Equipment Company Inc 806 745-4451
   10312 Fm 41 Wolfforth (79382) *(G-20908)*

Heritage Fmly Spclty Foods Inc 972 660-6511
   901 Santerre St Grand Prairie (75050) *(G-7889)*

Heritage Plas An Atkore Intl, Weatherford *Also called Atkore Plastic Pipe Corp* *(G-20577)*

Heritage Restorations, Waco *Also called Homestead Craftsmen LLC* *(G-20414)*

Heritage Stl Erction Fbrcation 817 790-5170
   4639 S Interstate 35 W Alvarado (76009) *(G-334)*

Heritage Wire Line Services 903 534-0671
   Hwy 155 South 10 Miles Tyler (75703) *(G-20097)*

Herman Miller Inc 214 855-0200
   2811 Mckinney Ave Ste 20 Dallas (75204) *(G-4453)*

Herman Packaging Co Inc 713 462-0228
   12822 Hempstead Rd Ste C Houston (77092) *(G-10159)*

Hermes Consolidated LLC (HQ) **303 894-9966**
   825 Town And Country Ln # 1500 Houston (77024) *(G-10160)*

Hermitage Operating LLC 337 852-0001
   720 Rusk St Ste 306 Houston (77002) *(G-10161)*

Hernandez Sandblasting 361 701-2522
   4957 County Road 403 Freer (78357) *(G-7227)*

Herndon Fabrication Works 713 941-3785
   911 Pennsylvania St South Houston (77587) *(G-19045)*

Herndon's Rod Iron Furniture, El Paso *Also called Robert F Herndon Corporation* *(G-5942)*

Hero Assemblers LP 210 628-4800
   1 Lone Star Pass Ste 1101 San Antonio (78264) *(G-18165)*

Herrin Haulers, Kilgore *Also called Herrin Welding Service Inc* *(G-13558)*

Herrin Welding Service Inc 903 984-7139
   11763 County Road 281 N Kilgore (75662) *(G-13558)*

Herring Construction Co, Houston *Also called Herring Enterprises Inc* *(G-10162)*

Herring Enterprises Inc 713 862-3614
   1122 W 20th St Houston (77008) *(G-10162)*

Herring Printing Co 830 257-7242
   615 Water St Kerrville (78028) *(G-13520)*

Herring Tank Company Inc (PA) **817 377-1851**
   7201 W Vickery Blvd Benbrook (76116) *(G-2041)*

Hesco Gathering Company L L C 361 883-8398
   500 N Shoreline Blvd Corpus Christi (78401) *(G-3547)*

Heseyeon LLC 214 483-3800
   1001 E Hbron Pkwy Ste 114 Carrollton (75010) *(G-2868)*

Heshka Oil LLC 936 760-3453
   2929 E Davis St Conroe (77301) *(G-3303)*

Hess Jerry Operating Company 940 759-4791
   310 N Magnolia St Muenster (76252) *(G-15670)*

Hess Corporation 713 496-4000
   1501 Mckinney St Houston (77010) *(G-10163)*

Hess Investments ND LLC 713 496-4000
   1501 Mckinney St Houston (77010) *(G-10164)*

Hess Midstream GP LP 713 496-4200
   1501 Mckinney St Houston (77010) *(G-10165)*

Heubach Corporation 214 291-0238
   2713 Industrial Ln Garland (75041) *(G-7511)*

Hewell Enterprises Inc 972 466-2442
   2722 N Josey Ln Ste 100 Carrollton (75007) *(G-2869)*

Hewlett Packard Enterprise Co (PA) **650 687-5817**
   11445 Compaq Center W Dr Houston (77070) *(G-10166)*

Hewlett-Packard Company 979 691-4540
   1700 Res Pkwy Ste 200 College Station (77845) *(G-3186)*

Hewlett-Packard Dev Co LP 281 370-0670
   10300 Energy Dr Spring (77389) *(G-19129)*

Hexa Containment LLC 281 884-8026
   709 S 16th St La Porte (77571) *(G-13743)*

Hexa Containment LLC 713 360-9221
   6900 Patillo Rd Nederland (77627) *(G-15754)*

Hexcel Reinforcements Corp (HQ) **830 379-1580**
   1913 N King St Seguin (78155) *(G-18843)*

Hexion Inc 936 829-5566
   100 W Borden St Diboll (75941) *(G-5467)*

Hexion Inc 281 727-3163
   5900 Highway 225 Deer Park (77536) *(G-5279)*

Hexion Inc 956 565-6301
   303 Industrial Park Mercedes (78570) *(G-15005)*

Hexion Inc 281 325-3368
   12650 Dirs Dr Ste 100 Stafford (77477) *(G-19325)*

Hexpol Compounding LLC 817 483-9797
   635 Tower Dr Kennedale (76060) *(G-13498)*

Heyday Beverage Company LLC 512 387-2399
   701 E 6th St Austin (78701) *(G-1201)*

HF Guyton Inc 713 869-6483
   6131 Corporate Dr Houston (77036) *(G-10167)*

Hfj Group LLC 833 777-3473
   4553 Aldine Bender Rd Houston (77032) *(G-10168)*

HFS Foods, Grand Prairie *Also called Heritage Fmly Spclty Foods Inc* *(G-7889)*

HFS Holding Corporation (PA) **214 634-8600**
   8900 Ambassador Row Dallas (75247) *(G-4454)*

Hg Solutions Inc 972 205-0888
   2020 Copper St Garland (75042) *(G-7512)*

Hg Tshirt Design Company 469 776-4995
   320 S Center St Apt 114 Grand Prairie (75051) *(G-7890)*

Hght Inc 281 446-1155
   14446 Smith Rd Humble (77396) *(G-12776)*

Hgm International, Houston *Also called Houston Grinding & Mfg Co* *(G-10235)*

Hh Oil Tools Inc 281 550-0633
   5322 Addicks Satsuma Rd A Houston (77084) *(G-10169)*

Hh Rigs and Services, Houston *Also called Honghua America LLC* *(G-10203)*

Hhbodu LLC 210 464-2669
   945 Bloomfield Dr Grand Prairie (75052) *(G-7891)*

Hhey Hay Farm, Harlingen *Also called Stitch Gallery Inc* *(G-8203)*

HI Tech Designers, Houston *Also called Dimensional Cnc LLC* *(G-9474)*

HI Tech Oil Blends Inc 972 231-5464
   1005 Hanover Dr Allen (75002) *(G-274)*

Hi-Crush Inc (PA) **713 980-6200**
   1330 Post Oak Blvd # 600 Houston (77056) *(G-10170)*

Hi-Crush Permian Sand LLC 713 960-4777
   1999 Bryan St Ste 900 Dallas (75201) *(G-4455)*

Hi-Crush Wyeville Oper LLC (HQ) **608 372-4705**
   1330 Post Oak Blvd # 600 Houston (77056) *(G-10171)*

Hi-Line Industries, Brenham *Also called HI Industries Inc* *(G-2257)*

Hi-Plains Canvas Products Inc 806 352-5345
   6337 Canyon Dr Amarillo (79110) *(G-492)*

Hi-Tech Champion Manufacturing (HQ) **713 644-2181**
   5565 Maudlin St Houston (77087) *(G-10172)*

Hi-Tech Metal Finishing, Denton *Also called Hi-Tech Metals Inc* *(G-5373)*

Hi-Tech Metals Inc 940 243-0516
   3100 Jim Christal Rd Denton (76207) *(G-5373)*

Hi-Tech Plastics, Mission *Also called Royal Technologies Corporation* *(G-15563)*

Hi-Tech Prcous Mtls Rfnery LLC (PA) **972 239-0597**
   13620 Gamma Rd Dallas (75244) *(G-4456)*

Hi-Tech Products Inc 512 450-1465
   1513 Brandi Ln Round Rock (78681) *(G-17662)*

Hibernia Energy III LLC 713 728-7911
   5599 San Felipe St # 1200 Houston (77056) *(G-10173)*

Hickham Industries 713 567-2700
   11518 Old La Porte Rd La Porte (77571) *(G-13744)*

Hickory Springs Mfg Co 817 831-1785
   3629 E 1st St Fort Worth (76111) *(G-6695)*

Hicks Post Co Inc 936 858-4228
   10690 Us Highway 69 S Alto (75925) *(G-316)*

Hicor Technologies Inc (PA) **281 727-0250**
   4140 World Hstn Pkwy # 100 Houston (77032) *(G-10174)*

Hid Global Corporation (HQ) **800 237-7769**
   611 Center Ridge Dr Austin (78753) *(G-1202)*

High End Systems Inc (HQ)......................512 836-2242
2105 Gracy Farms Ln Austin (78758) *(G-1203)*

High Fshion Decorative Fabrics, Houston Also called Levan Group I LP *(G-10628)*

High Grade Products LLC....................832 381-3455
25700 Interstate 45 # 121 Spring (77386) *(G-19215)*

High Line Ranch LLC....................830 875-5386
8526 N New Braunfels Ave San Antonio (78217) *(G-18166)*

High Plains Concrete Company (PA)..........806 293-8313
3200 Canyon St Plainview (79072) *(G-16757)*

High Plains Drilling Company.................806 935-2132
610 N Dumas Ave Dumas (79029) *(G-5521)*

High Plains Hydro Carbon....................806 948-4166
Hwy 119 Sunray (79086) *(G-19619)*

High Plins Cntrs MGT Group Inc (PA)........806 935-5858
414 S Dumas Ave Dumas (79029) *(G-5522)*

High Point Design LLC....................972 753-2622
2010 Century Center Blvd Irving (75062) *(G-13056)*

High Roller Sand Operating LLC..............936 632-6033
203 S 1st St Lufkin (75901) *(G-14530)*

High Roller Wells LLc....................936 598-5577
1008 Southview Cir Center (75935) *(G-2999)*

High Standard Manufacturing Co.............713 462-4200
5151 Mitchelldale St B14 Houston (77092) *(G-10175)*

High Tech Finishing, Houston Also called Result Enterprises Inc *(G-11614)*

High Tech Machine II Co LLC.................832 467-2806
6518 Wesco Way Houston (77041) *(G-10176)*

High Tech Services Inc....................972 231-8037
999 E Arapaho Rd Ste 200 Richardson (75081) *(G-17328)*

High Tide Oilfield Svcs LLC.................361 394-1731
5109 Highway 44 E Freer (78357) *(G-7228)*

High Voltage Power Systems Inc.............972 733-1700
2532 Highlander Way Carrollton (75006) *(G-2756)*

High-Tech Fabrication Inc....................281 351-0882
22206 Kobs Rd Tomball (77377) *(G-19981)*

Higher Planes Inc....................936 494-1717
513 Bryant Rd Conroe (77303) *(G-3304)*

Highland Concrete Co....................432 561-5858
10716 State Highway 191 # 7 Midland (79707) *(G-15246)*

Highlite Inc....................214 741-4116
4320 Action Dr Mesquite (75150) *(G-15051)*

Highmount Exploration Prod LLC.............325 387-3588
Highway 277 S 209 Pr 4489 Sonora (76950) *(G-19026)*

Highmount Exploration Prod LLC (HQ)........281 873-1500
1001 Fannin St Ste 800 Houston (77002) *(G-10177)*

Highpeak Energy Partners LP................817 850-9200
421 W 3rd St Ste 1000 Fort Worth (76102) *(G-6696)*

Highrise Systems Inc (PA)................817 927-8711
3313 May St Fort Worth (76110) *(G-6697)*

Hight Marine Products Inc....................817 431-4569
708 Katy Rd Unit B Fort Worth (76244) *(G-6698)*

Hightech Grafix Inc....................817 616-3204
7660 Pebble Dr Fort Worth (76118) *(G-6699)*

Hightech Signs, Texarkana Also called Double S Signs LLC *(G-19762)*

Hightech Signs, Richardson Also called Multi-Quest Inc *(G-17361)*

Hightech Signs, Austin Also called Abney Group Inc *(G-877)*

Hightech Signs, Texarkana Also called Sign Technologies Inc *(G-19773)*

Hightower Company, Flower Mound Also called CT Greggs and Sons LLC *(G-6264)*

Hightower Company....................972 874-2419
11111 Pleast Colny Dr 9 Apt 902 Houston (77065) *(G-10178)*

Hightower Metal Works Inc....................713 937-7181
9001 Taub Rd Houston (77064) *(G-10179)*

Highway Barricades & Svcs LLC (PA).........361 883-6300
7775 Leopard St Corpus Christi (78409) *(G-3548)*

Highwood Machine Tool LLC.................254 412-0512
600 Research Pkwy Waco (76705) *(G-20411)*

Higuchi International, San Antonio Also called Higuchi Manufacturing Amer LLC *(G-18167)*

Higuchi International Corp (HQ)..............210 633-2877
14901 Southton Rd Elmendorf (78112) *(G-6069)*

Higuchi Manufacturing Amer LLC.............210 633-2877
14901 Southton Rd San Antonio (78223) *(G-18167)*

Hii Mssion Drven Innvtive Slto, San Antonio Also called Camber Def SEC Systems Sltons *(G-17977)*

Hiland Dairy Foods Company LLC............903 565-0288
200 N Fuller Ave Tyler (75702) *(G-20098)*

Hiland Dairy Packaging, Tyler Also called Hiland Dairy Foods Company LLC *(G-20098)*

Hiland Gp LLC....................713 369-9000
1001 Louisiana St # 1000 Houston (77002) *(G-10180)*

Hiland Partners Holdings LLC (HQ)..........713 369-9000
1001 Louisiana St # 1000 Houston (77002) *(G-10181)*

Hilco, Harlingen Also called Alteca LLC *(G-8179)*

Hilco Metal Roofing Supply, Navasota Also called BD Hildebrandt Entps Inc *(G-15725)*

Hilcorp Energy Company....................979 548-2144
10201 County Road 359 Sweeny (77480) *(G-19627)*

Hilcorp Energy Company (PA)...............713 209-2400
1111 Travis St Houston (77002) *(G-10182)*

Hilcorp Energy I LP....................713 209-2400
1111 Travis St Houston (77002) *(G-10183)*

Hilcorp Energy I LP....................713 209-2400
1201 Louisiana St # 1400 Houston (77002) *(G-10184)*

Hilcorp Finance Company....................713 209-2400
1201 La St Ste 1400 Houston (77002) *(G-10185)*

Hilflo LLC....................936 756-2020
12076 Fm 3083 Rd Conroe (77301) *(G-3305)*

Hilite Industries Auto LP....................972 242-2116
1671 S Broadway St Carrollton (75006) *(G-2757)*

Hilite Industries Inc....................972 242-2116
990 S Saint Paul St Dallas (75201) *(G-4457)*

Hilite International Inc....................972 242-2116
1671 S Broadway St Carrollton (75006) *(G-2758)*

Hilite International Inc (HQ)................972 242-2116
1671 S Broadway St Carrollton (75006) *(G-2759)*

Hill & Smith Inc....................972 278-0553
2205 Hightower Dr Garland (75041) *(G-7513)*

Hill Cntry Bb Ch Drpping Sprng.............512 843-0035
100 Commons Rd Ste 4 Dripping Springs (78620) *(G-5507)*

Hill Country Cabinet Shop Inc................830 228-5062
18200 State Highway 46 W Spring Branch (78070) *(G-19270)*

Hill Country Directories Ltd.................512 864-2973
508 Cedar Dr Georgetown (78628) *(G-7656)*

Hill Country Insulation....................512 515-7707
20105 Algreg St Pflugerville (78660) *(G-16675)*

Hill Country Land Improvement..............512 766-8122
801 Carney Ln Wimberley (78676) *(G-20881)*

Hill Country News....................512 259-4449
715 Discovery Blvd # 304 Cedar Park (78613) *(G-2973)*

Hill Country Provisions LLC (PA)............512 564-3013
1800 S Congress Ave Austin (78704) *(G-1204)*

Hill Country Publishing Co (PA)..............512 556-6262
416 S Live Oak St Lampasas (76550) *(G-13834)*

Hill Country Site Supply LLC................512 608-0069
1202 Lakeway Dr Lakeway (78734) *(G-13816)*

Hill Country Steel LP....................210 667-9737
13638 E Ih 10 Unit 2 Converse (78109) *(G-3396)*

Hill County Animal Hospital, Helotes Also called JR Peterson Inc *(G-8239)*

Hill County Press Inc (PA)................254 582-3431
335 Country Club Dr Hillsboro (76645) *(G-8327)*

Hill Plastics Inc....................972 436-9717
1415 Crescent Ave Lewisville (75057) *(G-14052)*

Hill Print Solutions Ltd....................214 826-0092
915 S Peak St Dallas (75223) *(G-4458)*

Hill, W K Awning & Tent Co, Houston Also called C H V Corporation *(G-9029)*

Hillarys Sweet Temptations Inc..............972 485-1005
2677 Forest Ln Garland (75042) *(G-7514)*

Hillburn Defense Systems Inc...............512 636-8498
310 W View Dr Wimberley (78676) *(G-20882)*

Hillcresc Publishing, Abilene Also called Stone-Cmpbell Rest Mvment Pubg *(G-83)*

Hiller Measurements Inc....................512 394-8356
14141 W Hwy 290 Ste 100 Austin (78737) *(G-863)*

Hilliard Energy Inc (PA)................432 683-9100
125 W Missouri Ave Midland (79701) *(G-15247)*

Hillman Group Inc....................903 592-2826
6357 Reynolds Rd Tyler (75708) *(G-20099)*

Hillman Oyster Company, Dickinson Also called Hillman Shrimp and Oyster Co *(G-5475)*

Hillman Shrimp & Oyster Co................281 339-1506
10700 Hillman Dr Dickinson (77539) *(G-5474)*

Hillman Shrimp and Oyster Co..............281 339-1506
10700 Hillman Dr Dickinson (77539) *(G-5475)*

Hillsboro Reporter Inc....................254 582-3431
335 Country Club Dr Hillsboro (76645) *(G-8328)*

Hillshire Brands Company....................713 928-6281
235 N Norwood St Houston (77011) *(G-10186)*

Hillshire Brands Company....................817 427-7700
3900 Meacham Blvd Fort Worth (76117) *(G-6700)*

Hillshire Brands Company....................972 556-0392
9901 Valley Ranch Pkwy E Irving (75063) *(G-13057)*

Hillshire Brands Company....................972 416-4395
1820 N Josey Ln Carrollton (75006) *(G-2760)*

Hillstone Company....................512 746-5544
1946 County Rd 239 Jarrell (76537) *(G-13270)*

Hilltop Energy LLC (PA)................972 686-0369
4925 Grnvlle Ave Ste 1200 Dallas (75206) *(G-4459)*

Hilltop Texas Inc....................214 430-1311
1420 W Mcdermott Dr # 11 Allen (75013) *(G-275)*

Hilti of America Inc (HQ)................800 879-8000
7250 Dallas Pkwy Ste 1000 Plano (75024) *(G-16886)*

Hilton, Houston Also called University Houston - System *(G-12467)*

Hines Chaunte....................469 583-0985
2691 Hearthstone Dr Farmers Branch (75234) *(G-6202)*

Hinostroza Cabinet Shop, San Juan Also called Alfonso Hinostroza *(G-18670)*

Hipple Ice Company....................325 692-0101
5513 N 1st St Abilene (79603) *(G-50)*

Hipro Technologies Inc....................512 833-6600
13915 Burnet Rd Ste 308 Austin (78728) *(G-1205)*

Hiroko International Inc....................210 590-4411
6185 Camp Bullis Rd San Antonio (78257) *(G-18168)*

Hirschfeld Holdings LP (PA)................325 486-4201
112 W 29th St San Angelo (76903) *(G-17805)*

A
L
P
H
A
B
E
T
I
C

Hirschfeld Industries, San Angelo *Also called Hirschfeld Holdings LP* ***(G-17805)***
Hirschfeld of Nevada Inc 325 486-4201
112 W 29th St San Angelo (76903) ***(G-17806)***
Hirschfeld Steel, Abilene *Also called W&W-Afco Steel LLC* ***(G-92)***
His Company Inc 713 934-1600
10803 Vinecrest Dr # 190 Houston (77086) ***(G-10187)***
Hispanic Fmly Chrstn Ntwrk Inc 214 331-2800
8330 Lyndon B Johnson Fwy Dallas (75243) ***(G-4460)***
Hitachi America Ltd 972 488-3824
2315 Luna Rd Carrollton (75006) ***(G-2761)***
Hitech Fire Detection Corp 281 475-7289
18315 Trace Forest Dr Spring (77379) ***(G-19130)***
Hitech Integrated Solutions, Spring *Also called Hitech Fire Detection Corp* ***(G-19130)***
Hitech Truck Rigging, Houston *Also called 146 Business Park Inc* ***(G-8401)***
Hiway Neon Sign, Pharr *Also called Michael Egan Allen* ***(G-16707)***
Hixson Lumber Sales Inc 903 527-4010
1 Brewton Industrial Dr Caddo Mills (75135) ***(G-2624)***
Hj Plastering, Pasadena *Also called Hmj Plastering LLC* ***(G-16454)***
HK Energy Operating LLC 281 537-9920
1000 La St Ste 6700 Houston (77002) ***(G-10188)***
Hkn Inc (HQ) **817 424-2424**
180 State St Ste 200 Southlake (76092) ***(G-19074)***
Hl Industries Inc 979 836-2661
1208 Industrial Blvd Brenham (77833) ***(G-2257)***
Hlc Custom Processing LLC 432 556-2443
820 Sw 3001 Andrews (79714) ***(G-544)***
Hlcl Capital Corporation 972 660-4096
2113 109th St Grand Prairie (75050) ***(G-7892)***
Hlh Timber Company LLC 936 269-4199
380 County Road 3790 Joaquin (75954) ***(G-13311)***
Hli Energy Services, Cleburne *Also called Hli Resources LLC* ***(G-3095)***
Hli Resources LLC 817 240-4361
3600 W Highway 67 Cleburne (76033) ***(G-3095)***
HM Roustabout Service Inc 830 563-5449
8 W Louise Ave Eldorado (76936) ***(G-6046)***
HMC Capital Inc (PA) **936 441-2666**
27601 Commerce Oaks Dr The Woodlands (77385) ***(G-19872)***
HMC Instrmentation Contrls LLC 832 252-9280
16940 Grant Rd Cypress (77429) ***(G-3799)***
HMC Instrument & Mch Works Ltd 713 468-1426
2325 Blalock Rd Houston (77080) ***(G-10189)***
Hme, Grand Prairie *Also called Origin Instruments Corp* ***(G-7942)***
Hmh Supplemental Publishers 512 721-7000
10801 N Mopac Expy 3-150 Austin (78759) ***(G-1206)***
Hmj Plastering LLC 713 941-2807
716 Cavalier Ln Pasadena (77502) ***(G-16454)***
HMS Business Services, Irving *Also called Health Management Systems Inc* ***(G-13055)***
Hmt High Medical Tech USA Inc 512 721-4700
1301 S Cptl Of Tx Hwy 2 West Lake Hills (78746) ***(G-20682)***
Hmt LLC (PA) **281 681-7000**
19241 David Memorial Dr # 150 Shenandoah (77385) ***(G-18897)***
Hoarel Sign Co 806 373-2175
819 Ne 7th Ave Amarillo (79107) ***(G-434)***
Hobart Sales and Service Inc 210 829-5663
5407 Bandera Rd Ste 110 San Antonio (78238) ***(G-18169)***
Hobas Pipe Usa Inc 281 821-2200
1413 E Richey Rd Houston (77073) ***(G-10190)***
Hobbs Bonded Fibers LLC (PA) **254 741-0040**
200 Commerce Dr Waco (76710) ***(G-20412)***
Hobbs Bonded Fibers Na LLC (HQ) **254 741-0040**
200 Commerce Dr Waco (76710) ***(G-20413)***
Hobby Lobby Stores Inc 214 872-3184
5550 Preston Rd Frisco (75034) ***(G-7290)***
Hobby Q, Denton *Also called Reaper Miniatures Inc* ***(G-5397)***
Hockley County Publishing Co 806 894-3121
711 Austin St Levelland (79336) ***(G-14009)***
Hodyon LP (HQ) **512 225-0165**
2620 Brushy Creek Loop Cedar Park (78613) ***(G-2974)***
Hoelscher Weatherstrip Mfg Inc 713 869-6466
2400 S Persimmon St Tomball (77375) ***(G-19982)***
Hoerbiger Service Inc 281 442-2497
5405 Consulate Plaza Dr Houston (77032) ***(G-10191)***
Hoerbiger Service Inc 281 474-4458
12206 W Fairmont Pkwy La Porte (77571) ***(G-13745)***
Hoesman Industries Inc 512 247-4173
5264 Highway 71 E Del Valle (78617) ***(G-5331)***
Hoffa Inc 713 460-9000
4106 Campbell Rd Houston (77080) ***(G-10192)***
Hoffland Environmental Inc 936 856-4515
10391 Silver Springs Rd Conroe (77303) ***(G-3306)***
Hoffman Company 361 882-9281
1306 Laredo St Corpus Christi (78401) ***(G-3549)***
Hoffman Controls Corp 972 243-7425
2463 Merrell Rd Dallas (75229) ***(G-4461)***
Hoffman Industrial Electric (PA) **361 573-6365**
301 W Convent St Victoria (77901) ***(G-20272)***
Hoffman Lumber Company, Texas City *Also called Eason Properties I LLC* ***(G-19789)***
Hoffman Ventures Inc 281 339-2812
4403 15th St Bacliff (77518) ***(G-1732)***
Hogan Steel Erectors Inc (PA) **409 883-8208**
605 Dayton St West Orange (77630) ***(G-20694)***
Hogan, C H Drafting Service, West Orange *Also called Hogan Steel Erectors Inc* ***(G-20694)***
Hohmann & Barnard Inc 817 625-9781
2415 Cold Springs Rd Fort Worth (76106) ***(G-6701)***
Hoka Hey Fine Arts Foundry, Stephenville *Also called Hoka Hey Inc* ***(G-19416)***
Hoka Hey Inc 254 445-2017
1405 Parkwood Ct Stephenville (76401) ***(G-19416)***
Hokulia Shave Ice of Humble 832 527-2820
3540 Rayford Rd Spring (77386) ***(G-19216)***
Holcim Inc 713 672-4316
9600 Clinton Dr Houston (77029) ***(G-10193)***
Holcim (us) Inc 214 596-9760
15900 Dooley Rd Ste 200 Addison (75001) ***(G-134)***
Holcomb Candy Co, Jacksonville *Also called Jacksonville Candy Co Inc* ***(G-13244)***
Hold Phone LLC 281 304-4777
12320 Barker Cypress Rd Cypress (77429) ***(G-3800)***
Holdingcross 214 705-6502
3245 Main St Ste 235 Frisco (75034) ***(G-7291)***
Holdingcross.com, Frisco *Also called Holdingcross* ***(G-7291)***
Holdtite USA Inc 817 441-1723
1051 Fm 1187 S Fort Worth (76036) ***(G-6702)***
Hole Specialists Inc 281 290-7770
27950 Commercial Park Rd Tomball (77375) ***(G-19983)***
Holicks Manufacturing Co LLC 979 846-6721
4315 Wellborn Rd Bryan (77801) ***(G-2477)***
Holland and Associates LLC 806 892-3504
812 Mimosa Ave Idalou (79329) ***(G-12889)***
Holland Hitch, Wylie *Also called Saf-Holland Inc* ***(G-20947)***
Holland Jewelry Inc 325 655-3135
501 W Beauregard Ave San Angelo (76903) ***(G-17807)***
Hollimon Oil Corporation 210 829-8822
8833 Tradeway St San Antonio (78217) ***(G-18170)***
Hollimon, J Charles, San Antonio *Also called Hollimon Oil Corporation* ***(G-18170)***
Hollis Baker Sign Co Inc 512 835-5782
9711 Beck Cir Austin (78758) ***(G-1207)***
Hollman Inc (PA) **972 815-4000**
1825 W Walnut Hill Ln # 110 Irving (75038) ***(G-13058)***
Hollman Court Systems, Irving *Also called Hollman Inc* ***(G-13058)***
Holloman Corporation (PA) **281 878-2600**
333 N Sam Houston Pkwy E Houston (77060) ***(G-10194)***
Hollon Safe Company LLC 888 455-2337
227 44th St Corpus Christi (78405) ***(G-3550)***
Holloway Company Inc (PA) **817 232-8663**
1200 Jarvis Rd Saginaw (76179) ***(G-17746)***
Holloway Company Inc 713 453-4691
12660 La Rochelle Dr Houston (77015) ***(G-10195)***
Holloway Welding & Piping Co 972 562-5033
820 W Forest Grove Rd Allen (75002) ***(G-276)***
Holly Fabrication Inc 972 233-5362
4143 Billy Mitchell Dr Addison (75001) ***(G-135)***
Holly Yaupon Tea LLC 512 677-4907
202 N Front St Cat Spring (78933) ***(G-2930)***
Hollyfrontier Corporation (PA) **214 871-3555**
2828 N Harwood St # 1300 Dallas (75201) ***(G-4462)***
Hollyfrontier Ref & Mktg LLC (HQ) **214 871-3555**
2828 N Harwood St # 1300 Dallas (75201) ***(G-4463)***
Hollywood Ovrhd Door of Dallas (PA) **214 348-7240**
9525 White Rock Trl Dallas (75238) ***(G-4464)***
Hollywood Steel Inc 713 686-4325
6322 W 34th St Houston (77092) ***(G-10196)***
Holman Well Service LLC 806 665-3355
11401 Highway 152 Pampa (79065) ***(G-16325)***
Holmes Auto Supply Inc 432 689-8008
3301 Bankhead Hwy Midland (79701) ***(G-15248)***
Holmes Construction Co LP 806 376-8629
10221 Climer Cir Amarillo (79124) ***(G-435)***
Holmes Foods Inc (PA) **830 582-1551**
101 S Liberty Ave Nixon (78140) ***(G-15866)***
Holmes Foods Inc 830 437-5555
2170 Fm 108 S Gonzales (78629) ***(G-7755)***
Holmes Foods Inc 830 437-2555
108 South St Gonzales (78629) ***(G-7756)***
Holmes Rm, Houston *Also called Cemex Construction Mtls S LLC* ***(G-9126)***
Holmes Smokehouse, Houston *Also called Double R Brand Foods LLC* ***(G-9502)***
Holsey Mining Inc 936 545-1021
9812 State Highway 7 W Crockett (75835) ***(G-3719)***
Holt Texas Ltd (PA) **210 648-1111**
5665 Se Loop 410 San Antonio (78222) ***(G-18171)***
Holverstott Najee 210 769-5246
6435 Crestway Rd Lot 13 San Antonio (78239) ***(G-18172)***
Home Fragrance Holdings Inc (PA) **718 641-3759**
411 N Sam Houston Pkwy E # 300 Houston (77060) ***(G-10197)***
Home Mart Inc 956 724-4521
6419 Mcpherson Rd Laredo (78041) ***(G-13892)***
Home Treasures Inc 713 937-7716
5150 Ashley Ct Houston (77041) ***(G-10198)***
Homeart Designs Inc 956 724-4412
6419 Mcpherson Rd Laredo (78041) ***(G-13893)***

Homehardwareoutlet.com, San Antonio *Also called Allen and Allen LLC* ***(G-17894)***
Homeland Security Division, Richmond *Also called Azan Industries Inc* ***(G-17450)***
Homestead Craftsmen LLC (PA).....254 754-9600
308 Dry Creek Rd Waco (76705) ***(G-20414)***
Homestead Gristmill LLC.....254 829-2135
800 Dry Creek Rd Waco (76705) ***(G-20415)***
Homestead Heritage.....254 754-9665
800 Dry Creek Rd Waco (76705) ***(G-20416)***
Homestead Maintenance Services, Waco *Also called Homestead Heritage* ***(G-20416)***
Honcho Boots LLC.....915 855-9300
3505 Lee Blvd Ste E El Paso (79936) ***(G-5796)***
Hondo Anvil Herald, The, Hondo *Also called Associated Texas Newspapers* ***(G-8353)***
Honducar, San Antonio *Also called Egm Cleaning & Remodeling* ***(G-18084)***
Honeycomb One LLP.....817 649-7056
2800 E Randol Mill Rd Arlington (76011) ***(G-697)***
Honeywell Authorized Dealer, Houston *Also called Bates AC & Svc Co Inc* ***(G-8824)***
Honeywell Authorized Dealer, Odessa *Also called Darville Co* ***(G-15974)***
Honeywell Authorized Dealer, Dallas *Also called Air Performance Service Inc* ***(G-3907)***
Honeywell Authorized Dealer, Houston *Also called Custom Air Products & Svcs Inc* ***(G-9365)***
Honeywell Enraf Americas Inc.....281 885-7979
11201 Grens Crossing Blvd Houston (77067) ***(G-10199)***
Honeywell International Inc.....409 886-7445
3927 Farm Rd 1006 Orange (77630) ***(G-16246)***
Honeywell International Inc.....713 780-6500
8440 Westglen Dr Houston (77063) ***(G-10200)***
Honeywell International Inc.....972 792-1800
830 E Arapaho Rd Richardson (75081) ***(G-17329)***
Honeywell International Inc.....361 937-1082
308 Crecy St Corpus Christi (78419) ***(G-3551)***
Honeywell International Inc.....817 215-9800
100 Highway 287 N Mansfield (76063) ***(G-14682)***
Honeywell International Inc.....480 353-4053
3509 Durazno Ave El Paso (79905) ***(G-5797)***
Honeywell International Inc.....979 491-2802
Gate 34 Hgwy 35 Old Ocean (77463) ***(G-16217)***
Honeywell International Inc.....979 778-4477
6200 Mumford Rd Bryan (77807) ***(G-2478)***
Honeywell International Inc.....832 252-3500
1250 W S Houston Pkwy S Houston (77042) ***(G-10201)***
Honeywell International Inc.....480 592-2047
3518 Durazno Ave El Paso (79905) ***(G-5798)***
Honeywell International Inc.....915 778-7401
10 Leigh Fisher Blvd 9h El Paso (79906) ***(G-5799)***
Honeywell International Inc.....281 890-0088
21300 Northwest Fwy Cypress (77429) ***(G-3801)***
Honeywell International Inc.....915 544-6634
3509 Durazno Ave El Paso (79905) ***(G-5800)***
Honeywell International Inc.....480 592-2052
8260 S Hrdy Dr Golden Dv El Paso (79901) ***(G-5801)***
Honeywell International Inc.....480 592-7380
3509 Durazno Ave El Paso (79905) ***(G-5802)***
Honeywell International Inc.....972 896-0004
10318 Markison Rd Dallas (75238) ***(G-4465)***
Honeywell International Inc.....717 771-8100
3509 Durazno Ave El Paso (79905) ***(G-5803)***
Honeywell International Inc.....281 444-2282
14503 Bmmel N Hston Rd St Houston (77014) ***(G-10202)***
Honeywell International Inc.....512 301-8414
5307 Industrial Oaks Blvd # 430 Austin (78735) ***(G-1208)***
Honeywell International Inc.....409 833-4601
350 Pine St Ste 250 Beaumont (77701) ***(G-1904)***
Honeywell Security Monitoring, Carrollton *Also called Gtcr Golder Rauner LLC* ***(G-2749)***
Honeywell UOP, Houston *Also called UOP LLC* ***(G-12472)***
Honghua America LLC.....832 448-8100
5615 W Fuqua St Bldg A Houston (77085) ***(G-10203)***
Hons International Inc.....281 940-9184
14835 Walbrook Dr Sugar Land (77498) ***(G-19493)***
Hood County News Inc.....817 573-7066
1501 S Morgan St Granbury (76048) ***(G-7800)***
Hood Flexible Packaging Corp (PA).....903 593-1793
2410 N Lyndon Ave Tyler (75702) ***(G-20100)***
Hooken R LLC.....817 304-7645
186 Smith Ranch Rd Cuero (77954) ***(G-3761)***
Hooks Industeial Service Ctr.....361 299-6112
101 Industrial Ct Conroe (77301) ***(G-3307)***
Hoopeston Foods, Flower Mound *Also called Teasdale Foods Inc* ***(G-6288)***
Hoover Container Group, Houston *Also called Hoover Group Inc* ***(G-10204)***
Hoover Container Solutions, Houston *Also called Hoover Mtls Hdlg Group Inc* ***(G-10205)***
Hoover Group Inc (PA).....800 844-8683
2135 Highway 6 S Houston (77077) ***(G-10204)***
Hoover Mtls Hdlg Group Inc (HQ).....800 844-8683
2135 Highway 6 S Houston (77077) ***(G-10205)***
Hope Agri Products Inc.....214 371-7120
4930 River Oaks Rd Dallas (75241) ***(G-4466)***
Hope Agri Products of Texas, Dallas *Also called Hope Agri Products Inc* ***(G-4466)***
Hope Agri Products of Texas.....903 732-3361
6301 Us Highway 271 N Powderly (75473) ***(G-17199)***

Hopewell Operating Inc (PA).....214 691-6216
4600 Greenville Ave # 200 Dallas (75206) ***(G-4467)***
Hopkins County Echo, Sulphur Springs *Also called Echo Publishing Company* ***(G-19586)***
Horiba Instruments Inc.....949 250-4811
5390 Bay Oaks Dr Pasadena (77505) ***(G-16455)***
Horiba Instruments Inc.....408 730-4772
9701 Dessau Rd Ste 605 Austin (78754) ***(G-1209)***
Horiba Scientific, Pasadena *Also called Horiba Instruments Inc* ***(G-16455)***
Horiba Stec, Austin *Also called Horiba Instruments Inc* ***(G-1209)***
Horizon Exploration, Houston *Also called Horizon Resources LP* ***(G-10207)***
Horizon Global Americas Inc.....915 545-2720
8460 Grand Vis El Paso (79907) ***(G-5804)***
Horizon Industries, Tyler *Also called East Txas Lighthouse For Blind* ***(G-20082)***
Horizon Printing, Austin *Also called Westcave Printing Corporation* ***(G-1657)***
Horizon Production & Oper LLC.....713 522-5800
2727 Allen Pkwy Ste 1900 Houston (77019) ***(G-10206)***
Horizon Publications Inc.....325 236-6677
112 W 3rd St Sweetwater (79556) ***(G-19631)***
Horizon Resources LP (PA).....713 522-5800
2727 Allen Pkwy Ste 1900 Houston (77019) ***(G-10207)***
Horizon Structural Systems Inc.....830 629-8000
3950 W State Highway 46 New Braunfels (78132) ***(G-15803)***
Horizon Tech Industries Inc.....817 536-2263
2401 Ludelle St Fort Worth (76105) ***(G-6703)***
Horizon Trailers, Galveston *Also called Cnm Horizon Investments LLC* ***(G-7393)***
Horizon Worldwide Corporation.....713 647-7400
1765 Stebbins Dr Houston (77043) ***(G-10208)***
Hormel Foods Corp Svcs LLC.....817 465-4735
4601 Hollow Tree Dr # 10 Arlington (76018) ***(G-698)***
Hormel Foods Corp Svcs LLC.....210 495-0764
16414 San Pedro Ave # 50 San Antonio (78232) ***(G-18173)***
Hornbeek Enterprises Inc.....817 478-2447
7503 Us 287 Hwy Arlington (76001) ***(G-699)***
Hornsbys Custom Cabinets.....830 693-2420
2701 Commerce St Marble Falls (78654) ***(G-14744)***
Horse Creek Mfg & Fabrication.....903 572-4211
405 County Road 3095 Cookville (75558) ***(G-3404)***
Horsepower Services LLC.....713 582-2105
5847 San Felipe St Houston (77057) ***(G-10209)***
Horseshoe Operating Inc.....432 683-1448
110 W La Ave Ste 200 Midland (79701) ***(G-15249)***
Horticultural Printers, Mesquite *Also called Orora Visual TX LLC* ***(G-15065)***
Horton Automatics, Corpus Christi *Also called Overhead Door Corporation* ***(G-3586)***
Horton Draperies of Texas.....713 774-7477
6029 Jessamine St Houston (77081) ***(G-10210)***
Hose Master LLC.....713 926-2288
1903 Tellepsen St Houston (77023) ***(G-10211)***
Hose-Tex, Houston *Also called Reliable Hose Solutions LLC* ***(G-11590)***
Hoshizaki America Inc.....817 540-4665
15121 Frye Rd Fort Worth (76155) ***(G-6704)***
Hoshizaki Dallas DC, Fort Worth *Also called Hoshizaki America Inc* ***(G-6704)***
Hoskin & Muir Inc.....817 640-7220
825 Avenue H E Ste 115 Arlington (76011) ***(G-700)***
Hospital Forms & Systems, Dallas *Also called HFS Holding Corporation* ***(G-4454)***
Hot Biscuits, Waco *Also called Heart of Texas Biscuits Inc* ***(G-20410)***
Hot Hydraulics Inc.....713 722-7200
6800 Northwinds Dr Houston (77041) ***(G-10212)***
Hot Line, Houston *Also called 8228 Corporation* ***(G-8417)***
Hot Point Energy, Caldwell *Also called Novosad Enterprises Inc* ***(G-2633)***
Hotschedules, Austin *Also called Red Book Connect LLC* ***(G-1455)***
Hotschedulescom Inc.....512 904-4299
6504 Bridge Point Pkwy # 42 Austin (78730) ***(G-1210)***
Hotsy Equipment Company, San Antonio *Also called Smart Control Systems LLC* ***(G-18480)***
Hotwell Us LLC (PA).....281 598-9990
15905 Waverly Dr Houston (77032) ***(G-10213)***
Hou Fab & Maintenance Inc.....713 672-1993
716 Sundown Meadows St Crosby (77532) ***(G-3733)***
Hou-Stone Inc (PA).....713 827-8700
2142 Ojeman Rd Houston (77080) ***(G-10214)***
Hou-Tex Glass & Mirror, Houston *Also called Hou-Tex Newnom Inc* ***(G-10215)***
Hou-Tex Newnom Inc.....713 777-0748
1185 Brittmoore Rd Houston (77043) ***(G-10215)***
Houghton Mifflin Harcourt Pubg.....817 302-0006
301 Commerce St Ste 3700 Fort Worth (76102) ***(G-6705)***
Houma Armture Wrks Houston LLC.....713 748-0702
8100 Mchard Rd Houston (77053) ***(G-8384)***
House of Forgings LLC (PA).....281 443-4848
353 Greens Landing Dr Houston (77038) ***(G-10216)***
Housetech Inc.....281 879-0484
10865 Fallstone Rd Houston (77099) ***(G-10217)***
Houston - Pipe, Houston *Also called Hydro Conduit of Texas LP* ***(G-10304)***
Houston Anodes Intl LLC, Houston *Also called Gaus Anodes International LLC* ***(G-9906)***
Houston Building Supply, Houston *Also called Chemsystems Inc* ***(G-9172)***
Houston Business & Fincl Svcs.....713 398-6314
801 Travis St Ste 1900 Houston (77002) ***(G-10218)***
Houston Business Journals Inc.....214 696-5959
2515 Mckinney Ave Dallas (75201) ***(G-4468)***

ALPHABETIC

Houston Business Journals Inc (HQ) 713 688-8811
  5444 Westheimr Rd # 1000 Houston (77056) *(G-10219)*

Houston Cabinets Inc 713 349-0848
  5902 Royalton St Houston (77081) *(G-10220)*

Houston Calco Inc 713 236-8668
  9903 Daisy Clover Ct Houston (77089) *(G-10221)*

Houston Canvas and Awning Co 713 789-8712
  6015 Skyline Dr Houston (77057) *(G-10222)*

Houston Casing Specialities 713 433-3940
  195 Southbelt Indus Dr Houston (77047) *(G-10223)*

Houston Cement Company LP 713 754-8000
  9550 Clinton Dr Houston (77029) *(G-10224)*

Houston Chronicle, Houston *Also called Hearst Newspapers LLC (G-10144)*

Houston Chronicle 713 362-7171
  10635 Richmond Ave Houston (77042) *(G-10225)*

Houston Cnty Ready-Mix Con Co 936 544-7200
  Hwy 19 S Crockett (75835) *(G-3720)*

Houston Community Newspaper, Houston *Also called Asp Westward LP (G-8723)*

Houston Compression & Svcs LLC 713 550-1556
  16250 Tomball Pkwy Houston (77086) *(G-10226)*

Houston County Courier, Crockett *Also called Polk County Publishing Co (G-3722)*

Houston Custom Packaging LLC 713 827-1427
  14109 Lost Meadow Ln Houston (77079) *(G-10227)*

Houston D&J International Inc 713 678-7888
  5855 Sovereign Dr Ste F Houston (77036) *(G-10228)*

Houston Defender Newspaper Inc 713 663-6996
  3003 S Loop W Ste 320 Houston (77054) *(G-10229)*

Houston Digital Instruments, Houston *Also called Hdi Instruments LLC (G-10142)*

Houston Dynamic Service Inc 713 636-5587
  8150 Lawndale St Houston (77012) *(G-10230)*

Houston Elbow & Nipple Co Inc 713 225-2257
  1714 Hussion St Houston (77003) *(G-10231)*

Houston Energy LP 713 650-8008
  1200 Smith St Ste 2400 Houston (77002) *(G-10232)*

Houston Fab Truck Rigging RPS 713 455-6161
  1124 Keyport Ln Houston (77015) *(G-10233)*

Houston Foam Plastics Inc (PA) **713 224-3484**
  2019 Brooks St Houston (77026) *(G-10234)*

Houston Fullfillment Center, Houston *Also called R R Donnelley & Sons Company (G-11524)*

Houston Gate, Houston *Also called Meyer-Smith Inc (G-10862)*

Houston Gear USA Inc 281 495-8274
  12810 Mula Ln Stafford (77477) *(G-19326)*

Houston Global Heat Transf LLC 281 446-1155
  14446 Smith Rd Humble (77396) *(G-12777)*

Houston Grinding & Mfg Co 713 869-3573
  3544 W 12th St Houston (77008) *(G-10235)*

Houston Heat Treat, Houston *Also called Houston Thermal Processing LLC (G-10256)*

Houston House & Home, Houston *Also called Blue Thumb Inc (G-8921)*

Houston Jvic Operations 281 476-5775
  2217 Sens Rd La Porte (77571) *(G-13746)*

Houston Kik Inc 713 747-8710
  2921 Corder St Houston (77054) *(G-10236)*

Houston Label Company, Pasadena *Also called Excel Label LLC (G-16435)*

Houston Lifestyles & Homes, Stafford *Also called Fort Bend Publishing Group (G-19317)*

Houston Medical Testing Svcs, Houston *Also called Houston Medical Tstg Svcs Inc (G-10237)*

Houston Medical Tstg Svcs Inc (PA) **713 665-4687**
  2646 S Loop W Ste 550 Houston (77054) *(G-10237)*

Houston Mfg & Fabg Co 713 688-8383
  4734 Creekmont Dr Houston (77091) *(G-10238)*

Houston Mfg Specialty Co Inc 281 888-4635
  9909 Wallisville Rd Houston (77013) *(G-10239)*

Houston North Machine Inc 281 351-8108
  14202 Pine Meadow Ln Tomball (77377) *(G-19984)*

Houston North Remodel 936 314-4654
  13151 Walden Rd Apt 158 Montgomery (77356) *(G-15634)*

Houston North Sleep Center 713 688-3188
  2710 Mangum Rd Ste 300 Houston (77092) *(G-10240)*

Houston Numismatic Exchange 713 528-2135
  2486 Times Blvd Houston (77005) *(G-10241)*

Houston Operations, Houston *Also called Ethosenergy Tc Inc (G-9708)*

Houston Opicoil Inc (HQ) 713 840-7171
  3040 Post Oak Blvd # 800 Houston (77056) *(G-10242)*

Houston Pipe Benders LLC 281 449-8241
  14500 E Hardy Rd Houston (77039) *(G-10243)*

Houston Plant, Houston *Also called Arkema Inc (G-8698)*

Houston Plant, Houston *Also called American Roller Company LLC (G-8607)*

Houston Plant, Houston *Also called Inhance Technologies LLC (G-10365)*

Houston Plating & Coatings LLC 713 946-8920
  1311 Georgia St South Houston (77587) *(G-19046)*

Houston Plating & Coatings LLC (PA) **713 946-8920**
  1301 Georgia St South Houston (77587) *(G-19047)*

Houston Post Tension Inc 713 937-6990
  7015 San Antonio St Houston (77040) *(G-10244)*

Houston Powder Coaters LLC 281 676-3888
  14024 E Hardy Rd Houston (77039) *(G-10245)*

Houston Precision Fas I LP 713 462-2227
  4923 Cranswick Rd Houston (77041) *(G-10246)*

Houston Press, Houston *Also called Voice Media Group Inc (G-12580)*

Houston Press LP 713 280-2400
  2603 La Branch St Houston (77004) *(G-10247)*

Houston Products Proc Inc (PA) **281 487-0766**
  15201 East Fwy Ste 100 Channelview (77530) *(G-3026)*

Houston R-Co Incorporated 281 987-9909
  11840 Gloger St Houston (77039) *(G-10248)*

Houston Ready Mix LLC 832 532-7408
  140 Eldridge Rd Ste D Sugar Land (77478) *(G-19494)*

Houston Roll Pipe LLC 713 686-8970
  4128 Creekmont Dr Houston (77091) *(G-10249)*

Houston Service Industries Inc 713 947-1623
  15045 Lee Rd Houston (77032) *(G-10250)*

Houston Shared Services, Houston *Also called Cemex Materials LLC (G-9131)*

Houston Shutters LLC 713 723-7100
  7000 Grand Blvd Houston (77054) *(G-10251)*

Houston Sign & Service Inc 281 442-0175
  1536 Hartwick Rd Houston (77093) *(G-10252)*

Houston Sign Company, Houston *Also called Zspace LLC (G-12733)*

Houston Specialties Products 936 931-5256
  6239 Keyko St Houston (77041) *(G-10253)*

Houston Style Magazine, Houston *Also called Minority Print Media (G-10888)*

Houston Sysco Inc (HQ) **713 672-8080**
  10710 Grens Crossing Blvd Houston (77038) *(G-10254)*

Houston Technology Center, Houston *Also called Scientific Drilling Intl Inc (G-11787)*

Houston Technology Center, Houston *Also called Multi-Chem Inc (G-10937)*

Houston Texcast Inc 713 697-8006
  706 Lehman St Houston (77018) *(G-10255)*

Houston Thermal Processing LLC 281 590-9600
  13802 Chrisman Rd Houston (77039) *(G-10256)*

Houston Thermoseal Inc 713 997-8111
  3803 S Sam Houston Pkwy W Houston (77053) *(G-8385)*

Houston Trailer Inc 281 459-5350
  7600 E Sam Houston Pkwy N Houston (77049) *(G-10257)*

Houston Transformer Co Ltd 713 977-6009
  5725 Braxton Dr Houston (77036) *(G-10258)*

Houston Truck Tarps LLC 346 571-1832
  3421 Manitou Dr Houston (77013) *(G-10259)*

Houston Tsm Inc 713 691-5271
  8026 E Hardy Rd Houston (77093) *(G-10260)*

Houston Tubulars Inc (PA) **281 485-4014**
  13600 Hatfield Rd Pearland (77581) *(G-16569)*

Houston Uniform & Apparel Co, Houston *Also called Houston Canvas and Awning Co (G-10222)*

Houston Unlimited Metal Proc 979 836-7568
  9400 Highway 290 E Chappell Hill (77426) *(G-3046)*

Houston Vibrator Ltd 713 939-0404
  9921 Tanner Rd Bldg K Houston (77041) *(G-10261)*

Houston Vibrator MGT Inc 713 939-0404
  9921 Tanner Rd Houston (77041) *(G-10262)*

Houston Walls & Decor, Houston *Also called Piw Ventures Ltd (G-11340)*

Houston Well Screen Company 281 449-7261
  11939 Aldine Westfield Rd Houston (77093) *(G-10263)*

Houston Wifi C/Hston Cnstr Svc 832 444-8300
  18703 White Candle Dr Spring (77388) *(G-19131)*

Houston Wiper & Mill Supply Co 713 672-0571
  1234 Kress St Houston (77020) *(G-10264)*

Houston Wire Works Inc 713 946-2920
  1007 Kentucky St Houston (77087) *(G-10265)*

Houston Yard, Houston *Also called Vgcm LLC (G-12562)*

Houtex Hi-Temp Transformer LLC 713 271-8993
  6111 Corporate Dr Houston (77036) *(G-10266)*

Houtex Ready Mix 713 987-0303
  6262 S Acres Dr Houston (77048) *(G-10267)*

Hov Services Inc (HQ) **248 837-7100**
  2701 E Grauwyler Rd Irving (75061) *(G-13059)*

Howard Croft 936 258-3321
  201 County Road 2318 Dayton (77535) *(G-5229)*

Howard Field Services, Athens *Also called Howard Measurement Co Inc (G-827)*

Howard Keith Melton 972 222-1900
  2408 Liles Ln Mesquite (75181) *(G-15052)*

Howard Measurement Co Inc (PA) **903 677-0700**
  1637 Enterprise St Athens (75751) *(G-827)*

Howco Group, Houston *Also called Howco Metals Management LLC (G-10268)*

Howco Metals Management LLC (HQ) **281 649-8800**
  9611 Telge Rd Houston (77095) *(G-10268)*

Howell Corporation (HQ) **832 636-1000**
  1201 Lake Robbins Dr The Woodlands (77380) *(G-19873)*

Howell Oil & Gas Inc 903 935-0999
  3700 E End Blvd S Marshall (75672) *(G-14782)*

Howell Petroleum Corporation (HQ) **281 320-9096**
  1111 Fannin St Ste 1500 Houston (77002) *(G-10269)*

Howell Sand Company Inc 806 383-1721
  2300 E Hastings Ave Amarillo (79108) *(G-436)*

Howmedica Osteonics Corp 512 491-0222
  11500 Metric Blvd Ste 495 Austin (78758) *(G-1211)*

Howmet Aerospace Inc 866 385-2137
  25025 I 45 N Ste 575 The Woodlands (77380) *(G-19874)*

Howmet Aerospace Inc 940 243-4491
4401 N Elm St Denton (76207) *(G-5374)*

Howmet Aerospace Inc 903 832-8471
300 Alumax Dr Texarkana (75501) *(G-19765)*

Howmet Aerospace Inc 775 343-4010
14555 Old Crpus Chrsti Rd Elmendorf (78112) *(G-6070)*

Howmet Aerospace Inc 214 631-0200
8740 John Carpenter Fwy Dallas (75247) *(G-4469)*

Howmet Aerospace Inc 972 416-6500
2625 E Belt Line Rd Carrollton (75006) *(G-2762)*

Howmet Castings & Services Inc 940 855-8100
6200 Central Fwy Wichita Falls (76305) *(G-20771)*

Howmet Globl Fastening Systems 830 774-7156
2162 Cienegas Rd Del Rio (78840) *(G-5317)*

Howred Corporation 956 712-1003
5823 Northgate Ln # 2037 Laredo (78041) *(G-13894)*

Hoya Lens of America Inc (HQ) 972 221-4141
651 E Corporate Dr Lewisville (75057) *(G-14053)*

Hoya Optical Labs America Inc 972 221-4141
397 State Highway 121 Byp Lewisville (75067) *(G-14054)*

Hoyafam Holdings Ltd 281 447-0447
305 Hambrick Rd Houston (77060) *(G-10270)*

Hoyt Deryl 325 372-3825
2404 W Wallace St San Saba (76877) *(G-18717)*

HP, College Station *Also called Hewlett-Packard Company* *(G-3186)*

Hp Inc 512 432-8000
13620 Ranch Road 620 N B Austin (78717) *(G-1698)*

Hp Inc 970 898-0000
11445 Compaq Center W Dr Houston (77070) *(G-10271)*

Hp Inc 541 360-4763
10300 Energy Dr Spring (77389) *(G-19132)*

Hp Inc 972 604-3355
6901 Windcrest Dr Plano (75024) *(G-16887)*

HP Car Accessories & Atv Sales 903 675-0032
414 E Tyler St Athens (75751) *(G-828)*

Hpc Plating Company, South Houston *Also called Houston Plating & Coatings LLC (G-19047)*

Hpe, Houston *Also called Hewlett Packard Enterprise Co* *(G-10166)*

Hpi LLC (PA) 713 457-7500
15503 W Hardy Rd Houston (77060) *(G-10272)*

Hpp Recycle, Channelview *Also called Houston Products Proc Inc* *(G-3026)*

Hrh Door Corp 915 590-8997
1477 Lomaland Dr Ste B10 El Paso (79935) *(G-5805)*

Hrh Door Corp 281 821-8572
419 Century Plaza Dr # 230 Houston (77073) *(G-10273)*

Hrk Enterprises Inc 817 654-2008
5019 Mrtin Lther King Fwy Fort Worth (76119) *(G-6706)*

Hs, Houston *Also called High Standard Manufacturing Co* *(G-10175)*

Ht Energy LLC 806 771-7769
1415 Buddy Holly Ave Lubbock (79401) *(G-14419)*

Ht Intermediate Company LLC (PA) 512 328-2892
9825 Spectrum Dr Bldg 3 Austin (78717) *(G-1699)*

HTC Industries Inc 325 949-0645
1812 N Bell St San Angelo (76903) *(G-17808)*

Huawei Device USA Inc (HQ) 214 919-6688
5700 Tennyson Pkwy # 300 Plano (75024) *(G-16888)*

Huawei Mobile USA, Plano *Also called Huawei Device USA Inc* *(G-16888)*

Hub City Industries 903 938-8554
11441 State Highway 43 S Marshall (75670) *(G-14783)*

Hub Intrntnal Trnsp Insur Svcs 800 369-9010
70 Ne Loop 410 Ste 425 San Antonio (78216) *(G-18174)*

Hub Machine & Tool Inc 940 549-0155
800 380 Byp Graham (76450) *(G-7784)*

Hubbell Building Automtn Inc 512 450-1100
1812 Centre Creek Dr # 240 Austin (78754) *(G-1212)*

Hubbell Industrial Contrls Inc 281 391-6800
5713 13th St Katy (77493) *(G-13407)*

Huber Construction Company Inc 713 926-9623
5220 Texas St Houston (77011) *(G-10274)*

Huck International Inc 254 751-5283
8001 Imperial Dr Waco (76712) *(G-20417)*

Huckaby Enterprises Inc 817 732-5541
3805 W Vickery Blvd Fort Worth (76107) *(G-6707)*

Hudson & Hudson Neon Inc 281 720-0100
10500 Windfern Rd Houston (77064) *(G-10275)*

Hudson Abrasive Company 713 977-0037
8606 Windswept Ln Houston (77063) *(G-10276)*

Hudson Brothers Mining Company 903 876-4642
505 S Main St Rusk (75785) *(G-17731)*

Hudson Graphics Inc 903 758-1773
611 S Mobberly Ave Longview (75602) *(G-14248)*

Hudson Machine Works, Houston *Also called V & V Industries Inc* *(G-12509)*

Hudson Meat Market, Austin *Also called Hill Country Provisions LLC* *(G-1204)*

Hudson Products Corporation (HQ) 281 396-8195
9660 Grunwald Rd Beasley (77417) *(G-1841)*

Hudson Products Holdings Inc (HQ) 281 396-8100
9660 Grunwald Rd Beasley (77417) *(G-1842)*

Hudson Prtg & Graphic Design, Longview *Also called Hudson Graphics Inc* *(G-14248)*

Hudsons Embroidery 210 224-5504
330 Culebra Rd San Antonio (78201) *(G-18175)*

Huebner Road Quarry and Rdymx, San Antonio *Also called Legacy Vulcan LLC (G-18243)*

Hueco Quarry Inc 915 859-5767
15583 Faith Rd El Paso (79938) *(G-5806)*

Hufcor Inc 972 850-2200
454 W Mockingbird Ln Dallas (75247) *(G-4470)*

Huffco Industries Inc 713 827-1248
1400 W Sam Houston Pkwy N Houston (77043) *(G-10277)*

Huffco Metals & Machining, Houston *Also called Huffco Industries Inc (G-10277)*

Huffman & Huffman Inc 972 434-3640
243 Ridgeway Cir Lewisville (75067) *(G-14055)*

Huffman Company Ltd 432 332-5723
2373 W Interstate 20 Odessa (79766) *(G-16028)*

Hughes Dan A Company Lp (PA) 361 358-3752
208 E Houston St Beeville (78102) *(G-1985)*

Hughes Christensen, Corpus Christi *Also called Baker Hughes A GE Company LLC (G-3480)*

Hughes Christensen, Midland *Also called Baker Hughes A GE Company LLC (G-15132)*

Hughes Christensen, The Woodlands *Also called Baker Hughes A GE Company LLC (G-19834)*

Hughes Manufacturing Inc 979 542-0333
2301 W Highway 290 Giddings (78942) *(G-7696)*

Hughes Tank Company Inc 972 366-8684
157 South Hwy Venus (76084) *(G-20218)*

Huhtamaki Inc 903 427-5711
500 Industrial Blvd Clarksville (75426) *(G-3073)*

Huisache Energy Services Inc 361 299-2815
4528 County Road 56 Robstown (78380) *(G-17513)*

Hulk Oilfield Services Inc 432 803-7060
4911 S Arizona St Monahans (79756) *(G-15605)*

Hull Historical Inc 817 332-1495
201 Lipscomb St Fort Worth (76104) *(G-6708)*

Hull Supply Company Inc 512 385-1262
5117 E Cesar Chavez St Austin (78702) *(G-1213)*

Human Power of N Company 855 636-4040
1120 S Cap Of Tx Hwy Austin (78746) *(G-1214)*

Human Resource Micro Systems 415 362-8400
7301 State Highway 161 Irving (75039) *(G-13060)*

Humanetics II, Carrollton *Also called C H Industries Inc* *(G-2710)*

Humanetics II Ltd (HQ) 972 416-1304
1700 Columbian Club Dr Carrollton (75006) *(G-2763)*

Humanetics II Ltd 956 994-9200
7021 S Bentsen Rd McAllen (78503) *(G-14868)*

Humatech Inc (PA) 832 321-3098
19416 Park Row Ste 170 Houston (77084) *(G-10278)*

Humble Industries Inc 281 987-9175
2707 Wilson Rd Humble (77396) *(G-12778)*

Humble Texas Signs LLC 281 812-2100
20702 Townsen Blvd Humble (77338) *(G-12779)*

Humco Holding Group Inc (HQ) 903 831-7808
7400 Alumax Rd Texarkana (75501) *(G-19766)*

Humdinger Equipment Ltd 806 771-9944
3202 Clovis Rd Lubbock (79415) *(G-14420)*

Hunnicutt Digital Electronics 817 336-5449
4300 South Dr Fort Worth (76109) *(G-6709)*

Hunt Nlson Bnker Trust Estt-T (PA) 214 979-9072
3811 Trtl Crk Blvd Dallas (75219) *(G-4471)*

Hunt & Hunt Ltd (PA) 713 413-2500
14441 Almeda Rd Houston (77053) *(G-8386)*

Hunt Dominion Corporation (PA) 214 880-8400
1601 Elm St Ste 3900 Dallas (75201) *(G-4472)*

Hunt Engine Incorporated 713 721-9400
14805 Main St Houston (77035) *(G-10279)*

Hunt Exploration Mining Co 214 979-9072
1601 Elm St Ste 3650 Dallas (75201) *(G-4473)*

Hunt Marcellus LLC 214 978-8000
1900 N Akard St Dallas (75201) *(G-4474)*

Hunt Mining & Exploration, Dallas *Also called Nelson Hunt Bunker* *(G-4720)*

Hunt Oil Company 214 978-8000
1900 N Akard St Dallas (75201) *(G-4475)*

Hunt Oilfield Supply, Houston *Also called Halcon Operating Co Inc* *(G-10093)*

Hunt Petroleum Corporation (HQ) 214 880-8400
110 W 7th St Fort Worth (76102) *(G-6710)*

Hunt Petroleum Corporation 713 871-3400
1 Riverway Ste 700 Houston (77056) *(G-10280)*

Hunter Construction Inc 806 244-5331
Highway 54 W Dalhart (79022) *(G-3835)*

Hunter Inc 713 473-9333
802 Pasadena Fwy Pasadena (77506) *(G-16456)*

Hunter Industries Ltd (PA) 512 353-7757
4501 Hunter Rd San Marcos (78666) *(G-18695)*

Hunter Millworks Inc 806 792-4864
902 Ne Loop 289 Lubbock (79403) *(G-14421)*

Hunter Slings & Cables, Pasadena *Also called Hunter Inc* *(G-16456)*

Hunter Texas Stone, Abilene *Also called J P C Plastics Inc* *(G-53)*

Hunting Energy Services, Stafford *Also called National Coupling Company Inc (G-19356)*

Hunting Energy Services Inc 281 821-5577
1018 Rankin Rd Houston (77073) *(G-10281)*

A
L
P
H
A
B
E
T
I
C

Hunting Energy Services Inc...281 328-1400
16818 Ramsey Rd Crosby (77532) ***(G-3734)***
Hunting Energy Services Inc...281 569-3620
4400 N Sam Houston Pkwy W Houston (77086) ***(G-10282)***
Hunting Energy Services Inc...281 499-2583
1316 Staffordshire Rd Stafford (77477) ***(G-19327)***
Hunting Energy Services Inc...832 902-2266
555 Transport Dr Baytown (77523) ***(G-1791)***
Hunting Energy Services LLC...281 379-4289
7211 Spring Cypress Rd Spring (77379) ***(G-19133)***
Hunting Energy Services LLC (HQ)...**281 820-3838**
16825 Northchase Dr # 600 Houston (77060) ***(G-10283)***
Hunting Innova Inc...281 653-5500
8383 N Sam Houston Pkwy W Houston (77064) ***(G-10284)***
Hunting Oilfield Services, Houston *Also called Hunting Energy Services LLC* ***(G-10283)***
Hunting PLC USA (HQ)...**713 595-2950**
24 Waterway Ave Ste 700 The Woodlands (77380) ***(G-19875)***
Hunting Specialty Supply LP...281 970-8444
13730 Cypress N Huston Rd Cypress (77429) ***(G-3802)***
Hunting Titan Inc...281 463-5881
16825 Northchase Dr # 600 Houston (77060) ***(G-10285)***
Hunting Titan Inc...972 493-2580
143 Hcr 4361 Milford (76670) ***(G-15500)***
Huntington Foam LLC...512 581-7500
1278 Highway 71 W Bastrop (78602) ***(G-1758)***
Huntington Sky Production Ltd (PA)...**956 618-1800**
4117 N 10th St McAllen (78504) ***(G-14869)***
Huntington Solutions, Bastrop *Also called Huntington Foam LLC* ***(G-1758)***
Hunton Distribution Group, Houston *Also called Hunton Group Inc* ***(G-10286)***
Hunton Group Inc...806 788-1100
16335 Central Green Blvd Houston (77032) ***(G-10286)***
Huntsman Advnced Mtls Amrcas L (HQ)...**281 719-6000**
10003 Woodloch Forest Dr # 260 The Woodlands (77380) ***(G-19876)***
Huntsman Bldg Slutions USA LLC (HQ)...**817 640-4900**
3315 E Division St Arlington (76011) ***(G-701)***
Huntsman Chemical...936 539-1961
5451 Jefferson Chem Rd Conroe (77301) ***(G-3308)***
Huntsman Corporation...409 722-8381
Port Neches Operations Tio T Neches Opera Port Neches (77651) ***(G-17163)***
Huntsman Corporation (PA)...**281 719-6000**
10003 Woodloch Forest Dr # 260 The Woodlands (77380) ***(G-19877)***
Huntsman International LLC (HQ)...**281 719-6000**
10003 Woodloch Forest Dr # 260 The Woodlands (77380) ***(G-19878)***
Huntsman International LLC...713 924-6400
101 Concrete St Houston (77012) ***(G-10287)***
Huntsman Intl Trdg Corp...281 719-7400
8600 Gosling Rd The Woodlands (77381) ***(G-19879)***
Huntsman Intl Trdg Corp (HQ)...**281 719-6000**
10003 Woodloch Forest Dr # 260 The Woodlands (77380) ***(G-19880)***
Huntsman Petrochemical LLC...936 756-3381
5451 Jefferson Chem Rd Conroe (77301) ***(G-3309)***
Huntsman Petrochemical LLC...409 722-8381
2701 Spur 136 Port Neches (77651) ***(G-17164)***
Huntsman Petrochemical LLC...409 724-4474
6001 Highway 366 Port Neches (77651) ***(G-17165)***
Huntsman Pigments & Additives, The Woodlands *Also called Venator Americas LLC* ***(G-19935)***
Huntsville Item, Huntsville *Also called Newspaper Holding Inc* ***(G-12820)***
Hurd Enterprises Ltd...210 829-5255
7373 Broadway Ste 200 San Antonio (78209) ***(G-18176)***
Hurd Oil Field Service Inc...940 567-3131
500 S Main St Jacksboro (76458) ***(G-13221)***
Hurley International LLC...972 912-3040
820 W Stacy Rd Ste 201 Allen (75013) ***(G-277)***
Hurley International LLC...956 514-1700
5001 E Expressway 83 Mercedes (78570) ***(G-15006)***
Hurley Packaging Texas Inc...806 687-6179
2902 E Municipal Dr Lubbock (79403) ***(G-14422)***
Hurricane Office Supply & Prtg, Lubbock *Also called Trew Investments Inc* ***(G-14498)***
Hurst Hydraulics, Houston *Also called 820 Hydraulics LLC* ***(G-8416)***
Hurst Hydraulics Inc...713 863-0340
3714 Pinemont Dr Houston (77018) ***(G-10288)***
Hurst Terminal Us72, Hurst *Also called Lhoist North America Ala LLC* ***(G-12849)***
Hurst Terminal Us72, Hurst *Also called Lhoist North America Texas Ltd* ***(G-12850)***
Husa Accurate Mch Works Inc...713 691-0685
838 Dorchester St Houston (77022) ***(G-10289)***
Huse Country Meats, Malone *Also called Huse Processing Inc* ***(G-14638)***
Huse Processing Inc...254 533-2205
3697 State Highway 171 Malone (76660) ***(G-14638)***
Huss Services Inc...817 819-4138
3550 County Road 303 Jourdanton (78026) ***(G-13332)***
Hussmann Corporation...972 956-9045
925 Freeport Pkwy Ste 200 Coppell (75019) ***(G-3419)***
Hussy Media LLC...832 906-5816
9900 Spectrum Dr Austin (78717) ***(G-1700)***
Hutcheson Fabricating & Wldg...713 224-9703
15 N Hutcheson St Houston (77003) ***(G-10290)***
Hutchins Oil and Lube...972 225-0846
202 Myron Goff St Hutchins (75141) ***(G-12867)***
Hutchison Hayes Separation Inc...713 455-9600
3520 E Sam Houston Pkwy N Houston (77015) ***(G-10291)***
Hutto Holding Group Inc...512 832-8746
902 Tradesmens Park Loop Hutto (78634) ***(G-12879)***
Hvac Corrosion Tech LLC...214 790-9609
12160 Abrams Rd Ste 610 Dallas (75243) ***(G-4476)***
Hvac Manufacturing Inc...408 254-5420
1010 W Corsicana St Athens (75751) ***(G-829)***
Hvac Mechanical Svcs of Texas...713 266-3900
10555 Westpark Dr Houston (77042) ***(G-10292)***
Hvca, Addison *Also called Dean Technology Inc* ***(G-115)***
Hvm Technology Inc...830 626-5552
360 Mckenna Ave New Braunfels (78130) ***(G-15804)***
Hw Holdco LLC...972 536-6300
6191 N State Highway 161 Irving (75038) ***(G-13061)***
HWC Wire & Cable Company...713 453-8518
8641 Moers Rd Houston (77075) ***(G-10293)***
Hwm Hurst Inc...817 268-6111
645 W Hurst Blvd Hurst (76053) ***(G-12845)***
Hydessco LLC...903 983-2021
2505 N Longview St Kilgore (75662) ***(G-13559)***
Hydra-Rig, Fort Worth *Also called National Oilwell Varco Inc* ***(G-6861)***
Hydradyne LLC...210 661-4378
4235 S Ww White Rd San Antonio (78222) ***(G-18177)***
Hydradyne Hydraulics Inc (PA)...**713 937-8111**
1019 Rankin Rd Houston (77073) ***(G-10294)***
Hydrafab, Houston *Also called Hydraulic Fabrication Svcs Inc* ***(G-10297)***
Hydralift Amclyde Inc (HQ)...**713 375-3700**
10353 Richmond Ave Fl 21 Houston (77042) ***(G-10295)***
Hydraquip Custom Systems Inc...281 822-5000
16330 Central Green Blvd Houston (77032) ***(G-10296)***
Hydraulic and Pneumatic Eqp, Magnolia *Also called Hyvair Corporation* ***(G-14608)***
Hydraulic Fabrication Svcs Inc...832 844-3724
14490 Wagg Way Rd Houston (77041) ***(G-10297)***
Hydraulic Power Technology, Buda *Also called Dudley J Perio Inc* ***(G-2528)***
Hydraulic Pwr Technology-Texas...512 295-4234
18109 Foust Dr Buda (78610) ***(G-2530)***
Hydraulic Systems Inc (HQ)...**832 791-5000**
27601 Commerce Oaks Dr The Woodlands (77385) ***(G-19881)***
Hydraulics Inc...817 923-1965
3000 Saint Louis Ave Fort Worth (76110) ***(G-6711)***
Hydraulics of Texas, Houston *Also called Hot Hydraulics Inc* ***(G-10212)***
Hydril Company (HQ)...**713 670-3500**
302 Mccarty St Houston (77029) ***(G-10298)***
Hydril Company LP...281 449-2000
3300 N Sam Houston Pkwy E Houston (77032) ***(G-10299)***
Hydril Pressure Control, Houston *Also called Hydril USA Distribution LLC* ***(G-10300)***
Hydril USA Distribution LLC (HQ)...**281 449-2000**
3300 N Sam Houston Pkwy E Houston (77032) ***(G-10300)***
Hydril USA Distribution LLC...832 295-5557
5244 N Sam Houston Pkwy E Houston (77032) ***(G-10301)***
Hydril USA Distribution LLC...713 670-3500
302 Mccarty St Houston (77029) ***(G-10302)***
Hydrite Chemical Co...806 368-5660
2701 E 66th St Lubbock (79404) ***(G-14423)***
Hydro Conduit of Texas LP...832 590-5300
16701 Greenspoint Park Dr Houston (77060) ***(G-10303)***
Hydro Conduit of Texas LP...817 491-4321
8363 E Sam Lee Ln Northlake (76262) ***(G-15887)***
Hydro Conduit of Texas LP...832 590-5400
6560 Langfield Rd Bldg 3 Houston (77092) ***(G-10304)***
Hydro Conduit of Texas LP...979 885-7403
2735 Highway 36 Sealy (77474) ***(G-18808)***
Hydro Conduit of Texas LP...979 885-7403
2839 Highway 36 Sealy (77474) ***(G-18809)***
Hydro Conduit of Texas LP (HQ)...**832 590-5400**
6560 Langfield Rd 3-H Houston (77092) ***(G-10305)***
Hydro-Mulcher, Bowie *Also called Bowie Industries Incorporated* ***(G-2192)***
Hydrocrbon Exploration Dev LLC...281 453-5700
5825 N Sam Houston Pkwy W Houston (77086) ***(G-10306)***
Hydrocut Inc...979 849-5422
2015 County Road 220 Angleton (77515) ***(G-573)***
Hydroscience Technologies Inc...940 325-8221
6100 Columbia Rd Mineral Wells (76067) ***(G-15529)***
Hydrotex Holdings Inc...972 389-8500
12920 Senlac Dr Ste 190 Dallas (75234) ***(G-4477)***
Hydrotex Partners (PA)...**972 389-8500**
12920 Senlac Dr Ste 190 Farmers Branch (75234) ***(G-6203)***
Hyett Instrument Company, Bridge City *Also called Hyett Mfg & Instr Co Inc* ***(G-2285)***
Hyett Mfg & Instr Co Inc...409 735-5383
130 Granger Dr Bridge City (77611) ***(G-2285)***
Hygeia Dairy, Corpus Christi *Also called Dfa Dairy Brands Fluid LLC* ***(G-3513)***
Hygeia Dairy, Laredo *Also called Dfa Dairy Brands Fluid LLC* ***(G-13879)***
Hyghte Holdings, Irving *Also called Astura Medical* ***(G-12934)***
Hyper9 Inc...800 748-0685
9015 Mt Ridge Dr Ste 140 Austin (78759) ***(G-1215)***
Hyperion Energy LP (PA)...**214 750-3820**
12377 Merit Dr Ste 1200 Dallas (75251) ***(G-4478)***

Hyperion Resources Inc 214 750-1522
  5910 N Central Expy # 1520 Dallas (75206) *(G-4479)*

Hypertec Inc 940 564-5600
  301 E Main St Olney (76374) *(G-16221)*

Hyphen Solutions LLC (PA) **972 728-8100**
  1507 Lyndon B Johnson Fwy Dallas (75234) *(G-4480)*

Hyponex Corporation 936 291-6386
  1284 State Highway 75 N Huntsville (77320) *(G-12814)*

Hyseco Inc 713 991-4240
  5900 Almeda Genoa Rd Houston (77048) *(G-10307)*

Hyvair Corporation (PA) **281 259-7768**
  31341 Friendship Dr Magnolia (77355) *(G-14608)*

I & I Design Inc 713 667-6800
  7023 Rampart St Houston (77081) *(G-10308)*

I & R Machining Inc 512 281-2251
  401 Hwy 290 E Elgin (78621) *(G-6055)*

I 35 Sandpit Inc 817 790-2772
  4531 S Interstate 35 W Alvarado (76009) *(G-335)*

I A D C, Houston *Also called International Assn Drlg Contrs (G-10398)*

I C S, Waco *Also called Ics Jail Supplies Inc (G-20418)*

I Corp Inc 409 981-9090
  4933 Fannett Rd Beaumont (77705) *(G-1905)*

I D M Controls, Houston *Also called Schlumberger Rig Tech Inc (G-11771)*

I Do It With Ink 817 715-0681
  2433 Gelbray Pl Fort Worth (76131) *(G-6712)*

I F S, Tyler *Also called Integrated Flow Solutions LLC (G-20102)*

I Net Software Technologies 972 401-0100
  9901 Valley Ranch Pkwy E Irving (75063) *(G-13062)*

I O U Enterprises Inc 956 631-3366
  423 W Nolana Ave McAllen (78504) *(G-14870)*

I T D Precision, Houston *Also called Industrial Tool & Die Co Inc (G-10355)*

I T M, Schertz *Also called Instruments Tech McHy Inc (G-18750)*

I T Remarketing Inc 713 263-8800
  6600 Long Point Rd # 103 Houston (77055) *(G-10309)*

I W Marks Jewelers LP (PA) **713 668-5000**
  3841 Bellaire Blvd Houston (77025) *(G-10310)*

I&G Designs and Logistics LLC 214 543-4461
  14114 Dallas Pkwy Ste 420 Dallas (75254) *(G-4481)*

I2 Technologies Inc (HQ) **469 357-1000**
  11701 Luna Rd Dallas (75234) *(G-4482)*

I3 Plastic Cards, Dallas *Also called Motion Envelope Inc (G-4690)*

Iacx Energy LLC (PA) **972 960-3210**
  5001 Lyndon B Johnson Fwy Dallas (75244) *(G-4483)*

Iae International Inc 281 685-3091
  13300 Stonefield Dr Houston (77014) *(G-10311)*

Iag Energy Services, LP, Amarillo *Also called Integrated Advantage Group LP (G-493)*

Iai, Brownsville *Also called International Assembly Inc (G-2362)*

Iatid Inc 210 698-8500
  1732 Universal City Blvd Universal City (78148) *(G-20182)*

IB Supply LLC (PA) **469 709-9650**
  2933 Eisenhower St # 110 Carrollton (75007) *(G-2870)*

Ibac Interests LP 281 681-0122
  610 Todd St Oak Ridge North (77385) *(G-15889)*

Ibarra's Tortilleria, Fort Worth *Also called R Ibarras Inc (G-6931)*

Ibe Smt Equipment Inc 281 259-9660
  318 Corporate Wood Dr Magnolia (77354) *(G-14609)*

Iberon LLC 877 559-2140
  10333 Richmond Ave # 500 Houston (77042) *(G-10312)*

Ibex Inc 254 559-3355
  300 N Breckenridge Ave Breckenridge (76424) *(G-2229)*

Ibio Inc (PA) **979 446-0027**
  8800 Hsc Pkwy Bryan (77807) *(G-2479)*

IBM Global Systems Inc 972 468-1944
  1303 W Walnut Hill Ln # 13 Irving (75038) *(G-13063)*

Ibs, Lolita *Also called Integrted Bagging Systems Corp (G-14175)*

Ic Enable LLC 214 575-9400
  800 E Campbell Rd Richardson (75081) *(G-17330)*

Ic-I Remediate LLC 432 213-7813
  7600 Brandon Rd Big Spring (79720) *(G-2083)*

ICC, Houston *Also called Indochinese Culture Center (G-10343)*

Icci, La Marque *Also called Industrial Cmmssning Cons Intl (G-13708)*

Icd, Houston *Also called Independence Contract Drlg Inc (G-10338)*

ICEE Company 713 937-9496
  7121 Perimeter Park Dr # 210 Houston (77041) *(G-10313)*

Ichor Systems Inc 512 246-9092
  200 Parker Dr Ste C600 Austin (78728) *(G-1216)*

ICI Paints Store, San Antonio *Also called Akzo Nobel Inc (G-17879)*

ICI Paints Store, Houston *Also called Akzo Nobel Inc (G-8521)*

Icl Specialty Products Inc 281 471-4700
  902 Sens Rd La Porte (77571) *(G-13747)*

Icon Oilfield Services LLC (PA) **214 758-0315**
  5950 Berkshire Ln # 1401 Dallas (75225) *(G-4484)*

Iconic Sign Group LLC 361 883-7446
  5819 Leopard St Corpus Christi (78408) *(G-3552)*

Icotex, Houston *Also called Industrial Cmponents Texas LLC (G-10348)*

ICP Industries LLC (HQ) **210 226-1261**
  100 Business Park Ave San Antonio (78204) *(G-18178)*

Ics Enterprises Ltd 915 539-5415
  9560 Joe Rodriguez El Paso (79927) *(G-5807)*

Ics Enterprises LLP 915 239-9256
  12273 Gateway Blvd W El Paso (79936) *(G-5808)*

Ics Jail Supplies Inc 254 751-1566
  5804 Franklin Ave Waco (76710) *(G-20418)*

Ics Vmi Group, El Paso *Also called Ics Enterprises LLP (G-5808)*

Icsi, Willis *Also called International Coating Services (G-20850)*

Ict Energy Solutions LLC 432 203-0576
  2211 N County Road 1120 Midland (79706) *(G-15250)*

Ict Holdings LLC (PA) **713 652-6600**
  1861 Fm 54 Littlefield (79339) *(G-14145)*

Icu Medical Inc 512 255-2000
  3900 Howard Ln Austin (78728) *(G-1217)*

Icynene-Lapolla, Houston *Also called Lapolla Industries LLC (G-10599)*

ID Technology LLC (HQ) **817 626-7779**
  5051 N Sylvania Ave # 405 Fort Worth (76137) *(G-6713)*

Idaho Timber of Texas LLC 817 293-1001
  900 W Risinger Rd Fort Worth (76140) *(G-6714)*

Idcastings, Austin *Also called Prestige Tank & Pump Svcs Inc (G-1431)*

IDEA Corporation 915 845-6606
  1013 Ada Ln El Paso (79932) *(G-5809)*

Idea Incubator LP 512 892-3022
  4330 Gaines Ranch Loop Austin (78735) *(G-1218)*

Idea Planet LP (PA) **972 380-9867**
  18170 Hillcrest Rd Dallas (75252) *(G-3844)*

Idea Planet Collectibles, Dallas *Also called Idea Planet LP (G-3844)*

Ideal Plty Breeding Farms Inc 254 697-6677
  215 W Main St Cameron (76520) *(G-2642)*

Ideal Power Inc 512 264-1542
  4120 Freidrich Ln Ste 100 Austin (78744) *(G-1219)*

Ideal Printers Inc (PA) **713 880-8800**
  707 West Rd Houston (77038) *(G-10314)*

Ideal Signs 512 930-7446
  79 Eastview Dr Ste 101 Georgetown (78626) *(G-7657)*

Identitec, Southlake *Also called Distinctive Graphics Inc (G-19062)*

Identity Solutions Inc 972 926-0929
  3200 Broadway Blvd # 450 Garland (75043) *(G-7515)*

Idera Inc **713 523-4433**
  2950 North Loop W Ste 700 Houston (77092) *(G-10315)*

Idis America Co Ltd 866 986-1312
  801 Hammond St Ste 200 Coppell (75019) *(G-3420)*

IDM Control, Houston *Also called Omron Electronics LLC (G-11181)*

IDM Group LLC 972 578-1010
  2552 Summit Ave Ste 404 Plano (75074) *(G-16889)*

Idpl, Houston *Also called Ideal Printers Inc (G-10314)*

Idpro, Hurst *Also called Talbot Group Inc (G-12860)*

Idq Acquisition Corp 214 778-4600
  2447 Merritt Dr 200 Garland (75041) *(G-7516)*

Idx Corporation 314 739-4120
  621 Hall St Cedar Hill (75104) *(G-2943)*

Idx Dallas LLC 972 637-1525
  621 Hall St Cedar Hill (75104) *(G-2944)*

Ies Holdings Inc (PA) **713 860-1500**
  5433 Westheimer Rd # 500 Houston (77056) *(G-10316)*

Ies International Energy Svcs 713 928-5311
  7224 Lawndale St Houston (77012) *(G-10317)*

Ifco Systems, San Antonio *Also called Chep (usa) Inc (G-18002)*

Ifco Systems North America Inc 214 637-4840
  6909 Harry Hines Blvd Dallas (75235) *(G-4485)*

Ifco Systems North America Inc 713 937-9311
  6829 Flintlock Rd Houston (77040) *(G-10318)*

Ifco Systems North America Inc 806 335-1746
  9531 Whse Rd 1 Bldg 9531 Amarillo (79111) *(G-437)*

Ifco Systems North America Inc 806 291-9024
  3800 N Quincy St Plainview (79072) *(G-16758)*

Ifod, Irving *Also called Institute Flght Oprtons Dsptch (G-13064)*

Ifs, Pflugerville *Also called Integrated Flow Systems LLC (G-16676)*

Ifs Coatings Inc (HQ) **940 668-1062**
  3601 N Interstate 35 Gainesville (76240) *(G-7345)*

Ifs Industries Inc 972 864-2202
  2222 Lonnecker Dr Garland (75041) *(G-7517)*

Ig Holdings LP 940 565-8505
  4545 Airport Rd Denton (76207) *(G-5375)*

Igahu Inc 469 474-9490
  2607 Prince George Ave # 3601 Desoto (75115) *(G-5433)*

Igi The Intl Group Inc 281 573-9280
  7106 N Highway 146 Baytown (77523) *(G-1792)*

Iglehart Enterprises Inc 512 282-2559
  4219 Iriona Bnd Austin (78749) *(G-1220)*

Iglo LLC 214 893-8703
  4924 Cambridge Rd Fort Worth (76155) *(G-6715)*

Iglo Led, Fort Worth *Also called Iglo LLC (G-6715)*

Igloo Products Corp 713 461-5955
  30603 Katy Brookshire Rd Katy (77494) *(G-13364)*

Igloo Products Corp (HQ) **281 394-6800**
  777 Igloo Rd Katy (77494) *(G-13365)*

Ignite Combustion Technologies, Midland *Also called Ict Energy Solutions LLC (G-15250)*

A
L
P
H
A
B
E
T
I
C

Ignition Systems & Contrls Inc (HQ) 432 697-6472
6300 W Highway 80 Midland (79706) *(G-15251)*

Igt Global Solutions Corp 512 908-4310
5301 Riata Park Ct Ste E Austin (78727) *(G-1221)*

Ihs Energy, Houston Also called Ihs Global Inc *(G-10319)*

Ihs Global Inc 713 840-8282
5333 Westheimer Rd # 100 Houston (77056) *(G-10319)*

Iiat Services Company (HQ) 512 476-6281
1115 San Jacinto Blvd # 100 Austin (78701) *(G-1222)*

Ikey Ltd 512 837-0283
2621 Ridgepoint Dr # 235 Austin (78754) *(G-1223)*

Ikg Usa LLC (PA) 281 452-6637
1514 S Sheldon Rd Houston (77015) *(G-10320)*

Ikongps, Arlington Also called Vbi Group LLC *(G-808)*

Ilc Dover LP 281 333-8751
2101 Nasa Pkwy 1 Houston (77058) *(G-10321)*

Ili Technologies 2002 USA 713 960-0811
4900 Woodway Dr Ste 925 Houston (77056) *(G-10322)*

Illes Food Ingredients Ltd (PA) 800 683-4553
2200 Luna Rd Ste 120 Carrollton (75006) *(G-2764)*

Illes Seasonings & Flavors, Carrollton Also called Illes Food Ingredients Ltd *(G-2764)*

Illinois Tool Works Inc 713 797-2181
16200 Park Row Ste 120 Houston (77084) *(G-10323)*

Illinois Tool Works Inc 713 944-3200
3200 Awesome Ln La Porte (77571) *(G-13748)*

Illinois Tool Works Inc 281 580-1589
12055 Cutten Rd Houston (77066) *(G-10324)*

Illinois Tool Works Inc 956 215-2000
9601 International Blvd Pharr (78577) *(G-16700)*

Illinois Tool Works Inc 713 996-4200
9505 Bamboo Rd Houston (77041) *(G-10325)*

Illinois Tool Works Inc 714 870-8661
4401 Blue Mound Rd Fort Worth (76106) *(G-6716)*

Illinois Tool Works Inc 314 733-1110
12055 Cutten Rd Houston (77066) *(G-10326)*

Illinois Tool Works Inc 800 231-1024
1370 E 40th St Bldg 71 Houston (77022) *(G-10327)*

Illuminate Vintage LLC 903 948-1161
1121 Delano St Houston (77003) *(G-10328)*

Illuminations Lighting Design, Houston Also called Rulon Elc Illuminations Co Inc *(G-11697)*

Illumitex Inc 512 279-5020
6301 E Stassney Ln 6-400 Austin (78744) *(G-1224)*

Image Concrete Inc 817 430-0339
2030 Walnut Hill Ln Dallas (75229) *(G-4486)*

Image Display Systems Inc 281 395-9100
1403 Vanderwilt Ln Katy (77449) *(G-13408)*

Image Furnishings Inc 806 747-6500
3208 Oberlin St Lubbock (79415) *(G-14424)*

Image Imprinting Inc 972 243-8125
2675 Freewood Dr Dallas (75220) *(G-4487)*

Image Industries, Carrollton Also called Taconic Industries Corporation *(G-2823)*

Image Millworks, Lubbock Also called Image Furnishings Inc *(G-14424)*

Image Type Corporation 214 956-9050
1601 Prudential Dr Dallas (75235) *(G-4488)*

Imageair, Lindale Also called Benchmark Manufacturing Inc *(G-14133)*

Imagecraft Exhibits, Austin Also called Mike Davis and Associates Inc *(G-1343)*

Imagery Graphic Systems, Desoto Also called Precision Business Mchs Inc *(G-5440)*

Imagery Marketing Design Inc 817 576-3735
2372 Irving Blvd Dallas (75207) *(G-4489)*

Images Ink, Odessa Also called Ritchie-Vincent Inc *(G-16142)*

Imageset, Houston Also called Issgr Inc *(G-10429)*

Imageworks, Houston Also called Ndsventures LP *(G-11021)*

Imagination Station Inc 214 237-9300
8150 N Cntrl Expy # 2000 Dallas (75206) *(G-4490)*

Imagine Communications Corp (HQ) 469 803-4900
3001 Dallas Pkwy Ste 300 Frisco (75034) *(G-7292)*

Imaging Products Corp 214 631-8899
1850 Empire Central Dallas (75235) *(G-4491)*

IMC, Lubbock Also called Industrial Molding Corporation *(G-14426)*

Imerys Perlite Usa Inc 281 471-3122
201 N 18th St La Porte (77571) *(G-13749)*

Imerys Talc America Inc 281 272-7200
17509 Van Rd Houston (77049) *(G-10329)*

Imex Veterinary Inc 903 295-2196
1001 Mckesson Dr Longview (75604) *(G-14249)*

Imfab Inc 903 577-0510
3047 Farm Road 2348 N Mount Pleasant (75455) *(G-15651)*

IMI Z & J, Houston Also called Zimmermann & Jansen Inc *(G-12730)*

Immatics Us Inc 346 204-5400
2130 W Holcombe Blvd # 900 Houston (77030) *(G-10330)*

Immediatek Inc 888 661-6565
3301 Airport Fwy Ste 200 Bedford (76021) *(G-1974)*

Immi Turbines Inc 936 788-2229
1410 S Frazier St Conroe (77301) *(G-3310)*

Immunogenesis Inc 713 276-7600
909 Fannin St Ste 2000 Houston (77010) *(G-10331)*

Immunotek Bio Centers LLC 432 307-6774
1363 W University Blvd Odessa (79764) *(G-16029)*

Immunotek Bio Centers LLC 806 310-2859
1813 E Amarillo Blvd Amarillo (79107) *(G-438)*

Immunotek Bio Centers LLC 214 453-2748
8989 Forest Ln Ste 100 Dallas (75243) *(G-4492)*

Immunotek Bio Centers LLC 404 345-3570
1080 N Westmoreland Rd Dallas (75211) *(G-4493)*

Immunotek Bio Centers LLC 404 345-3570
1401 Brown Trl Bedford (76022) *(G-1975)*

Imodco Services, Houston Also called Sbm Offshore Usa Inc *(G-11762)*

Imogene Wagner Company Inc 210 669-8927
30520 Smithson Valley Rd San Antonio (78261) *(G-18179)*

Impac Systems Engineering LLP 713 784-3500
319 S 1st St Temple (76504) *(G-19682)*

Impact Composite Tech Ltd 806 385-1015
312 Phelps Ave Littlefield (79339) *(G-14146)*

Impact Energy Services, Weatherford Also called Select Energy Services LLC *(G-20620)*

Impact Energy Services, De Berry Also called Select Energy Services LLC *(G-5235)*

Impact Energy Services, Gainesville Also called Select Energy Services LLC *(G-7366)*

Impact Fire Services LLC 713 263-7535
1285 N Post Oak Rd # 102 Houston (77055) *(G-10332)*

Impact Fire Services LLC 254 857-4990
214 Mid Tex Rd Lorena (76655) *(G-14341)*

Impact Fire Services LLC 512 243-7788
14000 Summit Dr Ste 700 Austin (78728) *(G-1225)*

Impact Fluid Solutions LP (PA) 713 964-7736
2800 Post Oak Blvd Ste 20 Houston (77056) *(G-10333)*

Impact Printing & Graphics 214 904-0808
2618 Perth St Dallas (75220) *(G-4494)*

Impact Recovery Systems Inc 210 736-4477
4955 Stout Dr San Antonio (78219) *(G-18180)*

Imperial - Savannah, Sugar Land Also called Imperial Sugar Company *(G-19496)*

Imperial Bag & Paper Co LLC 713 223-5050
5707 Harvey Wilson Dr Houston (77020) *(G-10334)*

Imperial Dade, Houston Also called Imperial Bag & Paper Co LLC *(G-10334)*

Imperial Fabricating, Denton Also called Ig Holdings LP *(G-5375)*

Imperial Fabricating Company, Decatur Also called Imperial Group Mfg Inc *(G-5247)*

Imperial Group Mfg Inc (PA) 940 565-8505
4545 Airport Rd Denton (76207) *(G-5376)*

Imperial Group Mfg Inc 940 627-1700
2188 E Highway 380 Decatur (76234) *(G-5247)*

Imperial Outdoor Power Eqp, Sugar Land Also called Imperial Outdoor Power Eqp *(G-19495)*

Imperial Outdoor Power Eqp 832 939-9838
7822 Us 90 Alt Ste B Sugar Land (77498) *(G-19495)*

Imperial Pumps Co 806 791-5242
4716 79th St Lubbock (79424) *(G-14425)*

Imperial Sugar Company (HQ) 281 491-9181
3 Sugar Creek Center Blvd # 500 Sugar Land (77478) *(G-19496)*

Imperial Sugar Company 281 491-9181
8016 Highway 90a Sugar Land (77478) *(G-19497)*

Import Mdsg Concepts GP LLC 214 572-2000
15565 Wright Brothers Dr Addison (75001) *(G-136)*

Impreglon Surface Tech Inc (HQ) 713 466-9655
6421 Calle Lozano Dr Houston (77041) *(G-10335)*

Impresa Label Inc (PA) 915 592-4500
1410 Gail Borden Pl B1 El Paso (79935) *(G-5810)*

Impreso Inc (PA) 972 462-0100
652 Southwestern Blvd Coppell (75019) *(G-3421)*

Impression Inks Ltd 817 590-9711
7333 Jack Newell Blvd N # 200 Fort Worth (76118) *(G-6717)*

Impressive Image Works Inc (PA) 903 597-4599
2901 Teague Dr Tyler (75701) *(G-20101)*

IMS, Plainview Also called Rotom Inc *(G-16762)*

IMS, San Antonio Also called Information MGT Solutions LLC *(G-18182)*

Imunize El Paso 915 857-2474
1580 Grge Dter Dr Ste 102 El Paso (79936) *(G-5811)*

Inc Cse W-Industries, Jersey Village Also called Cse W-Industries Inc *(G-13297)*

Inc, Paragon Furniture, Arlington Also called Paragon Furniture Inc *(G-749)*

Incab America LLC 833 344-6222
640 107th St Arlington (76011) *(G-702)*

Incc, Richardson Also called Industrial Noise Control Corp *(G-17331)*

Incenergy LLC 512 327-2020
12012 Tech Blvd Ste 101 Austin (78727) *(G-1226)*

Inchbug LLC 512 837-1010
9421 Neils Thompson Dr Austin (78758) *(G-1227)*

Inchbug.com, Austin Also called Inchbug LLC *(G-1227)*

Incinerator International Inc 713 227-1466
2702 N Main St Houston (77009) *(G-10336)*

Inclusive Products Inc 281 650-7057
1802 Reseda Dr Houston (77062) *(G-10337)*

Incongruity LLC 954 889-6854
539 W Commerce St Dallas (75208) *(G-4495)*

Incora, Fort Worth Also called Wesco Aircraft Hardware Corp *(G-7136)*

Incounters Inc 325 675-5909
2364 Butternut St Abilene (79602) *(G-51)*

Incratools, Carrollton Also called Taylor Design Group Inc *(G-2825)*

Indatech, Houston Also called Snelson Oilfield Ltg Co Inc *(G-11930)*

Indeco Sales Inc (PA) 254 939-5742
805 E 4th Ave Belton (76513) *(G-2025)*

Indeco-Industrial Electric Co 325 653-4255
65 E Avenue K San Angelo (76903) *(G-17809)*

Indelect Corporation 903 656-2518
102 E Industrial Blvd Lone Star (75668) *(G-14183)*

Independence Contract Drlg Inc (PA) 281 598-1230
20475 State Highway 249 # 300 Houston (77070) *(G-10338)*

Independence Oilfield Chem LLC (HQ) 713 936-4340
2600 Tech Forest Blvd The Woodlands (77381) *(G-19882)*

Independence Oilfield Chem LLC 210 888-0300
472 Eagle Ford Dr Pleasanton (78064) *(G-17069)*

Independence Resources MGT LLC (HQ) 832 916-2300
11450 Cmpaq Ctr Dr W Bldg Houston (77070) *(G-10339)*

Independence Resources MGT LLC 832 916-2300
6914 N County Road 1294 Midland (79707) *(G-15252)*

Independent Door Co Inc 972 487-0511
525 N 5th St Garland (75040) *(G-7518)*

Independent Pipe Services LLC 281 436-0380
9025 Pineland Rd Houston (77044) *(G-10340)*

Independent Plastic Inc (PA) 713 329-9955
6611 Petropark Dr Houston (77041) *(G-10341)*

Independent Tele Dirctry Co (PA) 972 722-4796
2860 State Highway 66 Rockwall (75087) *(G-17550)*

Indepndent Insur Agnts Assn Tx, Austin *Also called Iiat Services Company (G-1222)*

Indepndent Rugh Trrain Ctr LLC 210 599-6541
103 Guadalupe Dr Cibolo (78108) *(G-3063)*

Indevco Plas - Longview LLC 903 291-1115
800 Jordan Valley Rd Longview (75604) *(G-14250)*

Index Skateboarding 817 887-9779
3312 S Riley Ct Hurst (76054) *(G-12846)*

Indian Aerospace Inc 817 265-5137
427a W Fork Dr Arlington (76012) *(G-703)*

Indian Industries LP (PA) 817 265-6731
432 W Fork Dr Ste A Arlington (76012) *(G-704)*

Indian Rubber, Arlington *Also called Indian Industries LP (G-704)*

Indian Rubber Company Inc 817 265-6732
440 W Fork Dr Arlington (76012) *(G-705)*

Indicom Buildings Inc 817 447-1213
721 N Burleson Blvd Burleson (76028) *(G-2582)*

Indies Coffee Bar & Speakeasy, League City *Also called Indies Productions LLC (G-13959)*

Indies Productions LLC 281 508-3920
2406 Lake Front Ct League City (77573) *(G-13959)*

Indigo Minerals LLC 713 237-5000
600 Travis St Ste 5500 Houston (77002) *(G-10342)*

Indo-Mim Inc (HQ) 609 580-9745
3902 Sw 36th St Ste 101 San Antonio (78226) *(G-18181)*

Indochinese Culture Center (PA) 713 522-7799
3333 Fannin St Ste 203 Houston (77004) *(G-10343)*

Indoormedia Inc 281 206-2500
17015 Park Row Houston (77084) *(G-10344)*

Indoormedia Inc (PA) 800 247-4793
1445 Langham Creek Dr Houston (77084) *(G-10345)*

Indorama Ventures Oxides LLC 346 365-6056
24 Waterway Ave Ste 1100 The Woodlands (77380) *(G-19883)*

Indumar Products Inc 713 977-4100
2230 W Governors Cir Houston (77092) *(G-10346)*

Indus Instruments 281 286-1130
721 Tristar Dr Ste C Webster (77598) *(G-20639)*

Industrial Accessories Inc 956 728-7524
1113 Park St Apt 1 Laredo (78040) *(G-13895)*

Industrial Alloy Fbrcation Inc 409 600-8222
3780 Milam St Beaumont (77701) *(G-1906)*

Industrial Castings Co Inc (PA) 713 747-5336
6910 Stearns St Houston (77021) *(G-10347)*

Industrial Chem Tex Inc 903 759-2642
117 Edgewood St Longview (75604) *(G-14251)*

Industrial Chemicals Corp 940 383-0035
1700 Shady Oaks Dr Ste A Denton (76205) *(G-5377)*

Industrial Cmmssning Cons Intl 833 873-4224
714 Highway 3 La Marque (77568) *(G-13708)*

Industrial Cmponents Texas LLC (PA) 936 755-5697
2121 W Sam Houston Pkwy N Houston (77043) *(G-10348)*

Industrial Cnvyor Fbrction Ltd 817 439-0735
646 Aviator Dr Fort Worth (76179) *(G-6718)*

Industrial Coils LLC 956 664-9496
809 E Fir Ave McAllen (78501) *(G-14871)*

Industrial Communications, Corpus Christi *Also called Sat Radio Communications Ltd (G-3615)*

Industrial Control Inc 713 464-8005
10808 Alcott Dr Houston (77043) *(G-10349)*

Industrial Control Instruments, Houston *Also called Cooper Crouse Hinds LLC (G-9304)*

Industrial Diamond Products Co (PA) 713 991-1600
9925 Moers Rd Houston (77075) *(G-10350)*

Industrial Electric Motor Co, Lone Star *Also called Indelect Corporation (G-14183)*

Industrial Fbrctors Crpus Chrs, Corpus Christi *Also called Tsgc Inc (G-3644)*

Industrial Info Resources Inc (PA) 713 783-5147
2277 Plaza Dr Ste 300 Sugar Land (77479) *(G-19498)*

Industrial Insptn Innovation 281 636-7215
10700 Deaf Smith St La Porte (77571) *(G-13750)*

Industrial Instrument Co, Baytown *Also called Gordon Martin Inc (G-1820)*

Industrial Insul & Shtmtl Inc 432 332-8203
3339 Kermit Hwy Odessa (79764) *(G-16030)*

Industrial Lumber and Box Inc 713 928-2096
7710 Bowie St Houston (77012) *(G-10351)*

Industrial Machine Repair Inc 713 937-7995
11407 Charles Rd Jersey Village (77041) *(G-13300)*

Industrial Machinery Service, Longview *Also called H L Hailey Enterprises Inc (G-14244)*

Industrial Material, Galveston *Also called Steven-Sharon Corporation (G-7409)*

Industrial Metal Co, Beaumont *Also called Pinchback Industrial Inc (G-1941)*

Industrial Mill Maint Sup Inc (PA) 800 537-1218
4401 Waco St Wake Village (75501) *(G-20486)*

Industrial Models Inc 940 665-7841
1711 Westaire Dr Gainesville (76240) *(G-7346)*

Industrial Molding Corporation (HQ) 806 474-1047
616 E Slaton Rd Lubbock (79404) *(G-14426)*

Industrial Neon Sign Corp 713 748-6600
6223 Saint Augustine St Houston (77021) *(G-10352)*

Industrial Noise Control Corp 972 494-1422
1023 Sunningdale Richardson (75081) *(G-17331)*

Industrial Olfld Mar Cmpnnts I 713 266-1900
906 S Persimmon St Tomball (77375) *(G-19985)*

Industrial Pipe Fittings LLC 800 241-4175
6040 Osborn St Houston (77033) *(G-10353)*

Industrial Pipe Fittings LLC 903 872-7890
305 N 7th St Corsicana (75110) *(G-3674)*

Industrial Pipe Fittings LLC (PA) 800 241-4175
10707 Corp Dr Ste 220 Stafford (77477) *(G-19328)*

Industrial Pro Fab LLC 713 205-7245
23735 Ayscough Ln Katy (77493) *(G-13409)*

Industrial Products Group, Houston *Also called Dresser LLC (G-9518)*

Industrial Safety Tech LLC 713 559-9200
4055 Tech Forest Blvd The Woodlands (77381) *(G-19884)*

Industrial Sand Products LLC 832 838-8095
11501 Crosby Rd Highlands (77562) *(G-8312)*

Industrial Spclty Svcs USA LLC 713 987-9117
4900 Railroad St Deer Park (77536) *(G-5280)*

Industrial Tape & Label Corp 713 748-3105
7025 W Tidwell Rd Ste 109 Houston (77092) *(G-10354)*

Industrial Thermal Svcs LLC 409 886-9700
2711 Highway 87 S Orange (77630) *(G-16247)*

Industrial Thermoform Inc 972 299-5391
1211 Industrial Way Cedar Hill (75104) *(G-2945)*

Industrial Tool & Die Co Inc (PA) 281 859-4499
9719 Telge Rd Houston (77095) *(G-10355)*

Industrial Tool & Die Co Inc 956 440-9960
818 N Fm 509 Harlingen (78550) *(G-8190)*

Industrial Vision Source, Dallas *Also called Mace Security Intl Inc (G-4624)*

Industrial Water Services, El Paso *Also called El Paso Water Indus Svcs Inc (G-5746)*

Industrial Welding Academy 713 944-0701
11001 Wallisville Rd Houston (77013) *(G-10356)*

Industrial Woodworking Mch, Garland *Also called SC Industrial Resource Group (G-7584)*

Industrias Lancermex SA De Cv, San Antonio *Also called Lancer Corporation (G-18236)*

Industrotech Inc 817 847-1358
1009 Wickwood Ct Fort Worth (76131) *(G-6719)*

Indy Construction, Fairfield *Also called Daniel Mike Construction Inc (G-6172)*

Ineos 979 415-8500
2305 N Brazosport Blvd Freeport (77541) *(G-7199)*

Ineos LLC 361 552-8205
13050 Texas Hwy 185 Port Lavaca (77979) *(G-17147)*

Ineos Americas LLC (HQ) 251 535-6600
2600 S Shore Blvd Ste 500 League City (77573) *(G-13960)*

Ineos Americas LLC 713 920-4300
3503 Pasadena Fwy Pasadena (77503) *(G-16457)*

Ineos Americas LLC 361 552-8244
S Of Bloomington Port Lavaca (77979) *(G-17148)*

Ineos Americas LLC 713 307-3000
1230 Independence Pkwy S La Porte (77571) *(G-13751)*

Ineos Americas LLC 713 767-5714
1514 Miller Cut Off Rd La Porte (77571) *(G-13752)*

Ineos Americas LLC 409 985-0863
2001 Gulfway Dr Port Arthur (77640) *(G-17113)*

Ineos Calabrian Corporation (HQ) 281 348-2303
1521 Green Oak Pl Ste 200 Kingwood (77339) *(G-13645)*

Ineos Calabrian Corporation 409 727-1471
5500 Highway 366 Port Neches (77651) *(G-17166)*

Ineos New Planet Bioenergy LLC 630 857-7143
2600 S Shore Blvd Ste 500 League City (77573) *(G-13961)*

Ineos Nitriles, League City *Also called Ineos Americas LLC (G-13960)*

Ineos Nitriles USA LLC 361 552-8200
13050 State Highway 185 N Port Lavaca (77979) *(G-17149)*

Ineos Nitriles USA LLC (HQ) 281 535-6600
2600 S Shore Blvd Ste 250 League City (77573) *(G-13962)*

Ineos Olgmers Chclat Bayou LLC (HQ) 281 535-6738
2600 S Shore Blvd Ste 250 League City (77573) *(G-13963)*

Ineos Oligomers, La Porte *Also called Ineos Americas LLC (G-13752)*

A
L
P
H
A
B
E
T
I
C

Ineos Oligomers USA LLC 281 581-3203
2 Miles S Of Fm 2917 Fm 2 Alvin (77512) *(G-366)*

Ineos Styrolution America LLC 281 474-1000
12222 Port Rd Pasadena (77507) *(G-16458)*

Ineos Styrolution America LLC 281 474-1009
2600 S Shore Blvd Ste 300 League City (77573) *(G-13964)*

Ineos USA LLC (HQ) **281 535-6600**
2600 S Shore Blvd Ste 500 League City (77573) *(G-13965)*

Ineos USA LLC 281 535-6600
2600 S Shore Blvd Ste 250 League City (77573) *(G-13966)*

Inexs, Houston *Also called Interctive Explrtion Solutions (G-10394)*

Infinity Carports Inc 903 765-2057
7977 Us Hwy 19 Edgewood (75117) *(G-5572)*

Infinity Marine Offshore, LLC, Houston *Also called US Joiner LLC (G-12484)*

Info-Power International Inc 972 424-4447
3345 Silverstone Dr Ste B Plano (75023) *(G-16890)*

Infocyte Inc 844 463-6298
3801 N Capital Of Texas H Austin (78746) *(G-1228)*

Infocyte Security, Austin *Also called Infocyte Inc (G-1228)*

Infomotion, Dallas *Also called Dobbs-Stanford Corporation (G-4269)*

Infor (us) LLC 800 915-3243
14185 Dallas Pkwy Ste 550 Dallas (75254) *(G-4496)*

Informacion Publishing Co Inc 713 272-0100
6065 Hillcroft St Ste 400 Houston (77081) *(G-10357)*

Information MGT Solutions LLC 210 826-4994
2416 Brockton St Ste 105 San Antonio (78217) *(G-18182)*

Information Store Inc (PA) **713 787-6798**
10777 Westheimer Rd # 250 Houston (77042) *(G-10358)*

Informcion-The Spanish Newsppr, Houston *Also called Informacion Publishing Co Inc (G-10357)*

Infosys Limited 281 454-0300
6002 Rogerdale Rd Ste 550 Houston (77072) *(G-10359)*

Infosys Limited (HQ) **214 306-2100**
2400 N Glnville Dr Ste C15 Richardson (75082) *(G-17332)*

Infovine Inc 713 223-9994
1100 W 23rd St Ste 100 Houston (77008) *(G-10360)*

Inframark LLC 281 579-4500
9550 Helms Trl Ste 800 Forney (75126) *(G-6309)*

Infrared Cameras Inc 409 861-0788
2105 W Cardinal Dr Beaumont (77705) *(G-1907)*

Infrared Thermal Imaging Inc 361 779-1197
703 W Richard Ave Kingsville (78363) *(G-13628)*

Infrared Training Institute, Beaumont *Also called Infrared Cameras Inc (G-1907)*

Infrastructure Networks Inc (PA) **832 598-6600**
5051 Westheimr Rd # 1700 Houston (77056) *(G-10361)*

Infratech Inc 214 503-1087
10440 Miller Rd Dallas (75238) *(G-4497)*

Infused Medical Technology Inc 214 330-4000
4559 S Westmoreland Rd Dallas (75237) *(G-4498)*

Ingalls Custom Lamps, Dallas *Also called Haleaux Inc (G-4428)*

Ingamia Inc 214 828-1660
4949 Beeman Ave Dallas (75223) *(G-4499)*

Ingenia Polymers Inc (HQ) **281 862-2111**
2222 Appelt Dr Houston (77015) *(G-10362)*

Ingenia Polymers Inc 281 862-2111
2222 Appelt Dr Houston (77015) *(G-10363)*

Ingersoll-Rand, Tyler *Also called Trane Technologies Company LLC (G-20163)*

Ingram Concrete LLC 325 677-2001
1801 N Danville Dr Abilene (79603) *(G-52)*

Ingram Industries Inc 903 848-8411
465 Vz County Road 2516 Canton (75103) *(G-2657)*

Ingram Ready Mix, Stephenville *Also called Childs Ready-Mix Concrete Co (G-19408)*

Ingram Ready Mix, Kingsville *Also called Ingram Readymix Inc (G-13629)*

Ingram Readymix Inc 830 379-2765
1316 N Bowie St Seguin (78155) *(G-18844)*

Ingram Readymix Inc 361 533-2225
5635 Holly Rd Corpus Christi (78412) *(G-3553)*

Ingram Readymix Inc 210 633-9161
9703 S Us Highway 181 San Antonio (78223) *(G-18183)*

Ingram Readymix Inc 830 606-9619
3580 Fm 482 New Braunfels (78132) *(G-15805)*

Ingram Readymix Inc 361 552-6071
3627 State Highway 35 S Port Lavaca (77979) *(G-17150)*

Ingram Readymix Inc 210 798-2676
8963 State Highway 211 San Antonio (78254) *(G-18184)*

Ingram Readymix Inc 830 672-6420
307 Theo St Gonzales (78629) *(G-7757)*

Ingram Readymix Inc 361 575-6358
4905 Houston Hwy Victoria (77901) *(G-20273)*

Ingram Readymix Inc 830 693-4396
2701 N Us Highway 281 Marble Falls (78654) *(G-14745)*

Ingram Readymix Inc 830 896-4525
2022 Sidney Baker St C Kerrville (78028) *(G-13521)*

Ingram Readymix Inc 210 659-4468
9450 Fm 78 Converse (78109) *(G-3397)*

Ingram Readymix Inc 830 334-3622
Hwy 81 N Pearsall (78061) *(G-16613)*

Ingram Readymix Inc 830 569-2187
1710 W Oaklawn Rd Pleasanton (78064) *(G-17070)*

Ingram Readymix Inc 956 722-8736
8719 San Dario Ave Laredo (78045) *(G-13896)*

Ingram Readymix Inc 210 492-8851
18679 Nw Military Hwy San Antonio (78257) *(G-18185)*

Ingram Readymix Inc 210 622-5621
10400 W Loop 1604 S San Antonio (78252) *(G-18186)*

Ingram Readymix Inc 830 249-3506
37345 Interstate 10 W Boerne (78006) *(G-2122)*

Ingram Readymix Inc 361 888-9281
101 Omaha Dr Corpus Christi (78408) *(G-3554)*

Ingram Readymix Inc 512 396-3136
3830 S Ih 35 San Marcos (78666) *(G-18696)*

Ingram Readymix Inc 830 997-6506
490 Fm 2093 Fredericksburg (78624) *(G-7183)*

Ingram Readymix Inc 361 516-1756
2601 E Corral Ave Kingsville (78363) *(G-13629)*

Ingram Sanco Materials, Robert Lee *Also called Sanco Materials Co (G-17498)*

Ingrids Custom Hand Woven 325 732-4370
Hwy 83 Paint Rock (76866) *(G-16291)*

Inhance Technologies LLC (HQ) **800 929-1743**
22008 N Berwick Dr Houston (77095) *(G-10364)*

Inhance Technologies LLC 713 678-7352
9830 East Fwy Houston (77029) *(G-10365)*

Inherent Software LLC 817 379-0328
2209 Lakeridge Ln Wylie (75098) *(G-20937)*

Ink It Printing 972 428-9623
402 E Trunk St Ste C Crandall (75114) *(G-3696)*

Ink Spot 817 831-4438
576 N Beach St Fort Worth (76111) *(G-6720)*

Inkjet Inc (PA) **936 856-6600**
11111 Inkjet Way Willis (77378) *(G-20848)*

Inkjet Inc 936 856-6600
11111 Inkjet Way Willis (77378) *(G-20849)*

Inkjet International, Dallas *Also called Inkjet Partners Inc (G-4500)*

Inkjet Partners Inc 972 991-4577
4443 Simonton Rd Dallas (75244) *(G-4500)*

Inkspot Printing, Pasadena *Also called Lagan Interests Inc (G-16470)*

Inland Boat Works Inc 409 988-0005
2842 E Roundbunch Rd Orange (77630) *(G-16248)*

Inland Machine 281 497-8871
1917 Highway 6 S Houston (77077) *(G-10366)*

Inland Products Inc 956 627-5700
3505 Xenops Ave McAllen (78504) *(G-14872)*

Inland Transport, McAllen *Also called Inland Products Inc (G-14872)*

Inline Technology, Amarillo *Also called Kruckeberg Corporation (G-496)*

Inman & Company Inc 713 224-4740
2424 Chapman St Houston (77009) *(G-10367)*

Inman Upholstery, Houston *Also called Inman & Company Inc (G-10367)*

Innco, Arlington *Also called Oil States Systems Inc (G-744)*

Inner Health Group Inc 210 661-8311
6003 Randolph Blvd San Antonio (78233) *(G-18187)*

Innocor Foam Tech - Acp Inc 972 563-1559
501 Industrial Blvd Terrell (75160) *(G-19738)*

Innocor Form Tech Brenham LLC 732 945-6222
1200 Rink St Brenham (77833) *(G-2258)*

Innosol Inc 281 859-4428
12231.5 Fm Rd 529 Houston (77041) *(G-10368)*

Innospec Inc 832 748-0284
2600 Tech Forest Blvd Spring (77381) *(G-19217)*

Innospec Oilfield Services, Spring *Also called Innospec Inc (G-19217)*

Innosync Inc 972 644-7962
13111 N Central Expy Dallas (75243) *(G-4501)*

Innova Electronics, Houston *Also called Hunting Innova Inc (G-10284)*

Innova Intgrated Solutions Inc 713 937-9999
6834 Flintlock Rd Houston (77040) *(G-10369)*

Innova Supply Inc (PA) **713 473-3345**
2739 Pasadena Blvd Pasadena (77502) *(G-16459)*

Innovate Quantum Group, Atascosa *Also called Quantum Corporation (G-817)*

Innovative Block S Texas Ltd 956 682-3181
1400 N Mccoll Rd Ste 201 McAllen (78501) *(G-14873)*

Innovative Block S Texas Ltd (PA) **956 797-4200**
240 E 1st St La Feria (78559) *(G-13691)*

Innovative Building Products 940 387-0408
2350 Bennett Rd Millsap (76066) *(G-15503)*

Innovative Electronics/Sfe, Missouri City *Also called Lucere LLc (G-15582)*

Innovative Gas Systems Inc (PA) **713 937-5200**
16250 State Highway 249 Houston (77086) *(G-10370)*

Innovative Gloves & Safety LLC 281 582-0700
11906 Brittmoore Park Dr A Houston (77041) *(G-10371)*

Innovative Hinge Products 817 598-4846
415 Jones Rd Weatherford (76088) *(G-20596)*

Innovative Idm LLC 281 880-2105
13770 Hollister Dr # 100 Houston (77086) *(G-10372)*

Innovative Idm LLC (PA) **214 574-9500**
301 W Vsta Rdge Mall Dr S Lewisville (75067) *(G-14056)*

Innovative Impressions Inc 817 838-6466
2333 Minnis Dr Ste D Fort Worth (76117) *(G-6721)*

Innovative Machine & Laser LLC 214 330-1141
3131 Winnequah St Dallas (75212) *(G-4502)*

(G-0000) Company's Geographic Section entry number

Innovative Millwork Systems......................................972 869-9892
11319 Tantor Rd A Dallas (75229) *(G-4503)*

Innovative Sand Solutions LLC...................................817 421-7428
201 Main St Ste 801 Fort Worth (76102) *(G-6722)*

Innovative Sftwr Solutions Inc...................................830 265-6835
27212 S Glenrose Rd San Antonio (78260) *(G-18188)*

Innovative Signal Analysis Inc (PA)..........................**972 231-5702**
3301 E Renner Rd Ste 200 Richardson (75082) *(G-17333)*

Innovative-Idm, Houston *Also called Innovative Idm LLC (G-10372)*

Innovex Downhole Solutions Inc (PA)........................**281 602-7815**
4310 N Sam Houston Pkwy E Houston (77032) *(G-10373)*

Innovtive Cnveyor Concepts Inc................................972 323-0797
910 Fountain Pkwy Grand Prairie (75050) *(G-7893)*

Innovtive Trnround Contrls Ltd..................................281 998-9547
3512 Fairmont Pkwy Pasadena (77504) *(G-16460)*

Innowave Rf LLC..737 200-7090
190 N Bagdad Rd Ste A Leander (78641) *(G-13992)*

Inogen Inc..972 616-5500
600 Shiloh Rd Plano (75074) *(G-16891)*

Inouii Alloy Fabrication Inc.....................................713 894-6662
1127 Jackson Ave Bacliff (77518) *(G-1733)*

Inova Geophysical Inc (HQ)...................................**281 568-2000**
13000 Executive Dr Sugar Land (77478) *(G-19499)*

Inovar Packaging Group LLC (HQ)...........................**817 277-6666**
10470 Miller Rd Dallas (75238) *(G-4504)*

Inpex Corporation..713 850-8480
2800 Post Oak Blvd # 2450 Houston (77056) *(G-10374)*

Inpex Eagle Ford LLC...713 850-8480
2800 Post Oak Blvd Ste 24 Houston (77056) *(G-10375)*

Inpro Fabrication Ltd..817 926-5050
5111 E California Pkwy Forest Hill (76119) *(G-6297)*

Input/Output, Stafford *Also called Ion Exploration Pdts USA Inc (G-19330)*

Inrock Drilling Systems Inc......................................713 690-5600
6000 Brittmoore Rd Houston (77041) *(G-10376)*

Insect Control Solutions Inc.....................................832 299-2400
612 Spring Cypress Rd Spring (77373) *(G-19134)*

Inservio LLC...713 344-1214
7211 Regency Square Blvd # 110 Houston (77036) *(G-10377)*

Inservio3 LLC (PA)..**213 439-9656**
624 S Austin Ave Ste 230 Georgetown (78626) *(G-7658)*

Insight Equity A P X L P (PA)................................**817 488-7775**
1400 Civic Pl Ste 250 Southlake (76092) *(G-19075)*

Insight Equity Holdings LLC.....................................512 372-9063
5910 Courtyard Dr Ste 210 Austin (78731) *(G-1229)*

Insight Equity LP (HQ)...**817 488-7775**
1400 Civic Pl Ste 250 Southlake (76092) *(G-19076)*

Insight Technology Division, Garland *Also called L3 Technologies Inc (G-7535)*

Insignia Marketing Inc..281 465-0040
32731 Egypt Ln Ste 301 Magnolia (77354) *(G-14610)*

Insituform Technologies Inc....................................636 530-8020
7330 Neuhaus St Houston (77061) *(G-10378)*

Inspection Oilfield Services, Houston *Also called Xxtreme Pipe Storage LLC (G-12712)*

Inspection Oilfield Services, Houston *Also called Ios/Pci LLC (G-10414)*

Inspectorate America Corp......................................281 291-9000
141 N Pasadena Blvd Pasadena (77506) *(G-16461)*

Inspired Elearning LLC..210 579-0224
4630 N Loop 1604 W # 401 San Antonio (78249) *(G-18189)*

Installed Building Pdts Inc.......................................210 937-1082
8135 Bracken Crk San Antonio (78266) *(G-18643)*

Installer Pro LLC...713 854-3656
3231 Allen Pkwy Apt 6302 Houston (77019) *(G-10379)*

Instant Embroidery..281 888-0485
159 Sharpstown Ctr Houston (77036) *(G-10380)*

Insteel Wire Products Company...............................936 258-7625
500 Klemp Rd Dayton (77535) *(G-5230)*

Institute Flght Oprtons Dsptch..................................817 967-4424
2300 Valley View Ln # 250 Irving (75062) *(G-13064)*

Instructional Materials Svc, College Station *Also called The Texas A&M University Sys (G-3207)*

Instrument & Valve Services Co................................281 998-6600
5404 Spencer Hwy Pasadena (77505) *(G-16462)*

Instrument & Valve Services Co................................281 884-8639
1465 E Sam Houston Pkwy S Pasadena (77503) *(G-16463)*

Instrument & Valve Services Co................................713 827-4395
1133 Bunker Hill Rd Houston (77055) *(G-10381)*

Instrument & Valve Services Co................................409 840-8400
4870 Romeda Rd Beaumont (77705) *(G-1908)*

Instrument & Valve Services Co................................903 753-9922
1300 E Whaley St Ste B Longview (75601) *(G-14252)*

Instrument Products Inc...281 491-0237
3727 Greenbriar Dr # 108 Stafford (77477) *(G-19329)*

Instrument Specialists Inc......................................830 249-9535
32390 Interstate 10 W Boerne (78006) *(G-2123)*

Instrument Tech Corp..972 458-8785
3333 Earhart Dr Ste 230 Carrollton (75006) *(G-2765)*

Instruments Tech McHy Inc......................................210 651-9066
5925 Corridor Pkwy Schertz (78154) *(G-18750)*

Insul-Fab, Coppell *Also called Concote Corporation (G-3412)*

Insul-Fab of Tyler, Tyler *Also called Concote Corporation (G-20070)*

Insul-Pipe Systems, Kyle *Also called Whitehorse Manufacturing Co (G-13688)*

Insulation Investors Inc...713 691-3661
1370 E 40th St Bldg 71 Houston (77022) *(G-10382)*

Insurgical Inc..512 318-2980
11002 Metric Blvd Ste C Austin (78758) *(G-1230)*

Insurgical Powered Instruments, Austin *Also called Insurgical Inc (G-1230)*

Intech Aerospace, Houston *Also called Can-AM Aero Support LLC (G-9084)*

Intech Aerospace LLC...281 810-4400
4750 World Hstn Pkwy # 100 Houston (77032) *(G-10383)*

Integ, Waco *Also called Anderton Group Inc (G-20362)*

Integ, Waco *Also called Anderton Group II Ltd (G-20361)*

Integer Holdings Corporation (PA)...........................**214 618-5243**
5830 Gran Pkwy Ste 1150 Plano (75024) *(G-16892)*

Integhearty Wheelchair Van Svc, Desoto *Also called Integhrty Whlchair Van Svc LLC (G-5434)*

Integhrty Whlchair Van Svc LLC..............................972 224-7017
1636 N Hampton Rd Ste 227 Desoto (75115) *(G-5434)*

Integrated Advantage Group LP (PA)........................**806 367-8031**
5700 Sw 45th Ave Amarillo (79109) *(G-493)*

Integrated Ctrl Systems & Svcs, Abilene *Also called Toro Company (G-89)*

Integrated Drive Systems L L C................................713 462-1400
6754 Willow Brook Park Houston (77066) *(G-10384)*

Integrated Flight Systems, Saginaw *Also called Rsg Products Inc (G-17755)*

Integrated Flow Solutions LLC (HQ)..........................**903 595-6511**
6461 Reynolds Rd Tyler (75708) *(G-20102)*

Integrated Flow Systems LLC.................................512 671-5002
1007 S Heatherwilde Blvd Pflugerville (78660) *(G-16676)*

Integrated McHy Solutions LLC................................877 693-7467
1500 Northwest Pkwy Azle (76020) *(G-1725)*

Integrated Metal Products Inc..................................512 259-4143
302 N Bagdad Rd Leander (78641) *(G-13993)*

Integrated MGT Concepts Inc...................................805 778-1629
3800 N Lamar Blvd Ste 200 Austin (78756) *(G-1231)*

Integrated Pipe & Supply LLC................................409 834-6123
13604 Highway 69 Village Mills (77663) *(G-20337)*

Integrated Power Services LLC................................281 471-4611
1500 E Main St La Porte (77571) *(G-13753)*

Integrated Power Services LLC................................409 833-9477
1320 Jim Gilligan Way Beaumont (77705) *(G-1909)*

Integrated Production Svcs Inc (HQ).........................**281 774-6700**
16800 Greenspt Pk Dr 200s Houston (77060) *(G-10385)*

Integrated Production Systems.................................817 385-0700
419 Duncan Perry Rd # 101 Arlington (76011) *(G-706)*

Integrated Roadway Svcs Inc...................................214 352-1937
11300 Kline Dr Dallas (75229) *(G-4505)*

Integrated Security Products, Houston *Also called Inclusive Products Inc (G-10337)*

Integrated Tax Solutions LLC...................................855 792-6657
8015 Bandera Rd Ste 103 San Antonio (78250) *(G-18190)*

Integrawood Inc..713 329-9949
6001 E Lowery Texas City (77591) *(G-19795)*

Integrity Bio-Chemicals LLC....................................408 396-7797
1100 N Cresson Hwy Cresson (76035) *(G-3709)*

Integrity Defense LLC...832 282-0993
700 Milam St Ste 1300 Houston (77002) *(G-10386)*

Integrity Delaware LLC (HQ).................................**361 595-5561**
2710 E Corral Ave Kingsville (78363) *(G-13630)*

Integrity Delaware Holdco, Kingsville *Also called Integrity Delaware LLC (G-13630)*

Integrity Intgration Resources, Plano *Also called Cates Control Systems Inc (G-16821)*

Integrity Plastics Inc...281 575-6688
10215 Landsbury Dr Houston (77099) *(G-10387)*

Integrity Precision Mch LLC.....................................832 859-4116
6946 Signat Dr Houston (77041) *(G-10388)*

Integrity Services LLC...432 682-0703
9701 Farm To Market 307 Et 3 Midland (79706) *(G-15253)*

Integrted Bagging Systems Corp (HQ)......................**361 874-3000**
101 Interplast Blvd Lolita (77971) *(G-14175)*

Integrted Crrsion Cmpanies Inc (PA).......................**713 789-9181**
601 Century Plaza Dr Houston (77073) *(G-10389)*

Integrted Mlding Solutions Inc.................................281 587-9761
6703 Theall Rd Houston (77066) *(G-10390)*

Intel Corporation..281 370-9355
6518 Castle Pine Ln Spring (77379) *(G-19135)*

Intel Corporation..512 362-1000
1300 S Mo Pac Expy Austin (78746) *(G-1232)*

Intel Corporation..972 987-2377
5000 Headquarters Dr Plano (75024) *(G-16893)*

Intel Corporation..281 251-7649
20475 State Highway 249 # 400 Houston (77070) *(G-10391)*

Intellicentrics Inc (PA)...**214 222-7484**
1420 Lakeside Pkwy # 110 Flower Mound (75028) *(G-6268)*

Intelliepi, Richardson *Also called Intelligent Epitaxy Tech Inc (G-17334)*

Intelligen...940 692-3334
3808b Kemp Blvd 308 Wichita Falls (76308) *(G-20772)*

Intelligent Epitaxy Tech Inc.....................................972 234-0068
1250 E Collins Blvd Richardson (75081) *(G-17334)*

Intelligent Package Systems, Grand Prairie *Also called M2I Systems LLC (G-7920)*

Intelligent Surveillance Corp...................................979 323-6900
122 Industrial Dr Forney (75126) *(G-6310)*

A
L
P
H
A
B
E
T
I
C

Intelligrated Systems Inc ... 972 899-9636
701 Canyon Dr Ste 110 Coppell (75019) ***(G-3422)***
Intense Wireline Solutions LLC ... 903 630-5440
100 Independence Pl # 405 Tyler (75703) ***(G-20103)***
Inteplast Group Corporation ... 361 874-3000
101 Interplast Blvd Lolita (77971) ***(G-14176)***
Inter-Wash-Garment Finishing, El Paso *Also called Ameri-Tech Dist Inc* ***(G-5643)***
Interact Inc ... 512 501-2680
9390 Res Blvd Ste Ii100 Austin (78759) ***(G-1233)***
Interact Software Systems, Austin *Also called Interact Inc* ***(G-1233)***
Interactive Life Forms LLC ... 888 804-4453
7000 Burleson Rd Ste C Austin (78744) ***(G-1234)***
Interav Inc ... 210 344-2785
106 E Rhapsody Dr San Antonio (78216) ***(G-18191)***
Intercarnes Texas Corporation ... 281 360-3825
12160 Rojas Dr Ste H El Paso (79936) ***(G-5812)***
Interceramic Inc (HQ) ... **214 503-5501**
1950 Parker Rd Carrollton (75010) ***(G-2871)***
Interco Products ... 972 613-6749
624 San Carlos Dr Garland (75043) ***(G-7519)***
Intercoastal Paint Co Inc ... 281 448-5258
14029 W Hardy Rd Houston (77060) ***(G-10392)***
Interconnect Wiring LLP ... 817 377-9473
5024 W Vickery Blvd Fort Worth (76107) ***(G-6723)***
Intercontinental Machine, Pearland *Also called Ronald L Jordan Company* ***(G-16597)***
Intercorr International Inc ... 281 444-2282
14503 Bammel N Houston Houston (77014) ***(G-10393)***
Intercramic Tile Stone Gallery, Carrollton *Also called Interceramic Inc* ***(G-2871)***
Interctive Explrtion Solutions ... 713 993-0676
1980 Post Oak Blvd # 2050 Houston (77056) ***(G-10394)***
Interface Lgic Tech Dcmnttion ... 713 446-3560
11607 Bay Ledge Dr Pearland (77584) ***(G-16570)***
Interfet Corporation ... 972 238-9700
715 N Glenville Dr # 400 Richardson (75081) ***(G-17335)***
Interglobal Plastics Inc ... 713 672-6055
8451 Market St Ste 138 Houston (77029) ***(G-10395)***
Intergulf Corporation (PA) ... **281 474-4210**
428 Highway 146 S La Porte (77571) ***(G-13754)***
Interior Fixture Installations ... 972 412-9773
3714 Big A Rd Rowlett (75089) ***(G-17707)***
Interlab, Spring *Also called International Lab Sup Ltd* ***(G-19218)***
Interlake Mecalux Inc ... 972 245-3910
12301 N Stemmons Fwy # 110 Dallas (75234) ***(G-4506)***
Interline Travel & Tour Inc (PA) ... **512 691-4500**
12708 Riata Vst Cira 125 Austin (78727) ***(G-1235)***
Interline Vacations, Austin *Also called Interline Travel & Tour Inc* ***(G-1235)***
Intermatic Incorporated ... 915 858-9204
12429 Rojas Dr Ste B El Paso (79928) ***(G-5813)***
Intermdal Repr Mdfcation Trckg ... 713 674-2179
11643 Wllsvlle Rd Unit 2b Houston (77013) ***(G-10396)***
Intermex Products Usa Ltd ... 972 660-2071
1375 Avenue S Ste 300 Grand Prairie (75050) ***(G-7894)***
Intermodal Repr Sales/Service, Houston *Also called Intermdal Repr Mdfcation Trckg* ***(G-10396)***
Intermoor Inc ... 832 399-5000
900 Threadneedle St # 300 Houston (77079) ***(G-10397)***
International Aerial Mapping ... 210 826-8681
2118 Mannix Dr San Antonio (78217) ***(G-18192)***
International Airmotive Holdg (HQ) ... **214 956-3000**
900 Nolen Dr Ste 100 Grapevine (76051) ***(G-8043)***
International Aluminum Corp ... 972 937-7032
202 Singleton Rd Waxahachie (75165) ***(G-20545)***
International Assembly Inc ... 956 525-4533
4402 Austin Rd Ste B Brownsville (78521) ***(G-2362)***
International Assn Drlg Contrs (PA) ... **713 292-1945**
3657 Briarpark Dr Ste 200 Houston (77042) ***(G-10398)***
International Beverage Inc ... 956 727-2995
1901 Aduanales Ln Laredo (78041) ***(G-13897)***
International Biomedical Ltd (PA) ... **512 873-0033**
8206 Cross Park Dr Austin (78754) ***(G-1236)***
International Biophysics Corp ... 512 326-3244
2101-2 E St Elmo Rd Ste 2 Austin (78744) ***(G-1237)***
International Builders Supply, Carrollton *Also called IB Supply LLC* ***(G-2870)***
International Business Publs ... 713 626-5369
18719 Ember Trails Dr Houston (77094) ***(G-10399)***
International Chemical Technol ... 432 339-9361
2710 W Hillmont Rd Odessa (79764) ***(G-16031)***
International Coating Services ... 936 344-9494
18150 Interstate 45 N Willis (77318) ***(G-20850)***
International Commodities ... 281 331-1252
301 E Highway 6 Alvin (77511) ***(G-367)***
International Daily News Inc ... 713 270-4855
9015 Bellaire Blvd 107a Houston (77036) ***(G-10400)***
International Do Foods Idf Inc ... 713 222-0598
101 Chartres St Houston (77002) ***(G-10401)***
International Energy Svcs LLC ... 281 973-9462
10309 Pineland Rd Houston (77044) ***(G-10402)***
International Envmtl Eqp Co, Houston *Also called Incinerator International Inc* ***(G-10336)***
International Extrusion Co, Waxahachie *Also called International Aluminum Corp* ***(G-20545)***
International Flatbed Svcs Inc (PA) ... **915 858-1200**
11425 Stockyard Dr El Paso (79927) ***(G-5814)***
International Gasket & Supply, La Porte *Also called Leader Gasket Technologies Inc* ***(G-13766)***
International Hanger, Austin *Also called International Innovations Inc* ***(G-1238)***
International Ingredient Corp ... 817 645-1328
2701 Pipeline Rd Cleburne (76033) ***(G-3096)***
International Innovations Inc ... 512 600-4517
3933 Spicewood Springs Rd Austin (78759) ***(G-1238)***
International Lab Sup Ltd ... 281 298-9410
26018 Budde Rd Spring (77380) ***(G-19218)***
International Machine Shop ... 956 838-1234
2250 Anglers Place Rd Brownsville (78521) ***(G-2363)***
International Paint LLC (HQ) ... **713 682-1711**
6001 Antoine Dr Houston (77091) ***(G-10403)***
International Paint LLC ... 817 834-0141
2951 Nthrn Cross Blvd Bld Fort Worth (76137) ***(G-6724)***
International Paint LLC ... 713 684-1500
11930 Proctor St Houston (77038) ***(G-10404)***
International Paper, Queen City *Also called Graphic Packaging Intl LLC* ***(G-17220)***
International Paper Company ... 972 417-1350
2605 E Belt Line Rd Carrollton (75006) ***(G-2766)***
International Paper Company ... 972 512-0400
1655 S I 35 Carrollton (75006) ***(G-2767)***
International Paper Company ... 956 383-3811
1501 N Closner Blvd Edinburg (78541) ***(G-5590)***
International Paper Company ... 713 996-9877
3000 Brittmoore Rd Houston (77043) ***(G-10405)***
International Paper Company ... 956 387-8100
1010 E Chapin St Edinburg (78541) ***(G-5591)***
International Paper Company ... 806 381-0121
4715 Ne 24th Ave Amarillo (79107) ***(G-439)***
International Paper Company ... 956 682-9406
200 N 26th St McAllen (78501) ***(G-14874)***
International Paper Company ... 210 225-2901
1111 At&T Center Pkwy San Antonio (78219) ***(G-18193)***
International Paper Company ... 210 661-8543
610 Pop Gunn St San Antonio (78219) ***(G-18194)***
International Paper Company ... 915 858-8877
9301 Billy The Kid St El Paso (79907) ***(G-5815)***
International Paper Company ... 979 885-4191
1485 Silliman St Sealy (77474) ***(G-18810)***
International Paper Company ... 972 416-8680
2015 Country Club Dr Carrollton (75006) ***(G-2768)***
International Paper Company ... 972 602-9880
1200 W North Carrier Pkwy Grand Prairie (75050) ***(G-7895)***
International Paper Company ... 817 338-4000
2400 Shamrock Ave Fort Worth (76107) ***(G-6725)***
International Paper Company ... 972 641-2972
1302 W North Carrier Pkwy Grand Prairie (75050) ***(G-7896)***
International Plant Svcs LLC ... 281 867-8400
1602 Old Underwood Rd La Porte (77571) ***(G-13755)***
International Steel Frmng LLC ... 817 591-0507
7108 Burns St Richland Hills (76118) ***(G-17438)***
International Sulphur Inc ... 903 577-5500
1386 N Frontage Rd Mount Pleasant (75455) ***(G-15652)***
International Tool & Mfg Co ... 800 753-1004
3218 Skylane Dr Ste 102 Carrollton (75006) ***(G-2769)***
International Tool & Supply, Sugar Land *Also called Global Oilfield Services Inc* ***(G-19488)***
International Well Testers ... 361 358-1990
3720 Highway 59 W Beeville (78102) ***(G-1986)***
International Wire Group Inc ... 915 877-5500
1700 Commerce Park Dr El Paso (79912) ***(G-5816)***
International Wood LLC ... 956 969-8666
2300 N Sugar Sweet Ave Weslaco (78596) ***(G-20660)***
Interntional Grains Cereal LLC ... 903 554-1003
6902 Hwy 66 Greenville (75402) ***(G-8077)***
Interntnal Arospc Coatings Inc ... 806 335-2616
10801 Baker St Amarillo (79111) ***(G-440)***
Interntnal Flvors Frgrnces Inc ... 496 557-7001
1620 W Crosby Rd Ste 102 Carrollton (75006) ***(G-2770)***
Interntnal Glvnzers Partnr Ltd ... 409 842-0216
5885 Industrial Rd Beaumont (77705) ***(G-1910)***
Interntnal Glvnzers Partnr Ltd (HQ) ... **817 810-0095**
3100 W 7th St Ste 500 Fort Worth (76107) ***(G-6726)***
Interntnal Prtein Colloids Inc ... 817 795-7744
370 English Trl Venus (76084) ***(G-20219)***
Interntnal Shpbreaking Ltd LLC ... 956 831-4112
18501 Rl Ostos Rd Brownsville (78521) ***(G-2364)***
Interntonal Garment Processors, El Paso *Also called JC Viramontes Inc* ***(G-5820)***
Interntonal Laminating Systems ... 713 645-0383
7013 Dixie Dr Houston (77087) ***(G-10406)***
Interntonal Resistive Texas LP ... 361 992-7900
4222 S Staples St Corpus Christi (78411) ***(G-3555)***
Interphase Corporation (PA) ... **214 654-5000**
4240 Intl Pkwy Ste 105 Carrollton (75007) ***(G-2872)***
Interplast Group, Lolita *Also called Inteplast Group Corporation* ***(G-14176)***
Interpress Technologies Inc ... 972 926-6768
3302 W Miller Rd Ste 100 Garland (75041) ***(G-7520)***

ALPHABETIC SECTION
Irwin Steel LLC

Intership Services Inc 713 645-2666
5630 Northdale St Houston (77087) *(G-10407)*
Interstate Batteries Inc (HQ) **972 991-1444**
12770 Merit Dr Ste 300 Dallas (75251) *(G-4507)*
Interstate Explorations LLC 254 442-1057
17010 Interstate 20 Cisco (76437) *(G-3067)*
Interstate Fittings Inc (PA) **214 637-6720**
2200 Singleton Blvd Dallas (75212) *(G-4508)*
Interstate Gas Treating Inc 432 362-9291
7141 Club Dr Odessa (79762) *(G-16032)*
Interstate Treating Inc 432 362-9291
2310 Prospect Odessa (79762) *(G-16033)*
Interstate Treating Inc (PA) **432 362-9291**
7141 Club Dr Odessa (79762) *(G-16034)*
Intertech Fluid Power Inc 817 329-9733
151 Central Ave Grapevine (76051) *(G-8044)*
Intertek Caleb Brett, Corpus Christi *Also called Intertek USA Inc (G-3556)*
Intertek Cnslting Trning USA I (HQ) **337 235-4493**
25025 Interstate 45 # 30 Spring (77380) *(G-19219)*
Intertek USA Inc 361 289-7474
4702 Westway Dr Corpus Christi (78408) *(G-3556)*
Intertek USA Inc 281 364-2800
25025 Interstate 45 Spring (77380) *(G-19220)*
Interventional Products, Houston *Also called Merit Medical Systems Inc (G-10837)*
Intervoice LLC 972 454-8000
17787 Waterview Pkwy Dallas (75252) *(G-3845)*
Intervoice LLC (HQ) **972 454-8000**
17787 Waterview Pkwy Dallas (75252) *(G-3846)*
Interwell US LLC 832 461-1500
6832 Bourgeois Rd Houston (77066) *(G-10408)*
Intesolv Inc 512 681-7272
8303 N Mopac Expy 127b Austin (78759) *(G-1239)*
Inteva Products LLC 248 655-8777
3501 Nafta Pkwy Ste C Brownsville (78526) *(G-2365)*
Intex United Inc 281 568-4000
12626 W Bellfort Ave Houston (77099) *(G-10409)*
Intrapack Corporation 214 348-7105
10650 Markison Rd Dallas (75238) *(G-4509)*
Intrapack Industries Inc 214 348-7105
10650 Markison Rd Dallas (75238) *(G-4510)*
Intrepid Drctnal Drlg Spclists, Midland *Also called Intrepid Drctnal Drlg Spclsts (G-15254)*
Intrepid Drctnal Drlg Spclsts (PA) **432 617-0593**
10314 State Highway 191 Midland (79707) *(G-15254)*
Intrepid Industries Inc 281 479-8301
2305 S Battleground Rd La Porte (77571) *(G-13756)*
Intrinsic Safety Eqp Texas Inc 281 488-0788
3902 Magnolia Pkwy Pearland (77584) *(G-16571)*
Introgen Therapeutics Inc 512 708-9310
301 Congress Ave Ste 1850 Austin (78701) *(G-1240)*
Intrusion Inc (PA) **972 234-6400**
1101 E Arapaho Rd Ste 200 Richardson (75081) *(G-17336)*
Intsel Steel Distributors LLC (HQ) **713 937-9500**
11310 W Little York Rd Houston (77041) *(G-10410)*
Intsel Steel West California, Houston *Also called Intsel Steel Distributors LLC (G-10410)*
Intuit Inc 214 387-2000
5601 Headquarters Dr Plano (75024) *(G-16894)*
Invensys Controls, Brownsville *Also called Robertshaw Controls Company (G-2402)*
Invensys Process Systems, Houston *Also called Schneider Elc Systems USA Inc (G-11781)*
Inventory Services Network 972 660-7365
175 Musket Livingston (77351) *(G-14157)*
Inverter Designs Inc 972 227-9085
2111 N Lncster Htchins Rd Lancaster (75134) *(G-13843)*
Investor Publications Inc (PA) **915 534-4422**
208 N Octavia St El Paso (79901) *(G-5817)*
Inview Technology Corporation (PA) **512 243-8751**
6201 E Oltorf St Ste 400 Austin (78741) *(G-1241)*
Invision Automated Systems Inc 713 461-6642
20434 Knolls Spring Trl Katy (77450) *(G-13410)*
Invisishield LLC (PA) **713 539-6700**
14750 Memorial Dr Houston (77079) *(G-10411)*
Invista Capital Management LLC 409 886-5080
2020 Western Ave West Orange (77630) *(G-20695)*
Invista Capital Management LLC 409 886-6982
Farm Market Road 1006 Orange (77631) *(G-16249)*
Invista Capital Management LLC 281 470-3434
12455 Strang Rd La Porte (77571) *(G-13757)*
Invista Capital Management LLC 361 572-1111
2695 Old Bloomington Rd N Victoria (77905) *(G-20274)*
Invista Capital Management LLC 409 886-9373
3055 Fm 1006 Orange (77630) *(G-16250)*
Invista Sarl - Victoria, Victoria *Also called Invista Capital Management LLC (G-20274)*
Involta LLC 817 937-8943
15770 Dallas Pkwy # 1100 Dallas (75248) *(G-4511)*
Inwell Inc 281 443-7614
504 Spring Hill Dr # 300 Spring (77386) *(G-19221)*
Inwesco Incorporated 817 538-0387
2824 N Sylvania Ave Fort Worth (76111) *(G-6727)*
Inwood Furniture Manufacturing 972 564-4444
11821 N Profit Row Forney (75126) *(G-6311)*
INX International Ink Co 817 375-0075
3701 New York Ave Ste 130 Arlington (76014) *(G-707)*
Inzer Advance Designs Inc 903 236-4012
124 W Tyler St Longview (75601) *(G-14253)*
Ioffice LP (PA) **713 526-1029**
5300 Memorial Dr Ste 300 Houston (77007) *(G-10412)*
Iom Components, Tomball *Also called Industrial Olfld Mar Cmpnnts I (G-19985)*
Ion Art Inc 512 326-9333
407 Radam Ln Ste A100 Austin (78745) *(G-1242)*
Ion Exploration Pdts USA Inc 281 933-3339
12300 Parc Crest Dr Stafford (77477) *(G-19330)*
Ion Geophysical Corporation (PA) **281 933-3339**
2105 Citywest Blvd # 100 Houston (77042) *(G-10413)*
Ion Geophysical Corporation 281 552-3000
12300 Parc Crest Dr Stafford (77477) *(G-19331)*
Ion Science Inc 877 864-7710
4153 Bluebonnet Dr Stafford (77477) *(G-19332)*
Iondesign Inc 512 260-5778
18700 White Rim Trl Jonestown (78645) *(G-13315)*
Ios Inspection 432 684-6440
2600 E I 20 Midland (79706) *(G-15255)*
Ios/Pci LLC (HQ) **281 310-5357**
7814 Miller Road 3 Houston (77049) *(G-10414)*
Iowa Beef Processors, Amarillo *Also called Tyson Fresh Meats Inc (G-470)*
Iowa Food Group LLC 712 600-3663
1205 Perdenalas Trl Westlake (76262) *(G-20696)*
Iowa Techniques Inc 512 846-2403
524 Tradesmens Park Dr Hutto (78634) *(G-12880)*
IPC Fabricators LLC 409 935-8800
12221 Highway 6 Unit C Santa Fe (77510) *(G-18735)*
Ipcelerate Inc 972 512-7100
6860 Dallas Pkwy Ste 200 Plano (75024) *(G-16895)*
Ipdisplays LLC 214 453-3570
817 S Greenville Ave Allen (75002) *(G-278)*
Ipf, Stafford *Also called Industrial Pipe Fittings LLC (G-19328)*
Ipr Energy Group, Irving *Also called Ipr Transoil Corporation (G-13065)*
Ipr Industrial LLC 281 362-1131
9400 Grogans Mill Rd # 205 The Woodlands (77380) *(G-19885)*
Ipr South Central, Houston *Also called RE Pipe Inc (G-11559)*
Ipr Transoil Corporation (PA) **972 257-1900**
909 Lake Carolyn Pkwy # 8 Irving (75039) *(G-13065)*
Ips International LLC 936 521-1981
2615 Industrial Ln Conroe (77301) *(G-3311)*
Ips Optimization, Houston *Also called Superior Energy Services Inc (G-12112)*
Ipsco Koppel Tubulars LLC 281 383-2603
2600 East Fwy 99 Baytown (77521) *(G-1822)*
Ipsco Tubulars (ky) Inc (HQ) **859 292-6000**
10120 Houston Oaks Dr Houston (77064) *(G-10415)*
Ipsco Tubulars Inc (HQ) **281 949-1023**
10120 Houston Oaks Dr Houston (77064) *(G-10416)*
Iq Enterprises Inc 866 789-0508
2521 5th Ave Fort Worth (76110) *(G-6728)*
Iq Graphics, El Paso *Also called Impresa Label Inc (G-5810)*
Iq Life Sciences Corporation 281 444-6454
16212 State Highway 249 Houston (77086) *(G-10417)*
Iq Scientific Corporation 281 444-6454
16212 State Highway 249 Houston (77086) *(G-10418)*
Irent 956 592-4061
3460 Southmost Rd Brownsville (78521) *(G-2366)*
Ireo Reproductions LLC 214 337-4731
633 Sunnyside Ave Dallas (75211) *(G-4512)*
Irex Group Ltd 512 835-1200
12317 Tech Blvd Ste 150 Austin (78727) *(G-1243)*
Irion County Plant (PA) **432 682-6311**
211 N Colorado St Midland (79701) *(G-15256)*
Iris Biotech LLC (HQ) **512 219-8020**
212 Technology Blvd Austin (78727) *(G-1244)*
Iris Usa Inc 972 329-0400
3401 Innovative Way Mesquite (75149) *(G-15053)*
Iron Hrse Olfled Svc Group LLC 832 224-4430
16815 Royal Crest Dr Houston (77058) *(G-10419)*
Iron Ram Services LLC 361 241-2346
8263 Leopard St Corpus Christi (78409) *(G-3557)*
Iron Sky 281 468-8255
2425 Ftn View Dr Ste 160 Houston (77057) *(G-10420)*
Ironforce Supply LLC 713 681-5600
7075 W 43rd St Houston (77092) *(G-10421)*
Ironhorse Unlimited Inc 903 489-2075
11101 State Highway 31 W Malakoff (75148) *(G-14635)*
Ironroc Energy Partners LLC 713 377-9860
2777 Allen Pkwy Ste 600 Houston (77019) *(G-10422)*
Ironwood Oil & Gas LLC 281 873-9378
16945 Northchase Dr # 1500 Houston (77060) *(G-10423)*
Irving Counter Inc 972 438-4343
101 N Irving Heights Dr Irving (75061) *(G-13066)*
Irving Tool & Mfg Co Inc 972 926-4000
2249 Wall St Garland (75041) *(G-7521)*
Irwin Steel LLC 817 636-2508
15740 Highway 114 Justin (76247) *(G-13344)*

ALPHABETIC

ISA, Richardson *Also called Innovative Signal Analysis Inc* ***(G-17333)***
Isabel/B & J, Frisco *Also called B & J Accessories Inc* ***(G-7269)***
Isabella Foods Inc (PA) **915 590-1899**
1133 Barranca Dr El Paso (79935) ***(G-5818)***
Isaiah 49 16 Inc 713 896-1765
9125 Emmott Rd Houston (77040) ***(G-10424)***
Isavela Enterprises Inc 800 918-8242
721 N Col Rowe Blvd McAllen (78501) ***(G-14875)***
ISC Industrial Manufacturing, Burleson *Also called ISC Manufacturing LLC* ***(G-2583)***
ISC Manufacturing LLC 817 641-0691
4133 Conveyor Dr Burleson (76028) ***(G-2583)***
Isco Industries Inc 817 477-2900
2441 Mathis Rd Mansfield (76063) ***(G-14683)***
Isco Systems, Plainview *Also called Ifco Systems North America Inc* ***(G-16758)***
ISE-Mag Tech, Pearland *Also called Intrinsic Safety Eqp Texas Inc* ***(G-16571)***
Isenberg Bath Corporation 888 342-2284
11927 Mustang Rd Ste 100 Dallas (75234) ***(G-4513)***
Isgas Incorporated 713 645-5886
5807 Northdale St Houston (77087) ***(G-10425)***
Iskandia Energy Operating Inc 832 209-8240
801 Travis St Ste 1818 Houston (77002) ***(G-10426)***
Islamic Services Foundation 972 414-5090
411 Industrial Dr Ste 105 Richardson (75081) ***(G-17337)***
Island Carriages 409 765-6951
2528 Post Office St Galveston (77550) ***(G-7401)***
Ism Industries Inc (PA) **409 769-7841**
16645 Ih 10 Vidor (77662) ***(G-20327)***
ISO Covers LLC 972 221-4410
711 E Jones St Ste A Lewisville (75057) ***(G-14057)***
ISO Machine Inc 281 568-1700
13050 Sugar Ridge Blvd Stafford (77477) ***(G-19333)***
ISO Tex Diagnostics, Friendswood *Also called Tex ISO Inc* ***(G-7250)***
ISO-Tex Diagnostics Inc 281 482-1231
1511 County Rd 129 Friendswood (77546) ***(G-7246)***
Isomedix Operations Inc 915 855-2001
1435 Isomedix Pl El Paso (79936) ***(G-5819)***
Isomeric Industries Inc (PA) **678 713-4275**
3400 Res Forest Dr Ste B4 Spring (77381) ***(G-19222)***
Isomeric Industries Inc 832 491-8106
3400 Research Forest Dr B4 The Woodlands (77381) ***(G-19886)***
Isotherm Inc 817 472-9922
7401 Commercial Blvd E Arlington (76001) ***(G-708)***
Isothrmal Prtctive Catings Inc 281 485-4440
1950 Oday Rd Pearland (77581) ***(G-16572)***
Isp Elastomers, Port Neches *Also called Ashland LLC* ***(G-17158)***
Isp Supplies LLC 855 947-7776
10770 State Highway 30 # 20 College Station (77845) ***(G-3187)***
Isramco Inc (HQ) **713 621-3882**
1001 West Loop S Ste 750 Houston (77027) ***(G-10427)***
Isramco Energy LLC 713 456-7892
1001 West Loop S Ste 750 Houston (77027) ***(G-10428)***
Issgr Inc 713 869-7700
6611 Portwest Dr Ste 190 Houston (77024) ***(G-10429)***
Istation, Dallas *Also called Imagination Station Inc* ***(G-4490)***
Istick Capital Management LLC 214 231-4000
600 N Pearl St Ste S226 Dallas (75201) ***(G-4514)***
Itafos Services LLC 713 242-8446
109 N Post Oak Ln Ste 405 Houston (77024) ***(G-10430)***
Itd Precision 956 440-9960
818 N Fm 509 Harlingen (78550) ***(G-8191)***
Itec Manufacturing LLC 903 365-6390
400 All Star Dr Winnsboro (75494) ***(G-20897)***
Itek Mobile, Houston *Also called Kingston I-Tek Solutions LLC* ***(G-10536)***
ITEX Piping Products LLC 832 604-7900
13411 West Rd Houston (77041) ***(G-10431)***
Itexaspolitics LLC 512 200-4035
5212 Elm St Colleyville (76034) ***(G-3214)***
ITI, Cedar Hill *Also called Industrial Thermoform Inc* ***(G-2945)***
Itl Infosys Limited, Richardson *Also called Infosys Limited* ***(G-17332)***
Itron Networked Solutions Inc 210 762-4400
300 Convent St Ste 1200 San Antonio (78205) ***(G-18195)***
Its Engineered Systems Inc 281 371-8026
6818 Fm 2855 Rd Katy (77493) ***(G-13411)***
Its Water Technology, Katy *Also called Its Engineered Systems Inc* ***(G-13411)***
ITT Bornemann Usa Inc 832 320-2500
12510 Sugar Ridge Blvd Stafford (77477) ***(G-19334)***
ITT LLC 469 221-1200
10661 Newkirk St Dallas (75220) ***(G-4515)***
ITT LLC 281 367-2800
309 Briar Rock Rd The Woodlands (77380) ***(G-19887)***
ITT LLC 281 504-6300
12510 Sugar Ridge Blvd Stafford (77477) ***(G-19335)***
ITW Blding Cmponents Group Inc 972 660-4422
2820 N Great Sw Pkwy Grand Prairie (75050) ***(G-7897)***
ITW EF&c Mexico- US Trading, Pharr *Also called Illinois Tool Works Inc* ***(G-16700)***
ITW Futura Coatings, Houston *Also called Illinois Tool Works Inc* ***(G-10326)***
ITW Global Brand, Houston *Also called Illinois Tool Works Inc* ***(G-10323)***
ITW Minigrip Inc 830 372-4400
1650 N Heideke St Seguin (78155) ***(G-18845)***
ITW Plymers Salants N Amer Inc (HQ) **972 438-9111**
420 Decker Dr Ste 160 Irving (75062) ***(G-13067)***
Iwc Oil & Refinery LLC 210 900-9928
8610 N New Braunfels Ave # 3 San Antonio (78217) ***(G-18196)***
Iwire, Haslet *Also called Ksh Enterprises Inc* ***(G-8220)***
Ixia, Austin *Also called Anue Systems Inc* ***(G-923)***
Ixpalia Inc 512 389-0389
3800 Promontory Point Dr Austin (78744) ***(G-1245)***
Ixrf Inc 512 386-6100
10421 Old Manchaca Rd Austin (78748) ***(G-1246)***
Ixrf Systems Inc 512 386-6100
10421 Old Manchaca Rd # 620 Austin (78748) ***(G-1247)***
Ixtapa Inc 956 782-9601
1500 Mid Cities Dr Pharr (78577) ***(G-16701)***
Izone, Temple *Also called Blind Dog Productions Ltd* ***(G-19671)***
J & A Manufacturing Inc 972 494-5552
2805 E Centerville Rd Garland (75040) ***(G-7522)***
J & B Industrial Services, Lubbock *Also called Csjb Holdings Inc* ***(G-14398)***
J & B Sausage Company Inc (PA) **830 788-7661**
100 Main Waelder (78959) ***(G-20484)***
J & B Sausage Company Inc 210 344-2212
10221 Desert Sands St # 302 San Antonio (78216) ***(G-18197)***
J & B Sausage Company Inc 979 725-6661
1078 Highway 90 Weimar (78962) ***(G-20649)***
J & E Welding Inc 409 794-2311
10930 E Clubb Rd Beaumont (77705) ***(G-1911)***
J & G Concrete LP 972 937-9200
1220 Solon Rd Waxahachie (75167) ***(G-20546)***
J & G Trybus Corporation (PA) **214 331-5248**
320 W Centre Park Blvd Desoto (75115) ***(G-5435)***
J & H Manufacturing Inc 830 665-5230
161 County Road 777 Devine (78016) ***(G-5450)***
J & J Fabricators, Dallas *Also called Jack Phipps* ***(G-4520)***
J & J Machining Inc (PA) **713 644-7916**
6520 Springer St Houston (77087) ***(G-10432)***
J & J Manufacturing Company 409 835-1330
5455 Ohio St Beaumont (77705) ***(G-1912)***
J & J Nameplate and Label LLC 972 939-1157
2425 Parker Rd Bldg 6 Carrollton (75010) ***(G-2873)***
J & J Stone Company 512 869-3527
4400 W Fm 487 Jarrell (76537) ***(G-13271)***
J & L Partners 972 417-3977
4246 Woodfin Dr Dallas (75220) ***(G-4516)***
J & L Sheet Metal Co Inc 713 864-7714
14102 Chrisman Rd Houston (77039) ***(G-10433)***
J & M Energy Services LP (PA) **432 943-7770**
1705 S Stockton Ave Monahans (79756) ***(G-15606)***
J & M Fixtures, Trenton *Also called JB Commercial Millwork Inc* ***(G-20017)***
J & N Welding and Fabricators 956 585-3992
507 S Main St Penitas (78576) ***(G-16629)***
J & P Services Inc 979 542-0500
1103 Private Road 7703 Giddings (78942) ***(G-7697)***
J & R Custom Processing LLC 325 456-1544
507 County Road 476 Rochelle (76872) ***(G-17522)***
J & R Grinding LLC 281 272-2344
15702 W Hardy Rd Ste 260 Houston (77060) ***(G-10434)***
J & R Valley Oilfield Svcs Inc 956 581-7235
8100 N Moorefield Rd Mission (78574) ***(G-15556)***
J & S Construction LLC 903 322-4942
10823 Hwy 75 S Buffalo (75831) ***(G-2544)***
J & S Contractors Inc (PA) **979 647-0040**
212 N Main St Sweeny (77480) ***(G-19628)***
J & S Plating and Repair Inc 972 784-8718
1318 County Road 655 Farmersville (75442) ***(G-6224)***
J & S Rides Inc 806 293-1353
1933 State Highway 194 Plainview (79072) ***(G-16759)***
J & W Services & Equipment Co (PA) **432 689-3947**
3510 E State Highway 158 Midland (79706) ***(G-15257)***
J & X Trucking LLC (PA) **830 583-0611**
1052 County Road 160 Kenedy (78119) ***(G-13488)***
J 2 Fabrications LLC 281 989-2984
327 Magnolia Bus Pk Dr Magnolia (77354) ***(G-14611)***
J B Edwards Company 281 429-7143
18960 Moorhead Rd Conroe (77302) ***(G-3312)***
J B Leasing, Waxahachie *Also called Top Quality Spindles LLC* ***(G-20566)***
J B Oil & Gas Well Service 830 378-5586
3387 County Rd 3700 Dilley (78017) ***(G-5482)***
J B R Enterprises Inc 972 542-3939
196 Industrial Blvd McKinney (75069) ***(G-14947)***
J B Smith Mfg Co LLC 713 928-5711
6618 Navigation Blvd Houston (77011) ***(G-10435)***
J Bar B Foods, Waelder *Also called J & B Sausage Company Inc* ***(G-20484)***
J Brandt Recognition Ltd 817 877-0513
2816 W Lancaster Ave Fort Worth (76107) ***(G-6729)***
J C Manufacturing Inc 903 473-3770
201 Prosperity Emory (75440) ***(G-6083)***

J C Ornamental Ironworks Inc	972 442-6293
130 Kristen Ln Wylie (75098) *(G-20938)*	
J Cleo Thmpson Jmes Cleo Thmp	432 550-8887
325 N Saint Paul St # 4300 Dallas (75201) *(G-4517)*	
J Connor Consulting Inc	281 578-3388
19219 Katy Fwy Ste 200 Houston (77094) *(G-10436)*	
J D Documents Inc	972 733-1080
17130 Dallas Pkwy Ste 115 Dallas (75248) *(G-4518)*	
J D Fields & Company Inc (PA)	281 558-7199
55 Waugh Dr Ste 1250 Houston (77007) *(G-10437)*	
J D Rush Corporation	281 558-8004
2 Northpoint Dr Ste 150 Houston (77060) *(G-10438)*	
J DS Machine Shop	903 532-6240
805 Mardell Ln Howe (75459) *(G-12734)*	
J E F Fabrication Inc	281 367-2032
25803 Oak Ridge Dr Spring (77380) *(G-19223)*	
J E Titus Company	713 991-1100
10425 Moers Rd Houston (77075) *(G-10439)*	
J Groomed, Boerne *Also called Jcjh LLC (G-2124)*	
J Harding & Co	713 862-9855
424 W 19th St Houston (77008) *(G-10440)*	
J I S Measurement & Operating (PA)	325 224-3036
2412 College Hills Blvd San Angelo (76904) *(G-17810)*	
J K Welding Service LLC	281 550-1008
18433 Fm 529 Rd Cypress (77433) *(G-3803)*	
J Keiths Jewelry Inc	806 791-0092
8001 Quaker Ave Ste H Lubbock (79424) *(G-14427)*	
J L Davis Company	432 399-4575
11703 Fm 846 Coahoma (79511) *(G-3165)*	
J L Proler Iron and Steel Co	713 675-3191
4401 Clinton Dr Houston (77020) *(G-10441)*	
J L Roberts Industries Inc	817 831-0676
2501 Ne 36th St Fort Worth (76111) *(G-6730)*	
J L Rushing Inc	903 759-6000
1106 Cherokee Trce White Oak (75693) *(G-20715)*	
J Leals Food Inc	214 412-3158
2515 W Jefferson St # 128 Grand Prairie (75051) *(G-7898)*	
J Lee Milligan Inc	806 373-5352
9200 Triangle Dr Amarillo (79108) *(G-441)*	
J Lewis Partners LP	972 702-7390
13355 Noel Rd Ste 1750 Dallas (75240) *(G-4519)*	
J M D, Aransas Pass *Also called J M Davidson Inc (G-592)*	
J M Davidson Inc (PA)	361 883-0983
2564 County Road 1960 Aransas Pass (78336) *(G-592)*	
J M Fabrication Company LLC	817 652-0526
415 Duncan Perry Rd Arlington (76011) *(G-709)*	
J M H Printing Company	972 263-1226
721 W Tarrant Rd Grand Prairie (75050) *(G-7899)*	
J M Saddler Inc (PA)	979 693-5114
9107 Riverstone Ct College Station (77845) *(G-3188)*	
J Morco Incorporated	817 596-3989
6650 Mineral Wells Hwy Weatherford (76088) *(G-20597)*	
J P C Plastics Inc	325 672-2895
8001 Us Highway 277 Abilene (79601) *(G-53)*	
J Patrick Services LLC	432 214-5443
7230 Manford Ln Odessa (79765) *(G-16035)*	
J Paul Horst & Associates	713 460-9386
5600 Nw Central Dr Houston (77092) *(G-10442)*	
J PS Fund Wear	806 794-5777
5120 69th St Lubbock (79424) *(G-14428)*	
J R & Adam Seitz Ltd	940 723-7303
813 8th St Ste 720 Wichita Falls (76301) *(G-20773)*	
J Rollins Construction Inc	936 258-3485
405 W Clayton St Dayton (77535) *(G-5231)*	
J S G, Houston *Also called J Simmons Group Inc (G-10443)*	
J S McKinney Inc	979 849-7283
571 Jimmy Phillips Blvd Angleton (77515) *(G-574)*	
J S Technology Inc	469 326-5900
3000 W Kingsley Rd Garland (75041) *(G-7523)*	
J S W, Baytown *Also called Jsw Steel (usa) Inc (G-1794)*	
J Simmons Group Inc	713 675-5100
7207 High Life Dr Houston (77066) *(G-10443)*	
J Suzette & Company Inc (PA)	972 359-0001
1293 Allen Station Pkwy Allen (75002) *(G-279)*	
J T Thorpe Company (HQ)	713 644-1247
6833 Kirbyville St Houston (77033) *(G-10444)*	
J T W Motor Co, Fort Worth *Also called Western Hauler Enterprises (G-7139)*	
J V I, Houston *Also called JVI Vibratory Equipment Inc (G-10491)*	
J V Plastics Inc	972 606-0500
2723 S Great Sw Pkwy Grand Prairie (75052) *(G-7900)*	
J W Drilling Inc	575 748-8704
10544 Kitsee Knoll Way Quinlan (75474) *(G-17223)*	
J W Hall Enterprises Inc	409 925-7712
17731 Elizabeth Rd Alvin (77511) *(G-368)*	
J W Hall Ltd Liability Co	281 337-6311
17731 Elizabeth Rd Alvin (77511) *(G-369)*	
J W Resources Inc	806 935-0185
7 Miles N Of Dumas Dumas (79029) *(G-5523)*	
J Waters Inc	502 896-0850
100 Arnold St Ennis (75119) *(G-6108)*	

J&A Fabrication	903 981-0136
510 N Edith St Longview (75601) *(G-14254)*	
J&A Trucking Co	713 854-0226
15911 Rogers Rd Willis (77378) *(G-20851)*	
J&D Interiors Inc (PA)	817 626-2365
2015 N Main St Fort Worth (76164) *(G-6731)*	
J&F Machine Shop Inc	713 466-1760
6300 W Little York Rd # 112 Houston (77091) *(G-10445)*	
J&J Weaver Co (PA)	254 756-2139
500 S Valley Mills Dr Waco (76711) *(G-20419)*	
J&J Welding & Awning	214 227-5606
2605 National Cir Garland (75041) *(G-7524)*	
J&P Ramirez Services LLC	361 526-2072
172 Highway 183 Refugio (78377) *(G-17243)*	
J&W Wellhead, Midland *Also called J & W Services & Equipment Co (G-15257)*	
J-Hobbs Machine Corporation	432 563-1526
3807 S C R 1297 Odessa (79765) *(G-16036)*	
J-III Concrete Co	956 787-5518
323 E Owassa Rd Pharr (78577) *(G-16702)*	
J-III Concrete Co (PA)	956 968-1371
1700 E 28th St Weslaco (78596) *(G-20661)*	
J-III Concrete Co	361 396-1951
6765 S Us Highway 281 Alice (78332) *(G-217)*	
J-Kraft Inc (PA)	281 876-2535
4643 E Richey Rd Humble (77338) *(G-12780)*	
J-M Manufacturing Company Inc	979 532-5640
10807 Us 59 Hwy Wharton (77488) *(G-20700)*	
J-Mac Tool Inc	817 237-6309
8701 Eagle Mountain Cir Fort Worth (76135) *(G-6732)*	
J-N Fence Co Inc	972 226-7205
305 Us Highway 80 E Mesquite (75150) *(G-15054)*	
J-Peam LLC	817 927-1819
3300 South Fwy Fort Worth (76110) *(G-6733)*	
J-W Energy Company (PA)	972 233-8191
16479 Dallas Pkwy Ste 850 Addison (75001) *(G-137)*	
J-W Gathering Company (HQ)	903 643-3413
122 Dovel Rd Longview (75603) *(G-14255)*	
J-W Operating Company (HQ)	972 233-8191
15505 Wright Brothers Dr Addison (75001) *(G-138)*	
J-W Operating Company	432 332-0111
250 Solo Rd Odessa (79762) *(G-16037)*	
J-W Operating Company	361 570-2788
4607 E Juan Linn St Victoria (77901) *(G-20275)*	
J-W Operating Company	281 592-2351
4748 Us Highway 59 S Cleveland (77327) *(G-3129)*	
J-W Power Company (HQ)	972 233-8191
16479 Dallas Pkwy Ste 850 Addison (75001) *(G-139)*	
J2 Fabrications, Magnolia *Also called J 2 Fabrications LLC (G-14611)*	
Ja Electronic Manufacturing Co, Stafford *Also called Bk/Ja Holdings Inc (G-19291)*	
Ja-En Enterprise Inc	956 782-0085
1305 Macco Dr Pharr (78577) *(G-16703)*	
Jab Rentals Inc	432 296-6464
2627 Faudree Rd Ste B Odessa (79765) *(G-16038)*	
Jab Services, Odessa *Also called Jab Rentals Inc (G-16038)*	
Jabil Inc	727 577-9749
130 Flecha Ln Laredo (78045) *(G-13898)*	
Jac Enterprises Inc	936 348-3997
1809 Interstate 45 N Madisonville (77864) *(G-14587)*	
Jac Enterprises Inc	936 348-3934
301 Crossroads Madisonville (77864) *(G-14588)*	
Jack Black LLC	469 341-2700
551 Sthwstern Blvd Ste 10 Coppell (75019) *(G-3423)*	
Jack Phipps	972 278-3186
11545 Pagemill Rd Ste 100 Dallas (75243) *(G-4520)*	
Jack Saunders	713 806-7997
4506 Adobe Ln Baytown (77521) *(G-1823)*	
Jack The Ripper Table Skirts, Stafford *Also called Quality Table Linen Inc (G-19365)*	
Jackal Merger Sub A LLC	737 704-2300
303 Colorado St Ste 3000 Austin (78701) *(G-1248)*	
Jackie Todaro	281 354-2581
1701 Northpark Dr Ste 15 Kingwood (77339) *(G-13646)*	
Jackrabbit Steel Products Inc	281 550-4551
9009 Jackrabbit Rd Houston (77095) *(G-10446)*	
Jackson County Herald Tribune	361 782-2131
306 N Wells St Edna (77957) *(G-5607)*	
Jackson Deerfield Mfg Corp	972 233-7513
14330 Midway Rd Ste 119 Dallas (75244) *(G-4521)*	
Jackson Promotions Inc	281 474-1313
1908 Hialeah Dr Ste A Seabrook (77586) *(G-18786)*	
Jackson Sign and Lighting Inc	254 751-0390
22007 Bush Industrial Par Woodway (76712) *(G-20921)*	
Jackson Steel Company, Elmendorf *Also called Trans-Tex Fabricating Co Inc (G-6072)*	
Jacksonville Candy Co Inc	903 586-8334
218 E Woodrow St 18 Jacksonville (75766) *(G-13244)*	
Jacksonville Daily Progress, Jacksonville *Also called Newspaper Holding Inc (G-13253)*	
Jacksonville Tool & Die Inc	903 586-6030
1044 E Loop 456 Jacksonville (75766) *(G-13245)*	
Jackup Structures Alliance Inc	713 910-7556
10850 Richmond Ave # 205 Houston (77042) *(G-10447)*	

A L P H A B E T I C

Jacob Stern & Sons Inc 713 926-8386
2104 75th St Houston (77011) *(G-10448)*

Jacqueline Construction Inc 469 258-4402
2302 Jacqueline Dr Garland (75042) *(G-7525)*

Jacqueline Thompson 210 269-1548
104 Fred Couples Dr Round Rock (78664) *(G-17663)*

Jadcap Machine Works Inc 210 932-1019
3621 Sw Military Dr San Antonio (78211) *(G-18198)*

Jade Services Inc 806 870-3883
701 N 1st St Lamesa (79331) *(G-13825)*

Jadtis Industries LP 214 905-9566
13365 Branch View Ln Farmers Branch (75234) *(G-6204)*

Jaeger Products Inc (HQ) **817 695-5680**
2201 E Lamar Blvd Ste 240 Arlington (76006) *(G-710)*

Jaffe Group Ltd 830 598-2413
1449 Airpark Horseshoe Bay (78657) *(G-8368)*

Jag Energy Company 832 997-0575
9894 Bissonnet St 100b Houston (77036) *(G-10449)*

Jag Energy Usa Inc 361 449-1400
1869 N Ih 37 Access Rd George West (78022) *(G-7625)*

Jagee Petro Inc 817 335-5881
2918 Wingate St Fort Worth (76107) *(G-6734)*

Jagged Peak Energy MGT LLC 720 215-3700
303 Colorado St Ste 3000 Austin (78701) *(G-1249)*

Jaguar Designs Inc 214 634-7733
9034 Diplomacy Row Dallas (75247) *(G-4522)*

Jaguar Energy Services LLC 337 250-4030
11890 W Ih 10 Marion (78124) *(G-14757)*

Jaguar Energy Services LLC 337 250-4030
1850 Roughneck Dr Bryan (77808) *(G-2480)*

Jaguar Exploration Inc 281 920-2668
440 Cobia Dr Ste 1204 Katy (77494) *(G-13366)*

Jaguar Hospitality Svcs Corp 214 295-3574
6009 W Parker Rd 149-130 Plano (75093) *(G-16896)*

Jahkur International LLC 832 431-3232
800 W Sam Houston Pkwy N Houston (77024) *(G-10450)*

Jahkur Services, Houston *Also called Jahkur International LLC* *(G-10450)*

Jake Harris & Sons Inc 281 471-0214
632 S 16th St La Porte (77571) *(G-13758)*

Jaks Machine Inc 361 575-2312
3302 Houston Hwy Victoria (77901) *(G-20276)*

Jalem Welding Service LLC 956 467-2355
414 Cottonwood Ave McAllen (78501) *(G-14876)*

Jam Construction, Dallas *Also called Jamco Services LLC* *(G-4523)*

Jamak Fabrication-Tex Ltd 817 594-8771
1401 N Bowie Dr Weatherford (76086) *(G-20598)*

Jamco Services LLC 432 242-6051
8080 Park Ln Ste 700 Dallas (75231) *(G-4523)*

James Avery Craftsman Inc 512 541-3823
9600 Interstate Hwy Austin (78748) *(G-1250)*

James Avery Craftsman Inc 956 509-2912
2355 N Xpwy Ste 1 Brownsville (78520) *(G-2367)*

James Barker III 936 298-2851
3301 Highway 105 Cleveland (77327) *(G-3130)*

James D Atkins 979 209-2121
3100 Leonard Rd Bryan (77803) *(G-2481)*

James D Vossler 281 376-6420
14022 Sunrise Arbor Ln Cypress (77429) *(G-3804)*

James Fisher Subsea Excav Inc 713 466-1233
6421 Cunningham Rd Houston (77041) *(G-10451)*

James Hardie Building Pdts Inc 972 923-9300
2425 N Highway 77 Waxahachie (75165) *(G-20547)*

James Hardie Building Pdts Inc 817 556-7000
820 Sparks Dr Cleburne (76033) *(G-3097)*

James L Rembert Jr Inc 281 240-7070
12832 Park One Dr Sugar Land (77478) *(G-19500)*

James Lee Davis (PA) **432 682-6311**
211 N Colorado St Midland (79701) *(G-15258)*

James Manufacturing Inc 903 872-2346
550 Hardy Ave Corsicana (75110) *(G-3675)*

James Puryear Weldng Fabrctn 325 672-2009
350 T And P Ln Abilene (79602) *(G-54)*

James Reneau Seed Company 806 256-3216
119 S Main St Shamrock (79079) *(G-18891)*

James Skinner Co 903 784-7174
2020 19th St Nw Paris (75460) *(G-16362)*

James Walker Oil & Gas Co 281 875-0002
26797 Hanna Rd Ste D7 Conroe (77385) *(G-3313)*

Jamestown North America LLC 713 672-6655
4550 Homestead Rd Houston (77028) *(G-10452)*

Jamestown Plastics Inc 956 831-8800
3200 Fm 511 Brownsville (78526) *(G-2368)*

Jamex Inc 214 265-7141
2871 Lake Vista Dr # 200 Lewisville (75067) *(G-14058)*

Jamieson Fence Supply, Dallas *Also called Jamieson Manufacturing Co* *(G-4524)*

Jamieson Manufacturing Co (HQ) 214 339-8384
3010 Lyndon B Johnson Fwy # 800 Dallas (75234) *(G-4524)*

Jan Pate Inc 903 683-5700
120 Birmingham Forest Dr Rusk (75785) *(G-17732)*

Jana Inc (PA) **210 616-0083**
1717 Universal City Blvd Universal City (78148) *(G-20183)*

Jana's Ministry, Spring *Also called Exxon Mobil Fuels Marketing Co* *(G-19115)*

Janak Packing Inc 361 798-2985
3116 Us Highway 90a W Hallettsville (77964) *(G-8123)*

Janis Litchfield 325 625-1001
4330 Gaines Ranch Loop # 120 Austin (78735) *(G-1251)*

Janssen Lease Service Inc 361 771-3556
204 York St Ganado (77962) *(G-7415)*

Janus International Group LLC 713 463-4427
1256 Brittmoore Rd Houston (77043) *(G-10453)*

Janus Signs 972 420-8770
1306 W Main St Lewisville (75067) *(G-14059)*

Janus Signs Inc (PA) **214 503-1333**
9742 Skillman St Dallas (75243) *(G-4525)*

Japan Arospc Exploration Agcy 281 333-5999
18050 Saturn Ln Ste 310 Houston (77058) *(G-10454)*

Jar Industries LLC 281 484-1777
12626 Fuqua St Houston (77034) *(G-10455)*

Jar-Tex Industries Inc 817 332-9922
204 E Daggett Ave Fort Worth (76104) *(G-6735)*

Jarco Steel Inc 713 644-4900
1011 Highway 6 S Ste 314 Houston (77077) *(G-10456)*

Jarden LLC 903 455-0691
7000 Industrial Dr Greenville (75402) *(G-8078)*

Jardine Foods Inc 512 295-4600
1 Chisholm Trl Buda (78610) *(G-2531)*

Jardine's Texas Foods, Buda *Also called Jardine Foods Inc* *(G-2531)*

Jaropamex 830 774-5920
2 A Fawcett Dr Del Rio (78842) *(G-5318)*

Jarvantech Inc 832 742-7220
2219 Sawdust Rd Ste 401 The Woodlands (77380) *(G-19888)*

Jarvis Industries Inc 281 370-5455
23924 Lenze Rd Spring (77389) *(G-19136)*

Jarvis Press Inc 214 637-2340
9112 Viscount Row Dallas (75247) *(G-4526)*

JAS Marketing Inc 281 879-1844
1328 Sheldon Rd Channelview (77530) *(G-3027)*

Jash Usa Inc (HQ) **281 962-6369**
6200 Savoy Dr Ste 750 Houston (77036) *(G-10457)*

Jasmine Lewis 325 200-5769
18551 Timber Forest Dr Humble (77346) *(G-12781)*

Jason Jones 903 753-6045
903 Memphis St Longview (75604) *(G-14256)*

Jasper Newsboy, Jasper *Also called Hearst Corporation* *(G-13277)*

Jaunt Air Mobility LLC 817 692-3030
2820 Rainforest Ct Southlake (76092) *(G-19077)*

Jax Ltd Inc 763 449-9699
3701 W Plano Pkwy Ste 100 Plano (75075) *(G-16897)*

Jaxa, Houston *Also called Japan Arospc Exploration Agcy* *(G-10454)*

Jay H Fixtures Inc 972 223-2245
305 N Beckley Rd De Soto (75115) *(G-5239)*

Jay Management Company LLC 936 258-2646
1252 Fm 1413 Dayton (77535) *(G-5232)*

Jayco Manufacturing, Grand Prairie *Also called Sage International Inc* *(G-7971)*

Jayco Manufacturing LLC 972 623-2004
1470 Avenue T Grand Prairie (75050) *(G-7901)*

Jayco Steel Services Inc 281 399-0189
22788 Antique Ln New Caney (77357) *(G-15842)*

Jayden Inc 214 389-7300
2632 Freewood Dr Dallas (75220) *(G-4527)*

Jaymaran Wholesale and Dist, Houston *Also called David* *(G-9407)*

Jayna Inc 972 417-8922
2555 Tarpley Rd Carrollton (75006) *(G-2771)*

Jayroe Litho Inc 972 243-3835
13240 Valley Branch Ln Dallas (75234) *(G-4528)*

Jayroe Printing, Dallas *Also called Jayroe Litho Inc* *(G-4528)*

Jayvic Inc (PA) **806 374-9402**
4210 Hester Dr Amarillo (79124) *(G-442)*

Jazzy's Southern Creations, Humble *Also called Jasmine Lewis* *(G-12781)*

JB Commercial Millwork Inc 903 989-2241
402 W Saunders St Trenton (75490) *(G-20017)*

Jbc Steel Products LLC 214 340-1510
10904 Sanden Dr Ste 102 Dallas (75238) *(G-4529)*

Jbd Bindery Inc 713 457-4606
5800 Corporate Dr Ste A4 Houston (77036) *(G-10458)*

Jbl Oil & Gas Operating LLC 281 516-3137
8500 Cypresswood Dr # 10 Spring (77379) *(G-19137)*

Jbm Specialties LLC 214 604-7646
302 W Obuch St Valley View (76272) *(G-20203)*

Jbs Packing Company Inc 409 982-5766
2170 Gulfway Dr Port Arthur (77640) *(G-17114)*

Jbs USA Food Company 817 306-9900
3906 Sandshell Dr Fort Worth (76137) *(G-6736)*

Jbs USA Food Company 903 434-1000
110 S Texas St Pittsburg (75686) *(G-16745)*

Jbs USA Food Company 806 966-5103
5950 Trails End Rd Cactus (79013) *(G-2622)*

Jbs USA Food Company.............................956 632-3800
6800 S Ware Rd Ste 109 McAllen (78503) *(G-14877)*

Jbt Aero Tech, El Paso *Also called John Bean Technologies Corp (G-5822)*

Jbt Aerotech, Houston *Also called John Bean Technologies Corp (G-10480)*

Jbt Aerotech Services, Conroe *Also called John Bean Technologies Corp (G-3315)*

JC Custom Boats Inc.............................361 785-6035
478 Cemetery Rd Seadrift (77983) *(G-18796)*

JC Millwork Inc.............................469 702-2570
501 Lakeside Pkwy Ste 150 Flower Mound (75028) *(G-6269)*

JC Viramontes Inc.............................915 857-4545
12651 Montana Ave El Paso (79938) *(G-5820)*

Jc/Fz Holdings Inc.............................713 948-6000
11951 Spectrum Blvd Houston (77047) *(G-10459)*

JCB Inc.............................254 687-2200
1199 E Main St Itasca (76055) *(G-13215)*

Jci Roofing LLC.............................956 227-1745
2916 N 1st Ln McAllen (78501) *(G-14878)*

Jcjh LLC.............................830 331-2240
1685 River Rd Ste 200 Boerne (78006) *(G-2124)*

Jcm Industries Inc.............................903 832-2581
200 Old Boston Rd Nash (75569) *(G-15722)*

JCs Marine Oilfield Svc Inc.............................281 338-7835
501 E Walker St League City (77573) *(G-13967)*

Jcv Manufacturing Corporation.............................281 201-4853
131 Eichwurzel Ln Bldg 1 Houston (77009) *(G-10460)*

JD Abrams LP (HQ).............................512 322-4000
5811 Trade Center Dr # 1 Austin (78744) *(G-1252)*

JD Abrams LP.............................512 243-1090
7300 Us Highway 183 S Austin (78744) *(G-1253)*

JD King Inc.............................800 805-6302
1300 Sw 2nd St Seminole (79360) *(G-18884)*

JD Murchison Interests Inc (PA).............................972 931-0700
7250 Dallas Pkwy Plano (75024) *(G-16898)*

JD Pro-Service LLC (PA).............................936 264-4003
17220 Highway 105 E Conroe (77306) *(G-3314)*

JDC Enterprises Inc.............................972 550-1880
2900 Gateway Dr Ste 625 Irving (75063) *(G-13068)*

Jdh Iron Designs LLC.............................254 486-9150
9685 N Lone Star Pkwy Valley Mills (76689) *(G-20201)*

Jdh Pacific Inc.............................562 926-8088
521 Ne Loop 289 Lubbock (79403) *(G-14429)*

JDM Designs Inc.............................281 356-6131
14135 Stagecoach Rd Stagecoach (77355) *(G-19401)*

Jdp Manufacturing Inc.............................817 529-4009
2016 Mrtin Lther King Fwy Fort Worth (76104) *(G-6737)*

Jdr Cable Systems Inc.............................832 220-4690
7906 N Sam Houston Pkwy W # 201 Houston (77064) *(G-10461)*

Jdw Services Inc (PA).............................903 845-5586
405 Riverside Dr Gladewater (75647) *(G-7723)*

Je Oilfield Services LLC.............................361 701-1324
183 County Road 162 Alice (78332) *(G-218)*

Jeb Originals, Winnsboro *Also called Jeb Sales Company Inc (G-20898)*

Jeb Sales Company Inc.............................903 342-3112
103 E Coke Rd Winnsboro (75494) *(G-20898)*

Jedco Building Systems Inc.............................281 591-2860
1645 Hill Rd Houston (77039) *(G-10462)*

Jeep Collins Jewelry Maker.............................830 997-3135
2089 N Llano St Fredericksburg (78624) *(G-7184)*

Jeeves Information Systems Inc.............................512 333-4418
7500 Rialto Blvd Ste 230 Austin (78735) *(G-1254)*

Jefes Welding Company.............................903 389-4036
234 County Road 1171 Fairfield (75840) *(G-6177)*

Jeff Bonner R & D Inc.............................210 590-3133
10525 Mopac Dr San Antonio (78217) *(G-18199)*

Jeff Bonner Research & Dev Co, San Antonio *Also called Jeff Bonner R & D Inc (G-18199)*

Jeffcoat Production Service.............................409 429-5900
11555 Fm 92 Spurger (77660) *(G-19278)*

Jefferson At Montfort Limited.............................972 789-3600
14332 Montfort Dr Dallas (75254) *(G-4530)*

Jefferson Electric Inc.............................956 542-5491
3330 E 14th St Brownsville (78521) *(G-2369)*

Jefferson Energy Company, The Woodlands *Also called Jefferson Refinery LLC (G-19889)*

Jefferson Gulf Coast Energy (HQ).............................281 677-4900
811 Louisiana St Ste 2300 Houston (77002) *(G-10463)*

Jefferson Refinery LLC (PA).............................281 677-4900
9595 Six Pines Dr # 6370 The Woodlands (77380) *(G-19889)*

Jeg Holdings LLC.............................972 532-6419
5080 Spectrum Dr Ste 510e Addison (75001) *(G-140)*

Jeh-Eas Inc.............................210 490-9156
12813 Wetmore Rd San Antonio (78247) *(G-18200)*

Jelco, Manchaca *Also called Jellison Inc (G-14639)*

Jeld-Wen Inc.............................972 623-1727
2510 W Main St Ste 300 Grand Prairie (75050) *(G-7902)*

Jeld-Wen Inc.............................903 885-0660
902 N Hillcrest Dr Sulphur Springs (75482) *(G-19590)*

Jeld-Wen Inc.............................972 272-3667
4409 Action St Garland (75042) *(G-7526)*

Jeld-Wen Doors, Garland *Also called Jeld-Wen Inc (G-7526)*

Jelec Inc (PA).............................713 977-6500
16901 Park Row Ste 200 Houston (77084) *(G-10464)*

Jell-Craft Products, San Antonio *Also called Son Beverage Company (G-18482)*

Jellison Inc.............................512 282-5256
11405 Conroy Ln Manchaca (78652) *(G-14639)*

Jemasco Inc.............................903 784-3014
11808 Farm Road 906 E Paris (75462) *(G-16363)*

Jenessco Industries Inc.............................281 498-8833
10589 Rockley Rd Houston (77099) *(G-10465)*

Jenkem Technology USA Inc.............................972 673-0603
4105 W Spring Creek Pkwy Plano (75024) *(G-16899)*

Jenkins Fabco Inc (PA).............................806 372-4336
820 Sw 6th Ave Amarillo (79101) *(G-443)*

Jennifer Harper, Corsicana *Also called Cor-Tex Steel (G-3662)*

Jennings Trailers Inc.............................903 473-4562
421 Rs County Road 1301 Emory (75440) *(G-6084)*

Jensar Corporation (PA).............................817 542-4327
2014 5th Ave Fort Worth (76110) *(G-6738)*

Jensco Transport Services LLC.............................325 234-1412
13880 Whitfield Rd Eola (76937) *(G-6124)*

Jensen, Cleburne *Also called Rangaire Manufacturing Co LP (G-3107)*

Jentek Water Treatment Inc.............................214 349-7111
11524 Pagemill Rd Dallas (75243) *(G-4531)*

Jerell Clothing Company LLC.............................214 349-1891
10367 Brockwood Rd Dallas (75238) *(G-4532)*

Jerell Clothing Multiples, Dallas *Also called Jerell Clothing Company LLC (G-4532)*

Jericho Systems Corporation.............................972 231-2000
25 Highland Park Vlg Dallas (75205) *(G-4533)*

Jericho Woodworks, Stafford *Also called Abuata Enterprises Inc (G-19280)*

Jerryco Boiler Works, Houston *Also called Jerryco Mch & Boiler Works LP (G-10466)*

Jerryco Mch & Boiler Works LP.............................713 224-7900
2403 Appelt Dr Houston (77015) *(G-10466)*

Jessco Solutions LLC.............................325 227-4196
4477 Christoval Rd San Angelo (76904) *(G-17811)*

Jesse C Taylor Oil Company, Fort Worth *Also called Taylor Distributing Co Inc (G-7037)*

Jesta Machine.............................903 721-9168
4373 Fm 1910 W Jacksonville (75766) *(G-13246)*

Jestex 2 LLC (PA).............................713 921-7187
8107 E Magnolia St Houston (77012) *(G-10467)*

Jet Learning Laboratory Inc (PA).............................713 524-6284
8236 Kirby Dr Ste 190 Houston (77054) *(G-10468)*

Jet Machine Works Inc.............................281 449-0046
1107 Aldine Mail Rte Houston (77039) *(G-10469)*

Jet Maintenance Inc.............................361 576-3226
4301 Houston Hwy Victoria (77901) *(G-20277)*

Jet Oil Producers Inc.............................936 653-3379
Hwy 150 Coldspring (77331) *(G-3166)*

Jet Research Center, Alvarado *Also called Halliburton Company (G-333)*

Jet Rubber Inc.............................713 673-5202
1240 Boyles St Houston (77020) *(G-10470)*

Jetstream of Houston LLP (HQ).............................832 590-1300
5905 Thomas Rd Houston (77041) *(G-10471)*

Jetta Operating Company Inc (PA).............................817 335-1179
640 Taylor St Ste 2400 Fort Worth (76102) *(G-6739)*

Jetta Production Company Inc (PA).............................817 335-1179
777 Taylor St Ph P1d Fort Worth (76102) *(G-6740)*

Jewell Concrete Products, Grapevine *Also called Oldcastle Apg Texas Inc (G-8049)*

Jewell Hudgens Inc.............................936 634-3731
1107 N Raguet St Lufkin (75904) *(G-14531)*

Jewell, An Oldcastle Company, Grapevine *Also called Old Castle Apg West (G-8048)*

Jewish Herald Voice Inc.............................713 630-0391
3403 Audley St Houston (77098) *(G-10472)*

JF Construction Inc.............................214 272-1902
1801 Mccord Way Apt 715 Frisco (75033) *(G-7293)*

Jf Filtration Inc.............................210 946-1688
4707 Nw Industrial San Antonio (78238) *(G-18201)*

Jf Filtration Inc.............................956 412-3234
2810 N Expwy 77 Ste C Harlingen (78552) *(G-8192)*

Jf Filtration Inc (PA).............................214 634-2200
4820 Memphis St Dallas (75207) *(G-4534)*

JG Media Inc.............................512 989-6808
16225 Impact Way Unit 1 Pflugerville (78660) *(G-16677)*

JGB Oilfield Services LLC.............................806 789-2796
5420 86th St Lubbock (79424) *(G-14430)*

Jgc Energy Development USA Inc.............................832 487-9965
3151 Briarpark Dr # 1050 Houston (77042) *(G-10473)*

Jgr Enterprises LLC.............................817 335-4629
108 South Fwy I35w Fort Worth (76104) *(G-6741)*

Jgt Services.............................432 553-5167
401 W Broadway St Andrews (79714) *(G-545)*

Jh Biotech Inc.............................830 557-4220
360 Koepsel Rd Mc Queeney (78123) *(G-14829)*

Ji Communications Inc.............................512 346-6921
9229 Wterford Ctr Ste 100 Austin (78758) *(G-1255)*

Jim Coleman Company (PA).............................713 683-9878
5842 W 34th St Houston (77092) *(G-10474)*

Jim Dandy Boxes Inc.............................817 608-9180
1750 Westpark Dr Ste 110 Grand Prairie (75050) *(G-7903)*

Jim McNabb Inc (PA) 512 365-2010
201 W 2nd St Taylor (76574) *(G-19658)*

Jim Melhart Piano and Organ Co 956 682-6147
3325 N 10th St McAllen (78501) *(G-14879)*

Jim R Reynolds & Assoc Inc 832 257-2312
25702 Aldine Westfield Rd Spring (77373) *(G-19138)*

Jim Ray Company Inc 713 941-2275
1207 Indiana St South Houston (77587) *(G-19048)*

Jim Warfield Electric, Carrollton *Also called Warfield Electric Texas Inc (G-2845)*

Jimco Sales & Mfg Inc 817 924-6173
3113 Saint Louis Ave Fort Worth (76110) *(G-6742)*

Jimmie Hahn Partnership Ltd (PA) 979 836-3664
1503 N Park St Brenham (77833) *(G-2259)*

Jimmy Smart (PA) 432 381-5450
3841 Nw Loop 338 Odessa (79764) *(G-16039)*

Jims Machine Service Inc 432 758-2611
102 County Road 402 Seminole (79360) *(G-18885)*

Jindal Saw Usa LLC (HQ) 281 573-3002
1411 S Fm 565 Rd Baytown (77523) *(G-1793)*

JIT Manufacturing Inc 903 887-0226
1420 S 3rd St Mabank (75147) *(G-14577)*

Jive Software Inc (HQ) 877 495-3700
401 Congress Ave Ste 2650 Austin (78701) *(G-1256)*

Jj of Dallas Manufacturing Inc 972 866-9866
4124 Billy Mitchell Dr Addison (75001) *(G-141)*

Jjm Oil & Gas Inc 832 740-4606
423 N Wayside Dr Houston (77020) *(G-10475)*

JK Manufacturing Inc 956 723-6893
1910 San Bernardo Ave Laredo (78040) *(G-13899)*

Jk Red Dirt Rentals LLC 214 530-3922
100 Gteway Hills Ln Ste A Granbury (76049) *(G-7801)*

Jl Bryan Eqp & Lease Svcs Inc 806 435-4511
806 S Industrial Hwy Perryton (79070) *(G-16638)*

Jlab Audio, Dallas *Also called Peag LLC (G-3850)*

JLK Industries Inc (PA) 713 462-7761
14545 Sommermeyer St Houston (77041) *(G-10476)*

JM Construction 956 518-2113
6304 Sioux Fls Brownsville (78521) *(G-2370)*

JM Cox Resources LP (PA) 432 682-9435
400 W Wall St Midland (79701) *(G-15259)*

JM Eagle, Wharton *Also called Pw Eagle Inc (G-20705)*

JM Eagle, Wharton *Also called J-M Manufacturing Company Inc (G-20700)*

JM Graphics LLC 817 460-7562
2407 S Cooper St Arlington (76015) *(G-711)*

JM Huber Corporation 830 693-3575
90 Avenue N Marble Falls (78654) *(G-14746)*

Jma Cattle Co, Abilene *Also called Alexander & Co (G-12)*

Jmd Oilfield & Rig Service LLC 469 261-2415
7035 Andrews Hwy Odessa (79765) *(G-16040)*

Jmd Oilfield and Rig Svc LLC 432 208-9941
7035 Andrews Hwy Odessa (79765) *(G-16041)*

Jmi Machine LLC 361 664-2848
600 S Johnson St Alice (78332) *(G-219)*

JMJ Organics Ltd (PA) 281 798-3056
1006 Spanish Cove Dr Crosby (77532) *(G-3735)*

Jmk International Inc (PA) 817 737-3703
1401 N Bowie Dr Weatherford (76086) *(G-20599)*

Jml Management Inc 936 591-9782
748 State Highway 7 W Center (75935) *(G-3000)*

Jml Services Inc 713 582-9500
2902 Skimmer Way Crosby (77532) *(G-3736)*

Jmn Energy Experts 817 703-9539
6229 Brentwood Dr Fort Worth (76112) *(G-6743)*

Jmr Industries Ltd (PA) 432 557-9721
3606 E State Highway 158 Midland (79706) *(G-15260)*

Jnb Machine Shop Inc 832 237-5000
20231 Hempstead Rd Houston (77065) *(G-10477)*

Joann Baik 281 469-1000
2777 Jones St Ste 140 Houston (77026) *(G-10478)*

Job Boss, Garland *Also called Robinson Engineering Co Inc (G-7580)*

Jobe Materials LP (PA) 915 298-9900
1150 Southview Dr Ste A El Paso (79928) *(G-5821)*

Jobe Systems Inc 713 344-1292
1701 Nance St Ste F&G Houston (77020) *(G-10479)*

Jobe's Company, The, Waco *Also called Easy Gardener Products Inc (G-20394)*

Jobran Unlimited LLC 956 541-1309
3009 J C S Industrial Dr Brownsville (78526) *(G-2371)*

Jodys Oilfield Service Inc 432 523-6866
110 Sw Mustang Dr Andrews (79714) *(G-546)*

Joe Bush & Associates Inc 512 238-0450
12 Indian Meadows Dr Round Rock (78665) *(G-17664)*

Joe Garcia 361 436-2130
100 S Nueces St George West (78022) *(G-7626)*

Joe Ross 903 450-9960
5430 Fm 118 Greenville (75401) *(G-8079)*

Joe Tipton Inc 972 271-6666
2202 Executive Dr Garland (75041) *(G-7527)*

Joe W. Fly Co., Dallas *Also called Jf Filtration Inc (G-4534)*

Joe White Tank Company Inc 817 624-1141
2710 N Nichols St Fort Worth (76106) *(G-6744)*

Joel G Gibbs Inc 281 595-3330
13730 County Road 48 Rosharon (77583) *(G-17606)*

Joes Industrial Mch Sp Inc 210 359-7500
1837 Rigsby Ave San Antonio (78210) *(G-18202)*

Joey Records Inc 210 432-7893
6703 W Commerce St San Antonio (78227) *(G-18203)*

Joey Records International, San Antonio *Also called Joey Records Inc (G-18203)*

John B Smith 830 620-9090
1320 Industrial Dr New Braunfels (78130) *(G-15806)*

John Bean Technologies Corp 936 441-2077
100 Interstate 45 N 152a Conroe (77301) *(G-3315)*

John Bean Technologies Corp 713 875-3735
6770 Imperl Vly Dr Ste 12 Houston (77060) *(G-10480)*

John Bean Technologies Corp 915 859-3776
6930 Market Ave Ste C El Paso (79915) *(G-5822)*

John Bludworth Shipyard LLC 361 887-7981
3909 Joe Fulton Intl Tc Corpus Christi (78402) *(G-3558)*

John C Maudlin Inc 281 334-7224
1207 Marina Bay Dr Kemah (77565) *(G-13476)*

John Charles Designs, Dallas *Also called Al Legacy Partners Inc (G-3916)*

John Christian Company, Austin *Also called Worldwide J R Wood LLC (G-867)*

John Cole Chemical Corporation 512 443-1037
6110 Trade Center Dr # 102 Austin (78744) *(G-1257)*

John Crane Inc 979 239-1201
115 Linda Ln Freeport (77541) *(G-7200)*

John Crane Inc 281 474-1700
4001 Fair Dr Pasadena (77507) *(G-16464)*

John D Blankenship 214 752-9191
1715 E Levee St Dallas (75207) *(G-4535)*

John Deere Authorized Dealer, Victoria *Also called K & K Repair Service LLC (G-20278)*

John Deere Authorized Dealer, Katy *Also called Brookside Equipment Sales Inc (G-13353)*

John Deere Authorized Dealer, Corpus Christi *Also called Doggett Heavy McHy Svcs LLC (G-3515)*

John Deere Authorized Dealer, Hockley *Also called Foster Farm & Equipment Supply (G-8345)*

John Deere Authorized Dealer, La Marque *Also called Land & Sea Services 1 Inc (G-13711)*

John Deere Authorized Dealer, Seguin *Also called Commercial Diesl Parts Svc Ltd (G-18830)*

John Galt Development Inc (PA) 312 701-9026
1919 Mckinney Ave Dallas (75201) *(G-4536)*

John H Hendrix Corporation (PA) 432 684-6631
6 Desta Dr Ste 2100 Midland (79705) *(G-15261)*

John H Sorola Inc 210 224-8597
523 W Cypress St San Antonio (78212) *(G-18204)*

John H Young Inc 713 236-8303
4605 Post Oak Place Dr # 250 Houston (77027) *(G-10481)*

John Henry Petroleum, Dallas *Also called Henry Oil LC (G-4449)*

John Hogan Interests Inc 214 637-0214
4561 Leston St Dallas (75247) *(G-4537)*

John Linder Operating Co LLC 903 845-4240
200 Griffin St Gladewater (75647) *(G-7724)*

John Oates Company Inc 806 878-3338
10398 S Stinnett Hwy Stinnett (79083) *(G-19427)*

John Roberts Designs, Pflugerville *Also called John Roberts Enterprises Inc (G-16678)*

John Roberts Enterprises Inc 512 252-0174
50063 Tictor Ste 100 Pflugerville (78660) *(G-16678)*

John Schexnayder, Austin *Also called Action Screen Graphics (G-886)*

John Sons Press, Fort Worth *Also called J-Peam LLC (G-6733)*

John Soules Foods Inc (PA) 903 592-9800
10150 Fm 14 Tyler (75706) *(G-20104)*

John W Gasparini Inc 972 466-4104
2720 Commodore Dr Ste 130 Carrollton (75007) *(G-2874)*

John Wiley & Sons Inc 972 245-0480
1649 W Frankford Rd Carrollton (75007) *(G-2875)*

John'crane, Pasadena *Also called John Crane Inc (G-16464)*

Johnnies Plastics Inc 210 533-8463
725 Florida St San Antonio (78210) *(G-18205)*

Johnny Baulch 409 938-8971
5305 Highway 6 Hitchcock (77563) *(G-8338)*

Johnnys Cabinet Shop Inc 940 686-2496
301 W Broad St Pilot Point (76258) *(G-16725)*

Johnnys Custom Cabinet 281 498-8950
9947 Mula Rd Ste 101 Stafford (77477) *(G-19336)*

Johns Dovetail Shop 972 557-0775
2123 Bridger Dr Mesquite (75149) *(G-15055)*

Johns Manville Corporation 817 645-9101
200 W Industrial Blvd Cleburne (76033) *(G-3098)*

Johnson & Ernst Operating Co 940 723-8127
807 8th St Ste 1200 Wichita Falls (76301) *(G-20774)*

Johnson Burns Co 806 372-5869
1310 Se 46th Ave Amarillo (79118) *(G-494)*

Johnson Cabinets & Woodworking 512 266-7099
15401 Storm Dr Austin (78734) *(G-1258)*

Johnson Cnstr Clearing LLC 281 659-1428
11 Deerfield Rd Huntsville (77340) *(G-12815)*

Johnson Contrls Authorized Dlr, Longview *Also called Morsco Supply LLC (G-14282)*

Johnson Contrls Authorized Dlr, Haltom City *Also called Ecolab Inc* (G-8138)

Johnson Contrls Authorized Dlr, Humble *Also called Century Arconditioning Sup L P* (G-12754)

Johnson Controls, Temple *Also called Clarios* (G-19676)

Johnson Controls, Fort Worth *Also called Clarios* (G-6522)

Johnson Controls, Houston *Also called Clarios* (G-9208)

Johnson Controls, Corpus Christi *Also called Clarios* (G-3500)

Johnson Controls Inc 713 934-2400
8323 N Eldridge Pkwy # 120 Houston (77041) (G-10482)

Johnson Controls Be Operation 956 782-3000
5201 George Mcvay Dr McAllen (78503) (G-14880)

Johnson Controls Inc 281 821-0121
2800 N Terminal Rd Houston (77032) (G-10483)

Johnson Controls Inc 512 973-3555
401 Center Ridge Dr # 400 Austin (78753) (G-1259)

Johnson Controls Inc 281 633-5700
4701 Ave I Richmond (77406) (G-17457)

Johnson Controls Inc 956 782-3000
5201 Gorge Mcvay Dr Ste I Mcallen (78503) (G-14881)

Johnson County Foam Inc 817 477-5061
565 Airport Dr Mansfield (76063) (G-14684)

Johnson County Pipe Inc 817 783-3444
800 County Road 209 Alvarado (76009) (G-336)

Johnson County Redi-Mix Ltd 817 556-9214
1905 N Main St Cleburne (76033) (G-3099)

Johnson Filtration Pdts Inc 806 371-8033
601 Ross St Amarillo (79102) (G-444)

Johnson Gear Inc 806 749-6400
1110 N Avenue T Lubbock (79415) (G-14431)

Johnson Machine & Tool Inc 972 843-5065
6930 Highway 78 S Nevada (75173) (G-15765)

Johnson Matthey Inc 281 291-7769
4106 New West Rd Pasadena (77507) (G-16465)

Johnson Ranches, Amarillo *Also called Johnson Burns Co* (G-494)

Johnson Tool Company Inc 432 267-7612
901 E 2nd St Big Spring (79720) (G-2084)

Johnston Products Dallas Inc 469 272-7212
604 Jealouse Way Cedar Hill (75104) (G-2946)

Joint Holdings/Basic Met Inds (PA) **713 937-7474**
11921 Fm 529 Rd Houston (77041) (G-10484)

Joists of Texas Inc 713 466-1212
16118 Singapore Ln Jersey Village (77040) (G-13301)

Jollyrhino Inc 909 732-8507
5100 Cuesta Verde Austin (78746) (G-1260)

Jolt Technologies, Irving *Also called IBM Global Systems Inc* (G-13063)

Jon Hart Design Co 210 226-8544
220 Burleson San Antonio (78202) (G-18206)

Jonell Filtration Products Inc 254 559-7591
900 Industrial Pkwy Breckenridge (76424) (G-2230)

Jones & Cook Stationers, Brownsville *Also called Gateway Printing & Off Sup Inc* (G-2359)

Jones Aluminum 409 866-5585
9805 Mallot Rd Beaumont (77713) (G-1913)

Jones Holt Enterprises Inc 210 657-5917
13715 Topper Cir San Antonio (78233) (G-18207)

Jones Lang Lasalle Ip Inc (HQ) **214 777-5100**
10440 N Central Expy # 1150 Dallas (75231) (G-4538)

Jones Manufacturing Inc 254 399-8940
640 Ruby Ave Waco (76710) (G-20420)

Jones Tape Duplicating Inc 281 351-8109
17408 Bobcat Trl Cypress (77429) (G-3805)

Jones, W D Drilling Co, Dumas *Also called High Plains Drilling Company* (G-5521)

Jones-Bell LLC 254 933-2270
2201 Taylors Valley Rd Belton (76513) (G-2026)

Jonsil Manufacturing Co, El Paso *Also called Shaudra Company Inc* (G-5957)

Jonsil Manufacturing Corp 915 544-4244
11812 Pete Rose Dr El Paso (79936) (G-5823)

Jordan Spooling Service Inc 432 366-6040
2400 W 56th St Odessa (79764) (G-16042)

Jordan Technologies LLC (PA) **502 267-8344**
16310 Bratton Ln Ste 350 Austin (78728) (G-1261)

Jordan Wire Rope, Odessa *Also called Jordan Spooling Service Inc* (G-16042)

Jordans Manufacturing Company 817 656-1033
4205 Garland Dr Fort Worth (76117) (G-6745)

Joren 713 300-0377
23031 S Waterlily Dr Richmond (77406) (G-17458)

Jorge Trevino 956 376-7114
1115 E 20th St Weslaco (78596) (G-20662)

Jormac Aerospace Inc 972 436-7069
820 W Sandy Lake Rd # 400 Coppell (75019) (G-3424)

Jorn Well Service 432 943-5699
412 W Sealy Ave Monahans (79756) (G-15607)

Josan Corporation 281 261-4747
1209 Moore Rd Stafford (77477) (G-19337)

Josco Products, Austin *Also called John Cole Chemical Corporation* (G-1257)

Jose Alfonsin 210 717-2306
10511 Sunflower Ln San Antonio (78213) (G-18208)

Jose Lucio Sandblasting & Pntg, Falls City *Also called B & M Oilfield Services LLC* (G-6182)

Jose Luis Villarreal 956 765-5535
641 Fm 496 E Zapata (78076) (G-20983)

Joseph McSweeny Entps LLC 214 334-8181
14920 Fm 156 S Justin (76247) (G-13345)

Josephine Tug Inc 409 744-1222
9723 Teichman Rd Galveston (77554) (G-7402)

Josephs Storehouse Baking Co 405 253-0669
3420 N Saint Marys St # 105 San Antonio (78212) (G-18209)

Josey Cypress Ranch, Houston *Also called Lenoir M Josey Inc* (G-10624)

Joshuas Respiratory Care Inc 469 916-9354
11880 Shiloh Rd Dallas (75228) (G-4539)

Journal Air Law Commerce 214 768-2570
3315 Daniel Ave Dallas (75205) (G-4540)

Journeyedcom Inc 800 876-3507
80 E Mcdermott Dr Allen (75002) (G-280)

Jovi Printing 713 467-4980
11177 Katy Fwy Ste C Houston (77079) (G-10485)

Joy Glbal Lngview Oprtions LLC (HQ) **903 237-7000**
2400 S Macarthur Dr Longview (75602) (G-14257)

Joy Glbal Lngview Oprtions LLC 903 237-7000
2400 Macarthur St Longview (75602) (G-14258)

Joy Global, Kilgore *Also called Komatsu Mining Corp* (G-13562)

Joy Pipe Usa LP (PA) **830 249-7400**
39850 Interstate 10 W Boerne (78006) (G-2125)

Joyson Safety Systems 830 703-7191
715 Frontera Rd Del Rio (78840) (G-5319)

Joyson Sfety Systems Acqstion 210 250-5000
4611 Wiseman Blvd San Antonio (78251) (G-18210)

JP Energy Partners LP (HQ) **972 444-0300**
600 Las Colinas Blvd E # 2000 Irving (75039) (G-13069)

JP Tubular Services Inc 281 426-8596
11621 Fm 2100 Crosby (77532) (G-3737)

Jp3 Measurement LLC 512 537-8450
4109 Todd Ln Ste 200 Austin (78744) (G-1262)

Jpm Eoc Opal LLC 303 861-8140
909 Fannin St Ste 1350 Houston (77010) (G-10486)

Jpon Glass Company Inc 214 349-1400
1825 S Jupiter Rd Garland (75042) (G-7528)

JPS Alliance Inc 817 534-0044
4625 Martin St Fort Worth (76119) (G-6746)

Jpt Graphics Inc 972 785-1013
212 W Irving Blvd Irving (75060) (G-13070)

JR Manufacturing LP 713 462-5900
6485 Thomas Rd Houston (77041) (G-10487)

JR Peterson Inc 210 695-4455
12410 Bandera Rd Helotes (78023) (G-8239)

JR Sheldon & Company Inc 940 368-5793
136 Bent Oak Dr Pottsboro (75076) (G-17197)

JR Simplot Company 361 987-2682
2301 Farm Market 1593 S Point Comfort (77978) (G-17087)

JR Simplot Company 979 826-8063
1275 Zach Rd Hempstead (77445) (G-8253)

Jr Thompson Inc 940 995-2245
450 Rock Quarry Rd Saint Jo (76265) (G-17763)

Jr3 Websmart LLC 254 759-1902
925 Columbus Ave Waco (76701) (G-20421)

Jrn Management LP 210 222-9511
726 Probandt San Antonio (78204) (G-18211)

Jro LLC 903 472-0924
6000 E End Blvd S Marshall (75672) (G-14784)

JRS Company Inc 626 967-2432
200 County Road 199 Hutto (78634) (G-12881)

Jspaz Guardian Energy Svcs LLC 432 606-5003
1009 W 5th St Big Spring (79720) (G-2085)

Jss Airbag, Del Rio *Also called Joyson Safety Systems* (G-5319)

Jst Global LLC (PA) **713 926-8386**
2104 75th St Houston (77011) (G-10488)

Jsw Steel (usa) Inc 281 383-2525
5200 E Mckinney Rd # 110 Baytown (77523) (G-1794)

Jt Oilfiled Manufacturing Co 713 947-7006
7443 Fauna St Houston (77061) (G-10489)

Jt Oilfiled Manufacturing Co (PA) **713 947-7006**
1882 Flat Rock St Friendswood (77546) (G-7247)

JT Swabbing Services Inc 956 580-8954
6803 Western Rd Mission (78574) (G-15557)

Jta Service 432 556-0091
1107 Maple Ave Midland (79705) (G-15262)

JTL Suplies, Round Rock *Also called Jacqueline Thompson* (G-17663)

Jtm Technologies Inc 972 635-6900
160 County Road 979 Royse City (75189) (G-17720)

Juan Garza 956 723-6687
4820 Mcpherson Rd Ste 1 Laredo (78041) (G-13900)

Judys Iron & Metal Inc (PA) **409 681-0500**
6755 N Highway 105 Vidor (77662) (G-20328)

Juggernaut Machinery LLC 210 399-3374
7475 W Fm 140 Jourdanton (78026) (G-13333)

Juiceus LLC 956 667-0153
3090 Pablo Kisel Blvd A Brownsville (78526) (G-2372)

Julie Keck 210 435-3535
1286 Bandera Rd San Antonio (78228) (G-18212)

A
L
P
H
A
B
E
T
I
C

Julios Corn Chips 325 486-9300
  1911 S Chadbourne St San Angelo (76903) *(G-17812)*

Junction Industries LLC (PA) **817 607-8873**
  3348 Peden Rd Ste 500 Fort Worth (76179) *(G-6747)*

Juniper Specialty Products LLC (PA) **346 310-6241**
  120 N Munger St Pasadena (77506) *(G-16466)*

Jupe Feeds Inc 254 773-5211
  405 S 2nd St Temple (76504) *(G-19683)*

Just Energy (us) Corp 713 850-6784
  5251 Westheimr Rd # 1000 Houston (77056) *(G-10490)*

Just Right Products, Haltom City Also called F W Promo *(G-8140)*

Justin Brands Inc 940 226-1706
  700 Avenue F Nw Childress (79201) *(G-3055)*

Justin Brands Inc (HQ) **817 332-4385**
  610 W Daggett Ave Fort Worth (76104) *(G-6748)*

Justin Brands Inc 915 778-8311
  1137 Tony Lama St El Paso (79915) *(G-5824)*

Justin Industries Inc 817 332-4385
  610 W Daggett Ave Fort Worth (76104) *(G-6749)*

Justin Industries Inc (HQ) **817 332-4101**
  3024 Acme Brick Plz Fort Worth (76109) *(G-6750)*

Justin Industries Inc 512 258-1474
  1800 W Whitestone Blvd Cedar Park (78613) *(G-2975)*

Justin Industries Inc 979 885-4124
  6005 Peters San Felipe Rd Sealy (77474) *(G-18811)*

Justin Original Work Boot, Fort Worth Also called Justin Brands Inc *(G-6748)*

Justiss Oil Company Inc 903 859-2111
  100 State Highway 64 E Arp (75750) *(G-812)*

JV Industrial Companies Ltd (HQ) **713 568-2600**
  527 Logwood Ave San Antonio (78221) *(G-18213)*

JV Industrial Companies Ltd 903 579-8900
  1001 E Northst Lp 323 2 Tyler (75708) *(G-20105)*

JV Industrial Companies Ltd 979 373-0376
  217 Commerce St Freeport (77541) *(G-7201)*

JV Industrial Companies Ltd 361 884-4022
  1920 N Port Ave Corpus Christi (78401) *(G-3559)*

JV Industrial Companies Ltd 281 417-7019
  2221 Sens Rd La Porte (77571) *(G-13759)*

JV Piping, San Antonio Also called JV Industrial Companies Ltd *(G-18213)*

JV Roustabout Inc 432 943-2999
  400 Houston Wickett (79788) *(G-20839)*

JV Tyler Engineers, Tyler Also called JV Industrial Companies Ltd *(G-20105)*

JVB Electronics Inc 972 877-8085
  3835 Conflans Rd Irving (75061) *(G-13071)*

JVI Vibratory Equipment Inc 832 467-3720
  11929 Brittmoore Park Dr Houston (77041) *(G-10491)*

Jvm Mechanical Inc 713 910-3839
  8889 W Monroe Rd Houston (77061) *(G-10492)*

JW Industries Ltd (PA) **972 291-7474**
  1001 Mount Lebanon Rd Cedar Hill (75104) *(G-2947)*

JW Nutritional LLC (PA) **214 221-0404**
  601 Century Pkwy Ste 300 Allen (75013) *(G-281)*

JW Williams Inc 307 237-8345
  901 S County Rd W Odessa (79763) *(G-16043)*

Jwacs Commercial Group, Austin Also called Ruben Arispe Jr *(G-1475)*

Jwb Consulting Service Inc 817 675-6419
  2116 S County Road 1122 Midland (79706) *(G-15263)*

Jwtmbg Enterprise LLC 817 230-2513
  1256 Main St Ste 210 Southlake (76092) *(G-19078)*

Jx Nippon Chemical Texas Inc 713 754-1000
  10500 Bay Area Blvd Pasadena (77507) *(G-16467)*

Jyoti Americas, Conroe Also called Jyoti International Inc *(G-3316)*

Jyoti International Inc 936 523-4700
  3575 Pollok Dr Conroe (77303) *(G-3316)*

K & B Steel, Clarksville Also called Wabb Industries Inc *(G-3078)*

K & C Meat Processing 936 825-6944
  124 Durden St Navasota (77868) *(G-15738)*

K & D Caps, Austin Also called Miller Uniforms & Emblems Inc *(G-1345)*

K & D Woodwork, Big Sandy Also called Kenneth M Burgin *(G-2065)*

K & H Fabricators Inc 512 237-5020
  170 Loop Rd Smithville (78957) *(G-18977)*

K & J Businesses Inc 254 628-9208
  401 Cheyenne Dr Killeen (76542) *(G-13609)*

K & J Woodworks LLC 512 668-4237
  86 S Old Spanish Trl Kyle (78640) *(G-13683)*

K & K Chemical Company Inc 972 635-2482
  1303 Industrial Dr Royse City (75189) *(G-17721)*

K & K Langham Ltd 512 835-5100
  11209 Metric Blvd Ste B Austin (78758) *(G-1263)*

K & K Machine Shop Inc 713 947-1705
  2622 Martinville Dr Houston (77017) *(G-10493)*

K & K Repair Service LLC 361 573-5027
  4855 Us Highway 87 S Victoria (77905) *(G-20278)*

K & L Precision Plastics Inc 972 234-4231
  410 N Grove Rd Richardson (75081) *(G-17338)*

K & N Engineering Inc 951 826-0000
  741 Refuge Way Grand Prairie (75050) *(G-7904)*

K & N Perforators Inc 361 578-8851
  508 Profit Dr Victoria (77901) *(G-20279)*

K & R Screen Graphics 214 821-9562
  3915 Main St Dallas (75226) *(G-4541)*

K & S Products Inc 972 820-0007
  1000 Crowley Dr Carrollton (75006) *(G-2772)*

K & T Printing Inc 281 988-8088
  10515 Bellaire Blvd Ste D Houston (77072) *(G-10494)*

K and M Manufacturing Co Inc 512 352-2588
  628 E Lake Dr Taylor (76574) *(G-19659)*

K C Crushed Concrete Inc 281 219-0820
  909 Pinafore Ln C Houston (77039) *(G-10495)*

K C Fab Inc (PA) **713 921-5333**
  2836 Delafield St Houston (77023) *(G-10496)*

K C Fab Inc 806 372-9281
  5601 S Washington St Amarillo (79110) *(G-495)*

K D M Hot Oil Service Inc 432 683-0831
  2400 Fm 715 Midland (79706) *(G-15264)*

K L Barton & Sons Tie Co 936 347-2744
  703 S Us Highway 59 Garrison (75946) *(G-7611)*

K M I L, Cameron Also called Milam Broadcasting Co Inc *(G-2643)*

K P A N Broadcasters 806 364-1860
  218 E 5th St Hereford (79045) *(G-8292)*

K S W Corp 214 350-1943
  2970 Blystone Ln Ste 101 Dallas (75220) *(G-4542)*

K T F Inc 713 932-6954
  1028 Campbell Rd Houston (77055) *(G-10497)*

K W Brock Directories Inc 806 687-6270
  7310 Slide Rd Lubbock (79424) *(G-14432)*

K W D Manufacturing Inc 210 924-5999
  2230 W Southcross Blvd San Antonio (78211) *(G-18214)*

K W Utility Cons Inc 903 564-5771
  26097 State Highway 56 Whitesboro (76273) *(G-20727)*

K&B Machine 281 456-0293
  8500 Miller Road 2 Houston (77049) *(G-10498)*

K&B Oilfield Services Inc (PA) **903 392-8213**
  120 Taylor St Henderson (75652) *(G-8266)*

K&F Equipment LLC 432 664-0758
  2310 College Ave Midland (79701) *(G-15265)*

K&L Contractors Inc 936 591-8333
  748 State Highway 7 W Center (75935) *(G-3001)*

K&P Oilfield Solutions 254 290-4862
  15207 Waverly Canyon Ct Cypress (77429) *(G-3806)*

K-3 Resources LP (PA) **281 585-2817**
  850 County Road 149 Alvin (77511) *(G-370)*

K-6 Machine Inc (PA) **254 386-3491**
  800 N Rice St Hamilton (76531) *(G-8166)*

K-6 Machine Inc 254 386-3491
  800 N Rice St Hamilton (76531) *(G-8167)*

K-Bin Inc 979 233-6610
  5616 E Highway 332 Freeport (77541) *(G-7202)*

K-C Lease Service Inc 979 323-9911
  128 S Fm 441 Rd Louise (77455) *(G-14352)*

K-Flex Systems, Allen Also called Thrailkill All Metals Fabg Inc *(G-302)*

K-I Cabinets, Fredericksburg Also called Kings Ltd *(G-7185)*

K-Line Machine Ltd 254 857-4848
  2919 Rosenthal Pkwy Lorena (76655) *(G-14342)*

K-T Bolt Mfg Co 281 391-2196
  1150 Katy Fort Bend Rd Katy (77493) *(G-13412)*

K-T Galvanizing Co Inc (PA) **281 391-9201**
  5105 3rd St Katy (77493) *(G-13413)*

K-T Galvanizing Co Inc 817 477-4434
  2500 Chambers St Venus (76084) *(G-20220)*

K2 Industrial Services Inc (HQ) **850 477-6437**
  1900 Old Underwood Rd La Porte (77571) *(G-13760)*

K3 Bmi, Alvin Also called K-3 Resources LP *(G-370)*

Kaba Ilco Corp 972 668-7996
  5750 Genesis Ct Ste 150 Frisco (75034) *(G-7294)*

Kadence Collective LLC 888 901-5343
  118 Broadway St Ste 627 San Antonio (78205) *(G-18215)*

Kady International LLC 210 860-1637
  306 Pueblo Pintado Helotes (78023) *(G-8240)*

Kager Industries, Fredericksburg Also called Alfred Kager *(G-7169)*

Kai, Houston Also called Kuraray America Inc *(G-10571)*

Kainer Export Crating Inc 713 641-2345
  6820 Lindbergh St Houston (77087) *(G-10499)*

Kainexus Inc (PA) **512 522-3940**
  4225 Wingren Dr Ste 115 Irving (75062) *(G-13072)*

Kairak, Fort Worth Also called Illinois Tool Works Inc *(G-6716)*

Kairak Inc 800 825-8220
  4401 Blue Mound Rd Fort Worth (76106) *(G-6751)*

Kairak Innovations, Fort Worth Also called Kairak Inc *(G-6751)*

Kaiser Aluminum Fab Pdts LLC 903 868-1556
  4300 Us Highway 75 Sherman (75090) *(G-18918)*

Kaiser Foodline LLC 972 705-9595
  1801 Reserve St Ste A Garland (75042) *(G-7529)*

Kajun Kuisine, San Antonio Also called David Lee Roberson *(G-18042)*

Kalamar Industries USA Inc 903 759-5490
  1301 Cherokee Trce White Oak (75693) *(G-20716)*

Kalco Machine & Mfg Co 940 761-1060
  5000 Cntl Fwy Wichita Fls Wichita Falls (76306) *(G-20775)*

Kale Naturals LLC...214 402-6040
3309 Villanova St Dallas (75225) ***(G-4543)***
Kalil Bottling Co...915 778-4413
7328 Boeing Dr El Paso (79925) ***(G-5825)***
Kalil Bottling Co of El Paso, El Paso *Also called Kalil Bottling Co* ***(G-5825)***
Kalle Enterprises Inc...210 340-1841
11811 Warfield St San Antonio (78216) ***(G-18216)***
Kalsi Engineering Incorporated...281 240-6500
745 Park Two Dr Sugar Land (77478) ***(G-19501)***
Kalyn Siebert, Gatesville *Also called Heil Trailer International LLC* ***(G-7618)***
Kam Controls Inc...713 784-0000
3939 Ann Arbor Dr Houston (77063) ***(G-10500)***
Kam-Fab LLC...512 332-2252
1941 Fm 20 Red Rock (78662) ***(G-17238)***
Kamal Incorporated (PA)...**210 695-2678**
13310 Western Oak Dr Helotes (78023) ***(G-8241)***
Kamico Instructional Media Inc...254 947-7283
4477 Fm 2843 Salado (76571) ***(G-17765)***
Kamma Group Inc...281 499-5888
335 Staffordshire Rd # 6 Stafford (77477) ***(G-19338)***
Kammok Gear LLC...512 947-7344
7301 Burnet Rd 101-161 Austin (78757) ***(G-1264)***
Kampus Books...936 560-0033
305 E College St Nacogdoches (75965) ***(G-15700)***
Kandi America, Garland *Also called SC Autosports LLC* ***(G-7583)***
Kaneka North America LLC (HQ)...**281 474-7084**
6161 Underwood Rd Pasadena (77507) ***(G-16468)***
Kap Project Services Ltd...877 527-7762
1200 Highway 146 S # 260 La Porte (77571) ***(G-13761)***
Kap Technologies Inc...972 359-7060
2500 Geiberger Dr Plano (75025) ***(G-16900)***
Kapstone, Mesquite *Also called US Corrugated Mesquite LLC* ***(G-15083)***
Karatech Cnc Machining LLC...281 337-1208
4211 21st St Dickinson (77539) ***(G-5476)***
Karatech Machining LLC...281 337-1208
4211 21st St Dickinson (77539) ***(G-5477)***
Karel Manufacturing Inc...210 651-6643
16742 Pawlin Dr Selma (78154) ***(G-18876)***
Karis Resources LLC...903 595-0900
3626 Rock Creek Dr Tyler (75707) ***(G-20106)***
Karlee Integration Facility...972 543-3175
2905 Miller Park N Garland (75042) ***(G-7530)***
Karltex Machine Inc...409 883-5889
10201 Fm 1130 Orange (77632) ***(G-16251)***
Karper Oil & Gas Corporation...940 549-0606
407 Elm St Graham (76450) ***(G-7785)***
Kaspar Die & Tool Inc...361 594-3327
959 State Highway 95 N Shiner (77984) ***(G-18941)***
Kaspar Machine LLC...254 836-1564
12431 Wortham Bend Rd Waco (76708) ***(G-20422)***
Kaspar Manufacturing, Shiner *Also called Kaspar Wire Works Inc* ***(G-18943)***
Kaspar Ranch Hand Eqp LLC (HQ)...**361 594-4608**
959 State Highway 95 N Shiner (77984) ***(G-18942)***
Kaspar Wire Works Inc (PA)...**361 594-3327**
959 State Highway 95 N Shiner (77984) ***(G-18943)***
Kaspar Wire Works Inc...361 594-3327
1127 Shorack Shiner (77984) ***(G-18944)***
Kasper Packing, Weimar *Also called Kaspers Meat Market Inc* ***(G-20650)***
Kasper Pro Vac Service Inc...956 796-0765
4440 E Del Mar Blvd Laredo (78041) ***(G-13901)***
Kaspers Meat Market Inc (PA)...**979 725-8227**
119 E Post Office St Weimar (78962) ***(G-20650)***
Kaston Fixs & Design Group LLC...972 243-5334
8610 Directors Row Dallas (75247) ***(G-4544)***
Kastros Wood Pallets Inc...915 855-8011
13781 Davidson Blvd El Paso (79938) ***(G-5826)***
Katch Filters LLC...713 425-7400
1414 Sakowitz St Houston (77020) ***(G-10501)***
Katco Vacuum Truck Service LP...361 527-4421
809 E Galbraith St Hebbronville (78361) ***(G-8235)***
Kathleen Sommers Designs Inc...210 271-7118
818 E Myrtle St San Antonio (78212) ***(G-18217)***
Kathrein Broadcast Usa Inc...541 879-2300
5 Cowboys Way Ste 300 Frisco (75034) ***(G-7295)***
Kathrein Holding Usa Inc...541 779-6500
2400 Lkeside Blvd Ste 650 Richardson (75082) ***(G-17339)***
Kathy & Janes Co...817 605-9335
5615 Colleyville Blvd # 340 Colleyville (76034) ***(G-3215)***
Katoen Ntie Specialty Chem Inc...281 941-1001
102 Old Underwood Rd La Porte (77571) ***(G-13762)***
Katoen Ntie Specialty Chem Inc (PA)...**281 470-5423**
10925 Sh 225 Bldg 5 La Porte (77571) ***(G-13763)***
Kats Coatings, Rockwall *Also called Whitmore Manufacturing Company* ***(G-17571)***
Kats Glass LLC...281 592-5211
901 E Houston St Ste A Cleveland (77327) ***(G-3131)***
Katy Ind Publications & Prtg...281 396-6250
5364 Franz Rd Katy (77493) ***(G-13414)***
Katy Magazine LLC...281 579-9840
605 Park Grove Dr Ste A Katy (77450) ***(G-13415)***
Katy Printers Inc...281 391-7072
5807 Highway Blvd Katy (77494) ***(G-13367)***
Katy Rm, Katy *Also called Cemex Construction Mtls S LLC* ***(G-13357)***
Katy Spring & Mfg Inc...281 391-1888
3535 Schlipf Rd Katy (77493) ***(G-13416)***
Katy Steel Co Incorporated (PA)...**281 391-7047**
28011 Highway Blvd 90 Katy (77494) ***(G-13368)***
Katy Stone & Gravel Inc...281 371-3003
4383 Katy Hockley Rd Katy (77493) ***(G-13417)***
Katysweet Confectioners Inc...979 242-5172
4321 W State Highway 71 La Grange (78945) ***(G-13697)***
Kaufman Independent School Dst...972 932-6940
1001 S Houston St Kaufman (75142) ***(G-13459)***
Kaufman Isd Print Shop, Kaufman *Also called Kaufman Independent School Dst* ***(G-13459)***
Kaurinas LLC...972 888-9990
4434 Mcewen Rd Dallas (75244) ***(G-4545)***
Kautex Inc...210 229-2300
1 Lone Star Pass Bldg 3 San Antonio (78264) ***(G-18218)***
Kawasaki Gas Turbines-Americas...281 970-3255
1200 Smith St Ste 1111 Houston (77002) ***(G-10502)***
Kawneer Company Inc...972 438-1212
3216 Royalty Row Irving (75062) ***(G-13073)***
Kawneer Company Inc...972 829-7160
710 Gateway Blvd Unit 140 Coppell (75019) ***(G-3425)***
Kawneer Company Inc...713 896-8906
6615 Roxburgh Dr Ste 400 Houston (77041) ***(G-10503)***
Kawneer North TX, Coppell *Also called Kawneer Company Inc* ***(G-3425)***
Kay Rock Bit Company (PA)...**512 478-2900**
2928 Manor Rd Austin (78722) ***(G-1265)***
Kayco Spray Booths Inc...830 779-2051
135 Industrial Dr La Vernia (78121) ***(G-13802)***
KB & KB Enterprises Inc...979 764-7446
404 University Dr E Ste C College Station (77840) ***(G-3189)***
KB Industries, Houston *Also called K&B Machine* ***(G-10498)***
KB Structures Inc...713 875-1024
23 Rd 602 I 10 Wallisville (77597) ***(G-20512)***
Kbg Management Company LP...806 627-4276
3071 Highway 86 Tulia (79088) ***(G-20035)***
Kbr Well Service, Kilgore *Also called Maverick Well Service LLC* ***(G-13572)***
Kbs Research LLC...214 984-3724
15770 Dallas Pkwy Ste 500 Dallas (75248) ***(G-4546)***
Kc Field Services Inc...903 322-9353
13498 N Us Highway 75 Buffalo (75831) ***(G-2545)***
Kcc Corrosion Control Co Ltd...281 550-1199
4018 Trey Dr Houston (77084) ***(G-10504)***
Kci, San Antonio *Also called Kinetic Concepts Inc* ***(G-18225)***
Kci, Odessa *Also called Kelleys Controls Incorporated* ***(G-16045)***
Kci, Grand Prairie *Also called Kitchen Cabinets Inc* ***(G-7905)***
Kci International Inc (HQ)...**210 524-9000**
12930 W Interstate 10 San Antonio (78249) ***(G-18219)***
Kci Usa Inc (HQ)...**800 275-4524**
12930 W Interstate 10 San Antonio (78249) ***(G-18220)***
Kcm Cabinets Inc...210 695-2213
5748 Grey Rock Dr San Antonio (78228) ***(G-18221)***
KCS Resources LLC...832 204-2700
1000 La St Ste 5600 Houston (77002) ***(G-10505)***
Kdh Companies Inc...281 583-8861
16920 Kuykendahl Rd # 218 Houston (77068) ***(G-10506)***
Kdl Medical Inc...972 783-7005
885 E Collins Blvd # 110 Richardson (75081) ***(G-17340)***
Kdm Holding Inc (HQ)...**817 732-8164**
3700 Hulen St Fort Worth (76107) ***(G-6752)***
Kdm Marine, Houston *Also called James Fisher Subsea Excav Inc* ***(G-10451)***
Kdr Outdoor & Leisure Pdts Inc...281 259-8033
30603 Beyette Rd Magnolia (77355) ***(G-14612)***
Kdr Supply Inc (PA)...**936 334-1353**
3112 Beaumont Ave Liberty (77575) ***(G-14120)***
Keaco Enterprises Inc...210 651-6688
1006 Assembly Cir Schertz (78154) ***(G-18751)***
Keal Cases Incorporated...512 244-9100
1100 W Old Settlers Blvd Round Rock (78681) ***(G-17665)***
Keane Frac Tx LLC (PA)...**713 960-0381**
2121 Sage Rd Houston (77056) ***(G-10507)***
Keane Frac Tx LLC...281 929-0370
5825 N Sam Houston Pkwy W # 600 Houston (77086) ***(G-10508)***
Keane Frac Tx LLC (PA)...**281 929-0370**
5825 N Sam Houston Pkwy W # 600 Houston (77086) ***(G-10509)***
Keane Group Holdings LLC...903 247-1053
4836 W Loop 281 S Longview (75603) ***(G-14259)***
Keane Group Holdings LLC...281 719-7200
8301 New Trils Dr Ste 151 The Woodlands (77381) ***(G-19890)***
Keane Group Holdings LLC (HQ)...**713 960-0381**
3990 Rogerdale Rd Houston (77042) ***(G-10510)***
Keane Group Holdings LLC...432 488-3800
8200 E Ih 20 Odessa (79766) ***(G-16044)***
Keane Group Holdings LLC...281 716-9152
20333 State Highway 249 Houston (77070) ***(G-10511)***
Keats Southwest Inc...915 599-2950
11425 Rojas Dr El Paso (79936) ***(G-5827)***

ALPHABETIC

Keca Metal Products Inc 713 249-3392
1227 Pine Walk Trl Spring (77388) ***(G-19139)***
Keddie Enterprises Inc 214 337-5387
4304 Shilling Way Dallas (75237) ***(G-4547)***
Keebler Company 817 868-2800
4300 Diplomacy Rd Ste 200 Fort Worth (76155) ***(G-6753)***
Keeling Homes Inc 806 655-2071
3101 N I 27 Canyon (79015) ***(G-2671)***
Keen Solutions Group Inc 903 253-0476
110 N College Ave Ste 203 Tyler (75702) ***(G-20107)***
Keeprite Refrigeration Inc 903 643-2261
1998 Fm 2011 Longview (75603) ***(G-14260)***
Kegspeed LLC 267 714-8854
12500 Pluto Ln Austin (78727) ***(G-1266)***
Keil An Arm Company, Plano *Also called Keil Software Inc* ***(G-16901)***
Keil Software Inc (HQ) **972 312-1107**
4965 Preston Park Blvd # 650 Plano (75093) ***(G-16901)***
Keiser Manufacturing Inc 830 303-3397
3501 N Hwy 123 Byp Seguin (78155) ***(G-18846)***
Keith & Company Inc 972 285-3588
1813 S Town East Blvd Mesquite (75149) ***(G-15056)***
Keith & Company Machining, Mesquite *Also called Keith & Company Inc* ***(G-15056)***
Keith Carrell Logging Inc 936 422-3375
1775 Pahal Rd Huntington (75949) ***(G-12810)***
Keith Darwin Raines (PA) **713 477-8534**
3309 Park Meadows Ave Deer Park (77536) ***(G-5281)***
Keith Properties Inc 254 883-2531
122 Live Oak St Marlin (76661) ***(G-14759)***
Keith Weighing Systems LLC 806 655-3033
10511 W Us Highway 60 Canyon (79015) ***(G-2672)***
Keizer Technologies Americas 817 685-7090
10908 S Pipeline Rd Euless (76040) ***(G-6148)***
Kel-Tech Inc (HQ) **432 684-4700**
3408 E State Highway 158 Midland (79706) ***(G-15266)***
Kelford Energy LLC 817 615-0263
8553 N Beach St 167 Fort Worth (76244) ***(G-6754)***
Keller Advg & Media Svcs 210 695-8767
1234 San Francisco San Antonio (78201) ***(G-18222)***
Keller Custom Signs & Designs, San Antonio *Also called Keller Advg & Media Svcs* ***(G-18222)***
Keller North America Inc 817 443-1465
15850 Highway 377 S Fort Worth (76126) ***(G-6755)***
Kellers Creamery LLC 903 347-4250
1015 E Broadway St Winnsboro (75494) ***(G-20899)***
Kelley Instrument Machine Inc 903 832-3332
120 Fairway St Texarkana (75501) ***(G-19767)***
Kelleys Controls Incorporated (PA) **432 362-7998**
210 E 57th St Odessa (79762) ***(G-16045)***
Kelli Kouri Leather, Dallas *Also called Europa Designs* ***(G-4336)***
Kellogg Brown & Root Intl Inc (HQ) **713 753-2000**
601 Jefferson St Ste 7911 Houston (77002) ***(G-10512)***
Kellogg Brown Root 361 758-2554
224 State Hwy 361 Aransas Pass (78335) ***(G-593)***
Kellogg Company 830 438-2254
5357 Honeysuckle Br Bulverde (78163) ***(G-2555)***
Kelly Associates 214 357-8752
4165 Meadowdale Ln Dallas (75229) ***(G-4548)***
Kelly B Pitts Jr 713 923-5555
3703 Reveille St Houston (77087) ***(G-10513)***
Kelly-Moore Paint Company Inc 817 268-1511
303 W Hurst Blvd Hurst (76053) ***(G-12847)***
Kelly-Moore Paint Company Inc 800 772-7408
305 Hurst Hurst (76053) ***(G-12848)***
Kelly-Moore Paints, Hurst *Also called Kelly-Moore Paint Company Inc* ***(G-12847)***
Kelly-Moore Paints, Hurst *Also called Kelly-Moore Paint Company Inc* ***(G-12848)***
Kelman Seismic Processing, Houston *Also called Kelman Technologies Inc* ***(G-10514)***
Kelman Technologies Inc 281 529-3204
10311 Westpark Dr Houston (77042) ***(G-10514)***
Kelmscott Communications LLC (HQ) **713 787-0977**
5858 Westheimer Rd # 410 Houston (77057) ***(G-10515)***
Kelye B Stites Inc (PA) **817 284-3499**
7115 Belton St Richland Hills (76118) ***(G-17439)***
Kem-Tron Technologies Inc 281 261-5778
10404 Cash Rd Ste B Stafford (77477) ***(G-19339)***
Kemet Electronics Corporation 956 548-7200
1705 Billy Mitchell Blvd Brownsville (78521) ***(G-2373)***
Kemlon Products & Dev Co (PA) **281 997-3300**
1424 N Main St Pearland (77581) ***(G-16573)***
Kemp-Meek Manufacturing Inc 903 569-9700
101 Park Central Rd Mineola (75773) ***(G-15509)***
Ken Garner Mfg - Vto Inc 361 485-0541
203 Wayne Watkins Rd Victoria (77905) ***(G-20280)***
Ken Jordan Custom Shutters, Dallas *Also called Ken Jordan Shutters Inc* ***(G-4549)***
Ken Jordan Shutters Inc 972 241-7776
10306 Hedgeway Dr Dallas (75229) ***(G-4549)***
Ken Ross Inc 972 442-3523
703 Cooper Dr Wylie (75098) ***(G-20939)***
Ken Ross International, Wylie *Also called Ken Ross Inc* ***(G-20939)***
Kenergy Oilfield Solutions LLC (PA) **979 574-6356**
1619 E Common St Ste 401 New Braunfels (78130) ***(G-15807)***
Kenergy Oilfield Solutions LLC 830 263-9951
806 Fm 1681 Nixon (78140) ***(G-15867)***
Keneric Healthcare, Irving *Also called Gwm Products LLC* ***(G-13047)***
Keneric Healthcare, Allen *Also called Gwm Products LLC* ***(G-272)***
Kenjer Inc (PA) **281 897-8600**
11275 Windfern Rd Ste B Houston (77064) ***(G-10516)***
Kenjer Sup-R-Jar, Houston *Also called Kenjer Inc* ***(G-10516)***
Kenmark Architectural Pdts Inc (PA) **800 788-8263**
9865 Chartwell Dr Dallas (75243) ***(G-4550)***
Kennedy Construction Co, Texarkana *Also called Bruce Kennedy Sand & Gravel Co* ***(G-19757)***
Kennedy Fabricating Inc 281 399-3008
25370 Fm 2090 Rd Splendora (77372) ***(G-19096)***
Kennedy Machine & Mfg Inc 972 241-7610
13112 Maida Vale Ln Haslet (76052) ***(G-8219)***
Kennedy Sausage Company, Santo *Also called Texas Best Proteins LP* ***(G-18739)***
Kennedy Wire Rope & Sling Co 210 527-0555
4202 Dividend San Antonio (78219) ***(G-18223)***
Kennedy Wire Rope & Sling Co 800 392-5510
5600 Surrey Square St Houston (77017) ***(G-10517)***
Kennedy Wire Rope & Sling Co (PA) **361 289-1444**
302 Flato Rd Corpus Christi (78405) ***(G-3560)***
Kenner Co Inc 432 333-1921
1103 N Texas Ave Odessa (79761) ***(G-16046)***
Kenner Well Svc of Palestine 903 729-3196
4329 S State Highway 19 Palestine (75801) ***(G-16300)***
Kennerprinting, Odessa *Also called Kenner Co Inc* ***(G-16046)***
Kenneth Cole Productions Inc 956 825-7116
5001 E Expy 83 Mercedes (78570) ***(G-15007)***
Kenneth Fox Supply Company (PA) **956 682-6176**
2200 Fox Dr McAllen (78504) ***(G-14882)***
Kenneth M Burgin 903 636-4086
381 Pine Rd Big Sandy (75755) ***(G-2065)***
Kenneth Wyatt Galleries 806 995-2239
310 Comanche Trl Tulia (79088) ***(G-20036)***
Kenney Industries Inc 214 421-4175
2110 Panoramic Cir Dallas (75212) ***(G-4551)***
Kenny's Seasonings, Wichita Falls *Also called Kennys All Purpose Seasoning* ***(G-20776)***
Kennymac LLC 214 732-4759
704 Smith Ln Seagoville (75159) ***(G-18801)***
Kennys All Purpose Seasoning 940 733-2200
5930 Us Highway 281 Wichita Falls (76310) ***(G-20776)***
Kennys Kustom Kards Inc 817 332-8639
5400 Airport Fwy Ste G Haltom City (76117) ***(G-8149)***
Kensing Iron Works Inc 830 625-2815
3950 W State Highway 46 New Braunfels (78132) ***(G-15808)***
Kent Moore Cabinets Inc (PA) **979 775-2906**
1460 Fountain Ave Bryan (77801) ***(G-2482)***
Kent Moore Cabinets Ltd 281 480-8883
1811 Frst Oaks St Ste 180 Richmond (77406) ***(G-17459)***
Kent Sporting Goods Co Inc 903 592-3853
3220 W Gentry Pkwy Tyler (75702) ***(G-20108)***
Kentec Composites, Sugar Land *Also called Saige Usa Inc* ***(G-19540)***
Kentex Fabrications 325 214-0025
220 Santa Anna Ave Coleman (76834) ***(G-3170)***
Kentucky Freight Systems Inc 972 475-6567
8309 Concord Dr Rowlett (75089) ***(G-17708)***
Kep Americas, Irving *Also called Celanese Americas LLC* ***(G-12963)***
Kepler Aerospace Ltd 855 553-7537
2908 Enterprise Ln Midland (79706) ***(G-15267)***
Kepler Spacecore Inc 855 553-7537
2908 Enterprise Ln Midland (79706) ***(G-15268)***
Keppel Amfels Inc (HQ) **956 838-3110**
20000 State Highway 48 Brownsville (78521) ***(G-2374)***
Keppel Letourneau Usa Inc 281 677-4482
5177 Richmond Ave Ste 950 Houston (77056) ***(G-10518)***
Keppel Offshore & Mar USA Inc (HQ) **713 600-8371**
5177 Richmond Ave # 1065 Houston (77056) ***(G-10519)***
Kerick Industries 214 432-2446
815 Wood River Rd Dallas (75232) ***(G-4552)***
Kerio Technologies Inc 408 496-4500
401 Congress Ave Ste 2650 Austin (78701) ***(G-1267)***
Kermit Concrete, Kermit *Also called Pb Materials Holdings Inc* ***(G-13513)***
Kern-Liebers Texas Inc 956 781-6563
400 E Nolana Loop Pharr (78577) ***(G-16704)***
Kerr Collection 817 572-4663
1100 E Rendon Crowley Rd Burleson (76028) ***(G-2584)***
Kerr Corporation 800 355-5063
800 W Sandy Lake Rd # 100 Coppell (75019) ***(G-3426)***
Kerr Energy Companies LLC 713 501-9555
258 S Post Oak Ln Houston (77056) ***(G-10520)***
Kerr Feed & Grain Company 940 538-4354
903 E Omega St Henrietta (76365) ***(G-8281)***
Kerr Oilfield Company 940 327-0447
7104 Highway 180 E Mineral Wells (76067) ***(G-15530)***
Kerr-Mcgee (nevada) LLC (HQ) **303 321-0683**
9950 Woodloch Forest Dr Spring (77380) ***(G-19224)***

Kerr-Mcgee Oil Gas Onshore LP	832 636-1000
1201 Lake Robbins Dr The Woodlands (77380) *(G-19891)*	
Kerrville Daily Times, Kerrville *Also called Southern Newspapers Inc (G-13526)*	
Kessler Enterprises, El Paso *Also called Kessler Industries Inc (G-5828)*	
Kessler Industries Inc	915 591-8161
8600 Gateway Blvd E Ste B El Paso (79907) *(G-5828)*	
Kessler Packaging Inc	915 591-8161
8600 Gateway Blvd E El Paso (79907) *(G-5829)*	
Kestran Inc	281 276-2700
12600 Executive Dr Stafford (77477) *(G-19340)*	
Kev Group Inc	866 891-9138
3000 S Hulen St Ste 124 Fort Worth (76109) *(G-6756)*	
Kevin Goss	281 812-1600
1881 Treble Dr Humble (77338) *(G-12782)*	
Kevin Hall	972 771-4246
254 Ranch Trl Rockwall (75032) *(G-17551)*	
Kevin M Ehringer Entps Inc	972 620-4997
1881 Valley View Ln # 100 Dallas (75234) *(G-4553)*	
Key 3 Casting LLC (HQ)	**817 332-9500**
301 Commerce St Ste 3200 Fort Worth (76102) *(G-6757)*	
Key Energy Drilling Inc	903 693-2622
1771 Ne Loop Carthage (75633) *(G-2910)*	
Key Energy Drilling Inc	432 639-2534
220 S Drake St Iraan (79744) *(G-12919)*	
Key Energy Drilling Inc (HQ)	**432 620-0300**
1301 Mckinney St Ste 1800 Houston (77010) *(G-10521)*	
Key Energy Drilling Inc	713 651-4300
111 State Highway 31 E Kilgore (75662) *(G-13560)*	
Key Energy Services Inc	979 542-3344
2144 Fm 448 Giddings (78942) *(G-7698)*	
Key Energy Services Inc	361 668-1526
511 Commerce St Alice (78332) *(G-220)*	
Key Energy Services Inc	432 381-1301
5347 W 42nd St Odessa (79764) *(G-16047)*	
Key Energy Services Inc	432 523-5155
100 Taylor Rd Andrews (79714) *(G-547)*	
Key Energy Services Inc	432 620-0300
6 Desta Dr Ste 4300 Midland (79705) *(G-15269)*	
Key Energy Services Inc	361 578-9975
1112 Us Highway 59 S Edna (77957) *(G-5608)*	
Key Energy Services Inc	713 651-4300
Hwy 59 El Campo (77437) *(G-5619)*	
Key Energy Services Inc	361 668-1818
4309 S Us Highway 281 Alice (78332) *(G-221)*	
Key Energy Services Inc (PA)	**713 651-4300**
1301 Mckinney St Ste 1800 Houston (77010) *(G-10522)*	
Key Energy Services Inc	432 586-2591
10202 W 42nd St Odessa (79764) *(G-16048)*	
Key Energy Services Inc	432 561-5682
12320 W Interstate 20 E Odessa (79765) *(G-16049)*	
Key Energy Services Inc	432 267-5291
3404 E F M 700 Big Spring (79720) *(G-2086)*	
Key Energy Services Inc	432 488-2800
12400 W Interstate 20 Odessa (79765) *(G-16050)*	
Key Energy Services Inc	432 558-3574
111th North Gaston St Crane (79731) *(G-3699)*	
Key Energy Services Inc	713 651-4300
12000 W Little York Rd Houston (77041) *(G-10523)*	
Key Energy Services Inc	806 872-6688
2015 S Highway 87 Lamesa (79331) *(G-13826)*	
Key Energy Services Inc	979 589-2594
4585 Andert Rd Bryan (77808) *(G-2483)*	
Key Energy Services Inc	325 236-6611
2210 W Broadway St Sweetwater (79556) *(G-19632)*	
Key Energy Services Inc	903 538-2280
8801 S Us Highway 79 Palestine (75801) *(G-16301)*	
Key Energy Services Inc	806 489-7452
Hwy 137 S Welch (79377) *(G-20655)*	
Key Energy Services Inc	806 872-8331
319 Big Spring Hwy 87 Lamesa (79331) *(G-13827)*	
Key Energy Services Inc	979 778-1800
6115 E State Highway 21 Bryan (77808) *(G-2484)*	
Key Energy Services Inc	903 963-5208
202 S Main Van (75790) *(G-20208)*	
Key Energy Services Inc	432 523-5155
1203 Sw Mustang Dr Andrews (79714) *(G-548)*	
Key Energy Services Inc	361 661-0488
135 County Road 336 Alice (78332) *(G-222)*	
Key Energy Services Inc	432 570-7440
1811 Garden City Hwy Midland (79701) *(G-15270)*	
Key Insulation, San Antonio *Also called Installed Building Pdts Inc (G-18643)*	
Key Insulation, San Antonio *Also called Valro-K LLC (G-18647)*	
Key Maps Incorporated	713 522-7949
5922 Richmond Ave Ste C Houston (77057) *(G-10524)*	
Key Maps of Houston, Houston *Also called Seawall Specialty Company Inc (G-11808)*	
Key Ovation LLC	512 259-5688
1320 Arrow Point Dr # 101 Cedar Park (78613) *(G-2976)*	
Key Products, The, Tyler *Also called Vincent Graphics & Supply Inc (G-20176)*	
Key Scientific Products	512 846-1440
1113 E Reynolds St Hutto (78634) *(G-12882)*	
Keylessco LLC	972 331-2773
1825 W Walnut Hill Ln # 10 Irving (75038) *(G-13074)*	
Keymex LLC	210 300-7056
915 Cormorant San Antonio (78245) *(G-18224)*	
Keynote Photonics, Allen *Also called Keynote Technologies LLC (G-282)*	
Keynote Technologies LLC	877 528-4747
400 W Bethany Dr Ste 110 Allen (75013) *(G-282)*	
Keys Corporation	713 864-7299
5400 Mitchelldale St A1 Houston (77092) *(G-10525)*	
Keys Upholstery, Houston *Also called Keys Corporation (G-10525)*	
Keyscan Inc	201 918-2396
6408 Richwood Rd Odessa (79762) *(G-16051)*	
Keyston Bros	713 692-2132
5250 N Sam Houston Pkwy W # 900 Houston (77086) *(G-10526)*	
Keystone Consolidated Inds	903 893-0191
428 Gibbons Rd Sherman (75092) *(G-18919)*	
Keystone Exploration Ltd	817 820-7029
777 Main St Ste 3100 Fort Worth (76102) *(G-6758)*	
Keystone Millwork Inc	979 823-4846
1740 Shiloh Ave Bryan (77803) *(G-2485)*	
Keystone Oilfield Fabrication, Rhome *Also called Keystone Synergy LLC (G-17256)*	
Keystone Synergy LLC	817 636-3300
1870 Illinois St Rhome (76078) *(G-17256)*	
Keytrak Inc	979 595-2600
200 Quality Cir College Station (77845) *(G-3190)*	
Kf Valves LLC	713 400-2200
11327 Tanner Rd Houston (77041) *(G-10527)*	
Kfl Promotions LLC	817 822-9116
4703 Mill Creek Dr Colleyville (76034) *(G-3216)*	
Kggt Management Corp	713 462-0900
13240 Hempstead Rd # 216 Houston (77040) *(G-10528)*	
Kgh Intermediate Holdco II LLC	432 563-1708
6913 N Fm 1788 Midland (79707) *(G-15271)*	
Kgm-Vto, Victoria *Also called Ken Garner Mfg - Vto Inc (G-20280)*	
Kgp Group Inc	817 349-3135
1401 Everman Pkwy Ste 130 Fort Worth (76140) *(G-6759)*	
Kgp Group Inc (PA)	**817 354-0766**
1000 Pennsylvania Ave Fort Worth (76104) *(G-6760)*	
Khanty Mansiysk Oil Corp	713 629-6600
5555 San Felipe St Houston (77056) *(G-10529)*	
Khoros LLC (PA)	**415 757-3100**
7300 Ranch Road 2222 # 1 Austin (78730) *(G-1268)*	
Khudairi Group Incorporated	713 782-1080
1616 S Voss Rd Ste 550 Houston (77057) *(G-10530)*	
Ki Memories Inc	972 333-3015
4343 Sigma Rd Dallas (75244) *(G-4554)*	
Kibo Software Inc (PA)	**707 780-1600**
717 N Harwood St Ste 1800 Dallas (75201) *(G-4555)*	
Kicstand Inc	210 324-0421
1631 Mccarty St Houston (77029) *(G-10531)*	
Kidasa Software Inc	512 368-2326
1114 Lost Creek Blvd # 300 Austin (78746) *(G-1269)*	
Kieschnick Industries Inc	409 833-5611
3050 W Cedar St Beaumont (77702) *(G-1914)*	
Kiger Bros Mch Tl & Die Works	281 447-1315
609 Carby Rd Houston (77037) *(G-10532)*	
Kiger Machine, Houston *Also called Kiger Bros Mch Tl & Die Works (G-10532)*	
Kik Custom Products, Houston *Also called Houston Kik Inc (G-10236)*	
Kikers Machine Works Inc	432 381-8142
4001 N Fm 1936 Odessa (79764) *(G-16052)*	
Kil-Tex Oilfield Services LLC	903 736-5051
524 Gladewater St Kilgore (75662) *(G-13561)*	
Killam Oil Co Ltd (PA)	**956 724-7141**
4320 University Blvd Laredo (78041) *(G-13902)*	
Killam Oil Co Ltd.	361 394-7680
3 Miles W Of Hwy 59 Freer (78357) *(G-7229)*	
Killeen Blueprint Co	254 634-2779
102 College St Killeen (76541) *(G-13610)*	
Killeen Crushed Stone	254 526-2526
4101 Trimmier Rd Killeen (76542) *(G-13611)*	
Killeen Daily Herald, Killeen *Also called Frank Mayborn Enterprises Inc (G-13607)*	
Killeen Marble	254 699-3408
450 N Roy Reynolds Dr F Killeen (76543) *(G-13612)*	
Killeen Ready Mix Ltd	254 634-4514
4101 Trimmier Rd Killeen (76542) *(G-13613)*	
Kim R Smith Logging Inc	903 947-6242
1155 E Johnson St Tatum (75691) *(G-19644)*	
Kimball Elec - Mexico Inc (HQ)	**956 205-4600**
9800 Intl Blvd Ste 120 Pharr (78577) *(G-16705)*	
Kimball Electronics Group, Pharr *Also called Kimball Elec - Mexico Inc (G-16705)*	
Kimbell Gin Machinery Company	806 763-6645
226 Ne Loop 289 232 Lubbock (79403) *(G-14433)*	
Kimbell-Bishard, Lubbock *Also called Kimbell Gin Machinery Company (G-14433)*	
Kimberly-Clark Corporation (PA)	**972 281-1200**
351 Phelps Dr Irving (75038) *(G-13075)*	
Kimberly-Clark Corporation	903 737-5100
2466 Farm Road 137 Paris (75460) *(G-16364)*	
Kimberly-Clark Corporation	817 847-0211
8715 Harmon Rd Fort Worth (76177) *(G-6761)*	

A L P H A B E T I C

Kimberly-Clark Worldwide Inc (HQ)......................972 281-1200
　351 Phelps Dr Irving (75038) *(G-13076)*

Kimray Inc...936 441-2468
　11133 I 45 S Ste A Conroe (77302) *(G-3317)*

Kimray Sales & Service, Conroe Also called Kimray Inc *(G-3317)*

Kin-Tek Analytical Inc..............................409 938-3627
　504 Laurel St La Marque (77568) *(G-13709)*

Kin-Tek Laboratories Inc...........................409 938-3627
　504 Laurel St La Marque (77568) *(G-13710)*

Kincer, L T Company, Lubbock Also called Denny Kincer Inc *(G-14401)*

Kinder Morgan (delaware) Inc......................806 272-3309
　Rr 2 Muleshoe (79347) *(G-15677)*

Kinetic Concepts Inc (HQ)..........................**800 531-5346**
　12930 W Interstate 10 San Antonio (78249) *(G-18225)*

King Capital, Addison Also called Geo Mesa Analysis LLC *(G-130)*

King Fabrication LLC................................281 209-0811
　19300 W Hardy Rd Houston (77073) *(G-10533)*

King Operating Corporation.........................214 420-3000
　6142 Campbell Rd Dallas (75248) *(G-4556)*

King Pipeline Services LLC.........................903 530-8667
　3805 Summercrest Dr Fort Worth (76109) *(G-6762)*

King Ranch Inc (PA)................................**832 681-5700**
　3 Riverway Ste 1600 Houston (77056) *(G-10534)*

King Ranch Holdings Inc (HQ).......................**832 681-5700**
　3 Riverway Ste 1600 Houston (77056) *(G-10535)*

King Roy Jr Logging Inc............................936 563-4899
　Rr 3 Box 399 Livingston (77351) *(G-14158)*

King Terrain Corporation...........................830 379-1480
　1502 E Walnut St Seguin (78155) *(G-18847)*

King Well Service Inc..............................806 323-6664
　10925 Us Highway 60 Canadian (79014) *(G-2652)*

King Workover Service Inc..........................979 543-5464
　2882 N Mechanic St El Campo (77437) *(G-5620)*

Kingdom Captain of Texas LLC.......................210 535-9480
　222 W Nakoma St San Antonio (78216) *(G-18226)*

Kingdom Coal LLC (PA)..............................**817 840-6646**
　8650 Freeport Pkwy # 100 Irving (75063) *(G-13077)*

Kingfisher Midstream LLC (HQ)......................**281 655-3200**
　2101 Cedar Springs Rd # 1100 Dallas (75201) *(G-4557)*

Kings Eco Plastics LLC.............................956 631-1115
　4001 W Military Hwy McAllen (78503) *(G-14883)*

Kings Ltd...830 990-0565
　401 S Lincoln St Fredericksburg (78624) *(G-7185)*

Kings Truck Beds Inc...............................940 433-2360
　1667 E Highway 114 Boyd (76023) *(G-2205)*

Kingsisle Entertainment Inc (PA)...................**972 265-1900**
　2745 Dallas Pkwy Ste 620 Plano (75093) *(G-16902)*

Kingston I-Tek Solutions LLC.......................281 656-4900
　9746 Whithorn Dr Houston (77095) *(G-10536)*

Kingsville Publishing Company......................361 592-4304
　1831 W Santa Gertrudis St Kingsville (78363) *(G-13631)*

Kingsville Record, Kingsville Also called Kingsville Publishing Company *(G-13631)*

Kinlau Sheet Metal Works Inc.......................940 552-5311
　2522 Frontage Rd Vernon (76384) *(G-20227)*

Kinro Composties...................................800 262-8827
　101 Mushroom Rd Waxahachie (75165) *(G-20548)*

Kinro Texas Ltd Partnership........................817 483-7791
　4381 W Green Oaks Blvd # 200 Arlington (76016) *(G-712)*

Kiolbassa Provision Company........................210 226-8127
　1325 S Brazos St San Antonio (78207) *(G-18227)*

Kior Inc (PA)......................................**281 694-8700**
　13001 Baypark Rd Pasadena (77507) *(G-16469)*

Kirby - Smith Machinery Inc........................817 378-0600
　1450 Ne Loop 820 Fort Worth (76106) *(G-6763)*

Kirby - Smith Machinery Inc........................806 373-1229
　3922 I 40 E Amarillo (79103) *(G-445)*

Kirby Midco Inc (PA)...............................214 688-0444
　9101 John W Carpenter Fwy Dallas (75247) *(G-4558)*

Kirby Stone Company LLC............................281 427-7990
　1300 Rollingbrook Dr # 500 Baytown (77521) *(G-1824)*

Kirchhoff Auto Dallas Inc (HQ).....................214 553-0208
　3901 W Miller Rd Ste 500 Garland (75041) *(G-7531)*

Kirchhoff Auto Dallas Inc..........................214 553-0208
　3901 W Miller Rd Ste 200 Garland (75041) *(G-7532)*

Kirk Construction Inc..............................281 392-4063
　26823 Willow Ln Katy (77494) *(G-13369)*

Kirk Root Designs, Austin Also called Roots Rocks Inc *(G-1473)*

Kirkland Sales Inc.................................972 864-1424
　2210 Sherwin St Garland (75041) *(G-7533)*

Kirks Machine Works...............................432 368-5333
　210 W 57th St Odessa (79764) *(G-16053)*

Kirkseys Sprint Prtg & Signs, Beaumont Also called Mail & Parcels Plus Inc *(G-1923)*

Kisabeth Furniture, Haltom City Also called Carl Kisabeth Co Inc *(G-8134)*

Kissaluvs, Houston Also called Sumehr Inc *(G-12093)*

Kistler Rods, Magnolia Also called Kdr Outdoor & Leisure Pdts Inc *(G-14612)*

Kit Professionals Inc..............................713 783-8700
　2000 W Sam Houston Pkwy S # 1400 Houston (77042) *(G-10537)*

Kitchen Bath Cbinets Doors Inc.....................915 852-0499
　13682 Nayarit Dr El Paso (79928) *(G-5830)*

Kitchen Cabinets Inc...............................972 660-6304
　2330 Nw Dallas St Grand Prairie (75050) *(G-7905)*

Kitchen Equipment Fabg Co..........................713 747-3611
　7007 Stearns St Houston (77021) *(G-10538)*

Kitchen Fare, Fort Worth Also called Regal Ware Inc *(G-6952)*

Kitchen Source, The, Dallas Also called Robert V Johns & Associates *(G-4905)*

Kite's Interiors, Fort Worth Also called Kites Draperies Inc *(G-6764)*

Kites Draperies Inc................................817 336-1027
　2711 White Settlement Rd Fort Worth (76107) *(G-6764)*

Kiuwan, Houston Also called Idera Inc *(G-10315)*

Kiva Construction & Engrg Inc......................409 252-3211
　600 Shipyard Rd Anahuac (77514) *(G-526)*

Kiva Stone, Dallas Also called GMI Stone LLC *(G-4411)*

Kiwienergy, Houston Also called Square Mile Energy LLC *(G-12029)*

Kiwo Holdings Inc (HQ).............................**281 474-9777**
　1929 Marvin Cir Seabrook (77586) *(G-18787)*

Kixx Rentals & Services LLC........................830 437-2959
　77 County Road 312 Gonzales (78629) *(G-7758)*

Kizer Energy Inc...................................281 712-2047
　1400 Broadfield Blvd # 225 Houston (77084) *(G-10539)*

Kj Energy LLC......................................214 297-5013
　8150 N Central Expy # 900 Dallas (75206) *(G-4559)*

Kj Rustic Designs LLC..............................832 477-6545
　6458 Dick Elliott Rd Bryan (77808) *(G-2486)*

Kjd Enterprises....................................325 641-0420
　2700 Virgil Gray Dr Brownwood (76801) *(G-2431)*

Kk Meier Co LLC....................................281 256-7366
　14030 Telge Rd Ste J Cypress (77429) *(G-3807)*

KLA Corporation....................................512 231-4200
　8834 N Capital Of Texas H Austin (78759) *(G-1270)*

Klabzuba Oil & Gas Inc (PA)........................**817 336-5757**
　100 Lexington St Ste 50 Fort Worth (76102) *(G-6765)*

Klabzuba, Robert, Fort Worth Also called Klabzuba Oil & Gas Inc *(G-6765)*

Klad Manufacturing Company, Pearland Also called PCC Klad LLC *(G-16588)*

Klean Corp International............................361 578-1524
　601 John Stockbauer Dr Victoria (77901) *(G-20281)*

Klein Products of Texas Inc........................903 589-4546
　16576 Us Highway 79 E Jacksonville (75766) *(G-13247)*

Kline Technical Consulting LLC (PA)................**505 310-2679**
　19826 Quarry Stone Ln Richmond (77407) *(G-17460)*

Klinger, Houston Also called Houston Thermoseal Inc *(G-8385)*

Kln Manufacturing LLC..............................210 227-4747
　1151 Empire Central Dr Dallas (75247) *(G-4560)*

Kln Steel Products Company LLC (PA)................**210 227-4747**
　1161 Empire Central Dr Dallas (75247) *(G-4561)*

Kloeckner Metals Corporation.......................713 633-7400
　7400 Mesa Dr Houston (77028) *(G-10540)*

Klose Cnstr & Fabrication..........................713 686-8720
　1355 Judiway St Ste B Houston (77018) *(G-10541)*

Kloudnation LLC....................................214 682-8692
　2611 Internet Blvd # 109 Frisco (75034) *(G-7296)*

Kluber Lubrication N Amer LP.......................903 534-8021
　9010 County Road 2120 Tyler (75707) *(G-20109)*

Kluber Lubrication NA LP...........................903 534-8021
　9010 County Road 2120 Tyler (75707) *(G-20110)*

Klx Energy Services LLC (HQ).......................**832 844-1015**
　1415 La St Ste 2900 Houston (77056) *(G-10542)*

Kmg Chemicals, Fort Worth Also called CMC Materials Inc *(G-6524)*

Kmg Electronic Chemicals Inc (HQ)..................**817 761-6100**
　300 Throckmorton St # 1800 Fort Worth (76102) *(G-6766)*

Kmg-Bernuth Inc (HQ)...............................**817 761-6100**
　300 Throckmorton St Fort Worth (76102) *(G-6767)*

Kmi Fabricators Inc................................940 325-7841
　410 Boyd Rd Mineral Wells (76067) *(G-15531)*

Kmp Graphics Inc...................................817 295-5350
　105 Black Jack Ln Burleson (76028) *(G-2585)*

Kmr Group LLC......................................713 932-6988
　1041 Blalock Rd Houston (77055) *(G-10543)*

Kmt Aqua-Dyne Inc..................................713 864-6929
　3620 W 11th St Houston (77008) *(G-10544)*

Kmt Wireless LLC...................................817 591-4600
　4055 Corporate Dr Ste 400 Grapevine (76051) *(G-8045)*

Kmtex, Crosby Also called Ramsey Properties LP *(G-3741)*

Kmtex, Port Arthur Also called Ramsey Properties LP *(G-17122)*

Kng LLC..713 263-1900
　2127 Harland Dr Ste B Houston (77055) *(G-10545)*

Knickerbocker Partition Corp.......................972 438-5330
　3230 Royalty Row Irving (75062) *(G-13078)*

Knife River Corp - South (HQ)......................**979 361-2900**
　1553 Greens Prairie Rd W College Station (77845) *(G-3191)*

Knife River Corporation............................979 779-1112
　9867 Fm 1227 Bryan (77806) *(G-2487)*

Knife River Corporation............................409 842-2100
　4825 Romeda Rd Beaumont (77705) *(G-1915)*

Knife River Corporation............................979 361-2900
　6310 W State Highway 21 Bryan (77807) *(G-2488)*

Knight Corporation.................................281 933-5363
　10885 Fallstone Rd Houston (77099) *(G-10546)*

Knight Energy Holdings LLC 713 466-6660
6003 Cunningham Rd Houston (77041) *(G-10547)*

Knight Energy Services LLC (PA) **832 678-8585**
6003 Cunningham Rd Houston (77041) *(G-10548)*

Knight Filter Corporation, Houston *Also called Knight Corporation (G-10546)*

Knight Industrial Services Inc 281 421-5049
6802 East Fwy Baytown (77521) *(G-1825)*

Knight Manufacturing Co Inc 903 561-0522
5401 Kent Dr Tyler (75707) *(G-20111)*

Knight Oil Tools LLC 432 530-1010
3700 N Fm 1936 Odessa (79764) *(G-16054)*

Knight Oil Tools LLC 361 668-8065
1270 Airport Rd Alice (78332) *(G-223)*

Knighten Industries, Odessa *Also called Knighten Machine and Svc Inc (G-16055)*

Knighten Machine and Svc Inc (PA) **877 457-7204**
3800 E 42nd St Ste 333 Odessa (79762) *(G-16055)*

Knights Landscaping LLC 972 971-4213
2000 Spring Mills Rd Mesquite (75181) *(G-15057)*

Knippa Quarry, Knippa *Also called Legacy Vulcan LLC (G-13661)*

Knit Rags LLC 713 249-9478
3120 Commerce St. Houston (77003) *(G-10549)*

Knives of Alaska Inc 903 786-7366
3100 Airport Dr Denison (75020) *(G-5341)*

Knoll Inc 713 629-5665
2800 Post Oak Blvd # 101 Houston (77056) *(G-10550)*

Knoll Inc 214 741-5819
1722 Routh St Ste 112 Dallas (75201) *(G-4562)*

Knot Hole , The, Killeen *Also called Knot Hole LLC (G-13614)*

Knot Hole LLC 254 634-0773
2802 Atkinson Ave Killeen (76543) *(G-13614)*

Knottsmith Construction Co Inc 214 499-5667
2620 Willowbrook Rd Dallas (75220) *(G-4563)*

Knowles Publishing Inc 817 838-0202
4708 Shadycreek Ln Colleyville (76034) *(G-3217)*

Knox Jr Leighton 806 327-5420
1683 Cr 29 Tahoka (79373) *(G-19641)*

Knust-Godwin LLC (HQ) **713 785-1060**
5686 Stone Ln Katy (77449) *(G-13418)*

Kobelco Compressors Amer Inc 713 470-1290
11817 W Fairmont Pkwy La Porte (77571) *(G-13764)*

Kobelco Construction McHy USA (HQ) **281 684-8761**
22350 Merchants Way Katy (77449) *(G-13419)*

Kobelco Cranes North Amer Inc 713 856-5755
22350 Merchants Way Katy (77449) *(G-13420)*

Kobelco Welding of America 281 240-5600
4755 Alpine Dr Ste 250 Stafford (77477) *(G-19341)*

Kobi Electric LLC 817 297-3200
301 E Risinger Rd Ste 109 Fort Worth (76140) *(G-6768)*

Koblend, San Antonio *Also called Thorne Electric Company (G-18551)*

Koch Filter Corporation 502 634-4796
4411 Darien St Ste A Houston (77028) *(G-10551)*

Koch Heat Transfer Company LP (HQ) **713 466-3535**
12602 Fm 529 Rd Houston (77041) *(G-10552)*

Koch Industries Inc 903 693-5172
606 S Shelby St Carthage (75633) *(G-2911)*

Koch Industries Inc 806 347-2645
072 S State Hwy 70 Matador (79244) *(G-14816)*

Koch Machine Tool Company 281 720-8500
8500 Westland West Blvd Houston (77041) *(G-10553)*

Koch Machinery, Houston *Also called Koch Machine Tool Company (G-10553)*

Koch Pulp & Paper Trading LLC 713 544-5070
20 Greenway Plz Ste 800 Houston (77046) *(G-10554)*

Koch Ranches Inc 210 858-9795
1999 Gulfmart St Ste 512 San Antonio (78217) *(G-18228)*

Koch Ranches Gourmet Cntry Str, San Antonio *Also called Koch Ranches Inc (G-18228)*

Koch Supply & Trading LP 713 544-4123
20 Greenway Plz Ste 850 Houston (77046) *(G-10555)*

Koch-Glitsch LP 281 445-7026
6611 Killough St Houston (77086) *(G-10556)*

Koch-Glitsch LP 214 583-3000
4900 Singleton Blvd Dallas (75212) *(G-4564)*

Koch-Otto York, Houston *Also called Koch-Glitsch LP (G-10556)*

Kodiak Assembly Solutions LLC 512 275-1700
2400 Grand Avenue Pkwy # 10 Austin (78728) *(G-1271)*

Kodiak Gas Services LLC (HQ) **936 539-3300**
15320 Highway 105 W # 210 Montgomery (77356) *(G-15635)*

Kodiak Networks Inc (HQ) **972 665-0200**
1501 10th St Ste 130 Plano (75074) *(G-16903)*

Kodiak Production Ltd 325 884-2040
303 N State Highway 137 Big Lake (76932) *(G-2058)*

Kodiak Trailer Components, Azle *Also called Dexter Brahma LLC (G-1723)*

Koehler Co 830 303-6256
1404 N Camp St Seguin (78155) *(G-18848)*

Koenig Welding Service Inc 979 532-4161
2305 N Richmond Rd Wharton (77488) *(G-20701)*

Kohler Co 920 457-4441
1820 High Prairie Rd Grand Prairie (75050) *(G-7906)*

Kohler Co 325 643-2661
4601 Highway 377 S Brownwood (76801) *(G-2432)*

Kohler Co 325 643-2661
Highway 37 Brownwood (76801) *(G-2433)*

Kohler Company Plumbing, Brownwood *Also called Kohler Co (G-2432)*

Kohlhaas Corporation 915 778-5357
6831 El Paso Dr El Paso (79905) *(G-5831)*

Kokomo Energy Inc 940 683-1102
101 Turkey Creek Trl Bridgeport (76426) *(G-2296)*

Kold Pack Incorporated 800 824-2661
5609 Azle Ave Fort Worth (76114) *(G-6769)*

Komatsu Mining Corp 903 983-7744
2320 State Highway 42 N Kilgore (75662) *(G-13562)*

Komatsu Mining Corp 903 237-7000
2400 Macarthur St Longview (75602) *(G-14261)*

Komax Corporation 915 591-4551
9641 Plaza Cir El Paso (79927) *(G-5832)*

Komplete Group Inc 214 252-8100
202 N Great Sw Pkwy Grand Prairie (75050) *(G-7907)*

Koncept Systems LLC (PA) **800 773-4910**
11555 Fuqua St Houston (77034) *(G-10557)*

Kone Inc 469 854-8861
450 Century Pkwy Ste 300 Allen (75013) *(G-283)*

Konecranes Inc 361 289-9400
1959 Saratoga Blvd Bldg 5 Corpus Christi (78417) *(G-3561)*

Konecranes Inc 281 631-0300
845 Greens Pkwy Ste 300 Houston (77067) *(G-10558)*

Konecranes Inc 800 486-7278
845 Greens Pkwy Ste 300 Houston (77067) *(G-10559)*

Konecranes America, Houston *Also called Morris Material Handling Inc (G-10923)*

Kongsberg Automotive, Willis *Also called Kongsberg Pwr Prod Systems I (G-20852)*

Kongsberg Pwr Prod Systems I 936 856-2971
300 S Cochran St Willis (77378) *(G-20852)*

Kontract Sftwr Solutions LLC 281 994-6104
1110 Nasa Pkwy Ste 450 Houston (77058) *(G-10560)*

Kony Inc (HQ) **512 792-2900**
9225 Bee Cave Rd Bldg As Austin (78733) *(G-1272)*

Koppel Steel Corp Baytown, Baytown *Also called Ipsco Koppel Tubulars LLC (G-1822)*

Koppers Inc 979 596-1321
Hwy 36 N And Cntry Rd 423 Somerville (77879) *(G-19022)*

Kopriva Cabinets, Troy *Also called,Pavliska Cabinets Inc (G-20032)*

Kordial Ntrnts Prof Spplements, Irving *Also called Progressive Laboratories Inc (G-13157)*

Kormachine, Waco *Also called Kaspar Machine LLC (G-20422)*

Kortivity, Austin *Also called Stone Cliff Technology LLC (G-1538)*

Kosmos Cement Company Inc (HQ) **713 722-1788**
929 Gessner Rd Ste 1900 Houston (77024) *(G-10561)*

Kosmos Energy LLC (PA) **214 445-9600**
8176 Park Ln Ste 500 Dallas (75231) *(G-4565)*

Kosmos Energy Holdings, Dallas *Also called Kosmos Energy LLC (G-4565)*

Kosmos Energy Ltd (PA) **214 445-9600**
8176 Park Ln Ste 500 Dallas (75231) *(G-4566)*

Kosta Oil Field Technologies, Stafford *Also called Asphwax Inc (G-19288)*

Kotara Mfg Inc 830 745-9007
8855 State Highway 123 S Stockdale (78160) *(G-19429)*

Kovach Enclosure Systems LLC 480 926-9292
1118 Sawdust Rd Spring (77380) *(G-19225)*

Kovach Enclosure Systems LLC 480 926-9292
2415 Kramer Ln Ste D Austin (78758) *(G-1273)*

Kovach Enclosure Systems LLC 480 926-9292
13649 Beta Rd Farmers Branch (75244) *(G-6205)*

Koy Concrete Ltd 281 391-2178
5013 3rd St Katy (77493) *(G-13421)*

Koza Inc 281 485-1462
2910 S Main St Pearland (77581) *(G-16574)*

Kpan Am/FM, Hereford *Also called K P A N Broadcasters (G-8292)*

Kpr & Rsw Investments Inc 281 499-2910
811 Success Ct Ste 400 Stafford (77477) *(G-19342)*

Kps Global LLC (PA) **817 281-5121**
4201 N Beach St Fort Worth (76137) *(G-6770)*

Kps Global LLC 817 339-2100
505 Pecan St Ste 200 Fort Worth (76102) *(G-6771)*

Kpt Inc 214 620-9700
700 Freeport Pkwy Ste 100 Coppell (75019) *(G-3427)*

Kpw Enterprises Inc 214 630-8088
9171 King Arthur Dr Dallas (75247) *(G-4567)*

Kraft Foods, Garland *Also called Kraft Heinz Company (G-7534)*

Kraft Foods, Irving *Also called Kraft Heinz Foods Company (G-13079)*

Kraft Heinz Company 972 272-7511
2340 Forest Ln Garland (75042) *(G-7534)*

Kraft Heinz Foods Company 847 646-2000
8150 Springwood Dr # 200 Irving (75063) *(G-13079)*

Kraft Heinz Foods Company 817 837-4100
1005 Railhead Dr Fort Worth (76177) *(G-6772)*

Kraken Oil & Gas LLC (PA) **713 360-7705**
9805 Katy Fwy Ste 300 Houston (77024) *(G-10562)*

Kraton Corporation (PA) **281 504-4700**
15710 John F Kennedy Blvd # 300 Houston (77032) *(G-10563)*

Kraton Polymers LLC 832 204-5400
700 Milam St Houston (77002) *(G-10564)*

Kraton Polymers LLC (HQ)........................**281 504-4700**
15710 John F Kennedy Blvd # 300 Houston (77032) *(G-10565)*

Kraton Polymers US LLC (HQ)....................**281 504-4700**
15710 John F Kennedy Blvd # 300 Houston (77032) *(G-10566)*

Kraton Polymers US LLC...............................281 668-3163
16400 Park Row Houston (77084) *(G-10567)*

Krenek Printing Company..............................281 463-8649
7102 Glen Chase Ct Houston (77095) *(G-10568)*

Krenekprinting.com, Houston *Also called Krenek Printing Company (G-10568)*

Kristen Distributing Co (PA)........................**979 775-6322**
8301 N State Highway 6 Bryan (77807) *(G-2489)*

Kroger Co..817 698-4357
900 S Main St Fort Worth (76104) *(G-6773)*

Kronos International Inc (HQ)......................**972 233-1700**
5430 Lyndon B Johnson Fwy Dallas (75240) *(G-4568)*

Kronos South Central, Irving *Also called Ultimate Kronos Group (G-13203)*

Kronos Worldwide Inc (HQ).........................**972 233-1700**
5430 Lbj Fwy Ste 1700 Dallas (75240) *(G-4569)*

Kronos Worldwide Inc..................................609 860-6200
5430 Lyndon B Johnson Fwy Dallas (75240) *(G-4570)*

Krown Manufacturing Inc.............................817 738-2485
3408 Indale Rd Fort Worth (76116) *(G-6774)*

Kruckeberg Corporation...............................806 352-9262
3229 Commerce St Amarillo (79109) *(G-496)*

Kruger Aluminum & Brass Fndry, Wichita Falls *Also called Kruger Aluminum & Brass Fndry (G-20777)*

Kruger Aluminum & Brass Fndry.................940 767-0432
1233 36th St Wichita Falls (76302) *(G-20777)*

Krypton Solutions LLC................................972 424-3880
3060 Summit Ave Plano (75074) *(G-16904)*

KS Little Shop...214 371-4113
5825 Spring Glen Dr Dallas (75232) *(G-4571)*

KSA Industries Inc (PA)..............................**713 881-3400**
4400 Post Oak Pkwy Fl 28 Houston (77027) *(G-10569)*

Ksc, Dallas *Also called Knottsmith Construction Co Inc (G-4563)*

Ksh Enterprises Inc.....................................817 313-0926
233 Ashmore Pl Haslet (76052) *(G-8220)*

Ksi, Garland *Also called Kirkland Sales Inc (G-7533)*

Ksw, Dallas *Also called K S W Corp (G-4542)*

Kt Foods LLC...409 293-3257
1520 Sabine Ave Port Arthur (77642) *(G-17115)*

Kta Services...832 368-0138
12296 S Us Highway 181 # 3 San Antonio (78223) *(G-18229)*

Ktb USA, Houston *Also called Megatron Inc (G-10824)*

Ktc Global, Richmond *Also called Kline Technical Consulting LLC (G-17460)*

Ktec Cleanroom Systems Inc.......................512 388-2396
5040 E State Highway 29 Georgetown (78626) *(G-7659)*

Ktech Products LLC......................................972 333-7092
5114 Heritage Oaks Dr Colleyville (76034) *(G-3218)*

Ktx Properties Inc.......................................281 328-3501
333 N Sam Houston Pkwy E Houston (77060) *(G-10570)*

Kuba-Tech Industries LLC............................817 924-5520
801 Ozona Ave Fort Worth (76108) *(G-6775)*

Kubota Authorized Dealer, Frisco *Also called Six & Mango Equipment LLP (G-7312)*

Kubys Sausage House Inc (PA)..................**214 363-2231**
6601 Snider Plz Dallas (75205) *(G-4572)*

Kudzookinect Inc...512 363-0704
1145 W 5th St Ste 200 Austin (78703) *(G-1274)*

Kuest Corporation..210 655-1220
10909 N Interstate 35 San Antonio (78233) *(G-18230)*

Kuhlman Cellars LLC....................................512 920-2675
1602 Sharon Ln Austin (78703) *(G-1275)*

Kunafin LLC..830 757-1181
13955 N Highway 277 Quemado (78877) *(G-17222)*

Kunka Enterprises LLC................................254 666-3576
7314 Bagby Ave Waco (76712) *(G-20423)*

Kuraray America Inc.....................................281 471-2771
12501 Strang Rd La Porte (77571) *(G-13765)*

Kuraray America Inc (HQ)...........................**800 423-9762**
2625 Bay Area Blvd Ste 60 Houston (77058) *(G-10571)*

Kurosky & Co Pntg Contrs Inc.....................817 834-7179
6220 Anderson Rd Fort Worth (76117) *(G-6776)*

Kurt Lupo..903 599-3181
118 Main St Streetman (75859) *(G-19434)*

Kurtz Printing Co, Victoria *Also called Thomas Kurtz (G-20310)*

Kuster Sign LLC...972 991-5841
4305 Lindbergh Dr Addison (75001) *(G-142)*

Kuykendall Btm Hole Pressure.....................432 563-5231
4917 S County Road 1305 Odessa (79765) *(G-16056)*

Kuzzy Industrial Supplier............................915 881-4105
2909 Alameda Ave El Paso (79905) *(G-5833)*

KVP International Inc....................................626 633-0077
1501 Corporate McKinney (75069) *(G-14948)*

Kw Industries Inc..281 240-0909
909 Industrial Blvd Sugar Land (77478) *(G-19502)*

Kw International LLC (PA)............................**713 468-9581**
11125 Equity Dr Ste 200 Houston (77041) *(G-10572)*

Kwest Rv LLC...512 294-2634
10777 Us Highway 183 S Austin (78747) *(G-1276)*

Kwik Kopy Printing, Houston *Also called Union Printers Inc (G-12436)*

Kwik Kopy Printing, Cypress *Also called Kwik-Kopy Corporation (G-3808)*

Kwik Kopy Printing, Cypress *Also called American Whl Thermographers (G-3772)*

Kwik-Kopy Corporation................................281 256-4100
1 Kwik Kopy Ln Cypress (77429) *(G-3808)*

Kwikool, Stafford *Also called Diversity Industries Inc (G-19306)*

Kwivik Inc..469 424-3144
5100 Eldorado Pkwy # 102 McKinney (75070) *(G-14949)*

Kws Manufacturing Company Ltd.................817 295-2247
3041 Conveyor Dr Burleson (76028) *(G-2586)*

Kyle Bunting Holdings Inc...........................512 264-1148
1340 Arprt Commrce Dr Austin (78741) *(G-1277)*

Kyocera Medical Tech Inc............................909 557-2360
10415 Morado Cir I350 Austin (78759) *(G-1278)*

Kysor Panel Systems, Fort Worth *Also called Welbilt Walk-Ins LP (G-7134)*

L & C Safety Inc...432 653-0393
2469 E 11th St Odessa (79761) *(G-16057)*

L & J Technology Inc...................................281 354-4800
22015 E Martin Dr Porter (77365) *(G-17178)*

L & L Pallet Supply Inc (PA).......................**806 272-5041**
1230 Us Highway 84 Muleshoe (79347) *(G-15678)*

L & L Pallet Supply Inc...............................806 272-5041
2795 E Fm 1151 Amarillo (79118) *(G-497)*

L & L Products Inc..972 475-5202
3210 Century Dr Rowlett (75088) *(G-17709)*

L & M Shtmtl & Stl Fabricators....................210 433-7131
1202 Saltillo St San Antonio (78207) *(G-18231)*

L & R Pre-Cast Con Works Inc.....................956 583-6293
3807 N Bentsen Palm Dr Mission (78574) *(G-15558)*

L & R Timber Company Inc..........................936 275-9701
240 Fm 3451 San Augustine (75972) *(G-18651)*

L 3 Cmncations Intgrtd Systms....................903 455-3450
1309 Ridge Rd Rockwall (75087) *(G-17552)*

L B Foster Company.....................................832 934-3107
21270 Fm 1488 Rd Magnolia (77355) *(G-14613)*

L B Foster Company.....................................254 296-6100
901 N Highway 77 Hillsboro (76645) *(G-8329)*

L B Pipe & Coupling Pdts LLC......................832 934-1850
549 Stonegate Dr Katy (77494) *(G-13370)*

L C Burkett Drilling.......................................806 948-4252
Fm 119 Sunray (79086) *(G-19620)*

L C Colormark..972 243-1919
1840 Hutton Dr Ste 208 Carrollton (75006) *(G-2773)*

L C S Production Company...........................325 692-3903
74 35 Hwy 277 S Abilene (79606) *(G-55)*

L E S Distribrs, Carrollton *Also called Iesco Distributing Inc (G-2776)*

L F Manufacturing Inc (PA).........................**979 542-8027**
5528 E Highway 290 Giddings (78942) *(G-7699)*

L G Electronics, Mission *Also called Lg Electronics Alabama Inc (G-15559)*

L G Pump Inc..432 550-3445
8400 Andrews Hwy Odessa (79765) *(G-16058)*

L J Machine Works Inc.................................713 928-5786
5510 Lawndale St Houston (77023) *(G-10573)*

L J Smith Inc...713 462-4653
6100 W By Northwest Blvd # 110 Houston (77040) *(G-10574)*

L L Machine Works Inc................................713 466-7100
9011 W Little York Rd Houston (77040) *(G-10575)*

L L O G Exploration Co, Houston *Also called SM Energy Company (G-11916)*

L L Pallets..469 916-7552
4060 Duncanville Rd Dallas (75236) *(G-4573)*

L L T Inc (PA)...**830 914-3800**
2462 W Interstate 20 Odessa (79763) *(G-16059)*

L P Printing, Houston *Also called Long Plan Printing Inc (G-10684)*

L R G Services Inc..713 504-4470
21830 Pinebrook Dr New Caney (77357) *(G-15843)*

L R S, Richardson *Also called Long Range Systems LLC (G-17349)*

L R W Fabricators, Wichita Falls *Also called Lake Road Welding Co (G-20778)*

L R West Manufacturing Co..........................281 485-6057
13823 1945 N Htfeld Rd Pearland (77581) *(G-16575)*

L S W Mfg Inc...817 232-4482
600 Burlington Rd Saginaw (76179) *(G-17747)*

L T D Explorations Inc..................................361 664-9108
690 N Highway 16 Freer (78357) *(G-7230)*

L V Controls Inc...713 691-4666
60 Rittenhouse St Houston (77076) *(G-10576)*

L&H Packing, San Antonio *Also called Leonard & Harral Packing Co (G-18247)*

L&R Midland Inc..713 680-0909
788 W Sam Houston Pkwy N # 200 Houston (77024) *(G-10577)*

L'Eggs - Hnes - Bali - Playtex, Hillsboro *Also called Hanesbrands Inc (G-8326)*

L'Etoile Children's Apparel, Dallas *Also called LEtoile Apparel Inc (G-3848)*

L-3 Mustang Technology, Plano *Also called Mustang Technology Group LP (G-16937)*

L3 Mobile-Vision Inc....................................973 263-1090
11375 S Sam Hston Pkwy W Houston (77031) *(G-10578)*

L3 Technologies Inc....................................512 251-3441
817 W Howard Ln Austin (78753) *(G-1279)*

L3 Technologies Inc....................................817 619-4756
2200 Arlington Downs Rd Arlington (76011) *(G-713)*

L3 Technologies Inc 972 722-7927
1700 Science Pl Rockwall (75032) (G-17553)

L3 Technologies Inc 817 619-2000
2200 Arlington Downs Rd Arlington (76011) (G-714)

L3 Technologies Inc 817 619-2000
2116 Arlington Downs Rd Arlington (76011) (G-715)

L3 Technologies Inc 903 457-4100
10001 Jack Finney Blvd Greenville (75402) (G-8080)

L3 Technologies Inc 972 840-5600
3414 Herrmann Dr Garland (75041) (G-7535)

L3 Technologies Inc 972 840-5600
9827 Chartwell Dr Dallas (75243) (G-4574)

L3 Technologies Inc 361 516-8396
614 Mccain St Kingsville (78363) (G-13632)

L3harris Technologies Inc 903 457-7461
10001 Jack Finney Blvd Greenville (75402) (G-8081)

L3harris Technologies Inc 972 550-2300
8105 N Belt Line Rd Ste 1 Irving (75063) (G-13080)

L3harris Technologies Inc 972 772-7501
1655 Science Pl Rockwall (75032) (G-17554)

L3harris Technologies Inc 254 799-5533
7500 Maehr Rd Waco (76705) (G-20424)

La Abuela Mexican Foods Inc 956 447-8289
1904 Joe Stephens Ave Weslaco (78599) (G-20663)

La Autentica Inc 202 415-6979
17806 W Interstate 10 San Antonio (78257) (G-18232)

La Bella Vida Inc 806 744-3600
901 17th St Lubbock (79401) (G-14434)

La Blanc Bob 972 492-1898
4309 Fairway Dr Carrollton (75010) (G-2876)

La Blue Crab Co Inc 972 422-7525
1111 Jupiter Rd Ste 100e Plano (75074) (G-16905)

La Bodega Restaurant, Midland Also called Aus-Mex Company Inc (G-15124)

La Brisa Ice Cream Company LLC 713 926-3450
7842 Canal St Houston (77012) (G-10579)

La Copa Field Services Inc 361 364-1608
500 W Fulton St Sinton (78387) (G-18963)

La Creme Coffee & Tea, Irving Also called La Creme Inc (G-13081)

La Creme Inc 214 352-8090
3225 Premier Dr Ste 100 Irving (75063) (G-13081)

La Diosa Cellars, Lubbock Also called La Bella Vida Inc (G-14434)

La Espiga De Oro - Georgia Inc (PA) 713 861-4200
1202 W 15th St Houston (77008) (G-10580)

La Fama Foods Inc 903 968-4500
7566 Us Highway 259 N Ore City (75683) (G-16274)

La Fama Tortilla Factory, Ore City Also called La Fama Foods Inc (G-16274)

La Famosa Tortilla 361 592-5596
620 E Alice Ave Kingsville (78363) (G-13633)

La Famosa Tortilla Factory, Kingsville Also called La Famosa Tortilla (G-13633)

La Feria News, Los Fresnos Also called Lfn LLC (G-14347)

La Frontera Molina 210 432-0855
727 Enrique M Barrera Pkw San Antonio (78237) (G-18233)

La Grange Con & Aggregates (PA) 979 836-3664
1503 N Park St Brenham (77833) (G-2260)

La Hacenda Mexican Fd Pdts Inc 214 353-0230
2604 Freewood Dr Dallas (75220) (G-4575)

La Hacienda Tortilla Factory 830 773-9151
2505 El Indio Hwy Eagle Pass (78852) (G-5548)

La India Packing Co 956 723-3772
1520 Marcella Ave Laredo (78040) (G-13903)

La King's Confectionery, Galveston Also called Candy Kings Inc (G-7391)

La Luz Marketing Group Inc 210 202-1800
12001 Network Blvd # 115 San Antonio (78249) (G-18234)

La Machine & Engineering Inc 903 764-5634
3202 An County Road 179 Elkhart (75839) (G-6060)

La Mexicana Tortilla Fctry Inc 214 943-7770
715 Skyline Dr Duncanville (75116) (G-5532)

La Nortena Inc 432 445-3273
211 E 3rd St Pecos (79772) (G-16621)

La Nortena Factory, Pecos Also called La Nortena Inc (G-16621)

La Nortena Restaurant, Pecos Also called La Nortena Tortilla Factory (G-16622)

La Nortena Tortilla Factory 432 445-3273
212 E 3rd St Pecos (79772) (G-16622)

La Nueva 106.5 FM, Dallas Also called Hispanic Fmly Chrstn Ntwrk Inc (G-4460)

La Nueva Riograndese Inc 817 921-0440
4241 Mccart Ave Fort Worth (76115) (G-6777)

La Original Tortilla Co Inc 361 570-8905
302 Profit Dr Victoria (77901) (G-20282)

La Paleteria 214 887-8278
4225 Ross Ave Dallas (75204) (G-4576)

La Pallet Recyclers 281 469-6070
9814 Frbanks Rd Houston (77064) (G-10581)

La Paloma Tortilla Factory (PA) 956 316-1515
621 E Cano St Edinburg (78539) (G-5592)

La Paloma Tortilla Fctry & Bky, Edinburg Also called La Paloma Tortilla Factory (G-5592)

La Ranchera Inc (PA) 713 699-4400
7710 N Shepherd Dr Houston (77088) (G-10582)

La Regia Tortilla Factory LLC 210 971-9190
1615 N Laredo St Ste 105 San Antonio (78207) (G-18235)

La Rotativa Tortilla Factory, El Paso Also called La Rotativa Tortilla Inc (G-5834)

La Rotativa Tortilla Inc 915 533-2317
2010 Montana Ave El Paso (79903) (G-5834)

La Subasta Incorporated 214 951-9500
502 N Haskell Ave Dallas (75246) (G-4577)

La Subasta Incorporated (PA) 713 777-1010
6120 Tarnef Dr Ste 100 Houston (77074) (G-10583)

La Subasta Newspaper, Houston Also called La Subasta Incorporated (G-10583)

La Superior Foods Inc 682 703-1165
500 E Central Ave Fort Worth (76164) (G-6778)

La Superior Tortillas Y Mas, Fort Worth Also called La Superior Foods Inc (G-6778)

La Tang Cuisine, Houston Also called Texpac Foods LLC (G-12261)

La Tapatia Inc 915 859-9616
8941 Old County Dr El Paso (79907) (G-5835)

La Tee Da, Marshall Also called Casey Products LLC (G-14770)

La Tee Da LLC 903 927-3500
1070 Pumpkin Center Rd Marshall (75672) (G-14785)

La Vakita, Houston Also called Castro Cheese Company Inc (G-9097)

La-Te-Da Frgrnce For HM L L C, Marshall Also called La Tee Da LLC (G-14785)

La-Z-Boy Furniture Galleries, Horseshoe Bay Also called Dbljs7 Inc (G-8366)

Labarge Coating LLC 713 378-7225
711 Shields St Channelview (77530) (G-3028)

Labarge Coating LLC 281 457-0200
400 S Sheldon Rd Channelview (77530) (G-3029)

Label Graphics, Fort Worth Also called Cash Engraving Co (G-6495)

Label Products Inc 713 869-2959
7511 Langtry St Houston (77040) (G-10584)

Labeling Equipment Specialists 903 734-5873
3115 Locust Rd Gilmer (75645) (G-7708)

Labelleco Fab LLC 409 225-5499
7335 Frint Dr Beaumont (77705) (G-1916)

Labelleco Fabrication, Beaumont Also called Labelleco Fab LLC (G-1916)

Labelmax Inc 956 718-3961
5601 Cerrito Prieto Ct Laredo (78041) (G-13904)

Labels Plus, El Paso Also called Darling Quick Print Inc (G-5714)

Labinal Salisbury LLC 410 548-7800
3790 Russell Newman Blvd # 100 Denton (76208) (G-5378)

Labuena Vida Vineyards, Grapevine Also called Bobby G Smith Do (G-8015)

Lac Fleet, Corpus Christi Also called Aransas Fuel LLC (G-3474)

Lacerte Software Corporation 214 387-2000
5601 Headquarters Dr Plano (75024) (G-16906)

Lachmann Vllneva Hldngs GP LLC 915 594-0500
45 Buttrfeld Trail Blvd S El Paso (79906) (G-5836)

Lacore Labs Inc 469 995-7791
901 Wilmeth Rd Mckinney (75069) (G-14950)

Lacy Construction Services LLC 903 498-0683
6012 Ashley Rd Kemp (75143) (G-13485)

Lacy Operations Ltd (PA) 903 758-8276
222 E Tyler St Longview (75601) (G-14262)

Lacy Operations Ltd 903 693-3501
657 Fm 2792 Beckville (75631) (G-1971)

Ladds Corporation 281 495-5200
12670 Jebbia Ln Stafford (77477) (G-19343)

Ladish Valve Company LLC 281 880-8560
7603 Bluff Point Dr Houston (77086) (G-10585)

Lady Hlth Ftness- Rockwall Inc (PA) 972 906-0400
4009 Old Denton Rd # 114 Carrollton (75007) (G-2877)

Lady Walton's Cookies, Dallas Also called Lwc Brands Inc (G-4613)

Lafargeholcim US, Addison Also called Holcim (us) Inc (G-134)

Lagan Interests Inc 713 472-1100
2301 Shaver St Pasadena (77502) (G-16470)

Lagarto Inc 915 598-2668
10787 Gateway Blvd W El Paso (79935) (G-5837)

Laguna Tubular Products Corp 832 734-0044
16952 Leonard Rd Houston (77049) (G-10586)

Laird Plastics Inc (HQ) 469 299-7000
5800 Campus Circle Dr E # 150 Irving (75063) (G-13082)

Lake Cities Sun, Lake Dallas Also called Sun Newspapers (G-13811)

Lake City Opitical & Vision, League City Also called Williams Optometrist (G-13982)

Lake County Newspaper 254 559-5412
114 E Elm St Breckenridge (76424) (G-2231)

Lake Ray Roberts Marina, Sanger Also called Wallace Marine of Texas Inc (G-18732)

Lake Region Medical Inc 978 570-6900
31 Butterfield Trail Blvd C El Paso (79906) (G-5838)

Lake Road Welding Co 940 692-4988
5615 State Highway 79 S Wichita Falls (76310) (G-20778)

Lake Services Inc 512 261-3625
109 Ranch Road 620 N Lakeway (78734) (G-13817)

Lakeland Paper Corporation 817 840-5470
600 109th St Arlington (76011) (G-716)

Lakeside Trailer Park, Nacogdoches Also called Lakeside Trailer Sales (G-15701)

Lakeside Trailer Sales 936 564-6252
7225 North St Nacogdoches (75965) (G-15701)

Lakland Paper, Arlington Also called Lakeland Paper Corporation (G-716)

Lala US Inc 469 804-3850
5301 Alpha Rd Ste 80-300 Dallas (75240) (G-4578)

A L P H A B E T I C

Lamar Hunt Trust Estate Inc..............214 720-1600
1601 Elm St Ste 4000 Dallas (75201) *(G-4579)*

Lamar Ranch, Dallas *Also called Hunt Oil Company* *(G-4475)*

Lambda Energy Resources LLC..............231 258-6425
12012 Wickchester Ln # 300 Houston (77079) *(G-10587)*

Lamesa Press Reporter, Lamesa *Also called Lamesa Reporter Inc* *(G-13828)*

Lamesa Reporter Inc..............806 872-2177
523 N 1st St Lamesa (79331) *(G-13828)*

Laminate Works Inc..............713 955-1310
8600 Telephone Rd Houston (77061) *(G-10588)*

Laminate Works Inc..............913 281-7474
4051 La Reunion Pkwy # 170 Dallas (75212) *(G-4580)*

Lamme's Candies, Austin *Also called Lammes Candies Since 1885 Inc* *(G-1280)*

Lammes Candies Since 1885 Inc (PA)..............512 310-1885
200b Parker Dr Ste B500 Austin (78728) *(G-1280)*

Lamons, Houston *Also called Lgc US Asset Holdings LLC* *(G-10631)*

Lamons Gasket Company (HQ)..............713 222-0284
7300 Airport Blvd Houston (77061) *(G-10589)*

Lamont Brands Inc..............281 286-7553
920 Gemini St Houston (77058) *(G-10590)*

Lamot Corporation..............816 792-1500
13650 N Promenade Blvd Stafford (77477) *(G-19344)*

Lampasas Building Components, Lampasas *Also called Claussen Inc* *(G-13833)*

Lamrite, Austin *Also called Hull Supply Company Inc* *(G-1213)*

Lamrite..............512 385-4455
5117 E Cesar Chavez St Austin (78702) *(G-1281)*

Lanbert's Ormamental Iron, Haltom City *Also called Southwest Fenter Inc* *(G-8158)*

Lancaster Flow Automation LLC..............832 237-9444
14041 West Rd Ste 100 Houston (77041) *(G-10591)*

Lancer Corporation (HQ)..............210 310-7250
6655 Lancer Blvd San Antonio (78219) *(G-18236)*

Land & Sea Industries LLC..............832 622-4216
19321 Stuebner Airline Rd Spring (77379) *(G-19140)*

Land & Sea Services 1 Inc..............409 935-9466
1900 Oak St La Marque (77568) *(G-13711)*

Land Enterprises Inc..............713 924-5929
5517 Dorbrandt St Houston (77023) *(G-10592)*

Land Industrial Trial Sevices..............281 385-2504
16940 County Line Old River Winfree (77535) *(G-16218)*

Land OLakes Inc..............281 342-2493
825 Highway 36 N Rosenberg (77471) *(G-17588)*

Landers Machine Co..............817 834-6383
3601 N Sylvania Ave Fort Worth (76111) *(G-6779)*

Landes Inc..............713 665-0655
4500 S Pinemont Dr Houston (77041) *(G-10593)*

Landmark Fabrication LP..............817 230-8857
3496 Gateway Dr Decatur (76234) *(G-5248)*

Landreth Fastner Corporation..............281 414-3103
8700 Scranton St Houston (77075) *(G-10594)*

Landreth Prcsion Machining Inc..............713 944-7464
8700 Scranton St Houston (77075) *(G-10595)*

Landry Corporation..............281 449-1052
1518 Hartwick Rd Houston (77093) *(G-10596)*

Landsberg Dallas Div 1053, Grapevine *Also called Orora North America* *(G-8050)*

Lane Supply Inc (PA)..............817 261-9116
120 Fairview St Arlington (76010) *(G-717)*

Lang & Mitchell Contrs Inc..............903 876-2882
1499 Us Highway 175 Frankston (75763) *(G-7167)*

Langes Legacy Home Ltd..............972 712-3949
23 Prestige Cir Allen (75002) *(G-284)*

Langford Construction Inc..............817 478-0218
5919 Woodmeadow Dr Arlington (76016) *(G-718)*

Langford Roustabout Svcs LLC..............940 864-3490
8348 Bus Us Hwy 277 N Haskell (79521) *(G-8213)*

Langham Creek Mch Works Inc..............281 550-9587
4408 Joyce Blvd Ste D Houston (77084) *(G-10597)*

Langley Energy..............214 221-2669
10405 E Northwest Hwy # 304 Dallas (75238) *(G-4581)*

Langley Manufacturing Inc..............936 569-8824
252 County Road 822 Nacogdoches (75964) *(G-15702)*

Lansa Inc..............630 874-7042
2950 North Loop W Ste 700 Houston (77092) *(G-10598)*

Lanxess Corporation..............281 383-7761
8500 W Bay Rd Baytown (77523) *(G-1795)*

Lap King LLC..............512 415-3034
2802 Flintrock Trce # 101 Austin (78738) *(G-1282)*

Lapaz Tortilla Factory..............432 337-7735
1112 S Crane Ave Odessa (79763) *(G-16060)*

Lapolla Industries LLC (HQ)..............281 219-4100
15402 Vantage Pkwy E # 322 Houston (77032) *(G-10599)*

Laporte Plant Us70, La Porte *Also called Chemical Lime-Southwest LLC* *(G-13727)*

Laredo Coca-Cola Bottling Co (HQ)..............956 726-2671
1402 Industrial Blvd Laredo (78041) *(G-13905)*

Laredo Coca-Cola Bottling Co..............361 693-4200
5126 Greenwood Dr Corpus Christi (78417) *(G-3562)*

Laredo Coca-Cola Bottling Co..............956 686-8827
2400 W Expressway 83 McAllen (78501) *(G-14884)*

Laredo Construction Inc (HQ)..............281 499-4333
13385 Murphy Rd Stafford (77477) *(G-19345)*

Laredo Energy IV Gp LLC (PA)..............713 600-6000
840 Houston Ave Houston (77007) *(G-10600)*

Laredo Morning Times, Laredo *Also called Hearst Corporation* *(G-13890)*

Laredo Petroleum Inc..............432 684-9955
508 W Wall St Ste 600 Midland (79701) *(G-15272)*

Laredo Ready Mix Ltd..............956 723-7429
18015 Mines Rd Laredo (78045) *(G-13906)*

Large Antennas Division, Kilgore *Also called CPI Satcom & Antenna Tech Inc* *(G-13539)*

Lariat Construction Services (PA)..............361 318-9104
12596 Fm 673 Pawnee (78145) *(G-16533)*

Lark Heat Treating, Houston *Also called Lark Industries Incorporated* *(G-10601)*

Lark Industrial LLC..............915 500-4347
7198 Merch Ave Ste C2 El Paso (79915) *(G-5839)*

Lark Industries Incorporated..............713 937-9089
6640 Mayard Rd Houston (77041) *(G-10601)*

Larkin Products Inc..............972 937-3640
1620 E Main St Waxahachie (75165) *(G-20549)*

Larry & Matt Inc (PA)..............806 665-4418
241 Western St Pampa (79065) *(G-16326)*

Larry Grimes Interest Inc..............281 331-3273
1006 Fm 517 Rd Alvin (77511) *(G-371)*

Larry McHorse Services LLC..............361 275-4978
401 2nd St Cuero (77954) *(G-3762)*

Larry Prters Cstm Intr Dsgns I..............409 296-3868
480 Broadway Winnie (77665) *(G-20888)*

Larsen Manufacturing LLC..............915 790-0762
12150 Rojas Dr Ste E El Paso (79936) *(G-5840)*

Larson International, Plainview *Also called J & S Rides Inc* *(G-16759)*

Larson-Juhl US LLC..............713 895-0296
9232 Baythorne Dr Houston (77041) *(G-10602)*

Larwel Industries Inc..............817 491-1200
3601 Haynes Rd Roanoke (76262) *(G-17486)*

Las Cruces Brand Products, El Paso *Also called Mexi-Snax Corporation* *(G-5874)*

Laselec Inc..............817 460-7830
2605 N Forum Dr Grand Prairie (75052) *(G-7908)*

Laser Care Inc..............817 640-6665
1222 W Corporate Dr Ste A Arlington (76006) *(G-719)*

Laser Drum Products Inc..............713 263-9050
6016 Centralcrest St Houston (77092) *(G-10603)*

Laser Graphics Arlington, Grand Prairie *Also called Printedd Products & Svcs Ltd* *(G-7954)*

Laser Image Inc..............214 267-1313
2451 N Stemmons Fwy Dallas (75207) *(G-4582)*

Laser Masters Inc..............832 467-4100
6039 Thomas Rd Ste D Houston (77041) *(G-10604)*

Laser Printing Inc..............972 235-2488
3002 W Campbell Rd Garland (75044) *(G-7536)*

Laser Pros International Corp..............715 369-5995
1402 Commerce St Marshall (75672) *(G-14786)*

Laser Prtrs & Mailing Svcs LLC..............210 590-6565
8701 Perrin Beitel Rd San Antonio (78217) *(G-18237)*

Laser Scientific LLC..............512 733-8709
210a Commerce Blvd Round Rock (78664) *(G-17666)*

Laser Shot Inc (PA)..............281 240-1122
4214 Bluebonnet Dr Stafford (77477) *(G-19346)*

Laser Ventures Inc (HQ)..............770 516-4600
9825 Spectrum Dr Bldg 3 Austin (78717) *(G-1701)*

Laser Welding Solutions LLC..............713 895-0800
7542 Fairview St Houston (77041) *(G-10605)*

Laserlight, Katy *Also called Laserweld Inc* *(G-13422)*

Laserweld Inc..............713 333-0804
1350 Schlipf Rd Katy (77493) *(G-13422)*

Lash Mfg & Dev Group LLC..............956 465-0330
2005 Matehuala Ct Brownsville (78526) *(G-2375)*

Lasko Products LLC..............817 625-6381
1700 Meacham Blvd Fort Worth (76106) *(G-6780)*

Lasmer Industries Inc..............830 895-4400
555 Mill Run Kerrville (78028) *(G-13522)*

Lassiter Industries Inc..............281 781-8708
321 Century Plaza Dr # 130 Houston (77073) *(G-10606)*

Lasso Technologies LLC..............866 392-0923
8750 N Central Expy # 300 Dallas (75231) *(G-4583)*

Lastrad LLC..............713 589-9477
1980 Post Oak Blvd Houston (77056) *(G-10607)*

Lastrad Oil & Gas Pdts & Svcs, Houston *Also called Lastrad LLC* *(G-10607)*

Latham Stairs & Millworks, Sanger *Also called Concierge Renovation Company* *(G-18724)*

Latham Stairs & Millworks Inc..............940 458-3075
1212 Ruby Lea Ln Fort Worth (76179) *(G-6781)*

Laticrete International Inc..............972 641-3266
1710 111th St Grand Prairie (75050) *(G-7909)*

Latin Orchid, Carrollton *Also called Chateau Noblesse Inc* *(G-2859)*

Latina Style Inc..............214 357-2186
2102 Empire Central Dallas (75235) *(G-4584)*

Latina Style Magazine, Dallas *Also called Latina Style Inc* *(G-4584)*

Lattimore Materials Company LP..............817 491-2400
1689 N Highway 377 Roanoke (76262) *(G-17487)*

Lattimore Materials Corp (HQ)..............972 221-4646
15900 Dooley Rd Addison (75001) *(G-143)*

Lattimore Materials Corp..............972 423-8359
1200 Ave N Plano (75074) *(G-16907)*

(G-0000) Company's Geographic Section entry number

Lattimore Materials Corp 972 569-4622
1000 E University Dr McKinney (75069) *(G-14951)*
Lattimore Materials Corp 972 346-3002
890 S Dallas Pkwy Prosper (75078) *(G-17214)*
Lattimore Materials Corp 903 868-9585
6102 Theresa Dr Sherman (75090) *(G-18920)*
Lattimore Ready Mix, Addison *Also called Lattimore Materials Corp (G-143)*
Lattimore Ready Mix, Plano *Also called Lattimore Materials Corp (G-16907)*
Latx Oilfield Services LLC (PA) **903 934-8263**
13927 Us Highway 80 E Waskom (75692) *(G-20518)*
Latx Operations LLC 903 927-2091
13927 Us Highway 80 E Waskom (75692) *(G-20519)*
Lauras Carousel Inc 940 365-1875
10459 Redfearn Rd Aubrey (76227) *(G-850)*
Lauren Concrete Inc 512 389-2113
4501 Shaw Ln Plant 2/9 29 Plant Austin (78744) *(G-1283)*
Lauren Concrete Inc 512 233-1348
2001 Picadilly Dr Round Rock (78664) *(G-17667)*
Lauren Concrete LP 512 389-2113
2001 Picadilly Dr Round Rock (78664) *(G-17668)*
Lauren Engineers & Constrs Inc 469 417-7600
1212 Corporate Dr Ste 100 Irving (75038) *(G-13083)*
Lauren Publications Inc 214 628-9720
4275 Kellway Cir Ste 146 Addison (75001) *(G-144)*
Lauson Drilling Services Inc 979 733-0345
4861 Highway 90 Alleyton (78935) *(G-310)*
Lavaca Pipe Line Company 361 987-8900
103 Fannin Rd Point Comfort (77978) *(G-17088)*
Lavender Enterprises Inc 214 631-8080
4939 Cash Rd Dallas (75247) *(G-4585)*
Laversab Inc 281 325-8300
505 Gillingham Blvd Sugar Land (77478) *(G-19503)*
Laverton Oilfield Services LLC 325 899-3556
124 Hill St Albany (76430) *(G-190)*
Law Publications Inc 800 527-0156
1100 Valwood Pkwy Ste 118 Carrollton (75006) *(G-2774)*
Lawe Industries LLC (PA) **210 833-9497**
24165 W Interstate 10 San Antonio (78257) *(G-18238)*
Lawe Industries LLC 512 262-1933
6170 Fm 2770 Kyle (78640) *(G-13684)*
Lawler Foods Ltd (HQ) **281 446-0059**
2200 S Houston Ave Humble (77396) *(G-12783)*
Lawler Foods Ltd 281 540-3321
1219 Carpenter Rd Humble (77396) *(G-12784)*
Lawler Foods Construction, Humble *Also called Lawler Foods Ltd (G-12784)*
Lawler's Dessert, Humble *Also called Lawler Foods Ltd (G-12783)*
Lawn Master Outdoor Living LLC (PA) **972 938-7100**
3841 S Intrstate Hwy 35 E Waxahachie (75165) *(G-20550)*
Lawrence Furniture Co Inc 361 572-3710
400 Warehouse Rd Victoria (77905) *(G-20283)*
Lay Cooley RE Holdings 1 LLC 972 721-4500
1000 E Airport Fwy Irving (75062) *(G-13084)*
Layline Petroleum LLC 713 465-4100
820 Gessner Rd Ste 1145 Houston (77024) *(G-10608)*
Laymor, Longview *Also called Mobile Products Inc (G-14278)*
Layne Christensen Company (HQ) **281 475-2600**
9303 New Trils Dr Ste 200 Spring (77381) *(G-19226)*
Layton Energy Inc 713 590-2820
2100 West Loop S Ste 1601 Houston (77027) *(G-10609)*
Lazarus Energy LLC 830 582-3202
801 Travis St Ste 2100 Houston (77002) *(G-10610)*
Lazarus Energy Holdings LLC (PA) **713 850-0500**
801 Travis St Ste 2100 Houston (77002) *(G-10611)*
Lazarus Energy Services, Houston *Also called Lazarus Energy Holdings LLC (G-10611)*
Lazel Inc (HQ) **214 932-9500**
17855 Dallas Pkwy Ste 400 Dallas (75287) *(G-3847)*
Lazio Design, Houston *Also called I & I Design Inc (G-10308)*
LB Foster Ball Winch Inc 936 228-0077
15786 N Highway 75 Willis (77378) *(G-20853)*
Lbs Enterprises LLC 903 845-6436
100 N Lee Dr Gladewater (75647) *(G-7725)*
Lc Sciences 713 664-7087
2575 W Bellfort Ave Houston (77054) *(G-10612)*
Lcra, Austin *Also called Lower Colorado River Authority (G-1305)*
Lcs, Kemp *Also called Lacy Construction Services LLC (G-13485)*
Lcs, Carrollton *Also called Logical Control Services LLP (G-2878)*
Lcw Automotive Corp 210 732-5466
1102 N Cherry St San Antonio (78202) *(G-18239)*
Lcy Elastomers LP 281 424-6100
4803 Decker Dr Baytown (77520) *(G-1826)*
Ldia Holdings LLC 512 247-3700
3019 Alvin Devane Blvd Austin (78741) *(G-1284)*
LDR Holding Corporation (HQ) **512 344-3333**
13785 Res Blvd Ste 200 Austin (78750) *(G-1285)*
Le Boufs Bindery Inc 281 485-0332
4101 Rice Drier Rd Ste E Pearland (77581) *(G-16576)*
Le Gourmet, Houston *Also called International Do Foods Idf Inc (G-10401)*
Le Ragge Ruggs Inc (PA) **512 858-4186**
1111 W Highway 290 Dripping Springs (78620) *(G-5508)*
Le Stitch N Designs Inc 214 340-1592
12215 Forestgate Dr # 101 Dallas (75243) *(G-4586)*
Leach Trailers LLP 254 687-2616
701 S Hill St Itasca (76055) *(G-13216)*
Leader Gasket Technologies Inc (HQ) **281 542-0600**
850 Sens Rd La Porte (77571) *(G-13766)*
Leader Gasket Technologies Inc 361 289-1614
5819 Leopard St Corpus Christi (78408) *(G-3563)*
Leading Testing Labs LLC (PA) **281 600-8227**
839 Fm 1489 Rd Brookshire (77423) *(G-2318)*
Leal Foods, Grand Prairie *Also called J Leals Food Inc (G-7898)*
Leam Drilling Systems LLC 936 539-1351
2027a Airport Rd Conroe (77301) *(G-3318)*
Leamco Bearing and Supply, Odessa *Also called Weatherford Artificia (G-16206)*
Lear Corporation 915 791-5400
11970 Pellicano Dr El Paso (79936) *(G-5841)*
Lear Corporation 915 307-9237
950 Loma Verde Dr El Paso (79936) *(G-5842)*
Lear Corporation 915 787-5012
950 Loma Verde Dr El Paso (79936) *(G-5843)*
Lear Corporation 817 419-3000
3120 N Great Sw Pkwy Grand Prairie (75050) *(G-7910)*
Lear Electrical Systems Group, El Paso *Also called Lear Corporation (G-5842)*
Lear Siegler Logistics Intl (PA) **210 490-0267**
333 Morris Witt Ste 1 San Antonio (78226) *(G-18240)*
Lear Trim LP 915 849-5660
1440 Don Haskins Dr El Paso (79936) *(G-5844)*
Learjet Inc 972 720-2400
3400 Waterview Pkwy # 320 Richardson (75080) *(G-17341)*
Learnsap A Texas Ltd Lblty Co 832 419-7371
1927 County Road 129 Pearland (77581) *(G-16577)*
Leather Leather, Dallas *Also called LP & M Group Inc (G-4607)*
Leatherwood Plastics 972 221-7656
1426 Crescent Ave Lewisville (75057) *(G-14060)*
Lebco Graphics Inc 830 755-8226
31400 Interstate 10 W Boerne (78006) *(G-2126)*
Lebus International Inc (PA) **903 758-5521**
215 Industrial Dr Longview (75602) *(G-14263)*
Lechi Foods 281 470-6200
10625 W Fairmont Pkwy La Porte (77571) *(G-13767)*
Lecolift Inc 713 676-1514
255 N Wayside Dr Houston (77020) *(G-10613)*
Led Illumination II, Waco *Also called Pruf Energy Solutions LLC (G-20450)*
Led OEM Partners LLC 832 769-0593
11857 Cutten Rd Houston (77066) *(G-10614)*
Leddy, M L Boot & Saddlery, San Angelo *Also called Franklin-Leddy Corporation (G-17800)*
Ledi2 Inc (PA) **713 636-9152**
10611 Harwin Dr Ste 402 Houston (77036) *(G-10615)*
Leds Unlimited, Lago Vista *Also called Light Emtting Dds-Nlimited LLC (G-13806)*
Ledsome Machine & Welding Co 325 646-4691
2508 Stephen F Austin Dr Brownwood (76801) *(G-2434)*
Ledwell & Son Enterprises Inc (PA) **903 838-6531**
3300 Waco St Texarkana (75501) *(G-19768)*
Ledwell Office Solutions, Texarkana *Also called Ledwell & Son Enterprises Inc (G-19768)*
Lee Container, Nacogdoches *Also called E-Coating Inc (G-15695)*
Lee Contracting Inc 281 456-9023
10818 Sheldon Rd Houston (77044) *(G-10616)*
Lee Custom Works Inc 210 432-1911
501 Culebra Rd San Antonio (78201) *(G-18241)*
Lee Dill Inc 325 677-0474
2631 Fm 3034 Abilene (79601) *(G-56)*
Lee Linco Plastics Inc 281 487-0377
1511 Genoa Red Bluff Rd Pasadena (77504) *(G-16471)*
Lee Products Inc 817 641-9893
4308 E Highway 67 Cleburne (76031) *(G-3100)*
Lee Quigley Company 512 762-4046
700 Rockmead Dr Ste 216 Austin (78745) *(G-1286)*
Lee Specialties (PA) **281 519-1719**
5119 Hiltonview Rd Houston (77086) *(G-10617)*
Lee Tech LLC 409 925-0553
5215 Fm 646 Rd S Santa Fe (77510) *(G-18736)*
Leeagra Inc 800 825-3446
117 E 70th St Lubbock (79404) *(G-14435)*
Leeco Precision Spring Mfg Co 713 692-6281
714 E Burress St Houston (77022) *(G-10618)*
Leeco Spring International, Houston *Also called Leeco Precision Spring Mfg Co (G-10618)*
Leedo Cabinetry, East Bernard *Also called Leedo Manufacturing Co LP (G-5559)*
Leedo Cabinetry, Stafford *Also called Leedo Manufacturing Co LP (G-19347)*
Leedo Manufacturing Co LP (PA) **866 465-3336**
16856 Cabinet Rd East Bernard (77435) *(G-5559)*
Leedo Manufacturing Co LP 866 995-3336
10707 Corp Dr Ste 250 Stafford (77477) *(G-19347)*
Leelinco Plastics Inc 281 487-0377
1511 Genoa Red Bluff Rd Pasadena (77504) *(G-16472)*
Leemah Corporation 214 570-7170
1001 E Arapaho Rd Richardson (75081) *(G-17342)*
Leemak LP 281 492-9555
17171 Park Row Ste 295 Houston (77084) *(G-10619)*

ALPHABETIC

Leeson Energy Services LLC 432 689-7000
2130 S Loop 250 W Ste 3 Midland (79703) ***(G-15273)***
Left Right Media LLC 972 897-6578
7910 Ceberry Dr Austin (78759) ***(G-1287)***
Legacy Aeronautics Inc 855 622-8600
2145 Chenault Dr Ste 110 Carrollton (75006) ***(G-2775)***
Legacy Automtn Pwr Design Inc 281 888-5402
11615 N Huston Rosslyn Rd Houston (77086) ***(G-10620)***
Legacy Blind Mfg, Carrollton *Also called K & S Products Inc* ***(G-2772)***
Legacy Energy Services, Jourdanton *Also called Green & Hansen LLC* ***(G-13331)***
Legacy Field Services LLC 903 694-9445
457 W Panola St Carthage (75633) ***(G-2912)***
Legacy Housing Corporation (PA) **817 799-4900**
1600 Airport Fwy Ste 100 Bedford (76022) ***(G-1976)***
Legacy Investments Inc (PA) **214 750-1522**
12377 Merit Dr Ste 1200 Dallas (75251) ***(G-4587)***
Legacy Lockers LLC 972 937-1088
4433 Bronze Way Dallas (75236) ***(G-4588)***
Legacy National Signs 972 790-8900
11330 Luna Rd Dallas (75229) ***(G-4589)***
Legacy Offshore International, League City *Also called Legacy Offshore LLC* ***(G-13968)***
Legacy Offshore LLC 281 334-2266
2951 Marina Bay Dr League City (77573) ***(G-13968)***
Legacy Reserves Inc (PA) **432 689-5200**
303 W Wall St Ste 1800 Midland (79701) ***(G-15274)***
Legacy Reserves LP 432 967-3490
1200 W County Road 114 Midland (79706) ***(G-15275)***
Legacy Reserves LP (HQ) **432 689-5200**
15 Smith Rd Ste 3000 Midland (79705) ***(G-15276)***
Legacy Reserves Oper GP LLC 432 689-5200
303 W Wall St Ste 1400 Midland (79701) ***(G-15277)***
Legacy Resources, Midland *Also called Legacy Reserves Oper GP LLC* ***(G-15277)***
Legacy Tubular LLC 281 363-1900
39013 Fm 1774 Rd Magnolia (77355) ***(G-14614)***
Legacy Vulcan LLC 830 693-2756
5525 E State Highway 71 Marble Falls (78654) ***(G-14747)***
Legacy Vulcan LLC 325 646-8526
377 S Brady Hwy Brownwood (76801) ***(G-2435)***
Legacy Vulcan LLC 830 278-6205
Hwy 90 W Fm 1022 Uvalde (78801) ***(G-20190)***
Legacy Vulcan LLC 254 629-2850
702 County Road 442 Eastland (76448) ***(G-5566)***
Legacy Vulcan LLC 817 594-4524
1111 Gilbert Pit Rd Millsap (76066) ***(G-15504)***
Legacy Vulcan LLC 325 676-0001
6301 E Hwy 80 Abilene (79601) ***(G-57)***
Legacy Vulcan LLC 210 349-3311
800 Isom Rd Ste 300 San Antonio (78216) ***(G-18242)***
Legacy Vulcan LLC 830 934-2625
10503 E Us Highway 90 Knippa (78870) ***(G-13661)***
Legacy Vulcan LLC 956 831-8888
10905 Rl Ostos Rd Brownsville (78521) ***(G-2376)***
Legacy Vulcan LLC 325 529-3785
14500 County Road 224 Abilene (79602) ***(G-58)***
Legacy Vulcan LLC 210 492-1053
12307 Huebner Rd San Antonio (78230) ***(G-18243)***
Legal Directories Pubg Co 214 321-3238
1313 Oates Dr Mesquite (75150) ***(G-15058)***
Legant Interior Inc 713 784-2647
7914 Westglen Dr Houston (77063) ***(G-10621)***
Legend Aircraft Mfg LP 903 885-7000
1810 Piper Ln Sulphur Springs (75482) ***(G-19591)***
Legend Energy Services LLC 432 523-6585
212 Nw 2000 Andrews (79714) ***(G-549)***
Legend Marine Mangement LLC 870 481-6750
107 Fm 3059 Streetman (75859) ***(G-19435)***
Legerity Holdings Inc 512 228-5400
4509 Freidrich Ln Ste 200 Austin (78744) ***(G-1288)***
Leggett & Platt Incorporated 817 378-0108
2107 Franklin Dr Fort Worth (76106) ***(G-6782)***
Leggett & Platt Incorporated 817 626-6690
307 W 7th St Ste 1800 Fort Worth (76102) ***(G-6783)***
Leggett & Platt Incorporated 214 391-3181
440 Hillburn Dr Dallas (75217) ***(G-4590)***
Leggett & Platt 0117, Fort Worth *Also called Leggett & Platt Incorporated* ***(G-6784)***
Leggett & Platt Incorporated 817 922-5000
5000 South Fwy Fort Worth (76115) ***(G-6784)***
Leggett & Platt Incorporated 972 875-8401
4100 S Interstate 45 Ennis (75119) ***(G-6109)***
Lehigh Cement Company LLC (HQ) **877 534-4442**
300 E John Carpenter Fwy Irving (75062) ***(G-13085)***
Lehigh Cement Company LLC 254 776-7162
100 Wickson Rd Waco (76712) ***(G-20425)***
Lehigh Cement Company LLC 254 772-9350
100 Wickson Rd Waco (76712) ***(G-20426)***
Lehigh Hanson Inc 713 466-6306
11201 Fm 529 Rd Houston (77041) ***(G-10622)***
Lehmberg Enterprises Inc 210 924-6811
919 Sw Military Dr # 100 San Antonio (78221) ***(G-18244)***
Leidos Inc 210 731-1438
1777 Ne Loop 410 Ste 912 San Antonio (78217) ***(G-18245)***
Leightner Electronics Inc 972 542-0176
1501 S Tennessee St McKinney (75069) ***(G-14952)***
Lektrotech Inc 972 225-2356
6800 Highway 66 Greenville (75402) ***(G-8082)***
Leland Southwest, Saginaw *Also called Bowlin Engineering Co* ***(G-17740)***
Leland Southwest, Saginaw *Also called L S W Mfg Inc* ***(G-17747)***
Leland Southwest, Saginaw *Also called Saginaw Machine Company* ***(G-17756)***
Lely Tank Waste Solutions LLC 800 367-5359
111 Lely Dr Troy (76579) ***(G-20029)***
Lemetrix Solutions LLC 281 381-0714
2800 Broadway St Ste C Pearland (77581) ***(G-16578)***
Lendflow Inc 512 265-1261
1525 Lakeville Dr Ste 121 Kingwood (77339) ***(G-13647)***
Lengston Corporation 713 757-1331
1010 Lamar St Ste 550 Houston (77002) ***(G-10623)***
Lengston Personnel, Houston *Also called Lengston Corporation* ***(G-10623)***
Lennox Industries Inc 806 412-4160
2435 S Loop 289 Ste 900 Lubbock (79423) ***(G-14436)***
Lennox International Inc 210 646-2399
10610 Sentinel St San Antonio (78217) ***(G-18246)***
Lennox International Inc (PA) **972 497-5000**
2140 Lake Park Blvd Richardson (75080) ***(G-17343)***
Lenoir M Josey Inc 713 526-3844
4202 Yoakum Blvd Houston (77006) ***(G-10624)***
Lenoir Water Transfer Inc 432 686-8200
400 E Loop 250 N Ste 107 Midland (79705) ***(G-15278)***
Lenorah Operators LLC 432 684-9822
5003 E State Highway 158 Midland (79706) ***(G-15279)***
Lenotre Bakery, Houston *Also called Martech Foods Inc* ***(G-10775)***
Lenscrafters, Austin *Also called Luxottica of America Inc* ***(G-1313)***
Leo Hicks Creosoting Co Inc 936 858-4419
11840 Us Highway 69 S Alto (75925) ***(G-317)***
Leon's Texas Cuisine, McKinney *Also called Leons Fine Foods Inc* ***(G-14953)***
Leonard & Harral Packing Co (HQ) **210 532-3241**
2001 S Laredo St San Antonio (78207) ***(G-18247)***
Leonard Elc Pdts Co Texas Inc 956 350-5650
2600 Old Alice Rd Ste E Brownsville (78521) ***(G-2377)***
Leonard Holding Company (HQ) **210 532-3241**
2001 S Laredo St San Antonio (78207) ***(G-18248)***
Leonard Ray Vaught 903 572-0352
1182 County Road 3425 Cookville (75558) ***(G-3405)***
Leonard Sloan & Associates Inc 214 350-2440
2720 Manor Way Dallas (75235) ***(G-4591)***
Leonard's Service Center, Breckenridge *Also called Breckenridge Auto & Engine Sup* ***(G-2224)***
Leons Fine Foods Inc (PA) **972 529-5050**
2100 Redbud Blvd McKinney (75069) ***(G-14953)***
Leons Signs Inc 903 597-7731
851 E Northeast Loop 323 Tyler (75708) ***(G-20112)***
Leopard Media LLC 713 993-9320
4545 Post Oak Place Dr # 210 Houston (77027) ***(G-10625)***
Lepco, Brownsville *Also called Leonard Elc Pdts Co Texas Inc* ***(G-2377)***
lesco Distributing Inc 972 446-1605
1628 W Crosby Rd Ste 115 Carrollton (75006) ***(G-2776)***
Letco Group LLC 817 490-6655
7761 Justin Rd Double Oak (75077) ***(G-5496)***
Letco Group LLC 972 274-2835
3150 S I 35 E Lancaster (75146) ***(G-13844)***
Letco Group LLC 409 584-2155
U S Hwy 96 Pineland (75968) ***(G-16740)***
Letco Group LLC 713 466-7360
5802 Crawford Rd Houston (77041) ***(G-10626)***
Letco Group LLC (PA) **972 506-8575**
1901 Cal Crossing Rd Dallas (75220) ***(G-4592)***
Letco Group LLC 972 869-4332
1901 California Xing Dallas (75220) ***(G-4593)***
Letco Group LLC 281 342-6113
1700 E Highway 90a Richmond (77406) ***(G-17461)***
Letco Group LLC 281 537-2377
12202 Cutten Rd Houston (77066) ***(G-10627)***
Letco Group LLC 281 431-3400
16138 Highway 6 Rosharon (77583) ***(G-17607)***
LEtoile Apparel Inc 972 701-8916
7503 Maribeth Dr Dallas (75252) ***(G-3848)***
Letourneau Lflike Orthtics Prs (PA) **409 832-5005**
2452 Calder St Beaumont (77702) ***(G-1917)***
Letourneau Tech Amer Inc 903 237-7000
2400 Macarthur St Longview (75602) ***(G-14264)***
Lets Gel Inc 512 628-1709
501 Precision Dr Waco (76710) ***(G-20427)***
Lets Gel Inc (PA) **512 628-1700**
11525b Stnholw Dr 200 Austin (78758) ***(G-1289)***
Levan Group I LP 713 528-3838
3100 Travis St Houston (77006) ***(G-10628)***
Level Up Transportation LLC 214 210-0701
405 State Highway 121 Byp Lewisville (75067) ***(G-14061)***

Levelfieldcom Inc 512 401-9200
8705 Shoal Creek Blvd # 205 Austin (78757) *(G-1290)*

Levelland Hockley News Press, Levelland *Also called Hockley County Publishing
Co* *(G-14009)*

Leverage Machine & Fabrication, Port Lavaca *Also called Endeavour Machine and Fab
Inc* *(G-17146)*

Levi Strauss & Co 817 262-6314
1600 Solana Blvd Ste 8200 Roanoke (76262) *(G-17488)*

Levi Strauss North America, Roanoke *Also called Levi Strauss & Co* *(G-17488)*

Lewis & Lambert LLLP 817 834-7146
5936 Eden Dr Haltom City (76117) *(G-8150)*

Lewis Casing Crews Inc (PA) **432 366-8077**
8931 Andrews Hwy Odessa (79765) *(G-16061)*

Lewis Company, Dallas *Also called J Lewis Partners LP* *(G-4519)*

Lewis Energy Group LP 956 728-6000
3 4 Mi W Hwy 44 Encinal (78019) *(G-6086)*

Lewis Engineering Company 903 938-6754
1608 E Houston St Marshall (75670) *(G-14787)*

Lewis Manufacturing Co, Dallas *Also called Creative Wood Concepts Inc* *(G-4184)*

Lewis Operating Co 940 723-0266
105 S E Ave Holliday (76366) *(G-8352)*

Lewis Petro Properties Inc 210 384-3200
10101 Reunion Pl Ste 1000 San Antonio (78216) *(G-18249)*

Lewis Sign Builders Inc 512 312-4555
16910 Interstate 35 Buda (78610) *(G-2532)*

Lewis, Larry, Holliday *Also called Lewis Operating Co* *(G-8352)*

Lewis-Quinn Cnstr Svcs Inc (PA) **936 321-8111**
11355 Highway 242 Conroe (77385) *(G-3319)*

Lexmark International Inc 214 257-0001
5215 N O Connor Blvd # 480 Irving (75039) *(G-13086)*

Lexus Group Inc 682 323-5942
6407 S Cooper St Ste 137b Arlington (76001) *(G-720)*

LFC Industries Inc 817 640-1322
1221 W Corporate Dr Arlington (76006) *(G-721)*

Lfm Industries Inc 713 928-5281
117 N Palmer St Houston (77003) *(G-10629)*

Lfn LLC 956 330-6838
203 N Arroyo Blvd Los Fresnos (78566) *(G-14347)*

Lft Panels Inc 713 984-9878
1606 Crestdale Dr Houston (77080) *(G-10630)*

Lg Electronics Alabama Inc 956 784-6500
3805 Plantation Grv Mission (78572) *(G-15559)*

Lgc US Asset Holdings LLC (PA) **713 222-0284**
7300 Airport Blvd Houston (77061) *(G-10631)*

Lgc US Holdings LLC 713 222-0284
7300 Airport Blvd Houston (77061) *(G-10632)*

LGS Technologies LP 972 224-9201
2950 W Wintergreen Rd Lancaster (75134) *(G-13845)*

Lhcn Inc (PA) **972 424-6565**
624 Krona Dr Ste 170 Plano (75074) *(G-16908)*

Lhoist North America Inc 830 625-2327
350 Apg Ln New Braunfels (78132) *(G-15809)*

Lhoist North America Inc 214 544-1717
205 S Mcdonald St McKinney (75069) *(G-14954)*

Lhoist North America Ala LLC (HQ) **817 732-8164**
5600 Clearfork Main St # 300 Fort Worth (76109) *(G-6785)*

Lhoist North America Ala LLC 817 268-1187
3110 S Precinct Line Rd Hurst (76053) *(G-12849)*

Lhoist North America MO Inc (HQ) **817 732-8164**
5600 Clearfork Main St # 300 Fort Worth (76109) *(G-6786)*

Lhoist North America Tenn Inc 254 486-2105
8759 5th St Crawford (76638) *(G-3704)*

Lhoist North America Tenn Inc 817 732-8164
5600 Clearfrk Main St 3 # 300 Fort Worth (76109) *(G-6787)*

Lhoist North America Texas Ltd 254 698-6610
11714 Highway Fm 439 Nolanville (76559) *(G-15871)*

Lhoist North America Texas Ltd 830 625-2327
350 Apg Ln New Braunfels (78132) *(G-15810)*

Lhoist North America Texas Ltd 512 756-8668
7829 S Us Highway 281 Burnet (78611) *(G-2611)*

Lhoist North America Texas Ltd 817 732-8164
3110 S Precinct Line Rd Hurst (76053) *(G-12850)*

Libcon Inc (PA) **956 724-6459**
8016 Killam Indus Blvd Laredo (78045) *(G-13907)*

Liberto Fun Foods, San Antonio *Also called Liberto Management Co Inc* *(G-18250)*

Liberto Management Co Inc 210 226-4167
830 S Presa St San Antonio (78210) *(G-18250)*

Liberty A&A 213 221-8110
24385 Wilderness Oak San Antonio (78258) *(G-18251)*

Liberty Cards LP 214 646-9923
2020 Singleton Blvd Dallas (75212) *(G-4594)*

Liberty Carton Co - Texas 817 577-6100
5100 Glenview Dr Haltom City (76117) *(G-8151)*

Liberty Company 817 921-0218
101 W Felix Fort Worth (76115) *(G-6788)*

Liberty County Precinct 4, Dayton *Also called County Barn Precinct 4* *(G-5224)*

Liberty Fishing Rentl Tls Inc 432 381-0551
313 E 96th St Odessa (79765) *(G-16062)*

Liberty Fluid Power Inc 972 623-0927
214 Nw 25th St Grand Prairie (75050) *(G-7911)*

Liberty Forge Inc 936 336-5785
1507 Fort Worth St Liberty (77575) *(G-14121)*

Liberty Label Company Inc 830 549-5459
964 E Kingsbury St Seguin (78155) *(G-18849)*

Liberty Lift Solutions LLC 713 575-2300
16420 Park Ten Pl Ste 300 Houston (77084) *(G-10633)*

Liberty Mask LLC 214 915-2133
8501 W State Highway 158 Midland (79707) *(G-15280)*

Liberty Materials Inc (PA) **281 572-4003**
18214 E River Rd Conroe (77302) *(G-3320)*

Liberty Packaging, Haltom City *Also called Liberty Carton Co - Texas* *(G-8151)*

Liberty Plant Maintenance Inc 281 923-5307
1939 Trinity St Liberty (77575) *(G-14122)*

Liberty Playing Cards LP 214 252-8175
1100 Avenue T Grand Prairie (75050) *(G-7912)*

Liberty Precision Company LLC 281 861-5530
12715 Fm 529 Rd Houston (77041) *(G-10634)*

Liberty Rverse Units Rentl Tls, Odessa *Also called Liberty Fishing Rentl Tls Inc* *(G-16062)*

Liberty Sand & Gravel Inc 972 924-8065
500 Highview Ln Anna (75409) *(G-584)*

Liberty Signs Inc 512 255-3887
1300 W Industrial Blvd B Round Rock (78681) *(G-17669)*

Liberty Tower & Flare Inc 281 339-1410
4815 6th St Bacliff (77518) *(G-1734)*

Libra Industries LLC 972 664-0900
1250 American Pkwy Richardson (75081) *(G-17344)*

Libra Leasing, Laredo *Also called Libcon Inc* *(G-13907)*

Libredigital Inc (HQ) **512 334-5100**
1835 Kramer Ln Ste B150 Austin (78758) *(G-1291)*

License Plates of Texas LLC 512 583-8585
7301 N Fm 620 Rd Ste 155 Austin (78726) *(G-1292)*

Lichtgitter Usa Inc 844 548-7911
12818 N Lake Houston Pkwy Houston (77044) *(G-10635)*

Liddell Industries Inc 325 646-7581
4306 Highway 377 S Brownwood (76801) *(G-2436)*

Lide Industries LLC (HQ) **254 562-0233**
2701 W Interstate 20 Odessa (79766) *(G-16063)*

Lide Industries LLC 254 562-0233
114 W Hillyard Rd Troy (76579) *(G-20030)*

Life Gas, San Antonio *Also called Linde Gas North America LLC* *(G-18252)*

Life Technologies, Austin *Also called Ambion Diagnostics Inc* *(G-912)*

Life Technologies Corporation 512 721-4857
2130 Woodward St Austin (78744) *(G-1293)*

Life-Tech Inc (PA) **281 491-6600**
365 Piney Point Rd Houston (77024) *(G-10636)*

Lifegas, Houston *Also called Linde Gas North America LLC* *(G-10645)*

Lifegas, Tyler *Also called Linde Gas North America LLC* *(G-20114)*

Lifegas, Temple *Also called Linde Gas North America LLC* *(G-19684)*

Lifelast Inc 512 628-2112
3813 Helios Way Ste 190 Pflugerville (78660) *(G-16679)*

Lifesells USA, Addison *Also called Yj USA Corp* *(G-175)*

Lifetime Filter Inc 281 391-8060
1005 Katyland Dr Katy (77493) *(G-13423)*

Lifoam Industries LLC 972 937-6512
1600 W Hwy 287 Byp Waxahachie (75165) *(G-20551)*

Lift Moore Inc 713 688-5533
7810 Pinemont Dr Houston (77040) *(G-10637)*

Lift-All Company Inc 281 445-2256
16803 Hedgecroft Dr Houston (77060) *(G-10638)*

Liftex Corporation 713 863-0900
7266 Wynnpark Dr Houston (77008) *(G-10639)*

Light & Champion Publishing (PA) **936 598-3377**
137 San Augustine St Center (75935) *(G-3002)*

Light Emtting Dds-Nlimited LLC 512 267-7315
3300 Parliament Cv Lago Vista (78645) *(G-13806)*

Light Gauge Solutions Inc 682 564-0378
1100 Eden Rd Arlington (76001) *(G-722)*

Light House Candles LLC (HQ) **713 467-4774**
1601 Gillingham Ln # 120 Sugar Land (77478) *(G-19504)*

Light House Home Products, Sugar Land *Also called Light House Candles LLC* *(G-19504)*

Lighthouse Converting, Dallas *Also called Lighthouse Distribution Inc* *(G-4595)*

Lighthouse Distribution Inc 214 630-1630
2176 French Settlement Rd Dallas (75212) *(G-4595)*

Lighthouse For The Blind, Austin *Also called Travis Assn For The Blind* *(G-1590)*

LIGHTHOUSE OF HOUSTON, Houston *Also called Lighthuse For The Blind Huston* *(G-10640)*

Lighthouse Seafood, Port Lavaca *Also called Palacios Processors Inc* *(G-17153)*

Lighthuse For The Blind Huston (PA) **713 284-8420**
3602 W Dallas St Houston (77019) *(G-10640)*

Lighting & Power Tech LLC 877 666-5267
7101 Whisperfield Dr Plano (75024) *(G-16909)*

Lighting Etc Inc 281 992-8308
8575 County Rd 128 Pearland (77584) *(G-16579)*

Lighting One, Conroe *Also called Carols Lighting and Fan Sp Inc* *(G-3274)*

Lightning Bolt & Supply Inc 713 920-2525
211 W Harris Ave Pasadena (77506) *(G-16473)*

Lightning Fluid Services Inc...361 396-0801
1310 Southwood St Alice (78332) *(G-224)*
Lightning Oilfield Svcs Inc...817 439-5558
9309 W I 20 Midland (79706) *(G-15281)*
Lightning Oilfield Svcs Inc (PA)...**817 439-5558**
11830 N Saginaw Blvd Saginaw (76179) *(G-17748)*
Lights Fantastic, Carrollton *Also called Fleco Industries LLC (G-2739)*
Lights Fantastic Pro...469 568-1111
2525 E State Highway 121 Lewisville (75056) *(G-14062)*
Lightside Games Inc...650 814-0293
1250 S Capital Of Texas H West Lake Hills (78746) *(G-20683)*
Lil' Dutch Maid Cookies, Abilene *Also called Abimar Foods Inc (G-8)*
Lilis Energy Inc (PA)...**817 585-9001**
201 Main St Ste 700 Fort Worth (76102) *(G-6789)*
Lilly Construction Inc...325 392-2669
603 Ave H Ozona (76943) *(G-16285)*
Lilly Machinery Inc...903 561-6733
10259 County Road 2213 Tyler (75707) *(G-20113)*
Lily of Desert Nutraceuitical, Denton *Also called O D C L Inc (G-5385)*
Lily of The Desert, Mercedes *Also called O D C L Inc (G-15009)*
Lilyrain Jewelry LLC (PA)...**713 467-5459**
8820b Wayfarer Ln Houston (77075) *(G-10641)*
Lima Refining Company...409 839-3500
9405 W Port Arthur Rd Beaumont (77705) *(G-1918)*
Lima Refining Company...409 985-1000
1801 Gulfway Dr Port Arthur (77640) *(G-17116)*
Lima Usa Inc...817 385-0777
2001 Ne Green Oaks Blvd Arlington (76006) *(G-723)*
Lime Holding Inc (HQ)...**817 732-8164**
3700 Hulen St Fort Worth (76107) *(G-6790)*
Lime Instrument, Houston *Also called Supreme Electrical Svcs Inc (G-12122)*
Lime Rock Resources A LP...713 292-9510
1111 Bagby St Ste 4600 Houston (77002) *(G-10642)*
Lime Rock Resources Iv-A LP...713 292-9500
1111 Bagby St Ste 4600 Houston (77002) *(G-10643)*
Limestone Exploration II LLC...432 695-6970
901 W Missouri Ave Midland (79701) *(G-15282)*
Lincoln Lumber LLC...409 384-2587
2500 Us Highway 96 S Jasper (75951) *(G-13278)*
Lincoln Lumber LLC (PA)...**936 539-4421**
1390 Fm 1314 Conroe (77301) *(G-3321)*
Lincoln Manufacturing Inc...713 514-0059
5301 Polk St Houston (77023) *(G-10644)*
Lincoln Manufacturing Inc (PA)...**281 252-9494**
31209 Fm 2978 Rd Magnolia (77354) *(G-14615)*
Lincoln Manufacturing Inc...281 357-1541
31209 2978 Rd Magnolia (77354) *(G-14616)*
Lincoln Press, Dallas *Also called Tejas Vsual Communications Inc (G-5047)*
Linde Gas North America LLC...866 543-3427
15150 Nautique Way Houston (77047) *(G-10645)*
Linde Gas North America LLC (PA)...**713 767-4100**
11603 Strang Rd La Porte (77571) *(G-13768)*
Linde Gas North America LLC...210 287-9788
5810 Rocky Pt San Antonio (78249) *(G-18252)*
Linde Gas North America LLC...903 939-0613
2107 Broussard St Tyler (75701) *(G-20114)*
Linde Gas North America LLC...254 718-5124
3301 Charter Oak Dr Temple (76502) *(G-19684)*
Linde Inc...281 478-1500
622 Tidal Rd Deer Park (77536) *(G-5282)*
Linde Inc...325 643-5813
813 Early Blvd Brownwood (76802) *(G-2437)*
Linde Inc...972 271-1531
2225 Lonnecker Dr Garland (75041) *(G-7537)*
Linde Inc...210 489-5800
1077 Central Pkwy S # 600 San Antonio (78232) *(G-18253)*
Linde Inc...409 963-0141
6710 Hogaboom Rd Groves (77619) *(G-8109)*
Linde Inc...281 471-4585
100 Strang Rd La Porte (77571) *(G-13769)*
Linde Inc...409 943-9280
2800s Loop 197 N Texas City (77590) *(G-19796)*
Linde Inc...281 203-3600
1585 Sawdust Rd Ste 300 Spring (77380) *(G-19227)*
Linde Inc...409 835-3939
3077 Calder St Beaumont (77702) *(G-1919)*
Linde Inc...979 774-0638
3030 E 29th St Ste 112 Bryan (77802) *(G-2490)*
Lindemann Drilling Co Inc...940 691-1344
518 N Center St Archer City (76351) *(G-596)*
Linden Steel LP...972 285-0200
12418 Fm 1641 Forney (75126) *(G-6312)*
Lindsay Forest Products Inc...903 693-7526
2113 Se Loop Carthage (75633) *(G-2913)*
Lindsayca Inc...713 467-9560
1602 Peach Leaf St Houston (77039) *(G-10646)*
Lindsey's Custom Upholstery, Houston *Also called Lindseys NW Off Furn Inc (G-10647)*
Lindseys NW Off Furn Inc (PA)...**713 957-2424**
12230 Northwest Fwy Houston (77092) *(G-10647)*
Lindsyca Oil Gas Int Solutions, Houston *Also called Lindsayca Inc (G-10646)*
Line Quest LLC...432 218-4980
7607 W Industrial Ave Midland (79706) *(G-15283)*
Line-X of West Ft Worth, Benbrook *Also called Friedson Hill Inc (G-2039)*
Lineage LLC...806 688-7384
11784 Highway 152 Pampa (79065) *(G-16327)*
Link Training & Simulation, Arlington *Also called L3 Technologies Inc (G-714)*
Link Training & Simulation, Arlington *Also called L3 Technologies Inc (G-715)*
Link World Technologies, Addison *Also called Link World Trade Inc (G-145)*
Link World Trade Inc...972 713-8000
3801 Arapaho Rd Addison (75001) *(G-145)*
Linn Acquisition Company LLC...281 840-4000
600 Travis St Ste 4900 Houston (77002) *(G-10648)*
Linn Energy Inc (HQ)...**281 840-4000**
600 Travis St Houston (77002) *(G-10649)*
Linn Energy Inc...405 241-2200
600 Travis St Ste 1400 Houston (77002) *(G-10650)*
Linn Energy Finance Corp...281 840-4000
600 Travis St Ste 5100 Houston (77002) *(G-10651)*
Linn Energy Holdings LLC (HQ)...**806 274-3074**
Jpmorgan Chase Twr 600 Tr Houston (77002) *(G-10652)*
Linnco LLC (PA)...**281 840-4000**
600 Travis St Ste 5100 Houston (77002) *(G-10653)*
Linux Tech Inc...972 907-0871
5050 Quorum Dr 700-360 Dallas (75254) *(G-4596)*
Lion Elastomers Orange LLC...409 924-4500
5713 Farm To Mkt Rd 1006 Orange (77630) *(G-16252)*
Lion Share LLP...281 888-5383
213 E Hamilton St Houston (77076) *(G-10654)*
Lippert Components Inc...972 232-3119
101 Mushroom Rd Waxahachie (75165) *(G-20552)*
Liquid Litigation MGT Inc...210 757-4881
1300 Guadalupe St Ste 100 Austin (78701) *(G-1294)*
Liquid Minerals, Huntsville *Also called Pilot Chemical Company Ohio (G-12822)*
Liquid Minerals Group Ltd...936 291-2424
37 Fm 2793 Rd Huntsville (77340) *(G-12816)*
Liquid Motors Inc...214 393-2323
1755 N Collins Blvd # 109 Richardson (75080) *(G-17345)*
Liquid-Stone Concrete...817 295-5151
221 Centre Dr Burleson (76028) *(G-2587)*
Liquidmtal Ctngs Solutions LLC (PA)...**281 359-1283**
20404 Whitewood Dr Spring (77373) *(G-19141)*
Lisam America Inc...979 307-7384
3091 University Dr E # 430 Bryan (77802) *(G-2491)*
Lisco LLP...806 762-5126
2101 E 50th St Lubbock (79404) *(G-14437)*
Lisco Tents, Lubbock *Also called Liscosports LLC (G-14438)*
Liscosports LLC...806 762-5126
2101 E 50th St Lubbock (79404) *(G-14438)*
Lisle Violin Shop (PA)...**281 487-7303**
4510 Burke Rd Ste A Pasadena (77504) *(G-16474)*
Listo Inc...469 544-4555
1025 W Commerce St Dallas (75208) *(G-4597)*
Lithic Industries Inc (PA)...**254 793-3791**
3450 Fm 2843 Florence (76527) *(G-6240)*
Litho Press Inc...210 333-1711
4334 Milling Rd San Antonio (78219) *(G-18254)*
Lithographics Inc...210 226-1722
500 N Alamo St San Antonio (78215) *(G-18255)*
Lithotripters Inc...888 252-6575
9825 Spectrum Dr Bldg 3 Austin (78717) *(G-1702)*
Littelfuse Inc...830 513-8775
1025 Adams Cir Eagle Pass (78852) *(G-5549)*
Little Green Apples Inc (PA)...**956 668-0028**
2201 W Dove Ave Ste 1 McAllen (78504) *(G-14885)*
Littlefield Brothers Con Cnstr...281 399-1488
15285 Fm 1485 Rd Conroe (77306) *(G-3322)*
Littlefield Brothers Mini Stor, Conroe *Also called Littlefield Brothers Con Cnstr (G-3322)*
Livanova Usa Inc (HQ)...**281 228-7200**
100 Cyberonics Blvd # 600 Houston (77058) *(G-10655)*
Live Oak Brewing Company LLC...512 385-2299
1615 Crozier Ln Del Valle (78617) *(G-5332)*
Live Oak Materials Inc...361 775-0065
Garrett Rd And Fm 2725 Ingleside (78362) *(G-12896)*
Live Soda LLC...512 888-9959
4020 S Industrial Dr # 133 Austin (78744) *(G-1295)*
Live Soda Kombucha, Austin *Also called Live Soda LLC (G-1295)*
Livengood Feeds Inc (PA)...**512 398-2351**
300 N Colorado St Lockhart (78644) *(G-14170)*
Liveo, Austin *Also called Kudzookinect Inc (G-1274)*
Living Company Holdings LLC...469 687-8991
2149 S Jupiter Rd Garland (75041) *(G-7538)*
Living Earth, Dallas *Also called Letco Group LLC (G-4592)*
Living Earth, Richmond *Also called Letco Group LLC (G-17461)*
Living Earth Technology, Lancaster *Also called Letco Group LLC (G-13844)*
Living Earth Technology Co, Houston *Also called Letco Group LLC (G-10626)*
Living Stream...972 257-1166
3600 Esters Rd Irving (75062) *(G-13087)*

Living Stream Ministry, Irving *Also called Living Stream (G-13087)*

Livingstone, Austin *Also called US Surface Warehouse (G-1617)*

Ljt Texas LLC 254 771-2253
   3601 Eberhardt Rd Temple (76504) *(G-19685)*

Lk252, Flower Mound *Also called Ruby Red Paint Inc (G-6279)*

Llano Estacado Winery Inc (PA) **806 745-2258**
   3426 E Fm 1585 Lubbock (79452) *(G-14439)*

Llano Operating Corporation 972 677-7690
   5944 Luther Ln Ste 1003 Dallas (75225) *(G-4598)*

Llanos Altos LLC 806 934-4534
   5901 W Road I Dumas (79029) *(G-5524)*

LLC, Dallas *Also called Southwest Diamond Cutters Inc (G-4989)*

LLC Battle Beaver 888 390-4363
   1161 Executive Dr W Richardson (75081) *(G-17346)*

LLC Huber Land 936 347-2744
   703 N Us Highway 59 Garrison (75946) *(G-7612)*

Llebroc Industries Inc 817 831-3158
   3601 Conway St Fort Worth (76111) *(G-6791)*

Llm, Austin *Also called Liquid Litigation MGT Inc (G-1294)*

Llog Exploration Company LLC 281 752-1100
   842 W Sam Houston Pkwy N Houston (77024) *(G-10656)*

Lloyd Company 281 590-8023
   14905 Willis St Houston (77039) *(G-10657)*

Lloyd's, Canton *Also called Valero Energy Corporation (G-2661)*

Lloyds Register Drilling Inte 281 675-3100
   1330 Enclave Pkwy Ste 200 Houston (77077) *(G-10658)*

LLT Inc 830 995-3465
   120 Hermann Sons Rd Comfort (78013) *(G-3239)*

LMC FABRICATION SERVICES, Longview *Also called Longview Mechanical Contrs Inc (G-14270)*

Lmp Readymix LLC 903 572-2500
   775 E 16th St Mount Pleasant (75455) *(G-15653)*

LMS Acquisitions LLC 512 371-7028
   2032 Centimeter Cir Austin (78758) *(G-1296)*

LMS Fulfillment, Austin *Also called LMS Acquisitions LLC (G-1296)*

Lmt Rustic & Western Imports 972 641-6700
   2920 N State Highway 360 # 200 Grand Prairie (75050) *(G-7913)*

Lnc Fabrication LLC 409 769-0403
   17970 Ih 10 Vidor (77662) *(G-20329)*

LNG Freeport Development L P (PA) **713 980-2888**
   333 Clay St Ste 5050 Houston (77002) *(G-10659)*

Load Systems Distribution, Houston *Also called Load Systems International (G-10660)*

Load Systems International 281 664-1330
   9633 Zaka Rd Houston (77064) *(G-10660)*

Loadcraft Industries Ltd 325 646-7581
   4306 Highway 377 S Brownwood (76801) *(G-2438)*

Loadcraft Industries Ltd (PA) **325 597-2911**
   3811 N Bridge St Brady (76825) *(G-2214)*

Loadcraft Industries Ltd 325 597-1930
   3811 N Brg Brady (76825) *(G-2215)*

Loadrite Inc 940 322-1003
   3014 Seymour Rd Wichita Falls (76309) *(G-20779)*

Lobato Studio LLC 512 483-1327
   1300 W Anderson Ln Austin (78757) *(G-1297)*

Lobo Tortilla Factory Inc 972 388-8000
   7777 Hines Pl Dallas (75235) *(G-4599)*

Lobo Tubing Tester Inc 432 943-5441
   1203 S Dwight Ave Monahans (79756) *(G-15608)*

Lobo Ventures Ltd 210 525-9595
   12027 Warfield St San Antonio (78216) *(G-18256)*

Lobues Rubber Stamp Co 713 652-0031
   1228 Mcgowen St Houston (77004) *(G-10661)*

Local Cuts Meat Company LLC 972 489-3832
   3620 Lakeside Dr Rockwall (75087) *(G-17555)*

Local Oven, Farmers Branch *Also called Bakeryworks LLC (G-6190)*

Local Phone Book 409 386-2244
   1250 Highway 96 S Silsbee (77656) *(G-18953)*

Lock Dock Inc 903 759-1288
   3506 W Loop 281 101 Longview (75604) *(G-14265)*

Lock Joint Tube LLC 254 771-2253
   3601 Eberhardt Rd Temple (76504) *(G-19686)*

Locke Investments LLC 832 804-7062
   700 Almeda Genoa Rd Houston (77047) *(G-10662)*

Locke Solutions, Houston *Also called Locke Investments LLC (G-10662)*

Lockhart Fine Foods, Lockhart *Also called Dgg Group LLC (G-14166)*

Lockhart Truss Co Inc 512 398-5300
   1505 Blackjack St Lockhart (78644) *(G-14171)*

Lockheed Martin 281 283-4400
   2625 Bay Area Blvd Houston (77058) *(G-10663)*

Lockheed Martin Corporation 972 603-1000
   1902 W Freeway St Grand Prairie (75051) *(G-7914)*

Lockheed Martin Corporation 210 736-6461
   4243 E Piedras Dr Ste 100 San Antonio (78228) *(G-18257)*

Lockheed Martin Corporation 817 763-3035
   1029 Lindstrom Dr Fort Worth (76131) *(G-6792)*

Lockheed Martin Corporation 281 283-4400
   18108 Point Lookout Dr A Houston (77058) *(G-10664)*

Lockheed Martin Corporation 281 335-2318
   4943 Mountain Timber Dr Friendswood (77546) *(G-7248)*

Lockheed Martin Corporation 817 655-8672
   3821 Ruth Rd Richland Hills (76118) *(G-17440)*

Lockheed Martin Corporation 817 763-2663
   4707 Mill Crossing W Colleyville (76034) *(G-3219)*

Lockheed Martin Corporation 281 218-3000
   1300 Hercules Ave Ste 100 Houston (77058) *(G-10665)*

Lockheed Martin Corporation 817 935-1363
   6937 Aspen Wood Trl Fort Worth (76132) *(G-6793)*

Lockheed Martin Corporation 210 581-6100
   1777 Ne Loop 410 Ste 912 San Antonio (78217) *(G-18258)*

Lockheed Martin Corporation 281 853-3000
   595 Gemini St Houston (77058) *(G-10666)*

Lockheed Martin Corporation 817 495-0200
   7000 Calmont Ave Fort Worth (76116) *(G-6794)*

Lockheed Martin Corporation 817 777-2000
   1 Lockheed Blvd Bldg 10 Fort Worth (76108) *(G-6795)*

Lockheed Martin Corporation 210 729-8600
   3203 General Hudnell Dr San Antonio (78226) *(G-18259)*

Lockheed Martin Corporation 210 445-5628
   485 Quentin Roosevelt Rd San Antonio (78226) *(G-18260)*

Lockheed Martin Corporation 817 777-2000
   Wilcox Plz 7000 Clmt Ave Wilcox Plaza Fort Worth (76116) *(G-6796)*

Lockheed Martin Corporation 334 347-4472
   4601 Jacobs Ln Killeen (76543) *(G-13615)*

Lockheed Martin Corporation 254 285-5503
   62nd Nrth Ave Bldg 26011 Fort Hood (76544) *(G-6325)*

Lockheed Martin Corporation 915 568-6264
   Abernathy Rd Bldg 5808 Fort Bliss (79916) *(G-6317)*

Lockheed Martin Corporation 817 763-4246
   810 Clearwater Ln Keller (76248) *(G-13468)*

Lockheed Martin Corporation 817 777-0786
   7501 Calmont Ave Fort Worth (76116) *(G-6797)*

Lockheed Martin Corporation 915 852-1100
   1 Ltv Dr El Paso (79928) *(G-5845)*

Lockheed Martin Corporation 432 358-4474
   21 Miles W Of Mrfa Hwy 90 Marfa (79843) *(G-14753)*

Lockheed Martin Corporation 281 218-6021
   2625 Bay Area Blvd 7 Houston (77058) *(G-10667)*

Lockheed Martin Corporation 972 603-1000
   1701 W Marshall Dr Grand Prairie (75051) *(G-7915)*

Lockheed Martin Corporation 817 777-4242
   2109 Amon Ct Azle (76020) *(G-1726)*

Lockheed Martin Corporation 817 777-2000
   6116 Southwest Blvd Benbrook (76109) *(G-2042)*

Lockheed Martin Corporation 817 777-2000
   6100 Western Pl Ste 700 Fort Worth (76107) *(G-6798)*

Lockheed Martin Corporation 956 425-4447
   2800 Airport Dr Harlingen (78550) *(G-8193)*

Lockheed Martin Corporation 210 581-6100
   1777 Ne Loop 410 Ste 300 San Antonio (78217) *(G-18261)*

Lockheed Martin Corporation 936 633-4800
   1008 N John Redditt Dr Lufkin (75904) *(G-14532)*

Lockheed Martin Missiles, Grand Prairie *Also called Lockheed Martin Corporation (G-7914)*

Lockheed Martin Space Company 281 283-4650
   2100 Park St Houston (77019) *(G-10668)*

Lockheed Martin Systems Co, Houston *Also called Lockheed Martin Space Company (G-10668)*

Lockheed Mrtin Crprtn-Rnautics, Fort Worth *Also called Lockheed Martin Corporation (G-6795)*

Lockheed Mrtin Space Oprations, Houston *Also called Lockheed Martin Corporation (G-10667)*

Lockney Beacon, Floydada *Also called Floyd County Hesperian-Beacon (G-6293)*

Loco Solutions LLC 817 437-6438
   5700 Sw 45th Ave Amarillo (79109) *(G-498)*

Lodor Enterprises Inc 214 651-1977
   635 Fort Worth Ave Dallas (75208) *(G-4600)*

LOEWS, Houston *Also called Diamond Offshore Drilling Inc (G-9453)*

Loftin Equipment Company 281 310-6858
   6113 Brittmoore Rd Houston (77041) *(G-10669)*

Loftin Mechanical Services, Crosby *Also called Jml Services Inc (G-3736)*

Loftus & Woosley Inc 214 631-1975
   8607 Ambtxdor Row Ste 190 Dallas (75247) *(G-4601)*

Loftwall Inc 214 239-3162
   2617 N Great Southwest Pk Grand Prairie (75050) *(G-7916)*

Logan Farms Inc (PA) **713 781-3773**
   1038 Winner Foster Rd Richmond (77406) *(G-17462)*

Logan Farms Honey Glazed Hams, Richmond *Also called Logan Farms Inc (G-17462)*

Logan Graphics, Grand Prairie *Also called Bdm Group LLC (G-7843)*

Logan International Inc 832 386-2500
   10613 W Sam Houston Pkwy Houston (77064) *(G-10670)*

Logan Oil Tools Inc (PA) **281 219-6613**
   11006 Lucerne St Houston (77016) *(G-10671)*

Loggins Meat Company Inc 903 595-1011
   1908 E Erwin St Tyler (75702) *(G-20115)*

Logic Control LLC 281 362-9600
   27331 Robinson Rd Conroe (77385) *(G-3323)*

Logic Services LLC............832 617-0805
800 Town And Country Blvd Houston (77024) *(G-10672)*
Logica North America, Houston *Also called Cgi Technologies Solutions Inc (G-9150)*
Logical Control Services LLP............972 820-0100
1421 Lemay Dr Carrollton (75007) *(G-2878)*
Logik Precision Inc............713 939-0061
5007 Steffani Ln Houston (77041) *(G-10673)*
Logitech Inc............512 347-9300
1601 S Mopac Expy Ste 100 Austin (78746) *(G-1298)*
Logitek Electronic Systems............713 664-4470
5622 Edgemoor Dr Houston (77081) *(G-10674)*
Logo Factory............972 642-4222
116 Nw 15th St Grand Prairie (75050) *(G-7917)*
Logo Masters LLC............830 822-8390
11031 Wye Dr Ste 108 San Antonio (78217) *(G-18262)*
Logo Pro, San Antonio *Also called Lone Star Special Tees LLC (G-18263)*
Logos In Thread, Harker Heights *Also called Military Customs LLC (G-8172)*
Lojack Corporation (HQ)............**781 302-4200**
2400 N Glnvlle Dr Ste 225 Richardson (75082) *(G-17347)*
Lojack Supply Chain Integrity, Richardson *Also called Sc-Integrity Inc (G-17393)*
Lok-Mor Inc............817 477-0232
661 Airport Dr Mansfield (76063) *(G-14685)*
Loloi Inc (PA)............**972 503-5656**
4501 Spring Valley Rd Dallas (75244) *(G-4602)*
Loloi Rugs, Dallas *Also called Loloi Inc (G-4602)*
Loma Rentals LLC (PA)............**817 964-1828**
433 Belle Grove Dr Richardson (75080) *(G-17348)*
Lomont Molding LLC............512 763-3600
107 Park Central Blvd Georgetown (78626) *(G-7660)*
Lone Star Aviation Corporation............682 518-8882
604 S Wisteria St Mansfield (76063) *(G-14686)*
Lone Star Bakery, Round Rock *Also called Round Rock Bakery Ltd (G-17686)*
Lone Star Bakery Inc (PA)............**210 648-6400**
6905 Us Highway 87 E China Grove (78263) *(G-3057)*
Lone Star Bakery Inc............210 648-6400
8100 Us Highway 87 E China Grove (78263) *(G-3058)*
Lone Star Beef Processors LP............325 658-5555
2150 E 37th St San Angelo (76903) *(G-17813)*
Lone Star Body Systems LLC............254 472-0852
1618 W Highway 84 Mexia (76667) *(G-15090)*
Lone Star Cast Mch Partners LP............903 986-8300
3102 Maverick Dr Kilgore (75662) *(G-13563)*
Lone Star Ceramics Company............972 247-3111
2408 Fruitland Ave Dallas (75234) *(G-4603)*
Lone Star Citrus Growers, Mission *Also called F and B Holdings LLC (G-15553)*
Lone Star Compressor Corp............713 947-9975
316 Old Course Dr Friendswood (77546) *(G-7249)*
Lone Star Container Sales Corp (PA)............**972 579-1551**
700 N Wildwood Dr Irving (75061) *(G-13088)*
Lone Star Corrosion Svcs Inc............281 955-1313
9216 Windmill Park Ln Houston (77064) *(G-10675)*
Lone Star Corrugated Cont Corp............972 579-1551
700 N Wildwood Dr Irving (75061) *(G-13089)*
Lone Star Cryogenics Inc............979 234-5001
500 Glen Flora Rd Eagle Lake (77434) *(G-5541)*
Lone Star Dairy Products LLC............806 567-5623
401 Highway 60 Canyon (79015) *(G-2673)*
Lone Star Emergency Group, Houston *Also called Hfj Group LLC (G-10168)*
Lone Star Fabrication, Willis *Also called S F L Inc (G-20863)*
Lone Star Faces Inc............713 706-3223
6100 Chapman St Houston (77022) *(G-10676)*
Lone Star Farm & Home Center, Nacogdoches *Also called Texas Farm Products Company (G-15715)*
Lone Star Fasteners LLC (HQ)............**281 353-1191**
24131 W Hardy Rd Spring (77373) *(G-19142)*
Lone Star Gasket and Sup Inc............432 333-1615
5012 Andrews Hwy Odessa (79762) *(G-16064)*
Lone Star Glass Inc (PA)............**713 661-0091**
3804 Bissonnet St Houston (77005) *(G-10677)*
Lone Star Heat Treating Corp (PA)............**713 672-6616**
3939 Blaffer St Houston (77026) *(G-10678)*
Lone Star Indus Corp Texas............915 779-7255
6985 Industrial Ave El Paso (79915) *(G-5846)*
Lone Star Industries Inc............512 917-8394
2320 Tom Miller St Austin (78723) *(G-1299)*
Lone Star Instrmnttion Elc Cor (PA)............**432 368-7827**
2222 W 42nd St Odessa (79764) *(G-16065)*
Lone Star INStrmnttn&elctrc............817 458-9347
1577 Ranger Hwy Weatherford (76086) *(G-20600)*
Lone Star Iron Doors, Plano *Also called Macgmc LLC (G-16916)*
Lone Star Livestock Eqp Co Inc............281 399-3550
20115 Ada Ln New Caney (77357) *(G-15844)*
Lone Star Machine and Tool Co............806 622-5106
10501 S Fm 1541 Amarillo (79118) *(G-499)*
Lone Star Medical Products Inc............281 340-6000
11211 Cash Rd Stafford (77477) *(G-19348)*
Lone Star Molding Inc............936 539-0008
12686 Fm 1314 Rd Conroe (77302) *(G-3324)*
Lone Star NGL Pipeline LP (HQ)............**210 403-7300**
1300 Main St 10 Houston (77002) *(G-10679)*
Lone Star NGL Rfinery Svcs LLC (HQ)............**210 403-7300**
1300 Main St Houston (77002) *(G-10680)*
Lone Star Oil & Gas Inc............432 686-9390
1003 N Big Spring St Midland (79701) *(G-15284)*
Lone Star Poultry Inc............713 868-3888
1222 Rutland St Houston (77008) *(G-10681)*
Lone Star Printing............956 535-2194
2004 W Jefferson Ave D Harlingen (78550) *(G-8194)*
Lone Star Ready-Mix LP (PA)............**512 260-0300**
9210 Fm 2243 Leander (78641) *(G-13994)*
Lone Star Ready-Mix LP............512 260-3629
7900 Old Manor Rd Austin (78724) *(G-1300)*
Lone Star Rebar Installers, Burleson *Also called Lsri LLC (G-2588)*
Lone Star Rigging LP............409 842-2263
4175 W Cardinal Dr Beaumont (77705) *(G-1920)*
Lone Star Rope, Buffalo *Also called Ls Rope LLC (G-2546)*
Lone Star Sales, Hebbronville *Also called Gray Sales Inc (G-8234)*
Lone Star Signs of West Texas............432 683-0016
1008 E Florida Ave Midland (79701) *(G-15285)*
Lone Star Special Tees LLC............210 402-0091
1011 N Frio St San Antonio (78207) *(G-18263)*
Lone Star Stone Texas Inc (PA)............**254 694-6613**
1073 Fm 1713 Whitney (76692) *(G-20730)*
Lone Star Technologies Inc (HQ)............**972 770-6401**
15660 Dallas Pkwy Ste 500 Dallas (75248) *(G-4604)*
Lone Star Wheel Components............903 654-1132
3129 E Hwy 31 Corsicana (75110) *(G-3676)*
Lonestar Aluminum Spc LLC............281 617-7177
8242 Warren Rd Houston (77040) *(G-10682)*
Lonestar Badge & Sign Inc............512 357-2261
301 Quail Run Rd Martindale (78655) *(G-14810)*
Lonestar Couplings Inc............713 690-1873
8306 Northcourt Rd Houston (77040) *(G-10683)*
Lonestar Energy Fabrication, Baytown *Also called Ls Energy Fabrication LLC (G-1796)*
Lonestar Energy Fabrication, Houston *Also called Ls Energy Fabrication LLC (G-8387)*
Lonestar Fencing and Wldg LLC............210 992-0441
7014 Valley Trl San Antonio (78250) *(G-18264)*
Lonestar Landscape Dfw LLC............817 863-5609
6807 Anglin Dr Forest Hill (76140) *(G-6298)*
Lonestar Logos MGT Co LLC............512 462-1310
3701 Bee Caves Rd Ste 202 West Lake Hills (78746) *(G-20684)*
Lonestar Pipe Fabrication Inc............817 439-5575
211 Sansom Blvd Saginaw (76179) *(G-17749)*
Lonestar Prestress Mfg Inc............713 896-0994
8892 Highway 159 E Bellville (77418) *(G-2010)*
Lonestar Prospects Ltd (HQ)............**817 279-1660**
4413 Carey St Fort Worth (76119) *(G-6799)*
Lonestar Recreational Vhcl Ctr, Harker Heights *Also called Shell Rapid Lube Lonestar Auto (G-8173)*
Lonestar Resources US Inc (PA)............**817 921-1889**
111 Boland St Ste 301 Fort Worth (76107) *(G-6800)*
Lonestar Shelter Manufacturing, Ponder *Also called Abac LLC (G-17092)*
Lonestar Windmills, Ross *Also called Travis Scott (G-17617)*
Long & Long Pier Drilling Co............972 422-4084
1712 Ave N Plano (75074) *(G-16910)*
Long Beach Shavings Co Inc (PA)............**936 231-4400**
14369 Fm 1314 Rd Conroe (77302) *(G-3325)*
Long Plan Printing Inc............713 797-1125
3029 Crossview Dr Houston (77063) *(G-10684)*
Long Range Systems LLC (PA)............**214 553-5308**
1155 Kas Dr Ste 150 Richardson (75081) *(G-17349)*
Long Trusts............903 984-5017
118 S Kilgore St Kilgore (75662) *(G-13564)*
Longer Protective LLC............832 987-1790
13215 Stafford Rd Ste 300 Missouri City (77489) *(G-15581)*
Longfellow Energy LP............972 590-9900
16803 Dallas Pkwy Addison (75001) *(G-146)*
Longhorn Custom Coating, Odessa *Also called Meister Industries Inc (G-16078)*
Longhorn Custom Coating, Odessa *Also called Meister Industries Inc (G-16079)*
Longhorn Drilling and Eqp Co............830 372-1910
1200 J Bar K Ln Seguin (78155) *(G-18850)*
Longhorn Fabrication Inc............972 225-6800
3200 Airport Rd Terrell (75160) *(G-19739)*
Longhorn Glass Mfg LP............713 679-7500
4202 Fidelity St Houston (77029) *(G-10685)*
Longhorn Leather Co, McKinney *Also called Simco Longhorn Leather (G-14974)*
Longhorn Leather Co............903 454-4866
1909 Interstate Hwy 30 W Greenville (75402) *(G-8083)*
Longhorn Mulching Inc............936 699-1160
7003 E State Highway 103 Lufkin (75901) *(G-14533)*
Longhorn Paper Converting LLC............214 988-3251
1123 W North Carrier Pkwy Grand Prairie (75050) *(G-7918)*
Longhorn Powder Coating I............817 759-2224
2516 Minnis Dr Ste 180 Haltom City (76117) *(G-8152)*
Longhorn Services Inc............956 655-2360
21377 N Moorefield Rd Edinburg (78541) *(G-5593)*

Longhorn Tube LP 972 556-0234
1891 Ryan Rd Dallas (75220) *(G-4605)*

Longview Asphalt Inc (HQ) **903 758-0065**
20 Robert Wilson Rd Longview (75602) *(G-14266)*

Longview Asphalt Inc. 903 758-4428
1301 Ray St Longview (75602) *(G-14267)*

Longview Brass & Aluminum Co 903 758-8171
4217 Estes Pkwy Longview (75603) *(G-14268)*

Longview Distribution I LLC (PA) **832 467-4600**
6650 Roxburgh Dr Ste 100 Houston (77041) *(G-10686)*

Longview Fab & Machine Inc 903 238-8300
57 Frj Dr Longview (75602) *(G-14269)*

Longview Mechanical Contrs Inc (PA) 903 759-1331
827 Fisher Rd Longview (75604) *(G-14270)*

Longview News Journal, Longview *Also called Texas Community Media LLC (G-14315)*

Longview News Journal 903 237-7711
320 E Methvin St Longview (75601) *(G-14271)*

Longview Photocopying, Longview *Also called Hart Engineering Company (G-14247)*

Longwood Elastomers Inc 979 830-1111
1901 Longwood Dr Brenham (77833) *(G-2261)*

Lons Welding 806 435-2278
522 N Main St Perryton (79070) *(G-16639)*

Lonza Inc 281 291-2300
9700 Bayport Blvd Pasadena (77507) *(G-16475)*

Lookout Services Inc 713 668-6200
4134 Bluebonnet Dr # 110 Stafford (77477) *(G-19349)*

Loomis Publishing Services 281 829-6825
18719 Ember Trails Dr Houston (77094) *(G-10687)*

Loop Tech International Ltd 936 295-7038
13802 N Highway 75 Willis (77378) *(G-20854)*

Looptech, Willis *Also called Loop Tech International Ltd (G-20854)*

Lopez Efrain 713 921-0057
7131 Harrisburg Blvd Houston (77011) *(G-10688)*

Lopez Houston Metals, El Paso *Also called Lopez Scrap Metal Inc (G-5847)*

Lopez Printing Incorporated 210 732-3232
427 Lombrano St San Antonio (78207) *(G-18265)*

Lopez Printing & Bindery Svc, San Antonio *Also called Lopez Printing Incorporated (G-18265)*

Lopez Ready Mix, Rio Grande City *Also called Erasmo Lopez Jr (G-17471)*

Lopez Scrap Metal Inc (PA) **915 859-0770**
351 N Nevarez Rd El Paso (79927) *(G-5847)*

Lopez Tank Lining LLC 936 257-9779
1199 County Road 615 Dayton (77535) *(G-5233)*

Lopez Tortilla Foods Inc 214 353-9538
9727 Brockbank Dr Dallas (75220) *(G-4606)*

Loredo Truss Company Inc 512 926-1782
2506 Ferguson Ln Austin (78754) *(G-1301)*

Lorelei Brewing Company LLC 361 445-1084
520 Nas Dr Corpus Christi (78418) *(G-3564)*

Lorena Machine, Lorena *Also called K-Line Machine Ltd (G-14342)*

LOrenta Nuts LLC 361 876-7570
2564 Macarthur Vw 101 San Antonio (78217) *(G-18266)*

Lorente International LLC 877 281-6469
4435 Simonton Rd Farmers Branch (75244) *(G-6206)*

Lorentson Manufacturing Co 956 399-8902
2101 Amistad Dr San Benito (78586) *(G-18659)*

LORENTSON MANUFACTURING COMPANY, INC., San Benito *Also called Lorentson Manufacturing Co (G-18659)*

Lorentson Mfg Co Southwest Inc 956 399-8902
2101 Amistad Dr San Benito (78586) *(G-18660)*

Lorenzo Textile Mills Inc 806 634-5506
417 Fillmore St Lorenzo (79343) *(G-14344)*

Lorillard Tobacco, Tyler *Also called R J Reynolds Tobacco Company (G-20144)*

Los Angles Tmes Cmmnctions LLC 512 476-7777
119 E 10th St Austin (78701) *(G-1302)*

Losoya Industries LLC 210 559-6066
205 Rosebud St Boerne (78006) *(G-2127)*

Lospinos Ranch Vineyards 903 855-1769
658 County Road 1334 Pittsburg (75686) *(G-16746)*

Loss Oil Field Services LLC 432 695-6914
307 E Texas Ave Midland (79701) *(G-15286)*

Lost Falls LLC 737 300-1965
2310 La Casa Dr Austin (78704) *(G-1303)*

Lottco Inc 832 773-4345
19747 Highway 59 N # 410 Humble (77338) *(G-12785)*

Lotus Lubes, Houston *Also called Globalpetrochem LLC (G-9983)*

Lotus Midstream LLC (HQ) **713 234-7865**
2150 Town Square Pl # 395 Sugar Land (77479) *(G-19505)*

Louis Barriga 817 923-7370
3244 Stuart Dr Fort Worth (76110) *(G-6801)*

Louis Hill Kennon Inc 713 926-2623
6952 Lawndale St Houston (77023) *(G-10689)*

Louisiana Purchase Foods, Selma *Also called Magi Foods LLC (G-18877)*

Louisiana Wild LLC 512 799-2537
13359 N Hwy 183 Ste 406b Austin (78750) *(G-1304)*

Louisiana-Pacific Corporation 409 383-0767
Hgwy 190 E Jasper (75951) *(G-13279)*

Love Good Fat, Austin *Also called Good Fat Co Ltd (G-1187)*

Lovelady Directional Drilling 936 675-4598
2946 Ted Trout Dr Lufkin (75904) *(G-14534)*

Lowe Offshore Inc 281 894-5454
1155 Dairy Ashford Rd # 315 Houston (77079) *(G-10690)*

Lowe Precast Inc 254 776-9690
24000 Woodway Dr Waco (76712) *(G-20428)*

Lower Colorado River Authority (PA) **512 473-3200**
3700 Lake Austin Blvd Austin (78703) *(G-1305)*

Lower Colorado River Authority 512 473-3270
815 Buchanan Plant Rd Buchanan Dam (78609) *(G-2518)*

Lown Brothers Inc 915 594-4499
11601 Pellicano Dr A15 El Paso (79936) *(G-5848)*

Lowrance Machine Shop Inc 281 449-6524
13510 E Hardy Rd Houston (77039) *(G-10691)*

Lozz Quatezz LLC 956 687-7446
105 E Interstate 2 Ste F Pharr (78577) *(G-16706)*

LP & M Group Inc 972 458-9393
13465 Inwood Rd Apt 1312 Dallas (75244) *(G-4607)*

LPC Crude Oil Inc 432 682-8555
303 W Wall St Ste 102 Midland (79701) *(G-15287)*

Lpmi, Bellville *Also called Lonestar Prestress Mfg Inc (G-2010)*

Lqc Pipe & Supply, Houston *Also called Lqc Pipe & Tube Ltd Partnr (G-10692)*

Lqc Pipe & Tube Ltd Partnr 832 559-7676
6410 Langfield Rd Ste X Houston (77092) *(G-10692)*

Lr Energy Inc (PA) **214 691-5800**
8150 N Central Expy Dallas (75206) *(G-4608)*

Lrr Energy LP 713 292-9510
1111 Bagby St Ste 4600 Houston (77002) *(G-10693)*

Ls Energy Fabrication LLC (PA) **281 573-9500**
2050 Fm 1405 Rd Baytown (77523) *(G-1796)*

Ls Energy Fabrication LLC 281 573-9500
8120 Mchard Rd Houston (77053) *(G-8387)*

Ls Packaging Design Inc 713 645-9177
6504 Mayfair St Houston (77087) *(G-10694)*

Ls Rope LLC 903 322-6580
213 Lanely Rd Buffalo (75831) *(G-2546)*

Lsc Communications Us LLC 817 640-9987
401 N Great Sw Pkwy Arlington (76011) *(G-724)*

Lsf8 Gypsum Holdings LP 703 480-3800
2711 N Haskell Ave Dallas (75204) *(G-4609)*

Lsg Sky Chefs N Amer Sltons In 972 793-9517
6191 N State Highway 161 Irving (75038) *(G-13090)*

LSI Corporation 817 430-5808
905 Trophy Club Dr # 204 Roanoke (76262) *(G-17489)*

LSI Graphic Solutions Plus, Houston *Also called LSI Integrated Graphics LP (G-10696)*

LSI Industries 513 793-3200
14902 Sommermeyer St # 120 Houston (77041) *(G-10695)*

LSI Integrated Graphics LP 713 744-4100
14902 Sommermeyer St # 120 Houston (77041) *(G-10696)*

Lsmw Lone Star Machine Works 844 837-4200
2048 S 3rd St Mabank (75147) *(G-14578)*

Lsp Products Group Inc (HQ) **775 884-4242**
2727 Chemsearch Blvd Irving (75062) *(G-13091)*

Lsri LLC 817 770-0937
417 N Rudd St Burleson (76028) *(G-2588)*

Lst Heat Treating LLC 903 757-2115
8 Gum Valley Cir Longview (75602) *(G-14272)*

Lt Seafood LP 713 328-1999
415 E Hamilton St Houston (77076) *(G-10697)*

Ltd Material LLC 512 933-9292
8115 Altoga Dr Ste A Austin (78724) *(G-1306)*

Ltl Group, Brookshire *Also called Leading Testing Labs LLC (G-2318)*

Ltn Industries Inc 713 849-1300
6829 Flintlock Rd B Houston (77040) *(G-10698)*

Lua Br LLC 404 610-0118
606 W 17th St Apt 307 Austin (78701) *(G-1307)*

Lubbock Artfl Limb & Brace Ltd, Lubbock *Also called Lubbock Artfl Limb & Brace Ltd (G-14440)*

Lubbock Artfl Limb & Brace Ltd 806 799-1518
4421 19th St Lubbock (79407) *(G-14440)*

Lubbock Gas & Building Inc 806 745-9695
8205 Avenue F Lubbock (79404) *(G-14441)*

Lubbock Gasket & Supply, Lubbock *Also called Panhandle Packing & Gasket Inc (G-14456)*

Lubbock Skylight Manufacturing 806 744-2300
701 N Interstate 27 Lubbock (79403) *(G-14442)*

Lubchem Inc 281 350-9600
23609 W Hardy Rd Spring (77373) *(G-19143)*

Lubri Tech Products 214 870-4070
1400 N County Road 1110 Midland (79706) *(G-15288)*

Lubrication Systems Texas LLC (HQ) **713 464-6266**
15150 West Dr Houston (77053) *(G-8388)*

Lubrication Technologies Inc 806 256-1600
6194 Us Highway 83 Shamrock (79079) *(G-18892)*

Lubrizol Corporation 281 479-2851
12801 Bay Area Blvd Pasadena (77507) *(G-16476)*

Lubrizol Production Plant, Pasadena *Also called Lubrizol Corporation (G-16476)*

Luc Urethanes Inc 936 539-2170
3411 Pollok Dr Conroe (77303) *(G-3326)*

Lucchese Inc......915 778-8585
40 Walter Jones Blvd El Paso (79906) *(G-5849)*

Lucchese Inc (HQ)......915 778-8585
40 Walter Jones Blvd El Paso (79906) *(G-5850)*

Lucchese Boot Co, El Paso *Also called Lucchese Inc (G-5850)*

Lucere LLc......281 240-7355
3803 Garden Way Missouri City (77459) *(G-15582)*

Lucias Oaks LP......832 616-3306
1908 Sawdust Rd Spring (77380) *(G-19228)*

Lucid Energy Group LLC......575 810-6025
3100 Mckinnon St Ste 800 Dallas (75201) *(G-4610)*

Lucid Energy Group II LLC (PA)......214 420-4950
3100 Mckinnon St Ste 800 Dallas (75201) *(G-4611)*

Lucid Iq, Dallas *Also called Solutions In Software Inc (G-4979)*

Lucite International Inc......409 729-1300
6350 N Twin City Hwy Nederland (77627) *(G-15755)*

Lucky Brand Dungarees LLC......512 393-2002
3939 S Interstate 35 # 1250 San Marcos (78666) *(G-18697)*

Lucy In Disguise With Diamonds, Austin *Also called Radtke Jenna (G-1450)*

Ludlum Measurements Inc (PA)......325 235-5494
501 Oak St Sweetwater (79556) *(G-19633)*

Ludlum Measurements Inc......325 235-1418
300 Crane St Sweetwater (79556) *(G-19634)*

Ludlum Measurements Inc......325 235-4276
1300 W Broadway St Sweetwater (79556) *(G-19635)*

Lueders Limestone LP......325 228-4370
3500 Fm 2843 Florence (76527) *(G-6241)*

Lueders Limestone Quarry, Florence *Also called Lueders Limestone LP (G-6241)*

Lueras Welding Service Inc......361 668-4572
3869 W State Highway 44 Alice (78332) *(G-225)*

Lufkin Armature Works Inc......936 632-6607
2300 N Timberland Dr Lufkin (75901) *(G-14535)*

Lufkin Armture Works Whsng Div, Lufkin *Also called Lufkin Armature Works Inc (G-14535)*

Lufkin Automation, Missouri City *Also called Lufkin Industries LLC (G-15583)*

Lufkin Automation, Kilgore *Also called Lufkin Industries LLC (G-13566)*

Lufkin Coca Cola Bottling Co......936 639-2355
704 Webber St Lufkin (75904) *(G-14536)*

Lufkin Creosoting Co Inc......936 634-2211
5865 S Us Highway 69 Lufkin (75901) *(G-14537)*

Lufkin Daily News, Lufkin *Also called Southern Newspapers Inc (G-14552)*

Lufkin Electric Co......936 639-2377
2300 N Timberland Dr Lufkin (75901) *(G-14538)*

Lufkin Gears LLC (PA)......936 634-2211
409 Ellis Ave Lufkin (75904) *(G-14539)*

Lufkin Gears LLC......936 634-2211
300 Winston Lufkin (75904) *(G-14540)*

Lufkin Ils......281 445-7676
11050 W Little York Rd Houston (77041) *(G-10699)*

Lufkin Industries LLC......806 592-2586
2811 State Highway 214 Denver City (79323) *(G-5420)*

Lufkin Industries LLC......903 986-9080
1120 Marvin A Smith Rd Kilgore (75662) *(G-13565)*

Lufkin Industries LLC......936 634-2211
Hwy 69 S Lufkin (75901) *(G-14541)*

Lufkin Industries LLC......281 495-1100
811 Willow Oak Dr 800 Missouri City (77489) *(G-15583)*

Lufkin Industries LLC......903 984-3875
7155 Hwy 42 N Kilgore (75662) *(G-13566)*

Lufkin Industries LLC......936 634-2211
3935 Fm 326 Lufkin (75901) *(G-14542)*

Lufkin-Oilfield, Lufkin *Also called Lufkin Industries LLC (G-14542)*

Lufkins Services, Denver City *Also called Lufkin Industries LLC (G-5420)*

Lufkins Six B Construction......936 632-3470
5168 Ted Trout Dr Lufkin (75904) *(G-14543)*

Lugra Inc......956 986-0958
3664 Commerce Dr Brownsville (78521) *(G-2378)*

Luig Energy Services LLC......940 264-6188
8039 Seymour Hwy Wichita Falls (76310) *(G-20780)*

Lukoil Intl Upstream W Inc (HQ)......713 877-8544
3200 Southwest Fwy # 3120 Houston (77027) *(G-10700)*

Luling Well Service......830 875-9181
1251 Hoover St Luling (78648) *(G-14562)*

Lululemon Athletica......713 863-1280
713 Heights Blvd Houston (77007) *(G-10701)*

Lulus Dessert Corporation......210 399-3767
1031 Hot Wells Blvd San Antonio (78223) *(G-18267)*

Lulus Dessert Factory, San Antonio *Also called Lulus Dessert Corporation (G-18267)*

Luma Vue Inc......214 842-8347
11625 Custer Rd Ste 150 Frisco (75035) *(G-7260)*

Lumadyne LLC......281 220-2409
1600 E Highway 6 Ste 425 Alvin (77511) *(G-372)*

Lumina Global Inc......713 783-7056
7115 Belgold St Ste F Houston (77066) *(G-10702)*

Luminant Generation Co LLC (HQ)......214 812-4600
6555 Sierra Dr Irving (75039) *(G-13092)*

Luminated Living LLC......512 523-5550
13247 Mesa Verde Dr Austin (78737) *(G-864)*

Luminator Aircraft Parts Div, Plano *Also called Luminator Holding LP (G-16911)*

Luminator Holding LP (HQ)......972 424-6511
900 Klein Rd Plano (75074) *(G-16911)*

Luminator Technology Group Inc......972 516-3154
900 Klein Rd Plano (75074) *(G-16912)*

Luminator Technology Group LLC (PA)......972 424-6511
900 Klein Rd Plano (75074) *(G-16913)*

Luminex Corporation......512 219-8020
12201 Technology Blvd Austin (78727) *(G-1308)*

Luminex Corporation (PA)......512 219-8020
12212 Technology Blvd Austin (78727) *(G-1309)*

Lummus Corporation......806 745-1191
501 E Hunter St Lubbock (79403) *(G-14443)*

Lumos Pharma Sub Inc......512 215-2630
4200 Marathon Blvd # 200 Austin (78756) *(G-1310)*

Luna Piena Inc......512 926-6346
8212 Bagby Dr Austin (78724) *(G-1311)*

Luna's Tortillas Y Hacienda, Dallas *Also called Lunas Tortillas Factory (G-4612)*

Lunar Lighting Solutions LLC......866 434-0732
100 Congress Ave Ste 2000 Austin (78701) *(G-1312)*

Lunas Tortillas Factory......214 747-2661
2225 Connector Dr Dallas (75220) *(G-4612)*

Lundy Services LLC......972 494-2554
221 Garvon St Garland (75040) *(G-7539)*

Luraco Inc......817 633-1080
1132 107th St Arlington (76011) *(G-725)*

Luraco Technologies, Arlington *Also called Luraco Inc (G-725)*

Lure Capital Corporation......713 729-2424
11144 S Post Oak Rd Houston (77035) *(G-10703)*

Luther M Creek......325 387-3295
912 S Crockett Ave Sonora (76950) *(G-19027)*

Luttrell Welding Services......940 433-3131
2840 E Highway 114 Boyd (76023) *(G-2206)*

Lutz Woodworks Llc......972 429-5521
700 Parker Rd Wylie (75098) *(G-20940)*

Luv Stuff, Greenville *Also called Shelbis Stuff Inc (G-8091)*

Luxottica of America Inc......512 450-1234
2206 Highland Mall Austin (78752) *(G-1313)*

Luxury Baths By Arrow, Houston *Also called Arrow Marble LLC (G-8705)*

Lwc Brands Inc......214 630-9101
151 Regal Row Ste 118 Dallas (75247) *(G-4613)*

Lwf Services LLC......432 425-9795
11231 W County Road 127 Odessa (79765) *(G-16066)*

Lwo Acquisitions Company LLC......972 573-1140
1920 Hurd Dr Irving (75038) *(G-13093)*

Lycra Company LLC......218 842-4613
12455 Strang Rd La Porte (77571) *(G-13770)*

Lyfe Tyme Products, Uvalde *Also called Marsha Kitchens (G-20191)*

Lynchburg Shipyard Inc......281 426-2474
999 Independence Pkwy N Baytown (77520) *(G-1827)*

Lynco Well Service Inc......936 336-7332
1590 Wallisville Rd Liberty (77575) *(G-14123)*

Lynn Electric Motor Co Inc......940 657-3511
1011 E Main St Knox City (79529) *(G-13664)*

Lynwood Farms, San Antonio *Also called Bolners Fiesta Products Inc (G-17962)*

Lynx Energy Company Inc......214 969-5555
2100 Ross Ave Ste 860 Dallas (75201) *(G-4614)*

Lynx Well Service Inc......409 735-2604
5443 Fm 408 Orangefield (77639) *(G-16271)*

Lyondell Chemical Company......281 597-8935
1221 Mckinney St Ste 700 Houston (77010) *(G-10704)*

Lyondell Chemical Company......361 242-8000
1501 Mckinney Rd Corpus Christi (78410) *(G-3565)*

Lyondell Chemical Company......281 474-4191
10801 Choate Rd Pasadena (77507) *(G-16477)*

Lyondell Chemical Company......979 245-1225
U.S Hwy 60 13 Mi S Of Bay City (77414) *(G-1774)*

Lyondell Chemical Company......361 572-2500
Old Bloomington Hwy Victoria (77901) *(G-20284)*

Lyondell Chemical Company (HQ)......713 309-7200
1221 Mckinney St Ste 300 Houston (77010) *(G-10705)*

Lyondell Chemical Company......281 291-1488
14403 Sugar Mill Cir Houston (77095) *(G-10706)*

Lyondell Chemical Company......281 385-7010
11815 Highway 146 Mont Belvieu (77535) *(G-15622)*

Lyondell Chemical Company......972 512-3171
4025 Midway Rd Carrollton (75007) *(G-2879)*

Lyondell Chemical Company......281 862-4000
8280 Sheldon Rd Channelview (77530) *(G-3030)*

Lyondell-Citgo Refining LLC......713 321-4111
12000 Lawndale St Houston (77017) *(G-10707)*

Lyondellbasell, Houston *Also called Lyondell Chemical Company (G-10705)*

Lyondellbasell, Houston *Also called Equistar Chemicals LP (G-9689)*

Lyondellbasell Acetyls LLC......713 309-7200
1221 Mckinney St Ste 300 Houston (77010) *(G-10708)*

Lyondellbasell Industries Inc......713 209-1248
1515 Miller Cut Off Rd La Porte (77571) *(G-13771)*

Lyondellbasell Industries Inc (HQ)......713 309-7200
1221 Mckinney St Ste 300 Houston (77010) *(G-10709)*

Lyondllbsell Advnced Plymers I (HQ).................713 309-7200
1221 Mckinney St Ste 300 Houston (77010) *(G-10710)*

Lyondllbsell Advnced Plymers I.................832 663-3104
24624 Interstate 45 Spring (77386) *(G-19229)*

Lyondllbsell Advnced Plymers I.................281 867-3000
1300 Mccabe Rd La Porte (77571) *(G-13772)*

Lyons Drilling Inc.................979 596-1898
120 E Bell Ave Rockdale (76567) *(G-17525)*

Lyons Manufacturing Inc.................214 381-8100
8900 Forney Rd Dallas (75227) *(G-4615)*

Lyris Technologies Inc (HQ).................510 844-1600
401 Congress Ave Ste 2650 Austin (78701) *(G-1314)*

M & B Oilfield Construction.................325 235-2514
2700 E Broadway St Sweetwater (79556) *(G-19636)*

M & D Companies Inc (PA).................936 347-2138
156 E Main St Garrison (75946) *(G-7613)*

M & F Gauge & Specialty Co Inc.................325 643-2655
3104 Morris Sheppard Dr Brownwood (76801) *(G-2439)*

M & F Wholesale Floral Sups (PA).................915 542-1238
212 S Oregon St Ste 212 # 212 El Paso (79901) *(G-5851)*

M & G Chemicals (HQ).................361 500-4747
450 Gears Rd Ste 240 Houston (77067) *(G-10711)*

M & G Development LP.................361 664-6122
2681 W Front St Alice (78332) *(G-226)*

M & G Resins Usa LLC (HQ).................281 873-5780
450 Gears Rd Ste 240 Houston (77067) *(G-10712)*

M & G Resins Usa LLC.................304 576-2041
7001 Joe Fulton Corpus Christi (78402) *(G-3566)*

M & H Crates Inc.................903 683-5351
4022 Farm Rd 347 Jacksonville (75766) *(G-13248)*

M & H Metal Specialities Inc.................972 296-9057
5711 W Ledbetter Dr Dallas (75236) *(G-4616)*

M & J Manufacturing, Humble *Also called Faith Manufacturing Co Inc* *(G-12766)*

M & J Valve Company (HQ).................281 469-0550
19191 Hempstead Hwy Houston (77065) *(G-10713)*

M & K Plating Inc.................817 332-6021
2621 Finley St Fort Worth (76111) *(G-6802)*

M & L Rose Enterprises Inc (PA).................214 637-8000
4639 N Lindhurst Ave Dallas (75229) *(G-4617)*

M & M Coastal Mfg Inc.................713 472-0700
8700 Hirsch Rd Houston (77016) *(G-10714)*

M & M Designs Inc.................936 295-2682
1981 Quality Blvd Huntsville (77320) *(G-12817)*

M & M Disposal, Stanton *Also called M & M Meter Service Inc* *(G-19403)*

M & M Italian Style Foods Inc.................817 439-8008
13794 Old Denton Rd Roanoke (76262) *(G-17490)*

M & M Lighting LP (PA).................713 667-5611
5620 S Rice Ave Houston (77081) *(G-10715)*

M & M Metals Inc.................210 341-1313
103 Braniff Dr San Antonio (78216) *(G-18268)*

M & M Meter Service Inc.................432 756-2801
108 N St Peter Stanton (79782) *(G-19403)*

M & M Upholstery Inc.................214 391-2666
8337 Lake June Rd Ste B Dallas (75217) *(G-4618)*

M & P Sealing Co (PA).................409 745-2002
11125 Interstate 10 E Orange (77630) *(G-16253)*

M & Q Oilfield Service Inc.................806 894-4025
1107 W Fm 300 Levelland (79336) *(G-14010)*

M & R Machine Works Inc.................713 462-0746
8511 Rannie Rd Houston (77080) *(G-10716)*

M & R USA (PA).................281 497-8973
6420 Richmond Ave Ste 203 Houston (77057) *(G-10717)*

M & S Mechanical Inc.................318 755-2431
136 County Road 1309 Pittsburg (75686) *(G-16747)*

M & T Natural Stone.................817 556-2107
5605 Thousand Oaks Dr Joshua (76058) *(G-13321)*

M & T Pallet Company Inc.................409 866-8136
11397 Highway 90 Beaumont (77713) *(G-1921)*

M & W Hot Oil Inc (PA).................432 447-2108
2902 Balmorhea Hwy Pecos (79772) *(G-16623)*

M A E W Inc.................956 627-3554
422 S 11th St McAllen (78501) *(G-14886)*

M A P A, Naples *Also called Mapa Manufacturing LLC* *(G-15719)*

M A R X Steel LLC (PA).................281 679-9700
11985 Fm 529 Rd Houston (77041) *(G-10718)*

M Alvarez Enterprises Inc.................972 514-2255
4287 Belt Line Rd Ste 360 Addison (75001) *(G-147)*

M and N Plastics Inc.................915 877-1900
7750 Trade Center Ave El Paso (79912) *(G-5852)*

M and S Mechanical, Pittsburg *Also called M & S Mechanical Inc* *(G-16747)*

M B & G Oilfld Fabrication Inc.................903 593-0400
2611 Us Highway 271 Tyler (75708) *(G-20116)*

M B C I, Houston *Also called Nci Group Inc* *(G-11016)*

M Brown Books Pubg Group Inc.................972 381-0009
16250 Knoll Trail Dr Dallas (75248) *(G-4619)*

M C R Oil Tools LLC.................817 701-5100
7315 Business Pl Arlington (76001) *(G-726)*

M C Systems Inc.................972 247-6785
2412 Richland Ave Ste 101 Dallas (75234) *(G-4620)*

M C(red)gibbins Inc.................940 872-1681
1007 E Wise St Bowie (76230) *(G-2197)*

M D I, Dallas *Also called Micro-Design Inc* *(G-4675)*

M E Ruby Jr Inc.................512 258-1601
15700 Anderson Mill Rd Cedar Park (78613) *(G-2977)*

M F I International, El Paso *Also called Mfi International Mfg LLC* *(G-5876)*

M Fab & Machine.................936 264-2388
17781 Highway 105 E Conroe (77306) *(G-3327)*

M G Bryan Equipment Co LP.................972 623-4300
1906 S Great Sw Pkwy Grand Prairie (75051) *(G-7919)*

M G Engineering LLC (PA).................626 913-1562
19678 County Road 4125 Lindale (75771) *(G-14135)*

M G Products Company (PA).................915 541-8950
6825 Cielo Vista Dr 25 El Paso (79925) *(G-5853)*

M Grill, San Marcos *Also called 3nine USA Inc* *(G-18676)*

M H & C Cabling, Mansfield *Also called Massey Holding & Consultants* *(G-14690)*

M H C X-Ploration Corporation.................903 595-4323
14609 Hwy 64 W Tyler (75704) *(G-20117)*

M Hastey Construction Co Inc.................806 296-7444
101 E 24th St Plainview (79072) *(G-16760)*

M I C Group, Brenham *Also called Magnetic Instruments Corp* *(G-2262)*

M J Celco Inc.................915 594-1777
1455 Vanderbilt Dr El Paso (79935) *(G-5854)*

M J M International Corp (PA).................956 781-5000
632 S Jackson Rd Edinburg (78539) *(G-5594)*

M K S Natural Gas Company.................817 599-9477
200 Cochran Rd Weatherford (76085) *(G-20601)*

M K Spcialty Metal Fabricators, Hutchins *Also called Mk Specialty Metal Fabricators* *(G-12869)*

M L Holdings Inc.................817 732-1708
5836 Camp Bowie Blvd Fort Worth (76107) *(G-6803)*

M N Gumbert Corporation.................214 340-8383
10750 Metric Dr Dallas (75243) *(G-4621)*

M P Energy Inc.................281 350-6350
3100 Weslayan St Ste 375 Houston (77027) *(G-10719)*

M P I, Austin *Also called Materials Products Inc* *(G-1329)*

M P I Label Systems of Texas, Grand Prairie *Also called Miller Products Inc* *(G-7929)*

M P Industries Inc.................903 561-4232
4939 Profit Dr Tyler (75707) *(G-20118)*

M P N Inc.................972 227-1210
101 Industrial St Lancaster (75134) *(G-13846)*

M Patel Enterprises Inc.................512 892-2721
5601 Brodie Ln Ste 1000 Sunset Valley (78745) *(G-19626)*

M Press, McKinney *Also called P & A Graphics LLC* *(G-14961)*

M R C, Midland *Also called MRC Global (us) Inc* *(G-15307)*

M R Fabrication.................940 427-4701
3640 County Road 2690 Alvord (76225) *(G-388)*

M R Sheet Metal, Houston *Also called Mason Road Sheet Metal Inc* *(G-10784)*

M S I Corporation.................512 243-9000
8704 Lava Hill Rd Ste B Austin (78744) *(G-1315)*

M Sosa White Cheese La Pintita.................956 546-7078
5294 Southmost Rd Brownsville (78521) *(G-2379)*

M T A, Euless *Also called Modern Tektronix Assembly* *(G-6150)*

M T C, El Paso *Also called Mexican Technologies Co Inc* *(G-5875)*

M T E, Houston *Also called Texas Metal Equipment Co Ltd* *(G-12241)*

M T S, Lubbock *Also called Module Truck Systems Inc* *(G-14448)*

M Tripple Oil Tool Inc.................432 337-1452
8317 Andrews Hwy Odessa (79765) *(G-16067)*

M W Butler Company.................817 572-3306
12390 Rendon Rd Burleson (76028) *(G-2589)*

M W Periscope Inc.................972 247-4202
2025 Royal Ln Ste 310 Dallas (75229) *(G-4622)*

M W Waldrop Co.................713 337-5600
8125 Kempwood Dr Houston (77055) *(G-10720)*

M&G Chemicals, Corpus Christi *Also called M & G Resins Usa LLC* *(G-3566)*

M&H Machining Inc.................512 930-9059
102 Meadow Dr Georgetown (78633) *(G-7661)*

M&I Electric LLC.................409 838-0441
4775 S Mlk Jr Pkwy Beaumont (77705) *(G-1922)*

M&I Electric Industries Inc (HQ).................832 241-6330
1250 Wood Branch Park Dr # 600 Houston (77079) *(G-10721)*

M&M Machine Shop LLC.................832 934-1542
101 Morris Rd Magnolia (77354) *(G-14617)*

M&M Manufacturing Inc (HQ).................817 336-2311
4001 Mark Iv Pkwy Fort Worth (76106) *(G-6804)*

M&M Manufacturing Inc.................972 485-1504
360 S Shiloh Rd Garland (75042) *(G-7540)*

M&M Manufacturing Inc.................817 334-0034
200 Adolph St Fort Worth (76107) *(G-6805)*

M&M Manufacturing Inc.................713 460-1677
5555 Guhn Rd Houston (77040) *(G-10722)*

M&M Manufacturing Company, Fort Worth *Also called M&M Manufacturing Inc* *(G-6804)*

M&M Prcsion Mtal Fbrcation Inc.................940 726-3379
12757 I 35 Frontage Rd Valley View (76272) *(G-20204)*

M&P Flange Pipe Protection Inc.................713 463-6339
9426 Katy Fwy Bldg 11 Houston (77055) *(G-10723)*

M&R Manufacturing LLC..281 590-7200
15040 Northgreen Blvd Houston (77032) *(G-10724)*

M-C Production and Drlg Co Inc...........................903 297-2251
Fm 1844 Longview (75604) *(G-14273)*

M-Files Inc...972 516-4210
6400 Intl Pkwy Ste 2500 Plano (75093) *(G-16914)*

M-I Drilling Fluids, Galveston *Also called M-I LLC (G-7403)*

M-I LLC..361 886-3400
1102 Heinsohn Rd Corpus Christi (78406) *(G-3567)*

M-I LLC (HQ)..281 561-1300
5950 N Course Dr Houston (77072) *(G-10725)*

M-I LLC..409 763-2249
4814 Port Industrial Blvd Galveston (77554) *(G-7403)*

M-I Swaco A Schlumberger Co, Houston *Also called M-I LLC (G-10725)*

M-I Swacor, Wharton *Also called Schlumberger (G-20706)*

M-Master LLC..915 242-2315
221 N Kansas St Ste 700 El Paso (79901) *(G-5855)*

M-Trigen Inc..713 469-5735
5050 Westway Park Blvd # 175 Houston (77041) *(G-10726)*

M. L. Leddy's, Fort Worth *Also called Franklin-Leddy Corporation (G-6648)*

M.T.T., Longview *Also called Missionary Tech Team (G-14277)*

M1 Support Services LP (PA).................................**940 323-1119**
300 N Elm St Ste 101 Denton (76201) *(G-5379)*

M2 Global Technology Ltd.......................................210 561-4800
5714 Epsilon San Antonio (78249) *(G-18269)*

M2I Systems LLC...214 412-1400
2122 113th St Grand Prairie (75050) *(G-7920)*

M2w Inc..972 407-1332
2318 N Belt Line Rd # 716 Mesquite (75150) *(G-15059)*

M3 Distribution Inc..281 357-0604
25116 Stanolind Rd Tomball (77375) *(G-19986)*

M3 Image LLC..915 845-7676
4709 Ripley Dr El Paso (79922) *(G-5856)*

M3 Midstream LLC (PA)...**713 783-3000**
600 Travis St Ste 5600 Houston (77002) *(G-10727)*

M3 Partners LLC (PA)..**602 561-6464**
6010 Royal Point Ct Kingwood (77345) *(G-13648)*

M3 Tooling LLC...210 946-4264
218 Roan Spg San Antonio (78258) *(G-18270)*

M3p Directional Services Ltd.................................432 561-8801
7600 W County Road 116 Midland (79706) *(G-15289)*

M3p Water Services LLC..432 570-7500
415 W Wall St Ste 835 Midland (79701) *(G-15290)*

M4 Performance Exhaust, Dallas *Also called M4 Products LLC (G-4623)*

M4 Products LLC...972 481-9300
2227 Joe Field Rd Dallas (75229) *(G-4623)*

M5 Louisiana Gathering LLC...................................713 783-3000
600 Travis St Ste 5600 Houston (77002) *(G-10728)*

Ma-Tex Wire Rope Co Inc (HQ)..............................**903 984-9691**
1975 Frm To Mkt Rd 1252 E Kilgore (75662) *(G-13567)*

Maas International, Houston *Also called Maass Flanges Corporation (G-10729)*

Maass Flanges Corporation (HQ)..........................**713 329-5500**
6202 Lumberdale Rd Houston (77092) *(G-10729)*

Mabco Equipment Ltd...817 599-7335
1219 Fort Worth Hwy Weatherford (76086) *(G-20602)*

Mac Fabricators...979 265-0235
617 Mockingbird Ln Clute (77531) *(G-3156)*

Mac Flotronics, Houston *Also called Schenck Process LLC (G-11765)*

Mac Machine and Gear Corp...................................972 790-7800
201 E Shady Grove Rd Grand Prairie (75050) *(G-7921)*

Mac Oil Field Company Inc.....................................325 754-5565
1007 W Dale St Winters (79567) *(G-20905)*

Mac Trailer Texas Inc...330 956-0171
5940 E Hwy 114 Rhome (76078) *(G-17257)*

Mac's Snacks, Arlington *Also called Evans Foods Inc (G-674)*

Mac-T of Texas, Inc., Rhome *Also called Mac Trailer Texas Inc (G-17257)*

Macadamia Beauty LLC (PA)...................................**800 807-3950**
5340 Legacy Dr Ste 180 Plano (75024) *(G-16915)*

Macadamia Natural Oil, Plano *Also called Macadamia Beauty LLC (G-16915)*

Macaulay Controls Company (PA)..........................281 282-0100
13920 Osprey Ct Ste E Webster (77598) *(G-20640)*

Macdermid Canning Ltd (HQ).................................**713 472-5081**
223 Brockman St Pasadena (77506) *(G-16478)*

Mace Security Intl Inc...800 627-6734
13710 Hutton Dr Dallas (75234) *(G-4624)*

Macgmc LLC...214 774-4455
6121 W Park Blvd Ste C226 Plano (75093) *(G-16916)*

Mach Industrial Group LP......................................713 695-6000
6119 Fulton St Houston (77022) *(G-10730)*

Mach International Inc...713 695-6000
6119 Fulton St Houston (77022) *(G-10731)*

Mach Speed Holdings LLC......................................214 978-3800
7200 Bishop Rd Ste 280 Plano (75024) *(G-16917)*

Machine Shop, Port Arthur *Also called Gulf Copper & Mfg Corp (G-17112)*

Machine Shop and Water Jet Div, Houston *Also called Logik Precision Inc (G-10673)*

Machine Tech Services Inc.....................................432 385-0891
3831 Nw Loop 338 Odessa (79764) *(G-16068)*

Machine Tech Services Inc (PA).............................325 573-1741
2708 25th St Snyder (79549) *(G-18993)*

Machining Solutions LLC (PA)................................**940 761-3030**
5000 Central Fwy Wichita Falls (76306) *(G-20781)*

Mack Bolt & Steel, Bryan *Also called Mack Larry (G-2492)*

Mack Larry...979 778-8088
5875 E State Highway 21 Bryan (77808) *(G-2492)*

Maclaskey Oil Field Services.................................817 594-8073
12600 Cleburne Hwy Weatherford (76086) *(G-20603)*

Maco Manufacturing Inc...254 939-5742
805 E 4th Ave Belton (76513) *(G-2027)*

Macro Tex Machine Works LLC...............................281 540-2141
2632 Wilson Rd Humble (77396) *(G-12786)*

Mactronix Inc..972 690-0028
735 N Plano Rd 105 Richardson (75081) *(G-17350)*

Madden Systems Inc..432 332-0255
1801 E Pearl St Odessa (79761) *(G-16069)*

Maddox Adams International, Dallas *Also called Maddox Metal Works Inc (G-4625)*

Maddox Enterprises Inc (PA)..................................**903 592-6531**
125 S Bonner Ave Tyler (75702) *(G-20119)*

Maddox Metal Works Inc (PA)................................**214 333-2311**
4116 Bronze Way Dallas (75237) *(G-4625)*

Maddox Residential & Coml Svcs, Tyler *Also called Maddox Enterprises Inc (G-20119)*

Made In America Mfg LLC..512 435-9952
8704 Lava Hill Rd Ste G Austin (78744) *(G-1316)*

Madewell LLC...713 674-1050
1330 Boyles St Houston (77020) *(G-10732)*

Madison Pipeline, Houston *Also called Farmers Oil Co (G-9764)*

Madisonville Service Contr LP...............................936 348-5506
3989 Interstate 45 N Madisonville (77864) *(G-14589)*

Madix Inc (PA)...214 515-5400
500 Airport Rd Terrell (75160) *(G-19740)*

Madmackenzie Solutions LLC................................281 615-8102
9119 Highway 6 Ste 230 Missouri City (77459) *(G-15584)*

Maersk Drilling USA Inc (HQ).................................**713 972-3300**
800 Town And Country Blvd # 500 Houston (77024) *(G-10733)*

Maersk Oil Houston Inc...713 346-5800
2500 Citywest Blvd # 100 Houston (77042) *(G-10734)*

Maevn Uniforms, Farmers Branch *Also called Asti Manufacturing Corp Inc (G-6189)*

Mag Flux Corporation (PA)......................................**972 272-8576**
1101 E Walnut St Garland (75040) *(G-7541)*

Magazine Fulfillment Service, Spring *Also called National Mail Advertising Inc (G-19152)*

Magdata Inc...425 372-2699
515 Congress Ave Ste 1510 Austin (78701) *(G-1317)*

Magee Machine & Mfg., Mesquite *Also called Magee Machine and Mfg Inc (G-15060)*

Magee Machine and Mfg Inc...................................972 285-2554
3535 Executive Blvd Mesquite (75149) *(G-15060)*

Magflux, Garland *Also called Mag Flux Corporation (G-7541)*

Maggie Chacon...915 857-3100
13351 Montana Ave El Paso (79938) *(G-5857)*

Magi Foods LLC..210 590-1308
17750 Lookout Rd Ste 205 Selma (78154) *(G-18877)*

Magic Aire, Wichita Falls *Also called United Electric Company LP (G-20823)*

Magic In Sky LLC..210 267-5371
26926 Hardy Run Boerne (78015) *(G-2128)*

Magic Valley Concrete LLC (PA).............................**956 432-0600**
3609 W Palma Vista Dr Palmview (78572) *(G-16311)*

Magna Leather Corp...915 772-0004
6841 Commerce Ave El Paso (79915) *(G-5858)*

Magnetic Field Effects LLC (PA)............................**713 856-8111**
14149 Westfair East Dr Houston (77041) *(G-10735)*

Magnetic Instruments Corp (HQ)..........................**800 836-6696**
3140 S Blue Bell Rd Brenham (77833) *(G-2262)*

Magnetic Technology Inc..214 544-2700
1627 Bray Central Dr McKinney (75069) *(G-14955)*

Magnetic Ticket & Label Corp (HQ).......................**214 634-8600**
8719 Diplomacy Row Dallas (75247) *(G-4626)*

Magnetrode, Jacksonville *Also called C & R Machine Inc (G-13231)*

Magnetrode Corporation...903 795-3378
2907 Fm 1910 W Jacksonville (75766) *(G-13249)*

Magni- Power Company...903 532-5533
1800 1900 N Collins Fwy Howe (75459) *(G-12735)*

Magni-Fab Southwest Co (HQ)...............................**903 532-5533**
811 N Collins Fwy Howe (75459) *(G-12736)*

Magnolia Brush Mfrs Inc...903 427-2261
1001 N Cedar St Clarksville (75426) *(G-3074)*

Magnolia Coca-Cola Bottling Co (PA)....................**915 593-2653**
11001 Gateway Blvd W El Paso (79935) *(G-5859)*

Magnolia Oil & Gas Oper LLC..................................713 842-9050
9 Greenway Plz Ste 1300 Houston (77046) *(G-10736)*

Magnum Custom Trailers, Austin *Also called Magnum Custom Trlr Mfg Co Inc (G-1318)*

Magnum Custom Trlr Mfg Co Inc (PA)...................**512 258-4101**
10806 N Fm 620 Rd Austin (78726) *(G-1318)*

Magnum Custom Trlr Mfg Co Inc...........................512 258-4101
11210 N Ih 35 San Antonio (78233) *(G-18271)*

Magnum Engineering Company..............................361 882-3858
500 N Shoreline Blvd # 32 Corpus Christi (78401) *(G-3568)*

Magnum Fabrications Inc..409 963-0161
6648 Gulfway Dr Port Arthur (77642) *(G-17117)*

Magnum Feeders Inc 281 261-0803
  6030 County Road 60 Rosharon (77583) *(G-17608)*

Magnum Fire & Safety Systems, Port Arthur *Also called Magnum Fabrications Inc* *(G-17117)*

Magnum Machine and Mfg Co 903 935-5300
  5029 Us Highway 59 N Marshall (75670) *(G-14788)*

Magnum Producing & Operating, Corpus Christi *Also called Magnum Engineering Company* *(G-3568)*

Magnum Producing LP (PA) 361 882-3858
  500 N Shoreline Blvd # 322 Corpus Christi (78401) *(G-3569)*

Magnum Terminal Tractor Div, White Oak *Also called Kalamar Industries USA Inc* *(G-20716)*

Magnum Trlrs Parts Equipments, San Antonio *Also called Magnum Custom Trlr Mfg Co Inc* *(G-18271)*

Magnus Mobility Systems Inc 800 527-5142
  2605 Joe Field Rd Dallas (75229) *(G-4627)*

Magseis Ff LLC 281 275-7500
  9811 Katy Fwy Ste 1100 Houston (77024) *(G-10737)*

Mahard Feed Mill Inc 903 523-4455
  27019 Us Highway 377 Gordonville (76245) *(G-7770)*

Mahle Behr Mfg MGT Inc 915 783-4213
  41 Butterfield Cir El Paso (79906) *(G-5860)*

Mahle Behr Mfg MGT Inc 248 735-3623
  48 Walter Jones Blvd El Paso (79906) *(G-5861)*

Mahle Behr Mfg MGT Inc 248 735-3623
  13701 Mines Rd Laredo (78045) *(G-13908)*

Mahle Behr Service America LLC (HQ) **817 624-7273**
  5020 Augusta Dr Fort Worth (76106) *(G-6806)*

Mahle Systema De Filtracion D 956 753-9100
  13493 Port Dr Laredo (78045) *(G-13909)*

Mail & Parcels Plus Inc 409 899-1771
  3865 W Lucas Dr Beaumont (77706) *(G-1923)*

Mail Contractors America Inc 214 742-6103
  1936 W Commerce St Dallas (75208) *(G-4628)*

Mail Mart Inc 214 630-9643
  4812 Top Line Dr Dallas (75247) *(G-4629)*

Mail Services Houston Inc 713 594-3362
  1 N Sampson St Houston (77003) *(G-10738)*

Main Event Inc 281 762-0854
  2033 Avenue H Rosenberg (77471) *(G-17589)*

Main Gate 409 832-1546
  1225 Main St Beaumont (77701) *(G-1924)*

Main Glass & Mirror Co 210 637-1011
  17341 Bell North Dr Schertz (78154) *(G-18752)*

Main Jewell LLC 713 623-0499
  5005 W 34th St Ste 100a Houston (77092) *(G-10739)*

Main Marine Repair Inc 713 645-3553
  1714 Broadway St Houston (77012) *(G-10740)*

Main Street Installers LLC 817 459-2001
  1133 W Main St Arlington (76013) *(G-727)*

Mainland Concrete Inc 281 337-7400
  5501 Century Blvd Texas City (77592) *(G-19797)*

Mainliners Welding Academy 409 229-1632
  10001 Porter Rd La Porte (77571) *(G-13773)*

Maintech International LLC 361 265-9901
  299 Gilliam St Corpus Christi (78409) *(G-3570)*

Maintenance Builders Sup Ltd (PA) **713 462-8213**
  1418 Brittmoore Rd Houston (77043) *(G-10741)*

Maintenance Tool & Supply Co (PA) **361 888-8801**
  1902 Mestina St Corpus Christi (78408) *(G-3571)*

Mainteniruav, San Antonio *Also called Jose Alfonsin* *(G-18208)*

Maison De Navar 512 266-6100
  7301 N Fm 620 Rd Austin (78726) *(G-1319)*

Majestic Petroleum Svcs LLC 432 686-2023
  3505 N County Road 1148 Midland (79705) *(G-15291)*

Major Metals Machining, Houston *Also called Coastal Mechanics Tl & Mch Inc* *(G-9228)*

Makerarm Inc 512 553-8033
  4019 Galena Hills Dr Round Rock (78681) *(G-17670)*

Makers Company Inc 817 834-5538
  2723 Weaver St Fort Worth (76117) *(G-6807)*

Makitso USA LLC 281 495-1300
  12850 Sugar Ridge Blvd Stafford (77477) *(G-19350)*

Mako Oilfield Services LLC (PA) **832 680-1300**
  12249-B Northwoods Pk Dr Houston (77041) *(G-10742)*

Maks Family Fun & Events LLC 254 518-0005
  14859 E Business 190 Copperas Cove (76522) *(G-3455)*

Malakoff Trading, Malakoff *Also called Ironhorse Unlimited Inc* *(G-14635)*

Malim Inc 210 654-3963
  3602 Highpoint San Antonio (78217) *(G-18272)*

Mallard Completions LLC 432 381-8508
  7100 I 20 Midland (79706) *(G-15292)*

Mallinckrodt LLC 915 298-6010
  9560 Joe Rodriguez El Paso (79927) *(G-5862)*

Mallorys Western & Leather Sup 817 558-0804
  328 N Broadway St Ste B Joshua (76058) *(G-13322)*

Malone Industrial Machine LLC 713 477-7737
  2902 E Pasadena Blvd Deer Park (77536) *(G-5283)*

Maloney Technical Products, Fort Worth *Also called S & B Technical Products Inc* *(G-6970)*

Malor Manufacturing Inc 817 926-0278
  3245 Saint Louis Ave Fort Worth (76110) *(G-6808)*

Mam LLC 512 407-9940
  404 W Powell Ln Ste 104 Austin (78753) *(G-1320)*

Man Energy Solutions USA Inc (HQ) **713 780-4200**
  1758 Twinwood Pkwy Brookshire (77423) *(G-2319)*

Man Energy Solutions USA Inc 713 780-4200
  1758 Twinwood Pkwy Brookshire (77423) *(G-2320)*

Management Controls Inc 281 590-5881
  15600 Jfk Blvd Ste 850 Houston (77032) *(G-10743)*

Management Services Intl 713 333-0200
  9000 Monroe Rd Houston (77061) *(G-10744)*

Manchaca Metals, Manchaca *Also called Property Works Central Texas* *(G-14640)*

Manco Structures Ltd 210 690-1705
  6106 Fm 3009 Schertz (78154) *(G-18753)*

Mancomm Inc 563 323-6245
  300 Bowie St Apt 2705 Austin (78703) *(G-1321)*

Manda Machine Co, Dallas *Also called Ellard John* *(G-4314)*

Manda Machine Company 214 352-5946
  2683 Myrtle Springs Ave Dallas (75220) *(G-4630)*

Manderscheid Inc 972 424-8701
  910 10th St Plano (75074) *(G-16918)*

Mangstor Inc 512 779-6999
  4201 W Parmer Ln Ste A200 Austin (78727) *(G-1322)*

Mangstor LLC 512 879-9241
  4201 W Parmer Ln Ste A200 Austin (78727) *(G-1323)*

Mangum Hunting Products, Rosharon *Also called Magnum Feeders Inc* *(G-17608)*

Mangums Oilfield Services 979 234-7327
  4321 Main St Eagle Lake (77434) *(G-5542)*

Mangums Oilfield Services Ltd 979 234-5203
  4321 Main St East Bernard (77435) *(G-5560)*

Manhattan Project LLC 469 678-8870
  2215 Sulphur St Dallas (75208) *(G-4631)*

Manhattan Project Beer Company, Dallas *Also called Manhattan Project LLC* *(G-4631)*

Manheim Companies Inc 972 387-4578
  13736 Beta Rd Dallas (75244) *(G-4632)*

Manheim Ruseau, Dallas *Also called Manheim Companies Inc* *(G-4632)*

Mani Little & Wortmann 210 403-9461
  300 Austin Hwy Ste 150 San Antonio (78209) *(G-18273)*

Manitex Inc (HQ) **512 942-3000**
  3000 S Austin Ave Georgetown (78626) *(G-7662)*

Manitou North America Inc 254 799-0232
  6401 Imperial Dr Waco (76712) *(G-20429)*

Mannatech Incorporated (PA) **972 471-7400**
  1410 Lkeside Pkwy Ste 200 Flower Mound (75028) *(G-6270)*

Manner Polymers Inc 972 542-6789
  500 Interchange St McKinney (75071) *(G-14956)*

Manning Navcomp Inc 877 680-1188
  12741 Res Blvd Ste 500 Austin (78750) *(G-1324)*

Manning Pool Service Inc 713 812-9098
  2121 Judiway St Houston (77018) *(G-10745)*

Mannings USA Inc 281 443-7474
  290 Beltway Green Blvd Pasadena (77503) *(G-16479)*

Mans Distributors, Carrollton *Also called MANS Distributors Inc* *(G-2777)*

MANS Distributors Inc 972 930-0330
  3120 Kellway Dr Ste 108 Carrollton (75006) *(G-2777)*

Mansfield Plumbing Pdts LLC 903 657-1436
  1505 Industrial Dr Henderson (75652) *(G-8267)*

Manti Operating Company 361 888-7708
  800 N Shoreline Blvd 900s Corpus Christi (78401) *(G-3572)*

Manti Resources Inc 361 888-7708
  2 Riverway Ste 1100 Houston (77056) *(G-10746)*

Manti Tarka Permian LP 832 460-0046
  2 Riverway Ste 1100 Houston (77056) *(G-10747)*

Mantua Manufacturing Co 713 672-9811
  5534 Armour Dr Houston (77020) *(G-10748)*

Manuels Tortilla Tamale Fctry, Odessa *Also called Odessa Tortilla & Tamale Fctry* *(G-16098)*

Manufactured Concrete Ltd 210 690-1705
  6106 Fm 3009 Schertz (78154) *(G-18754)*

Manufacturer, Bastrop *Also called Accurate Elastomer Pdts Inc* *(G-1748)*

Manufacturing, Weatherford *Also called J Morco Incorporated* *(G-20597)*

Manufacturing Global Resources 361 668-0111
  3707 S Us Highway 281 Alice (78332) *(G-227)*

Manufacturing Group Amer Inc 214 467-4444
  2841 Pierce St Dallas (75233) *(G-4633)*

Manufacturing Plant, Fort Worth *Also called Landers Machine Co* *(G-6779)*

Manufacturing Solutions Inc 409 842-4404
  9485 College St Beaumont (77707) *(G-1925)*

Manufacturing Systems, Austin *Also called M S I Corporation* *(G-1315)*

Manufctred Component Parts Ltd 713 880-0590
  3001 W 11th St Houston (77008) *(G-10749)*

Manufctring Oprations MGT Intl 682 521-5800
  3417 Raider Dr Ste 10 Hurst (76053) *(G-12851)*

Map Oil Tools Inc (PA) **337 560-8559**
  7942 Breen Dr Houston (77064) *(G-10750)*

Mapa Manufacturing LLC 903 897-2371
  103 W Cj Wise Pkwy Naples (75568) *(G-15719)*

Mapei Corporation 972 271-9500
  1501 Wall St Garland (75041) *(G-7542)*

Maple Industries LLC 972 745-2283
  2100 Century Cir Irving (75062) *(G-13094)*

A
L
P
H
A
B
E
T
I
C

Maposa Tinashe....512 704-4601
307 Greener Dr Leander Leander (78641) ***(G-13995)***
Maposa Services, Leander *Also called Maposa Tinashe* ***(G-13995)***
Mapsco Inc....214 476-5480
2521 Lakeshore Dr Flower Mound (75028) ***(G-6271)***
Mapspeople Inc....512 368-0038
3205 Industrial Ter # 100 Austin (78758) ***(G-1325)***
Maquila Magazine Inc....915 544-5845
114 S Oregon St El Paso (79901) ***(G-5863)***
Maquilaplex LLC....956 542-4138
2500 Courage Blvd Brownsville (78521) ***(G-2380)***
Mar-Con Services LLC....713 473-1800
1410 Preston Ave Ste H Pasadena (77503) ***(G-16480)***
Mar-Tek Industries Inc....214 350-9401
301 Industrial Dr Forney (75126) ***(G-6313)***
Maralo LLC (PA)....**713 622-5420**
4400 Post Oak Pkwy # 2550 Houston (77027) ***(G-10751)***
Maralo LLC....512 322-0041
1717 W 6th St Ste 470 Austin (78703) ***(G-1326)***
Marathon Battery, Waco *Also called Marathonnorco Aerospace Inc* ***(G-20431)***
Marathon Bindery Services Inc....713 690-6040
7511 Langtry St Ste 100 Houston (77040) ***(G-10752)***
Marathon International Oil Co (HQ)....**713 629-6600**
5555 San Felipe St # 2796 Houston (77056) ***(G-10753)***
Marathon Oil Company (HQ)....**713 629-6600**
5555 San Felipe St B1 Houston (77056) ***(G-10754)***
Marathon Oil Company....713 296-4336
5555 San Felipe St Houston (77056) ***(G-10755)***
Marathon Oil Corporation (PA)....**713 629-6600**
5555 San Felipe St Houston (77056) ***(G-10756)***
Marathon Oil Ef LLC....713 209-2458
5253 Prue Rd Ste 230 San Antonio (78240) ***(G-18274)***
Marathon Pipe Line, Houston *Also called Marathon Oil Company* ***(G-10754)***
Marathon Spa & Bath, Rosenberg *Also called Ptp Incorporated* ***(G-17595)***
Marathon Special Services Inc....713 784-4918
9515 Caraway Ln Houston (77036) ***(G-10757)***
Marathonnorco Aerospace Inc....254 776-0650
8301 Imperial Dr Waco (76712) ***(G-20430)***
Marathonnorco Aerospace Inc....254 315-7524
8301 Imperial Dr Waco (76712) ***(G-20431)***
Marathonnorco Aerospace Inc....254 772-7358
8301 Imperial Dr Waco (76712) ***(G-20432)***
Marberry Machine Inc....713 466-9666
6210 Cunningham Rd Houston (77041) ***(G-10758)***
Marble & Granite Resources....713 957-2646
3902 Black Locust Dr Houston (77088) ***(G-10759)***
Marble Falls Plant Us61, Burnet *Also called Chemical Lime-Southwest LLC* ***(G-2604)***
Marble Falls Plant Us61, Burnet *Also called Lhoist North America Texas Ltd* ***(G-2611)***
Marble Gallery Inc....903 759-4726
1229 Market St Longview (75604) ***(G-14274)***
Marble Masters of Texas Inc....830 303-7744
1334 Fieldcrest New Braunfels (78130) ***(G-15811)***
Marble Slab Creamery No 152....713 455-5786
11430 East Fwy Ste 400 Houston (77029) ***(G-10760)***
Marbros L L C....210 922-8383
623 New Laredo Hwy San Antonio (78211) ***(G-18275)***
Marc Climatic Controls Inc....713 464-8587
13415 Emmett Rd Houston (77041) ***(G-10761)***
Marc Johnsonusa Inc....713 780-8486
7480 Harwin Dr Houston (77036) ***(G-10762)***
March Resources Co....281 931-3986
11625 N Huston Rosslyn Rd Houston (77086) ***(G-10763)***
Marco Company, The, Fort Worth *Also called Marco Dsplay Specialists GP Lc* ***(G-6810)***
Marco Display Specialists LP....817 244-8300
3209 Marquita Dr Fort Worth (76116) ***(G-6809)***
Marco Dsplay Specialists GP Lc (PA)....**817 244-8300**
3209 Marquita Dr Fort Worth (76116) ***(G-6810)***
Marco Services Inc....806 344-4784
222 Northwest Dr Hereford (79045) ***(G-8293)***
Marcos N Suarez....214 357-2186
2102 Empire Central Dallas (75235) ***(G-4634)***
Mardel Souza Inc....956 459-3504
611 S International Blvd Weslaco (78596) ***(G-20664)***
Marelli Automotive Ltg USA LLC....915 872-1104
12112 Rojas Dr Ste B El Paso (79936) ***(G-5864)***
Maremont Exhaust Products Inc....865 458-4681
423 Bird House Hill Rd Schulenburg (78956) ***(G-18776)***
Marfield Inc....972 245-9122
1225 E Crosby Rd Ste B1 Carrollton (75006) ***(G-2778)***
Marfield Corporate Stationary, Carrollton *Also called Marfield Inc* ***(G-2778)***
Margarita Man, Bergheim *Also called Mmmix Ltd* ***(G-2049)***
Marian Fort Worth Inc....817 332-6151
1501 Northpark Dr Fort Worth (76102) ***(G-6811)***
Marian Graphics Inc....915 542-0033
11401 Pellicano Dr El Paso (79936) ***(G-5865)***
Marian Mexico Inc....915 591-8558
11401 Pellicano Dr El Paso (79936) ***(G-5866)***
Marick Foods Inc....915 593-2271
1013 Cedar St El Paso (79903) ***(G-5867)***
Marietta Martin Materials Inc....979 758-3960
6747 Highway 71 Garwood (77442) ***(G-7615)***
Marine Computation Svcs Kenny....281 646-4155
15115 Park Row Fl 3 Houston (77084) ***(G-10764)***
Marine Construction, Willis *Also called Shoreline Services Inc* ***(G-20865)***
Marine Rubber Inc (PA)....**281 446-4132**
2000 Wilson Rd Humble (77396) ***(G-12787)***
Marine Services LLC....713 923-6688
1714 Broadway St Houston (77012) ***(G-10765)***
Marine Specialties, Richmond *Also called Randolph Products Inc* ***(G-17464)***
Marine Urethane, Humble *Also called Marine Rubber Inc* ***(G-12787)***
Marine Well Containment Co LLC (PA)....**281 820-8800**
9807 Katy Fwy Ste 1200 Houston (77024) ***(G-10766)***
Mariner Gulf of Mexico LLC....713 954-5500
1 Briar Dale Ct Ste 2000 Houston (77027) ***(G-10767)***
Marion Energy Inc....435 789-6959
901 N Mcdonald St McKinney (75069) ***(G-14957)***
Mariposa Corporation....713 222-0220
10893 Shadow Wood Dr Houston (77043) ***(G-10768)***
Mark House of Hot Rods Inc....817 466-9942
2301 Highway 1187 Ste 101 Mansfield (76063) ***(G-14687)***
Mark Morales Shutter Source, Stafford *Also called Shutter Source Inc* ***(G-19378)***
Mark Prestigious....210 820-0093
850 Nor Tex Dr New Braunfels (78132) ***(G-15812)***
Mark's Plumbing Parts, Carrollton *Also called John W Gasparini Inc* ***(G-2874)***
Mark/Trece Inc....210 281-8348
3453 N Panam Expy Ste 203 San Antonio (78219) ***(G-18276)***
Markco Machine Works Inc (PA)....**432 362-8921**
6501 Golder Ave Odessa (79764) ***(G-16070)***
Market Avenue Packaging, El Paso *Also called Creative Molded Packaging LLC* ***(G-5705)***
Market Makers Inc....281 893-9261
6846 Theall Rd Ste 400 Houston (77066) ***(G-10769)***
Marketing 2 Wynne, Mesquite *Also called M2w Inc* ***(G-15059)***
Marketing and Service Assoc, Arlington *Also called Main Street Installers LLC* ***(G-727)***
Marketing Plus, Irving *Also called Marlo Sales Inc* ***(G-13095)***
Marketmap Inc....512 576-6403
9433 Fm 2244 Rd Bldg 1 Austin (78733) ***(G-1327)***
Marking Services Inc....281 424-6710
5518 Decker Dr Baytown (77520) ***(G-1828)***
Marking Services Inc....817 419-0061
5905 Polo Club Dr Arlington (76017) ***(G-728)***
Marking Systems Inc....972 475-0770
2601 Market St Garland (75041) ***(G-7543)***
Markle Mfg Co, San Antonio *Also called Markle Mfg Co San Antonio Inc* ***(G-18277)***
Markle Mfg Co San Antonio Inc....210 655-7130
10619 N Interstate 35 San Antonio (78233) ***(G-18277)***
Markload Systems Inc....281 485-8600
1118 N Main St Ste C Pearland (77581) ***(G-16580)***
Marks Floor Design Inc....713 974-2300
9927 Harwin Dr Houston (77036) ***(G-10770)***
Marks Machine Co Inc....979 543-9204
1101 N Blue Creek Rd El Campo (77437) ***(G-5621)***
Markwest Enrgy E Texas Gas LP....903 694-2225
3239 Sw Loop Carthage (75633) ***(G-2914)***
Markwest Javelina Company LLC....361 289-4900
5438 Union St Corpus Christi (78407) ***(G-3573)***
Marlin Controls Inc (PA)....**214 553-5700**
11011 Regency Crest Dr # 200 Dallas (75238) ***(G-4635)***
Marlin Environmental Products....214 493-9128
1406 Seminole Dr Richardson (75080) ***(G-17351)***
Marlink Inc....713 910-3352
3327 S Sam Houston Pkwy E # 100 Houston (77047) ***(G-10771)***
Marlo Sales Inc....972 721-9755
2511 Texas Dr Ste 100 Irving (75062) ***(G-13095)***
Marmon Highway Tech LLC....214 631-8810
3030 Irving Blvd Dallas (75247) ***(G-4636)***
Marrone & Co Inc....281 227-8400
14343 Interdrive E Houston (77032) ***(G-10772)***
Marroquin and Associates, Dallas *Also called Marroquin Custom Upholstery* ***(G-4637)***
Marroquin Custom Upholstery....214 905-0461
4835 Reading St Dallas (75247) ***(G-4637)***
Marroquin Tortilla Factory....361 883-7051
2737 Greenwood Dr Corpus Christi (78405) ***(G-3574)***
Marroquin's Tortilla Factory, Corpus Christi *Also called Marroquin Tortilla Factory* ***(G-3574)***
Mars Chocolate North Amer LLC....254 776-2100
1001 Texas Central Pkwy Waco (76712) ***(G-20433)***
Mars Petcare Us Inc....254 771-3366
3401 Eberhardt Rd Temple (76504) ***(G-19687)***
Mars Snackfood US, Waco *Also called Mars Chocolate North Amer LLC* ***(G-20433)***
Mars Transformers LLC (PA)....**281 648-1600**
83030 Mchard Rd Houston (77067) ***(G-10773)***
Mars Wrigley Conf US LLC....254 751-5404
1001 Texas Central Pkwy Waco (76712) ***(G-20434)***
Marsha Kitchens....830 278-7262
504 W Fannin St Uvalde (78801) ***(G-20191)***
Marshall & Winston Inc (PA)....**432 684-6373**
6 Desta Dr Ste 3100 Midland (79705) ***(G-15293)***
Marshall Brass, San Marcos *Also called S H Leggitt Company* ***(G-18708)***

Marshall Minerals Inc	903 938-8301
707 Evans St Marshall (75670) *(G-14789)*	
Marshall News Messenger Inc	903 935-7914
309 E Austin St Marshall (75670) *(G-14790)*	
Marshall Pottery Inc (HQ)	**903 938-9201**
4901 Elysian Fields Rd Marshall (75672) *(G-14791)*	
Marshall Prcsion Machining Inc	940 320-4240
403 Acker St Sanger (76266) *(G-18726)*	
Marshall R Young Oil Co (PA)	**817 335-1216**
200 Bailey Ave Ste 102 Fort Worth (76107) *(G-6812)*	
Marshall-Gruber Company LLC	682 518-7400
220 Airport Dr Mansfield (76063) *(G-14688)*	
Marsmith Enterprises Inc	972 488-9339
2403 Walnut Ridge St Dallas (75229) *(G-4638)*	
Marsol Technologies Inc	346 701-8268
14331 Fm 529 Rd Houston (77095) *(G-10774)*	
Martech Foods Inc	713 692-0077
7070 Allensby St Houston (77022) *(G-10775)*	
Martel's Machine Shop, Odessa *Also called Maxie Hodges (G-16074)*	
Martels Machine Shop	432 333-4556
330 S Grandview Ave Odessa (79761) *(G-16071)*	
Martex Fiber Southern Corp	956 831-7707
4656 Towerwood Dr Brownsville (78521) *(G-2381)*	
Martex Well Services LLP (PA)	**903 938-3574**
805 Cox Rd Marshall (75671) *(G-14792)*	
Martin Inc	972 247-7160
3108 Garden Brook Dr Dallas (75234) *(G-4639)*	
Martin Electric Co Inc	979 543-6421
1504 W Jackson St El Campo (77437) *(G-5622)*	
Martin Gas Sales Kilgore Texas, Kilgore *Also called Martin Underground Storage (G-13571)*	
Martin Marietta Materials Inc	210 208-4400
5710 W Hausman Rd Ste 121 San Antonio (78249) *(G-18278)*	
Martin Marietta Materials Inc	830 741-8227
4670 State Highway 173 N Hondo (78861) *(G-8355)*	
Martin Marietta Materials Inc	409 835-4933
5675 Fannett Rd Beaumont (77705) *(G-1926)*	
Martin Marietta Materials Inc	972 647-4985
245 Ward Rd Midlothian (76065) *(G-15484)*	
Martin Marietta Materials Inc	210 495-6224
4303 N Loop 1604 E San Antonio (78247) *(G-18279)*	
Martin Marietta Materials Inc	972 350-8200
1503 Lyndon B Johnson Fwy # 400 Dallas (75234) *(G-4640)*	
Martin Marietta Materials Inc	830 591-1887
4483 Ranch Road 1022 Uvalde (78801) *(G-20192)*	
Martin Marietta Materials Inc	713 896-8683
11913 Fm 529 Rd Houston (77041) *(G-10776)*	
Martin Midstream GP LLC	903 983-6200
4200 Stone Rd Kilgore (75662) *(G-13568)*	
Martin Midstream Partners LP (PA)	**903 983-6200**
4200 Stone Rd Kilgore (75662) *(G-13569)*	
Martin Midstream Partners LP	281 471-2211
2904 N 23rd St La Porte (77571) *(G-13774)*	
Martin Mrietta San Antonio Dst, San Antonio *Also called Martin Marietta Materials Inc (G-18278)*	
Martin Mrtta Mtls Suthwest LLC (HQ)	**210 208-4400**
5710 W Hausman Rd Ste 121 San Antonio (78249) *(G-18280)*	
Martin Mrtta Mtls Suthwest LLC	940 644-5084
856 Fm 2952 Chico (76431) *(G-3053)*	
Martin Mrtta Mtls Suthwest LLC	956 381-1459
35700 Fm 3250 Edinburg (78541) *(G-5595)*	
Martin Paul Inc	940 458-7976
9307 Interstate 35 Denton (76207) *(G-5380)*	
Martin Pedraza	281 814-3916
24202 Hampton Oaks Dr Spring (77389) *(G-19144)*	
MARTIN PREFERRED FOODS LP (PA)	**713 869-6191**
2011 Silver St Houston (77007) *(G-10777)*	
Martin Preferred Logistics, Houston *Also called MARTIN PREFERRED FOODS LP (G-10777)*	
Martin Resource Mgt Corp (PA)	**903 983-6200**
4200 Stone Rd Kilgore (75662) *(G-13570)*	
Martin Resource MGT Corp	432 381-0271
7589 W Murphy St Odessa (79763) *(G-16072)*	
Martin Sprocket & Gear Inc	817 473-1520
811 S 4th Ave Mansfield (76063) *(G-14689)*	
Martin Sprocket & Gear Inc	817 258-3000
9910 Bent Oak Dr Houston (77040) *(G-10778)*	
Martin Sprocket & Gear Inc	903 427-2217
300 Industrial Blvd Clarksville (75426) *(G-3075)*	
Martin Sprocket & Gear Inc	325 677-3591
4300 Fm 18 Abilene (79602) *(G-59)*	
Martin Sprocket & Gear Inc	817 258-3000
3600 Mccart Ave Fort Worth (76110) *(G-6813)*	
Martin Sprocket & Gear Inc	214 428-2191
2944 Oak Ln Dallas (75215) *(G-4641)*	
Martin Sprocket & Gear 15, Houston *Also called Martin Sprocket & Gear Inc (G-10778)*	
Martin Uav LLC (PA)	**972 381-2750**
5345 Towne Square Dr # 115 Plano (75024) *(G-16919)*	
Martin Underground Storage	903 983-1551
4200 Stone Rd Kilgore (75662) *(G-13571)*	

Martin's Gas Testers & Rental, Andrews *Also called Martins Fishing Tls & Rentals (G-550)*	
Martin's Mill Store, Mesquite *Also called Daniel Steel Industries Inc (G-15038)*	
Martin-Decker Totco Inc	903 534-3677
4912 Hightech Dr Tyler (75703) *(G-20120)*	
Martin-Decker Totco Inc (HQ)	**512 340-5000**
1200 Cypress Creek Rd Cedar Park (78613) *(G-2978)*	
Martinek Grain & Bins Inc	972 382-8500
104 W Ash St Celina (75009) *(G-2992)*	
Martinez Millworks Inc	281 988-9334
8503 Highway 6 S Houston (77083) *(G-10779)*	
Martinez Oil & Gas LLC (PA)	**361 384-9500**
223 Mdow Trl Orange Grv Orange Grove Orange Grove (78372) *(G-16268)*	
Martins Fishing Tls & Rentals	432 524-7456
5110 Se 2000 Andrews (79714) *(G-550)*	
Martins Fishing Tools	432 524-7456
5110 Se 2000 Andrews (79714) *(G-551)*	
Marubeni America Corporation	713 871-5700
2800 Post Oak Blvd # 6000 Houston (77056) *(G-10780)*	
Marubeni Oil & Gas (usa) LLC (HQ)	**832 379-1100**
945 Bunker Hill Rd # 700 Houston (77024) *(G-10781)*	
Marvel Communications Company	817 568-0177
6000 Old Hemphill Rd D Fort Worth (76134) *(G-6814)*	
Marvin Dace Company	281 482-1450
18315 W Clover Ln Alvin (77511) *(G-373)*	
Mary and Megan Food Co LLC (PA)	**972 921-9618**
314 N Bishop Ave Dallas (75208) *(G-4642)*	
Mary of Puddin Hill Inc	903 455-2651
512 N John St Palestine (75801) *(G-16302)*	
Maryfield Enterprises LP (PA)	**210 344-4151**
2161 Nw Loop 410 San Antonio (78213) *(G-18281)*	
Marygrove Awning LLC	713 697-0156
4617 N Shepherd Dr Houston (77018) *(G-10782)*	
Masco Cabinetry LLC	972 725-4298
520 Big Stone Gap Rd Duncanville (75137) *(G-5533)*	
Mascoat, Houston *Also called Mascorp Ltd (G-10783)*	
Mascorp Ltd	713 465-0304
4310 Campbell Rd Houston (77041) *(G-10783)*	
Mash Group Holdings LLC	314 638-4200
5329 Spanish Oaks Frisco (75034) *(G-7297)*	
Mash Oilfield Services LP	940 549-6152
3015 State Highway 16 S Graham (76450) *(G-7786)*	
Mason Bottling Company (PA)	**325 347-5150**
210 N Avenue A Mason (76856) *(G-14815)*	
Mason Brothers Cnstr Co Inc	806 495-3400
119 N Avenue H Post (79356) *(G-17191)*	
Mason Fencing and Cnstr LLC	432 272-8347
400 S Grandview Ave Odessa (79761) *(G-16073)*	
Mason Road Sheet Metal Inc	713 466-5054
6450 Clara Rd Ste 190 Houston (77041) *(G-10784)*	
Masonite International	972 686-5500
2300 Skyline Dr Mesquite (75149) *(G-15061)*	
Masonite International Corp	903 454-9500
6308 Industrial Dr Greenville (75402) *(G-8084)*	
Masonite International Corp	972 686-5500
11990 Shiloh Rd Dallas (75228) *(G-4643)*	
Masons Mill & Lumber Co Inc	713 462-6975
9885 Tanner Rd Houston (77041) *(G-10785)*	
Mass Transfer Limited (PA)	**281 991-8866**
5026 Railroad St Deer Park (77536) *(G-5284)*	
Massengale Armature Works Inc	210 732-5168
1031 Basse Rd San Antonio (78212) *(G-18282)*	
Massey Holding & Consultants	817 477-3176
4150 Britton Rd Mansfield (76063) *(G-14690)*	
Massey Industries, Houston *Also called Lfm Industries Inc (G-10629)*	
Massoud Furniture Mfg Co	214 388-8655
8351 Moberly Ln Dallas (75227) *(G-4644)*	
Mast Motorsports LLC	936 560-2218
330 Nw Stallings Dr Nacogdoches (75964) *(G-15703)*	
Master Builders LLC	972 228-7400
2355 W Longhorn Dr Lancaster (75134) *(G-13847)*	
Master Fabricators	832 294-8103
5524 Harvey Wilson Dr Houston (77020) *(G-10786)*	
Master Fibers Inc (HQ)	**915 544-2299**
1710 E Paisano Dr El Paso (79901) *(G-5868)*	
Master Flo	713 690-2789
8726 Fallbrook Dr Houston (77064) *(G-10787)*	
Master Halco, Dallas *Also called Master-Halco Inc (G-4645)*	
Master Hatters of Texas Inc	972 864-5523
2945 Market St Garland (75041) *(G-7544)*	
Master Machine Inc	713 690-3480
10101 Chickasaw Ln Houston (77041) *(G-10788)*	
Master Meter Inc	817 842-8000
101 Regency Pkwy Mansfield (76063) *(G-14691)*	
Master Precision Machining LLC	915 877-0776
4683 Pistolero Ln B El Paso (79912) *(G-5869)*	
Master Tubulars Ptp, Spring *Also called Pyramid Tubular Products LLC (G-19245)*	
Master Valve USA Inc	832 838-4999
23555 Clay Rd Katy (77493) *(G-13424)*	
Master Wall Inc	979 885-6905
914 Bartlett Rd Sealy (77474) *(G-18812)*	

A L P H A B E T I C

Master Woodcraft Cabinetry LLC (HQ)......................**903 935-0500**
 232 N Marshall Indus Blvd Marshall (75670) *(G-14793)*

Master-Halco Inc (HQ)......................................**972 714-7300**
 3010 Lbj Fwy Ste 800 Dallas (75234) *(G-4645)*

Master-Halco Inc...817 378-8086
 500 South Fwy Fort Worth (76104) *(G-6815)*

Master-Halco Inc...214 275-3100
 8330 Lovett Ave Dallas (75227) *(G-4646)*

Master-Halco Inc...214 391-3190
 8250 Lovett Ave Dallas (75227) *(G-4647)*

Masterco Inc..214 381-5690
 3925 Cresthill Rd Dallas (75227) *(G-4648)*

Mastercraft Wood Products LP................................903 935-0500
 232 N Marshall Indus Ave Marshall (75670) *(G-14794)*

Masterpiece Litho Inc...713 869-9990
 7220 Wynnwood Ln Houston (77008) *(G-10789)*

Masterpiece Machine and Mfg Co...........................713 952-4102
 10245 W Airport Blvd Stafford (77477) *(G-19351)*

Masterwerkes..214 315-6479
 100 N Shiloh Rd Ste 120 Garland (75042) *(G-7545)*

Matador Production Company..................................972 371-5200
 5400 Lbj Fwy Ste 1500l Dallas (75240) *(G-4649)*

Matador Ranch, Matador *Also called Koch Industries Inc (G-14816)*

Matador Resources Company, Dallas *Also called MRC Energy Company (G-4700)*

Matador Resources Company (PA)...........................**972 371-5200**
 5400 Lbj Fwy Ste 1500 Dallas (75240) *(G-4650)*

Matagorda Construction & Mtls, Louise *Also called K-C Lease Service Inc (G-14352)*

Mate Inc...281 855-0045
 8910 Point Six Cir Houston (77095) *(G-10790)*

Mateco Truck Equipment Co (HQ)...........................**713 692-3888**
 8222 North Fwy Houston (77037) *(G-10791)*

Matek Performance Inc..817 626-9006
 4920 Rondo Dr Fort Worth (76106) *(G-6816)*

Materia Inc..936 295-4040
 7629 Highway 75 S Huntsville (77340) *(G-12818)*

Material Control Inc..817 695-1400
 918 A 113th St Arlington (76011) *(G-729)*

Material Difference Tech LLC.................................713 640-2040
 6754 Kirbyville St Houston (77033) *(G-10792)*

Material Handling Concepts...................................512 836-6598
 16515 Bratton Ln Austin (78728) *(G-1328)*

Materials Products Inc (PA)...................................**512 821-3303**
 835 Kramer Ln Austin (78758) *(G-1329)*

Materials Transportation Co (PA)............................**800 433-3110**
 1408 S Commerce St Temple (76504) *(G-19688)*

Matex Co, Kilgore *Also called Ma-Tex Wire Rope Co Inc (G-13567)*

Matheson Tri-Gas Inc..361 887-0011
 4863 Baldwin Blvd Corpus Christi (78408) *(G-3575)*

Matheson Tri-Gas Inc..972 432-8800
 2040 California Xing Dallas (75220) *(G-4651)*

Matheson Tri-Gas Inc..713 869-7351
 2018 Houston Ave Houston (77007) *(G-10793)*

Matheson Tri-Gas Inc..281 474-1291
 13440 Bay Area Blvd Pasadena (77507) *(G-16481)*

Matheson Tri-Gas Inc..972 560-5700
 909 Lake Carolyn Pkwy # 1300 Irving (75039) *(G-13096)*

Matheson Tri-Gas Inc..512 385-0611
 3519 E 5th St Austin (78702) *(G-1330)*

Matheson Tri-Gas Inc..281 498-2310
 13045 Murphy Rd Stafford (77477) *(G-19352)*

Matheson Tri-Gas Inc..210 225-3151
 3566 N Panam Expy San Antonio (78219) *(G-18283)*

Matheson Tri-Gas Inc..281 471-2544
 2200 Houston Ave Houston (77007) *(G-10794)*

Matheson Tri-Gas Inc..817 354-9536
 2040 Cal Crossing Rd Dallas (75220) *(G-4652)*

Matheson Tri-Gas Inc..817 551-0550
 5932 South Fwy Fort Worth (76134) *(G-6817)*

Matheson Tri-Gas 506, Fort Worth *Also called Matheson Tri-Gas Inc (G-6817)*

Mathew Marine Inc...877 508-4004
 4001 Navigation Blvd Houston (77003) *(G-10795)*

Mathiesen, San Antonio *Also called Matthiesen Equipment Co (G-18284)*

Mathis & Son Inc...940 997-2137
 307 Amity Ave Rule (79547) *(G-17728)*

Mathis & Son Well Service, Rule *Also called Mathis & Son Inc (G-17728)*

Mathis Iron Works Inc...713 991-5846
 6003 Allison Rd Houston (77048) *(G-10796)*

Matica Biotechnology Inc.....................................979 321-7500
 1645 Grens Prrie Rd W Ste College Station (77845) *(G-3192)*

Matson Inc...817 478-1800
 5960 E Loop 820 S Fort Worth (76119) *(G-6818)*

Mattel Inc...817 302-3300
 501 Meacham Blvd Fort Worth (76106) *(G-6819)*

Mattel Inc...310 252-2000
 8702 Killam Indus Blvd Laredo (78045) *(G-13910)*

Matthew Warren Inc..800 364-0391
 7400 Pinemont Dr Houston (77040) *(G-10797)*

Matthews-Daniel Holdings Inc (PA)..........................**713 622-1633**
 4544 Post Oak Place Dr # 160 Houston (77027) *(G-10798)*

Matthiesen, San Antonio *Also called Modern Fabricating Inc (G-18315)*

Matthiesen Equipment Co.....................................210 333-1510
 566 N Ww White Rd San Antonio (78219) *(G-18284)*

Matutech Ltd Liability Company..............................832 989-3208
 5402 Creek Shadows Dr Kingwood (77339) *(G-13649)*

Maudlin Assets Management Inc..............................281 334-7566
 1929 Highway 146 Kemah (77565) *(G-13477)*

Maui Foods International Inc.................................214 823-6284
 2901 Summit Ave Ste 400 Plano (75074) *(G-16920)*

Mauser Packaging Solutions..................................817 473-0259
 1501 E Dallas St Mansfield (76063) *(G-14692)*

Mauser Usa LLC..936 273-1279
 410 S Trade Center Pkwy B13 Conroe (77385) *(G-3328)*

Mauser Usa LLC..713 670-2332
 4004 Homestead Rd Houston (77028) *(G-10799)*

Mavenir Prvate Holdings II Ltd...............................469 916-4393
 1700 Intl Pkwy Ste 200 Richardson (75081) *(G-17352)*

Maverick Business Forms Inc................................903 663-7503
 10401 Us Hwy 259 Diana (75640) *(G-5460)*

Maverick Companies LLC.....................................817 334-4100
 801 Cherry St Unit 2 Fort Worth (76102) *(G-6820)*

Maverick Concepts LLC.......................................972 418-7189
 3402 W Miller Rd Garland (75041) *(G-7546)*

Maverick Directional Services (PA)..........................**281 364-1212**
 25615 Oakhurst Dr Spring (77386) *(G-19230)*

Maverick Door and Millwork Inc.............................210 659-5553
 124 Pecan Dr Schertz (78154) *(G-18755)*

Maverick Enterprises..281 444-5010
 13727 Perry Rd Houston (77070) *(G-10800)*

Maverick Field Services LLC..................................432 685-5021
 3601 N County Road 1148 Midland (79705) *(G-15294)*

Maverick Hydraulics Machining, Grand Prairie *Also called George Hall (G-7882)*

Maverick Machining, Houston *Also called Maverick Precision Mfg Ltd (G-10801)*

Maverick Poles & Structure LLC.............................817 441-9688
 3559 Williams Rd Ste 106 Benbrook (76116) *(G-2043)*

Maverick Precision Mfg Ltd...................................713 433-3756
 13604 Almeda School Rd Houston (77047) *(G-10801)*

Maverick Solutions LLC.......................................817 334-4100
 801 Cherry St Unit 2 Fort Worth (76102) *(G-6821)*

Maverick Stainless LLC.......................................214 884-2700
 4525 Production Dr Dallas (75235) *(G-4653)*

Maverick Technical Systems Inc..............................903 845-5574
 315 E Us Highway 80 Gladewater (75647) *(G-7726)*

Maverick Trmnals Three Rvers L.............................956 371-6530
 14301 Rl Ostos Rd Brownsville (78521) *(G-2382)*

Maverick Tube Corporation (HQ).............................**713 767-4400**
 2200 West Loop S Ste 800 Houston (77027) *(G-10802)*

Maverick Tube Corporation...................................713 937-1800
 8204 Frbanks N Houston Rd Houston (77064) *(G-10803)*

Maverick Tube Corporation...................................936 539-2136
 699 Fm 3083 Rd Conroe (77301) *(G-3329)*

Maverick Well Pluggers LLC..................................432 458-3780
 3007 N Cr 110 Midland (79706) *(G-15295)*

Maverick Well Service LLC...................................903 983-6050
 300 Fm 1252 E Kilgore (75662) *(G-13572)*

Maviro Inc (HQ)...**713 485-5193**
 1102 Howard Dr Deer Park (77536) *(G-5285)*

Maxam North America Inc (HQ)..............................**801 233-6000**
 433 Las Colinas Blvd E # 900 Irving (75039) *(G-13097)*

Maxco LLC..832 554-0980
 6545 N Eldridge Pkwy Houston (77041) *(G-10804)*

Maxi Volt Corporation Inc....................................806 371-0722
 9350 S Georgia St Amarillo (79118) *(G-500)*

Maxie Hodges...432 333-4556
 330 S Grandview Ave Odessa (79761) *(G-16074)*

Maxim Integrated Products Inc...............................210 522-7000
 9651 Westover Hills Blvd San Antonio (78251) *(G-18285)*

Maxim Integrated Products Inc...............................214 458-0357
 6431 Longhorn Dr Irving (75063) *(G-13098)*

Maxim Integrated Products Inc...............................972 371-4000
 4345 Innovation Dr Dallas (75244) *(G-4654)*

Maxim Integrated Products Inc...............................512 249-0307
 8516 Anderson Mill Rd # 200 Austin (78729) *(G-1703)*

Maxim Silencers, Houston *Also called Maxco LLC (G-10804)*

Maxime International Foods, Plano *Also called Maui Foods International Inc (G-16920)*

Maxims Imports Inc..915 577-9228
 1001 E Missouri Ave El Paso (79902) *(G-5870)*

Maximum Industries Inc......................................214 614-6936
 1408 W Walnut Hill Ln Irving (75038) *(G-13099)*

Maxistrut of Texas Inc...713 880-4228
 1209 W 17th St Houston (77008) *(G-10805)*

Maxitrol Company..817 479-8505
 7415 Whitehall St Ste 124 Richland Hills (76118) *(G-17441)*

Maxmile Technologies LLC....................................512 961-1187
 10623 Winchelsea Dr Austin (78750) *(G-1331)*

Maxpower of Texas, Houston *Also called Qpower Incorporated (G-11486)*

Maxus Energy Corporation (HQ).............................**281 681-7200**
 10333 Richmond Ave # 1050 Houston (77042) *(G-10806)*

Maxus US Exploration Company..............................281 681-7200
 1330 Lake Robbins Dr # 300 The Woodlands (77380) *(G-19892)*

Maxwell Manufacturing Inc 512 357-2772
55 2nd St Ste 1 Maxwell (78656) *(G-14818)*

Maxwell Paper Products, Dallas *Also called Maxwell Papers LP (G-4655)*

Maxwell Papers LP 214 631-5550
615 Regal Row Dallas (75247) *(G-4655)*

Maxwell Papers Holdings LLLP (PA).............................**214 631-5550**
615 Regal Row Dallas (75247) *(G-4656)*

Maxxsafe Company, Dallas *Also called Corporate Records Management (G-4171)*

May Group International, Fort Worth *Also called Technographix LLC (G-7041)*

Mayco Inc 214 638-4848
2811 Mican Dr Dallas (75212) *(G-4657)*

Mayday Manufacturing Co 940 898-8301
3100 Jim Christal Rd Denton (76207) *(G-5381)*

Mayer Enterprises Inc 281 498-2600
5522 Mitchelldale St Houston (77092) *(G-10807)*

Mayfield Paper Company Inc 432 580-4118
2321 E 2nd St Odessa (79761) *(G-16075)*

Mayhan Fabricators Inc 903 734-4198
7525 Us Highway 271 S Gilmer (75645) *(G-7709)*

Mayo Mfg Corporation 903 838-0518
4101 Terry St Texarkana (75501) *(G-19769)*

Mayors Machine Works Inc 281 242-0636
2620 Charles Ln Sugar Land (77498) *(G-19506)*

MB Dustless Air Filter Co LLC 210 653-6901
6634 Mapleridge St Houston (77081) *(G-10808)*

MB Nutritional Sciences LLC 806 778-2697
6508 E Fm 40 Lubbock (79403) *(G-14444)*

MB Ranch King Blinds LLC 817 558-7320
4629 County Road 805 Joshua (76058) *(G-13323)*

MB Robinson Inc 432 267-5277
607 Main St Big Spring (79720) *(G-2087)*

MBK-Wi Inc 972 375-0253
1050 S State Highway 161 Grand Prairie (75051) *(G-7922)*

Mblh Marine LLC 409 962-1302
5848 Procter Ext Port Arthur (77642) *(G-17118)*

MBS Construction I Ltd 817 473-0328
1315 Fm 1187 Ste 115 Mansfield (76063) *(G-14693)*

Mbs Incoporated, Houston *Also called Maintenance Builders Sup Ltd (G-10741)*

Mbs Medical Technologies Inc 888 482-4201
6750 N Desert Blvd El Paso (79912) *(G-5871)*

Mc Coy Building Supply 451, McAllen *Also called McCoy Corporation (G-14890)*

Mc Creless Company (PA)...432 332-1213
1318 N Grant Ave Odessa (79761) *(G-16076)*

Mc Daniel Metals Inc 281 987-8400
1318 Buschong St Houston (77039) *(G-10809)*

Mc Hone Metal Fabricators Inc.....................................972 524-7775
10300 County Road 304 Terrell (75160) *(G-19741)*

Mc Manus Instrument Co Inc 409 834-2419
5088 Fm 3063 Village Mills (77663) *(G-20338)*

Mc Millan Company, Georgetown *Also called R D McMillan Company Inc (G-7671)*

Mc Quirk, Bob Watchmaker, Dallas *Also called Time Delay Corporation (G-5094)*

Mc Welding & Fabrication Inc 361 289-9605
8337 Up River Rd Ste A Corpus Christi (78409) *(G-3576)*

McAfee LLC 972 963-7000
5000 Headquarters Dr Plano (75024) *(G-16921)*

McAfee Public Sector LLC 972 963-7000
5000 Headquarters Dr Plano (75024) *(G-16922)*

McAllen Bag & Supply Company 956 686-6571
1608 Pecan Blvd McAllen (78501) *(G-14887)*

McAllen Metal Stamping Inc 956 682-3438
3500 W Military Hwy McAllen (78503) *(G-14888)*

McAllen P&Rs Service Center, McAllen *Also called GE Engine Svcs - McAllen L P (G-14864)*

McAllen Sports Inc (PA)...**956 687-5500**
108 S 16th St McAllen (78501) *(G-14889)*

McAps Inc 713 941-1300
102 Main St South Houston (77587) *(G-19049)*

McAps Automation and Power, South Houston *Also called McAps Inc (G-19049)*

McBee Operating Company LLC (PA)..............................214 526-1500
4301 Westside Dr Ste 200 Dallas (75209) *(G-4658)*

McBermett Milner LLC 325 643-2277
4501 Danhil Dr Brownwood (76801) *(G-2440)*

McBride Distribution, Wichita Falls *Also called Mpp Investments LLC (G-20784)*

McBroom Industries 817 645-2248
4385 S Highway 174 Cleburne (76033) *(G-3101)*

McC Holdings Inc 936 588-5301
9860 Johnson Rd Montgomery (77316) *(G-15636)*

McC Holdings Inc (HQ)..**936 271-6500**
4526 Res Frest Dr Ste 400 The Woodlands (77381) *(G-19893)*

McCamey Well Service Inc 432 208-2769
1368 E 24th St Mc Camey (79752) *(G-14819)*

McCarthy Print Inc 512 479-8938
1804 Chicon St Ste 106 Austin (78702) *(G-1332)*

McCartney Investment Corp 214 521-8410
6407 Hillcrest Ave Dallas (75205) *(G-4659)*

McCartney's University Spirit, Dallas *Also called McCartney Investment Corp (G-4659)*

McClinton Energy Group L L C 432 563-5500
12620 State Highway 191 Midland (79707) *(G-15296)*

McClinton Energy Group L L C (PA)...............................**432 563-5500**
11200 W Interstate 20 Odessa (79765) *(G-16077)*

McCord Printing Inc 214 631-1809
1111 Regal Row Dallas (75247) *(G-4660)*

McCormick & Company Inc 972 721-9318
3300 Century Cir Irving (75062) *(G-13100)*

McCormick & Company Inc 214 329-7044
200 Union Bower Ct # 214 Irving (75061) *(G-13101)*

McCormick Vision Centers, Austin *Also called Vision Centers PA (G-1638)*

McCoy, Boling *Also called Drawworks LP (G-2147)*

McCoy Corporation 956 618-3104
3209 W Business 83 McAllen (78501) *(G-14890)*

McCraw Materials, Telephone *Also called B Mayfield McCraw (G-19665)*

McCurdy Services Inc 903 729-5681
2223 W Point Tap Rd Palestine (75803) *(G-16303)*

McDermott International, Houston *Also called CB&i LLC (G-9105)*

McDermott International Inc (PA)....................................**281 588-6600**
915 N Eldridge Pkwy Houston (77079) *(G-10810)*

McDonald Extrusion Tooling 817 594-1290
116 Price Ln Weatherford (76085) *(G-20604)*

McDonald Lighting & Maint Sup 903 297-8181
1200 Regal Oak Dr Longview (75604) *(G-14275)*

McDonald Mch & Fabrications, Weatherford *Also called McDonald Extrusion Tooling (G-20604)*

McDonald Sales & Service, Longview *Also called McDonald Lighting & Maint Sup (G-14275)*

McDonald Welding Co 325 573-5329
1110 College Ave Snyder (79549) *(G-18994)*

McDowell Label, Plano *Also called McDowell Packg & Advg Co Inc (G-16923)*

McDowell Packg & Advg Co Inc 469 246-2700
2700 E Plano Pkwy Plano (75074) *(G-16923)*

McElroy Metal Mill Inc 214 703-3113
3014 Lincoln Ct Garland (75041) *(G-7547)*

McElroy Metal Mill Inc 972 226-7075
460 Clay Rd Mesquite (75182) *(G-15062)*

McElroy Plastics Inc 903 842-2180
725 Arp Dr Troup (75789) *(G-20025)*

McElvy Media, Houston *Also called McElvy Vasquez Inc (G-10811)*

McElvy Vasquez Inc 713 686-8494
3500 E T C Jester Blvd Houston (77018) *(G-10811)*

McEver Machine Works, Troup *Also called Carl R McEver (G-20023)*

McFa, Houston *Also called Mitsubshi Ctrpllar Frklift AME (G-10891)*

McFadden & Associates Inc 972 680-8333
515 N Interurban St # 103 Richardson (75081) *(G-17353)*

McFadden Stairs Inc 972 680-8333
515 N Interurban St # 103 Richardson (75081) *(G-17354)*

McGaskets & Ptfe Spc Inc 713 847-6700
6010 Dwyer Dr Humble (77396) *(G-12788)*

McGill Airflow LLC 254 580-1680
206 Pecos St Hillsboro (76645) *(G-8330)*

McGill Maint & Fabrication, Freeport *Also called McGill Maintenance Partnr Ltd (G-7203)*

McGill Maintenance Partnr Ltd (PA)...............................**979 233-5438**
6402 E Highway 332 Freeport (77541) *(G-7203)*

McGrew Energy Corporation 214 265-1135
4849 Grnvlle Ave Ste 1310 Dallas (75206) *(G-4661)*

McGuffy Energy Services LP 281 255-6955
18635 Telge Rd Cypress (77429) *(G-3809)*

McGuire Industries Inc 979 968-5131
4429 W State Highway 71 La Grange (78945) *(G-13698)*

MCI Flowtronex, Dallas *Also called Motor Controls Inc (G-4691)*

Mclp Industrial Entps Corp 832 767-4006
1122 N Main St Pearland (77581) *(G-16581)*

McKay Equipment Co 432 381-5510
3099 S Branch Rd Krum (76249) *(G-13674)*

McKee True Value Hdwr & Lbr 903 874-6581
104 N 7th St Corsicana (75110) *(G-3677)*

McKees Rock Forgings Division, Dallas *Also called Standard Forged Products LLC (G-5003)*

McKesson Corporation (PA)...**972 446-4800**
6555 State Highway 161 Irving (75039) *(G-13102)*

McKinley Iron Works Inc 817 335-1268
4720 Esco Dr Fort Worth (76140) *(G-6822)*

McKinley Paper Company 956 487-7424
1 E Sauz St Rio Grande City (78582) *(G-17473)*

McKinney Central Fire Dept, Mc Kinney *Also called City of McKinney (G-14827)*

McKinney Pipe & Steel, McKinney *Also called J B R Enterprises Inc (G-14947)*

McKinney/Frisco Overhead Door, McKinney *Also called Bochelle Inc (G-14928)*

McLeod Machine Works Inc 409 835-3429
5455 Ohio St Beaumont (77705) *(G-1927)*

McM, Houston *Also called Metal Construction Mtls Inc (G-10845)*

McMahan Trailer Sales, Cuero *Also called McMahan Welding Service Ltd (G-3763)*

McMahan Welding Service Ltd 361 275-0111
269 Us Highway 183 S Cuero (77954) *(G-3763)*

McMillan Welding 432 687-4625
110 N Mrenseld Ste 200 Midland (79701) *(G-15297)*

McMt LLC 903 592-9663
1810 W Southwest Loop 323 Tyler (75701) *(G-20121)*

McNeilus Truck and Mfg Inc 972 225-2313
1101 Hwy 45 S Hutchins (75141) *(G-12868)*

McNichols Company 877 884-4653
  3540 W Miller Rd Ste 240 Garland (75041) **(G-7548)**

McPherson Cellars Inc 806 687-9463
  1615 Texas Ave Lubbock (79401) **(G-14445)**

McQueary Industries Inc 817 335-1988
  3120 E 4th St Fort Worth (76111) **(G-6823)**

MCR Oil Tools LLC 817 704-6677
  7327 Business Pl Arlington (76001) **(G-730)**

MCS Kenny, Houston *Also called Marine Computation Svcs Kenny* **(G-10764)**

McV Sales Co L L C 713 785-0088
  7522 Kensico Rd Houston (77036) **(G-10812)**

McWane Inc 800 527-8478
  11910 County Road 492 Tyler (75706) **(G-20122)**

McWane Inc (HQ) **800 527-8478**
  11910 County Road 492 Tyler (75706) **(G-20123)**

McWane Inc 903 882-5511
  11721 Us Highway 69 N Tyler (75706) **(G-20124)**

McWhirter Wood Products Inc 713 861-1437
  5815 Schuler St Houston (77007) **(G-10813)**

McX Gulf of Mexico LLC 713 953-9292
  800 Gessner Rd Ste 800 # 800 Houston (77024) **(G-10814)**

MD Construction Inc 903 389-2595
  366 West St 27 Fairfield (75840) **(G-6178)**

MD Totco, Cedar Park *Also called National Oilwell Varco Inc* **(G-2980)**

MD Totco, Cedar Park *Also called Martin-Decker Totco Inc* **(G-2978)**

Md3 Industries Ltd 682 831-1414
  4901 Keller Haslet Rd Fort Worth (76244) **(G-6824)**

Mdi Security LLC 210 477-5400
  6800 Alamo Downs Pkwy San Antonio (78238) **(G-18286)**

Mds Printgraphics Inc 972 647-0043
  2641 N Forum Dr Grand Prairie (75052) **(G-7923)**

Mdt Replas, Houston *Also called Material Difference Tech LLC* **(G-10792)**

MDU Cnstruction Svcs Group Inc 817 447-8085
  5701 Highpoint Pkwy Burleson (76028) **(G-2590)**

Meador Products Inc 940 767-8541
  1901 Broday Rd Wichita Falls (76305) **(G-20782)**

Measurement Company, The, Houston *Also called Tmco Inc* **(G-12308)**

Measurement Services Inc 361 227-4998
  196 Arena Trl Alice (78332) **(G-228)**

Measurement Technologies Ltd 817 571-9981
  4843 Colleyville Blvd Colleyville (76034) **(G-3220)**

Measurementation 979 373-9991
  1744 W 4th St Ste 208 Freeport (77541) **(G-7204)**

Mec Services, Amarillo *Also called Moses Envmtl & Cnstr Svcs LLC* **(G-448)**

Mechanical Repair & Engrg LP (PA) **281 471-7811**
  202 N 18th St La Porte (77571) **(G-13775)**

Mechanical Sheet Metal Inc 972 524-6200
  3002 Tem Tex Blvd Terrell (75160) **(G-19742)**

Mechanical Technical Svcs LP 512 929-7090
  1720 Royston Ln Round Rock (78664) **(G-17671)**

Mechanism Exchange & Repr Inc 361 293-6452
  210 E Hochheim St Yoakum (77995) **(G-20968)**

Meco Inc 281 276-7600
  12505 Reed Rd Ste 100 Sugar Land (77478) **(G-19507)**

Meco Construction Company LLC 817 975-4599
  7113 Frenton Ter Fort Worth (76131) **(G-6825)**

Mecor Group, Spring *Also called Mecor Usa Inc* **(G-19231)**

Mecor Usa Inc (HQ) **713 817-0683**
  1776 Woodstead Ct Ste 109 Spring (77380) **(G-19231)**

Med Couture Inc 214 231-2500
  1901 Hutton Ct Ste 200 Farmers Branch (75234) **(G-6207)**

Med Logics Inc 949 582-3891
  1627 Enterprise St Athens (75751) **(G-830)**

Med-Loz Lease Service Inc 956 765-6029
  3050 N Us Highway 83 Zapata (78076) **(G-20984)**

Med-Loz Oil Field Supply, Zapata *Also called Med-Loz Lease Service Inc* **(G-20984)**

Medallion Delaware Basin LLC 972 746-4401
  222 Las Colinas Blvd W Irving (75039) **(G-13103)**

Medallion Midstream LLC (PA) **972 746-4401**
  909 Lake Carolyn Pkwy # 1 Irving (75039) **(G-13104)**

Medallion Oil Company Inc 713 654-0144
  1407 Fannin St Houston (77002) **(G-10815)**

Medapoint Inc 512 659-1117
  3005 S Lamar Blvd D109 Austin (78704) **(G-1333)**

Medassets Inc 972 813-7500
  5543 Legacy Dr Plano (75024) **(G-16924)**

Medc International 713 937-9772
  3413 N Sam Houston Pkwy W Houston (77086) **(G-10816)**

Medcalf Fabrication Inc 281 893-0775
  1703 Hugh Rd Houston (77067) **(G-10817)**

Medco Manufacturing LLC 281 379-3100
  8319 Thora Ln Hngr A1 Spring (77379) **(G-19145)**

Medcognition Inc 210 960-0930
  21750 Hardy Oak Blvd San Antonio (78258) **(G-18287)**

Medders Oil Company 940 692-6626
  4245 Kemp Blvd Ste 904 Wichita Falls (76308) **(G-20783)**

Medeanalytics Inc (PA) **469 476-5423**
  501 W President George Bu Richardson (75080) **(G-17355)**

Medek L L C 956 800-4366
  315 E Business Highway 83 Alamo (78516) **(G-180)**

Medex South 713 838-1989
  8588 Katy Fwy Ste 348 Houston (77024) **(G-10818)**

Medhab LLC 817 233-5271
  3216 Essex Dr Mansfield (76063) **(G-14694)**

Medhost Inc 972 560-3100
  6100 W Plano Pkwy # 3100 Plano (75093) **(G-16925)**

Media Displays Inc 210 495-6338
  14731 Bulverde Rd San Antonio (78247) **(G-18288)**

Media One, Mabank *Also called Monitor* **(G-14580)**

Media Palmer Inc 903 572-1705
  210 S Van Buren Ave Mount Pleasant (75455) **(G-15654)**

Media Recovery, Dallas *Also called Texas Mri LP* **(G-5077)**

Mediakind, Frisco *Also called Mk Systems USA Inc* **(G-7298)**

Mediana Technologies Corp 425 406-2262
  23510 Canyon Golf Rd # 103 San Antonio (78258) **(G-18289)**

Medical Components of America 830 237-6405
  292 Navarro Dr Seguin (78155) **(G-18851)**

Medical Concepts Dev Inc 651 735-0498
  1 Butterfield Trail Blvd El Paso (79906) **(G-5872)**

Medical Device Tech Inc (HQ) **800 338-0440**
  1445 Flat Creek Rd Athens (75751) **(G-831)**

Medical External Support Appls, San Antonio *Also called MESA Orthopedic Supplies* **(G-18292)**

Medical Extrusion Tech Inc 951 698-4346
  1400 Waters Ridge Dr Lewisville (75057) **(G-14063)**

Medical Plastics Laboratory 254 865-7221
  226 Fm 116 Gatesville (76528) **(G-7619)**

Medical Polymers, Austin *Also called Habitek International Inc* **(G-1196)**

Medical Practice Management, Cypress *Also called Blue Medical Services Inc* **(G-3781)**

Medical Present Value Inc 512 795-0015
  5000 Plaza On The Lk # 265 Austin (78746) **(G-1334)**

Medical Staffing Solutions, Killeen *Also called Teresa A McVicker Pc* **(G-13617)**

Medical Supplies, Commerce *Also called Covidien LP* **(G-3242)**

Medical Technology Inc 972 647-0884
  2601 Pinewood Dr Grand Prairie (75051) **(G-7924)**

Medical Textiles Inc 214 744-1246
  107 Pittsburg St Dallas (75207) **(G-4662)**

Medical Uniform Mfg Inc 713 838-2233
  4951 Terminal St Ste G Bellaire (77401) **(G-1998)**

Medical Web Experts LLC 619 819-8610
  5950 Sherry Ln Ste 405 Dallas (75225) **(G-4663)**

Medical Z 210 681-7912
  10625 Richmond Ave Houston (77042) **(G-10819)**

Medici Technologies LLC 800 768-8131
  7500 Rialto Blvd 2-100 Austin (78735) **(G-1335)**

Medifacts Inc 817 571-8181
  1105 S Airport Cir Ste B Colleyville (76034) **(G-3221)**

Medimobile 512 686-0817
  1918 Leander Rd Georgetown (78628) **(G-7663)**

Medinc of Texas LP 713 979-4364
  1771 Crosspoint Ave Houston (77054) **(G-10820)**

Meditrrnean Spcialty Foods LLC 214 680-8820
  6433 Norway Rd Dallas (75230) **(G-4664)**

Medivators Inc 936 539-0391
  3150 Pollok Dr Conroe (77303) **(G-3330)**

Medline Industries Inc 281 574-6200
  501 Commerce Pkwy Katy (77494) **(G-13371)**

Medplast Group Inc (PA) **480 553-6400**
  7865 Northcourt Rd # 100 Houston (77040) **(G-10821)**

Medstone International Inc 512 328-2892
  9825 Spectrum Dr Bldg 3 Austin (78717) **(G-1704)**

Medtex Converters Inc 903 670-3270
  1653 Enterprise St Athens (75751) **(G-832)**

Medtronic Minimed Inc 830 438-0383
  2880 John Charles Rd Bulverde (78163) **(G-2556)**

Medtronic PS Medical Inc 817 788-6400
  4620 N Beach St Haltom City (76137) **(G-8153)**

Medtronic Usa Inc 210 395-5769
  613 Nw Loop 410 Ste 660 San Antonio (78216) **(G-18290)**

Meera Enterprises Inc 972 385-3900
  15404 Midway Rd Addison (75001) **(G-148)**

Mega Compressor, Houston *Also called Megapower Inc* **(G-10822)**

Mega Metal Systems, Irving *Also called NCH Corporation* **(G-13118)**

Mega Oil Corporation 903 984-7050
  226 Hwy 42 W Access Rd Kilgore (75662) **(G-13573)**

Mega Systems Inc (PA) **210 684-2600**
  18668 Hwy 16 N Helotes (78023) **(G-8242)**

Mega-Lite, Helotes *Also called Mega Systems Inc* **(G-8242)**

Megaever Lighting, McKinney *Also called Yankon Lighting Inc* **(G-14992)**

Megalodon Services Inc 941 882-3108
  565 County Road 1591 Sunset (76270) **(G-19625)**

Megapower Inc 832 415-6995
  7120 Brittmoore Rd # 410 Houston (77041) **(G-10822)**

Megatrend Designs Inc 713 675-8838
  1250 Shotwell St Houston (77020) **(G-10823)**

Megatron Inc 281 558-0034
  11241 Richmond Ave Ste E1 Houston (77082) (G-10824)

Megger, Dallas Also called Avo Multi-AMP Corporation (G-3991)

Meggitt Control Systems, Addison Also called ACC-Kp LLC (G-98)

Megladon Mfg Group Ltd 512 491-0006
  12317 Tech Blvd Ste 100 Austin (78727) (G-1336)

MEI Micro Inc 972 690-9494
  4555 Excel Pkwy Ste 500 Addison (75001) (G-149)

Meister Industries Inc (PA) 432 366-2875
  2301 W 42nd St Odessa (79764) (G-16078)

Meister Industries Inc 432 425-0293
  4021 Rasco Ave Odessa (79764) (G-16079)

Mel Northey Co Inc 281 445-3485
  303 Gulf Bank Rd Houston (77037) (G-10825)

Melco Blowout Preventer Spc (PA) 432 362-0491
  4001 W County Rd Odessa (79764) (G-16080)

Melendy Yard, Houston Also called Martin Marietta Materials Inc (G-10776)

Melet Plastics Usa Inc 210 822-0460
  210 Laramie Dr San Antonio (78209) (G-18291)

Meletio Lighting and Elec Sup, Frisco Also called Dolan Northwest LLC (G-7257)

Melhart Music Center, McAllen Also called Jim Melhart Piano and Organ Co (G-14879)

Melissa Lighting Inc 214 388-7487
  4859 Olson Dr Dallas (75227) (G-4665)

Melissa Renewables LLC 432 563-0447
  3820 Sam Rayburn Hwy Melissa (75454) (G-14998)

Melvin Hammon 806 665-2667
  622 E Foster Ave Pampa (79065) (G-16328)

Memphis Electronic Inc 713 600-6080
  1225 North Loop W Ste 820 Houston (77008) (G-10826)

Men of Cloth LP 281 464-3141
  10725 Sagetree Dr Houston (77089) (G-10827)

Menard Industries LLC 512 628-1058
  12052 Homestead Rd Houston (77050) (G-10828)

Menard's Railroad Materials, Houston Also called Menard Industries LLC (G-10828)

Menasha Packaging Company LLC 330 419-3505
  2710 Edmonds Ln Lane42 Lewisville (75067) (G-14064)

Mendes Printing Co Inc 956 722-2222
  1020 Sanchez St Laredo (78040) (G-13911)

Mensor LP 512 396-4200
  201 Barnes Dr San Marcos (78666) (G-18698)

Mentor IMC (usa) Inc 713 425-6307
  3 Riverway Ste 725 Houston (77056) (G-10829)

Mentor Texas LP 972 252-6060
  3041 Skyway Cir N Irving (75038) (G-13105)

Mepco Enterprises Inc 713 943-9240
  11410 Dumas St Houston (77034) (G-10830)

Mepusa, Houston Also called Mitsui E&P USA LLC (G-10893)

Merc Medical Supply Co Inc 713 270-4936
  10518 Kipp Way Dr Ste D Houston (77099) (G-10831)

Mercer Controls Inc 361 782-7168
  804 Apollo Dr Edna (77957) (G-5609)

Mercer Metals LP 214 905-9915
  1249 Avenue R Grand Prairie (75050) (G-7925)

Mercer Well Service Inc 940 567-5991
  902 S Main St Jacksboro (76458) (G-13222)

Merch Legacy 817 682-6855
  3054 Se Loop 820 Fort Worth (76140) (G-6826)

Merchants Metals Inc 817 293-9641
  7000 Will Rogers Blvd Fort Worth (76140) (G-6827)

Merchants Moving & Storage Inc 361 293-7202
  4701 Us Highway 77a S Yoakum (77995) (G-20969)

Merchants Moving and Stor Inc 361 293-7202
  4701 Us Highway 77a S Yoakum (77995) (G-20970)

Merck & Co Inc 908 740-4000
  1414 W Bowie St Fort Worth (76110) (G-6828)

Merco Solutions Corporation 830 519-4260
  1078 Highway 304 Gonzales (78629) (G-7759)

Mercron Inc 972 690-6565
  610 Hanover Ln Irving (75062) (G-13106)

Mercury Companies, Houston Also called C K Kelley & Sons Inc (G-9030)

Mercury Operating LLC 214 935-1698
  6321 Campus Circle Dr E Irving (75063) (G-13107)

Mercury Signs and Display Ltd 713 462-1068
  12407 Sowden Rd Houston (77080) (G-10832)

Mercury Tool and Machine Inc 254 752-1639
  7420 Karl May Dr Waco (76708) (G-20435)

Merichem Company (PA) 713 428-5000
  5455 Old Spanish Trl Houston (77023) (G-10833)

Merichem Company 713 428-5201
  5450 Old Spanish Trl Houston (77023) (G-10834)

Meridian, Houston Also called Texas Furnace LLC (G-12231)

Meridian Brick LLC 281 442-8400
  1720 N Sam Houston Pkwy E Houston (77032) (G-10835)

Meridian Brick LLC 830 980-7071
  21455 Fm 2252 Schertz (78154) (G-18756)

Meridian Brick LLC 940 325-9466
  500 Ne 14th Ave Mineral Wells (76067) (G-15532)

Meridian Brick LLC 903 675-2256
  200 Athens Brick Rd Athens (75751) (G-833)

Meridian Brick LLC 972 245-1542
  1400 N Broadway St Carrollton (75006) (G-2779)

Meridian Construction Services 830 305-5700
  1075 York Crossing Rd Kingsbury (78638) (G-13620)

Meridian Energy Group Inc 281 291-0510
  9590 New Decade Dr Pasadena (77507) (G-16482)

Merisol LP 713 428-5652
  1914 Haden Rd Houston (77015) (G-10836)

Merit Energy Company LLC 940 683-4059
  9600 Fm 371 Gainesville (76240) (G-7347)

Merit Energy Company LLC 956 728-6206
  5919 State Highway 359 Laredo (78043) (G-13912)

Merit Energy Company LLC 903 923-7300
  886 Finklea Rd Hallsville (75650) (G-8129)

Merit Energy Company LLC 361 293-3586
  22629 Us Highway 77 S Yoakum (77995) (G-20971)

Merit Energy Company LLC 956 842-3649
  28808 N Fm 681 Edinburg (78541) (G-5596)

Merit Energy Company LLC (PA) 972 701-8377
  13737 Noel Rd Ste 1200 Dallas (75240) (G-4666)

Merit Energy Partners F-I LP 972 701-8377
  132727 Noel Rd Ste 500 Dallas (75240) (G-4667)

Merit Industries, Georgetown Also called Merit Sales Inc (G-7664)

Merit Medical Systems Inc 832 463-5100
  14646 Kirby Dr Houston (77047) (G-10837)

Merit Oil Field Services, Buna Also called Bailey & Harley Services LLC (G-2560)

Merit Sales Inc 512 863-8541
  119 Serenada Dr Georgetown (78628) (G-7664)

Merla LLC 281 931-6900
  706 Honea Egypt Rd Magnolia (77354) (G-14618)

Merla Wellhead Solutions, Magnolia Also called Merla LLC (G-14618)

Merrell Lease Service Inc 361 643-6911
  610 N Ave D Gregory (78359) (G-8101)

Merrick Engineering Inc 254 741-6330
  7325 Imperial Dr Waco (76712) (G-20436)

Merrills Southern Maid 409 755-2400
  690 S Main St Lumberton (77657) (G-14568)

Merrimac Manufacturing Inc 936 894-3900
  16749 Highway 105 E Plantersville (77363) (G-17059)

Merritt Prfrred Components Inc (PA) 903 983-1592
  703 Old Highway 135 S Kilgore (75662) (G-13574)

Mesa Distributors, Fort Worth Also called Ramann Enterprises Inc (G-6938)

Mesa Drilling Inc 713 993-7082
  1805 Kingfisher Ridge Cv Lago Vista (78645) (G-13807)

MESA Orthopedic Supplies 210 699-6911
  7319 Caribou San Antonio (78238) (G-18292)

Mesa Processing Inc 817 626-0319
  3701 N Grove St Ste G Fort Worth (76106) (G-6829)

Mesa Technologies LLC 713 895-7000
  5801 Dierker Dr Houston (77041) (G-10838)

Mesa Wireline LLC 970 257-0458
  11700 Katy Fwy Ste 330 Houston (77079) (G-10839)

Mesco Building Solutions, Southlake Also called Nci Group Inc (G-19080)

Mesco Metal Buildings, Irving Also called Nci Group Inc (G-13121)

Mesquite Concrete Inc 830 216-1530
  7566 Fm 541 E Falls City (78113) (G-6183)

Mesquite Energy Inc (PA) 713 756-2700
  700 Milam St Ste 600 Houston (77002) (G-10840)

Mesquite Oil Tools Inc (PA) 325 573-1705
  815 S County Road 221 Snyder (79549) (G-18995)

Mesquite Services LLC 806 368-7726
  6839 82nd St Ste 101 Lubbock (79424) (G-14446)

Messenger Office Supply, Decatur Also called Wise County Messenger Inc (G-5257)

Messenger Publishing Co Inc 254 865-5212
  116 S 6th St Gatesville (76528) (G-7620)

Messer LLC 281 837-0184
  100 S Airhart Dr Baytown (77520) (G-1829)

Messer LLC 713 767-4155
  11603 Strang Rd La Porte (77571) (G-13776)

Messer LLC 903 626-4877
  7149 Fm 39 N Jewett (75846) (G-13307)

Messina Hof Wine Cellars Inc (PA) 979 778-9463
  4545 Old Reliance Rd Bryan (77808) (G-2493)

Mestena Uranium LLC 361 884-2191
  500 N Shoreline Blvd Corpus Christi (78401) (G-3577)

Mestex Ltd 214 638-6010
  4830 Transport Dr Dallas (75247) (G-4668)

Met Company, Houston Also called Met International Trdg Co Inc (G-10841)

Met International Trdg Co Inc 281 445-5005
  922 Hill Rd Houston (77037) (G-10841)

Meta-Tech Industries Inc 713 467-6544
  8916 Spring Branch Dr Houston (77080) (G-10842)

Metal & Materials Proc LLC (PA) 713 664-0050
  1513 W Dallas St Ste 200 Houston (77019) (G-10843)

Metal Building Components Mbci, Lubbock Also called Nci Group Inc (G-14451)

Metal Coatings Corp (PA) 713 977-0123
  3700 Dunvale Rd Houston (77063) (G-10844)

Metal Construction Mtls Inc 281 550-8383
  7229 Jackrabbit Rd Houston (77095) (G-10845)

Metal Craft, Houston *Also called Partners Metalfab LP* *(G-11250)*

Metal Detail Inc 214 330-7757
4120 Shilling Way Dallas (75237) *(G-4669)*

Metal Fabrication, Rhome *Also called United Metal Services Inc (G-17263)*

Metal Finshining, Mansfield *Also called Aft Industries Inc (G-14654)*

Metal Improvement Company LLC 972 660-3692
1450 Avenue S Grand Prairie (75050) *(G-7926)*

Metal Improvement Company LLC 713 691-0257
9410 E Hardy Rd Houston (77093) *(G-10846)*

Metal Ink Wear Technologies, Buna *Also called Applied Maintenance Spc Inc (G-2559)*

Metal Kitchen Fabricators Inc 713 683-8375
5121 April Ln Houston (77092) *(G-10847)*

Metal Kitchens, Houston *Also called Metal Kitchen Fabricators Inc (G-10847)*

Metal Processing, Vinton *Also called Vinton Steel LLC (G-20342)*

Metal Processing Intl LP 956 205-0083
1108 Business Park Dr Mission (78572) *(G-15560)*

Metal Sales Manufacturing Corp 254 791-6650
3838 N General Bruce Dr Temple (76501) *(G-19689)*

Metal Specialties, Houston *Also called A&S Interests Inc (G-8430)*

Metal Specialties Inc (PA) **432 332-8762**
3345 Kermit Hwy Odessa (79764) *(G-16081)*

Metal Specialties Mfg Co, Grand Prairie *Also called Fleming & Son Corporation (G-7873)*

Metal Spinners Inc 817 847-0086
1300 E Industrial Ave Saginaw (76131) *(G-17750)*

Metal Supermarkets, Houston *Also called Galam Metals LLC (G-9893)*

Metal Transformation & Design 915 235-4645
5959 Gateway Blvd W # 315 El Paso (79925) *(G-5873)*

Metal Zinc LLC (PA) **832 252-9116**
19408 Kenswick Dr Humble (77338) *(G-12789)*

Metal Zinc LLC 281 449-2787
19300 Oil Center Blvd Houston (77073) *(G-10848)*

Metal-Prep, Houston *Also called Nci Group Inc (G-11018)*

Metalforms Ltd 409 842-1626
7218 Garth St Beaumont (77705) *(G-1928)*

Metallic Products Corporation 713 856-9696
7777 Hollister St Houston (77040) *(G-10849)*

Metalloid Corporation 800 686-3201
1720 N Quevado St Jacksonville (75766) *(G-13250)*

Metalloy Inc 800 828-0500
5800 Heiser St Houston (77087) *(G-10850)*

Metalplate Galvanizing LP 713 672-9480
10625 Needham St Houston (77013) *(G-10851)*

Metals Incorporated 713 923-9491
8411 Irvington Blvd Houston (77022) *(G-10852)*

Metalsa Light Truck Inc (HQ) **210 242-3403**
1 Lone Star Pass Bldg 4 San Antonio (78264) *(G-18293)*

Metapath Software Intl (HQ) **972 907-3600**
1755 N Collins Blvd # 400 Richardson (75080) *(G-17356)*

Metco Environmental, Carrollton *Also called Testamerica Air Emission Corp (G-2828)*

Metcon Inc 817 281-1620
8800 Kirk Ln Fort Worth (76182) *(G-6830)*

Metfab Inc 713 472-3900
314 Allen Genoa Rd Houston (77017) *(G-10853)*

Meticulous Machining Inc 512 756-7471
102 John Kelly St Burnet (78611) *(G-2612)*

Metl-Span LLC 972 221-6656
1720 Lakepointe Dr # 101 Lewisville (75057) *(G-14065)*

Metokote Corporation 210 628-1955
1 Lone Star Pass Bldg 37 San Antonio (78264) *(G-18294)*

Metric Medical Devices Inc 830 535-6300
846 Silver Spgs Helotes (78023) *(G-8243)*

Metric Standards & Odds, Houston *Also called Seal-Jet of Texas Inc (G-11804)*

Metrix Instrument Co LP (PA) **281 940-1802**
8824 Fallbrook Dr Houston (77064) *(G-10854)*

Metrix PMC/Beta (PA) **713 461-2131**
1711 Townhurst Dr Houston (77043) *(G-10855)*

Metro Coffee Grouppe Inc 972 263-8744
320 Se 26th St Grand Prairie (75050) *(G-7927)*

Metro Custom Plastics Inc 817 640-5646
615 109th St Arlington (76011) *(G-731)*

Metro Cutting and Sealing Inc 972 434-8722
1740 N Stemmons Fwy Lewisville (75067) *(G-14066)*

Metro Fire Apprtus Specialists 817 467-0911
1501 Heritage Pkwy # 103 Mansfield (76063) *(G-14695)*

Metro Gate & Mfg Co Inc (PA) **903 785-8911**
Hwy 82 W Paris (75460) *(G-16365)*

Metro Label Corporation (HQ) **214 369-9377**
3366 Miller Park S Garland (75042) *(G-7549)*

Metro Mats 817 640-6287
412 113th St Arlington (76011) *(G-732)*

Metro Mfg Support Svcs Inc 817 330-3430
8949 Forest Hill Dr Fort Worth (76140) *(G-6831)*

Metro Mini Courses Inc 214 826-2300
6400 Maple Ave Ste 850 Dallas (75235) *(G-4670)*

Metro Optics of Austin Inc 512 251-2386
15802 Vision Dr Pflugerville (78660) *(G-16680)*

Metro Plex Wood, Houston *Also called MPW Enterprises LLC (G-10932)*

Metro Ready Mix Ltd Company 713 991-6466
5421 Schurmier Rd Houston (77048) *(G-10856)*

Metro Sprocket & Gear Inc 972 723-3240
1258 Eastgate Rd Midlothian (76065) *(G-15485)*

Metro Store Fixtures, Dallas *Also called Cabfixco Inc (G-4075)*

Metro Sweet Products, Dallas *Also called Drafft Root Beer Inc (G-4278)*

Metro Tool & Manufacturing, Cross Plains *Also called Alexander Manufacturing Co (G-3746)*

Metro-Graphics Inc 214 638-6780
1311 Regal Row Dallas (75247) *(G-4671)*

Metro-Tex Fabricators Inc 713 473-3900
5107 Brookglen Dr Houston (77017) *(G-10857)*

Metroplex Cabinets Inc 940 321-5151
3100 Walton Dr Corinth (76208) *(G-3457)*

Metroplex Conveyor & Svcs LLC 972 584-0551
5710 State Highway 34 S Quinlan (75474) *(G-17224)*

Metroplex Graphics & Mktg Inc 817 831-7215
7451 Tower St Richland Hills (76118) *(G-17442)*

Metroplex Graphics and Svcs, Richland Hills *Also called Metroplex Graphics & Mktg Inc (G-17442)*

Metroplex Millworks Inc 214 358-1770
2665 Perth St Dallas (75220) *(G-4672)*

Metroplex Plastics, Arlington *Also called Contemporary Design Plastics (G-646)*

Metroplex Products Inc 817 923-8241
2901 Saint Louis Ave Fort Worth (76110) *(G-6832)*

Metroplex Roof and Fence Inc (PA) **469 417-8003**
6801 S Interstate 35 E Corinth (76210) *(G-3458)*

Metroplex Sand & Gravel Ltd (PA) **817 589-9001**
2620 Trinity Trail Way Fort Worth (76118) *(G-6833)*

Metroplex Sheet Metal Inc 972 276-6736
3701 Marquis Dr Ste 139 Garland (75042) *(G-7550)*

Metroplex Wood Products Ltd 817 538-0375
2201 W Risinger Rd Fort Worth (76134) *(G-6834)*

Metropolex Wood Specialty 214 339-5115
1357 N Walton Walker Blvd Dallas (75211) *(G-4673)*

Metropolitian Newsletter, Dallas *Also called Metro Mini Courses Inc (G-4670)*

Metrosoft, Pflugerville *Also called Metro Optics of Austin Inc (G-16680)*

Metso Minerals Industries Inc 210 491-9521
11451 Jnes Maltsberger Rd San Antonio (78216) *(G-18295)*

Mettle Filtration Products LLC 713 609-9370
8722 Pagewood Ln Houston (77063) *(G-10858)*

Mettler-Toledo LLC 972 727-8669
101 N Greenville Ave C Allen (75002) *(G-285)*

Metton America Inc 281 479-8078
2727 Miller Cut Off Rd La Porte (77571) *(G-13777)*

Mewborne Enrgy Prtners 04-A LP 903 561-2900
3901 S Broadway Ave Tyler (75701) *(G-20125)*

Mewbourne Holdings Inc (PA) **903 561-2900**
3901 S Broadway Ave Tyler (75701) *(G-20126)*

Mewbourne Oil Company, Tyler *Also called Mewborne Enrgy Prtners 04-A LP (G-20125)*

Mewbourne Oil Company 281 580-6608
3303 Fm 1960 Rd W Houston (77068) *(G-10859)*

Mewbourne Oil Company (HQ) **903 561-2900**
3620 Old Bullard Rd Tyler (75701) *(G-20127)*

Mewbourne Oil Company 432 682-3715
500 W Texas Ave Ste 1020 Midland (79701) *(G-15298)*

Mewbourne Oil Company 806 435-6881
143 E Loop Rd Perryton (79070) *(G-16640)*

Mexi-Snax Corporation 915 779-5709
6860 El Paso Dr El Paso (79905) *(G-5874)*

Mexia Daily News, Mexia *Also called Sun-Times Media Group Inc (G-15091)*

Mexican Snacks Inc 956 440-9127
826 N Fm 509 Harlingen (78550) *(G-8195)*

Mexican Technologies Co Inc 915 595-2285
8650 Yermoland Dr El Paso (79907) *(G-5875)*

Mexico Pacific Limited LLC 713 425-6500
5444 Westheimr Rd # 1685 Houston (77056) *(G-10860)*

Mexssub International Inc 713 278-2175
7500 San Felipe St # 600 Houston (77063) *(G-10861)*

Meyer Energy Services LLC (PA) **830 377-1099**
4311 E County Road 45 Midland (79705) *(G-15299)*

Meyer Energy Services LLC 830 377-1099
3001 W Loop 250 N Ste C10 Midland (79705) *(G-15300)*

Meyer Industries Inc 210 736-1811
3528 Fredericksburg Rd San Antonio (78201) *(G-18296)*

Meyer Machine Company, San Antonio *Also called Meyer Industries Inc (G-18296)*

Meyer Service Company, Corpus Christi *Also called Gjr Meyer Service Inc (G-3535)*

MEYER SMITH, Houston *Also called Yellow Rose Stl Fbricators Inc (G-12715)*

Meyer-Smith Inc (PA) **713 862-7339**
14239 Sommermeyer St Houston (77041) *(G-10862)*

Mezger Enterprises Ltd (PA) **254 547-8174**
Fm Rd 2808 Kempner (76539) *(G-13486)*

Mezger Enterprises Ltd 254 547-8207
1011 County Road 164 Lueders (79533) *(G-14518)*

Mf Guage, Brownwood *Also called M & F Gauge & Specialty Co Inc (G-2439)*

Mfg Chemical LLC 281 291-2300
9700 Bayport Blvd Pasadena (77507) *(G-16483)*

Mfi International Mfg LLC (PA) **915 858-0971**
9570 Pan American Dr El Paso (79927) *(G-5876)*

Mfs Piping and Indus Svcs LLC 979 472-7658
910 Columbus Rd Sealy (77474) *(G-18813)*

Mg Building Materials Ltd 210 798-0650
9405 New Laredo Hwy San Antonio (78211) *(G-18297)*

Mg Building Materials Ltd (HQ) **210 924-8604**
2651 Sw Military Dr San Antonio (78224) *(G-18298)*

Mg Doors & More LLC 972 291-4389
902 Kck Way Cedar Hill (75104) *(G-2948)*

Mg Industries, Houston Also called Alig LLC *(G-8538)*

Mg Truck Sales, San Antonio Also called Mg Building Materials Ltd *(G-18298)*

Mgc Inc 713 800-7300
6800 Sands Point Dr Houston (77074) *(G-10863)*

Mgc Electrical Services, Houston Also called Odysseus Holdings LLC *(G-11136)*

Mhc Kenworth- Wichita Falls, Wichita Falls Also called Texas Kenworth Co *(G-20816)*

Mhc Semiconductor Processing 512 331-6632
7801 N Lamar Blvd B155 Austin (78752) *(G-1337)*

Mhwirth Inc 281 371-2424
2201 N Sam Houston Pkwy W Houston (77038) *(G-10864)*

MI Inc 512 244-3676
2007 Lamar Dr Round Rock (78664) *(G-17672)*

MI T Fine Car Wash Inc 972 422-0707
1614 Custer Rd Plano (75075) *(G-16926)*

Mibo Fresh Foods LLC 817 882-9600
715 E 9th St Fort Worth (76102) *(G-6835)*

Mic Group LLC 979 277-7806
3140 S Blue Bell Rd Brenham (77833) *(G-2263)*

Mic Group LLC (PA) **979 277-7800**
3140 S Blue Bell Rd Brenham (77833) *(G-2264)*

Mic-All Machining Inc 979 830-8558
4254 E Fm 389 Rd Burton (77835) *(G-2619)*

Mica Steelworks Inc (PA) **817 529-5000**
5750 N Riverside Dr Fort Worth (76137) *(G-6836)*

Mica Steelworks Inc 817 581-9500
4201 Old Denton Rd Haltom City (76117) *(G-8154)*

Mica Steelworks Inc 972 287-5410
1200 Rand Rd Kaufman (75142) *(G-13460)*

Mica Steelworks Inc 817 267-9699
3501 House Anderson Rd Euless (76040) *(G-6149)*

Michael Angelo's Gourmet Foods, Austin Also called Bottom Line Fd Processors Inc *(G-1003)*

Michael Egan Allen 956 702-0692
1301 Macco Dr Pharr (78577) *(G-16707)*

Michael R Atteberry 214 222-3064
784 N Kealy Ave Lewisville (75057) *(G-14067)*

Michael Ray 832 567-2507
17070 Red Oak Dr Ste 211 Houston (77090) *(G-10865)*

Michael Roy 903 784-6362
12900 Farm Road 79 Sumner (75486) *(G-19607)*

Michaelholigan.com, Dallas Also called Hyphen Solutions LLC *(G-4480)*

Michaels Companies Inc (PA) **972 409-1300**
8000 Bent Branch Dr Irving (75063) *(G-13108)*

Michaels Naturopathic Programs, San Antonio Also called Inner Health Group Inc *(G-18187)*

Micheal J Arnold & Co 979 742-3030
3533 County Road 4 Damon (77430) *(G-5213)*

Michel's Tiffany, Fort Worth Also called El Habr Corporation *(G-6608)*

Michelin North America Inc 864 458-5000
1301 Horizon Blvd El Paso (79928) *(G-5877)*

Michelson Energy Company (PA) **210 826-0681**
7709 Broadway Apt 106 San Antonio (78209) *(G-18299)*

Michex International Inc 281 397-7770
3920 Cypress Creek Pkwy # 250 Houston (77068) *(G-10866)*

Mick & David Enterprises Inc 214 350-5765
9017 Diplomacy Row Dallas (75247) *(G-4674)*

Mico Group Ltd 713 460-3172
630 An County Road 1215 Grapeland (75844) *(G-8006)*

Micor Inc 281 476-0808
1001 Georgia Ave Deer Park (77536) *(G-5286)*

Micrel LLC 972 235-9166
2425 N Central Expy # 351 Richardson (75080) *(G-17357)*

Micro Engineering Inc 936 291-6891
511 Fm 3179 Rd Huntsville (77340) *(G-12819)*

Micro Hybrid Components, Austin Also called Mhc Semiconductor Processing *(G-1337)*

Micro Metl Corporation 903 248-4800
201 Kodak Blvd Longview (75602) *(G-14276)*

Micro Mold Plastics Inc 817 536-0930
2314 Ludelle St Fort Worth (76105) *(G-6837)*

Micro Mold Plastics Usa Inc 817 536-0930
2314 Ludelle St Fort Worth (76105) *(G-6838)*

Micro Precision of Texas Inc (PA) **713 462-7599**
4413 Campbell Rd Houston (77041) *(G-10867)*

Micro Star Technologies, Huntsville Also called Micro Engineering Inc *(G-12819)*

Micro Tesla Magnetic Field, Houston Also called Magnetic Field Effects LLC *(G-10735)*

Micro-Design Inc 972 488-8725
1805 Royal Ln Ste 111 Dallas (75229) *(G-4675)*

Micro-Smart Systems Inc 713 433-2277
5355 Anderson Rd Houston (77053) *(G-8389)*

Micro-Tes Inc 210 558-4757
12500 Network Blvd # 201 San Antonio (78249) *(G-18300)*

Microbes, The Woodlands Also called Promicom Inc *(G-19906)*

Microbes Inc 281 367-7500
1544 Sawdust Rd Ste 505 The Woodlands (77380) *(G-19894)*

Microchip Technology Inc 512 334-1931
10900b Stonelake Blvd Austin (78759) *(G-1338)*

Microlabs, Dallas Also called Ultratest International Inc *(G-5130)*

Micromed Technology Inc 713 838-9210
8965 Interchange Dr Houston (77054) *(G-10868)*

Micron Semiconductor Pdts Inc 512 248-8283
101 W Louis Henna Blvd # 210 Austin (78728) *(G-1339)*

Micron Semiconductor Pdts Inc 281 970-3202
16510 Avenplace Rd Tomball (77377) *(G-19987)*

Micron Technology Inc 972 521-5200
805 Central Expy S # 100 Allen (75013) *(G-286)*

Micron Technology Texas Llc 972 521-5200
805 Central Expy S # 100 Allen (75013) *(G-287)*

Micron Vision Corporation 281 546-9632
811 E Plano Pkwy Ste 113 Plano (75074) *(G-16927)*

Micron-Pro, The, Alvarado Also called Filtration Automation Inc *(G-332)*

Micropac Industries Inc (PA) **972 272-3571**
905 E Walnut St Garland (75040) *(G-7551)*

Micropac Industries Inc 972 272-3571
912 E Walnut St Garland (75040) *(G-7552)*

Micropower Global Corporation 512 245-8976
3055 Hunter Rd San Marcos (78666) *(G-18699)*

Microseismic Inc (PA) **713 781-2323**
10777 Westheimer Rd # 250 Houston (77042) *(G-10869)*

Microsemi Semiconductor (us) 512 228-5400
4509 Freidrich Ln Ste 200 Austin (78744) *(G-1340)*

Microsoft Corporation 210 402-0577
401 E Sonterra Blvd # 300 San Antonio (78258) *(G-18301)*

Microsoft Corporation 469 775-0000
7000 State Hwy Irving (75039) *(G-13109)*

Microsoft Corporation 469 775-0000
7100 State Highway 161 Irving (75039) *(G-13110)*

Microsoft Corporation 832 252-4300
2000 W S Houston Pkwy 3 Houston (77042) *(G-10870)*

Microsoft Corporation 210 346-2500
5150 Rogers Rd San Antonio (78251) *(G-18302)*

Microsoft Corporation 972 345-3610
7000 State Highway 161 Irving (75039) *(G-13111)*

Microspace Instruments Inc 214 388-0461
4751 Wilburton Dr Dallas (75227) *(G-4676)*

Micross Components, Austin Also called Austin Semiconductor Inc *(G-962)*

Micross Components-Tx LLC 512 833-5868
33 Cypress Blvd Ste 400 Round Rock (78665) *(G-17673)*

Microstaq Inc 512 628-2890
4120 Freidrich Ln Ste 225 Austin (78744) *(G-1341)*

Microtek Medical Inc 903 597-2568
2319 E Erwin St Tyler (75702) *(G-20128)*

Microteq Engineering Inc 210 736-2611
3003 Aniol St Ste 112 San Antonio (78219) *(G-18303)*

Microtransponder 214 280-9677
2802 Flintrock Trce Ste 2 Austin (78738) *(G-1342)*

Microtune Inc (HQ) **972 673-1600**
2201 10th St Plano (75074) *(G-16928)*

Microwave Networks Inc (HQ) **281 263-6500**
4000 Greenbriar Dr # 100 Stafford (77477) *(G-19353)*

Mid South Baking Company, Bryan Also called Bryan Baking Inc *(G-2461)*

Mid South Manufacturing LLC 903 759-5490
1301 Cherokee Trce White Oak (75693) *(G-20717)*

Mid South Roller, Arlington Also called Roy Johnson Incorporated *(G-773)*

Mid Tex Minerals Inc 361 865-3530
Barrium Ln Flatonia (78941) *(G-6233)*

Mid-America Pet Food LLC 903 572-5900
2024 N Frontage Rd Mount Pleasant (75455) *(G-15655)*

Mid-Coast Electric Supply Inc 830 333-7030
2022 E Main St Uvalde (78801) *(G-20193)*

Mid-County Ready Mix 830 876-3800
5940 N Us Hwy 83 Carrizo Springs (78834) *(G-2686)*

Mid-South Metals LLC 817 838-8000
3201 N Sylvania Ave Fort Worth (76111) *(G-6839)*

Mid-Valley Newspapers Inc 956 969-2543
401 S Kansas Ave Ste C2 Weslaco (78596) *(G-20665)*

Mid-Valley Towncrier, Weslaco Also called Mid-Valley Newspapers Inc *(G-20665)*

Mid-West Hose & Specialty 713 472-2900
2500 Pasadena Fwy Pasadena (77506) *(G-16484)*

Mid-West Hose & Specialty 214 638-3210
1132 Valwood Pkwy Ste 100 Carrollton (75006) *(G-2780)*

Mid-West Steel Building, Houston Also called Nci Group Inc *(G-11019)*

Mid-West Truck Center Inc 432 523-3451
801 N Main St Ste Q Andrews (79714) *(G-552)*

Midco Demolition Tool Co, Dallas Also called Kirby Midco Inc *(G-4558)*

Midco Machine 432 563-2010
11228 W County Road 127 Odessa (79765) *(G-16082)*

Midcoast Energy LLC 806 663-7700
1313 N Hobart St Pampa (79065) *(G-16329)*

Midcoast Energy LLC (HQ) 713 821-2000
1501 Mckinney St Ste 600 Houston (77010) *(G-10871)*

Midcoast Energy Partners LP (HQ) 713 821-2000
1100 La St Ste 3300 Houston (77002) *(G-10872)*

Midcoast Lease Service Inc 361 526-4636
1106 Old Brian Rd Refugio (78377) *(G-17244)*

Midcoast Operating LP 210 321-8000
10101 Reunion Pl Ste 200 San Antonio (78216) *(G-18304)*

Midessa Compression, Addison *Also called J-W Power Company (G-139)*

Midland Energy Inc 432 683-6686
110 N Marienfeld St # 101 Midland (79701) *(G-15301)*

Midland Roustabout Service Inc 432 682-5017
5800 E I 20 Midland (79706) *(G-15302)*

Midland Stamping and Fabg Corp 830 422-2052
2022 Cienegas Rd Del Rio (78840) *(G-5320)*

Midland Wellhead Inc 432 682-0856
40 E Industrial Loop Midland (79701) *(G-15303)*

Midlothian Lng LLC 818 450-3668
5091 Brookhollow Dr Midlothian (76065) *(G-15486)*

Midstar Energy LP 281 940-3022
1840 Snake River Rd Ste E Katy (77449) *(G-13425)*

Midstream Energy Holdings LLC (PA) 713 403-6460
10370 Richmond Ave # 510 Houston (77042) *(G-10873)*

Midstream Hess Operations LP (HQ) 713 496-4200
1501 Mckinney St Houston (77010) *(G-10874)*

Midstream Navarro Services LLC 956 728-6000
10101 Reunion Pl Ste 1000 San Antonio (78216) *(G-18305)*

Midstream Noble Services LLC (HQ) 281 872-3100
1001 Noble Energy Way Houston (77070) *(G-10875)*

Midtown Prtg & Graphics Inc 806 744-3382
7720 University Ave Lubbock (79423) *(G-14447)*

Midway Energy, Godley *Also called Midway Oilfield Constrs Inc (G-7736)*

Midway Energy Services, Midway *Also called Midway Oilfield Constrs Inc (G-15499)*

Midway Machine & Instr Co Inc 713 947-1312
701 Oregon St Ste B South Houston (77587) *(G-19050)*

Midway Machine & Wldg Sp Inc 817 447-0985
121 Industrial Park Blvd Burleson (76028) *(G-2591)*

Midway Oilfield Constrs Inc 817 389-2525
11400 Fm 2331 Godley (76044) *(G-7736)*

Midway Oilfield Constrs Inc (PA) 936 348-3721
12627 State Highway 21 E Midway (75852) *(G-15499)*

Midway Tire, Madisonville *Also called Jac Enterprises Inc (G-14588)*

Midway Trailer & Equipment, Madisonville *Also called Jac Enterprises Inc (G-14587)*

Midwest Asphalt Company, Gainesville *Also called Midwest Asphalt Corporation (G-7348)*

Midwest Asphalt Corporation 940 668-1480
3609 E Highway 82 Gainesville (76240) *(G-7348)*

Midwest Energy Emissions Corp (PA) 614 505-6115
1810 Jester Dr Corsicana (75109) *(G-3678)*

Midwest Fab & Construction Inc 806 335-9126
10720 E Amarillo Blvd Amarillo (79108) *(G-446)*

Midwest Folding Products Corp (HQ) 312 666-3366
1302 Industrial Blvd Temple (76504) *(G-19690)*

Midwest Industrial Rubber Inc 972 988-6700
1330 Post & Paddock Rd St Grand Prairie (75050) *(G-7928)*

Midwest Machine LLC 806 355-9400
6601 S Fm 1541 Amarillo (79118) *(G-501)*

Midwest Provisions Inc 903 891-6213
4700 S Us Highway 75 Sherman (75090) *(G-18921)*

Midwestern Services Inc 325 573-6666
8501 South Loop E Houston (77017) *(G-10876)*

Mighty Molding & Manufacturing, Eastland *Also called Mighty Molding & Mfg (G-5567)*

Mighty Molding & Mfg 254 629-2525
2016 Old Bankhead Hwy Eastland (76448) *(G-5567)*

Mighty Works Signage LLC 713 305-8355
7016 Hemlock St Houston (77087) *(G-10877)*

Mikada Cabinets LLC 713 681-6116
3724 Creekmont Dr Houston (77091) *(G-10878)*

Mike Conkles Custom Cabinets 817 483-9658
318 W Mansfield Hwy Kennedale (76060) *(G-13499)*

Mike Daniel Construction, Fairfield *Also called MD Construction Inc (G-6178)*

Mike Davis and Associates Inc (PA) 512 836-8442
15505 Long Vista Dr # 200 Austin (78728) *(G-1343)*

Mike Sandone Productions Inc 800 652-5635
403 S Haskell Ave Dallas (75226) *(G-4677)*

Mike Strand 940 482-3426
820 E Mccart St Krum (76249) *(G-13675)*

Mike's Custom Hatters, Longview *Also called C & C Western Wear Inc (G-14206)*

Mikel Machine Inc 281 354-2750
24792 Ford Rd Porter (77365) *(G-17179)*

Mikes Machine Works Inc 979 233-1257
403 S Avenue A Freeport (77541) *(G-7205)*

Mil Ltd (PA) 713 691-5200
1912 Buschong St Houston (77039) *(G-10879)*

Milagro Exploration Gp LLC 713 750-1600
1301 Mckinney St Ste 500 Houston (77010) *(G-10880)*

Milam Broadcasting Co Inc 254 697-6633
901 E 1st St Cameron (76520) *(G-2643)*

Mile 533 Marine Ways Inc 361 758-5379
748 E Goodnight Ave Aransas Pass (78336) *(G-594)*

Milestone International Inc 210 226-2122
1403 E Commerce St San Antonio (78205) *(G-18306)*

Milestone Metals Inc 281 448-9151
113 W Lorino St Houston (77037) *(G-10881)*

Military Aircraft Assmbly & De, Amarillo *Also called Bell Textron Inc (G-406)*

Military Customs LLC 254 699-8106
229 Cox Dr Harker Heights (76548) *(G-8172)*

Milke Manufacturing Jewelers 972 296-4319
106 S Cedar Ridge Dr Duncanville (75116) *(G-5534)*

Mill Ridge Golf Center, Livingston *Also called Forest Ogletree Products Inc (G-14155)*

Millar Inc (PA) 832 667-7000
6001 Gulf Fwy Ste A Houston (77023) *(G-10882)*

Millennium Exploration Co LLC 210 960-1000
211 N Loop 1604 E Ste 220 San Antonio (78232) *(G-18307)*

Millennium Plastics Tech LLC (PA) 915 834-2700
1305 Henry Brennan Dr El Paso (79936) *(G-5878)*

Millennium Recycling LLP 817 624-4307
3717 N Commerce St Fort Worth (76106) *(G-6840)*

Millennium Resources LP 432 687-4074
414 W Texas Ave Ste 411 Midland (79701) *(G-15304)*

Millennium Shopper 903 885-9966
115 Jefferson St E Sulphur Springs (75482) *(G-19592)*

Millennium Signs America LLC 903 944-7981
1832 W Gentry Pkwy Tyler (75702) *(G-20129)*

Miller Brewing 817 551-3300
7001 South Fwy Fort Worth (76134) *(G-6841)*

Miller Company, Burleson *Also called United Aviation ACC Inc (G-2600)*

Miller Coors, Fort Worth *Also called Miller Brewing (G-6841)*

Miller Equipment Co (PA) 469 366-4227
1000 N 1st St Garland (75040) *(G-7553)*

Miller Imging Dgital Solutions 512 381-5266
1000 E 7th St Austin (78702) *(G-1344)*

Miller Machine & Welding LLC 254 582-2185
256 Fm 3050 Whitney (76692) *(G-20731)*

Miller Mechanical Group 361 594-8080
7824 Fm 443 Shiner (77984) *(G-18945)*

Miller Milling Company LLC 817 847-8977
221 Fairmount St Saginaw (76179) *(G-17751)*

Miller Paper & Packaging, Amarillo *Also called Miller Paper Company (G-502)*

Miller Paper Company 806 353-0317
6511 S Washington St Amarillo (79118) *(G-502)*

Miller Power Equipment Co LLC 903 592-7201
3227 Old Jacksonville Rd Tyler (75701) *(G-20130)*

Miller Products Inc 972 988-0983
916 Avenue N Grand Prairie (75050) *(G-7929)*

Miller Seafood Co Inc (PA) 361 552-6423
1102 Broadway St Port Lavaca (77979) *(G-17151)*

Miller Sheet Metal Mfg, Dallas *Also called B & S Premium Sheet Metal Inc (G-3995)*

Miller Uniforms & Emblems Inc 512 302-5541
826 Rutland Dr Austin (78758) *(G-1345)*

Miller Waste Mills Inc 817 293-6163
1301 Joel East Rd Fort Worth (76140) *(G-6842)*

Miller's Sea Food, Port Lavaca *Also called Miller Seafood Co Inc (G-17151)*

Mills Machine Shop 940 479-2194
11619 Bois D Arc Ln Ponder (76259) *(G-17095)*

Millsap Waterproofing Inc 713 956-6677
2414 Mcallister Rd Houston (77092) *(G-10883)*

Millsource Inc 281 372-0311
4343 Kennedy Commerce Dr Houston (77032) *(G-10884)*

Milltech Manufacturing Company 972 276-1786
537 Easy St Garland (75042) *(G-7554)*

Millwood Cabinets LLP 903 567-3333
1200 1st Monday Ln Canton (75103) *(G-2658)*

Millwork Solutions Ltd 817 473-3934
1008 Magnolia St Mansfield (76063) *(G-14696)*

Milspec Works LLC 281 530-7002
11000 Stncliff Rd Ste 160 Houston (77099) *(G-10885)*

Milton Bernhard Meat Proc 830 367-2995
2590 Junction Hwy Ste D Kerrville (78028) *(G-13523)*

Milvian Solutions LLC 915 219-5260
2407 E Yandell Dr Ste A El Paso (79903) *(G-5879)*

Milwhite Inc (PA) 956 547-1970
5487 Padre Island Hwy Brownsville (78521) *(G-2383)*

Minae Products Inc 830 620-1303
863 N Interstate 35 J New Braunfels (78130) *(G-15813)*

Mindpower International Inc (PA) 469 287-2735
3832 Red Oak Trl Lewisville (75056) *(G-14068)*

Minearc Systems America LLC 214 337-5100
4850 W Ledbetter Dr Dallas (75236) *(G-4678)*

Mineola Packing Company 903 569-5355
906 E Broad St Mineola (75773) *(G-15510)*

Mineral Resource Tech Inc (HQ) 281 362-1060
929 Gessner Rd Ste 1900 Houston (77024) *(G-10886)*

Mineral Technologies Inc 432 685-3520
2052 Commerce Dr Midland (79703) *(G-15305)*

Mineraltech Gulf Coast Abr LLC (PA) 832 838-8623
11501 Crosby Lynchburg Highlands (77562) *(G-8313)*

Mineraltechllc.com, Highlands *Also called Mineraltech Gulf Coast Abr LLC (G-8313)*

Minergy LLC...832 800-6336
12000 Westheimer Rd # 303 Houston (77077) *(G-10887)*
Mingtel Inc...972 378-5559
4108 W Spring Creek Pkwy Plano (75024) *(G-16929)*
Miniconcrete Materials Inc...915 852-4468
15001 Horizon Blvd El Paso (79928) *(G-5880)*
Minom Inc...210 734-5124
200 Lombrano St San Antonio (78207) *(G-18308)*
Minority Opportunity News Inc...972 516-4191
1100 Summit Ave Ste 1201 Plano (75074) *(G-16930)*
Minority Print Media...713 748-6300
2646 S Loop W Ste 600 Houston (77054) *(G-10888)*
Minsa Corporation, Muleshoe *Also called Bunge Milling Southwest Inc (G-15676)*
Minute Maid Co, The, Sugar Land *Also called Coca-Cola Refreshments USA Inc (G-19460)*
Minute Man Press Southwest, Houston *Also called 3f Investments Co (G-8409)*
Minuteman Press, Houston *Also called Town & Country Printing Inc (G-12336)*
Minuteman Press, Georgetown *Also called Gipson Group LLC (G-7654)*
Minuteman Press...817 864-3000
2567 Gravel Dr Fort Worth (76118) *(G-6843)*
Minuteman Press Houston, Houston *Also called First National Trading Co LLC (G-9791)*
Mir, Grand Prairie *Also called Midwest Industrial Rubber Inc (G-7928)*
Miracon Technologies LLC...972 387-3099
401 S Sherman St Ste 101 Richardson (75081) *(G-17358)*
Miramar Wf LLC...940 626-4309
3858 N Us Highway 287 Alvord (76225) *(G-389)*
Miranda Energy Corporation...432 685-1953
24 Smith Rd Ste 601 Midland (79705) *(G-15306)*
Mirror Acquisitions LLC...713 686-4435
11510 Kilburn Rd Houston (77055) *(G-10889)*
Mirror Industries, Houston *Also called Mirror Acquisitions LLC (G-10889)*
Mirror Industries, Houston *Also called Finley Investments Inc (G-9788)*
Mirror Publishers Inc...281 486-6558
7500 Fm 1765 Texas City (77591) *(G-19798)*
Miscellaneous Specialties Inc...281 351-1177
11024 Mahaffey Rd Tomball (77375) *(G-19988)*
Miscellaneous Steel Inds Inc...512 268-2831
400 Bunton Creek Rd Kyle (78640) *(G-13685)*
Mission Candle Company, San Antonio *Also called Reed Candle Company (G-18417)*
Mission City Press Inc...210 614-7051
115 N Loop 1604 E Ste 220 San Antonio (78232) *(G-18309)*
Mission Clay Products LLC...830 393-2568
8854 County Road 128 Floresville (78114) *(G-6248)*
Mission Cycleplex LLC...210 250-0057
9800 San Pedro Ave San Antonio (78216) *(G-18310)*
Mission Foods, Irving *Also called Gruma Corporation (G-13043)*
Mission Foods, Irving *Also called Gruma Corporation (G-13044)*
Mission Foods, Dallas *Also called Gruma Corporation (G-4419)*
Mission Foods, San Antonio *Also called Gruma Corporation (G-18154)*
Mission Foods, Houston *Also called Gruma Corporation (G-10050)*
Mission Oil Company...210 224-4455
100 W Houston St Ste 1500 San Antonio (78205) *(G-18311)*
Mission Pharmacal Company (PA)...**210 696-8400**
10999 W Interstate 10 San Antonio (78230) *(G-18312)*
Mission Pharmacal Company...210 696-8400
1325 E Cesar E Chavez Blv San Antonio (78210) *(G-18313)*
Mission Pharmacal Company...210 696-8400
38505 Interstate 10 W Boerne (78006) *(G-2129)*
Mission Solar Energy LLC...210 531-8600
8303 S New Braunfels San Antonio (78235) *(G-18314)*
Mission Wrecker Service S A...210 341-0333
4535 Fm 1516 N Converse (78109) *(G-3398)*
Missionary Tech Team...903 757-4530
25 Frj Dr Longview (75602) *(G-14277)*
Mistaway Systems Inc...713 468-6464
2121 Brittmoore Rd # 5200 Houston (77043) *(G-10890)*
Mitchell Industries, Baytown *Also called Mitchell Well Service Inc (G-1797)*
Mitchell Machine & Fabricating...903 880-0249
16490 Fm 90 Mabank (75147) *(G-14579)*
Mitchell Manufacturing Inc...281 351-9641
22806 Commercial Ln Tomball (77375) *(G-19989)*
Mitchell Well Service Inc (PA)...**281 576-5007**
15555 Interstate 10 E Baytown (77523) *(G-1797)*
Mitek Corporation...972 875-8413
1601 Jack Mckay Blvd Ennis (75119) *(G-6110)*
Mitel Networks Inc...469 365-3000
5360 Legacy Dr Ste 300 Plano (75024) *(G-16931)*
Mitsubshi Ctrpllar Frklift AME (HQ)...**713 365-1000**
2121 W Sam Houston Pkwy N Houston (77043) *(G-10891)*
Mitsubshi Hvy Inds Cmprsr Intl...713 652-0300
14888 Kirby Dr Houston (77047) *(G-10892)*
Mitsui E&P USA LLC...713 960-0023
1300 Post Oak Blvd Ste 18 Houston (77056) *(G-10893)*
Mix Printing Company Inc...972 248-9000
2441 Midway Rd Carrollton (75006) *(G-2781)*
Mizkan America Inc...214 339-5551
4515 Bronze Way Dallas (75236) *(G-4679)*
Mizkan Americas Inc...214 339-5551
4647 Bronze Way Dallas (75236) *(G-4680)*

Mj Stone LLC...832 887-3575
5855 Shurmard Dr Houston (77092) *(G-10894)*
MJB Precision Wood Group, Coppell *Also called MJB Wood Group LLC (G-3428)*
MJB Supply, Cedar Hill *Also called Precision Wood Products Inc (G-2951)*
MJB Wood Group LLC (PA)...**972 401-0005**
3100 Olympus Blvd Ste 480 Coppell (75019) *(G-3428)*
MJM Sourcing LLC...214 769-7881
1050 Metro Media Pl Dallas (75247) *(G-4681)*
Mjs Manufacturing Inc...832 446-6440
6720 Theall Rd Houston (77066) *(G-10895)*
Mk Pallets Inc...903 537-2400
12525 Interstate Hwy 30 E Saltillo (75478) *(G-17766)*
Mk Specialty Metal Fabricators...972 225-6562
725 W Wintergreen Rd Hutchins (75141) *(G-12869)*
Mk Systems USA Inc (PA)...**469 626-9523**
3001 Dallas Pkwy Ste 300 Frisco (75034) *(G-7298)*
ML Industries Inc (PA)...**956 279-8678**
165 S Oak Trl Fredericksburg (78624) *(G-7186)*
Mlc Cad Systems LLC (PA)...**512 288-8511**
4625 W William Cannon Dr Austin (78749) *(G-1346)*
Mlc Operating LP...713 255-6200
8900 Eastloch Dr Ste 235 Spring (77379) *(G-19146)*
Mlc Signs LP...972 420-8770
1306 W Main St Lewisville (75067) *(G-14069)*
Mli Supply Inc...713 266-1400
3776 Greenbriar Dr Stafford (77477) *(G-19354)*
MMC, Kennedale *Also called Montgomery Mfg Co LLC (G-13500)*
Mmi, Richwood *Also called Mueller Manufacturing Inc (G-17469)*
Mmi Division 7, Houston *Also called Market Makers Inc (G-10769)*
Mmlj Inc (PA)...**713 869-2227**
5711 Schurmier Rd Houston (77048) *(G-10896)*
Mmmix Ltd...830 336-4252
33 Fm 3351 N Bergheim (78004) *(G-2049)*
Mmmpanadas, Austin *Also called Various Fields LLC (G-1624)*
MMS Traders LLC...832 433-7948
903 Port Houston St Houston (77029) *(G-10897)*
Mmw Fab Ltd...817 589-0881
1155 W Hurst Blvd Hurst (76053) *(G-12852)*
Mmw Industries, Hurst *Also called Mmw Fab Ltd (G-12852)*
MO Glass, Corpus Christi *Also called Morenos Auto Glass Inc (G-3579)*
MO Vac Service Co of Alice...361 668-8203
2 N Johnson St 31 Alice (78332) *(G-229)*
Mo-Vac Service Company (PA)...**956 682-6381**
3721 S Mccoll Rd Edinburg (78539) *(G-5597)*
Mo-Vac Service Company...830 583-3622
Hwy 181 Kenedy (78119) *(G-13489)*
Mo2 Inc (PA)...**214 575-7600**
13111 N Cntl Expy Ste 440 Dallas (75243) *(G-4682)*
Mobil Producing Texas and NM...713 871-5000
9 Greenway Plz 2700 Houston (77046) *(G-10898)*
Mobil Steel International Inc...713 991-0450
13830 S Wayside Dr Houston (77048) *(G-10899)*
Mobile Mini Inc...817 439-2288
11042 S Us Hwy Ste 287 Rhome (76078) *(G-17258)*
Mobile Mini Inc...512 251-2461
2851 S A W Grimes Blvd Austin (73301) *(G-1347)*
Mobile Mini Inc...480 894-6311
7020 Old Katy Rd Houston (77024) *(G-10900)*
Mobile Products Inc...800 323-0135
401 Capacity Dr Longview (75604) *(G-14278)*
Mobile Specialty Vehicles Inc...409 383-0521
811 County Road 2076 Newton (75966) *(G-15864)*
Mobile Surgical Tech Inc...972 735-8003
17817 Davenport Rd # 315 Dallas (75252) *(G-3849)*
Mobile Systems International, Richardson *Also called Metapath Software Intl (G-17356)*
Mobile Toys Inc...979 268-6066
909 University Dr E Ste B College Station (77840) *(G-3193)*
Mobility Works of Texas, Haltom City *Also called Wmk LLC (G-8162)*
Mobley Oilfield Services, Houston *Also called Tervita LLC (G-12210)*
Mobley Oilfield Services LP...903 234-2179
Fm Rd 2087 Longview (75603) *(G-14279)*
Mobotrex Inc...512 521-3060
301 W Howard Ln Ste 200 Austin (78753) *(G-1348)*
Mod-U-Serve, Houston *Also called Commercial Kitchens Inc (G-9250)*
Moda Midstream LLC...832 930-4838
1000 Louisiana St # 7100 Houston (77002) *(G-10901)*
Modco Industries Inc...936 539-9222
10650 Fm 1484 Rd Conroe (77303) *(G-3331)*
Modec International Inc (HQ)...**281 529-8100**
15011 Katy Fwy Ste 500 Houston (77094) *(G-10902)*
Modec Sofec, Houston *Also called Sofec Inc (G-11931)*
Modena Operating LLC...713 592-5000
2603 Augusta Dr Ste 430 Houston (77057) *(G-10903)*
Modern AG Products LLC...281 470-1903
816 W Barbours Cut Blvd La Porte (77571) *(G-13778)*
Modern Chemical, Houston *Also called Commercial Bev Concepts LLC (G-9249)*
Modern Concrete & Mtls LLC...409 840-2080
2090 W Cardinal Dr Beaumont (77705) *(G-1929)*

Modern Exploration Inc (PA) 903 893-1129
　4900 Texoma Pkwy Sherman (75090) *(G-18922)*
Modern Fabricating Inc 800 543-1581
　566 N Ww White Rd San Antonio (78219) *(G-18315)*
Modern Forge Texas LLC 817 268-0781
　733 W Hurst Blvd Hurst (76053) *(G-12853)*
Modern Group Ltd (PA) 800 231-8198
　1655 Louisiana St Beaumont (77701) *(G-1930)*
Modern Heat Treat Inc 817 616-0333
　2550 Austin Rd Richland Hills (76118) *(G-17443)*
Modern Iron Works Inc 915 778-6469
　2101 E Mills Ave El Paso (79901) *(G-5881)*
Modern Lantern 214 507-8608
　2212 Lipscomb St Fort Worth (76110) *(G-6844)*
Modern Machine Shop Inc 956 722-4656
　2000 Blaine St Laredo (78043) *(G-13913)*
Modern Print Shop Inc 713 861-7262
　2728 Columbia St Houston (77008) *(G-10904)*
Modern Shade LLC 512 385-4100
　4213 Felter Ln Austin (78744) *(G-1349)*
Modern Tektronix Assembly 817 868-7173
　1107 Pamela Dr Euless (76040) *(G-6150)*
Modern Welding Co of Texas 817 636-2215
　200 N Main St Rhome (76078) *(G-17259)*
Modern Welding Co Texas Inc 713 675-4211
　715 Sakowitz St Houston (77020) *(G-10905)*
Modernfold Door Specialties, Lewisville *Also called T R W Modernfold Company Inc (G-14096)*
Modine Jacksonville Inc 903 589-0009
　224 Talley Nichols Dr Jacksonville (75766) *(G-13251)*
Modine Manufacturing, Jacksonville *Also called Modine Jacksonville Inc (G-13251)*
Modisette Welding & Supply 903 984-2502
　3616 River Rd Kilgore (75662) *(G-13575)*
Modular Concepts Inc 817 945-1667
　6602 Plaza Pkwy Fort Worth (76116) *(G-6845)*
Module Truck Systems Inc (PA) 806 783-0777
　2010 E 50th St Lubbock (79404) *(G-14448)*
Modus Test LLC 972 914-7866
　651 N Plano Rd Ste 419 Richardson (75081) *(G-17359)*
Moehnke Custom Cabinetry 512 352-6506
　2210 W 2nd St Taylor (76574) *(G-19660)*
Moein Inc 817 341-1414
　1816 Barnett Dr Weatherford (76087) *(G-20605)*
Moffitt & Assoc Inc 361 884-9273
　615 Leopard St Ste 707 Corpus Christi (78401) *(G-3578)*
Moffitt West LLC 972 298-0531
　1146 S Cedar Ridge Dr Duncanville (75137) *(G-5535)*
Moffitt West LLC (HQ) 903 463-5700
　3100 Juanita Dr Denison (75020) *(G-5342)*
Mohave Oil and Gas Corporation (PA) 713 975-1725
　24 Waterway Ave Ste 350 Spring (77380) *(G-19232)*
Mohawk Industries Inc 210 564-8849
　4602 Perrin Crk Ste 1240 San Antonio (78217) *(G-18316)*
Mohawk Industries Inc 956 630-4709
　1201 N Jackson Rd McAllen (78501) *(G-14891)*
Mohawk Industries Inc 972 874-5820
　100 Enterprise Dr Ste 200 Flower Mound (75028) *(G-6272)*
Mohawk Industries Inc 214 309-4848
　7834 C F Hawn Fwy Dallas (75217) *(G-4683)*
Mohawk Laboratories Division, Irving *Also called Nch Corporation (G-13116)*
Mohawk Machine & Welding Inc 936 372-5103
　19111 Fm 362 Rd Waller (77484) *(G-20504)*
Mohf Manufacturing Inc 346 317-3618
　31 Roundtop Pl Spring (77381) *(G-19233)*
Mohr Research & Engrg Div, Houston *Also called Stress Engineering Svcs Inc (G-12079)*
Moil, Fort Worth *Also called Moncrief Oil International Inc (G-6848)*
Mokey Chem, Fairfield *Also called Halliburton Company (G-6176)*
Molded Fiber Glass Companies 940 668-0302
　3333 N I 35 Bldg 5 Gainesville (76240) *(G-7349)*
Molding Acquisition Corp (HQ) 209 723-5000
　685 John B Sias Mem Pkwy Fort Worth (76134) *(G-6846)*
Molecula Corp 512 649-9113
　4200 N Lamar Blvd Ste 225 Austin (78756) *(G-1350)*
Molecular Biologicals LLC 281 998-1227
　5413 Crenshaw Rd Ste 200 Pasadena (77505) *(G-16485)*
Molecular Structure, The Woodlands *Also called Rigaku Americas Corporation (G-19911)*
Molecular Templates Inc (PA) 512 869-1555
　9301 Amberglen Blvd # 100 Austin (78729) *(G-1705)*
Moleculin Biotech Inc 713 300-5160
　5300 Memorial Dr Ste 950 Houston (77007) *(G-10906)*
Molex LLC 512 345-1092
　9111 Jollyville Rd # 105 Austin (78759) *(G-1351)*
Molex LLC 915 591-5600
　11501 James Watt Dr El Paso (79936) *(G-5882)*
Molex Connector, Austin *Also called Molex LLC (G-1351)*
Moll McNeill Inc 214 748-7272
　3901 Main St Dallas (75226) *(G-4684)*
Moller Electric, Houston *Also called Copperlogic Inc (G-9310)*
Moller Supply Services, Houston *Also called Atlantic Pacific Marine Corp (G-8740)*

Molloy Corporation 713 771-9485
　9000 Suthwest Fwy Ste 320 Houston (77074) *(G-10907)*
Molson Coors Bev Co USA LLC 214 618-7400
　7800 Dallas Pkwy Ste 400 Plano (75024) *(G-16932)*
Molson Coors Bev Co USA LLC 817 551-3300
　7001 South Fwy Fort Worth (76134) *(G-6847)*
Moltroq International, Weslaco *Also called Jorge Trevino (G-20662)*
Momentum Chemical LLC 713 266-1042
　6 Tokeneke Trl Houston (77024) *(G-10908)*
Momentum Operating Co Inc 325 762-3331
　224 S Main St Albany (76430) *(G-191)*
Momentum Plastics LLC 713 678-7741
　5631 Old Clinton Rd Houston (77020) *(G-10909)*
Momentum Pressure Control LLC (HQ) 903 643-3700
　199 Corporate Rd Longview (75603) *(G-14280)*
Momentum Prssure Ctrl Rntl LLC 903 643-3700
　3820 Creekwood Cir Longview (75602) *(G-14281)*
Mometrix Media LLC (PA) 888 248-1219
　3827 Phelan Blvd Ste 179 Beaumont (77707) *(G-1931)*
Mometrix Test Preparation, Beaumont *Also called Mometrix Media LLC (G-1931)*
Monahans Electric Inc 432 943-3246
　3000 S Stockton Ave Monahans (79756) *(G-15609)*
Monahans News, The, Monahans *Also called Briggs News Alliance LLC (G-15601)*
Monahans Nipple-Up Service, Monahans *Also called Quell Petroleum Services Inc (G-15612)*
Monarch Separators, Houston *Also called Water Std Spration Systems LLC (G-12603)*
Moncrief Oil International Inc 817 348-8454
　950 Commerce St Fort Worth (76102) *(G-6848)*
Moncrief Partners LP (PA) 817 336-7232
　950 Commerce St Fort Worth (76102) *(G-6849)*
Moncrieff Oil, Fort Worth *Also called Moncrief Partners LP (G-6849)*
Moncries Faxel Oil Interests 817 335-5656
　777 Taylor St Ste 1030 Fort Worth (76102) *(G-6850)*
Mondelez Global LLC 713 749-0400
　6803 Almeda Rd Houston (77021) *(G-10910)*
Mondelez Global LLC 847 943-4000
　11210 Armour Dr Ste 3 El Paso (79935) *(G-5883)*
Moneyonmobile Inc 214 758-8600
　500 N Akard St Ste 2850 Dallas (75201) *(G-4685)*
Monico Monitoring Inc 281 350-8751
　18530 Klein Church Rd Spring (77379) *(G-19147)*
Monitor 903 887-4511
　1316 S 3rd St Ste 108 Mabank (75147) *(G-14580)*
Monitor Canopies Inc 903 893-6336
　200 Elliott Rd Sherman (75092) *(G-18923)*
Monitor Dynamics, San Antonio *Also called Mdi Security LLC (G-18286)*
Monitor, The, McAllen *Also called Aim Media Texas Operating LLC (G-14833)*
Monmouth Real Estate Inv Corp 281 784-4360
　16211 Air Center Blvd Houston (77032) *(G-10911)*
Monogram Orthopaedics Inc 512 399-2656
　3913 Todd Ln Ste 307 Austin (78744) *(G-1352)*
Monograms & More 979 693-7773
　1806 Welsh Ave Ste G College Station (77840) *(G-3194)*
Monolith Tech Holdings LLC (PA) 972 532-7387
　7164 Tech Dr Ste 100 Frisco (75033) *(G-7299)*
Monolithic Constructors Inc 972 483-7423
　177 Dome Park Pl Italy (76651) *(G-13214)*
Monolithic Dome Institute, Italy *Also called Monolithic Constructors Inc (G-13214)*
Monsanto Company 806 935-5623
　Hwy 87 W Dumas (79029) *(G-5525)*
Montague County Shopper, Bowie *Also called Shopper (G-2201)*
Montana Nelson Ready Mix LLC 936 328-5688
　709 Us 59 Loop S Livingston (77351) *(G-14159)*
Montana West USA 972 241-9998
　2606 Brenner Dr Dallas (75220) *(G-4686)*
Montano Investments Inc 956 630-1877
　4800 W Expressway 83 McAllen (78501) *(G-14892)*
Montecarlo Foods LLC 206 304-6771
　6421 Broadway San Antonio (78209) *(G-18317)*
Montecito Oilfield Svcs LLC 956 337-6082
　1505 Clle Dl Nrte 460 Laredo (78041) *(G-13914)*
Montega Ltd 713 692-1400
　1370 E 40th St 3 Houston (77022) *(G-10912)*
Monterey Oil & Gas Corporation 832 985-8723
　3737 Buffalo Speedway Houston (77098) *(G-10913)*
Monterrey Iron & Metal Ltd 210 927-2727
　2300 Frio City Rd San Antonio (78226) *(G-18318)*
Monterrey Products Company 210 435-2872
　803 S Zarzamora St San Antonio (78207) *(G-18319)*
Montes Machine Works LLC 346 320-4960
　706 Nebraska St South Houston (77587) *(G-19051)*
Montes Tortilla Factory 956 969-5792
　7536 N Fm 88 Weslaco (78599) *(G-20666)*
Montex Drilling Company (PA) 817 336-7232
　950 Commerce St Fort Worth (76102) *(G-6851)*
Montgomery Machine Company Inc 713 453-6381
　1005 Mae Dr Houston (77015) *(G-10914)*
Montgomery Manufacturing, Garland *Also called Fgl Group LLC (G-7489)*
Montgomery Mfg Co LLC 817 478-3221
　118 Industrial Ct Kennedale (76060) *(G-13500)*

Montoya Building Services Inc 713 367-0231
1400 Brdfeld Blvd Ste 200 Houston (77084) *(G-10915)*

Monument Chemical LLC 281 474-5550
10200 Bay Area Blvd Pasadena (77507) *(G-16486)*

Monument Chemical Houston LLC (HQ) **281 452-5951**
16717 Jacintoport Blvd Houston (77015) *(G-10916)*

Monument Chemical Houston LLC 832 376-2201
15635 Jacintoport Blvd Houston (77015) *(G-10917)*

Monument Chemicals Inc 281 452-5951
16717 Jacintoport Blvd Houston (77015) *(G-10918)*

Mooala Brands LLC 214 206-1902
2633 Mckinney Ave Ste 130 Dallas (75204) *(G-4687)*

Moody Compress & Warehouse Co, Pasadena *Also called Eugene B Smith & Co Inc (G-16432)*

Mooney Aerospace Group Ltd (PA) **830 896-6000**
165 Al Mooney Rd Kerrville (78028) *(G-13524)*

Mooney Airplane Company Inc 830 896-6000
165 Al Mooney Rd Kerrville (78028) *(G-13525)*

Mooney Saenger Enterprises 512 869-0979
40204 Industrial Park Cir Georgetown (78626) *(G-7665)*

Moontower Resources LLC 432 400-2445
303 Camp Craft Rd Ste 360 West Lake Hills (78746) *(G-20685)*

Moore Asphalt Co Inc 903 561-1321
5509 Old Jacksonville Hwy Tyler (75703) *(G-20131)*

Moore Business Forms, Nacogdoches *Also called R R Donnelley & Sons Company (G-15711)*

Moore Control Systems Inc 281 392-7747
1435 Katy Flewellen Rd Katy (77494) *(G-13372)*

Moore County News Press 806 935-4111
702 N Meredith Ave Dumas (79029) *(G-5526)*

Moore Fabrication Inc 713 643-7477
901 Bay Area Blvd Houston (77058) *(G-10919)*

Moore, T S Print-It, Mission *Also called T S Moore Printing Co Inc (G-15565)*

Mooreco Inc (HQ) **254 778-4727**
2885 Lorraine Ave Temple (76501) *(G-19691)*

Moores Machine Shop 281 489-2925
3806 Fm 1128 Rd Pearland (77584) *(G-16582)*

Morales Machine Sp & Trnsp LLC 956 722-4485
5795 State Highway 359 Laredo (78043) *(G-13915)*

Morefield Development Inc (PA) **713 869-2111**
2518 Mcallister Rd Houston (77092) *(G-10920)*

Moreman Community Gin Assn 361 552-9407
10254 State Highway 35 S Port Lavaca (77979) *(G-17152)*

Morenos Auto Glass Inc 361 855-1471
2617 Holly Rd Corpus Christi (78415) *(G-3579)*

Morgan Building & Spa Mfg Corp 254 629-1599
1117 Lower Seman Eastland (76448) *(G-5568)*

Morgan Building Transport 972 864-7300
12700 Hillcrest Rd Ste C Dallas (75230) *(G-4688)*

Morgan Buildings & Spas, Dallas *Also called Morgan Building Transport (G-4688)*

Morgan Buildings & Spas Inc (HQ) **972 864-7300**
1651 N Glenville Dr Richardson (75081) *(G-17360)*

Morgan Buildings &AMp Spas, Eastland *Also called Morgan Building & Spa Mfg Corp (G-5568)*

Morgan Cabinetry Inc 972 278-8836
2775 W Kingsley Rd Garland (75041) *(G-7555)*

Morgan Kinder Treating LP (HQ) **361 578-1312**
407 Holt Rd Victoria (77905) *(G-20285)*

Morgan Kinder Treating LP 432 563-2766
13405 E Highway 191 Odessa (79765) *(G-16083)*

Morgan Kinder Treating LP 713 369-8515
1001 La St Ste 1000 Houston (77002) *(G-10921)*

Morgan Newton Company LP 972 212-8080
3401 Wynwood Dr Plano (75074) *(G-16933)*

Morgan Performance 281 370-2465
6715 Klein Cemetary Rd Spring (77379) *(G-19148)*

Morgan Roofing 409 762-8068
1311 42nd St Galveston (77550) *(G-7404)*

Morgan Trim Inc 806 655-9777
18700 S Us Highway 87 Canyon (79015) *(G-2674)*

Morgan Truck Body LLC 903 872-7445
8051 Morgan Cir Corsicana (75109) *(G-3679)*

Morningstar Partners LP (PA) **817 334-7800**
400 W 7th St Fort Worth (76102) *(G-6852)*

Morrell Plating Co Inc 214 357-9850
2712 Anson Rd Dallas (75235) *(G-4689)*

Morris Communications Co LLC 806 376-4488
600 S Tyler St Ste 600 # 600 Amarillo (79101) *(G-447)*

Morris Export Crating Company (PA) **713 675-9101**
1225 Mccarty St Houston (77029) *(G-10922)*

Morris Export Services, Houston *Also called Morris Export Crating Company (G-10922)*

Morris Material Handling Inc 281 445-2225
7300 Chippewa Blvd Houston (77086) *(G-10923)*

Morris Ready-Mix Concrete, Abilene *Also called Ingram Concrete LLC (G-52)*

Morrison Architectural Sign, Dallas *Also called Martin Inc (G-4639)*

Morrison Energy Group LLC 713 344-9233
16285 Park Ten Pl Ste 100 Houston (77084) *(G-10924)*

Morrison Milling Company (HQ) **940 387-6111**
319 E Prairie St Denton (76201) *(G-5382)*

Morrison Products Inc 972 279-4000
3400 Us Highway 80 E Mesquite (75149) *(G-15063)*

Morrow Cabinets Inc 972 221-7551
136 E College St Lewisville (75057) *(G-14070)*

Morsco Supply LLC 903 234-2183
930 N Fredonia St Longview (75601) *(G-14282)*

Mortex Products Inc 817 624-0820
501 Terminal Rd Fort Worth (76106) *(G-6853)*

Mortin Printing, Victoria *Also called Altman & Nelson Prtg Co Inc (G-20238)*

Morton Printers Inc 210 223-4258
814 N Alamo St San Antonio (78215) *(G-18320)*

Morven Partners LP 325 372-5727
2803 W Wallace St San Saba (76877) *(G-18718)*

Moseley Machine Company Inc (PA) **713 228-1382**
3608 Polk St Houston (77003) *(G-10925)*

Moses Envmtl & Cnstr Svcs LLC 806 418-8525
3433 Plains Blvd Amarillo (79102) *(G-448)*

Mosielee Rm Dual, Houston *Also called Cemex Construction Mtls S LLC (G-9125)*

Mosites Rubber Company Inc 817 335-3451
2720 Tillar St Fort Worth (76107) *(G-6854)*

Mosquedas Coml & Indus Pnt, Pearland *Also called Mclp Industrial Entps Corp (G-16581)*

Mother Earth Labs Inc 210 695-3535
24165 Ih 10 W San Antonio (78257) *(G-18321)*

Mother Parker's Tea and Coffee, Fort Worth *Also called Mother Parkers Tea Cof USA Ltd (G-6855)*

Mother Parkers Tea Cof USA Ltd (HQ) **817 551-5500**
7800 Will Rogers Blvd Fort Worth (76140) *(G-6855)*

Mothers Journey Inc 877 279-7975
15922 Eldorado Pkwy # 50 Frisco (75035) *(G-7261)*

Motion Computing Inc 512 637-1100
8601 Rr 2222 Bldg Ii Austin (78730) *(G-1353)*

Motion Envelope Inc 214 634-2131
1628 Terre Colony Ct Dallas (75212) *(G-4690)*

Motion Gear Works LLC 713 585-5245
10511 Wndsor Ln Bldg A St Stafford (77477) *(G-19355)*

Motion Reps Inc 940 565-9411
3801 N Interstate 35 # 110 Denton (76207) *(G-5383)*

Motive Wireless Ltd Lblty Co 214 500-9242
8765 Spring Cypress Rd Spring (77379) *(G-19149)*

Motor City Tool & Die Corp 512 251-7700
20203 Algreg St Pflugerville (78660) *(G-16681)*

Motor Controls Inc 972 247-4440
10661 Newkirk St Dallas (75220) *(G-4691)*

Motor Crier Sfety Slutions Inc 956 726-3377
5717 Springfield Ave Laredo (78041) *(G-13916)*

Motor Pwr Prtction Systems Div, Georgetown *Also called Starks Welding & Mfg Svcs Inc (G-7681)*

Motor Trike Inc 903 842-3094
22667 Fm 15 Troup (75789) *(G-20026)*

Motorola Solutions Inc 713 783-6400
9800 Richmond Ave Houston (77042) *(G-10926)*

Motorola Solutions Inc 512 422-9028
2120 W Braker Ln Ste P Austin (78758) *(G-1354)*

Motorola Solutions Inc 512 895-2000
6501 W William Cannon Dr Austin (78735) *(G-1355)*

Motorola Solutions Inc 972 277-4600
1507 L B Johnson Fwy # 700 Dallas (75234) *(G-4692)*

Motorola Solutions Inc 972 587-5360
1701 Valley View Ln Dallas (75234) *(G-4693)*

Motorola Solutions Inc 915 872-1229
1220 Don Haskins Dr Ste A El Paso (79936) *(G-5884)*

Motorola Solutions Inc 512 821-1560
4515 Seton Center Pkwy # 330 Austin (78759) *(G-1356)*

Motorola Solutions Inc 817 245-6000
2101 Eagle Pkwy Fort Worth (76177) *(G-6856)*

Motts, Plano *Also called Motts LLP (G-16934)*

Motts LLP (HQ) **972 673-8088**
5301 Legacy Dr Plano (75024) *(G-16934)*

Mount Franklin Foods LLC 800 351-8178
9820 Railroad Dr El Paso (79924) *(G-5885)*

Mount Pleasant Daily Tribune, Mount Pleasant *Also called Media Palmer Inc (G-15654)*

Mount Vernon Mills Inc 361 275-2393
202 N Gazzie St Cuero (77954) *(G-3764)*

Mount Vernon Mills Inc 979 836-5255
1100 Highway 290 W Brenham (77833) *(G-2265)*

Mountain Commercial Graphics, Houston *Also called Mountain Products LP (G-10927)*

Mountain Products LP (PA) **713 895-1350**
12922 Hempstead Rd Houston (77040) *(G-10927)*

Mountain Pure TX LLC 903 723-1362
777 Willow Creek Pkwy Palestine (75801) *(G-16304)*

Movement Industries Corp 713 849-1300
6829 Flintlock Rd Houston (77040) *(G-10928)*

Moventas Gears Inc 432 517-4518
604 Owens St Big Spring (79720) *(G-2088)*

Moventas Gears Inc (HQ) **503 247-6107**
2002 Timberloch Pl # 200 Spring (77380) *(G-19234)*

Moyes & Co Inc 214 623-6700
8235 Douglas Ave Ste 1221 Dallas (75225) *(G-4694)*

ALPHABETIC

Mozaic Company 972 386-3332
1101 Avenue G Arlington (76011) *(G-733)*

Mozu, Austin *Also called Volusion LLC (G-1645)*

Mozzarella Company 214 741-4072
2944 Elm St Dallas (75226) *(G-4695)*

Mp Precision Services Inc 915 599-9188
11501 Rojas Dr Ste O El Paso (79936) *(G-5886)*

MPA International LP (PA) **915 474-7832**
7453 Le Conte Dr El Paso (79912) *(G-5887)*

Mpact Beverage Company, Spring *Also called Mpact Beverage Solutions LLC (G-19150)*

Mpact Beverage Solutions LLC (PA) **832 260-2342**
21240 Foster Rd Spring (77388) *(G-19150)*

Mpact Construction Services, Houston *Also called Mpact Strategic Consulting LLC (G-10929)*

Mpact Strategic Consulting LLC 866 361-7611
4635 Suthwest Fwy Ste 700 Houston (77027) *(G-10929)*

Mpck Machining Inc 254 938-7555
1709 Church Ave Troy (76579) *(G-20031)*

Mpi Marketing Inc 972 403-7801
3308 Preston Rd Ste 350 Plano (75093) *(G-16935)*

Mpi Wood, Plano *Also called Mpi Marketing Inc (G-16935)*

Mpl Industries Inc (PA) **214 253-2332**
10877 Rockwall Rd Dallas (75238) *(G-4696)*

Mpl Industries Inc 972 233-0757
10877 Rockwall Rd Dallas (75238) *(G-4697)*

Mpp Group of Companies, Corsicana *Also called Texas Mpp LP (G-3685)*

Mpp Investments LLC 940 691-0014
4517 Southwest Pkwy Wichita Falls (76308) *(G-20784)*

Mpr Products Inc (PA) **713 493-0252**
6124 Highway 6 N 119 Houston (77084) *(G-10930)*

MPS Dallas, Dallas *Also called Multi Packaging Solutions Inc (G-4704)*

MPS Group (PA) **210 344-0332**
12020 Warfield St San Antonio (78216) *(G-18322)*

MPW Corporation 713 640-2700
5814 Heffernan St Houston (77087) *(G-10931)*

MPW Enterprises LLC 713 671-9560
7501 Schneider St Houston (77093) *(G-10932)*

Mr Bird, New Braunfels *Also called John B Smith (G-15806)*

Mr Bird 830 620-9090
1197 Eikel St New Braunfels (78130) *(G-15814)*

Mr Maiz-Ito-Inc 915 873-9270
1901 E Yandell Dr Ste B El Paso (79903) *(G-5888)*

Mr Nams Foods Incorporated 214 689-4688
3435 Jane Ln Dallas (75247) *(G-4698)*

Mr Sign Inc (PA) **214 526-7446**
2629 Oak Lawn Ave Dallas (75219) *(G-4699)*

MRC Energy Company 972 371-5200
5400 Lyndon B Johnson Fwy Dallas (75240) *(G-4700)*

MRC Global (us) Inc 432 620-0059
511 W Missouri Ave Midland (79701) *(G-15307)*

Mrs Baird's Baking Co, Houston *Also called Bairds Mrs Bakeries Bus Tr (G-8791)*

Mrs Bairds Bakeries Bus Tr (HQ) **800 355-1260**
14401 Statler Blvd Fort Worth (76155) *(G-6857)*

Mrs John L Strong & Co LLC 212 838-3775
3245 Ella Lee Ln Houston (77019) *(G-10933)*

Mrs Rios Corn Products, San Angelo *Also called Armando G Martinez (G-17778)*

Ms Dallas Reprographics Inc 214 521-7000
1130 Dragon St Ste 110 Dallas (75207) *(G-4701)*

Ms Directional LLC (HQ) **936 442-2500**
3335 Pollok Dr Conroe (77303) *(G-3332)*

Ms Energy Services, Conroe *Also called Ms Directional LLC (G-3332)*

Ms Logging Inc 409 382-2424
1 Newton County Rd Bon Wier (75928) *(G-2149)*

MSA Industries Inc 432 337-6062
2742 W Interstate 20 Odessa (79763) *(G-16084)*

Msd Performance, El Paso *Also called Msdp Group LLC (G-5889)*

Msdp Group LLC (HQ) **915 857-5200**
1350 Pullman Dr 14 El Paso (79936) *(G-5889)*

Msf Electric Inc 210 781-4112
15500 Tradesman San Antonio (78249) *(G-18323)*

Msf Electric Inc 214 377-8710
9622 Chartwell Dr Dallas (75243) *(G-4702)*

Msh Printing, Houston *Also called Mail Services Houston Inc (G-10738)*

MSI, Garland *Also called Marking Systems Inc (G-7543)*

MSI, Harlingen *Also called Mexican Snacks Inc (G-8195)*

MSI, Beaumont *Also called Manufacturing Solutions Inc (G-1925)*

MSI Oilfield Products, Houston *Also called Nov MSI Pipe Prtction Tech Inc (G-11086)*

MSP Drilex Inc 281 377-4393
21227 Hfsmith Khrvil Rd Tomball (77375) *(G-19990)*

Mssl Wiring System Inc 830 776-9221
7 Zane Grey St Ste A El Paso (79906) *(G-5890)*

Mt Texas LLC 210 599-0060
3614 Highpoint San Antonio (78217) *(G-18324)*

MT&I Card Products, Dallas *Also called Magnetic Ticket & Label Corp (G-4626)*

Mtc America Enterprises Inc 972 926-0600
3302 W Miller Rd Ste 300 Garland (75041) *(G-7556)*

MTC Marketing Inc (PA) **972 488-0577**
1415 Hutton Dr Carrollton (75006) *(G-2782)*

Mtc Printing Inc (PA) **972 620-3212**
1840 Hutton Dr Ste 200 Carrollton (75006) *(G-2783)*

Mtech, Colleyville *Also called Measurement Technologies Ltd (G-3220)*

Mtech Comfort Systems, Round Rock *Also called Mechanical Technical Svcs LP (G-17671)*

MTI Materials, El Paso *Also called Hueco Quarry Inc (G-5806)*

MTI Ready Mix, El Paso *Also called Mullen-Telles Inc (G-5891)*

Mtlv Properties LLC 361 946-6145
15338 Dasmarinas Dr Corpus Christi (78418) *(G-3580)*

MTS Threaded Products Company, Corpus Christi *Also called Maintenance Tool & Supply Co (G-3571)*

Mtwd Holdings Inc 972 346-2242
10601 Clarence Dr Ste 100 Frisco (75033) *(G-7300)*

Mtx Electronics Inc 956 781-3476
100 S Austin Dr Ste A Pharr (78577) *(G-16708)*

Muchowich Offshore Oil Service, Clute *Also called Offshore Oil Services Inc (G-3157)*

Mud King, Houston *Also called Mud King Products Inc (G-10934)*

Mud King Products Inc 281 645-4158
15211 Woodham Dr Houston (77073) *(G-10934)*

Mud Technology Intl Inc 903 675-3240
2610 State Highway 31 W Athens (75751) *(G-834)*

Mudsmith 214 370-9535
2114 Greenville Ave Dallas (75206) *(G-4703)*

Mudsmith Ltd 432 687-6837
1309 W County Road 114 Midland (79706) *(G-15308)*

Mueller Co LLC 956 621-3086
3351 Ruben Torres Sr Blvd Brownsville (78526) *(G-2384)*

Mueller Construction Company 903 868-3585
5100 Marshall St Sherman (75090) *(G-18924)*

Mueller Manufacturing Inc (PA) **979 265-8303**
2200 Brazosport Blvd N Richwood (77531) *(G-17469)*

Mueller Supply Company Inc (PA) **325 365-3555**
1913 Hutchins Ave Ballinger (76821) *(G-1741)*

Mueller Supply Company Inc 936 344-9057
16355 N Highway 75 Willis (77378) *(G-20855)*

Mueller Supply Company Inc 512 308-9173
1455 Highway 71 W Bastrop (78602) *(G-1759)*

Mueller Supply Company Inc 325 690-7700
4625 Fm 18 Abilene (79602) *(G-60)*

Mueller Supply Company Inc 972 932-3208
3550 E Us Highway 175 Kaufman (75142) *(G-13461)*

Mueller Supply Company Inc 361 580-1427
9502 Us Highway 59 N Victoria (77905) *(G-20286)*

Mueller Supply Company Inc 915 886-3383
8810 S Desert Blvd Anthony (79821) *(G-588)*

Mueller Supply Company Inc 409 886-2233
6311 Ih 10 E Orange (77630) *(G-16254)*

Mueller Supply Company Inc 254 742-2754
6910 N General Bruce Dr Temple (76501) *(G-19692)*

Mueller Supply Company Inc 903 892-6222
110 E Hwy 82 Sherman (75092) *(G-18925)*

Muenster Drilling Company 940 759-4949
415 County Road 350 Muenster (76252) *(G-15671)*

Muilenburg Prosthetics Inc 713 524-3949
3900 La Branch St Houston (77004) *(G-10935)*

Mulberry Heart I Ltd (PA) **210 377-3335**
118 Irvington Dr San Antonio (78209) *(G-18325)*

Mullen-Telles Inc 915 859-5767
905 Loma Verde Dr El Paso (79936) *(G-5891)*

Mullins Machine & Mfg Co 713 672-0451
17214 Ash Butte Dr Houston (77090) *(G-10936)*

Mullins White Exploration Inc 817 442-5259
100 S Village Center Dr Southlake (76092) *(G-19079)*

Multalloy LLC (HQ) **713 943-3544**
3730 S Main St Pearland (77581) *(G-16583)*

Multi Packaging Solutions Inc 214 343-7600
13465 Jupiter Rd Dallas (75238) *(G-4704)*

Multi Packg Solutions Intl Ltd 214 634-2131
1455 Terre Colony Ct Dallas (75212) *(G-4705)*

Multi Plastics 972 402-9100
10554 King William Dr Dallas (75220) *(G-4706)*

Multi-Chem Inc 281 442-1222
3000 N Sam Houston Pkwy E Houston (77032) *(G-10937)*

Multi-Chem Group LLC (HQ) **281 871-4000**
3000 N Sam Houston Pkwy E P Houston (77032) *(G-10938)*

Multi-Machining Co Inc 972 429-6111
701 Business Way Wylie (75098) *(G-20941)*

Multi-Metal & Mfg Co Inc 972 771-1376
1500 E Interstate 30 Rockwall (75087) *(G-17556)*

Multi-Quest Inc (PA) **972 235-2356**
1111 Commerce Dr Richardson (75081) *(G-17361)*

Multi-Seal Corporation 281 591-0111
407 Alana Ln Spring (77386) *(G-19235)*

Multicam (HQ) **972 929-4070**
1025 Royal Ln Dallas (75261) *(G-4707)*

Multicopy Printing Company 210 923-8373
516 New Laredo Hwy San Antonio (78211) *(G-18326)*

Multilayer Technology, Irving *Also called JVB Electronics Inc (G-13071)*

Multiple Systems Inc (PA).....................806 373-7073
2716 Tee Anchor Blvd Amarillo (79104) *(G-449)*

Multiple Systems Inc.............................806 373-7073
2700 Tee Anchor Blvd Amarillo (79104) *(G-450)*

Multisources Ltd.................................979 247-4305
9305 Feydler Rd La Grange (78945) *(G-13699)*

Multisports Inc...................................713 460-8188
2612 Mckinney St Houston (77003) *(G-10939)*

Multitech Group Inc..............................817 496-5500
3705 W Green Oaks Blvd A Arlington (76016) *(G-734)*

Muncaster Capital Texas Inc (PA)..............214 515-5000
4101 S Interstate Hwy 45 Ennis (75119) *(G-6111)*

Munters Corporation.............................210 651-5018
16900 Jordan Selma (78154) *(G-18878)*

Munters Corporation.............................210 651-5018
16900 Jordan Selma (78154) *(G-18879)*

Murchison Oil & Gas, Plano Also called JD Murchison Interests Inc *(G-16898)*

Murchison Oil and Gas Inc.......................972 931-0700
7250 Dallas Pkwy Ste 1400 Plano (75024) *(G-16936)*

Murco Wall Products, Houston Also called Murphy Wall Products Intl Inc *(G-10943)*

Murex Petroleum Corporation (PA).............281 590-3313
363 N Sam Houston Pkwy E # 200 Houston (77060) *(G-10940)*

Muroc Systems Inc...............................214 295-9442
100 Highland Park Vlg Dallas (75205) *(G-4708)*

Murphy & Murphy Inc (PA).......................940 325-2666
315 Ne 9th Ave Mineral Wells (76067) *(G-15533)*

Murphy Connected Entps Inc....................512 821-0222
10423 Mckalla Pl Austin (78758) *(G-1357)*

Murphy Exploration & Prod Co...................281 675-9000
9805 Katy Fwy Ste G200 Houston (77024) *(G-10941)*

Murphy Exploration Prod - USA (HQ)...........281 675-9000
9805 Katy Fwy Ste G200 Houston (77024) *(G-10942)*

Murphy Fw.......................................281 633-4500
2105 Randon Dyer Rd Rosenberg (77471) *(G-17590)*

Murphy USA Inc..................................512 332-0622
490 Agnes St Bastrop (78602) *(G-1760)*

Murphy Wall Products Intl Inc...................713 694-8365
919 E Rittenhouse St Houston (77076) *(G-10943)*

Murphy's Readymix Concrete, Schertz Also called W P Murphy Inc *(G-18769)*

Murray Building & Crane Inds...................713 464-6506
2218 Pech Rd Houston (77055) *(G-10944)*

Murray Building & Crane Inds, Houston Also called Murray Building & Crane Inds *(G-10944)*

Murray Label & Printing Ltd.....................972 234-2220
10470 Miller Rd Dallas (75238) *(G-4709)*

Musshorn Enterprises Inc........................915 772-9007
7170 Copperqueen Dr El Paso (79915) *(G-5892)*

Mustang Exploration Co Inc.....................979 648-2641
106 N Orange Louise (77455) *(G-14353)*

Mustang Extreme Envmtl Svcs LL (PA).........830 393-1034
5049 Edwards Ranch Rd # 2 Fort Worth (76109) *(G-6858)*

Mustang Gas Compression LLC (PA)............903 218-4459
2500 Woodbine Dr Kilgore (75662) *(G-13576)*

Mustang Group Ltd..............................830 968-0291
4058 Adams Cir Eagle Pass (78852) *(G-5550)*

Mustang Manufacturing Corp....................903 482-5666
461 Martin Duke Rd Van Alstyne (75495) *(G-20211)*

Mustang Oilfield Services LLC...................903 389-4200
117 County Road 946 Fairfield (75840) *(G-6179)*

Mustang Technology Group LP..................972 747-0707
6900 K Ave Plano (75074) *(G-16937)*

Mustang Tubing Testers, Abilene Also called Red Diamond Energy Svcs Inc *(G-69)*

Mustang Well Service LLC........................432 524-6112
2681 Se 1000 Andrews (79714) *(G-553)*

Mustang Wireline Services, Wichita Falls Also called Luig Energy Services LLC *(G-20780)*

Muto Technology Inc.............................512 251-2211
2121 Grand Avenue Pkwy Austin (78728) *(G-1358)*

Mvc, Amarillo Also called Maxi Volt Corporation Inc *(G-500)*

Mvp Plastics Sa LLC.............................440 834-1790
4001 W Military Hwy McAllen (78503) *(G-14893)*

Mw Americas Inc., Plano Also called Exyte Americas Holding Inc *(G-16868)*

Mw Industries Inc................................281 233-0448
2400 Farrell Rd Houston (77073) *(G-10945)*

Mw Supply Inc....................................254 897-4590
100 Progress St Glen Rose (76043) *(G-7732)*

Mwp, Fort Worth Also called Metroplex Wood Products Ltd *(G-6834)*

My Jack Products, Mesquite Also called Technical Services Intl *(G-15079)*

My Magic Mud, New Braunfels Also called Carbon and Clay Company *(G-15777)*

My Plates, Austin Also called License Plates of Texas LLC *(G-1292)*

My Sons Laundry LLC............................214 634-2080
8700 Chancellor Row Dallas (75247) *(G-4710)*

Myco Plastics Inc................................903 586-0551
902 Cherokee Trl Jacksonville (75766) *(G-13252)*

Myedu Corporation...............................512 469-9777
1301 S Mo Pac Expy # 250 Austin (78746) *(G-1359)*

Mygi's Desserts, Seagoville Also called Kennymac LLC *(G-18801)*

Mygis Empire LLC................................972 674-9758
1807 Lost Crossing Trl Arlington (76002) *(G-735)*

Mykytyn Enterprise Inc..........................281 866-9263
12539 Hammill Path Dr Houston (77066) *(G-10946)*

Mylan Bertek Pharmaceuticals..................281 240-1000
12720 Dairy Ashford Rd Sugar Land (77478) *(G-19508)*

Mylan Institutional Inc..........................281 240-1000
12720 Dairy Ashford Rd Sugar Land (77478) *(G-19509)*

Myramid Analytical Inc..........................512 288-5093
12345 Pauls Valley Rd # 7 Austin (78737) *(G-865)*

Myrex Industries, Houston Also called Mil Ltd *(G-10879)*

Mystic Pharmaceuticals Inc.....................512 918-2900
2006 Windy Ter Ste A Cedar Park (78613) *(G-2979)*

N & N Services LLC...............................281 741-9714
1502 Mykawa Rd Pearland (77581) *(G-16584)*

N & P Sign System Inc...........................281 444-9535
7590 Fallbrook Dr Ste 1 Houston (77086) *(G-10947)*

N 2 The World....................................817 424-0799
3510 Hightimber Dr Grapevine (76051) *(G-8046)*

N A Petroflex Ltd.................................800 433-5711
1920 N Weaver St Gainesville (76240) *(G-7350)*

N A Petroflex Ltd (PA)...........................940 668-7283
1305 N Interstate 35 Gainesville (76240) *(G-7351)*

N C A, Houston Also called Norse Cutng & Abandonment Inc *(G-11070)*

N C A, Garland Also called National Circuit Assembly Inc *(G-7557)*

N C I, Houston Also called Cornerstone Bldg Brands Inc *(G-9321)*

N D Nolen Drilling LLC...........................210 585-1966
300 Convent St Ste 1330 San Antonio (78205) *(G-18327)*

N D Stovall & Son................................940 549-2616
605 3rd St Ste 200 Graham (76450) *(G-7787)*

N E C America Radio Division, Dallas Also called Nec Corporation of America *(G-4719)*

N L Industries Inc (HQ)..........................972 233-1700
5430 Lbj Fwy Ste 1700 Dallas (75240) *(G-4711)*

N M L Inc of Texas...............................713 753-1448
1221 Lamar St Ste 1175 Houston (77010) *(G-10948)*

N O V Wilson Tx19, Navasota Also called National Oilwell Varco LP *(G-15740)*

N S S, Austin Also called Neu Security Services LLC *(G-1364)*

N S S I, Houston Also called Nuclear Sources and Svcs Inc *(G-11096)*

N-Fab Inc...281 880-6322
12302 Shiloh Church Rd Houston (77066) *(G-10949)*

N2, Midland Also called Nitrogen Services LLC *(G-15320)*

N5 Wireline Service LLC.........................806 648-1505
1322 S Main St Perryton (79070) *(G-16641)*

NA Acquisition Company.........................817 231-1300
3400 Northern Cross Blvd Fort Worth (76137) *(G-6859)*

Nabisco, Houston Also called Mondelez Global LLC *(G-10910)*

Nabors Corporate Services Inc..................281 874-0035
515 W Greens Rd Ste 1100 Houston (77067) *(G-10950)*

Nabors Drilling International, Houston Also called Nabors International Inc *(G-10954)*

Nabors Drilling International.....................281 775-8506
515 W Greens Rd Ste 1200 Houston (77067) *(G-10951)*

Nabors Drilling Tech USA Inc (HQ)..............281 874-0035
515 W Greens Rd Ste 1200 Houston (77067) *(G-10952)*

Nabors Drilling Tech USA Inc....................281 462-1310
2100 Crosby Dayton Rd Crosby (77532) *(G-3738)*

Nabors Drilling Tech USA Inc....................281 874-0035
2500 Oregon St Odessa (79764) *(G-16085)*

Nabors Drilling Tech USA Inc....................281 259-8887
14703 Fm 1488 Rd Magnolia (77354) *(G-14619)*

Nabors Industries Inc (HQ)......................281 874-0035
515 W Greens Rd Ste 1200 Houston (77067) *(G-10953)*

Nabors International Inc (HQ)....................281 874-0035
515 W Greens Rd Ste 600 Houston (77067) *(G-10954)*

Nabors Offshore Corporation (HQ)..............281 874-0406
515 W Greens Rd Ste 1200 Houston (77067) *(G-10955)*

Nabors Oil Tools, Houston Also called Nabors Well Services Co *(G-10956)*

Nabors Well Services Co (HQ)...................281 874-0035
515 W Greens Rd Ste 1000 Houston (77067) *(G-10956)*

Nabors Well Services Co.........................325 884-2536
100 W Highway 67 Big Lake (76932) *(G-2059)*

Nabors Well Services Co.........................817 396-4310
12890 Cleburne Hwy Cresson (76035) *(G-3710)*

Nabors Well Services Co.........................940 626-3735
2273 N Highway 287 Decatur (76234) *(G-5249)*

Nabors Well Services Co.........................281 775-8506
672008 Box Houston (77267) *(G-10957)*

Nabors Well Services Ltd........................432 523-4420
701 Nw Mustang Dr Andrews (79714) *(G-554)*

Nabors Well Services Ltd........................325 387-2884
Hwy 277 S Sonora (76950) *(G-19028)*

Nabors Well Services Ltd........................325 573-2621
2857 W Us Highway 180 Snyder (79549) *(G-18996)*

Nabors Well Services Ltd........................432 943-2227
110 Industrail Monahans (79756) *(G-15610)*

Nabors Well Services Ltd (HQ)..................281 874-0035
515 W Greens Rd Ste 1200 Houston (77067) *(G-10958)*

Nabors Well Services Ltd........................432 683-5000
3300 N A St Bldg 2-200 Midland (79705) *(G-15309)*

Nabors Well Services Ltd........................806 592-9128
1161 State Hwy 83 Denver City (79323) *(G-5421)*

Nabors Well Services Ltd 325 651-9241
1214 Gas Plant Rd San Angelo (76904) ***(G-17814)***
Nabors Well Services Ltd 325 392-2313
Hwy 163 N Ozona (76943) ***(G-16286)***
Nabors Well Services Ltd 432 836-4332
Hwy 349 S Iraan (79744) ***(G-12920)***
Nabors Wells Service, Cresson *Also called Nabors Well Services Co* ***(G-3710)***
Nacco Industries Inc 440 449-9600
5340 Legacy Dr Ste 300 Plano (75024) ***(G-16938)***
Nacero Inc 346 200-7706
2050 W Sam Houston Pkwy S Houston (77042) ***(G-10959)***
Nacogdoches Coca Cola Btlg Co 936 564-0268
3321 Nw Stallings Dr Nacogdoches (75964) ***(G-15704)***
Nacogdoches Feed Mill, Nacogdoches *Also called Pilgrims Pride Corporation* ***(G-15710)***
Nacogdoches Oil and Gas Inc 936 560-4747
816 North St Nacogdoches (75961) ***(G-15705)***
Naegles Industrial Lea McHy Co 361 293-7015
405 Fm 3083 Yoakum (77995) ***(G-20972)***
Nail Therapie Htx 832 703-4386
9121a Stella Link Rd Houston (77025) ***(G-10960)***
Nailhead Spur Company Inc 512 588-6112
Polk St 1840 E Hwy 29 Burnet (78611) ***(G-2613)***
Nailit Millwork Inc 210 633-4659
205 E Nakoma St San Antonio (78216) ***(G-18328)***
Nailit Millwork Installation, San Antonio *Also called Nailit Millwork Inc* ***(G-18328)***
Nailor Industries Texas Inc (HQ) **281 590-1172**
4714 Winfield Rd Houston (77039) ***(G-10961)***
Nakent LLC 619 212-2277
25755 Velvet Crk San Antonio (78255) ***(G-18329)***
Nalco Champion, Odessa *Also called Championx LLC* ***(G-15959)***
Nalco Champion Wellchem 432 366-0971
6601 Trunk St Odessa (79762) ***(G-16086)***
Nalco Company LLC 210 493-0379
3523 Oakfort St San Antonio (78247) ***(G-18330)***
Nan Ya Plastics Corp America 979 532-5494
2081 Fm 102 Rd Wharton (77488) ***(G-20702)***
Nan Ya Plastics Corp America 281 727-7300
706 F M 102 Wharton (77488) ***(G-20703)***
Nan Ya Plastics Corp USA 979 532-5494
2081 Fm 102 Rd Wharton (77488) ***(G-20704)***
Nan Ya Plastics Corp USA 713 674-7822
8989 North Loop E Houston (77029) ***(G-10962)***
Nan Ya Plstic Corp Tpei Taiwan, Wharton *Also called Nan Ya Plastics Corp America* ***(G-20703)***
Nance International Inc 409 838-6127
2915 Milam St Beaumont (77701) ***(G-1932)***
Nance Marine & Industrial AC, Beaumont *Also called Nance International Inc* ***(G-1932)***
Nano Coat LP 281 217-5265
750 Rittiman Rd San Antonio (78209) ***(G-18331)***
Nano Instrs Div Dcg Systems, Richardson *Also called Fei Efa Inc* ***(G-17309)***
Nanoracks LLC 832 632-7754
503 Forge River Rd Webster (77598) ***(G-20641)***
Nap, San Antonio *Also called Nationwide Pnnant Flag Mfg Inc* ***(G-18337)***
Nap Industries LLC 940 668-8111
202 S Dixon St Ste 201 Gainesville (76240) ***(G-7352)***
NAPA Auto Parts, Conroe *Also called Wapco Inc* ***(G-3384)***
Napco Bag & Film Gp LLC (PA) **972 245-8190**
1435 Bradley Ln Ste 130 Carrollton (75007) ***(G-2880)***
Napco Chemical Company Inc 281 651-6800
2830 Spring Cypress Rd Spring (77388) ***(G-19151)***
Napco Precast LLC (PA) **210 424-4371**
6949 Low Bid Ln San Antonio (78250) ***(G-18332)***
Napco,, Wichita Falls *Also called North American Pipe Corp* ***(G-20787)***
Narco, Lewisville *Also called North American Research Corp* ***(G-14074)***
Narstco Inc (HQ) **972 775-5560**
300 Ward Rd Midlothian (76065) ***(G-15487)***
NASA, El Paso *Also called National Aeronautics* ***(G-5893)***
Nasco Steel, Fort Worth *Also called North American Steel Corp* ***(G-6866)***
Nash Manufacturing Inc (HQ) **817 926-5223**
6363 Lansdale Rd Fort Worth (76116) ***(G-6860)***
Nashtec LLC 361 777-2280
4633 Hwy 361 Gregory (78359) ***(G-8102)***
Nason Services LLC 940 495-2558
102 Hwy 287 E Electra (76360) ***(G-6048)***
Nat G CNG Solutions LLC (PA) **281 954-4600**
16504 Aldine Westfield Rd A1 Houston (77032) ***(G-10963)***
Nat G CNG Solutions LLC 512 998-9316
9402 Converse Business Ln Converse (78109) ***(G-3399)***
Nat'l Switchgear, Lewisville *Also called National Swtchgear Systems Inc* ***(G-14071)***
Natco, Snyder *Also called Cameron Solutions Inc* ***(G-18985)***
Natco, Houston *Also called Cameron Solutions Inc* ***(G-9079)***
Natco Group Inc (HQ) **713 849-7500**
11210 Equity Dr Ste 100 Houston (77041) ***(G-10964)***
Naterra International Inc 972 616-6100
1250 Freeport Pkwy Coppell (75019) ***(G-3429)***
Nathan Faulk 432 634-9223
735 Polk Dr Apt A Arlington (76011) ***(G-736)***

National Aeronautics 915 782-5250
8101 Boeing Dr El Paso (79925) ***(G-5893)***
National Art Service Co Inc 713 869-5861
726 Lawrence St Houston (77007) ***(G-10965)***
National Banner Company Inc (PA) **972 241-2131**
11938 Harry Hines Blvd Dallas (75234) ***(G-4712)***
National Banner Company Inc 972 241-2131
12023 Denton Dr Dallas (75234) ***(G-4713)***
National Banner Company Inc 903 378-2761
300 E Main St Honey Grove (75446) ***(G-8357)***
National Bedding Company LLC 281 345-6237
10710 Telge Rd Houston (77095) ***(G-10966)***
National Beverage, Houston *Also called Shasta Beverages Inc* ***(G-11847)***
National Buildings, Houston *Also called Shaun K Boyer* ***(G-11848)***
National Carport Industries, Sherman *Also called Prengler Ltd* ***(G-18928)***
National Circuit Assembly Inc (PA) **972 278-2009**
2908 National Dr Ste 100 Garland (75041) ***(G-7557)***
National Cnverting Fulfillment 972 875-5096
2708 Ne Main St Ennis (75119) ***(G-6112)***
National Coupling Company Inc 281 499-2583
1316 Staffordshire Rd Stafford (77477) ***(G-19356)***
National Crane Cmplnce Inspcto 888 720-6224
17512 Highway 6 Ste F15 Manvel (77578) ***(G-14735)***
National Dentex Corporation 903 597-3198
114 Jordan Plaza Blvd # 300 Tyler (75704) ***(G-20132)***
National Diamond Lab Texas Inc 214 638-1435
1435 Round Table Dr Dallas (75247) ***(G-4714)***
National Electric Coil Co LP 956 541-1759
3330 E 14th St Brownsville (78521) ***(G-2385)***
National Electronic Devices 936 273-4111
15 S Trade Center Pkwy Conroe (77385) ***(G-3333)***
National Elevator Company Inc 925 484-5050
6000 Pine Valley Dr Flower Mound (75022) ***(G-6273)***
National Energetics Inc 512 382-1894
2051 Gattis School Rd # 540 Round Rock (78664) ***(G-17674)***
National Enrgy Svcs Rnted Corp (PA) **832 925-3777**
777 Post Oak Blvd Ste 730 Houston (77056) ***(G-10967)***
National Flange & Fitting Co (PA) **713 688-2515**
4420 Creekmont Dr Houston (77091) ***(G-10968)***
National Food and Beverage Inc 214 905-9700
9030 Premier Row Dallas (75247) ***(G-4715)***
National Foundry & Mfg Co 432 558-3444
299 Foundry Rd Crane (79731) ***(G-3700)***
National Frame Rail Inc 940 482-9494
11919 Interstate 35 N Sanger (76266) ***(G-18727)***
National Gasket Company, Houston *Also called Mariposa Corporation* ***(G-10768)***
National Gypsum Company, Cleburne *Also called Ng Operations LLC* ***(G-3104)***
National Gypsum Company, Harper *Also called Ng Operations LLC* ***(G-8210)***
National Heat Treat LLC 281 809-9840
6923 Brittmoore Rd Houston (77041) ***(G-10969)***
National Hose & Accessory, Pasadena *Also called National Hose Aquisition Corp* ***(G-16487)***
National Hose Aquisition Corp (HQ) **713 920-2030**
1831 Richey St Pasadena (77502) ***(G-16487)***
National Hot Water, Dallas *Also called National Wholesale Supply Inc* ***(G-4716)***
National Instruments Corp 214 227-4788
505 Fairway Meadows Dr Garland (75044) ***(G-7558)***
National Instruments Corp (PA) **512 683-0100**
11500 N Mopac Expy Austin (78759) ***(G-1360)***
National Machine & Work Holdg, Manvel *Also called National Machine & Workholding* ***(G-14736)***
National Machine & Workholding 281 489-0490
7102 Bissell Rd Manvel (77578) ***(G-14736)***
National Mail Advertising Inc 713 869-8551
6706 River Lodge Dr Spring (77379) ***(G-19152)***
National Manufacturing LLC 281 856-7693
7131 Jackrabbit Rd Houston (77095) ***(G-10970)***
National Mri Shielding Inc 855 996-9820
1604 Kestrel Ave Ste 102 Desoto (75115) ***(G-5436)***
National Oil & Lube News Inc 806 762-4464
2345 50th St Lubbock (79412) ***(G-14449)***
National Oil Well, Houston *Also called National Oilwell Varco Inc* ***(G-10980)***
National Oilfield Fabricators, Trinity *Also called Xg Ventures LLC* ***(G-20020)***
National Oilwell Bowen Tls Div, Kilgore *Also called National Oilwell Varco Inc* ***(G-13577)***
National Oilwell Dht LP (HQ) **713 346-7500**
10000 Richmond Ave # 100 Houston (77042) ***(G-10971)***
National Oilwell Varco Inc 830 693-5312
1 N Ridge Loop Marble Falls (78654) ***(G-14748)***
National Oilwell Varco Inc 817 985-5000
1020 Emerman Pkwy Fort Worth (76140) ***(G-6861)***
National Oilwell Varco Inc 432 333-4196
1901 W 2nd St Odessa (79763) ***(G-16087)***
National Oilwell Varco Inc 432 528-4354
2040 Oregon St Odessa (79764) ***(G-16088)***
National Oilwell Varco Inc 432 563-2150
7636 Hwy 80 Odessa (79765) ***(G-16089)***
National Oilwell Varco Inc 713 799-8198
2000 W S Houston Pkwy S Houston (77051) ***(G-10972)***

National Oilwell Varco Inc 281 351-2222
10906 Fm 2920 Rd Tomball (77375) *(G-19991)*

National Oilwell Varco Inc 713 466-7999
7402 N Aldridge Pkwy Houston (77041) *(G-10973)*

National Oilwell Varco Inc 713 983-9281
8017 Breen Dr Houston (77064) *(G-10974)*

National Oilwell Varco Inc 432 381-4111
10720 W Interstate 20 Odessa (79765) *(G-16090)*

National Oilwell Varco Inc 361 664-8013
3267 County Road 48 Robstown (78380) *(G-17514)*

National Oilwell Varco Inc 713 935-8170
1230 W Sam Houston Pkwy N. Houston (77043) *(G-10975)*

National Oilwell Varco Inc 903 984-2553
3108 Maverick Dr Kilgore (75662) *(G-13577)*

National Oilwell Varco Inc 281 854-0300
8708 W Little York Rd # 100 Houston (77040) *(G-10976)*

National Oilwell Varco Inc 713 896-9115
6390 N Eldridge Pkwy Houston (77041) *(G-10977)*

National Oilwell Varco Inc 713 634-3327
9724 Beechnut St Ste 140 Houston (77036) *(G-10978)*

National Oilwell Varco Inc 325 573-2665
2004 84 Byp Snyder (79549) *(G-18997)*

National Oilwell Varco Inc 713 375-3700
7909 Parkwood Circle Dr Houston (77036) *(G-10979)*

National Oilwell Varco Inc 832 424-6000
6390 N Eldridge Pkwy Houston (77041) *(G-10980)*

National Oilwell Varco Inc 210 572-4012
7640 Us Highway 87 E San Antonio (78263) *(G-18333)*

National Oilwell Varco Inc 713 237-3766
100 Gillingham Ln Sugar Land (77478) *(G-19510)*

National Oilwell Varco Inc 432 563-1173
83 Groening St Odessa (79765) *(G-16091)*

National Oilwell Varco Inc 713 237-9793
12002 W Little York Rd Houston (77041) *(G-10981)*

National Oilwell Varco Inc 281 820-5400
650 Aldine Bender Rd Houston (77060) *(G-10982)*

National Oilwell Varco Inc 281 854-0537
10353 Richmond Ave Houston (77042) *(G-10983)*

National Oilwell Varco Inc 512 340-5000
1200 Cypress Creek Rd Cedar Park (78613) *(G-2980)*

National Oilwell Varco Inc 936 856-9180
500 Conroe Park West Dr Conroe (77303) *(G-3334)*

National Oilwell Varco Inc 281 943-5948
5130 N Sam Houston Pkwy W Houston (77086) *(G-10984)*

National Oilwell Varco Inc 409 842-2114
5780 Hagner Rd Beaumont (77705) *(G-1933)*

National Oilwell Varco Inc 713 482-0500
4310 N Sam Houston Pkwy E Houston (77032) *(G-10985)*

National Oilwell Varco Inc 713 849-8011
Fm 529 Houston (77041) *(G-10986)*

National Oilwell Varco Inc 281 599-4700
8018 Breen Dr Houston (77064) *(G-10987)*

National Oilwell Varco Inc (PA) **713 346-7500**
7909 Parkwood Circle Dr Houston (77036) *(G-10988)*

National Oilwell Varco Inc 325 884-2556
506 W Us Highway 67 Big Lake (76932) *(G-2060)*

National Oilwell Varco Inc 281 456-0751
10222 Sheldon Rd Houston (77049) *(G-10989)*

National Oilwell Varco Inc 936 444-4000
500 Conroe Park West Dr Conroe (77303) *(G-3335)*

National Oilwell Varco Inc 936 825-7070
9475 Fm 1227 Indus Park 1227 Industrial Navasota (77868) *(G-15739)*

National Oilwell Varco Inc 713 395-5000
10011 Madowglen Ste Mg 2a Houston (77042) *(G-10990)*

National Oilwell Varco Inc 940 761-2333
803 E Scott Ave Wichita Falls (76301) *(G-20785)*

National Oilwell Varco Inc 936 777-6100
3770 Pollok Dr Conroe (77303) *(G-3336)*

National Oilwell Varco Inc 281 456-8551
8600 Pineland Rd Houston (77044) *(G-10991)*

National Oilwell Varco Inc 817 389-2444
8000 County Road 1001 Godley (76044) *(G-7737)*

National Oilwell Varco Inc 281 878-8000
140 Cypress Station Dr # 220 Houston (77090) *(G-10992)*

National Oilwell Varco Inc 713 468-7328
11929 Fm 529 Rd Houston (77041) *(G-10993)*

National Oilwell Varco Inc 936 873-2600
6740 Highway 30 Anderson (77830) *(G-530)*

National Oilwell Varco Inc 281 209-4840
16211 Air Center Blvd Houston (77032) *(G-10994)*

National Oilwell Varco Inc 832 575-2000
500 Conroe Park West Dr Conroe (77303) *(G-3337)*

National Oilwell Varco Inc 936 441-0006
2800 N Frazier St Conroe (77303) *(G-3338)*

National Oilwell Varco Inc 361 576-3161
508 Mallard Rd Victoria (77905) *(G-20287)*

National Oilwell Varco Inc 432 683-6696
2206 W New Jersey Ave Midland (79701) *(G-15310)*

National Oilwell Varco LP 936 825-2211
9542 Interstate Dr Navasota (77868) *(G-15740)*

National Oilwell Varco LP 210 477-7500
17115 San Pedro Ave # 20 San Antonio (78232) *(G-18334)*

National Oilwell Varco LP 806 274-5293
301 Premier Rd Borger (79007) *(G-2180)*

National Oilwell Varco LP 817 203-8302
10586 N Highway 75 Willis (77378) *(G-20856)*

National Oilwell Varco LP 281 586-2046
5100 N Sam Houston Pkwy W Houston (77086) *(G-10995)*

National Oilwell Varco LP 713 346-7500
10000 Richmond Ave # 100 Houston (77042) *(G-10996)*

National Oilwell Varco LP 713 375-3700
9724 Beechnut St Ste 300 Houston (77036) *(G-10997)*

National Oilwell Varco LP 281 599-4700
8018 Breen Dr Houston (77064) *(G-10998)*

National Oilwell Varco LP 936 777-6200
3770 Pollock Dr Conroe (77303) *(G-3339)*

National Oilwell Varco LP 713 849-6121
6390 N Eldridge Pkwy Houston (77041) *(G-10999)*

National Oilwell Varco LP (HQ) **713 375-3700**
7909 Parkwood Circle Dr Houston (77036) *(G-11000)*

National Oilwell Varco LP 936 756-4800
2800 N Frazier St Conroe (77303) *(G-3340)*

National Oilwell Varco DHT, Houston *Also called National Oilwell Dht LP (G-10971)*

National Oilwell-Pft Div, Tomball *Also called National Oilwell Varco Inc (G-19991)*

National Olwell Vrco - Fibr GL, San Antonio *Also called National Oilwell Varco LP (G-18334)*

National Optcl & Scientfic Ins 210 590-9010
6508 Tri County Pkwy Schertz (78154) *(G-18757)*

National Pallet Company, Dallas *Also called Chep (usa) Inc (G-4109)*

National Plastic Molders Inc 281 346-1942
29313 Mckinnon Rd Richmond (77406) *(G-17463)*

National Presort LP (PA) **214 634-2288**
14901 Trinity Blvd Fort Worth (76155) *(G-6862)*

National Signage Affiliates, Corpus Christi *Also called Corpus Christi Stamp Works Inc (G-3509)*

National Signs LLC 832 433-4957
2611 El Camino St Houston (77054) *(G-11001)*

National Specialty Alloys Inc (HQ) **281 345-2115**
18250 Kieth Harrow Blvd Houston (77084) *(G-11002)*

National Specialty Alloys Nsa, Houston *Also called National Specialty Alloys Inc (G-11002)*

National Stage Equipment Co., Lorena *Also called Nsec LLC (G-14343)*

National Stone Ltd 214 651-7667
804 W Shady Grove Rd Grand Prairie (75050) *(G-7930)*

National Stone Inc 214 651-7667
1419 Chamberlain St Irving (75060) *(G-13112)*

National Stone TX, Grand Prairie *Also called National Stone Ltd (G-7930)*

National Strand Products LP 713 455-2888
12611 Cain Cir Houston (77015) *(G-11003)*

National Swtchgear Systems Inc (PA) **972 420-0149**
649 Franklin Lewisville (75057) *(G-14071)*

National Vinegar Company 713 223-4214
5242 Loch Lomond Dr Houston (77096) *(G-11004)*

National Well Supplies Co Inc (PA) **713 467-0462**
1625 Brittmoore Rd Houston (77043) *(G-11005)*

National Wholesale Supply Inc 469 517-0600
3500 S Intrstate Hwy 35 E Waxahachie (75165) *(G-20553)*

National Wholesale Supply Inc (PA) **972 331-7770**
1972 Cal Crossing Rd Dallas (75220) *(G-4716)*

Nations Cabinetry LLC 210 681-8477
4600 Timco E San Antonio (78238) *(G-18335)*

Nationwide Applications LLC 210 651-0202
17324 Bell North Dr Schertz (78154) *(G-18758)*

Nationwide Disc - Ntnwide Pres, Richland Hills *Also called Nationwide Press LLC (G-17444)*

Nationwide Pharmaceutical LLC 800 697-3329
1270 N Loop 1604 E # 1306 San Antonio (78232) *(G-18336)*

Nationwide Plastics, Arlington *Also called Curbell Plastics Inc (G-654)*

Nationwide Pnnant Flag Mfg Inc 210 684-3524
7325 Reindeer Trl San Antonio (78238) *(G-18337)*

Nationwide Press LLC 817 885-8855
7370 Dogwood Park Dr Richland Hills (76118) *(G-17444)*

Nationwide Tank & Pipe LLC 830 387-4027
3567 Ih 35 S New Braunfels (78132) *(G-15815)*

Native American Industries Inc 817 731-6786
3470 River Bend Blvd # 404 Fort Worth (76116) *(G-6863)*

Natural Cosmeceuticals of Amer 832 771-0882
2909 Hillcroft St Ste 250 Houston (77057) *(G-11006)*

Natural Energy Resources Inc 832 631-5013
20042 Cresent Creek Dr Katy (77449) *(G-13426)*

Natural Gas Anadarko Company 806 435-6818
1800 S Main St Perryton (79070) *(G-16642)*

Natural Gas Pipeline Amer LLC (HQ) **713 369-9000**
1001 Louisiana St Houston (77002) *(G-11007)*

Natural Gas Pipeline Amer LLC 903 758-0154
19935 Fm 449 Longview (75605) *(G-14283)*

Natural Gas Pipeline Amer LLC 361 897-1022
9819 State Highway 185 S Victoria (77905) *(G-20288)*

Natural Gas Services Group Inc (PA) **432 262-2700**
508 W Wall St Ste 550 Midland (79701) *(G-15311)*

A
L
P
H
A
B
E
T
I
C

Natural Gas Sltions N Amer LLC............832 590-2303
16240 Port Nw Houston (77041) ***(G-11008)***
Natural Gas Vehicles Texas Inc............214 630-1000
10733 Spangler Rd Dallas (75220) ***(G-4717)***
Natural Graphics Inc............713 661-5075
6376 Alder Dr Houston (77081) ***(G-11009)***
Natural Minerals Inc............432 283-2330
12900 E Interstate 10 Van Horn (79855) ***(G-20215)***
Natural Resource Partners LP (PA)............**713 751-7507**
1201 La St Ste 3400 Houston (77002) ***(G-11010)***
Natural Stone Inc............713 678-4407
1929 Dorsett St Houston (77029) ***(G-11011)***
Natural Technology Inc............972 551-2563
350 Apache Trl Terrell (75160) ***(G-19743)***
Nature's Source, Sherman *Also called Ball Dpf LLC* ***(G-18907)***
Naturelab Corp............972 417-3000
1606 Vantage Dr Carrollton (75006) ***(G-2784)***
Natures Eat, Boerne *Also called Texas Star Nut and Food Co Inc* ***(G-2140)***
Natures Finest LLC............972 673-1526
4701 Old Shepard Pl Frnt Plano (75093) ***(G-16939)***
Natures Way Resources Inc............936 273-1200
101 Sherbrook Cir Conroe (77385) ***(G-3341)***
Naturetech, Terrell *Also called Natural Technology Inc* ***(G-19743)***
Naturich Cosmetique Labs Inc............972 926-9200
2505 Merritt Dr Garland (75041) ***(G-7559)***
Naturich Labs, Garland *Also called Naturich Cosmetique Labs Inc* ***(G-7559)***
Natus Medical Incorporated............650 802-0400
2670 Firewheel Dr Ste B Flower Mound (75028) ***(G-6274)***
Natus Peloton, Flower Mound *Also called Natus Medical Incorporated* ***(G-6274)***
Nautical Control Solutions LP............281 209-3480
20358 Whitewood Dr Spring (77373) ***(G-19153)***
Navajo Skin Care, Austin *Also called Maison De Navar* ***(G-1319)***
Navarrete Industries LLC............432 332-0272
2300 E Murphy St Odessa (79761) ***(G-16092)***
Navasota Concrete Inc............936 825-8106
5970 Fm 3455 Rd Navasota (77868) ***(G-15741)***
Navco Oilfield Services LLC (PA)............**956 542-4426**
2500 Courage Blvd Brownsville (78521) ***(G-2386)***
Navigation Rm Dual, Houston *Also called Cemex Construction Mtls S LLC* ***(G-9129)***
Navistar Inc............972 377-1217
5850 Granite Pkwy Ste 760 Plano (75024) ***(G-16940)***
Navistar International Corp............972 487-6509
801 Easy St Garland (75042) ***(G-7560)***
Navitaire............512 617-2121
1501 S Mo Pac Expy # 300 Austin (78746) ***(G-1361)***
NBC, Lubbock *Also called Nci Building Systems LP* ***(G-14450)***
Nbl Permian LLC............979 542-5571
6 Desta Dr Ste 1100 Midland (79705) ***(G-15312)***
Nbl Permian LLC (HQ)............**281 872-3100**
1001 Noble Energy Way Houston (77070) ***(G-11012)***
Nbl Permian LLC............979 764-4030
707 Texas Ave S Ste 109a College Station (77840) ***(G-3195)***
Nbl Permian LLC............432 688-3430
6 Desta Dr Ste 1100 Midland (79705) ***(G-15313)***
Nbl Texas LLC (HQ)............**281 872-3100**
1001 Noble Energy Way Houston (77070) ***(G-11013)***
Nbr Sand LLC............903 593-3311
905 Interstate 20 W Tyler (75706) ***(G-20133)***
Nbr Wheels and Tires LLC............855 575-3879
9010 N Royal Ln Ste 100 Irving (75063) ***(G-13113)***
NC Group Inc............281 459-9418
12901 Beaumont Hwy Houston (77049) ***(G-11014)***
NC Millwork, Houston *Also called NC Group Inc* ***(G-11014)***
Ncc Nano LLC............512 491-9500
400 Parker Dr Ste 1110 Austin (78728) ***(G-1362)***
NCH Corporation (PA)............**972 438-0211**
2727 Chemsearch Blvd Irving (75062) ***(G-13114)***
NCH Corporation............972 438-0381
1400 E Northgate Dr Irving (75062) ***(G-13115)***
Nch Corporation............972 438-0551
2730 Carl Rd Irving (75062) ***(G-13116)***
Nch Corporation............972 438-0024
2500 Carl Rd Irving (75062) ***(G-13117)***
NCH Corporation............800 336-0450
1570 E Northgate Dr Irving (75062) ***(G-13118)***
NCH Corporation............972 438-0211
2727 Chemsearch Blvd Irving (75062) ***(G-13119)***
NCH Corporation............972 438-0211
2727 Chemsearch Blvd Irving (75062) ***(G-13120)***
Nci Building Systems LP............806 747-4291
5711 E Fm 40 Lubbock (79403) ***(G-14450)***
Nci Group Inc............817 481-2501
400 N Kimball Ave 114 Southlake (76092) ***(G-19080)***
Nci Group Inc............281 897-7788
14031 W Hardy Rd Houston (77060) ***(G-11015)***
Nci Group Inc (HQ)............**281 897-7788**
10943 N Sam Huston Pkwy W Houston (77064) ***(G-11016)***
Nci Group Inc............972 221-6656
1720 Lakepointe Dr # 101 Lewisville (75057) ***(G-14072)***
Nci Group Inc............806 747-4291
5711 E Fm 40 Lubbock (79403) ***(G-14451)***
Nci Group Inc............281 302-1900
7311 Fairview St Houston (77041) ***(G-11017)***
Nci Group Inc............713 921-7997
501 N Greenwood St Houston (77011) ***(G-11018)***
Nci Group Inc............972 299-5556
550 Murray St 287 Midlothian (76065) ***(G-15488)***
Nci Group Inc............817 488-8511
5244 Bear Creek Ct Irving (75061) ***(G-13121)***
Nci Group Inc............713 466-7788
7301 Fairview St Houston (77041) ***(G-11019)***
Nci Metal Depots Houston Hardy, Houston *Also called Nci Group Inc* ***(G-11015)***
Ncp Solutions LLC............210 694-1528
15955 La Cantera Pkwy San Antonio (78256) ***(G-18338)***
NCR Corporation............210 366-2959
1077 Central Pkwy S # 800 San Antonio (78232) ***(G-18339)***
NCR Solutions Llc............405 413-8278
3947 Spinnaker Run Pt Little Elm (75068) ***(G-14140)***
Ncs Multistage Holdings Inc (PA)............**281 453-2222**
19350 State Highway 249 # 200 Houston (77070) ***(G-11020)***
Ncs Pearson Inc............432 685-0033
3300 N A St Bldg 4-228 Midland (79705) ***(G-15314)***
Ncs Pearson Inc............210 339-5000
19500 Bulverde Rd Ste 100 San Antonio (78259) ***(G-18340)***
Ncti, Pasadena *Also called Jx Nippon Chemical Texas Inc* ***(G-16467)***
ND Industries Inc............817 633-2788
3611 Dalworth St Arlington (76011) ***(G-737)***
Ndsventures LP............713 395-0461
723 Main St Ste 801 Houston (77002) ***(G-11021)***
Ndustri.com, Houston *Also called Superior Shot Peening Inc* ***(G-12119)***
NEAL & ASSOCIATES, Dallas *Also called R Neal John & Associates Inc* ***(G-4855)***
Nearburg Producing Company (PA)............**214 739-1778**
5447 Glen Lakes Dr Dallas (75231) ***(G-4718)***
Nearburg Producing Company............432 686-8235
3300 N A St Bldg 2-120 Midland (79705) ***(G-15315)***
Nearly ME Technologies LLC............254 662-1752
200 N Industrial Dr Waco (76710) ***(G-20437)***
Neb Products LLC............281 528-9428
3336 Spring Stuebner Rd O Spring (77389) ***(G-19154)***
Nec, Houston *Also called Nipples Elbows & Couplings Inc* ***(G-11059)***
Nec America Inc............214 262-2387
1213 N 28th Ave Dfw Airport (75261) ***(G-5453)***
Nec Corporation of America............214 262-2387
1213 N 28th Ave Dallas (75261) ***(G-4719)***
Nec Signage Architectural Pdts, Houston *Also called Neon Electric Corporation* ***(G-11023)***
Neckover Trailer, Troup *Also called C Diamond F Inc* ***(G-20022)***
Needleworks Etc (PA)............**432 445-9313**
120 S Cedar St Pecos (79772) ***(G-16624)***
Nefab Companies, Coppell *Also called Nefab Packaging Inc* ***(G-3431)***
Nefab Companies Inc (HQ)............**866 332-4425**
204 Airline Dr Ste 100 Coppell (75019) ***(G-3430)***
Nefab Packaging Inc (HQ)............**469 444-5264**
204 Airline Dr Ste 100 Coppell (75019) ***(G-3431)***
Nei, Plano *Also called Unicom Engineering Inc* ***(G-17041)***
Neighborhood News Inc............210 558-3160
3740 Colony Dr Ste Ll100 San Antonio (78230) ***(G-18341)***
Nelco of Texas, Houston *Also called New England Lead Burning Inc* ***(G-11034)***
Nelson Bros Ready Mix Ltd............972 436-6558
721 E Main St Lewisville (75057) ***(G-14073)***
Nelson Facilities Inc............979 865-8596
12355 Highway 36 Bellville (77418) ***(G-2011)***
Nelson Hunt Bunker............214 979-9072
3811 Trtl Crk Blvd # 1825 Dallas (75219) ***(G-4720)***
Nelson Machine Products, Houston *Also called National Manufacturing LLC* ***(G-10970)***
Nelson Oil Field Eqp & Sup............361 375-2105
Pns St Pettus (78146) ***(G-16653)***
Nelson Oilfield Equipment, Pettus *Also called Yegua Oil Field Service Inc* ***(G-16654)***
Nema Enclosure Mfg Corp............713 921-2233
1118 Pleasantville Dr Houston (77029) ***(G-11022)***
Nemesis Uvc LLC............972 423-0075
3301 Wood Dr Ste 100 Garland (75041) ***(G-7561)***
Neofirma Inc............214 233-7111
2100 Alamo Rd Ste T Richardson (75080) ***(G-17362)***
Neogard, Conroe *Also called Hempel (usa) Inc* ***(G-3302)***
Neom LLC............210 372-3475
27711 Woodway Bnd Boerne (78006) ***(G-2130)***
Neon Electric Corporation............281 987-1144
1122 Lauder Rd Houston (77039) ***(G-11023)***
Neon Signs and Designs Inc............903 463-7446
103 E Crawford St Denison (75021) ***(G-5343)***
Neon Systems Inc (HQ)............**281 276-5900**
14100 Southwest Fwy # 500 Sugar Land (77478) ***(G-19511)***
Neopal LLC............281 219-9600
5100 Cross Continents Dr Houston (77032) ***(G-11024)***
Neopod Systems LLC............954 603-3100
7850 Old Bastrop Rd New Braunfels (78130) ***(G-15816)***

Neora LLC (HQ)...855 463-7486
4201 Spring Valley Rd Dallas (75244) *(G-4721)*
Neos Therapeutics Inc (PA)...972 408-1300
2940 N Highway 360 Grand Prairie (75050) *(G-7931)*
Neos Therapeutics LP...972 408-1300
2940 N State Highway 360 Grand Prairie (75050) *(G-7932)*
Neosem Technology Inc...512 257-5000
11001 Lakeline Blvd Austin (78717) *(G-1706)*
Neosen Energy LLC...972 422-0722
2637 Summit Ave 301 Plano (75074) *(G-16941)*
Neosensory Inc...401 257-9460
1302 Waugh Dr 447 Houston (77019) *(G-11025)*
Neotech, El Paso *Also called Epic Technologies LLC (G-5758)*
Neotek Energy Inc...469 206-3344
2600 Tech Dr Ste 400 Plano (75074) *(G-16942)*
Nerium Biotechnology Inc (PA)...210 822-7908
11467 Huebner Rd Ste 175 San Antonio (78230) *(G-18342)*
Nerium International, Dallas *Also called Neora LLC (G-4721)*
Nerium Skincare, San Antonio *Also called Nerium Biotechnology Inc (G-18342)*
Nerve Software LLC...972 231-4775
300 N Coit Rd Ste 1500 Richardson (75080) *(G-17363)*
Nes International, Frisco *Also called New ERA Solutions Intl LLC (G-7262)*
Nesr, Houston *Also called National Enrgy Svcs Rnted Corp (G-10967)*
Neste Oil Services Inc (HQ)...713 407-4411
3040 Post Oak Blvd Ste 17 Houston (77056) *(G-11026)*
Neste Petroleum, Houston *Also called Neste Oil Services Inc (G-11026)*
Neste Petroleum Inc...713 407-4400
3040 Post Oak Blvd # 1700 Houston (77056) *(G-11027)*
Nestle Distribution Center, Fort Worth *Also called Nestle Usa Inc (G-6865)*
Nestle Usa Inc...817 420-9971
1313 Samuels Ave Fort Worth (76102) *(G-6864)*
Nestle Usa Inc...817 491-5500
13600 Independence Pkwy Fort Worth (76177) *(G-6865)*
Neteffect Inc...512 302-0002
9211 Waterford Ctr Blvd Austin (78758) *(G-1363)*
Netfires LLC...972 603-2702
2400 W Marshall Dr Grand Prairie (75051) *(G-7933)*
Netgate, Austin *Also called Rubicon Communications LLC (G-1476)*
Netiq Corporation (HQ)...713 548-1700
515 Post Oak Blvd Ste 120 Houston (77027) *(G-11028)*
Netrake Corporation...214 291-1000
1255 W 15th St Ste 200 Plano (75075) *(G-16943)*
Netscout Systems Texas LLC...469 330-4000
915 Guardians Way Allen (75013) *(G-288)*
Nettlecombe Oil Co Inc...713 652-4040
3000 Wilcrest Dr Ste 240 Houston (77042) *(G-11029)*
Netvia Group LLC...972 573-1400
230 Irby Ln Irving (75061) *(G-13122)*
Netwatch Solutions Inc...214 446-8486
1101 E Arapaho Rd Ste 100 Richardson (75081) *(G-17364)*
Network Info Systems Inc (PA)...713 255-4800
410 Pierce St Ste 303 Houston (77002) *(G-11030)*
Neu Plumbing Inc...940 580-2200
1117 Foundation Dr Pilot Point (76258) *(G-16726)*
Neu Security Services LLC...512 469-9980
8206 Cross Park Dr # 300 Austin (78754) *(G-1364)*
Neuma Doors, Houston *Also called Nan Ya Plastics Corp USA (G-10962)*
Neuman & Esser Investments Inc (HQ)...281 497-5113
1502 E Summitry Cir Katy (77449) *(G-13427)*
Neuman & Esser Usa Inc (HQ)...281 497-5113
1502 E Summitry Cir Katy (77449) *(G-13428)*
Neumin Production Co...361 987-8900
103 Fannin Rd Point Comfort (77978) *(G-17089)*
Neuro Resource Group Intl Inc...972 665-1810
870 N Dorothy Dr Ste 708 Richardson (75081) *(G-17365)*
Neutex Advnced Enrgy Group Inc (PA)...281 227-2208
14340 Torrey Chase Blvd Houston (77014) *(G-11031)*
Neutex Advnced Enrgy Group Inc...281 227-2208
15700 Vickery Dr Houston (77032) *(G-11032)*
Neutral Posture Inc...979 778-0502
3904 N Texas Ave Bryan (77803) *(G-2494)*
Neutrex Inc...281 807-9449
11119 Jones Rd W Houston (77065) *(G-11033)*
Neuville, Shelbyville *Also called Afi Unlimited LLC (G-18894)*
Nev Holdings LLC...972 731-1100
3211 Internet Blvd # 200 Frisco (75034) *(G-7301)*
Nevins LLC...713 230-2100
14006 Newberg Rd Cat Spring (78933) *(G-2931)*
New Age, Kaufman *Also called New Altrnative Green Enrgy Inc (G-13462)*
New Altrnative Green Enrgy Inc...972 523-9970
9973 County Road 115 Kaufman (75142) *(G-13462)*
New Boston Concrete Inc (PA)...903 628-3556
100 S Mccoy Blvd New Boston (75570) *(G-15767)*
New Braunfels Machine Inc...830 226-7179
311 Fm 306 Bldg 3 New Braunfels (78130) *(G-15817)*
New Braunfels Plant Us62, New Braunfels *Also called Lhoist North America Texas Ltd (G-15810)*
New Braunfels Quarry, New Braunfels *Also called Cemex Construction Mtls S LLC (G-15779)*
New Braunfesl Plant Us62, New Braunfels *Also called Lhoist North America Inc (G-15809)*
New Canaan Farms Inc...512 858-7669
Hwy 290 W Dripping Springs (78620) *(G-5509)*
New Century Enterprises Inc...972 926-6062
601 Shepherd Dr Garland (75042) *(G-7562)*
New Century Exploration Inc...832 698-1374
20008 Champion Forest Dr # 701 Spring (77379) *(G-19155)*
New Concept Services Inc...903 342-5523
100 Park St Winnsboro (75494) *(G-20900)*
New Core Inc...956 421-2446
22673 Hand Rd Harlingen (78552) *(G-8196)*
New Crosslink LP...972 484-3322
11122 Morrison Ln Dallas (75229) *(G-4722)*
New Dairy Madisonville LLC...863 297-7342
8750 N Central Expy # 400 Dallas (75231) *(G-4723)*
New Dairy Ndh Transport LLC...214 459-1100
8750 N Central Expy # 400 Dallas (75231) *(G-4724)*
New Dairy Opco LLC (PA)...972 619-1535
8750 N Central Expy # 400 Dallas (75231) *(G-4725)*
New Dairy Texas LLC...214 459-1100
8750 N Central Expy # 400 Dallas (75231) *(G-4726)*
New Dairy Trademark Holdg LLC...803 297-7342
8750 N Central Expy Dallas (75231) *(G-4727)*
New Diry Clims Adjsting Svcs L...863 297-7342
8750 N Central Expy # 400 Dallas (75231) *(G-4728)*
New England Lead Burning Inc...713 675-3266
4600 Homestead Rd Houston (77028) *(G-11034)*
New ERA Solutions Intl LLC...972 360-6112
6686 Simon Ave Frisco (75035) *(G-7262)*
New Horizon Publishers...956 943-5545
101 E Maxan St Port Isabel (78578) *(G-17137)*
New Horizon Publishers Inc...956 399-2436
356 N Sam Houston Blvd San Benito (78586) *(G-18661)*
New Horizons Landscape MGT, Odessa *Also called Mason Fencing and Cnstr LLC (G-16073)*
New Icm LP (HQ)...979 578-0543
220 Sam Bishkin Rd El Campo (77437) *(G-5623)*
New ICM L P...979 578-0543
220 Sam Bishkin Rd El Campo (77437) *(G-5624)*
New Lifestyles Inc...214 824-0022
4144 N Cntl Expy Ste 1000 Dallas (75204) *(G-4729)*
New Mllennium Bldg Systems LLC...915 298-5050
6248 Edgemere Blvd El Paso (79925) *(G-5894)*
New National Dairy LLC...863 297-7342
8750 N Cntl Ex Way Ste 40 Dallas (75231) *(G-4730)*
New Options Inc...214 638-6422
1850 Diplomat Dr 100 Farmers Branch (75234) *(G-6208)*
New Options Sports, Farmers Branch *Also called New Options Inc (G-6208)*
New Phase Technologies, Sugar Land *Also called Baker Petrolite LLC (G-19448)*
New Phase Technologies, Sugar Land *Also called Baker Hughes A GE Company LLC (G-19447)*
New Process Steel LP (HQ)...713 686-9631
1322 N Post Oak Rd Houston (77055) *(G-11035)*
New Purple LLC...713 499-0422
11152 Wsheimer Rd Ste 804 Houston (77042) *(G-11036)*
New Railhead Manufacturing LLC...817 594-6663
1405 Mineral Wells Hwy Weatherford (76086) *(G-20606)*
New Saw Inc...972 288-2117
3248 Executive Blvd Mesquite (75149) *(G-15064)*
New Southwest Baking Co, Bryan *Also called Bryan Baking Company LLC (G-2462)*
New Tech Systems Inc (PA)...817 779-6262
603 S Wisteria St Mansfield (76063) *(G-14697)*
New Teraco Inc (HQ)...800 687-3999
2080 Commerce Dr Midland (79703) *(G-15316)*
New Tk Coatings LLC...713 666-1375
8411 Rannie Rd Houston (77080) *(G-11037)*
New Ventures Leasing LLC...940 577-7789
820 State Highway 101 Bowie (76230) *(G-2198)*
New World Jewelry Inc...972 243-2931
10830 Grissom Ln Ste 100 Dallas (75229) *(G-4731)*
New York Air Brake LLC...972 893-2400
5201 Regent Blvd Ste 130 Irving (75063) *(G-13123)*
New York Bagel Shop & Deli, Houston *Also called New York Bagles Inc (G-11038)*
New York Bagles Inc...713 723-5879
9724 Hillcroft St Houston (77096) *(G-11038)*
Newage Casting LP...281 565-0928
12630 W Arprt Blvd Ste 10 Sugar Land (77478) *(G-19512)*
Newark Paperboard Products, Atlanta *Also called Caraustar Industries Inc (G-841)*
Neway Valve Usa LP...281 969-5500
9757 Stafford Centre Dr Stafford (77477) *(G-19357)*
Newberry Bakers Inc...281 987-8985
14149 Interdrive W Houston (77032) *(G-11039)*
Newberry Bakers Inc (PA)...281 987-8985
14212 Interdrive W Houston (77032) *(G-11040)*
Newco Valves LLC...832 944-5930
4655 Wright Rd Ste 250 Stafford (77477) *(G-19358)*
Newco Valves LLC (HQ)...281 325-0041
13127 Trinity Dr Stafford (77477) *(G-19359)*

ALPHABETIC

Newcomb Spring Corp 972 241-6781
2831 Satsuma Dr Dallas (75229) *(G-4732)*

Newcomb Spring of Texas, Dallas *Also called Newcomb Spring Corp (G-4732)*

Newell Ltd 210 222-9511
726 Probandt San Antonio (78204) *(G-18343)*

Newfield, The Woodlands *Also called Ovintiv Exploration Inc (G-19899)*

Newfield Exploration Company 281 847-6000
24 Waterway Ave Ste 900 Spring (77380) *(G-19236)*

Newgen Biotech Usa Inc 972 241-1438
12901 Nicholson Rd # 100 Farmers Branch (75234) *(G-6209)*

Newhrm LP 713 978-7474
8625 Schumacher Ln Houston (77063) *(G-11041)*

Newinn Inc 713 473-8188
2300 Pasadena Fwy Ste 101 Pasadena (77506) *(G-16488)*

Newletter Company, The, Dallas *Also called Newsletter Company (G-4734)*

Newline Interactive Inc (PA) **972 468-9728**
101 E Park Blvd Ste 807 Plano (75074) *(G-16944)*

Newly Weds Foods Inc 903 577-3200
4125 Farm Road 3417 Mount Pleasant (75455) *(G-15656)*

Newman Company, Houston *Also called Precision Custom Machining Inc (G-11388)*

Newman Operating Co 361 394-5516
5002 Highway 44 E Freer (78357) *(G-7231)*

Newman Printing Company Inc (PA) **979 779-7700**
1300 E 29th St Bryan (77802) *(G-2495)*

Newmans, Stafford *Also called Newco Valves LLC (G-19358)*

Newmans, Stafford *Also called Newco Valves LLC (G-19359)*

Newmark International 14, Bellville *Also called Valmont Newmark Inc (G-2014)*

Newpark Drilling Fluids LLC 903 297-2210
211 Cherokee St Longview (75604) *(G-14284)*

Newpark Drlg Flids Prsonnel SE 405 721-0207
9320 Lakeside Blvd Spring (77381) *(G-19237)*

Newpark Environmental Svcs LLC 432 682-5411
3001 N Big Spring St Midland (79705) *(G-15317)*

Newpark Indus Blnding Sltons L 713 898-3829
9320 Lkeside Blvd Ste 100 The Woodlands (77381) *(G-19895)*

Newpark Mats Intgrted Svcs LLC (HQ) **281 362-6800**
9320 Lkeside Blvd Ste 100 The Woodlands (77381) *(G-19896)*

Newpark Mats Intgrted Svcs LLC 979 245-3894
Hwy 35 W Bay City (77414) *(G-1775)*

Newpark Mats Intgrted Svcs LLC 409 752-5800
16341 Highway 90 Beaumont (77713) *(G-1934)*

Newpark Resources Inc (PA) **281 362-6800**
9320 Lkeside Blvd Ste 100 The Woodlands (77381) *(G-19897)*

Newpart Drilling, Bay City *Also called Newpark Mats Intgrted Svcs LLC (G-1775)*

Newpoint Energy Solutions, Houston *Also called Standard Renewable Energy LP (G-12043)*

Newpoint Media Group LLC 770 962-7220
12912 Hill Country Blvd F-245 Austin (78738) *(G-1365)*

Newpro, Seguin *Also called Alx Imaging LLC (G-18824)*

News Gram 830 773-8610
2431 Del Rio Blvd Eagle Pass (78852) *(G-5551)*

News Korea Texas Inc 972 247-9111
2000 Royal Ln Ste 200 Dallas (75229) *(G-4733)*

News Printing Inc 817 275-5601
1007 Paula Dr Arlington (76012) *(G-738)*

News Publications Inc 713 668-9293
5160 Spruce St Bellaire (77401) *(G-1999)*

Newsco Intl Enrgy Svcs USA Inc 832 924-4020
12029 Brittmoore Park Dr Houston (77041) *(G-11042)*

Newsco USA, Houston *Also called Newsco Intl Enrgy Svcs USA Inc (G-11042)*

Newsletter Company 214 871-7997
4901 Cole Ave Dallas (75205) *(G-4734)*

Newspaper Holding Inc 817 645-2441
108 S Anglin St Cleburne (76031) *(G-3102)*

Newspaper Holding Inc 903 729-0281
519 N Elm St Palestine (75801) *(G-16305)*

Newspaper Holding Inc 903 586-2236
525 E Commerce St Jacksonville (75766) *(G-13253)*

Newspaper Holding Inc 817 594-7440
512 Palo Pinto St Weatherford (76086) *(G-20607)*

Newspaper Holding Inc 903 675-5626
201 S Prairieville St Athens (75751) *(G-835)*

Newspaper Holding Inc 903 455-4220
2305 King St Greenville (75401) *(G-8085)*

Newspaper Holding Inc 936 295-5407
1409 10th St Huntsville (77320) *(G-12820)*

Newspaper Holding Inc 903 886-3196
1219 Washington St Commerce (75428) *(G-3244)*

Newspaper Holding Inc 512 392-2458
1910 S Interstate 35 San Marcos (78666) *(G-18700)*

Newsstand.com, Austin *Also called Libredigital Inc (G-1291)*

Newtek Inc 210 370-8000
5131 Beckwith Blvd San Antonio (78249) *(G-18344)*

Newtek Partners Lp 210 370-8000
5131 Beckwith Blvd San Antonio (78249) *(G-18345)*

Newton Conveyors Inc 817 558-1722
1204 County Road 1123 Cleburne (76033) *(G-3103)*

Newton Pole Co Inc 409 379-2715
Hwy 877 08cr1001 Newton (75966) *(G-15865)*

Newwater Boatworks, Elmendorf *Also called Pro Line Newwater Inc (G-6071)*

Nexa Resources Us Inc 832 726-0160
3200 Southwest Fwy # 3030 Houston (77027) *(G-11043)*

Nexans, San Antonio *Also called Autoelectric of America Inc (G-17924)*

Nexen Energy Marketing USA Inc, Houston *Also called Cnooc Marketing USA Inc (G-9221)*

Nexen Energy Services USA Inc 832 714-5000
945 Bunker Hill Rd # 1000 Houston (77024) *(G-11044)*

Nexen Petroleum Offshr USA Inc, Dallas *Also called Cnooc Petroleum Offshr USA Inc (G-4132)*

Nexen Petroleum USA Inc (HQ) **972 450-4600**
945 Bunker Hill Rd # 1400 Houston (77024) *(G-11045)*

Nexeon Medsystems Inc 844 919-9990
1910 Pcf Ave Ste 20000 Dallas (75201) *(G-4735)*

Nexgen - Advnced Fuel Systems 281 789-2000
2430 Farrell Rd Houston (77073) *(G-11046)*

Nexgen Wtr Solutions Ltd Lblty (PA) **830 583-9915**
951 County Road 160 Kenedy (78119) *(G-13490)*

Nexgen Wtr Solutions Ltd Lblty 432 234-8404
4407 S County Road 1265 Midland (79706) *(G-15318)*

Nexlube Operating LLC 972 590-9908
16803 Dallas Pkwy Ste 30 Addison (75001) *(G-150)*

Nexnol LLC 833 463-9665
5250 Coffee Port Rd Brownsville (78521) *(G-2387)*

Next Century Screens Inc 972 496-4981
575 S Intl Rd Ste 200 Garland (75042) *(G-7563)*

Next Gen Compounding LLC 972 602-9717
2901 Eagle Dr Grand Prairie (75052) *(G-7934)*

Next Technologies Inc 888 615-5721
2251 Picadilly Dr Round Rock (78664) *(G-17675)*

Next Technologies Inc (PA) **512 212-7758**
2530 Shell Rd Georgetown (78628) *(G-7666)*

Nextdecade Corporation (PA) **713 574-1880**
1000 Louisiana St # 3900 Houston (77002) *(G-11047)*

Nextdesk, Georgetown *Also called Next Technologies Inc (G-7666)*

Nextech Solutions Inc 214 343-5300
10480 Markison Rd Dallas (75238) *(G-4736)*

Nextgenauto LLC 888 481-9756
1431 Greenlane Rd Ste 775 Irving (75038) *(G-13124)*

Nextgenbill, Irving *Also called Nextgenauto LLC (G-13124)*

Nextier Cmpltion Solutions Inc 830 277-1200
303 E Hindes Charlotte (78011) *(G-3048)*

Nextier Cmpltion Solutions Inc (HQ) **713 325-6000**
3990 Rogerdale Rd Houston (77042) *(G-11048)*

Nextier Oilfield Solutions Inc (PA) **713 325-6000**
3990 Rogerdale Rd Houston (77042) *(G-11049)*

Nextus Inc 512 288-9080
101 Halmar Cv Georgetown (78628) *(G-7667)*

Nexus Alarm & Suppression Inc 877 828-1200
10575 Vista Park Rd Dallas (75238) *(G-4737)*

Nexus Capacity Services Ulc 713 627-5040
5400 Westheimer Ct Houston (77056) *(G-11050)*

Nfs Inc 915 584-1440
6002 Doniphan Dr El Paso (79932) *(G-5895)*

Ng Operations LLC 325 735-2221
832 County Road 311 Rotan (79546) *(G-17618)*

Ng Operations LLC 817 645-3435
811 Sparks Dr Cleburne (76033) *(G-3104)*

Ng Operations LLC 972 660-7140
1502 W North Carrier Pkwy Grand Prairie (75050) *(G-7935)*

Ng Operations LLC 830 864-4100
5124 Gypsum Mine Rd Harper (78631) *(G-8210)*

Ngpl, Houston *Also called Natural Gas Pipeline Amer LLC (G-11007)*

Ngsg, Midland *Also called Natural Gas Services Group Inc (G-15311)*

Ngv Texas, Dallas *Also called Natural Gas Vehicles Texas Inc (G-4717)*

Niagara Conservation Corp (PA) **817 391-0800**
1200 Lkeside Pkwy Ste 450 Flower Mound (75028) *(G-6275)*

Niagara Screen Products, Houston *Also called Purolator Efp LLC (G-11474)*

Nialti Manufacturing LLC 281 894-4995
12018 Palmerton Dr Houston (77064) *(G-11051)*

Nibco Inc 936 564-8321
723 S Fredonia St Nacogdoches (75961) *(G-15706)*

Nibco Inc 574 295-3000
6410 S 33rd St McAllen (78503) *(G-14894)*

Niblett Enterprises Inc 940 383-2887
4400 W Highway 82 Gainesville (76240) *(G-7353)*

Nibletts Oilfield Services Inc 325 853-2521
Hwy 277 S Eldorado (76936) *(G-6047)*

Nichirin Coupler, El Paso *Also called Nichirin-Flex USA Inc (G-5896)*

Nichirin-Flex USA Inc 915 859-1199
9600 Plaza Cir El Paso (79927) *(G-5896)*

Nichols Enterprises Inc 979 543-4833
5731 N Sh 71 El Campo (77437) *(G-5625)*

Nichols Irrigation, El Campo *Also called Nichols Enterprises Inc (G-5625)*

Nicholson Metal Fabricators 214 920-3654
5127 Mercantile Row Dallas (75247) *(G-4738)*

Nickel Rock LLC 512 395-7416
2206 Old Ranch Road 12 D San Marcos (78666) *(G-18701)*

Nickens Brothers Racing Engs 936 441-1131
   200 Beach Airport Rd Conroe (77301) *(G-3342)*

Nicklos Drilling Company 713 224-5959
   2229 San Felipe St # 1401 Houston (77019) *(G-11052)*

Nicole Dionne 310 699-7556
   500 N Capitl Of Texas Hwy Austin (78746) *(G-1366)*

Nicor Inc 707 484-0835
   100 Commons Rd 7-355 Dripping Springs (78620) *(G-5510)*

Nielsen & Bainbridge LLC (HQ) 512 506-3900
   12303 Tech Blvd Ste 950 Austin (78727) *(G-1367)*

Nieman Printing Inc (PA) 972 506-7400
   10615 Newkirk St Ste 100 Dallas (75220) *(G-4739)*

Nigen International LLC 713 956-8022
   13938 Chrisman Rd Houston (77039) *(G-11053)*

Night Hawk Frozen Foods Inc 800 580-4166
   100 Nighthawk Cir Buda (78610) *(G-2533)*

Night Owls Print Shop LLC 281 741-7032
   4303 Southerland Rd Houston (77092) *(G-11054)*

Nighthawk, Carrollton *Also called AMI Investments LLC (G-2698)*

Nightngale Archtctral Dors Inc 972 875-1134
   100 Arnold St Ennis (75119) *(G-6113)*

Nike Inc 956 565-2446
   5001 E Expressway 83 Mercedes (78570) *(G-15008)*

Nike Inc 972 980-1946
   14241 Dallas Pkwy Ste 100 Dallas (75254) *(G-4740)*

Nikkiso Pumps, Houston *Also called Oliver Equipment Company LLC (G-11171)*

Nikkiso Pumps America Inc 281 310-6747
   3433 N Sm Hstn Pkwy W 4 Houston (77086) *(G-11055)*

Niltronix Circuits, Houston *Also called Circuit Services Inc (G-9195)*

Niltronix Circuits Inc 713 465-4216
   3715 Artdale St Houston (77063) *(G-11056)*

Nimco Instruments 713 723-5063
   4301 Town Plaza Dr Ste 1 Houston (77045) *(G-11057)*

Nine Energy Service, Fort Worth *Also called CDK Perforating LLC (G-6501)*

Nine Energy Service Inc (PA) 281 730-5100
   2001 Kirby Dr Ste 200 Houston (77019) *(G-11058)*

Nine Energy Service Inc 903 469-3922
   679 Callender Lake Dr Murchison (75778) *(G-15680)*

Nine Energy Service Inc 903 479-3155
   29119 State Highway 19 N Athens (75752) *(G-836)*

Nipco Inc (PA) 432 362-1936
   2104 W 42nd St Odessa (79764) *(G-16093)*

Nipples Elbows & Couplings Inc 281 405-8240
   7207 West Rd Houston (77086) *(G-11059)*

Nissan Chemical Houston Corp 281 291-0200
   12330 Bay Area Blvd Pasadena (77507) *(G-16489)*

Nitro AV, Austin *Also called Verge Labs Inc (G-1630)*

Nitro Downhole LLC 361 564-9282
   6001 Fm 240 Yorktown (78164) *(G-20978)*

Nitro Fiber LLC 888 906-4202
   2801 Tech Dr Ste 157 Plano (75074) *(G-16945)*

Nitro Fluids LLC (PA) 361 938-5300
   117 Broadway Nordheim (78141) *(G-15872)*

Nitro Well Service LLC 432 617-1128
   13020 State Highway 191 G Midland (79707) *(G-15319)*

Nitro-Phos Inc 713 228-1868
   7402 Neuhaus St Houston (77061) *(G-11060)*

Nitro-Phos Fertilizer, Houston *Also called Nitro-Phos Inc (G-11060)*

Nitrocision LLC 210 254-4100
   6766 Culebra Rd San Antonio (78238) *(G-18346)*

Nitrogen Services LLC 925 336-1560
   921 N Fairgrounds Rd Midland (79706) *(G-15320)*

Nitrous Express Inc 940 767-7694
   5411 Seymour Hwy Wichita Falls (76310) *(G-20786)*

Nivisys LLC 915 633-8354
   1120 Alza Dr El Paso (79907) *(G-5897)*

Nk Energy LLC 832 857-8228
   26897 Kings Pk Hollow Dr Kingwood (77339) *(G-13650)*

Nl Industries, Dallas *Also called N L Industries Inc (G-4711)*

NL INDUSTRIES, Dallas *Also called Compx International Inc (G-4154)*

Nmg Workspace Solutions LLC 281 240-1007
   2301 Caroline St Houston (77004) *(G-11061)*

Nn Inc V-S Products Division, El Paso *Also called PMC Acquisition Company Inc (G-5913)*

Noah Chemical, San Antonio *Also called Noah Technologies Corp Texas (G-18347)*

Noah Technologies Corp Texas 210 691-2000
   1 Noah Park San Antonio (78249) *(G-18347)*

Noahmaya Candle Co 210 341-7373
   13702 Chittim Woods San Antonio (78232) *(G-18348)*

Noahs Manufacturing Inc 713 926-3500
   4619 Navigation Blvd Houston (77011) *(G-11062)*

Noahs Service & Supply LLC 903 218-6888
   1092 Marvin A Smith Rd Kilgore (75662) *(G-13578)*

Nobix Inc 925 659-3500
   7916 Wichita Falls Blvd McKinney (75071) *(G-14958)*

Noble Drilling (us) Inc (HQ) 281 276-6100
   13135 Dairy Ashford Rd Sugar Land (77478) *(G-19513)*

Noble Drilling Corporation (HQ) 281 276-6100
   13135 Dairy Ashford Rd # 700 Sugar Land (77478) *(G-19514)*

Noble Drilling Holding LLC 281 276-6100
   13135 Dairy Ashford Rd Sugar Land (77478) *(G-19515)*

Noble Drilling Services Inc 281 276-6100
   13135 Dairy Ashford Rd # 800 Sugar Land (77478) *(G-19516)*

Noble Energy, Houston *Also called Samedan Oil Corporation (G-11739)*

Noble Energy Inc 800 234-3867
   12707 North Fwy Ste 165 Houston (77060) *(G-11063)*

Noble Energy Inc (HQ) 281 872-3100
   1001 Noble Energy Way Houston (77070) *(G-11064)*

Noble Flow Control LLC 432 638-5962
   5538 Club Park Way San Angelo (76904) *(G-17815)*

Noble Gent LLC 214 516-8609
   1801 N Hampton Rd Ste 365 Desoto (75115) *(G-5437)*

Noble Holding US Corporation (HQ) 281 276-6100
   3135 S Dairy Ashford Sugar Land (77478) *(G-19517)*

Noble International Finance Co 281 276-6142
   13135 Dairy Ashford Rd Sugar Land (77478) *(G-19518)*

Noble Machine Works, Orange *Also called Gary L Noble Inc (G-16244)*

Noel Duque 281 447-5789
   606 Hill Rd Houston (77037) *(G-11065)*

Noircroxx Biologicals LLC 406 471-0671
   4706 Oak Valley Dr Arlington (76016) *(G-739)*

Noisy Trumpet LLC 210 852-0505
   7550 W Interstate 10 San Antonio (78229) *(G-18349)*

Nokia Inc 214 496-0329
   6363 N State Highway 161 # 800 Irving (75038) *(G-13125)*

Nokia Slutions Networks US LLC (HQ) 972 374-3000
   3201 Olympus Blvd Coppell (75019) *(G-3432)*

Nolanville Plant Usf7, Nolanville *Also called Lhoist North America Texas Ltd (G-15871)*

Noles Davis Plating Co 214 358-1731
   2711 Manor Way Dallas (75235) *(G-4741)*

Noles Plating Co, Dallas *Also called Noles Davis Plating Co (G-4741)*

Noltex LLC 281 842-5000
   12220 Strang Rd La Porte (77571) *(G-13779)*

Noltex Truss Big Spring Inc 254 216-0904
   1705 E Main St Gatesville (76528) *(G-7621)*

Noltex Truss Big Spring Inc 432 267-4700
   1700 Rickabaugh Dr Big Spring (79720) *(G-2089)*

Noltex Truss Dfw Inc 817 866-3333
   8800 E Fm 916 Grandview (76050) *(G-8002)*

Noltex Truss Gatesville LP 713 926-7715
   6247 Navigation Blvd Houston (77011) *(G-11066)*

Noltex Truss Littlefield LP 432 687-1241
   3101 Garden City Hwy Midland (79701) *(G-15321)*

Noltex Truss Littlefield LP (PA) 806 385-5533
   1012 E Wylon Jnnings Blvd Littlefield (79339) *(G-14147)*

Non Typical Pipeline, Cleveland *Also called Non-Typical Pipeline Llc (G-3132)*

Non-Frrous Extrsion Scrap Mtls (PA) 713 869-9551
   9210 Emmott Rd Houston (77040) *(G-11067)*

Non-Typical Pipeline Llc 281 622-5002
   418 Fm 2025 Rd Cleveland (77328) *(G-3132)*

Noormac LLC 303 261-2818
   12309 Rojas Dr Unit B4b3 El Paso (79928) *(G-5898)*

Nor Tex Metal Finishing, Garland *Also called Wolters Holdings Inc (G-7610)*

Norak Inc 281 585-4091
   44 County Road 249 Alvin (77511) *(G-374)*

Noral Holding Company 972 392-7780
   5495 Belt Line Rd Dallas (75254) *(G-4742)*

Noram Drilling Company 281 598-9200
   8400 N Sam Houston Pkwy W # 120 Houston (77064) *(G-11068)*

Noramco, Montgomery *Also called North American Trade Corp (G-15637)*

Norbord Texas Limited, Jefferson *Also called Norbord Texas LP (G-13285)*

Norbord Texas LP 936 568-8009
   500 Nexfor Blvd Jefferson (75657) *(G-13285)*

Norbord Texas Nacogdoches Inc 936 568-8000
   2301 Se Stallings Dr Nacogdoches (75961) *(G-15707)*

Nordic Tankers 281 538-3250
   2551 S Shore Blvd Ste A League City (77573) *(G-13969)*

Norel Animal Nutrition USA Inc 281 741-8211
   5365 Bay Oaks Dr Pasadena (77505) *(G-16490)*

Noremac Gas LLC 281 248-6423
   22136 Westheimer Pkwy # 425 Katy (77450) *(G-13429)*

Noren Products Inc (PA) 650 322-9500
   205 S Edmond St Taylor (76574) *(G-19661)*

Norkol Inc 832 644-1481
   1731 Treble Dr Humble (77338) *(G-12790)*

Norkol Industrial Film, Humble *Also called Norkol Inc (G-12790)*

Norlus Group Inc 915 590-2041
   1217 Barranca Dr Ste A El Paso (79935) *(G-5899)*

Norm Pipe Inc 903 702-8966
   907 Cox Rd Marshall (75672) *(G-14795)*

Normans Well Service Inc 940 668-8201
   3728 E Highway 82 Gainesville (76240) *(G-7354)*

Norris Cylinder Company (HQ) 903 757-7633
   4818 W Loop 281 S Longview (75603) *(G-14285)*

Norris Production Solutions, Spring *Also called Apergy Artfl Lift Intl LLC (G-19195)*

Norriseal Controls, Houston *Also called Norriseal-Wellmark Inc (G-11069)*

Norriseal-Wellmark Inc (HQ) 713 466-3552
   11122 W Little York Rd Houston (77041) *(G-11069)*

Norse Cutng & Abandonment Inc 832 327-3640
5535 Brystone Dr Houston (77041) **(G-11070)**

Norstar Industries LLC 903 784-8900
5500 Farm Road 38 N Brookston (75421) **(G-2328)**

Nortex Corporation 713 658-1142
3009 Post Oak Blvd # 1212 Houston (77056) **(G-11071)**

Nortex Redimix LLC (PA) **214 681-5200**
2010 Valley View Ln Farmers Branch (75234) **(G-6210)**

Nortex Redimix LLC 214 681-5200
5191 Fm 2931 Aubrey (76227) **(G-851)**

North Amercn Tubular Svcs LLC 903 984-0625
991 Marvin A Smith Rd Kilgore (75662) **(G-13579)**

North America Packaging Corp 979 779-5900
1591 N Hrvey Mtchell Pkwy Bryan (77803) **(G-2496)**

North American Atk Corporation (HQ) **972 647-1400**
1102 W N Carrier Grand Prairie (75050) **(G-7936)**

North American Beverages Ltd (PA) **512 501-3890**
6500 River Place Blvd Austin (78730) **(G-1368)**

North American Coal Corp (HQ) **972 448-5400**
5340 Legacy Dr Ste 300 Plano (75024) **(G-16946)**

North American Coal Corp. 830 784-3545
9200 Peeler Ln Christine (78012) **(G-3059)**

North American Engineering Ctr, Webster *Also called Tri-Sen Systems Corporation* **(G-20648)**

North American Galvanizing, Hurst *Also called Azz Incorporated* **(G-12836)**

North American Interpipe Inc 713 333-0333
1800 West Loop S Ste 1350 Houston (77027) **(G-11072)**

North American Pipe Corp (HQ) **855 624-7473**
2801 Post Oak Blvd # 600 Houston (77056) **(G-11073)**

North American Pipe Corp. 940 855-4100
3348 Industrial Dr Wichita Falls (76306) **(G-20787)**

North American Plastics, Irving *Also called Laird Plastics Inc* **(G-13082)**

North American Precast Company 210 509-9100
6949 Low Bid Ln San Antonio (78250) **(G-18350)**

North American Research Corp 972 492-1800
519 Huffines Blvd Lewisville (75056) **(G-14074)**

North American Steel Corp 817 332-7069
1909 Northpark Dr Fort Worth (76102) **(G-6866)**

North American Tech Group Inc (PA) **972 996-5750**
429 S Memory Ln Marshall (75670) **(G-14796)**

North American Trade Corp 936 588-1010
18948 Freeport Dr Montgomery (77356) **(G-15637)**

North Amrcn Glvnzing Ctngs Inc 817 810-0095
3100 W 7th St Ste 500 Fort Worth (76107) **(G-6867)**

North Amrcn Sling Slutions LLC 817 984-8000
4116 Cockrell Ave Fort Worth (76133) **(G-6868)**

North Basin Coating Inc (PA) **806 894-1531**
2041 W State Road 300 Levelland (79336) **(G-14011)**

North Blue Oak Inc 844 778-2336
1306 Fm 1092 Rd Ste 508 Missouri City (77459) **(G-15585)**

North Canvas & Upholstery, Kemah *Also called John C Maudlin Inc* **(G-13476)**

North Crete Services, Longview *Also called Scott Newland Office* **(G-14307)**

North Houston Alcohol DRG Tstg 713 816-4990
440 Benmar Dr Ste 2289 Houston (77060) **(G-11074)**

North Lean Ltd 956 781-2029
401 E Nolana Loop Pharr (78577) **(G-16709)**

North Plains Agriculture, Dumas *Also called Moore County News Press* **(G-5526)**

North Shore Boat Works Inc 361 776-2525
1645 Main St Ingleside (78362) **(G-12897)**

North Shore Express Clean 832 418-0535
15119 Wallisville Rd # 1000 Houston (77049) **(G-11075)**

North Shore Steel, Houston *Also called North Shore Supply Company Inc* **(G-11076)**

North Shore Supply Company Inc (PA) **713 453-3533**
1566 Miles St Houston (77015) **(G-11076)**

North Shore Supply Company Inc 713 400-3320
13935 Industrial Rd Houston (77015) **(G-11077)**

North Side Electric Motors, Houston *Also called Morefield Development Inc* **(G-10920)**

North Texas Compression 940 683-5025
101 Turkey Creek Trl Bridgeport (76426) **(G-2297)**

North Texas Coring Inc 817 279-8930
315 Sun Valley Ct Granbury (76049) **(G-7802)**

North Texas Crushed Stone 940 665-9100
14 County Road 460 Gainesville (76240) **(G-7355)**

North Texas Epitaxy LLC 972 747-8603
301 Ridgemont Dr Allen (75002) **(G-289)**

North Texas Farm & Ranch 940 872-5922
200 Walnut St Bowie (76230) **(G-2199)**

North Texas Flameproof & Wood, Fort Worth *Also called Chicago Flameproof WD Spc Corp* **(G-6513)**

North Texas Health Care Ldry, Grand Prairie *Also called North Txas Hlth Care Ldry Coop* **(G-7938)**

North Texas Ingredients Inc 817 270-2397
308 Commerce St Ste C Azle (76020) **(G-1727)**

North Texas Llano Operating, Dallas *Also called Llano Operating Corporation* **(G-4598)**

North Texas Packing Co 972 660-2800
1350 Avenue S Ste 110 Grand Prairie (75050) **(G-7937)**

North Texas Plastics Inc 940 458-7954
503 W Chapman Dr Sanger (76266) **(G-18728)**

North Texas Tool and Machine, Sanger *Also called North Texas Plastics Inc* **(G-18728)**

North Texas Truss 806 385-5533
1012 E Wylon Jnnings Blvd Littlefield (79339) **(G-14148)**

North Texas Truss Co, Littlefield *Also called Noltex Truss Littlefield LP* **(G-14147)**

North Txas Hlth Care Ldry Coop 469 916-1150
1080 Post And Paddock St Grand Prairie (75050) **(G-7938)**

North Txas Intgrity Sptic Pmpg, Ponder *Also called Texas Integrity Waste* **(G-17096)**

North Txas Prssure Vessels Inc (PA) **940 327-0800**
301 Travis St Walters Ind K S Insdurial Pr Mineral Wells (76067) **(G-15534)**

Northast Txas McHning Wldg Hrd 903 427-2277
121 North St Clarksville (75426) **(G-3076)**

Northeast Gate Co Inc 903 739-8778
20364 Farm Road 79 Sumner (75486) **(G-19608)**

Northeast Texas Hydraulics 903 582-2692
11339 Texas Highway 11 W Sulphur Springs (75482) **(G-19593)**

Northern & Nye Printing Inc 254 662-2292
3115 Robinson Dr Waco (76706) **(G-20438)**

Northern Dental Supplies, Mission *Also called Ramon Guardiola* **(G-15562)**

Northern Offshore Ltd (HQ) **281 649-2600**
575 N Dairy Ashford Rd Houston (77079) **(G-11078)**

Northrop Grmman Coml Arcft Div, Dallas *Also called Northrop Grumman Systems Corp* **(G-4743)**

Northrop Grumman Corporation 214 524-0102
8710 Freport Pkwy Ste 200 Irving (75063) **(G-13126)**

Northrop Grumman Information, Irving *Also called Northrop Grumman Systems Corp* **(G-13127)**

Northrop Grumman Intl Trdg, Irving *Also called Northrop Grumman Corporation* **(G-13126)**

Northrop Grumman Systems Corp 512 374-4100
7745 Chevy Chase Dr # 100 Austin (78752) **(G-1369)**

Northrop Grumman Systems Corp 512 804-2153
4000 S Ih 35 Austin (78704) **(G-1370)**

Northrop Grumman Systems Corp 972 946-9000
9314 W Jefferson Blvd Dallas (75211) **(G-4743)**

Northrop Grumman Systems Corp 469 524-0109
8710 Freport Pkwy Ste 180 Irving (75063) **(G-13127)**

Northrup Grmman Technical Svcs 405 736-8207
8710 Freport Pkwy Ste 200 Irving (75063) **(G-13128)**

Northside Cultured Marble Inc 281 429-5288
19627 Fm 1314 Rd 1314th Conroe (77302) **(G-3343)**

Northstar Ceramic Trading, Carrollton *Also called Styleaccess LLC* **(G-2821)**

Northstar Graphix Inc 817 385-1902
305 W Fork Dr Arlington (76012) **(G-740)**

NORTHSTAR INDUSTRIES, Houston *Also called Marine Services LLC* **(G-10765)**

Northstar Interests LC 713 626-9696
11 Greenway Plz Ste 2800 Houston (77046) **(G-11079)**

Northwest Advantage Inc 713 622-4888
8802 W Rayford Rd Tomball (77375) **(G-19992)**

Northwest Drive Train Inc 713 937-8499
11432 Fm 529 Rd Jersey Village (77041) **(G-13302)**

Northwest Drive Train Service, Jersey Village *Also called Northwest Drive Train Inc* **(G-13302)**

Northwest Fastener and Sup Inc 281 921-7880
11320 Fm 529 Rd Ste F Houston (77041) **(G-11080)**

Northwest Independent Schl Dst 817 698-7300
1350 Eagle Dr Fort Worth (76111) **(G-6869)**

Northwest Machining Svcs LLC 281 894-5388
9101 Windmill Park Ln Houston (77064) **(G-11081)**

Northwest Metal and Steel Inc. 281 444-5269
6811 Theall Rd Ste A Houston (77066) **(G-11082)**

Northwest Pipe Company 817 847-1402
509 Burlington Rd Saginaw (76179) **(G-17752)**

Northwest Pipe Company 817 847-1402
351 Longhorn Rd Saginaw (76179) **(G-17753)**

Norton Drilling, Snyder *Also called Pattersn-Uti Drlg Svcs LP Lllp* **(G-18998)**

Nortonlifelock Inc 210 403-7800
911 Central Pkwy N # 300 San Antonio (78232) **(G-18351)**

Nortonlifelock Inc 650 527-8000
10111 Richmond Ave # 200 Houston (77042) **(G-11083)**

Norwex Usa Inc 214 614-6707
800 W Bethel Rd Ste 100 Coppell (75019) **(G-3433)**

Norwood Equipment Houston Inc 713 670-1320
1812 Mccarty St Houston (77029) **(G-11084)**

Norwood Quarry, Del Valle *Also called Cemex Construction Mtls S LLC* **(G-5329)**

Noshok Inc 281 897-6115
12777 Jones Rd Ste 297 Houston (77070) **(G-11085)**

Not Previous User, Nocona *Also called Peba Oil & Gas Co* **(G-15870)**

Notes-N-Quotes, Austin *Also called Paradigm Bks Lecture Notes Ltd* **(G-1396)**

Nottus Energy Resources Inc 940 687-5304
900 8th St Ste 916 Wichita Falls (76301) **(G-20788)**

Nov, Willis *Also called National Oilwell Varco LP* **(G-20856)**

Nov Asep Elmar, Houston *Also called Elmar Services Inc* **(G-9606)**

Nov Completion Prod Solutions, Borger *Also called National Oilwell Varco LP* **(G-2180)**

Nov Ctes, Conroe *Also called National Oilwell Varco LP* **(G-3339)**

Nov Fiberglass Systems, Mineral Wells *Also called Centron International Inc* **(G-15522)**

Nov MSI Pipe Prtction Tech Inc 281 890-4595
9035 Solon Rd Houston (77064) **(G-11086)**

Nov Rig Systems, Houston *Also called National Oilwell Varco Inc (G-10984)*

Nov Rolligon, Anderson *Also called National Oilwell Varco Inc (G-530)*

Nov Tuboscope, Houston *Also called National Oilwell Varco Inc (G-10989)*

Nov Tuboscope 713 799-5100
10000 Richmond Ave Houston (77042) *(G-11087)*

Nov Wellbore Technologies, Conroe *Also called National Oilwell Varco Inc (G-3334)*

Nova Chemicals Inc 281 474-1000
12222 Port Rd Pasadena (77507) *(G-16491)*

Nova Construction Co Inc 972 869-3041
1713 E Crosby Rd Carrollton (75006) *(G-2785)*

Nova Consulting 281 445-6393
623 Buffington St Houston (77060) *(G-11088)*

Nova Directional Inc 281 246-1149
12227 Fm 529 Rd Bldg lj Houston (77041) *(G-11089)*

Nova Drilling Technologies Inc 713 726-0151
11800 Fairmont St Houston (77035) *(G-11090)*

Nova Magnetics Inc (PA) **972 272-8287**
1101 E Walnut St Garland (75040) *(G-7564)*

Novacentrix, Austin *Also called Ncc Nano LLC (G-1362)*

Novak Commercial Cnstr LLC 512 688-5644
1500 Rivery Blvd Ste 2200 Georgetown (78628) *(G-7668)*

Novaria Group LLC (PA) **817 381-3810**
6300 Ridglea Pl Ste 800 Fort Worth (76116) *(G-6870)*

Novartis Pharmaceuticals Corp 817 293-0450
6201 South Fwy Fort Worth (76134) *(G-6871)*

Novartis Services Inc 817 293-0450
6201 South Fwy Fort Worth (76134) *(G-6872)*

Novolex Inc 972 686-5090
12118 Corporate Dr Dallas (75228) *(G-4744)*

Novomet Usa Inc (PA) **832 437-5998**
23567 Clay Rd Katy (77493) *(G-13430)*

Novosad Enterprises Inc 979 272-9203
2080 State Highway 21 W Caldwell (77836) *(G-2633)*

Novosci Corp 281 363-4949
2021 Airport Rd Conroe (77301) *(G-3344)*

Novvi LLC 281 488-0833
2525 Independence Pkwy Deer Park (77536) *(G-5287)*

Now Inc (PA) **281 823-4700**
7402 N Eldridge Pkwy Houston (77041) *(G-11091)*

Now Magazines LLC 972 937-8447
413 W Main St Corsicana (75151) *(G-3680)*

Nowiczewski, Joe, Houston *Also called Nova Consulting (G-11088)*

Npi Technologies Inc (PA) **972 968-0400**
1241 N Plano Rd Richardson (75081) *(G-17366)*

Npi Technologies 2 Inc 281 265-2815
12144 Dairy Ashford Rd Sugar Land (77478) *(G-19519)*

Nppi Intermediate Inc 512 476-7100
106 E 6th St Ste 300 Austin (78701) *(G-1371)*

NPS, Houston *Also called New Process Steel LP (G-11035)*

NRG Manufacturing Inc (HQ) **281 320-2525**
11311 Holderrieth Rd # 100 Tomball (77375) *(G-19993)*

NRG Manufacturing Inc 281 320-2525
18703 G H Cir Waller (77484) *(G-20505)*

Nri Inc 903 526-5800
218 N College Ave Tyler (75702) *(G-20134)*

Nrp, Houston *Also called Natural Resource Partners LP (G-11010)*

Nrp (gp) LP 713 751-7507
610 Jefferson St Ste 3600 Houston (77002) *(G-11092)*

Nrp (operating) LLC 713 751-7507
601 Jefferson St Ste 3600 Houston (77002) *(G-11093)*

Nrpc Operating LLC 512 428-4753
4925 Greenville Ave # 550 Dallas (75206) *(G-4745)*

NS Controls Inc 713 465-7591
5601 W Sam Houston Pkwy N Houston (77041) *(G-11094)*

Nsec LLC 254 756-0651
3854 Old Lorena Rd Lorena (76655) *(G-14343)*

Nsg Corporation (PA) **972 840-1233**
640 Shiloh Rd 2 Plano (75074) *(G-16947)*

Nsh Services Inc 817 961-5045
14501 North Fwy Fort Worth (76177) *(G-6873)*

NSM Inc 281 880-8188
1535 Industrial Dr Missouri City (77489) *(G-15586)*

NSM Industries Inc 713 697-2091
332 Martin St Houston (77018) *(G-11095)*

Ntl-Brands Ltd (PA) **214 631-0307**
3901 Pipestone Rd Dallas (75212) *(G-4746)*

Ntt Data Inc (HQ) **800 745-3263**
7950 Legacy Dr Ste 900 Plano (75024) *(G-16948)*

Ntw Services Inc 210 885-8637
4507 Lakebend West Dr San Antonio (78244) *(G-18352)*

Ntx Gates & Fences Inc 817 740-9449
632 S Cherry Ln Fort Worth (76108) *(G-6874)*

Ntxepi, Allen *Also called North Texas Epitaxy LLC (G-289)*

Nu Energy Services LP 817 832-0724
225 Jakes Trl Aledo (76008) *(G-200)*

Nubocam LLC 512 473-0500
4611 Bee Caves Rd Ste 202 West Lake Hills (78746) *(G-20686)*

Nucera Solutions LLC 281 275-7473
12645 W Airport Blvd Sugar Land (77478) *(G-19520)*

Nuclear Services Division, Dallas *Also called Saulsbury Industries Inc (G-4938)*

Nuclear Sources and Svcs Inc 713 641-0391
5711 Etheridge St Houston (77087) *(G-11096)*

Nuco, Fort Worth *Also called V I J Corporation (G-7096)*

Nuco Controls LLC 940 257-7092
1008 7th St Wichita Falls (76301) *(G-20789)*

Nuco Tool Inc (PA) **956 383-6620**
1408 E Upas Ave McAllen (78501) *(G-14895)*

Nuco2 Supply LLC 817 676-7580
3970 Business Park Dr Amarillo (79110) *(G-503)*

Nucon Steel Commercial Corp 940 891-3050
3570 Shelby Ln Denton (76207) *(G-5384)*

Nucor Bldg Systems Sls Corp 972 524-5407
600 Apache Trl Terrell (75160) *(G-19744)*

Nucor Building Systems Texas, Terrell *Also called Nucor Corporation (G-19745)*

Nucor Corporation 281 251-8857
16000 Stuebner Airline Rd # 520 Spring (77379) *(G-19156)*

Nucor Corporation 936 687-4665
175 County Road 2345 Grapeland (75844) *(G-8007)*

Nucor Corporation 903 626-4461
8812 Hwy 79 W Jewett (75846) *(G-13308)*

Nucor Corporation 972 524-5407
600 Apache Trl Terrell (75160) *(G-19745)*

Nucor Corporation 214 340-1883
7616 Lyndon B Johnson Fwy Dallas (75251) *(G-4747)*

Nucor Steel Longview LLC (HQ) **800 256-5757**
5400 W Loop 281 Bldg 52 Longview (75603) *(G-14286)*

Nueces Canyon Cattle Company, Brenham *Also called Nueces Canyon Companies (G-2266)*

Nueces Canyon Companies 979 289-5600
9501 Highway 290 W Brenham (77833) *(G-2266)*

Nueces County Record Star, Alice *Also called Alice Newspapers Inc (G-203)*

Nueces Valve Solutions LLC 361 248-1700
730 Diamond Cut Dr Ste A Corpus Christi (78409) *(G-3581)*

Nuevo Energy Company 713 579-6000
700 Milam St Ste 3100 Houston (77002) *(G-11097)*

Nuevo Leon Tortilla Factory 972 721-1984
820 E Irving Blvd Irving (75060) *(G-13129)*

Nukote Coating Systems Intl (PA) **832 770-7100**
4730 Consulate Plaza Dr # 100 Houston (77032) *(G-11098)*

Numerical Precision Inc (PA) **281 328-7343**
1630 E Stroker Rd Crosby (77532) *(G-3739)*

Numo Manufacturing Inc 800 253-0434
1072 E Us Highway 175 Kaufman (75142) *(G-13463)*

Nupi Americas Inc 281 590-4471
1511 Superior Way Houston (77039) *(G-11099)*

Nurse Assist LLC 800 649-6800
4409 Haltom Rd Haltom City (76117) *(G-8155)*

Nustar Gp LLC 210 370-2000
19003 W Interstate 10 San Antonio (78257) *(G-18353)*

Nut Place Inc 713 462-3147
6605 Gessner Rd Houston (77040) *(G-11100)*

Nutech Energy Alliance Ltd (PA) **281 812-4030**
4101 Interwood N Pkwy # 250 Houston (77032) *(G-11101)*

Nutrex America Inc 714 943-9119
24044 Cnco Vlg Ctr Blvd S Katy (77494) *(G-13373)*

Nutri-Feeds Inc 806 357-2288
Us 60 Rd I Hereford (79045) *(G-8294)*

Nutrition Plus LLP 806 655-0505
2308 10th Ave Canyon (79015) *(G-2675)*

Nutrition Supply Corp 936 334-0514
317 Industrial Cir Liberty (77575) *(G-14124)*

Nutritional Scientific, Liberty *Also called Nutrition Supply Corp (G-14124)*

Nuvectra Corporation (PA) **214 474-3103**
5830 Gran Pkwy Ste 1100 Plano (75024) *(G-16949)*

Nuview Systems Inc (PA) **978 296-6600**
401 Congress Ave Ste 2650 Austin (78701) *(G-1372)*

Nuvinair LLC 844 984-6247
5851 Legacy Cir Ste 600 Plano (75024) *(G-16950)*

Nuvo Athletic LLC 281 808-7650
3727 Greenbriar Dr # 111 Stafford (77477) *(G-19360)*

Nuzee Inc 760 295-2408
1401 Capital Ave Ste B Plano (75074) *(G-16951)*

Nvent Thermal LLC 800 545-6258
7433 Harwin Dr Houston (77036) *(G-11102)*

Nvidia Corporation 408 486-2000
740 E Campbell Rd Ste 300 Richardson (75081) *(G-17367)*

Nvidia Corporation 512 401-4762
11001 Lakeline Blvd # 100 Austin (78717) *(G-1707)*

NW Fabrics LLC 832 895-1110
8300 Telephone Rd Houston (77061) *(G-11103)*

NW Sign Industries Inc 972 602-9434
1170 109th St Grand Prairie (75050) *(G-7939)*

Nx Media Inc 713 270-1198
6118 Aletha Ln Houston (77081) *(G-11104)*

Nxp Semiconductors, Austin *Also called Nxp Usa Inc (G-1373)*

Nxp Semiconductors USA, Austin *Also called Nxp Usa Inc (G-1374)*

Nxp Usa Inc 512 933-6000
3501 Ed Bluestein Blvd Austin (78721) *(G-1373)*

A L P H A B E T I C

Nxp Usa Inc (HQ)...............................512 933-8214
 6501 W William Cannon Dr Austin (78735) *(G-1374)*

Nxp Usa Inc......................................512 996-4000
 7700 W Parmer Ln Austin (78729) *(G-1708)*

Nytex Automatic Products Inc..................830 997-8986
 535 E Ammann Rd Bulverde (78163) *(G-2557)*

Nzone Guidance LLC (PA).......................512 778-5353
 140 Falon Ln Liberty Hill (78642) *(G-14128)*

O & B Tank Co Inc (PA).........................806 624-3431
 511 W Hwy 15 Darrouzett (79024) *(G-5214)*

O & B Tank Co Inc..............................806 624-4781
 Hwy 15 W Darrouzett (79024) *(G-5215)*

O & C Equipment Inc............................281 232-4686
 2808 Hartledge Rd Rosenberg (77471) *(G-17591)*

O & D Manufacturing Inc........................903 295-2057
 1103 Cherokee Trce White Oak (75693) *(G-20718)*

O & I Fabrication Incorporated.................281 617-7732
 6417 Cunningham Rd Houston (77041) *(G-11105)*

O C C, Plano *Also called Applied Optical Systems Inc (G-16791)*

O D C L Inc (PA)................................940 566-9914
 1887 Geesling Rd Denton (76208) *(G-5385)*

O D C L Inc.....................................956 565-3131
 324 Industrial Park Mercedes (78570) *(G-15009)*

O E M Industries Inc...........................214 330-7271
 1015 N Justin Ave Dallas (75211) *(G-4748)*

O F M Pump Inc.................................432 381-7390
 2243 N Fm 1936 Odessa (79763) *(G-16094)*

O H M Orperating, Borger *Also called Ray Mac Energy (G-2184)*

O I Analytical, College Station *Also called OI Corporation (G-3196)*

O K Concrete, Vernon *Also called OK Concrete Company (G-20228)*

O M C International LLC.........................281 398-4281
 19302 Whspering Breeze Ln Houston (77094) *(G-11106)*

O S & S Operating Inc..........................940 495-3645
 1305 S Bailey St Electra (76360) *(G-6049)*

O Talk Texas Brands Inc........................325 655-6077
 1610 Roosevelt St San Angelo (76905) *(G-17816)*

O X Y, Dallas *Also called Occidental Chemical Corp (G-4751)*

O& M Manufacturing, Houston *Also called Ecodyne Heat Exchanger LLC (G-9577)*

O'Connell, James F, Amarillo *Also called Exploration Center Building (G-487)*

O'Connor Ready Mix Plant, San Antonio *Also called Martin Marietta Materials Inc (G-18279)*

O'Drill-Mcm Pump & Valve Mfg, Houston *Also called ODrill/Mcm Inc (G-11132)*

O-Tex Pumping LLC (PA).........................432 685-9901
 306 W Wall St Ste 700 Midland (79701) *(G-15322)*

O-Tex Pumping LLC..............................806 665-0552
 1865 Mccullough St Pampa (79065) *(G-16330)*

O. B. Macaroni Company, Fort Worth *Also called Jgr Enterprises LLC (G-6741)*

O9 Solutions Inc (PA)..........................214 838-3125
 1501 Lyndon B Johnson Fwy # 140 Dallas (75234) *(G-4749)*

Oak Cliff Office Sup Prtg Inc..................214 943-7421
 1876 Lone Star Dr Dallas (75212) *(G-4750)*

Oak Farms Dairy, San Antonio *Also called Dfa Dairy Brands Fluid LLC (G-18052)*

Oak Farms Dairy, Houston *Also called Dfa Dairy Brands Fluid LLC (G-9448)*

Oak Lease Service Co LLC.......................361 362-1429
 604 Osage St Refugio (78377) *(G-17245)*

Oaks Precision Fabricating Inc.................713 937-9190
 8550 Breen Dr Houston (77064) *(G-11107)*

Oakwood Steel Fabrication Inc..................903 545-2266
 491 W Us Highway 79 Oakwood (75855) *(G-15893)*

Oas, Sugar Land *Also called Oilfield Audit Services Inc (G-19521)*

Oasis Midstream Partners LP....................281 404-9500
 1001 Fannin St Ste 1500 Houston (77002) *(G-11108)*

Oasis Petroleum Inc (PA).......................281 404-9500
 1001 Fannin St Ste 1500 Houston (77002) *(G-11109)*

Oasis Petroleum LLC (HQ).......................281 404-9500
 1001 Fannin St Ste 1500 Houston (77002) *(G-11110)*

Oasis Petroleum North Amer LLC (HQ)............281 404-9500
 1001 Fannin St Ste 1500 Houston (77002) *(G-11111)*

Oasis Tires & Wheels, Socorro *Also called Otw-Ep Inc (G-19017)*

Ob Cues, Plano *Also called Owen-Bunnell Inc (G-16960)*

Ober & Sons Inc................................281 879-6760
 7755 Synott Rd Houston (77083) *(G-11112)*

OBrien Hogman Associates LLC...................972 823-1900
 9001 Sterling St Irving (75063) *(G-13130)*

Occidental Chemical Corp (HQ)..................972 404-3800
 14555 Dallas Pkwy Ste 400 Dallas (75254) *(G-4751)*

Occidental Chemical Corp.......................214 421-7607
 1100 Lenway St Dallas (75215) *(G-4752)*

Occidental Chemical Corp.......................512 476-2245
 604 W 14th St Austin (78701) *(G-1375)*

Occidental Chemical Corp.......................800 699-5123
 16300 Ledgemont Ln # 1403 Addison (75001) *(G-151)*

Occidental Chemical Corp.......................361 242-8000
 1501 Mckinzie Rd Corpus Christi (78410) *(G-3582)*

Occidental Chemical Corp.......................361 776-6000
 4133 Hwy 361 Gregory (78359) *(G-8103)*

Occidental Chemical Holdg Corp.................972 404-3800
 5005 Lb Johnson Fwy Fl 22 Flr 22 Dallas (75244) *(G-4753)*

Occidental Energy Mktg Inc (HQ)................713 215-7000
 5 Greenway Plz Ste 110 Houston (77046) *(G-11113)*

Occidental Oil and Gas Corp (HQ)...............713 215-7000
 5 Greenway Plz Ste 110 Houston (77046) *(G-11114)*

Occidental Oil and Gas Corp....................432 685-5600
 6001 Deauville Midland (79706) *(G-15323)*

Occidental Permian Ltd.........................432 523-7556
 711 Sw 7th Pl Andrews (79714) *(G-555)*

Occidental Permian Ltd.........................806 592-3777
 3 Mile N Hwy 214 Denver City (79323) *(G-5422)*

Occidental Permian Ltd.........................806 229-2501
 4 Miles West Fm 301 Sundown (79372) *(G-19613)*

Occidental Permian Ltd (HQ)....................713 215-7000
 5 Greenway Plz Ste 110 Houston (77046) *(G-11115)*

Occidental Petroleum Corp (PA).................713 215-7000
 5 Greenway Plz Ste 110 Houston (77046) *(G-11116)*

Occidental Petroleum Corp......................325 574-8567
 14005 Fm 1610 Ira (79527) *(G-12913)*

Occidental Petroleum Corp......................713 640-7500
 17320 Chanute Rd Houston (77032) *(G-11117)*

Occidntal Intl Explration Prod (HQ)............713 215-7600
 5 Greenway Plz Ste 2400 Houston (77046) *(G-11118)*

Occupational Marketing Inc.....................281 492-8250
 19424 Park Row Ste 110 Houston (77084) *(G-11119)*

Ocean Freedom Shipping Inc.....................281 579-3700
 16211 Park Ten Pl Houston (77084) *(G-11120)*

Ocean Ship Holding Inc.........................281 579-3700
 16211 Park Ten Pl Ste 200 Houston (77084) *(G-11121)*

Ocean Shipholdings Inc (PA)....................281 579-3700
 16211 Park Ten Pl Houston (77084) *(G-11122)*

Ocean Ships Inc................................281 579-3700
 16211 Park Ten Pl Houston (77084) *(G-11123)*

Ocean Spray Cranberries Inc....................903 885-8676
 419 Industrial Dr E Sulphur Springs (75482) *(G-19594)*

Oceaneering Deepwater Tech, Houston *Also called Oceaneering International Inc (G-11125)*

Oceaneering International Inc (PA)..............713 329-4500
 11911 Fm 529 Rd Houston (77041) *(G-11124)*

Oceaneering International Inc...................713 939-3682
 11915 Fm 529 Rd Houston (77041) *(G-11125)*

Oceaneering International Inc...................713 329-4318
 11917 Fm 529 Rd Houston (77041) *(G-11126)*

Oceaneering International Inc...................713 466-8853
 9342 Telge Rd Houston (77095) *(G-11127)*

Oceaneering International Inc...................281 228-5300
 16665 Space Center Blvd Houston (77058) *(G-11128)*

Oceaneering International Inc...................713 856-9375
 11800 Charles Rd Jersey Village (77041) *(G-13303)*

Oceaneering International Inc...................361 776-7251
 2552 4th St Ingleside (78362) *(G-12898)*

Oceaneering Multiflex USA, Jersey Village *Also called Oceaneering International Inc (G-13303)*

Oceaneering Reflange...........................713 682-5105
 11911 Fm 529 Rd Houston (77041) *(G-11129)*

Oceanus Automotive LLC.........................512 551-9726
 508 Oakland Ave Austin (78703) *(G-1376)*

Oci Beaumont LLC...............................409 723-1900
 5470 N Twin City Hwy Nederland (77627) *(G-15756)*

Oci Methanol Marketing LLC (PA)................409 723-1900
 2800 Post Oak Blvd # 3150 Houston (77056) *(G-11130)*

Oci Partners LP (HQ)...........................409 723-1900
 5470 N Twin City Hwy Nederland (77627) *(G-15757)*

OConn LLC......................................956 630-6116
 2104 Highland Ave McAllen (78501) *(G-14896)*

Octal Inc......................................972 985-4370
 4975 Preston Park Blvd # 850 Plano (75093) *(G-16952)*

Octane Energy Consulting LLC...................432 685-7736
 310 W Wall St Ste 810 Midland (79701) *(G-15324)*

Octg Material Hdlg Systems Inc.................432 687-5420
 2614 Flynt Midland (79701) *(G-15325)*

Ocusoft Inc....................................281 342-3350
 30444 Southwest Fwy Rosenberg (77471) *(G-17592)*

Odee Company...................................214 340-0415
 10630 Control Pl Dallas (75238) *(G-4754)*

Odeeco Ready Mix Concrete, Pearland *Also called Otis T Dickerson (G-16585)*

Odes Industries LLC............................866 572-8420
 2423 E Loop 820 N Fort Worth (76118) *(G-6875)*

Odessa American, Odessa *Also called Aim Media Texas LLC (G-15905)*

Odessa Babbitt Bearing Company.................432 366-2836
 6112 N County Rd W Odessa (79764) *(G-16095)*

Odessa Division, Odessa *Also called Brandon & Clark Inc (G-15942)*

Odessa JPK Investments Ltd.....................432 368-0888
 6830 E Business 20 Odessa (79762) *(G-16096)*

Odessa Separator Inc (PA)......................432 580-7111
 1001 E Pearl St Odessa (79761) *(G-16097)*

Odessa Service Center, Odessa *Also called Sulzer Pump Services (us) Inc (G-16168)*

Odessa Tortilla & Tamale Fctry.................432 332-6676
 1915 E 2nd St Odessa (79761) *(G-16098)*

Odl Inc..281 647-8300
 17000 Katy Fwy Ste 150 Houston (77094) *(G-11131)*

Odom Trailer Mfg Co Inc 936 756-3910
213 Porter Rd Conroe (77301) *(G-3345)*

ODrill/Mcm Inc 832 782-6300
5055 Cranswick Rd Houston (77041) *(G-11132)*

Ods International Inc 713 782-6767
10375 Richmond Ave # 800 Houston (77042) *(G-11133)*

Odwalla Inc 281 925-0189
11707 S Sam Houston Pkwy Houston (77031) *(G-11134)*

Odyssea Marine Holdings Inc 713 260-1100
2500 Citywest Blvd Houston (77042) *(G-11135)*

Odysseus Holdings LLC 281 769-2399
5523 Indigo St Houston (77096) *(G-11136)*

Odyssey Aerospace Components, Denton *Also called Greenpoint Precision Mch Inc (G-5369)*

Odyssey Precision Fabricating 713 849-3043
11669 Brittmoore Park Dr Houston (77041) *(G-11137)*

Oec LLC USA, Kingwood *Also called Orion Engineered Carbons LLC (G-13651)*

OEM, Houston *Also called Oilfield-Electric-Marine Inc (G-11165)*

OEM Components Inc 281 449-6258
14535 Chrisman Rd Houston (77039) *(G-11138)*

OEM Outsourcing LLC 972 742-7950
7809 Trixie Trail Dr McKinney (75070) *(G-14959)*

Oes Oilfield Services USA Inc 713 960-1339
4295 San Felipe St # 250 Houston (77027) *(G-11139)*

Ofd Engineering, Houston *Also called Oil Field Dev Engrg LLC (G-11151)*

Offenhauser Company (PA) **713 928-2981**
2201 Telephone Rd Houston (77023) *(G-11140)*

Office, Garland *Also called Hco Holding I Corporation (G-7508)*

Office Furn Cmpanies Texas LLC 281 724-1533
1309 W League City Pkwy League City (77573) *(G-13970)*

Office Printing & Supply Inc 512 474-2036
408 W 17th St Austin (78701) *(G-1377)*

Offshore Domestic Group, Houston *Also called Offshore Spclty Fbricators LLC (G-11144)*

Offshore Express Inc (PA) **985 868-1438**
20445 State Highway 249 # 280 Houston (77070) *(G-11141)*

Offshore Kinematics Inc 713 934-7300
16340 Park Ten Pl Ste 200 Houston (77084) *(G-11142)*

Offshore Oil Services Inc 979 265-3300
1608 Old Angleton Rd Clute (77531) *(G-3157)*

Offshore Service Vessels LLC 832 251-6665
2000 W Sam Houston Pkwy S Houston (77042) *(G-11143)*

Offshore Spclty Fbricators LLC (PA) **985 868-1438**
20445 State Highway 249 # 280 Houston (77070) *(G-11144)*

Offshore Wind Power Systems of 682 367-0652
1210 Woodmoor Ct Grapevine (76051) *(G-8047)*

Ofi Testing Equipment Inc 713 880-9885
11302 Steeplecrest Dr Houston (77065) *(G-11145)*

Ofite, Houston *Also called Ofi Testing Equipment Inc (G-11145)*

OFlaherty Holdings Inc (PA) **254 399-2100**
7601 Imperial Dr Waco (76712) *(G-20439)*

Ofs, Houston *Also called Oil Field Supply Pty Ltd (G-11152)*

Ofs Inc 281 456-0052
17211 Hall Shepperd Rd Houston (77049) *(G-11146)*

Ofs Global Inc 832 786-4728
5308 Oates Rd Houston (77013) *(G-11147)*

Ofs International, Houston *Also called Threading & Precision Mfg LLC (G-12282)*

Ofs International, Odessa *Also called Oilfield Services & Tech LLC (G-16100)*

Ofs International LLC 281 452-3036
7735 Miller Rd Ste 3 Houston (77049) *(G-11148)*

Oft Enterprises Inc (PA) **713 787-5373**
4950 Terminal St Bellaire (77401) *(G-2000)*

Ogburn Truck Parts LP 281 331-0005
19511 Highway 35 Alvin (77511) *(G-375)*

Ogf LLC 817 484-4004
3333 E Loop 820 S Fort Worth (76119) *(G-6876)*

Oginfocom LLC 361 904-0071
3802 Saturn Rd Corpus Christi (78413) *(G-3583)*

Ogletree Custom Cabinets 903 356-2611
7183 County Road 2294 Quinlan (75474) *(G-17225)*

Ogp Operating Inc 214 696-2393
8140 Walnut Hill Ln # 610 Dallas (75231) *(G-4755)*

Ogsna, Houston *Also called Orbital Gas Systems N Amer Inc (G-11191)*

Ohair Shutters, Lubbock *Also called Basileia Investments Inc (G-14365)*

Ohara Valente 830 775-8769
500 Veterans Blvd Del Rio (78840) *(G-5321)*

Ohenry Productions Inc 254 714-1103
3859 Chappel Hill Rd Waco (76705) *(G-20440)*

OHM Pharma Inc 940 325-4797
2940 Fm 3028 Mineral Wells (76067) *(G-15535)*

Ohmite Holding LLC 956 542-0276
2400 Courage Blvd # 1110 Brownsville (78521) *(G-2388)*

Ohmite Manufacturing, Brownsville *Also called Ohmite Holding LLC (G-2388)*

Ohmstede Industrial Svcs Inc 409 840-6644
2450 S Shore Blvd Ste 120 League City (77573) *(G-13971)*

Ohmstede Ltd 281 471-4140
12415 Highway 225 La Porte (77571) *(G-13780)*

Ohmstede Ltd 281 867-3260
801 Georgia Ave Deer Park (77536) *(G-5288)*

Ohmstede Ltd (HQ) **409 833-6375**
895 N Main St Beaumont (77701) *(G-1935)*

Ohmstede Ltd 361 289-1701
410 Flato Rd Corpus Christi (78405) *(G-3584)*

Ohmstede Ltd 409 840-6644
2450 S Shore Blvd League City (77573) *(G-13972)*

Ohs Energy Corp 832 871-5088
700 Milam St Ste 1300 Houston (77002) *(G-11149)*

OI Corporation (HQ) **979 690-1711**
151 Graham Rd College Station (77845) *(G-3196)*

Oil & Gas Consultants Intl Inc 832 426-1200
25403 Kingsland Blvd Katy (77494) *(G-13374)*

Oil & Gas Drilling Production, Odessa *Also called Ejr Consulting Services Inc (G-15986)*

Oil & Gas Producers Inc 214 696-2393
8140 Walnut Hill Ln # 610 Dallas (75231) *(G-4756)*

Oil & Gas Technology Fund Inc 281 671-7142
2600 S Shore Blvd Ste 300 League City (77573) *(G-13973)*

Oil Air Hydraulics, Houston *Also called Olaer Usa Inc (G-11167)*

Oil Chem Industrial Plastics, Borger *Also called Borger Oil Chemical Indus Plas (G-2165)*

Oil City Iron Works, Corsicana *Also called Grandor Corporation (G-3672)*

Oil City Iron Works Inc 903 872-6571
814 S Main St Corsicana (75110) *(G-3681)*

Oil Country Manufacturing Inc 432 563-8014
13400 W Highway 80 E Odessa (79765) *(G-16099)*

Oil Data Inc (PA) **713 461-7178**
1888 Stebbins Dr Houston (77043) *(G-11150)*

Oil Field Dev Engrg LLC 281 679-9060
12121 Wickchester Ln # 70 Houston (77079) *(G-11151)*

Oil Field Rental Svc. Co., Pearland *Also called U S Weatherford L P (G-16608)*

Oil Field Supply Pty Ltd 281 877-0049
450 Gears Rd Ste 777 Houston (77067) *(G-11152)*

Oil Patch Group Inc 361 576-0300
991 Industrial Park Dr Victoria (77905) *(G-20289)*

Oil School Services LLC 903 657-7600
800 Industrial Dr Henderson (75652) *(G-8268)*

Oil Spill Response USA Inc (HQ) **832 431-3191**
Citycentre One 800 # 1 Houston (77024) *(G-11153)*

Oil States Energy Services LLC 361 384-0041
405 E Orange Ave Orange Grove (78372) *(G-16269)*

Oil States Energy Services LLC 903 986-3791
3201 Goforth Rd Kilgore (75662) *(G-13580)*

Oil States Energy Services LLC (HQ) **713 425-2400**
333 Clay St Ste 2100 Houston (77002) *(G-11154)*

Oil States Energy Services LLC 432 563-1304
2601 S County Road 1257 Midland (79706) *(G-15326)*

Oil States Energy Services LLC 281 331-1800
1131 Fm 517 Rd Alvin (77511) *(G-376)*

Oil States Energy Services LLC 432 943-2556
3104 S Stockton Ave Monahans (79756) *(G-15611)*

Oil States Energy Services LLC 903 526-4777
9019 Us Highway 271 Tyler (75708) *(G-20135)*

Oil States Industries Inc 817 468-1400
1031 Commercial Blvd N Arlington (76001) *(G-741)*

Oil States Industries Inc 713 510-2200
13111 Nw Fwy Ste 220 Houston (77040) *(G-11155)*

Oil States Industries Inc 713 920-9800
7250 W 43rd St Houston (77092) *(G-11156)*

Oil States Industries Inc 713 445-2200
6120 E Orem Dr Houston (77048) *(G-11157)*

Oil States Industries Inc 713 510-2200
333 Clay St Ste 4620 Houston (77002) *(G-11158)*

Oil States Industries Inc 512 556-5471
1720 Central Texas Expy Lampasas (76550) *(G-13835)*

Oil States Industries Inc 817 468-1400
1115 Commercial Blvd S Arlington (76001) *(G-742)*

Oil States Industries Inc (HQ) **817 548-4200**
7701 S Cooper St Arlington (76001) *(G-743)*

Oil States Industries Inc 281 247-7400
16730 Jacintoport Blvd Houston (77015) *(G-11159)*

Oil States Industries Inc 713 445-2200
5819 Almeda Genoa Rd Houston (77048) *(G-11160)*

Oil States International Inc (PA) **713 652-0582**
333 Clay St Ste 4620 Houston (77002) *(G-11161)*

Oil States Systems Inc 713 445-2210
7701 S Cooper St Arlington (76001) *(G-744)*

Oil Sttes Houston Ship Channel, Houston *Also called Oil States Industries Inc (G-11159)*

Oil Sttes Qlty Conectr Systems, Houston *Also called Oil States Industries Inc (G-11156)*

Oil Tech Services Inc 281 456-9023
10818 Sheldon Rd Houston (77044) *(G-11162)*

Oil Tech Services Inc (PA) **713 789-5144**
800 Wilcrest Dr Ste 101 Houston (77042) *(G-11163)*

Oil Well Chemical Co Inc 940 592-2012
W Expressway At Cy Limits Iowa Park (76367) *(G-12907)*

Oilfield Anchor Company Inc 903 723-2833
600 N John St Palestine (75801) *(G-16306)*

Oilfield Audit Services Inc 281 242-9521
1933 Country Club Blvd Sugar Land (77478) *(G-19521)*

Oilfield Protectors Supply, La Porte *Also called Ponderosa Precision Plas Inc (G-13783)*

A
L
P
H
A
B
E
T
I
C

Oilfield Services & Tech LLC (PA)..........................281 452-3036
7735 Miller Road 3 Houston (77049) *(G-11164)*

Oilfield Services & Tech LLC 432 614-0076
3333 Brazos Ave Odessa (79764) *(G-16100)*

Oilfield Water Logistics LLC 214 292-2011
8201 Preston Rd Ste 520 Dallas (75225) *(G-4757)*

Oilfield-Electric-Marine Inc (HQ) 713 680-9659
6500 Brittmoore Rd Houston (77041) *(G-11165)*

Oilpatch Technologies, Houston *Also called Technologies Alliance Inc (G-12176)*

Oiltanking Texas City LP 409 797-1710
2800 Loop 197 S Texas City (77592) *(G-19799)*

Oiltek Systems LLC 325 200-0423
278 W 2nd St Colorado City (79512) *(G-3225)*

Oilwell Hydraulics Inc 281 602-8170
2002 Timberloch Pl Ste 50 The Woodlands (77380) *(G-19898)*

Oilwell Hydraulics Inc (PA) 432 334-8580
1460 Windway Odessa (79763) *(G-16101)*

Oilwell Tubular Consultants 281 328-6220
14630 Bohemian Hall Rd Crosby (77532) *(G-3740)*

OK Concrete Company (PA) 940 723-4324
2304 Sheppard Access Rd Wichita Falls (76306) *(G-20790)*

OK Concrete Company 940 552-5162
1620 Frontage Rd Vernon (76384) *(G-20228)*

Ok-Go Packaging Inc 915 440-2500
201 Inglwood Ave Bldg 1-A El Paso (79927) *(G-5900)*

OKelley Office Supply Inc 325 673-6422
290 Cypress St Abilene (79601) *(G-61)*

Oklahoma Pacific Ltd 713 209-1100
9805 Katy Fwy Ste 500 Houston (77024) *(G-11166)*

Ol Sonora Trading Company (PA)..........................325 387-2524
1203 End Of E 2nd St Sonora (76950) *(G-19029)*

Olaer Usa Inc (HQ) 713 937-8900
15102 Sommermeyer St # 125 Houston (77041) *(G-11167)*

Olaeris Inc 877 750-5500
717 Creekview Dr Burleson (76028) *(G-2592)*

Old Castle Apg Texas Inc 512 864-9601
15811 Hwy 195 Georgetown (78626) *(G-7669)*

Old Castle Apg West 844 576-1364
2561 Sw Grapevine Pkwy # 200 Grapevine (76051) *(G-8048)*

Old Df Inc 281 590-5467
20322 Hfsmith Khrville Rd Tomball (77375) *(G-19994)*

Old Dt Holdings 432 267-7141
2515 Apron Dr Big Spring (79720) *(G-2090)*

Old Frito-Lay Inc 972 334-7000
7701 Legacy Dr Plano (75024) *(G-16953)*

Old Nocona Boot Factory LLC (PA) 682 237-7644
304 N Oak St Roanoke (76262) *(G-17491)*

Old Strand Emporium, Galveston *Also called Conversation Pieces Inc (G-7394)*

Old Timber Table Company, Dallas *Also called Renever Inc (G-4887)*

Old World Design LLC 214 741-6858
134 Riveredge Dr Dallas (75207) *(G-4758)*

Oldcastle Apg Texas Inc 972 335-4122
9850 John W Elliott Dr Frisco (75033) *(G-7302)*

Oldcastle Apg Texas Inc (HQ) 817 545-8325
2561 Sw Grapevine Pkwy # 200 Grapevine (76051) *(G-8049)*

Oldcastle Building Envelope 972 647-4028
1101 Fountain Pkwy Grand Prairie (75050) *(G-7940)*

Oldcastle Buildingenvelope Inc 972 551-6100
803 Airport Rd Terrell (75160) *(G-19746)*

Oldcastle Buildingenvelope Inc 800 392-9815
4822 Southerland Rd Houston (77092) *(G-11168)*

Oldcastle Buildingenvelope Inc (HQ) 214 273-3400
5005 Lyndon B Johnson Fwy # 1050 Dallas (75244) *(G-4759)*

Oldcastle Buildingenvelope Inc 713 827-1965
4822 Southerland Rd Houston (77092) *(G-11169)*

Oldcastle GL Engnered Pdts Inc 972 563-2627
803 Airport Rd Terrell (75160) *(G-19747)*

Oldcastle Glass, Terrell *Also called Oldcastle Buildingenvelope Inc (G-19746)*

Oldcastle Infrastructure Inc 281 841-9187
1606 Greens Rd Ste 100 Houston (77032) *(G-11170)*

Oldcastle Infrastructure Inc 817 477-2914
1100 Heritage Pkwy Mansfield (76063) *(G-14698)*

Oldcastle Infrastructure Inc 210 922-7306
1900 Rilling Rd San Antonio (78214) *(G-18354)*

Oldcastle Infrastructure Inc 713 991-2400
2120 Fm 359 Rd S Brookshire (77423) *(G-2321)*

Olin Blue Cubellc 979 201-1789
2301 N Brazosport Blvd Freeport (77541) *(G-7206)*

Olio, San Angelo *Also called Hall Tree Antiques Inc (G-17803)*

Olive Packing Company Inc 409 293-3257
1500 Sabine Ave Port Arthur (77642) *(G-17119)*

Olive Packing Company, The, Port Arthur *Also called Olive Packing Company Inc (G-17119)*

Oliver Brothers Lumber Co, Huntsville *Also called Oliver Brothers Sawmill (G-12821)*

Oliver Brothers Sawmill..936 295-0931
1537 Us Highway 190 Huntsville (77340) *(G-12821)*

Oliver Equipment Company LLC (HQ) 713 856-9206
4620 Brittmoore Rd Houston (77041) *(G-11171)*

Oliver Machinery Inc 903 489-2250
10847 State Highway 31 W Malakoff (75148) *(G-14636)*

OLIVER MACHINERY INC DBA OLIVER MFG, Malakoff *Also called Oliver Machinery Inc (G-14636)*

Olivo Enterprises Inc 713 694-3077
9925 Aldine Westfield Rd Houston (77093) *(G-11172)*

Olmos Drilling Co, San Antonio *Also called Lewis Petro Properties Inc (G-18249)*

Olney Door & Screen Co 940 564-3543
1019 W Main St Olney (76374) *(G-16222)*

Olney Sales Inc 940 564-3592
1019 W Main St Olney (76374) *(G-16223)*

Olton Welding & Machine Inc 806 285-3006
1115 1st St Olton (79064) *(G-16227)*

Olympic Trophy Center, San Antonio *Also called Lehmberg Enterprises Inc (G-18244)*

Olympus Marble & Granite Svc, Houston *Also called Hou-Stone Inc (G-10214)*

Omc Americas Inc 713 893-7413
14655 Champion Forest Dr # 7 Houston (77069) *(G-11173)*

Omega Chemical Products Inc 219 208-0500
688 Hiner Rd Weatherford (76087) *(G-20608)*

Omega Dallas, Dallas *Also called Essilor of America Inc (G-4334)*

Omega Environmental Tech, Irving *Also called Auto Air Export Inc (G-12935)*

Omega Oilfield Services, Kilgore *Also called Mega Oil Corporation (G-13573)*

Omega Optical Co LP (PA) 972 241-4141
13515 N Stemmons Fwy Dallas (75234) *(G-4760)*

Omega Optics Inc 512 996-8833
8500 Shoal Creek Blvd 4-200 Austin (78757) *(G-1378)*

Omega Paving Contractor Inc 915 595-1280
428 Frederick Rd El Paso (79905) *(G-5901)*

Omega Printing LP 972 256-1234
2906 Story Rd W Irving (75038) *(G-13131)*

Omega Protein Corporation 713 940-6100
1717 Saint James Pl # 550 Houston (77056) *(G-11174)*

Omganics Inc 512 560-3262
1821 Waterston Ave Unit B Austin (78703) *(G-1379)*

OMI, Houston *Also called Occupational Marketing Inc (G-11119)*

OMI Crane Systems Inc (PA) 972 636-8000
1515 E Interstate 30 Fate (75189) *(G-6228)*

OMI Oilfield Investments LLC 806 648-4120
1201 S Ash St Perryton (79070) *(G-16643)*

Omimex Canada Ltd 817 460-7777
7950 John T White Rd Fort Worth (76120) *(G-6877)*

Omimex Energy Inc (HQ) 817 460-7777
7950 John T White Rd Fort Worth (76120) *(G-6878)*

Omimex Petroleum Inc 817 460-7777
7950 John T White Rd Fort Worth (76120) *(G-6879)*

Omimex Resources Inc (PA) 817 460-7777
7950 John T White Rd Fort Worth (76120) *(G-6880)*

Omk Tube Inc (HQ) 281 609-8150
8304 Sorrel Leaf Ln Houston (77055) *(G-11175)*

Omk Tube Inc 281 609-8970
16937 Leonard Rd Houston (77049) *(G-11176)*

Omni Air & Nitrogen Ltd 432 288-9087
8809 E Highway 80 Midland (79706) *(G-15327)*

Omni Contracting 972 890-4536
505 Chelsea Dr Midlothian (76065) *(G-15489)*

Omni Data Systems Ltd LLP 281 469-4365
11010 Neeshaw Dr Bldg B Houston (77065) *(G-11177)*

Omni Energy Services Corp 936 591-8598
1524 Shelbyville St Center (75935) *(G-3003)*

Omni Flow Computers Inc 281 240-6161
12320 Cardinal Mdw # 180 Sugar Land (77478) *(G-19522)*

Omni Gear, Houston *Also called Omni Usa Inc (G-11179)*

Omni Hotels, Dallas *Also called TRT Holdings Inc (G-5121)*

Omni Lubricants,, Argyle *Also called Triton Products LLC (G-604)*

Omni Precision Inc 713 688-3131
3721 Pinemont Dr Houston (77018) *(G-11178)*

Omni Surgical LP 512 327-6400
5000 Plaza On The Lk # 305 Austin (78746) *(G-1380)*

Omni Usa Inc 713 635-6331
3620 W 11th St Houston (77008) *(G-11179)*

Omni Water Solutions Inc 512 275-0804
4007 Coml Ctr Dr Ste 700 Austin (78744) *(G-1381)*

Omnibase Services of Texas (PA) 512 346-6511
7320 N Mo Pac Expy # 310 Austin (78731) *(G-1382)*

Omnidata Services Group LLC 281 469-4365
10682 Jones Rd Ste 200 Houston (77065) *(G-11180)*

Omnimax Holdings Inc 469 366-3208
300 Railhead Rd Fort Worth (76106) *(G-6881)*

Omnimax International Inc 817 481-3521
300 Railhead Rd Fort Worth (76106) *(G-6882)*

Omnimax International Inc 817 473-1541
700 S 2nd Ave Mansfield (76063) *(G-14699)*

Omnimax International Inc 469 366-3200
300 Railhead Rd Fort Worth (76106) *(G-6883)*

Omnimax International Inc 972 522-0148
3125 N Grt Sw Pkwy 300 Grand Prairie (75050) *(G-7941)*

Omnimax International Inc 817 481-3521
300 Railhead Rd Fort Worth (76106) *(G-6884)*

Omnisling, Frisco *Also called Greenbasket Inc (G-7259)*

Omp Specialties Inc 903 874-0045
2201 S Business 45 Corsicana (75110) *(G-3682)*
Omron Electronics LLC 713 849-1900
9510 N Houston Rosslyn Rd Houston (77088) *(G-11181)*
Omron Management Ctr Amer Inc 489 724-2899
2801 W Rchlle Rd Bldg 100 Dallas (75261) *(G-4761)*
On Line Agency, Austin *Also called Levelfieldcom Inc (G-1290)*
On Shore Qlty Ctrl Spclist LLC 512 443-3582
111 Congress Ave Ste 600 Austin (78701) *(G-1383)*
On Site Decals LLC 281 994-9000
12807 Royal Dr Ste 101 Stafford (77477) *(G-19361)*
On-Board Communications Inc 214 346-0300
12850 Spurling Dr Ste 280 Dallas (75230) *(G-4762)*
On-Site Bennett Services LLC 855 239-2505
4836 W Loop 281 S Longview (75603) *(G-14287)*
On-X Life Technologies Inc (HQ) **512 832-8548**
1300 E Anderson Ln Ste B Austin (78752) *(G-1384)*
Oncken & Sons Cabinet Shop 210 333-4611
203 Seale Rd San Antonio (78219) *(G-18355)*
One Book At A Time Pubg LLC 972 392-2679
4680 Belt Line Rd Addison (75001) *(G-152)*
One Focus Inc (PA) **817 750-7667**
900 Blue Mound Rd E Haslet (76052) *(G-8221)*
One Gas Inc 830 672-2921
619 N Saint Joseph St Gonzales (78629) *(G-7760)*
One Gas Inc 830 672-2256
225 Commerce Ct Gonzales (78629) *(G-7761)*
One Logos Education Solution, Austin *Also called Frh Consumer Services Inc (G-1172)*
One Semiconductor LLC 512 785-4456
3105 Scott Dr Unit 1 Austin (78734) *(G-1385)*
One Source Energy Services, Greenville *Also called Dve Management Inc (G-8071)*
One Source Mfg Tech LLC 512 259-3272
1106 Leander Dr Leander (78641) *(G-13996)*
One Source Recycling Inc 512 549-2812
7400 Fm 969 Austin (78724) *(G-1386)*
One Source SEC & Sound Inc (PA) **713 934-7400**
2925 Fm 1960 Rd E Humble (77338) *(G-12791)*
One Stop Printing Inc 817 338-1962
2904 Cullen St Fort Worth (76107) *(G-6885)*
One Ten Welding Inc 903 561-8549
14762 State Highway 110 S Whitehouse (75791) *(G-20726)*
One Water Source LLC (PA) **512 347-9280**
211 Rr 620 N Ste 140 Lakeway (78734) *(G-13818)*
One Wind Services (us) Inc 902 482-8687
2684 Shafer Rd San Benito (78586) *(G-18662)*
One World Foods Inc 512 480-0203
1219 W 6th St Austin (78703) *(G-1387)*
ONeal Oil Company 940 825-3716
200 Oaklawn Ave Nocona (76255) *(G-15869)*
Oneil Data Systems, Plano *Also called ONeil Digital Solutions LLC (G-16954)*
ONeil Digital Solutions LLC (HQ) **972 881-1282**
3100 E Plano Pkwy Plano (75074) *(G-16954)*
Oneok Inc 915 680-7200
4600 Pollard St El Paso (79930) *(G-5902)*
Onepointe Solutions LLC 866 222-7494
1112 Swenson Blvd Elgin (78621) *(G-6056)*
Onesubsea LLC 713 939-2282
4646 W Sam Houston Pkwy N Houston (77041) *(G-11182)*
Oneta Company (PA) **361 853-0123**
1401 S Padre Island Dr Corpus Christi (78416) *(G-3585)*
Online Construction LP 361 445-6161
411 Catholic Cemetery Rd George West (78022) *(G-7627)*
Online Training Solutions Inc 888 308-6874
315 Wooded Ct Argyle (76226) *(G-602)*
Onsiteview.com, Dallas *Also called Osv Investment LLC (G-4771)*
Onward LLC 281 535-2739
66 Harbor Ln Kemah (77565) *(G-13478)*
Onyx Contractors Operations LP 432 561-8900
1010 S Fm 1788 Midland (79706) *(G-15328)*
Onyx Venture Group LLC 281 395-4791
2719 Falcon Knoll Ln Katy (77494) *(G-13375)*
Op2 Labs LLC (PA) **888 448-8468**
601 Bridgewater St Euless Euless (76039) *(G-6151)*
Opal Resources LLC 713 647-7300
7600 W Tidwell Rd Ste 500 Houston (77040) *(G-11183)*
Open and Close Equipment, Rosenberg *Also called O & C Equipment Inc (G-17591)*
Open and Closed Equipment, Sugar Land *Also called Mayors Machine Works Inc (G-19506)*
Open Options LLC 972 818-7001
16650 Westgrove Dr # 150 Addison (75001) *(G-153)*
Open Road Mobility LLC (PA) **806 866-0275**
7411 82nd St Lubbock (79424) *(G-14452)*
Open Sky Media Inc 512 263-9133
1712 Rio Grande St Ste A Austin (78701) *(G-1388)*
Open-Plant, El Paso *Also called Cemex Construction Mtls S LLC (G-5689)*
Openconnect Systems Inc 972 484-5200
2711 Lbj Fwy Ste 700 Dallas (75234) *(G-4763)*
Operating Company, Corpus Christi *Also called Virtex Holdings LLP (G-3652)*
Operating Technical Elec 817 288-2600
1289 Hemphill St Ste 231 Fort Worth (76104) *(G-6886)*
Operations Rod Permian L C 432 367-4149
9009 N County Rd W Odessa (79764) *(G-16102)*
Opex, Stafford *Also called Output Acquisition Corp (G-19362)*
Opportune LP 713 772-0664
4424 W Sam Houston Pkwy N # 200 Houston (77041) *(G-11184)*
Opteconn LP 972 331-4627
2621 Summit Ave Ste 100 Plano (75074) *(G-16955)*
Optek Technology Inc (HQ) **972 323-2200**
1645 Wallace Dr Carrollton (75006) *(G-2786)*
Optex Systems Inc 972 629-1701
9827 Chartwell Dr Dallas (75243) *(G-4764)*
Optex Systems Inc (HQ) **972 764-5700**
1420 Presidential Dr Richardson (75081) *(G-17368)*
Optex Systems Holdings Inc (PA) **972 764-5700**
1420 Presidential Dr Richardson (75081) *(G-17369)*
Opti-Blast Inc 903 589-0452
4032 N Jackson St Jacksonville (75766) *(G-13254)*
Optiblend Industries Inc (HQ) **281 584-0047**
29738 Goynes Rd Katy (77493) *(G-13431)*
Optical Cable Corporation 972 509-1500
1700 Capital Ave Plano (75074) *(G-16956)*
Optical Cabling Systems, Plano *Also called Opteconn LP (G-16955)*
Optical Cabling Systems LC 972 331-4627
2621 Summit Ave Ste 100 Plano (75074) *(G-16957)*
Optical Filter Source LLC 512 248-0605
16920 Joe Barbee Dr # 2 Round Rock (78664) *(G-17676)*
Optimum Consultancy Svcs LLC 713 505-0300
9800 Richmond Ave Houston (77042) *(G-11185)*
Optimum Path Systems Inc 813 990-8204
8301 Bowspirit Ln Hurst (76053) *(G-12854)*
Optimum Steel Industries, Austin *Also called T&V Optimum LLC (G-1554)*
Optimus Steel LLC (HQ) **800 303-9543**
25219 Kuykendahl Rd # 290 The Woodlands (77375) *(G-19820)*
Opto Electronics Group, Garland *Also called Micropac Industries Inc (G-7552)*
Opulence Magazine, Austin *Also called AMC Publishing LLC (G-914)*
Opulent Transport LLC 713 551-1445
1430 Wedgewood St Houston (77093) *(G-11186)*
Oq Chemicals Bishop LLC 361 584-6920
U.S Highway 77 Business Bishop (78343) *(G-2108)*
Oq Chemicals Corporation 972 481-2771
2001 Fm 3057 Bay City (77414) *(G-1776)*
Oq Chemicals Corporation (HQ) **713 830-3135**
15375 Memorial Dr Houston (77079) *(G-11187)*
Oq Chemicals Holding Corp (HQ) **972 481-2700**
1505 Lyndon B Johnson Fwy Dallas (75234) *(G-4765)*
or Disposables, Irving *Also called Spectrum Lifesciences LLC (G-13188)*
Oracle America Inc 650 506-7000
613 Nw Loop 410 Ste 1000 San Antonio (78216) *(G-18356)*
Oracle America Inc 512 401-1000
5300 Riata Park Ct Austin (78727) *(G-1389)*
Oracle America Inc 972 980-7799
12750 Merit Dr Ste 800 Dallas (75251) *(G-4766)*
Oracle America Inc 972 580-0629
1431 Greenway Dr Ste 145 Irving (75038) *(G-13132)*
Oracle America Inc 214 494-4527
7460 Warren Pkwy Ste 300 Frisco (75034) *(G-7303)*
Oracle Corporation 817 422-5231
144 Mount Gilead Rd Keller (76248) *(G-13469)*
Oracle Corporation 512 372-8207
9600 N Mopac Expy Ste 700 Austin (78759) *(G-1390)*
Oracle Corporation 972 652-8000
7460 Warren Pkwy Ste 300 Frisco (75034) *(G-7304)*
Oracle Corporation (PA) **737 867-1000**
2300 Oracle Way Austin (78741) *(G-1391)*
Oracle Corporation 512 832-1599
11400 N Lamar Blvd Austin (78753) *(G-1392)*
Oracle Corporation 713 595-7656
2100 West Loop S Ste 900 Houston (77027) *(G-11188)*
Oracle Glass LLC 713 462-4759
4927 Cranswick Rd Houston (77041) *(G-11189)*
Oracle Systems Corporation 713 658-6925
6624 Sunrise Dr Lewisville (75056) *(G-14075)*
Orange County Industrial Inc 409 697-3559
4568 Farming Market 408 Orange (77630) *(G-16255)*
Orange County Publishing Co 409 769-5428
450 W Bolivar St Vidor (77662) *(G-20330)*
Orange Oilfield Supply, Orangefield *Also called Lynx Well Service Inc (G-16271)*
Orano Med LLC 301 841-1673
700 Klein Rd Plano (75074) *(G-16958)*
Orbis International Tech Inc 972 929-5705
2081 Hutton Dr Ste 201 Carrollton (75006) *(G-2787)*
Orbis Rpm LLC 940 387-6711
5071 Dakota Ln Denton (76207) *(G-5386)*
Orbit Industries Inc 806 744-8300
4106 N Fm 2528 Lubbock (79416) *(G-14453)*
Orbit Powder Coating, Lubbock *Also called Orbit Industries Inc (G-14453)*
Orbital Energy Group Inc (PA) **832 467-1420**
1924 Aldine Western Rd Houston (77038) *(G-11190)*

ALPHABETIC

Orbital Gas Systems N Amer Inc....................832 467-1420
 1924 Aldine Western Rd Houston (77038) *(G-11191)*

Orbital Sciences Corporation.....................281 218-6140
 16055 Space Center Blvd Houston (77062) *(G-11192)*

Orbital Systems LLC.............................972 915-3669
 3807 Carbon Rd Irving (75038) *(G-13133)*

Orbix Corporation..............................254 675-8651
 4450 S Hwy 6 Clifton (76634) *(G-3145)*

Orc Industries Inc.............................956 831-0618
 2807 N Central Ave Brownsville (78526) *(G-2389)*

Orcaconfig, Georgetown *Also called Trifectix Inc (G-7687)*

Ordermygear LLC...............................214 945-4000
 2211 Commerce St Ste 300 Dallas (75201) *(G-4767)*

Oregon Resources Corporation...................541 266-0875
 764 Salt Creek Rd Springtown (76082) *(G-19274)*

OReilly Automotive Stores Inc..................936 856-2409
 12275 N Highway 75 Willis (77378) *(G-20857)*

Organics By Gosh, Elgin *Also called Employee Owned Nursery Entps (G-6054)*

Origen Biomedical Inc..........................512 474-7278
 7000 Burleson Rd Bldg D Austin (78744) *(G-1393)*

Origin Bio Solutions LLC.......................432 570-4081
 1308 S Midkiff Rd Ste 229 Midland (79701) *(G-15329)*

Origin Instruments Corp........................972 606-8740
 854 Greenview Dr Grand Prairie (75050) *(G-7942)*

Original Services Inc..........................325 617-7400
 5986 Us Highway 87 N San Angelo (76901) *(G-17817)*

Originclear Inc (PA)...........................**323 939-6645**
 2535 E University Dr McKinney (75069) *(G-14960)*

Orion Communications...........................214 361-1203
 8350 N Central Expy # 700 Dallas (75206) *(G-4768)*

Orion Engineered Carbons LLC (HQ)..............**832 445-3300**
 4501 Magnolia Cove Dr Kingwood (77345) *(G-13651)*

Orion Engineered Carbons LLC...................409 883-9966
 1513 Echo Ave Orange (77632) *(G-16256)*

Orion Engineered Carbons LLC...................806 274-6347
 9440 Fm Hwy 1559 W Of Cy Borger (79007) *(G-2181)*

Orion Orrex, Odessa *Also called Orrex Plastics Company LLC (G-16104)*

Orion Pacific Inc (HQ).........................**432 332-0058**
 2525 E Pearl St Odessa (79761) *(G-16103)*

Orizon Industries Inc..........................281 375-7700
 7007 Fm 362 Rd Brookshire (77423) *(G-2322)*

Orora North America............................972 724-2828
 4151 State Hwy 121 N Grapevine (76051) *(G-8050)*

Orora Packaging Solutions......................281 517-8600
 10000 W Sam Huston Pkwy N Houston (77064) *(G-11193)*

Orora Visual TX LLC............................972 289-0705
 3210 Innovative Way Mesquite (75149) *(G-15065)*

Orora Visual TX LLC............................972 289-0705
 3638 Executive Blvd Mesquite (75149) *(G-15066)*

Orrex Plastics Company LLC (PA)................**432 332-1229**
 2800 S Orrex Ave Odessa (79766) *(G-16104)*

Ors Fluids LLC.................................903 535-9992
 809 E Erwin St Tyler (75702) *(G-20136)*

Ortega Bath Environments Inc...................806 763-5777
 2834 Clovis Rd Lubbock (79415) *(G-14454)*

Ortegas Custom Interiors Inc...................214 341-4003
 10885 Alder Cir Ste A Dallas (75238) *(G-4769)*

Orteq Energy Technologies LLC..................940 665-2316
 3401 W Highway 82 Gainesville (76240) *(G-7356)*

Orthodontic Technologies Inc...................800 522-4636
 3315 W 12th St Houston (77008) *(G-11194)*

Orthofix Inc...................................214 937-2000
 3451 Plano Pkwy Lewisville (75056) *(G-14076)*

Orthofix Inc...................................214 937-2000
 3451 Plano Pkwy Lewisville (75056) *(G-14077)*

Orthofix Inc (PA)..............................**214 937-2000**
 3451 Plano Pkwy Lewisville (75056) *(G-14078)*

Orthofix Medical Inc (PA)......................**214 937-2000**
 3451 Plano Pkwy Lewisville (75056) *(G-14079)*

Orthofix Spinal Implants, Lewisville *Also called Blackstone Medical Inc (G-14028)*

Orthorx Inc (HQ)...............................**214 501-0180**
 5204 Tennyson Pkwy # 100 Plano (75024) *(G-16959)*

Ortiz Inc......................................713 688-0374
 5380 W 34th St Houston (77092) *(G-11195)*

Oryx Midstream Services LLC....................432 684-4272
 4000 N Big Spring St # 400 Midland (79705) *(G-15330)*

Oryx Sthern Del Oil Gthring Tr.................432 684-4272
 4000 N Big Spring St # 300 Midland (79705) *(G-15331)*

ORYX TRANS PERMIAN, Midland *Also called Oryx Sthern Del Oil Gthring Tr (G-15331)*

Os Hood County News, Granbury *Also called Hood County News Inc (G-7800)*

Osaka Gas USA Corporation (HQ).................**713 354-9100**
 1330 Post Oak Blvd Fl 19 Houston (77056) *(G-11196)*

Osborn Heirs Company Ltd.......................210 826-0700
 1250 Ne Loop 410 Ste 1100 San Antonio (78209) *(G-18357)*

Osborne Bearing Technologies, Houston *Also called Pfi Molding Inc (G-11314)*

Osborne Cabinet & Millworks, Beaumont *Also called Osborne Cabinets & Millwork (G-1936)*

Osborne Cabinets & Millwork....................713 802-0092
 1420 Graham Ln Port Neches (77651) *(G-17167)*

Osborne Cabinets & Millwork (PA)...............**409 899-1191**
 8080 Eastex Fwy Beaumont (77708) *(G-1936)*

Osborne Cabinets Millwork, Port Neches *Also called Osborne Cabinets & Millwork (G-17167)*

Osburn Materials, San Antonio *Also called Osburn Sand Co (G-18358)*

Osburn Materials, San Antonio *Also called Superior Silica Sands LLC (G-18515)*

Osburn Sand Co.................................210 626-2045
 215 Wellesley Loop San Antonio (78231) *(G-18358)*

OSG Usa Inc (HQ)...............................**800 837-2223**
 1945 W Walnut Hill Ln Irving (75038) *(G-13134)*

Osies Inc (PA).................................**713 849-5131**
 12734 Tanner Rd Houston (77041) *(G-11197)*

Osisoft LLC....................................281 920-6170
 14701 Saint Marys Ln # 600 Houston (77079) *(G-11198)*

Oso Perforating LLC............................972 754-7773
 3225 Premier Dr Ste 150 Irving (75063) *(G-13135)*

Osr Services LP (PA)...........................**281 422-7206**
 2315 W Main St Baytown (77520) *(G-1830)*

Osseus Fusion Systems LLC......................888 330-5960
 1931 Greenville Ave Dallas (75206) *(G-4770)*

Osteocentric Technologies Inc..................800 969-0639
 11000 N Mopac Expy # 600 Austin (78759) *(G-1394)*

Osteogenics Biomedical Inc.....................806 796-1923
 4620 71st St Spc 78 Lubbock (79424) *(G-14455)*

Osteomed LLC...................................972 677-4600
 3885 Arapaho Rd Addison (75001) *(G-154)*

Osv Investment LLC.............................512 301-2848
 3333 Lee Pkwy Ste 600 Dallas (75219) *(G-4771)*

Ota Compression LLC (PA).......................**972 831-1300**
 102 Decker Ct Ste 204 Irving (75062) *(G-13136)*

Ota Compression LLC............................817 326-8250
 120 Industrial Ave Granbury (76049) *(G-7803)*

Otcr Inc.......................................713 685-3600
 909 Wirt Rd Houston (77024) *(G-11199)*

Ote, Fort Worth *Also called Operating Technical Elec (G-6886)*

Ote International Holdings LLC..................888 666-9361
 6695 County Road 4628 Athens (75752) *(G-837)*

Oteco Inc (PA).................................**713 695-3693**
 2828 Trout St Houston (77093) *(G-11200)*

Oteco Inc......................................713 695-3693
 2811 Trout St Houston (77093) *(G-11201)*

Otis Elevator Company..........................214 741-6207
 1444 N Cockrell Hill Rd # 102 Dallas (75211) *(G-4772)*

Otis Instruments Inc...........................432 563-0007
 3308 Norden Dr Midland (79706) *(G-15332)*

Otis T Dickerson...............................713 988-2533
 2818 Wagon Trail Rd Pearland (77584) *(G-16585)*

Otsi, Argyle *Also called Online Training Solutions Inc (G-602)*

Otto H Fenner & Associates, College Station *Also called Fenner & Associates Inc (G-3182)*

Otw-Ep Inc (PA)................................**915 858-0448**
 757 Horizon Blvd Socorro (79927) *(G-19017)*

Outdoor Furn Refinishing Inc...................713 741-9779
 6030 Inglewood St Houston (77021) *(G-11202)*

Outdoor Furniture Refinishing..................713 741-9779
 6010 Saint Augustine St Houston (77021) *(G-11203)*

Outdoor Lighting Services LP...................713 690-6301
 5115 Steadmont Dr Houston (77040) *(G-11204)*

Outdoor Systems Advertising, Houston *Also called Outfront Media LLC (G-11205)*

Outerwear USA..................................806 792-8891
 726 Donald Preston Dr Wolfforth (79382) *(G-20909)*

Outfront Media LLC.............................713 868-2284
 1600 Studemont St Houston (77007) *(G-11205)*

Outlaw Conversions Inc.........................254 968-5733
 1000 Airport Rd Stephenville (76401) *(G-19417)*

Outlaws Oilfield Service LLC...................432 445-0005
 415 W Wall St Ste 612 Midland (79701) *(G-15333)*

Output Acquisition Corp........................281 879-3609
 11104 W Airport Blvd # 160 Stafford (77477) *(G-19362)*

Outsmart Magazine, Houston *Also called Up & Out Communications (G-12473)*

Outstnding Grphic Slutions Inc.................972 255-2022
 4070 N Belt Line Rd Irving (75038) *(G-13137)*

Overflow Energy LLC............................806 658-7832
 723 W Industrial Rd Booker (79005) *(G-2157)*

Overhead Door Co Longview, TX, Longview *Also called WD Norton Inc (G-14332)*

Overhead Door Corporation (HQ).................**469 549-7100**
 2501 S State Hwy 121 Ste Lewisville (75067) *(G-14080)*

Overhead Door Corporation......................361 884-6640
 4242 Baldwin Blvd Corpus Christi (78405) *(G-3586)*

Overhead Door Corporation......................214 630-4669
 2170 French Settlement Rd Dallas (75212) *(G-4773)*

Overland Tank Inc..............................325 673-7132
 2700 E Interstate 20 Odessa (79766) *(G-16105)*

Overlay Product Systems Inc....................281 552-3500
 3657 Briarpark Dr Houston (77042) *(G-11206)*

Overnite Software Inc..........................979 319-8371
 1212 N Velasco St Ste 110 Angleton (77515) *(G-575)*

Overtime LLC...................................409 833-3300
 801 Laurel St Beaumont (77701) *(G-1937)*

Overton Energy LLC.............................713 580-7250
 4265 San Felipe St # 1040 Houston (77027) *(G-11207)*

Overton Enterprises LLC 512 394-6089
8201 E Riverside Dr # 125 Austin (78744) *(G-1395)*

Overwraps Packaging Inc 214 634-0427
3950 La Reunion Pkwy Dallas (75212) *(G-4774)*

Ovintiv Exploration Inc (HQ)..........................**281 210-5100**
4 Waterway Square Pl # 100 The Woodlands (77380) *(G-19899)*

Owen Oil Tools LP (HQ).................................**817 551-0540**
12001 County Road 1000 Godley (76044) *(G-7738)*

Owen-Bunnell Inc..972 578-9100
961 N Ave Ste 700 Plano (75074) *(G-16960)*

Owens Corning...940 723-5998
219 Randy Dr Wichita Falls (76306) *(G-20791)*

Owens Corning Sales LLC..............................972 937-1340
3700 N Ih 35 E Waxahachie (75165) *(G-20554)*

Owens Corning Sales LLC..............................806 622-1582
1701 Hollywood Rd Amarillo (79118) *(G-504)*

Owens Corning Sales LLC..............................972 438-1050
201 N Nursery Rd Irving (75061) *(G-13138)*

Owens Corning Sales LLC..............................903 538-2271
10658 W State Highway 294 Palestine (75801) *(G-16307)*

Owens Corning Sales LLC..............................713 672-8338
8360 Market St Houston (77029) *(G-11208)*

Owens Mach & Manufacturing..........................325 672-4161
917 Oil Center Dr Abilene (79601) *(G-62)*

Owens Machine & Manufacturing, Abilene *Also called Owens Mach & Manufacturing (G-62)*

Owens Machine and Tool Company.....................972 219-2354
561 N Cowan Ave Ste 201 Lewisville (75057) *(G-14081)*

Owens-Brockway Glass Cont Inc.......................956 717-4200
13711 Regional Dr Laredo (78045) *(G-13917)*

Owens-Brockway Glass Cont Inc.......................956 717-4200
5200 Tennyson Pkwy # 100 Plano (75024) *(G-16961)*

Owl Swd Operating, Dallas *Also called Oilfield Water Logistics LLC (G-4757)*

Oxbow Calcining LLC (HQ)..............................**281 907-9425**
1450 Lake Robbins Dr # 500 Spring (77380) *(G-19238)*

Oxbow Carbon Minerals, Spring *Also called Oxbow Calcining LLC (G-19238)*

Oxea Bishop, LLC, Bishop *Also called Oq Chemicals Bishop LLC (G-2108)*

Oxea Holding Corp, Dallas *Also called Oq Chemicals Holding Corp (G-4765)*

Oxidor Corporation Inc.................................972 424-6422
1825 E Plano Pkwy Ste 160 Plano (75074) *(G-16962)*

OXY, Houston *Also called Occidental Oil and Gas Corp (G-11114)*

OXY, Midland *Also called Occidental Oil and Gas Corp (G-15323)*

OXY Inc..432 685-5600
6001 Deauville Midland (79706) *(G-15334)*

OXY Inc (HQ)..**713 215-7000**
5 Greenway Plz Ste 2400 Houston (77046) *(G-11209)*

OXY Inc..956 728-6200
6213 State Highway 359 Laredo (78043) *(G-13918)*

OXY USA Inc...432 634-2247
4518 S Us Highway 87 Big Spring (79720) *(G-2091)*

OXY USA Inc...713 215-7000
5 Greenway Plz Ste 110 Houston (77046) *(G-11210)*

OXY USA Inc...956 429-0600
401 Dallas Ave McAllen (78501) *(G-14897)*

OXY USA Inc...806 637-5965
1056 Fm 1066 E Loop (79342) *(G-14340)*

OXY USA Wtp LP..713 366-5303
Karen Sinard Fl 20 Flr 20 Houston (77046) *(G-11211)*

OXY Vinyls LP (HQ).....................................**877 699-8465**
14555 Dallas Pkwy Ste 400 Dallas (75254) *(G-4775)*

OXY Vinyls LP...281 476-2927
2800 Park Rd 1836 La Porte (77571) *(G-13781)*

OXY Vinyls LP...281 476-8000
2400 Miller Cut Off Rd La Porte (77571) *(G-13782)*

OXY Vinyls LP...281 884-4000
4403 Pasadena Fwy Pasadena (77503) *(G-16492)*

OXY Vinyls LP...281 476-2640
5900 Highway 225 G8a Deer Park (77536) *(G-5289)*

Oxymar Inc..361 776-6321
Hwy 361 Ingleside (78362) *(G-12899)*

P & A Graphics LLC....................................972 632-2100
2100 Couch Dr McKinney (75069) *(G-14961)*

P & C Oil Field Service LLC...........................956 581-1725
1213 Blake St Mission (78572) *(G-15561)*

P & H Casters, Arlington *Also called P&H Sales Ltd (G-745)*

P & K Services LLC.....................................361 299-1800
5741 Leopard St Ste A Corpus Christi (78408) *(G-3587)*

P & L Cast Stone Inc...................................817 430-8114
210 James St Roanoke (76262) *(G-17492)*

P & L Enterprises, Roanoke *Also called P & L Cast Stone Inc (G-17492)*

P & L Rentals, Palestine *Also called Oilfield Anchor Company Inc (G-16306)*

P & M Blasting & Coating Inc.........................713 896-4691
7826 Harms Rd Houston (77041) *(G-11212)*

P & N Machine Company Inc...........................281 469-9140
12450 Windfern Rd Houston (77064) *(G-11213)*

P & W C, Wichita Falls *Also called Raytheon Technologies Corp (G-20801)*

P & W Quality Machines Inc (PA)......................**972 299-0500**
707 S Highway 67 Cedar Hill (75104) *(G-2949)*

P & W Sales Incorporated.............................817 244-6565
6676 Corp Pkwy Ste 100 Fort Worth (76126) *(G-6887)*

P A S, Houston *Also called Pas Group LLC (G-11254)*

P B I, San Antonio *Also called B Plan Inc (G-17933)*

P Diamond Enterprises Inc (PA).......................**325 643-5629**
3300 Milam Dr Brownwood (76801) *(G-2441)*

P E Moseley & Assoc, Houston *Also called Phillip E Mosley & Associates (G-11322)*

P I Components Corp...................................979 830-5400
1951 Highway 290 W Brenham (77833) *(G-2267)*

P M P E Ltd (PA).......................................**830 303-0056**
2251 Rudeloff Rd Seguin (78155) *(G-18852)*

P M T, El Paso *Also called Plastic Molding Technology Inc (G-5911)*

P M W Ventures Inc.....................................940 855-6100
9142 Powell Rd Wichita Falls (76305) *(G-20792)*

P N A, Gainesville *Also called N A Petroflex Ltd (G-7351)*

P N I Accuflow, Houston *Also called Pressure Point Service (G-11410)*

P P I, Cypress *Also called Professional Projects Inc (G-3814)*

P R S Pallet Repair Services, Boerne *Also called Taylormade Pllets Lgistics LLC (G-2139)*

P Rockin Enterprises Inc..............................915 886-4912
310 Valley Chili Rd Anthony (79821) *(G-589)*

P S I Extrusions, Olney *Also called PSI Industries Inc (G-16224)*

P S I Urethanes, Austin *Also called Plastic Specialties Inc (G-1420)*

P S M S, Rockwall *Also called Precision Sheet Metal Shop Inc (G-17561)*

P T I, Houston *Also called Proportional Technologies Inc (G-11450)*

P T Products & Services Inc...........................512 251-3592
20109 Algreg St Pflugerville (78660) *(G-16682)*

P T S, Houston *Also called Production Tech & Svcs Inc (G-11437)*

P W Platforms Inc......................................713 731-7155
4010 Broad St Houston (77087) *(G-11214)*

P&G Mining LLC..682 500-8986
2860 N Hwy Grand Prairie (75050) *(G-7943)*

P&H Sales Ltd..817 468-3850
1016 W Harris Rd Arlington (76001) *(G-745)*

P-Americas LLC...361 853-0123
1401 S Padre Island Dr Corpus Christi (78416) *(G-3588)*

P-Americas LLC...903 794-3883
3005 Magnolia St Texarkana (75503) *(G-19770)*

P-Mcom Incorporated..................................866 310-2556
685 John B Sias Mem Pkwy Fort Worth (76134) *(G-6888)*

P-R-O Management Inc.................................972 720-1475
13601 Preston Rd Ste 309e Dallas (75240) *(G-4776)*

P.S.i, San Antonio *Also called Pressure Systems International (G-18394)*

P2 Energy Solutions Inc..............................713 787-6300
1221 Lamar St Ste 1400 Houston (77010) *(G-11215)*

P2es Holdings LLC.....................................713 481-2000
1221 Lamar St Ste 1300 Houston (77010) *(G-11216)*

P2es Holdings LLC.....................................210 402-5900
1355 Central Pkwy S # 500 San Antonio (78232) *(G-18359)*

P3 Imaging Solutions LLC............................210 494-9998
1211 Safari St San Antonio (78216) *(G-18360)*

Pabst Brewing Company LLC..........................210 299-6708
110 E Houston St Fl 3 San Antonio (78205) *(G-18361)*

Pac, Houston *Also called Petroleum Analyzer Company LP (G-11304)*

Paccar Inc..940 566-7100
3200 Airport Rd Denton (76207) *(G-5387)*

Paccar Inc..940 591-4000
1700 Woodbrook St Denton (76205) *(G-5388)*

Paccar Inc..940 566-7329
2111 Redrock Dr Corinth (76210) *(G-3459)*

Paccar Inc..940 566-7752
2501 Mountainview Dr Corinth (76210) *(G-3460)*

Pacific Columns.......................................714 257-9600
6765 Horizon Rd Rockwall (75032) *(G-17557)*

Pacific Drilling Services Inc..........................713 334-6662
800 Town And Country Blvd # 5 Houston (77024) *(G-11217)*

Pacific Foam Technologies Div, El Paso *Also called Ufp Technologies Inc (G-6018)*

Pacific Mwd Inc..713 466-1616
8250 W Little York Rd Houston (77040) *(G-11218)*

Pacific Refining Company (PA)........................**713 877-6929**
9 Greenway Plz Houston (77046) *(G-11219)*

Pacific Resources Intl LLC............................214 504-3853
211 E Louisiana St McKinney (75069) *(G-14962)*

Pacific Sensor LLC.....................................972 242-5750
2501 Mayes Rd Ste 100 Carrollton (75006) *(G-2788)*

Pacific Valves..562 426-2531
4526 Res Frest Dr Ste 400 Spring (77381) *(G-19239)*

Pacifica T-Shirts Inc...................................714 508-4848
3000 Joe Dimaggio Blvd # 31 Round Rock (78665) *(G-17677)*

Paciugo Italian Gelato, Dallas *Also called Authentic Gelato LLC (G-3986)*

Package Conveyer Co Inc..............................817 332-7195
123 S Main St Fort Worth (76104) *(G-6889)*

Packaged Ice, Corpus Christi *Also called Reddy Ice Corporation (G-3607)*

Packaging Corporation America.......................210 798-1700
4671 W Us Highway 90 San Antonio (78237) *(G-18362)*

Packaging Corporation America.......................972 422-4270
1800 E Plano Pkwy Plano (75074) *(G-16963)*

Packaging Corporation America.......................214 227-5124
2510 W Miller Rd Garland (75041) *(G-7565)*

Packaging Corporation America................................817 640-1888
 1001 113th St Arlington (76011) *(G-746)*
Packaging Corporation America................................254 776-2360
 701 Texas Central Pkwy Waco (76712) *(G-20441)*
Packaging Corporation America................................469 568-7000
 1015 Hayden Dr Carrollton (75006) *(G-2789)*
Packaging Corporation America................................254 776-8890
 9200 Old Mcgregor Rd Waco (76712) *(G-20442)*
Packaging Corporation America................................956 464-5664
 2111 Hester Ave Ste A Donna (78537) *(G-5489)*
Packaging Corporation America................................915 779-1291
 21 Leigh Fisher Blvd El Paso (79906) *(G-5903)*
Packaging One Inc................................713 674-0302
 6016 Knute St Houston (77028) *(G-11220)*
Packaging Service Co Inc................................281 485-1458
 1904 Mykawa Rd Pearland (77581) *(G-16586)*
Packard International Inc................................281 399-8771
 22397 White Oak Dr Conroe (77306) *(G-3346)*
Packers Plus Enrgy Svcs USA In (HQ)................................**281 872-6999**
 11415 Spell Rd Tomball (77375) *(G-19995)*
Packless Industries, Waco *Also called Packless Metal Hose Inc (G-20443)*
Packless Metal Hose Inc (PA)................................**254 666-7700**
 8401 Imperial Dr Waco (76712) *(G-20443)*
Paco Label Systems Inc................................903 561-2125
 1 Hombre Dr Tyler (75707) *(G-20137)*
Paco Pumps By Grundfos, Brookshire *Also called Grundfos CBS Inc (G-2316)*
Pactiv LLC................................903 654-4745
 4501 E Hwy 31 Corsicana (75109) *(G-3683)*
Pactiv LLC................................254 770-4100
 3000 Pegasus Dr Temple (76501) *(G-19693)*
Pactiv LLC................................817 608-9009
 500 113th St Arlington (76011) *(G-747)*
Padgett Machine Tools Co Inc................................254 865-9771
 4212 E Us Highway 84 Gatesville (76528) *(G-7622)*
Pae Avation Technical Svcs LLC................................940 257-2836
 235 9th Ave Bldg 140 Sheppard Afb (76311) *(G-18902)*
Page Chester Ltd................................817 624-4001
 1401 S Cherry Ln Fort Worth (76108) *(G-6890)*
Page Design, Cedar Creek *Also called Duke Forms & Printing (G-2935)*
Page Eagle Industries Inc................................409 960-4310
 1520 Woodworth Blvd Port Arthur (77640) *(G-17120)*
Page's Printing, San Antonio *Also called Shannon Durin (G-18468)*
Page/Ntrntnal Cmmnications LLC................................713 341-6619
 2748 Bingle Rd Houston (77055) *(G-11221)*
Pai, Midland *Also called Petroplex Acidizing Inc (G-15348)*
Pain Du Jour French Bakery, Houston *Also called Adem Ruman Inc (G-8478)*
Painless Performance, Fort Worth *Also called Perfect Performance Pdts LLC (G-6902)*
Painted Pony, San Antonio *Also called Mulberry Heart I Ltd (G-18325)*
Painted Rock LLC (PA)................................**512 832-5057**
 1017 Innovation Way Cedar Park (78613) *(G-2981)*
Paisano Educational Trust................................210 690-9301
 14547 Roadrunner Way San Antonio (78249) *(G-18363)*
Paisano Service & Supply Inc................................361 572-0322
 751 Us Highway 183 S Cuero (77954) *(G-3765)*
PAISANO STUDENT NEWSPAPER, San Antonio *Also called Paisano Educational Trust (G-18363)*
Pak-Mor Ltd................................830 303-6238
 2191 Rudeloff Rd Seguin (78155) *(G-18853)*
Pak-Sher, Kilgore *Also called Command Packaging LLC (G-13536)*
Paksher, Kilgore *Also called Revolution Plastics LLC (G-13586)*
Paktronics Controls, Richland Hills *Also called Maxitrol Company (G-17441)*
PAL- LEASE & MANAGEMENT, Stephenville *Also called Pal-Con LLC (G-19418)*
Pal-Con LLC................................254 968-3335
 12425 N Hwy 377 Stephenville (76401) *(G-19418)*
Pal-Serv of Dallas LLC................................214 631-4600
 2150 S Peachtree Rd Balch Springs (75180) *(G-1738)*
Palacio Ivis................................214 402-6856
 811 Pleasant Hills Dr Dallas (75217) *(G-4777)*
Palacios & Sons LLC................................713 463-5851
 9101 Jameel Rd Ste 110 Houston (77040) *(G-11222)*
Palacios Processors Inc................................361 552-1231
 625 State Highway 316 Port Lavaca (77979) *(G-17153)*
Paladin Signs and Graphics Inc................................817 744-7361
 324 Rhineland Rd Benbrook (76126) *(G-2044)*
Palestine Concrete Tile Co, Palestine *Also called Headwaters Cnstr Mtls LLC (G-16299)*
Palestine Herald-Press, Palestine *Also called Newspaper Holding Inc (G-16305)*
Paleteria El Pibe................................281 541-8777
 636 E Crosstimbers St Houston (77022) *(G-11223)*
Palex, Dallas *Also called Ifco Systems North America Inc (G-4485)*
Palex Systems, Lubbock *Also called Chep (usa) Inc (G-14392)*
Pall Corporation................................713 896-9995
 17489 Village Green Dr Jersey Village (77040) *(G-13304)*
Palladium Exchange LLC................................214 421-8600
 1208 S Riverfront Blvd Dallas (75207) *(G-4778)*
Pallas Archtctral Wodworks LLC................................214 741-1125
 9008 Chancellor Row Dallas (75247) *(G-4779)*

Pallet & Crating Co Inc................................903 463-5786
 Fm 1417 Denison (75021) *(G-5344)*
Pallet Advisor LLC................................817 271-4840
 8770 S Central Expy Dallas (75241) *(G-4780)*
Pallet Depot................................972 336-0006
 2501 Dalworth St Ste B Grand Prairie (75050) *(G-7944)*
Pallet King Enterprises Inc................................972 723-3249
 107 N 5th St Midlothian (76065) *(G-15490)*
Pallet Logistics of America, San Antonio *Also called Crimstone AAA Operating Co LP (G-18030)*
Pallet Ops LLC................................713 554-6972
 4847 Blaffer St Houston (77026) *(G-11224)*
Pallet Ops - San Antonio LLC................................210 225-7882
 514 Merida St Ste 1 San Antonio (78207) *(G-18364)*
Pallet Repair Services Inc................................972 913-1110
 1012 W Wintergreen Rd Hutchins (75141) *(G-12870)*
Palletone Inc................................903 427-3030
 670 Us Highway 82 E Clarksville (75426) *(G-3077)*
Palletone of Texas LP................................903 628-5695
 1020 W Us Highway 82 New Boston (75570) *(G-15768)*
Pallets911 LLC................................956 203-2671
 602 S Indiana Ave Brownsville (78521) *(G-2390)*
Palm Inc................................713 410-1331
 5725 County Road 121 Rosharon (77583) *(G-17609)*
Palmer Industrial Products, Andrews *Also called Palmer of Texas Tanks Inc (G-556)*
Palmer of Texas Tanks Inc................................432 523-5904
 1701 N Us Highway 385 Andrews (79714) *(G-556)*
Palmer Steel Supplies Inc................................956 686-6575
 4300 Acapulco Ave McAllen (78503) *(G-14898)*
Palmetto Services LLC................................903 655-0900
 2905 County Road 205 N Henderson (75652) *(G-8269)*
Palo Petroleum Inc (PA)................................**214 691-3676**
 5944 Luther Ln Ste 900 Dallas (75225) *(G-4781)*
Palo Verde Oil Company (PA)................................**214 692-7052**
 5949 Sherry Ln Ste 850 Dallas (75225) *(G-4782)*
Paloma Lease Service Inc................................361 449-2815
 3466 Highway 281 George West (78022) *(G-7628)*
Paloma Partners III LLC................................713 650-8500
 1021 Main St Ste 2450 Houston (77002) *(G-11225)*
Palomar Modular Buildings LLC................................469 727-0727
 505 N Interstate 35 E Desoto (75115) *(G-5438)*
Pamco Ltd................................713 621-0002
 4550 Post Oak Place Dr Houston (77027) *(G-11226)*
Pamela Printing Co................................281 240-1313
 550 Jlie Rvers Dr Ste 310 Sugar Land (77478) *(G-19523)*
Pampa Concrete Co Inc................................806 669-3111
 220 W Tyng Ave Pampa (79065) *(G-16331)*
Pampa Machine & Supply Inc................................806 665-0013
 112 Western St Pampa (79065) *(G-16332)*
Pampa News, Pampa *Also called Pts Inc (G-16336)*
Pampillonia Designs II Inc................................214 503-7272
 1740 N Collins Blvd Richardson (75080) *(G-17370)*
Pamrod Products Company................................830 372-1500
 2511 N Heideke St Seguin (78155) *(G-18854)*
Pan American Industries Inc................................281 572-4842
 20194 Alexander Ln Porter (77365) *(G-17180)*
Pan American Wire Inc................................817 332-6486
 2301 Hemphill St Fort Worth (76110) *(G-6891)*
Pan Asian Chemicals Inc................................713 621-1888
 5444 Westheimr Rd # 1570 Houston (77056) *(G-11227)*
Pan Continental Resources (PA)................................**281 291-8100**
 2600 Red Bluff Rd Seabrook (77586) *(G-18788)*
Pan Ector Industries LLC................................940 566-1414
 1017 Shady Oaks Dr Denton (76205) *(G-5389)*
Pan Inc................................713 589-6850
 24 Greenway Plz Ste 965 Houston (77046) *(G-11228)*
Pan-America Hyperbarics Inc................................972 423-0377
 1607 Capital Ave Plano (75074) *(G-16964)*
Panamerican Indus Svcs Co Inc................................210 666-3542
 5290 New Sulphur Sprng Rd San Antonio (78222) *(G-18365)*
Panasonic Avionics Corporation................................346 242-1599
 3340 Greens Rd Ste D700 Houston (77032) *(G-11229)*
Panasonic Corp North America................................956 984-3432
 4900 Gorge Mcvay Dr Ste C Mcallen (78503) *(G-14899)*
Panasonic Corp North America................................956 984-3700
 2600 Network Blvd Ste 600 Frisco (75034) *(G-7305)*
Panasonic Indus Dvcs Sls Amer, Frisco *Also called Panasonic Corp North America (G-7305)*
Panchitas Tortilla Factory................................325 655-2138
 2504 N Chadbourne St San Angelo (76903) *(G-17818)*
Panda Ethanol Inc (PA)................................**972 361-1200**
 4100 Spring Valley Rd # 675 Dallas (75244) *(G-4783)*
Panda Power Fund, Dallas *Also called Panda Pwr Gnrtion Infrstrcture (G-4784)*
Panda Pwr Gnrtion Infrstrcture................................972 361-2000
 5001 Spring Valley Rd 1150w Dallas (75244) *(G-4784)*
Panda-Brandywine L P................................972 980-7159
 4100 Spring Valley Rd Dallas (75244) *(G-4785)*
Pandemx LLC................................432 638-3055
 10008 W County Road 150 Midland (79706) *(G-15335)*
Panel Processing Texas Inc................................903 586-2423
 1010 S Bolton St Jacksonville (75766) *(G-13255)*

Panel Specialists Inc 254 774-9197
  3601 Range Rd Temple (76504) *(G-19694)*

Panel Specialists Inc (HQ) **254 774-9800**
  3115 Range Rd Temple (76504) *(G-19695)*

Panel Truss of Longview Inc 903 657-7000
  700 Kilgore Dr Henderson (75652) *(G-8270)*

Panel Truss Texas Inc 903 657-7000
  700 Kilgore Dr Henderson (75652) *(G-8271)*

Panel-Tech Incorporated (PA) **713 896-6900**
  7800 Breen Dr Houston (77064) *(G-11230)*

Panelmatic Texas Inc 281 890-1678
  9826 Windmill Park Ln Houston (77064) *(G-11231)*

Pangea Enterprises Inc 956 542-9494
  5333 Westheimr Rd # 1050 Houston (77056) *(G-11232)*

Panhandle Eastrn Pipe Line LP 713 627-5400
  1221 Mckinney St Ste 2252 Houston (77010) *(G-11233)*

Panhandle Milling LLC (PA) **806 243-4211**
  4805 Fm 809 Dawn (79025) *(G-5217)*

Panhandle Milling LLC 806 258-7253
  4805 Fm 809 Dawn (79025) *(G-5218)*

Panhandle Milling Co, Dawn *Also called Panhandle Milling LLC (G-5217)*

Panhandle Packing & Gasket Inc 806 763-2801
  402 19th St Lubbock (79401) *(G-14456)*

Panhandle Slim, Fort Worth *Also called Westmoor Mfg Co (G-7143)*

Panini America Inc (HQ) **817 662-5300**
  5325 F A A Blvd Ste 100 Irving (75061) *(G-13139)*

Panola Equipment Inc 903 633-2545
  County Rte 335 Panola (75685) *(G-16349)*

Panola Wire Line Services Inc 903 693-3966
  Hwy 79 Carthage (75633) *(G-2915)*

Pantera Energy Company 806 376-6625
  817 S Polk St Ste 201 Amarillo (79101) *(G-451)*

Pantex Ennerflo Systems Inc 832 861-7700
  8110 Mchard Rd Houston (77053) *(G-8390)*

Pantex Manufacturing, Kaufman *Also called Advance Tabco Inc (G-13456)*

Pantheon Construction Inc 940 458-9183
  7880 Rector Rd Sanger (76266) *(G-18729)*

Panya Fabricate Welding & Mch, Fort Worth *Also called Panyanouvong Jose & Le Malysa (G-6892)*

Panyanouvong Jose & Le Malysa 310 279-7065
  2804 N Nichols St Fort Worth (76106) *(G-6892)*

Papa Bears Pizza 512 351-5421
  1420 Colorado Bend Dr Cedar Park (78613) *(G-2982)*

Papa Grande Gourmet Foods LLC 210 349-6262
  3444 E Commerce St San Antonio (78220) *(G-18366)*

Papa Jose, Houston *Also called Cuatro Cinco Enterprises LLC (G-9355)*

Paper City Magazine, Dallas *Also called Urban Publishers Inc (G-5146)*

Paper Network Inc (PA) **972 239-6567**
  4652 Nall Rd Dallas (75244) *(G-4786)*

Paper Planet 817 451-8898
  6515 E Lancaster Ave Fort Worth (76112) *(G-6893)*

Paper Plate Incorporated 972 296-7888
  1670 N Hampton Rd Ste 106 Desoto (75115) *(G-5439)*

Paper Source Inc 469 304-5168
  1900 Preston Rd Ste 211 Plano (75093) *(G-16965)*

Paper Tubes & Sales Co 214 631-0973
  Hinton St Dallas (75235) *(G-4787)*

Papercity Magazine, Houston *Also called Urban Publishers Inc (G-12477)*

Papergraphics Ltd (PA) **254 526-4303**
  904 S 31st St Temple (76504) *(G-19696)*

Pappys Sand & Gravel Inc 972 486-4400
  13851 Hwy 34 W Scurry (75158) *(G-18783)*

Par Hawaii Refining LLC (HQ) **281 899-4800**
  825 Town And Country Ln # 150 Houston (77024) *(G-11234)*

Par Pacific Holdings Inc (PA) **281 899-4800**
  825 Town And Country Ln # 1500 Houston (77024) *(G-11235)*

Par Petroleum LLC (HQ) **281 899-4800**
  825 Town And Country Ln # 1500 Houston (77024) *(G-11236)*

Parabellum Energy LLC 832 460-6521
  1302 Waugh Dr Ste 161 Houston (77019) *(G-11237)*

Paradigm Bks Lecture Notes Ltd (PA) **217 344-4433**
  407 W 24th St Austin (78705) *(G-1396)*

Paradigm Concept LLC 817 896-7729
  1613 Monte Carlo Dr Mansfield (76063) *(G-14700)*

Paradigm Metals Incorporated (PA) **512 255-2622**
  15811 Vision Dr Pflugerville (78660) *(G-16683)*

Paradigm Ses LLC 713 402-6140
  1001 West Loop S Ste 700k Houston (77027) *(G-11238)*

Paradigm SRP LLC 877 677-9899
  11811 Brantly Ave Houston (77034) *(G-11239)*

Paradigm Traffic Systems Inc (PA) **817 831-9406**
  2201 E Div St Arlington (76011) *(G-748)*

Paragon Directional Drlg LLC 903 880-7398
  3501 Old Granbury Rd Granbury (76049) *(G-7804)*

Paragon Fabricators Inc 409 935-6602
  500 Main St La Marque (77568) *(G-13712)*

Paragon Furniture Inc 817 633-3242
  2224 E Randol Mill Rd Arlington (76011) *(G-749)*

Paragon Industries LP 972 288-7557
  2011 S Town East Blvd Mesquite (75149) *(G-15067)*

Paragon Industries Inc 972 288-7557
  2011 S Town East Blvd Mesquite (75149) *(G-15068)*

Paragon Offshore PLC (HQ) **832 783-4000**
  3151 Briarpark Dr Ste 700 Houston (77042) *(G-11240)*

Paragon Packaging Inc (PA) **817 477-5211**
  1500 E Broad St Mansfield (76063) *(G-14701)*

Paragon Printing & Mailing, Austin *Also called Murphy Connected Entps Inc (G-1357)*

Paragon Rio Grande LLC 956 831-8249
  5295 Commercial Dr Brownsville (78521) *(G-2391)*

Parallel Petroleum LLC (PA) **432 684-3727**
  1004 N Big Spring St Midland (79701) *(G-15336)*

Paramount Millwork Corporation 817 429-1145
  3220 May St Fort Worth (76110) *(G-6894)*

Paramount Petroleum Corp 800 882-6541
  704 Sheldon Rd Ste B Channelview (77530) *(G-3031)*

Paramount Rental Services LLC 940 264-8379
  900 8th St Ste 1002 Wichita Falls (76301) *(G-20793)*

Parco Double-E LLC 214 631-2290
  1261 Profit Dr Dallas (75247) *(G-4788)*

Paris Construction LLC 832 752-5271
  16518 House Hahl Rd Cypress (77433) *(G-3810)*

Paris News, Paris *Also called Southern Newspapers Inc (G-16370)*

Paris Texas Hardware, Dallas *Also called Pt Hardware Inc (G-4834)*

Parish International Inc 281 463-9233
  1100 Zach Rd Hempstead (77445) *(G-8254)*

Park of Penske Logistics, Laredo *Also called Aptiv Services Us LLC (G-13860)*

Park Tank Trucks Service, Iowa Park *Also called Oil Well Chemical Co Inc (G-12907)*

Parker & Par, Midland *Also called Pioneer Ntral Rsources USA Inc (G-15357)*

Parker Business Forms Inc 409 842-5251
  30 Interstate 10 N Beaumont (77702) *(G-1938)*

Parker County Shopper, Weatherford *Also called Weatherford Advertising Inc (G-20629)*

Parker Drilling Company (PA) **281 406-2000**
  5 Greenway Plz Ste 100 Houston (77046) *(G-11241)*

Parker Drilling MGT Svcs Ltd 281 406-2000
  5 Greenway Plz Ste 100 Houston (77046) *(G-11242)*

Parker Drilling Offshr Co LLC 281 406-2000
  5 Greenway Plz Ste 100 Houston (77046) *(G-11243)*

Parker Petroleum Pros Inc 903 360-5450
  526 Springcreek Rd Grand Saline (75140) *(G-7998)*

Parker Pgi, Houston *Also called Pgi International Ltd (G-11316)*

Parker School Uniforms LLC 713 465-1635
  12524 Memorial Dr Houston (77024) *(G-11244)*

Parker Systems Inc 800 262-4891
  6601 Harrisburg Blvd Houston (77011) *(G-11245)*

Parker-Hannifin Corporation 936 560-8900
  403 Industrial Dr Nacogdoches (75964) *(G-15708)*

Parker-Hannifin Corporation 817 625-5081
  4700 Lone Star Blvd Fort Worth (76106) *(G-6895)*

Parker-Hannifin Corporation 817 232-1040
  304 E Mcleroy Blvd Saginaw (76179) *(G-17754)*

Parker-Hannifin Corporation 409 924-0300
  16101 Vallen Dr Houston (77041) *(G-11246)*

Parkerlane Directional Drlg LP 817 235-4050
  2504 Kodiak Cir Euless (76039) *(G-6152)*

Parking Sense Usa Inc 830 428-0299
  37535 Interstate 10 W # 2 Boerne (78006) *(G-2131)*

Parkline Inc 409 935-5743
  5235 Delany Rd Hitchcock (77563) *(G-8339)*

Parkline Inc 409 935-1037
  4725 Lawndale St La Marque (77568) *(G-13713)*

Parks Metal Fabricators Inc 903 838-0535
  5702 W 7th St Wake Village (75501) *(G-20487)*

Parks Printing Co 806 747-2881
  1715 19th St Lubbock (79401) *(G-14457)*

Parland Inc 903 843-3467
  1205 Industrial Blvd Gilmer (75644) *(G-7710)*

Parlevel Systems Inc 210 200-8873
  114 E Cevallos San Antonio (78204) *(G-18367)*

Parman Capital Group LLC 713 751-2700
  1000 La St Ste 5900 Houston (77002) *(G-11247)*

Parrot Inc 512 514-6840
  7000 N Mopac Fl 2 Flr 2 Austin (78731) *(G-1397)*

Parsec Technologies Inc 972 804-4600
  820 Jupiter Rd Plano (75074) *(G-16966)*

Parsley Energy Inc (HQ) **737 704-2300**
  303 Colorado St Ste 3000 Austin (78701) *(G-1398)*

Parsley Energy LLC (HQ) **432 818-2100**
  1703 E County Road 120 Midland (79706) *(G-15337)*

Parsley Energy Operations LLC 432 818-2100
  1703 E County Road 120 Midland (79706) *(G-15338)*

Parsleys Shtmtl & Roofg Co 806 669-6461
  214 E Tyng Ave Pampa (79065) *(G-16333)*

Part of Collins Aerospace, A, Haltom City *Also called Goodrich Corporation (G-8142)*

Partee Enterprises 432 263-0632
  110 W 22nd St Ste A Big Spring (79720) *(G-2092)*

Parten Operating Inc 936 624-3100
  19354 State Highway 21 W Crockett (75835) *(G-3721)*

Parten Operating Inc (PA) **281 874-2101**
211 Hghland Crotx Dr Ste Houston (77073) *(G-11248)*

Particle Drilling Tech Inc 713 223-3031
11050 W Little York Rd Q Houston (77041) *(G-11249)*

Partner Metalfab LP 409 933-0026
319 Volney St La Marque (77568) *(G-13714)*

Partners Converting Inc 469 568-5000
1800 Kelly Blvd Carrollton (75006) *(G-2790)*

Partners Metalfab LP 713 672-6888
1309 Akron St Houston (77029) *(G-11250)*

Partners Specialties Inc 281 922-9102
12405 Fuqua St Houston (77034) *(G-11251)*

Partrac Geomarine Inc 713 338-3495
16225 Park Ten Pl Ste 500 Houston (77084) *(G-11252)*

Parts Krafters Co (PA) **515 981-4749**
13130 Glenside Dr Dallas (75234) *(G-4789)*

Parts Suppliers Inc 830 773-5069
2913 Diaz St Eagle Pass (78852) *(G-5552)*

Partsmaster, Irving *Also called NCH Corporation (G-13115)*

Party Ice Co, Mission *Also called Trevino Jr Gustavo (G-15569)*

Party Pig Superstore, Sunset Valley *Also called M Patel Enterprises Inc (G-19626)*

Party Props Inc 713 868-5433
4025 Willowbend Blvd # 30 Houston (77025) *(G-11253)*

Pas Group LLC (PA) **281 286-6565**
13100 Space Center Blvd Houston (77059) *(G-11254)*

Pasadena Refining System Inc (HQ) **713 920-1874**
10350 Richmond Ave # 1400 Houston (77042) *(G-11255)*

Pasadena Service Center, Pasadena *Also called Tdw Services Inc (G-16517)*

Pasadena Tank Corporation 281 457-3996
1301 Transport Dr Baytown (77523) *(G-1798)*

Paso Del Norte Hardware LLC 915 591-6200
2200 N Yarbrough Dr E43 El Paso (79925) *(G-5904)*

Paso Del Norte Publishing Inc 915 838-1601
1801 Texas Ave El Paso (79901) *(G-5905)*

Pason Offshore, Houston *Also called Petron Industries Inc (G-11310)*

Pason Systems USA Corp (HQ) **713 693-8700**
7701 W Little York Rd # 800 Houston (77040) *(G-11256)*

Passare Inc 325 695-3412
6550 Directors Pkwy Abilene (79606) *(G-63)*

Pastusek Industries Inc 972 291-0511
2008 Mrtin Lther King Fwy Fort Worth (76104) *(G-6896)*

Pat and Gail Jackowski 830 278-6247
508 S Wood St Uvalde (78801) *(G-20194)*

Pat Garcia 254 559-2815
6512 Us Highway 180 W Breckenridge (76424) *(G-2232)*

Pat Tank Inc 409 982-7319
2146 5th Ave Port Arthur (77642) *(G-17121)*

Patara Oil & Gas LLC 214 295-6704
333 Clay St Ste 3960 Dallas (75219) *(G-4790)*

Patara Stone Inc 713 681-2301
6550 Long Point Rd Ste A Houston (77055) *(G-11257)*

Patco Machine & Fab Inc 281 443-2837
2002 Humble Westfield Rd Houston (77073) *(G-11258)*

Pate Trucking Co Inc 432 758-2166
104 N Hwy 214 Seminole (79360) *(G-18886)*

Pate Trucking Co LLC 575 392-4441
4025 112th St Lubbock (79423) *(G-14458)*

Patek Grocery and Market 361 594-3171
224 S Avenue E Shiner (77984) *(G-18946)*

Pathmark Traffic Equipment LLC 512 392-2090
4435 Hunter Rd San Marcos (78666) *(G-18702)*

Pathway Control Products Inc 281 354-3699
22262 Cuttler Rd New Caney (77357) *(G-15845)*

Patient Conversation Media Inc (PA) **512 522-0966**
4315 Guadalupe St Ste 200 Austin (78751) *(G-1399)*

Patina Metals Inc 713 462-6117
9303 Clay Rd Houston (77080) *(G-11259)*

Patio One Furniture LP (PA) **713 789-8080**
10520 Harwin Dr Houston (77036) *(G-11260)*

Patricia Wolf Designs, Smithville *Also called Wolf & Sons Design Inc (G-18979)*

Patrick Industries Inc 254 799-5717
1500 Fort Graham Rd Waco (76705) *(G-20444)*

Patrick S Molak Corp 830 606-0093
1612 Hunter Rd New Braunfels (78130) *(G-15818)*

Patriot Erectors LLC 512 858-9100
3023 W Highway 290 Dripping Springs (78620) *(G-5511)*

Patriot Oilfield Services LLC (PA) **979 648-2416**
1 Oconnor Plz Ste 300 Victoria (77901) *(G-20290)*

Patriot Parent LLC 512 858-9100
3023 W Highway 290 Dripping Springs (78620) *(G-5512)*

Patriot Premium Threading Serv 432 250-6001
8300 W Highway 80 Midland (79706) *(G-15339)*

Patriot Resources Inc 432 686-9801
110 W La Ave Ste 500 Midland (79701) *(G-15340)*

Patriot Trinity LLC 936 594-5948
104 Industrial Blvd Trinity (75862) *(G-20019)*

Pattern Bioscience Inc 512 905-9527
9600 Great Hills Trl 160e Austin (78759) *(G-1400)*

Pattersn-Uti Drlg Svcs LP Lllp (HQ) **325 573-1104**
4500 Lamesa Hwy Snyder (79549) *(G-18998)*

Pattersn-Uti Drlg Svcs LP Lllp 361 576-6896
844 Bob White Rd Victoria (77905) *(G-20291)*

Patterson Drilling Company 325 651-6603
4105 S Chadbourne St San Angelo (76904) *(G-17819)*

Patterson Manufacturing Inc 903 757-0523
3794 Bell Meadows Dr Longview (75605) *(G-14288)*

Patterson Tubular Services Inc (HQ) **281 452-5443**
539 S Sheldon Rd Channelview (77530) *(G-3032)*

Patterson Well Service Co LLC 361 575-9600
1501 E Mockingbird Ln # 3 Victoria (77904) *(G-20292)*

Patterson-Uti Acquisition LLC 432 561-9382
9915 W Industrial Ave Midland (79706) *(G-15341)*

Patterson-Uti Drilling, Tyler *Also called Patterson-Uti Energy Inc (G-20138)*

Patterson-Uti Drilling Co LLC 325 574-6300
4510 Lamesa Hwy Snyder (79549) *(G-18999)*

Patterson-Uti Drlg Intl Inc 214 765-5530
10713 W Sam Houston Pkwy Houston (77064) *(G-11261)*

Patterson-Uti Energy Inc 432 561-9382
9915 W Industrial Ave Midland (79706) *(G-15342)*

Patterson-Uti Energy Inc 817 556-5300
3205 Windmill Rd Cleburne (76033) *(G-3105)*

Patterson-Uti Energy Inc (PA) **281 765-7100**
10713 W Sam Houston Pkwy Houston (77064) *(G-11262)*

Patterson-Uti Energy Inc 903 877-3659
11940 Constantine Ave Tyler (75708) *(G-20138)*

Patterson-Uti Energy Inc 432 682-9401
410 N Loraine St Midland (79701) *(G-15343)*

Patterson-Uti MGT Svcs LLC 325 574-6300
4510 Lamesa Hwy Snyder (79549) *(G-19000)*

Patton Cabinet Doors, Austin *Also called Patton Manufactured Pdts LP (G-1401)*

Patton Enterprises Inc 832 619-1890
12130 Highway 3 Bldg 4 Webster (77598) *(G-20642)*

Patton Manufactured Pdts LP 512 918-3737
10206b N Interstate 35 Austin (78753) *(G-1401)*

Pattonair Usa Inc 817 284-4449
1900 Robotics Pl Fort Worth (76118) *(G-6897)*

Pattty Brinlee 940 600-0878
1715 Vintage Dr Corinth (76210) *(G-3461)*

Pattycakes Sweettreats, Corinth *Also called Pattty Brinlee (G-3461)*

Paty Investments Inc (PA) **713 688-7686**
4540 S Pinemont Dr # 110 Houston (77041) *(G-11263)*

Paul Krivoy 361 854-7911
2106 Cord 20b Corpus Christi (78415) *(G-3589)*

Paul Musslewhite Trckg Co LLC 806 894-3151
1700 10th St Levelland (79336) *(G-14012)*

Paul Musslewhite Trucking Co, Levelland *Also called Gravity Oilfield Services LLC (G-14007)*

Paul Smoke 281 422-4228
6730 Independence Blvd # 300 Baytown (77521) *(G-1831)*

Pauluhn Electric Mfg LLP 281 485-4311
1616 N Main St Pearland (77581) *(G-16587)*

Pave/Lock/Plus LLC 281 239-3033
1705 Cottonwood School Rd Rosenberg (77471) *(G-17593)*

Pavement Tool Mfg Inc 903 734-7531
6339 Scrub Pine Rd Big Sandy (75755) *(G-2066)*

Paver Connection, Katy *Also called Tropiscapes Inc (G-13452)*

Pavestone LLC 281 769-5098
830 Brookline Katy (77494) *(G-13376)*

Pavestone LLC 512 558-7283
1900 Clovis Barker Rd San Marcos (78666) *(G-18703)*

Pavestone LLC 817 481-5802
3215 State Highway 360 Grapevine (76051) *(G-8051)*

Pavliska Cabinets Inc 254 773-4461
I-35 N Pendleton Rd Troy (76579) *(G-20032)*

Paw Depot Incorporated 214 440-6324
955 E Campbell Rd Richardson (75081) *(G-17371)*

Pawnee Gas Plant, Pawnee *Also called Pioneer Ntral Rsources USA Inc (G-16534)*

Pay-N-Save, Alba *Also called Valero Energy Corporation (G-183)*

PAYMENT SYSTEMS, Irving *Also called Touchpay Holdings LP (G-13196)*

Payton Interests Inc (PA) **512 244-3221**
1609 Chisholm Trail Rd # 40 Round Rock (78681) *(G-17678)*

Payton Machine & Supply Inc 806 274-5221
3100 S Cedar Borger (79007) *(G-2182)*

Pb Materials Holdings Inc (PA) **432 563-8036**
4001 E 42nd St Ste 100 Odessa (79762) *(G-16106)*

Pb Materials Holdings Inc 806 745-5332
2803 114th St Lubbock (79423) *(G-14459)*

Pb Materials Holdings Inc 432 208-2761
602 N East Ave Kermit (79745) *(G-13513)*

Pb Unlimited LLC 817 831-4336
1659 Hickory Dr Ste H Haltom City (76117) *(G-8156)*

Pbi Labs, Denton *Also called Permian Basin Instruments Inc (G-5392)*

Pbp Inc 832 902-2231
5151 E Grand Pkwy S Baytown (77523) *(G-1799)*

Pbp Fabrication Inc 432 381-5542
1117 S Tripp Ave Odessa (79763) *(G-16107)*

Pbr Inc 830 401-4523
1903 N Austin St Seguin (78155) *(G-18855)*

Pbv Valve, Stafford *Also called Pbv-Usa Inc (G-19363)*

Pbv-Usa Inc 800 231-3530
  12735 Dairy Ashford Rd Stafford (77477) *(G-19363)*

PC Cable Connexion Inc 281 338-5400
  202 Reynolds Ave League City (77573) *(G-13974)*

PC Calendar 2010 LLC (PA) **214 491-5103**
  2501 N Harwood St # 2600 Dallas (75201) *(G-4791)*

PC Connexion, League City *Also called Behemoth Corporation (G-13949)*

PC Legal Tools Inc 415 808-8800
  5001 Plz On The Lk Ste 11 Austin (78746) *(G-1402)*

PCA, San Antonio *Also called Packaging Corporation America (G-18362)*

PCA, Arlington *Also called Packaging Corporation America (G-746)*

PCA/Donna 319, Donna *Also called Packaging Corporation America (G-5489)*

PCA/El Paso 327, El Paso *Also called Packaging Corporation America (G-5903)*

Pca/Garland 322, Garland *Also called Packaging Corporation America (G-7565)*

PCA/Plano 374, Plano *Also called Packaging Corporation America (G-16963)*

Pca/Regional Design Center, Waco *Also called Packaging Corporation America (G-20442)*

PCC Klad LLC 713 433-5151
  1710 Mykawa Rd Pearland (77581) *(G-16588)*

Pccfasteners, Arlington *Also called Progressive Incorporated (G-762)*

Pccs Printing Solutions Inc 210 340-1841
  11811 Warfield St San Antonio (78216) *(G-18368)*

PCI, Beasley *Also called Pipe Coatings Intl LLC (G-1843)*

PCI, Fort Worth *Also called An Authorized Affiliate of PRI (G-6387)*

PCI, Austin *Also called Publications Communications Inc (G-1437)*

PCI Industries Inc (PA) **817 509-2300**
  5101 Blue Mound Rd Fort Worth (76106) *(G-6898)*

PCI Manufacturing LLC 903 439-1080
  906 N Hillcrest Dr Sulphur Springs (75482) *(G-19595)*

PCI Manufacturing LLC 903 885-6772
  903 I 30 E Sulphur Springs (75482) *(G-19596)*

PCI Nitrogen LLC 713 920-5300
  2001 Jackson Rd Pasadena (77506) *(G-16493)*

PCL Air Technology, Humble *Also called Tecalemit Inc (G-12801)*

Pcore Exploration Prod II LLC 469 802-1400
  2200 Ross Ave Ste 4900e Dallas (75201) *(G-4792)*

Pcs Ferguson Inc 432 334-8580
  1460 W Interstate 20 Odessa (79763) *(G-16108)*

Pcs Oilfield Services LLC 806 323-8007
  10918 Shanna St Canadian (79014) *(G-2653)*

Pcs Telecom Inc (PA) **281 469-3367**
  1726 Richey St Pasadena (77502) *(G-16494)*

Pcx Aerostructures Tx LP 817 583-8820
  800 S 6th Ave Mansfield (76063) *(G-14702)*

Pd Supply Inc 713 435-6100
  10803 Vinecrest Dr Ste 1 Houston (77086) *(G-11264)*

PDC Logic, Midland *Also called Taurex Drill Bits LLC (G-15431)*

Pdn Ssl LLC 915 629-9100
  11445 Cedar Oak Dr El Paso (79936) *(G-5906)*

PDQ Machine Shop Inc 832 327-4455
  15151 Henry Rd Houston (77060) *(G-11265)*

Pdvsa Services Inc 281 531-0004
  1293 Eldridge Pkwy Houston (77077) *(G-11266)*

Pdx Printing, El Paso *Also called Porfirio Diaz Exit LP (G-5916)*

Pe Ceramics, Austin *Also called Progressive Mfg Tech Inc (G-1435)*

Peached Tortilla Mobile LLC 512 297-8635
  5350 Burnet Rd Apt 425 Austin (78756) *(G-1403)*

Peaches, Farmers Branch *Also called Med Couture Inc (G-6207)*

Peacock Alley Inc (PA) **214 744-0399**
  2050 Postal Way Dallas (75212) *(G-4793)*

Peacock Alley Dsign Stdio Atln, Dallas *Also called Peacock Alley Inc (G-4793)*

Peacock Plastics Company 903 586-2531
  225 Cash St Jacksonville (75766) *(G-13256)*

Peacock Press LLC 972 272-7764
  538 Shepherd Dr Garland (75042) *(G-7566)*

Peag LLC (PA) **858 683-3634**
  17950 Preston Rd Ste 360 Dallas (75252) *(G-3850)*

Peak Completion Tech Inc 361 668-8383
  159 Enterprise Dr Victoria (77905) *(G-20293)*

Peak Completion Tech Inc 817 529-2030
  309 W 7th St Ste 720 Fort Worth (76102) *(G-6899)*

Peak Completion Tech Inc 325 574-1170
  1802 Mccowen St Snyder (79549) *(G-19001)*

Peak Industrial Services Inc 409 729-0345
  3525 Tanner Ln Nederland (77627) *(G-15758)*

Peak Nanosystems LLC (PA) **469 464-4504**
  8951 Cypress Waters Blvd Coppell (75019) *(G-3434)*

Peak Oilfield Services LLC (HQ) **940 683-1627**
  1502 10th St Bridgeport (76426) *(G-2298)*

Peak Pressure Control LLC 432 563-5800
  12914 W County Road 91 Midland (79707) *(G-15344)*

Pearland Alternator Inc 281 485-8871
  1221 N Main St Pearland (77581) *(G-16589)*

Pearland American Door, Houston *Also called Pearland Industries Inc (G-8391)*

Pearland Arts League 713 304-0672
  3519 Liberty Dr Pearland (77581) *(G-16590)*

Pearland Industries Inc 713 434-9898
  14510 Almeda Rd Houston (77053) *(G-8391)*

Pearland Mri and Imaging Ctr 281 412-3916
  8633 Broadway St Ste 209 Pearland (77584) *(G-16591)*

Pearson Company, San Antonio *Also called Ncs Pearson Inc (G-18340)*

Pearson Education Inc 281 496-0657
  11999 Katy Fwy Houston (77079) *(G-11267)*

Pearson Education Inc 512 989-5300
  400 Center Ridge Dr Ste F Austin (78753) *(G-1404)*

Pearson Education Inc 866 565-4879
  2535 Ridgepoint Dr Austin (78754) *(G-1405)*

Pearson Education Inc 972 870-1048
  6025 Commerce Dr Ste 550 Irving (75063) *(G-13140)*

Pearson's Livestock Equipment, Vernon *Also called Pearsons Inc (G-20229)*

Pearsons Inc 308 645-2231
  122 Wilbarger St Vernon (76384) *(G-20229)*

Peba Oil & Gas Co 940 825-4825
  313 Clay St Nocona (76255) *(G-15870)*

PEC Manufacturing 830 693-7879
  4401 W Innovation Loop Marble Falls (78654) *(G-14749)*

Pechal Cabinets LLC 254 773-4460
  18451 Se H K Dodgen Loop Temple (76501) *(G-19697)*

Pechal Pallets LLC 254 773-4460
  3205 E Adams Ave Temple (76501) *(G-19698)*

Peck & Company 713 526-2590
  98 Dennis St Houston (77006) *(G-11268)*

Pecofacet (us) Inc (HQ) **940 325-2575**
  118 Washington Ave Mineral Wells (76067) *(G-15536)*

Pecofacet US, Mineral Wells *Also called Pecofacet (us) Inc (G-15536)*

Pederson Kronseder LLC 254 386-4790
  1207 S Rice St Hamilton (76531) *(G-8168)*

Pederson Natural Farms Inc 254 386-4790
  1207 S Rice St Hamilton (76531) *(G-8169)*

Pedley Nets Inc 940 328-0448
  4711 S Highway 281 Mineral Wells (76067) *(G-15537)*

Pedraza Hvac Inc 281 970-4834
  11318 Timber Crest Dr Houston (77065) *(G-11269)*

Peeco, Corpus Christi *Also called Process Engineered Eqp Co (G-3597)*

Peek Traffic Corporation 281 453-0200
  5401 N Sam Houston Pkwy W Houston (77086) *(G-11270)*

Peerless Mfg Co 940 566-9029
  1115 Duncan St Denton (76205) *(G-5390)*

Peerless Mfg Co (HQ) **214 357-6181**
  14651 Dallas Pkwy Ste 50 Dallas (75254) *(G-4794)*

Peerless Mfg Co Inc 972 559-6380
  5450 Dakota Ln Denton (76207) *(G-5391)*

Pegasus Automation Inc 972 390-9548
  130 Danbury Ct Allen (75002) *(G-290)*

Pegasus Food 972 961-5200
  1635 Innovation Dr Rockwall (75032) *(G-17558)*

Pegasus Optmztion Managers LLC 979 213-4101
  15320 Highway 105 W # 210 Montgomery (77356) *(G-15638)*

Pegicorn Enterprises LLC 512 821-3300
  9110 Burnet Rd Austin (78758) *(G-1406)*

Pelican Asphalt Refining, Houston *Also called Pelican Refining Company LLC (G-11273)*

Pelican Energy Partners LP (PA) **713 559-7110**
  2050 W Sam Houston Pkwy S # 1550 Houston (77042) *(G-11271)*

Pelican Industrial Inc 832 678-4808
  8550 Westland West Blvd Houston (77041) *(G-11272)*

Pelican Refining Company LLC (PA) **713 877-7777**
  4400 Post Oak Pkwy Ste 26 Houston (77027) *(G-11273)*

Pelican Tank Parts Inc 713 862-5557
  14710 Hathrow Forest Pkwy Houston (77032) *(G-11274)*

Pelican Worldwide, Houston *Also called Pelican Tank Parts Inc (G-11274)*

Pelican Worldwide Incorporated 713 862-5557
  14710 Hathrow Forest Pkwy Houston (77032) *(G-11275)*

Pelletizer Knives (PA) **281 859-4492**
  9703 Telge Rd Houston (77095) *(G-11276)*

Peloton Therapeutics Inc 972 629-4100
  2330 Inwood Rd Ste 226 Dallas (75235) *(G-4795)*

Pem-Tech Inc 281 494-2079
  12144 Dairy Ashford Rd # 200 Sugar Land (77478) *(G-19524)*

Pemco, Houston *Also called Powell Electrical Systems Inc (G-11372)*

Pen Tech Assembly LLC 512 275-0590
  2400 Grand Avenue Pkwy # 103 Austin (78728) *(G-1407)*

Penatek, Odessa *Also called Odessa JPK Investments Ltd (G-16096)*

Penatek LLC 432 368-0888
  6830 Cargo Rd Odessa (79762) *(G-16109)*

Penatek Foundry & Machining 432 368-0888
  6830 E Business 20 Odessa (79762) *(G-16110)*

Pencco Inc (PA) **979 885-0005**
  831 Bartlett Rd Sealy (77474) *(G-18814)*

Pencil Cup Office Products Inc 915 838-0026
  1220 Texas Ave El Paso (79901) *(G-5907)*

Pendleton Woolen Mills Inc 903 581-7742
  909 E Northeast Loop 323 Tyler (75708) *(G-20139)*

Peninsula Steel Inc 956 795-1966
  4119 Free Trade St Ste A Laredo (78045) *(G-13919)*

Peninsula Steel Elm Tree, Laredo *Also called Peninsula Steel Inc (G-13919)*

Penn Machine of Texas, Houston *Also called Texas Pmw Inc (G-12245)*

Penn Virginia Corporation (PA) 713 722-6500
  16285 Park Ten Pl Ste 500 Houston (77084) *(G-11277)*
Penn Virginia Mc Corporation 713 722-6500
  14701 Saint Marys Ln # 275 Houston (77079) *(G-11278)*
Penn Virginia Mc Energy LLC 713 722-6500
  14701 Saint Marys Ln # 275 Houston (77079) *(G-11279)*
Penn Virginia Oil & Gas LP (HQ) 713 722-6500
  16285 Park Ten Pl Ste 500 Houston (77084) *(G-11280)*
Penn Virginia Oil & Gas Corp (HQ) 610 687-8900
  14701 Saint Marys Ln # 275 Houston (77079) *(G-11281)*
Penn Virginia Oil & Gas GP LLC 713 722-6500
  14701 Saint Marys Ln # 275 Houston (77079) *(G-11282)*
Pennar Global Inc 281 362-2707
  21 Waterway Ave Ste 300 The Woodlands (77380) *(G-19900)*
Pennbarry, Plano *Also called Air System Components Inc (G-16781)*
Penntex Industries Inc 817 589-7501
  7620 Flagstone St Fort Worth (76118) *(G-6900)*
Penntex Midstream Partners LLC 214 981-0700
  11931 Wickchester Ln Houston (77043) *(G-11283)*
Pennwell C & E, Houston *Also called Clarion Events Inc (G-9207)*
Penny Record, Bridge City *Also called Bjhr Inc (G-2280)*
Pennzoil-Quaker State Company (HQ) 800 237-8645
  150 N Dairy Ashford Rd Houston (77079) *(G-11284)*
Penspen Corporation (PA) 713 953-7007
  122 N Holderrieth Blvd Tomball (77375) *(G-19996)*
Penta Industries Inc 512 834-2421
  20202 Mashburn St Pflugerville (78660) *(G-16684)*
Pentagon Energy LLC 203 451-8382
  7441 E Orem Dr Houston (77075) *(G-11285)*
Pentair Filtration Solutions, Conroe *Also called Pentair Rsdntial Fltration LLC (G-3347)*
Pentair Rsdntial Fltration LLC 936 525-2310
  4301 W Davis St Conroe (77304) *(G-3347)*
Pentair Valves & Controls, Stafford *Also called Emerson Automation Solutions (G-19310)*
Pentair Valves & Controls LLC (HQ) 713 986-4665
  10707 Clay Rd Ste 200 Houston (77041) *(G-11286)*
People News Papers, Dallas *Also called City Newspapers Management LLC (G-4123)*
Peopleadmin (HQ) 877 637-5800
  805 Las Cimas Pkwy # 400 Austin (78746) *(G-1408)*
Peopleanswers, Dallas *Also called Infor (us) LLC (G-4496)*
Pepco Promotional Products, Lane City *Also called Perma Pom Partnership Ltd (G-13851)*
Pepper Springs Spice Co, Wylie *Also called Carmies Kitchen Inc (G-20930)*
Pepperidge Farm Incorporated 713 385-2010
  1303 Rosemeadow Houston (77094) *(G-11287)*
Pepsi Beverages Company 210 661-5311
  6100 Ne Loop 410 San Antonio (78218) *(G-18369)*
Pepsi Bottling Company 210 662-3418
  6100 Ne Loop 410 San Antonio (78218) *(G-18370)*
Pepsi Bottling Group 214 324-8500
  4532 Interstate 30 Mesquite (75150) *(G-15069)*
Pepsi Cola Bottling Co Laredo 956 722-9934
  4700 Santa Maria Ave Laredo (78041) *(G-13920)*
Pepsi Cola Sales & Dist 909 472-4060
  735 E Trinity Blvd # 100 Grand Prairie (75050) *(G-7945)*
Pepsi Logistics Company Inc 972 963-1920
  5600 Headquarters Dr Plano (75024) *(G-16967)*
Pepsi-Cola, Laredo *Also called Pepsi Cola Bottling Co Laredo (G-13920)*
Pepsi-Cola, Corpus Christi *Also called Oneta Company (G-3585)*
Pepsi-Cola Bottling Group 254 953-7433
  612 N Twin Creek Dr Killeen (76543) *(G-13616)*
Pepsi-Cola Btlg Crpus Chrsti V 361 853-0123
  1401 S Padre Island Dr Corpus Christi (78416) *(G-3590)*
Pepsi-Cola Metro Btlg Co Inc 409 842-2111
  2750 W Cardinal Dr Beaumont (77705) *(G-1939)*
Pepsi-Cola Metro Btlg Co Inc 817 640-4445
  1000 113th St Arlington (76011) *(G-750)*
Pepsi-Cola Metro Btlg Co Inc 210 661-5311
  6100 Ne Loop 410 San Antonio (78218) *(G-18371)*
Pepsi-Cola Metro Btlg Co Inc 361 575-2661
  3811 E Rio Grande St Victoria (77901) *(G-20294)*
Pepsi-Cola Metro Btlg Co Inc 214 324-8500
  4532 Us Highway 67 Mesquite (75150) *(G-15070)*
Pepsi-Cola Metro Btlg Co Inc 979 779-6324
  1801 Shiloh Ave Bryan (77803) *(G-2497)*
Pepsi-Cola Metro Btlg Co Inc 806 745-7711
  131 Se Loop 289 Lubbock (79404) *(G-14460)*
Pepsi-Cola Metro Btlg Co Inc 972 801-1730
  7701 Legacy Dr Plano (75024) *(G-16968)*
Pepsi-Cola Metro Btlg Co Inc 713 645-4111
  9300 La Porte Fwy Houston (77017) *(G-11288)*
Pepsi-Cola Metro Btlg Co Inc 817 625-4101
  5201 Blue Mound Rd Fort Worth (76106) *(G-6901)*
Pepsi-Cola Metro Btlg Co Inc 936 522-4400
  222 N Loop 336 E Conroe (77301) *(G-3348)*
Pepsi-Cola Metro Btlg Co Inc 806 372-8717
  8115 E Amarillo Blvd Amarillo (79107) *(G-452)*
Pepsi-Cola Metro Btlg Co Inc 979 836-3755
  Geers Rd Brenham (77833) *(G-2268)*
Pepsi-Cola Metro Btlg Co Inc 361 798-3651
  1415 Us Highway 90a E Hallettsville (77964) *(G-8124)*

Pepsi-Cola Metro Btlg Co Inc 915 590-6965
  10841 Pellicano Dr El Paso (79935) *(G-5908)*
Pepsi-Cola Metro Btlg Co Inc 903 892-3030
  4817 Marshall St Sherman (75090) *(G-18926)*
Pepsi-Cola Sales and Dist Inc 817 640-4445
  1000 113th St Arlington (76011) *(G-751)*
Pepsico, Wharton *Also called Dr Pepper/Seven Up Inc (G-20699)*
Pepsico, Grand Prairie *Also called Pepsi Cola Sales & Dist (G-7945)*
Pepsico, San Angelo *Also called Ab-Tex Beverage Ltd (G-17769)*
Pepsico, Victoria *Also called Pepsi-Cola Metro Btlg Co Inc (G-20294)*
Pepsico, Killeen *Also called Pepsi-Cola Bottling Group (G-13616)*
Pepsico, Houston *Also called Pepsi-Cola Metro Btlg Co Inc (G-11288)*
Pepsico, Fort Worth *Also called Pepsi-Cola Metro Btlg Co Inc (G-6901)*
Pepsico, Corpus Christi *Also called P-Americas LLC (G-3588)*
Pepsico, Mesquite *Also called Pepsi Bottling Group (G-15069)*
Pepsico, Texarkana *Also called P-Americas LLC (G-19770)*
Pepsico, Brenham *Also called Pepsi-Cola Metro Btlg Co Inc (G-2268)*
Pepsico, Hallettsville *Also called Pepsi-Cola Metro Btlg Co Inc (G-8124)*
Pepsico, Sherman *Also called Pepsi-Cola Metro Btlg Co Inc (G-18926)*
Pepsico Inc 972 963-1000
  5600 Headquarters Dr Plano (75024) *(G-16969)*
Pepsico Inc 972 334-4140
  7701 Legacy Dr Plano (75024) *(G-16970)*
Pepsico Americas Foods, Plano *Also called Frito-Lay North America Inc (G-16874)*
Perales Group Ventures Inc (PA) 830 780-3336
  506 W 3rd St Karnes City (78118) *(G-13346)*
Perception Software Inc 512 593-6996
  8310 N Capital Of Tx Hwy Austin (78731) *(G-1409)*
Percomonline Incorporated 325 480-2617
  149 N Willis St Ste 10 Abilene (79603) *(G-64)*
Perdue Acoustic, Amarillo *Also called Jayvic Inc (G-442)*
Perdure Petroleum LLC 281 668-8488
  1101 Central Expy S # 150 Allen (75013) *(G-291)*
Peregrine Petroleum LLC (PA) 214 231-6800
  2101 Cedar Springs Rd Dallas (75201) *(G-4796)*
Peregrine Petroleum LLC 713 630-8965
  2929 Allen Pkwy Ste 1520 Houston (77019) *(G-11289)*
Peregrine Petroleum Group, Houston *Also called Peregrine Petroleum LLC (G-11289)*
Peregrine Stimulation Svcs LLC 713 201-6787
  30510 Cedar Woods St Fulshear (77441) *(G-7329)*
Perennial Design LLC 512 387-1582
  2105 Donley Dr Ste 100 Austin (78758) *(G-1410)*
Perfect Ink Inc 281 376-4781
  17126 Stuebner Airline Rd Spring (77379) *(G-19157)*
Perfect Performance Pdts LLC 817 244-6898
  2501 Ludelle St Fort Worth (76105) *(G-6902)*
Perfect Quilt, Houston *Also called Bronx Industries Inc (G-8994)*
Perfect Surface of Austin (PA) 512 339-9937
  6800 West Gate Blvd # 132 Austin (78745) *(G-1411)*
Perfect Weather Htg & Coolg, El Paso *Also called S & M Aire LLC (G-5951)*
Perfect Windows Inc 817 277-0014
  2400c Roosevelt Dr Ste C Arlington (76016) *(G-752)*
Perfectfitmeals LLC (PA) 713 868-5300
  10370 Richmond Ave Ste 13 Houston (77042) *(G-11290)*
Perfection Wholesale Supply, Houston *Also called Fireplace Installers Inc (G-9789)*
Perfomix LLC 713 893-8310
  1 Greenway Plz Ste 930 Bellaire (77401) *(G-2001)*
Performance Companies LP 214 665-1000
  2929 N Stemmons Fwy Dallas (75247) *(G-4797)*
Performance Elastomers Inc 817 293-7503
  1300 Forum Way S Ste G Fort Worth (76140) *(G-6903)*
Performance Gear Hdqtr LLC 281 402-6816
  17689 Telge Rd Cypress (77429) *(G-3811)*
Performance Label Company, Lubbock *Also called Sides Printing Company Inc (G-14479)*
Performance Label Company 806 763-1663
  311 E 40th St Lubbock (79404) *(G-14461)*
Performance Metal Works Inc 903 967-2622
  Hwy 37 Quitman Quitman (75783) *(G-17228)*
Performance Pipe, Brownwood *Also called Chevron Phillips Chem Co LP (G-2427)*
Performance Pop, Dallas *Also called Performance Companies LP (G-4797)*
Performance Pressure Pumping 409 980-8188
  5320 Gorman Rd Beaumont (77705) *(G-1940)*
Performance Specialty Service, Dallas *Also called Barron Manufacturing Inc (G-4007)*
Performax Custom Accessories, Wylie *Also called Performax Custom Trailers (G-20942)*
Performax Custom Trailers 972 442-3527
  1825 E Fm 544 Wylie (75098) *(G-20942)*
Pergan 903 938-5141
  710 Bussey Rd Marshall (75670) *(G-14797)*
Perigee Health, The Colony *Also called Apex Custom Software Inc (G-19809)*
Periscope Holdings, Austin *Also called Periscope Intermediate Corp (G-1412)*
Periscope Intermediate Corp 512 717-0684
  5000 Plz On The Lk # 100 Austin (78746) *(G-1412)*
Peritus Inc 817 726-4626
  222 Las Colinas Blvd W # 745 Irving (75039) *(G-13141)*
Perkup Coffees LLC 281 445-6744
  11600 Big John St Houston (77038) *(G-11291)*

Perma Pom Partnership Ltd 979 532-3106
 9611 S State Hwy 60 Lane City (77453) *(G-13851)*

Perma Tone, Houston *Also called Corev America Inc (G-9319)*

Perma-Pier Fndation Repr Texas, Arlington *Also called Construct Capital LLC (G-645)*

Perma-Pier Foundation Repair O, Houston *Also called Construct Capital LLC (G-9278)*

Perma-Pier Foundation Repair O, San Antonio *Also called Construct Capital LLC (G-18024)*

Permian Anchors Inc 432 563-0205
 4915 S County Road 1303 Odessa (79765) *(G-16111)*

Permian Basin Derrick Svcs LP 432 332-2315
 1532 S Redondo Ave Odessa (79763) *(G-16112)*

Permian Basin Eqp & Sup LLC 432 563-1044
 4 Casa Loma Odessa (79765) *(G-16113)*

Permian Basin Instruments Inc 432 687-4445
 5014 Oak Bend Cir Denton (76208) *(G-5392)*

Permian Basin Joint Ventr LLC 713 296-6000
 2000 Post Oak Blvd B Houston (77056) *(G-11292)*

Permian Basin Materials LLC (PA) **432 614-6201**
 4001 E 42nd St Ste 100 Odessa (79762) *(G-16114)*

Permian Bsin Hmes Land Mag LLC 737 256-0799
 865 Power Dr Odessa (79761) *(G-16115)*

Permian Enterprises Ltd 432 332-0903
 2121 W Murphy St Odessa (79763) *(G-16116)*

Permian H2o Solutions LLC (PA) **432 214-4520**
 875 Central Dr Ste 7a Odessa (79761) *(G-16117)*

Permian Limestone 254 547-8207
 Fm 2808 Kempner (76539) *(G-13487)*

Permian Ndt Inc 432 563-3638
 14950 Heathrow Forest Pkw Houston (77032) *(G-11293)*

Permian Petroleum Services Inc 432 682-0434
 4601 S State Highway 349 Midland (79706) *(G-15345)*

Permian Power Tong Inc 432 550-7386
 4512 E Us Highway 158 Gardendale (79758) *(G-7421)*

Permian Sign Co Inc 432 563-3072
 4111 S County Road 1276 Midland (79706) *(G-15346)*

Permian Tank & Mfg Inc 432 550-7317
 8800 Nw Loop 338 Odessa (79764) *(G-16118)*

Permian Tank & Mfg Inc (PA) **432 580-1050**
 2701 W Interstate 20 Odessa (79766) *(G-16119)*

Permian Tank & Mfg Inc 903 984-2516
 3405 S Henderson Blvd Kilgore (75662) *(G-13581)*

Permin Tanks, Troy *Also called Lide Industries LLC (G-20030)*

Permocast Corporation 254 778-5216
 3110 Center St Temple (76504) *(G-19699)*

Peroxychem LLC 281 474-4171
 12000 Bay Area Blvd Pasadena (77507) *(G-16495)*

Perry Slingsby Systems Inc 561 743-7000
 10642 W Little York Rd Houston (77041) *(G-11294)*

Perryman Group Inc (PA) **254 751-9595**
 510 N Vly Mills Dr # 300 Waco (76710) *(G-20445)*

Perryton Feeders LLC 806 435-5466
 13210 Highway 70 Perryton (79070) *(G-16644)*

Personal Advisor, The, Austin *Also called Viserv Inc (G-1637)*

Personalized Printing Inc 903 886-7173
 1300 Bonham St Commerce (75428) *(G-3245)*

Pesa Labeling Systems Inc 956 544-3323
 4401 Paredes Line Rd Brownsville (78526) *(G-2392)*

Pestroutes Opco LLC 404 800-7378
 4500 Eldorado Pkwy Ste 3 McKinney (75070) *(G-14963)*

Petco, Breckenridge *Also called B B L Ltd (G-2220)*

Petco Petroleum Corporation 806 669-3947
 Se Of City Pampa (79065) *(G-16334)*

Pete Sanchez, Houston *Also called Budget Ready Mix LLC (G-9010)*

Peter Paul Petroleum Company 713 209-1100
 9805 Katy Fwy Ste 500 Houston (77024) *(G-11295)*

Petersen Aluminum Corporation 903 581-6228
 10551 Pac Rd Tyler (75707) *(G-20140)*

Peterson Beckner Inds Inc 281 872-1806
 1310 Spears Rd Houston (77067) *(G-11296)*

Peterson Construction 254 227-0738
 2682 Highway 31 Axtell (76624) *(G-1718)*

Peterson Drilling and Tstg Inc (PA) **806 342-4911**
 1700 Se 22nd Ave Amarillo (79103) *(G-453)*

Petex, Breckenridge *Also called Petroleum Exploration Co Ltd (G-2233)*

Pethonesty LLC 909 435-6574
 600 Congress Ave Fl 14 Austin (78701) *(G-1413)*

Petmate Holdings Co (PA) **817 467-5116**
 2300 E Randol Mill Rd Arlington (76011) *(G-753)*

Petnair Valves & Controls 713 986-8468
 10707 Clay Rd Ste 200 Houston (77041) *(G-11297)*

PETnet Houston LLC 713 791-1734
 1028 Dreyfus St Houston (77030) *(G-11298)*

Petra Land LLC 832 791-5495
 10200 Grogans Mill Rd # 125 The Woodlands (77380) *(G-19901)*

Petra Oil Company Inc 888 738-7261
 11085 Regency Green Dr Cypress (77429) *(G-3812)*

Petrasoft Counsulting 832 448-5600
 738 Highway 6 S Houston (77079) *(G-11299)*

Petro Chem Industries Inc 713 645-5024
 5629 Cheswood St Houston (77087) *(G-11300)*

Petro Harvester Oper Co LLC (HQ) **214 618-7600**
 5005 Lyndon B Johnson Fwy # 700 Dallas (75244) *(G-4798)*

Petro Land Group Inc 903 595-4293
 3400 G E Dr Tyler (75701) *(G-20141)*

Petro Mechanical Services LLC 800 727-1398
 2451 N Fm 1936 Odessa (79763) *(G-16120)*

Petro Mechanical Supply, Odessa *Also called Petro Mechanical Services LLC (G-16120)*

Petro-Hunt LLC 903 629-3205
 6524 Fm 69 Como (75431) *(G-3249)*

Petro-Hunt LLC (HQ) **214 880-8400**
 2101 Cedar Springs Rd # 60 Dallas (75201) *(G-4799)*

Petro-Tech Environmental LLC 713 926-9986
 8502 Cypress St Bldg 3 Houston (77012) *(G-11301)*

Petrobal Omega 1 LLC 972 284-5120
 6191 N State Highway 161 Irving (75038) *(G-13142)*

Petrochem Energy LLC 713 234-7814
 13914 Abbey Ln Sugar Land (77498) *(G-19525)*

Petrochem Field Services Inc 281 441-2550
 2429 Wilson Rd Humble (77396) *(G-12792)*

Petrofuels Quality Mktg LP 409 722-6880
 2300 Highway 365 Ste 400 Nederland (77627) *(G-15759)*

Petroh2o Recovery LLC 817 778-8413
 2225 W Southlake Blvd Southlake (76092) *(G-19081)*

Petrohab Llc (PA) **281 407-3800**
 4930 Dacoma St Ste G Houston (77092) *(G-11302)*

Petrohawk Energy Corporation (HQ) **713 961-8500**
 1360 Post Oak Blvd Ste 15 Houston (77056) *(G-11303)*

Petrolegacy Energy II LLC 512 735-9000
 6101 W Courtyard Dr # 212 Austin (78730) *(G-1414)*

Petroleum Analyzer Company LP (PA) **281 940-1803**
 8824 Fallbrook Dr Houston (77064) *(G-11304)*

Petroleum College Intl 361 575-4882
 3302 N Ben Wilson St Victoria (77901) *(G-20295)*

Petroleum Elastomers Inc 281 591-1500
 757 Kenrick Dr Ste 124 Houston (77060) *(G-11305)*

Petroleum Engineers Intl (HQ) **337 984-2603**
 1030 Regional Park Dr Houston (77060) *(G-11306)*

Petroleum Exploration Co Ltd 254 559-5453
 220 W Elm St Breckenridge (76424) *(G-2233)*

Petroleum Financial Inc 817 339-1075
 100 Throckmorton St # 400 Fort Worth (76102) *(G-6904)*

Petroleum Geo-Services, Houston *Also called Pgs Americas Inc (G-11317)*

Petroleum Geo-Services Inc (HQ) **281 509-8000**
 15375 Memorial Dr Ste 100 Houston (77079) *(G-11307)*

Petroleum Industry Inspectors 713 377-2637
 1817 Tidwell Ln Houston (77093) *(G-11308)*

Petroleum Listing Service, Houston *Also called Pls Inc (G-11349)*

Petroleum Machinery, Houston *Also called Petroluem Machinery Inc (G-11309)*

Petroleum Network Solutions, Arlington *Also called Tomdao Llc (G-800)*

Petroleum Products & Svcs Inc (PA) **281 448-1000**
 23518 Coons Rd Tomball (77375) *(G-19997)*

Petrolima LLC 432 695-9989
 203 W Wall St Ste 1100 Midland (79701) *(G-15347)*

Petroluem Machinery Inc 713 697-4999
 6005 N Shepherd Dr Ste H2 Houston (77091) *(G-11309)*

Petron Industries Inc (HQ) **713 693-8700**
 7701 W Little York Rd Houston (77040) *(G-11310)*

Petronash Americas LLC (HQ) **281 566-6600**
 12633 Reed Rd Sugar Land (77478) *(G-19526)*

Petroplex Acidizing Inc (PA) **432 563-1200**
 3716 S Canny Rd S 1305 1305 S Midland (79705) *(G-15348)*

Petroplex Cabinets Inc 432 333-2025
 2710 Henderson Ave Odessa (79764) *(G-16121)*

Petroplex Energy Inc 432 687-2222
 3011 Garden City Hwy Midland (79701) *(G-15349)*

Petroplex Pipe & Cnstr Inc (PA) **432 697-4540**
 2802 W County Road 111 Midland (79706) *(G-15350)*

Petrosantander Colombia, Houston *Also called Petrosantander Inc (G-11311)*

Petrosantander Inc (PA) **713 784-8700**
 6363 Woodway Dr Ste 350 Houston (77057) *(G-11311)*

Petrosaudi Oil Services, Houston *Also called Procurement Services Del Inc (G-11434)*

Petrosaurus Inc 210 624-2750
 20905 State Highway 16 S Von Ormy (78073) *(G-20348)*

Petroskills, Katy *Also called Oil & Gas Consultants Intl Inc (G-13374)*

Petrostar Services LLC 903 247-6390
 1740 Callahan Rd Longview (75602) *(G-14289)*

Petrotel Inc (PA) **972 473-2767**
 5240 Tennyson Pkwy # 207 Plano (75024) *(G-16971)*

Petrotel USA, Plano *Also called Petrotel Inc (G-16971)*

Petrotrim Services LLC 281 821-2111
 1881 Treble Dr Humble (77338) *(G-12793)*

Petrovalve, Houston *Also called Turbeco Inc (G-12407)*

Petrovisor, Houston *Also called Datagration Solutions Inc (G-9405)*

Petrustech Oil & Gas LLC (PA) **281 781-0020**
 5500 N Sam Houston Pkwy W Houston (77086) *(G-11312)*

Pettigrews Custom Iron & Mtls 214 637-1494
 7301 Hines Pl Dallas (75235) *(G-4800)*

Peyton Salas & Mendoza LLC 512 784-5875
 10101 Southwest Fwy # 400 Houston (77074) *(G-11313)*

Pfi, Tomball *Also called Precision Fluorocarbon Inc (G-20001)*

Pfi Molding Inc...713 946-3300
8777 Tallyho Rd Ste 200 Houston (77061) *(G-11314)*

Pfizer Inc...817 293-8887
6601 Will Rogers Blvd A Fort Worth (76140) *(G-6905)*

Pfizer Inc...212 733-2323
1301 Solana Blvd Ste 2330 Roanoke (76262) *(G-17493)*

Pfizer Inc...817 491-8400
7 Village Trl Roanoke (76262) *(G-17494)*

Pfj, Houston *Also called Pineforest Jewelry Inc (G-11333)*

Pfm LLC (PA)..**713 664-7767**
3200 Southwest Fwy # 3300 Houston (77027) *(G-11315)*

Pft Systems, Deer Park *Also called Fd-Thru Power Systems Cnnctors (G-5273)*

Pgi International Ltd..713 466-0056
16101 Vallen Dr Houston (77041) *(G-11316)*

Pgs Americas, Houston *Also called Petroleum Geo-Services Inc (G-11307)*

Pgs Americas Inc...512 670-8700
12555 Harris Branch Pkwy Manor (78653) *(G-14648)*

Pgs Americas Inc (HQ).....................................**281 509-8000**
15375 Memorial Dr Ste 100 Houston (77079) *(G-11317)*

Pgs Finance Inc..281 509-8000
15150 Memorial Dr Houston (77079) *(G-11318)*

Pgs Imaging Inc..281 509-8000
15375 Memorial Dr Ste 100 Houston (77079) *(G-11319)*

Pgs Onshore, Houston *Also called Geokinetics Acquisition Co (G-9934)*

Pharmscript LLC...281 492-7220
1718 Fry Rd Ste 125 Houston (77084) *(G-11320)*

Pharos Marine Autmtc Pwr Inc (HQ).................**713 228-5208**
10810 W Little York Rd Houston (77041) *(G-11321)*

Phase 1 Prototypes LLC....................................972 406-9988
10580 Newkirk St Ste 301 Dallas (75220) *(G-4801)*

Phase Dynamics Inc..972 680-1550
1251 Columbia Dr Richardson (75081) *(G-17372)*

Phase Electric Motors Inc.................................972 291-9221
1105 S Cedar Hill Rd Cedar Hill (75104) *(G-2950)*

Phaseware Inc...214 432-9043
1700 Redbud Blvd Ste 120 McKinney (75069) *(G-14964)*

Phazr Inc...972 693-7829
8 Prestige Cir Ste 104 Allen (75002) *(G-292)*

PHD Crane Systems, Haslet *Also called Product Handling Design Inc (G-8222)*

PHD Energy Inc...800 318-3639
6026 Ronchamps Dr Round Rock (78681) *(G-17679)*

Pheasant Rubber Company Inc..........................432 367-5137
2426 W 40th St Odessa (79764) *(G-16122)*

Phil Dollar Oilfield Services..............................806 435-3373
2025 W Hwy 15 Perryton (79070) *(G-16645)*

Philadelphia Gear, Houston *Also called Timken Gears & Services Inc (G-12292)*

Philbo Enterprises Inc.......................................214 747-7018
1201 S Ervay St Dallas (75215) *(G-4802)*

Philco Tubing Testers, Cedar Park *Also called Triple D Services LLC (G-2989)*

Philip Morris USA Inc..210 530-7100
84 Ne Loop 410 San Antonio (78216) *(G-18372)*

Philips Consumer Electronic Co........................915 298-4111
12430 Mercantile Ave El Paso (79928) *(G-5909)*

Philips Lighting, El Paso *Also called Philips North America LLC (G-5910)*

Philips Lighting, Dallas *Also called Signify North America Corp (G-4961)*

Philips North America LLC................................956 541-1224
1000 Billy Mitchell Blvd Brownsville (78521) *(G-2393)*

Philips North America LLC................................915 298-4111
12430 Mercantile Ave El Paso (79928) *(G-5910)*

Philips North America LLC................................800 526-2731
2828 Trade Ctr Ste 130 Carrollton (75007) *(G-2881)*

Phillip E Mosley & Associates..........................281 496-1249
12121 Wickchester Ln # 300 Houston (77079) *(G-11322)*

Phillip Townsend Assoc Inc (PA)......................**281 873-8733**
509 N Sam Houston Pkwy E # 600 Houston (77060) *(G-11323)*

Phillips 66 (PA)...**281 293-6600**
2331 Citywest Blvd Houston (77042) *(G-11324)*

Phillips 66 Carrier LLC......................................855 283-9237
3010 Briarpark Dr Houston (77042) *(G-11325)*

Phillips 66 Partners LP (HQ)............................855 283-9237
2331 Citywest Blvd Houston (77042) *(G-11326)*

Phillips Consumer Electronics, El Paso *Also called Philips Consumer Electronic Co (G-5909)*

Phillips Fabrication Inc.....................................432 264-6600
1305 E Airpark Dr Big Spring (79720) *(G-2093)*

Phillips Iron Works Inc......................................337 364-2337
2903 Gano St Houston (77009) *(G-11327)*

Phillips Signs, Grand Prairie *Also called Richard Phillips Inc (G-7966)*

Phillips Smika Plyprpylene LLC (PA)................**832 813-4100**
10001 Six Pines Dr The Woodlands (77380) *(G-19902)*

Phillys, Lubbock *Also called World of Jeans & Tops (G-14514)*

Phlur Inc (PA)...**888 771-9434**
2400 E Cesar Chavez St Austin (78702) *(G-1415)*

Phoeben Inc..832 486-9500
10601 S Sam Huston Pkwy W Houston (77071) *(G-11328)*

Phoenix Construction Services, Alvin *Also called Phoenix Millwork LLC (G-377)*

Phoenix EMB & Screen Prtg, Edinburg *Also called Rley Enterprises Inc (G-5599)*

Phoenix Fund Inc..210 828-4373
8626 Tesoro Dr Ste 801 San Antonio (78217) *(G-18373)*

Phoenix Hydrocarbons Operating.....................936 258-2646
1252 Fm 1413 Dayton (77535) *(G-5234)*

Phoenix Metalworks LP....................................979 992-3909
1135 Dunlavy Rd Cat Spring (78933) *(G-2932)*

Phoenix Mfg Inc..214 544-7507
2880 Country Club Rd Allen (75002) *(G-293)*

Phoenix Millwork LLC......................................281 388-2211
1901 E House St Alvin (77511) *(G-377)*

Phoenix Mobile Air Inc.....................................972 418-6444
2320 Apollo Cir Carrollton (75006) *(G-2791)*

Phoenix Plastics LP...936 760-2311
5400 Jefferson Chem Rd Conroe (77301) *(G-3349)*

Phoenix Production Tech, Corpus Christi *Also called Polk Production Tech Inc (G-3593)*

Phoenix Services LLC (PA)..............................**713 952-5533**
10260 Westheimer Rd # 460 Houston (77042) *(G-11329)*

Phoenix Technology Svcs USA (HQ).................**713 337-0600**
1805 Brittmoore Rd Houston (77043) *(G-11330)*

Photo Etch, Fort Worth *Also called Airco Industries, Inc. (G-6358)*

Photodigm Inc...972 235-7584
1155 E Collins Blvd # 20 Richardson (75081) *(G-17373)*

Photonic Inc..956 722-3326
1907 Aduanales Ln Laredo (78041) *(G-13921)*

Photronics Inc...469 675-8520
601 Millenium Dr Allen (75013) *(G-294)*

Photronics Texas Allen Inc................................972 889-6275
601 Millenium Dr Allen (75013) *(G-295)*

Php Systems & Design, Houston *Also called Portable Pipe Hangers Inc (G-11366)*

Phunware Inc...512 693-4199
7800 Shoal Creek Blvd 230s Austin (78757) *(G-1416)*

Phx Grp - Txas Div Ttanium Fab, Houston *Also called Titanium Fabrication Corp (G-12300)*

Physicians Wellness Group Inc.........................817 703-2102
1431 Greenway Dr Ste 800 Irving (75038) *(G-13143)*

Phyto-Source LP...281 474-7500
12502 Bay Area Blvd Pasadena (77507) *(G-16496)*

Phyton Biotech LLC..817 900-4050
3909 Hulen St Fort Worth (76107) *(G-6906)*

PI Holdings Inc...903 586-2408
1613 N Bolton St Jacksonville (75766) *(G-13257)*

PI Tape Texas LLC (PA)...................................**903 266-9204**
10235 Robinson Dr Tyler (75703) *(G-20142)*

Pi-Co Prcision Fabrication Inc..........................512 759-1026
223 Tradesmen Dr Hutto (78634) *(G-12883)*

Pic Texas, Brenham *Also called P I Components Corp (G-2267)*

Picco Coatings Co..281 447-8877
20738 Stokes Rd Waller (77484) *(G-20506)*

Pick Instrument Products Co.............................713 672-1686
102 Eastway St Galena Park (77547) *(G-7381)*

Pick-A-Prof, Austin *Also called Myedu Corporation (G-1359)*

Pickens Company Inc..214 369-7471
8111 Preston Rd Ste 800 Dallas (75225) *(G-4803)*

Pickens Energy Corporation.............................214 503-1271
10100 N Cntl Expy Ste 200 Dallas (75231) *(G-4804)*

Pickle Juice Company......................................972 755-0289
206 S Town East Blvd Mesquite (75149) *(G-15071)*

Pickle Juice Sport, Mesquite *Also called Pickle Juice Company (G-15071)*

Pickup Outfitters, Waco *Also called J&J Weaver Co (G-20419)*

Pico Sales and Dist LLC..................................800 591-2796
320 N Glenwood Blvd Tyler (75702) *(G-20143)*

Pico Technology, Tyler *Also called Pico Sales and Dist LLC (G-20143)*

Pictsweet Company..210 833-9618
4231 Profit St Ste C San Antonio (78219) *(G-18374)*

Pid Group Inc..936 699-4743
400 Southpark Dr Lufkin (75904) *(G-14544)*

Pied Piper Animal Trap, Weatherford *Also called Pipers Welding Service Inc (G-20609)*

Piedra Operating LLC (PA)..............................**432 685-9005**
400 W Illinois Ave # 1070 Midland (79701) *(G-15351)*

Piedras Negras Tortilla Fctry............................830 773-6706
340 N Pierce St Eagle Pass (78852) *(G-5553)*

Pier 19 Marine Field...409 763-5423
19 Pier Galveston (77550) *(G-7405)*

Pier 19 Marine Fuel, Galveston *Also called Pier 19 Marine Field (G-7405)*

Pier 99, Corpus Christi *Also called Tandem Marketing Services Inc (G-3635)*

Pierce Arrow Inc...940 538-5643
549 Us Highway 287 S Henrietta (76365) *(G-8282)*

Pierce Construction Inc (PA)............................**903 678-3748**
4324 State Hwy 149 Beckville (75631) *(G-1972)*

Pierce Corporation (PA)...................................**541 998-0300**
3407 Steen St San Antonio (78219) *(G-18375)*

Pierce Manufacturing Company, San Antonio *Also called Pierce Corporation (G-18375)*

Pierce Packaging Co..815 636-5656
9020 Jackrabbit Rd Houston (77095) *(G-11331)*

Pierce Pump Company, Dallas *Also called Fcx Performance Inc (G-4357)*

Pierce Sales, Henrietta *Also called Pierce Arrow Inc (G-8282)*

Pieter Andries Jewelries, Southlake *Also called H P Creations (G-19073)*

Pietro Fiorenpini...832 299-6075
10077 Grogans Mill Rd # 275 Spring (77380) *(G-19240)*

Pigs Unlimited Intl Inc 281 351-2749
  15719 Treichel Rd Tomball (77377) *(G-19998)*

Pileworks LLC 936 372-9760
  24430 Fm 1488 Rd Ste A Magnolia (77355) *(G-14620)*

Pilgrim's Pride Chicken Operat, Center *Also called Pilgrims Pride Corporation (G-3004)*

Pilgrim's Pride Rendering/By-P, Mount Pleasant *Also called Pilgrims Pride Corporation (G-15658)*

Pilgrims Pride Corporation 936 598-3356
  1102 Logansport St Center (75935) *(G-3004)*

Pilgrims Pride Corporation 903 575-1000
  1000 S Otyson St Mt Pleasant (75455) *(G-15667)*

Pilgrims Pride Corporation 936 564-3306
  928 Martin Luther King Jr Nacogdoches (75961) *(G-15709)*

Pilgrims Pride Corporation 254 412-5800
  2500 E Lake Shore Dr Waco (76705) *(G-20446)*

Pilgrims Pride Corporation 936 560-3901
  Fm 1275 S Nacogdoches (75963) *(G-15710)*

Pilgrims Pride Corporation 936 639-1174
  1800 W Frank Ave Lufkin (75904) *(G-14545)*

Pilgrims Pride Corporation 214 565-8600
  1900 S Central Expy Dallas (75215) *(G-4805)*

Pilgrims Pride Corporation 903 575-3540
  1107 Monticello Rd Mount Pleasant (75455) *(G-15657)*

Pilgrims Pride Corporation 936 248-5600
  Hwy 59 Tenaha (75974) *(G-19724)*

Pilgrims Pride Corporation 919 774-7333
  110 S Texas St Pittsburg (75686) *(G-16748)*

Pilgrims Pride Corporation 903 575-3403
  1030 Pilgrim St Mount Pleasant (75455) *(G-15658)*

Pilgrims Pride Corporation 903 434-1000
  4840 Us Highway 271 N Pittsburg (75686) *(G-16749)*

Pilgrims Pride Corporation 210 633-2412
  11850 Center Rd Frzr 4 4 Freezer San Antonio (78223) *(G-18376)*

Pilgrims Pride Corporation 903 575-3748
  1210 Pilgrim St Mount Pleasant (75455) *(G-15659)*

Pilgrims Pride Prpred Fods Div, Nacogdoches *Also called Pilgrims Pride Corporation (G-15709)*

Pilgrims Pride Prpred Fods Div, Waco *Also called Pilgrims Pride Corporation (G-20446)*

Pilot Chemical Company Ohio 936 291-2424
  37 Fm 2793 Rd Huntsville (77340) *(G-12822)*

Pilot Logistic Services, Fort Worth *Also called Pilot Thomas Logistics LLC (G-6908)*

Pilot Plastics LLC 800 918-6765
  4360 Western Center Blvd Fort Worth (76137) *(G-6907)*

Pilot Point Wood Design, Pilot Point *Also called Johnnys Cabinet Shop Inc (G-16725)*

Pilot Thomas Logistics LLC (HQ) 817 877-8300
  201 N Rupert St Ste 101 Fort Worth (76107) *(G-6908)*

Pilot Thomas Logistics LLC 432 741-1514
  7316 S County Road 1270 Midland (79706) *(G-15352)*

Pin Oak Caregivers LLC 713 301-3481
  4811 Mcdermed Dr Houston (77035) *(G-11332)*

Pinchback Industrial Inc 409 860-1964
  695 Pinchback Rd Beaumont (77707) *(G-1941)*

Pine Street Salvage Co (PA) 325 677-8831
  3833 Pine St Abilene (79601) *(G-65)*

Pine Street Salvage Co 806 372-5678
  95 Browning St Amarillo (79104) *(G-454)*

Pineforest Jewelry Inc 713 451-1321
  1141 Uvalde Rd Houston (77015) *(G-11333)*

Piney Forest Products LLC 936 275-9751
  201 Farm Market 3451 San Augustine (75972) *(G-18652)*

Pinnacle Frames & Accents, Austin *Also called Nielsen & Bainbridge LLC (G-1367)*

Pinnacle Gas Treating LLC 903 928-1200
  1760 An County Road 2608 Tennessee Colony (75861) *(G-19726)*

Pinnacle Graphics Inc 972 418-1202
  4098 Lindbergh Dr Ste A Addison (75001) *(G-155)*

Pinner Wire & Cable Inc 972 494-3333
  932 N Shiloh Rd Garland (75042) *(G-7567)*

Pinnergy Ltd 830 569-1997
  1012 W Oaklawn Rd Unit A Pleasanton (78064) *(G-17071)*

Pinnergy Ltd 903 693-6300
  1156 Hills Lake Rd Carthage (75633) *(G-2916)*

Pinnergy Ltd 817 389-2105
  9913 N Highway 171 Godley (76044) *(G-7739)*

Pinnergy Ltd (PA) 512 343-8880
  111 Congress Ave Ste 2020 Austin (78701) *(G-1417)*

Pinnergy Ltd 903 693-8400
  325 W Sabine St Ste G Carthage (75633) *(G-2917)*

Pioneer Balloon Co, Dallas *Also called Continental American Corp (G-4157)*

Pioneer Concrete Plant, Richardson *Also called Hanson Aggregates LLC (G-17326)*

Pioneer Drilling Services Ltd (HQ) 210 828-7689
  1250 Ne Loop 410 Ste 1000 San Antonio (78209) *(G-18377)*

Pioneer Drilling Services Ltd 432 684-7360
  4401 E Highway 80 Midland (79706) *(G-15353)*

Pioneer Drilling Services Ltd 361 289-9241
  334 Flato Rd Corpus Christi (78405) *(G-3591)*

Pioneer Energy Services Corp (PA) 855 884-0575
  1250 Ne Loop 410 Ste 1000 San Antonio (78209) *(G-18378)*

Pioneer Energy Services Corp 281 880-9988
  16430 N Eldridge Pkwy E Tomball (77377) *(G-19999)*

Pioneer Exploration Company (PA) **281 893-9400**
  1900 Saint James Pl # 800 Houston (77056) *(G-11334)*

Pioneer Frozen Foods Inc (HQ) 972 298-4281
  627 Big Stone Gap Rd Duncanville (75137) *(G-5536)*

Pioneer Gas Pipeline Inc 325 655-3300
  217 W Beauregard Ave San Angelo (76903) *(G-17820)*

Pioneer Mill Works Inc 806 622-3201
  3850 Mack Rd Amarillo (79118) *(G-505)*

Pioneer Millwork Inc 806 622-3100
  3850 Mack Rd Amarillo (79118) *(G-506)*

Pioneer Millworks, Amarillo *Also called Pioneer Mill Works Inc (G-505)*

Pioneer Natural Resources Co, Irving *Also called Pioneer Water Management LLC (G-13147)*

Pioneer Natural Resources Co 432 683-4768
  3617 N Big Spring St Midland (79705) *(G-15354)*

Pioneer Natural Resources Co (PA) **972 444-9001**
  777 Hidden Rdg Irving (75038) *(G-13144)*

Pioneer Natural Resources Co 432 571-2800
  4815 E Highway 80 Midland (79706) *(G-15355)*

Pioneer Natural Resources Co 432 535-2444
  24500 E Farm Market 309 Midkiff (79755) *(G-15096)*

Pioneer Ntral Rsources USA Inc 432 683-4768
  3617 N Big Spring St Midland (79705) *(G-15356)*

Pioneer Ntral Rsources USA Inc 432 684-0023
  3617 N Big Spring St Midland (79705) *(G-15357)*

Pioneer Ntral Rsources USA Inc 361 456-7201
  2 Mi S On Hwy 673 Pawnee (78145) *(G-16534)*

Pioneer Ntral Rsrces Pmpg Svcs 972 444-9001
  777 Hidden Rdg Irving (75038) *(G-13145)*

Pioneer Sands LLC 325 597-0721
  1000 Oglebay Norton Dr Brady (76825) *(G-2216)*

Pioneer Sands LLC (HQ) **972 444-9001**
  777 Hidden Rdg Irving (75038) *(G-13146)*

Pioneer Water Management LLC 800 242-2607
  777 Hidden Rdg Irving (75038) *(G-13147)*

Pioneer West Texas Division, Midland *Also called Pioneer Drilling Services Ltd (G-15353)*

Pioneer Wireline Services LLC (HQ) **210 828-7689**
  1250 Ne Loop 410 Ste 1000 San Antonio (78209) *(G-18379)*

Pioner Ntrl Rsrc Wll Srvcs LLC 972 969-3670
  5205 N O Connor Blvd # 200 Irving (75039) *(G-13148)*

PIP Printing, Austin *Also called Process Industry Practices (G-1434)*

Pipe Coatings Intl LLC 979 387-3150
  9028 Vincik Ehlert Rd Beasley (77417) *(G-1843)*

Pipe Division, Harlingen *Also called Alamo Concrete Products Ltd (G-8175)*

Pipe Pros LLC (PA) **361 289-9090**
  1729 N Clarkwood Rd # 10 Corpus Christi (78409) *(G-3592)*

Pipe Pros LLC 432 699-4245
  2716 S County Road 1207 Midland (79706) *(G-15358)*

Pipe Pros LLC 903 981-7801
  3000 State Highway 42 Kilgore (75662) *(G-13582)*

Pipe Welding Specialist, Lufkin *Also called T & B Construction Svcs LLC (G-14553)*

Pipeline Inspection Company 713 681-5837
  1919 Antoine Dr Houston (77055) *(G-11335)*

Pipeline Seal & Insulator Inc 713 747-6948
  6455 Clara Rd Ste 300 Houston (77041) *(G-11336)*

Pipeline Technique LLC 281 570-1363
  6605 Rankin Rd Humble (77396) *(G-12794)*

Pipers Welding Service Inc 940 682-4663
  445 Garner Adell Rd Weatherford (76088) *(G-20609)*

Piping Accessories Inc 409 842-5000
  7322 Garth St Beaumont (77705) *(G-1942)*

Piping Technology & Pdts Inc 713 731-0030
  3770 South Loop E Houston (77021) *(G-11337)*

Piping Technology & Pdts Inc (PA) **800 787-5914**
  3701 Holmes Rd Houston (77051) *(G-11338)*

Piping Technology & Products, Houston *Also called Sweco Fab Inc (G-12130)*

Piq Machine LLC 281 354-9873
  22800 Gabriel New Caney (77357) *(G-15846)*

Piranha Scientific LLC 855 585-5200
  11910 State Highway 191 Midland (79707) *(G-15359)*

Pirate Oilfield Services Inc 432 260-9040
  3303 E County Road 44 Midland (79705) *(G-15360)*

Pita Pal Industries Inc 713 777-7482
  3100 Canal St Houston (77003) *(G-11339)*

Pitcock Inc (PA) **940 549-3344**
  166 Elm St Graham (76450) *(G-7788)*

Pitney Bowes Inc 512 823-0833
  11400 Burnet Rd Bldg 7 Austin (78758) *(G-1418)*

Pitts Energy Group, Dallas *Also called Dallas Production Inc (G-4224)*

Pitts Oil Company Inc 214 369-9266
  4600 Greenville Ave # 300 Dallas (75206) *(G-4806)*

Pitts Oilfield Pdts & Svcs LLC 325 340-4401
  2710 Smith Blvd San Angelo (76905) *(G-17821)*

Pitts Sand & Gravel Inc 940 692-3290
  6007 Seymour Hwy Wichita Falls (76310) *(G-20794)*

Pittsburg Steel LLC 903 855-7515
  3489 Fm 557 Pittsburg (75686) *(G-16750)*

Pittsburgh Corning LLC 281 437-6000
  810 Fm 521 Rd Fresno (77545) *(G-7240)*

A
L
P
H
A
B
E
T
I
C

Pitzer Family Ltd Partnership................214 398-1491
  8388 C F Hawn Fwy Dallas (75217) *(G-4807)*

Pivot Corporation................972 475-4747
  2913 Singleton St Rowlett (75088) *(G-17710)*

Pivot3 Inc................281 516-6000
  6605 Cypresswood Dr Spring (77379) *(G-19158)*

Piw Ventures Ltd (PA)................**713 932-9311**
  9311 Katy Fwy Ste H Houston (77024) *(G-11340)*

Pixel and Texel LLC................214 240-0013
  2933 Commerce St Dallas (75226) *(G-4808)*

Pixels & Powertools LLC................844 458-1847
  4201 S Congress Ave # 316 Austin (78745) *(G-1419)*

Pixelworks Corporation................210 826-5375
  8603 Botts St San Antonio (78217) *(G-18380)*

Pj Piping Inc................713 730-3457
  651 N Shepherd Dr Ste 440 Houston (77007) *(G-11341)*

Pk Manufacturing, Houston Also called Ameriforge Corporation *(G-8615)*

Pkc Group, San Antonio Also called Aees Inc *(G-17871)*

Pks Designs Inc................817 429-5174
  9329 County Road 519 Alvarado (76009) *(G-337)*

Plains Dairy LLC................806 374-0385
  300 N Taylor St Amarillo (79107) *(G-455)*

Plains Exploration & Prod Co (PA)................**713 579-6000**
  700 Milam St Ste 3100 Houston (77002) *(G-11342)*

Plains GP Holdings LP (PA)................**713 646-4100**
  333 Clay St Ste 1600 Houston (77002) *(G-11343)*

Plains Meat Co Ltd................806 765-5595
  812 Avenue G Lubbock (79401) *(G-14462)*

Plains Resources Inc (PA)................**713 579-5000**
  700 Milam St Ste 3100 Houston (77002) *(G-11344)*

Plainview Bioenergy LLC................806 296-8000
  2698 E Us Highway 70 Plainview (79072) *(G-16761)*

Planet Resource Recovery Inc................281 996-5315
  8815 Industrial Dr Pearland (77584) *(G-16592)*

Planeview-Wmi LLC................936 588-8988
  13639 Poplar Cir Ste 101 Conroe (77304) *(G-3350)*

Plank Coatings Inc................432 530-1234
  4103 N Tripp Ave Odessa (79764) *(G-16123)*

Plano Acquisition LLC................214 343-0131
  3601 E Plano Pkwy Ste 200 Plano (75074) *(G-16972)*

Plano Door Service Inc................972 422-1695
  1100 N Central Expy Ste A Plano (75074) *(G-16973)*

Plano Profile, Plano Also called Wishbone Graphics Inc *(G-17052)*

Plano Sports Soccer Inc (PA)................**972 519-0222**
  1820 Coit Rd Ste 125 Plano (75075) *(G-16974)*

Plano Star Courier, Plano Also called Lhcn Inc *(G-16908)*

Plano Synergy Holding Inc (PA)................**469 733-1868**
  602 Fountain Pkwy Ste C Grand Prairie (75050) *(G-7946)*

Plant Fabricators Inc................830 393-3064
  6893 Us Highway 181 N Floresville (78114) *(G-6249)*

Plant Process Equipment Inc (PA)................**281 332-2589**
  280 Reynolds Ave League City (77573) *(G-13975)*

Plantation Shutter................214 341-3677
  11649 Chairman Dr Ste 1 Dallas (75243) *(G-4809)*

Plantex Machine LLC................936 894-0226
  15622 Fm 1774 Plantersville (77363) *(G-17060)*

Plaque World, Fort Worth Also called One Stop Printing Inc *(G-6885)*

Plas II, Irving Also called Plastronics Interconnections *(G-13153)*

Plas Mac Inc................806 447-0065
  3696 Us Highway 83 Wellington (79095) *(G-20656)*

Plaskolite Texas LLC................903 962-7573
  5300 Us Hwy 80 Grand Saline (75140) *(G-7999)*

Plasscon, San Antonio Also called Plastcos Arco Iris of San Antn *(G-18381)*

Plastcos Arco Iris of San Antn................210 308-6500
  2819 Woodcliffe St # 100 San Antonio (78230) *(G-18381)*

Plastech Corporation................972 490-1155
  15606 Wright Brothers Dr Addison (75001) *(G-156)*

Plasteco Inc................713 673-7710
  8535 Market St Houston (77029) *(G-11345)*

Plasti Fab Inc................817 485-0156
  6430 Wuliger Way Ste J Richland Hills (76180) *(G-17445)*

Plastic Bagging & Packaging, Baytown Also called Pbp Inc *(G-1799)*

Plastic Forming Inc................817 284-7878
  2100 Reeves Pl Richland Hills (76118) *(G-17446)*

Plastic Industries Inc................817 477-5211
  1500 E Broad St Mansfield (76063) *(G-14703)*

Plastic Industries Mansfield, Mansfield Also called Plastic Industries Inc *(G-14703)*

Plastic Molded Products Inc................254 840-3721
  110 Ne 1st St Mc Gregor (76657) *(G-14821)*

Plastic Molding Technology Inc................915 593-6922
  12280 Rojas Dr Ste A El Paso (79936) *(G-5911)*

Plastic Pipe Plant, Waco Also called Certainteed Corporation *(G-20382)*

Plastic Specialties Inc................512 835-5873
  10503 Metropolitan Dr Austin (78758) *(G-1420)*

Plastic Specialties & Tech Inc................254 772-6979
  700 Jewell Dr Waco (76712) *(G-20447)*

Plastic Tubing Inds Texas Inc................979 921-9990
  18121 Cochran Rd Hempstead (77445) *(G-8255)*

Plastic Vacuum Forming Inc................210 344-8531
  104 Trailcrest St San Antonio (78232) *(G-18382)*

Plastic Welding & Fabrication, Buda Also called Pwf Enterprises *(G-2534)*

Plastic-Mart.com, Fort Worth Also called P-Mcom Incorporated *(G-6888)*

Plastics Holdings, Inc., Jacksonville Also called Pl Holdings Inc *(G-13257)*

Plastiform Inc (PA)................**972 241-2593**
  3418 International Pl Irving (75062) *(G-13149)*

Plastiform Inc................972 579-8803
  3245 Royalty Row Irving (75062) *(G-13150)*

Plastipak Packaging Inc................972 276-8660
  3201 Miller Park N Garland (75042) *(G-7568)*

Plastix Plus LLC................281 469-3451
  10818 Barely Ln Ste A Houston (77070) *(G-11346)*

Plastronics Co................972 986-0474
  3251 Story Rd W Irving (75038) *(G-13151)*

Plastronics Interconnections (PA)................**972 258-2580**
  2601 Texas Dr Irving (75062) *(G-13152)*

Plastronics Interconnections................972 255-1964
  2920 Story Rd W Irving (75038) *(G-13153)*

Plate Cut Inc................713 802-1291
  2190 North Loop W Ste 106 Houston (77018) *(G-11347)*

Platform Group Gallery , The, Houston Also called 101 Products LLC *(G-8400)*

Platinum Energy Resources Inc................713 364-7822
  Galleria Tower 1 270 Houston (77056) *(G-11348)*

Platinum Press Inc................469 733-1506
  4251 Empire Rd Fort Worth (76155) *(G-6909)*

Platinum Pressure Services Inc (HQ)................**866 943-2204**
  2618 S Highway 287 Decatur (76234) *(G-5250)*

Platinum Underground LLC................512 770-9410
  3200 Vortac Ln Georgetown (78628) *(G-7670)*

Platron Manufacturing and Pltg................512 989-1362
  13930 Immanuel Rd Ste A Pflugerville (78660) *(G-16685)*

Platts Welding and Cnstr LLC................972 333-5830
  431 E Parnell St Denison (75021) *(G-5345)*

Players Media Group Inc................509 254-4949
  5960 Berkshire Ln Dallas (75225) *(G-4810)*

Playground Constructors Inc................915 585-6336
  205 Teramar Way El Paso (79922) *(G-5912)*

Playgrund Shade Structures Inc................512 642-6124
  505 Trdesmen Pk Dr Ste A Hutto (78634) *(G-12884)*

Playnet Inc................817 358-7580
  1901 Central Dr Ste 600 Bedford (76021) *(G-1977)*

Playwood Outdoor Fun................512 250-8819
  10208 N Fm 620 Rd Ste 1a Austin (78726) *(G-1421)*

PLbennett Entp & Inv Fund A................903 405-1940
  15732 S State Hwy 121 Trenton (75490) *(G-20018)*

Plci, Plano Also called Pepsi Logistics Company Inc *(G-16967)*

Pleasant Fencing & Cnstr................903 572-0352
  1182 County Road 3425 Cookville (75558) *(G-3406)*

Pleasant Pallet, Cookville Also called Leonard Ray Vaught *(G-3405)*

Pleasanton Express, Pleasanton Also called Wilkerson Publishing Company *(G-17078)*

Plotter Depot Corporation................469 608-9747
  90 Windsor Dr Rockwall (75032) *(G-17559)*

PLPS Inc (PA)................**866 992-7577**
  8321 Industrial Dr Pearland (77584) *(G-16593)*

Pls Inc................713 650-1212
  10850 Richmond Ave # 300 Houston (77042) *(G-11349)*

Plsi, Midland Also called Production Lift Systems Inc *(G-15364)*

Plugged In LLC................512 380-0900
  8701 Shoal Creek Blvd # 101 Austin (78757) *(G-1422)*

Plumbline Architecture Wdwrk, Houston Also called Plumbline Inc *(G-11350)*

Plumbline Inc................713 462-9500
  11422 Craighead Dr Ste B Houston (77025) *(G-11350)*

Plumlee Place LLC................254 662-4021
  802 N Robinson Dr Robinson (76706) *(G-17501)*

Plunkett Energy & Industrial S................806 395-3205
  9723 Highway 62 Wolfforth (79382) *(G-20910)*

Plunkett Oil & Energy Svc Co, Wolfforth Also called Plunkett Energy & Industrial S *(G-20910)*

Plunkett Research Ltd................713 932-0000
  4102 Bellaire Blvd Houston (77025) *(G-11351)*

Plus One Robotics Inc................937 287-5060
  311 N Frank Luke Dr # 101 San Antonio (78226) *(G-18383)*

Plus Therapeutics Inc (PA)................**737 255-7194**
  4200 Marathon Blvd # 200 Austin (78756) *(G-1423)*

Pluspetrol International Inc................713 961-1095
  5599 San Felipe St # 100 Houston (77056) *(G-11352)*

Ply Gem Industries Inc................979 361-3514
  615 W Carson St Bryan (77801) *(G-2498)*

Ply-Tech Inc................830 625-3913
  1630 W State Highway 46 New Braunfels (78132) *(G-15819)*

PM Assembly LLC................972 814-3727
  17141 County Road 566 Farmersville (75442) *(G-6225)*

Pmc Inc................817 695-5680
  2201 E Lamar Blvd Ste 240 Arlington (76006) *(G-754)*

PMC Acquisition Company Inc................915 225-8758
  11355 Rojas Dr Ste 13-14 El Paso (79936) *(G-5913)*

PMC Beta, Houston Also called Metrix PMC/Beta *(G-10855)*

PMC Service Company, Grand Prairie Also called Polk Mechanical Company LLC *(G-7947)*

PMG Digital Inc 806 747-7446
  6011 43rd St Lubbock (79407) *(G-14463)*

PMI, Houston *Also called Printmailers Inc (G-11422)*

PMI Oil Tools, Karnes City *Also called Perales Group Ventures Inc (G-13346)*

PMI Pump Parts LLC 817 441-7787
  178 Bear Cat Rd Aledo (76008) *(G-201)*

Pml Exploration Services LLC (PA) **405 606-2701**
  19059 Champion Forest Dr # 103 Spring (77379) *(G-19159)*

Pmq Alternatives Inc 713 690-7672
  6120 W By Northwest Blvd # 190 Houston (77040) *(G-11353)*

Pmr Global Inc (PA) **817 484-1100**
  4290 E Fm 1187 Burleson (76028) *(G-2593)*

Pmr Global Aerospace, Burleson *Also called Cordova Corporation (G-2577)*

Pneumatech Safety Systems, Charlotte *Also called Fla Safety & Prod Svcs Inc (G-3047)*

Poco Graphite Holdings LLC 940 627-2121
  300 Old Greenwood Rd Decatur (76234) *(G-5251)*

Poco Grathite, Decatur *Also called Entegris Inc (G-5246)*

Pohaku Classic - Oklahoma LLC 972 840-8660
  2914 National Ct Garland (75041) *(G-7569)*

Pointsmith Pnt-F-Prchase MGT S 281 599-5900
  21202 Park Row Dr Katy (77449) *(G-13432)*

Pointwise Inc 817 377-2807
  213 S Jennings Ave Fort Worth (76104) *(G-6910)*

Pol-Tex International, Mont Belvieu *Also called Poly-America LP (G-15620)*

Pol-Tex International Division, Grand Prairie *Also called Poly-America LP (G-7948)*

Polar Corporation 972 635-2464
  1012 Industrial Dr Royse City (75189) *(G-17722)*

Polar Ice Inc 979 830-1954
  2106 Longwood Dr Brenham (77833) *(G-2269)*

Polar Service Centers, Houston *Also called Entrans International LLC (G-9665)*

Polara Engineering Inc 951 547-5500
  1497 County Road 2178 Greenville (75402) *(G-8086)*

Polara Enterprises LLC 903 366-0300
  1497 County Road 2178 Greenville (75402) *(G-8087)*

Polaris Exploration Corp 361 857-7176
  2863 Central Ln Beeville (78102) *(G-1987)*

Polaris Led Inc 832 582-6263
  7787 Pinemont Dr Ste B Houston (77040) *(G-11354)*

Polibrid Coatings Inc 956 831-7818
  6700 Ruben Torres Sr Blvd Brownsville (78526) *(G-2394)*

Politics & Religion Broadcast, Plano *Also called Endtime Inc (G-16861)*

Polk County Publishing Co 409 283-2516
  205 W Bluff St Woodville (75979) *(G-20916)*

Polk County Publishing Co (PA) **936 327-4357**
  100 E Calhoun St Livingston (77351) *(G-14160)*

Polk County Publishing Co 936 544-0540
  102 S 7th St Crockett (75835) *(G-3722)*

Polk Mechanical Company LLC (PA) **972 339-1200**
  2425 Dillard St Grand Prairie (75051) *(G-7947)*

Polk Production Tech Inc 361 815-1245
  4910 Leopard St Ste 500 Corpus Christi (78408) *(G-3593)*

Pollok Inc 915 592-5700
  21 Butterfield Trail Blvd El Paso (79906) *(G-5914)*

Pollok Electronics, El Paso *Also called Pollok Inc (G-5914)*

Pollution System Solutions Inc 713 574-6661
  2170 Buckthorne Pl # 160 Spring (77380) *(G-19241)*

Pollution Systems, Spring *Also called Pollution System Solutions Inc (G-19241)*

Polly Knapp Pig Inc 713 222-0146
  1209 Hardy St Houston (77020) *(G-11355)*

Polobrid Coating, Brownsville *Also called Polibrid Coatings Inc (G-2394)*

Polsys Services Inc 713 999-1100
  2170 Buckthorne Pl # 165 The Woodlands (77380) *(G-19903)*

Poly America, Grand Prairie *Also called Poly-Flex Construction Inc (G-7950)*

Poly Sac Inc 713 978-7888
  7920 Westpark Dr Houston (77063) *(G-11356)*

Poly U Molding & Mfg LP 817 701-0779
  1016 W Harris Rd Arlington (76001) *(G-755)*

Poly-America LP (PA) **972 337-7100**
  2000 W Marshall Dr Grand Prairie (75051) *(G-7948)*

Poly-America LP 972 337-7107
  1350 S State Highway 161 Grand Prairie (75051) *(G-7949)*

Poly-America LP 281 385-3700
  13830 Hatcherville Rd Mont Belvieu (77521) *(G-15620)*

Poly-Flex Construction Inc 972 647-4374
  2000 W Marshall Dr Grand Prairie (75051) *(G-7950)*

Polycom Inc 512 372-7000
  7700 W Parmer Ln Austin (78729) *(G-1709)*

Polycom of Austin, Austin *Also called Polycom Inc (G-1709)*

Polyfab Inc 361 594-3535
  514 W Runk St Shiner (77984) *(G-18947)*

Polyflow LLC 432 686-2001
  2309 E Interstate 20 Midland (79701) *(G-15361)*

Polyglass Coatings Limited LLC 832 736-9243
  1616 N Main St Pearland (77581) *(G-16594)*

Polyguard Products, Ennis *Also called Muncaster Capital Texas Inc (G-6111)*

Polyguard Products Inc (HQ) **972 875-8421**
  3801 S Interstate Hwy 45 Ennis (75119) *(G-6114)*

Polymed Therapeutics Inc 713 777-7088
  6200 Savoy Dr Ste 1200 Houston (77036) *(G-11357)*

Polymer Dynamics Inc 281 894-6382
  11211 Neeshaw Dr Houston (77065) *(G-11358)*

Polymer Products LP 972 647-1000
  432 W Fork Dr Ste A Arlington (76012) *(G-756)*

Polymerica Ltd 915 845-6288
  6055 Luckett Ct El Paso (79932) *(G-5915)*

Polymers Sales & Logistics LLC 281 874-8072
  450 Gears Rd Ste 240 Houston (77067) *(G-11359)*

Polynt Composites USA Inc 903 938-9571
  5851 Fm 1998 Marshall (75672) *(G-14798)*

Polynt Composites USA Inc 713 799-1800
  2434 Holmes Rd Houston (77051) *(G-11360)*

Polynt Composites USA Inc 972 875-8634
  201 Cedar Rd Ennis (75119) *(G-6115)*

Polyone Corporation 281 474-2831
  5306 Highway 146 Seabrook (77586) *(G-18789)*

Polyone Corporation 281 474-2831
  5110 Hwy 146 Seabrook (77586) *(G-18790)*

Polyspec (tx) LLC 281 397-0033
  1255 Cutten Rd Houston (77066) *(G-11361)*

Polyspede Electronics Corp 214 363-7245
  6770 Twin Hills Ave Dallas (75231) *(G-4811)*

Polytex Fibers Corp 713 690-9055
  9341 Baythorne Dr Houston (77041) *(G-11362)*

Polytex Fibers International 713 690-9055
  9333 Baythorne Dr Houston (77041) *(G-11363)*

Polytrnix McHning Fbrction LLC (PA) **972 436-0422**
  735 N Plano Rd 200 Richardson (75081) *(G-17374)*

Polyweld USA Inc 281 821-4156
  1620 E Richey Rd Houston (77073) *(G-11364)*

Pond King Inc 940 668-2573
  5924 W Us Highway 82 Gainesville (76240) *(G-7357)*

Ponderosa Precision Plas Inc 281 471-3221
  106 N 15th St La Porte (77571) *(G-13783)*

Pony Xpress Printing LLC 214 221-7669
  2485 Merritt Dr Garland (75041) *(G-7570)*

Poo-Pourri, Addison *Also called Scentsible LLC (G-161)*

Pool & Electrical Products Inc 512 707-0109
  407 Radam Ln Austin (78745) *(G-1424)*

Pool Custom Iron Works Inc 936 756-4292
  923 S 1st St Conroe (77301) *(G-3351)*

Pool Energy Corporation 512 249-9252
  12885 N Hwy 183 Ste 104 Austin (78750) *(G-1425)*

Poole Chemical Co Inc (PA) **806 362-4261**
  111 N 1st St Texline (79087) *(G-19808)*

Poole Chemical Co Inc 806 647-2121
  Hwy 194 Se Dimmitt (79027) *(G-5485)*

Pop Star LLC 214 244-2502
  1350 Manufacturing St # 212 Dallas (75207) *(G-4812)*

Pop's Bkry/Grcias Trtlla Fctry, San Angelo *Also called Pops Bakery Inc (G-17822)*

Popes Cleaners LLC (PA) **210 923-7785**
  6218 S Flores St San Antonio (78214) *(G-18384)*

Pops Bakery Inc 325 655-1170
  208 E Avenue J San Angelo (76903) *(G-17822)*

Pore Technology Inc 903 601-4466
  498 Fm 881 Jefferson (75657) *(G-13286)*

Porfirio Diaz Exit LP 915 544-6688
  208 N Octavia St El Paso (79901) *(G-5916)*

Porous Metal Filters Inc 866 288-2522
  19994 Hickory Twig Way Spring (77388) *(G-19160)*

Port Arthur Refinery, Port Arthur *Also called Total Ptrchemicals Ref USA Inc (G-17129)*

Port City Inc 713 673-7272
  2075 N Wayside Dr Houston (77020) *(G-11365)*

Port City Cabinet Works, Houston *Also called Port City Inc (G-11365)*

Port Isabel Press, Port Isabel *Also called New Horizon Publishers (G-17137)*

Port Isabel Rm, Port Isabel *Also called Cemex Construction Mtls S LLC (G-17136)*

Port Lavaca Wave 361 552-9788
  107 E Austin St Port Lavaca (77979) *(G-17154)*

Port Plastics Inc 817 834-7678
  6312 Airport Fwy Ste C Fort Worth (76117) *(G-6911)*

Portable Pipe Hangers Inc 713 672-5088
  5534 Harvey Wilson Dr Houston (77020) *(G-11366)*

Portacool LLC (HQ) **936 598-5651**
  711 Fm 2468 Center (75935) *(G-3005)*

Portacool LLC 936 598-6353
  721 Fm 2468 Center (75935) *(G-3006)*

Portage Plastics Corporation 956 504-6102
  1900 Billy Mitchell Blvd Brownsville (78521) *(G-2395)*

Portele Printing Company Inc 936 441-3738
  3606 N Frazier St Conroe (77303) *(G-3352)*

Porter Ready Mix Spring Plant, Houston *Also called Porter Ready-Mix Inc (G-11367)*

Porter Ready-Mix Inc (PA) **281 354-5181**
  25152 Loop 494 Porter (77365) *(G-17181)*

Porter Ready-Mix Inc 281 443-6363
  1601 Westfield Loop Rd Houston (77073) *(G-11367)*

Porter Seal Company, Irving *Also called Elder Rubber Incorporated (G-13013)*

A
L
P
H
A
B
E
T
I
C

Porterfield Timber Harvesting 936 598-4203
  349 County Road 1005 Center (75935) *(G-3007)*

Portersville Sales & Testing 806 373-6811
  114 Se 46th Ave Amarillo (79118) *(G-507)*

Portsmouth Trading Co Inc 713 957-0470
  3526 E T C Jester Blvd Houston (77018) *(G-11368)*

Positive Marketing (usa) Inc 877 284-4488
  11277 N Stemmons Fwy Dallas (75229) *(G-4813)*

Posse Energy, Houston *Also called Oklahoma Pacific Ltd (G-11166)*

Post Newspaper, The, Texas City *Also called D & V Day Investments Corp (G-19787)*

Post Oak Energy Capital LP (PA) **713 571-9393**
  34 S Wynden Dr Ste 300 Houston (77056) *(G-11369)*

Post Oak Graphics, Houston *Also called Post Oak Graphics Inc (G-11370)*

Post Oak Graphics Inc 713 850-3563
  16010 Barkers Point Ln # 150 Houston (77079) *(G-11370)*

Post Printing & Publishing, Dallas *Also called Texas Jewish Post Ltd (G-5074)*

Post Up Town Inc 214 965-6565
  3000 Mckinney Ave Dallas (75204) *(G-4814)*

Posture Beauty Sleep Products, Fort Worth *Also called Dynasty Consolidated Inds Inc (G-6599)*

Potbelly Corporation 281 277-2515
  1815 Highway 6 Sugar Land (77478) *(G-19527)*

Potters Industries LLC 903 785-1633
  1601 19th St Nw Paris (75460) *(G-16366)*

Potters Industries LLC 325 752-6711
  5650 Highway 279 Brownwood (76801) *(G-2442)*

Pottorff, Fort Worth *Also called PCI Industries Inc (G-6898)*

Powder Coaters of Texas Inc 979 387-2049
  8723 Loop 540 Beasley (77417) *(G-1844)*

Powder Finishes Inc (PA) **254 968-5601**
  645 W Lingleville Rd Stephenville (76401) *(G-19419)*

Powder Metallurgy Company Inc 972 436-3502
  201 E College St Lewisville (75057) *(G-14082)*

Powell Apparatus Service Div, Houston *Also called Powell Electrical Systems Inc (G-11375)*

Powell Electrical Systems Inc 713 599-0324
  4201 Southwest Fwy Houston (77027) *(G-11371)*

Powell Electrical Systems Inc (HQ) **713 944-6900**
  8550 Mosley Rd Houston (77075) *(G-11372)*

Powell Electrical Systems Inc 713 790-1700
  7232 Airport Blvd Houston (77061) *(G-11373)*

Powell Electrical Systems Inc 281 452-4885
  16535 Jacintoport Blvd Houston (77015) *(G-11374)*

Powell Electrical Systems Inc 713 944-6900
  7232 Airport Blvd Houston (77061) *(G-11375)*

Powell Industries, Houston *Also called Powell Electrical Systems Inc (G-11373)*

Powell Industries Inc (PA) **713 944-6900**
  8550 Mosley Rd Houston (77075) *(G-11376)*

Powell Manufacturing Company 972 278-9507
  2720 Industrial Ln Garland (75041) *(G-7571)*

Powell Offshore, Houston *Also called Powell Electrical Systems Inc (G-11374)*

Power Pipe and Tank LLC 417 447-4508
  511 Sw 48th Ave Amarillo (79110) *(G-508)*

Power Generation, Houston *Also called Continental Turbine Services (G-9290)*

Power Line Infrstrcture Svcs I 432 586-2518
  422 W Austin St Kermit (79745) *(G-13514)*

Power Packaging of Texas, Grand Prairie *Also called Exel N Amercn Logistics Inc (G-7867)*

Power Plastic Inc 713 957-3695
  5879 W 34th St Houston (77092) *(G-11377)*

Power Process Developments Inc 713 926-5840
  100 Hutcheson St Houston (77003) *(G-11378)*

Power Repair Service Inc 361 289-1471
  314 Mcbride Ln Corpus Christi (78408) *(G-3594)*

Power Seal 940 767-5566
  701 Pleasant View Dr Wichita Falls (76306) *(G-20795)*

Power Service Products Inc (PA) **817 599-9486**
  513 Peaster Hwy Weatherford (76086) *(G-20610)*

Power Steel, Tomball *Also called A&T Steel Fabricators Inc (G-19953)*

Power Temp Systems Inc 281 617-7889
  1428 N Sam Houston Pkwy E # 170 Houston (77032) *(G-11379)*

Power Well Services, Longview *Also called Expro Americas LLC (G-14233)*

Powerhouse Ready-Mix LLC 832 620-1922
  2710 W Eagle Dr Rosenberg (77471) *(G-17594)*

Powerohm Resistors, Katy *Also called Hubbell Industrial Contrls Inc (G-13407)*

Powers Embroidery Inc 254 754-2498
  2825 Gholson Rd Waco (76704) *(G-20448)*

Powerseal Pipeline Pdts Corp 940 767-5566
  701 Pleasant View Dr Wichita Falls (76306) *(G-20796)*

Powersecure Inc 203 683-6222
  8655 Corporate Dr Frisco (75033) *(G-7306)*

Powersecure Lighting, Frisco *Also called Powersecure Inc (G-7306)*

Powersource, Sugar Land *Also called Fifth Rock Software Inc (G-19483)*

Powersteering Software, Austin *Also called Upland Software I Inc (G-1612)*

Powertech Components Inc 210 521-0799
  403 E Ramsey Rd Ste 205 San Antonio (78216) *(G-18385)*

Pp Exit LLC (PA) **817 701-3555**
  1130 Avenue H E Arlington (76011) *(G-757)*

Ppc Insulators, Houston *Also called Ppc Usa Inc (G-11380)*

Ppc Usa Inc 281 257-8222
  363 N Sam Houston Pkwy E # 700 Houston (77060) *(G-11380)*

Ppe LLC 979 353-7300
  3201 S Blue Bell Rd Brenham (77833) *(G-2270)*

PPG 8302, Pasadena *Also called PPG Industries Inc (G-16497)*

PPG 8304, Tomball *Also called PPG Industries Inc (G-20000)*

PPG 8314, Universal City *Also called PPG Industries Inc (G-20184)*

PPG 8318, Lubbock *Also called PPG Industries Inc (G-14464)*

PPG 8323, Houston *Also called PPG Industries Inc (G-11383)*

PPG 8325, Houston *Also called PPG Industries Inc (G-11381)*

PPG 8327, College Station *Also called PPG Industries Inc (G-3197)*

PPG 8328, Sugar Land *Also called PPG Industries Inc (G-19528)*

PPG 8329, Amarillo *Also called PPG Industries Inc (G-509)*

PPG 8331, Plano *Also called PPG Industries Inc (G-16975)*

PPG 8334, Corpus Christi *Also called PPG Industries Inc (G-3595)*

PPG 8338, Round Rock *Also called PPG Industries Inc (G-17680)*

PPG 8339, Conroe *Also called PPG Industries Inc (G-3353)*

PPG 8344, Dallas *Also called PPG Industries Inc (G-4815)*

PPG 8351, McKinney *Also called PPG Industries Inc (G-14965)*

PPG 8358, Austin *Also called PPG Industries Inc (G-1426)*

PPG 8362, Weatherford *Also called PPG Industries Inc (G-20611)*

PPG 9657, Laredo *Also called PPG Industries Inc (G-13922)*

PPG 9714, Wichita Falls *Also called PPG Industries Inc (G-20797)*

PPG Aerospace, Grand Prairie *Also called PRC - Desoto International Inc (G-7953)*

PPG Aerospace, Arlington *Also called Texstars LLC (G-796)*

PPG Arspace Eldorado Solutions, McKinney *Also called PRC-Desoto International Inc (G-14966)*

PPG Industries Inc. 940 665-9590
  3333 N Interstate 35 C Gainesville (76240) *(G-7358)*

PPG Industries Inc. 806 467-9707
  2511 Paramount Blvd B2 Amarillo (79109) *(G-509)*

PPG Industries Inc. 979 693-7097
  3800 State Highway 6 S # 200 College Station (77845) *(G-3197)*

PPG Industries Inc. 936 441-1533
  910 W Dallas St Conroe (77301) *(G-3353)*

PPG Industries Inc. 361 225-2250
  6764 Weber Rd Corpus Christi (78413) *(G-3595)*

PPG Industries Inc. 214 902-8922
  2515 Willowbrook Rd # 109 Dallas (75220) *(G-4815)*

PPG Industries Inc. 713 683-8025
  3423 N Sam Houston Pkwy W # 301 Houston (77086) *(G-11381)*

PPG Industries Inc. 806 794-0180
  5920 66th St Unit 1 Lubbock (79424) *(G-14464)*

PPG Industries Inc. 214 544-0700
  921 Redbud Blvd Ste 100 McKinney (75069) *(G-14965)*

PPG Industries Inc. 713 576-8418
  3530 Lang Rd Houston (77092) *(G-11382)*

PPG Industries Inc. 512 288-5505
  7401 W Highway 71 Ste 115 Austin (78735) *(G-1426)*

PPG Industries Inc. 281 487-6416
  5334 Spencer Hwy Pasadena (77505) *(G-16497)*

PPG Industries Inc. 512 218-9551
  399 Texas Ave Round Rock (78664) *(G-17680)*

PPG Industries Inc. 210 656-5541
  1705 Pat Booker Rd # 223 Universal City (78148) *(G-20184)*

PPG Industries Inc. 281 265-5333
  2601 Cordes Dr Sugar Land (77479) *(G-19528)*

PPG Industries Inc. 281 357-0455
  24914 Tomball Pkwy # 160 Tomball (77375) *(G-20000)*

PPG Industries Inc. 281 890-4481
  13306 Fm 1960 Rd W Houston (77065) *(G-11383)*

PPG Industries Inc. 817 613-1860
  2201 Tin Top Rd Ste 375 Weatherford (76087) *(G-20611)*

PPG Industries Inc. 972 517-2226
  909 W Spring Creek Pkwy # 330 Plano (75023) *(G-16975)*

PPG Industries Inc. 940 322-5201
  1810 9th St Wichita Falls (76301) *(G-20797)*

PPG Industries Inc. 956 791-1191
  719 Gale St Laredo (78041) *(G-13922)*

PPG Industries Inc. 281 842-9518
  11505 Highway 225 La Porte (77571) *(G-13784)*

Ppsi, Houston *Also called Professionalized Pdts & Svcs (G-11440)*

Practice Interactive Inc (PA) **844 413-2602**
  1701 Dirs Blvd Ste 110 Austin (78744) *(G-1427)*

Prairie Dog Pet Products LLC 972 606-9050
  907 Avenue R Grand Prairie (75050) *(G-7951)*

Prairie Ptfood Ingredients LLC 469 383-5182
  3111 Se Mckinney St Rice (75155) *(G-17266)*

Praseks Hillje Smokehouse 979 543-8312
  29714 Us 59 Hwy El Campo (77437) *(G-5626)*

Praters, Lubbock *Also called Usm Manufacturing LLC (G-14505)*

Pratt & Whitney Dallas Dist, Dallas *Also called Pratt Whtney Line Mint Svcs In (G-4817)*

Pratt & Whitney Eng Svcs Inc 972 343-1300
  1177 N Great Sw Pkwy Grand Prairie (75050) *(G-7952)*

Pratt Industries Inc 972 296-2900
  3700 Eagle Place Dr # 800 Dallas (75236) *(G-4816)*

Pratt Industries Inc 210 651-6309
 6389 Fm 3009 Ste 100 Schertz (78154) (G-18759)
Pratt Industries USA Inc 940 387-7291
 1401 S Mayhill Rd Denton (76208) (G-5393)
Pratt Rockwall Corrugating LLC 770 918-5678
 3400 Discovery Blvd Rockwall (75032) (G-17560)
Pratt Whtney Line Mint Svcs In 972 894-0139
 2701 Regent Blvd Ste 300 Dallas (75261) (G-4817)
Prause Market LLC 979 968-3259
 2036 W Guenther Ln La Grange (78945) (G-13700)
Prause's Market, La Grange Also called Prause Market LLC (G-13700)
Praxair, Deer Park Also called Linde Inc (G-5282)
Praxair, Brownwood Also called Linde Inc (G-2437)
Praxair, San Antonio Also called Linde Inc (G-18253)
Praxair, Groves Also called Linde Inc (G-8109)
Praxair, Texas City Also called Linde Inc (G-19796)
Praxair, Spring Also called Linde Inc (G-19227)
Praxair, Beaumont Also called Linde Inc (G-1919)
Praxair, Bryan Also called Linde Inc (G-2490)
Praxair Inc 936 295-3912
 1223 Financial Plz Huntsville (77340) (G-12823)
Praxair Inc Freeport Psa 281 203-3682
 5619 E Highway 332 Freeport (77541) (G-7207)
Praxair Surface Tech Inc 713 849-9474
 7615 Fairview St Houston (77041) (G-11384)
Praxis Fabrication Inc 806 883-7621
 1475 County Rd W White Deer (79097) (G-20710)
PRC - Desoto International Inc 817 640-1067
 2750 114th St Ste 400 Grand Prairie (75050) (G-7953)
PRC-Desoto International Inc 972 540-0360
 200 Industrial Blvd McKinney (75069) (G-14966)
Pre Management Inc 512 891-0300
 7600 Burnet Rd Ste 160 Austin (78757) (G-1428)
Precise Connections Inc 972 298-1040
 1114 Explorer St Duncanville (75137) (G-5537)
Precise Food Ingredients Inc 972 323-4951
 1432 Wainwright Way # 150 Carrollton (75007) (G-2882)
Precise Hard Chrome, Temple Also called Texas Hydraulics Inc (G-19712)
Precise Hard Chrome, Waco Also called Texas Hydraulics Inc (G-20466)
Precise Hard Chrome 254 756-6879
 6613 N 19th St Waco (76708) (G-20449)
Precise Industrial Maintenance, Cleveland Also called James Barker III (G-3130)
Precise Machine & Fabrications 936 298-2851
 3301 Highway 105 Cleveland (77327) (G-3133)
Precise Machining Co, Leander Also called EW & WG LP (G-13989)
Precise Steel Inc 713 673-6300
 1335 Boyles St Ste 110 Houston (77020) (G-11385)
Precision Additives Inc 713 896-0606
 1441 Park Ten Blvd Houston (77084) (G-11386)
Precision Alloys Corporation 800 321-0759
 811 Regal Row Dallas (75247) (G-4818)
Precision Business Mchs Inc 972 224-9119
 1509 Falcon Dr Ste 106 Desoto (75115) (G-5440)
Precision Coatings 432 362-7696
 9019 N County Rd W Odessa (79764) (G-16124)
Precision Components, Houston Also called Prism Resources Inc (G-11423)
Precision Components 888 554-4999
 7311 Old Galveston Rd # 110 Houston (77034) (G-11387)
Precision Custom Machining Inc 713 462-8622
 14237 Aston St Houston (77040) (G-11388)
Precision Dcment Solutions Inc (PA) 866 916-1177
 2452 Lacy Ln Ste 100 Carrollton (75006) (G-2792)
Precision Def Components LLC 870 949-8590
 5911 Richmond Rd Apt 4103 Texarkana (75503) (G-19771)
Precision Directional Svcs Inc 713 975-1209
 10350 Richmond Ave # 700 Houston (77042) (G-11389)
Precision Drilling, Houston Also called Precision Tech (G-11395)
Precision Drilling Company LP 817 396-4714
 1415 Hughie Long Rd Cresson (76035) (G-3711)
Precision Drilling Company LP (HQ) 713 435-6100
 10350 Richmond Ave # 700 Houston (77042) (G-11390)
Precision Drilling Corporation (HQ) 713 435-6100
 10370 Richmond Ave # 600 Houston (77042) (G-11391)
Precision Drilling US, Houston Also called Precision Drilling Company LP (G-11390)
Precision Energy Services Inc 281 892-0600
 2442 Greens Rd Houston (77032) (G-11392)
Precision Energy Services Inc (HQ) 713 693-4000
 2000 Saint James Pl Houston (77056) (G-11393)
Precision Enterprise, Woodville Also called Temple Precision Enterpise Inc (G-20918)
Precision Flow Inc 432 332-0266
 1609 W 2nd St Odessa (79763) (G-16125)
Precision Fluorocarbon Inc 281 351-4070
 9930 Fm 2920 Rd Tomball (77375) (G-20001)
Precision Formed Plastics Inc 972 579-8803
 3245 Royalty Row Irving (75062) (G-13154)
Precision Formulations LLC 972 393-7170
 9660 Dilworth Rd Dallas (75243) (G-4819)

Precision Frac LLC 855 967-1023
 10008 W County Road 150 Midland (79706) (G-15362)
Precision Helicopter Svcs Inc 210 525-9595
 12027 Warfield St San Antonio (78216) (G-18386)
Precision Iron, Seguin Also called TH Precision LLC (G-18868)
Precision Iron Fabrication LLC 972 636-7581
 1215 Industrial Dr Royse City (75189) (G-17723)
Precision Joint Solution Inc 972 351-0470
 3903 S Congress Ave # 42108 Austin (78704) (G-1429)
Precision M/C Mfg Inc 972 429-6200
 700 Sanden Blvd Wylie (75098) (G-20943)
Precision M/C Products Inc 972 429-6200
 700 Sanden Blvd Wylie (75098) (G-20944)
Precision Machine 903 675-2300
 6815 Stewart Rd Galveston (77551) (G-7406)
Precision Machine Works, Wichita Falls Also called P M W Ventures Inc (G-20792)
Precision Mfg Co Fort Worth, Fort Worth Also called Essner Precision Mfg LLC (G-6619)
Precision Mold & Tool Group, San Antonio Also called Royberg Inc (G-18435)
Precision Mold Builders, Fort Worth Also called Louis Barriga (G-6801)
Precision Mold TI Gvrnment Div, San Antonio Also called Lobo Ventures Ltd (G-18256)
Precision Motor Rebuilder, Fort Worth Also called Rays Chmpn Spring & Mtr Svc (G-6943)
Precision Orthodonics, Euless Also called Scott Mc Gaha (G-6157)
Precision Oxygen & Supply, Dallas Also called Ws Group Inc (G-5204)
Precision Pack 214 553-8044
 10725 Sandhill Rd Ste 102 Dallas (75238) (G-4820)
Precision Parts Center, Corpus Christi Also called Paul Krivoy (G-3589)
Precision Pearl Inlay Inc 512 442-4941
 7208 Cooper Ln Austin (78745) (G-1430)
Precision Polymer Engrg Ltd 713 482-0123
 4702 N Sam Houston Pkwy W Houston (77086) (G-11394)
Precision Power Associates 972 234-6165
 1758 Firman Dr 200 Richardson (75081) (G-17375)
Precision Print & Office Sup, Navasota Also called Precision Printing & Off Sup (G-15742)
Precision Printing, Conroe Also called Portele Printing Company Inc (G-3352)
Precision Printing & Off Sup 936 825-2488
 206 E Washington Ave Navasota (77868) (G-15742)
Precision Prosthetic Inc (PA) 915 544-2961
 1501 E Missouri Ave El Paso (79902) (G-5917)
Precision Ready Mix Ltd 210 872-6053
 3714 Fossil Crk San Antonio (78261) (G-18387)
Precision Set Incorporated 972 385-6732
 13711 Omega Rd Dallas (75244) (G-4821)
Precision Sheet Metal Shop Inc 972 771-1423
 2650 Observation Trl Rockwall (75032) (G-17561)
Precision Specialties Company 800 527-3295
 1201 E Pecan St Sherman (75090) (G-18927)
Precision Tackle Inc 936 597-6145
 13100 Fm 149 Rd Ste 109 Montgomery (77316) (G-15639)
Precision Tech 281 227-5750
 14041 Vickery Dr Houston (77032) (G-11395)
Precision Technology Inc 214 343-0131
 3601 E Plano Pkwy Ste 200 Plano (75074) (G-16976)
Precision Turning 817 472-7999
 6301 Calender Rd Arlington (76001) (G-758)
Precision Water Tech Inc 972 488-6755
 1225 Capital Dr Ste 180 Carrollton (75006) (G-2793)
Precision Welding & Iron, Royse City Also called Precision Iron Fabrication LLC (G-17723)
Precision Well Logging Inc 713 681-3435
 924 Wakefield Dr Houston (77018) (G-11396)
Precision Wire Products LLC (PA) 214 436-4923
 108 Muntain View Indus Ln Frisco (75034) (G-7307)
Precision Wldg & Fabrication, Houston Also called Grazco LLC (G-10023)
Precision Wood Products Inc 972 293-2252
 1585 High Meadows Way Cedar Hill (75104) (G-2951)
Precision-Hayes Intl Inc (HQ) 972 287-2390
 704 W Simonds Rd Seagoville (75159) (G-18802)
Preco Turbine Comprsr Svcs Inc 281 821-9620
 17619 Aldine Westfield Rd Houston (77073) (G-11397)
Predictech, Houston Also called Provibtech (G-11466)
Predominant Pumps & Automation 281 987-0204
 910 Pinafore Ln Houston (77039) (G-11398)
Preferred Beef Group LP 806 658-4561
 910 E Industrial Rd Booker (79005) (G-2158)
Preferred Oilfield Services 325 884-5700
 3027 Southwest Blvd San Angelo (76904) (G-17823)
Preferred Plastics, Shiner Also called Polyfab Inc (G-18947)
Preferred Plastics Inc 361 594-3535
 514 W Runk St Shiner (77984) (G-18948)
Preferred Pump & Equipment LP (HQ) 817 536-9800
 2201 Scott Ave Ste 100 Fort Worth (76103) (G-6912)
Preferred Stampings of Texas 512 255-7803
 1602 N A W Grimes Blvd Round Rock (78665) (G-17681)
Premark Health Science Inc 972 894-0020
 3200 Story Rd W Irving (75038) (G-13155)
Premcor Refining, Beaumont Also called Lima Refining Company (G-1918)
Premcor Refining Group Inc (HQ) 210 345-2000
 1 Valero Way San Antonio (78249) (G-18388)

ALPHABETIC

Premex Door Supply Inc 214 341-2212
3630 W Miller Rd Ste 320 Garland (75041) *(G-7572)*

Premier Antique Stucco LLC 210 602-8054
1114 Delgado St San Antonio (78207) *(G-18389)*

Premier Board Inc 361 883-6553
138 45th St Corpus Christi (78405) *(G-3596)*

Premier Christmas, Carrollton *Also called Premier Lighting Entps LLC (G-2794)*

Premier Coatings, Houston *Also called Denso North America USA Inc (G-9437)*

Premier Coil Solutions Inc 713 677-0209
18993 G H Cir Waller (77484) *(G-20507)*

Premier Company, The, Houston *Also called Premier Printing & Ltr Svc Inc (G-11404)*

Premier Concrete Products Inc 713 641-2727
5102 Galveston Rd Houston (77017) *(G-11399)*

Premier Corporate Housing, Beaumont *Also called Akcorp Inc (G-1848)*

Premier Digital Design LLC 210 774-5456
8523 Speedway Dr San Antonio (78230) *(G-18390)*

Premier Directional Drlg LP 281 673-4000
363 N Sam Houston Pkwy E # 300 Houston (77060) *(G-11400)*

Premier Election Solutions Inc (HQ) 469 675-8990
1253 Allen Station Pkwy Allen (75002) *(G-296)*

Premier Emblem, San Antonio *Also called Premier Uniform Inc (G-18392)*

Premier Emblem & Insignia Inc 210 253-3406
2111 West Ave San Antonio (78201) *(G-18391)*

Premier Entry Systems LLC 817 422-5908
5001 Mosson Rd Fort Worth (76119) *(G-6913)*

Premier Lighting Entps LLC 855 426-4544
1300 Hutton Dr Ste 104 Carrollton (75006) *(G-2794)*

Premier Machining Services 281 558-3242
16230 Westpark Dr Houston (77082) *(G-11401)*

Premier Manufacturing LP 972 355-3285
3151 Justin Rd Flower Mound (75028) *(G-6276)*

Premier Oilfield Group LLC (PA) 713 492-2057
11335 Clay Rd Ste 180 Houston (77041) *(G-11402)*

Premier Pipe LLC (HQ) 832 300-8100
15600 John F Kennedy Blvd Houston (77032) *(G-11403)*

Premier Plastics Dallas Inc (PA) 972 554-1597
2109 Vanco Dr Irving (75061) *(G-13156)*

Premier Pressure Pumping LLC 903 981-0081
2310 Industrial Blvd Kilgore (75662) *(G-13583)*

Premier Printing, Dallas *Also called Loftus & Woosley Inc (G-4601)*

Premier Printing & Ltr Svc Inc 713 868-6300
815 Live Oak St Houston (77003) *(G-11404)*

Premier Silica, Irving *Also called Pioneer Sands LLC (G-13146)*

Premier Technical Plastics, Irving *Also called Premier Plastics Dallas Inc (G-13156)*

Premier Uniform Inc (PA) 210 253-3406
2111 West Ave San Antonio (78201) *(G-18392)*

Premier Worldwide Inc 281 752-0014
3819 Honea Egypt Rd Montgomery (77316) *(G-15640)*

Premiere Inc 817 326-3500
215 Industrial Ave Granbury (76049) *(G-7805)*

Premiere Well Service 806 669-3227
2101 Mccullough St Pampa (79065) *(G-16335)*

Premium Oilfield Tech LLC (HQ) 281 670-5200
5727 Brittmoore Rd Houston (77041) *(G-11405)*

Premium Valve Services LLC (HQ) 281 457-2565
260 N Sam Houston Pkwy E Houston (77060) *(G-11406)*

Premium Weld Services Inc 940 329-0222
16119 S Fm 4 Santo (76472) *(G-18738)*

Premium Welding Inc 713 957-2724
4122 Creekmont Dr Houston (77091) *(G-11407)*

Premium Welding & Mfg Inc 713 957-2724
4122 Creekmont Dr Houston (77091) *(G-11408)*

Prengler Ltd 972 965-5188
14871 State Highway 56 Sherman (75092) *(G-18928)*

Prentex Alloy Fabricators Inc 214 748-7837
3108 Sylvan Ave Dallas (75212) *(G-4822)*

Prentice Hall, Irving *Also called Pearson Education Inc (G-13140)*

Presco, Sherman *Also called Precision Specialties Company (G-18927)*

Presco Polymers Opco Inc 903 957-2263
1201 E Pecan St Sherman (75090) *(G-18929)*

Prescotts Limbs & Braces (PA) 210 224-0726
6715 San Pedro Ave San Antonio (78216) *(G-18393)*

Prescrption Dspensing Labs Inc 512 219-0724
101 Commercial Pkwy Cedar Park (78613) *(G-2983)*

Preservo Pnt & Coatings Mfg Co, Houston *Also called Envirokind Inc (G-9668)*

Presidential Billiards LP 281 572-4733
20221 Caroline Way New Caney (77357) *(G-15847)*

Presidio Custom Metal Works 512 284-8549
903 Brandi Ln Round Rock (78681) *(G-17682)*

Presidio Ntwrked Sltons Group 469 549-3800
1955 Lakeway Dr Ste 220 Lewisville (75057) *(G-14083)*

Presidio Petroleum LLC 814 589-3550
500 W 7th St Fort Worth (76102) *(G-6914)*

Press Masters Inc (PA) 713 661-9100
3814 Bissonnet St Houston (77005) *(G-11409)*

Press Stop, San Antonio *Also called Milestone International Inc (G-18306)*

Pressman Toy Corporation (HQ) 732 562-1590
1111 Digital Dr Ste 150 Richardson (75081) *(G-17376)*

Pressure Point Service 713 641-2325
6430 Springer St Houston (77087) *(G-11410)*

Pressure Products Inc 817 249-1338
15920 Highway 377 S A Fort Worth (76126) *(G-6915)*

Pressure Systems International 210 222-1926
4323 Interstate Way San Antonio (78219) *(G-18394)*

Prestige Ameritech Ltd 817 427-2700
7201 Iron Horse Blvd North Richland Hills (76180) *(G-15879)*

Prestige Custom Cabinetry 832 674-8074
18902 Fm 529 Rd Ste D Cypress (77433) *(G-3813)*

Prestige Embossing Company Inc 713 864-0578
9777 W Gulf Bank Rd # 900 Houston (77040) *(G-11411)*

Prestige Kitchen Inc 972 366-3322
1404 S Fm 157 Venus (76084) *(G-20221)*

Prestige Printers, Houston *Also called Royal Publishing Inc (G-11683)*

Prestige Tank & Pump Svcs Inc 512 698-9645
1600 S 8th St Austin (78718) *(G-1431)*

Presto Printing, San Antonio *Also called Chandler Consultants Inc (G-17999)*

Presto Products Company, Carrollton *Also called Reynolds Presto Products Inc (G-2807)*

Preston Exploration Ltd Lblty 281 367-8697
1717 Woodstead Ct Ste 207 The Woodlands (77380) *(G-19904)*

Preston Oil Company LP 281 367-8697
1717 Woodstead Ct Ste 207 The Woodlands (77380) *(G-19905)*

Pretzels Inc 972 416-3660
2305 E Belt Line Rd # 210 Carrollton (75006) *(G-2795)*

PRI, McKinney *Also called Pacific Resources Intl LLC (G-14962)*

Price Drilling Company Inc 361 256-3363
Hwy 359 E Benavides (78341) *(G-2035)*

Pricevision Inc 972 770-0000
1505 Wallace Dr Ste 140 Carrollton (75006) *(G-2796)*

Pride Refining Inc 325 677-5444
1209 N 4th St Abilene (79601) *(G-66)*

Priefert Complex Designs, Mount Pleasant *Also called Priefert Mfg Co Inc (G-15660)*

Priefert Mfg Co Inc 903 572-1741
2630 S Jefferson Ave Mount Pleasant (75455) *(G-15660)*

Primac Systems, Dallas *Also called Vercom Software Inc (G-5161)*

Primalscream Music, Austin *Also called Nicole Dionne (G-1366)*

Primary Color LLC 214 630-8800
9239 Premier Row Dallas (75247) *(G-4823)*

Primary Sourcing Corp (HQ) 713 952-5405
2930 Rogerdale Rd Houston (77042) *(G-11412)*

Prime Deli, Lewisville *Also called Warabeya Texas Inc (G-14110)*

Prime Downhole Mfg LLC (PA) 832 957-3200
800 Northpark Central Dr Houston (77073) *(G-11413)*

Prime Energy Management, Houston *Also called Sterling Drlg Fund 1983-1 LP (G-12059)*

Prime Equipment Services, Arlington *Also called Skl Prime Services LLC (G-782)*

Prime Flexible Products, Houston *Also called Wellstream Inc (G-12633)*

Prime Lables, Farmers Branch *Also called Dallas Label and Packaging Inc (G-6192)*

Prime Momento LLC 832 643-4605
19901 Southwest Fwy # 124 Sugar Land (77479) *(G-19529)*

Prime Natural Resources Inc 832 531-8555
1201 La St Ste 2700 Houston (77002) *(G-11414)*

Prime Natural Resources LLC (PA) 713 953-3200
1201 La St Ste 2700 Houston (77002) *(G-11415)*

Prime Operating Company (HQ) 713 735-0000
9821 Katy Fwy Ste 1050 Houston (77024) *(G-11416)*

Prime Operating Company 830 876-2441
1595 Hwy 83 S Carrizo Springs (78834) *(G-2687)*

Prime Products Inc 979 743-6555
601 S Main St Schulenburg (78956) *(G-18777)*

Prime Source Office Solutions, Houston *Also called HF Guyton Inc (G-10167)*

Prime Time LLC 210 250-3000
301 Avenue E San Antonio (78205) *(G-18395)*

Prime Turbines LLC (HQ) 972 406-2100
1615 Diplomat Dr Ste 120 Carrollton (75006) *(G-2797)*

Primed Up Nitrogen Svcs LLC 361 543-0747
230 Barrow White Rd Anahuac (77514) *(G-527)*

Primeenergy Corporation 830 876-2441
1684 S Us Highway 83 Carrizo Springs (78834) *(G-2688)*

Primeenergy Corporation (PA) 713 735-0000
9821 Katy Fwy Ste 1050 Houston (77024) *(G-11417)*

Primera Energy LLC 210 490-8200
446 Forest Sq Longview (75605) *(G-14290)*

Primera Fabrication Inc 956 367-8690
15671 Primera Rd Harlingen (78552) *(G-8197)*

Primexx Operating Corporation (PA) 214 369-5909
4849 Grnvlle Ave Ste 1600 Dallas (75206) *(G-4824)*

Primexx Operating Corporation 432 445-7860
2131 Barilla Rd Pecos (79772) *(G-16625)*

Primo Microphones Inc (HQ) 972 548-9807
1805 Couch Dr McKinney (75069) *(G-14967)*

Prince Energy LLC (HQ) 713 955-5398
15311 Vantage Pkwy W # 3 Houston (77032) *(G-11418)*

Prince Manufacturing Corp 915 217-2664
6248 Edgemere Blvd El Paso (79925) *(G-5918)*

Prince Minerals LLC (HQ) 646 747-4222
15311 Vantage Pkwy W # 3 Houston (77032) *(G-11419)*

Prince Plastics Inc 281 240-6400
455 Julie Rivers Dr Sugar Land (77478) *(G-19530)*

Prince Signs LLC 281 345-4488
6432 Cunningham Rd Houston (77041) *(G-11420)*

Principal Led, San Angelo Also called 2v Led LLC *(G-17767)*

Principal Led, San Angelo Also called Principal Lighting Group LLC *(G-17824)*

Principal Lighting Group LLC 325 227-4577
3490 Venture Dr San Angelo (76905) *(G-17824)*

Print Art, McKinney Also called Accurate Die Cutting Inc *(G-14922)*

Print Graphics, Grand Prairie Also called Mds Printgraphics Inc *(G-7923)*

Print Group 817 847-7860
4296 Western Center Blvd Fort Worth (76137) *(G-6916)*

Print Place, Arlington Also called Pp Exit LLC *(G-757)*

Print Premium 972 292-7227
555 Republic Dr Ste 200 Plano (75074) *(G-16977)*

Print Shop, Garland Also called Garland Independent School Dst *(G-7494)*

Print Shop 903 295-2727
214 S Bolivar St Marshall (75670) *(G-14799)*

Print Shop, The, Lampasas Also called Hill Country Publishing Co *(G-13834)*

Print Systems Inc (PA) **713 812-8126**
4537 Brittmoore Rd Houston (77041) *(G-11421)*

Print World Inc 817 446-9555
6025 E Lancaster Ave Fort Worth (76112) *(G-6917)*

Print X Press, Laredo Also called Juan Garza *(G-13900)*

Printcitycom 214 728-1230
9020 Directors Row Dallas (75247) *(G-4825)*

Printdallas Inc 214 363-1101
3001 Knox St Ste 102 Dallas (75205) *(G-4826)*

Printed Products, Austin Also called Printedd Products & Svcs Ltd *(G-1432)*

Printed Supplies Inc 210 946-2977
10530 Sentinel St San Antonio (78217) *(G-18396)*

Printedd Products & Svcs Ltd (PA) **972 660-3800**
2641 N Forum Dr Grand Prairie (75052) *(G-7954)*

Printedd Products & Svcs Ltd 512 835-2253
2400 Forbes Dr Ste 100 Austin (78754) *(G-1432)*

Printegra Corp 800 972-1175
3301 Avenue E E Arlington (76011) *(G-759)*

Printer Solutions, San Antonio Also called MPS Group *(G-18322)*

Printers Service Florida Inc 817 477-1291
6740 Exchange Dr Mansfield (76063) *(G-14704)*

Printing Corner, The, El Paso Also called Beck-Drennan Inc *(G-5660)*

Printing Edge The, Fort Worth Also called Print Group *(G-6916)*

Printing Plus, Burleson Also called Wahoo Inc *(G-2601)*

Printing Research Corporation 214 353-9000
10760 Shady Trl Ste 300 Dallas (75220) *(G-4827)*

Printing X-Press, Houston Also called Molloy Corporation *(G-10907)*

Printmailers Inc 832 201-2000
707 West Rd Houston (77038) *(G-11422)*

Printmailpro.com, Austin Also called Printmpro Ltd *(G-1433)*

Printmpro Ltd 512 821-9000
9011 Tuscany Way Ste 200 Austin (78754) *(G-1433)*

Printpack Inc 409 883-9325
4715 Fm 1006 Orange (77630) *(G-16257)*

Printpack Inc 972 602-8421
2006 Great Southwest Pkwy Grand Prairie (75051) *(G-7955)*

Printpack Inc 972 641-4421
2005 S Great Sw Pkwy Grand Prairie (75051) *(G-7956)*

Priority Signs and Graphics, Southlake Also called Cjhorak Enterprises Inc *(G-19059)*

Prism Enterprises (HQ) **210 520-8051**
6952 Fairgrounds Pkwy San Antonio (78238) *(G-18397)*

Prism Industries LLC 956 425-3300
2901 N Expressway 77 Harlingen (78552) *(G-8198)*

Prism Microwave Inc 972 745-7222
440 Wrangler Dr Ste 500 Coppell (75019) *(G-3435)*

Prism Resources Inc 713 947-2800
7301 Galveston Rd Houston (77034) *(G-11423)*

Prism Technologies, San Antonio Also called Prism Enterprises *(G-18397)*

Pristech Products Inc 210 520-8051
6952 Fairgrounds Pkwy # 107 San Antonio (78238) *(G-18398)*

Pristine Cast Stone Inc 972 772-9490
900 Sids Rd Rockwall (75032) *(G-17562)*

Pritchett LP 214 239-9600
8150 N Central Expy Dallas (75206) *(G-4828)*

Privacy Inc 214 760-8700
12720 Hillcrest Rd # 720 Dallas (75230) *(G-4829)*

Privileged Culture LLC 682 252-5173
3700 Trailwood Ct Apt 832 Arlington (76014) *(G-760)*

Pro Chem Cleaning Systems, Arlington Also called Pro-Chem of Dfw Inc *(G-761)*

Pro Coat, Carrollton Also called Quality Powder Coating Inc *(G-2801)*

Pro Connect Technology LLC 972 543-2603
1700 Capital Ave Plano (75074) *(G-16978)*

Pro Digi Embroidery 713 339-4373
5755 Bonhomme Rd Ste 410 Houston (77036) *(G-11424)*

Pro Directional, Conroe Also called Professnal Drctional Entps Inc *(G-3354)*

Pro Directional, Midland Also called Professnal Drctional Entps Inc *(G-15365)*

Pro Fab, Magnolia Also called Professional Fabrication Inc *(G-14622)*

Pro Field Services Inc (PA) 361 798-5552
212 E 2nd St Hallettsville (77964) *(G-8125)*

Pro Field Services Inc 361 575-0348
22905 Nw Zac Lentz Pkwy Victoria (77905) *(G-20296)*

Pro Inspection Inc 432 362-2247
6975 E Commerce St Odessa (79762) *(G-16126)*

Pro Line Newwater Inc 210 648-2206
13406 Donop Rd Elmendorf (78112) *(G-6071)*

Pro Line Products Inc 972 488-4200
11625 Columbia Center Dr # 1 Dallas (75229) *(G-4830)*

Pro Machine LP 713 466-3210
6119 Brittmoore Rd Houston (77041) *(G-11425)*

Pro Oilfield Services LLC (PA) **281 496-5810**
25700 Interstate 45 # 460 Spring (77386) *(G-19242)*

Pro Panels, Dallas Also called Mick & David Enterprises Inc *(G-4674)*

Pro Pavers Houston LLC 281 665-4718
22603 Beckendorff Rd Katy (77449) *(G-13433)*

Pro Print & Label Group, El Paso Also called Ramirez Everardo *(G-5926)*

Pro Print A Sasch Company, Dallas Also called Sasch Inc *(G-4935)*

Pro Soap, Rockwall Also called Texas Nova-Chem Corporation *(G-17569)*

Pro Star Industries Inc (HQ) **979 779-9399**
1590a N Harvey Mitchell Bryan (77803) *(G-2499)*

Pro Tech Mwd Services Inc 817 568-1038
9729 South Fwy Fort Worth (76140) *(G-6918)*

Pro Techniques, Midland Also called Core Laboratories LP *(G-15178)*

Pro-Chem of Dfw Inc 817 695-1660
609 112th St Arlington (76011) *(G-761)*

Pro-Form, Quitman Also called Performance Metal Works Inc *(G-17228)*

Pro-Grind Inc 713 645-2966
5637 Hogue St Houston (77087) *(G-11426)*

Pro-Ject Chemicals Inc 832 403-2560
1800 Hughes Landing Blvd Spring (77380) *(G-19243)*

Pro-Kleen Inc 713 855-2760
4800 Fidelity St Houston (77029) *(G-11427)*

Pro-Kleen Industries, Houston Also called Pro-Kleen Inc *(G-11427)*

Pro-Plastics Inc 713 690-9000
9530 Baythorne Dr Houston (77041) *(G-11428)*

Pro-Plastics Inc (PA) **713 690-9000**
9530 Baythorne Dr Houston (77041) *(G-11429)*

Pro-Steel Inc 817 572-4959
5121 Kaltenbrun Rd Fort Worth (76119) *(G-6919)*

Pro-Tem Inc 281 334-5547
2525 S Shore Blvd Ste 401 League City (77573) *(G-13976)*

Pro-Test Inc (PA) **903 986-8404**
454 Fm 1252 E Kilgore (75662) *(G-13584)*

Proactive Technologies Inc 972 416-6298
2833 Trinty Sq Dr Ste 105 Carrollton (75006) *(G-2798)*

Probe Technology Services Inc (PA) **817 568-8528**
1132 Everman Pkwy Ste 100 Fort Worth (76140) *(G-6920)*

Probity Energy Partners LLC 432 570-1122
3407 Caldera Blvd Midland (79707) *(G-15363)*

Procam Controls Inc 972 422-1212
2605 Tech Dr Ste 300 Plano (75074) *(G-16979)*

Procegas LLC 832 652-2129
111 Berry Rd Houston (77022) *(G-11430)*

Procella Logging 409 787-2325
1440 Hwy 184 Hemphill (75948) *(G-8247)*

Procera Networks Inc (HQ) **510 230-2777**
5800 Granite Pkwy Ste 170 Plano (75024) *(G-16980)*

Process Automation Design Inc (PA) **817 283-1500**
3508 Raider Dr Hurst (76053) *(G-12855)*

Process Engineered Eqp Co 361 289-8891
438 Mcbride Ln Corpus Christi (78408) *(G-3597)*

Process Industry Practices 512 232-3041
3925 W Braker Ln R4500 Austin (78759) *(G-1434)*

Process Level Technology Ltd 281 332-6241
888 Clear Creek Ave League City (77573) *(G-13977)*

Process Manufacturing Corp 713 426-1403
415a N Wayside Dr Ste A Houston (77020) *(G-11431)*

Process Products, La Porte Also called Puffer-Sweiven Holdings Inc *(G-13785)*

Process Recovery Systems Inc 281 448-8180
5930 Par Four Dr Houston (77088) *(G-11432)*

Processing Division, Waco Also called Sanderson Farms Inc *(G-20457)*

Procial, Austin Also called Practice Interactive Inc *(G-1427)*

Proco Inc 361 516-1112
129 W Huisache Ave Kingsville (78363) *(G-13634)*

Procon Construction Co Inc 281 375-6829
2875 Woods Rd Brookshire (77423) *(G-2323)*

Procraft Cabinetry Inc 832 203-5736
4647 Pine Timbers St Houston (77041) *(G-11433)*

Procraft Cabinetry Dallas LLC 469 607-2588
2330 Alberta Dr 100 Dallas (75229) *(G-4831)*

Procurement Services Del Inc 832 243-6330
363 N Sam Houston Pkwy E Houston (77060) *(G-11434)*

Procyrion Inc 713 579-9224
3900 Essex Ln Ste 850 Houston (77027) *(G-11435)*

Prodektive Specialty Svcs LLC 713 425-3075
1110 Nasa Pkwy Ste 450 Houston (77058) *(G-11436)*

A
L
P
H
A
B
E
T
I
C

Prodigy Painting......817 277-2468
2309 Superior Dr Pantego (76013) ***(G-16351)***
Producers Midstream LP......214 238-5740
2311 Cedar Springs Rd # 100 Dallas (75201) ***(G-4832)***
Product Handling Design Inc (PA)......**972 231-4628**
6650 E State Highway 114 Haslet (76052) ***(G-8222)***
Product Quality Management LLC......713 538-3028
1710 Preston Ave Ste 160 Pasadena (77503) ***(G-16498)***
Production Downhole Svcs Inc......806 592-0032
1602 State Route 83 Denver City (79323) ***(G-5423)***
Production Facilities Eqp Inc......281 356-1107
28010 Fm 2978 Rd Magnolia (77354) ***(G-14621)***
Production Lift Systems Inc......432 699-1200
14 E Industrial Loop Midland (79701) ***(G-15364)***
Production Logging Inc......325 573-4441
2268 N State Highway 208 Snyder (79549) ***(G-19002)***
Production Machine & Tool LP......940 767-9400
2450 Burkburnett Rd Wichita Falls (76306) ***(G-20798)***
Production Manufacturing Inc......915 629-9668
1515 Goodyear Dr El Paso (79936) ***(G-5919)***
Production Mch & Tl MGT LLC......940 767-9400
2450 Burkburnett Rd Wichita Falls (76306) ***(G-20799)***
Production Meter & Testing......254 559-7271
506 E Walker St Breckenridge (76424) ***(G-2234)***
Production Pump, Odessa *Also called Machine Tech Services Inc* ***(G-16068)***
Production Services, Aransas Pass *Also called Kellogg Brown Root* ***(G-593)***
Production Tech & Svcs Inc......281 498-7399
1463 Highway 6 S Ths Houston (77077) ***(G-11437)***
Production Warehousing Inc......915 779-1405
320 N Clark Dr El Paso (79905) ***(G-5920)***
Productioneered Products Co......281 364-1086
25531 Richards Rd Spring (77386) ***(G-19244)***
Productos Real, El Paso *Also called Rd Food Manufacturing Inc* ***(G-5930)***
Profab, Lubbock *Also called American Petroleum Welding Inc* ***(G-14361)***
Professional Ambulance Sls Svc, Comanche *Also called Youghall Enterprises Inc* ***(G-3237)***
Professional Coating Tech Inc......972 291-7474
1001 Mount Lebanon Rd Cedar Hill (75104) ***(G-2952)***
Professional Fabrication Inc......936 321-7070
714c Honea Egypt Rd Ste C Magnolia (77354) ***(G-14622)***
Professional Machine Works......713 645-7562
7583 Morley St Houston (77061) ***(G-11438)***
Professional Machines Co, El Paso *Also called Norlus Group Inc* ***(G-5899)***
Professional Projects Inc......281 351-6315
18115 Telge Rd Cypress (77429) ***(G-3814)***
Professional Rebuild & Optimal......806 358-3636
14115 Indian Hill Rd Amarillo (79124) ***(G-456)***
Professional Rental Tools LLC (PA)......**713 808-9756**
1111 North Loop W Ste 140 Houston (77008) ***(G-11439)***
Professional Supplements, Frisco *Also called Prosupps USA LLC* ***(G-7308)***
Professionalized Pdts & Svcs......281 933-9427
10905 Brooklet Dr Houston (77099) ***(G-11440)***
Professnal Drctional Entps Inc (PA)......**936 441-7266**
850 Conroe Park West Dr Conroe (77303) ***(G-3354)***
Professnal Drctional Entps Inc......432 695-6152
3001 S County Road 1260 Midland (79706) ***(G-15365)***
Professnal Rbild Optmal Svc LL (PA)......**806 749-7761**
2523 86th St Lubbock (79423) ***(G-14465)***
Proficiency Testing, Brownsville *Also called Serafy Laboratories Ltd* ***(G-2405)***
Profile Labels & Tags, Schulenburg *Also called Schulenburg Prtg Off Sups Inc* ***(G-18778)***
Profitable Decisions Inc......281 972-3030
7814 Nairn St Houston (77074) ***(G-11441)***
Profitgarden, Houston *Also called E-Ceptionist Inc* ***(G-9554)***
Proform Group Inc......214 206-4100
2400 Skyline Dr Mesquite (75149) ***(G-15072)***
Progress Drilling Inc......830 875-3442
1575 N Magnolia Ave Luling (78648) ***(G-14563)***
Progress Rail Services Corp......817 693-2550
13601 North Fwy Ste 100 Fort Worth (76177) ***(G-6921)***
Progress Rail Services Corp......806 335-3900
12100 Walls Rd Amarillo (79118) ***(G-510)***
Progressive, Arlington *Also called SPS Technologies LLC* ***(G-786)***
Progressive Coml Aquatics Inc (PA)......**281 982-0212**
2510 Farrell Rd Houston (77073) ***(G-11442)***
Progressive Components Inc......972 775-6932
1010 Eastgate Rd Midlothian (76065) ***(G-15491)***
Progressive Incorporated......817 465-3221
1030 Commercial Blvd N Arlington (76001) ***(G-762)***
Progressive Laboratories Inc......972 518-9660
3131 Story Rd W Irving (75038) ***(G-13157)***
Progressive Machine Works Ltd......281 209-9990
19515 Oil Center Blvd Houston (77073) ***(G-11443)***
Progressive Mfg Tech Inc......512 380-1991
5507 Honey Dew Ter Austin (78749) ***(G-1435)***
Progressive Millworks Inc......512 832-0551
11118 N Lamar Blvd Ste A Austin (78753) ***(G-1436)***
Progressive Resources Inc (PA)......**915 778-9548**
7713 Alameda Ave El Paso (79915) ***(G-5921)***
Progressive Sales Inc (PA)......**432 333-6631**
1201 S County Rd W Odessa (79763) ***(G-16127)***
Progressive Steel & Wire LLC (HQ)......**972 999-8778**
1321 Greenway Dr Irving (75038) ***(G-13158)***
Progrssive Mdia Communications......254 675-3336
310 W 5th St Clifton (76634) ***(G-3146)***
Project Services Group Inc......972 812-7370
2040 Century Center Blvd # 10 Irving (75062) ***(G-13159)***
Prolift Equipment Inc......214 682-3327
1314 Heather Glen St Duncanville (75137) ***(G-5538)***
Proline Hs, Dallas *Also called Pro Line Products Inc* ***(G-4830)***
Prolux LLC......801 955-7070
3125 N Great Southwest Pk Grand Prairie (75050) ***(G-7957)***
Proman Usa Inc (HQ)......**713 943-2200**
600 Travis St Ste 3680 Houston (77002) ***(G-11444)***
Proman USA (pampa) LLC (HQ)......**713 943-2200**
600 Travis St Ste 3600 Houston (77002) ***(G-11445)***
Promar LP (PA)......**361 727-3300**
4305 Highway 35 S Rockport (78382) ***(G-17531)***
Promaxima Manufacturing Ltd (PA)......**800 231-6652**
5310 Ashbrook Dr Houston (77081) ***(G-11446)***
Promaxima Mfg LLP Prom......713 667-9606
5310 Ashbrook Dr Houston (77081) ***(G-11447)***
Prometheus Energy Group Inc (HQ)......**832 456-6500**
10305 Richmond Ave # 825 Houston (77042) ***(G-11448)***
Prometheus SEC Group Globl, Austin *Also called Ldia Holdings LLC* ***(G-1284)***
Promicom Inc (PA)......**832 544-0855**
1544 Sawdust Rd Ste 301 The Woodlands (77380) ***(G-19906)***
Promos Distributors Inc......972 478-7298
2520 Tarpley Rd Ste 500 Carrollton (75006) ***(G-2799)***
Promotional Products Assn Intl......972 252-0404
3125 Skyway Cir N Irving (75038) ***(G-13160)***
Prompt Printers Inc......210 223-9177
503 Chestnut St San Antonio (78202) ***(G-18399)***
Pronav Inc (PA)......**361 727-3300**
4305 Hwy 35 S Rockport (78382) ***(G-17532)***
Pronto Publishings & Prtg Co......210 658-6857
304 Crown Ct Converse (78109) ***(G-3400)***
Propel Energy LLC (PA)......**713 463-6500**
1923 Woodhead St Houston (77019) ***(G-11449)***
Propell American LLC......817 573-3550
4801 Glen Rose Hwy Granbury (76048) ***(G-7806)***
Proper Storage Systems LLC......830 372-1380
2200 E Us Highway 90 Seguin (78155) ***(G-18856)***
Property Works Central Texas......512 940-9353
12928 Lowden Ln Unit G Manchaca (78652) ***(G-14640)***
Propetro Holding Corp (PA)......**432 688-0012**
1706 S Midkiff Rd Ste B Midland (79701) ***(G-15366)***
Propetro Services Inc......432 685-0059
4 S Industrial Loop Midland (79701) ***(G-15367)***
Propetro Services Inc (HQ)......**432 688-0012**
1706 S Midkiff Rd Ste B Midland (79701) ***(G-15368)***
Proportion Foods LLC (PA)......**512 735-9800**
101 Chisholm Trail Rd Round Rock (78681) ***(G-17683)***
Proportional Technologies Inc......713 747-7324
12233 Robin Blvd Houston (77045) ***(G-11450)***
Props By Tops, Austin *Also called Texas Office Pdts & Sup Inc* ***(G-1569)***
Proptester Incorporated (PA)......**281 256-8880**
17222 Huffmeister Rd B Cypress (77429) ***(G-3815)***
Prorock Granite & Cabinets Inc......832 486-9414
8620 Windswept Ln Houston (77063) ***(G-11451)***
Pros Inc......713 335-5151
3200 Kirby Dr Houston (77098) ***(G-11452)***
Pros Company, Lubbock *Also called Professnal Rbild Optmal Svc LL* ***(G-14465)***
Pros Holdings Inc (PA)......**713 335-5151**
3200 Kirby Dr Ste 600 Houston (77098) ***(G-11453)***
Prosep Technologies Inc......281 504-2040
5512 Clara Rd Houston (77041) ***(G-11454)***
Proserv Anchor Crane Group, Irving *Also called Proserv Crane & Equipment Inc* ***(G-13161)***
Proserv Anchor Crane Group, Houston *Also called Proserv Crane & Equipment Inc* ***(G-11455)***
Proserv Crane & Equipment Inc......972 438-5100
2020 E Grauwyler Rd Irving (75061) ***(G-13161)***
Proserv Crane & Equipment Inc (PA)......**281 405-9048**
455 Aldine Bender Rd Houston (77060) ***(G-11455)***
Proserv Operations Inc......337 984-8054
15151 Sommermeyer St Houston (77041) ***(G-11456)***
Proserv Operations Inc......832 467-3110
15151 Sommermeyer St Houston (77041) ***(G-11457)***
Proserv Operations Inc......713 468-8778
1231 Lumpkin Rd Houston (77043) ***(G-11458)***
Proserv Operations Inc......713 983-7222
15151 Sommermeyer St Houston (77041) ***(G-11459)***
Proserv Operations Inc......281 807-2100
2437 Peyton Rd Houston (77032) ***(G-11460)***
Prosigns, Garland *Also called Identity Solutions Inc* ***(G-7515)***
Proske Plastic Products Inc......713 926-9941
6701 Supply Row Houston (77011) ***(G-11461)***
Prosource Industries Inc......972 660-1400
1700 111th St Grand Prairie (75050) ***(G-7958)***

Prostar Manufacturing Inc (PA) 281 910-0110
  5519 Bay Oaks Dr Pasadena (77505) *(G-16499)*

Prostar Manufacturing Inc 936 585-0737
  5519 Bay Oaks Dr Pasadena (77505) *(G-16500)*

Prosupps USA LLC (HQ) 214 310-1188
  5757 Main St Ste 205 Frisco (75034) *(G-7308)*

Protec, Webster *Also called Patton Enterprises Inc (G-20642)*

Protech Diamond Usa Inc 972 602-0080
  1600 109th St Grand Prairie (75050) *(G-7959)*

Protech Global, El Paso *Also called Compass Electronics Group LLC (G-5701)*

Protech Globl Solutions GP LLC, El Paso *Also called Lachmann Vllneva Hldngs GP LLC (G-5836)*

Protechnics, Kilgore *Also called Core Laboratories LP (G-13538)*

Protechnics (PA) 713 328-2320
  6510 W Sam Houston Pkwy N Houston (77041) *(G-11462)*

Protect Controls Inc 713 691-5183
  3212 Old Highway 105 E Conroe (77301) *(G-3355)*

Protective Concepts Inc 832 843-7619
  17803 Grant Rd Cypress (77429) *(G-3816)*

Protective Industries Inc 281 399-2600
  19233 Fm 1485 Rd New Caney (77357) *(G-15848)*

Protective Packaging Corp Inc 972 446-2247
  1746 W Crosby Rd Ste 108 Carrollton (75006) *(G-2800)*

Protective Powder Coatings LLC 361 854-7911
  502 Mccampbell Rd Corpus Christi (78408) *(G-3598)*

Protege Energy III LLC (PA) 918 728-3092
  55 Waugh Dr Ste 400 Houston (77007) *(G-11463)*

Protek Specialty Company 713 667-6691
  10315 Brighton Ln Houston (77031) *(G-11464)*

Proto Industrial Tools, Dallas *Also called Stanley Industrial & Auto LLC (G-5007)*

Protocol Feeds, Bridgeport *Also called Protocol Technologies Inc (G-2299)*

Protocol Technologies Inc 940 683-8123
  210 Lake Rd Bridgeport (76426) *(G-2299)*

Protoline Inc 281 561-0802
  10650 Stancliff Rd Houston (77099) *(G-11465)*

Protom International Inc (PA) 972 410-3551
  610 Parker Sq Flower Mound (75028) *(G-6277)*

Protorque Energy Inc (PA) 432 208-1404
  2606 E Interstate 20 Midland (79706) *(G-15369)*

Prototype Machine Co 512 282-1590
  2119 W Fm 1626 Manchaca (78652) *(G-14641)*

Provence Hardware Corporation 817 572-4663
  1112 E Rendon Crowley Rd Burleson (76028) *(G-2594)*

Provibtech Inc (PA) 713 830-7601
  7636 Harwin Dr Ste 112 Houston (77036) *(G-11466)*

Providence Energy Corporation 214 522-9131
  14860 Montfort Dr Ste 115 Dallas (75254) *(G-4833)*

Provident Rmnfcturing Svcs Inc 940 239-7775
  2141 Collins Rd Ste 301 Denton (76208) *(G-5394)*

Provimi North America Inc 817 594-9628
  1050 Vigortone Blvd Weatherford (76086) *(G-20612)*

Proworx Inc 713 666-3131
  12309 Hodges St Houston (77085) *(G-11467)*

Proworx Architectural Signage, Houston *Also called Proworx Inc (G-11467)*

Proximity Systems Inc 281 370-5004
  11301 Boudreaux Rd Tomball (77375) *(G-20002)*

Prt Offshore, Houston *Also called Professional Rental Tools LLC (G-11439)*

Prucka-Laney Inc (PA) 432 687-0799
  3204 Sunburst Dr Midland (79707) *(G-15370)*

Prudent Speculator, The, Austin *Also called Afam Capital Inc (G-900)*

Pruf Energy Solutions LLC 254 870-0400
  215 Cotton Dr Waco (76712) *(G-20450)*

Prysmian Cbles Systems USA LLC 281 209-1070
  1610 Greens Rd Houston (77032) *(G-11468)*

Prytime Medical Devices Inc (PA) 210 340-0116
  229 N Main St Boerne (78006) *(G-2132)*

PSC, Azle *Also called Allen Prfmce Resources Inc (G-1719)*

Psd3 Enterprises LLC 830 995-3894
  50502 Ih 10 W Comfort (78013) *(G-3240)*

Psde LLC 972 429-7160
  941 Hensley Ln Wylie (75098) *(G-20945)*

PSI, Houston *Also called Pipeline Seal & Insulator Inc (G-11336)*

PSI, Temple *Also called Panel Specialists Inc (G-19695)*

PSI Automation, Celina *Also called Rda Corporation (G-2993)*

PSI Concrete Construction LLC 210 204-1529
  130 Talavera Pkwy # 1032 San Antonio (78232) *(G-18400)*

PSI Industries Inc 940 564-3563
  1436 W Main St Olney (76374) *(G-16224)*

PSI Midstream Partners LP 713 554-2880
  114 Fawnlake Dr Houston (77079) *(G-11469)*

PSM, Houston *Also called Peyton Salas & Mendoza LLC (G-11313)*

Psp Engineering, Schertz *Also called Psp Industries Inc (G-18760)*

Psp Industries Inc (HQ) 210 651-9595
  9885 Doerr Ln Schertz (78154) *(G-18760)*

Pt Hardware Inc 214 744-4491
  4030 La Reunion Pkwy Dallas (75212) *(G-4834)*

Pt Trucks Inc 713 338-1375
  6509 Romona Blvd Houston (77086) *(G-11470)*

Pti Pvment Repr Pdts Aka Pvptc, Missouri City *Also called David L Jennings (G-15579)*

Pti Systems, League City *Also called Pro-Tem Inc (G-13976)*

Ptp Incorporated 281 342-8775
  1549 Highway 36 N Rosenberg (77471) *(G-17595)*

Pts Inc 806 669-2525
  403 W Atchison Ave Pampa (79065) *(G-16336)*

Pts - Power Temp Systems Inc 337 806-9779
  1646 Rankin Rd Ste 300 Houston (77073) *(G-11471)*

Pts Vam Co, Houston *Also called Vam Usa LLC (G-12525)*

Public Steel Inc 806 376-8221
  1012 Sw 4th Ave Amarillo (79101) *(G-457)*

Publictions Communications Inc 512 250-9023
  13552 N Hwy 183 Ste A Austin (78750) *(G-1437)*

Publishing Concepts LP 214 530-0335
  4835 Lbj Fwy Ste 1100 Dallas (75244) *(G-4835)*

Pudding On Smiles, Arlington *Also called Mygis Empire LLC (G-735)*

Puff & Stuff Candles, San Antonio *Also called Scentchips Inc (G-18456)*

Puffer-Sweiven Holdings Inc 281 470-2000
  903 Highway 146 S La Porte (77571) *(G-13785)*

Puffer-Sweiven Holdings Inc 361 883-6215
  621 Navigation Blvd Corpus Christi (78408) *(G-3599)*

Puffer-Sweiven LP Inc 281 240-2000
  4230 Greenbriar Dr Stafford (77477) *(G-19364)*

Pugh Acquisition Company 361 884-9351
  5878 Agnes St Corpus Christi (78406) *(G-3600)*

Pulido Associates Inc 817 249-6728
  7601 Benbrook Pkwy Benbrook (76126) *(G-2045)*

Pulido Tortilla Factory, Benbrook *Also called Pulido Associates Inc (G-2045)*

Pull Rite Trailers LLC (HQ) 903 502-5000
  9350 State Highway 31 E Murchison (75778) *(G-15681)*

Pump Arts Inc 713 946-0500
  10034 Easthaven Blvd Houston (77075) *(G-11472)*

Pump Station, Lewisville *Also called City of Colony The (G-14037)*

Pumpco Inc 979 542-9054
  1209 S Main St Giddings (78942) *(G-7700)*

Pumping Unit Technologies, Midland *Also called Endeavor Energy Resources LP (G-15212)*

Pumps Plus Pump & Valve Repair 903 987-9232
  508 S Commerce St Kilgore (75662) *(G-13585)*

Pumpworks Castings LLC 936 634-4206
  1001 E Park Ave Lufkin (75901) *(G-14546)*

Purchasing Dept 956 318-2626
  2802 S Hwy Business 281 Edinburg (78539) *(G-5598)*

Pure & Gentle Inc 830 379-1937
  2460 Crossroads Blvd Seguin (78155) *(G-18857)*

Pure Biofuels Corp 281 540-9317
  3811 Shadow Trace Cir Houston (77082) *(G-11473)*

Pure Element Water, Dumas *Also called Llanos Altos LLC (G-5524)*

Pure Party Ice LP 210 223-6400
  1902 S Laredo St Bldg 5 San Antonio (78207) *(G-18401)*

Pure River LLC 469 853-4867
  1045 County Road 456 Princeton (75407) *(G-17211)*

Purina Animal Nutrition LLC 817 492-9159
  5500 South Fwy Ste 180 Fort Worth (76115) *(G-6922)*

Purina Animal Nutrition LLC 817 878-0280
  1501 E 4th St Fort Worth (76102) *(G-6923)*

Purina Animal Nutrition LLC 830 672-6565
  1402 E Sarah Dewitt Dr Gonzales (78629) *(G-7762)*

Purina Animal Nutrition LLC 806 761-7200
  212 E Harvard St Lubbock (79403) *(G-14466)*

Purina Animal Nutrition LLC 254 840-3276
  1135 E Mcgregor Dr Mc Gregor (76657) *(G-14822)*

Purina Mills LLC 281 342-6758
  825 Highway 36 N Rosenberg (77471) *(G-17596)*

Purina Mills LLC 830 672-6565
  1402 E Sarah Dewitt Dr Gonzales (78629) *(G-7763)*

Purity Oilfield Services LLC (HQ) 214 880-8400
  2101 Cedar Springs Rd # 650 Dallas (75201) *(G-4836)*

Purity Oilfield Services LLC 844 221-1500
  11109 W County Road 46 Midland (79707) *(G-15371)*

Purocol LLC 310 926-9007
  2001 Platinum St Garland (75042) *(G-7573)*

Purolator Efp LLC (HQ) 713 977-0610
  8733 Daffodil St Houston (77063) *(G-11474)*

Pursuit Oil & Gas LLC 832 706-2299
  840 Gessner Rd Ste 850 Houston (77024) *(G-11475)*

Pursuit Safety Inc 972 772-4747
  4947 State Highway 276 Royse City (75189) *(G-17724)*

Purvis Industries LLC (PA) 214 358-5500
  10500 N Stemmons Fwy Dallas (75220) *(G-4837)*

Pushnami LLC (PA) 512 961-7042
  6600 N Lamar Blvd Austin (78752) *(G-1438)*

Put-In-Cups LLC 800 506-7891
  14510 Whitman Pond Corpus Christi (78418) *(G-3601)*

Pv American Inc 713 270-7772
  1907 Upland Dr Ofc Houston (77043) *(G-11476)*

Pvf Extruders, San Antonio *Also called Plastic Vacuum Forming Inc (G-18382)*

Pvh Corp 512 392-2036
  4015 S Ih 35 Ste 1050 San Marcos (78666) *(G-18704)*

Pw Eagle Inc 979 532-5640
  10807 Us 59 Hwy Wharton (77488) *(G-20705)*

PWC Industries Inc 361 289-0557
  6650 Leopard St Corpus Christi (78409) *(G-3602)*

Pwf Enterprises 512 295-6412
  2457 S Loop 4 Ste 3b Buda (78610) *(G-2534)*

Pwg, Irving Also called Physicians Wellness Group Inc *(G-13143)*

Pwr Technologies LLC 469 609-3537
  18601 Lbj Fwy Ste 700 Mesquite (75150) *(G-15073)*

Pxp Gulf Coast Inc (HQ) **713 579-6000**
  700 Milam St Ste 3100 Houston (77002) *(G-11477)*

Pxp Offshore LLC 713 579-6000
  700 Milam St Ste 3100 Houston (77002) *(G-11478)*

Pyco Industries Inc (PA) **806 747-3434**
  2901 Avenue A Lubbock (79404) *(G-14467)*

Pyle Machine Company Inc 817 485-6011
  4201 Clay Ave Fort Worth (76117) *(G-6924)*

Pyramid Gom Inc 281 822-0801
  1800 West Loop S Ste 1950 Houston (77027) *(G-11479)*

Pyramid Stone Co Inc 210 533-3511
  9011 Old Crpus Chrsti Hwy San Antonio (78223) *(G-18402)*

Pyramid Tubular Products LLC 281 405-8090
  480 Wildwood Forest Dr # 700 Spring (77380) *(G-19245)*

Pyranha Inc 832 467-3840
  6602 Cunningham Rd Houston (77041) *(G-11480)*

Pyranha Insecticides, Houston Also called Pyranha Inc *(G-11480)*

Pysz Enterprises Inc 972 964-3980
  2305 Trellis Ln Plano (75075) *(G-16981)*

Python Pressure Pumping LLC 940 549-6900
  111 Hyde Park Blvd # 500 Cleburne (76033) *(G-3106)*

Q C Graphics Inc 972 931-4100
  1501 N Plano Rd Ste 300 Richardson (75081) *(G-17377)*

Q Cabinets Inc 915 859-5252
  10050 N Loop Dr Socorro (79927) *(G-19018)*

Q M Company Inc 713 673-1917
  4846 W O S T Dr Houston (77013) *(G-11481)*

Q'Max America Envmtl Solutions, Houston Also called QMax America Inc *(G-11483)*

Q-West Energy Company 972 233-8191
  15505 Wright Brothers Dr Addison (75001) *(G-157)*

Q2 Artificial Lift Svcs LLC 903 983-1432
  3611 E State Highway 158 Midland (79706) *(G-15372)*

Q2 Holdings Inc (PA) **512 275-0072**
  13785 Res Blvd Ste 150 Austin (78750) *(G-1439)*

Qa Support LP 281 307-1000
  11005 W Fairmont Pkwy La Porte (77571) *(G-13786)*

Qae Inc 281 436-5500
  16945 Northchase Dr # 2200 Houston (77060) *(G-11482)*

Qar Industries Inc (PA) **940 325-3301**
  101 Se 25th Ave Mineral Wells (76067) *(G-15538)*

Qc Graphics, Richardson Also called Q C Graphics Inc *(G-17377)*

Qdi Stone, Houston Also called Quarries Direct Intl LLC *(G-11509)*

QEP Co Inc 817 477-1183
  300 S 6th Ave Mansfield (76063) *(G-14705)*

Qes Pressure Control LLC 903 643-0700
  5104 Estes Pkwy Longview (75603) *(G-14291)*

Qes Pressure Control LLC 361 580-5400
  376 Enterprise Dr Victoria (77905) *(G-20297)*

Qes Wireline LLC 903 720-8805
  291 Johnny Clark Rd Longview (75603) *(G-14292)*

Qes Wireline LLC (HQ) **817 546-4970**
  801 Cherry St Ste 800 Fort Worth (76102) *(G-6925)*

Qes Wireline LLC 432 813-6088
  12052 Cleburne Hwy Cresson (76035) *(G-3712)*

Qfc Industries Inc (PA) **817 640-2151**
  3201 E Arkansas Ln 111 Arlington (76010) *(G-763)*

Qfc Plastics Inc 817 375-5774
  4304 Larry Ln Arlington (76017) *(G-764)*

Qg Printing Corp 936 634-3357
  3001 Atkinson Dr Lufkin (75901) *(G-14547)*

QMax America Inc 817 732-2423
  11700 Katy Fwy Enrgy Twr Houston (77079) *(G-11483)*

QMax Solutions Inc 832 672-4459
  1315 W Sam Houston Pkwy N S Houston (77043) *(G-11484)*

QMF Steel Inc 903 455-3618
  3846 E Interstate 30 Campbell (75422) *(G-2646)*

QMF Supply Fab Manufacturing, Campbell Also called QMF Steel Inc *(G-2646)*

Qnet Inc 214 341-7638
  12021 Plano Rd Ste 150 Dallas (75243) *(G-4838)*

Qnet Information Services, Dallas Also called Qnet Inc *(G-4838)*

QO Inc (PA) **713 224-7823**
  10402 Valley Forge Dr Houston (77042) *(G-11485)*

Qorvo Inc 336 678-5099
  4345 Innovation Dr Bldg D Farmers Branch (75234) *(G-6211)*

Qorvo Logistics, Farmers Branch Also called Qorvo Inc *(G-6211)*

Qorvo Texas LLC 972 994-8200
  500 W Renner Rd Richardson (75080) *(G-17378)*

Qorvo US, Richardson Also called Qorvo Texas LLC *(G-17378)*

Qpower Incorporated 713 266-5295
  5610 Savoy Dr Houston (77036) *(G-11486)*

Qri International LLC (HQ) **713 485-8800**
  909 Fannin St Ste 2200 Houston (77010) *(G-11487)*

QSD Manufacturing Inc 713 957-0599
  5700 Mitchelldale St Houston (77092) *(G-11488)*

Qsfirst Inc 210 362-1983
  10203 Kotzebue St Ste 106 San Antonio (78217) *(G-18403)*

Qsi Custom Cabinets LP 512 443-3303
  3800 Drossett Dr Ste B Austin (78744) *(G-1440)*

Qt Dog LLC 214 333-4477
  4419 Mint Way Dallas (75236) *(G-4839)*

Qt Industries LLC 972 221-0537
  7410 Ambassador Row Dallas (75247) *(G-4840)*

Qti Apparel & Promotions LLC 254 662-3076
  300 S Valley Mills Dr Waco (76710) *(G-20451)*

Qti Apparel and Promotions, Waco Also called Qti Apparel & Promotions LLC *(G-20451)*

Qti Promotions and Apparel Inc 254 756-4444
  300 S Valley Mills Dr Waco (76710) *(G-20452)*

Qti-Powers 254 662-3076
  300 S Valley Mills Dr Waco (76710) *(G-20453)*

Qtran Corp 817 870-1855
  1334 E 4th St Fort Worth (76102) *(G-6926)*

Qtrco Inc 281 516-0277
  13120 Theis Ln Tomball (77375) *(G-20003)*

Qts LLC 713 462-7072
  5084 Steadmont Dr Houston (77040) *(G-11489)*

Quacito LLC (PA) **210 695-0795**
  11802 Warfield St San Antonio (78216) *(G-18404)*

Quad/Graphics Inc 972 892-3803
  6700 Denton Dr Dallas (75235) *(G-4841)*

Quadrabyte LLC 469 619-0749
  700 Lavaca St Ste 1401 Austin (78701) *(G-1441)*

Quadrangle Press Inc 210 828-8191
  9111 Broadway San Antonio (78217) *(G-18405)*

Quadrant Chemical, McKinney Also called Vertrauen Chemie Solutions Inc *(G-14986)*

Quail Construction, Andrews Also called Quail Energy Services LP *(G-557)*

Quail Energy Services LP (PA) **432 523-3742**
  2495 N Us Highway 385 Andrews (79714) *(G-557)*

Quail Tools LP 361 579-0244
  7701 Us Highway 59 N Victoria (77905) *(G-20298)*

Quail Tools LP 281 445-1777
  15401 Vantage Pkwy W # 100 Houston (77032) *(G-11490)*

Quail Well Service Inc 325 677-0323
  110 Caddo Dr Abilene (79602) *(G-67)*

Quaint Energy, Rosenberg Also called Quaint Slutions Trdg Ltd Lblty *(G-17597)*

Quaint Slutions Trdg Ltd Lblty 832 758-3074
  1201 Nantere Ct Rosenberg (77471) *(G-17597)*

Quaker Oats Company 214 333-1200
  2822 Glenfield Ave Dallas (75233) *(G-4842)*

Quaker State Investment Corp 713 546-4000
  700 Milam St Houston (77002) *(G-11491)*

Qualcomm Technologies Inc 512 623-3700
  9600 Mo Pac Dr Austin (78731) *(G-1442)*

Quali-Tex Ball & Seat Co 432 332-3755
  3300 N Fm 1936 Odessa (79764) *(G-16128)*

Qualico Steel Company Inc 972 775-1400
  2800 Miller Rd Midlothian (76065) *(G-15492)*

Quality Access Control Systems 830 981-5400
  28993 Interstate 10 W Boerne (78006) *(G-2133)*

Quality Bakery Products Inc 281 449-4977
  14330 Interdrive W Houston (77032) *(G-11492)*

Quality Bedding Company, Houston Also called Quality Mattress Company Inc *(G-11497)*

Quality Biologicals, Seguin Also called Quality Bioresources Inc *(G-18858)*

Quality Bioresources Inc 830 372-4797
  1015 N Austin St Seguin (78155) *(G-18858)*

Quality Brewers, Houston Also called C Villanueva Company LLc *(G-9035)*

Quality Bumper Service Dallas 214 824-7300
  1155 S Haskell Ave Dallas (75223) *(G-4843)*

Quality Business Solutions 972 285-2000
  2830 Anchor Dr Mesquite (75150) *(G-15074)*

Quality Case & Fixture Inc 409 832-3200
  2070 Gulf St Beaumont (77703) *(G-1943)*

Quality Cases & Containers LLC 972 690-9911
  1800 Jay Ell Dr Ste 100 Richardson (75081) *(G-17379)*

Quality Cast Metals Inc 817 921-3595
  3000 S Jones St Fort Worth (76104) *(G-6927)*

Quality Concrete Products, Commerce Also called Randolph D & L Company LLC *(G-3246)*

Quality Copper & Alloys LLC 346 223-1032
  515 Garden Oaks Blvd Houston (77018) *(G-11493)*

Quality Custom Fabricators 817 649-8020
  1750 Westpark Dr Ste 100 Grand Prairie (75050) *(G-7960)*

Quality Fabrication Design LP 972 304-3266
  955 Freeport Pkwy Ste 400 Coppell (75019) *(G-3436)*

Quality Fiberglass Inc 817 473-3563
  105 Industrial Blvd Mansfield (76063) *(G-14706)*

Quality For Dressing Co, Spring Also called Quality Fur Dressing *(G-19246)*

Quality Foundation Repair Inc 512 363-7769
  9906 Gray Blvd Ste A Austin (78758) *(G-1443)*

Quality Fur Dressing 281 292-2617
  1012 Rayford Rd Ste E Spring (77386) *(G-19246)*

Quality Graphics & Forms Inc 915 592-4500
1410 Gail Borden Pl B1 El Paso (79935) *(G-5922)*

Quality Hand Bindery Inc 281 445-8682
8520 Sweetwater Ln E42 Houston (77037) *(G-11494)*

Quality Honeycomb LP 817 640-1190
624 107th St Arlington (76011) *(G-765)*

Quality Hot Mix Inc (PA) **979 543-6464**
1805 N Blue Creek Rd El Campo (77437) *(G-5627)*

Quality Industries Inc 615 708-4980
1550 N Wstn Blvd Ste 190 Denton (76207) *(G-5395)*

QUALITY INDUSTRIES, INCORPORATED, Denton *Also called Quality Industries Inc* *(G-5395)*

Quality Ingredients, Richardson *Also called Steven M Riley* *(G-17402)*

Quality Ironworks Inc 214 688-0180
1607 W Commerce St Dallas (75208) *(G-4844)*

Quality Lighting 512 799-2341
1611 Clovis R Barker Rd San Marcos (78666) *(G-18705)*

Quality Lnings Fabrication Inc (PA) **713 863-7013**
3601 W 12th St Houston (77008) *(G-11495)*

Quality Logging Inc 432 682-7168
1800 Dayton Rd Midland (79706) *(G-15373)*

Quality Machine Shop LLC 979 885-6932
3213 Highway 36 Sealy (77474) *(G-18815)*

Quality Manufacturing Inc 940 592-5790
5873 Fm 369 N Iowa Park (76367) *(G-12908)*

Quality Mat Company (PA) **409 898-1170**
6550 Tram Rd Beaumont (77713) *(G-1944)*

Quality Mat Company 713 455-3990
14214 East Fwy Houston (77015) *(G-11496)*

Quality Mattress Company Inc 713 433-9155
5331 Prudence Dr Ste A Houston (77045) *(G-11497)*

Quality Mill of Texas LLC 409 722-4594
550 Tram Rd Beaumont (77713) *(G-1945)*

Quality Powder Coating Inc (PA) **972 466-0655**
1838 Forms Dr Carrollton (75006) *(G-2801)*

Quality Precision Coatings LLC 713 631-8141
9105 Ley Rd Houston (77078) *(G-11498)*

Quality Product Finishing Inc 281 469-6970
9610 Frbanks N Houston Rd Houston (77064) *(G-11499)*

Quality Readymix Ltd LLP 361 289-2515
333 Mcbride Ln Corpus Christi (78408) *(G-3603)*

Quality Roller Supply Inc 817 783-5100
9620 E Fm Hwy 917 Alvarado (76009) *(G-338)*

Quality Running Gear, Royse City *Also called Polar Corporation* *(G-17722)*

Quality Sausage Company Inc (PA) **214 634-3400**
1925 Lone Star Dr Dallas (75212) *(G-4845)*

Quality Sausage Company Inc 214 634-3400
1919 Lone Star Dr Dallas (75212) *(G-4846)*

Quality Signs Inc 713 671-9222
10205 Market St Houston (77029) *(G-11500)*

Quality Star Products Ltd 214 680-7448
3930 Miller Park Dr Garland (75042) *(G-7574)*

Quality Steel Fab, San Antonio *Also called SA Quality Fence Ltd* *(G-18440)*

Quality Stone Co, Florence *Also called Lithic Industries Inc* *(G-6240)*

Quality Store Equipment Inc 713 278-8634
7800 Harwin Dr Ste C Houston (77036) *(G-11501)*

Quality Table Linen Inc 281 240-1024
4003 Greenbriar Dr Ste A Stafford (77477) *(G-19365)*

Quality Tool, Dallas *Also called Qt Industries LLC* *(G-4840)*

Quality Trailer Products LP (HQ) **817 444-4518**
604 W Main St Azle (76020) *(G-1728)*

Quality Trailer Products LP 903 572-7932
609 E 16th St Mount Pleasant (75455) *(G-15661)*

Quality Trbchrger Cmpnents LLC 713 849-4200
6902 Signat Dr Houston (77041) *(G-11502)*

Quality Tubing Inc (HQ) **281 456-0751**
10303 Sheldon Rd Houston (77049) *(G-11503)*

Quality Welding & Fabrication, New Braunfels *Also called BCAD Zion Corporation* *(G-15775)*

Quality Wood Products, Huntsville *Also called Falcon Wood Products 2 Ltd* *(G-12811)*

Qualtex Laboratories 210 736-8952
6211 W Interstate 10 San Antonio (78201) *(G-18406)*

Quanex Building Products Corp (PA) **731 961-4600**
1800 West Loop S Ste 1500 Houston (77027) *(G-11504)*

Quanex Homeshield, LLC, Houston *Also called Quanex Screens LLC* *(G-11505)*

Quanex Screens LLC (HQ) **713 961-4600**
1800 West Loop S Ste 1500 Houston (77027) *(G-11505)*

Quantex Instrument Company 936 544-5732
1503 E Loop 304 Crockett (75835) *(G-3723)*

Quantum Corporation 210 622-9235
12081 Barker Rd Atascosa (78002) *(G-817)*

Quantum Fitness Corporation 281 495-3003
126 Eldridge Rd Ste B Sugar Land (77478) *(G-19531)*

Quantum Ink Company 713 688-2288
16802 Barker Springs Rd # 900 Houston (77084) *(G-11506)*

Quantum Investment Group Inc (PA) **281 994-5400**
16600 Park Row Houston (77084) *(G-11507)*

Quantum Materials Corp 512 245-6646
3055 Hunter Rd San Marcos (78666) *(G-18706)*

Quantum Reservoir Impact LLC (PA) **713 485-8800**
909 Fannin St Ste 2200 Houston (77010) *(G-11508)*

Quarries Direct International 602 269-7900
2605 Freewood Dr Dallas (75220) *(G-4847)*

Quarries Direct Intl LLC 713 808-9849
5800 Centralcrest St Houston (77092) *(G-11509)*

Quasar Energy Services Inc 940 612-3336
3288 Fm 51 Gainesville (76240) *(G-7359)*

Quatrefoil Partners LLC 214 631-7117
5521 Maple Ave Dallas (75235) *(G-4848)*

Quatro Oil and Gas Inc 940 767-4443
700 Lamar St Wichita Falls (76301) *(G-20800)*

Quell Petroleum Services Inc 432 943-8400
700 N Loop 464 Monahans (79756) *(G-15612)*

Quemetco Metals Limited Inc 214 631-6070
2777 N Stemmons Fwy # 1800 Dallas (75207) *(G-4849)*

Quesco Turbo Machinery Svcs, Houston *Also called Power Process Developments Inc* *(G-11378)*

Quest and Sons Inc 806 744-2351
222 E 34th St Lubbock (79404) *(G-14468)*

Quest Drape, Frisco *Also called Bkbl Holdings Ltd* *(G-7270)*

Quest Medical Inc 800 627-0226
1 Allentown Pkwy Allen (75002) *(G-297)*

Quest Software Inc 949 754-8000
15950 Dallas Pkwy Ste 350 Dallas (75248) *(G-4850)*

Quest-TEC Solutions Inc (HQ) **281 240-0440**
13960 S Wayside Dr Houston (77048) *(G-11510)*

Questech Services Corporation 972 278-8006
2201 Executive Dr Garland (75041) *(G-7575)*

Questspecialty Corporation (PA) **713 896-8188**
2001 E Tom Green St Brenham (77833) *(G-2271)*

Quexco Incorporated (PA) **214 688-4000**
2777 N Stemmons Fwy # 18 Dallas (75207) *(G-4851)*

Quick Connectors, Houston *Also called Innovex Downhole Solutions Inc* *(G-10373)*

Quick Intrnet Sftwr Sltons Inc 979 846-3008
3206 Earl Rudder Fwy S College Station (77845) *(G-3198)*

Quick Tick International Inc 832 249-6400
10541 Fm 1960 Rd W # 501 Houston (77070) *(G-11511)*

Quick Turn Machining Inc 281 355-8876
428 S Persimmon St Tomball (77375) *(G-20004)*

Quickfilter Technologies Inc 972 442-3964
3103 Stonehenge Dr Richardson (75082) *(G-17380)*

Quickie Manufacturing Corp 915 859-2522
12058 Rojas Dr Ste A El Paso (79936) *(G-5923)*

Quicksilver Arena, Paris *Also called Metro Gate & Mfg Co Inc* *(G-16365)*

Quicksilver Resources Inc (PA) **817 665-5000**
801 Cherry St Unit 19 Fort Worth (76102) *(G-6928)*

Quiet Logistics Inc 860 841-3892
10750 Denton Dr Dallas (75220) *(G-4852)*

Quietaire Cooling Inc 713 228-9421
505 N Hutcheson St Houston (77003) *(G-11512)*

Quietaire Corporation (PA) **713 228-9421**
505 N Hutcheson St Houston (77003) *(G-11513)*

Quietflex Manufacturing Co LP 877 694-3669
4518 Brittmoore Rd Houston (77041) *(G-11514)*

Quik Print of Austin Inc (PA) **512 467-9382**
8508 Cross Park Dr Austin (78754) *(G-1444)*

Quik Print Prtg & Copying Ctr, Austin *Also called Quik Print of Austin Inc* *(G-1444)*

Quikrete 210 208-1511
6981 E Evans Rd San Antonio (78266) *(G-18644)*

Quikrete Companies LLC 936 587-4450
203119 Highway 90 E Raywood (77582) *(G-17235)*

Quikrete Companies LLC 979 732-8210
1083 Kleimann Columbus (78934) *(G-3232)*

Quikrete Companies LLC 325 672-4634
794 Fm 2404 Abilene (79601) *(G-68)*

Quikrete Companies LLC 432 694-5432
3517 W Industrial Ave Midland (79703) *(G-15374)*

Quikrete Companies LLC 817 783-3010
1008 E Highway 67 Alvarado (76009) *(G-339)*

Quiktrip Corporation 817 378-8410
2501 Ne 28th St Fort Worth (76106) *(G-6929)*

Quilters Emporium LLC 281 491-0016
11925 Ste 11 Sw Fwy Stafford (77477) *(G-19366)*

Quinn Printing Co Inc 972 788-4266
2001 Midway Rd Ste 128 Carrollton (75006) *(G-2802)*

Quinstar Corporation 512 326-1011
2024 E Saint Elmo Rd Austin (78744) *(G-1445)*

Quintana Energy Services Inc 832 518-4094
1415 La St Ste 2900 Houston (77002) *(G-11515)*

Quintana Energy Services LP (PA) **832 518-4094**
1415 La St Ste 2900 Houston (77002) *(G-11516)*

Quintana Minerals Brazil LLC (HQ) **713 751-7500**
1415 La St Ste 2400 Houston (77002) *(G-11517)*

Quintana Minerals Corporation 713 751-7500
1415 La St Ste 2400 Houston (77002) *(G-11518)*

Quintessential Chocolates Inc 830 990-9382
251 W Main St Fredericksburg (78624) *(G-7187)*

Quizno's Subs, Katy *Also called Onyx Venture Group LLC* *(G-13375)*

Quva Pharma Inc (PA) **888 339-0874**
1075 W Park One Dr # 100 Sugar Land (77478) *(G-19532)*

Quva Pharma Inc 201 306-4412
  5920 S General Bruce Dr # 100 Temple (76502) *(G-19700)*

Qvinci Software 512 637-7337
  1601 S Mo Pac Expy Austin (78746) *(G-1446)*

R & B Electronics Inc 906 632-1542
  2358 Nw Dallas St Grand Prairie (75050) *(G-7961)*

R & B Energy LLC 254 647-3358
  2817 Highway 101 Ranger (76470) *(G-17231)*

R & C Machine LLC 254 694-9278
  1104 Hwy 22 Whitney (76692) *(G-20732)*

R & D Advantage Inc 713 836-4000
  2000 Saint James Pl Houston (77056) *(G-11519)*

R & D Machine Shop, Dallas Also called Amfan Corporation *(G-3947)*

R & E Tooling & Plastics Inc 817 834-2858
  3939 Broadway Ave Fort Worth (76117) *(G-6930)*

R & F Industries Inc 830 875-6927
  402 W Davis St Luling (78648) *(G-14564)*

R & I Enterprises Inc 956 544-7948
  233 Paredes Line Rd Brownsville (78521) *(G-2396)*

R & N Manufacturing Ltd 713 466-6252
  21235 Fm 529 Rd Cypress (77433) *(G-3817)*

R & R Contractors, Corpus Christi Also called R & R Oilfield Services Inc *(G-3604)*

R & R Custom Cabinets Inc 972 247-4697
  1213 Wiltshire Dr Carrollton (75007) *(G-2883)*

R & R Design Inc 972 524-1789
  1112 S Virginia St Terrell (75160) *(G-19748)*

R & R Heat Exchangers Inc 281 951-0003
  1414 E Richey Rd Bldg C Houston (77073) *(G-11520)*

R & R Lease Service Inc 361 562-8379
  1791 Martin L King Blvd Alice (78332) *(G-230)*

R & R Oilfield Services Inc 361 289-5892
  7619 Up River Rd Corpus Christi (78409) *(G-3604)*

R & R Sheet Metal and Mch Sp 806 274-2361
  110 E Grand St Borger (79007) *(G-2183)*

R & S Steel Fabricating Co 713 675-9007
  9900 Beaumont Hwy Houston (77078) *(G-11521)*

R A Beaird Oil Co (PA) **325 928-5220**
  410 Oak Merkel (79536) *(G-15016)*

R A D Roustabout Service LLC 432 664-2430
  1508 S Jefferson St Midland (79701) *(G-15375)*

R A M, Cisco Also called Research Advanced Methods Inds *(G-3068)*

R B Converting, Dallas Also called RB Converting Inc *(G-4863)*

R B Testers Inc (PA) **432 582-2500**
  8705 N County Rd W Odessa (79764) *(G-16129)*

R C Schmidt & Son Inc 713 673-5911
  1215 Akron St Houston (77029) *(G-11522)*

R C T Inc 972 231-9698
  11527 Hillguard Rd Dallas (75243) *(G-4853)*

R C Technical, Stafford Also called R C Technical Welding & Fabr *(G-19367)*

R C Technical Welding & Fabr 281 933-6004
  12814 Mula Ln Stafford (77477) *(G-19367)*

R C W, The Colony Also called Rcw Energy Services LLC *(G-19812)*

R Chem Company, Dallas Also called Rchemco Inc *(G-4864)*

R Construction Company (PA) **903 322-4639**
  1313 W Us Highway 79 Buffalo (75831) *(G-2547)*

R D McMillan Company Inc 512 863-0231
  7075 Ranch Road 2338 Georgetown (78633) *(G-7671)*

R D Moxie LLc (PA) **210 633-2300**
  13515 Blue Wing Rd San Antonio (78223) *(G-18407)*

R D Screw Machine Products Inc 210 337-8942
  1054 Grubb St San Antonio (78219) *(G-18408)*

R D T, Midland Also called Roxwell Performance Drlg LLC *(G-15389)*

R E Janes Gravel Co 325 736-5008
  Fm 126 Merkel (79536) *(G-15017)*

R E M Industries Inc 915 544-2233
  2025 E Yandell Dr El Paso (79903) *(G-5924)*

R F Higginbotham Inc 512 836-8985
  8723 N Lamar Blvd Austin (78753) *(G-1447)*

R Guerra Construction Inc 956 854-4038
  6700 N Mile 3 1/2 W Weslaco (78599) *(G-20667)*

R Ibarras Inc 817 625-8962
  5410 Basswood Blvd 21 Fort Worth (76137) *(G-6931)*

R J C Enterprises Inc 806 793-8238
  5404 4th St Lubbock (79416) *(G-14469)*

R J Machine Company Inc 830 693-7493
  130 Northridge Rd Marble Falls (78654) *(G-14750)*

R J Mangold Grain Co Inc 830 985-3323
  16112 S Front St La Coste (78039) *(G-13690)*

R J Reynolds Tobacco Company 877 703-0386
  5400 University Dr Tyler (75707) *(G-20144)*

R J Smelley Company Inc 817 295-4241
  123 N Commerce St Burleson (76028) *(G-2595)*

R Jones and Associates Inc 214 951-0091
  3054 Irving Blvd Dallas (75247) *(G-4854)*

R K Texas Leather Mfg Inc 903 378-2100
  104 E Main St Honey Grove (75446) *(G-8358)*

R Lacy Inc 903 758-8276
  222 E Tyler St Longview (75601) *(G-14293)*

R Lacy Services Ltd (PA) **903 758-8276**
  222 E Tyler St Longview (75601) *(G-14294)*

R Lute S Inc 281 595-3777
  803 E Fm 1462 Rd Rosharon (77583) *(G-17610)*

R Lutes Inc (PA) **281 595-3777**
  803 W Fm 1462 Rosharon (77583) *(G-17611)*

R M S Inc 713 467-2043
  1624 Oak Tree Dr Houston (77080) *(G-11523)*

R Neal John & Associates Inc 214 340-1464
  10610 Boomer Cir Dallas (75238) *(G-4855)*

R P M, Lockhart Also called Reed Prototype and Model Inc *(G-14172)*

R R Donnelley, Houston Also called R R Donnelley & Sons Company *(G-11525)*

R R Donnelley, Lewisville Also called R R Donnelley & Sons Company *(G-14085)*

R R Donnelley, Lewisville Also called R R Donnelley & Sons Company *(G-14086)*

R R Donnelley & Sons Company 972 459-1493
  1550 Lakeway Dr Ste 500 Lewisville (75057) *(G-14084)*

R R Donnelley & Sons Company 936 564-4683
  5903 North St Nacogdoches (75965) *(G-15711)*

R R Donnelley & Sons Company 979 836-4451
  1903 Fm 389 Brenham (77833) *(G-2272)*

R R Donnelley & Sons Company 214 521-4767
  3500 Maple Ave Ste 810 Dallas (75219) *(G-4856)*

R R Donnelley & Sons Company 713 957-8910
  6600 Long Point Rd # 103 Houston (77055) *(G-11524)*

R R Donnelley & Sons Company 713 630-1000
  2001 Kirby Dr Ste 400 Houston (77019) *(G-11525)*

R R Donnelley & Sons Company 972 459-1400
  1550 Lakeway Dr Ste 200 Lewisville (75057) *(G-14085)*

R R Donnelley & Sons Company 713 468-7175
  1645 W Sam Houston Pkwy N Houston (77043) *(G-11526)*

R R Donnelley & Sons Company 713 354-1300
  6315 W By Northwest Blvd Houston (77040) *(G-11527)*

R R Donnelley & Sons Company 972 353-6130
  1550 Lakeway Dr Ste 100 Lewisville (75057) *(G-14086)*

R R Ramsower Inc 979 849-6441
  1413 S Hwy 288b Angleton (77515) *(G-576)*

R S D Supply, Houston Also called RSD Supply Inc *(G-11691)*

R S Global Inc 972 406-2930
  3373 Garden Brook Dr Dallas (75234) *(G-4857)*

R S Graphic Services Inc 817 921-6266
  3300 S Jones St Fort Worth (76110) *(G-6932)*

R Slater Enterprises LLC 832 456-4900
  14119 Fm 529 Rd Houston (77041) *(G-11528)*

R T L X LLC (HQ) **214 778-6400**
  6100 Tennyson Pkwy # 150 Plano (75024) *(G-16982)*

R T M Interests LLC 432 683-7700
  550 W Texas Ave Ste 945 Midland (79701) *(G-15376)*

R T P Company, Fort Worth Also called Miller Waste Mills Inc *(G-6842)*

R Triplett Construction, Dallas Also called Rick Triplett *(G-4899)*

R W Gonzalez Office Pdts Inc (PA) **512 300-2300**
  600 Congress Ave Ste 1400 Austin (78701) *(G-1448)*

R W Machine Inc 281 784-1600
  1414 E Richey Rd Houston (77073) *(G-11529)*

R W McNamara, Euless Also called Davis Machine & Mfg Co *(G-6140)*

R Y N O, Tyler Also called Athletic Bag Company LP *(G-20051)*

R Young Fabrications, Midland Also called Randco Industries Inc *(G-15377)*

R&D Futures LLC 214 473-9955
  5760 Legacy Dr Ste B14 Plano (75024) *(G-16983)*

R&M Energy Systems, Willis Also called Robbins Myers Enrgy Systems LP *(G-20862)*

R&M Retro Services, Lewisville Also called Michael R Atteberry *(G-14067)*

R&R Machine, Dalhart Also called Dalhart R & R Mch Works Inc *(G-3834)*

R&R Millwork Inc 903 873-6600
  304 Bluebird Pkwy Wills Point (75169) *(G-20876)*

R-5 Metal Fabricators Inc 903 873-2633
  21121 Us Highway 80 Wills Point (75169) *(G-20877)*

R-D Sheet Metal Inc 817 332-2177
  200 N Foch St Fort Worth (76107) *(G-6933)*

R-Interests LLC 940 759-4181
  621 W Division St Muenster (76252) *(G-15672)*

R-J Typesetters Inc 915 562-4461
  2717 E Missouri Ave El Paso (79903) *(G-5925)*

R-O Mfg Co 817 293-6150
  7701 Will Rogers Blvd Fort Worth (76140) *(G-6934)*

R-Tex Services LLC 817 774-3333
  8124 Fm 1902 Joshua (76058) *(G-13324)*

R.C.T. & Company, New London Also called Reclamation Contractors Texas *(G-15851)*

R.G. Morgan & Son Central Ark, Dallas Also called Beta Arkansas LLC *(G-4022)*

R2 Fabrication Inc 817 230-2015
  804 S Blue Mound Rd Fort Worth (76131) *(G-6935)*

R2r and D LLC 432 264-7500
  610 S Main St Big Spring (79720) *(G-2094)*

R2sonic LLC 512 891-0000
  5307 Industrial Oaks Blvd Austin (78735) *(G-1449)*

R3 Edge, Odessa Also called R3 Energy Services LLC *(G-16130)*

R3 Energy Services LLC 432 335-7800
  5075 E 52nd St Apt A204 Odessa (79762) *(G-16130)*

R360 Envmtl Solutions LLC (HQ) **281 872-7360**
  3 Waterway Square Pl # 110 The Woodlands (77380) *(G-19907)*

Ra-Lock Security Solutions Inc.................................972 775-6301
  3570 N Highway 67 Ste B Midlothian (76065) *(G-15493)*

RAC Materials LLC 281 255-8500
  31350 Sh 249 Tomball (77375) *(G-20005)*

Rack Industries LLC 432 687-1868
  701 W Murphy St Odessa (79763) *(G-16131)*

Rack Solutions Inc 903 453-0800
  6725 Fm 1570 W Greenville (75402) *(G-8088)*

Rack Technology Inc 817 468-2233
  1001 Enterprise Pl Arlington (76001) *(G-766)*

Rackmount Solutions, Plano *Also called Bogey Free LLC (G-16809)*

Radco Operations LP 409 287-1277
  165 S Merchant St Sour Lake (77659) *(G-19033)*

Radford Manufacturing Inc 817 536-7706
  1800 Duval St Fort Worth (76104) *(G-6936)*

Radia Enterprises Inc (PA).....................................713 645-3600
  3800 Juniper St Houston (77087) *(G-11530)*

Radial Drilling Services Inc (PA)...........................281 374-7507
  4921 Spring Cypress Rd Spring (77379) *(G-19161)*

Radiant Indus Solutions Inc 713 972-0196
  2121 Brittmoore Rd # 3900 Houston (77043) *(G-11531)*

Radiant Uv, Houston *Also called Radiant Indus Solutions Inc (G-11531)*

Radiation Sys Prec Cntrls 972 907-9599
  1219 Digital Dr Ste 101 Richardson (75081) *(G-17381)*

Radiology Associates N Texas (PA)........................817 321-0300
  816 W Cannon St Fort Worth (76104) *(G-6937)*

Radioshack, Fort Worth *Also called General Wreless Operations Inc (G-6664)*

Radius Display Products, Dallas *Also called Display Products Inc (G-4262)*

Radius Hdd Direct LLC 800 892-9114
  2525 Ranger Hwy Weatherford (76088) *(G-20613)*

Radix Engineering and Software, Houston *Also called Radix Us LLC (G-11532)*

Radix Us LLC 832 377-9601
  820 Gessner Ster 875 Houston (77024) *(G-11532)*

Radixon Inc 855 723-4966
  4144 N Central Expy # 600 Dallas (75204) *(G-4858)*

Radke Machine & Tool Inc 254 576-2513
  603 Ne 4th St Hubbard (76648) *(G-12737)*

Radley Electric Inc 409 781-7172
  105 S Fannin St Sour Lake (77659) *(G-19034)*

Radtke Jenna 512 444-2002
  1506 S Congress Ave Austin (78704) *(G-1450)*

Rae Energy, Katy *Also called Subsea Services Intl Inc (G-13446)*

Rae Energy Inc 281 578-6523
  1621 Prime West Pkwy Katy (77449) *(G-13434)*

Rae Energy Solutions Inc 281 440-3434
  10757 Cutten Rd Bldg 1 Houston (77066) *(G-11533)*

Ragsdale Vision Ctr 940 387-9595
  526 N Locust St Ste B Denton (76201) *(G-5396)*

Ragsdale, Mark S Od, Denton *Also called Ragsdale Vision Ctr (G-5396)*

Rai of Sunshine LLC 832 271-0144
  11314 White Gate Ln Houston (77067) *(G-11534)*

Raider Manufacturing Inc 806 762-3227
  2008 E 50th St Lubbock (79404) *(G-14470)*

Raider Services LP 830 996-0016
  6215 County Road 120 Gordon (76453) *(G-7769)*

Rail Products Intl Inc 956 541-1759
  3600 E 14th St Brownsville (78521) *(G-2397)*

Rain Cii Carbon LLC (HQ)..281 318-2400
  2627 Chestnut Ridge Dr # 200 Kingwood (77339) *(G-13652)*

Rainbow Building Systems, Dallas *Also called Akidco Inc (G-3915)*

Rainbow Lake Aquaculture Co, Austin *Also called William B Sides (G-1667)*

Rainfost, Grand Prairie *Also called Bexter Enterprises LLC (G-7846)*

Rains County Leader 903 473-2653
  239 N Texas St Emory (75440) *(G-6085)*

Rainsoft Corpus Christi, Corpus Christi *Also called Texas Air & Water LLC (G-3636)*

Ral & Associates Inc 903 833-5191
  14750 State Highway 64 Ben Wheeler (75754) *(G-2034)*

Ralph Cordova Company 972 771-7281
  131 Mark Ln Royse City (75189) *(G-17725)*

Ram, Sealy *Also called Reactive & Alloy Mtls Inds Inc (G-18816)*

Ram Indstries Acquisitions LLC 281 495-9056
  5615 W Fuqua St Bldg C Houston (77085) *(G-11535)*

Ram International Inc 361 688-1966
  1848 Suntide Rd Corpus Christi (78409) *(G-3605)*

Ram Winch and Hoist Ltd 281 999-8665
  14603 Chrisman Rd Houston (77039) *(G-11536)*

Ram-Bro Contracting Inc 361 387-2795
  904 Industrial Ave Robstown (78380) *(G-17515)*

Ram-Gear Manufacturing Inc 361 668-0235
  6150 E Highway 44 Alice (78332) *(G-231)*

Rama Fabrication, Odessa *Also called Interstate Treating Inc (G-16033)*

Rama Fabrication Inc (PA).......................................432 362-9291
  2310 Prospect Odessa (79762) *(G-16132)*

Raman Systems Inc 512 673-7364
  7301 N Fm 620 Rd Ste 155 Austin (78726) *(G-1451)*

Ramann Enterprises Inc (PA)...................................817 560-4222
  3134 Marquita Dr Fort Worth (76116) *(G-6938)*

Rambler Newspapers Inc 972 870-1992
  627 S Rogers Rd Irving (75060) *(G-13162)*

Ramco Roustabout Inc 325 884-5734
  1401 E 3rd St Big Lake (76932) *(G-2061)*

Ramin Corporation 281 356-5178
  39019 Fm 149 Rd Magnolia (77354) *(G-14623)*

Ramirez Everardo 915 593-5349
  8701 Castner Dr El Paso (79907) *(G-5926)*

Ramirez Pecan Farm LLC 915 851-2003
  13709 N Loop Dr Clint (79836) *(G-3147)*

Ramon Guardiola 956 330-8026
  2545 E Griffin Pkwy U146 Mission (78572) *(G-15562)*

Rampak Group Inc 713 678-8898
  1356 Kress St Houston (77020) *(G-11537)*

Ramrod Enterprises LLC 936 756-4846
  12286 Highway 105 E Conroe (77306) *(G-3356)*

Ramses Lubr Repackaging LLC 972 672-8717
  861 S Great Sw Pkwy Grand Prairie (75051) *(G-7962)*

Ramsey Properties LP (PA)......................................281 328-3501
  16503 Ramsey Rd Crosby (77532) *(G-3741)*

Ramsey Properties LP 409 985-4200
  2450 Gulfway Dr Port Arthur (77640) *(G-17122)*

Ramtech Building Systems Inc 817 473-9376
  1400 Highway 287 S Mansfield (76063) *(G-14707)*

Ran Technologies Inc 281 530-3248
  10627 Kinghurst Dr Houston (77099) *(G-11538)*

Ranch Hand Truck Accessories, Shiner *Also called Kaspar Ranch Hand Eqp LLC (G-18942)*

Ranch House Jerky LLC 512 347-8999
  4201 Hidden Canyon Cv Austin (78746) *(G-1452)*

Ranch House Meat Company LLC 325 396-4536
  303 W San Saba Ave Menard (76859) *(G-15000)*

Rancho Lpg Holdings LLC 713 993-5331
  333 Clay St Ste 1600 Houston (77002) *(G-11539)*

Ranco Industries Inc 713 228-5543
  3421 Rusk St Houston (77003) *(G-11540)*

Ranco Rhino Mats & Matting 713 228-5543
  3421 Rusk St Houston (77003) *(G-11541)*

Randall & Dewey Jefferis 281 774-2000
  3 Allen Ctr 333 Clay 10 Houston (77002) *(G-11542)*

Randco Industries Inc 432 520-0820
  2702 W County Road 130 Midland (79706) *(G-15377)*

Randolph D & L Company LLC 903 886-3055
  915 Bois D Arc St Commerce (75428) *(G-3246)*

Randolph Door & Hearth Shoppe, Corpus Christi *Also called RDHS Inc (G-3606)*

Randolph Products Inc 713 468-6070
  27110 Shamrock Ct Richmond (77406) *(G-17464)*

Randy Drive Shaft Service, Houston *Also called Chalks Truck Parts Inc (G-9154)*

Randy L Gardner Inc 409 837-5111
  301 S Wheeler Colmesneil (75938) *(G-3222)*

Randy Myers Enterprises Inc 903 897-0681
  511 County Road 4311 Naples (75568) *(G-15720)*

Randy Smith Training Solutions, Spring *Also called Intertek Cnslting Trning USA I (G-19219)*

Randy Wrecker Service Inc 713 690-4000
  10127 Sussex Ln Houston (77041) *(G-11543)*

Randy's Drive Shaft Service, Houston *Also called Chalks Truck Parts Inc (G-9153)*

Ranews Texas Incorporated 770 229-5090
  940 Best Dr Seguin (78155) *(G-18859)*

Rangaire Manufacturing Co LP 817 556-6500
  501 S Wilhite St Cleburne (76031) *(G-3107)*

Range Production Parent Co (HQ)...........................817 870-2601
  100 Throckmorton St # 120 Fort Worth (76102) *(G-6939)*

Range Resources, Fort Worth *Also called Range Production Parent Co (G-6939)*

Range Resources - La Inc (HQ)................................713 588-8300
  100 Throckmorton St # 1200 Fort Worth (76102) *(G-6940)*

Range Resources Corporation (PA)..........................817 870-2601
  100 Throckmorton St # 1200 Fort Worth (76102) *(G-6941)*

Range Resources Corporation 817 870-2601
  100 Throckmorton St # 1200 Fort Worth (76102) *(G-6942)*

Ranger Aerodesign, Fort Worth *Also called Rsg Aerodesign LLC (G-6969)*

Ranger Air Aviation LLC 972 245-6699
  2670 Edmonds Ln Ste 200 Lewisville (75067) *(G-14087)*

Ranger Coml Con Contrs LLC 210 831-7052
  771 Brand Rd Rc Bulverde (78163) *(G-2558)*

Ranger Conveying & Supply Co (PA).......................713 671-0004
  4701 Clinton Dr Houston (77020) *(G-11544)*

Ranger Energy Services Inc (PA)............................713 935-8900
  10350 Richmond Ave # 550 Houston (77042) *(G-11545)*

Ranger Energy Services Inc 830 569-1940
  4740 County Road 430 Pleasanton (78064) *(G-17072)*

Ranger Energy Services LLC 713 461-9000
  10350 Richmond Ave # 550 Houston (77042) *(G-11546)*

Ranger Gate Company, Yoakum *Also called Merchants Moving & Storage Inc (G-20969)*

Ranger Gate Company, Yoakum *Also called Merchants Moving and Stor Inc (G-20970)*

Ranger Lift Trucks LLC (PA)....................................281 424-2111
  2100 I 10 E Baytown (77521) *(G-1832)*

Ranger Oilfield Products Inc 936 856-4182
  224 Longstreet Rd Willis (77378) *(G-20858)*

Ranger Opco, Baytown *Also called Ranger Lift Trucks LLC (G-1832)*

ALPHABETIC

Ranger Plastic Extrusions Inc 817 640-6067
  801 N Great Sw Pkwy Arlington (76011) *(G-767)*

Ranger Ready Mix LLC (PA) **512 363-7630**
  40206 Industrial Park Cir Georgetown (78626) *(G-7672)*

Ranger Security Detectors Inc 915 590-4441
  11900 Montana Ave El Paso (79936) *(G-5927)*

Ranger Signs, Porter *Also called Right Signs Inc* *(G-17182)*

Ranger Steel Supply LP (PA) **713 633-1306**
  1225 North Loop W Ste 650 Houston (77008) *(G-11547)*

Ranger Times, Eastland *Also called Eastland County Newspaper Inc* *(G-5564)*

Rap, Stafford *Also called Regional Acid Production LP* *(G-19368)*

Rapid Filter, Austin *Also called Janis Litchfield* *(G-1251)*

Rapid Hose 713 468-4673
  10207 Oakpoint Dr Houston (77043) *(G-11548)*

Rapid Reprographics LP 214 357-5444
  156 Kingston Cir Coppell (75019) *(G-3437)*

Rapid Service Inc (PA) **432 367-7283**
  2724 W 40th St Odessa (79764) *(G-16133)*

Rapid Turn Laser & Machine Ltd (PA) **281 447-5000**
  757 Kenrick Dr Ste 100 Houston (77060) *(G-11549)*

Rapid Wristbands, Houston *Also called Velocity Promotions LLC* *(G-12545)*

Raptor, Hutto *Also called Utility Composites Inc* *(G-12887)*

Raqcs, Houston *Also called Russian-American Quality* *(G-11700)*

Rare Enterprises, Dallas *Also called Ruben Reyes* *(G-4918)*

Rasch Graphic Services Corp 713 785-5750
  8648 Glenmont Dr Ste 100 Houston (77036) *(G-11550)*

Raschig Jaeger Technologies, Arlington *Also called Pmc Inc* *(G-754)*

Rashidah LLC 281 469-5277
  13214 Walnut Lake Rd Houston (77065) *(G-11551)*

Rast Iron Work Company Inc 210 659-6704
  6430 Railway San Antonio (78244) *(G-18409)*

Ratec Inc 903 687-3811
  935 W Texas Ave Waskom (75692) *(G-20520)*

Rathole Drilling Inc (PA) **361 664-9995**
  2427 N Us Highway 281 Alice (78332) *(G-232)*

Rational Systems LLC 832 476-8468
  8 Greenway Plz Ste 702 Houston (77046) *(G-11552)*

Ratliff Industries Inc 409 755-1830
  9514 Ratliff St Lumberton (77657) *(G-14569)*

Raul Gonzalez 956 793-5359
  300 E 5th St Elsa (78543) *(G-6080)*

Ravago Americas LLC 817 635-4770
  616 111th St Arlington (76011) *(G-768)*

Ravago Mfg Americas LLC 281 443-6220
  1031 Goodnight Trl Houston (77060) *(G-11553)*

Rave Gear LLC 830 421-3295
  425 Strempel St Seguin (78155) *(G-18860)*

Rave Gears, Seguin *Also called Rave Gear LLC* *(G-18860)*

Raven Butene-1 LLC 251 414-6955
  9520 East Fwy Baytown (77521) *(G-1833)*

Raw Services, Lubbock *Also called Ht Energy LLC* *(G-14419)*

Rawlins Monument Inc 817 594-2726
  111 Palo Pinto St Weatherford (76086) *(G-20614)*

Ray Cannedy SEC Investigations, Wichita Falls *Also called Cannedy Contemporary Svcs Inc (G-20749)*

Ray Mac Energy 806 274-5881
  1601 Fairlanes Blvd Borger (79007) *(G-2184)*

Raybar Services LLC 409 698-2548
  105 Don Woods Dr Brookeland (75931) *(G-2308)*

Raydon Inc (PA) **254 559-5012**
  300 Fm 3099 N Breckenridge (76424) *(G-2235)*

Raydon Construction, Breckenridge *Also called Raydon Inc* *(G-2235)*

Raymer Enterprises Inc 972 242-8863
  3355 Garden Brook Dr Dallas (75234) *(G-4859)*

Rays Chmpn Spring & Mtr Svc 817 921-3600
  3336 South Fwy Fort Worth (76110) *(G-6943)*

Rays Flow Control LLC 832 827-3427
  9700 Richmond Ave Ste 104 Houston (77042) *(G-11554)*

Rays Valve, Houston *Also called Rays Flow Control LLC* *(G-11554)*

Rays Welding Shop Inc 972 775-2822
  530 Curtis Ray Rd Midlothian (76065) *(G-15494)*

Rayson Company 713 680-0540
  7914 Breen Dr Houston (77064) *(G-11555)*

Raytheon Company 972 952-4195
  2816 Commodore Dr Carrollton (75007) *(G-2884)*

Raytheon Company 781 522-3000
  1309 Harvest Glen Dr Plano (75023) *(G-16984)*

Raytheon Company 972 231-4931
  2105 Belleview Ct Richardson (75082) *(G-17382)*

Raytheon Company 972 494-2073
  1110 Sunset Dr Garland (75040) *(G-7576)*

Raytheon Company 972 205-8846
  3400 Louis Dr Plano (75023) *(G-16985)*

Raytheon Company 972 205-4277
  6000 Lemmon Ave Dallas (75209) *(G-4860)*

Raytheon Company 972 344-2591
  6600 Chase Oaks Blvd Plano (75023) *(G-16986)*

Raytheon Company 972 344-3000
  13588 N Central Expy Dallas (75243) *(G-4861)*

Raytheon Company 915 771-5466
  1727 Cityline Dr Richardson (75082) *(G-17383)*

Raytheon Company 817 735-1251
  6500 West Fwy Ste 400 Fort Worth (76116) *(G-6944)*

Raytheon Company 719 638-2756
  1727 Cityline Dr Richardson (75082) *(G-17384)*

Raytheon Company 972 344-9133
  13510 N Central Expy Dallas (75243) *(G-4862)*

Raytheon Company 361 348-2712
  281 1 Mile S Premont (78375) *(G-17204)*

Raytheon Company 972 952-2007
  2501 W University Dr McKinney (75071) *(G-14968)*

Raytheon Company 915 779-7666
  7201 Montana Ave El Paso (79925) *(G-5928)*

Raytheon Company 972 272-0515
  1717 Cityline Dr Richardson (75082) *(G-17385)*

Raytheon Company 781 522-3000
  6625 Excellence Way Plano (75023) *(G-16987)*

Raytheon Company 703 525-1550
  621 Six Flags Dr Ste 100 Arlington (76011) *(G-769)*

Raytheon Company 972 344-8000
  1601 N Plano Rd Richardson (75081) *(G-17386)*

Raytheon Company 972 952-2007
  2501 W University Dr McKinney (75071) *(G-14969)*

Raytheon Company 877 291-9990
  4101 E Plano Pkwy Plano (75074) *(G-16988)*

Raytheon Company 972 952-4067
  2501 W University Dr McKinney (75071) *(G-14970)*

Raytheon Technologies Corp 210 680-0283
  6948 Fairgrounds Pkwy San Antonio (78238) *(G-18410)*

Raytheon Technologies Corp 940 761-9200
  3101 Hammon Rd Wichita Falls (76310) *(G-20801)*

Razberi Technologies Inc 469 828-3380
  13755 Hutton Dr Ste 500 Farmers Branch (75234) *(G-6212)*

Razor Specialties LLC 888 578-9656
  4553 N Loop 1604 W # 1227 San Antonio (78249) *(G-18411)*

RB Converting Inc (HQ) **800 543-7690**
  12855 Valley Branch Ln Dallas (75234) *(G-4863)*

RB Machine Works Inc 281 446-1414
  2407 Wilson Rd Humble (77396) *(G-12795)*

RB Processing LLc (PA) **281 992-3500**
  740 Bradfield Rd Houston (77060) *(G-11556)*

Rbc Music Company 210 736-6902
  4415 Centerview San Antonio (78228) *(G-18412)*

Rbc/H & H Sheet Music Centers, San Antonio *Also called Rbc Music Company* *(G-18412)*

Rbf, Houston *Also called Renewable Biofuels Inc* *(G-11599)*

Rbf Port Neches LLC (HQ) **713 386-2600**
  2229 San Felipe St # 950 Houston (77019) *(G-11557)*

Rbr Machine, Houston *Also called Reliable Bus Resources LLC* *(G-11588)*

Rbt Industries LLC (PA) **512 600-5994**
  800 Interchange Blvd # 101 Austin (78721) *(G-1453)*

RC Christopher Industries Inc 972 875-6555
  1504 S Kaufman St Ennis (75119) *(G-6116)*

RC Donuts 972 422-3379
  700 W Spring Creek Pkwy Plano (75023) *(G-16989)*

Rchemco Inc 817 791-7304
  2633 Mckinney Ave 130-411 Dallas (75204) *(G-4864)*

Rci, Houston *Also called Rotary Components Intl Inc* *(G-11668)*

Rcl Technologies Inc 214 870-3703
  103 E Pioneer Dr Irving (75061) *(G-13163)*

Rcss 210 661-8474
  2919 Fm 1516 N Converse (78109) *(G-3401)*

Rct Global Inc 915 595-8750
  1520 Goodyear Dr Ste S El Paso (79936) *(G-5929)*

Rcw Energy Services LLC (HQ) **972 394-1000**
  6270 Morning Star Dr # 100 The Colony (75056) *(G-19812)*

Rd Food Manufacturing Inc 915 594-4488
  1100 Pendale Rd El Paso (79907) *(G-5930)*

Rda Corporation 281 474-2881
  4295 County Road 86 # 180 Celina (75009) *(G-2993)*

RDG Real Estate & Construction 469 629-9919
  5955 Alpha Rd 1109 Dallas (75240) *(G-4865)*

RDHS Inc 361 852-4094
  6767 Weber Rd Corpus Christi (78413) *(G-3606)*

Rdl Supply, Dallas *Also called Cook & Boardman Group LLC* *(G-4165)*

Rdrtec Incorporated 214 353-8755
  3737 Atwell St Ste 208 Dallas (75209) *(G-4866)*

RDS, Spring *Also called Radial Drilling Services Inc* *(G-19161)*

RDS Metal LP 817 539-7400
  911 S 5th Ave Mansfield (76063) *(G-14708)*

RDS Products Inc 817 656-8277
  4301 Clay Ave Fort Worth (76117) *(G-6945)*

Rdt Inc 979 387-3223
  9022 Vincik Ehlert Beasley (77417) *(G-1845)*

Rdt General Contractors, Strawn *Also called Red Dog Track Inc* *(G-19432)*

Rdt-USA, Houston *Also called Rotary Drilling Tools USA LLC* *(G-11669)*

(G-0000) Company's Geographic Section entry number

ALPHABETIC SECTION
Reddy Ice Group Inc

RE Campbell Company Ltd 713 957-8721
3502 Pinemont Dr Houston (77018) *(G-11558)*
RE Pipe Inc 713 634-0439
7600 S Santa Fe Dr Ste E Houston (77061) *(G-11559)*
RE Watson & Associates Inc 817 478-4401
620 Tower Dr Kennedale (76060) *(G-13501)*
Reactive & Alloy Mtls Inds Inc 979 885-2244
829 Bartlett Rd Sealy (77474) *(G-18816)*
Reactive Downhole Tls USA Inc 281 821-6566
19945 Aldine Westfield Rd Humble (77338) *(G-12796)*
Reactive Metals Corp 979 849-7197
2115 County Road 233 Angleton (77515) *(G-577)*
Reactor Services International 281 824-0841
200 Avenue I Bldg G Alvin (77511) *(G-378)*
Ready Cable of Houston Inc 713 856-5132
11315 W Little York Rd # 2 Houston (77041) *(G-11560)*
Ready Products Resaw Mill, Weatherford *Also called Ready Seal Inc (G-20615)*
Ready Seal Inc 817 594-8198
801 W Interstate 20 Weatherford (76087) *(G-20615)*
Readyone Industries Inc 915 858-7277
1414 Ability Dr El Paso (79936) *(G-5931)*
Reagan National Advertising, Austin *Also called Reagan Outdoor Advertising (G-1454)*
Reagan Outdoor Advertising 512 926-7740
7301 Burleson Rd Austin (78744) *(G-1454)*
Reagens Usa Inc 281 291-8484
9640 Bayport Blvd Pasadena (77507) *(G-16501)*
Reagent Chemical & RES Inc 713 626-1843
1300 Post Oak Blvd Houston (77056) *(G-11561)*
Reagent Chemical & RES Inc 409 962-1116
18950 Ih 10 Vidor (77662) *(G-20331)*
Reagent Chemical & RES Inc 281 862-9464
2710 Appelt Dr Houston (77015) *(G-11562)*
Reagent Chemical & RES Inc 432 458-3403
2833 Ih 20 South Svc Rd Stanton (79782) *(G-19404)*
Reagent Chemical & RES Inc 409 899-3400
210 Office Park Dr Beaumont (77707) *(G-1946)*
Real Energy Solutions Inc (PA) **713 864-9076**
438 Heights Blvd Houston (77007) *(G-11563)*
Real Estate Foreclosures 210 733-4262
2007 Candlelight Ln San Antonio (78213) *(G-18413)*
Real Estate Invstmnts/Vni Prpt, Houston *Also called Victor Nicolle Inc (G-12566)*
Real Granite Inc 210 732-8350
848 W Rhapsody Dr San Antonio (78216) *(G-18414)*
Real Industry, Dallas *Also called Elah Holdings Inc (G-4307)*
Real Log Com, Arlington *Also called Langford Construction Inc (G-718)*
Real Products, Brownsville *Also called Jefferson Electric Inc (G-2369)*
Reality Publishing Co 281 493-4105
1322 Eagle Point Dr Georgetown (78628) *(G-7673)*
Realpage Inc (PA) **972 820-3000**
2201 Lakeside Blvd Richardson (75082) *(G-17387)*
Reama Inc (PA) **409 744-9222**
5320 Sealy St Galveston (77551) *(G-7407)*
Reaper Miniatures Inc 940 484-6464
9062 Teasley Ln Denton (76210) *(G-5397)*
Reatta Energy Inc 432 682-7495
306 W Wall St Ste 1100 Midland (79701) *(G-15378)*
REB Technologies Inc 817 285-7740
1500 Brown Trl Ste 100 Bedford (76022) *(G-1978)*
Rebar Supply Company Ltd 713 937-8999
7834 Fairview St Houston (77041) *(G-11564)*
Rebel Athletic Inc 972 418-0827
2554 Tarpley Rd Ste 114 Carrollton (75006) *(G-2803)*
Rebel Testers, Midland *Also called Basic Energy Services Inc (G-15135)*
Rebirth Leathers, Honey Grove *Also called R K Texas Leather Mfg Inc (G-8358)*
Rebtech, Bedford *Also called REB Technologies Inc (G-1978)*
Rebuilding Tgether El Paso Inc 915 342-3882
6400 Airport Rd Ste G El Paso (79925) *(G-5932)*
Recaro Arcft Sting Amricas LLC (HQ) **817 490-9160**
2275 Eagle Pkwy Fort Worth (76177) *(G-6946)*
Reclaimed Textiles Co 214 638-7551
10777 Shady Trl Dallas (75220) *(G-4867)*
Reclamation Contractors Texas 903 895-4584
10503 Hwy 323 New London (75682) *(G-15851)*
Recognition Express, Richardson *Also called Drsk Limited Partnership (G-17302)*
Recon Coating Solutions LLC 979 277-8455
3984 N Us Highway 287 Alvord (76225) *(G-390)*
Recon Exploration Inc 972 960-8600
15506 Wright Brothers Dr # 100 Addison (75001) *(G-158)*
Reconditioned Couplings Inc 832 878-6255
102 Whites Lk Estates Dr Highlands (77562) *(G-8314)*
Reconserve of Texas Inc 214 339-4755
3610 Duncanville Rd Dallas (75236) *(G-4868)*
Recorder Publishing Co Inc 817 926-5351
3032 S Jones St Fort Worth (76104) *(G-6947)*
Recovered Water Industries, Gainesville *Also called Site Safe Solutions Ltd (G-7368)*
Recovered Water Industries LLC 940 668-8200
202 Suth Dixon St Ste 203 Gainesville (76240) *(G-7360)*
Recs Signs LLC 832 226-8000
1523 Vanderwilt Ln Katy (77449) *(G-13435)*
Rectorseal LLC (HQ) **713 263-8001**
2601 Spenwick Dr Houston (77055) *(G-11565)*
Recycle To Conserve, Tx, Inc., Dallas *Also called Reconserve of Texas Inc (G-4868)*
Red Arrow Energy LLC 713 580-7250
4265 San Felipe St # 1040 Houston (77027) *(G-11566)*
Red Book Connect LLC 877 741-9610
6504 Bridge Point Pkwy # 42 Austin (78730) *(G-1455)*
Red Diamond Energy Svcs Inc (PA) **325 690-0053**
402 S 7th St Abilene (79602) *(G-69)*
Red Diamond Oilfld Svcs L L C 903 687-4000
1268 Magnolia Rd Waskom (75692) *(G-20521)*
Red Diamond Pressure Ctrl LLC 903 687-4000
1268 Magnolia Rd Waskom (75692) *(G-20522)*
Red Dog Studios, Fort Worth *Also called Doyle & Hamilton Inc (G-6592)*
Red Dog Track Inc 254 672-5261
3271 State Highway 108 Strawn (76475) *(G-19432)*
Red Energy Services LP 432 943-2746
1005 W 31st St Monahans (79756) *(G-15613)*
Red Express Pallet Company, Waco *Also called Kunka Enterprises LLC (G-20423)*
Red Mountain Resources Inc (PA) **214 871-0400**
6334 Maple Ave Ste 500 Dallas (75235) *(G-4869)*
Red News Inc 281 888-1448
2537 S Gessner Rd Ste 126 Houston (77063) *(G-11567)*
Red River Commodities Inc 806 763-9747
212 Ne Loop 289 Lubbock (79403) *(G-14471)*
Red River Compression LLC (PA) **832 831-0532**
8300 Cypress Creek Pkwy # 450 Houston (77070) *(G-11568)*
Red River Compression Svcs LLC (PA) **832 831-0532**
8300 Cypress Creek Pkwy # 450 Houston (77070) *(G-11569)*
Red River Manufacturing, Houston *Also called Red River Compression LLC (G-11568)*
Red River Publishing, Paris *Also called Roger Hooper (G-16368)*
Red River Tea Company 214 956-0373
13375 Branch View Ln Dallas (75234) *(G-4870)*
Red Rock Oilfield Service LLC 325 933-0224
199 S Fm 1229 Colorado City (79512) *(G-3226)*
Red Steel Company 972 243-4242
10566 Spangler Rd Dallas (75220) *(G-4871)*
Red Technology Alliance LLC 713 839-4689
2101 Cy W Blvd Bldg Fl 2 Houston (77042) *(G-11570)*
Red The Uniform Tailor (PA) **972 660-8433**
1630 111th St Grand Prairie (75050) *(G-7963)*
Red Watson Logging Inc 409 565-2484
Hwy 63 E Wiergate (75977) *(G-20840)*
Red Willow Offshore LLC 281 822-7500
1415 La St Ste 3650 Houston (77002) *(G-11571)*
Redbud E&P Inc (PA) **832 698-4234**
16000 Stuebner Airline Rd # 320 Spring (77379) *(G-19162)*
Redcastle Manufacturing LLC 817 350-6300
1501 Heritage Pkwy # 103 Mansfield (76063) *(G-14709)*
Redcliff Midstream LLC 713 655-9500
1331 Lamar St Ste 1675 Houston (77010) *(G-11572)*
Redco Distribution LLC (PA) **832 320-4950**
2155 Silber Rd Ste 100 Houston (77055) *(G-11573)*
Redco Endeavors Inc 832 421-8549
4200 State Highway 155 S Gilmer (75645) *(G-7711)*
Redco Pallet Inc 903 561-2075
413 Top Hill Dr Tyler (75703) *(G-20145)*
Redding Machine Shop Inc 940 691-5218
5720 Seymour Hwy Wichita Falls (76310) *(G-20802)*
Reddy Ice Corporation 956 428-6666
1409 N 28th St Harlingen (78550) *(G-8199)*
Reddy Ice Corporation 956 723-3838
4301 Jaime Zapata Memoria Laredo (78043) *(G-13923)*
Reddy Ice Corporation 940 686-5259
309 Enterprise Dr Pilot Point (76258) *(G-16727)*
Reddy Ice Corporation 915 532-2495
1621 Texas Ave El Paso (79901) *(G-5933)*
Reddy Ice Corporation 210 532-3232
1106 E Cesar E Chavez Blv San Antonio (78210) *(G-18415)*
Reddy Ice Corporation 361 578-3032
507 E Sabine St Victoria (77901) *(G-20299)*
Reddy Ice Corporation 972 296-4271
4320 Duncanville Rd Dallas (75236) *(G-4872)*
Reddy Ice Corporation 713 691-2773
6004 N Shepherd Dr Ste B Houston (77091) *(G-11574)*
Reddy Ice Corporation 214 526-6740
8750 N Cntl Expy Ste 1800 Dallas (75231) *(G-4873)*
Reddy Ice Corporation 432 943-4541
1310 E Sealy Ave Monahans (79756) *(G-15614)*
Reddy Ice Corporation (HQ) **214 526-6740**
5710 Lbj Fwy Ste 300 Dallas (75240) *(G-4874)*
Reddy Ice Corporation 361 289-0276
5874 State Highway 44 Byp Corpus Christi (78406) *(G-3607)*
Reddy Ice Corporation 817 654-9020
601 N Sylvania Ave Fort Worth (76111) *(G-6948)*
Reddy Ice Group Inc 254 753-7378
6 19th St W Jefferson (75657) *(G-13287)*
Reddy Ice Group Inc 903 732-3231
89 County Road 35725 Powderly (75473) *(G-17200)*

ALPHABETIC

Reddy Ice Group Inc 972 263-4359
  4320 Duncanville Rd Dallas (75236) *(G-4875)*

Reddy Ice Group Inc (HQ) **877 295-0024**
  5720 Lbj Fwy Ste 200 Dallas (75240) *(G-4876)*

Reddy Ice Holdings Inc (HQ) **214 526-6740**
  5720 Lbj Fwy Ste 200 Dallas (75240) *(G-4877)*

Redemption Oil & Gas LLC 210 572-2988
  401 E Sonterra Blvd # 165 San Antonio (78258) *(G-18416)*

Redhouse Virtual Education LLC 210 872-4989
  701 Commerce St Dallas (75202) *(G-4878)*

Redi Services 432 272-1583
  8001 E Interstate 20 Odessa (79765) *(G-16134)*

Redi Smok Electric Cookers, Houston *Also called Burkhead Manufacturing Company (G-9019)*

Redi-Mix LLC 210 651-4141
  7998 Jethro Ln Garden Ridge (78266) *(G-7419)*

Redi-Mix LLC (HQ) **817 835-4105**
  331 N Main St Euless (76039) *(G-6153)*

Redi-Mix Concrete, Euless *Also called Redi-Mix LLC (G-6153)*

Redi-Mix Concrete, Euless *Also called Redi-Mix LP (G-6154)*

Redi-Mix LP 972 335-2060
  14800 State Highway 121 Frisco (75035) *(G-7263)*

Redi-Mix LP 817 561-9785
  4040 S Eden Rd Kennedale (76060) *(G-13502)*

Redi-Mix LP (HQ) **972 242-4550**
  1445 Mac Arthur Dr # 136 Carrollton (75007) *(G-2885)*

Redi-Mix LP 817 485-4850
  1100 Westpark Way Ste 100 Euless (76040) *(G-6154)*

Rediform Inc 972 393-8080
  555 Airline Dr Coppell (75019) *(G-3438)*

Redline Instruments Inc 979 776-7200
  10350 State Highway 30 College Station (77845) *(G-3199)*

Redman Energy Corporation 713 782-2870
  10375 Richmond Ave # 920 Houston (77042) *(G-11575)*

Redman Pipe Organs LLC (PA) **817 332-2953**
  816 E Vickery Blvd Fort Worth (76104) *(G-6949)*

Redondo Manufacturing, Converse *Also called Rcss (G-3401)*

Redox Chemicals LLC 972 923-7734
  116 N Rogers St Waxahachie (75165) *(G-20555)*

Redrock Microsystems LLC 817 490-1326
  5230 Kelly Dr Roanoke (76262) *(G-17495)*

Redstone Impressions Inc 817 921-6266
  3300 S Jones St Fort Worth (76110) *(G-6950)*

Redstone Visual Impressions, Fort Worth *Also called R S Graphic Services Inc (G-6932)*

Redwine Resources Inc 214 691-5800
  8214 Westchester Dr # 740 Dallas (75225) *(G-4879)*

Redzone Coil Tubing LLC (HQ) **936 632-2645**
  203 S 1st St Lufkin (75901) *(G-14548)*

Redzone Holdco LLC 936 632-2645
  203 S 1st St Lufkin (75901) *(G-14549)*

REE Holding Inc 409 840-5650
  5420 Gorman Rd Beaumont (77705) *(G-1947)*

Reed Candle Company 210 737-7156
  1531 W Poplar St San Antonio (78207) *(G-18417)*

Reed Fiberglass Inc 432 332-8265
  102 Reed Ave Odessa (79761) *(G-16135)*

Reed Prototype and Model Inc 512 457-0560
  303 W San Antonio St Lockhart (78644) *(G-14172)*

Reed Tool, Houston *Also called Schlumberger International (G-11766)*

Reed-Hycalog 832 422-4070
  6806 Willow Brook Park Houston (77066) *(G-11576)*

Reedholm Instruments Co 512 869-1935
  4 Sierra Way St Georgetown (78626) *(G-7674)*

Reef Chemical Corporation Inc 432 560-5600
  7906 W Highway 80 Midland (79706) *(G-15379)*

Reef Exploration LP 972 437-6792
  1901 N Cent Expy Ste 300 Richardson (75080) *(G-17388)*

Reef Industries Inc (PA) **713 507-4200**
  9209 Almeda Genoa Rd Houston (77075) *(G-11577)*

Reef Industries Inc 713 507-4329
  10020 Mykawa Rd Houston (77048) *(G-11578)*

Reef Industries Inc 956 399-1352
  1951 Amistad Dr San Benito (78586) *(G-18663)*

Reef Oil & Gas Companies, Richardson *Also called Reef Exploration LP (G-17388)*

Reef Oil & Gas Partners LLC 972 437-6792
  1901 N Central Expy Ste 3 Richardson (75080) *(G-17389)*

Reef Process Systems LLC (PA) **972 874-9300**
  2604 Long Prairie Rd # 300 Flower Mound (75022) *(G-6278)*

Reef Services LLC 325 573-1133
  1600th Ave Q Snyder (79549) *(G-19003)*

Reef Services LLC (HQ) **432 560-5600**
  1515 W Sam Houston Pkwy N Houston (77043) *(G-11579)*

Reel Power Oil & Gas Inc 713 937-4494
  8780 West Rd Houston (77064) *(G-11580)*

Reel-Logix LLC 713 369-3139
  227 Hambrick Rd Houston (77060) *(G-11581)*

REEL-LOGIX SOLUTIONS, Houston *Also called Reel-Logix LLC (G-11581)*

Reeves Roofing Equipment Co 210 695-3567
  1025 Forest Park Dr Weatherford (76087) *(G-20616)*

Ref Machining Ltd Partnr LLP 512 251-9954
  2210 Patterson Indus Dr Pflugerville (78660) *(G-16686)*

Refined Industrial Services, League City *Also called Refined Industrial Supply Inc (G-13978)*

Refined Industrial Supply Inc 409 789-1794
  3312 Delesandri Ln League City (77573) *(G-13978)*

Reflange Gulf Coast, Houston *Also called Oceaneering Reflange (G-11129)*

Reflection Printing, Houston *Also called Barrport Properties Inc (G-8818)*

Reflections of Dallas, Garland *Also called Career Concepts Inc (G-7453)*

Refocus Group Inc (PA) **214 368-0200**
  10210 N Cntl Expy Ste 400 Dallas (75231) *(G-4880)*

Refocus Ocular, Dallas *Also called Refocus Group Inc (G-4880)*

Refregration Design Tech, Waxahachie *Also called Refrigeration Design Inc (G-20556)*

Refresco Beverages US Inc 210 333-4310
  4238 Director Dr San Antonio (78219) *(G-18418)*

Refresco Beverages US Inc 817 359-4500
  15200 Trinity Blvd Fort Worth (76155) *(G-6951)*

Refrigeration Design Inc 972 937-3240
  1808 Fm 66 Waxahachie (75167) *(G-20556)*

Refrigeration Gaskets Texas Inc (PA) **713 880-8066**
  729 W 22nd St Houston (77008) *(G-11582)*

Refrigrtion Vlves Systems Corp, Bryan *Also called Refrigrtion Vssels Systems Cor (G-2500)*

Refrigrtion Vssels Systems Cor 979 778-0095
  1520 Crosswind Dr Bryan (77808) *(G-2500)*

Refuge Industries LLC 512 961-4907
  4310 Willow Springs Rd Austin (78745) *(G-1456)*

Regal Beloit America Inc 956 213-0503
  6901 S International Pkwy McAllen (78503) *(G-14900)*

Regal Beloit America Inc 715 284-9801
  1305 Industrial Blvd Eagle Pass (78852) *(G-5554)*

Regal Beloit America Inc 417 847-4775
  11206 Farmer 2182 Eagle Pass (78852) *(G-5555)*

Regal Beloit Corporation 830 774-2677
  532 Industrial Blvd Del Rio (78840) *(G-5322)*

Regal Beloit Corporation 412 968-0100
  1265 Peter Cooper Dr El Paso (79936) *(G-5934)*

Regal Chef, Houston *Also called Regal Interests Inc (G-11583)*

Regal Hardwoods Inc (PA) **972 620-8833**
  1540 Selene Dr Ste 110 Carrollton (75006) *(G-2804)*

Regal Interests Inc 713 222-8231
  3515 Eastex Fwy Houston (77026) *(G-11583)*

Regal Machine, Mfg, Tyler *Also called TW Stamping & Tool Inc (G-20166)*

Regal Marble Co 361 572-8498
  2498 Guadalupe Rd Victoria (77905) *(G-20300)*

Regal Plastic Supply Co Inc 210 599-8291
  4041 Rittiman Rd San Antonio (78218) *(G-18419)*

Regal Plastic Supply Co Inc 512 836-3629
  9311 Metric Blvd Austin (78758) *(G-1457)*

Regal Research and Mfg Co LLC 972 494-0359
  1200 E Plano Pkwy Plano (75074) *(G-16990)*

Regal Ware Inc 817 652-8151
  4300 Amon Carter Blvd # 100 Fort Worth (76155) *(G-6952)*

Regency Conversions Inc 800 839-7551
  4709 Lone Star Blvd Fort Worth (76106) *(G-6953)*

Regency Crude Marketing LLC 806 665-3491
  8442 County Road 3 Pampa (79065) *(G-16337)*

Regency Desoto-Hesco Svcs LLC 281 408-1200
  1415 La St Ste 2700 Houston (77002) *(G-11584)*

Regency Energy Partners LP 806 665-2551
  220 N Ballard St Pampa (79065) *(G-16338)*

Regency Energy Partners LP (HQ) **214 750-1771**
  8111 Westchester Dr # 600 Dallas (75225) *(G-4881)*

Regency Field Services, Pampa *Also called Regency Energy Partners LP (G-16338)*

Regency Plastics - Ubly Inc 915 860-1997
  1101 Burgundy Dr El Paso (79907) *(G-5935)*

Regency Plz Prtg & Off Sup Inc 214 939-3456
  2797 Irving Blvd Ste 118 Dallas (75207) *(G-4882)*

Regency Purchasing Inc 713 973-0315
  8419 Bascom Ln Houston (77080) *(G-11585)*

Regency Rv, Fort Worth *Also called Regency Conversions Inc (G-6953)*

Regency Wraps Inc 214 357-0099
  2731 Satsuma Dr Dallas (75229) *(G-4883)*

Regional Acid Production LP 281 381-7866
  4755 Alpine Dr Ste 150b Stafford (77477) *(G-19368)*

Regis Manufacturing Company 214 421-5171
  1500 Corinth St Dallas (75215) *(G-4884)*

Register Tapes Unlimited LP 281 206-2500
  1445 Langham Creek Dr Houston (77084) *(G-11586)*

Rehab Plus Thrapeutic Pdts Inc 806 791-2288
  726 Donald Preston Dr Wolfforth (79382) *(G-20911)*

Reher-Morrison Racing Engines 817 467-7171
  1120 Enterprise Pl Arlington (76001) *(G-770)*

Rehme Custom Doors & Ltg Inc 512 916-0511
  3914 Crawford Rd Spicewood (78669) *(G-19093)*

Rehme Steel Windows & Doors, Spicewood *Also called Rehme Custom Doors & Ltg Inc (G-19093)*

Rehrig Pacific Company 214 631-7943
  625 W Mockingbird Ln Dallas (75247) *(G-4885)*

Reichert Corporation....972 267-1300
1625 Crescent Cir Ste 210 Carrollton (75006) ***(G-2805)***
Reichhold Industries Inc....713 453-5431
1503 Haden Rd Houston (77015) ***(G-11587)***
Reinforced Earth Company....254 836-1847
136 Waco Sand Rd Waco (76708) ***(G-20454)***
Reinfro LLC....956 838-9814
3320 E 14th St Brownsville (78521) ***(G-2398)***
Relentless Oilfield Svcs LLC....432 242-1160
12165 W Drvers Hall Of Fa Odessa (79763) ***(G-16136)***
Reliable Bus Resources LLC....281 469-6400
6327 N Sam Houston Pkwy W Houston (77086) ***(G-11588)***
Reliable Design Services LP....972 584-0551
5710 State Highway 34 S Quinlan (75474) ***(G-17226)***
Reliable Edm Ltd (PA)....**713 692-5454**
6940 Fulton St Houston (77022) ***(G-11589)***
Reliable Hose Solutions LLC (PA)....**713 983-9090**
5097 Ashley Ct Houston (77041) ***(G-11590)***
Reliable Manufacturing Inc (PA)....**512 255-6572**
1900 N A W Grimes Blvd Round Rock (78665) ***(G-17684)***
Reliable Pump Consultants Inc....713 640-2718
12951 South Fwy Houston (77047) ***(G-11591)***
Reliable Well Svc N Texas LLC (PA)....**940 692-9511**
7774 Seymour Hwy Wichita Falls (76310) ***(G-20803)***
Reliable Wireline LLC....713 280-7995
2656 S Loop W Ste 395 Houston (77054) ***(G-11592)***
Reliance Coated Fabrics Inc....817 453-8829
950 S 6th Ave Mansfield (76063) ***(G-14710)***
Reliance Energy Inc (PA)....**432 683-4816**
300 N Marienfeld St # 1100 Midland (79701) ***(G-15380)***
Reliance Fall Protection, Deer Park *Also called Reliance Industries LLC* ***(G-5290)***
Reliance Industrial, Midland *Also called Applied US Energy Inc* ***(G-15117)***
Reliance Industrial Products, Houston *Also called Applied US Energy Inc* ***(G-8669)***
Reliance Industries Inc (PA)....**281 499-9926**
1900 Fm 1092 Rd Ste A Missouri City (77459) ***(G-15587)***
Reliance Industries LLC....281 930-8000
2101 S Battle Ground Rd Deer Park (77536) ***(G-5290)***
Reliance Mixers, Missouri City *Also called Reliance Industries Inc* ***(G-15587)***
Reliance Prcision Mfg Partners....281 894-0044
10541 Cypress Creek Pkwy # 402 Houston (77070) ***(G-11593)***
Reliance Steel & Aluminum Co....972 276-2676
410 Mars Dr Garland (75040) ***(G-7577)***
Reliant Labels and Prtg Inc....915 595-2999
11400 Rojas Dr Ste B El Paso (79936) ***(G-5936)***
Reliant NDT, Linden *Also called Wells Family Holding Co LLC* ***(G-14137)***
Reliant Worldwide Plastics LLC....214 382-9672
4430 W Highway 82 Gainesville (76240) ***(G-7361)***
Relocation Systems Inc....972 241-2300
8904 N Royal Ln Irving (75063) ***(G-13164)***
Remington Health Products LLC....817 847-0606
808 S Blue Mound Rd Fort Worth (76131) ***(G-6954)***
Remington Oil and Gas Corp....281 618-0400
400 N Sam Houston Pkwy E # 601 Houston (77060) ***(G-11594)***
Remlap Manufacturing Inc....713 462-3199
5757 Teague Rd Houston (77041) ***(G-11595)***
Remnant Oil Company LLC....432 695-6997
6 Desta Dr Ste 5100 Midland (79705) ***(G-15381)***
Remora Energy Management LLC....832 325-2300
5709 Val Verde St 100 Houston (77057) ***(G-11596)***
Remora Royalties Inc....512 579-3590
807 Las Cimas Pkwy Ii Austin (78746) ***(G-1458)***
Remsa Usa Inc....915 855-8621
14500 Sam Hawken Rd El Paso (79938) ***(G-5937)***
Remtex Inc....903 758-0461
23 Frj Dr Longview (75602) ***(G-14295)***
Remtex Precision Machining, Longview *Also called Remtex Inc* ***(G-14295)***
Renaissance Cmpt Group Not Inc....713 256-6067
2747 Briargrove Dr # 940 Houston (77057) ***(G-11597)***
Renaissance Offshore LLC....832 333-7700
920 Mmrial Cy Way Ste 800 Houston (77024) ***(G-11598)***
Renaissance Printing....972 234-0347
1215 Commerce St Dallas (75202) ***(G-4886)***
Renco Tool Co Inc....806 648-2903
21 S Industrial Hwy Perryton (79070) ***(G-16646)***
Rendevous, Dallas *Also called Glen Oaks Industries Inc* ***(G-4409)***
Reneau Publishing Inc....409 385-5278
404 Highway 96 S Silsbee (77656) ***(G-18954)***
Renegade Well Services LLC....940 626-4498
4348 Us Highway 380 Decatur (76234) ***(G-5252)***
Renegade Well Services LLC....830 378-5977
2799 W Fm 117 Dilley (78017) ***(G-5483)***
Renegade Well Services LLC....817 389-2496
7501 County Road 1128 Godley (76044) ***(G-7740)***
Renegade Well Services LLC (HQ)....**682 936-4466**
3301 E Us Highway 377 # 202 Granbury (76049) ***(G-7807)***
Renegade Wireline Services, Levelland *Also called Rwls LLC* ***(G-14014)***
Renegade Wireline Services, Odessa *Also called Rwls LLC* ***(G-16146)***
Renesas Electronics Amer Inc....408 432-8888
900 S Cpitl Of Txas Hwy S West Lake Hills (78746) ***(G-20687)***
Renever Inc....214 761-1882
908 Dragon St Dallas (75207) ***(G-4887)***
Renewable Biofuels Inc (PA)....**713 386-2600**
2229 San Felipe St # 950 Houston (77019) ***(G-11599)***
Renfro Foods Inc....817 336-3849
815 Stella St Fort Worth (76104) ***(G-6955)***
Renfro Industries Inc....972 563-4295
102 Metro Dr Terrell (75160) ***(G-19749)***
Renfro Logging I Ltd....936 208-6177
1404 E Denman Ave Lufkin (75901) ***(G-14550)***
Renfro Street Holdings Ltd (PA)....**817 295-6100**
645 E Renfro St Burleson (76028) ***(G-2596)***
Renfrow & Co Inc....361 884-5541
1123 Agnes St Corpus Christi (78401) ***(G-3608)***
Renfrow Metalsmiths LLC....832 724-8517
37 Lyerly St Houston (77022) ***(G-11600)***
Renlita Doors North Amer LLC....903 583-7500
2430 Albert Broadfoot St Bonham (75418) ***(G-2154)***
Reno Machine Works LLC....903 224-6275
275 Key West Rd Reno (75462) ***(G-17252)***
Renovated Homes Inc....214 678-9114
4829 Top Line Dr Dallas (75247) ***(G-4888)***
Rensco, Houston *Also called Resource Energy Service Corp* ***(G-11608)***
Rentech Boiler Services Inc (PA)....**325 672-2900**
5025 C East Business 20 Abilene (79601) ***(G-70)***
Rentech Nitrogen, Pasadena *Also called Agrifos LLC* ***(G-16379)***
Repco Replacement Parts Inc....817 293-3639
1021 W Enon Ave Fort Worth (76140) ***(G-6956)***
Repcon Inc (HQ)....**361 289-6342**
7501 Up River Rd Corpus Christi (78409) ***(G-3609)***
Repcoreplacement, Fort Worth *Also called Repco Replacement Parts Inc* ***(G-6956)***
Repsol Energy North Amer Corp (HQ)....**832 442-1000**
2455 Tech Forest Blvd The Woodlands (77381) ***(G-19908)***
Repsol Oil & Gas Usa LLC (HQ)....**832 442-1000**
2455 Tech Forest Blvd Spring (77381) ***(G-19247)***
Repsol Services Company....832 442-1000
2455 Tech Forest Blvd The Woodlands (77381) ***(G-19909)***
Reptrax, Flower Mound *Also called Intellicentrics Inc* ***(G-6268)***
Republic Bag, Houston *Also called Republic Mfg Group Inc* ***(G-11602)***
Republic Blower Systems, Dallas *Also called Republic Sales & Manufacturing* ***(G-4890)***
Republic Energy Inc....214 369-4800
2621 State St Dallas (75204) ***(G-4889)***
Republic Heat Treat Inc....713 692-3308
8902 N Main St Houston (77022) ***(G-11601)***
Republic Industries, Marshall *Also called Republic Nat Inds Texas LP* ***(G-14800)***
Republic Mfg Group Inc....713 847-7542
8419 Tewantin Dr Houston (77061) ***(G-11602)***
Republic Nat Inds Texas LP (HQ)....**903 935-3680**
1400 Warren Dr Marshall (75672) ***(G-14800)***
Republic National Cabinet Corp (PA)....**903 935-3680**
1400 Warren Dr Marshall (75672) ***(G-14801)***
Republic Plastics Ltd (PA)....**830 557-5574**
355 Schumann Rd Mc Queeney (78123) ***(G-14830)***
Republic Print & Mail, Austin *Also called Colvin Painovich LP* ***(G-1057)***
Republic Sales & Manufacturing....214 631-8070
5131 Cash Rd Dallas (75247) ***(G-4890)***
Republic Title of Texas Inc (HQ)....**972 578-8611**
2701 W Plano Pkwy Ste 100 Plano (75075) ***(G-16991)***
Republic Tube LLC....832 672-6000
11200 Mesa Dr Houston (77078) ***(G-11603)***
Requejo Construction Svcs LLC....210 459-5161
820 County Road 3822 San Antonio (78253) ***(G-18420)***
Required Team Gear LLC....817 922-8448
2600 Cherry Ln Fort Worth (76116) ***(G-6957)***
REr Apparel Inc (PA)....**417 673-5786**
7527 Bromwich Ct Dallas (75252) ***(G-3851)***
Resa Power LLC (PA)....**832 900-8340**
8300 Cypress Pkwy Ste 225 Houston (77070) ***(G-11604)***
Resa Service, Houston *Also called Resa Power LLC* ***(G-11604)***
Rescue Rescue LLC....210 648-2722
6223 Us Highway 87 E San Antonio (78222) ***(G-18421)***
Research & Technology, La Porte *Also called Total Ptrchemicals Ref USA Inc* ***(G-13797)***
Research Advanced Methods Inds....254 442-1008
808 E 6th St Cisco (76437) ***(G-3068)***
Research and Development, The Woodlands *Also called Keane Group Holdings LLC* ***(G-19890)***
Reserve Analysts Assoc Inc....281 438-3000
2130 Glenn Lakes Ln Missouri City (77459) ***(G-15588)***
Reserve Compression Corp....713 783-8851
13310 Hempstead Rd Houston (77040) ***(G-11605)***
Reserve Equipment, Houston *Also called Reserve Compression Corp* ***(G-11605)***
Reserve Equipment Inc....713 939-8988
13310 Hempstead Rd Houston (77040) ***(G-11606)***
Reservoir Group....281 776-5300
12950 S Kirkwood Rd # 160 Stafford (77477) ***(G-19369)***
Reservoir Marine LLC....281 277-7575
13313 Southwest Fwy # 285 Sugar Land (77478) ***(G-19533)***

A L P H A B E T I C

Resideo Technologies Inc (PA) 512 726-3500
  901 E 6th St Austin (78702) *(G-1459)*

Resistol Hats, Garland *Also called Rhe Hatco Inc (G-7579)*

Reslink, Houston *Also called Schlumberger Norge As (G-11769)*

Resmetrics LLC 832 592-1900
  6801 Portwest Dr Ste 190 Houston (77024) *(G-11607)*

Resolute Natural Resources LLC 432 684-7475
  4000 N Big Spring St # 500 Midland (79705) *(G-15382)*

Resonant Inc (PA) 805 308-9803
  10900 Stnlake Blvd Ste 10 Austin (78759) *(G-1460)*

Resonant Tech Partners LLC 210 477-3671
  16103 University Oak # 100 San Antonio (78249) *(G-18422)*

Resource Energy Service Corp 713 953-5300
  11200 Westheimer Rd # 525 Houston (77042) *(G-11608)*

Resource Metals Company, Houston *Also called Resource Oilfield Pdts Co Inc (G-11610)*

Resource Metals Company 281 442-8600
  14311 Reevestan Rd Houston (77039) *(G-11609)*

Resource Oilfield Pdts Co Inc 281 442-8600
  14311 Reevestan Rd Houston (77039) *(G-11610)*

Resource Royalty LLC 214 691-5234
  5949 Sherry Ln Ste 1100 Dallas (75225) *(G-4891)*

Respiratory Technology Corp (PA) 858 673-3700
  11011 Brooklet Dr Ste 300 Houston (77099) *(G-11611)*

Responsible Prtg & Signs LLC 713 722-0100
  1403 Brittmoore Rd Houston (77043) *(G-11612)*

Restaurant Depot LLC 512 454-5600
  820 Blackson Ave Austin (78752) *(G-1461)*

Restaurant Services, Arlington *Also called RSI Partners LLC (G-777)*

Restech, Houston *Also called Respiratory Technology Corp (G-11611)*

Restline Bedding Products Inc 713 921-1900
  5401 Gulf Fwy Houston (77023) *(G-11613)*

Restonic-Houston, Houston *Also called Continntal Silverline Pdts LLC (G-9291)*

Result Enterprises Inc (PA) 713 666-0550
  6201 Royalton St Houston (77081) *(G-11614)*

Results Fitness For Women, Carrollton *Also called Lady Hlth Ftness- Rockwall Inc (G-2877)*

Retail Concepts Inc 512 467-2782
  2438 W Anderson Ln B1a Austin (78757) *(G-1462)*

Retco Tool Company Inc 214 358-5039
  9030 Viscount Row Dallas (75247) *(G-4892)*

Retractable Technologies Inc 972 294-1010
  511 Lobo Ln Little Elm (75068) *(G-14141)*

Retro Ltg & Conservation Lc 281 302-6431
  3407 Autumn Bend Dr Sugar Land (77479) *(G-19534)*

Retronix Global Inc 512 808-5659
  11221 Blairview Ln Austin (78748) *(G-1463)*

Retronix Inc, Austin *Also called Retronix Global Inc (G-1463)*

Revak Keene Turbomachinery LP (PA) 281 427-8800
  12204 W Fairmont Pkwy La Porte (77571) *(G-13787)*

Revak Turbo Machinery, La Porte *Also called Hoerbiger Service Inc (G-13745)*

Revenue Technology Svcs Corp (PA) 972 573-1600
  6404 Intl Pkwy 2000 Plano (75093) *(G-16992)*

Revere Smelting & Ref Corp 214 631-6070
  2777 N Stemmons Fwy # 1800 Dallas (75207) *(G-4893)*

Revision LLC 972 756-1026
  5930 Campus Circle Dr W Irving (75063) *(G-13165)*

Revisions Skin Care, Irving *Also called Revision LLC (G-13165)*

Revitalu International LLC 469 270-5533
  5830 Granite Pkwy Ste 110 Plano (75024) *(G-16993)*

Revolution Plastics LLC 903 984-8596
  2500 N Longview St Kilgore (75662) *(G-13586)*

Revolution Retail Systems LLC 469 317-2910
  1400 Valwood Pkwy Ste 100 Carrollton (75006) *(G-2806)*

Revolution Screening In Texas, Katy *Also called Revolution Screening Inc (G-13436)*

Revolution Screening Inc 916 712-4458
  21821 Katy Fwy Ste 102a Katy (77450) *(G-13436)*

Rex Mechanical Inc 979 793-3340
  8806 Main St Needville (77461) *(G-15763)*

Rex Supply Company, Houston *Also called RSC Acquisitions (G-11690)*

Rex-Hide Incorporated (PA) 903 593-7387
  705 S Lyons Ave Tyler (75702) *(G-20146)*

Rex-Hide Industries Inc (HQ) 903 593-7387
  705 S Lyons Ave Tyler (75702) *(G-20147)*

Rexcel Coatings Corporation (PA) 915 581-2797
  4600 Ripley Dr El Paso (79922) *(G-5938)*

Rextac LLC (PA) 432 332-0058
  2501 S Grandview Ave Odessa (79766) *(G-16137)*

Reycomp Inc 972 606-4600
  2525 Dalworth St Grand Prairie (75050) *(G-7964)*

Reyes Automotive Group LLC 210 228-2500
  1 Lone Star Pass Bldg 28 San Antonio (78264) *(G-18423)*

Reyes Automotive Group II LLC 210 228-2500
  1 Lone Star Pass Bldg 28 San Antonio (78264) *(G-18424)*

Reyes-Amtex Automotive LLC (PA) 210 628-4900
  1 Lone Star Pass Bldg 30 San Antonio (78264) *(G-18425)*

Reyniers French Bakery Inc 972 401-3600
  2156 W Northwest Hwy # 304 Dallas (75220) *(G-4894)*

Reynolds Brothers Ltd (PA) 432 682-7393
  315 N Colorado St Midland (79701) *(G-15383)*

Reynolds Consumer Products LLC 254 770-4100
  3000 Pegasus Dr Temple (76501) *(G-19701)*

Reynolds Lift Technologies LLC 866 629-6298
  14043 S Gessner Rd Missouri City (77489) *(G-15589)*

Reynolds Metals Company LLC 361 777-2200
  4633 Hwy 361 Gregory (78359) *(G-8104)*

Reynolds Mfg Corp Inc 325 698-7300
  5489 N 3rd St Abilene (79603) *(G-71)*

Reynolds Presto Products Inc 972 416-6500
  2625 E Belt Line Rd Carrollton (75006) *(G-2807)*

Reynolds Scrapers LLC 830 303-0794
  2191 Rudeloff Rd Seguin (78155) *(G-18861)*

Rf Code Inc 512 439-2200
  9229 Waterford Centre Blv Austin (78758) *(G-1464)*

Rf Identity LLC 512 689-1586
  413 Ridgetop Bnd Cedar Park (78613) *(G-2984)*

Rf Manufacturing LLC 817 479-1950
  4212 Glenview Dr Haltom City (76117) *(G-8157)*

Rf Monolithics Inc (HQ) 972 233-2903
  4100 Midway Rd Ste 2050 Carrollton (75007) *(G-2886)*

Rf Saw Inc 469 227-0322
  1725 Old Mason Rd Fredericksburg (78624) *(G-7188)*

Rfc Drilling LLC 432 276-3505
  6001 W Murphy St Odessa (79763) *(G-16138)*

Rfm, Carrollton *Also called Rf Monolithics Inc (G-2886)*

Rfmicron Inc 512 535-4647
  6101 W Courtyard Dr # 1 Austin (78730) *(G-1465)*

Rfr Vertex LLC 713 851-2060
  11355 Fm 830 Rd Willis (77318) *(G-20859)*

Rfv Enterprises Inc 281 842-1877
  425 N 10th St La Porte (77571) *(G-13788)*

RG Builders, Elsa *Also called Raul Gonzalez (G-6080)*

RG Exploration LLC 405 650-1207
  10 Desta Dr Ste 260e Midland (79705) *(G-15384)*

Rg-5 Company LP 903 753-3456
  2912 S Access Rd Longview (75602) *(G-14296)*

Rg3 Meter Company, Longview *Also called Rg-5 Company LP (G-14296)*

Rgv Optical Lab, McAllen *Also called I O U Enterprises Inc (G-14870)*

Rgvsg, Santa Rosa *Also called Rio Grande Vly Sug Growers Inc (G-18737)*

RH Tamlyn & Sons (PA) 281 499-9604
  13623 Pike Rd Stafford (77477) *(G-19370)*

RH Tamlyn & Sons LP 214 348-9676
  10940 Petal St Dallas (75238) *(G-4895)*

Rh Well Service 432 393-5305
  7608 S Service Rd I20 Big Spring (79720) *(G-2095)*

Rhe Hatco Inc 903 753-2631
  302 Huntsman Way Longview (75602) *(G-14297)*

Rhe Hatco Inc (PA) 972 494-0511
  601 Marion Dr Garland (75042) *(G-7578)*

Rhe Hatco Inc 972 494-0511
  601 Marion Dr Garland (75042) *(G-7579)*

Rheaco Inc 972 264-4748
  1801 W Jefferson St Grand Prairie (75051) *(G-7965)*

Rheaco Oil Company Ltd 409 287-1225
  395 Highway 105 W Sour Lake (77659) *(G-19035)*

Rheem Container, Bryan *Also called North America Packaging Corp (G-2496)*

Rheonics Inc 713 364-5427
  3 Sugar Creek Center Blvd Sugar Land (77478) *(G-19535)*

Rhimco Industries Inc (PA) 817 477-3176
  4150 Britton Rd Mansfield (76063) *(G-14711)*

Rhino Machine Shop Inc 281 290-7858
  402 Carrell St Tomball (77375) *(G-20006)*

Rhino Rush 3gs LLC 817 793-9400
  7115 Lake Hill Trl Sachse (75048) *(G-17734)*

Rhizogen LLC (PA) 281 367-7500
  4200 Res Frest Dr Ste 100 The Woodlands (77381) *(G-19910)*

Rhodes Building Systems Inc 979 596-1451
  1607 Ave E Thor Somerville (77879) *(G-19023)*

Rhonda Griffin 936 715-0735
  5093 County Road 411 Nacogdoches (75961) *(G-15712)*

Rhos Inc 979 542-5420
  716 E Austin St Giddings (78942) *(G-7701)*

Rhr Acquisition Co LLC (PA) 713 699-3892
  6910 Fulton St Houston (77022) *(G-11615)*

Rhr Acquisition Co LLC 936 856-6607
  4400 N Frazier St Conroe (77303) *(G-3357)*

Riazul Imports LLC 713 894-9177
  16402 Falcons Cove Dr Houston (77095) *(G-11616)*

Rib Ranger Products of Texas, Denton *Also called Texas Rib Rangers Product (G-5406)*

Riba Foods Inc (PA) 713 975-7001
  3701 Arc St Houston (77063) *(G-11617)*

Rice Addict, Houston *Also called Nx Media Inc (G-11104)*

Rice Metal Fabricators Inc 713 462-1978
  13824 Hempstead Rd Houston (77040) *(G-11618)*

Ricetec Inc (PA) 281 756-3300
  1925 Fm 2917 Rd Alvin (77511) *(G-379)*

Rich Products Corporation 956 542-0001
  3555 E 14th St Brownsville (78521) *(G-2399)*

(G-0000) Company's Geographic Section entry number

Rich Products Corporation................................281 835-7100
14847 Fairway Pines Dr Missouri City (77489) *(G-15590)*

Rich Products Corporation................................281 410-6600
13221 S Gessner Rd Missouri City (77489) *(G-15591)*

Rich Transport LLC.......................................214 819-3082
4444 Irving Blvd Dallas (75247) *(G-4896)*

Richard E Colgin I Ltd....................................214 951-8687
4111 Mint Way Dallas (75237) *(G-4897)*

Richard Eric LLC..214 477-5230
1808 E Park Blvd Plano (75074) *(G-16994)*

Richard H Smith LLC......................................817 267-6750
2221 Regal Pkwy Euless (76040) *(G-6155)*

Richard Phillips Inc......................................972 264-5315
116 Ne 6th St Grand Prairie (75050) *(G-7966)*

Richard's Hot Oil Service, Giddings *Also called Rhos Inc (G-7701)*

Richard's Rainwater, Austin *Also called Tank Town LLC (G-1555)*

Richard-Marcus Inc.......................................972 484-0406
13821 Diplomat Dr Dallas (75234) *(G-4898)*

Richards Signs & Cranes Inc.............................940 325-6585
1215 Sw 1st St Mineral Wells (76067) *(G-15539)*

Richardson Milling Inc...................................806 258-7227
Fm 809 At Fm 1062 Dawn (79025) *(G-5219)*

Richardson Timbers, Dallas *Also called Sawmill Partners LLC (G-4939)*

Richardson Trident Company LLC (HQ)..................**972 231-5176**
1301 Apollo Rd Richardson (75081) *(G-17390)*

Richco Acidizing Services, Snyder *Also called Steven C Rich LLC (G-19010)*

Richman Oil, Austin *Also called Pool Energy Corporation (G-1425)*

Richmond Materials Inc..................................281 238-5488
5251 Ransom Rd Richmond (77469) *(G-17465)*

Richmond Printing LLC...................................713 952-0800
5825 Schumacher Ln Houston (77057) *(G-11619)*

Richmonds American Svc Ctr Inc........................972 681-2222
8600 Verona Dr McKinney (75071) *(G-14971)*

Richs Machinery Company Inc...........................903 758-0531
1207 Fm 1845 S Longview (75603) *(G-14298)*

Rick Triplett...214 823-2830
802 S Haskell Ave Dallas (75223) *(G-4899)*

Rickett Ricky Sand & Gravel.............................281 356-3103
41922 N Mill Dr Magnolia (77354) *(G-14624)*

Ricos Manufacturing Co Inc.............................210 226-4168
600 Tittle Dr Lewisville (75056) *(G-14088)*

Ricos Products Co Inc (HQ)............................**210 222-1415**
830 S Presa St San Antonio (78210) *(G-18426)*

Riddles Dehi & Chem Svc Co LLC........................903 986-3904
1873 Fm 1252 E Kilgore (75662) *(G-13587)*

Ridge Oil Company Inc...................................254 559-2297
6628 Us Highway 180 E Breckenridge (76424) *(G-2236)*

Ridgewood Energy Corporation..........................281 293-8488
1254 Enclave Pkwy Ste 600 Houston (77077) *(G-11620)*

Ridley Block Operations, Buffalo *Also called Ridley USA Inc (G-2548)*

Ridley Block Operations, Fort Worth *Also called Ridley USA Inc (G-6958)*

Ridley USA Inc...903 322-4228
125 Industrial Blvd Buffalo (75831) *(G-2548)*

Ridley USA Inc...817 625-6680
5100 Blue Mound Rd Fort Worth (76106) *(G-6958)*

Rife Energy Operating Inc...............................940 964-2822
167 County Road 345 Forestburg (76239) *(G-6300)*

Rig Qa International Inc (PA)..........................**936 856-5614**
12725 Cude Cemetery Rd Willis (77318) *(G-20860)*

Rig Technology Inc.......................................432 362-2789
4422 Johnson Rd Odessa (79764) *(G-16139)*

Rig Testers Inc (PA)....................................**325 673-2771**
5333 N 3rd St Abilene (79603) *(G-72)*

Rig Works Inc...432 366-4501
2310 Steven Rd Odessa (79764) *(G-16140)*

Rigaku Americas Corporation (HQ)....................**281 362-2300**
9009 New Trails Dr The Woodlands (77381) *(G-19911)*

Rigamonti Trailer Parts, Victoria *Also called Rigamonti Welding Services (G-20301)*

Rigamonti Welding Services..............................361 578-0397
5180 Hanselman Rd Victoria (77905) *(G-20301)*

Rigba International Inc (PA)...........................**915 239-1070**
820 Hawkins Blvd Ste G El Paso (79915) *(G-5939)*

Riggs Machine and Welding Inc..........................254 965-3910
307 East Rd Stephenville (76401) *(G-19420)*

Right Machine Company, Houston *Also called Harrison Mullane Inc (G-10128)*

Right Pathways LLC......................................817 522-3600
106 N Denton Tap Rd Coppell (75019) *(G-3439)*

Right Signs Inc...281 429-3683
17218 Porter Ln Porter (77365) *(G-17182)*

Rigid Global Buildings LLC (PA).......................**281 443-9065**
18933 Aldine Westfield Rd Houston (77073) *(G-11621)*

Rignet Inc (PA)..**281 674-0100**
15115 Park Row Ste 300 Houston (77084) *(G-11622)*

Rik-Mar Fabricators Inc.................................979 779-1616
400 Stone City Dr Bryan (77803) *(G-2501)*

Ril USA Inc...713 430-8700
2000 W Sam Houston Pkwy S # 700 Houston (77042) *(G-11623)*

Rilco Manufacturing Co Inc.............................713 466-4777
5446 1st St Katy (77493) *(G-13437)*

Rilco Manufacturing Co Inc (PA)......................**713 466-4777**
12700 Tanner Rd Houston (77041) *(G-11624)*

Riley Exploration Group LLC............................512 481-7676
111 Congress Ave Austin (78701) *(G-1466)*

Riley Industrial Services Inc............................432 332-9630
1251 Oibc Dr Odessa (79766) *(G-16141)*

Riley-Built Inc..806 798-9684
7802 Genoa Ave Lubbock (79424) *(G-14472)*

Rim Manufacturing LLC...................................817 599-6521
901 W Interstate 20 Weatherford (76087) *(G-20617)*

Rimrock Energy LLC......................................303 308-1300
5128 Apache Plume Rd # 300 Fort Worth (76109) *(G-6959)*

Ring Energy Inc (PA)..................................**432 682-7464**
901 W Wall St Fl 3 Midland (79701) *(G-15385)*

Ring Energy Inc..432 682-7464
200 N Loraine St Ste 1245 Midland (79701) *(G-15386)*

Ringdale Inc (HQ)....................................**512 288-9080**
101 Halmar Cv Georgetown (78628) *(G-7675)*

Ringers Gloves, Houston *Also called Ringers Technology Group Inc (G-11625)*

Ringers Technology Group Inc (PA)...................**281 953-5300**
3443 N Sam Houston Pkwy W Houston (77086) *(G-11625)*

Ringo Drilling I Lp.......................................325 232-5807
12900 Preston Rd Ste 730 Dallas (75230) *(G-4900)*

Ringwood Containers LP..................................817 625-7214
841 Railhead Rd Fort Worth (76106) *(G-6960)*

Rinker Materials, Sealy *Also called Hydro Conduit of Texas LP (G-18809)*

Rinker Materials, Castroville *Also called Cemex Materials LLC (G-2926)*

Rinker Materials Con Pipe Div, San Antonio *Also called Cemex Materials LLC (G-17991)*

Rinker Materials Con Pipe Div, Houston *Also called Hydro Conduit of Texas LP (G-10305)*

Rio Grande Container Inc...............................956 447-5949
1405 E Expressway 83 Weslaco (78599) *(G-20668)*

Rio Grande Imaging Center Inc.........................956 668-6900
101 E Ridge Rd McAllen (78503) *(G-14901)*

Rio Grande Mining Company.............................432 229-4737
97243 Us Hwy 67 Marfa (79843) *(G-14754)*

Rio Grande Portland Cement, El Paso *Also called Gcc Rio Grande Inc (G-5779)*

Rio Grande Steel, Pharr *Also called Commercial Metals Company (G-16696)*

Rio Grande Steel Ltd....................................956 361-4443
1980 E Business Rd 77 San Benito (78586) *(G-18664)*

Rio Grande Stucco Product, El Paso *Also called Western Stucco Product (G-6036)*

Rio Grande Tool Co, Brownsville *Also called Paragon Rio Grande LLC (G-2391)*

Rio Grande Valley Business.............................956 546-5113
1300 Wildrose Ln Brownsville (78520) *(G-2400)*

Rio Grande Vly Sug Growers Inc........................956 636-1411
2.5 Miles W Hwy 107 Santa Rosa (78593) *(G-18737)*

Rio Oil and Gas II LLC..................................832 616-3726
3 Waterway Square Pl # 500 The Woodlands (77380) *(G-19912)*

Rio Oil and Gas LLC.....................................832 616-3717
3 Waterway Square Pl # 500 Spring (77380) *(G-19248)*

Rio Petroleum...806 356-8033
2805 Sw 15th Ave Amarillo (79102) *(G-458)*

Rio Plastics Inc...956 831-2715
2700 Rl Ostos Rd Brownsville (78521) *(G-2401)*

Rio Resources LLC.......................................830 438-4841
1171 Gruene Rd Ste 105 New Braunfels (78130) *(G-15820)*

Rio Services, Odessa *Also called Everett LLC (G-15994)*

Rio Star Foods Inc.......................................214 630-4455
3251 W Commerce St Dallas (75212) *(G-4901)*

Rio Truss LP...956 682-9822
100 N Bentsen Rd McAllen (78501) *(G-14902)*

Rio Valley Biofuel Transport............................915 791-8720
3500 Doniphan Dr El Paso (79922) *(G-5940)*

Rio Valley Biofuels LLC..................................915 791-8720
3500 Doniphan Dr El Paso (79922) *(G-5941)*

Rio Valley Pipe LLC (PA)..............................**956 580-3466**
3609 W Palma Vista Dr Palmview (78572) *(G-16312)*

Rio Valley Pipe LLC......................................956 519-4960
3100 N Tom Gill Rd Penitas (78576) *(G-16630)*

Rios Packaging Corp......................................214 920-9851
4557 Leston St Dallas (75247) *(G-4902)*

Rise n Shine Donuts......................................806 745-5282
7803 University Ave Lubbock (79423) *(G-14473)*

Rising S Bunkers, Murchison *Also called Rising S Company LLC (G-15682)*

Rising S Company LLC (PA)............................**214 455-0560**
9350 State Highway 31 E Murchison (75778) *(G-15682)*

Rising S Company LLC....................................903 469-4452
17729 Interstate 20 Canton (75103) *(G-2659)*

Risk Management Armored SEC..........................817 932-5923
8909 County Road 109 Alvarado (76009) *(G-340)*

Riso Inc..800 942-7476
2081 Hutton Dr Ste 208 Carrollton (75006) *(G-2808)*

Rister Crnkshaft Spcialist Ltd..........................361 289-0588
5317 Leopard St Corpus Christi (78408) *(G-3610)*

Rita Barber Inc..325 698-0111
133 Wall St Abilene (79603) *(G-73)*

Ritchie-Vincent Inc (PA)..............................**432 337-5133**
301 S Lincoln Ave Odessa (79761) *(G-16142)*

Rite Weld Supply, Dallas *Also called J & L Partners (G-4516)*

Riteks Inc 972 529-1118
415 Interchange St McKinney (75071) *(G-14972)*

Ritescreen Company LLC 903 482-9200
787 E Village Pkwy Van Alstyne (75495) *(G-20212)*

Rittal Corp 937 399-0500
13810 Hollister Dr # 170 Houston (77086) *(G-11626)*

Riva Services LLC 713 675-2525
12231 1/2 Fm 529 Rd Houston (77041) *(G-11627)*

Rival Prcsion Mnfctrng RPM LLC 817 487-9694
4545 J D Mouser Pkwy Alvarado (76009) *(G-341)*

River Aggregates LLC 936 446-2000
13070 Sh 242 Conroe (77302) *(G-3358)*

River Cement Sales Company 325 288-4224
202 County Road 306 Maryneal (79535) *(G-14811)*

River City Cabinets Inc 512 442-9990
115 E Saint Elmo Rd Ste D Austin (78745) *(G-1467)*

River City Industries, San Antonio *Also called Rivercity Waterjet Inc (G-18428)*

River City Manufacturing Inc 512 335-5194
1255 E State Highway 29 Bertram (78605) *(G-2053)*

River City Ready Mix Inc 210 520-1941
5745 Easterling San Antonio (78251) *(G-18427)*

River Oaks Printing Co Inc 817 738-5461
4706 Barbara Rd River Oaks (76114) *(G-17479)*

Rivercity Donuts, Del Rio *Also called Ohara Valente (G-5321)*

Rivercity Sportswear LLC (PA) **512 754-8039**
1705 S I 35 Exit 202 San Marcos (78666) *(G-18707)*

Rivercity Waterjet Inc 210 590-0300
11734 Nacogdoches Rd San Antonio (78217) *(G-18428)*

Riverside Engineering Inc (PA) **210 227-9090**
121 Interpark Blvd # 604 San Antonio (78216) *(G-18429)*

Riverside Machine Shop Inc 409 246-1600
4002 Highway 327 Kountze (77625) *(G-13672)*

Riviana Foods, Houston *Also called Riviana International Inc (G-11630)*

Riviana Foods Inc 713 529-3251
1702 Taylor St Houston (77007) *(G-11628)*

Riviana Foods Inc (HQ) **713 529-3251**
2777 Allen Pkwy Fl 15 Houston (77019) *(G-11629)*

Riviana International Inc (HQ) **713 529-3251**
2777 Allen Pkwy Fl 15 Houston (77019) *(G-11630)*

Riviera Operating LLC (HQ) **713 227-1868**
600 Travis St Ste 5100 Houston (77002) *(G-11631)*

Riviera Resources Inc (PA) **281 840-4000**
717 Texas St Ste 2000 Houston (77002) *(G-11632)*

Rj & RC Associates LLC 214 352-4690
4103 Crossing Ln Dallas (75220) *(G-4903)*

RJ Global Wika LP 281 897-9222
10910 W Sam Houston Pkwy Houston (77064) *(G-11633)*

Rk Global Inc 972 339-8016
726 Cheshire Dr Coppell (75019) *(G-3440)*

Rk Petroleum Corp 432 683-4319
406 N Main St Midland (79701) *(G-15387)*

Rk Ranco Industries LLC 903 831-5992
294 Cantrell St Nash (75569) *(G-15723)*

Rki Inc (PA) **713 688-4414**
2301 Central Pkwy Houston (77092) *(G-11634)*

Rkr Technologies Ltd 817 640-5340
724 111th St Arlington (76011) *(G-771)*

Rkt Operating LLC 903 686-0284
2706 E Marshall Ave Longview (75601) *(G-14299)*

Rley Enterprises Inc 956 715-8228
1012 E Owassa Rd Ste B Edinburg (78542) *(G-5599)*

Rlf Salado Quarries LLC 254 793-3355
3500 Fm 2843 Florence (76527) *(G-6242)*

Rln Consulting Enterprises LLC 713 515-3638
2791 E Highway 199 Springtown (76082) *(G-19275)*

Rln Fabricators, Springtown *Also called Rln Consulting Enterprises LLC (G-19275)*

Rlra Inc 817 783-3335
3813 Easy St Alvarado (76009) *(G-342)*

Rm Manifold Group Inc 817 897-5330
120 S Sylvania Ave Ste A Fort Worth (76111) *(G-6961)*

RMA, Houston *Also called Ravago Mfg Americas LLC (G-11553)*

RMC Plastics Inc 713 722-9322
629 Aldine Mail Rd Houston (77037) *(G-11635)*

RMC Reliable Machinists Corp 281 444-2181
7102 Belgold St Houston (77066) *(G-11636)*

RMC Usa Inc (HQ) **713 650-6200**
920 Memorial City Way Houston (77024) *(G-11637)*

Rmd Manufacturing Ltd 817 477-5321
1402 Highway 287 S Mansfield (76063) *(G-14712)*

Rmf Manufacturing LLC 713 910-9777
7922 Hansen Rd Houston (77061) *(G-11638)*

Rmg Enterprise Solutions Inc (HQ) **877 796-6634**
15770 Dallas Pkwy # 1100 Dallas (75248) *(G-4904)*

Rmg Networks, Dallas *Also called Rmg Enterprise Solutions Inc (G-4904)*

Rmg Networks Holding Corp (HQ) **800 827-9666**
15301 Dallas Pkwy Ste 500 Addison (75001) *(G-159)*

Rmi Titanium Company LLC 713 466-8222
7600 S Santa Fe Dr Ste C Houston (77061) *(G-11639)*

Rmis, Deer Park *Also called Maviro Inc (G-5285)*

Rmor Energy Corporation 361 318-0151
116 Highway 183 Refugio (78377) *(G-17246)*

RMS Solutions Group LLC 469 964-7127
320 Rs County Road 4310 Point (75472) *(G-17080)*

Rnb Controls Inc 325 388-6023
4623 W Ranch Road 1431 Kingsland (78639) *(G-13622)*

Rncc, Marshall *Also called Republic National Cabinet Corp (G-14801)*

Ro Mac Oil Co Inc 940 849-2261
104 W High St Throckmorton (76483) *(G-19946)*

Ro SA Vacuum Trucks Inc 956 584-8685
15751 Wallace Rd Edinburg (78541) *(G-5600)*

Road Kare International LP 972 647-8300
530 Jesse St Grand Prairie (75051) *(G-7967)*

Road Rescue, Uvalde *Also called Blades Group LLC (G-20188)*

Road Runner Service Point 713 675-5110
4926 N Mccarty St Houston (77013) *(G-11640)*

Roadclipper Enterprises Inc (PA) **903 572-2834**
4006 Farm Road 3417 Mount Pleasant (75455) *(G-15662)*

Roadrunner Rubber Corp 713 697-0633
4824 Downs Ln Houston (77093) *(G-11641)*

Roadway Specialties Inc 512 280-6666
14152 Fm 1826 Austin (78737) *(G-866)*

Roastery, The, Wolfforth *Also called Daily Offrngs Cof Roastery LLC (G-20907)*

Robbco Pumps Inc 806 892-2290
12610 N Fm 400 Idalou (79329) *(G-12890)*

Robbins & Myers Inc (HQ) **936 890-1064**
10586 Highway 75 N Willis (77378) *(G-20861)*

Robbins Metal Fabricators, La Marque *Also called Partner Metalfab LP (G-13714)*

Robbins Myers Enrgy Systems LP 936 890-1064
10586 N Highway 75 Willis (77378) *(G-20862)*

Roberson Wireline Inc 806 435-3087
314 Se 9th Ave Perryton (79070) *(G-16647)*

Robert Bosch Auto Steering LLC 956 857-4436
11302 Eastpoint Dr Ste C Laredo (78045) *(G-13924)*

Robert Bosch LLC 956 753-6082
11302 Eastpoint Dr Ste C Laredo (78045) *(G-13925)*

Robert Early Welding 325 573-0029
5140 County Road 475 Snyder (79549) *(G-19004)*

Robert F Herndon Corporation 915 779-7905
7360 Stiles Dr El Paso (79915) *(G-5942)*

Robert J Jenkins Co 281 332-3566
906 W Medical Center Blvd Webster (77598) *(G-20643)*

Robert K Dean 713 681-2218
5707 Garden Ln Ste B Houston (77092) *(G-11642)*

Robert L Rowan & Associates 713 681-5811
3816 Dacoma St Houston (77092) *(G-11643)*

Robert Leshea Inc 803 407-9284
24319 Bay Hill Blvd Katy (77494) *(G-13377)*

Robert Marshall Cnstr Inc 361 747-5253
980 Rr 8054c Bruni (78344) *(G-2450)*

Robert Shaw Mfg Co Inc 817 927-2557
2820 Bryan Ave Fort Worth (76104) *(G-6962)*

Robert U Neese 281 342-2884
307 Wollschlaeger Dr Boerne (78006) *(G-2134)*

Robert V Johns & Associates (PA) **214 741-1912**
1544 Slocum St Dallas (75207) *(G-4905)*

Robertshaw Controls Company 956 831-9000
5845 Padre Island Hwy Brownsville (78521) *(G-2402)*

Robertshaw Controls Company 956 724-4400
13602 N Unitec Dr Laredo (78045) *(G-13926)*

Robertson-Ceco II Corporation (HQ) **281 897-7788**
10943 N Sam Huston Pkwy W Houston (77064) *(G-11644)*

Robin Guitars, Houston *Also called Portsmouth Trading Co Inc (G-11368)*

Robinson Aerospace Inc 817 253-0639
539 W Commerce St Dallas (75208) *(G-4906)*

Robinson Drilling Texas Ltd 432 267-5277
1200 N Fm 700 Big Spring (79720) *(G-2096)*

Robinson Engineering Co Inc 972 272-2001
1914 Silver St Garland (75042) *(G-7580)*

Robinson Fans Inc 325 437-3267
2424 Oak St Abilene (79602) *(G-74)*

Robinson Media Company LLC 254 757-5757
900 Franklin Ave Waco (76701) *(G-20455)*

Robinson Pipe & Sign, Houston *Also called Robinson Pipe & Supply Inc (G-11645)*

Robinson Pipe & Supply Inc 713 672-4152
915 Mccarty St Houston (77029) *(G-11645)*

Robogistics LLC (PA) **409 234-1033**
363 N Sam Houston Pkwy E # 1100 Houston (77060) *(G-11646)*

Robogistics LLC 713 364-4430
3451 57th St Port Arthur (77642) *(G-17123)*

Robotic Welding Solutions LLC 281 706-5967
1525 Airport Rd Conroe (77301) *(G-3359)*

Robroy Industries Inc 412 828-2100
1100 Us Highway 271 S Gilmer (75644) *(G-7712)*

Robroy Industries - Texas LP, Gilmer *Also called Robroy Industries-Texas LLC (G-7713)*

Robroy Industries-Texas LLC 903 843-5591
1100 Us Highway 271 S Gilmer (75644) *(G-7713)*

ROC Carbon Company, Houston *Also called ROC Industries Inc (G-11647)*

ROC Industries Inc 713 468-7743
  1605 Brittmoore Rd Houston (77043) *(G-11647)*

ROC Service Company LLC (HQ)................................ **940 683-0159**
  191 Energy Way Bridgeport (76426) *(G-2300)*

ROC Software LP (PA).. **512 336-4200**
  3305 Northland Dr Ste 105 Austin (78731) *(G-1468)*

ROC Software Systems, Austin *Also called ROC Software LP (G-1468)*

Roca Precision Mfg Inc 281 240-2020
  12830 Century Dr Stafford (77477) *(G-19371)*

Roca Printed Circuits, Stafford *Also called Roca Precision Mfg Inc (G-19371)*

Roca USA Inc 713 983-8008
  7100 Business Park Dr Houston (77041) *(G-11648)*

Roche Rouge Company L L C 512 326-1670
  600 E Saint Elmo Rd Austin (78745) *(G-1469)*

Rochester Gauges LLC (HQ)..................................... **972 280-8478**
  11616 Harry Hines Blvd Dallas (75229) *(G-4907)*

Rock Crushers Inc 979 289-3768
  7000 Fm 390 Rd W Burton (77835) *(G-2620)*

Rock Fin Countertops Inc 713 460-4441
  5830 Gessner Rd Ste A Houston (77041) *(G-11649)*

Rock Fin Minerals, Houston *Also called Rock Fin Countertops Inc (G-11649)*

Rock Island Donut Shop 972 254-5069
  2336 Rock Island Rd Irving (75060) *(G-13166)*

Rock Solid Crushed Stone Inc 903 587-3448
  110 W Cottonwood St Leonard (75452) *(G-14002)*

Rock Water Energy, Snyder *Also called Reef Services LLC (G-19003)*

Rock-Tenn Folding Carton, Greenville *Also called Westrock Rkt LLC (G-8096)*

Rock-Tenn Paperboard Products, Dallas *Also called Westrock Rkt LLC (G-5184)*

Rocka Solutions Inc 514 602-9449
  14005 Sandy Point Ln El Paso (79938) *(G-5943)*

Rockall Energy LLC (PA)... **214 618-7600**
  5005 Lyndon B Johnson Fwy # 700 Dallas (75244) *(G-4908)*

Rockcliff Energy MGT LLC 713 351-0525
  717 Texas St Houston (77002) *(G-11650)*

Rockdale Reporter Inc 512 446-5838
  221225 E Cameron St Rockdale (76567) *(G-17526)*

Rocket Air Supply Division, Arlington *Also called Rkr Technologies Ltd (G-771)*

Rocket Distribution LLC 817 688-9454
  344 Mcdonnell St Lewisville (75057) *(G-14089)*

Rockies Environmental LLC 469 715-2642
  860 Dentwood Trl Prosper (75078) *(G-17215)*

Rocking Horse Designs, Aubrey *Also called Lauras Carousel Inc (G-850)*

Rocking T Saddlery 903 455-6629
  2210 Highway 34 N Greenville (75401) *(G-8089)*

Rockmm Manufacturing Inc 346 888-6188
  1620 N Main St Pearland (77581) *(G-16595)*

Rockpoint Apparel Company 713 699-9896
  9925 Aldine Westfield Rd Houston (77093) *(G-11651)*

Rockpoint Marketplace, Houston *Also called Rockpoint Apparel Company (G-11651)*

Rockport Pilot, Rockport *Also called Hartman Newspapers LP (G-17530)*

Rocksolid LLC 855 282-8880
  1 Cowboys Way Ste 190 Frisco (75034) *(G-7309)*

Rocksprings Short Stop, Rocksprings *Also called Valero Energy Corporation (G-17533)*

Rockstar Welding, Pilot Point *Also called Rs Welding LLC (G-16728)*

Rockwall Chrysler Dodge 469 698-2100
  970 E Interstate 30 Rockwall (75087) *(G-17563)*

Rockwell American, Mount Pleasant *Also called Quality Trailer Products LP (G-15661)*

Rockwell Automation Inc 713 353-2400
  4325 W S Houston Pky N100 Houston (77043) *(G-11652)*

Rockwell Automation Inc 972 417-5400
  6601 Cascades Ct Ste 130 Lewisville (75056) *(G-14090)*

Rockwell Collins Inc 325 695-0308
  7318 Dafb Abilene (79607) *(G-75)*

Rockwell Collins Inc 972 705-3156
  3200 E Renner Rd Richardson (75082) *(G-17391)*

Rockwell Medical Tech Inc 972 874-2130
  4051 Freport Pkwy Ste 100 Grapevine (76051) *(G-8052)*

Rockwell Precision Inc 281 890-9331
  8926 Solon Rd Houston (77064) *(G-11653)*

Rockwood Shutters, Houston *Also called Houston Shutters LLC (G-10251)*

Rocky Mountain High Brands Inc (PA)........................ **800 260-9062**
  1000 Shiloh Rd Ste 200 Plano (75074) *(G-16995)*

Rocla Concrete Tie Inc 806 383-7071
  1601 Holly St Amarillo (79108) *(G-459)*

Roco Drilling and Service Inc 903 963-7036
  160 W Main St Van (75790) *(G-20209)*

Roda Deaco Valve Inc 780 465-4429
  8824 Fallbrook Dr Houston (77064) *(G-11654)*

Rodbouban Corporation 972 841-8989
  5211 Kleinbrook Dr Houston (77066) *(G-11655)*

Rodco-Brandt Manufacturing 817 477-4118
  600 S 2nd Ave Mansfield (76063) *(G-14713)*

Roddie Wool Scouring Inc 325 597-2138
  601 Grand Ave Brady (76825) *(G-2217)*

Roddy Information Services, Addison *Also called Foreclosure Listing Service (G-125)*

Rodens All Star Mch & Mfg Inc 817 927-2825
  3998 Fairview Rd Millsap (76066) *(G-15505)*

Rodeo Plastic Bag & Film LLC 972 216-3331
  3328 Executive Blvd Mesquite (75149) *(G-15075)*

Rodessa Operating Company Inc (PA)........................ **903 534-4765**
  4085 Emil St Robstown (78380) *(G-17516)*

Rodgers Ornamental Iron Inc 817 535-2127
  2248 E Lancaster Ave Fort Worth (76103) *(G-6963)*

Rodgers-Wade Mfg Co Inc 903 739-2500
  1401 3rd St Sw Paris (75460) *(G-16367)*

Rodney Hunt, Houston *Also called Jash Usa Inc (G-10457)*

Rodriguez Foods Ltd 817 626-3961
  2901 Decatur Ave Fort Worth (76106) *(G-6964)*

Rodrill Inc 210 667-2130
  11670 Interstate 10 E Converse (78109) *(G-3402)*

Rodrill Manufacturing, Converse *Also called Rodrill Inc (G-3402)*

Rods Service LLC 979 775-5000
  7932 W State Highway 21 Bryan (77807) *(G-2502)*

Roes of San Antonio LLC 210 224-5441
  1922 S Laredo St San Antonio (78207) *(G-18430)*

Roger D Stevens Contractor 830 796-3714
  587 Fm 3240 Bandera (78003) *(G-1744)*

Roger Hooper 903 784-3328
  101 Lamar Ave Paris (75460) *(G-16368)*

Rogers Lumber Co Inc 409 745-1953
  8330 Old Highway 90 Orange (77630) *(G-16258)*

Rogers Manufacturing Corp 901 301-4936
  4223 Rocky Bend Dr Sugar Land (77479) *(G-19536)*

Rogers Manufacturing Inc 940 325-7806
  109 Sw Mrtn Lther King Jr Mineral Wells (76067) *(G-15540)*

Rogers Wade, Paris *Also called Rodgers-Wade Mfg Co Inc (G-16367)*

Rogii Inc 346 714-8694
  11750 Katy Fwy Ste 1010 Houston (77079) *(G-11656)*

Rogupe Sasa Molding, El Paso *Also called Sasa Molding Inc (G-5952)*

Rohart Company 713 695-5333
  150 Bennington St Houston (77022) *(G-11657)*

Rohde & Schwarz Usa Inc 469 713-5300
  410 Freeport Pkwy Coppell (75019) *(G-3441)*

Rohm and Haas Texas Inc (HQ)................................ **281 476-8304**
  6600 La Porte Fwy Deer Park (77536) *(G-5291)*

Roi Telephony LLC 214 364-2425
  4951 Airport Pkwy Ste 660 Addison (75001) *(G-160)*

Roicom Usa LLC 915 471-3071
  1414 Ability Dr El Paso (79936) *(G-5944)*

Rok Protective Systems Inc 713 467-6999
  2313 W Sam Houston Pkwy S Houston (77042) *(G-11658)*

Roka Sports Inc 877 985-7652
  2214 W Braker Ln Ste A Austin (78758) *(G-1470)*

Roland Curtains Inc 817 607-0080
  3212 Pinewood Dr Arlington (76010) *(G-772)*

Roldan Drilling Fluids R&D 832 918-6267
  3600 College Park Dr # 10206 The Woodlands (77384) *(G-19913)*

Roldan Midstream Services LLC 832 918-6267
  123 N Misty Dawn Dr The Woodlands (77385) *(G-19914)*

Roll Master Corp 817 292-4319
  7432 Ranger Way Fort Worth (76133) *(G-6965)*

Roll-A-Cone Mfg Distrg Co Ltd 806 668-4722
  7655 Roll A Cone Rd Tulia (79088) *(G-20037)*

Rollac Shutter of Texas Inc 281 485-1911
  5331 W Orange St Pearland (77581) *(G-16596)*

Rolland Centuries of Security, Dallas *Also called Rolland Safe & Lock Co LLC (G-4909)*

Rolland Safe & Lock Co LLC (PA)............................... **972 243-3711**
  3140 Towerwood Dr Dallas (75234) *(G-4909)*

Rolligon Nov LP 936 873-2600
  6740 Highway 30 Anderson (77830) *(G-531)*

Rolling Frito-Lay Sales LP 972 334-2513
  7701 Legacy Dr Plano (75024) *(G-16996)*

Rolltchs Spcialty Vehicles LLC 210 651-5700
  7451 Fm 3009 Schertz (78154) *(G-18761)*

Rolltex Inc 432 570-7576
  901 W Florida Ave Midland (79701) *(G-15388)*

Rolltex Bearing, Midland *Also called Rolltex Inc (G-15388)*

Roltrans Group America, Arlington *Also called Roland Curtains Inc (G-772)*

Rom Industrial Inc 915 875-1186
  2120 E Paisano Dr Ste D El Paso (79905) *(G-5945)*

Roma Steam Bath Inc 281 578-9945
  10555 W Little York Rd Houston (77041) *(G-11659)*

Romar/Mec LLC 281 440-1725
  218 Richey Rd Houston (77090) *(G-11660)*

Romco Manufacturing Inc 281 479-9600
  100 W 1st St Deer Park (77536) *(G-5292)*

Romco Manufacturing Inc 281 479-9600
  100 W 1st St Deer Park (77536) *(G-5293)*

Romeo Engineering Incorporated 817 656-0048
  4217 Hahn Blvd Fort Worth (76117) *(G-6966)*

Romines & Warner, Pampa *Also called Copan Corporation (G-16319)*

Romix Chemical & Brush, Euless *Also called Romix Chemicals Inc (G-6156)*

Romix Chemicals Inc 817 685-0006
  3608 Liston Ln Euless (76040) *(G-6156)*

Romtex Enterprises Inc 281 494-0373
  16322 W Bellfort St Sugar Land (77498) *(G-19537)*

A
L
P
H
A
B
E
T
I
C

Ron T Felt (PA)..512 258-5523
  8820 Burnet Rd Ste 504 Austin (78757) *(G-1471)*

Ron T Felt...512 335-7446
  13497 N Hwy 183 Ste 301 Austin (78750) *(G-1472)*

Ronald L Jordan Company.............................281 485-6626
  4271 Magnolia Pkwy Pearland (77584) *(G-16597)*

Ronald Noles...281 489-7727
  7042 Bissell Rd Manvel (77578) *(G-14737)*

Ronco Machine and Mfg Inc.............................713 697-8717
  10833 W Hardy Rd Houston (77076) *(G-11661)*

Rooftop Systems Inc....................................972 247-7447
  1625 Diplomat Dr Carrollton (75006) *(G-2809)*

Roots Rocks Inc..512 346-1780
  10000 Res Blvd Ste 126 Austin (78759) *(G-1473)*

Ropak Southwest Inc...................................817 473-0259
  1501 E Dallas St Mansfield (76063) *(G-14714)*

Ros Vacuum Services, Sour Lake *Also called Radley Electric Inc (G-19034)*

Rosado Welding Inc.......................................469 730-2222
  6632 Fireflame Dr Dallas (75248) *(G-4910)*

Rosco Laboratories Inc.................................512 388-5299
  1600 Chisholm Trail Rd # 200 Round Rock (78681) *(G-17685)*

Rose Electronics..281 933-7673
  10707 Stancliff Rd Houston (77099) *(G-11662)*

Rose Machine & Fab Inc (PA)...........................713 670-9007
  9031 Ley Rd Houston (77078) *(G-11663)*

Rose Tree Linen, Dallas *Also called M & L Rose Enterprises Inc (G-4617)*

Rosemount Inc..713 396-8700
  10241 W Little York Rd Houston (77040) *(G-11664)*

Rosemount Inc..281 240-2000
  12603 Southwest Fwy # 400 Stafford (77477) *(G-19372)*

Rosemunt Tank Gging N Amer Inc.....................281 988-4000
  6005 Rogerdale Rd Sc200.2 Houston (77072) *(G-11665)*

Rosetta Resources Offshore LLC......................713 335-2400
  1111 Bagby St Ste 1600 Houston (77002) *(G-11666)*

Rosetta Resources Operating LP......................281 872-3100
  1001 Noble Energy Way Houston (77070) *(G-11667)*

Rosewood Prvate Invstments Inc (PA)...............214 849-9000
  2101 Cedar Springs Rd # 16 Dallas (75201) *(G-4911)*

Rosewood Resources (HQ)..............................214 849-9300
  2101 Cedar Springs Rd # 1500 Dallas (75201) *(G-4912)*

Ross Co Services Company Inc.........................806 894-1511
  2341 E Ellis St Levelland (79336) *(G-14013)*

Ross Lumber Ltd..936 254-2575
  2770 Fm 1645 Timpson (75975) *(G-19949)*

Ross Metal Works, Houston *Also called Better Burglar Bars Inc (G-8867)*

Ross Optical Industries Inc...........................915 595-5417
  1410 Gail Borden Pl A3 El Paso (79935) *(G-5946)*

Rotary Components Intl Inc.............................281 590-6484
  814 Logandale Ln Houston (77032) *(G-11668)*

Rotary Drilling Tools USA LLC (HQ)...................979 387-3223
  1201 Louisiana St Fl 28 Houston (77002) *(G-11669)*

Rotary Exploration Inc...................................210 248-9892
  19276 Redland Rd San Antonio (78259) *(G-18431)*

Rothe Enterprises Inc (PA)............................210 310-0447
  4535 E Houston St San Antonio (78220) *(G-18432)*

Rothe Joint Venture Lp.................................281 483-3852
  2101 Nasa Pkwy Bldg 9 Houston (77058) *(G-11670)*

Rothe Joint Venture Lp (PA)..........................210 648-3131
  4614 Sinclair Rd San Antonio (78222) *(G-18433)*

Roto-Flex Oven Co :.......................................210 222-2278
  135 E Cevallos San Antonio (78204) *(G-18434)*

Roto-Versal Compression Svcs.........................713 538-2800
  13223 Fm 529 Rd Houston (77041) *(G-11671)*

Rotom Inc...806 293-7331
  200 W 24th St Plainview (79072) *(G-16762)*

Rotoplas, Fort Worth *Also called Molding Acquisition Corp (G-6846)*

Rotor-Tech Inc...713 984-8900
  10613 Stebbins Cir Houston (77043) *(G-11672)*

Rotork Controls Inc.......................................713 353-7887
  1811 Brittmoore Rd # 100 Houston (77043) *(G-11673)*

Rotork Controls Inc.......................................713 983-7381
  9777 W Gulf Bank Rd # 15 Houston (77040) *(G-11674)*

Rough Country Accessories............................325 365-5258
  1408 N 8th St Ballinger (76821) *(G-1742)*

Rough Hats, Longview *Also called Rhe Hatco Inc (G-14297)*

Roughrider, Dallas *Also called Circle T Western Wear Ltd (G-4121)*

Round Rock Bakery Ltd...................................512 255-3629
  106 W Liberty St Round Rock (78664) *(G-17686)*

Round Rock Dnuts - Liberty LLC.......................512 255-3629
  106 W Liberty Ave Round Rock (78664) *(G-17687)*

Round Rock Screen Printing, Round Rock *Also called Payton Interests Inc (G-17678)*

Roundhouse Elc & Eqp Co Inc..........................432 333-3923
  2224 S Grandview Ave Odessa (79766) *(G-16143)*

Rounhouse Corporation...................................281 593-1118
  18488 Highway 105 Cleveland (77328) *(G-3134)*

Rover Oilfield Services LLC...........................979 533-7195
  118 Alex Way Abilene (79602) *(G-76)*

Rovop Inc..281 231-2626
  13719 Fm 529 Rd Houston (77041) *(G-11675)*

Rowan Companies LLC (HQ)............................713 621-7800
  5847 San Felipe St # 330 Houston (77057) *(G-11676)*

Rowan Drilling Company Inc (HQ)......................713 621-7800
  2800 Post Oak Blvd # 5450 Houston (77056) *(G-11677)*

Rowan Marine Drilling Inc...............................713 621-7800
  2800 Post Oak Blvd # 5450 Houston (77056) *(G-11678)*

Rowan Oil Operator, Van *Also called Al Rowan (G-20205)*

Rowan Petroleum Inc......................................713 621-7800
  2800 Post Oak Blvd Fl 54 Houston (77056) *(G-11679)*

Rowan, Robt L & Assoc, Houston *Also called Robert L Rowan & Associates (G-11643)*

Rowe Equipment Inc.......................................281 255-0555
  19534 Bauer Rd Hockley (77447) *(G-8347)*

Roxar Inc..281 879-2600
  6005 Rogerdale Rd Houston (77072) *(G-11680)*

Roxar Flow Measurement, Houston *Also called Roxar Inc (G-11680)*

Roxwell Performance Drlg LLC..........................432 617-0419
  7613 W Industrial Ave Midland (79706) *(G-15389)*

Roy B Wheeler Company Inc.............................713 692-9729
  911 Martin St Houston (77018) *(G-11681)*

Roy C Garrett Inc...210 659-6701
  411 Fm 1103 Cibolo (78108) *(G-3064)*

Roy Johnson Incorporated.............................817 468-2939
  1108 Enterprise Pl Arlington (76001) *(G-773)*

Royal Bath Mfg, Buda *Also called Royal Baths Mfg Co Ltd (G-2535)*

Royal Baths Manufacturing Co (PA)...................281 442-3400
  14635 Chrisman Rd Houston (77039) *(G-11682)*

Royal Baths Mfg Co Ltd...................................512 707-0094
  199 Park 35 Cv N Buda (78610) *(G-2535)*

Royal Baths Mfg Co Ltd...................................817 589-7300
  7112 Burns St Richland Hills (76118) *(G-17447)*

Royal Business Forms Inc...............................817 640-5253
  2801 Avenue E E Arlington (76011) *(G-774)*

Royal Case Company Inc (PA)...........................903 868-0288
  419 E Lamar St Sherman (75090) *(G-18930)*

Royal Case Company Inc................................903 364-5231
  124 E Grand St Whitewright (75491) *(G-20728)*

Royal Case Company Inc................................903 328-3371
  309 E Houston St Sherman (75090) *(G-18931)*

Royal Chemical Company Ltd..........................214 358-1861
  2851 Reward Ln Dallas (75220) *(G-4913)*

Royal Cup Inc...817 261-7527
  2112 E Randol Mill Rd Arlington (76011) *(G-775)*

Royal Cup of Coffee, Arlington *Also called Royal Cup Inc (G-775)*

Royal Manufacturing, Houston *Also called Royal Baths Manufacturing Co (G-11682)*

Royal Metal Bldg Components, San Benito *Also called Royal Metal Bldg Components (G-18665)*

Royal Metal Bldg Components (PA) 956 399-2271
  2031 Amistad Dr San Benito (78586) *(G-18665)*

Royal Natnwde PRNtng&bus, Arlington *Also called Royal Business Forms Inc (G-774)*

Royal Oak Enterprises LLC..............................903 455-5803
  7000 Industrial Dr Greenville (75402) *(G-8090)*

Royal Printing Group Inc...............................972 241-5686
  2035 Royal Ln Ste 250 Dallas (75229) *(G-4914)*

Royal Production Company Inc (HQ)...................361 888-4792
  500 N Shoreline Blvd # 807 Corpus Christi (78401) *(G-3611)*

Royal Publishing Inc.....................................713 895-9727
  3560 Lang Rd Houston (77092) *(G-11683)*

Royal Purple, Porter *Also called Calumet Branded Products LLC (G-17171)*

Royal Sleep Products Ltd (PA)........................817 834-7522
  900 Haltom Rd Fort Worth (76117) *(G-6967)*

Royal Technocrats Inc....................................713 776-8300
  7447 Harwin Dr Ste 270 Houston (77036) *(G-11684)*

Royal Technologies Corporation.......................956 424-9388
  1200 Trinity St Mission (78572) *(G-15563)*

Royal White Cement Inc (HQ)...........................713 676-0000
  8316 East Fwy Houston (77029) *(G-11685)*

Royal Window Fashions, San Antonio *Also called Drapery Man Corporation (G-18071)*

Royalty Clearinghouse Ltd.............................800 877-5122
  201 W 5th St Ste 1350 Austin (78701) *(G-1474)*

Royalty Metal Finishing Inc...........................281 208-4455
  10050 W Gulf Bank Rd # 200 Houston (77040) *(G-11686)*

Royalty Supply, Grandfalls *Also called Royalty Well Service Inc (G-8000)*

Royalty Well Service Inc (PA)..........................432 547-2926
  Fm 1219 Grandfalls (79742) *(G-8000)*

Royberg Inc (PA)..210 525-0094
  315 N Park Dr San Antonio (78216) *(G-18435)*

Royce Tower Service Inc.................................409 684-1913
  2323 Madison Ave Port Bolivar (77650) *(G-17134)*

Royce Williams Logging, Lufkin *Also called Williams Logging (G-14556)*

Royco Industries Inc......................................713 413-9191
  802 Riley Rd Houston (77047) *(G-11687)*

Royomartin, Corrigan *Also called Corrigan Osb LLC (G-3659)*

Roywell LLC (HQ)...713 661-4747
  1600 Highway 6 Ste 220 Sugar Land (77478) *(G-19538)*

Roywell LLC..432 332-0703
  2425 E Interstate 20 Odessa (79766) *(G-16144)*

Rp Machine Shop...713 939-7522
  8628 Rannie Rd Houston (77080) *(G-11688)*

Rp Welding Inc 940 315-1024
   9000 King Ranch Dr Crossroads (76227) *(G-3749)*

Rpc Inc 361 289-7088
   820 Mcbride Ln Corpus Christi (78408) *(G-3612)*

Rpc Inc 817 689-7660
   1616 Grantland Cir Fort Worth (76112) *(G-6968)*

Rpc Inc 210 310-1330
   5251 Tacco San Antonio (78244) *(G-18436)*

Rpc Inc 325 573-7022
   2545 County Road 226 Snyder (79549) *(G-19005)*

RPC Logistics Express, Fort Worth *Also called Rpc Inc (G-6968)*

Rpe, Arlington *Also called Ranger Plastic Extrusions Inc (G-767)*

RPM Services Inc 281 595-3165
   27920 Highway 288 Rosharon (77583) *(G-17612)*

Rpm-Tronics, Carrollton *Also called Rpmtronics Incorporated (G-2810)*

Rpmtronics Incorporated 972 865-1330
   2201 Midway Rd Ste 108s Carrollton (75006) *(G-2810)*

RPR Products Inc (PA) **713 697-7003**
   407 Delz St Houston (77018) *(G-11689)*

RPS Composites Alabama Inc (PA) **979 265-4262**
   1402 County Road 434 Clute (77531) *(G-3158)*

RPS Environmental Solutions LP 972 247-1556
   12200 N Stemmons Fwy Dallas (75234) *(G-4915)*

RPS Manufacturing Solutions, Wolfforth *Also called Rehab Plus Thrapeutic Pdts Inc (G-20911)*

RR Design, Carrollton *Also called MTC Marketing Inc (G-2782)*

RR Donnelley Global, Houston *Also called R R Donnelley & Sons Company (G-11527)*

Rrs, Carrollton *Also called Rooftop Systems Inc (G-2809)*

Rs Logistics LLC 318 347-5915
   512 Kingscote Ct Arlington (76010) *(G-776)*

Rs Welding LLC 940 488-4144
   8490 Highway 377 Pilot Point (76258) *(G-16728)*

RSC Acquisitions (HQ) **713 222-2251**
   14751 Kirby Dr Houston (77047) *(G-11690)*

RSD Security Scanners LLC 915 590-4441
   11900 Montana Ave El Paso (79936) *(G-5947)*

RSD Supply Inc 713 983-6363
   13225 Fm 529 Rd Ste N Houston (77041) *(G-11691)*

Rsg Aerodesign LLC 817 625-9000
   3901 N Main St Hngr 2s Fort Worth (76106) *(G-6969)*

Rsg Products Inc 817 624-6600
   440 West Ln Ste 100 Saginaw (76131) *(G-17755)*

Rsg Southwest, Dallas *Also called R S Global Inc (G-4857)*

RSI, Alvin *Also called Reactor Services International (G-378)*

Rsi Inc (PA) **512 268-7500**
   1670 Kohlers Xing Kyle (78640) *(G-13686)*

RSI Inspection LLC 325 673-9800
   402 S Treadaway Blvd Abilene (79602) *(G-77)*

RSI Partners LLC 817 640-5415
   2901 E Randol Mill Rd Arlington (76011) *(G-777)*

RSI Precision Controls, Richardson *Also called Radiation Sys Prec Cntrls (G-17381)*

RSI Visual Systems Inc 817 510-0350
   615 Freeport Pkwy Coppell (75019) *(G-3442)*

RSI Visuals, Coppell *Also called RSI Visual Systems Inc (G-3442)*

Rsp Permian Inc (HQ) **432 683-7443**
   600 W Illinois Ave Midland (79701) *(G-15390)*

Rsp Permian LLC 432 818-1300
   200 N Loraine St Ste 800 Midland (79701) *(G-15391)*

Rsp Permian LLC (HQ) **214 252-2700**
   3141 Hood St Ste 700 Dallas (75219) *(G-4916)*

Rt Precision Machinery LP 281 354-0910
   3227 Glade Springs Dr Kingwood (77339) *(G-13653)*

Rt Technical Solutions LLC 409 721-9100
   4484 Hodgson Rd Nederland (77627) *(G-15760)*

RTC Manufacturing Inc 817 860-1217
   1016 Enterprise Pl Arlington (76001) *(G-778)*

Rti, Houston *Also called Royal Technocrats Inc (G-11684)*

Rti Energy Systems Inc 281 379-4289
   7211 Spring Cypress Rd Spring (77379) *(G-19163)*

Rti Extrusions Inc 713 641-6010
   7600 S Santa Fe Dr Ste C Houston (77061) *(G-11692)*

Rti Fabrication, Houston *Also called Rti Extrusions Inc (G-11692)*

Rtic Custom Shop, Cypress *Also called Performance Gear Hdqtr LLC (G-3811)*

RTS, Plano *Also called Revenue Technology Svcs Corp (G-16992)*

RTS Packaging LLC 214 331-6555
   4105 Bronze Way Dallas (75237) *(G-4917)*

Rtui, Houston *Also called Indoormedia Inc (G-10345)*

Ruben Arispe Jr 512 543-3444
   8300 Thaxton Rd Austin (78747) *(G-1475)*

Ruben Reyes 214 331-4307
   4707 S Cockrell Hill Rd Dallas (75236) *(G-4918)*

Rubens Electroplating Inc 915 779-3796
   1040 Hawkins Blvd El Paso (79915) *(G-5948)*

Rubicon Communications LLC 512 646-4100
   4616 W Howard Ln Ste 900 Austin (78728) *(G-1476)*

Rubicon Olfld Intl Hldings LLC (PA) **832 386-2500**
   10613 W Sam Hston Pkwy600 Houston (77064) *(G-11693)*

Rubrix LLC 512 581-5513
   110 E Houston St San Antonio (78205) *(G-18437)*

Ruby Automation LLC 972 881-9663
   801 Klein Rd Ste 100 Plano (75074) *(G-16997)*

Ruby Red Paint Inc 972 221-8665
   5312 Meadow Chase Ln Flower Mound (75028) *(G-6279)*

Ruckus Wireless Inc 972 546-1700
   101 E Park Blvd Ste 758 Plano (75074) *(G-16998)*

Rudd Welding Inc 806 435-5501
   12485 Spur 192 Perryton (79070) *(G-16648)*

Ruddock Brothers, El Paso *Also called Ruddock Manufacturing Co Inc (G-5949)*

Ruddock Manufacturing Co Inc 915 544-3530
   1801 Magoffin Ave El Paso (79901) *(G-5949)*

Ruddock Manufacturing Co Inc 915 544-3530
   1825 Magoffin Ave El Paso (79901) *(G-5950)*

Rudinger Enterprises Inc 713 939-1234
   10018 Talley Ln Houston (77041) *(G-11694)*

Rudinger Enterprises Inc (PA) **281 356-6219**
   10010 Talley Ln Houston (77041) *(G-11695)*

Rudolph Foods Company Inc 214 638-2204
   3660 Pipestone Rd Dallas (75212) *(G-4919)*

Rudolphs Market & Sausage Co 214 741-1874
   2924 Elm St Dallas (75226) *(G-4920)*

Rudys Custom Uphl & Design 210 821-5156
   4334 Mccullough Ave San Antonio (78212) *(G-18438)*

Ruiz Distributing Co 713 682-7008
   7515 Long Point Rd Ste 3 Houston (77055) *(G-11696)*

Rulon Elc Illuminations Co Inc 713 863-1133
   607 Durham Dr Houston (77007) *(G-11697)*

Rumber Materials, Muenster *Also called R-Interests LLC (G-15672)*

Rumber Materials Incorporated 940 759-4181
   621 W Division St Muenster (76252) *(G-15673)*

Rummler-Brache Group, Dallas *Also called Pritchett LP (G-4828)*

Runnels Carpet and Tile Inc 903 392-8026
   414 Us Highway 79 N Henderson (75652) *(G-8272)*

Rupert Neve Designs LLC 512 847-3013
   511 Flite Acres Rd Wimberley (78676) *(G-20883)*

Rus Industrial LLC 281 864-9070
   16030 Bear Bayou Dr Channelview (77530) *(G-3033)*

Rush Apparel LLC 713 208-5194
   1810 Cattle Dr Magnolia (77354) *(G-14625)*

Rush Eye Associates Pllc 806 353-0125
   7308 Fleming Ave Ste A Amarillo (79106) *(G-460)*

Rush Overland Manufacturing, Odessa *Also called Rush Sales Company (G-16145)*

Rush Sales Company 432 337-2397
   2700 E I 20 Service Rd Odessa (79766) *(G-16145)*

Rushin Truss Ltd 972 442-3544
   15590 County Road 543 Nevada (75173) *(G-15766)*

Rushing Machine Shop, White Oak *Also called J L Rushing Inc (G-20715)*

Rushman Draperies Inc 214 943-1000
   8600 Preston Rd Ste 106 Plano (75024) *(G-16999)*

Rusk County Well Service Inc 903 984-5017
   118 S Kilgore St Kilgore (75662) *(G-13588)*

Ruskin Company 972 247-7448
   2405 Mciver Ln Carrollton (75006) *(G-2811)*

Russell E Womack Inc 806 747-2581
   1300 E 42nd St Lubbock (79404) *(G-14474)*

Russell Industries Inc (PA) **713 692-7225**
   6125 Nordling Rd Houston (77076) *(G-11698)*

Russell Marine LLC 281 860-0011
   16828 Market St Channelview (77530) *(G-3034)*

Russell Mfg & Fabg Inc 281 590-8185
   14518 Reeveston Rd Houston (77039) *(G-11699)*

Russell Oilfield Equipment Co 281 540-8982
   1910 Humble Place Dr Humble (77338) *(G-12797)*

Russell's Maintenance, Tomball *Also called RAC Materials LLC (G-20005)*

Russells Bakery and Coffee Bar 512 419-7877
   3339 Hancock Dr Austin (78731) *(G-1477)*

Russian Spirit Inc 214 334-3018
   13644 Neutron Rd Dallas (75244) *(G-4921)*

Russian-American Quality 713 522-0453
   2441 Del Monte Dr Houston (77019) *(G-11700)*

Rustex Inc 979 778-7551
   1776 Frieda Ln Bryan (77808) *(G-2503)*

Rustic Creations, Streetman *Also called Kurt Lupo (G-19434)*

Ruth Vending Inc 972 905-3523
   6300 Fallwater Trl # 100 The Colony (75056) *(G-19813)*

Rutherford Oil Corporation (PA) **713 622-5555**
   8 Greenway Plz Ste 1400 Houston (77046) *(G-11701)*

Rutherford Oil Corporation 830 334-8396
   1825 Private Road 1500 Pearsall (78061) *(G-16614)*

Rutherford-Moran Exploration 859 254-4775
   8 Greenway Plz Ste 1400 Houston (77046) *(G-11702)*

Rv Station Ltd (PA) **979 778-8000**
   4520 State Highway 6 S College Station (77845) *(G-3200)*

Rvg Prodirect LLC 956 627-6161
   1913 W Houston Ave McAllen (78501) *(G-14903)*

Rvo Manufacturing LLC 832 229-5114
   15040 Northgreen Blvd Houston (77032) *(G-11703)*

RW Cox Inc...903 739-8088
1690 19th St Sw Paris (75460) ***(G-16369)***
Rw Dirk Engineering, Tuleta *Also called Dirnett Inc* ***(G-20033)***
Rwc Material LLC...210 219-2987
2514 Irvin Rd Fowlerton (78021) ***(G-7162)***
Rwg (repair Overhauls USA Inc (HQ)...**713 538-9700**
6223 W Sam Houston Pkwy N Houston (77041) ***(G-11704)***
RWG Incorporated...972 461-1920
2807 Capital St Wylie (75098) ***(G-20946)***
Rwi, Gainesville *Also called Recovered Water Industries LLC* ***(G-7360)***
Rwls LLC (PA)...**806 897-0231**
14 Crockett Cir Levelland (79336) ***(G-14014)***
Rwls LLC...432 664-0020
2811 E Pearl St Odessa (79761) ***(G-16146)***
Rwn Contractors LLC...817 523-7900
8700 W Highway 199 Springtown (76082) ***(G-19276)***
RWS Cabinets LLC...936 760-2407
5797 Rolling Hills Rd Conroe (77303) ***(G-3360)***
Ryan Manufacturing Company Inc...817 613-1890
213 Old Agnes Rd Weatherford (76088) ***(G-20618)***
Ryc Foods LLC...210 731-8854
7700 Broadway Ste 200 San Antonio (78209) ***(G-18439)***
Rydar Inc (PA)...**979 877-0703**
979 Brazos Crossing Ln Sealy (77474) ***(G-18817)***
S & A Systems Inc...972 722-1009
992 Sids Rd Rockwall (75032) ***(G-17564)***
S & B Technical Products Inc...800 432-8213
1300 E Berry St Fort Worth (76119) ***(G-6970)***
S & G Disposal...806 894-6044
1001 8th St Levelland (79336) ***(G-14015)***
S & G Plastics Inc...713 467-8766
8399 Kempwood Dr Houston (77055) ***(G-11705)***
S & H Manufacturing Co, Houston *Also called S & H Shtmtl & Fabg Co Inc* ***(G-11706)***
S & H Shtmtl & Fabg Co Inc...713 926-8805
7218 Canal St Houston Houston (77011) ***(G-11706)***
S & M Aire LLC...915 921-9677
13340 Ayla Rd El Paso (79938) ***(G-5951)***
S & N Pump Company...281 445-2243
8002 Breen Dr Houston (77064) ***(G-11707)***
S & S Cabinet Shop Inc...325 655-6757
3201 Lake Dr San Angelo (76903) ***(G-17825)***
S & S Construction, Midland *Also called Slaughter & Stanley Cnstr Inc* ***(G-15410)***
S & S Contract Pumping Svc Inc...956 386-0211
1204 S Mccoll Rd Edinburg (78539) ***(G-5601)***
S & S Electric, Plainview *Also called Gauntlett Inc* ***(G-16754)***
S & S Hvac, Freer *Also called Super-Tech Hvac LLC* ***(G-7234)***
S & S Machine Inc...972 438-6282
450 Gates Dr Irving (75061) ***(G-13167)***
S & S Machine Shop, Irving *Also called S & S Machine Inc* ***(G-13167)***
S & S McHining Fabrication Inc...254 729-3685
1331 N Highway 14 Groesbeck (76642) ***(G-8108)***
S & S Operating Co Inc...409 296-9571
46436 Interstate 10 Winnie (77665) ***(G-20889)***
S & S Technologies, Big Spring *Also called S C S Technologies LLC* ***(G-2097)***
S & S X-Ray Products Inc (PA)...**281 815-1300**
10625 Telge Rd Houston (77095) ***(G-11708)***
S & T International Inc...409 745-4990
7376 Cohenour Rd Orange (77632) ***(G-16259)***
S & V Well Service Inc...940 872-3535
1500 Nugent St Bowie (76230) ***(G-2200)***
S + S Industries Inc (PA)...**713 643-8888**
5614 Nunn St Houston (77087) ***(G-11709)***
S + S Instruments Inc...281 463-1600
19001 Fm 529 Rd Cypress (77433) ***(G-3818)***
S 5 Manufacturing LLC...940 592-2100
500 W Highway St Iowa Park (76367) ***(G-12909)***
S A Fabtecmex C V...956 504-0707
4200 Las Palmas Cir # 327 Brownsville (78521) ***(G-2403)***
S A I, Tomball *Also called SAI Power Systems Inc* ***(G-20007)***
S A S, San Antonio *Also called San Antonio Shoe Inc* ***(G-18450)***
S and S Pallets...972 382-8142
11189 County Road 95 Celina (75009) ***(G-2994)***
S B I Fine Fabric Finishing, Athens *Also called Schneider-Banks Inc* ***(G-838)***
S C S C Inc...214 398-1199
301 Pleasant Dr Dallas (75217) ***(G-4922)***
S C S Technologies LLC...432 264-6500
3423 Ih 20 E Big Spring (79720) ***(G-2097)***
S C Terminals, Houston *Also called South Coast Terminals LP* ***(G-11963)***
S D I, Wylie *Also called Specialty Devices Incorporated* ***(G-20951)***
S F L Inc...936 856-1433
410 Lindley Dr Willis (77378) ***(G-20863)***
S F Sulphur Company...979 233-3555
608 E 2nd St Freeport (77541) ***(G-7208)***
S G & P Incorporated...979 233-7491
1022 N Avenue G Freeport (77541) ***(G-7209)***
S H Leggitt Company (PA)...**956 504-6440**
1000 Civic Center Loop San Marcos (78666) ***(G-18708)***
S J Manufacturing, Houston *Also called Southern Jwly Mfg Houston Co* ***(G-11975)***
S K Industries Inc...713 462-6997
11934 Hempstead Rd Houston (77092) ***(G-11710)***
S K Resources Inc...713 782-1075
7700 San Felipe St # 500 Houston (77063) ***(G-11711)***
S L P Backhoe Service...903 643-8258
12961 State Highway 149 Longview (75603) ***(G-14300)***
S N D Manufacturing Ltd...214 340-1592
12215 Forestgate Dr # 101 Dallas (75243) ***(G-4923)***
S O A Pump & Supply Inc...432 381-2380
3361 Nw Loop 338 Odessa (79764) ***(G-16147)***
S P (texas) Inc...713 666-5166
7121 Chimney Rock Rd Houston (77081) ***(G-11712)***
S P M, Georgetown *Also called Spm Technology Inc* ***(G-7679)***
S P TX General Comm Printer, Houston *Also called S P (texas) Inc* ***(G-11712)***
S Q I Inc...432 366-9264
820 W 83rd St Odessa (79764) ***(G-16148)***
S R A, Orange *Also called Sabine River Authority Texas* ***(G-16261)***
S R Hill and Assoc Intl Inc...713 960-6617
4265 San Felipe St # 1100 Houston (77027) ***(G-11713)***
S S I, Odessa *Also called Standard Structures Inc* ***(G-16164)***
S S T, Houston *Also called Subsea Technology Inc* ***(G-12089)***
S T I, Lago Vista *Also called Semiconductor Technology Inc* ***(G-13808)***
S T I, Boerne *Also called Separation Technology Inc* ***(G-2136)***
S T S, Dallas *Also called Spectra Test Solutions LLC* ***(G-4995)***
S T S, La Porte *Also called Specialty Tank Services Ltd* ***(G-13791)***
S W Galleries Corp...972 788-2743
4500 Sigma Rd Dallas (75244) ***(G-4924)***
S Y G Corporation...361 884-4927
105 Villa Dr Corpus Christi (78408) ***(G-3613)***
S&K Residential Rmdlg Repr Co, Port Arthur *Also called Stephen Jones* ***(G-17126)***
S&L Designs, Dallas *Also called Sibbitt and Lott Inc* ***(G-4958)***
S&M Energy Services LLC...318 210-5166
153 Private Road 8202 Gary (75643) ***(G-7616)***
S&M International Co Inc...281 749-8289
22422 Crescent Cove Ct Katy (77494) ***(G-13378)***
S&S Industries Inc...972 438-7150
2204 Century Center Blvd Irving (75062) ***(G-13168)***
S-TEC Corporation...800 872-7832
1 S Tec Way Mineral Wells (76067) ***(G-15541)***
S.S.T. Enterprises, Mabank *Also called Simplfied Strl Thrmforming Inc* ***(G-14581)***
S/M, Dallas *Also called Scott-Merriman Inc* ***(G-4944)***
S/T Health Group Consulting...281 491-5555
3033 Chimney Rock Rd # 550 Houston (77056) ***(G-11714)***
S2w Contracting LLC...940 745-1421
136 Miramar Cir Weatherford (76085) ***(G-20619)***
S2w Field Services, Weatherford *Also called S2w Contracting LLC* ***(G-20619)***
SA Quality Fence Ltd...210 545-6767
13115 Wetmore Rd San Antonio (78247) ***(G-18440)***
Sa-Alc/Ldae-adtic, San Antonio *Also called US Dept of the Air Force* ***(G-18580)***
Sabalo Explrtion Operating LLC (PA)...**361 888-7708**
800 N Shoreline Blvd Corpus Christi (78401) ***(G-3614)***
Saber Security Systems Inc...512 341-8700
2111 Greenhill Dr Ste 100 Round Rock (78664) ***(G-17688)***
Saber Systems, Round Rock *Also called Saber Security Systems Inc* ***(G-17688)***
Saberex Group Ltd...512 623-4694
12317 Tech Blvd Ste 100 Austin (78727) ***(G-1478)***
Sabfi, San Antonio *Also called San Antonio Broom Factory Inc* ***(G-18446)***
Sabine Hub Services LLC...214 721-9474
2811 Hayes Rd Houston (77082) ***(G-11715)***
Sabine Investor Holdings LLC...832 242-9600
1415 La St Ste 1600 Houston (77002) ***(G-11716)***
Sabine Mining Company...903 660-4200
6501 Fm 968 W Hallsville (75650) ***(G-8130)***
Sabine Mud Logging Inc...903 693-2912
1018 University Cir Carthage (75633) ***(G-2918)***
Sabine Oil & Gas Corporation (HQ)...**832 242-9600**
1415 Louisiana St # 1600 Houston (77002) ***(G-11717)***
Sabine Oil & Gas LLC...832 242-9600
1415 La St Ste 1600 Houston (77002) ***(G-11718)***
Sabine River & Northern RR Co...409 746-2453
5830 Old Highway 87 Orange (77632) ***(G-16260)***
Sabine River Authority Texas (PA)...**409 746-2192**
12777 Highway 87 N Orange (77632) ***(G-16261)***
Sabine River Works, Orange *Also called E I Du Pont De Nemours & Co* ***(G-16240)***
Sabio Environmental LLC...512 869-0544
21 Cypress Blvd Ste 1130 Round Rock (78665) ***(G-17689)***
Sable Natural Resources Corp...972 770-4700
12222 Merit Dr Ste 1850 Dallas (75251) ***(G-4925)***
Sable Permian Resources LLC (PA)...**713 579-8000**
700 Milam St Ste 3100 Houston (77002) ***(G-11719)***
Sable Prmian Resources Fin LLC (HQ)...**713 579-8000**
700 Milam St Ste 3100 Houston (77002) ***(G-11720)***
Sabre Alloys LP...281 405-8580
6039 Thomas Rd Ste B Houston (77041) ***(G-11721)***
Sabre Communications, Alvarado *Also called Sabre Industries Inc* ***(G-343)***
Sabre Industries Inc (HQ)...**817 852-1700**
8653 E Highway 67 Alvarado (76009) ***(G-343)***

Sabre Industries Inc 817 852-1950
  8669 E Highway 67 Alvarado (76009) *(G-344)*

Sabre Sentinel Intl LLC (PA) **972 529-6570**
  321 N Central Expy # 204 McKinney (75070) *(G-14973)*

Sac Manufacturing Inc 903 643-9100
  10730 State Highway 149 Longview (75603) *(G-14301)*

Sachem Inc (PA) **512 421-4900**
  821 Woodward St Austin (78704) *(G-1479)*

Sachem Inc. 512 421-4946
  5700 S Mopac Bldg B Austin (78749) *(G-1480)*

Sachem Inc. 817 202-3200
  2311 Pipeline Rd Cleburne (76033) *(G-3108)*

Saddle Creek Corp 817 306-2000
  5000 Low Iron Crossing Dr Fort Worth (76131) *(G-6971)*

SAE Towers Ltd (HQ) **281 763-2282**
  16945 Northchase Dr # 1910 Houston (77060) *(G-11722)*

Saexploration Holdings Inc (PA) **281 258-4400**
  1160 Dairy Ashford Rd # 160 Houston (77079) *(G-11723)*

Saf Evac, Royse City *Also called Texas Medical Industries Inc (G-17726)*

Saf-Holland Inc 972 442-3556
  1301 Martinez Ln Wylie (75098) *(G-20947)*

Safe PC Solutions, Plano *Also called Excelente Inc (G-16867)*

Safe-T-Pet Inc 903 569-0590
  224 County Road 2455 Mineola (75773) *(G-15511)*

Safeguard Business Systems Inc (HQ) **800 523-2422**
  8585 N Stemmons Fwy 600n Dallas (75247) *(G-4926)*

Safeplex Systems Inc 832 582-7029
  10801 Hammerly Blvd # 242 Houston (77043) *(G-11724)*

Safequip, Austin *Also called Hasse Enterprises Inc (G-1199)*

Safertek Software LLC 972 331-2984
  153 E State Highway 121 # 100 Coppell (75019) *(G-3443)*

Safespace Concepts Inc 713 956-0820
  1424 N Post Oak Rd Houston (77055) *(G-11725)*

Safety Design Usa Inc 940 757-0238
  3029 Cromwell Ave Wichita Falls (76309) *(G-20804)*

Safety N95 LLC 281 624-1812
  5300 N Braeswood Blvd Houston (77096) *(G-11726)*

Safety Rx Services & Sup Corp (PA) **281 487-0505**
  2835 E Sam Houston Pkwy S Pasadena (77503) *(G-16502)*

Safety Seal Piston Ring Co (PA) **903 938-9241**
  4000 S Airport Rd Marshall (75672) *(G-14802)*

Safety Seal Piston Ring Co. 817 283-1574
  10736 S Pipeline Rd Hurst (76053) *(G-12856)*

Safety Supply Inc 210 650-9033
  11827 Tech Com Rd Ste 114 San Antonio (78233) *(G-18441)*

Safety Wear Ltd 832 243-0100
  11050 W Little York Rd B2 Houston (77041) *(G-11727)*

Safety-Kleen Systems Inc (HQ) **800 669-5740**
  1651 N Glnvlle Dr Ste 210 Richardson (75081) *(G-17392)*

Safety-Kleen Systems Inc. 254 772-4419
  22006 Woodway Dr Waco (76712) *(G-20456)*

Safoco Inc 713 956-5936
  9901 Regal Row Houston (77040) *(G-11728)*

Safran Elec & Pwr USA LLC (HQ) **940 272-5700**
  3790 Russell Newman Blvd Denton (76208) *(G-5398)*

Safran Elec Def Avnics USA LLC (HQ) **972 314-3600**
  2802 Safran Dr Grand Prairie (75052) *(G-7968)*

Safran Helicopter Engines USA 972 606-7600
  2709 N Forum Dr Grand Prairie (75052) *(G-7969)*

Safran Power Units Dallas Inc 972 606-7681
  2709 N Forum Dr Grand Prairie (75052) *(G-7970)*

Safran Seats USA LLC (HQ) **940 668-4825**
  2000 Weber Dr Gainesville (76240) *(G-7362)*

Safran Usa Inc 469 941-8150
  2201 W Royal Ln Ste 150 Irving (75063) *(G-13169)*

Safran Usa Inc. 469 941-8150
  2201 W Royal Ln Ste 150 Irving (75063) *(G-13170)*

Safzone Field Services LLC 210 569-6699
  18615 Tuscany Stone # 38 San Antonio (78258) *(G-18442)*

Saga Petro Ltd Lblty Co Colo 432 687-6200
  200 N Loraine St Ste 1300 Midland (79701) *(G-15392)*

Sage Energy Company 979 567-7629
  1516 Fm 166 Caldwell (77836) *(G-2634)*

Sage Energy Company (PA) **210 404-2828**
  100 Ne Loop 410 Ste 1300 San Antonio (78216) *(G-18443)*

Sage International Inc (PA) **972 623-2004**
  1470 Avenue T Ste 1222 Grand Prairie (75050) *(G-7971)*

Sage Software Inc. 512 331-0723
  10800 Pecan Park Blvd # 400 Austin (78750) *(G-1481)*

Sage Surfaces LLC 281 907-8766
  6700 The Wdlnds Pkwy Ste The Woodlands (77382) *(G-19915)*

Sagem Communications USA LLC 972 386-4641
  14651 Dallas Pkwy Ste 900 Dallas (75254) *(G-4927)*

Saginaw Machine Company (PA) **817 232-4482**
  600 Burlington Rd Saginaw (76179) *(G-17756)*

Sagl Enterprises Inc 281 496-3737
  24 Greenway Plz Ste 800 Houston (77046) *(G-11729)*

Sago Christie LP 281 240-8444
  14090 Southwest Fwy # 460 Sugar Land (77478) *(G-19539)*

Sago Energy LLC 325 473-5161
  209 Ne Railroad St Bronte (76933) *(G-2306)*

Sagus International Inc (HQ) **630 413-5540**
  1302 Industrial Blvd Temple (76504) *(G-19702)*

Sahara Operating Company 432 697-0967
  306 W Wall St Ste 1025 Midland (79701) *(G-15393)*

SAI Power Systems Inc 281 516-3130
  11311 Holderrieth Rd # 200 Tomball (77375) *(G-20007)*

Saifee Corporation 713 674-2000
  1220 Shotwell St Houston (77020) *(G-11730)*

Saige Usa Inc 281 980-8393
  3202 Deer Creek Dr Sugar Land (77478) *(G-19540)*

Sailpoint Tech Holdings Inc (PA) **512 346-2000**
  11120 Four Points Dr # 10 Austin (78726) *(G-1482)*

Sailpoint Technologies Inc (HQ) **512 346-2000**
  11120 Four Points Dr # 100 Austin (78726) *(G-1483)*

Saint Arnold Brewing Company 713 686-9494
  2000 Lyons Ave Houston (77020) *(G-11731)*

Saint-Gobain Abrasives Inc 956 541-5285
  1505 Morningside Rd Brownsville (78521) *(G-2404)*

Saint-Gobain Abrasives Inc. 956 519-5047
  6100 Intl Pkwy Ste 300 Mcallen (78503) *(G-14904)*

Saint-Gobain Abrasives Inc. 254 918-2307
  2770 W Washington St Stephenville (76401) *(G-19421)*

Saint-Gobain Prfmce Plas Corp 903 572-3475
  1300 Industrial Rd Mount Pleasant (75455) *(G-15663)*

Saipem America Inc (HQ) **281 552-5600**
  1311 Broadfield Blvd Fl 6 Houston (77084) *(G-11732)*

Salado Operations LLC 254 793-3355
  3500 Fm 2843 Florence (76527) *(G-6243)*

Salado Quarry, Florence *Also called Rlf Salado Quarries LLC (G-6242)*

Salazar Service and Trckg Corp (PA) **432 523-9658**
  5511 Starboard Dr Midland (79706) *(G-15394)*

Salco Products Inc 630 783-2570
  11747 Windfern Rd Ste 500 Houston (77064) *(G-11733)*

Sales Office, Houston *Also called Superior Energy Services LLC (G-12113)*

Sales R Up Media Inc 817 326-3282
  3609 Acton Hwy Ste 24 Granbury (76049) *(G-7808)*

Salient Global Technologies 925 526-1234
  11252 Leo Ln Dallas (75229) *(G-4928)*

Salient Systems Corporation 512 617-4800
  4616 W Howard Ln 1-100 Austin (78728) *(G-1484)*

Salof Companies, New Braunfels *Also called Folas Inc (G-15793)*

Salsa Xochitl, Irving *Also called Xochitl Inc (G-13211)*

Salt Creek Midstream LLC 281 655-3200
  20329 State Highway 249 4thf Houston (77070) *(G-11734)*

Saltel-Industries Inc 432 238-1076
  6213 W County Road 112 Midland (79706) *(G-15395)*

Salter Precision Machining 281 391-4118
  1115 Glenwood Dr Katy (77493) *(G-13438)*

Salzgtter Mnnsmann Stnless Tbe 713 466-7278
  12050 W Little York Rd Houston (77041) *(G-11735)*

Sam, El Paso *Also called Southanchor Manufacturing LLC (G-5970)*

Sam & Sons Truck Equipment, Houston *Also called Olivo Enterprises Inc (G-11172)*

Sam and Sab Inc 713 983-7500
  6919 Maynard Rd Houston (77041) *(G-11736)*

Sam Group Inc 817 481-1968
  213 E Northwest Hwy Grapevine (76051) *(G-8053)*

Sam Stevens Inc 806 872-8365
  2101 Lubbock Hwy Lamesa (79331) *(G-13829)*

SAM&m Group LLC (PA) **346 204-5786**
  1112 Staffordshire Rd Stafford (77477) *(G-19373)*

Samco Enterprises Inc (PA) **281 443-6505**
  16115 Aldine Westfield Rd Houston (77032) *(G-11737)*

Samco Sales Inc 713 733-5700
  7444 Calhoun Rd Houston (77033) *(G-11738)*

Same Day Dumpster Rental LLC 866 223-6227
  6725 S Fry Rd Ste 700-310 Katy (77494) *(G-13379)*

Samedan Oil Corporation (PA) **580 223-4110**
  1001 Noble Energy Way Houston (77070) *(G-11739)*

Sample House & Candle Shop, Dallas *Also called Sample House & Resale Shop Inc (G-4929)*

Sample House & Resale Shop Inc (PA) **214 688-0751**
  4722 Bengal St Dallas (75235) *(G-4929)*

Samsill Corporation (PA) **817 536-1906**
  5740 Hartman Rd Fort Worth (76119) *(G-6972)*

Samson Controls Inc (HQ) **281 383-3677**
  4111 Cedar Blvd Baytown (77523) *(G-1800)*

Samson Project Engineering, Baytown *Also called Samson Controls Inc (G-1800)*

Samson Resources Company 806 435-7200
  922 Se 9th Ave Perryton (79070) *(G-16649)*

Samsung SDS Globl Scl Amer Inc 201 263-3000
  3033 W Pres Grge Bush Pkw Plano (75075) *(G-17000)*

Samuel Son & Co (usa) Inc 972 438-3949
  2303 Century Center Blvd Irving (75062) *(G-13171)*

Samuel Son & Co (usa) Inc. 713 462-5000
  5022 Ashley Ct Houston (77041) *(G-11740)*

Samuel Jackson Incorporated 806 795-5218
  3900 Upland Ave Lubbock (79407) *(G-14475)*

A L P H A B E T I C

Samuel Jackson Mfg Co 806 795-5218
  3900 Upland Ave Lubbock (79407) *(G-14476)*

San Angelo Standard Times, San Angelo *Also called EW Scripps Company* *(G-17798)*

San Antnio Lghthouse For Blind (PA) **210 533-5195**
  2305 Roosevelt Ave San Antonio (78210) *(G-18444)*

San Antonio Armature Works Inc 210 227-0291
  1015 N Colorado St San Antonio (78207) *(G-18445)*

San Antonio Bag & Burlap, McAllen *Also called Kenneth Fox Supply Company* *(G-14882)*

San Antonio Broom Factory Inc 210 226-9762
  3535 N Panam Expy Ste 117 San Antonio (78219) *(G-18446)*

San Antonio Business Journal, San Antonio *Also called Business Jrnl Publications Inc* *(G-17974)*

San Antonio Current, San Antonio *Also called Euclid Media Group LLC* *(G-18097)*

San Antonio Express News, San Antonio *Also called Hearst Corporation* *(G-18162)*

San Antonio Foam Fabricators, San Antonio *Also called Jones Holt Enterprises Inc* *(G-18207)*

San Antonio Light, San Antonio *Also called Hearst Corporation* *(G-18161)*

San Antonio Packing Company, San Antonio *Also called Roes of San Antonio LLC* *(G-18430)*

San Antonio Refinery LLC 512 350-7898
  7811 S Presa St San Antonio (78223) *(G-18447)*

San Antonio Refinery LLC (PA) **210 918-7436**
  1 Bda Xing Ste 100 San Antonio (78235) *(G-18448)*

San Antonio Shoe Inc 210 223-0166
  101 Alamo Plz San Antonio (78205) *(G-18449)*

San Antonio Shoe Inc 210 921-8274
  1717 Sas Dr 2 San Antonio (78224) *(G-18450)*

San Antonio Shoe Inc 830 768-7200
  100 Johnson Blvd Del Rio (78840) *(G-5323)*

San Antonio Shoes 121, Del Rio *Also called San Antonio Shoe Inc* *(G-5323)*

San Antonio Woman, San Antonio *Also called Pixelworks Corporation* *(G-18380)*

San Bay Studio Inc 940 387-4466
  1427 Oakland St Denton (76201) *(G-5399)*

San Benito News, San Benito *Also called New Horizon Publishers Inc* *(G-18661)*

San Benito Textile Inc 956 361-0282
  201 N Travis St San Benito (78586) *(G-18666)*

San Jac Marine LLC 281 862-9764
  17112 Market St Channelview (77530) *(G-3035)*

San Marcos Daily Record, San Marcos *Also called San Marcos Publishing LP* *(G-18709)*

San Marcos Daily Record, San Marcos *Also called Community Newspapers Holdings* *(G-18682)*

San Marcos Daily Record, San Marcos *Also called Newspaper Holding Inc* *(G-18700)*

San Marcos Publishing LP 512 392-2458
  1910 S Ih 35 San Marcos (78666) *(G-18709)*

San Martino Winery & Vineyards 972 772-6043
  12512 Highway 205 N Rockwall (75087) *(G-17565)*

San Mateo Midstream LLC 972 371-5203
  5400 Lbj Fwy Ste 1500 Dallas (75240) *(G-4930)*

San Miguel Lignite Mine, Christine *Also called North American Coal Corp* *(G-3059)*

San Patricio Co Drain 361 364-4268
  701 S San Patricio St Sinton (78387) *(G-18964)*

San Patricio Publishing Co Inc (PA) **361 364-1270**
  117 S Rachal St Sinton (78387) *(G-18965)*

San Saba Pecan, San Saba *Also called Morven Partners LP* *(G-18718)*

San Saba Printing, San Saba *Also called Hoyt Deryl* *(G-18717)*

San-Co Steel Ltd 956 464-7766
  9221 N Fm 493 Donna (78537) *(G-5490)*

Sanara Medtech Inc (PA) **817 529-2300**
  1200 Summit Ave Ste 414 Fort Worth (76102) *(G-6973)*

Sanare Energy Partners LLC 713 626-9696
  777 N Eldridge Pkwy # 300 Houston (77079) *(G-11741)*

Sanbar Balls & Seats Inc 432 332-3755
  3300 N Fm 1936 Odessa (79764) *(G-16149)*

Sanchez Energy, Houston *Also called Mesquite Energy Inc* *(G-10840)*

Sanchez Oil & Gas Corporation (PA) **713 783-8000**
  1360 Post Oak Blvd # 2400 Houston (77056) *(G-11742)*

Sanchez Oil & Gas Corporation 210 208-1300
  30888 S Us Hwy 83 Catarina (78836) *(G-2933)*

Sanchez Oil & Gas Corporation 713 783-8000
  1111 Bagy 1600 Houston (77002) *(G-11743)*

Sanchez Tire Shop 5 ....956 423-0047
  622 S F St Harlingen (78550) *(G-8200)*

Sanco Materials Co 325 453-2901
  1681 Valley View Rd Robert Lee (76945) *(G-17498)*

Sanco Metal Fabricators LLC 806 745-9674
  9102 Highway 87 Lubbock (79423) *(G-14477)*

Sancus Energy and Power LLC (PA) **832 460-1000**
  11767 Katy Fwy Ste 700 Houston (77079) *(G-11744)*

Sand Creek Timber Frames LLC 210 698-6156
  613 State Highway 46 E Boerne (78006) *(G-2135)*

Sand Express, Columbus *Also called Quikrete Companies LLC* *(G-3232)*

Sand Socks 512 284-7706
  5381 Industrial Way Dr Buda (78610) *(G-2536)*

Sandalwood Exploration LP 713 759-6095
  1220 Augusta Dr Ste 400 Houston (77057) *(G-11745)*

Sandalwood Oil & Gas Inc (PA) **713 759-6095**
  1220 Augusta Dr Ste 400 Houston (77057) *(G-11746)*

Sanday Corporation 832 717-4412
  9111 Memorial Grove Dr Spring (77379) *(G-19164)*

Sanden International USA Inc (HQ) **972 442-8400**
  601 Sanden Blvd Wylie (75098) *(G-20948)*

Sandenvendo America Inc (HQ) **800 344-7216**
  10710 Sanden Dr Dallas (75238) *(G-4931)*

Sanderson Farms Inc 903 723-2112
  400 Sanderson Farms Pkwy Palestine (75803) *(G-16308)*

Sanderson Farms Inc 254 412-3800
  301 Aviation Pkwy Waco (76705) *(G-20457)*

Sanderson Farms Inc Proc Div 979 361-3410
  2000 Shiloh Ave Bryan (77803) *(G-2504)*

Sanderson Farms Inc Prod Div 979 778-5730
  701 Capitol Pkwy Bryan (77807) *(G-2505)*

Sanderson Farms Proc Plant, Palestine *Also called Sanderson Farms Inc* *(G-16308)*

Sandford Prepress Systems 214 808-3070
  4656 Leston St Ste 511 Dallas (75247) *(G-4932)*

Sandifers LP Gas & Svc Co Inc 409 963-1269
  5812 Gulfway Dr Port Arthur (77642) *(G-17124)*

Sandpaper of Texas, Dallas *Also called M N Gumbert Corporation* *(G-4621)*

Sandvik Mining & Cnstr USA LLC 817 453-2800
  1300 Heritage Pkwy Mansfield (76063) *(G-14715)*

Sandy Hill Redi-Mix Con Co (PA) **940 627-8769**
  3812 S Highway 287 Decatur (76234) *(G-5253)*

Sandy's Baking Company, El Paso *Also called Marick Foods Inc* *(G-5867)*

Sanford Howard Litho, Dallas *Also called Sandford Prepress Systems* *(G-4932)*

Sani-Safe Products Inc (PA) **210 826-1344**
  2723 Old Ranch Rd San Antonio (78217) *(G-18451)*

Sani-Safe Products Inc 210 646-6706
  11311 Wayland Way San Antonio (78233) *(G-18452)*

Sani-Weld Inc 281 442-0667
  1614 Isom St Houston (77039) *(G-11747)*

Sanijet, Irving *Also called Maple Industries LLC* *(G-13094)*

Sanitary Tortilla Mfg Co 210 226-9209
  623 Urban Loop San Antonio (78204) *(G-18453)*

Sanitation Department, Pasadena *Also called City of Pasadena* *(G-16409)*

Sanitizenow Inc 602 699-3150
  10502 Fallstone Rd Houston (77099) *(G-11748)*

Sanitz Enterprises Inc 719 439-2183
  2054 Willow City Loop Willow City (78675) *(G-20871)*

Sanmina Corporation 408 964-3500
  417 Union Pacific Blvd Laredo (78045) *(G-13927)*

Sanmina Corporation 408 964-3500
  11901 Gavin Rd Laredo (78045) *(G-13928)*

Sanmina Corporation 512 997-1100
  9100 Cameron Rd Austin (78754) *(G-1485)*

Sanmina Corporation 972 512-3333
  1201 W Crosby Rd Carrollton (75006) *(G-2812)*

Sanmina Corporation 210 623-5081
  10501 Fischer Rd Von Ormy (78073) *(G-20349)*

Sanmina Corporation 956 523-6800
  11921 Hayter Rd Laredo (78045) *(G-13929)*

Sanmina-Sci, Austin *Also called Sanmina Corporation* *(G-1485)*

Sanmina-Sci Shared Services, Laredo *Also called Sanmina Corporation* *(G-13929)*

Sanofi-Aventis US LLC 800 981-2491
  211 Quality Cir College Station (77845) *(G-3201)*

Sanotech 360 LLC 817 697-7116
  1000 Frest Pk Blvd Ste 40 Fort Worth (76110) *(G-6974)*

Santa Cruz Biotechnology Inc (PA) **214 902-3900**
  10410 Finnell St Dallas (75220) *(G-4933)*

Santanna Energy Services, Austin *Also called Santanna Natural Gas Corp* *(G-1710)*

Santanna Natural Gas Corp (PA) **512 346-2500**
  7701 San Felipe Blvd # 2 Austin (78729) *(G-1710)*

Santech Industries LLC 817 589-1212
  1401 Valley View Ln # 100 Irving (75061) *(G-13172)*

Santin Auto and Truck Repr Ctr 210 648-4100
  9822 Perrin Beitel Rd San Antonio (78217) *(G-18454)*

Santos CMI Inc (usa) 713 273-4140
  400 N Sam Houston Pkwy E # 590 Houston (77060) *(G-11749)*

Santos, A E De Mexico, Laredo *Also called A E Santos & Co* *(G-13852)*

Santre Export USA LLC 811 053-1165
  319 E Coma Ave Ste 844 Hidalgo (78557) *(G-8309)*

Santte Foods, Shenandoah *Also called Santte Labs LLC* *(G-18898)*

Santte Labs LLC 832 585-1862
  250 Ed English Dr Ste C Shenandoah (77385) *(G-18898)*

Sanvig Sawmill, Sulphur Springs *Also called Gary Sanvig* *(G-19588)*

Sanwa Electronics USA Corp 972 503-3031
  4012 Preston Rd Ste 200 Plano (75093) *(G-17001)*

Sanwa Usa Inc (HQ) **972 503-3031**
  4012 Preston Rd Ste 200 Plano (75093) *(G-17002)*

Saoza's Market, Channelview *Also called Hasco Marine* *(G-3025)*

Sapling Systems Inc 512 323-6565
  2815 Exposition Blvd Austin (78703) *(G-1486)*

Saputo Dairy Foods Usa LLC 903 885-0881
  300 Industrial Dr E Sulphur Springs (75482) *(G-19597)*

Saputo Dairy Foods Usa LLC 214 433-3978
1107 Como St S Sulphur Springs (75482) *(G-19598)*
Saputo Dairy Foods Usa LLC (HQ) **214 863-2300**
2711 N Haskell Ave # 370 Dallas (75204) *(G-4934)*
Sara Lee Coffee & Tea, Houston *Also called Hillshire Brands Company (G-10186)*
Sara's Mediterranean Foods, Richardson *Also called Bayan Imports Inc (G-17278)*
Saracen Energy Advisors LP 713 285-2900
3033 W Alabama St Houston (77098) *(G-11750)*
Sarais Spreads Superfood LLC 552 163-6178
2202 Timberloch Pl # 133 The Woodlands (77380) *(G-19916)*
Saratoga Resources Inc (PA) **713 458-1560**
9225 Katy Fwy Ste 100 Houston (77024) *(G-11751)*
Sarbali Alloys LLC 281 384-3500
8860 Scranton St Houston (77075) *(G-11752)*
Sardisco Enterprises Inc 281 419-9229
27635 Commerce Oaks Dr Oak Ridge North (77385) *(G-15890)*
Sartartia Fabrication Inc 281 240-1222
730 Sartartia Rd Sugar Land (77479) *(G-19541)*
Sas Global Corporation 903 643-9111
9486 Fm 2011 Longview (75603) *(G-14302)*
Sas Institute Inc 512 258-5171
1801 E 6th St Fl 5 Austin (78702) *(G-1487)*
Sasa Molding Inc 915 726-9290
32 Via Placita El Paso (79927) *(G-5952)*
Sasch Inc 214 388-7000
8101a Moberly Ln Dallas (75227) *(G-4935)*
Sasi, Houston *Also called Southern Archtctral Systems In (G-11972)*
Sasol (usa) Corporation (HQ) **281 588-3000**
12120 Wickchester Ln Houston (77079) *(G-11753)*
Sasol Chemicals (usa) LLC 713 428-5652
11821 East Fwy Ste 600 Houston (77029) *(G-11754)*
Sasol Chemicals (usa) LLC 713 428-5400
1914 Haden Rd Houston (77015) *(G-11755)*
Sasol Chemicals (usa) LLC (HQ) **281 588-3000**
12120 Wickchester Ln Houston (77079) *(G-11756)*
Sasol Chemicals (usa) LLC 409 296-9091
14322 Rollins Rd Winnie (77665) *(G-20890)*
Sasol Chemicals North Amer LLC 281 588-3000
12120 Wickchester Ln Houston (77079) *(G-11757)*
Sat Radio Communications Ltd 361 853-9943
730 Diamond Cut Dr Ste F Corpus Christi (78409) *(G-3615)*
Sat-Lite Technologies Ltd 903 295-3400
1969 Willow Lk White Oak (75693) *(G-20719)*
Satake USA Inc (HQ) **281 276-3600**
10900 Cash Rd Stafford (77477) *(G-19374)*
Satco Products Inc 972 247-2437
2000 Valwood Pkwy Dallas (75234) *(G-4936)*
Satco South 1 LLC 361 961-1181
Ste Tc 12b Bldg 1824 Corpus Christi (78419) *(G-3616)*
Satellink Inc 972 487-1434
3525 Miller Park Dr Garland (75042) *(G-7581)*
Satori Home Limited LLC 855 472-8674
13612 Midway Rd Ste 515 Dallas (75244) *(G-4937)*
Satpro Network Inc 972 675-8475
7406 Spicewood Dr Garland (75044) *(G-7582)*
Satterwhite Companies Inc (PA) **903 663-1729**
8405 Us Highway 259 Longview (75605) *(G-14303)*
Satterwhite Log Homes, Longview *Also called Satterwhite Companies Inc (G-14303)*
Saturn Machine Inc 281 391-7800
4815 Front St Brookshire (77423) *(G-2324)*
Saturn Manufacturing Corp 817 267-3961
3608 Raider Dr Hurst (76053) *(G-12857)*
Saturn Polymers Inc 936 334-0675
3718 E Highway 90 Liberty (77575) *(G-14125)*
Saturn Shredders, Grand Prairie *Also called Granutch-Sturn Systems Corp AM (G-7884)*
Saucedas Prcision Grinding Inc 956 399-1572
2800 E Business 77 San Benito (78586) *(G-18667)*
Sauder Management Co (PA) **940 723-8125**
900 8th St Ste 202 Wichita Falls (76301) *(G-20805)*
Saudi Basic Industries Corp 713 532-4999
19706 Gulfwind Dr Houston (77094) *(G-11758)*
Saulsbury Industries Inc 972 884-6000
3010 L B Johnson Fwy # 1100 Dallas (75234) *(G-4938)*
Saulsbury Industries Inc 903 392-2248
2800 County Road 205 N Henderson (75652) *(G-8273)*
Savage Companies 806 381-0261
8400 N Lakeside Dr Amarillo (79108) *(G-461)*
Savage Prcsion Fabrication Inc 972 429-0993
1415 Martinez Ln Wylie (75098) *(G-20949)*
Savanna Drilling LLC 432 614-1055
1500 Windway Odessa (79763) *(G-16150)*
Savanna Energy Svcs USA Corp (HQ) **281 907-4800**
2445 Tech Frest B Ste 200 The Woodlands (77381) *(G-19917)*
Savant Alaska LLC (HQ) **907 868-1258**
4601 Washington Ave # 220 Houston (77007) *(G-11759)*
Savara Inc (PA) **512 614-1848**
6836 Bee Caves Rd 3-200 Austin (78746) *(G-1488)*
Savvy, Houston *Also called Texas Medplast LLC (G-12240)*
Saw Custom Millwork Inc 972 288-2118
3248 Executive Blvd Mesquite (75149) *(G-15076)*
Sawmill Partners LLC 214 358-2314
7557 Rambler Rd Ste 1020 Dallas (75231) *(G-4939)*
Sawyer Crystal, Conroe *Also called Sawyer Technical Materials LLC (G-3361)*
Sawyer Industries, Brownwood *Also called Sawyer Oilfield Products LLC (G-2443)*
Sawyer Metal, Tyler *Also called FE Sawyer Bldg Systems Inc (G-20087)*
Sawyer Oilfield Products LLC 254 644-7261
2700 Virgil Gray Dr Brownwood (76801) *(G-2443)*
Sawyer Technical Materials LLC 936 756-8886
1601 Airport Rd Conroe (77301) *(G-3361)*
Saxet Petroleum Inc 713 783-4883
510 Bering Dr Ste 600 Houston (77057) *(G-11760)*
Saxon Drilling LP (HQ) **281 712-4529**
23400 Clnl Pkwy Bldg H222 Katy (77493) *(G-13439)*
Saxon Engineering Inc 713 466-7500
6946 Signat Dr Houston (77041) *(G-11761)*
Saxon Technologies, Houston *Also called Saxon Engineering Inc (G-11761)*
Saybolt LP 281 478-1300
201 Deerwood Glen Dr Deer Park (77536) *(G-5294)*
Saybolt LP 409 948-3166
220 Texas Ave Texas City (77590) *(G-19800)*
Sb Southern Welding LLC 469 517-0410
3941 Windmill Rd Joshua (76058) *(G-13325)*
Sbi Industrial LLC 972 284-1250
21739 State Highway 64 Canton (75103) *(G-2660)*
Sbi Precision Components LLC 713 715-6111
17643 Telge Rd Cypress (77429) *(G-3819)*
Sbm Offshore Usa Inc (HQ) **281 848-6000**
1255 Enclave Pkwy Houston (77077) *(G-11762)*
Sbu Group LP 281 564-6464
10852 Kinghurst Dr Houston (77099) *(G-11763)*
SC Autosports LLC 972 271-0888
3101 W Miller Rd Garland (75041) *(G-7583)*
SC Industrial Resource Group 972 272-4521
601 Shepherd Dr Garland (75042) *(G-7584)*
SC Manufacturing Texas LLC 817 556-3689
6401 County Road 912 Joshua (76058) *(G-13326)*
Sc-Integrity Inc 214 612-7000
1301 W President George B Richardson (75080) *(G-17393)*
Scada Products LLC 888 649-4283
800 S Blue Mound Rd Fort Worth (76131) *(G-6975)*
Scalable Software Inc 512 501-2828
600 Congress Ave Ste C100 Austin (78701) *(G-1489)*
Scale Free Company Inc 281 873-5555
16420 W Hardy Rd Ste 100 Houston (77060) *(G-11764)*
Scan Drilling Company Inc 903 597-5368
9395 Fm 2767 Tyler (75708) *(G-20148)*
Scan-Pac Mfg Inc 281 356-1640
31502 Sugar Bend Dr Magnolia (77355) *(G-14626)*
Scanlin Sign Service Inc 281 561-9924
13123 Mula Ct Stafford (77477) *(G-19375)*
Scantron Corporation 770 593-5050
15955 La Cantera Pkwy San Antonio (78256) *(G-18455)*
Scarab, White Deer *Also called Praxis Fabrication Inc (G-20710)*
Scarab International Lllp 806 883-7621
1475 County Rd W White Deer (79097) *(G-20711)*
Scent Chips, San Antonio *Also called Noahmaya Candle Co (G-18348)*
Scent Shop Inc 972 271-4661
2614 National Pl Garland (75041) *(G-7585)*
Scentchips Inc 210 341-7373
301 Breesport St San Antonio (78216) *(G-18456)*
Scentsible LLC 972 818-8200
4901 Keller Springs Rd Addison (75001) *(G-161)*
Schaefer Art Bronze LP 817 460-1102
132 S Collins St Ste 132 # 132 Arlington (76010) *(G-779)*
Schaefer Mold Inc 817 534-7461
2358 Blue Smoke Ct N Fort Worth (76105) *(G-6976)*
Schaefer Outfitters, Fort Worth *Also called Schaefer Ventures LLC (G-6977)*
Schaefer Ventures LLC 800 426-2074
6715 Cpration Pkwy Ste A Fort Worth (76126) *(G-6977)*
Schenck Process LLC 816 891-9300
13813 Fm 529 Rd Houston (77041) *(G-11765)*
Schepps Dairy, Dallas *Also called Southern Foods Group LLC (G-4986)*
Schill Steel Services, Houston *Also called Manufctred Component Parts Ltd (G-10749)*
Schirm USA Inc 972 878-4400
4101 Knighthurst St Ennis (75119) *(G-6117)*
Schlachter Oil, Dallas *Also called Schlachter Operating Corp (G-4940)*
Schlachter Operating Corp 214 692-1567
6211 W Nw Hwy Ste C256 Dallas (75225) *(G-4940)*
Schlemmer Usa Inc (HQ) **210 491-4800**
4709 Marco Dr San Antonio (78218) *(G-18457)*
Schlumberger, Houston *Also called Smith International Inc (G-11923)*
Schlumberger, Sugar Land *Also called Thrubit LLC (G-19566)*
Schlumberger, Houston *Also called Geoservices Incorporated (G-9944)*
Schlumberger 979 531-8141
1506 N Alabama Rd Wharton (77488) *(G-20706)*
Schlumberger CMF, Frisco *Also called Schlumberger Technology Corp (G-7310)*
Schlumberger International (HQ) **713 747-4000**
7030 Ardmore St Houston (77054) *(G-11766)*

ALPHABETIC

Schlumberger Limited (HQ) 713 513-2000
5599 San Felipe St Fl 17 Houston (77056) *(G-11767)*

Schlumberger Limited 713 513-2000
1430 Enclave Pkwy Houston (77077) *(G-11768)*

Schlumberger Nam Financial Ctr, Sugar Land *Also called Schlumberger Technology Corp (G-19550)*

Schlumberger Norge As 281 227-9854
1121 Buschong St Houston (77039) *(G-11769)*

Schlumberger Oilfield Services, Sugar Land *Also called Schlumberger Technology Corp (G-19542)*

Schlumberger Oilfield Services, Sugar Land *Also called Schlumberger Technology Corp (G-19543)*

Schlumberger Oilfield Services, Sugar Land *Also called Schlumberger Technology Corp (G-19545)*

Schlumberger Oilfield Services, Midland *Also called Schlumberger Technology Corp (G-15396)*

Schlumberger Oilfield Services, Longview *Also called Schlumberger Technology Corp (G-14304)*

Schlumberger Oilfield Services, San Antonio *Also called Schlumberger Technology Corp (G-18459)*

Schlumberger Omnes Inc 281 285-5176
14910 Airline Rd Rosharon (77583) *(G-17613)*

Schlumberger Omnes Inc (HQ) 713 375-3400
5599 San Felipe St Fl 17 Houston (77056) *(G-11770)*

Schlumberger Recruiting, Sugar Land *Also called Schlumberger Technology Corp (G-19544)*

Schlumberger Rig Tech Inc (HQ) 713 849-1700
6650 Bingle Rd Houston (77092) *(G-11771)*

Schlumberger Technology Corp (HQ) 281 285-8500
300 Schlumberger Dr Sugar Land (77478) *(G-19542)*

Schlumberger Technology Corp 281 285-8500
121 Industrial Blvd Sugar Land (77478) *(G-19543)*

Schlumberger Technology Corp 361 210-6200
2725 County Road 342 Alice (78332) *(G-233)*

Schlumberger Technology Corp 281 285-7400
12808 W Airport Blvd Sugar Land (77478) *(G-19544)*

Schlumberger Technology Corp 281 285-5200
14910 Airline Rd Rosharon (77583) *(G-17614)*

Schlumberger Technology Corp 281 285-8400
300 Schlumberger Dr Sugar Land (77478) *(G-19545)*

Schlumberger Technology Corp 830 569-8046
203 Wyoming Blvd Pleasanton (78064) *(G-17073)*

Schlumberger Technology Corp 432 694-0000
4704 W Hwy 80 Midland (79703) *(G-15396)*

Schlumberger Technology Corp 312 237-2810
6415 Babcock Rd San Antonio (78249) *(G-18458)*

Schlumberger Technology Corp 210 623-4975
10310 Fischer Rd Von Ormy (78073) *(G-20350)*

Schlumberger Technology Corp 956 744-4029
206 Oil Rd Pleasanton (78064) *(G-17074)*

Schlumberger Technology Corp 832 310-2155
1200 Enclave Pkwy Houston (77077) *(G-11772)*

Schlumberger Technology Corp 940 442-6566
3011 Internet Blvd # 200 Frisco (75034) *(G-7310)*

Schlumberger Technology Corp 713 482-0700
6350 W Sam Houston Pkwy N # 200 Houston (77041) *(G-11773)*

Schlumberger Technology Corp 210 623-9400
10625 Fischer Rd Von Ormy (78073) *(G-20351)*

Schlumberger Technology Corp 281 285-8500
105 Industrial Blvd Sugar Land (77478) *(G-19546)*

Schlumberger Technology Corp 281 285-4823
200 Gillingham Ln Sugar Land (77478) *(G-19547)*

Schlumberger Technology Corp 817 870-9040
100 Throckmorton St # 150 Fort Worth (76102) *(G-6978)*

Schlumberger Technology Corp 325 692-1930
5445 N 3rd St Abilene (79603) *(G-78)*

Schlumberger Technology Corp 713 513-2000
5599 San Felipe St # 100 Houston (77056) *(G-11774)*

Schlumberger Technology Corp 903 590-4500
9965 State Highway 31 E Tyler (75705) *(G-20149)*

Schlumberger Technology Corp 903 297-0222
301 Capacity Dr Longview (75604) *(G-14304)*

Schlumberger Technology Corp 713 513-2000
5599 San Felipe St Fl 16 Houston (77056) *(G-11775)*

Schlumberger Technology Corp 281 285-6370
110 Schlumberger Dr Sugar Land (77478) *(G-19548)*

Schlumberger Technology Corp 281 369-3800
22535 N Highway 288b Angleton (77515) *(G-578)*

Schlumberger Technology Corp 210 824-7921
777 E Sonterra Blvd # 200 San Antonio (78258) *(G-18459)*

Schlumberger Technology Corp 432 683-0047
7104 W County Road 116 Midland (79706) *(G-15397)*

Schlumberger Technology Corp 361 664-3458
1126 Airport Rd Alice (78332) *(G-234)*

Schlumberger Technology Corp 281 285-8500
555 Industrial Blvd Sugar Land (77478) *(G-19549)*

Schlumberger Technology Corp 903 297-0222
301 Capacity Dr Longview (75604) *(G-14305)*

Schlumberger Technology Corp 713 747-1040
7275 Grand Blvd Houston (77054) *(G-11776)*

Schlumberger Technology Corp 432 571-4600
1204 W Scharbauer Dr Midland (79705) *(G-15398)*

Schlumberger Technology Corp 713 747-4000
7030 Ardmore St Houston (77054) *(G-11777)*

Schlumberger Technology Corp 281 285-8226
100 Gillingham Ln Sugar Land (77478) *(G-19550)*

Schlumberger Technology Corp 281 285-8500
150 Gillingham Ln Md1 Sugar Land (77478) *(G-19551)*

Schlumberger Technology Corp 281 285-4551
225 Schlumberger Dr Sugar Land (77478) *(G-19552)*

Schlumberger Technology Corp 281 285-8500
145 Industrial Blvd Sugar Land (77478) *(G-19553)*

Schlumberger Technology Corp 281 285-1300
4646 W Sam Houston Pkwy N Houston (77041) *(G-11778)*

Schlumberger Technology Corp 281 285-3501
4501 S Pinemont Dr # 106 Houston (77041) *(G-11779)*

Schlumberger Technology Corp 281 285-8500
3600 Briarpark Dr Houston (77042) *(G-11780)*

Schlumberger Well Services, Pleasanton *Also called Schlumberger Technology Corp (G-17074)*

Schlumberger Well Services, Abilene *Also called Schlumberger Technology Corp (G-78)*

Schlumberger Well Services, Midland *Also called Schlumberger Technology Corp (G-15397)*

Schlumberger Wireline & Tstg, Tyler *Also called Schlumberger Technology Corp (G-20149)*

Schlumberger, Well Completions, Houston *Also called Schlumberger Technology Corp (G-11776)*

Schlumberger, Well Completions, Houston *Also called Schlumberger Technology Corp (G-11777)*

Schlumbrger Rsrvoir Cmpletions, Rosharon *Also called Schlumberger Technology Corp (G-17614)*

Schmidt Manufacturing Inc 281 431-0581
6330 West Loop S Ste 900 Bellaire (77401) *(G-2002)*

Schmidt Tool & Mfg Co 936 856-5897
13967 Fm 1097 Rd W Willis (77318) *(G-20864)*

Schneder Elc Bldngs Amrcas Inc 859 243-8254
5914 San Bernardo Ave Laredo (78041) *(G-13930)*

Schneder Elc Bldngs Amrcas Inc (HQ) 972 323-1111
1650 W Crosby Rd Carrollton (75006) *(G-2813)*

Schneider Elc Systems USA Inc (HQ) 713 329-1600
10900 Equity Dr Houston (77041) *(G-11781)*

Schneider Electric 915 834-6451
1601 Northwestern Dr El Paso (79912) *(G-5953)*

Schneider Electric 956 205-7533
5801 George Mcvay Dr C McAllen (78503) *(G-14905)*

Schneider Electric It USA Inc 888 994-8867
12121 Wickchester Ln # 40 Houston (77079) *(G-11782)*

Schneider Electric Systems USA 281 709-1200
17146 Feathercraft Ln Webster (77598) *(G-20644)*

Schneider Electric Usa Inc 972 323-1111
1650 W Crosby Rd Carrollton (75006) *(G-2814)*

Schneider Electric Usa Inc 512 295-8060
576 Commercial Dr Buda (78610) *(G-2537)*

Schneider Electric Usa Inc 972 236-0300
204 Airline Dr Ste 300 Coppell (75019) *(G-3444)*

Schneider Electric Usa Inc 877 248-3781
1215 San Dario Ave Laredo (78040) *(G-13931)*

Schneider Electric Usa Inc 361 887-5055
555 N Carancahua St # 230 Corpus Christi (78401) *(G-3617)*

Schneider Optical Machines Inc 972 247-4000
6644 All Stars Ave Ste 10 Frisco (75033) *(G-7311)*

Schneider-Banks Inc 903 675-1440
1108 Commercial St Athens (75751) *(G-838)*

School Specialty, Cameron *Also called Texwood Ltd (G-2644)*

Schrader Electronics Limited 817 608-2289
13601 Independence Pkwy Fort Worth (76177) *(G-6979)*

Schroeder Welding & Cnstr 361 573-4322
2303 Lone Tree Rd Victoria (77901) *(G-20302)*

Schroeder Welding & Cnstr 361 575-4992
3112 Pleasant Green Dr Victoria (77901) *(G-20303)*

Schry-Way Cases 806 622-0066
10525 S Washington St Amarillo (79118) *(G-511)*

Schuhmacher Publishing, San Antonio *Also called Beernet Communications (G-17944)*

Schuhmacher Publishing Co Inc 210 805-8006
909 Ne Loop 410 Ste 720 San Antonio (78209) *(G-18460)*

Schulenburg Prtg Off Sups Inc 979 743-4511
705 Upton Ave Schulenburg (78956) *(G-18778)*

Schulenburgh Sticker Inc 979 743-3450
405 N Main St Schulenburg (78956) *(G-18779)*

Schulte Building Systems Inc (PA) 281 304-6111
17600 Badtke Rd Hockley (77447) *(G-8348)*

Schultz Industries Inc (PA) 254 666-5155
131 Ava Dr Hewitt (76643) *(G-8300)*

Schumacher Company Inc 713 923-5548
5610 Polk St Houston (77023) *(G-11783)*

Schumacher International Inc (PA) 713 923-5548
5610 Polk St Houston (77023) *(G-11784)*

Schunk Semiconductor, Georgetown *Also called Schunk Xycarb Technology Inc (G-7676)*

Schunk Xycarb Technology Inc 512 863-0033
  101 Se Inner Loop Georgetown (78626) *(G-7676)*

Schusters of Texas Inc 325 648-2267
  2109 Priddy Rd Goldthwaite (76844) *(G-7744)*

Schutz Container Systems Inc 281 474-5200
  5000 Underwood Rd Pasadena (77507) *(G-16503)*

Schwan's Food Manufacturing, Pasadena Also called Sfc Global Supply Chain Inc *(G-16505)*

Schwarze Industries Inc 830 379-1480
  1627 E Walnut St Seguin (78155) *(G-18862)*

Schweitzer Engrg Labs Inc 509 334-8154
  10110 W Sam Houston Pkwy Houston (77064) *(G-11785)*

Schweizer Rsg LLC 817 405-2100
  3901 N Main St 2s Fort Worth (76106) *(G-6980)*

Schwob Energy Services LLC 469 917-9023
  2346 Glenda Ln Dallas (75229) *(G-4941)*

Scicron Technologies LLC 806 372-8300
  501 W Amarillo Blvd Amarillo (79107) *(G-462)*

Science Applications Intl Corp 469 557-8249
  2440 Marsh Ln Carrollton (75006) *(G-2815)*

Scientific Climate Systems, Houston Also called AB Bellco Corporation *(G-8440)*

Scientific Drilling Intl Inc (PA) **281 443-3300**
  16071 Grnspint Pk Dr Ste Houston (77060) *(G-11786)*

Scientific Drilling Intl Inc 281 214-7600
  1100 Rankin Rd Houston (77073) *(G-11787)*

Scientific Drilling Intl Inc 432 563-1339
  2034 Trade Dr Midland (79706) *(G-15399)*

Scientific Glass & Plastic, Freeport Also called S G & P Incorporated *(G-7209)*

Scientific Machine & Wldg Inc 512 926-8400
  3404 Duke Rd Austin (78724) *(G-1490)*

Scientific Test Inc 972 479-1300
  1110 E Collins Blvd # 130 Richardson (75081) *(G-17394)*

Sclm Enterprises Inc 972 243-1688
  11252 Leo Ln Dallas (75229) *(G-4942)*

SCM, Galena Park Also called South Coast Manufacturing LLC *(G-7382)*

Scomi Equipment Inc (HQ) **281 260-6016**
  6607 Theall Rd Houston (77066) *(G-11788)*

Scorpion Flowback LLC 432 302-1628
  2318 E County Road 123 Midland (79706) *(G-15400)*

Scorpion Hydraulic, Houston Also called Bar Yam Engineering Inc *(G-8816)*

Scorpion Oiltools Inc 281 999-2222
  13913 Faber St Houston (77037) *(G-11789)*

Scot Hone Corporation 903 639-2551
  Hwy 250 E Lone Star (75668) *(G-14184)*

Scot Industries, Lone Star Also called Scot Hone Corporation *(G-14184)*

Scotch Corporation 214 943-4605
  1255 Viceroy Dr Dallas (75247) *(G-4943)*

Scotia Group Inc (PA) **281 448-6188**
  411 N Sam Houston Pkwy E # 130 Houston (77060) *(G-11790)*

Scott Environmental Svcs Inc 903 663-4635
  4804 Judson Rd Ste B Longview (75605) *(G-14306)*

Scott Fennell Inc 817 822-1283
  7322 County Road 118 Iola (77861) *(G-12900)*

Scott Fetzer Company 713 996-7331
  4300 Windfern Rd Houston (77041) *(G-11791)*

Scott Fetzer Company 432 523-5511
  Seminole Hwy N Andrews (79714) *(G-558)*

Scott Manufacturing Inc 806 747-3395
  10609 Fm 1585 Wolfforth (79382) *(G-20912)*

Scott Mc Gaha 817 540-2309
  700 S Main St Euless (76040) *(G-6157)*

Scott Measurement Service Inc (PA) **817 326-2361**
  5718 Acton Cir Granbury (76049) *(G-7809)*

Scott Newland Office 903 758-1500
  3920 Fm 2879 Longview (75605) *(G-14307)*

Scott Publishing LLC 817 632-8100
  1612 Summit Ave Ste 150 Fort Worth (76102) *(G-6981)*

Scott Studios Corporation 972 620-2211
  701 Canyon Dr Ste 120 Coppell (75019) *(G-3445)*

Scott Traffic LLC 972 937-6040
  307 Brown St Waxahachie (75165) *(G-20557)*

Scott-Merriman Inc 972 484-7113
  2930 Merrell Rd Dallas (75229) *(G-4944)*

Scotts Miracle-Gro Company 281 821-1022
  16518 Aldine Westfield Rd Houston (77032) *(G-11792)*

Scotts Miracle-Gro Company 830 591-0299
  90 Fm 1403 Uvalde (78801) *(G-20195)*

Scout Downhole, Conroe Also called Turbo Drill Industries Inc *(G-3375)*

Scout Downhole Inc 936 756-3255
  1125 Beach Airport Rd Conroe (77301) *(G-3362)*

Scout Energy Management LLC (PA) **972 277-1397**
  4901 Lyndon B Johnson Fwy # 300 Dallas (75244) *(G-4945)*

Scout Energy Partners, Dallas Also called Scout Energy Management LLC *(G-4945)*

Scout Goods & Design LLC 512 865-8775
  4819 R O Dr Ste 202 Spicewood (78669) *(G-19094)*

Scout Lightning and Design, Spicewood Also called Scout Goods & Design LLC *(G-19094)*

Scp International Inc 817 326-0257
  1447 Fm 1010 Rd Cleveland (77327) *(G-3135)*

Screen Play Promotions Inc 817 788-8608
  420 Greatvine Hwy Ste 118 Hurst (76054) *(G-12858)*

Screen Visions, Arlington Also called Cenikor Foundation *(G-640)*

Screened Images Inc 979 260-9891
  725 E Vlla Mria Rd Ste 23 Bryan (77801) *(G-2506)*

Screenfab LLC (PA) **972 438-2860**
  610 N Wildwood Dr Irving (75061) *(G-13173)*

Scripps Texas Newspapers LP 325 653-1221
  34 W Harris Ave San Angelo (76903) *(G-17826)*

Scripps Texas Newspapers LP 325 673-4271
  100 Cypress St Abilene (79601) *(G-79)*

Scruples Prof Salon Pdts Inc 952 469-4646
  20411 Imperial Valley Dr Houston (77073) *(G-11793)*

Scs Machine & Fabricating, Houston Also called American Roller Company LLC *(G-8608)*

Sctray Company 817 473-0233
  949 S 6th Ave Mansfield (76063) *(G-14716)*

Scurry Midstream LLC 214 238-5740
  2311 Cedar Springs Rd # 10 Dallas (75201) *(G-4946)*

Sdi, Houston Also called System Development Inc *(G-12139)*

Sdmi, Hurst Also called Sons Design & Mfg Inc *(G-12859)*

Sdrg Controls Inc 713 242-0822
  8234 Braniff St Houston (77061) *(G-11794)*

SDS Energy Services LLC 903 747-3837
  1406 Rice Rd Ste 400 Tyler (75703) *(G-20150)*

Sdtx, Wichita Falls Also called Safety Design Usa Inc *(G-20804)*

Sea Eagle Ford LLC 720 390-6244
  1155 Dairy Ashford Rd # 2 Houston (77079) *(G-11795)*

Sea Lion Inc 409 948-4351
  5700 Century Blvd Texas City (77591) *(G-19801)*

Sea Pak Shrimp Company, Brownsville Also called Rich Products Corporation *(G-2399)*

Seabed Geosolutions (us) Inc (PA) **713 904-2244**
  10350 Richmond Ave # 800 Houston (77042) *(G-11796)*

Seaboard Controls LLC 281 328-8620
  4807 Highway 90 Crosby (77532) *(G-3742)*

Seaboard Holdings Inc (HQ) **713 644-3535**
  13822 Furman Rd Houston (77047) *(G-11797)*

Seaboard International Inc (HQ) **713 644-3535**
  13815 South Fwy Houston (77047) *(G-11798)*

Seaboard Oil Co 432 684-7005
  3100 N A St Ste B-200 Midland (79705) *(G-15401)*

Seaboard Operating, Midland Also called Seaboard Oil Co *(G-15401)*

Seaboard Operating Inc 432 684-7005
  3100 N A St Bldg B Midland (79705) *(G-15402)*

Seabreeze Culvert 409 296-4675
  3836 Texas 124 Winnie (77665) *(G-20891)*

Seabreeze Culvert Inc 409 296-4098
  3836 State Hwy 124 Stowell (77661) *(G-19431)*

Seabrook Marina Inc 281 694-0001
  1900 Shipyard Dr Seabrook (77586) *(G-18791)*

Seabrook Seafood Inc 281 334-2546
  1419 Lawrence Rd Kemah (77565) *(G-13479)*

Seabrook Shipyard, Seabrook Also called Seabrook Marina Inc *(G-18791)*

Seadrift Coke LP 361 552-8887
  8618 Hwy 185 N Port Lavaca (77979) *(G-17155)*

Seadrill Americas Inc (HQ) **713 407-8900**
  11025 Equity Dr Ste 150 Houston (77041) *(G-11799)*

Seaflex Inc 281 448-8821
  14325 W Hardy Rd Houston (77060) *(G-11800)*

Seah Steel California LLC 281 873-7800
  14550 Torrey Chase Blvd # 345 Houston (77014) *(G-11801)*

Seah Steel USA LLC (HQ) **832 734-0044**
  16952 Leonard Rd Houston (77049) *(G-11802)*

Seahawk Drilling Inc (PA) **713 369-7300**
  5 Greenway Plz Ste 2700 Houston (77046) *(G-11803)*

Seal-Jet of Texas Inc 713 983-7233
  4702 Steffani Ln Houston (77041) *(G-11804)*

Sealant Solution Inc 214 886-6688
  4809 Neptune Ct Flower Mound (75022) *(G-6280)*

Sealed Air Corporation 940 851-6060
  3800 Central Fwy Wichita Falls (76306) *(G-20806)*

Sealed Air Corporation 817 540-2020
  2401 Dillard St Grand Prairie (75051) *(G-7972)*

Sealed Air Corporation 940 592-2111
  1301 W Magnolia Ave Iowa Park (76367) *(G-12910)*

Sealing Technology Inc 281 330-6363
  11152 Westheimer Rd # 762 Houston (77042) *(G-11805)*

Sealy - Precast, Sealy Also called Hydro Conduit of Texas LP *(G-18808)*

Sealy Concrete Inc 281 391-3435
  4460 Ne I 10 Frontage Rd Sealy (77474) *(G-18818)*

Sealy Precision Machining Inc 979 885-7380
  2060 Highway 90 W Sealy (77474) *(G-18819)*

Seapac Inc 281 383-2400
  4000 Cedar Blvd Baytown (77523) *(G-1801)*

Seaport Steel Fab Inc 361 884-1670
  333 45th St Corpus Christi (78405) *(G-3618)*

Season Group Usa LLC 210 522-1116
  8001 Mainland Dr San Antonio (78250) *(G-18461)*

Season Group Usa LLC (PA) **210 522-1116**
  8001 Mainland Dr San Antonio (78250) *(G-18462)*

A
L
P
H
A
B
E
T
I
C

Seatrax Inc (HQ)..713 896-6500
13223 Fm 529 Rd Houston (77041) *(G-11806)*

Seatrax Inc..713 896-6500
13218 Weiman Rd Houston (77041) *(G-11807)*

Seawall Specialty Company Inc............................713 522-9064
5922 Richmond Ave Ste C Houston (77057) *(G-11808)*

Seawalt Butane, Brownwood *Also called Bobs Fuels Inc (G-2426)*

Seawolf Rswd Resources LP................................713 518-1763
811 Main St Fl 18 Houston (77002) *(G-11809)*

Seawolf Transport LP...713 518-1763
811 Main St Fl 18 Houston (77002) *(G-11810)*

SEC Energy Products & Svcs LP (HQ)...................281 890-9977
9523 Frbanks N Houston Rd Houston (77064) *(G-11811)*

Secco Inc..361 289-1722
1411 Corn Pdts Rd Rear Corpus Christi (78409) *(G-3619)*

Sechrist-Hall Company (PA)................................361 884-5264
102 Omaha Dr Corpus Christi (78408) *(G-3620)*

Second Gnration ARC Spark Wldg........................979 778-1999
7502 E State Highway 21 Bryan (77808) *(G-2507)*

Secure Control Systems Inc................................210 530-5245
16103 University Oak San Antonio (78249) *(G-18463)*

Securetech Systems Inc......................................817 869-0569
4500 Fuller Dr Ste 135 Irving (75038) *(G-13174)*

Securetech, Ssi, Irving *Also called Securetech Systems Inc (G-13174)*

Security Cameras Direct, Austin *Also called Supercircuits Inc (G-1548)*

See You At The Top Inc......................................210 556-5452
17422 Oconnor Rd Ste 200 San Antonio (78247) *(G-18464)*

Seebridge Media LLC..832 201-2000
707 West Rd Houston (77038) *(G-11812)*

Sefton Steel LP..281 449-8677
1830 Aldine Mail Rte Houston (77039) *(G-11813)*

Seguin Fiberglass, Seguin *Also called Seguins Budget Auto Inc (G-18863)*

Seguin Gazette Enterprises, Seguin *Also called Southern Newspapers Inc (G-18864)*

Seguins Budget Auto Inc....................................830 372-1790
1440 N King St Seguin (78155) *(G-18863)*

Segundo Navarro Drilling Ltd..............................210 384-3200
10101 Reunion Pl Ste 1000 San Antonio (78216) *(G-18465)*

Seguro Well Service Inc......................................830 672-8025
183 South St Gonzales (78629) *(G-7764)*

SEI Heat Treat, Houston *Also called Rhr Acquisition Co LLC (G-11615)*

SEI Heat Treat, Conroe *Also called Rhr Acquisition Co LLC (G-3357)*

SEI Oilfields, Fort Worth *Also called Sitton Enterprises LLC (G-6991)*

Seidler Oil & Gas LP..817 259-1777
7140 E Fm 917 Alvarado (76009) *(G-345)*

Seidls Bindery Inc..713 681-3815
8035 Blankenship Dr Houston (77055) *(G-11814)*

Seisa Medical Inc (PA)..915 774-4321
9005 Montana Ave El Paso (79925) *(G-5954)*

Seismic Eqp Solutions Inc...................................832 288-4427
3402 Bacor Rd Houston (77084) *(G-11815)*

Seismic Exchange Inc (PA)..................................832 590-5100
4805 Westway Park Blvd Houston (77041) *(G-11816)*

Seismic Products Inc (PA)...................................903 675-8571
518 Progress Way Athens (75751) *(G-839)*

Seitel..832 295-8300
10811 Westview Dr Bldg C Houston (77043) *(G-11817)*

Seitel Inc (HQ)...713 881-8900
10811 S Westview Circle D Houston (77043) *(G-11818)*

Seitel Management Inc..713 881-8900
10811 S Westview Cir Houston (77043) *(G-11819)*

Sekisui Spcialty Chem Amer LLC..........................713 456-1525
1423 Pasadena Fwy Pasadena (77506) *(G-16504)*

Sekisui Spcialty Chem Amer LLC (HQ)...................972 277-2900
1501 Lyndon B Johnson Fwy Dallas (75234) *(G-4947)*

Sel Corporate Enterprises Inc.............................214 348-8784
10660 Plano Rd Ste 118 Dallas (75238) *(G-4948)*

Seldon Energy Partners LLC................................503 807-4300
6610 Malibu Dr Houston (77092) *(G-11820)*

Select Butter & Packaging LLC............................214 568-9000
1926 Fm 54 Littlefield (79339) *(G-14149)*

Select Energy Services Inc..................................432 447-0602
2400 Moore St Pecos (79772) *(G-16626)*

Select Energy Services Inc (PA)...........................713 235-9500
1233 West Loop S Ste 1400 Houston (77027) *(G-11821)*

Select Energy Services Inc..................................903 766-2600
1820 N Interstate 35 Gainesville (76240) *(G-7363)*

Select Energy Services LLC................................956 286-7100
321 Wildcat Laredo (78043) *(G-13932)*

Select Energy Services Inc..................................713 296-1000
1233 West Loop S Ste 1400 Houston (77027) *(G-11822)*

Select Energy Services LLC (HQ)..........................940 668-1818
1820 N I 35 Gainesville (76240) *(G-7364)*

Select Energy Services LLC................................817 523-0136
6150 N Fm 51 Weatherford (76085) *(G-20620)*

Select Energy Services LLC................................361 701-8465
7740 E State Highway 21 Bryan (77808) *(G-2508)*

Select Energy Services LLC................................325 949-0326
3001 W Harris Ave San Angelo (76901) *(G-17827)*

Select Energy Services LLC................................318 949-5080
175 Private Road 7336 De Berry (75639) *(G-5235)*

Select Energy Services LLC................................940 665-8223
4337 E Us Highway 82 Gainesville (76240) *(G-7365)*

Select Energy Services LLC................................940 665-1767
4506 S Interstate 35 Gainesville (76240) *(G-7366)*

Select Energy Services LLC................................956 723-4900
6010 Mcpherson Rd Ste 100 Laredo (78041) *(G-13933)*

Select Energy Services LLC................................830 457-2215
15386 Hwy 85 W Big Wells (78830) *(G-2104)*

Select Energy Services LLC................................940 627-2066
1826 E Highway 380 Decatur (76234) *(G-5254)*

Select Industries Inc..940 855-0461
4163 Airport Dr Wichita Falls (76305) *(G-20807)*

Select Mat LLC..833 205-1515
30355 Old Hockley Rd Magnolia (77355) *(G-14627)*

Select Millwork Inc..972 445-8287
300 Union Bower Ct # 310 Irving (75061) *(G-13175)*

Select Oilfield Construction, Big Wells *Also called Select Energy Services LLC (G-2104)*

Select Plastics LLC (HQ)....................................817 595-3804
8800 South Fwy Fort Worth (76140) *(G-6982)*

Select Power Sport Inc.......................................936 967-2332
4400 Us Highway 190 W Livingston (77351) *(G-14161)*

Select Sands America Corp (PA)...........................501 276-5928
363 N Sm Hstn Pkwy E 1050 Houston (77060) *(G-11823)*

Selectouch Corporation......................................972 924-3289
105 Fourth St Anna (75409) *(G-585)*

Self Industries..713 672-2559
6900 Cavalcade St Houston (77028) *(G-11824)*

Selkirk Corporation..972 943-6100
1301 Presidential Dr Richardson (75081) *(G-17395)*

Sellers Lease Service Inc....................................361 865-2142
2033 Fm 609 Flatonia (78941) *(G-6234)*

Sellers' Pump & Supply, Flatonia *Also called Sellers Lease Service Inc (G-6234)*

Sellmark Corporation...817 225-0310
2201 Heritage Pkwy Mansfield (76063) *(G-14717)*

Selman & Associates Ltd....................................432 563-0084
10114 Liberator Ln Midland (79706) *(G-15403)*

Selon Plating, Manvel *Also called Ronald Noles (G-14737)*

Seltek International Inc.......................................915 772-8444
2301 Wyoming Ave El Paso (79903) *(G-5955)*

Semasys Inc (HQ)..713 869-8331
4480 Blalock Rd Houston (77041) *(G-11825)*

Semes America Inc...512 251-3188
13400 Immanuel Rd Ste 1 Pflugerville (78660) *(G-16687)*

Semicon Phtmtrlogy Sltions LLC..........................214 957-0295
413 Trails Ct Garland (75043) *(G-7586)*

Semiconductor Support Svcs Co..........................512 267-7087
4715 Steiner Ranch Blvd Austin (78732) *(G-1491)*

Semiconductor Technology Inc............................512 468-8687
1924 American Dr Lago Vista (78645) *(G-13808)*

Semmt Inc..713 966-5829
3900 Essex Ln Ste 250 Houston (77027) *(G-11826)*

Semtech Corporation..972 231-1606
681 N Plano Rd Ste 121 Richardson (75081) *(G-17396)*

Sencha Inc..713 523-4433
2950 North Loop W Ste 700 Houston (77092) *(G-11827)*

Sendero Industries LLC......................................713 868-6960
6814 Thornwall St Houston (77092) *(G-11828)*

Seneca Resources Company LLC (HQ)...................713 654-2600
1201 La St Ste 2600 Houston (77002) *(G-11829)*

Seneca Resources Corporation............................713 374-6300
1201 Louisiana St Ste 400 Houston (77002) *(G-11830)*

Senior Flextronics Pathway, New Braunfels *Also called Senior Operations LLC (G-15822)*

Senior Operations LLC..830 629-8080
2400 Longhorn Indus Dr New Braunfels (78130) *(G-15821)*

Senior Operations LLC..830 629-8080
2311 Lifehaus Indus Dr New Braunfels (78130) *(G-15822)*

Seno Medical Instruments Inc.............................210 615-6501
8023 Vantage Dr Ste 1000 San Antonio (78230) *(G-18466)*

Senox Corporation (PA)......................................512 251-3333
15409 Long Vista Dr Austin (78728) *(G-1492)*

Sensata Technologies Inc....................................817 608-2289
13601 Indpdnc Pkwy 400 Fort Worth (76177) *(G-6983)*

Sensatronics LLC...800 633-1033
13091 Pond Springs Rd Austin (78729) *(G-1711)*

Sensia LLC (HQ)...866 773-6742
200 Westlake Park Blvd # 1400 Houston (77079) *(G-11831)*

Sensortran Inc...281 876-2323
10110-C W Samhouston Pkwy Austin (78744) *(G-1493)*

Sentech Archtctral Systems LLC..........................512 266-7045
4421 Supply Ct Ste 100 Austin (78744) *(G-1494)*

Sentinel Midstream LLC......................................214 712-2141
740 E Campbell Rd Ste 200 Richardson (75081) *(G-17397)*

Sentinel Plating Inc...972 276-2780
610 N 1st St Garland (75040) *(G-7587)*

Sentrimax Centrifuges USA Inc...........................817 453-8112
108 Sentry Dr Mansfield (76063) *(G-14718)*

Sentry Energy Production LLC.............................972 380-1600
4570 Westgrove Dr Ste 220 Addison (75001) *(G-162)*

Sentry Oil & Gas LLC 212 753-6367
170 Pr 1731 Ste 100 Mico (78056) *(G-15094)*

Sentry Oil and Gas, Mico *Also called Sentry Oil & Gas LLC (G-15094)*

Sentry Supply Inc 409 840-4800
4855 Fannett Rd Beaumont (77705) *(G-1948)*

Sentry Wellhead Systems LLC (PA) **281 210-0070**
1780 Hughes Landing Blvd # 675 Spring (77380) *(G-19249)*

Sentry Wellhead Systems LLC 432 661-5810
11016 E Interstate 20 Odessa (79765) *(G-16151)*

Sep Operating Company, The Woodlands *Also called Spartan Operating Company LLC (G-19924)*

Separation Technology Inc 830 249-0772
1261 N Main St Boerne (78006) *(G-2136)*

Sepco, Spring *Also called Swn Production Company LLC (G-19173)*

Sepra-Chem Corporation 478 788-9789
10975 Spur 248 Tyler (75707) *(G-20151)*

Sepsa Precast Solutions Corp 832 291-8930
5503 Fry Rd Katy (77449) *(G-13440)*

Septh Group LLC 713 988-4200
8125 Mcgee Ln Houston (77071) *(G-11832)*

Serafy Laboratories Ltd 956 546-5313
205 W Levee St Brownsville (78520) *(G-2405)*

Serampore Inds Private Ltd Inc (HQ) **713 923-6111**
8876 Gulf Fwy Ste 500 Houston (77017) *(G-11833)*

Sercel Inc (HQ) **281 492-6688**
17200 Park Row Houston (77084) *(G-11834)*

Seremedi Inc 832 671-8622
2450 Holcombe Blvd Ste J Houston (77021) *(G-11835)*

Serenity Candles 281 565-0130
226 Scarlet Maple Dr Sugar Land (77479) *(G-19554)*

Seretti Dental Lab Inc 512 452-8989
1820 W 35th St Austin (78703) *(G-1495)*

Serimax North America LLC 832 230-2700
11315 W Little York Rd # 4 Houston (77041) *(G-11836)*

Serious Cigars Llc 281 397-9800
6608 Fm 1960 Rd W Ste D Houston (77069) *(G-11837)*

Sermatech Dynamic 713 849-9474
7615 Fairview St Houston (77041) *(G-11838)*

Serpa Fabrication Inc 361 883-2266
1302 Mary St Corpus Christi (78401) *(G-3621)*

Serta Mattress, Houston *Also called National Bedding Company LLC (G-10966)*

Serta Mattress Company, Lockhart *Also called Dormae Products Inc (G-14167)*

Serva Corporation 940 761-3361
1500 Fisher Rd Ste A Wichita Falls (76305) *(G-20808)*

Service Center, Houston *Also called Honeywell Enraf Americas Inc (G-10199)*

Service Drilling Southwest LLC 806 878-2052
Hwy 152 Stinnett (79083) *(G-19428)*

Service Electric, Kilgore *Also called A & R Enterprises Inc (G-13530)*

Service Electric Supply Inc 972 620-2821
10929 Grissom Ln Dallas (75229) *(G-4949)*

Service Metal Products Company 281 499-3020
3500 E Crosstimbers St Houston (77093) *(G-11839)*

Service Photo Copy Inc 713 225-1988
815 Walker St Ste 101 Houston (77002) *(G-11840)*

Service Rubber Group, Plano *Also called Gren Industries Inc (G-16881)*

Service Shade Shop, San Antonio *Also called Ybarra Group Inc (G-18629)*

Service, Visual Communication, Houston *Also called Service Photo Copy Inc (G-11840)*

Servomex Company 281 295-5800
12300 Dairy Ashford Rd # 400 Sugar Land (77478) *(G-19555)*

SES Foam LLC (PA) **713 239-0252**
2400 Spring Stuebner Rd Spring (77389) *(G-19165)*

SES Operating Inc 432 687-6560
223 W Wall St Fl 9 Midland (79701) *(G-15404)*

Sesi, Longview *Also called Scott Environmental Svcs Inc (G-14306)*

Sevco Security Inc 512 413-2211
6302 Lost Horizon Dr Austin (78759) *(G-1496)*

Seven Construction Inc 806 894-5685
102 Duval Dr Levelland (79336) *(G-14016)*

Seven Q Seven Ltd 210 930-4040
11827 Tech Com Rd Ste 220 San Antonio (78233) *(G-18467)*

Seven Up Bottling Company, Corpus Christi *Also called American Bottling Company (G-3472)*

Sevendipity Jewelry Mfg LLC 915 594-8500
1528 Sioux Dr Ste A El Paso (79925) *(G-5956)*

Severe Service Valve Inc 832 390-2380
2800 Post Oak Blvd Houston (77056) *(G-11841)*

Sew-Eurodrive Inc 214 330-4824
202 W Danieldale Rd Desoto (75115) *(G-5441)*

Sey Tec Inc 817 595-1949
8825 Bud Jenson Dr North Richland Hills (76180) *(G-15880)*

Sfc Global Supply Chain Inc 713 740-7200
1251 Scarborough Ln Pasadena (77506) *(G-16505)*

Sfc Global Supply Chain Inc 713 740-7536
612 Georgia Ave Deer Park (77536) *(G-5295)*

SFG Management Ltd Lblty Co 214 824-8163
3114 S Haskell Ave Dallas (75223) *(G-4950)*

Sfi Gray Steel, Houston *Also called Sfi-Gray Steel LLC (G-11842)*

Sfi-Gray Steel LLC 713 864-6450
3511 W 12th St Houston (77008) *(G-11842)*

Sfp Hydraulics Inc (PA) **281 347-8080**
22240 Merchants Way # 100 Katy (77449) *(G-13441)*

Sg Interest, Houston *Also called Gordy Gas Corporation (G-10004)*

Sg Interests, Houston *Also called Gordy Oil Company (G-10005)*

Sg Interests I Ltd (PA) **713 951-0100**
100 Waugh Dr Ste 400 Houston (77007) *(G-11843)*

Sgm Corporation 281 313-6111
12831 Royal Dr Stafford (77477) *(G-19376)*

Sgp, El Paso *Also called Signs & Graphics Plus LLC (G-5961)*

SGS, Richardson *Also called Southern Graphic Systems LLC (G-17400)*

Sgt LLC 281 751-1071
17155 Feathercraft Ln # 100 Webster (77598) *(G-20645)*

Sgt. Pepperoni's, Waller *Also called Alpha Foods Co (G-20491)*

Shade Shop Inc 713 623-0750
4122 Richmond Ave Houston (77027) *(G-11844)*

Shade Structures Inc 214 905-9500
8319 Chancellor Row Dallas (75247) *(G-4951)*

Shadow Fax Graphics, Dallas *Also called T Rich Inc (G-5033)*

Shadowgraph Inc 281 208-1280
1545 Industrial Dr Missouri City (77489) *(G-15592)*

Shadowsoft Inc 972 841-2469
7750 N Macarthur Blvd # 1 Irving (75063) *(G-13176)*

Shafter Mine, Marfa *Also called Rio Grande Mining Company (G-14754)*

Shakun Solutions LLC 936 756-3738
3606 N Frazier St Conroe (77303) *(G-3363)*

Shale Flow Specialties LLC (PA) **903 218-6120**
300 Marvin A Smith Rd Kilgore (75662) *(G-13589)*

Shallow Sport Boats, Los Fresnos *Also called Shallow Sport of Texas Inc (G-14348)*

Shallow Sport of Texas Inc 956 233-9489
41146 Schafer Rd Los Fresnos (78566) *(G-14348)*

Shame Lingerie 214 823-1454
8330 Moberly Ln Dallas (75227) *(G-4952)*

Shamrock Industries Ltd 817 336-1413
400 E Vickery Blvd Ste A Fort Worth (76104) *(G-6984)*

Shamrock Precision Usa LLC 972 241-4226
14850 Venture Dr Farmers Branch (75234) *(G-6213)*

Shaneda Machine Inc 432 333-7083
2500 E Pearl St Odessa (79761) *(G-16152)*

Shannon Dunn 210 653-7222
1810 N Pine St San Antonio (78208) *(G-18468)*

Shany Cosmetics, Stafford *Also called Shany Enterprises Inc (G-19377)*

Shany Enterprises Inc 713 772-1345
10302 Mula Rd Stafford (77477) *(G-19377)*

Shape Corp 616 846-8700
3901 W Miller Rd Garland (75041) *(G-7588)*

Sharco Technologies Inc (PA) **512 258-0573**
1010 Old Austin Hutto Rd Pflugerville (78660) *(G-16688)*

Shared Services, Laredo *Also called Sanmina Corporation (G-13927)*

Shared Svcs Accounts Payable, Fort Worth *Also called Bell Textron Inc (G-6443)*

Sharewell LP 281 288-2560
1111 North Loop W Ste 705 Houston (77008) *(G-11845)*

Sharewell Energy Services, Houston *Also called Sharewell LP (G-11845)*

Sharewell Hdd LLC 281 288-2560
21315 W Hardy Rd Houston (77073) *(G-11846)*

Sharewell Hdd Services, Houston *Also called Sharewell Hdd LLC (G-11846)*

Sharidge Inc 325 573-4242
Hwy 350 Ira (79527) *(G-12914)*

Sharon Young Inc (PA) **214 349-1891**
10367 Brockwood Rd Dallas (75238) *(G-4953)*

Sharp Chemical Co, Houston *Also called Ultra Chem Ltd (G-12429)*

Sharp Iron Group LLC 940 855-2710
4140 Reilly Rd Wichita Falls (76305) *(G-20809)*

Sharp Iron Group LLC (PA) **940 766-4545**
1206 Hatton Rd Wichita Falls (76302) *(G-20810)*

Sharp Oilfield Services LLC 877 742-7784
212 W Main St Gainesville (76240) *(G-7367)*

Sharp Roustabout & Cnstr LLC 432 528-6360
4304 E County Road 130 Midland (79706) *(G-15405)*

Sharp-Bilt LLC 409 886-0066
6902 Interstate 10 W Orange (77632) *(G-16262)*

Shasta Beverages Inc 713 634-0094
7333 Major St Houston (77061) *(G-11847)*

Shattuck Labs Inc (PA) **919 864-2700**
1018 W 11th St Ste 100 Austin (78703) *(G-1497)*

Shaudra Company Inc 915 544-4244
11812 Pete Rose Dr El Paso (79936) *(G-5957)*

Shaun K Boyer 281 442-3800
11730 Aldine Westfield Rd Houston (77093) *(G-11848)*

Shaw Acquisition Holdings LLC 337 562-3471
19450 Sh 249 N Ste 450 Houston (77070) *(G-11849)*

Shaw Fabricators Inc 713 991-5313
7705 Hall Rd Houston (77075) *(G-11850)*

Shaw Group, The, Houston *Also called Shaw Acquisition Holdings LLC (G-11849)*

Shaw Pipeline Services, Houston *Also called Shawcor Pipe Protection LLC (G-11851)*

Shawcor Company, Houston *Also called Bredero Shaw LLC (G-8982)*

Shawcor Pipe Protection LLC 281 485-8321
1122 N Main St Pearland (77581) *(G-16598)*

Shawcor Pipe Protection LLC 281 940-0700
5175 World Houston Pkwy # 100 Houston (77032) *(G-11851)*

Shawcor Pipe Protection LLC 713 378-7200
711 Shields St Channelview (77530) *(G-3036)*

Shawcor Pipe Protection LLC (HQ) **281 886-2350**
5875 N Sam Houston Pkwy W # 200 Houston (77086) *(G-11852)*

Shawdashian Group LLC 832 649-3800
7322 Suthwest Fwy Ste 710 Houston (77074) *(G-11853)*

Shawn Austin Furnishings, Burleson *Also called Provence Hardware Corporation (G-2594)*

Shayne Foods Incorporated 210 442-8776
4225 Gatecrest San Antonio (78217) *(G-18469)*

Shayne Foods Market, San Antonio *Also called Shayne Foods Incorporated (G-18469)*

SHD Oil & Gas LLC 713 595-4274
1415 La St Ste 3410 Houston (77002) *(G-11854)*

Shearwater Geoservices Inc 281 921-8000
945 Bunker Hill Rd # 650 Houston (77024) *(G-11855)*

Sheepskin Ranch Inc 817 738-2485
3408 Indale Rd Fort Worth (76116) *(G-6985)*

Sheet Metal Air Plus Co LLC 915 566-8131
4016 Johnson Ave El Paso (79930) *(G-5958)*

Shekinah Oilfield Services Inc 325 762-2205
140 Hill St Albany (76430) *(G-192)*

Shelbis Stuff Inc 903 450-1300
2310 Stonewall St Greenville (75401) *(G-8091)*

Sheldon Containers, Houston *Also called Sheldon Industries Inc (G-11856)*

Sheldon Industries Inc 713 398-2427
6016 Knute St Houston (77028) *(G-11856)*

Shell Catalysts & Tech LP (HQ) **713 241-3000**
910 Louisiana St Ste 2900 Houston (77002) *(G-11857)*

Shell Chemical LP (HQ) **855 697-4355**
910 Louisiana St Houston (77002) *(G-11858)*

Shell Chemicals, Houston *Also called Shell Chemical LP (G-11858)*

Shell Gulf of Mexico Inc 713 241-6161
777 Walker St Houston (77002) *(G-11859)*

Shell Machine Works Inc 361 883-7073
5317 Agnes St Corpus Christi (78405) *(G-3622)*

Shell Oil Company (HQ) **713 241-6161**
150 N Dairy Ashford Rd A Houston (77079) *(G-11860)*

Shell Oil Company 713 241-6471
7510 Ardmore St Houston (77054) *(G-11861)*

Shell Oil Company 713 332-7606
9255 Riddlewood Ln Houston (77025) *(G-11862)*

Shell Oil Company 713 246-6462
5900 Highway 225 Deer Park (77536) *(G-5296)*

Shell Oil Company 713 546-4000
700 Milam St 125 Houston (77002) *(G-11863)*

Shell Oil Company 713 721-6282
5521 Gasmer Dr Houston (77035) *(G-11864)*

Shell Oil Products U S, Houston *Also called Equilon Enterprises LLC (G-9685)*

Shell Rapid Lube Lonestar Auto 254 953-4360
611 E Central Texas Expy Harker Heights (76548) *(G-8173)*

Shenandoah Petroleum Corp 432 685-1964
24 Smith Rd Ste 601 Midland (79705) *(G-15406)*

Sheperd Maury 713 921-3456
2221 Canada Dry St Houston (77023) *(G-11865)*

Shepherd Shutter Company Inc 806 799-3458
4411 Brownfield Dr Lubbock (79410) *(G-14478)*

Shepherd Shutters, Lubbock *Also called Shepherd Shutter Company Inc (G-14478)*

Sheridan Prod Partners I-A LP 432 683-5271
200 N Loraine St Ste 530 Midland (79701) *(G-15407)*

Sheridan Prod Partners I-A LP (PA) **713 548-1000**
1360 Post Oak Blvd Ste 25 Houston (77056) *(G-11866)*

Sheridan Production Co LLC 806 842-3521
2131 County Road 109 Lorenzo (79343) *(G-14345)*

Sheridan Production Co LLC 432 263-4301
400 Ranch Road 33 Big Spring (79720) *(G-2098)*

Sheridan Production Co LLC 325 453-2108
900 Gas Plant Rd Robert Lee (76945) *(G-17499)*

Sheridan Production Co LLC (PA) **713 548-1000**
1360 Post Oak Blvd # 2500 Houston (77056) *(G-11867)*

Sheridan Production Co LLC 979 567-7629
1516 Fm 166 Caldwell (77836) *(G-2635)*

Sherman Branson Construction 432 684-4740
10400 W County Road 77 Midland (79707) *(G-15408)*

Sherman Machine Inc 903 892-2889
1622 S First St Sherman (75090) *(G-18932)*

Sherman Roto Tank LLC 281 648-0909
8521 Industrial Dr Pearland (77584) *(G-16599)*

Sherman Wire, West Plant, Sherman *Also called Keystone Consolidated Inds (G-18919)*

Shermco Industries Inc 512 267-2324
1705 Hur Industrial Blvd Cedar Park (78613) *(G-2985)*

Shermco System Integration LLC 940 322-2206
1411 Twin Oaks St Wichita Falls (76302) *(G-20811)*

Sherrod Rv Center Inc 409 385-5689
1000 Highway 327 E Silsbee (77656) *(G-18955)*

Sherrod Services LLC 254 729-3177
311 Lcr 730 Thornton (76687) *(G-19943)*

Sherwin Alumina Company Div, Gregory *Also called Allied Alumina Group Inc (G-8098)*

Sherwin Alumina Company LLC 361 777-2200
4633 Hwy 361 Gregory (78359) *(G-8105)*

Sheshunoff Information Svcs, Austin *Also called Alex Esolutions Inc (G-907)*

Sheynne Bag & Accessories, Joshua *Also called Mallorys Western & Leather Sup (G-13322)*

Shf Inc 832 456-2000
8103 Red Bluff Rd Pasadena (77507) *(G-16506)*

Shi International Corp 732 764-8888
13737 Noel Rd Ste 210 Dallas (75240) *(G-4954)*

Shi/Government Solutions Inc 512 634-8100
3828 Pecana Trl Austin (78749) *(G-1498)*

Shield Bearer Inc (PA) **817 868-1400**
1316 Shirley Way Bedford (76022) *(G-1979)*

Shieldcoat Technologies Inc 936 633-6387
308 Ellen Trout Dr Lufkin (75904) *(G-14551)*

Shiftsmart Inc 817 271-3604
16000 Dallas Pkwy Ste 550 Dallas (75248) *(G-4955)*

Shimadzu Scientific Instrs Inc 713 467-1151
9940 W Sam Houston Pkwy S Houston (77099) *(G-11868)*

Shine Lighting Group Usa Inc 973 865-5893
1445 Ross Ave Ste 3700 Dallas (75202) *(G-4956)*

Shiner Beer, Shiner *Also called Gambrinus Company (G-18940)*

Shiner Bock, San Antonio *Also called Gambrinus Company (G-18133)*

Shiner Candy Company, Shiner *Also called D S D Services Inc (G-18939)*

Shinn and Gregory Inc 254 965-7585
3237 N Us Highway 281 Stephenville (76401) *(G-19422)*

Shintech Incorporated (HQ) **713 965-0713**
3 Greenway Plz Ste 1150 Houston (77046) *(G-11869)*

Shintech Incorporated 979 233-7861
5618 E Highway 332 Freeport (77541) *(G-7210)*

Shioleno Industries Inc (PA) **817 465-9361**
1715 Peyco Dr N Arlington (76001) *(G-780)*

Shipcom Wireless Inc (PA) **281 558-5252**
11200 Richmond Ave # 552 Houston (77082) *(G-11870)*

Shipley Do - Nuts 281 499-5234
1701 Texas Pkwy Missouri City (77489) *(G-15593)*

Shipley Do-Nut Flour Sup Inc 281 575-1766
1128 West Rd Houston (77038) *(G-11871)*

Shipley Do-Nut Flour Sup Inc 713 728-9366
10517 S Post Oak Rd Houston (77035) *(G-11872)*

Shipley Do-Nut Flour Sup Inc 713 729-2381
5847 W Airport Blvd Houston (77035) *(G-11873)*

Shipley Do-Nuts, Missouri City *Also called Shipley Do - Nuts (G-15593)*

Shipley Donut Shops, Houston *Also called Shipley Do-Nut Flour Sup Inc (G-11871)*

Shipley Donut Shops, Houston *Also called Shipley Do-Nut Flour Sup Inc (G-11873)*

Shipley's Do-Nut Shop, Houston *Also called C & K Management Co Inc (G-9025)*

Shippers Carline Div, Longview *Also called American Railcar Inds Inc (G-14194)*

Shipping Department, Houston *Also called FMC Technologies Inc (G-9827)*

Shl, Houston *Also called Subsea Hydraulic Leads LLC (G-12088)*

Sho Rack, Shiner *Also called Kaspar Wire Works Inc (G-18944)*

Shockwatch Inc (HQ) **214 630-9625**
5501 Lyndon B Johnson Fwy Dallas (75240) *(G-4957)*

Shoco Production LP 903 759-0082
1518 Colony Cir Longview (75604) *(G-14308)*

Shook Mobile Technology, Schertz *Also called Rolltchs Spcialty Vehicles LLC (G-18761)*

Shopper 940 872-6186
30 Lyndsey St Bowie (76230) *(G-2201)*

Shoreline Inc 361 643-3135
2361 Willow Dr Portland (78374) *(G-17187)*

Shoreline Services Inc 936 856-4880
12435 Fm 830 Rd Willis (77318) *(G-20865)*

Shores Lift Solutions, Goldsmith *Also called Waters & Waters Services Inc (G-7743)*

Short-Line Corporation 210 492-6088
1206 W Blanco Rd San Antonio (78232) *(G-18470)*

Shortes Inc 940 658-3576
Hwy 222 E Knox City (79529) *(G-13665)*

Shorthorn Resources Inc 713 668-0550
2636 S Loop W 50 Houston (77054) *(G-11874)*

Showcase Cstm Vnyl Wndows Door, Houston *Also called Showcase Windows & Doors Inc (G-11875)*

Showcase Windows & Doors Inc 713 926-8500
1702 Cullen Blvd Houston (77023) *(G-11875)*

Shower Doors of Dallas, Richardson *Also called Ganten Group LLC (G-17320)*

Shumate Energy Tech LLC 936 539-9533
12060 Fm 3083 Rd Conroe (77301) *(G-3364)*

Shure Brothers, El Paso *Also called Shure Electronics (G-5959)*

Shure Electronics 915 782-2800
12425 Rojas Dr 1 El Paso (79928) *(G-5959)*

Shutter Source Inc 281 403-2012
10404 Cash Rd Ste B Stafford (77477) *(G-19378)*

Shutters Manufacturers, Garland *Also called American Eagle Enteprise (G-7434)*

Shweiki Media Inc (PA) **210 804-0390**
4954 Space Center Dr San Antonio (78218) *(G-18471)*

Si Funeral Svcs & Con Precast, Cedar Hill *Also called Wilbert Funeral Services Inc (G-2956)*

Si Group Inc 979 238-8000
702 Fm 523 Rd Freeport (77541) *(G-7211)*

Si Precast Concrete, Ennis *Also called Wilbert Funeral Services Inc (G-6123)*
Si Printing LP 817 375-9016
  7316 Business Pl Arlington (76001) *(G-781)*
Siana Oil & Gas Co LLC 713 568-1082
  400 N Sam Houston Pkwy E # 601 Houston (77060) *(G-11876)*
Siana Operating, Houston *Also called Siana Oil & Gas Co LLC (G-11876)*
Sibbitt and Lott Inc 214 742-6949
  1813 W Commerce St Dallas (75208) *(G-4958)*
Sid Richardson Carbn Enrgy Co, Big Spring *Also called Tokai Carbon CB Ltd (G-2100)*
Sidco Minerals Inc 903 838-4493
  2801 Richmond Rd Ste 51 Texarkana (75503) *(G-19772)*
Sides Printing Company Inc 806 765-8168
  313 E 40th St Lubbock (79404) *(G-14479)*
Sidewinder Drilling Inc (HQ) **832 320-7600**
  20475 State Highway 249 # 300 Houston (77070) *(G-11877)*
Sidwell Operating Company LP 806 371-7513
  712 Sw 9th Ave Amarillo (79101) *(G-463)*
Siemens Energy Inc 281 328-3777
  16530 Peninsula St Bldg 3 Houston (77015) *(G-11878)*
Siemens Energy Inc 972 929-5044
  8600 N Royal Ln Unit 100 Irving (75063) *(G-13177)*
Siemens Industry Inc 972 947-7100
  2700 Esters Blvd Ste 200b Dfw Airport (75261) *(G-5454)*
Siemens Industry Inc 512 339-6991
  1826 Kramer Ln Ste D Austin (78758) *(G-1499)*
Siemens Industry Inc 956 797-5075
  2805 W Expy 83 Ste A La Feria (78559) *(G-13692)*
Siemens Industry Inc 512 837-8300
  9225 Bee Cave Rd Bldg B Austin (78733) *(G-1500)*
Siemens Industry Inc 817 633-4430
  501 Fountain Pkwy Grand Prairie (75050) *(G-7973)*
Siemens Industry Inc 972 947-7000
  2700 Esters Blvd Ste 200b Dallas (75261) *(G-4959)*
Siemens Industry Inc 713 671-9510
  7222 Clinton Dr Houston (77020) *(G-11879)*
Siemens Industry Inc 915 790-0219
  9494 Escobar Dr Ste A El Paso (79907) *(G-5960)*
Siemens Industry Inc 972 550-8488
  8600 N Royal Ln Unit 100 Irving (75063) *(G-13178)*
Siemens Industry Software Inc (HQ) **972 987-3000**
  5800 Granite Pkwy Ste 600 Plano (75024) *(G-17003)*
Siemens Industry Software Inc 972 391-2476
  2805 Dallas Pkwy Plano (75093) *(G-17004)*
Siemens Logistics LLC 972 947-7100
  2700 Esters Blvd Ste 200b Dfw Airport (75261) *(G-5455)*
Siemens Water Technology, Houston *Also called Siemens Industry Inc (G-11879)*
Sienergy LP 281 778-6250
  3 Lakeway Centre Ct # 110 Lakeway (78734) *(G-13819)*
Sienko Precision Inc 713 462-7482
  10102 Sussex Ln Houston (77041) *(G-11880)*
Sierra Blnco Trtlla Fctry Prod, Houston *Also called Lopez Efrain (G-10688)*
Sierra Chemical, Houston *Also called Cummings Inv Bankers Inc (G-8376)*
Sierra Dust Control LLC (PA) **903 836-4642**
  1155 E Johnson St Tatum (75691) *(G-19645)*
Sierra Dust Control LLC 903 836-4642
  8197 Fm 794 Harwood (78632) *(G-8212)*
Sierra Industries Ltd 210 805-3188
  1770 Skyplace Blvd San Antonio (78216) *(G-18472)*
Sierra Nevada Corporation 775 331-0222
  1100 Jupiter Rd Ste 200 Plano (75074) *(G-17005)*
Sierra Nevada Corporation 210 523-6500
  4801 Nw Loop 410 Ste 250 San Antonio (78229) *(G-18473)*
Sierra Pacific Engrg & Pdts, Lancaster *Also called SPEP Acquisition Corp (G-13848)*
Sierra Plastics, El Paso *Also called Regency Plastics - Ubly Inc (G-5935)*
Sierra Resources LLC 713 365-6100
  333 Clay St Ste 3600 Houston (77002) *(G-11881)*
Sifco Applied Srfc Cncepts LLC 281 444-6500
  7620 Bluff Point Dr Houston (77086) *(G-11882)*
Sigga USA LLC 855 744-4287
  13135 Dairy Ashford Rd # 525 Sugar Land (77478) *(G-19556)*
Sigma Corporation 281 987-1200
  5000 Askins Ln Houston (77093) *(G-11883)*
Sigma Drilling Tech LLC 281 656-9298
  1004 Avenue A Katy (77493) *(G-13442)*
Sigma Electronics Inc (PA) **800 874-7121**
  10830 Kinghurst Dr Houston (77099) *(G-11884)*
Sigma Fasteners Inc 281 214-8800
  16723 Aldine Westfield Rd Houston (77032) *(G-11885)*
Sigma Industrial Automtn Inc (PA) **210 659-5000**
  5450 Fm 1103 Schertz (78108) *(G-18762)*
Sigma MBL Granite-Houston Inc 713 290-8530
  5930 Centralcrest St Houston (77092) *(G-11886)*
Sigma Tube & Bar LLC (PA) **281 369-5525**
  363 N Sam Houston Pkwy E Houston (77060) *(G-11887)*
Sigma Valves, Houston *Also called Array Holdings Inc (G-8704)*
Sigma-Genosys of Texas LLC 281 363-3693
  9186 Six Pines Dr Ste 100 Spring (77380) *(G-19250)*
Sigmapro Engineering & Mfg LLC 682 888-1234
  13241 Harmon Rd Fort Worth (76177) *(G-6986)*

Sigmasense 844 248-9081
  3939 Bee Caves Rd Ste A6 West Lake Hills (78746) *(G-20688)*
Sigmatron International Inc 830 775-5524
  103 Avenue J Del Rio (78840) *(G-5324)*
Sigmund Kane & Hatch Inc 713 782-1075
  7700 San Felipe St # 500 Houston (77063) *(G-11888)*
Sign & Awning Services Inc 817 926-7270
  2100 E Richmond Ave Fort Worth (76104) *(G-6987)*
Sign City Inc 281 338-1203
  1851 Fm 528 Rd Webster (77598) *(G-20646)*
Sign Company, Euless *Also called Sign Erection Ltd (G-6158)*
Sign Crafters Inc 512 392-0900
  2401 S Interstate 35 San Marcos (78666) *(G-18710)*
Sign Depot, The, Pharr *Also called Lozz Quatezz LLC (G-16706)*
Sign Erection Ltd 817 267-1554
  11128 S Pipeline Rd Euless (76040) *(G-6158)*
Sign Express, Houston *Also called Fusion Led Inc (G-9877)*
Sign Factory Inc 713 849-4575
  5101 Ashley Ct Houston (77041) *(G-11889)*
Sign International Express, Beaumont *Also called Sign International Inc (G-1949)*
Sign International Inc 409 832-0117
  7398 College St Beaumont (77707) *(G-1949)*
Sign Pro of Lubbock Ltd 806 798-7446
  110 E Highway 62 Wolfforth (79382) *(G-20913)*
Sign Shop 325 641-2424
  4300 Fm 3021 Brownwood (76801) *(G-2444)*
Sign System Tech, Houston *Also called N & P Sign System Inc (G-10947)*
Sign Technologies Inc 903 838-8999
  3502 New Boston Rd Texarkana (75501) *(G-19773)*
Sign Wave Corporation 214 890-4444
  10225 N Central Expy Dallas (75231) *(G-4960)*
Sign-Ad, Houston *Also called Signad Inc (G-11890)*
Signacert Inc 512 577-4894
  12912 Hill Country Blvd Austin (78738) *(G-1501)*
Signad Inc 713 861-6013
  1010 North Loop Houston (77009) *(G-11890)*
Signal Group Inc (PA) **281 453-0200**
  5401 N Sam Houston Pkwy W Houston (77086) *(G-11891)*
Signal Metal Industries Inc (PA) **972 438-1022**
  850 E Pioneer Dr Irving (75061) *(G-13179)*
Signal Peak Silica LLC 281 822-4568
  4605 Post Oak Place Dr Houston (77027) *(G-11892)*
Signature Arch & Blind 281 469-2500
  10720 Jones Rd Houston (77065) *(G-11893)*
Signature Cards LP 972 783-7600
  1299 Commerce Dr Bldg B Richardson (75081) *(G-17398)*
Signature Envelope Company Inc 713 538-1177
  13180 State Highway 150 W Coldspring (77331) *(G-3167)*
Signature Millwork, Dallas *Also called Growth Holdings LLC (G-4418)*
Signature Mldngs Millworks Inc (PA) **210 967-8400**
  1400 Currency St San Antonio (78219) *(G-18474)*
Signature Molding, San Antonio *Also called Signature Partners Ltd (G-18475)*
Signature Moulding & Millworks, San Antonio *Also called Signature Mldngs Millworks Inc (G-18474)*
Signature Partners Ltd 210 967-8400
  4234 Profit St San Antonio (78219) *(G-18475)*
Signature Plating Ltd 210 380-0020
  1135 Guadalupe Dr Cibolo (78108) *(G-3065)*
Signature Press Inc 713 956-8555
  3300 Kingswood St Houston (77092) *(G-11894)*
Signature Stair Parts, Plano *Also called Pysz Enterprises Inc (G-16981)*
Signature Systems Group LLC (HQ) **972 684-5736**
  1201 Lkeside Pkwy Ste 150 Flower Mound (75028) *(G-6281)*
Signature Window Coverings, Houston *Also called Signature Arch & Blind (G-11893)*
Signazon Corporation 214 296-0022
  4000 E Plano Pkwy Ste A Plano (75074) *(G-17006)*
Signazon.com, Plano *Also called Signazon Corporation (G-17006)*
Signgrafx, Addison *Also called Andax Corp (G-104)*
Signicast Hutchins, Hutchins *Also called Consolidated Casting LLC (G-12865)*
Signify North America Corp 800 235-2314
  1611 Clovis Barker Rd San Marcos (78666) *(G-18711)*
Signify North America Corp 214 647-7880
  10911 Petal St Dallas (75238) *(G-4961)*
Signit Inc 817 589-9988
  3100 Handley Ederville Rd Richland Hills (76118) *(G-17448)*
Signmaster Wholesale Sign Co, Dallas *Also called Masterco Inc (G-4648)*
Signmaxx, Katy *Also called Image Display Systems Inc (G-13408)*
Signode Industrial Group LLC 409 745-2600
  19440 Fm 1130 Orange (77632) *(G-16263)*
Signquick, Seabrook *Also called Jackson Promotions Inc (G-18786)*
Signs & Graphics Plus LLC 915 590-7446
  1302 Gail Borden Pl Ste B El Paso (79935) *(G-5961)*
Signs 2 Go Lakeway, Lakeway *Also called Stokes Sign Company Inc (G-13821)*
Signs and Designs, Stephenville *Also called Day Night Signs Inc (G-19409)*
Signs By Tomorrow, Tomball *Also called Northwest Advantage Inc (G-19992)*
Signs Manufacturing Corp (PA) **214 339-2227**
  4550 Mint Way Dallas (75236) *(G-4962)*

A
L
P
H
A
B
E
T
I
C

Signs Now Corporation..972 398-8648
701 E Plano Pkwy Ste 113 Plano (75074) *(G-17007)*

Signs On Go...806 722-7446
304 County Road 7200 Lubbock (79404) *(G-14480)*

Signs Universe...972 880-2884
3733 N Josey Ln Ste 105 Carrollton (75007) *(G-2887)*

Signs West Inc..512 282-5001
11926 Wirth Rd Austin (78748) *(G-1502)*

Signtex Imaging Inc...281 351-2776
1225 Alma St Ste C Tomball (77375) *(G-20008)*

Signtex Outdoor Inc...281 351-8023
1225 Alma St Ste D Tomball (77375) *(G-20009)*

Sika Corporation..972 387-4500
13524 Welch Rd Dallas (75244) *(G-4963)*

Sikes Fabricating Co Inc..409 941-0727
3416 3rd Ave S Texas City (77590) *(G-19802)*

Sikes Machine Shop Inc...806 828-6568
265 N Terry Dr Slaton (79364) *(G-18973)*

Sikorsky Aircraft Corporation................................817 377-7500
7000 Calmont Ave 300 Fort Worth (76116) *(G-6988)*

Silco Inc (PA)...**713 785-6272**
1215 Gessner Rd Houston (77055) *(G-11895)*

Silent Partners Inc...512 458-1191
8727 Shoal Creek Blvd A Austin (78757) *(G-1503)*

Silentaire Technology, Houston Also called Werther International Inc *(G-12634)*

Silgan Plastics of Texas (PA)...............................**713 242-0923**
6814 Kirbyville St Houston (77033) *(G-11896)*

Silicon Hills Design Inc...512 836-1088
8504 Cross Park Dr Austin (78754) *(G-1504)*

Silicon Laboratories Inc (PA)................................**512 416-8500**
400 W Cesar Chavez St Austin (78701) *(G-1505)*

Silicon Space Technology Corp.............................512 347-1814
1501 S Mopac Expy Ste 350 Austin (78746) *(G-1506)*

Silsbee Bee, Silsbee Also called Reneau Publishing Inc *(G-18954)*

Silsbee Tube Plant, Silsbee Also called Caraustar Industrial and Con *(G-18950)*

Silva Technologies Inc...713 869-3631
3228 Maxroy St Houston (77008) *(G-11897)*

Silver Creek Machine Ltd......................................817 238-0131
6216 Frank Christian Rd Azle (76020) *(G-1729)*

Silver Creek Materials (PA)...................................**817 246-2426**
2251 Silver Creek Rd Fort Worth (76108) *(G-6989)*

Silver Creek Oil & Gas LLC..................................972 573-1630
5525 N Macarthur Blvd # 7 Irving (75038) *(G-13180)*

Silver Creek Resources, Irving Also called Silver Creek Oil & Gas LLC *(G-13180)*

Silver Hill Enrgy Partners LLC..............................214 865-6555
5949 Sherry Ln Ste 1550 Dallas (75225) *(G-4964)*

Silver Spring Networks, San Antonio Also called Itron Networked Solutions Inc *(G-18195)*

Silver Star I Pwr Partners LLC..............................713 354-2168
700 Louisiana St Houston (77002) *(G-11898)*

Silverbow Resources Inc (PA)...............................**281 874-2700**
575 N Dairy Ashford Rd Houston (77079) *(G-11899)*

Silvertip Completion Svcs LLC..............................432 701-9020
9816 W County Road 146 Midland (79706) *(G-15409)*

Silverwell Technology Inc......................................281 389-3020
6824 N Sam Houston Pkwy W Houston (77064) *(G-11900)*

Simco Longhorn Leather..972 542-8700
1425 N Tennessee St McKinney (75069) *(G-14974)*

Simdesk Technologies Inc.....................................713 244-0850
3900 Essex Ln Fl 5 Houston (77027) *(G-11901)*

Simmons Custom Boats LLC..................................832 864-2331
800 Peach Pt Freeport (77541) *(G-7212)*

Simon Printing Company..713 666-1296
10810 Craighead Dr Houston (77025) *(G-11902)*

Simple Booth, Austin Also called Smpl Inc *(G-1513)*

Simplelegal Inc...415 763-5366
1360 Post Oak Blvd # 2200 Houston (77056) *(G-11903)*

Simplex Time Recorder LLC...................................210 402-6311
1070 Arion Cir Ste 102 San Antonio (78216) *(G-18476)*

Simplfied Strl Thrmforming Inc.............................903 887-8546
14062 State Highway 198 Mabank (75147) *(G-14581)*

Simplot Grower Solutions, Point Comfort Also called JR Simplot Company *(G-17087)*

Simplot Growers Solutions, Hempstead Also called JR Simplot Company *(G-8253)*

Simply 7 Snacks LLC..713 988-2900
13843 Stafford Rd Stafford (77477) *(G-19379)*

Simply Donuts...281 955-6374
11711 Jones Rd Houston (77070) *(G-11904)*

Simply Nuc Inc..512 766-0402
495 Round Rock West Dr Round Rock (78681) *(G-17690)*

Simplyfresco LLC...210 494-8443
12867 Wetmore Rd San Antonio (78247) *(G-18477)*

Simpro, Arlington Also called B and D Index Inc *(G-628)*

Simpson Helmets Inc...830 625-1774
328 Fm 306 New Braunfels (78130) *(G-15823)*

Simpson Stone Company..512 746-2204
3410 W Fm 487 Jarrell (76537) *(G-13272)*

Simpson Strong-Tie Company Inc.........................972 542-0326
2221 Country Ln McKinney (75069) *(G-14975)*

Sims Aviation Inc...972 733-3828
4390 Sunbelt Dr Addison (75001) *(G-163)*

Simtek Inc...817 283-1801
1505 Royal Pkwy Euless (76040) *(G-6159)*

Singer Data Products Inc.......................................915 594-7650
3800 Buckner St El Paso (79925) *(G-5962)*

Singleton ML Inc...409 755-0893
568 N Lhs Dr Lumberton (77657) *(G-14570)*

Singleton Mouldings Inc..254 559-7541
1895 E Us Highway 180 Breckenridge (76424) *(G-2237)*

Sinochem American Holdings (HQ)........................**713 263-8880**
1330 Post Oak Blvd # 2500 Houston (77056) *(G-11905)*

Sinochem Petroleum USA LP.................................832 742-8670
1330 Post Oak Blvd # 600 Houston (77056) *(G-11906)*

Sip Industries, Houston Also called Serampore Inds Private Ltd Inc *(G-11833)*

Sipco, Webster Also called Standard Industrial Pdts Co *(G-20647)*

Siplast Inc (HQ)...**469 995-2200**
1000 Rochelle Blvd Irving (75062) *(G-13181)*

Sips By LLC...214 208-0184
2215 W Braker Ln Austin (78758) *(G-1507)*

Sir Hc20 Inc..817 228-9449
3201 Wstn Ctr Blvd Ste 10 Fort Worth (76137) *(G-6990)*

Sir Speedy, Richardson Also called Thompson Family Partnership *(G-17411)*

Sir Speedy, Houston Also called Kggt Management Corp *(G-10528)*

Sir Speedy, Carrollton Also called Quinn Printing Co Inc *(G-2802)*

Sir Speedy, Amarillo Also called Bernadette Debrango *(G-408)*

Sir Speedy 4043, Carrollton Also called Egh Printing LLC *(G-2728)*

Sir Speedy 4092...512 338-9818
3818 Far West Blvd # 105 Austin (78731) *(G-1508)*

Siri Granite Inc...832 203-8322
4849 Cranswick Rd Houston (77041) *(G-11907)*

SIS, Grand Prairie Also called Southwest Indus Surfaces Inc *(G-7974)*

Sister2sster Dstiny Trnspt LLC.............................346 337-6637
11510 Homestead Rd # 299 Houston (77016) *(G-11908)*

Site Safe Solutions Ltd (PA)................................**940 612-2286**
202 S Dixon St Ste 214 Gainesville (76240) *(G-7368)*

Sitepro LLC...806 687-5326
9502 Highway 87 Lubbock (79423) *(G-14481)*

Siteselect Inc...956 207-5587
1100 E Jasmine Ave # 105 McAllen (78501) *(G-14906)*

Siteselect Medical Tech, McAllen Also called Siteselect Inc *(G-14906)*

Siteworks Incorporated..281 931-1000
363 W Canino Rd Houston (77037) *(G-11909)*

Sitton Enterprises LLC (PA).................................**817 737-8500**
4055 International Plz # 410 Fort Worth (76109) *(G-6991)*

Sivalls Inc (PA)..**432 337-3571**
2200 E 2nd St Odessa (79761) *(G-16153)*

Sivalls Inc...325 643-3621
2300 Dickman Dr Brownwood (76801) *(G-2445)*

Sivco Inc...713 466-1100
5713 Cunningham Rd Houston (77041) *(G-11910)*

Six & Mango Equipment LLP (PA).........................**972 335-2731**
8741 Main St Frisco (75034) *(G-7312)*

Six B Construction,, Lufkin Also called Lufkins Six B Construction *(G-14543)*

Six B Labels Corporation.......................................214 349-7824
12200 Forestgate Dr Dallas (75243) *(G-4965)*

Sjoc, Wichita Falls Also called Stephens & Johnson Oper Co *(G-20812)*

Sk Energy Houston, Houston Also called Sk Gc Americas Inc *(G-11911)*

Sk Gc Americas Inc (HQ).......................................**713 341-5820**
11700 Katy Fwy Ste 900 Houston (77079) *(G-11911)*

Sk Global Software LLC...301 963-7300
940 Gemini St Ste 200 Houston (77058) *(G-11912)*

Skagen Designs Ltd (HQ)......................................**775 336-5667**
10615 Sanden Dr Dallas (75238) *(G-4966)*

Skaps Matrix, Seguin Also called Pbr Inc *(G-18855)*

Skeeter Boats, Kilgore Also called Skeeter Products Inc *(G-13590)*

Skeeter Products Inc (HQ).....................................**903 984-0541**
1 Skeeter Rd Kilgore (75662) *(G-13590)*

Skeletal Kinetics LLC...408 366-5000
3885 Arapaho Rd Addison (75001) *(G-164)*

Sketchers, Richardson Also called Fossil Partners LP *(G-17315)*

SKF Machine Tool Services, Houston Also called SKF USA Inc *(G-11913)*

SKF USA Inc..281 506-3250
3443 N Sam Houston Pkwy W Houston (77086) *(G-11913)*

Skh Management, Houston Also called Sigmund Kane & Hatch Inc *(G-11888)*

Skh Management LP..713 782-1075
7600 San Felipe St 200 Houston (77063) *(G-11914)*

Skh Resources, Houston Also called Skh Management LP *(G-11914)*

Skipper Industries Inc..254 897-1292
650 Bo Gibbs Blvd Glen Rose (76043) *(G-7733)*

Skiva Technologies Inc...214 441-3517
2010 Valley View Ln # 320 Dallas (75234) *(G-4967)*

Skl Prime Services LLC..469 733-1540
1121 108th St Arlington (76011) *(G-782)*

Skledar-Greene LLC...817 454-4214
4243 Fm 1173 Krum (76249) *(G-13676)*

Skorpios Technologies Inc.....................................512 356-2000
2706 Montopolis Dr Austin (78741) *(G-1509)*

Skudo USA Distribution LLC 972 993-0777
11120 Zodiac Ln Dallas (75229) *(G-4968)*

SKW Alliance Med LLC 972 358-5171
2256 Longwood Dr Carrollton (75010) *(G-2888)*

SKW Manufacturing LLC 806 763-8118
4224 Adrian St Lubbock (79415) *(G-14482)*

Sky Glass Aluminum, Dallas *Also called Sky Glass Inc (G-4969)*

Sky Glass Inc (PA) 972 807-9616
2600 Manana Dr Dallas (75220) *(G-4969)*

Sky TEC Ltd 817 573-2250
350 Howard Clemmons Rd Granbury (76048) *(G-7810)*

Skycam LLC 817 984-6840
2751 Northern Cross Blvd # 333 Fort Worth (76137) *(G-6992)*

Skygrid LLC 844 205-7173
4030 W Braker Ln Ste 400 Austin (78759) *(G-1510)*

Skylights Over Texas LLC (PA) 210 402-0500
319 E Nakoma St Ste 1 San Antonio (78216) *(G-18478)*

Skyline Cabinetry Inc (HQ) 972 620-8880
12301 N Stemmons Fwy # 100 Farmers Branch (75234) *(G-6214)*

Skyline Cabinetry Inc 972 620-8880
2230 Lbj Fwy Ste 400 Dallas (75234) *(G-4970)*

Skyline Cabinets, Farmers Branch *Also called Skyline Cabinetry Inc (G-6214)*

Skyven Technologies Inc 972 861-0893
1201 Intl Pkwy Ste 300 Richardson (75081) *(G-17399)*

Skyway Aviation Group LLC 830 278-4481
1770 Skyplace Blvd San Antonio (78216) *(G-18479)*

Skyway Group Inc (PA) 830 278-4481
122 Howard Langford Dr Uvalde (78801) *(G-20196)*

Slab Fabricators, Dallas *Also called Stonemode Granite LLC (G-5012)*

Slate Mill Wine Collective, Fredericksburg *Also called 1851 Vineyards LLC (G-7168)*

Slater Gate and Fence, Houston *Also called R Slater Enterprises LLC (G-11528)*

Slaughter & Stanley Cnstr Inc 432 264-0031
921 N Fairgrounds Rd Midland (79706) *(G-15410)*

Sle Electronics-Usa Inc 915 594-4998
9641 Plaza Cir Ste A El Paso (79927) *(G-5963)*

Sleep Disorder Centers LLC 972 390-2014
7900 Henneman Way Ste 220 McKinney (75070) *(G-14976)*

Slinggrip, Rosharon *Also called DMD Products LLC (G-17604)*

Sloan Energy Services LLC 432 653-0205
4803 Plaza Blvd Ste 802 Odessa (79762) *(G-16154)*

Slocum Printing Incorporated 214 748-2238
909 Lorene Dr Wylie (75098) *(G-20950)*

Slovacek Foods LP 979 272-8625
Hwy 60 W Snook (77878) *(G-18981)*

Slovacek Sausage, Snook *Also called Slovacek Foods LP (G-18981)*

Slpc Inc 281 398-6655
1454 E Summitry Cir Katy (77449) *(G-13443)*

Slz Rebar LLC 832 427-5860
7719 Serene Wood Ln Cypress (77433) *(G-3820)*

SM Energy Company 432 688-1700
6301 Holiday Hill Rd # 1 Midland (79707) *(G-15411)*

SM Energy Company 281 677-2800
580 Westlake Park Blvd Houston (77079) *(G-11915)*

SM Energy Company 281 677-2800
777 N Eldridge Pkwy # 1100 Houston (77079) *(G-11916)*

SMA Distributors 281 442-0890
6519 Mohawk St Houston (77016) *(G-11917)*

Smalley Bill Drilling & Trckg, Albany *Also called Bill Smalley Drilling & Trckg (G-185)*

Smalley Drilling & Trckg Corp 325 762-3409
160 Fm 1084 Albany (76430) *(G-193)*

Smart City Locating Inc 214 586-0519
1619 N Hall St Dallas (75204) *(G-4971)*

Smart Control Systems LLC 210 224-4906
3005 Interstate Dr San Antonio (78219) *(G-18480)*

Smart Family Cooling Products, Humble *Also called Combined Rfrgn Resources Inc (G-12761)*

Smart Imaging Technologies Co 713 589-3500
1770 Saint James Pl # 414 Houston (77056) *(G-11918)*

Smart Packager Inc 713 316-4903
600 Congress Ave Ste C100 Austin (78701) *(G-1511)*

Smart Pipe Company Inc 281 945-5700
6955 High Life Dr Houston (77066) *(G-11919)*

Smart Sand Inc (PA) 281 231-2660
1725 Hughes Landing Blvd # 800 The Woodlands (77380) *(G-19918)*

Smartdraw Software LLC 858 225-3300
1780 Hughes Landing Blvd The Woodlands (77380) *(G-19919)*

Smartdrone Corporation 443 655-5556
2014 Deerbrook Dr Tyler (75703) *(G-20152)*

Smarter Sorting, Austin *Also called Waste Repurposing Intl Inc (G-1647)*

Smartstyle, San Antonio *Also called A&S New Braunfels LLC (G-17849)*

Smarttruck Systems, Fort Worth *Also called Smarttruck Undertray Systems (G-6993)*

Smarttruck Undertray Systems 864 990-0781
201 Main St Ste 2600 Fort Worth (76102) *(G-6993)*

Smartz Printing Services, El Paso *Also called Tre Stars Incorporated (G-6014)*

Smbg Corsicana LLC 254 262-4400
3501 Crscana Crssngs Blvd Corsicana (75109) *(G-3684)*

SMC Industries Inc 281 860-9950
2260 Appelt Dr Houston (77015) *(G-11920)*

Smco L & M LP 432 550-7116
6600 N County Rd W Odessa (79764) *(G-16155)*

Smead Manufacturing Company 956 631-1418
3801 W Military Hwy McAllen (78503) *(G-14907)*

SMI Manufacturing Inc (HQ) 281 449-0345
13312 E Hardy Rd Houston (77039) *(G-11921)*

SMI-Carr Inc 325 677-0491
2573 Pine St Abilene (79601) *(G-80)*

Smith & Company, Conroe *Also called Dmg Equipment Company LLC (G-3295)*

Smith & Nephew Inc 512 358-5975
7000 W William Cannon Dr Austin (78735) *(G-1512)*

Smith & Nephew Inc 817 900-4000
5600 Clearfork Main St Fort Worth (76109) *(G-6994)*

Smith & Nephew Biotherapeutics, Fort Worth *Also called Smith & Nephew Inc (G-6994)*

Smith & Nephew Wound MGT 800 876-1261
4900 W Vickery Blvd Fort Worth (76107) *(G-6995)*

Smith and Nephew, Austin *Also called Smith & Nephew Inc (G-1512)*

Smith Bits Division, Odessa *Also called Smith International Inc (G-16156)*

Smith Design and Mfg Inc 903 433-4444
208 E College St Gunter (75058) *(G-8116)*

Smith Energy Company 713 651-9102
1001 Sannin St Ste 3850 Houston (77002) *(G-11922)*

Smith Energy Services Inc (PA) 903 693-8872
932 S Shelby St Carthage (75633) *(G-2919)*

Smith Equipment Rental & Svcs, Carthage *Also called Smith Energy Services Inc (G-2919)*

Smith Fans Inc 806 872-8465
501 S Dallas Ave Lamesa (79331) *(G-13830)*

Smith Fibercast, San Antonio *Also called Fiber Glass Systems LP (G-18112)*

Smith Industries Inc 432 683-9722
3601 E State Highway 158 Midland (79706) *(G-15412)*

Smith International (HQ) 281 443-3370
1310 Rankin Rd Houston (77073) *(G-11923)*

Smith International Inc 409 724-2471
6405 Highway 347 Beaumont (77705) *(G-1950)*

Smith International Inc 432 337-5541
2120 Maurice Rd Odessa (79763) *(G-16156)*

Smith International Inc 254 697-4488
468 Kenny Rd 143 Missouri City (77459) *(G-15594)*

Smith International Inc 903 693-2596
114 Wilson St Carthage (75633) *(G-2920)*

Smith International Inc 432 550-6909
8700 Nw Loop 338 Odessa (79764) *(G-16157)*

Smith Lester Management, Houston *Also called Smith Energy Company (G-11922)*

Smith Millworks Solutions, Mansfield *Also called Millwork Solutions Ltd (G-14696)*

Smith Oilfield Services Inc 940 683-5722
172 County Road 3503 Bridgeport (76426) *(G-2301)*

Smith Production Inc (PA) 281 583-0196
14425 Torrey Chase Blvd # 190 Houston (77014) *(G-11924)*

Smith Production Inc 281 296-5600
8708 Tech Forest Pl 15 The Woodlands (77381) *(G-19920)*

Smith Pump Company Inc 817 589-2060
4624 Martin St 100 Fort Worth (76119) *(G-6996)*

Smith Services Incorporated 361 526-2615
103 Highway 183 Refugio (78377) *(G-17247)*

Smith Services Red Baron 361 396-0521
2225 Energy Ave Alice (78332) *(G-235)*

Smith System Manufacturing Co 800 328-1061
1150 Luna Rd Carrollton (75006) *(G-2816)*

Smith Tank & Equipment Company 903 597-5541
9887 Us Highway 271 Tyler (75708) *(G-20153)*

Smith Tool & Manufacturing, Wylie *Also called Vlj Inc (G-20955)*

Smith Vacuum Service 325 573-7437
3642 W Us Highway 180 Snyder (79549) *(G-19006)*

Smith Wood Products Inc 817 581-5200
4220 Clay Ave Fort Worth (76117) *(G-6997)*

Smith-Hamm Inc 409 740-3314
320 77th St Galveston (77554) *(G-7408)*

Smithfield Bioenergy LLC (HQ) 817 558-9255
3102 Windmill Rd Cleburne (76033) *(G-3109)*

Smob, Midland *Also called Brinkerhoff Inspection Inc (G-15150)*

Smob, Midland *Also called Brinkerhoff Inspection Inc (G-15151)*

Smocker's, San Antonio *Also called Bexar Manufacturing & Trdg Co (G-17951)*

Smokehouse Salt Company, Fort Worth *Also called Trothyhide LLC (G-7080)*

Smolecule Inc 512 262-9938
1003 Ruthven St Houston (77019) *(G-11925)*

Smoothie King, The Colony *Also called Smoothie King (G-19814)*

Smoothie King 214 469-1552
4770 State Highway 121 The Colony (75056) *(G-19814)*

Smpl Inc 402 525-5078
902 E 5th St Ste 202 Austin (78702) *(G-1513)*

Smu Electron Microprobe Lab, Dallas *Also called Southern Methodist University (G-4988)*

Smurfit Kappa Bates LLC (HQ) 817 498-3200
6433 Davis Blvd North Richland Hills (76182) *(G-15881)*

Smurfit Kappa Bates LLC 903 234-1100
2811 Robert Cargill Dr Longview (75602) *(G-14309)*

Smurfit Kappa Bates LLC 210 436-7777
10600 Fischer Rd Von Ormy (78073) *(G-20352)*

Smurfit Kappa Forney, Forney *Also called Smurfit Kappa North Amer LLC (G-6314)*

Smurfit Kappa Houston, Houston *Also called Smurfit Kappa North Amer LLC* **(G-11926)**
Smurfit Kappa North Amer LLC 214 515-6400
855 E Us Highway 80 Forney (75126) **(G-6314)**
Smurfit Kappa North Amer LLC (HQ) **800 306-8326**
125 E John Carpenter Fwy # 925 Irving (75062) **(G-13182)**
Smurfit Kappa North Amer LLC 713 869-5900
7800 Washington Ave Houston (77007) **(G-11926)**
Smw, Pasadena *Also called Standard Machine Works Inc* **(G-16512)**
Sn & Db Holdings Inc 713 645-3370
8400 Villa Dr Houston (77061) **(G-11927)**
Sn Midstream LLC 713 783-8000
700 Milam St Ste 600 Houston (77002) **(G-11928)**
Sn Operating LLC 713 951-0233
700 Milam St Ste 600 Houston (77002) **(G-11929)**
Snap Drape Brands, Flower Mound *Also called CFS Brands LLC* **(G-6262)**
Snap Oilfield Services LLC 956 322-1210
3605 N 42nd Ln McAllen (78501) **(G-14908)**
Snapp Tool & Die Inc 915 821-2046
10885 Dyer St Ste A El Paso (79934) **(G-5964)**
Snd Operating LLC 214 691-3072
13140 Coit Rd Ste 225 Dallas (75240) **(G-4972)**
Sneaky Chef Foods LLC 203 768-5654
6610 Lancret Hill Dr Austin (78745) **(G-1514)**
Sneed Shipbuilding Inc (PA) **281 862-2266**
17112 Market St Channelview (77530) **(G-3037)**
Snelick Quality Tool Inc 972 221-0537
7410 Ambassador Row Dallas (75247) **(G-4973)**
Snelson Oilfield Ltg Co Inc (PA) **817 926-0571**
3619 Alice St Fort Worth (76110) **(G-6998)**
Snelson Oilfield Ltg Co Inc 713 937-3600
14655 Chmpn Frest Dr Apt Houston (77069) **(G-11930)**
Snf Inc (PA) **817 402-8040**
2800 Golden Triangle Blvd Fort Worth (76177) **(G-6999)**
Snf Flomin, Baytown *Also called Flomin Inc* **(G-1787)**
Snider Industries LLP 903 938-9221
3311 Sue Belle Lake Rd Marshall (75670) **(G-14803)**
Sniper Drilling Motors, Houston *Also called Iae International Inc* **(G-10311)**
Snoe Inc Machining & Welding 979 567-0808
215 County Road 300 Caldwell (77836) **(G-2636)**
Snoke Special Products Co Inc (PA) **903 586-3618**
2050 N Jackson St Jacksonville (75766) **(G-13258)**
Snow Flake & Co, Baytown *Also called Snow Flake Bakery* **(G-1834)**
Snow Flake Bakery 281 427-4423
1906 N Alexander Dr Baytown (77520) **(G-1834)**
Snowball Lighting Inc 915 227-7210
1555 Goodyear Dr Ste A El Paso (79936) **(G-5965)**
Snowden-Pencer, El Paso *Also called Carefusion 213 LLC* **(G-5683)**
Sns Plating, Houston *Also called S + S Industries Inc* **(G-11709)**
Snw Operating Company Inc 806 273-2667
1621 N Main St Borger (79007) **(G-2185)**
Snyder Daily News 325 573-5486
3600 College Ave Snyder (79549) **(G-19007)**
Snyder Drilling Corp 325 762-2389
Throckmorton Hwy Aka Albany (76430) **(G-194)**
Snyder Iron Metal 325 573-6862
208 N Old Post Rd Snyder (79549) **(G-19008)**
Snyders-Lance Inc 214 638-2378
3276 Quebec St Dallas (75247) **(G-4974)**
Soc Industries LLC 432 620-0040
2324 Fm 715 Midland (79706) **(G-15413)**
Soccer 4 All Inc 281 376-7890
6700 Louetta Rd Ste C Spring (77379) **(G-19166)**
Soccer Corner, The, Plano *Also called Plano Sports Soccer Inc* **(G-16974)**
Sock Club Enterprises LLC 919 619-4981
2200 Tillery St B Austin (78723) **(G-1515)**
Socomore, Rhome *Also called Dysol Inc* **(G-17255)**
Socorro Exploration Inc 806 798-2790
8008 Slide Rd Ste 37b Lubbock (79424) **(G-14483)**
Sofec Inc (HQ) **713 510-6600**
15011 Katy Fwy Ste 500 Houston (77094) **(G-11931)**
Soff Corporation 469 467-9700
2828 W Parker Rd Ste 101b Plano (75075) **(G-17008)**
Soff Corporation (PA) **469 467-9700**
520 Central Pkwy E # 300 Plano (75074) **(G-17009)**
Soft Air Usa Inc 817 717-4300
4265 Trade Center Dr # 130 Grapevine (76051) **(G-8054)**
Softech Controls Inc 713 553-0365
15710 Cascading Brook Way Cypress (77433) **(G-3821)**
Softest Designs Corporation 210 697-8828
5807 Sebastian Pl San Antonio (78249) **(G-18481)**
Software Construction Co Inc (PA) **214 495-7387**
1024 S Greenville Ave # 160 Allen (75002) **(G-298)**
Software Consulting, Trophy Club *Also called Software Development Tech* **(G-20021)**
Software Development Tech 650 906-6135
10 Rochester Ct Trophy Club (76262) **(G-20021)**
Software Global Ltd 832 274-0478
2000 S Interstate 35 A Austin (78704) **(G-1516)**
Soho 713 526-3755
2528 Amherst St Houston (77005) **(G-11932)**

Soil Mender Products L P 806 627-4276
3071 Highway 86 Tulia (79088) **(G-20038)**
Soil Mender Products L P (PA) **806 627-4276**
7355 Fm 928 Tulia (79088) **(G-20039)**
Sojitz Energy Venture Inc 713 963-9101
2000 Houston Ave Houston (77007) **(G-11933)**
Sojourner Drilling Corporation 325 672-2832
810 Anson Ave Abilene (79601) **(G-81)**
Sol Marketing, Tomball *Also called Enthusiastic Sales LLC* **(G-19978)**
Sola Prosthetics Inc 972 492-7652
4541 N Josey Ln Ste 240 Carrollton (75010) **(G-2889)**
Solais Lighting Group, Frisco *Also called Solais Lighting LLC* **(G-7313)**
Solais Lighting LLC 469 294-1516
8655 Corporate Dr Ste 100 Frisco (75033) **(G-7313)**
Solamotor of Texas 432 426-3246
Hc 74 Box 117 Fort Davis (79734) **(G-6319)**
Solano Furniture Incorporated 713 849-4855
8211 Fairbanks White Oak Houston (77040) **(G-11934)**
Solansky Welding and Pump Inc 830 374-3318
501 W Zavala St Crystal City (78839) **(G-3757)**
Solar Accessories Corporation 972 524-2099
109 Silent Wings Blvd Terrell (75160) **(G-19750)**
Solar Streetscapes, Austin *Also called Valen Light LLC* **(G-1621)**
Solar Turbines Incorporated 972 228-5500
215 E Centre Park Blvd Desoto (75115) **(G-5442)**
Solar Turbines Incorporated 903 880-1461
904 Fm 90 Mabank (75147) **(G-14582)**
Solar Turbines Incorporated 713 895-2300
10203 Sam Houston Park Dr # 300 Houston (77064) **(G-11935)**
Solar Turbines Incorporated 281 860-6703
16504 De Zavalla Rd Channelview (77530) **(G-3038)**
Solar Turbines Incorporated 800 851-6594
2912 S County Road 1255 Midland (79706) **(G-15414)**
Solar Turbines Incorporated 903 880-1200
904 Solar Turbine Way # 90 Mabank (75147) **(G-14583)**
Solara Doors, Dallas *Also called Solara Ironworks LLC* **(G-4975)**
Solara Ironworks LLC (PA) **214 744-9900**
142 Howell St Dallas (75207) **(G-4975)**
Solarbridge Technologies, Austin *Also called Sunpower Corporation* **(G-1545)**
Solarcraft Inc 281 340-1224
12300 Dairy Ashford Rd Sugar Land (77478) **(G-19557)**
Solaris Oilfield Tech LLC 281 501-3070
9811 Katy Fwy Ste 900 Houston (77024) **(G-11936)**
Solaris Olfld Infrstrcture Inc (PA) **281 501-3070**
9811 Katy Fwy Ste 700 Houston (77024) **(G-11937)**
Solaro Energy Inc 575 838-3813
1704 S Fredonia St Nacogdoches (75964) **(G-15713)**
Solarwinds Corporation (PA) **512 682-9300**
7171 Sw Pkwy Bldg 400 Austin (78735) **(G-1517)**
Solarwinds Holdings Inc (HQ) **512 682-9300**
7171 Sw Pkwy Bldg 400 Austin (78735) **(G-1518)**
Solarwinds North America Inc (HQ) **512 682-9300**
7171 Southwest Pkwy Austin (78735) **(G-1519)**
Solarwinds Worldwide LLC 512 682-9300
7171 Southwest Pkwy Austin (78735) **(G-1520)**
Solavanti Lighting, Dallas *Also called Solavanti Trading LLC* **(G-4976)**
Solavanti Trading LLC 214 221-9405
9659 Wendell Rd Dallas (75243) **(G-4976)**
Solectron USA, Austin *Also called Flextronics America LLC* **(G-1159)**
Solenis LLC 713 991-3722
6121 Almeda Genoa Rd Houston (77048) **(G-11938)**
Solenis LLC 713 738-6815
6060 South Loop E Ste 212 Houston (77033) **(G-11939)**
Solera Co 915 637-6471
500 W Overland Ave # 250 El Paso (79901) **(G-5966)**
Solid Crate LLC 713 475-9926
409 Pasadena Fwy Pasadena (77506) **(G-16507)**
Solid Distribution LLC 915 235-4357
8900 Viscount Blvd # 722 El Paso (79925) **(G-5967)**
Solid Integrations LLC 915 235-4357
7101 N Mesa St El Paso (79912) **(G-5968)**
Solid Rock Ready Mix Inc 281 931-3003
5515 Breen Dr Houston (77086) **(G-11940)**
Solid Rocks Properties LLC 940 779-3700
20115 State Highway 337 Graford (76449) **(G-7773)**
Solidiform Inc 817 831-2626
3928 Lawnwood St Fort Worth (76111) **(G-7000)**
Solidwood Forest Ltd (PA) **281 351-0271**
16801 Fm 2920 Rd Tomball (77377) **(G-20010)**
Solmax Geosynthetics LLC 281 443-8564
19103 Gundle Rd Houston (77073) **(G-11941)**
Solnexus Chemical LLC 432 689-6180
6001 W Industrial Ave Midland (79706) **(G-15415)**
Solo Cup Operating Corporation 214 339-3131
4444 W Ledbetter Dr Dallas (75236) **(G-4977)**
Soloco-Mallard, Beaumont *Also called Newpark Mats Intgrted Svcs LLC* **(G-1934)**
Solofill LLC (PA) **832 675-9862**
3515 Avignon Ct Houston (77082) **(G-11942)**

Solomon Transformers LLC 512 763-3306
100 W Cooperative Way Georgetown (78626) *(G-7677)*

Soloprotect Us LLC 866 632-6577
701 Canyon Dr Ste 100 Coppell (75019) *(G-3446)*

Solorider Golf Carts, Plano *Also called Regal Research and Mfg Co LLC* *(G-16990)*

Solovis Inc (HQ) **678 234-4583**
5030 Riverside Dr Ste 200 Irving (75039) *(G-13183)*

Solrac Corporation 915 772-3073
19 Leigh Fisher Blvd B El Paso (79906) *(G-5969)*

Solugen Inc (PA) **713 380-2134**
14549 Minetta St Houston (77035) *(G-11943)*

Solution Integrated Chem LLC (PA) **361 584-5000**
5398 County Road 4 Bishop (78343) *(G-2109)*

Solution Tech Harn Group LLC 214 221-0323
11601 Plano Rd Ste 107 Dallas (75243) *(G-4978)*

Solutions In Software Inc 214 221-9995
2201 Main St Ste 1120 Dallas (75201) *(G-4979)*

Solutions Pest & Lawn, Pasadena *Also called Innova Supply Inc* *(G-16459)*

Solutions Pest Pet and Pools, Pasadena *Also called Control Solutions Inc* *(G-16413)*

Solvay America, Houston *Also called Solvay Chemicals Inc* *(G-11945)*

Solvay America Inc (HQ) **713 525-4000**
3737 Buffalo Speedway # 800 Houston (77098) *(G-11944)*

Solvay Chemicals Inc (HQ) **713 525-6800**
3737 Buffalo Speedway Houston (77098) *(G-11945)*

Solvay Chemicals Inc 713 307-3800
1130 Independence Pkwy S La Porte (77571) *(G-13789)*

Solvay Fluorides Llc 713 525-6700
3737 Buffalo Spdwy Ste 80 Houston (77098) *(G-11946)*

Solvay Info Svcs Nafta LLC 713 525-6000
3737 Buffalo Spdwy Ste 80 Houston (77098) *(G-11947)*

Solvay North America, Houston *Also called Solvay America Inc* *(G-11944)*

Solvay North America LLC 713 525-6000
3737 Buffalo Spdwy Ste 80 Houston (77098) *(G-11948)*

Solvay Spclty Polymers USA LLC 770 772-8200
600 Spur 119 N Borger (79007) *(G-2186)*

Solvay USA Inc 325 515-7609
506 County Road 137 Snyder (79549) *(G-19009)*

Solvay USA Inc 281 984-3030
5761 Underwood Rd Ste B Pasadena (77507) *(G-16508)*

Solvay USA Inc 940 552-9911
201 Harrison St Vernon (76384) *(G-20230)*

Solvay USA Inc 281 882-4700
2645 Tech Forest Blvd The Woodlands (77381) *(G-19921)*

Solvchem Inc (HQ) **281 485-5377**
1904 Mykawa Rd Pearland (77581) *(G-16600)*

Somani Texas Inc 214 698-0556
1505 Federal St Ste 150 Dallas (75201) *(G-4980)*

Somerset Fine Art, Fulshear *Also called Somerset House Publishing Inc* *(G-7330)*

Somerset House Publishing Inc 281 346-8900
29370 Mckinnon Rd Fulshear (77406) *(G-7330)*

Somerset House Publishing Inc 713 932-6847
10688 Haddington Dr Houston (77043) *(G-11949)*

Son and Daughters Inc 956 423-2689
313 Hanmore Indus Pkwy Harlingen (78550) *(G-8201)*

Son Beverage Company 210 733-7761
6896 Fairgrounds Pkwy San Antonio (78238) *(G-18482)*

Son-Lan Industries Inc 972 937-8162
419 E Madison St Waxahachie (75165) *(G-20558)*

Sonardyne Inc 281 890-2120
8280 Willow Place Dr N # 130 Houston (77070) *(G-11950)*

Sonatest Inc 210 697-0335
12775 Cogburn San Antonio (78249) *(G-18483)*

Sond Industries LLC 281 372-8220
6403 Brittmoore Rd Houston (77041) *(G-11951)*

Songa Drilling, Houston *Also called Songa Offshore* *(G-11952)*

Songa Offshore 713 781-0670
2925 Briarpark Dr Ste 100 Houston (77042) *(G-11952)*

Sonias Accessories 832 443-7586
21714 Denali Range Ct Katy (77449) *(G-13444)*

Sonic Surveys Ltd 281 385-6500
10601 Langston Dr Baytown (77523) *(G-1802)*

Sonoco Industrial Products, Irving *Also called Sonoco Products Company* *(G-13184)*

Sonoco Products Company 817 461-5616
5111 Frye Rd Irving (75061) *(G-13184)*

Sonoco Products Company 903 665-3966
Hwy 59 S Jefferson (75657) *(G-13288)*

Sonoco Products Company 972 416-2595
1925 Country Club Dr Carrollton (75006) *(G-2817)*

Sonoco Products Company 254 666-4777
6501 Texas Central Pkwy Waco (76712) *(G-20458)*

Sons Design & Mfg Inc 817 595-9800
1541 Central Park Dr Hurst (76053) *(G-12859)*

Sonterra Grp Zppelinn Enrgy LP 210 930-3111
901 Ne Loop 410 Ste 500 San Antonio (78209) *(G-18484)*

Sony Electronics Inc 858 942-2400
11302 Eastpoint Dr Laredo (78045) *(G-13934)*

Sooner Pipe LLC 281 328-4877
1919 Highway 90 Crosby (77532) *(G-3743)*

Sooner Trading Inc 806 235-3904
Hwy 385 N Channing (79018) *(G-3045)*

Sopus Products, Houston *Also called Pennzoil-Quaker State Company* *(G-11284)*

Sor Inc 409 842-3334
5175 Ashley Ct Houston (77041) *(G-11953)*

Sor Inc 281 272-5333
5175 Ashley Ct Houston (77041) *(G-11954)*

Sorb All Company 713 223-4575
2300 Nance St Houston (77020) *(G-11955)*

Sorcerers Apprentice Inc 210 377-1212
10839 Vandale St San Antonio (78216) *(G-18485)*

Sorensen Industries Inc 940 365-9999
301 S Highway 377 Crossroads (76227) *(G-3750)*

Sorita Enterprises Inc 817 860-2679
2407 S Cooper St Arlington (76015) *(G-783)*

Sorrell Cnstr Eqp & Mtls LLC 979 233-6655
2101 Oyster Creek Bnd Freeport (77541) *(G-7213)*

Sort-Rite International Inc 956 423-2427
825 W Jefferson Ave Harlingen (78550) *(G-8202)*

SOS Cuetara USA Inc 281 272-8800
10700 North Fwy Ste 800 Houston (77037) *(G-11956)*

SOS Environmental 281 723-8282
719 Sawdust Rd Ste 331 Spring (77380) *(G-19251)*

Sound Bridge Acoustic Labs Inc 972 937-2030
3501 S Intrstate Hwy 35 E Waxahachie (75165) *(G-20559)*

Source Operations Group LLC 888 557-7079
11807 Westheimer Rd # 550 Houston (77077) *(G-11957)*

Source Vital LLC 713 622-2190
1291 N Post Oak Rd # 125 Houston (77055) *(G-11958)*

Sourceday Inc 512 361-7029
9737 Great Hills Trl # 100 Austin (78759) *(G-1521)*

South Bay Resources LLC (PA) **713 785-8700**
952 Echo Ln Ste 375 Houston (77024) *(G-11959)*

South Bay Solutions Inc 936 494-0180
2600 Tech Forest Blvd The Woodlands (77381) *(G-19922)*

South Belt Ellington Leader, Houston *Also called South Belt Press Inc* *(G-11960)*

South Belt Press Inc 281 484-4337
11555 Beamer Rd Ste 200 Houston (77089) *(G-11960)*

South By Midwest Ret Partners 281 465-8480
9595 Six Pines Dr # 1035 Spring (77380) *(G-19252)*

South Coast Grinding Co LLC 713 649-0001
5730 Ledbetter St Houston (77087) *(G-11961)*

South Coast Manufacturing LLC 713 670-0900
502 S Main St Galena Park (77547) *(G-7382)*

South Coast Products LP 713 434-2141
20 Southbelt Indus Dr Houston (77047) *(G-11962)*

South Coast Products & PDT Dev, Houston *Also called South Coast Products LP* *(G-11962)*

South Coast Terminals LP (PA) **713 672-2401**
7402 Wallisville Rd Houston (77020) *(G-11963)*

South Coast Terminals LP 281 842-1286
10900 Strang Rd La Porte (77571) *(G-13790)*

South East Pallet Inc 713 645-6131
6519 Rupley Cir Houston (77087) *(G-11964)*

South Hampton Resources Inc (HQ) **409 385-1400**
7752 Fm 418 Silsbee (77656) *(G-18956)*

South Houston Concrete Pipe Co 713 946-2831
828 Old Gnoa Red Bluff Rd Houston (77034) *(G-11965)*

South Jetty, Port Aransas *Also called Southern Publishing Inc* *(G-17100)*

South Plains Compost Inc 806 745-3559
5407 E Highway 84 Slaton (79364) *(G-18974)*

South Texas Bindery 210 340-1110
9914 Mccullough Ave San Antonio (78216) *(G-18486)*

South Texas Bolt & Fitting Inc 713 673-5376
4845 Homestead Rd Ste 500 Houston (77028) *(G-11966)*

South Texas Concrete (PA) **956 381-9886**
1420 S 28th Ave Edinburg (78542) *(G-5602)*

South Texas Concrete 956 485-2301
122 El Faro Rd Sullivan City (78595) *(G-19577)*

South Texas Concrete 956 464-4440
E Expy 83 Donna (78537) *(G-5491)*

South Texas Eye Cons Pllc (PA) **361 992-9400**
5402 S Staples St Ste 100 Corpus Christi (78411) *(G-3623)*

South Texas Machine Shop Inc 361 664-8902
1714 S Us Highway 281 Alice (78332) *(G-236)*

South Texas Mining Venture LLP 361 888-8235
500 N Shoreline Blvd # 800 Corpus Christi (78401) *(G-3624)*

South Texas Moulding Inc (PA) **956 464-0560**
940 W Expressway 83 Donna (78537) *(G-5492)*

South Texas Moulding Inc 956 831-0340
4668 Ruben Torres Sr Blvd Brownsville (78526) *(G-2406)*

South Texas Moulding Inc 361 857-7770
6525 Ayers St Corpus Christi (78415) *(G-3625)*

South Texas Moulding & Plywood, Brownsville *Also called South Texas Moulding Inc* *(G-2406)*

South Texas Neon Sign, Pharr *Also called Ixtapa Inc* *(G-16701)*

South Texas Neon Signs Co 956 723-4665
317 Masterson Rd Laredo (78046) *(G-13935)*

South Texas Oil Field Maint 361 526-2822
135 Fairgrounds Rd Refugio (78377) *(G-17248)*

A
L
P
H
A
B
E
T
I
C

South Texas Oilfield Svcs LLC...........................361 701-7064
  5115 Hwy 59 Freer (78357) *(G-7232)*
South Texas Paper LLC....................................956 239-1473
  9102 Seguin Dr Pharr (78577) *(G-16710)*
South Texas Precision Inc................................713 939-0101
  6989 W Little York Rd K Houston (77040) *(G-11967)*
South Texas Sports Academy.............................361 992-3364
  525 Belleview Dr Corpus Christi (78412) *(G-3626)*
South Texas Steel Svc Co LLC............................713 699-2500
  226 E Tidwell Rd Houston (77022) *(G-11968)*
South Txas Lghthouse For Blind (PA)....................361 883-6553
  4421 Agnes St Corpus Christi (78405) *(G-3627)*
South Txas Olfld Solutions LLC..........................361 396-1777
  411 Flournoy Rd 102 Alice (78332) *(G-237)*
South Wire Coleman Cable, El Paso *Also called Coleman Cable LLC (G-5699)*
South Wstn Stl Rolling Door Co, Dallas *Also called Hollywood Ovrhd Door of Dallas (G-4464)*
South-Tex Concrete Ready Mix, Edinburg *Also called South Texas Concrete (G-5602)*
Southanchor Manufacturing LLC.........................915 590-6718
  525 Canal Rd Ste C El Paso (79901) *(G-5970)*
Southast Vcational Aliance Inc (PA)....................713 847-0697
  6018 Nunn St Houston (77087) *(G-11969)*
Southcross Ala Pipeline LLC (HQ).......................214 979-3700
  1700 Pacific Ave Ste 5200 Dallas (75201) *(G-4981)*
Southcross Ccng Gathering Ltd..........................214 953-9500
  2501 Cedar Springs Rd # 600 Dallas (75201) *(G-4982)*
Southcross Enrgy Prtners GP LL.........................214 979-3792
  2103 Citywest Blvd Houston (77042) *(G-11970)*
Southcross Gathering Ltd................................214 979-3700
  1700 Pacific Ave Ste 2900 Dallas (75201) *(G-4983)*
Southcross Marketing Co Ltd.............................214 979-3700
  1700 Pacific Ave Ste 2900 Dallas (75201) *(G-4984)*
Southdown Inc...713 650-6200
  1200 Smith St Ste 2400 Houston (77002) *(G-11971)*
Southeast Land Services LLC............................724 256-9259
  1200 Lake Haven Dr Little Elm (75068) *(G-14142)*
Southeast Prtr Connection LLC (PA)....................256 880-9991
  2400 Dallas Pkwy Ste 230 Plano (75093) *(G-17010)*
Southeast Texas Indus Svcs, Bridge City *Also called Stis Inc (G-2287)*
Southeast Texas Industries Inc..........................409 783-0009
  635 Old Highway 90 W Vidor (77662) *(G-20332)*
Southeast Texas Industries Inc..........................409 722-7351
  9561 Viterbo Rd Beaumont (77705) *(G-1951)*
Southeast Texas Industries Inc (PA)....................409 994-3570
  35911 Us Highway 96 S Buna (77612) *(G-2562)*
Southeast Texas Industries Inc..........................409 792-0084
  325 Nevils St Bridge City (77611) *(G-2286)*
Southeast Wood Georgia Pacific, Mineola *Also called Southeast Wood Treating Inc (G-15512)*
Southeast Wood Treating Inc............................903 569-9441
  701 Freeman St Mineola (75773) *(G-15512)*
Southeastern Metals Mfg Co Inc.........................210 651-6331
  18757 Bracken Dr San Antonio (78266) *(G-18645)*
Souther Equipment Sales Inc.............................972 296-5231
  5409 W Ledbetter Dr Dallas (75236) *(G-4985)*
Southeran Plains Power, Amarillo *Also called Cummins Southern Plains LLC (G-419)*
Southern Archtctral Systems In..........................713 462-6379
  10038 Talley Ln Houston (77041) *(G-11972)*
Southern Associates, Longview *Also called Sac Manufacturing Inc (G-14301)*
Southern Avionics Co.....................................409 842-1717
  5055 Belmont St Beaumont (77707) *(G-1952)*
Southern Bleacher Company Inc..........................940 549-0733
  801 5th St Graham (76450) *(G-7789)*
Southern Cabinets...254 799-2271
  405 N Lacy Dr Waco (76705) *(G-20459)*
Southern Champion, Carrollton *Also called Buzzballz LLC (G-2707)*
Southern Champion Tray LP..............................512 442-2337
  4140 S Congress Ave Austin (78745) *(G-1522)*
Southern Champion Tray LP..............................817 477-3485
  949 S 6th Ave Mansfield (76063) *(G-14719)*
Southern Chinese Daily News, Houston *Also called Southern Chnese Nwspapers Pubg (G-11973)*
Southern Chnese Nwspapers Pubg........................281 498-4310
  11122 Bellaire Blvd Houston (77072) *(G-11973)*
Southern Energy Homes of Texas, Fort Worth *Also called Al/Tex Homes Inc (G-6361)*
Southern Fields Aloe Inc.................................956 565-5102
  Mile 2 E & Mile 6 N St Mi Mercedes (78570) *(G-15010)*
Southern Flger Dtntion Eqp LLC.........................210 533-1231
  4634 S Presa St San Antonio (78223) *(G-18487)*
Southern Flow, Carrizo Springs *Also called Zedi US Inc (G-2689)*
Southern Flow, Houston *Also called Zedi US Inc (G-12724)*
Southern Foods Group LLC (HQ)........................214 824-8163
  3114 S Haskell Ave Dallas (75223) *(G-4986)*
Southern Foods Group LLC...............................214 941-0302
  1114 N Lancaster Ave Dallas (75203) *(G-4987)*
Southern Foodservice MGT Inc..........................903 463-1313
  2600 N State Highway 91 Denison (75020) *(G-5346)*
Southern Forest Products, Bon Wier *Also called Texas Timberjack Inc (G-2151)*

Southern Forest Products LLC...........................409 634-3365
  Fm 2626 N St Bon Wier (75928) *(G-2150)*
Southern Frac LLC..877 576-0821
  1805 Howard Rd Waxahachie (75165) *(G-20560)*
Southern Glazers Wine and Sp (HQ).....................972 277-2000
  2001 Diplomat Dr Farmers Branch (75234) *(G-6215)*
Southern Graphic Systems LLC..........................214 565-9000
  1101 E Arapaho Rd Ste 220 Richardson (75081) *(G-17400)*
Southern Gulf Solutions LLC.............................979 299-8808
  1227 Highway 332 Ste 8 Clute (77531) *(G-3159)*
Southern Heat Exchanger Corp..........................281 668-4619
  4206 Fidelity St Houston (77029) *(G-11974)*
Southern Ionics Incorporated............................281 474-4826
  12901 Baypark Rd Pasadena (77507) *(G-16509)*
Southern Jwly Mfg Houston Co...........................713 460-5533
  9830 Clay Rd Houston (77080) *(G-11975)*
Southern Lease Service Ltd..............................361 449-3048
  100 County Rd 121 George West (78022) *(G-7629)*
Southern Maid Donut, Lumberton *Also called Merrills Southern Maid (G-14568)*
Southern Manufacturing Co LLC.........................409 962-4501
  6287 Gulfway Dr Groves (77619) *(G-8110)*
SOUTHERN METALS COMPANY, Dallas *Also called Mpl Industries Inc (G-4696)*
Southern Methodist University...........................214 768-2756
  3225 Daniel Ave Dallas (75205) *(G-4988)*
Southern Newspapers Inc................................830 896-7000
  429 Jefferson St Kerrville (78028) *(G-13526)*
Southern Newspapers Inc................................830 625-5232
  1342 Industrial Dr New Braunfels (78130) *(G-15824)*
Southern Newspapers Inc................................830 625-9144
  549 Landa St New Braunfels (78130) *(G-15825)*
Southern Newspapers Inc................................830 379-5402
  1012 Schriewer Seguin (78155) *(G-18864)*
Southern Newspapers Inc................................281 422-8302
  1301 Memorial Dr Baytown (77520) *(G-1835)*
Southern Newspapers Inc................................979 237-0100
  720 S Main St Clute (77531) *(G-3160)*
Southern Newspapers Inc................................936 632-6631
  300 Ellis Ave Lufkin (75904) *(G-14552)*
Southern Newspapers Inc................................903 785-6900
  5050 Se Loop 286 Paris (75460) *(G-16370)*
Southern Noodle Company................................281 988-7778
  6518 Wilcrest Dr Houston (77072) *(G-11976)*
Southern Nut N Tree Equipment.........................325 938-5460
  324 State Highway 16 S Goldthwaite (76844) *(G-7745)*
Southern Patrolling Labs, Venus *Also called Southern Petroleum Labs Inc (G-20222)*
Southern Petroleum Labs Inc............................817 539-2168
  2440 Chambers St Unit A Venus (76084) *(G-20222)*
Southern Petroleum Labs Inc............................903 693-6242
  1595 S Us Highway 79 Carthage (75633) *(G-2921)*
Southern Plains Power, Odessa *Also called Cummins Southern Plains LLC (G-15973)*
Southern Plains Power, San Antonio *Also called Cummins Southern Plains LLC (G-18035)*
Southern Plastics Inc.....................................903 984-6229
  1010 Energy Dr Kilgore (75662) *(G-13591)*
Southern Product Finishing, Pearland *Also called Columns Inc (G-16547)*
Southern Publishing Inc..................................361 749-5131
  141 W Cotter Ave Port Aransas (78373) *(G-17100)*
Southern Shutters & Blinds, Manor *Also called Southern Shutters Inc (G-14649)*
Southern Shutters Inc....................................512 272-9711
  12804 Beltex Rd Manor (78653) *(G-14649)*
Southern Spring Manufacturing...........................713 692-7191
  915 Pinemont Dr Houston (77018) *(G-11977)*
Southern Star, Sugar Land *Also called Argos USA LLC (G-19446)*
Southern Star Concrete, Irving *Also called Hanson Aggregates LLC (G-13049)*
Southern Star Concrete, Irving *Also called Argos USA LLC (G-12932)*
Southern Star Concrete, Houston *Also called Argos USA LLC (G-8690)*
Southern State Steel Co..................................409 866-1409
  9675 Walden Rd Beaumont (77707) *(G-1953)*
Southern Steel Fabricators, Donna *Also called San-Co Steel Ltd (G-5490)*
Southern Strtch Frming Fbrctio (PA)....................940 591-0410
  9070 Teasley Ln Denton (76210) *(G-5400)*
Southern Stud Weld Inc..................................972 790-3339
  3645 Conflans Rd Irving (75061) *(G-13185)*
Southern Transformers...................................713 923-1191
  15200 North Fwy Houston (77090) *(G-11978)*
Southern Tube LLC.......................................713 231-2929
  13500 Industrial Rd Houston (77015) *(G-11979)*
Southern Utilities Company..............................903 593-2588
  218 N Broadway Ave Frnt Tyler (75702) *(G-20154)*
Southern Welding LLC....................................469 517-0410
  300 Howard Rd Ste 100 Waxahachie (75165) *(G-20561)*
Southland Athletic Mfg Co...............................972 563-3321
  714 E Grove St Terrell (75160) *(G-19751)*
Southtex Treaters, Odessa *Also called Morgan Kinder Treating LP (G-16083)*
Southtex Treaters Inc (PA)..............................432 563-2766
  13405 E Highway 191 Odessa (79765) *(G-16158)*
Southwest Air Products, Euless *Also called Blakeman Industries Inc (G-6133)*
Southwest Beanmakers, Saginaw *Also called CTI Saginaw I LLC (G-17744)*

Southwest Cabinet Corporation..........817 460-8681
2002 W Pioneer Pkwy Pantego (76013) *(G-16352)*

Southwest Canners Texas Inc..........936 569-9737
617 Industrial Dr Nacogdoches (75964) *(G-15714)*

Southwest Canvas Mfg Co (PA)..........**806 747-0201**
1325 E 37th St Lubbock (79404) *(G-14484)*

Southwest Center of Excellence, Irving Also called Advanced Arm Dynamics *(G-12923)*

Southwest Companies, Alvin Also called Southwest Refractory Texas LP *(G-380)*

Southwest Concrete Products, Alleyton Also called Headwaters Cnstr Mtls LLC *(G-308)*

Southwest Concrete Products Co..........888 464-9341
Ih 10 E Columbus (78934) *(G-3233)*

Southwest Cutters LLC..........915 858-2200
1430 Gail Borden Pl 1c El Paso (79935) *(G-5971)*

Southwest Data Systems Inc..........817 370-9966
2501 Parkview Dr Ste 317 Fort Worth (76102) *(G-7001)*

Southwest Diamond Cutters Inc..........972 387-1078
13721 Omega Rd Dallas (75244) *(G-4989)*

Southwest Displays and Events, Carrollton Also called Cree Visual Marketing Company *(G-2720)*

Southwest Dist & Winery LLC..........214 440-4144
9761 Clifford Dr Dallas (75220) *(G-4990)*

Southwest Division, Abilene Also called Legacy Vulcan LLC *(G-58)*

Southwest Door & Window, Garland Also called Premex Door Supply Inc *(G-7572)*

Southwest Earth Resources..........325 251-6598
Hwy 501 Pontotoc (76869) *(G-17098)*

Southwest Elctronic Enrgy Corp..........281 240-4000
823 Buffalo Run Missouri City (77489) *(G-15595)*

Southwest Fenter Inc..........817 577-3837
4201 Hahn Blvd Haltom City (76117) *(G-8158)*

Southwest Formseal, Houston Also called Deterling Company Inc *(G-8378)*

Southwest Formseal Inc..........832 399-3900
4323 South Dr Houston (77053) *(G-8392)*

Southwest Fountain Supply, Irving Also called American Bottling Company *(G-12929)*

Southwest Fountain Supply Co, Houston Also called American Bottling Company *(G-8590)*

Southwest Gallery, Dallas Also called S W Galleries Corp *(G-4924)*

Southwest Galvanizing Inc (PA)..........**800 799-8413**
737 Aleen St Houston (77029) *(G-11980)*

Southwest Heat Treat, Houston Also called Swht LLC *(G-12132)*

Southwest Impreglon R Inc..........281 441-2000
15014 Lee Rd Humble (77396) *(G-12798)*

Southwest Index Tab Co Inc..........972 228-8227
300 N Rogers St Waxahachie (75165) *(G-20562)*

Southwest Indus Surfaces Inc (PA)..........**972 641-4393**
1165 111th St Grand Prairie (75050) *(G-7974)*

Southwest Industrial Eqp Svc, Garland Also called Contract Powder Coating Inc *(G-7462)*

Southwest Industrial Svcs Inc..........817 332-6481
2413 Whitmore St Fort Worth (76107) *(G-7002)*

Southwest Machine, Stafford Also called Kpr & Rsw Investments Inc *(G-19342)*

Southwest Machine & Mfg Co Inc..........972 254-2014
108 N Rogers Rd Irving (75061) *(G-13186)*

Southwest Machine Works Inc..........713 433-6824
60 Southbelt Indus Dr Houston (77047) *(G-11981)*

Southwest Maintenance LLC..........254 662-3966
803 S Robinson Dr Robinson (76706) *(G-17502)*

Southwest Manufacturing Corp..........214 638-0323
8720 Empress Row Dallas (75247) *(G-4991)*

Southwest Marble & Granite Inc..........512 918-0135
13240 Pond Springs Rd Austin (78729) *(G-1712)*

Southwest Metal Systems LLC..........903 569-8811
485 E Loop 564 Mineola (75773) *(G-15513)*

Southwest Metal Treating Corp..........817 551-1004
9516 Lynwood St Fort Worth (76134) *(G-7003)*

Southwest Metrics Inc (PA)..........**817 281-7697**
4209 Hahn Blvd Fort Worth (76117) *(G-7004)*

Southwest Metrics Inc..........817 581-4474
4212 Murray Ave Fort Worth (76117) *(G-7005)*

Southwest Mtal Systems Sthwest, Mineola Also called Southwest Metal Systems LLC *(G-15513)*

Southwest Nipple Company Inc..........210 333-3720
2831 S Ww White Rd San Antonio (78222) *(G-18488)*

Southwest Ocean Services Inc..........713 671-9101
5721 Harvey Wilson Dr Houston (77020) *(G-11982)*

Southwest Oilfield Pdts Inc..........254 559-8667
1000 Industrial Pkwy Breckenridge (76424) *(G-2238)*

Southwest Precision Prtrs LP..........713 777-3333
1055 Conrad Sauer Dr Houston (77043) *(G-11983)*

Southwest Prof Vehicles (PA)..........**214 371-3474**
3910 E Overton Rd Dallas (75216) *(G-4992)*

Southwest Quality Molding LP..........281 643-4500
7900 Bissell Rd Manvel (77578) *(G-14738)*

Southwest Quartz Ltd Co..........512 863-8415
6024 Williams Dr Ste 110 Georgetown (78633) *(G-7678)*

Southwest Refractory Texas LP..........979 285-7219
2443 N Gordon St Ste A Alvin (77511) *(G-380)*

Southwest Resources..........979 836-5500
205 N Market St Ste 207 Brenham (77833) *(G-2273)*

Southwest Royalties Inc..........325 573-4977
County Rd 3138 Ira (79527) *(G-12915)*

Southwest Sign Group Inc (PA)..........210 648-3221
7208 S Ww White Rd San Antonio (78222) *(G-18489)*

Southwest Signal Supply Inc..........713 946-7162
1107 Jackson St South Houston (77587) *(G-19052)*

Southwest Solutions Group Inc (PA)..........972 250-1970
2535 E State Highway 121 110b Lewisville (75056) *(G-14091)*

Southwest Spice Company LLC..........713 860-5300
12010 Taylor Rd Houston (77041) *(G-11984)*

Southwest Spray Inc..........972 875-5665
1702 Jack Mckay Blvd Ennis (75119) *(G-6118)*

Southwest Tactical LLC..........915 726-0634
11201 Armour Dr Ste D El Paso (79935) *(G-5972)*

Southwest Textiles Inc (PA)..........**806 687-4001**
4606 91st St Lubbock (79424) *(G-14485)*

Southwest Tool Co, Big Spring Also called Johnson Tool Company Inc *(G-2084)*

Southwest Truck Rigging & Eqp, Houston Also called Rudinger Enterprises Inc *(G-11695)*

Southwest Wire Rope, Houston Also called HWC Wire & Cable Company *(G-10293)*

Southwestern Diversified Lsg, Plainview Also called M Hastey Construction Co Inc *(G-16760)*

Southwestern Energy Company (PA)..........**832 796-1000**
10000 Energy Dr Spring (77389) *(G-19167)*

Southwestern Foam Tech Inc..........254 939-6379
1106 Industrial Park Rd Belton (76513) *(G-2028)*

Southwestern Laser Charge, Houston Also called Laser Drum Products Inc *(G-10603)*

Southwestern Machine Products, Odessa Also called S Q I Inc *(G-16148)*

Southwestern Nameplate Mfg Co..........972 924-3289
4th St Anna (75409) *(G-586)*

Southwestern Paint Panels LLC..........281 442-0000
2019 Sandydale Ln Houston (77039) *(G-11985)*

Southwestern Petroleum Corp (PA)..........**817 348-7233**
534 N Main St Fort Worth (76164) *(G-7006)*

Southwestern Plating Company..........713 223-1331
1312 Halpern St Houston (77009) *(G-11986)*

Southwestern Wldg & Machining, San Antonio Also called Edward Bloch Ltd *(G-18083)*

Southwire Company LLC..........940 328-1047
3800 Se Industrial Pkwy Mineral Wells (76067) *(G-15542)*

Souza Bakery..........214 631-0669
9000 Diplomacy Row Dallas (75247) *(G-4993)*

Sovereign Pharmaceuticals LLC..........817 284-0429
7590 Sand St Fort Worth (76118) *(G-7007)*

Sowell & Co LP..........214 871-3320
1601 Elm St Ste 3500 Dallas (75201) *(G-4994)*

Sp Foundry, Houston Also called Star Pipe Usa LLC *(G-12047)*

Space Age Lmnating Bindery Inc..........713 868-1471
3400 White Oak Dr Houston (77007) *(G-11987)*

Space City Machine & Tool Co..........713 939-0011
8101 Leghorn St Houston (77040) *(G-11988)*

Space City Publishing..........281 480-3600
17045 El Camino Real # 103 Houston (77058) *(G-11989)*

Space Enterprises LLC (PA)..........**800 559-2923**
26310 Oak Rdg Ste 38 San Antonio (78229) *(G-18490)*

Space Enterprises LLC..........281 846-9613
26310 Oak Ridge Dr Ste 38 The Woodlands (77380) *(G-19923)*

Space Exploration Tech Corp..........310 363-6000
8550 Case Rd Mc Gregor (76657) *(G-14823)*

Space Exploration Tech Corp..........310 363-6000
13100 Space Center Blvd Houston (77059) *(G-11990)*

Space Saver Racks, Houston Also called Houston Wire Works Inc *(G-10265)*

Spaceman Home & Office Inc..........713 688-8808
3556 W T C Jester Blvd Houston (77018) *(G-11991)*

Spacex Rocket Dev Test Fcilty..........254 840-5771
1 Rocket Rd Mc Gregor (76657) *(G-14824)*

Spaeth Machine Shop Inc..........972 438-3804
2120 E Grauwyler Rd Irving (75061) *(G-13187)*

Spaeth Pump & Equipment Co, Irving Also called Spaeth Machine Shop Inc *(G-13187)*

Spansion LLC..........512 934-6427
5204 E Ben White Blvd Austin (78741) *(G-1523)*

Sparkle Lighting Services..........713 856-8500
7938 Wright Rd Houston (77041) *(G-11992)*

Sparkler Group Inc (PA)..........**936 756-4471**
101 N Loop 336 E Conroe (77301) *(G-3365)*

Sparkletts, Katy Also called Ds Services of America Inc *(G-13360)*

Sparkletts, Houston Also called Ds Services of America Inc *(G-9533)*

Sparklist, Austin Also called Lyris Technologies Inc *(G-1314)*

Sparkman Industries Inc..........361 573-0001
169 Aviation Dr Victoria (77904) *(G-20304)*

Sparkman Well Service Inc (PA)..........**361 572-4833**
6811 Us Highway 59 N Victoria (77905) *(G-20305)*

Sparrows Group, Houston Also called Sparrows Offshore LLC *(G-11993)*

Sparrows Offshore LLC (HQ)..........**832 467-7300**
6758 Northwinds Dr Houston (77041) *(G-11993)*

Spartan Energy Partners LP..........281 466-3310
9595 Six Pines Dr Spring (77380) *(G-19253)*

Spartan Energy Services LLC..........830 281-8505
511 Corgey Rd Pleasanton (78064) *(G-17075)*

Spartan Operating Company LLC..........281 466-3310
24 Waterway Ave Ste 850 The Woodlands (77380) *(G-19924)*

A
L
P
H
A
B
E
T
I
C

Spartan Printing Inc (PA) 817 640-6341
320 109th St Arlington (76011) *(G-784)*

Spartan Pumps Inc 713 858-9887
2435 W 42nd St Odessa (79764) *(G-16159)*

Spartan Reinforcing LLC (PA) 832 271-1721
15840 Fm 529 Rd Ste 303 Houston (77095) *(G-11994)*

Spartan Reinforcing LLC 915 269-5222
1955 Fm 2001 Ste 320 Buda (78610) *(G-2538)*

Spartan Structures LLC (PA) 936 591-9280
1084 State Highway 7 E Center (75935) *(G-3008)*

Spartech Polycom (texas) Inc 817 640-5600
1121 108th St Arlington (76011) *(G-785)*

Spc Rentals, Alice *Also called Warrior Energy Services Corp (G-245)*

Speakermax Inc 281 880-9922
17203 Bamwood Dr Houston (77090) *(G-11995)*

Speakermax.com, Houston *Also called Speakermax Inc (G-11995)*

Spears Manufacturing Co 469 528-3000
1000 Lakeside Pkwy Flower Mound (75028) *(G-6282)*

Spears Manufacturing Co 817 293-0292
3132 Wichita Ct K Fort Worth (76140) *(G-7008)*

Speartex Grain Company 806 659-3711
405 Collard St Spearman (79081) *(G-19087)*

Spec Americas LLC 281 812-7732
340 N Sam Houston Pkwy E # 110 Houston (77060) *(G-11996)*

Special Products & Mfg Inc (PA) 972 771-8851
2625 Discovery Blvd Rockwall (75032) *(G-17566)*

Specialized Cnstr Svcs LLC 210 262-7263
8715 Business Cir Ste 1 Converse (78109) *(G-3403)*

Specialized Manufacturing Ltd 713 864-2551
1209 W 17th St Houston (77008) *(G-11997)*

Specialty Advertisers, Brownsville *Also called Lugra Inc (G-2378)*

Specialty Billings, Lufkin *Also called Dreamwrks Ansthesia Assoc Pllc (G-14525)*

Specialty Bindery and Printing, Houston *Also called Specialty Bindery Service Inc (G-11998)*

Specialty Bindery Service Inc 713 869-0594
2211 Norfolk St Ste 805 Houston (77098) *(G-11998)*

Specialty Coils LLC 903 212-2645
5902 Old Highway 80 Longview (75604) *(G-14310)*

Specialty Composites Group LLC 254 752-3622
302 S 27th St Waco (76710) *(G-20460)*

Specialty Comprsr & Eng Co Inc (PA) 806 274-7135
2 Industrial Blvd Borger (79007) *(G-2187)*

Specialty Devices Incorporated 972 429-7240
2905 Capital St Wylie (75098) *(G-20951)*

Specialty Electrical LLC 817 355-5315
14900 Grand River Rd # 124 Fort Worth (76155) *(G-7009)*

Specialty Heat Treat Inc 713 937-3101
11307 W Little York Rd Houston (77041) *(G-11999)*

Specialty Hose Fittings, Pasadena *Also called Shf Inc (G-16506)*

Specialty Locomotive Services 281 425-9850
115 N Main St Baytown (77520) *(G-1836)*

Specialty Machine, Lago Vista *Also called Cryer Limited Partnership (G-13805)*

Specialty Metal Finishing Inc 713 528-5428
1915 W Dallas St Houston (77019) *(G-12000)*

Specialty Packaging Inc 817 922-9727
3250 W Seminary Dr Fort Worth (76133) *(G-7010)*

Specialty Process Eqp Corp 281 812-7732
1931 Humble Place Dr # 207 Humble (77338) *(G-12799)*

Specialty Products Division, South Houston *Also called Jim Ray Company Inc (G-19048)*

Specialty Research Associates 817 441-6044
426 Circle Dr Aledo (76008) *(G-202)*

Specialty Sand Company 979 234-7431
1096 Parker Rd Eagle Lake (77434) *(G-5543)*

Specialty Sand Company Inc (PA) 281 456-9553
16601 Garrett Rd Houston (77044) *(G-12001)*

Specialty Services, Edinburg *Also called Longhorn Services Inc (G-5593)*

Specialty Sup Installation Co, Willis *Also called Unlimited Supply Inc (G-20868)*

Specialty Supply, Cypress *Also called Ss Machine LP (G-3822)*

Specialty Tank Services Ltd 281 470-4880
2225 Sens Rd La Porte (77571) *(G-13791)*

Specialty Tower Lighting Ltd 713 722-8123
1630 Elmview Dr Houston (77080) *(G-12002)*

Specialty Valve Group LLC 281 385-8200
3550 W T C Jester Blvd Houston (77018) *(G-12003)*

Specialty Welding and Machine, Pampa *Also called Swm International Inc (G-16340)*

Specialty Wldg & Fabrication, Waskom *Also called Ratec Inc (G-20520)*

Specialty Woood Mouldings Inc 254 642-3835
16999 E Us Highway 190 Rogers (76569) *(G-17574)*

Specility Locomotive Service, Baytown *Also called Specialty Locomotive Services (G-1836)*

Specilty Adhesives Coating Inc 972 641-7600
1164 N Great Sw Pkwy Grand Prairie (75050) *(G-7975)*

Specktrum 832 892-0863
301 Wilcrest Dr Houston (77042) *(G-12004)*

Specs Family Partners Ltd 713 669-1722
2314 W Holcombe Blvd Houston (77030) *(G-12005)*

Specs Liquor Stores, Houston *Also called Specs Family Partners Ltd (G-12005)*

Specter Instruments, Austin *Also called Quinstar Corporation (G-1445)*

Specter Instruments Inc 512 326-1011
4020 S Industrial Dr # 120 Austin (78744) *(G-1524)*

Spectra Dynamics Corporation 512 255-2233
315 Craigen Rd Liberty Hill (78642) *(G-14129)*

Spectra Engineering Inc 432 367-8413
825 W 68th St Odessa (79764) *(G-16160)*

Spectra Metal Sales Inc 972 556-2564
11425 Mathis Ave 406 Farmers Branch (75234) *(G-6216)*

Spectra Test Solutions LLC (PA) 214 349-0288
10810 Alder Cir Dallas (75238) *(G-4995)*

Spectral Md Inc 972 499-4934
2515 Mckinney Ave # 1000 Dallas (75201) *(G-4996)*

Spectraseis Inc 303 658-9171
10815 Woodedge Dr Houston (77070) *(G-12006)*

Spectrasensors Inc (HQ) 713 466-3172
4333 W Sam Houston Pkwy N Houston (77043) *(G-12007)*

Spectrum Batteries Inc 281 533-9735
6910 Sprigg St Fulshear (77441) *(G-7331)*

Spectrum Brand Global Autocare, Garland *Also called Spectrum Brands Inc (G-7589)*

Spectrum Brands Inc 214 778-4600
2447 Merritt Dr 200 Garland (75041) *(G-7589)*

Spectrum Corporation (PA) 713 944-6200
10048 Easthaven Blvd Houston (77075) *(G-12008)*

Spectrum Lifesciences LLC 214 492-0506
3400 Royalty Row Irving (75062) *(G-13188)*

Spectrum Message Centers, Houston *Also called Spectrum Corporation (G-12008)*

Spectrum Printing, Killeen *Also called K & J Businesses Inc (G-13609)*

Spectrum Quality Standards 281 578-7575
17360 Groschke Rd Houston (77084) *(G-12009)*

Spectrum Semiconductor Tech Lc 972 562-2552
404 Mckinney Pkwy Ste C McKinney (75071) *(G-14977)*

Spectrum Technologies USA Inc 817 232-2373
3934 Sandshell Dr Fort Worth (76137) *(G-7011)*

Speed Printing & Office Supply, Conroe *Also called Speed Printing Conroe Inc (G-3366)*

Speed Printing Conroe Inc (PA) 936 441-2248
1105 W Dallas St Conroe (77301) *(G-3366)*

Speed-Fab-Crete Corp Intl 817 572-0351
1150 E Kennedale Pkwy Kennedale (76060) *(G-13503)*

Speedcast Americas Inc (HQ) 281 340-2057
4400 S Sam Houston Pkwy E Houston (77048) *(G-12010)*

Speedorange Inc 281 448-5900
2406 Pasadena Fwy Pasadena (77506) *(G-16510)*

Speedtech Lights Inc 800 757-2581
2809 Business Park Dr Buda (78610) *(G-2539)*

Speedway Copying & Printing, Austin *Also called Bisi Inc (G-992)*

Speedway LLC 713 943-9002
2454 Delwin St Houston (77034) *(G-12011)*

Speedway LLC 432 758-6700
100 Nw 7th St Seminole (79360) *(G-18887)*

Speedway LLC 877 609-4255
1201 Louisiana St Ste 700 Houston (77002) *(G-12012)*

Speedway LLC 713 496-4000
1501 Mckinney St Houston (77010) *(G-12013)*

Speedy Printing K T F, Houston *Also called K T F Inc (G-10497)*

Speedy Products, Jacksonville *Also called Peacock Plastics Company (G-13256)*

SPEP Acquisition Corp 310 608-0693
2986 S Longhorn Dr Lancaster (75134) *(G-13848)*

Speqtrum, Fort Worth *Also called Kgp Group Inc (G-6760)*

Spf, Garland *Also called Stillers Prcision Firearms LLC (G-7592)*

Spf Corporation of America 713 983-9373
6529 Cunningham Rd # 2105 Houston (77041) *(G-12014)*

Spfm LP (PA) 210 805-8931
4310 West Ave San Antonio (78213) *(G-18491)*

SPI Brand, Austin *Also called Overton Enterprises LLC (G-1395)*

Spicewood Quarry & Asphalt, Marble Falls *Also called Legacy Vulcan LLC (G-14747)*

Spiceworks Inc 512 346-7743
3700 N Capital Of Texas Austin (78746) *(G-1525)*

Spigit Inc 855 774-4480
12301 Res Blvd Ste 5-101 Austin (78759) *(G-1526)*

Spike Electric and Contrls LLC 832 243-5372
5914 E Sam Houston Pkwy S Houston (77034) *(G-12015)*

Spike Electrical Supply, Houston *Also called Spike Electric and Contrls LLC (G-12015)*

Spillar Boatdocks & Boatlifts, Spicewood *Also called Spillar Welding Inc (G-19095)*

Spillar Welding Inc 512 264-0351
Rr 3 Spicewood (78669) *(G-19095)*

Spindletop Drilling Company 972 644-2581
12850 Spurling Dr Ste 200 Dallas (75230) *(G-4997)*

Spindletop Oil & Gas Co (PA) 972 644-2581
12850 Spurling Dr Ste 200 Dallas (75230) *(G-4998)*

Spine 360, Austin *Also called Omni Surgical LP (G-1380)*

Spinesmith Holdings LLC (PA) 512 637-2073
4719 S Congress Ave # 100 Austin (78745) *(G-1527)*

Spinner Printing Co (PA) 972 380-0789
3335 Keller Springs Rd # 1 Carrollton (75006) *(G-2818)*

Spinner The Printer, Carrollton *Also called Spinner Printing Co (G-2818)*

Spinning Wheel Shop, Houston *Also called Vinh Ho Machine Shop Inc (G-12569)*

Spiral Diners 817 332-8834
1314 W Magnolia Ave Fort Worth (76104) *(G-7012)*

Spiral X LLC 855 346-8823
3532 Miller Park Dr Garland (75042) *(G-7590)*

Spire Marketing Inc (HQ)..................................346 308-7549
   3773 Richmond Ave Ste 300 Houston (77046) *(G-12016)*
Spirit Aerosystems Inc.....................................316 523-4221
   1900 1st Ave San Antonio (78216) *(G-18492)*
Spirit Globl Enrgy Sltions Inc.............................432 522-2288
   1460 Windway Odessa (79763) *(G-16161)*
Spirit Industries Inc.......................................936 597-5144
   21973 Eva St Montgomery (77356) *(G-15641)*
Spirit Pin, Mineola *Also called Safe-T-Pet Inc (G-15511)*
Spirited Cocktails Corporation............................512 256-0150
   8201 Carranzo Dr Austin (78735) *(G-1528)*
Spitzer Industries Inc.....................................713 230-4200
   13863 Industrial Rd Houston (77015) *(G-12017)*
Spitzer Industries Inc.....................................713 466-1518
   10543 Fisher Rd Houston (77041) *(G-12018)*
Spitzer Industries Inc (PA)................................832 783-7000
   12141 Wickc Ln Ste 750 Houston (77079) *(G-12019)*
Spitzer Industries Inc.....................................713 856-9208
   11433 Brittmoore Park Dr Houston (77041) *(G-12020)*
Spivey Stake & Supply Inc (PA).............................903 822-3888
   16384 Us Highway 259 S Mount Enterprise (75681) *(G-15645)*
Spl, Carthage *Also called Southern Petroleum Labs Inc (G-2921)*
Splendora Pipe Services LLC...............................281 432-1400
   26670 Midline Rd Cleveland (77328) *(G-3136)*
Splunk Inc...972 244-8806
   5360 Legacy Dr Ste 250 Plano (75024) *(G-17011)*
Spm, Houston *Also called Bace Manufacturing Inc (G-8787)*
Spm Division, Houston *Also called Bace Manufacturing Inc (G-8786)*
SPM Flow Control Inc (HQ).................................817 246-2461
   7601 Wyatt Dr Fort Worth (76108) *(G-7013)*
SPM Flow Control Inc.....................................903 984-8153
   1102 State Highway 31 W Kilgore (75662) *(G-13592)*
SPM Flow Control Inc.....................................432 580-3887
   2424 E Ih 20 Odessa (79766) *(G-16162)*
SPM Flow Control Inc.....................................817 246-2461
   920 Seaco Ave Deer Park (77536) *(G-5297)*
SPM Flow Control Inc.....................................281 820-7807
   8300 Cypress Creek Pkwy # 450 Houston (77070) *(G-12021)*
Spm Technology Inc......................................512 931-0201
   300 Park Central Blvd Georgetown (78626) *(G-7679)*
Spooltech LLC...281 861-6800
   9325 Highway 6 N Houston (77095) *(G-12022)*
Sport Source Inc...972 509-5707
   400 W Virginia St Ste 200 McKinney (75069) *(G-14978)*
Sports Cave, New Braunfels *Also called Great American Products Ltd (G-15797)*
Sports Magic Inc...903 832-1975
   8523 S Lake Dr Texarkana (75501) *(G-19774)*
Sports Solutions Inc.....................................214 351-2834
   2536 Manana Dr Dallas (75220) *(G-4999)*
Sports Wear Graphics Inc.................................817 870-9900
   110 Saint Louis Ave Fort Worth (76104) *(G-7014)*
Sportswear Graphics, Fort Worth *Also called Sports Wear Graphics Inc (G-7014)*
Sportzone, The, Spearman *Also called Texas 28 LLC (G-19088)*
Spotsee, Dallas *Also called Shockwatch Inc (G-4957)*
Spotted Dog Printing Inc (PA)...........................972 234-3033
   1750 Alma Rd Ste 118 Richardson (75081) *(G-17401)*
Spotted Dog Printing Inc................................972 234-4391
   14648 Snowshill Dr Frisco (75035) *(G-7264)*
Spotted Lakes LLC.......................................817 441-9900
   1995 Ranger Hwy Weatherford (76088) *(G-20621)*
Spraying Systems Co......................................903 535-5036
   15592 Timberline Dr Tyler (75703) *(G-20155)*
Spraymetal Inc...713 923-2000
   5610 Polk St Houston (77023) *(G-12023)*
Sprecher & Schuh Inc (HQ)..............................281 442-9000
   15910 Intl Plz Dr Houston (77032) *(G-12024)*
Sprecher Schuh, Houston *Also called Sprecher & Schuh Inc (G-12024)*
Spring Bolt and Nut Mfg Ltd............................281 448-4440
   3280 Wheat St Houston (77086) *(G-12025)*
Spring Branch Shtmtl Co Inc.............................281 469-8855
   7960 Fallbrook Dr Houston (77064) *(G-12026)*
Spring Engineers Houston Ltd (PA)......................713 690-9488
   9740 Tanner Rd Houston (77041) *(G-12027)*
Spring Guns and Ammo, Spring *Also called Bayou Arms Inc (G-19102)*
Spring Products International, Navasota *Also called Exper-Tech Products Company (G-15734)*
Spring Rm Dual, Spring *Also called Cemex Construction Mtls S LLC (G-19104)*
Springhill Pallets LLC...................................903 297-6090
   164 Sven Pines Cut Off Rd Longview (75605) *(G-14311)*
Springs Window Fashions LLC.............................608 826-7052
   9601 International Blvd Pharr (78577) *(G-16711)*
Sprint Bindery, Houston *Also called Jbd Bindery Inc (G-10458)*
Spruce Creek Company, Austin *Also called Senox Corporation (G-1492)*
Spruiell Drilling Co (PA)................................940 592-5471
   307 N Wall St Iowa Park (76367) *(G-12911)*
SPS Technologies LLC....................................817 467-0031
   1030 Commercial Blvd N Arlington (76001) *(G-786)*
Spur Environmental Services, Cresson *Also called Spur Industrial LLC (G-3713)*

Spur Industrial LLC......................................817 293-1515
   1420 Hughie Long Rd Cresson (76035) *(G-3713)*
Spur Machine Works Inc..................................903 597-8757
   3182 Spur 124 Tyler (75707) *(G-20156)*
Spurlock Logging Inc...................................409 429-4333
   201 Sutton St Woodville (75979) *(G-20917)*
SPX Dock Products Inc...................................972 466-0707
   1612 Hutton Dr Ste 140 Carrollton (75006) *(G-2819)*
SPX Flow Control, Houston *Also called M & J Valve Company (G-10713)*
SPX Flow Technology Usa Inc.............................281 897-2964
   8800 Westplain Dr Houston (77041) *(G-12028)*
Sqs Ndt LP..940 726-1107
   1641 Melton Rd Sanger (76266) *(G-18730)*
Sqs Ndt LP (PA)...432 614-9920
   2600 W I 20 Odessa (79763) *(G-16163)*
Square Cabinetry LLC....................................214 838-2225
   2405 Crown Rd Dallas (75229) *(G-5000)*
Square Mile Energy LLC.................................713 266-3685
   5847 San Felipe St # 2949 Houston (77057) *(G-12029)*
Square One Machine Inc..................................254 968-5600
   6420 S Us Highway 377 Stephenville (76401) *(G-19423)*
Square Root, Austin *Also called Oceanus Automotive LLC (G-1376)*
Square's Gourmet Meat, Abilene *Also called Squares Distributing Inc (G-82)*
Squares Distributing Inc................................325 692-4797
   4801 Buffalo Gap Rd Abilene (79606) *(G-82)*
Squaw Creek Materials LP................................254 897-3505
   4448 E Highway 67 Rainbow (76077) *(G-17229)*
Srg Solutions, Houston *Also called Srg Ventures LLC (G-12030)*
Srg Ventures LLC.......................................281 214-8560
   565 W 38th St Houston (77018) *(G-12030)*
Srh Tools LLC...432 686-1058
   1104 N County Road 1090 Midland (79706) *(G-15416)*
SRI Energy Inc...832 742-7500
   12565 W Airport Blvd Sugar Land (77478) *(G-19558)*
SRI Monogramming Inc....................................512 388-4989
   2303 County Road 172 Round Rock (78681) *(G-17691)*
Srj Holdings LLC..972 747-8613
   301 Ridgemont Dr Allen (75002) *(G-299)*
Ss Electric Inc...915 217-2200
   3650 Buckner St El Paso (79925) *(G-5973)*
Ss Equipment Services II LLC............................830 483-0187
   1162 Fm 3408 Cotulla (78014) *(G-3691)*
Ss Machine LP...281 970-8444
   13730 Cypress N Huston Rd Cypress (77429) *(G-3822)*
Ssab Texas Inc..713 341-7700
   13609 Industrial Rd # 114 Houston (77015) *(G-12031)*
Ssb Manufacturing Company...............................972 874-9666
   4255 Patriot Dr Ste 100 Grapevine (76051) *(G-8055)*
SSC Signs & Lighting LLC...............................972 219-2495
   2090 Mcgee Ln Lewisville (75077) *(G-14092)*
Ssi Artificial Lift USA, Midland *Also called Ssi Lift USA Ltd (G-15417)*
Ssi Interests LLC.......................................713 221-3488
   3770 Gramercy St Houston (77025) *(G-12032)*
Ssi Lift USA Ltd..432 488-6427
   9702 E County Rd 97 Midland (79706) *(G-15417)*
Ssi Maxim Company Inc...................................903 984-5600
   312 Higginbotham Rd Kilgore (75662) *(G-13593)*
SSP Developers Inc......................................956 456-4415
   420 Jay St San Benito (78586) *(G-18668)*
SSS Co., Austin *Also called Semiconductor Support Svcs Co (G-1491)*
Sst Truck Company LLC...................................972 487-2900
   4030 Forest Ln Garland (75042) *(G-7591)*
St Andrew, Euless *Also called Commscope Technologies LLC (G-6138)*
St Elmo Brewing Company, Austin *Also called Lost Falls LLC (G-1303)*
St Fastening Systems, Tyler *Also called Hillman Group Inc (G-20099)*
St George Software L L C................................512 442-6794
   5003 Tahoe Trl Austin (78745) *(G-1529)*
St Jude Candle Company LP..............................281 768-7800
   4851 Homestead Rd Ste 102 Houston (77028) *(G-12033)*
St Jude Medical LLC....................................512 732-7400
   6300 Bee Caves Rd # 210 Austin (78746) *(G-1530)*
St Ready Mix LLC.......................................830 480-0933
   2585 S State Highway 16 Jourdanton (78026) *(G-13334)*
Stabil Drill Specialties LLC............................281 583-0127
   608 Richey Rd Houston (77090) *(G-12034)*
Stabilis Energy Inc (PA)................................832 456-6500
   10375 Richmond Ave # 700 Houston (77042) *(G-12035)*
Stabilis Energy LLC (HQ)...............................409 833-1115
   10375 Richmond Ave # 700 Houston (77042) *(G-12036)*
Stabilis Energy Services, Houston *Also called Stabilis Energy LLC (G-12036)*
Staccato 2011 LLC (PA).................................512 819-0656
   114 Halmar Cv Georgetown (78628) *(G-7680)*
Stadium Chair Co LLC....................................432 682-4682
   206 N Midkiff Rd Ste 2b Midland (79701) *(G-15418)*
Stage 3 Separation LLC.................................713 868-4040
   2000 Silber Rd Houston (77055) *(G-12037)*
Stagecoach Trailers, Naples *Also called Randy Myers Enterprises Inc (G-15720)*
Stained Glass Studio, San Antonio *Also called Cavallini Co Inc (G-17988)*

Stainless Drains Com, Caddo Mills *Also called East Creek Corporation (G-2623)*

Stainless Mfg & Seals Svc 806 795-8932
1431 N Gary Ave Lubbock (79415) *(G-14486)*

Stainless Steel Concepts LLC 214 630-4430
8908 Sovereign Row Dallas (75247) *(G-5001)*

Stainless Steel Products Inc 361 884-1281
502 Westchester Dr Corpus Christi (78408) *(G-3628)*

Stainless Stl Cstm Fbrctors In 713 433-0495
2116 Almeda Genoa Rd Houston (77047) *(G-12038)*

Stainless Stl Fabricators Ltd 903 595-6625
11967 State Highway 64 W Tyler (75704) *(G-20157)*

Stair Solutions LLC 972 347-5151
474 N Hays Rd Ste 8 Prosper (75078) *(G-17216)*

Stairways Inc 713 680-3110
4166 Pinemont Dr Houston (77018) *(G-12039)*

Stakeholder Gas Utility LLC 210 444-9664
401 E Sonterra Blvd San Antonio (78258) *(G-18493)*

Stakeholder Midstream LLC 210 444-9664
401 E Sonterra Blvd # 215 San Antonio (78258) *(G-18494)*

Staley Steel Inc 940 686-6000
9620 Saint John Rd Pilot Point (76258) *(G-16729)*

Stalker Radar, Richardson *Also called Applied Concepts Inc (G-17270)*

Stallion Boot Co Inc 915 532-6268
100 N Cotton St El Paso (79901) *(G-5974)*

Stallion Oilfield Cnstr LLC (PA) **713 528-5544**
950 Corbindale Rd Ste 400 Houston (77024) *(G-12040)*

Stallion Oilfield Holdings Ltd (PA) **713 528-5544**
950 Corbindale Rd Ste 400 Houston (77024) *(G-12041)*

Stallion Oilfield Services 361 578-7500
10205 Us Highway 59 N Victoria (77905) *(G-20306)*

Stallion Oilfield Services Ltd 830 583-6927
204 Private Road 1125 1 Kenedy (78119) *(G-13491)*

Stallion Oilfield Services Ltd (HQ) **713 528-5544**
950 Corbindale Rd Ste 400 Houston (77024) *(G-12042)*

Stamp Shop Inc 210 824-7373
8800 Broadway Ste 106 San Antonio (78217) *(G-18495)*

Stampcoat Inc 915 591-0346
10863 Pellicano Dr El Paso (79935) *(G-5975)*

Stan Thompson Investments 713 910-2320
2106 Hickory Ln Pasadena (77502) *(G-16511)*

Stanbio Laboratory LP (HQ) **830 824-0772**
1261 N Main St Boerne (78006) *(G-2137)*

Stanco Manufacturing Inc 903 796-7936
2004 W Main St Atlanta (75551) *(G-845)*

Stanco Marine Inc 979 233-1614
1201 E Brazos St Freeport (77541) *(G-7214)*

Stand By Systems Inc 214 346-2980
5956 Sherry Ln Ste 1000 Dallas (75225) *(G-5002)*

Standard Alloys Incorporated (HQ) **409 983-3201**
201 Lakeshore Dr Port Arthur (77640) *(G-17125)*

Standard Alloys Incorporated 409 769-7850
22389 Ih 10 Vidor (77662) *(G-20333)*

Standard E&S LLC (PA) **806 741-1080**
2310 Fordham St Lubbock (79415) *(G-14487)*

Standard Forged Products LLC (HQ) **214 631-4420**
500 N Akard St Dallas (75201) *(G-5003)*

Standard Indus Mfg Prtners LLC 682 500-1718
8500 Silver Spur Ct Cresson (76035) *(G-3714)*

Standard Indus Mfg Prtners LLC 940 580-3512
1804 Independence Ave Gainesville (76240) *(G-7369)*

Standard Indus Mfg Prtners LLC 817 598-1500
3600 N Fm 51 Weatherford (76085) *(G-20622)*

Standard Industrial Pdts Co (PA) **281 280-0147**
12610 Galveston Rd Webster (77598) *(G-20647)*

Standard Industries Inc 972 851-0460
14911 Quorum Dr Ste 600 Dallas (75254) *(G-5004)*

Standard Machine Works, Houston *Also called Texas Honing Inc (G-12234)*

Standard Machine Works Inc 713 673-1111
2823 Strawberry Rd Pasadena (77502) *(G-16512)*

Standard Meat Company LLC (PA) **214 561-0561**
5105 Investment Dr Dallas (75236) *(G-5005)*

Standard Motor Products Inc 972 316-8100
1801 Waters Ridge Dr Lewisville (75057) *(G-14093)*

Standard Motor Products Inc 972 316-8100
1801 Waters Ridge Dr Lewisville (75057) *(G-14094)*

Standard Motor Products Inc 972 316-8100
1801 Waters Ridge Dr Lewisville (75057) *(G-14095)*

Standard Paints Inc 817 477-5060
940 S 6th Ave Mansfield (76063) *(G-14720)*

Standard Renewable Energy LP (HQ) **281 763-2020**
4460 W 12th St Houston (77055) *(G-12043)*

Standard Safety & Supply, Odessa *Also called L & C Safety Inc (G-16057)*

Standard Structures Inc (PA) **432 580-5353**
1500 W Interstate 20 Odessa (79763) *(G-16164)*

Standard Textile Co Inc 956 831-9040
3300 Nafta Pkwy Ste C Brownsville (78526) *(G-2407)*

Standard Waste Services LLC 210 619-7962
5610 Fm 1346 San Antonio (78220) *(G-18496)*

Standards Testing Labs Inc 325 651-4946
4321 S Chadbourne St San Angelo (76904) *(G-17828)*

Standex International Corp. 972 908-6100
1307 N Watters Rd Allen (75013) *(G-300)*

Stanley Black & Decker Inc 972 247-1367
12827 Valley Branch Ln Dallas (75234) *(G-5006)*

Stanley Industrial & Auto LLC 972 247-1367
12827 Valley Branch Ln Dallas (75234) *(G-5007)*

Stanley Jeans Corp (PA) **936 544-5521**
908 S 4th St Crockett (75835) *(G-3724)*

Stanmar Manufacturing Inc 936 967-3040
5800 Us Highway 190 W Livingston (77351) *(G-14162)*

Star Award Ribbon Company, Ennis *Also called Ennis Inc (G-6098)*

Star Builders Supply, Donna *Also called Velas Builders LLC (G-5495)*

Star Delta Motor Controls Inc 210 479-3550
11135 Iota Dr San Antonio (78217) *(G-18497)*

Star Engraving Company Inc 281 951-5808
500 Century Plaza Dr # 145 Houston (77073) *(G-12044)*

Star Glass and Metal Svcs LLC 770 490-9055
7601 Churchill Way # 439 Dallas (75251) *(G-5008)*

Star Manufacturing Ltd 830 401-5951
1001 Crossroads Blvd Seguin (78155) *(G-18865)*

Star Pipe LLC (PA) **281 558-3000**
4018 Westhollow Pkwy Houston (77082) *(G-12045)*

Star Pipe Products, Houston *Also called Star Pipe LLC (G-12045)*

Star Pipe Products Ltd (PA) **281 558-3000**
4018 Westhollow Pkwy Houston (77082) *(G-12046)*

Star Pipe Usa LLC (HQ) **620 251-5700**
4018 Westhollow Pkwy Houston (77082) *(G-12047)*

Star-Telegram Operating Ltd 817 215-2100
685 John B Sias Mem Pkwy Fort Worth (76134) *(G-7015)*

Star-Telegram Operating Ltd (HQ) **817 390-7400**
808 Throckmorton St Fort Worth (76102) *(G-7016)*

Starcorr Sheets LLC 254 598-7800
4515 Wendland Rd Temple (76504) *(G-19703)*

Starion USA Inc 956 283-1289
3805 Plntn Grv Blvd Mission (78572) *(G-15564)*

Starjb 713 408-8327
10419 Gold Point Dr Houston (77064) *(G-12048)*

Stark Heating & Air, North Richland Hills *Also called DFW Comfort Experts Inc (G-15876)*

Stark Holdings Inc 512 329-8109
1705 S Capital Of Texas H Austin (78746) *(G-1531)*

Starke Machine Co 817 625-6821
2109 Brennan Ave Fort Worth (76106) *(G-7017)*

Starkey Laboratories Inc 956 541-1917
615 Elca Ln Ste A Brownsville (78521) *(G-2408)*

Starks Welding & Mfg Svcs Inc 512 863-2424
1255 Old 1460 Trl Georgetown (78626) *(G-7681)*

Starline Costumes, San Antonio *Also called Julie Keck (G-18212)*

Starlite Sign LP 817 430-8359
7923 E Mckinney St Denton (76208) *(G-5401)*

Starmark Solutions LLC 877 823-7847
200 County Road 197 Hutto (78634) *(G-12885)*

Starpak Plastics Inc 713 329-9183
9690 W Wingfoot Rd Houston (77041) *(G-12049)*

Starr Aircraft Products Inc 903 893-1106
5236 N Hwy 1417 Sherman (75092) *(G-18933)*

Starrfoam Manufacturing Inc 915 886-4636
1004 Omar St Anthony (79821) *(G-590)*

Starrfoam Manufacturing Inc (HQ) **817 654-4688**
3220 Avenue F Arlington (76011) *(G-787)*

Stars Information Solutions, San Antonio *Also called Jeh-Eas Inc (G-18200)*

Startex Linen Co 713 782-4419
7011 Lozier St Houston (77021) *(G-12050)*

Startkleen Legacy LLC 903 207-1079
193 Wall Street Rd Gunter (75058) *(G-8117)*

Stasswender's, Austin *Also called Southwest Marble & Granite Inc (G-1712)*

Statacorp LLC 979 696-4600
4905 Lakeway Dr College Station (77845) *(G-3202)*

State House Printing Inc 512 472-5331
2117 E Cesar Chavez St Austin (78702) *(G-1532)*

State Rbr Envmtl Solutions LLC 806 592-3803
1390 County Rd 344 Denver City (79323) *(G-5424)*

State Sign Corporation 713 943-1831
7630 Hansen Rd Houston (77061) *(G-12051)*

States Inc (PA) **254 559-3355**
300 N Breckenridge Ave Breckenridge (76424) *(G-2239)*

Statewide Traffic Signal Co 713 680-2875
1509 W 34th St Houston (77018) *(G-12052)*

Stationary Power Systems Inc (PA) **877 924-4949**
1115 Sturgeon Ct Ste 119 Arlington (76001) *(G-788)*

Statoil Exploration Company, Austin *Also called Equinor Exploration Company (G-1135)*

Statoil Oil & Gas Services Inc 512 427-3300
6300 Bridge Point Pkwy 2-500 Austin (78730) *(G-1533)*

Statoil USA E&P, Inc., Houston *Also called Equinor USA E&P Inc (G-9688)*

Stauffer/Freeport, Freeport *Also called S F Sulphur Company (G-7208)*

Stay-Tuff Fence Mfg Inc 830 608-9302
1067 Fm 306 Ste 102 New Braunfels (78130) *(G-15826)*

Stb, Houston *Also called South Texas Bolt & Fitting Inc (G-11966)*

Steady Flow Testers Llc 432 258-1184
1518 E County Road 140 Midland (79706) *(G-15419)*

Stealth Oilwell Services LLC 432 333-3600
7668 W 42nd St Odessa (79764) (G-16165)

Stealth Power LLC (PA) 512 306-0088
1201 Old Bastrop Hwy Austin (78742) (G-1534)

Stealth Products LLC 512 715-9995
104 John Kelly St Burnet (78611) (G-2614)

Stealth Pump & Supply LLC 432 385-7770
7680 W 42nd St Odessa (79764) (G-16166)

Steel Building Supply Inc 936 598-6373
1154 State Highway 7 E Center (75935) (G-3009)

Steel Designs Inc (PA) 713 937-3006
13303 Emmett Rd Houston (77041) (G-12053)

Steel Effects LLC 713 729-1100
12300 Zavalla St Houston (77085) (G-12054)

Steel Insulator Group LLC 409 284-4407
7870 College St Beaumont (77707) (G-1954)

Steel Metal Daddy, Como Also called Steel Metal Dairy Inc (G-3250)

Steel Metal Dairy Inc 903 866-2536
3362 County Road 2346 Como (75431) (G-3250)

Steel Specialties Inc 915 590-2337
750 Pendale Rd El Paso (79907) (G-5976)

Steelfab Texas Inc (HQ) 972 562-7720
301 S Mcdonald St McKinney (75069) (G-14979)

Steelfast Inc (PA) 972 243-5312
11281 Leo Ln Dallas (75229) (G-5009)

Steelhead Inc 210 628-1066
10322 Moursund Blvd San Antonio (78221) (G-18498)

Steelman Industries Inc 903 984-3061
2800 State Highway 135 N Kilgore (75662) (G-13594)

Steeltex Fabricators LLC 817 225-0973
6840 N Fm 157 Venus (76084) (G-20223)

Steeltron Metal Works 210 774-4127
402 Kraft St San Antonio (78220) (G-18499)

Steelway International LLC 972 563-2000
2990 Tem Tex Blvd Terrell (75160) (G-19752)

Steelwedge Software, Austin Also called E2open LLC (G-1109)

Steely Lumber Co Inc 936 295-5898
1405 Southwood Dr Huntsville (77340) (G-12824)

Steeplechase Diagnostic Center 281 955-0440
10694 Jones Rd Ste 150 Houston (77065) (G-12055)

Steffani Metals Inc 713 896-9160
6811 Satsuma Dr Houston (77041) (G-12056)

Steinberger Drilling Company 940 423-6900
10063 State Highway 25 E Windthorst (76389) (G-20886)

Stelco Industries Inc 972 923-3603
1313 N Intrstate Hwy 35 E Waxahachie (75165) (G-20563)

Stella Hasegawa 915 594-7633
9801 Montwood Dr El Paso (79925) (G-5977)

Stellar Automation Inc 432 517-4502
711 E 3rd St Big Spring (79720) (G-2099)

Stellar Micro Devices Inc 512 997-7781
9210 Cameron Rd Ste 300 Austin (78754) (G-1535)

Stem Cell Innovations Inc (PA) 281 679-7000
11222 Richmond Ave # 180 Houston (77082) (G-12057)

Stemco, La Grange Also called Multisources Ltd (G-13699)

Stemco Motor Wheel, Longview Also called Stemco Products Inc (G-14312)

Stemco Products Inc (HQ) 903 758-9981
300 Industrial Dr Longview (75602) (G-14312)

Sten Corporation 903 586-0914
4555 N Jackson St Jacksonville (75766) (G-13259)

Step Energy Services USA Ltd (HQ) 210 477-1517
70 Ne Loop 410 Ste 1070 San Antonio (78216) (G-18500)

Step Energy Services USA Ltd., San Antonio Also called Step Energy Services USA
Ltd (G-18500)

Step Energy Svcs Holdings Ltd 918 423-4300
70 Ne Loop 410 Ste 1070 San Antonio (78216) (G-18501)

Step Energy Svcs Holdings Ltd (HQ) 281 606-3600
480 Wildwood Forest Dr Spring (77380) (G-19254)

Stephen Jones 409 460-8609
4105 Ferndale Dr Port Arthur (77642) (G-17126)

Stephens & Johnson Oper Co 940 723-2166
811 6th St Ste 300 Wichita Falls (76301) (G-20812)

Stephens A-1 Lbr & Pallet Inc 281 440-6444
16701 Mathis Church Rd Houston (77090) (G-12058)

Stephens Pneumatics Inc 817 636-9004
147 County Road 4840 Haslet (76052) (G-8223)

Stephenville Empire Tribune, Stephenville Also called Erath Publishers Inc (G-19410)

Stephenville Printing Company (PA) 254 965-5012
1193 W South Loop Stephenville (76401) (G-19424)

Stephenville Printing Company 254 968-3115
1193 W South Loop Stephenville (76401) (G-19425)

Sterigenics US LLC 817 293-0999
3125 Wichita Ct Fort Worth (76140) (G-7018)

Sterling Bv Inc 210 490-1669
1075 Arion Pkwy San Antonio (78216) (G-18502)

Sterling Drlg Fund 1983-1 LP 203 358-5700
9821 Katy Fwy Ste 1050 Houston (77024) (G-12059)

Sterling Fabrication Tech 713 591-9004
2707 W Mockingbird Ln Dallas (75235) (G-5010)

Sterling Foods, San Antonio Also called Sterling Bv Inc (G-18502)

Sterling Foods LLC (HQ) 210 490-1669
1075 Arion Pkwy San Antonio (78216) (G-18503)

Sterling Foods II Inc (HQ) 210 490-1669
1075 Arion Pkwy San Antonio (78216) (G-18504)

Sterling Group LP (PA) 713 877-8257
9 Greenway Plz Ste 2400 Houston (77046) (G-12060)

Sterling Manufacturing, Houston Also called Rohart Company (G-11657)

Sterling Shipyard LP 409 727-2009
906 Main St Port Neches (77651) (G-17168)

Sterlings Vacuum Service 979 657-4633
11708 Fm 1301 Rd Boling (77420) (G-2148)

Stern Empire Dental Laboratory, Tyler Also called National Dentex Corporation (G-20132)

Sterno Group LLC 903 223-3400
303 Falvey Ave Texarkana (75501) (G-19775)

Stetson Hats, Garland Also called Rhe Hatco Inc (G-7578)

Stetson International LP 281 592-4788
21189 Highway 321 Cleveland (77327) (G-3137)

Steve Gibson 713 937-8838
12826 Fm 529 Rd Houston (77041) (G-12061)

Steve Jackson Games Inc (PA) 512 447-7866
3735 Promontory Point Dr Austin (78744) (G-1536)

Steven C Rich LLC 325 573-6653
1345 N College Ave Snyder (79549) (G-19010)

Steven M Riley 972 741-0971
789 N Grove Rd Ste 113 Richardson (75081) (G-17402)

Steven-Sharon Corporation 409 744-4538
7701 Harborside Dr Galveston (77554) (G-7409)

Stevens Technology LLC (PA) 817 831-3500
4205 Stadium Dr Ste 300 Fort Worth (76133) (G-7019)

Steves & Sons Inc 210 921-1400
211 New Laredo Hwy San Antonio (78211) (G-18505)

Steves & Sons Inc 210 924-5111
113 Humble Ave San Antonio (78225) (G-18506)

Steves Doors & Windows, San Antonio Also called Steves & Sons Inc (G-18505)

Steward Cable, Midland Also called Steward Enterprises Inc (G-15420)

Steward Energy II LLC 214 297-0500
2600 Dallas Pkwy Ste 400 Frisco (75034) (G-7314)

Steward Enterprises Inc 432 687-2553
1921 Alta Vista Dr Midland (79706) (G-15420)

Steward Printing & Advg Inc 214 348-1200
10775 Sanden Dr Dallas (75238) (G-5011)

Stewart & Stevenson LLC (HQ) 713 751-2700
55 Waugh Dr Ste 1000 Houston (77007) (G-12062)

Stewart Efi LLC 915 775-2558
27 Leigh Fisher Blvd El Paso (79906) (G-5978)

Stewart Efi Finishing LLC 915 775-2558
44 Butterfield Cir El Paso (79906) (G-5979)

Stewart Stevenson Capitl Corp 713 868-7700
601 W 38th St Houston (77018) (G-12063)

Stewart Stevenson Pwr Pdts LLC 903 838-9966
80 Bilek Dr Texarkana (75501) (G-19776)

Stewart Stevenson Pwr Pdts LLC 361 299-6839
6530 Agnes St Corpus Christi (78406) (G-3629)

Stewart Stevenson Pwr Pdts LLC 915 790-1848
11100 Gateway Blvd E El Paso (79927) (G-5980)

Stewart Stevenson Pwr Pdts LLC 504 347-4326
55 Waugh Dr Ste 1000 Houston (77007) (G-12064)

Stewart Stevenson Pwr Pdts LLC (HQ) 713 751-2600
55 Waugh Dr Ste 800 Houston (77007) (G-12065)

Stewart Tubular Products LLC 713 682-1486
5951 N Houston Rosslyn Rd Houston (77091) (G-12066)

STI, Austin Also called Superconductor Tech Inc (G-1549)

STI Graphics Inc 281 351-2776
1225 Alma St Ste C Tomball (77375) (G-20011)

STI Group, Vidor Also called Southeast Texas Industries Inc (G-20332)

STI Group, Buna Also called Southeast Texas Industries Inc (G-2562)

STI International, Georgetown Also called Staccato 2011 LLC (G-7680)

STI Vibration Monitoring Inc 281 334-0766
1010 E Main St League City (77573) (G-13979)

Stillers Prcision Firearms LLC 972 429-5000
543 N 5th St Garland (75040) (G-7592)

Stinger Auto Appearance Pdts, Houston Also called Stinger Chemical LLC (G-12067)

Stinger Chemical LLC 713 227-1340
1100 Pleasantville Dr Houston (77029) (G-12067)

Stingray Import, Addison Also called Stingray Worldwide LLC (G-165)

Stingray Worldwide LLC 972 818-6025
4300 Wiley Post Rd Addison (75001) (G-165)

Stis Inc 409 697-3350
3127 Texas Ave Bridge City (77611) (G-2287)

Stitch Gallery Inc 512 550-6172
1200 Lakeway Dr Ste 2 Lakeway (78734) (G-13820)

Stitch Gallery Inc 956 412-3087
113 S 77 Sunshinestrip Harlingen (78550) (G-8203)

Stitch Texas, Austin Also called Vikay Group LLC (G-1634)

Stitches Inc 915 591-9260
360 Ridgemont Dr El Paso (79912) (G-5981)

Stitt Spark Plug Company Inc 936 441-7796
204 N Loop 336 E Conroe (77301) *(G-3367)*

Stmicrlctrnics N Amer Hldg Inc 972 466-6000
1310 Electronics Dr Carrollton (75006) *(G-2820)*

Stock Building Sup Texas LLC (HQ) **512 444-3172**
4501 Burleson Rd Austin (78744) *(G-1537)*

Stokes Sign Company Inc (PA) **512 263-7446**
1909 Ranch Road 620 S C Lakeway (78734) *(G-13821)*

Stoller Group Inc (PA) **713 461-1493**
9090 Katy Fwy Ste 400 Houston (77024) *(G-12068)*

Stoller International Inc (HQ) **713 461-1493**
9090 Katy Fwy Ste 400 Houston (77024) *(G-12069)*

Stone Art, Bertram *Also called Antiquestone Inc (G-2051)*

Stone Bond Technologies 713 622-8798
1021 Main St Ste 1550 Houston (77002) *(G-12070)*

Stone Cast Inc 713 683-6780
2300 Karbach St Bldg B Houston (77092) *(G-12071)*

Stone Cliff Technology LLC (PA) **512 640-0650**
500 N Capital Hwy Bldg 2 Austin (78746) *(G-1538)*

Stone Images, Dallas *Also called Lavender Enterprises Inc (G-4585)*

Stone Machinery Movers Inc 936 446-2805
13905 Henry Harris Rd Conroe (77306) *(G-3368)*

Stone Masters 915 216-1702
1201 Berryville St El Paso (79928) *(G-5982)*

Stone Production Inc 512 990-9800
13810 N Interstate 35 Austin (78728) *(G-1539)*

Stone Systems Centl Texas LLC 512 295-2950
4101 Smith School Rd # 2 Austin (78744) *(G-1540)*

Stone Well Service Inc 361 874-4211
Fm 1593 3 Mi N Fm 15 St Lolita (77971) *(G-14177)*

Stone-Cmpbell Rest Mvment Pubg 325 674-2720
1626 Campus Ct Abilene (79601) *(G-83)*

Stonefab Intl LLC 806 352-3416
4005 W Amarillo Blvd Amarillo (79106) *(G-464)*

Stonehouse Signs, Arlington *Also called Acp International Inc (G-608)*

Stonemode Granite LLC 214 484-8820
2840 Reward Ln Dallas (75220) *(G-5012)*

Stoneridge Inc 915 778-1331
21 Butterfield Trail Blvd A El Paso (79906) *(G-5983)*

Stoneridge Electronics Inc 915 621-6111
21 Buttrfeld Blvd 1 # 100 El Paso (79906) *(G-5984)*

Stoneridge Electronics NA, El Paso *Also called Stoneridge Electronics Inc (G-5984)*

Stonexpressions LLC 214 366-2216
2647 Andjon Dr Dallas (75220) *(G-5013)*

Stop It Pipe Repair System, Houston *Also called Indumar Products Inc (G-10346)*

Storage & Processors Inc 832 360-2800
8500 Clinton Dr Houston (77029) *(G-12072)*

Storagetek, Dallas *Also called Oracle America Inc (G-4766)*

Store Dcor Inc - Rtailgraphics 972 475-4404
5050 Boyd Blvd Rowlett (75088) *(G-17711)*

Store Front Printers Inc 281 367-3373
25723 Lake Lawn Dr Spring (77380) *(G-19255)*

Stork Technical Svcs USA Inc (HQ) **832 781-5700**
3350 Rogerdale Rd Ste G Houston (77042) *(G-12073)*

Storm Vulcan Inc 214 637-1430
2225 Burbank St Dallas (75235) *(G-5014)*

Straight Line Construction Inc (PA) **361 394-7656**
5115 N Hwy 59 Freer (78357) *(G-7233)*

Straight Line Sawing & Sealing 972 590-8922
114 Ne 28th St Grand Prairie (75050) *(G-7976)*

Strand Energy LC 713 658-8096
440 Louisiana St Ste 2600 Houston (77002) *(G-12074)*

Strata Control Services Inc 337 785-0000
1450 Lake Robbins Dr # 400 Spring (77380) *(G-19256)*

Stratas Foods LLC 713 671-0057
1302 Harris St Houston (77020) *(G-12075)*

Stratas Foods LLC 469 341-7055
2210 Saint Germain Rd Dallas (75212) *(G-5015)*

Stratasys Direct Inc 512 821-1112
9715 Burnet Rd Ste A500 Austin (78758) *(G-1541)*

Stratasys Direct Manufacturing, Belton *Also called Harvest Incorporated (G-2024)*

Strategic SEC Intelligence Co, McKinney *Also called Sabre Sentinel Intl LLC (G-14973)*

Stratfor Enterprises LLC 512 744-4300
7708 Rialto Blvd Unit 200 Austin (78735) *(G-1542)*

Stratgic Ltigation Partners LP 713 995-8225
21324 Provincial Blvd Katy (77450) *(G-13445)*

Strathmore Products Inc 281 269-9658
1250 Justin Rd Rockwall (75087) *(G-17567)*

Strattec Security Corporation 915 790-5400
12170 Rojas Dr Ste E El Paso (79936) *(G-5985)*

Stratum Energy Romania LLC 832 813-8947
445 Edgewood Dr Montgomery (77356) *(G-15642)*

Strawn Transport & Acid Co 806 495-2422
1103 E Main St Post (79356) *(G-17192)*

Strc Oilfield Technology LLC 817 599-6155
327 N Denton St Ste 100 Weatherford (76086) *(G-20623)*

Stream-Flo USA LLC 903 753-6785
701 Glencrest Ln Longview (75601) *(G-14313)*

Stream-Flo USA LLC 361 362-2600
3102 Highway 59 E Beeville (78102) *(G-1988)*

Stream-Flo USA LLC 903 983-2992
3000 Synergy Blvd Kilgore (75662) *(G-13595)*

Stream-Flo USA LLC (HQ) **903 912-1022**
8726 Fallbrook Dr Houston (77064) *(G-12076)*

Streamline Energy Services LLC 361 852-0907
2610 Holly Rd Corpus Christi (78415) *(G-3630)*

Streamline Innovations Inc (PA) **888 787-6569**
21252 Gathering Oak # 101 San Antonio (78260) *(G-18507)*

Streamline Innovations Inc 888 787-6569
20079 Stone Oak Pkwy San Antonio (78258) *(G-18508)*

Streamline Polymers LLC 832 376-4500
16950 Wallisville Rd Houston (77049) *(G-12077)*

Streamline Prod Systems Inc (HQ) **800 780-4011**
1447 Highway 69 S Kountze (77625) *(G-13673)*

Streamline Production Svcs Inc 409 834-6096
13604 Hwy 69 N Village Mills (77663) *(G-20339)*

Streamline Supply Inc 713 914-0330
10711 Valley Forge Dr Houston (77042) *(G-12078)*

Street Cos,, Graham *Also called Corporate Texas Co LLC (G-7778)*

Streetloc Inc 254 274-2500
13101 Preston Rd 110-3 Dallas (75240) *(G-5016)*

Stress Engineering Svcs Inc 713 466-1527
13062 Westwind E Blvd Houston (77041) *(G-12079)*

Strickland Bridge Inc 940 864-2677
175 Business Us Highway 2 Haskell (79521) *(G-8214)*

Stricklin Company, Dallas *Also called Baldwin Metals Company Inc (G-4000)*

Strike LLC 888 353-1444
5101 W County Rd S Odessa (79766) *(G-16167)*

Strike LLC 888 353-1444
1130 S Highway 77 Robstown (78380) *(G-17517)*

Strike LLC 888 353-1444
5436 Old Pearsall Rd San Antonio (78242) *(G-18509)*

Strike LLC 888 353-1444
2605 N Closner Blvd Edinburg (78541) *(G-5603)*

Strike LLC 888 353-1444
1525 Gilman Rd Fort Worth (76140) *(G-7020)*

Strike LLC 888 353-1444
10919 I 10 E Baytown (77520) *(G-1837)*

Strike LLC 361 939-0800
7619 Up River Rd Corpus Christi (78409) *(G-3631)*

Stromberg Architectural Produc 903 454-0904
2142 County Road 3124 Greenville (75402) *(G-8092)*

Stromberg Archtctral Pdts Stha (PA) **903 454-8682**
4400 Oneal St Greenville (75401) *(G-8093)*

Strombergs Architectural Pdts, Greenville *Also called Stromberg Archtctral Pdts Stha (G-8093)*

Strong Concrete Services Inc (PA) **281 847-9304**
13617 Ralph Culver Rd Houston (77086) *(G-12080)*

Strong Industries Inc 281 448-9315
13617 Ralph Culver Rd Houston (77086) *(G-12081)*

Strong Ready Mix Ltd 325 260-6935
108 County Road 583 Abilene (79606) *(G-84)*

Strong Services LP (PA) **903 693-3966**
3784 S Us Highway 79 Carthage (75633) *(G-2922)*

Strong Ventures, Houston *Also called Mrs John L Strong & Co LLC (G-10933)*

Strongarm Industries Inc 409 835-1330
790 Highway 1131 Vidor (77662) *(G-20334)*

Strongfab Solutions Inc 713 856-6511
9209 Windfern Rd Houston (77064) *(G-12082)*

Structural & Stl Pdts Mfg Ltd 817 869-2301
3001 W Pafford St Fort Worth (76110) *(G-7021)*

Structural Fabrications Inc 903 868-2979
111 Cody Ln Sherman (75092) *(G-18934)*

Structural Glass Division, Houston *Also called Offenhauser Company (G-11140)*

Structural Metals Inc 830 372-8200
1 Steel Mill Dr Seguin (78155) *(G-18866)*

Structural Steel Services, El Paso *Also called Maggie Chacon (G-5857)*

Stryker Communications Inc (HQ) **972 410-7000**
571 Silveron Flower Mound (75028) *(G-6283)*

Stryker Corporation 214 461-4663
15160 Marsh Ln Addison (75001) *(G-166)*

Stryker Orthopaedics, Austin *Also called Howmedica Osteonics Corp (G-1211)*

Stryker Orthopaedics, Addison *Also called Stryker Corporation (G-166)*

Stuart Hose & Pipe Ltd 214 631-6682
2621 Irving Blvd Dallas (75207) *(G-5017)*

Stuart Pressure Control 713 678-0154
10077 Grogans Mill Rd # 100 The Woodlands (77380) *(G-19925)*

Stuart-Dean Co Inc 972 513-9781
460 S Belt Line Rd # 430 Irving (75060) *(G-13189)*

Stuarts Sheet Metal Inc 512 491-0112
9623 Beck Cir Austin (78758) *(G-1543)*

Stubbs Legendary Kitchen, Austin *Also called One World Foods Inc (G-1387)*

Stuckey Terry & Associates 281 590-8628
2511 Lauder Rd Houston (77039) *(G-12083)*

Stuckey's Specialty Tool, Houston *Also called Stuckey Terry & Associates (G-12083)*

Study Breaks Magazine, San Antonio *Also called Shweiki Media Inc (G-18471)*

ALPHABETIC SECTION Sun-Times Media Group Inc

Sturdisteel Company, Hewitt *Also called Schultz Industries Inc* ***(G-8300)***
Sturgeon Services Texas Inc......661 322-4408
1100 E County Road 140 Midland (79706) ***(G-15421)***
Sturm Welding Inc......940 686-2492
111 E Liberty St Pilot Point (76258) ***(G-16730)***
Sturrock & Robson USA Svcs Inc......281 907-8928
1420 Lkeside Pkwy Ste 109 Flower Mound (75028) ***(G-6284)***
Sturrock and Robson Mfg, Flower Mound *Also called Sturrock & Robson USA Svcs Inc* ***(G-6284)***
Stx - Office, Laredo *Also called Select Energy Services LLC* ***(G-13933)***
Stx Beef Company LLC......361 241-5000
9001 Leopard St Corpus Christi (78409) ***(G-3632)***
Stx Service Americas LLC......713 637-4030
11995 Fm 529 Rd Houston (77041) ***(G-12084)***
Style Magazine, Houston *Also called Style Publications* ***(G-12085)***
Style Publications......713 748-6300
2646 S Loop W Ste 270 Houston (77054) ***(G-12085)***
Style Publishing Group LLC......972 335-1181
8020 Main St Frisco Frisco (75033) ***(G-7315)***
Styleaccess LLC......972 392-3800
1613 Hutton Dr Ste 110 Carrollton (75006) ***(G-2821)***
Styrochem Canada......817 847-8254
400 Minton Rd Saginaw (76179) ***(G-17757)***
Styrochem International, Saginaw *Also called Styrochem Canada* ***(G-17757)***
Sub Assembly Group......214 420-8367
1035 Nicholson Rd Garland (75042) ***(G-7593)***
Submersible Oil Services Inc......432 699-1506
2707 S County Road 1208 Midland (79706) ***(G-15422)***
Subsea 7 (us) LLC (HQ)......**713 430-1100**
17220 Katy Fwy Ste 100 Houston (77094) ***(G-12086)***
Subsea Company......281 324-0558
4527 Brittmoore Rd Houston (77041) ***(G-12087)***
Subsea Hydraulic Leads LLC......832 327-4853
6401 Cunningham Rd Houston (77041) ***(G-12088)***
Subsea Services Intl Inc......281 578-6523
1621 Prime West Pkwy Katy (77449) ***(G-13446)***
Subsea Services Western Region, Houston *Also called FMC Technologies Inc* ***(G-9823)***
Subsea Technology, Houston *Also called Proserv Operations Inc* ***(G-11459)***
Subsea Technology Inc......281 498-7399
6911 Signat Dr Houston (77041) ***(G-12089)***
Suburban Sheet Metal Ltd......817 478-0801
528 Eden Rd Kennedale (76060) ***(G-13504)***
Subway, Livingston *Also called Food Group Ventures LLC* ***(G-14153)***
Success Partners Holding Co......800 752-2030
5800 Democracy Dr Plano (75024) ***(G-17012)***
Sudaglass Fiber Technology......281 496-5427
14714 Perthshire Rd A Houston (77079) ***(G-12090)***
Suez Wts Services Usa Inc......214 339-2135
4740 Bronze Way Dallas (75236) ***(G-5018)***
Suez Wts Usa Inc......409 866-4756
W Hwy 90 Beaumont (77713) ***(G-1955)***
Sugar Krystles LLC......817 368-6869
120 Turtle Creek Blvd Dallas (75207) ***(G-5019)***
Sugar Land Product Center, Sugar Land *Also called Schlumberger Technology Corp* ***(G-19547)***
Suhm Spring of Dallas, Dallas *Also called Suhm Spring Works Inc* ***(G-5020)***
Suhm Spring Works Inc (PA)......**713 224-9293**
14650 Hathrow Forest Pkwy Houston (77032) ***(G-12091)***
Suhm Spring Works Inc......214 330-9111
1601 Terre Colony Ct Dallas (75212) ***(G-5020)***
Suits Drilling Company (HQ)......**325 573-1104**
4510 Lamesa Way Snyder (79549) ***(G-19011)***
Sullivan Welding Inc......512 259-3440
9250 Fm 2243 Leander (78641) ***(G-13997)***
Sullys Lone Star Office Pdts (PA)......**512 835-9506**
10200 Mckalla Pl Ste 400 Austin (78758) ***(G-1544)***
Sulphur River Exploration Inc (PA)......**214 373-1091**
4851 Lyndon B Johnson Fwy # 550 Dallas (75244) ***(G-5021)***
Sulphur River Exploration Inc......903 734-7248
2186 State Highway 300 Gilmer (75645) ***(G-7714)***
Sulphur River Gathering LP......806 663-7700
1313 N Hobart St Pampa (79065) ***(G-16339)***
Sulphur Springs Cultured Spc, Dallas *Also called Saputo Dairy Foods Usa LLC* ***(G-4934)***
Sulta Manufacturing Company......903 885-2139
159 Putman St Sulphur Springs (75482) ***(G-19599)***
Sulzer Electro-Mechanical Serv (HQ)......**713 473-3231**
1910 Jasmine Dr Pasadena (77503) ***(G-16513)***
Sulzer Electro-Mechanical Serv......409 882-9112
3904 Tulane Rd Orange (77630) ***(G-16264)***
Sulzer Grayson, Pasadena *Also called Sulzer Electro-Mechanical Serv* ***(G-16513)***
Sulzer Grayson, Orange *Also called Sulzer Electro-Mechanical Serv* ***(G-16264)***
Sulzer Pump Services (us) Inc......432 614-2574
340 S Meadow Ave Odessa (79761) ***(G-16168)***
Sulzer Pumps Houston Inc......281 934-6014
800 Koomey Rd Brookshire (77423) ***(G-2325)***
Sulzer Turbo Svcs Houston Inc......713 567-2700
11518 Old La Porte Rd La Porte (77571) ***(G-13792)***
Sulzer USA Inc......832 886-2300
1255 Enclave Pkwy Ste 300 Houston (77077) ***(G-12092)***
Sulzermedica USA, Austin *Also called Zimmer* ***(G-1717)***
Sumehr Inc......713 849-5528
12302 Sienna Rosa Ln Houston (77041) ***(G-12093)***
Sumitomo Elc Wirg Systems Inc......915 845-7700
6500 N Desert Blvd El Paso (79912) ***(G-5986)***
Sumitomo Elc Wirg Systems Inc......210 507-3395
6903 Ne Loop 410 San Antonio (78219) ***(G-18510)***
Sumitomo Elc Wirg Systems Inc......915 859-0555
12110 Esther Lama Dr # 100 El Paso (79936) ***(G-5987)***
Sumitomo Precision Usa Inc......972 228-9300
1639 Falcon Dr Desoto (75115) ***(G-5443)***
Summa Group LLC (PA)......**713 524-2768**
1485 E Sam Houston Pkwy S Pasadena (77503) ***(G-16514)***
Summit, Fort Worth *Also called Mortex Products Inc* ***(G-6853)***
Summit Casing Equipment, Fort Worth *Also called Summit Casing Services LLC* ***(G-7022)***
Summit Casing Services LLC (PA)......**877 860-0969**
6575 Corporation Pkwy Fort Worth (76126) ***(G-7022)***
Summit Defense Systems Group, Plano *Also called Summit Night Vision Group Inc* ***(G-17013)***
Summit Electric Supply Co Inc......325 691-9600
3202 S Treadaway Blvd Abilene (79602) ***(G-85)***
Summit Energy Equipment......903 951-1217
41 Pioneer Pkwy Sulphur Springs (75482) ***(G-19600)***
Summit Industrial Products, Tyler *Also called Kluber Lubrication N Amer LP* ***(G-20109)***
Summit Industrial Products, Tyler *Also called Kluber Lubrication NA LP* ***(G-20110)***
Summit Mechanical......903 267-7949
5200 County Road 31100 Sumner (75486) ***(G-19609)***
Summit Metals Corporation......940 433-8788
3587 E Highway 114 Rhome (76078) ***(G-17260)***
Summit Midstream Partners LP (PA)......**832 413-4770**
910 Louisiana St Ste 4200 Houston (77002) ***(G-12094)***
Summit Night Vision Group Inc......972 992-0046
1845 Summit Ave Ste 403 Plano (75074) ***(G-17013)***
Summit Petroleum LLC......432 682-9800
550 W Texas Ave Ste 700 Midland (79701) ***(G-15423)***
Summit Pump & Safety Inc......979 567-7867
1203 Commerce St Caldwell (77836) ***(G-2637)***
Summit Seals Inc......409 769-8151
760 Archie St Vidor (77662) ***(G-20335)***
Summit Sportswear Inc......281 335-5370
406 Dunes Ridge Way League City (77573) ***(G-13980)***
Summit Springs Bottled Water......559 277-1239
1501 N Plano Rd Ste 100 Richardson (75081) ***(G-17403)***
Summit Steel Fabricators Inc......713 451-6960
2004 Federal Rd Houston (77015) ***(G-12095)***
Summit Steel Services, Houston *Also called Summit Steel Fabricators Inc* ***(G-12095)***
Summma International LLC (HQ)......**630 519-3632**
710 Union Pacific Blvd Laredo (78045) ***(G-13936)***
Sumner Manufacturing Co Inc, Houston *Also called Sumner Manufacturing Co LLC* ***(G-12096)***
Sumner Manufacturing Co LLC......281 999-6900
7514 Alabonson Rd Houston (77088) ***(G-12096)***
Sun & Ski Sports Expo, Austin *Also called Retail Concepts Inc* ***(G-1462)***
Sun Chemical Corporation......972 647-1641
1505 109th St Grand Prairie (75050) ***(G-7977)***
Sun Chemical Corporation......972 270-6735
12010 Corporate Dr Dallas (75228) ***(G-5022)***
Sun Coast Resources Inc (PA)......**713 844-9600**
6405 Cavalcade St Bldg 1 Houston (77026) ***(G-12097)***
Sun Energy Services LLC......432 701-9000
10303 W County Road 148 Midland (79706) ***(G-15424)***
Sun Fun Enclosures, Stafford *Also called Aluminum Techniques Inc* ***(G-19285)***
Sun Gro Horticulture Dist Inc......903 938-7348
1010 Commerce St Marshall (75672) ***(G-14804)***
Sun Machine Ltd......832 448-1201
11220 Charles Rd Jersey Village (77041) ***(G-13305)***
Sun Manufacturing Company, Jersey Village *Also called Sun Machine Ltd* ***(G-13305)***
Sun Microsystems, San Antonio *Also called Oracle America Inc* ***(G-18356)***
Sun Microsystems, Austin *Also called Oracle America Inc* ***(G-1389)***
Sun Microsystems, Irving *Also called Oracle America Inc* ***(G-13132)***
Sun Newspapers......940 497-4141
275 Market St Lake Dallas (75065) ***(G-13811)***
Sun Products Corporation......281 474-9855
12400 Bay Area Blvd Pasadena (77507) ***(G-16515)***
Sun Splash, Corpus Christi *Also called T L R Group* ***(G-3634)***
Sun System, Georgetown *Also called Williamson County Sun Inc* ***(G-7689)***
Sun West Mud Company Inc (PA)......**432 689-0777**
3002 W Front St Midland (79701) ***(G-15425)***
Sun West Mud Company Inc......817 594-9758
112 W Scenic Trl Weatherford (76088) ***(G-20624)***
Sun-Star Electric Inc......806 793-2812
7722 34th St Lubbock (79407) ***(G-14488)***
Sun-Times Media Group Inc......254 562-2868
214 N Railroad St Mexia (76667) ***(G-15091)***

ALPHABETIC

Sunbeam Products Inc 830 774-4517
1653 Frontera Rd Plant126 Del Rio (78840) *(G-5325)*
Sunbelt Custom Mineral LLC 903 438-2340
79 County Road 2306 Sulphur Springs (75482) *(G-19601)*
Sunbelt Design & Dev Inc 210 227-9162
730 Perez St San Antonio (78207) *(G-18511)*
Sunbelt Design Holdings LLC 210 227-9162
730 Perez St San Antonio (78207) *(G-18512)*
Sunbelt Hot Tubs LLC 281 575-9814
3924 Dunvale Rd Houston (77063) *(G-12098)*
Sunbelt Laboratories, Stafford *Also called Josan Corporation* *(G-19337)*
Sunbelt Letterpress, Dallas *Also called Sclm Enterprises Inc* *(G-4942)*
Sunbelt Machine Works Corp 281 499-0051
13411 Redfish Ln Stafford (77477) *(G-19380)*
Sunbelt Mixes Inc 972 529-5155
2100 Redbud Blvd McKinney (75069) *(G-14980)*
Sunbelt Modular, Garland *Also called Amtex Corp* *(G-7437)*
Sunbelt Plastics Incorporated 972 335-4100
8940 Alpha Ave Frisco (75034) *(G-7316)*
Sunbelt Spas, Houston *Also called Sunbelt Hot Tubs LLC* *(G-12098)*
Sunbelt Stud Welding Inc 713 939-8903
6381 Windfern Rd Houston (77040) *(G-12099)*
Sunbelt Transformer Ltd 713 481-5500
1922 S Martin Luther King Temple (76504) *(G-19704)*
Sunbelt Transformer Ltd (PA) **800 433-3128**
1922 S Mrtn Lther King Jr Temple (76504) *(G-19705)*
Sunbelt Vacuum Services Inc 972 449-3830
2551 S Good Latimer Expy Dallas (75215) *(G-5023)*
Suncoast A/C & Rfrgn Inc 956 428-1190
28020 S Dilworth Rd Harlingen (78552) *(G-8204)*
Suncoast Post-Tension Ltd 972 287-0307
2215 E Pioneer Dr D Irving (75061) *(G-13190)*
Suncoast Post-Tension Ltd (HQ) **281 445-8886**
509 N Sam Houston Pkwy E # 300 Houston (77060) *(G-12100)*
Suncoast Post-Tension Ltd 281 445-8886
15422 Lillja Rd Houston (77060) *(G-12101)*
Suncoast Post-Tension Ltd 512 259-7908
1500 Leander Dr Leander (78641) *(G-13998)*
Sundown Cnc Inc 281 342-8314
3210 Horak St Needville (77461) *(G-15764)*
Sundown Operating Inc 806 229-6102
304 Richardson Sundown (79372) *(G-19614)*
Sunetics Intl Mktg Group LLC 888 266-2232
1700 Alma Dr Ste 400 Plano (75075) *(G-17014)*
Sungold Foods Inc 806 748-2500
901 E 66th St Lubbock (79404) *(G-14489)*
Sunline Product 281 398-6655
1454 E Summitry Cir Katy (77449) *(G-13447)*
Sunline Products, Katy *Also called Slpc Inc* *(G-13443)*
Sunny Delight Beverages Co 903 893-5764
300 W Fm 1417 Sherman (75092) *(G-18935)*
Sunny Sky Products LLC (PA) **713 683-9399**
11747 Windfern Rd Ste 100 Houston (77064) *(G-12102)*
Sunnyvale Fence, Forney *Also called Vrt Investments Inc* *(G-6316)*
Sunpower Corporation 512 294-3859
9229 Wtrford Cntre Blvd S Austin (78758) *(G-1545)*
Sunpower Corporation 512 735-0119
2900 Esprnza Crssing 2nd Flr 2 Austin (78758) *(G-1546)*
Sunrgy LLC 832 786-5051
12763 Capricorn St # 100 Stafford (77477) *(G-19381)*
Sunrgy Solar Distribution, Stafford *Also called Sunrgy LLC* *(G-19381)*
Sunrise Chemical LLC 713 754-1000
10500 Bay Area Blvd Pasadena (77507) *(G-16516)*
Sunrise Woods Designs (PA) **972 842-3579**
410 N Interstate Hwy 45 Ferris (75125) *(G-6232)*
Sunset Well Service Inc 432 561-8600
4318 S County Road 1290 Odessa (79765) *(G-16169)*
Sunshine Custom Cabinets Inc 817 572-5201
5212 Saunders Rd Ste C Fort Worth (76119) *(G-7023)*
Sunshine Machine Inc 281 445-0326
13515 Ann Louise Rd Houston (77086) *(G-12103)*
Sunshine Paper Corp 956 283-9999
90 N Main St Donna (78537) *(G-5493)*
Suntec Industries, Dallas *Also called Coronet Enterprises Inc* *(G-4170)*
Sunterra International LLC 210 501-9510
21720 Hardy Oak Blvd San Antonio (78258) *(G-18513)*
Suntronic Inc 281 879-9562
10501 Kipp Way Dr Ste 350 Houston (77099) *(G-12104)*
Suntronic Electronic Assembly, Houston *Also called Suntronic Inc* *(G-12104)*
Supa Doors, Universal City *Also called Iatid Inc* *(G-20182)*
Supaks Inc 979 968-5654
907 E State Highway 71 La Grange (78945) *(G-13701)*
Super Color Digital LLC 702 242-6335
2010 Valley View Ln # 230 Farmers Branch (75234) *(G-6217)*
Super Heaters LLC 713 952-5533
10260 Westheimer Rd # 460 Houston (77042) *(G-12105)*
Super Imprint Solutions LLC 877 570-5573
1980 Post Oak Blvd Ste 15 Houston (77056) *(G-12106)*

Super Lopez Tortillas LLC 713 921-1237
7314 Harrisburg Blvd Houston (77011) *(G-12107)*
Super Sack Bag Inc 903 965-7713
512 Hwy 56 Savoy (75479) *(G-18741)*
Super Sack Bag Inc (PA) **214 340-7060**
11510 Data Dr Dallas (75218) *(G-5024)*
Super Seed Foods LLC 512 698-7907
3005 S Lamar Blvd Austin (78704) *(G-1547)*
Super Soft, Wichita Falls *Also called TRC Recreation LP* *(G-20820)*
Super Strong Products Inc 972 342-6921
601 E Rock Island Rd Grand Prairie (75050) *(G-7978)*
Super-Tech Hvac LLC 361 394-5549
611 Huisache St Freer (78357) *(G-7234)*
Superbag USA Corp (PA) **713 462-1173**
9291 Baythorne Dr Houston (77041) *(G-12108)*
Superbag USA Corp 713 462-1173
9201 Baythorne Dr Houston (77041) *(G-12109)*
Superblue.net, Dallas *Also called Printing Research Corporation* *(G-4827)*
Supercircuits Inc (HQ) **877 995-2288**
15505 Long Vista Dr # 250 Austin (78728) *(G-1548)*
Superconductor Tech Inc (PA) **512 650-7775**
15511 W State Highway 71 Austin (78738) *(G-1549)*
Superior Air Parts Inc 800 420-4727
621 S Royal Ln Ste 100 Coppell (75019) *(G-3447)*
Superior Cladding Products LLC 281 405-9400
11505 Todd St Houston (77055) *(G-12110)*
Superior Coils, Longview *Also called Keeprite Refrigeration Inc* *(G-14260)*
Superior Completion Services, Houston *Also called Superior Energy Services*
LLC (G-12114)
Superior Con Fence Texas Inc 817 558-6658
2020 S Highway 171 Cleburne (76031) *(G-3110)*
Superior Con Fence Texas Inc (PA) **817 277-9255**
1203 Raider Dr Euless (76040) *(G-6160)*
Superior Concrete Products, Euless *Also called Superior Con Fence Texas Inc* *(G-6160)*
Superior Controls Inc 432 332-4051
2103 W Murphy St Odessa (79763) *(G-16170)*
Superior Cooling Services Inc (PA) **214 637-2162**
2227 Irving Blvd Dallas (75207) *(G-5025)*
Superior Die Cast LLC 903 586-0637
1020 S Bolton St Jacksonville (75766) *(G-13260)*
Superior Energies Inc (PA) **409 962-8549**
3115 Main Ave Groves (77619) *(G-8111)*
Superior Energy Services Inc 281 784-5717
16610 Aldine Westfield Rd Houston (77032) *(G-12111)*
Superior Energy Services Inc 940 668-5100
3333 N I 35 Bldg F Gainesville (76240) *(G-7370)*
Superior Energy Services Inc (PA) **713 654-2200**
1001 La St Ste 2900 Houston (77002) *(G-12112)*
Superior Energy Services LLC 281 999-0047
11000 Equity Dr Ste 150 Houston (77041) *(G-12113)*
Superior Energy Services LLC 432 385-3000
2723 W Hillmont Rd Odessa (79764) *(G-16171)*
Superior Energy Services LLC 281 784-5700
16610 Aldine Westfield Rd Houston (77032) *(G-12114)*
Superior Energy Services LLC 281 934-2181
3943 Fm 362 Rd Brookshire (77423) *(G-2326)*
Superior Essex Communications, Brownwood *Also called Superior Essex Intl LP* *(G-2446)*
Superior Essex Intl LP 325 646-8591
2900 Morris Sheppard Dr Brownwood (76801) *(G-2446)*
Superior Grating Inc 713 686-9475
3006 April Ln Houston (77092) *(G-12115)*
Superior Information Systems 713 524-8998
7100 Regency Square Blvd # 125 Houston (77036) *(G-12116)*
Superior Is, Houston *Also called Superior Information Systems* *(G-12116)*
Superior It Solutions LLC 713 501-1260
16350 Park Ten Pl Houston (77084) *(G-12117)*
Superior Label Systems Inc 214 330-7770
3530 Pipestone Rd Dallas (75212) *(G-5026)*
Superior McHning Fbrcation Inc 940 759-5066
15551 W Hwy 82 Muenster (76252) *(G-15674)*
Superior Optimization Ltd 817 244-4900
2100 N Main St Ste 212 Fort Worth (76164) *(G-7024)*
Superior Pattern Works Inc 281 442-1422
21614 Tophill Dr Spring (77388) *(G-19168)*
Superior Pipeline Company 806 323-8145
15041 Fm 3044 Canadian (79014) *(G-2654)*
Superior Pllet Wichita FLS Ltd (PA) **940 569-5244**
160 Gresham Rd Burkburnett (76354) *(G-2564)*
Superior Pressure Pumping Svcs, Brookshire *Also called Superior Energy Services*
LLC (G-2326)
Superior Processing Service 713 759-6900
1100 Louisiana St Ste 350 Houston (77002) *(G-12118)*
Superior Rex, Plano *Also called Air System Components Inc* *(G-16782)*
Superior Shot Peening Inc 281 432-0900
2350 Security Forest Dr Cleveland (77328) *(G-3138)*
Superior Shot Peening Inc (PA) **281 449-6559**
13930 Luthe Rd Houston (77039) *(G-12119)*
Superior Sign & Lighting, El Paso *Also called Pdn Ssl LLC* *(G-5906)*

Superior Signs	210 646-7799
6606 Topper Rd San Antonio (78233) *(G-18514)*	
Superior Silica Sands LLC	210 626-2045
215 Wellesley Loop San Antonio (78231) *(G-18515)*	
Superior Stone Inc	512 746-2608
455 County Road 344 Jarrell (76537) *(G-13273)*	
Superior Stone Inc (PA)	512 327-4509
7011 Fm 2244 Rd Austin (78746) *(G-1550)*	
Superior Supply & Steel, Beaumont Also called Sentry Supply Inc *(G-1948)*	
Superior Systems & Tech, Merkel Also called Transition Superior Systems Lc *(G-15018)*	
Superior Threaded Products LP	281 459-3131
9045 E Sam Houston Pkwy N Houston (77044) *(G-12120)*	
Superior Trailer Sales Co	713 674-2676
4624 N Mccarty St Houston (77013) *(G-12121)*	
Superior Tubing Tester	361 668-4611
4783 S Us Highway 281 Alice (78332) *(G-238)*	
Superior Weighting Pdts LLC	361 880-7160
4030 Rincon Rd Corpus Christi (78402) *(G-3633)*	
Superior Welding Inc	432 523-2038
1010 S Us Highway 385 Andrews (79714) *(G-559)*	
Superlife Products Inc (PA)	**281 298-5550**
25143 Melda Rd Bldg A Spring (77380) *(G-19257)*	
Supermedia LLC (HQ)	**972 453-7000**
2200 W Airfield Dr Dfw Airport (75261) *(G-5456)*	
Supermedia Services Inc	972 453-7000
2200 W Airfield Dr Dallas (75261) *(G-5027)*	
Supply Chain Solutions Ltd	281 288-0658
4503 Spring Cypress Rd Spring (77388) *(G-19169)*	
Supply Pro Sorbents LLC	713 672-9080
4102 Ivymist Ct Sugar Land (77479) *(G-19559)*	
Supply Solutions Inc	214 766-6866
1800 Preston Park Blvd # 1 Plano (75093) *(G-17015)*	
Supplynet Inc	484 582-1004
1631 Record Crossing Rd Dallas (75235) *(G-5028)*	
Supplynet Inc	214 637-0160
1608 Plantation Rd Dallas (75235) *(G-5029)*	
Supplyone El Paso, El Paso Also called Supplyone Tucson Inc *(G-5988)*	
Supplyone Tucson Inc	915 860-9911
12135 Esther Lama Dr El Paso (79936) *(G-5988)*	
Supreme Armored, Cleburne Also called Supreme Corporation of Texas *(G-3112)*	
Supreme Corporation of Texas (HQ)	**817 641-6282**
500 Commerce Blvd Cleburne (76033) *(G-3111)*	
Supreme Corporation of Texas	817 641-8002
3001 N Main St Cleburne (76033) *(G-3112)*	
Supreme Electrical Svcs Inc	713 676-2588
1187 Brittmoore Rd Houston (77043) *(G-12122)*	
Supreme Manufacturing Company	281 447-3153
7102 Chippewa Blvd Houston (77086) *(G-12123)*	
Supreme Meat Purveyors, San Antonio Also called Tejas Supreme Meat *(G-18525)*	
Supreme Printing Company	214 742-2511
148 Pittsburg St Dallas (75207) *(G-5030)*	
Supreme Rubber Products, Houston Also called Supreme Manufacturing Company *(G-12123)*	
Sure Cast Inc	512 756-6500
200 Sure Cast Burnet (78611) *(G-2615)*	
Sure Trac Inc	254 666-6732
1037 Industrial Blvd Hewitt (76643) *(G-8301)*	
Sure Trac of Texas, Hewitt Also called Sure Trac Inc *(G-8301)*	
Surf Subsea Inc	281 305-4411
5010 Honea Egypt Rd Montgomery (77316) *(G-15643)*	
Surface Burial Vault Monument	361 275-3213
1319 E Broadway St Cuero (77954) *(G-3766)*	
Surface Burial Vaults Monu Co, Cuero Also called Surface Burial Vault Monument *(G-3766)*	
Surface Techniques Inc	713 932-8050
1545 Blalock Rd Houston (77080) *(G-12124)*	
Surface Well Control LLC (PA)	**903 526-2522**
6290b Reynolds Rd Tyler (75708) *(G-20158)*	
Surfrac, Grand Prairie Also called Sweco *(G-7979)*	
Surge Operating LLC (PA)	**832 333-2300**
7850 N Sam Houston Pkwy W S Houston (77064) *(G-12125)*	
Surgical Notes Inc	214 821-3850
3100 Monticello Ave # 450 Dallas (75205) *(G-5031)*	
Surgitech Inc	800 975-6850
13225 Fm 529 Rd Ste E Houston (77041) *(G-12126)*	
Surlean Foods, San Antonio Also called Surlean Meat Company *(G-18516)*	
Surlean Meat Company (HQ)	**210 227-4370**
1545 S San Marcos San Antonio (78207) *(G-18516)*	
Surveys & Analysis Inc	508 842-4011
800 Town And Country Blvd # 500 Houston (77024) *(G-12127)*	
Susies South Forty Confections (PA)	**432 570-4040**
401 S Marienfeld St Midland (79701) *(G-15426)*	
Sustain Ability Solutions Inc	888 657-7582
1200 Lkeside Pkwy Ste 425 Flower Mound (75028) *(G-6285)*	
Sustainable Modular MGT Inc	972 619-7300
7500 Dallas Pkwy Ste 175 Plano (75024) *(G-17016)*	
Sutton Bros Inc	325 387-2053
210 E Pecan St Sonora (76950) *(G-19030)*	
Sva Logistics, Houston Also called Southast Vcational Aliance Inc *(G-11969)*	
Svtronics Inc	214 440-1234
3465 Technology Dr Plano (75074) *(G-17017)*	
SW Fluids, Midland Also called Sun West Mud Company Inc *(G-15425)*	
SW Foam LLC	915 751-1000
9900 Railroad Dr El Paso (79924) *(G-5989)*	
SW Health Care Solutions LLC	832 578-6694
6418 Star Shadow Ln Houston (77066) *(G-12128)*	
SW Technology, Dallas Also called Linux Tech Inc *(G-4596)*	
Swabco Inc	806 894-1511
2341 E Ellis St Levelland (79336) *(G-14017)*	
Swaby Manufacturing Company	281 479-7500
921 Seaco Ct Deer Park (77536) *(G-5298)*	
Swaco, Corpus Christi Also called M-I LLC *(G-3567)*	
Swagelok Austin, Cedar Park Also called Painted Rock LLC *(G-2981)*	
Swan Products LLC	254 772-6979
700 Jewell Dr Waco (76712) *(G-20461)*	
Swanner Properties	940 723-7714
2608 Kemp Blvd Ste E Wichita Falls (76309) *(G-20813)*	
Swans Production Inc	940 567-3147
518 Us Highway 281 N Jacksboro (76458) *(G-13223)*	
Swarco-Reflex LLC (HQ)	**254 562-9879**
900 N Denton St Mexia (76667) *(G-15092)*	
Swarco-Reflex LLC	254 562-9879
Hwy 84 Mexia (76667) *(G-15093)*	
Swat Inc	409 296-4976
9835 State Highway 97 W Floresville (78114) *(G-6250)*	
Sway Water Inc	512 693-7588
6500 Cannonleague Dr Austin (78745) *(G-1551)*	
Swc Industries Inc	903 657-1436
1505 Industrial Dr Henderson (75652) *(G-8274)*	
Swd Enterprises LLC	281 846-6851
1148 Arlington St Houston (77008) *(G-12129)*	
Sweco	817 202-0350
1850 Westpark Dr Grand Prairie (75050) *(G-7979)*	
Sweco Fab Inc	713 731-0030
3701 Holmes Rd Houston (77051) *(G-12130)*	
Swedish Match North Amer LLC	817 416-7017
541 Silicon Dr Ste 100 Southlake (76092) *(G-19082)*	
Sweeney Enterprises Inc	830 537-4631
321 Waring Welfare Rd Boerne (78006) *(G-2138)*	
Sweet	713 647-9338
801 Town And Country Blvd A120 Houston (77024) *(G-12131)*	
Sweet Dreams Inc	956 687-2737
1300 E Upas Ave McAllen (78501) *(G-14909)*	
Sweet Ritual LLC	512 923-1930
8711 Burnet Rd Ste H100 Austin (78757) *(G-1552)*	
Sweeth2o - Office, Decatur Also called Select Energy Services LLC *(G-5254)*	
Sweetwater Machine and Welding	325 235-2922
711 W Broadway St Sweetwater (79556) *(G-19637)*	
Sweetwater Ready-Mix Con Co (PA)	**325 236-6200**
105 W 12th St Sweetwater (79556) *(G-19638)*	
Sweetwater Reporter, Sweetwater Also called Horizon Publications Inc *(G-19631)*	
Swepco, Fort Worth Also called Southwestern Petroleum Corp *(G-7006)*	
Swht LLC	281 442-6694
1733 Lauder Rd Houston (77039) *(G-12132)*	
Swift, Carrollton Also called America Ilsin Tech LLC *(G-2696)*	
Swift Beef Plant, Cactus Also called Jbs USA Food Company *(G-2622)*	
Swift Sales Office, Fort Worth Also called Jbs USA Food Company *(G-6736)*	
Swift Screen Printing Inc	972 494-1144
3848 Marquis Dr Garland (75042) *(G-7594)*	
Swiftex Manufacturing Corp	512 321-2574
Hwy 71 Bastrop (78602) *(G-1761)*	
Swiftwater Energy Services LLC	405 203-5419
2401 N County Road 1287 Midland (79707) *(G-15427)*	
Swifty Printing & Graphics, Arlington Also called JM Graphics LLC *(G-711)*	
Swim Swam Partners LLC	512 827-9040
7308 Seneca Falls Loop Austin (78739) *(G-1553)*	
Swimswam.com, Austin Also called Swim Swam Partners LLC *(G-1553)*	
Swinger Gate Company, Fort Worth Also called Ntx Gates & Fences Inc *(G-6874)*	
Swire Oilfield Services LLC (PA)	**281 210-5598**
28420 Hardy Toll Rd # 100 Spring (77373) *(G-19170)*	
Swirl-Way, Henderson Also called Swc Industries Inc *(G-8274)*	
Swiss Pastry Shop	817 732-5661
3936 W Vickery Blvd Fort Worth (76107) *(G-7025)*	
Swiss-American Cdmo LLC	214 239-2280
2055 Luna Rd Ste 126 Carrollton (75006) *(G-2822)*	
Swm International Inc	806 665-8747
2225 Alcock St Pampa (79065) *(G-16340)*	
Swn International LLC	832 796-1000
10000 Energy Dr Spring (77389) *(G-19171)*	
Swn Production (arkansas) LLC	832 796-1000
10000 Energy Dr Spring (77389) *(G-19172)*	
Swn Production Company LLC (HQ)	**281 618-4700**
2350 N Sam Houston Pkwy E S Houston (77032) *(G-12133)*	
Swn Production Company LLC (HQ)	**832 796-1000**
10000 Energy Dr Spring (77389) *(G-19173)*	
Sword Company	903 561-1921
19981 Us Highway 69 S Tyler (75703) *(G-20159)*	

A
L
P
H
A
B
E
T
I
C

Swos, Houston *Also called Southwest Ocean Services Inc (G-11982)*

Swye360 Learning Inc 214 263-2932
6782 Irongate Pl Frisco (75036) *(G-7317)*

Sybron Dental Specialties Inc 469 635-6100
800 W Sandy Lake Rd # 100 Coppell (75019) *(G-3448)*

Sylvan Energy LLC 412 222-9600
920 Mmrial Cy Way Ste 200 Houston (77024) *(G-12134)*

Symantec, San Antonio *Also called Nortonlifelock Inc (G-18351)*

Symantec, Houston *Also called Nortonlifelock Inc (G-11083)*

Symonds Flags & Poles Inc 214 596-1900
7503 Flagstone St Bldg 30 Fort Worth (76118) *(G-7026)*

Synaptic Cloud LLC (PA) **972 591-0151**
5900 S Lake Forest Dr # 120 McKinney (75070) *(G-14981)*

Syndiant Inc (PA) **972 248-3331**
18325 Waterview Pkwy A101 Dallas (75252) *(G-3852)*

Syneo, Angleton *Also called Technical Innovations LLC (G-580)*

Syneo LLC 979 849-8700
3601 Galaznik Rd Angleton (77515) *(G-579)*

Synergen Health LLC 214 643-6002
3131 Mckinney Ave Ste 602 Dallas (75204) *(G-5032)*

Synergy Catalyst LLC 248 786-7145
1122 W Bethel Rd Ste 400 Coppell (75019) *(G-3449)*

Synergy Environmental Svcs LLC 972 513-1118
2500 E Randol Mill Rd Arlington (76011) *(G-789)*

Synergy Industries LP 817 295-1161
12963 Oak Grove Rd S Burleson (76028) *(G-2597)*

Synergy Oil & Gas LP 713 827-9988
9821 Katy Fwy Ste 805 Houston (77024) *(G-12135)*

Synergy Signs & Services LLC 817 745-2330
2815 Prestige Rd Fort Worth (76244) *(G-7027)*

Synergy Telecom Service Co Inc 210 599-7743
12126 El Sendero St San Antonio (78233) *(G-18517)*

Syntech Chemicals Inc 713 433-5818
14822 Hooper Rd Houston (77047) *(G-12136)*

Syntex Super Materials Inc 281 821-9495
2020 Rankin Rd Houston (77073) *(G-12137)*

Synthesis Energy Systems Inc (PA) **713 579-0600**
3 Riverway Ste 300 Houston (77056) *(G-12138)*

Syntheticomp, Bellaire *Also called Medical Uniform Mfg Inc (G-1998)*

Syrgis Holdings Inc (PA) **361 438-1139**
1607 Junction Hwy Kerrville (78028) *(G-13527)*

Systagenix Wound MGT US Inc 617 774-5500
12930 W Interstate 10 San Antonio (78249) *(G-18518)*

Systel Inc 281 207-7619
1655 Industrial Blvd Sugar Land (77478) *(G-19560)*

System & Tech Integration Ctr, Fort Worth *Also called Sikorsky Aircraft Corporation (G-6988)*

System Development Inc 713 266-5667
3603 Westcenter Dr # 100 Houston (77042) *(G-12139)*

System Sensor 915 778-1301
1101b Burgundy Dr El Paso (79907) *(G-5990)*

Systems Automated Controls Inc 818 898-1900
1512 Interstate 35 W # 108 Denton (76207) *(G-5402)*

Systems Integration Inc 817 468-1494
7316 Business Pl Arlington (76001) *(G-790)*

Systems International Inc 281 424-2700
4318 Fm 1985 Anahuac (77514) *(G-528)*

Systems Product Co Houston N, McAllen *Also called Atlas Copco Compressors LLC (G-14839)*

Systum Inc 406 600-3684
555 Republic Dr Ste 200 Plano (75074) *(G-17018)*

Sytek Electric Corporaiton 713 862-8813
1233 W 34th St Houston (77018) *(G-12140)*

Syzygy Plasmonics Inc 806 470-5779
9000 Kirby Dr Houston (77054) *(G-12141)*

T & B Construction Svcs LLC 936 824-3914
4188 Fm 326 Lufkin (75901) *(G-14553)*

T & H Construction Inc 830 535-6111
863 Roller Coaster Pipe Creek (78063) *(G-16742)*

T & L Lease Service Ltd 281 331-8221
427 E South St Alvin (77511) *(G-381)*

T & R Chemicals Inc 915 851-2761
700 Celum Rd Clint (79836) *(G-3148)*

T & S Machines and Tools Inc 940 668-1002
12 Whitleys Ridge Ln Gainesville (76240) *(G-7371)*

T & S Manufacturing Inc 940 342-2005
8044 State Highway 114 Jermyn (76459) *(G-13290)*

T & S Randall and Sons LP 713 466-6951
27760 Commercial Park Rd Tomball (77375) *(G-20012)*

T & T Airport Services, Fort Worth *Also called Thyssenkrupp Arprt Systems Inc (G-7061)*

T & T Marine, Galveston *Also called Josephine Tug Inc (G-7402)*

T & T Marine Salvage Inc 409 621-4500
2915 Todd Rd Galveston (77554) *(G-7410)*

T & T Offshore, Galveston *Also called T & T Marine Salvage Inc (G-7410)*

T & T Testers Inc 432 682-5456
1302 Dayton Rd Midland (79706) *(G-15428)*

T & T Transports Inc 325 728-2669
2308 N State Highway 208 Colorado City (79512) *(G-3227)*

T & W Tire LLC 940 683-3558
1908 Chico Hwy Bridgeport (76426) *(G-2302)*

T 2 C 3 Group, El Paso *Also called IDEA Corporation (G-5809)*

T A F, Bellaire *Also called Texas Automatic Foods Inc (G-2003)*

T A P, San Antonio *Also called Texas Air Products Ltd (G-18532)*

T A S, Houston *Also called Turbine Air Systems Ltd (G-12408)*

T and L Environmental, Alvin *Also called T & L Lease Service Ltd (G-381)*

T and S Machine Company 936 264-1030
19160 Fm 1484 Rd 105 Cut and Shoot (77303) *(G-3768)*

T B W, Granbury *Also called Bionic Welder LLC (G-7793)*

T C R, Houston *Also called Turbine Component Repair Inc (G-12409)*

T D A, Irving *Also called Taylor - Deal Aviation LLC (G-13191)*

T E M A, Plano *Also called Toyota Mtr Engrg Mfg N Amer In (G-17037)*

T F E Company Inc 979 836-6111
1311 Highway 290 W Brenham (77833) *(G-2274)*

T G & P Inc 979 778-8255
2600 Fm 2223 Bryan (77808) *(G-2509)*

T G Industries Inc 281 356-2001
31714 Industrial Park Dr Pinehurst (77362) *(G-16735)*

T G M Inc 972 761-9101
1810 N Glnvlle Dr Ste 108 Richardson (75081) *(G-17404)*

T Hangers Inc 830 741-8383
3095 County Road 251 Hondo (78861) *(G-8356)*

T Hill Production Svcs Inc 325 884-2670
1700 N State Highway 137 Big Lake (76932) *(G-2062)*

T I Tex, Houston *Also called Titex Inc (G-12302)*

T J Manufacturing Co 806 348-7546
200 Broadway St Roaring Springs (79256) *(G-17497)*

T L Precision Welding Inc 713 896-4500
10533 Fisher Rd Houston (77041) *(G-12142)*

T L R Group (PA) **361 500-4136**
3149 Crestwater Dr Corpus Christi (78415) *(G-3634)*

T L Tedford Enterprises Inc 817 808-8052
206 S Madison St Aurora (76078) *(G-854)*

T L W Archery Inc 830 227-5171
41000 Fm 3159 Canyon Lake (78133) *(G-2680)*

T M D, Waco *Also called Texas Meter and Device Co LLC (G-20467)*

T M T, Highlands *Also called Tubular Makeup Technology Inc (G-8315)*

T N T Printing, Houston *Also called TNT Printing (G-12315)*

T O F Enterprises Inc 281 328-2553
1609 Kennings Rd Crosby (77532) *(G-3744)*

T P E, Megargel *Also called Team Pride Extrusions Inc (G-14994)*

T P S, Alvarado *Also called Total Pallet Solutions LLC (G-347)*

T R W Modernfold Company Inc 214 357-2572
1501 Fairway Dr 100 Lewisville (75057) *(G-14096)*

T Rich Inc 214 748-8700
4834 Reading St Dallas (75247) *(G-5033)*

T S A, Victoria *Also called Aci Worldwide Corp (G-20234)*

T S K Innovations Company 915 581-9718
1057 Doniphan Park Cir B El Paso (79922) *(G-5991)*

T S K Innovations Company 915 581-9718
9641 Plaza Cir Ste B El Paso (79927) *(G-5992)*

T S Moore Printing Co Inc 956 687-6868
2311 Amethyst Ave Mission (78574) *(G-15565)*

T Shirts N Trends 972 272-2581
2050 Forest Ln Ste 320 Garland (75042) *(G-7595)*

T Squared Mfg Inc 254 732-9039
7400 Imperial Dr Waco (76712) *(G-20462)*

T W Design & Construction, Dallas *Also called Theatrical Warehouse Inc (G-5082)*

T W Havens Metals Inc 817 834-2621
6360 Airport Fwy Ste 100 Fort Worth (76117) *(G-7028)*

T W O, Dallas *Also called Window Outfitters LP (G-5193)*

T X I, Fort Worth *Also called Texas Industries Inc (G-7048)*

T X I, Wills Point *Also called Texas Industries Inc (G-20878)*

T X I, Weatherford *Also called Texas Industries Inc (G-20625)*

T X I, Dallas *Also called Texas Industries Inc (G-5063)*

T X I, Longview *Also called Texas Industries Inc (G-14316)*

T X I, Greenville *Also called Texas Industries Inc (G-8094)*

T X I, Paradise *Also called Texas Industries Inc (G-16354)*

T X I, Stafford *Also called Texas Industries Inc (G-19385)*

T X I, Dallas *Also called Texas Industries Inc (G-5064)*

T X P Inc 325 944-9844
3150 Executive Dr San Angelo (76904) *(G-17829)*

T&B Boiler Inc 972 576-1920
816 Vinson Ln Red Oak (75154) *(G-17236)*

T&V Optimum LLC 512 398-5271
10202 Spicewood Mesa Austin (78759) *(G-1554)*

T-3 Energy Services Inc (HQ) **713 944-5950**
140 Cypress Station Dr # 225 Houston (77090) *(G-12143)*

T-B & S Mfg Co 817 281-9315
4901 Blue Mound Rd Fort Worth (76106) *(G-7029)*

T-C Oil Company 361 526-4693
427 Fm 774 Refugio (78377) *(G-17249)*

T-P Rentals LLC 432 558-7218
1204 Se County Rd Crane (79731) *(G-3701)*

T-Rey Properties Inc 432 570-6822
3700 E Hwy 158 Midland (79706) *(G-15429)*

T-System Inc	972 503-8899
6509 Windcrest Dr Ste 165 Plano (75024) *(G-17019)*	
T-Tex Equipment LP	713 991-7070
8302 Almeda Genoa Rd Houston (77075) *(G-12144)*	
Ta Chen International Inc	713 672-0177
9525 Wallisville Rd Houston (77013) *(G-12145)*	
Ta Fabrication LLC	330 301-6800
2307 Harrington Ct Euless (76039) *(G-6161)*	
Tabco Machines Inc	806 749-5649
1114 N Avenue T Lubbock (79415) *(G-14490)*	
Tableaux, Austin *Also called Luna Piena Inc (G-1311)*	
Tables Manufacturing Inc	972 932-4148
2000 S Houston St Kaufman (75142) *(G-13464)*	
Tabors of San Angelo Inc	325 942-1696
4816 Knickerbocker Rd San Angelo (76904) *(G-17830)*	
TAC Services, Copperas Cove *Also called Tach Services Inc (G-3456)*	
Tach Services Inc	254 547-7121
103 Wolf Rd Copperas Cove (76522) *(G-3456)*	
Tackaberry Dooley Systems (HQ)	**281 479-9700**
1515 W 13th St Deer Park (77536) *(G-5299)*	
Tacki Mac Grips	281 358-6738
22000 Northpark Dr Humble (77339) *(G-12800)*	
Taco & Tortilla Factory Inc	713 706-3233
6154 Westheimer Rd Houston (77057) *(G-12146)*	
Taco Garcia Mexican Cafe, Amarillo *Also called G Tacos Inc (G-427)*	
Taco Tote, Houston *Also called Taco & Tortilla Factory Inc (G-12146)*	
Taconic Industries Corporation	972 241-5200
2151 Hutton Dr Carrollton (75006) *(G-2823)*	
Tacony Corporation	817 551-0700
3101 Wichita Ct Fort Worth (76140) *(G-7030)*	
Tacor, Ponder *Also called Tulsa Arspc Cmpnent Ovrhaul RE (G-17097)*	
Taf Incorporated (PA)	713 896-4040
5427 Gessner Rd Houston (77041) *(G-12147)*	
Taft Tribune, Sinton *Also called San Patricio Publishing Co Inc (G-18965)*	
Tag Holdings Inc (HQ)	**214 469-3300**
883 Trinity Dr The Colony (75056) *(G-19815)*	
Tag Waterblock LLC	281 862-0300
16023 East Fwy Ste 7 Channelview (77530) *(G-3039)*	
Tahwahkaro Distilling Co LLC	479 871-2565
541 Industrial Blvd Ste C Grapevine (76051) *(G-8056)*	
Taiga Coolers LLC	214 762-3648
2200 Big Town Blvd # 130 Mesquite (75149) *(G-15077)*	
Tailwind Business Ventures LLC	210 268-2717
11901 W Parmer Ln Ste 220 Cedar Park (78613) *(G-2986)*	
Tait Radio Communications	281 944-3539
15340 Park Row Houston (77084) *(G-12148)*	
Tajas Machine, Garland *Also called Gil-Mar & Associates Inc (G-7505)*	
Takata Seat Belts, San Antonio *Also called Joyson Sfety Systems Acqstion (G-18210)*	
Takumi Stamping Inc	210 380-1087
1930 Hormel Dr San Antonio (78219) *(G-18519)*	
Takumi Stamping Inc (HQ)	**210 924-3110**
1 Lone Star Pass Bldg 40 San Antonio (78264) *(G-18520)*	
Talajak Inc	325 632-5341
809 N 5th St Mertzon (76941) *(G-15021)*	
Talalay Global Inc	940 851-0107
8600 Central Fwy N Wichita Falls (76305) *(G-20814)*	
Talbot Group Inc	866 866-5020
421 W Harwood Rd Ste 110 Hurst (76054) *(G-12860)*	
Talco Industries, Fort Worth *Also called Aviation Products Inc (G-6413)*	
Talk OTexas Brands Inc	325 655-6077
1610 Roosevelt St San Angelo (76905) *(G-17831)*	
Talke Usa Inc	832 260-8325
13822 Hatcherville Rd Mont Belvieu (77521) *(G-15621)*	
Tall City Well Service Co LP	432 618-9937
303 Veterans Airpark Ln # 4105 Midland (79705) *(G-15430)*	
Talla-Com Industries, Fort Worth *Also called Talla-Com Tllhssee Cmmnctns I (G-7031)*	
Talla-Com Tllhssee Cmmnctns I (HQ)	**817 234-6726**
4700 Marine Creek Pkwy Fort Worth (76179) *(G-7031)*	
Tallahassee Technologies Inc (HQ)	**817 234-6726**
4700 Marine Creek Pkwy Fort Worth (76179) *(G-7032)*	
Tallannquest LLC	972 423-8455
538 Haggard St Ste 406 Plano (75074) *(G-17020)*	
Tallent Enterprises Inc	936 594-2591
3736 Hwy 19 Riverside (77367) *(G-17480)*	
Tallent Sausage and Grocery, Riverside *Also called Tallent Enterprises Inc (G-17480)*	
Tally Energy Services (PA)	**832 530-4880**
5611 Baird Ct Houston (77041) *(G-12149)*	
Tallyho Plastics Inc (PA)	**903 586-2263**
1020 S Bolton St Jacksonville (75766) *(G-13261)*	
Talon, Houston *Also called S & S X-Ray Products Inc (G-11708)*	
Talon Oil & Gas LLC	214 323-8360
3131 Mckinney Ave Ste 750 Dallas (75204) *(G-5034)*	
Talon/Lpe Ltd	806 372-6600
301 S Polk St Amarillo (79101) *(G-465)*	
Talon/Lpe Ltd (PA)	**806 467-0607**
921 N Bivins St Amarillo (79107) *(G-466)*	
Talon/Lpe Ltd	210 253-7200
13111 Lookout Way San Antonio (78233) *(G-18521)*	
Talos Energy Inc (PA)	**713 328-3000**
333 Clay St Ste 3300 Houston (77002) *(G-12150)*	
Talos Energy LLC (HQ)	**713 328-3000**
500 Dallas St Ste 2000 Houston (77002) *(G-12151)*	
Talos Ert LLC (HQ)	**281 618-0590**
500 Dallas St Ste 2000 Houston (77002) *(G-12152)*	
Talos Petroleum LLC	281 872-1999
16800 Greenspt Pk Dr 225s Houston (77060) *(G-12153)*	
Talos Production LLC (HQ)	**713 328-3000**
500 Dallas St Ste 2000 Houston (77002) *(G-12154)*	
Tam International Inc (PA)	**713 462-7617**
4620 Southerland Rd Houston (77092) *(G-12155)*	
Tam International Inc	713 462-7617
6935 Pinemont Dr Houston (77092) *(G-12156)*	
Tamra Group Inc	817 453-3370
1052 S 2nd Ave Ste 200 Mansfield (76063) *(G-14721)*	
Tams Industries LLC (HQ)	**281 370-3087**
8303 Thora Ln Spring (77379) *(G-19174)*	
Tan Boots LLC	512 921-0720
10904 Casitas Dr Austin (78717) *(G-1713)*	
Tana Exploration Company LLC	469 276-8262
4001 Maple Ave Ste 600 Dallas (75219) *(G-5035)*	
Tandem Marketing Services Inc (PA)	**361 949-7703**
2822 N Shoreline Blvd Corpus Christi (78402) *(G-3635)*	
Tanglewood Moms LLC	817 247-1474
3200 Sweetbriar Ln Fort Worth (76109) *(G-7033)*	
Tango Networks Inc (PA)	**469 920-2100**
2801 Network Blvd Ste 200 Frisco (75034) *(G-7318)*	
Tank and Vessel Builders LP	325 854-8450
100 E Tp Ln Baird (79504) *(G-1736)*	
Tank Town LLC	512 894-0861
1621 E 6th St Apt 1149 Austin (78702) *(G-1555)*	
Tank Wind-Down Corp	936 539-1747
498 N Loop 336 E Conroe (77301) *(G-3369)*	
Tankheads Inc	817 636-2085
147 County Road 4840 Haslet (76052) *(G-8224)*	
Tanner Timber Products, Kountze *Also called Cadre Timber Products Inc (G-13669)*	
Tanos Energy LLC	903 597-7667
821 E Se Loop 323 Ste 400 Tyler (75701) *(G-20160)*	
Taos Resources Oper Co LLC	713 993-0774
10700 North Fwy Ste 930 Houston (77037) *(G-12157)*	
Taotao Usa Inc (PA)	**214 635-3980**
2201 Luna Rd Carrollton (75006) *(G-2824)*	
Tapcoenpro LLC (HQ)	**281 247-8100**
16315 Market St Channelview (77530) *(G-3040)*	
Tapcoenpro International Inc	281 247-8100
16315 Market St Channelview (77530) *(G-3041)*	
Tape Innovations LLC (PA)	**817 568-1212**
201 E Risinger Rd Ste 101 Fort Worth (76140) *(G-7034)*	
Taper-Lok Corporation (HQ)	**713 467-3333**
945 Bunker Hill Rd # 500 Houston (77024) *(G-12158)*	
Taprite Inc (HQ)	**210 523-0800**
3248 Northwestern San Antonio (78238) *(G-18522)*	
Taprite-Fassco Mfg Inc	830 914-2539
105 S Center St Marion (78124) *(G-14758)*	
Taramar Products, Fort Worth *Also called Harris Cabinet & Wdwkg Inc (G-6690)*	
Targa Gas Marketing LLC	713 584-1000
1000 La St Ste 4300 Houston (77002) *(G-12159)*	
Targa Ppline Mid-Continent LLC	432 535-2484
17400 E Fm 2401 Midkiff (79755) *(G-15097)*	
Targa Resources, Crane *Also called Tri Resources Inc (G-3703)*	
Targa Resources, Houston *Also called Tri Resources Inc (G-12362)*	
Targa Resources Corp	713 584-1053
16514 De Zavalla Rd Ste B Channelview (77530) *(G-3042)*	
Targa Resources GP LLC	713 873-1000
811 Louisiana St Ste 2100 Houston (77002) *(G-12160)*	
Targa Term Channelview, Channelview *Also called Targa Resources Corp (G-3042)*	
Target Stone LLC	832 827-8663
11514 Hempstead Rd Houston (77092) *(G-12161)*	
Target Well Services Inc (PA)	**361 883-8100**
212 Flat Crk Canyon Lake (78133) *(G-2681)*	
Tarkett Inc	800 366-2689
1705 Oliver St Houston (77007) *(G-12162)*	
Tarmac Materials LLC	281 342-9314
6130 Fm 2218 Rd Richmond (77469) *(G-17466)*	
Tarps LLC	833 469-8277
12910 Broadmeade Ave Austin (78729) *(G-1714)*	
Tarquin Polymers & Colors Inc	281 240-0202
13313 Southwest Fwy # 194 Sugar Land (77478) *(G-19561)*	
Tarrant Concrete Co Inc (HQ)	**817 926-6660**
5400 Thelin St Fort Worth (76115) *(G-7035)*	
Tarsco Construction Corp (HQ)	**515 225-3003**
25000 Pitkin Rd Ste 100 Spring (77386) *(G-19258)*	
Tascon Inc	713 937-0900
7607 Fairview St Houston (77041) *(G-12163)*	
Tascon Industries, Houston *Also called Tascon Inc (G-12163)*	
Tasman Amarillo, Amarillo *Also called Tasman Industries Inc (G-512)*	
Tasman Industries Inc	806 372-3850
102 Beefco Rd Amarillo (79118) *(G-512)*	

A
L
P
H
A
B
E
T
I
C

Tasting Room Cafe, Laredo *Also called La India Packing Co* *(G-13903)*

Tasus Corporation 512 869-7766
211 Tasus Way Georgetown (78626) *(G-7682)*

Tasus Texas Corporation 512 869-7766
211 Tasus Way Georgetown (78626) *(G-7683)*

Tatex Inc 254 799-4911
2800 Gholson Rd Waco (76704) *(G-20463)*

Tatex Thermographers, Waco *Also called Tatex Inc* *(G-20463)*

Tauber Exploration & Prod Co 713 869-5656
55 Waugh Dr Ste 600 Houston (77007) *(G-12164)*

Tauren Exploration Inc 972 681-8047
9870 Plano Rd Dallas (75238) *(G-5036)*

Taurex Drill Bits LLC 432 684-4711
9 E Industrial Loop Midland (79701) *(G-15431)*

Taurus Industrial Group LLC 713 554-0157
3810 Underwood Rd La Porte (77571) *(G-13793)*

Taurus Oil Inc 432 685-3520
2052 Commerce Dr Midland (79703) *(G-15432)*

Tavhealth, San Antonio *Also called Triple Aim Ventures LLC* *(G-18569)*

Taxa Inc 713 861-2540
1830 W 15th St Houston (77008) *(G-12165)*

Taxsation Inc 888 829-1120
7606 Lairds Ln Dallas (75248) *(G-5037)*

Taylor - Deal Aviation LLC 972 220-0943
911 Maryland Dr Irving (75061) *(G-13191)*

Taylor Cmmnctons Scure Cstmer 817 283-9500
4401 Cambridge Rd Fort Worth (76155) *(G-7036)*

Taylor Coml Foodservice Inc 972 937-1820
2275 N Highway 77 Waxahachie (75165) *(G-20564)*

Taylor Communications Inc 972 581-7711
8750 Autobahn Dr Dallas (75237) *(G-5038)*

Taylor Communications Inc 713 456-4089
13105 Nw Fwy Ste 1110 Houston (77040) *(G-12166)*

Taylor Communications Inc 214 275-3200
4808 Eastover Cir Ste 101 Mesquite (75149) *(G-15078)*

Taylor Communications Inc 800 755-6405
1609 S Blue Bell Rd Brenham (77833) *(G-2275)*

Taylor Craft Cabinet & Door 512 352-6355
1353 W 2nd St Taylor (76574) *(G-19662)*

Taylor Daily Press, Taylor *Also called Blacklands Publications Inc* *(G-19650)*

Taylor Design Group Inc 972 243-7943
1605 Crescent Cir Ste 400 Carrollton (75006) *(G-2825)*

Taylor Distributing Co Inc 817 831-0601
3701 N Sylvania Ave Fort Worth (76137) *(G-7037)*

Taylor Foundry, Wichita Falls *Also called Meador Products Inc* *(G-20782)*

Taylor Industries LLC (HQ) 918 266-7301
801 Cherry St Unit 2 Fort Worth (76102) *(G-7038)*

Taylor Iron-Machine Works 512 365-3646
208 Bland St Taylor (76574) *(G-19663)*

Taylor Made Bit Co LLC 432 362-4471
4519 Brazos Ave Odessa (79764) *(G-16172)*

Taylor Meat Company, Taylor *Also called Centex Meat Company LP* *(G-19652)*

Taylor Metal Works & Pipe Co 409 736-3555
215 W Highway 365 Port Arthur (77640) *(G-17127)*

Taylor Oil Co Ltd Partnership (PA) 806 948-4166
Fm 119 Fm 1 St Sunray (79086) *(G-19621)*

Taylor Oil Field Supply, Sunray *Also called Taylor Oil Inc* *(G-19622)*

Taylor Oil Inc 806 948-4166
Fm 119 Sunray (79086) *(G-19622)*

Taylor Press Products Company 512 746-5556
13675 N Interstate 35 Jarrell (76537) *(G-13274)*

Taylor Publishing Company (HQ) 214 637-2800
1550 W Mockingbird Ln Dallas (75235) *(G-5039)*

Taylor Publishing Company 325 486-5300
3490 Venture Dr San Angelo (76905) *(G-17832)*

Taylor Publishing Company 210 659-7505
1136 Berry Creek Dr Schertz (78154) *(G-18763)*

Taylor Publishing Company 713 782-0700
2211 Norfolk St Ste 603 Houston (77098) *(G-12167)*

Taylor, Gordon Oil Co, Sunray *Also called Taylor Oil Co Ltd Partnership* *(G-19621)*

Taylor-Wharton America Inc 281 738-2863
1411 Transport Dr Baytown (77523) *(G-1803)*

Taylormade Pllets Lgistics LLC 210 566-3833
30023 Fairway Vista Dr Boerne (78015) *(G-2139)*

Taylors Oilfield Mfg Inc 281 442-4084
14401 Interdrive E Houston (77032) *(G-12168)*

Taysha Gene Therapies Inc 214 612-0000
2280 Inwood Rd Dallas (75235) *(G-5040)*

Tb Woods Incorporated 512 352-4000
2000 Clovis Barker Rd San Marcos (78666) *(G-18712)*

Tb Woods Incorporated 512 353-4000
2000 Clovis R Barker Rd San Marcos (78666) *(G-18713)*

Tbc Brinadd, Houston *Also called Tbc-Brinadd LLC* *(G-8393)*

Tbc-Brinadd LLC 281 438-2565
5035 Mchard Rd Houston (77053) *(G-8393)*

Tbk Materials LLC (PA) 214 239-4916
5208 Tennyson Pkwy # 130 Plano (75024) *(G-17021)*

Tbx Employee Benefits LLC 972 248-9030
7500 Dallas Pkwy Ste 500 Plano (75024) *(G-17022)*

Tc Sanitizer Co LLC 832 296-4561
16711 Hollister St Ste I Houston (77066) *(G-12169)*

Tc Signs Inc 972 492-2801
1620 E State Highway 121 Lewisville (75056) *(G-14097)*

Tcc, Groveton *Also called Texas Concrete Chemical Inc* *(G-8113)*

Tcca Inc (PA) **361 668-9636**
1023 E Main St Alice (78332) *(G-239)*

TCI Coatings Inc 806 762-0871
4501 Bradley St Lubbock (79415) *(G-14491)*

TCI Garment Division, Huntsville *Also called Texas Dept Criminal Justice* *(G-12825)*

Tcm Investments Inc 432 366-5433
2121 W 44th St Odessa (79764) *(G-16173)*

TCO Field Service Inc 432 682-5355
3601 Garden City Hwy Midland (79706) *(G-15433)*

Tcr Business Systems 972 807-8000
1801 Royal Ln Ste 600 Dallas (75229) *(G-5041)*

Tcw Investments Inc 409 796-1883
8505 Hwy 365 Beaumont (77705) *(G-1956)*

Tdi LLC 972 877-5780
4816 Pack Saddle Way Flower Mound (75028) *(G-6286)*

Tdindustries Ltd 972 888-9500
13850 Diplomat Dr Dallas (75234) *(G-5042)*

Tdk Rf Solutions Inc 512 258-9478
1101 Cypress Creek Rd Cedar Park (78613) *(G-2987)*

Tdr Services Inc (PA) **422 606-6084**
4 Golden Gate Ste 3 Midland (79707) *(G-15434)*

Tdw Services Inc 281 291-8156
9409 New Century Dr Pasadena (77507) *(G-16517)*

Te Connectivity Corporation 469 568-0657
1628 W Crosby Rd Ste 100 Carrollton (75006) *(G-2826)*

Te Connectivity Corporation 610 893-9800
1321 Joe Battle Blvd El Paso (79936) *(G-5993)*

TE&s Limited (PA) **817 573-3550**
4801 Glen Rose Hwy Granbury (76048) *(G-7811)*

Teale Pipewell Solutions, Magnolia *Also called Tpws Inc* *(G-14632)*

Team Inc 409 840-9955
3875 W Cardinal Dr Beaumont (77705) *(G-1957)*

Team Alloys LLC 713 360-1060
7350 Roundhouse Ln Houston (77078) *(G-12170)*

Team Cooperheat-Mqs Inc (HQ) **713 673-3660**
5858 Westheimer Rd # 625 Houston (77057) *(G-12171)*

Team Fabricators LLC 409 962-0266
650 Main Ave Port Arthur (77642) *(G-17128)*

Team Go Figure LLP 972 276-6700
6140 Goliad Ave Dallas (75214) *(G-5043)*

Team Golf, Carrollton *Also called Golf Time LLC* *(G-2746)*

Team IMS, Azle *Also called Integrated McHy Solutions LLC* *(G-1725)*

Team Industrial Services, Beaumont *Also called Team Inc* *(G-1957)*

Team Manufacturing Inc 903 583-7722
1438 N State Highway 78 Bonham (75418) *(G-2155)*

Team Mncuso Pwrsports Gulf Fwy, Houston *Also called 9650 Nf Ltd* *(G-8418)*

Team Oil Tools LLC 918 461-8104
4310 N Sam Houston Pkwy E Houston (77032) *(G-12172)*

Team Pride Extrusions Inc 940 562-2205
10472 Fm 210 Megargel (76370) *(G-14994)*

Team Promark LLC 303 926-1328
5001 North Fwy Ste C Fort Worth (76106) *(G-7039)*

Team Pvf LLC 281 714-1582
7350 Roundhouse Ln Houston (77078) *(G-12173)*

Teamsupport.com, Dallas *Also called Muroc Systems Inc* *(G-4708)*

Teasdale Foods Inc (PA) **209 358-5616**
3041 Churchill Dr Ste 100 Flower Mound (75022) *(G-6287)*

Teasdale Foods Inc 915 821-2500
8000 Ashley Rd El Paso (79934) *(G-5994)*

Teasdale Foods Inc 952 854-0903
3041 Churchill Dr Ste 100 Flower Mound (75022) *(G-6288)*

Teasdale Latin Foods, Flower Mound *Also called Teasdale Foods Inc* *(G-6287)*

Teazzers, Dallas *Also called Red River Tea Company* *(G-4870)*

Tebo Concre Fence LLC 512 219-1018
11800 N Highway 183 Florence (76527) *(G-6244)*

TEC Utility Supply & Services, Georgetown *Also called Texas Electric Coops Inc* *(G-7685)*

Tecal Manufacturing LLC 915 593-1413
9100 Mayflower Ave Ste E El Paso (79925) *(G-5995)*

Tecalemit Inc 281 446-7300
6324 Greens Rd Humble (77396) *(G-12801)*

Tech Dogs LLC 972 985-4730
1200 Placid Ave Ste 500 Plano (75074) *(G-17023)*

Tech Fab, Houston *Also called Greenwood Manufacturing Inc* *(G-10038)*

Tech Lite, Lancaster *Also called Inverter Designs Inc* *(G-13843)*

Tech Lite Mfg, Cleburne *Also called DA Schoggin Inc* *(G-3086)*

Tech Management, Odessa *Also called Globe Chemical LLC* *(G-16015)*

Tech Power International Co 281 494-4242
4147 Greenbriar Dr Stafford (77477) *(G-19382)*

Tech Specialty, Irving *Also called Lsp Products Group Inc* *(G-13091)*

Tech Tool Plastics Inc 817 246-4694
7800 Skyline Park Dr Fort Worth (76108) *(G-7040)*

Tech-Lab Industries Inc 972 660-1111
2371 Nw Dallas St Ste 400 Grand Prairie (75050) *(G-7980)*

(G-0000) Company's Geographic Section entry number

Techcomp (usa) Inc 512 215-8335
  4801 Southwest Pkwy # 125 Austin (78735) *(G-1556)*

Techemet LP 281 991-8300
  6025 Genoa Red Bluff Rd Pasadena (77507) *(G-16518)*

Techlight, Dallas *Also called DA Schoggin Inc (G-4204)*

Techline Sports Lighting LLC 512 977-8880
  15303 Storm Dr Austin (78734) *(G-1557)*

Techmar Industries LLC 832 246-6200
  5510 Spring Stuebner Rd Spring (77389) *(G-19175)*

Technical Automtn Svcs Co Ltd (PA)...........281 474-3232
  2000 Nasa Pkwy Seabrook (77586) *(G-18792)*

Technical Composite Corp 210 832-0200
  2107 Danbury St San Antonio (78217) *(G-18523)*

Technical Innovations LLC 979 849-8700
  3601 Galaznik Rd Angleton (77515) *(G-580)*

Technical Services Intl 972 285-7400
  1522 Mclead Dr Mesquite (75149) *(G-15079)*

Technicolor Usa Inc 915 872-8001
  12430 Mercantile Ave El Paso (79928) *(G-5996)*

Technicolor Usa Inc 915 841-7233
  11751 Alameda Ave Socorro (79927) *(G-19019)*

Techniek LLC 832 618-7085
  2215 Harbor St Houston (77020) *(G-12174)*

Technimark Reynosa LLC 336 498-4171
  9600 International Blvd Pharr (78577) *(G-16712)*

Technip S&W International Inc 281 870-1111
  11740 Katy Fwy Ste 100 Houston (77079) *(G-12175)*

Technipfmc, Houston *Also called FMC Technologies Inc (G-9820)*

Techniplex Conference Center 281 565-5566
  4810 Techniplex Dr Stafford (77477) *(G-19383)*

Technocycle, Houston *Also called I T Remarketing Inc (G-10309)*

Technographix LLC 817 336-5671
  1200 Forum Way S Fort Worth (76140) *(G-7041)*

Technologies Alliance Inc (HQ)..................281 442-8825
  6401 N Eldridge Pkwy Houston (77041) *(G-12176)*

Technology Container Corp 972 228-1617
  1221 E Cntre Pk Blvd Bldg Desoto (75115) *(G-5444)*

Technology Fleet Products Inc 713 907-8394
  2331 Watts St Houston (77030) *(G-12177)*

Technology Media Group Inc 469 463-7647
  1262 Viceroy Dr Dallas (75247) *(G-5044)*

Technology Media Group Inc (PA).............800 777-9091
  1208 Viceroy Dr Dallas (75247) *(G-5045)*

Technology Plastics, Bryan *Also called Bryan Container Company Inc (G-2463)*

Technology Printing, Dallas *Also called Technology Media Group Inc (G-5045)*

Technos Inc 210 651-9393
  7016 Fm 3009 Schertz (78154) *(G-18764)*

Techstar Molding, Pasadena *Also called Lee Linco Plastics Inc (G-16471)*

Techstyles Inc 972 732-7694
  16415 Addison Rd Ste 660 Addison (75001) *(G-167)*

Techsys Chassis Inc 903 395-4155
  524 S Church St Paris (75460) *(G-16371)*

Techtrade Solutions, Houston *Also called Cloud Ninjas LLC (G-9217)*

Techworks Inc 512 349-1300
  11100 Metric Blvd Ste 750 Austin (78758) *(G-1558)*

Tecmag Inc 713 667-8747
  10161 Harwin Dr Ste 150 Houston (77036) *(G-12178)*

Tecni-Quip Carts, Seguin *Also called Tqi LLC (G-18869)*

Tecnon Supply LLC 281 888-9045
  1185 Brittmoore Rd Houston (77043) *(G-12179)*

Tecnotrat Metal Processing LLC 281 894-9189
  9429 Frbanks N Houston Rd Houston (77064) *(G-12180)*

Tecnoval LLC 956 782-1111
  3805 Plntn Grv Blvd # 43 Mission (78572) *(G-15566)*

Teco Metal Products LLC 214 221-5020
  11477 Pagemill Rd Dallas (75243) *(G-5046)*

Tecpac Plastics & Seals LLC 281 547-0620
  22955 State Highway 249 # 25 Tomball (77375) *(G-20013)*

Tecpetrol Corporation 713 974-3322
  2200 West Loop S Ste 400 Houston (77027) *(G-12181)*

Tecplate LP 972 487-0636
  3609 Marquis Dr Garland (75042) *(G-7596)*

Teda Tpco America Corporation 361 826-2610
  5431 Highway 35 Gregory (78359) *(G-8106)*

Teebaud Co LLC 713 682-5161
  8732 Clay Rd Ste 109 Houston (77080) *(G-12182)*

Teems Rig Manufacturing LLC 806 379-6904
  14290 S Us Highway 287 Amarillo (79118) *(G-513)*

Teer Logging Inc 936 632-6862
  9793 E State Highway 103 Lufkin (75901) *(G-14554)*

Teer, Wilbern, Lufkin *Also called Teer Logging Inc (G-14554)*

Tefco II Lc 281 398-9684
  19407 Park Row Ste 120 Houston (77084) *(G-12183)*

Tefkab Footwear LLC 281 988-0977
  9330 W Arprt Blvd Ste 190 Houston (77031) *(G-12184)*

Tegraexcel Energy Services LLC 412 508-0690
  2807 Douglas Dr Midland (79701) *(G-15435)*

Tegron Holding LLC (HQ).........................903 759-1088
  5912 Old Highway 80 Ste B Longview (75604) *(G-14314)*

Teifs Wall Systems, San Antonio *Also called Texas Eifs LLC (G-18536)*

Teikoku USA Inc 713 983-9901
  5880 Bingle Rd Houston (77092) *(G-12185)*

Tejas Alloys LLC 830 303-4422
  285 Navarro Dr Seguin (78155) *(G-18867)*

Tejas Boiler Services Inc 713 631-8200
  7206 Elbert St Houston (77028) *(G-12186)*

Tejas Casing Ltd 281 215-1500
  8740 Miller Road 2 Houston (77049) *(G-12187)*

Tejas Industries Inc 806 293-4431
  E Of City Plainview (79072) *(G-16763)*

Tejas Industries Inc 806 322-2822
  3783 Fm 2943 Hereford (79045) *(G-8295)*

Tejas Machines Inc 281 350-8890
  2115 Riley Fuzzel Rd Spring (77386) *(G-19259)*

Tejas Oilfield Service, Gainesville *Also called Select Energy Services LLC (G-7365)*

Tejas PMS, San Antonio *Also called Tejas Precision Metalfabricatn (G-18524)*

Tejas Precision Metalfabricatn 210 648-1555
  2818 Se Loop 410 San Antonio (78222) *(G-18524)*

Tejas Production Services Inc 361 572-3127
  7303 Houston Hwy Victoria (77901) *(G-20307)*

Tejas Signs Wetz 830 609-6246
  20286 Fm 2252 San Antonio (78266) *(G-18646)*

Tejas Supreme Meat 210 224-9672
  222 E Cevallos San Antonio (78204) *(G-18525)*

Tejas Trucking Inc 432 523-5786
  2185 E State Highway 176 Andrews (79714) *(G-560)*

Tejas Tubular Products, Houston *Also called Tejas Casing Ltd (G-12187)*

Tejas Tubular Products Inc 254 965-5162
  600 Caporal Dr Stephenville (76401) *(G-19426)*

Tejas Tubular Products Inc (PA)...............281 822-3400
  8799 North Loop E Ste 300 Houston (77029) *(G-12188)*

Tejas Utility Construction Inc 281 299-5097
  8503 Pines Place Dr Humble (77346) *(G-12802)*

Tejas Vsual Communications Inc 972 243-6612
  9020 Directors Row Dallas (75247) *(G-5047)*

Tejon Exploration Co 325 673-6429
  400 Pine St Ste 900 Abilene (79601) *(G-86)*

Tejones Operating Corporation 210 824-5957
  17 Bitterblue Ln San Antonio (78218) *(G-18526)*

Tek Turbine, Brownsville *Also called Torqon Inc (G-2414)*

Tekmos Inc 512 342-9871
  7901 E Riverside Dr # 150 Austin (78744) *(G-1559)*

Tekna Impact 956 213-8285
  5800 S 42nd St Ste E McAllen (78503) *(G-14910)*

Tekni-Plex Inc 214 337-4711
  4700 S Westmoreland Rd Dallas (75237) *(G-5048)*

Teknor Color Company 903 586-0583
  4545 N Jackson St Jacksonville (75766) *(G-13262)*

Tektronix Inc 713 691-3658
  4500 S Wayside Dr Houston (77087) *(G-12189)*

Tektronix Inc 512 926-7625
  2324 Ridgepoint Dr Ste D Austin (78754) *(G-1560)*

Tekvox Inc 512 808-0845
  108 Wild Basin Rd Ste 215 West Lake Hills (78746) *(G-20689)*

Tel Mnfacturing Engrg Amer Inc 972 643-2000
  600 Millenium Dr Allen (75013) *(G-301)*

Telco Intercontinental Corp 281 500-8270
  9812 Whithorn Dr Houston (77095) *(G-12190)*

Telecom Management Corp 281 404-5610
  1110 Arden Forest Dr Spring (77379) *(G-19176)*

Telecom Products, Garland *Also called TPI (G-7604)*

Telecom Site Solutions LLC 888 779-9069
  7841 Hawn Fwy Dallas (75217) *(G-5049)*

Telecore Inc 972 238-9000
  1600 Jay Ell Dr Richardson (75081) *(G-17405)*

Teledrill Inc 281 550-0434
  18303 W Little York Rd Katy (77449) *(G-13448)*

Teledyne Bolt, Houston *Also called Teledyne Instruments Inc (G-12191)*

Teledyne Detcon Inc 281 367-4100
  4055 Tech Frest Blvd Ste The Woodlands (77381) *(G-19926)*

Teledyne Instruments Inc 713 666-2561
  5825 Chimney Rock Rd Houston (77081) *(G-12191)*

Teledyne Real Time Systems Inc 830 990-2340
  103 Industrial Loop # 1100 Fredericksburg (78624) *(G-7189)*

Telefuel, San Antonio *Also called Rubrix LLC (G-18437)*

Teleometrics International 254 776-2060
  4567 Lake Shore Dr Waco (76710) *(G-20464)*

Telephone Directory of Texas 903 586-2987
  404 Wynn Dr Jacksonville (75766) *(G-13263)*

Teleprime Advanced Communicati 512 271-9503
  7500 Rialto Blvd Ste 250 Austin (78735) *(G-1561)*

Telespace LLC 210 489-6600
  1354 N Loop 1604 E # 103 San Antonio (78232) *(G-18527)*

Telkin Piping System, Houston *Also called Telkin Sheetmetal Inc (G-12192)*

Telkin Sheetmetal Inc 713 691-3707
  7313 Domino Ln Houston (77076) *(G-12192)*

Tellabs Inc (HQ).......................................800 690-2324
  4240 Intl Pkwy Ste 105 Carrollton (75007) *(G-2890)*

Tellabs Enterprise Inc 972 588-7951
  4240 Intl Pkwy Ste 105 Carrollton (75007) **(G-2891)**

Telltales Magazines, Kemah *Also called Waterfront Publishing Inc* **(G-13482)**

Tellurian Inc (PA)...832 962-4000
  1201 La St Ste 3100 Houston (77002) **(G-12193)**

Tellurian Investments Inc (HQ).............................832 962-4000
  1201 Louisiana St # 3100 Houston (77002) **(G-12194)**

Telsco Industries Inc (PA)....................................972 278-6131
  3301 W Kingsley Rd Garland (75041) **(G-7597)**

Telxon Corporation 713 868-5511
  9000 Hempstead Rd Ste 220 Houston (77008) **(G-12195)**

Tema Oil and Gas Company (HQ).............................281 829-3206
  16200 Park Row Ste 300 Houston (77084) **(G-12196)**

Temperatsure LLC 502 715-2819
  1520 Luna Rd Ste 126 Carrollton (75006) **(G-2827)**

Temperture Measurement Systems 800 967-6498
  1502 E Royall Blvd Malakoff (75148) **(G-14637)**

Temple Bottling Company Ltd (PA).........................254 773-3376
  3510 Parkway Dr Temple (76504) **(G-19706)**

Temple Bottling Company Ltd 979 778-1203
  1820 Roughneck Dr Bryan (77808) **(G-2510)**

Temple Freightliner LP 254 770-1422
  4848 N General Bruce Dr Temple (76501) **(G-19707)**

Temple Generation I LLC 254 598-3700
  2892 Panda Dr Temple (76501) **(G-19708)**

Temple Machine Shop Inc 254 774-8099
  1401 N 14th St Temple (76501) **(G-19709)**

Temple Precision Enterpise Inc 409 283-8163
  1036 Hwy 69 N Woodville (75979) **(G-20918)**

Temple Tag II Ltd 254 982-4212
  1110 Industrial Blvd Temple (76504) **(G-19710)**

Temple Water Treatment 254 939-2161
  4820 Parkside Dr Temple (76502) **(G-19711)**

Temples Trailer Sales Inc 903 885-7301
  3964 Texas Highway 154 S Sulphur Springs (75482) **(G-19602)**

Tempo Semiconductor Inc 512 827-3440
  8627 N Mopac Expy Ste 130 Austin (78759) **(G-1562)**

Temptation Publishing, Houston *Also called TM Luckett Enterprises LLC* **(G-12307)**

Tenaha Feed Mill, Tenaha *Also called Pilgrims Pride Corporation* **(G-19724)**

Tenaris, Houston *Also called Maverick Tube Corporation* **(G-10802)**

Tenaris, Houston *Also called Maverick Tube Corporation* **(G-10803)**

Tenaris, Conroe *Also called Maverick Tube Corporation* **(G-3329)**

Tenaris Coiled Tubes LLC 713 460-1500
  8700 Clay Rd Houston (77080) **(G-12197)**

Tenaris Coiled Tubes LLC 281 458-2883
  8615 E Sam Houston Pkwy N Houston (77044) **(G-12198)**

Tenaris Global Svcs USA Corp 936 525-3101
  302 Mccarty St Houston (77029) **(G-12199)**

Tenaris Global Svcs USA Corp (HQ).......................713 767-4400
  2200 West Loop S Ste 800 Houston (77027) **(G-12200)**

Tenaris Hydril, Houston *Also called Hydril Company* **(G-10298)**

Tenaris Rods (usa) Inc 713 767-4400
  2200 West Loop S Ste 800 Houston (77027) **(G-12201)**

Tendeka Inc 832 827-4211
  6650 W Sam Houston Pkwy N # 420 Houston (77041) **(G-12202)**

Tendenci Inc (PA)...281 497-6567
  611 Dairy Ashford Rd # 4 Houston (77079) **(G-12203)**

Tender Mercies, Dallas *Also called Ferreira Holding Group LLC* **(G-4359)**

Tenneco Automotive Oper Co Inc 210 304-9390
  1 Lone Star Pass San Antonio (78264) **(G-18528)**

Tenneco Automotive Oper Co Inc 979 691-7732
  211 Quality Cir College Station (77845) **(G-3203)**

Tenneco Inc 915 832-4661
  7801 Trade Center Ave A El Paso (79912) **(G-5997)**

Tennessee Pipeline Cnstr Inc 361 364-2703
  917 S San Patricio St Sinton (78387) **(G-18966)**

Tension Envelope Corporation 817 451-5811
  5900 Tension Dr Fort Worth (76112) **(G-7042)**

Tent Company LLC 832 623-8958
  2333 Wirtcrest Ln Ste F Houston (77055) **(G-12204)**

Tent Rental, Waco *Also called Aquila & Priscilla Tentmakers* **(G-20363)**

Tenth Frame Inc 979 743-6585
  233 College St Schulenburg (78956) **(G-18780)**

Tenth Street Industries LP 972 578-5155
  901 10th St Plano (75074) **(G-17024)**

Tents of Southwest Inc 713 692-8565
  5920 Killough St Houston (77086) **(G-12205)**

Tep Barnett Usa LLC 817 720-1130
  301 Commerce St Ste 3700 Fort Worth (76102) **(G-7043)**

Tepee Petroleum Company Inc 713 659-8300
  3700 Buffalo Speedway # 1010 Houston (77098) **(G-12206)**

Teraco, Inc., Midland *Also called New Teraco Inc* **(G-15316)**

Teradyne Inc 972 231-5384
  2701 W Plano Pkwy Ste 700 Plano (75075) **(G-17025)**

Teradyne Inc 512 891-9600
  5700 S Mo Pac Expy # 400 Austin (78749) **(G-1563)**

Tercel Oilfield Pdts USA LLC (HQ).........................832 386-2500
  10613 W Sam Houston Pkwy Houston (77064) **(G-12207)**

Teresa A McVicker Pc 254 526-2823
  1008 N 4th St Killeen (76541) **(G-13617)**

Terex Corporation 903 786-2981
  3501 N Fm 1417 Denison (75020) **(G-5347)**

Ternium Usa Inc (HQ)..318 698-7500
  2200 West Loop S Ste 945 Houston (77027) **(G-12208)**

Terra Biochem LLC 409 489-1700
  610 Mcqueen St Jasper (75951) **(G-13280)**

Terra Energy Partners LLC (PA).............................281 936-0355
  3050 Post Oak Blvd # 1500 Houston (77056) **(G-12209)**

Terra Metrics Ltd 432 337-3412
  1300 N Texas Ave Odessa (79761) **(G-16174)**

Terrace Energy LLC 817 546-7490
  301 Commerce Ste 3635 Fort Worth (76102) **(G-7044)**

Terrell Tribune, Terrell *Also called Hartman Newspapers LP* **(G-19737)**

Terry Costa Inc (PA)..972 385-6100
  12817 Preston Rd Ste 138 Dallas (75230) **(G-5050)**

Tervita LLC (HQ)..832 399-4500
  10613 W Sam Houston Pkwy Houston (77064) **(G-12210)**

Tervita LLC 817 783-2777
  7912 S Ih 35 W Alvarado (76009) **(G-346)**

Tesco Corporation (HQ)...713 359-7000
  515 W Greens Rd 1200 Houston (77067) **(G-12211)**

Tesco Corporation (us) (HQ).................................713 359-7000
  515 W Greens Rd Ste 1200 Houston (77067) **(G-12212)**

Tesco Drilling Tech U S A, Houston *Also called Tesco Corporation (us)* **(G-12212)**

Tesco Industries Lp 979 865-2163
  1035 E Hacienda St Bellville (77418) **(G-2012)**

Tesco Services Inc 903 983-1007
  104 Longview St Kilgore (75662) **(G-13596)**

Tesoro, Donna *Also called AAA Electrical Signs* **(G-5486)**

Tesoro Corp 956 682-7831
  2407 E Business Hwy 83 Donna (78537) **(G-5494)**

Tesoro Lgstics NW Pipeline LLC 210 249-9123
  19100 Ridgewood Pkwy San Antonio (78259) **(G-18529)**

Tesoro Refining & Mktg Co LLC (HQ).....................210 828-8484
  19100 Ridgewood Pkwy San Antonio (78259) **(G-18530)**

Tessco, Kermit *Also called Power Line Infrstrcture Svcs I* **(G-13514)**

Test Automation & Controls, Houston *Also called Test Incorporated* **(G-12213)**

Test Engineering, San Antonio *Also called Turbomasters Inc* **(G-18572)**

Test Equipment USA, Houston *Also called Gil Automations LLC* **(G-9957)**

Test Incorporated 713 983-2800
  6213 W Sam Houston Pkwy N Houston (77041) **(G-12213)**

Test Spectrum Inc 512 472-6750
  9701 Brodie Ln Ste 101 Austin (78748) **(G-1564)**

Testamerica Air Emission Corp (HQ)......................800 394-1194
  3226 Commander Dr Carrollton (75006) **(G-2828)**

Testco Well Services LLC 361 396-0626
  6016 E Hwy 44 Laredo (78043) **(G-13937)**

Testequity LLC 972 247-2470
  2434 Mciver Ln Carrollton (75006) **(G-2829)**

Testforce Usa Inc 925 281-3501
  15020 Beltway Dr Addison (75001) **(G-168)**

Testing Laboratory, Pasadena *Also called Product Quality Management LLC* **(G-16498)**

Testmasters Inc 713 896-1885
  5711 Cunningham Rd Houston (77041) **(G-12214)**

Testronics Consolidated Inc 972 542-3111
  903 N Bowser Rd Ste 300 Richardson (75081) **(G-17406)**

Teton Buildings LLC 307 473-7543
  2701 Magnet St Houston (77054) **(G-12215)**

Tetra Pak CPS, Denton *Also called Tetra Pak Inc* **(G-5404)**

Tetra Pak Global Information 940 565-8800
  3300 Airport Rd Bldg 900b Denton (76207) **(G-5403)**

Tetra Pak Inc (HQ)...940 565-8800
  3300 Airport Rd Denton (76207) **(G-5404)**

Tetra Pak Materials LP 940 565-8800
  3300 Airport Rd Denton (76207) **(G-5405)**

Tetra Production Tstg Svcs LLC 281 367-1983
  24955 Interstate 45 The Woodlands (77380) **(G-19927)**

Tetra Services, Converse *Also called Epica Applied Technologies LLC* **(G-3393)**

Tetra Technologies, Converse *Also called Epica Applied Technologies LLC* **(G-3392)**

Tetra Technologies Inc (PA)...................................281 367-1983
  24955 Interstate 45 The Woodlands (77380) **(G-19928)**

Tetra Technologies Inc 903 693-9500
  1743 Ne Loop Carthage (75633) **(G-2923)**

Tewa LLC 915 886-9973
  251 Valley Chili Rd Vinton (79821) **(G-20341)**

Tex Air Filters, Fort Worth *Also called Air Relief Technologies Inc* **(G-6357)**

Tex Cnp/Seal Inc (PA)...214 688-7770
  8435 Directors Row Dallas (75247) **(G-5051)**

Tex Co, Rockwall *Also called Tex-Co Resin Distribution Inc* **(G-17568)**

Tex ISO Inc 281 482-1231
  1511 County Rd 129 Friendswood (77546) **(G-7250)**

Tex Styles International Inc 713 787-9955
  12725 Royal Dr Stafford (77477) **(G-19384)**

Tex Sun Manufacturing Co 830 393-5186
  1912 Virginia Ln Floresville (78114) **(G-6251)**

Tex Tan Western Co Yoakum Inc......................361 293-2314
601 Hickey St Yoakum (77995) *(G-20973)*

Tex Tan Western Leather Co, Yoakum *Also called Tex Tan Western Co Yoakum Inc (G-20973)*

Tex Tech Environmental Inc..........................817 295-3701
1125 S Burleson Blvd Burleson (76028) *(G-2598)*

Tex Webb LLC..214 770-7073
7324 Gaston Ave 124-42 Dallas (75214) *(G-5052)*

Tex-Art Stone Inc....................................817 481-9602
8900 Davis Blvd Keller (76248) *(G-13470)*

Tex-Co Resin Distribution Inc........................972 722-8603
105 Industrial Blvd Rockwall (75087) *(G-17568)*

Tex-Lam Manufacturing Inc..........................713 695-5975
7219 Stuebner Airline Rd Houston (77091) *(G-12216)*

Tex-Lam Toilet Partition Mfg, Houston *Also called Tex-Lam Manufacturing Inc (G-12216)*

Tex-Mex Cold Storage Inc (PA).....................956 831-4531
21 Poinsettia Pl Brownsville (78520) *(G-2409)*

Tex-Pac Hide & Skin, Fort Worth *Also called Texpac Hide & Skin Ltd (G-7052)*

Tex-Rite, Houston *Also called Texas Cement Products Inc (G-12225)*

Tex-Sun Shade Specialties Inc.......................972 279-0132
12150 Shiloh Rd Ste 104 Dallas (75228) *(G-5053)*

Tex-Tube Company...................................713 686-4351
1503 N Post Oak Rd Houston (77055) *(G-12217)*

Texaco Exploration & Prod Inc (HQ)...............**800 962-1223**
1500 Louisiana St Houston (77002) *(G-12218)*

Texakoma Financial Inc..............................972 701-9106
5601 Granite Pkwy Ste 600 Plano (75024) *(G-17026)*

Texakoma Operating LP..............................972 701-9106
5601 Granite Pkwy Ste 600 Plano (75024) *(G-17027)*

Texaloy Foundry Company...........................830 393-6679
710 4th St Floresville (78114) *(G-6252)*

Texan Accent, San Antonio *Also called Monterrey Products Company (G-18319)*

Texan Electric Co Inc................................713 645-6560
7011 Dixie Dr Houston (77087) *(G-12219)*

Texan News The, Colleyville *Also called Itexaspolitics LLC (G-3214)*

Texan Waste Equipment Inc.........................210 224-5800
503 Pop Gunn St San Antonio (78219) *(G-18531)*

Texana Feeders Ltd..................................830 947-3396
3493 Fm 539 Floresville (78114) *(G-6253)*

Texans Agri Products, Conroe *Also called Ramrod Enterprises LLC (G-3356)*

Texarkan Fence......................................870 779-0660
359 Dodd St Nash (75569) *(G-15724)*

Texarkana Door & Window Inc......................903 793-6011
6509 Farmers Ln Texarkana (75503) *(G-19777)*

Texarkana EMB & Graphics.........................903 792-1144
21 Lambeth Rd Texarkana (75503) *(G-19778)*

Texarkana Machine Inc..............................903 831-4355
277 White Rd E Texarkana (75503) *(G-19779)*

Texarkana Recycling Plant, Texarkana *Also called Caraustar Industries Inc (G-19758)*

Texarome Inc..830 232-6079
1585 E Ranch Rd Leakey (78873) *(G-13983)*

Texas 2 Stitch.......................................972 599-1717
3100 Independence Pkwy # 207 Plano (75075) *(G-17028)*

Texas 21st Century Transport &....................432 607-2071
708 N Lamesa Hwy Stanton (79782) *(G-19405)*

Texas 21st Century Trnsp, Stanton *Also called Texas 21st Century Transport & (G-19405)*

Texas 28 LLC..806 644-9663
719 W 7th Ave Spearman (79081) *(G-19088)*

Texas Aeroplastics..................................817 430-3651
1803 E Highway 114 Boyd (76023) *(G-2207)*

Texas Aggregates LP................................512 303-4215
420 Old Perkins Rd Bastrop (78602) *(G-1762)*

Texas Agri Machine & Indus Mfg...................806 296-5765
1317 Andy Taylor Rd Plainview (79072) *(G-16764)*

Texas Air & Water LLC..............................361 814-3131
3818 Wow Rd Corpus Christi (78413) *(G-3636)*

Texas Air Products Ltd (PA)........................**210 495-8100**
11122 Gordon Rd San Antonio (78216) *(G-18532)*

Texas Almet LP......................................817 649-7056
2800 E Randol Mill Rd Arlington (76011) *(G-791)*

Texas Aluminum Foundry Inc........................817 834-5568
204 Penland St Fort Worth (76111) *(G-7045)*

Texas Aluminum Industries Inc......................713 941-7186
2900 Patio Dr Houston (77017) *(G-12220)*

Texas Ammo, Taylor *Also called Babeco Inc (G-19648)*

Texas and Oklahoma Elc Svc LLC..................972 222-2229
11233 N Stemmons Fwy Dallas (75229) *(G-5054)*

Texas Archtctral Aggregate Inc (PA)...............**325 372-5105**
Hwy 190 E San Saba (76877) *(G-18719)*

Texas Armoring Corporation.........................210 333-0211
4323 Factory Hill St San Antonio (78219) *(G-18533)*

Texas Australian Power Inc..........................940 723-4122
5018 Ditto Ln Wichita Falls (76302) *(G-20815)*

Texas Auto Trim.....................................713 661-5557
6025 Bissonnet St Houston (77081) *(G-12221)*

Texas Automatic Foods Inc..........................713 432-1331
1331 N 1st St Bellaire (77401) *(G-2003)*

Texas Automation Products Inc......................972 289-0300
300 Nichols Dr Hutchins (75141) *(G-12871)*

Texas Aviation Tech LLC............................210 680-8181
1731 S San Marcos # 912 San Antonio (78207) *(G-18534)*

Texas Barricade Service.............................915 355-6653
6621 Doniphan Dr Canutillo (79835) *(G-2665)*

Texas Best Panels Inc...............................512 752-3777
15614 N Highway 183 Lometa (76853) *(G-14178)*

Texas Best Proteins LP..............................940 769-2028
5775 Fm 2201 Santo (76472) *(G-18739)*

Texas Big Game Processing Inc......................210 366-0638
15603 Legend Springs Dr San Antonio (78247) *(G-18535)*

Texas Bolt & Nut Company Ltd.....................713 869-7111
6300 W By Northwest Blvd # 600 Houston (77040) *(G-12222)*

Texas Book Company................................972 825-4781
1123 Sycamore St Waxahachie (75165) *(G-20565)*

Texas Brine Baytown Company, Mont Belvieu *Also called Texas Brine Company LLC (G-15619)*

Texas Brine Company LLC (HQ)....................**713 877-2700**
4800 San Felipe St Houston (77056) *(G-12223)*

Texas Brine Company LLC...........................281 385-6048
401 W Winfree Rd Mont Belvieu (77580) *(G-15619)*

Texas Building Products Inc.........................254 672-5262
3261 State Highway 108 Strawn (76475) *(G-19433)*

Texas By-Products Partnership (PA)................**214 871-0600**
2621 State St Dallas (75204) *(G-5055)*

Texas Cabinet Inc...................................972 293-2450
1001 Cedarview Dr Cedar Hill (75104) *(G-2953)*

Texas Cabinet Doors, Cedar Hill *Also called Texas Cabinet Inc (G-2953)*

Texas Capital Bancshares Inc.......................214 706-6780
2350 Lakeside Blvd Frnt Richardson (75082) *(G-17407)*

Texas Carved Stone LP..............................254 793-2384
6621 Hwy 195 Florence (76527) *(G-6245)*

Texas Catholic Herald Inc...........................713 659-5461
1700 San Jacinto St Houston (77002) *(G-12224)*

Texas Catholic Herald The, Houston *Also called Texas Catholic Herald Inc (G-12224)*

Texas Cement Products Inc (PA)...................**713 682-8411**
4000 Pinemont Dr Houston (77018) *(G-12225)*

Texas Cementing Services Inc.......................361 516-1127
2620 E Corral Ave Kingsville (78363) *(G-13635)*

Texas Circuitry Inc..................................972 278-3838
2960 Market St Garland (75041) *(G-7598)*

Texas Citrus Exchange..............................956 585-8321
702 E Interstate 2 Mission (78572) *(G-15567)*

Texas City Newspapers Inc..........................409 945-3441
7800 Emmett F Lowry Expy Texas City (77591) *(G-19803)*

Texas City Sun, The, Texas City *Also called Texas City Newspapers Inc (G-19803)*

Texas Clothing Holding Corp (PA)..................**214 956-4494**
11511 Luna Rd Dallas (75234) *(G-5056)*

Texas Coastal Energy Co LLC.......................214 429-3700
9330 Lyndon B J Fwy 900 Dallas (75243) *(G-5057)*

Texas Coffee Company..............................409 835-3434
3297 S M L King Jr Pkwy Beaumont (77705) *(G-1958)*

Texas Coffee Traders, Austin *Also called Coffee Traders Inc (G-1056)*

Texas Coin and Commercial Ldry, Dallas *Also called My Sons Laundry LLC (G-4710)*

Texas Community Media LLC........................903 757-3311
320 E Methvin St Longview (75601) *(G-14315)*

Texas Community Newspapers, Fort Worth *Also called Connor Media Group LLC (G-6542)*

Texas Compression Services, Houston *Also called Houston Compression & Svcs LLC (G-10226)*

Texas Concrete Chemical Inc........................936 638-4273
7780 Grvton Flat Prrie Rd Groveton (75845) *(G-8113)*

Texas Concrete Enterprise LLC......................713 227-1122
3506 Cherry St Houston (77026) *(G-12226)*

Texas Concrete Entp Rdymx Inc.....................713 227-1122
6001 Homestead Rd Houston (77028) *(G-12227)*

Texas Concrete Partners LP.........................361 573-9145
4702 N Vine St Victoria (77904) *(G-20308)*

Texas Concrete Partners LP (PA)...................**254 822-1351**
1690 Mesquite Tree Rd Elm Mott (76640) *(G-6065)*

Texas Concrete Tank, Del Valle *Also called Hoesman Industries Inc (G-5331)*

Texas Corrugated Box Packg LLC...................817 454-2037
1624 Intermodal Pkwy Fort Worth (76177) *(G-7046)*

Texas Couplings.....................................281 350-2494
1835 Old Holzwarth Rd Spring (77388) *(G-19177)*

Texas Covers, Olden *Also called Creative MENus&folders LLC (G-16219)*

Texas Crude Energy Inc.............................713 599-9900
2803 Buffalo Spdwy # 105 Houston (77098) *(G-12228)*

Texas Crude Energy LLC............................713 599-9900
2803 Buffalo Speedway # 105 Houston (77098) *(G-12229)*

Texas Crumb and Food Products, Carrollton *Also called Das Brot Inc (G-2721)*

Texas Crushed Stone Company (PA)................**512 255-4405**
5300 S Interstate 35 Georgetown (78626) *(G-7684)*

Texas Custom Coach, Pipe Creek *Also called Coachworks LLC (G-16741)*

Texas Custom Coaters Inc...........................936 825-7211
9468 Interstate Dr Navasota (77868) *(G-15743)*

Texas Dental Association Inc........................512 443-3675
1946 S Interstate 35 # 400 Austin (78704) *(G-1565)*

Texas Department Trnsp............................512 486-5887
1101 W Anderson Ln Austin (78757) *(G-1566)*

Texas Dept Criminal Justice 936 295-6371
Wine Unit Huntsville (77349) *(G-12825)*

Texas Die Casting LLC 903 845-2224
600 S Loop 485 Gladewater (75647) *(G-7727)*

Texas Digital Copy and Print, San Antonio *Also called Copy Center LLC (G-18026)*

Texas Digital Systems Inc 979 693-0933
400 Technology Pkwy College Station (77845) *(G-3204)*

Texas Drect Bndery Letterpress, Houston *Also called Kng LLC (G-10545)*

Texas Eagle Construction, Haltom City *Also called USA Eagle Carports Inc (G-8161)*

Texas Eagle Star MGT Inc 915 858-3144
10747 Ululani Dr El Paso (79927) *(G-5998)*

Texas Economic Publishers, Waco *Also called Perryman Group Inc (G-20445)*

Texas Eifs LLC (PA) **210 472-2935**
220 Burleson San Antonio (78202) *(G-18536)*

Texas Electric Coops Inc (PA) **512 454-0311**
1122 Colorado St Ste 2400 Austin (78701) *(G-1567)*

Texas Electric Coops Inc 409 384-4633
2240 Bevil Loop Jasper (75951) *(G-13281)*

Texas Electric Coops Inc 512 868-8610
100 W Cooperative Way Georgetown (78626) *(G-7685)*

Texas Electric Eqp Co Ltd 281 479-6086
9401 Highway 225 La Porte (77571) *(G-13794)*

Texas Electrical, Dallas *Also called Texas and Oklahoma Elc Svc LLC (G-5054)*

Texas Electrical Machinery Co, Houston *Also called Land Enterprises Inc (G-10592)*

Texas Electronics Inc 214 327-2566
4230 Shilling Way Dallas (75237) *(G-5058)*

Texas Energy Holdings Inc (PA) **214 231-4000**
3320 Oak Grove Ave # 100 Dallas (75204) *(G-5059)*

Texas Energy Services LP (PA) **361 664-5020**
4932 N Us Hwy 281 Alice (78332) *(G-240)*

Texas Enterprise Mfg & Mch 281 342-0027
2505 County Road 235 Wharton (77488) *(G-20707)*

Texas Envelope Company 214 358-5661
10655 Shady Trl Dallas (75220) *(G-5060)*

Texas Environmental Tech LLC 817 534-4275
3453 E Vickery Blvd Fort Worth (76105) *(G-7047)*

Texas Extrusion Service Inc 281 350-2288
20803 Sunshine Ln Spring (77388) *(G-19178)*

Texas Fabco Solutions Inc 979 255-3530
178 Ranch Road 962 E Round Mountain (78663) *(G-17619)*

Texas Farm Bureau 254 751-2251
7420 Fish Pond Rd Waco (76710) *(G-20465)*

Texas Farm Products Company (PA) **936 564-3711**
915 S Fredonia St Nacogdoches (75964) *(G-15715)*

Texas Finishing Company 972 416-2961
1801 Surveyor Blvd Carrollton (75006) *(G-2830)*

Texas Firecrckrs Fstptch Softb 713 818-4661
11093 Darby Loop Conroe (77385) *(G-3370)*

Texas First Indus Corp Inc 281 934-1190
32473 Morton Rd Brookshire (77423) *(G-2327)*

Texas Fish Game Pubg Co L L C 281 227-3001
247 Airtex Dr Houston (77090) *(G-12230)*

Texas Fixtures and Interiors 512 846-1998
3874 Limmer Loop Hutto (78634) *(G-12886)*

Texas Flameproofing Inc 214 630-1088
5131 Sharp St Dallas (75247) *(G-5061)*

Texas Fluorescents, Dallas *Also called Fleco Industries LLC (G-4368)*

Texas Foam Inc 512 581-7500
1278 Highway 71 W Bastrop (78602) *(G-1763)*

Texas Food Solutions LLC 713 579-5634
25002 Clay Rd Katy (77493) *(G-13449)*

Texas Friction Materials, Magnolia *Also called Scan-Pac Mfg Inc (G-14626)*

Texas Furnace LLC 713 466-1504
7037 Brittmoore Rd Houston (77041) *(G-12231)*

Texas Galvanizing, Brenham *Also called Valmont Industries Inc (G-2278)*

Texas Gas Service Company, Gonzales *Also called One Gas Inc (G-7760)*

Texas Gas Service Company, Gonzales *Also called One Gas Inc (G-7761)*

Texas Gas Service Company 956 444-3900
5602 E Grimes St Harlingen (78550) *(G-8205)*

Texas Gas Utilities LLC 281 252-6700
9750 Fm 1488 Rd Magnolia (77354) *(G-14628)*

Texas Gasket and Packing Co 713 674-7531
1255 Lathrop St Houston (77020) *(G-12232)*

Texas Gate and Panel, Bryan *Also called T G & P Inc (G-2509)*

Texas Geologic Services LLC 979 542-3893
2946 E Austin St Giddings (78942) *(G-7702)*

Texas Global Systems Inc (PA) **832 403-4238**
8700 Commerce Park Dr # 201 Houston (77036) *(G-12233)*

Texas Gravel Co, Sullivan City *Also called South Texas Concrete (G-19577)*

Texas Heat Treating Inc (PA) **512 255-5884**
155 Texas Ave Round Rock (78664) *(G-17692)*

Texas High Roller Inc 979 778-7460
13810 S State Highway 6 Bryan (77807) *(G-2511)*

Texas Highways Magazine, Austin *Also called Texas Department Trnsp (G-1566)*

Texas Hills Vineyard Inc 830 868-2321
878 Ranch Rd 2766 Johnson City (78636) *(G-13313)*

Texas Home & Projects LLC 956 546-8400
2685 N Coria St Rear Brownsville (78520) *(G-2410)*

Texas Honing Inc (HQ) **281 485-8339**
1710 Mykawa Rd Pearland (77581) *(G-16601)*

Texas Honing Inc 713 673-1111
5602 Arapahoe St Houston (77020) *(G-12234)*

Texas Honing Inc 281 953-5900
2000 Aldine Western Rd Houston (77038) *(G-12235)*

Texas Hot Oilers Inc 979 542-9341
Hwy 77 Giddings (78942) *(G-7703)*

Texas Hydraulic & Eqp Co Inc 214 748-7551
810 Skyline Dr Hutchins (75141) *(G-12872)*

Texas Hydraulics Inc (HQ) **254 778-4701**
3410 Range Rd Temple (76504) *(G-19712)*

Texas Hydraulics Inc 254 756-6879
6613 N 19th St Waco (76708) *(G-20466)*

Texas Ice Cream, Justin *Also called Joseph McSweeny Entps LLC (G-13345)*

Texas Incinerator Co Inc 432 687-5045
2401 Neill Ave Midland (79701) *(G-15436)*

Texas Industrial Choice LLC 432 231-7313
2291 S Bickley Ave Pecos (79772) *(G-16627)*

Texas Industrial Remcor Inc 254 982-4236
1807 N Highway 95 Little River Academy (76554) *(G-14143)*

Texas Industries Inc 972 775-3449
245 Ward Rd Midlothian (76065) *(G-15495)*

Texas Industries Inc 940 683-4277
1795 S Hwy 101 Bridgeport (76426) *(G-2303)*

Texas Industries Inc 817 838-4212
3601 Lawnwood St Fort Worth (76111) *(G-7048)*

Texas Industries Inc 903 873-2849
201 Vz County Road 3805 Wills Point (75169) *(G-20878)*

Texas Industries Inc (HQ) **972 647-6700**
1503 Lyndon B Johnson Fwy Dallas (75234) *(G-5062)*

Texas Industries Inc 936 564-8301
1211 Bennett Clark Rd Nacogdoches (75961) *(G-15716)*

Texas Industries Inc 903 843-2327
320 Walnut St Gilmer (75644) *(G-7715)*

Texas Industries Inc 512 396-4244
7781 Fm 1102 New Braunfels (78132) *(G-15827)*

Texas Industries Inc 817 596-4307
5211 New Tin Top Rd Weatherford (76087) *(G-20625)*

Texas Industries Inc 972 556-0751
10610 Spangler Rd Dallas (75220) *(G-5063)*

Texas Industries Inc 903 758-7351
433 E College St Longview (75601) *(G-14316)*

Texas Industries Inc 903 454-2029
6500 Fm 1570 W Greenville (75402) *(G-8094)*

Texas Industries Inc 940 969-6021
2939 W Highway 114 Paradise (76073) *(G-16354)*

Texas Industries Inc 512 276-7990
18601 Fm 969 Manor (78653) *(G-14650)*

Texas Industries Inc 281 261-0790
13908 Pike Rd Stafford (77477) *(G-19385)*

Texas Industries Inc 972 263-5077
2202 Chalk Hill Rd Dallas (75212) *(G-5064)*

Texas Ine Inc (PA) **281 601-4884**
6438 Long Dr Houston (77087) *(G-12236)*

Texas Ingredient Corporation 817 645-1328
2701 Pipeline Rd Cleburne (76033) *(G-3113)*

Texas Ingredients, Cleburne *Also called Texas Ingredient Corporation (G-3113)*

Texas Injection Molding LLC 281 489-4292
8820 Frey Rd Houston (77034) *(G-12237)*

Texas Instrs Philippines LLC 972 995-3773
12500 T I Blvd Dallas (75243) *(G-5065)*

Texas Instruments Incorporated 972 995-2011
7800 Banner Dr Dallas (75251) *(G-5066)*

Texas Instruments Incorporated (PA) **972 995-3773**
12500 Ti Blvd Dallas (75243) *(G-5067)*

Texas Instruments Incorporated 512 434-1560
108 Wild Basin Rd West Lake Hills (78746) *(G-20690)*

Texas Instruments Incorporated 214 480-4691
4317 Brady Dr Plano (75024) *(G-17029)*

Texas Instruments Incorporated 214 479-3773
13020 Ti Blvd Dallas (75243) *(G-5068)*

Texas Instruments Incorporated 214 966-9759
330 Valley View Trl Double Oak (75077) *(G-5497)*

Texas Instruments Incorporated 214 567-5185
13532 N Central Expy Dallas (75243) *(G-5069)*

Texas Instruments Incorporated 972 995-2011
13570 N Central Expy Dallas (75243) *(G-5070)*

Texas Instruments Incorporated 832 939-2000
13905 University Blvd Sugar Land (77479) *(G-19562)*

Texas Instruments Incorporated 972 995-2011
12201 Southwest Fwy Stafford (77477) *(G-19386)*

Texas Instruments Incorporated 972 644-5580
8330 Lbj Fwy Ms3123 Dallas (75243) *(G-5071)*

Texas Instruments Incorporated 817 401-5563
13536 N Central Expy Dallas (75243) *(G-5072)*

Texas Instruments Incorporated 972 995-2011
13588 N Central Expy Dallas (75243) *(G-5073)*

Texas Instruments Incorporated 972 995-2011
6500 Chase Oaks Blvd Plano (75023) *(G-17030)*

Texas Instruments Incorporated 214 567-2075
300 W Renner Rd Richardson (75080) *(G-17408)*

Texas Instruments Incorporated 214 567-9863
6550 Chase Oaks Blvd Plano (75023) *(G-17031)*

Texas Integrity Waste 940 479-0189
7588 Fm 2449 Ponder (76259) *(G-17096)*

Texas Intl Gas & Oil Co 915 860-8803
124 W Castellano Dr # 211 El Paso (79912) *(G-5999)*

Texas Intrnal Pipe Coating LLC 936 348-2508
8463 Highway 75 S Madisonville (77864) *(G-14590)*

Texas Iron & Steel LLC 903 758-9498
288 Pr 2317 Longview (75603) *(G-14317)*

Texas Iron & Steel Hauling, Longview *Also called Texas Iron & Steel LLC (G-14317)*

Texas Jewish Post Ltd (PA) **972 458-7283**
7920 Belt Line Rd Ste 680 Dallas (75254) *(G-5074)*

Texas Kenworth Co 940 767-0001
1901 Central Fwy E Wichita Falls (76302) *(G-20816)*

Texas Kenworth Co 432 381-3300
5251 W Interstate 20 Odessa (79763) *(G-16175)*

Texas Label and Tag, Carrollton *Also called J & J Nameplate and Label LLC (G-2873)*

Texas Lamp Manufacturers Inc 972 564-5267
505 E Us Highway 80 Forney (75126) *(G-6315)*

Texas Landfill Management LLC 210 651-6115
14080 Nacogdoches Rd # 314 San Antonio (78247) *(G-18537)*

Texas Lawyer, Dallas *Also called Alm Media LLC (G-3928)*

Texas Leather Trim Inc 817 535-5883
2422 Blue Smoke Ct S Fort Worth (76105) *(G-7049)*

Texas Lehigh Cement Company LP 512 434-9330
336 Scenic Way Wimberley (78676) *(G-20884)*

Texas Lehigh Cement Company LP 512 295-6111
701 Cement Plant Rd Buda (78610) *(G-2540)*

Texas Lehigh Cement Company LP (HQ) **512 295-6111**
1000 Jack C Hays Trl Buda (78610) *(G-2541)*

Texas Lightsmith Inc 512 264-2266
3410 Andtree Blvd Austin (78724) *(G-1568)*

Texas Lime Company (HQ) **972 385-1335**
5429 Lyndon B Johnson Fwy # 230 Dallas (75240) *(G-5075)*

Texas Lime Company 817 641-4433
15865 Farm Road 1434 Cleburne (76033) *(G-3114)*

Texas Liner Service LLC 281 445-5050
6618 Spindle Dr Houston (77086) *(G-12238)*

Texas Logic Inc 956 682-3466
4200 N Bicentennial Dr A McAllen (78504) *(G-14911)*

Texas Lumber Construction 979 732-2063
939 Fannin St Columbus (78934) *(G-3234)*

Texas Machinery Co 972 792-0166
451 Vz County Road 3803 Wills Point (75169) *(G-20879)*

Texas Marble Manufacturing, Hallsville *Also called Churchill Manufacturing Inc (G-8128)*

Texas Marine Holdings Ltd (PA) **817 589-7547**
2177 E Loop 820 N Fort Worth (76118) *(G-7050)*

Texas Marine Shipyard LLC 409 457-6260
5200 27th St Dickinson (77539) *(G-5478)*

Texas Marking Products Inc 281 364-7100
26019 Interstate 45 The Woodlands (77380) *(G-19929)*

Texas Materials Group Inc 214 372-7700
8201 S Central Expy Dallas (75241) *(G-5076)*

Texas Mattress Makers, Houston *Also called Noahs Manufacturing Inc (G-11062)*

Texas Meat Purveyors, San Antonio *Also called Buckhead Meat of San Antonio (G-17970)*

Texas Medical Industries Inc 972 636-9556
1409 Industrial Dr Royse City (75189) *(G-17726)*

Texas Medical Technology LLC 832 512-7727
6115 Skyline Dr Ste C Houston (77057) *(G-12239)*

Texas Medplast LLC 832 288-2106
6630 Roxburgh Dr Ste 171 Houston (77041) *(G-12240)*

Texas Metal Casting Co (PA) **936 639-1131**
5400 Lotus Ln Lufkin (75904) *(G-14555)*

Texas Metal Equipment Co Ltd (PA) **713 466-8722**
6707 Mayard Rd Houston (77041) *(G-12241)*

Texas Metal Equipment Co Ltd 214 446-7200
8704 N Royal Ln Irving (75063) *(G-13192)*

Texas Metal Industries Inc 972 288-2333
1331 Us Highway 80 E # 15 Mesquite (75150) *(G-15080)*

Texas Metal Processing Intl, Mission *Also called Metal Processing Intl LP (G-15560)*

Texas Meter and Device Co LLC 254 732-1305
300 S 8th St Waco (76701) *(G-20467)*

Texas Monthly Magazine, Austin *Also called GP Tm Acquisition LLC (G-1190)*

Texas Mpp LP (PA) **903 874-5781**
2900 E State Highway 31 Corsicana (75109) *(G-3685)*

Texas Mri LP (PA) **940 549-5462**
510 Corporate Dr Graham (76450) *(G-7790)*

Texas Mri LP 214 630-9625
1111 W Mockingbird Ln # 1050 Dallas (75247) *(G-5077)*

Texas Music Magazine 903 838-3838
120 Cherokee Trl Apt 5 Texarkana (75501) *(G-19780)*

Texas Nameplate Company Inc 214 428-8341
2200 W Longhorn Dr Lancaster (75134) *(G-13849)*

Texas National Fleet Pnt & Bdy, Houston *Also called Randy Wrecker Service Inc (G-11543)*

Texas National Solutions, Houston *Also called Tns Industries Inc (G-12313)*

Texas Natural Rainwtr Hrvstng 512 772-1981
125 Kellar Rd Smithville (78957) *(G-18978)*

Texas Neighbors, Waco *Also called Texas Farm Bureau (G-20465)*

Texas Neon Advertising Company 210 734-6694
245 W Josephine St San Antonio (78212) *(G-18538)*

Texas Nom Limited Partnership 210 687-1900
6002 Camp Bullis Rd San Antonio (78257) *(G-18539)*

Texas Nova-Chem Corporation 972 771-1161
2020 Industrial Blvd Rockwall (75087) *(G-17569)*

Texas Office Pdts & Sup Inc 512 472-1340
1300 E 5th St Austin (78702) *(G-1569)*

Texas Offset Printing LP (PA) **214 628-7430**
6730 Oakbrook Blvd Dallas (75235) *(G-5078)*

Texas Oil & Chemical Co II Inc 409 385-1400
7752 Fm 418 Silsbee (77656) *(G-18957)*

Texas Oil Group Ltd Co 281 645-9398
17806 W Interstate 10 San Antonio (78257) *(G-18540)*

Texas Oiltech Laboratories Inc 281 495-2400
10630 Fallstone Rd Houston (77099) *(G-12242)*

Texas Orthopaedic PDT Svcs LLC 972 772-8776
805 Riding Club Rd Rockwall (75087) *(G-17570)*

Texas Orthopedic Products, Rockwall *Also called Texas Orthopaedic PDT Svcs LLC (G-17570)*

Texas Orthotics, Plano *Also called Orthorx Inc (G-16959)*

Texas Pacific Group, Fort Worth *Also called Tpg Capital Management LP (G-7069)*

Texas Pack Inc 956 943-5461
508 Port Rd Port Isabel (78578) *(G-17138)*

Texas Packing, San Angelo *Also called 7 S Packing LLC (G-17768)*

Texas Perforators Inc 361 516-0541
2005 N 14th St Kingsville (78363) *(G-13636)*

Texas Petrochemicals LP (HQ) **713 477-9211**
500 Dallas St Ste 2000 Houston (77002) *(G-12243)*

Texas Petrochemicals LP 409 724-4857
2102 Spur 136 Port Neches (77651) *(G-17169)*

Texas Petrochemicals LP 713 627-7474
3 Riverway Ste 1500 Houston (77056) *(G-12244)*

Texas Photonics Inc 972 412-7111
2202 Lkeview Pkwy Ste 106 Rowlett (75088) *(G-17712)*

Texas Pipe Fabricators Inc 361 882-5541
709 High Starr Dr Corpus Christi (78408) *(G-3637)*

Texas Pipe Works Inc (PA) **936 825-6571**
2810 Bill Owens Pkwy # 400 Longview (75605) *(G-14318)*

Texas Pipe Works Inc 936 825-0652
9444 Industrial Dr Navasota (77868) *(G-15744)*

Texas Pipeline Webb 210 298-2222
17806 Ih 10 W Ste 210 San Antonio (78257) *(G-18541)*

Texas Pit Crafters, Pinehurst *Also called TPC Acquisition Partners LP (G-16736)*

Texas Plywood and Lumber Co, Grand Prairie *Also called BMC Stock Holdings Inc (G-7847)*

Texas Pmw Inc 713 679-7900
315 N Wayside Dr Houston (77020) *(G-12245)*

Texas Pneumatic Systems Inc 817 794-0068
1001 Commercial Blvd N Arlington (76001) *(G-792)*

Texas Pneumatic Systems Inc (PA) **817 794-0068**
2404 Superior Dr Pantego (76013) *(G-16353)*

Texas Pocket Springs Tech Inc 817 645-7666
460 County Rd 318 Keene (76059) *(G-13465)*

Texas Poly Inc 817 540-2351
1375 Westpark Way Euless (76040) *(G-6162)*

Texas Powder Coating Inc 713 690-6226
10010 Chickasaw Ln Houston (77041) *(G-12246)*

Texas Precision Metalcraft Inc 281 240-9191
810 Industrial Blvd Sugar Land (77478) *(G-19563)*

Texas Precision Mfg Inc 806 741-1166
610 28th St Lubbock (79404) *(G-14492)*

Texas Precision Plating Inc 972 494-1547
3002 Benton St Garland (75042) *(G-7599)*

Texas Precision Polymers Inc 936 588-4333
13843 Highway 105 W # 423 Conroe (77304) *(G-3371)*

Texas Priming LLC 903 893-6200
14989 State Highway 56 Sherman (75092) *(G-18936)*

Texas Printing Company, Austin *Also called D R & J Inc (G-1083)*

Texas Profab Corporation 972 241-5050
2151 Hutton Dr Carrollton (75006) *(G-2831)*

Texas Protein, Booker *Also called Preferred Beef Group LP (G-2158)*

Texas Publishing Co 361 991-1306
4455 S Padre Island Dr 21-O Corpus Christi (78411) *(G-3638)*

Texas Quarries, Cedar Park *Also called Justin Industries Inc (G-2975)*

Texas R P M Services, Rosharon *Also called RPM Services Inc (G-17612)*

Texas Rapid LLC 432 837-1049
10 Los Ranchos Dr Alpine (79830) *(G-312)*

Texas Real Estate Magazine, Granbury *Also called Sales R Up Media Inc (G-7808)*

Texas Refinery Corp 682 518-1405
500 Airport Dr Mansfield (76063) *(G-14722)*

Texas Republic Signs LLC 832 727-5415
2211 Pech Rd Houston (77055) *(G-12247)*

Texas Responsible Energy & 903 266-9103
705 Sutherland Dr Tyler (75703) *(G-20161)*

A
L
P
H
A
B
E
T
I
C

Texas Rib Rangers Product...............................940 565-1983
2402 Sherwood St Denton (76209) *(G-5406)*

Texas Right of Way Association, Fort Worth *Also called Trwa Inc (G-7084)*

Texas Roof Management Inc...............................972 272-7663
728 Lingco Dr Richardson (75081) *(G-17409)*

Texas Roofing Supply, Stafford *Also called Trs Distribution LLC (G-19389)*

Texas Saddlebags Inc...............................817 649-2626
3600 E Randol Mill Rd Arlington (76011) *(G-793)*

Texas Sampling Inc...............................361 575-8087
3706 E Rio Grande St Victoria (77901) *(G-20309)*

Texas Scenic Company Inc (PA)...............................**210 684-0091**
8053 Potranco Rd San Antonio (78251) *(G-18542)*

Texas Scientific Products...............................972 757-2304
11941 Hilltop Rd Argyle (76226) *(G-603)*

Texas Seal Supply Co Inc...............................817 640-1193
330 Westway Pl Ste 446 Arlington (76018) *(G-794)*

Texas SEC & Surveillance Inc (PA)...............................**512 693-4003**
2111 Sam Bass Rd Ste 400a Round Rock (78681) *(G-17693)*

Texas Sewing Inc...............................713 271-5466
9210 Clarewood Dr Houston (77036) *(G-12248)*

Texas Shapes Inc...............................713 641-1000
6470 Rupley Cir Houston (77087) *(G-12249)*

Texas Sheet Metal Works...............................806 765-8404
1102 E 50th St Lubbock (79404) *(G-14493)*

Texas Smoked Meats, Ballinger *Also called Dankworth Packing Co Inc (G-1740)*

Texas Sodium Bentonite Inc...............................325 885-2339
18301 Highway 16 Comanche (76442) *(G-3236)*

Texas Solar Resources Inc...............................281 846-4968
2310 Lees Ct League City (77573) *(G-13981)*

Texas Source Group Inc...............................713 464-9702
207 Stratford St Houston (77006) *(G-12250)*

Texas Spa Covers Inc...............................512 756-2043
1801 S Water St Burnet (78611) *(G-2616)*

Texas Stairs and Rails Inc...............................281 987-2115
11365 Eastex Fwy Houston (77093) *(G-12251)*

Texas Star Envelope Inc...............................210 293-8820
610 Lanark Dr Ste 204 San Antonio (78218) *(G-18543)*

Texas Star Nut and Food Co Inc...............................830 249-8300
206 Market Ave Boerne (78006) *(G-2140)*

Texas Starwares Inc...............................972 641-2100
2606 Aviation Pkwy Grand Prairie (75052) *(G-7981)*

Texas State Historical Assn (PA)...............................**512 471-2600**
3001 Lake Austin Blvd # 3116 Austin (78703) *(G-1570)*

Texas State University...............................512 245-3487
203 Pleasant St San Marcos (78666) *(G-18714)*

Texas Steel Conversion Inc (PA)...............................**713 733-6013**
3101 Holmes Rd Houston (77051) *(G-12252)*

Texas Steel Conversion Inc...............................832 230-8228
110 Cypress Station Dr # 160 Houston (77090) *(G-12253)*

Texas Steel Conversion Inc...............................281 452-2260
7203 Miller Road 2 Houston (77049) *(G-12254)*

Texas Steel Conversion Inc...............................281 459-2905
7401 C E King Pkwy Houston (77044) *(G-12255)*

Texas Steel Fabricators Inc...............................936 372-1616
28306 Fm 2920 Rd Waller (77484) *(G-20508)*

Texas Steel Tech LLC...............................817 894-7041
6620 Mineral Wells Hwy Weatherford (76088) *(G-20626)*

Texas Sthwind Vnyrd Winery LLC...............................361 526-4662
16375 Us 183 Refugio (78377) *(G-17250)*

Texas Stone Designs Inc...............................817 265-4011
2001 W Mayfield Rd Arlington (76015) *(G-795)*

Texas Stress Inc (PA)...............................**281 930-0897**
1304 Underwood Rd La Porte (77571) *(G-13795)*

Texas Stud Welding LLC...............................210 300-2500
7780 Fm 3175 Somerset (78069) *(G-19021)*

Texas Tank Trucks Co...............................254 559-5404
4500 Blue Heron Ct Granbury (76049) *(G-7812)*

Texas Tape & Label, Waco *Also called Garner & Golding Corporation (G-20406)*

Texas Technical Ceramics Inc...............................936 856-2903
303 Industrial Park Ln Willis (77378) *(G-20866)*

Texas Tempered Glass Inc...............................713 697-2828
1901 Little York Rd Houston (77093) *(G-12256)*

Texas Thermowell, Houston *Also called Parker-Hannifin Corporation (G-11246)*

Texas Thread Manufacturing Co...............................956 412-4999
2222 Wilson Rd Harlingen (78552) *(G-8206)*

Texas Timberjack Inc...............................409 397-4221
Fm 2626 Bon Wier (75928) *(G-2151)*

Texas Tissue Converting LLC...............................281 821-0429
1521 Greens Rd Ste 300 Houston (77032) *(G-12257)*

Texas Titos Inc...............................830 626-1123
1411 Fm 1101 Ste A New Braunfels (78130) *(G-15828)*

Texas Tool & Die, Dallas *Also called Dallas Texas Tool and Die Inc (G-4227)*

Texas Toolmakers Inc...............................210 494-3651
11411 E Coker Loop San Antonio (78216) *(G-18544)*

Texas Transmitter, Kemah *Also called Triseal Inc (G-13480)*

Texas Tripe Inc...............................903 674-8042
110 2nd St Sw Detroit (75436) *(G-5448)*

Texas Trophies Inc (PA)...............................**210 674-6099**
2525 Renwick Dr San Antonio (78227) *(G-18545)*

Texas Turbine Inc...............................817 444-5528
624 Profit St Azle (76020) *(G-1730)*

Texas Twist, Carrollton *Also called Pretzels Inc (G-2795)*

Texas Underground Inc...............................281 485-9900
1617 Garden Rd Pearland (77581) *(G-16602)*

Texas Uniform Manufacture, Houston *Also called Texas Sewing Inc (G-12248)*

Texas United Corporation (PA)...............................**713 877-1793**
4800 San Felipe St Houston (77056) *(G-12258)*

Texas Vessels Fabrication LLC...............................903 541-4883
1991 Us Highway 175 W Jacksonville (75766) *(G-13264)*

Texas Welded Wire LLC, Hurst *Also called Azz - Texas Welded Wire LLC (G-12835)*

Texas Westmoreland Coal Co...............................903 626-5485
4336 Farm Rd 39 Jewett (75846) *(G-13309)*

Texas Wipers & Rags LLC...............................956 554-7500
739 Mcnair Family Dr Brownsville (78520) *(G-2411)*

Texas Wire, Schertz *Also called Unified Screening & Crushing - (G-18767)*

Texas Wireline Mfg LLC...............................817 546-0772
8821 Forum Way Ste 101 Fort Worth (76140) *(G-7051)*

Texas Wood Supply, Donna *Also called South Texas Moulding Inc (G-5492)*

Texas-Agri Mch Indus Manufact, Plainview *Also called Texas Agri Machine & Indus Mfg (G-16764)*

Texastone Quarries LLC...............................432 354-2569
1400 Sherrod Rd Garden City (79739) *(G-7417)*

Texco Trim Inc...............................713 861-1892
1407 W Patton St Houston (77009) *(G-12259)*

Texcon Ready Mix Inc...............................281 572-1712
20783 Fm 1314 Rd Porter (77365) *(G-17183)*

Texcorr, Waxahachie *Also called Castell LP (G-20535)*

Texcraft Inc...............................806 744-6651
3917 Clovis Rd Lubbock (79415) *(G-14494)*

Texforce Restoration Svcs LLC...............................817 775-3556
5424 Rufe Snow Dr Ste 410 North Richland Hills (76180) *(G-15882)*

Texgulmarco Co Inc...............................956 943-2673
400 E Washington St Port Isabel (78578) *(G-17139)*

Texian Press, Waco *Also called Davis Brothers Pubg Co Ltd (G-20393)*

Texla Energy Management Inc...............................713 655-9900
1100 La St Ste 4700 Houston (77002) *(G-12260)*

Texland Petroleum LP...............................806 894-4657
6812 Wayne Ave Ste F Lubbock (79424) *(G-14495)*

Texmark Chemicals Inc...............................713 455-1206
900 Clinton Dr Galena Park (77547) *(G-7383)*

Texod Energy LLC...............................214 998-5360
1920 Mckinney Ave Fl 7 Dallas (75201) *(G-5079)*

Texoil Services...............................979 242-5571
4449 W State Highway 71 La Grange (78945) *(G-13702)*

Texokan Operating Inc...............................214 484-2322
5646 Milton St Ste 130 Dallas (75206) *(G-5080)*

Texolon, Houston *Also called Enpro Industries Inc (G-9650)*

Texon Icx, Denton *Also called Motion Reps Inc (G-5383)*

Texon Partners...............................940 264-3019
7645 Seymour Hwy Wichita Falls (76310) *(G-20817)*

Texpac Foods LLC...............................713 780-4876
3824 Artdale St Houston (77063) *(G-12261)*

Texpac Hide & Skin Ltd (PA)...............................**817 626-6586**
601 Ne 29th St Fort Worth (76106) *(G-7052)*

Texpak, Conroe *Also called Long Beach Shavings Co Inc (G-3325)*

Texpert Machine Co Inc...............................713 263-7000
6018 Gardendale Dr Houston (77092) *(G-12262)*

Texseis Inc...............................713 465-3181
2618 Hollow Hook Rd Houston (77080) *(G-12263)*

Texstar Energy Corporation...............................830 875-5919
402 W Davis St Luling (78648) *(G-14565)*

Texstar International LLC...............................817 740-9072
1624 Intermodal Pkwy Haslet (76052) *(G-8225)*

Texstars LLC...............................972 647-1366
925 Avenue H E Arlington (76011) *(G-796)*

Texton Inc...............................972 494-5941
114 S Kirby St Garland (75042) *(G-7600)*

Textool Company...............................713 923-5595
1124 Hackney St Houston (77023) *(G-12264)*

Textray & Strut Ltd...............................713 864-2551
1209 W 17th St Houston (77008) *(G-12265)*

Textron Inc...............................210 229-2303
1 Lone Star Pass Bldg 3 San Antonio (78264) *(G-18546)*

Textruss Component Bldg Inc...............................512 836-4830
12201 Dorsett Rd Austin (78727) *(G-1571)*

Texweld & Fabrication Inc...............................903 586-1775
200 N Gillespie Ave Jacksonville (75766) *(G-13265)*

Texwood Ltd...............................888 388-3224
1110 Industrial Blvd Cameron (76520) *(G-2644)*

TF Hudgins Holdings Inc (PA)...............................**713 682-3651**
4405 Directors Row Houston (77092) *(G-12266)*

Tfp Corporation...............................281 598-2330
10183 Windfern Rd Houston (77064) *(G-12267)*

Tfw Industrial Sup Cnc Mch LLC...............................817 898-9140
1133 S Madison Ave Dallas (75208) *(G-5081)*

Tgbtx, Los Indios *Also called Toyoda Gsei Brwnsvlle Txas LLC (G-14350)*

Tgc Industries 903 464-9908
  3375 Juanita Dr Denison (75020) (G-5348)
Tgcs, Houston Also called Hpi LLC (G-10272)
Tgs-Nopec Geophysical Company (HQ) **713 860-2100**
  10451 Clay Rd Houston (77041) (G-12268)
Tgs-Nopec Geophysical Company 281 319-4944
  2345 Atascocita Rd Humble (77396) (G-12803)
TH Precision LLC 830 549-5864
  2579 Old Lehmann Rd Seguin (78155) (G-18868)
Thacker Jewelry, Roaring Springs Also called T J Manufacturing Co (G-17497)
The Copy Center, Alice Also called Tcca Inc (G-239)
The Cumming Company Inc 817 737-2393
  6300 Ridglea Pl Ste 800 Fort Worth (76116) (G-7053)
The Dallas Greensheet, Dallas Also called Helen Gordon Interests Ltd (G-4446)
The Hot Bagel Shop, Houston Also called Dmv Wicks Inc (G-9488)
The Pallet Place Inc 903 963-4026
  303 Park Row St Van (75790) (G-20210)
The San Angelo Standard-Times, San Angelo Also called Scripps Texas Newspapers
LP (G-17826)
The San Antonio Truss Company 210 736-9629
  1010 Culebra Rd San Antonio (78201) (G-18547)
The Terrill Mfg Co Inc 325 655-7133
  2816 Mrtin Lther King Blv San Angelo (76903) (G-17833)
The Texas A&M University Sys 979 845-3414
  1 Sippel Rd College Station (77843) (G-3205)
The Texas A&M University Sys 979 845-1436
  4354 Tamu College Station (77843) (G-3206)
The Texas A&M University Sys 979 845-6601
  2588 Tamus College Station (77843) (G-3207)
The Wylie News, Wylie Also called C & S Media Inc (G-20928)
Thea Test, Austin Also called Pearson Education Inc (G-1405)
Theag North Arlington LLC 817 261-3027
  803 E Lamar Blvd Arlington (76011) (G-797)
Theatrical Warehouse Inc 214 634-2965
  2808 Mcgowan St Dallas (75203) (G-5082)
Theriot Inc 979 233-6391
  315 E Park St Freeport (77541) (G-7215)
Therm All Insulation, Dallas Also called Therm-All Inc (G-5084)
Therm Processes Inc 214 942-3131
  1609 E 8th St Dallas (75203) (G-5083)
Therm-All Inc 214 630-4800
  4884 Duncanville Rd Ste B Dallas (75236) (G-5084)
Therm-O-Disc Incorporated 915 860-9167
  12425 Rojas Dr El Paso (79928) (G-6000)
Therm-O-Link Inc 915 860-9933
  1295 Henry Brennan Dr El Paso (79936) (G-6001)
Thermacor Process Inc (PA) **817 847-7300**
  1670 E Hicks Field Rd Fort Worth (76179) (G-7054)
Thermafoam Operating LLC 254 582-2730
  1240 N Highway 77 Hillsboro (76645) (G-8331)
Thermal Designs Inc (PA) **713 433-6003**
  5352 Prudence Dr Houston (77045) (G-12269)
Thermal Edge Inc 972 580-0200
  1800 Hurd Dr Irving (75038) (G-13193)
Thermal Solutions Texas LLC 281 351-4328
  14306 Mary Jane Ln Tomball (77377) (G-20014)
Thermal Specialties Texas LLC 918 836-4800
  212 Page Ave Fort Worth (76110) (G-7055)
Thermo Disc, El Paso Also called Therm-O-Disc Incorporated (G-6000)
Thermo Elctron Process Systems 713 272-0404
  9303 W Sam Houston Pkwy S Houston (77099) (G-12270)
Thermo Finnigan LLC 512 251-1400
  2215 Grand Avenue Pkwy Austin (78728) (G-1572)
Thermo Fisher Scientific, Austin Also called Life Technologies Corporation (G-1293)
Thermo Fisher Scientific Inc 512 251-1525
  2215 Grand Avenue Pkwy Austin (78728) (G-1573)
Thermo Fisher Scientific Inc 972 437-3327
  900 Alpha Dr Ste 420 Richardson (75081) (G-17410)
Thermo Flow Systems, Sugar Land Also called Thermo Process Instruments LP (G-19564)
Thermo Industrial, Houston Also called Michael Ray (G-10865)
Thermo Materials, Lindale Also called Thermo Mfg Systems LLLC (G-14136)
Thermo Mfg Systems LLC 903 881-8771
  301 Walnut Springs Rd Lindale (75771) (G-14136)
Thermo Plastics Corporation 817 281-9010
  4101 Hahn Blvd Fort Worth (76117) (G-7056)
Thermo Process Instruments LP 713 272-0404
  12320 Cardinal Mdw # 150 Sugar Land (77478) (G-19564)
Thermo Sensors Corporation (PA) **972 494-1566**
  405 Gautney St Garland (75040) (G-7601)
Thermo-Mold Inc 713 944-6336
  5801 Berry Brook Dr Houston (77017) (G-12271)
Thermo-Serv Inc 214 631-0307
  3901 Pipestone Rd Dallas (75212) (G-5085)
Thermocontrol Inc 713 780-8600
  5700 Hartsdale Dr Houston (77036) (G-12272)
Thermolink, El Paso Also called Therm-O-Link Inc (G-6001)
Thermon Inc (HQ) **512 396-5801**
  100 Thermon Dr San Marcos (78666) (G-18715)

Thermon Industries Inc 512 396-5801
  100 Thermon Dr San Marcos (78666) (G-18716)
Thermoserv, Dallas Also called Ntl-Brands Ltd (G-4746)
Thermtech Inc 281 359-7555
  14723 Ashland Pines Ln Humble (77396) (G-12804)
Thi Acquisition Inc 281 485-8339
  1710 Mykawa Rd Pearland (77581) (G-16603)
Thick n Thin Lumber Co Inc 281 592-0437
  8591 Fm 787 Rd W Cleveland (77327) (G-3139)
Thiel Co. 817 310-3110
  531 Industrial Blvd Grapevine (76051) (G-8057)
Thiink Biig Tax Service Inc 832 606-3380
  21919 Clay Rd Apt 4211 Katy (77449) (G-13450)
Think Energy, Houston Also called Engie Retail LLC (G-9645)
Think Plastics LLC 713 771-7700
  602 Piedmont St Sugar Land (77478) (G-19565)
Thinkgeo LLC (PA) **785 727-4133**
  2770 Main St Ste 185 Frisco (75033) (G-7319)
Thinksmart LLC 888 489-4284
  5001 Plz On The Lk Ste 11 Austin (78746) (G-1574)
Thinkwell Corporation 888 416-8880
  505 E Huntland Dr Ste 150 Austin (78752) (G-1575)
Third Coast Packaging Inc 281 412-0275
  1871 Mykawa Rd Pearland (77581) (G-16604)
Third Coast Rx Inc 361 749-6337
  3845 S Padre Island Dr Corpus Christi (78415) (G-3639)
Third Coast Services LLC 832 934-0240
  36530 Coleman Rd Magnolia (77355) (G-14629)
Third Coast Terminals, Pearland Also called Third Coast Packaging Inc (G-16604)
Thirlwall Sheet Metal Co, Brownsville Also called Thur-Co Inc (G-2412)
Thom-Bat-Ler Enterprises 972 660-4056
  2622 Skyway Dr Ste 3d Grand Prairie (75052) (G-7982)
Thomas Bus Gulf Coast GP Inc 713 580-8600
  8806 Mississippi St Houston (77029) (G-12273)
Thomas Graphics Inc 512 719-3535
  9501 N Interstate 35 Austin (78753) (G-1576)
Thomas Instrument Incorporated 830 331-1325
  110 Commerce Ave Boerne (78006) (G-2141)
Thomas Kurtz 361 578-2594
  102 Cozzi Cir Victoria (77901) (G-20310)
Thomas Lease Service 806 202-1800
  2602 S Hayden St Amarillo (79109) (G-514)
Thomas M Niland Company 915 779-1405
  320 N Clark Dr El Paso (79905) (G-6002)
Thomas Oilfield Services LLC (PA) **855 778-5940**
  4250 Se Loop 281 Longview (75602) (G-14319)
Thomas Oilfield Services LLC 903 806-0582
  5327 W 42nd St Odessa (79764) (G-16176)
Thomas Plastics Inc 817 654-3238
  4121 Stadium Dr Fort Worth (76133) (G-7057)
Thomas Printworks 832 201-2000
  707 West Rd Houston (77038) (G-12274)
Thomas Redi-Mix Company Inc 806 381-8485
  N Western & Loop 335 Amarillo (79108) (G-467)
Thomas Reprographics Inc 210 829-7000
  1223 Arion Pkwy San Antonio (78216) (G-18548)
Thomas Reprographics Inc 713 977-6363
  3232 Chimney Rock Rd Houston (77056) (G-12275)
Thomas Reprographics Inc 281 875-2500
  361 Greens Rd Houston (77060) (G-12276)
Thomas Steel Drums Inc 817 838-6891
  2517 Ne 35th St Fort Worth (76111) (G-7058)
Thomason Family Corporation 713 223-4575
  2300 Nance St Houston (77020) (G-12277)
Thompson & Thompson (PA) **214 953-1177**
  325 N Saint Paul St # 4300 Dallas (75201) (G-5086)
Thompson & Thompson 214 953-1177
  117 W Yukon Rd Odessa (79764) (G-16177)
Thompson & Thompson 325 392-3721
  117 Ave H Ozona (76943) (G-16287)
Thompson Business Forms Inc 210 734-5356
  5818 Rocky Pt San Antonio (78249) (G-18549)
Thompson Family Partnership 972 238-7664
  620 N Glenville Dr Richardson (75081) (G-17411)
Thompson Hard Metal Service, Odessa Also called Thompson Welding (G-16178)
Thompson J Cleo, Dallas Also called Thompson Petroleum Corporation (G-5087)
Thompson J Cleo Oil Producers, Odessa Also called Thompson & Thompson (G-16177)
Thompson Jr Inc 940 665-2533
  3500 N Grand Ave Gainesville (76240) (G-7372)
Thompson Paper Pdts Texas Inc 713 869-6636
  3800 Tanglewilde St # 407 Houston (77063) (G-12278)
Thompson Petroleum Corporation (PA) **214 953-1177**
  325 N Saint Paul St # 4300 Dallas (75201) (G-5087)
Thompson Pipe Group - Pressure, Grand Prairie Also called Tpg Pressure Inc (G-7984)
Thompson Pipe Group - Pressure, Grand Prairie Also called Tpg Pressure Inc (G-7985)
Thompson Print Solutions, San Antonio Also called Thompson Business Forms
Inc (G-18549)
Thompson Scale Company 713 932-9071
  9000 Jameel Rd Ste 190 Houston (77040) (G-12279)

Thompson Welding 432 381-1531
  3602 W 11th St Odessa (79763) *(G-16178)*

Thompson's Quick Print, Carrollton *Also called Mtc Printing Inc (G-2783)*

Thompsons Cstm Meats & Proc LP 254 445-4180
  111 W Elm St Dublin (76446) *(G-5517)*

Thompsons Custom Meats & Proc, Dublin *Also called Thompsons Cstm Meats & Proc LP (G-5517)*

Thomson Reuters Corporation 972 250-7000
  2395 Midway Rd Carrollton (75006) *(G-2832)*

Thomson Rters Tax Accnting Inc (HQ) **800 431-9025**
  2395 Midway Rd Carrollton (75006) *(G-2833)*

Thor Energy Group Inc 210 277-0368
  710 Lightstone Dr San Antonio (78258) *(G-18550)*

Thorne Electric Company 210 590-1226
  610 Lanark Dr Ste 205 San Antonio (78218) *(G-18551)*

Thornton Drum Ring, Houston *Also called Self Industries (G-11824)*

Thornton Steel Holdings Inc 817 926-3324
  2700 W Pafford St Fort Worth (76110) *(G-7059)*

Thorntree LP (PA) **713 690-8200**
  10105 W Gulf Bank Rd Houston (77040) *(G-12280)*

Thorntree Slate & Marble, Houston *Also called Thorntree LP (G-12280)*

Thorpe Plant Services Inc (HQ) **713 644-1247**
  6833 Kirbyville St Houston (77033) *(G-12281)*

Thrailkill All Metals Fabg Inc 972 747-1230
  200 Allentown Pkwy Allen (75002) *(G-302)*

Thrasher Inc 806 296-2609
  1209 E 24th St Plainview (79072) *(G-16765)*

Thrasher Ready Mix, Plainview *Also called Thrasher Inc (G-16765)*

Threading & Precision Mfg LLC 281 452-3036
  7735 Miller Road 3 Houston (77049) *(G-12282)*

Threads In Motion 972 422-4607
  1240 Shiloh Rd Ste 200 Plano (75074) *(G-17032)*

Three Brothers Bakery Inc (PA) **713 666-2253**
  4036 S Braeswood Blvd Houston (77025) *(G-12283)*

Three Chiefs & No Indians LLC 909 465-6314
  2800 112th St Ste 100 Grand Prairie (75050) *(G-7983)*

Three D Finishing Inc 972 475-2726
  5020 Grisham Dr Rowlett (75088) *(G-17713)*

Three Leaf Studio, Addison *Also called From Here Inc (G-128)*

Three P Operating Company 940 846-3326
  620 Broadway St Newcastle (76372) *(G-15863)*

Three Rivers Operating Co LLC 512 600-3190
  5301 Sw Pkwy Ste 400 Austin (78735) *(G-1577)*

Three Span Oil & Gas Inc 432 684-6511
  400 W Illinois Ave # 1250 Midland (79701) *(G-15437)*

Three Streams Energy LLC 469 917-1777
  3811 Turtle Creek Blvd Dallas (75219) *(G-5088)*

Threet Pallet LLC 972 489-6887
  801 Lakeway Dr Ennis (75119) *(G-6119)*

Threshold Development Company 817 870-1483
  777 Taylor St Fort Worth (76102) *(G-7060)*

Threshold Group, Rockwall *Also called Kevin Hall (G-17551)*

Thrifty Nckel Want ADS Crpus C 361 980-0008
  1308 Airline Rd Corpus Christi (78412) *(G-3640)*

Thrifty Nckel Want ADS Vctoria, Victoria *Also called Want ADS of Colorado Springs (G-20318)*

Thrifty Nickel, Fort Worth *Also called Want ADS of Fort Worth Inc (G-7124)*

Thrifty Nickel, Temple *Also called American Classifieds (G-19668)*

Thrifty Nickel Want ADS, Abilene *Also called West Texas Want Ads Inc (G-94)*

Thrifty Nickel Want ADS, Amarillo *Also called American Classifieds (G-480)*

Thrifty Nickel Want ADS, San Angelo *Also called Want ADS of San Angelo Inc (G-17837)*

Thrifty Nickel Want Ads Inc 915 751-3494
  10921 Pellicano Dr # 100 El Paso (79935) *(G-6003)*

Thriftynickel.com, El Paso *Also called Thrifty Nickel Want Ads Inc (G-6003)*

Thrillworks Inc (PA) **916 663-1749**
  1391 Flat Creek Rd Athens (75751) *(G-840)*

Thru Inc 214 496-0100
  909 Lake Carolyn Pkwy # 750 Irving (75039) *(G-13194)*

Thru Holding Company LLC (PA) **214 496-0100**
  909 Lake Carolyn Pkwy # 7 Irving (75039) *(G-13195)*

Thru Tubing Solutions Inc 361 883-4600
  6769 Ih 37 Access Rd Corpus Christi (78409) *(G-3641)*

Thrubit LLC 713 874-9600
  150 Gillingham Ln Sugar Land (77478) *(G-19566)*

Thrubit LLC (PA) **713 538-9500**
  150 Gillingham Ln Sugar Land (77478) *(G-19567)*

Thrubit Logging Solutions, Sugar Land *Also called Thrubit LLC (G-19567)*

Thrustmaster of Texas Inc 713 937-6295
  6900 Thrustmaster Dr Houston (77041) *(G-12284)*

Thryv Inc 903 593-5400
  1001 E Se Loop 323 # 420 Tyler (75701) *(G-20162)*

Thryv Inc 281 312-3258
  1521 Green Oak Pl Ste 210 Kingwood (77339) *(G-13654)*

Thryv Inc (HQ) **972 453-7000**
  2200 W Airfield Dr Dfw Airport (75261) *(G-5457)*

Thryv Holdings Inc (PA) **972 453-7000**
  2200 W Airfield Dr Dfw Airport (75261) *(G-5458)*

Thug City Records 832 264-4892
  204 E 30th St Houston (77018) *(G-12285)*

Thunderbird Food Machinery 214 331-3000
  4602 Brass Way Dallas (75236) *(G-5089)*

Thunderco Inc 713 681-4686
  909 Fisher St Houston (77018) *(G-12286)*

Thur-Co Inc 956 982-4424
  225 Industrial Dr Brownsville (78521) *(G-2412)*

Thurmond-Mcglothlin LLC (PA) **806 665-5700**
  1428 N Banks St Pampa (79065) *(G-16341)*

Thursby Software Systems LLC 817 478-5070
  4901 S Collins St Arlington (76018) *(G-798)*

Thybar Corporation 972 416-6220
  13801 Senlac Dr Ste 100 Dallas (75234) *(G-5090)*

Thyssenkrupp Arprt Systems Inc 817 834-6984
  3201 N Sylvania Ave # 117 Fort Worth (76111) *(G-7061)*

Thyssenkrupp Elevator Corp 512 486-1000
  3615 Willow Springs Rd F Austin (78704) *(G-1578)*

Thyssenkrupp Elevator Corp 817 922-9590
  7425 Pebble Dr Fort Worth (76118) *(G-7062)*

TI Group Auto Systems LLC 956 686-5400
  3900 W Ursula Ave McAllen (78503) *(G-14912)*

Tianhai Electric N Amer Inc 915 881-9740
  19 Leigh Fisher Blvd El Paso (79906) *(G-6004)*

Tibco Software Inc 713 344-2045
  1600 Smith St Ste 3890 Houston (77002) *(G-12287)*

Ticona Polymers Inc 972 443-4000
  1601 Lyndon B Johnson Fwy Dallas (75234) *(G-5091)*

Tidal Energy Marketing US LLC 713 650-8900
  1100 La St Ste 3600 Houston (77002) *(G-12288)*

Tidal Logistics Inc 940 668-1818
  12319 Us 287 Bus Fort Worth (76179) *(G-7063)*

Tidel Engineering LP 972 484-3358
  2025 W Belt Line Rd # 114 Carrollton (75006) *(G-2834)*

Tideland Signal Corporation (HQ) **713 681-6101**
  7100 Bus Pk Dr Ste B Houston (77041) *(G-12289)*

Tideline Designs Inc 214 275-3958
  623 107th St Arlington (76011) *(G-799)*

Tiendas Sindicales, San Antonio *Also called Spfm LP (G-18491)*

Tiernan Aeration Inc 806 372-4051
  1722 Ne 3rd Ave Amarillo (79107) *(G-468)*

Tiernan Outdoor Products, Amarillo *Also called Tieman Aeration Inc (G-468)*

Tierra Lease Service LLC 830 583-3717
  311 S Sunset Strip St Kenedy (78119) *(G-13492)*

Tiet Jens Lone Star Truck Eqp, La Grange *Also called Tietjen Inc (G-13703)*

Tietek Global LLC 281 444-3494
  429 S Memory Ln Marshall (75670) *(G-14805)*

Tietjen Inc 979 249-3888
  6035 State Highway 159 La Grange (78945) *(G-13703)*

Tiffs Treats Rbd Inc 512 614-3200
  8900 Shoal Creek Blvd Austin (78757) *(G-1579)*

Tifs Treats 512 473-2600
  1806 Nueces St Austin (78701) *(G-1580)*

Tig Real Estate Services Inc 972 661-0232
  2500 Dallas Pkwy Ste 2060 Dallas (75254) *(G-5092)*

Tige Boats Inc 325 676-7777
  1801 State Highway 36 Abilene (79602) *(G-87)*

Tiger Construction 915 999-1260
  688 Bluff Canyon Cir El Paso (79912) *(G-6005)*

Tiger Industries Inc 713 896-9300
  11955 Fm 529 Rd Houston (77041) *(G-12290)*

Tiger Manufacturing, Abilene *Also called Beall Construction Company Inc (G-16)*

Tiger Manufacturing, Abilene *Also called Lee Dill Inc (G-56)*

Tiger Offshore Rentals LLC (PA) **409 951-4048**
  1655 Louisiana St Beaumont (77701) *(G-1959)*

Tiger Ridge Manufacturing Inc 903 364-1810
  12656 State Highway 11 Whitewright (75491) *(G-20729)*

Tiger Tails, Grapevine *Also called Dbs Group Inc (G-8026)*

Tiger Tower Services LLC 281 951-2500
  1605 S Battleground Rd La Porte (77571) *(G-13796)*

Tiger Valve Houston Co LLC 281 227-9911
  15862 Diplomatic Plaza Dr Houston (77032) *(G-12291)*

Tigerflow Systems LLC (PA) **214 337-8780**
  4034 Mint Way Dallas (75237) *(G-5093)*

Tigua Enterprises Inc (HQ) **915 298-0700**
  12 Leigh Fisher Blvd El Paso (79906) *(G-6006)*

Tillery & Parks Company LP 432 366-2700
  8836 Andrews Hwy Odessa (79765) *(G-16179)*

Tillman Learning LLC 866 540-9677
  5700 W Plano Pkwy # 3200 Plano (75093) *(G-17033)*

Tim Yockey 281 252-6175
  32550 Decker Prairie Rd Magnolia (77355) *(G-14630)*

Timber Blinds Mfg Ltd (PA) **972 569-9100**
  800 Elm St McKinney (75069) *(G-14982)*

Timberblindmetroshade, McKinney *Also called Timber Blinds Mfg Ltd (G-14982)*

Timco Services Inc 903 693-9400
  850 S Shelby St Carthage (75633) *(G-2924)*

Time Delay Corporation 214 369-4063
  10440 N Cntl Expy Ste 210 Dallas (75231) *(G-5094)*

Timeclock Plus LLC (PA) 325 223-9300
1 Time Clock Dr San Angelo (76904) *(G-17834)*
Timekeepers Inc 830 331-1224
115 Bess St Boerne (78006) *(G-2142)*
Timekeepers Security, Boerne *Also called Timekeepers Inc (G-2142)*
Timesaver Templates Inc 972 620-2197
5920 Preston Valley Dr Dallas (75240) *(G-5095)*
Timken Gears & Services Inc 713 224-4900
10830 Train Ct Houston (77041) *(G-12292)*
Timkensteel Material Svcs LLC 281 449-0319
14730 Yarberry St Houston (77039) *(G-12293)*
Tims South Texas LLC (PA) 830 278-3368
4055 E Main St Uvalde (78801) *(G-20197)*
Tims South Texas LLC 830 468-3860
6627 S Us Highway 83 Asherton (78827) *(G-814)*
Tiny Pies LLC 512 297-2690
3736 Bee Caves Rd Ste 8b West Lake Hills (78746) *(G-20691)*
Tip Top Sheet Metal Inc 281 931-7823
2309 W Mount Houston Rd Houston (77038) *(G-12294)*
Tippen Steel Services Inc 940 433-3132
100 E Lawrence Ave Boyd (76023) *(G-2208)*
Tips Incorporated 512 863-3653
2402 Williams Dr Georgetown (78628) *(G-7686)*
Tips Iron & Steel Co Inc 512 478-8511
300 Baylor St Austin (78703) *(G-1581)*
Tiptop Quality, Tyler *Also called Tyler Packing Co Inc (G-20171)*
Tisdale AC & Htg Co 936 856-1500
5111 N Frazier St Conroe (77303) *(G-3372)*
Tisdale Company, Conroe *Also called Tisdale AC & Htg Co (G-3372)*
Titan Bop Rubber Products Inc 713 895-9230
9447 Bamboo Rd Houston (77041) *(G-12295)*
Titan Chair LLC (PA) 888 848-2630
1001 W Crosby Rd Carrollton (75006) *(G-2835)*
Titan Chemical Corporation 713 747-3134
6710 Cadillac St Houston (77021) *(G-12296)*
Titan Corrugated Inc 214 513-2691
801 Lakeside Pkwy Flower Mound (75028) *(G-6289)*
Titan Custom Products Inc 214 678-9105
2560 W Commerce St Dallas (75212) *(G-5096)*
Titan Environmental USA LLC 713 849-1311
15847 Kimberlee St Houston (77049) *(G-12297)*
Titan Fence & Supply, Crossroads *Also called Sorensen Industries Inc (G-3750)*
Titan International Inc 956 541-7500
6700 Paredes Line Rd Brownsville (78526) *(G-2413)*
Titan Solutions 281 973-9653
825 Town And Country Ln # 1200 Houston (77024) *(G-12298)*
Titan Tire Corp of Texas, Brownsville *Also called Titan International Inc (G-2413)*
Titan Tool & Die Company 713 849-4300
10050 W Gulf Bank Rd # 200 Houston (77040) *(G-12299)*
Titanchair.com, Carrollton *Also called Titan Chair LLC (G-2835)*
Titanium Emergency Group LLP 940 613-2653
1600 11th St Wichita Falls (76301) *(G-20818)*
Titanium Fabrication Corp 832 375-1800
5121 Hiltonview Rd Houston (77086) *(G-12300)*
Titanium Metals Corporation 972 233-1700
5430 Lyndon B Johnson Fwy # 1700 Dallas (75240) *(G-5097)*
Titanium Welding Services LLC 281 380-7043
5871 Belneath St Houston (77033) *(G-12301)*
Titex Inc 713 678-8890
4800 Clinton Dr Houston (77020) *(G-12302)*
Titus, Horizon City *Also called Air System Components Inc (G-8362)*
Titus Group Inc 469 289-1773
14580 Midway Rd Dallas (75244) *(G-5098)*
Titus Industrial, Dallas *Also called Titus Group Inc (G-5098)*
Tiw Corporation (HQ) 713 939-7711
6401 N Eldridge Pkwy Houston (77041) *(G-12303)*
Tiw International Inc (HQ) 713 729-2110
6401 N Eldridge Pkwy Houston (77041) *(G-12304)*
TJ Blackburn Syrup Works Inc 903 665-2541
22382 Hwy 49 W Jefferson (75657) *(G-13289)*
Tj Machine & Tool Ltd 817 444-5540
11220 S Fm 730 Azle (76020) *(G-1731)*
Tjp Enterprises LLC 817 779-4360
5225 Teague Rd Fort Worth (76140) *(G-7064)*
Tk Holdings Inc (HQ) 210 509-0762
4611 Wiseman Blvd San Antonio (78251) *(G-18552)*
Tko Sports Group USA Limited 713 895-9270
4660 Pine Timbers St # 198 Houston (77041) *(G-12305)*
Tko Telesystems LLC 972 484-4900
12801 N Stemmons Fwy Dallas (75234) *(G-5099)*
TLC Tonerland LP 713 692-6650
3990 North Fwy Houston (77022) *(G-12306)*
Tlmi Corporation 512 833-7075
2111 W Braker Ln Ste 500 Austin (78758) *(G-1582)*
Tlr Energy Services Inc (PA) 940 969-2400
122 County Road 3341 Paradise (76073) *(G-16355)*
Tlr Welding & Fabricating Inc 940 969-2400
122 County Road 3341 Paradise (76073) *(G-16356)*
Tlt Leather, Fort Worth *Also called Texas Leather Trim Inc (G-7049)*
Tm Chemicals Ltd Partnership 281 930-2525
2525 Independence Pkwy S Deer Park (77536) *(G-5300)*
Tm Deer Park Services, Deer Park *Also called Tm Chemicals Ltd Partnership (G-5300)*
TM Luckett Enterprises LLC 866 216-7278
5444 Westheimr Rd # 1080 Houston (77056) *(G-12307)*
Tmbr/Sharp Drilling, Midland *Also called Patterson-Uti Acquisition LLC (G-15341)*
TMC Foundation Inc (PA) 214 212-4645
190 Industrial Blvd McKinney (75069) *(G-14983)*
Tmco Inc 713 465-3255
4100 N Sam Houston Pkwy W Houston (77086) *(G-12308)*
Tmd Manufacturing Inc 903 919-0600
46 Pioneer Pkwy Sulphur Springs (75482) *(G-19603)*
Tmf Graphics Inc 817 483-0237
408 W Kennedale Pkwy Kennedale (76060) *(G-13505)*
TMI LLC 469 231-6918
2324 Barton Creek Blvd The Colony (75056) *(G-19816)*
Tmk Completions, Houston *Also called Oilfield Services & Tech LLC (G-11164)*
Tmk Ipsco, Houston *Also called Ipsco Tubulars (ky) Inc (G-10415)*
Tmk North America Inc 281 949-1023
10120 Houston Oaks Dr Houston (77064) *(G-12309)*
Tmp Truck & Trailer LP 432 686-2500
2700 Rankin Hwy Midland (79706) *(G-15438)*
Tmr Services LLC 432 693-2175
1400 N Hwy 349 Rankin (79778) *(G-17233)*
Tms International LLC 409 768-1241
100 Old Hwy 90 Beaumont (77707) *(G-1960)*
Tnc, Lancaster *Also called Texas Nameplate Company Inc (G-13849)*
Tng GP 210 226-9333
5130 Commerce Pkwy San Antonio (78218) *(G-18553)*
Tnn Machining Company LLC 713 849-0062
8330 W Little York Rd Houston (77040) *(G-12310)*
Tnn Manufacturing Company Inc 713 849-0062
8330 W Little York Rd Houston (77040) *(G-12311)*
Tnn New World 281 598-6680
6834 Flintlock Rd Houston (77040) *(G-12312)*
Tns Industries Inc 713 690-4000
6818 Satsuma Dr Houston (77041) *(G-12313)*
TNT Directional Drilling Inc 972 333-3410
5435 N Garland Ave 140-205 Garland (75040) *(G-7602)*
TNT Machine 713 722-0622
1105 Upland Dr Ste B2 Houston (77043) *(G-12314)*
TNT Printing 281 449-9090
2111 Hartwick Rd Houston (77093) *(G-12315)*
Toastmasters International 325 949-3782
1819 Knickerbocker Rd San Angelo (76904) *(G-17835)*
Todays Children Food Program 214 562-4702
1205 Briarbrook Dr Desoto (75115) *(G-5445)*
Todd Weldings, Beeville *Also called TW Tanks and Construction Co (G-1989)*
Toff, Dallas *Also called Artlux Inc (G-3968)*
TOFS LLC 806 543-9833
5802 E Highway 62 Lubbock (79403) *(G-14496)*
Toilet Partitions Washroom ACC, Irving *Also called Knickerbocker Partition Corp (G-13078)*
Tokai Carbon CB Ltd (HQ) 817 390-8600
301 Commerce St Ste 500 Fort Worth (76102) *(G-7065)*
Tokai Carbon CB Ltd 432 263-7389
1211 N Midway Rd Big Spring (79720) *(G-2100)*
Tokai Carbon CB Ltd 806 274-7213
9455 Fm 1559 Rd 1559th Borger (79007) *(G-2188)*
Tokyo Electron America Inc (HQ) 512 424-1000
2400 Grove Blvd Austin (78741) *(G-1583)*
Tokyo Electron America Inc 512 424-1000
3910 S Industrial Dr Austin (78744) *(G-1584)*
Tokyo Electron US Holdings Inc (HQ) 512 424-1000
2400 Grove Blvd Austin (78741) *(G-1585)*
Tokyo Seimitsu Co Ltd (HQ) 214 459-1688
2280 Campbell Crk Richardson (75082) *(G-17412)*
Tolbert Electric Motor Company 972 272-6541
3822 Dividend Dr Garland (75042) *(G-7603)*
Tolteq Group LLC 512 331-4241
1200 Cypress Creek Rd Cedar Park (78613) *(G-2988)*
Tom and Jerry, El Campo *Also called New Icm LP (G-5623)*
Tom Daenen Inc 409 978-2132
7531 Fm 2004 Rd Hitchcock (77563) *(G-8340)*
Tom James Company 325 695-0190
2401 S Willis St Ste 117 Abilene (79605) *(G-88)*
Tom Lanham Software 254 773-2513
2801 W Avenue T Temple (76504) *(G-19713)*
Tom McGee Corp 806 658-4591
319 W Industrial Rd Booker (79005) *(G-2159)*
Tom Thorp Transports 325 392-8323
102 Bob White Dr Ozona (76943) *(G-16288)*
Tomball Forest, Tomball *Also called Solidwood Forest Ltd (G-20010)*
Tomball Sheet Metal LP 281 356-1200
24620 Hardin Store Rd Magnolia (77354) *(G-14631)*
Tombstone Welding 325 573-8446
1015 N Avenue M Snyder (79549) *(G-19012)*
Tomcat Drilling LLC 316 262-8554
716 Grandview Dr Corsicana (75109) *(G-3686)*

A L P H A B E T I C

Tomcat Global Corporation (PA) 432 694-7070
2160 Commerce Dr Midland (79703) *(G-15439)*

Tomdao Llc 817 888-6167
4401 Little Rd 550-324 Arlington (76016) *(G-800)*

Tomlinson Oilfield Service 956 802-0030
14414 Us Highway 87 W 3c La Vernia (78121) *(G-13803)*

Tommy Chappell LLC 432 967-2469
8 Santa Fe Pl Odessa (79765) *(G-16180)*

Tommy Lewis Industries 806 291-4433
208 S Columbia St Plainview (79072) *(G-16766)*

Tonatco Cryogenic Services 281 651-0305
1906 Old Holzwarth Rd Spring (77388) *(G-19179)*

Tony Lama Company Inc 915 778-8311
1137 Tony Lama St El Paso (79915) *(G-6007)*

Tool and Die By H&H Inc 713 943-0545
1216 Illinios St S Houston (77002) *(G-12316)*

Tool Tech, Beaumont Also called *REE Holding Inc (G-1947)*

Tool-Flo Manufacturing Inc 713 941-1080
14745 Kirby Dr Houston (77047) *(G-12317)*

Toolco Precision Machine Inc 713 433-3700
14701 Park Almeda Dr Houston (77047) *(G-12318)*

Toolex Inc 713 644-8071
7570 Morley St Houston (77061) *(G-12319)*

Tooling Designs Inc 281 354-0421
21790 E Wallis Dr Porter (77365) *(G-17184)*

Tooling Manufacturing, Fort Worth Also called *Fort Worth Forging Die LP (G-6644)*

Tooling Technologies Mfg LLC 713 722-8501
11680 Brittmoore Park Dr Houston (77041) *(G-12320)*

Toon LLC 817 609-0672
2312 Monarch Dr Apt 616 Fort Worth (76119) *(G-7066)*

Tootie Pie Company Inc (PA) 210 737-6600
129 Industrial Dr Boerne (78006) *(G-2143)*

Tootie Pie Gourmet Cafe, Boerne Also called *Tootie Pie Company Inc (G-2143)*

Top Cat Ready Mix LLC 972 486-3162
2040 Dowdy Ferry Rd Dallas (75217) *(G-5100)*

Top Cat Well Transport 903 295-7000
513 S Sun Camp Rd White Oak (75693) *(G-20720)*

Top Coat Inc 979 233-9558
9720 Hwy 36 Freeport (77541) *(G-7216)*

Top Deck Inc 409 745-3955
10861 Highway 62 N Orange (77632) *(G-16265)*

Top Golf USA Inc 214 494-6310
3760 Blair Oaks Dr The Colony (75056) *(G-19817)*

Top Level Printing Ink Inc 214 267-9010
1343 Round Table Dr Dallas (75247) *(G-5101)*

Top O Texas Oilfield Services (PA) 806 665-2501
408 S Price Rd Pampa (79065) *(G-16342)*

Top Quality Spindles LLC 972 937-2126
2650 Fm 878 Waxahachie (75165) *(G-20566)*

Top Shelf Industries Oper Ltd 806 995-2224
907 E Service Rd Tulia (79088) *(G-20040)*

Top Threading Services Inc 281 426-8461
11613 Fm 2100 Crosby (77532) *(G-3745)*

Top-Co Cementing Products Inc 832 300-3660
10613 W Sam Houston Pkwy Houston (77064) *(G-12321)*

Topgolf International Inc 832 200-0106
560 Spring Park Ctr Blvd Spring (77373) *(G-19180)*

Toppan Photomasks Inc 972 398-0411
555 Republic Dr Ste 312 Plano (75074) *(G-17034)*

Toppan Photomasks Inc 512 310-6000
400 Texas Ave Round Rock (78664) *(G-17694)*

Toppan Photomasks Inc (HQ) 512 310-6500
131 E Old Settlers Blvd Round Rock (78664) *(G-17695)*

Tops Printing Inc 979 779-1234
2023 S Texas Ave Bryan (77802) *(G-2512)*

Tops Software Corporation 972 739-8677
1301 Central Expy S # 200 Allen (75013) *(G-303)*

Tops Well Services LLC (PA) 979 627-7434
3077 Outlet Center Dr Sealy (77474) *(G-18820)*

Topsail Energy Mktg Group LLC 832 823-2380
25775 Oak Ridge Dr # 150 The Woodlands (77380) *(G-19930)*

Topway Global Inc 713 784-1808
8738 Westpark Dr Houston (77063) *(G-12322)*

Tor Minerals International Inc (PA) 361 883-5591
722 Burleson St Corpus Christi (78402) *(G-3642)*

Torans Precision Fabricating 281 371-2352
5230 E 5th St Katy (77493) *(G-13451)*

Toray Composite Mtls Amer Inc 972 899-2930
700 Parker Sq Ste 275 Lewisville (75028) *(G-14098)*

Torcsill Foundations LLC (PA) 281 825-5200
12000 Aerospace Ave # 115 Houston (77034) *(G-12323)*

Tornado Production Svcs LLC 361 384-9020
1587 W Fm 624 Orange Grove (78372) *(G-16270)*

Toro Company 915 231-7200
9455 Railroad Dr El Paso (79924) *(G-6008)*

Toro Company 325 673-8762
500 Chestnut St Ste 400 Abilene (79602) *(G-89)*

Torqon Inc (PA) 956 546-3239
253 W Elizabeth St Brownsville (78520) *(G-2414)*

Torr NA Lochs LLC 832 606-7575
7055 W State Highway 29 Burnet (78611) *(G-2617)*

Torr NA Lochs Vinyrd & Winery, Burnet Also called *Torr NA Lochs LLC (G-2617)*

Torrent Energy Services LLC 512 722-3439
173 Fm 3237 Ste B Wimberley (78676) *(G-20885)*

Torres Brothers 713 732-4237
4247 Fuqua St Houston (77048) *(G-12324)*

Tortillas Olivo LLC 956 702-8388
502 S San Antonio Ave San Juan (78589) *(G-18675)*

Tortillas Santos LLC 956 712-3800
606 Amistad Dr Laredo (78041) *(G-13938)*

Tortilleria Cuauhtemoc 915 886-4480
809 Westway Blvd Canutillo (79835) *(G-2666)*

Tortilleria La Campera, Houston Also called *Montega Ltd (G-10912)*

Tortillria Monterrey Groceries 956 544-7222
364 Us Highway 281 Brownsville (78520) *(G-2415)*

Tortuga Operating Co (PA) 713 680-3600
7412 Shadyvilla Ln Houston (77055) *(G-12325)*

Toshiba International Corp 713 466-0277
10510 Okanella St Houston (77041) *(G-12326)*

Toshiba International Corp (HQ) 800 231-1412
13131 W Little York Rd Houston (77041) *(G-12327)*

Toshiba International Corp 713 466-0277
10435 Okanella St Houston (77041) *(G-12328)*

Total Alloy Foundry Inc 806 259-2255
2100 Greenwood St Memphis (79245) *(G-14999)*

Total E&P RES & Tech USA LLC 713 647-3000
1201 La St Ste 1800 Houston (77002) *(G-12329)*

Total E&P Usa Inc 713 647-3000
1201 La St Ste 1800 Houston (77002) *(G-12330)*

Total Equipment and Service, Granbury Also called *TE&s Limited (G-7811)*

Total Flow Products Div, Houston Also called *ABB Inc (G-8443)*

Total Grow Control, Alvin Also called *Total Grow Holdings LLC (G-382)*

Total Grow Holdings LLC 281 585-9500
2190 Washington Ave Alvin (77511) *(G-382)*

Total Holdings Usa Inc (HQ) 713 483-5000
1201 La St Ste 1800 Houston (77002) *(G-12331)*

Total Innvtive Cntrls Solution, Houston Also called *Sam and Sab Inc (G-11736)*

Total Instrumentation Contrls, Houston Also called *Tubular Instrumentat (G-12402)*

Total Lubrication MGT Co, Houston Also called *Lubrication Systems Texas LLC (G-8388)*

Total Machining Solutions LLC (PA) 281 355-7700
19129 Northpine Dr Spring (77388) *(G-19181)*

Total Metal Products Inc 214 330-7453
4071 Shilling Way Dallas (75237) *(G-5102)*

Total Oilfield Eqp & Sup LLC 361 442-2922
2653 Highway 44 Robstown (78380) *(G-17518)*

Total Oilfield Services, Lubbock Also called *TOFS LLC (G-14496)*

Total Operations Prod Svcs LLC 432 332-9777
12614 W County Road 91 Midland (79707) *(G-15440)*

Total Orthtic Prsthtic Sltions (PA) 915 541-8677
900 E Yandell Dr El Paso (79902) *(G-6009)*

Total Pallet Solutions LLC 817 783-5565
3532 S Burleson Blvd Alvarado (76009) *(G-347)*

Total Production Services Inc 361 572-0484
2501 E Real Grant Victoria (77901) *(G-20311)*

Total Ptrchemicals Ref USA Inc (HQ) 713 483-5000
1201 La St Ste 1800 Houston (77002) *(G-12332)*

Total Ptrchemicals Ref USA Inc 409 291-7296
11455 Ih 10 Beaumont (77705) *(G-1961)*

Total Ptrchemicals Ref USA Inc 281 542-9542
1902 Independence Pkwy S La Porte (77571) *(G-13797)*

Total Ptrchemicals Ref USA Inc 409 963-6837
Hwy 366 And 32nd St Port Arthur (77642) *(G-17129)*

Total Ptrchemicals Ref USA Inc 281 452-8577
8280 Sheldon Rd Channelview (77530) *(G-3043)*

Total Ptrchemicals Ref USA Inc 281 476-3700
1818 Battleground Rd Deer Park (77536) *(G-5301)*

Total Ptrchemicals Ref USA Inc 409 963-6800
7600 32nd St Port Arthur (77642) *(G-17130)*

Total Ptrchemicals SEC USA Inc 713 483-5000
1201 La St Ste 1800 Houston (77002) *(G-12333)*

Total Ptrchmcals USA Fundation 713 483-5000
1818 Independence Pkwy S La Porte (77571) *(G-13798)*

Total Quality Machining, Gilmer Also called *Parland Inc (G-7710)*

Total Rod Concepts Inc 432 689-0300
2800 S County Road 1207 Midland (79706) *(G-15441)*

Total Sand Services LLC 817 420-7474
300 Throckmorton St # 300 Fort Worth (76102) *(G-7067)*

Total Spcalty Publications LLC 813 405-2610
5120 State Highway 6 Riesel (76682) *(G-17470)*

Total Specialties Usa Inc (HQ) 713 969-4651
1201 La St Ste 1800 Houston (77002) *(G-12334)*

Total Steel Fabrication LLC 972 846-4703
2705 Brombeck Ennis (75119) *(G-6120)*

Total Wellhead & Rentl Tls LLC 806 435-3800
401 S Juniper St Perryton (79070) *(G-16650)*

Tote Systems International LP 817 447-9110
8821 Forum Way Ste 113 Fort Worth (76140) *(G-7068)*

Toter LLC 830 775-3411
  1661 Frontera Rd Del Rio (78840) *(G-5326)*

Toucan Recycling, San Antonio *Also called Monterrey Iron & Metal Ltd (G-18318)*

Touch International Inc 512 832-8292
  2222 W Rundberg Ln # 200 Austin (78758) *(G-1586)*

Touchmate Inc 512 949-3330
  7703 N Lamar Blvd Ste 100 Austin (78752) *(G-1587)*

Touchpay Holdings LP 972 215-0133
  7801 Mesquite Bend Dr # 101 Irving (75063) *(G-13196)*

Touchshare Inc (PA) **626 639-5460**
  815 Briarpark Dr Houston (77042) *(G-12335)*

Touchtec, Rockwall *Also called Dallas Decal Inc (G-17546)*

Tourtexas.com, Spring *Also called Ajr Media Group LLC (G-19194)*

Toutatis Aztec Solutions 972 484-3060
  2101 Cedar Springs Rd Dallas (75201) *(G-5103)*

Tovar Printing Inc 915 584-5900
  1230 Texas Ave El Paso (79901) *(G-6010)*

Tower Elevator Systems Inc 512 266-6200
  2000a Picadilly Dr Round Rock (78664) *(G-17696)*

Tower Extrusions Ltd 972 442-3535
  930 Hensley Ln Wylie (75098) *(G-20952)*

Tower Extrusions Ltd (PA) **940 564-5681**
  1003 State Highway 79 S Olney (76374) *(G-16225)*

Tower Extrusions Ltd 972 442-7200
  1405 Martinez Ln Wylie (75098) *(G-20953)*

Tower Semicdtr San Antonio Inc 210 522-7000
  9651 Westover Hills Blvd San Antonio (78251) *(G-18554)*

Town & Country Printing Inc 713 973-6666
  1171 Brittmoore Rd Houston (77043) *(G-12336)*

Townsend International Inc (PA) **432 381-8750**
  5381 W 42nd St Odessa (79764) *(G-16181)*

Townsend Oilfield Services LP 361 449-1444
  3122 Highway 281 George West (78022) *(G-7630)*

Towsley and Bailey Inc 972 563-5400
  10415 County Road 305 Terrell (75160) *(G-19753)*

Toyo Ink America LLC 979 778-1538
  2400 N Hrvey Mtchell Pkwy Bryan (77807) *(G-2513)*

Toyoda Gosei 210 628-1337
  15800 Applewhite Rd San Antonio (78264) *(G-18555)*

Toyoda Gosei Texas LLC 210 302-4600
  1 Lone Star Pass Bldg 31 San Antonio (78264) *(G-18556)*

Toyoda Gsei Brwnsvlle Txas LLC 956 290-8802
  107 Joaquin Cavazos Rd Los Indios (78567) *(G-14350)*

Toyota Motor North America Inc 859 746-4351
  5360 Legacy Dr Plano (75024) *(G-17035)*

Toyota Motor North America Inc (HQ) **469 292-4000**
  6565 Headquarters Dr Plano (75024) *(G-17036)*

Toyota Mtr Engrg Mfg N Amer In (HQ) **469 292-1074**
  6565 Hdqtr Dr W1 3c 1 W Plano (75024) *(G-17037)*

Toyotetsu Texas Inc 210 231-5515
  1 Lone Star Pass Bldg 38 San Antonio (78264) *(G-18557)*

TPC Acquisition Partners LP 281 356-2168
  31909 Decker Indus Dr Pinehurst (77362) *(G-16736)*

Tpe Solutions Inc 978 425-3033
  616 111th St Arlington (76011) *(G-801)*

Tpg Capital Management LP (PA) **817 871-4000**
  301 Commerce St Ste 3300 Fort Worth (76102) *(G-7069)*

Tpg Pressure Inc 972 262-3600
  1004 Macarthur Blvd Grand Prairie (75050) *(G-7984)*

Tpg Pressure Inc (PA) **972 262-3600**
  1003 Macarthur Blvd Grand Prairie (75050) *(G-7985)*

Tpg Software Inc 713 974-1375
  5858 Westheimer Rd # 620 Houston (77057) *(G-12337)*

TPI 972 276-2901
  1136 N 1st St Garland (75040) *(G-7604)*

Tpi Mexico LLC (HQ) **915 881-5808**
  700 N Zaragoza Rd Ste N El Paso (79907) *(G-6011)*

Tpm, Conroe *Also called Tubular Prfrting Mfr of Conroe (G-3374)*

Tpv International (usa) Inc (PA) **512 241-1508**
  3737 Executive Center Dr # 261 Austin (78731) *(G-1588)*

Tpws Inc 713 291-5518
  21602 Timber Ridge Dr Magnolia (77355) *(G-14632)*

Tqi LLC 830 401-4400
  960 Crossroads Blvd Seguin (78155) *(G-18869)*

Trace Metal Industries Inc 817 921-6251
  2944 S Main St Fort Worth (76110) *(G-7070)*

Tracerco, Pasadena *Also called Johnson Matthey Inc (G-16465)*

Tracey Technologies Corp 281 445-1666
  16720 Hedgecroft Dr # 208 Houston (77060) *(G-12338)*

Track What Matters LLC 817 430-9201
  2652 Fm 407 E Ste 215 Bartonville (76226) *(G-1747)*

Tracker, Austin *Also called PC Legal Tools Inc (G-1402)*

Tracker Energy Services Inc 830 837-0806
  1312 Havenwood Blvd New Braunfels (78132) *(G-15829)*

Tracy and Associates 817 559-9274
  3408 Sundance Ct Granbury (76049) *(G-7813)*

Tradco Inc 713 333-9300
  9400 Bamboo Rd Houston (77041) *(G-12339)*

Trade Mart, Dallas *Also called Dallas Market Center Co Ltd (G-4219)*

Trade Source International (HQ) 972 393-3800
  650 S Royal Ln Ste 200 Coppell (75019) *(G-3450)*

Trade-Mark Industrial LLC 519 650-7444
  1 Lone Star Pass Lot C12 San Antonio (78264) *(G-18558)*

Trademarks Promotional Pdts LP 713 255-6506
  11333 Todd St Houston (77055) *(G-12340)*

Trader Sam LLC 214 537-0885
  3928 Lost Creek Dr Plano (75074) *(G-17038)*

Tradesorg LLC 512 729-3544
  3605 Menchaca Rd Austin (78704) *(G-1589)*

Tradewinds Petrotrade LLC 713 465-7590
  8955 Katy Fwy Ste 220 Houston (77024) *(G-12341)*

Traeger Wood Pellets 409 384-5331
  606 Mcqueen St Jasper (75951) *(G-13282)*

Trafco Industries Inc 979 234-5713
  413 W Main St Eagle Lake (77434) *(G-5544)*

Traffic & Transportation, Irving *Also called City of Irving (G-12972)*

Traffic Supply Inc 979 234-5509
  500 Highway 3013 W Eagle Lake (77434) *(G-5545)*

Trafficware, Sugar Land *Also called Cubic Its Inc (G-19471)*

Trailer Jockey, Longview *Also called Capacity of Texas Inc (G-14207)*

Trailers By Southern LLC 469 517-0410
  3941 Windmill Rd Joshua (76058) *(G-13327)*

Trainup.com, Plano *Also called Tillman Learning LLC (G-17033)*

Trajan Scientific Americas Inc (HQ) **512 837-7190**
  1421 W Wlls Br Pkwy Ste 1 Pflugerville (78660) *(G-16689)*

Trajan Scientific and Medical, Pflugerville *Also called Trajan Scientific Americas Inc (G-16689)*

Trampoline USA Inc 800 872-6765
  9010 Interstate 10 W Orange (77632) *(G-16266)*

Trampolines Usa Inc (HQ) **409 745-3139**
  8672 Interstate 10 W Orange (77632) *(G-16267)*

Trane Company 956 968-6425
  1240 Vo Tech Dr Weslaco (78599) *(G-20669)*

Trane Company 915 593-3484
  1405 Vanderbilt Dr El Paso (79935) *(G-6012)*

Trane Company, The, El Paso *Also called Trane US Inc (G-6013)*

Trane Global Parts, El Paso *Also called Trane Company (G-6012)*

Trane Supply, Dallas *Also called Trane US Inc (G-5104)*

Trane Technologies, San Antonio *Also called Trane US Inc (G-18559)*

Trane Technologies Company LLC 903 730-4000
  6200 Troup Hwy Tyler (75707) *(G-20163)*

Trane US Inc 239 277-7400
  1617 Hutton Dr Carrollton (75006) *(G-2836)*

Trane US Inc 903 581-3200
  6200 Troup Hwy Tyler (75707) *(G-20164)*

Trane US Inc 903 316-8033
  1211 Woodland Hills Dr Tyler (75701) *(G-20165)*

Trane US Inc 972 892-3900
  11011 Regency Crest Dr Dallas (75238) *(G-5104)*

Trane US Inc 832 747-2000
  16335 Central Green Blvd Houston (77032) *(G-12342)*

Trane US Inc 713 266-3900
  10555 Westpark Dr Houston (77042) *(G-12343)*

Trane US Inc 817 838-1310
  4200 N Sylvania Ave Fort Worth (76137) *(G-7071)*

Trane US Inc 210 657-0901
  9535 Ball St San Antonio (78217) *(G-18559)*

Trane US Inc 469 758-3128
  1617 Hutton Dr Carrollton (75006) *(G-2837)*

Trane US Inc 915 593-3484
  1405 Vanderbilt Dr El Paso (79935) *(G-6013)*

Trane US Inc 254 299-6300
  182 Cotton Belt Pkwy Mc Gregor (76657) *(G-14825)*

Trans Cable International Inc 903 449-4622
  800 E 2nd St Bonham (75418) *(G-2156)*

Trans Continental Cold Storage, Amarillo *Also called Tyson Fresh Meats Inc (G-469)*

Trans Tool LLC 210 225-6745
  110 Connelly St San Antonio (78203) *(G-18560)*

Trans-Gulf Drilling Svcs Inc 903 759-0010
  1201 W Loop 281 Ste 200 Longview (75604) *(G-14320)*

Trans-Mate LLC 800 867-9274
  5949 Sherry Ln Ste 540 Dallas (75225) *(G-5105)*

Trans-Mountain Equipment, Austin *Also called JD Abrams LP (G-1252)*

Trans-Pecos Pipeline LLC 713 989-2606
  1300 Main St Houston (77002) *(G-12344)*

Trans-TEC Machine Ltd 713 643-9114
  6320 Ridgemont St Houston (77087) *(G-12345)*

Trans-Tel Central Inc 405 447-5025
  10930 Wye Dr Ste 104 San Antonio (78217) *(G-18561)*

Trans-Tex Cementing Svcs LLC 432 699-4400
  5019 Basin St Midland (79703) *(G-15442)*

Trans-Tex Fabricating Co Inc 210 633-0100
  13165 Donop Rd Elmendorf (78112) *(G-6072)*

Trans-Tex Fabricating Co Inc (PA) **210 924-4431**
  549 Heimer Rd Ste 100 San Antonio (78232) *(G-18562)*

Trans-Texas Tire LLC (PA) **903 572-0267**
  1106 Industrial Rd Mount Pleasant (75455) *(G-15664)*

A
L
P
H
A
B
E
T
I
C

Trans-Texas Tire Mt Pleasant, Mount Pleasant *Also called Trans-Texas Tire LLC* ***(G-15664)***
Transamerican Natural Gas Corp....281 372-5304
1300 N Sam Houston Pkwy E Houston (77032) ***(G-12346)***
Transatlantic Petro USA Corp (HQ)....**214 220-4323**
16803 Dallas Pkwy Addison (75001) ***(G-169)***
Transatlantic Petroleum Ltd (PA)....**214 220-4323**
16803 Dallas Pkwy Addison (75001) ***(G-170)***
Transcanada Turbines Inc....281 880-2900
11221 Cutten Rd Bldg 4 Houston (77066) ***(G-12347)***
Transcanada USA Services Inc....832 320-5000
700 Louisiana St Ste 700 # 700 Houston (77002) ***(G-12348)***
Transcean Offshore Dpwter Drlg (HQ)....**713 232-7500**
1414 Enclave Pkwy Houston (77077) ***(G-12349)***
Transcend Drilling Company Inc....432 618-1100
1118 S Fm 1788 Midland (79706) ***(G-15443)***
Transcend Solutions Llc....936 689-5618
14432 John F Kennedy Blvd Houston (77032) ***(G-12350)***
Transcendia Inc....800 659-4254
2001 Westgate Dr Ste 100 Carrollton (75006) ***(G-2838)***
Transcom Packaging Inc....979 885-1800
2893 Fm 1094 Rd Sealy (77474) ***(G-18821)***
Transcontinental Energy Corp....713 856-6755
9000 Emmott Rd Ste E Houston (77040) ***(G-12351)***
Transdata Inc....972 418-7717
2560 Tarpley Rd Carrollton (75006) ***(G-2839)***
Transfer Graphics Inc....940 566-2679
1024 Dallas Dr Denton (76205) ***(G-5407)***
Transfield Services, Houston *Also called Broadspectrum Downstream Servi* ***(G-8989)***
Transformation Enzyme, Houston *Also called Dicqie M Fuller Looney* ***(G-9465)***
Transformer Components, Harlingen *Also called Asphalt Products Inc* ***(G-8181)***
Transformer Division, Lubbock *Also called Brandon & Clark Inc* ***(G-14381)***
Transilwrap Texas, Carrollton *Also called Transcendia Inc* ***(G-2838)***
Transit Ready Mix LLC....956 584-0039
7205 N La Homa Rd Mission (78574) ***(G-15568)***
Transition Superior Systems Lc....325 690-0248
274 County Road 287 Merkel (79536) ***(G-15018)***
Transitions Industries LLC....806 698-6200
4415 66th St Ste 101 Lubbock (79414) ***(G-14497)***
Transmedia Dynamics Inc....512 971-2313
7212 Goforth Rd Ste 109 Kyle (78640) ***(G-13687)***
Transmix Redi Mix, Dalhart *Also called Hunter Construction Inc* ***(G-3835)***
Transnorm System Inc....972 606-0303
2810 Avenue E E Arlington (76011) ***(G-802)***
Transocean, Houston *Also called Global Marine Inc* ***(G-9974)***
Transocean Inc (HQ)....**713 232-7500**
4 Greenway Plz Ste 700 Houston (77046) ***(G-12352)***
Transocean Offshore USA Inc....713 232-7500
4 Greenway Plz Ste 700 Houston (77046) ***(G-12353)***
Transocean Sedco Forex, Houston *Also called Transcean Offshore Dpwter Drlg* ***(G-12349)***
Transplant Technology Inc (PA)....**210 696-7616**
5335 Castroville Rd San Antonio (78227) ***(G-18563)***
Transport Boats....361 972-6629
1729 1st St Palacios (77465) ***(G-16292)***
Transportation Testing, San Angelo *Also called Standards Testing Labs Inc* ***(G-17828)***
Transportation Texas Dept....940 937-2571
1700 Avenue F Nw Childress (79201) ***(G-3056)***
Transtar Oilfield Services LLC....281 456-7822
10402 Vrana Dr Houston (77049) ***(G-12354)***
Transtex LLC (HQ)....**832 369-6986**
1111 Louisiana Ste 4520 Irving (75038) ***(G-13197)***
Transworld Worldwide Inc....713 232-7500
4 Greenway Plz Houston (77046) ***(G-12355)***
Tranter Inc (HQ)....**940 723-7125**
1900 Old Burk Hwy Wichita Falls (76306) ***(G-20819)***
Traulsen & Co Inc....817 625-9671
4401 Blue Mound Rd Fort Worth (76106) ***(G-7072)***
Traulsen Companies, Fort Worth *Also called Traulsen & Co Inc* ***(G-7072)***
Travelhost Printing Inc....972 556-0541
433 Las Colinas Blvd E Irving (75039) ***(G-13198)***
Travis Assn For The Blind (PA)....**512 442-2329**
2307 Business Center Dr Austin (78744) ***(G-1590)***
Travis Body and Trailer Inc....713 466-5888
13955 Fm 529 Rd Houston (77041) ***(G-12356)***
Travis Millwork Inc....210 525-8088
235 W Turbo Dr San Antonio (78216) ***(G-18564)***
Travis Peak Resources LLC....512 814-0345
1100 La St Ste 5100 Houston (77002) ***(G-12357)***
Travis Scott....254 829-0651
16629 N Interstate 35 Ross (76684) ***(G-17617)***
Travis Software Inc....281 496-3737
24 Greenway Plz Ste 800 Houston (77046) ***(G-12358)***
Travis Trailers, Houston *Also called Travis Body and Trailer Inc* ***(G-12356)***
Travisoft, Houston *Also called Sagl Enterprises Inc* ***(G-11729)***
Travistin Inc....512 275-4812
5609 Lakeshore Dr Lago Vista (78645) ***(G-13809)***
Traw Machine Works LLC....281 893-1710
18635 Telge Rd Cypress (77429) ***(G-3823)***
Trax Holdings Inc....855 999-7828
3051 Churchill Dr Ste 116 Flower Mound (75022) ***(G-6290)***
Traxis Machining & Fabrication, Austin *Also called Traxis Manufacturing LLC* ***(G-1591)***
Traxis Manufacturing LLC....512 383-0089
511 E Saint Elmo Rd Austin (78745) ***(G-1591)***
Traxsales LLC....713 466-7177
6830 N Eldridge Pkwy # 3 Houston (77041) ***(G-12359)***
Tray-Tec Inc....281 441-7314
2598 Wilson Rd Humble (77396) ***(G-12805)***
TRC Consultants Lc (PA)....**830 249-9968**
120 Dietert Ave Ste 100 Boerne (78006) ***(G-2144)***
TRC Recreation LP (PA)....**940 322-4463**
908 N Beverly Dr Wichita Falls (76306) ***(G-20820)***
Tre Printing, Garland *Also called Georgia Tre Magazine LLC* ***(G-7502)***
Tre Stars Incorporated....915 351-1433
6800 Gateway Blvd E El Paso (79915) ***(G-6014)***
Treaty Oak Brewing Distlg LLC....512 680-1606
16604 Fitzhugh Rd Dripping Springs (78620) ***(G-5513)***
Treaty Oak Distilling Company, Dripping Springs *Also called Treaty Oak Brewing Distlg LLC* ***(G-5513)***
Trecora Chemical Inc....281 474-7500
12500 Bay Area Blvd Pasadena (77507) ***(G-16519)***
Trecora Resources (PA)....**281 980-5522**
1650 Highway 6 Ste 190 Sugar Land (77478) ***(G-19568)***
Treffinger Inc....972 286-8852
12650 Ravenview Rd Dallas (75253) ***(G-5106)***
Trek Resources Inc....214 373-0318
4925 Greenville Ave # 915 Dallas (75206) ***(G-5107)***
Trelleborg Offshore Us Inc....281 774-2600
10375 Richmond Ave # 1725 Houston (77042) ***(G-12360)***
Tremetrics, Austin *Also called Thermo Finnigan LLC* ***(G-1572)***
Trench-Tech Ltd (PA)....**817 491-0621**
330 Benson Ln Roanoke (76262) ***(G-17496)***
Trencor Enterprises Inc....806 659-3911
1103 W 7th Spearman (79081) ***(G-19089)***
Trend Gathering & Treating LP (HQ)....**817 885-2524**
810 Houston St Ste 2000 Fort Worth (76102) ***(G-7073)***
Trend Micro Incorporated (HQ)....**408 257-1500**
225 E John Carpenter Fwy # 1500 Irving (75062) ***(G-13199)***
TREND OFFSET PRINTING SERVICES INCORPORATED, Carrollton *Also called Trend Offset Printing Svcs Inc* ***(G-2840)***
Trend Offset Printing Svcs Inc....972 243-3556
2323 Mcdaniel Dr Ste 100 Carrollton (75006) ***(G-2840)***
Trend Services Inc....361 396-0048
3230 W Highway 44 Alice (78332) ***(G-241)***
Trendsetter Construction Inc (PA)....**903 759-4955**
2173 Turkey Rd Gladewater (75647) ***(G-7728)***
Trendsetter Recycling Services, Gladewater *Also called Trendsetter Construction Inc* ***(G-7728)***
Trenton Plastics, Trenton *Also called Gudgel & Sons Inc* ***(G-20016)***
Tres Outlaws, El Paso *Also called Falconhead Boots Belts Buckles* ***(G-5762)***
Tres Palacios Marine LP....361 972-3097
111 Friery Rd Palacios (77465) ***(G-16293)***
Treska Inc (PA)....**682 647-0352**
3801 Austin Ln Fort Worth (76111) ***(G-7074)***
Tresu Americas, Grapevine *Also called Tresu Royse Inc* ***(G-8058)***
Tresu Royse Inc....214 631-2844
635 Westport Pkwy Ste 300 Grapevine (76051) ***(G-8058)***
Trevino Industries Inc....281 489-1754
5302 Bailey Rd Pearland (77584) ***(G-16605)***
Trevino Jr Gustavo....956 585-2522
4200 W Mile 3 Rd Mission (78574) ***(G-15569)***
Trevinos Painting Inc....956 571-3999
2038 E Richardson Rd Edinburg (78542) ***(G-5604)***
Trevinos Welding....806 250-3669
701 W 11th St Friona (79035) ***(G-7254)***
Trevway Inc....832 687-6269
6725 S Fry Rd Ste 700538 Katy (77494) ***(G-13380)***
Trew Investments Inc....806 749-3200
1407 E Fm 1585 Lubbock (79423) ***(G-14498)***
Trey Industries Inc....409 948-8891
5201 Emmett F Lowry Expy Texas City (77591) ***(G-19804)***
Trey Industry SW....915 591-5100
1221 Barranca Dr El Paso (79935) ***(G-6015)***
Trey Resources Inc....432 570-6898
601 N Marienfeld St # 400 Midland (79701) ***(G-15444)***
Trey Trucks Ltd....432 558-7966
1160 Sw 6th St Crane (79731) ***(G-3702)***
Tri Capital Energy Corporation....972 996-7486
1 Galleria Tower Dallas (75240) ***(G-5108)***
Tri Cities Ready Mix Div, Breckenridge *Also called Breckenridge Ready Mix Inc* ***(G-2226)***
Tri Element Incorporated....361 664-5000
1216 Airport Rd Alice (78332) ***(G-242)***
Tri Gas, Houston *Also called Matheson Tri-Gas Inc* ***(G-10794)***
Tri Leaf Industries LLC....830 742-3700
6140 Highway 6 Ste 178 Missouri City (77459) ***(G-15596)***
Tri Resources Inc....713 584-1000
1000 La St Ste 4300 Houston (77002) ***(G-12361)***

Tri Resources Inc..940 644-2233
  383 County Road 1745 Chico (76431) *(G-3054)*

Tri Resources Inc..432 558-3996
  5880 Fm 1233 Crane (79731) *(G-3703)*

Tri Resources Inc..432 688-0555
  6 Desta Dr Ste 3300 Midland (79705) *(G-15445)*

Tri Resources Inc..903 845-2617
  3018 Barrow Ln Gladewater (75647) *(G-7729)*

Tri Resources Inc..281 385-3200
  10119 Highway 146 Mont Belvieu (77535) *(G-15623)*

Tri Resources Inc..806 323-9125
  3 Mi S On Hwy 60 Canadian (79014) *(G-2655)*

Tri Resources Inc..940 549-8340
  2209 Us Highway 180 E Breckenridge (76424) *(G-2240)*

Tri Resources Inc (HQ).......................................**713 584-1000**
  811 Louisiana St Ste 2100 Houston (77002) *(G-12362)*

Tri Resources Inc..903 687-2513
  155 Private Rd Ste 1133 Waskom (75692) *(G-20523)*

Tri Resources Inc..254 559-7533
  4 Market Rd 2231 Breckenridge (76424) *(G-2241)*

Tri Star Diversified, Lewisville *Also called Arnold Stone Inc (G-14024)*

Tri Star Metals Inc...940 433-2173
  554 S Allen St Boyd (76023) *(G-2209)*

Tri State Pressure Control, Longview *Also called Petrostar Services LLC (G-14289)*

Tri Tool Inc..281 499-1188
  13330 Pike Rd Stafford (77477) *(G-19387)*

Tri-C Resources, Houston *Also called Otcr Inc (G-11199)*

Tri-City Investments, Beaumont *Also called Tcw Investments Inc (G-1956)*

Tri-City Welding & Fabrication, Beaumont *Also called Walston Ventures LLC (G-1968)*

Tri-Construction Co Inc......................................979 233-7211
  5550 E Highway 332 Freeport (77541) *(G-7217)*

Tri-Cor Industries Inc...210 979-0552
  2929 Mossrock Ste 105 San Antonio (78230) *(G-18565)*

Tri-Max Corporation...713 937-8808
  6324 Cunningham Rd Houston (77041) *(G-12363)*

Tri-Pak Machinery Inc..956 423-5140
  1102 N Commerce St Harlingen (78550) *(G-8207)*

Tri-Sen Systems Corporation (HQ)......................**832 632-1211**
  109 Magellan Cir Webster (77598) *(G-20648)*

Tri-Star Petroleum Company................................713 222-0011
  9 Greenway Plz Ste 3100 Houston (77046) *(G-12364)*

Tri-Tex Cabinets Inc..940 686-2617
  900 N Highway 377 Pilot Point (76258) *(G-16731)*

Tri-Tex Enterprises Inc (PA)...............................**214 744-1246**
  4909 Lakawana St Dallas (75247) *(G-5109)*

Tri-Tex Enterprises Inc.......................................214 744-1246
  202 N College Ave Eastland (76448) *(G-5569)*

Tri-Win Outsourcing Inc......................................214 826-2244
  4301 Simonton Rd Ste 100 Dallas (75244) *(G-5110)*

Triangel Food, Houston *Also called Villpac Inc (G-12568)*

Triangle Blue Print Company..............................409 835-6810
  1123 Calder St Beaumont (77701) *(G-1962)*

Triangle Bolt, Beaumont *Also called Colgan-Wilson Metals LLC (G-1873)*

Triangle Pump Components Inc (PA)...................**817 202-8530**
  3644 W Highway 67 Cleburne (76033) *(G-3115)*

Triangle Reproductions Inc (PA)........................**713 780-0236**
  8168 Westpark Dr Ste A Houston (77063) *(G-12365)*

Triangle Reproductions of San...........................713 780-0236
  2203 Ceegee St San Antonio (78217) *(G-18566)*

Triangle Resources Inc.......................................409 861-2267
  9869 Highway 90 Beaumont (77713) *(G-1963)*

Triangle Well Servicing Co..................................806 665-8459
  129 S Price Rd Pampa (79065) *(G-16343)*

Triarch Industries Inc (PA)..................................**713 690-9977**
  9550 W Wingfoot Rd # 140 Houston (77041) *(G-12366)*

Triathlon Btry Solutions Inc................................469 301-2128
  2025 Midway Rd Ste 200 Lewisville (75056) *(G-14099)*

Triaz Digital Printing LLC....................................512 491-7000
  2013 Wlls Br Pkwy Ste 307 Austin (78728) *(G-1592)*

Tribocor Technologies Inc..................................281 277-7200
  12950 Royal Dr Stafford (77477) *(G-19388)*

Tribute Energy Inc...281 768-5300
  2100 West Loop S Ste 1500 Houston (77027) *(G-12367)*

Trican Well Service LP.......................................281 716-9152
  5825 N Sam Houston Pkwy W # 600 Houston (77086) *(G-12368)*

Trican Wells Service, Houston *Also called Keane Group Holdings LLC (G-10511)*

Trico Technologies Corporation (HQ)..................**956 544-2722**
  1995 Billy Mitchell Blvd Brownsville (78521) *(G-2416)*

Tricon Energy, Houston *Also called Tricon International Ltd (G-12371)*

Tricon Energy Inc (PA).......................................**713 963-0066**
  777 Post Oak Blvd Ste 550 Houston (77056) *(G-12369)*

Tricon Energy Ltd...713 963-0066
  777 Post Oak Blvd Ste 550 Houston (77056) *(G-12370)*

Tricon International Ltd (HQ)..............................**713 963-0066**
  777 Post Oak Blvd Ste 550 Houston (77056) *(G-12371)*

Tricor Industrial Inc...936 273-2661
  3517 N Loop 336 W Conroe (77304) *(G-3373)*

Tricounty Materials & Svcs LP............................972 446-1816
  14459 Intrstate 35 Frntag Sanger (76266) *(G-18731)*

Trident Crating & Services Inc............................281 227-3999
  14320 Interdrive E Houston (77032) *(G-12372)*

Trident Laboratories Inc.....................................972 226-4986
  200 Adell Blvd Mesquite (75182) *(G-15081)*

Trident Process Systems LLC.............................940 372-1535
  2300 N I 35 Gainesville (76240) *(G-7373)*

Trident Water Services LLC...............................817 889-4334
  325 Trinidad Ct Benbrook (76126) *(G-2046)*

Trifecta Environmental Svcs, Floresville *Also called Trifecta Oilfield Services LLC (G-6254)*

Trifecta Oilfield Services LLC.............................930 730-4800
  2840 Bus Loop 181 N Ste 1 Floresville (78114) *(G-6254)*

Trifectix Inc...512 580-2809
  20126 West Lake Pkwy Georgetown (78628) *(G-7687)*

Trifusion, Round Rock *Also called Connectione LLC (G-17636)*

Trilliant Surgical LLC..800 495-2919
  727 N Shepherd Dr Ste 100 Houston (77007) *(G-12373)*

Trillium US Inc..512 441-6893
  1340 Arprt Commrce Dr # 175 Austin (78741) *(G-1593)*

Trimco Master Millwork Inc................................915 855-8501
  3500 Lee Blvd El Paso (79936) *(G-6016)*

Trimira LLC..713 984-8994
  952 Echo Ln Ste 333 Houston (77024) *(G-12374)*

Trimmings Inc...903 872-1556
  2030 Haggar St Corsicana (75110) *(G-3687)*

Trinidad Benham Holding Co...............................903 569-2283
  322 Freeman St Mineola (75773) *(G-15514)*

Trinity Asphalt Inc...903 657-2391
  8621 Hwy 2276 Henderson (75652) *(G-8275)*

Trinity Casting Service Inc..................................214 631-4248
  2127 Cartwright St Dallas (75212) *(G-5111)*

Trinity Coatings LLC..281 845-0022
  25225 Hwy 288 Rosharon Rosharon (77583) *(G-17615)*

Trinity Environmental Svcs LLC (PA)...................**512 582-8050**
  6300 Bridge Point Pkwy 2-210 Austin (78730) *(G-1594)*

Trinity Envmtl Ctarina Swd LLC...........................512 524-7281
  113343 Hwy 71 W Austin (78738) *(G-1595)*

Trinity Esc, Arlington *Also called Trnlwb LLC (G-805)*

Trinity Fellowship (PA)..**806 355-8955**
  5000 Hollywood Rd Amarillo (79118) *(G-515)*

Trinity Forge Inc..817 473-1515
  947 Trinity Dr Mansfield (76063) *(G-14723)*

Trinity Industrial Svcs LLC (PA)..........................**409 722-6700**
  13071 W Port Arthur Rd Beaumont (77705) *(G-1964)*

Trinity Industries Inc (PA)..................................**214 631-4420**
  14221 Dallas Pkwy Ste 11 Dallas (75254) *(G-5112)*

Trinity Industries Inc..817 665-1499
  2548 Ne 28th St Fort Worth (76111) *(G-7075)*

Trinity Industries 068...903 295-0356
  708 Jordan Valley Rd Longview (75604) *(G-14321)*

Trinity Industries Intl..214 589-8967
  14221 Dallas Pkwy Dallas (75254) *(G-5113)*

Trinity Industries Plant 181.................................214 631-4420
  140 Shady Brook Ln Longview (75602) *(G-14322)*

Trinity Millennium Group Inc..............................210 615-1606
  2424 Babcock Rd Ste 300 San Antonio (78229) *(G-18567)*

Trinity Parts & Components, Fort Worth *Also called Trinity Industries Inc (G-7075)*

Trinity Parts & Components LLC (HQ)..................**817 378-2003**
  2548 Ne 28th St Fort Worth (76111) *(G-7076)*

Trinity Powder Coating.......................................214 703-3609
  2850 Industrial Ln Garland (75041) *(G-7605)*

Trinity Rail Group LLC (HQ)...............................**214 631-4420**
  14221 Dallas Pkwy # 1100 Dallas (75254) *(G-5114)*

Trinity River Distillery LLC...................................214 293-6011
  1734 E El Paso St Ste 130 Fort Worth (76102) *(G-7077)*

Trinity River Energy LLC (HQ)............................**817 872-7898**
  15021 Katy Fwy Ste 200 Houston (77094) *(G-12375)*

Trinity River Energy Oper LLC (HQ).....................**817 872-7800**
  15021 Katy Fwy Ste 200 Houston (77094) *(G-12376)*

Trinity Services LLC..903 687-4350
  18149 Us Highway 80 E Waskom (75692) *(G-20524)*

Trinity Services Group Inc..................................903 277-7128
  2819 W 7th St Texarkana (75501) *(G-19781)*

Trinity Services LLC-Admin, Waskom *Also called Trinity Services LLC (G-20524)*

Trinity Sling Authority Inc...................................817 589-2404
  3508 Avenue F Arlington (76011) *(G-803)*

Trinity Specialty Products Inc.............................210 304-2100
  647 N Ww White Rd San Antonio (78219) *(G-18568)*

Trinity Stairs Inc (PA)...**972 335-0700**
  12750 Preston Rd Ste 1100 Frisco (75033) *(G-7320)*

Trinity Storage Services, Austin *Also called Trinity Environmental Svcs LLC (G-1594)*

Trinity Tool, Mason *Also called Flotek Industries Inc (G-14814)*

Trinitys Covenant LLC..210 620-3694
  1603 Sweden Ln Laredo (78045) *(G-13939)*

Trinkote Indus Finishes Inc.................................817 396-4747
  800 Hughie Long Rd Cresson (76035) *(G-3715)*

Triofab Inc...713 417-1205
  6515 Carson Rd Houston (77048) *(G-12377)*

Tripac International Inc......................................817 534-9278
  9000 Forum Way Fort Worth (76140) *(G-7078)*

A
L
P
H
A
B
E
T
I
C

Triple - C Fence Llc 817 439-9500
1803 Avondale Haslet Rd Haslet (76052) *(G-8226)*

Triple Aim Ventures LLC 210 417-4170
100 Ne Loop 410 Ste 100 # 100 San Antonio (78216) *(G-18569)*

Triple C Concrete Lubbock Ltd 806 762-3227
2008 E 50th St Lubbock (79404) *(G-14499)*

Triple C Hardware & Lumber Inc 325 392-4123
1116 Ave E Ozona (76943) *(G-16289)*

Triple C Hauling, Lewisville Also called Elmer Christy *(G-14048)*

Triple C Industries Inc 936 931-1171
36296 1/2 Old Highway 290 Hockley (77447) *(G-8349)*

Triple C Sheetmetal, Brenham Also called 6-K Inc *(G-2242)*

Triple Crown Resources LLC 972 444-8808
1722 Routh St Ste 1750 Dallas (75201) *(G-5115)*

Triple D Services LLC 512 750-6052
2930 Grand Oaks Loop # 2002 Cedar Park (78613) *(G-2989)*

Triple Diamond Energy Oper LLC 972 267-8600
17855 Dallas Pkwy Ste 140 Dallas (75287) *(G-3853)*

Triple J Oilfield Services Inc 956 585-1949
300 Trinity St Mission (78572) *(G-15570)*

Triple N Services Inc 432 687-1994
1110 W County Road 114 Midland (79706) *(G-15446)*

Triple Nickel Inc 806 272-5589
413 E American Blvd Muleshoe (79347) *(G-15679)*

Triple R Welding LLC 432 336-5289
2215 W 9th St Fort Stockton (79735) *(G-6330)*

Triple S Manufacturing Company 817 281-0602
4208 Murray Ave Fort Worth (76117) *(G-7079)*

Triple S Onshore Oprations LLC 903 658-0489
117 Pecan Valley Dr Bullard (75757) *(G-2552)*

Triple S Ready Mix LLC 830 769-2629
2585 S State Highway 16 Jourdanton (78026) *(G-13335)*

Triple S Welding Co 210 464-2878
18303 Wisdom Rd Lytle (78052) *(G-14574)*

Triple/S Dynamics Inc 214 828-8600
4215 Gurley St Dallas (75223) *(G-5116)*

Triple/S Dynamics Inc (PA) **214 828-8600**
1031 S Haskell Ave Dallas (75223) *(G-5117)*

Tripp Construction Inc 432 381-2440
1073 N Fm 1936 Odessa (79763) *(G-16182)*

Tripp Research Inc 512 321-9445
529 Kelley Rd Bastrop (78602) *(G-1764)*

Triseal Inc 713 589-5380
900 Anders Ln Ste 9 Kemah (77565) *(G-13480)*

Triseum LLC 979 773-8909
1733 Briarcrest Dr # 213 Bryan (77802) *(G-2514)*

Tristar Globl Enrgy Sltons Inc 713 463-9200
12600 N Featherwood Dr # 330 Houston (77034) *(G-12378)*

Tristar Group Inc 972 392-2848
5220 Spring Valley Rd # 190 Dallas (75254) *(G-5118)*

Tristar Packaging Inc 281 540-2613
1731 Treble Dr Humble (77338) *(G-12806)*

Tristar Web Graphics Inc 713 691-0001
4010 Airline Dr Houston (77022) *(G-12379)*

Tristream Energy LLC (PA) **281 240-8444**
10370 Richmond Ave # 400 Houston (77042) *(G-12380)*

Tritan Productz Ltd 940 224-1575
2006 Avondale St Wichita Falls (76308) *(G-20821)*

Tritech Software Development 972 680-2223
1205 S Greenville Ave Allen (75002) *(G-304)*

Tritex Grass LLC 817 573-6676
5901 E Us Highway 377 Granbury (76049) *(G-7814)*

Tritex Technologies Inc 214 346-6200
1201 N Bowser Rd Richardson (75081) *(G-17413)*

Triton Barn Systems, Fort Worth Also called Pilot Plastics LLC *(G-6907)*

Triton Consolidated Inc 972 362-1711
815 Mercury Ave Duncanville (75137) *(G-5539)*

Triton Data Services Inc 281 578-9700
17171 Park Row Ste 320 Houston (77084) *(G-12381)*

Triton Distribution, Richardson Also called Wages White Lion Invstmnts LLC *(G-17425)*

Triton Equipment & Services 281 681-9797
2847 W Wildwind Cir Spring (77380) *(G-19260)*

Triton Products LLC 940 455-2800
4014 Brooks Ct Ste 200 Argyle (76226) *(G-604)*

Triump Group, Grand Prairie Also called Triumph Accssory Svcs - Grnd P *(G-7986)*

Triumph Inc 361 946-4658
445 44th St Corpus Christi (78405) *(G-3643)*

Triumph Accssory Svcs - Grnd P 972 623-9300
1038 Santerre St Grand Prairie (75050) *(G-7986)*

Triumph Aerostructures LLC 972 595-9900
1601 W Marshall Dr Grand Prairie (75051) *(G-7987)*

Triumph Aerostructures LLC (HQ) **972 515-8276**
300 Austin Blvd Red Oak (75154) *(G-17237)*

Triumph Energy Partners LLC 918 986-8283
14001 Dallas Pkwy # 1200 Dallas (75240) *(G-5119)*

Triumph Group Inc 610 251-1000
899 Cassatt Rd Ste 210 Dallas (75265) *(G-5120)*

Triumph Group Inc 817 804-9400
1401 Nolan Ryan Expy Arlington (76011) *(G-804)*

Trix & Kix Dannys 281 353-6618
3400 Fm 2920 Rd Spring (77388) *(G-19182)*

Triyards, Houston Also called Goodcrane Corporation *(G-9997)*

Trnlwb LLC (PA) **800 581-3117**
1112 E Cpeland Rd Ste 500 Arlington (76011) *(G-805)*

Tronics Mems Inc 469 872-0300
15050 E Beltwood Pkwy Addison (75001) *(G-171)*

Tronox Incorporated 903 794-5169
2513 Buchanan Rd Texarkana (75501) *(G-19782)*

Tronox Incorporated 432 263-4301
Hc 63 Big Spring (79720) *(G-2101)*

Tropar Manufacturing Co Inc 972 875-5831
2313 N Preston St Ennis (75119) *(G-6121)*

Tropical Fusions Inc 830 203-5116
2712 Harwood Rd Gonzales (78629) *(G-7765)*

Tropiscapes Inc 281 371-2955
25810 Clay Rd Katy (77493) *(G-13452)*

Trosby of Georgia Inc 713 526-7332
4029 Ella Lee Ln Houston (77027) *(G-12382)*

Trothyhide LLC (PA) **817 455-1118**
5371 Rendon Rd Fort Worth (76140) *(G-7080)*

Trotti Service Company Inc 281 894-5095
9210 Meadow Vista Blvd Houston (77064) *(G-12383)*

Troubleshooters, The, Houston Also called Vickery Street Fabricators Inc *(G-12564)*

Troux Technologies Inc (PA) **512 346-8600**
12301 Res Blvd Bldg Vste Austin (78759) *(G-1596)*

Troy Barbell and Fitness, Houston Also called USA Sports Inc *(G-12502)*

Troy Helen Texas Corporation (HQ) **915 225-8000**
1 Helen Of Troy Plz El Paso (79912) *(G-6017)*

Troy Vines Incorporated 432 682-7031
2817 S State Highway 349 Midland (79706) *(G-15447)*

Trpg Inc 713 477-6995
909 Shaver St Pasadena (77506) *(G-16520)*

Trs Distribution LLC 281 372-8479
12002 Southwest Fwy Stafford (77477) *(G-19389)*

TRT Holdings Inc (PA) **214 283-8500**
4001 Maple Ave Ste 600 Dallas (75219) *(G-5121)*

Tru 254 831-6002
520 Sparta Rd Belton (76513) *(G-2029)*

Tru Turn, Deer Park Also called Romco Manufacturing Inc *(G-5292)*

Tru-Form Optics Inc (PA) **817 267-9261**
400 Harwood Rd Bedford (76021) *(G-1980)*

Tru-Test Inc 940 327-8020
528 Grant Rd Mineral Wells (76067) *(G-15543)*

Tru-Vision Plastics Inc 979 836-1091
401 W Blue Bell Rd Brenham (77833) *(G-2276)*

Truck Accessory Store, Dallas Also called Dfw Camper Corral Inc *(G-4255)*

Truckpro LLC 512 836-0482
8151 N Lamar Blvd Austin (78753) *(G-1597)*

Trucoastal Oil and Gas Svcs 432 413-9950
5002 Basin St Midland (79703) *(G-15448)*

True Grit Redi Mix Ltd 817 439-5914
12150 N Saginaw Blvd Fort Worth (76179) *(G-7081)*

True Grit Transportation Inc 682 708-5847
2724 E Renfro St Burleson (76028) *(G-2599)*

True Grit Works 978 604-4915
10236 Fm 274 Ravenna (75476) *(G-17234)*

True Integration Limited, San Antonio Also called Steelhead Inc *(G-18498)*

True Shot LLC 972 505-0433
10901 W County Road 125 Odessa (79765) *(G-16183)*

True Value, Pittsburg Also called B & S Hardware Inc *(G-16744)*

True Value, Seguin Also called D&D Retail LP *(G-18835)*

True Value Company LLC 903 872-8365
2601 E Highway 31 Corsicana (75109) *(G-3688)*

True Velocity Ammunition LLC 972 487-6500
2735 Forest Ln Garland (75042) *(G-7606)*

Truform Metalservice Inc 512 258-1675
13496 Pond Springs Rd B Austin (78729) *(G-1715)*

Truglo Inc 972 774-0300
525 International Pkwy Richardson (75081) *(G-17414)*

Trulite Inc 713 432-7238
3731 Linkview Dr Houston (77025) *(G-12384)*

Trulite GL Alum Solutions LLC 800 395-4224
3333 Holly Hall St Houston (77021) *(G-12385)*

Trulite GL Alum Solutions LLC 210 653-7790
5807 Business Park # 100 San Antonio (78218) *(G-18570)*

Trumed Technologies Inc 952 882-0611
1801 Big Town Blvd # 100 Mesquite (75149) *(G-15082)*

Trumer Brauerei, San Antonio Also called Comeback Brewing II Inc *(G-18020)*

Trupoint Well Services LLC 940 683-2871
851 W Harrison Rd Longview (75604) *(G-14323)*

Trupply LLC 281 516-8100
2956 Farrell Rd Houston (77073) *(G-12386)*

Trusource Labs LLC (HQ) **512 487-7103**
13011 Mccallen Pass A Austin (78753) *(G-1598)*

Truss Ops North LLC 479 824-8787
700 Kilgore Dr Henderson (75652) *(G-8276)*

Trussway LLC Central 713 691-6900
9411 Alcorn St Houston (77093) *(G-12387)*

Trussway LLC East...713 691-6900
9411 Alcorn St Houston (77093) *(G-12388)*

Trussway Holdings Inc (PA).................................713 691-6900
9411 Alcorn St Houston (77093) *(G-12389)*

Trussway Manufacturing Inc (HQ).....................719 322-9662
9411 Alcorn St Houston (77093) *(G-12390)*

Trussway Transportation Inc...............................713 691-6900
9411 Alcorn St Houston (77093) *(G-12391)*

Trust Printshop Inc..817 453-3121
2506 Tillar St Fort Worth (76107) *(G-7082)*

Trustkey Solutions Inc..214 865-9354
2100 Alamo Rd Ste T Richardson (75080) *(G-17415)*

Truth Chemical LLC..281 292-6900
2170 Buckthorne Pl # 400 The Woodlands (77380) *(G-19931)*

TRW Vssi, Pharr *Also called ZF Passive Safety Systems US (G-16717)*

Trwa Inc (PA)...817 361-8839
925 N University Dr Fort Worth (76114) *(G-7083)*

Trwa Inc...817 361-8839
6502 Sabrosa Ct E Fort Worth (76133) *(G-7084)*

Trx Industries Inc...254 694-6256
1130 Fm 1713 Whitney (76692) *(G-20733)*

Tryer Process Equipment Ltd............................940 432-0130
1730 City View Dr Wichita Falls (76306) *(G-20822)*

Trylene Inc...281 980-0400
10650 Stancliff Rd Houston (77099) *(G-12392)*

Tryton Tools USA Inc..830 372-2755
3517 W Us Highway 90 Seguin (78155) *(G-18870)*

Tryton Tools USA Inc (PA).................................832 717-7125
20329 State Highway 249 # 125 Houston (77070) *(G-12393)*

TS Distributors Inc (PA).....................................832 467-5400
4404 Windfern Rd Houston (77041) *(G-12394)*

TS Grinding, Houston *Also called Prince Energy LLC (G-11418)*

TSA Griddle System, Carrollton *Also called CPM Acquisition Corp (G-2719)*

TSA Griddle Systems Inc....................................972 243-8070
2009 Mckenzie Dr Ste 116 Carrollton (75006) *(G-2841)*

Tsar Operating Company.....................................817 731-9595
6500 West Fwy Ste 222 Fort Worth (76116) *(G-7085)*

TSC Manufacturing and Sup LLC (HQ)...............832 456-3900
13788 West Rd Ste 100 Houston (77041) *(G-12395)*

TSC Offshore Corporation (PA)..........................832 456-3900
7611 Railhead Ln Houston (77086) *(G-12396)*

TSC Offshore Corporation..................................832 456-3900
13788 West Rd Ste 100 Houston (77041) *(G-12397)*

TSC Superior Hdd, Houston *Also called Texas Steel Conversion Inc (G-12254)*

Tsgc Inc...361 289-0901
300 Mcbride Ln Corpus Christi (78408) *(G-3644)*

Tsha, Austin *Also called Texas State Historical Assn (G-1570)*

Tsi Aquisitions, Arlington *Also called Tsi Products Inc (G-806)*

Tsi Flow Products Inc...903 984-2870
322 S Longview St Kilgore (75662) *(G-13597)*

Tsi Prime, Coppell *Also called Trade Source International (G-3450)*

Tsi Products Inc..817 649-2626
809 110th St Arlington (76011) *(G-806)*

Tsm Houston, Houston *Also called Houston Tsm Inc (G-10260)*

Tsrc Specialty Materials LLC (HQ).....................281 754-5800
12012 Wickchester Ln # 28 Houston (77079) *(G-12398)*

Tssands, Fort Worth *Also called Total Sand Services LLC (G-7067)*

TST NA Trim Llc..956 843-3500
401 E Olmos Ave Hidalgo (78557) *(G-8310)*

Tst/Impreso Inc (HQ)..972 462-0100
652 Southwestern Blvd Coppell (75019) *(G-3451)*

Tsti, Fort Worth *Also called Arcosa Wind Towers Inc (G-6398)*

Tstimpreso, Coppell *Also called Impreso Inc (G-3421)*

Tsunami Rig Wash LLC..512 280-1649
9313 Circle Dr Austin (78736) *(G-1599)*

Ttc Trammell Co Inc..713 921-7121
109 Engel St Houston (77011) *(G-12399)*

TTI, Azle *Also called Texas Turbine Inc (G-1730)*

TTI Oil, Houston *Also called Texas Ine Inc (G-12236)*

Ttl Subsea Inc...713 960-3655
10700 Corp Dr Ste 108 Stafford (77477) *(G-19390)*

Ttna, San Antonio *Also called Toyotetsu Texas Inc (G-18557)*

Tts Pediatrics Pdn, Houston *Also called Inservio LLC (G-10377)*

Ttwf LP...713 960-9111
2801 Post Oak Blvd Houston (77056) *(G-12400)*

Tubal Cain Hydraulic Solutions, Magnolia *Also called Tubal Cain Industries Inc (G-14633)*

Tubal Cain Industries Inc...................................281 789-7087
706 Honea Egypt Rd Magnolia (77354) *(G-14633)*

Tubal Cain Industries Inc (PA)...........................409 786-1783
5665 N Main St Vidor (77662) *(G-20336)*

Tubal-Cain, Vidor *Also called Tubal Cain Industries Inc (G-20336)*

Tube Products Inc...817 489-2264
1471 Fm 718 Aurora (76078) *(G-855)*

Tubing Testers Inc..940 574-2177
801 N Center Archer City (76351) *(G-597)*

Tuboscope, Houston *Also called Varco LP (G-12534)*

Tuboscope (holding US) LLC (PA)......................713 799-5100
2919 Holmes Rd Houston (77051) *(G-12401)*

Tuboscope Pipeline Svcs Inc.............................432 337-1570
2269 S Fulton Ave Odessa (79766) *(G-16184)*

Tuboscope Pipeline Svcs Inc.............................936 870-3680
9574 Fm 1227 Rd Navasota (77868) *(G-15745)*

Tubscope Nov, Corpus Christi *Also called Varco LP (G-3650)*

Tubular Instrumentat..832 467-3110
15151 Sommermeyer St Houston (77041) *(G-12402)*

Tubular Makeup Technology Inc.........................281 452-5211
1105 N Main St Highlands (77562) *(G-8315)*

Tubular Prfrting Mfr of Conroe...........................936 441-8660
2611 Industrial Ln Conroe (77301) *(G-3374)*

Tubular Repair LLC (HQ).....................................979 387-3223
1201 Louisiana St Fl 28 Houston (77002) *(G-12403)*

Tubular Resource Inc..281 240-3343
1108 Soldiers Field Dr Sugar Land (77479) *(G-19569)*

Tubular Services LLC (HQ).................................713 675-6212
1010 Mccarty St Houston (77029) *(G-12404)*

Tubular Services LLC..281 452-4353
2030 Jacintoport Blvd Houston (77015) *(G-12405)*

Tubular Solutions Inc...713 391-8005
1401 Brittmoore Rd Houston (77043) *(G-12406)*

Tucker Saddlery Inc..361 293-3501
201 W Morris St Yoakum (77995) *(G-20974)*

Tucker Saddlery & Western AP, Yoakum *Also called Tucker Saddlery Inc (G-20974)*

Tucker Technologies, Spring *Also called Step Energy Svcs Holdings Ltd (G-19254)*

Tucson Industrial Plastics, Houston *Also called Industrial Pipe Fittings LLC (G-10353)*

Tuff Shed Inc...903 236-9126
2719 E Marshall Ave Longview (75601) *(G-14324)*

Tuffronts, The Colony *Also called Ruth Vending Inc (G-19813)*

Tuffy Products, Hurst *Also called Delta Rigging & Tools Inc (G-12844)*

Tuffys AC & Htg Svc Inc.....................................817 596-0150
4017 Azle Hwy Weatherford (76085) *(G-20627)*

Tufline, The Woodlands *Also called Xomox Corporation (G-19942)*

Tulia Ready Mix Concrete Co, Plainview *Also called High Plains Concrete Company (G-16757)*

Tulsa Arspc Cmpnent Ovrhaul RE.....................940 479-2000
8086 Fm 2449 Ponder (76259) *(G-17097)*

Tulsa Power, Houston *Also called Reel Power Oil & Gas Inc (G-11580)*

Turbeco Inc (HQ)...713 849-9911
8846 N Sam Houston Pkwy W # 150 Houston (77064) *(G-12407)*

Turbine Air Systems Ltd.....................................713 877-8700
6110 Cullen Blvd Houston (77021) *(G-12408)*

Turbine Aircraft Marketing Inc...........................972 248-3108
4550 Jimmy Doolittle Dr Addison (75001) *(G-172)*

Turbine Component Repair Inc...........................713 895-9551
3608 Pinemont Dr Houston (77018) *(G-12409)*

Turbine Fuel Systems, Arlington *Also called Texas Pneumatic Systems Inc (G-792)*

Turbine Resources Inc..817 540-0249
1005 Stanley Dr Euless (76040) *(G-6163)*

Turbine Supply Company....................................806 763-5901
2222 N Interstate 27 Lubbock (79403) *(G-14500)*

Turbine Tool Corporation...................................512 385-5311
157 Privada Dr Del Valle (78617) *(G-5333)*

Turbo Drill Industries Inc (PA)...........................936 756-3210
1125 Beach Airport Rd Conroe (77301) *(G-3375)*

Turbo Mach R & D II Inc......................................210 340-4773
143 W Rhapsody Dr San Antonio (78216) *(G-18571)*

Turbo Machine Technology Inc...........................281 443-4646
16038 Waverly Dr Houston (77032) *(G-12410)*

Turbo Refrigerating, Lewisville *Also called Vogt Ice LLC (G-14109)*

Turbo Tech Engineering, Bryan *Also called James D Atkins (G-2481)*

Turbochef Technologies Inc...............................214 379-6000
4240 Intl Pkwy Ste 105 Carrollton (75007) *(G-2892)*

Turbochef Technologies Inc (HQ)......................214 379-6000
2801 Trade Ctr Carrollton (75007) *(G-2893)*

Turbomasters Inc..210 690-1958
12718 Cimarron Path San Antonio (78249) *(G-18572)*

Turboweld..713 896-6467
6951 W Little York Rd Houston (77040) *(G-12411)*

Turf Technologies LLC..419 422-4356
1525 Hinton St Dallas (75235) *(G-5122)*

Turn Right Tools LLC (PA)..................................432 704-5490
2408 S County Road 1245 Midland (79706) *(G-15449)*

Turn-Key Coatings, Houston *Also called New Tk Coatings LLC (G-11037)*

Turn-Tech Inc..281 356-1290
32007 Industrial Park Dr Pinehurst (77362) *(G-16737)*

Turn-Tex Machine & Tool Inc..............................903 759-0989
5910b Old Highway 80 Longview (75604) *(G-14325)*

Turnamatic Machine Inc.....................................972 235-1923
1725 Jay Ell Dr Richardson (75081) *(G-17416)*

Turnbow Oil Field Services LLC..........................817 880-3833
3510 Woodrow Rd Lubbock (79423) *(G-14501)*

Turner Bros Crane & Rigging, Marshall *Also called Frontier Tubular Solutions LLC (G-14778)*

Turner Capital Inc...281 488-4900
17305 El Camino Real Houston (77058) *(G-12412)*

A L P H A B E T I C

Turner Company LLC 817 638-9053
11049 S Us Hwy 287 Rhome (76078) *(G-17261)*

Turner Energy Services LLC 806 323-8844
111 Airport Rd Canadian (79014) *(G-2656)*

Turner Industries Group LLC 903 782-9379
1200 19th St Sw Paris (75460) *(G-16372)*

Turner Manufacturing Co Inc 254 840-2891
1288 N Lone Star Pkwy Mc Gregor (76657) *(G-14826)*

Turner Sign Systems Inc 817 222-0033
1302 Avenue R Grand Prairie (75050) *(G-7988)*

Turnkey Anticorrosion, Magnolia Also called Tim Yockey (G-14630)

Turrubiartes Benedicto 832 675-1569
7600 S Santa Fe Dr Bldg 1 Houston (77061) *(G-12413)*

Tuttle & Bailey, Richardson Also called Air System Components Inc (G-17268)

TV Ammo, Garland Also called True Velocity Ammunition LLC (G-7606)

TW Stamping & Tool Inc 903 877-2353
10893 Us Highway 271 Tyler (75708) *(G-20166)*

TW Tanks and Construction Co 361 358-8869
671 W Fm 351 Beeville (78102) *(G-1989)*

Twbm Holding Co Inc (PA) 469 916-9430
8500 N Stemmons Fwy Dallas (75247) *(G-5123)*

TWC Architectural Moldings Ltd 210 662-2800
8523 Ne Loop 410 San Antonio (78219) *(G-18573)*

TWC Print Shop 512 927-0002
4405 Springdale Rd Austin (78723) *(G-1600)*

Twe Nonwovens Us Inc 210 651-3735
6389 Fm 3009 Ste B202 Schertz (78154) *(G-18765)*

Tweco, Denton Also called Victor Technologies Group Inc (G-5410)

Tweco-Arcair, Denton Also called Victor Technologies Intl Inc (G-5411)

Twg, Austin Also called Whitley Group LLC (G-1663)

Twg Solutions LLC (PA) 512 472-8972
4129 Coml Ctr Dr Ste 400 Austin (78744) *(G-1601)*

Twilight Services LLC (PA) 817 326-4806
5401 Old Granbury Rd Granbury (76049) *(G-7815)*

Twin Distributing Inc 903 463-1194
2545 E Fm 120 Denison (75021) *(G-5349)*

Twin Eagle Sand Logistics LLC (HQ) 713 341-7300
8847 W Sam Houston Pkwy N Houston (77040) *(G-12414)*

Twin Hill Acquisition Co Inc 888 206-0699
5630 Renwick Dr Houston (77081) *(G-12415)*

Twinstar Bakery, Missouri City Also called Rich Products Corporation (G-15591)

Twisted R Oilfield Svcs LLC 432 312-3110
1008 Clemente Ct Midland (79706) *(G-15450)*

Twisted S Services Inc 817 473-6959
7864 Retta Mansfield Rd Mansfield (76063) *(G-14724)*

Two Elk Investments LLC 972 465-3608
6025 Commerce Dr Ste 510 Irving (75063) *(G-13200)*

Two Hills Studio Inc 512 707-7571
2706 S Lamar Blvd Austin (78704) *(G-1602)*

Two Old Goats LLC (PA) 817 520-4230
4117 Murray Ave Haltom City (76117) *(G-8159)*

Two Talents Image Plus Prtg 817 379-5926
12001 Katy Rd Fort Worth (76244) *(G-7086)*

Twr Lighting Inc 713 973-6905
10810 W Little York Rd # 13 Houston (77041) *(G-12416)*

TX 7 Engine Treatment, Houston Also called Polymer Dynamics Inc (G-11358)

TX Quality Products LLC 979 234-7979
1134 Pioneer Plant Rd Eagle Lake (77434) *(G-5546)*

TX Tinman Enterprises LLC 817 288-6116
6731 Bridge St Ste 64 Fort Worth (76112) *(G-7087)*

Txco Resources Inc 210 822-8864
2001 Ross Ave Ste 400 Dallas (75201) *(G-5124)*

TXG Industries Inc 713 222-0220
10893 Shadow Wood Dr Houston (77043) *(G-12417)*

Txi, Bridgeport Also called Texas Industries Inc (G-2303)

Txi, Dallas Also called Texas Industries Inc (G-5062)

Txi Operations LP 936 295-7672
51 Champion Woodyard Rd Huntsville (77340) *(G-12826)*

Txi Operations LP (HQ) 972 647-6700
1341 W Mockingbird Ln 700w Dallas (75247) *(G-5125)*

Txsyn Int LLC 210 884-3895
7232 Eckhert Rd San Antonio (78238) *(G-18574)*

Txsyn Labs Stsfy Lqds / Pur La, San Antonio Also called Txsyn Int LLC (G-18574)

Txtb Tech Llc 832 928-5740
17350 Sunset Ranch Dr Montgomery (77316) *(G-15644)*

Txu Energy Services Co LLC 903 389-6074
488 Fm 2570 Fairfield (75840) *(G-6180)*

Tyco Engineered Pdts & Svcs (HQ) 609 720-4200
9600 W Gulf Bank Rd Houston (77040) *(G-12418)*

Tyco Fire Products LP 806 472-2400
8902 N Interstate 27 Lubbock (79403) *(G-14502)*

Tyco Fire Products LP 806 472-2400
8902 N Interstate 27 Lubbock (79403) *(G-14503)*

Tyco Fire Protection Products, Lubbock Also called Tyco Fire Products LP (G-14503)

Tyco International MGT Co LLC 361 575-9565
202 John Stockbauer Dr Victoria (77901) *(G-20312)*

Tyco International MGT Co LLC 713 644-8872
8323 N Aldrich Pkwy Houston (77041) *(G-12419)*

Tyco Simplexgrinnell 903 759-4417
6618 Navigation Blvd Houston (77011) *(G-12420)*

Tyco Thermal Controls, Houston Also called Nvent Thermal LLC (G-11102)

Tyco Valves & Controls, Houston Also called Pentair Valves & Controls LLC (G-11286)

TYG Products LP 972 542-1828
1800 N Mcdonald St McKinney (75071) *(G-14984)*

Tykhe Foods, Dallas Also called Meditrmean Spcialty Foods LLC (G-4664)

Tyler Building Systems LP (PA) 903 561-3000
3535 Shiloh Rd Tyler (75707) *(G-20167)*

Tyler Candle Company LLC 903 877-2298
11733 State Highway 155 N Tyler (75708) *(G-20168)*

Tyler Corrugated Box Inc 903 581-4950
5710 Reed Rd Tyler (75707) *(G-20169)*

Tyler County Booster, Woodville Also called Polk County Publishing Co (G-20916)

Tyler Iron & Metal Ltd 903 592-8144
1630 W Northwest Loop 323 Tyler (75702) *(G-20170)*

Tyler Packing Co Inc 903 593-9592
2209 E Erwin St Ste 11 Tyler (75702) *(G-20171)*

Tyler Pipe Company, Tyler Also called McWane Inc (G-20123)

Tyler Products Sales Inc 903 593-8633
10383 Spur 164 Tyler (75709) *(G-20172)*

Tyler Public Safety, Lubbock Also called Tyler Technologies Inc (G-14504)

Tyler Technologies Inc (PA) 972 713-3700
5101 Tennyson Pkwy Plano (75024) *(G-17039)*

Tyler Technologies Inc 903 753-4292
911 E Loop 281 Longview (75605) *(G-14326)*

Tyler Technologies Inc 972 713-3770
6500 Intl Pkwy Ste 2000 Plano (75093) *(G-17040)*

Tyler Technologies Inc 806 797-0761
5519 53rd St Lubbock (79414) *(G-14504)*

Tymco International Inc 254 799-5546
225 E Industrial Blvd Waco (76705) *(G-20468)*

Type Excellence Inc 830 833-9005
20406 Wilson Rd Coupland (78615) *(G-3693)*

Tyr Usa LLC 956 274-9380
3800 Canan Weslaco (78596) *(G-20670)*

Tyrex Group Ltd (PA) 512 623-4694
12317 Tech Blvd Ste 100 Austin (78727) *(G-1603)*

Tyson Farms of Texas Inc 936 598-2474
1019 Shelbyville St Center (75935) *(G-3010)*

Tyson Foods Inc 817 485-8912
6350 Browning Ct North Richland Hills (76180) *(G-15883)*

Tyson Foods Inc 936 569-7967
2208 Se Stallings Dr Nacogdoches (75961) *(G-15717)*

Tyson Foods Inc 903 859-4030
15131 E Ridge Rd Arp (75750) *(G-813)*

Tyson Foods Inc 214 331-1010
4114 Mint Way Dallas (75237) *(G-5126)*

Tyson Foods Inc 903 297-4200
1484 Ne Loop Carthage (75633) *(G-2925)*

Tyson Foods Inc 830 672-6548
2504 Church St Gonzales (78629) *(G-7766)*

Tyson Foods Inc 830 401-8800
1200 W Kingsbury St Seguin (78155) *(G-18871)*

Tyson Foods Inc 940 553-1811
700 Wheeler St Vernon (76384) *(G-20231)*

Tyson Foods Inc 936 248-2081
7665 Us Highway 96 N Tenaha (75974) *(G-19725)*

Tyson Foods Inc 817 568-9000
7401 Will Rogers Blvd Fort Worth (76140) *(G-7088)*

Tyson Foods Inc 713 678-1893
300 Portwall St Houston (77029) *(G-12421)*

Tyson Foods Inc 903 891-6001
4700 S Us Highway 75 Sherman (75090) *(G-18937)*

Tyson Foods Inc 817 656-5507
6350 Browning Ct Fort Worth (76180) *(G-7089)*

Tyson Fresh Meats Inc 806 335-7492
1912 E Fm Rd Hwy 60 Amarillo (79187) *(G-469)*

Tyson Fresh Meats Inc 806 335-7322
5000 N Sm 1912 Amarillo (79187) *(G-470)*

Tyson Fresh Meats Inc 806 335-2301
2201 B Ave Amarillo (79111) *(G-471)*

Tyson Globl Trnspt & Cnstr LLC 470 481-6161
15507 Stallion Point Cir Cypress (77429) *(G-3824)*

Tzc Services LLC 432 517-1212
200 W Illinois Ave # 260 Midland (79701) *(G-15451)*

U of H Newspaper, Houston Also called University of Houston System (G-12468)

U S A, Houston Also called United Structures America Inc (G-12458)

U S A, Texas City Also called United Service Alliance Inc (G-19805)

U S A Frametek, Liberty Hill Also called USA Frametek LLC (G-14130)

U S Alloy Co 877 711-9274
4855 Alpine Dr Ste 100 Stafford (77477) *(G-19391)*

U S C, Houston Also called United Salt Baytown LLC (G-12453)

U S Companies Inc (PA) 214 891-3300
17210 Campbell Rd Ste 100 Dallas (75252) *(G-3854)*

U S Energy Development Corp 682 305-2868
1521 N Cooper St Ste 700 Arlington (76011) *(G-807)*

U S Foam Inc (PA) 903 753-3901
800 E Cotton St Longview (75602) *(G-14327)*

U S Ink Division, Dallas *Also called Sun Chemical Corporation* **(G-5022)**

U S Machine Shop Inc 940 495-3964
501 E Cleveland Ave Electra (76360) **(G-6050)**

U S Plating LLP 972 871-2800
2215 Century Cir Irving (75062) **(G-13201)**

U S Silica Company (HQ) **301 682-0600**
24275 Katy Fwy Ste 100 Katy (77494) **(G-13381)**

U S Silica Company 806 470-2035
300 County Road 11 Lamesa (79331) **(G-13831)**

U S Silica Company 254 375-2225
Farm To Market Road 2749 R 27 Kosse (76653) **(G-13667)**

U S Weatherford L P 903 729-2106
2013 State Highway 135 N Kilgore (75662) **(G-13598)**

U S Weatherford L P 817 293-5192
751 Eight Twenty Blvd # 103 Fort Worth (76106) **(G-7090)**

U S Weatherford L P 281 331-5505
2548 E Highway 6 Alvin (77511) **(G-383)**

U S Weatherford L P 281 674-6500
4420 W Greens Rd Houston (77066) **(G-12422)**

U S Weatherford L P 361 289-1551
6002 Hopkins Rd Corpus Christi (78409) **(G-3645)**

U S Weatherford L P 806 592-3407
1251 State Hwy 83 Denver City (79323) **(G-5425)**

U S Weatherford L P 281 443-5627
18155 Chisholm Trl Houston (77060) **(G-12423)**

U S Weatherford L P 432 561-8892
10000 Pilot Ave Midland (79706) **(G-15452)**

U S Weatherford L P 903 984-5541
2013 Hwy 135 N Kilgore (75662) **(G-13599)**

U S Weatherford L P 432 550-9297
710 S Faudree Rd Odessa (79766) **(G-16185)**

U S Weatherford L P 281 348-1000
22001 Northpark Dr 100a Kingwood (77339) **(G-13655)**

U S Weatherford L P 713 983-5000
11909 Spencer Rd Fm529 Houston (77041) **(G-12424)**

U S Weatherford L P 817 293-5192
3044 Wichita Ct Fort Worth (76140) **(G-7091)**

U S Weatherford L P 281 348-1090
22001 Northpark Dr Kingwood (77339) **(G-13656)**

U S Weatherford L P 281 652-1300
3810 Magnolia Pkwy Pearland (77584) **(G-16606)**

U S Weatherford L P 832 590-4130
9600 W Gulf Bank Rd Houston (77040) **(G-12425)**

U S Weatherford L P 832 424-0000
1040 Schlipf Rd Katy (77493) **(G-13453)**

U S Weatherford L P 361 289-5111
5821 Agnes St Corpus Christi (78406) **(G-3646)**

U S Weatherford L P 281 485-1899
3632 S Main St Pearland (77581) **(G-16607)**

U S Weatherford L P 432 530-4900
8870 Nw Loop 338 Odessa (79764) **(G-16186)**

U S Weatherford L P 940 626-4698
2045 E Highway 380 # 300 Decatur (76234) **(G-5255)**

U S Weatherford L P 936 435-8118
7587 State Highway 75 S Huntsville (77340) **(G-12827)**

U S Weatherford L P 432 682-7321
10 Desta Dr Ste 350e Midland (79705) **(G-15453)**

U S Weatherford L P 281 449-1383
918 Hodgkins St Houston (77032) **(G-12426)**

U S Weatherford L P 817 249-7200
500 Winscott Rd Benbrook (76126) **(G-2047)**

U S Weatherford L P 361 668-8362
19685 Interstate 37 S Elmendorf (78112) **(G-6073)**

U S Weatherford L P 325 387-3280
3269 Selfservice Rd Sonora (76950) **(G-19031)**

U S Weatherford L P 936 295-0080
7587 Highway 75 S Huntsville (77340) **(G-12828)**

U S Weatherford L P 432 332-4798
2263 W Bell St Odessa (79766) **(G-16187)**

U S Weatherford L P 281 847-0121
10655 Bammel N Houston Rd Houston (77086) **(G-12427)**

U S Weatherford L P 325 392-3715
211 Crockett Ln Ozona (76943) **(G-16290)**

U S Weatherford L P 281 485-0500
3808 Magnolia Pkwy Pearland (77584) **(G-16608)**

U T M B Biocommunication, Galveston *Also called University of TX Med Brnch Gal* **(G-7411)**

U-Gas, Houston *Also called Synthesis Energy Systems Inc* **(G-12138)**

U.S. Completion & Production, Houston *Also called Nabors Corporate Services Inc* **(G-10950)**

U.S. Energy Development, Arlington *Also called U S Energy Development Corp* **(G-807)**

U.S. Zinc-Houston Dust Plant, Houston *Also called US Zinc North America Inc* **(G-12494)**

U.S. Zinc-Houston Metal Plant, Houston *Also called US Zinc North America Inc* **(G-12495)**

Ually LLC 936 252-7476
718 Bordeaux Dr Euless (76039) **(G-6164)**

Ubalde Concrete, Carrizo Springs *Also called Mid-County Ready Mix* **(G-2686)**

Udelhoven Inc 210 635-8833
1210 Fm 537 Floresville (78114) **(G-6255)**

Udfc, Lewisville *Also called Universal Display and Fix Co* **(G-14101)**

Udundi LLC 917 727-4220
101 Colorado St Austin (78701) **(G-1604)**

Ufp Dallas LLC (HQ) **817 825-6512**
2829 Sea Harbor Rd Dallas (75212) **(G-5127)**

Ufp Dallas LLC 972 232-1711
2829 Sea Harbor Rd Dallas (75212) **(G-5128)**

Ufp New Waverly LLC 936 295-3411
146b Fm 2793 New Waverly (77358) **(G-15861)**

Ufp Schertz LLC 830 606-4300
21700 Fm 2252 Schertz (78154) **(G-18766)**

Ufp Technologies Inc 915 598-7377
1400 Henry Brennan Dr El Paso (79936) **(G-6018)**

Uglypress L L C 806 322-1050
3608 Mockingbird Ln Amarillo (79109) **(G-516)**

Uhnder Inc (PA) **512 722-6353**
3409 Executive Center Dr # 205 Austin (78731) **(G-1605)**

Uhu Technologies LLC 972 523-2701
1201 Executive Dr W Richardson (75081) **(G-17417)**

Ulterra Drilling Tech LP (HQ) **817 293-7555**
201 Main St Ste 1660 Fort Worth (76102) **(G-7092)**

Ultimate Banners, Conroe *Also called Ultimate Decals Inc* **(G-3376)**

Ultimate Comfort Manufacturing 713 641-0100
8510 South Loop E Houston (77017) **(G-12428)**

Ultimate Control Solutions Inc 972 383-9414
13601 Preston Rd Ste 310e Dallas (75240) **(G-5129)**

Ultimate Decals Inc 936 539-5719
808 W Dallas St Ste B Conroe (77301) **(G-3376)**

Ultimate Imaging, Austin *Also called William Totah Printing LLC* **(G-1668)**

Ultimate Kronos Group 469 221-1823
600 Las Colinas Blvd E Irving (75039) **(G-13202)**

Ultimate Kronos Group 469 221-1800
600 E John Carpenter Fwy Irving (75062) **(G-13203)**

Ultimate Trining Munitions Inc 908 392-5390
1555 N Central Ave Ste A Brownsville (78521) **(G-2417)**

Ultra Chem Ltd 713 641-1444
6700 Dixie Dr Houston (77087) **(G-12429)**

Ultra Clean Technology Systems 512 252-6100
500 Center Ridge Dr # 400 Austin (78753) **(G-1606)**

Ultra Fine Silica LP 936 444-7338
2251 N Loop 336 W Ste B Conroe (77304) **(G-3377)**

Ultra Seating Company (HQ) **469 865-2010**
602 Fountain Pkwy Ste B Grand Prairie (75050) **(G-7989)**

Ultraflote LLC (PA) **713 461-2100**
3640 W 12th St Houston (77008) **(G-12430)**

Ultrafryer Systems Inc 210 731-5000
302 Spencer Ln San Antonio (78201) **(G-18575)**

Ultramar Inc (HQ) **210 345-2000**
1 Valero Way San Antonio (78249) **(G-18576)**

Ultramation Inc 254 772-4860
221 Cotton Dr Waco (76712) **(G-20469)**

Ultrapak, Houston *Also called Polytex Fibers Corp* **(G-11362)**

Ultratest International Inc 214 340-5252
7326 Craigshire Ave Dallas (75231) **(G-5130)**

Ultravision International 214 260-4500
4542 Mcewen Rd Dallas (75244) **(G-5131)**

UM Abrasives Inc 817 572-1344
831 Trent St Kennedale (76060) **(G-13506)**

Umax Pipeline Contractors, Houston *Also called Serimax North America LLC* **(G-11836)**

Umbilicals International Inc 281 275-6600
10711 Cash Rd Stafford (77477) **(G-19392)**

Umbra Winery, Grapevine *Also called Crossroads Winery* **(G-8024)**

Umc Energy Solutions Inc (PA) **432 524-2456**
461 N Broadway St Joshua (76058) **(G-13328)**

Umphres Production Services 956 765-8409
607 Falcon Ave Zapata (78076) **(G-20985)**

Umps, Granbury *Also called Counter Club Inc* **(G-7795)**

Unconvntonal Gas Solutions LLC 346 353-1048
10002 Windfern Rd Houston (77064) **(G-12431)**

Underwriters Indemnity 713 961-1300
2925 Richmond Ave # 1600 Houston (77098) **(G-12432)**

UNI-Fab LLC 936 344-2800
15890 N Highway 75 Willis (77378) **(G-20867)**

UNI-Form Components Co (HQ) **281 456-9724**
10703 Sheldon Rd Houston (77044) **(G-12433)**

Unicat Catalyst Tech LLC 281 331-2231
5918 S Highway 35 Alvin (77511) **(G-384)**

Unichem, Borger *Also called Baker Hughes* **(G-2162)**

Unicom Engineering Inc 972 673-1345
3501 E Plano Pkwy Plano (75074) **(G-17041)**

Unicor, Seagoville *Also called Federal Prison Industries* **(G-18800)**

Unicor, Big Spring *Also called Federal Prison Industries* **(G-2082)**

Unicor, Bastrop *Also called Federal Prison Industries* **(G-1757)**

Unified Screening & Crushing - 210 946-6900
9235 Margies Ln Schertz (78154) **(G-18767)**

Unified Supply & Services Co 972 355-8299
124 Capital Ln Rhome (76078) **(G-17262)**

Unifirst Corporation 817 834-7386
2900 N Beach St Haltom City (76111) **(G-8160)**

A L P H A B E T I C

Unifirst Corporation 281 261-9632
13513 S Gessner Rd Missouri City (77489) **(G-15597)**

Unifirst Corporation 979 774-0577
12700 Highway 30 Bldg 100 College Station (77845) **(G-3208)**

Unifix Inc 817 645-3435
811 Sparks Dr Cleburne (76033) **(G-3116)**

Uniform Concepts Inc 512 345-5793
5206 Backtrail Dr Austin (78731) **(G-1607)**

Uniforms Inc 214 630-0924
1489 Prudential Dr Dallas (75235) **(G-5132)**

Unifrax I LLC 281 251-5595
2340 E Trinty Mls Rd # 300 Carrollton (75006) **(G-2842)**

Unilin North America LLC (HQ) **214 398-1411**
7834 C F Hawn Fwy Dallas (75217) **(G-5133)**

Union Carbide Corporation 361 553-2000
7501 State Hwy 185 N Seadrift (77983) **(G-18797)**

Union Carbide Corporation (HQ) **281 966-2727**
1254 Enclave Pkwy Houston (77077) **(G-12434)**

Union Carbide Corporation 713 849-7000
10235 W Little York Rd # 230 Houston (77040) **(G-12435)**

Union Drilling Inc 432 682-6111
9105 W County Road 127 Midland (79706) **(G-15454)**

Union Printers Inc 713 526-6364
4001 San Jacinto St Houston (77004) **(G-12436)**

Union Slaughter House Inc 830 774-0065
1000 Plaza Ave Del Rio (78840) **(G-5327)**

Union Tank Car Company 281 592-6424
604 County Road 2205 Cleveland (77327) **(G-3140)**

Union Tank Car Company 281 456-9381
10515 Sheldon Rd Houston (77044) **(G-12437)**

Union Tank Car Company 713 926-6980
2011 Clinton Dr Galena Park (77547) **(G-7384)**

Union Tank Car Company 281 847-8200
16923 Beaumont Hwy Houston (77049) **(G-12438)**

Union Tech Co LLC 281 583-7601
11727 Veterans Mem Dr Houston (77067) **(G-12439)**

Unipal Intl Ltd Co Texas 850 232-5586
5202 Red Bluff Rd Pasadena (77503) **(G-16521)**

Unique Cabinets Inc 512 251-3058
16001 N Interstate 35 Pflugerville (78660) **(G-16690)**

Unique Machine Shop Inc 254 456-2972
101 Baird St Oglesby (76561) **(G-16216)**

Unique Products Mfg LLC 915 590-2444
8650 Yermoland Dr El Paso (79907) **(G-6019)**

Unique Stainless Designs LLC 972 254-8424
259 Gilbert Cir Grand Prairie (75050) **(G-7990)**

Unique System LLC 713 937-6193
5355 W Sam Houston Pkwy N # 320 Houston (77041) **(G-12440)**

Unique Wood Products Inc 713 462-5045
9915 Tanner Rd Houston (77041) **(G-12441)**

Unique Woodworks Inc 940 686-5547
1024 N Highway 377 Pilot Point (76258) **(G-16732)**

Uniseal Division, Fort Worth Also called Pattonair Usa Inc **(G-6897)**

Unisert Multi Wall Systems Inc 936 441-7722
13295 Rocky Rd Conroe (77306) **(G-3378)**

Unisorb Corporation 713 943-3753
1310 Genoa St South Houston (77587) **(G-19053)**

Unistar Plastics LLC 713 242-8377
6415 Allegheny St Houston (77021) **(G-12442)**

Unit Corporation 432 362-0901
6005 Eastridge Rd Ste 160 Odessa (79762) **(G-16188)**

Unit Corporation 806 658-2262
112 S Main St Booker (79005) **(G-2160)**

Unit Drilling Company 713 960-8870
110 Cypress Station Dr # 11 Houston (77090) **(G-12443)**

Unit Petroleum, Booker Also called Unit Corporation **(G-2160)**

Unit Petroleum, Houston Also called Unit Drilling Company **(G-12443)**

Unit Petroleum Company 713 960-8870
110 Cypress Station Dr # 113 Houston (77090) **(G-12444)**

United 1 International Labs, Carrollton Also called United Laboratories Mfg LLC **(G-2843)**

United Advg Publications Inc 214 269-0788
6500 Intl Pkwy Ste 1000 Plano (75093) **(G-17042)**

United Amercn Acquisition Corp 859 987-5389
400 Austin Ave Waco (76701) **(G-20470)**

United Aviation ACC Inc 817 447-8000
2075 S Burleson Blvd Burleson (76028) **(G-2600)**

United Casing Incorporated 432 682-0110
3610 E State Highway 158 Midland (79706) **(G-15455)**

United Casing Incorporated 281 456-0212
10901 Sheldon Rd Houston (77044) **(G-12445)**

United Casing Tubular Services, Midland Also called United Casing Incorporated **(G-15455)**

United Casing Tubular Services 281 456-0212
10901 Sheldon Rd Houston (77044) **(G-12446)**

United Cast Stone Company, Gainesville Also called Niblett Enterprises Inc **(G-7353)**

United Commercial Cast Stone 940 668-8133
4400 W Highway 82 Gainesville (76240) **(G-7374)**

United Commodities LLC 956 621-1798
44 Fireside Dr Brownsville (78521) **(G-2418)**

United Copper Industries LLC 940 243-8200
2727 Geesling Rd Denton (76208) **(G-5408)**

United Elec Instrmentation Ltd (HQ) **979 265-1256**
622 Commerce St Clute (77531) **(G-3161)**

United Electric Company LP 940 397-2100
501 Galveston St Wichita Falls (76301) **(G-20823)**

United Energex Inc 254 629-8560
517 Spur 490 Cisco (76437) **(G-3069)**

United Energex Inc (HQ) **210 826-0681**
7709 Broadway St Apt 106 San Antonio (78209) **(G-18577)**

United Energy Group LLC 281 839-0080
8010 Needlepoint Rd Baytown (77521) **(G-1838)**

United Film Solutions Inc 713 715-4197
15864 W Hardy Rd Ste 760 Houston (77060) **(G-12447)**

United Galvanizing Inc 713 466-4161
6123 Cunningham Rd Houston (77041) **(G-12448)**

United Group Printing 972 428-3000
14001 Distribution Way Dallas (75234) **(G-5134)**

United Industrial Products, Houston Also called United Oilfield Supply LLC **(G-12450)**

United Industries Inc (PA) **432 362-2361**
3926 N County Rd W Odessa (79764) **(G-16189)**

United Insul Sls Fbrcation Inc (HQ) **409 727-3191**
6401 N Twin City Hwy Port Arthur (77642) **(G-17131)**

United Interior Resources, Dallas Also called United Office Interiors Inc **(G-5136)**

United Laboratories Mfg LLC (HQ) **972 490-3300**
1541 Champion Dr Carrollton (75006) **(G-2843)**

United Launch Alliance LLC 956 425-4447
2800 Airport Dr Harlingen (78550) **(G-8208)**

United Leather Usa Inc 214 698-8270
1233 E Levee St Dallas (75207) **(G-5135)**

United Lynn-Con Corporation 972 223-2540
1308 S Hampton Rd Desoto (75115) **(G-5446)**

United Machine Works, New Waverly Also called Craig Godwin Inc **(G-15858)**

United Machine Works, New Waverly Also called Craig Godwin Inc **(G-15859)**

United Machining Services Inc 936 760-1153
1009 Ivey St Conroe (77301) **(G-3379)**

United Marine Enterprise Inc 409 833-0303
1440 Spindletop Rd Beaumont (77705) **(G-1965)**

United Marine Shipyard, Beaumont Also called United Marine Enterprise Inc **(G-1965)**

United Marine Shipyard, Port Arthur Also called Bgi Contractors Inc **(G-17102)**

United Metal Services Inc 817 932-3330
8333 S Us Highway 287 A Rhome (76078) **(G-17263)**

United Metro Media LLC 210 315-6046
4242 Woodcock Dr Ste 202 San Antonio (78228) **(G-18578)**

United Minerals and Prpts Inc 713 881-9466
14047 Industrial Rd Houston (77015) **(G-12449)**

United Office Interiors Inc (PA) **214 381-0101**
8200 Lovett Ave Dallas (75227) **(G-5136)**

United Oil Corporation 303 856-6444
6300 Fm 2244 Rd Bldg 500 Austin (78746) **(G-1608)**

United Oilfield Supply LLC 713 489-2000
630 Brittmoore Rd Houston (77079) **(G-12450)**

United Parcel Service Inc 817 490-7300
13700 Independence Pkwy Fort Worth (76177) **(G-7093)**

United Petro Transports Inc 817 540-6178
3520 S Main St Euless (76040) **(G-6165)**

United Plastics Group Inc 713 466-5563
7865 Northcourt Rd Houston (77040) **(G-12451)**

United Plastics Inc 713 222-2186
2005 Canal St Houston (77003) **(G-12452)**

United Rtorcraft Solutions LLC 940 627-0626
1942 N Trinity St Decatur (76234) **(G-5256)**

United Salt Baytown LLC (HQ) **713 877-2600**
4800 San Felipe St # 100 Houston (77056) **(G-12453)**

United Salt Baytown LLC 936 372-3931
14002 Warren Ranch Rd Hockley (77447) **(G-8350)**

United Salt Baytown LLC 281 303-1101
7901 Fm 1405 Rd Baytown (77523) **(G-1804)**

United Salt Carlsbad LLC 713 877-2600
4800 San Felipe St # 100 Houston (77056) **(G-12454)**

United Salt Corporation 713 877-2600
4800 San Felipe St Houston (77056) **(G-12455)**

United Salt Hockley LLC 713 877-2781
14002 Warren Ranch Rd Hockley (77447) **(G-8351)**

United Salt Saltville LLC 713 877-2600
4800 San Felipe St # 100 Houston (77056) **(G-12456)**

United Scaffolding, Houston Also called Brock Services LLC **(G-8991)**

United Service Alliance Inc 409 935-9500
5245 Emmett F Lowry Expy Texas City (77591) **(G-19805)**

United Shtdown Sfety Texas Inc (HQ) **877 805-5155**
6104 Red Bluff Rd Pasadena (77505) **(G-16522)**

United States Gypsum Company 713 308-5400
1201 Mayo Shell Rd Galena Park (77547) **(G-7385)**

United States Gypsum Company 214 424-2500
255 Regal Row Dallas (75247) **(G-5137)**

United States Lime & Minerals, Cleburne Also called Texas Lime Company **(G-3114)**

United States Lime & Mnrl Inc (HQ) **972 991-8400**
5429 Lbj Fwy Ste 230 Dallas (75240) **(G-5138)**

United States Mineral Pdts Co 713 462-1709
3340 Bingle Rd Houston (77055) **(G-12457)**

United States Steel Corp 903 656-6521
  6866 Us Highway 259 S Lone Star (75668) *(G-14185)*
United Structures America Inc (PA) 281 442-8247
  1912 Buschong St Houston (77039) *(G-12458)*
United Structures America Inc 281 442-8247
  3717 Sunset Blvd Houston (77005) *(G-12459)*
United Vision Logistics, Houston *Also called Uv Logistics LLC (G-12508)*
United Worth Hydrochem Corp 682 518-6200
  350 English Trl Ste C Venus (76084) *(G-20224)*
Unitex Oil & Gas LLC 432 685-0014
  508 W Wall St Ste 1000 Midland (79701) *(G-15456)*
Unitra Inc 281 240-1500
  12601 Exchange Dr Ste 100 Stafford (77477) *(G-19393)*
Unitron LP 214 221-9094
  10925 Miller Rd Dallas (75238) *(G-5139)*
Unity Hunt Inc 214 720-1600
  5956 Sherry Ln Ste 1500 Dallas (75225) *(G-5140)*
Unity Lab Services, Houston *Also called Halliburton Company (G-10098)*
Unity Manufacturing, Garland *Also called Buferd Company Inc (G-7451)*
Univar Solutions USA Inc 281 297-0678
  3 Waterway Square Pl # 1000 Spring (77380) *(G-19261)*
Univation Technologies LLC (HQ) **713 892-3650**
  5555 San Felipe St # 1950 Houston (77056) *(G-12460)*
Universal Blanchers LLC 254 445-4021
  1033 County Road 343 6w Dublin (76446) *(G-5518)*
Universal Display & Fixs Co 972 221-5157
  726 E Hwy 121 Lewisville (75057) *(G-14100)*
Universal Display & Fixs Co 972 829-2366
  200 Northpoint Dr Ste 100 Coppell (75019) *(G-3452)*
Universal Display and Fix Co (PA) **972 434-8067**
  726 E Hwy 121 Lewisville (75057) *(G-14101)*
Universal Display and Fix Co 972 221-5157
  1650 Lakeside Pkwy # 200 Flower Mound (75028) *(G-6291)*
Universal Enclosure Systems, Duncanville *Also called Moffitt West LLC (G-5535)*
Universal Ensco Inc (HQ) **713 425-6000**
  4848 Loop Central Dr # 137 Houston (77081) *(G-12461)*
Universal Forest Products, Schertz *Also called Ufp Schertz LLC (G-18766)*
Universal Forest Products, Dallas *Also called Ufp Dallas LLC (G-5128)*
Universal Forest Products, Cedar Hill *Also called Idx Dallas LLC (G-2944)*
Universal Graphics Inc 915 591-8943
  1217 Barranca Dr Ste B El Paso (79935) *(G-6020)*
Universal Kids LLC 832 374-1082
  21369 Kings Guild Ln Kingwood (77339) *(G-13657)*
Universal Lifting Products, Houston *Also called Bridon-American Corporation (G-8984)*
Universal Machining Inds Inc 940 759-2430
  810 E Division St Muenster (76252) *(G-15675)*
Universal Management Svcs LLC 979 481-5711
  201 N Walker St Angleton (77515) *(G-581)*
Universal Metal Products Inc 956 283-7200
  101 W Eldora Rd Pharr (78577) *(G-16713)*
Universal Oilfield Services 936 636-2324
  160 E Houston St Lovelady (75851) *(G-14355)*
Universal Ornaments Inc 713 699-1500
  2305 Bennington St Houston (77093) *(G-12462)*
Universal Outlets Inc 903 983-3261
  200 Smackover St Kilgore (75662) *(G-13600)*
Universal Pen & Print Inc 210 656-4000
  5351 Brewster St San Antonio (78233) *(G-18579)*
Universal Pressure Pumping Inc 432 699-3205
  4517 W Industrial Ave Midland (79703) *(G-15457)*
Universal Pressure Pumping Inc (HQ) **432 221-7000**
  10713 W Sam Huston Pkwy N Houston (77064) *(G-12463)*
Universal Rectifiers Inc 281 342-8471
  1631 Cottonwood School Rd Rosenberg (77471) *(G-17598)*
Universal Solar Technology Inc 832 764-8260
  10685 Hazelhurst Dr # 21698 Houston (77043) *(G-12464)*
Universal Tech 832 584-9460
  200 County Road 120 Floresville (78114) *(G-6256)*
Universal Transformer Company 972 784-7700
  411 Welch Dr Farmersville (75442) *(G-6226)*
Universal Valve Company Inc 432 689-6341
  3501 W Industrial Ave Midland (79703) *(G-15458)*
Universal Vlve Crane Spcalists, Midland *Also called Universal Valve Company Inc (G-15458)*
Universal Well Service LLC 432 272-6686
  1101 E Pool Rd Odessa (79766) *(G-16190)*
Universal Well Svc Holdings 325 573-6209
  3704 W Highway 180 Snyder (79549) *(G-19013)*
Universal Wire Works Inc 713 649-3828
  15 Drennan St Houston (77003) *(G-12465)*
Universal Wldg & Fabrication, Angleton *Also called Universal Management Svcs LLC (G-581)*
Universal Wllhead Svcs Hldngs 361 299-1100
  5729 Leopard St Bldg 9 Corpus Christi (78408) *(G-3647)*
Universalpegasus International, Houston *Also called Universal Ensco Inc (G-12461)*
Universe Tchncal Trnsltion Inc 713 827-8800
  9225 Katy Fwy Ste 400 Houston (77024) *(G-12466)*
University Houston - System 713 741-2447
  4450 University Dr Houston (77204) *(G-12467)*

University of Houston System 713 221-8192
  1 Main St Houston (77002) *(G-12468)*
University of Houston System 713 743-2841
  4880 Calhoun Rd Ste 2 Houston (77204) *(G-12469)*
University of Texas At Austin 800 252-3206
  3001 Lake Austin Blvd Austin (78703) *(G-1609)*
University of Texas At Austin 512 471-1865
  2500 Whitis Ave Rm 3200 Austin (78712) *(G-1610)*
University of TX Med Brnch Gal 409 772-5900
  1902 Harborside Dr # 2104 Galveston (77550) *(G-7411)*
University Press, College Station *Also called The Texas A&M University Sys (G-3206)*
University Star, The, San Marcos *Also called Texas State University (G-18714)*
Uniwell Laboratories LLC 817 510-1850
  14801 Sovereign Rd Fort Worth (76155) *(G-7094)*
Uniwell Labs, Fort Worth *Also called Uniwell Laboratories LLC (G-7094)*
Unlimited Cabinets and Doors, Longview *Also called E & A Ventures LLC (G-14225)*
Unlimited Custom Embroidery 713 773-0111
  10507 Fallstone Rd Houston (77099) *(G-12470)*
Unlimited Frac Sand Llc 800 560-1246
  4210 Cnty Rd 1286 Ste 401 Odessa (79765) *(G-16191)*
Unlimited Stone LLC 903 297-0829
  114 Stevens St Longview (75604) *(G-14328)*
Unlimited Supply Inc 936 890-8997
  12511 Fm 830 Rd Willis (77318) *(G-20868)*
Uno Network LLC 844 885-5000
  9999 Bellaire Blvd # 1122 Houston (77036) *(G-12471)*
Unocal, Houston *Also called Chevron Corporation (G-9177)*
Unocal, Van *Also called Chevron Corporation (G-20206)*
Unocal, Andrews *Also called Chevron Corporation (G-543)*
UOP LLC 832 551-9638
  2101 Citywest Blvd Bldg 1 Houston (77042) *(G-12472)*
Up & Out Communications (PA) **713 520-7237**
  3406 Audubon Pl Houston (77006) *(G-12473)*
Up 1 Trucking LLC 833 398-7825
  11816 Inwood Rd Dallas (75244) *(G-5141)*
Upay Inc (PA) **972 888-6052**
  3010 Lbj Fwy Dallas (75234) *(G-5142)*
Upely Traders 832 998-8432
  3811 Turtle Creek Blvd Dallas (75219) *(G-5143)*
Upex Auto Supply 214 741-2400
  3036 Elm St Dallas (75226) *(G-5144)*
Upg Company LLC (HQ) **713 466-5563**
  7865 Northcourt Rd # 100 Houston (77040) *(G-12474)*
Upham Oil & Gas Company LP (PA) **940 325-4491**
  999 Energy Ave Mineral Wells (76067) *(G-15544)*
Upland Software Inc (PA) **833 875-2631**
  401 Congress Ave Ste 1850 Austin (78701) *(G-1611)*
Upland Software I Inc 617 494-5515
  401 Congress Ave Ste 1850 Austin (78701) *(G-1612)*
Uplogix Inc 512 857-7000
  7600b N Cpitl Of Txas Hwy Austin (78731) *(G-1613)*
Upper Crust Bakery Inc 512 467-0102
  4508 Burnet Rd Austin (78756) *(G-1614)*
Upright Lighting LLC 408 472-6379
  1513 Jamison Dr Allen (75013) *(G-305)*
UPS, Fort Worth *Also called United Parcel Service Inc (G-7093)*
Ups Inc 713 222-7300
  1605 Nagle St Houston (77003) *(G-12475)*
UPS Stores, The, Kingwood *Also called M3 Partners LLC (G-13648)*
Upstart Acquisitions Corp 281 469-0815
  10225 Woodedge Dr Houston (77070) *(G-12476)*
Upstream International LLC 281 265-0033
  15140 Southwest Fwy Ste C Sugar Land (77478) *(G-19570)*
Uptime Devices Inc 512 328-1800
  11724 Dunfries Ln Austin (78754) *(G-1615)*
Uptime Solutions Inc 214 497-9635
  2809 Sunset Rdg McKinney (75072) *(G-14993)*
Uptown Popcorn LLC (PA) **972 291-4767**
  10880 Rockwall Rd Ste 200 Dallas (75238) *(G-5145)*
Uranium Energy Corp (PA) **361 888-8235**
  500 N Shoreline Blvd # 800 Corpus Christi (78401) *(G-3648)*
Uranium Resources Inc 972 219-3330
  650 S Edmonds Ln Ste 108 Lewisville (75067) *(G-14102)*
Urban Oil & Gas Group LLC (PA) **972 543-8800**
  1000 14th St Fl 3 Plano (75074) *(G-17043)*
Urban Publishers Inc 214 521-3439
  3303 Lee Pkwy Ste 340 Dallas (75219) *(G-5146)*
Urban Publishers Inc (PA) **713 524-0606**
  3411 Richmond Ave Ste 600 Houston (77046) *(G-12477)*
Urban Sheet Metal Inc (PA) **713 522-6441**
  4512 Montrose Blvd Houston (77006) *(G-12478)*
Urbanovsky Advanced Cnstr LLC 817 556-3288
  4301 County Road 312b Cleburne (76031) *(G-3117)*
Uribe Steel 281 452-5696
  7213 Miller Road 2 Houston (77049) *(G-12479)*
Urman Inc 832 246-8810
  8350 Ashlane Way Ste 104 The Woodlands (77382) *(G-19932)*
Ursa Resources Group II LLC (PA) **713 456-3000**
  602 Sawyer St Ste 710 Houston (77007) *(G-12480)*

A
L
P
H
A
B
E
T
I
C

US American Resources Inc 972 662-9070
  3839 Briargrove Ln # 6305 Dallas (75287) *(G-3855)*

US Bellows Inc 713 731-0030
  3701 Holmes Rd Houston (77051) *(G-12481)*

US Bioservices 214 572-8300
  3101 Gaylord Pkwy Frisco (75034) *(G-7321)*

US Bolt Manufacturing Inc 713 726-1000
  12895 Main St Houston (77035) *(G-12482)*

US Citrus LLC 956 252-3101
  30232 Fm 493 Hargill (78549) *(G-8171)*

US Composite Pipe Inc 817 783-3444
  800 County Rd Ste 209 Alvarado (76009) *(G-348)*

US Concrete Inc (PA) **817 835-4105**
  331 N Main St Euless (76039) *(G-6166)*

US Concrete Inc 806 373-4951
  100 S Van Buren St Amarillo (79101) *(G-472)*

US Corrugated Mesquite LLC 801 798-7331
  700 N Sam Houston Rd Mesquite (75149) *(G-15083)*

US Dept of the Air Force 210 925-4401
  404 Greig St 178 San Antonio (78226) *(G-18580)*

US Fabrication East Texas Inc 903 531-0000
  5624 American Legion Rd Tyler (75708) *(G-20173)*

US Farathane Holdings Corp 734 656-9000
  820 W Howard Ln Austin (78753) *(G-1616)*

US Galvanizing LLC 817 268-6111
  2525 N Stemmons Fwy Dallas (75207) *(G-5147)*

US Galvanizing LP 817 572-2280
  1530 Gilman Rd Kennedale (76060) *(G-13507)*

US Home Systems Inc (HQ) **214 488-6300**
  2951 Kinwest Pkwy Irving (75063) *(G-13204)*

US Hose Corp 281 458-0400
  2020 Greens Rd Ste 400 Houston (77032) *(G-12483)*

US Joiner LLC 713 330-1700
  12775 Nimitz St Bldg A Houston (77015) *(G-12484)*

US Lbm Holdings LLC 713 650-6200
  929 Gessner Rd Ste 1900 Houston (77024) *(G-12485)*

US Led, Houston *Also called US Led Ltd (G-12486)*

US Led Ltd 713 972-9191
  6807 Portwest Dr Houston (77024) *(G-12486)*

US Machinery Parts Sales Inc 972 551-3551
  2144 N Belt Line Rd Ste H Mesquite (75150) *(G-15084)*

US Minerals Inc 409 740-3355
  5712 Harborside Dr Galveston (77554) *(G-7412)*

US Operating Inc (HQ) 214 393-3992
  17210 Campbell Rd Ste 100 Dallas (75252) *(G-3856)*

US Petrochemicals Inc 713 871-1951
  5075 Westheimer Rd # 675 Houston (77056) *(G-12487)*

US Pipe Fabrication 817 232-5858
  7030 Old Pearsall Rd San Antonio (78252) *(G-18581)*

US Polyco Inc 972 875-9300
  3901 S Interstate Hwy 45 Ennis (75119) *(G-6122)*

US Remodelers Inc 214 488-6300
  405 State Highway 121 Byp A250 Lewisville (75067) *(G-14103)*

US Rubber Corporation 936 756-1977
  211 N Loop 336 E Conroe (77301) *(G-3380)*

US Sand LLC 713 333-3001
  5177 Richmond Ave # 1220 Houston (77056) *(G-12488)*

US Signs Inc (PA) **713 977-7900**
  6807 Portwest Dr Houston (77024) *(G-12489)*

US SILICA, Katy *Also called US Silica Holdings Inc (G-13382)*

US Silica Holdings Inc 281 258-2170
  12012 Wickchester Ln # 300 Houston (77079) *(G-12490)*

US Silica Holdings Inc (PA) **281 258-2170**
  24275 Katy Fwy Ste 600 Katy (77494) *(G-13382)*

US Surface Warehouse 866 433-2229
  4601 Spicewood Springs Rd 1-100 Austin (78759) *(G-1617)*

US VT 713 856-9171
  6828 Flintlock Rd Houston (77040) *(G-12491)*

US VT Severe Service Valves, Houston *Also called US VT (G-12491)*

US Well Services Inc (PA) 832 562-3730
  1360 Post Oak Blvd # 1800 Houston (77056) *(G-12492)*

US Zinc Corporation (PA) 713 926-1705
  2727 Allen Pkwy Ste 800 Houston (77019) *(G-12493)*

US Zinc North America Inc 713 926-1705
  6020 Esperson St Houston (77011) *(G-12494)*

US Zinc North America Inc 713 926-1705
  6020 Navigation Blvd Houston (77011) *(G-12495)*

US Zinc North America Inc (PA) 713 926-1705
  2727 Allen Pkwy Ste 800 Houston (77019) *(G-12496)*

USA Capitol, Belton *Also called Capitol Seating Company (G-2022)*

USA Compression Partners LLC (HQ) 512 369-1380
  111 Congress Ave Ste 2400 Austin (78701) *(G-1618)*

USA Compression Partners LP (PA) **512 473-2662**
  111 Congress Ave Ste 2400 Austin (78701) *(G-1619)*

USA Eagle Carports Inc 817 788-5395
  5700 E Belknap St Haltom City (76117) *(G-8161)*

USA Frametek LLC 512 515-6500
  1300 County Road 257 Liberty Hill (78642) *(G-14130)*

USA Harness Inc 903 342-3767
  1201 E Coke Rd Winnsboro (75494) *(G-20901)*

USA Machine Inc 972 636-7400
  2503 Circle Dr Royse City (75189) *(G-17727)*

USA Millennium LP 409 840-6801
  2710 S 11th St Beaumont (77701) *(G-1966)*

USA Petroleum Equipment Sup Co 281 893-2471
  40 Fm 1960 Rd W 181 Houston (77090) *(G-12497)*

USA Petrovalve Inc 713 466-9881
  10603 W Sam Houston Pkwy Houston (77064) *(G-12498)*

USA Precision LLC 281 458-7304
  8028 Van Hut Ln Houston (77044) *(G-12499)*

USA Precision Machining Co, Houston *Also called USA Precision LLC (G-12499)*

USA Printing Corporation (PA) **281 498-4310**
  11122 Bellaire Blvd Houston (77072) *(G-12500)*

USA Promlite Technology Inc 832 868-8866
  7001 Corporate Dr Ste 213 Houston (77036) *(G-12501)*

USA Rock Bit Inc (PA) **940 574-2238**
  507 N Center Archer City (76351) *(G-598)*

USa Screen Printing Chem Inc 281 474-9777
  1929 Marvin Cir Seabrook (77586) *(G-18793)*

USA Securglass Corporation 214 907-9445
  15504 Wright Brothers Dr Addison (75001) *(G-173)*

USA Shade, Dallas *Also called Shade Structures Inc (G-4951)*

USA Sports Inc 713 957-2882
  10600 Shadow Wood Dr # 301 Houston (77043) *(G-12502)*

Usac Leasing 2 LLC 512 473-2662
  100 Congress Ave Ste 450 Austin (78701) *(G-1620)*

Usc, Houston *Also called United Salt Carlsbad LLC (G-12454)*

Usdatwing Aerial Analytics LLC 210 495-5577
  18615 Tuscany Stone # 200 San Antonio (78258) *(G-18582)*

User Friendly Phone Book LLC (PA) **281 465-5400**
  10200 Grogans Mill Rd # 440 The Woodlands (77380) *(G-19933)*

USF, Longview *Also called U S Foam Inc (G-14327)*

USI Integrated Trnsp LLC 956 781-6606
  301 E Milano Pharr (78577) *(G-16714)*

Usm Inc 281 619-0144
  12303 Fuqua St Houston (77034) *(G-12503)*

Usm Manufacturing LLC 806 791-0220
  2206 114th St Lubbock (79423) *(G-14505)*

Uson Lp (PA) **281 671-2000**
  8640 N Eldridge Pkwy Houston (77041) *(G-12504)*

Usplabs LLC 469 484-1927
  10761 King William Dr Dallas (75220) *(G-5148)*

USS Holdings Inc 301 682-0600
  24275 Katy Fwy Ste 100 Katy (77494) *(G-13383)*

Ussery Printing Company Inc 972 438-8344
  4201 Airborn Dr Addison (75001) *(G-174)*

Ust-Mamiya Inc 817 267-2219
  14950 Faa Blvd Ste 200 Fort Worth (76155) *(G-7095)*

Utax Software LLC (PA) **844 440-8829**
  11985 Pellicano Dr G123 El Paso (79936) *(G-6021)*

Utex Industries Inc (HQ) **713 467-1000**
  10810 Katy Fwy Ste 100 Houston (77043) *(G-12505)*

Utex Industries Inc 979 725-8503
  605 Utex Dr Weimar (78962) *(G-20651)*

Utex Industries Inc 713 559-0203
  6840 N Fm 157 Venus (76084) *(G-20225)*

Utex Industries Inc 432 333-4151
  1104 Market Ave Odessa (79761) *(G-16192)*

Utex Industries Inc 936 760-4100
  116a Industrial Ct Conroe (77301) *(G-3381)*

Utex Industries Inc 832 358-0350
  4330 Brittmoore Rd Houston (77041) *(G-12506)*

Utility Agency & Import Inc 817 477-9888
  2417 Fm 917 Mansfield (76063) *(G-14725)*

Utility Composites Inc 512 846-4027
  888 County Road 108 Hutto (78634) *(G-12887)*

Utlx Manufacturing LLC 281 847-8200
  16923 Old Beaumont 90 Houston (77049) *(G-12507)*

Uv Country Inc 713 649-0556
  2616 Tx 35 Alvin (77511) *(G-385)*

Uv Logistics LLC 281 436-2310
  15005 Crosby Fwy Houston (77049) *(G-12508)*

Uvalde Concrete Inc (PA) **830 278-9200**
  3043 Fm 1052 Benson Rd Uvalde (78801) *(G-20198)*

Uvalde Leader News 830 334-3644
  321 E San Marcos St Pearsall (78061) *(G-16615)*

Uvalde Meat Processing Plant, Uvalde *Also called Pat and Gail Jackowski (G-20194)*

Uvc Manufacturing Group LLC 281 969-6059
  3430 Rolling Terrace Dr Spring (77388) *(G-19183)*

Uvc Pwersports Trctrs Outdoors, Alvin *Also called Uv Country Inc (G-385)*

V & V Industries Inc 713 224-1751
  1419 Hays St Houston (77009) *(G-12509)*

V & V Products Inc 361 865-3841
  12705 N Hwy 5 Flatonia (78941) *(G-6235)*

V & V Sausage, Flatonia *Also called V & V Products Inc (G-6235)*

V Fab, Venus *Also called Venus Fabrication Inc (G-20226)*

V Gas LLC 713 896-8531
  12221 Fm 529 Rd Houston (77041) *(G-12510)*

V I J Corporation..817 838-2020
1700 Hickory Dr Fort Worth (76117) *(G-7096)*

V P Sales & Company LP...................................361 664-2999
2733 San Diego Hwy 44 W Alice (78332) *(G-243)*

V Respect...281 780-6267
4351 Richmeadow Dr Houston (77048) *(G-12511)*

V S I, Fort Worth *Also called Vision Systems Intl LLC (G-7107)*

V S T, Midland *Also called Tall City Well Service Co LP (G-15430)*

V T I of Texas Inc...979 778-2804
6201 Mumford Rd Bryan (77807) *(G-2515)*

V&G Dynamic Machine LLC..............................830 693-4743
701 Industrial Blvd Marble Falls (78654) *(G-14751)*

V&L Industrail Services Inc............................409 724-3336
511 S 3rd St Nederland (77627) *(G-15761)*

V-F Petroleum Inc..432 683-3344
500 W Texas Ave Ste 350 Midland (79701) *(G-15459)*

V-J Electronic Assemblies, Stafford *Also called Sgm Corporation (G-19376)*

V-Kool Inc...713 856-8333
8515 Jackrabbit Rd Ste B Houston (77095) *(G-12512)*

V-S Precision Usa LLC......................................915 590-2707
2150 Trawood Dr El Paso (79935) *(G-6022)*

V-Teq Manufacturing Inc..................................713 466-0660
5218 Brittmoore Rd Houston (77041) *(G-12513)*

Vaalco Energy Inc (PA)....................................713 623-0801
9800 Richmond Ave Ste 700 Houston (77042) *(G-12514)*

Vaalco Gabon (etame) Inc................................713 623-0801
9800 Richmond Ave Ste 700 Houston (77042) *(G-12515)*

Vac-U-Rat Oilfield Svcs LLC............................214 850-1042
3860 W Northwest Hwy # 325 Dallas (75220) *(G-5149)*

Vacation Publications Inc (PA).........................713 974-6903
5851 San Felipe St # 500 Houston (77057) *(G-12516)*

Vacuumpodscom Inc...972 986-8876
135 Hunter Dr Cedar Hill (75104) *(G-2954)*

Vah Distributing, Richardson *Also called Vent-A-Hood Ltd (G-17419)*

Vaign Designer Street AP LLC..........................832 490-8510
1205 Blaydon Ct Rosenberg (77471) *(G-17599)*

Val and Val Inc...361 852-8992
5815a A Weber Rd Corpus Christi (78413) *(G-3649)*

Val Verde Publishing LLC.................................830 774-2198
2116 Veterans Blvd Del Rio (78840) *(G-5328)*

Valaris Hereunder Ensco Intl, Houston *Also called Ensco International Inc (G-9652)*

Valco Instruments Company (PA).....................713 688-9345
7811 Westview Dr Houston (77055) *(G-12517)*

Valco Instruments Company.............................713 688-9345
8300 Waterbury Dr Ste 400 Houston (77055) *(G-12518)*

Valen Light LLC..512 222-5550
2101 E Saint Elmo Rd # 3 Austin (78744) *(G-1621)*

Valence Midstream Ltd......................................281 359-3659
600 Rockmead Dr Ste 200 Kingwood (77339) *(G-13658)*

Valence Operating Company (PA).....................281 359-3659
600 Rockmead Dr Ste 200 Kingwood (77339) *(G-13659)*

Valence Surface Tech LLC (PA)........................855 370-5920
1790 Hughes Landing Blvd The Woodlands (77380) *(G-19934)*

Valeo North America Inc...................................915 774-9340
5 Zane Grey St El Paso (79906) *(G-6023)*

Valeo North America Inc...................................972 574-1900
2520 Esters Blvd Ste 100 Dallas (75261) *(G-5150)*

Valeo North America Inc...................................915 779-1625
5a Zane Grey St El Paso (79906) *(G-6024)*

Valeo Wiper Systems, El Paso *Also called Valeo North America Inc (G-6023)*

Valeo Wipers Systems, El Paso *Also called Valeo North America Inc (G-6024)*

Valerian Technologies, Richardson *Also called Signature Cards LP (G-17398)*

Valero Energy Corporation (PA).......................210 345-2000
1 Valero Way San Antonio (78249) *(G-18583)*

Valero Energy Corporation...............................903 567-6001
310 E Hwy 243 Canton (75103) *(G-2661)*

Valero Energy Corporation...............................903 765-2900
182 S Fm 17 Alba (75410) *(G-183)*

Valero Energy Corporation...............................325 347-6561
Hwy 55 Rocksprings (78880) *(G-17533)*

Valero Energy Corporation...............................806 935-1307
6701 Fm 119 Sunray (79086) *(G-19623)*

Valero Energy Corporation...............................936 594-6233
225 Hwy 19 Riverside (77367) *(G-17481)*

Valero Marketing and Supply Co......................877 882-5376
7201 Canyon Dr Amarillo (79110) *(G-517)*

Valero McKee Refinery, Sunray *Also called Valero Energy Corporation (G-19623)*

Valero Port Arthur, San Antonio *Also called Premcor Refining Group Inc (G-18388)*

Valero Ref Company-California (HQ)..................210 345-2000
1 Valero Way San Antonio (78249) *(G-18584)*

Valero Ref Company-New Jersey (HQ)..............210 345-2000
1 Valero Way San Antonio (78249) *(G-18585)*

Valero Refining Company (HQ).........................210 345-2000
1 Valero Way San Antonio (78249) *(G-18586)*

Valero Refining-Texas LP (HQ).........................210 345-2000
1 Valero Way San Antonio (78249) *(G-18587)*

Valero Refining-Texas LP.................................713 923-6641
9701 Manchester St Houston (77012) *(G-12519)*

Valero Refining-Texas LP.................................409 945-4451
1301 Loop 197 S Texas City (77590) *(G-19806)*

Valero Refining-Texas LP.................................281 470-4900
1200 N Broadway St La Porte (77571) *(G-13799)*

Valero Renewable Fuels Co LLC (HQ)...............210 345-2000
1 Valero Way San Antonio (78249) *(G-18588)*

Valero Rfining-New Orleans LLC (HQ)...............210 345-2000
1 Valero Way San Antonio (78249) *(G-18589)*

Valero Services Inc...210 345-2000
1 Valero Way San Antonio (78249) *(G-18590)*

Valerus Compression Svcs LP..........................817 598-1600
1303 Azle Hwy Weatherford (76085) *(G-20628)*

Valerus Feld Sltions Hldngs LLC (HQ)..............713 744-6100
919 Milam St Ste 1000 Houston (77002) *(G-12520)*

Valerus Field Solutions LP (HQ).......................877 983-7500
919 Milam St Ste 1000 Houston (77002) *(G-12521)*

Vales Welding Service.......................................936 336-5148
301 Industrial Pl Liberty (77575) *(G-14126)*

Valet Parking By Vally Park, Mission *Also called Vally Park USA Corp (G-15572)*

Valhi Inc (HQ)...972 233-1700
5430 Lbj Fwy Ste 1700 Dallas (75240) *(G-5151)*

Valhi Timet, Dallas *Also called Titanium Metals Corporation (G-5097)*

Valiant Artfl Lift Sltions LLC............................432 253-2233
2806 N County Road 1148 Midland (79705) *(G-15460)*

Valkyrie Systems Aerospace Inc.......................888 426-2113
17440 Dallas Pkwy Ste 230 Dallas (75287) *(G-3857)*

Valley Armature & Elc Co Inc............................956 393-2233
1313 N Expressway 281 Edinburg (78542) *(G-5605)*

Valley Bargain Book, Brownsville *Also called Gatehouse Media LLC (G-2358)*

Valley By Products Inc......................................915 877-3131
7740 Kiely Rd Canutillo (79835) *(G-2667)*

Valley Caliche Products Inc..............................956 581-2751
3656 Iowa Rd Mission (78574) *(G-15571)*

Valley Crating & Packaging, Houston *Also called Ifco Systems North America Inc (G-10318)*

Valley Die Castings Inc.....................................956 630-0268
5216 N 26th St McAllen (78504) *(G-14913)*

Valley Farm Service Inc....................................806 364-6900
3510 Us Highway 385 Hereford (79045) *(G-8296)*

Valley Feed Mill Inc Paris (PA).........................903 785-3501
315 W Center St Paris (75460) *(G-16373)*

Valley Herbal Products Inc...............................956 631-8869
2601 Zinnia Ave McAllen (78504) *(G-14914)*

Valley Media Inc (PA)..956 546-5113
2494 Central Blvd Ste A Brownsville (78520) *(G-2419)*

Valley Morning Star, Harlingen *Also called Aim Media Texas Operating LLC (G-8174)*

Valley Orthopedic Inc.......................................512 771-1970
10910 Domain Dr Ste 300 Austin (78758) *(G-1622)*

Valley Orthpd & Prosthetics (PA)......................956 686-0032
2216 N 10th St McAllen (78501) *(G-14915)*

Valley Outdoor Power Eqp Inc..........................956 787-0469
1012 E Ferguson St Pharr (78577) *(G-16715)*

Valley Proteins Inc..432 334-0449
2441 Catalina Dr Odessa (79763) *(G-16193)*

Valley Proteins Inc..325 653-3858
8394 Fm 380 San Angelo (76905) *(G-17836)*

Valley Proteins (de) Inc....................................469 580-0864
515 Pontiac Ave Dallas (75203) *(G-5152)*

Valley Proteins (de) Inc....................................540 247-2798
8415 Se 1st Ave Amarillo (79118) *(G-518)*

Valley Proteins (de) Inc....................................806 379-6001
80 N Lakeside Dr Amarillo (79118) *(G-519)*

Valley Roller Company Inc................................817 453-8950
101 Sentry Dr Mansfield (76063) *(G-14726)*

Valley Swabbing & Flowback Svc, Mission *Also called J & R Valley Oilfield Svcs Inc (G-15556)*

Valley View Productions, Grapevine *Also called Sam Group Inc (G-8053)*

Valley Welding & Crane Service, Palmview *Also called Valley Welding Service (G-16313)*

Valley Welding Service......................................956 585-1043
1313 N Moorefield Rd Palmview (78572) *(G-16313)*

Vallourec Drilling Pdts USA, Houston *Also called Vallourec Drlg Pdts USA Inc (G-12522)*

Vallourec Drlg Pdts USA Inc.............................713 844-3700
6300-6230 Navigation Blvd Houston (77011) *(G-12522)*

Vallourec Tube-Alloy LLC (HQ).........................713 462-7613
1050 E Richey Rd Houston (77073) *(G-12523)*

Vallourec USA Corporation (HQ).......................713 479-3200
2107 Citywest Blvd # 130 Houston (77042) *(G-12524)*

Vally Park USA Corp...956 994-0000
3504 Santa Inez Cir Mission (78572) *(G-15572)*

Valmont Industries Inc......................................979 836-9395
2551 Valmont Dr Brenham (77833) *(G-2277)*

Valmont Industries Inc......................................979 277-3359
2569 Valmont Dr Brenham (77833) *(G-2278)*

Valmont Industries Inc......................................979 865-9137
11308 Highway 36 Bellville (77418) *(G-2013)*

Valmont Newmark Inc.......................................979 865-9137
11308 Highway 36 Bellville (77418) *(G-2014)*

Valor Built, San Antonio *Also called Nationwide Pharmaceutical LLC (G-18336)*

Valor Containments LLC....................................432 202-4220
1207 S Midland Dr Midland (79703) *(G-15461)*

ALPHABETIC

Valor Plastics LLC 512 663-2489
307 Industrial Blvd Burnet (78611) ***(G-2618)***
Valro-K LLC 210 937-1082
8135 Bracken Crk San Antonio (78266) ***(G-18647)***
Valron Strength Films, Houston *Also called Illinois Tool Works Inc* ***(G-10325)***
Valtek Industries Inc 432 339-8481
2120 W 44th St Odessa (79764) ***(G-16194)***
Valtrek Group LLC 915 201-7559
3523 Confederate Rd El Paso (79936) ***(G-6025)***
Valve Index International Inc 281 712-8246
14039 S Gessner Rd Missouri City (77489) ***(G-15598)***
Valves and Control Systems Inc 713 378-0311
1202 Washington St South Houston (77587) ***(G-19054)***
Vam Usa LLC (HQ) **281 821-5510**
4424 W Sam Houston Pkwy N S Houston (77041) ***(G-12525)***
Van Foods, Dallas *Also called Van Oriental Food Inc* ***(G-5153)***
Van Heusen, San Marcos *Also called Pvh Corp* ***(G-18704)***
Van London Company (HQ) **713 772-6641**
10540 Rockley Rd Houston (77099) ***(G-12526)***
Van London Company Inc 713 772-6641
10540 Rockley Rd Ste 100 Houston (77099) ***(G-12527)***
Van London-Phoenix Company, Houston *Also called Van London Company* ***(G-12526)***
Van Nu Technology Inc 817 276-3300
2155 Highway 1187 Mansfield (76063) ***(G-14727)***
Van Operating Ltd 325 762-3353
216 Hill St Albany (76430) ***(G-195)***
Van Oriental Food Inc 214 630-0333
4828 Reading St Dallas (75247) ***(G-5153)***
Van Rob Dallas, Garland *Also called Kirchhoff Auto Dallas Inc* ***(G-7532)***
Van Tone Creative Flavors Inc 972 563-2600
200 Metro Dr Terrell (75160) ***(G-19754)***
Van Zandt Newspapers LLC (PA) **903 567-4000**
109 N 5th St Wills Point (75169) ***(G-20880)***
Vanco Ring Gsket Spclty Corp I 281 499-1543
10138 Cash Rd Stafford (77477) ***(G-19394)***
Vandervoort Dairy, Fort Worth *Also called Kroger Co* ***(G-6773)***
Vanguard Defense Inds LLC 281 298-6672
2455 Fm 2920 Rd Ste A Spring (77388) ***(G-19184)***
Vanguard Machinery Intl LLC 713 462-5800
3609 Clinton Dr Houston (77020) ***(G-12528)***
Vanguard Metal Technologies 713 641-1859
5737 Heffernan St Houston (77087) ***(G-12529)***
Vanguard Permian LLC 432 362-2209
4001 Penbrook St Ste 201 Odessa (79762) ***(G-16195)***
Vanguard Pharmaceutical McHy 281 528-8885
21755 Interstate 45 # 6 Spring (77388) ***(G-19185)***
Vanguard Resources Inc 325 372-3142
606 E Wallace St San Saba (76877) ***(G-18720)***
Vans Inc 713 436-7925
11200 Broadway St # 1355 Pearland (77584) ***(G-16609)***
Vant Marketing Inc 830 217-2523
193 1/2 W San Antonio St # 306 New Braunfels (78130) ***(G-15830)***
Vantacore Partners LLC (HQ) **215 751-1403**
1201 La St Ste 3400 Houston (77002) ***(G-12530)***
VANTAGE DEEPWATER DRILLING, Houston *Also called Vantage Drilling Intl Inc* ***(G-12532)***
Vantage Driller I Co 281 404-4700
777 Post Oak Blvd Ste 800 Houston (77056) ***(G-12531)***
Vantage Drilling Intl Inc (PA) **281 404-4700**
777 Post Oak Blvd Ste 800 Houston (77056) ***(G-12532)***
Vantage Energy Services Inc 281 404-4700
777 Post Oak Blvd Ste 800 Houston (77056) ***(G-12533)***
Vantage Industries, Houston *Also called Vantage Energy Services Inc* ***(G-12533)***
Vantran Industries Inc 254 772-9740
7711 Imperial Dr Waco (76712) ***(G-20471)***
Vantran Transformers, Waco *Also called Vantran Industries Inc* ***(G-20471)***
Vanzandt Controls (HQ) **806 655-9367**
700 Highway 60 Canyon (79015) ***(G-2676)***
Vapor Io Inc 512 600-1123
6200 Brdgpint Pkwy Bldg F Austin (78730) ***(G-1623)***
Vaquero Midstream LLC 214 855-5546
2602 Mckinney Ave Ste 400 Dallas (75204) ***(G-5154)***
Varco LP 432 550-6802
4710 Andrews Hwy Odessa (79762) ***(G-16196)***
Varco LP (HQ) **713 799-5272**
2835 Holmes Rd Houston (77051) ***(G-12534)***
Varco LP 432 362-0581
2400 Steven Rd Odessa (79764) ***(G-16197)***
Varco LP 432 367-9726
100 E 61st St Odessa (79762) ***(G-16198)***
Varco LP 432 337-1570
2269 S Fulton Ave Odessa (79766) ***(G-16199)***
Varco LP 361 854-1167
401 Saratoga Blvd Corpus Christi (78417) ***(G-3650)***
Varco BJ Oil Tools, Houston *Also called A Varco Shaffer Co* ***(G-8429)***
Varco Shaffer Inc 713 672-1711
875 Lockwood Dr Houston (77020) ***(G-12535)***
Varco Shaffer Inc 713 937-5000
12950 W Little York Rd Houston (77041) ***(G-12536)***
Varel Energy Solutions, Houston *Also called Varel International Ind LLC* ***(G-12538)***
Varel Energy Solutions (HQ) **972 242-1160**
4730 Consulate Plaza Dr # 190 Houston (77032) ***(G-12537)***
Varel International Ind LLC (HQ) **281 272-6000**
4730 Consulate Plaza Dr # 190 Houston (77032) ***(G-12538)***
Varel International Ind LLC 713 304-5813
4531 Ayers St Corpus Christi (78415) ***(G-3651)***
Varel International Ind LLC 432 550-4816
2415 W 44th St Odessa (79764) ***(G-16200)***
Varel Intl Enrgy Svcs Inc, Houston *Also called Varel Energy Solutions* ***(G-12537)***
Varel Mining and Indus LLC (HQ) **469 476-4870**
1625 W Crosby Rd Ste 124 Carrollton (75006) ***(G-2844)***
Vari Doc Management Group LLC 214 528-9925
737 Regal Row Dallas (75247) ***(G-5155)***
Vari-Lite LLC 214 647-7880
10911 Petal St Dallas (75238) ***(G-5156)***
Varidesk, Coppell *Also called Gemmy Industries Corporation* ***(G-3417)***
Varieon Inc 469 916-1099
565 E Church St Lewisville (75057) ***(G-14104)***
Variosystems Inc (HQ) **817 416-7535**
901 S Kimball Ave Southlake (76092) ***(G-19083)***
Various Fields LLC 512 788-2228
1301 Broadmoor Dr Austin (78723) ***(G-1624)***
Varmicon Industries, Harlingen *Also called Alamo Concrete Products Ltd* ***(G-8176)***
Varo LLC 972 840-5506
2800 W Kingsley Rd Garland (75041) ***(G-7607)***
Vastar Resources Inc 281 584-6000
15375 Memorial Dr Houston (77079) ***(G-12539)***
Vastav Inc 972 466-2442
2722 N Josey Ln Ste 100 Carrollton (75007) ***(G-2894)***
Vatco, Houston *Also called Van London Company Inc* ***(G-12527)***
Vaughan Investments Inc 956 546-5175
3800 International Blvd Brownsville (78521) ***(G-2420)***
Vaughan Investments Inc 956 686-3725
108 E Us Highway 83 McAllen (78501) ***(G-14916)***
Vaughn Energy Services 936 539-9096
500 N Loop 336 E Ste 100 Conroe (77301) ***(G-3382)***
Vault 55 ....512 482-8810
710 Colorado St Ste 150 Austin (78701) ***(G-1625)***
Vax-Immune LLC 832 423-0055
3718 Sunset Blvd Ste 301 Houston (77005) ***(G-12540)***
Vbi Group LLC (PA) **817 533-3180**
1161 W Corp Dr Ste 130 Arlington (76006) ***(G-808)***
Vce Company LLC (HQ) **972 656-5300**
1500 N Grnvlle Ave Ste 11 Richardson (75081) ***(G-17418)***
VCM Industries Inc 713 462-7444
6202 Lumberdale Rd Houston (77092) ***(G-12541)***
Veco Printing Inc 956 968-1589
33840 S Garcia St # 866 Port Isabel (78578) ***(G-17140)***
Vector Group Inc 713 979-4444
4301 S Pinemont Dr # 104 Houston (77041) ***(G-12542)***
Vector Industrial Group LLC 281 967-1093
803 Marina Bay Dr Kemah (77565) ***(G-13481)***
Vector Seismic Data Processing (PA) **303 571-1515**
10001 Richmond Ave Houston (77042) ***(G-12543)***
Vector Systems Inc 214 544-9500
411 Mckinney Pkwy McKinney (75071) ***(G-14985)***
Vectornav Technologies LLC 512 772-3615
10501 Markison Rd Dallas (75238) ***(G-5157)***
Vedero Software Inc 972 309-9870
4100 Midway Rd Ste 2050 Carrollton (75007) ***(G-2895)***
Vee Interests LLC 832 864-2001
1911 Jasmine Dr Pasadena (77503) ***(G-16523)***
Veeder-Root Fuelquest LLC 713 222-5700
8 Greenway Plz Ste 300 Houston (77046) ***(G-12544)***
Veggie Noodle Co LLC 512 200-3337
3714 Bluestein Dr Ste 631 Austin (78721) ***(G-1626)***
Veka South Inc 972 551-2030
107 Metrocrest Way Terrell (75160) ***(G-19755)***
Velas Builders LLC 956 464-7827
2617 E Expressway 83 Donna (78537) ***(G-5495)***
Velocity Aerospace Group Inc (PA) **214 988-9898**
7460 Warren Pkwy Ste 180 Frisco (75034) ***(G-7322)***
Velocity Manufacturing, Houston *Also called Ltn Industries Inc* ***(G-10698)***
Velocity Promotions LLC 800 523-8078
1100 Hercules Ave Ste 320 Houston (77058) ***(G-12545)***
Venable Corporation 512 949-3144
8656 W Highway 71 Bldg E Austin (78735) ***(G-1627)***
Venable Instruments, Austin *Also called Venable Corporation* ***(G-1627)***
Venable's Welding & Roustabout, Amarillo *Also called Venables Construction Inc* ***(G-520)***
Venables Construction Inc (PA) **806 381-2121**
7410 Continental Pkwy Amarillo (79119) ***(G-520)***
Venado Oil & Gas LLC (PA) **512 518-2900**
13301 Galleria Cir # 300 Austin (78738) ***(G-1628)***
Venado Oil & Gas LLC 512 518-2900
490 E Hindes Ave Charlotte (78011) ***(G-3049)***
Venator Americas LLC (HQ) **281 465-6700**
10001 Woodloch Forest Dr The Woodlands (77380) ***(G-19935)***
Venator Americas LLC 281 719-6000
10003 Woodloch Forest Dr The Woodlands (77380) ***(G-19936)***

Venator Chemicals LLC 979 233-8183
  302 Midway Rd Freeport (77541) *(G-7218)*

Venator Materials LLC 281 465-6700
  10003 Woodloch Forest Dr The Woodlands (77380) *(G-19937)*

Vencorex Holding France, Freeport Also called Vencorex Us Inc *(G-7219)*

Vencorex Us Inc (HQ) 979 233-7871
  6213 E Highway 332 Freeport (77541) *(G-7219)*

Vencorex Us Inc 979 233-7871
  6213 E Highway 332 Freeport (77541) *(G-7220)*

Vendor Guide, The, Irving Also called JDC Enterprises Inc *(G-13068)*

Venetian Blind Flr Cvg Sp Ltd 713 528-2404
  2504 Bissonnet St Houston (77005) *(G-12546)*

Venetian Marble Co Lubbock Inc (PA) ... 806 763-5777
  2834 Clovis Rd Lubbock (79415) *(G-14506)*

Venetian Marble Kitchen & Bath, Lubbock Also called Ortega Bath Environments Inc *(G-14454)*

Venetian Marble of San Antonio, Helotes Also called Kamal Incorporated *(G-8241)*

Venetian of Lubbock, Lubbock Also called Venetian Marble Co Lubbock Inc *(G-14506)*

Venkel Ltd (PA) 512 794-0081
  5900 Shepherd Mountain Cv Austin (78730) *(G-1629)*

Vent-A-Hood Ltd (PA) 888 557-8368
  1000 N Greenville Ave Richardson (75081) *(G-17419)*

Ventamatic Ltd (PA) 940 325-7887
  100 Washington Ave Mineral Wells (76067) *(G-15545)*

Ventil USA Inc 281 280-0141
  906 Gemini St Houston (77058) *(G-12547)*

Ventilation Service Inc 713 683-1003
  14723 Silver Sands St Houston (77095) *(G-12548)*

Ventura Foods LLC 817 232-6800
  3201 Ne Loop 820 Ste 150 Fort Worth (76137) *(G-7097)*

Ventura Foods LLC 817 232-5450
  1100 Defiel Rd Saginaw (76179) *(G-17758)*

Venture Precision, Humble Also called Kevin Goss *(G-12782)*

Venture Products Co, Sugar Land Also called James L Rembert Jr Inc *(G-19500)*

Venture Research Inc 469 246-4000
  3001 Summit Ave Ste 100 Plano (75074) *(G-17044)*

Venus Beauty Inc 301 503-4052
  1041 S Jupiter Rd Garland (75042) *(G-7608)*

Venus Fabrication Inc 972 366-3565
  18901 County Road 620 Venus (76084) *(G-20226)*

Venus Marble Co Inc (PA) 972 223-8008
  1101 S Hampton Rd Desoto (75115) *(G-5447)*

Venus Spa 214 469-1615
  4770 State Highway 121 Lewisville (75056) *(G-14105)*

Veolia North America Reg Serv 915 782-5550
  6501 Trowbridge Dr El Paso (79905) *(G-6026)*

Vera Bradley Inc 713 647-0323
  303 Memorial City Ste 303 # 303 Houston (77024) *(G-12549)*

Veracity USA Incoporated 972 786-6771
  17000 Preston Rd Ste 260 Dallas (75248) *(G-5158)*

Verado Energy Inc (PA) 214 368-5322
  8150 N Central Expy # 850 Dallas (75206) *(G-5159)*

Verado Oil and Gas Corporation 214 368-5322
  8150 N Central Expy # 900 Dallas (75206) *(G-5160)*

Vercom Software Inc 972 661-9336
  13355 Noel Rd Ste 1100 Dallas (75240) *(G-5161)*

Verdad Oil & Gas Corporation (PA) 214 357-0333
  5950 Sherry Ln Ste 700 Dallas (75225) *(G-5162)*

Verdia Inc 713 999-5090
  11133 Interstate 45 S Conroe (77302) *(G-3383)*

Verdun Oil Company LLC 713 554-4577
  55 Waugh Dr Ste 400 Houston (77007) *(G-12550)*

Vere Technology LLC (PA) 832 532-6745
  4541 Brittmoore Rd Houston (77041) *(G-12551)*

Verge Labs Inc 512 707-0001
  209 E Ben White Blvd # 114 Austin (78704) *(G-1630)*

Verge Ventures LLC 972 200-1707
  49 Dunrobin Richardson (75082) *(G-17420)*

Vericast Corp (HQ) 210 697-8888
  15955 La Cantera Pkwy San Antonio (78256) *(G-18591)*

Veriovox Corporation 713 409-7216
  608 Pederson Rd Katy (77494) *(G-13384)*

Veripos (us) Inc 281 966-7600
  15990 N Barkers Houston (77079) *(G-12552)*

Verity Instruments Inc 972 446-9990
  2901 Eisenhower St Carrollton (75007) *(G-2896)*

Verizon, Dfw Airport Also called Supermedia LLC *(G-5456)*

Vermeer Equipment Texas LLC 512 244-0505
  1945 Louis Henna Blvd Round Rock (78664) *(G-17697)*

Vermeer Texas-Louisiana, Round Rock Also called Vermeer Equipment Texas LLC *(G-17697)*

Vermillion, Austin Also called Aspira Womens Health Inc *(G-940)*

Vernon E Faulconer Inc (PA) 903 581-4382
  1001 E Se Loop 323 # 160 Tyler (75701) *(G-20174)*

Vernor Material & Eqp Co Inc 409 233-3366
  545 County Road 227a Freeport (77541) *(G-7221)*

Verope USA Inc 832 831-0132
  1101 Pleasantville Dr B Houston (77029) *(G-12553)*

Versa Printing Inc 972 243-5353
  2631 Brenner Dr Dallas (75220) *(G-5163)*

Versabar Inc (PA) 713 937-3100
  11349 Fm 529 Rd Houston (77041) *(G-12554)*

Versalift East LLC (HQ) 254 399-2100
  7601 Imperial Dr Waco (76712) *(G-20472)*

Versalift Southwest LLC (HQ) 254 399-2100
  1200 Texas Central Pkwy Waco (76712) *(G-20473)*

Versata Inc (HQ) 512 524-6149
  401 Congress Ave Ste 2600 Austin (78701) *(G-1631)*

Versatrac, Houston Also called American Door Products Inc *(G-8594)*

Vertec Polymers Inc 866 283-7832
  6880 Wynnwood Ln Houston (77008) *(G-12555)*

Vertex Aerospace LLC 210 652-4541
  1851 5th St W Bldg 58 Randolph (75475) *(G-17230)*

Vertex Aerospace LLC 210 652-6717
  5th St Hngr 7 Universal City (78148) *(G-20185)*

Vertex Energy Inc (PA) 866 660-8156
  1331 Gemini St Ste 250 Houston (77058) *(G-12556)*

Vertical Computer Systems Inc (PA) 972 437-5200
  101 W Renner Rd Ste 200 Richardson (75082) *(G-17421)*

Vertical Nerve Inc 800 330-9450
  8350 N Central Expy Dallas (75206) *(G-5164)*

Vertical Trbine Spcialists Inc 806 743-5555
  1802 E 50th St Unit 106 Lubbock (79404) *(G-14507)*

Vertiv Corporation 956 683-2948
  5109 Tanya Ave Bldg B McAllen (78503) *(G-14917)*

Vertrauen Chemie Solutions Inc (PA) ... 469 283-0789
  200 Industrial Blvd McKinney (75069) *(G-14986)*

Vesco Business Products, La Porte Also called Rfv Enterprises Inc *(G-13788)*

Vessel Repair, Port Arthur Also called Mblh Marine LLC *(G-17118)*

Vessel Technology 903 643-9111
  9486 Fm 2011 Longview (75603) *(G-14329)*

Vestal Steel Specialties Inc 210 651-4333
  17993 Red Iron Schertz (78154) *(G-18768)*

Vesuvius U S A Corporation 903 597-7237
  1812 E Duncan St Tyler (75702) *(G-20175)*

Vesuvius U S A Corporation 903 597-7237
  210 Pecos St Hillsboro (76645) *(G-8332)*

Vetco Gray LLC 281 445-8968
  12221 N Huston Rosslyn Rd Houston (77086) *(G-12557)*

Vetco Gray LLC (HQ) 281 448-4410
  12221 N Huston Rosslyn Rd Houston (77086) *(G-12558)*

Veterans Mfg LLC 713 854-9261
  5446 1st St Ste A Katy (77493) *(G-13454)*

Veterinary Diagnostic Lab, College Station Also called The Texas A&M University Sys *(G-3205)*

Vetoquinol USA Inc (HQ) 817 529-7500
  4250 N Sylvania Ave Fort Worth (76137) *(G-7098)*

Vexa Pak LLC 713 671-1100
  6902 Palestine St A Houston (77020) *(G-12559)*

Vf Industrial Park Inc 979 826-8277
  805 Factory Outlet Dr Hempstead (77445) *(G-8256)*

Vf Industrial Park Inc 936 327-7881
  440 Highway 59 Loop S Livingston (77351) *(G-14163)*

Vf Outdoor LLC 817 348-0567
  125 S Jennings Ave Fort Worth (76104) *(G-7099)*

Vf Outdoor LLC 817 336-7201
  509 W Vickery Blvd Fort Worth (76104) *(G-7100)*

Vf Outdoor LLC 830 278-2535
  510 S Highway 83 Uvalde (78801) *(G-20199)*

Vf Outdoor LLC 817 810-4401
  9400 Blue Mound Rd Fort Worth (76131) *(G-7101)*

Vf Outdoor LLC 817 491-4949
  201 Intermodal Pkwy Fort Worth (76177) *(G-7102)*

Vf Sagebrush Enterprises LLC (HQ) 817 336-7201
  319 Lipscomb St Fort Worth (76104) *(G-7103)*

Vfl Energy Technologies Inc 713 466-9883
  12431 Taylor Rd Houston (77041) *(G-12560)*

Vfuels Solutions Inc 713 456-3443
  12221 Fm 529 Rd Houston (77041) *(G-12561)*

Vgcm LLC 713 455-1465
  14047 Industrial Rd Houston (77015) *(G-12562)*

Vhp Foods Company, McAllen Also called Valley Herbal Products Inc *(G-14914)*

Vhsc Cement LLC (PA) 281 419-2422
  2204 Timberloch Pl # 248 The Woodlands (77380) *(G-19938)*

Viant Medical Inc 830 792-1156
  200 Holdsworth Dr Kerrville (78028) *(G-13528)*

Viant San Antonio Inc 210 684-7553
  7027 Fairgrounds Pkwy San Antonio (78238) *(G-18592)*

Viarden Lab LLC 956 294-0260
  2005 E Griffin Pkwy Mission (78572) *(G-15573)*

Viatech Pubg Solutions Inc (PA) 214 827-8151
  11935 N Stemmons Fwy # 1 Dallas (75234) *(G-5165)*

Viatran Inc 512 832-8400
  404 W Powell Ln Ste 408 Austin (78753) *(G-1632)*

Viavi Solutions Inc 972 907-8882
  900 Alpha Dr Ste 420 Richardson (75081) *(G-17422)*

Vibra-Whirl Sports Ltd 806 537-3526
  94 Main St Panhandle (79068) *(G-16348)*

(PA)=Parent Co (HQ)=Headquarters (DH)=Div Headquarters

Vibration Management Corp................................713 983-8462
5930 Thomas Rd Houston (77041) *(G-12563)*

Vic West Importers Ltd Co................................888 698-6463
512 E Rverside Dr Ste 200 Austin (78704) *(G-1633)*

Viceroy Inc (HQ)...**713 475-4518**
3225 Pasadena Blvd Pasadena (77503) *(G-16524)*

Viceroy Petroleum LP.....................................832 783-5790
4359 Roans Chapel Rd College Station (77845) *(G-3209)*

Vickery Street Fabricators Inc........................713 695-9195
4525 Saunders Rd Houston (77093) *(G-12564)*

Vicky Cakes Pancake Mix LLC.........................469 573-2773
4601 Langland Rd Ste 103 Farmers Branch (75244) *(G-6218)*

Victaulic Co of America, Stafford *Also called Victaulic Company (G-19395)*

Victaulic Company...281 494-5000
13833 N Promenade Blvd # 500 Stafford (77477) *(G-19395)*

Victaulic-Bermad LLC.....................................713 856-1700
9424 W Little York Rd Houston (77040) *(G-12565)*

Victor Equipment Company (HQ)......................**940 566-2000**
2800 Airport Rd Denton (76207) *(G-5409)*

Victor Nicolle Inc..713 896-4911
15255 Vntage Prsrve Pkwy Houston (77070) *(G-12566)*

Victor Technologies, Denton *Also called Victor Equipment Company (G-5409)*

Victor Technologies Group Inc.........................940 566-2000
2800 Airport Rd Denton (76207) *(G-5410)*

Victor Technologies Intl Inc (HQ)....................**940 381-1353**
2800 Airport Rd Denton (76207) *(G-5411)*

Victoria Advocate News Bureau.......................361 575-1451
1 Oconnor Plz Ste 1200 Victoria (77901) *(G-20313)*

Victoria Advocate Pubg Co (PA).......................**361 575-1451**
1 Oconnor Plz Ste 1200 Victoria (77901) *(G-20314)*

Victoria Well Service, Victoria *Also called Sparkman Industries Inc (G-20304)*

Victorious Music Co...713 450-3306
11811i 10th St Ste 330 Houston (77044) *(G-12567)*

Victory Awning Inc..817 759-1600
6801 Old Randol Mill Rd Fort Worth (76120) *(G-7104)*

Victory Climate Systems LLC..........................817 293-3331
8912 South Fwy Ste C Fort Worth (76140) *(G-7105)*

Videotex Systems Inc......................................214 349-6399
10255 Miller Rd Dallas (75238) *(G-5166)*

Vidorian, The, Vidor *Also called Orange County Publishing Co (G-20330)*

Viewcastcom Inc (PA).....................................**972 488-7200**
756 Port America Pl # 400 Grapevine (76051) *(G-8059)*

Vikay Group LLC...512 291-8234
321 W Ben White Blvd # 112 Austin (78704) *(G-1634)*

Viking Archery, Canyon Lake *Also called T L W Archery Inc (G-2680)*

Viking Coil Tubing LLC....................................432 580-7555
335 S County Rd W Odessa (79763) *(G-16201)*

Viking International Limited.............................214 220-4323
5910 N Central Expy Dallas (75206) *(G-5167)*

Villa At Messina Hof, Bryan *Also called Messina Hof Wine Cellars Inc (G-2493)*

Village Farms LP...432 426-2301
State Highway 17 S Fort Davis (79734) *(G-6320)*

Village News, Bellaire *Also called News Publications Inc (G-1999)*

Villarreal Production Service, Zapata *Also called Jose Luis Villarreal (G-20983)*

Villatoro Construction LLC.............................214 350-7900
2851 Whiteley Rd Wylie (75098) *(G-20954)*

Villpac Inc..713 672-1255
1101 Mercury Dr Houston (77029) *(G-12568)*

Vince Hagan Company (PA)...............................**214 330-4601**
330 Clay Rd Sunnyvale (75182) *(G-19615)*

Vincent Graphics & Supply Inc (PA)..................**903 882-3123**
12979 State Highway 110 N Tyler (75704) *(G-20176)*

Vindicator, The, Liberty *Also called Hartman Newspapers LP (G-14119)*

Vine Oil & Gas LP (PA).....................................**469 606-0540**
5800 Granite Pkwy Ste 550 Plano (75024) *(G-17045)*

Vines Ready Mix, Midland *Also called Troy Vines Incorporated (G-15447)*

Vineyard At Florence, The, Florence *Also called Dionysus Group LLLP (G-6239)*

Vinh Ho Machine Shop Inc................................713 896-7828
4941 Gessner Rd Houston (77041) *(G-12569)*

Vinson Process Controls Co LP (PA).................**972 459-8200**
2747 Highpoint Oaks Dr Lewisville (75067) *(G-14106)*

Vintage Air Inc..210 296-2302
18865 Goll St San Antonio (78266) *(G-18648)*

Vinton Steel LLC..915 886-2000
8100 Border Steel Rd Vinton (79821) *(G-20342)*

Vinyard Water Service......................................806 256-2766
709 E 11 St Shamrock (79079) *(G-18893)*

Violet Care LLC..210 482-0237
14603 Bassett Ln San Antonio (78231) *(G-18593)*

VIP Samples Incorporated................................972 647-8888
2800 112th St Ste 100 Grand Prairie (75050) *(G-7991)*

Viper Blasting & Coating Inc...........................432 337-9711
2700 E Interstate 20 Odessa (79766) *(G-16202)*

Viper Drilling International...............................832 917-5804
8524 Highway 6 N Ste 478 Houston (77095) *(G-12570)*

Viper Energy Partners LP.................................432 221-7400
500 W Texas Ave Ste 1200 Midland (79701) *(G-15462)*

Viper Oil & Gas, El Campo *Also called Viper Well Services LLC (G-5628)*

Viper Petroleum LLC.......................................832 917-5804
13423 Blanco Rd 348 San Antonio (78216) *(G-18594)*

Viper Well Services LLC...................................979 541-5262
402 Dam Rd El Campo (77437) *(G-5628)*

Vira Insight LLC (PA).......................................**800 366-2345**
2701 S Valley Pkwy Lewisville (75067) *(G-14107)*

Vira Insight LLC..800 366-2345
2701 S Valley Pkwy Lewisville (75067) *(G-14108)*

Virbac Animal Health, Westlake *Also called Virbac Corporation (G-20697)*

Virbac Corporation (HQ)...................................**800 338-3659**
1301 Solana Blvd Ste 2400 Westlake (76262) *(G-20697)*

Virgin Fields LLC...972 322-7902
7236 Yellowstone Dr Frisco (75033) *(G-7323)*

Viron International Corp...................................254 773-9292
3100 Lucius Mccelvey Dr Temple (76504) *(G-19714)*

Virtex Assembly Services Inc..........................512 835-6772
12234 N Interstate 35 A Austin (78753) *(G-1635)*

Virtex Enterprises LP (PA)...............................**512 835-6772**
12234 N Interstate 35 Austin (78753) *(G-1636)*

Virtex Holdings LLP...361 882-3046
615 N Upper Broadway St # 525 Corpus Christi (78401) *(G-3652)*

Virtual Realities..409 599-7863
2706 Wilmington Dr Ste A Dickinson (77539) *(G-5479)*

Virus Armor, Fort Worth *Also called Virus Light Rx LLC (G-7106)*

Virus Light Rx LLC...817 917-2800
4924 Cambridge Rd Fort Worth (76155) *(G-7106)*

Viserv Inc..512 454-7403
2211 S Interstate 35 # 205 Austin (78741) *(G-1637)*

Visicare, Magnolia *Also called Insignia Marketing Inc (G-14610)*

Vision Centers PA (PA).....................................**512 258-2020**
12701 Research Blvd Austin (78759) *(G-1638)*

Vision Oil Field Services Lc.............................361 578-1901
1908 N Laurent St Ste 200 Victoria (77901) *(G-20315)*

Vision Openings, San Antonio *Also called Travis Millwork Inc (G-18564)*

Vision Products Inc (PA)..................................**830 755-4719**
12726 Cimarron Path San Antonio (78249) *(G-18595)*

Vision Systems Intl LLC...................................817 234-6600
4700 Marine Creek Pkwy Fort Worth (76179) *(G-7107)*

Vision-Ease Lens, Southlake *Also called Insight Equity A P X L P (G-19075)*

Visionael Corporation......................................650 963-0960
401 Congress Ave Ste 2950 Austin (78701) *(G-1639)*

Visionmonitor Software LLC (PA).....................**713 935-0500**
11451 Katy Fwy Ste 510 Houston (77079) *(G-12571)*

Visionworks of America Inc (HQ)......................**800 669-1183**
175 E Houston St San Antonio (78205) *(G-18596)*

Vison Tech Products LLC..................................832 850-6085
6464 Cunningham Rd Houston (77041) *(G-12572)*

Vista Cntrs & Closures LLC..............................713 609-9250
4003 Leeland St Houston (77023) *(G-12573)*

Vista Machining Company LLC.........................817 710-2987
3559 Williams Rd Ste 101 Fort Worth (76116) *(G-7108)*

Vista Proppants Logistics LLC (HQ)..................**817 563-3500**
4413 Carey St Fort Worth (76119) *(G-7109)*

Vista Sand, Fort Worth *Also called Lonestar Prospects Ltd (G-6799)*

Vistawall, Terrell *Also called Oldcastle GL Engnered Pdts Inc (G-19747)*

Vistech Corporation...972 231-1746
858 N Glenville Dr Richardson (75081) *(G-17423)*

Vistech Mfg Solutions LLC...............................210 225-9900
3345b N Panam Expy San Antonio (78219) *(G-18597)*

Visual Bi Solutions Inc....................................972 232-2233
5920 Windhaven Pkwy # 200 Plano (75093) *(G-17046)*

Visual Click Software Inc.................................512 231-9990
3267 Bee Caves Rd Austin (78746) *(G-1640)*

Visual Comfort & Co., Houston *Also called Visual Comfort of America LLC (G-12574)*

Visual Comfort of America LLC.........................713 686-5999
22400 Nw Lake Dr Houston (77095) *(G-12574)*

Visual Lighting Technologies, Cedar Park *Also called Drw Holdings (G-2966)*

Visualml Operations LLC.................................855 847-8256
301 Spring Creek Dr Liberty Hill (78642) *(G-14131)*

Vita International Inc.......................................281 591-1300
12050 Proctor St Houston (77038) *(G-12575)*

Vita Nonwovens Texas Plant, Schertz *Also called Twe Nonwovens Us Inc (G-18765)*

Vital Farms Inc...877 455-3063
3601 S Congress Ave C1 Austin (78704) *(G-1641)*

Vital Fuels, El Paso *Also called Global Alternative Fuels LLC (G-5787)*

Vitality Construction, Fort Worth *Also called Cabinets By Michael Inc (G-6485)*

Vitalpure Labs LLC..573 469-1302
100 Industrial Dr Junction (76849) *(G-13340)*

Vitaltech Affiliates LLC...................................214 886-5249
6652 Pinecrest Dr Ste 400 Plano (75024) *(G-17047)*

Vitesco Technologies Usa LLC.........................830 379-8850
3740 N Austin St Seguin (78155) *(G-18872)*

Vitex Wireline Services Inc..............................361 575-1233
3802 E Rio Grande St Victoria (77901) *(G-20316)*

Vitol Americas Corp (HQ).................................**713 230-1000**
2925 Richmond Ave Ste 11 Houston (77098) *(G-12576)*

Vitro Architectural Glass.................................940 851-4374
7400 Central Fwy N Wichita Falls (76305) *(G-20824)*

Vitro Flat Glass LLC 940 855-3804
7400 Central Fwy N Wichita Falls (76305) *(G-20825)*
Vitruvian Exploration II LLC (PA) **832 458-3100**
13814 Riverton Manor Ct Cypress (77429) *(G-3825)*
Vitruvian Exploration IV LLC 832 458-3100
13814 Riverton Manor Ct Cypress (77429) *(G-3826)*
Vitruvian II Woodford LLC 832 458-3100
4 Waterway Square Pl # 400 The Woodlands (77380) *(G-19939)*
Vitzrocellusa Inc 832 850-7095
10804 Fallstone Rd # 200 Houston (77099) *(G-12577)*
Viva Support Services, Andrews *Also called Viva Well Servicing II L P* *(G-561)*
Viva Well Servicing Company LP 432 552-0800
3747 W 8th St Odessa (79763) *(G-16203)*
Viva Well Servicing II L P 432 524-2781
1501 W Broadway St Andrews (79714) *(G-561)*
Vivace International Corp 504 613-4329
22211 W Interstate 10 San Antonio (78257) *(G-18598)*
Vivicom, Seabrook *Also called Technical Automtn Svcs Co Ltd* *(G-18792)*
Vixen Creations Inc 512 928-4933
4803 Commercial Park Dr Austin (78724) *(G-1642)*
Vixxo Corporation 713 977-7900
4801 Woodway Dr Ste 160w Houston (77056) *(G-12578)*
Vizza Wash Services LLC 512 246-8822
1322 Round Rock Ave Round Rock (78681) *(G-17698)*
Vlgc LLC 817 926-5209
6811 Corporation Pkwy Fort Worth (76126) *(G-7110)*
Vlj Inc 972 442-4673
116 Regency Dr Wylie (75098) *(G-20955)*
Vls Marine Services, Port Arthur *Also called Vls Recovery Services LLC* *(G-17132)*
Vls Recovery Services LLC 409 962-8800
8700 Yacht Club Rd Port Arthur (77642) *(G-17132)*
Vlsip Technologies Inc (PA) **972 437-5506**
750 Presidential Dr Richardson (75081) *(G-17424)*
Vmc Group, The, Houston *Also called Amber/Booth Inc* *(G-8577)*
Vmc Signs Inc 361 575-0548
102 E Mockingbird Ln Victoria (77904) *(G-20317)*
VME, Freeport *Also called Vernor Material & Eqp Co Inc* *(G-7221)*
Vmg Welding 832 605-3933
5035 Jefferson St Houston (77023) *(G-12579)*
Voestalpine Texas LLC 361 704-9000
2800 Kay Bley Htchison Rd Portland (78374) *(G-17188)*
Vog Palo Verde LP 512 518-2900
13301 Galleria Cir # 300 Austin (78738) *(G-1643)*
Vogler Sheet Metal Company 713 861-1154
1331 Lemm Road 1 Spring (77373) *(G-19186)*
Vogt Ice LLC 940 387-4301
522 S Edmonds Ln Ste 102 Lewisville (75067) *(G-14109)*
Vogt Valves Inc 346 304-2566
13800 N Promenade Blvd Stafford (77477) *(G-19396)*
Voice Media Group, Dallas *Also called Dallas Observer LP* *(G-4222)*
Voice Media Group Inc 713 280-2400
2603 La Branch St Houston (77004) *(G-12580)*
Voice Publishing Co Inc 214 754-8710
1825 Market Center Blvd # 240 Dallas (75207) *(G-5168)*
Voidform Products Inc 817 429-0888
6151 Cowley Rd Fort Worth (76119) *(G-7111)*
Voip Tel LP 512 543-9556
7801 N Lamar Blvd B168 Austin (78752) *(G-1644)*
Volcano Corporation 210 582-5820
12829 Wetmore Rd San Antonio (78247) *(G-18599)*
Volks Resources LLC 972 636-1880
7460 Warren Pkwy Ste 100 Frisco (75034) *(G-7324)*
Vollara LLC (HQ) **800 989-2299**
4100 Alpha Rd Ste 1100 Dallas (75244) *(G-5169)*
Volta LLC 832 369-2420
1616 Gears Rd Houston (77067) *(G-12581)*
Volume Feed & Seed Inc 325 676-3302
249 S 11th St Abilene (79602) *(G-90)*
Volusion LLC (HQ) **800 646-3517**
1835 Kramer Ln Ste 100 Austin (78758) *(G-1645)*
Voom Group Inc 972 424-8887
1825 E Plano Pkwy Ste 250 Plano (75074) *(G-17048)*
Vorago Technologies, Austin *Also called Silicon Space Technology Corp* *(G-1506)*
Vortech Contracting Inc 409 296-3219
42408 Ih 10 Winnie (77665) *(G-20892)*
Voss Catering Inc 713 257-9898
5422 Bellaire Blvd Bellaire (77401) *(G-2004)*
Votorantim Metais N Amer Inc, Houston *Also called US Zinc North America Inc* *(G-12496)*
Votorantim Us, Inc., Houston *Also called Nexa Resources Us Inc* *(G-11043)*
Votronics Inc 972 509-8494
1505 Capital Ave Plano (75074) *(G-17049)*
Vought Commercial Division, Grand Prairie *Also called Triumph Aerostructures LLC* *(G-7987)*
Voyager, Dallas *Also called Cambium Learning Inc* *(G-3840)*
Voyager, Dallas *Also called Lazel Inc* *(G-3847)*
Voyager Energy Services LLC 830 583-9590
1 Airport Rd Kenedy (78119) *(G-13493)*
Voyager Learning Company (HQ) **214 932-9500**
17855 Dallas Pkwy Ste 400 Dallas (75287) *(G-3858)*
Voyant Beauty, Fort Worth *Also called CBI Laboratories Inc* *(G-6497)*
Vp Racing Fuels Inc (HQ) **210 635-7744**
204 E Rhapsody Dr San Antonio (78216) *(G-18600)*
Vrc Technologies Inc (PA) **325 643-8038**
1412 Custer Rd Brownwood (76801) *(G-2447)*
Vrt Investments Inc 972 226-1981
10600 W Us Highway 80 Forney (75126) *(G-6316)*
VSE Corporation 903 831-0192
154 Service New Boston (75570) *(G-15769)*
VSI, Houston *Also called Ventilation Service Inc* *(G-12548)*
VSI Solutions Inc 855 712-7677
5900 S Lake Forest Dr # 300 McKinney (75070) *(G-14987)*
Vtech Communications Inc 210 244-0600
1143 At&T Center Pkwy San Antonio (78219) *(G-18601)*
Vts Pumps, Lubbock *Also called Vertical Trbine Spcialists Inc* *(G-14507)*
Vu Enterprise Inc 713 944-0384
1016 Virginia St South Houston (77587) *(G-19055)*
Vulcan Construction Mtls LLC 210 492-1053
12307 Huebner Rd San Antonio (78230) *(G-18602)*
Vulcan Construction Mtls LLC 254 629-2850
702 County Road 442 Eastland (76448) *(G-5570)*
Vulcan Finned Tubes LP 281 255-4775
27951 Commercial Park Rd Tomball (77375) *(G-20015)*
Vulcan Industrial Holdings LLC (PA) **715 294-3200**
1990 Post Oak Blvd # 2400 Houston (77056) *(G-12582)*
Vulcan Materials Company 713 631-7200
6505 Homestead Rd Houston (77028) *(G-12583)*
Vulcan Materials Company 830 624-4944
19347 N Interstate 35 New Braunfels (78132) *(G-15831)*
Vulcan Materials Company 409 833-4177
1399 Carroll St Beaumont (77701) *(G-1967)*
Vulcan Materials Company 972 335-0008
6601 Eubanks St Frisco (75034) *(G-7325)*
Vulcan Materials Company 325 529-3785
14500 County Road 224 Abilene (79602) *(G-91)*
Vulcan Materials Company 940 683-4996
2560 S State Highway 101 Bridgeport (76426) *(G-2304)*
Vulcan Materials Company 210 695-3081
11602 Rainbow Rdg Helotes (78023) *(G-8244)*
Vulcan Materials Company 210 349-3311
800 Isom Rd Ste 300 San Antonio (78216) *(G-18603)*
Vulcan Materials Company 210 494-9555
4303 N Loop 1604 E San Antonio (78247) *(G-18604)*
Vulcan Materials Plant 363, Uvalde *Also called Legacy Vulcan LLC* *(G-20190)*
Vulcraft, Spring *Also called Nucor Corporation* *(G-19156)*
Vulcraft Carrier Corporation 936 687-4665
N Main St Ext Grapeland (75844) *(G-8008)*
Vutex Inc 210 476-1700
1 Lone Star Pass Ste 1102 San Antonio (78264) *(G-18605)*
Vysk Communications Inc 210 832-8322
13750 San Pedro Ave # 27 San Antonio (78232) *(G-18606)*
W & D, Hutchins *Also called Williams & Davis Boilers Inc* *(G-12873)*
W & R Industrial Services Inc 806 637-8204
720 W Broadway St Brownfield (79316) *(G-2332)*
W & S Precision Finishing Co 214 339-7181
4138 Shilling Way Dallas (75237) *(G-5170)*
W & W Fiberglass Tank Company 806 669-1128
100 N Price Rd Pampa (79065) *(G-16344)*
W & W Silkscreening Inc 817 590-4479
2451 Riverbend West Dr Fort Worth (76118) *(G-7112)*
W & W Steel Co, Lubbock *Also called W&W-Afco Steel LLC* *(G-14508)*
W A Neel Co Inc 903 503-5834
2199 Farm Rd I 20 20 I Scottsville (75688) *(G-18781)*
W B Mason Co Inc 888 926-2766
1215 W Wells Branch Pkwy Pflugerville (78660) *(G-16691)*
W B Mason Co Inc 888 926-2766
5425 Faa Blvd Irving (75061) *(G-13205)*
W B Mason Co Inc 888 926-2766
8518 W Little York Rd Houston (77040) *(G-12584)*
W B Osborn Oil Gas Oprtons L 210 826-8654
1250 Ne Loop 410 Ste 600 San Antonio (78209) *(G-18607)*
W C Hodges Logging 936 867-4550
County Rd 2707 Wells (75976) *(G-20658)*
W E Hayden Lease Service Inc 361 771-3684
281 Hwy 172 S Ganado (77962) *(G-7416)*
W J Denims, Dallas *Also called Aalfs Manufacturing Inc* *(G-3874)*
W L Flowers Mch Wldg Co Inc 361 664-6527
2585 S Us Highway 281 Alice (78332) *(G-244)*
W M Greens Construction Svcs 713 692-2291
611 Cravens St Houston (77076) *(G-12585)*
W O I, Houston *Also called Welding Outlets Inc* *(G-12630)*
W O M, Houston *Also called Worldwide Oilfield Machine Inc* *(G-12694)*
W P C Services L L C 903 686-0597
5810 W Marshall Ave Longview (75604) *(G-14330)*
W P Murphy Inc 210 658-4947
11695 E Fm 1518 N Schertz (78108) *(G-18769)*
W P T, Mansfield *Also called Walton Process Tech Inc* *(G-14728)*

ALPHABETIC

W Promotions 254 753-3411
906 Austin Ave Waco (76701) **(G-20474)**

W R Grace & Co-Conn............................... 713 223-8353
4323 Crites St Houston (77003) **(G-12586)**

W R Grace & Co-Conn............................... 713 675-6445
4750 Blaffer St Houston (77026) **(G-12587)**

W R Grace Construction Pdts, Houston Also called W R Grace & Co-Conn **(G-12586)**

W R Grace Davison Chemical Div, Houston Also called W R Grace & Co-Conn **(G-12587)**

W R Meadows Inc...................................... 817 834-1969
2555 Ne 33rd St Fort Worth (76111) **(G-7113)**

W R Watson Corporation............................ 281 495-2800
12902 Mula Ln Stafford (77477) **(G-19397)**

W S I, Vinton Also called W Silver Inc **(G-20343)**

W Silver Inc... 915 886-3553
9059 Doniphan Dr Vinton (79821) **(G-20343)**

W Silver Recycling, El Paso Also called W Silver Recycling Inc **(G-6027)**

W Silver Recycling Inc (PA)....................... **915 532-5643**
1720 Magoffin Ave El Paso (79901) **(G-6027)**

W T Fiber Link Company, Seminole Also called WT Fiber Link LLC **(G-18888)**

W T Harris Company Inc............................. 325 646-7521
2908 Stephen F Austin Dr Brownwood (76801) **(G-2448)**

W T Porter Corp.. 713 946-4174
1211 Virginia St South Houston (77587) **(G-19056)**

W T Waggoner Estate................................. 940 552-2521
1700 Deaf Smith St Vernon (76384) **(G-20232)**

W V Grant Intl Ministries............................ 214 333-2176
5600 W Lovers Ln Ste 116 Dallas (75209) **(G-5171)**

W W Metal Products Inc............................. 903 838-4329
1226 N Fm 2148 Texarkana (75501) **(G-19783)**

W W Wood Inc... 830 569-2501
1799 Corgey Rd Pleasanton (78064) **(G-17076)**

W&S Finishing, Dallas Also called W & S Precision Finishing Co **(G-5170)**

W&T Offshore Inc (PA).............................. **713 626-8525**
5718 Westheimer Rd # 700 Houston (77057) **(G-12588)**

W&W, Pampa Also called W & W Fiberglass Tank Company **(G-16344)**

W&W-Afco Steel LLC.................................. 325 676-1422
771 Virgil St Abilene (79602) **(G-92)**

W&W-Afco Steel LLC.................................. 806 765-5781
2221 Erskine St Lubbock (79415) **(G-14508)**

W-Industries of Louisiana.......................... 281 921-3067
6602 Petropark Dr Houston (77041) **(G-12589)**

W-Industries of Louisiana (PA)................... **713 466-9463**
11500 Charles Rd Jersey Village (77041) **(G-13306)**

W-Tek, Irving Also called Netvia Group LLC **(G-13122)**

W. Pat Crow Forgings, Fort Worth Also called Crow Precision Components LLC **(G-6562)**

W.B. Osborn Oil Gas Operations, San Antonio Also called W B Osborn Oil Gas Oprtons L **(G-18607)**

W.T. Harris Company, Brownwood Also called W T Harris Company Inc **(G-2448)**

Wabash National Trlr Ctrs Inc.................... 972 923-2200
4675 N I 35 Waxahachie (75165) **(G-20567)**

Wabb Industries Inc.................................. 903 427-3980
525 Industrial Blvd Clarksville (75426) **(G-3078)**

Wabtec Corporation.................................. 713 222-0792
7402 Eastex Fwy Houston (77093) **(G-12590)**

Wabtec Global Services, Houston Also called Wabtec Corporation **(G-12590)**

Wabtec Mfg Solutions LLC......................... 814 449-9619
16201 Three Wide Dr Fort Worth (76177) **(G-7114)**

Wachs Subsea LLC.................................... 713 983-0784
15331 Vantage Pkwy E Houston (77032) **(G-12591)**

Waco Composites, Waco Also called Specialty Composites Group LLC **(G-20460)**

Waco Composites....................................... 866 688-3088
302 S 27th St Waco (76710) **(G-20475)**

Waco Publications Inc............................... 254 752-0334
3901 W Waco Dr Waco (76710) **(G-20476)**

Waco Tribune-Herald, Waco Also called Robinson Media Company LLC **(G-20455)**

Waddington N Amer - Houston.................... 713 686-6700
14345 Nw Fwy Houston (77040) **(G-12592)**

Wade Choate Office, Midland Also called Choate Co Inc **(G-15165)**

Wages White Lion Invstmnts LLC................ 214 880-6440
789 N Grove Rd Ste 111 Richardson (75081) **(G-17425)**

Waggoner Land Services........................... 817 763-8112
316 Bailey Ave Ste 100 Fort Worth (76107) **(G-7115)**

Waggoner Ranch, Vernon Also called W T Waggoner Estate **(G-20232)**

Wagner & Brown Ltd (PA).......................... **432 682-7936**
200 N Loraine St Ste 950 Midland (79701) **(G-15463)**

Wagner Materials & Cnstr, San Antonio Also called Imogene Wagner Company Inc **(G-18179)**

Wagner Oil Company (PA).......................... **817 335-2222**
500 Commerce St Ste 600 Fort Worth (76102) **(G-7116)**

Wagner Plate Works LLC (PA).................... **713 462-1946**
6250 N Rosslyn Rd Houston (77091) **(G-12593)**

Wahoo Inc.. 817 332-2310
149 Loy St Burleson (76028) **(G-2601)**

Walcott Drywall, Stamford Also called Walcott Enterprises Inc **(G-19402)**

Walcott Enterprises Inc............................. 325 773-5212
211 N Swenson St Stamford (79553) **(G-19402)**

Waldrop Company, Houston Also called M W Waldrop Co **(G-10720)**

Walker Creek-Ppdc, Pittsburg Also called Pilgrims Pride Corporation **(G-16749)**

Walker Industrial Machining....................... 713 434-5000
4949 W Orem Dr Ofc Houston (77045) **(G-12594)**

Walker Neer, Wichita Falls Also called Walker-Neer Manufacturing Co **(G-20826)**

Walker-Neer Manufacturing Co.................. 940 723-0711
1520 Old Iowa Park Rd Wichita Falls (76306) **(G-20826)**

Walkup Company.. 713 675-6383
5945 Armour Dr Houston (77020) **(G-12595)**

Wall-Tech, Austin Also called Sullys Lone Star Office Pdts **(G-1544)**

Wallace Foundation, The, Austin Also called Quality Foundation Repair Inc **(G-1443)**

Wallace Marine of Texas Inc...................... 940 458-7343
1399 Marina Cir Sanger (76266) **(G-18732)**

Wallace Monument Company (PA)............... **806 874-2442**
213 E 2nd St Clarendon (79226) **(G-3071)**

Wallace-Thompson Company...................... 903 683-2223
514 Henderson St Rusk (75785) **(G-17733)**

Wallis Concrete LLC.................................. 979 478-6734
646 Wallis Concrete Rd Wallis (77485) **(G-20510)**

Walls & Forms Inc..................................... 972 745-0800
15000 Grand River Rd Fort Worth (76155) **(G-7117)**

Walls Across Texas I Ltd............................ 210 826-4123
10203 Kotzebue St Ste 120 San Antonio (78217) **(G-18608)**

Walls Industries LLC (HQ).......................... **844 259-2557**
125 S Jennings Ave Fort Worth (76104) **(G-7118)**

Walls Industries LLC.................................. 817 357-8040
301 E Risinger Rd Fort Worth (76140) **(G-7119)**

Walls Printing Company, Dallas Also called Kpw Enterprises Inc **(G-4567)**

Walming Inc... 713 690-9000
9530 Baythorne Dr Houston (77041) **(G-12596)**

Walsh & Watts, Fort Worth Also called Walsh Oil Co **(G-7123)**

Walsh and Watts Inc (PA).......................... **817 335-5417**
500 W 7th St Ste 1007 Fort Worth (76102) **(G-7120)**

Walsh Company... 817 335-3741
500 W 7th St Unit 27 Fort Worth (76102) **(G-7121)**

Walsh F Howard Jr Oper Co Inc.................. 817 336-2062
500 W 7th St Ste 1007 Fort Worth (76102) **(G-7122)**

Walsh Oil Co.. 817 336-2062
500 W 7th St Ste 1007 Fort Worth (76102) **(G-7123)**

Walsh Petroleum Inc.................................. 432 684-5937
301 N Colorado St Ste 359 Midland (79701) **(G-15464)**

Walsh Welding Inc (PA).............................. **325 387-2357**
1603 S Crockett Ave Sonora (76950) **(G-19032)**

Walston Ventures LLC................................ 409 796-1883
8505 Fm 365 Rd Beaumont (77705) **(G-1968)**

Walter Oil & Gas Corporation..................... 713 659-1221
1100 Louisiana St Ste 200 Houston (77002) **(G-12597)**

Walter Oil & Gas Weather Data, Houston Also called Walter Oil & Gas Corporation **(G-12597)**

Walter Solomon... 903 938-2096
505 Price St Marshall (75670) **(G-14806)**

Walton Process Tech Inc........................... 682 518-9002
300 S Wisteria St Mansfield (76063) **(G-14728)**

Walton Signage Ltd................................... 210 886-0644
10101 Reunion Pl Ste 200 San Antonio (78216) **(G-18609)**

Want ADS of Colorado Springs.................. 361 575-6400
2708 N Ben Wilson St Victoria (77901) **(G-20318)**

Want ADS of Fort Worth Inc (PA)............... **817 870-0055**
2800 W Lancaster Ave Fort Worth (76107) **(G-7124)**

Want ADS of San Angelo Inc...................... 325 944-7653
15 N Tyler St San Angelo (76901) **(G-17837)**

Wapco Inc (PA).. **936 539-6272**
201 S Frazier St Conroe (77301) **(G-3384)**

Wapiti Energy, Houston Also called Wapiti Operating LLC **(G-12598)**

Wapiti Operating LLC (PA).......................... **713 365-8500**
800 Gessner Rd Ste 700 Houston (77024) **(G-12598)**

Waples Holdings Inc.................................. 817 568-1600
8900 Forum Way Fort Worth (76140) **(G-7125)**

Waples Manufacturing, Fort Worth Also called Waples Holdings Inc **(G-7125)**

Warabeya Texas Inc.................................. 972 219-7110
1301a Ridgeview Ste 200 Lewisville (75057) **(G-14110)**

Ward Leonard, Houston Also called Houma Armture Wrks Houston LLC **(G-8384)**

Ward Mc Carty Inc..................................... 936 336-3132
4408 N Main St Liberty (77575) **(G-14127)**

Ward Packaging of Fort Worth.................... 817 334-0484
2848 Cullen St Fort Worth (76107) **(G-7126)**

Ward Vessel and Exchanger Corp............... 713 413-8416
6900 Mchard Rd Houston (77053) **(G-8394)**

Warehouse, Mansfield Also called Texas Refinery Corp **(G-14722)**

Wareing Athon & Co................................... 713 222-8804
2229 San Felipe St Houston (77019) **(G-12599)**

Warfab Oilfield Services Inc....................... 903 295-1011
607 Fisher Rd Longview (75604) **(G-14331)**

Warfield Electric Texas Inc........................ 214 637-1200
1221 Champion Cir Ste 105 Carrollton (75006) **(G-2845)**

Wargaming America (HQ)........................... **510 962-6747**
10415 Morado Cir 3-110 Austin (78759) **(G-1646)**

Warminster Fiberglass, Jacksonville Also called WFC Company Inc **(G-13267)**

Warner Bailey Inc...................................... 936 867-4801
4736 Us Highway 69 S Alto (75925) **(G-318)**

Warner Electric LLC 940 767-2000
2800 Fisher Rd Wichita Falls (76302) *(G-20827)*

Warner Electric LLC 940 723-3400
2800 Fisher Rd Wichita Falls (76302) *(G-20828)*

Warner Group, Dallas *Also called Republic Energy Inc (G-4889)*

Warren Laboraties LLC 254 580-9990
1656 Ih 35 S Abbott (76621) *(G-1)*

Warren Resources Inc (PA) **214 393-9688**
5420 Lbj Fwy Ste 600 Dallas (75240) *(G-5172)*

Warren Watts Technology LLC 817 924-1370
1911 Windsor Pl Fort Worth (76110) *(G-7127)*

Warren's Southern Gardens, Crosby *Also called JMJ Organics Ltd (G-3735)*

Warrior Energy Services Corp 903 984-9093
3306 Goforth Rd Kilgore (75662) *(G-13601)*

Warrior Energy Services Corp 972 687-9057
5050 Quorum Dr Ste 700 Dallas (75254) *(G-5173)*

Warrior Energy Services Corp 830 569-2096
4541 County Road 430 Pleasanton (78064) *(G-17077)*

Warrior Energy Services Corp 504 220-8080
4242 N Capistrano Dr # 17 Dallas (75287) *(G-3859)*

Warrior Energy Services Corp 817 237-9223
908 Cecilia St Alice (78332) *(G-245)*

Warrior G Industries 409 594-5258
1008 N Nellius St Woodville (75979) *(G-20919)*

Warrior Systems Division, Dallas *Also called L3 Technologies Inc (G-4574)*

Warrior Technologies LLC 432 818-0498
400 W Illinois Ave # 1120 Midland (79701) *(G-15465)*

Wartsila North America Inc (HQ) **281 233-6200**
11710 N Gessner Rd Ste A Houston (77064) *(G-12600)*

Washington Alloy, Stafford *Also called U S Alloy Co (G-19391)*

Washita Valley Enterprises Inc 817 220-0450
3064 W Highway 199 Springtown (76082) *(G-19277)*

Waskom Gas Processing Company 903 687-2513
155 Private Road 1133 Waskom (75692) *(G-20525)*

Waste Repurposing Intl Inc 760 525-7180
4901 E Cesar Chavez St Austin (78702) *(G-1647)*

Waste Water Treatment Plant, Jefferson *Also called City of Jefferson (G-13283)*

Wastequip Manufacturing Co LLC 214 905-9101
3920 Singleton Blvd Dallas (75212) *(G-5174)*

Watchguard Inc 972 423-9777
415 E Exchange Pkwy Allen (75002) *(G-306)*

Watchguard Video, Allen *Also called Watchguard Inc (G-306)*

Watco Tanks Inc 830 947-0101
5877 Fm 539 Floresville (78114) *(G-6257)*

Water 2 Wine, San Antonio *Also called Burke Texgals LLC (G-17973)*

Water Cleaning Service, Midland *Also called M3p Water Services LLC (G-15290)*

Water Energy Technologies 713 464-7117
9741 Tappenbeck Dr Houston (77055) *(G-12601)*

Water Event Gulf Coast LLC 713 937-8630
2109 Luna Rd Ste 100 Carrollton (75006) *(G-2846)*

Water Source One, Lakeway *Also called One Water Source LLC (G-13818)*

Water Standard MGT US Inc (HQ) **713 400-4777**
4265 San Felipe St # 620 Houston (77027) *(G-12602)*

Water Std Spration Systems LLC 713 433-7441
5410 Trafalgar Dr Houston (77045) *(G-12603)*

Water Street Millworks Inc 512 321-5741
910 Water St B Bastrop (78602) *(G-1765)*

Waterfall International Inc 844 627-2438
401 Congress Avo Sto 1860 Austin (78701) *(G 1648)*

Waterfleet LLC 855 744-5222
5110 Se Loop 410 San Antonio (78222) *(G-18610)*

Waterford Operating LLC 713 255-6200
3555 Timmons Ln Ste 1115 Houston (77027) *(G-12604)*

Waterfront Publishing Inc (PA) **281 334-2202**
228 Marina Bay Dr Ste B Kemah (77565) *(G-13482)*

Waterloo Sparkling Water Corp 512 910-8990
2612 E Cesar Chavez St # 200 Austin (78702) *(G-1649)*

Watermark Graphics Inc (PA) **361 576-6874**
9201 Us Highway 59 N Victoria (77905) *(G-20319)*

Watermark Group Inc 210 599-0400
4271 Gatecrest San Antonio (78217) *(G-18611)*

Waters & Waters Services Inc (PA) **432 827-3354**
616 N Odessa St Goldsmith (79741) *(G-7743)*

Watkins Metal Fabrication Inc 940 325-6008
544 Grant Rd Mineral Wells (76067) *(G-15546)*

Watkins Ornamental Iron Inc 972 931-5350
3219 Commander Dr Ste 120 Carrollton (75006) *(G-2847)*

Watson & Chalin Holding Corp (PA) **972 547-6020**
725 E University Dr McKinney (75069) *(G-14988)*

Watson & Chalin Mfg Inc (HQ) **972 547-6020**
725 E University Dr McKinney (75069) *(G-14989)*

Watson Grinding and Mfg Co 713 466-3053
4525 Gessner Rd Houston (77041) *(G-12605)*

Watts Industries Houston, Houston *Also called Watts Water Technologies Inc (G-12606)*

Watts Water Qulty & Cond Pdts, San Antonio *Also called Watts Wtr Qulty Cond Pdts Inc (G-18612)*

Watts Water Technologies Inc 713 943-0688
8550 Hansen Rd Houston (77075) *(G-12606)*

Watts Wtr Qulty Cond Pdts Inc 210 677-0618
13700 W Us Highway 90 San Antonio (78245) *(G-18612)*

Wattstock LLC 713 248-4148
4925 Grnvlle Ave Ste 1020 Dallas (75206) *(G-5175)*

Waukesha-Pearce Industries Inc, Houston *Also called Waukesha-Pearce Industries LLC (G-12607)*

Waukesha-Pearce Industries Inc 512 989-4900
16029 Ih 35 Pflugerville (78660) *(G-16692)*

Waukesha-Pearce Industries LLC (HQ) **713 723-1050**
12320 Main St Houston (77035) *(G-12607)*

Wave Quantum Def & Tech LLC 512 505-2339
11701 Fm 2244 Ste 124 Austin (78738) *(G-1650)*

Waveware Technologies Inc 972 479-1702
2630 National Dr Garland (75041) *(G-7609)*

Wayne - Dalton of El Paso, El Paso *Also called Hrh Door Corp (G-5805)*

Wayne - Dalton of Houston, Houston *Also called Hrh Door Corp (G-10273)*

Wayne Fueling Systems LLC 512 388-8446
401 Parker Dr Ste A Austin (78728) *(G-1651)*

Wayne Fueling Systems LLC (HQ) **512 388-8311**
3814 Jarrett Way Austin (78728) *(G-1652)*

Wayne Services Group, Austin *Also called Wayne Fueling Systems LLC (G-1651)*

Wayne Services Group, Austin *Also called Wayne Fueling Systems LLC (G-1652)*

Wayne Wilk 570 326-1164
8807 W Sam Houston Pkwy N S Houston (77040) *(G-12608)*

Wbc Media LP 214 764-2000
8350 N Central Expy Dallas (75206) *(G-5176)*

Wcc Energy LLC (PA) **432 208-2839**
11848 County Road 372 Anson (79501) *(G-587)*

Wccog Corp 903 667-0264
75 County Road 3303 De Kalb (75559) *(G-5237)*

Wce Wholesale Caps, Etc, Houston *Also called Kelly B Pitts Jr (G-10513)*

WCI Construction Inc 432 530-4009
3408 S County Rd W Odessa (79766) *(G-16204)*

Wcn Inc 830 216-4519
1012 C St Floresville (78114) *(G-6258)*

Wcs Oil & Gas Corporation 979 542-0021
451 Cactus St Giddings (78942) *(G-7704)*

Wcsa Inc 806 383-1060
2349 E Loop 335 N Amarillo (79108) *(G-473)*

Wcsc LLC 915 774-0348
150 E Sunset Rd El Paso (79922) *(G-6028)*

WD Norton Inc 903 758-0301
1000 W Cotton St Longview (75604) *(G-14332)*

We Hereford LLC 806 360-7400
3748 S Progressive Rd Hereford (79045) *(G-8297)*

Wearable Etc, Houston *Also called Wearables Etc Inc (G-12609)*

Wearables Etc Inc 713 339-1373
8130 Westglen Dr Ste 100 Houston (77063) *(G-12609)*

Wearalloy Inc 979 543-1133
1313 Lombardy St Houston (77023) *(G-12610)*

Wearform, Houston *Also called Ghashim Capital Ventures Corp (G-9949)*

Weather-Matic, Garland *Also called Telsco Industries Inc (G-7597)*

Weatherford, Houston *Also called Houston Well Screen Company (G-10263)*

Weatherford Advertising Inc 817 594-7440
512 Palo Pinto St Weatherford (76086) *(G-20629)*

Weatherford Aerospace Inc 817 598-0044
610 W 3rd St Weatherford (76086) *(G-20630)*

Weatherford Aerospace Inc (HQ) **817 594-5464**
1020 E Columbia St Weatherford (76086) *(G-20631)*

Weatherford Artificia 432 561-5505
10000 Pilot Ave Midland (79706) *(G-15466)*

Weatherford Artificia 817 624-7810
800 Railhead Rd Ste 328 Fort Worth (76106) *(G-7128)*

Weatherford Artificia (HQ) **713 836-4000**
2000 Saint James Pl Houston (77056) *(G-12611)*

Weatherford Artificia 817 882-9955
300 Burnett St Ste 350 Fort Worth (76102) *(G-7129)*

Weatherford Artificia 918 224-7428
22001 Northpark Dr Kingwood (77339) *(G-13660)*

Weatherford Artificia 432 550-6118
2818 W 42nd St Odessa (79764) *(G-16205)*

Weatherford Artificia 432 368-3865
8866 Nw Loop 338 Odessa (79764) *(G-16206)*

Weatherford Artificia 903 935-2416
5605 Medco Dr Marshall (75672) *(G-14807)*

Weatherford Artificial Lift, Kingwood *Also called Eproduction Solutions LLC (G-13641)*

WEATHERFORD ARTIFICIAL LIFT SY, Houston *Also called Weatherford International Ltd (G-12621)*

Weatherford Completion, Huntsville *Also called Weatherford International LLC (G-12830)*

Weatherford Completion, Houston *Also called Weatherford International LLC (G-12616)*

Weatherford Concrete, Willow Park *Also called Childs Ready-Mix Concrete Co (G-20872)*

Weatherford CPS, Huntsville *Also called U S Weatherford L P (G-12827)*

Weatherford CPS, Elmendorf *Also called U S Weatherford L P (G-6073)*

Weatherford Democrat, Weatherford *Also called Newspaper Holding Inc (G-20607)*

Weatherford Enterra, Corpus Christi *Also called U S Weatherford L P (G-3645)*

Weatherford Enterra, Denver City *Also called U S Weatherford L P (G-5425)*

A
L
P
H
A
B
E
T
I
C

Weatherford Enterra, Odessa *Also called U S Weatherford L P (G-16185)*

Weatherford Fracturing Tech.................................817 882-9955
300 Burnett St Ste 350 Fort Worth (76102) *(G-7130)*

Weatherford International, Fort Worth *Also called U S Weatherford L P (G-7090)*

Weatherford International LLC...............................903 353-9700
219 Industrial Dr Longview (75602) *(G-14333)*

Weatherford International LLC...............................281 652-1300
12227 Fm 529 Rd Ste A Houston (77041) *(G-12612)*

Weatherford International LLC...............................985 493-6100
7587 State Highway 75 S Huntsville (77340) *(G-12829)*

Weatherford International LLC...............................713 693-4000
7587 Hwy 785 S Huntsville (77340) *(G-12830)*

Weatherford International LLC...............................281 485-1899
3632 S Main St Bldg 1 Pearland (77581) *(G-16610)*

Weatherford International LLC...............................817 568-0282
3044 Wichita Ct Fort Worth (76140) *(G-7131)*

Weatherford International LLC...............................210 306-3431
19685 Interstate 37 S Elmendorf (78112) *(G-6074)*

Weatherford International LLC...............................432 332-1318
2263 W Bell St Odessa (79766) *(G-16207)*

Weatherford International LLC (HQ).......................**713 693-4000**
2000 Saint James Pl Houston (77056) *(G-12613)*

Weatherford International LLC...............................361 576-5641
435 Leeper Ln Victoria (77904) *(G-20320)*

Weatherford International LLC...............................281 759-5100
738 Highway 6 S Houston (77079) *(G-12614)*

Weatherford International LLC...............................806 435-6801
14425 E Loop 143 Perryton (79070) *(G-16651)*

Weatherford International LLC...............................817 443-3000
7500 Benbrook Pkwy Benbrook (76126) *(G-2048)*

Weatherford International LLC...............................832 955-0000
12227 Spencer Rd Houston (77041) *(G-12615)*

Weatherford International LLC...............................661 589-2146
6325 Highway 380 W Greenville (75401) *(G-8095)*

Weatherford International LLC...............................361 815-2104
2650 Old Airport Rd Alice (78332) *(G-246)*

Weatherford International LLC...............................210 621-2156
4420 S Flores Rd Elmendorf (78112) *(G-6075)*

Weatherford International LLC...............................832 590-4000
9600 W Gulf Bank Rd Houston (77040) *(G-12616)*

Weatherford International LLC...............................281 260-5700
16134 W Hardy Rd Houston (77060) *(G-12617)*

Weatherford International LLC...............................281 460-7863
2442 Greens Rd Houston (77032) *(G-12618)*

Weatherford International LLC...............................281 260-2707
16210 W Hardy Rd Houston (77060) *(G-12619)*

Weatherford International LLC...............................432 563-0598
8860 Nw Loop 338 Odessa (79764) *(G-16208)*

Weatherford International Inc................................361 693-6800
210 S Carancahua St Corpus Christi (78401) *(G-3653)*

Weatherford International Inc (PA).........................**713 836-4000**
2000 Saint James Pl Houston (77056) *(G-12620)*

Weatherford International Ltd................................713 836-4000
2000 Saint James Pl Houston (77056) *(G-12621)*

Weatherford International Ltd................................210 626-0831
4426 S Flores Rd Elmendorf (78112) *(G-6076)*

Weatherford US LP...210 306-3400
19685 Ih 37 S Elmendorf (78112) *(G-6077)*

Weatherford Well Screen Techno..........................281 670-0005
11939 Aldine Westfield Rd Houston (77093) *(G-12622)*

Weathrford Artfl Lift Systems..............................432 334-4500
905 S Grandview Ave Odessa (79761) *(G-16209)*

Weathrford Artfl Lift Systems..............................903 663-1966
Fm 2751 Longview (75601) *(G-14334)*

Weathrford Artfl Lift Systems..............................432 586-3883
159 W Hwy 302 Kermit (79745) *(G-13515)*

Weathrford Artfl Lift Systems..............................281 630-5919
5611 Baird Ct Houston (77041) *(G-12623)*

Weathrford Engneered Chemistry, Elmendorf *Also called Weatherford International LLC (G-6075)*

Web Devices, Houston *Also called Willingham Systems LLC (G-12671)*

Web Technology Inc...214 343-9238
11464 Pagemill Rd Dallas (75243) *(G-5177)*

Webb Automation, Dallas *Also called Webb Technology Inc (G-5178)*

Webb Technology Inc...214 348-8678
11411 Plano Rd Dallas (75243) *(G-5178)*

Webb, Shannon & Haas Assoc, Houston *Also called Wsh Land Inc (G-12700)*

Webb-Mason Inc..214 205-1123
4131 N Central Expy # 600 Dallas (75204) *(G-5179)*

Webb-Mason Inc..800 992-2665
3125 W Bolt St Fort Worth (76110) *(G-7132)*

Webbmason...682 432-0548
3125 W Bolt St Fort Worth (76110) *(G-7133)*

Websense LLC (HQ)..**858 320-8000**
10900 Stonelake Blvd Austin (78759) *(G-1653)*

Websiteradiotraffic.com, Waxahachie *Also called Scott Traffic LLC (G-20557)*

Webvent Inc..617 418-4126
2540 King Arthur Blvd 209h Lewisville (75056) *(G-14111)*

Wedding Oak Winery LLC.....................................325 372-4050
301 E Wallace St Ste 205 San Saba (76877) *(G-18721)*

Wedge M & C Services, Houston *Also called Wedge Measurement Systems LLC (G-12625)*

Wedge Measurement & Control LP.........................713 490-9555
1415 La St Ste 1500 Houston (77002) *(G-12624)*

Wedge Measurement Systems LLC (HQ)................**713 490-9444**
1415 La St Ste 1500 Houston (77002) *(G-12625)*

WEI-Chuan USA Inc...713 690-3677
7439 Langtry St Houston (77040) *(G-12626)*

Weimar Industries Inc...979 725-8503
505 S Eagle St Weimar (78962) *(G-20652)*

Weimar Manufacturing, Weimar *Also called Weimar Industries Inc (G-20652)*

Weir Bros Pit, Aubrey *Also called Weir Brothers Contracting LLC (G-852)*

Weir Brothers Contracting LLC.............................940 440-2931
4523 Fm 2931 Aubrey (76227) *(G-852)*

Weir Oil & Gas, Fort Worth *Also called SPM Flow Control Inc (G-7013)*

Weir Seaboard, Houston *Also called Seaboard Holdings Inc (G-11797)*

Weir Seaboard International, Houston *Also called Seaboard International Inc (G-11798)*

Weissker Mfg Ltd Lblty Co..................................903 538-2271
10658 W State Highway 294 Palestine (75801) *(G-16309)*

Welasco Inc...903 784-5562
1950 19th St Sw Paris (75460) *(G-16374)*

Welbilt Walk-Ins LP (HQ)....................................**817 281-5121**
4201 N Beach St Fort Worth (76137) *(G-7134)*

Welbor Technology Inc.......................................713 980-2345
15045 Woodham Dr Houston (77073) *(G-12627)*

Welch Hvac Incorporated...................................214 222-8600
118 Lynn Ave Ste 602 Lewisville (75057) *(G-14112)*

Weld Revolution LLC..832 585-1244
19511 Wied Rd Spring (77388) *(G-19187)*

Weld-Tech Engineering, Spring *Also called Rti Energy Systems Inc (G-19163)*

Welder Exploration & Prod Inc (PA).....................**210 354-1515**
100 W Olmos Dr San Antonio (78212) *(G-18613)*

Welder Rob & Bessie Wildlife............................361 364-2643
10429 Welder Wildlife Sinton (78387) *(G-18967)*

Weldfit Corporation...713 460-3700
4133 Southerland Rd Houston (77092) *(G-12628)*

Weldforce Fabricators LLC.................................713 270-7733
14875 Waterloo Dr Houston (77053) *(G-8395)*

Welding Material Sales Inc.................................713 672-4166
8811 Wallisville Rd Ste C Houston (77029) *(G-12629)*

Welding Outlets Inc...281 590-0190
1341 Hill Rd Houston (77039) *(G-12630)*

Welding Works Intl Inc.......................................956 838-5636
7620 Victoria Ct Ste 4 Brownsville (78521) *(G-2421)*

Weldon Manufacturing Inc..................................817 834-2229
3488 Bethlehem St Fort Worth (76111) *(G-7135)*

Weldon Quality Truck Sleepers, Fort Worth *Also called Weldon Manufacturing Inc (G-7135)*

Welfab Inc...361 552-4033
3839 Fm 2541 Port Lavaca (77979) *(G-17156)*

Welker Inc...281 491-2331
13839 W Bellfort St Sugar Land (77498) *(G-19571)*

Well Body Purify LLC...443 847-6501
3663 Nasa Pkwy Apt 706 Seabrook (77586) *(G-18794)*

Well Completion Technologies, Houston *Also called U S Weatherford L P (G-12425)*

Well-Foam Inc...432 276-3290
4215 N Sierra Ave Odessa (79764) *(G-16210)*

Well-Pro Services LP...903 759-6071
1907 E Us Highway 80 White Oak (75693) *(G-20721)*

Wella Organics, Lockhart *Also called Garnea Llc (G-14168)*

Wellbore Fishing Rentl Tls LLC...........................432 563-1478
12100 Jordy Rd Midland (79707) *(G-15467)*

Wellborn Sign Inc (PA)......................................**806 331-3563**
700 Se 10th Ave Amarillo (79101) *(G-474)*

Wellco Holdings Inc...254 772-1740
600 Texas Central Pkwy Waco (76712) *(G-20477)*

Welldog, Houston *Also called Gas Sensing Technology Corp (G-9902)*

Welldynamics Inc (HQ)......................................**281 297-1211**
3000 N Sam Houston Pkwy E Houston (77032) *(G-12631)*

Wellflex Energy Solutions, Rhome *Also called Wellflex Enrgy Prtners Fort Wr (G-17264)*

Wellflex Enrgy Prtners Fort Wr...........................817 730-5111
500 Randall St Rhome (76078) *(G-17264)*

Wellhead Control Products Inc............................713 475-2283
501 N Richey St Pasadena (77506) *(G-16525)*

Wellhead Distributors Intl, Tomball *Also called Petroleum Products & Svcs Inc (G-19997)*

Wellpath Solutions, Carthage *Also called Fieldco Energy Services Inc (G-2907)*

Wells Cargo Texas Div, Waco *Also called Wellco Holdings Inc (G-20477)*

Wells Family Holding Co LLC..............................903 756-5656
3551 Texas Highway 11 Linden (75563) *(G-14137)*

Wells Manufacturing, McAllen *Also called Wells Vehicle Electronics LP (G-14918)*

Wells Manufacturing LLC....................................713 690-4204
14425 Wagg Way Houston Houston (77041) *(G-12632)*

Wells Mfg, Houston *Also called Wells Manufacturing LLC (G-12632)*

Wells Vehicle Electronics LP..............................956 630-4310
4312 W Military Hwy McAllen (78503) *(G-14918)*

Wells/Mccoy Steel Services Inc..........................469 742-0888
423 Metro Park Dr McKinney (75071) *(G-14990)*

Wellsite Automation 432 218-9361
1513 W Montgomery Ave Midland (79701) *(G-15468)*

Wellsmith Inc 866 266-7793
2901 Via Fortuna Ste 600 Austin (78746) *(G-1654)*

Wellstream Inc (PA) **281 249-0900**
11202 Equity Dr Ste 350 Houston (77041) *(G-12633)*

Welltec Inc (HQ) **281 371-1200**
22440 Merchants Way Katy (77449) *(G-13455)*

Wendland's Farm Products, Temple *Also called Jupe Feeds Inc (G-19683)*

Wenglar Services Inc 979 648-2225
700 North St Louise (77455) *(G-14354)*

Weno Healthcare Inc 210 912-8143
9403 Longvale Dr Austin (78729) *(G-1716)*

Wenzel Associates Inc (HQ) **512 835-2038**
2215 Kramer Ln Austin (78758) *(G-1655)*

Wenzel Spine Inc 512 469-0600
1130 Rutherford Ln # 200 Austin (78753) *(G-1656)*

Weq Britco LP 254 741-6701
1101 Foundation Dr Waco (76712) *(G-20478)*

Werner & Pfleiderer, Houston *Also called Coperion Corporation (G-9309)*

Werner - North Coast Logistics, Socorro *Also called Werner Co (G-19020)*

Werner Co 915 851-4933
11751 Alameda Ave Ste C Socorro (79927) *(G-19020)*

Werther International Inc 800 655-4781
8614 Veterans Memorial Dr Houston (77088) *(G-12634)*

Wes Tex Drilling Company LLC 325 677-9121
400 Pine St Ste 700 Abilene (79601) *(G-93)*

Wes-Tex Manufacturing Inc 806 749-3795
6201 Martin L King Blvd Lubbock (79404) *(G-14509)*

Wes-Tex Pure Minerals Inc 432 250-7010
4900 W Expy 83 Ste 231 McAllen (78501) *(G-14919)*

Wesco, Dallas *Also called Dalla Compress Ener Solutio LL (G-4209)*

Wesco Acquisition Partners Inc 713 688-5551
2333 Clinton Dr Galena Park (77547) *(G-7386)*

Wesco Aircraft Hardware Corp (HQ) **661 775-7200**
2601 Meacham Blvd Ste 400 Fort Worth (76137) *(G-7136)*

Wesco Chemicals Inc 972 938-0913
103 Industrial Dr Waxahachie (75165) *(G-20568)*

Wesco Equipment, Galena Park *Also called Wesco Acquisition Partners Inc (G-7386)*

Wesco Industries Inc 817 551-7063
8717 Forum Way Ste 101 Fort Worth (76140) *(G-7137)*

Wesco International Inc 432 699-2680
3303 W Illinois Ave Midland (79703) *(G-15469)*

Wesco Refractories Inc 682 518-5035
301 S 6th Ave Mansfield (76063) *(G-14729)*

Wesco Valve & Manufacturing Co (HQ) **903 938-9241**
4000 S Airport Rd Marshall (75672) *(G-14808)*

Wesmar Corporation 915 599-1572
4720 Osborne Dr Ste 300 El Paso (79922) *(G-6029)*

Wessely-Thompson Hardware Inc 210 344-3081
102 Interloop Rd San Antonio (78216) *(G-18614)*

Wesso Metals, Conroe *Also called Planeview-Wmi LLC (G-3350)*

West Ltd 409 794-9090
11025 Highway 124 Beaumont (77705) *(G-1969)*

West Coast Group Inc 281 447-2020
9134 North Fwy Houston (77037) *(G-12635)*

West Craft Manufacturing Inc 936 858-4426
506 Palestine Rd Alto (75925) *(G-319)*

West Fraser Inc 903 657-4575
609 Industrial Dr Henderson (75652) *(G-8277)*

West Fraser Inc 903 628-2506
Hwy 82 E New Boston (75570) *(G-15770)*

West Gulf Marine Ltd 409 744-0492
6000 Harborside Dr Galveston (77554) *(G-7413)*

West Machine & Tool Inc 903 758-5401
211 Industrial Dr Longview (75602) *(G-14335)*

West Phalia Market Inc 512 846-1155
409 W Front St Hutto (78634) *(G-12888)*

West Texas Anchor Inc 325 884-3402
103 S Utah Ave Big Lake (76932) *(G-2063)*

West Texas Boring, Odessa *Also called Wtb LLC (G-16214)*

West Texas Chaptr of Archtctrl 915 833-9922
275 Rio West Dr El Paso (79932) *(G-6030)*

West Texas Container Corp 915 859-6712
12345 Rojas Dr El Paso (79928) *(G-6031)*

West Texas Drum Company Ltd II 281 383-1901
8950 Fm 1405 Rd Baytown (77523) *(G-1805)*

West Texas Energy Sevices LLC 432 267-3126
3215 S Us Highway 87 Big Spring (79720) *(G-2102)*

West Texas Lee Co Inc 800 825-3346
117 E 70th St Lubbock (79404) *(G-14510)*

West Texas Printing Company 325 646-3598
2909 Stephen F Austin Dr Brownwood (76801) *(G-2449)*

West Texas Steel and Sup Inc 325 651-7322
6617 S Us Highway 277 San Angelo (76904) *(G-17838)*

West Texas Want Ads Inc (PA) **325 673-4521**
1634 N 1st St Abilene (79601) *(G-94)*

West Txas Lighthouse For Blind 325 653-4231
2001 Austin St San Angelo (76903) *(G-17839)*

West U Marble Company, Houston *Also called West University Marble Co (G-8396)*

West U Marble LLC 713 433-4424
14715 Park Almeda Dr Houston (77047) *(G-12636)*

West University Marble Co 713 433-2240
14715 Almeda Rd Houston (77053) *(G-8396)*

West-Com Nrse Call Systems Inc 713 731-2500
6060 South Loop E Ste 216 Houston (77033) *(G-12637)*

West-Reeves, Ltd. 972 938-9623
1616 E Main St Waxahachie (75165) *(G-20569)*

West-Ward Pharmaceutical Corp 800 631-2174
3030 Lyndon B Johnson Fwy Dallas (75234) *(G-5180)*

WESTA, Austin *Also called Westlake Enes Scence Tech Assn (G-1659)*

Westar Graphics Inc 713 957-4575
2500 Central Pkwy Ste D Houston (77092) *(G-12638)*

Westbrook & Associates Inc 972 840-0858
3309 Essex Dr Ste 100 Richardson (75082) *(G-17426)*

Westbrook Hot Shot Service Inc 903 987-1400
579 Cargill Rd Kilgore (75662) *(G-13602)*

Westbrook Sales & Distrg Corp 713 675-6438
11 Lockwood Ave Houston (77020) *(G-12639)*

Westcave Printing Corporation 512 989-0006
2111 Grand Avenue Pkwy Austin (78728) *(G-1657)*

Westec Sterling Co, Abilene *Also called Wes Tex Drilling Company LLC (G-93)*

Westech Bearing, Odessa *Also called Westech Seal Inc (G-16211)*

Westech Heavy Machinery Div, Houston *Also called Control Flow Inc (G-9295)*

Westech Seal Inc 432 367-1188
7200 Sprague Rd Odessa (79764) *(G-16211)*

Westerly Exploration Inc 817 738-1917
6640 Camp Bowie Blvd Fort Worth (76116) *(G-7138)*

Westerly Exploration Inc (PA) **713 524-7755**
3701 Kirby Dr Ste 514 Houston (77098) *(G-12640)*

Western AG Sales Co Inc 806 293-2517
327 W 24th St Plainview (79072) *(G-16767)*

Western Atlas Intl Inc (PA) **713 972-4000**
3900 Essex Ln Houston (77027) *(G-12641)*

Western Bowl 806 359-5211
5120 Canyon Dr Amarillo (79109) *(G-521)*

Western Cabinets Inc (PA) **469 916-5350**
3444 Morse Dr Dallas (75236) *(G-5181)*

Western Cabinets Inc 972 293-2450
1001 Cedarview Dr Cedar Hill (75104) *(G-2955)*

Western Chemical Trading LLC 405 923-4211
14493 S Padre Island Dr A Corpus Christi (78418) *(G-3654)*

Western Container Corporation (HQ) **346 309-3238**
2277 Plaza Dr Ste 270 Sugar Land (77479) *(G-19572)*

Western Container Corporation 432 263-8361
1600 W 1st St Big Spring (79720) *(G-2103)*

Western Container Corporation 713 691-0730
3801 Distribution Blvd Houston (77018) *(G-12642)*

Western Falcon LLC (PA) **832 391-9461**
1304 Langham Creek Dr # 122 Houston (77084) *(G-12643)*

Western Forge & Flange Co Inc (HQ) **800 352-6433**
687 County Road 2201 Cleveland (77327) *(G-3141)*

Western Gas Resources Inc 432 395-2448
S On Fm 2023 Fort Stockton (79735) *(G-6331)*

Western Gas Resources Inc 432 693-2302
Hc 34 Box 20 Midkiff (79755) *(G-15098)*

Western Gas Resources Inc 432 395-2973
3368310 Gomez Rd Fort Stockton (79735) *(G-6332)*

Western Geophysical, Houston *Also called Western Atlas Intl Inc (G-12641)*

Western Glass LLC 512 820-2475
3871 E University Ave # 185 Georgetown (78626) *(G-7688)*

Western Grinding Co Inc 214 631-3090
9000 S Hampton Rd Dallas (75232) *(G-5182)*

Western Group, The, Fort Worth *Also called Western Wire Works Inc (G-7141)*

Western Hauler Enterprises 817 332-1121
2420 White Settlement Rd Fort Worth (76107) *(G-7139)*

Western Horseman Magazine 817 737-6397
2112 Montgomery St Fort Worth (76107) *(G-7140)*

Western Industries Corporation 512 837-0240
4616 W Howard Ln 7-750 Austin (78728) *(G-1658)*

Western Industries Corporation 214 503-8322
2161 Hutton Dr Ste 116 Carrollton (75006) *(G-2848)*

Western Intl Gas Cylinders Inc (HQ) **979 865-5991**
7173 Highway 159 E Bellville (77418) *(G-2015)*

Western Leather Goods Inc (PA) **800 717-1853**
1740 E Expressway 83 Mercedes (78570) *(G-15011)*

Western Leather Goods Inc 956 565-2618
1750 E Expy 83 Mercedes (78570) *(G-15012)*

Western Marketing Inc 817 232-8626
816 S Blue Mound Rd Saginaw (76131) *(G-17759)*

Western Midstream Partners LP (PA) **832 636-6000**
9950 Woodloch Forest Dr The Woodlands (77380) *(G-19940)*

Western Precast Concrete Inc 915 859-9362
9101 Roseway Dr El Paso (79907) *(G-6032)*

Western Pulp Products Co 903 586-3608
1577 N Bolton St Jacksonville (75766) *(G-13266)*

Western Ready Mix LLC 830 433-1963
6411 Ih 10 W Seguin (78155) *(G-18873)*

Western Ref Cnan Gathering LLC..........210 626-6000
19100 Ridgewood Pkwy San Antonio (78259) *(G-18615)*

Western Refining Inc (HQ)..........**915 775-3300**
212 N Clark Dr El Paso (79905) *(G-6033)*

Western Refining Company LP..........915 775-3246
6550 Gateway Blvd E El Paso (79905) *(G-6034)*

Western Refining Company LP (HQ)..........**915 534-1400**
212 N Clark Dr El Paso (79905) *(G-6035)*

Western Rental and Fishing Tls, Wichita Falls *Also called Western Well Service Inc (G-20830)*

Western Repair Service, Odessa *Also called Empire Tubing Tongs Inc (G-15988)*

Western Rubber and Mfg Co..........936 588-3033
7015 Old Highway 105 W Conroe (77304) *(G-3385)*

Western Sheet Metal Inc..........804 732-0230
2406 Hinton Dr Irving (75061) *(G-13206)*

Western Sls Tstg Amarillo Inc..........806 373-6811
114 Se 46th Ave 16 Amarillo (79118) *(G-522)*

Western Stress, La Porte *Also called Analytic Stress Relieving Inc (G-13724)*

Western Stucco Product..........915 858-3494
9151 Roseway Dr El Paso (79907) *(G-6036)*

Western Texas Forge Flange Co, Kountze *Also called Forged Components Inc (G-13670)*

Western Towers, San Angelo *Also called Wilbur L Anderson Inc (G-17841)*

Western Towing Company..........713 435-1800
18350 Market St Channelview (77530) *(G-3044)*

Western Truck & Equipment..........940 723-2555
2213 East Rd 79s Wichita Falls (76305) *(G-20829)*

Western Valve Inc (PA)..........**806 373-6811**
114 Se 46th Ave Amarillo (79118) *(G-523)*

Western Valve Inc..........806 373-6811
6701 Mccormick Amarillo (79118) *(G-524)*

Western Well Service Inc..........940 723-2550
2213 East Rd 79s Wichita Falls (76305) *(G-20830)*

Western Well Tool, Houston *Also called Wwt International Inc (G-12701)*

Western Well Tool, Houston *Also called Wwt International Inc (G-12702)*

Western Wire Works Inc..........817 654-3373
4921 Rondo Dr Fort Worth (76106) *(G-7141)*

Westerngeco LLc (HQ)..........**713 789-9600**
10001 Richmond Ave Houston (77042) *(G-12644)*

Westex Welding Company..........254 826-5343
210 Cottonwood Rd West (76691) *(G-20672)*

Westfield Engrg & Svcs Inc..........281 438-2047
8310 Mchard Rd Houston (77053) *(G-8397)*

Westgate Graphics..........713 688-1292
2500 Central Pkwy Ste D Houston (77092) *(G-12645)*

Westlake CA&o, Houston *Also called Westlake Vinyls Inc (G-12654)*

Westlake Chemical, Houston *Also called Westlake Longview Corporation (G-12649)*

Westlake Chemical Corporation..........903 242-7513
2290 Callahan Rd Longview (75602) *(G-14336)*

Westlake Chemical Corporation (PA)..........**713 960-9111**
2801 Post Oak Blvd Ste 60 Houston (77056) *(G-12646)*

Westlake Chemical Opco LP (HQ)..........**713 960-9111**
2801 Post Oak Blvd Houston (77056) *(G-12647)*

Westlake Chemical Partners LP (HQ)..........**713 585-2900**
2801 Post Oak Blvd Ste 60 Houston (77056) *(G-12648)*

Westlake Enes Scence Tech Assn..........512 751-5049
304 N Laurelwood Dr Austin (78733) *(G-1659)*

Westlake Longview Corpora..........903 242-7500
2290 Callahan Rd Longview (75602) *(G-14337)*

Westlake Longview Corporation..........713 960-9111
2801 Post Oak Blvd # 650 Houston (77056) *(G-12649)*

Westlake Monomers Corp..........270 395-4151
2801 Post Oak Blvd Houston (77056) *(G-12650)*

Westlake Olefins Corporation (HQ)..........**713 960-9111**
2801 Post Oak Blvd Fl 6 Houston (77056) *(G-12651)*

Westlake Polymers LLC (HQ)..........**713 960-9111**
2801 Post Oak Blvd # 650 Houston (77056) *(G-12652)*

Westlake Power Washing, Austin *Also called Tsunami Rig Wash LLC (G-1599)*

Westlake Pvc Corporation (HQ)..........**713 960-9111**
2801 Post Oak Blvd Houston (77056) *(G-12653)*

Westlake Vinyls Inc..........800 321-8550
2801 Post Oak Blvd # 600 Houston (77056) *(G-12654)*

Westlake Vinyls Company LP (HQ)..........**713 960-9111**
2801 Post Oak Blvd Ste 60 Houston (77056) *(G-12655)*

Westland Printers, Houston *Also called Consolidated Graphics Inc (G-9275)*

Westmoor Corp (PA)..........**817 625-2841**
4901 North Fwy Fort Worth (76106) *(G-7142)*

Westmoor Mfg Co..........817 625-2841
4901 North Fwy Fort Worth (76106) *(G-7143)*

Westport Dallas, Dallas *Also called Westport Innovations (us) (G-5183)*

Westport Innovations (us) (HQ)..........**214 231-1450**
2180 French Settlement Rd Dallas (75212) *(G-5183)*

Westrade Usa Inc..........713 785-0053
6363 Woodway Dr Ste 150 Houston (77057) *(G-12656)*

Westrock Container LLC..........972 285-8865
700 N Sam Houston Rd Mesquite (75149) *(G-15085)*

Westrock Cp LLC..........915 778-7350
7350 Stiles Dr El Paso (79915) *(G-6037)*

Westrock Cp LLC..........817 568-0918
6701 South Fwy Fort Worth (76134) *(G-7144)*

Westrock Cp LLC..........281 830-0131
8440 Tewantin Dr Houston (77061) *(G-12657)*

Westrock Cp LLC..........281 893-8918
1180 West Loop N Houston (77055) *(G-12658)*

Westrock Cp LLC..........915 778-7350
7350 Stiles Dr El Paso (79915) *(G-6038)*

Westrock Mwv LLC..........409 276-3243
1913 Hwy 105 S Evadale (77615) *(G-6167)*

Westrock Mwv LLC..........409 276-3000
4594 Old Evadale Rd Silsbee (77656) *(G-18958)*

Westrock Rkt LLC..........903 455-0147
6702 Hwy 66 Greenville (75402) *(G-8096)*

Westrock Rkt LLC..........214 941-3400
1120 E Clarendon Dr Dallas (75203) *(G-5184)*

Westside Graphics, Houston *Also called Westgate Graphics (G-12645)*

Westside Welding Inc..........915 877-5345
141 El Chanate Dr Canutillo (79835) *(G-2668)*

Westwater Resources Inc..........361 279-3307
3021 County Road 333 San Diego (78384) *(G-18669)*

Westway Feed Products LLC..........903 885-5541
206 League St N Sulphur Springs (75482) *(G-19604)*

Westway Feed Products LLC..........713 514-1000
9325 E Avenue S Houston (77012) *(G-12659)*

Westway Feed Products LLC..........806 364-5200
3588 County Road H Hereford (79045) *(G-8298)*

Westway Group, Houston *Also called Contanda LLC (G-9281)*

Westway Terminal, Houston *Also called Westway Feed Products LLC (G-12659)*

Westx Packaging Company..........806 686-4447
508 Lubbock Bus Pk Blvd Lubbock (79403) *(G-14511)*

Wet, Houston *Also called Water Energy Technologies (G-12601)*

Wetmore & Company, Houston *Also called R R Donnelley & Sons Company (G-11526)*

Wets, Sweetwater *Also called Wind Energy Turbine Services (G-19639)*

Wetz Sign & Lighting Service..........830 609-6246
20286 Fm 2252 San Antonio (78266) *(G-18649)*

Weyerhaeuser Company..........972 929-8581
8800 Sterling St Irving (75063) *(G-13207)*

Weyerhaeuser Company..........972 641-3891
1200 W N Carrier Pkwy Grand Prairie (75050) *(G-7992)*

Weyerhaeuser Company..........940 230-4670
5007 Airport Rd Denton (76207) *(G-5412)*

WFC Company Inc..........903 586-0476
1428 Elberta St Jacksonville (75766) *(G-13267)*

Wfi International, Houston *Also called Bonney Forge Texas LP (G-8951)*

Wfms Inc..........281 491-2445
13901 W Bellfort St Sugar Land (77498) *(G-19573)*

Wgi Innovations Ltd..........469 733-1868
602 Fountain Pkwy Grand Prairie (75050) *(G-7993)*

Wheco Controls, Lakeside *Also called Wheco Electric Inc (G-13813)*

Wheco Electric Inc..........817 244-6660
8501 Jacksboro Hwy Lakeside (76135) *(G-13813)*

Wheel Innovationz Inc..........408 390-2871
5905 Sir Ivor Cv Austin (78746) *(G-1660)*

Wheel Rack..........210 342-0333
6127 San Pedro Ave San Antonio (78216) *(G-18616)*

Wheel-A-Rama Inc..........325 655-7373
2015 Austin St San Angelo (76903) *(G-17840)*

Wheels America Alloy Wheel (PA)..........**214 330-9866**
3939 Platinum Way Dallas (75237) *(G-5185)*

Wheels and Fitness In Motion..........210 828-4542
8522 Broadway Ste 101 San Antonio (78217) *(G-18617)*

Whelan Group, The, Austin *Also called Twg Solutions LLC (G-1601)*

Where To Retire Magazine, Houston *Also called Vacation Publications Inc (G-12516)*

Whip Industries Inc (PA)..........**817 289-1404**
3010 S Main St Fort Worth (76110) *(G-7145)*

Whipped Up Inc..........361 248-4639
4101 Intrstate Hwy 69 Acc Corpus Christi (78410) *(G-3655)*

Whirlwind Building Components, Houston *Also called Whirlwind Holding Company Inc (G-12660)*

Whirlwind Building Systems, Houston *Also called Whirlwind Steel Buildings Inc (G-12661)*

Whirlwind Holding Company Inc (PA)..........**713 946-7140**
8234 Hansen Rd Houston (77075) *(G-12660)*

Whirlwind Steel Buildings Inc (HQ)..........**713 946-7140**
8234 Hansen Rd Houston (77075) *(G-12661)*

Whiskey Hollow, Valley View *Also called Jbm Specialties LLC (G-20203)*

Whistling Duck Vneyards Winery..........512 913-4813
1241 County Road 212 Weimar (78962) *(G-20653)*

Whit-Co Checks, Amarillo *Also called Foust Incorporated (G-424)*

Whitaker Metal Deck Sales..........972 938-1445
800 Fm 879 Waxahachie (75165) *(G-20570)*

White Cement, Waco *Also called Lehigh Cement Company LLC (G-20426)*

White Cloud Security Inc..........512 887-8783
1464 E Whitestone Blvd Cedar Park (78613) *(G-2990)*

White Energy Hereford, Hereford *Also called We Hereford LLC (G-8297)*

White Energy Holding Co LLC (PA)..........**972 715-6490**
2595 Dallas Pkwy Ste 310 Frisco (75034) *(G-7326)*

White Oak Energy, Houston *Also called White Oak Operating Co LLC* ***(G-12662)***
White Oak Operating Co LLC.....281 876-2025
16945 Northchase Dr # 17 Houston (77060) ***(G-12662)***
White Rock Networks Inc A De.....972 543-6900
1301 W Pres G Bush Hwy Richardson (75080) ***(G-17427)***
White Star Pump Company LLC.....281 357-4999
41499 Cyrus Ln Waller (77484) ***(G-20509)***
White Star Steel Inc.....713 675-6501
2200 Harbor St Houston (77020) ***(G-12663)***
White Water Resources, San Antonio *Also called Whitewater Resources LLC* ***(G-18618)***
White Wing Inspection Inc.....979 421-8255
12505 New Wehdem Rd Brenham (77833) ***(G-2279)***
White Wing Weaponry LLC.....940 382-0830
1629 W Hebron Pkwy Carrollton (75010) ***(G-2897)***
Whitecap Wastewater Treatment.....361 826-4142
13409 Whitecap Blvd Corpus Christi (78418) ***(G-3656)***
Whitefield Plastics Corp.....281 214-8510
2300 Ww Thorne Blvd Houston (77073) ***(G-12664)***
Whitehawk Machine & Tools Inc.....903 450-1060
6008 Hwy 66 Greenville (75402) ***(G-8097)***
Whitehill Manufacturing Inc.....281 240-2003
12603 Executive Dr # 810 Stafford (77477) ***(G-19398)***
Whitehorse Manufacturing Co.....512 376-2112
15000 Camino Real Kyle (78640) ***(G-13688)***
Whites Trucking, Texarkana *Also called Whites Wood Group Inc* ***(G-19784)***
Whites Wood Group Inc.....903 793-1603
2723 W 7th St Texarkana (75501) ***(G-19784)***
Whiteside Cnstr Svcs Amarillo, Amarillo *Also called Wcsa Inc* ***(G-473)***
Whitewater Midstream LLC (PA).....**512 953-2100**
100 Congress Ave Ste 2200 Austin (78701) ***(G-1661)***
Whitewater Resources LLC.....210 290-9005
8700 Crownhill Blvd # 408 San Antonio (78209) ***(G-18618)***
Whitley & Siddons (PA).....**512 477-9491**
11612 Fm 2244 Rd 1-230 Austin (78738) ***(G-1662)***
Whitley Group LLC.....512 476-7101
4129 Coml Ctr Dr Ste 400 Austin (78744) ***(G-1663)***
Whitley Siddons Hwy Cnstr Info, Austin *Also called Whitley & Siddons* ***(G-1662)***
Whitlock Instruments, Odessa *Also called Terra Metrics Ltd* ***(G-16174)***
Whitmore Manufacturing Company (HQ).....**972 771-1000**
930 Whitmore Dr Rockwall (75087) ***(G-17571)***
Whitney Oil & Gas LLC.....504 218-2929
920 Mmrial Cy Way Ste 200 Houston (77024) ***(G-12665)***
Whm Custom Services Inc (PA).....**254 854-2111**
8720 County Road 421 Grandview (76050) ***(G-8003)***
Whole Tomato Software Inc.....512 226-8080
10801-1 N Mpac Expy Bldg Austin (78759) ***(G-1664)***
Wholearth Organic Composting.....210 621-2411
20805 Lamm Rd Elmendorf (78112) ***(G-6078)***
Wholesale Envelope Inc.....806 762-2255
2410 Rice St Lubbock (79415) ***(G-14512)***
Wholesaler Oilfield Equipment, McAllen *Also called Bersal Energy LLC* ***(G-14841)***
Wholesome Group LLC.....214 937-4750
5850 Granite Pkwy Ste 150 Plano (75024) ***(G-17050)***
Whrzt Inc.....888 507-9985
2418 Marsh Ln Ste 106 Carrollton (75006) ***(G-2849)***
WHW Properties Inc.....903 572-4161
100 S Edwards Ave Mount Pleasant (75455) ***(G-15665)***
Wiatrek Dunn Kutac Inc.....830 484-2888
200 County Rd 220 Poth (78147) ***(G-17196)***
Wic, Carrollton *Also called Western Industries Corporation* ***(G-2848)***
Wichita Clutch, Wichita Falls *Also called Warner Electric LLC* ***(G-20828)***
Wichita Falls Mfg Inc.....940 322-4491
2000 Old Burk Hwy Wichita Falls (76306) ***(G-20831)***
Wichita Falls Times Record.....940 767-8341
1301 Lamar St Wichita Falls (76301) ***(G-20832)***
Wichita Metal Products Inc (PA).....**940 322-9611**
1020 Vermont St Wichita Falls (76306) ***(G-20833)***
Wichita Tank Mfg Inc.....940 692-5791
8321 Seymour Hwy Wichita Falls (76310) ***(G-20834)***
Wicked Voodoo Espresso LLC.....360 631-1447
1975 Lou Ann Dr New Braunfels (78130) ***(G-15832)***
Wigwag LLC.....512 814-6459
5707 Southwest Pkwy 1-100 Austin (78735) ***(G-1665)***
Wika Instrument LP.....713 475-0022
950 Hall Ct Deer Park (77536) ***(G-5302)***
Wika USA, Houston *Also called RJ Global Wika LP* ***(G-11633)***
Wikoff Color Corporation.....972 647-1371
1710 Robinson Rd Grand Prairie (75051) ***(G-7994)***
Wil Call Services Ltd.....903 322-2911
12762 Fm 2539 Buffalo (75831) ***(G-2549)***
Wil-Cor Inc.....281 487-6547
2823 Randolph Rd Pasadena (77503) ***(G-16526)***
Wilbanks, Bruce A Company, Midland *Also called Bruce A Wilbanks Company Inc* ***(G-15152)***
Wilbert Burial Vault Corp.....817 481-3577
827 Dawn Ln Grapevine (76051) ***(G-8060)***
Wilbert Funeral Services Inc.....972 291-7854
611 Jealouse Way Cedar Hill (75104) ***(G-2956)***
Wilbert Funeral Services Inc.....806 762-1162
2301 Auburn St Lubbock (79415) ***(G-14513)***
Wilbert Funeral Services Inc.....210 922-2122
5111 Se Loop 410 San Antonio (78222) ***(G-18619)***
Wilbert Funeral Services Inc.....972 875-9605
5203 N Interstate Hwy 45 Ennis (75119) ***(G-6123)***
Wilbert of North Texas, Grapevine *Also called A & W Industries Inc* ***(G-8010)***
Wilbert of San Antonio, San Antonio *Also called Wilbert Funeral Services Inc* ***(G-18619)***
Wilborn Steel Company.....210 532-6852
2315 Dan Ct San Antonio (78223) ***(G-18620)***
Wilbur L Anderson Inc.....325 658-6539
320 W 26th St San Angelo (76903) ***(G-17841)***
Wilbur-Ellis Company LLC.....830 663-3644
265 Interstate 35 S Devine (78016) ***(G-5451)***
Wilbur-Ellis Company LLC.....956 748-2382
21204 Reynolds Rio Hondo (78583) ***(G-17476)***
Wilbur-Ellis Company LLC.....979 279-3486
1100 W Brown St Hearne (77859) ***(G-8233)***
Wilbur-Ellis Nutrition LLC.....979 849-6757
1500 E Cedar St Angleton (77515) ***(G-582)***
Wilcor and Armor Plate, Pasadena *Also called Armor Plate Inc* ***(G-16390)***
Wildcat Manufacturing Inc.....806 327-5602
1683 County Rd 29 Tahoka (79373) ***(G-19642)***
Wildcat Midstream Oper LLC.....214 310-1213
8333 Douglas Ave Ste 400 Dallas (75225) ***(G-5186)***
Wildcat Minerals Holdings LLC.....214 706-3553
2950 N Harwood St # 2200 Dallas (75201) ***(G-5187)***
Wildcat Oil Tools LLC.....432 332-4241
1400 Windway Odessa (79763) ***(G-16212)***
Wildcat Wireline.....830 879-5100
6159 N Interstate 35 Cotulla (78014) ***(G-3692)***
Wilder Systems LLC.....713 825-7348
5811 Techni Center Dr # 5 Austin (78721) ***(G-1666)***
Wilderado Wind LLC.....806 267-0746
6798 County Rd 42 Vega (79092) ***(G-20216)***
Wilderado Wind Ranch, Vega *Also called Wilderado Wind LLC* ***(G-20216)***
Wildhorse Resources LLC.....713 568-4910
920 Mmrial Cy Way Ste 700 Houston (77024) ***(G-12666)***
Wildkat Precision LLC.....936 890-9572
14357 N Highway 75 Willis (77378) ***(G-20869)***
Wiley Holdings Group Inc.....214 443-0908
4650 Cole Ave Apt 105 Dallas (75205) ***(G-5188)***
Wiley Lease Co Ltd.....830 277-0112
903 W State Highway 97 Jourdanton (78026) ***(G-13336)***
Wiley Lease Service, Jourdanton *Also called Wiley Lease Co Ltd* ***(G-13336)***
Wiley Printing, Dallas *Also called Wiley Holdings Group Inc* ***(G-5188)***
Wilkens Weather Technologies, Houston *Also called Dtn LLC* ***(G-9535)***
Wilkerson Publishing Company.....830 281-2341
114 W Goodwin St Pleasanton (78064) ***(G-17078)***
Wilkins & Associates Inc.....713 472-6585
1128 Pasadena Blvd Pasadena (77506) ***(G-16527)***
Willamar Plant, Lyford *Also called Citation Oil & Gas Corp* ***(G-14571)***
Willbanks Metals Inc.....817 625-6161
2400 Ne 36th St Fort Worth (76111) ***(G-7146)***
Willbanks Metals Inc (PA).....**817 625-6161**
1155 Ne 28th St Fort Worth (76106) ***(G-7147)***
Willbnks Fncl Cnslting Group L.....469 444-0170
3635 Eden Dr Dallas (75287) ***(G-3860)***
Willborn Bros Co LLC.....806 372-4311
105 S Houston St Amarillo (79102) ***(G-475)***
Willcox-U S Hose Div, Houston *Also called US Hose Corp* ***(G-12483)***
Willda Beast LLC.....979 268-6760
15823 Fm 244 Iola (77861) ***(G-12901)***
William B Sides.....512 385-3826
8908 Ramirez Ln Austin (78742) ***(G-1667)***
William G Burns.....972 233-4700
4601 Langland Rd Ste 106 Dallas (75244) ***(G-5189)***
William Grant Tank Vessel Inc.....903 657-6100
915 Cr 201 W W Henderson (75652) ***(G-8278)***
William L Arrington.....806 669-3324
408 W Kingsmill Ave 171a Pampa (79065) ***(G-16345)***
William L Bonnell Company Inc.....409 543-0600
902 Gladys St El Campo (77437) ***(G-5629)***
William Price Distlg Co LLC.....713 364-9225
970 Wakefield Dr Houston (77018) ***(G-12667)***
William Totah Printing LLC.....512 916-9780
10024 Austral Cv Austin (78739) ***(G-1668)***
Williams & Davis Boilers, Greenville *Also called Lektrotech Inc* ***(G-8082)***
Williams & Davis Boilers Inc.....972 225-2356
2044 Interstate 45 S Hutchins (75141) ***(G-12873)***
Williams Alloy & Welding.....713 896-9096
11425 W Little York Rd Houston (77041) ***(G-12668)***
Williams Companies Inc.....281 444-6441
4233 W Richey Rd Houston (77066) ***(G-12669)***
Williams Field Services Co LLC.....979 843-7724
2200 Avenue A Bay City (77414) ***(G-1777)***
Williams Field Services-Gulf C, Houston *Also called Williams Gas Pipeline-Transco* ***(G-12670)***
Williams Fire Hazard Ctrl Inc (HQ).....**409 745-3232**
9605 Richard Wycoff Port Arthur (77640) ***(G-17133)***

ALPHABETIC

Williams Gas Pipeline-Transco (HQ)............................713 215-2000
2800 Post Oak Blvd # 300 Houston (77056) *(G-12670)*

Williams Indus Svcs Group Inc............................281 884-8364
130 W San Augustine St Deer Park (77536) *(G-5303)*

Williams Logging............................936 632-6891
401 E Denman Ave Lufkin (75901) *(G-14556)*

Williams Machine Inc............................713 462-2229
19738 Ashley Terrace Ln Cypress (77433) *(G-3827)*

Williams Optometrist............................281 332-6021
910 W Main St League City (77573) *(G-13982)*

Williams Printing............................210 599-6204
4733 Rittiman Rd San Antonio (78218) *(G-18621)*

Williams Products Inc............................214 630-3131
2127 Exchange Dr Arlington (76011) *(G-809)*

Williamson Conference Center............................512 341-7000
1209 N Interstate 35 Round Rock (78664) *(G-17699)*

Williamson County Sun Inc............................512 930-3072
707 S Main St Georgetown (78626) *(G-7689)*

Williamsrdm Inc............................817 872-1500
200 Greenleaf St Fort Worth (76107) *(G-7148)*

Willingham Systems LLC............................713 928-3936
9201 Winkler Dr Houston (77017) *(G-12671)*

Willow Bend Bakery Inc............................214 353-0889
6607 Duffield Dr Dallas (75248) *(G-5190)*

Willow Creek Signs Inc............................817 847-0571
2633 Blue Mound Rd W Haslet (76052) *(G-8227)*

Willow Creek Signs Inc............................817 847-0571
213 E Mcleroy Blvd Saginaw (76179) *(G-17760)*

Wills Pro Custom Mfg Inc............................817 534-6009
4920 Northeast Pkwy Fort Worth (76106) *(G-7149)*

Wilmot Printing Company Inc............................915 843-6424
10618 Montwood Dr El Paso (79935) *(G-6039)*

Wilson Art, Dallas *Also called Wilsonart LLC (G-5192)*

Wilson County Holdings LLC (HQ)............................512 402-7273
111 Congress Ave Ste 400 Austin (78701) *(G-1669)*

Wilson County News, Floresville *Also called Wcn Inc (G-6258)*

Wilson Culverts Inc............................903 764-5605
699 Fm 1817 Elkhart (75839) *(G-6061)*

Wilson Electronics LLC............................800 204-4104
750 International Pkwy Richardson (75081) *(G-17428)*

Wilson Environmental MGT Inc............................713 984-0800
9613 Maribelle Way Houston (77055) *(G-12672)*

Wilson International Inc............................281 823-4700
7402 N Eldridge Pkwy Houston (77041) *(G-12673)*

Wilson Metal Fabricators Inc............................972 227-0200
1925 N Lncstr Hutchins Rd Dallas (75220) *(G-5191)*

Wilson Precision Mch Works LP............................832 721-9918
16321 Loch Katrine Ln E1 Houston (77084) *(G-12674)*

Wilson Steel Services LLC............................903 275-2995
13501 County Road 3300 Brownsboro (75756) *(G-2333)*

Wilson Supply Corporate Office............................713 237-3309
7402 N Eldridge Pkwy Houston (77041) *(G-12675)*

Wilson Systems Inc............................432 684-5567
3100 N A St Bldg A Midland (79705) *(G-15470)*

Wilsonart Engineered Surfaces, Temple *Also called Wilsonart LLC (G-19719)*

Wilsonart Intl Holdings Inc............................254 207-7000
2400 Wilson Pl Temple (76504) *(G-19715)*

Wilsonart Intl Holdings LLC (HQ)............................254 207-7000
2501 Wilsonart Dr Temple (76504) *(G-19716)*

Wilsonart Intl Holdings LLC............................254 207-6000
10501 Nw H K Dodgen Loop Temple (76504) *(G-19717)*

Wilsonart Intl Holdings LLC............................254 207-7000
2400 Wilson Pl Temple (76504) *(G-19718)*

Wilsonart Jordan Holdings Inc............................512 302-6500
13413 Galleria Cir # 200 Austin (78738) *(G-1670)*

Wilsonart LLC (HQ)............................254 207-7000
2501 Wilsonart Dr Temple (76504) *(G-19719)*

Wilsonart LLC............................254 742-2451
2400 Wilson Pl Temple (76504) *(G-19720)*

Wilsonart LLC............................214 634-2310
4051 La Reunion Pkwy # 140 Dallas (75212) *(G-5192)*

Wilsonart LLC............................254 207-7000
1110 Industrial Blvd Temple (76504) *(G-19721)*

Wilsonart LLC............................254 207-0207
500 E Ridge Blvd Temple (76502) *(G-19722)*

Wilsonart LLC............................713 576-5500
552 Garden Oaks Blvd Houston (77018) *(G-12676)*

Win-911 Software, Austin *Also called Specter Instruments Inc (G-1524)*

Win-911 Software............................512 326-1011
2024 E Saint Elmo Rd Austin (78744) *(G-1671)*

Win-Holt Equipment Corp............................972 641-4658
1169 N Great Sw Pkwy Grand Prairie (75050) *(G-7995)*

Win-Holt Equipment Inc S W, Grand Prairie *Also called Win-Holt Equipment Corp (G-7995)*

Win-Tex Lease Services Inc............................409 296-4194
18195 County Line Rd Winnie (77665) *(G-20893)*

Winchester Safes, Mansfield *Also called Granite Security Products Inc (G-14677)*

Winco Machine & Repair Inc............................903 844-2200
1011 E Commerce Ave Gladewater (75647) *(G-7730)*

Wincor Nixdorf Inc............................512 252-5622
12521 Harris Branch Pkwy Manor (78653) *(G-14651)*

Wincor Nixdorf Inc (HQ)............................512 676-5000
12345 N Lamar Blvd # 200 Austin (78753) *(G-1672)*

Wind Clean Corp............................325 625-1899
8465 E Fm 916 Grandview (76050) *(G-8004)*

Wind Energy Turbine Services............................325 235-1555
2503 E Broadway St Sweetwater (79556) *(G-19639)*

Windlass Metalworks LLC............................713 849-9292
7042 Satsuma Dr Houston (77041) *(G-12677)*

Window Gang, San Antonio *Also called M3 Tooling LLC (G-18270)*

Window On Wall Street, Richardson *Also called Window On Wallstreet Inc (G-17429)*

Window On Wallstreet Inc............................972 727-3626
1820 N Glenville Dr # 100 Richardson (75081) *(G-17429)*

Window Outfitters LP............................469 619-0892
10405 Shady Trl Ste 300 Dallas (75220) *(G-5193)*

Windsor Mold Texas, Pharr *Also called Windsor Mold USA Inc (G-16716)*

Windsor Mold USA Inc (HQ)............................956 787-8737
9200 S Austin Dr Pharr (78577) *(G-16716)*

Windstorm Industries & Assoc............................214 298-6342
7474 S Lancaster Rd 8a Dallas (75241) *(G-5194)*

Windy Cove Energy LLC............................281 402-1880
11757 Katy Fwy Ste 300 Houston (77079) *(G-12678)*

Windy Hill Spirits Inc............................615 678-4785
4301 W William Cannon Dr Austin (78749) *(G-1673)*

Winfield Laboratories Inc............................972 234-0940
1221 W Campbell Rd # 201 Richardson (75080) *(G-17430)*

Wingate Archtectural Millworks............................936 560-1040
7516 Us Highway 59 N Nacogdoches (75964) *(G-15718)*

Wingate Partners LP (PA)............................214 720-1313
750 N Saint Paul St # 1200 Dallas (75201) *(G-5195)*

Wingate Partners V LP (HQ)............................214 720-1313
750 N Saint Paul St # 1200 Dallas (75201) *(G-5196)*

Wingate WIlmson Conference Ctr, Round Rock *Also called Williamson Conference Center (G-17699)*

Wings Sportswear Inc............................210 696-1824
12814 Cogburn San Antonio (78249) *(G-18622)*

Wingspan, Ingleside *Also called D J Young Publishing (G-12893)*

Winifred S Hayes Incorporated............................215 855-0615
2711 N Haskell Ave # 145 Dallas (75204) *(G-5197)*

Winkel & Son Inc............................903 928-2560
1159 Fm 645 Tennessee Colony (75861) *(G-19727)*

Winklman Wnkleman Partners LLC (PA)............................817 831-0170
5600 Midway Rd Fort Worth (76117) *(G-7150)*

Winn Exploration Co Inc............................361 844-6900
800 N Shoreline Blvd 1900n Corpus Christi (78401) *(G-3657)*

Winnie Wldg Works & Cnstr Inc............................409 296-2953
25949 Highway 73 Winnie (77665) *(G-20894)*

Winnsboro Spclty Prts Intl Inc............................903 342-3551
301 Park St Winnsboro (75494) *(G-20902)*

Winston Land & Cattle Co Inc............................936 634-6321
4501 Us Highway 59 N Lufkin (75901) *(G-14557)*

Winston/Royal Guard Corp (PA)............................903 757-7341
1604 Cherokee Trce White Oak (75693) *(G-20722)*

Winsupply San Antonio............................210 481-8123
10000 Iota Dr San Antonio (78217) *(G-18623)*

Winsystems Inc............................817 274-7553
2890 112th St Ste 100 Grand Prairie (75050) *(G-7996)*

Wintegra Inc............................512 345-3808
6850 Austin Center Blvd # 215 Austin (78731) *(G-1674)*

Winters Instruments, Houston *Also called Winters Instruments Inc (G-12679)*

Winters Instruments Inc............................281 880-8607
5400 W Sam Houston Pkwy N Houston (77041) *(G-12679)*

Winzen Film Inc............................214 340-7060
11510 Data Dr Dallas (75218) *(G-5198)*

Winzer Corporation (HQ)............................214 341-2122
4060 E Plano Pkwy Plano (75074) *(G-17051)*

Wipco Acquisition LLC............................936 327-8250
3373 Us Highway 59 S Livingston (77351) *(G-14164)*

Wire Mesh Sales LLC (HQ)............................706 922-5179
25219 Kuykendahl Rd # 290 The Woodlands (77375) *(G-19821)*

Wire Products Supply, Sherman *Also called Wire Sales Inc (G-18938)*

Wire Sales Inc............................903 892-9473
4707 Gibbons Rd Sherman (75092) *(G-18938)*

Wireless Maniac............................817 209-9524
11532 Harry Hines Blvd Dallas (75229) *(G-5199)*

Wireless Seismic Inc (PA)............................832 532-5080
12503 Exchange Dr Ste 500 Stafford (77477) *(G-19399)*

Wireline Incorporated............................903 663-1963
710 Skinner Ln Longview (75605) *(G-14338)*

Wireline Supply, Midland *Also called A P Manufacturing Incorporated (G-15101)*

Wireline Truck Fab LP............................830 372-3626
2200 Ilka Switch Seguin (78155) *(G-18874)*

Wiscast, Grand Prairie *Also called Firstex Industries Inc (G-7872)*

Wisco Moran Drilling Co Inc............................281 431-2600
125 Post Rosharon (77583) *(G-17616)*

Wise County Messenger Inc............................940 627-5987
115 S Trinity St Decatur (76234) *(G-5257)*

Wise County Power Company LLC............................940 374-9925
800 Boones Creek Ln Poolville (76487) *(G-17099)*

(G-0000) Company's Geographic Section entry number

Wise Products Co Inc (PA) 903 378-2233
400 Commerce St E Honey Grove (75446) *(G-8359)*

Wise Ready Mix Concrete (PA) 940 683-5260
2005 16th St Bridgeport (76426) *(G-2305)*

Wiseman House Chocolates, Hico *Also called Wiseman House Companies Inc* *(G-8303)*

Wiseman House Companies Inc (PA) 254 796-2565
406 W Grubbs St Hico (76457) *(G-8303)*

Wishbone Graphics Inc 972 769-7272
1413 Gables Ct Plano (75075) *(G-17052)*

Wizetrade Group 407 206-6500
6900 Dallas Pkwy Ste 600 Plano (75024) *(G-17053)*

WL Plastics Corporation 325 574-6100
2160 S Hwy Bus 84 Snyder (79549) *(G-19014)*

Wl Plastics Corporation 940 872-8300
1110 Old Wise Rd Bowie (76230) *(G-2202)*

Wldg Wilkerson & Fabrication 817 528-1032
10702 County Road 173 N Overton (75684) *(G-16277)*

Wmc Steel LLC 706 922-5179
18490 Old Harvey Rd Conroe (77385) *(G-3386)*

Wmc Waco Holdings Inc 254 753-7301
1801 W Waco Dr Waco (76707) *(G-20479)*

Wmk LLC 817 429-1273
2110 N Beach St Haltom City (76111) *(G-8162)*

Wna Cups Illustrated Inc 972 224-8407
2155 W Longhorn Dr Lancaster (75134) *(G-13850)*

Wna Lancaster, Lancaster *Also called Wna Cups Illustrated Inc* *(G-13850)*

Wnco Valve International Inc 432 362-2136
5114 Golder Ave Odessa (79764) *(G-16213)*

WO Energy of Nevada Inc (HQ) 806 665-8298
11705 Highway 152 Pampa (79065) *(G-16346)*

Wo Operating, Pampa *Also called WO Energy of Nevada Inc* *(G-16346)*

Wolar Industrial Inc (PA) 713 926-2440
1313 Lombardy St Houston (77023) *(G-12680)*

Wolf & Sons Design Inc 512 237-3388
314 Main St Smithville (78957) *(G-18979)*

Wolf Oil Field Services Inc 979 242-5341
Hwy 77 Warda (78960) *(G-20513)*

Wolf-Solutions, Krum *Also called Skledar-Greene LLC* *(G-13676)*

Wolford, Carroll L., Garland *Also called T Shirts N Trends* *(G-7595)*

Wolfson Microelectronics Inc 408 329-9800
800 W 6th St Austin (78701) *(G-1675)*

Wolters Holdings Inc 972 272-4600
1917 Silver St Garland (75042) *(G-7610)*

Wom, Houston *Also called Worldwide Oilfield Machine Inc* *(G-12695)*

Womack Machine Supply Co (HQ) 800 569-9800
13835 Senlac Dr Farmers Branch (75234) *(G-6219)*

Womble Company Inc 713 636-8700
12821 Industrial Rd Houston (77015) *(G-12681)*

Wondercide LLC 877 896-7426
9415 Neils Thompson Dr Austin (78758) *(G-1676)*

Wonderduck Decoys, Marshall *Also called Walter Solomon* *(G-14806)*

Wonderful Citrus Packing LLC 956 205-7300
4000 E Goodwin Rd Mission (78574) *(G-15574)*

Wonton Food Corporation 832 366-1280
2902 Caroline St Houston (77004) *(G-12682)*

Woo Kee Foods Inc 832 818-6988
11243 S Gessner Rd Ste A Houston (77071) *(G-12683)*

Wood County Energy LLC 281 994-5400
16600 Park Row Houston (77084) *(G-12684)*

Wood Gallery Inc 972 869-9161
10724 Goodnight Ln Dallas (75220) *(G-5200)*

Wood Group Management Svcs Inc (HQ) 281 828-3500
17325 Park Row Houston (77084) *(G-12685)*

Wood Group Power Gp LLC (HQ) 281 828-3500
17420 Katy Fwy Ste 300 Houston (77094) *(G-12686)*

Wood Group Usa Inc (HQ) 832 809-8000
17325 Park Row Houston (77084) *(G-12687)*

Wood Group Usa Inc 281 647-8300
17420 Katy Fwy Ste 300 Houston (77094) *(G-12688)*

Wood House Bay Spa Plano, Plano *Also called R&D Futures LLC* *(G-16983)*

Wood Printing Company Inc 214 421-7393
1418 Seegar St Dallas (75215) *(G-5201)*

Wood Shed Truss 903 569-2147
1345 N Us Highway 69 Mineola (75773) *(G-15515)*

Wood Shed Trusse 903 569-2147
Hwy 69 Mineola (75773) *(G-15516)*

Woodard Furniture, Coppell *Also called Woodard—Cm LLC* *(G-3453)*

Woodard—Cm LLC (HQ) 972 393-3800
650 S Royal Ln Ste 100 Coppell (75019) *(G-3453)*

Woodbridge Group, The, El Paso *Also called Woodbridge Sales & Engrg Inc* *(G-6040)*

Woodbridge Sales & Engrg Inc 915 751-1000
9900 Railroad Dr El Paso (79924) *(G-6040)*

Woodco Millwork Ltd 210 298-9663
1210 Arion Pkwy San Antonio (78216) *(G-18624)*

Woodcrafters Home Products LLC (HQ) 956 565-6329
3700 Camino De Verdad Rd Weslaco (78596) *(G-20671)*

Wooden Pallets Ltd 409 385-1234
3840 Henry Reed Rd Silsbee (77656) *(G-18959)*

Woodfield Pharmaceutical LLC 281 530-3077
10863 Rockley Rd Houston (77099) *(G-12689)*

Woodhaus Inc 972 245-8117
1207 Tappan Cir Ste 104 Carrollton (75006) *(G-2850)*

Woodhead, El Paso *Also called Molex LLC* *(G-5882)*

Woodland Midstream II LLC 832 592-1202
24 Waterway Ave Ste 1460 Spring (77380) *(G-19262)*

Woodland Publishing Inc 281 485-7501
2407 Park Ave Pearland (77581) *(G-16611)*

Woodlands Apothecary, Dallas *Also called Executive Enterprises LLC* *(G-4346)*

Woodlawn Manufacturing Inc 903 938-1882
275 N Marshall Indus Ave Marshall (75670) *(G-14809)*

Woodmont Cabinetry, Dallas *Also called Western Cabinets Inc* *(G-5181)*

Woodrose Winery Inc 830 644-2539
662 Woodrose Ln Stonewall (78671) *(G-19430)*

Woods Tool and Machine Co Inc (PA) 817 275-4541
423 Dodson Lake Dr Arlington (76012) *(G-810)*

Woods Tool Company, Arlington *Also called Woods Tool and Machine Co Inc* *(G-810)*

Woodshop of Texas, Texas City *Also called Integrawood* *(G-19795)*

Woodshop of Texas Ltd 409 938-7875
6001 Emmett F Lowry Expy Texas City (77591) *(G-19807)*

Woodside Energy (usa) Inc 713 963-8490
5151 San Felipe St # 1200 Houston (77056) *(G-12690)*

Woodville Hardwoods 409 283-6106
4937 Us Highway 69 S Woodville (75979) *(G-20920)*

Woodwright Hardwood Flr Co Inc 214 630-8811
425 Regal Row Dallas (75247) *(G-5202)*

Woody's Accessories & Off-Road, Tyler *Also called McMt LLC* *(G-20121)*

Woolley Fishing Tool Inc 903 984-3553
3000 Laird Hill Rd Kilgore (75662) *(G-13603)*

Woolley Tool Inc (PA) 903 984-3553
3000 Laird Hill Rd Kilgore (75662) *(G-13604)*

Word Constructors LLC 830 693-2933
Hwy 281 Marble Falls (78654) *(G-14752)*

Wordyisms Inc 512 835-6695
601 Olympic Dr Pflugerville (78660) *(G-16693)*

Work Area Protection, Garland *Also called Hill & Smith Inc* *(G-7513)*

Work Services Corporation (PA) 940 766-3207
1343 Hatton Rd Wichita Falls (76302) *(G-20835)*

Workiva Inc 817 308-1153
600 Las Colinas Blvd E # 900 Irving (75039) *(G-13208)*

Workover Solutions Inc 361 947-8695
10011 Windfern Rd Houston (77064) *(G-12691)*

Worksite Lighting LLC 225 313-3711
4109 Murray Ave Haltom City (76117) *(G-8163)*

World Class Awards, Farmers Branch *Also called Lorente International LLC* *(G-6206)*

World Division USA, Dallas *Also called National Banner Company Inc* *(G-4712)*

World Division USA, Dallas *Also called National Banner Company Inc* *(G-4713)*

World Energy Magazine, Houston *Also called International Business Publs* *(G-10399)*

World Jewelry Associates, Dallas *Also called New World Jewelry Inc* *(G-4731)*

World Journal La LLC 713 771-4363
10415 Westpark Dr Apt A Houston (77042) *(G-12692)*

World Journel of Texas, Houston *Also called World Journal La LLC* *(G-12692)*

World of Jeans & Tops 806 788-1233
6002 Slide Rd Lubbock (79414) *(G-14514)*

World Research Company Inc (PA) 903 581-3720
4926 Profit Dr Tyler (75707) *(G-20177)*

World Wide Celebrity Mag LLP 832 305-8716
846 Rayford Rd Spring (77386) *(G-19263)*

World Wide Filtration Inc 281 421-7676
5340 East Rd Baytown (77521) *(G-1839)*

Worldfab Inc 281 446-9777
2626 Wilson Rd Humble (77396) *(G-12807)*

Worlds of Wow LLC 817 380-4215
1800 Shady Oaks Dr Denton (76205) *(G-5413)*

Worldwide Dpwter Solutions LLC 281 238-6000
6023 Carolyn Ln Richmond (77406) *(G-17467)*

Worldwide Instrument, Livingston *Also called Wipco Acquisition LLC* *(G-14164)*

Worldwide J R Wood LLC 512 858-2556
14101 W Hwy 290 Ste 900 Austin (78737) *(G-867)*

Worldwide Locking Systems Inc 972 775-6320
3570 N Highway 67 Ste A Midlothian (76065) *(G-15496)*

Worldwide Manufacturing Inc 713 645-6552
3721 Lapas Dr Houston (77023) *(G-12693)*

Worldwide Oilfield Machine Inc (PA) 713 729-9200
11809 Canemont St Houston (77035) *(G-12694)*

Worldwide Oilfield Machine Inc. 713 721-5200
11625 Fairmont St Houston (77035) *(G-12695)*

Worldwide Oilfield Machine Inc. 713 937-0795
5800 Cunningham Rd Houston (77041) *(G-12696)*

Worldwide Sorbent Products Inc 409 983-7800
6600 Tram Rd Ste 2 Beaumont (77713) *(G-1970)*

Worldwide Spanish Literature 940 692-4933
4212 Fairway Blvd Wichita Falls (76308) *(G-20836)*

Worldwide Stffing Slutions LLC 210 293-3600
11502 Jnes Maltsberger Rd San Antonio (78216) *(G-18625)*

Worldwide Wndows Tratments LLC (PA) 718 893-9370
4030 La Reunion Pkwy # 100 Dallas (75212) *(G-5203)*

Worth Beauty LLC ... 713 660-0025
3101 Richmond Ave Ste 200 Houston (77098) ***(G-12697)***
Worth Eqp Parts & Svc Co Inc ... 817 473-7266
812 S 2nd Ave Mansfield (76063) ***(G-14730)***
Worth Trailer Parts Inc ... 817 496-7841
4312 E Loop 820 S Fort Worth (76119) ***(G-7151)***
Woven Metal Products Inc (PA) ... **281 331-4466**
1201 Fm 517 Alvin (77511) ***(G-386)***
Woven Remembrance, Fort Worth *Also called Vlgc LLC* ***(G-7110)***
Wow Funscapes, Denton *Also called Worlds of Wow LLC* ***(G-5413)***
Wp Resources LLC ... 512 913-7234
340 Rancho Rd New Braunfels (78130) ***(G-15833)***
Wp Resources Consulting, New Braunfels *Also called Wp Resources LLC* ***(G-15833)***
Wpt LLC (HQ) ... **713 960-9111**
2801 Postoakblvd Ste 600 Houston (77056) ***(G-12698)***
Wpt Power Corporation ... 940 761-1971
1600 Fisher Rd Wichita Falls (76305) ***(G-20837)***
Wr Meadows of Texas, Fort Worth *Also called W R Meadows Inc* ***(G-7113)***
Wrangler Hats, Garland *Also called Master Hatters of Texas Inc* ***(G-7544)***
Wraps Gorilla ... 817 652-2882
615 Six Flags Dr Arlington (76011) ***(G-811)***
WRB Refining LP (PA) ... **281 293-6600**
2331 Citywest Blvd Houston (77042) ***(G-12699)***
Wren Oilfield Services Inc ... 903 759-3086
1500 Cherokee Trce White Oak (75693) ***(G-20723)***
Wrico Stamping of Texas, Grapevine *Also called Griffiths Corporation* ***(G-8041)***
Wright Landscaping & Cnst LLC ... 254 213-3912
4100 S Clear Creek Rd Killeen (76549) ***(G-13618)***
Wright Materials, Robstown *Also called Wt Mining Company Inc* ***(G-17521)***
Wright Materials Inc ... 361 387-1511
5706 Fm 3088 Robstown (78380) ***(G-17519)***
Wrights Ammunitions LLC ... 972 257-1111
2300 Valley View Ln # 213 Irving (75062) ***(G-13209)***
Wrights Printing & Mktg LLP ... 281 367-6060
2407 Timberloch Pl Ste A The Woodlands (77380) ***(G-19941)***
Wrights Well Control Svcs LLC ... 337 502-4160
28019 Buena Way Spring (77386) ***(G-19264)***
Wristband Connection, Houston *Also called McV Sales Co L L C* ***(G-10812)***
Wristbands With A Message Inc ... 281 494-2424
10200 W Airport Blvd # 100 Stafford (77477) ***(G-19400)***
Wrkco Inc ... 817 624-8000
4675 Railhead Rd Fort Worth (76106) ***(G-7152)***
Wrs Group Ltd ... 254 776-6461
624 Texas Central Pkwy Waco (76712) ***(G-20480)***
Wrs Group Ltd (PA) ... **254 776-6461**
624 Texas Central Pkwy Waco (76712) ***(G-20481)***
Ws Energy Services LLC ... 361 348-3488
3913 Fm 1889 Robstown (78380) ***(G-17520)***
Ws Group Inc (PA) ... **214 337-4761**
2829 Fort Worth Ave Dallas (75211) ***(G-5204)***
Wsh Land Inc (PA) ... **713 622-4823**
2727 Allen Pkwy Ste 1815 Houston (77019) ***(G-12700)***
Wsi Cased Hole Specialist Inc ... 800 658-9674
4668 Fm 1607 Snyder (79549) ***(G-19015)***
WT Fiber Link LLC ... 432 758-2700
807 Se Avenue P Seminole (79360) ***(G-18888)***
Wt Lease Services Inc ... 361 348-3525
1123 Orion Dr Portland (78374) ***(G-17189)***
Wt Mining Company Inc ... 361 767-4095
5706 Fm 3088 Robstown (78380) ***(G-17521)***
Wtb, Midland *Also called Sherman Branson Construction* ***(G-15408)***
Wtb LLC ... 432 366-1026
1201 Oicd Dr Odessa (79766) ***(G-16214)***
Wte Services LLC ... 432 547-2300
7662 Fm 1219 S Monahans (79756) ***(G-15615)***
Wtg Fuels Inc ... 432 837-2518
3001 N State Highway 118 Alpine (79830) ***(G-313)***
Wtg Gas Processing LP (PA) ... **432 682-4349**
211 N Colorado St Midland (79701) ***(G-15471)***
Wtg Gas Processing LP ... 325 473-5161
209 Ne Railroad St Bronte (76933) ***(G-2307)***
Wtg Suth Permian Midstream LLC ... 432 682-4349
211 N Colorado St Midland (79701) ***(G-15472)***
Wtx Oilfield Services ... 325 227-4656
36 W Beauregard Ave # 604 San Angelo (76903) ***(G-17842)***
Ww Electronics Solutions LLC ... 214 396-6636
10167 County Road 3705 Quinlan (75474) ***(G-17227)***
Ww Wireline Co Inc (PA) ... **956 712-9473**
1719 Guadalupe St Laredo (78043) ***(G-13940)***
Wwl Industries Inc ... 432 362-0326
2412 W 42nd St Odessa (79764) ***(G-16215)***
Wwt International Inc ... 281 345-8019
9817 Whithorn Dr Houston (77095) ***(G-12701)***
Wwt International Inc (PA) ... **281 345-8019**
9758 Whithorn Dr Houston (77095) ***(G-12702)***
Www.carbidetech, Pasadena *Also called Carbide Technologies Inc* ***(G-16400)***
Www.wtrt.net/Handrmfg, Hereford *Also called H & R Black Mfg Co LLC* ***(G-8290)***
Wwwhoustonsignmakercom ... 281 990-7446
4208 Washington Ave Houston (77007) ***(G-12703)***
Wyatt Resources Inc ... 281 346-6100
5623 Fm Rd 359 Fulshear (77441) ***(G-7332)***
Wylie & Son Inc (PA) ... **806 667-3566**
101 N Main St Petersburg (79250) ***(G-16652)***
Wylie & Son Inc ... 325 695-0000
3542 S Treadaway Blvd Abilene (79602) ***(G-95)***
Wylie Implement, Abilene *Also called Wylie & Son Inc* ***(G-95)***
Wylie Sprayers of Amarillo, Petersburg *Also called Wylie & Son Inc* ***(G-16652)***
Wynnewood Energy Company LLC ... 281 207-3200
2277 Plaza Dr Ste 500 Sugar Land (77479) ***(G-19574)***
Wynnewood Refining Company LLC (HQ) ... **281 207-3444**
2277 Plaza Dr Ste 500 Sugar Land (77479) ***(G-19575)***
Wyoming Refining Company, Houston *Also called Hermes Consolidated LLC* ***(G-10160)***
X Press Bags Inc ... 972 513-9899
707 Robbie Dr Ste 150 Irving (75061) ***(G-13210)***
X-Analog Communications Inc ... 409 925-4702
1835 Algoa Friendswood Rd Alvin (77511) ***(G-387)***
X-Fab Texas Inc (HQ) ... **806 747-4400**
2301 N University Ave Lubbock (79415) ***(G-14515)***
Xact Technologies USA Corp ... 403 862-3383
9851 Fllbrook Pnes Dr Ste Houston (77064) ***(G-12704)***
Xact Xpressions Inc ... 972 242-6332
13995 Diplomat Dr Ste 200 Dallas (75234) ***(G-5205)***
Xarmr Corporation (PA) ... **972 385-7899**
5900 S Lake Forest Dr McKinney (75070) ***(G-14991)***
Xceed Resources, El Paso *Also called Border Tm Industries Inc* ***(G-5671)***
XCEL Metal Finishing Inc ... 972 772-4440
2065 Kristy Ln Rockwall (75032) ***(G-17572)***
XCL Resources LLC ... 346 335-1081
600 N Shepherd Dr Ste 390 Houston (77007) ***(G-12705)***
Xedia Process Solutions LLC ... 832 356-8347
5773 Woodway Dr 181 Houston (77057) ***(G-12706)***
Xella Aircrete North Amer Inc ... 229 896-1593
833 Isom Rd San Antonio (78216) ***(G-18626)***
Xencom Energy Management LLC ... 469 429-1111
1609 Precision Dr # 3000 Plano (75074) ***(G-17054)***
Xenex Disinfection Svcs Inc (PA) ... **800 553-0069**
1074 Arion Cir Ste 116 San Antonio (78216) ***(G-18627)***
Xentaur Corporation ... 631 345-3434
4140 World Hstn Pkwy # 180 Houston (77032) ***(G-12707)***
Xerxes Corporation ... 830 372-0090
2001 Proform Rd Seguin (78155) ***(G-18875)***
Xg Ventures LLC ... 936 744-1800
101 Martin Ct Trinity (75862) ***(G-20020)***
Xgrafx LLC (PA) ... **210 681-7177**
2643 Mossrock Ste 1 San Antonio (78230) ***(G-18628)***
Xit Sand and Gravel LLC ... 806 249-8743
3212 Us Highway 54 Dalhart (79022) ***(G-3836)***
Xjian Inc ... 972 618-6096
4500 Staten Island Ct Plano (75024) ***(G-17055)***
Xl Oilfield Services LLC ... 830 672-6644
530 Seydler St Gonzales (78629) ***(G-7767)***
Xl Technology LLC ... 972 369-1359
210 Security Ct Wylie (75098) ***(G-20956)***
Xochitl Inc ... 214 800-3551
6020 Colwell Blvd Irving (75039) ***(G-13211)***
Xog Operating LLC ... 432 683-3171
1801 W Texas Ave Midland (79701) ***(G-15473)***
Xomox Corporation (HQ) ... **936 271-6500**
4526 Res Frest Dr Ste 400 The Woodlands (77381) ***(G-19942)***
Xplicit Treasure, Houston *Also called Ariel Kennard* ***(G-8693)***
Xplore Technologies Corp (HQ) ... **512 637-1100**
8601 Rr 2222 Ste 1 Austin (78730) ***(G-1677)***
Xqz, San Angelo *Also called Wtx Oilfield Services* ***(G-17842)***
Xstar Resources LLC ... 817 495-9306
4237 Salt Creek Rd Jacksboro (76458) ***(G-13224)***
Xtenti LLC ... 818 434-5239
17304 Preston Rd Ste 800 Dallas (75252) ***(G-3861)***
Xtera Inc ... 972 649-5000
500 W Bethany Dr Ste 100 Allen (75013) ***(G-307)***
Xtera Subsea, Allen *Also called Xtera Inc* ***(G-307)***
Xterra Fishing & Rental Tls Co ... 817 334-4100
801 Cherry St Unit 2 Fort Worth (76102) ***(G-7153)***
Xterra Industries LLC ... 281 998-0442
5385 Bay Oaks Dr Pasadena (77505) ***(G-16528)***
Xterra Trench Shields, Pasadena *Also called Xterra Industries LLC* ***(G-16528)***
Xto Energy Inc ... 817 885-2195
210 W 6th St Fort Worth (76102) ***(G-7154)***
Xto Energy Inc ... 817 870-2800
1 Riverway Ste 700 Houston (77056) ***(G-12708)***
Xto Energy Inc ... 432 682-8873
6401 Holiday Hill Rd # 5 Midland (79707) ***(G-15474)***
Xto Energy Inc ... 505 333-3100
600 E Exchange Ave Fort Worth (76164) ***(G-7155)***
Xto Energy Inc ... 806 367-1047
888 County Road 121 Tokio (79376) ***(G-19950)***
Xto Energy Inc ... 979 828-1963
14596 Hilltop Ln Bryan (77803) ***(G-2516)***

Xto Energy Inc 903 939-1200
6141 Paluxy Dr Tyler (75703) *(G-20178)*

Xto Energy Inc 903 553-3800
5652 Fm 2208 S Longview (75605) *(G-14339)*

Xto Energy Inc (HQ) **817 870-2800**
22777 Sprngwoods Vlg Pkwy Spring (77389) *(G-19188)*

Xto Energy Inc 903 983-8800
700 State Highway 31 E Kilgore (75662) *(G-13605)*

Xto Energy Inc 432 524-6545
1584 Sw 5900 Andrews (79714) *(G-562)*

Xto Energy Inc 936 858-3533
12642 Us Highway 69 S Alto (75925) *(G-320)*

Xto Energy Inc 713 871-3453
600 E Exchange Ave Fort Worth (76164) *(G-7156)*

Xto Energy Inc 817 740-0488
3250 Love Field Dr Dallas (75235) *(G-5206)*

Xtralight Manufacturing Ltd 713 943-9927
8812 Frey Rd Houston (77034) *(G-12709)*

Xtreme Force Inc 281 397-0073
1234 N Post Oak Rd Houston (77055) *(G-12710)*

Xtreme Force Wheel, Houston Also called Xtreme Force Inc *(G-12710)*

Xtreme High Prfmce Catings Inc 281 695-8880
7410 Miller Road 2 Houston (77049) *(G-12711)*

Xtreme Lashes LLC 281 907-0689
24127 W Hardy Rd Ste C Spring (77373) *(G-19189)*

Xtreme Powder Coating, Garland Also called Swift Screen Printing Inc *(G-7594)*

Xtreme Strctres Fbrication LLC 903 438-1100
300 Cmh Sulphur Springs (75482) *(G-19605)*

Xxtreme Pipe Storage LLC 281 452-9015
7814 Miller Road 3 Houston (77049) *(G-12712)*

Xytex Inc 361 394-5524
690 N Highway 16 Freer (78357) *(G-7235)*

Xytronics, San Antonio Also called Season Group Usa LLC *(G-18461)*

Y 8 Foundry, Tulia Also called Kenneth Wyatt Galleries *(G-20036)*

Yadblue LLC 214 542-6140
1716 Water Lily Dr Southlake (76092) *(G-19084)*

Yale E Key, Odessa Also called Key Energy Services Inc *(G-16047)*

Yamhill Valley Vineyards Inc 281 822-9463
7786 Blankenship Dr # 700 Houston (77055) *(G-12713)*

Yancey Ready-Mix, Conroe Also called Conroe Concrete Ltd *(G-3281)*

Yankon Lighting Inc 469 248-0749
1581 Corporate Dr Ste 100 McKinney (75069) *(G-14992)*

Yarrington Road Materials 512 754-3573
1401 Yarrington Rd Kyle (78640) *(G-13689)*

Yarrington Road Materials LP 512 306-7800
2705 Bee Caves Rd Ste 130 Austin (78746) *(G-1678)*

Yash & Lujan Consulting Inc 800 519-5221
100 Congress Ave Ste 2000 Austin (78701) *(G-1679)*

Yates Carpet Incorporated 806 795-9942
1901 W Loop 289 Ste 11 Lubbock (79407) *(G-14516)*

Yates Flooring Center, Lubbock Also called Yates Carpet Incorporated *(G-14516)*

Yazaki North America Inc 618 512-8723
12435 Rojas Dr El Paso (79928) *(G-6041)*

Ybarra Group Inc 210 533-5323
10104 Huebner Rd San Antonio (78240) *(G-18629)*

Yci Methanol One LLC 832 924-1998
10777 Westheimer Rd # 800 Houston (77042) *(G-12714)*

Yegua Oil Field Service Inc 361 375-2105
S Hwy 181 And Pins St Pettus (78146) *(G-16654)*

Yegua Well Service, Pettus Also called Nelson Oil Field Eqp & Sup *(G-16653)*

Yellow Folder LLC 214 431-3600
1617 W Crosby Rd Ste 100 Carrollton (75006) *(G-2851)*

Yellow Page Consultants, Rockwall Also called Independent Tele Dirctry Co *(G-17550)*

Yellow Rose Stl Fbricators Inc 713 862-7339
14239 Sommermeyer St Houston (77041) *(G-12715)*

Yellowjacket Oilfield Svcs LLC 432 523-3692
300 Nw Mustang Dr Andrews (79714) *(G-563)*

Yellowjacket Oilfield Svcs LLC 361 485-0625
5500 Sw Moody St Victoria (77905) *(G-20321)*

Yellowjacket Oilfield Svcs LLC 432 381-0104
5151 Katy Fwy Ste 206 Houston (77007) *(G-12716)*

Yellowjacket Oilfield Svcs LLC 432 242-7615
102 Avenue Q Levelland (79336) *(G-14018)*

Yellowstone Brands Ltd (PA) **713 650-0065**
777 Post Oak Blvd Ste 250 Houston (77056) *(G-12717)*

Yerico Manufacturing Inc (PA) **512 285-3444**
619 Mogonye Ln Elgin (78621) *(G-6057)*

Yes Lighting LLC 972 807-9197
11220 Grader St Ste 500 Dallas (75238) *(G-5207)*

Yeti Coolers LLC (HQ) **512 394-9384**
7601 Southwest Pkwy Austin (78735) *(G-1680)*

Yeti Holdings Inc (PA) **512 394-8220**
7601 Southwest Pkwy Austin (78735) *(G-1681)*

Yj USA Corp (PA) **877 927-8777**
3970 Lindbergh Dr Addison (75001) *(G-175)*

YKK AP America Inc 972 245-9551
346 E Belt Line Rd # 600 Coppell (75019) *(G-3454)*

Yoakum Herald Times, Yoakum Also called Yoakum Herald-Times Inc *(G-20975)*

Yoakum Herald-Times Inc (PA) **361 293-5266**
312 Lott St Yoakum (77995) *(G-20975)*

Yogurt Technologies LLC 409 621-2060
1202 Post Office St Galveston (77550) *(G-7414)*

Yohawk Energy LLC 817 484-9642
6209 Sandra Dr Fort Worth (76133) *(G-7157)*

Yokogawa Corporation America, Houston Also called Yokogawa Leisure Analysis Div *(G-12718)*

Yokogawa Corporation America (HQ) **281 340-3800**
12530 W Airport Blvd Sugar Land (77478) *(G-19576)*

Yokogawa Corporation America 936 653-2120
35 Petroleum Rd Coldspring (77331) *(G-3168)*

Yokogawa Leisure Analysis Div 281 488-0409
910 Gemini St Houston (77058) *(G-12718)*

Yoolotto LLC 469 383-6488
13760 Noel Rd Ste 855 Dallas (75240) *(G-5208)*

York Group Inc 412 995-1600
24406 Bay Hill Blvd Katy (77494) *(G-13385)*

Yotta Solar Inc 512 856-7788
3512 Montopolis Dr B Austin (78744) *(G-1682)*

Youghall Enterprises Inc 325 356-2233
309 Highway 3381 Comanche (76442) *(G-3237)*

Younger Colorpress Inc 817 923-1331
4050 Hildring Dr W Fort Worth (76109) *(G-7158)*

Youngs Tank Incorporated 800 345-7952
3500 E Hwy 114 Boyd (76023) *(G-2210)*

Younicos Inc 512 268-8191
3100 Alvin Devane Blvd Austin (78741) *(G-1683)*

Your Ideas Inc 325 673-5860
825 Oak St Abilene (79602) *(G-96)*

Yoyo Management Inc 512 447-1455
2113 Cimarron Trl Austin (78745) *(G-1684)*

Yp LLC 713 867-6500
2525 North Loop W Ste 600 Houston (77008) *(G-12719)*

Ysleta Del Sur Pblo Ltd Prtnr, El Paso Also called Big Bear Oil Company Inc *(G-5662)*

Ytec, Galveston Also called Yogurt Technologies LLC *(G-7414)*

Z Fab USA Inc 817 380-1156
5929 S Hampshire Blvd Fort Worth (76112) *(G-7159)*

Z Fabulous Inc 972 385-0202
1700 Coit Rd Plano (75075) *(G-17056)*

Z S L, Floresville Also called Camino Agave Inc *(G-6246)*

Z-Modular Killeen LLC 254 833-6645
710 Swanner Loop Killeen (76543) *(G-13619)*

Zach's Spice Company, Deer Park Also called Micor Inc *(G-5286)*

Zachry Associates Inc 325 677-1342
3457 Curry Ln Abilene (79606) *(G-97)*

Zachry Consolidated LLC 210 588-5000
527 Logwood Ave San Antonio (78221) *(G-18630)*

Zachry Construction & Mtls Inc (PA) **210 479-1027**
2330 N Loop 1604 W San Antonio (78248) *(G-18631)*

Zachry Holdings Inc 806 322-4100
6440 S Fm 1541 Amarillo (79118) *(G-525)*

Zachry Holdings Inc (PA) **210 588-5000**
527 Logwood Ave San Antonio (78221) *(G-18632)*

Zack Burkett Co 940 322-2101
2600 Old Burk Hwy Wichita Falls (76306) *(G-20838)*

Zack Burkett Co Asp Plant 1, Wichita Falls Also called Zack Burkett Co *(G-20838)*

Zackson Resources Inc 713 782-1075
7600 San Felipe St 200 Houston (77063) *(G-12720)*

Zamo Inc 210 667-1717
16102 E Lupon Rd Saint Hedwig (78152) *(G-17761)*

Zamorano Enterprises Inc 210 924-2320
8603 S Flores St San Antonio (78221) *(G-18633)*

Zapco Inc 512 237-5521
403 Zapalac Rd Smithville (78957) *(G-18980)*

Zarsky Lumber Company Inc 361 882-2575
510 N Port Ave Corpus Christi (78408) *(G-3658)*

Zarsky Lumber Company Inc (HQ) **361 573-2479**
604 E Rio Grande St Victoria (77901) *(G-20322)*

Zarsky Oil Field, Corpus Christi Also called Zarsky Lumber Company Inc *(G-3658)*

Zarvona Energy LLC 713 600-0600
1001 Mckinney St Ste 1800 Houston (77002) *(G-12721)*

Zaza Energy LLC (HQ) **713 595-1900**
1301 Mckinney St Ste 2800 Houston (77010) *(G-12722)*

Zaza Energy Corporation (PA) **713 595-1900**
1301 Mckinney St Ste 2850 Houston (77010) *(G-12723)*

Zdscada LP 903 526-1100
1918 Sybil Ln Tyler (75703) *(G-20179)*

Zebra Technologies Corporation 512 716-3088
3729 Galena Hills Loop Round Rock (78681) *(G-17700)*

Zebra Technologies Corporation 956 630-0315
2705 Ebony Ave McAllen (78501) *(G-14920)*

Zebra Technologies Corporation 956 571-3770
5400 George Mcvay Dr McAllen (78503) *(G-14921)*

Zedi US Inc 830 876-2777
3415 N Hwy 277 Carrizo Springs (78834) *(G-2689)*

Zedi US Inc 361 575-4528
3001 N Cameron St Victoria (77901) *(G-20323)*

Zedi US Inc 713 527-9591
  5875 N Sam Houston Pkwy W Houston (77086) *(G-12724)*

Zemer International LLC 214 227-2320
  1800 Dove Ln Midlothian (76065) *(G-15497)*

Zemer International MO Inc 214 227-2320
  1800 Dove Ln Midlothian (76065) *(G-15498)*

Zentech Dallas LLC 972 907-2727
  1717 Firman Dr Ste 200 Richardson (75081) *(G-17431)*

Zeon Chemicals LP 281 474-9693
  11235 Choate Rd Pasadena (77507) *(G-16529)*

Zeon Chemicals Texas Inc (HQ) **502 775-2000**
  11235 Choate Rd Pasadena (77507) *(G-16530)*

Zeotech Corporation 361 274-3357
  Hwy 72 W Tilden (78072) *(G-19947)*

Zephyr Gas Services LLC 281 376-2980
  20405 State Highway 249 # 2 Houston (77070) *(G-12725)*

Zero Fasteners, Houston *Also called Zero Products Inc* *(G-12726)*

Zero Products Inc 713 675-0123
  219 Baywood St Houston (77011) *(G-12726)*

Zesty-Calco Marketing Service, Houston *Also called Calco Taiwan Marketing*
Service *(G-9048)*

Zeta Energy LLC 732 581-0838
  5300 N Braeswood Blvd Houston (77096) *(G-12727)*

Zeus Development Corp 713 952-9500
  16 Courtlandt Pl Houston (77006) *(G-12728)*

Zevex Corporation 512 322-9039
  510 Hearn St Ste 300 Austin (78703) *(G-1685)*

ZF Elec Sys Plsnt Praire LLC 915 790-5000
  12420 Mercantile Ave El Paso (79928) *(G-6042)*

ZF Passive Safety Systems US 956 566-7680
  9600 International Blvd Pharr (78577) *(G-16717)*

ZF Passive Safety US Inc 956 632-8100
  9600 International Blvd Pharr (78577) *(G-16718)*

ZF Passive Safety US Inc 734 582-1139
  9780 Plaza Cir Ste A El Paso (79927) *(G-6043)*

ZF TRW Auto Holdings Corp 956 632-8100
  9600 Intl Blvd Docks 5/8 58 Docks Pharr (78577) *(G-16719)*

Ziften Technologies Inc 512 298-5501
  801 Barton Springs Rd 9 Austin (78704) *(G-1686)*

Zilkha Biomass Fuels I LLC 713 979-9961
  1001 Mckinney St Ste 1925 Houston (77002) *(G-12729)*

Zilks Foods LLC 512 633-8904
  1807 W Slaughter Ln # 495 Austin (78748) *(G-1687)*

Zimair Dsplay Systems Florplan, Fort Worth *Also called Zimair LP* *(G-7160)*

Zimair LP 817 624-7245
  2024 Belle Ave Fort Worth (76164) *(G-7160)*

Zimco Elc Sup A Div Brder Stte, Odessa *Also called Border States Industries Inc* *(G-15940)*

Zimco Marine LLC 956 831-7828
  1170 Bayou Ct Brownsville (78521) *(G-2422)*

Zimmer (HQ) **800 613-6131**
  9900 Spectrum Dr Austin (78717) *(G-1717)*

Zimmermann & Jansen Inc 281 446-8000
  4525 Kennedy Commerce Dr Houston (77032) *(G-12730)*

Zinepak LLC 212 706-8621
  1902 Forest Trl Austin (78703) *(G-1688)*

Zinsmeyer Mech & Wldg Ltd 830 985-3498
  2891 Us Highway 90 E Castroville (78009) *(G-2929)*

Zion Oil & Gas Inc (PA) **214 221-4610**
  12655 N Cntl Expy Ste 100 Dallas (75243) *(G-5209)*

Zip Print, Amarillo *Also called Easy Print Inc* *(G-421)*

Zix Corporation (PA) **214 370-2000**
  2711 N Haskell Ave # 2300 Dallas (75204) *(G-5210)*

Zixcorp Systems Inc (HQ) **214 370-2000**
  2711 N Haskell Ave Dallas (75204) *(G-5211)*

Zochem LLC 615 446-8791
  109 N Post Oak Ln Ste 415 Houston (77024) *(G-12731)*

Zodiac Seats California LLC 909 652-9700
  8595 Milliken Ave Ste 101 Gainesville (76240) *(G-7375)*

Zodiac Stone LLC 972 243-2112
  11125 Zodiac Ln Dallas (75229) *(G-5212)*

Zoetis Inc 817 293-8887
  5430 Faa Blvd Ste 140 Irving (75061) *(G-13212)*

Zor N Terprize 832 304-0504
  5955 Ridgeway Dr Houston (77033) *(G-12732)*

Zrc Ltd 325 949-7625
  1821 Knickerbocker Rd D San Angelo (76904) *(G-17843)*

Zspace LLC 713 662-3123
  5801 Chimney Rock Rd Houston (77081) *(G-12733)*

Zti Merger Subsidiary III Inc (HQ) **510 777-7000**
  5700 Tennyson Pkwy # 400 Plano (75024) *(G-17057)*

Zubie Wear 210 590-8892
  1516 Universal City Blvd Universal City (78148) *(G-20186)*

Zurn Industries LLC 972 277-0900
  2055 Luna Rd Ste 182 Carrollton (75006) *(G-2852)*

Zw, Pampa *Also called Crall Products Inc* *(G-16320)*

Zxp Technologies LLC 281 426-8800
  409 E Wallisville Rd Highlands (77562) *(G-8316)*

Zxp Technologies LLC 281 426-8800
  409 Wallisville Rd Highlands (77562) *(G-8317)*

Zynex Inc 972 221-5050
  421 S Mill St Pmb 167 Lewisville (75057) *(G-14113)*

Zyvex Corporation 972 235-7881
  1301 N Plano Rd Richardson (75081) *(G-17432)*

Zyvex Instruments LLC 972 792-1625
  1321 N Plano Rd Richardson (75081) *(G-17433)*

PRODUCT INDEX

• Product categories are listed in alphabetical order.

A

ABRASIVES
ABRASIVES: Synthetic
ABRASIVES: Tungsten Carbide
ACCELERATION INDICATORS & SYSTEM COMPONENTS: Aerospace
ACCOUNTING MACHINES & CASH REGISTERS
ACETONE: Synthetic
ACIDS: Battery
ACIDS: Inorganic
ACIDS: Nitric
ACIDS: Sulfuric, Oleum
ACOUSTICAL BOARD & TILE
ACRYLIC RESINS
ACRYLONITRILE BUTADIENE STYRENE RESINS
ACTUATORS: Indl, NEC
ADAPTERS: Well
ADDITIVE BASED PLASTIC MATERIALS: Plasticizers
ADHESIVES
ADHESIVES & SEALANTS
ADHESIVES & SEALANTS WHOLESALERS
ADHESIVES: Epoxy
ADVERTISING AGENCIES
ADVERTISING AGENCIES: Consultants
ADVERTISING DISPLAY PRDTS
ADVERTISING MATERIAL DISTRIBUTION
ADVERTISING REPRESENTATIVES: Electronic Media
ADVERTISING REPRESENTATIVES: Media
ADVERTISING REPRESENTATIVES: Newspaper
ADVERTISING REPRESENTATIVES: Printed Media
ADVERTISING SPECIALTIES, WHOLESALE
ADVERTISING SVCS: Billboards
ADVERTISING SVCS: Direct Mail
ADVERTISING SVCS: Display
ADVERTISING SVCS: Outdoor
ADVERTISING SVCS: Transit
ADVERTISING: Aerial
AERIAL WORK PLATFORMS
AGENTS, BROKERS & BUREAUS: Personal Service
AGRICULTURAL DISINFECTANTS
AGRICULTURAL EQPT: BARN, SILO, POULTRY, DAIRY/LIVESTOCK MACH
AGRICULTURAL EQPT: Barn Cleaners
AGRICULTURAL EQPT: Barn Stanchions & Standards
AGRICULTURAL EQPT: Fertilizing Machinery
AGRICULTURAL EQPT: Fertilizng, Sprayng, Dustng/Irrigatn Mach
AGRICULTURAL EQPT: Grade, Clean & Sort Machines, Fruit/Veg
AGRICULTURAL EQPT: Grounds Mowing Eqpt
AGRICULTURAL EQPT: Irrigation Eqpt, Self-Propelled
AGRICULTURAL EQPT: Loaders, Manure & General Utility
AGRICULTURAL EQPT: Planting Machines
AGRICULTURAL EQPT: Soil Preparation Mach, Exc Turf & Grounds
AGRICULTURAL EQPT: Soil Sampling Machines
AGRICULTURAL EQPT: Spreaders, Fertilizer
AGRICULTURAL EQPT: Tractors, Farm
AGRICULTURAL EQPT: Trailers & Wagons, Farm
AGRICULTURAL EQPT: Turf Eqpt, Commercial
AGRICULTURAL MACHINERY & EQPT REPAIR
AGRICULTURAL MACHINERY & EQPT: Wholesalers
AIR CLEANING SYSTEMS
AIR CONDITIONERS, AUTOMOTIVE: Wholesalers
AIR CONDITIONERS: Motor Vehicle
AIR CONDITIONING & VENTILATION EQPT & SPLYS: Wholesales
AIR CONDITIONING EQPT
AIR CONDITIONING EQPT, WHOLE HOUSE: Wholesalers
AIR CONDITIONING REPAIR SVCS
AIR CONDITIONING UNITS: Complete, Domestic Or Indl
AIR COOLERS: Metal Plate
AIR CURTAINS
AIR DUCT CLEANING SVCS
AIR MATTRESSES: Plastic
AIR POLLUTION CONTROL EQPT & SPLYS WHOLE-SALERS
AIR POLLUTION MEASURING SVCS

AIR PURIFICATION EQPT
AIR-CONDITIONING SPLY SVCS
AIRBOATS
AIRCRAFT & AEROSPACE FLIGHT INSTRUMENTS & GUID-ANCE SYSTEMS
AIRCRAFT & HEAVY EQPT REPAIR SVCS
AIRCRAFT ASSEMBLY PLANTS
AIRCRAFT AUTOMATIC PILOT SYSTEMS
AIRCRAFT CLEANING & JANITORIAL SVCS
AIRCRAFT CONTROL SYSTEMS:
AIRCRAFT CONTROL SYSTEMS: Electronic Totalizing Coun-ters
AIRCRAFT DEALERS
AIRCRAFT ENGINES & ENGINE PARTS: Air Scoops
AIRCRAFT ENGINES & ENGINE PARTS: Research & Devel-opment, Mfr
AIRCRAFT ENGINES & PARTS
AIRCRAFT EQPT & SPLYS WHOLESALERS
AIRCRAFT FLIGHT INSTRUMENT REPAIR SVCS
AIRCRAFT FLIGHT INSTRUMENTS
AIRCRAFT LIGHTING
AIRCRAFT MAINTENANCE & REPAIR SVCS
AIRCRAFT PARTS & AUXILIARY EQPT: Aircraft Training Eqpt
AIRCRAFT PARTS & AUXILIARY EQPT: Assys, Subassem-blies/Parts
AIRCRAFT PARTS & AUXILIARY EQPT: Beaching Gear
AIRCRAFT PARTS & AUXILIARY EQPT: Blades, Prop, Metal Or Wood
AIRCRAFT PARTS & AUXILIARY EQPT: Body & Wing Assys & Parts
AIRCRAFT PARTS & AUXILIARY EQPT: Body Assemblies & Parts
AIRCRAFT PARTS & AUXILIARY EQPT: Brakes
AIRCRAFT PARTS & AUXILIARY EQPT: Elevators
AIRCRAFT PARTS & AUXILIARY EQPT: Gears, Power Trans-mission
AIRCRAFT PARTS & AUXILIARY EQPT: Military Eqpt & Arma-ment
AIRCRAFT PARTS & AUXILIARY EQPT: Oxygen Systems
AIRCRAFT PARTS & AUXILIARY EQPT: Research & Devel-opment, Mfr
AIRCRAFT PARTS & EQPT, NEC
AIRCRAFT PARTS WHOLESALERS
AIRCRAFT RADIO EQPT REPAIR SVCS
AIRCRAFT SEATS
AIRCRAFT SERVICING & REPAIRING
AIRCRAFT TURBINES
AIRCRAFT: Airplanes, Fixed Or Rotary Wing
AIRCRAFT: Motorized
AIRCRAFT: Research & Development, Manufacturer
AIRLINE TRAINING
AIRPORTS, FLYING FIELDS & SVCS
ALARMS: Fire
ALCOHOL, GRAIN: For Beverage Purposes
ALCOHOL: Amyl
ALCOHOL: Ethyl & Ethanol
ALCOHOL: Methyl & Methanol, Synthetic
ALKALIES & CHLORINE
ALLOYS: Additive, Exc Copper Or Made In Blast Furnaces
ALTERNATORS & GENERATORS: Battery Charging
ALTERNATORS: Automotive
ALUMINUM
ALUMINUM PRDTS
ALUMINUM: Coil & Sheet
ALUMINUM: Pigs
ALUMINUM: Rolling & Drawing
AMBLYGONITE MINING
AMBULANCE SVCS
AMMONIUM NITRATE OR AMMONIUM SULFATE
AMMONIUM PHOSPHATE
AMMUNITION
AMMUNITION: Cartridges Case, 30 mm & Below
AMMUNITION: Small Arms
AMPLIFIERS
AMPLIFIERS: Parametric
AMPLIFIERS: RF & IF Power
AMUSEMENT & RECREATION SVCS: Amusement Arcades
AMUSEMENT & RECREATION SVCS: Archery Lanes

AMUSEMENT & RECREATION SVCS: Baseball Batting Cage
AMUSEMENT & RECREATION SVCS: Card & Game Svcs
AMUSEMENT & RECREATION SVCS: Diving Instruction, Un-derwater
AMUSEMENT & RECREATION SVCS: Exhibition Operation
AMUSEMENT & RECREATION SVCS: Fishing Lakes & Piers, Op
AMUSEMENT & RECREATION SVCS: Hunting Club, Mem-bership
AMUSEMENT & RECREATION SVCS: Mechanical Games, Coin-Operated
AMUSEMENT & RECREATION SVCS: Tour & Guide
AMUSEMENT MACHINES: Coin Operated
AMUSEMENT PARK DEVICES & RIDES
AMUSEMENT PARK DEVICES & RIDES: Carnival Mach & Eqpt, NEC
ANALYZERS: Coulometric, Indl Process
ANALYZERS: Electrical Testing
ANALYZERS: Petroleum Prdts
ANESTHESIA EQPT
ANIMAL FEED & SUPPLEMENTS: Livestock & Poultry
ANIMAL FEED: Wholesalers
ANIMAL FOOD & SUPPLEMENTS: Bird Food, Prepared
ANIMAL FOOD & SUPPLEMENTS: Dog
ANIMAL FOOD & SUPPLEMENTS: Dog & Cat
ANIMAL FOOD & SUPPLEMENTS: Feed Concentrates
ANIMAL FOOD & SUPPLEMENTS: Feed Supplements
ANIMAL FOOD & SUPPLEMENTS: Livestock
ANIMAL FOOD & SUPPLEMENTS: Mineral feed supplements
ANIMAL FOOD & SUPPLEMENTS: Pet, Exc Dog & Cat, Canned
ANIMAL FOOD & SUPPLEMENTS: Pet, Exc Dog & Cat, Dry
ANIMAL FOOD & SUPPLEMENTS: Pet, Exc Dog & Cat, Frozen
ANIMAL FOOD & SUPPLEMENTS: Poultry
ANIMAL FOOD & SUPPLEMENTS: Pulverized Oats
ANIMAL FOOD & SUPPLEMENTS: Stock Feeds, Dry
ANIMAL FOOD/SUPPLEMENTS: Feeds Fm Meat/Meat/Veg Combnd Meals
ANIMAL OILS: Medicinal Grade, Refined Or Concentrated
ANODIZING EQPT
ANODIZING SVC
ANTENNA REPAIR & INSTALLATION SVCS
ANTENNAS: Radar Or Communications
ANTENNAS: Receiving
ANTENNAS: Satellite, Household Use
ANTI-GLARE MATERIAL
ANTI-OXIDANTS
ANTIFREEZE
ANTIQUE FURNITURE RESTORATION & REPAIR
ANTIQUE SHOPS
ANTISCALING COMPOUNDS, BOILER
ANTISEPTICS, MEDICINAL
APARTMENT LOCATING SVCS
APLITE MINING
APPAREL ACCESS STORES
APPAREL DESIGNERS: Commercial
APPAREL FILLING MATERIALS: Cotton Waste, Kapok/Re-lated Matl
APPLIANCES, HOUSEHOLD: Drycleaning Machines, Incl Coin-Op
APPLIANCES, HOUSEHOLD: Kitchen, Major, Exc Refrigs & Stoves
APPLIANCES: Household, NEC
APPLIANCES: Household, Refrigerators & Freezers
APPLIANCES: Major, Cooking
APPLIANCES: Small, Electric
APPLICATIONS SOFTWARE PROGRAMMING
AQUARIUMS & ACCESS: Glass
ARCHITECT'S SUPPLIES WHOLESALERS
ARCHITECTURAL PANELS OR PARTS: Porcelain Enameled
ARCHITECTURAL SVCS
ARCHITECTURAL SVCS: Engineering
ARMATURE REPAIRING & REWINDING SVC
ARMORED CAR SVCS
AROMATIC CHEMICAL PRDTS
ART DEALERS & GALLERIES
ART DESIGN SVCS

ART GOODS, WHOLESALE
ART MARBLE: Concrete
ART SPLY STORES
ARTIFICIAL FLOWER SHOPS
ARTISTS' AGENTS & BROKERS
ARTISTS' MATERIALS, WHOLESALE
ARTISTS' MATERIALS: Pastels
ARTWORK: Framed
ASBESTOS & ASBESTOS CEMENT: Tubing & Piping
ASBESTOS PRDTS: Roofing, Felt Roll
ASBESTOS PRDTS: Tape
ASBESTOS REMOVAL EQPT
ASPHALT & ASPHALT PRDTS
ASPHALT COATINGS & SEALERS
ASPHALT MINING & BITUMINOUS STONE QUARRYING SVCS
ASPHALT MIXTURES WHOLESALERS
ASPHALT PLANTS INCLUDING GRAVEL MIX TYPE
ASSOCIATION FOR THE HANDICAPPED
ASSOCIATIONS: Business
ASSOCIATIONS: Dentists'
ASSOCIATIONS: Real Estate Management
ASSOCIATIONS: Trade
ATOMIZERS
ATTENUATORS
AUCTION SVCS: Motor Vehicle
AUDIO & VIDEO EQPT, EXC COMMERCIAL
AUDIO & VIDEO TAPES WHOLESALERS
AUDIO ELECTRONIC SYSTEMS
AUDIO-VISUAL PROGRAM PRODUCTION SVCS
AUTO & HOME SUPPLY STORES: Auto & Truck Eqpt & Parts
AUTO & HOME SUPPLY STORES: Auto Air Cond Eqpt, Sell/Install
AUTO & HOME SUPPLY STORES: Automotive Access
AUTO & HOME SUPPLY STORES: Automotive parts
AUTO & HOME SUPPLY STORES: Batteries, Automotive & Truck
AUTO & HOME SUPPLY STORES: Speed Shops, Incl Race Car Splys
AUTO & HOME SUPPLY STORES: Trailer Hitches, Automotive
AUTO & HOME SUPPLY STORES: Truck Eqpt & Parts
AUTO SPLYS & PARTS, NEW, WHSLE: Exhaust Sys, Mufflers, Etc
AUTOMATED TELLER MACHINE OR ATM REPAIR SVCS
AUTOMATIC REGULATING CONTROL: Building Svcs Monitoring, Auto
AUTOMATIC REGULATING CONTROLS: AC & Refrigeration
AUTOMATIC REGULATING CONTROLS: Electric Heat
AUTOMATIC REGULATING CONTROLS: Energy Cutoff, Residtl/Comm
AUTOMATIC REGULATING CONTROLS: Hardware, Environmental Reg
AUTOMATIC REGULATING CONTROLS: Hydronic Pressure Or Temp
AUTOMATIC REGULATING CONTROLS: Oil & Hydronic, Combination
AUTOMATIC REGULATING CONTROLS: Pneumatic Relays, Air-Cond
AUTOMATIC REGULATING CONTROLS: Pressure, Air-Cond Sys
AUTOMATIC REGULATING CONTROLS: Refrigeration, Pressure
AUTOMATIC REGULATING CONTROLS: Vapor Heating
AUTOMATIC REGULATING CTRLS: Damper, Pneumatic Or Electric
AUTOMATIC TELLER MACHINES
AUTOMOBILE FABRICS, WHOLESALE
AUTOMOBILE RECOVERY SVCS
AUTOMOBILES & OTHER MOTOR VEHICLES WHOLESALERS
AUTOMOBILES: Wholesalers
AUTOMOTIVE & TRUCK GENERAL REPAIR SVC
AUTOMOTIVE AIR CONDITIONING REPAIR SHOPS
AUTOMOTIVE BATTERIES WHOLESALERS
AUTOMOTIVE BODY SHOP
AUTOMOTIVE BODY, PAINT & INTERIOR REPAIR & MAINTENANCE SVC
AUTOMOTIVE CUSTOMIZING SVCS, NONFACTORY BASIS
AUTOMOTIVE GLASS REPLACEMENT SHOPS
AUTOMOTIVE PAINT SHOP
AUTOMOTIVE PARTS, ACCESS & SPLYS
AUTOMOTIVE PARTS: Plastic
AUTOMOTIVE PRDTS: Rubber
AUTOMOTIVE RADIATOR REPAIR SHOPS

AUTOMOTIVE REPAIR SHOPS: Brake Repair
AUTOMOTIVE REPAIR SHOPS: Diesel Engine Repair
AUTOMOTIVE REPAIR SHOPS: Electrical Svcs
AUTOMOTIVE REPAIR SHOPS: Engine Rebuilding
AUTOMOTIVE REPAIR SHOPS: Engine Repair
AUTOMOTIVE REPAIR SHOPS: Frame Repair Shops
AUTOMOTIVE REPAIR SHOPS: Machine Shop
AUTOMOTIVE REPAIR SHOPS: Powertrain Components Repair Svcs
AUTOMOTIVE REPAIR SHOPS: Tire Repair Shop
AUTOMOTIVE REPAIR SHOPS: Trailer Repair
AUTOMOTIVE REPAIR SHOPS: Truck Engine Repair, Exc Indl
AUTOMOTIVE REPAIR SHOPS: Turbocharger & Blower Repair
AUTOMOTIVE REPAIR SVC
AUTOMOTIVE REPAIR SVCS, MISCELLANEOUS
AUTOMOTIVE SPLYS & PARTS, NEW, WHOL: Auto Servicing Eqpt
AUTOMOTIVE SPLYS & PARTS, NEW, WHOL: Auto Svc Station Eqpt
AUTOMOTIVE SPLYS & PARTS, NEW, WHOLESALE: Brakes
AUTOMOTIVE SPLYS & PARTS, NEW, WHOLESALE: Bumpers
AUTOMOTIVE SPLYS & PARTS, NEW, WHOLESALE: Engines/Eng Parts
AUTOMOTIVE SPLYS & PARTS, NEW, WHOLESALE: Filters, Air & Oil
AUTOMOTIVE SPLYS & PARTS, NEW, WHOLESALE: Hardware
AUTOMOTIVE SPLYS & PARTS, NEW, WHOLESALE: Pumps, Oil & Gas
AUTOMOTIVE SPLYS & PARTS, NEW, WHOLESALE: Radiators
AUTOMOTIVE SPLYS & PARTS, NEW, WHOLESALE: Seat Belts
AUTOMOTIVE SPLYS & PARTS, NEW, WHOLESALE: Splys
AUTOMOTIVE SPLYS & PARTS, NEW, WHOLESALE: Tools & Eqpt
AUTOMOTIVE SPLYS & PARTS, NEW, WHOLESALE: Trailer Parts
AUTOMOTIVE SPLYS & PARTS, USED, WHOLESALE
AUTOMOTIVE SPLYS & PARTS, USED, WHOLESALE: Access, NEC
AUTOMOTIVE SPLYS & PARTS, USED, WHOLESALE: Tools & Eqpt
AUTOMOTIVE SPLYS & PARTS, WHOLESALE, NEC
AUTOMOTIVE SPLYS/PARTS, NEW, WHOL: Body Rpr/Paint Shop Splys
AUTOMOTIVE SVCS, EXC REPAIR & CARWASHES: Fuel Sys Conv
AUTOMOTIVE SVCS, EXC REPAIR & CARWASHES: Glass Tinting
AUTOMOTIVE SVCS, EXC REPAIR & CARWASHES: Lubrication
AUTOMOTIVE SVCS, EXC REPAIR & CARWASHES: Maintenance
AUTOMOTIVE SVCS, EXC REPAIR & CARWASHES: Trailer Maintenance
AUTOMOTIVE SVCS, EXC REPAIR: Carwash, Self-Service
AUTOMOTIVE SVCS, EXC REPAIR: Washing & Polishing
AUTOMOTIVE SVCS, EXC RPR/CARWASHES: High Perf Auto Rpr/Svc
AUTOMOTIVE TOWING SVCS
AUTOMOTIVE TRANSMISSION REPAIR SVC
AUTOMOTIVE WELDING SVCS
AUTOMOTIVE: Bodies
AUTOMOTIVE: Seat Frames, Metal
AUTOMOTIVE: Seating
AUTOTRANSFORMERS: Electric
AVIATION PROPELLER & BLADE REPAIR SVCS
AWNING REPAIR SHOP
AWNINGS & CANOPIES
AWNINGS & CANOPIES: Awnings, Fabric, From Purchased Matls
AWNINGS & CANOPIES: Canopies, Fabric, From Purchased Matls
AWNINGS & CANOPIES: Fabric
AWNINGS: Fiberglass
AWNINGS: Metal
AXLES
AXLES: Rolled Or Forged, Made In Steel Mills

B

BABBITT (METAL)
BABY FORMULA
BACKHOES
BADGES, WHOLESALE
BADGES: Identification & Insignia
BAGS & CONTAINERS: Textile, Exc Sleeping
BAGS: Canvas
BAGS: Cement, Made From Purchased Materials
BAGS: Duffle, Canvas, Made From Purchased Materials
BAGS: Food Storage & Frozen Food, Plastic
BAGS: Garment, Plastic Film, Made From Purchased Materials
BAGS: Paper
BAGS: Paper, Made From Purchased Materials
BAGS: Plastic
BAGS: Plastic & Pliofilm
BAGS: Plastic, Made From Purchased Materials
BAGS: Pliofilm, Made From Purchased Materials
BAGS: Rubber Or Rubberized Fabric
BAGS: Textile
BAGS: Trash, Plastic Film, Made From Purchased Materials
BAGS: Vacuum cleaner, Made From Purchased Materials
BAKERIES, COMMERCIAL: On Premises Baking Only
BAKERIES: On Premises Baking & Consumption
BAKERY FOR HOME SVC DELIVERY
BAKERY MACHINERY
BAKERY PRDTS: Bagels, Fresh Or Frozen
BAKERY PRDTS: Bakery Prdts, Partially Cooked, Exc frozen
BAKERY PRDTS: Biscuits, Baked, Baking Powder & Raised
BAKERY PRDTS: Bread, All Types, Fresh Or Frozen
BAKERY PRDTS: Buns, Bread Type, Fresh Or Frozen
BAKERY PRDTS: Cakes, Bakery, Exc Frozen
BAKERY PRDTS: Cakes, Bakery, Frozen
BAKERY PRDTS: Cookies
BAKERY PRDTS: Cookies & crackers
BAKERY PRDTS: Doughnuts, Exc Frozen
BAKERY PRDTS: Dry
BAKERY PRDTS: Frozen
BAKERY PRDTS: Pies, Bakery, Frozen
BAKERY PRDTS: Pretzels
BAKERY PRDTS: Rusk, Machine Made
BAKERY PRDTS: Sponge Goods, Bakery, Exc Frozen
BAKERY PRDTS: Wholesalers
BAKERY: Wholesale Or Wholesale & Retail Combined
BALANCING SVC
BALERS
BALLASTS: Lighting
BALLOONS: Novelty & Toy
BALLOONS: Rubber Laminated Metal Foil
BALLOONS: Toy & Advertising, Rubber
BALLS: Rubber, Exc Athletic
BANNERS: Fabric
BANQUET HALL FACILITIES
BAR
BAR FIXTURES: Wood
BARBECUE EQPT
BARBER SHOPS
BARGES BUILDING & REPAIR
BARITE MINING
BARRICADES: Metal
BARS & BAR SHAPES: Steel, Cold-Finished, Own Hot-Rolled
BARS & BAR SHAPES: Steel, Hot-Rolled
BARS, COLD FINISHED: Steel, From Purchased Hot-Rolled
BARS, PLATES & SHEETS: Zinc & Zinc Alloy Bars, Plates, Etc
BARS: Cargo, Stabilizing, Metal
BARS: Concrete Reinforcing, Fabricated Steel
BARS: Iron, Made In Steel Mills
BASES, BEVERAGE
BATCHING PLANTS: Aggregate Concrete & Bulk Cement
BATH SHOPS
BATHROOM ACCESS & FITTINGS: Vitreous China & Earthenware
BATHROOM FIXTURES: Plastic
BATTERIES, EXC AUTOMOTIVE: Wholesalers
BATTERIES: Alkaline, Cell Storage
BATTERIES: Dry
BATTERIES: Rechargeable
BATTERIES: Storage
BATTERIES: Wet
BATTERY CHARGERS
BEARINGS
BEARINGS & PARTS Ball

INDEX

CABLE: Fiber
CABLE: Fiber Optic
CABLE: Nonferrous, Shipboard
CABLE: Noninsulated
CABLE: Ropes & Fiber
CABLE: Steel, Insulated Or Armored
CAGES: Wire
CALIBRATING SVCS, NEC
CAMERAS & RELATED EQPT: Photographic
CANDLE SHOPS
CANDLES
CANDLES: Wholesalers
CANDY & CONFECTIONS: Candy Bars, Including Chocolate Covered
CANDY & CONFECTIONS: Chocolate Candy, Exc Solid Chocolate
CANDY & CONFECTIONS: Popcorn Balls/Other Trtd Popcorn Prdts
CANDY, NUT & CONFECTIONERY STORE: Popcorn, Incl Caramel Corn
CANDY, NUT & CONFECTIONERY STORES: Candy
CANDY, NUT & CONFECTIONERY STORES: Nuts
CANNED SPECIALTIES
CANOPIES: Sheet Metal
CANS: Aluminum
CANS: Fiber
CANS: Metal
CANVAS PRDTS
CANVAS PRDTS, WHOLESALE
CAPACITORS & CONDENSERS
CAPACITORS: NEC
CAPACITORS: Series
CAPS: Plastic
CAR WASH EQPT
CAR WASH EQPT & SPLYS WHOLESALERS
CAR WASHES
CARBIDES
CARBON & GRAPHITE PRDTS, NEC
CARBON BLACK
CARBON PAPER & INKED RIBBONS
CARBON REMOVING SOLVENT
CARBON SPECIALTIES Electrical Use
CARDIOVASCULAR SYSTEM DRUGS, EXC DIAGNOSTIC
CARDS: Color
CARDS: Greeting
CARDS: Identification
CARDS: Playing
CARPET & RUG CLEANING & REPAIRING PLANTS
CARPET & UPHOLSTERY CLEANING PLANTS
CARPET & UPHOLSTERY CLEANING SVCS
CARPET & UPHOLSTERY CLEANING SVCS: Carpet/Furniture, On Loc
CARPETS & RUGS: Tufted
CARPETS, RUGS & FLOOR COVERING
CARPORTS: Prefabricated Metal
CARRIAGES: Horse Drawn
CARRIER EQPT: Telephone Or Telegraph
CARRYING CASES, WHOLESALE
CARS & TRUCKS: Indl Mining
CASES, WOOD
CASES: Carrying
CASES: Carrying, Clothing & Apparel
CASES: Packing, Nailed Or Lock Corner, Wood
CASES: Plastic
CASES: Shipping, Nailed Or Lock Corner, Wood
CASING-HEAD BUTANE & PROPANE PRODUCTION
CASING: Boiler, Metal Plate
CASINGS: Sheet Metal
CASINGS: Storage, Missile & Missile Components
CASKETS & ACCESS
CASKETS WHOLESALERS
CAST STONE: Concrete
CASTERS
CASTINGS GRINDING: For The Trade
CASTINGS: Aerospace Investment, Ferrous
CASTINGS: Aerospace, Aluminum
CASTINGS: Aerospace, Nonferrous, Exc Aluminum
CASTINGS: Aluminum
CASTINGS: Brass, NEC, Exc Die
CASTINGS: Bronze, NEC, Exc Die
CASTINGS: Commercial Investment, Ferrous
CASTINGS: Die, Aluminum
CASTINGS: Die, Magnesium & Magnesium-Base Alloy
CASTINGS: Die, Nonferrous
CASTINGS: Die, Zinc

CASTINGS: Ductile
CASTINGS: Gray Iron
CASTINGS: Machinery, Aluminum
CASTINGS: Precision
CASTINGS: Rubber
CASTINGS: Steel
CASTINGS: Zinc
CATALOG & MAIL-ORDER HOUSES
CATALOG SALES
CATALYSTS: Chemical
CATCH BASIN COVERS: Concrete
CATERERS
CAULKING COMPOUNDS
CEILING SYSTEMS: Luminous, Commercial
CEMENT & CONCRETE RELATED PRDTS & EQPT: Bituminous
CEMENT ROCK: Crushed & Broken
CEMENT, EXC LINOLEUM & TILE
CEMENT: Hydraulic
CEMENT: Masonry
CEMENT: Portland
CEMETERIES: Real Estate Operation
CEMETERY MEMORIAL DEALERS
CERAMIC FIBER
CERAMIC FLOOR & WALL TILE WHOLESALERS
CERAMIC SCHOOLS
CHAIN: Welded, Made From Purchased Wire
CHAINS: Forged
CHAMBERS & CAISSONS
CHAMBERS OF COMMERCE
CHANDELIERS: Residential
CHANGE MAKING MACHINES
CHANNELS: Furring
CHARCOAL
CHARCOAL: Activated
CHASSIS: Automobile Trailer
CHASSIS: Motor Vehicle
CHEESE WHOLESALERS
CHEMICAL CLEANING SVCS
CHEMICAL ELEMENTS
CHEMICAL INDICATORS
CHEMICAL PROCESSING MACHINERY & EQPT
CHEMICAL SPLYS FOR FOUNDRIES
CHEMICAL: Sodm Compnds/Salts, Inorg, Exc Rfnd Sodm Chloride
CHEMICALS & ALLIED PRDTS WHOLESALERS, NEC
CHEMICALS & ALLIED PRDTS, WHOL: Chemical, Organic, Synthetic
CHEMICALS & ALLIED PRDTS, WHOL: Gases, Compressed/Liquefied
CHEMICALS & ALLIED PRDTS, WHOLESALE: Acids
CHEMICALS & ALLIED PRDTS, WHOLESALE: Ammonia
CHEMICALS & ALLIED PRDTS, WHOLESALE: Carbon Dioxide
CHEMICALS & ALLIED PRDTS, WHOLESALE: Chemical Additives
CHEMICALS & ALLIED PRDTS, WHOLESALE: Chemicals, Indl
CHEMICALS & ALLIED PRDTS, WHOLESALE: Chemicals, Indl & Heavy
CHEMICALS & ALLIED PRDTS, WHOLESALE: Concrete Additives
CHEMICALS & ALLIED PRDTS, WHOLESALE: Detergent/Soap
CHEMICALS & ALLIED PRDTS, WHOLESALE: Detergents
CHEMICALS & ALLIED PRDTS, WHOLESALE: Drilling Mud
CHEMICALS & ALLIED PRDTS, WHOLESALE: Essential Oils
CHEMICALS & ALLIED PRDTS, WHOLESALE: Indl Gases
CHEMICALS & ALLIED PRDTS, WHOLESALE: Manmade Fibers
CHEMICALS & ALLIED PRDTS, WHOLESALE: Metal Polishes
CHEMICALS & ALLIED PRDTS, WHOLESALE: Oil Additives
CHEMICALS & ALLIED PRDTS, WHOLESALE: Oxygen
CHEMICALS & ALLIED PRDTS, WHOLESALE: Plastics Film
CHEMICALS & ALLIED PRDTS, WHOLESALE: Plastics Materials, NEC
CHEMICALS & ALLIED PRDTS, WHOLESALE: Plastics Prdts, NEC
CHEMICALS & ALLIED PRDTS, WHOLESALE: Plastics Sheets & Rods
CHEMICALS & ALLIED PRDTS, WHOLESALE: Plastics, Basic Shapes
CHEMICALS & ALLIED PRDTS, WHOLESALE: Polyurethane Prdts

CHEMICALS & ALLIED PRDTS, WHOLESALE: Resins
CHEMICALS & ALLIED PRDTS, WHOLESALE: Resins, Plastics
CHEMICALS & ALLIED PRDTS, WHOLESALE: Sealants
CHEMICALS & ALLIED PRDTS, WHOLESALE: Silicon Lubricants
CHEMICALS & ALLIED PRDTS, WHOLESALE: Spec Clean/Sanitation
CHEMICALS & ALLIED PRDTS, WHOLESALE: Syn Resin, Rub/Plastic
CHEMICALS, AGRICULTURE: Wholesalers
CHEMICALS/ALLIED PRDTS, WHOL: Coal Tar Prdts, Prim/Intermdt
CHEMICALS: Agricultural
CHEMICALS: Alcohols
CHEMICALS: Alkali Metals, Lithium, Cesium, Francium/Rubidium
CHEMICALS: Alkalies
CHEMICALS: Aluminum Oxide
CHEMICALS: Anhydrous Ammonia
CHEMICALS: Brine
CHEMICALS: Bromine, Elemental
CHEMICALS: Calcium Chloride
CHEMICALS: Fire Retardant
CHEMICALS: Fluorine, Elemental
CHEMICALS: Formaldehyde
CHEMICALS: Fuel Tank Or Engine Cleaning
CHEMICALS: High Purity Grade, Organic
CHEMICALS: High Purity, Refined From Technical Grade
CHEMICALS: Hydrogen Peroxide
CHEMICALS: Hypophosphites
CHEMICALS: Inorganic, NEC
CHEMICALS: Medicinal, Organic, Uncompounded, Bulk
CHEMICALS: Metal Compounds Or Salts, Inorganic, NEC
CHEMICALS: NEC
CHEMICALS: Nonmetallic Compounds
CHEMICALS: Organic, NEC
CHEMICALS: Phenol
CHEMICALS: Phosphorus, Elemental
CHEMICALS: Potassium Compound/Salt, Exc Hydroxide/Carbonate
CHEMICALS: Reagent Grade, Refined From Technical Grade
CHEMICALS: Silica Compounds
CHEMICALS: Soda Ash
CHEMICALS: Sodium Bicarbonate
CHEMICALS: Sodium/Potassium Cmpnds,Exc Bleach,Alkalies/Alum
CHEMICALS: Sulfur, Incl Rcvrd/Refined, Fm Sour Natural Gas
CHEMICALS: Water Treatment
CHESTS: Bank, Metal
CHESTS: Steel
CHICKEN SLAUGHTERING & PROCESSING
CHLORINATED RUBBERS: Synthetic
CHLORINE
CHOCOLATE, EXC CANDY FROM BEANS: Chips, Powder, Block, Syrup
CHOCOLATE, EXC CANDY FROM PURCH CHOC: Chips, Powder, Block
CHRISTMAS TREES WHOLESALERS
CHRISTMAS TREES: Artificial
CHROMATOGRAPHY EQPT
CHUCKS
CHUTES & TROUGHS
CIGAR STORES
CIGARETTE & CIGAR PRDTS & ACCESS
CIRCUIT BOARDS, PRINTED: Television & Radio
CIRCUIT BOARDS: Wiring
CIRCUIT BREAKERS
CIRCUITS: Electronic
CLAIMS ADJUSTING SVCS
CLAMPS: Metal
CLAY PRDTS: Architectural
CLAY, PETROLEUM REFINING: Chemically Processed
CLAY: Ground Or Treated
CLAYS, EXC KAOLIN & BALL
CLEANERS: Pipe & Cigarette Holder
CLEANING & DYEING PLANTS, EXC RUGS
CLEANING COMPOUNDS: Rifle Bore
CLEANING EQPT: Blast, Dustless
CLEANING EQPT: Commercial
CLEANING EQPT: Floor Washing & Polishing, Commercial
CLEANING EQPT: High Pressure
CLEANING OR POLISHING PREPARATIONS, NEC
CLEANING PRDTS: Automobile Polish
CLEANING PRDTS: Bleaches, Household, Dry Or Liquid

COMPUTER SOFTWARE DEVELOPMENT & APPLICATIONS
COMPUTER SOFTWARE SYSTEMS ANALYSIS & DESIGN: Custom
COMPUTER STORAGE DEVICES, NEC
COMPUTER SYSTEMS ANALYSIS & DESIGN
COMPUTER TERMINALS
COMPUTER TERMINALS: CRT
COMPUTER-AIDED DESIGN SYSTEMS SVCS
COMPUTER-AIDED MANUFACTURING SYSTEMS SVCS
COMPUTERS, NEC
COMPUTERS, NEC, WHOLESALE
COMPUTERS, PERIPH & SOFTWARE, WHLSE: Personal & Home Entrtn
COMPUTERS, PERIPHERALS & SOFTWARE, WHOLESALE: Printers
COMPUTERS, PERIPHERALS & SOFTWARE, WHOLESALE: Software
COMPUTERS: Mini
COMPUTERS: Personal
CONCENTRATES, DRINK
CONCRETE BUILDING PRDTS WHOLESALERS
CONCRETE CURING & HARDENING COMPOUNDS
CONCRETE MIXERS
CONCRETE PLANTS
CONCRETE PRDTS
CONCRETE PRDTS, PRECAST, NEC
CONCRETE REINFORCING MATERIAL
CONCRETE: Asphaltic, Not From Refineries
CONCRETE: Dry Mixture
CONCRETE: Ready-Mixed
CONDENSERS & CONDENSING UNITS: Air Conditioner
CONDENSERS: Fixed Or Variable
CONDENSERS: Heat Transfer Eqpt, Evaporative
CONDENSERS: Refrigeration
CONDUITS & FITTINGS: Electric
CONFECTIONERY PRDTS WHOLESALERS
CONFECTIONS & CANDY
CONFINEMENT SURVEILLANCE SYS MAINTENANCE & MONITORING SVCS
CONNECTORS & TERMINALS: Electrical Device Uses
CONNECTORS: Electrical
CONNECTORS: Electronic
CONNECTORS: Power, Electric
CONSTRUCTION & MINING MACHINERY WHOLESALERS
CONSTRUCTION EQPT REPAIR SVCS
CONSTRUCTION EQPT: Attachments
CONSTRUCTION EQPT: Backhoes, Tractors, Cranes & Similar Eqpt
CONSTRUCTION EQPT: Crane Carriers
CONSTRUCTION EQPT: Cranes
CONSTRUCTION EQPT: Dozers, Tractor Mounted, Material Moving
CONSTRUCTION EQPT: Hammer Mills, Port, Incl Rock/Ore Crush
CONSTRUCTION EQPT: Loaders, Shovel, Self-Propelled
CONSTRUCTION EQPT: Rakes, Land Clearing, Mechanical
CONSTRUCTION EQPT: Rock Crushing Machinery, Portable
CONSTRUCTION EQPT: Roofing Eqpt
CONSTRUCTION EQPT: SCRAPERS, GRADERS, ROLLERS & SIMILAR EQPT
CONSTRUCTION EQPT: Tractors
CONSTRUCTION MATERIALS WHOLESALERS
CONSTRUCTION MATERIALS, WHOL: Concrete/Cinder Bldg Prdts
CONSTRUCTION MATERIALS, WHOLESALE: Aggregate
CONSTRUCTION MATERIALS, WHOLESALE: Air Ducts, Sheet Metal
CONSTRUCTION MATERIALS, WHOLESALE: Awnings
CONSTRUCTION MATERIALS, WHOLESALE: Block, Concrete & Cinder
CONSTRUCTION MATERIALS, WHOLESALE: Brick, Exc Refractory
CONSTRUCTION MATERIALS, WHOLESALE: Building Stone
CONSTRUCTION MATERIALS, WHOLESALE: Building Stone, Granite
CONSTRUCTION MATERIALS, WHOLESALE: Building Stone, Marble
CONSTRUCTION MATERIALS, WHOLESALE: Building, Exterior
CONSTRUCTION MATERIALS, WHOLESALE: Building, Interior
CONSTRUCTION MATERIALS, WHOLESALE: Cement

CONSTRUCTION MATERIALS, WHOLESALE: Clay, Exc Refractory
CONSTRUCTION MATERIALS, WHOLESALE: Door Frames
CONSTRUCTION MATERIALS, WHOLESALE: Doors, Garage
CONSTRUCTION MATERIALS, WHOLESALE: Doors, Sliding
CONSTRUCTION MATERIALS, WHOLESALE: Eavestroughing, Part/Sply
CONSTRUCTION MATERIALS, WHOLESALE: Fiberglass Building Mat
CONSTRUCTION MATERIALS, WHOLESALE: Glass
CONSTRUCTION MATERIALS, WHOLESALE: Gravel
CONSTRUCTION MATERIALS, WHOLESALE: Hardboard
CONSTRUCTION MATERIALS, WHOLESALE: Insulation, Thermal
CONSTRUCTION MATERIALS, WHOLESALE: Limestone
CONSTRUCTION MATERIALS, WHOLESALE: Metal Buildings
CONSTRUCTION MATERIALS, WHOLESALE: Millwork
CONSTRUCTION MATERIALS, WHOLESALE: Molding, All Materials
CONSTRUCTION MATERIALS, WHOLESALE: Paving Materials
CONSTRUCTION MATERIALS, WHOLESALE: Prefabricated Structures
CONSTRUCTION MATERIALS, WHOLESALE: Roof, Asphalt/Sheet Metal
CONSTRUCTION MATERIALS, WHOLESALE: Roofing & Siding Material
CONSTRUCTION MATERIALS, WHOLESALE: Sand
CONSTRUCTION MATERIALS, WHOLESALE: Septic Tanks
CONSTRUCTION MATERIALS, WHOLESALE: Sewer Pipe, Clay
CONSTRUCTION MATERIALS, WHOLESALE: Stone, Crushed Or Broken
CONSTRUCTION MATERIALS, WHOLESALE: Stucco
CONSTRUCTION MATERIALS, WHOLESALE: Tile & Clay Prdts
CONSTRUCTION MATERIALS, WHOLESALE: Tile, Clay/Other Ceramic
CONSTRUCTION MATERIALS, WHOLESALE: Tile, Structural Clay
CONSTRUCTION MATERIALS, WHOLESALE: Veneer
CONSTRUCTION MATERIALS, WHOLESALE: Wallboard
CONSTRUCTION MATERIALS, WHOLESALE: Window Frames
CONSTRUCTION MATERIALS, WHOLESALE: Windows
CONSTRUCTION MATL, WHOLESALE: Structural Assy, Prefab, Wood
CONSTRUCTION MATLS, WHOL: Composite Board Prdts, Woodboard
CONSTRUCTION MATLS, WHOL: Lumber, Rough, Dressed/Finished
CONSTRUCTION MATLS, WHOLESALE: Soil Erosion Cntrl Fabrics
CONSTRUCTION MTRLS, WHOL: Exterior Flat Glass, Plate/Window
CONSTRUCTION SAND MINING
CONSTRUCTION SITE PREPARATION SVCS
CONSTRUCTION: Apartment Building
CONSTRUCTION: Athletic & Recreation Facilities
CONSTRUCTION: Athletic & Recreation Facilities
CONSTRUCTION: Athletic Field
CONSTRUCTION: Bridge
CONSTRUCTION: Cable Television Line
CONSTRUCTION: Chemical Facility
CONSTRUCTION: Commercial & Institutional Building
CONSTRUCTION: Commercial & Office Building, New
CONSTRUCTION: Commercial & Office Buildings, Prefabricated
CONSTRUCTION: Concrete Patio
CONSTRUCTION: Curb
CONSTRUCTION: Dam
CONSTRUCTION: Dams, Waterways, Docks & Other Marine
CONSTRUCTION: Dock
CONSTRUCTION: Drainage System
CONSTRUCTION: Electric Power Line
CONSTRUCTION: Factory
CONSTRUCTION: Food Prdts Manufacturing or Packing Plant
CONSTRUCTION: Foundation & Retaining Wall
CONSTRUCTION: Grain Elevator
CONSTRUCTION: Heavy
CONSTRUCTION: Heavy Highway & Street
CONSTRUCTION: Indl Building & Warehouse
CONSTRUCTION: Indl Building, Prefabricated

CONSTRUCTION: Indl Buildings, New, NEC
CONSTRUCTION: Indl Plant
CONSTRUCTION: Indoor Athletic Court
CONSTRUCTION: Institutional Building
CONSTRUCTION: Irrigation System
CONSTRUCTION: Land Preparation
CONSTRUCTION: Marine
CONSTRUCTION: Mausoleum
CONSTRUCTION: Mine Loading & Discharging Station
CONSTRUCTION: Multi-Family Housing
CONSTRUCTION: Multi-family Dwellings, New
CONSTRUCTION: Natural Gas Compressor Station
CONSTRUCTION: Nonresidential Buildings, Custom
CONSTRUCTION: Oil & Gas Line & Compressor Station
CONSTRUCTION: Oil & Gas Pipeline Construction
CONSTRUCTION: Parking Lot
CONSTRUCTION: Pharmaceutical Manufacturing Plant
CONSTRUCTION: Pipeline, NEC
CONSTRUCTION: Power & Communication Transmission Tower
CONSTRUCTION: Power Plant
CONSTRUCTION: Railroad & Subway
CONSTRUCTION: Railway Roadbed
CONSTRUCTION: Refineries
CONSTRUCTION: Residential, Nec
CONSTRUCTION: Restaurant
CONSTRUCTION: Retaining Wall
CONSTRUCTION: Roads, Gravel or Dirt
CONSTRUCTION: Sewer Line
CONSTRUCTION: Sidewalk
CONSTRUCTION: Single-Family Housing
CONSTRUCTION: Single-family Housing, New
CONSTRUCTION: Steel Buildings
CONSTRUCTION: Street Sign Installation & Mntnce
CONSTRUCTION: Street Surfacing & Paving
CONSTRUCTION: Telephone & Communication Line
CONSTRUCTION: Transmitting Tower, Telecommunication
CONSTRUCTION: Tunnel
CONSTRUCTION: Utility Line
CONSTRUCTION: Warehouse
CONSTRUCTION: Waste Water & Sewage Treatment Plant
CONSTRUCTION: Water & Sewer Line
CONSULTING SVC: Actuarial
CONSULTING SVC: Business, NEC
CONSULTING SVC: Chemical
CONSULTING SVC: Computer
CONSULTING SVC: Data Processing
CONSULTING SVC: Educational
CONSULTING SVC: Engineering
CONSULTING SVC: Financial Management
CONSULTING SVC: Human Resource
CONSULTING SVC: Management
CONSULTING SVC: Marketing Management
CONSULTING SVC: Online Technology
CONSULTING SVC: Personnel Management
CONSULTING SVC: Telecommunications
CONSULTING SVCS, BUSINESS: Economic
CONSULTING SVCS, BUSINESS: Energy Conservation
CONSULTING SVCS, BUSINESS: Environmental
CONSULTING SVCS, BUSINESS: Indl Development Planning
CONSULTING SVCS, BUSINESS: Publishing
CONSULTING SVCS, BUSINESS: Safety Training Svcs
CONSULTING SVCS, BUSINESS: Sys Engnrg, Exc Computer/Prof
CONSULTING SVCS, BUSINESS: Systems Analysis & Engineering
CONSULTING SVCS, BUSINESS: Test Development & Evaluation
CONSULTING SVCS, BUSINESS: Traffic
CONSULTING SVCS: Geological
CONSULTING SVCS: Geophysical
CONSULTING SVCS: Oil
CONSULTING SVCS: Scientific
CONSUMER PURCHASING SVCS
CONTACT LENSES
CONTAINERS, GLASS: Food
CONTAINERS: Air Cargo, Metal
CONTAINERS: Cargo, Wood
CONTAINERS: Cargo, Wood & Metal Combination
CONTAINERS: Corrugated
CONTAINERS: Food & Beverage
CONTAINERS: Food, Wood Wirebound
CONTAINERS: Frozen Food & Ice Cream
CONTAINERS: Glass
CONTAINERS: Ice Cream, Made From Purchased Materials

CONVENTION & TRADE SHOW SVCS
CONVERTERS: Data
CONVERTERS: Frequency
CONVERTERS: Phase Or Rotary, Electrical
CONVERTERS: Power, AC to DC
CONVERTERS: Torque, Exc Auto
CONVEYOR SYSTEMS
CONVEYOR SYSTEMS: Belt, General Indl Use
CONVEYOR SYSTEMS: Bucket Type
CONVEYOR SYSTEMS: Bulk Handling
CONVEYOR SYSTEMS: Pneumatic Tube
CONVEYORS & CONVEYING EQPT
COOKING & FOOD WARMING EQPT: Commercial
COOKING & FOODWARMING EQPT: Coffee Brewing
COOKING & FOODWARMING EQPT: Commercial
COOKING & FOODWARMING EQPT: Microwave Ovens, Commercial
COOKING & FOODWARMING EQPT: Popcorn Machines, Commercial
COOKING EQPT, HOUSEHOLD: Convection Ovens, Incldg Portable
COOKWARE, STONEWARE: Coarse Earthenware & Pottery
COOLERS & ICE CHESTS: Metal
COOLERS & ICE CHESTS: Polystyrene Foam
COOLING TOWERS: Wood
COPINGS: Concrete
COPPER ORE MINING
COPPER ORES
COPPER: Blister
COPPER: Cathodes, Primary
COPY MACHINES WHOLESALERS
COPYRIGHT BUYING & LICENSING
COPYRIGHT PROTECTION SVCS
CORD & TWINE
CORD & TWINE: Fiber, Hard
CORES: Fiber, Made From Purchased Materials
CORNICES: Sheet Metal
CORRECTIONAL INSTITUTIONS
CORRECTIONAL INSTITUTIONS, GOVERNMENT: Prison, government
CORRUGATED PRDTS: Boxes, Partition, Display Items, Sheet/Pad
COSMETIC PREPARATIONS
COSMETICS & TOILETRIES
COSMETICS WHOLESALERS
COSMETOLOGY & PERSONAL HYGIENE SALONS
COSTUME JEWELRY & NOVELTIES: Apparel, Exc Precious Metals
COSTUME JEWELRY & NOVELTIES: Bracelets, Exc Precious Metals
COSTUME JEWELRY & NOVELTIES: Costume Novelties
COSTUME JEWELRY & NOVELTIES: Exc Semi & Precious
COSTUME JEWELRY & NOVELTIES: Keychains, Exc Precious Metal
COSTUME JEWELRY & NOVELTIES: Rings, Finger, Gold Plated Wire
COSTUMES & WIGS STORES
COTTON COMPRESSES & WAREHOUSES
COUNTER & SINK TOPS
COUNTERS & COUNTING DEVICES
COUNTERS OR COUNTER DISPLAY CASES, EXC WOOD
COUNTERS OR COUNTER DISPLAY CASES, WOOD
COUNTING DEVICES: Controls, Revolution & Timing
COUNTING DEVICES: Odometers
COUNTING DEVICES: Speed Indicators & Recorders, Vehicle
COUNTING DEVICES: Vehicle Instruments
COUPLINGS: Hose & Tube, Hydraulic Or Pneumatic
COUPLINGS: Pipe
COUPLINGS: Shaft
COURIER OR MESSENGER SVCS
COURIER SVCS, AIR: Package Delivery, Private
COURIER SVCS: Air
COURIER SVCS: Ground
COURIER SVCS: Motorcycle
COURT REPORTING SVCS
COVERS: Automobile Seat
CRACKED CASTING REPAIR SVCS
CRANE & AERIAL LIFT SVCS
CRANES & MONORAIL SYSTEMS
CRANES: Indl Plant
CRANES: Indl Truck
CRANES: Locomotive
CRANES: Overhead
CRATING SVCS: Shipping
CREATIVE SVCS: Advertisers, Exc Writers

CREDIT & OTHER FINANCIAL RESPONSIBILITY INSURANCE
CREDIT INSTITUTIONS, SHORT-TERM BUS: Wrkg Capital Finance
CREDIT INSTITUTIONS, SHORT-TERM BUSINESS: Mercantile Finance
CROWNS & CLOSURES
CRUDE PETROLEUM & NATURAL GAS PRODUCTION
CRUDE PETROLEUM & NATURAL GAS PRODUCTION
CRUDE PETROLEUM PRODUCTION
CRUDES: Cyclic, Organic
CRYSTALS
CULTURE MEDIA
CULVERTS: Sheet Metal
CUPS & PLATES: Foamed Plastics
CUPS: Paper
CUPS: Plastic Exc Polystyrene Foam
CURBING: Granite Or Stone
CURTAIN & DRAPERY FIXTURES: Poles, Rods & Rollers
CURTAIN WALLS: Building, Steel
CURTAINS: Knit
CURTAINS: Window, From Purchased Materials
CUSHIONS & PILLOWS
CUSHIONS & PILLOWS: Bed, From Purchased Materials
CUSHIONS: Carpet & Rug, Foamed Plastics
CUSHIONS: Textile, Exc Spring & Carpet
CUSTOM COMPOUNDING OF RUBBER MATERIALS
CUT STONE & STONE PRODUCTS
CUTLERY
CUTTING EQPT: Glass Cutters
CUTTING SVC: Paper, Exc Die-Cut
CYCLIC CRUDES & INTERMEDIATES
CYLINDER & ACTUATORS: Fluid Power
CYLINDERS: Pressure

D

DAIRY EQPT
DAIRY PRDTS STORE: Cheese
DAIRY PRDTS STORE: Ice Cream, Packaged
DAIRY PRDTS STORES
DAIRY PRDTS WHOLESALERS: Fresh
DAIRY PRDTS: Butter
DAIRY PRDTS: Butter Oil
DAIRY PRDTS: Buttermilk, Cultured
DAIRY PRDTS: Cheese
DAIRY PRDTS: Condensed Milk
DAIRY PRDTS: Cream Substitutes
DAIRY PRDTS: Custard, Frozen
DAIRY PRDTS: Dietary Supplements, Dairy & Non-Dairy Based
DAIRY PRDTS: Dips, Cheese-Based
DAIRY PRDTS: Evaporated Milk
DAIRY PRDTS: Frozen Desserts & Novelties
DAIRY PRDTS: Ice Cream & Ice Milk
DAIRY PRDTS: Ice Cream, Bulk
DAIRY PRDTS: Ice Cream, Packaged, Molded, On Sticks, Etc.
DAIRY PRDTS: Milk & Cream, Cultured & Flavored
DAIRY PRDTS: Milk, Condensed & Evaporated
DAIRY PRDTS: Milk, Fluid
DAIRY PRDTS: Milk, Processed, Pasteurized, Homogenized/Btld
DAIRY PRDTS: Natural Cheese
DAIRY PRDTS: Processed Cheese
DAIRY PRDTS: Sour Cream
DAIRY PRDTS: Yogurt Mix
DAIRY PRDTS: Yogurt, Exc Frozen
DAMAGED MERCHANDISE SALVAGING, SVCS ONLY
DATA ENTRY SVCS
DATA PROCESSING & PREPARATION SVCS
DATA PROCESSING SVCS
DECALS, WHOLESALE
DECORATIVE WOOD & WOODWORK
DEFENSE SYSTEMS & EQPT
DEGREASING MACHINES
DEHYDRATION EQPT
DELIVERY SVCS, BY VEHICLE
DENTAL EQPT
DENTAL EQPT & SPLYS
DENTAL EQPT & SPLYS WHOLESALERS
DENTAL EQPT & SPLYS: Compounds
DENTAL EQPT & SPLYS: Dental Hand Instruments, NEC
DENTAL EQPT & SPLYS: Dental Materials
DENTAL EQPT & SPLYS: Glue
DENTAL EQPT & SPLYS: Investment Materials

DENTAL EQPT & SPLYS: Laboratory
DENTAL EQPT & SPLYS: Orthodontic Appliances
DENTISTS' OFFICES & CLINICS
DEPARTMENT STORES
DEPARTMENT STORES: Army-Navy Goods
DERMATOLOGICALS
DERRICKS: Oil & Gas Field
DESICCANTS, CLAY: Activated
DESIGN SVCS, NEC
DESIGN SVCS: Commercial & Indl
DESIGN SVCS: Computer Integrated Systems
DESIGN SVCS: Hand Tools
DETECTION APPARATUS: Electronic/Magnetic Field, Light/Heat
DETECTIVE & ARMORED CAR SERVICES
DETECTORS: Water Leak
DETONATORS: Detonators, high explosives
DIAGNOSTIC SUBSTANCES
DIAGNOSTIC SUBSTANCES OR AGENTS: Enzyme & Isoenzyme
DIAGNOSTIC SUBSTANCES OR AGENTS: Hematology
DIAGNOSTIC SUBSTANCES OR AGENTS: In Vitro
DIAGNOSTIC SUBSTANCES OR AGENTS: Microbiology & Virology
DIAGNOSTIC SUBSTANCES OR AGENTS: Radioactive
DIAMONDS: Cutting & Polishing
DIAPERS: Cloth
DIE CUTTING SVC: Paper
DIE SETS: Presses, Metal Stamping
DIES & TOOLS: Special
DIES: Cutting, Exc Metal
DIES: Diamond, Metalworking
DIES: Plastic Forming
DIES: Steel Rule
DIODES & RECTIFIERS
DIODES: Light Emitting
DIODES: Solid State, Germanium, Silicon, Etc
DIRECT SELLING ESTABLISHMENTS, NEC
DIRECT SELLING ESTABLISHMENTS: Appliances, House-To-House
DIRECT SELLING ESTABLISHMENTS: Food Svcs
DIRECT SELLING ESTABLISHMENTS: Home Related Prdts
DISASTER SVCS
DISHWASHING EQPT: Commercial
DISINFECTING SVCS
DISK DRIVES: Computer
DISPENSERS: Soap
DISPENSING EQPT & PARTS, BEVERAGE: Beer
DISPENSING EQPT & PARTS, BEVERAGE: Coolers, Milk/Water, Elec
DISPENSING EQPT & PARTS, BEVERAGE: Fountain/Other Beverage
DISPLAY CASES: Refrigerated
DISPLAY FIXTURES: Wood
DISPLAY ITEMS: Corrugated, Made From Purchased Materials
DISTILLATES: Hardwood
DISTILLATION PRDTS: Wood
DISTILLERS DRIED GRAIN & SOLUBLES
DISTRIBUTORS: Motor Vehicle Engine
DOCK EQPT & SPLYS, INDL
DOCKS: Prefabricated Metal
DOCUMENT DESTRUCTION SVC
DOCUMENT STORAGE SVCS
DOCUMENTATION CENTER
DOLLIES: Industrial
DOOR & WINDOW REPAIR SVCS
DOOR FRAMES: Wood
DOOR OPERATING SYSTEMS: Electric
DOORS & WINDOWS WHOLESALERS: All Materials
DOORS & WINDOWS: Screen & Storm
DOORS & WINDOWS: Storm, Metal
DOORS: Fiberglass
DOORS: Fire, Metal
DOORS: Folding, Plastic Or Plastic Coated Fabric
DOORS: Garage, Overhead, Metal
DOORS: Garage, Overhead, Wood
DOORS: Glass
DOORS: Rolling, Indl Building Or Warehouse, Metal
DOORS: Safe & Vault, Metal
DOORS: Screen, Metal
DOORS: Wooden
DRAFTING SVCS
DRAINAGE PRDTS: Concrete
DRAPERIES & CURTAINS

FABRICS: Felts, Blanketing & Upholstery, Wool
FABRICS: Fiberglass, Broadwoven
FABRICS: Filter Cloth, Cotton
FABRICS: Glass & Fiberglass, Broadwoven
FABRICS: Glove, Cotton
FABRICS: Metallized
FABRICS: Nonwoven
FABRICS: Polyester, Broadwoven
FABRICS: Polypropylene, Broadwoven
FABRICS: Resin Or Plastic Coated
FABRICS: Rubberized
FABRICS: Scrub Cloths
FABRICS: Surgical Fabrics, Cotton
FABRICS: Trimmings
FABRICS: Wall Covering, From Manmade Fiber Or Silk
FABRICS: Warp Knit, Lace & Netting
FABRICS: Woven Wire, Made From Purchased Wire
FACIAL SALONS
FACILITIES SUPPORT SVCS
FAMILY CLOTHING STORES
FANS, VENTILATING: Indl Or Commercial
FANS: Ceiling
FARM & GARDEN MACHINERY WHOLESALERS
FARM MACHINERY REPAIR SVCS
FARM PRDTS, RAW MATERIAL, WHOLESALE: Tobacco &
    Tobacco Prdts
FARM PRDTS, RAW MATERIALS, WHOLESALE: Nuts & Nut
    By-Prdts
FARM PRDTS, RAW MTRLS, WHOLESALE: Peanuts, Un-
    roasted, Bulk
FARM SPLY STORES
FARM SPLYS WHOLESALERS
FARM SPLYS, WHOLESALE: Feed
FARM SPLYS, WHOLESALE: Fertilizers & Agricultural Chemi-
    cals
FARM SPLYS, WHOLESALE: Greenhouse Eqpt & Splys
FARM SPLYS, WHOLESALE: Insecticides
FARM SPLYS, WHOLESALE: Phosphate Rock, Ground
FARM SPLYS, WHOLESALE: Saddlery
FASTENERS WHOLESALERS
FASTENERS: Brads, Alum, Brass/Other Nonferrous
    Metal/Wire
FASTENERS: Metal
FASTENERS: Metal
FASTENERS: Notions, NEC
FELT PARTS
FELT: Acoustic
FENCE POSTS: Iron & Steel
FENCES & FENCING MATERIALS
FENCES OR POSTS: Ornamental Iron Or Steel
FENCING DEALERS
FENCING MATERIALS: Docks & Other Outdoor Prdts, Wood
FENCING MATERIALS: Plastic
FENCING MATERIALS: Wood
FENCING: Chain Link
FERROUS METALS: Reclaimed From Clay
FERTILIZER MINERAL MINING
FERTILIZER, AGRICULTURAL: Wholesalers
FERTILIZERS: NEC
FERTILIZERS: Nitrogenous
FERTILIZERS: Phosphatic
FIBER & FIBER PRDTS: Acetate & Triacetate
FIBER & FIBER PRDTS: Elastomeric
FIBER & FIBER PRDTS: Organic, Noncellulose
FIBER & FIBER PRDTS: Polyester
FIBER & FIBER PRDTS: Polyvinylidene Chloride
FIBER & FIBER PRDTS: Synthetic Cellulosic
FIBER OPTICS
FIBER: Vulcanized
FIBERS: Carbon & Graphite
FIDELITY OR SURETY BONDING
FILE FOLDERS
FILLERS & SEALERS: Putty
FILM & SHEET: Unsuppported Plastic
FILM: Motion Picture
FILM: Rubber
FILTER CLEANING SVCS
FILTER ELEMENTS: Fluid & Hydraulic Line
FILTERS
FILTERS & SOFTENERS: Water, Household
FILTERS & STRAINERS: Pipeline
FILTERS: Air
FILTERS: Air Intake, Internal Combustion Engine, Exc Auto
FILTERS: Gasoline, Internal Combustion Engine, Exc Auto
FILTERS: General Line, Indl

FILTRATION DEVICES: Electronic
FILTRATION SAND MINING
FINANCIAL INVEST ACTIVITY: Protective Assoc, Royalty
    Owner
FINANCIAL INVESTMENT ACTIVITIES, NEC: Security Trans-
    fer
FINANCIAL INVESTMENT ADVICE
FINANCIAL SVCS
FINDINGS & TRIMMINGS Waistbands, Trouser
FINDINGS & TRIMMINGS: Fabric
FINDINGS & TRIMMINGS: Furniture, Fabric
FINGERNAILS, ARTIFICIAL
FINISHING SVCS
FIRE ALARM MAINTENANCE & MONITORING SVCS
FIRE ARMS, SMALL: Guns Or Gun Parts, 30 mm & Below
FIRE ARMS, SMALL: Pistols Or Pistol Parts, 30 mm & below
FIRE ARMS, SMALL: Rifles Or Rifle Parts, 30 mm & below
FIRE CONTROL OR BOMBING EQPT: Electronic
FIRE DETECTION SYSTEMS
FIRE EXTINGUISHER CHARGES
FIRE EXTINGUISHER SVC
FIRE EXTINGUISHERS, WHOLESALE
FIRE EXTINGUISHERS: Portable
FIRE OR BURGLARY RESISTIVE PRDTS
FIRE PROTECTION EQPT
FIRE PROTECTION SVCS: Contracted
FIRE PROTECTION, GOVERNMENT: State
FIREARMS & AMMUNITION, EXC SPORTING, WHOLESALE
FIREARMS: Small, 30mm or Less
FIREFIGHTING APPARATUS
FIREPLACE EQPT & ACCESS
FIREWORKS
FIRST AID SPLYS, WHOLESALE
FIRST AID SVCS
FISH & SEAFOOD MARKETS
FISH & SEAFOOD PROCESSORS: Canned Or Cured
FISH & SEAFOOD PROCESSORS: Fresh Or Frozen
FISH FOOD
FISHING EQPT: Lures
FITTINGS & ASSEMBLIES: Hose & Tube, Hydraulic Or Pneu-
    matic
FITTINGS & SPECIALTIES: Steam
FITTINGS: Pipe
FITTINGS: Pipe, Fabricated
FIXTURES & EQPT: Kitchen, Metal, Exc Cast Aluminum
FIXTURES: Cut Stone
FLAGPOLES
FLAGS: Fabric
FLAGSTONES
FLARES
FLAT GLASS: Building
FLAT GLASS: Construction
FLAT GLASS: Float
FLAT GLASS: Laminated
FLAT GLASS: Skylight
FLAT GLASS: Strengthened Or Reinforced
FLAT GLASS: Tempered
FLAT GLASS: Window, Clear & Colored
FLAVORS OR FLAVORING MATERIALS: Synthetic
FLIGHT RECORDERS
FLOOR CLEANING & MAINTENANCE EQPT: Household
FLOOR COVERING STORES
FLOOR COVERING STORES: Carpets
FLOOR COVERING STORES: Floor Tile
FLOOR COVERING STORES: Rugs
FLOOR COVERINGS WHOLESALERS
FLOOR COVERINGS: Aircraft & Automobile
FLOOR COVERINGS: Asphalted-Felt Base, Linoleum Or Car-
    pet
FLOOR COVERINGS: Rubber
FLOOR COVERINGS: Textile Fiber
FLOORING & GRATINGS: Open, Construction Applications
FLOORING & SIDING: Metal
FLOORING: Hard Surface
FLOORING: Hardwood
FLOORING: Tile
FLORISTS
FLOWER ARRANGEMENTS: Artificial
FLOWERS, ARTIFICIAL, WHOLESALE
FLOWERS: Artificial & Preserved
FLUID METERS & COUNTING DEVICES
FLUID POWER PUMPS & MOTORS
FLUID POWER VALVES & HOSE FITTINGS
FLUXES
FOAM CHARGE MIXTURES

FOAM RUBBER
FOAM RUBBER, WHOLESALE
FOAMS & RUBBER, WHOLESALE
FOOD PRDTS, BREAKFAST: Cereal, Rice: Cereal Breakfast
    Food
FOOD PRDTS, CANNED OR FRESH PACK: Fruit Juices
FOOD PRDTS, CANNED OR FRESH PACK: Vegetable
    Juices
FOOD PRDTS, CANNED, NEC
FOOD PRDTS, CANNED: Barbecue Sauce
FOOD PRDTS, CANNED: Bean Sprouts
FOOD PRDTS, CANNED: Beans & Bean Sprouts
FOOD PRDTS, CANNED: Beans, Baked Without Meat
FOOD PRDTS, CANNED: Chow Mein
FOOD PRDTS, CANNED: Ethnic
FOOD PRDTS, CANNED: Fruit Juices, Fresh
FOOD PRDTS, CANNED: Fruits
FOOD PRDTS, CANNED: Fruits
FOOD PRDTS, CANNED: Fruits & Fruit Prdts
FOOD PRDTS, CANNED: Jams, Including Imitation
FOOD PRDTS, CANNED: Jams, Jellies & Preserves
FOOD PRDTS, CANNED: Jellies, Edible, Including Imitation
FOOD PRDTS, CANNED: Macaroni
FOOD PRDTS, CANNED: Mexican, NEC
FOOD PRDTS, CANNED: Olives
FOOD PRDTS, CANNED: Poultry
FOOD PRDTS, CANNED: Soups
FOOD PRDTS, CANNED: Spaghetti & Other Pasta Sauce
FOOD PRDTS, CANNED: Spanish
FOOD PRDTS, CANNED: Tamales
FOOD PRDTS, CANNED: Tomato Sauce.
FOOD PRDTS, CANNED: Tomatoes
FOOD PRDTS, CANNED: Vegetables
FOOD PRDTS, CONFECTIONERY, WHOLESALE: Candy
FOOD PRDTS, CONFECTIONERY, WHOLESALE: Nuts,
    Salted/Roasted
FOOD PRDTS, CONFECTIONERY, WHOLESALE: Potato
    Chips
FOOD PRDTS, CONFECTIONERY, WHOLESALE: Snack
    Foods
FOOD PRDTS, CONFECTIONERY, WHOLESALE: Syrups,
    Fountain
FOOD PRDTS, DAIRY, WHOLESALE: Frozen Dairy Desserts
FOOD PRDTS, FISH & SEAFOOD, WHOLESALE: Fresh
FOOD PRDTS, FISH & SEAFOOD, WHOLESALE: Seafood
FOOD PRDTS, FISH & SEAFOOD: Crabmeat, Fresh, Pkgd
    Nonsealed
FOOD PRDTS, FISH & SEAFOOD: Fish, Fresh, Prepared
FOOD PRDTS, FISH & SEAFOOD: Fresh, Prepared
FOOD PRDTS, FISH & SEAFOOD: Seafood, Frozen, Pre-
    pared
FOOD PRDTS, FISH & SEAFOOD: Shellfish, Frozen, Pre-
    pared
FOOD PRDTS, FISH & SEAFOOD: Shrimp, Fresh, Prepared
FOOD PRDTS, FISH & SEAFOOD: Shrimp, Preserved &
    Cured
FOOD PRDTS, FROZEN: Breakfasts, Packaged
FOOD PRDTS, FROZEN: Dinners, Packaged
FOOD PRDTS, FROZEN: Ethnic Foods, NEC
FOOD PRDTS, FROZEN: Fruits
FOOD PRDTS, FROZEN: Fruits, Juices & Vegetables
FOOD PRDTS, FROZEN: Lunches, Packaged
FOOD PRDTS, FROZEN: NEC
FOOD PRDTS, FROZEN: Pizza
FOOD PRDTS, FROZEN: Potato Prdts
FOOD PRDTS, FROZEN: Snack Items
FOOD PRDTS, FROZEN: Vegetables, Exc Potato Prdts
FOOD PRDTS, FRUITS & VEGETABLES, FRESH, WHOLE-
    SALE
FOOD PRDTS, FRUITS & VEGETABLES, FRESH, WHOLE-
    SALE: Vegetable
FOOD PRDTS, MEAT & MEAT PRDTS, WHOLESALE: Cured
    Or Smoked
FOOD PRDTS, MEAT & MEAT PRDTS, WHOLESALE: Fresh
FOOD PRDTS, MEAT & MEAT PRDTS, WHOLESALE: Lard
FOOD PRDTS, POULTRY, WHOLESALE:
    Live/Dressed/Frozen, Unpkgd
FOOD PRDTS, POULTRY, WHOLESALE: Poultry Prdts, NEC
FOOD PRDTS, WHOL: Canned Goods, Fruit, Veg,
    Seafood/Meats
FOOD PRDTS, WHOLESALE: Beans, Field
FOOD PRDTS, WHOLESALE: Beverage Concentrates
FOOD PRDTS, WHOLESALE: Beverages, Exc Coffee & Tea
FOOD PRDTS, WHOLESALE: Breakfast Cereals
FOOD PRDTS, WHOLESALE: Chocolate

FURNITURE: Office, Exc Wood
FURNITURE: Office, Wood
FURNITURE: Outdoor, Wood
FURNITURE: Picnic Tables Or Benches, Park
FURNITURE: Restaurant
FURNITURE: School
FURNITURE: Sofa Beds Or Convertible Sofas)
FURNITURE: Stadium
FURNITURE: Table Tops, Marble
FURNITURE: Tables, Office, Wood
FURNITURE: Upholstered
FURNITURE: Vehicle
FURNITURE: Wicker & Rattan
FUSES & FUSE EQPT

G

GAMES & TOYS: Banks
GAMES & TOYS: Bingo Boards
GAMES & TOYS: Board Games, Children's & Adults'
GAMES & TOYS: Craft & Hobby Kits & Sets
GAMES & TOYS: Electronic
GAMES & TOYS: Game Machines, Exc Coin-Operated
GAMES & TOYS: Go-Carts, Children's
GAMES & TOYS: Kits, Science, Incl Microscopes/Chemistry Sets
GAMES & TOYS: Models, Boat & Ship, Toy & Hobby
GAMES & TOYS: Toy Guns
GARAGES: Portable, Prefabricated Metal
GARBAGE CONTAINERS: Plastic
GARBAGE DISPOSALS: Household
GARNET MINING SVCS
GAS & HYDROCARBON LIQUEFACTION FROM COAL
GAS & OIL FIELD EXPLORATION SVCS
GAS & OIL FIELD SVCS, NEC
GAS & OTHER COMBINED SVCS
GAS FIELD MACHINERY & EQPT
GAS PROCESSING SVC
GAS PRODUCTION & DISTRIBUTION
GAS PRODUCTION & DISTRIBUTION: Liq Petroleum, Distrib-Mains
GAS STATIONS
GAS: Refinery
GASES & LIQUIFIED PETROLEUM GASES
GASES: Acetylene
GASES: Carbon Dioxide
GASES: Flourinated Hydrocarbon
GASES: Hydrogen
GASES: Indl
GASES: Nitrogen
GASES: Oxygen
GASKET MATERIALS
GASKETS
GASKETS & SEALING DEVICES
GASOLINE BLENDING PLANT
GASOLINE FILLING STATIONS
GASOLINE WHOLESALERS
GATES: Ornamental Metal
GAUGES
GAUGES: Pressure
GEARS
GEARS & GEAR UNITS: Reduction, Exc Auto
GEARS: Power Transmission, Exc Auto
GEM STONES MINING, NEC: Natural
GENERAL COUNSELING SVCS
GENERAL ECONOMIC PROG ADMIN, GOVT: Consumer Protection
GENERAL MERCHANDISE, NONDURABLE, WHOLESALE
GENERATING APPARATUS & PARTS: Electrical
GENERATION EQPT: Electronic
GENERATOR REPAIR SVCS
GENERATOR SETS: Motor
GENERATORS SETS: Steam
GENERATORS: Automotive & Aircraft
GENERATORS: Electric
GENERATORS: Electrochemical, Fuel Cell
GIFT SHOP
GIFT, NOVELTY & SOUVENIR STORES: Gifts & Novelties
GIFT, NOVELTY & SOUVENIR STORES: Party Favors
GIFT, NOVELTY & SOUVENIR STORES: Trading Cards, Sports
GIFTS & NOVELTIES: Wholesalers
GIFTWARE: Brass
GILSONITE MINING SVCS
GLASS FABRICATORS

GLASS PRDTS, FROM PURCHASED GLASS: Glass Beads, Reflecting
GLASS PRDTS, FROM PURCHASED GLASS: Glassware
GLASS PRDTS, FROM PURCHASED GLASS: Glassware, Indl
GLASS PRDTS, FROM PURCHASED GLASS: Insulating
GLASS PRDTS, FROM PURCHASED GLASS: Mirrored
GLASS PRDTS, PRESSED OR BLOWN: Blocks & Bricks
GLASS PRDTS, PRESSED OR BLOWN: Furnishings & Access
GLASS PRDTS, PRESSED OR BLOWN: Glassware, Art Or Decorative
GLASS PRDTS, PRESSED OR BLOWN: Glassware, Novelty
GLASS PRDTS, PRESSED OR BLOWN: Lighting Eqpt Parts
GLASS PRDTS, PRESSED OR BLOWN: Scientific Glassware
GLASS PRDTS, PRESSED OR BLOWN: Yarn, Fiberglass
GLASS PRDTS, PURCHD GLASS: Furniture Top, Cut, Beveld/Polshd
GLASS PRDTS, PURCHSD GLASS: Ornamental, Cut, Engraved/Décor
GLASS STORE: Leaded Or Stained
GLASS STORES
GLASS: Fiber
GLASS: Flat
GLASS: Indl Prdts
GLASS: Pressed & Blown, NEC
GLASS: Stained
GLASS: Structural
GLASS: Tempered
GLASSWARE: Laboratory & Medical
GLOBAL POSITIONING SYSTEMS & EQPT
GLOVES: Fabric
GLOVES: Leather
GLOVES: Leather, Work
GLOVES: Plastic
GLOVES: Safety
GLUE
GOLD ORE MINING
GOLF COURSES: Public
GOLF EQPT
GOURMET FOOD STORES
GOVERNMENT, EXECUTIVE OFFICES: Mayors'
GOVERNMENT, GENERAL: Administration
GRANITE: Crushed & Broken
GRANITE: Cut & Shaped
GRANITE: Dimension
GRAPHIC ARTS & RELATED DESIGN SVCS
GRAPHIC LAYOUT SVCS: Printed Circuitry
GRASSES: Artificial & Preserved
GRATINGS: Open Steel Flooring
GRATINGS: Tread, Fabricated Metal
GRAVE VAULTS, METAL
GRAVEL & PEBBLE MINING
GRAVEL MINING
GREASES & INEDIBLE FATS, RENDERED
GREENHOUSES: Prefabricated Metal
GREENSAND MINING SVCS
GRILLES & REGISTERS: Ornamental Metal Work
GRILLS & GRILLWORK: Woven Wire, Made From Purchased Wire
GRINDING SVC: Precision, Commercial Or Indl
GRINDING SVCS: Ophthalmic Lens, Exc Prescription
GRIPS OR HANDLES: Rubber
GRITS: Crushed & Broken
GROCERIES WHOLESALERS, NEC
GROCERIES, GENERAL LINE WHOLESALERS
GUARD SVCS
GUARDRAILS
GUIDED MISSILES & SPACE VEHICLES
GUIDED MISSILES & SPACE VEHICLES: Research & Development
GUIDED MISSILES/SPACE VEHICLE PARTS/AUX EQPT: Research/Devel
GUM & WOOD CHEMICALS
GUN SIGHTS: Optical
GUN STOCKS: Wood
GUN SVCS
GUNSMITHS
GUTTERS
GUTTERS: Sheet Metal
GYPSUM BOARD
GYPSUM MINING
GYPSUM PRDTS

H

HAIR & HAIR BASED PRDTS
HAIR CARE PRDTS
HAIR CARE PRDTS: Hair Coloring Preparations
HAIR DRYERS: Beauty Shop
HAIRDRESSERS
HAND TOOLS, NEC: Wholesalers
HANDBAG STORES
HANDBAGS
HANDBAGS: Women's
HANDLES: Wood
HANGERS: Garment, Home & Store, Wooden
HARD RUBBER PRDTS, NEC
HARDWARE
HARDWARE & BUILDING PRDTS: Plastic
HARDWARE & EQPT: Stage, Exc Lighting
HARDWARE STORES
HARDWARE STORES: Builders'
HARDWARE STORES: Door Locks & Lock Sets
HARDWARE STORES: Pumps & Pumping Eqpt
HARDWARE STORES: Tools
HARDWARE WHOLESALERS
HARDWARE, WHOLESALE: Bolts
HARDWARE, WHOLESALE: Builders', NEC
HARDWARE, WHOLESALE: Casters & Glides
HARDWARE, WHOLESALE: Furniture, NEC
HARDWARE, WHOLESALE: Nozzles
HARDWARE, WHOLESALE: Power Tools & Access
HARDWARE, WHOLESALE: Screws
HARDWARE, WHOLESALE: Security Devices, Locks
HARDWARE: Aircraft
HARDWARE: Aircraft & Marine, Incl Pulleys & Similar Items
HARDWARE: Builders'
HARDWARE: Door Opening & Closing Devices, Exc Electrical
HARDWARE: Furniture
HARDWARE: Furniture, Builders' & Other Household
HARDWARE: Harness
HARDWARE: Locking Systems, Security Cable
HARNESS ASSEMBLIES: Cable & Wire
HARNESS WIRING SETS: Internal Combustion Engines
HARNESSES, HALTERS, SADDLERY & STRAPS
HARVESTING MACHINERY & EQPT WHOLESALERS
HEADPHONES: Radio
HEALTH AIDS: Exercise Eqpt
HEALTH FOOD & SUPPLEMENT STORES
HEARING AIDS
HEAT EMISSION OPERATING APPARATUS
HEAT EXCHANGERS
HEAT EXCHANGERS: After Or Inter Coolers Or Condensers, Etc
HEAT TREATING: Metal
HEATERS: Swimming Pool, Electric
HEATING & AIR CONDITIONING EQPT & SPLYS WHOLESALERS
HEATING & AIR CONDITIONING UNITS, COMBINATION
HEATING EQPT & SPLYS
HEATING EQPT: Complete
HEATING EQPT: Induction
HEATING PADS, ELECTRIC
HEATING PADS: Nonelectric
HEATING UNITS & DEVICES: Indl, Electric
HEATING UNITS: Gas, Infrared
HEELS, BOOT OR SHOE: Plastic
HEELS, BOOT OR SHOE: Rubber, Composition Or Fiber
HELICOPTERS
HELMETS: Athletic
HELP SUPPLY SERVICES
HERMETICS REPAIR SVCS
HIGH ENERGY PARTICLE PHYSICS EQPT
HIGHWAY & STREET MAINTENANCE SVCS
HIGHWAY SIGNALS: Electric
HITCHES: Trailer
HOBBY, TOY & GAME STORES: Arts & Crafts & Splys
HOBBY, TOY & GAME STORES: Ceramics Splys
HOBBY, TOY & GAME STORES: Dolls & Access
HOBBY, TOY & GAME STORES: Toys & Games
HOISTING SLINGS
HOISTS
HOLDERS, PAPER TOWEL, GROCERY BAG, ETC: Plastic
HOLDING COMPANIES: Investment, Exc Banks
HOLDING COMPANIES: Personal, Exc Banks
HOLLOWARE, STAINLESS STEEL
HOME CENTER STORES
HOME ENTERTAINMENT EQPT: Electronic, NEC

HOME FURNISHINGS WHOLESALERS
HOME HEALTH CARE SVCS
HOME IMPROVEMENT & RENOVATION CONTRACTOR AGENCY
HOMEBUILDERS & OTHER OPERATIVE BUILDERS
HOMEFURNISHING STORE: Bedding, Sheet, Blanket,Spread/Pillow
HOMEFURNISHING STORES: Beddings & Linens
HOMEFURNISHING STORES: Cookware, Exc Aluminum
HOMEFURNISHING STORES: Cutlery
HOMEFURNISHING STORES: Lighting Fixtures
HOMEFURNISHING STORES: Metalware
HOMEFURNISHING STORES: Mirrors
HOMEFURNISHING STORES: Pictures, Wall
HOMEFURNISHING STORES: Pottery
HOMEFURNISHING STORES: Venetian Blinds
HOMEFURNISHING STORES: Vertical Blinds
HOMEFURNISHING STORES: Wicker, Rattan, Or Reed
HOMEFURNISHING STORES: Window Furnishings
HOMEFURNISHING STORES: Window Shades, NEC
HOMEFURNISHINGS, WHOLESALE: Blinds, Venetian
HOMEFURNISHINGS, WHOLESALE: Blinds, Vertical
HOMEFURNISHINGS, WHOLESALE: Carpets
HOMEFURNISHINGS, WHOLESALE: Draperies
HOMEFURNISHINGS, WHOLESALE: Fireplace Eqpt & Access
HOMEFURNISHINGS, WHOLESALE: Floor Cushion & Padding
HOMEFURNISHINGS, WHOLESALE: Linens, Table
HOMEFURNISHINGS, WHOLESALE: Pillowcases
HOMEFURNISHINGS, WHOLESALE: Pottery
HOMEFURNISHINGS, WHOLESALE: Rugs
HOMEFURNISHINGS, WHOLESALE: Window Covering Parts & Access
HOMEFURNISHINGS, WHOLESALE: Wood Flooring
HOMES, MODULAR: Wooden
HOMES: Log Cabins
HONES
HOPPERS: Metal Plate
HORNS: Marine, Compressed Air Or Steam
HORSE & PET ACCESSORIES: Textile
HOSE: Air Line Or Air Brake, Rubber Or Rubberized Fabric
HOSE: Automobile, Rubber
HOSE: Fabric
HOSE: Flexible Metal
HOSE: Garden, Plastic
HOSE: Plastic
HOSE: Pneumatic, Rubber Or Rubberized Fabric, NEC
HOSE: Rubber
HOSES & BELTING: Rubber & Plastic
HOSIERY STORES
HOSPITAL EQPT REPAIR SVCS
HOSPITALS: Medical & Surgical
HOSPITALS: Rehabilitation, Drug Addiction
HOT TUBS
HOT TUBS: Plastic & Fiberglass
HOTELS & MOTELS
HOUSEHOLD APPLIANCE STORES
HOUSEHOLD APPLIANCE STORES: Garbage Disposals
HOUSEHOLD ARTICLES, EXC FURNITURE: Cut Stone
HOUSEHOLD ARTICLES, EXC KITCHEN: Pottery
HOUSEHOLD ARTICLES: Metal
HOUSEHOLD FURNISHINGS, NEC
HOUSES: Rooming & Boarding
HOUSEWARES, ELECTRIC: Air Purifiers, Portable
HOUSEWARES, ELECTRIC: Cooking Appliances
HOUSEWARES, ELECTRIC: Dehumidifiers, Room
HOUSEWARES, ELECTRIC: Fans, Exhaust & Ventilating
HOUSEWARES, ELECTRIC: Grills Or Griddles
HOUSEWARES, ELECTRIC: Heaters, Sauna
HOUSEWARES, ELECTRIC: Heating Units, Electric Appliances
HOUSEWARES, ELECTRIC: Heating, Bsbrd/Wall, Radiant Heat
HOUSEWARES, ELECTRIC: Massage Machines, Exc Beauty/Barber
HOUSEWARES: Dishes, Plastic
HOUSEWARES: Food Dishes & Utensils, Pressed & Molded Pulp
HOUSEWARES: Toothpicks, Wood
HOUSINGS: Business Machine, Sheet Metal
HUB CAPS: Automobile, Stamped Metal
HUMIDIFIERS & DEHUMIDIFIERS
HYDRAULIC EQPT REPAIR SVC
HYDRAULIC FLUIDS: Synthetic Based

Hard Rubber & Molded Rubber Prdts

I

ICE
ICE CREAM & ICES WHOLESALERS
ICE WHOLESALERS
IDENTIFICATION PLATES
IDENTIFICATION TAGS, EXC PAPER
IGNEOUS ROCK: Crushed & Broken
IGNITION APPARATUS & DISTRIBUTORS
IGNITION CONTROLS: Gas Appliance
IGNITION SYSTEMS: High Frequency
IGNITION SYSTEMS: Internal Combustion Engine
INCENSE
INCINERATORS
INDL & PERSONAL SVC PAPER WHOLESALERS
INDL & PERSONAL SVC PAPER, WHOL: Bags, Paper/Disp Plastic
INDL & PERSONAL SVC PAPER, WHOL: Boxes, Corrugtd/Solid Fiber
INDL & PERSONAL SVC PAPER, WHOL: Boxes, Paperbrd/Plastic
INDL & PERSONAL SVC PAPER, WHOL: Container, Paper/Plastic
INDL & PERSONAL SVC PAPER, WHOL: Paper, Wrap/Coarse/Prdts
INDL & PERSONAL SVC PAPER, WHOLESALE: Cardboard & Prdts
INDL & PERSONAL SVC PAPER, WHOLESALE: Disposable
INDL & PERSONAL SVC PAPER, WHOLESALE: Paper Tubes & Cores
INDL & PERSONAL SVC PAPER, WHOLESALE: Shipping Splys
INDL EQPT CLEANING SVCS
INDL EQPT SVCS
INDL GASES WHOLESALERS
INDL MACHINERY & EQPT WHOLESALERS
INDL MACHINERY REPAIR & MAINTENANCE
INDL PATTERNS: Foundry Patternmaking
INDL PROCESS INSTR: Transmit, Process Variables
INDL PROCESS INSTRUMENTS: Absorp Analyzers, Infrared, X-Ray
INDL PROCESS INSTRUMENTS: Analyzers
INDL PROCESS INSTRUMENTS: Chromatographs
INDL PROCESS INSTRUMENTS: Control
INDL PROCESS INSTRUMENTS: Controllers, Process Variables
INDL PROCESS INSTRUMENTS: Data Loggers
INDL PROCESS INSTRUMENTS: Digital Display, Process Variables
INDL PROCESS INSTRUMENTS: Fluidic Devices, Circuit & Systems
INDL PROCESS INSTRUMENTS: Indl Flow & Measuring
INDL PROCESS INSTRUMENTS: Level & Bulk Measuring
INDL PROCESS INSTRUMENTS: Manometers
INDL PROCESS INSTRUMENTS: On-Stream Gas Or Liquid Analysis
INDL PROCESS INSTRUMENTS: Temperature
INDL PROCESS INSTRUMENTS: Water Quality Monitoring/Cntrl Sys
INDL SPLYS WHOLESALERS
INDL SPLYS, WHOL: Fasteners, Incl Nuts, Bolts, Screws, Etc
INDL SPLYS, WHOLESALE: Abrasives
INDL SPLYS, WHOLESALE: Abrasives & Adhesives
INDL SPLYS, WHOLESALE: Adhesives, Tape & Plasters
INDL SPLYS, WHOLESALE: Bearings
INDL SPLYS, WHOLESALE: Bottler Splys
INDL SPLYS, WHOLESALE: Filters, Indl
INDL SPLYS, WHOLESALE: Fittings
INDL SPLYS, WHOLESALE: Gaskets
INDL SPLYS, WHOLESALE: Gaskets & Seals
INDL SPLYS, WHOLESALE: Hydraulic & Pneumatic Pistons/Valves
INDL SPLYS, WHOLESALE: Mill Splys
INDL SPLYS, WHOLESALE: Pipeline Wrappings, Anti-Corrosive
INDL SPLYS, WHOLESALE: Plastic Bottles
INDL SPLYS, WHOLESALE: Power Transmission, Eqpt & Apparatus
INDL SPLYS, WHOLESALE: Rubber Goods, Mechanical
INDL SPLYS, WHOLESALE: Seals
INDL SPLYS, WHOLESALE: Signmaker Eqpt & Splys
INDL SPLYS, WHOLESALE: Springs
INDL SPLYS, WHOLESALE: Sprockets
INDL SPLYS, WHOLESALE: Tanks, Pressurized

INDL SPLYS, WHOLESALE: Tools
INDL SPLYS, WHOLESALE: Tools, NEC
INDL SPLYS, WHOLESALE: Valves & Fittings
INDL TRUCK REPAIR SVCS
INDUCTORS
INDUSTRIAL & COMMERCIAL EQPT INSPECTION SVCS
INFANTS' WEAR STORES
INFORMATION BUREAU SVCS
INFORMATION RETRIEVAL SERVICES
INFORMATION SVCS: Consumer
INGOT, EXTRUSION: Extrusion ingot, aluminum: rolling mills
INK OR WRITING FLUIDS
INK: Printing
INSECTICIDES & PESTICIDES
INSPECTION & TESTING SVCS
INSTRUMENTS & ACCESSORIES: Surveying
INSTRUMENTS & METERS: Measuring, Electric
INSTRUMENTS, LABORATORY: Analyzers, Automatic Chemical
INSTRUMENTS, LABORATORY: Analyzers, Thermal
INSTRUMENTS, LABORATORY: Electrophoresis
INSTRUMENTS, LABORATORY: Gas Analyzing
INSTRUMENTS, LABORATORY: Gas Chromatographic
INSTRUMENTS, LABORATORY: Infrared Analytical
INSTRUMENTS, LABORATORY: Integrators, Mathematical
INSTRUMENTS, LABORATORY: Microprobes
INSTRUMENTS, LABORATORY: Protein Analyzers
INSTRUMENTS, MEASURING & CNTRG: Plotting, Drafting/Map Rdg
INSTRUMENTS, MEASURING & CNTRL: Auto Turnstiles
INSTRUMENTS, MEASURING & CNTRL: Geophysical & Meteorological
INSTRUMENTS, MEASURING & CNTRL: Geophysical/Meteorological
INSTRUMENTS, MEASURING & CNTRL: Radiation & Testing, Nuclear
INSTRUMENTS, MEASURING & CNTRL: Testing, Abrasion, Etc
INSTRUMENTS, MEASURING & CNTRLG: Aircraft & Motor Vehicle
INSTRUMENTS, MEASURING & CNTRLG: Thermometers/Temp Sensors
INSTRUMENTS, MEASURING & CNTRLNG: Press & Vac Ind, Acft Eng
INSTRUMENTS, MEASURING & CONTROLLING: Fuel System, Aircraft
INSTRUMENTS, MEASURING & CONTROLLING: Gas Detectors
INSTRUMENTS, MEASURING & CONTROLLING: Ion Chambers
INSTRUMENTS, MEASURING & CONTROLLING: Leak Detection, Liquid
INSTRUMENTS, MEASURING & CONTROLLING: Magnetometers
INSTRUMENTS, MEASURING & CONTROLLING: Reactor Controls, Aux
INSTRUMENTS, MEASURING & CONTROLLING: Seismoscopes
INSTRUMENTS, MEASURING & CONTROLLING: Surveying & Drafting
INSTRUMENTS, MEASURING & CONTROLLING: Ultrasonic Testing
INSTRUMENTS, MEASURING & CONTROLLING: Weather Tracking
INSTRUMENTS, MEASURING/CNTRLNG: Med Diagnostic Sys, Nuclear
INSTRUMENTS, OPTICAL: Coating, Lens
INSTRUMENTS, OPTICAL: Elements & Assemblies, Exc Ophthalmic
INSTRUMENTS, OPTICAL: Lenses, All Types Exc Ophthalmic
INSTRUMENTS, OPTICAL: Sighting & Fire Control
INSTRUMENTS, OPTICAL: Test & Inspection
INSTRUMENTS, SURGICAL & MED: Needles & Syringes, Hypodermic
INSTRUMENTS, SURGICAL & MEDICAL: Blood & Bone Work
INSTRUMENTS, SURGICAL & MEDICAL: Blood Pressure
INSTRUMENTS, SURGICAL & MEDICAL: Catheters
INSTRUMENTS, SURGICAL & MEDICAL: Cystoscopes
INSTRUMENTS, SURGICAL & MEDICAL: Holders, Surgical Needle
INSTRUMENTS, SURGICAL & MEDICAL: Inhalation Therapy
INSTRUMENTS, SURGICAL & MEDICAL: Knives
INSTRUMENTS, SURGICAL & MEDICAL: Lasers, Ophthalmic
INSTRUMENTS, SURGICAL & MEDICAL: Lasers, Surgical

INSTRUMENTS, SURGICAL & MEDICAL: Ophthalmic
INSTRUMENTS, SURGICAL & MEDICAL: Oxygen Tents
INSTRUMENTS, SURGICAL/MED: Microsurgical, Exc Electromedical
INSTRUMENTS: Airspeed
INSTRUMENTS: Analytical
INSTRUMENTS: Analyzers, Internal Combustion Eng, Electronic
INSTRUMENTS: Analyzers, Radio Apparatus, NEC
INSTRUMENTS: Combustion Control, Indl
INSTRUMENTS: Digital Panel Meters, Electricity Measuring
INSTRUMENTS: Electrolytic Conductivity, Indl
INSTRUMENTS: Endoscopic Eqpt, Electromedical
INSTRUMENTS: Flow, Indl Process
INSTRUMENTS: Indl Process Control
INSTRUMENTS: Instrument Relays, All Types
INSTRUMENTS: Laser, Scientific & Engineering
INSTRUMENTS: Liquid Level, Indl Process
INSTRUMENTS: Measurement, Indl Process
INSTRUMENTS: Measuring & Controlling
INSTRUMENTS: Measuring Electricity
INSTRUMENTS: Measuring, Electrical Energy
INSTRUMENTS: Measuring, Electrical Power
INSTRUMENTS: Medical & Surgical
INSTRUMENTS: Meteorological
INSTRUMENTS: Nautical
INSTRUMENTS: Pressure Measurement, Indl
INSTRUMENTS: Radio Frequency Measuring
INSTRUMENTS: Recorders, Oscillographic
INSTRUMENTS: Seismographs
INSTRUMENTS: Standards & Calibration, Electrical Measuring
INSTRUMENTS: Sweep Oscillators
INSTRUMENTS: Temperature Measurement, Indl
INSTRUMENTS: Test, Digital, Electronic & Electrical Circuits
INSTRUMENTS: Test, Electronic & Electric Measurement
INSTRUMENTS: Test, Electronic & Electrical Circuits
INSTRUMENTS: Testing, Semiconductor
INSTRUMENTS: Thermal Conductive, Indl
INSTRUMENTS: Transducers, Volts, Amperes, Watts, VARs & Freq
INSTRUMENTS: Transformers, Portable
INSTRUMENTS: Vibration
INSTRUMENTS: Viscometer, Indl Process
INSULATING BOARD, CELLULAR FIBER
INSULATING BOARD, HARD PRESSED
INSULATION & CUSHIONING FOAM: Polystyrene
INSULATION & ROOFING MATERIALS: Wood, Reconstituted
INSULATION MATERIALS WHOLESALERS
INSULATION: Fiberglass
INSULATORS & INSULATION MATERIALS: Electrical
INSULATORS, PORCELAIN: Electrical
INSURANCE AGENCIES & BROKERS
INSURANCE CARRIERS: Automobile
INSURANCE INFORMATION & CONSULTING SVCS
INSURANCE PROFESSIONAL STANDARDS SVCS
INSURANCE: Agents, Brokers & Service
INTEGRATED CIRCUITS, SEMICONDUCTOR NETWORKS, ETC
INTERCOMMUNICATION EQPT REPAIR SVCS
INTERCOMMUNICATIONS SYSTEMS: Electric
INTERIOR DECORATING SVCS
INTERIOR DESIGN SVCS, NEC
INTERIOR DESIGNING SVCS
INVENTORY STOCKING SVCS
INVERTERS: Nonrotating Electrical
INVERTERS: Rotating Electrical
INVESTMENT FIRM: General Brokerage
INVESTMENT FUNDS, NEC
INVESTMENT FUNDS: Open-Ended
INVESTORS, NEC
INVESTORS: Real Estate, Exc Property Operators
IRON & STEEL PRDTS: Hot-Rolled
IRON ORE MINING
IRRADIATION EQPT: Beta Ray
IRRIGATION EQPT WHOLESALERS
IRRIGATION SYSTEMS, NEC Impounding Reservoir
IRRIGATION SYSTEMS, NEC Water Distribution Or Sply Systems

J

JANITORIAL & CUSTODIAL SVCS
JANITORIAL EQPT & SPLYS WHOLESALERS
JEWELERS' FINDINGS & MATERIALS: Castings

JEWELERS' FINDINGS & MTLS: Jewel Prep, Instr, Tools, Watches
JEWELERS' FINDINGS/MTRLS: Gem Prep, Settings, Real/Imitation
JEWELRY & PRECIOUS STONES WHOLESALERS
JEWELRY APPAREL
JEWELRY FINDINGS & LAPIDARY WORK
JEWELRY REPAIR SVCS
JEWELRY STORES
JEWELRY STORES: Precious Stones & Precious Metals
JEWELRY STORES: Silverware
JEWELRY STORES: Watches
JEWELRY, PRECIOUS METAL: Bracelets
JEWELRY, PRECIOUS METAL: Cigar & Cigarette Access
JEWELRY, PRECIOUS METAL: Mountings & Trimmings
JEWELRY, PRECIOUS METAL: Rings, Finger
JEWELRY, WHOLESALE
JEWELRY: Decorative, Fashion & Costume
JEWELRY: Precious Metal
JIGS & FIXTURES
JIGS: Welding Positioners
JOB PRINTING & NEWSPAPER PUBLISHING COMBINED
JOB TRAINING & VOCATIONAL REHABILITATION SVCS
JOINTS & COUPLINGS
JOINTS: Expansion
JOINTS: Expansion, Pipe
JOISTS: Fabricated Bar
JOISTS: Long-Span Series, Open Web Steel

K

KAOLIN MINING
KAOLIN: Ground Or Otherwise Treated
KEYBOARDS: Computer Or Office Machine
KILNS & FURNACES: Ceramic
KITCHEN CABINET STORES, EXC CUSTOM
KITCHEN CABINETS WHOLESALERS
KITCHEN UTENSILS: Food Handling & Processing Prdts, Wood
KITCHENWARE: Plastic
KNIVES: Agricultural Or indl
KNOBS: Porcelain

L

LABELS: Cotton, Printed
LABELS: Paper, Made From Purchased Materials
LABOR RESOURCE SVCS
LABORATORIES, TESTING: Hydrostatic
LABORATORIES, TESTING: Prdt Certification, Sfty/Performance
LABORATORIES, TESTING: Product Testing
LABORATORIES, TESTING: Soil Analysis
LABORATORIES, TESTING: X-ray Inspection Svc, Indl
LABORATORIES: Biological Research
LABORATORIES: Biotechnology
LABORATORIES: Commercial Nonphysical Research
LABORATORIES: Dental
LABORATORIES: Dental & Medical X-Ray
LABORATORIES: Electronic Research
LABORATORIES: Environmental Research
LABORATORIES: Medical
LABORATORIES: Physical Research, Commercial
LABORATORIES: Testing
LABORATORIES: Testing
LABORATORY APPARATUS & FURNITURE
LABORATORY APPARATUS, EXC HEATING & MEASURING
LABORATORY APPARATUS: Melting Point
LABORATORY APPARATUS: Physics, NEC
LABORATORY CHEMICALS: Organic
LABORATORY EQPT, EXC MEDICAL: Wholesalers
LABORATORY EQPT: Clinical Instruments Exc Medical
LABORATORY EQPT: Incubators
LABORATORY EQPT: Measuring
LABORATORY EQPT: Sterilizers
LADDERS: Metal
LADDERS: Permanent Installation, Metal
LADDERS: Portable, Metal
LADLES: Metal Plate
LAMINATED PLASTICS: Plate, Sheet, Rod & Tubes
LAMINATING SVCS
LAMP & LIGHT BULBS & TUBES
LAMP BULBS & TUBES, ELECTRIC: Electric Light
LAMP BULBS & TUBES, ELECTRIC: Health, Infrared/Ultraviolet
LAMP BULBS & TUBES, ELECTRIC: Light, Complete

LAMP BULBS & TUBES/PARTS, ELECTRIC: Generalized Applications
LAMP FIXTURES: Ultraviolet
LAMP SHADES: Glass
LAMP SHADES: Metal
LAMPS: Desk, Residential
LAMPS: Floor, Residential
LAMPS: Incandescent, Filament
LAND SUBDIVIDERS & DEVELOPERS: Commercial
LAND SUBDIVIDERS & DEVELOPERS: Residential
LAND SUBDIVISION & DEVELOPMENT
LASER SYSTEMS & EQPT
LASERS: Welding, Drilling & Cutting Eqpt
LATEX: Foamed
LATH: Expanded Metal
LAUNDRY & DRYCLEANER AGENTS
LAUNDRY & GARMENT SVCS, NEC: Garment Making, Alter & Repair
LAUNDRY EQPT: Commercial
LAUNDRY SVC: Indl Eqpt
LAWN & GARDEN EQPT
LAWN & GARDEN EQPT STORES
LAWN & GARDEN EQPT: Grass Catchers, Lawn Mower
LAWN & GARDEN EQPT: Tractors & Eqpt
LAWN MOWER REPAIR SHOP
LEAD & ZINC
LEAD & ZINC ORES
LEAD PENCILS & ART GOODS
LEAD-IN WIRES: Electric Lamp
LEASING & RENTAL SVCS: Computer Hardware, Exc Finance
LEASING & RENTAL SVCS: Cranes & Aerial Lift Eqpt
LEASING & RENTAL SVCS: Oil Field Eqpt
LEASING & RENTAL SVCS: Oil Well Drilling
LEASING & RENTAL: Computers & Eqpt
LEASING & RENTAL: Construction & Mining Eqpt
LEASING & RENTAL: Medical Machinery & Eqpt
LEASING & RENTAL: Mobile Home Sites
LEASING & RENTAL: Other Real Estate Property
LEASING & RENTAL: Trucks, Without Drivers
LEASING: Passenger Car
LEASING: Residential Buildings
LEATHER GOODS, EXC FOOTWEAR, GLOVES, LUGGAGE/BELTING, WHOL
LEATHER GOODS: Belting & Strapping
LEATHER GOODS: Boots, Horse
LEATHER GOODS: Cases
LEATHER GOODS: Checkbook Covers
LEATHER GOODS: Garments
LEATHER GOODS: Holsters
LEATHER GOODS: Key Cases
LEATHER GOODS: Personal
LEATHER GOODS: Saddles Or Parts
LEATHER GOODS: Seat Belts
LEATHER GOODS: Stirrups, Wood Or Metal
LEATHER TANNING & FINISHING
LEATHER, LEATHER GOODS & FURS, WHOLESALE
LEATHER: Accessory Prdts
LEATHER: Bag
LEATHER: Processed
LEATHER: Shoe
LECTURING SVCS
LEGAL OFFICES & SVCS
LEGAL PROCESS SERVERS
LENSES: Plastic, Exc Optical
LICENSE TAGS: Automobile, Stamped Metal
LIFE INSURANCE AGENTS
LIFE RAFTS: Rubber
LIGHT DISTILLATES
LIGHT SENSITIVE DEVICES
LIGHTER FLUID
LIGHTERS, CIGARETTE & CIGAR, WHOLESALE
LIGHTING EQPT: Motor Vehicle
LIGHTING EQPT: Motor Vehicle, Headlights
LIGHTING EQPT: Motor Vehicle, NEC
LIGHTING EQPT: Outdoor
LIGHTING FIXTURES WHOLESALERS
LIGHTING FIXTURES, NEC
LIGHTING FIXTURES: Airport
LIGHTING FIXTURES: Arc
LIGHTING FIXTURES: Decorative Area
LIGHTING FIXTURES: Fluorescent, Commercial
LIGHTING FIXTURES: Indl & Commercial
LIGHTING FIXTURES: Marine
LIGHTING FIXTURES: Motor Vehicle

INDEX

MACHINERY, COMMERCIAL LAUNDRY: Extractors
MACHINERY, EQPT & SUPPLIES: Parking Facility
MACHINERY, FOOD PRDTS: Beverage
MACHINERY, FOOD PRDTS: Dairy & Milk
MACHINERY, FOOD PRDTS: Food Processing, Smokers
MACHINERY, FOOD PRDTS: Mills, Food
MACHINERY, FOOD PRDTS: Ovens, Bakery
MACHINERY, FOOD PRDTS: Packing House
MACHINERY, FOOD PRDTS: Processing, Fish & Shellfish
MACHINERY, FOOD PRDTS: Slicers, Commercial
MACHINERY, LUBRICATION: Automatic
MACHINERY, MAILING: Postage Meters
MACHINERY, METALWORKING: Assembly, Including Robotic
MACHINERY, METALWORKING: Coiling
MACHINERY, METALWORKING: Screw Driving
MACHINERY, OFFICE: Perforators
MACHINERY, OFFICE: Stapling, Hand Or Power
MACHINERY, OFFICE: Time Clocks &Time Recording Devices
MACHINERY, PACKAGING: Packing & Wrapping
MACHINERY, PACKAGING: Wrapping
MACHINERY, PAPER INDUSTRY: Coating & Finishing
MACHINERY, PAPER INDUSTRY: Converting, Die Cutting & Stampng
MACHINERY, PAPER INDUSTRY: Paper Mill, Plating, Etc
MACHINERY, PRINTING TRADES: Plates
MACHINERY, PRINTING TRADES: Printing Trade Parts & Attchts
MACHINERY, SEWING: Sewing & Hat & Zipper Making
MACHINERY, TEXTILE: Embroidery
MACHINERY, TEXTILE: Fiber & Yarn Preparation
MACHINERY, TEXTILE: Printing
MACHINERY, TEXTILE: Silk Screens
MACHINERY, TEXTILE: Warping
MACHINERY, WOODWORKING: Box Making, For Wooden Boxes
MACHINERY, WOODWORKING: Lathes, Wood Turning Includes Access
MACHINERY/EQPT, INDL, WHOL: Cleaning, High Press, Sand/Steam
MACHINERY: Ammunition & Explosives Loading
MACHINERY: Assembly, Exc Metalworking
MACHINERY: Automobile Garage, Frame Straighteners
MACHINERY: Automotive Maintenance
MACHINERY: Automotive Related
MACHINERY: Banking
MACHINERY: Binding
MACHINERY: Blasting, Electrical
MACHINERY: Boot Making & Repairing
MACHINERY: Bottle Washing & Sterilzing
MACHINERY: Brick Making
MACHINERY: Bridge Or Gate, Hydraulic
MACHINERY: Cement Making
MACHINERY: Centrifugal
MACHINERY: Concrete Prdts
MACHINERY: Construction
MACHINERY: Cotton Ginning
MACHINERY: Cryogenic, Industrial
MACHINERY: Custom
MACHINERY: Die Casting
MACHINERY: Electronic Component Making
MACHINERY: Extruding
MACHINERY: Extruding, Synthetic Filament
MACHINERY: Gas Producers
MACHINERY: Gas Separators
MACHINERY: Gear Cutting & Finishing
MACHINERY: General, Industrial, NEC
MACHINERY: Grinding
MACHINERY: Ice Making
MACHINERY: Industrial, NEC
MACHINERY: Labeling
MACHINERY: Lapping
MACHINERY: Leather Working
MACHINERY: Metalworking
MACHINERY: Milling
MACHINERY: Mining
MACHINERY: Ozone
MACHINERY: Packaging
MACHINERY: Paper Industry Miscellaneous
MACHINERY: Pharmaciutical
MACHINERY: Photographic Reproduction
MACHINERY: Plastic Working
MACHINERY: Printing Presses
MACHINERY: Recycling
MACHINERY: Road Construction & Maintenance

MACHINERY: Robots, Molding & Forming Plastics
MACHINERY: Rubber Working
MACHINERY: Screening Eqpt, Electric
MACHINERY: Semiconductor Manufacturing
MACHINERY: Sheet Metal Working
MACHINERY: Specialty
MACHINERY: Textile
MACHINERY: Voting
MACHINERY: Wire Drawing
MACHINERY: Woodworking
MACHINES: Forming, Sheet Metal
MACHINISTS' TOOLS & MACHINES: Measuring, Metalworking Type
MACHINISTS' TOOLS: Measuring, Precision
MACHINISTS' TOOLS: Precision
MACHINISTS' TOOLS: Scales, Measuring, Precision
MAGNETIC INK & OPTICAL SCANNING EQPT
MAGNETIC RESONANCE IMAGING DEVICES: Nonmedical
MAGNETIC TAPE, AUDIO: Prerecorded
MAGNETS: Permanent
MAIL PRESORTING SVCS
MAIL-ORDER HOUSE, NEC
MAIL-ORDER HOUSES: Books, Exc Book Clubs
MAIL-ORDER HOUSES: Computer Software
MAIL-ORDER HOUSES: Religious Merchandise
MAILBOX RENTAL & RELATED SVCS
MAILING & MESSENGER SVCS
MAILING SVCS, NEC
MANAGEMENT CONSULTING SVCS: Automation & Robotics
MANAGEMENT CONSULTING SVCS: Business
MANAGEMENT CONSULTING SVCS: Business Planning & Organizing
MANAGEMENT CONSULTING SVCS: Construction Project
MANAGEMENT CONSULTING SVCS: Food & Beverage
MANAGEMENT CONSULTING SVCS: Foreign Trade
MANAGEMENT CONSULTING SVCS: General
MANAGEMENT CONSULTING SVCS: Hospital & Health
MANAGEMENT CONSULTING SVCS: Industrial & Labor
MANAGEMENT CONSULTING SVCS: Industry Specialist
MANAGEMENT CONSULTING SVCS: Information Systems
MANAGEMENT CONSULTING SVCS: Maintenance
MANAGEMENT CONSULTING SVCS: Management Engineering
MANAGEMENT CONSULTING SVCS: Manufacturing
MANAGEMENT CONSULTING SVCS: Public Utilities
MANAGEMENT CONSULTING SVCS: Quality Assurance
MANAGEMENT CONSULTING SVCS: Real Estate
MANAGEMENT CONSULTING SVCS: Training & Development
MANAGEMENT CONSULTING SVCS: Transportation
MANAGEMENT SERVICES
MANAGEMENT SVCS, FACILITIES SUPPORT: Environ Remediation
MANAGEMENT SVCS: Administrative
MANAGEMENT SVCS: Business
MANAGEMENT SVCS: Construction
MANAGEMENT SVCS: Financial, Business
MANAGEMENT SVCS: Industrial
MANHOLES & COVERS: Metal
MANHOLES COVERS: Concrete
MANICURE PREPARATIONS
MANIFOLDS: Pipe, Fabricated From Purchased Pipe
MANUFACTURED & MOBILE HOME DEALERS
MANUFACTURING INDUSTRIES, NEC
MAPS
MAPS & CHARTS, WHOLESALE
MARBLE BOARD
MARBLE, BUILDING: Cut & Shaped
MARBLE: Crushed & Broken
MARINE BASIN OPERATIONS
MARINE CARGO HANDLING SVCS: Ship Hold Cleaning
MARINE ENGINE REPAIR SVCS
MARINE RELATED EQPT
MARINE RELATED EQPT: Cranes, Ship
MARINE SPLY DEALERS
MARINE SPLYS WHOLESALERS
MARKERS
MARKETS: Meat & fish
MARKING DEVICES
MARKING DEVICES: Canceling Stamps, Hand, Rubber Or Metal
MARKING DEVICES: Embossing Seals & Hand Stamps
MARKING DEVICES: Letters, Metal
MARKING DEVICES: Seal Presses, Notary & Hand
MASQUERADE OR THEATRICAL COSTUMES STORES

MASSAGE MACHINES, ELECTRIC: Barber & Beauty Shops
MASSAGE PARLORS
MASTIC FLOOR COMPOSITION
MASTIC ROOFING COMPOSITION
MATCHES & MATCH BOOKS
MATERIALS HANDLING EQPT WHOLESALERS
MATS & MATTING, MADE FROM PURCHASED WIRE
MATS, MATTING & PADS: Aircraft, Floor, Exc Rubber Or Plastic
MATS, MATTING & PADS: Auto, Floor, Exc Rubber Or Plastic
MATS, MATTING & PADS: Nonwoven
MATS: Blasting, Rope
MATTRESS STORES
MAUSOLEUMS
MEAT & FISH MARKETS: Food & Freezer Plans, Meat
MEAT & FISH MARKETS: Seafood
MEAT & MEAT PRDTS WHOLESALERS
MEAT CUTTING & PACKING
MEAT MARKETS
MEAT PRDTS: Bacon, Slab & Sliced, From Slaughtered Meat
MEAT PRDTS: Boneless Meat, From Purchased Meat
MEAT PRDTS: Boxed Beef, From Slaughtered Meat
MEAT PRDTS: Calf's Foot Jelly, From Purchased Meat
MEAT PRDTS: Canned
MEAT PRDTS: Canned Exc Baby Food, From Slaughtered Meat
MEAT PRDTS: Cooked Meats, From Purchased Meat
MEAT PRDTS: Frozen
MEAT PRDTS: Head Cheese, From Purchased Meat
MEAT PRDTS: Meat By-Prdts, From Slaughtered Meat
MEAT PRDTS: Pork, Cured, From Purchased Meat
MEAT PRDTS: Pork, From Slaughtered Meat
MEAT PRDTS: Prepared Beef Prdts From Purchased Beef
MEAT PRDTS: Prepared Pork Prdts, From Purchased Meat
MEAT PRDTS: Sausage Casings, Natural
MEAT PRDTS: Sausages & Related Prdts, From Purchased Meat
MEAT PRDTS: Sausages, From Purchased Meat
MEAT PRDTS: Sausages, From Slaughtered Meat
MEAT PRDTS: Smoked
MEAT PRDTS: Snack Sticks, Incl Jerky, From Purchased Meat
MEAT PROCESSED FROM PURCHASED CARCASSES
MEAT PROCESSING MACHINERY
MEATS, PACKAGED FROZEN: Wholesalers
MECHANICAL INSTRUMENT REPAIR SVCS
MEDIA: Magnetic & Optical Recording
MEDICAL & HOSPITAL EQPT WHOLESALERS
MEDICAL & HOSPITAL SPLYS: Radiation Shielding Garments
MEDICAL & SURGICAL SPLYS: Abdominal Support, Braces/Trusses
MEDICAL & SURGICAL SPLYS: Bandages & Dressings
MEDICAL & SURGICAL SPLYS: Braces, Orthopedic
MEDICAL & SURGICAL SPLYS: Clothing, Fire Resistant & Protect
MEDICAL & SURGICAL SPLYS: Cotton & Cotton Applicators
MEDICAL & SURGICAL SPLYS: Dressings, Surgical
MEDICAL & SURGICAL SPLYS: Hosiery, Support, Orthopedic
MEDICAL & SURGICAL SPLYS: Hydrotherapy
MEDICAL & SURGICAL SPLYS: Ligatures
MEDICAL & SURGICAL SPLYS: Limbs, Artificial
MEDICAL & SURGICAL SPLYS: Live Preservers, Exc Cork & Inflat
MEDICAL & SURGICAL SPLYS: Orthopedic Appliances
MEDICAL & SURGICAL SPLYS: Personal Safety Eqpt
MEDICAL & SURGICAL SPLYS: Prosthetic Appliances
MEDICAL & SURGICAL SPLYS: Supports, Abdominal, Ankle, Etc
MEDICAL & SURGICAL SPLYS: Swabs, Sanitary Cotton
MEDICAL & SURGICAL SPLYS: Tape, Adhesive, Non-Medicated
MEDICAL EQPT REPAIR SVCS, NON-ELECTRIC
MEDICAL EQPT: Diagnostic
MEDICAL EQPT: Electromedical Apparatus
MEDICAL EQPT: Electrotherapeutic Apparatus
MEDICAL EQPT: Laser Systems
MEDICAL EQPT: Lithotripters
MEDICAL EQPT: MRI/Magnetic Resonance Imaging Devs, Nuclear
MEDICAL EQPT: Patient Monitoring
MEDICAL EQPT: Sterilizers
MEDICAL EQPT: TENS Units/Transcutaneous Elec Nerve Stimulatr
MEDICAL EQPT: Ultrasonic Scanning Devices

INDEX

MOTOR VEHICLES, WHOLESALE: Ambulances
MOTOR VEHICLES, WHOLESALE: Commercial
MOTOR VEHICLES, WHOLESALE: Recreational, All-Terrain
MOTOR VEHICLES, WHOLESALE: Trailers, Truck, New & Used
MOTOR VEHICLES, WHOLESALE: Truck bodies
MOTORCYCLE & BICYCLE PARTS: Saddles & Seat Posts
MOTORCYCLE DEALERS
MOTORCYCLE REPAIR SHOPS
MOTORCYCLES & RELATED PARTS
MOTORS: Electric
MOTORS: Fluid Power
MOTORS: Generators
MOTORS: Pneumatic
MOTORS: Rocket, Guided Missile
MOTORS: Timing, Synchronous, Electric
MOUNTING SVC: Swatches & Samples
MOVING SVC & STORAGE: Local
MOVING SVC: Local
MULTIPLEXERS: Telephone & Telegraph
MUSEUMS & ART GALLERIES
MUSIC BROADCASTING SVCS
MUSICAL INSTRUMENT LESSONS
MUSICAL INSTRUMENT REPAIR
MUSICAL INSTRUMENTS & ACCESS: NEC
MUSICAL INSTRUMENTS & PARTS: Percussion
MUSICAL INSTRUMENTS & SPLYS STORES
MUSICAL INSTRUMENTS & SPLYS STORES: Pianos
MUSICAL INSTRUMENTS: Electric & Electronic
MUSICAL INSTRUMENTS: Organs
MUSICAL INSTRUMENTS: Violins & Parts
MUTUAL FUND MANAGEMENT

N

NAILS: Steel, Wire Or Cut
NAME PLATES: Engraved Or Etched
NAMEPLATES
NAPHTHA
NATIONAL SECURITY FORCES
NATIONAL SECURITY, GOVERNMENT: Air Force
NATURAL BUTANE PRODUCTION
NATURAL GAS COMPRESSING SVC, On-Site
NATURAL GAS DISTRIBUTION TO CONSUMERS
NATURAL GAS LIQUID FRACTIONATING SVC
NATURAL GAS LIQUIDS PRODUCTION
NATURAL GAS LIQUIDS PRODUCTION
NATURAL GAS POWER BROKER
NATURAL GAS PRODUCTION
NATURAL GAS STORAGE SVCS
NATURAL GAS TRANSMISSION
NATURAL GAS TRANSMISSION & DISTRIBUTION
NATURAL GASOLINE PRODUCTION
NATURAL LIQUEFIED PETROLEUM GAS PRODUCTION
NATURAL PROPANE PRODUCTION
NAVIGATIONAL SYSTEMS & INSTRUMENTS
NETTING: Cargo
NETTING: Mosquito
NETTING: Rope
NEW & USED CAR DEALERS
NEWS DEALERS & NEWSSTANDS
NEWSPAPERS, WHOLESALE
NICKEL ALLOY
NICKEL ORE MINING
NIPPLES: Rubber
NONAROMATIC CHEMICAL PRDTS
NONCURRENT CARRYING WIRING DEVICES
NONFERROUS: Rolling & Drawing, NEC
NONMETALLIC MINERALS DEVELOPMENT & TEST BORING SVC
NONMETALLIC MINERALS: Support Activities, Exc Fuels
NOTARIES PUBLIC
NOTEBOOKS, MADE FROM PURCHASED MATERIALS
NOTIONS: Pins, Hair, Exc Rubber
NOVELTIES
NOVELTIES & SPECIALTIES: Metal
NOVELTIES: Paper, Made From Purchased Materials
NOVELTIES: Plastic
NOVELTY SHOPS
NOZZLES & SPRINKLERS Lawn Hose
NOZZLES: Fire Fighting
NOZZLES: Spray, Aerosol, Paint Or Insecticide
NUCLEAR CORE STRUCTURALS: Metal Plate
NUCLEAR DETECTORS: Solid State
NUCLEAR REACTORS: Military Or Indl

NURSERIES & LAWN & GARDEN SPLY STORE, RET: Lawn/Garden Splys
NURSERIES & LAWN & GARDEN SPLY STORES, RETAIL
NURSERIES & LAWN & GARDEN SPLY STORES, RETAIL: Fertilizer
NURSERIES & LAWN & GARDEN SPLY STORES, RETAIL: Top Soil
NURSERIES & LAWN/GARDEN SPLY STORE, RET: Lawn-mowers/Tractors
NURSERIES/LAWN/GARDEN SPLY STORES, RET: Hydroponic Eqpt/Sply
NURSERIES/LAWN/GRDN SPLY STORE, RET: Nursery Stck, Seed/Bulb
NURSERY & GARDEN CENTERS
NUTRITION SVCS
NUTS: Metal
NYLON FIBERS
NYLON RESINS

O

OFFICE EQPT WHOLESALERS
OFFICE EQPT, WHOLESALE: Photocopy Machines
OFFICE FIXTURES: Wood
OFFICE FURNITURE REPAIR & MAINTENANCE SVCS
OFFICE SPLY & STATIONERY STORES: Office Forms & Splys
OFFICE SPLYS, NEC, WHOLESALE
OFFICES & CLINICS OF DOCTORS OF MEDICINE: Ophthalmologist
OFFICES & CLINICS OF DOCTORS OF MEDICINE: Radiologist
OFFICES & CLINICS OF DOCTORS, MEDICINE: Gen & Fam Practice
OFFICES & CLINICS OF DRS OF MEDICINE: Physician, Orthopedic
OFFICES & CLINICS OF DRS, MED: Specialized Practitioners
OFFICES & CLINICS OF HEALTH PRACTITIONERS: Nutrition
OFFICES & CLINICS OF HEALTH PRACTITIONERS: Paramedic
OFFICES & CLINICS OF HEALTH PRACTITIONERS: Psychotherapist
OIL & GAS FIELD EQPT: Drill Rigs
OIL & GAS FIELD MACHINERY
OIL ABSORPTION Eqpt
OIL FIELD MACHINERY & EQPT
OIL FIELD SVCS, NEC
OIL LEASES, BUYING & SELLING ON OWN ACCOUNT
OIL ROYALTY TRADERS
OIL TREATING COMPOUNDS
OILS & ESSENTIAL OILS
OILS & GREASES: Blended & Compounded
OILS & GREASES: Lubricating
OILS: Cutting
OILS: Essential
OILS: Lubricating
OILS: Lubricating
OILS: Mineral, Natural
OILS: Vegetable Oils, Vulcanized Or Sulfurized
OINTMENTS
OLEFINS
ON-LINE DATABASE INFORMATION RETRIEVAL SVCS
OPERATIVE BUILDERS: Condominiums
OPERATOR TRAINING, COMPUTER
OPERATOR: Apartment Buildings
OPERATOR: Nonresidential Buildings
OPHTHALMIC GOODS
OPHTHALMIC GOODS WHOLESALERS
OPHTHALMIC GOODS, NEC, WHOLESALE: Lenses
OPHTHALMIC GOODS: Eyewear, Protective
OPHTHALMIC GOODS: Frames & Parts, Eyeglass & Spectacle
OPHTHALMIC GOODS: Frames, Lenses & Parts, Eyeglasses
OPTICAL GOODS STORES
OPTICAL GOODS STORES: Contact Lenses, Prescription
OPTICAL GOODS STORES: Eyeglasses, Prescription
OPTICAL INSTRUMENT REPAIR SVCS
OPTICAL INSTRUMENTS & APPARATUS
OPTICAL INSTRUMENTS & LENSES
OPTICAL SCANNING SVCS
OPTOMETRISTS' OFFICES
ORDNANCE
ORDNANCE: Flame Throwers
ORGANIZATIONS & UNIONS: Labor

ORGANIZATIONS: Physical Research, Noncommercial
ORGANIZATIONS: Professional
ORGANIZATIONS: Religious
ORGANIZATIONS: Research Institute
ORGANIZATIONS: Scientific Research Agency
OSCILLATORS
OSICIZERS: Inorganic
OVENS: Distillation, Charcoal & Coke
OVENS: Surveillance, Powder Aging & Testing

P

PACKAGED FROZEN FOODS WHOLESALERS, NEC
PACKAGING & LABELING SVCS
PACKAGING MATERIALS, INDL: Wholesalers
PACKAGING MATERIALS, WHOLESALE
PACKAGING MATERIALS: Paper
PACKAGING MATERIALS: Paper, Coated Or Laminated
PACKAGING MATERIALS: Plastic Film, Coated Or Laminated
PACKAGING MATERIALS: Polystyrene Foam
PACKAGING: Blister Or Bubble Formed, Plastic
PACKING & CRATING SVC
PACKING & CRATING SVCS: Containerized Goods For Shipping
PACKING MATERIALS: Mechanical
PACKING SVCS: Shipping
PACKING: Rubber
PADS: Mattress
PAGERS: One-way
PAINT & PAINTING SPLYS STORE
PAINT STORE
PAINTING SVC: Metal Prdts
PAINTS & ADDITIVES
PAINTS & ALLIED PRODUCTS
PAINTS, VARNISHES & SPLYS WHOLESALERS
PAINTS, VARNISHES & SPLYS, WHOLESALE: Colors & Pigments
PAINTS, VARNISHES & SPLYS, WHOLESALE: Paints
PAINTS: Asphalt Or Bituminous
PAINTS: Lead-In-Oil
PAINTS: Marine
PAINTS: Oil Or Alkyd Vehicle Or Water Thinned
PALLET REPAIR SVCS
PALLETS
PALLETS & SKIDS: Wood
PALLETS: Corrugated
PALLETS: Plastic
PALLETS: Wooden
PANEL & DISTRIBUTION BOARDS & OTHER RELATED APPARATUS
PANELS & SECTIONS: Prefabricated, Concrete
PANELS, FLAT: Plastic
PANELS: Building, Metal
PANELS: Building, Plastic, NEC
PANELS: Building, Wood
PANELS: Control & Metering, Generator
PANELS: Wood
PAPER & BOARD: Die-cut
PAPER CONVERTING
PAPER MANUFACTURERS: Exc Newsprint
PAPER PRDTS: Book Covers
PAPER PRDTS: Facial Tissue
PAPER PRDTS: Infant & Baby Prdts
PAPER PRDTS: Molded Pulp Prdts
PAPER PRDTS: Sanitary
PAPER PRDTS: Sanitary Tissue Paper
PAPER PRDTS: Towels, Napkins/Tissue Paper, From Purchd Mtrls
PAPER: Adding Machine Rolls, Made From Purchased Materials
PAPER: Adhesive
PAPER: Art
PAPER: Cardboard
PAPER: Coated & Laminated, NEC
PAPER: Coated, Exc Photographic, Carbon Or Abrasive
PAPER: Corrugated
PAPER: Envelope
PAPER: Gift Wrap
PAPER: Insulation Siding
PAPER: Offset
PAPER: Packaging
PAPER: Printer
PAPER: Specialty
PAPER: Wallpaper
PAPER: Wrapping
PAPERBOARD

INDEX

PRECIOUS STONES WHOLESALERS
PRECISION INSTRUMENT REPAIR SVCS
PREFABRICATED BUILDING DEALERS
PREPARING SHAFTS OR TUNNELS, METAL MINING
PRERECORDED TAPE, COMPACT DISC & RECORD
  STORES: Compact Disc
PRERECORDED TAPE, COMPACT DISC & RECORD
  STORES: Records
PRESSED FIBER & MOLDED PULP PRDTS, EXC FOOD
  PRDTS
PRESSES
PRESTRESSED CONCRETE PRDTS
PRIMARY FINISHED OR SEMIFINISHED SHAPES
PRIMARY METAL PRODUCTS
PRINT CARTRIDGES: Laser & Other Computer Printers
PRINTED CIRCUIT BOARDS
PRINTERS & PLOTTERS
PRINTERS' SVCS: Folding, Collating, Etc
PRINTERS: Computer
PRINTERS: Magnetic Ink, Bar Code
PRINTING & BINDING: Books
PRINTING & BINDING: Textbooks
PRINTING & EMBOSSING: Plastic Fabric Articles
PRINTING & ENGRAVING: Financial Notes & Certificates
PRINTING & ENGRAVING: Invitation & Stationery
PRINTING & ENGRAVING: Poster & Decal
PRINTING & STAMPING: Fabric Articles
PRINTING & WRITING PAPER WHOLESALERS
PRINTING INKS WHOLESALERS
PRINTING MACHINERY
PRINTING MACHINERY, EQPT & SPLYS: Wholesalers
PRINTING TRADES MACHINERY & EQPT REPAIR SVCS
PRINTING, COMMERCIAL Newspapers, NEC
PRINTING, COMMERCIAL: Announcements, NEC
PRINTING, COMMERCIAL: Business Forms, NEC
PRINTING, COMMERCIAL: Catalogs, NEC
PRINTING, COMMERCIAL: Decals, NEC
PRINTING, COMMERCIAL: Directories, Exc Telephone, NEC
PRINTING, COMMERCIAL: Directories, Telephone, NEC
PRINTING, COMMERCIAL: Imprinting
PRINTING, COMMERCIAL: Invitations, NEC
PRINTING, COMMERCIAL: Labels & Seals, NEC
PRINTING, COMMERCIAL: Letterpress & Screen
PRINTING, COMMERCIAL: Literature, Advertising, NEC
PRINTING, COMMERCIAL: Magazines, NEC
PRINTING, COMMERCIAL: Promotional
PRINTING, COMMERCIAL: Publications
PRINTING, COMMERCIAL: Screen
PRINTING, COMMERCIAL: Stationery, NEC
PRINTING, COMMERCIAL: Tags, NEC
PRINTING, LITHOGRAPHIC: Advertising Posters
PRINTING, LITHOGRAPHIC: Circulars
PRINTING, LITHOGRAPHIC: Color
PRINTING, LITHOGRAPHIC: Decals
PRINTING, LITHOGRAPHIC: Forms & Cards, Business
PRINTING, LITHOGRAPHIC: Forms, Business
PRINTING, LITHOGRAPHIC: Letters, Circular Or Form
PRINTING, LITHOGRAPHIC: Maps
PRINTING, LITHOGRAPHIC: Offset & photolithographic print-
  ing
PRINTING, LITHOGRAPHIC: On Metal
PRINTING, LITHOGRAPHIC: Posters
PRINTING, LITHOGRAPHIC: Promotional
PRINTING, LITHOGRAPHIC: Schedules, Transportation
PRINTING, LITHOGRAPHIC: Tags
PRINTING, LITHOGRAPHIC: Tickets
PRINTING, LITHOGRAPHIC: Transfers, Decalcomania Or Dry
PRINTING: Books
PRINTING: Books
PRINTING: Broadwoven Fabrics. Cotton
PRINTING: Checkbooks
PRINTING: Commercial, NEC
PRINTING: Engraving & Plate
PRINTING: Flexographic
PRINTING: Gravure, Business Form & Card
PRINTING: Gravure, Cards, Exc Greeting
PRINTING: Gravure, Cards, Playing
PRINTING: Gravure, Color
PRINTING: Gravure, Envelopes
PRINTING: Gravure, Imprinting
PRINTING: Gravure, Labels
PRINTING: Gravure, Rotogravure
PRINTING: Gravure, Stationery
PRINTING: Laser
PRINTING: Letterpress

PRINTING: Lithographic
PRINTING: Manmade Fiber & Silk, Broadwoven Fabric
PRINTING: Offset
PRINTING: Pamphlets
PRINTING: Photo-Offset
PRINTING: Screen, Broadwoven Fabrics, Cotton
PRINTING: Screen, Fabric
PRINTING: Screen, Manmade Fiber & Silk, Broadwoven Fab-
  ric
PRINTING: Thermography
PRODUCT STERILIZATION SVCS
PRODUCTS: Petroleum & coal, NEC
PROFESSIONAL EQPT & SPLYS, WHOLESALE: Analytical
  Instruments
PROFESSIONAL EQPT & SPLYS, WHOLESALE: Engineers',
  NEC
PROFESSIONAL EQPT & SPLYS, WHOLESALE: Optical
  Goods
PROFESSIONAL EQPT & SPLYS, WHOLESALE: Scientific &
  Engineerg
PROFESSIONAL EQPT & SPLYS, WHOLESALE: Theatrical
PROFESSIONAL INSTRUMENT REPAIR SVCS
PROFILE SHAPES: Unsupported Plastics
PROGRAMMERS: Indl Process
PROMOTERS OF SHOWS & EXHIBITIONS
PROPELLERS: Boat & Ship, Cast
PROPELLERS: Boat & Ship, Machined
PROPERTY DAMAGE INSURANCE
PROPULSION UNITS: Guided Missiles & Space Vehicles
PROPYLENE & BUTYLENE
PROTECTION EQPT: Lightning
PUBLIC FINANCE, TAXATION & MONETARY POLICY OF-
  FICES
PUBLIC ORDER/SAFETY OFFICES, GOVT: Public Sfty Stats
  Ctr
PUBLIC RELATIONS SVCS
PUBLIC STENOGRAPHY SVCS
PUBLISHERS: Art Copy
PUBLISHERS: Art Copy & Poster
PUBLISHERS: Book
PUBLISHERS: Books, No Printing
PUBLISHERS: Catalogs
PUBLISHERS: Comic Books, No Printing
PUBLISHERS: Directories, NEC
PUBLISHERS: Directories, Telephone
PUBLISHERS: Guides
PUBLISHERS: Magazines, No Printing
PUBLISHERS: Maps
PUBLISHERS: Miscellaneous
PUBLISHERS: Music Book & Sheet Music
PUBLISHERS: Music, Book
PUBLISHERS: Music, Sheet
PUBLISHERS: Newsletter
PUBLISHERS: Newspaper
PUBLISHERS: Newspapers, No Printing
PUBLISHERS: Pamphlets, No Printing
PUBLISHERS: Periodical, With Printing
PUBLISHERS: Periodicals, Magazines
PUBLISHERS: Periodicals, No Printing
PUBLISHERS: Sheet Music
PUBLISHERS: Shopping News
PUBLISHERS: Technical Manuals
PUBLISHERS: Technical Manuals & Papers
PUBLISHERS: Telephone & Other Directory
PUBLISHERS: Television Schedules, No Printing
PUBLISHERS: Textbooks, No Printing
PUBLISHERS: Trade journals, No Printing
PUBLISHING & BROADCASTING: Internet Only
PUBLISHING & PRINTING: Book Clubs
PUBLISHING & PRINTING: Books
PUBLISHING & PRINTING: Directories, NEC
PUBLISHING & PRINTING: Directories, Telephone
PUBLISHING & PRINTING: Magazines: publishing & printing
PUBLISHING & PRINTING: Newsletters, Business Svc
PUBLISHING & PRINTING: Newspapers
PUBLISHING & PRINTING: Pamphlets
PUBLISHING & PRINTING: Posters
PUBLISHING & PRINTING: Shopping News
PUBLISHING & PRINTING: Technical Manuals
PUBLISHING & PRINTING: Textbooks
PUBLISHING & PRINTING: Trade Journals
PUBLISHING & PRINTING: Yearbooks
PULLEYS: Metal
PULP MILLS
PULP MILLS: Chemical & Semichemical Processing

PULP MILLS: Mechanical & Recycling Processing
PUMP JACKS & OTHER PUMPING EQPT: Indl
PUMPS
PUMPS & PARTS: Indl
PUMPS & PUMPING EQPT REPAIR SVCS
PUMPS & PUMPING EQPT WHOLESALERS
PUMPS, HEAT: Electric
PUMPS: Aircraft, Hydraulic
PUMPS: Domestic, Water Or Sump
PUMPS: Fluid Power
PUMPS: Gasoline, Measuring Or Dispensing
PUMPS: Hydraulic Power Transfer
PUMPS: Measuring & Dispensing
PUMPS: Oil Well & Field
PUMPS: Oil, Measuring Or Dispensing
PUMPS: Vacuum, Exc Laboratory
PURCHASING SVCS
PURIFICATION & DUST COLLECTION EQPT
PURLINS: Steel, Light Gauge
PURSES: Women's

Q

QUARTZ CRYSTAL MINING SVCS
QUARTZ CRYSTALS: Electronic
QUICKLIME
QUILTING SVC
QUILTING SVC & SPLYS, FOR THE TRADE

R

RACE CAR OWNERS
RACKS: Book & Magazine, Wood
RACKS: Display
RACKS: Railroad Car, Vehicle Transportation, Steel
RADAR SYSTEMS & EQPT
RADIATORS, EXC ELECTRIC
RADIATORS: Stationary Engine
RADIO & TELEVISION COMMUNICATIONS EQUIPMENT
RADIO & TELEVISION REPAIR
RADIO BROADCASTING & COMMUNICATIONS EQPT
RADIO BROADCASTING STATIONS
RADIO COMMUNICATIONS: Carrier Eqpt
RADIO RECEIVING SETS
RADIO REPAIR & INSTALLATION SVCS
RADIO, TELEVISION & CONSUMER ELECTRONICS
  STORES: TV Sets
RADIO, TV & CONSUMER ELEC STORES: Automotive
  Sound Eqpt
RADIO, TV & CONSUMER ELEC STORES: High Fidelity
  Stereo Eqpt
RADIO, TV & CONSUMER ELECTRONICS: VCR & Access
RADIO, TV/CONSUMER ELEC STORES: Marine
  Radios/Radar Eqpt
RADIOS WHOLESALERS
RAIL & STRUCTURAL SHAPES: Aluminum rail & structural
  shapes
RAILINGS: Prefabricated, Metal
RAILINGS: Wood
RAILROAD CAR RENTING & LEASING SVCS
RAILROAD CAR REPAIR SVCS
RAILROAD CARGO LOADING & UNLOADING SVCS
RAILROAD EQPT
RAILROAD EQPT & SPLYS WHOLESALERS
RAILROAD EQPT, EXC LOCOMOTIVES
RAILROAD EQPT: Cars & Eqpt, Dining
RAILROAD EQPT: Cars & Eqpt, Train, Freight Or Passenger
RAILROAD EQPT: Cars, Motor
RAILROAD EQPT: Cars, Tank Freight & Eqpt
RAILROAD EQPT: Locomotives & Parts, Electric Or Nonelec-
  tric
RAILROAD TIES: Concrete
RAILROAD TIES: Wood
RAILROADS: Long Haul
RAILS: Steel Or Iron
REACTORS: Current Limiting
REAL ESTATE AGENCIES & BROKERS
REAL ESTATE AGENCIES: Buying
REAL ESTATE AGENCIES: Commercial
REAL ESTATE AGENTS & MANAGERS
REAL ESTATE APPRAISERS
REAL ESTATE INVESTMENT TRUSTS
REAL ESTATE OPERATORS, EXC DEVELOPERS: Commer-
  cial/Indl Bldg
RECEIVERS: Radio Communications
RECLAIMED RUBBER: Reworked By Manufacturing Process
RECORD BLANKS: Phonographic

RECORDING TAPE: Video, Blank
RECORDS & TAPES: Prerecorded
RECORDS OR TAPES: Masters
RECOVERY SVCS: Metal
RECREATIONAL SPORTING EQPT REPAIR SVCS
RECREATIONAL VEHICLE DEALERS
RECREATIONAL VEHICLE PARTS & ACCESS STORES
RECREATIONAL VEHICLE REPAIRS
RECREATIONAL VEHICLE: Wholesalers
RECTIFIERS: Electronic, Exc Semiconductor
RECYCLING: Paper
REELS: Cable, Metal
REELS: Wood
REFINERS & SMELTERS: Aluminum
REFINERS & SMELTERS: Copper
REFINERS & SMELTERS: Copper, Secondary
REFINERS & SMELTERS: Gold
REFINERS & SMELTERS: Lead, Secondary
REFINERS & SMELTERS: Magnesium, Secondary
REFINERS & SMELTERS: Nonferrous Metal
REFINERS & SMELTERS: Platinum Group Metals, Secondary
REFINERS & SMELTERS: Zinc, Secondary
REFINING LUBRICATING OILS & GREASES, NEC
REFINING: Petroleum
REFRACTORIES: Cement
REFRACTORIES: Clay
REFRACTORIES: Graphite, Carbon Or Ceramic Bond
REFRACTORIES: Nonclay
REFRACTORIES: Plastic
REFRACTORY MATERIALS WHOLESALERS
REFRIGERATION & HEATING EQUIPMENT
REFRIGERATION EQPT & SPLYS WHOLESALERS
REFRIGERATION EQPT & SPLYS, WHOL: Refrig Units, Motor Veh
REFRIGERATION EQPT & SPLYS, WHOLESALE: Beverage Dispensers
REFRIGERATION EQPT & SPLYS, WHOLESALE: Commercial Eqpt
REFRIGERATION EQPT & SPLYS, WHOLESALE: Ice Cream Cabinets
REFRIGERATION EQPT: Complete
REFRIGERATION REPAIR SVCS
REFRIGERATION SVC & REPAIR
REFRIGERATORS & FREEZERS WHOLESALERS
REFUSE SYSTEMS
REGISTERS: Air, Metal
REGULATION & ADMINISTRATION, GOVT: Transp Dept, Nonoperating
REGULATORS: Generator Voltage
REGULATORS: Line Voltage
REGULATORS: Power
RELAYS & SWITCHES: Indl, Electric
RELAYS: Control Circuit, Ind
RELAYS: Electric Power
RELAYS: Electronic Usage
REMOTE DATABASE INFORMATION RETRIEVAL SVCS
RENDERING PLANT
RENT-A-CAR SVCS
RENTAL CENTERS: Furniture
RENTAL CENTERS: General
RENTAL CENTERS: Party & Banquet Eqpt & Splys
RENTAL CENTERS: Tools
RENTAL SVCS: Aircraft
RENTAL SVCS: Aircraft & Indl Truck
RENTAL SVCS: Audio-Visual Eqpt & Sply
RENTAL SVCS: Business Machine & Electronic Eqpt
RENTAL SVCS: Clothing
RENTAL SVCS: Costume
RENTAL SVCS: Musical Instrument
RENTAL SVCS: Oil Eqpt
RENTAL SVCS: Propane Eqpt
RENTAL SVCS: Recreational Vehicle
RENTAL SVCS: Sign
RENTAL SVCS: Stores & Yards Eqpt
RENTAL SVCS: Tent & Tarpaulin
RENTAL SVCS: Work Zone Traffic Eqpt, Flags, Cones, Etc
RENTAL: Trucks, With Drivers
REPAIR TRAINING, COMPUTER
REPRODUCTION SVCS: Video Tape Or Disk
RESEARCH & DEVELOPMENT SVCS, COMMERCIAL: Engineering Lab
RESEARCH, DEV & TESTING SVCS, COMM: Chem Lab, Exc Testing
RESEARCH, DEVELOPMENT & TEST SVCS, COMM: Cmptr Hardware Dev

RESEARCH, DEVELOPMENT & TEST SVCS, COMM: Research, Exc Lab
RESEARCH, DEVELOPMENT & TESTING SVCS, COMM: Agricultural
RESEARCH, DEVELOPMENT & TESTING SVCS, COMM: Bus Economic Sve
RESEARCH, DEVELOPMENT & TESTING SVCS, COMM: Natural Resource
RESEARCH, DEVELOPMENT & TESTING SVCS, COMM: Research Lab
RESEARCH, DEVELOPMENT & TESTING SVCS, COMMERCIAL: Business
RESEARCH, DEVELOPMENT & TESTING SVCS, COMMERCIAL: Education
RESEARCH, DEVELOPMENT & TESTING SVCS, COMMERCIAL: Energy
RESEARCH, DEVELOPMENT & TESTING SVCS, COMMERCIAL: Food
RESEARCH, DEVELOPMENT & TESTING SVCS, COMMERCIAL: Medical
RESEARCH, DEVELOPMENT & TESTING SVCS, COMMERCIAL: Physical
RESEARCH, DVLPT & TEST SVCS, COMM: Mkt Analysis or Research
RESIDENTIAL REMODELERS
RESINS: Custom Compound Purchased
RESISTORS
RESPIRATORS
RESTAURANT EQPT REPAIR SVCS
RESTAURANT EQPT: Carts
RESTAURANT EQPT: Food Wagons
RESTAURANT EQPT: Sheet Metal
RESTAURANT RESERVATION SVCS
RESTAURANTS: Fast Food
RESTAURANTS:Full Svc, American
RESTAURANTS:Full Svc, Barbecue
RESTAURANTS:Full Svc, Cajun
RESTAURANTS:Full Svc, Diner
RESTAURANTS:Full Svc, Family
RESTAURANTS:Full Svc, Family, Independent
RESTAURANTS:Full Svc, Mexican
RESTAURANTS:Full Svc, Seafood
RESTAURANTS:Full Svc, Steak & Barbecue
RESTAURANTS:Limited Svc, Carry-Out Only, Exc Pizza
RESTAURANTS:Limited Svc, Coffee Shop
RESTAURANTS:Limited Svc, Fast-Food, Chain
RESTAURANTS:Limited Svc, Fast-Food, Independent
RESTAURANTS:Limited Svc, Grill
RESTAURANTS:Limited Svc, Health Food
RESTAURANTS:Limited Svc, Ice Cream Stands Or Dairy Bars
RESTAURANTS:Limited Svc, Sandwiches & Submarines Shop
RESTAURANTS:Ltd Svc, Ice Cream, Soft Drink/Fountain Stands
RETAIL BAKERY: Bagels
RETAIL BAKERY: Bread
RETAIL BAKERY: Cakes
RETAIL BAKERY: Cookies
RETAIL BAKERY: Doughnuts
RETAIL FIREPLACE STORES
RETAIL LUMBER YARDS
RETAIL STORES: Air Purification Eqpt
RETAIL STORES: Alcoholic Beverage Making Eqpt & Splys
RETAIL STORES: Architectural Splys
RETAIL STORES: Artificial Limbs
RETAIL STORES: Awnings
RETAIL STORES: Banners
RETAIL STORES: Batteries, Non-Automotive
RETAIL STORES: Business Machines & Eqpt
RETAIL STORES: Canvas Prdts
RETAIL STORES: Children's Furniture, NEC
RETAIL STORES: Christmas Lights & Decorations
RETAIL STORES: Cleaning Eqpt & Splys
RETAIL STORES: Coins
RETAIL STORES: Communication Eqpt
RETAIL STORES: Concrete Prdts, Precast
RETAIL STORES: Decals
RETAIL STORES: Drafting Eqpt & Splys
RETAIL STORES: Electronic Parts & Eqpt
RETAIL STORES: Engine & Motor Eqpt & Splys
RETAIL STORES: Engines & Parts, Air-Cooled
RETAIL STORES: Farm Eqpt & Splys
RETAIL STORES: Farm Machinery, NEC
RETAIL STORES: Fiberglass Materials, Exc Insulation

RETAIL STORES: Fire Extinguishers
RETAIL STORES: Flags
RETAIL STORES: Foam & Foam Prdts
RETAIL STORES: Gems & Precious Stones
RETAIL STORES: Hair Care Prdts
RETAIL STORES: Hearing Aids
RETAIL STORES: Ice
RETAIL STORES: Insecticides
RETAIL STORES: Maps & Charts
RETAIL STORES: Medical Apparatus & Splys
RETAIL STORES: Mobile Telephones & Eqpt
RETAIL STORES: Monuments, Finished To Custom Order
RETAIL STORES: Motors, Electric
RETAIL STORES: Orthopedic & Prosthesis Applications
RETAIL STORES: Pet Food
RETAIL STORES: Pet Splys
RETAIL STORES: Picture Frames, Ready Made
RETAIL STORES: Pipe Store, Tobacco
RETAIL STORES: Plumbing & Heating Splys
RETAIL STORES: Safety Splys & Eqpt
RETAIL STORES: Spas & Hot Tubs
RETAIL STORES: Swimming Pools, Above Ground
RETAIL STORES: Technical Aids For The Handicapped
RETAIL STORES: Telephone & Communication Eqpt
RETAIL STORES: Telephone Eqpt & Systems
RETAIL STORES: Tents
RETAIL STORES: Vaults & Safes
RETAIL STORES: Water Purification Eqpt
RETAIL STORES: Welding Splys
RETAINERS OR HOUSINGS: Rotor
REUPHOLSTERY & FURNITURE REPAIR
REWINDING SVCS
RIBBONS, NEC
RIBBONS: Machine, Inked Or Carbon
RINGS: Angle
RIVETS: Metal
ROAD MATERIALS: Bituminous, Not From Refineries
ROBOTS, SERVICES OR NOVELTY, WHOLESALE
ROBOTS: Assembly Line
ROBOTS: Indl Spraying, Painting, Etc
ROCK SALT MINING
ROCKETS: Space & Military
ROD & BAR: Aluminum
RODS: Plastic
RODS: Rolled, Aluminum
RODS: Steel & Iron, Made In Steel Mills
RODS: Welding
ROLL COVERINGS: Rubber
ROLL FORMED SHAPES: Custom
ROLLING MILL EQPT: Galvanizing Lines
ROLLING MILL EQPT: Plate
ROLLING MILL EQPT: Rod Mills
ROLLING MILL MACHINERY
ROLLING MILL ROLLS: Cast Steel
ROLLS & ROLL COVERINGS: Rubber
ROOF DECKS
ROOFING MATERIALS: Asphalt
ROOFING MATERIALS: Sheet Metal
ROOFING MEMBRANE: Rubber
ROPE
ROTORS: Motor
RUBBER
RUBBER PRDTS
RUBBER PRDTS: Appliance, Mechanical
RUBBER PRDTS: Automotive, Mechanical
RUBBER PRDTS: Mechanical
RUBBER PRDTS: Medical & Surgical Tubing, Extrudd & Lathe-Cut
RUBBER PRDTS: Oil & Gas Field Machinery, Mechanical
RUBBER PRDTS: Silicone
RUBBER PRDTS: Sponge
RUBBER STAMP, WHOLESALE
RUGS : Braided & Hooked
RUGS : Hand & Machine Made
RUGS : Machine Woven

S

SADDLERY STORES
SAFE DEPOSIT BOXES
SAFES & VAULTS: Metal
SAFETY EQPT & SPLYS WHOLESALERS
SAFETY INSPECTION SVCS
SALES PROMOTION SVCS
SALT
SALT MINING: Common

SAMPLE BOOKS
SAND & GRAVEL
SAND LIME PRDTS
SAND MINING
SAND: Hygrade
SAND: Silica
SANDBLASTING EQPT
SANDBLASTING SVC: Building Exterior
SANDSTONE: Crushed & Broken
SANITARY SVC, NEC
SANITARY SVCS: Chemical Detoxification
SANITARY SVCS: Environmental Cleanup
SANITARY SVCS: Hazardous Waste, Collection & Disposal
SANITARY SVCS: Nonhazardous Waste Disposal Sites
SANITARY SVCS: Oil Spill Cleanup
SANITARY SVCS: Refuse Collection & Disposal Svcs
SANITARY SVCS: Sewage Treatment Facility
SANITARY SVCS: Toxic Or Hazardous Waste Cleanup
SANITARY SVCS: Waste Materials, Recycling
SANITARY WARE: Metal
SANITATION CHEMICALS & CLEANING AGENTS
SASHES: Door Or Window, Metal
SATELLITE COMMUNICATIONS EQPT
SATELLITES: Communications
SAW BLADES
SAWDUST & SHAVINGS
SAWING & PLANING MILLS
SAWING & PLANING MILLS: Custom
SAWS & SAWING EQPT
SCAFFOLDS: Mobile Or Stationary, Metal
SCALES & BALANCES, EXC LABORATORY
SCANNING DEVICES: Optical
SCHOOLS & EDUCATIONAL SVCS, NEC
SCHOOLS: Vocational, NEC
SCIENTIFIC INSTRUMENTS WHOLESALERS
SCRAP & WASTE MATERIALS, WHOLESALE: Auto Wrecking For Scrap
SCRAP & WASTE MATERIALS, WHOLESALE: Ferrous Metal
SCRAP & WASTE MATERIALS, WHOLESALE: Metal
SCRAP & WASTE MATERIALS, WHOLESALE: Nonferrous Metals Scrap
SCRAP & WASTE MATERIALS, WHOLESALE: Paper
SCRAP & WASTE MATERIALS, WHOLESALE: Plastics Scrap
SCRAP & WASTE MATERIALS, WHOLESALE: Rags
SCREENS: Door, Wood Frame
SCREENS: Window, Metal
SCREENS: Window, Wood Framed
SCREENS: Woven Wire
SCREW MACHINE PRDTS
SCREWS: Metal
SEALANTS
SEALING COMPOUNDS: Sealing, synthetic rubber or plastic
SEALS: Hermetic
SEALS: Oil, Rubber
SEARCH & DETECTION SYSTEMS, EXC RADAR
SEARCH & NAVIGATION SYSTEMS
SEAT BELTS: Automobile & Aircraft
SEATING: Bleacher, Portable
SEATING: Transportation
SECRETARIAL & COURT REPORTING
SECURE STORAGE SVC: Document
SECURITIES DEALING
SECURITY CONTROL EQPT & SYSTEMS
SECURITY DEVICES
SECURITY EQPT STORES
SECURITY GUARD SVCS
SECURITY PROTECTIVE DEVICES MAINTENANCE & MONITORING SVCS
SECURITY SYSTEMS SERVICES
SEEDS & BULBS WHOLESALERS
SELF-DEFENSE & ATHLETIC INSTRUCTION SVCS
SELF-PROPELLED AIRCRAFT DEALER
SEMICONDUCTOR & RELATED DEVICES: Random Access Memory Or RAM
SEMICONDUCTOR CIRCUIT NETWORKS
SEMICONDUCTOR DEVICES: Wafers
SEMICONDUCTORS & RELATED DEVICES
SENSORS: Infrared, Solid State
SENSORS: Radiation
SENSORS: Temperature, Exc Indl Process
SEPARATORS: Metal Plate
SEPTIC TANK CLEANING SVCS
SEPTIC TANKS: Concrete
SEPTIC TANKS: Plastic

SEWAGE & WATER TREATMENT EQPT
SEWAGE FACILITIES
SEWAGE TREATMENT SYSTEMS & EQPT
SEWER CLEANING & RODDING SVC
SEWER CLEANING EQPT: Power
SEWING CONTRACTORS
SEWING MACHINES & PARTS: Household
SEWING, NEEDLEWORK & PIECE GOODS STORE: Needlework Gds/Sply
SEWING, NEEDLEWORK & PIECE GOODS STORES: Fabric, Remnants
SHADES: Lamp & Light, Residential
SHADES: Lamp Or Candle
SHADES: Window
SHAFTS: Flexible
SHALE MINING, COMMON
SHALE: Expanded
SHAPES & PILINGS, STRUCTURAL: Steel
SHEET METAL SPECIALTIES, EXC STAMPED
SHEET MUSIC STORES
SHEET MUSIC, WHOLESALE
SHEETING: Laminated Plastic
SHEETING: Window, Plastic
SHEETS & STRIPS: Aluminum
SHEETS: Solid Fiber, Made From Purchased Materials
SHELLAC
SHELTERED WORKSHOPS
SHELVING, MADE FROM PURCHASED WIRE
SHELVING: Office & Store, Exc Wood
SHIP BLDG & RPRG: Drilling & Production Platforms, Oil/Gas
SHIP BLDG/RPRG: Submersible Marine Robots, Manned/Unmanned
SHIP BUILDING & REPAIRING: Cargo, Commercial
SHIP BUILDING & REPAIRING: Dredges
SHIP BUILDING & REPAIRING: Fishing Vessels, Large
SHIP BUILDING & REPAIRING: Landing
SHIP BUILDING & REPAIRING: Offshore Sply Boats
SHIP BUILDING & REPAIRING: Radar Towers, Floating
SHIP BUILDING & REPAIRING: Rigging, Marine
SHIP BUILDING & REPAIRING: Tankers
SHIP BUILDING & REPAIRING: Towboats
SHIP BUILDING & REPAIRING: Transport Vessels, Troop
SHIP BUILDING & REPAIRING: Tugboats
SHIPBUILDING & REPAIR
SHOE & BOOT ACCESS
SHOE MATERIALS: Counters
SHOE MATERIALS: Rubber
SHOE STORES
SHOE STORES: Boots, Men's
SHOE STORES: Orthopedic
SHOE STORES: Women's
SHOES & BOOTS WHOLESALERS
SHOES: Athletic, Exc Rubber Or Plastic
SHOES: Canvas, Rubber Soled
SHOES: Infants' & Children's
SHOES: Men's
SHOES: Plastic Or Rubber
SHOES: Plastic Or Rubber Soles With Fabric Uppers
SHOES: Women's
SHOES: Women's, Sandals
SHOPPING CENTERS & MALLS
SHOT PEENING SVC
SHOWCASES & DISPLAY FIXTURES: Office & Store
SHOWER STALLS: Plastic & Fiberglass
SHREDDERS: Indl & Commercial
SHUTTERS, DOOR & WINDOW: Metal
SHUTTERS, DOOR & WINDOW: Plastic
SHUTTERS: Door, Wood
SHUTTERS: Window, Wood
SIDING & STRUCTURAL MATERIALS: Wood
SIDING MATERIALS
SIDING: Precast Stone
SIDING: Sheet Metal
SIGN LETTERING & PAINTING SVCS
SIGN PAINTING & LETTERING SHOP
SIGNALING APPARATUS: Electric
SIGNALS: Traffic Control, Electric
SIGNALS: Transportation
SIGNS & ADVERTISING SPECIALTIES
SIGNS & ADVERTISING SPECIALTIES: Artwork, Advertising
SIGNS & ADVERTISING SPECIALTIES: Letters For Signs, Metal
SIGNS & ADVERTISING SPECIALTIES: Novelties
SIGNS & ADVERTISING SPECIALTIES: Scoreboards, Electric

SIGNS & ADVERTISING SPECIALTIES: Signs
SIGNS & ADVERTSG SPECIALTIES: Displays/Cutouts Window/Lobby
SIGNS, ELECTRICAL: Wholesalers
SIGNS, EXC ELECTRIC, WHOLESALE
SIGNS: Electrical
SIGNS: Neon
SILICA MINING
SILICON
SILICON WAFERS: Chemically Doped
SILICON: Pure
SILICONES
SILK SCREEN DESIGN SVCS
SILO STAVES: Concrete Or Cast Stone
SILVER ORE MINING
SIMULATORS: Flight
SKIDS: Wood
SKILL TRAINING CENTER
SKIN CARE PRDTS: Suntan Lotions & Oils
SKYLIGHTS
SLAB & TILE, ROOFING: Concrete
SLAB & TILE: Precast Concrete, Floor
SLAB, CROSSING: Concrete
SLAG PRDTS
SLAG: Crushed Or Ground
SLATE PRDTS
SLAUGHTERING & MEAT PACKING
SLIDES & EXHIBITS: Prepared
SLINGS: Lifting, Made From Purchased Wire
SLINGS: Rope
SLIP RINGS
SLOT MACHINES
SMOKE DETECTORS
SNOWMOBILE DEALERS
SOAPS & DETERGENTS
SOCIAL SVCS: Individual & Family
SODA ASH MINING: Natural
SOFT DRINKS WHOLESALERS
SOFTWARE PUBLISHERS: Application
SOFTWARE PUBLISHERS: Business & Professional
SOFTWARE PUBLISHERS: Computer Utilities
SOFTWARE PUBLISHERS: Education
SOFTWARE PUBLISHERS: Home Entertainment
SOFTWARE PUBLISHERS: NEC
SOFTWARE PUBLISHERS: Operating Systems
SOFTWARE PUBLISHERS: Publisher's
SOFTWARE PUBLISHERS: Word Processing
SOFTWARE TRAINING, COMPUTER
SOLAR CELLS
SOLAR HEATING EQPT
SOLVENTS
SONAR SYSTEMS & EQPT
SOUND EQPT: Electric
SOUND RECORDING STUDIOS
SOUND REPRODUCING EQPT
SOUVENIR SHOPS
SPACE RESEARCH & TECHNOLOGY, GOVERNMENT: Federal
SPACE SUITS
SPACE VEHICLE EQPT
SPACE VEHICLES
SPARK PLUGS: Internal Combustion Engines
SPAS
SPEAKER MONITORS
SPEAKER SYSTEMS
SPECIAL PRODUCT SAWMILLS, NEC
SPECIALIZED LEGAL SVCS
SPECIALTY FOOD STORES: Coffee
SPECIALTY FOOD STORES: Health & Dietetic Food
SPECIALTY FOOD STORES: Juices, Fruit Or Vegetable
SPECIALTY FOOD STORES: Vitamin
SPECIALTY OUTPATIENT CLINICS, NEC
SPECIALTY SAWMILL PRDTS
SPECULATIVE BUILDERS: Single-Family Housing
SPICE & HERB STORES
SPONGES: Bleached & Dyed
SPOOLS: Indl
SPORTING & ATHLETIC GOODS: Bags, Golf
SPORTING & ATHLETIC GOODS: Bowling Alleys & Access
SPORTING & ATHLETIC GOODS: Bowling Balls
SPORTING & ATHLETIC GOODS: Bows, Archery
SPORTING & ATHLETIC GOODS: Camping Eqpt & Splys
SPORTING & ATHLETIC GOODS: Cases, Gun & Rod
SPORTING & ATHLETIC GOODS: Driving Ranges, Golf, Electronic

SPORTING & ATHLETIC GOODS: Dumbbells & Other Weight Eqpt
SPORTING & ATHLETIC GOODS: Exercising Cycles
SPORTING & ATHLETIC GOODS: Fishing Tackle, General
SPORTING & ATHLETIC GOODS: Football Eqpt & Splys, NEC
SPORTING & ATHLETIC GOODS: Gymnasium Eqpt
SPORTING & ATHLETIC GOODS: Hunting Eqpt
SPORTING & ATHLETIC GOODS: Pools, Swimming, Exc Plastic
SPORTING & ATHLETIC GOODS: Pools, Swimming, Plastic
SPORTING & ATHLETIC GOODS: Protectors, Baseball, Etc
SPORTING & ATHLETIC GOODS: Rods & Rod Parts, Fishing
SPORTING & ATHLETIC GOODS: Shafts, Golf Club
SPORTING & ATHLETIC GOODS: Shooting Eqpt & Splys, General
SPORTING & ATHLETIC GOODS: Shuffleboards & Shuffleboard Eqpt
SPORTING & ATHLETIC GOODS: Skateboards
SPORTING & ATHLETIC GOODS: Softball Eqpt, Splys
SPORTING & ATHLETIC GOODS: Targets, Archery & Rifle Shooting
SPORTING & ATHLETIC GOODS: Team Sports Eqpt
SPORTING & ATHLETIC GOODS: Track & Field Athletic Eqpt
SPORTING & ATHLETIC GOODS: Trampolines & Eqpt
SPORTING & ATHLETIC GOODS: Treadmills
SPORTING & REC GOODS, WHOLESALE: Camping Eqpt & Splys
SPORTING & RECREATIONAL GOODS & SPLYS WHOLESALERS
SPORTING & RECREATIONAL GOODS, WHOLESALE: Bicycle Parts
SPORTING & RECREATIONAL GOODS, WHOLESALE: Boat Access & Part
SPORTING & RECREATIONAL GOODS, WHOLESALE: Exercise
SPORTING & RECREATIONAL GOODS, WHOLESALE: Fitness
SPORTING & RECREATIONAL GOODS, WHOLESALE: Golf
SPORTING & RECREATIONAL GOODS, WHOLESALE: Golf & Skiing
SPORTING & RECREATIONAL GOODS, WHOLESALE: Hunting
SPORTING & RECREATIONAL GOODS, WHOLESALE: Watersports
SPORTING FIREARMS WHOLESALERS
SPORTING GOODS
SPORTING GOODS STORES, NEC
SPORTING GOODS STORES: Ammunition
SPORTING GOODS STORES: Archery Splys
SPORTING GOODS STORES: Bait & Tackle
SPORTING GOODS STORES: Camping & Backpacking Eqpt
SPORTING GOODS STORES: Firearms
SPORTING GOODS STORES: Hunting Eqpt
SPORTING GOODS STORES: Soccer Splys
SPORTING GOODS STORES: Specialty Sport Splys, NEC
SPORTING GOODS STORES: Tennis Goods & Eqpt
SPORTING GOODS STORES: Trampolines & Eqpt
SPORTING GOODS: Archery
SPORTING GOODS: Hammocks & Other Net Prdts
SPORTING GOODS: Sleeping Bags
SPORTS APPAREL STORES
SPRAYING & DUSTING EQPT
SPRAYING EQPT: Agricultural
SPRINGS: Coiled Flat
SPRINGS: Furniture, Unassembled
SPRINGS: Leaf, Automobile, Locomotive, Etc
SPRINGS: Mechanical, Precision
SPRINGS: Precision
SPRINGS: Steel
SPRINGS: Torsion Bar
SPRINGS: Wire
SPRINKLING SYSTEMS: Fire Control
SPROCKETS: Power Transmission
STACKING MACHINES: Automatic
STAGE LIGHTING SYSTEMS
STAINLESS STEEL
STAINLESS STEEL WARE
STAIRCASES & STAIRS, WOOD
STAMPED ART GOODS FOR EMBROIDERING
STAMPINGS: Automotive
STAMPINGS: Metal
STAPLES
STARTERS & CONTROLLERS: Motor, Electric
STARTERS: Motor

STATIONARY & OFFICE SPLYS, WHOL: Computer/Photocopying Splys
STATIONARY & OFFICE SPLYS, WHOL: Writing Instruments & Splys
STATIONERY & OFFICE SPLYS WHOLESALERS
STATIONERY ARTICLES: Pottery
STATIONERY PRDTS
STATORS REWINDING SVCS
STATUARY & OTHER DECORATIVE PRDTS: Nonmetallic
STEAM SPLY SYSTEMS SVCS INCLUDING GEOTHERMAL
STEEL & ALLOYS: Tool & Die
STEEL FABRICATORS
STEEL MILLS
STEEL SHEET: Cold-Rolled
STEEL WOOL
STEEL, HOT-ROLLED: Sheet Or Strip
STEEL: Cold-Rolled
STEEL: Galvanized
STEEL: Laminated
STENCILS
STILLS: Pressure, Metal Plate
STITCHING SVCS
STITCHING SVCS: Custom
STOCK QUOTATION SVCS
STOCK SHAPES: Plastic
STONE: Cast Concrete
STONE: Dimension, NEC
STONE: Quarrying & Processing, Own Stone Prdts
STONES: Abrasive
STORE FIXTURES, EXC REFRIGERATED: Wholesalers
STORE FIXTURES: Exc Wood
STORE FIXTURES: Wood
STORE FRONTS: Prefabricated, Metal
STORE FRONTS: Prefabricated, Wood
STORES: Auto & Home Supply
STORES: Drapery & Upholstery
STRAPPING
STRAWS: Drinking, Made From Purchased Materials
STRUCTURAL SUPPORT & BUILDING MATERIAL: Concrete
STUCCO
STUDS & JOISTS: Sheet Metal
STYRENE
STYRENE RESINS, NEC
STYRENE-BUTADIENE RUBBERS, OVER 50% BUTADIENE
SUBMARINE BUILDING & REPAIR
SUNDRIES & RELATED PRDTS: Medical & Laboratory, Rubber
SUPERMARKETS & OTHER GROCERY STORES
SURFACE ACTIVE AGENTS
SURFACE ACTIVE AGENTS: Oils & Greases
SURGICAL & MEDICAL INSTRUMENTS WHOLESALERS
SURGICAL APPLIANCES & SPLYS
SURGICAL APPLIANCES & SPLYS
SURGICAL EQPT: See Also Instruments
SURGICAL IMPLANTS
SURGICAL INSTRUMENT REPAIR SVCS
SURVEYING & MAPPING: Land Parcels
SURVEYING INSTRUMENTS WHOLESALERS
SURVEYING SVCS: Aerial Digital Imaging
SURVEYORS, MARINE CARGO
SUSPENSION SYSTEMS: Acoustical, Metal
SVC ESTABLISHMENT EQPT, WHOL: Cleaning & Maint Eqpt & Splys
SVC ESTABLISHMENT EQPT, WHOL: Funeral Director's Eqpt/Splys
SVC ESTABLISHMENT EQPT, WHOLESALE: Firefighting Eqpt
SVC ESTABLISHMENT EQPT, WHOLESALE: Laundry Eqpt & Splys
SVC ESTABLISHMENT EQPT, WHOLESALE: Restaurant Splys
SVC ESTABLISHMENT EQPT, WHOLESALE: Shredders, Indl & Comm
SVC ESTABLISHMENT EQPT, WHOLESALE: Sprinkler Systems
SVC ESTABLISHMENT EQPT, WHOLESALE: Voting Machines
SWIMMING POOL & HOT TUB CLEANING & MAINTENANCE SVCS
SWIMMING POOL EQPT: Filters & Water Conditioning Systems
SWIMMING POOL SPLY STORES
SWIMMING POOLS, EQPT & SPLYS: Wholesalers
SWITCHBOARD APPARATUS, EXC INSTRUMENTS
SWITCHES

SWITCHES: Electric Power
SWITCHES: Electronic
SWITCHES: Electronic Applications
SWITCHES: Solenoid
SWITCHES: Time, Electrical Switchgear Apparatus
SWITCHGEAR & SWITCHBOARD APPARATUS
SWITCHGEAR & SWITCHGEAR ACCESS, NEC
SYNTHETIC RESIN FINISHED PRDTS, NEC
SYRUPS, DRINK
SYRUPS, FLAVORING, EXC DRINK
SYSTEMS ENGINEERING: Computer Related
SYSTEMS INTEGRATION SVCS
SYSTEMS INTEGRATION SVCS: Local Area Network
SYSTEMS INTEGRATION SVCS: Office Computer Automation
SYSTEMS SOFTWARE DEVELOPMENT SVCS

T

TABLE OR COUNTERTOPS, PLASTIC LAMINATED
TABLECLOTHS & SETTINGS
TABLETS: Bronze Or Other Metal
TABULATING SVCS
TAGS & LABELS: Paper
TAGS: Paper, Blank, Made From Purchased Paper
TAILORS: Custom
TALC
TALC MINING
TANK COMPONENTS: Military, Specialized
TANK RECOVERY VEHICLES
TANK REPAIR & CLEANING SVCS
TANK REPAIR SVCS
TANKS & OTHER TRACKED VEHICLE CMPNTS
TANKS: Concrete
TANKS: Cryogenic, Metal
TANKS: For Tank Trucks, Metal Plate
TANKS: Fuel, Including Oil & Gas, Metal Plate
TANKS: Lined, Metal
TANKS: Plastic & Fiberglass
TANKS: Standard Or Custom Fabricated, Metal Plate
TANKS: Water, Metal Plate
TAPE PRINT UNITS: Computer
TAPE: Instrumentation Type, Blank
TAPES, ADHESIVE: Masking, Made From Purchased Materials
TAPES: Coated Fiberglass, Pipe Sealing Or Insulating
TAPES: Magnetic
TAPES: Plastic Coated
TAPES: Pressure Sensitive
TAPES: Pressure Sensitive, Rubber
TAR PAPER: Roofing
TARGET DRONES
TARPAULINS
TAX RETURN PREPARATION SVCS
TAXI CABS
TAXIDERMISTS
TECHNICAL INSTITUTE
TECHNICAL WRITING SVCS
TELECOMMUNICATION EQPT REPAIR SVCS, EXC TELEPHONES
TELECOMMUNICATION SYSTEMS & EQPT
TELECOMMUNICATIONS CARRIERS & SVCS: Wired
TELECOMMUNICATIONS CARRIERS & SVCS: Wireless
TELEGRAPH OR TELEPHONE CARRIER & REPEATER EQPT
TELEMARKETING BUREAUS
TELEMETERING EQPT
TELEPHONE ANSWERING MACHINES
TELEPHONE EQPT INSTALLATION
TELEPHONE EQPT: Modems
TELEPHONE EQPT: NEC
TELEPHONE EQPT: PBX, Manual & Automatic
TELEPHONE SET REPAIR SVCS
TELEPHONE STATION EQPT & PARTS: Wire
TELEPHONE SVCS
TELEPHONE SWITCHING EQPT
TELEPHONE: Automatic Dialers
TELEPHONE: Fiber Optic Systems
TELEPHONE: Sets, Exc Cellular Radio
TELEVISION BROADCASTING & COMMUNICATIONS EQPT
TELEVISION BROADCASTING STATIONS
TELEVISION SETS
TELEVISION: Cameras
TELEVISION: Closed Circuit Eqpt
TENTS: All Materials
TERRA COTTA: Architectural

INDEX

TESTERS: Battery
TESTERS: Environmental
TESTERS: Gas, Exc Indl Process
TESTERS: Ignition Eqpt
TESTERS: Integrated Circuit
TESTERS: Logic Circuit
TESTERS: Physical Property
TEXTILE & APPAREL SVCS
TEXTILE BAGS WHOLESALERS
TEXTILE FINISH: Chem Coat/Treat, Fire Resist, Manmade
TEXTILE FINISHING: Bleaching, Broadwoven, Cotton
TEXTILE FINISHING: Chem Coat/Treat, Man, Broadwoven, Cotton
TEXTILE FINISHING: Chem Coating/Treating, Broadwoven, Cotton
TEXTILE FINISHING: Chemical Coating Or Treating
TEXTILE FINISHING: Embossing, Cotton, Broadwoven
TEXTILE: Finishing, Cotton Broadwoven
TEXTILE: Finishing, Raw Stock NEC
TEXTILE: Goods, NEC
TEXTILES
TEXTILES: Fibers, Textile, Rcvrd From Mill Waste/Rags
TEXTILES: Jute & Flax Prdts
TEXTILES: Linen Fabrics
TEXTILES: Mill Waste & Remnant
TEXTILES: Recovering Textile Fibers From Clippings & Rags
THEATER COMPANIES
THEATRICAL PRODUCERS & SVCS
THEATRICAL SCENERY
THERMISTORS, EXC TEMPERATURE SENSORS
THERMOCOUPLES
THERMOELECTRIC DEVICES: Solid State
THERMOMETERS: Medical, Digital
THERMOPLASTIC MATERIALS
THERMOPLASTICS
THERMOSETTING MATERIALS
THREAD: Thread, From Manmade Fiber
TILE: Brick & Structural, Clay
TILE: Building, clay
TILE: Floor Or Wall, Enamel, Clay
TILE: Mosaic, Ceramic
TILE: Quarry, Clay
TIMING DEVICES: Electronic
TIRE CORD & FABRIC
TIRE CORD & FABRIC: Fabric, Reinforcing
TIRE CORD & FABRIC: Steel
TIRE DEALERS
TIRE INFLATORS: Hand Or Compressor Operated
TIRE INNER-TUBES
TIRE RECAPPING & RETREADING
TIRE SUNDRIES OR REPAIR MATERIALS: Rubber
TIRES & INNER TUBES
TIRES & TUBES WHOLESALERS
TIRES & TUBES, WHOLESALE: Truck
TIRES: Auto
TIRES: Cushion Or Solid Rubber
TIRES: Indl Vehicles
TIRES: Truck
TITANIUM MILL PRDTS
TITLE ABSTRACT & SETTLEMENT OFFICES
TOBACCO & TOBACCO PRDTS WHOLESALERS
TOBACCO THRASHING
TOBACCO: Chewing
TOBACCO: Cigarettes
TOBACCO: Cigars
TOILET FIXTURES: Plastic
TOILET PREPARATIONS
TOILETRIES, COSMETICS & PERFUME STORES
TOILETS: Portable Chemical, Plastics
TOLL OPERATIONS
TOOL & DIE STEEL
TOOL REPAIR SVCS
TOOLS: Carpenters', Including Levels & Chisels, Exc Saws
TOOLS: Hand
TOOLS: Hand, Hammers
TOOLS: Hand, Jewelers'
TOOLS: Hand, Mechanics
TOOLS: Hand, Plumbers'
TOOLS: Hand, Power
TOOLS: Soldering
TOOTHPASTES, GELS & TOOTHPOWDERS
TOPS, DISPENSER OR SHAKER, ETC: Plastic
TOUR OPERATORS
TOWELETTES: Premoistened
TOWELS: Indl

TOWERS, SECTIONS: Transmission, Radio & Television
TOWERS: Bubble, Cooling, Fractionating, Metal Plate
TOWERS: Cooling, Sheet Metal
TOWING & TUGBOAT SVC
TOWING SVCS: Marine
TOYS
TOYS & HOBBY GOODS & SPLYS, WHOLESALE: Playing Cards
TOYS & HOBBY GOODS & SPLYS, WHOLESALE: Toys & Games
TOYS & HOBBY GOODS & SPLYS, WHOLESALE: Toys, NEC
TOYS & HOBBY GOODS & SPLYS, WHOLESALE: Video Games
TOYS: Dolls, Stuffed Animals & Parts
TOYS: Kites
TOYS: Paint Sets, Children's
TOYS: Rubber
TOYS: Video Game Machines
TRADE SHOW ARRANGEMENT SVCS
TRADERS: Commodity, Contracts
TRAFFIC CONTROL FLAGGING SVCS
TRAILER COACHES: Automobile
TRAILERS & CHASSIS: Camping
TRAILERS & PARTS: Boat
TRAILERS & PARTS: Horse
TRAILERS & PARTS: Truck & Semi's
TRAILERS & TRAILER EQPT
TRAILERS OR VANS: Horse Transportation, Fifth-Wheel Type
TRAILERS: Bodies
TRAILERS: Bus, Tractor Type
TRAILERS: Camping, Tent-Type
TRAILERS: Semitrailers, Missile Transportation
TRAILERS: Semitrailers, Truck Tractors
TRAILERS: Truck, Chassis
TRANSDUCERS: Electrical Properties
TRANSFORMERS: Distribution
TRANSFORMERS: Distribution, Electric
TRANSFORMERS: Electric
TRANSFORMERS: Electronic
TRANSFORMERS: Furnace, Electric
TRANSFORMERS: Instrument
TRANSFORMERS: Power Related
TRANSFORMERS: Specialty
TRANSFORMERS: Voltage Regulating
TRANSISTORS
TRANSLATION & INTERPRETATION SVCS
TRANSMISSION FLUID, MADE FROM PURCHASED MATERIALS
TRANSPORTATION EPQT & SPLYS, WHOL: Aircraft Engs/Eng Parts
TRANSPORTATION EPQT & SPLYS, WHOLESALE: Acft/Space Vehicle
TRANSPORTATION EPQT & SPLYS, WHOLESALE: Helicopter Parts
TRANSPORTATION EPQT & SPLYS, WHOLESALE: Marine Crafts/Splys
TRANSPORTATION EPQT & SPLYS, WHOLESALE: Tanks & Tank Compnts
TRANSPORTATION EPQT/SPLYS, WHOL: Marine Propulsn Mach/Eqpt
TRANSPORTATION EQPT & SPLYS WHOLESALERS, NEC
TRANSPORTATION EQUIPMENT, NEC
TRANSPORTATION PROGRAM REGULATION & ADMIN, GOVT: State
TRANSPORTATION PROGRAMS REGULATION & ADMINISTRATION SVCS
TRANSPORTATION SVCS, AIR, NONSCHEDULED: Air Cargo Carriers
TRANSPORTATION SVCS, DEEP SEA: Intercoastal, Freight
TRANSPORTATION SVCS, NEC
TRANSPORTATION SVCS, WATER: Boathouses, Commercial
TRANSPORTATION SVCS, WATER: Canal & Intracoastal, Freight
TRANSPORTATION SVCS, WATER: Cleaning
TRANSPORTATION SVCS, WATER: Salvaging & Surveying, Marine
TRANSPORTATION SVCS, WATER: Ship Cleaning
TRANSPORTATION SVCS, WATER: Ship Dismantling
TRANSPORTATION: Coastal Domestic Freight
TRANSPORTATION: Deep Sea Foreign Freight
TRAP ROCK: Crushed & Broken
TRAPS: Animal & Fish, Wire
TRAVEL TRAILERS & CAMPERS

TRAVELER ACCOMMODATIONS, NEC
TROPHIES, NEC
TROPHIES: Metal, Exc Silver
TROPHY & PLAQUE STORES
TRUCK & BUS BODIES: Ambulance
TRUCK & BUS BODIES: Cement Mixer
TRUCK & BUS BODIES: Garbage Or Refuse Truck
TRUCK & BUS BODIES: Motor Vehicle, Specialty
TRUCK & BUS BODIES: Stake Platform Truck
TRUCK & BUS BODIES: Truck Beds
TRUCK & BUS BODIES: Truck, Motor Vehicle
TRUCK & BUS BODIES: Van Bodies
TRUCK & FREIGHT TERMINALS & SUPPORT ACTIVITIES
TRUCK BODIES: Body Parts
TRUCK BODY SHOP
TRUCK DRIVER SVCS
TRUCK DRIVING TRAINING
TRUCK FINANCE LEASING
TRUCK GENERAL REPAIR SVC
TRUCK PAINTING & LETTERING SVCS
TRUCK PARTS & ACCESSORIES: Wholesalers
TRUCKING & HAULING SVCS: Contract Basis
TRUCKING & HAULING SVCS: Hazardous Waste
TRUCKING & HAULING SVCS: Heavy, NEC
TRUCKING & HAULING SVCS: Liquid Petroleum, Exc Local
TRUCKING & HAULING SVCS: Liquid Transfer Svc
TRUCKING & HAULING SVCS: Liquid, Local
TRUCKING & HAULING SVCS: Lumber & Log, Local
TRUCKING & HAULING SVCS: Lumber & Timber
TRUCKING & HAULING SVCS: Machinery, Heavy
TRUCKING & HAULING SVCS: Mobile Homes
TRUCKING & HAULING SVCS: Petroleum, Local
TRUCKING, AUTOMOBILE CARRIER
TRUCKING, DUMP
TRUCKING: Except Local
TRUCKING: Local, With Storage
TRUCKING: Local, Without Storage
TRUCKS & TRACTORS: Industrial
TRUCKS, INDL: Wholesalers
TRUCKS: Forklift
TRUCKS: Indl
TRUSSES & FRAMING: Prefabricated Metal
TRUSSES: Wood, Floor
TRUSSES: Wood, Roof
TRUST MANAGEMENT SVCS: Educational
TUB CONTAINERS: Plastic
TUBE & PIPE MILL EQPT
TUBE & TUBING FABRICATORS
TUBES: Extruded Or Drawn, Aluminum
TUBES: Finned, For Heat Transfer
TUBES: Gas Or Vapor
TUBES: Paper
TUBES: Paper Or Fiber, Chemical Or Electrical Uses
TUBES: Steel & Iron
TUBES: Welded, Aluminum
TUBES: Wrought, Welded Or Lock Joint
TUBING: Copper
TUBING: Flexible, Metallic
TUBING: Plastic
TUBING: Rubber
TUBING: Seamless
TUGBOAT SVCS
TUMBLERS: Plastic
TUNGSTEN CARBIDE
TURBINE GENERATOR SET UNITS: Hydraulic, Complete
TURBINES & TURBINE GENERATOR SET UNITS, COMPLETE
TURBINES & TURBINE GENERATOR SET UNITS: Gas, Complete
TURBINES & TURBINE GENERATOR SETS
TURBINES & TURBINE GENERATOR SETS & PARTS
TURBINES: Gas, Mechanical Drive
TURBINES: Hydraulic, Complete
TURBINES: Steam
TURNKEY VENDORS: Computer Systems
TYPESETTING SVC
TYPESETTING SVC: Computer

U

ULTRASONIC EQPT: Cleaning, Exc Med & Dental
UMBRELLAS: Garden Or Wagon
UNDERGROUND IRON ORE MINING
UNDERGROUND SILVER MINING
UNIFORM SPLY SVCS: Indl
UNIFORM STORES

UNISEX HAIR SALONS
UNIVERSITY
UPHOLSTERY FILLING MATERIALS
UPHOLSTERY WORK SVCS
URANIUM ORE MINING, NEC
URBAN PLANNING & COMMUNITY & RURAL DEVELOPMENT SVCS
USED BOOK STORES
USED CLOTHING STORES
USED MERCHANDISE STORES
USED MERCHANDISE STORES: Rare Books
UTILITY TRAILER DEALERS

V

VACUUM CLEANER REPAIR SVCS
VACUUM CLEANER STORES
VACUUM CLEANERS: Household
VACUUM CLEANERS: Indl Type
VACUUM CLEANERS: Wholesalers
VACUUM SYSTEMS: Air Extraction, Indl
VALUE-ADDED RESELLERS: Computer Systems
VALVE REPAIR SVCS, INDL
VALVES
VALVES & PARTS: Gas, Indl
VALVES & PIPE FITTINGS
VALVES & REGULATORS: Pressure, Indl
VALVES Solenoid
VALVES: Aerosol, Metal
VALVES: Aircraft, Hydraulic
VALVES: Control, Automatic
VALVES: Engine
VALVES: Fluid Power, Control, Hydraulic & pneumatic
VALVES: Gas Cylinder, Compressed
VALVES: Indl
VALVES: Plumbing & Heating
VALVES: Regulating & Control, Automatic
VALVES: Regulating, Process Control
VALVES: Water Works
VAN CONVERSIONS
VARIETY STORE MERCHANDISE, WHOLESALE
VARIETY STORES
VAULTS & SAFES WHOLESALERS
VEHICLES: All Terrain
VEHICLES: Recreational
VENDING MACHINE OPERATORS: Candy & Snack Food
VENDING MACHINE OPERATORS: Cold Drinks
VENDING MACHINE OPERATORS: Food
VENDING MACHINES & PARTS
VENETIAN BLINDS & SHADES
VENTILATING EQPT: Metal
VENTILATING EQPT: Sheet Metal
VENTURE CAPITAL COMPANIES
VESSELS: Process, Indl, Metal Plate
VETERINARY PHARMACEUTICAL PREPARATIONS
VETERINARY PRDTS: Instruments & Apparatus
VIBRATORS: Concrete Construction
VIDEO & AUDIO EQPT, WHOLESALE
VIDEO TRIGGERS EXC REMOTE CONTROL TV DEVICES
VINYL RESINS, NEC
VISUAL COMMUNICATIONS SYSTEMS
VITAMINS: Natural Or Synthetic, Uncompounded, Bulk
VITAMINS: Pharmaceutical Preparations
VOCATIONAL REHABILITATION AGENCY

W

WALKWAYS: Moving
WALL & CEILING SQUARES: Concrete
WALL COVERINGS WHOLESALERS
WALLBOARD: Gypsum
WALLPAPER STORE
WALLS: Curtain, Metal
WAREHOUSING & STORAGE FACILITIES, NEC
WAREHOUSING & STORAGE, REFRIGERATED: Cold Storage Or Refrig
WAREHOUSING & STORAGE, REFRIGERATED: Frozen Or Refrig Goods

WAREHOUSING & STORAGE: Bulk St & Termnls, Hire, Petro/Chem
WAREHOUSING & STORAGE: General
WAREHOUSING & STORAGE: General
WAREHOUSING & STORAGE: Liquid
WAREHOUSING & STORAGE: Miniwarehouse
WAREHOUSING & STORAGE: Self Storage
WARFARE COUNTER-MEASURE EQPT
WARM AIR HEATING & AC EQPT & SPLYS, WHOLESALE Air Filters
WARM AIR HEATING & AC EQPT & SPLYS, WHOLESALE Heat Exchgrs
WARRANTY INSURANCE: Automobile
WASHERS: Metal
WASHERS: Plastic
WATCHES & PARTS, WHOLESALE
WATER HEATERS
WATER PURIFICATION EQPT: Household
WATER PURIFICATION PRDTS: Chlorination Tablets & Kits
WATER SOFTENER SVCS
WATER SOFTENING WHOLESALERS
WATER SPLY: Irrigation
WATER SUPPLY
WATER TREATMENT EQPT: Indl
WATER: Distilled
WATER: Mineral, Carbonated, Canned & Bottled, Etc
WATER: Pasteurized & Mineral, Bottled & Canned
WATER: Pasteurized, Canned & Bottled, Etc
WATERPROOFING COMPOUNDS
WAVEGUIDE STRUCTURES: Accelerating
WAXES: Petroleum, Not Produced In Petroleum Refineries
WEATHER STRIPS: Metal
WEIGHING MACHINERY & APPARATUS
WELDING & CUTTING APPARATUS & ACCESS, NEC
WELDING EQPT
WELDING EQPT & SPLYS WHOLESALERS
WELDING EQPT & SPLYS: Electrodes
WELDING EQPT & SPLYS: Gas
WELDING EQPT & SPLYS: Resistance, Electric
WELDING EQPT & SPLYS: Wire, Bare & Coated
WELDING EQPT REPAIR SVCS
WELDING EQPT: Electric
WELDING EQPT: Electrical
WELDING MACHINES & EQPT: Ultrasonic
WELDING REPAIR SVC
WELDING SPLYS, EXC GASES: Wholesalers
WELDING TIPS: Heat Resistant, Metal
WELL LOGGING EQPT
WELL SURVEYING EQPT
WESTERN APPAREL STORES
WHEEL BALANCING EQPT: Automotive
WHEELCHAIR LIFTS
WHEELCHAIRS
WHEELS
WHEELS: Abrasive
WHIRLPOOL BATHS: Hydrotherapy
WICKER PRDTS
WINCHES
WINDINGS: Coil, Electronic
WINDMILLS: Electric Power Generation
WINDMILLS: Farm Type
WINDOW & DOOR FRAMES
WINDOW BLIND REPAIR SVCS
WINDOW CLEANING SVCS
WINDOW FRAMES & SASHES: Plastic
WINDOW FRAMES, MOLDING & TRIM: Vinyl
WINDOW FURNISHINGS WHOLESALERS
WINDOW SASHES, WOOD
WINDOW SCREENING: Plastic
WINDOWS: Frames, Wood
WINDOWS: Wood
WINDSHIELD WIPER SYSTEMS
WINE & DISTILLED ALCOHOLIC BEVERAGES WHOLESALERS
WINE CELLARS, BONDED: Wine, Blended
WIRE

WIRE & CABLE: Aluminum
WIRE & CABLE: Nonferrous, Aircraft
WIRE & CABLE: Nonferrous, Building
WIRE & WIRE PRDTS
WIRE CLOTH & WOVEN WIRE PRDTS, MADE FROM PURCHASED WIRE
WIRE CLOTH: Cylinder, Made From Purchased Wire
WIRE CLOTH: Fourdrinier, Made From Purchased Wire
WIRE FABRIC: Welded Steel
WIRE FENCING & ACCESS WHOLESALERS
WIRE MATERIALS: Copper
WIRE MATERIALS: Steel
WIRE PRDTS: Ferrous Or Iron, Made In Wiredrawing Plants
WIRE PRDTS: Steel & Iron
WIRE WHOLESALERS
WIRE WINDING OF PURCHASED WIRE
WIRE: Barbed & Twisted
WIRE: Communication
WIRE: Mesh
WIRE: Nonferrous
WIRE: Wire, Ferrous Or Iron
WOMEN'S & CHILDREN'S CLOTHING WHOLESALERS, NEC
WOMEN'S & GIRLS' SPORTSWEAR WHOLESALERS
WOMEN'S CLOTHING STORES
WOMEN'S CLOTHING STORES: Ready-To-Wear
WOMEN'S SPECIALTY CLOTHING STORES
WOOD CARVINGS, WHOLESALE
WOOD CHIPS, PRODUCED AT THE MILL
WOOD FENCING WHOLESALERS
WOOD PRDTS: Applicators
WOOD PRDTS: Flour
WOOD PRDTS: Furniture Inlays, Veneers
WOOD PRDTS: Jalousies, Glass, Wood Framed
WOOD PRDTS: Laundry
WOOD PRDTS: Moldings, Unfinished & Prefinished
WOOD PRDTS: Mulch Or Sawdust
WOOD PRDTS: Mulch, Wood & Bark
WOOD PRDTS: Poles
WOOD PRDTS: Saddle Trees
WOOD PRDTS: Signboards
WOOD PRDTS: Survey Stakes
WOOD PRDTS: Trim
WOOD PRDTS: Trophy Bases
WOOD PRDTS: Wood Wool, Excelsior
WOOD PRODUCTS: Reconstituted
WOOD SHAVINGS BALES, MULCH TYPE, WHOLESALE
WOOD TREATING: Creosoting
WOOD TREATING: Millwork
WOOD TREATING: Railroad Cross Bridges & Switch Ties
WOOD TREATING: Railroad Cross-Ties
WOOD TREATING: Structural Lumber & Timber
WOODWORK & TRIM: Exterior & Ornamental
WOODWORK & TRIM: Interior & Ornamental
WOODWORK: Carved & Turned
WOODWORK: Interior & Ornamental, NEC
WOODWORK: Ornamental, Cornices, Mantels, Etc.
WOOLEN & WORSTED YARNS, WHOLESALES
WOVEN WIRE PRDTS, NEC

X

X-RAY EQPT & TUBES

Y

YARN & YARN SPINNING
YARN: Cotton, Spun
YARN: Embroidery, Spun
YARN: Manmade & Synthetic Fiber, Spun
YARN: Polyester, Spun From Purchased Staple
YARN: Polypropylene Filament, Throw, Twist, Windg/Spool
YOGURT WHOLESALERS

Z

ZIRCONIUM

INDEX

PRODUCT SECTION

Product category ⟶ **BOXES:** *Folding*
Edgar & Son Paperboard ....G...... 999 999-9999
Yourtown *(G-11480)*
Ready Box Co ....E....... 999 999-9999
City ⟶ Anytown *(G-7097)*

Indicates approximate employment figure
A = Over 500 employees, B = 251-500
C = 101-250, D = 51-100, E = 20-50
F = 10-19, G =9

Business phone

Geographic Section entry number where full
company information appears.

See footnotes for symbols and codes identification.

• Refer to the Industrial Product Index preceding this section to locate product headings.

ABRASIVES

Asset Guard Products Inc ....E 940 627-1400
Decatur *(G-5242)*
Carbo Ceramics Inc ....B 281 921-6400
Houston *(G-9091)*
Custom Abrasives LLC ....F 281 286-7200
Houston *(G-9362)*
Dunn Enterprises Inc ....E 713 869-4841
Porter *(G-17174)*
Gulf States Abrasive Mfg ....D 713 869-4841
Porter *(G-17177)*
Hartwell Industries Inc ....E 713 771-4311
Houston *(G-10134)*
Saint-Gobain Abrasives Inc ....C 956 541-5285
Brownsville *(G-2404)*
Saint-Gobain Abrasives Inc ....F 956 519-5047
Mcallen *(G-14904)*
Saint-Gobain Abrasives Inc ....A 254 918-2307
Stephenville *(G-19421)*
UM Abrasives Inc ....F 817 572-1344
Kennedale *(G-13506)*
US Minerals Inc ....F 409 740-3355
Galveston *(G-7412)*

ABRASIVES: Synthetic

Opti-Blast Inc ....F 903 589-0452
Jacksonville *(G-13254)*

ABRASIVES: Tungsten Carbide

Cerametals Carbide LLC ....E 713 937-3801
Houston *(G-9144)*
Dynalloy Industries Inc ....E 936 825-2532
Navasota *(G-15729)*
Dynalloy Industries Inc ....E 936 825-2532
Navasota *(G-15730)*
Dynalloy Industries Inc ....F 713 856-9377
Houston *(G-9545)*
Syntex Super Materials Inc ....E 281 821-9495
Houston *(G-12137)*

ACCELERATION INDICATORS & SYSTEM COMPONENTS: Aerospace

Marathonnorco Aerospace Inc ....C 254 315-7524
Waco *(G-20431)*
P T Products & Services Inc ....E 512 251-3592
Pflugerville *(G-16682)*
Skygrid LLC ....F 844 205-7173
Austin *(G-1510)*
Thomas Instrument Incorporated ....E 830 331-1325
Boerne *(G-2141)*

ACCOUNTING MACHINES & CASH REGISTERS

Revolution Retail Systems LLC ....G 469 317-2910
Carrollton *(G-2806)*

ACETONE: Synthetic

Braskem America Inc ....C 713 255-4747
Houston *(G-8976)*
Braskem America Inc ....G 215 841-3100
Port Lavaca *(G-17142)*
Braskem America Inc ....F 979 705-2532
Freeport *(G-7193)*
Ineos Americas LLC ....C 251 535-6600
League City *(G-13960)*

ACIDS: Battery

Revere Smelting & Ref Corp ....C 214 631-6070
Dallas *(G-4893)*

ACIDS: Inorganic

El Dorado Chemical Company ....C 254 445-2720
Dublin *(G-5516)*

ACIDS: Nitric

El Dorado Nitrogen LP ....F 281 383-1807
Baytown *(G-1786)*

ACIDS: Sulfuric, Oleum

Chemtrade Refinery Svcs Inc ....E 409 835-6641
Beaumont *(G-1869)*
Eco Services Operations Corp ....F 844 812-1812
The Woodlands *(G-19860)*
Eco Services Operations Corp ....C 713 924-1401
Houston *(G-9576)*
Eco Services Operations LLC ....B 800 642-4200
Spring *(G-19210)*
Veolia North America Reg Serv ....E 915 782-5550
El Paso *(G-6026)*

ACOUSTICAL BOARD & TILE

Jayvic Inc ....F 806 374-9402
Amarillo *(G-442)*

ACRYLIC RESINS

Dianal America Inc ....E 713 758-8100
Pasadena *(G-16416)*
Lucite International Inc ....C 409 729-1300
Nederland *(G-15755)*
Octal Inc ....F 972 985-4370
Plano *(G-16952)*
Sani-Safe Products Inc ....E 210 646-6706
San Antonio *(G-18452)*

ACRYLONITRILE BUTADIENE STYRENE RESINS

Eastman Chemical Texas Cy Inc ....E 409 942-3307
Texas City *(G-19791)*

ACTUATORS: Indl, NEC

Rotork Controls Inc ....F 713 983-7381
Houston *(G-11674)*
Stoneridge Inc ....B 915 778-1331
El Paso *(G-5983)*
Tyco Engineered Pdts & Svcs ....D 609 720-4200
Houston *(G-12418)*
Ultramation Inc ....G 254 772-4860
Waco *(G-20469)*
Vanzandt Controls ....G 806 655-9367
Canyon *(G-2676)*
Wesco Acquisition Partners Inc ....E 713 688-5551
Galena Park *(G-7386)*
Williams Machine Inc ....F 713 462-2229
Cypress *(G-3827)*

ADAPTERS: Well

Shf Inc ....C 832 456-2000
Pasadena *(G-16506)*

ADDITIVE BASED PLASTIC MATERIALS: Plasticizers

Britec Solutions Inc ....G 903 707-7471
Tyler *(G-20061)*
LyondlIbsell Advnced Plymers I ....C 281 867-3000
La Porte *(G-13772)*

ADHESIVES

Aviation Products Inc ....F 817 457-2040
Fort Worth *(G-6413)*
Championx LLC ....A 281 632-6500
Sugar Land *(G-19455)*
Edge Adhesives Inc ....D 817 232-2026
Fort Worth *(G-6604)*
HB Fuller Cnstr Pdts Inc ....E 713 926-3125
Houston *(G-10139)*
Holdtite USA Inc ....F 817 441-1723
Fort Worth *(G-6702)*
Mapei Corporation ....D 972 271-9500
Garland *(G-7542)*
Mar-Tek Industries Inc ....G 214 350-9401
Forney *(G-6313)*
PRC - Desoto International Inc ....E 817 640-1067
Grand Prairie *(G-7953)*
Precision Additives Inc ....E 713 896-0606
Houston *(G-11386)*
QEP Co Inc ....E 817 477-1183
Mansfield *(G-14705)*
Rex-Hide Incorporated ....F 903 593-7387
Tyler *(G-20146)*
Rocka Solutions Inc ....F 514 602-9449
El Paso *(G-5943)*
Specilty Adhesives Coating Inc ....F 972 641-7600
Grand Prairie *(G-7975)*

ADHESIVES & SEALANTS

Akfix USA Inc ....D 972 276-9600
Garland *(G-7431)*
American Indus Mfrs Bldg Mate ....C 214 254-4720
Plano *(G-16787)*
Armor Plate Inc ....E 281 487-2023
Pasadena *(G-16390)*
Denovus LLC ....E 214 789-5725
Ennis *(G-6092)*
Hexpol Compounding LLC ....D 817 483-9797
Kennedale *(G-13498)*
Igi The Intl Group Inc ....E 281 573-9280
Baytown *(G-1792)*
Illinois Tool Works Inc ....D 281 580-1589
Houston *(G-10324)*
Lapolla Industries LLC ....E 281 219-4100
Houston *(G-10599)*
Orrex Plastics Company LLC ....E 432 332-1229
Odessa *(G-16104)*
Silco Inc ....G 713 785-6272
Houston *(G-11895)*
Vertrauen Chemie Solutions Inc ....E 469 283-0789
McKinney *(G-14986)*
W R Grace & Co-Conn ....E 713 675-6445
Houston *(G-12587)*
Wilsonart LLC ....F 214 634-2310
Dallas *(G-5192)*

ADHESIVES & SEALANTS WHOLESALERS

Progressive Components Inc ....F 972 775-6932
Midlothian *(G-15491)*
RH Tamlyn & Sons ....E 281 499-9604
Stafford *(G-19370)*

PRODUCT

ADHESIVES: Epoxy

His Company Inc............................F...... 713 934-1600
Houston (G-10187)

Wil-Cor Inc...................................F...... 281 487-6547
Pasadena (G-16526)

ADVERTISING AGENCIES

EPM Live Inc................................C....... 425 452-1111
Austin (G-1133)

Fource Communications Limited..........F...... 214 630-2125
Dallas (G-4374)

Gatehouse Media LLC....................F...... 956 546-5113
Brownsville (G-2358)

Gemstar Stoneworks Inc.................E...... 281 257-6500
Spring (G-19124)

Hudson Graphics Inc......................E...... 903 758-1773
Longview (G-14248)

JDC Enterprises Inc.......................E...... 972 550-1880
Irving (G-13068)

Thryv Inc.....................................C....... 972 453-7000
Dfw Airport (G-5457)

Waco Publications Inc.....................E...... 254 752-0334
Waco (G-20476)

William G Burns............................F...... 972 233-4700
Dallas (G-5189)

ADVERTISING AGENCIES: Consultants

Beehive Specialty Co......................F...... 512 912-7940
Austin (G-985)

C & B Printing Co..........................F...... 806 374-6262
Amarillo (G-410)

Horizon Worldwide Corporation..........D...... 713 647-7400
Houston (G-10208)

Lugra Inc....................................F...... 956 986-0958
Brownsville (G-2378)

Mission Pharmacal Company............E...... 210 696-8400
San Antonio (G-18313)

Zachry Associates Inc....................E...... 325 677-1342
Abilene (G-97)

ADVERTISING DISPLAY PRDTS

Cree Visual Marketing Company..........E...... 214 905-8485
Carrollton (G-2720)

Insignia Marketing Inc....................F...... 281 465-0040
Magnolia (G-14610)

Mash Group Holdings LLC................E...... 314 638-4200
Frisco (G-7297)

ADVERTISING MATERIAL DISTRIBUTION

All Star Caps Inc...........................F...... 210 509-9086
San Antonio (G-17893)

Arygin Corporation.........................F...... 940 597-8275
Denton (G-5350)

Beehive Specialty Co......................F...... 512 912-7940
Austin (G-985)

Indoormedia Inc............................B...... 800 247-4793
Houston (G-10345)

Register Tapes Unlimited LP.............C...... 281 206-2500
Houston (G-11586)

Success Partners Holding Co.............C...... 800 752-2030
Plano (G-17012)

ADVERTISING REPRESENTATIVES: Electronic Media

A H Belo Corporation......................D...... 214 977-8222
Dallas (G-3871)

ADVERTISING REPRESENTATIVES: Media

Ajr Media Group LLC......................F...... 713 942-7676
Spring (G-19194)

ADVERTISING REPRESENTATIVES: Newspaper

Arbol Publishing LP........................F...... 512 476-8636
Austin (G-929)

C & S Media Inc.............................G...... 972 442-5515
Wylie (G-20928)

Cnhi LLC.....................................E...... 806 273-5611
Borger (G-2169)

Cnhi LLC.....................................E...... 940 665-5511
Gainesville (G-7339)

Dmn Inc......................................E...... 214 745-8383
Garland (G-7480)

Hartman Newspapers LP..................E...... 281 232-3737
Rosenberg (G-17587)

Hartman Newspapers LP..................F...... 972 563-6476
Terrell (G-19737)

Hearst Corporation.........................F...... 409 384-3441
Jasper (G-13277)

La Subasta Incorporated.................F...... 214 951-9500
Dallas (G-4577)

Marcos N Suarez...........................E...... 214 357-2186
Dallas (G-4634)

Polk County Publishing Co................F...... 409 283-2516
Woodville (G-20916)

University of Texas At Austin.............E...... 512 471-1865
Austin (G-1610)

Want ADS of San Angelo Inc.............F...... 325 944-7653
San Angelo (G-17837)

ADVERTISING REPRESENTATIVES: Printed Media

Calrock Music...............................D...... 432 213-8822
Houston (G-9054)

D Custom....................................F...... 214 523-0300
Dallas (G-4202)

Shweiki Media Inc..........................E...... 210 804-0390
San Antonio (G-18471)

ADVERTISING SPECIALTIES, WHOLESALE

A J L Advertising Specialties.............E...... 512 320-0070
Austin (G-872)

Bells Advertising Inc......................E...... 512 454-9663
Austin (G-989)

Bob Hughes Displays LLC................F...... 713 468-7726
Marble Falls (G-14739)

Bob Lillys Prof Mktg Group Inc...........E...... 214 231-2082
Garland (G-7449)

Cfj Manufacturing LP......................D...... 817 625-9559
Fort Worth (G-6506)

Cfj Manufacturing LP......................E...... 817 232-9251
Saginaw (G-17741)

Doyle & Hamilton Inc......................F...... 817 882-8080
Fort Worth (G-6592)

G and G Investments Inc.................F...... 325 949-7864
San Angelo (G-17801)

Insignia Marketing Inc....................F...... 281 465-0040
Magnolia (G-14610)

Mc Creless Company......................E...... 432 332-1213
Odessa (G-16076)

Merit Sales Inc..............................D...... 512 863-8541
Georgetown (G-7664)

Midtown Prtg & Graphics Inc.............E...... 806 744-3382
Lubbock (G-14447)

Pacifica T-Shirts Inc.......................F...... 714 508-4848
Round Rock (G-17677)

Premier Printing & Ltr Svc Inc...........E...... 713 868-6300
Houston (G-11404)

Sam Group Inc..............................F...... 817 481-1968
Grapevine (G-8053)

Slpc Inc......................................E...... 281 398-6655
Katy (G-13443)

Trademarks Promotional Pdts LP........D...... 713 255-6506
Houston (G-12340)

ADVERTISING SVCS: Billboards

Allied Advertising Agency Inc............E...... 210 732-7874
San Antonio (G-17897)

Reagan Outdoor Advertising.............E...... 512 926-7740
Austin (G-1454)

ADVERTISING SVCS: Direct Mail

Anderton Group II Ltd.....................F...... 254 751-1012
Waco (G-20361)

Associated Publishing Company.........E...... 432 687-1756
Midland (G-15121)

Clear Visions Inc...........................D...... 210 496-6006
San Antonio (G-18012)

College Port Enterprises Inc..............F...... 979 848-3070
Angleton (G-568)

Corporate Bus Solutions Inc.............E...... 817 701-1390
Arlington (G-647)

Fgs - Dallas Inc............................E...... 972 375-0253
Grand Prairie (G-7871)

Harte Hanks Inc............................E...... 512 343-1100
Austin (G-1198)

Infovine Inc..................................F...... 713 223-9994
Houston (G-10360)

Laser Image Inc............................E...... 214 267-1313
Dallas (G-4582)

ADVERTISING SVCS: Display

Adcorp Sign Systems LLC................F...... 936 321-4888
Conroe (G-3252)

Andax Corp..................................F...... 972 392-3999
Addison (G-104)

Cree Visual Marketing Company..........E...... 214 905-8485
Carrollton (G-2720)

Daryan Design Inc..........................F...... 214 905-6022
Dallas (G-4239)

Mick & David Enterprises Inc.............F...... 214 350-5765
Dallas (G-4674)

ADVERTISING SVCS: Outdoor

D-Signs Inc..................................E...... 214 327-2373
Garland (G-7473)

Lozz Quatezz LLC..........................F...... 956 687-7446
Pharr (G-16706)

Outfront Media LLC.........................D...... 713 868-2284
Houston (G-11205)

ADVERTISING SVCS: Transit

M2w Inc......................................D...... 972 407-1332
Mesquite (G-15059)

Thryv Holdings Inc.........................A...... 972 453-7000
Dfw Airport (G-5458)

ADVERTISING: Aerial

Idea Planet LP..............................E...... 972 380-9867
Dallas (G-3844)

AERIAL WORK PLATFORMS

Versalift Southwest LLC...................D...... 254 399-2100
Waco (G-20473)

AGENTS, BROKERS & BUREAUS: Personal Service

Advanced Control Systems LLC..........E...... 832 529-2234
Houston (G-8487)

Dallas Flag & Flagpole Co Lc.............F...... 972 607-0958
Dallas (G-4216)

Fisher Energy Partners LLC...............E...... 713 937-6838
Houston (G-9792)

Nipco Inc.....................................E...... 432 362-1936
Odessa (G-16093)

Wave Quantum Def & Tech LLC..........F...... 512 505-2339
Austin (G-1650)

AGRICULTURAL DISINFECTANTS

Disingerm Inc...............................F...... 214 482-9135
Ennis (G-6093)

Ecofusion Inc...............................G...... 972 403-7449
Plano (G-16855)

AGRICULTURAL EQPT: BARN, SILO, POULTRY, DAIRY/LIVESTOCK MACH

Harris Fabrication LLC....................F...... 361 547-6910
Mathis (G-14817)

Hcr Electronics Inc.........................E...... 512 756-8164
Burnet (G-2610)

AGRICULTURAL EQPT: Barn Cleaners

County Barn Precinct 4....................F...... 936 258-5202
Dayton (G-5224)

AGRICULTURAL EQPT: Barn Stanchions & Standards

Dasilveira Southwest Inc..................E...... 936 349-1900
Madisonville (G-14586)

AGRICULTURAL EQPT: Fertilizing Machinery

Bowie Industries Incorporated...........E...... 940 872-1106
Bowie (G-2192)

Texas High Roller Inc......................E...... 979 778-7460
Bryan (G-2511)

AGRICULTURAL EQPT: Fertilizng, Sprayng, Dustng/Irrigatn Mach

Compliant Power Systems LLC...........F...... 903 427-0071
Clarksville (G-3072)

H & H Landscape Services LLC..........F...... 832 831-9133
Hockley (G-8346)

Toro Company ....D....... 325 673-8762
  Abilene (G-89)

Valley Farm Service Inc ....F....... 806 364-6900
  Hereford (G-8296)

AGRICULTURAL EQPT: Grade, Clean & Sort Machines, Fruit/Veg

Delta Technology Corporation.............E....... 713 464-7407
  Houston (G-9436)

AGRICULTURAL EQPT: Grounds Mowing Eqpt

Alamo Group (tx) Inc ....B....... 800 882-5762
  Seguin (G-18822)

AGRICULTURAL EQPT: Irrigation Eqpt, Self-Propelled

Pierce Corporation........................E....... 541 998-0300
  San Antonio (G-18375)

Telsco Industries Inc ....G....... 972 278-6131
  Garland (G-7597)

Toro Company ....C....... 915 231-7200
  El Paso (G-6008)

AGRICULTURAL EQPT: Loaders, Manure & General Utility

Heritage Equipment Company Inc ....D....... 806 745-4451
  Wolfforth (G-20908)

AGRICULTURAL EQPT: Planting Machines

W & R Industrial Services Inc ....E....... 806 637-8204
  Brownfield (G-2332)

AGRICULTURAL EQPT: Soil Preparation Mach, Exc Turf & Grounds

Bigham Brothers Inc.......................D....... 806 745-0334
  Lubbock (G-14373)

Texas Incinerator Co Inc ....F....... 432 687-5045
  Midland (G-15436)

AGRICULTURAL EQPT: Soil Sampling Machines

Triangle Resources Inc....................E....... 409 861-2267
  Beaumont (G-1963)

AGRICULTURAL EQPT: Spreaders, Fertilizer

Boyd AG LLC..............................F....... 512 863-2589
  Georgetown (G-7642)

AGRICULTURAL EQPT: Tractors, Farm

Roadclipper Enterprises Inc ....D....... 903 572-2834
  Mount Pleasant (G-15662)

Techsys Chassis Inc ....E....... 903 395-4155
  Paris (G-16371)

West Texas Lee Co Inc ....E....... 800 825-3346
  Lubbock (G-14510)

AGRICULTURAL EQPT: Trailers & Wagons, Farm

Dugan Trailer ....F....... 254 729-3253
  Groesbeck (G-8107)

AGRICULTURAL EQPT: Turf Eqpt, Commercial

Manitou North America Inc ....D....... 254 799-0232
  Waco (G-20429)

AGRICULTURAL MACHINERY & EQPT REPAIR

H & H Water Well Service Inc ....G....... 806 659-5577
  Spearman (G-19086)

Kimbell Gin Machinery Company.........D....... 806 763-6645
  Lubbock (G-14433)

AGRICULTURAL MACHINERY & EQPT: Wholesalers

Caldwell Machine and Gear Inc ....F....... 903 572-1660
  Mount Pleasant (G-15648)

Tru-Test Inc ....E....... 940 327-8020
  Mineral Wells (G-15543)

AIR CLEANING SYSTEMS

3nine USA Inc ....F....... 512 667-6146
  San Marcos (G-18676)

Airflow Systems Inc ....D....... 800 818-6185
  Dallas (G-3911)

Clean Air Consultants Inc ....D....... 972 278-2664
  Garland (G-7458)

Metroplex Products Inc ....F....... 817 923-8241
  Fort Worth (G-6832)

AIR CONDITIONERS, AUTOMOTIVE: Wholesalers

American Cooling Tech Inc ....F....... 717 767-2775
  Haslet (G-8215)

ARA Automotive Systems Inc ....E....... 214 537-1659
  Garland (G-7440)

CW Davis Enterprises Inc ....E....... 972 723-1247
  Midlothian (G-15477)

E3rivers LLC..............................E....... 817 247-5828
  Decatur (G-5245)

AIR CONDITIONERS: Motor Vehicle

American Cooling Tech Inc ....F....... 717 767-2775
  Haslet (G-8215)

Auto Air Export Inc ....D....... 972 812-7000
  Irving (G-12935)

Bus Air LLC ....E....... 817 636-2308
  Haslet (G-8217)

Cold Air Products Inc ....E....... 817 531-2665
  Fort Worth (G-6530)

E3rivers LLC..............................E....... 817 247-5828
  Decatur (G-5245)

Tripac International Inc ....E....... 817 534-9278
  Fort Worth (G-7078)

Valeo North America Inc ....E....... 972 574-1900
  Dallas (G-5150)

AIR CONDITIONING & VENTILATION EQPT & SPLYS: Wholesales

Champion Cooler Corporation ....C....... 903 465-3294
  Denison (G-5337)

Compressors Unlimited Intl LLC ....F....... 972 286-2264
  Dallas (G-4152)

Maverick Enterprises ....F....... 281 444-5010
  Houston (G-10800)

Munters Corporation ....D....... 210 651-5018
  Selma (G-18879)

AIR CONDITIONING EQPT

A-1 Smf LLC ....E....... 512 288-9900
  Austin (G-874)

Air System Components Inc ....C....... 972 212-4888
  Plano (G-16780)

Air System Components Inc ....B....... 915 852-1358
  Horizon City (G-8362)

Air System Components Inc ....B....... 972 212-4700
  Plano (G-16781)

Air System Components Inc ....B....... 972 680-9128
  Richardson (G-17268)

Air System Components Inc ....B....... 972 212-4800
  Plano (G-16782)

All State Fire Eqp Texas Inc ....F....... 972 412-0770
  Wylie (G-20924)

American Air Services LLC ....F....... 832 715-8025
  Houston (G-8583)

Aspen Manufacturing LLC ....C....... 281 441-6500
  Humble (G-12748)

Century Arconditioning Sup L P ....F....... 281 446-7820
  Humble (G-12754)

Coburn Supply Company Inc ....C....... 409 838-6363
  Houston (G-9233)

Custom Controls Company ....E....... 713 666-3258
  Houston (G-9368)

Diversity Industries Inc ....E....... 713 667-9595
  Stafford (G-19306)

Goodman Global Holdings Inc ....F....... 713 861-2500
  Waller (G-20500)

Goodman Manufacturing Co LP ....F....... 936 372-5224
  Waller (G-20501)

Hvac Manufacturing Inc ....F....... 408 254-5420
  Athens (G-829)

Idq Acquisition Corp ....E....... 214 778-4600
  Garland (G-7516)

Keeprite Refrigeration Inc ....D....... 903 643-2261
  Longview (G-14260)

Maverick Enterprises.......................F....... 281 444-5010
  Houston (G-10800)

Mechanical Technical Svcs LP ....E....... 512 929-7090
  Round Rock (G-17671)

National Wholesale Supply Inc ....E....... 972 331-7770
  Dallas (G-4716)

Phoenix Mobile Air Inc ....F....... 972 418-6444
  Carrollton (G-2791)

Rex Mechanical Inc ....E....... 979 793-3340
  Needville (G-15763)

Suncoast A/C & Rfrgn Inc ....F....... 956 428-1190
  Harlingen (G-8204)

Texas Air Products Ltd ....F....... 210 495-8100
  San Antonio (G-18532)

Thermal Edge Inc ....F....... 972 580-0200
  Irving (G-13193)

Winsupply San Antonio ....F....... 210 481-8123
  San Antonio (G-18623)

AIR CONDITIONING EQPT, WHOLE HOUSE: Wholesalers

Amber/Booth Inc ....D....... 713 466-0003
  Houston (G-8577)

Auto Air Export Inc ....D....... 972 812-7000
  Irving (G-12935)

Bois DArc International Trade ....E....... 903 758-2647
  Longview (G-14203)

Century Arconditioning Sup L P ....F....... 281 446-7820
  Humble (G-12754)

Coburn Supply Company Inc ....C....... 409 838-6363
  Houston (G-9233)

Combined Rfrgn Resources Inc ....E....... 281 540-7552
  Humble (G-12761)

Darville Co ....F....... 432 580-9675
  Odessa (G-15974)

Goodman Manufacturing Co LP ....F....... 936 372-5224
  Waller (G-20501)

PCI Industries Inc.........................C....... 817 509-2300
  Fort Worth (G-6898)

AIR CONDITIONING REPAIR SVCS

Air Performance Service Inc ....E....... 972 387-3334
  Dallas (G-3907)

Blade Runner Turbomachinery SE........E....... 713 669-1155
  Navasota (G-15726)

Corsicana Sheet Metal Co Inc ....F....... 903 872-8434
  Corsicana (G-3666)

E Tamez Coml Rfrgn & AC Inc ....G....... 210 884-5059
  San Antonio (G-18079)

Eastern Star Group LLC ....E....... 972 729-9955
  Allen (G-263)

Johnson Controls Inc ....E....... 512 973-3555
  Austin (G-1259)

Miller Mechanical Group ....F....... 361 594-8080
  Shiner (G-18945)

Rex Mechanical Inc ....E....... 979 793-3340
  Needville (G-15763)

Suncoast A/C & Rfrgn Inc ....E....... 956 428-1190
  Harlingen (G-8204)

Synergy Environmental Svcs LLC ....E....... 972 513-1118
  Arlington (G-789)

Trotti Service Company Inc ....F....... 281 894-5095
  Houston (G-12383)

Tuffys AC & Htg Svc Inc ....F....... 817 596-0150
  Weatherford (G-20627)

AIR CONDITIONING UNITS: Complete, Domestic Or Indl

Bergstrom Climate Systems LLC ....E....... 210 507-5670
  San Antonio (G-17948)

Carrier Corporation........................C....... 903 510-7300
  Tyler (G-20063)

Carrier Corporation........................E....... 210 495-2600
  San Antonio (G-17985)

Ces Industrial LLC ....F....... 281 615-5621
  Stafford (G-19293)

Compressors Unlimited Intl LLC ....F....... 972 286-2264
  Dallas (G-4152)

Danhard Inc ....F....... 214 328-8541
  Dallas (G-4233)

Goodman Manufacturing Co LP ....B....... 713 263-5556
  Houston (G-9998)

Goodman Manufacturing Co LP ....C....... 713 861-2500
  Waller (G-20502)

Goodman Manufacturing Co LP ....F....... 713 263-5416
  Houston (G-9999)

PRODUCT

Jmn Energy Experts ....E 817 703-9539
Fort Worth *(G-6743)*

Marc Climatic Controls Inc ....F 713 464-8587
Houston *(G-10761)*

AIR COOLERS: Metal Plate

Hudson Products Holdings Inc ....E 281 396-8100
Beasley *(G-1842)*

Sartartia Fabrication Inc ....E 281 240-1222
Sugar Land *(G-19541)*

Sierra Industries Ltd ....D 210 805-3188
San Antonio *(G-18472)*

AIR CURTAINS

Atlantic Blowers LLC ....F 214 233-0280
Dallas *(G-3979)*

AIR DUCT CLEANING SVCS

Christopher RAD Nader ....F 512 442-5326
Cedar Park *(G-2963)*

Filter Maintenance Company Inc ....E 713 432-7969
Houston *(G-9786)*

AIR MATTRESSES: Plastic

M & G Resins Usa LLC ....E 281 873-5780
Houston *(G-10712)*

M & G Resins Usa LLC ....F 304 576-2041
Corpus Christi *(G-3566)*

Prime Products Inc ....D 979 743-6555
Schulenburg *(G-18777)*

Ravago Mfg Americas LLC ....E 281 443-6220
Houston *(G-11553)*

Royal Case Company Inc ....G 903 328-3371
Sherman *(G-18931)*

AIR POLLUTION CONTROL EQPT & SPLYS WHOLESALERS

Clean Air Consultants Inc ....D 972 278-2664
Garland *(G-7458)*

Gulf Coast Envmtl Systems LLC ....E 832 476-9024
Conroe *(G-3299)*

AIR POLLUTION MEASURING SVCS

Clean Air Consultants Inc ....D 972 278-2664
Garland *(G-7458)*

Enrud Resources Inc ....F 713 943-1600
Pasadena *(G-16429)*

AIR PURIFICATION EQPT

Air Oasis LLC ....E 806 373-7788
Amarillo *(G-477)*

Air Quality Systems LLC ....F 214 495-9991
Allen *(G-248)*

Airbox LLC ....G 512 968-5496
Austin *(G-901)*

American Green Technology Inc ....E 269 340-9975
Houston *(G-8598)*

Braided Green Brokerage LLC ....F 480 729-5506
Murphy *(G-15683)*

Psp Industries Inc ....F 210 651-9595
Schertz *(G-18760)*

Radiant Indus Solutions Inc ....F 713 972-0196
Houston *(G-11531)*

Skyven Technologies Inc ....E 972 861-0893
Richardson *(G-17399)*

Thermtech Inc ....E 281 359-7555
Humble *(G-12804)*

Viron International Corp ....D 254 773-9292
Temple *(G-19714)*

AIR-CONDITIONING SPLY SVCS

Suncoast A/C & Rfrgrn Inc ....F 956 428-1190
Harlingen *(G-8204)*

AIRBOATS

American Airboat Corporation ....E 409 883-7725
Orange *(G-16231)*

AIRCRAFT & AEROSPACE FLIGHT INSTRUMENTS & GUIDANCE SYSTEMS

Bae Systems Info & Elec Sys ....D 972 994-4176
Dallas *(G-3838)*

Fieldtech Avionics Instrs Inc ....E 817 740-7110
Fort Worth *(G-6629)*

Genesys Aerosystems Group Inc ....C 800 872-7832
Mineral Wells *(G-15526)*

GKN Aerospace Inc ....F 972 432-1900
Irving *(G-13038)*

Honeywell International Inc ....D 409 886-7445
Orange *(G-16246)*

Jaunt Air Mobility LLC ....F 817 692-3030
Southlake *(G-19077)*

L 3 Cmncations Intgrtd Systms ....C 903 455-3450
Rockwall *(G-17552)*

L3harris Technologies Inc ....A 903 457-7461
Greenville *(G-8081)*

Lockheed Martin Space Company ....A 281 283-4650
Houston *(G-10668)*

Marathonnorco Aerospace Inc ....D 254 772-7358
Waco *(G-20432)*

Mtc America Enterprises Inc ....F 972 926-0600
Garland *(G-7556)*

Northrop Grumman Corporation ....D 214 524-0102
Irving *(G-13126)*

Orbital Sciences Corporation ....A 281 218-6140
Houston *(G-11192)*

Rothe Joint Venture Lp ....D 281 483-3852
Houston *(G-11670)*

Rothe Joint Venture Lp ....G 210 648-3131
San Antonio *(G-18433)*

S-TEC Corporation ....A 800 872-7832
Mineral Wells *(G-15541)*

Valkyrie Systems Aerospace Inc ....F 888 426-2113
Dallas *(G-3857)*

Williamsrdm Inc ....F 817 872-1500
Fort Worth *(G-7148)*

AIRCRAFT & HEAVY EQPT REPAIR SVCS

3-D Honing Inc ....G 281 391-8989
Katy *(G-13386)*

Aeroxchange Ltd ....E 972 556-8500
Farmers Branch *(G-6185)*

Ahlers Aerospace Inc ....F 817 553-2155
Hurst *(G-12832)*

Airbus Helicopters Inc ....B 972 641-0000
Grand Prairie *(G-7824)*

C & F Tool & Die Co LLC ....E 210 522-9310
San Antonio *(G-17975)*

Currentech ....F 214 693-6751
Arlington *(G-655)*

Dallas Airmotive Inc ....B 214 956-2505
Dallas *(G-4211)*

Evans Composites Inc ....E 817 477-9014
Mansfield *(G-14670)*

H & H Machine Service LLC ....F 979 836-2599
Brenham *(G-2256)*

Harris Composites Inc ....E 817 279-9546
Granbury *(G-7799)*

International Airmotive Holdg ....F 214 956-3000
Grapevine *(G-8043)*

James Manufacturing Inc ....E 903 872-2346
Corsicana *(G-3675)*

L3 Technologies Inc ....C 512 251-3441
Austin *(G-1279)*

Lebus International Inc ....D 903 758-5521
Longview *(G-14263)*

Payton Machine & Supply Inc ....E 806 274-5221
Borger *(G-2182)*

Safran Power Units Dallas Inc ....F 972 606-7681
Grand Prairie *(G-7970)*

Texas Pneumatic Systems Inc ....F 817 794-0068
Arlington *(G-792)*

Texas Pneumatic Systems Inc ....D 817 794-0068
Pantego *(G-16353)*

Tymco International Inc ....C 254 799-5546
Waco *(G-20468)*

Velocity Aerospace Group Inc ....D 214 988-9898
Frisco *(G-7322)*

AIRCRAFT ASSEMBLY PLANTS

Aero Brigham LLC ....F 940 626-4849
Decatur *(G-5240)*

Aerostar International Inc ....E 903 885-0728
Sulphur Springs *(G-19578)*

Be-Technologies Ltd ....F 972 242-1853
Carrollton *(G-2704)*

Boeing Arospc Operations Inc ....A 210 932-6990
San Antonio *(G-17960)*

Boeing Company ....A 281 226-4057
Houston *(G-8940)*

Boeing Company ....A 210 677-0900
San Antonio *(G-17961)*

Boeing Company ....B 972 491-5442
Plano *(G-16808)*

Boeing Company ....B 713 658-0831
Houston *(G-8941)*

Boeing Company ....B 915 834-1000
El Paso *(G-5665)*

Boeing Company ....A 972 344-7249
Richardson *(G-17280)*

Boeing Company ....D 281 226-4000
Houston *(G-8944)*

Boeing Company ....F 325 696-5771
Abilene *(G-21)*

Bombardier Aerospace Corp ....F 972 960-3810
Dallas *(G-4040)*

Bombardier Services Corp ....D 214 331-9400
Dallas *(G-4041)*

Broadwing Aviation LLC ....E 817 332-0011
Fort Worth *(G-6472)*

Carter Aerospace Dev LLC ....F 940 691-0819
Wichita Falls *(G-20750)*

Dean Baldwin Pntg Ltd Partnr ....E 210 293-3528
San Antonio *(G-18045)*

Draken International LLC ....E 863 289-0849
Fort Worth *(G-6593)*

Evans Composites Inc ....E 817 477-9014
Mansfield *(G-14670)*

Gulfstream Aerospace Corp ....A 912 965-3000
Dallas *(G-4422)*

Gulfstream Aerospace Corp ....A 972 899-1625
Coppell *(G-3418)*

Gulfstream Aerospace Corp ....A 214 902-7520
Dallas *(G-4423)*

H6 Aircraft LLC ....F 830 741-3836
D Hanis *(G-3829)*

Harris Composites Inc ....E 817 279-9546
Granbury *(G-7799)*

Jaffe Group Ltd ....E 830 598-2413
Horseshoe Bay *(G-8368)*

Learjet Inc ....A 972 720-2400
Richardson *(G-17341)*

Legend Aircraft Mfg LP ....E 903 885-7000
Sulphur Springs *(G-19591)*

Lockheed Martin Corporation ....C 956 425-4447
Harlingen *(G-8193)*

Lockheed Martin Corporation ....A 972 603-1000
Grand Prairie *(G-7914)*

Lockheed Martin Corporation ....E 915 852-1100
El Paso *(G-5845)*

Mooney Aerospace Group Ltd ....E 830 896-6000
Kerrville *(G-13524)*

Mooney Airplane Company Inc ....B 830 896-6000
Kerrville *(G-13525)*

Olaeris Inc ....F 877 750-5500
Burleson *(G-2592)*

R & B Electronics Inc ....E 906 632-1542
Grand Prairie *(G-7961)*

Rf Manufacturing LLC ....E 817 479-1950
Haltom City *(G-8157)*

Sabre Sentinel Intl LLC ....E 972 529-6570
McKinney *(G-14973)*

Seven Q Seven Ltd ....E 210 930-4040
San Antonio *(G-18467)*

Skyway Group Inc ....F 830 278-4481
Uvalde *(G-20196)*

Taylor - Deal Aviation LLC ....D 972 220-0943
Irving *(G-13191)*

Textron Inc ....D 210 229-2303
San Antonio *(G-18546)*

Triumph Aerostructures LLC ....A 972 515-8276
Red Oak *(G-17237)*

Valkyrie Systems Aerospace Inc ....F 888 426-2113
Dallas *(G-3857)*

Velocity Aerospace Group Inc ....D 214 988-9898
Frisco *(G-7322)*

Vertex Aerospace LLC ....F 210 652-4541
Randolph *(G-17230)*

Vertex Aerospace LLC ....E 210 652-6717
Universal City *(G-20185)*

W T Porter Corp ....G 713 946-4174
South Houston *(G-19056)*

AIRCRAFT AUTOMATIC PILOT SYSTEMS

Vanguard Defense Inds LLC ....F 281 298-6672
Spring *(G-19184)*

AIRCRAFT CLEANING & JANITORIAL SVCS

Thiink Biig Tax Service Inc ....F 832 606-3380
Katy *(G-13450)*

AIRCRAFT CONTROL SYSTEMS:

Triumph Group Inc ....E 817 804-9400
Arlington *(G-804)*

AIRCRAFT CONTROL SYSTEMS: Electronic Totalizing Counters

Currentech ....F 214 693-6751
Arlington *(G-655)*
Honeywell International Inc ....E 832 252-3500
Houston *(G-10201)*
Honeywell International Inc ....A 281 890-0088
Cypress *(G-3801)*
L3 Technologies Inc ....A 817 619-2000
Arlington *(G-715)*
L3harris Technologies Inc ....A 972 772-7501
Rockwall *(G-17554)*

AIRCRAFT DEALERS

Dar International Inc ....F 972 402-0493
Irving *(G-12991)*
Legend Aircraft Mfg LP ....E 903 885-7000
Sulphur Springs *(G-19591)*
W T Porter Corp ....G 713 946-4174
South Houston *(G-19056)*

AIRCRAFT ENGINES & ENGINE PARTS: Air Scoops

Sierra Industries Ltd ....D 210 805-3188
San Antonio *(G-18472)*

AIRCRAFT ENGINES & ENGINE PARTS: Research & Development, Mfr

Jet Learning Laboratory Inc ....G 713 524-6284
Houston *(G-10468)*
Safran Usa Inc ....D 469 941-8150
Irving *(G-13170)*
Seven Q Seven Ltd ....E 210 930-4040
San Antonio *(G-18467)*
Sunbelt Design & Dev Inc ....D 210 227-9162
San Antonio *(G-18511)*

AIRCRAFT ENGINES & PARTS

Addison Jet Maintenance Inc ....F 972 559-1000
Addison *(G-99)*
Aero Capital Solutions Inc ....E 737 717-0624
Austin *(G-898)*
Aeromax Industries Inc ....F 818 701-9500
Fort Worth *(G-6352)*
Aircraft Engine & Accessory Co ....F 972 243-7404
Dallas *(G-3910)*
Aviation Products Inc ....F 817 457-2040
Fort Worth *(G-6413)*
BP Aero Engine Services LLC ....E 972 252-2800
Irving *(G-12951)*
Broadwing Aviation LLC ....E 817 332-0011
Fort Worth *(G-6472)*
Chromalloy Component Svcs Inc ....E 210 331-2300
San Antonio *(G-18006)*
Chromalloy Gas Turbine LLC ....F 972 241-2501
Dallas *(G-4114)*
D & D Machinery and Sales Inc ....F 830 438-2309
San Antonio *(G-18039)*
Dallas Airmotive Inc ....B 214 956-2505
Dallas *(G-4211)*
Fore Machine LLC ....D 817 834-6251
Haltom City *(G-8141)*
GE Engine Svcs - McAllen L P ....A 956 971-5200
McAllen *(G-14864)*
General Electric Company ....G 325 794-5100
Abilene *(G-43)*
Honeywell Enraf Americas Inc ....F 281 885-7979
Houston *(G-10199)*
Honeywell International Inc ....B 713 780-6500
Houston *(G-10200)*
Honeywell International Inc ....B 972 792-1800
Richardson *(G-17329)*
Honeywell International Inc ....A 361 937-1082
Corpus Christi *(G-3551)*
Honeywell International Inc ....A 817 215-9800
Mansfield *(G-14682)*
Honeywell International Inc ....D 480 353-4053
El Paso *(G-5797)*
Honeywell International Inc ....E 979 491-2802
Old Ocean *(G-16217)*
Honeywell International Inc ....C 480 592-2047
El Paso *(G-5798)*

Honeywell International Inc ....E 915 778-7401
El Paso *(G-5799)*
Honeywell International Inc ....A 281 890-0088
Cypress *(G-3801)*
Honeywell International Inc ....E 915 544-6634
El Paso *(G-5800)*
Honeywell International Inc ....F 480 592-2052
El Paso *(G-5801)*
Honeywell International Inc ....E 480 592-7380
El Paso *(G-5802)*
Honeywell International Inc ....D 972 896-0004
Dallas *(G-4465)*
Honeywell International Inc ....A 717 771-8100
El Paso *(G-5803)*
Honeywell International Inc ....E 281 444-2282
Houston *(G-10202)*
Honeywell International Inc ....E 512 301-8414
Austin *(G-1208)*
Honeywell International Inc ....E 409 833-4601
Beaumont *(G-1904)*
International Airmotive Holdg ....F 214 956-3000
Grapevine *(G-8043)*
L3 Technologies Inc ....C 512 251-3441
Austin *(G-1279)*
Lobo Ventures Ltd ....E 210 525-9595
San Antonio *(G-18256)*
M W Butler Company ....F 817 572-3306
Burleson *(G-2589)*
Mooney Airplane Company Inc ....B 830 896-6000
Kerrville *(G-13525)*
Mt Texas LLC ....E 210 599-0060
San Antonio *(G-18324)*
Page Chester Ltd ....C 817 624-4001
Fort Worth *(G-6890)*
Polytrnix McHning Fbrction LLC ....F 972 436-0422
Richardson *(G-17374)*
Pratt & Whitney Eng Svcs Inc ....B 972 343-1300
Grand Prairie *(G-7952)*
Prime Turbines LLC ....E 972 406-2100
Carrollton *(G-2797)*
Qsfirst Inc ....F 210 362-1983
San Antonio *(G-18403)*
Quality Honeycomb LP ....E 817 640-1190
Arlington *(G-765)*
Ranger Air Aviation LLC ....F 972 245-6699
Lewisville *(G-14087)*
Raytheon Technologies Corp ....B 210 680-0283
San Antonio *(G-18410)*
Safran Helicopter Engines USA ....B 972 606-7600
Grand Prairie *(G-7969)*
Superior Air Parts Inc ....E 800 420-4727
Coppell *(G-3447)*
Techmar Industries LLC ....F 832 246-6200
Spring *(G-19175)*
Texas Almet LP ....D 817 649-7056
Arlington *(G-791)*
Triumph Accssory Svcs - Grnd P ....D 972 623-9300
Grand Prairie *(G-7986)*
Triumph Group Inc ....E 817 804-9400
Arlington *(G-804)*
Tru ....E 254 831-6002
Belton *(G-2029)*

AIRCRAFT EQPT & SPLYS WHOLESALERS

Cinch Connectors Inc ....B 956 686-1151
McAllen *(G-14847)*
Complete Tchncal Rprsnttion In ....E 972 621-1111
Carrollton *(G-2718)*
Dar International Inc ....F 972 402-0493
Irving *(G-12991)*
Instrument Tech Corp ....F 972 458-8785
Carrollton *(G-2765)*

AIRCRAFT FLIGHT INSTRUMENT REPAIR SVCS

Dfw Instrument LLC ....F 214 217-7600
Addison *(G-116)*
Mooney Aerospace Group Ltd ....E 830 896-6000
Kerrville *(G-13524)*
Sims Aviation Inc ....F 972 733-3828
Addison *(G-163)*

AIRCRAFT FLIGHT INSTRUMENTS

Castlberry Instrs Avionics LLC ....E 512 251-5322
Pflugerville *(G-16663)*
Instrument Tech Corp ....F 972 458-8785
Carrollton *(G-2765)*

AIRCRAFT LIGHTING

Fenner Technologies Inc ....C 972 264-0368
Grand Prairie *(G-7870)*
Luminator Holding LP ....C 972 424-6511
Plano *(G-16911)*
Luminator Technology Group LLC ....C 972 424-6511
Plano *(G-16913)*

AIRCRAFT MAINTENANCE & REPAIR SVCS

Baileys Premier Services LLC ....C 817 292-2423
Fort Worth *(G-6419)*
Fellfab Corporation ....E 817 595-7408
Fort Worth *(G-6627)*
Interconnect Wiring LLP ....C 817 377-9473
Fort Worth *(G-6723)*
Seven Q Seven Ltd ....E 210 930-4040
San Antonio *(G-18467)*

AIRCRAFT PARTS & AUXILIARY EQPT: Aircraft Training Eqpt

Institute Flght Oprtons Dsptch ....G 817 967-4424
Irving *(G-13064)*
Sierra Industries Ltd ....D 210 805-3188
San Antonio *(G-18472)*

AIRCRAFT PARTS & AUXILIARY EQPT: Assys, Subassemblies/Parts

Albany Engnered Composites Inc ....D 830 249-4400
Boerne *(G-2113)*
Alcor Inc ....F 210 349-6491
San Antonio *(G-17890)*
DK Drill I Management Co LLC ....E 817 539-2500
Mansfield *(G-14666)*
Heldoorn Manufacturing Inc ....F 817 275-0835
Arlington *(G-696)*
R & B Electronics Inc ....E 906 632-1542
Grand Prairie *(G-7961)*
Rsg Aerodesign LLC ....D 817 625-9000
Fort Worth *(G-6969)*
Turbine Tool Corporation ....E 512 385-5311
Del Valle *(G-5333)*
V I J Corporation ....E 817 838-2020
Fort Worth *(G-7096)*

AIRCRAFT PARTS & AUXILIARY EQPT: Beaching Gear

Rave Gear LLC ....D 830 421-3295
Seguin *(G-18860)*

AIRCRAFT PARTS & AUXILIARY EQPT: Blades, Prop, Metal Or Wood

Blackland Aerospace LP ....C 972 980-5970
Dallas *(G-4028)*

AIRCRAFT PARTS & AUXILIARY EQPT: Body & Wing Assys & Parts

Progressive Incorporated ....B 817 465-3221
Arlington *(G-762)*
Triumph Group Inc ....F 610 251-1000
Dallas *(G-5120)*
Triumph Group Inc ....E 817 804-9400
Arlington *(G-804)*

AIRCRAFT PARTS & AUXILIARY EQPT: Body Assemblies & Parts

Cw Aerotech Services ....F 817 595-1949
North Richland Hills *(G-15875)*
Ogf LLC ....F 817 484-4004
Fort Worth *(G-6876)*
S & S Machine Inc ....D 972 438-6282
Irving *(G-13167)*

AIRCRAFT PARTS & AUXILIARY EQPT: Brakes

Honeywell International Inc ....A 281 890-0088
Cypress *(G-3801)*

AIRCRAFT PARTS & AUXILIARY EQPT: Elevators

Triton Consolidated Inc ....F 972 362-1711
Duncanville *(G-5539)*

PRODUCT

AIRCRAFT PARTS & AUXILIARY EQPT:
Gears, Power Transmission

M1 Support Services LP ....D 940 323-1119
Denton *(G-5379)*

AIRCRAFT PARTS & AUXILIARY EQPT:
Military Eqpt & Armament

Contract Fabrication ....E 972 736-2260
Princeton *(G-17206)*
General Aviation Inds Inc ....E 817 598-4848
Weatherford *(G-20595)*
Texas Starwares Inc ....F 972 641-2100
Grand Prairie *(G-7981)*
US Dept of the Air Force ....B 210 925-4401
San Antonio *(G-18580)*
Vanguard Defense Inds LLC ....F 281 298-6672
Spring *(G-19184)*
VSE Corporation ....D 903 831-0192
New Boston *(G-15769)*

AIRCRAFT PARTS & AUXILIARY EQPT:
Oxygen Systems

ACC-Kp LLC ....D 972 407-1234
Addison *(G-98)*

AIRCRAFT PARTS & AUXILIARY EQPT:
Research & Development, Mfr

Bell Textron Inc ....F 817 280-1587
Hurst *(G-12837)*
Jeff Bonner R & D Inc ....C 210 590-3133
San Antonio *(G-18199)*
Precision Def Components LLC ....F 870 949-8590
Texarkana *(G-19771)*
Wesco Aircraft Hardware Corp ....B 661 775-7200
Fort Worth *(G-7136)*
Wilder Systems LLC ....F 713 825-7348
Austin *(G-1666)*

AIRCRAFT PARTS & EQPT, NEC

Acerts Inc ....F 866 938-5599
Southlake *(G-19057)*
Advanced Integration Tech GP ....E 972 522-6363
Grand Prairie *(G-7822)*
Advanced Integration Tech Inc ....C 972 423-8354
Plano *(G-16772)*
Advanced Integration Tech LP ....D 972 423-8354
Plano *(G-16773)*
Advanced Integration Tech LP ....E 210 762-3777
San Antonio *(G-17868)*
Advanced Integration Tech SA ....D 210 762-3777
San Antonio *(G-17869)*
Advantage Aviation Tech ....E 972 647-7300
Dallas *(G-3892)*
Advantage Aviation Tech II LLC ....E 972 647-7300
Dallas *(G-3893)*
Aereos Inc ....D 817 267-1371
Euless *(G-6126)*
Aero Components LLC ....D 817 834-6251
Fort Worth *(G-6351)*
Aero Composites Structures Inc ....F 972 694-5330
Carrollton *(G-2695)*
Aero Dynamix Inc ....D 817 571-0729
Euless *(G-6127)*
Aerospace & Coml Tech Inc ....F 817 560-6600
Fort Worth *(G-6353)*
Aerospace Fasteners Inc ....E 903 723-0693
Palestine *(G-16295)*
Aerospace Products SE Inc ....F 210 924-2907
San Antonio *(G-17873)*
Aerotech Engineering Inc ....E 817 267-1371
Euless *(G-6128)*
Aeroxchange Ltd ....F 972 556-8500
Farmers Branch *(G-6185)*
AGH Industries Inc ....E 817 284-1742
Euless *(G-6129)*
Air Power Inc ....E 817 557-5855
Arlington *(G-613)*
Airco Industries, Inc. ....D 817 332-3806
Fort Worth *(G-6358)*
Aircraft Engine & Accessory Co ....F 972 243-7404
Dallas *(G-3910)*
Aircraft On Ground Inc ....E 214 350-5334
San Antonio *(G-17877)*
Aircraft Technologies Inc ....E 210 590-6858
San Antonio *(G-17878)*

Airtech Supply Inc ....E 501 525-7707
North Richland Hills *(G-15873)*
Alcocer LLC ....D 210 930-4580
San Antonio *(G-17889)*
American Armtive Cmponents Inc .....E 281 442-7791
Houston *(G-8585)*
Applied Avionics Inc ....D 817 451-1141
Fort Worth *(G-6392)*
Arlington Intl AVI Pdts LLC ....E 817 465-9880
Arlington *(G-625)*
Aviation Dvcs Elctrnic Cmpnnts ....E 817 738-9161
Fort Worth *(G-6412)*
Bae Systems Inc ....D 512 276-3100
Austin *(G-972)*
Be-Technologies Ltd ....F 972 242-1853
Carrollton *(G-2704)*
Bell Boeing Joint Project Off ....E 301 866-6835
Amarillo *(G-403)*
Bell Helicopter Textron Inc ....F 806 341-3400
Amarillo *(G-404)*
Bell Helicopter Textron Inc ....F 817 280-4700
Amarillo *(G-405)*
Bell Textron Inc ....E 817 837-4700
Fort Worth *(G-6443)*
Bell Textron Inc ....C 817 280-2011
Austin *(G-987)*
Bell Textron Inc ....D 817 280-2011
Grand Prairie *(G-7845)*
Bell Textron Inc ....A 817 280-2011
Fort Worth *(G-6444)*
Bell Textron Inc ....E 817 280-2011
Hurst *(G-12838)*
Bell Textron Inc ....C 806 341-3400
Amarillo *(G-406)*
Bell Textron Inc ....D 817 280-2011
Hurst *(G-12839)*
Bell Textron Inc ....C 806 341-3400
Amarillo *(G-407)*
Bell Textron Services Inc ....F 817 280-2011
Fort Worth *(G-6446)*
Benz Companies Ltd ....F 817 280-0000
Fort Worth *(G-6447)*
Berry Machine Shop ....E 817 572-0948
Burleson *(G-2571)*
Beta Engineering Inc ....F 817 265-3367
Arlington *(G-631)*
Blackhawk Modifications Inc ....E 254 755-6711
Waco *(G-20369)*
BP Aerospace LLC ....D 972 252-2800
Irving *(G-12952)*
Broadwing Aviation LLC ....E 817 332-0011
Fort Worth *(G-6472)*
C & F Tool & Die Co LLC ....E 210 522-9310
San Antonio *(G-17975)*
Calcomp Inc ....E 817 862-9311
Fort Worth *(G-6486)*
Calkins Aero Service Inc ....F 281 579-6674
Houston *(G-9050)*
Can-AM Aero Support LLC ....D 281 810-4400
Houston *(G-9084)*
Century Components Corporation .....F 817-831-8301
Fort Worth *(G-6505)*
Coastal Mechanics Company Inc ......C 713 784-0111
Houston *(G-9227)*
Composite Technology Inc ....E 972 456-6900
Dallas *(G-4151)*
Crown Aerospace Inc ....F 281 351-7068
Tomball *(G-19972)*
Decatur Machine Services Inc ....E 940 627-1062
Decatur *(G-5244)*
Direct International ....G 817 284-7722
Fort Worth *(G-6587)*
Enflite LLC ....D 512 868-3399
Georgetown *(G-7650)*
Esna LLC ....B 817 281-8816
North Richland Hills *(G-15877)*
Essner Precision Mfg LLC ....E 817 529-2580
Fort Worth *(G-6619)*
Euless Aero Components LLC ....D 817 267-1371
Euless *(G-6143)*
Fore Machine LLC ....D 817 834-6251
Haltom City *(G-8141)*
Ftg Aerospace Inc ....D 818 577-6126
Fort Worth *(G-6651)*
Gas Turbine Engines Inc ....F 281 824-9200
Alvin *(G-363)*
Gdc Technics LLC ....D 210 496-5614
Fort Worth *(G-6663)*
Genesys Aerosystems Group Inc .....C 800 872-7832
Mineral Wells *(G-15526)*

GI Legacy LLC ....F 817 222-1414
Fort Worth *(G-6668)*
Goodrich Corporation ....C 512 754-3658
San Marcos *(G-18690)*
Goodrich Corporation ....F 214 689-9588
Dallas *(G-4413)*
Goodrich Corporation ....C 682 730-4270
Haltom City *(G-8142)*
Greenpoint Precision Mch Inc ....E 940 382-3933
Denton *(G-5369)*
Greiner Aerospace Inc ....D 817 686-3100
Fort Worth *(G-6680)*
Gulfstream Aerospace Corp ....A 214 902-7520
Dallas *(G-4423)*
H T A Aerostructures Inc ....C 512 754-3600
San Marcos *(G-18692)*
Halsey Manufacturing ....D 940 566-3306
Denton *(G-5371)*
Heartland Enterprises Ltd ....E 830 997-9434
Fredericksburg *(G-7182)*
Higher Planes Inc ....G 936 494-1717
Conroe *(G-3304)*
Intech Aerospace LLC ....E 281 810-4400
Houston *(G-10383)*
K W D Manufacturing Inc ....E 210 924-5999
San Antonio *(G-18214)*
Kaspar Machine LLC ....E 254 836-1564
Waco *(G-20422)*
Kepler Aerospace Ltd ....E 855 553-7537
Midland *(G-15267)*
Kepler Spacecore Inc ....E 855 553-7537
Midland *(G-15268)*
L3 Technologies Inc ....C 512 251-3441
Austin *(G-1279)*
L3harris Technologies Inc ....A 254 799-5533
Waco *(G-20424)*
Labinal Salisbury LLC ....A 410 548-7800
Denton *(G-5378)*
Legacy Aeronautics Inc ....E 855 622-8600
Carrollton *(G-2775)*
Lockheed Martin Corporation ....E 915 852-1100
El Paso *(G-5845)*
Lockheed Martin Corporation ....D 817 777-2000
Benbrook *(G-2042)*
Lockheed Martin Corporation ....B 817 777-2000
Fort Worth *(G-6798)*
Lone Star Aviation Corporation ....F 682 518-8882
Mansfield *(G-14686)*
Maddox Metal Works Inc ....D 214 333-2311
Dallas *(G-4625)*
Marathonnorco Aerospace Inc ....C 254 776-0650
Waco *(G-20430)*
Mayday Manufacturing Co ....C 940 898-8301
Denton *(G-5381)*
Merritt Prfrred Components Inc ....D 903 983-1592
Kilgore *(G-13574)*
Mooney Aerospace Group Ltd ....E 830 896-6000
Kerrville *(G-13524)*
Novaria Group LLC ....E 817 381-3810
Fort Worth *(G-6870)*
Pae Avation Technical Svcs LLC ....F 940 257-2836
Sheppard Afb *(G-18902)*
Panasonic Avionics Corporation ....F 346 242-1599
Houston *(G-11229)*
Pcx Aerostructures Tx LP ....E 817 583-8820
Mansfield *(G-14702)*
Precision Helicopter Svcs Inc ....E 210 525-9595
San Antonio *(G-18386)*
REB Technologies Inc ....F 817 285-7740
Bedford *(G-1978)*
Recaro Arcft Sting Amricas LLC ....C 817 490-9160
Fort Worth *(G-6946)*
Rf Manufacturing LLC ....E 817 479-1950
Haltom City *(G-8157)*
Rkr Technologies Ltd ....D 817 640-5340
Arlington *(G-771)*
Rsg Products Inc ....E 817 624-6600
Saginaw *(G-17755)*
RSI Visual Systems Inc ....D 817 510-0350
Coppell *(G-3442)*
S-TEC Corporation ....C 800 872-7832
Mineral Wells *(G-15541)*
Safran Elec & Pwr USA LLC ....A 940 272-5700
Denton *(G-5398)*
Safran Elec Def Avnics USA LLC ......C 972 314-3600
Grand Prairie *(G-7968)*
Safran Seats USA LLC ....A 940 668-4825
Gainesville *(G-7362)*
Sky TEC Ltd ....F 817 573-2250
Granbury *(G-7810)*

Spirit Aerosystems Inc ....D 316 523-4221
  San Antonio (G-18492)

Starr Aircraft Products Inc ....C 903 893-1106
  Sherman (G-18933)

Sumitomo Precision Usa Inc ....G 972 228-9300
  Desoto (G-5443)

Sunbelt Design Holdings LLC ....E 210 227-9162
  San Antonio (G-18512)

T-B & S Mfg Co ....F 817 281-9315
  Fort Worth (G-7029)

Texas Aeroplastics ....F 817 430-3651
  Boyd (G-2207)

Texas Almet LP ....D 817 649-7056
  Arlington (G-791)

Texas Aviation Tech LLC ....F 210 680-8181
  San Antonio (G-18534)

Texstars LLC ....E 972 647-1366
  Arlington (G-796)

Textool Company ....E 713 923-5595
  Houston (G-12264)

Triumph Accssory Svcs - Grnd P .....D 972 623-9300
  Grand Prairie (G-7986)

Triumph Aerostructures LLC ....C 972 595-9900
  Grand Prairie (G-7987)

Triumph Aerostructures LLC ....A 972 515-8276
  Red Oak (G-17237)

Tulsa Arspc Cmpnent Ovrhaul RE .....G 940 479-2000
  Ponder (G-17097)

Turbine Aircraft Marketing Inc ....F 972 248-3108
  Addison (G-172)

Turbo Mach R & D II Inc ....F 210 340-4773
  San Antonio (G-18571)

Weatherford Aerospace Inc ....C 817 598-0044
  Weatherford (G-20630)

Weatherford Aerospace Inc ....E 817 594-5464
  Weatherford (G-20631)

Williamsrdm Inc ....D 817 872-1500
  Fort Worth (G-7148)

Zodiac Seats California LLC ....C 909 652-9700
  Gainesville (G-7375)

AIRCRAFT PARTS WHOLESALERS

Bombardier Aerospace Corp ....F 972 960-3810
  Dallas (G-4040)

Broadwing Aviation LLC ....E 817 332-0011
  Fort Worth (G-6472)

Esna LLC ....B 817 281-8816
  North Richland Hills (G-15877)

Indian Aerospace Inc ....F 817 265-5137
  Arlington (G-703)

L3 Technologies Inc ....C 512 251-3441
  Austin (G-1279)

Ranger Air Aviation LLC ....F 972 245-6699
  Lewisville (G-14087)

Wesco Aircraft Hardware Corp ....B 661 775-7200
  Fort Worth (G-7136)

AIRCRAFT RADIO EQPT REPAIR SVCS

Fieldtech Avionics Instrs Inc ....E 817 740-7110
  Fort Worth (G 6620)

AIRCRAFT SEATS

United Aviation ACC Inc ....E 817 447-8000
  Burleson (G-2600)

United Rtorcraft Solutions LLC ....E 940 627-0626
  Decatur (G-5256)

AIRCRAFT SERVICING & REPAIRING

Can-AM Aero Support LLC ....D 281 810-4400
  Houston (G-9084)

Composite Technology Inc ....E 972 456-6900
  Dallas (G-4151)

Interntnal Arospc Coatings Inc ....F 806 335-2616
  Amarillo (G-440)

Texas Pneumatic Systems Inc ....F 817 794-0068
  Arlington (G-792)

Texas Pneumatic Systems Inc ....D 817 794-0068
  Pantego (G-16353)

Wood Group Power Gp LLC ....E 281 828-3500
  Houston (G-12686)

AIRCRAFT TURBINES

Pantex Ennerflo Systems Inc ....E 832 861-7700
  Houston (G-8390)

Raytheon Technologies Corp ....C 940 761-9200
  Wichita Falls (G-20801)

Vanguard Defense Inds LLC ....F 281 298-6672
  Spring (G-19184)

Wood Group Power Gp LLC ....E 281 828-3500
  Houston (G-12686)

AIRCRAFT: Airplanes, Fixed Or Rotary Wing

Boeing Company ....A 281 226-4000
  Houston (G-8939)

Boeing Company ....A 936 756-0505
  Conroe (G-3263)

Boeing Company ....B 281 244-3056
  Houston (G-8943)

Cockrell Resources Inc ....E 713 454-1400
  Houston (G-9236)

Gulfstream Aerospace Corp GA ....A 214 350-4177
  Dallas (G-4424)

Sierra Industries Ltd ....D 210 805-3188
  San Antonio (G-18472)

AIRCRAFT: Motorized

Ace Aeronautics LLC ....F 972 641-0835
  Grand Prairie (G-7821)

B R L Consultants Inc ....F 210 341-3442
  San Antonio (G-17934)

Bell Textron Inc ....F 817 280-1587
  Hurst (G-12837)

Interntnal Arospc Coatings Inc ....F 806 335-2616
  Amarillo (G-440)

M1 Support Services LP ....D 940 323-1119
  Denton (G-5379)

Martin Uav LLC ....E 972 381-2750
  Plano (G-16919)

Vanguard Defense Inds LLC ....F 281 298-6672
  Spring (G-19184)

AIRCRAFT: Research & Development, Manufacturer

Lockheed Martin Corporation ....D 817 777-2000
  Benbrook (G-2042)

Lockheed Martin Corporation ....B 817 777-2000
  Fort Worth (G-6798)

AIRLINE TRAINING

L3 Technologies Inc ....A 817 619-4756
  Arlington (G-713)

AIRPORTS, FLYING FIELDS & SVCS

Aircraft Engine & Accessory Co ....F 972 243-7404
  Dallas (G-3910)

M1 Support Services LP ....D 940 323-1119
  Denton (G-5379)

ALARMS: Fire

Impact Fire Services LLC ....E 254 857-4990
  Lorena (G-14341)

Impact Fire Services LLC ....E 512 243-7788
  Austin (G-1225)

Warren Watts Technology LLC ....E 817 924-1370
  Fort Worth (G-7127)

Ww Electronics Solutions LLC ....F 214 396-6636
  Quinlan (G-17227)

ALCOHOL, GRAIN: For Beverage Purposes

Alamo Premium Distillery Inc ....F 210 325-7853
  San Antonio (G-17886)

ALCOHOL: Amyl

Ethyl Corporation ....D 713 740-8300
  Pasadena (G-16431)

ALCOHOL: Ethyl & Ethanol

Green Plains Hereford LLC ....D 806 258-7800
  Hereford (G-8289)

Hereford Biofuels LP ....D 972 980-7159
  Dallas (G-4452)

Kior Inc ....E 281 694-8700
  Pasadena (G-16469)

Panda Ethanol Inc ....F 972 361-1200
  Dallas (G-4783)

Plainview Bioenergy LLC ....E 806 296-8000
  Plainview (G-16761)

Texas Ingredient Corporation ....D 817 645-1328
  Cleburne (G-3113)

We Hereford LLC ....E 806 360-7400
  Hereford (G-8297)

ALCOHOL: Methyl & Methanol, Synthetic

Ampco Services LLC ....B 281 872-8324
  Houston (G-8627)

Oci Beaumont LLC ....C 409 723-1900
  Nederland (G-15756)

ALKALIES & CHLORINE

Buckeye International Inc ....F 281 873-4200
  Houston (G-9007)

Dow Chemical Company ....E 979 238-2011
  Freeport (G-7196)

Occidental Chemical Corp ....E 512 476-2245
  Austin (G-1375)

Occidental Chemical Corp ....C 800 699-5123
  Addison (G-151)

Solvay Fluorides Llc ....D 713 525-6700
  Houston (G-11946)

Westlake Vinyls Company LP ....C 713 960-9111
  Houston (G-12655)

ALLOYS: Additive, Exc Copper Or Made In Blast Furnaces

Elah Holdings Inc ....F 805 435-1255
  Dallas (G-4307)

ALTERNATORS & GENERATORS: Battery Charging

Batteries Concord ....F 281 931-4488
  Houston (G-8827)

Delta Electronics (usa) Inc ....E 469 330-9100
  Plano (G-16837)

Interstate Batteries Inc ....C 972 991-1444
  Dallas (G-4507)

PHD Energy Inc ....E 800 318-3639
  Round Rock (G-17679)

ALTERNATORS: Automotive

Alterstart Systems Inc ....G 214 330-2277
  Dallas (G-3933)

Pearland Alternator Inc ....E 281 485-8871
  Pearland (G-16589)

Penntex Industries Inc ....E 817 589-7501
  Fort Worth (G-6900)

ALUMINUM

Aastek Electronics Corp ....F 903 953-0888
  Emory (G-6081)

Howmet Aerospace Inc ....B 866 385-2137
  The Woodlands (G-19874)

Kaiser Aluminum Fab Pdts LLC ....C 903 868-1556
  Sherman (G-18918)

Quality Cast Metals Inc ....E 817 921-3595
  Fort Worth (G-6927)

TPI ....E 972 276-2901
  Garland (G-7604)

ALUMINUM PRDTS

Affinity Chemical LLC ....F 214 696-1037
  Dallas (G-3901)

American Extrusion Company ....F 713 869-9551
  Houston (G-8596)

Atrium Windows and Doors Inc ....D 214 583-1840
  Dallas (G-3983)

Bielas Glass & Aluminum Pdts ....E 210 333-8040
  San Antonio (G-17952)

Brandon Industries Inc ....E 972 542-3000
  McKinney (G-14929)

C E Shepherd Company LP ....D 713 924-4300
  Houston (G-9028)

Columbia Alum Processors Co JV ....E 972 771-7150
  Rockwall (G-17543)

Crh Americas Inc ....E 903 765-2212
  Alba (G-181)

Crown Cork & Seal Usa Inc ....E 281 240-4838
  Sugar Land (G-19469)

Crown Cork & Seal Usa Inc ....C 936 539-5401
  Conroe (G-3287)

Everlite Inc ....E 903 297-3444
  Longview (G-14232)

Hudson & Hudson Neon Inc ....E 281 720-0100
  Houston (G-10275)

Innovative Building Products ....E 940 387-0408
  Millsap (G-15503)

International Aluminum Corp ....C 972 937-7032
  Waxahachie (G-20545)

Employee Codes: A=Over 500 employees, B=251-500
C=101-250, D=51-100, E=20-50, F=10-19, G=9

2021 Harris Texas
Manufacturers Directory

1385

PRODUCT

ALUMINUM PRDTS (continued)

Justiss Oil Company Inc ....D 903 859-2111
Arp (G-812)

Kaiser Aluminum Fab Pdts LLC ....C 903 868-1556
Sherman (G-18918)

Oldcastle Buildingenvelope Inc ....A 972 551-6100
Terrell (G-19746)

Omnimax International Inc ....E 817 473-1541
Mansfield (G-14699)

PSI Industries Inc ....E 940 564-3563
Olney (G-16224)

Quality Cast Metals Inc ....E 817 921-3595
Fort Worth (G-6927)

Texas Aluminum Industries Inc ....B 713 941-7186
Houston (G-12220)

Tower Extrusions Ltd ....B 972 442-3535
Wylie (G-20952)

Tower Extrusions Ltd ....C 940 564-5681
Olney (G-16225)

Tower Extrusions Ltd ....C 972 442-7200
Wylie (G-20953)

TPI ....E 972 276-2901
Garland (G-7604)

William L Bonnell Company Inc ....B 409 543-0600
El Campo (G-5629)

ALUMINUM: Coil & Sheet

RDS Metal LP ....F 817 539-7400
Mansfield (G-14708)

ALUMINUM: Pigs

Pigs Unlimited Intl Inc ....E 281 351-2749
Tomball (G-19998)

ALUMINUM: Rolling & Drawing

Alcoa USA Corp ....C 512 446-8681
Rockdale (G-17524)

Quality Cast Metals Inc ....E 817 921-3595
Fort Worth (G-6927)

Ultraflote LLC ....E 713 461-2100
Houston (G-12430)

AMBLYGONITE MINING

Texas United Corporation ....E 713 877-1793
Houston (G-12258)

AMBULANCE SVCS

Hfj Group LLC ....E 833 777-3473
Houston (G-10168)

AMMONIUM NITRATE OR AMMONIUM SULFATE

Brenntag Pacific Inc ....F 281 474-5400
Pasadena (G-16399)

Oci Partners LP ....F 409 723-1900
Nederland (G-15757)

AMMONIUM PHOSPHATE

PCI Nitrogen LLC ....D 713 920-5300
Pasadena (G-16493)

AMMUNITION

Expal USA Inc ....E 903 472-4970
Irving (G-13020)

AMMUNITION: Cartridges Case, 30 mm & Below

Expansion Industries LLC ....E 888 707-9343
Carrollton (G-2735)

AMMUNITION: Small Arms

True Velocity Ammunition LLC ....D 972 487-6500
Garland (G-7606)

Wrights Ammunitions LLC ....D 972 257-1111
Irving (G-13209)

AMPLIFIERS

Jim Melhart Piano and Organ Co ....E 956 682-6147
McAllen (G-14879)

AMPLIFIERS: Parametric

Reedholm Instruments Co ....E 512 869-1935
Georgetown (G-7674)

AMPLIFIERS: RF & IF Power

Good Sportsman Marketing LLC ....E 877 269-8490
Irving (G-13040)

Micropac Industries Inc ....D 972 272-3571
Garland (G-7551)

Satellink Inc ....E 972 487-1434
Garland (G-7581)

AMUSEMENT & RECREATION SVCS: Amusement Arcades

Maks Family Fun & Events LLC ....E 254 518-0005
Copperas Cove (G-3455)

AMUSEMENT & RECREATION SVCS: Archery Lanes

T L W Archery Inc ....G 830 227-5171
Canyon Lake (G-2680)

AMUSEMENT & RECREATION SVCS: Baseball Batting Cage

Nueces Canyon Companies ....F 979 289-5600
Brenham (G-2266)

AMUSEMENT & RECREATION SVCS: Card & Game Svcs

Carta Mundi Inc ....D 214 330-7761
Dallas (G-4087)

AMUSEMENT & RECREATION SVCS: Diving Instruction, Underwater

Precision Frac LLC ....F 855 967-1023
Midland (G-15362)

AMUSEMENT & RECREATION SVCS: Exhibition Operation

Dallas Market Center Co Ltd ....C 214 655-6100
Dallas (G-4219)

AMUSEMENT & RECREATION SVCS: Fishing Lakes & Piers, Op

William B Sides ....F 512 385-3826
Austin (G-1667)

AMUSEMENT & RECREATION SVCS: Hunting Club, Membership

American Trphy Hnters Assn Inc ....E 210 523-8500
San Antonio (G-17904)

AMUSEMENT & RECREATION SVCS: Mechanical Games, Coin-Operated

Everi Games Inc ....D 512 439-3100
Austin (G-1142)

AMUSEMENT & RECREATION SVCS: Tour & Guide

Brenham Repair Center LLC ....F 979 277-9071
Brenham (G-2247)

AMUSEMENT MACHINES: Coin Operated

Kelye B Stites Inc ....E 817 284-3499
Richland Hills (G-17439)

Tooling Technologies Mfg LLC ....F 713 722-8501
Houston (G-12320)

AMUSEMENT PARK DEVICES & RIDES

America Industrial Pdts LLC ....F 832 974-4153
Houston (G-8580)

Arbor Resources LLC ....F 936 632-9914
Pollok (G-17091)

Dynamic Attractions Inc ....F 817 652-1212
Arlington (G-667)

Kevin Goss ....E 281 812-1600
Humble (G-12782)

AMUSEMENT PARK DEVICES & RIDES: Carnival Mach & Eqpt, NEC

J & S Rides Inc ....E 806 293-1353
Plainview (G-16759)

ANALYZERS: Coulometric, Indl Process

Cosa Xentaur Corporation ....E 713 947-9591
Houston (G-9327)

ANALYZERS: Electrical Testing

Venable Corporation ....F 512 949-3144
Austin (G-1627)

ANALYZERS: Petroleum Prdts

Petroleum Analyzer Company LP ....D 281 940-1803
Houston (G-11304)

ANESTHESIA EQPT

Bay Area Anesthesia Associates ....F 361 857-8588
Corpus Christi (G-3482)

Dreamwrks Ansthesia Assoc Pllc ....F 936 639-3036
Lufkin (G-14525)

Teresa A McVicker Pc ....G 254 526-2823
Killeen (G-13617)

ANIMAL FEED & SUPPLEMENTS: Livestock & Poultry

Abilene AG Service & Sup Inc ....D 325 677-4371
Abilene (G-4)

American Dehydrated Foods Inc ....G 903 838-0366
Hooks (G-8360)

Archer-Daniels-Midland Company ....D 806 723-5117
Lubbock (G-14363)

Bryant Grain Co ....E 817 441-9782
Aledo (G-196)

Cargill Incorporated ....F 806 364-3891
Hereford (G-8285)

Cargill Incorporated 325 672-3271
Abilene (G-29)

Cargill Incorporated ....F 254 774-9022
Temple (G-19673)

Crystal Feed Mills Inc ....E 903 488-3261
Como (G-3247)

Dairy Manufacturers Inc ....F 972 347-2878
Prosper (G-17213)

Darling Ingredients Inc ....D 313 928-7400
Irving (G-12993)

Darling Ingredients Inc ....E 214 948-7501
Dallas (G-4238)

International Ingredient Corp ....F 817 645-1328
Cleburne (G-3096)

J M Saddler Inc ....G 979 693-5114
College Station (G-3188)

Kunafin LLC ....F 830 757-1181
Quemado (G-17222)

Land OLakes Inc ....E 281 342-2493
Rosenberg (G-17588)

Leonard & Harral Packing Co ....B 210 532-3241
San Antonio (G-18247)

Livengood Feeds Inc ....E 512 398-2351
Lockhart (G-14170)

Marshall Minerals Inc ....E 903 938-8301
Marshall (G-14789)

Nutri-Feeds Inc ....E 806 357-2288
Hereford (G-8294)

Prairie Ptfood Ingredients LLC ....F 469 383-5182
Rice (G-17266)

Provimi North America Inc ....G 817 594-9628
Weatherford (G-20612)

Purina Animal Nutrition LLC ....E 817 492-9159
Fort Worth (G-6922)

Purina Animal Nutrition LLC ....D 817 878-0280
Fort Worth (G-6923)

Purina Animal Nutrition LLC ....E 830 672-6565
Gonzales (G-7762)

Purina Animal Nutrition LLC ....E 806 761-7200
Lubbock (G-14466)

Purina Animal Nutrition LLC ....E 254 840-3276
Mc Gregor (G-14822)

Purina Mills LLC ....F 281 342-6758
Rosenberg (G-17596)

Purina Mills LLC ....D 830 672-6565
Gonzales (G-7763)

R J Mangold Grain Co Inc ....F 830 985-3323
La Coste (G-13690)

Red River Commodities Inc ....E 806 763-9747
  Lubbock **(G-14471)**

Ridley USA Inc ....F 817 625-6680
  Fort Worth **(G-6958)**

Tejas Industries Inc ....E 806 293-4431
  Plainview **(G-16763)**

TX Quality Products LLC ....F 979 234-7979
  Eagle Lake **(G-5546)**

Tyson Foods Inc ....E 936 248-2081
  Tenaha **(G-19725)**

Valley Feed Mill Inc Paris ....E 903 785-3501
  Paris **(G-16373)**

Valley Proteins (de) Inc ....E 806 379-6001
  Amarillo **(G-519)**

Volume Feed & Seed Inc ....E 325 676-3302
  Abilene **(G-90)**

Westway Feed Products LLC ....F 903 885-5541
  Sulphur Springs **(G-19604)**

Westway Feed Products LLC ....E 713 514-1000
  Houston **(G-12659)**

ANIMAL FEED: Wholesalers

Cargill Incorporated ....E 325 672-3271
  Abilene **(G-29)**

Ecofusion Inc ....G 972 403-7449
  Plano **(G-16855)**

Precision Joint Solution Inc ....F 972 351-0470
  Austin **(G-1429)**

R J Smelley Company Inc ....F 817 295-4241
  Burleson **(G-2595)**

Ridley USA Inc ....F 903 322-4228
  Buffalo **(G-2548)**

Westway Feed Products LLC ....F 806 364-5200
  Hereford **(G-8298)**

Wilbur-Ellis Nutrition LLC ....E 979 849-6757
  Angleton **(G-582)**

ANIMAL FOOD & SUPPLEMENTS: Bird Food, Prepared

John B Smith ....C 830 620-9090
  New Braunfels **(G-15806)**

Mr Bird ....F 830 620-9090
  New Braunfels **(G-15814)**

ANIMAL FOOD & SUPPLEMENTS: Dog

Bark To Basics LLC ....F 913 825-1760
  Irving **(G-12944)**

Mars Petcare Us Inc ....D 254 771-3366
  Temple **(G-19687)**

Paw Depot Incorporated ....F 214 440-6324
  Richardson **(G-17371)**

Prairie Dog Pet Products LLC ....B 972 606-9050
  Grand Prairie **(G-7951)**

Tejas Industries Inc ....E 806 322-2822
  Hereford **(G-8295)**

ANIMAL FOOD & SUPPLEMENTS: Dog & Cat

Pethonesty LLC ....F 909 435-6574
  Austin **(G-1413)**

Summma International LLC ....F 630 519-3632
  Laredo **(G-13936)**

Texas Farm Products Company ....C 936 564-3711
  Nacogdoches **(G-15715)**

Valley Proteins (de) Inc ....E 806 379-6001
  Amarillo **(G-519)**

ANIMAL FOOD & SUPPLEMENTS: Feed Concentrates

Economy Mills Ltd ....F 806 765-5547
  Lubbock **(G-14406)**

Pegasus Food ....F 972 961-5200
  Rockwall **(G-17558)**

ANIMAL FOOD & SUPPLEMENTS: Feed Supplements

Animal Science Products Inc ....E 936 560-0003
  Nacogdoches **(G-15685)**

Contanda LLC ....E 832 699-4001
  Houston **(G-9281)**

Global Animal Products Inc ....E 806 622-9600
  Amarillo **(G-489)**

Norel Animal Nutrition USA Inc ....F 281 741-8211
  Pasadena **(G-16490)**

Nutrition Plus LLP ....G 806 655-0505
  Canyon **(G-2675)**

Precision Joint Solution Inc ....F 972 351-0470
  Austin **(G-1429)**

Protocol Technologies Inc ....F 940 683-8123
  Bridgeport **(G-2299)**

Westway Feed Products LLC ....F 806 364-5200
  Hereford **(G-8298)**

ANIMAL FOOD & SUPPLEMENTS: Livestock

Angelo Pellets Inc ....F 325 655-5751
  San Angelo **(G-17777)**

E Barr Feeds Inc ....F 830 672-6515
  Gonzales **(G-7752)**

East Bernard Milling Co LLC ....G 979 335-7554
  East Bernard **(G-5557)**

Ezell-Key Grain Company Inc ....E 325 573-9373
  Snyder **(G-18991)**

Feeders Supply ....F 806 889-3391
  Lubbock **(G-14409)**

Gorman Milling Co Inc ....D 254 734-2252
  Gorman **(G-7772)**

Mahard Feed Mill Inc ....G 903 523-4455
  Gordonville **(G-7770)**

MB Nutritional Sciences LLC ....G 806 778-2697
  Lubbock **(G-14444)**

Mid-America Pet Food LLC ....E 903 572-5900
  Mount Pleasant **(G-15655)**

R J Smelley Company Inc ....F 817 295-4241
  Burleson **(G-2595)**

Ridley USA Inc ....F 903 322-4228
  Buffalo **(G-2548)**

Sooner Trading Inc ....E 806 235-3904
  Channing **(G-3045)**

ANIMAL FOOD & SUPPLEMENTS: Mineral feed supplements

Sunbelt Custom Mineral LLC ....F 903 438-2340
  Sulphur Springs **(G-19601)**

ANIMAL FOOD & SUPPLEMENTS: Pet, Exc Dog & Cat, Canned

Eznectar LLC ....F 210 732-6400
  San Antonio **(G-18101)**

ANIMAL FOOD & SUPPLEMENTS: Pet, Exc Dog & Cat, Dry

Hamlin Pet Worx LLC ....F 855 430-9888
  Hamlin **(G-8170)**

ANIMAL FOOD & SUPPLEMENTS: Pet, Exc Dog & Cat, Frozen

Koch Ranches Inc ....F 210 858-9795
  San Antonio **(G-18228)**

ANIMAL FOOD & SUPPLEMENTS: Poultry

Behrends Feed & Fertilizer LLC ....E 830 997-3410
  Fredericksburg **(G-7172)**

Jupe Feeds Inc ....E 254 773-5211
  Temple **(G-19683)**

ANIMAL FOOD & SUPPLEMENTS: Pulverized Oats

Reconserve of Texas Inc ....E 214 339-4755
  Dallas **(G-4868)**

ANIMAL FOOD & SUPPLEMENTS: Stock Feeds, Dry

Scotts Miracle-Gro Company ....E 830 591-0299
  Uvalde **(G-20195)**

ANIMAL FOOD/SUPPLEMENTS: Feeds Fm Meat/Meat/Veg Combnd Meals

Tyson Foods Inc ....F 940 553-1811
  Vernon **(G-20231)**

Tyson Foods Inc ....B 713 678-1893
  Houston **(G-12421)**

ANIMAL OILS: Medicinal Grade, Refined Or Concentrated

Darling Ingredients Inc ....D 313 928-7400
  Irving **(G-12993)**

Diamond Green Diesel LLC (jv) ....E 210 345-2009
  San Antonio **(G-18055)**

ANODIZING EQPT

Rack Technology Inc ....E 817 468-2233
  Arlington **(G-766)**

ANODIZING SVC

Alkote Inc ....E 713 695-3609
  Houston **(G-8539)**

Anadite Cal Restoration Tr ....F 817 282-9171
  Hurst **(G-12833)**

Cynco Specialty Inc ....G 281 499-0519
  Stafford **(G-19298)**

Dixie Electro Plating Company ....E 713 224-1826
  Houston **(G-9483)**

Surface Techniques Inc ....F 713 932-8050
  Houston **(G-12124)**

T G Industries Inc ....F 281 356-2001
  Pinehurst **(G-16735)**

ANTENNA REPAIR & INSTALLATION SVCS

Crown Castle Intl Corp ....F 713 570-3000
  Houston **(G-9346)**

Innovative Idm LLC ....E 214 574-9500
  Lewisville **(G-14056)**

Innovative Idm LLC ....E 281 880-2105
  Houston **(G-10372)**

ANTENNAS: Radar Or Communications

Freeflight Acquisition Corp ....F 254 662-0000
  Irving **(G-13035)**

ANTENNAS: Receiving

Cloud Ninjas LLC ....F 832 478-9158
  Houston **(G-9217)**

Orbital Systems LLC ....E 972 915-3669
  Irving **(G-13133)**

Texas Photonics Inc ....G 972 412-7111
  Rowlett **(G-17712)**

ANTENNAS: Satellite, Household Use

ASC Signal Corporation ....E 214 291-7654
  Plano **(G-16795)**

Satpro Network Inc ....E 972 675-8475
  Garland **(G-7582)**

ANTI-GLARE MATERIAL

Tackaberry Dooley Systems ....C 281 479-9700
  Deer Park **(G-5299)**

ANTI-OXIDANTS

Planet Resource Recovery Inc ....E 281 996-5315
  Pearland **(G-16592)**

Univar Solutions USA Inc ....E 281 297-0678
  Spring **(G-19261)**

ANTIFREEZE

BASF Corporation ....C 800 794-1019
  Houston **(G-8821)**

ANTIQUE FURNITURE RESTORATION & REPAIR

AA Flood Masters LLC ....E 409 796-2620
  Beaumont **(G-1847)**

ANTIQUE SHOPS

Wiseman House Companies Inc ....F 254 796-2565
  Hico **(G-8303)**

ANTISCALING COMPOUNDS, BOILER

Wesco Chemicals Inc ....F 972 938-0913
  Waxahachie **(G-20568)**

ANTISEPTICS, MEDICINAL

Allied Bioscience Inc ....E 214 432-5580
  Plano **(G-16783)**

APARTMENT LOCATING SVCS

Smart City Locating Inc ....E 214 586-0519
  Dallas **(G-4971)**

APLITE MINING

U S Silica Company ....E 301 682-0600
  Katy (G-13381)

APPAREL ACCESS STORES

Conversation Pieces Inc ....G 409 762-2799
  Galveston (G-7394)

Treska Inc ....E 682 647-0352
  Fort Worth (G-7074)

APPAREL DESIGNERS: Commercial

ML Industries Inc ....G 956 279-8678
  Fredericksburg (G-7186)

APPAREL FILLING MATERIALS: Cotton Waste, Kapok/Related Matl

Hobbs Bonded Fibers LLC.............E 254 741-0040
  Waco (G-20412)

Hobbs Bonded Fibers Na LLC.........D 254 741-0040
  Waco (G-20413)

APPLIANCES, HOUSEHOLD: Drycleaning Machines, Incl Coin-Op

North Shore Express Clean ....F 832 418-0535
  Houston (G-11075)

APPLIANCES, HOUSEHOLD: Kitchen, Major, Exc Refrigs & Stoves

Handcrafted Metal Inc ....F 512 386-5433
  Converse (G-3395)

APPLIANCES: Household, NEC

Automated Ceiling Registers ....F 972 509-2400
  Richardson (G-17274)

APPLIANCES: Household, Refrigerators & Freezers

Arctic Cooler-Freezer Repr Inc ....F 817 492-0200
  Fort Worth (G-6399)

Brand Commercial Services Inc ....E 844 232-7263
  Lewisville (G-14029)

Chill King ....E 512 303-1529
  Bastrop (G-1750)

APPLIANCES: Major, Cooking

Turbochef Technologies Inc ....E 214 379-6000
  Carrollton (G-2892)

APPLIANCES: Small, Electric

Aerus Holdings LLC.....................F 214 378-4000
  Dallas (G-3896)

Burkhead Manufacturing Company ....E 713 227-5248
  Houston (G-9019)

Hydrocut Inc ....F 979 849-5422
  Angleton (G-573)

Lasko Products LLC.....................B 817 625-6381
  Fort Worth (G-6780)

Regal Ware Inc ....E 817 652-8151
  Fort Worth (G-6952)

Requejo Construction Svcs LLC ....F 210 459-5161
  San Antonio (G-18420)

Starion USA Inc ....E 956 283-1289
  Mission (G-15564)

Vollara LLC ....E 800 989-2299
  Dallas (G-5169)

APPLICATIONS SOFTWARE PROGRAMMING

Avolin LLC ....C 512 524-6149
  Austin (G-970)

Compu-Data International LLC.............E 281 292-1333
  Houston (G-9263)

Esi Technologies LLC....................G 512 633-2897
  Austin (G-1138)

Jarvantech Inc ....F 832 742-7220
  The Woodlands (G-19888)

Jose Alfonsin ....F 210 717-2306
  San Antonio (G-18208)

Kainexus Inc ....F 512 522-3940
  Irving (G-13072)

Network Info Systems Inc ....E 713 255-4800
  Houston (G-11030)

Pwr Technologies LLC ....F 469 609-3537
  Mesquite (G-15073)

AQUARIUMS & ACCESS: Glass

Fiberglass Creations Inc ....E 903 657-6616
  Henderson (G-8262)

Tideline Designs Inc ....F 214 275-3958
  Arlington (G-799)

ARCHITECT'S SUPPLIES WHOLESALERS

Thomas Reprographics Inc................D 210 829-7000
  San Antonio (G-18548)

ARCHITECTURAL PANELS OR PARTS: Porcelain Enameled

Wood Gallery Inc.......................E 972 869-9161
  Dallas (G-5200)

ARCHITECTURAL SVCS

Classic Industries LP....................E 972 564-2192
  Forney (G-6305)

Exyte Americas Holding Inc................E 972 535-7300
  Plano (G-16868)

Graphtec Inc ....E 713 690-9999
  Houston (G-10019)

Kenmark Architectural Pdts Inc ....F 800 788-8263
  Dallas (G-4550)

Sentech Archtctral Systems LLC ....E 512 266-7045
  Austin (G-1494)

Texas Neon Advertising Company ....F 210 734-6694
  San Antonio (G-18538)

ARCHITECTURAL SVCS: Engineering

Global Technical Solutions USA ....F 832 410-4488
  Spring (G-19126)

ARMATURE REPAIRING & REWINDING SVC

Alliance Machine & Spc Inc ....F 432 367-9113
  Odessa (G-15911)

Amerimex Motor & Controls LLC ....D 713 225-4300
  Houston (G-8618)

Blade Runner Turbomachinery SE...........E 713 669-1155
  Navasota (G-15726)

General Electric Company ....D 412 469-6080
  Southlake (G-19071)

H L Hailey Enterprises Inc ....F 903 759-1881
  Longview (G-14244)

Heights Armature Works Inc................F 713 937-7676
  Houston (G-10147)

Houma Armture Wrks Houston LLC.....F 713 748-0702
  Houston (G-8384)

Industrial Spclty Svcs USA LLC ....F 713 987-9117
  Deer Park (G-5280)

ARMORED CAR SVCS

Cannedy Contemporary Svcs Inc...........E 940 322-3856
  Wichita Falls (G-20749)

AROMATIC CHEMICAL PRDTS

Chevron Phillips Chem Co LP ....A 832 813-4100
  The Woodlands (G-19845)

ART DEALERS & GALLERIES

Kenneth Wyatt Galleries...................F 806 995-2239
  Tulia (G-20036)

S W Galleries Corp ....E 972 788-2743
  Dallas (G-4924)

ART DESIGN SVCS

Mighty Works Signage LLC ....G 713 305-8355
  Houston (G-10877)

ART GOODS, WHOLESALE

Idea Planet LP ....E 972 380-9867
  Dallas (G-3844)

Kiwo Holdings Inc ....E 281 474-9777
  Seabrook (G-18787)

USa Screen Printing Chem Inc ....E 281 474-9777
  Seabrook (G-18793)

ART MARBLE: Concrete

37 Building Products Ltd ....C 817 341-3130
  Weatherford (G-20571)

ART SPLY STORES

Greater Southwest Art Center ....G 915 566-2410
  El Paso (G-5790)

ARTIFICIAL FLOWER SHOPS

Fosters Point Inc.........................E 281 353-6696
  Tomball (G-19979)

Schusters of Texas Inc ....F 325 648-2267
  Goldthwaite (G-7744)

ARTISTS' AGENTS & BROKERS

Dirt Road Music Group LLC...............F 678 525-3982
  Arlington (G-663)

Lee Tech LLC............................F 409 925-0553
  Santa Fe (G-18736)

ARTISTS' MATERIALS, WHOLESALE

Greater Southwest Art Center ....G 915 566-2410
  El Paso (G-5790)

ARTISTS' MATERIALS: Pastels

Pearland Arts League ....F 713 304-0672
  Pearland (G-16590)

ARTWORK: Framed

Michaels Companies Inc ....D 972 409-1300
  Irving (G-13108)

ASBESTOS & ASBESTOS CEMENT: Tubing & Piping

Chevron Phillips Chem Co LP ....A 832 813-4100
  The Woodlands (G-19845)

MCR Oil Tools LLC.......................E 817 704-6677
  Arlington (G-730)

ASBESTOS PRDTS: Roofing, Felt Roll

Certainteed LLC ....D 214 630-7377
  Dallas (G-4103)

ASBESTOS PRDTS: Tape

Builders Post-Tension Inc..................E 281 873-9500
  Houston (G-9014)

ASBESTOS REMOVAL EQPT

Advanced Cntinment Systems Inc...........C 713 987-0336
  Houston (G-8486)

ASPHALT & ASPHALT PRDTS

Bryan & Bryan Asp Rd Oil Co...............E 903 657-2391
  Henderson (G-8259)

Capitol Aggregates Inc ....C 210 871-6100
  San Antonio (G-17981)

Cleveland Asphalt Products Inc.............E 936 628-6200
  Shepherd (G-18900)

Csa Materials Inc.........................D 325 655-4511
  San Angelo (G-17793)

David L Jennings ....D 281 778-3223
  Missouri City (G-15579)

Dmg Equipment Company LLC.............C 936 756-6960
  Conroe (G-3295)

Gulf States Asphalt Company LP ....D 713 941-4410
  South Houston (G-19042)

Hunter Industries Ltd.....................B 512 353-7757
  San Marcos (G-18695)

Longview Asphalt Inc ....F 903 758-0065
  Longview (G-14266)

Longview Asphalt Inc ....G 903 758-4428
  Longview (G-14267)

Omega Paving Contractor Inc ....F 915 595-1280
  El Paso (G-5901)

Quality Hot Mix Inc......................F 979 543-6464
  El Campo (G-5627)

US Lbm Holdings LLC ....C 713 650-6200
  Houston (G-12485)

Valley Caliche Products Inc ....D 956 581-2751
  Mission (G-15571)

Vantacore Partners LLC ....F 215 751-1403
  Houston (G-12530)

Zack Burkett Co ....E 940 322-2101
  Wichita Falls (G-20838)

ASPHALT COATINGS & SEALERS

American Indus Mfrs Bldg Mate .....C 214 254-4720
Plano (G-16787)
Asphalt Products Inc .....F 956 423-8315
Harlingen (G-8181)
Henry Company .....E 972 272-5488
Garland (G-7510)
Owens Corning Sales LLC .....C 972 438-1050
Irving (G-13138)
Standard Industries Inc .....C 972 851-0460
Dallas (G-5004)

ASPHALT MINING & BITUMINOUS STONE QUARRYING SVCS

Evans Sons Prtble Rock Crshing .....F 830 214-3629
Euless (G-6144)
Rlf Salado Quarries LLC .....E 254 793-3355
Florence (G-6242)

ASPHALT MIXTURES WHOLESALERS

Asphalt Inc LLC .....E 512 428-5739
Austin (G-939)
Csa Materials Inc .....D 325 655-4511
San Angelo (G-17793)
Kohlhaas Corporation .....E 915 778-5357
El Paso (G-5831)
Moore Asphalt Co Inc .....E 903 561-1321
Tyler (G-20131)
US Lbm Holdings LLC .....E 713 650-6200
Houston (G-12485)

ASPHALT PLANTS INCLUDING GRAVEL MIX TYPE

D and H Equipment Ltd .....E 830 833-5366
Blanco (G-2110)
Fordyce Ltd .....E 956 581-0672
Palmview (G-16310)
Thompson Jr Inc .....E 940 665-2533
Gainesville (G-7372)
Western Refining Company LP .....F 915 775-3246
El Paso (G-6034)

ASSOCIATION FOR THE HANDICAPPED

Beacon Lighthouse Inc .....D 940 767-0888
Wichita Falls (G-20743)
Dallas Lghthouse For Blind Inc .....C 214 821-2375
Dallas (G-4217)

ASSOCIATIONS: Business

Rumber Materials Incorporated .....G 940 759-4181
Muenster (G-15673)

ASSOCIATIONS: Dentists'

Texas Dental Association Inc .....E 512 443-3675
Austin (G-1565)

ASSOCIATIONS: Real Estate Management

Carter Lee Properties LLC .....F 713 385-8092
Richmond (G-17452)

ASSOCIATIONS: Trade

Associated Locksmiths Amer Inc .....F 214 819-9733
Dallas (G-3973)
Channl-Track Tube-Way Inds Inc .....F 361 798-4979
Hallettsville (G-8120)
International Assn Drlg Contrs .....E 713 292-1945
Houston (G-10398)
Promotional Products Assn Intl .....D 972 252-0404
Irving (G-13160)

ATOMIZERS

Act Global Tech Industries .....F 210 651-2543
San Antonio (G-17864)
Advanced Aero Coatings LLC .....F 940 367-5963
Ponder (G-17093)
Advanced Telesensors Inc .....F 888 292-2208
Austin (G-895)
Aequs Oil and Gas LLC .....F 832 616-3110
Paris (G-16357)
Auto Fit Inc .....F 713 696-9000
Houston (G-8752)
B&B Custom Fabrication LLC .....E 214 773-9240
Grand Saline (G-7997)

Dcp Operating Company LP .....C 361 584-8509
Bishop (G-2107)
Deansteel Manufacturing Co .....C 210 226-8271
San Antonio (G-18046)
Duna USA Inc .....E 281 383-3862
Baytown (G-1785)
Enerflex Services Inc .....E 281 345-9300
Houston (G-9633)
Global Operations Texas LP .....F 915 595-2250
San Antonio (G-18148)
H Rosen Usa LLC .....B 281 442-8282
Houston (G-10085)
Ineos USA LLC .....C 281 535-6600
League City (G-13965)
Insight Equity Holdings LLC .....C 512 372-9063
Austin (G-1229)
Intelligen .....E 940 692-3334
Wichita Falls (G-20772)
Mortex Products Inc .....B 817 624-0820
Fort Worth (G-6853)
Noltex LLC .....E 281 842-5000
La Porte (G-13779)
P I Components Corp .....D 979 830-5400
Brenham (G-2267)
Ravago Mfg Americas LLC .....F 281 443-6220
Houston (G-11553)
Tex-Tube Company .....C 713 686-4351
Houston (G-12217)
Top Shelf Industries Oper Ltd .....F 806 995-2224
Tulia (G-20040)
Townsend Oilfield Services LP .....F 361 449-1444
George West (G-7630)
Twin Eagle Sand Logistics LLC .....E 713 341-7300
Houston (G-12414)
Vee Interests LLC .....F 832 864-2001
Pasadena (G-16523)
Weatherford Well Screen Techno .....F 281 670-0005
Houston (G-12622)

ATTENUATORS

L3 Technologies Inc .....B 972 840-5600
Garland (G-7535)
L3 Technologies Inc .....B 972 840-5600
Dallas (G-4574)

AUCTION SVCS: Motor Vehicle

Lexus Group Inc .....F 682 323-5942
Arlington (G-720)

AUDIO & VIDEO EQPT, EXC COMMERCIAL

51 Home Technologies LLC .....F 713 589-5747
Fresno (G-7236)
Ce Labs LLC .....E 469 429-9200
Garland (G-7455)
Commscope Technologies LLC .....A 214 634-8502
Dallas (G-4149)
Conference Technologies Inc .....C 512 584-8275
Austin (G-1061)
Custom Electronics Inc .....F 512 454-8824
Pflugerville (G-16667)
Dm Home Entertainment LLC .....G 972 992-3155
Carrollton (G-2866)
Peag LLC .....E 858 683-3634
Dallas (G-3850)
Satellink Inc .....E 972 487-1434
Garland (G-7581)
Sound Bridge Acoustic Labs Inc .....E 972 937-2030
Waxahachie (G-20559)
Technicolor Usa Inc .....C 915 872-8001
El Paso (G-5996)
Technicolor Usa Inc .....C 915 841-7233
Socorro (G-19019)
Videotex Systems Inc .....F 214 349-6399
Dallas (G-5166)

AUDIO & VIDEO TAPES WHOLESALERS

Digital Speech Systems Inc .....E 972 235-2999
Allen (G-262)

AUDIO ELECTRONIC SYSTEMS

Dynamic Intgrtons Ctrl Systems .....F 512 716-0817
Round Rock (G-17650)
Koncept Systems LLC .....E 800 773-4910
Houston (G-10557)
Ksh Enterprises Inc .....F 817 313-0926
Haslet (G-8220)
Iesco Distributing Inc .....F 972 446-1605
Carrollton (G-2776)

Mega Systems Inc .....E 210 684-2600
Helotes (G-8242)
Panasonic Corp North America .....A 956 984-3432
Mcallen (G-14899)
Rupert Neve Designs LLC .....F 512 847-3013
Wimberley (G-20883)

AUDIO-VISUAL PROGRAM PRODUCTION SVCS

EPM Live Inc .....C 425 452-1111
Austin (G-1133)

AUTO & HOME SUPPLY STORES: Auto & Truck Eqpt & Parts

A G Van & Truck Eqp Inc .....E 214 638-8805
Dallas (G-3870)
Riggs Machine and Welding Inc .....F 254 965-3910
Stephenville (G-19420)
Texas Kenworth Co .....G 940 767-0001
Wichita Falls (G-20816)
Tmp Truck & Trailer LP .....E 432 686-2500
Midland (G-15438)
Vaughan Investments Inc .....F 956 686-3725
McAllen (G-14916)

AUTO & HOME SUPPLY STORES: Auto Air Cond Eqpt, Sell/Install

Auto Air Export Inc .....D 972 812-7000
Irving (G-12935)
Bus Air LLC .....E 817 636-2308
Haslet (G-8217)
Mahle Behr Service America LLC .....E 817 624-7273
Fort Worth (G-6806)
Vintage Air Inc .....D 210 296-2302
San Antonio (G-18648)

AUTO & HOME SUPPLY STORES: Automotive Access

Team Promark LLC .....E 303 926-1328
Fort Worth (G-7039)
Wmk LLC .....F 817 429-1273
Haltom City (G-8162)

AUTO & HOME SUPPLY STORES: Automotive parts

A & B Auto Electric Inc .....F 713 928-3219
Houston (G-8422)
C C Battery Company Inc .....E 361 882-5561
Corpus Christi (G-3492)
Matek Performance Inc .....E 817 626-9006
Fort Worth (G-6816)
OReilly Automotive Stores Inc .....F 936 856-2409
Willis (G-20857)
Upex Auto Supply .....F 214 741-2400
Dallas (G-5144)
Wapco Inc .....F 936 539-6272
Conroe (G-3384)

AUTO & HOME SUPPLY STORES: Batteries, Automotive & Truck

Battery Solutions Inc .....F 806 771-3777
Lubbock (G-14366)
Interstate Batteries Inc .....C 972 991-1444
Dallas (G-4507)

AUTO & HOME SUPPLY STORES: Speed Shops, Incl Race Car Splys

Audio and Prfmce Solutions LLC .....E 210 549-4242
San Antonio (G-17922)

AUTO & HOME SUPPLY STORES: Trailer Hitches, Automotive

Dfw Camper Corral Inc .....F 972 241-6443
Dallas (G-4255)
Magnum Custom Trlr Mfg Co Inc .....F 512 258-4101
San Antonio (G-18271)

AUTO & HOME SUPPLY STORES: Truck Eqpt & Parts

American Tire Distributors Inc .....F 281 872-0397
Houston (G-8612)

PRODUCT

ARC Rite Welding & Fabrication ....F 830 774-6058
  Del Rio *(G-5305)*
Dealers Truck Equipment Co Inc..........F 512 312-2100
  Buda *(G-2527)*
Dealers Truck Equipment Co Inc..........F 903 758-4451
  Longview *(G-14223)*
Friedson Hill Inc ....F 817 244-6500
  Benbrook *(G-2039)*
Indepndent Rugh Trrain Ctr LLC..........C 210 599-6541
  Cibolo *(G-3063)*
J&J Weaver Co ....E 254 756-2139
  Waco *(G-20419)*
Magnum Custom Trlr Mfg Co Inc..........D 512 258-4101
  Austin *(G-1318)*
Module Truck Systems Inc ....E 806 783-0777
  Lubbock *(G-14448)*
Northwest Drive Train Inc ....F 713 937-8499
  Jersey Village *(G-13302)*
Ogburn Truck Parts LP ....F 281 331-0005
  Alvin *(G-375)*
Quality Bumper Service Dallas ....E 214 824-7300
  Dallas *(G-4843)*

AUTO SPLYS & PARTS, NEW, WHSLE: Exhaust Sys, Mufflers, Etc

Maremont Exhaust Products Inc..........C 865 458-4681
  Schulenburg *(G-18776)*

AUTOMATED TELLER MACHINE OR ATM REPAIR SVCS

Access Atm Inc..........F 713 463-9033
  Houston *(G-8456)*

AUTOMATIC REGULATING CONTROL: Building Svcs Monitoring, Auto

APS Building Services Inc ....D 713 979-0720
  Houston *(G-8670)*
City of Houston ....C 713 221-0404
  Houston *(G-9203)*
Clarios ....F 361 289-9675
  Corpus Christi *(G-3500)*
Divcon Ems Austin LLC ....E 214 821-6958
  Farmers Branch *(G-6193)*
Evolve Holdings Inc ....E 832 375-0099
  Houston *(G-9720)*
Logical Control Services LLP ....E 972 820-0100
  Carrollton *(G-2878)*

AUTOMATIC REGULATING CONTROLS: AC & Refrigeration

A-Action Aire Inc ....F 210 648-3801
  San Antonio *(G-17850)*
Ademco Inc..........E 972 402-8612
  Farmers Branch *(G-6184)*
Ademco Inc..........F 713 861-9418
  Houston *(G-8479)*
Ademco Inc..........C 915 872-5542
  El Paso *(G-5637)*
Crisp Air ....E 903 530-4385
  Winona *(G-20903)*
Johnson Controls Be Operation..........A 956 782-3000
  McAllen *(G-14880)*
Schneder Elc Bldngs Amrcas Inc..........B 972 323-1111
  Carrollton *(G-2813)*
Siemens Industry Inc..........D 956 797-5075
  La Feria *(G-13692)*
Siemens Industry Inc..........B 972 947-7000
  Dallas *(G-4959)*
Siemens Industry Inc..........C 972 550-8488
  Irving *(G-13178)*
Super-Tech Hvac LLC..........F 361 394-5549
  Freer *(G-7234)*

AUTOMATIC REGULATING CONTROLS: Electric Heat

Eml Manufacturing Llc ....E 281 880-7517
  Houston *(G-9617)*

AUTOMATIC REGULATING CONTROLS: Energy Cutoff, Residtl/Comm

Jefferson Gulf Coast Energy ....E 281 677-4900
  Houston *(G-10463)*
Standard Renewable Energy LP..........D 281 763-2020
  Houston *(G-12043)*

AUTOMATIC REGULATING CONTROLS: Hardware, Environmental Reg

Burly Corp ....E 817 295-1128
  Burleson *(G-2573)*
Nailor Industries Texas Inc ....C 281 590-1172
  Houston *(G-10961)*
Qa Support LP ....E 281 307-1000
  La Porte *(G-13786)*

AUTOMATIC REGULATING CONTROLS: Hydronic Pressure Or Temp

Momentum Prssure Ctrl Rntl LLC ....D 903 643-3700
  Longview *(G-14281)*

AUTOMATIC REGULATING CONTROLS: Oil & Hydronic, Combination

Texas Ine Inc..........D 281 601-4884
  Houston *(G-12236)*

AUTOMATIC REGULATING CONTROLS: Pneumatic Relays, Air-Cond

Parkline Inc..........D 409 935-5743
  Hitchcock *(G-8339)*

AUTOMATIC REGULATING CONTROLS: Pressure, Air-Cond Sys

George Wood and Company Inc ....E 713 672-7270
  Houston *(G-9943)*
Rampak Group Inc..........F 713 678-8898
  Houston *(G-11537)*

AUTOMATIC REGULATING CONTROLS: Refrigeration, Pressure

Altech Controls Corporation..........F 281 207-2775
  Missouri City *(G-15575)*
Convergentz Bldg Systems LLC ....E 713 266-3900
  Houston *(G-9297)*
RMS Solutions Group LLC ....F 469 964-7127
  Point *(G-17080)*

AUTOMATIC REGULATING CONTROLS: Vapor Heating

Jessco Solutions LLC ....F 325 227-4196
  San Angelo *(G-17811)*

AUTOMATIC REGULATING CTRLS: Damper, Pneumatic Or Electric

Lower Colorado River Authority..........F 512 473-3270
  Buchanan Dam *(G-2518)*
Peerless Mfg Co ....D 214 357-6181
  Dallas *(G-4794)*

AUTOMATIC TELLER MACHINES

Access Atm Inc ....F 713 463-9033
  Houston *(G-8456)*
American Pos Alliance LLC ....F 817 350-4714
  Grapevine *(G-8011)*
Cannedy Contemporary Svcs Inc..........E 940 322-3856
  Wichita Falls *(G-20749)*
Diebold Nixdorf Incorporated ....F 210 242-6100
  San Antonio *(G-18058)*
Ganart Technologies Inc ....E 972 512-6933
  Carrollton *(G-2744)*
One Source SEC & Sound Inc ....E 713 934-7400
  Humble *(G-12791)*
Touchpay Holdings LP ....E 972 215-0133
  Irving *(G-13196)*
Wincor Nixdorf Inc ....G 512 252-5622
  Manor *(G-14651)*

AUTOMOBILE FABRICS, WHOLESALE

Keyston Bros ....F 713 692-2132
  Houston *(G-10526)*

AUTOMOBILE RECOVERY SVCS

Intertek USA Inc ....F 281 364-2800
  Spring *(G-19220)*

AUTOMOBILES & OTHER MOTOR VEHICLES WHOLESALERS

Jac Enterprises Inc ....F 936 348-3997
  Madisonville *(G-14587)*
Select Power Sport Inc ....F 936 967-2332
  Livingston *(G-14161)*
Southwest Prof Vehicles ....F 214 371-3474
  Dallas *(G-4992)*

AUTOMOBILES: Wholesalers

Toyota Motor North America Inc..........E 469 292-4000
  Plano *(G-17036)*

AUTOMOTIVE & TRUCK GENERAL REPAIR SVC

Cannon Engineering Inc..........F 818 508-0123
  Austin *(G-1023)*
Freedom Wheels Inc ....F 713 864-1460
  Houston *(G-9860)*
Goodyear Tire & Rubber Company ....A 361 289-8251
  Corpus Christi *(G-3537)*
Great Dane LLC ....E 713 675-6577
  Houston *(G-10025)*
Heil Trailer International LLC ....C 254 865-7235
  Gatesville *(G-7618)*
McMt LLC..........F 903 592-9663
  Tyler *(G-20121)*
Pegicorn Enterprises LLC ....F 512 821-3300
  Austin *(G-1406)*
Rays Chmpn Spring & Mtr Svc ....E 817 921-3600
  Fort Worth *(G-6943)*
Stewart Stevenson Pwr Pdts LLC ....F 915 790-1848
  El Paso *(G-5980)*
Western Hauler Enterprises..........F 817 332-1121
  Fort Worth *(G-7139)*

AUTOMOTIVE AIR CONDITIONING REPAIR SHOPS

Standard Motor Products Inc..........C 972 316-8100
  Lewisville *(G-14095)*

AUTOMOTIVE BATTERIES WHOLESALERS

Exide Technologies LLC ....E 281 443-0382
  Houston *(G-9724)*
Exide Technologies LLC ....F 972 870-0337
  Irving *(G-13019)*

AUTOMOTIVE BODY SHOP

G Kustoms Auto Customizing LLC ....F 682 703-1583
  Fort Worth *(G-6658)*
Randy Wrecker Service Inc..........F 713 690-4000
  Houston *(G-11543)*

AUTOMOTIVE BODY, PAINT & INTERIOR REPAIR & MAINTENANCE SVC

Auto Wax Company Inc..........E 214 631-4000
  Dallas *(G-3988)*
Joe Ross ....F 903 450-9960
  Greenville *(G-8079)*

AUTOMOTIVE CUSTOMIZING SVCS, NONFACTORY BASIS

Clegg Industries Inc..........E 361 578-0291
  Victoria *(G-20253)*
Freedom Wheels Inc ....F 713 864-1460
  Houston *(G-9860)*
Uv Country Inc ....E 713 649-0556
  Alvin *(G-385)*

AUTOMOTIVE GLASS REPLACEMENT SHOPS

Glass Magic Inc ....F 806 535-4724
  Lubbock *(G-14416)*
Lone Star Glass Inc ....F 713 661-0091
  Houston *(G-10677)*
Morenos Auto Glass Inc ....F 361 855-1471
  Corpus Christi *(G-3579)*

AUTOMOTIVE PAINT SHOP

Dusold Designs Inc..........F 972 221-1455
  Lewisville *(G-14045)*

International Assembly Inc ....F 956 525-4533
Brownsville (G-2362)

AUTOMOTIVE PARTS, ACCESS & SPLYS

Adell Corporation.........................E 972 226-4600
Mesquite (G-15024)

Adient US LLC.............................E 210 271-2428
San Antonio (G-17866)

Aer Manufacturing Inc..................B 972 418-6499
Carrollton (G-2694)

Al Knoch Interiors Inc..................D 915 886-5800
Canutillo (G-2662)

Albany Engnered Composites Inc.....D 830 249-4400
Boerne (G-2113)

Allen Prfmce Resources Inc ....F 817 270-0102
Azle (G-1719)

Alps Electric North Amer Inc ....D 956 217-6500
Mcallen (G-14835)

American Friction Inc...................F 713 818-5919
Humble (G-12745)

Aptiv Services Us LLC.................B 956 366-4600
Los Indios (G-14349)

Aptiv Services Us LLC.................C 915 783-4201
Laredo (G-13859)

Aptiv Services Us LLC.................E 915 783-4200
El Paso (G-5646)

Aptiv Services Us LLC.................C 956 693-3300
Laredo (G-13860)

Aptiv Services Us LLC.................C 915 783-4769
El Paso (G-5647)

Aptiv Services Us LLC.................E 956 237-9066
Laredo (G-13861)

Aptiv Services Us LLC.................F 915 783-4787
El Paso (G-5648)

Behr Service America...................F 817 624-7273
Fort Worth (G-6442)

Bendco Inc.................................E 713 473-1557
Pasadena (G-16398)

Beta Engineering Inc ....F 817 265-3367
Arlington (G-631)

Borgwarner Pds Anderson LLC ....D 765 778-6499
Laredo (G-13870)

Borgwarner Transm Systems LLC ....F 915 217-9268
El Paso (G-5672)

Brenham Auto Ltd.........................F 979 836-4524
Brenham (G-2245)

Bumper Manufacturing Co Inc.........E 817 831-4401
Fort Worth (G-6477)

C C Battery Company Inc..............E 361 882-5561
Corpus Christi (G-3492)

Cadillac Products Inc ....F 248 813-8200
Schertz (G-18747)

Cameron International Corp ....E 806 665-1647
Pampa (G-16318)

Chromalloy Component Svcs Inc.......C 210 331-2300
San Antonio (G-18005)

Component Parts Machine Co Inc.......E 817 834-4771
Fort Worth (G-6534)

Continental Auto Systems Inc ....B 847 862-0366
Laredo (G-13875)

Continental Auto Systems Inc ....A 830 372-7000
Seguin (G-18833)

Cooper-Standard Automotive Inc.......F 956 717-3835
Laredo (G-13876)

Covercraft Industries Inc...............D 940 763-2535
Wichita Falls (G-20757)

Cummins Inc...............................G 615 986-2596
Arlington (G-652)

Cummins Southern Plains LLC.......E 800 286-6467
Dallas (G-4193)

Cummins Southern Plains LLC.......E 210 655-5420
San Antonio (G-18035)

Cylinder Heads International ....F 972 264-3449
Grand Prairie (G-7861)

Dallas Towing and Autonet Inc.........E 972 219-8484
Lewisville (G-14040)

Dana Global Products Inc ....G 915 860-7204
El Paso (G-5712)

Dealers Truck Equipment Co Inc.......F 903 758-4451
Longview (G-14223)

Delphi Powertrain Systems LLC.......F 915 783-4733
El Paso (G-5718)

Delphi Powertrain Systems LLC.......E 915 783-4769
El Paso (G-5719)

Dfw Camper Corral Inc ....F 972 241-6443
Dallas (G-4255)

Dlhbowles Inc.............................F 410 800-6548
Laredo (G-13881)

Don Hardy Race Cars Inc ....F 806 983-3774
Floydada (G-6292)

Dus Operating Inc........................B 956 371-3057
Brownsville (G-2351)

Emissions Technology Inc ....F 713 691-1211
Houston (G-9616)

EMLS Incorporated ....C 940 566-9500
Denton (G-5364)

Enduro Products Inc.....................E 817 704-7346
Arlington (G-670)

Fisher & Company Incorporated ......E 586 746-1961
Brownsville (G-2357)

Flex-N-Gate Texas LLC.................E 817 652-3400
Grand Prairie (G-7874)

Flex-N-Gate Texas LLC.................E 817 652-3400
Grand Prairie (G-7875)

General Motors LLC.....................A 817 652-2182
Arlington (G-691)

Gentherm (texas) Inc ....D 830 774-3512
Del Rio (G-5315)

Go Industries Inc.........................E 972 783-7444
Richardson (G-17323)

Hart Heat Transfer Pdts Inc ....D 713 675-9848
Houston (G-10133)

Harwood Industries Inc ....E 903 566-6001
Tyler (G-20094)

Hilite Industries Auto LP ....D 972 242-2116
Carrollton (G-2757)

Hilite Industries Inc ....E 972 242-2116
Dallas (G-4457)

Hilite International Inc ....B 972 242-2116
Carrollton (G-2758)

Hilite International Inc ....F 972 242-2116
Carrollton (G-2759)

Honeywell International Inc ....A 281 890-0088
Cypress (G-3801)

Imperial Group Mfg Inc.................C 940 627-1700
Decatur (G-5247)

Insight Equity A P X L P ....E 817 488-7775
Southlake (G-19075)

Insight Equity LP.........................E 817 488-7775
Southlake (G-19076)

Inteva Products LLC.....................B 248 655-8777
Brownsville (G-2365)

J&J Weaver Co............................E 254 756-2139
Waco (G-20419)

Johnson Controls Inc....................C 956 782-3000
Mcallen (G-14881)

K & N Engineering Inc ....E 951 826-0000
Grand Prairie (G-7904)

Kaspar Ranch Hand Eqp LLC.........C 361 594-4608
Shiner (G-18942)

Kautex Inc..................................E 210 229-2300
San Antonio (G-18218)

Lay Cooley RE Holdings 1 LLC........E 972 721-4500
Irving (G-13084)

Lear Corporation..........................B 915 791-5400
El Paso (G-5841)

Lear Corporation..........................B 915 307-9237
El Paso (G-5842)

Lear Corporation..........................B 915 787-5012
El Paso (G-5843)

Lear Corporation..........................B 817 419-3000
Grand Prairie (G-7910)

Lear Siegler Logistics Intl ....F 210 490-0267
San Antonio (G-18240)

Lear Trim LP...............................G 915 849-5660
El Paso (G-5844)

Mahle Behr Mfg MGT Inc...............F 248 735-3623
El Paso (G-5861)

Mahle Behr Mfg MGT Inc...............F 248 735-3623
Laredo (G-13908)

Marmon Highway Tech LLC............E 214 631-8810
Dallas (G-4636)

Metalsa Light Truck Inc ....F 210 242-3403
San Antonio (G-18293)

Michex International Inc ....F 281 397-7770
Houston (G-10866)

Modern Welding Co Texas Inc ....E 713 675-4211
Houston (G-10905)

Nat G CNG Solutions LLC..............F 281 954-4600
Houston (G-10963)

Nat G CNG Solutions LLC..............F 512 998-9316
Converse (G-3399)

Nichirin-Flex USA Inc ....B 915 859-1199
El Paso (G-5896)

North American Atk Corporation........D 972 647-1400
Grand Prairie (G-7936)

Pearland Alternator Inc ....E 281 485-8871
Pearland (G-16589)

PEC Manufacturing ....F 830 693-7879
Marble Falls (G-14749)

Phillips Iron Works Inc ....E 337 364-2337
Houston (G-11327)

Pierce Arrow Inc.........................F 940 538-5643
Henrietta (G-8282)

Pollok Inc...................................A 915 592-5700
El Paso (G-5914)

Pressure Systems International ....D 210 222-1926
San Antonio (G-18394)

Quality Trailer Products LP.............D 817 444-4518
Azle (G-1728)

Regis Manufacturing Company ....F 214 421-5171
Dallas (G-4884)

Reher-Morrison Racing Engines ....E 817 467-7171
Arlington (G-770)

Reyes Automotive Group II LLC........C 210 228-2500
San Antonio (G-18424)

Robert Bosch Auto Steering LLC......E 956 857-4436
Laredo (G-13924)

Robert Bosch LLC.......................F 956 753-6082
Laredo (G-13925)

Saf-Holland Inc............................C 972 442-3556
Wylie (G-20947)

Santech Industries LLC.................E 817 589-1212
Irving (G-13172)

Schrader Electronics Limited ....B 817 608-2289
Fort Worth (G-6979)

Solrac Corporation ....A 915 772-3073
El Paso (G-5969)

Standard Motor Products Inc ....C 972 316-8100
Lewisville (G-14094)

Standard Motor Products Inc ....C 972 316-8100
Lewisville (G-14095)

Sumitomo Elc Wirg Systems Inc ....F 915 859-0555
El Paso (G-5987)

Sunshine Machine Inc ....F 281 445-0326
Houston (G-12103)

Tenneco Automotive Oper Co Inc ....C 979 691-7732
College Station (G-3203)

Tenneco Inc................................A 915 832-4661
El Paso (G-5997)

Texas Saddlebags Inc...................D 817 649-2626
Arlington (G-793)

Texas Spa Covers Inc ....G 512 756-2043
Burnet (G-2616)

TI Group Auto Systems LLC............E 956 686-5400
McAllen (G-14912)

Tianhai Electric N Amer Inc.............E 915 881-9740
El Paso (G-6004)

Toyoda Gosei Texas LLC................C 210 302-4600
San Antonio (G-18556)

Toyotetsu Texas Inc.....................D 210 231-5515
San Antonio (G-18557)

Trey Industry SW.........................F 915 591-5100
El Paso (G-6015)

TYG Products LP.........................D 972 542-1828
McKinney (G-14984)

United States Steel Corp ....D 903 656-6521
Lone Star (G-14185)

Victory Climate Systems LLC...........C 817 293-3331
Fort Worth (G-7105)

Vitesco Technologies Usa LLC..........A 830 379-8850
Seguin (G-18872)

Watson & Chalin Holding Corp..........E 972 547-6020
McKinney (G-14988)

Watson & Chalin Mfg Inc................D 972 547-6020
McKinney (G-14989)

Xerxes Corporation ....E 830 372-0090
Seguin (G-18875)

Youngs Tank Incorporated ....E 800 345-7952
Boyd (G-2210)

ZF Elec Sys Plsnt Praire LLC...........F 915 790-5000
El Paso (G-6042)

ZF Passive Safety US Inc ....F 956 632-8100
Pharr (G-16718)

ZF Passive Safety US Inc ....B 734 582-1139
El Paso (G-6043)

ZF TRW Auto Holdings Corp............D 956 632-8100
Pharr (G-16719)

AUTOMOTIVE PARTS: Plastic

Aer Manufacturing LP...................F 972 392-4130
Addison (G-101)

Baileys Premier Services LLC..........C 817 292-2423
Fort Worth (G-6419)

Cool Cruisers of Texas ....F 972 772-5517
Rockwall (G-17545)

Coverlay Manufacturing Inc ....E 325 659-4697
San Angelo (G-17791)

G Kustoms Auto Customizing LLC ......F 682 703-1583
Fort Worth (G-6658)

GL Automotive LLC ....F 925 360-3937
San Antonio (G-18141)
Illinois Tool Works Inc ....B 956 215-2000
Pharr (G-16700)
Jacqueline Thompson ....F 210 269-1548
Round Rock (G-17663)
Schlemmer Usa Inc ....D 210 491-4800
San Antonio (G-18457)
TYG Products LP ....D 972 542-1828
McKinney (G-14984)

AUTOMOTIVE PRDTS: Rubber

Dacon Industries Co ....E 903 589-7456
Jacksonville (G-13235)
Parker-Hannifin Corporation ....C 936 560-8900
Nacogdoches (G-15708)
Rex-Hide Incorporated ....F 903 593-7387
Tyler (G-20146)

AUTOMOTIVE RADIATOR REPAIR SHOPS

Centennial Radiator Inc ....E 214 634-8262
Dallas (G-4096)
Hght Inc ....G 281 446-1155
Humble (G-12776)

AUTOMOTIVE REPAIR SHOPS: Brake Repair

Heitman Company Inc ....F 713 675-9001
Houston (G-10148)

AUTOMOTIVE REPAIR SHOPS: Diesel Engine Repair

Cummins Inc ....E 915 791-6600
El Paso (G-5707)
Cummins Southern Plains LLC ....E 817 624-2107
Fort Worth (G-6566)
Stx Service Americas LLC ....F 713 637-4030
Houston (G-12084)

AUTOMOTIVE REPAIR SHOPS: Electrical Svcs

Auto Electric Systems Inc ....F 972 241-2077
Plano (G-16796)
Ies Holdings Inc ....D 713 860-1500
Houston (G-10316)
Ksh Enterprises Inc ....F 817 313-0926
Haslet (G-8220)
North Amrcn Glvnzing Ctngs Inc ....A 817 810-0095
Fort Worth (G-6867)

AUTOMOTIVE REPAIR SHOPS: Engine Rebuilding

Cameron International Corp ....E 806 665-1647
Pampa (G-16318)

AUTOMOTIVE REPAIR SHOPS: Engine Repair

Man Energy Solutions USA Inc ....F 713 780-4200
Brookshire (G-2319)
Stewart Stevenson Pwr Pdts LLC ....C 504 347-4326
Houston (G-12064)

AUTOMOTIVE REPAIR SHOPS: Frame Repair Shops

Conglobal Industries LLC ....E 713 675-7587
Galena Park (G-7379)

AUTOMOTIVE REPAIR SHOPS: Machine Shop

Component Parts Machine Co Inc ....F 817 834-4771
Fort Worth (G-6535)
Joel G Gibbs Inc ....F 281 595-3330
Rosharon (G-17606)
M&R Manufacturing LLC ....F 281 590-7200
Houston (G-10724)
Mic Group LLC ....D 979 277-7800
Brenham (G-2264)
Sunshine Machine Inc ....F 281 445-0326
Houston (G-12103)
Vaughan Investments Inc ....E 956 546-5175
Brownsville (G-2420)
Wapco Inc ....F 936 539-6272
Conroe (G-3384)

AUTOMOTIVE REPAIR SHOPS: Powertrain Components Repair Svcs

Brazos Valley Drivelines Inc ....F 979 775-3535
Bryan (G-2459)
Northwest Drive Train Inc ....F 713 937-8499
Jersey Village (G-13302)

AUTOMOTIVE REPAIR SHOPS: Tire Repair Shop

T & W Tire LLC ....G 940 683-3558
Bridgeport (G-2302)

AUTOMOTIVE REPAIR SHOPS: Trailer Repair

Ace Welding and Trailer Co ....E 210 667-1171
San Antonio (G-17858)
Beall Construction Company Inc ....D 325 677-2112
Abilene (G-16)
Bill Gilmore Welding Inc ....E 940 592-4945
Iowa Park (G-12903)
Buck Dandy Co ....E 903 784-6362
Sumner (G-19606)
Campbell Trailers & Leasing ....F 806 250-3611
Friona (G-7251)
City Machine & Welding Inc ....E 806 358-7293
Amarillo (G-416)
Houston Truck Tarps LLC ....E 346 571-1832
Houston (G-10259)
Magnum Custom Trlr Mfg Co Inc ....F 512 258-4101
San Antonio (G-18271)
McMahan Welding Service Ltd ....F 361 275-0111
Cuero (G-3763)
Olivo Enterprises Inc ....D 713 694-3077
Houston (G-11172)
Portersville Sales & Testing ....E 806 373-6811
Amarillo (G-507)
Santin Auto and Truck Repr Ctr ....E 210 648-4100
San Antonio (G-18454)
Worth Trailer Parts Inc ....E 817 496-7841
Fort Worth (G-7151)

AUTOMOTIVE REPAIR SHOPS: Truck Engine Repair, Exc Indl

Thomas Bus Gulf Coast GP Inc ....E 713 580-8600
Houston (G-12273)

AUTOMOTIVE REPAIR SHOPS: Turbocharger & Blower Repair

Man Energy Solutions USA Inc ....F 713 780-4200
Brookshire (G-2319)
Quality Trbchrger Cmpnents LLC ....E 713 849-4200
Houston (G-11502)

AUTOMOTIVE REPAIR SVC

Goodyear Tire & Rubber Company ....A 361 289-8251
Corpus Christi (G-3537)
Lay Cooley RE Holdings 1 LLC ....E 972 721-4500
Irving (G-13084)
Millennium Plastics Tech LLC ....E 915 834-2700
El Paso (G-5878)
Rays Chmpn Spring & Mtr Svc ....E 817 921-3600
Fort Worth (G-6943)

AUTOMOTIVE REPAIR SVCS, MISCELLANEOUS

Ma-Tex Wire Rope Co Inc ....E 903 984-9691
Kilgore (G-13567)
Santin Auto and Truck Repr Ctr ....E 210 648-4100
San Antonio (G-18454)

AUTOMOTIVE SPLYS & PARTS, NEW, WHOL: Auto Servicing Eqpt

Conslidated Rigworks LP ....E 817 446-5272
Fort Worth (G-6543)
Ogburn Truck Parts LP ....F 281 331-0005
Alvin (G-375)

AUTOMOTIVE SPLYS & PARTS, NEW, WHOL: Auto Svc Station Eqpt

Werther International Inc ....F 800 655-4781
Houston (G-12634)

AUTOMOTIVE SPLYS & PARTS, NEW, WHOLESALE: Brakes

Austin Brake & Clutch Supply ....F 512 836-0482
Austin (G-951)
Truckpro LLC ....F 512 836-0482
Austin (G-1597)

AUTOMOTIVE SPLYS & PARTS, NEW, WHOLESALE: Bumpers

Quality Bumper Service Dallas ....E 214 824-7300
Dallas (G-4843)

AUTOMOTIVE SPLYS & PARTS, NEW, WHOLESALE: Engines/Eng Parts

Hartmanns Inc ....F 325 695-7641
Abilene (G-46)

AUTOMOTIVE SPLYS & PARTS, NEW, WHOLESALE: Filters, Air & Oil

Taylor Distributing Co Inc ....E 817 831-0601
Fort Worth (G-7037)
TF Hudgins Holdings Inc ....C 713 682-3651
Houston (G-12266)

AUTOMOTIVE SPLYS & PARTS, NEW, WHOLESALE: Hardware

Northwest Drive Train Inc ....F 713 937-8499
Jersey Village (G-13302)

AUTOMOTIVE SPLYS & PARTS, NEW, WHOLESALE: Pumps, Oil & Gas

Kdr Supply Inc ....F 936 334-1353
Liberty (G-14120)

AUTOMOTIVE SPLYS & PARTS, NEW, WHOLESALE: Radiators

Centennial Radiator Inc ....E 214 634-8262
Dallas (G-4096)

AUTOMOTIVE SPLYS & PARTS, NEW, WHOLESALE: Seat Belts

ZF Passive Safety Systems US ....E 956 566-7680
Pharr (G-16717)

AUTOMOTIVE SPLYS & PARTS, NEW, WHOLESALE: Splys

Therm Processes Inc ....F 214 942-3131
Dallas (G-5083)

AUTOMOTIVE SPLYS & PARTS, NEW, WHOLESALE: Tools & Eqpt

Equalizer Industries Inc ....E 512 388-7715
Round Rock (G-17656)

AUTOMOTIVE SPLYS & PARTS, NEW, WHOLESALE: Trailer Parts

Ledwell & Son Enterprises Inc ....C 903 838-6531
Texarkana (G-19768)
Lee Products Inc ....F 817 641-9893
Cleburne (G-3100)
Quality Trailer Products LP ....D 817 444-4518
Azle (G-1728)
Tmp Truck & Trailer LP ....E 432 686-2500
Midland (G-15438)
Worth Trailer Parts Inc ....E 817 496-7841
Fort Worth (G-7151)

AUTOMOTIVE SPLYS & PARTS, USED, WHOLESALE

Holmes Auto Supply Inc ....F 432 689-8008
Midland (G-15248)

AUTOMOTIVE SPLYS & PARTS, USED, WHOLESALE: Access, NEC

International Assembly Inc ....F 956 525-4533
Brownsville (G-2362)

AUTOMOTIVE SPLYS & PARTS, USED, WHOLESALE: Tools & Eqpt

Hh Oil Tools Inc ....F 281 550-0633
Houston **(G-10169)**

AUTOMOTIVE SPLYS & PARTS, WHOLESALE, NEC

A & B Auto Electric Inc ....F 713 928-3219
Houston **(G-8422)**

A G Van & Truck Eqp Inc ....E 214 638-8805
Dallas **(G-3870)**

American Engine & Grinding Co ....F 713 224-5326
Houston **(G-8595)**

Auto Fit Inc ....F 713 696-9000
Houston **(G-8752)**

Blaines Motor Supply Inc ....D 214 426-4400
Dallas **(G-4029)**

Breckenridge Auto & Engine Sup ......F 254 559-8241
Breckenridge **(G-2224)**

Dallas Towing and Autonet Inc ....E 972 219-8484
Lewisville **(G-14040)**

Emergency Vehicles Texas Inc ....F 817 281-4172
Haltom City **(G-8139)**

Hfj Group LLC ....E 833 777-3473
Houston **(G-10168)**

Penntex Industries Inc ....E 817 589-7501
Fort Worth **(G-6900)**

Stewart Stevenson Capitl Corp ....D 713 868-7700
Houston **(G-12063)**

Texas Spa Covers Inc ....E 512 756-2043
Burnet **(G-2616)**

Tripac International Inc ....E 817 534-9278
Fort Worth **(G-7078)**

Upex Auto Supply ....F 214 741-2400
Dallas **(G-5144)**

Vaughan Investments Inc ....E 956 546-5175
Brownsville **(G-2420)**

Vaughan Investments Inc ....F 956 686-3725
McAllen **(G-14916)**

Wapco Inc ....F 936 539-6272
Conroe **(G-3384)**

Yazaki North America Inc ....F 618 512-8723
El Paso **(G-6041)**

AUTOMOTIVE SPLYS/PARTS, NEW, WHOL: Body Rpr/Paint Shop Splys

1-Fast Rspnse Rntals Oil Feld ....D 210 437-2473
San Antonio **(G-17844)**

AUTOMOTIVE SVCS, EXC REPAIR & CARWASHES: Fuel Sys Conv

Nat G CNG Solutions LLC ....F 512 998-9316
Converse **(G-3399)**

Nat G CNG Solutions LLC ....F 281 954-4600
Houston **(G-10963)**

AUTOMOTIVE SVCS, EXC REPAIR & CARWASHES: Glass Tinting

Jimmy Smart ....E 432 381-5450
Odessa **(G-16039)**

McMt LLC ....E 903 592-9663
Tyler **(G-20121)**

AUTOMOTIVE SVCS, EXC REPAIR & CARWASHES: Lubrication

Zxp Technologies LLC ....B 281 426-8800
Highlands **(G-8317)**

AUTOMOTIVE SVCS, EXC REPAIR & CARWASHES: Maintenance

Metro Fire Apprtus Specialists ....G 817 467-0911
Mansfield **(G-14695)**

AUTOMOTIVE SVCS, EXC REPAIR & CARWASHES: Trailer Maintenance

Worth Trailer Parts Inc ....E 817 496-7841
Fort Worth **(G-7151)**

AUTOMOTIVE SVCS, EXC REPAIR: Carwash, Self-Service

Southwest Prof Vehicles ....F 214 371-3474
Dallas **(G-4992)**

AUTOMOTIVE SVCS, EXC REPAIR: Washing & Polishing

MI T Fine Car Wash Inc ....E 972 422-0707
Plano **(G-16926)**

Stinger Chemical LLC ....D 713 227-1340
Houston **(G-12067)**

Vizza Wash Services LLC ....E 512 246-8822
Round Rock **(G-17698)**

AUTOMOTIVE SVCS, EXC RPR/CARWASHES: High Perf Auto Rpr/Svc

Homestead Heritage ....E 254 754-9665
Waco **(G-20416)**

AUTOMOTIVE TOWING SVCS

Hight Marine Products Inc ....G 817 431-4569
Fort Worth **(G-6698)**

AUTOMOTIVE TRANSMISSION REPAIR SVC

Grooms & Grooms Inc ....G 806 358-8119
Amarillo **(G-490)**

Rays Chmpn Spring & Mtr Svc ....E 817 921-3600
Fort Worth **(G-6943)**

Standard Motor Products Inc ....C 972 316-8100
Lewisville **(G-14094)**

AUTOMOTIVE WELDING SVCS

Ace Welding and Trailer Co ....E 210 667-1171
San Antonio **(G-17858)**

Houston Truck Tarps LLC ....F 346 571-1832
Houston **(G-10259)**

Laserweld Inc ....E 713 333-0804
Katy **(G-13422)**

Prime Downhole Mfg LLC ....E 832 957-3200
Houston **(G-11413)**

Sb Southern Welding LLC ....E 469 517-0410
Joshua **(G-13325)**

Solansky Welding and Pump Inc ....E 830 374-3318
Crystal City **(G-3757)**

AUTOMOTIVE: Bodies

Harwood Industries Inc ....E 903 566-6001
Tyler **(G-20094)**

Lcw Automotive Corp ....D 210 732-5466
San Antonio **(G-18239)**

Toyoda Gsei Brwnsvlle Txas LLC ......F 956 290-8802
Los Indios **(G-14350)**

AUTOMOTIVE: Seat Frames, Metal

Complete Tchncal Rprsnttion In ....E 972 621-1111
Carrollton **(G-2718)**

Fleming & Son Corporation ....E 972 263-1713
Grand Prairie **(G-7873)**

AUTOMOTIVE: Seating

Clarios ....D 254 774-9287
Temple **(G-19676)**

Clarios ....D 817 733-4326
Fort Worth **(G-6522)**

Clarios ....C 281 518-8053
Houston **(G-9208)**

Fleming & Son Corporation ....E 972 263-1713
Grand Prairie **(G-7873)**

Johnson Controls Inc ....F 281 821-0121
Houston **(G-10483)**

Llebroc Industries Inc ....E 817 831-3158
Fort Worth **(G-6791)**

Pan Inc ....E 713 589-6850
Houston **(G-11228)**

Ultra Seating Company ....F 469 865-2010
Grand Prairie **(G-7989)**

AUTOTRANSFORMERS: Electric

Panda-Brandywine L P ....E 972 980-7159
Dallas **(G-4785)**

AVIATION PROPELLER & BLADE REPAIR SVCS

Pratt & Whitney Eng Svcs Inc ....B 972 343-1300
Grand Prairie **(G-7952)**

AWNING REPAIR SHOP

Southwest Canvas Mfg Co ....F 806 747-0201
Lubbock **(G-14484)**

AWNINGS & CANOPIES

Awntech Corporation ....E 817 354-9600
Euless **(G-6132)**

Presidio Custom Metal Works ....F 512 284-8549
Round Rock **(G-17682)**

AWNINGS & CANOPIES: Awnings, Fabric, From Purchased Matls

American Canvas Products Inc ....F 817 429-3108
Fort Worth **(G-6378)**

C H V Corporation ....F 713 526-1347
Houston **(G-9029)**

Centex Manufacturing Co ....F 254 752-2531
Waco **(G-20379)**

Coronet Enterprises Inc ....E 214 630-1116
Dallas **(G-4170)**

Hendee Enterprises Inc ....D 713 796-2322
Houston **(G-10153)**

Marygrove Awning LLC ....E 713 697-0156
Houston **(G-10782)**

Matson Inc ....E 817 478-1800
Fort Worth **(G-6818)**

Plumlee Place LLC ....F 254 662-4021
Robinson **(G-17501)**

Sign & Awning Services Inc ....E 817 926-7270
Fort Worth **(G-6987)**

Southwest Canvas Mfg Co ....F 806 747-0201
Lubbock **(G-14484)**

Victory Awning Inc ....E 817 759-1600
Fort Worth **(G-7104)**

AWNINGS & CANOPIES: Canopies, Fabric, From Purchased Matls

Tent Company LLC ....F 832 623-8958
Houston **(G-12204)**

AWNINGS & CANOPIES: Fabric

Awntech Corporation ....E 817 354-9600
Euless **(G-6132)**

Corradi USA Inc ....E 972 466-0721
Carrollton **(G-2860)**

Double C Canvas & Repairs Inc ....G 972 723-8000
Midlothian **(G-15479)**

Houston Canvas and Awning Co ....E 713 789-8712
Houston **(G-10222)**

Inpro Fabrication Ltd ....F 817 926-5050
Forest Hill **(G-6297)**

Jones Aluminum ....F 409 866-5585
Beaumont **(G-1913)**

Mike Sandone Productions Inc ....E 800 652-5635
Dallas **(G-4677)**

Modern Shade LLC ....E 512 385-4100
Austin **(G-1349)**

Richmonds American Svc Ctr Inc ....F 972 681-2222
McKinney **(G-14971)**

Roche Rouge Company L L C ....F 512 326-1670
Austin **(G-1469)**

AWNINGS: Fiberglass

Neon Electric Corporation ....D 281 987-1144
Houston **(G-11023)**

AWNINGS: Metal

A & E Venetian Blind Company ....F 940 767-1449
Wichita Falls **(G-20735)**

Sign & Awning Services Inc ....E 817 926-7270
Fort Worth **(G-6987)**

Texas Aluminum Industries Inc ....B 713 941-7186
Houston **(G-12220)**

AXLES

Horizon Global Americas Inc ....E 915 545-2720
El Paso **(G-5804)**

Northwest Drive Train Inc ....F 713 937-8499
Jersey Village **(G-13302)**

PRODUCT

Polar Corporation ....D....... 972 635-2464
Royse City (G-17722)
Techsys Chassis Inc ....E....... 903 395-4155
Paris (G-16371)

AXLES: Rolled Or Forged, Made In Steel Mills

Standard Forged Products LLC.........E....... 214 631-4420
Dallas (G-5003)

BABBITT (METAL)

Shaneda Machine Inc ....E....... 432 333-7083
Odessa (G-16152)

BABY FORMULA

Ajooo Inc ....F....... 469 494-7317
Dallas (G-3914)
Bristol-Myers Squibb Company ....E....... 212 546-4000
Houston (G-8986)
Lone Star Dairy Products LLC..........D....... 806 567-5623
Canyon (G-2673)

BACKHOES

Howard Keith Melton ....F....... 972 222-1900
Mesquite (G-15052)

BADGES, WHOLESALE

All Color Press Texas Inc ....F....... 214 744-2258
Dallas (G-3920)
Drsk Limited Partnership ....F....... 972 644-1490
Richardson (G-17302)

BADGES: Identification & Insignia

Big City Manufacturing Inc ....F....... 713 649-7769
Houston (G-8881)
D & W Nameplate Service Inc ....F....... 713 681-6616
Houston (G-9389)
Lonestar Badge & Sign Inc ....F....... 512 357-2261
Martindale (G-14810)

BAGS & CONTAINERS: Textile, Exc Sleeping

Kenneth Fox Supply Company.............C....... 956 682-6176
McAllen (G-14882)
McAllen Bag & Supply Company ....F....... 956 686-6571
McAllen (G-14887)

BAGS: Canvas

Kerick Industries ....F....... 214 432-2446
Dallas (G-4552)

BAGS: Cement, Made From Purchased Materials

Vhsc Cement LLC ....F....... 281 419-2422
The Woodlands (G-19938)

BAGS: Duffle, Canvas, Made From Purchased Materials

Athletic Bag Company LP ....E....... 903 520-3343
Tyler (G-20051)
Landes Inc ....E....... 713 665-0655
Houston (G-10593)

BAGS: Food Storage & Frozen Food, Plastic

Cardet Wholesale Inc.................D....... 713 266-9834
Brookshire (G-2312)
El Chilito Foods Inc ....F....... 512 391-0550
Austin (G-1118)
Reynolds Consumer Products LLC ....F....... 254 770-4100
Temple (G-19701)

BAGS: Garment, Plastic Film, Made From Purchased Materials

Starpak Plastics Inc ....D....... 713 329-9183
Houston (G-12049)

BAGS: Paper

Knight Corporation ....E....... 281 933-5363
Houston (G-10546)
Protective Packaging Corp Inc ....E....... 972 446-2247
Carrollton (G-2800)

Super Sack Bag Inc ....F....... 903 965-7713
Savoy (G-18741)
Westx Packaging Company ....F....... 806 686-4447
Lubbock (G-14511)

BAGS: Paper, Made From Purchased Materials

B & H Bag Company ....E....... 713 641-0921
Brookshire (G-2310)
C-L & Associates Inc ....E....... 903 831-4311
Wake Village (G-20485)
Tristar Packaging Inc ....F....... 281 540-2613
Humble (G-12806)

BAGS: Plastic

Berry Global Films LLC ....C....... 972 576-8193
Waxahachie (G-20529)
C-L & Associates Inc ....E....... 903 831-4311
Wake Village (G-20485)
Caraustar Industries Inc ....E....... 903 793-6231
Texarkana (G-19758)
Command Packaging LLC ....F....... 903 984-8596
Kilgore (G-13536)
Express Plastic Corporation.................F....... 713 664-9588
Houston (G-9732)
Global Entp Worldwide LLC.................F....... 713 260-9687
Houston (G-9972)
Houston Custom Packaging LLC..........E....... 713 827-1427
Houston (G-10227)
Houston D&J International Inc ....F....... 713 678-7888
Houston (G-10228)
Integrity Plastics Inc ....E....... 281 575-6688
Houston (G-10387)
Interglobal Plastics Inc.................F....... 713 672-6055
Houston (G-10395)
ITW Minigrip Inc ....C....... 830 372-4400
Seguin (G-18845)
Momentum Plastics LLC ....C....... 713 678-7741
Houston (G-10909)
Pactiv LLC ....G....... 254 770-4100
Temple (G-19693)
Phillips Smika Plyprpylene LLC ....C....... 832 813-4100
The Woodlands (G-19902)
Poly Sac Inc ....E....... 713 978-7888
Houston (G-11356)
Printpack Inc ....C....... 409 883-9325
Orange (G-16257)
Printpack Inc ....C....... 972 602-8421
Grand Prairie (G-7955)
Printpack Inc ....E....... 972 641-4421
Grand Prairie (G-7956)
Reynolds Presto Products Inc.............B....... 972 416-6500
Carrollton (G-2807)
Sealed Air Corporation ....D....... 940 592-2111
Iowa Park (G-12910)
Supplynet Inc ....E....... 484 582-1004
Dallas (G-5028)
Supplynet Inc ....D....... 214 637-0160
Dallas (G-5029)
Tyco International MGT Co LLC ....C....... 361 575-9565
Victoria (G-20312)
Tyr Usa LLC ....E....... 956 274-9380
Weslaco (G-20670)
Unistar Plastics LLC ....D....... 713 242-8377
Houston (G-12442)
Westlake Polymers LLC ....C....... 713 960-9111
Houston (G-12652)

BAGS: Plastic & Pliofilm

Global Empire Incorporated.................F....... 713 503-5545
Houston (G-9971)
Prince Plastics Inc ....E....... 281 240-6400
Sugar Land (G-19530)
Tristar Packaging Inc ....F....... 281 540-2613
Humble (G-12806)

BAGS: Plastic, Made From Purchased Materials

Advance Polybag (nevada) Inc.............F....... 702 642-1110
Sugar Land (G-19437)
Advance Polybag (texas) Inc ....E....... 713 580-4800
Sugar Land (G-19438)
Advance Polybag North East Inc..........F....... 410 796-8551
Sugar Land (G-19439)
Agribag Inc ....F....... 713 847-8008
Houston (G-8504)

American Film & Printing Ltd ....D....... 817 783-7600
Alvarado (G-323)
API Industries Inc ....C....... 845 365-2200
Sulphur Springs (G-19579)
Better Bags Inc ....E....... 713 864-8200
Houston (G-8866)
Continental Poly Inc ....E....... 281 277-6550
Sugar Land (G-19467)
Handgards LLC ....C....... 915 779-6606
El Paso (G-5794)
Hood Flexible Packaging Corp ....D....... 903 593-1793
Tyler (G-20100)
Novolex Inc ....C....... 972 686-5090
Dallas (G-4744)
Pro-Plastics Inc ....D....... 713 690-9000
Houston (G-11428)
Pro-Plastics Inc ....E....... 713 690-9000
Houston (G-11429)
Republic Mfg Group Inc ....D....... 713 847-7542
Houston (G-11602)
S & G Plastics Inc ....E....... 713 467-8766
Houston (G-11705)
Super Sack Bag Inc ....F....... 214 340-7060
Dallas (G-5024)
Superbag USA Corp ....B....... 713 462-1173
Houston (G-12108)
Superbag USA Corp ....C....... 713 462-1173
Houston (G-12109)
Texas Poly Inc ....E....... 817 540-2351
Euless (G-6162)
Titex Inc ....E....... 713 678-8890
Houston (G-12302)
Walming Inc ....E....... 713 690-9000
Houston (G-12596)
Winzen Film Inc ....E....... 214 340-7060
Dallas (G-5198)

BAGS: Pliofilm, Made From Purchased Materials

United Plastics Inc ....E....... 713 222-2186
Houston (G-12452)

BAGS: Rubber Or Rubberized Fabric

Advanced Rubber Molding Inc ....E....... 972 647-4040
Grand Prairie (G-7823)

BAGS: Textile

Bags Elite Inc ....E....... 972 279-7798
Mesquite (G-15029)
Flying Circle Bag Co ....E....... 830 249-2480
Boerne (G-2121)
Gulf Coast Bag Inc ....F....... 281 556-8500
Houston (G-10057)
Polytex Fibers Corp ....C....... 713 690-9055
Houston (G-11362)
Southast Vcational Aliance Inc.................D....... 713 847-0697
Houston (G-11969)

BAGS: Trash, Plastic Film, Made From Purchased Materials

Poly-America LP ....A....... 972 337-7100
Grand Prairie (G-7948)

BAGS: Vacuum cleaner, Made From Purchased Materials

Mosites Rubber Company Inc ....E....... 817 335-3451
Fort Worth (G-6854)

BAKERIES, COMMERCIAL: On Premises Baking Only

AB Mauri Food Inc.................E....... 903 454-3891
Greenville (G-8061)
Affiliated Foods Inc.................C....... 806 372-3851
Amarillo (G-476)
Bluebonnet Bakery Inc ....F....... 817 731-4233
Fort Worth (G-6458)
Bridgford Foods Corporation ....D....... 214 428-1535
Dallas (G-4051)
Brill Inc ....C....... 214 343-4816
Dallas (G-4055)
Cake Craft Factory LLC ....E....... 469 782-2500
Garland (G-7452)
Campbell Soup Company ....C....... 903 784-3341
Paris (G-16359)

Capt Nemos Steak Submarines............F 972 438-7777
  Irving *(G-12959)*

CH Guenther & Son LLC ....B 210 227-1401
  San Antonio *(G-17997)*

Churro Factory LLC ....G 214 566-5894
  Dallas *(G-4116)*

Dibella Baking Company LLC.............F 281 987-8985
  Houston *(G-9461)*

Empire Baking Company L P.................E 972 851-5677
  Dallas *(G-4320)*

Exquisita Tortillas Inc 956 383-3011
  Edinburg *(G-5587)*

Flowers Bakeries LLC...........................E 915 533-8434
  El Paso *(G-5771)*

Flowers Baking Co Denton LLC...........F 214 343-6796
  Dallas *(G-4371)*

Flowers Baking Co Tyler LLC ....F 903 758-2369
  Longview *(G-14236)*

Flowers Baking Co Tyler LLC ....C 903 677-2455
  Athens *(G-826)*

H & M Baking LLC................................G 713 568-5674
  Houston *(G-10079)*

H E Butt Grocery Company 956 702-2289
  Alamo *(G-179)*

Lone Star Bakery Inc ....B 210 648-6400
  China Grove *(G-3057)*

Mrs Bairds Bakeries Bus Tr ....B 800 355-1260
  Fort Worth *(G-6857)*

Pops Bakery Inc ....E 325 655-1170
  San Angelo *(G-17822)*

Reyniers French Bakery Inc ....F 972 401-3600
  Dallas *(G-4894)*

Round Rock Dnuts - Liberty LLC ....F 512 255-3629
  Round Rock *(G-17687)*

Sterling Bv Inc ....D 210 490-1669
  San Antonio *(G-18502)*

Sterling Foods LLC..............................C 210 490-1669
  San Antonio *(G-18503)*

Swiss Pastry Shop ....F 817 732-5661
  Fort Worth *(G-7025)*

Willow Bend Bakery Inc ....F 214 353-0889
  Dallas *(G-5190)*

BAKERIES: On Premises Baking & Consumption

Bairds Mrs Bakeries Bus Tr ....B 713 996-5000
  Houston *(G-8791)*

Campbell Soup Company ....C 903 784-3341
  Paris *(G-16359)*

Curse of Good Taste Inc ....F 512 327-9660
  Austin *(G-1078)*

Droubis Bakery & Deli Inc ....F 713 988-5897
  Houston *(G-9532)*

Flowers Baking Co Houston LLC ....F 713 869-5701
  Houston *(G-9812)*

H E Butt Grocery Company....................C 956 702-2289
  Alamo *(G-179)*

Pepperidge Farm Incorporated.............E 713 385-2010
  Houston *(G-11287)*

Praseks Hillje Smokehouse ....D 979 543-8312
  El Campo *(G-5626)*

Snow Flake Bakery ....E 281 427-4423
  Baytown *(G-1834)*

Upper Crust Bakery Inc ....E 512 467-0102
  Austin *(G-1614)*

BAKERY FOR HOME SVC DELIVERY

Spiral Diners..F 817 332-8834
  Fort Worth *(G-7012)*

BAKERY MACHINERY

Bakery Equipment & Svc Co Inc ....E 210 734-5124
  San Antonio *(G-17937)*

BAKERY PRDTS: Bagels, Fresh Or Frozen

New York Bagles Inc.............................E 713 723-5879
  Houston *(G-11038)*

BAKERY PRDTS: Bakery Prdts, Partially Cooked, Exc frozen

Epic Source Food Company LLC.........F 214 407-7154
  Frisco *(G-7283)*

James Skinner Co ....F 903 784-7174
  Paris *(G-16362)*

BAKERY PRDTS: Biscuits, Baked, Baking Powder & Raised

Bakeryworks LLC..................................E 972 250-1818
  Farmers Branch *(G-6190)*

Frito-Lay North America Inc ....B 214 331-7000
  Dallas *(G-4381)*

BAKERY PRDTS: Bread, All Types, Fresh Or Frozen

Ashcrft-Uropean Bky Ltd Partnr ....D 281 403-5040
  Stafford *(G-19287)*

Bimbo Bakeries Usa Inc ....A 903 785-6401
  Paris *(G-16358)*

Flowers Baking Co Tyler LLC ....C 903 595-2421
  Tyler *(G-20088)*

Flowers Bkg Co San Antonio LLC.........B 210 661-2361
  San Antonio *(G-18118)*

Marick Foods Inc.................................D 915 593-2271
  El Paso *(G-5867)*

BAKERY PRDTS: Buns, Bread Type, Fresh Or Frozen

Bryan Baking Inc.................................C 979 778-6600
  Bryan *(G-2461)*

Bryan Baking Company LLC ....B 979 778-6600
  Bryan *(G-2462)*

BAKERY PRDTS: Cakes, Bakery, Exc Frozen

Cheesecake Royale Inc ....E 214 328-9102
  Dallas *(G-4107)*

Kennymac LLC......................................F 214 732-4759
  Seagoville *(G-18801)*

Sterling Foods II Inc............................E 210 490-1669
  San Antonio *(G-18504)*

Sugar Krystles LLC ....F 817 368-6869
  Dallas *(G-5019)*

BAKERY PRDTS: Cakes, Bakery, Frozen

Quality Bakery Products Inc ....D 281 449-4977
  Houston *(G-11492)*

Sweet ....F 713 647-9338
  Houston *(G-12131)*

Whipped Up Inc....................................G 361 248-4639
  Corpus Christi *(G-3655)*

BAKERY PRDTS: Cookies

Ashcrft-Uropean Bky Ltd Partnr ....D 281 403-5040
  Stafford *(G-19287)*

Food Group Ventures LLC ....G 936 327-4443
  Livingston *(G-14153)*

Frito-Lay Inc ....B 972 334-7000
  Plano *(G-16873)*

Keebler Company ....E 817 868-2800
  Fort Worth *(G-6753)*

Lwc Brands Inc ....E 214 630-9101
  Dallas *(G-4613)*

Old Frito-Lay Inc ....A 972 334-7000
  Plano *(G-16953)*

Pepperidge Farm Incorporated.............E 713 385-2010
  Houston *(G-11287)*

Riviana Foods Inc ....C 713 529-3251
  Houston *(G-11629)*

Santte Labs LLC...................................F 832 585-1862
  Shenandoah *(G-18898)*

Southern Noodle Company ....F 281 988-7778
  Houston *(G-11976)*

Sterling Bv Inc ....D 210 490-1669
  San Antonio *(G-18502)*

Sterling Foods LLC..............................C 210 490-1669
  San Antonio *(G-18503)*

Sterling Foods II Inc............................E 210 490-1669
  San Antonio *(G-18504)*

BAKERY PRDTS: Cookies & crackers

Bluebonnet Bakery Inc ....F 817 731-4233
  Fort Worth *(G-6458)*

Campbell Soup Company ....C 903 784-3341
  Paris *(G-16359)*

Dgg Group LLC ....F 512 398-4523
  Lockhart *(G-14166)*

Hillarys Sweet Temptations Inc ....F 972 485-1005
  Garland *(G-7514)*

Mondelez Global LLC ....A 713 749-0400
  Houston *(G-10910)*

Pepsico Inc ....D 972 963-1000
  Plano *(G-16969)*

Tiffs Treats Rbd Inc ....E 512 614-3200
  Austin *(G-1579)*

Tifs Treats ....E 512 473-2600
  Austin *(G-1580)*

BAKERY PRDTS: Doughnuts, Exc Frozen

Ashley Donuts & Ice Cream Inc............F 281 486-5644
  Houston *(G-8719)*

C & K Management Co Inc ....F 713 774-7429
  Houston *(G-9025)*

Lua Br LLC..G 404 610-0118
  Austin *(G-1307)*

Merrills Southern Maid ....G 409 755-2400
  Lumberton *(G-14568)*

Ohara Valente 830 775-8769
  Del Rio *(G-5321)*

RC Donuts ....G 972 422-3379
  Plano *(G-16989)*

Rise n Shine Donuts ....F 806 745-5282
  Lubbock *(G-14473)*

Rock Island Donut Shop ....F 972 254-5069
  Irving *(G-13166)*

Shipley Do - Nuts ....F 281 499-5234
  Missouri City *(G-15593)*

Shipley Do-Nut Flour Sup Inc ....G 281 575-1766
  Houston *(G-11871)*

Shipley Do-Nut Flour Sup Inc ....G 713 728-9366
  Houston *(G-11872)*

Shipley Do-Nut Flour Sup Inc ....F 713 729-2381
  Houston *(G-11873)*

Simply Donuts ....F 281 955-6374
  Houston *(G-11904)*

BAKERY PRDTS: Dry

ABC Ingredients Corp ....F 972 602-2427
  Grand Prairie *(G-7819)*

CH Guenther & Son LLC ....B 210 227-1401
  San Antonio *(G-17997)*

Fxm International LLC ....F 832 886-0003
  Houston *(G-9880)*

BAKERY PRDTS: Frozen

Blue Ribbon Products Inc ....D 214 647-1825
  Rockwall *(G-17540)*

Fgf LLC ....E 210 475-9981
  San Antonio *(G-18111)*

Lawler Foods Ltd ....C 281 446-0059
  Humble *(G-12783)*

Lone Star Bakery Inc ....B 210 648-6400
  China Grove *(G-3057)*

Lone Star Bakery Inc ....C 210 648-6400
  China Grove *(G-3058)*

Newberry Bakers Inc ....D 281 987-8985
  Houston *(G-11039)*

Newberry Bakers Inc ....C 281 987-8985
  Houston *(G-11040)*

Pepperidge Farm Incorporated.............E 713 385-2010
  Houston *(G-11287)*

Pretzels Inc ....E 972 416-3660
  Carrollton *(G-2795)*

Rich Products Corporation ....F 281 835-7100
  Missouri City *(G-15590)*

Rich Products Corporation ....C 281 410-6600
  Missouri City *(G-15591)*

BAKERY PRDTS: Pies, Bakery, Frozen

Tootie Pie Company Inc ....D 210 737-6600
  Boerne *(G-2143)*

BAKERY PRDTS: Pretzels

Pretzels Inc ....E 972 416-3660
  Carrollton *(G-2795)*

BAKERY PRDTS: Rusk, Machine Made

Ellard John ....F 214 352-5946
  Dallas *(G-4314)*

BAKERY PRDTS: Sponge Goods, Bakery, Exc Frozen

Bakery Express Centl Texas LP ....D 972 221-8394
  Lewisville *(G-14025)*

PRODUCT

BAKERY PRDTS: Wholesalers

Droubis Bakery & Deli Inc ....F 713 988-5897
  Houston *(G-9532)*

Flowers Baking Co Houston LLC ....E 713 869-5701
  Houston *(G-9812)*

Lulus Dessert Corporation ....D 210 399-3767
  San Antonio *(G-18267)*

BAKERY: Wholesale Or Wholesale & Retail Combined

Adem Ruman Inc ....G 713 266-8584
  Houston *(G-8478)*

Bairds Mrs Bakeries Bus Tr ....B 713 996-5000
  Houston *(G-8791)*

Bayan Imports Inc ....E 972 437-1122
  Richardson *(G-17278)*

Bimbo Bakeries Usa Inc ....F 254 750-2500
  Waco *(G-20368)*

CCS Cupcake Heaven ....F 817 732-2993
  Fort Worth *(G-6499)*

David ....E 713 357-6393
  Houston *(G-9407)*

Dessert Dreams Inc ....E 972 313-2138
  Irving *(G-12996)*

Droubis Bakery & Deli Inc ....F 713 988-5897
  Houston *(G-9532)*

Fgf LLC ....A 210 475-9981
  San Antonio *(G-18110)*

Flowers Bakeries LLC ....E 361 814-0558
  Corpus Christi *(G-3532)*

Flowers Baking Co Denton LLC ....E 972 263-3363
  Grand Prairie *(G-7876)*

Flowers Baking Co Denton LLC ....C 940 383-5280
  Denton *(G-5366)*

Flowers Baking Co El Paso LLC ....F 915 533-8434
  El Paso *(G-5772)*

Flowers Baking Co Houston LLC ....E 713 869-5701
  Houston *(G-9812)*

Fr Hruska Store ....E 979 378-2333
  Ellinger *(G-6062)*

Fxm International LLC ....F 832 886-0003
  Houston *(G-9880)*

Hillarys Sweet Temptations Inc ....F 972 485-1005
  Garland *(G-7514)*

Lawler Foods Ltd ....C 281 540-3321
  Humble *(G-12784)*

Martech Foods Inc ....F 713 692-0077
  Houston *(G-10775)*

Mary and Megan Food Co LLC ....E 972 921-9618
  Dallas *(G-4642)*

Mary of Puddin Hill Inc ....F 903 455-2651
  Palestine *(G-16302)*

Mygis Empire LLC ....F 972 674-9758
  Arlington *(G-735)*

Pattty Brinlee ....F 940 600-0878
  Corinth *(G-3461)*

Round Rock Bakery Ltd ....F 512 255-3629
  Round Rock *(G-17686)*

Russells Bakery and Coffee Bar ....F 512 419-7877
  Austin *(G-1477)*

Souza Bakery ....F 214 631-0669
  Dallas *(G-4993)*

Three Brothers Bakery Inc ....F 713 666-2253
  Houston *(G-12283)*

Tootie Pie Company Inc ....D 210 737-6600
  Boerne *(G-2143)*

Upper Crust Bakery Inc ....E 512 467-0102
  Austin *(G-1614)*

Voss Catering Inc ....D 713 257-9898
  Bellaire *(G-2004)*

BALANCING SVC

Technos Inc ....E 210 651-9393
  Schertz *(G-18764)*

BALERS

K and M Manufacturing Co Inc ....E 512 352-2588
  Taylor *(G-19659)*

BALLASTS: Lighting

Philips North America LLC ....E 915 298-4111
  El Paso *(G-5910)*

BALLOONS: Novelty & Toy

M Patel Enterprises Inc ....E 512 892-2721
  Sunset Valley *(G-19626)*

BALLOONS: Rubber Laminated Metal Foil

Classic Balloon Corporation ....C 972 242-2711
  Dallas *(G-4127)*

BALLOONS: Toy & Advertising, Rubber

Continental American Corp ....C 214 630-3121
  Dallas *(G-4157)*

Gayla Industries Inc ....D 713 681-2411
  Houston *(G-9907)*

Spirit Industries Inc ....E 936 597-5144
  Montgomery *(G-15641)*

BALLS: Rubber, Exc Athletic

Baari Inc ....F 214 566-5165
  Plano *(G-16797)*

BANNERS: Fabric

Banner Supply Inc ....F 713 802-2225
  Houston *(G-8814)*

Design Center Signs Inc ....F 903 561-4995
  Tyler *(G-20075)*

Multi-Quest Inc ....F 972 235-2356
  Richardson *(G-17361)*

Powers Embroidery Inc ....D 254 754-2498
  Waco *(G-20448)*

BANQUET HALL FACILITIES

Delaney Vineyards Inc ....F 817 421-0950
  Grapevine *(G-8028)*

BAR

Brazos Valley Brewing Co LLC ....F 979 353-5361
  Brenham *(G-2244)*

Emerald Pt Marina Partners Ltd ....C 512 266-1535
  Austin *(G-1123)*

Patrick S Molak Corp ....F 830 606-0093
  New Braunfels *(G-15818)*

BAR FIXTURES: Wood

Liberty Company ....E 817 921-0218
  Fort Worth *(G-6788)*

BARBECUE EQPT

Brand Commercial Services Inc ....E 844 232-7263
  Lewisville *(G-14029)*

Burkhead Manufacturing Company ......E 713 227-5248
  Houston *(G-9019)*

Burris Custom Smokers & Grills ....F 806 893-3360
  Abernathy *(G-2)*

Circle J Fabrication Inc ....E 817 367-3877
  Fort Worth *(G-6519)*

Klose Cnstr & Fabrication ....F 713 686-8720
  Houston *(G-10541)*

Marsha Kitchens ....E 830 278-7262
  Uvalde *(G-20191)*

Sunbeam Products Inc ....E 830 774-4517
  Del Rio *(G-5325)*

TPC Acquisition Partners LP ....E 281 356-2168
  Pinehurst *(G-16736)*

Trampolines Usa Inc ....F 409 745-3139
  Orange *(G-16267)*

BARBER SHOPS

Jcjh LLC ....F 830 331-2240
  Boerne *(G-2124)*

BARGES BUILDING & REPAIR

Arcosa Inc ....C 972 942-6500
  Dallas *(G-3958)*

Arcosa Marine Products Inc ....C 214 631-4420
  Dallas *(G-3961)*

Gates Fuel Services LLC ....E 409 925-8897
  Santa Fe *(G-18734)*

Griffin Barge Line LLC ....E 713 560-6874
  Houston *(G-10043)*

Keppel Offshore & Mar USA Inc ....E 713 600-8371
  Houston *(G-10519)*

Mblh Marine LLC ....D 409 962-1302
  Port Arthur *(G-17118)*

San Jac Marine LLC ....C 281 862-9764
  Channelview *(G-3035)*

Trinity Industries Inc ....B 214 631-4420
  Dallas *(G-5112)*

West Gulf Marine Ltd ....D 409 744-0492
  Galveston *(G-7413)*

Western Towing Company ....E 713 435-1800
  Channelview *(G-3044)*

BARITE MINING

Barite Logistics LLC ....F 281 635-0584
  Seabrook *(G-18784)*

BARRICADES: Metal

Buyers Barricades Inc ....E 817 535-3939
  Grapevine *(G-8016)*

Cowtown Traffic Control Inc ....G 817 924-4524
  Fort Worth *(G-6553)*

Dallas Lite and Barricade Inc ....E 214 748-5791
  Dallas *(G-4218)*

Gibraltar Global LLC ....F 512 715-9650
  Marble Falls *(G-14743)*

Highway Barricades & Svcs LLC ....D 361 883-6300
  Corpus Christi *(G-3548)*

BARS & BAR SHAPES: Steel, Cold-Finished, Own Hot-Rolled

Harris Rebar ....E 936 258-8221
  Dayton *(G-5228)*

Interstate Fittings Inc ....D 214 637-6720
  Dallas *(G-4508)*

BARS & BAR SHAPES: Steel, Hot-Rolled

Commercial Metals Company ....F 830 372-8200
  Seguin *(G-18831)*

Structural Metals Inc ....A 830 372-8200
  Seguin *(G-18866)*

Texas Industries Inc ....D 817 838-4212
  Fort Worth *(G-7048)*

Vinton Steel LLC ....B 915 886-2000
  Vinton *(G-20342)*

BARS, COLD FINISHED: Steel, From Purchased Hot-Rolled

Confederate Steel Corporation ....F 713 643-8526
  Houston *(G-9269)*

Promicom Inc ....G 832 544-0855
  The Woodlands *(G-19906)*

BARS, PLATES & SHEETS: Zinc & Zinc Alloy Bars, Plates, Etc

US Zinc North America Inc ....C 713 926-1705
  Houston *(G-12494)*

US Zinc North America Inc ....D 713 926-1705
  Houston *(G-12495)*

US Zinc North America Inc ....E 713 926-1705
  Houston *(G-12496)*

BARS: Cargo, Stabilizing, Metal

Benchmark Completions LLC ....E 281 537-8483
  Spring *(G-19200)*

BARS: Concrete Reinforcing, Fabricated Steel

Adobe Fab Consultants Inc ....E 936 447-6400
  Conroe *(G-3253)*

Delzotto Products Texas Inc ....E 903 981-0400
  Gladewater *(G-7721)*

Effective Metal Services LLC ....F 832 962-8626
  Houston *(G-9584)*

Fortitude Specialty Mfg LLC ....D 713 465-3370
  Houston *(G-9839)*

Hogan Steel Erectors Inc ....E 409 883-8208
  West Orange *(G-20694)*

Ironforce Supply LLC ....F 713 681-5600
  Houston *(G-10421)*

Meridian Construction Services ....F 830 305-5700
  Kingsbury *(G-13620)*

Modern Machine Shop Inc ....D 956 722-4656
  Laredo *(G-13913)*

Omp Specialties Inc ....E 903 874-0045
  Corsicana *(G-3682)*

Rik-Mar Fabricators Inc ....F 979 779-1616
  Bryan *(G-2501)*

Slz Rebar LLC ....F 832 427-5860
  Cypress *(G-3820)*

Son-Lan Industries Inc ....G 972 937-8162
  Waxahachie *(G-20558)*

Spartan Reinforcing LLC ....E 832 271-1721
Houston (G-11994)
Steelway International LLC ....E 972 563-2000
Terrell (G-19752)
Tubal Cain Industries Inc ....D 409 786-1783
Vidor (G-20336)
Worldfab Inc ....F 281 446-9777
Humble (G-12807)

BARS: Iron, Made In Steel Mills

Conner Steel Products Inc ....B 325 655-8225
Houston (G-9271)
Lnc Fabrication LLC ....F 409 769-0403
Vidor (G-20329)

BASES, BEVERAGE

Bartush-Schnitzius Foods Co ....E 972 219-1270
Lewisville (G-14026)
Epic Bottling LLC ....E 512 947-8608
Coppell (G-3416)
Mooala Brands LLC ....F 214 206-1902
Dallas (G-4687)

BATCHING PLANTS: Aggregate Concrete & Bulk Cement

Gcc Permian LLC ....D 432 385-2800
Odessa (G-16012)
Hanson Aggregates LLC ....E 979 758-3662
Garwood (G-7614)
Xit Sand and Gravel LLC ....G 806 249-8743
Dalhart (G-3836)

BATH SHOPS

Knickerbocker Partition Corp ....F 972 438-5330
Irving (G-13078)
Royal Baths Mfg Co Ltd ....E 512 707-0094
Buda (G-2535)

BATHROOM ACCESS & FITTINGS: Vitreous China & Earthenware

Arrow Marble LLC ....D 832 467-4345
Houston (G-8705)

BATHROOM FIXTURES: Plastic

Venetian Marble Co Lubbock Inc ....E 806 763-5777
Lubbock (G-14506)

BATTERIES, EXC AUTOMOTIVE: Wholesalers

Exide Technologies LLC ....F 678 566-9000
The Woodlands (G-19863)
Grace IV Albert Thomas ....F 940 500-4323
Wichita Falls (G-20768)
Pharos Marine Autmtc Pwr Inc ....E 713 228-5208
Houston (G-11321)
Pronav Inc ....D 361 727-3300
Rockport (G-17532)

BATTERIES: Alkaline, Cell Storage

Vitzrocellusa Inc ....F 832 850-7095
Houston (G-12577)

BATTERIES: Dry

Panasonic Corp North America ....D 956 984-3700
Frisco (G-7305)

BATTERIES: Rechargeable

Otw-Ep Inc ....E 915 858-0448
Socorro (G-19017)
Zeta Energy LLC ....F 732 581-0838
Houston (G-12727)

BATTERIES: Storage

Battery Solutions Inc ....F 806 771-3777
Lubbock (G-14366)
Continental Battery Company ....D 214 631-5701
Dallas (G-4158)
Eestor Inc ....G 512 259-7601
Cedar Park (G-2967)
Enersys ....F 972 245-6601
Carrollton (G-2731)

Ereplacements LLC ....F 214 935-3591
Grapevine (G-8032)
Exide Technologies LLC ....F 972 633-6900
Irving (G-13018)
Exide Technologies LLC ....F 678 566-9000
The Woodlands (G-19863)
Ideal Power Inc ....F 512 264-1542
Austin (G-1219)
Integer Holdings Corporation ....D 214 618-5243
Plano (G-16892)
Panasonic Corp North America ....F 956 984-3700
Frisco (G-7305)
Southwest Elctronic Enrgy Corp ....D 281 240-4000
Missouri City (G-15595)
Spectrum Brands Inc ....D 214 778-4600
Garland (G-7589)
Triathlon Btry Solutions Inc ....E 469 301-2128
Lewisville (G-14099)

BATTERIES: Wet

CSB Energy Tech Americas Ltd ....E 817 244-7777
Haltom City (G-8135)
Grace IV Albert Thomas ....F 940 500-4323
Wichita Falls (G-20768)
Integer Holdings Corporation ....D 214 618-5243
Plano (G-16892)
OReilly Automotive Stores Inc ....F 936 856-2409
Willis (G-20857)
Southwest Elctronic Enrgy Corp ....D 281 240-4000
Missouri City (G-15595)
Spectrum Batteries Inc ....E 281 533-9735
Fulshear (G-7331)

BATTERY CHARGERS

Cooper Crouse-Hinds Mtl Inc ....C 281 571-8065
Houston (G-9306)
Englobal Constant Power Inc ....C 713 880-6200
Houston (G-9647)
Exide Technologies LLC ....E 281 443-0382
Houston (G-9724)
Exide Technologies LLC ....F 972 633-6900
Irving (G-13018)
Exide Technologies LLC ....F 210 662-8999
San Antonio (G-18099)
Exide Technologies LLC ....F 972 870-0337
Irving (G-13019)
Exide Technologies LLC ....F 678 566-9000
The Woodlands (G-19863)

BEARINGS

Odessa Babbitt Bearing Company ....E 432 366-2836
Odessa (G-16095)

BEARINGS & PARTS Ball

Westech Seal Inc ....F 432 367-1188
Odessa (G-16211)

BEARINGS: Ball & Roller

Gulf Coast Bearing & Seal Inc ....F 832 399-4227
Houston (G-10058)

BEAUTY & BARBER SHOP EQPT

Aloterra Energy LLC ....F 713 412-5311
The Woodlands (G-19823)
Austin Industries Inc ....B 512 288-1831
Austin (G-857)
Autistic Treatment Ctr ....E 972 644-2076
Dallas (G-3987)
Bartos Industries Ltd ....F 800 858-8497
Richland Hills (G-17436)
Bhc Industries of Texas Inc ....F 817 556-2306
Alvarado (G-325)
Bluestone Industries LLC ....E 469 916-8090
McKinney (G-14927)
C&S Lease Service LC ....E 903 988-8642
Kilgore (G-13534)
Dmi International Inc ....F 936 591-8006
Center (G-2997)
Eakin Industries LLC ....G 281 620-8625
Porter (G-17175)
Goodman Manufacturing Co LP ....F 936 372-5224
Waller (G-20501)
Gtx Technologies LLC ....F 806 367-7074
Amarillo (G-491)
Gulf Copper & Mfg Corp ....G 409 941-6200
Galveston (G-7399)

Hadlock & Fox Mfg Co L L C ....E 830 778-6017
Del Rio (G-5316)
Holicks Manufacturing Co LLC ....F 979 846-6721
Bryan (G-2477)
Howco Metals Management LLC ....C 281 649-8800
Houston (G-10268)
Isomeric Industries Inc ....F 678 713-4275
Spring (G-19222)
Lacore Labs Inc ....F 469 995-7791
Mckinney (G-14950)
Lawe Industries LLC ....F 210 833-9497
San Antonio (G-18238)
Loadcraft Industries Ltd ....F 325 597-1930
Brady (G-2215)
Luraco Inc ....E 817 633-1080
Arlington (G-725)
M&R Manufacturing LLC ....F 281 590-7200
Houston (G-10724)
Mustang Group Ltd ....F 830 968-0291
Eagle Pass (G-5550)
Mykytyn Enterprise Inc ....F 281 866-9263
Houston (G-10946)
Pacific Resources Intl LLC ....B 214 504-3853
McKinney (G-14962)
PCI Manufacturing LLC ....F 903 439-1080
Sulphur Springs (G-19595)
Peerless Mfg Co Inc ....F 972 559-6380
Denton (G-5391)
Prostar Manufacturing Inc ....F 936 585-0737
Pasadena (G-16500)
Shermco Industries Inc ....G 512 267-2324
Cedar Park (G-2985)
Siemens Industry Inc ....E 512 837-8300
Austin (G-1500)
Supply Solutions Inc ....D 214 766-6866
Plano (G-17015)
Tag Waterblock LLC ....E 281 862-0300
Channelview (G-3039)
Valtek Industries Inc ....F 432 339-8481
Odessa (G-16194)
Victaulic Company ....F 281 494-5000
Stafford (G-19395)

BEAUTY & BARBER SHOP EQPT & SPLYS WHOLESALERS

Chateau Noblesse Inc ....D 972 365-7017
Carrollton (G-2859)
Goodier Cosmetics LLC ....C 214 630-1803
Irving (G-13041)
Mykytyn Enterprise Inc ....F 281 866-9263
Houston (G-10946)

BEAUTY SALONS

Indochinese Culture Center ....F 713 522-7799
Houston (G-10343)
Revision LLC ....F 972 756-1026
Irving (G-13165)

BED & BREAKFAST INNS

Fredericksburg Brewing Company ....D 830 997-1646
Fredericksburg (G-7178)
Nueces Canyon Companies ....F 979 289-5600
Brenham (G-2266)

BED SHEETING, COTTON

Lauras Carousel Inc ....F 940 365-1875
Aubrey (G-850)

BEDDING, BEDSPREADS, BLANKETS & SHEETS

Childress Furniture & Fabr Inc ....D 214 565-0900
Addison (G-109)
Encompass Group LLC ....F 972 732-7694
Addison (G-120)
Ladds Corporation ....F 281 495-5200
Stafford (G-19343)
Peacock Alley Inc ....D 214 744-0399
Dallas (G-4793)
Shelbis Stuff Inc ....F 903 450-1300
Greenville (G-8091)
Techstyles Inc ....E 972 732-7694
Addison (G-167)

BEDDING, BEDSPREADS, BLANKETS & SHEETS: Comforters & Quilts

Tabors of San Angelo Inc ....E 325 942-1696
San Angelo (G-17830)

BEDS & ACCESS STORES

Cantwell Mattress Company ....F 361 883-8525
Corpus Christi (G-3496)

Deansteel Manufacturing Co ....C 210 226-8271
San Antonio (G-18046)

BEDS: Hospital

C H Industries Inc ....D 972 416-1304
Carrollton (G-2709)

Chiron Holdings Inc ....E 210 524-9000
San Antonio (G-18003)

Transitions Industries LLC ....F 806 698-6200
Lubbock (G-14497)

BEDS: Institutional

Kci International Inc ....E 210 524-9000
San Antonio (G-18219)

BEDSPREADS & BED SETS, FROM PURCHASED MATERIALS

Bronx Industries Inc ....G 713 467-6155
Houston (G-8994)

Tri-Tex Enterprises Inc ....E 214 744-1246
Dallas (G-5109)

BEDSPREADS, COTTON

Tri-Tex Enterprises Inc ....D 214 744-1246
Eastland (G-5569)

BEDSPREADS, FROM SILK OR MANMADE FIBER

Hc Interiors Inc ....E 214 350-0468
Carrollton (G-2754)

BEER & ALE, WHOLESALE: Beer & Other Fermented Malt Liquors

Gambrinus Company ....D 210 483-5100
San Antonio (G-18133)

Kristen Distributing Co ....E 979 775-6322
Bryan (G-2489)

Live Oak Brewing Company LLC ....E 512 385-2299
Del Valle (G-5332)

BEER, WINE & LIQUOR STORES

Big Buck Brewery & Steakhouse ....D 972 691-5100
Grapevine (G-8014)

BEER, WINE & LIQUOR STORES: Beer, Packaged

Guadalupe Brewing Company LLC ......G 512 878-9214
New Braunfels (G-15798)

BEER, WINE & LIQUOR STORES: Hard Liquor

Specs Family Partners Ltd ....F 713 669-1722
Houston (G-12005)

BEER, WINE & LIQUOR STORES: Wine

Delaney Vineyards Inc ....F 817 421-0950
Grapevine (G-8028)

Torr NA Lochs LLC ....F 832 606-7575
Burnet (G-2617)

Whistling Duck Vneyards Winery ....G 512 913-4813
Weimar (G-20653)

BEER, WINE & LIQUOR STORES: Wine & Beer

Fredericksburg Brewing Company ....D 830 997-1646
Fredericksburg (G-7178)

Live Oak Brewing Company LLC ....E 512 385-2299
Del Valle (G-5332)

BEESWAX PROCESSING

Juniper Specialty Products LLC ....F 346 310-6241
Pasadena (G-16466)

BELLOWS

Bellows Systems Inc ....F 281 721-2947
Houston (G-8854)

BELTING: Rubber

Eastex Rubber & Gasket Co ....F 409 727-6800
Nederland (G-15752)

BELTS & BELT PRDTS

Reliance Industries LLC ....E 281 930-8000
Deer Park (G-5290)

BELTS: Conveyor, Made From Purchased Wire

All-State Belting LLC ....F 713 433-1272
Houston (G-8371)

Conveyor Aggregate Pdts Corp ....E 214 358-5588
Dallas (G-4164)

US Rubber Corporation ....E 936 756-1977
Conroe (G-3380)

BELTS: Seat, Automotive & Aircraft

Joyson Safety Systems ....E 830 703-7191
Del Rio (G-5319)

Tk Holdings Inc ....D 210 509-0762
San Antonio (G-18552)

ZF Passive Safety US Inc ....F 956 632-8100
Pharr (G-16718)

ZF Passive Safety US Inc ....B 734 582-1139
El Paso (G-6043)

BENCHES, WORK : Factory

Onepointe Solutions LLC ....F 866 222-7494
Elgin (G-6056)

BENZENE

US Petrochemicals Inc ....F 713 871-1951
Houston (G-12487)

BEVERAGE BASES & SYRUPS

Collins Gold Label Inc ....G 972 960-7346
Addison (G-111)

ICEE Company ....F 713 937-9496
Houston (G-10313)

O D C L Inc ....F 940 566-9914
Denton (G-5385)

O D C L Inc ....E 956 565-3131
Mercedes (G-15009)

BEVERAGE POWDERS

John Hogan Interests Inc ....E 214 637-0214
Dallas (G-4537)

BEVERAGE PRDTS: Brewers' Grain

Texas Ingredient Corporation ....D 817 645-1328
Cleburne (G-3113)

BEVERAGE STORES

Cardet Wholesale Inc ....D 713 266-9834
Brookshire (G-2312)

Farmer Bros Co ....E 817 640-8111
Arlington (G-675)

Royal Cup Inc ....F 817 261-7527
Arlington (G-775)

BEVERAGES, ALCOHOLIC: Beer

Anheuser-Busch LLC ....C 713 670-1629
Houston (G-8644)

Anheuser-Busch LLC ....C 713 675-2311
Houston (G-8645)

Bluebonnet Beer Company LLC ....F 512 774-4258
Round Rock (G-17627)

Brazos Valley Brewing Co LLC ....F 979 353-5361
Brenham (G-2244)

C Villanueva Company LLc ....F 281 974-2361
Houston (G-9035)

Comeback Brewing Inc ....F 210 490-9128
San Antonio (G-18019)

Comeback Brewing II Inc ....D 210 490-9128
San Antonio (G-18020)

Deep Ellum Brewing Company LLC ......E 214 888-3322
Dallas (G-4245)

Fredericksburg Brewing Company ....D 830 997-1646
Fredericksburg (G-7178)

Gambrinus Company ....D 361 594-3383
Shiner (G-18940)

Gambrinus Company ....D 210 483-5100
San Antonio (G-18133)

Goliad Brewing Company Inc ....F 936 441-6100
Goliad (G-7747)

Guadalupe Brewing Company LLC ....G 512 878-9214
New Braunfels (G-15798)

Live Oak Brewing Company LLC ....E 512 385-2299
Del Valle (G-5332)

Lost Falls LLC ....F 737 300-1965
Austin (G-1303)

Manhattan Project LLC ....E 469 678-8870
Dallas (G-4631)

Miller Brewing ....E 817 551-3300
Fort Worth (G-6841)

Molson Coors Bev Co USA LLC ....C 214 618-7400
Plano (G-16932)

Molson Coors Bev Co USA LLC ....D 817 551-3300
Fort Worth (G-6847)

Pabst Brewing Company LLC ....E 210 299-6708
San Antonio (G-18361)

Saint Arnold Brewing Company ....G 713 686-9494
Houston (G-11731)

Southern Glazers Wine and Sp ....C 972 277-2000
Farmers Branch (G-6215)

Sway Water Inc ....F 512 693-7588
Austin (G-1551)

Treaty Oak Brewing Distlg LLC ....E 512 680-1606
Dripping Springs (G-5513)

BEVERAGES, ALCOHOLIC: Beer & Ale

Big Buck Brewery & Steakhouse ....D 972 691-5100
Grapevine (G-8014)

Lorelei Brewing Company LLC ....G 361 445-1084
Corpus Christi (G-3564)

Refresco Beverages US Inc ....D 817 359-4500
Fort Worth (G-6951)

BEVERAGES, ALCOHOLIC: Bourbon Whiskey

Tahwahkaro Distilling Co LLC ....G 479 871-2565
Grapevine (G-8056)

BEVERAGES, ALCOHOLIC: Cocktails

Barmac LLC ....G 903 454-3166
Greenville (G-8064)

Mpact Beverage Solutions LLC ....F 832 260-2342
Spring (G-19150)

BEVERAGES, ALCOHOLIC: Distilled Liquors

Azar Distilling LLC ....F 210 403-5142
San Antonio (G-17926)

Balcones Distilling LLC ....E 254 755-6003
Waco (G-20366)

Bendt Distilling LLC ....E 214 814-0545
Lewisville (G-14027)

BJ Hookers Distilleries LLC ....F 713 249-2022
Spring (G-19201)

C Villanueva Company LLc ....F 281 974-2361
Houston (G-9035)

Ckl Distilling LLC ....E 512 963-2373
Driftwood (G-5499)

Diageo North America Inc ....E 972 716-7700
Addison (G-117)

Firestone Robertson Distlg LLC ....E 817 840-9140
Fort Worth (G-6632)

Jbm Specialties LLC ....F 214 604-7646
Valley View (G-20203)

Riazul Imports LLC ....F 713 894-9177
Houston (G-11616)

Russian Spirit Inc ....F 214 334-3018
Dallas (G-4921)

Southwest Dist & Winery LLC ....F 214 440-4144
Dallas (G-4990)

Treaty Oak Brewing Distlg LLC ....E 512 680-1606
Dripping Springs (G-5513)

Trinity River Distillery LLC ....F 214 293-6011
Fort Worth (G-7077)

William Price Distlg Co LLC ....G 713 364-9225
Houston (G-12667)

BEVERAGES, ALCOHOLIC: Vodka

Buzzballz LLC ....D 972 242-3777
Carrollton **(G-2707)**
Spirited Cocktails Corporation ....F 512 256-0150
Austin **(G-1528)**

BEVERAGES, ALCOHOLIC: Wines

2018 Kidwell LLC ....E 214 824-9463
Dallas **(G-3864)**
Ambiente Opco LLC ....F 512 835-2299
Austin **(G-910)**
Augusta Vin LLC ....F 830 307-1007
Fredericksburg **(G-7170)**
Barons Creek Vineyards LLC ....F 830 304-3000
Fredericksburg **(G-7171)**
Bell Mountain Vineyards Inc ....G 830 685-3297
Willow City **(G-20870)**
Blue Ostrich Wineries LLC ....F 940 995-3100
Saint Jo **(G-17762)**
Bobby G Smith Do ....F 817 481-9463
Grapevine **(G-8015)**
Burke Texgals LLC ....F 210 344-9463
San Antonio **(G-17973)**
Cap Rock Winery Inc ....F 806 863-2704
Lubbock **(G-14388)**
Crossroads Winery ....G 817 421-2999
Grapevine **(G-8024)**
Delaney Vineyards Inc ....F 817 421-0950
Grapevine **(G-8028)**
Dionysus Group LLLP ....F 512 572-7000
Florence **(G-6239)**
Driftwood Estate Winery LLC ....F 512 692-6229
Driftwood **(G-5500)**
Future Proof Brands LLC ....E 512 790-9967
Austin **(G-1174)**
Gcv Enterprise LLC ....D 830 644-2710
Fredericksburg **(G-7180)**
Georgetown Winery LLC ....G 512 869-8600
Georgetown **(G-7652)**
Kuhlman Cellars LLC ....E 512 920-2675
Austin **(G-1275)**
La Bella Vida Inc ....F 806 744-3600
Lubbock **(G-14434)**
Llano Estacado Winery Inc ....E 806 745-2258
Lubbock **(G-14439)**
Lospinos Ranch Vineyards ....F 903 855-1769
Pittsburg **(G-16746)**
McPherson Cellars Inc ....F 806 687-9463
Lubbock **(G-14445)**
Messina Hof Wine Cellars Inc ....E 979 778-9463
Bryan **(G-2493)**
Patrick S Molak Corp ....F 830 606-0093
New Braunfels **(G-15818)**
San Martino Winery & Vineyards ......F 972 772-6043
Rockwall **(G-17565)**
Texas Hills Vineyard Inc ....F 830 868-2321
Johnson City **(G-13313)**
Texas Sthwind Vnyrd Winery LLC ....F 361 526-4662
Refugio **(G-17250)**
Torr NA Lochs LLC ....F 832 606-7575
Burnet **(G-2617)**
Wedding Oak Winery LLC ....F 325 372-4050
San Saba **(G-18721)**
Whistling Duck Vneyards Winery ....G 512 913-4813
Weimar **(G-20653)**
Woodrose Winery Inc ....F 830 644-2539
Stonewall **(G-19430)**
Yamhill Valley Vineyards Inc ....F 281 822-9463
Houston **(G-12713)**

BEVERAGES, NONALCOHOLIC: Bottled & canned soft drinks

Austin Coca-Cola Bottling Co ....D 979 543-2522
El Campo **(G-5611)**
Austin Coca-Cola Bottling Co ....E 512 832-2652
Austin **(G-953)**
Austin Coca-Cola Bottling Co ....E 713 799-7296
Houston **(G-8749)**
Austin Coca-Cola Bottling Co ....B 210 225-2601
San Antonio **(G-17923)**
Austin Coca-Cola Bottling Co ....E 409 899-5080
Beaumont **(G-1855)**
Austin Coca-Cola Bottling Co ....D 903 597-9325
Tyler **(G-20053)**
Austin Coca-Cola Bottling Co ....A 817 232-8600
Fort Worth **(G-6410)**
Austin Coca-Cola Bottling Co ....D 713 805-9722
Houston **(G-8750)**

Austin Coca-Cola Bottling Co ....E 512 836-0870
Austin **(G-954)**
Coca Cola Btlg Co of Southwest ....C 210 229-0555
San Antonio **(G-18015)**
Coca Cola Btlg of Shreveport ....C 214 902-2600
Dallas **(G-4134)**
Coca Cola Btlg of Shreveport ....D 956 632-3773
McAllen **(G-14849)**
Coca-Cola Bottling Co ....G 830 775-8561
Del Rio **(G-5313)**
Coca-Cola Company ....D 281 302-4317
Sugar Land **(G-19459)**
Coca-Cola Company ....B 817 847-3000
Fort Worth **(G-6526)**
Coca-Cola Company ....C 713 799-7332
Houston **(G-9234)**
Coca-Cola Company ....C 214 351-4797
Dallas **(G-4135)**
Coca-Cola Company ....D 254 666-5500
Waco **(G-20388)**
Coca-Cola Enterprises ....E 817 232-8600
Fort Worth **(G-6527)**
Coca-Cola Enterprises Bottling ....C 214 253-5747
Dallas **(G-4136)**
Coca-Cola Refreshments USA Inc ......E 903 893-0194
Sherman **(G-18911)**
Coca-Cola Refreshments USA Inc ......F 800 438-2653
Sugar Land **(G-19460)**
Coca-Cola Refreshments USA Inc ......D 214 253-5600
Dallas **(G-4137)**
Coca-Cola Refreshments USA Inc ......D 281 452-7635
Channelview **(G-3016)**
Coca-Cola Refreshments USA Inc ......E 325 672-3232
Abilene **(G-33)**
Coca-Cola Refreshments USA Inc ......D 903 276-1295
Texarkana **(G-19759)**
Coca-Cola Refreshments USA Inc ......D 806 324-5300
Amarillo **(G-417)**
Coca-Cola Refreshments USA Inc ......E 806 472-3200
Lubbock **(G-14395)**
Coca-Cola Refreshments USA Inc ......D 325 437-5000
Abilene **(G-34)**
Coca-Cola Refreshments USA Inc ......D 940 720-3907
Wichita Falls **(G-20755)**
Coca-Cola Southwest Bevs LLC ....C 214 902-2600
Dallas **(G-4138)**
Coca-Cola Southwest Bevs LLC ....B 214 388-6000
Dallas **(G-4139)**
Dr Ppper Btlg Wichita FLS Inc ....D 940 322-5416
Wichita Falls **(G-20760)**
Ewb International Inc ....F 972 764-5252
Addison **(G-122)**
H2eco Bulk LLC ....F 713 812-8400
Houston **(G-10087)**
Heyday Beverage Company LLC ....F 512 387-2399
Austin **(G-1201)**
Laredo Coca-Cola Bottling Co ....C 956 726-2671
Laredo **(G-13905)**
Laredo Coca-Cola Bottling Co ....F 361 693-4200
Corpus Christi **(G-3562)**
Laredo Coca-Cola Bottling Co ....C 956 686-8827
McAllen **(G-14884)**
Lufkin Coca Cola Bottling Co ....D 936 639-2355
Lufkin **(G-14536)**
Magnolia Coca-Cola Bottling Co ....E 915 593-2653
El Paso **(G-5859)**
Marsmith Enterprises Inc ....F 972 488-9339
Dallas **(G-4638)**
Mason Bottling Company ....F 325 347-5150
Mason **(G-14815)**
Nacogdoches Coca Cola Btlg Co ....D 936 564-0268
Nacogdoches **(G-15704)**
Odwalla Inc ....G 281 925-0189
Houston **(G-11134)**
Pepsi-Cola Metro Btlg Co Inc ....E 903 892-3030
Sherman **(G-18926)**
Pepsico Inc ....D 972 963-1000
Plano **(G-16969)**
Pickle Juice Company ....F 972 755-0289
Mesquite **(G-15071)**
Quaker Oats Company ....C 214 333-1200
Dallas **(G-4842)**
Rocky Mountain High Brands Inc ......G 800 260-9062
Plano **(G-16995)**
Ruiz Distributing Co ....F 713 682-7008
Houston **(G-11696)**
Son Beverage Company ....F 210 733-7761
San Antonio **(G-18482)**
Texas Natural Rainwtr Hrvstng ....F 512 772-1981
Smithville **(G-18978)**

BEVERAGES, NONALCOHOLIC: Carbonated

Ab-Tex Beverage Ltd ....E 325 655-9588
San Angelo **(G-17769)**
Dr Pepper/Seven Up Inc ....C 979 532-8801
Wharton **(G-20699)**
Frito-Lay North America Inc ....A 972 334-7000
Plano **(G-16874)**
Oneta Company ....C 361 853-0123
Corpus Christi **(G-3585)**
P-Americas LLC ....E 361 853-0123
Corpus Christi **(G-3588)**
P-Americas LLC ....D 903 794-3883
Texarkana **(G-19770)**
Pepsi Beverages Company ....G 210 661-5311
San Antonio **(G-18369)**
Pepsi Bottling Company ....D 210 662-3418
San Antonio **(G-18370)**
Pepsi Bottling Group ....D 214 324-8500
Mesquite **(G-15069)**
Pepsi Cola Bottling Co Laredo ....E 956 722-9934
Laredo **(G-13920)**
Pepsi Cola Sales & Dist ....G 909 472-4060
Grand Prairie **(G-7945)**
Pepsi Logistics Company Inc ....C 972 963-1920
Plano **(G-16967)**
Pepsi-Cola Bottling Group ....E 254 953-7433
Killeen **(G-13616)**
Pepsi-Cola Metro Btlg Co Inc ....E 409 842-2111
Beaumont **(G-1939)**
Pepsi-Cola Metro Btlg Co Inc ....D 817 640-4445
Arlington **(G-750)**
Pepsi-Cola Metro Btlg Co Inc ....C 210 661-5311
San Antonio **(G-18371)**
Pepsi-Cola Metro Btlg Co Inc ....E 979 779-6324
Bryan **(G-2497)**
Pepsi-Cola Metro Btlg Co Inc ....E 806 745-7711
Lubbock **(G-14460)**
Pepsi-Cola Metro Btlg Co Inc ....D 972 801-1730
Plano **(G-16968)**
Pepsi-Cola Metro Btlg Co Inc ....C 713 645-4111
Houston **(G-11288)**
Pepsi-Cola Metro Btlg Co Inc ....E 817 625-4101
Fort Worth **(G-6901)**
Pepsi-Cola Metro Btlg Co Inc ....D 936 522-4400
Conroe **(G-3348)**
Pepsi-Cola Metro Btlg Co Inc ....E 806 372-8717
Amarillo **(G-452)**
Pepsi-Cola Metro Btlg Co Inc ....G 915 590-6965
El Paso **(G-5908)**
Pepsi-Cola Sales and Dist Inc ....D 817 640-4445
Arlington **(G-751)**
Pepsico Inc ....D 972 334-4140
Plano **(G-16970)**

BEVERAGES, NONALCOHOLIC: Carbonated, Canned & Bottled, Etc

Beer Dudes Canning Co LLC ....F 972 342-4819
Denton **(G-5353)**
Birch B LLC ....F 646 942-8058
Houston **(G-8889)**
Dps Holdings Inc ....E 972 673-7000
Plano **(G-16848)**
Global Dispense ....F 210 310-2337
San Antonio **(G-18146)**
International Beverage Inc ....F 956 727-2995
Laredo **(G-13897)**
Refresco Beverages US Inc ....C 210 333-4310
San Antonio **(G-18418)**
Rhino Rush 3gs LLC ....F 817 793-9400
Sachse **(G-17734)**
Sunny Sky Products LLC ....D 713 683-9399
Houston **(G-12102)**
Temple Bottling Company Ltd ....G 979 778-1203
Bryan **(G-2510)**

BEVERAGES, NONALCOHOLIC: Flavoring extracts & syrups, nec

Adams Flvors Fods Ingrdnts LLC ......C 830 672-1850
Gonzales **(G-7748)**
Agrana Fruit Us Inc ....D 817 625-9053
Fort Worth **(G-6355)**
American Bottling Company ....D 713 799-1024
Houston **(G-8590)**
Bcw Food Products Inc ....E 214 350-3320
Dallas **(G-4010)**
Chemicals Incorporated ....D 281 576-5000
Baytown **(G-1813)**

PRODUCT

Coca-Cola Company ....C 214 351-4797
Dallas (G-4135)
Consolidated Mills Inc ....E 713 896-4196
Houston (G-9276)
Dr Pepper/Seven Up Inc ....B 972 673-7000
Plano (G-16850)
Flotek Industries Inc ....E 713 849-9911
Houston (G-9806)
Illes Food Ingredients Ltd ....D 800 683-4553
Carrollton (G-2764)
North American Beverages Ltd ....F 512 501-3890
Austin (G-1368)
Pepsico Inc ....D 972 963-1000
Plano (G-16969)
Ricos Products Co Inc ....C 210 222-1415
San Antonio (G-18426)
Solvay USA Inc ....C 325 515-7609
Snyder (G-19009)
Solvay USA Inc ....D 940 552-9911
Vernon (G-20230)
TJ Blackburn Syrup Works Inc ....D 903 665-2541
Jefferson (G-13289)

BEVERAGES, NONALCOHOLIC: Fruit Drnks, Under 100% Juice, Can

Mountain Pure TX LLC ....E 903 723-1362
Palestine (G-16304)
Smoothie King ....G 214 469-1552
The Colony (G-19814)
Tropical Fusions Inc ....E 830 203-5116
Gonzales (G-7765)

BEVERAGES, NONALCOHOLIC: Soft Drinks, Canned & Bottled, Etc

Ab-Tex Beverage Ltd ....E 830 775-1543
Del Rio (G-5304)
Ab-Tex Beverage Ltd ....C 325 673-7171
Abilene (G-3)
Ab-Tex Beverage Ltd ....E 956 722-9934
Laredo (G-13853)
Ab-Tex Beverage Ltd ....E 940 322-5416
Wichita Falls (G-20736)
American Bottling Company ....D 956 423-2705
Harlingen (G-8180)
American Bottling Company ....C 210 662-4400
San Antonio (G-17902)
American Bottling Company ....D 512 385-4477
Austin (G-915)
American Bottling Company ....D 972 579-1024
Irving (G-12928)
American Bottling Company ....E 903 893-6536
Sherman (G-18906)
American Bottling Company ....C 254 412-1900
Waco (G-20360)
American Bottling Company ....C 972 721-8197
Irving (G-12929)
American Bottling Company ....E 214 330-0491
Dallas (G-3938)
American Bottling Company ....D 361 851-9977
Corpus Christi (G-3472)
American Bottling Company ....D 713 799-1024
Houston (G-8590)
American Bottling Company ....E 409 842-6061
Beaumont (G-1851)
American Bottling Company ....E 903 874-5666
Corsicana (G-3660)
American Bottling Company ....C 972 673-7000
Plano (G-16785)
Beaumont Coca-Cola Bottling Co ....C 409 899-5080
Beaumont (G-1860)
Big Red Inc ....G 713 791-9886
Houston (G-8884)
Dr Pepper Snpple Group Emplyee ....C 972 673-7000
Plano (G-16849)
Dublin Bottling Works Inc ....E 254 445-3939
Dublin (G-5515)
Kalil Bottling Co ....E 915 778-4413
El Paso (G-5825)
Old Frito-Lay Inc ....A 972 334-7000
Plano (G-16953)
Pepsi-Cola Metro Btlg Co Inc ....F 361 575-2661
Victoria (G-20294)
Pepsi-Cola Metro Btlg Co Inc ....B 214 324-8500
Mesquite (G-15070)
Pepsi-Cola Metro Btlg Co Inc ....E 979 836-3755
Brenham (G-2268)
Pepsi-Cola Metro Btlg Co Inc ....E 361 798-3651
Hallettsville (G-8124)

Shasta Beverages Inc ....E 713 634-0094
Houston (G-11847)
Southwest Canners Texas Inc ....D 936 569-9737
Nacogdoches (G-15714)
Temple Bottling Company Ltd ....D 254 773-3376
Temple (G-19706)

BEVERAGES, NONALCOHOLIC: Tea, Iced, Bottled & Canned, Etc

Live Soda LLC ....F 512 888-9959
Austin (G-1295)

BEVERAGES, WINE & DISTILLED ALCOHOLIC, WHOLESALE: Wine

C K Higgs ....E 713 666-5739
Bellaire (G-1992)
Torr NA Lochs LLC ....F 832 606-7575
Burnet (G-2617)

BIBLE SCHOOL

Trinity Fellowship ....C 806 355-8955
Amarillo (G-515)

BICYCLE SHOPS

McAllen Sports Inc ....E 956 687-5500
McAllen (G-14889)

BICYCLES, PARTS & ACCESS

Bell Sports Corp ....E 469 417-6600
Irving (G-12946)
Fallbrook Technologies Inc ....E 512 714-1964
Leander (G-13990)

BILLIARD & POOL TABLES & SPLYS

Owen-Bunnell Inc ....F 972 578-9100
Plano (G-16960)
Presidential Billiards LP ....F 281 572-4733
New Caney (G-15847)

BILLING & BOOKKEEPING SVCS

Kpt Inc ....D 214 620-9700
Coppell (G-3427)

BINDING SVC: Books & Manuals

Alliance Press Leasing Inc ....E 713 957-3349
Houston (G-8546)
ARC Document Solutions LLC ....B 713 988-9200
Houston (G-8678)
ARC Document Solutions LLC ....F 713 787-1244
Houston (G-8679)
Beeville Publishing Company ....E 361 358-2550
Beeville (G-1984)
Bookbinding & Laminating Spc ....F 806 785-1126
Lubbock (G-14378)
Brenholb Inc ....E 210 349-4024
San Antonio (G-17965)
Brunswick Press Inc ....E 713 462-0600
Houston (G-9000)
Business Printing Inc ....F 214 445-5000
Carrollton (G-2706)
Capital Printing LLC ....D 512 442-1415
Austin (G-1027)
Central Texas Printing Inc ....E 254 754-4653
Waco (G-20381)
Cenveo Worldwide Limited ....C 210 923-7591
San Antonio (G-17994)
Cenveo Worldwide Limited ....D 806 376-4347
Amarillo (G-414)
Clear Visions Inc ....D 210 496-6006
San Antonio (G-18012)
Cloud Printing Co of Abilene ....G 325 676-9396
Abilene (G-32)
Cockrell Printing Co ....D 817 336-0571
Fort Worth (G-6528)
Company Printing ....F 325 949-9941
San Angelo (G-17788)
Curry Printing Ltd ....E 817 540-5252
Euless (G-6139)
Easy Print Inc ....E 806 374-7711
Amarillo (G-421)
Fedex Office & Print Svcs Inc ....E 210 821-6911
San Antonio (G-18107)
Fedex Office & Print Svcs Inc ....E 713 977-2666
Houston (G-9773)

Fedex Office & Print Svcs Inc ....E 512 476-3242
Austin (G-1150)
Fedex Office & Print Svcs Inc ....F 806 359-9684
Amarillo (G-488)
Fedex Office & Print Svcs Inc ....F 281 463-8433
Houston (G-9775)
Fedex Office & Print Svcs Inc ....F 713 521-9465
Houston (G-9772)
Fedex Office & Print Svcs Inc ....E 254 776-7763
Waco (G-20401)
Fedex Office & Print Svcs Inc ....E 512 452-3600
Austin (G-1152)
Fedex Office & Print Svcs Inc ....E 817 543-0833
Arlington (G-678)
Finishing & Mailing Center LLC ....E 214 747-6244
Dallas (G-4362)
Gainesville Printing Co Inc ....E 940 665-5517
Gainesville (G-7344)
Grafikshop Corporation ....E 713 977-2555
Houston (G-10012)
Graphic Image Inc ....E 563 285-5214
Flower Mound (G-6267)
Hewell Enterprises Inc ....E 972 466-2442
Carrollton (G-2869)
J M H Printing Company ....E 972 263-1226
Grand Prairie (G-7899)
K & T Printing Inc ....E 281 988-8088
Houston (G-10494)
Kenner Co Inc ....F 432 333-1921
Odessa (G-16046)
L C Colormark ....D 972 243-1919
Carrollton (G-2773)
Lebco Graphics Inc ....E 830 755-8226
Boerne (G-2126)
Lithographics Inc ....G 210 226-1722
San Antonio (G-18255)
Odee Company ....E 214 340-0415
Dallas (G-4754)
Premier Printing & Ltr Svc Inc ....E 713 868-6300
Houston (G-11404)
Quadrangle Press Inc ....E 210 828-8191
San Antonio (G-18405)
Quality Hand Bindery Inc ....F 281 445-8682
Houston (G-11494)
Rapid Reprographics LP ....F 214 357-5444
Coppell (G-3437)
Reynolds Brothers Ltd ....E 432 682-7393
Midland (G-15383)
S P (texas) Inc ....G 713 666-5166
Houston (G-11712)
Simon Printing Company ....E 713 666-1296
Houston (G-11902)
Spartan Printing Inc ....E 817 640-6341
Arlington (G-784)
Thomas Reprographics Inc ....D 210 829-7000
San Antonio (G-18548)
TNT Printing ....G 281 449-9090
Houston (G-12315)
Transfer Graphics Inc ....F 940 566-2679
Denton (G-5407)

BINDING SVC: Trade

Seidls Bindery Inc ....E 713 681-3815
Houston (G-11814)

BINGO HALL

Brown and Anthony Inc ....F 806 762-1975
Lubbock (G-14384)

BINS: Prefabricated, Metal Plate

Entrans International LLC ....E 281 459-5350
Houston (G-9665)
Fabcorp Inc ....E 713 466-3962
Houston (G-9746)
Kohlhaas Corporation ....E 915 778-5357
El Paso (G-5831)
R & N Manufacturing Ltd ....D 713 466-6252
Cypress (G-3817)

BIOLOGICAL PRDTS: Blood Derivatives

Csl Plasma Inc ....E 972 329-0186
Dallas (G-4188)
Immunotek Bio Centers LLC ....E 432 307-6774
Odessa (G-16029)
Immunotek Bio Centers LLC ....E 806 310-2859
Amarillo (G-438)
Immunotek Bio Centers LLC ....E 214 453-2748
Dallas (G-4492)

Immunotek Bio Centers LLC ....F 404 345-3570
Dallas (G-4493)
Immunotek Bio Centers LLC ....F 404 345-3570
Bedford (G-1975)

BIOLOGICAL PRDTS: Exc Diagnostic

Aeglea Development Company Inc ....F 512 942-2935
Austin (G-897)
Ambion Inc ....C 512 651-0200
Austin (G-911)
American Animal Health Inc ....F 972 641-5420
Grand Prairie (G-7829)
Assure Labs Inc ....D 713 561-5529
Houston (G-8728)
Bellicum Pharmaceuticals Inc ....D 832 384-1100
Houston (G-8853)
Cone Bioproducts Seguin LLC ....F 830 379-0197
Seguin (G-18832)
Dnatrix Inc ....F 832 930-2401
Houston (G-9489)
Ecm Biosurgery Inc ....F 281 229-0348
Houston (G-9574)
Fujifilm Diosynth Biotechnolog ....F 979 431-3500
College Station (G-3183)
International Lab Sup Ltd ....E 281 298-9410
Spring (G-19218)
Matica Biotechnology Inc ....F 979 321-7500
College Station (G-3192)
Micro-Tes Inc ....F 210 558-4757
San Antonio (G-18300)
Peloton Therapeutics Inc ....D 972 629-4100
Dallas (G-4795)
Qualtex Laboratories ....E 210 736-8952
San Antonio (G-18406)
Santa Cruz Biotechnology Inc ....C 214 902-3900
Dallas (G-4933)
Sigma-Genosys of Texas LLC ....C 281 363-3693
Spring (G-19250)
Vax-Immune LLC ....F 832 423-0055
Houston (G-12540)

BIOLOGICAL PRDTS: Vaccines

American Animal Health Inc ....F 817 293-6363
Grand Prairie (G-7828)
Astrotech Corporation ....G 512 485-9530
Webster (G-20633)
Caliber Biotherapeutics LLC ....E 979 314-7740
Bryan (G-2465)

BIOLOGICAL PRDTS: Vaccines & Immunizing

Imunize El Paso ....F 915 857-2474
El Paso (G-5811)
SKW Alliance Med LLC ....G 972 358-5171
Carrollton (G-2888)

BIOLOGICAL PRDTS: Veterinary

DSM Nutritional Products LLC ....F 979 373-5010
Freeport (G-7197)
Futursarch Trials Neurology LP ....F 512 380-9925
Austin (G-1175)
Vetoquinol USA Inc ....E 817 529-7500
Fort Worth (G-7098)
Wondercide LLC ....F 877 896-7426
Austin (G-1676)

BITUMINOUS LIMESTONE QUARRYING SVCS

Continental Quarries ....F 325 228-4180
Lueders (G-14517)

BLACKBOARDS & CHALKBOARDS

T R W Modernfold Company Inc ....F 214 357-2572
Lewisville (G-14096)

BLACKPLATE

Carols Mch & Fabrication Inc ....E 713 921-7266
Wharton (G-20698)

BLADES: Knife

Ddr Manufacturing Inc ....G 469 728-7242
Forney (G-6307)

BLANKBOOKS & LOOSELEAF BINDERS

AMA Printing / Finishing Inc ....E 254 776-8860
Waco (G-20359)
B and D Binder and Index Inc ....E 817 261-8227
Arlington (G-627)
Clarke Harland Corp ....D 210 697-8888
Houston (G-9210)
Data Print Ltd ....E 806 324-4350
Amarillo (G-420)
Firmin Business Forms Inc ....F 254 776-5742
Waco (G-20402)
JPS Alliance Inc ....F 817 534-0044
Fort Worth (G-6746)
Printegra Corp ....E 800 972-1175
Arlington (G-759)
Samsill Corporation ....C 817 536-1906
Fort Worth (G-6972)
Travis Assn For The Blind ....C 512 442-2329
Austin (G-1590)

BLANKBOOKS: Account

Thompson Business Forms Inc ....E 210 734-5356
San Antonio (G-18549)

BLANKBOOKS: Albums

Panini America Inc ....D 817 662-5300
Irving (G-13139)

BLANKBOOKS: Checkbooks & Passbooks, Bank

Vericast Corp ....D 210 697-8888
San Antonio (G-18591)

BLANKETS & BLANKETING, COTTON

Powers Embroidery Inc ....D 254 754-2498
Waco (G-20448)
Wmc Waco Holdings Inc ....E 254 753-7301
Waco (G-20479)

BLAST FURNACE & RELATED PRDTS

Mineraltech Gulf Coast Abr LLC ....E 832 838-8623
Highlands (G-8313)

BLAST SAND MINING

Specialty Sand Company ....G 979 234-7431
Eagle Lake (G-5543)
Specialty Sand Company Inc ....E 281 456-9553
Houston (G-12001)

BLASTING SVC: Sand, Metal Parts

Arrow Construction Co Inc ....E 325 573-3571
Snyder (G-18982)
F & W Industries Inc ....F 432 563-8895
Odessa (G-15997)
Genes Paul Enterprises Inc ....E 817 558-7868
Cleburne (G-3091)
Knight Industrial Services Inc ....C 281 421-5049
Baytown (G-1825)
P & M Blasting & Coating Inc ....F 713 896-4691
Houston (G-11212)
Riley Industrial Services Inc ....C 432 332-9630
Odessa (G-16141)
Trevinos Painting Inc ....E 956 571-3999
Edinburg (G-5604)
Trinity Powder Coating ....F 214 703-3609
Garland (G-7605)
West Ltd ....F 409 794-9090
Beaumont (G-1969)

BLINDS & SHADES: Mini

Piw Ventures Ltd ....F 713 932-9311
Houston (G-11340)
Yates Carpet Incorporated ....E 806 795-9942
Lubbock (G-14516)

BLINDS & SHADES: Vertical

Drapery Man Corporation ....E 210 733-5444
San Antonio (G-18071)
Plantation Shutter ....F 214 341-3677
Dallas (G-4809)
Springs Window Fashions LLC ....F 608 826-7052
Pharr (G-16711)
Tex Sun Manufacturing Co ....E 830 393-5186
Floresville (G-6251)

Texton Inc ....D 972 494-5941
Garland (G-7600)
Vertical Nerve Inc ....F 800 330-9450
Dallas (G-5164)

BLINDS : Window

Alpha Door and Rail Inc ....F 817 358-8687
Aurora (G-853)
Aramco Home Improvement LLC ....E 409 762-9652
Galveston (G-7387)
Custom Drapery Company Inc ....D 713 225-9221
Houston (G-9370)
K & S Products Inc ....F 972 820-0007
Carrollton (G-2772)
Ral & Associates Inc ....E 903 833-5191
Ben Wheeler (G-2034)
Tex-Sun Shade Specialties Inc ....F 972 279-0132
Dallas (G-5053)
Timber Blinds Mfg Ltd ....B 972 569-9100
McKinney (G-14982)

BLINDS, WOOD

American Eagle Enteprise ....F 972 494-3357
Garland (G-7434)
Custom Shutters Inc ....E 903 488-3224
Como (G-3248)
Ken Jordan Shutters Inc ....E 972 241-7776
Dallas (G-4549)
Shepherd Shutter Company Inc ....G 806 799-3458
Lubbock (G-14478)

BLOCK & BRICK: Sand Lime

Hmj Plastering LLC ....F 713 941-2807
Pasadena (G-16454)

BLOCKS & BRICKS: Concrete

Acme Brick Company ....E 512 255-2573
Elgin (G-6051)
Acme Brick Company ....D 512 281-5744
Elgin (G-6052)
Alamo Concrete Tile Inc ....E 210 534-8821
San Antonio (G-17883)
Arcosa Inc ....C 972 942-6500
Dallas (G-3958)
Big D Concrete Inc ....E 972 737-7976
Dallas (G-4023)
Brick Dudes LLC ....F 214 592-7904
Allen (G-258)
Cemex Inc ....B 713 650-6200
Houston (G-9120)
Headwaters Cnstr Mtls LLC ....C 713 393-3300
Alleyton (G-308)
Headwaters Incorporated ....F 713 393-3328
Alleyton (G-309)
Houston Products Proc Inc ....E 281 487-0766
Channelview (G-3026)
Innovative Block S Texas Ltd ....F 956 682-3181
McAllen (G-14873)
Innovative Block S Texas Ltd ....G 956 797-4200
La Feria (G-13691)
Justin Industries Inc ....D 817 332-4101
Fort Worth (G-6750)
Meridian Brick LLC ....E 830 980-7071
Schertz (G-18756)
Meridian Brick LLC ....D 940 325-9466
Mineral Wells (G-15532)
Metro Cutting and Sealing Inc ....E 972 434-8722
Lewisville (G-14066)
RMC Usa Inc ....F 713 650-6200
Houston (G-11637)
Southwest Concrete Products Co ....C 888 464-9341
Columbus (G-3233)
Trnlwb LLC ....G 800 581-3117
Arlington (G-805)

BLOCKS: Drystack Interlocking, Concrete

PC Calendar 2010 LLC ....E 214 491-5103
Dallas (G-4791)

BLOCKS: Landscape Or Retaining Wall, Concrete

Lonestar Landscape Dfw LLC ....F 817 863-5609
Forest Hill (G-6298)
Mason Fencing and Cnstr LLC ....E 432 272-8347
Odessa (G-16073)
Napco Precast LLC ....C 210 424-4371
San Antonio (G-18332)

PRODUCT

PSI Concrete Construction LLC ....F 210 204-1529
San Antonio (G-18400)

Trevway Inc ....F 832 687-6269
Katy (G-13380)

BLOCKS: Paving

Cemex El Paso Inc ....C 915 565-4681
El Paso (G-5691)

Dlc Construction Inc ....F 915 771-7580
El Paso (G-5722)

BLOCKS: Paving, Composition

Ram-Bro Contracting Inc ....E 361 387-2795
Robstown (G-17515)

BLOCKS: Paving, Concrete

Mar-Con Services LLC ....D 713 473-1800
Pasadena (G-16480)

Pavestone LLC ....E 512 558-7283
San Marcos (G-18703)

Southwest Maintenance LLC ....F 254 662-3966
Robinson (G-17502)

BLOCKS: Sewer & Manhole, Concrete

Dfw Infrastructure Inc ....F 888 739-9070
Alvarado (G-328)

Turner Company LLC ....E 817 638-9053
Rhome (G-17261)

BLOCKS: Standard, Concrete Or Cinder

Acme Brick Company ....E 214 637-2720
Dallas (G-3883)

Alamo Concrete Products Ltd ....E 210 208-1580
San Antonio (G-18636)

Camp Logan Cement Works Inc ....E 713 869-3385
Houston (G-9080)

Cemex Construction Mtls S LLC ....A 713 650-6200
Houston (G-9128)

Del Norte Masonry Products Inc ....E 915 584-4453
El Paso (G-5716)

Featherlite Building Pdts Corp ....B 512 472-2424
Austin (G-1147)

Headwaters Cnstr Mtls LLC ....E 903 729-2217
Palestine (G-16299)

Oldcastle Apg Texas Inc ....E 817 545-8325
Grapevine (G-8049)

Tex-Art Stone Inc ....F 817 481-9602
Keller (G-13470)

Texas Building Products Inc ....E 254 672-5262
Strawn (G-19433)

Texas Industries Inc ....E 972 775-3449
Midlothian (G-15495)

Texas Industries Inc ....E 903 873-2849
Wills Point (G-20878)

Texas Industries Inc ....F 903 758-7351
Longview (G-14316)

Texas Industries Inc ....F 903 454-2029
Greenville (G-8094)

Texas Industries Inc ....D 817 838-4212
Fort Worth (G-7048)

Txi Operations LP ....C 972 647-6700
Dallas (G-5125)

BLOCKS: Tackle, Metal

Block Division Inc ....F 940 723-7308
Wichita Falls (G-20746)

BLOWERS & FANS

Aerus LLC ....E 214 378-4000
Dallas (G-3897)

Airfoil Impellers Corporation ....E 979 822-6418
Bryan (G-2452)

Attic Breeze LLC ....E 254 865-9999
Gatesville (G-7617)

Bill West Properties Inc ....E 713 726-0151
Houston (G-8885)

Bullen Pump Inc ....E 281 274-1800
Houston (G-9017)

Carols Lighting and Fan Sp Inc ....F 281 292-1661
Conroe (G-3274)

Carrier Corporation ....C 903 510-7300
Tyler (G-20063)

Commscope Technologies LLC ....A 214 634-8502
Dallas (G-4149)

Custom Air Products & Svcs Inc ....D 281 802-7419
Houston (G-9365)

Goodman Global Holdings Inc ....F 713 861-2500
Waller (G-20500)

Lasko Products LLC ....B 817 625-6381
Fort Worth (G-6780)

Magnetic Technology Inc ....E 214 544-2700
McKinney (G-14955)

Morrison Products Inc ....D 972 279-4000
Mesquite (G-15063)

Oliver Equipment Company LLC ....E 713 856-9206
Houston (G-11171)

Polsys Services Inc ....F 713 999-1100
The Woodlands (G-19903)

Regal Beloit America Inc ....C 417 847-4775
Eagle Pass (G-5555)

Republic Sales & Manufacturing ....E 214 631-8070
Dallas (G-4890)

Selkirk Corporation ....B 972 943-6100
Richardson (G-17395)

Technos Inc ....E 210 651-9393
Schertz (G-18764)

Toro Company ....C 915 231-7200
El Paso (G-6008)

Winston/Royal Guard Corp ....E 903 757-7341
White Oak (G-20722)

BLOWERS & FANS

Gardner Denver Inc ....B 432 366-5433
Odessa (G-16010)

Houston Service Industries Inc ....E 713 947-1623
Houston (G-10250)

Robinson Fans Inc ....E 325 437-3267
Abilene (G-74)

Smith Fans Inc ....F 806 872-8465
Lamesa (G-13830)

BLOWERS, TURBO: Indl

Hanwha Pwr Systems Amricas Inc ......F 281 599-3377
Houston (G-10121)

BLUEPRINTING SVCS

ARC Document Solutions LLC ....B 713 988-9200
Houston (G-8678)

ARC Document Solutions LLC ....F 713 787-1244
Houston (G-8679)

Complete Reprographics Inc ....F 915 779-5000
El Paso (G-5702)

El Paso Reprographics LLC ....F 915 532-6255
El Paso (G-5740)

H & B Copies Inc ....E 979 694-2679
College Station (G-3185)

Killeen Blueprint Co ....E 254 634-2779
Killeen (G-13610)

Ms Dallas Reprographics Inc ....E 214 521-7000
Dallas (G-4701)

Reynolds Brothers Ltd ....E 432 682-7393
Midland (G-15383)

Thomas Reprographics Inc ....F 713 977-6363
Houston (G-12275)

Triangle Blue Print Company ....F 409 835-6810
Beaumont (G-1962)

BOAT & BARGE COMPONENTS: Metal, Prefabricated

Tres Palacios Marine LP ....E 361 972-3097
Palacios (G-16293)

BOAT BUILDING & REPAIR

Austin Boats & Motors Inc ....F 512 263-1266
Lakeway (G-13814)

Burton Shipyard Inc ....E 409 735-2491
Bridge City (G-2281)

Crumplers Shipbuilding Co Inc ....E 409 886-7934
Orange (G-16237)

Es Custom Boats LLC ....F 832 864-2331
Kemah (G-13473)

Forterra Pipe & Precast LLC ....D 713 466-6324
Houston (G-9838)

Four Brothers Boat Works Inc ....F 409 229-4302
Galveston (G-7397)

Gpd Marine Inc ....F 512 266-1834
Austin (G-1191)

Gulf Copper & Mfg Corp ....F 409 989-0300
Port Arthur (G-17111)

Hards Marine Service Ltd ....D 281 452-0848
Hull (G-12741)

Hart Heat Transfer Pdts Inc ....D 713 675-9848
Houston (G-10133)

Inland Boat Works Inc ....F 409 988-0005
Orange (G-16248)

JC Custom Boats Inc ....F 361 785-6035
Seadrift (G-18796)

Josephine Tug Inc ....E 409 744-1222
Galveston (G-7402)

Mile 533 Marine Ways Inc ....F 361 758-5379
Aransas Pass (G-594)

North Shore Boat Works Inc ....G 361 776-2525
Ingleside (G-12897)

Pond King Inc ....F 940 668-2573
Gainesville (G-7357)

R & R Design Inc ....E 972 524-1789
Terrell (G-19748)

Seabrook Marina Inc ....F 281 694-0001
Seabrook (G-18791)

Shallow Sport of Texas Inc ....F 956 233-9489
Los Fresnos (G-14348)

Shoreline Services Inc ....F 936 856-4880
Willis (G-20865)

Simmons Custom Boats LLC ....F 832 864-2331
Freeport (G-7212)

Texas Marine Holdings Ltd ....E 817 589-7547
Fort Worth (G-7050)

Transport Boats ....F 361 972-6629
Palacios (G-16292)

Wallace Marine of Texas Inc ....E 940 458-7343
Sanger (G-18732)

BOAT BUILDING & REPAIRING: Fiberglass

Land & Sea Services 1 Inc ....G 409 935-9466
La Marque (G-13711)

Skeeter Products Inc ....B 903 984-0541
Kilgore (G-13590)

BOAT BUILDING & REPAIRING: Kits, Not Models

Dargel Boats Inc ....E 956 464-2263
Donna (G-5488)

BOAT BUILDING & REPAIRING: Motorboats, Inboard Or Outboard

American Airboat Corporation ....E 409 883-7725
Orange (G-16231)

Tige Boats Inc ....C 325 676-7777
Abilene (G-87)

BOAT BUILDING & REPAIRING: Motorized

David Keels ....E 409 316-9265
Hitchcock (G-8336)

BOAT BUILDING & RPRG: Fishing, Small, Lobster, Crab, Oyster

Legend Marine Mangement LLC ....E 870 481-6750
Streetman (G-19435)

Pro Line Newwater Inc ....F 210 648-2206
Elmendorf (G-6071)

BOAT DEALERS

American Airboat Corporation ....E 409 883-7725
Orange (G-16231)

Gpd Marine Inc ....F 512 266-1834
Austin (G-1191)

BOAT DEALERS: Jet Skis

D & S Cycle of Arlington Inc ....F 817 465-5454
Arlington (G-657)

BOAT DEALERS: Motor

Austin Boats & Motors Inc ....F 512 263-1266
Lakeway (G-13814)

Dargel Boats Inc ....E 956 464-2263
Donna (G-5488)

Texas Marine Holdings Ltd ....E 817 589-7547
Fort Worth (G-7050)

BOAT LIFTS

Emerald Pt Marina Partners Ltd ....C 512 266-1535
Austin (G-1123)

Hight Marine Products Inc ....G 817 431-4569
Fort Worth (G-6698)

BOAT REPAIR SVCS

Austin Boats & Motors Inc ....F 512 263-1266
Lakeway (G-13814)
Dargel Boats Inc ....E 956 464-2263
Donna (G-5488)
Mathew Marine Inc ....F 877 508-4004
Houston (G-10795)
Mile 533 Marine Ways Inc ....F 361 758-5379
Aransas Pass (G-594)
Seabrook Marina Inc ....F 281 694-0001
Seabrook (G-18791)
Zimco Marine LLC ....F 956 831-7828
Brownsville (G-2422)

BOAT YARD: Boat yards, storage & incidental repair

Gulf Copper & Mfg Corp ....C 409 982-6122
Port Arthur (G-17112)
Seabrook Marina Inc ....F 281 694-0001
Seabrook (G-18791)
Wallace Marine of Texas Inc ....E 940 458-7343
Sanger (G-18732)

BOATS & OTHER MARINE EQPT: Plastic

Amphion Inc ....F 210 771-8116
San Antonio (G-17906)
David Keels ....E 409 316-9265
Hitchcock (G-8336)
Pat Garcia ....F 254 559-2815
Breckenridge (G-2232)

BODIES: Truck & Bus

AA Truck Sleeper LLC ....F 817 834-4781
Kennedale (G-13495)
Ace Welding and Trailer Co ....E 210 667-1171
San Antonio (G-17858)
Comprobe Inc ....F 817 293-7333
Fort Worth (G-6538)
Crosby Group LLC ....B 918 834-4611
Longview (G-14216)
Dallas Towing and Autonet Inc ....E 972 219-8484
Lewisville (G-14040)
Energy Fabrication Inc ....E 432 362-0591
Odessa (G-15990)
Everlite Inc ....E 903 297-3444
Longview (G-14232)
Houston Fab Truck Rigging RPS ....E 713 455-6161
Houston (G-10233)
Imperial Group Mfg Inc ....C 940 627-1700
Decatur (G-5247)
Industrial Models Inc ....C 940 665-7841
Gainesville (G-7346)
J L Roberts Industries Inc ....F 817 831-0676
Fort Worth (G-6730)
Jac Enterprises Inc ....F 936 348-3934
Madisonville (G-14588)
Lone Star Body Systems LLC ....E 254 472-0852
Mexia (G-15090)
Lufkin Industries LLC ....B 936 634-2211
Lufkin (G-14541)
Module Truck Systems Inc ....E 806 783-0777
Lubbock (G-14448)
Navistar Inc ....E 972 377-1217
Plano (G-16940)
Pak-Mor Ltd ....E 830 303-6238
Seguin (G-18853)
Rudinger Enterprises Inc ....F 713 939-1234
Houston (G-11694)
Saf-Holland Inc ....C 972 442-3556
Wylie (G-20947)
Sst Truck Company LLC ....B 972 487-2900
Garland (G-7591)
Synergy Industries LP ....D 817 295-1161
Burleson (G-2597)
Tietjen Inc ....E 979 249-3888
La Grange (G-13703)
Toyota Mtr Engrg Mfg N Amer In ....C 469 292-1074
Plano (G-17037)

BODY PARTS: Automobile, Stamped Metal

ABC Exclusive Inc ....D 972 485-8182
Garland (G-7425)
Anderton Castings LLC ....B 254 938-2541
Troy (G-20027)
Batterson Truck Equipment LLC ......F 281 598-6588
Houston (G-8829)

Caldwell Upfitters LLC ....F 832 203-5658
Houston (G-9049)
Caldwell Upfitters LLC ....F 254 773-1959
Temple (G-19672)
CW Sehorn Enterprises Ltd ....E 713 895-8834
Houston (G-9379)
HP Car Accessories & Atv Sales ....F 903 675-0032
Athens (G-828)
Illinois Tool Works Inc ....B 956 215-2000
Pharr (G-16700)
Kirchhoff Auto Dallas Inc ....C 214 553-0208
Garland (G-7531)
Kirchhoff Auto Dallas Inc ....C 214 553-0208
Garland (G-7532)
Mahle Systema De Filtracion D ....G 956 753-9100
Laredo (G-13909)
Toyoda Gosei ....F 210 628-1337
San Antonio (G-18555)
TYG Products LP ....D 972 542-1828
McKinney (G-14984)

BOILER & HEATING REPAIR SVCS

American Steam Inc ....E 972 442-4499
Wylie (G-20926)
Colt Services LP ....E 281 471-9099
La Porte (G-13729)
Colt Services LP ....F 409 842-6929
Beaumont (G-1874)

BOILER REPAIR SHOP

Alamo Welding & Boiler Work ....F 210 227-6502
San Antonio (G-17888)
Cisco Boiler Service Co Inc ....E 713 928-5700
Houston (G-9196)
Huber Construction Company Inc ....E 713 926-9623
Houston (G-10274)
Jerryco Mch & Boiler Works LP ....D 713 224-7900
Houston (G-10466)
Rentech Boiler Services Inc ....C 325 672-2900
Abilene (G-70)
Tejas Boiler Services Inc ....E 713 631-8200
Houston (G-12186)
Williams & Davis Boilers Inc ....E 972 225-2356
Hutchins (G-12873)

BOILERS & BOILER SHOP WORK

Cisco Boiler Service Co Inc ....E 713 928-5700
Houston (G-9196)
Peyton Salas & Mendoza LLC ....E 512 784-5875
Houston (G-11313)
Tejas Boiler Services Inc ....E 713 631-8200
Houston (G-12186)
Williams & Davis Boilers Inc ....E 972 225-2356
Hutchins (G-12873)

BOILERS: Low-Pressure Heating, Steam Or Hot Water

A O Smith Corporation ....E 915 400-2800
El Paso (G-5634)
American Steam Inc ....E 972 442-4499
Wylie (G-20926)
Cisco Boiler Service Co Inc ....E 713 928-5700
Houston (G-9196)
Huber Construction Company Inc ....E 713 926-9623
Houston (G-10274)
Skyven Technologies Inc ....E 972 861-0893
Richardson (G-17399)

BOLTS: Metal

Aab Mfg Holdings LP ....F 281 438-1599
Houston (G-8438)
All-Pro Threaded Products ....F 817 467-5700
Arlington (G-614)
All-Spec Sales Inc ....F 972 641-4053
Grand Prairie (G-7827)
Colgan-Wilson Metals LLC ....F 409 882-9296
Beaumont (G-1873)
Corpus Chrsti Gsket Fstner Inc ....C 361 884-6366
Corpus Christi (G-3510)
Dan-Loc Group LLC ....D 713 356-3500
Houston (G-9399)
Dan-Loc, LLC ....C 713 356-3500
Houston (G-9400)
Efi Inc ....E 940 380-8000
Denton (G-5362)
Frontier Bolt Company Texas ....F 817 477-5319
Mansfield (G-14674)

K-T Bolt Mfg Co ....E 281 391-2196
Katy (G-13412)
Mw Industries Inc ....E 281 233-0448
Houston (G-10945)
Robert L Rowan & Associates ....F 713 681-5811
Houston (G-11643)
South Texas Bolt & Fitting Inc ....E 713 673-5376
Houston (G-11966)
Texas Bolt & Nut Company Ltd ....E 713 869-7111
Houston (G-12222)
Tubal Cain Industries Inc ....D 409 786-1783
Vidor (G-20336)

BONE CHINA

En Plast Technology LLC ....F 832 730-4606
Houston (G-9622)

BOOK STORES

Bookstore Manager Software ....E 325 673-2826
Abilene (G-22)
Half Price Bks Rec Mgzines Inc ....F 512 244-0203
Round Rock (G-17661)
Paradigm Bks Lecture Notes Ltd ......F 217 344-4433
Austin (G-1396)

BOOK STORES: Children's

Beecon Learning LLC ....F 877 923-3266
Dallas (G-4014)

BOOK STORES: College

Kampus Books ....F 936 560-0033
Nacogdoches (G-15700)

BOOK STORES: Comic

Ben Dunn Corporation ....F 210 614-0396
San Antonio (G-17946)

BOOK STORES: Religious

Baptist Sunday Schl Committee ....E 903 792-2783
Texarkana (G-19756)
Half Price Bks Rec Mgzines Inc ....F 713 340-0094
Pearland (G-16567)
Trinity Fellowship ....C 806 355-8955
Amarillo (G-515)

BOOKS, WHOLESALE

Bisi Inc ....G 512 478-3334
Austin (G-992)

BOOTHS: Spray, Sheet Metal, Prefabricated

Dusold Designs Inc ....F 972 221-1455
Lewisville (G-14045)
Ekj Enterprises LP ....C 972 772-1919
Rockwall (G-17547)
Givco Inc ....G 830 624-8598
New Braunfels (G-15795)
J B Edwards Company ....G 281 429-7143
Conroe (G-3312)
Kayco Spray Booths Inc ....F 830 779-2051
La Vernia (G-13802)

BOOTS: Men's

Anderson Bean Boot Co Inc ....F 956 565-2618
Mercedes (G-15003)
Cowtown Boot Company ....D 915 593-2929
El Paso (G-5704)
Falconhead Boots Belts Buckles ....F 915 544-2727
El Paso (G-5762)
Franklin-Leddy Corporation ....D 817 624-3149
Fort Worth (G-6648)
Holicks Manufacturing Co LLC ....F 979 846-6721
Bryan (G-2477)
Justin Brands Inc ....C 817 332-4385
Fort Worth (G-6748)
Justin Brands Inc ....A 915 778-8311
El Paso (G-5824)
Justin Industries Inc ....B 817 332-4385
Fort Worth (G-6749)
Lagarto Inc ....E 915 598-2668
El Paso (G-5837)
Lucchese Inc ....B 915 778-8585
El Paso (G-5849)
Lucchese Inc ....B 915 778-8585
El Paso (G-5850)

Employee Codes: A=Over 500 employees, B=251-500
C=101-250, D=51-100, E=20-50, F=10-19, G=9

2021 Harris Texas
Manufacturers Directory

PRODUCT

1403

Stallion Boot Co Inc ....E 915 532-6268
El Paso (G-5974)
Tony Lama Company Inc ....A 915 778-8311
El Paso (G-6007)
Western Leather Goods Inc ....D 800 717-1853
Mercedes (G-15011)
Western Leather Goods Inc ....E 956 565-2618
Mercedes (G-15012)
Westmoor Corp ....E 817 625-2841
Fort Worth (G-7142)

BOOTS: Plastic

Handgards LLC ....C 915 779-6606
El Paso (G-5794)

BOOTS: Women's

Anderson Bean Boot Co Inc ....F 956 565-2618
Mercedes (G-15003)
Justin Brands Inc ....C 817 332-4385
Fort Worth (G-6748)
Lucchese Inc ....B 915 778-8585
El Paso (G-5849)
Lucchese Inc ....B 915 778-8585
El Paso (G-5850)
Stallion Boot Co Inc ....E 915 532-6268
El Paso (G-5974)

BORING MILL

Dynamic Precision Mfg LLC ....E 713 466-4545
Houston (G-9549)
Thi Acquisition Inc ....C 281 485-8339
Pearland (G-16603)

BOTTLE CAPS & RESEALERS: Plastic

Berry Global Inc ....C 409 794-1011
Beaumont (G-1863)
Covalnce Spcalty Adhesives LLC ....E 713 676-0085
Houston (G-9331)

BOTTLED GAS DEALERS: Liquefied Petro, Dlvrd To Customers

Martin Resource Mgt Corp ....C 903 983-6200
Kilgore (G-13570)

BOTTLED GAS DEALERS: Propane

Lubbock Gas & Building Inc ....F 806 745-9695
Lubbock (G-14441)
Matheson Tri-Gas Inc ....F 281 498-2310
Stafford (G-19352)
Sandifers LP Gas & Svc Co Inc ......F 409 963-1269
Port Arthur (G-17124)

BOTTLED WATER DELIVERY

Culligan Southeast Texas Water .....E 409 838-6261
Beaumont (G-1879)
Ds Services of America Inc ....E 281 391-3770
Katy (G-13360)

BOTTLES: Plastic

Bkh Enterprises LLC ....D 979 743-6577
Schulenburg (G-18772)
Cal Sierra International LLC ....F 832 615-6002
Houston (G-9047)
CKS Packaging Inc ....C 817 924-2205
Fort Worth (G-6521)
CKS Packaging Inc ....E 214 358-2441
Dallas (G-4125)
Graham Packaging Company LP .....C 713 869-5471
Houston (G-10013)
Houston Kik Inc ....C 713 747-8710
Houston (G-10236)
Paragon Packaging Inc ....E 817 477-5211
Mansfield (G-14701)
Plastcos Arco Iris of San Antn ....E 210 308-6500
San Antonio (G-18381)
Plastic Industries Inc ....D 817 477-5211
Mansfield (G-14703)
Plastipak Packaging Inc ....C 972 276-8660
Garland (G-7568)
Polymers Sales & Logistics LLC .....F 281 874-8072
Houston (G-11359)
Ringwood Containers LP ....E 817 625-7214
Fort Worth (G-6960)
Thomas Plastics Inc ....D 817 654-3238
Fort Worth (G-7057)

Western Container Corporation ....B 346 309-3238
Sugar Land (G-19572)
Western Container Corporation ....C 432 263-8361
Big Spring (G-2103)
Western Container Corporation ....C 713 691-0730
Houston (G-12642)

BOULDER: Crushed & Broken

Attoyac Rock LLC ....F 936 275-3636
San Augustine (G-18650)
Avila Stone LLC ....E 956 453-4747
Donna (G-5487)
Hard Rock Crushing ....F 806 383-1721
Amarillo (G-433)
Killeen Crushed Stone ....E 254 526-2526
Killeen (G-13611)

BOWLING EQPT & SPLYS

Dacos Bowling International ....E 972 394-6507
Carrollton (G-2863)

BOXES & CRATES: Rectangular, Wood

B & B Box and Lumber Company ......E 903 592-7369
Tyler (G-20054)
DMd Custom Crates & Bxs Inc ....F 915 849-1744
Horizon City (G-8364)
Ics Enterprises LLP ....B 915 239-9256
El Paso (G-5808)
Ifco Systems North America Inc ......E 713 937-9311
Houston (G-10318)
Nefab Companies Inc ....E 866 332-4425
Coppell (G-3430)
Nefab Packaging Inc ....E 469 444-5264
Coppell (G-3431)
Relocation Systems Inc ....E 972 241-2300
Irving (G-13164)
Solid Crate LLC ....E 713 475-9926
Pasadena (G-16507)
Superior Pllet Wichita FLS Ltd ....F 940 569-5244
Burkburnett (G-2564)
Ufp Schertz LLC ....E 830 606-4300
Schertz (G-18766)

BOXES & SHOOK: Nailed Wood

Apache Products Inc ....D 409 385-7021
Silsbee (G-18949)
Bell Wooden Products Inc ....E 214 388-5421
Dallas (G-4016)
Ifco Systems North America Inc ......E 713 937-9311
Houston (G-10318)
Industrial Lumber and Box Inc ....F 713 928-2096
Houston (G-10351)
Kainer Export Crating Inc ....F 713 641-2345
Houston (G-10499)
Morris Export Crating Company ....D 713 675-9101
Houston (G-10922)
Nefab Companies Inc ....E 866 332-4425
Coppell (G-3430)
Nefab Packaging Inc ....E 469 444-5264
Coppell (G-3431)
Pallet & Crating Co Inc ....E 903 463-5786
Denison (G-5344)
Superior Pllet Wichita FLS Ltd ....F 940 569-5244
Burkburnett (G-2564)

BOXES: Cigar, Wood & Part Wood

Serious Cigars Llc ....G 281 397-9800
Houston (G-11837)

BOXES: Corrugated

Action Box Co Inc ....C 713 869-7701
Houston (G-8469)
Age Industries Ltd ....E 254 939-5828
Belton (G-2017)
Age Industries Ltd ....E 956 399-8279
San Benito (G-18654)
Age Industries Ltd ....D 817 477-5266
Cleburne (G-3079)
Age Industries Ltd ....D 210 659-1301
Cibolo (G-3060)
Age Industries Ltd ....E 713 460-3060
Houston (G-8502)
Age Industries Ltd ....E 915 852-9099
Horizon City (G-8361)
All Star Corrugated ....E 817 551-5580
Fort Worth (G-6371)

All Star Corrugated ....D 817 454-8640
Burleson (G-2566)
Amarillo Custom Box Co ....E 806 371-9111
Amarillo (G-393)
American Carton Company Inc ....E 817 473-2992
Mansfield (G-14655)
Amerisource Companies LP ....E 972 380-2000
Carrollton (G-2856)
Apple Corrugated Packaging Inc .....E 214 331-9000
Duncanville (G-5528)
Benson Box Inc ....F 210 662-6383
San Antonio (G-17947)
Buckeye Corrugated Inc ....D 713 869-9121
Houston (G-9006)
Capital City Container Corp ....F 512 312-1222
Buda (G-2523)
Central Texas Corrugated Inc ....C 254 776-6902
Waco (G-20380)
Corrugated Concepts Packg Inc ......E 713 462-5600
Houston (G-9326)
D & S Container Inc ....D 214 637-7957
Dallas (G-4199)
Danhil Containers II Ltd ....C 254 773-0704
Temple (G-19678)
Durabox Corrugated Pdts Inc ....F 915 440-4409
El Paso (G-5725)
East Texas Containers Inc ....E 903 595-6444
Tyler (G-20079)
Ecd Acquisitions Inc ....D 254 776-2360
Waco (G-20395)
Georgia-Pacific LLC ....C 972 937-8804
Waxahachie (G-20543)
Green Bay Packaging Inc ....C 817 551-1934
Fort Worth (G-6675)
Hager Containers L P ....D 972 417-7660
Carrollton (G-2750)
Harris Packaging Corporation ....D 817 429-6262
Haltom City (G-8148)
Herman Packaging Co Inc ....E 713 462-0228
Houston (G-10159)
Hurley Packaging Texas Inc ....E 806 687-6179
Lubbock (G-14422)
International Paper Company ....C 972 417-1350
Carrollton (G-2766)
International Paper Company ....D 806 381-0121
Amarillo (G-439)
International Paper Company ....C 956 682-9406
McAllen (G-14874)
Jim Dandy Boxes Inc ....E 817 608-9180
Grand Prairie (G-7903)
Kessler Packaging Inc ....E 915 591-8161
El Paso (G-5829)
Liberty Carton Co - Texas ....C 817 577-6100
Haltom City (G-8151)
Lone Star Container Sales Corp ....F 972 579-1551
Irving (G-13088)
Lone Star Corrugated Cont Corp ......C 972 579-1551
Irving (G-13089)
Ok-Go Packaging Inc ....E 915 440-2500
El Paso (G-5900)
Orora North America ....E 972 724-2828
Grapevine (G-8050)
Orora Packaging Solutions ....D 281 517-8600
Houston (G-11193)
Packaging Corporation America ....C 210 798-1700
San Antonio (G-18362)
Packaging Corporation America ....C 972 422-4270
Plano (G-16963)
Packaging Corporation America ....E 214 227-5124
Garland (G-7565)
Packaging Corporation America ....E 817 640-1888
Arlington (G-746)
Packaging Corporation America ....C 254 776-8890
Waco (G-20442)
Packaging Corporation America ....D 956 464-5664
Donna (G-5489)
Packaging Corporation America ....E 915 779-1291
El Paso (G-5903)
Pratt Industries Inc ....E 972 296-2900
Dallas (G-4816)
Pratt Industries Inc ....D 210 651-6309
Schertz (G-18759)
Pratt Rockwall Corrugating LLC ....C 770 918-5678
Rockwall (G-17560)
Rio Grande Container Inc ....E 956 447-5949
Weslaco (G-20668)
Smurfit Kappa Bates LLC ....C 817 498-3200
North Richland Hills (G-15881)
Smurfit Kappa Bates LLC ....F 903 234-1100
Longview (G-14309)

Smurfit Kappa Bates LLC..................D...... 210 436-7777
Von Ormy (G-20352)

Smurfit Kappa North Amer LLC..........B...... 214 515-6400
Forney (G-6314)

Smurfit Kappa North Amer LLC..........B...... 800 306-8326
Irving (G-13182)

Supplynet Inc.................................D...... 214 637-0160
Dallas (G-5029)

Technology Container Corp................E...... 972 228-1617
Desoto (G-5444)

Texas Corrugated Box Packg LLC......E...... 817 454-2037
Fort Worth (G-7046)

Titan Corrugated Inc......................E...... 214 513-2691
Flower Mound (G-6289)

Tyler Corrugated Box Inc.................E...... 903 581-4950
Tyler (G-20169)

US Corrugated Mesquite LLC............F...... 801 798-7331
Mesquite (G-15083)

Ward Packaging of Fort Worth ....E...... 817 334-0484
Fort Worth (G-7126)

West Texas Container Corp...............E...... 915 859-6712
El Paso (G-6031)

Westrock Container LLC...................D...... 972 285-8865
Mesquite (G-15085)

Westrock Cp LLC............................B...... 915 778-7350
El Paso (G-6037)

Westrock Cp LLC............................C...... 817 568-0918
Fort Worth (G-7144)

Westrock Cp LLC............................D...... 281 830-0131
Houston (G-12657)

Westrock Cp LLC............................E...... 281 893-8918
Houston (G-12658)

Westrock Cp LLC............................E...... 915 778-7350
El Paso (G-6038)

Westrock Mwv LLC..........................C...... 409 276-3243
Evadale (G-6167)

Westrock Rkt LLC...........................C...... 214 941-3400
Dallas (G-5184)

Weyerhaeuser Company...................C...... 972 641-3891
Grand Prairie (G-7992)

Wrkco Inc.....................................F...... 817 624-8000
Fort Worth (G-7152)

BOXES: Mail Or Post Office, Collection/Storage, Sheet Metal

Brandon Industries Inc....................E...... 972 542-3000
McKinney (G-14929)

Mel Northey Co Inc.........................F...... 281 445-3485
Houston (G-10825)

United Parcel Service Inc..................F...... 817 490-7300
Fort Worth (G-7093)

BOXES: Packing & Shipping, Metal

Airline Mortuary Associates ....G...... 281 540-4141
Humble (G-12744)

Jerryco Mch & Boiler Works LP..........D...... 713 224-7900
Houston (G-10466)

Karlee Integration Facility.................E...... 972 543-3175
Garland (G-7530)

SA Quality Fence Ltd......................D...... 210 545-6767
San Antonio (G-18440)

BOXES: Paperboard, Folding

Abox Paperboard Company................D...... 972 932-9800
Forney (G-6301)

Age Industries Ltd.........................E...... 915 852-9099
Horizon City (G-8361)

Ics Enterprises Ltd........................E...... 915 539-5415
El Paso (G-5807)

Morgan Truck Body LLC...................D...... 903 872-7445
Corsicana (G-3679)

P & A Graphics LLC........................F...... 972 632-2100
McKinney (G-14961)

Sctray Company.............................D...... 817 473-0233
Mansfield (G-14716)

Smurfit Kappa North Amer LLC..........B...... 214 515-6400
Forney (G-6314)

Smurfit Kappa North Amer LLC..........B...... 800 306-8326
Irving (G-13182)

Westrock Rkt LLC...........................C...... 903 455-0147
Greenville (G-8096)

BOXES: Paperboard, Set-Up

Abox Paperboard Company................D...... 972 932-9800
Forney (G-6301)

BOXES: Plastic

Kaston Fixs & Design Group LLC.......E...... 972 243-5334
Dallas (G-4544)

Plastic Molded Products Inc..............E...... 254 840-3721
Mc Gregor (G-14821)

BOXES: Wirebound, Wood

Cougar Pallet Inc...........................D...... 281 442-1177
Houston (G-9330)

BOXES: Wooden

Bana Inc......................................C...... 817 232-3750
Saginaw (G-17739)

Pierce Packaging Co.......................E...... 815 636-5656
Houston (G-11331)

BRAKE LININGS

Ogburn Truck Parts LP....................F...... 281 331-0005
Alvin (G-375)

BRAKES & BRAKE PARTS

Austin Brake & Clutch Supply ....F...... 512 836-0482
Austin (G-951)

Truckpro LLC................................F...... 512 836-0482
Austin (G-1597)

Warner Electric LLC........................D...... 940 723-3400
Wichita Falls (G-20828)

BRAKES: Electromagnetic

Warner Electric LLC........................D...... 940 767-2000
Wichita Falls (G-20827)

BRASS & BRONZE PRDTS: Die-casted

Coastal Foundry Company.................E...... 713 695-4008
Houston (G-9226)

Kruger Aluminum & Brass Fndry ....F...... 940 767-0432
Wichita Falls (G-20777)

BRASS FOUNDRY, NEC

A&B Foundry LLC...........................F...... 972 247-3579
Dallas (G-3872)

BRASS GOODS, WHOLESALE

Robert F Herndon Corporation...........F...... 915 779-7905
El Paso (G-5942)

BRAZING SVCS

Mp Precision Services Inc.................F...... 915 599-9188
El Paso (G-5886)

BRAZING: Metal

Bodycote Thermal Proc Inc ....E...... 214 904-2420
Dallas (G-4038)

Bodycote Thermal Proc Inc ....E...... 817 265-5878
Arlington (G-633)

Bodycote Usa Inc...........................D...... 214 904-2420
Dallas (G-4039)

Chromalloy Gas Turbine LLC ....F...... 972 241-2501
Dallas (G-4114)

Lark Industries Incorporated ....E...... 713 937-9089
Houston (G-10601)

Lst Heat Treating LLC.....................G...... 903 757-2115
Longview (G-14272)

BREAKER POINT SETS: Internal Combustion Engines

Manning Navcomp Inc......................E...... 877 680-1188
Austin (G-1324)

BRICK, STONE & RELATED PRDTS WHOLESALERS

Alamo Concrete Products Ltd ....F...... 361 572-0231
Victoria (G-20236)

Alamo Concrete Products Ltd ....E...... 361 289-9200
Corpus Christi (G-3471)

Childs Ready-Mix Concrete Co...........E...... 817 477-5151
Cleburne (G-3083)

Decorum Tile & Stone Inc ....F...... 512 344-9235
Austin (G-1087)

Live Oak Materials Inc....................E...... 361 775-0065
Ingleside (G-12896)

Old Castle Apg Texas Inc ....E...... 512 864-9601
Georgetown (G-7669)

R E Janes Gravel Co.......................E...... 325 736-5008
Merkel (G-15017)

Ralph Cordova Company...................E...... 972 771-7281
Royse City (G-17725)

Thrasher Inc.................................F...... 806 296-2609
Plainview (G-16765)

United States Gypsum Company..........E...... 214 424-2500
Dallas (G-5137)

Weir Brothers Contracting LLC...........F...... 940 440-2931
Aubrey (G-852)

BRICK: Bauxite

Able Supply Co..............................F...... 713 926-9623
Houston (G-8448)

BRICKS & BLOCKS: Structural

Acme Brick Company.......................D...... 817 332-4101
El Paso (G-5636)

Acme Brick Company.......................D...... 325 949-7685
San Angelo (G-17770)

Acme Brick Company.......................C...... 817 332-4101
Fort Worth (G-6343)

BRICKS: Clay

Justin Industries Inc......................D...... 817 332-4101
Fort Worth (G-6750)

Meridian Brick LLC.........................E...... 903 675-2256
Athens (G-833)

Texas Industries Inc.......................C...... 512 396-4244
New Braunfels (G-15827)

BRICKS: Concrete

Featherlite Corp............................E...... 409 727-8800
Port Neches (G-17160)

J & G Concrete LP.........................E...... 972 937-9200
Waxahachie (G-20546)

BRIDAL SHOPS

Brides & Belles of Tyler...................G...... 903 581-8211
Tyler (G-20060)

BRIDGE COMPONENTS: Bridge sections, prefabricated, highway

Insight Equity A P X L P..................F...... 817 488-7775
Southlake (G-19075)

Insight Equity LP...........................E...... 817 488-7775
Southlake (G-19076)

Seismic Products Inc.......................E...... 903 675-8571
Athens (G-839)

BROADCASTING & COMMS EQPT: Antennas, Transmitting/Comms

Alpha Satcom Inc...........................F...... 903 238-8888
Longview (G-14193)

Antenna Products Corporation ....D...... 940 325-3301
Mineral Wells (G-15518)

CPI Satcom & Antenna Tech Inc..........B...... 903 984-0555
Kilgore (G-13539)

CPI Satcom & Antenna Tech Inc..........C...... 972 852-5300
Plano (G-16830)

CPI Satcom & Antenna Tech Inc..........D...... 903 984-0555
Kilgore (G-13540)

CPI Satcom & Antenna Tech Inc..........D...... 254 765-3304
Wortham (G-20922)

Kathrein Holding Usa Inc..................D...... 541 779-6500
Richardson (G-17339)

Marvel Communications Company ....E...... 817 568-0177
Fort Worth (G-6814)

Parsec Technologies Inc...................F...... 972 804-4600
Plano (G-16966)

Qar Industries Inc..........................F...... 940 325-3301
Mineral Wells (G-15538)

Radiation Sys Prec Cntrls.................A...... 972 907-9599
Richardson (G-17381)

BROADCASTING & COMMS EQPT: Trnsmttng TV Antennas/Grndng Eqpt

Isp Supplies LLC............................E...... 855 947-7776
College Station (G-3187)

BROADCASTING & COMMUNICATION EQPT: Transmit-Receiver, Radio

EF Johnson Company ....C 972 819-0700
Irving (G-13010)

BROADCASTING & COMMUNICATIONS EQPT: Cellular Radio Telephone

AT&T Inc ....A 210 821-4105
Dallas (G-3978)

Front End Services ....E 214 672-0600
Grand Prairie (G-7879)

Fujitsu Ntwrk Cmmnications Inc ....A 972 479-6000
Richardson (G-17318)

Huawei Device USA Inc ....C 214 919-6688
Plano (G-16888)

BROADCASTING & COMMUNICATIONS EQPT: Light Comms Eqpt

Teleprime Advanced Communicati ....G 512 271-9503
Austin (G-1561)

BROADCASTING & COMMUNICATIONS EQPT: Studio Eqpt, Radio & TV

Broadcast Technical Svcs Inc ....F 832 467-0002
Houston (G-8988)

Falcon Events LLC ....D 800 895-6934
Irving (G-13022)

BROADCASTING STATIONS, RADIO: Music Format

K P A N Broadcasters ....F 806 364-1860
Hereford (G-8292)

Milam Broadcasting Co Inc ....F 254 697-6633
Cameron (G-2643)

BROKERS' SVCS

Evo IDT LLC ....E 817 637-0149
Mansfield (G-14671)

BROKERS: Business

W&W-Afco Steel LLC ....C 806 765-5781
Lubbock (G-14508)

BROKERS: Commodity Contracts

Pdvsa Services Inc ....D 281 531-0004
Houston (G-11266)

Source Operations Group LLC ....E 888 557-7079
Houston (G-11957)

BROKERS: Food

Circle U Foods Inc ....F 817 626-6918
Fort Worth (G-6520)

Five Star Custom Foods Ltd ....E 682 647-2700
Fort Worth (G-6635)

Fortune One Foods Inc ....E 713 426-1133
Houston (G-9840)

Fountain Valley Foods Inc ....F 281 592-0610
Livingston (G-14156)

BROKERS: Loan

Valero Ref Company-New Jersey ....B 210 345-2000
San Antonio (G-18585)

BROKERS: Printing

Colordynamics Inc ....B 972 390-6500
Allen (G-259)

Digital Copy LLC ....E 214 740-2480
Dallas (G-4258)

Duke Forms & Printing ....F 512 985-6587
Cedar Creek (G-2935)

LMS Acquisitions LLC ....F 512 371-7028
Austin (G-1296)

Sasch Inc ....F 214 388-7000
Dallas (G-4935)

BROKERS: Security

Texakoma Financial Inc ....E 972 701-9106
Plano (G-17026)

BROOMS

Quickie Manufacturing Corp ....D 915 859-2522
El Paso (G-5923)

San Antonio Broom Factory Inc ....E 210 226-9762
San Antonio (G-18446)

BROOMS & BRUSHES

Birdwell Cleaning Products Inc ....D 800 722-8006
Burleson (G-2572)

Bz & Sons Sweeping & Wshg Inc ....G 903 732-9882
Powderly (G-17198)

Eagle Brush & Chemical Inc ....F 972 484-0391
Dallas (G-4289)

BROOMS & BRUSHES: Household Or Indl

Bluebonnet Industrial Brush Co ....F 713 923-2855
Houston (G-8922)

Magnolia Brush Mfrs Inc ....D 903 427-2261
Clarksville (G-3074)

BROOMS & BRUSHES: Paint & Varnish

True Value Company LLC ....C 903 872-8365
Corsicana (G-3688)

BROOMS & BRUSHES: Street Sweeping, Hand Or Machine

All Washed Up Inc ....F 512 288-5522
Austin (G-908)

Harman Property Services LLC ....F 469 446-2909
Dallas (G-4436)

Mobile Products Inc ....E 800 323-0135
Longview (G-14278)

BUCKETS: Plastic

Caterpillar Work Tools Inc ....D 254 297-2321
Waco (G-20378)

BUCKLES & PARTS

Creative Casting Inc ....F 903 463-6160
Denison (G-5339)

BUILDING & OFFICE CLEANING SVCS

Montoya Building Services Inc ....E 713 367-0231
Houston (G-10915)

BUILDING & STRUCTURAL WOOD MBRS: Timbers, Struct, Lam Lumber

Sand Creek Timber Frames LLC ....E 210 698-6156
Boerne (G-2135)

Unifix Inc ....E 817 645-3435
Cleburne (G-3116)

BUILDING & STRUCTURAL WOOD MEMBERS

Aries Acrylic Mfg Inc ....F 972 771-6286
Rockwall (G-17538)

B & S Hardware Inc ....E 903 856-3552
Pittsburg (G-16744)

BMC West LLC ....D 325 698-4465
Abilene (G-18)

Builders Firstsource Inc ....E 972 621-2233
Irving (G-12953)

Builders Firstsource Inc ....E 817 625-1200
Fort Worth (G-6476)

Component Structures Inc ....E 940 566-1166
Denton (G-5356)

Connor Sports Flooring LLC ....F 817 944-0269
Southlake (G-19061)

Contractors Service Ltd ....F 325 692-4317
Abilene (G-36)

Esco Laminating Texas Inc ....D 254 296-0500
Waco (G-20397)

Steel Building Supply Inc ....E 936 598-6373
Center (G-3009)

Stock Building Sup Texas LLC ....B 512 444-3172
Austin (G-1537)

Ufp New Waverly LLC ....D 936 295-3411
New Waverly (G-15861)

BUILDING CLEANING & MAINTENANCE SVCS

Clarios ....C 281 518-8053
Houston (G-9208)

Holverstott Najee ....F 210 769-5246
San Antonio (G-18172)

BUILDING COMPONENTS: Structural Steel

Associated Stl Fabricators Inc ....F 281 516-0909
Tomball (G-19961)

Atascosa Steel Industries Inc ....F 830 276-4322
Poteet (G-17193)

Baker Steel Company Inc ....E 713 479-9399
Katy (G-13351)

Bludau Fabrication Inc ....E 361 798-4339
Hallettsville (G-8119)

Buzzard Industries Inc ....F 936 264-1010
Conroe (G-3268)

C & F Steel Company Inc ....E 254 386-8847
Hamilton (G-8165)

Cherokee Steel Fabricators Inc ....E 903 759-3844
White Oak (G-20712)

Cody Builders Supply Inc ....E 512 339-9834
Austin (G-1055)

Contractors Metal Works Inc ....F 713 856-6600
Houston (G-9293)

E-Z Line Pipe Support Co LLC ....E 713 675-6693
Manvel (G-14733)

Eagle Fabricators Inc ....D 281 442-8787
Houston (G-9556)

Efficient-Tec Intl LLC ....E 214 221-9405
Dallas (G-4302)

Ernmex Interntational Inc ....E 281 458-0152
Houston (G-9693)

Express Fabricators LLC ....F 972 734-3855
Farmersville (G-6222)

Ford Steel LLC ....D 281 354-3011
Porter (G-17176)

Four-Star Fabrication Inc ....G 214 748-3494
Dallas (G-4373)

Gavin Steel Fabricating Inc ....E 210 695-9672
Helotes (G-8237)

Gordons Specialties Inc ....E 972 225-1660
Hutchins (G-12866)

Guardiar USA LLC ....D 972 878-7000
Ennis (G-6106)

Hefco Enterprises Inc ....E 281 431-1571
Fresno (G-7238)

Henderson Fabrication Inc ....E 979 245-5350
Bay City (G-1773)

Hollywood Steel Inc ....E 713 686-4325
Houston (G-10196)

Jackrabbit Steel Products Inc ....E 281 550-4551
Houston (G-10446)

Jackup Structures Alliance Inc ....G 713 910-7556
Houston (G-10447)

JV Industrial Companies Ltd ....D 713 568-2600
San Antonio (G-18213)

King Fabrication LLC ....D 281 209-0811
Houston (G-10533)

Labelleco Fab LLC ....D 409 225-5499
Beaumont (G-1916)

Larwel Industries Inc ....F 817 491-1200
Roanoke (G-17486)

Nci Building Systems LP ....D 806 747-4291
Lubbock (G-14450)

Orizon Industries Inc ....C 281 375-7700
Brookshire (G-2322)

Palmer Steel Supplies Inc ....C 956 686-6575
McAllen (G-14898)

Patriot Trinity LLC ....E 936 594-5948
Trinity (G-20019)

Pinchback Industrial Inc ....E 409 860-1964
Beaumont (G-1941)

Prism Resources Inc ....E 713 947-2800
Houston (G-11423)

Process Manufacturing Corp ....D 713 426-1403
Houston (G-11431)

Rising S Company LLC ....E 214 455-0560
Murchison (G-15682)

Rln Consulting Enterprises LLC ....F 713 515-3638
Springtown (G-19275)

San-Co Steel Ltd ....C 956 464-7766
Donna (G-5490)

Starks Welding & Mfg Svcs Inc ....E 512 863-2424
Georgetown (G-7681)

Structural Fabrications Inc ....E 903 868-2979
Sherman (G-18934)

Sulta Manufacturing Company ....E 903 885-2139
Sulphur Springs (G-19599)
T & B Construction Svcs LLC ....D 936 824-3914
Lufkin (G-14553)
Thorpe Plant Services Inc ....E 713 644-1247
Houston (G-12281)
Truform Metalservice Inc ....D 512 258-1675
Austin (G-1715)
United Metal Services Inc ....F 817 932-3330
Rhome (G-17263)
W&W-Afco Steel LLC ....C 806 765-5781
Lubbock (G-14508)
West Texas Steel and Sup Inc ....E 325 651-7322
San Angelo (G-17838)
Wichita Metal Products Inc ....E 940 322-9611
Wichita Falls (G-20833)
Wilborn Steel Company ....E 210 532-6852
San Antonio (G-18620)
Wind Clean Corp ....E 325 625-1899
Grandview (G-8004)
Zachry Holdings Inc ....A 210 588-5000
San Antonio (G-18632)

BUILDING EXTERIOR CLEANING SVCS

Harman Property Services LLC ....F 469 446-2909
Dallas (G-4436)

BUILDING ITEM REPAIR SVCS, MISCELLANEOUS

City Sign Services Inc ....E 214 826-4475
Dallas (G-4124)
Otis Elevator Company ....F 214 741-6207
Dallas (G-4772)

BUILDING PRDTS & MATERIALS DEALERS

A & B Sheet Metal Inc ....G 512 365-7870
Taylor (G-19646)
Alamo Concrete Products Ltd ....F 361 572-0231
Victoria (G-20236)
Arlington Cast Stone Inc ....F 817 284-5933
Hurst (G-12834)
Associated Supply Company Inc ....E 512 272-8922
Manor (G-14643)
Associated Truss Company ....D 972 226-1973
Mesquite (G-15028)
B & S Hardware Inc ....E 903 856-3552
Pittsburg (G-16744)
Bielas Glass & Aluminum Pdts ....E 210 333-8040
San Antonio (G-17952)
BMC West LLC ....E 817 952-3124
Hurst (G-12840)
Builders Firstsource Inc ....E 214 880-3500
Dallas (G-4066)
Clarks Hardwood Lumber Co LP ....F 713 862-6628
Houston (G-9211)
Cokers Doors & Mouldings Inc ....F 409 727-4600
Nederland (G-15750)
Dfw A-1 Pallet Inc ....D 972 401-3502
Irving (G-12998)
Hanson Aggregates LLC ....E 903 794-6161
Texarkana (G-19764)
Independent Door Co Inc ....F 972 487-0511
Garland (G-7518)
King Ranch Holdings Inc ....E 832 681-5700
Houston (G-10535)
Materials Products Inc ....F 512 821-3303
Austin (G-1329)
Mg Building Materials Ltd ....B 210 924-8604
San Antonio (G-18298)
Spivey Stake & Supply Inc ....E 903 822-3888
Mount Enterprise (G-15645)
Stock Building Sup Texas LLC ....B 512 444-3172
Austin (G-1537)
Texarkana Door & Window Inc ....F 903 793-6011
Texarkana (G-19777)
Zarsky Lumber Company Inc ....E 361 573-2479
Victoria (G-20322)

BUILDING PRDTS: Concrete

David L Jennings ....D 281 778-3223
Missouri City (G-15579)
Lyons Manufacturing Inc ....E 214 381-8100
Dallas (G-4615)
Quanex Building Products Corp ....E 731 961-4600
Houston (G-11504)
Texas Eifs LLC ....F 210 472-2935
San Antonio (G-18536)

BUILDING PRDTS: Stone

Choice Fabricated Stone LLC ....E 817 222-2201
Fort Worth (G-6515)
Import Mdsg Concepts GP LLC ....F 214 572-2000
Addison (G-136)

BUILDING SCALES MODELS

Safety-Kleen Systems Inc ....B 800 669-5740
Richardson (G-17392)

BUILDINGS & COMPONENTS: Prefabricated Metal

Alvarez & Marsal Inc ....C 212 759-4433
Houston (G-8575)
Berridge Manufacturing Company ....E 830 401-5200
Seguin (G-18826)
Bluff Manufacturing Inc ....D 817 293-3018
Fort Worth (G-6461)
Carolina Carports Inc ....E 800 670-4262
Emory (G-6082)
Cornerstone Bldg Brands Inc ....G 281 897-7726
Houston (G-9321)
Cozart Mtal Bldngs Systems Inc ....G 817 237-2282
Fort Worth (G-6555)
Diamond Door Products Ltd ....E 979 826-0238
Hempstead (G-8251)
FE Sawyer Bldg Systems Inc ....E 903 531-0182
Tyler (G-20087)
Fehrs Industrial Mfg LLC ....D 432 758-0068
Seminole (G-18883)
Jedco Building Systems Inc ....E 281 591-2860
Houston (G-10462)
Lane Supply Inc ....D 817 261-9116
Arlington (G-717)
McElroy Metal Mill Inc ....B 214 703-3113
Garland (G-7547)
McElroy Metal Mill Inc ....F 972 226-7075
Mesquite (G-15062)
Mobile Mini Inc ....E 817 439-2288
Rhome (G-17258)
Morgan Buildings & Spas Inc ....F 972 864-7300
Richardson (G-17360)
Mueller Supply Company Inc ....G 409 886-2233
Orange (G-16254)
Mueller Supply Company Inc ....F 254 742-2754
Temple (G-19692)
Mueller Supply Company Inc ....F 903 892-6222
Sherman (G-18925)
Nci Group Inc ....E 972 299-5556
Midlothian (G-15488)
Northast Txas McHning Wldg Hrd ....F 903 427-2277
Clarksville (G-3076)
Nucor Bldg Systems Sls Corp ....C 972 524-5407
Terrell (G-19744)
Omnimax International Inc ....E 817 481-3521
Fort Worth (G-6882)
Palomar Modular Buildings LLC ....C 469 727-0727
Desoto (G-5438)
Parkline Inc ....D 409 935-5743
Hitchcock (G-8339)
Parkline Inc ....D 409 935-1037
La Marque (G-13713)
Powell Electrical Systems Inc ....E 281 452-4885
Houston (G-11374)
Ramtech Building Systems Inc ....E 817 473-9376
Mansfield (G-14707)
Rhodes Building Systems Inc ....E 979 596-1451
Somerville (G-19023)
Rigid Global Buildings LLC ....B 281 443-9065
Houston (G-11621)
Shaun K Boyer ....F 281 442-3800
Houston (G-11848)
Southwest Metal Systems LLC ....E 903 569-8811
Mineola (G-15513)
Steel Building Supply Inc ....E 936 598-6373
Center (G-3009)
Techmar Industries LLC ....E 832 246-6200
Spring (G-19175)
Unique Stainless Designs LLC ....F 972 254-8424
Grand Prairie (G-7990)
USA Frametek LLC ....E 512 515-6500
Liberty Hill (G-14130)
Xg Ventures LLC ....F 936 744-1800
Trinity (G-20020)

BUILDINGS, PREFABRICATED: Wholesalers

Custom Building Products Inc ....D 972 641-6996
Grand Prairie (G-7860)

BUILDINGS: Farm & Utility

D & R Custom Wldg & Cnstr Inc ....E 830 997-1058
Fredericksburg (G-7175)

BUILDINGS: Mobile, For Commercial Use

Atomic Container Homes Inc ....E 915 433-4817
El Paso (G-5653)
Bristlecone Ventures 2 LLC ....E 512 231-9603
Manor (G-14646)
G-Con LLC ....F 214 220-4303
College Station (G-3184)

BUILDINGS: Portable

Abac LLC ....F 940 479-9163
Ponder (G-17092)
Apache Construction Inc ....F 903 839-2242
Whitehouse (G-20725)
Atlas Building Systems Inc ....F 903 597-4211
Tyler (G-20052)
Atlas Building Systems Inc ....E 903 865-1153
Wills Point (G-20873)
Atomic Container Homes Inc ....E 915 433-4817
El Paso (G-5653)
Bathsystem America LLC ....E 713 382-8585
Houston (G-8825)
Cornerstone Bldg Brands Inc ....D 713 466-0712
Houston (G-9322)
Doyles Construction & Mfg Inc ....F 940 549-5517
Graham (G-7780)
Floyd Tate A ....F 409 745-3256
Orange (G-16243)
General Shlters of Bvlle Texas ....E 936 598-3389
Center (G-2998)
Ghm Corp ....C 972 840-1200
Dallas (G-4406)
Hawk Portable Buildings Inc ....E 325 893-5120
Clyde (G-3163)
Indicom Buildings Inc ....D 817 447-1213
Burleson (G-2582)
Lakeside Trailer Sales ....F 936 564-6252
Nacogdoches (G-15701)
Lubbock Gas & Building Inc ....F 806 745-9695
Lubbock (G-14441)
Minearc Systems America LLC ....F 214 337-5100
Dallas (G-4678)
Mobile Mini Inc ....F 512 251-2461
Austin (G-1347)
Modular Concepts Inc ....F 817 945-1667
Fort Worth (G-6845)
Nci Group Inc ....C 817 481-2501
Southlake (G-19080)
Nci Group Inc ....B 281 897-7788
Houston (G-11016)
Nci Group Inc ....E 806 747-4291
Lubbock (G-14451)
Nci Group Inc ....B 713 466-7788
Houston (G-11019)
Protect Controls Inc ....C 713 691-5183
Conroe (G-3355)
Robertson-Ceco II Corporation ....C 281 897-7788
Houston (G-11644)
Schulte Building Systems Inc ....D 281 304-6111
Hockley (G-8348)
Standard Structures Inc ....D 432 580-5353
Odessa (G-16164)
United Structures America Inc ....B 281 442-8247
Houston (G-12458)
United Structures America Inc ....C 281 442-8247
Houston (G-12459)
Whirlwind Holding Company Inc ....B 713 946-7140
Houston (G-12660)
Whirlwind Steel Buildings Inc ....B 713 946-7140
Houston (G-12661)

BUILDINGS: Prefabricated, Metal

Athens Steel Building Corp ....E 903 675-5733
Athens (G-820)
Berrys Tin Shop Inc ....F 903 586-3552
Jacksonville (G-13229)
Capco Steel Inc ....E 210 493-9992
San Antonio (G-17979)
Cato Construction Company ....E 979 830-1398
Brenham (G-2250)

PRODUCT

Cornerstone Bldg Brands Inc ....C 281 897-7788
  Houston (G-9320)
Cotton Construction Inc ....F 936 931-2510
  Waller (G-20496)
Geometrica Inc ....F 832 220-1200
  Cypress (G-3795)
Guard-All Bldg Sltions Mfg LLC ....E 877 397-1594
  Dallas (G-4420)
Horizon Structural Systems Inc ....G 830 629-8000
  New Braunfels (G-15803)
Infinity Carports Inc ....F 903 765-2057
  Edgewood (G-5572)
M&I Electric LLC ....C 409 838-0441
  Beaumont (G-1922)
Mg Building Materials Ltd ....G 210 798-0650
  San Antonio (G-18297)
Nci Group Inc ....E 281 897-7788
  Houston (G-11015)
Nci Group Inc ....D 817 488-8511
  Irving (G-13121)
Supaks Inc ....E 979 968-5654
  La Grange (G-13701)
Tyler Building Systems LP ....E 903 561-3000
  Tyler (G-20167)

BUILDINGS: Prefabricated, Wood

Cook Sales Inc ....E 512 321-2888
  Bastrop (G-1751)
Gfrc 360 LLC ....E 972 494-9000
  Garland (G-7503)
Morgan Building Transport ....E 972 864-7300
  Dallas (G-4688)
Murray Building & Crane Inds ....D 713 464-6506
  Houston (G-10944)
Neon Electric Corporation ....D 281 987-1144
  Houston (G-11023)
Neopod Systems LLC ....F 954 603-3100
  New Braunfels (G-15816)
Oldcastle Buildingenvelope Inc ....A 972 551-6100
  Terrell (G-19746)
Palomar Modular Buildings LLC ....C 469 727-0727
  Desoto (G-5438)
Ramtech Building Systems Inc ....E 817 473-9376
  Mansfield (G-14707)
Raul Gonzalez ....F 956 793-5359
  Elsa (G-6080)
Sustainable Modular MGT Inc ....F 972 619-7300
  Plano (G-17016)
Tuff Shed Inc ....E 903 236-9126
  Longview (G-14324)

BUILDINGS: Prefabricated, Wood

Atlas Building Systems Inc ....F 903 597-4211
  Tyler (G-20052)
Atlas Building Systems Inc ....E 903 865-1153
  Wills Point (G-20873)
General Shlters of Bvlle Texas ....E 936 598-3389
  Center (G-2998)
Hawk Portable Buildings Inc ....E 325 893-5120
  Clyde (G-3163)
Indicom Buildings Inc ....D 817 447-1213
  Burleson (G-2582)
Morgan Building & Spa Mfg Corp ....D 254 629-1599
  Eastland (G-5568)

BUMPERS: Motor Vehicle

Road Kare International LP ....E 972 647-8300
  Grand Prairie (G-7967)
Tietjen Inc ....E 979 249-3888
  La Grange (G-13703)

BURGLAR ALARM MAINTENANCE & MONITORING SVCS

Enterprise SEC Sltions Txas Inc ....E 940 320-3778
  Justin (G-13343)
Texas SEC & Surveillance Inc ....E 512 693-4003
  Round Rock (G-17693)
Timekeepers Inc ....D 830 331-1224
  Boerne (G-2142)

BURIAL VAULTS: Concrete Or Precast Terrazzo

A & W Industries Inc ....E 817 481-3577
  Grapevine (G-8010)
Buena Vista Burial Park Inc ....F 956 542-5271
  Brownsville (G-2342)

Hauck Enterprises Ltd ....E 409 727-2227
  Port Neches (G-17162)
Surface Burial Vault Monument ....F 361 275-3213
  Cuero (G-3766)
Vault 55 ....F 512 482-8810
  Austin (G-1625)
Wallace Monument Company ....F 806 874-2442
  Clarendon (G-3071)
Wilbert Burial Vault Corp ....E 817 481-3577
  Grapevine (G-8060)
Wilbert Funeral Services Inc ....F 972 291-7854
  Cedar Hill (G-2956)
Wilbert Funeral Services Inc ....E 806 762-1162
  Lubbock (G-14513)
Wilbert Funeral Services Inc ....E 210 922-2122
  San Antonio (G-18619)
Wilbert Funeral Services Inc ....E 972 875-9605
  Ennis (G-6123)

BURNERS: Gas-Oil, Combination

Reatta Energy Inc ....F 432 682-7495
  Midland (G-15378)

BURS: Dental

Sybron Dental Specialties Inc ....A 469 635-6100
  Coppell (G-3448)

BUS BARS: Electrical

Ies Holdings Inc ....D 713 860-1500
  Houston (G-10316)
Powell Industries Inc ....B 713 944-6900
  Houston (G-11376)
Schneider Electric Usa Inc ....C 972 236-0300
  Coppell (G-3444)

BUSHINGS & BEARINGS

Baart Industrial Group ....F 713 690-1690
  Houston (G-8783)
Esna LLC ....B 817 281-8816
  North Richland Hills (G-15877)
J DS Machine Shop ....F 903 532-6240
  Howe (G-12734)
Jc/Fz Holdings Inc ....E 713 948-6000
  Houston (G-10459)

BUSINESS ACTIVITIES: Non-Commercial Site

A E & Sons LLC ....F 281 898-4021
  Pearland (G-16535)
Akhu Therapeutics Inc ....G 979 820-2740
  College Station (G-3173)
Alltrans Port Trucking Inc ....E 713 673-3844
  Houston (G-8559)
Ambassador Facility Svcs LLC ....E 210 849-7677
  Cibolo (G-3061)
Arismendy Josias ....E 817 353-1244
  Fort Worth (G-6401)
Biotool LLC ....F 713 732-2181
  Houston (G-8887)
Bless-Scent Candle Company LLC ....F 832 431-9923
  Cypress (G-3779)
C&D Bobcat and Backhoe LLC ....F 512 358-0163
  Austin (G-1018)
Caballo Loco Midstream LLC ....F 432 262-1011
  Midland (G-15154)
Cavern Solutions Inc ....F 713 393-7733
  Houston (G-9103)
Cuda Express II Inc ....E 806 433-1896
  Bushland (G-2621)
Deep Imaging Technologies Inc ....F 281 290-0492
  Tomball (G-19973)
Diamond P Lease & Well Svc Inc ....D 979 884-6111
  Dime Box (G-5484)
E Z Roustabout ....F 432 556-8419
  Midland (G-15201)
Eclectic Innvtive Slutions LLC ....F 737 999-1907
  Dripping Springs (G-5505)
Edmonds Pubg & Media Group LLC ....F 214 460-7560
  Colleyville (G-3213)
Education Advanced Inc ....G 903 858-4497
  Tyler (G-20083)
Eduspark Inc ....E 512 535-6139
  Austin (G-1116)
El Tejano Hispanic Community ....F 361 884-2238
  Corpus Christi (G-3518)
Epic Provisions LLC ....F 512 944-8502
  Austin (G-1129)

Fishbowl Games LLC ....F 469 449-3275
  Dallas (G-4366)
Forge Tech Inc ....G 888 854-8414
  Kemah (G-13474)
G & G Logging LLC ....E 936 269-9086
  Joaquin (G-13310)
Gill Assoc Prprty MGT Systems ....G 832 644-9751
  Humble (G-12770)
Greenbasket Inc ....E 212 203-3302
  Frisco (G-7259)
Hall-Houston Exploration LP ....G 713 333-0975
  Houston (G-10095)
Hempstead Halide Inc ....E 409 572-2505
  Galveston (G-7400)
High Plins Cntrs MGT Group Inc ....E 806 935-5858
  Dumas (G-5522)
Homeart Designs Inc ....F 956 724-4412
  Laredo (G-13893)
Huffman & Huffman Inc ....G 972 434-3640
  Lewisville (G-14055)
JD Pro-Service LLC ....F 936 264-4003
  Conroe (G-3314)
JMJ Organics Ltd ....F 281 798-3056
  Crosby (G-3735)
Jose Alfonsin ....F 210 717-2306
  San Antonio (G-18208)
Jwb Consulting Service Inc ....F 817 675-6419
  Midland (G-15263)
K-C Lease Service Inc ....E 979 323-9911
  Louise (G-14352)
Kmr Group LLC ....G 713 932-6988
  Houston (G-10543)
Light Emtting Dds-Nlimited LLC ....F 512 267-7315
  Lago Vista (G-13806)
Lightning Fluid Services Inc ....F 361 396-0801
  Alice (G-224)
M2w Inc ....D 972 407-1332
  Mesquite (G-15059)
Marvin Dace Company ....F 281 482-1450
  Alvin (G-373)
Measurement Services Inc ....F 361 227-4998
  Alice (G-228)
Mooala Brands LLC ....F 214 206-1902
  Dallas (G-4687)
Nicole Dionne ....F 310 699-7556
  Austin (G-1366)
Nu Energy Services LP ....F 817 832-0724
  Aledo (G-200)
Paragon Directional Drlg LLC ....F 903 880-7398
  Granbury (G-7804)
Percomonline Incorporated ....F 325 480-2617
  Abilene (G-64)
Petrochem Energy LLC ....F 713 234-7814
  Sugar Land (G-19525)
Peyton Salas & Mendoza LLC ....E 512 784-5875
  Houston (G-11313)
Precision Joint Solution Inc ....F 972 351-0470
  Austin (G-1429)
R-Interests LLC ....F 940 759-4181
  Muenster (G-15672)
Rock Solid Crushed Stone Inc ....F 903 587-3448
  Leonard (G-14002)
Scott Fennell Inc ....E 817 822-1283
  Iola (G-12900)
Sherrod Services LLC ....F 254 729-3177
  Thornton (G-19943)
Sigma Drilling Tech LLC ....F 281 656-9298
  Katy (G-13442)
Slz Rebar LLC ....F 832 427-5860
  Cypress (G-3820)
Threet Pallet LLC ....E 972 489-6887
  Ennis (G-6119)
Transition Superior Systems Lc ....F 325 690-0248
  Merkel (G-15018)
Ultimate Control Solutions Inc ....F 972 383-9414
  Dallas (G-5129)
Virtual Realities ....F 409 599-7863
  Dickinson (G-5479)
Visualml Operations LLC ....G 855 847-8256
  Liberty Hill (G-14131)
Well-Foam Inc ....C 432 276-3290
  Odessa (G-16210)
White Cloud Security Inc ....F 512 887-8783
  Cedar Park (G-2990)
Yadblue LLC ....F 214 542-6140
  Southlake (G-19084)

BUSINESS FORMS WHOLESALERS

Brunswick Press Inc ....E 713 462-0600
  Houston (G-9000)

Colvin Painovich LP ....F 512 459-4139
Austin (G-1057)
HFS Holding Corporation ....F 214 634-8600
Dallas (G-4454)
Rediform Inc ....E 972 393-8080
Coppell (G-3438)
Safeguard Business Systems Inc ....C 800 523-2422
Dallas (G-4926)

BUSINESS FORMS: Printed, Continuous

Data Print Ltd ....E 806 324-4350
Amarillo (G-420)
Impressive Image Works Inc ....E 903 597-4599
Tyler (G-20101)
Tst/Impreso Inc ....D 972 462-0100
Coppell (G-3451)

BUSINESS FORMS: Printed, Manifold

Blumbergexcelsior Inc ....E 817 462-1530
Arlington (G-632)
Cash Engraving Co ....F 817 831-8585
Fort Worth (G-6495)
Ennis Inc ....A 972 775-9801
Midlothian (G-15480)
Impreso Inc ....D 972 462-0100
Coppell (G-3421)
Label Products Inc ....E 713 869-2959
Houston (G-10584)
Quality Graphics & Forms Inc ....F 915 592-4500
El Paso (G-5922)
R R Donnelley & Sons Company ....C 936 564-4683
Nacogdoches (G-15711)
R R Donnelley & Sons Company ....D 972 353-6130
Lewisville (G-14086)
Rediform Inc ....E 972 393-8080
Coppell (G-3438)
Royal Business Forms Inc ....E 817 640-5253
Arlington (G-774)
Taylor Communications Inc ....E 972 581-7711
Dallas (G-5038)
Weyerhaeuser Company ....D 972 929-8581
Irving (G-13207)
Wood Printing Company Inc ....F 214 421-7393
Dallas (G-5201)
Wrs Group Ltd ....E 254 776-6461
Waco (G-20481)

BUSINESS MACHINE REPAIR, ELECTRIC

Laser Pros International Corp ....E 715 369-5995
Marshall (G-14786)
National Presort LP ....D 214 634-2288
Fort Worth (G-6862)
Precision Dcment Solutions Inc ....E 866 916-1177
Carrollton (G-2792)

BUSINESS SUPPORT SVCS

Ash Automated Ctrl Systems LLC ....F 281 346-1400
Fulshear (G-7327)
Hughes Tank Company Inc ....F 972 366-8684
Venus (G-20218)
Movement Industries Corp ....F 713 849-1300
Houston (G-10928)
Nakent LLC ....F 619 212-2277
San Antonio (G-18329)

BUSINESS TRAINING SVCS

Kwik-Kopy Corporation ....C 281 256-4100
Cypress (G-3808)
Tillman Learning LLC ....F 866 540-9677
Plano (G-17033)

BUTADIENE RUBBERS: Polybutadiene

Lion Elastomers Orange LLC ....C 409 924-4500
Orange (G-16252)

BUTADIENE: Indl, Organic, Chemical

Lyondell Chemical Company ....D 361 572-2500
Victoria (G-20284)
Texas Petrochemicals LP ....E 713 477-9211
Houston (G-12243)

CABINETS & CASES: Show, Display & Storage, Exc Wood

BAC Products Inc ....E 832 230-1463
Houston (G-8785)

Classic Millwork and Products ....E 915 833-9922
El Paso (G-5696)
Kcm Cabinets Inc ....F 210 695-2213
San Antonio (G-18221)
Thom-Bat-Ler Enterprises ....F 972 660-4056
Grand Prairie (G-7982)

CABINETS: Bathroom Vanities, Wood

Brandom Holdings LLC ....C 800 366-8001
Hillsboro (G-8323)
Cameron Knight ....F 972 636-7172
Royse City (G-17717)
Donovan White Cabinets Inc ....F 903 569-5611
Mineola (G-15506)
Dunlaps Custom Cabinets Inc ....F 254 829-2279
Elm Mott (G-6063)
Fixture Exchange Corporation ....F 817 429-2496
Joshua (G-13320)
Kent Moore Cabinets Inc ....E 979 775-2906
Bryan (G-2482)
Leedo Manufacturing Co LP ....C 866 465-3336
East Bernard (G-5559)
Leedo Manufacturing Co LP ....B 866 995-3336
Stafford (G-19347)
Manufacturing Group Amer Inc ....A 214 467-4444
Dallas (G-4633)
Moehnke Custom Cabinetry ....F 512 352-6506
Taylor (G-19660)
Pavliska Cabinets Inc ....F 254 773-4461
Troy (G-20032)
Republic Nat Inds Texas LP ....C 903 935-3680
Marshall (G-14800)
West-Reeves, Ltd. ....C 972 938-9623
Waxahachie (G-20569)
Woodcrafters Home Products LLC ......D 956 565-6329
Weslaco (G-20671)

CABINETS: Entertainment

Unique Cabinets Inc ....E 512 251-3058
Pflugerville (G-16690)

CABINETS: Entertainment Units, Household, Wood

Cabinets Deluxe By Dale Inc ....D 512 259-2531
Freeport (G-7195)
Clearmediaone Inc ....E 713 622-9393
Houston (G-9214)
Knot Hole LLC ....E 254 634-0773
Killeen (G-13614)
Texas Home & Projects LLC ....G 956 546-8400
Brownsville (G-2410)

CABINETS: Factory

G2 Automated Technologies LLC ....E 972 479-0699
Dallas (G-4390)
Image Furnishings Inc ....F 806 747-6500
Lubbock (G-14424)
Kuba-Tech Industries LLC ....F 817 924-5520
Fort Worth (G-6775)
Larry Prters Cstm Intr Dsgns I ....F 409 296-3868
Winnie (G-20888)
Metroplex Millworks Inc ....F 214 358-1770
Dallas (G-4672)
Robinson Aerospace Inc ....F 817 253-0639
Dallas (G-4906)
Travis Millwork Inc ....E 210 525-8088
San Antonio (G-18564)

CABINETS: Filing, Wood

Hayes Building Service Inc ....F 940 484-7775
Crossroads (G-3748)

CABINETS: Kitchen, Metal

Asmar Custom Cabinets Inc ....F 972 241-7676
Dallas (G-3971)
Badj Inc ....F 254 918-5397
Stephenville (G-19407)
Jormac Aerospace Inc ....E 972 436-7069
Coppell (G-3424)

CABINETS: Kitchen, Wood

3 L Designs Inc ....E 214 920-9223
Dallas (G-3867)
3 Star Custom Cabinets Inc ....F 940 686-2124
Pilot Point (G-16720)

34 Oaks Fine Cabinetry LLC ....D 469 533-0730
Dallas (G-3868)
A & C Cabinet Co ....E 817 244-4303
Fort Worth (G-6334)
Alamo City Counter Tops Inc ....E 210 732-4800
San Antonio (G-17880)
All Wood Custom Cabinets Inc ....F 940 686-2795
Pilot Point (G-16721)
American Woodmark Corporation ....C 469 635-1960
Coppell (G-3409)
Americana Cabinets LLC ....G 281 973-8255
Humble (G-12746)
B & W Remodeling Inc ....E 817 485-0444
North Richland Hills (G-15874)
Bassett Woodworks ....F 915 855-2144
El Paso (G-5659)
Benedettini Cabinets LP ....C 281 633-8200
Rosenberg (G-17575)
Bentwood Companies Inc ....D 972 227-6855
Lancaster (G-13839)
Builders Firstsource-Ohio Vall ....C 214 880-3500
Dallas (G-4067)
C K Higgs ....E 713 666-5739
Bellaire (G-1992)
Cabinet Creation Inc ....E 830 709-4116
Lytle (G-14573)
Cabinettech Inc ....F 325 670-0414
Abilene (G-28)
Central Renovation Solutions ....F 469 567-2400
Lancaster (G-13842)
Champion Custom Cabinets Inc ....F 817 834-8552
Fort Worth (G-6507)
Classic Millwork and Products ....E 915 833-9922
El Paso (G-5696)
Cmcabco LLC ....F 972 617-8605
Waxahachie (G-20536)
Coleman Wood Products Inc ....E 940 440-2300
Aubrey (G-849)
Colony Cabinets Inc ....E 903 753-2488
Longview (G-14211)
Creative Custom Cabinets Inc ....F 512 821-0300
Round Rock (G-17639)
Creative Wood Concepts Inc ....F 972 539-2555
Dallas (G-4184)
Custom Cabinet Doors Inc ....E 940 686-2808
Pilot Point (G-16723)
D & H Quality Cabinets ....F 903 882-0274
Lindale (G-14134)
Daycor Enterprises Inc ....F 972 838-2700
Melissa (G-14996)
Delta Millwork ....E 713 849-2281
Houston (G-9432)
Dozier Cabinet Works Inc ....E 940 566-5315
Sanger (G-18725)
Dutch Marble Creations ....F 956 399-6767
San Benito (G-18656)
E & A Ventures LLC ....E 903 297-0829
Longview (G-14225)
Elite Cabinets & Closets ....F 903 737-0848
Paris (G-16361)
Encore Cabinets Ltd ....E 979 968-9482
La Grange (G-13694)
Espitias Cabinet & Door Makers ....E 713 329-9515
Houston (G-9699)
Evans Cabinet and Door Ltd ....E 979 836-6934
Brenham (G-2253)
Global Casework Mfg Inc ....E 281 494-6181
Sugar Land (G-19487)
Gracy Cabinets ....F 972 843-3123
Lavon (G-13943)
Graham Custom Cabinets LLC ....F 940 549-4311
Graham (G-7782)
Greenhaw Cabinets Inc ....F 325 646-8319
Brownwood (G-2430)
Growth Holdings LLC ....F 972 241-9535
Dallas (G-4418)
Gulf Coast Cabinet Doors LLC ....F 979 265-1519
Clute (G-3155)
Gunckel Archtectural Millworks ....E 830 303-0688
Seguin (G-18839)
Hartsfield & Pierce Cabinet Co ....F 972 288-5487
Irving (G-13053)
Heartland Furniture Inc ....E 817 483-6161
Arlington (G-695)
Hill Country Cabinet Shop Inc ....F 830 228-5062
Spring Branch (G-19270)
Home Mart Inc ....F 956 724-4521
Laredo (G-13892)
Homeart Designs Inc ....F 956 724-4412
Laredo (G-13893)

PRODUCT

Hornbeek Enterprises Inc ....F 817 478-2447
  Arlington *(G-699)*

Hornsbys Custom Cabinets ....F 830 693-2420
  Marble Falls *(G-14744)*

Houston Cabinets Inc ....E 713 349-0848
  Houston *(G-10220)*

Interior Fixture Installations ....E 972 412-9773
  Rowlett *(G-17707)*

J-Kraft Inc ....E 281 876-2535
  Humble *(G-12780)*

JB Commercial Millwork Inc ....E 903 989-2241
  Trenton *(G-20017)*

Jim R Reynolds & Assoc Inc ....E 832 257-2312
  Spring *(G-19138)*

Johnnys Cabinet Shop Inc ....F 940 686-2496
  Pilot Point *(G-16725)*

Johnnys Custom Cabinet ....F 281 498-8950
  Stafford *(G-19336)*

Johnson Cabinets & Woodworking .....F 512 266-7099
  Austin *(G-1258)*

Jormac Aerospace Inc ....E 972 436-7069
  Coppell *(G-3424)*

Kamma Group Inc ....G...... 281 499-5888
  Stafford *(G-19338)*

Keeling Homes Inc ....F 806 655-2071
  Canyon *(G-2671)*

Kenneth M Burgin ....F 903 636-4086
  Big Sandy *(G-2065)*

Kent Moore Cabinets Ltd ....F 281 480-8883
  Richmond *(G-17459)*

Killeen Marble ....E 254 699-3408
  Killeen *(G-13612)*

Knot Hole LLC ....E 254 634-0773
  Killeen *(G-13614)*

Lawrence Furniture Co Inc ....F 361 572-3710
  Victoria *(G-20283)*

Lundy Services LLC ....E 972 494-2554
  Garland *(G-7539)*

Maryfield Enterprises LP ....D 210 344-4151
  San Antonio *(G-18281)*

Masco Cabinetry LLC ....C 972 725-4298
  Duncanville *(G-5533)*

Master Woodcraft Cabinetry LLC ....D 903 935-0500
  Marshall *(G-14793)*

Mastercraft Wood Products LP ....B 903 935-0500
  Marshall *(G-14794)*

Metroplex Cabinets Inc ....D 940 321-5151
  Corinth *(G-3457)*

Metroplex Millworks Inc ....F 214 358-1770
  Dallas *(G-4672)*

Mikada Cabinets LLC ....D 713 681-6116
  Houston *(G-10878)*

Mike Conkles Custom Cabinets ....E 817 483-9658
  Kennedale *(G-13499)*

Millwood Cabinets LLP ....E 903 567-3333
  Canton *(G-2658)*

MJB Wood Group LLC ....E 972 401-0005
  Coppell *(G-3428)*

Morrow Cabinets Inc ....F 972 221-7551
  Lewisville *(G-14070)*

Nations Cabinetry LLC ....E 210 681-8477
  San Antonio *(G-18335)*

New Saw Inc ....E 972 288-2117
  Mesquite *(G-15064)*

OBrien Hogman Associates LLC ....F 972 823-1900
  Irving *(G-13130)*

Ogletree Custom Cabinets ....G...... 903 356-2611
  Quinlan *(G-17225)*

Oncken & Sons Cabinet Shop ....F 210 333-4611
  San Antonio *(G-18355)*

Osborne Cabinets & Millwork ....E 713 802-0092
  Port Neches *(G-17167)*

Osborne Cabinets & Millwork ....E 409 899-1191
  Beaumont *(G-1936)*

Patterson Manufacturing Inc ....F 903 757-0523
  Longview *(G-14288)*

Pechal Cabinets LLC ....F 254 773-4460
  Temple *(G-19697)*

Petroplex Cabinets Inc ....G...... 432 333-2025
  Odessa *(G-16121)*

Plano Door Service Inc ....F 972 422-1695
  Plano *(G-16973)*

Prestige Custom Cabinetry ....G...... 832 674-8074
  Cypress *(G-3813)*

Procraft Cabinetry Inc ....F 832 203-5736
  Houston *(G-11433)*

Procraft Cabinetry Dallas LLC ....F 469 607-2588
  Dallas *(G-4831)*

Progressive Millworks Inc ....D 512 832-0551
  Austin *(G-1436)*

Prorock Granite & Cabinets Inc ....F 832 486-9414
  Houston *(G-11451)*

Q Cabinets Inc ....F 915 859-5252
  Socorro *(G-19018)*

Qsi Custom Cabinets LP ....E 512 443-3303
  Austin *(G-1440)*

R & R Custom Cabinets Inc ....F 972 247-4697
  Carrollton *(G-2883)*

Republic National Cabinet Corp ....F 903 935-3680
  Marshall *(G-14801)*

Rick Triplett ....F 214 823-2830
  Dallas *(G-4899)*

River City Cabinets Inc ....F 512 442-9990
  Austin *(G-1467)*

Robert V Johns & Associates ....F 214 741-1912
  Dallas *(G-4905)*

RWS Cabinets LLC ....F 936 760-2407
  Conroe *(G-3360)*

S & S Cabinet Shop Inc ....F 325 655-6757
  San Angelo *(G-17825)*

Skyline Cabinetry Inc ....F 972 620-8880
  Farmers Branch *(G-6214)*

Skyline Cabinetry Inc ....F 972 620-8880
  Dallas *(G-4970)*

Southern Cabinets ....G...... 254 799-2271
  Waco *(G-20459)*

Square Cabinetry LLC ....E 214 838-2225
  Dallas *(G-5000)*

Sunshine Custom Cabinets Inc ....F 817 572-5201
  Fort Worth *(G-7023)*

Taylor Craft Cabinet & Door ....E 512 352-6355
  Taylor *(G-19662)*

Texas Home & Projects LLC ....G...... 956 546-8400
  Brownsville *(G-2410)*

Thom-Bat-Ler Enterprises ....F 972 660-4056
  Grand Prairie *(G-7982)*

Tri-Tex Cabinets Inc ....D 940 686-2617
  Pilot Point *(G-16731)*

Unique Cabinets Inc ....E 512 251-3058
  Pflugerville *(G-16690)*

US Remodelers Inc ....E 214 488-6300
  Lewisville *(G-14103)*

W R Watson Corporation ....F 281 495-2800
  Stafford *(G-19397)*

Walcott Enterprises Inc ....E 325 773-5212
  Stamford *(G-19402)*

Western Cabinets Inc ....C 469 916-5350
  Dallas *(G-5181)*

Western Cabinets Inc ....E 972 293-2450
  Cedar Hill *(G-2955)*

Zamo Inc ....E 210 667-1717
  Saint Hedwig *(G-17761)*

CABINETS: Office, Metal

Spaceman Home & Office Inc ....F 713 688-8808
  Houston *(G-11991)*

CABINETS: Office, Wood

Alamo City Counter Tops Inc ....E 210 732-4800
  San Antonio *(G-17880)*

Aris Designs Inc ....F 361 881-8131
  Corpus Christi *(G-3475)*

Cabinets By Michael Inc ....F 817 485-1962
  Fort Worth *(G-6485)*

Cabinets Deluxe By Dale Inc ....D 512 259-2531
  Freeport *(G-7195)*

Hill Country Cabinet Shop Inc ....F 830 228-5062
  Spring Branch *(G-19270)*

J C Manufacturing Inc ....F 903 473-3770
  Emory *(G-6083)*

Keystone Millwork Inc ....E 979 823-4846
  Bryan *(G-2485)*

Kuba-Tech Industries LLC ....F 817 924-5520
  Fort Worth *(G-6775)*

Southwest Cabinet Corporation ....D 817 460-8681
  Pantego *(G-16352)*

CABINETS: Radio & Television, Metal

AAe Manufacturing Co Inc ....F 956 748-0033
  Rio Hondo *(G-17474)*

CABINETS: Show, Display, Etc, Wood, Exc Refrigerated

Aircraft Composite Inc ....F 214 638-0138
  Dallas *(G-3909)*

Amarillo Plstic Fbricators Ltd ....F 806 372-1207
  Amarillo *(G-397)*

Bentwood Companies Inc ....D 972 227-6855
  Lancaster *(G-13839)*

E and H Originals In Wood Inc ....F 832 203-7629
  Houston *(G-9552)*

F C Designs Inc ....F 713 462-1442
  Houston *(G-9743)*

Falcon Wood Products 2 Ltd ....E 936 295-9381
  Huntsville *(G-12811)*

Kitchen Cabinets Inc ....D 972 660-6304
  Grand Prairie *(G-7905)*

Morgan Cabinetry Inc ....F 972 278-8836
  Garland *(G-7555)*

Quality Case & Fixture Inc ....E 409 832-3200
  Beaumont *(G-1943)*

Sunrise Woods Designs ....D 972 842-3579
  Ferris *(G-6232)*

Texas Fixtures and Interiors ....D 512 846-1998
  Hutto *(G-12886)*

CABLE & OTHER PAY TELEVISION DISTRIBUTION

Addvantage Tech Group Inc ....E 918 251-9121
  Carrollton *(G-2853)*

CABLE & PAY TV SVCS: Satellite Master Antenna Sys/SMATV

Mo2 Inc ....F 214 575-7600
  Dallas *(G-4682)*

Satpro Network Inc ....E 972 675-8475
  Garland *(G-7582)*

CABLE TELEVISION PRDTS

Addvantage Tech Group Inc ....E 918 251-9121
  Carrollton *(G-2853)*

National Electronic Devices ....F 936 273-4111
  Conroe *(G-3333)*

Sigmatron International Inc ....F 830 775-5524
  Del Rio *(G-5324)*

CABLE: Aluminum, Made In Rolling Mills

General Cable Corporation ....E 903 938-8151
  Marshall *(G-14780)*

Southwire Company LLC ....F 940 328-1047
  Mineral Wells *(G-15542)*

CABLE: Coaxial

B Comm Constructors LLC ....E 210 257-0102
  San Antonio *(G-17929)*

Trans Cable International Inc ....E 903 449-4622
  Bonham *(G-2156)*

CABLE: Fiber

Accurate Connections Inc ....E 972 484-8500
  Plano *(G-16769)*

Federal Prison Industries ....C 432 466-2300
  Big Spring *(G-2082)*

Kevin M Ehringer Entps Inc ....D 972 620-4997
  Dallas *(G-4553)*

CABLE: Fiber Optic

Applied Optical Systems Inc ....D 972 509-1500
  Plano *(G-16791)*

Global Teknicians Inc ....E 407 504-9087
  Houston *(G-9978)*

Incab America LLC ....E 833 344-6222
  Arlington *(G-702)*

Jacqueline Construction Inc ....F 469 258-4402
  Garland *(G-7525)*

Megladon Mfg Group Ltd ....E 512 491-0006
  Austin *(G-1336)*

Optical Cable Corporation ....E 972 509-1500
  Plano *(G-16956)*

Sanwa Electronics USA Corp ....G...... 972 503-3031
  Plano *(G-17001)*

Scott Fennell Inc ....E 817 822-1283
  Iola *(G-12900)*

CABLE: Nonferrous, Shipboard

Geo Space LP ....F 713 939-7093
  Houston *(G-9933)*

Xact Technologies USA Corp ....F 403 862-3383
  Houston *(G-12704)*

CABLE: Noninsulated

Bridon-American Corporation ....E 713 921-4101
  Houston (G-8984)
Falcon Fine Wire Wire Pdts Inc ....D 214 771-3441
  Rockwall (G-17548)

CABLE: Ropes & Fiber

Southwest Ocean Services Inc.............E 713 671-9101
  Houston (G-11982)

CABLE: Steel, Insulated Or Armored

Geo Space LP ....F 713 939-7093
  Houston (G-9933)
Suncoast Post-Tension Ltd.................C 281 445-8886
  Houston (G-12100)
Suncoast Post-Tension Ltd.................C 281 445-8886
  Houston (G-12101)
Textray & Strut Ltd ....F 713 864-2551
  Houston (G-12265)

CAGES: Wire

Bright Coop Inc ....C 936 564-8378
  Nacogdoches (G-15686)

CALIBRATING SVCS, NEC

Dnv GL Noble Denton Usa LLC ....B 281 396-1000
  Katy (G-13396)
Gil Automations LLC ....F 713 904-4600
  Houston (G-9957)

CAMERAS & RELATED EQPT: Photographic

Infrared Cameras Inc ....F 409 861-0788
  Beaumont (G-1907)
Osv Investment LLC ....E 512 301-2848
  Dallas (G-4771)
Varieon Inc ....F 469 916-1099
  Lewisville (G-14104)

CANDLE SHOPS

Bless-Scent Candle Company LLC ....F 832 431-9923
  Cypress (G-3779)
Candle Cottage.................................G 409 720-7087
  Orange (G-16233)

CANDLES

Al Root Company...............................F 210 223-2948
  San Antonio (G-17876)
Bless-Scent Candle Company LLC ....F 832 431-9923
  Cypress (G-3779)
Calyan Wax Company LLC ....F 817 455-0895
  Arlington (G-638)
Candle Cottage.................................G 409 720-7087
  Orange (G-16233)
Circle E Candles Inc ....F 830 990-4478
  Fredericksburg (G-7173)
DDB Candles Inc ....F 817 927-3377
  Fort Worth (G-6579)
From Here Inc..................................F 805 368-3363
  Addison (G-128)
Gaines Group LLC ....D 713 467-4774
  Houston (G-9891)
Home Fragrance Holdings Inc ....B 718 641-3759
  Houston (G-10197)
Light House Candles LLC ....E 713 467-4774
  Sugar Land (G-19504)
Natures Finest LLC ....E 972 673-1526
  Plano (G-16939)
Noahmaya Candle Co ....F 210 341-7373
  San Antonio (G-18348)
Reed Candle Company........................C 210 737-7156
  San Antonio (G-18417)
Scentchips Inc ....G 210 341-7373
  San Antonio (G-18456)
Serenity Candles ....F 281 565-0130
  Sugar Land (G-19554)
South Txas Lghthouse For Blind ....C 361 883-6553
  Corpus Christi (G-3627)
St Jude Candle Company LP ....D 281 768-7800
  Houston (G-12033)
Tyler Candle Company LLC ....F 903 877-2298
  Tyler (G-20168)

CANDLES: Wholesalers

Bless-Scent Candle Company LLC ....F 832 431-9923
  Cypress (G-3779)

DDB Candles Inc ....F 817 927-3377
  Fort Worth (G-6579)
Hall Tree Antiques Inc ....D 325 944-4794
  San Angelo (G-17803)

CANDY & CONFECTIONS: Candy Bars, Including Chocolate Covered

Snyders-Lance Inc ....E 214 638-2378
  Dallas (G-4974)

CANDY & CONFECTIONS: Chocolate Candy, Exc Solid Chocolate

Lammes Candies Since 1885 Inc..........F 512 310-1885
  Austin (G-1280)

CANDY & CONFECTIONS: Popcorn Balls/Other Trtd Popcorn Prdts

Amplify Snack Brands Inc...................E 512 600-9893
  Austin (G-920)
Ricos Manufacturing Co Inc ....E 210 226-4168
  Lewisville (G-14088)
Uptown Popcorn LLC ....F 972 291-4767
  Dallas (G-5145)

CANDY, NUT & CONFECTIONERY STORE: Popcorn, Incl Caramel Corn

Uptown Popcorn LLC ....F 972 291-4767
  Dallas (G-5145)

CANDY, NUT & CONFECTIONERY STORES: Candy

Candy Kings Inc ....F 409 762-6100
  Galveston (G-7391)
Flightsafety International Inc ....C 817 571-5925
  Fort Worth (G-6638)
Lammes Candies Since 1885 Inc..........F 512 310-1885
  Austin (G-1280)
Quintessential Chocolates Inc..............F 830 990-9382
  Fredericksburg (G-7187)

CANDY, NUT & CONFECTIONERY STORES: Nuts

Birdsong Corporation.........................E 254 734-2266
  Gorman (G-7771)
Birdsong Corporation.........................F 806 637-7200
  Brownfield (G-2330)
Morven Partners LP ....F 325 372-5727
  San Saba (G-18718)
Ramirez Pecan Farm LLC ....F 915 851-2003
  Clint (G-3147)

CANNED SPECIALTIES

Houston Calco Inc ....G 713 236-8668
  Houston (G-10221)
Texas Titos Inc ....F 830 626-1123
  New Braunfels (G-15828)

CANOPIES: Sheet Metal

Carports Childers & Structures ....F 713 460-2181
  Houston (G-9094)
Heat Shield Inc ....F 903 845-4066
  Gladewater (G-7722)
Metallic Products Corporation...............D 713 856-9696
  Houston (G-10849)

CANS: Aluminum

Palladium Exchange LLC ....F 214 421-8600
  Dallas (G-4778)
Reynolds Metals Company LLC ....A 361 777-2200
  Gregory (G-8104)

CANS: Fiber

Paper Tubes & Sales Co ....E 214 631-0973
  Dallas (G-4787)

CANS: Metal

Ball Metal Beverage Cont Corp ....C 936 760-2255
  Conroe (G-3261)
Ball Metal Beverage Cont Corp ....C 817 551-3100
  Fort Worth (G-6425)

Bway..F 979 779-5900
  Bryan (G-2464)
Crown Cork & Seal Usa Inc ....C 281 240-4838
  Sugar Land (G-19469)
Crown Cork & Seal Usa Inc ....C 936 539-5401
  Conroe (G-3287)
Hoover Group Inc ....E 800 844-8683
  Houston (G-10204)
Kegspeed LLC ....F 267 714-8854
  Austin (G-1266)
Mauser Packaging Solutions ....F 817 473-0259
  Mansfield (G-14692)
Weldforce Fabricators LLC ....E 713 270-7733
  Houston (G-8395)

CANVAS PRDTS

All American Awnings Inc ....E 214 388-5444
  Dallas (G-3919)
Athletic Bag Company LP ....E 903 520-3343
  Tyler (G-20051)
C Cushions Inc ....F 361 729-1244
  Rockport (G-17527)
Canvas USA Inc ....F 361 729-0638
  Rockport (G-17528)
Carports Childers & Structures ....F 713 460-2181
  Houston (G-9094)
Covercraft Industries Inc ....D 940 763-2535
  Wichita Falls (G-20757)
Guard-Line Inc ....C 903 796-4111
  Atlanta (G-843)
Hi-Plains Canvas Products Inc ....E 806 352-5345
  Amarillo (G-492)
Houston Truck Tarps LLC ....F 346 571-1832
  Houston (G-10259)
John C Maudlin Inc ....F 281 334-7224
  Kemah (G-13476)
Lift-All Company Inc ....E 281 445-2256
  Houston (G-10638)
Reef Industries Inc ....D 956 399-1352
  San Benito (G-18663)
Shade Structures Inc ....G 214 905-9500
  Dallas (G-4951)
Southwest Tactical LLC.......................C 915 726-0634
  El Paso (G-5972)
Tarps LLC ....F 833 469-8277
  Austin (G-1714)

CANVAS PRDTS, WHOLESALE

Centex Manufacturing Co ....F 254 752-2531
  Waco (G-20379)
Mick & David Enterprises Inc...............F 214 350-5765
  Dallas (G-4674)

CAPACITORS & CONDENSERS

Cordyne Inc ....D 713 460-5151
  Houston (G-9313)

CAPACITORS: NEC

Integer Holdings Corporation................D 214 618-5243
  Plano (G-16892)
Kemet Electronics Corporation.............F 956 548-7200
  Brownsville (G-2373)
Panasonic Corp North America.............A 956 984-3432
  Mcallen (G-14899)
Steelman Industries Inc ....E 903 984-3061
  Kilgore (G-13594)
Venkel Ltd.......................................E 512 794-0081
  Austin (G-1629)

CAPACITORS: Series

Universal Rectifiers Inc ....E 281 342-8471
  Rosenberg (G-17598)

CAPS: Plastic

Vista Cntrs & Closures LLC ....F 713 609-9250
  Houston (G-12573)

CAR WASH EQPT

Colemn-Hnna Crwash Systems LLC......E 713 683-9878
  Houston (G-9244)
MI T Fine Car Wash Inc.......................E 972 422-0707
  Plano (G-16926)
Twin Distributing Inc ....E 903 463-1194
  Denison (G-5349)
Vizza Wash Services LLC....................E 512 246-8822
  Round Rock (G-17698)

PRODUCT

CAR WASH EQPT & SPLYS WHOLESALERS

Jim Coleman Company ....E 713 683-9878
Houston (G-10474)

CAR WASHES

Genes Paul Enterprises Inc ....E 817 558-7868
Cleburne (G-3091)

CARBIDES

Carbide Grinding Inc ....F 713 944-0015
Houston (G-9090)
Carbide Specialists Inc ....F 281 354-5585
Porter (G-17172)

CARBON & GRAPHITE PRDTS, NEC

Cabot Corporation ....C...... 806 661-3100
Pampa (G-16317)
Carbon Carbn Advanced Tech Inc........E 817 985-2500
Arlington (G-639)
Continental Carbon Company ....D...... 281 647-3700
Houston (G-9283)
E Z Filter Base Manufacturing ....F 972 272-5800
Garland (G-7482)
Poco Graphite Holdings LLC ....B 940 627-2121
Decatur (G-5251)
ROC Industries Inc............................E 713 468-7743
Houston (G-11647)
Winston/Royal Guard Corp ....E 903 757-7341
White Oak (G-20722)

CARBON BLACK

Cabot Corporation ....C...... 806 661-3100
Pampa (G-16317)
Continental Carbon Company ....D....... 281 647-3700
Houston (G-9283)
Engineered Carbons Inc ....D....... 806 274-6347
Borger (G-2178)
Federal Reserve Bank Dallas...............A 214 922-6000
Dallas (G-4358)
G V C Holdings Inc............................B 409 722-8321
Port Neches (G-17161)
Orion Engineered Carbons LLC ....D...... 832 445-3300
Kingwood (G-13651)
Orion Engineered Carbons LLC ....D...... 409 883-9966
Orange (G-16256)
Orion Engineered Carbons LLC ....D...... 806 274-6347
Borger (G-2181)
Tokai Carbon CB Ltd ....E 817 390-8600
Fort Worth (G-7065)
Tokai Carbon CB Ltd ....D...... 432 263-7389
Big Spring (G-2100)
Tokai Carbon CB Ltd ....C...... 806 274-7213
Borger (G-2188)
Venator Americas LLC.......................F 281 719-6000
The Woodlands (G-19936)

CARBON PAPER & INKED RIBBONS

Advanced Materials Group Inc ....D...... 469 246-4100
Garland (G-7428)

CARBON REMOVING SOLVENT

Alcor Inc..F 210 349-6491
San Antonio (G-17890)

CARBON SPECIALTIES Electrical Use

Carbonyx Inc ....E 972 943-3355
Plano (G-16820)

CARDIOVASCULAR SYSTEM DRUGS, EXC DIAGNOSTIC

Bristol-Myers Squibb Company ....E 212 546-4000
Houston (G-8986)

CARDS: Color

Panini America Inc ....D...... 817 662-5300
Irving (G-13139)

CARDS: Greeting

Quad/Graphics Inc ....C...... 972 892-3803
Dallas (G-4841)

CARDS: Identification

Lonestar Badge & Sign Inc ....F 512 357-2261
Martindale (G-14810)
Multi Packg Solutions Intl Ltd............E 214 634-2131
Dallas (G-4705)
New Teraco Inc ....E 800 687-3999
Midland (G-15316)
Signature Cards LP...........................D...... 972 783-7600
Richardson (G-17398)
Talbot Group Inc ....E 866 866-5020
Hurst (G-12860)

CARDS: Playing

Carta Mundi Inc................................D...... 214 330-7761
Dallas (G-4087)

CARPET & RUG CLEANING & REPAIRING PLANTS

Exclusive Oriental Rugs Inc.................F 214 747-5557
Dallas (G-4342)

CARPET & UPHOLSTERY CLEANING PLANTS

Ambassador Facility Svcs LLC ....E 210 849-7677
Cibolo (G-3061)

CARPET & UPHOLSTERY CLEANING SVCS

Boriack Interiors Inc ....E 214 376-1814
Dallas (G-4044)
Christopher RAD Nader.......................F 512 442-5326
Cedar Park (G-2963)
E Z Cleaning Solutions ....F 214 841-9626
Dallas (G-4286)

CARPET & UPHOLSTERY CLEANING SVCS: Carpet/Furniture, On Loc

Melvin Hammon ....F 806 665-2667
Pampa (G-16328)

CARPETS & RUGS: Tufted

Mohawk Industries Inc ....C....... 210 564-8849
San Antonio (G-18316)
Mohawk Industries Inc ....C....... 956 630-4709
McAllen (G-14891)
Mohawk Industries Inc ....F 972 874-5820
Flower Mound (G-6272)
Mohawk Industries Inc ....E 214 309-4848
Dallas (G-4683)

CARPETS, RUGS & FLOOR COVERING

Clover Group Inc...............................E 915 590-2525
El Paso (G-5698)
Elk Corporation of Texas....................C....... 972 875-9611
Ennis (G-6095)
Elk Corporation of Texas....................D...... 972 851-0500
Dallas (G-4312)
Loloi Inc..C....... 972 503-5656
Dallas (G-4602)
Metro Mats ....E 817 640-6287
Arlington (G-732)
R S Global Inc..................................D...... 972 406-2930
Dallas (G-4857)

CARPORTS: Prefabricated Metal

American Steel Carports Inc................E 866 471-8761
Joshua (G-13317)
Carports Childers & Structures ....F 713 460-2181
Houston (G-9094)
Chism Company ....F 210 824-6315
San Antonio (G-18004)
Metal Construction Mtls Inc................F 281 550-8383
Houston (G-10845)
Peterson Construction ....F 254 227-0738
Axtell (G-1718)
Prengler Ltd ....F 972 965-5188
Sherman (G-18928)
R Slater Enterprises LLC....................F 832 456-4900
Houston (G-11528)
USA Eagle Carports Inc......................F 817 788-5395
Haltom City (G-8161)

CARRIAGES: Horse Drawn

Big Shot LLC ....E 504 877-2335
Lancaster (G-13840)
Island Carriages ....F 409 765-6951
Galveston (G-7401)

CARRIER EQPT: Telephone Or Telegraph

Cuda Express II Inc............................E 806 433-1896
Bushland (G-2621)
Xtera Inc ....E 972 649-5000
Allen (G-307)

CARRYING CASES, WHOLESALE

Quality Cases & Containers LLC ....F 972 690-9911
Richardson (G-17379)

CARS & TRUCKS: Indl Mining

Rockwall Chrysler Dodge....................F 469 698-2100
Rockwall (G-17563)

CASES, WOOD

Schry-Way Cases ....F 806 622-0066
Amarillo (G-511)
Trident Crating & Services Inc.............E 281 227-3999
Houston (G-12372)

CASES: Carrying

Royal Case Company Inc ....C....... 903 868-0288
Sherman (G-18930)

CASES: Carrying, Clothing & Apparel

Bio World Merchandising Inc ....C....... 972 488-0655
Irving (G-12948)
Esip Group LLC.................................F 281 965-4942
Richmond (G-17455)
Richard Eric LLC ....F 214 477-5230
Plano (G-16994)

CASES: Packing, Nailed Or Lock Corner, Wood

Erwin Containers Inc ....E 817 295-5256
Burleson (G-2578)

CASES: Plastic

Tdi LLC...E 972 877-5780
Flower Mound (G-6286)
Team Promark LLC ....E 303 926-1328
Fort Worth (G-7039)

CASES: Shipping, Nailed Or Lock Corner, Wood

Corsicana Box Company Inc ....F 903 874-5615
Corsicana (G-3665)
Main Gate..E 409 832-1546
Beaumont (G-1924)

CASING-HEAD BUTANE & PROPANE PRODUCTION

Irion County Plant.............................G 432 682-6311
Midland (G-15256)

CASING: Boiler, Metal Plate

Ios Inspection ....E 432 684-6440
Midland (G-15255)

CASINGS: Sheet Metal

10-4 Tubular Inc................................E 281 436-0380
Houston (G-8399)

CASINGS: Storage, Missile & Missile Components

Top-Co Cementing Products Inc ....C....... 832 300-3660
Houston (G-12321)

CASKETS & ACCESS

Esser Casket Co LLC ....E 713 225-5548
Houston (G-9701)
Freeman Metal Products Inc ....E 877 278-2275
Greenville (G-8074)

York Group Inc ....F 412 995-1600
Katy (G-13385)

CASKETS WHOLESALERS

Wise Products Co Inc ....F 903 378-2233
Honey Grove (G-8359)

CAST STONE: Concrete

American Cast-Stone Inc ....E 817 695-1800
Arlington (G-615)
Cast Fireplaces ....F 713 937-1080
Houston (G-9095)
Dallas Cast Stone II Corp ....E 940 382-6922
Dallas (G-4213)
Pyramid Stone Co Inc 210 533-3511
San Antonio (G-18402)
Rcss ....D 210 661-8474
Converse (G-3401)

CASTERS

Magnus Mobility Systems Inc ....F 800 527-5142
Dallas (G-4627)
P&H Sales Ltd ....E 817 468-3850
Arlington (G-745)
Roll Master Corp ....D 817 292-4319
Fort Worth (G-6965)

CASTINGS GRINDING: For The Trade

Campbell Grinding & Machine ....F 972 221-2211
Lewisville (G-14032)
Serampore Inds Private Ltd Inc ....E 713 923-6111
Houston (G-11833)
South Coast Grinding Co LLC ....F 713 649-0001
Houston (G-11961)
Texas Honing Inc ....E 281 953-5900
Houston (G-12235)
Western Grinding Co Inc ....F 214 631-3090
Dallas (G-5182)

CASTINGS: Aerospace Investment, Ferrous

Howmet Castings & Services Inc ....B 940 855-8100
Wichita Falls (G-20771)
Lone Star Cast Mch Partners LP ....F 903 986-8300
Kilgore (G-13563)
Netfires LLC ....F 972 603-2702
Grand Prairie (G-7933)

CASTINGS: Aerospace, Aluminum

Be-Technologies Ltd ....F 972 242-1853
Carrollton (G-2704)
Cytec Engineered Materials Inc ....C 903 457-8500
Greenville (G-8068)
Gamma Aerospace LLC ....C 817 477-2193
Mansfield (G-14675)
Harlow Arostructures Texas LLC ....D 817 583-8820
Mansfield (G-14679)
Honeycomb One LLP ....D 817 649-7056
Arlington (G-697)
Skyway Aviation Group LLC ....D 830 278-4481
San Antonio (G-18479)

CASTINGS: Aerospace, Nonferrous, Exc Aluminum

Clear Lk Program Solutions LLC ....F 713 784-0111
Webster (G-20636)
Kgp Group Inc ....F 817 349-3135
Fort Worth (G-6759)

CASTINGS: Aluminum

A&B Foundry LLC ....F 972 247-3579
Dallas (G-3872)
Alloy Casting Co Inc ....E 800 527-1318
Mesquite (G-15025)
Anadite Cal Restoration Tr ....F 817 282-9171
Hurst (G-12833)
Arsham Metal Industries Inc ....E 713 896-8585
Jersey Village (G-13292)
Blaylock Industries Inc ....E 817 831-0170
Fort Worth (G-6456)
Cole Industries Inc ....F 972 271-0280
Garland (G-7460)
Denison Industries Inc ....C 903 786-4444
Denison (G-5340)
Gaus Anodes International LLC ....E 832 243-0700
Houston (G-9906)

Key 3 Casting LLC ....D 817 332-9500
Fort Worth (G-6757)
Longview Brass & Aluminum Co ....F 903 758-8171
Longview (G-14268)
Texas Aluminum Foundry Inc ....E 817 834-5568
Fort Worth (G-7045)
Winklman Wnkleman Partners LLC ....E 817 831-0170
Fort Worth (G-7150)

CASTINGS: Brass, NEC, Exc Die

Longview Brass & Aluminum Co ....F 903 758-8171
Longview (G-14268)

CASTINGS: Bronze, NEC, Exc Die

Deep In Heart Art Foundry ....E 512 321-7868
Bastrop (G-1755)
Hoka Hey Inc ....F 254 445-2017
Stephenville (G-19416)
Schaefer Art Bronze LP ....F 817 460-1102
Arlington (G-779)

CASTINGS: Commercial Investment, Ferrous

Consolidated Casting LLC ....C 972 225-7305
Hutchins (G-12865)
Houston Texcast Inc ....E 713 697-8006
Houston (G-10255)
Sure Cast Inc ....D 512 756-6500
Burnet (G-2615)
Texas Precision Metalcraft Inc ....E 281 240-9191
Sugar Land (G-19563)

CASTINGS: Die, Aluminum

Brown Die Casting & Mfg Inc ....E 972 636-9575
Royse City (G-17716)
Coastal Foundry Company ....E 713 695-4008
Houston (G-9226)
Kruger Aluminum & Brass Fndry ....F 940 767-0432
Wichita Falls (G-20777)
Quality Cast Metals Inc ....E 817 921-3595
Fort Worth (G-6927)
Shamrock Industries Ltd ....E 817 336-1413
Fort Worth (G-6984)
Superior Die Cast LLC ....E 903 586-0637
Jacksonville (G-13260)
Texas Die Casting LLC ....C 903 845-2224
Gladewater (G-7727)

CASTINGS: Die, Magnesium & Magnesium-Base Alloy

Anadite Cal Restoration Tr ....F 817 282-9171
Hurst (G-12833)
Quality Cast Metals Inc ....E 817 921-3595
Fort Worth (G-6927)

CASTINGS: Die, Nonferrous

Fisher Controls Intl LLC ....B 972 542-5512
McKinney (G-14943)
Fore Machine LLC ....D 817 834-6251
Haltom City (G-8141)
Resource Oilfield Pdts Co Inc ....F 281 442-8600
Houston (G-11610)
Wichita Falls Mfg Inc ....E 940 322-4491
Wichita Falls (G-20831)

CASTINGS: Die, Zinc

Gaus Anodes International LLC ....E 832 243-0700
Houston (G-9906)
Superior Die Cast LLC ....E 903 586-0637
Jacksonville (G-13260)
Valley Die Castings Inc ....F 956 630-0268
McAllen (G-14913)

CASTINGS: Ductile

Ebaa Iron Inc ....B 254 629-1737
Eastland (G-5565)
Gas Equipment Company Inc ....C 972 241-2333
Dallas (G-4393)
Metso Minerals Industries Inc ....E 210 491-9521
San Antonio (G-18295)
Prestige Tank & Pump Svcs Inc ....E 512 698-9645
Austin (G-1431)

CASTINGS: Gray Iron

Frazier & Frazier Inds Inc ....B 254 786-2293
Coolidge (G-3407)

Harris Industries Incorporated ....D 903 759-4485
Dallas (G-4437)
Jdh Pacific Inc ....E 562 926-8088
Lubbock (G-14429)
Key 3 Casting LLC ....D 817 332-9500
Fort Worth (G-6757)
Lufkin Gears LLC ....B 936 634-2211
Lufkin (G-14539)
Lufkin Industries LLC ....F 281 495-1100
Missouri City (G-15583)
McKinley Iron Works Inc ....E 817 335-1268
Fort Worth (G-6822)
Meador Products Inc ....D 940 767-8541
Wichita Falls (G-20782)
Texaloy Foundry Company ....E 830 393-6679
Floresville (G-6252)

CASTINGS: Machinery, Aluminum

Airfoil Impellers Corporation ....E 979 822-6418
Bryan (G-2452)
Anodico Corporation ....F 713 690-6100
Houston (G-8647)

CASTINGS: Precision

V-S Precision Usa LLC ....B 915 590-2707
El Paso (G-6022)

CASTINGS: Rubber

Core International LLC ....F 281 880-0200
Houston (G-9314)

CASTINGS: Steel

American Spincast Inc ....D 254 939-0292
Belton (G-2018)
Centrifugal Castings Inc ....E 254 773-9068
Temple (G-19675)
Delta Centrifugal LLC ....C 254 773-9055
Temple (G-19679)
Lone Star Cast Mch Partners LP ....F 903 986-8300
Kilgore (G-13563)
Pumpworks Castings LLC ....E 936 634-4206
Lufkin (G-14546)
Shumate Energy Tech LLC ....E 936 539-9533
Conroe (G-3364)
Star Pipe Usa LLC ....D 620 251-5700
Houston (G-12047)

CASTINGS: Zinc

Anodico Corporation ....F 713 690-6100
Houston (G-8647)
Galvotec Alloys Inc ....C 956 630-3500
McAllen (G-14863)

CATALOG & MAIL-ORDER HOUSES

Casey Products LLC ....E 903 927-3500
Marshall (G-14770)

CATALOG SALES

Finck Cigar Co ....D 210 226-4191
San Antonio (G-18115)

CATALYSTS: Chemical

Albemarle Corporation ....F 281 480-4747
Houston (G-8530)
Brookshire Chemical Svcs LLC ....E 281 371-2600
Brookshire (G-2311)
Eurecat U S Incorporated ....F 281 218-0669
Houston (G-9710)
Eurecat U S Incorporated ....F 281 842-6700
Pasadena (G-16433)
Haldor Topsoe Inc ....C 281 228-5000
Houston (G-10094)
Haldor Topsoe Inc ....C 281 228-5000
Pasadena (G-16452)
Shell Catalysts & Tech LP ....D 713 241-3000
Houston (G-11857)
Syzygy Plasmonics Inc ....F 806 470-5779
Houston (G-12141)
Unicat Catalyst Tech LLC ....E 281 331-2231
Alvin (G-384)
Univation Technologies LLC ....C 713 892-3650
Houston (G-12460)
UOP LLC ....E 832 551-9638
Houston (G-12472)
Whm Custom Services Inc ....D 254 854-2111
Grandview (G-8003)

Employee Codes: A=Over 500 employees, B=251-500
C=101-250, D=51-100, E=20-50, F=10-19, G=9

2021 Harris Texas
Manufacturers Directory

PRODUCT

1413

CATCH BASIN COVERS: Concrete

Atlas Sand Company LLC ....E 432 276-3990
Austin (G-946)

CATERERS

Bluebonnet Bakery Inc ....F 817 731-4233
Fort Worth (G-6458)

Kubys Sausage House Inc ....F 214 363-2231
Dallas (G-4572)

Louisiana Wild LLC ....G 512 799-2537
Austin (G-1304)

Thiink Biig Tax Service Inc ....F 832 606-3380
Katy (G-13450)

Voss Catering Inc ....D 713 257-9898
Bellaire (G-2004)

CAULKING COMPOUNDS

Centennial Moisture Ctrl Inc ....D 214 350-7689
Irving (G-12967)

Dap Products Inc ....D 214 349-9951
Dallas (G-4237)

Gardner-Gibson Mfg Inc ....E 713 637-4791
Houston (G-9900)

Gardner-Gibson Mfg Inc ....F 972 878-1602
Ennis (G-6103)

CEILING SYSTEMS: Luminous, Commercial

Lights Fantastic Pro ....G 469 568-1111
Lewisville (G-14062)

USA Promlite Technology Inc ....F 832 868-8866
Houston (G-12501)

CEMENT & CONCRETE RELATED PRDTS & EQPT: Bituminous

Ammann America Inc ....F 253 266-4023
Houston (G-8625)

Spartan Structures LLC ....E 936 591-9280
Center (G-3008)

W R Grace & Co-Conn ....E 713 223-8353
Houston (G-12586)

CEMENT ROCK: Crushed & Broken

Caprock Materials LLC ....F 806 778-0343
Lubbock (G-14390)

Kirby Stone Company LLC ....E 281 427-7990
Baytown (G-1824)

Rock Solid Crushed Stone Inc ....F 903 587-3448
Leonard (G-14002)

CEMENT, EXC LINOLEUM & TILE

Royal White Cement Inc ....E 713 676-0000
Houston (G-11685)

CEMENT: Hydraulic

Alamo Cement Company ....C 210 208-1880
San Antonio (G-18635)

Ardex Engineered Cements Inc ....D 817 435-5020
Mansfield (G-14656)

Cemex Inc ....D 830 625-7338
New Braunfels (G-15778)

Cemex Construction Mtls S LLC ....F 936 372-0493
Hockley (G-8342)

Cemex Construction Mtls S LLC ....E ......
Houston (G-9126)

Custom Building Products Inc ....D 972 641-6996
Grand Prairie (G-7860)

Eagle Materials Inc ....C 214 432-2000
Dallas (G-4292)

Giant Cement Holding Inc ....E 571 302-7150
Houston (G-9954)

Hanson Aggregates LLC ....F 210 658-3533
New Braunfels (G-15802)

Holcim Inc ....G 713 672-4316
Houston (G-10193)

James Hardie Building Pdts Inc ....C 972 923-9300
Waxahachie (G-20547)

Knife River Corporation ....D 979 361-2900
Bryan (G-2488)

Quikrete Companies LLC ....D 817 783-3010
Alvarado (G-339)

Quikrete Companies LLC ....E 979 732-8210
Columbus (G-3232)

Saudi Basic Industries Corp ....F 713 532-4999
Houston (G-11758)

Southdown Inc ....B 713 650-6200
Houston (G-11971)

Texas Industries Inc ....D 817 838-4212
Fort Worth (G-7048)

Texas Industries Inc ....E 936 564-8301
Nacogdoches (G-15716)

Texas Industries Inc ....E 903 843-2327
Gilmer (G-7715)

Texas Industries Inc ....C 512 396-4244
New Braunfels (G-15827)

Texas Industries Inc ....E 972 775-3449
Midlothian (G-15495)

CEMENT: Masonry

Ahi Supply Inc ....D 281 331-0088
Alvin (G-350)

Ash Grove Cement Company ....E 713 674-4100
Houston (G-8717)

Florencio Villanueva ....C 210 534-4879
San Antonio (G-18117)

Giant Cement Company ....F 843 851-9898
Houston (G-9953)

Houston Cement Company LP ....F 713 754-8000
Houston (G-10224)

Old Castle Apg West ....D 844 576-1364
Grapevine (G-8048)

Texas Industries Inc ....C 972 647-6700
Dallas (G-5062)

CEMENT: Portland

Buzzi Unicem USA Inc ....E 214 638-8391
Dallas (G-4069)

Capitol Aggregates Inc ....C 210 871-6100
San Antonio (G-17981)

Cemex Cement Inc ....B 713 650-6200
Houston (G-9121)

Cemex Construction Mtls S LLC ....E 281 651-6426
Spring (G-19104)

Holcim (us) Inc ....F 214 596-9760
Addison (G-134)

Lehigh Cement Company LLC ....C 877 534-4442
Irving (G-13085)

Lone Star Industries Inc ....F 512 917-8394
Austin (G-1299)

River Cement Sales Company ....F 325 288-4224
Maryneal (G-14811)

Texas Lehigh Cement Company LP ....D 512 434-9330
Wimberley (G-20884)

Texas Lehigh Cement Company LP ....C 512 295-6111
Buda (G-2540)

Texas Lehigh Cement Company LP ....C 512 295-6111
Buda (G-2541)

Zachry Consolidated LLC ....A 210 588-5000
San Antonio (G-18630)

Zachry Construction & Mtls Inc ....D 210 479-1027
San Antonio (G-18631)

CEMETERIES: Real Estate Operation

Buena Vista Burial Park Inc ....F 956 542-5271
Brownsville (G-2342)

CEMETERY MEMORIAL DEALERS

Buena Vista Burial Park Inc ....F 956 542-5271
Brownsville (G-2342)

Southwest Marble & Granite Inc ....G 512 918-0135
Austin (G-1712)

Stone Production Inc ....F 512 990-9800
Austin (G-1539)

CERAMIC FIBER

Scan-Pac Mfg Inc ....E 281 356-1640
Magnolia (G-14626)

Texas Technical Ceramics Inc ....E 936 856-2903
Willis (G-20866)

Texas United Corporation ....E 713 877-1793
Houston (G-12258)

Unifrax I LLC ....E 281 251-5595
Carrollton (G-2842)

CERAMIC FLOOR & WALL TILE WHOLESALERS

American Marazzi Tile Inc ....G 972 232-3800
Fort Worth (G-6381)

Arizona Tile LLC ....E 713 292-1001
Houston (G-8696)

Creative Tile Inc ....G 214 827-0552
Dallas (G-4182)

Dal-Tile Corporation ....F 972 578-1600
Plano (G-16836)

Dal-Tile Corporation ....F 817 831-6935
Haltom City (G-8136)

Roca USA Inc ....F 713 983-8008
Houston (G-11648)

CERAMIC SCHOOLS

Overnite Software Inc ....E 979 319-8371
Angleton (G-575)

CHAIN: Welded, Made From Purchased Wire

Land & Sea Industries LLC ....F 832 622-4216
Spring (G-19140)

CHAINS: Forged

Franklin Machine & Gear Corp ....F 281 441-3177
Humble (G-12768)

CHAMBERS & CAISSONS

AB Bellco Corporation ....E 713 781-6447
Houston (G-8440)

CHAMBERS OF COMMERCE

Mozaic Company ....E 972 386-3332
Arlington (G-733)

CHANDELIERS: Residential

Crow Chandeliers Inc ....F 214 744-5488
Dallas (G-4186)

Scout Goods & Design LLC ....F 512 865-8775
Spicewood (G-19094)

CHANGE MAKING MACHINES

Cummins - Allison Corp ....F 972 661-5390
Dallas (G-4192)

CHANNELS: Furring

Custom Manufacturing Company ....E 214 428-5173
Dallas (G-4196)

CHARCOAL

Clorox Sales Company ....F 972 915-0430
Irving (G-12973)

CHARCOAL: Activated

A E Santos & Co ....E 956 723-8359
Laredo (G-13852)

Cabot Norit Americas Inc ....C 903 938-9211
Marshall (G-14765)

Cabot Norit Americas Inc ....C 800 641-9245
Marshall (G-14766)

CHASSIS: Automobile Trailer

Horizon Global Americas Inc ....F 915 545-2720
El Paso (G-5804)

CHASSIS: Motor Vehicle

Cool City Inc ....F 940 682-1122
Weatherford (G-20583)

Norwood Equipment Houston Inc ....F 713 670-1320
Houston (G-11084)

CHEESE WHOLESALERS

Cheesemakers Inc ....E 281 593-1319
Cleveland (G-3122)

Columbia Packing Co Inc ....E 214 946-8171
Dallas (G-4144)

Dfa Dairy Brands Fluid LLC ....D 806 765-8833
Lubbock (G-14404)

CHEMICAL CLEANING SVCS

B C Williams Industries Inc ....F 214 352-4255
Dallas (G-3996)

Blast Envmtl & Indus Svcs ....E 281 557-1000
League City (G-13950)

Industrial Cmmssning Cons Intl ....F 833 873-4224
La Marque (G-13708)

Klean Corp International ....E 361 578-1524
Victoria (G-20281)

Nch Corporation ....C 972 438-0551
Irving (G-13116)

CHEMICAL ELEMENTS

Atlantic Dwntwn Dllas Vntr LLC ....E 469 399-1049
Dallas *(G-3980)*

Pergan ....D 903 938-5141
Marshall *(G-14797)*

CHEMICAL INDICATORS

Saturn Polymers Inc ....G 936 334-0675
Liberty *(G-14125)*

CHEMICAL PROCESSING MACHINERY & EQPT

B Plan Inc ....F 210 256-1700
San Antonio *(G-17933)*

B&P Littleford LLC ....F 713 433-3304
Houston *(G-8781)*

Championx LLC ....A 281 632-6500
Sugar Land *(G-19455)*

JAS Marketing Inc ....F 281 879-1844
Channelview *(G-3027)*

Merichem Company ....E 713 428-5201
Houston *(G-10834)*

Stanmar Manufacturing Inc ....F 936 967-3040
Livingston *(G-14162)*

CHEMICAL SPLYS FOR FOUNDRIES

Advanced Rupture Disk Tech Inc ....G 281 591-6700
Katy *(G-13388)*

Biosuite LLC ....F 713 849-5319
Sugar Land *(G-19450)*

Fqe Chemicals Inc ....F 281 476-9249
Deer Park *(G-5275)*

Marubeni America Corporation ....E 713 871-5700
Houston *(G-10780)*

Oiltanking Texas City LP ....F 409 797-1710
Texas City *(G-19799)*

Pan Asian Chemicals Inc ....F 713 621-1888
Houston *(G-11227)*

Shoreline Inc ....F 361 643-3135
Portland *(G-17187)*

Turf Technologies LLC ....E 419 422-4356
Dallas *(G-5122)*

CHEMICAL: Sodm Compnds/Salts, Inorg, Exc Rfnd Sodm Chloride

Texas Sodium Bentonite Inc ....G 325 885-2339
Comanche *(G-3236)*

CHEMICALS & ALLIED PRDTS WHOLESALERS, NEC

Allied Bioscience Inc ....E 214 432-5580
Plano *(G-16783)*

Angelo Bolt and Indus Sup Inc ....E 325 655-0075
San Angelo *(G-17776)*

Biocope Inc ....F 806 655-2933
Canyon *(G-2869)*

Blue Line Corporation ....E 210 225-0400
San Antonio *(G-17958)*

Catalyst Partners Inc ....G 940 644-5625
Chico *(G-3052)*

Celanese Americas LLC ....F 972 443-4000
Irving *(G-12963)*

Chevron Phillips Chem Co LP ....A 832 813-4100
The Woodlands *(G-19845)*

Crain Chemical Company Inc ....E 214 358-3301
Dallas *(G-4180)*

Evco Partners LP ....E 409 766-1900
Texas City *(G-19793)*

Independence Oilfield Chem LLC ....E 713 936-4340
The Woodlands *(G-19882)*

Indorama Ventures Oxides LLC ....A 346 365-6056
The Woodlands *(G-19883)*

Ineos Calabrian Corporation ....F 281 348-2303
Kingwood *(G-13645)*

K & K Chemical Company Inc ....E 972 635-2482
Royse City *(G-17721)*

Koch Industries Inc ....F 806 347-2645
Matador *(G-14816)*

Lone Star Corrosion Svcs Inc ....D 281 955-1313
Houston *(G-10675)*

Lyondellbasell Industries Inc ....F 713 209-1248
La Porte *(G-13771)*

Marubeni America Corporation ....E 713 871-5700
Houston *(G-10780)*

Nissan Chemical Houston Corp ....F 281 291-0200
Pasadena *(G-16489)*

Oil Well Chemical Co Inc ....F 940 592-2012
Iowa Park *(G-12907)*

Pencco Inc ....E 979 885-0005
Sealy *(G-18814)*

Romix Chemicals Inc ....E 817 685-0006
Euless *(G-6156)*

S&M International Co Inc ....E 281 749-8289
Katy *(G-13378)*

Scotch Corporation ....E 214 943-4605
Dallas *(G-4943)*

Secco Inc ....G 361 289-1722
Corpus Christi *(G-3619)*

South Coast Terminals LP ....D 713 672-2401
Houston *(G-11963)*

Texas Concrete Chemical Inc ....E 936 638-4273
Groveton *(G-8113)*

Titan Chemical Corporation ....F 713 747-3134
Houston *(G-12296)*

Tribute Energy Inc ....F 281 768-5300
Houston *(G-12367)*

Tricor Industrial Inc ....E 936 273-2661
Conroe *(G-3373)*

Venator Americas LLC ....D 281 465-6700
The Woodlands *(G-19935)*

Venator Americas LLC ....E 281 719-6000
The Woodlands *(G-19936)*

CHEMICALS & ALLIED PRDTS, WHOL: Chemical, Organic, Synthetic

Arkema Inc ....D 281 328-3561
Crosby *(G-3725)*

Optiblend Industries Inc ....E 281 584-0047
Katy *(G-13431)*

Sinochem American Holdings ....E 713 263-8880
Houston *(G-11905)*

CHEMICALS & ALLIED PRDTS, WHOL: Gases, Compressed/Liquefied

Airgas Inc ....E 281 893-9353
Houston *(G-8516)*

CHEMICALS & ALLIED PRDTS, WHOLESALE: Acids

Roywell LLC ....E 713 661-4747
Sugar Land *(G-19538)*

CHEMICALS & ALLIED PRDTS, WHOLESALE: Ammonia

Oci Beaumont LLC ....C 409 723-1900
Nederland *(G-15756)*

CHEMICALS & ALLIED PRDTS, WHOLESALE: Carbon Dioxide

Coca-Cola Refreshments USA Inc ....E 806 472-3200
Lubbock *(G-14395)*

CHEMICALS & ALLIED PRDTS, WHOLESALE: Chemical Additives

CEo Performance Chem LLC ....E 281 457-2020
Houston *(G-9143)*

Chemstation International Inc ....F 281 457-2020
Houston *(G-9171)*

Mudsmith Ltd ....F 432 687-6837
Midland *(G-15308)*

Precision Additives Inc ....E 713 896-0606
Houston *(G-11386)*

CHEMICALS & ALLIED PRDTS, WHOLESALE: Chemicals, Indl

Ace Cmpltion Enhncmnt Svcs LP ....C 432 653-0732
Odessa *(G-15900)*

Allchem Services Incorporated ....E 713 796-8000
Houston *(G-8542)*

Artlux Inc ....F 214 716-1990
Dallas *(G-3968)*

Avastar Brands LLC ....E 512 804-9337
Austin *(G-968)*

BBC Biochemical Corporation ....C 360 542-8400
McKinney *(G-14925)*

Benchmark Research & Tech Inc ....C 432 697-8171
Midland *(G-15138)*

Care Laboratories Inc ....F 281 835-9600
Missouri City *(G-15577)*

Chemax Corporation ....E 409 866-4232
Beaumont *(G-1868)*

Dx Service Company Inc ....E 281 457-4888
Houston *(G-9542)*

Ecofusion Inc ....G 972 403-7449
Plano *(G-16855)*

Fastserv Supply Inc ....E 800 527-4126
Plano *(G-16870)*

Gc3 Specialty Chemicals Inc ....F 713 802-1761
Houston *(G-9909)*

Progressive Coml Aquatics Inc ....D 281 982-0212
Houston *(G-11442)*

Total Ptrchemicals Ref USA Inc ....C 281 476-3700
Deer Park *(G-5301)*

Truth Chemical LLC ....F 281 292-6900
The Woodlands *(G-19931)*

Westrade Usa Inc ....F 713 785-0053
Houston *(G-12656)*

Winzer Corporation ....E 214 341-2122
Plano *(G-17051)*

CHEMICALS & ALLIED PRDTS, WHOLESALE: Chemicals, Indl & Heavy

Foster Testing Co Inc ....F 806 435-6876
Farnsworth *(G-6227)*

Kmg-Bernuth Inc ....F 817 761-6100
Fort Worth *(G-6767)*

Macdermid Canning Ltd ....E 713 472-5081
Pasadena *(G-16478)*

Solvchem Inc ....E 281 485-5377
Pearland *(G-16600)*

CHEMICALS & ALLIED PRDTS, WHOLESALE: Concrete Additives

Mineral Resource Tech Inc ....F 281 362-1060
Houston *(G-10886)*

CHEMICALS & ALLIED PRDTS, WHOLESALE: Detergent/Soap

Sasol Chemicals (usa) LLC ....C 713 428-5652
Houston *(G-11754)*

Sasol Chemicals (usa) LLC ....C 281 588-3000
Houston *(G-11756)*

CHEMICALS & ALLIED PRDTS, WHOLESALE: Detergents

Anko Products Company of Texas ....F 972 227-4466
Lancaster *(G-13837)*

CHEMICALS & ALLIED PRDTS, WHOLESALE: Drilling Mud

Ambar Inc ....C 281 873-7600
Houston *(G-8576)*

Dixie Chemical Company Inc ....E 281 474-3271
Pasadena *(G-16418)*

Dx Holding Company Inc ....E 713 863-1947
Houston *(G-9540)*

CHEMICALS & ALLIED PRDTS, WHOLESALE: Essential Oils

Grayden Cedarworks Inc ....E 325 446-3366
Junction *(G-13339)*

CHEMICALS & ALLIED PRDTS, WHOLESALE: Indl Gases

Air Liquide America LP ....B 713 438-6000
Pasadena *(G-16381)*

Airgas Usa LLC ....E 972 660-0500
Grand Prairie *(G-7825)*

Airgas Usa LLC ....E 281 474-8300
Pasadena *(G-16382)*

Messer LLC ....E 281 837-0184
Baytown *(G-1829)*

Western Intl Gas Cylinders Inc ....C 979 865-5991
Bellville *(G-2015)*

CHEMICALS & ALLIED PRDTS, WHOLESALE: Manmade Fibers

CNA Holdings LLC ....E 972 443-4000
Irving *(G-12976)*

CHEMICALS & ALLIED PRDTS, WHOLESALE: Metal Polishes

M N Gumbert Corporation.....................E....... 214 340-8383
Dallas (G-4621)

CHEMICALS & ALLIED PRDTS, WHOLESALE: Oil Additives

National Oilwell Varco Inc......................E....... 713 482-0500
Houston (G-10985)

CHEMICALS & ALLIED PRDTS, WHOLESALE: Oxygen

Matheson Tri-Gas Inc.............................E....... 512 385-0611
Austin (G-1330)

McDonald Welding Co ....F....... 325 573-5329
Snyder (G-18994)

CHEMICALS & ALLIED PRDTS, WHOLESALE: Plastics Film

Curbell Plastics Inc................................E....... 214 239-3870
Arlington (G-654)

CHEMICALS & ALLIED PRDTS, WHOLESALE: Plastics Materials, NEC

Brisco Plastics and Chem LLC..............F....... 713 395-7081
Houston (G-8985)

C-L & Associates Inc ....E....... 903 831-4311
Wake Village (G-20485)

Ineos Calabrian Corporation...................F....... 281 348-2303
Kingwood (G-13645)

Laird Plastics Inc ....B....... 469 299-7000
Irving (G-13082)

Pore Technology Inc ....E....... 903 601-4466
Jefferson (G-13286)

Sinochem American Holdings ....E....... 713 263-8880
Houston (G-11905)

Tyco International MGT Co LLC ....C....... 361 575-9565
Victoria (G-20312)

CHEMICALS & ALLIED PRDTS, WHOLESALE: Plastics Prdts, NEC

Bruegmann Usa Inc ....E....... 713 742-0788
Houston (G-8997)

Core Pacific Inc ....E....... 800 860-1637
Houston (G-9318)

Daxwell LLC...E....... 281 669-0622
Houston (G-9411)

Gem-Tech Inc ....E....... 817 329-3586
Grapevine (G-8040)

Gemini Incorporated ....D....... 512 352-5207
Taylor (G-19656)

Port Plastics Inc ....F....... 817 834-7678
Fort Worth (G-6911)

Regal Plastic Supply Co Inc....................F....... 210 599-8291
San Antonio (G-18419)

Regal Plastic Supply Co Inc....................F....... 512 836-3629
Austin (G-1457)

CHEMICALS & ALLIED PRDTS, WHOLESALE: Plastics Sheets & Rods

Novolex Inc..C....... 972 686-5090
Dallas (G-4744)

Wilsonart LLC..F....... 214 634-2310
Dallas (G-5192)

CHEMICALS & ALLIED PRDTS, WHOLESALE: Plastics, Basic Shapes

Border Assembly Inc ....E....... 915 592-1172
El Paso (G-5667)

CHEMICALS & ALLIED PRDTS, WHOLESALE: Polyurethane Prdts

SES Foam LLC ....E....... 713 239-0252
Spring (G-19165)

CHEMICALS & ALLIED PRDTS, WHOLESALE: Resins

F & F Composite Group Inc ....E....... 817 379-4411
Fort Worth (G-6622)

John Cole Chemical Corporation............E....... 512 443-1037
Austin (G-1257)

CHEMICALS & ALLIED PRDTS, WHOLESALE: Resins, Plastics

Axiomagnets LLC.....................................F....... 956 283-5920
McAllen (G-14840)

Octal Inc..F....... 972 985-4370
Plano (G-16952)

CHEMICALS & ALLIED PRDTS, WHOLESALE: Sealants

East Texas Acoustical Inc ....F....... 903 663-3820
Longview (G-14226)

CHEMICALS & ALLIED PRDTS, WHOLESALE: Silicon Lubricants

Regal Plastic Supply Co Inc....................F....... 512 836-3629
Austin (G-1457)

Univar Solutions USA Inc ....E....... 281 297-0678
Spring (G-19261)

CHEMICALS & ALLIED PRDTS, WHOLESALE: Spec Clean/Sanitation

Ankem of Texas Inc ....E....... 903 802-7133
Farmers Branch (G-6186)

Montoya Building Services Inc.................E....... 713 367-0231
Houston (G-10915)

CHEMICALS & ALLIED PRDTS, WHOLESALE: Syn Resin, Rub/Plastic

Shintech Incorporated ....C....... 979 233-7861
Freeport (G-7210)

US Petrochemicals Inc ....F....... 713 871-1951
Houston (G-12487)

CHEMICALS, AGRICULTURE: Wholesalers

Bonus Crop Fertilizer Inc ....E....... 903 455-9439
Greenville (G-8065)

Helena Agri-Enterprises LLC ....G....... 806 365-4433
Hartley (G-8211)

Univar Solutions USA Inc ....E....... 281 297-0678
Spring (G-19261)

CHEMICALS/ALLIED PRDTS, WHOL: Coal Tar Prdts, Prim/Intermdt

Texas Electric Coops Inc.........................D....... 409 384-4633
Jasper (G-13281)

CHEMICALS: Agricultural

Agpro Systems Inc ....F....... 903 636-5545
Big Sandy (G-2064)

Akzo Nobel Inc ....E....... 817 625-1500
Fort Worth (G-6360)

American Plant Food Corp ....F....... 817 624-7132
Fort Worth (G-6383)

BASF Corporation....................................D....... 409 981-5000
Beaumont (G-1858)

BASF Corporation....................................C....... 800 794-1019
Houston (G-8821)

Bayer Cropscience LP.............................D....... 806 741-2010
Lubbock (G-14367)

Bayer Cropscience LP.............................E....... 806 765-8846
Lubbock (G-14368)

Celanese US Holdings LLC ....A....... 972 443-4000
Dallas (G-4094)

Chemours Company Fc LLC....................F....... 281 471-2771
La Porte (G-13728)

Control Solutions Inc...............................E....... 281 892-2500
Pasadena (G-16413)

E I Du Pont De Nemours & Co ....A....... 409 886-6442
Orange (G-16240)

E I Du Pont De Nemours & Co ....B....... 281 471-2771
Missouri City (G-15580)

E I Du Pont De Nemours & Co ....G....... 713 413-0000
Houston (G-9553)

Easy Gardener Products Inc....................D....... 254 753-5353
Waco (G-20394)

Global Chemliquidations LLC...................E....... 832 539-3969
Houston (G-9968)

Humatech Inc ....F....... 832 321-3098
Houston (G-10278)

JR Simplot Company ....E....... 361 987-2682
Point Comfort (G-17087)

JR Simplot Company ....D....... 979 826-8063
Hempstead (G-8253)

Kuraray America Inc ....E....... 281 471-2771
La Porte (G-13765)

Monsanto Company ....E....... 806 935-5623
Dumas (G-5525)

Occidental Chemical Holdg Corp ....E....... 972 404-3800
Dallas (G-4753)

Ramsey Properties LP.............................E....... 409 985-4200
Port Arthur (G-17122)

Solugen Inc ....D....... 713 380-2134
Houston (G-11943)

Stoller International Inc ....E....... 713 461-1493
Houston (G-12069)

Westrade Usa Inc ....F....... 713 785-0053
Houston (G-12656)

Zxp Technologies LLC ....B....... 281 426-8800
Highlands (G-8317)

CHEMICALS: Alcohols

Monument Chemical LLC ....E....... 281 474-5550
Pasadena (G-16486)

Pandemx LLC...E....... 432 638-3055
Midland (G-15335)

CHEMICALS: Alkali Metals, Lithium, Cesium, Francium/Rubidium

Fujifilm Ultra Pure Sltons Inc ....E....... 972 245-3797
Carrollton (G-2742)

Peak Nanosystems LLC ....E....... 469 464-4504
Coppell (G-3434)

Solvay USA Inc ....D....... 940 552-9911
Vernon (G-20230)

CHEMICALS: Alkalies

Tricon Energy Inc....................................D....... 713 963-0066
Houston (G-12369)

CHEMICALS: Aluminum Oxide

Sherwin Alumina Company LLC ....A....... 361 777-2200
Gregory (G-8105)

CHEMICALS: Anhydrous Ammonia

Agrium US Inc ....D....... 806 274-5204
Borger (G-2161)

Poole Chemical Co Inc ....F....... 806 647-2121
Dimmitt (G-5485)

CHEMICALS: Brine

Tetra Technologies Inc ....C....... 281 367-1983
The Woodlands (G-19928)

Wilson Systems Inc ....F....... 432 684-5567
Midland (G-15470)

CHEMICALS: Bromine, Elemental

Albemarle Corporation.............................E....... 281 480-4747
Houston (G-8529)

CHEMICALS: Calcium Chloride

Ambar Inc ....C....... 281 873-7600
Houston (G-8576)

CHEMICALS: Fire Retardant

Flame Seal Products Inc ....F....... 713 668-4291
Houston (G-8380)

Flamestop Inc ....E....... 817 306-1222
Fort Worth (G-6636)

CHEMICALS: Fluorine, Elemental

Solvay Fluorides Llc ....D....... 713 525-6700
Houston (G-11946)

CHEMICALS: Formaldehyde

Foremark Performance Chem Inc ....E....... 281 867-1330
League City (G-13957)

Foremark Performance Chem Inc ....E....... 281 867-1330
La Porte (G-13737)

CHEMICALS: Fuel Tank Or Engine Cleaning

Huss Services Inc ....F....... 817 819-4138
Jourdanton (G-13332)

CHEMICALS: *High Purity Grade, Organic*

Sierra Dust Control LLC ....F 903 836-4642
Tatum *(G-19645)*

CHEMICALS: *High Purity, Refined From Technical Grade*

Chemquest Chemicals LLC ....E 281 291-9966
Pasadena *(G-16407)*

Fino Oilfield Services Corp ....E 361 394-7700
Freer *(G-7224)*

Noah Technologies Corp Texas ....D 210 691-2000
San Antonio *(G-18347)*

SOS Environmental Inc ....F 281 723-8282
Spring *(G-19251)*

CHEMICALS: *Hydrogen Peroxide*

Solvay Chemicals Inc ....C 713 525-6800
Houston *(G-11945)*

CHEMICALS: *Hypophosphites*

Avastar Brands LLC ....E 512 804-9337
Austin *(G-968)*

CHEMICALS: Inorganic, NEC

Access Chemicals & Svcs LLC ....F 713 270-7215
Houston *(G-8457)*

Air Liquide Electronics US LP ....A 972 301-5200
Dallas *(G-3905)*

Albemarle Corporation ....F 713 740-1866
Pasadena *(G-16384)*

Albemarle Corporation ....B 281 474-2864
Pasadena *(G-16385)*

Albemarle Corporation ....A 713 740-1000
Pasadena *(G-16386)*

Altivia Chemicals LLC ....E 713 658-9000
Houston *(G-8570)*

Altivia Corporation ....F 713 658-9000
Houston *(G-8571)*

Altivia Specialty Chem LLC ....D 713 658-9000
Houston *(G-8572)*

Aqua/Process Inc ....E 713 910-2977
Houston *(G-8672)*

Arkema Inc ....D 409 838-3981
Beaumont *(G-1854)*

Arkema Inc ....C 713 751-7340
Pasadena *(G-16389)*

Arkema Inc ....D 713 455-1211
Houston *(G-8698)*

Arkema Inc ....D 281 328-3561
Crosby *(G-3725)*

Arrow-Magnolia Intl Inc ....E 972 247-7111
Dallas *(G-3967)*

Artlux Inc ....F 214 716-1990
Dallas *(G-3968)*

Asarco LLC ....A 806 468-4000
Amarillo *(G-401)*

Athlon Solutions LLC ....F 713 457-2400
Pasadena *(G-16391)*

Austin White Lime Company ....F 512 255-3646
Austin *(G-966)*

Baikowski Malakoff Inc ....F 903 489-1910
Malakoff *(G-14634)*

Baker Petrolite LLC ....D 281 474-5166
Pasadena *(G-16392)*

BASF Corporation ....A 800 794-1019
Houston *(G-8821)*

Biotics Research Corporation ....D 281 344-0909
Rosenberg *(G-17577)*

Cadre Material Products LLC ....D 301 682-0600
Katy *(G-13354)*

Cadre Material Products LLC ....C 325 400-2793
Voca *(G-20344)*

Carbonfree Chemicals Spe I LLC ....G 210 476-5906
San Antonio *(G-17983)*

Carbonfree Chemicals Spe I LLC ....E 210 476-5906
San Antonio *(G-17984)*

Celanese Americas LLC ....E 361 584-6000
Bishop *(G-2105)*

Celanese Americas LLC ....E 979 241-4000
Bay City *(G-1770)*

Celanese Americas LLC ....E 972 443-4000
Irving *(G-12963)*

Celanese Corporation ....B 972 443-4000
Irving *(G-12964)*

Celanese Eva Performance ....F 972 443-4000
Irving *(G-12965)*

Celanese International Corp ....A 972 443-4000
Irving *(G-12966)*

Celanese US Holdings LLC ....A 972 443-4000
Dallas *(G-4094)*

Championx LLC ....D 432 363-9105
Odessa *(G-15959)*

Chemical Exchange Inds Inc ....E 713 455-1206
Galena Park *(G-7378)*

Chemicals Incorporated ....D 281 576-5000
Baytown *(G-4621)*

Chemtrade Chemicals US LLC ....F 361 368-2200
Odem *(G-15894)*

Clariant Corporation ....B 832 753-3042
Pasadena *(G-16410)*

Cis Indstrial Purification LLC ....E 281 538-4669
League City *(G-13953)*

CNA Holdings LLC ....E 972 443-4000
Irving *(G-12976)*

Continental Carbon Company ....F 281 647-3728
Houston *(G-9284)*

Continental Carbon Company ....E 806 935-4174
Sunray *(G-19616)*

Diamond Shamrock Ref & Mktg Co .....B 361 786-2536
Three Rivers *(G-19944)*

Dixie Chemical Company Inc ....E 281 474-3271
Pasadena *(G-16418)*

Dow Chemical Company ....D 281 474-4495
La Porte *(G-13732)*

Dow Chemical Company ....E 979 238-2011
Freeport *(G-7196)*

Dow Chemical Company ....B 281 228-2800
Deer Park *(G-5268)*

Dow Chemical Company ....D 713 767-1615
Deer Park *(G-5269)*

Dow Chemical Company ....D 409 948-5886
Texas City *(G-19788)*

Dow Chemical Company ....A 281 228-3060
Deer Park *(G-5270)*

Dow Chemical Company ....E 713 246-0369
La Porte *(G-13733)*

Dow Chemical Company ....G 713 826-5234
Houston *(G-9506)*

Dow Chemical Company ....D 713 751-7285
Pasadena *(G-16420)*

Dow Chemical Company ....D 409 722-3451
Beaumont *(G-1884)*

Dpc Enterprises LP ....E 713 863-1947
Houston *(G-9511)*

Dupont Specialty Pdts USA LLC ....E 281 474-8614
Pasadena *(G-16421)*

Dx Holding Company Inc ....E 713 863-1947
Houston *(G-9540)*

Dx Service Company Inc ....E 281 457-4888
Houston *(G-9542)*

Dynalloy Industries Inc ....E 936 825-2532
Navasota *(G-15729)*

Dynalloy Industries Inc ....E 936 825-2532
Navasota *(G-15730)*

E I Du Pont De Nemours & Co ....B 409 883-8411
Orange *(G-16241)*

E I Du Pont De Nemours & Co ....E 281 470-2371
La Porte *(G-13734)*

Enviro-Tech Specialties Inc ....F 281 476-9803
Channelview *(G-3019)*

Finoric LLC ....D 855 346-6742
Beasley *(G-1840)*

Freeport Minerals Corporation ....C 915 778-9881
El Paso *(G-5774)*

Frontier Chemical LLC ....E 325 672-0072
Abilene *(G-42)*

Global Chemliquidations LLC ....E 832 539-3969
Houston *(G-9968)*

Huntsman International LLC ....E 713 924-6400
Houston *(G-10287)*

Hyett Mfg & Instr Co Inc ....F 409 735-5383
Bridge City *(G-2285)*

Imerys Perlite Usa Inc ....F 281 471-3122
La Porte *(G-13749)*

Ineos Calabrian Corporation ....F 281 348-2303
Kingwood *(G-13645)*

Ineos Calabrian Corporation ....E 409 727-1471
Port Neches *(G-17166)*

Inhance Technologies LLC ....E 713 678-7352
Houston *(G-10365)*

JM Huber Corporation ....D 830 693-3575
Marble Falls *(G-14746)*

K & K Chemical Company Inc ....E 972 635-2482
Royse City *(G-17721)*

Klean Corp International ....E 361 578-1524
Victoria *(G-20281)*

Kuraray America Inc ....E 281 471-2771
La Porte *(G-13765)*

Lanxess Corporation ....E 281 383-7761
Baytown *(G-1795)*

Liquid Minerals Group Ltd ....E 936 291-2424
Huntsville *(G-12816)*

Lubchem Inc ....E 281 350-9600
Spring *(G-19143)*

M N Gumbert Corporation ....E 214 340-8383
Dallas *(G-4621)*

Martinek Grain & Bins Inc ....F 972 382-8500
Celina *(G-2992)*

Merichem Company ....C 713 428-5000
Houston *(G-10833)*

N L Industries Inc ....E 972 233-1700
Dallas *(G-4711)*

Napco Chemical Company Inc ....E 281 651-6800
Spring *(G-19151)*

Nashtec LLC ....E 361 777-2280
Gregory *(G-8102)*

Nch Corporation ....C 972 438-0551
Irving *(G-13116)*

Nerium Biotechnology Inc ....F 210 822-7908
San Antonio *(G-18342)*

OXY Vinyls LP ....E 877 699-8465
Dallas *(G-4775)*

Pencco Inc ....E 979 885-0005
Sealy *(G-18814)*

Peroxychem LLC ....D 281 474-4171
Pasadena *(G-16495)*

Phillip Townsend Assoc Inc ....E 281 873-8733
Houston *(G-11323)*

Phyton Biotech LLC ....E 817 900-4050
Fort Worth *(G-6906)*

Pilot Chemical Company Ohio ....E 936 291-2424
Huntsville *(G-12822)*

Precision Additives Inc ....E 713 896-0606
Houston *(G-11386)*

Prince Energy LLC ....E 713 955-5398
Houston *(G-11418)*

RB Processing LLc ....G 281 992-3500
Houston *(G-11556)*

Reagent Chemical & RES Inc ....F 409 899-3400
Beaumont *(G-1946)*

Redox Chemicals LLC ....F 972 923-7734
Waxahachie *(G-20555)*

Rohm and Haas Texas Inc ....C 281 476-8304
Deer Park *(G-5291)*

Royal Chemical Company Ltd ....F 214 358-1861
Dallas *(G-4913)*

S F Sulphur Company ....F 979 233-3555
Freeport *(G-7208)*

Sasol Chemicals (usa) LLC ....C 713 428-5400
Houston *(G-11755)*

Sasol Chemicals (usa) LLC ....E 409 296-9091
Winnie *(G-20890)*

Scotch Corporation ....E 214 943-4605
Dallas *(G-4943)*

Select Industries Inc ....E 940 855-0461
Wichita Falls *(G-20807)*

Solvay America Inc ....E 713 525-4000
Houston *(G-11944)*

Solvay Info Svcs Nafta LLC ....D 713 525-6000
Houston *(G-11947)*

Solvay North America LLC ....B 713 525-6000
Houston *(G-11948)*

Solvay Spclty Polymers USA LLC ....E 770 772-8200
Borger *(G-2186)*

Solvay USA Inc ....E 281 984-3030
Pasadena *(G-16508)*

Solvay USA Inc ....G 281 882-4700
The Woodlands *(G-19921)*

Southern Ionics Incorporated ....E 281 474-4826
Pasadena *(G-16509)*

Syntech Chemicals Inc ....E 713 433-5818
Houston *(G-12136)*

Tbc-Brinadd LLC ....F 281 438-2565
Houston *(G-8393)*

Terra Biochem LLC ....F 409 489-1700
Jasper *(G-13280)*

Texas Brine Company LLC ....F 281 385-6048
Mont Belvieu *(G-15619)*

Texas Materials Group Inc ....D 214 372-7700
Dallas *(G-5076)*

Texmark Chemicals Inc ....E 713 455-1206
Galena Park *(G-7383)*

Tor Minerals International Inc ....D 361 883-5591
Corpus Christi *(G-3642)*

Total Ptrchemicals Ref USA Inc ....G 281 452-8577
Channelview *(G-3043)*

PRODUCT

Tri Element Incorporated...............F 361 664-5000
Alice *(G-242)*

U S Silica Company.......................F 806 470-2035
Lamesa *(G-13831)*

USS Holdings Inc ....F 301 682-0600
Katy *(G-13383)*

Venator Chemicals LLC.................F 979 233-8183
Freeport *(G-7218)*

CHEMICALS: Medicinal, Organic, Uncompounded, Bulk

Peroxychem LLC............................D 281 474-4171
Pasadena *(G-16495)*

CHEMICALS: Metal Compounds Or Salts, Inorganic, NEC

Blue Line Corporation...................E 210 225-0400
San Antonio *(G-17958)*

Lonza Inc ....D 281 291-2300
Pasadena *(G-16475)*

CHEMICALS: NEC

Afton Chemical Corporation ....F 281 475-1040
Spring *(G-19193)*

Agribiofuels LLC..........................F 936 257-0826
Dayton *(G-5220)*

Akzo Nobel Inc ....E 713 433-7289
Houston *(G-8370)*

Albemarle Corporation ....B 281 474-2864
Pasadena *(G-16385)*

Allchem Services Incorporated ......E 713 796-8000
Houston *(G-8542)*

Allied Bioscience Inc....................E 214 432-5580
Plano *(G-16783)*

Aqua Solutions Inc ....E 800 256-2586
Deer Park *(G-5261)*

Arkema Inc...................................D 409 838-3981
Beaumont *(G-1854)*

Ashburn Industries ....E 832 399-1000
Houston *(G-8718)*

Ask Industries Inc ....F 432 686-2520
Fort Worth *(G-6403)*

Athlon Solutions LLC....................C 713 457-2400
Houston *(G-8735)*

Baker Hghes Olfld Oprtions LLC....F 713 879-1000
Houston *(G-8796)*

Baker Hughes A GE Company LLC ..B 713 625-4200
Houston *(G-8801)*

Baker Petrolite LLC......................D 281 474-5166
Pasadena *(G-16392)*

Banner Technology Inc ....F 713 675-3100
Houston *(G-8815)*

Benchmark Research & Tech Inc .....C 432 697-8171
Midland *(G-15138)*

Big Lake Fuels LLC.......................E 713 943-2200
Houston *(G-8882)*

Bio-RAD Laboratories Inc ....D 972 596-6165
Plano *(G-16805)*

Blentech Corporation ....E 713 673-3436
Houston *(G-8914)*

Buckeye International Inc ....F 281 873-4200
Houston *(G-9007)*

Calhoun Chemical LLC..................E 713 254-8974
Port Lavaca *(G-17143)*

Carpenter Chemical Co Inc ....E 281 474-5111
Pasadena *(G-16401)*

CEo Performance Chem LLC..........E 281 457-2020
Houston *(G-9143)*

Chemax Corporation ....E 409 866-4232
Beaumont *(G-1868)*

Chemicals Incorporated ....D 281 576-5000
Baytown *(G-1813)*

Chemquest Chemicals LLC............E 281 291-9966
Pasadena *(G-16407)*

Chemstation International Inc ....F 281 457-2020
Houston *(G-9171)*

Chemsystems Inc ....F 713 329-9066
Houston *(G-9172)*

Chevron Phillips Chem Co LP ....A 281 421-6500
Baytown *(G-1814)*

CMC Materials Inc ....D 817 761-6100
Fort Worth *(G-6524)*

Corrpro Companies Inc ....C 713 460-6000
Houston *(G-9325)*

Custom Building Products Inc ....D 972 641-6996
Grand Prairie *(G-7860)*

Cytec Industries Inc ....D 281 296-1622
Spring *(G-19206)*

Cytec Industries Inc ....A 903 454-2004
Greenville *(G-8069)*

Diamond Shamrock Ref & Mktg Co ...B 361 786-2536
Three Rivers *(G-19944)*

Dome Petrochemical Lc ....F 713 540-9075
Baytown *(G-1784)*

Dorf Ketal Chemicals LLC ....E 713 343-2377
Houston *(G-9499)*

Dow Chemical Company ....E 979 238-2011
Freeport *(G-7196)*

Dow Chemical Company ....D 409 722-3451
Beaumont *(G-1884)*

Economy Mud Products Company ....D 800 231-2066
Houston *(G-9580)*

Equistar Chemicals LP ....E 281 862-4000
Channelview *(G-3020)*

Equistar Chemicals LP ....E 281 474-4040
Pasadena *(G-16430)*

Ethyl Corporation.........................D 713 740-8300
Pasadena *(G-16431)*

Evonik Corporation ....C 713 477-6841
Pasadena *(G-16434)*

Fgl Group LLC..............................F 817 481-7857
Grapevine *(G-8034)*

Flomin Inc ....F 281 573-6401
Baytown *(G-1787)*

Flotek Industries Inc ....B 713 849-9911
Houston *(G-9806)*

Fritz Industries Inc ....B 972 285-5471
Mesquite *(G-15042)*

Fritz Industries Inc ....C 214 244-7822
Greenville *(G-8075)*

Fritz Industries Inc ....C 972 288-5425
Mesquite *(G-15043)*

Genesis Cstm Chem Blending LLC....F 469 309-2790
Ennis *(G-6104)*

Globe Chemical LLC ....F 432 684-4939
Odessa *(G-16015)*

Green Stream Solutions LLC ....D 832 404-2436
Houston *(G-10030)*

Hampshire Chemical Corp ....D 281 479-9525
Deer Park *(G-5278)*

Haverhill Chemicals LLC ....C 281 885-8900
Houston *(G-10137)*

Hexion Inc...................................E 936 829-5566
Diboll *(G-5467)*

Honeywell International Inc ....D 409 886-7445
Orange *(G-16246)*

Honeywell International Inc ....F 979 778-4477
Bryan *(G-2478)*

Humco Holding Group Inc ....C 903 831-7808
Texarkana *(G-19766)*

Huntsman International LLC ....E 713 924-6400
Houston *(G-10287)*

Hydrite Chemical Co......................E 806 368-5660
Lubbock *(G-14423)*

Ifs Coatings Inc ....F 940 668-1062
Gainesville *(G-7345)*

Immatics Us Inc............................E 346 204-5400
Houston *(G-10330)*

Independence Oilfield Chem LLC.....E 713 936-4340
The Woodlands *(G-19882)*

Independence Oilfield Chem LLC.....G 210 888-0300
Pleasanton *(G-17069)*

Ineos Nitriles USA LLC..................C 361 552-8200
Port Lavaca *(G-17149)*

Integrity Delaware LLC..................E 361 595-5561
Kingsville *(G-13630)*

Jentek Water Treatment Inc ....F 214 349-7111
Dallas *(G-4531)*

Jx Nippon Chemical Texas Inc ....D 713 754-1000
Pasadena *(G-16467)*

Katoen Ntie Specialty Chem Inc ......E 281 941-1001
La Porte *(G-13762)*

Katoen Ntie Specialty Chem Inc ......F 281 470-5423
La Porte *(G-13763)*

Kiwo Holdings Inc.........................E 281 474-9777
Seabrook *(G-18787)*

Kmg Electronic Chemicals Inc ....E 817 761-6100
Fort Worth *(G-6766)*

Kronos Worldwide Inc ....E 609 860-6200
Dallas *(G-4570)*

Laticrete International Inc ....E 972 641-3266
Grand Prairie *(G-7909)*

Linde Gas North America LLC ....D 713 767-4100
La Porte *(G-13768)*

Loco Solutions LLC ....E 817 437-6438
Amarillo *(G-498)*

Lubrizol Corporation ....E 281 479-2851
Pasadena *(G-16476)*

M & G Chemicals..........................F 361 500-4747
Houston *(G-10711)*

Macdermid Canning Ltd ....E 713 472-5081
Pasadena *(G-16478)*

Mesa Processing Inc ....F 817 626-0319
Fort Worth *(G-6829)*

Nalco Company LLC.......................G 210 493-0379
San Antonio *(G-18330)*

Newpark Indus Blnding Sltons L ......E 713 898-3829
The Woodlands *(G-19895)*

Ng Operations LLC ....F 972 660-7140
Grand Prairie *(G-7935)*

Noah Technologies Corp Texas.......D 210 691-2000
San Antonio *(G-18347)*

Nuclear Sources and Svcs Inc ....E 713 641-0391
Houston *(G-11096)*

Oq Chemicals Bishop LLC..............E 361 584-6920
Bishop *(G-2108)*

Oq Chemicals Holding Corp ....G 972 481-2700
Dallas *(G-4765)*

OXY Vinyls LP ....F 281 476-8000
La Porte *(G-13782)*

OXY Vinyls LP ....F 877 699-8465
Dallas *(G-4775)*

R & F Industries Inc ....F 830 875-6927
Luling *(G-14564)*

Ramsey Properties LP ....C 281 328-3501
Crosby *(G-3741)*

Reagens Usa Inc ....E 281 291-8484
Pasadena *(G-16501)*

Riteks Inc....................................F 972 529-1118
McKinney *(G-14972)*

Rohm and Haas Texas Inc ....C 281 476-8304
Deer Park *(G-5291)*

Sachem Inc ....D 817 202-3200
Cleburne *(G-3108)*

Scale Free Company Inc ....F 281 873-5555
Houston *(G-11764)*

Scotch Corporation ....E 214 943-4605
Dallas *(G-4943)*

Seapac Inc ....D 281 383-2400
Baytown *(G-1801)*

Sekisui Spcialty Chem Amer LLC .....F 713 456-1525
Pasadena *(G-16504)*

Sekisui Spcialty Chem Amer LLC .....E 972 277-2900
Dallas *(G-4947)*

Solnexus Chemical LLC ....F 432 689-6180
Midland *(G-15415)*

Solution Integrated Chem LLC ....F 361 584-5000
Bishop *(G-2109)*

Solvay USA Inc ....C 325 515-7609
Snyder *(G-19009)*

Solvchem Inc ....E 281 485-5377
Pearland *(G-16600)*

South Coast Terminals LP ....D 713 672-2401
Houston *(G-11963)*

Strata Control Services Inc ....E 337 785-0000
Spring *(G-19256)*

Sun Chemical Corporation ....E 972 647-1641
Grand Prairie *(G-7977)*

Syntech Chemicals Inc ....E 713 433-5818
Houston *(G-12136)*

Talke Usa Inc ....E 832 260-8325
Mont Belvieu *(G-15621)*

Texas Materials Group Inc ....D 214 372-7700
Dallas *(G-5076)*

Third Coast Packaging Inc ....E 281 412-0275
Pearland *(G-16604)*

Tm Chemicals Ltd Partnership ....C 281 930-2525
Deer Park *(G-5300)*

Tokai Carbon CB Ltd ....D 432 263-7389
Big Spring *(G-2100)*

Total Ptrchemicals Ref USA Inc ....B 713 483-5000
Houston *(G-12332)*

Total Ptrchemicals Ref USA Inc ....C 281 542-9542
La Porte *(G-13797)*

Total Ptrchemicals Ref USA Inc ....B 409 963-6800
Port Arthur *(G-17130)*

Trecora Chemical Inc ....D 281 474-7500
Pasadena *(G-16519)*

Tricon Energy Inc ....D 713 963-0066
Houston *(G-12369)*

Tricon Energy Ltd ....D 713 963-0066
Houston *(G-12370)*

United Salt Baytown LLC ....E 936 372-3931
Hockley *(G-8350)*

USA Petrovalve Inc ....F 713 466-9881
Houston *(G-12498)*

USa Screen Printing Chem Inc ....E 281 474-9777
Seabrook *(G-18793)*

Valero Refining-Texas LP ....C 281 470-4900
La Porte *(G-13799)*

Valhi Inc ....E 972 233-1700
Dallas *(G-5151)*

Vitalpure Labs LLC ....E 573 469-1302
Junction *(G-13340)*

Yci Methanol One LLC ....D 832 924-1998
Houston *(G-12714)*

Zxp Technologies LLC ....C 281 426-8800
Highlands *(G-8316)*

CHEMICALS: Nonmetallic Compounds

Martin Resource MGT Corp ....F 432 381-0271
Odessa *(G-16072)*

Mineral Resource Tech Inc ....F 281 362-1060
Houston *(G-10886)*

Questspecialty Corporation ....D 713 896-8188
Brenham *(G-2271)*

CHEMICALS: Organic, NEC

AA Scientific Inc ....F 979 696-8080
College Station *(G-3171)*

Access Chemicals & Svcs LLC ....F 713 270-7215
Houston *(G-8457)*

Akzo Nobel Inc ....E 281 584-0093
Houston *(G-8521)*

Albemarle Corporation ....A 713 740-1000
Pasadena *(G-16386)*

Altivia Specialty Chem LLC ....C 713 658-9000
La Porte *(G-13720)*

American Acryl LP ....D 281 909-2600
Pasadena *(G-16387)*

Aqua/Process Inc ....E 713 910-2977
Houston *(G-8672)*

Arkema Inc ....D 713 455-1211
Houston *(G-8698)*

Arkema Inc ....D 409 838-3981
Beaumont *(G-1854)*

Ashland LLC ....C 973 628-3245
Port Neches *(G-17158)*

Baker Petrolite LLC ....B 281 276-5400
Sugar Land *(G-19448)*

BASF Corporation ....C 800 794-1019
Houston *(G-8821)*

BASF Corporation ....F 409 960-5000
Port Arthur *(G-17101)*

BASF Corporation ....D 713 383-4500
Houston *(G-8822)*

BASF Corporation ....F 973 245-6000
Carrollton *(G-2702)*

BASF Corporation ....D 409 981-5000
Beaumont *(G-1858)*

BASF Corporation ....E 281 884-4400
Pasadena *(G-16393)*

Baze Chemical Inc ....E 903 723-3146
Palestine *(G-16296)*

Beacon Energy (texas) Corp ....F 817 558-9255
Cleburne *(G-3081)*

Black Diamond Structures LLC ....F 512 900-3822
Austin *(G-858)*

Celanese Ltd ....E 281 474-0554
Pasadena *(G-16403)*

Centauri Technologies LP ....E 281 474-4675
Pasadena *(G-16404)*

Chemicals Incorporated ....E 979 244-0100
Bay City *(G-1771)*

Chemicals Incorporated ....D 281 576-5000
Baytown *(G-1813)*

Chryso Inc ....E 972 772-6010
Rockwall *(G-17542)*

Dixie Chemical Company Inc ....E 281 474-3271
Pasadena *(G-16418)*

Dow Chemical Company ....C 281 452-5951
Houston *(G-9505)*

Dow Chemical Company ....D 409 722-3451
Beaumont *(G-1884)*

Dpc Enterprises LP ....E 713 863-1947
Houston *(G-9511)*

Dx Holding Company Inc ....E 713 863-1947
Houston *(G-9540)*

E I Du Pont De Nemours & Co ....E 361 776-1872
Ingleside *(G-12895)*

E R Carpenter LP ....C 804 359-0800
Temple *(G-19680)*

Eastman Chemical Company ....E 423 229-2000
Longview *(G-14230)*

Eastman Chemical Texas Cy Inc ....E 409 942-3307
Texas City *(G-19791)*

Equistar Chemicals LP ....G 361 572-2547
Victoria *(G-20261)*

Evonik Corporation ....C 713 477-6841
Pasadena *(G-16434)*

Flint Hills Resources LP ....D 903 239-5200
Longview *(G-14235)*

Hampshire Chemical Corp ....D 281 479-9525
Deer Park *(G-5278)*

Hexion Inc ....E 936 829-5566
Diboll *(G-5467)*

Hexion Inc ....F 956 565-6301
Mercedes *(G-15005)*

Hexion Inc ....E 281 325-3368
Stafford *(G-19325)*

Huntsman International LLC ....E 713 924-6400
Houston *(G-10287)*

Ict Holdings LLC ....E 713 652-6600
Littlefield *(G-14145)*

Ineos Calabrian Corporation ....E 409 727-1471
Port Neches *(G-17166)*

Ineos Nitriles USA LLC ....E 361 552-8200
Port Lavaca *(G-17149)*

Kmg-Bernuth Inc ....F 817 761-6100
Fort Worth *(G-6767)*

Ktx Properties Inc ....E 281 328-3501
Houston *(G-10570)*

Kuraray America Inc ....E 281 471-2771
La Porte *(G-13765)*

Lanxess Corporation ....E 281 383-7761
Baytown *(G-1795)*

Lyondell Chemical Company ....E 281 597-8935
Houston *(G-10704)*

Lyondell Chemical Company ....D 281 474-4191
Pasadena *(G-16477)*

Lyondell Chemical Company ....E 979 245-1225
Bay City *(G-1774)*

Lyondell Chemical Company ....F 281 385-7010
Mont Belvieu *(G-15622)*

Lyondell Chemical Company ....F 281 862-4000
Channelview *(G-3030)*

Lyondellbasell Acetyls LLC ....F 713 309-7200
Houston *(G-10708)*

M-I LLC ....B 281 561-1300
Houston *(G-10725)*

Master Builders LLC ....C 972 228-7400
Lancaster *(G-13847)*

Merisol LP ....E 713 428-5652
Houston *(G-10836)*

Nissan Chemical Houston Corp ....F 281 291-0200
Pasadena *(G-16489)*

Occidental Chemical Holdg Corp ....E 972 404-3800
Dallas *(G-4753)*

Odysseus Holdings LLC ....F 281 769-2399
Houston *(G-11136)*

Oiltek Systems LLC ....E 325 200-0423
Colorado City *(G-3225)*

Olin Blue Cubellc ....F 979 201-1789
Freeport *(G-7206)*

Oq Chemicals Corporation ....C 972 481-2771
Bay City *(G-1776)*

Oq Chemicals Corporation ....E 713 830-3135
Houston *(G-11187)*

Pergan ....D 903 938-5141
Marshall *(G-14797)*

Regional Acid Production LP ....D 281 381-7866
Stafford *(G-19368)*

Rohm and Haas Texas Inc ....C 281 476-8304
Deer Park *(G-5291)*

Royal Chemical Company Ltd ....F 214 358-1861
Dallas *(G-4913)*

Sachem Inc ....E 512 421-4900
Austin *(G-1479)*

Sachem Inc ....D 512 421-4946
Austin *(G-1480)*

Sachem Inc ....D 817 202-3200
Cleburne *(G-3108)*

Sasol Chemicals (usa) LLC ....C 713 428-5400
Houston *(G-11755)*

Sasol Chemicals (usa) LLC ....G 409 296-9091
Winnie *(G-20890)*

Sasol Chemicals North Amer LLC ....F 281 588-3000
Houston *(G-11757)*

Sea Lion Inc ....D 409 948-4351
Texas City *(G-19801)*

Serafy Laboratories Ltd ....E 956 546-5313
Brownsville *(G-2405)*

Shell Catalysts & Tech LP ....D 713 241-3000
Houston *(G-11857)*

Shell Chemical LP ....E 855 697-4355
Houston *(G-11858)*

Si Group Inc ....C 979 238-8000
Freeport *(G-7211)*

Sierra Dust Control LLC ....F 903 836-4642
Harwood *(G-8212)*

Smithfield Bioenergy LLC ....E 817 558-9255
Cleburne *(G-3109)*

Solvay Fluorides Llc ....D 713 525-6700
Houston *(G-11946)*

Ssi Maxim Company Inc ....G 903 984-5600
Kilgore *(G-13593)*

Sunrise Chemical LLC ....D 713 754-1000
Pasadena *(G-16516)*

Syntech Chemicals Inc ....E 713 433-5818
Houston *(G-12136)*

T & R Chemicals Inc ....E 915 851-2761
Clint *(G-3148)*

Texas Petrochemicals LP ....C 409 724-4857
Port Neches *(G-17169)*

Texas Petrochemicals LP ....D 713 627-7474
Houston *(G-12244)*

Total Ptrchemicals Ref USA Inc ....G 281 452-8577
Channelview *(G-3043)*

Total Ptrchemicals Ref USA Inc ....B 409 963-6800
Port Arthur *(G-17130)*

Transcendia Inc ....E 800 659-4254
Carrollton *(G-2838)*

Trecora Chemical Inc ....D 281 474-7500
Pasadena *(G-16519)*

Ultra Chem Ltd ....F 713 641-1444
Houston *(G-12429)*

Union Carbide Corporation ....D 361 553-2000
Seadrift *(G-18797)*

Vencorex Us Inc ....E 979 233-7871
Freeport *(G-7219)*

Vencorex Us Inc ....E 979 233-7871
Freeport *(G-7220)*

Vrc Technologies Inc ....F 325 643-8038
Brownwood *(G-2447)*

CHEMICALS: Phenol

Ineos Americas LLC ....C 251 535-6600
League City *(G-13960)*

Si Group Inc ....C 979 238-8000
Freeport *(G-7211)*

Solvay USA Inc ....D 940 552-9911
Vernon *(G-20230)*

Solvay USA Inc ....C 325 515-7609
Snyder *(G-19009)*

CHEMICALS: Phosphorus, Elemental

Icl Specialty Products Inc ....E 281 471-4700
La Porte *(G-13747)*

CHEMICALS: Potassium Compound/Salt, Exc Hydroxide/Carbonate

Occidental Petroleum Corp ....G 325 574-8567
Ira *(G-12913)*

Occidental Petroleum Corp ....E 713 640-7500
Houston *(G-11117)*

CHEMICALS: Reagent Grade, Refined From Technical Grade

Aceschem Inc ....F 817 863-6948
Frisco *(G-7265)*

BBC Biochemical Corporation ....C 360 542-8400
McKinney *(G-14925)*

Kem-Tron Technologies Inc ....E 281 261-5778
Stafford *(G-19339)*

Mfg Chemical LLC ....E 281 291-2300
Pasadena *(G-16483)*

Smolecule Inc ....F 512 262-9938
Houston *(G-11925)*

CHEMICALS: Silica Compounds

US Silica Holdings Inc ....F 281 258-2170
Houston *(G-12490)*

CHEMICALS: Soda Ash

FMC Corporation ....D 281 591-4470
Houston *(G-9819)*

FMC Corporation ....F 936 559-0031
Nacogdoches *(G-15697)*

Solvay Chemicals Inc ....D 713 307-3800
La Porte *(G-13789)*

Solvay USA Inc ....D 940 552-9911
Vernon *(G-20230)*

Employee Codes: A=Over 500 employees, B=251-500
C=101-250, D=51-100, E=20-50, F=10-19, G=9

2021 Harris Texas
Manufacturers Directory

PRODUCT

1419

CHEMICALS: Sodium Bicarbonate

Genesis Alkali LLC ....D....... 713 860-2500
Houston (G-9930)

CHEMICALS: Sodium/Potassium Cmpnds,Exc Bleach,Alkalies/Alum

Basin Water Inc ....F....... 877 312-8950
Kingwood (G-13640)
Brenntag Pacific Inc ....F....... 281 474-5400
Pasadena (G-16399)
Chemtrade Solutions LLC.....................E....... 972 775-2307
Midlothian (G-15476)
Eastman Chemical Texas Cy Inc ....E....... 409 942-3307
Texas City (G-19791)
Texas United Corporation ....E....... 713 877-1793
Houston (G-12258)

CHEMICALS: Sulfur, Incl Rcvrd/Refined, Fm Sour Natural Gas

Ctci Americas Inc...................................F....... 281 870-9998
Houston (G-9354)
International Sulphur Inc........................E....... 903 577-5500
Mount Pleasant (G-15652)
Martin Midstream Partners LP ....F....... 281 471-2211
La Porte (G-13774)
Reagent Chemical & RES Inc................F....... 713 626-1843
Houston (G-11561)
Reagent Chemical & RES Inc................E....... 409 962-1116
Vidor (G-20331)
Reagent Chemical & RES Inc................E....... 281 862-9464
Houston (G-11562)
Reagent Chemical & RES Inc................F....... 432 458-3403
Stanton (G-19404)

CHEMICALS: Water Treatment

Alpha Labs Inc ....F....... 806 744-1960
Lubbock (G-14359)
Baker Petrolite LLC................................B....... 281 276-5400
Sugar Land (G-19448)
Baker Petrolite LLC................................B....... 713 599-7400
Houston (G-8809)
C Treat Offshore Watermakers ....E....... 281 367-2800
The Woodlands (G-19837)
Chemtrade Sulfate Chem Inc ....E....... 416 496-4176
Celina (G-2991)
Chemtreat Inc ....E....... 409 724-1111
Nederland (G-15748)
Garratt-Callahan Company ....G....... 972 661-5006
Dallas (G-4391)
Global Wstewater Solutions Inc ....G....... 832 286-4600
Houston (G-9981)
Hercules LLC...D....... 409 866-4778
Beaumont (G-1903)
NCH Corporation.....................................A....... 972 438-0211
Irving (G-13114)
NCH Corporation.....................................A....... 972 438-0381
Irving (G-13115)
Pencco Inc ....E....... 979 885-0005
Sealy (G-18814)
Solenis LLC ....F....... 713 991-3722
Houston (G-11938)
Solenis LLC ....F....... 713 738-6815
Houston (G-11939)
Suez Wts Usa Inc ....E....... 409 866-4756
Beaumont (G-1955)
United Worth Hydrochem Corp ....F....... 682 518-6200
Venus (G-20224)
Whitecap Wastewater Treatment..........F....... 361 826-4142
Corpus Christi (G-3656)

CHESTS: Bank, Metal

Acero Fab Inc..F....... 956 584-1166
Mission (G-15548)

CHESTS: Steel

Rising S Company LLC ....E....... 214 455-0560
Murchison (G-15682)
Tidel Engineering LP ....C....... 972 484-3358
Carrollton (G-2834)

CHICKEN SLAUGHTERING & PROCESSING

Gold Taste Foods Inc ....D....... 713 378-0198
Houston (G-9991)
Tig Real Estate Services Inc ....E....... 972 661-0232
Dallas (G-5092)

Tyson Foods Inc ....F....... 940 553-1811
Vernon (G-20231)
Tyson Foods Inc ....B....... 713 678-1893
Houston (G-12421)

CHLORINATED RUBBERS: Synthetic

G V C Holdings Inc.................................B....... 409 722-8321
Port Neches (G-17161)

CHLORINE

Occidental Chemical Corp ....B....... 972 404-3800
Dallas (G-4751)
Occidental Chemical Corp ....F....... 361 776-6000
Gregory (G-8103)
Occidental Petroleum Corp....................G....... 325 574-8567
Ira (G-12913)
Occidental Petroleum Corp....................E....... 713 640-7500
Houston (G-11117)

CHOCOLATE, EXC CANDY FROM BEANS: Chips, Powder, Block, Syrup

Candy Kings Inc......................................F....... 409 762-6100
Galveston (G-7391)
Mars Chocolate North Amer LLC ....A....... 254 776-2100
Waco (G-20433)
Susies South Forty Confections ....D....... 432 570-4040
Midland (G-15426)

CHOCOLATE, EXC CANDY FROM PURCH CHOC: Chips, Powder, Block

La India Packing Co................................E....... 956 723-3772
Laredo (G-13903)
Wiseman House Companies Inc............F....... 254 796-2565
Hico (G-8303)

CHRISTMAS TREES WHOLESALERS

Daryan Design Inc..................................F....... 214 905-6022
Dallas (G-4239)

CHRISTMAS TREES: Artificial

Barcana Inc..F....... 800 638-4533
Irving (G-12943)

CHROMATOGRAPHY EQPT

Spectra Dynamics Corporation ....F....... 512 255-2233
Liberty Hill (G-14129)

CHUCKS

Qti Apparel & Promotions LLC ....E....... 254 662-3076
Waco (G-20451)

CHUTES & TROUGHS

Electro-Mechanical Inds Inc...................E....... 281 894-1600
Houston (G-9592)
G Fabricating LLC ....E....... 281 421-3100
Crosby (G-3731)

CIGAR STORES

Serious Cigars Llc ....G....... 281 397-9800
Houston (G-11837)

CIGARETTE & CIGAR PRDTS & ACCESS

Permian Basin Eqp & Sup LLC..............E....... 432 563-1044
Odessa (G-16113)

CIRCUIT BOARDS, PRINTED: Television & Radio

Best Circuit Boards Inc ....D....... 214 291-1427
Wylie (G-20927)
Canyon Manufacturing Svcs Inc ....E....... 281 876-7105
Houston (G-9086)
Circuit Services Inc................................F....... 713 465-4216
Houston (G-9195)
Dynalyst Corporation ....E....... 512 365-1203
Taylor (G-19653)
Dynalyst Manufacturing Corp................E....... 281 293-7980
Houston (G-9546)
Dynalyst Manufacturing Corp................E....... 512 365-1230
Taylor (G-19654)
Eagle Circuits Inc ....E....... 214 349-0288
Dallas (G-4290)

Epic Technologies LLC ....C....... 915 791-5326
El Paso (G-5757)
Iondesign Inc ....F....... 512 260-5778
Jonestown (G-13315)
Niltronix Circuits Inc..............................F....... 713 465-4216
Houston (G-11056)
Protoline Inc ....F....... 281 561-0802
Houston (G-11465)
Roca Precision Mfg Inc ....F....... 281 240-2020
Stafford (G-19371)
Sanmina Corporation ....F....... 512 997-1100
Austin (G-1485)
Silicon Hills Design Inc ....E....... 512 836-1088
Austin (G-1504)
Texas Circuitry Inc.................................E....... 972 278-3838
Garland (G-7598)
Variosystems Inc....................................C....... 817 416-7535
Southlake (G-19083)

CIRCUIT BOARDS: Wiring

Q C Graphics Inc....................................E....... 972 931-4100
Richardson (G-17377)

CIRCUIT BREAKERS

Circuit Breaker Sales LLC.....................C....... 940 665-4444
Gainesville (G-7338)
Elah Holdings Inc ....F....... 805 435-1255
Dallas (G-4307)
Ema Electromechanics Inc ....E....... 325 235-8000
Sweetwater (G-19629)
Schneider Electric Usa Inc ....C....... 972 236-0300
Coppell (G-3444)
Texas Instruments Incorporated ....A....... 972 995-3773
Dallas (G-5067)
Texas Instruments Incorporated ....E....... 214 567-2075
Richardson (G-17408)
Utility Agency & Import Inc ....F....... 817 477-9888
Mansfield (G-14725)

CIRCUITS: Electronic

Alphabet McD Division ....E....... 915 593-2011
El Paso (G-5642)
Apx Plastics Inc ....F....... 817 275-3883
Arlington (G-620)
Atron Group LLC.....................................D....... 214 292-9840
Dallas (G-3984)
Austin American Tech Corp ....F....... 512 756-4150
Burnet (G-2603)
Bench Tree Group LLC ....E....... 512 869-6900
Georgetown (G-7640)
Benning Power Electronics Inc ....D....... 214 553-1444
Richardson (G-17279)
Clairex Technologies Inc ....F....... 972 265-4905
Plano (G-16825)
Concurrent Mfg Solutions LLC..............E....... 512 310-9139
Round Rock (G-17635)
Cordyne Inc ....D....... 713 460-5151
Houston (G-9313)
Creation Technologies Kentucky ....B....... 859 253-3066
Plano (G-16831)
Delta Group Electronics Inc ....D....... 972 606-2102
Grand Prairie (G-7863)
Dfm Technology Pvt USA Inc ....F....... 713 547-0114
Houston (G-9449)
E-M Design Time Inc ....F....... 972 279-4720
Dallas (G-4287)
Elcom Inc ....F....... 915 298-2000
El Paso (G-5749)
Engineering Spectrum Inc ....F....... 210 697-8828
San Antonio (G-18090)
High Point Design LLC ....F....... 972 753-2622
Irving (G-13056)
Indus Instruments...................................F....... 281 286-1130
Webster (G-20639)
Infratech Inc..F....... 214 503-1087
Dallas (G-4497)
Lachmann Vllneva Hldngs GP LLC ....F....... 915 594-0500
El Paso (G-5836)
Lee Tech LLC ....F....... 409 925-0553
Santa Fe (G-18736)
Leonard Elc Pdts Co Texas Inc.............F....... 956 350-5650
Brownsville (G-2377)
Lucere LLc ....E....... 281 240-7355
Missouri City (G-15582)
Lwo Acquisitions Company LLC ....D....... 972 573-1140
Irving (G-13093)
Mdi Security LLC....................................F....... 210 477-5400
San Antonio (G-18286)

Modern Tektronix Assembly ....E 817 868-7173
Euless (G-6150)
Mtx Electronics Inc ....F 956 781-3476
Pharr (G-16708)
Orbis International Tech Inc ....E 972 929-5705
Carrollton (G-2787)
Parsec Technologies Inc ....F 972 804-4600
Plano (G-16966)
Petron Industries Inc ....D 713 693-8700
Houston (G-11310)
Polara Engineering Inc ....D 951 547-5500
Greenville (G-8086)
Polara Enterprises LLC ....F 903 366-0300
Greenville (G-8087)
Regal Research and Mfg Co LLC ....C 972 494-0359
Plano (G-16990)
Season Group Usa LLC.....................D 210 522-1116
San Antonio (G-18462)
Stoneridge Electronics Inc ....A 915 621-6111
El Paso (G-5984)
Tech Power International Co................D 281 494-4242
Stafford (G-19382)
Texas Mri LP ....C 940 549-5462
Graham (G-7790)
Toppan Photomasks Inc ....C 512 310-6000
Round Rock (G-17694)
Trylene Inc ....E 281 980-0400
Houston (G-12392)
Unitron LP ....D 214 221-9094
Dallas (G-5139)
Wolfson Microelectronics Inc ....B 408 329-9800
Austin (G-1675)
Yazaki North America Inc ....F 618 512-8723
El Paso (G-6041)

CLAIMS ADJUSTING SVCS

Matthews-Daniel Holdings Inc ....D 713 622-1633
Houston (G-10798)

CLAMPS: Metal

Indumar Products Inc ....F 713 977-4100
Houston (G-10346)

CLAY PRDTS: Architectural

Kenmark Architectural Pdts Inc ....F 800 788-8263
Dallas (G-4550)

CLAY, PETROLEUM REFINING: Chemically Processed

Tribute Energy Inc............................F 281 768-5300
Houston (G-12367)

CLAY: Ground Or Treated

Bentonite Performance Mnrl LLC.........F 281 871-7900
Houston (G-8858)

CLAYS, EXC KAOLIN & BALL

Mid Tex Minerals Inc ....F 361 865-3530
Flatonia (G-6233)
Zeotech Corporation..........................F 361 274-3357
Tilden (G-19947)

CLEANERS: Pipe & Cigarette Holder

Polk Mechanical Company LLC............C 972 339-1200
Grand Prairie (G-7947)

CLEANING & DYEING PLANTS, EXC RUGS

Popes Cleaners LLC..........................F 210 923-7785
San Antonio (G-18384)
R J C Enterprises Inc........................E 806 793-8238
Lubbock (G-14469)

CLEANING COMPOUNDS: Rifle Bore

E Z Cleaning Solutions ....F 214 841-9626
Dallas (G-4286)

CLEANING EQPT: Blast, Dustless

Mmlj Inc...F 713 869-2227
Houston (G-10896)
Reliable Pump Consultants Inc ....E 713 640-2718
Houston (G-11591)

CLEANING EQPT: Commercial

Advanced MBL Fltrtion Svcs LLC ....F 800 484-4590
Fort Worth (G-6348)
Cummings Inv Bankers Inc...................F 281 416-3007
Houston (G-8376)
Falcon Prosolutions Inc ....E 210 547-2741
San Antonio (G-18103)
Keizer Technologies Americas ....F 817 685-7090
Euless (G-6148)
Trans Tool LLC ....F 210 225-6745
San Antonio (G-18560)

CLEANING EQPT: Floor Washing & Polishing, Commercial

Tacony Corporation ....D 817 551-0700
Fort Worth (G-7030)

CLEANING EQPT: High Pressure

APS Pressure Systems LLC ....E 281 290-9950
Tomball (G-19960)
Grayloc Products LLC ....E 713 466-8853
Houston (G-10021)
Jetstream of Houston LLP ....D 832 590-1300
Houston (G-10471)
Smart Control Systems LLC ....F 210 224-4906
San Antonio (G-18480)

CLEANING OR POLISHING PREPARATIONS, NEC

Allied Assets Corporation....................E 713 413-9700
Houston (G-8548)
Amrep Inc ....D 972 227-3304
Desoto (G-5428)
Beacon Lighthouse Inc ....D 940 767-0888
Wichita Falls (G-20743)
Chemax Corporation ....E 409 866-4232
Beaumont (G-1868)
Cobb Carpet Supply Co ....F 214 634-2622
Dallas (G-4133)
Envirocon Technologies Inc ....E 512 382-9842
Austin (G-1127)
Industrial Chem Tex Inc......................G 903 759-2642
Longview (G-14251)
McDonald Lighting & Maint Sup............G 903 297-8181
Longview (G-14275)
Norwex Usa Inc ....C 214 614-6707
Coppell (G-3433)
Ntw Services Inc ....G 210 885-8637
San Antonio (G-18352)
Pro Star Industries Inc........................E 979 779-9399
Bryan (G-2499)
Romix Chemicals Inc ....E 817 685-0006
Euless (G-6156)
Texas Nova-Chem Corporation ....F 972 771-1161
Rockwall (G-17569)
Titan Chemical Corporation ....F 713 747-3134
Houston (G-12296)

CLEANING PRDTS: Automobile Polish

Nuvinair LLC ....E 844 984-6247
Plano (G-16950)
Stinger Chemical LLC ....D 713 227-1340
Houston (G-12067)

CLEANING PRDTS: Bleaches, Household, Dry Or Liquid

Clorox Manufacturing Company ....D 713 674-5042
Houston (G-9216)
Houston Kik Inc ....C 713 747-8710
Houston (G-10236)

CLEANING PRDTS: Disinfectants, Household Or Indl Plant

Disingerm Inc ....F 214 482-9135
Ennis (G-6093)
Lighthuse For The Blind Huston ....E 713 284-8420
Houston (G-10640)

CLEANING PRDTS: Drycleaning Preparations

Ashmore & Ashmore Properties ....D 214 327-9228
Dallas (G-3970)

Cliff Dunta Bros Inc ....F 940 325-4855
Mineral Wells (G-15523)

CLEANING PRDTS: Indl Plant Disinfectants Or Deodorants

Josan Corporation ....F 281 261-4747
Stafford (G-19337)

CLEANING PRDTS: Laundry Preparations

R J C Enterprises Inc..........................E 806 793-8238
Lubbock (G-14469)

CLEANING PRDTS: Polishing Preparations & Related Prdts

Auto Wax Company Inc ....E 214 631-4000
Dallas (G-3988)

CLEANING PRDTS: Sanitation Preparations

City of Pasadena ....E 713 475-7884
Pasadena (G-16409)
East Texas Municpl Utility Dst ....F 903 877-3644
Tyler (G-20080)
Purocol LLC......................................F 310 926-9007
Garland (G-7573)
Sanitizenow Inc ....E 602 699-3150
Houston (G-11748)

CLEANING PRDTS: Sanitation Preps, Disinfectants/Deodorants

E-Mist Innovations Inc ....F 844 563-6478
Fort Worth (G-6601)
Envirocleanse LLC ....E 713 840-0404
Katy (G-13400)
Mbs Medical Technologies Inc ....E 888 482-4201
El Paso (G-5871)
Nexnol LLC ....F 833 463-9665
Brownsville (G-2387)
Scentsible LLC ....D 972 818-8200
Addison (G-161)
Tc Sanitizer Co LLC ....D 832 296-4561
Houston (G-12169)
Viarden Lab LLC ....F 956 294-0260
Mission (G-15573)
Virus Light Rx LLC ....F 817 917-2800
Fort Worth (G-7106)
Well Body Purify LLC ....F 443 847-6501
Seabrook (G-18794)

CLEANING PRDTS: Specialty

B C Williams Industries Inc ....F 214 352-4255
Dallas (G-3996)
Buckeye International Inc ....F 512 870-8555
Austin (G-1014)
Buckeye International Inc ....F 281 873-4200
Houston (G-9007)
Care Laboratories Inc ....E 281 835-9600
Missouri City (G-15577)
Ecoclean Supply & Services LLC.........F 800 245-9896
Southlake (G-19065)
Jimmy Smart ....E 432 381-5450
Odessa (G-16039)
K2 Industrial Services Inc ....F 850 477-6437
La Porte (G-13760)
Kiwo Holdings Inc ....E 281 474-9777
Seabrook (G-18787)
Montoya Building Services Inc...............E 713 367-0231
Houston (G-10915)
NCH Corporation ....A 972 438-0211
Irving (G-13114)
Nch Corporation ....E 972 438-0024
Irving (G-13117)
NCH Corporation ....F 972 438-0211
Irving (G-13119)
NCH Corporation ....F 972 438-0211
Irving (G-13120)
NCH Corporation ....A 972 438-0381
Irving (G-13115)
Pro-Chem of Dfw Inc...........................F 817 695-1660
Arlington (G-761)
Thomason Family Corporation..............F 713 223-4575
Houston (G-12277)
USa Screen Printing Chem Inc ....E 281 474-9777
Seabrook (G-18793)
Whitmore Manufacturing Company ......F 972 771-1000
Rockwall (G-17571)

Employee Codes: A=Over 500 employees, B=251-500
C=101-250, D=51-100, E=20-50, F=10-19, G=9

2021 Harris Texas
Manufacturers Directory

1421

PRODUCT

CLEANING PRDTS: Window Cleaning Preparations

Ambassador Facility Svcs LLC ....E 210 849-7677
Cibolo *(G-3061)*

CLEANING SVCS

Big Shot LLC ....E 504 877-2335
Lancaster *(G-13840)*

Bright Initiatives LLC ....F 512 466-4734
Austin *(G-1008)*

CLEANING SVCS: Industrial Or Commercial

Blue Box Air LLC ....D 424 241-3060
Dallas *(G-4031)*

Jahkur International LLC ....E 832 431-3232
Houston *(G-10450)*

Wcsa Inc ....F 806 383-1060
Amarillo *(G-473)*

CLOSURES: Closures, Stamped Metal

Self Industries ....E 713 672-2559
Houston *(G-11824)*

CLOTHES HANGERS, WHOLESALE

International Innovations Inc ....D 512 600-4517
Austin *(G-1238)*

CLOTHING & ACCESS, WOMEN, CHILD & INFANT, WHOL: Diapers

Diaper Sports Group LLC ....F 214 871-5131
Dallas *(G-4257)*

Sumehr Inc ....F 713 849-5528
Houston *(G-12093)*

CLOTHING & ACCESS, WOMEN, CHILD/INFANT, WHOLESALE: Child

Ingamia Inc ....F 214 828-1660
Dallas *(G-4499)*

CLOTHING & ACCESS, WOMEN, CHILDREN & INFANT, WHOL: Access

Fossil Partners LP ....A 972 234-2525
Richardson *(G-17317)*

Fossil Partners LP ....B 972 234-2525
Richardson *(G-17314)*

CLOTHING & ACCESS, WOMEN, CHILDREN & INFANT, WHOL: Uniforms

Medical Uniform Mfg Inc ....G 713 838-2233
Bellaire *(G-1998)*

Uniform Concepts Inc ....F 512 345-5793
Austin *(G-1607)*

CLOTHING & ACCESS, WOMEN, CHILDREN & INFANTS, WHOL: Purses

Mallorys Western & Leather Sup ....F 817 558-0804
Joshua *(G-13322)*

CLOTHING & ACCESS, WOMEN, CHILDREN/INFANT, WHOL: Swimsuits

Roka Sports Inc ....E 877 985-7652
Austin *(G-1470)*

CLOTHING & ACCESS: Costumes, Masquerade

Radtke Jenna ....E 512 444-2002
Austin *(G-1450)*

CLOTHING & ACCESS: Costumes, Theatrical

Claudia Rodriguez ....F 956 381-0845
Edinburg *(G-5583)*

CLOTHING & ACCESS: Handicapped

Vikay Group LLC ....F 512 291-8234
Austin *(G-1634)*

CLOTHING & ACCESS: Hospital Gowns

Border Opprtnity Sver Systems ....E 830 775-1225
Del Rio *(G-5308)*

Encompass Group LLC ....F 972 732-7694
Addison *(G-120)*

Essential Safety Ppe LLC ....D 844 372-3377
Spring *(G-19113)*

Stitches Inc ....E 915 591-9260
El Paso *(G-5981)*

Techstyles Inc ....E 972 732-7694
Addison *(G-167)*

CLOTHING & ACCESS: Men's Miscellaneous Access

Athletic Sewing Center Inc ....F 210 681-9744
San Antonio *(G-17920)*

Best Made Designs LLC ....E 432 943-9995
Monahans *(G-15600)*

Fossil Partners LP ....A 972 234-2525
Richardson *(G-17317)*

Fossil Partners LP ....B 972 234-2525
Richardson *(G-17314)*

Guess Inc ....E 915 877-1948
Canutillo *(G-2664)*

MJM Sourcing LLC ....F 214 769-7881
Dallas *(G-4681)*

Montana West USA ....F 972 241-9998
Dallas *(G-4686)*

MTC Marketing Inc ....F 972 488-0577
Carrollton *(G-2782)*

Tripp Research Inc ....F 512 321-9445
Bastrop *(G-1764)*

World of Jeans & Tops ....F 806 788-1233
Lubbock *(G-14514)*

CLOTHING & ACCESS: Regalia

McCartney Investment Corp ....F 214 521-8410
Dallas *(G-4659)*

CLOTHING & ACCESS: Suspenders

Overton Enterprises LLC ....F 512 394-6089
Austin *(G-1395)*

CLOTHING & APPAREL STORES: Custom

Directors Assistant LLC ....F 972 816-5553
Dallas *(G-4261)*

Gallery One Point LLC ....E 512 428-5710
Pflugerville *(G-16674)*

Military Customs LLC ....E 254 699-8106
Harker Heights *(G-8172)*

Rivercity Sportswear LLC ....E 512 754-8039
San Marcos *(G-18707)*

CLOTHING & FURNISHINGS, MEN'S & BOYS', WHOLESALE: Caps

Jj of Dallas Manufacturing Inc ....E 972 866-9866
Addison *(G-141)*

CLOTHING & FURNISHINGS, MEN'S & BOYS', WHOLESALE: Gloves

Mallorys Western & Leather Sup ....F 817 558-0804
Joshua *(G-13322)*

CLOTHING & FURNISHINGS, MEN'S & BOYS', WHOLESALE: Shirts

Athletic Sewing Center Inc ....F 210 681-9744
San Antonio *(G-17920)*

Beaver Graphix LLC ....F 325 227-3014
San Angelo *(G-17780)*

Esskay Manufacturing Co ....D 210 222-9585
San Antonio *(G-18096)*

H & H T-Shirt Printing Inc ....G 254 628-1453
Belton *(G-2023)*

CLOTHING & FURNISHINGS, MEN'S & BOYS', WHOLESALE: Trousers

Glen Oaks Industries Inc ....F 214 631-1340
Dallas *(G-4409)*

CLOTHING & FURNISHINGS, MEN'S & BOYS', WHOLESALE: Uniforms

Asti Manufacturing Corp Inc ....E 972 241-3055
Farmers Branch *(G-6189)*

Boy Scouts of America ....A 972 580-2000
Irving *(G-12950)*

Ghashim Capital Ventures Corp ....F 713 266-1888
Houston *(G-9949)*

Ics Jail Supplies Inc ....E 254 751-1566
Waco *(G-20418)*

Medical Uniform Mfg Inc ....G 713 838-2233
Bellaire *(G-1998)*

Uniform Concepts Inc ....F 512 345-5793
Austin *(G-1607)*

CLOTHING & FURNISHINGS, MEN/BOY, WHOL: Hats, Scarves/Gloves

Headcovers Unlimited Inc ....F 281 334-4287
League City *(G-13958)*

CLOTHING ACCESS STORES: Belts, Custom

Big Bend Saddlery Inc ....F 432 837-5551
Alpine *(G-311)*

CLOTHING STORES: Caps & Gowns

A J L Advertising Specialties ....E 512 320-0070
Austin *(G-872)*

G and G Investments Inc ....E 325 949-7864
San Angelo *(G-17801)*

CLOTHING STORES: Lingerie & Corsets, Underwear

Shame Lingerie ....F 214 823-1454
Dallas *(G-4952)*

CLOTHING STORES: Lingerie, Outerwear

Ce Soir Lingerie Co Inc ....D 512 953-4500
Austin *(G-1035)*

CLOTHING STORES: Shirts, Custom Made

Bond Clothier Inc ....E 713 784-7121
Houston *(G-8949)*

CLOTHING STORES: T-Shirts, Printed, Custom

Beaver Graphix LLC ....F 325 227-3014
San Angelo *(G-17780)*

Campus Design Incorporated ....F 806 744-9998
Lubbock *(G-14387)*

H & H T-Shirt Printing Inc ....G 254 628-1453
Belton *(G-2023)*

Jovi Printing ....F 713 467-4980
Houston *(G-10485)*

Kruckeberg Corporation ....G 806 352-9262
Amarillo *(G-496)*

Qti Apparel & Promotions LLC ....E 254 662-3076
Waco *(G-20451)*

Uniforms Inc ....F 214 630-0924
Dallas *(G-5132)*

CLOTHING STORES: Uniforms & Work

Startex Linen Co ....F 713 782-4419
Houston *(G-12050)*

CLOTHING STORES: Unisex

1 Play Away LLC ....E 972 532-6226
Desoto *(G-5426)*

Gallery One Point LLC ....E 512 428-5710
Pflugerville *(G-16674)*

CLOTHING: Access

Game Day Sports Apparel LLC ....E 214 499-0028
Grapevine *(G-8037)*

New Purple LLC ....E 713 499-0422
Houston *(G-11036)*

Privileged Culture LLC ....F 682 252-5173
Arlington *(G-760)*

CLOTHING: Access, Women's & Misses'

B Bad Sports Inc ....E 713 664-3838
Houston *(G-8773)*

Fossil Partners LP ....B 972 234-2525
Richardson **(G-17314)**

Fossil Partners LP ....B 469 587-2627
Richardson **(G-17316)**

Fossil Partners LP ....A 972 234-2525
Richardson **(G-17317)**

Helens Heart LLC ....F 972 247-1414
Dallas **(G-4447)**

I&G Designs and Logistics LLC ....F 214 543-4461
Dallas **(G-4481)**

Jerell Clothing Company LLC ....F 214 349-1891
Dallas **(G-4532)**

Jon Hart Design Co ....E 210 226-8544
San Antonio **(G-18206)**

Rai of Sunshine LLC ....D 832 271-0144
Houston **(G-11534)**

World of Jeans & Tops ....F 806 788-1233
Lubbock **(G-14514)**

CLOTHING: Aprons, Harness

Premier Emblem & Insignia Inc ....F 210 253-3406
San Antonio **(G-18391)**

Willingham Systems LLC ....D 713 928-3936
Houston **(G-12671)**

CLOTHING: Aprons, Waterproof, From Purchased Materials

Handgards LLC ....C 915 779-6606
El Paso **(G-5794)**

CLOTHING: Athletic & Sportswear, Men's & Boys'

8228 Corporation ....E 713 465-1303
Houston **(G-8417)**

Baw Athletic Wear LP ....F 281 391-3335
Katy **(G-13389)**

Bexar Manufacturing & Trdg Co ....F 210 977-9585
San Antonio **(G-17951)**

Double D Ranchwear Inc ....F 361 293-2394
Yoakum **(G-20963)**

Ennis Inc ....A 972 775-9801
Midlothian **(G-15480)**

Gmyp Manufacturing LLC ....F 682 313-3023
Farmers Branch **(G-6197)**

Hurley International LLC ....C 972 912-3040
Allen **(G-277)**

Hurley International LLC ....C 956 514-1700
Mercedes **(G-15006)**

J & G Trybus Corporation ....F 214 331-5248
Desoto **(G-5435)**

Lululemon Athletica ....F 713 863-1280
Houston **(G-10701)**

Trademarks Promotional Pdts LP ....D 713 255-6506
Houston **(G-12340)**

CLOTHING: Athletic & Sportswear, Women's & Girls'

8228 Corporation ....E 713 465-1303
Houston **(G-8417)**

Cheerleading Company Inc ....E 800 411-4105
Dallas **(G-4106)**

Couture American Lifestyle ....E 972 487-1641
Garland **(G-7469)**

Fashion Works Inc ....F 972 596-5815
Plano **(G-16869)**

Lululemon Athletica ....F 713 863-1280
Houston **(G-10701)**

Zrc Ltd ....F 325 949-7625
San Angelo **(G-17843)**

CLOTHING: Baker, Barber, Lab/Svc Ind Apparel, Washable, Men

A&S New Braunfels LLC ....E 832 206-4202
San Antonio **(G-17849)**

Gallery One Point LLC ....E 512 428-5710
Pflugerville **(G-16674)**

CLOTHING: Band Uniforms

Band Mans Co Southwest Inc ....F 214 350-0631
Dallas **(G-4003)**

Cheerleading Company Inc ....E 800 411-4105
Dallas **(G-4106)**

Directors Assistant LLC ....F 972 816-5553
Dallas **(G-4261)**

Rebel Athletic Inc ....F 972 418-0827
Carrollton **(G-2803)**

CLOTHING: Bathing Suits & Swimwear, Knit

Body Language Fashions Inc ....F 713 974-0960
Houston **(G-8936)**

CLOTHING: Beachwear, Knit

Enthusiastic Sales LLC ....F 832 698-1608
Tomball **(G-19978)**

CLOTHING: Belts

3-D Belt Company LP ....E 979 743-4567
Schulenburg **(G-18770)**

Brushy Creek Belt & Buckle Co ....F 361 293-2345
Yoakum **(G-20960)**

Circle Y Saddles Inc ....F 361 293-3501
Yoakum **(G-20961)**

Cowtown Western Belt Inc ....E 817 625-4411
Fort Worth **(G-6554)**

Lagarto Inc ....E 915 598-2668
El Paso **(G-5837)**

Mallorys Western & Leather Sup ....F 817 558-0804
Joshua **(G-13322)**

Maxims Imports Inc ....F 915 577-9228
El Paso **(G-5870)**

Stallion Boot Co Inc ....E 915 532-6268
El Paso **(G-5974)**

Travis Assn For The Blind ....C 512 442-2329
Austin **(G-1590)**

CLOTHING: Blouses, Women's & Girls'

Chapman Shameka ....F 281 507-8790
Pearland **(G-16543)**

David McNeff Inc ....F 972 562-0607
McKinney **(G-14935)**

Readyone Industries Inc ....A 915 858-7277
El Paso **(G-5931)**

Treska Inc ....E 682 647-0352
Fort Worth **(G-7074)**

Vf Sagebrush Enterprises LLC ....E 817 336-7201
Fort Worth **(G-7103)**

CLOTHING: Blouses, Womens & Juniors, From Purchased Mtrls

Pvh Corp ....G 512 392-2036
San Marcos **(G-18704)**

Westmoor Corp ....E 817 625-2841
Fort Worth **(G-7142)**

Westmoor Mfg Co ....E 817 625-2841
Fort Worth **(G-7143)**

CLOTHING: Burial

Rita Barber Inc ....F 325 698-0111
Abilene **(G-73)**

Vlgc LLC ....E 817 926-5209
Fort Worth **(G-7110)**

CLOTHING: Caps, Baseball

Vanguard Resources Inc ....F 325 372-3142
San Saba **(G-18720)**

CLOTHING: Children & Infants'

Ingamia Inc ....F 214 828-1660
Dallas **(G-4499)**

Paty Investments Inc ....E 713 688-7686
Houston **(G-11263)**

Quatrefoil Partners LLC ....F 214 631-7117
Dallas **(G-4848)**

Universal Kids LLC ....E 832 374-1082
Kingwood **(G-13657)**

CLOTHING: Children's, Girls'

Asics America Corporation ....E 972 678-0200
Allen **(G-252)**

Dallas Bias Fabrics Inc ....E 214 824-2036
Dallas **(G-4212)**

LEtoile Apparel Inc ....E 972 701-8916
Dallas **(G-3848)**

Paty Investments Inc ....E 713 688-7686
Houston **(G-11263)**

Tag Holdings Inc ....C 214 469-3300
The Colony **(G-19815)**

Team Go Figure LLP ....E 972 276-6700
Dallas **(G-5043)**

Walls Industries LLC ....D 844 259-2557
Fort Worth **(G-7118)**

Westmoor Corp ....E 817 625-2841
Fort Worth **(G-7142)**

CLOTHING: Coats & Jackets, Leather & Sheep-Lined

Wolf & Sons Design Inc ....E 512 237-3388
Smithville **(G-18979)**

CLOTHING: Coats & Suits, Men's & Boys'

Haggar Clothing Co ....B 214 352-8481
Texas City **(G-19794)**

Ingamia Inc ....F 214 828-1660
Dallas **(G-4499)**

Walls Industries LLC ....D 844 259-2557
Fort Worth **(G-7118)**

CLOTHING: Costumes

Cowan Costumes Inc ....F 817 641-3126
Cleburne **(G-3085)**

CLOTHING: Culottes & Shorts, Children's

Westmoor Mfg Co ....E 817 625-2841
Fort Worth **(G-7143)**

CLOTHING: Dresses

David McNeff Inc ....F 972 562-0607
McKinney **(G-14935)**

G-III Apparel Group Ltd ....F 281 256-3661
Cypress **(G-3794)**

Moll McNeill Inc ....G 214 748-7272
Dallas **(G-4684)**

Sharon Young Inc ....E 214 349-1891
Dallas **(G-4953)**

Terry Costa Inc ....E 972 385-6100
Dallas **(G-5050)**

CLOTHING: Garments, Indl, Men's & Boys

Vf Outdoor LLC ....B 817 348-0567
Fort Worth **(G-7099)**

CLOTHING: Hats & Caps, NEC

Bio World Merchandising Inc ....C 972 488-0655
Irving **(G-12948)**

C & C Western Wear Inc ....F 903 753-8991
Longview **(G-14206)**

Rhe Hatco Inc ....C 903 753-2631
Longview **(G-14297)**

Rhe Hatco Inc ....B 972 494-0511
Garland **(G-7579)**

Rockpoint Apparel Company ....F 713 699-9896
Houston **(G-11651)**

CLOTHING: Hats & Caps, Uniform

Choice Cap Inc ....F 832 251-9551
Houston **(G-9185)**

CLOTHING: Hats & Headwear, Knit

Bio World Merchandising Inc ....C 972 488-0655
Irving **(G-12948)**

Gall Art Novelties LLC ....F 956 290-3124
Laredo **(G-13888)**

Headcovers Unlimited Inc ....F 281 334-4287
League City **(G-13958)**

Virtual Realities ....F 409 599-7863
Dickinson **(G-5479)**

CLOTHING: Hats, Harvest, Straw

Ahc Western Hatters Ltd Lblty ....E 940 872-2404
Bowie **(G-2190)**

CLOTHING: Hospital, Men's

Armbrust Inc ....E 512 807-0744
Pflugerville **(G-16658)**

Asti Manufacturing Corp Inc ....E 972 241-3055
Farmers Branch **(G-6189)**

Blue Medical Services Inc ....E 954 417-5442
Cypress **(G-3781)**

Medical Uniform Mfg Inc ....G 713 838-2233
Bellaire **(G-1998)**

Radia Enterprises Inc ....E 713 645-3600
Houston **(G-11530)**

PRODUCT

Texas Sewing Inc ....G 713 271-5466
Houston *(G-12248)*

CLOTHING: Jackets & Vests, Exc Fur & Leather, Women's

Moll McNeill Inc ....G 214 748-7272
Dallas *(G-4684)*

CLOTHING: Jackets, Field, Military

Advantage Supplies Inc ....F 972 250-1339
Carrollton *(G-2854)*

CLOTHING: Jeans, Men's & Boys'

Ameri-Tech Dist Inc ....E 915 772-9090
El Paso *(G-5643)*
Guess Inc ....E 915 877-1948
Canutillo *(G-2664)*
Haggar Clothing Co ....B 214 352-8481
Farmers Branch *(G-6199)*
Stanley Jeans Corp ....D 936 544-5521
Crockett *(G-3724)*

CLOTHING: Jogging & Warm-Up Suits, Knit

Brazos Running Company LLC ....G 979 485-9830
College Station *(G-3178)*

CLOTHING: Leather & sheep-lined clothing

C N A Inc ....E 915 533-2425
El Paso *(G-5675)*
Distinctive Inds Texas Inc ....E 512 491-3500
Austin *(G-1096)*
Double J Saddlery Inc ....D 361 293-6364
Yoakum *(G-20964)*

CLOTHING: Men's & boy's underwear & nightwear

J & G Trybus Corporation ....F 214 331-5248
Desoto *(G-5435)*

CLOTHING: Mens & Boys Jackets, Sport, Suede, Leatherette

Dilly Letter Jackets ....F 713 334-3232
Houston *(G-9473)*
H & R Black Mfg Co LLC ....F 806 364-2040
Hereford *(G-8290)*
Vf Sagebrush Enterprises LLC ....E 817 336-7201
Fort Worth *(G-7103)*

CLOTHING: Neckwear

Cortwear Sports AP & Eqp LLC ....F 361 728-1868
Kingsville *(G-13624)*

CLOTHING: Outerwear, Lthr, Wool/Down-Filled, Men, Youth/Boy

Aerostar International Inc ....E 903 885-0728
Sulphur Springs *(G-19578)*

CLOTHING: Outerwear, Women's & Misses' NEC

Asics America Corporation ....E 972 678-0200
Allen *(G-252)*
Charles De Vuae Inc ....F 713 789-8485
Houston *(G-9164)*
Conversation Pieces Inc ....G 409 762-2799
Galveston *(G-7394)*
David McNeff Inc ....F 972 562-0607
McKinney *(G-14935)*
Double D Ranchwear Inc ....F 361 293-9239
Yoakum *(G-20962)*
Double D Ranchwear Inc ....F 361 293-2394
Yoakum *(G-20963)*
FSI Apparel Inc ....E 562 906-3000
Southlake *(G-19070)*
LEtoile Apparel Inc ....E 972 701-8916
Dallas *(G-3848)*
Needleworks Etc ....F 432 445-9313
Pecos *(G-16624)*
REr Apparel Inc ....E 417 673-5786
Dallas *(G-3851)*
Ruddock Manufacturing Co Inc ....C 915 544-3530
El Paso *(G-5949)*

Tag Holdings Inc ....C 214 469-3300
The Colony *(G-19815)*
Vf Outdoor LLC ....B 817 348-0567
Fort Worth *(G-7099)*
Vf Outdoor LLC ....A 817 336-7201
Fort Worth *(G-7100)*
Vf Outdoor LLC ....E 817 491-4949
Fort Worth *(G-7102)*

CLOTHING: Overalls & Coveralls

Aztec Fr Apparel Inc ....B 830 422-1775
Del Rio *(G-5306)*
Earls Apparel Inc ....D 936 544-5521
Crockett *(G-3717)*

CLOTHING: Pants, Work, Men's, Youths' & Boys'

REr Apparel Inc ....E 417 673-5786
Dallas *(G-3851)*

CLOTHING: Service Apparel, Women's

Directors Assistant LLC ....F 972 816-5553
Dallas *(G-4261)*

CLOTHING: Shirts

Asics America Corporation ....E 972 678-0200
Allen *(G-252)*
Dos Carolinas Inc ....E 210 222-9117
San Antonio *(G-18065)*
Earls Apparel Inc ....D 936 544-5521
Crockett *(G-3717)*
Haggar Clothing Co ....B 214 352-8481
Farmers Branch *(G-6199)*
Haggar Clothing Co ....B 214 352-8481
Texas City *(G-19794)*
Haggar Corp ....A 214 352-8481
Farmers Branch *(G-6200)*
Hamilton Shirt Interests Ltd ....E 713 780-8222
Houston *(G-10113)*
J & G Trybus Corporation ....F 214 331-5248
Desoto *(G-5435)*
Ruddock Manufacturing Co Inc ....C 915 544-3530
El Paso *(G-5949)*
Texas Clothing Holding Corp ....E 214 956-4494
Dallas *(G-5056)*
Westmoor Corp ....E 817 625-2841
Fort Worth *(G-7142)*

CLOTHING: Shirts, Dress, Men's & Boys'

Apparel Group Ltd ....C 214 469-3300
Lewisville *(G-14022)*
Bond Clothier Inc ....E 713 784-7121
Houston *(G-8949)*
Pvh Corp ....E 512 392-2036
San Marcos *(G-18704)*
Ruddock Manufacturing Co Inc ....C 915 544-3530
El Paso *(G-5950)*
Tag Holdings Inc ....E 214 469-3300
The Colony *(G-19815)*
Vf Sagebrush Enterprises LLC ....E 817 336-7201
Fort Worth *(G-7103)*
Westmoor Mfg Co ....E 817 625-2841
Fort Worth *(G-7143)*

CLOTHING: Shirts, Sports & Polo, Men's & Boys'

Rockpoint Apparel Company ....F 713 699-9896
Houston *(G-11651)*

CLOTHING: Shirts, Women's & Juniors', From Purchased Mtrls

Circle T Western Wear Ltd ....F 214 808-1100
Dallas *(G-4121)*
Moll McNeill Inc ....G 214 748-7272
Dallas *(G-4684)*

CLOTHING: Skirts

Circle T Western Wear Ltd ....F 214 808-1100
Dallas *(G-4121)*

CLOTHING: Sleeping Garments, Men's & Boys'

New Icm LP ....E 979 578-0543
El Campo *(G-5623)*

CLOTHING: Sleeping Garments, Women's & Children's

New Icm LP ....E 979 578-0543
El Campo *(G-5623)*
New ICM L P ....C 979 578-0543
El Campo *(G-5624)*

CLOTHING: Socks

Celeste Stein Designs Inc ....E 409 763-1009
Galveston *(G-7392)*
Sand Socks ....F 512 284-7706
Buda *(G-2536)*
Sock Club Enterprises LLC ....G 919 619-4981
Austin *(G-1515)*

CLOTHING: Sportswear, Women's

Apparel Group Ltd ....C 214 469-3300
Lewisville *(G-14022)*
B & J Accessories Inc ....E 972 494-6939
Frisco *(G-7269)*
J Suzette & Company Inc ....F 972 359-0001
Allen *(G-279)*
Kathleen Sommers Designs Inc ....F 210 271-7118
San Antonio *(G-18217)*
Nuvo Athletic LLC ....G 281 808-7650
Stafford *(G-19360)*

CLOTHING: Suits, Men's & Boys', From Purchased Materials

Esskay Manufacturing Co ....D 210 222-9585
San Antonio *(G-18096)*
Tom James Company ....F 325 695-0190
Abilene *(G-88)*

CLOTHING: Sweatshirts & T-Shirts, Men's & Boys'

A-Z Graphics LLC ....F 210 495-3468
San Antonio *(G-17852)*
Business Print Center Inc ....E 505 864-3553
Converse *(G-3390)*

CLOTHING: Swimwear, Men's & Boys'

Roka Sports Inc ....E 877 985-7652
Austin *(G-1470)*

CLOTHING: Swimwear, Women's & Misses'

Roka Sports Inc ....E 877 985-7652
Austin *(G-1470)*

CLOTHING: T-Shirts & Tops, Knit

Hg Tshirt Design Company ....F 469 776-4995
Grand Prairie *(G-7890)*

CLOTHING: T-Shirts & Tops, Women's & Girls'

A-Z Graphics LLC ....F 210 495-3468
San Antonio *(G-17852)*
Ennis Inc ....A 972 775-9801
Midlothian *(G-15480)*

CLOTHING: Tailored Suits & Formal Jackets

Directors Assistant LLC ....F 972 816-5553
Dallas *(G-4261)*
Haggar Clothing Co ....B 214 352-8481
Farmers Branch *(G-6199)*
Haggar Corp ....A 214 352-8481
Farmers Branch *(G-6200)*
Texas Clothing Holding Corp ....E 214 956-4494
Dallas *(G-5056)*

CLOTHING: Trousers & Slacks, Men's & Boys'

Bellagio Menswear LLC ....G 512 496-8322
Austin *(G-988)*

Earls Apparel Inc....................D.......936 544-5521
  Crockett (G-3717)
Fashion Works Inc.................F.......972 596-5815
  Plano (G-16869)
Glen Oaks Industries Inc.................F.......214 631-1340
  Dallas (G-4409)
Haggar Clothing Co...................B.......214 352-8481
  Texas City (G-19794)
J & G Trybus Corporation.................F.......214 331-5248
  Desoto (G-5435)
Vf Industrial Park Inc.................F.......979 826-8277
  Hempstead (G-8256)

CLOTHING: Underwear, Men's & Boys'

Inzer Advance Designs Inc.................E.......903 236-4012
  Longview (G-14253)

CLOTHING: Uniforms & Vestments

Bric Mc Mann Industries Inc.................F.......830 775-9153
  Del Rio (G-5309)
Gavson Inc.................E.......214 341-0440
  Dallas (G-4394)
Parker School Uniforms LLC.................E.......713 465-1635
  Houston (G-11244)

CLOTHING: Uniforms, Ex Athletic, Women's, Misses' & Juniors'

Career Concepts Inc.................E.......972 276-9332
  Garland (G-7453)
Leonard Sloan & Associates Inc.................F.......214 350-2440
  Dallas (G-4591)

CLOTHING: Uniforms, Firemen's, From Purchased Materials

Red The Uniform Tailor.................E.......972 660-8433
  Grand Prairie (G-7963)
Safety Supply Inc.................F.......210 650-9033
  San Antonio (G-18441)

CLOTHING: Uniforms, Men's & Boys'

Ics Jail Supplies Inc.................E.......254 751-1566
  Waco (G-20418)
Roicom Usa LLC.................E.......915 471-3071
  El Paso (G-5944)
Rvg Prodirect LLC.................F.......956 627-6161
  McAllen (G-14903)

CLOTHING: Uniforms, Military, Men/Youth, Purchased Materials

Advantage Supplies Inc.................F.......972 250-1339
  Carrollton (G-2854)
El Paso Lighthouse For Blind.................E.......915 532-4495
  El Paso (G-5736)
Marlo Sales Inc.................F.......972 721-9755
  Irving (G-13095)
Readyone Industries Inc.................A.......915 858-7277
  El Paso (G-5931)

CLOTHING: Uniforms, Team Athletic

Nsg Corporation.................C.......972 840-1233
  Plano (G-16947)
Southland Athletic Mfg Co.................D.......972 563-3321
  Terrell (G-19751)

CLOTHING: Uniforms, Work

Ashley Worldwide Inc.................E.......956 383-0636
  Edinburg (G-5575)
Med Couture Inc.................D.......214 231-2500
  Farmers Branch (G-6207)
Newinn Inc.................F.......713 473-8188
  Pasadena (G-16488)
Twin Hill Acquisition Co Inc.................E.......888 206-0699
  Houston (G-12415)

CLOTHING: Vests

Neosensory Inc.................F.......401 257-9460
  Houston (G-11025)

CLOTHING: Waterproof Outerwear

Alamo Waterproofing Svcs Inc.................F.......210 648-2100
  San Antonio (G-17887)
Forum Industries Inc.................D.......210 225-9600
  San Antonio (G-18124)

Orc Industries Inc.................D.......956 831-0618
  Brownsville (G-2389)
Precision Frac LLC.................F.......855 967-1023
  Midland (G-15362)
Walls Industries LLC.................D.......844 259-2557
  Fort Worth (G-7118)

CLOTHING: Work Apparel, Exc Uniforms

Maquilaplex LLC.................F.......956 542-4138
  Brownsville (G-2380)
Safety Supply Inc.................F.......210 650-9033
  San Antonio (G-18441)
Schaefer Ventures LLC.................G.......800 426-2074
  Fort Worth (G-6977)

CLOTHING: Work, Men's

Border Apparel Laundry Ltd.................E.......915 772-7170
  El Paso (G-5666)
Guard-Line Inc.................C.......903 796-4111
  Atlanta (G-843)
Handgards LLC.................C.......915 779-6606
  El Paso (G-5794)
Le Stitch N Designs Inc.................E.......214 340-1592
  Dallas (G-4586)
Medline Industries Inc.................C.......281 574-6200
  Katy (G-13371)
Ruddock Manufacturing Co Inc.................C.......915 544-3530
  El Paso (G-5949)
Southland Athletic Mfg Co.................D.......972 563-3321
  Terrell (G-19751)
Stanco Manufacturing Inc.................D.......903 796-7936
  Atlanta (G-845)
Stanley Jeans Corp.................D.......936 544-5521
  Crockett (G-3724)
Stitches Inc.................E.......915 591-9260
  El Paso (G-5981)
Unifirst Corporation.................E.......281 261-9632
  Missouri City (G-15597)
Uniforms Inc.................F.......214 630-0924
  Dallas (G-5132)
Vf Industrial Park Inc.................E.......936 327-7881
  Livingston (G-14163)
Vf Outdoor LLC.................A.......817 336-7201
  Fort Worth (G-7100)
Vf Outdoor LLC.................C.......817 810-4401
  Fort Worth (G-7101)
Vf Outdoor LLC.................E.......817 491-4949
  Fort Worth (G-7102)
Vf Outdoor LLC.................E.......830 278-2535
  Uvalde (G-20199)
Walls Industries LLC.................D.......844 259-2557
  Fort Worth (G-7118)
Walls Industries LLC.................E.......817 357-8040
  Fort Worth (G-7119)

CLUTCHES, EXC VEHICULAR

Bk Power Systems LLC.................F.......713 225-6661
  Houston (G-8898)
Clutchco International Inc.................E.......281 446-1297
  Humble (G-12758)
Clutchco USA.................F.......936 588-3501
  Humble (G-12759)
Warner Electric LLC.................D.......940 767-2000
  Wichita Falls (G-20827)

COAL & OTHER MINERALS & ORES WHOLESALERS

Airtrust Intl Systems Corp.................F.......713 491-4455
  Texas City (G-19785)
C & C Wood Company Inc.................F.......361 865-3444
  Waelder (G-20482)

COAL GASIFICATION

Synthesis Energy Systems Inc.................F.......713 579-0600
  Houston (G-12138)

COAL MINING EXPLORATION SVCS: Anthracite

Enerquest Resources LLC.................E.......432 685-3116
  Midland (G-15219)

COAL MINING EXPLORATION SVCS: Bituminous Or Lignite

M H C X-Ploration Corporation.................F.......903 595-4323
  Tyler (G-20117)

COAL MINING SERVICES

Far East Energy Corporation.................F.......832 598-0470
  Houston (G-9762)
Hunt Dominion Corporation.................C.......214 880-8400
  Dallas (G-4472)
Kingdom Coal LLC.................F.......817 840-6646
  Irving (G-13077)
Savage Companies.................E.......806 381-0261
  Amarillo (G-461)
Squaw Creek Materials LP.................E.......254 897-3505
  Rainbow (G-17229)
Texas Westmoreland Coal Co.................D.......903 626-5485
  Jewett (G-13309)

COAL MINING: Bituminous Coal & Lignite-Surface Mining

El Paso CNG Company LLC.................F.......713 420-2600
  Houston (G-9586)
Knife River Corporation.................D.......979 361-2900
  Bryan (G-2488)
Natural Resource Partners LP.................E.......713 751-7507
  Houston (G-11010)
North American Coal Corp.................D.......972 448-5400
  Plano (G-16946)
North American Coal Corp.................C.......830 784-3545
  Christine (G-3059)
Nrp (gp) LP.................B.......713 751-7507
  Houston (G-11092)
Nrp (operating) LLC.................D.......713 751-7507
  Houston (G-11093)
Sabine Mining Company.................C.......903 660-4200
  Hallsville (G-8130)

COAL MINING: Bituminous Underground

BHP Mineral Resources Inc.................D.......713 961-8500
  Houston (G-8877)
BHP Minerals International LLC.................B.......713 961-8500
  Houston (G-8878)
Clariant Corporation.................E.......281 465-9100
  The Woodlands (G-19846)
Williams Gas Pipeline-Transco.................C.......713 215-2000
  Houston (G-12670)

COAL MINING: Bituminous, Surface, NEC

Williams Gas Pipeline-Transco.................C.......713 215-2000
  Houston (G-12670)

COAL MINING: Lignite, Strip

Caddo Creek Resources Co LLC.................G.......903 927-1130
  Marshall (G-14767)

COAL MINING: Underground, Semianthracite

American Natural Resources Co.................E.......832 320-5000
  Houston (G-8603)

COAL, MINERALS & ORES, WHOLESALE: Coal

Savage Companies.................E.......806 381-0261
  Amarillo (G-461)

COAL, MINERALS & ORES, WHOLESALE: Sulfur

US Petrochemicals Inc.................F.......713 871-1951
  Houston (G-12487)

COATING COMPOUNDS: Tar

Ark-La-Tex Custom Coatings.................F.......903 845-6436
  Gladewater (G-7717)
Coatings Group Inc.................C.......817 633-7383
  Grand Prairie (G-7857)
JW Industries Ltd.................F.......972 291-7474
  Cedar Hill (G-2947)
Professional Coating Tech Inc.................F.......972 291-7474
  Cedar Hill (G-2952)

COATING OR WRAPPING SVC: Steel Pipe

A&A Coating Inc.................E.......903 656-2581
  Lone Star (G-14181)
APAC International Inc.................F.......940 696-2525
  Wichita Falls (G-20738)
Bredero Shaw LLC.................E.......281 886-2350
  Houston (G-8982)

Employee Codes: A=Over 500 employees, B=251-500
C=101-250, D=51-100, E=20-50, F=10-19, G=9

2021 Harris Texas
Manufacturers Directory

PRODUCT

1425

LB Foster Ball Winch Inc..................D...... 936 228-0077
  Willis (G-20853)
Nov Tuboscope.................................F...... 713 799-5100
  Houston (G-11087)
Shawcor Pipe Protection LLC............F...... 281 485-8321
  Pearland (G-16598)
Shawcor Pipe Protection LLC............E...... 281 940-0700
  Houston (G-11851)
Shawcor Pipe Protection LLC............F...... 713 378-7200
  Channelview (G-3036)
Shawcor Pipe Protection LLC............D...... 281 886-2350
  Houston (G-11852)
Tim Yockey.......................................F...... 281 252-6175
  Magnolia (G-14630)
Varco LP..E...... 432 367-9726
  Odessa (G-16198)
Varco LP..E...... 432 337-1570
  Odessa (G-16199)
Varco LP..C...... 713 799-5272
  Houston (G-12534)

COATING SVC

Elite Coating Services.......................F...... 469 431-3353
  Alvarado (G-329)
Nano Coat LP....................................F...... 281 217-5265
  San Antonio (G-18331)

COATING SVC: Aluminum, Metal Prdts

Keith Darwin Raines..........................F...... 713 477-8534
  Deer Park (G-5281)
Son-Lan Industries Inc......................G...... 972 937-8162
  Waxahachie (G-20558)

COATING SVC: Electrodes

E-Coating Inc....................................F...... 936 715-0700
  Nacogdoches (G-15695)
Electro-Coatings of Iowa Inc.............G...... 800 806-6059
  San Antonio (G-18086)
Land Industrial Trial Sevices.............F...... 281 385-2504
  Old River Winfree (G-16218)

COATING SVC: Hot Dip, Metals Or Formed Prdts

Azz Inc...E...... 832 467-3772
  Houston (G-8771)
Azz Incorporated...............................D...... 817 268-2414
  Hurst (G-12836)
National Oilwell Varco Inc..................E...... 281 456-8551
  Houston (G-10991)

COATING SVC: Metals & Formed Prdts

3M Company.....................................F...... 979 848-8489
  Angleton (G-564)
3p Industries LLC..............................E...... 903 877-3960
  Tyler (G-20042)
A-1 Powder Coat Paint Inc.................F...... 972 494-6861
  Garland (G-7424)
AAA Blast-Cote Inc............................E...... 281 482-1236
  Friendswood (G-7241)
Accurate Inc.....................................D...... 512 352-5278
  Taylor (G-19647)
American Powder Coating Corp..........F...... 817 446-9400
  Fort Worth (G-6384)
American Roller Company LLC...........F...... 262 878-2445
  Houston (G-8607)
American Roller Company LLC...........E...... 713 466-0550
  Houston (G-8608)
Apache Global Painting Inc................C...... 713 450-9307
  Houston (G-8658)
Armadillo Blast Coat Inc....................E...... 281 485-2743
  Pearland (G-16539)
Bdm Metal Coaters LLC......................D...... 713 400-2300
  Houston (G-8844)
Berridge Manufacturing Company.......E...... 210 650-7056
  San Antonio (G-17949)
Berridge Manufacturing Company.......F...... 713 223-4971
  Houston (G-8861)
C&F Fabrication Indus Svcs LLC.........E...... 409 994-2135
  Buna (G-2561)
Cincinnati Thermal Spray Inc.............F...... 281 431-1629
  Rosharon (G-17603)
Coating Industries Inc.......................E...... 713 937-8581
  Houston (G-9230)
Coiling Technologies Inc....................D...... 713 849-4000
  Houston (G-9241)
Contract Powder Coating Inc..............F...... 972 494-4444
  Garland (G-7462)

Corev America Inc.............................E...... 713 849-3671
  Houston (G-9319)
Corrosion Prtction Prcsses of............F...... 713 869-9454
  Houston (G-9324)
Crosslink McKnney Pwdr Cting L.........F...... 972 542-5441
  McKinney (G-14933)
Crosslink Pwdr Cting Astin Ltd...........G...... 512 989-6458
  Pflugerville (G-16664)
Daggett Street Properties...................F...... 817 332-5604
  Fort Worth (G-6572)
Dean-Chem Inc..................................F...... 713 644-3882
  Houston (G-9419)
Deq Coatings Inc...............................F...... 713 645-1777
  Houston (G-9438)
Dobbs Coating Systems Inc................F...... 817 341-1777
  Weatherford (G-20587)
El Paso Pwdr Cting Hydrgrphics.........F...... 915 313-9333
  El Paso (G-5739)
Ford Contract Services Inc.................E...... 713 862-2960
  Livingston (G-14154)
Fusion Operations LP.........................D...... 713 691-6547
  Houston (G-9878)
G&C Coatings & Industrial Serv..........D...... 832 916-6070
  Houston (G-9887)
Gartner Coatings Inc.........................E...... 281 997-3500
  Pearland (G-16563)
General Magnaplate Corporation.........D...... 817 640-1761
  Arlington (G-687)
General Magnaplate Texas Inc............E...... 817 649-8989
  Arlington (G-688)
General Magnaplate Wisconsin...........F...... 800 441-6173
  Arlington (G-689)
Gfk Interests Ltd...............................D...... 713 225-0010
  Houston (G-9947)
Grothe Industrial Coating LLC............F...... 281 354-1574
  Crosby (G-3732)
Gulf Coast Powdr Gelworks Inc...........E...... 409 962-1211
  Port Arthur (G-17110)
Gull Industries Inc............................E...... 713 224-2430
  Houston (G-10074)
Houston Powder Coaters LLC..............E...... 281 676-3888
  Houston (G-10245)
Houston Unlimited Metal Proc.............F...... 979 836-7568
  Chappell Hill (G-3046)
Impreglon Surface Tech Inc................E...... 713 466-9655
  Houston (G-10335)
Jar-Tex Industries Inc........................E...... 817 332-9922
  Fort Worth (G-6735)
K-T Galvanizing Co Inc.......................E...... 281 391-9201
  Katy (G-13413)
Labarge Coating LLC..........................D...... 713 378-7225
  Channelview (G-3028)
Labarge Coating LLC..........................E...... 281 457-0200
  Channelview (G-3029)
Lifelast Inc......................................G...... 512 628-2112
  Pflugerville (G-16679)
Liquidmtal Ctngs Solutions LLC..........F...... 281 359-1283
  Spring (G-19141)
Longhorn Powder Coating I.................F...... 817 759-2224
  Haltom City (G-8152)
Meister Industries Inc........................F...... 432 425-0293
  Odessa (G-16079)
Metal Coatings Corp..........................D...... 713 977-0123
  Houston (G-10844)
Metal Processing Intl LP.....................E...... 956 205-0083
  Mission (G-15560)
Metalplate Galvanizing LP..................E...... 713 672-9480
  Houston (G-10851)
Metokote Corporation........................F...... 210 628-1955
  San Antonio (G-18294)
Modine Jacksonville Inc.....................E...... 903 589-0009
  Jacksonville (G-13251)
ND Industries Inc..............................D...... 817 633-2788
  Arlington (G-737)
Orbit Industries Inc...........................F...... 806 744-8300
  Lubbock (G-14453)
Paul Krivoy......................................E...... 361 854-7911
  Corpus Christi (G-3589)
Polibrid Coatings Inc.........................F...... 956 831-7818
  Brownsville (G-2394)
Polymer Dynamics Inc........................F...... 281 894-6382
  Houston (G-11358)
Powder Finishes Inc..........................F...... 254 968-5601
  Stephenville (G-19419)
Praxair Surface Tech Inc....................E...... 713 849-9474
  Houston (G-11384)
Precision Coatings............................F...... 432 362-7696
  Odessa (G-16124)
Prince Manufacturing Corp.................C...... 915 217-2664
  El Paso (G-5918)

Protective Powder Coatings LLC.........F...... 361 854-7911
  Corpus Christi (G-3598)
Quality Powder Coating Inc................G...... 972 466-0655
  Carrollton (G-2801)
Quality Product Finishing Inc.............E...... 281 469-6970
  Houston (G-11499)
Royalty Metal Finishing Inc................E...... 281 208-4455
  Houston (G-11686)
Southwest Impreglon R Inc.................E...... 281 441-2000
  Humble (G-12798)
Southwest Spray Inc..........................E...... 972 875-5665
  Ennis (G-6118)
Spraymetal Inc..................................F...... 713 923-2000
  Houston (G-12023)
Ternium Usa Inc................................C...... 318 698-7500
  Houston (G-12208)
Texas Custom Coaters Inc..................F...... 936 825-7211
  Navasota (G-15743)
Texas Finishing Company...................E...... 972 416-2961
  Carrollton (G-2830)
Texas Intrnal Pipe Coating LLC...........E...... 936 348-2508
  Madisonville (G-14590)
Thermal Designs Inc..........................E...... 713 433-6003
  Houston (G-12269)
United Galvanizing Inc.......................C...... 713 466-4161
  Houston (G-12448)
Womble Company Inc.........................B...... 713 636-8700
  Houston (G-12681)
XCEL Metal Finishing Inc....................F...... 972 772-4440
  Rockwall (G-17572)

COATING SVC: Metals, With Plastic Or Resins

Alliance Coatings LLC.......................E...... 817 834-8817
  Fort Worth (G-6372)
C E Shepherd Company LP..................D...... 713 924-4300
  Houston (G-9028)
Cobra Coating..................................F...... 432 332-0272
  Odessa (G-15963)
El Paso Tool & Die Co Inc...................E...... 915 591-0346
  El Paso (G-5744)
Meister Industries Inc........................E...... 432 366-2875
  Odessa (G-16078)
Nipco Inc...F...... 432 362-1936
  Odessa (G-16093)

COATING SVC: Rust Preventative

Ceram-Kote Coatings Inc...................E...... 432 263-8497
  Big Spring (G-2074)
F & W Industries Inc..........................F...... 432 563-8895
  Odessa (G-15997)
International Paint LLC.......................C...... 713 684-1500
  Houston (G-10404)

COATINGS: Air Curing

Hvac Corrosion Tech LLC....................F...... 214 790-9609
  Dallas (G-4476)
Illinois Tool Works Inc.......................F...... 314 733-1110
  Houston (G-10326)
Rexcel Coatings Corporation..............F...... 915 581-2797
  El Paso (G-5938)
Triarch Industries Inc........................E...... 713 690-9977
  Houston (G-12366)

COATINGS: Epoxy

Anc Ion Coating Inc...........................F...... 281 207-0300
  Houston (G-8638)
F & L Coatings and Con LLC................F...... 281 316-2203
  League City (G-13956)
Ifs Coatings Inc................................E...... 940 668-1062
  Gainesville (G-7345)

COATINGS: Polyurethane

Carlisle Ctngs Wtrproofing Inc...........D...... 972 442-6545
  Wylie (G-20929)
Dow Chemical Company......................E...... 713 246-0369
  La Porte (G-13733)
Metroplex Roof and Fence Inc............F...... 469 417-8003
  Corinth (G-3458)
Nukote Coating Systems Intl..............E...... 832 770-7100
  Houston (G-11098)

COCKTAIL LOUNGE

Noble Gent LLC.................................F...... 214 516-8609
  Desoto (G-5437)
Western Bowl....................................E...... 806 359-5211
  Amarillo (G-521)

COFFEE SVCS

Cactus Coin ....F 817 640-1791
Arlington (G-637)
CPI Importers Inc ....F 214 353-0328
Dallas (G-4179)
Metro Coffee Grouppe Inc ....F 972 263-8744
Grand Prairie (G-7927)

COIL WINDING SVC

Bayou Processing & Storage LP ....E 713 450-8401
Houston (G-8836)
Cudd Pumping Services Inc ....B 432 580-3544
Odessa (G-15972)

COILS & ROD: Extruded, Aluminum

Sigmatron International Inc ....F 830 775-5524
Del Rio (G-5324)

COILS & TRANSFORMERS

Amkin Technologies LLC ....F 281 755-2046
Cypress (G-3774)
B I Products LLC ....D 972 359-4000
Allen (G-255)
Benchmark Manufacturing Inc ....E 903 882-4311
Lindale (G-14133)
Cooper Power Systems LLC ....C 936 569-9422
Nacogdoches (G-15692)
Ets-Lindgren Inc ....C 512 531-6400
Cedar Park (G-2968)
Houston Transformer Co Ltd ....D 713 977-6009
Houston (G-10258)
Martin-Decker Totco Inc ....B 512 340-5000
Cedar Park (G-2978)
Polara Engineering Inc ....D 951 547-5500
Greenville (G-8086)
Sigma Electronics Inc ....E 800 874-7121
Houston (G-11884)
Tecal Manufacturing LLC ....F 915 593-1413
El Paso (G-5995)

COILS: Electric Motors Or Generators

Benchmark Manufacturing Inc ....E 903 882-4311
Lindale (G-14133)
G B Coil Inc ....E 903 212-2645
Longview (G-14238)
Lennox International Inc ....C 972 497-5000
Richardson (G-17343)
Musshorn Enterprises Inc ....C 915 772-9007
El Paso (G-5892)
National Electric Coil Co LP ....E 956 541-1759
Brownsville (G-2385)

COILS: Pipe

Oil School Services LLC ....F 903 657-7600
Henderson (G-8268)
Peyton Salas & Mendoza LLC ....E 512 784-5875
Houston (G-11313)
Storage & Processors Inc ....D 832 360-2800
Houston (G-12072)

COKE OVEN PRDTS, NEC

Seadrift Coke LP ....C 361 552-8887
Port Lavaca (G-17155)

COKE: Calcined Petroleum, Made From Purchased Materials

Rain Cii Carbon LLC ....E 281 318-2400
Kingwood (G-13652)

COKE: Petroleum

Oxbow Calcining LLC ....E 281 907-9425
Spring (G-19238)

COLOR PIGMENTS

Adtec Colorant Corporation ....F 817 633-3004
Arlington (G-610)

COLORS: Pigments, Inorganic

Acme Brick Company ....D 817 332-4101
El Paso (G-5636)
American Roller Company LLC ....F 262 878-2445
Houston (G-8607)

Kronos International Inc ....F 972 233-1700
Dallas (G-4568)
Lonza Inc ....D 281 291-2300
Pasadena (G-16475)
Teknor Color Company ....D 903 586-0583
Jacksonville (G-13262)

COLORS: Pigments, Organic

Venator Materials LLC ....A 281 465-6700
The Woodlands (G-19937)

COMMERCIAL & INDL SHELVING WHOLESALERS

Comac Fixtures Inc ....F 806 376-4511
Amarillo (G-418)

COMMERCIAL & LITERARY WRITINGS

M Brown Books Pubg Group Inc ....F 972 381-0009
Dallas (G-4619)

COMMERCIAL & OFFICE BUILDINGS RENOVATION & REPAIR

Eklunds Inc ....E 817 949-2030
Southlake (G-19067)
Stella Hasegawa ....F 915 594-7633
El Paso (G-5977)

COMMERCIAL ART & GRAPHIC DESIGN SVCS

Big Star Branding Inc ....E 210 590-2662
San Antonio (G-17953)
Bob Lillys Prof Mktg Group Inc ....E 214 231-2082
Garland (G-7449)
Brick Stone Graphics By Gartex ....F 214 343-0573
Dallas (G-4049)
C & B Printing Co ....F 806 374-6262
Amarillo (G-410)
Corporate Bus Solutions Inc ....E 817 701-1390
Arlington (G-647)
El Paso Reprographics LLC ....F 915 532-6255
El Paso (G-5740)
Genti Studios Inc ....E 214 951-9696
Dallas (G-4402)
Hewell Enterprises Inc ....E 972 466-2442
Carrollton (G-2869)
Insignia Marketing Inc ....F 281 465-0040
Magnolia (G-14610)
Iq Enterprises Inc ....E 866 789-0508
Fort Worth (G-6728)
Kingdom Captain of Texas LLC ....F 210 535-9480
San Antonio (G-18226)
L C Colormark ....D 972 243-1919
Carrollton (G-2773)
M3 Partners LLC ....E 602 561-6464
Kingwood (G-13648)
Multi-Quest Inc ....F 972 235-2356
Richardson (G-17361)
Natural Graphics Inc ....E 713 661-5075
Houston (G-11009)
Pan Ector Industries LLC ....F 940 566-1414
Denton (G-5389)
R S Graphic Services Inc ....E 817 921-6266
Fort Worth (G-6932)
Siemens Industry Software Inc ....E 972 391-2476
Plano (G-17004)
Sports Wear Graphics Inc ....G 817 870-9900
Fort Worth (G-7014)
Texas Carved Stone LP ....F 254 793-2384
Florence (G-6245)
Thomas Graphics Inc ....D 512 719-3535
Austin (G-1576)

COMMERCIAL ART & ILLUSTRATION SVCS

Complete Reprographics Inc ....F 915 779-5000
El Paso (G-5702)

COMMERCIAL CONTAINERS WHOLESALERS

Mauser Usa LLC ....D 936 273-1279
Conroe (G-3328)
West Texas Drum Company Ltd II ......E 281 383-1901
Baytown (G-1805)

COMMERCIAL EQPT & SPLYS, WHOLESALE: Hotel

Builders Depot Direct LLC ....F 832 384-7272
Houston (G-9012)

COMMERCIAL EQPT WHOLESALERS, NEC

Blaze Equipment LLC ....F 817 439-0453
Lake Worth (G-13812)
Compostology LLC ....F 318 787-7442
Waco (G-20389)
Miller Equipment Co ....F 469 366-4227
Garland (G-7553)

COMMERCIAL EQPT, WHOLESALE: Bakery Eqpt & Splys

Bakery Equipment & Svc Co Inc ....E 210 734-5124
San Antonio (G-17937)
Dawn Food Products Inc ....E 972 485-8004
Garland (G-7477)

COMMERCIAL EQPT, WHOLESALE: Coffee Brewing Eqpt & Splys

CPI Importers Inc ....F 214 353-0328
Dallas (G-4179)
Farmer Bros Co ....E 817 640-8111
Arlington (G-675)
La Creme Inc ....E 214 352-8090
Irving (G-13081)
Metro Coffee Grouppe Inc ....F 972 263-8744
Grand Prairie (G-7927)
Wicked Voodoo Espresso LLC ....E 360 631-1447
New Braunfels (G-15832)

COMMERCIAL EQPT, WHOLESALE: Comm Cooking & Food Svc Eqpt

Hobart Sales and Service Inc ....E 210 829-5663
San Antonio (G-18169)
Houston Sysco Inc ....E 713 672-8080
Houston (G-10254)
Ricos Products Co Inc ....C 210 222-1415
San Antonio (G-18426)
Win-Holt Equipment Corp ....C 972 641-4658
Grand Prairie (G-7995)

COMMERCIAL EQPT, WHOLESALE: Mannequins

Medical Plastics Laboratory ....B 254 865-7221
Gatesville (G-7619)

COMMERCIAL EQPT, WHOLESALE: Parking Meters

Associated Time Instrs Co Inc ....F 713 263-1366
Houston (G-8726)
Associated Time Instrs Co Inc ....E 214 637-2763
Dallas (G-3975)

COMMERCIAL EQPT, WHOLESALE: Restaurant, NEC

MANS Distributors Inc ....F 972 930-0330
Carrollton (G-2777)
Restaurant Depot LLC ....E 512 454-5600
Austin (G-1461)
RSI Partners LLC ....D 817 640-5415
Arlington (G-777)

COMMERCIAL EQPT, WHOLESALE: Scales, Exc Laboratory

Bastrop Scale Company Inc ....F 512 321-3443
Bastrop (G-1749)

COMMERCIAL EQPT, WHOLESALE: Store Fixtures & Display Eqpt

Abbco Display Company ....G 214 319-8148
Dallas (G-3876)
Ion Science Inc ....F 877 864-7710
Stafford (G-19332)
Thom-Bat-Ler Enterprises ....F 972 660-4056
Grand Prairie (G-7982)

PRODUCT

COMMERCIAL EQPT, WHOLESALE: Vending Machines, Coin-Operated

Coca Cola Btlg of Shreveport ....C 214 902-2600
Dallas (G-4134)

Kaspar Wire Works Inc ....A 361 594-3327
Shiner (G-18944)

COMMERCIAL PRINTING & NEWSPAPER PUBLISHING COMBINED

Azle Tri-County Advertiser ....F 817 270-3340
Azle (G-1720)

Barton Publications Inc ....E 512 262-1110
Kyle (G-13679)

Bay City Tribune ....F 979 245-2920
Bay City (G-1768)

Bcs Eagle ....F 979 776-4444
Bryan (G-2456)

Blacklands Publications Inc ....E 512 352-8535
Taylor (G-19650)

Community Newspapers Holdings ....D 512 392-6143
San Marcos (G-18682)

Community Ventures Inc ....F 817 441-7661
Weatherford (G-20582)

Cox Texas Newspapers LP ....C 903 237-7777
Longview (G-14215)

Eastland County Newspaper Inc ....F 254 629-1707
Eastland (G-5564)

Echo Publishing Company ....E 903 885-2030
Sulphur Springs (G-19586)

Fannin County Leader LLC ....F 903 583-3280
Bonham (G-2153)

Fayette County Record Inc ....G 979 968-3155
La Grange (G-13695)

Focus Newspapers of Dfw Inc ....E 972 223-9175
Desoto (G-5431)

Fredericksburg Publishing Co ....E 830 997-2155
Fredericksburg (G-7179)

Galveston Newspapers Inc ....D 409 683-5200
Galveston (G-7398)

Granite Publications LLC ....F 512 352-8285
Taylor (G-19657)

Guadalupe Valley Publishing Co ....G 830 672-2861
Gonzales (G-7754)

Kingsville Publishing Company ....F 361 592-4304
Kingsville (G-13631)

Lake County Newspaper ....F 254 559-5412
Breckenridge (G-2231)

Monitor ....E 903 887-4511
Mabank (G-14580)

New Century Enterprises Inc ....F 972 926-6062
Garland (G-7562)

New Horizon Publishers ....F 956 943-5545
Port Isabel (G-17137)

Orange County Publishing Co ....F 409 769-5428
Vidor (G-20330)

Paso Del Norte Publishing Inc ....D 915 838-1601
El Paso (G-5905)

Progrssive Mdia Communications ....F 254 675-3336
Clifton (G-3146)

Schulenburgh Sticker Inc ....F 979 743-3450
Schulenburg (G-18779)

Southern Newspapers Inc ....E 830 625-9144
New Braunfels (G-15825)

Southern Newspapers Inc ....D 936 632-6631
Lufkin (G-14552)

Sun-Times Media Group Inc ....F 254 562-2868
Mexia (G-15091)

Wcn Inc ....E 830 216-4519
Floresville (G-6258)

Wilkerson Publishing Company ....F 830 281-2341
Pleasanton (G-17078)

Wise County Messenger Inc ....E 940 627-5987
Decatur (G-5257)

COMMODITY CONTRACTS BROKERS, DEALERS

United Commodities LLC ....F 956 621-1798
Brownsville (G-2418)

COMMON SAND MINING

Granville R Damron Trucking ....E 806 842-3519
Slaton (G-18971)

Granville R Damron Trucking ....F 806 842-3519
Slaton (G-18972)

Hanson Aggregates LLC ....D 940 683-4294
Bridgeport (G-2295)

Johnny Baulch ....F 409 938-8971
Hitchcock (G-8338)

Metroplex Sand & Gravel Ltd ....D 817 589-9001
Fort Worth (G-6833)

Wright Materials Inc ....D 361 387-1511
Robstown (G-17519)

COMMUNICATION HEADGEAR: Telephone

Motive Wireless Ltd Lblty Co ....F 214 500-9242
Spring (G-19149)

Telecom Management Corp ....F 281 404-5610
Spring (G-19176)

Tko Telesystems LLC ....F 972 484-4900
Dallas (G-5099)

COMMUNICATIONS EQPT & SYSTEMS, NEC

Texas Barricade Service ....F 915 355-6653
Canutillo (G-2665)

COMMUNICATIONS EQPT REPAIR & MAINTENANCE

Gerber Technology Inc ....C 972 238-7211
Dallas (G-4405)

COMMUNICATIONS EQPT WHOLESALERS

D C A E Inc ....E 972 278-0202
Garland (G-7472)

COMMUNICATIONS EQPT: Microwave

M2 Global Technology Ltd ....F 210 561-4800
San Antonio (G-18269)

Microwave Networks Inc ....E 281 263-6500
Stafford (G-19353)

Nec America Inc ....E 214 262-2387
Dfw Airport (G-5453)

Nec Corporation of America ....E 214 262-2387
Dallas (G-4719)

Prism Microwave Inc ....D 972 745-7222
Coppell (G-3435)

COMMUNICATIONS SVCS: Cellular

AT&T Inc ....A 210 821-4105
Dallas (G-3978)

Enterprise ESP Svc Prvider LLC ....F 469 619-3114
Plano (G-16863)

Metapath Software Intl ....F 972 907-3600
Richardson (G-17356)

COMMUNICATIONS SVCS: Data

Aim Media Texas Operating LLC ....B 956 683-4000
McAllen (G-14833)

Broadcast Technical Svcs Inc ....F 832 467-0002
Houston (G-8988)

Calix Inc ....G 707 766-3000
Richardson (G-17282)

Crown Castle Intl Corp ....F 713 570-3000
Houston (G-9346)

Enterprise ESP Svc Prvider LLC ....F 469 619-3114
Plano (G-16863)

Imagine Communications Corp ....D 469 803-4900
Frisco (G-7292)

Jive Software Inc ....D 877 495-3700
Austin (G-1256)

Rignet Inc ....F 281 674-0100
Houston (G-11622)

Sharco Technologies Inc ....F 512 258-0573
Pflugerville (G-16688)

COMMUNICATIONS SVCS: Internet Connectivity Svcs

Calix Inc ....G 707 766-3000
Richardson (G-17282)

Dzs Inc ....C 469 327-1531
Plano (G-16854)

Pwr Technologies LLC ....F 469 609-3537
Mesquite (G-15073)

Rignet Inc ....C 281 674-0100
Houston (G-11622)

Voip Tel LP ....F 512 543-9556
Austin (G-1644)

Warren Watts Technology LLC ....F 817 924-1370
Fort Worth (G-7127)

COMMUNICATIONS SVCS: Online Svc Providers

Awesome Paging Inc ....G 361 576-2255
Victoria (G-20240)

Playnet Inc ....E 817 358-7580
Bedford (G-1977)

COMMUNICATIONS SVCS: Signal Enhancement Network Svcs

Infrastructure Networks Inc ....E 832 598-6600
Houston (G-10361)

Itron Networked Solutions Inc ....F 210 762-4400
San Antonio (G-18195)

Pcs Telecom Inc ....F 281 469-3367
Pasadena (G-16494)

Ringdale Inc ....F 512 288-9080
Georgetown (G-7675)

COMMUNICATIONS SVCS: Telephone Or Video

Trans-Tel Central Inc ....F 405 447-5025
San Antonio (G-18561)

COMMUNICATIONS SVCS: Telephone, Broker

Front End Services ....E 214 672-0600
Grand Prairie (G-7879)

COMMUNICATIONS SVCS: Telephone, Data

Absolute Cmmnctons Ntwrk Sltion ....E 361 888-6776
Corpus Christi (G-3464)

COMMUNICATIONS SVCS: Telephone, Local & Long Distance

AT&T Inc ....A 210 821-4105
Dallas (G-3978)

COMMUNICATIONS SVCS: Telephone, Long Distance

Cypress Telecommunications ....E 281 449-4000
Spring (G-19205)

COMMUNICATIONS SVCS: Telephone, Voice

Enterprise ESP Svc Prvider LLC ....F 469 619-3114
Plano (G-16863)

COMMUNICATIONS SVCS: Television Antenna Construction & Rent

Wilbur L Anderson Inc ....E 325 658-6539
San Angelo (G-17841)

COMMUNITY CENTERS: Adult

Indochinese Culture Center ....F 713 522-7799
Houston (G-10343)

COMPACT LASER DISCS: Prerecorded

Austin Dvd Inc ....F 512 246-8759
Round Rock (G-17625)

Casscom Media LP ....F 903 455-2555
Greenville (G-8066)

COMPOST

Back To Nature Inc ....E 806 745-3559
Slaton (G-18969)

Dairymans Choice Organics Inc ....F 817 641-2015
Godley (G-7734)

East Side Compost Pedallers ....F 512 436-3884
Austin (G-1111)

Employee Owned Nursery Entps ....F 512 276-1211
Elgin (G-6054)

Kbg Management Company LP ....G 806 627-4276
Tulia (G-20035)

Letco Group LLC ....D 713 466-7360
Houston (G-10626)

Letco Group LLC ....D 972 506-8575
Dallas (G-4592)

Letco Group LLC ....E 972 869-4332
Dallas (G-4593)

Letco Group LLC ....D 281 431-3400
Rosharon (G-17607)

COMPRESSORS: Air & Gas (continued)

Natures Way Resources Inc ....F 936 273-1200
Conroe (G-3341)
Soil Mender Products L P ....E 806 627-4276
Tulia (G-20038)
Soil Mender Products L P ....E 806 627-4276
Tulia (G-20039)
Wholearth Organic Composting ....F 210 621-2411
Elmendorf (G-6078)

COMPRESSORS: Air & Gas

Air Power Sales & Service LLC ....E 903 236-0500
Longview (G-14190)
Alegacy Equipment LLC ....E 832 916-3700
Waller (G-20490)
Angelo Bolt and Indus Sup Inc ....E 325 655-0075
San Angelo (G-17776)
Atlas Copco Compressors LLC ....F 281 453-6800
Houston (G-8743)
Atlas Copco Compressors LLC ....E 281 453-6800
Houston (G-8744)
Atlas Copco Compressors LLC ....B 281 453-6800
McAllen (G-14839)
Atlas Copco Rental LLC ....E 800 736-8267
Deer Park (G-5262)
Atron Group LLC ....D 214 292-9840
Dallas (G-3984)
Baker Hughes Energy Svcs LLC ......D 713 439-8600
Houston (G-8803)
Cameron International Corp ....D 281 582-9500
Houston (G-9064)
Cameron International Corp ....E 713 939-2282
Houston (G-9072)
Cameron International Corp ....E 713 571-3100
Waller (G-20495)
Cameron International Corp ....C 713 354-1900
Houston (G-9068)
Cameron International Corp ....E 806 665-1647
Pampa (G-16318)
Com-Pac Systems Inc ....F 432 332-4515
Odessa (G-15964)
Compressor Designs Inc ....F 432 425-0044
Odessa (G-15965)
Compressor Elements Service ....F 432 943-6701
Monahans (G-15602)
Cook Compression ....F 432 367-7786
Odessa (G-15966)
Csi Compressco Sub Inc ....E 361 576-6827
Victoria (G-20256)
Csi Compressco Sub Inc ....A 432 563-1170
Midland (G-15185)
Diversified Industrial Svc Co ....E 806 274-2214
Borger (G-2174)
Dresser-Rand Company ....F 713 354-6100
Houston (G-9520)
Dresser-Rand Company ....D 713 468-4210
Houston (G-9521)
Dresser-Rand Group Inc ....C 713 354-6100
Houston (G-9522)
Dresser-Rand LLC ....E 713 467-2221
Houston (G-9523)
Dresser-Rand LLC ....A 713 354-6100
Houston (G-9524)
Enerflex Energy Systems Inc ....F 806 826-0126
Wheeler (G-20708)
Enerflex Energy Systems Inc ....B 281 345-9300
Houston (G-9631)
Enerflex Energy Systems Inc ....D 281 758-4900
Cypress (G-3787)
Fluxmetals LLC ....D 832 948-4307
Houston (G-9818)
Gardner Denver Inc ....D 832 421-5469
Pasadena (G-16446)
Heartland Enterprises Ltd ....E 830 997-9434
Fredericksburg (G-7182)
Hicor Technologies Inc ....E 281 727-0250
Houston (G-10174)
Houston Compression & Svcs LLC ......F 713 550-1556
Houston (G-10226)
Imperial Pumps Co ....F 806 791-5242
Lubbock (G-14425)
Knox Jr Leighton ....E 806 327-5420
Tahoka (G-19641)
Kobelco Compressors Amer Inc ....C 713 470-1290
La Porte (G-13764)
Natural Gas Services Group Inc ....C 432 262-2700
Midland (G-15311)
Neuman & Esser Investments Inc ......E 281 497-5113
Katy (G-13427)
Neuman & Esser Usa Inc ....E 281 497-5113
Katy (G-13428)

Onesubsea LLC ....A 713 939-2282
Houston (G-11182)
Petro Chem Industries Inc ....E 713 645-5024
Houston (G-11300)
Productioneered Products Co ....E 281 364-1086
Spring (G-19244)
Red River Compression LLC ....F 832 831-0532
Houston (G-11568)
Sanden International USA Inc ....A 972 442-8400
Wylie (G-20948)
SEC Energy Products & Svcs LP ....E 281 890-9977
Houston (G-11811)
Texas Turbine Inc ....E 817 444-5528
Azle (G-1730)
Trillium US Inc ....D 512 441-6893
Austin (G-1593)
Unconvntonal Gas Solutions LLC ....F 346 353-1048
Houston (G-12431)
Werther International Inc ....F 800 655-4781
Houston (G-12634)

COMPRESSORS: Air & Gas, Including Vacuum Pumps

Fcx Performance Inc ....E 214 320-3604
Dallas (G-4357)
Gardner Denver Inc ....B 432 366-5433
Odessa (G-16010)
Global Compressor LP ....E 713 983-8773
Houston (G-9969)
J-W Power Company ....C 972 233-8191
Addison (G-139)
Lone Star Compressor Corp ....E 713 947-9975
Friendswood (G-7249)
Trane Technologies Company LLC ......E 903 730-4000
Tyler (G-20163)
United Industries Inc ....E 432 362-2361
Odessa (G-16189)

COMPRESSORS: Refrigeration & Air Conditioning Eqpt

American Envircon Inc ....G 214 634-1744
Dallas (G-3940)
CW Davis Enterprises Inc ....E 972 723-1247
Midlothian (G-15477)
Delta Industries Inc ....D 214 941-3135
Denton (G-5357)
Hodyon LP ....F 512 225-0165
Cedar Park (G-2974)

COMPRESSORS: Repairing

Atron Group LLC ....D 214 292-9840
Dallas (G-3984)
Community Motors Inc ....F 281 354-8087
New Caney (G-15837)
E J Reynolds Company Inc ....F 281 331-4556
Alvin (G-361)
Enerflex Energy Systems Inc ....F 806 826-0126
Wheeler (G-20708)
Enerflex Energy Systems Inc ....B 281 345-9300
Houston (G-9631)
Enerflex Energy Systems Inc ....D 281 758-4900
Cypress (G-3787)
Evans Enterprises Inc ....F 254 772-4710
Waco (G-20399)
H & S Valve ....E 432 362-0486
Odessa (G-16021)
Hodyon LP ....F 512 225-0165
Cedar Park (G-2974)
Petro Chem Industries Inc ....E 713 645-5024
Houston (G-11300)
Texas Turbine Inc ....E 817 444-5528
Azle (G-1730)
USA Compression Partners LP ....E 512 473-2662
Austin (G-1619)

COMPRESSORS: Wholesalers

Archrock Inc ....F 903 389-5666
Fairfield (G-6168)
Borger Oil Chemical Indus Plas ....F 806 273-9518
Borger (G-2165)
Fitz Torque Convertors Inc ....E 432 362-3261
Odessa (G-16003)
James L Rembert Jr Inc ....F 281 240-7070
Sugar Land (G-19500)
Marathon Special Services Inc ....F 713 784-4918
Houston (G-10757)

Samco Enterprises Inc ....E 281 443-6505
Houston (G-11737)
Specialty Comprsr & Eng Co Inc ......E 806 274-7135
Borger (G-2187)
Werther International Inc ....F 800 655-4781
Houston (G-12634)

COMPUTER & COMPUTER SOFTWARE STORES

At-Integration Inc ....G 512 819-4629
Georgetown (G-7637)
Gamestop Corp ....C 817 424-2000
Grapevine (G-8038)
Gamestop Holdings Corp ....B 817 424-2159
Grapevine (G-8039)
Nationwide Press LLC ....F 817 885-8855
Richland Hills (G-17444)
Wincor Nixdorf Inc ....D 512 676-5000
Austin (G-1672)

COMPUTER & COMPUTER SOFTWARE STORES: Peripheral Eqpt

Alx Imaging LLC ....E 210 651-5000
Seguin (G-18824)
EMC Corporation ....F 512 343-3332
Austin (G-1122)
Southeast Prtr Connection LLC ....E 256 880-9991
Plano (G-17010)
Tyler Technologies Inc ....E 903 753-4292
Longview (G-14326)

COMPUTER & COMPUTER SOFTWARE STORES: Personal Computers

Journeyedcom Inc ....D 800 876-3507
Allen (G-280)

COMPUTER & COMPUTER SOFTWARE STORES: Software & Access

Jose Alfonsin ....F 210 717-2306
San Antonio (G-18208)

COMPUTER & COMPUTER SOFTWARE STORES: Software, Bus/Non-Game

Behemoth Corporation ....E 281 332-4798
League City (G-13949)
Cloud Logix LLC ....E 682 310-0665
Irving (G-12974)
H Rosen Usa LLC ....B 281 442-8282
Houston (G-10085)
System Development Inc ....E 713 266-5667
Houston (G-12139)

COMPUTER & DATA PROCESSING EQPT REPAIR & MAINTENANCE

Jeh-Eas Inc ....G 210 490-9156
San Antonio (G-18200)
Laser Drum Products Inc ....F 713 263-9050
Houston (G-10603)
Quacito LLC ....F 210 695-0795
San Antonio (G-18404)
Southeast Prtr Connection LLC ....E 256 880-9991
Plano (G-17010)

COMPUTER & OFFICE MACHINE MAINTENANCE & REPAIR

Abacus Computer Co Inc ....E 713 467-2136
Houston (G-8442)
Acer America Corporation ....C 254 298-4000
Temple (G-19666)
Alpha Laser Recharge Inc ....F 713 861-2425
Houston (G-8562)
Excelente Inc ....E 855 209-1970
Plano (G-16867)
Jack Saunders ....F 713 806-7997
Baytown (G-1823)
Omnidata Services Group LLC ....E 281 469-4365
Houston (G-11180)
PC Cable Connexion Inc ....E 281 338-5400
League City (G-13974)

COMPUTER DISKETTES WHOLESALERS

Cramer Computer Supplies Ltd ....E 806 371-7310
Amarillo (G-485)

Employee Codes: A=Over 500 employees, B=251-500
C=101-250, D=51-100, E=20-50, F=10-19, G=9

2021 Harris Texas
Manufacturers Directory

1429

PRODUCT

COMPUTER FACILITIES MANAGEMENT SVCS

Onyx Venture Group LLC ....F 281 395-4791
Katy (G-13375)

COMPUTER FORMS

Gulf Business Forms Inc ....D 512 353-8313
San Marcos (G-18691)

Printegra Corp ....E 800 972-1175
Arlington (G-759)

Renfrow & Co Inc ....E 361 884-5541
Corpus Christi (G-3608)

COMPUTER GRAPHICS SVCS

Ajr Media Group LLC ....F 713 942-7676
Spring (G-19194)

Cme Printing Inc ....E 713 271-7700
Houston (G-9218)

Ets Zone ....F 713 559-1400
Spring (G-19211)

Iq Enterprises Inc ....E 866 789-0508
Fort Worth (G-6728)

Issgr Inc ....E 713 869-7700
Houston (G-10429)

Missionary Tech Team ....F 903 757-4530
Longview (G-14277)

Renaissance Cmpt Group Not Inc ....F 713 256-6067
Houston (G-11597)

Salient Systems Corporation ....F 512 617-4800
Austin (G-1484)

Style Publications ....F 713 748-6300
Houston (G-12085)

University of TX Med Brnch Gal ....D 409 772-5900
Galveston (G-7411)

Visual Bi Solutions Inc ....E 972 232-2233
Plano (G-17046)

COMPUTER INTERFACE EQPT: Indl Process

Emicon Corporation ....F 915 857-5128
El Paso (G-5753)

Emicon Corporation ....F 915 593-6422
El Paso (G-5754)

Umc Energy Solutions Inc ....E 432 524-2456
Joshua (G-13328)

W A Neel Co Inc ....F 903 503-5834
Scottsville (G-18781)

COMPUTER PAPER WHOLESALERS

Cramer Computer Supplies Ltd ....E 806 371-7310
Amarillo (G-485)

COMPUTER PERIPHERAL EQPT REPAIR & MAINTENANCE

Cypress Technologies LP ....E 512 267-9973
Leander (G-13986)

Omni Data Systems Ltd LLP ....F 281 469-4365
Houston (G-11177)

COMPUTER PERIPHERAL EQPT, NEC

Access Imaging Solutions LLC ....F 210 590-8338
San Antonio (G-17857)

Acer America Corporation ....C 214 383-3194
Allen (G-247)

Advanced Tracking Tech Inc ....E 800 279-0035
Houston (G-8492)

Agent Systems Inc ....G 972 774-0400
Dallas (G-3902)

Augmentix Corporation ....D 512 334-0111
Austin (G-948)

Automation Solutions LP ....E 281 286-6017
Houston (G-8754)

Black Box Corporation ....F 713 307-4000
Houston (G-8900)

Brady Corporation ....G 214 275-9595
Mesquite (G-15033)

Bt5 Technologies LLC ....F 832 727-5214
Houston (G-9001)

Cisco Systems Inc ....A 210 357-2500
San Antonio (G-18008)

Cisco Systems Inc ....C 469 255-0000
Richardson (G-17287)

Cisco Systems Inc ....A 512 378-1112
Austin (G-1051)

Cisco Systems Inc ....A 800 553-6387
Lubbock (G-14393)

Cisco Systems Inc ....A 972 393-0874
Houston (G-9197)

Corvalent Corporation ....E 512 456-2400
Cedar Park (G-2965)

Crossroads Systems (texas) ....C 512 349-0300
Austin (G-1074)

Cypress Technologies LP ....E 512 267-9973
Leander (G-13986)

Data Connection Inc ....F 972 231-2185
Dallas (G-4240)

Datatronic Control Corporation ....E 972 475-7879
Rowlett (G-17704)

Dell Inc ....A 800 289-3355
Round Rock (G-17642)

Dell Technologies Inc ....C 800 289-3355
Round Rock (G-17646)

Delta Group Electronics Inc ....D 972 606-2102
Grand Prairie (G-7863)

Denali Intermediate Inc ....A 713 627-0933
Round Rock (G-17648)

Digital Speech Systems Inc ....E 972 235-2999
Allen (G-262)

Dynatouch Corporation ....E 210 828-8343
San Antonio (G-18076)

E J Ward Inc ....E 210 824-7383
San Antonio (G-18078)

E Major Tech LLC ....F 972 385-6466
Farmers Branch (G-6194)

Epicor Software Corporation ....D 949 585-4000
Austin (G-1131)

Hp Inc ....B 512 432-8000
Austin (G-1698)

Intel Corporation ....D 281 370-9355
Spring (G-19135)

Intel Corporation ....D 512 362-1000
Austin (G-1232)

Intel Corporation ....F 972 987-2377
Plano (G-16893)

Intel Corporation ....F 281 251-7649
Houston (G-10391)

Intrusion Inc ....E 972 234-6400
Richardson (G-17336)

Keyscan Inc ....F 201 918-2396
Odessa (G-16051)

Lap King LLC ....F 512 415-3034
Austin (G-1282)

Laser Pros International Corp ....E 715 369-5995
Marshall (G-14786)

Mesa Technologies LLC ....E 713 895-7000
Houston (G-10838)

Microsoft Corporation ....D 210 346-2500
San Antonio (G-18302)

Motion Computing Inc ....C 512 637-1100
Austin (G-1353)

Motorola Solutions Inc ....E 915 872-1229
El Paso (G-5884)

Mtwd Holdings Inc ....F 972 346-2242
Frisco (G-7300)

National Instruments Corp ....A 512 683-0100
Austin (G-1360)

Nationwide Press LLC ....F 817 885-8855
Richland Hills (G-17444)

Nextus Inc ....E 512 288-9080
Georgetown (G-7667)

Omni Data Systems Ltd LLP ....F 281 469-4365
Houston (G-11177)

Pason Systems USA Corp ....D 713 693-8700
Houston (G-11256)

Photonic Inc ....E 956 722-3326
Laredo (G-13921)

Ringdale Inc ....F 512 288-9080
Georgetown (G-7675)

Rose Electronics ....C 281 933-7673
Houston (G-11662)

Salient Systems Corporation ....F 512 617-4800
Austin (G-1484)

Samsill Corporation ....C 817 536-1906
Fort Worth (G-6972)

Sigma Industrial Automtn Inc ....F 210 659-5000
Schertz (G-18762)

Singer Data Products Inc ....E 915 594-7650
El Paso (G-5962)

South Txas Lghthouse For Blind ....C 361 883-6553
Corpus Christi (G-3627)

Systel Inc ....E 281 207-7619
Sugar Land (G-19560)

Techworks Inc ....F 512 349-1300
Austin (G-1558)

Touch International Inc ....D 512 832-8292
Austin (G-1586)

Tpv International (usa) Inc ....F 512 241-1508
Austin (G-1588)

Tri-Cor Industries Inc ....E 210 979-0552
San Antonio (G-18565)

Unicom Engineering Inc ....D 972 673-1345
Plano (G-17041)

Uptime Devices Inc ....F 512 328-1800
Austin (G-1615)

Venture Research Inc ....E 469 246-4000
Plano (G-17044)

Viewcastcom Inc ....E 972 488-7200
Grapevine (G-8059)

Warren Watts Technology LLC ....F 817 924-1370
Fort Worth (G-7127)

Wincor Nixdorf Inc ....D 512 676-5000
Austin (G-1672)

Yokogawa Corporation America ....E 281 340-3800
Sugar Land (G-19576)

COMPUTER PERIPHERAL EQPT, WHOLESALE

Axxion Group Corporation ....D 915 225-8888
El Paso (G-5656)

Cypress Technologies LP ....E 512 267-9973
Leander (G-13986)

Gemmy Industries Corporation ....C 972 538-4200
Coppell (G-3417)

Hbs Systems Inc ....D 972 234-4444
Richardson (G-17327)

Hp Inc ....B 512 432-8000
Austin (G-1698)

Omni Data Systems Ltd LLP ....F 281 469-4365
Houston (G-11177)

Omnidata Services Group LLC ....F 281 469-4365
Houston (G-11180)

Photonic Inc ....E 956 722-3326
Laredo (G-13921)

COMPUTER PERIPHERAL EQPT: Graphic Displays, Exc Terminals

Newline Interactive Inc ....F 972 468-9728
Plano (G-16944)

Texas Digital Systems Inc ....D 979 693-0933
College Station (G-3204)

COMPUTER PERIPHERAL EQPT: Input Or Output

Bowens Reed and Calloway Inc ....F 214 389-0002
Dallas (G-4045)

Interphase Corporation ....D 214 654-5000
Carrollton (G-2872)

COMPUTER PROCESSING SVCS

Synergen Health LLC ....F 214 643-6002
Dallas (G-5032)

Thomas Reprographics Inc ....D 210 829-7000
San Antonio (G-18548)

COMPUTER PROGRAMMING SVCS

Advanced Tracking Tech Inc ....E 800 279-0035
Houston (G-8492)

Alert Technologies Inc ....E 281 326-9900
Houston (G-8534)

Annapurna Solutions LLC ....F 916 905-3144
Houston (G-8646)

Birch Grove Software Inc ....D 888 907-0301
Austin (G-991)

BMC Software Inc ....E 512 343-1961
Austin (G-999)

BMC Software Inc ....A 713 918-8800
Houston (G-8924)

Bradmark Technologies Inc ....E 713 621-2808
Houston (G-8975)

Carbo Ceramics Inc ....B 281 921-6400
Houston (G-9091)

Conloop Inc ....F 940 322-2206
Wichita Falls (G-20756)

Cooper Consulting Company ....E 512 527-1000
Austin (G-1065)

Dairy LLC ....E 214 442-5928
Frisco (G-7278)

Digital Speech Systems Inc ....E 972 235-2999
Allen *(G-262)*

Eixsys LLC.................................G.... 512 666-3574
Austin *(G-1117)*

Ets Zone ....F 713 559-1400
Spring *(G-19211)*

Filecontrol Partners Ltd ....F 713 355-1111
Houston *(G-9785)*

Hendricks BTS Corporation ....F 713 516-8716
Pearland *(G-16568)*

Impac Systems Engineering LLP .....F 713 784-3500
Temple *(G-19682)*

Intrusion Inc ....E 972 234-6400
Richardson *(G-17336)*

Ldia Holdings LLC ....E 512 247-3700
Austin *(G-1284)*

Management Controls Inc ....C 281 590-5881
Houston *(G-10743)*

NCR Corporation ....E 210 366-2959
San Antonio *(G-18339)*

NCR Solutions Llc.......................F 405 413-8278
Little Elm *(G-14140)*

Odysseus Holdings LLC ....E 281 769-2399
Houston *(G-11136)*

Origin Instruments Corp ....F 972 606-8740
Grand Prairie *(G-7942)*

Osisoft LLC................................F 281 920-6170
Houston *(G-11198)*

Qnet Inc....................................D 214 341-7638
Dallas *(G-4838)*

Quacito LLC...............................E 210 695-0795
San Antonio *(G-18404)*

Rational Systems LLC ....E 832 476-8468
Houston *(G-11552)*

Renaissance Cmpt Group Not Inc.....F 713 256-6067
Houston *(G-11597)*

Sagl Enterprises Inc ....E 281 496-3737
Houston *(G-11729)*

Sharco Technologies Inc ....F 512 258-0573
Pflugerville *(G-16688)*

Siemens Industry Software Inc........F 972 391-2476
Plano *(G-17004)*

Smart Imaging Technologies Co .....E 713 589-3500
Houston *(G-11918)*

Stark Holdings Inc ....F 512 329-8109
Austin *(G-1531)*

Tailwind Business Ventures LLC.......C 210 268-2717
Cedar Park *(G-2986)*

Test Spectrum Inc ....F 512 472-6750
Austin *(G-1564)*

Upland Software I Inc ....D 617 494-5515
Austin *(G-1612)*

Vercom Software Inc ....E 972 661-9336
Dallas *(G-5161)*

WT Fiber Link LLC ....D 432 758-2700
Seminole *(G-18888)*

COMPUTER PROGRAMMING SVCS: Custom

Timeclock Plus LLC.....................D 325 223-9300
San Angelo *(G-17834)*

COMPUTER RELATED MAINTENANCE SVCS

Excelente Inc ....E 855 209-1970
Plano *(G-16867)*

Hewlett Packard Enterprise Co.........C 650 687-5817
Houston *(G-10166)*

NCR Corporation ....F 210 366-2959
San Antonio *(G-18339)*

NCR Solutions Llc.......................F 405 413-8278
Little Elm *(G-14140)*

Noisy Trumpet LLC ....F 210 852-0505
San Antonio *(G-18349)*

Oiltek Systems LLC ....E 325 200-0423
Colorado City *(G-3225)*

Onyx Venture Group LLC ....F 281 395-4791
Katy *(G-13375)*

Qnet Inc....................................D 214 341-7638
Dallas *(G-4838)*

Rignet Inc..................................C 281 674-0100
Houston *(G-11622)*

Software Global Ltd ....F 832 274-0478
Austin *(G-1516)*

Tech Dogs LLC ....F 972 985-4730
Plano *(G-17023)*

Upland Software I Inc ....D 617 494-5515
Austin *(G-1612)*

COMPUTER RELATED SVCS, NEC

Annapurna Solutions LLC..............F 916 905-3144
Houston *(G-8646)*

COMPUTER SOFTWARE DEVELOPMENT

Anderson Software LLC ....F 936 569-0447
Kerrville *(G-13518)*

Bio-RAD Laboratories Inc ....D 972 596-6165
Plano *(G-16805)*

Capitalsoft Inc ....F 972 220-1560
Richardson *(G-17284)*

CDM Software Solutions Inc ....E 972 469-3082
Frisco *(G-7272)*

Checkfree Corporation ....D 281 333-9800
Houston *(G-9167)*

Cimarron Software Services Inc.......E 281 226-5100
Houston *(G-9190)*

Cistera Networks Inc ....F 972 381-4699
Plano *(G-16823)*

Cme Printing Inc ....F 713 271-7700
Houston *(G-9218)*

Correlog Inc ....F 239 514-3331
Houston *(G-9323)*

Crescent Systems Inc ....E 972 437-0400
Richardson *(G-17294)*

Diyatech Corp ....E 214 769-6933
Dallas *(G-4264)*

Embarcadero Technologies Inc ....C 512 226-8080
Austin *(G-1121)*

Espy Corporation ....E 512 261-1016
Austin *(G-861)*

Esw Holdings Inc ....F 512 524-6149
Austin *(G-1140)*

Exigo Office Inc ....F 214 367-9999
Dallas *(G-4347)*

Falconstor Software Inc ....E 631 777-5188
Austin *(G-1146)*

Global Shop Solutions Inc ....D 281 681-1959
The Woodlands *(G-19868)*

Gresham Enterprise Storage Inc.......E 512 250-0916
Austin *(G-1194)*

Human Resource Micro Systems .....F 415 362-8400
Irving *(G-13060)*

Iberon LLC.................................F 877 559-2140
Houston *(G-10312)*

Idera Inc ....D 713 523-4433
Houston *(G-10315)*

Info-Power International Inc............G 972 424-4447
Plano *(G-16890)*

Infosys Limited...........................F 281 454-0300
Houston *(G-10359)*

Infosys Limited...........................D 214 306-2100
Richardson *(G-17332)*

Keynote Technologies LLC............F 877 528-4747
Allen *(G-282)*

Lacerte Software Corporation ....C 214 387-2000
Plano *(G-16906)*

Lansa Inc ....C 630 874-7042
Houston *(G-10598)*

Lisam America Inc ....E 979 307-7384
Bryan *(G-2491)*

Manning Navcomp Inc ....E 877 680-1188
Austin *(G-1324)*

MEI Micro Inc ....E 972 690-9494
Addison *(G-149)*

Neofirma Inc ....F 214 233-7111
Richardson *(G-17362)*

Oil & Gas Consultants Intl Inc ....F 832 426-1200
Katy *(G-13374)*

Optimum Path Systems Inc ....F 813 990-8204
Hurst *(G-12854)*

Paradigm Ses LLC ....F 713 402-6140
Houston *(G-11238)*

Peritus Inc.................................C 817 726-4626
Irving *(G-13141)*

Petrasoft Counsulting ....F 832 448-5600
Houston *(G-11299)*

Procera Networks Inc ....E 510 230-2777
Plano *(G-16980)*

Professionalized Pdts & Svcs.........E 281 933-9427
Houston *(G-11440)*

Pros Holdings Inc ....C 713 335-5151
Houston *(G-11453)*

Rmg Enterprise Solutions Inc.........E 877 796-6634
Dallas *(G-4904)*

ROC Software LP ....E 512 336-4200
Austin *(G-1468)*

Rogii Inc....................................E 346 714-8694
Houston *(G-11656)*

Roxar Inc...................................E 281 879-2600
Houston *(G-11680)*

Samsung SDS Globl Scl Amer Inc ......E 201 263-3000
Plano *(G-17000)*

Science Applications Intl Corp ....F 469 557-8249
Carrollton *(G-2815)*

Software Global Ltd ....F 832 274-0478
Austin *(G-1516)*

Statacorp LLC............................C 979 696-4600
College Station *(G-3202)*

Thinkgeo LLC ....F 785 727-4133
Frisco *(G-7319)*

Thomson Rters Tax Accnting Inc ......B 800 431-9025
Carrollton *(G-2833)*

Touchmate Inc ....E 512 949-3330
Austin *(G-1587)*

Tritech Software Development ....E 972 680-2223
Allen *(G-304)*

Troux Technologies Inc ....D 512 346-8600
Austin *(G-1596)*

Vedero Software Inc ....G 972 309-9870
Carrollton *(G-2895)*

Window On Wallstreet Inc.............E 972 727-3626
Richardson *(G-17429)*

COMPUTER SOFTWARE DEVELOPMENT & APPLICATIONS

Advent Global Solutions Inc ....F 281 970-3000
Houston *(G-8495)*

American Vapor Company LLC ....F 512 596-1892
Pflugerville *(G-16657)*

Automatize Logistics LLC..............E 817 221-8106
Grapevine *(G-8013)*

Candeo Interactive LLC ....F 214 394-8499
Forney *(G-6303)*

Centrax International Corp ....E 281 465-0781
Spring *(G-19203)*

City of Arlington.........................A 817 459-5700
Arlington *(G-644)*

Dnv GL Noble Denton Usa LLC ....B 281 396-1000
Katy *(G-13396)*

Four Cornerstone Solutions LLC ......E 817 377-1144
Fort Worth *(G-6646)*

Happy Shopper Inc ....F 281 751-7138
Houston *(G-10122)*

Involta LLC................................F 817 937-8943
Dallas *(G-4511)*

Jones Lang Lasalle Ip Inc ....E 214 777-5100
Dallas *(G-4538)*

La Nortena Inc ....G 432 445-3273
Pecos *(G-16621)*

Law Publications Inc ....F 800 527-0156
Carrollton *(G-2774)*

Netiq Corporation ....D 713 548-1700
Houston *(G-11028)*

Pixel and Texel LLC ....E 214 240-0013
Dallas *(G-4808)*

Premier Digital Design LLC............G 210 774-5456
San Antonio *(G-18390)*

Redhouse Virtual Education LLC ......E 210 872-4989
Dallas *(G-4878)*

Rubrix LLC.................................E 512 581-5513
San Antonio *(G-18437)*

Stone Cliff Technology LLC ....E 512 640-0650
Austin *(G-1538)*

Texas Air & Water LLC.................F 361 814-3131
Corpus Christi *(G-3636)*

Tpg Software Inc ....E 713 974-1375
Houston *(G-12337)*

Venture Research Inc ....E 469 246-4000
Plano *(G-17044)*

Visual Bi Solutions Inc ....F 972 232-2233
Plano *(G-17046)*

Western Midstream Partners LP.........F 832 636-6000
The Woodlands *(G-19940)*

COMPUTER SOFTWARE SYSTEMS ANALYSIS & DESIGN: Custom

1-Stop Enterprises LLC ....E 678 485-9873
Little Elm *(G-14138)*

Aim Solutions Inc........................F 214 373-6084
Dallas *(G-3904)*

Ambernet Technologies Inc ....F 972 707-4000
Dallas *(G-3936)*

Baxter Planning Systems Inc...........E 512 323-5959
Austin *(G-977)*

Broadaxis Inc ....F 469 688-2272
Plano *(G-16814)*

Centaur Technology Inc ....D ... 512 418-5700
    Austin *(G-1037)*

Coda Global LLC ....E ... 844 366-8250
    Southlake *(G-19060)*

Convergepoint Inc ....F ... 347 948-4258
    Houston *(G-9298)*

Eclectic Innvtive Slutions LLC ....F ... 737 999-1907
    Dripping Springs *(G-5505)*

Election Systems & Sftwr LLC ....D ... 469 675-8990
    Allen *(G-264)*

Harris N Computer Corporation ....F ... 903 535-8222
    Tyler *(G-20093)*

Hiller Measurements Inc ....C ... 512 394-8356
    Austin *(G-863)*

Information Store Inc ....F ... 713 787-6798
    Houston *(G-10358)*

Keen Solutions Group Inc ....E ... 903 253-0476
    Tyler *(G-20107)*

Optimum Consultancy Svcs LLC ....F ... 713 505-0300
    Houston *(G-11185)*

Pason Systems USA Corp ....D ... 713 693-8700
    Houston *(G-11256)*

Radix Us LLC ....E ... 832 377-9601
    Houston *(G-11532)*

Royal Technocrats Inc ....E ... 713 776-8300
    Houston *(G-11684)*

Systel Inc ....E ... 281 207-7619
    Sugar Land *(G-19560)*

System Development Inc ....E ... 713 266-5667
    Houston *(G-12139)*

Systum Inc ....F ... 406 600-3684
    Plano *(G-17018)*

Tendenci Inc ....E ... 281 497-6567
    Houston *(G-12203)*

Verge Ventures LLC ....F ... 972 200-1707
    Richardson *(G-17420)*

Yadblue LLC ....F ... 214 542-6140
    Southlake *(G-19084)*

COMPUTER STORAGE DEVICES, NEC

Bogey Free LLC ....F ... 972 272-6631
    Plano *(G-16809)*

Cd3 Inc ....E ... 512 252-2592
    Austin *(G-1034)*

Dell Inc ....A ... 800 289-3355
    Round Rock *(G-17642)*

Denali Intermediate Inc ....A ... 713 627-0933
    Round Rock *(G-17648)*

Dinamica Inc ....E ... 281 564-5100
    Houston *(G-9476)*

EMC Corporation ....F ... 512 343-3332
    Austin *(G-1122)*

EMC Corporation ....C ... 972 892-7700
    Dallas *(G-4317)*

EMC Corporation ....E ... 713 621-9800
    Houston *(G-9609)*

Filecontrol Partners Ltd ....F ... 713 355-1111
    Houston *(G-9785)*

Hendricks BTS Corporation ....F ... 713 516-8716
    Pearland *(G-16568)*

Hewlett Packard Enterprise Co ....C ... 650 687-5817
    Houston *(G-10166)*

Keyscan Inc ....F ... 201 918-2396
    Odessa *(G-16051)*

Mangstor Inc ....E ... 512 779-6999
    Austin *(G-1322)*

N L Industries Inc ....E ... 972 233-1700
    Dallas *(G-4711)*

Onyx Venture Group LLC ....F ... 281 395-4791
    Katy *(G-13375)*

Proactive Technologies Inc ....F ... 972 416-6298
    Carrollton *(G-2798)*

Quantum Corporation ....C ... 210 622-9235
    Atascosa *(G-817)*

Synaptic Cloud LLC ....E ... 972 591-0151
    McKinney *(G-14981)*

Toshiba International Corp ....A ... 800 231-1412
    Houston *(G-12327)*

Vce Company LLC ....C ... 972 656-5300
    Richardson *(G-17418)*

Verge Labs Inc ....F ... 512 707-0001
    Austin *(G-1630)*

Viewcastcom Inc ....E ... 972 488-7200
    Grapevine *(G-8059)*

COMPUTER SYSTEMS ANALYSIS & DESIGN

Asna Inc ....E ... 210 408-0212
    San Antonio *(G-17917)*

Hendricks BTS Corporation ....F ... 713 516-8716
    Pearland *(G-16568)*

Tdk Rf Solutions Inc ....E ... 512 258-9478
    Cedar Park *(G-2987)*

Tendenci Inc ....E ... 281 497-6567
    Houston *(G-12203)*

COMPUTER TERMINALS

Behemoth Corporation ....E ... 281 332-4798
    League City *(G-13949)*

IDEA Corporation ....F ... 915 845-6606
    El Paso *(G-5809)*

NCR Corporation ....E ... 210 366-2959
    San Antonio *(G-18339)*

NCR Solutions Llc ....F ... 405 413-8278
    Little Elm *(G-14140)*

Rose Electronics ....C ... 281 933-7673
    Houston *(G-11662)*

Singer Data Products Inc ....E ... 915 594-7650
    El Paso *(G-5962)*

Verity Instruments Inc ....D ... 972 446-9990
    Carrollton *(G-2896)*

COMPUTER TERMINALS: CRT

Telco Intercontinental Corp ....E ... 281 500-8270
    Houston *(G-12190)*

COMPUTER-AIDED DESIGN SYSTEMS SVCS

Hi-Tech Products Inc ....F ... 512 450-1465
    Round Rock *(G-17662)*

Mlc Cad Systems LLC ....E ... 512 288-8511
    Austin *(G-1346)*

Q C Graphics Inc ....E ... 972 931-4100
    Richardson *(G-17377)*

COMPUTER-AIDED MANUFACTURING SYSTEMS SVCS

Rct Global Inc ....F ... 915 595-8750
    El Paso *(G-5929)*

COMPUTERS, NEC

Acer America Corporation ....C ... 254 298-4000
    Temple *(G-19666)*

Boomi Inc ....E ... 800 289-3355
    Round Rock *(G-17628)*

Convey Computer Corporation ....E ... 214 576-9630
    Dallas *(G-4163)*

Corvalent Corporation ....E ... 512 456-2400
    Cedar Park *(G-2965)*

Cray Inc ....E ... 512 651-7020
    Austin *(G-1071)*

Crescent Systems Inc ....E ... 972 437-0400
    Richardson *(G-17294)*

Daniel Industries Inc ....E ... 713 467-6000
    Houston *(G-9401)*

Daniel Measurement & Ctrl LLC ....B ... 713 827-5033
    Houston *(G-9402)*

Dell America Latina Corp ....E ... 512 799-1022
    Round Rock *(G-17641)*

Dell Inc ....G ... 817 408-5725
    Arlington *(G-658)*

Dell Marketing LP ....C ... 512 513-9022
    Round Rock *(G-17644)*

Dell Products LP ....A ... 866 413-3355
    Round Rock *(G-17645)*

Dell USA LP ....F ... 512 728-3366
    Austin *(G-1088)*

Dell USA LP ....D ... 512 725-1829
    Round Rock *(G-17647)*

Focus Wireless Inc ....F ... 586 907-5323
    Richardson *(G-17310)*

Foxconn Assembly LLC ....D ... 281 668-1668
    Houston *(G-9848)*

Foxconn Corporation ....E ... 281 668-1668
    Houston *(G-9849)*

Futuremedia Group Inc ....E ... 972 770-0000
    Carrollton *(G-2743)*

Gazoo Inc ....F ... 979 220-7753
    Bryan *(G-2475)*

General Dynmics Mssion Systems ....C ... 210 524-8200
    San Antonio *(G-18137)*

Gtech Precision Inds USA Ltd ....F ... 817 539-8014
    Mansfield *(G-14678)*

Hewlett-Packard Company ....D ... 979 691-4540
    College Station *(G-3186)*

Keil Software Inc ....F ... 972 312-1107
    Plano *(G-16901)*

Laversab Inc ....E ... 281 325-8300
    Sugar Land *(G-19503)*

Link World Trade Inc ....C ... 972 713-8000
    Addison *(G-145)*

Linux Tech Inc ....F ... 972 907-0871
    Dallas *(G-4596)*

PC Cable Connexion Inc ....F ... 281 338-5400
    League City *(G-13974)*

Rfmicron Inc ....E ... 512 535-4647
    Austin *(G-1465)*

Rsi Inc ....E ... 512 268-7500
    Kyle *(G-13686)*

Salient Global Technologies ....D ... 925 526-1234
    Dallas *(G-4928)*

Skiva Technologies Inc ....E ... 214 441-3517
    Dallas *(G-4967)*

Touchmate Inc ....E ... 512 949-3330
    Austin *(G-1587)*

Tri-Cor Industries Inc ....E ... 210 979-0552
    San Antonio *(G-18565)*

Winsystems Inc ....E ... 817 274-7553
    Grand Prairie *(G-7996)*

COMPUTERS, NEC, WHOLESALE

Alecom Technologies Group Inc ....G ... 972 870-9400
    Flower Mound *(G-6259)*

P2es Holdings LLC ....D ... 713 481-2000
    Houston *(G-11216)*

Safeguard Business Systems Inc ....C ... 800 523-2422
    Dallas *(G-4926)*

Texas Logic Inc ....F ... 956 682-3466
    McAllen *(G-14911)*

COMPUTERS, PERIPH & SOFTWARE, WHLSE: Personal & Home Entrtn

Galaxy Electronics Company ....F ... 972 234-0065
    Richardson *(G-17319)*

COMPUTERS, PERIPHERALS & SOFTWARE, WHOLESALE: Printers

An Authorized Affiliate of PRI ....G ... 817 430-6202
    Fort Worth *(G-6387)*

Laser Pros International Corp ....E ... 715 369-5995
    Marshall *(G-14786)*

COMPUTERS, PERIPHERALS & SOFTWARE, WHOLESALE: Software

Cgi Technologies Solutions Inc ....B ... 866 344-3221
    Houston *(G-9150)*

Cimarron Software Services Inc ....E ... 281 226-5100
    Houston *(G-9190)*

Exigo Office Inc ....F ... 214 367-9999
    Dallas *(G-4347)*

Guardian Compliance ....A ... 713 641-2020
    Deer Park *(G-5277)*

Jericho Systems Corporation ....E ... 972 231-2000
    Dallas *(G-4533)*

Network Info Systems Inc ....E ... 713 255-4800
    Houston *(G-11030)*

ONeil Digital Solutions LLC ....B ... 972 881-1282
    Plano *(G-16954)*

Quick Intrnet Sftwr Sltons Inc ....F ... 979 846-3008
    College Station *(G-3198)*

Shi/Government Solutions Inc ....E ... 512 634-8100
    Austin *(G-1498)*

Trend Micro Incorporated ....C ... 408 257-1500
    Irving *(G-13199)*

Trusource Labs LLC ....E ... 512 487-7103
    Austin *(G-1598)*

COMPUTERS: Mini

Dell Inc ....A ... 800 289-3355
    Round Rock *(G-17642)*

Denali Intermediate Inc ....A ... 713 627-0933
    Round Rock *(G-17648)*

Oracle Corporation ....A ... 737 867-1000
    Austin *(G-1391)*

Simply Nuc Inc ....E ... 512 766-0402
    Round Rock *(G-17690)*

COMPUTERS: Personal

Dell Inc ....C ... 512 324-0137
    Round Rock *(G-17643)*

Enterprise Svcs Ltin Amer Corp ....E ... 703 245-9675
    Houston *(G-9664)*

Hp Inc ....E ... 970 898-0000
    Houston *(G-10271)*

Hp Inc ....A 541 360-4763
Spring *(G-19132)*

Hp Inc ....B 972 604-3355
Plano *(G-16887)*

Jack Saunders ....F 713 806-7997
Baytown *(G-1823)*

Mingtel Inc ....F 972 378-5559
Plano *(G-16929)*

CONCENTRATES, DRINK

Aloe Laboratories Inc ....D 956 428-8416
Harlingen *(G-8178)*

Chameleon Cold Brew LLC .....E 512 323-0345
Austin *(G-1042)*

Coca-Cola Refreshments USA Inc ....E 806 472-3200
Lubbock *(G-14395)*

Drafft Root Beer Inc ....F 214 638-8442
Dallas *(G-4278)*

CONCRETE BUILDING PRDTS WHOLESALERS

Erect-A-Line Inc ....F 214 630-1154
Dallas *(G-4330)*

CONCRETE CURING & HARDENING COMPOUNDS

Concrete Producers Solutions ....F 281 398-6244
Pearland *(G-16549)*

Miracon Technologies LLC ......F 972 387-3099
Richardson *(G-17358)*

CONCRETE MIXERS

Domatex Inc ....D 281 219-1800
Houston *(G-9493)*

CONCRETE PLANTS

Construction Eqp Mfg Co Inc ......E 940 257-6215
Olney *(G-16220)*

Kirk Construction Inc ....F 281 392-4063
Katy *(G-13369)*

Scott Newland Office ....F 903 758-1500
Longview *(G-14307)*

Souther Equipment Sales Inc ......F 972 296-5231
Dallas *(G-4985)*

Trinity Industries Inc ....B 214 631-4420
Dallas *(G-5112)*

Vince Hagan Company ....F 214 330-4601
Sunnyvale *(G-19615)*

CONCRETE PRDTS

Al Tex Concrete Products Inc ......F 830 964-5150
Canyon Lake *(G-2677)*

Alamo Concrete Products Ltd ......E 956 423-6388
Harlingen *(G-8175)*

Alamo Concrete Products Ltd ......E 210 208-1500
San Antonio *(G-17881)*

Alamo Concrete Products Ltd ......E 956 423-6380
Harlingen *(G-8176)*

Alamo Concrete Products Co ......E 210 208-1500
San Antonio *(G-18637)*

Alamo Concrete Products Co ......F 281 443-2644
Houston *(G-8522)*

Argos USA LLC ....D 972 299-5274
Cedar Hill *(G-2936)*

Cemex Inc ....B 713 650-6200
Houston *(G-9120)*

Cemex Materials LLC ....E 979 885-7403
Sealy *(G-18807)*

Concrete ASAP LLC ....F 713 222-6216
Houston *(G-9268)*

Custom Crete Inc ....F 713 937-3966
Houston *(G-9369)*

Del Norte Masonry Products Inc ....E 915 584-4453
El Paso *(G-5716)*

Delzotto Products Minn Inc ....E 903 981-0400
Gladewater *(G-7720)*

Diversitech Corporation ....D 678 542-3600
Columbus *(G-3231)*

Dumpzit LLC ....F 817 238-6563
Fort Worth *(G-6596)*

Espinoza Cast Stone Inc ....F 214 396-5280
Waxahachie *(G-20542)*

Forterra Pipe & Precast LLC ......C 972 263-2181
Grand Prairie *(G-7877)*

Forterra Pipe & Precast LLC ......B 972 262-1571
Grand Prairie *(G-7878)*

Gate Precast Company ....C 254 582-7200
Hillsboro *(G-8325)*

Genesis Granite Inc ....F 940 692-0611
Wichita Falls *(G-20767)*

Gfrc 360 LLC ....E 972 494-9000
Garland *(G-7503)*

Hanson Aggregates LLC ....E 972 556-0735
Dallas *(G-4433)*

Heldenfels Enterprises Inc ......C 512 396-2376
San Marcos *(G-18694)*

Holcim (us) Inc ....F 214 596-9760
Addison *(G-134)*

Hydro Conduit of Texas LP ......E 817 491-4321
Northlake *(G-15887)*

Hydro Conduit of Texas LP ......E 832 590-5400
Houston *(G-10304)*

Hydro Conduit of Texas LP ......E 979 885-7403
Sealy *(G-18808)*

Lattimore Materials Corp ....D 972 569-4622
McKinney *(G-14951)*

New England Lead Burning Inc ......F 713 675-3266
Houston *(G-11034)*

North Texas Coring Inc ....F 817 279-8930
Granbury *(G-7802)*

Pavestone LLC ....E 281 769-5098
Katy *(G-13376)*

Pavestone LLC ....E 512 558-7283
San Marcos *(G-18703)*

Pb Materials Holdings Inc ....E 432 563-8036
Odessa *(G-16106)*

Premier Concrete Products Inc ......F 713 641-2727
Houston *(G-11399)*

Quanex Screens LLC ....D 713 961-4600
Houston *(G-11505)*

Quikrete Companies LLC ....E 936 587-4450
Raywood *(G-17235)*

Quikrete Companies LLC ....E 432 694-5432
Midland *(G-15374)*

Ranger Ready Mix LLC ....E 512 363-7630
Georgetown *(G-7672)*

Ready Cable of Houston Inc ......D 713 856-5132
Houston *(G-11560)*

Royal Metal Bldg Components ......E 956 399-2271
San Benito *(G-18665)*

Siteworks Incorporated ....E 281 931-1000
Houston *(G-11909)*

Speed-Fab-Crete Corp Intl ......C 817 572-0351
Kennedale *(G-13503)*

Stromberg Architectural Produc ......D 903 454-0904
Greenville *(G-8092)*

Stromberg Archtctral Pdts Stha ......E 903 454-8682
Greenville *(G-8093)*

Suncoast Post-Tension Ltd ......E 512 259-7908
Leander *(G-13998)*

Superior Cladding Products LLC ......E 281 405-9400
Houston *(G-12110)*

Superior Con Fence Texas Inc ......E 817 558-6658
Cleburne *(G-3110)*

Texas Cement Products Inc ......E 713 682-8411
Houston *(G-12225)*

Texas Concrete Chemical Inc ......E 936 638-4273
Groveton *(G-8113)*

Transit Ready Mix LLC ....F 956 584-0039
Mission *(G-15568)*

Trinity Stairs Inc ....E 972 335-0700
Frisco *(G-7320)*

United Commercial Cast Stone ......F 940 668-8133
Gainesville *(G-7374)*

US Concrete Inc ....E 817 835-4105
Euless *(G-6166)*

Vulcan Materials Company ......F 210 349-3311
San Antonio *(G-18603)*

Vulcan Materials Company ......F 210 494-9555
San Antonio *(G-18604)*

W R Meadows Inc ....E 817 834-1969
Fort Worth *(G-7113)*

Western Ready Mix LLC ....F 830 433-1963
Seguin *(G-18873)*

Wise Products Co Inc ....F 903 378-2233
Honey Grove *(G-8359)*

Xella Aircrete North Amer Inc ......E 229 896-1593
San Antonio *(G-18626)*

CONCRETE PRDTS, PRECAST, NEC

Acme Brick Company ....E 512 255-2573
Elgin *(G-6051)*

Alamo Concrete Tile Inc ....E 210 534-8821
San Antonio *(G-17883)*

American Maatco Ltd ....E 817 284-7222
Richland Hills *(G-17435)*

Ark-Concrete Specialties Inc ......E 713 692-6736
Houston *(G-8697)*

Beltran Precast Inc ....E 915 599-8777
El Paso *(G-5661)*

CFS Forming Structure Company ......D 210 698-9252
San Antonio *(G-17996)*

Coast Precast LLC ....F 936 890-5500
Conroe *(G-3278)*

Coreslab Structures Texas Inc ......C 512 250-0755
Cedar Park *(G-2964)*

Creative Stone Inc ....E 512 303-7866
Bastrop *(G-1752)*

East Texas Precast Company ......C 281 463-0654
Hempstead *(G-8252)*

Enterprise Concrete Pdts LLC ......D 214 631-7006
Dallas *(G-4326)*

Enterprise Prcast Con Txas LLC ......E 903 875-1077
Corsicana *(G-3671)*

Erect-A-Line Inc ....F 214 630-1154
Dallas *(G-4330)*

Featherlite Corporation ....C 817 332-4101
Fort Worth *(G-6625)*

Fencecrete America Inc ....C 281 438-1444
Houston *(G-9776)*

Fencecrete America Inc ....C 210 492-7911
San Antonio *(G-18109)*

First Texas Precast Inc ....E 214 350-5612
Dallas *(G-4364)*

Flexicore of Texas Inc ....C 281 437-5700
Houston *(G-8381)*

Form and Fiber Inc ....F 888 314-8852
Gun Barrel City *(G-8114)*

L & R Pre-Cast Con Works Inc ......E 956 583-6293
Mission *(G-15558)*

Lowe Precast Inc ....E 254 776-9690
Waco *(G-20428)*

Manco Structures Ltd ....D 210 690-1705
Schertz *(G-18753)*

Napco Precast LLC ....C 210 424-4371
San Antonio *(G-18332)*

North American Precast Company ......C 210 509-9100
San Antonio *(G-18350)*

Oldcastle Infrastructure Inc ......E 281 841-9187
Houston *(G-11170)*

Oldcastle Infrastructure Inc ......D 817 477-2914
Mansfield *(G-14698)*

Oldcastle Infrastructure Inc ......E 210 922-7306
San Antonio *(G-18354)*

Oldcastle Infrastructure Inc ......E 713 991-2400
Brookshire *(G-2321)*

Pavestone LLC ....D 817 481-5802
Grapevine *(G-8051)*

RMC Usa Inc ....F 713 650-6200
Houston *(G-11637)*

S C S C Inc ....E 214 398-1199
Dallas *(G-4922)*

Superior Con Fence Texas Inc ......F 817 277-9255
Euless *(G-6160)*

Tex-Art Stone Inc ....F 817 481-9602
Keller *(G-13470)*

Western Precast Concrete Inc ......D 915 859-9362
El Paso *(G-6032)*

CONCRETE REINFORCING MATERIAL

Dorstener Wire Tech Inc ....F 281 651-6226
Spring *(G-19111)*

Wire Mesh Sales LLC ....E 706 922-5179
The Woodlands *(G-19821)*

CONCRETE: Asphaltic, Not From Refineries

Caprock Materials LLC ....F 806 778-0343
Lubbock *(G-14390)*

Guerro Ready Mix ....F 281 342-4022
Rosenberg *(G-17583)*

Martin Mrtta Mtls Suthwest LLC ......B 210 208-4400
San Antonio *(G-18280)*

CONCRETE: Dry Mixture

James Hardie Building Pdts Inc ......C 817 556-7000
Cleburne *(G-3097)*

Quikrete Companies LLC ....E 979 732-8210
Columbus *(G-3232)*

Quikrete Companies LLC ....E 325 672-4634
Abilene *(G-68)*

Vison Tech Products LLC ....F 832 850-6085
Houston *(G-12572)*

Employee Codes: A=Over 500 employees, B=251-500
C=101-250, D=51-100, E=20-50, F=10-19, G=9

2021 Harris Texas
Manufacturers Directory

1433

PRODUCT

CONCRETE: Ready-Mixed

849 Red Baron Supply Co LLC	E	903 882-1700	
Lindale *(G-14132)*			
Affordable Asphalt Paving Inc	F	903 596-7003	
Tyler *(G-20044)*			
Alamo Concrete Products Ltd	E	512 444-2464	
Austin *(G-904)*			
Alamo Concrete Products Ltd	F	210 208-1880	
San Antonio *(G-17882)*			
Alamo Concrete Products Ltd	F	361 578-9678	
Victoria *(G-20237)*			
Alamo Concrete Products Ltd	F	830 773-6334	
Eagle Pass *(G-5547)*			
Alamo Concrete Products Ltd	F	361 552-9525	
Port Lavaca *(G-17141)*			
Alamo Concrete Products Ltd	D	512 444-2464	
Austin *(G-905)*			
Alamo Concrete Products Ltd	E	210 208-1580	
San Antonio *(G-18636)*			
Alamo Concrete Products Ltd	F	979 245-8365	
Bay City *(G-1767)*			
Alamo Concrete Products Ltd	F	979 345-4631	
West Columbia *(G-20673)*			
Alamo Concrete Products Ltd	F	979 849-6378	
West Columbia *(G-20674)*			
Alamo Concrete Products Ltd	E	210 208-1500	
San Antonio *(G-17881)*			
Alamo Concrete Products Ltd	E	361 289-9200	
Corpus Christi *(G-3471)*			
Alamo Concrete Products Ltd	F	361 572-0231	
Victoria *(G-20236)*			
Alamo Concrete Products L	G	361 592-5114	
Kingsville *(G-13623)*			
Alamo Lumber Company	F	361 275-2321	
Cuero *(G-3758)*			
Alamo Ready Mix LLC	E	713 330-3000	
Houston *(G-8523)*			
Alleyton Resource Company LLC	E	281 238-1010	
Columbus *(G-3228)*			
Alpha Ready Mix LLC	F	512 846-2221	
Hutto *(G-12875)*			
Ameron International Corp	E	713 375-3700	
Houston *(G-8623)*			
Ant Enterprises Incorporated	D	281 456-7446	
Baytown *(G-1778)*			
Arcosa Aggregates Inc	E	254 662-1025	
Waco *(G-20364)*			
Arcosa Aggregates Inc	F	972 287-4343	
Seagoville *(G-18798)*			
Arcosa Aggregates Inc	F	254 982-4158	
Rogers *(G-17573)*			
Arcosa Lw Ky LLC	E	214 631-4420	
Dallas *(G-3960)*			
Argos USA LLC	D	713 664-4527	
Jersey Village *(G-13291)*			
Argos USA LLC	D	817 551-0931	
Fort Worth *(G-6400)*			
Argos USA LLC	D	817 468-1333	
Arlington *(G-623)*			
Argos USA LLC	F	281 391-4554	
Katy *(G-13350)*			
Argos USA LLC	F	713 273-2700	
Sugar Land *(G-19446)*			
Argos USA LLC	F	972 621-0999	
Irving *(G-12932)*			
Argos USA LLC	F	972 436-3026	
Lewisville *(G-14023)*			
Argos USA LLC	G	713 692-4408	
Houston *(G-8689)*			
Argos USA LLC	D	817 329-8550	
Grapevine *(G-8012)*			
Argos USA LLC	D	972 256-6571	
Irving *(G-12933)*			
Argos USA LLC	F	972 285-8823	
Mesquite *(G-15027)*			
Argos USA LLC	F	713 273-2800	
Houston *(G-8690)*			
Argos USA LLC	E	972 556-0735	
Dallas *(G-3965)*			
Art Mix LLC	G	713 552-9028	
Houston *(G-8708)*			
Austin Ready-Mix LLC	F	512 386-7187	
Austin *(G-958)*			
B & B Ready Mix Inc	E	972 287-9998	
Seagoville *(G-18799)*			
B Mayfield McCraw	D	903 664-2332	
Telephone *(G-19665)*			
Bell Concrete Products Co	F	903 885-3126	
Sulphur Springs *(G-19581)*			

Bodin Concrete LP	E	972 463-7348	
Rowlett *(G-17702)*			
Borger Redi-Mix Con Co Inc	E	806 273-2874	
Borger *(G-2166)*			
Boyd Ready Mix Inc	E	979 778-5199	
Bryan *(G-2458)*			
Breckenridge Ready Mix Inc	F	254 559-3775	
Breckenridge *(G-2226)*			
Brenham Ready Mix Inc	F	979 830-1989	
Brenham *(G-2246)*			
Brm Concrete	F	346 570-2975	
Houston *(G-8987)*			
Brookhollow Rental Co Inc	E	214 631-6883	
Dallas *(G-4059)*			
Budget Ready Mix	F	281 452-5233	
Channelview *(G-3014)*			
Budget Ready Mix LLC	E	281 452-5233	
Houston *(G-9010)*			
Bullet Concrete Materials Inc	F	281 367-9747	
Conroe *(G-3267)*			
Burnco Texas LLC	E	940 242-3100	
Irving *(G-12954)*			
Cajun Ready Mix Ltd	E	936 597-8455	
Montgomery *(G-15627)*			
Campbell Concrete & Mtls LP	E	281 277-0022	
Sugar Land *(G-19453)*			
Campbell Concrete & Mtls LP	F	713 734-6600	
Houston *(G-9081)*			
Campbell Concrete & Mtls LP	E	281 424-5650	
Baytown *(G-1810)*			
Campbell Concrete & Mtls LP	E	281 592-5201	
Houston *(G-9082)*			
Campbell Concrete & Mtls LP	G	713 783-4761	
Houston *(G-9083)*			
Campbell Concrete & Mtls LP	E	281 391-4700	
Katy *(G-13391)*			
Campbell Concrete & Mtls LP	E	281 356-5444	
Magnolia *(G-14593)*			
Campbell Concrete & Mtls LP	E	281 491-7376	
Richmond *(G-17451)*			
Canadian Redi-Mix Inc	F	806 323-5379	
Canadian *(G-2647)*			
Cementos Ready Mix	G	432 385-7477	
Odessa *(G-15956)*			
Cemex Inc	F	713 332-4070	
Jersey Village *(G-13295)*			
Cemex Inc	D	830 625-7338	
New Braunfels *(G-15778)*			
Cemex Inc	B	713 650-6200	
Houston *(G-9120)*			
Cemex Cement Inc	D	432 385-2800	
Odessa *(G-15957)*			
Cemex Cement Inc	B	713 650-6200	
Houston *(G-9121)*			
Cemex Construction Mtls LP	F	713 650-6200	
Houston *(G-9122)*			
Cemex Construction Mtls S LLC	F	956 386-1452	
Edinburg *(G-5581)*			
Cemex Construction Mtls S LLC	E	915 855-9658	
El Paso *(G-5689)*			
Cemex Construction Mtls S LLC	F	281 457-0031	
Channelview *(G-3015)*			
Cemex Construction Mtls S LLC	E	713 650-6200	
Houston *(G-9123)*			
Cemex Construction Mtls S LLC	E	915 565-4681	
El Paso *(G-5690)*			
Cemex Construction Mtls S LLC	E	713 967-5416	
Houston *(G-9124)*			
Cemex Construction Mtls S LLC	E	956 943-2472	
Port Isabel *(G-17136)*			
Cemex Construction Mtls S LLC	E	281 260-9651	
Houston *(G-9125)*			
Cemex Construction Mtls S LLC	E	501 350-2696	
Levelland *(G-14005)*			
Cemex Construction Mtls S LLC	E	210 250-4100	
New Braunfels *(G-15780)*			
Cemex Construction Mtls S LLC	F	281 391-2655	
Katy *(G-13357)*			
Cemex Construction Mtls S LLC	F	512 247-3400	
Del Valle *(G-5329)*			
Cemex Construction Mtls S LLC	E	281 444-8306	
Houston *(G-9127)*			
Cemex Construction Mtls S LLC	G	713 767-7983	
Houston *(G-9129)*			
Cemex Construction Mtls S LLC	A	713 650-6200	
Houston *(G-9128)*			
Cemex El Paso Inc	C	915 565-4681	
El Paso *(G-5691)*			
Cemex International Trdg LLC	E	713 650-6200	
Houston *(G-9130)*			

Cemex Materials LLC	E	713 650-6200	
Houston *(G-9131)*			
Cemex Materials LLC	E	210 677-8191	
Castroville *(G-2926)*			
Cemex Materials LLC	E	210 677-8191	
San Antonio *(G-17991)*			
Cemex Materials LLC	D	832 590-5400	
Houston *(G-9132)*			
Cemex Materials LLC	E	940 665-8355	
Gainesville *(G-7337)*			
Cemex Southeast LLC	C	713 722-5818	
Houston *(G-9133)*			
Cemex Trading LLC	F	713 650-6200	
Houston *(G-9134)*			
Cemex USA Inc	C	432 385-2892	
Odessa *(G-15958)*			
Centex Materials LLC	E	512 251-5106	
Austin *(G-1038)*			
Centex Materials LLC	E	512 444-9591	
Austin *(G-1039)*			
Centex Materials LLC	E	512 460-3003	
Austin *(G-1040)*			
Centex Materials LLC	E	512 295-4801	
Buda *(G-2525)*			
Central Ready Mix Concrete Co	E	956 383-2261	
San Juan *(G-18672)*			
Central Ready Mix Concrete Co	E	956 541-6082	
San Benito *(G-18655)*			
Charleys Concrete Co Ltd	E	817 431-2016	
Euless *(G-6135)*			
Charleys Concrete Co Ltd	E	817 431-3515	
Fort Worth *(G-6510)*			
Charleys Concrete Co Ltd	E	972 734-6300	
Princeton *(G-17205)*			
Charleys Concrete Co Ltd	E	817 568-2400	
Crowley *(G-3753)*			
Childs Ready-Mix Concrete Co	F	254 968-4755	
Stephenville *(G-19408)*			
Childs Ready-Mix Concrete Co	F	817 594-3832	
Willow Park *(G-20872)*			
Chryso Inc	E	972 772-6010	
Rockwall *(G-17542)*			
City Concrete Inc	F	817 636-2690	
Rhome *(G-17253)*			
City Ready Mix Inc	E	956 722-6315	
Laredo *(G-13874)*			
Coastal Crushed Concrete LLC	E	713 941-3232	
Houston *(G-9224)*			
Coastal Ready Mix Inc	E	409 287-3307	
Nederland *(G-15749)*			
Concho Concrete Company Inc	E	325 653-3354	
San Angelo *(G-17790)*			
Concrete Mobility LLC	F	325 728-5858	
Colorado City *(G-3223)*			
Conroe Concrete Ltd	D	936 539-1761	
Conroe *(G-3281)*			
Continntal Con Mxer Sltons LLC	E	859 234-1100	
Austin *(G-1062)*			
Contractors Supplies Inc	E	936 634-3341	
Lufkin *(G-14523)*			
Contractors Supplies Inc	E	903 753-5766	
Longview *(G-14213)*			
Contractors Supplies Inc	E	903 597-1308	
Tyler *(G-20072)*			
Contractors Supplies Inc	F	903 670-1085	
Athens *(G-824)*			
Cooper Concrete Co	E	972 276-1167	
Garland *(G-7463)*			
Cowboys Ready Mix LLC	E	281 972-7000	
Wallisville *(G-20511)*			
Cowtown Redi Mix Inc	F	817 759-1919	
Fort Worth *(G-6552)*			
Coyote Ready Mix LLC	F	832 432-2025	
Magnolia *(G-14598)*			
Crh Americas Materials Inc	C	409 866-1444	
Beaumont *(G-1878)*			
Custom Crete Inc	C	972 243-4466	
Dallas *(G-4195)*			
Custom Crete Inc	E	512 443-5787	
Austin *(G-1079)*			
Custom Crete Inc	F	713 937-3966	
Houston *(G-9369)*			
Ddm Materials Inc	F	970 726-1122	
Valley View *(G-20202)*			
Dorsett Bros Concrete Sup Inc	E	281 487-0264	
Pasadena *(G-16419)*			
Eagle Materials Inc	C	214 432-2000	
Dallas *(G-4292)*			
El Paso Star Ready-Mix	E	915 860-8555	
El Paso *(G-5742)*			

Erasmo Lopez Jr	E	956 487-3366
Rio Grande City (G-17471)		
Far South Mining LLC	G	210 688-2607
San Antonio (G-18104)		
Farris Concrete Company	D	972 838-2217
Melissa (G-14997)		
Few Ready Mix Corp	D	936 560-5675
Nacogdoches (G-15696)		
Fritz-Pak Corporation	F	214 221-9494
Mesquite (G-15044)		
G E Huebner Concrete Inc	F	979 865-2274
Bellville (G-2009)		
Gcc Rio Grande Inc	F	915 544-1750
El Paso (G-5779)		
Granchelli Construction LLC	F	956 928-1122
McAllen (G-14867)		
Great Southern Ready Mix LLC	E	281 689-9339
New Caney (G-15841)		
Gulf Coast Con & Shell Inc	D	281 238-8883
Manvel (G-14734)		
Halls Lumber Inc	F	806 285-2393
Olton (G-16226)		
Hanson Aggregates LLC	E	806 372-8114
Amarillo (G-432)		
Hanson Aggregates LLC	E	972 875-9590
Ennis (G-6107)		
Hanson Aggregates LLC	F	254 622-3239
Clifton (G-3144)		
Hanson Aggregates LLC	E	713 692-4408
Houston (G-10118)		
Hanson Aggregates LLC	E	713 937-7405
Houston (G-10119)		
Hanson Aggregates LLC	F	281 238-4759
Richmond (G-17456)		
Hanson Aggregates LLC	C	469 417-1200
Irving (G-13049)		
Hanson Aggregates LLC	F	972 644-6415
Richardson (G-17326)		
Hanson Aggregates LLC	F	972 263-2181
Grand Prairie (G-7887)		
Hanson Aggregates LLC	F	281 367-4557
Conroe (G-3301)		
Hanson Aggregates LLC	E	972 256-6571
Irving (G-13050)		
Hanson Aggregates LLC	F	972 556-0735
Dallas (G-4433)		
Hanson Aggregates LLC	E	903 794-6161
Texarkana (G-19764)		
Hanson Aggregates New York LLC	E	972 621-0345
Irving (G-13051)		
Hanson Concrete Balch Springs	F	972 289-0601
Mesquite (G-15048)		
Hanson Lehigh Inc	G	281 491-7376
Dallas (G-4434)		
Hanson Lehigh Inc	B	972 653-5500
Irving (G-13052)		
Hanson Lehigh Inc	E	281 616-0700
Houston (G-10120)		
Heath Transit Mix Concrete Co	F	432 283-2127
Van Horn (G-20214)		
High Plains Concrete Company	F	806 293-8313
Plainview (G-16757)		
Highland Concrete Co	E	432 561-5858
Midland (G-15246)		
Houston Cnty Ready-Mix Con Co	F	936 544-7200
Crockett (G-3720)		
Houston Ready Mix LLC	F	832 532-7408
Sugar Land (G-19494)		
Houtex Ready Mix	E	713 987-0303
Houston (G-10267)		
Hueco Quarry Inc	F	915 859-5767
El Paso (G-5806)		
Hunter Construction Inc	D	806 244-5331
Dalhart (G-3835)		
Image Concrete Inc	E	817 430-0339
Dallas (G-4486)		
Ingram Concrete LLC	E	325 677-2001
Abilene (G-52)		
Ingram Readymix Inc	F	830 379-2765
Seguin (G-18844)		
Ingram Readymix Inc	E	361 533-2225
Corpus Christi (G-3553)		
Ingram Readymix Inc	E	210 633-9161
San Antonio (G-18183)		
Ingram Readymix Inc	E	830 606-9619
New Braunfels (G-15805)		
Ingram Readymix Inc	E	361 552-6071
Port Lavaca (G-17150)		
Ingram Readymix Inc	E	210 798-2676
San Antonio (G-18184)		
Ingram Readymix Inc	E	830 672-6420
Gonzales (G-7757)		
Ingram Readymix Inc	F	361 575-6358
Victoria (G-20273)		
Ingram Readymix Inc	E	830 693-4396
Marble Falls (G-14745)		
Ingram Readymix Inc	F	830 896-4525
Kerrville (G-13521)		
Ingram Readymix Inc	E	210 659-4468
Converse (G-3397)		
Ingram Readymix Inc	F	830 569-2187
Pleasanton (G-17070)		
Ingram Readymix Inc	F	956 722-8736
Laredo (G-13896)		
Ingram Readymix Inc	E	210 492-8851
San Antonio (G-18185)		
Ingram Readymix Inc	F	830 249-3506
Boerne (G-2122)		
Ingram Readymix Inc	F	361 888-9281
Corpus Christi (G-3554)		
Ingram Readymix Inc	E	512 396-3136
San Marcos (G-18696)		
Ingram Readymix Inc	F	830 997-6506
Fredericksburg (G-7183)		
Ingram Readymix Inc	F	361 516-1756
Kingsville (G-13629)		
Ingram Readymix Inc	F	830 334-3622
Pearsall (G-16613)		
Ingram Readymix Inc	E	210 622-5621
San Antonio (G-18186)		
J-III Concrete Co	F	956 787-5518
Pharr (G-16702)		
J-III Concrete Co	F	956 968-1371
Weslaco (G-20661)		
J-III Concrete Co	G	361 396-1951
Alice (G-217)		
Jimmie Hahn Partnership Ltd	E	979 836-3664
Brenham (G-2259)		
Jobe Materials LP	B	915 298-9900
El Paso (G-5821)		
Johnson County Redi-Mix Ltd	F	817 556-9214
Cleburne (G-3099)		
K C Crushed Concrete Inc	E	281 219-0820
Houston (G-10495)		
Killeen Ready Mix Ltd	E	254 634-4514
Killeen (G-13613)		
Knife River Corp - South	F	979 361-2900
College Station (G-3191)		
Knife River Corporation	D	979 779-1112
Bryan (G-2487)		
Knife River Corporation	D	409 842-2100
Beaumont (G-1915)		
Knife River Corporation	D	979 361-2900
Bryan (G-2488)		
Kosmos Cement Company Inc	F	713 722-1788
Houston (G-10561)		
Koy Concrete Ltd	E	281 391-2178
Katy (G-13421)		
La Grange Con & Aggregates	F	979 836-3664
Brenham (G-2260)		
Laredo Ready Mix Ltd	D	956 723-7429
Laredo (G-13906)		
Lattimore Materials Company LP	E	817 491-2400
Roanoke (G-17487)		
Lattimore Materials Corp	C	972 221-4646
Addison (G-143)		
Lattimore Materials Corp	E	972 423-8359
Plano (G-16907)		
Lattimore Materials Corp	D	972 569-4622
McKinney (G-14951)		
Lattimore Materials Corp	E	972 346-3002
Prosper (G-17214)		
Lattimore Materials Corp	F	903 868-9585
Sherman (G-18920)		
Lauren Concrete Inc	D	512 389-2113
Austin (G-1283)		
Lauren Concrete Inc	E	512 233-1348
Round Rock (G-17667)		
Lauren Concrete LP	F	512 389-2113
Round Rock (G-17668)		
Legacy Vulcan LLC	F	830 693-2756
Marble Falls (G-14747)		
Legacy Vulcan LLC	F	254 629-2850
Eastland (G-5566)		
Legacy Vulcan LLC	E	817 594-4524
Millsap (G-15504)		
Legacy Vulcan LLC	E	325 676-0001
Abilene (G-57)		
Legacy Vulcan LLC	E	210 349-3311
San Antonio (G-18242)		
Legacy Vulcan LLC	F	830 934-2625
Knippa (G-13661)		
Legacy Vulcan LLC	F	956 831-8888
Brownsville (G-2376)		
Legacy Vulcan LLC	D	210 492-1053
San Antonio (G-18243)		
Lehigh Cement Company LLC	E	254 776-7162
Waco (G-20425)		
Lehigh Cement Company LLC	D	254 772-9350
Waco (G-20426)		
Lehigh Cement Company LLC	C	877 534-4442
Irving (G-13085)		
Lehigh Hanson Inc	D	713 466-6306
Houston (G-10622)		
Liberty Materials Inc	E	281 572-4003
Conroe (G-3320)		
Lilly Construction Inc	E	325 392-2669
Ozona (G-16285)		
Liquid-Stone Concrete	E	817 295-5151
Burleson (G-2587)		
Live Oak Materials Inc	E	361 775-0065
Ingleside (G-12896)		
Lmp Readymix LLC	F	903 572-2500
Mount Pleasant (G-15653)		
Lone Star Ready-Mix LP	F	512 260-0300
Leander (G-13994)		
Lone Star Ready-Mix LP	E	512 260-3629
Austin (G-1300)		
Magic Valley Concrete LLC	E	956 432-0600
Palmview (G-16311)		
Mainland Concrete Inc	E	281 337-7400
Texas City (G-19797)		
Martin Marietta Materials Inc	E	830 741-8227
Hondo (G-8355)		
Martin Marietta Materials Inc	E	409 835-4933
Beaumont (G-1926)		
Martin Marietta Materials Inc	F	972 647-4985
Midlothian (G-15484)		
Martin Mrtta Mtls Suthwest LLC	B	210 208-4400
San Antonio (G-18280)		
Mesquite Concrete Inc	F	830 216-1530
Falls City (G-6183)		
Metro Ready Mix Ltd Company	F	713 991-6466
Houston (G-10856)		
Mid-County Ready Mix	E	830 876-3800
Carrizo Springs (G-2686)		
Miniconcrete Materials Inc	F	915 852-4468
El Paso (G-5880)		
Modern Concrete & Mtls LLC	F	409 840-2080
Beaumont (G-1929)		
Montana Nelson Ready Mix LLC	G	936 328-5688
Livingston (G-14159)		
Mullen-Telles Inc	D	915 859-5767
El Paso (G-5891)		
Murphy & Murphy Inc	F	940 325-2666
Mineral Wells (G-15533)		
Navasota Concrete Inc	F	936 825-8106
Navasota (G-15741)		
Nelson Bros Ready Mix Ltd	D	972 436-6558
Lewisville (G-14073)		
New Boston Concrete Inc	F	903 628-3556
New Boston (G-15767)		
Newhrm LP	E	713 978-7474
Houston (G-11041)		
Nortex Redimix LLC	E	214 681-5200
Farmers Branch (G-6210)		
Nortex Redimix LLC	E	214 681-5200
Aubrey (G-851)		
OK Concrete Company	E	940 723-4324
Wichita Falls (G-20790)		
OK Concrete Company	F	940 552-5162
Vernon (G-20228)		
Old Castle Apg Texas Inc	E	512 864-9601
Georgetown (G-7669)		
Otis T Dickerson	F	713 988-2533
Pearland (G-16585)		
Pampa Concrete Co Inc	F	806 669-3111
Pampa (G-16331)		
Pb Materials Holdings Inc	E	806 745-5332
Lubbock (G-14459)		
Pb Materials Holdings Inc	D	432 208-2761
Kermit (G-13513)		
Porter Ready-Mix Inc	E	281 354-5181
Porter (G-17181)		
Porter Ready-Mix Inc	F	281 443-6363
Houston (G-11367)		
Powerhouse Ready-Mix LLC	F	832 620-1922
Rosenberg (G-17594)		
Precision Ready Mix Ltd	F	210 872-6053
San Antonio (G-18387)		

Quality Readymix Ltd LLP ....F 361 289-2515
Corpus Christi *(G-3603)*

Redi-Mix LLC ....E 210 651-4141
Garden Ridge *(G-7419)*

Redi-Mix LLC ....D 817 835-4105
Euless *(G-6153)*

Redi-Mix LP ....E 972 335-2060
Frisco *(G-7263)*

Redi-Mix LP ....E 817 561-9785
Kennedale *(G-13502)*

Redi-Mix LP ....E 972 242-4550
Carrollton *(G-2885)*

Redi-Mix LP ....E 817 485-4850
Euless *(G-6154)*

Richmond Materials Inc ....E 281 238-5488
Richmond *(G-17465)*

River City Ready Mix Inc ....F 210 520-1941
San Antonio *(G-18427)*

RMC Usa Inc ....F 713 650-6200
Houston *(G-11637)*

Roger D Stevens Contractor ....F 830 796-3714
Bandera *(G-1744)*

Sandy Hill Redi-Mix Con Co ....E 940 627-8769
Decatur *(G-5253)*

Sealy Concrete Inc ....E 281 391-3435
Sealy *(G-18818)*

Solid Rock Ready Mix Inc ....F 281 931-3003
Houston *(G-11940)*

South Texas Concrete ....D 956 381-9886
Edinburg *(G-5602)*

South Texas Concrete ....F 956 464-4440
Donna *(G-5491)*

South Texas Concrete 956 485-2301
Sullivan City *(G-19577)*

Southdown Inc ....B 713 650-6200
Houston *(G-11971)*

St Ready Mix LLC ....E 830 480-0933
Jourdanton *(G-13334)*

Strickland Bridge Inc ....F 940 864-2677
Haskell *(G-8214)*

Strong Ready Mix Ltd ....F 325 260-6935
Abilene *(G-84)*

Sweetwater Ready-Mix Con Co ....F 325 236-6200
Sweetwater *(G-19638)*

Tarrant Concrete Co Inc ....D 817 926-6660
Fort Worth *(G-7035)*

Texas Aggregates LP ....F 512 303-4215
Bastrop *(G-1762)*

Texas Concrete Enterprise LLC ....F 713 227-1122
Houston *(G-12226)*

Texas Concrete Entp Rdymx Inc ....E 713 227-1122
Houston *(G-12227)*

Texas Industries Inc ....E 972 775-3449
Midlothian *(G-15495)*

Texas Industries Inc ....C 940 683-4277
Bridgeport *(G-2303)*

Texas Industries Inc ....E 903 873-2849
Wills Point *(G-20878)*

Texas Industries Inc ....D 972 556-0751
Dallas *(G-5063)*

Texas Industries Inc ....F 903 758-7351
Longview *(G-14316)*

Texas Industries Inc ....F 903 454-2029
Greenville *(G-8094)*

Texas Industries Inc ....E 512 276-7990
Manor *(G-14650)*

Texas Industries Inc ....D 817 838-4212
Fort Worth *(G-7048)*

Texas Industries Inc ....C 972 647-6700
Dallas *(G-5062)*

Texcon Ready Mix Inc ....D 281 572-1712
Porter *(G-17183)*

Thomas Redi-Mix Company Inc ....E 806 381-8485
Amarillo *(G-467)*

Top Cat Ready Mix LLC ....D 972 486-3162
Dallas *(G-5100)*

Torres Brothers ....F 713 732-4237
Houston *(G-12324)*

Treffinger Inc ....E 972 286-8852
Dallas *(G-5106)*

Triple C Concrete Lubbock Ltd ....E 806 762-3227
Lubbock *(G-14499)*

Triple S Ready Mix LLC ....E 830 769-2629
Jourdanton *(G-13335)*

Troy Vines Incorporated ....F 432 682-7031
Midland *(G-15447)*

True Grit Redi Mix Ltd ....E 817 439-5914
Fort Worth *(G-7081)*

Txi Operations LP ....C 936 295-7672
Huntsville *(G-12826)*

Txi Operations LP ....C 972 647-6700
Dallas *(G-5125)*

US Concrete Inc ....E 817 835-4105
Euless *(G-6166)*

US Concrete Inc ....E 806 373-4951
Amarillo *(G-472)*

Uvalde Concrete Inc ....E 830 278-9200
Uvalde *(G-20198)*

Vulcan Construction Mtls LLC ....F 210 492-1053
San Antonio *(G-18602)*

Vulcan Construction Mtls LLC ....E 254 629-2850
Eastland *(G-5570)*

Vulcan Materials Company ....F 713 631-7200
Houston *(G-12583)*

Vulcan Materials Company ....F 409 833-4177
Beaumont *(G-1967)*

Vulcan Materials Company ....F 972 335-0008
Frisco *(G-7325)*

Vulcan Materials Company ....F 325 529-3785
Abilene *(G-91)*

Vulcan Materials Company ....F 210 695-3081
Helotes *(G-8244)*

Vulcan Materials Company ....F 210 349-3311
San Antonio *(G-18603)*

Vulcan Materials Company ....F 210 494-9555
San Antonio *(G-18604)*

W P Murphy Inc ....F 210 658-4947
Schertz *(G-18769)*

Wise Ready Mix Concrete ....F 940 683-5260
Bridgeport *(G-2305)*

Yarrington Road Materials LP ....F 512 306-7800
Austin *(G-1678)*

CONDENSERS & CONDENSING UNITS: Air Conditioner

Marvin Dace Company ....F 281 482-1450
Alvin *(G-373)*

United Electric Company LP ....C 940 397-2100
Wichita Falls *(G-20823)*

CONDENSERS: Fixed Or Variable

Seaport Steel Fab Inc ....F 361 884-1670
Corpus Christi *(G-3618)*

CONDENSERS: Heat Transfer Eqpt, Evaporative

Air Flow Products LP ....F 713 305-0258
Houston *(G-8508)*

Champion Cooler Corporation ....C 903 465-3294
Denison *(G-5337)*

East Texas Radiator Inc ....E 903 753-7286
Longview *(G-14228)*

East Texas Radiator Inc ....F 903 759-3877
Longview *(G-14229)*

Noren Products Inc ....E 650 322-9500
Taylor *(G-19661)*

Ota Compression LLC ....E 972 831-1300
Irving *(G-13136)*

Ota Compression LLC ....F 817 326-8250
Granbury *(G-7803)*

CONDENSERS: Refrigeration

Emerson Climate Tech Inc ....C 817 277-7764
Arlington *(G-668)*

CONDUITS & FITTINGS: Electric

Appleton Grp LLC ....C 281 774-3700
Houston *(G-8665)*

Fielder Electric Supply Co Inc ....E 281 485-6599
Pearland *(G-16560)*

Regal Beloit America Inc ....F 956 213-0503
McAllen *(G-14900)*

Robroy Industries Inc ....C 412 828-2100
Gilmer *(G-7712)*

CONFECTIONERY PRDTS WHOLESALERS

CPT International (usa) LLC ....D 713 747-4773
Sugar Land *(G-19468)*

Ricos Products Co Inc ....C 210 222-1415
San Antonio *(G-18426)*

CONFECTIONS & CANDY

B & G Inc ....F 713 944-1200
Houston *(G-8772)*

Bettera Brands LLC ....F 800 344-6225
Plano *(G-16802)*

Candy Kings Inc ....F 409 762-6100
Galveston *(G-7391)*

CPT International (usa) LLC ....D 713 747-4773
Sugar Land *(G-19468)*

Cyclone Cotton Candy LLC ....E 281 748-9163
Houston *(G-9383)*

Elamex Usa Corp ....A 915 298-3061
El Paso *(G-5748)*

Goodart Candy Inc ....F 806 747-2600
Lubbock *(G-14418)*

Jacksonville Candy Co Inc ....E 903 586-8334
Jacksonville *(G-13244)*

Katysweet Confectioners Inc ....E 979 242-5172
La Grange *(G-13697)*

Kraft Heinz Company ....B 972 272-7511
Garland *(G-7534)*

Mars Chocolate North Amer LLC ....A 254 776-2100
Waco *(G-20433)*

Mars Wrigley Conf US LLC ....E 254 751-5404
Waco *(G-20434)*

Mary of Puddin Hill Inc ....F 903 455-2651
Palestine *(G-16302)*

Monterrey Products Company ....F 210 435-2872
San Antonio *(G-18319)*

Mount Franklin Foods LLC ....B 800 351-8178
El Paso *(G-5885)*

North Blue Oak Inc ....F 844 778-2336
Missouri City *(G-15585)*

Quintessential Chocolates Inc ....F 830 990-9382
Fredericksburg *(G-7187)*

Red River Commodities Inc ....E 806 763-9747
Lubbock *(G-14471)*

Susies South Forty Confections ....D 432 570-4040
Midland *(G-15426)*

CONFINEMENT SURVEILLANCE SYS MAINTENANCE & MONITORING SVCS

Comsovereign Holding Corp ....E 469 930-2661
Dallas *(G-4155)*

Core Laboratories Holding Inc ....B 713 328-2673
Houston *(G-9316)*

Omnidata Services Group LLC ....F 281 469-4365
Houston *(G-11180)*

CONNECTORS & TERMINALS: Electrical Device Uses

3h Manufacturing Inc ....E 281 342-1478
Richmond *(G-17449)*

AF Technologies Inc ....C 817 649-2500
Arlington *(G-611)*

Cinch Connectors Inc ....B 956 686-1151
McAllen *(G-14847)*

Galaxy Electronics Company ....F 972 234-0065
Richardson *(G-17319)*

Kemlon Products & Dev Co ....B 281 997-3300
Pearland *(G-16573)*

Nicor Inc ....F 707 484-0835
Dripping Springs *(G-5510)*

Safran Usa Inc ....E 469 941-8150
Irving *(G-13169)*

Teradyne Inc ....D 972 231-5384
Plano *(G-17025)*

Teradyne Inc ....D 512 891-9600
Austin *(G-1563)*

Tricon International Ltd ....E 713 963-0066
Houston *(G-12371)*

CONNECTORS: Electrical

Rhimco Industries Inc ....E 817 477-3176
Mansfield *(G-14711)*

CONNECTORS: Electronic

ADI Electronics Inc ....F 214 818-4720
Dallas *(G-3889)*

Airborn Interconnect Inc ....B 512 863-5585
Georgetown *(G-7633)*

Amphenol Corporation ....B 214 547-2400
Allen *(G-251)*

Capital City Appliance LLC ....F 512 491-7600
Austin *(G-1026)*

Cinch Connectors Inc ....B 956 686-1151
McAllen *(G-14847)*

Fastener Specialty Inc ....F 972 988-0064
North Richland Hills *(G-15878)*

Fd-Thru Power Systems Cnnctors ....E 281 476-9100
Deer Park *(G-5273)*

Kemp-Meek Manufacturing Inc ....F 903 569-9700
Mineola *(G-15509)*

Lwo Acquisitions Company LLC ....D 972 573-1140
Irving *(G-13093)*

Molex LLC ....F 512 345-1092
Austin *(G-1351)*

Simpson Strong-Tie Company Inc ....C 972 542-0326
McKinney *(G-14975)*

Solution Tech Harn Group LLC ....E 214 221-0323
Dallas *(G-4978)*

Te Connectivity Corporation ....D 610 893-9800
El Paso *(G-5993)*

Teledyne Instruments Inc ....C 713 666-2561
Houston *(G-12191)*

Welding Outlets Inc ....D 281 590-0190
Houston *(G-12630)*

CONNECTORS: Power, Electric

Molex LLC ....D 915 591-5600
El Paso *(G-5882)*

CONSTRUCTION & MINING MACHINERY WHOLESALERS

Brookside Equipment Sales Inc ....F 281 391-2165
Katy *(G-13353)*

Caterpillar Work Tools Inc ....D 254 297-2321
Waco *(G-20378)*

Excel Machinery Ltd ....F 806 335-1553
Amarillo *(G-486)*

Foster Farm & Equipment Supply ....F 281 256-6900
Hockley *(G-8345)*

Hiroko International Inc ....E 210 590-4411
San Antonio *(G-18168)*

K & K Repair Service LLC ....E 361 573-5027
Victoria *(G-20278)*

Land & Sea Services 1 Inc ....G 409 935-9466
La Marque *(G-13711)*

Lincoln Manufacturing Inc ....C 713 514-0059
Houston *(G-10644)*

Preferred Pump & Equipment LP ....E 817 536-9800
Fort Worth *(G-6912)*

CONSTRUCTION EQPT REPAIR SVCS

Beta Arkansas LLC ....F 972 490-2340
Dallas *(G-4022)*

Holt Texas Ltd ....B 210 648-1111
San Antonio *(G-18171)*

Proserv Crane & Equipment Inc ....D 972 438-5100
Irving *(G-13161)*

W T Porter Corp ....G 713 946-4174
South Houston *(G-19056)*

CONSTRUCTION EQPT: Attachments

Schwarze Industries Inc ....F 830 379-1480
Seguin *(G-18862)*

CONSTRUCTION EQPT: Backhoes, Tractors, Cranes & Similar Eqpt

Associated Supply Company Inc ....E 512 272-8922
Manor *(G-14643)*

Crocker Crane Rentals LP ....E 512 258-1323
Leander *(G-13985)*

Dealers Truck Equipment Co Inc ....F 512 312-2100
Buda *(G-2527)*

Elizondo Enterprises Inc ....G 956 831-7174
Brownsville *(G-2353)*

M G Bryan Equipment Co LP ....F 972 623-4300
Grand Prairie *(G-7919)*

Material Handling Concepts ....F 512 836-6598
Austin *(G-1328)*

Proserv Crane & Equipment Inc ....D 972 438-5100
Irving *(G-13161)*

Waukesha-Pearce Industries Inc ....E 512 989-4900
Pflugerville *(G-16692)*

CONSTRUCTION EQPT: Crane Carriers

Frontier Tubular Solutions LLC ....E 903 236-2100
Marshall *(G-14778)*

Precision Wire Products LLC ....F 214 436-4923
Frisco *(G-7307)*

CONSTRUCTION EQPT: Cranes

3ps Inc ....D 512 610-5200
Cedar Park *(G-2958)*

Coastal Hydraulic Cranes Inc ....F 281 448-8998
Spring *(G-19106)*

Favelle Favco Cranes Usa Inc ....D 956 428-7488
Harlingen *(G-8188)*

Global Crane Sales ....F 832 364-8301
Houston *(G-9970)*

Sparrows Offshore LLC ....E 832 467-7300
Houston *(G-11993)*

CONSTRUCTION EQPT: Dozers, Tractor Mounted, Material Moving

Holt Texas Ltd ....B 210 648-1111
San Antonio *(G-18171)*

CONSTRUCTION EQPT: Hammer Mills, Port, Incl Rock/Ore Crush

Imogene Wagner Company Inc ....E 210 669-8927
San Antonio *(G-18179)*

CONSTRUCTION EQPT: Loaders, Shovel, Self-Propelled

Rowan Companies LLC ....C 713 621-7800
Houston *(G-11676)*

CONSTRUCTION EQPT: Rakes, Land Clearing, Mechanical

Raybar Services LLC ....F 409 698-2548
Brookeland *(G-2308)*

CONSTRUCTION EQPT: Rock Crushing Machinery, Portable

Epcs Environmental LLC ....F 817 975-5790
Arlington *(G-672)*

Excel Machinery Ltd ....F 806 335-1553
Amarillo *(G-486)*

CONSTRUCTION EQPT: Roofing Eqpt

Longview Mechanical Contrs Inc ....E 903 759-1331
Longview *(G-14270)*

Reeves Roofing Equipment Co ....E 210 695-3567
Weatherford *(G-20616)*

CONSTRUCTION EQPT: SCRAPERS, GRADERS, ROLLERS & SIMILAR EQPT

Clarendon Mfg & Distrg Co Inc ....F 806 874-3584
Clarendon *(G-3070)*

CONSTRUCTION EQPT: Tractors

Famco Logistics Inc ....F 915 307-2536
El Paso *(G-5763)*

CONSTRUCTION MATERIALS WHOLESALERS

Permian Limestone ....E 254 547-8207
Kempner *(G-13487)*

Texas Carved Stone LP ....F 254 793-2384
Florence *(G-6245)*

CONSTRUCTION MATERIALS, WHOL: Concrete/Cinder Bldg Prdts

Big D Concrete Inc ....E 972 737-7976
Dallas *(G-4023)*

CONSTRUCTION MATERIALS, WHOLESALE: Aggregate

Knife River Corporation ....D 409 842-2100
Beaumont *(G-1915)*

Lehigh Cement Company LLC ....C 877 534-4442
Irving *(G-13085)*

Tricounty Materials & Svcs LP ....F 972 446-1816
Sanger *(G-18731)*

CONSTRUCTION MATERIALS, WHOLESALE: Air Ducts, Sheet Metal

B G Metals Inc ....E 210 648-5071
San Antonio *(G-17930)*

J & G Concrete LP ....E 972 937-9200
Waxahachie *(G-20546)*

Playground Constructors Inc ....F 915 585-6336
El Paso *(G-5912)*

CONSTRUCTION MATERIALS, WHOLESALE: Awnings

Rollac Shutter of Texas Inc ....D 281 485-1911
Pearland *(G-16596)*

CONSTRUCTION MATERIALS, WHOLESALE: Block, Concrete & Cinder

Borger Redi-Mix Con Co Inc ....E 806 273-2874
Borger *(G-2166)*

Hanson Aggregates LLC ....E 903 794-6161
Texarkana *(G-19764)*

CONSTRUCTION MATERIALS, WHOLESALE: Brick, Exc Refractory

Acme Brick Company ....D 325 949-7685
San Angelo *(G-17770)*

Acme Brick Company ....C 817 332-4101
Fort Worth *(G-6343)*

Del Norte Masonry Products Inc ....E 915 584-4453
El Paso *(G-5716)*

Detering Company of Houston LP ....C 713 869-3761
Houston *(G-9446)*

Justin Industries Inc ....D 817 332-4101
Fort Worth *(G-6750)*

Lhoist North America Texas Ltd ....E 254 698-6610
Nolanville *(G-15871)*

CONSTRUCTION MATERIALS, WHOLESALE: Building Stone

Ahi Supply Inc ....D 281 331-0088
Alvin *(G-350)*

Continental Stone LLC ....E 713 462-5700
Houston *(G-9289)*

Custom Crete Inc ....C 972 243-4466
Dallas *(G-4195)*

Custom Crete Inc ....E 512 443-5787
Austin *(G-1079)*

Espinoza Stone Inc ....D 830 629-2530
New Braunfels *(G-15791)*

CONSTRUCTION MATERIALS, WHOLESALE: Building Stone, Granite

Arlington Cast Stone Inc ....F 817 284-5933
Hurst *(G-12834)*

Choice Fabricated Stone LLC ....E 817 222-2201
Fort Worth *(G-6515)*

Delta Granite and Marble Inc ....D 210 829-7171
San Antonio *(G-18050)*

Import Mdsg Concepts GP LLC ....F 214 572-2000
Addison *(G-136)*

Ortega Bath Environments Inc ....E 806 763-5777
Lubbock *(G-14454)*

CONSTRUCTION MATERIALS, WHOLESALE: Building Stone, Marble

Golden Stones LP ....E 713 934-7887
Houston *(G-9994)*

Irving Counter Inc ....E 972 438-4343
Irving *(G-13066)*

Patara Stone Inc ....E 713 681-2301
Houston *(G-11257)*

CONSTRUCTION MATERIALS, WHOLESALE: Building, Exterior

Allied Truss LLC ....E 903 586-1982
Jacksonville *(G-13225)*

Chicago Flameproof WD Spc Corp ....F 817 534-9800
Fort Worth *(G-6513)*

Detering Company of Houston LP ....C 713 869-3761
Houston *(G-9446)*

James Hardie Building Pdts Inc ....C 972 923-9300
Waxahachie *(G-20547)*

PRODUCT

RH Tamlyn & Sons ....E 281 499-9604
Stafford (G-19370)

RMC Usa Inc ....F 713 650-6200
Houston (G-11637)

CONSTRUCTION MATERIALS, WHOLESALE: Building, Interior

Irving Counter Inc ....E 972 438-4343
Irving (G-13066)

CONSTRUCTION MATERIALS, WHOLESALE: Cement

Cemex Inc ....B 713 650-6200
Houston (G-9120)

Quikrete Companies LLC ....D 817 783-3010
Alvarado (G-339)

CONSTRUCTION MATERIALS, WHOLESALE: Clay, Exc Refractory

Aguado Stone Incorporated ....D 512 746-5094
Georgetown (G-7632)

CONSTRUCTION MATERIALS, WHOLESALE: Door Frames

Maintenance Builders Sup Ltd ....E 713 462-8213
Houston (G-10741)

CONSTRUCTION MATERIALS, WHOLESALE: Doors, Garage

Hollywood Ovrhd Door of Dallas ...E 214 348-7240
Dallas (G-4464)

CONSTRUCTION MATERIALS, WHOLESALE: Doors, Sliding

Houston Shutters LLC ....B 713 723-7100
Houston (G-10251)

CONSTRUCTION MATERIALS, WHOLESALE: Eavestroughing, Part/Sply

Beach Sheet Metal Company Inc ...E 972 226-4440
Mesquite (G-15030)

CONSTRUCTION MATERIALS, WHOLESALE: Fiberglass Building Mat

Awntech Corporation ....E 817 354-9600
Euless (G-6132)

CONSTRUCTION MATERIALS, WHOLESALE: Glass

Glass Samuels Company LLC ....D 210 227-2481
San Antonio (G-18142)

Glasscraft Door Mfg Corp ....C 713 690-8282
Houston (G-9962)

Guardian Industries LLC ....B 903 872-4871
Corsicana (G-3673)

Oldcastle Building Envelope ....E 972 647-4028
Grand Prairie (G-7940)

Potters Industries LLC ....D 903 785-1633
Paris (G-16366)

CONSTRUCTION MATERIALS, WHOLESALE: Gravel

Hanson Aggregates LLC ....C 469 417-1200
Irving (G-13049)

Rwc Material LLC ....F 210 219-2987
Fowlerton (G-7162)

CONSTRUCTION MATERIALS, WHOLESALE: Hardboard

Masons Mill & Lumber Co Inc ....D 713 462-6975
Houston (G-10785)

CONSTRUCTION MATERIALS, WHOLESALE: Insulation, Thermal

Border Assembly Inc ....E 915 592-1172
El Paso (G-5667)

Distribution International Inc ....E 214 637-0151
Dallas (G-4263)

Protective Concepts Inc ....F 832 843-7619
Cypress (G-3816)

CONSTRUCTION MATERIALS, WHOLESALE: Limestone

Charles Barton ....E 512 759-1231
Hutto (G-12877)

Lhoist North America Ala LLC ......E 817 268-1187
Hurst (G-12849)

Superior Stone Inc ....F 512 746-2608
Jarrell (G-13273)

CONSTRUCTION MATERIALS, WHOLESALE: Metal Buildings

Horizon Structural Systems Inc ....G 830 629-8000
New Braunfels (G-15803)

Mueller Supply Company Inc ....C 325 365-3555
Ballinger (G-1741)

Shaun K Boyer ....F 281 442-3800
Houston (G-11848)

South Texas Moulding Inc ....F 956 831-0340
Brownsville (G-2406)

Southwest Metal Systems LLC .....F 903 569-8811
Mineola (G-15513)

CONSTRUCTION MATERIALS, WHOLESALE: Millwork

Bee Builders Supply Inc ....E 972 422-4960
Plano (G-16801)

Osborne Cabinets & Millwork ....F 713 802-0092
Port Neches (G-17167)

Smith Wood Products Inc ....E 817 581-5200
Fort Worth (G-6997)

CONSTRUCTION MATERIALS, WHOLESALE: Molding, All Materials

Fox Valley Molding Inc ....E 956 428-2506
Harlingen (G-8189)

Singleton Mouldings Inc ....F 254 559-7541
Breckenridge (G-2237)

CONSTRUCTION MATERIALS, WHOLESALE: Paving Materials

Longview Asphalt Inc ....G 903 758-4428
Longview (G-14267)

Pavement Tool Mfg Inc ....F 903 734-7531
Big Sandy (G-2066)

Pavestone LLC ....E 281 769-5098
Katy (G-13376)

Pavestone LLC ....E 512 558-7283
San Marcos (G-18703)

CONSTRUCTION MATERIALS, WHOLESALE: Prefabricated Structures

Materials Products Inc ....F 512 821-3303
Austin (G-1329)

Oldcastle Buildingenvelope Inc ....A 972 551-6100
Terrell (G-19746)

CONSTRUCTION MATERIALS, WHOLESALE: Roof, Asphalt/Sheet Metal

Custom Bilt Holdings LLC ....F 214 699-4876
Irving (G-12987)

Elkcorp ....E 972 851-0500
Dallas (G-4313)

Owens Corning Sales LLC ....C 972 438-1050
Irving (G-13138)

Parsleys Shtmtl & Roofg Co ....E 806 669-6461
Pampa (G-16333)

Tip Top Sheet Metal Inc ....E 281 931-7823
Houston (G-12294)

CONSTRUCTION MATERIALS, WHOLESALE: Roofing & Siding Material

Allied Truss LLC ....E 903 586-1982
Jacksonville (G-13225)

CONSTRUCTION MATERIALS, WHOLESALE: Sand

Cemex El Paso Inc ....C 915 565-4681
El Paso (G-5691)

E & A Materials Inc ....E 940 692-3290
Wichita Falls (G-20761)

Pappys Sand & Gravel Inc ....E 972 486-4400
Scurry (G-18783)

Sweetwater Ready-Mix Con Co .....F 325 236-6200
Sweetwater (G-19638)

Valley Caliche Products Inc ....D 956 581-2751
Mission (G-15571)

CONSTRUCTION MATERIALS, WHOLESALE: Septic Tanks

Edwards Sptic Grease Trck Svcs ...F 903 643-7585
Kilgore (G-13549)

Gicon Pumps & Equipment Ltd .....G 806 373-0478
Amarillo (G-428)

CONSTRUCTION MATERIALS, WHOLESALE: Sewer Pipe, Clay

Argos USA LLC ....D 972 299-5274
Cedar Hill (G-2936)

CONSTRUCTION MATERIALS, WHOLESALE: Stone, Crushed Or Broken

Fort Worth Crushed Stone LLC .....F 817 596-5512
Weatherford (G-20593)

Hanson Aggregates LLC ....F 210 658-3533
New Braunfels (G-15802)

Hillstone Company ....E 512 746-5544
Jarrell (G-13270)

Metroplex Sand & Gravel Ltd ....D 817 589-9001
Fort Worth (G-6833)

Sorrell Cnstr Eqp & Mtls LLC ....D 979 233-6655
Freeport (G-7213)

Texas Archtctral Aggregate Inc ....E 325 372-5105
San Saba (G-18719)

Yarrington Road Materials LP ....F 512 306-7800
Austin (G-1678)

CONSTRUCTION MATERIALS, WHOLESALE: Stucco

Colorado Stone Pdts Texas Inc .....D 972 434-2515
Carrollton (G-2716)

CONSTRUCTION MATERIALS, WHOLESALE: Tile & Clay Prdts

Styleaccess LLC ....D 972 392-3800
Carrollton (G-2821)

CONSTRUCTION MATERIALS, WHOLESALE: Tile, Clay/Other Ceramic

IB Supply LLC ....F 469 709-9650
Carrollton (G-2870)

CONSTRUCTION MATERIALS, WHOLESALE: Tile, Structural Clay

Interceramic Inc ....B 214 503-5501
Carrollton (G-2871)

CONSTRUCTION MATERIALS, WHOLESALE: Veneer

Halbert Mill Company Texas Inc ....F 903 683-2788
Jacksonville (G-13243)

CONSTRUCTION MATERIALS, WHOLESALE: Wallboard

American Gypsum Company ....C 214 530-5500
Dallas (G-3943)

CONSTRUCTION MATERIALS, WHOLESALE: Window Frames

South Texas Moulding Inc ....E 956 464-0560
Donna (G-5492)

South Texas Moulding Inc ....F 361 857-7770
Corpus Christi (G-3625)

CONSTRUCTION MATERIALS, WHOLESALE: Windows

Advanced Window and Glass Mfg ...G 210 735-9959
San Antonio (G-17870)

B & B Windows Inc ....F 817 237-2212
  Fort Worth *(G-6417)*
Lock Dock Inc ....F 903 759-1288
  Longview *(G-14265)*

CONSTRUCTION MATL, WHOLESALE: Structural Assy, Prefab, Wood

Manufacturing Group Amer Inc ....A 214 467-4444
  Dallas *(G-4633)*
Trussway Manufacturing Inc ....C 719 322-9662
  Houston *(G-12390)*

CONSTRUCTION MATLS, WHOL: Composite Board Prdts, Woodboard

Be-Technologies Ltd ....F 972 242-1853
  Carrollton *(G-2704)*

CONSTRUCTION MATLS, WHOL: Lumber, Rough, Dressed/Finished

Alamo Concrete Products Ltd ....F 361 572-0231
  Victoria *(G-20236)*
American Wholesale Lbr & Mfg ....E 281 342-7020
  Needville *(G-15762)*
Bayou City Lumber Company ....F 713 991-2377
  Houston *(G-8834)*
Brazos Forest Products LP ....E 512 443-0777
  Austin *(G-1006)*
Builders Firstsource Inc ....D 972 621-2233
  Irving *(G-12953)*
Builders Firstsource-Ohio Vall ....C 214 880-3500
  Dallas *(G-4067)*
Builders Frstsrc-Txas Group LP ....B 817 640-1234
  Arlington *(G-634)*
Building Products Plus LLC ....E 713 946-7939
  Houston *(G-9016)*
Cedar Supply Inc ....E 972 242-6561
  Carrollton *(G-2711)*
Central Hardwoods Inc ....E 972 241-3571
  Dallas *(G-4098)*
Clarks Hardwood Lumber Co LP ....F 713 862-6628
  Houston *(G-9211)*
Conner Industries Inc ....E 817 439-3555
  Fort Worth *(G-6541)*
Conner Industries Inc ....E 956 781-0215
  Alamo *(G-178)*
Connor Sports Flooring LLC ....F 817 944-0269
  Southlake *(G-19061)*
Idaho Timber of Texas LLC ....D 817 293-1001
  Fort Worth *(G-6714)*
Keith Carrell Logging Inc ....E 936 422-3375
  Huntington *(G-12810)*
Lincoln Lumber LLC ....D 936 539-4421
  Conroe *(G-3321)*
Southeast Wood Treating Inc ....F 903 569-9441
  Mineola *(G-15512)*
Stock Building Sup Texas LLC ....B 512 444-3172
  Austin *(G-1537)*
West Fraser Inc ....C 903 628-2506
  New Boston *(G-15770)*

CONSTRUCTION MATLS, WHOLESALE: Soil Erosion Cntrl Fabrics

Hill Country Site Supply LLC ....G 512 608-0069
  Lakeway *(G-13816)*

CONSTRUCTION MTRLS, WHOL: Exterior Flat Glass, Plate/Window

A & B Glass LLC ....F 432 517-4565
  Big Spring *(G-2067)*
Hartung Glass Industries Inc ....G 972 629-6890
  Farmers Branch *(G-6201)*
Trulite GL Alum Solutions LLC ....E 210 653-7790
  San Antonio *(G-18570)*

CONSTRUCTION SAND MINING

Capitol Aggregates Inc ....F 830 693-3533
  Marble Falls *(G-14741)*
Capitol Aggregates Inc ....C 210 871-6100
  San Antonio *(G-17981)*
Cemex El Paso Inc ....C 915 564-8400
  El Paso *(G-5692)*
Centex Materials LLC ....E 512 251-5106
  Austin *(G-1038)*
Centex Materials LLC ....E 512 444-9591
  Austin *(G-1039)*

Centex Materials LLC ....F 512 460-3003
  Austin *(G-1040)*
Challenger Services Inc ....F 361 874-4433
  Lolita *(G-14174)*
Wt Mining Company Inc ....F 361 767-4095
  Robstown *(G-17521)*
Zachry Consolidated LLC ....A 210 588-5000
  San Antonio *(G-18630)*

CONSTRUCTION SITE PREPARATION SVCS

Eggemeyer Land Clearing LLC ....E 210 366-4100
  New Braunfels *(G-15789)*
Longhorn Mulching Inc ....E 936 699-1160
  Lufkin *(G-14533)*
Property Works Central Texas ....F 512 940-9353
  Manchaca *(G-14640)*
Robert Marshall Cnstr Inc ....F 361 747-5253
  Bruni *(G-2450)*
Trendsetter Construction Inc ....C 903 759-4955
  Gladewater *(G-7728)*
Universal Management Svcs LLC ....E 979 481-5711
  Angleton *(G-581)*

CONSTRUCTION: Apartment Building

Hutto Holding Group Inc ....D 512 832-8746
  Hutto *(G-12879)*
Requejo Construction Svcs LLC ....F 210 459-5161
  San Antonio *(G-18420)*

CONSTRUCTION: Athletic & Recreation Facilities

Hollman Inc ....C 972 815-4000
  Irving *(G-13058)*

CONSTRUCTION: Athletic & Recreation Facilities

Capco Steel Inc ....E 210 493-9992
  San Antonio *(G-17979)*
Electric Submersible Pump Inc ....F 325 573-8101
  Snyder *(G-18990)*
Laserweld Inc ....E 713 333-0804
  Katy *(G-13422)*
Trendsetter Construction Inc ....C 903 759-4955
  Gladewater *(G-7728)*

CONSTRUCTION: Athletic Field

Vibra-Whirl Sports Ltd ....E 806 537-3526
  Panhandle *(G-16348)*

CONSTRUCTION: Bridge

Hirschfeld Holdings LP ....A 325 486-4201
  San Angelo *(G-17805)*
JD Abrams LP ....E 512 322-4000
  Austin *(G-1252)*
Mar-Con Services LLC ....D 713 473-1800
  Pasadena *(G-16480)*
Strickland Bridge Inc ....F 940 864-2677
  Haskell *(G-8214)*
Zachry Consolidated LLC ....A 210 588-5000
  San Antonio *(G-18630)*
Zachry Construction & Mtls Inc ....D 210 479-1027
  San Antonio *(G-18631)*

CONSTRUCTION: Cable Television Line

B Comm Constructors LLC ....E 210 257-0102
  San Antonio *(G-17929)*

CONSTRUCTION: Chemical Facility

Amec Foster Wheeler USA Corp ....E 713 929-5000
  Houston *(G-8578)*
Repcon Inc ....B 361 289-6342
  Corpus Christi *(G-3609)*

CONSTRUCTION: Commercial & Institutional Building

Bgi Enterprise Inc ....E 409 833-0303
  Beaumont *(G-1865)*
Centex Corporation ....C 214 981-5000
  Dallas *(G-4097)*
Climax Investors LLC ....E 832 582-9622
  Dallas *(G-4130)*
Crisp Industries Inc ....D 830 372-1110
  Seguin *(G-18834)*

Homestead Craftsmen LLC ....D 254 754-9600
  Waco *(G-20414)*
Hunter Construction Inc ....D 806 244-5331
  Dalhart *(G-3835)*
Torcsill Foundations LLC ....D 281 825-5200
  Houston *(G-12323)*
Trinity Services Group Inc ....C 903 277-7128
  Texarkana *(G-19781)*
Tyler Building Systems LP ....E 903 561-3000
  Tyler *(G-20167)*
Zachry Construction & Mtls Inc ....D 210 479-1027
  San Antonio *(G-18631)*

CONSTRUCTION: Commercial & Office Building, New

Boyd Industries Inc ....E 940 433-2315
  Boyd *(G-2203)*
Cato Construction Company ....E 979 830-1398
  Brenham *(G-2250)*
Central Texas Ex Metalwork LLC ....E 210 337-2260
  San Antonio *(G-17992)*
Classic Industries LP ....E 972 564-2192
  Forney *(G-6305)*
Cnc Fabrication and Maint ....F 817 295-9055
  Burleson *(G-2575)*
Herring Enterprises Inc ....F 713 862-3614
  Houston *(G-10162)*
High Plins Cntrs MGT Group Inc ....E 806 935-5858
  Dumas *(G-5522)*
Knights Landscaping LLC ....F 972 971-4213
  Mesquite *(G-15057)*
Knottsmith Construction Co Inc ....E 214 499-5667
  Dallas *(G-4563)*
Mason Brothers Cnstr Co Inc ....E 806 495-3400
  Post *(G-17191)*
Monolithic Constructors Inc ....E 972 483-7423
  Italy *(G-13214)*
Nationwide Pharmaceutical LLC ....F 800 697-3329
  San Antonio *(G-18336)*
Neom LLC ....F 210 372-3475
  Boerne *(G-2130)*
Palomar Modular Buildings LLC ....C 469 727-0727
  Desoto *(G-5438)*
Ramtech Building Systems Inc ....E 817 473-9376
  Mansfield *(G-14707)*
Requejo Construction Svcs LLC ....F 210 459-5161
  San Antonio *(G-18420)*
Rhodes Building Systems Inc ....E 979 596-1451
  Somerville *(G-19023)*
Speed-Fab-Crete Corp Intl ....C 817 572-0351
  Kennedale *(G-13503)*
Spur Industrial LLC ....E 817 293-1515
  Cresson *(G-3713)*

CONSTRUCTION: Commercial & Office Buildings, Prefabricated

Atomic Container Homes Inc ....E 915 433-4817
  El Paso *(G-5653)*

CONSTRUCTION: Concrete Patio

Moses Envmtl & Cnstr Svcs LLC ....E 806 418-8525
  Amarillo *(G-448)*
PSI Concrete Construction LLC ....F 210 204-1529
  San Antonio *(G-18400)*
Requejo Construction Svcs LLC ....F 210 459-5161
  San Antonio *(G-18420)*

CONSTRUCTION: Curb

Redco Endeavors Inc ....F 832 421-8549
  Gilmer *(G-7711)*

CONSTRUCTION: Dam

JD Abrams LP ....E 512 322-4000
  Austin *(G-1252)*
Zachry Consolidated LLC ....A 210 588-5000
  San Antonio *(G-18630)*
Zachry Construction & Mtls Inc ....D 210 479-1027
  San Antonio *(G-18631)*

CONSTRUCTION: Dams, Waterways, Docks & Other Marine

American Fincl Mktg Group Inc ....F 866 679-9241
  League City *(G-13945)*
Amphion Inc ....F 210 771-8116
  San Antonio *(G-17906)*

Cox Tank Construction Co Inc..............E...... 361 528-3524
Taft (G-19640)
Mpact Strategic Consulting LLC ....E...... 866 361-7611
Houston (G-10929)

CONSTRUCTION: Dock

Spillar Welding Inc.................................E...... 512 264-0351
Spicewood (G-19095)

CONSTRUCTION: Drainage System

Construct Capital LLC..........................C...... 214 637-1444
Arlington (G-645)
Construct Capital LLC..........................D...... 713 322-6714
Houston (G-9278)
Construct Capital LLC..........................D...... 210 654-4400
San Antonio (G-18024)

CONSTRUCTION: Electric Power Line

Cotton Utility Constructors...................F...... 281 659-5707
Shepherd (G-18901)
Farm & Ranch Construction LLC ....E...... 254 364-2226
Iredell (G-12921)

CONSTRUCTION: Factory

Iacx Energy LLC....................................F...... 972 960-3210
Dallas (G-4483)

CONSTRUCTION: Food Prdts Manufacturing or Packing Plant

Cnc Fabrication and Maint....................F...... 817 295-9055
Burleson (G-2575)
Hilltop Texas Inc...................................E...... 214 430-1311
Allen (G-275)

CONSTRUCTION: Foundation & Retaining Wall

Construct Capital LLC..........................C...... 214 637-1444
Arlington (G-645)
Construct Capital LLC..........................D...... 713 322-6714
Houston (G-9278)
Construct Capital LLC..........................D...... 210 654-4400
San Antonio (G-18024)

CONSTRUCTION: Grain Elevator

M Hastey Construction Co Inc...............E...... 806 296-7444
Plainview (G-16760)

CONSTRUCTION: Heavy

International Energy Svcs LLC..............E...... 281 973-9462
Houston (G-10402)

CONSTRUCTION: Heavy Highway & Street

Baker & Company Cnstr LLC.................E...... 903 561-1763
Tyler (G-20056)
Berry Gp Inc..A...... 361 693-2100
Corpus Christi (G-3484)
Dunn Services Inc................................E...... 361 275-3952
Cuero (G-3760)
Gtl Supply Solutions LLC......................F...... 214 644-2402
Allen (G-271)
H & H Sign Co Inc.................................E...... 254 752-1801
Waco (G-20409)
Longhorn Services Inc..........................E...... 956 655-2360
Edinburg (G-5593)
Merrell Lease Service Inc......................D...... 361 643-6911
Gregory (G-8101)
Outdoor Lighting Services LP ....C...... 713 690-6301
Houston (G-11204)
PSI Concrete Construction LLC ....F...... 210 204-1529
San Antonio (G-18400)
Raydon Inc...E...... 254 559-5012
Breckenridge (G-2235)
South Texas Oil Field Maint..................E...... 361 526-2822
Refugio (G-17248)
Vernor Material & Eqp Co Inc................D...... 409 233-3366
Freeport (G-7221)
W P Murphy Inc....................................F...... 210 658-4947
Schertz (G-18769)

CONSTRUCTION: Indl Building & Warehouse

Bgi Enterprise Inc................................E...... 409 833-0303
Beaumont (G-1865)
Cains Welding Service Inc.....................E...... 281 303-9517
Mont Belvieu (G-15616)

Centex Corporation..............................C...... 214 981-5000
Dallas (G-4097)
Climax Investors LLC............................E...... 832 582-9622
Dallas (G-4130)
Fasterra Group LP................................C...... 940 240-5800
Argyle (G-600)
Hydril USA Distribution LLC..................F...... 832 295-5557
Houston (G-10301)
Lauren Engineers & Constrs Inc...........E...... 469 417-7600
Irving (G-13083)
Marlin Environmental Products.............F...... 214 493-9128
Richardson (G-17351)
Monolithic Constructors Inc..................E...... 972 483-7423
Italy (G-13214)
South Texas Oil Field Maint..................E...... 361 526-2822
Refugio (G-17248)
United Marine Enterprise Inc................D...... 409 833-0303
Beaumont (G-1965)

CONSTRUCTION: Indl Building, Prefabricated

Deer Park Cnstr Assoc Inc....................E...... 281 839-0020
Baytown (G-1815)
Modular Concepts Inc ....F...... 817 945-1667
Fort Worth (G-6845)
Platts Welding and Cnstr LLC ....F...... 972 333-5830
Denison (G-5345)

CONSTRUCTION: Indl Buildings, New, NEC

Berry Gp Inc..A...... 361 693-2100
Corpus Christi (G-3484)
Berry Holdings LP.................................A...... 361 693-2100
Corpus Christi (G-3485)
Big M Constructors Inc.........................E...... 281 469-9770
Houston (G-8883)
Delta Fabrication and Mch Inc...............D...... 903 645-3994
Daingerfield (G-3831)
Echo Maintenance LLC..........................C...... 409 724-0456
Port Arthur (G-17106)
Elite Specialty Welding LLC...................D...... 832 649-4251
Pasadena (G-16423)
Entech Technology Inc..........................E...... 972 542-0210
Dallas (G-4325)
Fisher Construction..............................E...... 432 332-7532
Odessa (G-16001)
Granchelli Construction LLC.................F...... 956 928-1122
McAllen (G-14867)
Holloman Corporation...........................E...... 281 878-2600
Houston (G-10194)
J M Davidson Inc..................................C...... 361 883-0983
Aransas Pass (G-592)
Process Industry Practices....................G...... 512 232-3041
Austin (G-1434)
Rhodes Building Systems Inc................E...... 979 596-1451
Somerville (G-19023)
T R W Modernfold Company Inc............F...... 214 357-2572
Lewisville (G-14096)

CONSTRUCTION: Indl Plant

Bgi Contractors Inc..............................C...... 409 833-0303
Port Arthur (G-17102)
Bgi Enterprise Inc................................E...... 409 833-0303
Beaumont (G-1865)
Conner Machine and Welding Inc ....C...... 806 274-2281
Borger (G-2171)
George Bros Fabrication Co Inc............F...... 432 563-3390
Odessa (G-16014)
Interstate Treating Inc.........................D...... 432 362-9291
Odessa (G-16034)
Trans-Tel Central Inc...........................F...... 405 447-5025
San Antonio (G-18561)
Tri-Construction Co Inc........................C...... 979 233-7211
Freeport (G-7217)

CONSTRUCTION: Indoor Athletic Court

Vibra-Whirl Sports Ltd..........................E...... 806 537-3526
Panhandle (G-16348)

CONSTRUCTION: Institutional Building

Aj Commercial Services Inc...................G...... 361 336-2113
Corpus Christi (G-3470)
Mpact Strategic Consulting LLC ....E...... 866 361-7611
Houston (G-10929)

CONSTRUCTION: Irrigation System

H & H Landscape Services LLC.............F...... 832 831-9133
Hockley (G-8346)

CONSTRUCTION: Land Preparation

Bayside Industrial Inc...........................E...... 832 632-2815
League City (G-13948)
Hill Country Land Improvement ....E...... 512 766-8122
Wimberley (G-20881)
Reclamation Contractors Texas ....E...... 903 895-4584
New London (G-15851)

CONSTRUCTION: Marine

Beacon Maritime Inc.............................A...... 409 670-1060
West Orange (G-20693)
Helix Enrgy Slutions Group Inc.............C...... 281 618-0400
Houston (G-10150)
J & S Contractors Inc...........................F...... 979 647-0040
Sweeny (G-19628)
Laredo Construction Inc.......................F...... 281 499-4333
Stafford (G-19345)
Russell Marine LLC..............................C...... 281 860-0011
Channelview (G-3034)
Subsea 7 (us) LLC................................C...... 713 430-1100
Houston (G-12086)

CONSTRUCTION: Mausoleum

Gifford Monument Works Inc.................F...... 972 544-6305
Wylie (G-20936)

CONSTRUCTION: Mine Loading & Discharging Station

Arnold Stone Inc..................................F...... 972 248-1953
Lewisville (G-14024)

CONSTRUCTION: Multi-Family Housing

JD Murchison Interests Inc....................E...... 972 931-0700
Plano (G-16898)

CONSTRUCTION: Multi-family Dwellings, New

Willbnks Fncl Cnslting Group L ....F...... 469 444-0170
Dallas (G-3860)

CONSTRUCTION: Natural Gas Compressor Station

Sancus Energy and Power LLC..............E...... 832 460-1000
Houston (G-11744)

CONSTRUCTION: Nonresidential Buildings, Custom

JM Construction...................................E...... 956 518-2113
Brownsville (G-2370)

CONSTRUCTION: Oil & Gas Line & Compressor Station

Schwob Energy Services LLC ....D...... 469 917-9023
Dallas (G-4941)

CONSTRUCTION: Oil & Gas Pipeline Construction

Allegiant Industrial LLC........................E...... 409 782-7963
Beaumont (G-1849)
Charger Services LLC ....E...... 432 218-7674
Midland (G-15158)
Flint Energy Services Inc......................C...... 361 449-2405
George West (G-7624)
George Bartee Cnstr Co Inc..................E...... 936 687-4811
Grapeland (G-8005)
Holloman Corporation...........................E...... 281 878-2600
Houston (G-10194)
J Rollins Construction Inc......................D...... 936 253-3485
Dayton (G-5231)
JF Construction Inc..............................E...... 214 272-1902
Frisco (G-7293)
Lons Welding.......................................E...... 806 435-2278
Perryton (G-16639)
Merrell Lease Service Inc......................D...... 361 643-6911
Gregory (G-8101)
Midway Oilfield Constrs Inc..................B...... 936 348-3721
Midway (G-15499)
Palmetto Services LLC ....D...... 903 655-0900
Henderson (G-8269)
Partners Specialties Inc ....E...... 281 922-9102
Houston (G-11251)

Petroplex Pipe & Cnstr Inc .... D 432 697-4540
  Midland (G-15350)
Raybar Services LLC .... F 409 698-2548
  Brookeland (G-2308)
Tennessee Pipeline Cnstr Inc .... C 361 364-2703
  Sinton (G-18966)
Venables Construction Inc .... C 806 381-2121
  Amarillo (G-520)

CONSTRUCTION: Parking Lot

Nova Construction Co Inc .... E 972 869-3041
  Carrollton (G-2785)

CONSTRUCTION: Pharmaceutical Manufacturing Plant

Innova Supply Inc .... E 713 473-3345
  Pasadena (G-16459)

CONSTRUCTION: Pipeline, NEC

C&S Lease Service LC .... E 903 988-8642
  Kilgore (G-13534)
Dyna Torque Technologies Inc .... F 713 937-6699
  Houston (G-9543)
Insituform Technologies Inc .... F 636 530-8020
  Houston (G-10378)
Ipr Industrial LLC .... E 281 362-1131
  The Woodlands (G-19885)
McDermott International Inc .... B 281 588-6600
  Houston (G-10810)
Pumpco Inc .... C 979 542-9054
  Giddings (G-7700)
Zachry Consolidated LLC .... A 210 588-5000
  San Antonio (G-18630)
Zachry Construction & Mtls Inc .... D 210 479-1027
  San Antonio (G-18631)

CONSTRUCTION: Power & Communication Transmission Tower

Trans-Tel Central Inc .... F 405 447-5025
  San Antonio (G-18561)

CONSTRUCTION: Power Plant

Evolve Holdings Inc .... E 832 375-0099
  Houston (G-9720)
Halliburton Company .... C 817 783-5111
  Alvarado (G-333)
Halliburton Company .... E 432 571-8600
  Odessa (G-16024)
Halliburton Delaware Inc .... D 713 759-2600
  Houston (G-10108)
Industrial Cmmssning Cons Intl .... F 833 873-4224
  La Marque (G-13708)
Quaint Slutions Trdg Ltd Lblty .... F 832 758-3074
  Rosenberg (G-17597)
Viceroy Inc .... E 713 475-4518
  Pasadena (G-16524)
Wartsila North America Inc .... C 281 233-6200
  Houston (G-12600)

CONSTRUCTION: Railroad & Subway

Ardent Mills LLC .... D 817 847-3400
  Saginaw (G-17737)
Ctc Inc .... E 817 886-8210
  Fort Worth (G-6564)

CONSTRUCTION: Railway Roadbed

Winkel & Son Inc .... E 903 928-2560
  Tennessee Colony (G-19727)

CONSTRUCTION: Refineries

Chemex Modular LLC .... D 801 565-8099
  New Waverly (G-15856)
Fife Services Inc .... E 432 827-3601
  Goldsmith (G-7742)
International Plant Svcs LLC .... B 281 867-8400
  La Porte (G-13755)
Keppel Amfels Inc .... A 956 838-3110
  Brownsville (G-2374)
Shortes Inc .... E 940 658-3576
  Knox City (G-13665)
Spur Industrial LLC .... E 817 293-1515
  Cresson (G-3713)
Trey Industries Inc .... C 409 948-8891
  Texas City (G-19804)

CONSTRUCTION: Residential, Nec

Assocted Bldrs Cntrs Grter Hst .... F 713 523-6222
  Houston (G-8727)
Atlas Building Systems Inc .... F 903 597-4211
  Tyler (G-20052)
Atlas Building Systems Inc .... E 903 865-1153
  Wills Point (G-20873)
C Bar Contractors I Ltd .... F 409 925-5757
  Hitchcock (G-8334)
Centex Corporation .... C 214 981-5000
  Dallas (G-4097)
Climax Investors LLC .... E 832 582-9622
  Dallas (G-4130)
Fasterra Group LP .... C 940 240-5800
  Argyle (G-600)
Homestead Heritage .... E 254 754-9665
  Waco (G-20416)
Jahkur International LLC .... E 832 431-3232
  Houston (G-10450)
Regal Marble Co .... E 361 572-8498
  Victoria (G-20300)
Talon/Lpe Ltd .... F 806 372-6600
  Amarillo (G-465)
Tricounty Materials & Svcs LP .... E 972 446-1816
  Sanger (G-18731)

CONSTRUCTION: Restaurant

Willbnks Fncl Cnslting Group L .... F 469 444-0170
  Dallas (G-3860)

CONSTRUCTION: Retaining Wall

Materials Products Inc .... F 512 821-3303
  Austin (G-1329)
Pavestone LLC .... E 512 558-7283
  San Marcos (G-18703)

CONSTRUCTION: Roads, Gravel or Dirt

Farm & Ranch Construction LLC .... E 254 364-2226
  Iredell (G-12921)
Streamline Energy Services LLC .... F 361 852-0907
  Corpus Christi (G-3630)

CONSTRUCTION: Sewer Line

AAA Pipe Cleaning Corporation .... E 281 476-5200
  La Porte (G-13715)
Raydon Inc .... E 254 559-5012
  Breckenridge (G-2235)

CONSTRUCTION: Sidewalk

Mpact Strategic Consulting LLC .... E 866 361-7611
  Houston (G-10929)

CONSTRUCTION: Single-Family Housing

A Sklar Company Inc .... E 361 573-5775
  Victoria (G-20233)
All Wood Custom Cabinets Inc .... F 940 686-2795
  Pilot Point (G-16721)
Apache Construction Inc .... F 903 839-2242
  Whitehouse (G-20725)
Argio Roofing & Cnstr Lllc .... F 956 434-6411
  Rio Hondo (G-17475)
Homestead Craftsmen LLC .... D 254 754-9600
  Waco (G-20414)
Hutto Holding Group Inc .... D 512 832-8746
  Hutto (G-12879)
Knife River Corp - South .... F 979 361-2900
  College Station (G-3191)
Knights Landscaping LLC .... F 972 971-4213
  Mesquite (G-15057)
Petersen Aluminum Corporation .... E 903 581-6228
  Tyler (G-20140)
Venus Marble Co Inc .... D 972 223-8008
  Desoto (G-5447)

CONSTRUCTION: Single-family Housing, New

Big Spring Cat Cnstr Inc .... F 432 394-4161
  Coahoma (G-3164)
Cabinets By Michael Inc .... F 817 485-1962
  Fort Worth (G-6485)
Doyles Construction & Mfg Inc .... F 940 549-5517
  Graham (G-7780)
JD Murchison Interests Inc .... E 972 931-0700
  Plano (G-16898)

Koehler Co .... E 830 303-6256
  Seguin (G-18848)
Langford Construction Inc .... F 817 478-0218
  Arlington (G-718)
Monolithic Constructors Inc .... E 972 483-7423
  Italy (G-13214)
Satterwhite Companies Inc .... D 903 663-1729
  Longview (G-14303)

CONSTRUCTION: Steel Buildings

Atomic Container Homes Inc .... E 915 433-4817
  El Paso (G-5653)
CK Kustoms Iron Works Inc .... F 281 850-6118
  Rockport (G-17529)
Graywolf Industrial Inc .... E 281 441-5400
  Humble (G-12771)
Houston Wifi C/Hston Cnstr Svc .... F 832 444-8300
  Spring (G-19131)
Jedco Building Systems Inc .... E 281 591-2860
  Houston (G-10462)
Joe Bush & Associates Inc .... F 512 238-0450
  Round Rock (G-17664)
Patriot Erectors LLC .... C 512 858-9100
  Dripping Springs (G-5511)
Patriot Parent LLC .... B 512 858-9100
  Dripping Springs (G-5512)

CONSTRUCTION: Street Sign Installation & Mntnce

Dallas Lite and Barricade Inc .... E 214 748-5791
  Dallas (G-4218)

CONSTRUCTION: Street Surfacing & Paving

Holmes Construction Co LP .... D 806 376-8629
  Amarillo (G-435)
Nova Construction Co Inc .... E 972 869-3041
  Carrollton (G-2785)
Thrasher Inc .... E 806 296-2609
  Plainview (G-16765)
Tropiscapes Inc .... E 281 371-2955
  Katy (G-13452)

CONSTRUCTION: Telephone & Communication Line

Cline Construction Inc .... E 432 267-6006
  Big Spring (G-2075)

CONSTRUCTION: Transmitting Tower, Telecommunication

Black Star Energy Services LLC .... E 432 272-3395
  Odessa (G-15936)
Royce Tower Service Inc .... F 409 684-1913
  Port Bolivar (G-17134)

CONSTRUCTION: Tunnel

BP Surface Solutions LLC .... D 325 387-3881
  San Angelo (G-17786)

CONSTRUCTION: Utility Line

Challenger Drilling Inc .... F 281 290-8335
  Tomball (G-19969)
D & L Quality Painting Inc .... E 281 458-3588
  Houston (G-9387)
Echo Maintenance LLC .... C 409 724-0456
  Port Arthur (G-17106)
Facilities Rehab Inc .... F 512 352-6035
  Taylor (G-19655)
Fisher Construction .... E 432 332-7532
  Odessa (G-16001)
Layne Christensen Company .... D 281 475-2600
  Spring (G-19226)
Shortes Inc .... E 940 658-3576
  Knox City (G-13665)

CONSTRUCTION: Warehouse

EMLS Incorporated .... C 940 566-9500
  Denton (G-5364)

CONSTRUCTION: Waste Water & Sewage Treatment Plant

Gracon Construction Inc .... D 972 222-8533
  Mesquite (G-15046)

PRODUCT

L F Manufacturing Inc.................................D 979 542-8027
Giddings **(G-7699)**

Lakeside Trailer Sales............................F 936 564-6252
Nacogdoches **(G-15701)**

Lower Colorado River Authority..................A 512 473-3200
Austin **(G-1305)**

CONSTRUCTION: Water & Sewer Line

Dfw Infrastructure Inc...............................F 888 739-9070
Alvarado **(G-328)**

CONSULTING SVC: Actuarial

AA Flood Masters LLC ....E 409 796-2620
Beaumont **(G-1847)**

United Casing Incorporated......................E 432 682-0110
Midland **(G-15455)**

CONSULTING SVC: Business, NEC

1 Play Away LLC ....E 972 532-6226
Desoto **(G-5426)**

Arcanum Corp..F 214 507-3433
Carrollton **(G-2857)**

Bentley Consultants Co Inc ....F 972 289-2750
Mesquite **(G-15032)**

Blackbaud Inc..F 512 652-7969
Austin **(G-995)**

Chemical Data LLC..................................F 713 683-3900
Houston **(G-9170)**

E-M Design Time Inc................................F 972 279-4720
Dallas **(G-4287)**

Ejr Consulting Services Inc ....F 432 634-2905
Odessa **(G-15986)**

Endeavor Energy Resources LP ....E 432 687-1575
Midland **(G-15210)**

Excelente Inc...E 855 209-1970
Plano **(G-16867)**

Frontera Resources Corporation ....F 713 585-3200
Houston **(G-9868)**

Global Shop Solutions Inc ....D 281 681-1959
The Woodlands **(G-19868)**

Gps International LLC ....F 832 319-1730
The Woodlands **(G-19870)**

Grace Shursen Moore Assoc Inc...........G 806 358-6894
Amarillo **(G-429)**

Hart Energy Publishing LLC ....D 713 993-9320
Houston **(G-10130)**

Hewlett-Packard Company......................D 979 691-4540
College Station **(G-3186)**

Houston R-Co Incorporated....................F 281 987-9909
Houston **(G-10248)**

Intertek Cnslting Trning USA I ....E 337 235-4493
Spring **(G-19219)**

Jarvantech Inc...F 832 742-7220
The Woodlands **(G-19888)**

Jwb Consulting Service Inc ....F 817 675-6419
Midland **(G-15263)**

Manufctring Oprations MGT Intl..........F 682 521-5800
Hurst **(G-12851)**

Micro-Tes Inc..F 210 558-4757
San Antonio **(G-18300)**

Millennium Exploration Co LLC..............F 210 960-1000
San Antonio **(G-18307)**

Mpact Strategic Consulting LLC ....E 866 361-7611
Houston **(G-10929)**

Pan Continental Resources ....E 281 291-8100
Seabrook **(G-18788)**

Quacito LLC...F 210 695-0795
San Antonio **(G-18404)**

Rational Systems LLC ....E 832 476-8468
Houston **(G-11552)**

Red Willow Offshore LLC.........................D 281 822-7500
Houston **(G-11571)**

Tallannquest LLC.....................................G 972 423-8455
Plano **(G-17020)**

Tim Yockey..F 281 252-6175
Magnolia **(G-14630)**

Titan Solutions..F 281 973-9653
Houston **(G-12298)**

Tray-Tec Inc...E 281 441-7314
Humble **(G-12805)**

Viceroy Inc..F 713 475-4518
Pasadena **(G-16524)**

CONSULTING SVC: Chemical

Honeywell International Inc ....F 979 778-4477
Bryan **(G-2478)**

CONSULTING SVC: Computer

Advent Global Solutions Inc ....F 281 970-3000
Houston **(G-8495)**

Allan Banks ....F 936 337-4020
Willis **(G-20841)**

Arcanum Corp..F 214 507-3433
Carrollton **(G-2857)**

Baxter Planning Systems Inc..................F 512 323-5959
Austin **(G-977)**

Beicip Inc..F 281 293-8550
Houston **(G-8852)**

Bresa Tech LLC..E 866 728-2889
Plano **(G-16811)**

Broadaxis Inc ....F 469 688-2272
Plano **(G-16814)**

Broadband Technology Corp....................E 806 698-0396
Lubbock **(G-14383)**

Carreker Corporation..............................C 800 486-1981
Dallas **(G-4086)**

Cgi Technologies Solutions Inc...............B 866 344-3221
Houston **(G-9150)**

Cityon Systems Inc ....E 972 519-1673
Plano **(G-16824)**

Compu-Data International LLC ....E 281 292-1333
Houston **(G-9263)**

Covey Software Systems Inc ....F 972 353-8716
Irving **(G-12982)**

Csi Techs Inc ....D 210 875-7978
San Antonio **(G-18033)**

Dell Inc ....A 800 289-3355
Round Rock **(G-17642)**

Espy Corporation ....E 512 261-1016
Austin **(G-861)**

Four Cornerstone Solutions LLC ....E 817 377-1144
Fort Worth **(G-6646)**

Infosys Limited ....D 214 306-2100
Richardson **(G-17332)**

Infosys Limited ....F 281 454-0300
Houston **(G-10359)**

Jones Lang Lasalle Ip Inc ....E 214 777-5100
Dallas **(G-4538)**

Linux Tech Inc ....F 972 907-0871
Dallas **(G-4596)**

Mindpower International Inc ....F 469 287-2735
Lewisville **(G-14068)**

Ntt Data Inc ....C 800 745-3263
Plano **(G-16948)**

Optimum Consultancy Svcs LLC ....F 713 505-0300
Houston **(G-11185)**

Oracle Corporation ....A 737 867-1000
Austin **(G-1391)**

Phillip E Mosley & Associates ....F 281 496-1249
Houston **(G-11322)**

Pwr Technologies LLC ....F 469 609-3537
Mesquite **(G-15073)**

Quadrabyte LLC ....E 469 619-0749
Austin **(G-1441)**

Royal Technocrats Inc ....E 713 776-8300
Houston **(G-11684)**

Veeder-Root Fuelquest LLC ....F 713 222-5700
Houston **(G-12544)**

Wincor Nixdorf Inc ....D 512 676-5000
Austin **(G-1672)**

CONSULTING SVC: Data Processing

Gresham Enterprise Storage Inc...........E 512 250-0916
Austin **(G-1194)**

Hov Services Inc ....E 248 837-7100
Irving **(G-13059)**

CONSULTING SVC: Educational

Allan Banks ....F 936 337-4020
Willis **(G-20841)**

Kamico Instructional Media Inc ....E 254 947-7283
Salado **(G-17765)**

CONSULTING SVC: Engineering

Acute Technological Svcs Inc ....D 713 983-9353
Houston **(G-8473)**

Airtrust Intl Systems Corp ....F 713 491-4455
Texas City **(G-19785)**

Bowlin Engineering Co............................F 817 232-2020
Saginaw **(G-17740)**

E-Spectrum Technologies Inc.................F 210 696-8848
San Antonio **(G-18080)**

Four Cornerstone Solutions LLC ....E 817 377-1144
Fort Worth **(G-6646)**

Gw Marine (usa) LLC ....E 281 809-6213
Houston **(G-10077)**

H J Gruy and Associates Inc ....F 713 739-1000
Bellaire **(G-1997)**

Heath Consultants Incorporated ....C 713 844-1300
Houston **(G-10146)**

Highrise Systems Inc ....E 817 927-8711
Fort Worth **(G-6697)**

Hp Inc ....B 512 432-8000
Austin **(G-1698)**

J Simmons Group Inc ....E 713 675-5100
Houston **(G-10443)**

Kalsi Engineering Incorporated.............E 281 240-6500
Sugar Land **(G-19501)**

Pacific Resources Intl LLC ....B 214 504-3853
McKinney **(G-14962)**

Partrac Geomarine Inc ....F 713 338-3495
Houston **(G-11252)**

Qa Support LP ....E 281 307-1000
La Porte **(G-13786)**

Quaint Slutions Trdg Ltd Lblty ....F 832 758-3074
Rosenberg **(G-17597)**

Ramin Corporation ....F 281 356-5178
Magnolia **(G-14623)**

Specialty Devices Incorporated ....F 972 429-7240
Wylie **(G-20951)**

Stress Engineering Svcs Inc ....E 713 466-1527
Houston **(G-12079)**

Stuckey Terry & Associates ....E 281 590-8628
Houston **(G-12083)**

Technical Automtn Svcs Co Ltd ....D 281 474-3232
Seabrook **(G-18792)**

Turbomasters Inc ....F 210 690-1958
San Antonio **(G-18572)**

Wood Group Usa Inc ....A 832 809-8000
Houston **(G-12687)**

CONSULTING SVC: Financial Management

Alvarez & Marsal Inc ....C 212 759-4433
Houston **(G-8575)**

Jollyrhino Inc...F 909 732-8507
Austin **(G-1260)**

Specktrum ....F 832 892-0863
Houston **(G-12004)**

CONSULTING SVC: Human Resource

Chequedcom Inc ....E 888 412-0699
Dallas **(G-4110)**

Fervid Group LLC ....F 713 364-3378
Houston **(G-9779)**

Tillman Learning LLC ....E 866 540-9677
Plano **(G-17033)**

CONSULTING SVC: Management

Bresa Tech LLC..E 866 728-2889
Plano **(G-16811)**

Broadaxis Inc ....F 469 688-2272
Plano **(G-16814)**

Broadband Technology Corp....................E 806 698-0396
Lubbock **(G-14383)**

C & K Management Co Inc ....F 713 774-7429
Houston **(G-9025)**

Carbo Ceramics Inc ....B 281 921-6400
Houston **(G-9091)**

Casteel & Associates Inc ....F 214 352-7446
Dallas **(G-4091)**

Chemtrusion Inc......................................D 713 675-1616
Houston **(G-9173)**

Cordova Corporation ....E 817 484-1100
Burleson **(G-2577)**

Eship Global Inc ....F 972 518-1775
Dallas **(G-3842)**

Hart Energy Publishing Lllp....................F 713 952-9500
Houston **(G-10131)**

Mentor IMC (usa) Inc..............................E 713 425-6307
Houston **(G-10829)**

Mpact Strategic Consulting LLC ....E 866 361-7611
Houston **(G-10929)**

Ods International Inc ....D 713 782-6767
Houston **(G-11133)**

Pritchett LP ....E 214 239-9600
Dallas **(G-4828)**

Sable Prmian Resources Fin LLC ....F 713 579-8000
Houston **(G-11720)**

Santech Industries LLC ....E 817 589-1212
Irving **(G-13172)**

Viceroy Inc..E 713 475-4518
Pasadena **(G-16524)**

Zeus Development Corp..............F......713 952-9500
Houston **(G-12728)**

Ziften Technologies Inc..............E......512 298-5501
Austin **(G-1686)**

CONSULTING SVC: Marketing Management

1 Play Away LLC..............E......972 532-6226
Desoto **(G-5426)**

Ambernet Technologies Inc..............F......972 707-4000
Dallas **(G-3936)**

Benton Oil Co..............F......806 763-5302
Lubbock **(G-14370)**

Candeo Interactive LLC..............F......214 394-8499
Forney **(G-6303)**

Client Connect LLC..............E......214 295-4940
Plano **(G-16826)**

Digital Marketer Labs LLC..............E......512 892-3022
Austin **(G-1093)**

Fource Communications Limited..............F......214 630-2125
Dallas **(G-4374)**

Hightech Grafix Inc..............G......817 616-3204
Fort Worth **(G-6699)**

Idea Planet LP..............E......972 380-9867
Dallas **(G-3844)**

La Luz Marketing Group Inc..............F......210 202-1800
San Antonio **(G-18234)**

M2w Inc..............D......972 407-1332
Mesquite **(G-15059)**

Revitalu International LLC..............F......469 270-5533
Plano **(G-16993)**

Shawdashian Group LLC..............E......832 649-3800
Houston **(G-11853)**

Tradesorg LLC..............E......512 729-3544
Austin **(G-1589)**

Yoolotto LLC..............E......469 383-6488
Dallas **(G-5208)**

CONSULTING SVC: Online Technology

B&B Worldwide Technology..............F......713 471-2387
Cibolo **(G-3062)**

Docresources LLC..............F......832 802-6008
Crosby **(G-3729)**

Eclectic Innvtive Slutions LLC..............F......737 999-1907
Dripping Springs **(G-5505)**

Houston Wifi C/Hston Cnstr Svc..............F......832 444-8300
Spring **(G-19131)**

Involta LLC..............F......817 937-8943
Dallas **(G-4511)**

Sun-Star Electric Inc..............D......806 793-2812
Lubbock **(G-14488)**

Tradesorg LLC..............E......512 729-3544
Austin **(G-1589)**

Virgin Fields LLC..............E......972 322-7902
Frisco **(G-7323)**

CONSULTING SVC: Personnel Management

Behavioral Science Res Press..............F......972 243-8543
Dallas **(G-4015)**

Human Resource Micro Systems..............F......415 362-8400
Irving **(G-13060)**

CONSULTING SVC: Telecommunications

Airtrust Intl Systems Corp..............F......713 491-4455
Texas City **(G-19785)**

B Comm Constructors LLC..............E......210 257-0102
San Antonio **(G-17929)**

BBS Telecom LC..............G......512 328-9500
Austin **(G-981)**

Digital I M..............F......281 855-4933
Houston **(G-9472)**

Pwr Technologies LLC..............F......469 609-3537
Mesquite **(G-15073)**

Sharco Technologies Inc..............F......512 258-0573
Pflugerville **(G-16688)**

Teleprime Advanced Communicati..............G......512 271-9503
Austin **(G-1561)**

Volks Resources LLC..............F......972 636-1880
Frisco **(G-7324)**

CONSULTING SVCS, BUSINESS: Economic

Perryman Group Inc..............E......254 751-9595
Waco **(G-20445)**

CONSULTING SVCS, BUSINESS: Energy Conservation

Broadband Technology Corp..............E......806 698-0396
Lubbock **(G-14383)**

Etech Envmtl Safety Solutions..............E......432 563-2200
Odessa **(G-15993)**

Everything Energy LLC..............E......713 537-3000
Houston **(G-9718)**

CONSULTING SVCS, BUSINESS: Environmental

Aquila Environmental LLC..............G......817 953-3171
Fort Worth **(G-6397)**

Banks Petroleum Inc..............E......512 478-0059
Austin **(G-974)**

Best Drilling Services (bds)..............E......713 864-3900
Houston **(G-8862)**

Clean Air Consultants Inc..............D......972 278-2664
Garland **(G-7458)**

Epcs Environmental LLC..............F......817 975-5790
Arlington **(G-672)**

Evans - Hamilton Inc..............E......281 448-6188
Houston **(G-9715)**

Evergreen Solutions Inc..............E......512 389-0625
Austin **(G-1141)**

Inframark LLC..............F......281 579-4500
Forney **(G-6309)**

Layne Christensen Company..............D......281 475-2600
Spring **(G-19226)**

Oiltek Systems LLC..............G......325 200-0423
Colorado City **(G-3225)**

Partrac Geomarine Inc..............F......713 338-3495
Houston **(G-11252)**

Rain Cii Carbon LLC..............E......281 318-2400
Kingwood **(G-13652)**

Talon/Lpe Ltd..............F......806 372-6600
Amarillo **(G-465)**

Talon/Lpe Ltd..............D......806 467-0607
Amarillo **(G-466)**

Talon/Lpe Ltd..............F......210 253-7200
San Antonio **(G-18521)**

Technip S&W International Inc..............E......281 870-1111
Houston **(G-12175)**

CONSULTING SVCS, BUSINESS: Indl Development Planning

Trinity Industrial Svcs LLC..............B......409 722-6700
Beaumont **(G-1964)**

CONSULTING SVCS, BUSINESS: Publishing

Downey Publishing Inc..............F......817 416-6661
Southlake **(G-19064)**

CONSULTING SVCS, BUSINESS: Safety Training Svcs

Nuclear Sources and Svcs Inc..............E......713 641-0391
Houston **(G-11096)**

Occupational Marketing Inc..............G......281 492-8250
Houston **(G-11119)**

CONSULTING SVCS, BUSINESS: Sys Engnrg, Exc Computer/Prof

Global Technical Solutions USA..............F......832 410-4488
Spring **(G-19126)**

Transmedia Dynamics Inc..............E......512 971-2313
Kyle **(G-13687)**

CONSULTING SVCS, BUSINESS: Systems Analysis & Engineering

Bresa Tech LLC..............E......866 728-2889
Plano **(G-16811)**

Four Cornerstone Solutions LLC..............E......817 377-1144
Fort Worth **(G-6646)**

Metapath Software Intl..............F......972 907-3600
Richardson **(G-17356)**

Superior Information Systems..............F......713 524-8998
Houston **(G-12116)**

CONSULTING SVCS, BUSINESS: Test Development & Evaluation

Intercorr International Inc..............E......281 444-2282
Houston **(G-10393)**

Osteogenics Biomedical Inc..............F......806 796-1923
Lubbock **(G-14455)**

CONSULTING SVCS, BUSINESS: Traffic

Buyers Barricades Houston LLC..............E......817 535-3939
Grapevine **(G-8017)**

CONSULTING SVCS: Geological

Exploration Center Building..............E......806 353-9123
Amarillo **(G-487)**

Partrac Geomarine Inc..............F......713 338-3495
Houston **(G-11252)**

Pason Systems USA Corp..............D......713 693-8700
Houston **(G-11256)**

CONSULTING SVCS: Geophysical

Cgg Marine (us) Inc..............F......713 369-5600
Houston **(G-9148)**

E & E Polaris Services Inc..............G......281 367-6000
Spring **(G-19209)**

Gw Marine (usa) LLC..............E......281 809-6213
Houston **(G-10077)**

Shearwater Geoservices Inc..............F......281 921-8000
Houston **(G-11855)**

CONSULTING SVCS: Oil

Accessesp LLC..............E......713 589-2599
Stafford **(G-19281)**

Allstream Envmtl Svcs LLC..............F......713 408-7237
San Antonio **(G-17899)**

Astrimar Consultants LLC..............E......281 994-7816
Houston **(G-8729)**

Astrimar Consultants LLC..............E......281 994-7816
Houston **(G-8730)**

Banks Petroleum Inc..............E......512 478-0059
Austin **(G-974)**

Barnett Gathering LLC..............F......817 870-2800
Fort Worth **(G-6427)**

Bc Johnson Assoc LLC..............G......281 489-4894
Houston **(G-8841)**

Blackstar Envmtl Indus Svcs LL..............F......713 280-0590
Houston **(G-8911)**

Camac International Corp..............E......713 965-5100
Houston **(G-9059)**

Cavern Solutions Inc..............F......713 393-7733
Houston **(G-9103)**

Cnooc Marketing USA Inc..............D......713 380-4800
Houston **(G-9221)**

Compliance Group Inc..............F......936 447-6100
Montgomery **(G-15628)**

Dan Blocker Petroleum Cons..............D......903 234-2093
Longview **(G-14222)**

Deepwater Subsea LLC..............E......832 356-6781
Katy **(G-13359)**

Delta Marine Technologies..............E......936 582-7237
Montgomery **(G-15631)**

Dixon Services Inc..............F......903 579-9300
Tyler **(G-20077)**

Edge Integrity Services LLC..............G......817 585-1007
Fort Worth **(G-6605)**

Elite Upstream LLC..............F......832 674-3050
Houston **(G-9603)**

Energy Operators Inc..............C......281 351-1780
Tomball **(G-19976)**

Energy Solutions Inc..............E......281 257-2994
Tomball **(G-19977)**

Extech Consulting LLC..............E......940 613-6461
Henrietta **(G-8280)**

G E Oil Technology Inc..............E......713 774-0340
Houston **(G-9886)**

Grace Shursen Moore Assoc Inc..............G......806 358-6894
Amarillo **(G-429)**

Gw Marine (usa) LLC..............E......281 809-6213
Houston **(G-10077)**

Hilliard Energy Inc..............E......432 683-9100
Midland **(G-15247)**

Houston Business & Fincl Svcs..............F......713 398-6314
Houston **(G-10218)**

J Connor Consulting Inc..............E......281 578-3388
Houston **(G-10436)**

Jeffcoat Production Service..............F......409 429-5900
Spurger **(G-19278)**

Jwb Consulting Service Inc..............E......817 675-6419
Midland **(G-15263)**

Kizer Energy Inc..............E......281 712-2047
Houston **(G-10539)**

Mexssub International Inc..............C......713 278-2175
Houston **(G-10861)**

Nova Consulting..............F......281 445-6393
Houston **(G-11088)**

PRODUCT

O M C International LLC ....E 281 398-4281
Houston *(G-11106)*

Octane Energy Consulting LLC ....F 432 685-7736
Midland *(G-15324)*

Onward LLC ....F 281 535-2739
Kemah *(G-13478)*

Opportune LP ....D 713 772-0664
Houston *(G-11184)*

Partrac Geomarine Inc ....F 713 338-3495
Houston *(G-11252)*

Petroleum Financial Inc ....E 817 339-1075
Fort Worth *(G-6904)*

Phillip E Mosley & Associates ....F 281 496-1249
Houston *(G-11322)*

Proptester Incorporated ....F 281 256-8880
Cypress *(G-3815)*

QO Inc ....F 713 224-7823
Houston *(G-11485)*

Randall & Dewey Jefferis ....D 281 774-2000
Houston *(G-11542)*

Reserve Analysts Assoc Inc ....F 281 438-3000
Missouri City *(G-15588)*

S R Hill and Assoc Intl Inc ....F 713 960-6617
Houston *(G-11713)*

Scotia Group Inc ....F 281 448-6188
Houston *(G-11790)*

Smith Services Red Baron ....F 361 396-0521
Alice *(G-235)*

Step Energy Svcs Holdings Ltd ....F 918 423-4300
San Antonio *(G-18501)*

Summa Group LLC ....G 713 524-2768
Pasadena *(G-16514)*

Talon/Lpe Ltd ....F 806 372-6600
Amarillo *(G-465)*

Tetra Production Tstg Svcs LLC ....B 281 367-1983
The Woodlands *(G-19927)*

Thurmond-Mcglothlin LLC ....G 806 665-5700
Pampa *(G-16341)*

Trinity Envmtl Ctarina Swd LLC ....E 512 524-7281
Austin *(G-1595)*

Upstream International LLC ....B 281 265-0033
Sugar Land *(G-19570)*

Volks Resources LLC ....F 972 636-1880
Frisco *(G-7324)*

Wells Family Holding Co LLC ....E 903 756-5656
Linden *(G-14137)*

Wood Group Management Svcs Inc ....E 281 828-3500
Houston *(G-12685)*

CONSULTING SVCS: Scientific

SOS Environmental Inc ....F 281 723-8282
Spring *(G-19251)*

CONSUMER PURCHASING SVCS

Be-Technologies Ltd ....F 972 242-1853
Carrollton *(G-2704)*

CONTACT LENSES

Alcon Vision LLC ....D 817 293-0450
Fort Worth *(G-6368)*

Ciba Vision Corporation ....A 817 551-6881
Fort Worth *(G-6517)*

Ciba Vision Inc ....A 847 294-3000
Fort Worth *(G-6518)*

Metro Optics of Austin Inc ....E 512 251-2386
Pflugerville *(G-16680)*

Tru-Form Optics Inc ....E 817 267-9261
Bedford *(G-1980)*

CONTAINERS, GLASS: Food

Jarden LLC ....C 903 455-0691
Greenville *(G-8078)*

CONTAINERS: Air Cargo, Metal

GP Terminals LLC ....F 713 209-7780
Galena Park *(G-7380)*

John Bean Technologies Corp ....C 713 875-3735
Houston *(G-10480)*

CONTAINERS: Cargo, Wood

Apache Products Inc ....D 409 385-7021
Silsbee *(G-18949)*

Superior Pllet Wichita FLS Ltd ....F 940 569-5244
Burkburnett *(G-2564)*

CONTAINERS: Cargo, Wood & Metal Combination

Intermdal Repr Mdfcation Trckg ....F 713 674-2179
Houston *(G-10396)*

Keal Cases Incorporated ....E 512 244-9100
Round Rock *(G-17665)*

CONTAINERS: Corrugated

101 Products LLC ....F 832 247-7979
Houston *(G-8400)*

Corrugated Services Garland ....G 972 494-4059
Garland *(G-7465)*

Edi Weyerhaeuser McAllen ....G 956 682-9406
McAllen *(G-14855)*

Green Bay Packaging Inc ....G 915 822-9700
El Paso *(G-5791)*

International Paper Company ....C 972 641-2972
Grand Prairie *(G-7896)*

Menasha Packaging Company LLC ....E 330 419-3505
Lewisville *(G-14064)*

Packaging Corporation America ....C 254 776-2360
Waco *(G-20441)*

Packaging Corporation America ....D 469 568-7000
Carrollton *(G-2789)*

Perennial Design LLC ....F 512 387-1582
Austin *(G-1410)*

Smurfit Kappa North Amer LLC ....E 713 869-5900
Houston *(G-11926)*

CONTAINERS: Food & Beverage

Ball Corporation ....C 817 551-3100
Fort Worth *(G-6424)*

CONTAINERS: Food, Wood Wirebound

Industrial Lumber and Box Inc ....F 713 928-2096
Houston *(G-10351)*

CONTAINERS: Frozen Food & Ice Cream

Various Fields LLC ....F 512 788-2228
Austin *(G-1624)*

CONTAINERS: Glass

Owens-Brockway Glass Cont Inc ....E 956 717-4200
Laredo *(G-13917)*

Owens-Brockway Glass Cont Inc ....E 956 717-4200
Plano *(G-16961)*

CONTAINERS: Ice Cream, Made From Purchased Materials

Huhtamaki Inc ....B 903 427-5711
Clarksville *(G-3073)*

CONTAINERS: Laminated Phenolic & Vulcanized Fiber

Transcom Packaging Inc ....F 979 885-1800
Sealy *(G-18821)*

CONTAINERS: Liquid Tight Fiber, From Purchased Materials

Equipment Storage Service Inc ....F 214 374-3995
Dallas *(G-4329)*

CONTAINERS: Metal

Hoover Group Inc ....E 800 844-8683
Houston *(G-10204)*

Keal Cases Incorporated ....E 512 244-9100
Round Rock *(G-17665)*

Mobile Mini Inc ....D 480 894-6311
Houston *(G-10900)*

Modern AG Products LLC ....E 281 470-1903
La Porte *(G-13778)*

Schmidt Manufacturing Inc ....F 281 431-0581
Bellaire *(G-2002)*

Self Industries ....E 713 672-2559
Houston *(G-11824)*

Westrock Cp LLC ....D 281 830-0131
Houston *(G-12657)*

Weyerhaeuser Company ....C 972 641-3891
Grand Prairie *(G-7992)*

CONTAINERS: Plastic

Altium Packaging ....F 281 391-4244
Katy *(G-13349)*

Altium Packaging ....E 817 491-9229
Fort Worth *(G-6375)*

Altium Packaging ....G 214 333-4179
Dallas *(G-3934)*

Altium Packaging ....E 903 870-7080
Sherman *(G-18905)*

Altium Packaging LP ....C 678 742-4600
Houston *(G-8569)*

Amcor Rigid Packaging Usa LLC .....D 817 267-5917
Fort Worth *(G-6377)*

Bayland Inc ....F 281 489-1930
Manvel *(G-14732)*

Berry Global Inc ....C 361 575-9565
Victoria *(G-20246)*

Berry Global Films LLC ....C 972 576-8193
Waxahachie *(G-20529)*

CKS Packaging Inc ....C 817 924-2205
Fort Worth *(G-6521)*

CKS Packaging Inc ....C 214 358-2441
Dallas *(G-4125)*

Clarion Tech Lonestar Inc ....D 972 278-9700
Garland *(G-7457)*

Consolidated Containment LLC ....E 409 781-4254
Beaumont *(G-1876)*

Core Pacific Inc ....E 800 860-1637
Houston *(G-9318)*

Detroit Forming Inc ....E 903 832-4653
Nash *(G-15721)*

Enduro Composites Inc ....D 713 358-4000
Houston *(G-9630)*

Epak International Inc ....A 512 231-8083
Austin *(G-1128)*

Gajeske Inc ....F 972 314-8100
Grand Prairie *(G-7881)*

Genpak LLC ....C 903 693-7151
Carthage *(G-2908)*

Graham Packaging Company LP ......C 713 869-5471
Houston *(G-10013)*

Helmy Associates & Co Inc ....E 210 681-0101
San Antonio *(G-18164)*

Hoover Group Inc ....E 800 844-8683
Houston *(G-10204)*

Hoover Mtls Hdlg Group Inc ....D 800 844-8683
Houston *(G-10205)*

Iris Usa Inc ....E 972 329-0400
Mesquite *(G-15053)*

Mighty Molding & Mfg ....F 254 629-2525
Eastland *(G-5567)*

Momentum Plastics LLC ....C 713 678-7741
Houston *(G-10909)*

Nan Ya Plastics Corp USA ....D 713 674-7822
Houston *(G-10962)*

Numo Manufacturing Inc ....C 800 253-0434
Kaufman *(G-13463)*

P-Mcom Incorporated ....F 866 310-2556
Fort Worth *(G-6888)*

Reef Industries Inc ....D 713 507-4329
Houston *(G-11578)*

Rodeo Plastic Bag & Film LLC ....D 972 216-3331
Mesquite *(G-15075)*

Silgan Plastics of Texas ....F 713 242-0923
Houston *(G-11896)*

Spears Manufacturing Co ....E 469 528-3000
Flower Mound *(G-6282)*

Tekni-Plex Inc ....C 214 337-4711
Dallas *(G-5048)*

Tsi Products Inc ....E 817 649-2626
Arlington *(G-806)*

West Texas Drum Company Ltd II ....E 281 383-1901
Baytown *(G-1805)*

CONTAINERS: Plywood & Veneer, Wood

Age Industries Ltd ....D 210 659-1301
Cibolo *(G-3060)*

CONTAINERS: Sanitary, Food

MANS Distributors Inc ....F 972 930-0330
Carrollton *(G-2777)*

Smith Tank & Equipment Company ......E 903 597-5541
Tyler *(G-20153)*

Tetra Pak Materials LP ....C 940 565-8800
Denton *(G-5405)*

CONTAINERS: Shipping, Bombs, Metal Plate

FR Global Trading Co Inc ....E 214 281-8668
Dallas *(G-4376)*

CONTAINERS: Wood

Age Industries Ltd ....E 956 399-8279
San Benito *(G-18654)*

Bell Wooden Products Inc ....E 214 388-5421
Dallas *(G-4016)*

Cargo Crating Company Ltd ....F 713 699-0172
Houston *(G-9092)*

Conner Industries Inc ....E 817 439-3555
Fort Worth *(G-6541)*

Keal Cases Incorporated ....E 512 244-9100
Round Rock *(G-17665)*

Leonard Ray Vaught ....E 903 572-0352
Cookville *(G-3405)*

Pallet & Crating Co Inc ....E 903 463-5786
Denison *(G-5344)*

Ufp Dallas LLC ....E 817 825-6512
Dallas *(G-5127)*

W T Harris Company Inc ....E 325 646-7521
Brownwood *(G-2448)*

Western Industries Corporation ....D 214 503-8322
Carrollton *(G-2848)*

CONTAINMENT VESSELS: Reactor, Metal Plate

Hexa Containment LLC ....E 713 360-9221
Nederland *(G-15754)*

Robbins & Myers Inc ....E 936 890-1064
Willis *(G-20861)*

CONTRACT FOOD SVCS

Champion Food Service 2 Inc ....F 210 736-2190
Von Ormy *(G-20346)*

CONTRACTOR: Dredging

Johnny Baulch ....F 409 938-8971
Hitchcock *(G-8338)*

US Lbm Holdings LLC ....C 713 650-6200
Houston *(G-12485)*

CONTRACTOR: Rigging & Scaffolding

Blaze Equipment LLC ....F 817 439-0453
Lake Worth *(G-13812)*

Crocker Crane Rentals LP ....E 512 258-1323
Leander *(G-13985)*

Prodektive Specialty Svcs LLC ....E 713 425-3075
Houston *(G-11436)*

CONTRACTORS: Access Control System Eqpt

Associated Time Instrs Co Inc ....E 214 637-2763
Dallas *(G-3975)*

Dsx Access Systems Inc ....E 214 553-6140
Dallas *(G-4282)*

Hid Global Corporation ....C 800 237-7769
Austin *(G-1202)*

Meyer-Smith Inc ....F 713 862-7339
Houston *(G-10862)*

Quality Access Control Systems ....F 830 981-5400
Boerne *(G-2133)*

CONTRACTORS: Acoustical & Insulation Work

Kenmark Architectural Pdts Inc ....F 800 788-8263
Dallas *(G-4550)*

Protective Concepts Inc ....F 832 843-7619
Cypress *(G-3816)*

CONTRACTORS: Antenna Installation

Alpha Satcom Inc ....F 903 238-8888
Longview *(G-14193)*

Commscope Technologies LLC ....A 214 634-8502
Dallas *(G-4149)*

Talon/Lpe Ltd ....F 210 253-7200
San Antonio *(G-18521)*

CONTRACTORS: Asphalt

David L Jennings ....D 281 778-3223
Missouri City *(G-15579)*

Longview Asphalt Inc ....G 903 758-4428
Longview *(G-14267)*

CONTRACTORS: Awning Installation

Chism Company ....F 210 824-6315
San Antonio *(G-18004)*

CONTRACTORS: Blasting, Exc Building Demolition

Brock Enterprises LLC ....E 409 729-6353
Nederland *(G-15747)*

Kellogg Brown & Root Intl Inc ....F 713 753-2000
Houston *(G-10512)*

Riley Industrial Services Inc ....E 432 332-9630
Odessa *(G-16141)*

CONTRACTORS: Boiler & Furnace

Furnace Systems Inc ....F 972 423-7800
Plano *(G-16875)*

CONTRACTORS: Boiler Maintenance Contractor

Triple S Manufacturing Company ....F 817 281-0602
Fort Worth *(G-7079)*

CONTRACTORS: Boring, Building Construction

Clean Hrbors Explrtion Svcs In ....F 281 478-2600
Deer Park *(G-5264)*

CONTRACTORS: Building Eqpt & Machinery Installation

Assa Abloy Entrance Systems US ....F 713 934-9095
Houston *(G-8725)*

Bandana Installation LP ....E 903 764-2933
Elkhart *(G-6058)*

Brush Mechanical Inc ....F 713 937-9027
Jersey Village *(G-13294)*

Forge Tech Inc ....G 888 854-8414
Kemah *(G-13474)*

Freer Iron Works Inc ....E 361 394-7273
Freer *(G-7225)*

Hep Mechanical Services LLC ....F 903 278-6826
Queen City *(G-17221)*

Jayco Steel Services Inc ....E 281 399-0189
New Caney *(G-15842)*

Ledsome Machine & Welding Co ....F 325 646-4691
Brownwood *(G-2434)*

Multitech Group Inc ....F 817 496-5500
Arlington *(G-734)*

Otis Elevator Company ....F 214 741-6207
Dallas *(G-4772)*

Unique Stainless Designs LLC ....F 972 254-8424
Grand Prairie *(G-7990)*

CONTRACTORS: Building Fireproofing

Brock Services LLC ....C 281 807-8200
Houston *(G-8991)*

D & L Quality Painting Inc ....E 281 458-3588
Houston *(G-9387)*

CONTRACTORS: Building Front Installation, Metal

Floyd Tate A ....F 409 745-3256
Orange *(G-16243)*

Houston Tsm Inc ....E 713 691-5271
Houston *(G-10260)*

Richard Phillips Inc ....E 972 264-5315
Grand Prairie *(G-7966)*

CONTRACTORS: Building Sign Installation & Mntnce

AAA Electrical Signs ....F 956 464-3221
Donna *(G-5486)*

Accent Graphics Inc ....E 972 399-0333
Grand Prairie *(G-7820)*

Accent Sign & Awning Co LLC ....F 713 780-1151
Houston *(G-8455)*

Badmoon Enterprises LLC ....E 817 548-0561
Arlington *(G-629)*

Baker Macy Edward ....F 817 572-7346
Fort Worth *(G-6420)*

Budget Signs Ltd ....E 210 349-7446
San Antonio *(G-17971)*

Comet Signs LLC ....C 210 341-7244
San Antonio *(G-18021)*

Comet Signs LLC ....E 281 492-6581
Houston *(G-9247)*

Creative Signworks Inc ....E 850 785-8899
San Angelo *(G-17792)*

Dallas Lite and Barricade Inc ....E 214 748-5791
Dallas *(G-4218)*

Gem Sign Service Inc ....F 830 609-1052
New Braunfels *(G-15794)*

Gulf Coast Sign Inc ....E 956 399-0755
San Benito *(G-18658)*

H & H Sign Co Inc ....E 254 752-1801
Waco *(G-20409)*

Hoarel Sign Co ....F 806 373-2175
Amarillo *(G-434)*

Iconic Sign Group LLC ....F 361 883-7446
Corpus Christi *(G-3552)*

Identity Solutions Inc ....E 972 926-0929
Garland *(G-7515)*

Jackson Sign and Lighting Inc ....G 254 751-0390
Woodway *(G-20921)*

Liberty Signs Inc ....E 512 255-3887
Round Rock *(G-17669)*

Mighty Works Signage LLC ....G 713 305-8355
Houston *(G-10877)*

Neon Signs and Designs Inc ....F 903 463-7446
Denison *(G-5343)*

Pdn Ssl LLC ....E 915 629-9100
El Paso *(G-5906)*

Richard Phillips Inc ....E 972 264-5315
Grand Prairie *(G-7966)*

Sign Technologies Inc ....F 903 838-8999
Texarkana *(G-19773)*

Sparkle Lighting Services ....E 713 856-8500
Houston *(G-11992)*

State Sign Corporation ....D 713 943-1831
Houston *(G-12051)*

Third Coast Services LLC ....D 832 934-0240
Magnolia *(G-14629)*

Vmc Signs Inc ....F 361 575-0548
Victoria *(G-20317)*

Willow Creek Signs Inc ....E 817 847-0571
Saginaw *(G-17760)*

CONTRACTORS: Building Site Preparation

Big 4 Inc ....E 409 787-2733
Hemphill *(G-8245)*

Superior Welding Inc ....E 432 523-2038
Andrews *(G-559)*

CONTRACTORS: Cable Laying

Csi Techs Inc ....D 210 875-7978
San Antonio *(G-18033)*

CONTRACTORS: Carpentry Work

Lundy Services LLC ....E 972 494-2554
Garland *(G-7539)*

Progressive Millworks Inc ....D 512 832-0551
Austin *(G-1436)*

CONTRACTORS: Carpentry, Cabinet & Finish Work

Alfonso Hinostroza ....E 956 781-1845
San Juan *(G-18670)*

Asmar Custom Cabinets Inc ....F 972 241-7676
Dallas *(G-3971)*

Bentwood Companies Inc ....D 972 227-6855
Lancaster *(G-13839)*

Brownsvlle Architectural Mllwk ....E 956 592-5423
Brownsville *(G-2341)*

Coleman Wood Products Inc ....E 940 440-2300
Aubrey *(G-849)*

Graham Custom Cabinets LLC ....F 940 549-4311
Graham *(G-7782)*

Image Furnishings Inc ....F 806 747-6500
Lubbock *(G-14424)*

Incounters Inc ....E 325 675-5909
Abilene *(G-51)*

Innovative Millwork Systems ....E 972 869-9892
Dallas *(G-4503)*

J-Kraft Inc ....E 281 876-2535
Humble *(G-12780)*

Johnnys Custom Cabinet ....F 281 498-8950
Stafford *(G-19336)*

Employee Codes: A=Over 500 employees, B=251-500
C=101-250, D=51-100, E=20-50, F=10-19, G=9   2021 Harris Texas
Manufacturers Directory   1445

Liberty Company...............................E........ 817 921-0218
  Fort Worth *(G-6788)*
Moehnke Custom Cabinetry................F........ 512 352-6506
  Taylor *(G-19660)*
US Home Systems Inc......................E........ 214 488-6300
  Irving *(G-13204)*

CONTRACTORS: *Carpentry, Cabinet Building & Installation*

Artisans Cabinetry & Woodwork..........D........ 512 626-7311
  Georgetown *(G-7636)*
Daycor Enterprises Inc.....................F........ 972 838-2700
  Melissa *(G-14996)*
John D Blankenship...........................E........ 214 752-9191
  Dallas *(G-4535)*
Maryfield Enterprises LP....................D........ 210 344-4151
  San Antonio *(G-18281)*
Mike Conkles Custom Cabinets...........E........ 817 483-9658
  Kennedale *(G-13499)*
Millwood Cabinets LLP......................E........ 903 567-3333
  Canton *(G-2658)*
New Saw Inc..................................E........ 972 288-2117
  Mesquite *(G-15064)*
Saw Custom Millwork Inc...................E........ 972 288-2118
  Mesquite *(G-15076)*
Unique Cabinets Inc.........................E........ 512 251-3058
  Pflugerville *(G-16690)*

CONTRACTORS: *Carpentry, Finish & Trim Work*

AW Installers Inc.............................E........ 210 649-1618
  Adkins *(G-176)*
Morgan Trim Inc..............................F........ 806 655-9777
  Canyon *(G-2674)*

CONTRACTORS: *Carpet Laying*

United Lynn-Con Corporation...............F........ 972 223-2540
  Desoto *(G-5446)*
Yates Carpet Incorporated.................E........ 806 795-9942
  Lubbock *(G-14516)*

CONTRACTORS: *Coating, Caulking & Weather, Water & Fire*

ABG Contracting Group LLC................E........ 281 431-7223
  Pearland *(G-16536)*
Hanitatek LLC................................G........ 214 351-5818
  Carrollton *(G-2753)*
K2 Industrial Services Inc..................F........ 850 477-6437
  La Porte *(G-13760)*

CONTRACTORS: *Commercial & Office Building*

Capco Steel Inc..............................E........ 210 493-9992
  San Antonio *(G-17979)*
Ferreira Holding Group LLC................E........ 214 293-9233
  Dallas *(G-4359)*
Granchelli Construction LLC...............F........ 956 928-1122
  McAllen *(G-14867)*
Health Care Temporaries Inc..............A........ 713 631-7106
  Houston *(G-10143)*
Houston Wifi C/Hston Cnstr Svc..........F........ 832 444-8300
  Spring *(G-19131)*
Jahkur International LLC....................E........ 832 431-3232
  Houston *(G-10450)*
JD Murchison Interests Inc................E........ 972 931-0700
  Plano *(G-16898)*
Koehler Co....................................E........ 830 303-6256
  Seguin *(G-18848)*
Odysseus Holdings LLC.....................F........ 281 769-2399
  Houston *(G-11136)*
Onyx Contractors Operations LP.........D........ 432 561-8900
  Midland *(G-15328)*
Talon/Lpe Ltd.................................F........ 210 253-7200
  San Antonio *(G-18521)*
Wccog Corp...................................F........ 903 667-0264
  De Kalb *(G-5237)*

CONTRACTORS: *Communications Svcs*

Tellabs Inc....................................E........ 800 690-2324
  Carrollton *(G-2890)*

CONTRACTORS: *Computer Installation*

Behemoth Corporation......................E........ 281 332-4798
  League City *(G-13949)*

Csi Techs Inc.................................D........ 210 875-7978
  San Antonio *(G-18033)*
Data Connection Inc.........................F........ 972 231-2185
  Dallas *(G-4240)*
Intrapack Corporation.......................E........ 214 348-7105
  Dallas *(G-4509)*

CONTRACTORS: *Concrete*

Acme Brick Company........................D........ 817 332-4101
  El Paso *(G-5636)*
Bgi Enterprise Inc...........................E........ 409 833-0303
  Beaumont *(G-1865)*
Builders Post-Tension Inc..................E........ 281 873-9500
  Houston *(G-9014)*
Cemex Construction Mtls S LLC..........F........ 936 372-0493
  Hockley *(G-8342)*
Childs Ready-Mix Concrete Co............F........ 254 968-4755
  Stephenville *(G-19408)*
Detsco Inc....................................F........ 713 999-5260
  Jersey Village *(G-13298)*
Forterra Pipe & Precast LLC...............D........ 713 466-6324
  Houston *(G-9838)*
Forterra Pipe & Precast LLC...............E........ 469 458-7973
  Irving *(G-13033)*
Gfrc 360 LLC.................................E........ 972 494-9000
  Garland *(G-7503)*
Holmes Construction Co LP................D........ 806 376-8629
  Amarillo *(G-435)*
Houston Wifi C/Hston Cnstr Svc..........F........ 832 444-8300
  Spring *(G-19131)*
International Energy Svcs LLC..............E........ 281 973-9462
  Houston *(G-10402)*
Keller North America Inc....................E........ 817 443-1465
  Fort Worth *(G-6755)*
Koy Concrete Ltd............................E........ 281 391-2178
  Katy *(G-13421)*
Metro Cutting and Sealing Inc.............E........ 972 434-8722
  Lewisville *(G-14066)*
Modern Concrete & Mtls LLC..............F........ 409 840-2080
  Beaumont *(G-1929)*
Murphy & Murphy Inc.......................E........ 940 325-2666
  Mineral Wells *(G-15533)*
Ram-Bro Contracting Inc...................E........ 361 387-2795
  Robstown *(G-17515)*
Southwest Indus Surfaces Inc.............E........ 972 641-4393
  Grand Prairie *(G-7974)*
Superior Con Fence Texas Inc.............F........ 817 277-9255
  Euless *(G-6160)*
Tri-Construction Co Inc.....................C........ 979 233-7211
  Freeport *(G-7217)*
Venetian Blind Flr Cvg Sp Ltd..............E........ 713 528-2404
  Houston *(G-12546)*

CONTRACTORS: *Concrete Block Masonry Laying*

Fencecrete America Inc.....................C........ 210 492-7911
  San Antonio *(G-18109)*
Fencecrete America Inc.....................E........ 281 438-1444
  Houston *(G-9776)*
Hmj Plastering LLC..........................F........ 713 941-2807
  Pasadena *(G-16454)*

CONTRACTORS: *Concrete Breaking, Street & Highway*

North Texas Coring Inc......................E........ 817 279-8930
  Granbury *(G-7802)*

CONTRACTORS: *Concrete Reinforcement Placing*

37 Building Products Ltd....................C........ 817 341-3130
  Weatherford *(G-20571)*

CONTRACTORS: *Concrete Repair*

Ea Services Inc...............................D........ 866 711-1001
  Pearland *(G-16557)*

CONTRACTORS: *Construction Site Cleanup*

Etech Envmtl Safety Solutions.............E........ 432 563-2200
  Odessa *(G-15993)*
Fun Da Mentals For Educatn LLC..........E........ 832 368-3345
  Houston *(G-9874)*
Gill Assoc Prprty MGT Systems...........G........ 832 644-9751
  Humble *(G-12770)*
Green & Hansen LLC........................D........ 210 289-2482
  Jourdanton *(G-13331)*

Redco Endeavors Inc.......................F........ 832 421-8549
  Gilmer *(G-7711)*
SSP Developers Inc..........................F........ 956 456-4415
  San Benito *(G-18668)*
Wright Landscaping & Cnst LLC...........E........ 254 213-3912
  Killeen *(G-13618)*

CONTRACTORS: *Construction Site Metal Structure Coating*

Custom Pipe Coating Inc....................E........ 713 675-2324
  Houston *(G-9373)*
Top Deck Inc..................................E........ 409 745-3955
  Orange *(G-16265)*

CONTRACTORS: *Core Drilling & Cutting*

M H C X-Ploration Corporation.............F........ 903 595-4323
  Tyler *(G-20117)*

CONTRACTORS: *Countertop Installation*

Artistic Counters Inc........................C........ 210 651-3281
  Garden Ridge *(G-7418)*
Bmp & Associates Inc.......................E........ 713 779-8677
  Houston *(G-8927)*
Creative Tile Inc.............................G........ 214 827-0552
  Dallas *(G-4182)*
Incounters Inc................................E........ 325 675-5909
  Abilene *(G-51)*
Johnnies Plastics Inc........................E........ 210 533-8463
  San Antonio *(G-18205)*
Regal Marble Co..............................F........ 361 572-8498
  Victoria *(G-20300)*
Sage Surfaces LLC...........................F........ 281 907-8766
  The Woodlands *(G-19915)*
Siri Granite Inc...............................E........ 832 203-8322
  Houston *(G-11907)*
Stone Production Inc.........................F........ 512 990-9800
  Austin *(G-1539)*
Stone Systems Centl Texas LLC...........E........ 512 295-2950
  Austin *(G-1540)*
Target Stone LLC.............................E........ 832 827-8663
  Houston *(G-12161)*

CONTRACTORS: *Curb & Sidewalk*

JD King Inc....................................C........ 800 805-6302
  Seminole *(G-18884)*

CONTRACTORS: *Demolition, Building & Other Structures*

Detsco Inc....................................F........ 713 999-5260
  Jersey Village *(G-13298)*
Gill Assoc Prprty MGT Systems...........G........ 832 644-9751
  Humble *(G-12770)*
Sorrell Cnstr Eqp & Mtls LLC..............D........ 979 233-6655
  Freeport *(G-7213)*
Wcsa Inc......................................F........ 806 383-1060
  Amarillo *(G-473)*

CONTRACTORS: *Dewatering*

Griffin Dewatering LLC......................E........ 713 676-8000
  Houston *(G-10044)*
Nitrogen Services LLC.......................C........ 925 336-1560
  Midland *(G-15320)*

CONTRACTORS: *Directional Oil & Gas Well Drilling Svc*

Aim Directional Services LLC...............E........ 432 934-0628
  Midland *(G-15110)*
Aim Directional Services LLC...............D........ 361 653-6500
  Corpus Christi *(G-3467)*
Austral Integrated Services................F........ 936 266-0945
  Conroe *(G-3259)*
Axon Ep Inc...................................E........ 281 855-3200
  Houston *(G-8762)*
B & T Directional Drilling Inc...............F........ 903 629-3406
  Winnsboro *(G-20896)*
Big 6 Drilling Company......................E........ 713 783-2300
  Houston *(G-8880)*
Blue Line Drilling Co LLC....................D........ 325 653-1891
  San Angelo *(G-17782)*
Cathedral Energy Services Inc.............E........ 303 825-1001
  Houston *(G-9102)*
Challenger Drilling Inc.......................F........ 281 290-8335
  Tomball *(G-19969)*
Coastal Drilling Company L L C.............C........ 361 852-6195
  Corpus Christi *(G-3503)*

Copan Corporation ....G...... 806 665-1267
  Pampa (G-16319)
Crescent Directional Drlg LP ....D...... 281 668-9500
  Houston (G-9342)
D & S Drilling Ltd ....F...... 806 794-8866
  Lubbock (G-14400)
Dallas Directional Drlg Inc ....F...... 214 254-6985
  Dallas (G-4215)
Directional Prj Support Inc ....G...... 281 259-7819
  Magnolia (G-14601)
Double K Well Service LP ....F...... 940 567-2855
  Jacksboro (G-13219)
Drillchem Drlg Solutions LLC ....G...... 281 713-8941
  The Woodlands (G-19852)
Exceed Drilling Tech LLC ....F...... 512 656-9669
  Austin (G-1144)
Hayhurst Bros Drilling Co ....F...... 325 340-1865
  Abilene (G-47)
Inwell Inc ....F...... 281 443-7614
  Spring (G-19221)
JF Construction Inc ....E...... 214 272-1902
  Frisco (G-7293)
Longhorn Drilling and Eqp Co ....F...... 830 372-1910
  Seguin (G-18850)
Lovelady Directional Drilling ....F...... 936 675-4598
  Lufkin (G-14534)
M3p Directional Services Ltd ....F...... 432 561-8801
  Midland (G-15289)
Maverick Directional Services ....E...... 281 364-1212
  Spring (G-19230)
Mhwirth Inc ....F...... 281 371-2424
  Houston (G-10864)
Midstar Energy LP ....E...... 281 940-3022
  Katy (G-13425)
Muenster Drilling Company ....F...... 940 759-4949
  Muenster (G-15671)
Nabors Drilling Tech USA Inc ....C...... 281 874-0035
  Houston (G-10952)
Nicklos Drilling Company ....D...... 713 224-5959
  Houston (G-11052)
Nitrogen Services LLC ....C...... 925 336-1560
  Midland (G-15320)
Noram Drilling Company ....E...... 281 598-9200
  Houston (G-11068)
Nova Directional Inc ....E...... 281 246-1149
  Houston (G-11089)
Parkerlane Directional Drlg LP ....E...... 817 235-4050
  Euless (G-6152)
Particle Drilling Tech Inc ....F...... 713 223-3031
  Houston (G-11249)
Patterson Drilling Company ....A...... 325 651-6603
  San Angelo (G-17819)
Patterson-Uti Energy Inc ....D...... 432 561-9382
  Midland (G-15342)
Patterson-Uti Energy Inc ....E...... 281 765-7100
  Houston (G-11262)
Patterson-Uti Energy Inc ....E...... 903 877-3659
  Tyler (G-20138)
Patterson-Uti Energy Inc ....F...... 432 682-9401
  Midland (G-15343)
Phoenix Technology Svcs USA ....F...... 713 337-0600
  Houston (G-11330)
Precision Directional Svcs Inc ....F...... 713 975-1209
  Houston (G-11389)
Precision Drilling Corporation ....A...... 713 435-6100
  Houston (G-11391)
Premier Directional Drlg LP ....C...... 281 673-4000
  Houston (G-11400)
Progress Drilling Inc ....E...... 830 875-3442
  Luling (G-14563)
Quintana Energy Services LP ....F...... 832 518-4094
  Houston (G-11516)
Resource Energy Service Corp ....D...... 713 953-5300
  Houston (G-11608)
Ringo Drilling I Lp ....C...... 325 232-5807
  Dallas (G-4900)
Robinson Drilling Texas Ltd ....E...... 432 267-5277
  Big Spring (G-2096)
Rowan Drilling Company Inc ....F...... 713 621-7800
  Houston (G-11677)
Schlumberger Limited ....E...... 713 513-2000
  Houston (G-11767)
Schlumberger Limited ....F...... 713 513-2000
  Houston (G-11768)
Scientific Drilling Intl Inc ....C...... 281 443-3300
  Houston (G-11786)
Scientific Drilling Intl Inc ....E...... 432 563-1339
  Midland (G-15399)
Sentry Energy Production LLC ....F...... 972 380-1600
  Addison (G-162)

Sparkman Well Service Inc ....C...... 361 572-4833
  Victoria (G-20305)
Spruiell Drilling Co ....F...... 940 592-5471
  Iowa Park (G-12911)
Steinberger Drilling Company ....E...... 940 423-6900
  Windthorst (G-20886)
Sterling Drlg Fund 1983-1 LP ....C...... 203 358-5700
  Houston (G-12059)
Tally Energy Services ....F...... 832 530-4880
  Houston (G-12149)
TNT Directional Drilling Inc ....F...... 972 333-3410
  Garland (G-7602)
Trinity River Energy LLC ....F...... 817 872-7898
  Houston (G-12375)
Wil Call Services Ltd ....D...... 903 322-2911
  Buffalo (G-2549)
XCL Resources LLC ....E...... 346 335-1081
  Houston (G-12705)

CONTRACTORS: Dock Eqpt Installation, Indl

Trade-Mark Industrial LLC ....D...... 519 650-7444
  San Antonio (G-18558)

CONTRACTORS: Drapery Track Installation

Nsec LLC ....F...... 254 756-0651
  Lorena (G-14343)

CONTRACTORS: Drywall

Phoenix Millwork LLC ....D...... 281 388-2211
  Alvin (G-377)
United Office Interiors Inc ....D...... 214 381-0101
  Dallas (G-5136)
Walcott Enterprises Inc ....E...... 325 773-5212
  Stamford (G-19402)
Walls Across Texas I Ltd ....E...... 210 826-4123
  San Antonio (G-18608)

CONTRACTORS: Earthmoving

George Bartee Cnstr Co Inc ....E...... 936 687-4811
  Grapeland (G-8005)
Hudson Brothers Mining Company ....F...... 903 876-4642
  Rusk (G-17731)
Jamco Services LLC ....D...... 432 242-6051
  Dallas (G-4523)
Lang & Mitchell Contrs Inc ....F...... 903 876-2882
  Frankston (G-7167)

CONTRACTORS: Electric Power Systems

Advanced Control Systems LLC ....E...... 832 529-2234
  Houston (G-8487)
Electric Pwr Systems Intl Inc ....E...... 972 907-3783
  Richardson (G-17305)
Larry & Matt Inc ....D...... 806 665-4418
  Pampa (G-16326)

CONTRACTORS: Electrical

Acm Hub LLC ....F...... 210 248-9631
  San Antonio (G-17860)
Big M Constructors Inc ....E...... 281 469-9770
  Houston (G-8883)
Bmf Oil & Gas Services Inc ....F...... 832 443-2089
  Houston (G-8926)
Commercial Armature Works ....F...... 713 672-7873
  Houston (G-9248)
Crawford Electric Sup Co Inc ....E...... 512 593-4000
  Round Rock (G-17638)
D&G Energy Corporation ....F...... 956 686-6040
  McAllen (G-14852)
Designed Security Inc ....E...... 512 321-4426
  Bastrop (G-1756)
Electric Submersible Pump Inc ....F...... 325 573-8101
  Snyder (G-18990)
ESP Enterprises Inc ....D...... 281 444-2377
  Houston (G-9697)
Houma Armture Wrks Houston LLC ...E...... 713 748-0702
  Houston (G-8384)
Innosync Inc ....E...... 972 644-7962
  Dallas (G-4501)
Msf Electric Inc ....D...... 210 781-4112
  San Antonio (G-18323)
Msf Electric Inc ....E...... 214 377-8710
  Dallas (G-4702)
National Circuit Assembly Inc ....D...... 972 278-2009
  Garland (G-7557)
National Swtchgear Systems Inc ....E...... 972 420-0149
  Lewisville (G-14071)

Nmg Workspace Solutions LLC ....E...... 281 240-1007
  Houston (G-11061)
R-Tex Services LLC ....D...... 817 774-3333
  Joshua (G-13324)
RMS Solutions Group LLC ....F...... 469 964-7127
  Point (G-17080)
Rus Industrial LLC ....C...... 281 864-9070
  Channelview (G-3033)
Schneider Electric Usa Inc ....C...... 512 295-8060
  Buda (G-2537)
Ss Electric Inc ....F...... 915 217-2200
  El Paso (G-5973)
Systems Integration Inc ....E...... 817 468-1494
  Arlington (G-790)
Thiel Co ....F...... 817 310-3110
  Grapevine (G-8057)
Udelhoven Inc ....D...... 210 635-8833
  Floresville (G-6255)
WT Fiber Link LLC ....D...... 432 758-2700
  Seminole (G-18888)

CONTRACTORS: Electronic Controls Installation

Electro-Quip Service Inc ....D...... 281 456-8600
  Houston (G-9593)
Port City Inc ....E...... 713 673-7272
  Houston (G-11365)
Schneider Elc Bldngs Amrcas Inc ......B...... 972 323-1111
  Carrollton (G-2813)
Skledar-Greene LLC ....F...... 817 454-4214
  Krum (G-13676)
Texan Electric Co Inc ....D...... 713 645-6560
  Houston (G-12219)

CONTRACTORS: Energy Management Control

ROC Service Company LLC ....C...... 940 683-0159
  Bridgeport (G-2300)

CONTRACTORS: Epoxy Application

Composite Lining Systems LP ....C...... 432 617-0242
  Midland (G-15174)

CONTRACTORS: Erection & Dismantling, Poured Concrete Forms

Epic Energy Services LLC ....C...... 361 222-1226
  Odem (G-15895)

CONTRACTORS: Excavating

Duane Ollinger ....E...... 806 935-6786
  Dumas (G-5520)
Earth Haulers Inc ....F...... 817 540-2777
  Euless (G-6141)
H & M Dirt Contractors Inc ....E...... 806 495-3293
  Post (G-17190)
Halls Lumber Inc ....F...... 806 285-2393
  Olton (G-16226)
J & S Contractors Inc ....F...... 979 647-0040
  Sweeny (G-19628)
JD King Inc ....C...... 800 805-6302
  Seminole (G-18884)
Larry McHorse Services LLC ....F...... 361 275-4978
  Cuero (G-3762)
Longhorn Mulching Inc ....E...... 936 699-1160
  Lufkin (G-14533)
Nova Construction Co Inc ....E...... 972 869-3041
  Carrollton (G-2785)
R-Tex Services LLC ....D...... 817 774-3333
  Joshua (G-13324)
Ram-Bro Contracting Inc ....E...... 361 387-2795
  Robstown (G-17515)
Raydon Inc ....E...... 254 559-5012
  Breckenridge (G-2235)
Satterwhite Companies Inc ....D...... 903 663-1729
  Longview (G-14303)
Sherrod Services LLC ....E...... 254 729-3177
  Thornton (G-19943)
Venables Construction Inc ....C...... 806 381-2121
  Amarillo (G-520)
Wcsa Inc ....F...... 806 383-1060
  Amarillo (G-473)

CONTRACTORS: Excavating Slush Pits & Cellars Svcs

Johnson Cnstr Clearing LLC ....E 281 659-1428
Huntsville (G-12815)
Med-Loz Lease Service Inc ....C 956 765-6029
Zapata (G-20984)
Winkel & Son Inc ....E 903 928-2560
Tennessee Colony (G-19727)

CONTRACTORS: Exterior Concrete Stucco

Hmj Plastering LLC ....F 713 941-2807
Pasadena (G-16454)
Metroplex Roof and Fence Inc...........F 469 417-8003
Corinth (G-3458)

CONTRACTORS: Exterior Painting

Gill Assoc Prprty MGT Systems ....G... 832 644-9751
Humble (G-12770)

CONTRACTORS: Exterior Wall System Installation

Lacy Construction Services LLC...........F 903 498-0683
Kemp (G-13485)
Shaun K Boyer ....F 281 442-3800
Houston (G-11848)

CONTRACTORS: Fence Construction

Baker & Company Cnstr LLC................E 903 561-1763
Tyler (G-20056)
Buzz Services LLC ....E 817 263-9788
Fort Worth (G-6480)
Fencecrete America Inc......................C 281 438-1444
Houston (G-9776)
Huckaby Enterprises Inc ....F 817 732-5541
Fort Worth (G-6707)
J-N Fence Co Inc ....E 972 226-7205
Mesquite (G-15054)
Mason Fencing and Cnstr LLC ....E 432 272-8347
Odessa (G-16073)
Master-Halco Inc ....D...... 972 714-7300
Dallas (G-4645)
Metroplex Roof and Fence Inc..............F 469 417-8003
Corinth (G-3458)
Neu Security Services LLC..................D...... 512 469-9980
Austin (G-1364)
Ntx Gates & Fences Inc ....E 817 740-9449
Fort Worth (G-6874)
Presidio Custom Metal Works ....F 512 284-8549
Round Rock (G-17682)
Quality Access Control Systems...........F 830 981-5400
Boerne (G-2133)
SA Quality Fence Ltd.........................D...... 210 545-6767
San Antonio (G-18440)
Sorensen Industries Inc......................E 940 365-9999
Crossroads (G-3750)
Triple - C Fence Llc.............................E 817 439-9500
Haslet (G-8226)
WD Norton Inc ....F 903 758-0301
Longview (G-14332)

CONTRACTORS: Fiber Optic Cable Installation

Accurate Connections Inc...................E 972 484-8500
Plano (G-16769)
B Comm Constructors LLC...................E 210 257-0102
San Antonio (G-17929)
Btm Services LLC ....E 281 773-6060
Houston (G-9004)
Kevin M Ehringer Entps Inc.................D...... 972 620-4997
Dallas (G-4553)
Pcs Telecom Inc ....F 281 469-3367
Pasadena (G-16494)
Scott Fennell Inc ....E 817 822-1283
Iola (G-12900)
Trans-Tel Central Inc..........................F 405 447-5025
San Antonio (G-18561)
Villatoro Construction LLC ....E 214 350-7900
Wylie (G-20954)

CONTRACTORS: Fiberglass Work

F & F Composite Group Inc ....E 817 379-4411
Fort Worth (G-6622)
Quietflex Manufacturing Co LP ....B...... 877 694-3669
Houston (G-11514)

Wil-Cor Inc...F 281 487-6547
Pasadena (G-16526)

CONTRACTORS: Fire Detection & Burglar Alarm Systems

Allestec Corporation...........................F 281 359-1519
Kingwood (G-13637)
Drone Labs LLC ....F 214 538-1467
Katy (G-13397)
Eisenbeck Corporation ....F 972 526-5235
Garland (G-7485)
Logical Control Services LLP ....E 972 820-0100
Carrollton (G-2878)
Nexus Alarm & Suppression Inc ....E 877 828-1200
Dallas (G-4737)
Tackaberry Dooley Systems ....C 281 479-9700
Deer Park (G-5299)
Ww Electronics Solutions LLC..............F 214 396-6636
Quinlan (G-17227)

CONTRACTORS: Fire Sprinkler System Installation Svcs

Advantage Interests Inc ....D...... 713 983-7253
Houston (G-8494)
Frontier Fire Systems Inc ....E 214 343-9500
Dallas (G-4382)
Nexus Alarm & Suppression Inc ....E 877 828-1200
Dallas (G-4737)
Texas SEC & Surveillance Inc.............E 512 693-4003
Round Rock (G-17693)
Tyco International MGT Co LLC ....F 713 644-8872
Houston (G-12419)

CONTRACTORS: Floor Laying & Other Floor Work

American Marble Mosaic Company ....E 713 747-7634
Houston (G-8600)
Bmp & Associates Inc ....E 713 779-8677
Houston (G-8927)
Signature Systems Group LLC.............E 972 684-5736
Flower Mound (G-6281)
Southwest Indus Surfaces Inc..............E 972 641-4393
Grand Prairie (G-7974)

CONTRACTORS: Flooring

Nmg Workspace Solutions LLC ....E 281 240-1007
Houston (G-11061)
Target Stone LLC ....E 832 827-8663
Houston (G-12161)

CONTRACTORS: Food Svcs Eqpt Installation

Professional Fabrication Inc ....E 936 321-7070
Magnolia (G-14622)
RSI Partners LLC ....D...... 817 640-5415
Arlington (G-777)
Systems Integration Inc ....E 817 468-1494
Arlington (G-790)

CONTRACTORS: Foundation & Footing

Ats Drilling LP ....D...... 817 498-0040
Haltom City (G-8132)
Libcon Inc ....D...... 956 724-6459
Laredo (G-13907)
Littlefield Brothers Con Cnstr..............E 281 399-1488
Conroe (G-3322)
One Source SEC & Sound Inc ....E 713 934-7400
Humble (G-12791)
Shinn and Gregory Inc ....G 254 965-7585
Stephenville (G-19422)
TMC Foundation Inc ....F 214 212-4645
McKinney (G-14983)

CONTRACTORS: Foundation Building

Keller North America Inc ....E 817 443-1465
Fort Worth (G-6755)

CONTRACTORS: Garage Doors

Accent Door Co Inc.............................E 913 780-5800
San Antonio (G-17856)

CONTRACTORS: Gas Detection & Analysis Svcs

Oil & Gas Consultants Intl Inc ....F 832 426-1200
Katy (G-13374)
Streamline Innovations Inc ....E 888 787-6569
San Antonio (G-18507)

CONTRACTORS: Gas Field Svcs, NEC

Andeavor Rio Holdings LLC ....F 281 566-3000
Sugar Land (G-19444)
Bison Energy Partners Inc ....F 281 873-9100
Houston (G-8894)
Black Horse Test Services ....F 903 938-8554
Marshall (G-14764)
Bmf Oil & Gas Services Inc..................E 832 443-2089
Houston (G-8926)
C P Bailey Cnstr Co Inc ....G 936 348-3627
Madisonville (G-14585)
Cadena Services LLC ....F 956 727-9391
Laredo (G-13872)
Cameron Solutions Inc ....F 325 573-8521
Snyder (G-18985)
Car-Tex Transport & Vacuum Svc ....D...... 903 693-6271
Carthage (G-2901)
Chemex Modular LLC..........................D...... 801 565-8099
New Waverly (G-15856)
Clean Combustion Inc ....F 832 333-7800
Dayton (G-5223)
Clean Harbors San Leon Inc ....D...... 281 339-1352
Dickinson (G-5473)
Copperbeck Energy Partners LLC ....E 214 238-4881
Dallas (G-4166)
Cornerstone Synergy LLC ....F 806 679-9178
Panhandle (G-16347)
CW Ford Rentals LP ....E 903 935-7608
Kilgore (G-13543)
Dnv GL Noble Denton Usa LLC ....B...... 281 396-1000
Katy (G-13396)
Eagle Ford Reclamation Co LLC ....E 361 786-3960
Three Rivers (G-19945)
Enersys Corporation ....F 281 598-7100
Stafford (G-19311)
Ensign Management LLC ....E 281 403-6304
Houston (G-9656)
Fowlerton Energy Services LLC............G 830 570-4507
Fowlerton (G-7161)
Gel Technologies Corp ....F 432 683-1881
Midland (G-15236)
H G Nichols Construction Co ....F 903 876-2527
Poynor (G-17202)
Howard Measurement Co Inc................E 903 677-0700
Athens (G-827)
Integrated Advantage Group LP............F 806 367-8031
Amarillo (G-493)
Jade Services Inc................................E 806 870-3883
Lamesa (G-13825)
Jmd Oilfield & Rig Service LLC.............E 469 261-2415
Odessa (G-16040)
John Linder Operating Co LLC..............E 903 845-4240
Gladewater (G-7724)
Johnson Matthey Inc ....D...... 281 291-7769
Pasadena (G-16465)
M & S Mechanical Inc ....E 318 755-2431
Pittsburg (G-16747)
Natural Gas Services Group Inc............C 432 262-2700
Midland (G-15311)
Natural Gas Sltions N Amer LLC ....A...... 832 590-2303
Houston (G-11008)
Ncs Multistage Holdings Inc ....F 281 453-2222
Houston (G-11020)
Oil States Energy Services LLC.............F 432 943-2556
Monahans (G-15611)
Outlaws Oilfield Service LLC ....E 432 445-0005
Midland (G-15333)
Pantheon Construction Inc ....E 940 458-9183
Sanger (G-18729)
Penspen Corporation ....F 713 953-7007
Tomball (G-19996)
Petroh2o Recovery LLC ....E 817 778-8413
Southlake (G-19081)
Professional Projects Inc ....D...... 281 351-6315
Cypress (G-3814)
R A Beaird Oil Co ....F 325 928-5220
Merkel (G-15016)
Roto-Versal Compression Svcs............E 713 538-2800
Houston (G-11671)
Sardisco Enterprises Inc......................F 281 419-9229
Oak Ridge North (G-15890)

Seawolf Rswd Resources LP............F 713 518-1763
　Houston (G-11809)
Seven Construction Inc....................G...... 806 894-5685
　Levelland (G-14016)
Sherman Branson Construction............D...... 432 684-4740
　Midland (G-15408)
Stabil Drill Specialties LLC.............E...... 281 583-0127
　Houston (G-12034)
Stellar Automation Inc...................F...... 432 517-4502
　Big Spring (G-2099)
Sterlings Vacuum Service.................F...... 979 657-4633
　Boling (G-2148)
Swd Enterprises LLC......................E...... 281 846-6851
　Houston (G-12129)
Tejon Exploration Co.....................G...... 325 673-6429
　Abilene (G-86)
Torcsill Foundations LLC.................D...... 281 825-5200
　Houston (G-12323)
TRC Consultants Lc.......................F...... 830 249-9968
　Boerne (G-2144)
Trident Water Services LLC...............E...... 817 889-4334
　Benbrook (G-2046)
Trifecta Oilfield Services LLC...........C...... 930 730-4800
　Floresville (G-6254)
Tristream Energy LLC.....................E...... 281 240-8444
　Houston (G-12380)
Triumph Inc..............................E...... 361 946-4658
　Corpus Christi (G-3643)
Universal Ensco Inc......................E...... 713 425-6000
　Houston (G-12461)
Wcc Energy LLC...........................E...... 432 208-2839
　Anson (G-587)
Wp Resources LLC.........................F...... 512 913-7234
　New Braunfels (G-15833)
Yegua Oil Field Service Inc..............F...... 361 375-2105
　Pettus (G-16654)

CONTRACTORS: Gasoline Condensation Removal Svcs

Forum Energy Technologies Inc...........F...... 817 602-1174
　Argyle (G-601)
Fts International Inc....................B...... 903 590-2440
　Flint (G-6237)
Mesa Wireline LLC........................E...... 970 257-0458
　Houston (G-10839)
N5 Wireline Service LLC..................F...... 806 648-1505
　Perryton (G-16641)
Wildcat Wireline.........................D...... 830 879-5100
　Cotulla (G-3692)

CONTRACTORS: General Electric

A & R Enterprises Inc....................F...... 903 984-9057
　Kilgore (G-13530)
AAA Electrical Signs.....................F...... 956 464-3221
　Donna (G-5486)
Accurate Air Solutions LLC...............E...... 325 672-2966
　Abilene (G-9)
Amarillo Elc Specialists Inc.............F...... 806 372-3798
　Amarillo (G-394)
Arns Holdings Ltd........................D...... 713 863-0600
　Houston (G-8701)
Energy Retrofitters Inc..................F...... 817 319-2796
　Fort Worth (G-6614)
Gauntlett Inc............................G...... 806 293-9849
　Plainview (G-16754)
Ies Holdings Inc.........................D...... 713 860-1500
　Houston (G-10316)
J M Davidson Inc.........................C...... 361 883-0983
　Aransas Pass (G-592)
M&I Electric Industries Inc..............D...... 832 241-6330
　Houston (G-10721)
Maddox Enterprises Inc...................E...... 903 592-6531
　Tyler (G-20119)
Martin Electric Co Inc...................E...... 979 543-6421
　El Campo (G-5622)
Musshorn Enterprises Inc.................C...... 915 772-9007
　El Paso (G-5892)
Outdoor Lighting Services LP.............C...... 713 690-6301
　Houston (G-11204)
Specialty Electrical LLC.................F...... 817 355-5315
　Fort Worth (G-7009)
Texas and Oklahoma Elc Svc LLC...........E...... 972 222-2229
　Dallas (G-5054)
United Elec Instrmentation Ltd...........D...... 979 265-1256
　Clute (G-3161)
Wheco Electric Inc.......................E...... 817 244-6660
　Lakeside (G-13813)

CONTRACTORS: Geothermal Drilling

Air Drilling Associates Inc..............F...... 832 957-6093
　Houston (G-8505)

CONTRACTORS: Glass Tinting, Architectural & Automotive

Southern Shutters Inc....................F...... 512 272-9711
　Manor (G-14649)
V-Kool Inc...............................G...... 713 856-8333
　Houston (G-12512)

CONTRACTORS: Glass, Glazing & Tinting

A & B Glass LLC..........................F...... 432 517-4565
　Big Spring (G-2067)
Arrow Mirror & Glass Inc.................C...... 832 467-4345
　Houston (G-8706)
Arrowall Company.........................D...... 713 462-1751
　San Antonio (G-18639)
ASAP Glass & Door LLC....................F...... 214 770-8266
　Denton (G-5351)
Bielas Glass & Aluminum Pdts.............E...... 210 333-8040
　San Antonio (G-17952)
Country Glass & Mirror Inc...............E...... 972 216-9100
　Mesquite (G-15035)
Houston Wifi C/Hston Cnstr Svc...........F...... 832 444-8300
　Spring (G-19131)
Jpon Glass Company Inc...................E...... 214 349-1400
　Garland (G-7528)
Kovach Enclosure Systems LLC.............D...... 480 926-9292
　Spring (G-19225)
Kovach Enclosure Systems LLC.............D...... 480 926-9292
　Austin (G-1273)
Kovach Enclosure Systems LLC.............D...... 480 926-9292
　Farmers Branch (G-6205)
Lone Star Glass Inc......................F...... 713 661-0091
　Houston (G-10677)
Morenos Auto Glass Inc...................F...... 361 855-1471
　Corpus Christi (G-3579)

CONTRACTORS: Gutters & Downspouts

Senox Corporation........................E...... 512 251-3333
　Austin (G-1492)
Vogler Sheet Metal Company...............E...... 713 861-1154
　Spring (G-19186)

CONTRACTORS: Heating & Air Conditioning

Christopher RAD Nader....................F...... 512 442-5326
　Cedar Park (G-2963)
Concord Mechanical Inc...................F...... 817 319-5575
　Boyd (G-2204)
Eastern Star Group LLC...................F...... 972 729-9955
　Allen (G-263)
Graco Mechanical Inc.....................D...... 713 978-7000
　Houston (G-10011)
Miller Mechanical Group..................F...... 361 594-8080
　Shiner (G-18945)
Mortex Products Inc......................B...... 817 624-0820
　Fort Worth (G-6853)
Munters Corporation......................D...... 210 651-5018
　Selma (G-18878)
R2 Fabrication Inc.......................F...... 817 230-2015
　Fort Worth (G-6935)
Saber Security Systems Inc...............F...... 512 341-8700
　Round Rock (G-17688)
Welch Hvac Incorporated..................F...... 214 222-8600
　Lewisville (G-14112)

CONTRACTORS: Heating Systems Repair & Maintenance Svc

Cimarron Energy Holding Co LLC...........E...... 432 563-9700
　Odessa (G-15961)
Convergentz Bldg Systems LLC.............D...... 713 266-3900
　Houston (G-9297)
Qtran Corp...............................F...... 817 870-1855
　Fort Worth (G-6926)
Synergy Environmental Svcs LLC...........E...... 972 513-1118
　Arlington (G-789)

CONTRACTORS: Highway & Street Construction, General

Crh Americas Materials Inc...............C...... 409 866-1444
　Beaumont (G-1878)
Gobbato Builders LLC.....................F...... 737 843-4327
　Austin (G-1185)

Hunter Industries Ltd....................B...... 512 353-7757
　San Marcos (G-18695)
JD Abrams LP.............................E...... 512 322-4000
　Austin (G-1252)
JD Abrams LP.............................E...... 512 243-1090
　Austin (G-1253)
Metroplex Roof and Fence Inc.............F...... 469 417-8003
　Corinth (G-3458)
Straight Line Construction Inc...........E...... 361 394-7656
　Freer (G-7233)
Tach Services Inc........................E...... 254 547-7121
　Copperas Cove (G-3456)
Tri-Construction Co Inc..................C...... 979 233-7211
　Freeport (G-7217)
Winston Land & Cattle Co Inc.............F...... 936 634-6321
　Lufkin (G-14557)
Zachry Consolidated LLC..................A...... 210 588-5000
　San Antonio (G-18630)
Zachry Construction & Mtls Inc...........D...... 210 479-1027
　San Antonio (G-18631)

CONTRACTORS: Highway & Street Paving

Aj Commercial Services Inc...............G...... 361 336-2113
　Corpus Christi (G-3470)
Berry Holdings LP........................A...... 361 693-2100
　Corpus Christi (G-3485)
Cline Construction Inc...................E...... 432 267-6006
　Big Spring (G-2075)
Dmg Equipment Company LLC................C...... 936 756-6960
　Conroe (G-3295)
Halliburton Delaware Inc.................D...... 713 759-2600
　Houston (G-10108)
Highway Barricades & Svcs LLC............D...... 361 883-6300
　Corpus Christi (G-3548)
Littlefield Brothers Con Cnstr...........F...... 281 399-1488
　Conroe (G-3322)

CONTRACTORS: Home & Office Intrs Finish, Furnish/Remodel

Cast Fireplaces..........................F...... 713 937-1080
　Houston (G-9095)
Lundy Services LLC.......................F...... 972 494-2554
　Garland (G-7539)

CONTRACTORS: Hot Shot Svcs

Tejas Utility Construction Inc...........F...... 281 299-5097
　Humble (G-12802)
Westbrook Hot Shot Service Inc...........G...... 903 987-1400
　Kilgore (G-13602)

CONTRACTORS: Hotel & Motel Renovation

Trans-Tel Central Inc....................F...... 405 447-5025
　San Antonio (G-18561)

CONTRACTORS: Hotel, Motel/Multi-Famly Home Renovtn/Remodel

Gobbato Builders LLC.....................F...... 737 843-4327
　Austin (G-1185)
Tradesorg LLC............................F...... 512 729-3544
　Austin (G-1589)

CONTRACTORS: Hydraulic Eqpt Installation & Svcs

DSM Fluid Power Inc......................E...... 512 243-1986
　Austin (G-1104)
HMC Capital Inc..........................G...... 936 441-2666
　The Woodlands (G-19872)
Hydraulic Systems Inc....................E...... 832 791-5000
　The Woodlands (G-19881)
K&B Oilfield Services Inc................F...... 903 392-8213
　Henderson (G-8266)
Wilson Supply Corporate Office...........F...... 713 237-3309
　Houston (G-12675)

CONTRACTORS: Hydraulic Well Fracturing Svcs

Alamo Pressure Pumping LLC...............B...... 432 695-6210
　Midland (G-15111)
Calfrac Well Services Corp...............C...... 210 268-0800
　Converse (G-3391)
Fts International Inc....................B...... 817 862-2000
　Fort Worth (G-6652)
Step Energy Svcs Holdings Ltd............F...... 281 606-3600
　Spring (G-19254)

PRODUCT

Unlimited Frac Sand Llc ....E 800 560-1246
Odessa (G-16191)

US Well Services Inc ....F 832 562-3730
Houston (G-12492)

CONTRACTORS: Indl Building Renovation, Remodeling & Repair

Centennial Moisture Ctrl Inc ....D 214 350-7689
Irving (G-12967)

Ggctr Inc ....E 832 456-4585
Pasadena (G-16448)

Gill Assoc Prprty MGT Systems ....G 832 644-9751
Humble (G-12770)

Trinitys Covenant LLC ....F 210 620-3694
Laredo (G-13939)

CONTRACTORS: Insulation Installation, Building

Bmf Oil & Gas Services Inc ....F 832 443-2089
Houston (G-8926)

Hill Country Insulation ....G 512 515-7707
Pflugerville (G-16675)

Houston R-Co Incorporated ....F 281 987-9909
Houston (G-10248)

Industrial Insul & Shtmtl Inc ....E 432 332-8203
Odessa (G-16030)

Mueller Construction Company ....E 903 868-3585
Sherman (G-18924)

Superior Energies Inc ....E 409 962-8549
Groves (G-8111)

CONTRACTORS: Kitchen & Bathroom Remodeling

Cruising Kitchens LLC ....G 210 920-2658
San Antonio (G-18032)

Graham Custom Cabinets LLC ....F 940 549-4311
Graham (G-7782)

Tradesorg LLC ....E 512 729-3544
Austin (G-1589)

CONTRACTORS: Kitchen Cabinet Installation

US Remodelers Inc ....E 214 488-6300
Lewisville (G-14103)

CONTRACTORS: Lighting Conductor Erection

Texas Neon Advertising Company ......F 210 734-6694
San Antonio (G-18538)

CONTRACTORS: Lighting Syst

One Source SEC & Sound Inc ....E 713 934-7400
Humble (G-12791)

Rulon Elc Illuminations Co Inc ....E 713 863-1133
Houston (G-11697)

Third Coast Services LLC ....D 832 934-0240
Magnolia (G-14629)

CONTRACTORS: Lightweight Steel Framing Installation

Requejo Construction Svcs LLC ....F 210 459-5161
San Antonio (G-18420)

CONTRACTORS: Machine Rigging & Moving

Dynamic Crane Svc Fbrction Inc ....E 713 849-1341
Houston (G-9547)

CONTRACTORS: Machinery Installation

Action Rigging and Pump Svc LP ......F 512 670-9567
Austin (G-885)

BS Fab & Mechanical Inc ....E 817 373-2879
Rio Vista (G-17477)

Lubrication Systems Texas LLC ....D 713 464-6266
Houston (G-8388)

Texas Extrusion Service Inc ....F 281 350-2288
Spring (G-19178)

CONTRACTORS: Maintenance, Parking Facility Eqpt

Parking Sense Usa Inc ....F 830 428-0299
Boerne (G-2131)

CONTRACTORS: Marble Installation, Interior

Aspen Marble Inc ....F 817 478-5140
Fort Worth (G-6404)

Northside Cultured Marble Inc ....G 281 429-5288
Conroe (G-3343)

Pks Designs Inc ....F 817 429-5174
Alvarado (G-337)

Siri Granite Inc ....F 832 203-8322
Houston (G-11907)

Stone Production Inc ....F 512 990-9800
Austin (G-1539)

Stonexpressions LLC ....G 214 366-2216
Dallas (G-5013)

Target Stone LLC ....E 832 827-8663
Houston (G-12161)

CONTRACTORS: Marble Masonry, Exterior

Dallas Marble Company Inc ....D 972 291-9145
Midlothian (G-15478)

Delta Granite and Marble Inc ....D 210 829-7171
San Antonio (G-18050)

Killeen Marble ....E 254 699-3408
Killeen (G-13612)

CONTRACTORS: Masonry & Stonework

Acme Brick Company ....D 817 332-4101
El Paso (G-5636)

Arismendy Josias ....E 817 353-1244
Fort Worth (G-6401)

JMJ Organics Ltd ....E 281 798-3056
Crosby (G-3735)

CONTRACTORS: Mechanical

Bmf Oil & Gas Services Inc ....F 832 443-2089
Houston (G-8926)

Four-Star Fabricators & Svc Co ....E 903 965-4309
Bells (G-2006)

G W Vines Company Inc ....E 214 742-8371
Dallas (G-4389)

Gonzalez Mechanical Contr LLC ....G 915 345-1282
El Paso (G-5788)

H & H Machine Service LLC ....F 979 836-2599
Brenham (G-2256)

Jml Services Inc ....F 713 582-9500
Crosby (G-3736)

M & S Mechanical Inc ....E 318 755-2431
Pittsburg (G-16747)

Maddox Enterprises Inc ....E 903 592-6531
Tyler (G-20119)

Mechanical Technical Svcs LP ....E 512 929-7090
Round Rock (G-17671)

Polk Mechanical Company LLC ....C 972 339-1200
Grand Prairie (G-7947)

Roy C Garrett Inc ....F 210 659-6701
Cibolo (G-3064)

RW Cox Inc ....E 903 739-8088
Paris (G-16369)

Welfab Inc ....E 361 552-4033
Port Lavaca (G-17156)

CONTRACTORS: Millwrights

Colliers Top of Texas Inc ....E 806 363-2867
Hereford (G-8287)

Longview Fab & Machine Inc ....E 903 238-8300
Longview (G-14269)

M & S Mechanical Inc ....E 318 755-2431
Pittsburg (G-16747)

Mueller Construction Company ....E 903 868-3585
Sherman (G-18924)

CONTRACTORS: Multi-Family Home Remodeling

Health Care Temporaries Inc ....A 713 631-7106
Houston (G-10143)

JM Construction ....E 956 518-2113
Brownsville (G-2370)

CONTRACTORS: Office Furniture Installation

Nmg Workspace Solutions LLC ....E 281 240-1007
Houston (G-11061)

CONTRACTORS: Oil & Gas Aerial Geophysical Exploration Svcs

Arena Offshore LP ....D 218 210-3138
The Woodlands (G-19832)

Cnpc USA Corporation ....E 713 465-7382
Houston (G-9222)

Freeport-Mcmoran Oil & Gas LLC ....C 713 579-6000
Houston (G-9862)

Jay Management Company LLC ....G 936 258-2646
Dayton (G-5232)

Ovintiv Exploration Inc ....C 281 210-5100
The Woodlands (G-19899)

Petra Land LLC ....F 832 791-5495
The Woodlands (G-19901)

Pioneer Natural Resources Co ....C 432 683-4768
Midland (G-15354)

Wartsila North America Inc ....C 281 233-6200
Houston (G-12600)

CONTRACTORS: Oil & Gas Building, Repairing & Dismantling Svc

Atlantic Pacific Marine Corp ....F 713 346-4300
Houston (G-8740)

Baker Petrolite LLC ....F 979 567-9859
Caldwell (G-2627)

Basic Energy Services LP ....D 432 530-0907
Odessa (G-15928)

Basic Energy Services LP ....D 806 592-4287
Denver City (G-5416)

Basic Energy Services LP ....E 817 334-4100
Fort Worth (G-6433)

Cameron Solutions Inc ....C 713 849-7500
Houston (G-9079)

Cogent Energy Services LLC ....E 713 554-1200
Houston (G-9238)

Cs Well Service LLC ....F 325 242-2438
Colorado City (G-3224)

Daniel Mike Construction Inc ....E 903 389-2595
Fairfield (G-6172)

Davis Energy Services LLC ....C 903 935-9269
Marshall (G-14774)

Diamond Refractory Svcs LLC ....E 713 378-9200
Houston (G-9458)

FDL Operating LLC ....E 469 453-7346
Irving (G-13023)

Flat Creek Resources LLC ....E 817 310-8570
Fort Worth (G-6637)

Gds International LLC ....E 713 623-1449
Houston (G-9910)

Gibbons Inc ....F 940 872-2452
Bowie (G-2196)

Gravity Oilfield Services LLC ....C 432 218-7889
Midland (G-15240)

High Roller Wells LLc ....E 936 598-5577
Center (G-2999)

Jbl Oil & Gas Operating LLC ....F 281 516-3137
Spring (G-19137)

Jmi Machine LLC ....F 361 664-2848
Alice (G-219)

Kellogg Brown & Root Intl Inc ....F 713 753-2000
Houston (G-10512)

Keppel Amfels Inc ....A 956 838-3110
Brownsville (G-2374)

Kiva Construction & Engrg Inc ....E 409 252-3211
Anahuac (G-526)

Merrell Lease Service Inc ....D 361 643-6911
Gregory (G-8101)

Moffitt & Assoc Inc ....E 361 884-9273
Corpus Christi (G-3578)

Oil States Industries Inc ....C 817 548-4200
Arlington (G-743)

Oil States Industries Inc ....C 713 445-2200
Houston (G-11160)

Palmetto Services LLC ....D 903 655-0900
Henderson (G-8269)

Patterson-Uti Energy Inc ....D 281 765-7100
Houston (G-11262)

Pierce Construction Inc ....D 903 678-3748
Beckville (G-1972)

Pipe Pros LLC ....E 361 289-9090
Corpus Christi (G-3592)

Pipeline Technique LLC ....C 281 570-1363
Humble (G-12794)

Pirate Oilfield Services Inc ....E 432 260-9040
Midland (G-15360)

Premier Worldwide Inc ....F 281 752-0014
Montgomery (G-15640)

Proserv Operations Inc ....F 713 983-7222
Houston (G-11459)

Red Energy Services LP ....F 432 943-2746
Monahans (G-15613)

Renco Tool Co Inc ....F 806 648-2903
Perryton (G-16646)

Russian-American Quality ....E 713 522-0453
Houston *(G-11700)*

Rustex Inc ....E 979 778-7551
Bryan *(G-2503)*

Sentry Wellhead Systems LLC ....E 281 210-0070
Spring *(G-19249)*

Sentry Wellhead Systems LLC ....F 432 661-5810
Odessa *(G-16151)*

Sherrod Services LLC ....E 254 729-3177
Thornton *(G-19943)*

Streamline Energy Services LLC ....F 361 852-0907
Corpus Christi *(G-3630)*

Surface Well Control LLC ....F 903 526-2522
Tyler *(G-20158)*

Tan Boots LLC ....F 512 921-0720
Austin *(G-1713)*

Team Inc ....E 409 840-9955
Beaumont *(G-1957)*

Tejas Production Services Inc ....F 361 572-3127
Victoria *(G-20307)*

Tetra Technologies Inc ....C 281 367-1983
The Woodlands *(G-19928)*

Texas 21st Century Transport & ....C 432 607-2071
Stanton *(G-19405)*

Thomas Lease Service ....F 806 202-1800
Amarillo *(G-514)*

Umphres Production Services ....F 956 765-8409
Zapata *(G-20985)*

Vortech Contracting Inc ....C 409 296-3219
Winnie *(G-20892)*

CONTRACTORS: *Oil & Gas Field Fire Fighting Svcs*

Giddings Volunteer Fire Dept ....E 979 492-1156
Giddings *(G-7695)*

Hamilton Oilfield Services Inc ....E 325 944-2540
San Angelo *(G-17804)*

Jmr Industries Ltd ....F 432 557-9721
Midland *(G-15260)*

L & C Safety Inc ....D 432 653-0393
Odessa *(G-16057)*

Ods International Inc ....D 713 782-6767
Houston *(G-11133)*

Proserv Operations Inc ....B 337 984-8054
Houston *(G-11456)*

Proserv Operations Inc ....B 281 807-2100
Houston *(G-11460)*

CONTRACTORS: *Oil & Gas Field Geological Exploration Svcs*

BP International Ltd ....C 281 366-2000
Houston *(G-8970)*

Chroma Energy Inc ....F 281 340-6100
Sugar Land *(G-19457)*

Cinco Oil & Gas LLC ....E 214 520-7727
Dallas *(G-4118)*

Cudd Pumping Services Inc ....B 432 580-3544
Odessa *(G-15972)*

Dataseismic Corporation ....E 713 650-3200
Houston *(G-9406)*

Downunder Gosolutions Amer LLC ......G 832 582-3221
Houston *(G-9510)*

Dtn LLC ....E 713 430-7100
Houston *(G-9535)*

Element Markets LLC ....E 281 207-7200
Houston *(G-9598)*

Energy Precision Tstg Lab LLC ....F 806 665-0750
Amarillo *(G-422)*

Exploration Center Building ....E 806 353-9123
Amarillo *(G-487)*

Falcon Seaboard Holdings LLC ....E 713 622-0055
Houston *(G-9755)*

Fervid Group LLC ....F 713 364-3378
Houston *(G-9779)*

Goldston Oil Corporation ....E 713 355-3408
Houston *(G-9995)*

Great Basin Petroleum Svcs LP ....D 432 561-9702
Odessa *(G-16018)*

H J Gruy and Associates Inc ....E 713 739-1000
Bellaire *(G-1997)*

Hibernia Energy III LLC ....F 713 728-7911
Houston *(G-10173)*

Odl Inc ....G 281 647-8300
Houston *(G-11131)*

Oginfocom LLC ....E 361 904-0071
Corpus Christi *(G-3583)*

Paloma Partners III LLC ....F 713 650-8500
Houston *(G-11225)*

Schlumberger Technology Corp ....C 281 285-8500
Sugar Land *(G-19549)*

Shell Oil Company ....F 713 241-6471
Houston *(G-11861)*

Sinochem Petroleum USA LP ....F 832 742-8670
Houston *(G-11906)*

Texas Geologic Services LLC ....E 979 542-3893
Giddings *(G-7702)*

Triple Diamond Energy Oper LLC ....F 972 267-8600
Dallas *(G-3853)*

Vaughn Energy Services ....F 936 539-9096
Conroe *(G-3382)*

Vitruvian Exploration IV LLC ....E 832 458-3100
Cypress *(G-3826)*

CONTRACTORS: *Oil & Gas Field Geophysical Exploration Svcs*

Breckenridge Exploration Co ....E 254 559-7566
Breckenridge *(G-2225)*

Cgg Marine (us) Inc ....F 713 369-5600
Houston *(G-9148)*

Dawson Geophysical Company ....C 432 684-3000
Midland *(G-15187)*

E & E Polaris Services Inc ....G 281 367-6000
Spring *(G-19209)*

Elite Wellsite Services LLC ....F 940 393-2116
Bridgeport *(G-2292)*

Fairfield Industries Inc ....F 281 275-7500
Houston *(G-9752)*

Geokinetics Inc ....E 713 850-7600
Houston *(G-9935)*

Geophyscal Explrtion Technolgy ....D 713 979-9900
Houston *(G-9939)*

Ggm Exploration Inc ....E 817 338-1137
Fort Worth *(G-6667)*

J & X Trucking LLC ....F 830 583-0611
Kenedy *(G-13488)*

Layton Energy Inc ....F 713 590-2820
Houston *(G-10609)*

M H C X-Ploration Corporation ....F 903 595-4323
Tyler *(G-20117)*

Magseis Ff LLC ....C 281 275-7500
Houston *(G-10737)*

Oil Spill Response USA Inc ....F 832 431-3191
Houston *(G-11153)*

Pgs Imaging Inc ....B 281 509-8000
Houston *(G-11319)*

Preston Exploration Ltd Lblty ....F 281 367-8697
The Woodlands *(G-19904)*

Schlumberger Limited ....E 713 513-2000
Houston *(G-11767)*

Schlumberger Limited ....F 713 513-2000
Houston *(G-11768)*

Schlumberger Technology Corp ....A 281 285-8500
Sugar Land *(G-19542)*

Schlumberger Technology Corp ....E 281 285-8400
Sugar Land *(G-19545)*

Schlumberger Technology Corp ....C 312 237-2810
San Antonio *(G-18458)*

Schlumberger Technology Corp ....C 832 310-2155
Houston *(G-11772)*

Schlumberger Technology Corp ....E 281 285-8226
Sugar Land *(G-19550)*

Schlumberger Technology Corp ....C 281 285-3501
Houston *(G-11779)*

Schlumberger Technology Corp ....C 281 285-8500
Houston *(G-11780)*

Seabed Geosolutions (us) Inc ....E 713 904-2244
Houston *(G-11796)*

Shearwater Geoservices Inc ....F 281 921-8000
Houston *(G-11855)*

Spectraseis Inc ....E 303 658-9171
Houston *(G-12006)*

Talos Production LLC ....G 713 328-3000
Houston *(G-12154)*

CONTRACTORS: *Oil & Gas Field Salt Water Impound/Storing Svc*

Advance Hydrocarbon Corp ....F 979 778-8100
Bryan *(G-2451)*

Advance Hydrocarbon Corp ....F 979 542-1520
Giddings *(G-7690)*

Advance Hydrocarbon Corp ....F 979 690-2226
Houston *(G-8483)*

Ecostream LLC ....E 832 429-5317
Southlake *(G-19066)*

Oilfield Water Logistics LLC ....D 214 292-2011
Dallas *(G-4757)*

Rcw Energy Services LLC ....E 972 394-1000
The Colony *(G-19812)*

S & G Disposal ....F 806 894-6044
Levelland *(G-14015)*

Smith Vacuum Service ....F 325 573-7437
Snyder *(G-19006)*

Swiftwater Energy Services LLC ....G 405 203-5419
Midland *(G-15427)*

CONTRACTORS: *Oil & Gas Field Tools Fishing Svcs*

Baker Hughes A GE Company LLC ......B 713 625-4200
Houston *(G-8801)*

C Hinton Enterprises Inc ....E 432 339-0411
Odessa *(G-15950)*

Cagle Fishing & Rental Tls Inc ....F 432 381-3061
Odessa *(G-15952)*

Klx Energy Services LLC ....D 832 844-1015
Houston *(G-10542)*

Martins Fishing Tls & Rentals ....F 432 524-7456
Andrews *(G-550)*

U S Weatherford L P ....E 903 984-5541
Kilgore *(G-13599)*

CONTRACTORS: *Oil & Gas Well Casing Cement Svcs*

B & S Services Inc ....F 281 342-1052
Boling *(G-2146)*

Baker Hughes ....F 806 273-6531
Borger *(G-2162)*

Big E Services LLC ....F 432 550-2443
Odessa *(G-15934)*

Birch Operations Inc ....F 832 701-1776
Houston *(G-8890)*

Brittany Energy LLC ....D 210 785-2893
San Antonio *(G-17968)*

CDI Vessel Holdings LLC ....A 713 361-2600
Houston *(G-9113)*

Compass Well Services LLC ....E 325 387-2940
Sonora *(G-19025)*

Compass Well Services LLC ....D 817 244-2555
Fort Worth *(G-6532)*

Compass Well Services LLC ....E 432 561-5970
Midland *(G-15173)*

Concho Oilfield Services LLC ....E 325 762-3300
Albany *(G-186)*

Conner Machine and Welding Inc ....C 806 274-2281
Borger *(G-2171)*

Ecoloop Energy Inc ....E 972 885-5130
Plano *(G-16856)*

Gep Haynesville LLC ....E 281 363-9161
The Woodlands *(G-19867)*

Horsepower Services LLC ....E 713 582-2105
Houston *(G-10209)*

Houston Casing Specialities ....F 713 433-3940
Houston *(G-10223)*

Ironhorse Unlimited Inc ....C 903 489-2075
Malakoff *(G-14635)*

K&F Equipment LLC ....F 432 664-0758
Midland *(G-15265)*

Lewis Casing Crews Inc ....F 432 366-8077
Odessa *(G-16061)*

Oilwell Hydraulics Inc ....F 281 602-8170
The Woodlands *(G-19898)*

Pacific Sensor LLC ....F 972 242-5750
Carrollton *(G-2788)*

Pate Trucking Co Inc ....E 432 758-2166
Seminole *(G-18886)*

Preco Turbine Comprsr Svcs Inc ....C 281 821-9620
Houston *(G-11397)*

Roywell LLC ....E 713 661-4747
Sugar Land *(G-19538)*

Safzone Field Services LLC ....E 210 569-6699
San Antonio *(G-18442)*

Schlumberger Technology Corp ....D 281 285-4551
Sugar Land *(G-19552)*

Schlumberger Technology Corp ....C 281 285-8500
Sugar Land *(G-19549)*

Seah Steel California LLC ....F 281 873-7800
Houston *(G-11801)*

Srh Tools LLC ....E 432 686-1058
Midland *(G-15416)*

Talon/Lpe Ltd ....F 210 253-7200
San Antonio *(G-18521)*

Top-Co Cementing Products Inc ....E 832 300-3660
Houston *(G-12321)*

Trans-Tex Cementing Svcs LLC ....D 432 699-4400
Midland *(G-15442)*

PRODUCT

Zarvona Energy LLC .... F 713 600-0600
Houston *(G-12721)*

CONTRACTORS: *Oil & Gas Well Drilling Svc*

5 Elements Drilling LLC .... E 281 203-0405
Houston *(G-8413)*

Acme Energy Services Inc .... A 432 561-5271
Midland *(G-15104)*

AES Drilling Fluids LLC .... C 888 556-4533
Houston *(G-8499)*

Aly Centrifuge Inc .... F 972 382-4400
San Angelo *(G-17775)*

Applied Drilling Tech Inc .... D 281 925-7100
Houston *(G-8667)*

Aquila Drilling Co LP .... C 940 761-3153
Wichita Falls *(G-20739)*

Archer Well Company Inc .... D 713 856-4222
Houston *(G-8682)*

Aries One LLC .... F 832 564-3628
Houston *(G-8695)*

Athens Group Holdings LLC .... G 512 345-0600
Austin *(G-945)*

Atlantic Maritime Services LLC ... F 713 621-7800
Houston *(G-8739)*

Atlantica Management USA Inc ... E 832 494-2200
Houston *(G-8741)*

Atlas Ptro Explrtion Worldwide ... E 281 579-5200
Houston *(G-8745)*

Atlas Well Service LLC .... E 432 683-3835
Midland *(G-15123)*

Ats Drilling LP .... D 817 498-0040
Haltom City *(G-8132)*

Atwood Oceanics Management LLC ... F 281 749-7800
Houston *(G-8747)*

Axxis Drilling Inc .... E 985 868-6969
Houston *(G-8765)*

Baker Hghes Olfld Oprtions LLC ... F 713 879-1000
Houston *(G-8796)*

Baker Hughes A GE Company LLC ... B 713 625-4200
Houston *(G-8801)*

Big Tex Well Services LLC .... E 817 599-6155
Weatherford *(G-20578)*

Bison Drlg & Field Svcs LLC ...... C 405 463-6912
Odessa *(G-15935)*

Black Diamond Energy Inc .... E 307 684-2910
Katy *(G-13352)*

Black Sail Holdings Corp .... F 281 315-4955
Shenandoah *(G-18895)*

Bluff Creek Petroleum LLC .... F 325 676-5557
Abilene *(G-17)*

Bmlcrude Inc .... F 325 676-3355
Abilene *(G-20)*

BP America Production Company ... D 806 935-8810
Dumas *(G-5519)*

Brucemark Petroleum Inc .... F 630 339-5490
Addison *(G-108)*

C&D Bobcat and Backhoe LLC .... F 512 358-0163
Austin *(G-1018)*

Cantera Energy LLC .... E 832 246-6100
The Woodlands *(G-19838)*

Cantera Operating LLC .... F 832 246-6100
The Woodlands *(G-19839)*

Capital Well Service LLC .... C 830 767-2036
Jourdanton *(G-13329)*

Cavern Solutions Inc .... F 713 393-7733
Houston *(G-9103)*

Charger Services LLC .... E 432 218-7674
Midland *(G-15158)*

Crimson Exploration Inc .... E 713 236-7400
Houston *(G-9344)*

Cude Oilfield Contractors Inc ...... F 281 298-0600
Conroe *(G-3288)*

Dallas Oil .... E 214 638-9055
Dallas *(G-4223)*

Deen Drilling Company .... F 940 574-2561
Archer City *(G-595)*

Deepwell Energy Services LLC .... F 337 780-8297
Beaumont *(G-1882)*

Deepwell Energy Services LLC .... E 817 796-9970
Grapevine *(G-8027)*

Denbury Onshore LLC .... F 281 482-7581
Alvin *(G-358)*

Devon Energy Corporation .... F 903 693-7196
Carthage *(G-2906)*

Dewbre Petroleum Corporation ... F 361 888-7978
Corpus Christi *(G-3512)*

DH Braman III .... E 361 578-6271
Victoria *(G-20258)*

Diamond Offshore Company .... C 281 492-5300
Houston *(G-9452)*

Diamond Offshore Drilling Inc ..... C 281 492-5300
Houston *(G-9453)*

Diamond Offshore Drlg Svcs Inc ... E 281 492-5300
Houston *(G-9454)*

Diamond Offshore Finance Co ..... B 281 492-5300
Barker *(G-1746)*

Diamond Offshore General Co ..... B 281 492-5300
Houston *(G-9455)*

Diamond Offshore Management Co ... B 281 492-5300
Houston *(G-9456)*

Diamond Offshore Nthrlands B U ... B 281 492-5300
Houston *(G-9457)*

Dillard Kay R & Estate AR D ...... E 940 716-5100
Wichita Falls *(G-20759)*

Djh Services LLC .... E 713 228-5911
Houston *(G-9485)*

Don H Wilson Inc .... F 903 478-3860
Elkhart *(G-6059)*

Double K Drilling LLC .... F 940 567-2855
Jacksboro *(G-13218)*

Downhole Energy Inc .... G 469 250-7179
Garland *(G-7481)*

Duffco Oil Tools Inc .... D 325 672-2446
Abilene *(G-39)*

E & H Drilling Co .... F 940 549-0370
Graham *(G-7781)*

Eagle Oilfield Welding .... E 830 965-4255
Dilley *(G-5480)*

Edf Trading North America LLC ... F 830 351-5075
Luling *(G-14560)*

EGI Resources Inc .... F 432 687-6560
Midland *(G-15207)*

Emas Chiyoda Subsea Inc .... D 832 487-7300
Houston *(G-9607)*

Energy Reserves Group LLC .... E 713 659-7800
Houston *(G-9636)*

Ensco International Inc .... D 800 423-8006
Houston *(G-9652)*

Ensign United States Drlg Inc ..... E 303 292-1206
Houston *(G-9657)*

Ensign US Southern Drlg LLC ..... F 303 292-1206
Houston *(G-9658)*

Enterprise Offshore Drlg LLC ...... B 832 399-6500
Houston *(G-9662)*

Epic Energy Resources Inc .... C 281 419-3742
Houston *(G-9681)*

Erin Energy Corporation .... D 713 797-2940
Houston *(G-9692)*

Exxonmobil Development Company ... E 713 656-3636
Houston *(G-9740)*

Faith Drilling LLC .... E 432 758-6352
Seminole *(G-18882)*

Falcon Seaboard Oil & Gas LLC ... F 713 622-0055
Houston *(G-9756)*

Ferza Company LLC .... G 956 686-7100
Hidalgo *(G-8307)*

Finley Resources Inc .... F 817 336-1924
Fort Worth *(G-6631)*

Flocap Injection Services LLC ..... F 432 614-1609
Midland *(G-15232)*

Forge Energy LLC .... F 210 478-5950
San Antonio *(G-18121)*

Fox Nde .... F 325 690-1633
Abilene *(G-41)*

Foxxe Energy Services LLC .... D 713 960-0381
Houston *(G-9850)*

Friedel Drilling Co .... F 361 293-5545
Yoakum *(G-20966)*

Frontera Resources Corporation ... F 713 585-3200
Houston *(G-9868)*

Global Marine Inc .... D 713 232-7500
Houston *(G-9974)*

Global Santa Fe Drilling Co .... D 281 925-6821
Houston *(G-9976)*

Global Santa Fe Inc .... B 281 925-6000
Houston *(G-9977)*

Goodrich Drillers LLC .... E 713 659-3680
Houston *(G-10000)*

Guenther Family LP .... E 210 829-1800
San Antonio *(G-18155)*

Halliburton Company .... E 281 297-1200
Spring *(G-19214)*

Halliburton Company .... C 281 297-1200
Houston *(G-10100)*

Halliburton Company .... E 281 871-2699
Houston *(G-10107)*

Halliburton International Inc .... A 214 759-2600
Dallas *(G-4429)*

Hazelett Drilling and Sup Corp .... E 512 398-6682
Lockhart *(G-14169)*

Hb2 Energy Inc .... E 713 377-9860
Houston *(G-10140)*

Hdd Rotary Sales LLC .... E 936 446-1200
Houston *(G-10141)*

Heart Land Petroleum Corp .... D 325 437-8430
Abilene *(G-48)*

Helmerich & Payne Inc .... G 830 379-5858
Seguin *(G-18841)*

Helmerich & Payne Intl Drlg Co ... C 361 664-0114
Seguin *(G-18842)*

Helmerich & Payne Intl Drlg Co ... B 832 782-6800
Houston *(G-10151)*

Hercules Drilling Company LLC ... A 713 350-5100
Houston *(G-10157)*

Hercules Offshore Inc .... A 713 350-5100
Houston *(G-10158)*

Hess Jerry Operating Company ... F 940 759-4791
Muenster *(G-15670)*

Ht Energy LLC .... E 806 771-7769
Lubbock *(G-14419)*

Impact Fluid Solutions LP .... E 713 964-7736
Houston *(G-10333)*

Independence Contract Drlg Inc ... D 281 598-1230
Houston *(G-10338)*

Inpex Eagle Ford LLC .... D 713 850-8480
Houston *(G-10375)*

Integrity Services LLC .... D 432 682-0703
Midland *(G-15253)*

Intrepid Drctnal Drlg Spclsts ...... E 432 617-0593
Midland *(G-15254)*

J W Drilling Inc .... D 575 748-8704
Quinlan *(G-17223)*

J W Resources Inc .... G 806 935-0185
Dumas *(G-5523)*

J-W Energy Company .... D 972 233-8191
Addison *(G-137)*

Jamex Inc .... F 214 265-7141
Lewisville *(G-14058)*

Johnson Burns Co .... F 806 372-5869
Amarillo *(G-494)*

Jp3 Measurement LLC .... E 512 537-8450
Austin *(G-1262)*

Keane Frac Tx LLC .... F 713 960-0381
Houston *(G-10507)*

Keane Group Holdings LLC .... D 713 960-0381
Houston *(G-10510)*

Kelford Energy LLC .... F 817 615-0263
Fort Worth *(G-6754)*

Kenner Well Svc of Palestine ...... E 903 729-3196
Palestine *(G-16300)*

Keppel Letourneau Usa Inc .... E 281 677-4482
Houston *(G-10518)*

Key Energy Drilling Inc .... E 432 639-2534
Iraan *(G-12919)*

Key Energy Drilling Inc .... G 713 651-4300
Kilgore *(G-13560)*

Key Energy Services Inc .... F 432 570-7440
Midland *(G-15270)*

Key Energy Services Inc .... C 713 651-4300
Houston *(G-10522)*

Key Energy Services Inc .... D 432 586-2591
Odessa *(G-16048)*

Key Energy Services Inc .... E 432 561-5682
Odessa *(G-16049)*

Key Energy Services Inc .... D 432 267-5291
Big Spring *(G-2086)*

Key Energy Services Inc .... E 713 651-4300
Houston *(G-10523)*

Key Energy Services Inc .... D 903 538-2280
Palestine *(G-16301)*

Key Energy Services Inc .... D 806 872-8331
Lamesa *(G-13827)*

Key Energy Services Inc .... E 903 963-5208
Van *(G-20208)*

Kodiak Production Ltd .... E 325 884-2040
Big Lake *(G-2058)*

Lauson Drilling Services Inc .... E 979 733-0345
Alleyton *(G-310)*

Lewis Petro Properties Inc .... D 210 384-3200
San Antonio *(G-18249)*

Lindemann Drilling Co Inc .... F 940 691-1344
Archer City *(G-596)*

Logan International Inc .... C 832 386-2500
Houston *(G-10670)*

Lyons Drilling Inc .... E 979 596-1898
Rockdale *(G-17525)*

M K S Natural Gas Company ...... E 817 599-9477
Weatherford *(G-20601)*

M P Energy Inc .... F 281 350-6350
Houston *(G-10719)*

Maersk Drilling USA Inc	F	713 972-3300
Houston (G-10733)		
Maxus US Exploration Company	E	281 681-7200
The Woodlands (G-19892)		
MB Robinson Inc	E	432 267-5277
Big Spring (G-2087)		
McClinton Energy Group L L C	C	432 563-5500
Midland (G-15296)		
McClinton Energy Group L L C	E	432 563-5500
Odessa (G-16077)		
Medallion Oil Company Inc	F	713 654-0144
Houston (G-10815)		
Miramar Wf LLC	F	940 626-4309
Alvord (G-389)		
Mlc Operating LP	E	713 255-6200
Spring (G-19146)		
Modern Exploration Inc	F	903 893-1129
Sherman (G-18922)		
Morningstar Partners LP	E	817 334-7800
Fort Worth (G-6852)		
Ms Directional LLC	D	936 442-2500
Conroe (G-3332)		
Mudsmith Ltd	F	432 687-6837
Midland (G-15308)		
Nabors Corporate Services Inc	C	281 874-0035
Houston (G-10950)		
Nabors Drilling Tech USA Inc	E	281 462-1730
Crosby (G-3738)		
Nabors Industries Inc	C	281 874-0035
Houston (G-10953)		
Nabors International Inc	E	281 874-0035
Houston (G-10954)		
Noble Drilling (us) Inc	D	281 276-6100
Sugar Land (G-19513)		
Noble Drilling Corporation	B	281 276-6100
Sugar Land (G-19514)		
Noble Drilling Holding LLC	F	281 276-6100
Sugar Land (G-19515)		
Noble Drilling Services Inc	B	281 276-6100
Sugar Land (G-19516)		
Noble Holding US Corporation	C	281 276-6100
Sugar Land (G-19517)		
Noble International Finance Co	F	281 276-6142
Sugar Land (G-19518)		
Northern Offshore Ltd	E	281 649-2600
Houston (G-11078)		
Nova Drilling Technologies Inc	F	713 726-0151
Houston (G-11090)		
Nri Inc	F	903 526-5800
Tyler (G-20134)		
Nzone Guidance LLC	F	512 778-5353
Liberty Hill (G-14128)		
Oasis Midstream Partners LP	C	281 404-9500
Houston (G-11108)		
Octane Energy Consulting LLC	F	432 685-7736
Midland (G-15324)		
Odyssea Marine Holdings Inc	A	713 260-1100
Houston (G-11135)		
Oil Field Supply Pty Ltd	F	281 877-0049
Houston (G-11152)		
Pacific Drilling Services Inc	D	713 334-6662
Houston (G-11241)		
Parker Drilling Company	C	281 406-2000
Houston (G-11241)		
Parker Drilling MGT Svcs Ltd	C	281 406-2000
Houston (G-11242)		
Parker Drilling Offshr Co LLC	E	281 406-2000
Houston (G-11243)		
Pattersn-Uti Drlg Svcs LP Lllp	D	325 573-1104
Snyder (G-18998)		
Pattersn-Uti Drlg Svcs LP Lllp	E	361 576-6896
Victoria (G-20291)		
Patterson-Uti Acquisition LLC	B	432 561-9382
Midland (G-15341)		
Patterson-Uti Drlg Intl Inc	D	214 765-5530
Houston (G-11261)		
Patterson-Uti MGT Svcs LLC	F	325 574-6300
Snyder (G-19000)		
Petroleum Engineers Intl	E	337 984-2603
Houston (G-11306)		
Petroplex Energy Inc	F	432 687-2222
Midland (G-15349)		
Piedra Operating LLC	F	432 685-9005
Midland (G-15351)		
Pioneer Drilling Services Ltd	E	210 828-7689
San Antonio (G-18377)		
Pioneer Drilling Services Ltd	F	432 684-7360
Midland (G-15353)		
Pioneer Drilling Services Ltd	C	361 289-9241
Corpus Christi (G-3591)		
Pioneer Energy Services Corp	D	281 880-9988
Tomball (G-19999)		
Pioneer Wireline Services LLC	D	210 828-7689
San Antonio (G-18379)		
Precision Drilling Company LP	E	817 396-4714
Cresson (G-3711)		
Precision Drilling Company LP	D	713 435-6100
Houston (G-11390)		
Precision Tech	D	281 227-5750
Houston (G-11395)		
Price Drilling Company Inc	D	361 256-3363
Benavides (G-2035)		
Primera Energy LLC	F	210 490-8200
Longview (G-14290)		
Professnal Drctional Entps Inc	C	936 441-7266
Conroe (G-3354)		
Qes Pressure Control LLC	F	903 643-0700
Longview (G-14291)		
Qri International LLC	F	713 485-8800
Houston (G-11487)		
Radco Operations LP	F	409 287-1277
Sour Lake (G-19033)		
Rfc Drilling LLC	C	432 276-3505
Odessa (G-16138)		
RG Exploration LLC	G	405 650-1207
Midland (G-15384)		
Roco Drilling and Service Inc	D	903 963-7036
Van (G-20209)		
Rotary Exploration Inc	F	210 248-9892
San Antonio (G-18431)		
Rowan Companies LLC	C	713 621-7800
Houston (G-11676)		
Rowan Marine Drilling Inc	C	713 621-7800
Houston (G-11678)		
Rowan Petroleum Inc	C	713 621-7800
Houston (G-11679)		
Roxwell Performance Drlg LLC	F	432 617-0419
Midland (G-15389)		
Rutherford-Moran Exploration	E	859 254-4775
Houston (G-11702)		
Sage Energy Company	F	979 567-7629
Caldwell (G-2634)		
Sage Energy Company	E	210 404-2828
San Antonio (G-18443)		
Savanna Drilling LLC	F	432 614-1055
Odessa (G-16150)		
Savanna Energy Svcs USA Corp	F	281 907-4800
The Woodlands (G-19917)		
Saxon Drilling LP	E	281 712-4529
Katy (G-13439)		
Scientific Drilling Intl Inc	E	281 214-7600
Houston (G-11787)		
Seadrill Americas Inc	D	713 407-8900
Houston (G-11799)		
Seahawk Drilling Inc	F	713 369-7300
Houston (G-11803)		
Sentry Oil & Gas LLC	E	212 753-6367
Mico (G-15094)		
Service Drilling Southwest LLC	F	806 878-2052
Stinnett (G-19428)		
SES Operating Inc	E	432 687-6560
Midland (G-15404)		
Sidewinder Drilling Inc	D	832 320-7600
Houston (G-11877)		
Smalley Drilling & Trckg Corp	E	325 762-3409
Albany (G-193)		
Snyder Drilling Corp	F	325 762-2389
Albany (G-194)		
Songa Offshore	E	713 781-0670
Houston (G-11952)		
Steward Energy II LLC	F	214 297-0500
Frisco (G-7314)		
Suits Drilling Company	F	325 573-1104
Snyder (G-19011)		
Sunset Well Service Inc	E	432 561-8600
Odessa (G-16169)		
Surge Operating LLC	E	832 333-2300
Houston (G-12125)		
Swans Production Inc	F	940 567-3147
Jacksboro (G-13223)		
Synergy Oil & Gas LP	F	713 827-9988
Houston (G-12135)		
T X P Inc	G	325 944-9844
San Angelo (G-17829)		
Tesco Corporation (us)	D	713 359-7000
Houston (G-12212)		
Texas 21st Century Transport &	C	432 607-2071
Stanton (G-19405)		
Texas Australian Power Inc	E	940 723-4122
Wichita Falls (G-20815)		
Texokan Operating Inc	F	214 484-2322
Dallas (G-5080)		
Texstar Energy Corporation	G	830 875-5919
Luling (G-14565)		
Total E&P Usa Inc	C	713 647-3000
Houston (G-12330)		
Total Operations Prod Svcs LLC	F	432 332-9777
Midland (G-15440)		
Trans-Gulf Drilling Svcs Inc	G	903 759-0010
Longview (G-14320)		
Transcean Offshore Dpwter Drlg	G	713 232-7500
Houston (G-12349)		
Transcend Drilling Company Inc	D	432 618-1100
Midland (G-15443)		
Transocean Inc	C	713 232-7500
Houston (G-12352)		
Transocean Offshore USA Inc	D	713 232-7500
Houston (G-12353)		
Transworld Worldwide Inc	B	713 232-7500
Houston (G-12355)		
Trey Resources Inc	E	432 570-6898
Midland (G-15444)		
Tri Resources Inc	C	713 584-1000
Houston (G-12362)		
Tsar Operating Company	F	817 731-9595
Fort Worth (G-7085)		
Tuboscope (holding US) LLC	F	713 799-5100
Houston (G-12401)		
Turn Right Tools LLC	E	432 704-5490
Midland (G-15449)		
Txco Resources Inc	F	210 822-8864
Dallas (G-5124)		
Union Drilling Inc	C	432 682-6111
Midland (G-15454)		
Universal Pressure Pumping Inc	F	432 699-3205
Midland (G-15457)		
Universal Pressure Pumping Inc	D	432 221-7000
Houston (G-12463)		
Vaalco Gabon (etame) Inc	E	713 623-0801
Houston (G-12515)		
Vantage Driller I Co	E	281 404-4700
Houston (G-12531)		
Vantage Energy Services Inc	E	281 404-4700
Houston (G-12533)		
Varel Energy Solutions	F	972 242-1160
Houston (G-12537)		
Villatoro Construction LLC	E	214 350-7900
Wylie (G-20954)		
Viper Petroleum LLC	F	832 917-5804
San Antonio (G-18594)		
Weatherford International Inc	G	713 836-4000
Houston (G-12620)		
West Texas Energy Sevices LLC	F	432 267-3126
Big Spring (G-2102)		
Wisco Moran Drilling Co Inc	D	281 431-2600
Rosharon (G-17616)		
Yohawk Energy LLC	G	817 484-9642
Fort Worth (G-7157)		
Zarsky Lumber Company Inc	E	361 882-2575
Corpus Christi (G-3658)		

CONTRACTORS: Oil & Gas Well Flow Rate Measurement Svcs

Aim Oilfield Services	F	281 814-9787
Pearland (G-16537)		
Charts Ltd	E	432 697-7801
Midland (G-15159)		
Five Star Field Services LLC	D	817 594-9799
Weatherford (G-20591)		
Jag Energy Usa Inc	E	361 449-1400
George West (G-7625)		
Martin-Decker Totco Inc	F	903 534-3677
Tyler (G-20120)		
Measurement Services Inc	F	361 227-4998
Alice (G-228)		
Promar LP	C	361 727-3300
Rockport (G-17531)		
S & S Contract Pumping Svc Inc	F	956 386-0211
Edinburg (G-5601)		
Wedge Measurement Systems LLC	C	713 490-9444
Houston (G-12625)		
Zdscada LP	F	903 526-1100
Tyler (G-20179)		

CONTRACTORS: Oil & Gas Well On-Site Foundation Building Svcs

Aggregate Plant Products Co	D	210 333-1111
San Antonio (G-17874)		

Employee Codes: A=Over 500 employees, B=251-500
C=101-250, D=51-100, E=20-50, F=10-19, G=9

2021 Harris Texas
Manufacturers Directory

1453

PRODUCT

Burns Welding Works Inc ....F 432 682-0495
Midland *(G-15153)*

Capps Construction and Gas Co..........F 903 693-2580
Carthage *(G-2900)*

Complete Solids Control LLC ....F 817 372-2702
Fort Worth *(G-6533)*

Crawford Industrial Svcs LLC ....F 409 925-9580
Santa Fe *(G-18733)*

DFI Piling Inc ....F 877 334-7453
Conroe *(G-3291)*

Epic Energy Services LLC ....C 361 222-1226
Odem *(G-15895)*

Farm & Ranch Construction LLC ....E 254 364-2226
Iredell *(G-12921)*

J & X Trucking LLC ....E 830 583-0611
Kenedy *(G-13488)*

Jamco Services LLC ....D 432 242-6051
Dallas *(G-4523)*

Overton Energy LLC ....F 713 580-7250
Houston *(G-11207)*

Partners Specialties Inc ....E 281 922-9102
Houston *(G-11251)*

Renegade Well Services LLC ....E 682 936-4466
Granbury *(G-7807)*

ROC Service Company LLC ....C 940 683-0159
Bridgeport *(G-2300)*

Salt Creek Midstream LLC ....F 281 655-3200
Houston *(G-11734)*

Santos CMI Inc (usa) ....F 713 273-4140
Houston *(G-11749)*

Techniplex Conference Center ....G 281 565-5566
Stafford *(G-19383)*

Udelhoven Inc ....D 210 635-8833
Floresville *(G-6255)*

CONTRACTORS: Oil & Gas Well Plugging & Abandoning Svcs

Delta Seaboard LLC ....G 713 782-1468
Houston *(G-9435)*

Downing Well Service Inc ....F 830 665-4923
Devine *(G-5449)*

Epica Applied Technologies LLC ....E 281 367-1983
Converse *(G-3392)*

Interwell US LLC ....E 832 461-1500
Houston *(G-10408)*

Maverick Well Pluggers LLC ....E 432 458-3780
Midland *(G-15295)*

Pason Systems USA Corp ....D 713 693-8700
Houston *(G-11256)*

Ranger Energy Services LLC ....B 713 461-9000
Houston *(G-11546)*

Reliable Wireline LLC ....E 713 280-7995
Houston *(G-11592)*

Superior Energy Services LLC ....E 432 385-3000
Odessa *(G-16171)*

Superior Energy Services LLC ....D 281 784-5700
Houston *(G-12114)*

Superior Energy Services LLC ....E 281 934-2181
Brookshire *(G-2326)*

Whitney Oil & Gas LLC ....F 504 218-2929
Houston *(G-12665)*

CONTRACTORS: Oil & Gas Well Redrilling

Rotary Components Intl Inc ....F 281 590-6484
Houston *(G-11668)*

Tomcat Drilling LLC ....D 316 262-8554
Corsicana *(G-3686)*

Unit Drilling Company ....E 713 960-8870
Houston *(G-12443)*

CONTRACTORS: Oil & Gas Well reworking

Busters Well Service Inc ....D 432 586-2533
Kermit *(G-13510)*

Dhw Well Service Inc ....C 830 876-9615
Carrizo Springs *(G-2685)*

Interwell US LLC ....E 832 461-1500
Houston *(G-10408)*

J B Oil & Gas Well Service ....F 830 378-5586
Dilley *(G-5482)*

Nabors Offshore Corporation ....E 281 874-0406
Houston *(G-10955)*

Radial Drilling Services Inc ....E 281 374-7507
Spring *(G-19161)*

Viper Well Services LLC ....E 979 541-5262
El Campo *(G-5628)*

Western Well Service Inc ....E 940 723-2550
Wichita Falls *(G-20830)*

CONTRACTORS: Oil & Gas Wells Pumping Svcs

B J Services Company USA ....A 713 625-4200
Houston *(G-8775)*

B J Services Company USA ....E 281 357-2700
Tomball *(G-19963)*

B J Services Company USA ....A 713 879-1727
Houston *(G-8776)*

B J Services Company USA ....A 713 439-8600
Houston *(G-8777)*

CL&f Offshore LLC ....F 281 873-9378
Houston *(G-9204)*

CL&f Operating LLC ....F 281 873-9378
Houston *(G-9205)*

Hotwell Us LLC ....F 281 598-9990
Houston *(G-10213)*

Kodiak Gas Services LLC ....B 936 539-3300
Montgomery *(G-15635)*

Pioneer Ntral Rsrces Pmpg Svcs ....D 972 444-9001
Irving *(G-13145)*

Seawolf Transport LP ....F 713 518-1763
Houston *(G-11810)*

Stephens & Johnson Oper Co ....E 940 723-2166
Wichita Falls *(G-20812)*

Texas Industrial Choice LLC ....E 432 231-7313
Pecos *(G-16627)*

CONTRACTORS: Oil & Gas Wells Svcs

A and M Services Inc ....F 432 290-5536
Andrews *(G-532)*

A E & Sons LLC ....F 281 898-4021
Pearland *(G-16535)*

Accurate Pmpg Contractings Inc ....F 254 562-9747
Mexia *(G-15086)*

All City Well Service ....F 432 332-8863
Odessa *(G-15908)*

All Points Equipment Co LLC ....E 337 369-6314
Houston *(G-8540)*

Allied Well Service Inc ....F 361 664-6122
Alice *(G-204)*

Allpoints Oilfield Svcs LLC ....F 713 393-4200
Houston *(G-8558)*

Altus Intervention USA Inc ....E 346 231-0060
Houston *(G-8573)*

American Safety Services Inc ....C 432 552-7625
Odessa *(G-15914)*

ARC Pressure Data Inc ....F 432 563-2371
Aubrey *(G-846)*

Arpco Valves & Controls LLC ....F 903 834-7007
Kilgore *(G-13532)*

Axis Well Services LLC ....E 903 759-0082
Longview *(G-14199)*

B & E Roustabout Inc ....E 432 393-5672
Big Spring *(G-2070)*

Baker Hghes Olfld Oprtions LLC ....F 713 879-1000
Houston *(G-8796)*

Basic Energy Services Inc ....E 361 348-3320
Premont *(G-17203)*

Basic Energy Services Inc ....D 817 334-4100
Fort Worth *(G-6429)*

Basic Esa Inc ....D 817 334-4100
Knox City *(G-13663)*

Beckman Well Servicing Company ....E 806 435-2543
Perryton *(G-16634)*

Brothers Well Service Ltd ....E 979 543-6851
El Campo *(G-5613)*

Central Texas Oilfield Sup Co ....G 254 562-5522
Mexia *(G-15089)*

Chief Oilfield Tech LLC ....F 432 614-4481
Midland *(G-15164)*

Clements Fluids Henderson Ltd ....E 903 581-5110
Tyler *(G-20068)*

Concho Services LLC ....F 325 869-5242
Eden *(G-5571)*

Copan Corporation ....G 806 665-1267
Pampa *(G-16319)*

Cwr Management LLC ....E 512 212-9737
San Marcos *(G-18683)*

Dcp Midstream LLC ....E 432 343-7112
Coyanosa *(G-3695)*

Duoline Technologies LLC ....E 903 734-1371
Gilmer *(G-7706)*

Duval Well Service Inc ....E 361 394-7079
Freer *(G-7223)*

Extreme Well Testing LLC ....E 956 969-4452
Weslaco *(G-20659)*

First Energy Services Company ....B 817 334-4100
Fort Worth *(G-6633)*

Flint Energy Services Inc ....C 361 449-2405
George West *(G-7624)*

FMC Technologies Offshore LLC ....E 713 341-7742
Houston *(G-9828)*

Fortay Inc ....F 806 948-4166
Sunray *(G-19617)*

Hacker Brothers Well Service ....G 940 759-4196
Muenster *(G-15669)*

Heritage Wire Line Services ....G 903 534-0671
Tyler *(G-20097)*

Ic-I Remediate LLC ....F 432 213-7813
Big Spring *(G-2083)*

Jmd Oilfield and Rig Svc LLC ....E 432 208-9941
Odessa *(G-16041)*

Jta Service ....F 432 556-0091
Midland *(G-15262)*

K & N Perforators Inc ....E 361 578-8851
Victoria *(G-20279)*

K&B Oilfield Services Inc ....F 903 392-8213
Henderson *(G-8266)*

Kc Field Services Inc ....E 903 322-9353
Buffalo *(G-2545)*

Key Energy Services Inc ....D 979 542-3344
Giddings *(G-7698)*

Key Energy Services Inc ....F 432 620-0300
Midland *(G-15269)*

Key Energy Services Inc ....E 361 578-9975
Edna *(G-5608)*

Key Energy Services Inc ....C 713 651-4300
Houston *(G-10522)*

Key Energy Services Inc ....D 432 586-2591
Odessa *(G-16048)*

Key Energy Services Inc ....E 432 561-5682
Odessa *(G-16049)*

Key Energy Services Inc ....E 432 267-5291
Big Spring *(G-2086)*

Key Energy Services Inc ....E 432 558-3574
Crane *(G-3699)*

Key Energy Services Inc ....E 713 651-4300
Houston *(G-10523)*

Key Energy Services Inc ....E 979 589-2594
Bryan *(G-2483)*

Key Energy Services Inc ....E 806 489-7452
Welch *(G-20655)*

Key Energy Services Inc ....D 806 872-8331
Lamesa *(G-13827)*

Key Energy Services Inc ....F 432 523-5155
Andrews *(G-548)*

King Well Service Inc ....D 806 323-6664
Canadian *(G-2652)*

Knight Energy Services LLC ....E 832 678-8585
Houston *(G-10548)*

Lloyds Register Drilling Inte ....B 281 675-3100
Houston *(G-10658)*

Luling Well Service ....F 830 875-9181
Luling *(G-14562)*

M & W Hot Oil Inc ....E 432 447-2108
Pecos *(G-16623)*

Magnum Producing LP ....F 361 882-3858
Corpus Christi *(G-3569)*

Majestic Petroleum Svcs LLC ....D 432 686-2023
Midland *(G-15291)*

Marine Well Containment Co LLC ....E 281 820-8800
Houston *(G-10766)*

Mason Brothers Cnstr Co Inc ....E 806 495-3400
Post *(G-17191)*

Maverick Solutions LLC ....C 817 334-4100
Fort Worth *(G-6821)*

Mercer Well Service Inc ....D 940 567-5991
Jacksboro *(G-13222)*

Merrimac Manufacturing Inc ....E 936 894-3900
Plantersville *(G-17059)*

Michelson Energy Company ....F 210 826-0681
San Antonio *(G-18299)*

Mitchell Well Service Inc ....E 281 576-5007
Baytown *(G-1797)*

Ms Directional LLC ....D 936 442-2500
Conroe *(G-3332)*

Nabors Corporate Services Inc ....C 281 874-0035
Houston *(G-10950)*

Nabors Industries Inc ....C 281 874-0035
Houston *(G-10953)*

Nabors Offshore Corporation ....E 281 874-0406
Houston *(G-10955)*

Nabors Well Services Ltd ....E 281 874-0035
Houston *(G-10958)*

Nabors Well Services Ltd ....E 432 836-4332
Iraan *(G-12920)*

Normans Well Service Inc ....F 940 668-8201
Gainesville *(G-7354)*

Omni Air & Nitrogen Ltd ....F 432 288-9087
Midland **(G-15327)**

Peregrine Stimulation Svcs LLC ......G...... 713 201-6787
Fulshear **(G-7329)**

Petro Mechanical Services LLC.....D 800 727-1398
Odessa **(G-16120)**

Petroplex Acidizing Inc ....E 432 563-1299
Midland **(G-15348)**

Pioner Ntrl Rsrc WII Srvcs LLC ....E 972 969-3670
Irving **(G-13148)**

Primed Up Nitrogen Svcs LLC ....F 361 543-0747
Anahuac **(G-527)**

Q2 Artificial Lift Svcs LLC ....D 903 983-1432
Midland **(G-15372)**

Quail Well Service Inc ....E 325 677-0323
Abilene **(G-67)**

R-Tex Services LLC ....D 817 774-3333
Joshua **(G-13324)**

Recovered Water Industries LLC ......E 940 668-8200
Gainesville **(G-7360)**

Reef Chemical Corporation Inc ....C 432 560-5600
Midland **(G-15379)**

Renegade Well Services LLC ....E 940 626-4498
Decatur **(G-5252)**

Renegade Well Services LLC ....E 830 378-5977
Dilley **(G-5483)**

Renegade Well Services LLC ....E 817 389-2496
Godley **(G-7740)**

Rhos Inc ....F 979 542-5420
Giddings **(G-7701)**

Roco Drilling and Service Inc ....D 903 963-7036
Van **(G-20209)**

Rusk County Well Service Inc ....E 903 984-5017
Kilgore **(G-13588)**

S & V Well Service Inc ....F 940 872-3535
Bowie **(G-2200)**

Salazar Service and Trckg Corp ......E 432 523-9658
Midland **(G-15394)**

Seguro Well Service Inc ....F 830 672-8025
Gonzales **(G-7764)**

Sellers Lease Service Inc ....F 361 865-2142
Flatonia **(G-6234)**

Shoco Production LP ....F 903 759-0082
Longview **(G-14308)**

Smco L & M LP ....E 432 550-7116
Odessa **(G-16155)**

Southern Lease Service Ltd ....F 361 449-3048
George West **(G-7629)**

Step Energy Services USA Ltd ....F 210 477-1517
San Antonio **(G-18500)**

Strike LLC ....E 888 353-1444
Odessa **(G-16167)**

Strike LLC ....E 888 353-1444
Robstown **(G-17517)**

Strike LLC ....E 888 353-1444
San Antonio **(G-18509)**

Strike LLC ....E 888 353-1444
Edinburg **(G-5603)**

Strike LLC ....D 888 353-1444
Fort Worth **(G-7020)**

Strike LLC ....B 888 353-1444
Baytown **(G-1837)**

Superior Energy Services Inc ....D 713 654-2200
Houston **(G-12112)**

Superior Energy Services LLC ....E 281 999-0047
Houston **(G-12113)**

Superior Tubing Tester ....F 361 668-4611
Alice **(G-238)**

Targa Resources GP LLC ....E 713 873-1000
Houston **(G-12160)**

Tdr Services Inc ....D 422 606-6084
Midland **(G-15434)**

Texas Global Systems Inc ....F 832 403-4238
Houston **(G-12233)**

Total Production Services Inc ....C 361 572-0484
Victoria **(G-20311)**

Total Sand Services LLC ....G 817 420-7474
Fort Worth **(G-7067)**

Tri Resources Inc ....F 903 845-2617
Gladewater **(G-7729)**

Trupoint Well Services LLC ....E 940 683-2871
Longview **(G-14323)**

United Energex Inc ....E 254 629-8560
Cisco **(G-3069)**

United Energex Inc ....E 210 826-0681
San Antonio **(G-18577)**

Universal Oilfield Services ....E 936 636-2324
Lovelady **(G-14355)**

USA Rock Bit Inc ....G 940 574-2238
Archer City **(G-598)**

Viper Petroleum LLC ....F 832 917-5804
San Antonio **(G-18594)**

Western Truck & Equipment ....E 940 723-2555
Wichita Falls **(G-20829)**

Wireline Incorporated ....E 903 663-1963
Longview **(G-14338)**

CONTRACTORS: *Oil Field Haulage Svcs*

Acme Energy Services Inc ....A 432 561-5271
Midland **(G-15104)**

Acme Truck Line Inc ....F 361 576-2934
Victoria **(G-20235)**

Aransas Fuel LLC ....E 361 992-5223
Corpus Christi **(G-3474)**

Arkhoma Transports Inc ....E 806 435-2380
Perryton **(G-16633)**

BCM & Associates Inc ....E 432 580-7161
Odessa **(G-15931)**

Cosi Energy Services LLC ....F 956 765-6729
Zapata **(G-20981)**

Diamond Tank Rental Inc ....E 432 337-0011
Odessa **(G-15976)**

Drag N Fly Trucking ....F 903 987-0027
Kilgore **(G-13546)**

Dugga Boys Inc ....E 361 364-4311
Sinton **(G-18962)**

E L Farmer & Company ....F 432 366-2010
Odessa **(G-15981)**

E Z Roustabout ....F 432 556-8419
Midland **(G-15201)**

E&R Vacuum Truck Services LLC ......F 956 618-9590
Edinburg **(G-5585)**

Five Star Consolidated Co Ltd ....C 806 592-3113
Denver City **(G-5419)**

Flint Energy Services Inc ....C 830 569-8453
Pleasanton **(G-17067)**

Forbes Energy Services Ltd ....F 361 664-0549
Alice **(G-215)**

G & W Trucking Inc ....E 325 573-6338
Snyder **(G-18992)**

GM Oilfield & Trckg Svcs LLC ....E 432 934-6525
Midland **(G-15237)**

Key Energy Services Inc ....D 903 538-2280
Palestine **(G-16301)**

Marco Services Inc ....F 806 344-4784
Hereford **(G-8293)**

O & B Tank Co Inc ....F 806 624-4781
Darrouzett **(G-5215)**

Oil Well Chemical Co Inc ....F 940 592-2012
Iowa Park **(G-12907)**

Paisano Service & Supply Inc ....E 361 572-0322
Cuero **(G-3765)**

Paul Musslewhite Trckg Co LLC........A 806 894-3151
Levelland **(G-14012)**

Pro Field Services Inc ....F 361 575-0348
Victoria **(G-20296)**

Relentless Oilfield Svcs LLC ....F 432 242-1160
Odessa **(G-16136)**

Ro SA Vacuum Trucks Inc ....E 956 584-8685
Edinburg **(G-5600)**

Sancus Energy and Power LLC ....E 832 460-1000
Houston **(G-11744)**

Tegraexcel Energy Services LLC ....F 412 508-0690
Midland **(G-15435)**

Texas Tank Trucks Co ....E 254 559-5404
Granbury **(G-7812)**

Trey Trucks Ltd ....D 432 558-7966
Crane **(G-3702)**

Turner Energy Services LLC ....F 806 323-8844
Canadian **(G-2656)**

United Petro Transports Inc ....E 817 540-6178
Euless **(G-6165)**

Uv Logistics LLC ....G 281 436-2310
Houston **(G-12508)**

Whitewater Midstream LLC ....E 512 953-2100
Austin **(G-1661)**

Willda Beast LLC ....F 979 268-6760
Iola **(G-12901)**

CONTRACTORS: *Oil Field Lease Tanks: Erectg, Clng/Rprg Svcs*

Bbb Tank Services LLC ....C 832 695-2132
Baytown **(G-1808)**

Big C Rentals LLC ....G 432 266-8834
Andrews **(G-538)**

Bobbitt Construction Inc ....E 903 769-4513
Hawkins **(G-8228)**

Brown and Anthony Inc ....F 806 762-1975
Lubbock **(G-14384)**

Camino Agave Inc ....C 830 393-1051
Floresville **(G-6246)**

Camino Agave Inc ....D 956 765-4635
Zapata **(G-20979)**

Chachos Lease Service Inc ....F 361 661-1143
Alice **(G-205)**

Cierra Tank Services LLC ....E 713 568-4028
Houston **(G-8375)**

K-C Lease Service Inc ....E 979 323-9911
Louise **(G-14352)**

Lufkin Industries LLC ....E 806 592-2586
Denver City **(G-5420)**

Peak Industrial Services Inc ....E 409 729-0345
Nederland **(G-15758)**

Rotary Components Intl Inc ....F 281 590-6484
Houston **(G-11668)**

South Coast Terminals LP ....D 713 672-2401
Houston **(G-11963)**

Swn Production Company LLC ....F 832 796-1000
Spring **(G-19173)**

Tristar Globl Enrgy Sltons Inc ....E 713 463-9200
Houston **(G-12378)**

WCI Construction Inc ....F 432 530-4009
Odessa **(G-16204)**

CONTRACTORS: *Oil Field Mud Drilling Svcs*

Anderson Mud Logging Service ....F 903 693-5817
Carthage **(G-2898)**

BEg Liquid Mud Services Corp ....F 979 542-7000
Giddings **(G-7692)**

C&J Well Services Inc ....E 817 573-3550
Granbury **(G-7794)**

Champion Drilling Fluids Inc ....F 580 225-3450
Houston **(G-9156)**

Mo-Vac Service Company ....D 956 682-6381
Edinburg **(G-5597)**

Mo-Vac Service Company ....F 830 583-3622
Kenedy **(G-13489)**

National Oilwell Varco Inc ....E 713 482-0500
Houston **(G-10985)**

Patriot Oilfield Services LLC ....E 979 648-2416
Victoria **(G-20290)**

Pml Exploration Services LLC ....C 405 606-2701
Spring **(G-19159)**

QMax America Inc ....E 817 732-2423
Houston **(G-11483)**

Quintana Energy Services Inc ....A 832 518-4094
Houston **(G-11515)**

Sabine Mud Logging Inc ....F 903 693-2912
Carthage **(G-2918)**

Selman & Associates Ltd ....C 432 563-0084
Midland **(G-15403)**

Stage 3 Separation LLC ....D 713 868-4040
Houston **(G-12037)**

Zarsky Lumber Company Inc ....E 361 573-2479
Victoria **(G-20322)**

CONTRACTORS: *Oil Field Pipe Testing Svcs*

Advanced Hydrstatic Svcs L L C ....E 940 337-7950
Wichita Falls **(G-20737)**

Applied US Energy Inc ....E 713 466-1538
Houston **(G-8669)**

Applied US Energy Inc ....F 432 689-0102
Midland **(G-15117)**

Blaze Sales and Service Inc ....F 713 828-1685
Houston **(G-8913)**

Choat Enterprises Inc ....E 432 367-8459
Odessa **(G-15960)**

Core Laboratories Holding Inc ....B 713 328-2673
Houston **(G-9316)**

De Laune Drilling Service Ltd ....F 361 664-0106
Alice **(G-208)**

Dorsal Services Inc ....E 361 394-6300
Alice **(G-209)**

Dve Management Inc ....E 214 957-1095
Greenville **(G-8071)**

Express Energy Svcs Oper LP ....E 830 569-8606
Pleasanton **(G-17066)**

Fasterra Group LP ....C 940 240-5800
Argyle **(G-600)**

Houston Tubulars Inc ....D 281 485-4014
Pearland **(G-16569)**

J Rollins Construction Inc ....D 936 258-3485
Dayton **(G-5231)**

Longhorn Services Inc ....E 956 655-2360
Edinburg **(G-5593)**

M & G Development LP ....F 361 664-6122
Alice **(G-226)**

National Oilwell Varco Inc ....F 325 573-2665
Snyder **(G-18997)**

North Amercn Tubular Svcs LLC	F	903 984-0625	Baker Petrolite LLC	F	409 935-2248	Endeavor Energy Resources LP	E	432 563-5000

North Amercn Tubular Svcs LLC........F.......903 984-0625
Kilgore (G-13579)

Novomet Usa Inc........F.......832 437-5998
Katy (G-13430)

Ofs International LLC........B.......281 452-3036
Houston (G-11148)

On Shore Qlty Ctrl Spclist LLC........D.......512 443-3582
Austin (G-1383)

Petroleum Industry Inspectors........E.......713 377-2637
Houston (G-11308)

Production Meter & Testing........F.......254 559-7271
Breckenridge (G-2234)

R B Testers Inc........F.......432 582-2500
Odessa (G-16129)

Rapid Service Inc........F.......432 367-7283
Odessa (G-16133)

Rdt Inc........D.......979 387-3223
Beasley (G-1845)

Safety Design Usa Inc........E.......940 757-0238
Wichita Falls (G-20804)

Soc Industries LLC........E.......432 620-0040
Midland (G-15413)

T-P Rentals LLC........E.......432 558-7218
Crane (G-3701)

Testco Well Services LLC........D.......361 396-0626
Laredo (G-13937)

Testmasters Inc........E.......713 896-1885
Houston (G-12214)

Tubing Testers Inc........E.......940 574-2177
Archer City (G-597)

Walker-Neer Manufacturing Co........F.......940 723-0711
Wichita Falls (G-20826)

Wayne Fueling Systems LLC........F.......512 388-8311
Austin (G-1652)

White Wing Inspection Inc........E.......979 421-8255
Brenham (G-2279)

Woolley Fishing Tool Inc........E.......903 984-3553
Kilgore (G-13603)

Woolley Tool Inc........F.......903 984-3553
Kilgore (G-13604)

Xxtreme Pipe Storage LLC........E.......281 452-9015
Houston (G-12712)

CONTRACTORS: Oil Sampling Svcs

Badger Pressure Control LLC........E.......903 687-4100
Waskom (G-20515)

Southern Petroleum Labs Inc........E.......903 693-6242
Carthage (G-2921)

CONTRACTORS: Oil/Gas Field Casing, Tube/Rod Running, Cut/Pull

Basic Energy Services LP........D.......432 264-1212
Big Spring (G-2073)

Permian Power Tong Inc........E.......432 550-7386
Gardendale (G-7421)

Timco Services Inc........E.......903 693-9400
Carthage (G-2924)

Tubular Services LLC........E.......713 675-6212
Houston (G-12404)

Tubular Services LLC........C.......281 452-4353
Houston (G-12405)

CONTRACTORS: Oil/Gas Well Construction, Rpr/Dismantling Svcs

4-A Oilfield Enterprises........F.......903 668-3815
Longview (G-14186)

A F C Lease Service Inc........E.......361 364-2547
Sinton (G-18960)

Abasco LLC........E.......281 446-1500
Humble (G-12742)

Abshier Energy LLC........G.......432 352-4338
Bowie (G-2189)

Aker Solutions Inc........C.......713 685-5700
Houston (G-8519)

Alterman Energy Services Inc........F.......210 496-6888
San Antonio (G-17901)

Anything Goes Enterprises LLC........F.......210 608-1741
San Antonio (G-17908)

Anzures Welding Roustabout A........G.......432 385-4122
Odessa (G-15916)

Auto Fire and Safety Cons........G.......832 585-0423
Conroe (G-3260)

Avk Construction Group Inc........F.......972 255-9464
Irving (G-12939)

Badger Bmb Services Inc........D.......432 447-0498
Pecos (G-16617)

Bailey & Harley Services LLC........E.......409 994-5857
Buna (G-2560)

Baker Petrolite LLC........F.......409 935-2248
La Marque (G-13706)

Barrera Contractors Inc........F.......432 639-2516
Iraan (G-12916)

Basic Energy Services Inc........E.......361 578-3503
Victoria (G-20244)

Bastion Technologies Inc........E.......281 283-9330
Houston (G-8823)

Big D Equipment Company Ltd........D.......432 682-1664
Midland (G-15139)

Big Shot LLC........E.......504 877-2335
Lancaster (G-13840)

Billy R Coats Inc........E.......432 523-3861
Andrews (G-539)

Blakely Construction Co Inc........C.......432 363-6650
Odessa (G-15937)

Bml Inc........E.......325 676-3355
Abilene (G-19)

Bobcat Contracting LLC........C.......254 582-0205
Hillsboro (G-8322)

Bold Production Services LLC........E.......281 615-6799
Houston (G-8945)

BP Surface Solutions LLC........D.......325 387-3881
San Angelo (G-17786)

Brandt A Varco Company........E.......940 683-6286
Bridgeport (G-2289)

Britt Dirt Contracting Inc........F.......806 872-5194
Lamesa (G-13824)

Broncs Inc........F.......432 614-8305
Odessa (G-15945)

Bryant Industrial Services LLC........E.......956 838-5120
Port Isabel (G-17135)

Butchs Oilfield Services Inc........E.......956 381-8409
Edinburg (G-5580)

C & A Contractors Inc........E.......817 441-4178
Aledo (G-197)

Canyon Offshore Inc........D.......713 856-6010
Houston (G-9088)

CIC Construction Inc........E.......979 648-2968
Louise (G-14351)

CK Kustoms Iron Works Inc........F.......281 850-6118
Rockport (G-17529)

Cline Construction Inc........E.......432 267-6006
Big Spring (G-2075)

Colt Services LP........F.......409 842-6929
Beaumont (G-1874)

Colt Services LP........E.......281 471-9099
La Porte (G-13729)

Commercial Diesl Parts Svc Ltd........E.......830 372-1594
Seguin (G-18830)

Completion Technologies Inc........F.......936 760-2734
Conroe (G-3279)

Cothran AG Services LLC........E.......254 625-1715
Teague (G-19664)

Crab Ventures LLC........E.......979 571-0258
Bryan (G-2467)

Craft Wireline Services Inc........E.......432 943-5150
Monahans (G-15603)

Crowder Construction Co Inc........E.......254 629-1688
Eastland (G-5562)

Cyclone Construction LLC........E.......512 288-0430
Austin (G-859)

David Keels........E.......409 316-9265
Hitchcock (G-8336)

Deer Park Cnstr Assoc Inc........E.......281 839-0020
Baytown (G-1815)

Detsco Inc........F.......713 999-5260
Jersey Village (G-13298)

Diamante Construction & Design........F.......361 449-7072
Laredo (G-13880)

Digco Utility Construction LP........F.......281 833-2000
Houston (G-9468)

Don Spencer Co........C.......817 389-4413
Godley (G-7735)

Double D Tongs Inc........E.......432 381-0602
Odessa (G-15979)

Double R Construction Inc........F.......903 452-7890
Kilgore (G-13545)

Downhole Innovations LLC........F.......936 537-4640
Houston (G-9508)

Downhole Technology LLC........D.......281 820-2545
Houston (G-9509)

Dynasty Wireline Services LLC........E.......432 363-3100
Midland (G-15200)

Eastern Oil Well Service Corp........E.......203 358-5700
Houston (G-9570)

Electric Submersible Pump Inc........F.......325 573-8101
Snyder (G-18990)

Ems Usa Inc........E.......713 595-7600
Pasadena (G-16427)

Endeavor Energy Resources LP........E.......432 563-5000
Midland (G-15214)

Environmental Floors Inc........F.......713 956-5526
Georgetown (G-7651)

Etech Envmtl Safety Solutions........E.......432 563-2200
Odessa (G-15993)

Evers and Sons Inc........D.......979 596-2139
Caldwell (G-2632)

Fesco Ltd........E.......956 383-8378
Edinburg (G-5588)

Fesco Ltd........E.......432 332-3211
Odessa (G-16000)

Fesco Ltd........E.......361 526-4644
Refugio (G-17241)

Fleaux Services Louisiana LLC........F.......432 694-0004
Midland (G-15231)

Flint Energy Services Inc........C.......940 683-4181
Pleasanton (G-17068)

Franklin Howard Intl LLC........F.......281 815-1527
Houston (G-9856)

Fun Da Mentals For Educatn LLC........E.......832 368-3345
Houston (G-9874)

Global Industries Inc........G.......972 236-1366
Carrollton (G-2745)

Globalogix Inc........E.......713 987-7630
Houston (G-9982)

Gobbato Builders LLC........F.......737 843-4327
Austin (G-1185)

Gt Oilfield Repair Inc........E.......361 782-7300
Edna (G-5606)

Gulf Island Fabrication Inc........B.......713 714-6100
Houston (G-10065)

H2o Greenworks LLC........F.......817 884-7788
Arlington (G-694)

Halliburton International Inc........A.......214 759-2600
Dallas (G-4429)

Healthtronics Service Ctr LLC........B.......512 328-2892
Austin (G-1697)

Hercules Offshore Inc........A.......713 350-5100
Houston (G-10158)

Holverstott Najee........F.......210 769-5246
San Antonio (G-18172)

Hooken R LLC........D.......817 304-7645
Cuero (G-3761)

Houston North Remodel........F.......936 314-4654
Montgomery (G-15634)

Huisache Energy Services Inc........F.......361 299-2815
Robstown (G-17513)

Infrastructure Networks Inc........E.......832 598-6600
Houston (G-10361)

Integrated Production Svcs Inc........E.......281 774-6700
Houston (G-10385)

Intertek USA Inc........F.......281 364-2800
Spring (G-19220)

J & P Services Inc........F.......979 542-0500
Giddings (G-7697)

JD King Inc........C.......800 805-6302
Seminole (G-18884)

Jgt Services........E.......432 553-5167
Andrews (G-545)

JM Construction........E.......956 518-2113
Brownsville (G-2370)

Key Energy Services Inc........D.......361 668-1818
Alice (G-221)

Key Energy Services Inc........E.......361 661-0488
Alice (G-222)

Kj Rustic Designs LLC........D.......832 477-6545
Bryan (G-2486)

L R G Services Inc........F.......713 504-4470
New Caney (G-15843)

Lariat Construction Services........G.......361 318-9104
Pawnee (G-16533)

Lilly Construction Inc........E.......325 392-2669
Ozona (G-16285)

Lowe Offshore Inc........D.......281 894-5454
Houston (G-10690)

Lsri LLC........D.......817 770-0937
Burleson (G-2588)

Lufkin Industries LLC........E.......903 986-9080
Kilgore (G-13565)

Manufacturing Global Resources........F.......361 668-0111
Alice (G-227)

McDermott International Inc........B.......281 588-6600
Houston (G-10810)

MD Construction Inc........C.......903 389-2595
Fairfield (G-6178)

Meco Construction Company LLC........E.......817 975-4599
Fort Worth (G-6825)

Moses Envmtl & Cnstr Svcs LLC........E.......806 418-8525
Amarillo (G-448)

Mpact Strategic Consulting LLC ....E 866 361-7611
Houston (G-10929)

Newpark Mats Intgrted Svcs LLC ....E 409 752-5800
Beaumont (G-1934)

Newpark Resources Inc ....E 281 362-6800
The Woodlands (G-19897)

Nitro Downhole LLC ....F 361 564-9282
Yorktown (G-20978)

Non-Typical Pipeline Llc.....................E 281 622-5002
Cleveland (G-3132)

Norm Pipe Inc ....D 903 702-8966
Marshall (G-14795)

Novak Commercial Cnstr LLC ....F 512 688-5644
Georgetown (G-7668)

Oak Lease Service Co LLC ....F 361 362-1429
Refugio (G-17245)

Oil Patch Group Inc ....E 361 576-0300
Victoria (G-20289)

Paris Construction LLC........................F 832 752-5271
Cypress (G-3810)

Permian Basin Derrick Svcs LP ....G 432 332-2315
Odessa (G-16112)

Prime Operating Company ....E 713 735-0000
Houston (G-11416)

Primeenergy Corporation ....F 830 876-2441
Carrizo Springs (G-2688)

Quality Foundation Repair Inc ....F 512 363-7769
Austin (G-1443)

Rathole Drilling Inc ....E 361 664-9995
Alice (G-232)

RDG Real Estate & Construction..........F 469 629-9919
Dallas (G-4865)

Robert Marshall Cnstr Inc ....F 361 747-5253
Bruni (G-2450)

Rpc Inc ....E 210 310-1330
San Antonio (G-18436)

Ruben Arispe Jr ....F 512 543-3444
Austin (G-1475)

Saltel-Industries Inc...........................F 432 238-1076
Midland (G-15395)

Schlumberger ....F 979 531-8141
Wharton (G-20706)

Schlumberger Omnes Inc ....B 713 375-3400
Houston (G-11770)

Schlumberger Technology Corp ....D 210 623-9400
Von Ormy (G-20351)

Schlumberger Technology Corp ....F 817 870-9040
Fort Worth (G-6978)

Schwob Energy Services LLC ....D 469 917-9023
Dallas (G-4941)

Scout Downhole Inc............................F 936 756-3255
Conroe (G-3362)

Select Energy Services LLC ....D 325 949-0326
San Angelo (G-17827)

Sparkman Industries Inc ....D 361 573-0001
Victoria (G-20304)

Specialized Cnstr Svcs LLC.................E 210 262-7263
Converse (G-3403)

Ss Equipment Services II LLC..............E 830 483-0187
Cotulla (G-3691)

SSP Developers Inc ....F 956 456-4415
San Benito (G-18668)

Steel Insulator Group LLC ....F 409 284-4407
Beaumont (G-1954)

Stephen Jones ....F 409 460-8609
Port Arthur (G-17126)

Stewart Stevenson Pwr Pdts LLC ....C 713 751-2600
Houston (G-12065)

Stewart Stevenson Pwr Pdts LLC ....F 903 838-9966
Texarkana (G-19776)

T & H Construction Inc ....G 830 535-6111
Pipe Creek (G-16742)

T & L Lease Service Ltd ....C 281 331-8221
Alvin (G-381)

Tejas Machines Inc ....E 281 350-8890
Spring (G-19259)

Texas Capital Bancshares Inc ....A 214 706-6780
Richardson (G-17407)

Texas Lumber Construction ....F 979 732-2063
Columbus (G-3234)

Texforce Restoration Svcs LLC............F 817 775-3556
North Richland Hills (G-15882)

Tomdao Llc ....F 817 888-6167
Arlington (G-800)

Tracker Energy Services Inc ....E 830 837-0806
New Braunfels (G-15829)

Trend Services Inc ....G 361 396-0048
Alice (G-241)

Tri Resources Inc ....F 713 584-1000
Houston (G-12361)

Trinitys Covenant LLC.........................F 210 620-3694
Laredo (G-13939)

Triple S Onshore Oprations LLC ....E 903 658-0489
Bullard (G-2552)

Tryton Tools USA Inc ....F 830 372-2755
Seguin (G-18870)

Tryton Tools USA Inc ....E 832 717-7125
Houston (G-12393)

Underwriters Indemnity ....E 713 961-1300
Houston (G-12432)

US Joiner LLC ....E 713 330-1700
Houston (G-12484)

W M Greens Construction Svcs ....E 713 692-2291
Houston (G-12585)

Weatherford International LLC ....E 281 759-5100
Houston (G-12614)

Willbnks Fncl Cnslting Group L ....F 469 444-0170
Dallas (G-3860)

Wood Group Usa Inc ....A 832 809-8000
Houston (G-12687)

Wt Lease Services Inc ....E 361 348-3525
Portland (G-17189)

Zarsky Lumber Company Inc................E 361 882-2575
Corpus Christi (G-3658)

CONTRACTORS: On-Site Welding

Advanced Metal Fusion Inc..................F 512 422-0888
Cedar Park (G-2959)

American Fence and Sup Co Inc ....F 512 930-4000
Georgetown (G-7634)

ARC Marine LLC..................................G 713 489-7719
Dickinson (G-5469)

BCAD Zion Corporation ....E 210 657-9090
New Braunfels (G-15775)

Brandon Wldg & Fabrication Inc ....E 361 242-3344
Corpus Christi (G-3488)

Burns Welding Works Inc ....F 432 682-0495
Midland (G-15153)

C&J Cladding LLC ....E 281 987-2383
Houston (G-9039)

Canales Sheetmetal & Welding ....F 512 556-8613
Lampasas (G-13832)

CK Kustoms Iron Works Inc ....F 281 850-6118
Rockport (G-17529)

Conslidated Rigworks LP ....E 817 446-5272
Fort Worth (G-6543)

Dcu Inc ....F 972 816-6667
Wylie (G-20932)

Diamond Fab ....F 936 441-9353
Conroe (G-3293)

Dunn Services Inc ....E 361 275-3952
Cuero (G-3760)

Everlite Inc ....E 903 297-3444
Longview (G-14232)

Fusion Services Inc ....E 512 444-4283
Austin (G-1173)

H & H Machine Service LLC ....F 979 836-2599
Brenham (G-2256)

Harris Fabrication LLC ....F 361 547-6910
Mathis (G-14817)

Harrison Fabricators Inc ....F 214 374-1684
Dallas (G-4438)

J K Welding Service LLC ....E 281 550-1008
Cypress (G-3803)

J&A Fabrication ....F 903 981-0136
Longview (G-14254)

JD Pro-Service LLC ....F 936 264-4003
Conroe (G-3314)

Justiss Oil Company Inc ....D 903 859-2111
Arp (G-812)

Longview Fab & Machine Inc................E 903 238-8300
Longview (G-14269)

Lueras Welding Service Inc ....E 361 668-4572
Alice (G-225)

M Fab & Machine.................................F 936 264-2388
Conroe (G-3327)

Mc Welding & Fabrication Inc ....F 361 289-9605
Corpus Christi (G-3576)

McGill Maintenance Partnr Ltd ....C 979 233-5438
Freeport (G-7203)

McMahan Welding Service Ltd ....F 361 275-0111
Cuero (G-3763)

Miller Machine & Welding LLC..............E 254 582-2185
Whitney (G-20731)

Ober & Sons Inc ....F 281 879-6760
Houston (G-11112)

Paris Construction LLC........................F 832 752-5271
Cypress (G-3810)

Platts Welding and Cnstr LLC ....F 972 333-5830
Denison (G-5345)

Premium Weld Services Inc ....F 940 329-0222
Santo (G-18738)

R C Technical Welding & Fabr ....E 281 933-6004
Stafford (G-19367)

Schroeder Welding & Cnstr ....E 361 573-4322
Victoria (G-20302)

Shade Structures Inc ....G 214 905-9500
Dallas (G-4951)

Sullivan Welding Inc ....F 512 259-3440
Leander (G-13997)

Tlr Energy Services Inc ....F 940 969-2400
Paradise (G-16355)

Trencor Enterprises Inc ....F 806 659-3911
Spearman (G-19089)

TW Tanks and Construction Co ....F 361 358-8869
Beeville (G-1989)

Venables Construction Inc ....C 806 381-2121
Amarillo (G-520)

CONTRACTORS: Ornamental Metal Work

A Zahner Company ....F 469 348-2000
Grand Prairie (G-7817)

Johnston Products Dallas Inc ....E 469 272-7212
Cedar Hill (G-2946)

Quality Ironworks Inc ....D 214 688-0180
Dallas (G-4844)

Rising S Company LLC ....E 214 455-0560
Murchison (G-15682)

Texas Metal Industries Inc ....E 972 288-2333
Mesquite (G-15080)

Vickery Street Fabricators Inc ....E 713 695-9195
Houston (G-12564)

CONTRACTORS: Painting & Wall Covering

Batterson Iron Works L L P ....D 713 688-5433
Houston (G-8828)

Bmf Oil & Gas Services Inc ....F 832 443-2089
Houston (G-8926)

Brock Enterprises LLC ....E 409 729-6353
Nederland (G-15747)

Circuit Breaker Sales LLC ....C 940 665-4444
Gainesville (G-7338)

Genes Paul Enterprises Inc ....E 817 558-7868
Cleburne (G-3091)

Gulf Copper & Mfg Corp ....C 409 982-6122
Port Arthur (G-17112)

Gulfstream Aerospace Corp GA ....A 214 350-4177
Dallas (G-4424)

JM Construction ....E 956 518-2113
Brownsville (G-2370)

Travis Millwork Inc ....E 210 525-8088
San Antonio (G-18564)

Zimair LP ....D 817 624-7245
Fort Worth (G-7160)

CONTRACTORS: Painting, Aircraft

United Rtorcraft Solutions LLC ....E 940 627-0626
Decatur (G-5256)

CONTRACTORS: Painting, Commercial

Kurosky & Co Pntg Contrs Inc ....E 817 834-7179
Fort Worth (G-6776)

Requejo Construction Svcs LLC............F 210 459-5161
San Antonio (G-18420)

Stella Hasegawa ....F 915 594-7633
El Paso (G-5977)

CONTRACTORS: Painting, Commercial, Exterior

Riley Industrial Services Inc ....E 432 332-9630
Odessa (G-16141)

CONTRACTORS: Painting, Indl

Brock Services LLC ....C 281 807-8200
Houston (G-8991)

CB&i LLC ....D 832 513-1848
Houston (G-9104)

Custom Pipe Coating Inc ....E 713 675-2324
Houston (G-9373)

Cy-Fair Coatings Inc ....F 281 351-7427
Cypress (G-3784)

D & L Quality Painting Inc ....E 281 458-3588
Houston (G-9387)

F & L Coatings and Con LLC ....F 281 316-2203
League City (G-13956)

J E Titus Company ....F 713 991-1100
Houston (G-10439)

PRODUCT

Pro-Kleen Inc...E.......713 855-2760
Houston *(G-11427)*
Top Coat Inc...E.......979 233-9558
Freeport *(G-7216)*
Top Deck Inc...E.......409 745-3955
Orange *(G-16265)*
Trevinos Painting Inc..............................E.......956 571-3999
Edinburg *(G-5604)*
Triple C Industries Inc...........................E.......936 931-1171
Hockley *(G-8349)*

CONTRACTORS: Painting, Residential, Interior

Ferreira Holding Group LLC.................E.......214 293-9233
Dallas *(G-4359)*

CONTRACTORS: Parking Lot Maintenance

Crabtree Barricade Systems Inc...........E.......409 842-2073
Beaumont *(G-1877)*
Southwest Maintenance LLC................F.......254 662-3966
Robinson *(G-17502)*

CONTRACTORS: Patio & Deck Construction & Repair

Aries Acrylic Mfg Inc.............................F.......972 771-6286
Rockwall *(G-17538)*
Jones Aluminum......................................F.......409 866-5585
Beaumont *(G-1913)*
Metroplex Roof and Fence Inc..............F.......469 417-8003
Corinth *(G-3458)*

CONTRACTORS: Pavement Marking

Crabtree Barricade Systems Inc...........E.......409 842-2073
Beaumont *(G-1877)*

CONTRACTORS: Petroleum Storage Tank Install, Underground

Fabrication & Cnstr Svcs LP.................E.......936 257-0466
Dayton *(G-5226)*

CONTRACTORS: Pile Driving

DFI Piling Inc...F.......877 334-7453
Conroe *(G-3291)*
Shinn and Gregory Inc...........................G.......254 965-7585
Stephenville *(G-19422)*

CONTRACTORS: Pipe & Boiler Insulating

Gregg Indus Insulators Inc....................B.......903 757-5754
Longview *(G-14243)*
Power Pipe and Tank LLC......................E.......417 447-4508
Amarillo *(G-508)*
Protective Concepts Inc.........................F.......832 843-7619
Cypress *(G-3816)*

CONTRACTORS: Pipe Laying

Nichols Enterprises Inc..........................F.......979 543-4833
El Campo *(G-5625)*

CONTRACTORS: Pipeline Wrapping

Ea Services Inc.......................................D.......866 711-1001
Pearland *(G-16557)*
EZ Pipe Paddler Padding Mch...............E.......432 333-9587
Odessa *(G-15996)*
Larry McHorse Services LLC..................F.......361 275-4978
Cuero *(G-3762)*
Smart Pipe Company Inc........................F.......281 945-5700
Houston *(G-11919)*

CONTRACTORS: Playground Construction & Eqpt Installation

Playgrund Shade Structures Inc............G.......512 642-6124
Hutto *(G-12884)*
Worlds of Wow LLC................................E.......817 380-4215
Denton *(G-5413)*

CONTRACTORS: Plumbing

AAA Pipe Cleaning Corporation.............E.......281 476-5200
La Porte *(G-13715)*
Graco Interests Inc.................................B.......713 978-7000
Houston *(G-10010)*
Neu Plumbing Inc....................................D.......940 580-2200
Pilot Point *(G-16726)*

Walcott Enterprises Inc..........................E.......325 773-5212
Stamford *(G-19402)*

CONTRACTORS: Post Disaster Renovations

Christopher RAD Nader...........................F.......512 442-5326
Cedar Park *(G-2963)*
Munters Corporation...............................D.......210 651-5018
Selma *(G-18879)*

CONTRACTORS: Power Generating Eqpt Installation

Evolve Holdings Inc................................E.......832 375-0099
Houston *(G-9720)*
Viceroy Inc..E.......713 475-4518
Pasadena *(G-16524)*

CONTRACTORS: Precast Concrete Struct Framing & Panel Placing

Napco Precast LLC.................................C.......210 424-4371
San Antonio *(G-18332)*
North American Precast Company..........C.......210 509-9100
San Antonio *(G-18350)*

CONTRACTORS: Prefabricated Fireplace Installation

Accent Door Co Inc.................................E.......913 780-5800
San Antonio *(G-17856)*
RDHS Inc..F.......361 852-4094
Corpus Christi *(G-3606)*

CONTRACTORS: Prefabricated Window & Door Installation

Austin Window Fashion Inc.....................F.......512 836-3388
Austin *(G-967)*
Door Control Services.............................F.......210 732-1214
Ben Wheeler *(G-2032)*
Elite Entrances LLC................................E.......832 922-7444
Magnolia *(G-14603)*
Hou-Tex Newnom Inc..............................D.......713 777-0748
Houston *(G-10215)*
Maintenance Builders Sup Ltd................E.......713 462-8213
Houston *(G-10741)*
Premex Door Supply Inc.........................F.......214 341-2212
Garland *(G-7572)*
WD Norton Inc...F.......903 758-0301
Longview *(G-14332)*

CONTRACTORS: Protective Lining Install, Underground Sewage

GSE Environmental Inc...........................D.......281 443-8564
Houston *(G-10053)*
GSE International Inc..............................F.......281 443-8564
Houston *(G-10055)*

CONTRACTORS: Refractory or Acid Brick Masonry

J T Thorpe Company................................C.......713 644-1247
Houston *(G-10444)*
Southwest Refractory Texas LP.............E.......979 285-7219
Alvin *(G-380)*
Thermal Specialties Texas LLC.............G.......918 836-4800
Fort Worth *(G-7055)*

CONTRACTORS: Refrigeration

Colair Inc...F.......956 631-9889
Mission *(G-15550)*
Enerflex Inc...E.......801 292-0493
Houston *(G-9632)*
United Elec Instrmentation Ltd...............D.......979 265-1256
Clute *(G-3161)*

CONTRACTORS: Renovation, Aircraft Interiors

United Rtorcraft Solutions LLC...............E.......940 627-0626
Decatur *(G-5256)*

CONTRACTORS: Right-Of-Way Cutting

JD King Inc..C.......800 805-6302
Seminole *(G-18884)*

CONTRACTORS: Roofing

A & B Sheet Metal Inc............................G.......512 365-7870
Taylor *(G-19646)*
Con-Tex Builders Inc..............................E.......281 847-3336
Houston *(G-9266)*
J K Welding Service LLC.........................E.......281 550-1008
Cypress *(G-3803)*
Metroplex Roof and Fence Inc..............F.......469 417-8003
Corinth *(G-3458)*
Morgan Roofing.......................................E.......409 762-8068
Galveston *(G-7404)*
Ntw Services Inc.....................................G.......210 885-8637
San Antonio *(G-18352)*
Owens Corning Sales LLC......................C.......972 438-1050
Irving *(G-13138)*
Parsleys Shtmtl & Roofg Co...................E.......806 669-6461
Pampa *(G-16333)*
Sechrist-Hall Company............................E.......361 884-5264
Corpus Christi *(G-3620)*
Texas Roof Management Inc...................C.......972 272-7663
Richardson *(G-17409)*

CONTRACTORS: Roustabout Svcs

Absolute Roustabout Svc LLC................D.......432 488-8788
Midland *(G-15103)*
Allred Construction Company..................D.......806 435-5817
Perryton *(G-16631)*
B & B Roustabout Inc.............................D.......806 872-7276
Lamesa *(G-13822)*
Bassler Energy Services Inc...................E.......979 535-4593
Caldwell *(G-2628)*
Black Widow Energy LLC........................F.......956 378-5363
Edinburg *(G-5579)*
Cjr Contractors Inc.................................C.......806 592-2232
Denver City *(G-5417)*
Collins Roustabout & Well Svc...............F.......325 754-4237
Winters *(G-20904)*
Comac Well Service Inc..........................E.......806 274-2259
Borger *(G-2170)*
Convoy Servicing Co...............................F.......214 638-3050
Irving *(G-12979)*
Devonian Dirt Works LLC........................G.......432 253-7777
Odessa *(G-15975)*
Ds Oilfield Construction LLC..................F.......361 396-0089
Alice *(G-210)*
HM Roustabout Service Inc....................F.......830 563-5449
Eldorado *(G-6046)*
Holloman Corporation.............................E.......281 878-2600
Houston *(G-10194)*
Langford Roustabout Svcs LLC.............F.......940 864-3490
Haskell *(G-8213)*
M & Q Oilfield Service Inc......................F.......806 894-4025
Levelland *(G-14010)*
Midland Roustabout Service Inc............D.......432 682-5017
Midland *(G-15302)*
Petroplex Pipe & Cnstr Inc....................D.......432 697-4540
Midland *(G-15350)*
R A D Roustabout Service LLC...............G.......432 664-2430
Midland *(G-15375)*
Ramco Roustabout Inc...........................E.......325 884-5734
Big Lake *(G-2061)*
Raydon Inc...E.......254 559-5012
Breckenridge *(G-2235)*
Trendsetter Construction Inc.................C.......903 759-4955
Gladewater *(G-7728)*
Turnbow Oil Field Services LLC.............F.......817 880-3833
Lubbock *(G-14501)*
Venables Construction Inc.....................C.......806 381-2121
Amarillo *(G-520)*

CONTRACTORS: Safety & Security Eqpt

ABC Fire Systems LLC............................G.......830 625-3473
New Braunfels *(G-15771)*
Enterprise SEC Sltons Txas Inc............E.......940 320-3778
Justin *(G-13343)*
Reyes-Amtex Automotive LLC................E.......210 628-4900
San Antonio *(G-18425)*
Risk Management Armored SEC.............F.......817 932-5923
Alvarado *(G-340)*
Siemens Industry Inc.............................B.......972 947-7000
Dallas *(G-4959)*
Tyco International MGT Co LLC..............F.......713 644-8872
Houston *(G-12419)*

CONTRACTORS: Sandblasting Svc, Building Exteriors

Cor-Pro Systems Inc...............................E.......713 896-1091
Houston *(G-9312)*

(G-0000) Company's Geographic Section entry number

Kurosky & Co Pntg Contrs Inc ....E 817 834-7179
  Fort Worth *(G-6776)*
Pro-Kleen Inc ....E 713 855-2760
  Houston *(G-11427)*
Triple C Industries Inc ....E 936 931-1171
  Hockley *(G-8349)*

CONTRACTORS: Screening, Window & Door

Better Burglar Bars Inc ....E 713 699-9543
  Houston *(G-8867)*

CONTRACTORS: Seismograph Survey Svcs

Baker Hghes Olfld Oprtions LLC ....E 432 694-7761
  Midland *(G-15129)*
Baker Hghes Olfld Oprtions LLC ....E 361 573-2493
  Victoria *(G-20242)*
Baker Hghes Olfld Oprtions LLC ....D 972 466-2673
  Carrollton *(G-2701)*
Baker Hughes A GE Company LLC ......D 361 573-2493
  Victoria *(G-20243)*
Baker Hughes A GE Company LLC ......D 979 826-3621
  Hempstead *(G-8249)*
Cgg Services (us) Inc ....B 832 351-8300
  Houston *(G-9149)*
Dawson Geophysical Company ....F 713 917-6772
  Houston *(G-9410)*
Geokinetics Acquisition Co ....C 281 509-8000
  Houston *(G-9934)*
Kelman Technologies Inc ....E 281 529-3204
  Houston *(G-10514)*
Meridian Energy Group Inc ....E 281 291-0510
  Pasadena *(G-16482)*
Oil Data Inc ....E 713 461-7178
  Houston *(G-11150)*
Seismic Eqp Solutions Inc ....E 832 288-4427
  Houston *(G-11815)*
Seismic Exchange Inc ....E 832 590-5100
  Houston *(G-11816)*
Seitel Inc ....E 713 881-8900
  Houston *(G-11818)*
Steward Enterprises Inc ....C 432 687-2553
  Midland *(G-15420)*
Texseis Inc ....G 713 465-3181
  Houston *(G-12263)*
Triton Data Services Inc ....F 281 578-9700
  Houston *(G-12381)*
Vector Seismic Data Processing ....F 303 571-1515
  Houston *(G-12543)*
Western Atlas Intl Inc ....B 713 972-4000
  Houston *(G-12641)*
Westerngeco Llc ....A 713 789-9600
  Houston *(G-12644)*

CONTRACTORS: Septic System

Gicon Pumps & Equipment Ltd ....G 806 373-0478
  Amarillo *(G-428)*
Sherrod Services LLC ....E 254 729-3177
  Thornton *(G-19943)*
Tyler Products Sales Inc ....E 903 593-8633
  Tyler *(G-20172)*
Wilbert Funeral Services Inc ....E 972 875-9605
  Ennis *(G-6123)*

CONTRACTORS: Sheet Metal Work, NEC

Abilene Sheet Metal Inc ....F 325 677-2654
  Abilene *(G-7)*
Amtech Manufacturing Inc ....E 817 563-1251
  Fort Worth *(G-6386)*
Beach Sheet Metal Company Inc ....E 972 226-4440
  Mesquite *(G-15030)*
Berrys Tin Shop Inc ....F 903 586-3552
  Jacksonville *(G-13229)*
Bryne Sheet Metal Inc ....D 281 354-1100
  Humble *(G-12749)*
Canales Sheetmetal & Welding ....F 512 556-8613
  Lampasas *(G-13832)*
Corsicana Sheet Metal Co Inc ....F 903 872-8434
  Corsicana *(G-3666)*
G N P Inc Sheet Metal ....E 972 564-0450
  Forney *(G-6308)*
Gst Manufacturing Ltd ....C 817 335-1401
  Haltom City *(G-8146)*
J & L Sheet Metal Co Inc ....E 713 864-7714
  Houston *(G-10433)*
M & M Metals Inc ....D 210 341-1313
  San Antonio *(G-18268)*
Texas Pipe Fabricators Inc ....E 361 882-5541
  Corpus Christi *(G-3637)*

Turrubiartes Benedicto......................G 832 675-1569
  Houston *(G-12413)*
United Elec Instrmentation Ltd ....D 979 265-1256
  Clute *(G-3161)*

CONTRACTORS: Sheet metal Work, Architectural

A Zahner Company ....F 469 348-2000
  Grand Prairie *(G-7817)*
BD Hildebrandt Entps Inc ....F 936 825-0500
  Navasota *(G-15725)*
Chaparral Wldg Fabrication Inc............E 972 243-7747
  Dallas *(G-4104)*
Thur-Co Inc ....F 956 982-4424
  Brownsville *(G-2412)*

CONTRACTORS: Ship Boiler & Tank Cleaning & Repair

Lynchburg Shipyard Inc ....E 281 426-2474
  Baytown *(G-1827)*

CONTRACTORS: Shoring & Underpinning

Trevway Inc ....F 832 687-6269
  Katy *(G-13380)*

CONTRACTORS: Siding

Jones Aluminum ....F 409 866-5585
  Beaumont *(G-1913)*

CONTRACTORS: Single-Family Home Fire Damage Repair

Trinitys Covenant LLC ....F 210 620-3694
  Laredo *(G-13939)*

CONTRACTORS: Single-family Home General Remodeling

B & W Remodeling Inc ....E 817 485-0444
  North Richland Hills *(G-15874)*
Darville Co ....F 432 580-9675
  Odessa *(G-15974)*
Mike Strand ....F 940 482-3426
  Krum *(G-13675)*

CONTRACTORS: Skylight Installation

Birdview Skylights ....F 817 439-9266
  Fort Worth *(G-6453)*
Cerda-Fied Specialists Inc ....F 281 392-8063
  Brookshire *(G-2313)*
Skylights Over Texas LLC ....F 210 402-0500
  San Antonio *(G-18478)*

CONTRACTORS: Solar Reflecting Insulation Film Installation

Paladin Signs and Graphics Inc ....F 817 744-7361
  Benbrook *(G-2044)*

CONTRACTORS: Sound Eqpt Installation

Dallas Sight and Sound Inc ....E 972 392-3202
  Dallas *(G-4225)*

CONTRACTORS: Spa & Hot Tub Construction & Installation

Ghm Corp ....C 972 840-1200
  Dallas *(G-4406)*

CONTRACTORS: Sprinkler System

ABC Fire Systems LLC......................G 830 625-3473
  New Braunfels *(G-15771)*

CONTRACTORS: Standby Or Emergency Power Specialization

Abshier Energy LLC ....G 432 352-4338
  Bowie *(G-2189)*

CONTRACTORS: Steel Oil Tank Dismantling

Bay Area Industrial Contrs LP ....C 281 471-0400
  La Porte *(G-13725)*

CONTRACTORS: Storage Tank Erection, Metal

CB&i LLC ....C 713 649-4277
  Houston *(G-9106)*
CB&i LLC ....C 713 375-8000
  Houston *(G-9107)*
CB&i LLC ....C 713 485-1000
  Houston *(G-9108)*
Challenger Process Systems Co ....C 903 839-7291
  Troup *(G-20024)*
Herring Tank Company Inc ....E 817 377-1851
  Benbrook *(G-2041)*
Hmt LLC 281 681-7000
  Shenandoah *(G-18897)*
Holloway Company Inc ....E 817 232-8663
  Saginaw *(G-17746)*
Holloway Company Inc ....F 713 453-4691
  Houston *(G-10195)*
Justiss Oil Company Inc ....D 903 859-2111
  Arp *(G-812)*
Pat Tank Inc ....D 409 982-7319
  Port Arthur *(G-17121)*
Summit Seals Inc ....F 409 769-8151
  Vidor *(G-20335)*
Willborn Bros Co LLC ....E 806 372-4311
  Amarillo *(G-475)*

CONTRACTORS: Store Fixture Installation

Jay H Fixtures Inc ....E 972 223-2245
  De Soto *(G-5239)*

CONTRACTORS: Store Front Construction

Morenos Auto Glass Inc ....F 361 855-1471
  Corpus Christi *(G-3579)*

CONTRACTORS: Structural Steel Erection

Advanced Diversified Svcs Inc.............E 817 377-2718
  Benbrook *(G-2036)*
Aj Commercial Services Inc..................G 361 336-2113
  Corpus Christi *(G-3470)*
Amco Steel Fabrication LLC ....F 210 488-9023
  Elmendorf *(G-6066)*
Basden Steel and Erection Inc ....E 817 295-6100
  Burleson *(G-2569)*
Beck Steel Inc ....C 806 762-3255
  Lubbock *(G-14369)*
C & F Steel Company Inc ....E 254 386-8847
  Hamilton *(G-8165)*
CB&i LLC ....C 409 980-5500
  Beaumont *(G-1867)*
CB&i LLC ....E 281 456-5700
  Houston *(G-9105)*
D & D Fabrication & Erection ....F 817 237-3306
  Fort Worth *(G-6568)*
Daltons Welding Service Inc ....F 940 682-7237
  Weatherford *(G-20586)*
Dennis Steel Inc ....D 512 259-4001
  Leander *(G-13987)*
Graywolf Industrial Inc ....E 281 441-5400
  Humble *(G-12771)*
Heritage Stl Erction Fbrcation ....E 817 790-5170
  Alvarado *(G-334)*
Hollywood Steel Inc ....E 713 686-4325
  Houston *(G-10196)*
Hou-Stone Inc ....D 713 827-8700
  Houston *(G-10214)*
J & N Welding and Fabricators ....E 956 585-3992
  Penitas *(G-16629)*
J & S Contractors Inc ....F 979 647-0040
  Sweeny *(G-19628)*
Palmer Steel Supplies Inc ....E 956 686-6575
  McAllen *(G-14898)*
Patriot Erectors LLC ....C 512 858-9100
  Dripping Springs *(G-5511)*
Patriot Parent LLC ....B 512 858-9100
  Dripping Springs *(G-5512)*
Platts Welding and Cnstr LLC ....F 972 333-5830
  Denison *(G-5345)*
Public Steel Inc ....E 806 376-8221
  Amarillo *(G-457)*
Septh Group LLC ....E 713 988-4200
  Houston *(G-11832)*
Slz Rebar LLC ....F 832 427-5860
  Cypress *(G-3820)*
Splendora Pipe Services LLC ....D 281 432-1400
  Cleveland *(G-3136)*
Spur Industrial LLC ....E 817 293-1515
  Cresson *(G-3713)*

Employee Codes: A=Over 500 employees, B=251-500
C=101-250, D=51-100, E=20-50, F=10-19, G=9

2021 Harris Texas
Manufacturers Directory

1459

PRODUCT

Systems Integration Inc ....E 817 468-1494
Arlington (G-790)

Texas Steel Conversion Inc ....C 281 459-2905
Houston (G-12255)

TH Precision LLC ....E 830 549-5864
Seguin (G-18868)

Tippen Steel Services Inc ....E 940 433-3132
Boyd (G-2208)

Westside Welding Inc ....E 915 877-5345
Canutillo (G-2668)

Zinsmeyer Mech & Wldg Ltd ....E 830 985-3498
Castroville (G-2929)

CONTRACTORS: Stucco, Interior

JM Construction ....E 956 518-2113
Brownsville (G-2370)

CONTRACTORS: Svc Station Eqpt Installation, Maint & Repair

Consolidated Pressure Ctrl LLC ....D 281 893-5900
Conroe (G-3285)

Detsco Inc ....F 713 999-5260
Jersey Village (G-13298)

CONTRACTORS: Svc Well Drilling Svcs

Air Drilling Associates Inc ....F 832 957-6093
Houston (G-8505)

Big Red Engineering LLC ....F 817 539-9560
Fort Worth (G-6450)

Big Rock Energy Services Inc ....E 432 235-8509
Midland (G-15141)

Bill Smalley Drilling & Trckg ....E 325 762-3409
Albany (G-185)

Construct Capital LLC ....C 214 637-1444
Arlington (G-645)

Construct Capital LLC ....D 713 322-6714
Houston (G-9278)

Construct Capital LLC ....D 210 654-4400
San Antonio (G-18024)

Envirotech Drilling Services ....F 832 493-8063
Houston (G-9670)

Estill Inc ....G 806 789-1548
Lubbock (G-14408)

Garcias Well Servicing Inc ....E 432 527-3748
Wink (G-20887)

H & K Well Service LLC ....F 361 394-7165
Freer (G-7226)

J & S Construction LLC ....E 903 322-4942
Buffalo (G-2544)

Lottco Inc ....E 832 773-4345
Humble (G-12785)

Lynco Well Service Inc ....E 936 336-7332
Liberty (G-14123)

Martinez Oil & Gas LLC ....E 361 384-9500
Orange Grove (G-16268)

Mustang Well Service LLC ....F 432 524-6112
Andrews (G-553)

Patterson-Uti Drilling Co LLC ....E 325 574-6300
Snyder (G-18999)

Permian H2o Solutions LLC ....F 432 214-4520
Odessa (G-16117)

Propetro Services Inc ....F 432 685-0059
Midland (G-15367)

Vantage Drilling Intl Inc ....E 281 404-4700
Houston (G-12532)

Weatherford International Ltd ....E 713 836-4000
Houston (G-12621)

CONTRACTORS: Switchgear & Related Device Installation

Sytek Electric Corporaiton ....E 713 862-8813
Houston (G-12140)

CONTRACTORS: Terrazzo Work

American Marble Mosaic Company ......E 713 747-7634
Houston (G-8600)

CONTRACTORS: Tile Installation, Ceramic

Arizona Tile LLC ....E 713 292-1001
Houston (G-8696)

Creative Tile Inc ....G 214 827-0552
Dallas (G-4182)

Delta Granite and Marble Inc ....D 210 829-7171
San Antonio (G-18050)

CONTRACTORS: Tuck Pointing & Restoration

Texforce Restoration Svcs LLC ....F 817 775-3556
North Richland Hills (G-15882)

CONTRACTORS: Underground Utilities

Mar-Con Services LLC ....D 713 473-1800
Pasadena (G-16480)

Ram-Bro Contracting Inc ....E 361 387-2795
Robstown (G-17515)

CONTRACTORS: Ventilation & Duct Work

6-K Inc ....F 979 830-0251
Brenham (G-2242)

Brownsville Sheet Metal Works ....E 956 546-4517
Brownsville (G-2340)

Lewis & Lambert LLLP ....C 817 834-7146
Haltom City (G-8150)

CONTRACTORS: Warm Air Heating & Air Conditioning

A-Action Aire Inc ....F 210 648-3801
San Antonio (G-17850)

Abilene Sheet Metal Inc ....F 325 677-2654
Abilene (G-7)

Accurate Air Solutions LLC ....F 325 672-2966
Abilene (G-9)

Air Performance Service Inc ....E 972 387-3334
Dallas (G-3907)

Alexs Air Conditioning Inc ....E 409 935-2496
La Marque (G-13705)

Bates AC & Svc Co Inc ....E 713 869-5521
Houston (G-8824)

Berrys Tin Shop Inc ....F 903 586-3552
Jacksonville (G-13229)

Corsicana Sheet Metal Co Inc ....F 903 872-8434
Corsicana (G-3666)

Darville Co ....F 432 580-9675
Odessa (G-15974)

Hvac Mechanical Svcs of Texas ....E 713 266-3900
Houston (G-10292)

Johnson Controls Inc ....E 512 973-3555
Austin (G-1259)

Logical Control Services LLP ....F 972 820-0100
Carrollton (G-2878)

Qsfirst Inc ....E 210 362-1983
San Antonio (G-18403)

Trotti Service Company Inc ....F 281 894-5095
Houston (G-12383)

Truform Metalservice Inc ....E 512 258-1675
Austin (G-1715)

Zinsmeyer Mech & Wldg Ltd ....E 830 985-3498
Castroville (G-2929)

CONTRACTORS: Water Intake Well Drilling Svc

Axis Energy Services LLC ....F 903 643-3700
Longview (G-14198)

Coastal Plains Exploration LLC ....F 361 553-9000
Port Lavaca (G-17144)

Talon/Lpe Ltd ....D 806 467-0607
Amarillo (G-466)

Varel International Ind LLC ....E 281 272-6000
Houston (G-12538)

CONTRACTORS: Water Well Drilling

Aqua Drill International LLC ....D 281 337-0900
Dickinson (G-5468)

Blue Quail Energy Services LLC ....E 432 684-0999
Midland (G-15143)

Busters Well Service Inc ....D 432 586-2533
Kermit (G-13510)

Challenger Drilling Inc ....F 281 290-8335
Tomball (G-19969)

Charger Services LLC ....E 432 218-7674
Midland (G-15158)

Coastal Plains Exploration LLC ....F 361 553-9000
Port Lavaca (G-17144)

Friedel Drilling Co ....F 361 293-5545
Yoakum (G-20966)

Hazelett Drilling and Sup Corp ....E 512 398-6682
Lockhart (G-14169)

High Plains Drilling Company ....F 806 935-2132
Dumas (G-5521)

L C Burkett Drilling ....F 806 948-4252
Sunray (G-19620)

Lottco Inc ....E 832 773-4345
Humble (G-12785)

M H C X-Ploration Corporation ....F 903 595-4323
Tyler (G-20117)

Premier Directional Drlg LP ....C 281 673-4000
Houston (G-11400)

CONTRACTORS: Water Well Servicing

Alsay Incorporated ....E 210 628-1090
San Antonio (G-17900)

Layne Christensen Company ....D 281 475-2600
Spring (G-19226)

Strawn Transport & Acid Co ....F 806 495-2422
Post (G-17192)

Talon/Lpe Ltd ....D 806 467-0607
Amarillo (G-466)

CONTRACTORS: Waterproofing

Centennial Moisture Ctrl Inc ....D 214 350-7689
Irving (G-12967)

Market Makers Inc ....F 281 893-9261
Houston (G-10769)

Millsap Waterproofing Inc ....D 713 956-6677
Houston (G-10883)

CONTRACTORS: Weather Stripping

Hoelscher Weatherstrip Mfg Inc ....D 713 869-6466
Tomball (G-19982)

CONTRACTORS: Well Acidizing Svcs

Advanced Stimulation Tech Inc ....D 432 617-3250
Midland (G-15106)

John Oates Company Inc ....G 806 878-3338
Stinnett (G-19427)

Quintana Energy Services LP ....F 832 518-4094
Houston (G-11516)

Steven C Rich LLC ....F 325 573-6653
Snyder (G-19010)

Strawn Transport & Acid Co ....F 806 495-2422
Post (G-17192)

CONTRACTORS: Well Bailing, Cleaning, Swabbing & Treating Svc

Encore Wellhead Systems LLC ....F 832 742-1350
Houston (G-9625)

Encore Wellhead Systems LLC ....E 832 742-1325
Angleton (G-571)

Encore Wellhead Systems LLC ....E 903 983-4481
Kilgore (G-13550)

JT Swabbing Services Inc ....F 956 580-8954
Mission (G-15557)

Savanna Drilling LLC ....F 432 614-1055
Odessa (G-16150)

Savanna Energy Svcs USA Corp ....F 281 907-4800
The Woodlands (G-19917)

CONTRACTORS: Well Casings Perforating Svcs

Anderson Perforating Ltd ....E 830 569-1120
Pleasanton (G-17061)

Byrd Oilfield Services LLC ....E 325 690-0053
Abilene (G-27)

CDK Perforating ....E 817 945-1051
Fort Worth (G-6500)

Wsi Cased Hole Specialist Inc ....E 800 658-9674
Snyder (G-19015)

CONTRACTORS: Well Chemical Treating Svcs

Chemical Service Company ....E 432 523-5290
Andrews (G-542)

Corrosion Ltd ....E 432 561-8504
Odessa (G-15969)

Crudechem Technology LLC ....F 832 206-0790
Pattison (G-16531)

Foster Testing Co Inc ....F 806 435-6876
Farnsworth (G-6227)

Tornado Production Svcs LLC ....D 361 384-9020
Orange Grove (G-16270)

Zephyr Gas Services LLC ....E 281 376-2980
Houston (G-12725)

CONTRACTORS: Well Cleaning Svcs

Belarco Indus Clg Odessa LLC ....E 432 381-0999
  Odessa **(G-15932)**
D & L Well Service Inc ....F 432 336-8101
  Fort Stockton **(G-6329)**
Tsunami Rig Wash LLC ....E 512 280-1649
  Austin **(G-1599)**

CONTRACTORS: Well Logging Svcs

Coastal Wireline Services Inc ....F 281 485-6548
  Pearland **(G-16546)**
Continental Laboratories Inc ....E 713 460-0780
  Houston **(G-9285)**
Gowell International LLC ....E 713 909-2555
  Houston **(G-10007)**
Gray Energy Services LLC ....A 806 894-6008
  Levelland **(G-14008)**
Halliburton Company ....E 281 575-5000
  Corpus Christi **(G-3544)**
Helix Enrgy Slutions Group Inc ....C 281 618-0400
  Houston **(G-10150)**
Jose Luis Villarreal ....E 956 765-5535
  Zapata **(G-20983)**
Madden Systems Inc ....F 432 332-0255
  Odessa **(G-16069)**
Production Logging Inc ....E 325 573-4441
  Snyder **(G-19002)**
Qes Wireline LLC ....F 817 546-4970
  Fort Worth **(G-6925)**
Qes Wireline LLC ....F 432 813-6088
  Cresson **(G-3712)**
Quality Logging Inc ....D 432 682-7168
  Midland **(G-15373)**
Schlumberger Limited ....E 713 513-2000
  Houston **(G-11767)**
Schlumberger Limited ....F 713 513-2000
  Houston **(G-11768)**
Schlumberger Technology Corp 432 694-0000
  Midland **(G-15396)**
Schlumberger Technology Corp ....D 903 590-4500
  Tyler **(G-20149)**
Schlumberger Technology Corp ....A 281 285-8500
  Sugar Land **(G-19542)**
Schlumberger Technology Corp ....C 281 285-8500
  Houston **(G-11780)**
Sonic Surveys Ltd ....F 281 385-6500
  Baytown **(G-1802)**
Texas Perforators Inc ....E 361 516-0541
  Kingsville **(G-13636)**
Warrior Energy Services Corp ....F 903 984-9093
  Kilgore **(G-13601)**
Western Atlas Intl Inc ....B 713 972-4000
  Houston **(G-12641)**
Wren Oilfield Services Inc ....F 903 759-3086
  White Oak **(G-20723)**

CONTRACTORS: Well Surveying Svcs

Ark La Tex Surveying Co Inc ....F 903 938-9939
  Marshall **(G-14762)**
Collins Surveying and Mapping ....E 903 234-8051
  Longview **(G-14210)**
Deep Imaging Technologies Inc ....F 281 290-0492
  Tomball **(G-19973)**
Scientific Drilling Intl Inc ....C 281 443-3300
  Houston **(G-11786)**

CONTRACTORS: Well Swabbing Svcs

Border Swabbing Inc ....F 361 575-7852
  Victoria **(G-20248)**

CONTRACTORS: Window Treatment Installation

Highlite Inc ....F 214 741-4116
  Mesquite **(G-15051)**
Stella Hasegawa ....F 915 594-7633
  El Paso **(G-5977)**

CONTRACTORS: Windows & Doors

Airtite Products Llc ....F 325 672-5774
  Abilene **(G-11)**
Allstar Door & Maintenance LP ....F 817 748-0667
  Colleyville **(G-3210)**

CONTRACTORS: Wood Floor Installation & Refinishing

Ace Hardwood Flooring Inc ....F 512 719-3555
  West Lake Hills **(G-20676)**
Arismendy Josias ....E 817 353-1244
  Fort Worth **(G-6401)**
Woodwright Hardwood Flr Co Inc ....E 214 630-8811
  Dallas **(G-5202)**

CONTRACTORS: Wrecking & Demolition

C&F Fabrication Indus Svcs LLC ....E 409 994-2135
  Buna **(G-2561)**
Epcs Environmental LLC ....F 817 975-5790
  Arlington **(G-672)**
Mission Wrecker Service S A ....E 210 341-0333
  Converse **(G-3398)**
Moses Envmtl & Cnstr Svcs LLC ....E 806 418-8525
  Amarillo **(G-448)**
Trendsetter Construction Inc ....C 903 759-4955
  Gladewater **(G-7728)**
Vernor Material & Eqp Co Inc ....D 409 233-3366
  Freeport **(G-7221)**

CONTROL CIRCUIT DEVICES

Control Alternative Solutions ....F 512 858-9603
  Dripping Springs **(G-5503)**
Electrolab Inc ....E 210 824-5364
  Boerne **(G-2118)**

CONTROL EQPT: Electric

Ace Controls LLC ....F 713 589-5494
  Humble **(G-12743)**
Aphthoria Solutions Inc ....D 214 821-8607
  Dallas **(G-3950)**
Electronic Power Design Inc ....D 713 923-1191
  Houston **(G-9596)**
ITT LLC ....E 281 367-2800
  The Woodlands **(G-19887)**
Maverick Technical Systems Inc ....G 903 845-5574
  Gladewater **(G-7726)**
NS Controls Inc ....E 713 465-7591
  Houston **(G-11094)**
Nuco Controls LLC ....F 940 257-7092
  Wichita Falls **(G-20789)**
Powell Electrical Systems Inc ....A 713 944-6900
  Houston **(G-11372)**
Process Automation Design Inc ....E 817 283-1500
  Hurst **(G-12855)**
Southern Transformers ....E 713 923-1191
  Houston **(G-11978)**
Thunderco Inc ....G 713 681-4686
  Houston **(G-12286)**
Total Grow Holdings LLC ....F 281 585-9500
  Alvin **(G-382)**

CONTROL EQPT: Electric Buses & Locomotives

Luminator Holding LP ....C 972 424-6511
  Plano **(G-16911)**

CONTROL EQPT: Noise

Vibration Management Corp ....E 713 983-8462
  Houston **(G-12563)**

CONTROL PANELS: Electrical

Accurate Control Company LLC ....E 713 699-3799
  Houston **(G-8461)**
Aphthoria Solutions Inc ....D 214 821-8607
  Dallas **(G-3950)**
Cates Control Systems Inc ....D 972 665-3200
  Plano **(G-16821)**
Conloop Inc ....F 940 322-2206
  Wichita Falls **(G-20756)**
Control Panels USA Inc ....E 512 852-8280
  Austin **(G-1063)**
Coordnated Designs Contrls Inc ....F 713 921-0220
  Houston **(G-9308)**
Coyote Electronics Inc ....F 817 485-3336
  Azle **(G-1722)**
Crown Texas Inc ....D 972 905-4680
  Garland **(G-7471)**
Cse W-Industries Inc ....C 713 466-9463
  Jersey Village **(G-13297)**
Custom Controls Company ....E 713 666-3258
  Houston **(G-9368)**

Gil Automations LLC ....F 713 904-4600
  Houston **(G-9957)**
H Lorimer Corporation ....E 903 643-3239
  Longview **(G-14245)**
Lft Panels Inc ....F 713 984-9878
  Houston **(G-10630)**
Logic Control LLC ....E 281 362-9600
  Conroe **(G-3323)**
Lower Colorado River Authority ....A 512 473-3200
  Austin **(G-1305)**
M&I Electric LLC ....C 409 838-0441
  Beaumont **(G-1922)**
Mico Group Ltd ....F 713 460-3172
  Grapeland **(G-8006)**
Panelmatic Texas Inc ....E 281 890-1678
  Houston **(G-11231)**
Parkline Inc ....D 409 935-1037
  La Marque **(G-13713)**
Parkline Inc ....D 409 935-5743
  Hitchcock **(G-8339)**
Quality Lnings Fabrication Inc ....E 713 863-7013
  Houston **(G-11495)**
Ran Technologies Inc ....E 281 530-3248
  Houston **(G-11538)**
Rnb Controls Inc ....E 325 388-6023
  Kingsland **(G-13622)**
Sdrg Controls Inc ....F 713 242-0822
  Houston **(G-11794)**
Shermco System Integration LLC ....C 940 322-2206
  Wichita Falls **(G-20811)**
Skledar-Greene LLC ....E 817 454-4214
  Krum **(G-13676)**
Ss Electric Inc ....F 915 217-2200
  El Paso **(G-5973)**
Vector Systems Inc ....D 214 544-9500
  McKinney **(G-14985)**

CONTROLS & ACCESS: Indl, Electric

Capable Controls Inc ....E 915 594-7659
  El Paso **(G-5678)**
Edwin Jones Company Inc ....G 214 361-4000
  Dallas **(G-4301)**
L V Controls Inc ....F 713 691-4666
  Houston **(G-10576)**
Rockwell Automation Inc ....D 972 417-5400
  Lewisville **(G-14090)**
Ss Electric Inc ....G 915 217-2200
  El Paso **(G-5973)**
Superior Controls Inc ....G 432 332-4051
  Odessa **(G-16170)**
Tcw Investments Inc ....F 409 796-1883
  Beaumont **(G-1956)**
Tech Power International Co ....D 281 494-4242
  Stafford **(G-19382)**

CONTROLS & ACCESS: Motor

Advanced Control Systems LLC ....E 832 529-2234
  Houston **(G-8487)**
Capsonic Automotive Inc ....E 915 872-3585
  El Paso **(G-5680)**
Eaton Corporation ....B 262 765-9764
  El Paso **(G-5731)**
McAps Inc ....F 713 941-1300
  South Houston **(G-19049)**
Northwest Independent Schl Dst ....C 817 698-7300
  Fort Worth **(G-6869)**
Powell Industries Inc ....B 713 944-6900
  Houston **(G-11376)**

CONTROLS: Access, Motor

Electro-Quip Service Inc ....D 281 456-8600
  Houston **(G-9593)**

CONTROLS: Air Flow, Refrigeration

Concord Mechanical Inc ....F 817 319-5575
  Boyd **(G-2204)**
Miller Mechanical Group ....F 361 594-8080
  Shiner **(G-18945)**

CONTROLS: Automatic Temperature

Climatic Systems Inc ....F 972 206-2590
  Grand Prairie **(G-7853)**
Controlled Systems Sales Co ....F 972 234-6767
  Richardson **(G-17291)**
Maxitrol Company ....E 817 479-8505
  Richland Hills **(G-17441)**
Schneider Elc Systems USA Inc ....D 713 329-1600
  Houston **(G-11781)**

PRODUCT

Ultimate Control Solutions Inc ....F 972 383-9414
Dallas (G-5129)

CONTROLS: Crane & Hoist, Including Metal Mill

Markload Systems Inc ....F 281 485-8600
Pearland (G-16580)

Robinson Engineering Co Inc.............E 972 272-2001
Garland (G-7580)

CONTROLS: Electric Motor

Appliance Controls Texas Corp............E 214 501-3880
Garland (G-7439)

Elliott Electric Supply Inc..................E 512 246-8001
Round Rock (G-17652)

Hubbell Industrial Contrls Inc............D 281 391-6800
Katy (G-13407)

Omron Electronics LLC ....D 713 849-1900
Houston (G-11181)

Schlumberger Rig Tech Inc................D 713 849-1700
Houston (G-11771)

Siemens Industry Inc ....E 817 633-4430
Grand Prairie (G-7973)

Sprecher & Schuh Inc ....E 281 442-9000
Houston (G-12024)

CONTROLS: Environmental

Absolute Acstic Noise Ctrl LLC...........F 817 594-4446
Weatherford (G-20573)

Ademco Inc.....................................D 915 875-0091
El Paso (G-5638)

Apergy Artfl Lift Intl LLC ....D 713 466-3552
Houston (G-8662)

Aqua Quality Water Systems ....G 210 493-4545
San Antonio (G-17911)

Ash Automated Ctrl Systems LLC ....F 281 346-1400
Fulshear (G-7327)

C3 Environmental Spc LP ....E 210 653-7801
Schertz (G-18746)

Digital Air Control Inc ....E 713 975-8160
Houston (G-9471)

Environmental Fuel Systems ....F 800 375-7747
Boerne (G-2119)

Incenergy LLC ....F 512 327-2020
Austin (G-1226)

Johnson Controls Inc ....E 281 633-5700
Richmond (G-17457)

Johnson Controls Inc ....E 512 973-3555
Austin (G-1259)

Ldia Holdings LLC ....E 512 247-3700
Austin (G-1284)

Maddox Enterprises Inc ....E 903 592-6531
Tyler (G-20119)

Midwest Energy Emissions Corp ....F 614 505-6115
Corsicana (G-3678)

Repco Replacement Parts Inc ....E 817 293-3639
Fort Worth (G-6956)

Robertshaw Controls Company ....C 956 831-9000
Brownsville (G-2402)

Robinson Engineering Co Inc.............E 972 272-2001
Garland (G-7580)

Ruskin Company ....F 972 247-7448
Carrollton (G-2811)

Weimar Industries Inc.......................G 979 725-8503
Weimar (G-20652)

Whitewater Resources LLC ....F 210 290-9005
San Antonio (G-18618)

Xencom Energy Management LLC.......F 469 429-1111
Plano (G-17054)

CONTROLS: Hydronic

Sabine River Authority Texas ....E 409 746-2192
Orange (G-16261)

CONTROLS: Marine & Navy, Auxiliary

Industrial Olfld Mar Cmpnnts I..............F 713 266-1900
Tomball (G-19985)

CONTROLS: Positioning, Electric

Contrinex Inc ....F 574 340-7089
Coppell (G-3413)

CONTROLS: Relay & Ind

A & B Auto Electric Inc ....F 713 928-3219
Houston (G-8422)

Air Starter Components Inc ....E 281 261-7939
Stafford (G-19282)

Antx Inc ....F 512 255-2800
Cedar Park (G-2960)

Apergy Artfl Lift Intl LLC ....D 713 466-3552
Houston (G-8662)

B I Products LLC ....D 972 359-4000
Allen (G-255)

Bk/Ja Holdings Inc ....E 281 879-9903
Stafford (G-19291)

BI Technology Inc ....E 832 698-8000
Tomball (G-19967)

C-B-Gear & Machine Inc ....E 281 449-0777
Houston (G-9040)

Clairex Technologies Inc ....F 972 265-4905
Plano (G-16825)

Conloop Inc ....F 940 322-2206
Wichita Falls (G-20756)

Copperlogic Inc ....E 713 933-0999
Houston (G-9310)

Cse W-Industries Inc ....C 713 466-9463
Jersey Village (G-13297)

DK Controls LLC ....E 972 580-9300
Irving (G-13000)

Dresser LLC ....E 832 590-2306
Houston (G-9518)

Eaton Corporation ....B 915 779-4524
El Paso (G-5730)

Eaton Corporation ....C 915 881-0259
El Paso (G-5733)

Elliott Control Company Ltd ....F 713 589-3102
Willis (G-20846)

Emerson Atmtn Sltons Fnal Ctrl..........B 713 986-4665
Houston (G-9612)

Emerson Automation Solutions ....G 512 835-2190
Round Rock (G-17653)

Evans Enterprises Inc ....D 325 235-1776
Abilene (G-40)

Fisher Controls Intl LLC ....B 972 542-5512
McKinney (G-14943)

Fisher-Rosemount Systems Inc ....A 512 835-2190
Round Rock (G-17657)

Glo-Jo Electrical Products Inc.............E 210 673-3583
San Antonio (G-18144)

Kelleys Controls Incorporated.............F 432 362-7998
Odessa (G-16045)

Longview Distribution I LLC ....E 832 467-4600
Houston (G-10686)

M&I Electric Industries Inc ....D 832 241-6330
Houston (G-10721)

Maxitrol Company ....E 817 479-8505
Richland Hills (G-17441)

Moore Control Systems Inc ....D 281 392-7747
Katy (G-13372)

Overhead Door Corporation ....B 361 884-6640
Corpus Christi (G-3586)

Pegasus Automation Inc ....F 972 390-9548
Allen (G-290)

Powell Electrical Systems Inc..............A 713 790-1700
Houston (G-11373)

Powell Electrical Systems Inc..............F 713 944-6900
Houston (G-11375)

Ringdale Inc ....F 512 288-9080
Georgetown (G-7675)

Rockwell Automation Inc ....F 713 353-2400
Houston (G-11652)

Schenck Process LLC ....D 816 891-9300
Houston (G-11765)

Schmidt Manufacturing Inc ....F 281 431-0581
Bellaire (G-2002)

Schneider Electric Usa Inc ....C 972 236-0300
Coppell (G-3444)

Shermco System Integration LLC ....C 940 322-2206
Wichita Falls (G-20811)

Siemens Industry Inc ....B 972 947-7000
Dallas (G-4959)

Singer Data Products Inc ....E 915 594-7650
El Paso (G-5962)

Watts Water Technologies Inc ....D 713 943-0688
Houston (G-12606)

Wgi Innovations Ltd..........................E 469 733-1868
Grand Prairie (G-7993)

CONTROLS: Thermostats

Texas Instruments Incorporated ....A 972 995-3773
Dallas (G-5067)

Texas Instruments Incorporated ....E 214 567-2075
Richardson (G-17408)

CONTROLS: Thermostats, Exc Built-in

Aqua Electric Inc.............................F 972 243-2162
Dallas (G-3956)

CONVENIENCE STORES

Mobile Mini Inc ....E 817 439-2288
Rhome (G-17258)

Valero Services Inc ....A 210 345-2000
San Antonio (G-18590)

CONVENTION & TRADE SHOW SVCS

Mike Davis and Associates Inc.............E 512 836-8442
Austin (G-1343)

CONVERTERS: Data

Calrock Music..................................D 432 213-8822
Houston (G-9054)

Cisco Systems Inc ....D 469 420-4700
Irving (G-12971)

Cisco Systems Inc ....A 817 490-6062
Roanoke (G-17484)

Enseo LLC ....E 972 234-2513
Plano (G-16862)

Evans - Hamilton Inc.........................E 281 448-6188
Houston (G-9715)

Fotown Productions ....F 225 773-1894
Cypress (G-3791)

Sigmatron International Inc ....F 830 775-5524
Del Rio (G-5324)

Telxon Corporation ....C 713 868-5511
Houston (G-12195)

CONVERTERS: Frequency

Controlled Systems Sales Co ....F 972 234-6767
Richardson (G-17291)

CONVERTERS: Phase Or Rotary, Electrical

Precision Power Associates ....G 972 234-6165
Richardson (G-17375)

CONVERTERS: Power, AC to DC

M&I Electric LLC ....C 409 838-0441
Beaumont (G-1922)

Varo LLC ....B 972 840-5506
Garland (G-7607)

CONVERTERS: Torque, Exc Auto

Fitz Torque Convertors Inc ....E 432 362-3261
Odessa (G-16003)

CONVEYOR SYSTEMS

Laserweld Inc ....E 713 333-0804
Katy (G-13422)

Redcastle Manufacturing LLC ....F 817 350-6300
Mansfield (G-14709)

Souther Equipment Sales Inc ....F 972 296-5231
Dallas (G-4985)

Unified Supply & Services Co..............F 972 355-8299
Rhome (G-17262)

CONVEYOR SYSTEMS: Belt, General Indl Use

B W Sinclair Inc ....E 940 766-2556
Wichita Falls (G-20742)

Cnc Fabrication and Maint ....F 817 295-9055
Burleson (G-2575)

Cugar Machine Inc...........................F 817 927-0411
Fort Worth (G-6565)

Kws Manufacturing Company Ltd........C 817 295-2247
Burleson (G-2586)

Meyer Industries Inc ....D 210 736-1811
San Antonio (G-18296)

Siemens Logistics LLC ....A 972 947-7100
Dfw Airport (G-5455)

CONVEYOR SYSTEMS: Bucket Type

Frazier & Son LP ....F 936 494-4040
Conroe (G-3298)

CONVEYOR SYSTEMS: Bulk Handling

Apergy Artfl Lift Intl LLC ....E 281 403-5742
Spring (G-19195)

Coperion Corporation ....F 281 449-9944
Houston *(G-9309)*

Edelhoff Technologies USA LLC ....F 713 947-6469
Houston *(G-9582)*

ISC Manufacturing LLC ....E 817 641-0691
Burleson *(G-2583)*

JVI Vibratory Equipment Inc ....F 832 467-3720
Houston *(G-10491)*

Metso Minerals Industries Inc ....E 210 491-9521
San Antonio *(G-18295)*

Systems Integration Inc ....E 817 468-1494
Arlington *(G-790)*

CONVEYOR SYSTEMS: Pneumatic Tube

Communications Conveyor Co Inc ......E 940 498-1850
Lake Dallas *(G-13810)*

Dover Equipment Inc ....E 713 690-5200
Houston *(G-9504)*

Hou Fab & Maintenance Inc ....G 713 672-1993
Crosby *(G-3733)*

J & J Manufacturing Company ....D 409 835-1330
Beaumont *(G-1912)*

Lee Contracting Inc ....F 281 456-9023
Houston *(G-10616)*

Schenck Process LLC ....D 816 891-9300
Houston *(G-11765)*

CONVEYORS & CONVEYING EQPT

Action Rigging and Pump Svc LP ....F 512 670-9567
Austin *(G-885)*

Alimak Group USA Inc ....D 713 640-8500
Webster *(G-20632)*

All-State Belting LLC ....F 713 433-1272
Houston *(G-8371)*

Ammeraal Beltech Inc ....F 972 647-8996
Grand Prairie *(G-7831)*

Bowlin Engineering Co ....F 817 232-2020
Saginaw *(G-17740)*

Conveyor Aggregate Pdts Corp ....F 713 856-5600
Houston *(G-9299)*

Dallas A C Horn & Company Inc ....D 214 630-3311
Dallas *(G-4210)*

Eckels - Bilt Inc ....F 817 246-4555
Fort Worth *(G-6603)*

Esco Group LLC ....E 903 984-3726
Kilgore *(G-13551)*

Glidepath LLC ....D 972 641-4200
Arlington *(G-692)*

HI Industries Inc ....E 979 836-2661
Brenham *(G-2257)*

Industrial Cnvyor Fbrction Ltd ....F 817 439-0735
Fort Worth *(G-6718)*

Innovtive Cnveyor Concepts Inc ....F 972 323-0797
Grand Prairie *(G-7893)*

Intelligrated Systems Inc ....B 972 899-9636
Coppell *(G-3422)*

J Morco Incorporated ....E 817 596-3989
Weatherford *(G-20597)*

M2I Systems LLC ....F 214 412-1400
Grand Prairie *(G-7920)*

Martin Sprocket & Gear Inc ....D 817 473-1520
Mansfield *(G-14689)*

Martin Sprocket & Gear Inc ....C 817 258-3000
Fort Worth *(G-6813)*

Metroplex Conveyor & Svcs LLC ....F 972 584-0551
Quinlan *(G-17224)*

Midwest Industrial Rubber Inc ....F 972 988-6700
Grand Prairie *(G-7928)*

Midwest Machine LLC ....E 806 355-9400
Amarillo *(G-501)*

Mueller Construction Company ....E 903 868-3585
Sherman *(G-18924)*

Multitech Group Inc ....F 817 496-5500
Arlington *(G-734)*

Newton Conveyors Inc ....F 817 558-1722
Cleburne *(G-3103)*

Package Conveyer Co Inc ....F 817 332-7195
Fort Worth *(G-6889)*

Plant Fabricators Inc ....E 830 393-3064
Floresville *(G-6249)*

Ranger Conveying & Supply Co ....D 713 671-0004
Houston *(G-11544)*

Siemens Industry Inc ....D 972 947-7100
Dfw Airport *(G-5454)*

Systems Automated Controls Inc ....E 818 898-1900
Denton *(G-5402)*

Transnorm System Inc ....D 972 606-0303
Arlington *(G-802)*

Triple/S Dynamics Inc ....E 214 828-8600
Dallas *(G-5117)*

COOKING & FOOD WARMING EQPT: Commercial

Custom-Built Equipment Co Inc ....F 713 222-0342
Houston *(G-9377)*

Filtration Automation Inc ....E 817 999-8190
Alvarado *(G-332)*

Hobart Sales and Service Inc ....E 210 829-5663
San Antonio *(G-18169)*

Metal Kitchen Fabricators Inc ....F 713 683-8375
Houston *(G-10847)*

Professional Fabrication Inc ....E 936 321-7070
Magnolia *(G-14622)*

Project Services Group Inc ....D 972 812-7370
Irving *(G-13159)*

Renfro Industries Inc ....D 972 563-4295
Terrell *(G-19749)*

Restaurant Depot LLC ....E 512 454-5600
Austin *(G-1461)*

RSI Partners LLC ....D 817 640-5415
Arlington *(G-777)*

Steelhead Inc ....E 210 628-1066
San Antonio *(G-18498)*

Sterno Group LLC ....C 903 223-3400
Texarkana *(G-19775)*

Tri Star Metals Inc ....E 940 433-2173
Boyd *(G-2209)*

Ultrafryer Systems Inc ....C 210 731-5000
San Antonio *(G-18575)*

COOKING & FOODWARMING EQPT: Coffee Brewing

Solofill LLC ....F 832 675-9862
Houston *(G-11942)*

COOKING & FOODWARMING EQPT: Commercial

Advance Tabco Inc ....F 972 932-4148
Kaufman *(G-13456)*

H & K International Inc ....C 214 818-3500
Mesquite *(G-15047)*

Regency Wraps Inc ....E 214 357-0099
Dallas *(G-4883)*

Turbochef Technologies Inc ....E 214 379-6000
Carrollton *(G-2892)*

COOKING & FOODWARMING EQPT: Microwave Ovens, Commercial

Turbochef Technologies Inc ....E 214 379-6000
Carrollton *(G-2893)*

COOKING & FOODWARMING EQPT: Popcorn Machines, Commercial

Dallas A C Horn & Company Inc ....D 214 630-3311
Dallas *(G-4210)*

Liberto Management Co Inc ....E 210 226-4167
San Antonio *(G-18250)*

COOKING EQPT, HOUSEHOLD: Convection Ovens, Incldg Portable

Turbochef Technologies Inc ....E 214 379-6000
Carrollton *(G-2893)*

COOKWARE, STONEWARE: Coarse Earthenware & Pottery

Harris Potteries LP ....D 903 938-8884
Marshall *(G-14781)*

COOLERS & ICE CHESTS: Metal

Bags Elite Inc ....E 972 279-7798
Mesquite *(G-15029)*

COOLERS & ICE CHESTS: Polystyrene Foam

Bags Elite Inc ....E 972 279-7798
Mesquite *(G-15029)*

Igloo Products Corp ....A 281 394-6800
Katy *(G-13365)*

Yeti Coolers LLC ....C 512 394-9384
Austin *(G-1680)*

Yeti Holdings Inc ....E 512 394-8220
Austin *(G-1681)*

COOLING TOWERS: Wood

Enrud Resources Inc ....F 713 943-1600
Pasadena *(G-16429)*

Jml Services Inc ....F 713 582-9500
Crosby *(G-3736)*

Roy C Garrett Inc ....F 210 659-6701
Cibolo *(G-3064)*

Zachry Holdings Inc ....F 806 322-4100
Amarillo *(G-525)*

COPINGS: Concrete

Noel Duque ....E 281 447-5789
Houston *(G-11065)*

COPPER ORE MINING

Freeport Minerals Corporation ....C 915 778-9881
El Paso *(G-5774)*

COPPER ORES

BHP Minerals International LLC ....B 713 961-8500
Houston *(G-8878)*

COPPER: Blister

Reaper Miniatures Inc ....E 940 484-6464
Denton *(G-5397)*

COPPER: Cathodes, Primary

Deepwater Mfg USA Inc ....E 713 983-7117
Houston *(G-9425)*

COPY MACHINES WHOLESALERS

Alpha Laser Recharge Inc ....F 713 861-2425
Houston *(G-8562)*

Hill Country Publishing Co ....E 512 556-6262
Lampasas *(G-13834)*

Montano Investments Inc ....E 956 630-1877
McAllen *(G-14892)*

COPYRIGHT BUYING & LICENSING

Haggar Corp ....A 214 352-8481
Farmers Branch *(G-6200)*

COPYRIGHT PROTECTION SVCS

Corrpro Companies Inc ....C 713 460-6000
Houston *(G-9325)*

CORD & TWINE

Delta Rigging & Tools Inc ....D 877 889-8833
Hurst *(G-12844)*

CORD & TWINE: Fiber, Hard

Equibrand Products Group LP ....D 817 573-1884
Granbury *(G-7796)*

CORES: Fiber, Made From Purchased Materials

Impact Composite Tech Ltd ....E 806 385-1015
Littlefield *(G-14146)*

CORNICES: Sheet Metal

R F Higginbotham Inc ....E 512 836-8985
Austin *(G-1447)*

CORRECTIONAL INSTITUTIONS

Federal Prison Industries ....F 972 287-4040
Seagoville *(G-18800)*

Federal Prison Industries ....C 432 466-2300
Big Spring *(G-2082)*

Federal Prison Industries ....B 512 321-3903
Bastrop *(G-1757)*

CORRECTIONAL INSTITUTIONS, GOVERNMENT: Prison, government

Texas Dept Criminal Justice ....A 936 295-6371
Huntsville *(G-12825)*

CORRUGATED PRDTS: Boxes, Partition, Display Items, Sheet/Pad

America Empack Inc ....E 956 618-3922
McAllen *(G-14837)*
Fairbanks Packaging LLC ....G 817 849-1366
Grand Prairie *(G-7869)*
Ics Enterprises LLP ....B 915 239-9256
El Paso *(G-5808)*
National Cnverting Fulfillment ....E 972 875-5096
Ennis *(G-6112)*
Sbu Group LP ....F 281 564-6464
Houston *(G-11763)*

COSMETIC PREPARATIONS

Aloe Vera of America Inc ....C 956 585-9704
Alton *(G-321)*
Aroma Alternatives Ltd Co ....F 512 535-3646
Austin *(G-934)*
Atlantis Laboratories Inc ....F 936 760-1255
Conroe *(G-3258)*
Beauty Mfg Solutions Corp ....C 972 241-9665
Coppell *(G-3410)*
Cosmetic Laboratories Inc ....E 972 986-9098
Irving *(G-12981)*
Dhaliwal Laboratories LLC ....C 214 446-5862
Dallas *(G-4256)*
Gdmi Inc ....D 972 494-7477
Garland *(G-7498)*
Goodier Cosmetics LLC ....C 214 630-1803
Irving *(G-13041)*
Inner Health Group Inc ....E 210 661-8311
San Antonio *(G-18187)*
Jack Black LLC ....D 469 341-2700
Coppell *(G-3423)*
Natural Cosmeceuticals of Amer ....F 832 771-0882
Houston *(G-11006)*
Naturich Cosmetique Labs Inc ....F 972 926-9200
Garland *(G-7559)*
Shany Enterprises Inc ....E 713 772-1345
Stafford *(G-19377)*
Southern Fields Aloe Inc ....F 956 565-5102
Mercedes *(G-15010)*
United Laboratories Mfg LLC ....C 972 490-3300
Carrollton *(G-2843)*
Warren Laboraties LLC ....F 254 580-9990
Abbott *(G-1)*

COSMETICS & TOILETRIES

Aloe Queen Inc ....E 956 631-8869
McAllen *(G-14834)*
Aloecorp Inc ....E 956 223-6931
Mercedes *(G-15001)*
Colgate-Palmolive Company ....B 903 832-8615
Texarkana *(G-19760)*
Eltamd Inc ....D 972 385-2900
Addison *(G-119)*
Humco Holding Group Inc ....C 903 831-7808
Texarkana *(G-19766)*
Jahkur International LLC ....E 832 431-3232
Houston *(G-10450)*
Kale Naturals LLC ....F 214 402-6040
Dallas *(G-4543)*
Maison De Navar ....G 512 266-6100
Austin *(G-1319)*
Naterra International Inc ....D 972 616-6100
Coppell *(G-3429)*
Neora LLC ....F 855 463-7486
Dallas *(G-4721)*
Ocusoft Inc ....D 281 342-3350
Rosenberg *(G-17592)*
Phlur Inc ....F 888 771-9434
Austin *(G-1415)*
Premark Health Science Inc ....E 972 894-0020
Irving *(G-13155)*
R&D Futures LLC ....E 214 473-9955
Plano *(G-16983)*
Scent Shop Inc ....E 972 271-4661
Garland *(G-7585)*
Scentsible LLC ....D 972 818-8200
Addison *(G-161)*
Source Vital LLC ....F 713 622-2190
Houston *(G-11958)*
Spfm LP ....D 210 805-8931
San Antonio *(G-18491)*
Txsyn Int LLC ....E 210 884-3895
San Antonio *(G-18574)*
Worth Beauty LLC ....F 713 660-0025
Houston *(G-12697)*

COSMETICS WHOLESALERS

Fruit of Earth Inc ....E 817 510-1600
Grand Prairie *(G-7880)*
Kale Naturals LLC ....F 214 402-6040
Dallas *(G-4543)*
Natural Technology Inc ....E 972 551-2563
Terrell *(G-19743)*
Neora LLC ....F 855 463-7486
Dallas *(G-4721)*
Ocusoft Inc ....D 281 342-3350
Rosenberg *(G-17592)*
Revision LLC ....F 972 756-1026
Irving *(G-13165)*

COSMETOLOGY & PERSONAL HYGIENE SALONS

Chateau Noblesse Inc ....D 972 365-7017
Carrollton *(G-2859)*

COSTUME JEWELRY & NOVELTIES: Apparel, Exc Precious Metals

Worldwide J R Wood LLC ....E 512 858-2556
Austin *(G-867)*

COSTUME JEWELRY & NOVELTIES: Bracelets, Exc Precious Metals

Wristbands With A Message Inc ....F 281 494-2424
Stafford *(G-19400)*

COSTUME JEWELRY & NOVELTIES: Costume Novelties

Julie Keck ....F 210 435-3535
San Antonio *(G-18212)*

COSTUME JEWELRY & NOVELTIES: Exc Semi & Precious

Treska Inc ....E 682 647-0352
Fort Worth *(G-7074)*

COSTUME JEWELRY & NOVELTIES: Keychains, Exc Precious Metal

Dyna Group International Inc ....D 830 620-4400
New Braunfels *(G-15788)*

COSTUME JEWELRY & NOVELTIES: Rings, Finger, Gold Plated Wire

Creative Casting Inc ....F 903 463-6160
Denison *(G-5339)*

COSTUMES & WIGS STORES

Headcovers Unlimited Inc ....F 281 334-4287
League City *(G-13958)*

COTTON COMPRESSES & WAREHOUSES

Eugene B Smith & Co Inc ....E 409 763-6401
Pasadena *(G-16432)*

COUNTER & SINK TOPS

77 Stone ....F 915 590-0770
El Paso *(G-5631)*
Alamo City Counter Tops Inc ....E 210 732-4800
San Antonio *(G-17880)*
Ameritek Design Inc ....E 281 442-7767
Houston *(G-8621)*
Bmp & Associates Inc ....E 713 779-8677
Houston *(G-8927)*
Cabinet Creation Inc ....E 830 709-4116
Lytle *(G-14573)*
Dale Nichols Marble Inc ....F 817 341-8970
Weatherford *(G-20585)*
Johnnies Plastics Inc ....E 210 533-8463
San Antonio *(G-18205)*
Keystone Millwork Inc ....F 979 823-4846
Bryan *(G-2485)*
Stonefab Intl LLC ....G 806 352-3416
Amarillo *(G-464)*
US Surface Warehouse ....E 866 433-2229
Austin *(G-1617)*
Wilsonart LLC ....F 254 207-7000
Temple *(G-19721)*

COUNTERS & COUNTING DEVICES

Orbital Energy Group Inc ....E 832 467-1420
Houston *(G-11190)*
Welbor Technology Inc ....F 713 980-2345
Houston *(G-12627)*

COUNTERS OR COUNTER DISPLAY CASES, EXC WOOD

Fab-Tex Fixture & Mfg Co ....E 972 660-6304
Grand Prairie *(G-7868)*
Incounters Inc ....E 325 675-5909
Abilene *(G-51)*
R & R Custom Cabinets Inc ....F 972 247-4697
Carrollton *(G-2883)*
R C T Inc ....E 972 231-9698
Dallas *(G-4853)*
V T I of Texas Inc ....E 979 778-2804
Bryan *(G-2515)*

COUNTERS OR COUNTER DISPLAY CASES, WOOD

Gunckel Archtectural Millworks ....E 830 303-0688
Seguin *(G-18839)*
Wilsonart Intl Holdings LLC ....D 254 207-7000
Temple *(G-19716)*
Wilsonart LLC ....F 254 207-7000
Temple *(G-19719)*

COUNTING DEVICES: Controls, Revolution & Timing

Schlumberger Limited ....E 713 513-2000
Houston *(G-11767)*
Schlumberger Technology Corp ....C 281 285-8500
Sugar Land *(G-19549)*

COUNTING DEVICES: Odometers

Thermo Finnigan LLC ....D 512 251-1400
Austin *(G-1572)*

COUNTING DEVICES: Speed Indicators & Recorders, Vehicle

Applied Concepts Inc ....C 972 398-3750
Richardson *(G-17270)*

COUNTING DEVICES: Vehicle Instruments

Hamar Industries Inc ....E 817 756-8990
Fort Worth *(G-6685)*

COUPLINGS: Hose & Tube, Hydraulic Or Pneumatic

Direct Prchase Qick Cplngs Inc ....E 281 388-0253
Alvin *(G-360)*
Subsea Hydraulic Leads LLC ....G 832 327-4853
Houston *(G-12088)*

COUPLINGS: Pipe

L B Pipe & Coupling Pdts LLC ....E 832 934-1850
Katy *(G-13370)*
Nipples Elbows & Couplings Inc ....E 281 405-8240
Houston *(G-11059)*
Ofs International LLC ....B 281 452-3036
Houston *(G-11148)*
Reconditioned Couplings Inc ....F 832 878-6255
Highlands *(G-8314)*
Texas Pipe Works Inc ....G 936 825-6571
Longview *(G-14318)*

COUPLINGS: Shaft

Texas Precision Mfg Inc ....E 806 741-1166
Lubbock *(G-14492)*

COURIER OR MESSENGER SVCS

B Plan Inc ....F 210 256-1700
San Antonio *(G-17933)*
Cannedy Contemporary Svcs Inc ....E 940 322-3856
Wichita Falls *(G-20749)*

COURIER SVCS, AIR: Package Delivery, Private

Sierra Industries Ltd ....D...... 210 805-3188
San Antonio *(G-18472)*

COURIER SVCS: Air

Wareing Athon & Co ....B...... 713 222-8804
Houston *(G-12599)*

COURIER SVCS: Ground

Fedex Office & Print Svcs Inc ....F...... 512 528-9690
Cedar Park *(G-2969)*
San Antonio Broom Factory Inc ....E...... 210 226-9762
San Antonio *(G-18446)*

COURIER SVCS: Motorcycle

2nd Chance Pallets LLC ....F...... 817 847-8005
Saginaw *(G-17735)*

COURT REPORTING SVCS

Exhibitco Inc ....F...... 713 830-8989
Houston *(G-9723)*

COVERS: Automobile Seat

Mfi International Mfg LLC ....A...... 915 858-0971
El Paso *(G-5876)*
Texas Auto Trim ....E...... 713 661-5557
Houston *(G-12221)*

CRACKED CASTING REPAIR SVCS

RSI Inspection LLC ....E...... 325 673-9800
Abilene *(G-77)*

CRANE & AERIAL LIFT SVCS

Basden Steel and Erection Inc ....E...... 817 295-6100
Burleson *(G-2569)*
David Keels ....E...... 409 316-9265
Hitchcock *(G-8336)*
General Crane Service Inc ....E...... 713 649-4088
Houston *(G-9921)*
Gh Cranes & Components USA Inc ......E...... 972 563-8333
Terrell *(G-19735)*
Kirby - Smith Machinery Inc ....F...... 817 378-0600
Fort Worth *(G-6763)*
Kirby - Smith Machinery Inc ....F...... 806 373-1229
Amarillo *(G-445)*
Marmon Highway Tech LLC ....E...... 214 631-8810
Dallas *(G-4636)*
Proserv Crane & Equipment Inc ....D...... 281 405-9048
Houston *(G-11455)*

CRANES & MONORAIL SYSTEMS

Gh Cranes & Components USA Inc ......E...... 972 563-8333
Terrell *(G-19735)*
Hydralift Amclyde Inc ....D...... 713 375-3700
Houston *(G-10295)*

CRANES: Indl Plant

Gulf Special Services Inc ....E...... 956 541-1445
Brownsville *(G-2361)*
Hiroko International Inc ....F...... 210 590-4411
San Antonio *(G-18168)*

CRANES: Indl Truck

Craneworks Inc ....E...... 281 219-7779
Houston *(G-9334)*
Manitex Inc ....C...... 512 942-3000
Georgetown *(G-7662)*
On-Site Bennett Services LLC ....D...... 855 239-2505
Longview *(G-14287)*

CRANES: Locomotive

Goodcrane Corporation ....D...... 713 434-3322
Houston *(G-9997)*

CRANES: Overhead

Deshazo LLC ....E...... 281 227-6200
Houston *(G-9442)*
General Crane Service Inc ....E...... 713 649-4088
Houston *(G-9921)*
Morris Material Handling Inc ....C...... 281 445-2225
Houston *(G-10923)*

Proserv Crane & Equipment Inc ....D...... 972 438-5100
Irving *(G-13161)*
Proserv Crane & Equipment Inc ....D...... 281 405-9048
Houston *(G-11455)*

CRATING SVCS: Shipping

Cargo Crating Company Ltd ....F...... 713 699-0172
Houston *(G-9092)*

CREATIVE SVCS: Advertisers, Exc Writers

Pointsmith Pnt-F-Prchase MGT S..........C...... 281 599-5900
Katy *(G-13432)*

CREDIT & OTHER FINANCIAL RESPONSIBILITY INSURANCE

American Homestar Corporation ....E...... 281 334-9700
League City *(G-13946)*

CREDIT INSTITUTIONS, SHORT-TERM BUS: Wrkg Capital Finance

Kwik-Kopy Corporation ....C...... 281 256-4100
Cypress *(G-3808)*

CREDIT INSTITUTIONS, SHORT-TERM BUSINESS: Mercantile Finance

Affiliated Foods Inc ....C...... 806 372-3851
Amarillo *(G-476)*

CROWNS & CLOSURES

Modco Industries Inc ....E...... 936 539-9222
Conroe *(G-3331)*
Screen Play Promotions Inc ....G...... 817 788-8608
Hurst *(G-12858)*

CRUDE PETROLEUM & NATURAL GAS PRODUCTION

Adams Resources & Energy Inc............E...... 713 881-3600
Houston *(G-8475)*
Baker Hghes Olfld Oprtions LLC ....F...... 713 879-1000
Houston *(G-8796)*
Bg Brasilia LLC ....F...... 713 599-4000
Houston *(G-8868)*
BP Exploration & Prod Inc ....E...... 800 333-3991
Houston *(G-8969)*
Browning Offshore Inc ....F...... 214 739-3481
Dallas *(G-4061)*
Caelus Energy Alaska LLC ....E...... 214 368-6050
Dallas *(G-4077)*
Callon Petroleum Company ....D...... 281 589-5200
Houston *(G-9051)*
Cantera Energy LLC ....E...... 832 246-6100
The Woodlands *(G-19838)*
Cantera Operating LLC ....F...... 832 246-6100
The Woodlands *(G-19839)*
Catocon Inc ....E...... 903 348-3350
Sulphur Springs *(G-19582)*
Delaware River Swd LLC ....D...... 432 683-7443
Midland *(G-15189)*
Denbury Inc ....G...... 972 673-2000
Plano *(G-16838)*
E B R Energy LP ....F...... 281 265-6500
Sugar Land *(G-19481)*
Edmar Company LLC ....F...... 432 686-8888
Midland *(G-15206)*
Elevation Resources LLC ....G...... 432 686-7500
Midland *(G-15208)*
Energy Xxi Gulf Coast Inc ....F...... 713 351-3000
Houston *(G-9640)*
Enervest Ltd ....D...... 713 659-3500
Houston *(G-9643)*
Eog Resources Inc ....E...... 979 245-2201
Bay City *(G-1772)*
Eog Resources Inc ....E...... 830 879-4614
Cotulla *(G-3690)*
Eog Resources Inc ....D...... 432 686-3600
Midland *(G-15223)*
Federal Royalty Partners Ltd ....E...... 713 529-3729
Houston *(G-9771)*
Founders Oil & Gas Oper LLC ....F...... 817 390-1800
Arlington *(G-680)*
Fred Brown Methanol Inc ....F...... 806 665-0034
Pampa *(G-16323)*
Frostwood Energy LLC ....G...... 713 623-7133
Houston *(G-9871)*

Gmt Exploration Co Texas LLC ....F...... 713 334-6001
Houston *(G-9988)*
Goodrich Petroleum Company LLC ....D...... 713 780-9494
Houston *(G-10002)*
Hallwood Petroleum LLC ....E...... 214 528-5588
Dallas *(G-4431)*
Inpex Eagle Ford LLC ....D...... 713 850-8480
Houston *(G-10375)*
J & L Partners......................................E...... 972 417-3977
Dallas *(G-4516)*
Jamex Inc ....F...... 214 265-7141
Lewisville *(G-14058)*
Killam Oil Co Ltd ....E...... 956 724-7141
Laredo *(G-13902)*
Morgan Kinder Treating LP ....F...... 432 563-2766
Odessa *(G-16083)*
Murphy Exploration Prod - USA ....B...... 281 675-9000
Houston *(G-10942)*
Nbl Permian LLC ....F...... 979 764-4030
College Station *(G-3195)*
Occidental Permian Ltd ....E...... 806 229-2501
Sundown *(G-19613)*
Ohs Energy Corp ....G...... 832 871-5088
Houston *(G-11149)*
Par Petroleum LLC ....G...... 281 899-4800
Houston *(G-11236)*
Primeenergy Corporation ....E...... 713 735-0000
Houston *(G-11417)*
Quicksilver Resources Inc ....D...... 817 665-5000
Fort Worth *(G-6928)*
Quintana Minerals Brazil LLC ....F...... 713 751-7500
Houston *(G-11517)*
Ray Mac Energy ....F...... 806 274-5881
Borger *(G-2184)*
Remora Royalties Inc ....E...... 512 579-3590
Austin *(G-1458)*
Rockcliff Energy MGT LLC ....F...... 713 351-0525
Houston *(G-11650)*
Sandalwood Oil & Gas Inc ....F...... 713 759-6095
Houston *(G-11746)*
Savant Alaska LLC ....E...... 907 868-1258
Houston *(G-11759)*
Scout Energy Management LLC ....F...... 972 277-1397
Dallas *(G-4945)*
Silverbow Resources Inc ....D...... 281 874-2700
Houston *(G-11899)*
Topsail Energy Mktg Group LLC ....F...... 832 823-2380
The Woodlands *(G-19930)*
Transworld Worldwide Inc ....B...... 713 232-7500
Houston *(G-12355)*
Vitol Americas Corp ....D...... 713 230-1000
Houston *(G-12576)*
Williams Field Services Co LLC ....E...... 979 843-7724
Bay City *(G-1777)*
Wtg Gas Processing LP ....F...... 325 473-5161
Bronte *(G-2307)*

CRUDE PETROLEUM & NATURAL GAS PRODUCTION

Allied Natural Gas Corporation ....F...... 713 658-1144
Houston *(G-8550)*
Amplify Acquisitionco Inc ....E...... 713 490-8900
Houston *(G-8628)*
Amplify Energy Holdings LLC ....F...... 713 490-8900
Houston *(G-8630)*
Andeavor LLC ....C...... 210 626-6000
San Antonio *(G-17907)*
Apache Crude Oil Marketing ....E...... 713 296-6000
Houston *(G-8653)*
Apollo Resources Intl Inc ....E...... 214 389-9800
Dallas *(G-3952)*
Approach Resources Inc ....E...... 817 989-9000
Fort Worth *(G-6395)*
Approach Resources Inc ....F...... 325 392-8900
Ozona *(G-16278)*
Aroc Inc ....D...... 832 538-0300
Houston *(G-8702)*
Athlon Energy Inc ....E...... 817 984-8200
Fort Worth *(G-6407)*
Atlas Energy Group LLC ....F...... 412 489-0006
Fort Worth *(G-6408)*
Atlas Growth Partners Gp LLC ....E...... 412 489-0006
Fort Worth *(G-6409)*
Bainbridge Uinta LLC ....E...... 214 580-2059
Dallas *(G-3998)*
Bass Enterprises Production Co.............E...... 432 586-2563
Kermit *(G-13509)*
Belvan Partners LP ....F...... 432 682-4349
Midland *(G-15137)*

PRODUCT

Big Bear Oil Company Inc...............F....... 915 775-1945
  El Paso *(G-5662)*

Blue Bell Energy LLC.....................F....... 713 661-1040
  Houston *(G-8917)*

Blue Mountain Midstream LLC..........F....... 281 377-8770
  Houston *(G-8919)*

Brigham Minerals Inc.....................E....... 512 220-6350
  Austin *(G-1007)*

Brushy Resources Inc.....................F....... 210 999-5400
  San Antonio *(G-17969)*

Cabot Oil & Gas Corporation...........C....... 281 589-4600
  Houston *(G-9041)*

Caprock Permian Processing LLC.....F....... 832 914-1679
  Humble *(G-12752)*

Centurion Pipeline LP....................E....... 713 215-7000
  Houston *(G-9140)*

Chevron Corporation......................C....... 907 276-7600
  Houston *(G-9177)*

Cnooc Energy Holdings USA Inc.......E....... 713 380-4800
  Houston *(G-9220)*

Coastline Petroleum LLC.................F....... 281 844-4272
  Houston *(G-9229)*

Cobra Oil & Gas Corporation............E....... 940 723-4331
  Wichita Falls *(G-20754)*

Concho Oil & Gas LLC....................C....... 432 683-7443
  Midland *(G-15175)*

Concho Resources Inc....................B....... 432 683-7443
  Midland *(G-15177)*

Conocophillips.............................A....... 281 293-1000
  Houston *(G-9272)*

Contango Oil & Gas Company...........E....... 713 236-7400
  Houston *(G-9282)*

Copano Company...........................E....... 361 578-6271
  Victoria *(G-20254)*

Copano Company...........................E....... 361 526-2115
  Refugio *(G-17239)*

Daniel H Braman Jr Estate..............E....... 361 578-6271
  Victoria *(G-20257)*

Dcp NGL Services LP......................F....... 713 735-3600
  Houston *(G-9416)*

Denbury Onshore LLC.....................F....... 281 482-7581
  Alvin *(G-358)*

Diamond M Drlg Exploration Co........F....... 210 310-3135
  San Antonio *(G-18056)*

Diamondback Energy Inc.................E....... 432 221-7400
  Midland *(G-15193)*

Double Eagle Lone Star LLC............F....... 817 928-3260
  Fort Worth *(G-6591)*

E R Carpenter LP..........................C....... 804 359-0800
  Temple *(G-19680)*

Eagle Rock Energy G&P LLC............F....... 281 408-1200
  Houston *(G-9561)*

Eagle Rock Field Services LP...........F....... 806 323-5381
  Canadian *(G-2648)*

Eaglehawk Field Services LLC..........C....... 832 204-2700
  Houston *(G-9568)*

Eclipse Resources Holdings LP.........C....... 814 308-9754
  Irving *(G-13006)*

Ecostim Inc.................................D....... 281 531-7200
  Katy *(G-13399)*

El Paso Cgp Company LLC...............E....... 713 420-2600
  Houston *(G-9585)*

Emerald Gathering & Trnsp LLC.......F....... 713 621-2242
  Houston *(G-9611)*

Endeavour International Corp............E....... 713 307-8700
  Houston *(G-9627)*

Energy Xxi Ltd.............................E....... 713 351-3000
  Houston *(G-9641)*

Eni Petroleum US LLC....................C....... 713 393-6100
  Houston *(G-9648)*

Enlink Midstream Partners LP..........F....... 817 599-3492
  Weatherford *(G-20589)*

Eog Resources Inc........................E....... 210 403-7700
  San Antonio *(G-18093)*

Ep Energy LLC..............................F....... 713 997-1200
  Houston *(G-9675)*

Equinor Exploration Company...........F....... 512 427-3300
  Austin *(G-1135)*

Exxon Mobil Fuels Marketing Co........F....... 703 846-3000
  Spring *(G-19115)*

Fairway Rsrces Prtners III LLC.........E....... 817 416-1946
  Southlake *(G-19068)*

Far East Energy Corporation............F....... 832 598-0470
  Houston *(G-9762)*

Farmers Oil Co.............................E....... 281 874-2101
  Houston *(G-9764)*

Five - Jab Inc..............................D....... 281 356-7767
  Magnolia *(G-14607)*

Four Sevens Operating Co Ltd..........F....... 817 870-9088
  Fort Worth *(G-6647)*

Freedom Oil & Gas Inc...................F....... 832 783-5700
  Houston *(G-9859)*

Galveston Bay Gathering LLC...........F....... 281 408-1200
  Houston *(G-9896)*

Gip II Blue Holding Partnr LP............C....... 713 496-4200
  Houston *(G-9959)*

Glori Energy Inc...........................E....... 713 237-8880
  Houston *(G-8383)*

Goodrich Petroleum Corporation.......C....... 713 780-9494
  Houston *(G-10003)*

Hep El Dorado LLC.........................F....... 214 871-3555
  Dallas *(G-4451)*

Hess Midstream GP LP....................C....... 713 496-4200
  Houston *(G-10165)*

High Line Ranch LLC.......................D....... 830 875-5386
  San Antonio *(G-18166)*

Inpex Corporation.........................F....... 713 850-8480
  Houston *(G-10374)*

Iwc Oil & Refinery LLC....................E....... 210 900-9928
  San Antonio *(G-18196)*

Jackal Merger Sub A LLC................D....... 737 704-2300
  Austin *(G-1248)*

Johnson & Ernst Operating Co..........E....... 940 723-8127
  Wichita Falls *(G-20774)*

KCS Resources LLC........................F....... 832 204-2700
  Houston *(G-10505)*

Kerr-Mcgee (nevada) LLC................D....... 303 321-0683
  Spring *(G-19224)*

Kinder Morgan (delaware) Inc..........F....... 806 272-3309
  Muleshoe *(G-15677)*

L T D Explorations Inc....................G....... 361 664-9108
  Freer *(G-7230)*

Legacy Reserves Inc......................F....... 432 689-5200
  Midland *(G-15274)*

Legacy Reserves LP.......................D....... 432 689-5200
  Midland *(G-15276)*

LNG Freeport Development L P...........E....... 713 980-2888
  Houston *(G-10659)*

Lone Star Oil & Gas Inc..................E....... 432 686-9390
  Midland *(G-15284)*

Lonestar Resources US Inc..............E....... 817 921-1889
  Fort Worth *(G-6800)*

Lrr Energy LP...............................C....... 713 292-9510
  Houston *(G-10693)*

Marathon Oil Corporation................A....... 713 629-6600
  Houston *(G-10756)*

Mariner Gulf of Mexico LLC..............E....... 713 954-5500
  Houston *(G-10767)*

Matador Resources Company............E....... 972 371-5200
  Dallas *(G-4650)*

Matthews-Daniel Holdings Inc...........E....... 713 622-1633
  Houston *(G-10798)*

Maverick Field Services LLC.............F....... 432 685-5021
  Midland *(G-15294)*

MB Robinson Inc...........................E....... 432 267-5277
  Big Spring *(G-2087)*

Mesquite Energy Inc......................E....... 713 756-2700
  Houston *(G-10840)*

Midcoast Energy Partners LP...........F....... 713 821-2000
  Houston *(G-10872)*

Millennium Exploration Co LLC..........E....... 210 960-1000
  San Antonio *(G-18307)*

Mineral Technologies Inc................F....... 432 685-3520
  Midland *(G-15305)*

Mobil Producing Texas and NM..........A....... 713 871-5000
  Houston *(G-10898)*

Monterey Oil & Gas Corporation.......E....... 832 985-8723
  Houston *(G-10913)*

MRC Global (us) Inc.......................E....... 432 620-0059
  Midland *(G-15307)*

Nacero Inc..................................D....... 346 200-7706
  Houston *(G-10959)*

Natural Gas Pipeline Amer LLC.........F....... 903 758-0154
  Longview *(G-14283)*

Natural Gas Pipeline Amer LLC.........F....... 361 897-1022
  Victoria *(G-20288)*

Nbl Permian LLC...........................F....... 979 542-5571
  Midland *(G-15312)*

Neofirma Inc...............................E....... 214 233-7111
  Richardson *(G-17362)*

Newfield Exploration Company..........D....... 281 847-6000
  Spring *(G-19236)*

Noble Energy Inc..........................C....... 281 872-3100
  Houston *(G-11064)*

Noble Energy Inc..........................D....... 800 234-3867
  Houston *(G-11063)*

Oil & Gas Producers Inc..................F....... 214 696-2393
  Dallas *(G-4756)*

Patterson-Uti Energy Inc................D....... 281 765-7100
  Houston *(G-11262)*

Phillips 66.................................C....... 281 293-6600
  Houston *(G-11324)*

Phillips 66 Partners LP...................F....... 855 283-9237
  Houston *(G-11326)*

Pioneer Gas Pipeline Inc.................F....... 325 655-3300
  San Angelo *(G-17820)*

Prime Natural Resources LLC...........F....... 713 953-3200
  Houston *(G-11415)*

Prosep Technologies Inc.................E....... 281 504-2040
  Houston *(G-11454)*

Pxp Gulf Coast Inc........................C....... 713 579-6000
  Houston *(G-11477)*

Q-West Energy Company..................G....... 972 233-8191
  Addison *(G-157)*

Quatro Oil and Gas Inc...................F....... 940 767-4443
  Wichita Falls *(G-20800)*

Quintana Energy Services Inc...........A....... 832 518-4094
  Houston *(G-11515)*

Regency Crude Marketing LLC..........D....... 806 665-3491
  Pampa *(G-16337)*

Regency Desoto-Hesco Svcs LLC......E....... 281 408-1200
  Houston *(G-11584)*

Remnant Oil Company LLC...............F....... 432 695-6997
  Midland *(G-15381)*

Ring Energy Inc............................E....... 432 682-7464
  Midland *(G-15386)*

Sable Natural Resources Corp..........F....... 972 770-4700
  Dallas *(G-4925)*

Saga Petro Ltd Lblty Co Colo............F....... 432 687-6200
  Midland *(G-15392)*

Saracen Energy Advisors LP............F....... 713 285-2900
  Houston *(G-11750)*

Sea Eagle Ford LLC.......................E....... 720 390-6244
  Houston *(G-11795)*

Sg Interests I Ltd.........................F....... 713 951-0100
  Houston *(G-11843)*

Siana Oil & Gas Co LLC...................F....... 713 568-1082
  Houston *(G-11876)*

Sienergy LP................................F....... 281 778-6250
  Lakeway *(G-13819)*

Sn Operating LLC..........................E....... 713 951-0233
  Houston *(G-11929)*

Southcross Gathering Ltd................F....... 214 979-3700
  Dallas *(G-4983)*

Sowell & Co LP............................E....... 214 871-3320
  Dallas *(G-4994)*

Speedway LLC..............................F....... 713 496-4000
  Houston *(G-12013)*

Spindletop Oil & Gas Co..................E....... 972 644-2581
  Houston *(G-4998)*

Statoil Oil & Gas Services Inc..........D....... 512 427-3300
  Austin *(G-1533)*

Streamline Innovations Inc..............G....... 888 787-6569
  San Antonio *(G-18508)*

Summit Midstream Partners LP.........E....... 832 413-4770
  Houston *(G-12094)*

Targa Gas Marketing LLC................F....... 713 584-1000
  Houston *(G-12159)*

Tep Barnett Usa LLC......................C....... 817 720-1130
  Fort Worth *(G-7043)*

Terra Energy Partners LLC..............E....... 281 936-0355
  Houston *(G-12209)*

Texas Nom Limited Partnership.........E....... 210 687-1900
  San Antonio *(G-18539)*

Thor Energy Group Inc....................F....... 210 277-0368
  San Antonio *(G-18550)*

Tidal Energy Marketing US LLC.........C....... 713 650-8900
  Houston *(G-12288)*

Total E&P Usa Inc.........................C....... 713 647-3000
  Houston *(G-12330)*

Total Holdings Usa Inc....................E....... 713 483-5000
  Houston *(G-12331)*

Tri Resources Inc.........................E....... 432 558-3996
  Crane *(G-3703)*

W&T Offshore Inc.........................C....... 713 626-8525
  Houston *(G-12588)*

Wapiti Operating LLC.....................D....... 713 365-8500
  Houston *(G-12598)*

Western Midstream Partners LP.........E....... 832 636-6000
  The Woodlands *(G-19940)*

Xto Energy Inc.............................E....... 713 871-3453
  Fort Worth *(G-7156)*

Zion Oil & Gas Inc.........................F....... 214 221-4610
  Dallas *(G-5209)*

CRUDE PETROLEUM PRODUCTION

3-T Exploration Inc.......................F....... 940 691-5091
  Wichita Falls *(G-20734)*

Abraxas Petroleum Corporation.........D....... 210 490-4788
  San Antonio *(G-17855)*

Abraxas Petroleum Corporation ....G...... 325 573-6010
 Ira (G-12912)
Addax Petro Cameroon Co LLC ....C...... 713 245-1263
 Houston (G-8477)
Adexco Operating Company ....G...... 817 332-3891
 Fort Worth (G-6345)
Aix Energy Inc ....F...... 214 292-3482
 Dallas (G-3913)
Al Rowan ....D...... 903 963-7036
 Van (G-20205)
Alexander Production Company ....F...... 210 271-3691
 San Antonio (G-17891)
Allar Company ....G...... 940 549-0077
 Graham (G-7775)
Alpar Energy LP ....G...... 806 435-6566
 Perryton (G-16632)
Anadarko Holding Company ....F...... 832 636-7200
 Houston (G-8633)
Anadarko Petroleum Corporation ......E...... 432 684-2800
 Midland (G-15115)
Anadarko Petroleum Corporation ......C...... 832 636-1000
 The Woodlands (G-19830)
Anadarko Petroleum Corporation ......F...... 979 828-1668
 Franklin (G-7163)
Anadarko Petroleum Corporation ......F...... 979 567-7013
 Caldwell (G-2626)
Anderson Oil Ltd ....F...... 713 652-5746
 Houston (G-8641)
Apache Corporation ....A...... 713 296-6000
 Houston (G-8650)
Apache Corporation ....F...... 432 524-2277
 Andrews (G-536)
Apache Corporation ....F...... 713 296-6000
 Midland (G-15116)
Apache Corporation ....E...... 325 835-2323
 Mertzon (G-15019)
Apache Corporation ....F...... 432 558-2065
 Crane (G-3697)
Apache Corporation ....F...... 432 558-2572
 Crane (G-3698)
Apache Corporation ....E...... 800 272-2434
 Houston (G-8651)
Apache Corporation ....F...... 713 296-6000
 Houston (G-8652)
Apache Corporation ....F...... 806 229-3010
 Sundown (G-19611)
Apache Corporation ....F...... 806 755-2231
 Welch (G-20654)
Apache Corporation ....F...... 806 234-2058
 Lubbock (G-14362)
Apache Corporation ....F...... 979 543-4391
 El Campo (G-5610)
Apache Deepwater LLC ....E...... 713 296-6000
 Houston (G-8654)
Apache Gathering Company ....A...... 713 296-6000
 Houston (G-8657)
Apache International LLC ....E...... 713 296-6000
 Houston (G-8659)
Armor Petroleum Inc ....G...... 940 692-5001
 Wichita Falls (G-20740)
Aruba Petroleum Inc ....F...... 940 466-9438
 Decatur (G-5241)
Aruba Petroleum Inc ....E...... 972 312-9366
 Plano (G-16794)
Atropos Exploration Company ....F...... 214 691-2377
 Dallas (G-3985)
Axess North America Inc ....E...... 281 994-0364
 Houston (G-8758)
B B L Ltd ....E...... 254 559-3355
 Breckenridge (G-2220)
Baker Operating Inc ....G...... 432 367-5808
 Odessa (G-15924)
Ballard Exploration Co Inc ....E...... 713 651-0181
 Houston (G-8810)
Basa Resources Inc ....F...... 936 655-2477
 Kennard (G-13494)
Basa Resources Inc ....F...... 254 559-3366
 Breckenridge (G-2221)
Battalion Oil Corporation ....E...... 832 538-0300
 Houston (G-8826)
Bennett Production Corp ....F...... 940 872-1183
 Bowie (G-2191)
Berry Corporation (bry) ....E...... 661 616-3900
 Dallas (G-4021)
Beta Operating Company LLC ....E...... 562 628-8900
 Houston (G-8864)
Bettis Boyle & Stovall Inc ....F...... 940 549-0780
 Graham (G-7777)
BHP Billiton Petro N Amer Inc ....C...... 713 961-8500
 Houston (G-8875)

Bison Development Company ....F...... 806 355-8253
 Amarillo (G-481)
Black Stone Energy Company LLC .....E...... 713 658-0647
 Houston (G-8906)
Blue Star Ltd ....E...... 281 893-6035
 Houston (G-8920)
BP America Production Company ....F...... 903 927-8999
 Hallsville (G-8127)
BP Corporation North Amer Inc ....A...... 281 366-2000
 Houston (G-8965)
BP Corporation North Amer Inc ....A...... 281 366-2000
 Houston (G-8967)
Bpz Resources Inc ....E...... 281 556-6200
 Houston (G-8973)
Bradley Operating Company ....F...... 806 665-7130
 Pampa (G-16316)
Brayton Operating Corp ....F...... 361 884-8741
 Corpus Christi (G-3489)
Brazco Development Inc ....F...... 432 684-8031
 Midland (G-15149)
Breck Operating Company ....E...... 254 559-3355
 Breckenridge (G-2223)
Bridwell Oil Management LLC ....E...... 325 672-1512
 Abilene (G-24)
Bright Industries LLC ....E...... 972 410-6500
 Lewisville (G-14030)
Broken Hill Propty USA Inc ....D...... 713 961-8500
 Houston (G-8992)
Brown Fndtion Repr In Cnslting ....E...... 972 271-2621
 Dallas (G-4060)
Brown Oil & Gas Co Inc ....F...... 254 562-2818
 Mexia (G-15087)
Browning Oil Company Inc ....F...... 214 739-3481
 Dallas (G-4062)
Bruce A Wilbanks Company Inc ....F...... 432 682-7582
 Midland (G-15152)
Buck Production ....F...... 940 567-3005
 Jacksboro (G-13217)
Buffco Production Inc ....F...... 903 988-8199
 Longview (G-14204)
Burk Royalty Co Ltd ....E...... 940 397-8600
 Wichita Falls (G-20748)
Burlington Resources LLC ....C...... 281 293-1000
 Houston (G-9020)
Burnett Oil Co Inc ....E...... 817 332-5108
 Fort Worth (G-6479)
Callon Petroleum Operating Co ....E...... 601 442-1601
 Houston (G-9053)
Centennial Resource Dev Inc ....E...... 281 302-5048
 Sugar Land (G-19454)
Chaparral Energy LLC ....D...... 806 435-7533
 Perryton (G-16635)
Chesapeake Energy Corporation ....E...... 817 502-5000
 Fort Worth (G-6512)
Chesapeake Operating LLC ....E...... 806 273-5820
 Borger (G-2167)
Chevron Corporation ....E...... 903 963-8631
 Van (G-20206)
Chevron Corporation ....B...... 713 754-3998
 Houston (G-9178)
CHI Energy Inc ....G...... 432 685-5001
 Midland (G-15163)
Chief Oil & Gas LLC ....E...... 214 265-9590
 Dallas (G-4112)
Choctaw II Oil & Gas Ltd ....F...... 713 632-0222
 Houston (G-9184)
Cholla Petroleum Inc ....E...... 214 692-7052
 Dallas (G-4113)
Citation Oil & Gas Corp ....F...... 432 262-7600
 Midland (G-15167)
Citation Oil & Gas Corp ....C...... 281 891-1000
 Houston (G-9199)
Citation Oil & Gas Corp ....G...... 956 248-5741
 Lyford (G-14571)
Clajon Holding Corp ....C...... 432 682-6324
 Midland (G-15168)
Clear Fork Incorporated ....F...... 325 677-1309
 Abilene (G-31)
Coates Energy Trust ....G...... 210 820-0113
 San Antonio (G-18014)
Cockrell Oil Corporation ....E...... 713 209-7300
 Houston (G-9235)
Comstock Oil & Gas Llc ....E...... 972 668-8800
 Frisco (G-7273)
Comstock Resources Inc ....D...... 972 668-8800
 Frisco (G-7274)
Concho Resources Inc ....F...... 432 221-0400
 Midland (G-15176)
Concord Oil Co ....F...... 210 224-4455
 San Antonio (G-18022)

Continental Operating Co ....F...... 713 209-1110
 Houston (G-9287)
Corporate Texas Co LLC ....F...... 940 549-1400
 Graham (G-7778)
Courson Oil & Gas Inc ....F...... 806 435-2910
 Perryton (G-16636)
Crawford Energy Inc ....F...... 713 626-2637
 Houston (G-9335)
Crimson Exploration Inc ....E...... 713 236-7400
 Houston (G-9344)
Cw Resources Inc ....F...... 903 759-8822
 Longview (G-14218)
Dale Operating Company ....E...... 214 979-9010
 Dallas (G-4208)
Dallas Production Inc ....F...... 940 328-1241
 Mineral Wells (G-15524)
Dallas Production Inc ....E...... 214 369-9266
 Dallas (G-4224)
Dcp Midstream LLC ....E...... 806 228-6241
 Spearman (G-19085)
Dcp Operating Company LP ....C...... 361 584-8509
 Bishop (G-2107)
Delray Oil Inc ....F...... 210 824-7214
 San Antonio (G-18048)
Delta Oil & Gas Ltd ....E...... 254 559-9841
 Breckenridge (G-2228)
Denbury Onshore LLC ....C...... 972 673-2000
 Plano (G-16840)
Devon Energy Corporation ....F...... 903 693-7196
 Carthage (G-2906)
Devon Permian Corporation ....C...... 432 685-0727
 Midland (G-15191)
Dirnett Inc ....F...... 361 375-2194
 Tuleta (G-20033)
Djh Services LLC ....F...... 325 392-3671
 Ozona (G-16281)
Djh Services LLC ....F...... 713 228-5911
 Houston (G-9485)
Dorado Oil Company ....E...... 361 241-3200
 Corpus Christi (G-3516)
Dorchester Minerals LP ....E...... 214 559-0300
 Dallas (G-4273)
Doyle Hartman Oil Producer ....F...... 432 684-4011
 Midland (G-15196)
Dstj Corporation ....F...... 936 447-1174
 Montgomery (G-15632)
Dubai Petroleum Company ....A...... 281 293-1000
 Houston (G-9537)
Duncan Drilling Company ....G...... 432 263-7721
 Big Spring (G-2081)
Durham Inc ....F...... 432 684-5557
 Midland (G-15198)
Dynamic Inc ....E...... 817 838-1800
 Fort Worth (G-6597)
Dynamic Production ....E...... 817 838-1800
 Fort Worth (G-6598)
Dyne Oil & Gas Inc ....F...... 806 274-2952
 Borger (G-2176)
E & H Drilling Co ....E...... 940 549-0370
 Graham (G-7781)
Eagle Oil & Gas Co ....F...... 940 723-7322
 Wichita Falls (G-20762)
Eagle Rock Pipeline LP ....E...... 281 408-1200
 Houston (G-9565)
Eastland Oil Co ....E...... 432 683-6293
 Midland (G-15205)
Eclipse Resources I LP ....F...... 814 308-9754
 Irving (G-13007)
El Paso CNG Company LLC ....F...... 713 420-2600
 Houston (G-9586)
Elgie Company Inc ....F...... 214 691-6216
 Dallas (G-4310)
Elm Ridge Resources Inc ....F...... 972 889-2100
 Dallas (G-4316)
Endeavor Energy Resources LP ....E...... 432 687-1575
 Midland (G-15210)
Endeavor Energy Resources LP ....D...... 432 221-9300
 Midland (G-15211)
Endeavor Energy Resources LP ....F...... 432 687-1575
 Midland (G-15213)
Energen Corporation ....F...... 205 326-2700
 Midland (G-15216)
Energen Resources Corporation ....C...... 432 687-1155
 Midland (G-15217)
Eog Resources Inc ....C...... 713 651-7000
 Houston (G-9671)
Eog Resources Inc ....D...... 361 866-4300
 Corpus Christi (G-3519)
Eog Resources Inc ....E...... 940 696-6000
 Bowie (G-2194)

PRODUCT

Ep Energy Corporation..........................F 713 997-1000
  Houston (G-9673)
Esenjay Petroleum Corporation..............F 361 883-7464
  Corpus Christi (G-3521)
Excel Production Co..............................F 806 665-0366
  Pampa (G-16322)
Exco Holdings Inc.................................B 214 368-2084
  Dallas (G-4343)
Falcon Seaboard Holdings LLC.............E 713 622-0055
  Houston (G-9755)
Faulconer Energy Joint Ventr S.............D 903 581-4382
  Tyler (G-20085)
Faulconer Resources Corp.....................F 903 581-4382
  Tyler (G-20086)
Fayetteville-Floyd Gas Company...........D 432 682-6685
  Midland (G-15229)
Foothills Resources Inc........................F 713 621-9408
  Houston (G-9831)
Fortson Oil Company ....E 817 335-5641
  Fort Worth (G-6645)
Fuller Production Inc............................F 432 683-5661
  Midland (G-15233)
G S Petroleum Inc ....E 936 336-4114
  Liberty (G-14118)
Garvon Inc ....F 214 691-0711
  Dallas (G-4392)
Gas Acquisition & Supply Inc ....F 940 872-1183
  Bowie (G-2195)
Gene Powell Investments Inc.................F 903 234-1155
  Longview (G-14240)
Geo Halcon Holdings LLC......................D 832 538-0300
  Houston (G-9932)
George R Brown Partnership..................F 713 652-4901
  Houston (G-9942)
Geosouthern Energy Corporation..........E 281 363-9161
  The Woodlands (G-19866)
Glen Rose Petroleum Corp ....F 832 437-0701
  Houston (G-9964)
Global Marine Inc.................................D 713 232-7500
  Houston (G-9974)
Golden Oil Company ....E 713 626-1110
  Houston (G-9993)
Goldston Oil Corporation......................E 713 355-3408
  Houston (G-9995)
GP II Energy Inc...................................F 432 684-4748
  Midland (G-15238)
Granite Operating Company ....E 806 323-9118
  Canadian (G-2651)
Grizzly Energy LLC...............................E 832 327-2255
  Houston (G-10047)
GSM Enterprises Inc.............................E 806 358-6894
  Amarillo (G-430)
Gunn Oil Company ....F 940 723-5585
  Wichita Falls (G-20769)
H L Brown Jr ....F 432 683-5216
  Midland (G-15243)
H R Stasney & Sons Ltd ....F 325 762-3311
  Albany (G-189)
Halcon Gulf States LLC.........................F 832 538-0300
  Houston (G-10091)
Halcon Holdings Inc.............................E 832 538-0300
  Houston (G-10092)
Halcon Operating Co Inc.......................D 832 538-0300
  Houston (G-10093)
Halres LLC..C 832 538-0300
  Houston (G-10111)
Hamill Resources Inc............................F 281 556-9581
  Houston (G-10112)
Haynes International Inc.......................F 713 937-7597
  Houston (G-10138)
Headington Oil Company ....E 214 696-0606
  Dallas (G-4442)
Headington Oil Limited 1993 LP.............D 214 696-0606
  Dallas (G-4443)
Headingtron Oil LP...............................D 214 696-0606
  Dallas (G-4444)
Helix Enrgy Slutions Group Inc.............C 281 618-0400
  Houston (G-10150)
Herd Producing Co Inc..........................E 903 509-3456
  Tyler (G-20095)
Hilcorp Energy Company ....F 713 209-2400
  Houston (G-10182)
Hilcorp Energy Company ....F 979 548-2144
  Sweeny (G-19627)
Hkn Inc..F 817 424-2424
  Southlake (G-19074)
Hopewell Operating Inc.........................F 214 691-6216
  Dallas (G-4467)
Horseshoe Operating Inc.......................F 432 683-1448
  Midland (G-15249)

Houston Opicoil Inc..............................F 713 840-7171
  Houston (G-10242)
Howell Corporation...............................D 832 636-1000
  The Woodlands (G-19873)
Howell Oil & Gas Inc.............................F 903 935-0999
  Marshall (G-14782)
Howell Petroleum Corporation...............D 281 320-9096
  Houston (G-10269)
Hudson Brothers Mining Company..........F 903 876-4642
  Rusk (G-17731)
Hughes Dan A Company Lp ....F 361 358-3752
  Beeville (G-1985)
Hunt Nlson Bnker Trust Estt-T..............F 214 979-9072
  Dallas (G-4471)
Hunt Dominion Corporation...................C 214 880-8400
  Dallas (G-4472)
Hunt Petroleum Corporation..................C 214 880-8400
  Fort Worth (G-6710)
Hunt Petroleum Corporation..................E 713 871-3400
  Houston (G-10280)
Hurd Enterprises Ltd............................F 210 829-5255
  San Antonio (G-18176)
Hyperion Energy LP..............................F 214 750-3820
  Dallas (G-4478)
Hyperion Resources Inc........................F 214 750-1522
  Dallas (G-4479)
Ibex Inc..F 254 559-3355
  Breckenridge (G-2229)
Isramco Inc..F 713 621-3882
  Houston (G-10427)
J R & Adam Seitz Ltd.............................F 940 723-7303
  Wichita Falls (G-20773)
J-W Energy Company ....D 972 233-8191
  Addison (G-137)
J-W Operating Company ....D 972 233-8191
  Addison (G-138)
J-W Operating Company ....E 361 570-2788
  Victoria (G-20275)
Jagee Petro Inc....................................F 817 335-5881
  Fort Worth (G-6734)
James Lee Davis...................................D 432 682-6311
  Midland (G-15258)
James Reneau Seed Company................F 806 256-3216
  Shamrock (G-18891)
JD Murchison Interests Inc....................E 972 931-0700
  Plano (G-16898)
Jet Oil Producers Inc............................F 936 653-3379
  Coldspring (G-3166)
Jetta Operating Company Inc.................D 817 335-1179
  Fort Worth (G-6739)
Jetta Production Company Inc................E 817 335-1179
  Fort Worth (G-6740)
JM Cox Resources LP............................F 432 682-9435
  Midland (G-15259)
John H Hendrix Corporation...................G 432 684-6631
  Midland (G-15261)
John H Young Inc..................................F 713 236-8303
  Houston (G-10481)
John Oates Company Inc.......................G 806 878-3338
  Stinnett (G-19427)
Jpm Eoc Opal LLC.................................E 303 861-8140
  Houston (G-10486)
Karper Oil & Gas Corporation................F 940 549-0606
  Graham (G-7785)
Kerr-Mcgee Oil Gas Onshore LP.............E 832 636-1000
  The Woodlands (G-19891)
Key Energy Services Inc........................C 713 651-4300
  Houston (G-10522)
King Ranch Holdings Inc........................E 832 681-5700
  Houston (G-10535)
Klabzuba Oil & Gas Inc..........................F 817 336-5757
  Fort Worth (G-6765)
Koch Industries Inc..............................F 806 347-2645
  Matador (G-14816)
KSA Industries Inc................................D 713 881-3400
  Houston (G-10569)
L C S Production Company ....D 325 692-3903
  Abilene (G-55)
Lamar Hunt Trust Estate Inc..................D 214 720-1600
  Dallas (G-4579)
Langley Energy....................................F 214 221-2669
  Dallas (G-4581)
Legacy Investments Inc.........................E 214 750-1522
  Dallas (G-4587)
Lenoir M Josey Inc................................G 713 526-3844
  Houston (G-10624)
Lewis Operating Co...............................F 940 723-0266
  Holliday (G-8352)
Lime Rock Resources Iv-A LP.................C 713 292-9500
  Houston (G-10643)

Long Trusts..F 903 984-5017
  Kilgore (G-13564)
Lynx Energy Company Inc......................F 214 969-5555
  Dallas (G-4614)
M P Energy Inc......................................F 281 350-6350
  Houston (G-10719)
M-C Production and Drlg Co Inc.............E 903 297-2251
  Longview (G-14273)
Magnum Engineering Company.............G 361 882-3858
  Corpus Christi (G-3568)
Magnum Producing LP...........................F 361 882-3858
  Corpus Christi (G-3569)
Maralo LLC...E 713 622-5420
  Houston (G-10751)
Marathon Oil Company ....A 713 629-6600
  Houston (G-10754)
Marshall & Winston Inc.........................F 432 684-6373
  Midland (G-15293)
Marshall R Young Oil Co ....F 817 335-1216
  Fort Worth (G-6812)
Maxus Energy Corporation....................E 281 681-7200
  Houston (G-10806)
McBee Operating Company LLC.............F 214 526-1500
  Dallas (G-4658)
McGrew Energy Corporation...................G 214 265-1135
  Dallas (G-4661)
Medallion Oil Company Inc.....................F 713 654-0144
  Houston (G-10815)
Medders Oil Company ....G 940 692-6626
  Wichita Falls (G-20783)
Melvin Hammon....................................F 806 665-2667
  Pampa (G-16328)
Merit Energy Company LLC....................E 940 683-4059
  Gainesville (G-7347)
Merit Energy Company LLC....................E 956 728-6206
  Laredo (G-13912)
Merit Energy Company LLC....................E 903 923-7300
  Hallsville (G-8129)
Merit Energy Company LLC....................F 361 293-3586
  Yoakum (G-20971)
Merit Energy Company LLC....................F 956 842-3649
  Edinburg (G-5596)
Merit Energy Company LLC....................C 972 701-8377
  Dallas (G-4666)
Mewbourne Holdings Inc.......................E 903 561-2900
  Tyler (G-20126)
Mewbourne Oil Company ....E 281 580-6608
  Houston (G-10859)
Mewbourne Oil Company ....E 903 561-2900
  Tyler (G-20127)
Michelson Energy Company ....F 210 826-0681
  San Antonio (G-18299)
Midland Energy Inc...............................E 432 683-6686
  Midland (G-15301)
Miranda Energy Corporation..................F 432 685-1953
  Midland (G-15306)
Mission Oil Company ....F 210 224-4455
  San Antonio (G-18311)
Modern Exploration Inc.........................F 903 893-1129
  Sherman (G-18922)
Moncrief Partners LP............................E 817 336-7232
  Fort Worth (G-6849)
Moncries Faxel Oil Interests..................F 817 335-5656
  Fort Worth (G-6850)
Montex Drilling Company ....F 817 336-7232
  Fort Worth (G-6851)
Mustang Exploration Co Inc...................F 979 648-2641
  Louise (G-14353)
N D Stovall & Son.................................G 940 549-2616
  Graham (G-7787)
N M L Inc of Texas................................D 713 753-1448
  Houston (G-10948)
Natural Gas Anadarko Company.............E 806 435-6818
  Perryton (G-16642)
Nearburg Producing Company................F 214 739-1778
  Dallas (G-4718)
Nearburg Producing Company................F 432 686-8235
  Midland (G-15315)
Nelson Oil Field Eqp & Sup.....................F 361 375-2105
  Pettus (G-16653)
Neumin Production Co...........................E 361 987-8900
  Point Comfort (G-17089)
Newman Operating Co...........................D 361 394-5516
  Freer (G-7231)
Nexen Petroleum USA Inc......................E 972 450-4600
  Houston (G-11045)
Nortex Corporation...............................G 713 658-1142
  Houston (G-11071)
Oasis Petroleum Inc.............................D 281 404-9500
  Houston (G-11109)

Company	Code	Phone
Oasis Petroleum LLC Houston (G-11110)	F	281 404-9500
Oasis Petroleum North Amer LLC Houston (G-11111)	D	281 404-9500
Occidental Oil and Gas Corp Houston (G-11114)	E	713 215-7000
Occidental Oil and Gas Corp Midland (G-15323)	B	432 685-5600
Occidental Permian Ltd Andrews (G-555)	F	432 523-7556
Occidental Permian Ltd Denver City (G-5422)	E	806 592-3777
Occidental Permian Ltd Houston (G-11115)	C	713 215-7000
Occidental Petroleum Corp Houston (G-11116)	A	713 215-7000
Occidental Petroleum Corp Ira (G-12913)	G	325 574-8567
Occidental Petroleum Corp Houston (G-11117)	F	713 640-7500
Occidntal Intl Explration Prod Houston (G-11118)	B	713 215-7600
Omimex Canada Ltd Fort Worth (G-6877)	E	817 460-7777
Omimex Energy Inc Fort Worth (G-6878)	F	817 460-7777
Omimex Resources Inc Fort Worth (G-6880)	F	817 460-7777
Osborn Heirs Company Ltd San Antonio (G-18357)	E	210 826-0700
OXY Inc Midland (G-15334)	F	432 685-5600
OXY Inc Houston (G-11209)	C	713 215-7000
OXY Inc Laredo (G-13918)	E	956 728-6200
OXY USA Inc Big Spring (G-2091)	F	432 634-2247
OXY USA Inc Houston (G-11210)	C	713 215-7000
OXY USA Inc McAllen (G-14897)	C	956 429-0600
OXY USA Inc Loop (G-14340)	C	806 637-5965
P-R-O Management Inc Dallas (G-4776)	E	972 720-1475
Palo Petroleum Inc Dallas (G-4781)	F	214 691-3676
Palo Verde Oil Company Dallas (G-4782)	D	214 692-7052
Pantera Energy Company Amarillo (G-451)	E	806 376-6625
Par Pacific Holdings Inc Houston (G-11235)	D	281 899-4800
Parallel Petroleum LLC Midland (G-15336)	E	432 684-3727
Parsley Energy Inc Austin (G-1398)	D	737 704-2300
Parsley Energy LLC Midland (G-15337)	E	432 818-2100
Partee Enterprises Big Spring (G-2092)	F	432 263-0632
Parten Operating Company Houston (G-11248)	F	281 874-2101
Patriot Resources Inc Midland (G-15340)	F	432 686-9801
Patterson-Uti Energy Inc Midland (G-15343)	F	432 682-9401
Penn Virginia Mc Corporation Houston (G-11278)	D	713 722-6500
Perdure Petroleum LLC Allen (G-291)	F	281 668-8488
Petco Petroleum Corporation Pampa (G-16334)	D	806 669-3947
Peter Paul Petroleum Company Houston (G-11295)	E	713 209-1100
Petro Harvester Oper Co LLC Dallas (G-4798)	E	214 618-7600
Petro-Hunt LLC Como (G-3249)	E	903 629-3205
Petro-Hunt LLC Dallas (G-4799)	D	214 880-8400
Petrohawk Energy Corporation Houston (G-11303)	G	713 961-8500
Petrosantander Inc Houston (G-11311)	F	713 784-8700
Petrosaurus Inc Von Ormy (G-20348)	F	210 624-2750
Phoenix Fund Inc San Antonio (G-18373)	F	210 828-4373
Phoenix Hydrocarbons Operating Dayton (G-5234)	F	936 258-2646
Pickens Company Inc Dallas (G-4803)	F	214 369-7471
Pickens Energy Corporation Dallas (G-4804)	F	214 503-1271
Pioneer Drilling Services Ltd Corpus Christi (G-3591)	C	361 289-9241
Pioneer Exploration Company Houston (G-11334)	E	281 893-9400
Pioneer Natural Resources Co Irving (G-13144)	B	972 444-9001
Pioneer Natural Resources Co Midland (G-15355)	C	432 571-2800
Pioneer Natural Resources Co Midkiff (G-15096)	D	432 535-2444
Pioneer Ntral Rsources USA Inc Midland (G-15356)	D	432 683-4768
Pioneer Ntral Rsources USA Inc Pawnee (G-16534)	F	361 456-7201
Pioneer Water Management LLC Irving (G-13147)	F	800 242-2607
Pitcock Inc Graham (G-7788)	F	940 549-3344
Pitts Oil Company LLC Dallas (G-4806)	F	214 369-9266
Plains Resources Inc Houston (G-11344)	G	713 579-5000
Preston Oil Company LP The Woodlands (G-19905)	E	281 367-8697
Primexx Operating Corporation Dallas (G-4824)	F	214 369-5909
Primexx Operating Corporation Pecos (G-16625)	F	432 445-7860
Quantum Investment Group Inc Houston (G-11507)	E	281 994-5400
R A Beaird Oil Co Merkel (G-15016)	F	325 928-5220
Range Production Parent Co Fort Worth (G-6939)	E	817 870-2601
Red Mountain Resources Inc Dallas (G-4869)	E	214 871-0400
Reef Exploration LP Richardson (G-17388)	E	972 437-6792
Reef Oil & Gas Partners LLC Richardson (G-17389)	F	972 437-6792
Reliance Energy Inc Midland (G-15380)	E	432 683-4816
Republic Energy Inc Dallas (G-4889)	E	214 369-4800
Ridge Oil Company Inc Breckenridge (G-2236)	F	254 559-2297
Ring Energy Inc Midland (G-15385)	E	432 682-7464
Rk Petroleum Corp Midland (G-15387)	F	432 683-4319
Rosewood Resources Inc Dallas (G-4912)	E	214 849-9300
Royal Production Company Inc Corpus Christi (G-3611)	F	361 888-4792
Royalty Well Service Inc Grandfalls (G-8000)	D	432 547-2926
Rsp Permian Inc Midland (G-15390)	F	432 683-7443
Rutherford Oil Corporation Houston (G-11701)	F	713 622-5555
Sabine Investor Holdings LLC Houston (G-11716)	B	832 242-9600
Sabine Oil & Gas Corporation Houston (G-11717)	F	832 242-9600
Sabine Oil & Gas LLC Houston (G-11718)	F	832 242-9600
Sage Energy Company Caldwell (G-2634)	F	979 567-7629
Sage Energy Company San Antonio (G-18443)	E	210 404-2828
Sahara Operating Company Midland (G-15393)	F	432 697-0967
Samedan Oil Corporation Houston (G-11739)	F	580 223-4110
Saratoga Resources Inc Houston (G-11751)	F	713 458-1560
Sauder Management Co Wichita Falls (G-20805)	F	940 723-8125
Schlachter Operating Corp Dallas (G-4940)	G	214 692-1567
Seaboard Oil Co Midland (G-15401)	F	432 684-7005
Sellers Lease Service Inc Flatonia (G-6234)	F	361 865-2142
Sentry Oil & Gas LLC Mico (G-15094)	E	212 753-6367
Shell Oil Company Houston (G-11860)	A	713 241-6161
Shenandoah Petroleum Corp Midland (G-15406)	F	432 685-1964
Sidwell Operating Company LP Amarillo (G-463)	G	806 371-7513
SM Energy Company Midland (G-15411)	D	432 688-1700
SM Energy Company Houston (G-11916)	F	281 677-2800
Smalley Drilling & Trckg Corp Albany (G-193)	E	325 762-3409
Smith Energy Company Houston (G-11922)	F	713 651-9102
Snw Operating Company Inc Borger (G-2185)	F	806 273-2667
Socorro Exploration Inc Lubbock (G-14483)	G	806 798-2790
Sojitz Energy Venture Inc Houston (G-11933)	F	713 963-9101
Sojourner Drilling Corporation Abilene (G-81)	E	325 672-2832
Southern Petroleum Labs Inc Venus (G-20222)	F	817 539-2168
Southern Utilities Company Tyler (G-20154)	F	903 593-2588
Southwest Resources Brenham (G-2273)	F	979 836-5500
Southwest Royalties Inc Ira (G-12915)	F	325 573-4977
Southwestern Energy Company Spring (G-19167)	D	832 796-1000
Speartex Grain Company Spearman (G-19087)	E	806 659-3711
Speedway LLC Houston (G-12011)	D	713 943-9002
Speedway LLC Seminole (G-18887)	F	432 758-6700
Spruiell Drilling Co Iowa Park (G-12911)	F	940 592-5471
States Inc Breckenridge (G-2239)	E	254 559-3355
Strand Energy LC Houston (G-12074)	F	713 658-8096
Sulphur River Exploration Inc Dallas (G-5021)	F	214 373-1091
Sulphur River Exploration Inc Gilmer (G-7714)	F	903 734-7248
Swanner Properties Wichita Falls (G-20813)	G	940 723-7714
Swn International LLC Spring (G-19171)	A	832 796-1000
Swn Production (arkansas) LLC Spring (G-19172)	A	832 796-1000
Swn Production Company LLC Houston (G-12133)	E	281 618-4700
Synergy Oil & Gas LP Houston (G-12135)	F	713 827-9988
T-C Oil Company Refugio (G-17249)	E	361 526-4693
Talos Energy Inc Houston (G-12150)	C	713 328-3000
Talos Ert LLC Houston (G-12152)	F	281 618-0590
Talos Production LLC Houston (G-12154)	G	713 328-3000
Tauber Exploration & Prod Co Houston (G-12164)	F	713 869-5656
Taylor Oil Co Ltd Partnership Sunray (G-19621)	G	806 948-4166
Tepee Petroleum Company Inc Houston (G-12206)	G	713 659-8300
Tesoro Lgstics NW Pipeline LLC San Antonio (G-18529)	E	210 249-9123
Texas Crude Energy Inc Houston (G-12228)	F	713 599-9900
Texas Crude Energy LLC Houston (G-12229)	E	713 599-9900
Thompson & Thompson Dallas (G-5086)	E	214 953-1177
Thompson & Thompson Odessa (G-16177)	F	214 953-1177
Thompson & Thompson Ozona (G-16287)	F	325 392-3721
Thompson Petroleum Corporation Dallas (G-5087)	F	214 953-1177
Three P Operating Company Newcastle (G-15863)	F	940 846-3326

Threshold Development Company ....F 817 870-1483
Fort Worth (G-7060)

Tom McGee Corp ....G....... 806 658-4591
Booker (G-2159)

Tortuga Operating Co ....G....... 713 680-3600
Houston (G-12325)

Transatlantic Petroleum Ltd ....E 214 220-4323
Addison (G-170)

Trend Gathering & Treating LP ....F 817 885-2524
Fort Worth (G-7073)

Triple Crown Resources LLC ....F 972 444-8808
Dallas (G-5115)

Tronox Incorporated ....D 903 794-5169
Texarkana (G-19782)

Tronox Incorporated ....F 432 263-4301
Big Spring (G-2101)

U S Companies Inc ....F 214 891-3300
Dallas (G-3854)

Unit Corporation ....G....... 806 658-2262
Booker (G-2160)

United Oil Corporation ....F 303 856-6444
Austin (G-1608)

Unity Hunt Inc ....E 214 720-1600
Dallas (G-5140)

Upham Oil & Gas Company LP ....E 940 325-4491
Mineral Wells (G-15544)

V-F Petroleum Inc ....F 432 683-3344
Midland (G-15459)

Vaalco Energy Inc ....E 713 623-0801
Houston (G-12514)

Valence Operating Company ....E 281 359-3659
Kingwood (G-13659)

Van Operating Ltd ....E 325 762-3353
Albany (G-195)

Verado Energy Inc ....F 214 368-5322
Dallas (G-5159)

Verdad Oil & Gas Corporation ....E 214 357-0333
Dallas (G-5162)

Vernon E Faulconer Inc ....F 903 581-4382
Tyler (G-20174)

Viper Energy Partners LP ....C....... 432 221-7400
Midland (G-15462)

Virtex Holdings LLP ....E 361 882-3046
Corpus Christi (G-3652)

W B Osborn Oil Gas Oprtons L ....F 210 826-8654
San Antonio (G-18607)

W T Waggoner Estate ....C....... 940 552-2521
Vernon (G-20232)

Wagner & Brown Ltd ....D 432 682-7936
Midland (G-15463)

Wagner Oil Company ....E 817 335-2222
Fort Worth (G-7116)

Walsh and Watts Inc ....D 817 335-5417
Fort Worth (G-7120)

Walsh Company ....E 817 335-3741
Fort Worth (G-7121)

Walsh F Howard Jr Oper Co Inc ....D 817 336-2062
Fort Worth (G-7122)

Walsh Oil Co ....E 817 336-2062
Fort Worth (G-7123)

Walsh Petroleum Inc ....F 432 684-5937
Midland (G-15464)

Walter Oil & Gas Corporation ....E 713 659-1221
Houston (G-12597)

Wcs Oil & Gas Corporation ....F 979 542-0021
Giddings (G-7704)

Welder Rob & Bessie Wildlife ....F 361 364-2643
Sinton (G-18967)

Wes Tex Drilling Company LLC ....F 325 677-9121
Abilene (G-93)

Westerly Exploration Inc ....F 817 738-1917
Fort Worth (G-7138)

Westerly Exploration Inc ....F 713 524-7755
Houston (G-12640)

Western Ref Cnan Gathering LLC ....F 210 626-6000
San Antonio (G-18615)

William L Arrington ....G....... 806 669-3324
Pampa (G-16345)

Winn Exploration Co Inc ....F 361 844-6900
Corpus Christi (G-3657)

Winston Land & Cattle Co Inc ....F 936 634-6321
Lufkin (G-14557)

WO Energy of Nevada Inc ....G....... 806 665-8298
Pampa (G-16346)

Xto Energy Inc ....E 817 885-2195
Fort Worth (G-7154)

Xto Energy Inc ....E 817 870-2800
Houston (G-12708)

Xto Energy Inc ....C....... 432 682-8873
Midland (G-15474)

Xto Energy Inc ....D 806 367-1047
Tokio (G-19950)

Xto Energy Inc ....E 979 828-1963
Bryan (G-2516)

Xto Energy Inc ....D 903 939-1200
Tyler (G-20178)

Xto Energy Inc ....D 903 553-3800
Longview (G-14339)

Xto Energy Inc ....B 817 870-2800
Spring (G-19188)

Xto Energy Inc ....G....... 903 983-8800
Kilgore (G-13605)

Xto Energy Inc ....F 432 524-6545
Andrews (G-562)

Xto Energy Inc ....E 936 858-3533
Alto (G-320)

Xto Energy Inc ....E 817 740-0488
Dallas (G-5206)

Zackson Resources Inc ....F 713 782-1075
Houston (G-12720)

Zevex Corporation ....F 512 322-9039
Austin (G-1685)

CRUDES: Cyclic, Organic

Baker Petrolite ....E 903 389-2903
Fairfield (G-6169)

Jeg Holdings LLC ....C....... 972 532-6419
Addison (G-140)

CRYSTALS

Abracon LLC ....F 512 371-6159
Spicewood (G-19090)

Futaba Corporation of America ....F 915 771-7858
El Paso (G-5776)

CULTURE MEDIA

Digital Forge Media LLC ....F 432 559-6068
Odessa (G-15977)

Players Media Group Inc ....F 509 254-4949
Dallas (G-4810)

CULVERTS: Sheet Metal

American Fence and Sup Co Inc ....F 512 930-4000
Georgetown (G-7634)

Contech Engnered Solutions LLC ....E 940 888-3871
Seymour (G-18889)

Holmes Construction Co LP ....D 806 376-8629
Amarillo (G-435)

Nova Construction Co Inc ....E 972 869-3041
Carrollton (G-2785)

Pine Street Salvage Co ....F 806 372-5678
Amarillo (G-454)

Wilson Culverts Inc ....E 903 764-5605
Elkhart (G-6061)

CUPS & PLATES: Foamed Plastics

Quality Cases & Containers LLC ....F 972 690-9911
Richardson (G-17379)

Wna Cups Illustrated Inc ....C....... 972 224-8407
Lancaster (G-13850)

CUPS: Paper

Solo Cup Operating Corporation ....A 214 339-3131
Dallas (G-4977)

CUPS: Plastic Exc Polystyrene Foam

Ntl-Brands Ltd ....D 214 631-0307
Dallas (G-4746)

Thermo-Serv Inc ....C....... 214 631-0307
Dallas (G-5085)

CURBING: Granite Or Stone

Wallace Monument Company ....F 806 874-2442
Clarendon (G-3071)

CURTAIN & DRAPERY FIXTURES: Poles, Rods & Rollers

Awntech Corporation ....E 817 354-9600
Euless (G-6132)

Boriack Interiors Inc ....E 214 376-1814
Dallas (G-4044)

Fleuron Enterprises Inc ....E 214 678-0805
Dallas (G-4369)

Kites Draperies Inc ....E 817 336-1027
Fort Worth (G-6764)

Plumlee Place LLC ....F 254 662-4021
Robinson (G-17501)

Satori Home Limited LLC ....E 855 472-8674
Dallas (G-4937)

CURTAIN WALLS: Building, Steel

Baker Metal Products Inc ....C....... 972 241-3553
Dallas (G-3999)

CURTAINS: Knit

Center-Line Curtains Inc ....F 972 299-5902
Cedar Hill (G-2937)

CURTAINS: Window, From Purchased Materials

Austin Window Fashion Inc ....F 512 836-3388
Austin (G-967)

Perfect Windows Inc ....F 817 277-0014
Arlington (G-752)

CUSHIONS & PILLOWS

Banyan Industries Inc ....E 817 413-7945
Fort Worth (G-6426)

Blazing Needles LP ....E 817 831-2668
Fort Worth (G-6457)

Brunton International Inc ....E 214 638-4600
Dallas (G-4063)

Carpenter Co ....D 512 365-5833
Taylor (G-19651)

Easy Way Leisure Corporation ....C....... 956 831-6442
Brownsville (G-2352)

Loloi Inc ....C....... 972 503-5656
Dallas (G-4602)

Mozaic Company ....E 972 386-3332
Arlington (G-733)

Nielsen & Bainbridge LLC ....E 512 506-3900
Austin (G-1367)

S N D Manufacturing Ltd ....D 214 340-1592
Dallas (G-4923)

Wmc Waco Holdings Inc ....E 254 753-7301
Waco (G-20479)

CUSHIONS & PILLOWS: Bed, From Purchased Materials

Clark Pillow Company ....E 409 842-5767
Beaumont (G-1870)

Sweet Dreams Inc ....D 956 687-2737
McAllen (G-14909)

CUSHIONS: Carpet & Rug, Foamed Plastics

E R Carpenter LP ....C....... 281 474-7257
Pasadena (G-16422)

E R Carpenter LP ....C....... 804 359-0800
Temple (G-19680)

CUSHIONS: Textile, Exc Spring & Carpet

Starr Aircraft Products Inc ....C....... 903 893-1106
Sherman (G-18933)

CUSTOM COMPOUNDING OF RUBBER MATERIALS

Eutsler Technical Products Inc ....D 713 686-8209
Houston (G-9713)

Next Gen Compounding LLC ....E 972 602-9717
Grand Prairie (G-7934)

CUT STONE & STONE PRODUCTS

77 Stone ....F 915 590-0770
El Paso (G-5631)

A J Brauer Stone ....D 512 746-5792
Jarrell (G-13268)

American Marble Mosaic Company ....E 713 747-7634
Houston (G-8600)

Bonanza Industries Inc ....D 713 466-7900
Houston (G-8948)

Colorado Stone Pdts Texas Inc ....D 972 434-2515
Carrollton (G-2716)

Continental Cut Stone Inc ....E 254 793-2329
Florence (G-6238)

Custom Crete Inc ....F 713 937-3966
Houston (G-9369)

Dallas Cast Stone II Corp ....E 940 382-6922
Dallas (G-4213)

Delta Granite and Marble Inc ....D 210 829-7171
San Antonio *(G-18050)*

Fort Worth Crushed Stone LLC ....F 817 596-5512
Weatherford *(G-20593)*

GMI Stone LLC ....F 469 360-8847
Dallas *(G-4411)*

Incounters Inc ....E 325 675-5909
Abilene *(G-51)*

Irving Counter Inc ....E 972 438-4343
Irving *(G-13066)*

Justin Industries Inc ....D 512 258-1474
Cedar Park *(G-2975)*

Killeen Marble ....E 254 699-3408
Killeen *(G-13612)*

Lavender Enterprises Inc ....E 214 631-8080
Dallas *(G-4585)*

Mezger Enterprises Ltd ....D 254 547-8207
Lueders *(G-14518)*

Mj Stone LLC ....F 832 887-3575
Houston *(G-10894)*

National Stone Ltd ....E 214 651-7667
Grand Prairie *(G-7930)*

Permian Limestone ....E 254 547-8207
Kempner *(G-13487)*

Quarries Direct International ....E 602 269-7900
Dallas *(G-4847)*

Quarries Direct Intl LLC ....E 713 808-9849
Houston *(G-11509)*

Ralph Cordova Company ....E 972 771-7281
Royse City *(G-17725)*

Red Dog Track Inc ....E 254 672-5261
Strawn *(G-19432)*

Royal Baths Manufacturing Co ....B 281 442-3400
Houston *(G-11682)*

S C S C Inc ....E 214 398-1199
Dallas *(G-4922)*

Sawyer Technical Materials LLC ....D 936 756-8886
Conroe *(G-3361)*

Siteworks Incorporated ....E 281 931-1000
Houston *(G-11909)*

Stone Masters ....F 915 216-1702
El Paso *(G-5982)*

Texas Archtctral Aggregate Inc ....E 325 372-5105
San Saba *(G-18719)*

Venetian Marble Co Lubbock Inc ....E 806 763-5777
Lubbock *(G-14506)*

West Coast Group Inc ....F 281 447-2020
Houston *(G-12635)*

CUTLERY

Angel Sword Corp ....E 512 847-9679
Driftwood *(G-5498)*

Dexas International Ltd ....D 469 635-8100
Coppell *(G-3415)*

CUTTING EQPT: Glass Cutters

Texas Tempered Glass Inc ....E 713 697-2828
Houston *(G-12256)*

CUTTING SVC: Paper, Exc Die-Cut

Paper Network Inc ....E 972 239-6567
Dallas *(G-4786)*

CYCLIC CRUDES & INTERMEDIATES

Akzo Nobel Inc ....E 713 433-7289
Houston *(G-8370)*

Baker Hughes A GE Company LLC ......B 713 625-4200
Houston *(G-8801)*

Braskem America Inc ....C 713 255-4747
Houston *(G-8976)*

Braskem America Inc ....G 215 841-3100
Port Lavaca *(G-17142)*

Braskem America Inc ....F 979 705-2532
Freeport *(G-7193)*

Celanese Ltd ....E 281 474-0554
Pasadena *(G-16403)*

Eastman Chemical Company ....E 423 229-2000
Longview *(G-14230)*

Evonik Corporation ....C 713 477-6841
Pasadena *(G-16434)*

Kuraray America Inc ....E 281 471-2771
La Porte *(G-13765)*

Lonza Inc ....D 281 291-2300
Pasadena *(G-16475)*

M-I LLC ....B 281 561-1300
Houston *(G-10725)*

Noah Technologies Corp Texas ....D 210 691-2000
San Antonio *(G-18347)*

Sierra Dust Control LLC ....F 903 836-4642
Harwood *(G-8212)*

CYLINDER & ACTUATORS: Fluid Power

Automation Technology Inc ....E 713 934-0171
Cypress *(G-3777)*

Camozzi Pneumatics Inc ....E 972 548-8885
McKinney *(G-14931)*

Dresser LLC ....C 262 549-2626
Houston *(G-9517)*

Hannon Hydraulics Inc ....E 713 849-4445
Houston *(G-10116)*

Manitou North America Inc ....D 254 799-0232
Waco *(G-20429)*

Noremac Gas LLC ....F 281 248-6423
Katy *(G-13429)*

Xomox Corporation ....C 936 271-6500
The Woodlands *(G-19942)*

CYLINDERS: Pressure

Norris Cylinder Company ....C 903 757-7633
Longview *(G-14285)*

DAIRY EQPT

Agpro Inc ....E 903 785-5531
Reno *(G-17251)*

Steel Metal Dairy Inc ....E 903 866-2536
Como *(G-3250)*

DAIRY PRDTS STORE: Cheese

Mozzarella Company ....E 214 741-4072
Dallas *(G-4695)*

DAIRY PRDTS STORE: Ice Cream, Packaged

Marble Slab Creamery No 152 ....F 713 455-5786
Houston *(G-10760)*

DAIRY PRDTS STORES

Dean Holding Company ....E 214 303-3400
Dallas *(G-4243)*

DAIRY PRDTS WHOLESALERS: Fresh

Dairy Manufacturers Inc ....F 972 347-2878
Prosper *(G-17213)*

Dean Holding Company ....E 214 303-3400
Dallas *(G-4243)*

Dfa Dairy Brands Fluid LLC ....F 361 854-4561
Corpus Christi *(G-3513)*

DAIRY PRDTS: Butter

Kellers Creamery LLC ....E 903 347-4250
Winnsboro *(G-20899)*

New Dairy Trademark Holdg LLC ....F 803 297-7342
Dallas *(G-4727)*

DAIRY PRDTS: Butter Oil

Ingenia Polymers Inc ....E 281 862-2111
Houston *(G-10363)*

DAIRY PRDTS: Buttermilk, Cultured

Vital Farms Inc ....C 877 455-3063
Austin *(G-1641)*

DAIRY PRDTS: Cheese

Bridgford Industries Inc ....E 214 428-1535
Dallas *(G-4053)*

Cheesemakers Inc ....E 281 593-1319
Cleveland *(G-3122)*

DAIRY PRDTS: Condensed Milk

Eagle Family Foods Group LLC ....C 915 584-7189
El Paso *(G-5729)*

DAIRY PRDTS: Cream Substitutes

Saputo Dairy Foods Usa LLC ....C 214 433-3978
Sulphur Springs *(G-19598)*

Saputo Dairy Foods Usa LLC ....C 214 863-2300
Dallas *(G-4934)*

DAIRY PRDTS: Custard, Frozen

Freddys Frz Cstard Stakburgers ....E 210 521-5400
San Antonio *(G-18126)*

DAIRY PRDTS: Dietary Supplements, Dairy & Non-Dairy Based

Bio Trust Nutrition LLC ....E 800 766-5086
Dallas *(G-4025)*

Cheers Health Inc ....E 518 379-6133
Houston *(G-9168)*

Compass Alpha LLC ....E 512 557-9138
Austin *(G-1059)*

Cosmax Nbt Usa Inc ....C 469 661-9700
Garland *(G-7466)*

Cosmax Nbt USA Inc ....D 469 298-2222
Garland *(G-7467)*

Europa Sports Products Inc ....F 214 388-7444
Mesquite *(G-15041)*

Formulife Inc ....C 214 221-4911
Allen *(G-269)*

JW Nutritional LLC ....D 214 221-0404
Allen *(G-281)*

Naturelab Corp ....G 972 417-3000
Carrollton *(G-2784)*

Op2 Labs LLC ....F 888 448-8468
Euless *(G-6151)*

Specktrum ....F 832 892-0863
Houston *(G-12004)*

Usplabs LLC ....E 469 484-1927
Dallas *(G-5148)*

Valley Herbal Products Inc ....E 956 631-8869
McAllen *(G-14914)*

DAIRY PRDTS: Dips, Cheese-Based

Fountain Valley Foods Inc ....F 281 592-0610
Livingston *(G-14156)*

DAIRY PRDTS: Evaporated Milk

Nestle Usa Inc ....C 817 420-9971
Fort Worth *(G-6864)*

Nestle Usa Inc ....C 817 491-5500
Fort Worth *(G-6865)*

DAIRY PRDTS: Frozen Desserts & Novelties

Authentic Gelato LLC ....F 214 654-9501
Dallas *(G-3986)*

Candy Kings Inc ....F 409 762-6100
Galveston *(G-7391)*

Country Fresh LLC ....B 616 243-0173
Dallas *(G-4175)*

Epic Source Food Company LLC ....F 214 407-7154
Frisco *(G-7283)*

Gooeys ....F 832 788-9644
Cypress *(G-3798)*

Ja-En Enterprise Inc ....F 956 782-0085
Pharr *(G-16703)*

Joseph McSweeny Entps LLC ....G 214 334-8181
Justin *(G-13345)*

Kathy & Janes Co ....G 817 605-9335
Colleyville *(G-3215)*

Kaurinas LLC ....F 972 888-9990
Dallas *(G-4545)*

Kk Meier Co LLC ....F 281 256-7366
Cypress *(G-3807)*

Pop Star LLC ....F 214 244-2502
Dallas *(G-4812)*

Sweet Ritual LLC ....G 512 923-1930
Austin *(G-1552)*

DAIRY PRDTS: Ice Cream & Ice Milk

Dairy Queen ....F 281 481-8505
Houston *(G-9396)*

Dfa Dairy Brands Ice Cream LLC ....G 214 905-5003
Richardson *(G-17300)*

Marble Slab Creamery No 152 ....F 713 455-5786
Houston *(G-10760)*

DAIRY PRDTS: Ice Cream, Bulk

Montecarlo Foods LLC ....F 206 304-6771
San Antonio *(G-18317)*

DAIRY PRDTS: Ice Cream, Packaged, Molded, On Sticks, Etc.

Blue Bell Creameries LP ....F 806 749-9005
Lubbock *(G-14375)*

Paleteria El Pibe ....F 281 541-8777
Houston *(G-11223)*

PRODUCT

DAIRY PRDTS: Milk & Cream, Cultured & Flavored

Dfa Dairy Brands Fluid LLC .... D 956 686-0511
McAllen (G-14853)

DAIRY PRDTS: Milk, Condensed & Evaporated

Dean Foods Company .... B 214 303-3400
Dallas (G-4242)
Dean Holding Company .... E 214 303-3400
Dallas (G-4243)
Dfa Dairy Brands Distrg N LLC .... E 214 303-3400
Dallas (G-4250)
Dfa Dairy Brands Distrg S LLC .... E 214 303-3400
Dallas (G-4251)
Dfa Dairy Brands Distrg W LLC .... E 214 303-3400
Dallas (G-4252)
Dfa Dairy Brands Ip LLC .... C 214 303-3400
Dallas (G-4253)
Dfa Dairy Brands Trnsp LLC .... C 214 303-3400
Dallas (G-4254)
Kaneka North America LLC .... C 281 474-7084
Pasadena (G-16468)
Kellers Creamery LLC .... E 903 347-4250
Winnsboro (G-20899)
Lala US Inc .... B 469 804-3850
Dallas (G-4578)
New Dairy Opco LLC .... D 972 619-1535
Dallas (G-4725)
New Diry Clims Adjsting Svcs L ...... F 863 297-7342
Dallas (G-4728)
New National Dairy LLC .... F 863 297-7342
Dallas (G-4730)
Premark Health Science Inc .... E 972 894-0020
Irving (G-13155)

DAIRY PRDTS: Milk, Fluid

Affiliated Foods Inc .... C 806 372-3851
Amarillo (G-476)
Dairy Farmers America Inc .... D 979 743-4161
Schulenburg (G-18775)
Dairy Farmers America Inc .... E 817 410-4500
Grapevine (G-8025)
Dean Foods Company .... C 214 944-4960
Fort Worth (G-6580)
Dean Intllctual Prprty Svcs II .... A 214 303-3400
Dallas (G-4244)
Dfa Dairy Brands Fluid LLC .... B 210 732-1111
San Antonio (G-18052)
Dfa Dairy Brands Fluid LLC .... F 956 722-1718
Laredo (G-13879)
Dfa Dairy Brands Fluid LLC .... E 512 755-6015
Austin (G-1089)
Dfa Dairy Brands Fluid LLC .... F 972 542-9391
McKinney (G-14936)
Dfa Dairy Brands Fluid LLC .... G 903 758-8211
Longview (G-14224)
Kady International LLC .... E 210 860-1637
Helotes (G-8240)
Lala US Inc .... B 469 804-3850
Dallas (G-4578)
Southern Foods Group LLC .... D 214 941-0302
Dallas (G-4987)

DAIRY PRDTS: Milk, Processed, Pasteurized, Homogenized/Btld

Borden Dairy Company .... E 855 311-1583
Dallas (G-4042)
Borden Transport Co Ohio LLC .... D 214 459-1100
Dallas (G-4043)
Country Fresh LLC .... B 616 243-0173
Dallas (G-4175)
Daisy Brand LLC .... C 972 726-0800
Dallas (G-4207)
Daisy Brand LLC .... D 972 271-7314
Garland (G-7475)
Dean Foods Company .... B 214 303-3400
Dallas (G-4242)
Dean Foods Company .... B 817 684-3600
Fort Worth (G-6581)
Dfa Dairy Brands Distrg N LLC .... E 214 303-3400
Dallas (G-4250)
Dfa Dairy Brands Distrg S LLC .... E 214 303-3400
Dallas (G-4251)
Dfa Dairy Brands Distrg W LLC .... E 214 303-3400
Dallas (G-4252)

Dfa Dairy Brands Fluid LLC .... F 361 854-4561
Corpus Christi (G-3513)
Dfa Dairy Brands Fluid LLC .... D 806 765-8833
Lubbock (G-14404)
Dfa Dairy Brands Fluid LLC .... B 713 223-5296
Houston (G-9448)
Dfa Dairy Brands Ip LLC .... C 214 303-3400
Dallas (G-4253)
Dfa Dairy Brands Trnsp LLC .... C 214 303-3400
Dallas (G-4254)
Gh Dairy .... C 915 790-2609
El Paso (G-5785)
Hiland Dairy Foods Company LLC ... D 903 565-0288
Tyler (G-20098)
Kroger Co .... C 817 698-4357
Fort Worth (G-6773)
Plains Dairy LLC .... A 806 374-0385
Amarillo (G-455)
Saputo Dairy Foods Usa LLC .... E 903 885-0881
Sulphur Springs (G-19597)
SFG Management Ltd Lblty Co .... A 214 824-8163
Dallas (G-4950)

DAIRY PRDTS: Natural Cheese

Mozzarella Company .... E 214 741-4072
Dallas (G-4695)

DAIRY PRDTS: Processed Cheese

Castro Cheese Company Inc .... E 713 460-0329
Houston (G-9097)
M Sosa White Cheese La Pintita ...... G 956 546-7078
Brownsville (G-2379)
Mondelez Global LLC .... C 847 943-4000
El Paso (G-5883)

DAIRY PRDTS: Sour Cream

Saputo Dairy Foods Usa LLC .... C 214 863-2300
Dallas (G-4934)
Southern Foods Group LLC .... C 214 824-8163
Dallas (G-4986)

DAIRY PRDTS: Yogurt Mix

Yogurt Technologies LLC .... F 409 621-2060
Galveston (G-7414)

DAIRY PRDTS: Yogurt, Exc Frozen

Danone Us LLC .... C 817 336-2320
Fort Worth (G-6576)
Danone Us LLC .... C 817 332-1264
Fort Worth (G-6577)

DAMAGED MERCHANDISE SALVAGING, SVCS ONLY

Capital Returns Inc .... D 414 466-2418
Fort Worth (G-6493)

DATA ENTRY SVCS

Peritus Inc .... C 817 726-4626
Irving (G-13141)
Shipcom Wireless Inc .... D 281 558-5252
Houston (G-11870)

DATA PROCESSING & PREPARATION SVCS

Access Imaging Solutions LLC .... F 210 590-8338
San Antonio (G-17857)
Banks Petroleum Inc .... E 512 478-0059
Austin (G-974)
Baxter Planning Systems Inc .... E 512 323-5959
Austin (G-977)
Dairy LLC .... E 214 442-5928
Frisco (G-7278)
Defense Solutions Group Inc .... F 800 382-7571
Cleburne (G-3087)
Fiserv Solutions LLC .... C 281 242-8569
Stafford (G-19313)
Health Management Systems Inc .... C 214 453-3000
Irving (G-13055)
Health Management Systems Inc .... E 512 407-9680
Austin (G-1200)
Hov Services Inc .... E 248 837-7100
Irving (G-13059)
NCR Corporation .... D 210 366-2959
San Antonio (G-18339)
NCR Solutions Llc .... F 405 413-8278
Little Elm (G-14140)

Qnet Inc .... D 214 341-7638
Dallas (G-4838)
Rlra Inc .... F 817 783-3335
Alvarado (G-342)
Touchpay Holdings LP .... E 972 215-0133
Irving (G-13196)
Usdatwing Aerial Analytics LLC ...... F 210 495-5577
San Antonio (G-18582)
Verge Ventures LLC .... F 972 200-1707
Richardson (G-17420)
Zix Corporation .... D 214 370-2000
Dallas (G-5210)

DATA PROCESSING SVCS

Arygin Corporation .... F 940 597-8275
Denton (G-5350)
Data Dallas Corporation .... E 214 662-5165
Dallas (G-4241)
EMC Corporation .... F 972 892-7700
Dallas (G-4317)
Fairfield Industries Inc .... C 281 275-7500
Houston (G-9752)
Geokinetics Inc .... E 713 850-7600
Houston (G-9935)
Laser Image Inc .... E 214 267-1313
Dallas (G-4582)
Mail Mart Inc .... D 214 630-9643
Dallas (G-4629)
Saexploration Holdings Inc .... F 281 258-4400
Houston (G-11723)
Safeguard Business Systems Inc .... C 800 523-2422
Dallas (G-4926)
Tri-Cor Industries Inc .... E 210 979-0552
San Antonio (G-18565)

DECALS, WHOLESALE

Armadillo Blast Coat Inc .... E 281 485-2743
Pearland (G-16539)

DECORATIVE WOOD & WOODWORK

Brazos Walking Sticks .... E 254 799-7119
Waco (G-20371)
Harris Cabinet & Wdwkg Inc .... G 817 561-2959
Fort Worth (G-6690)
Hayes Carpentry L L C .... E 713 944-2608
South Houston (G-19044)
Hw Holdco LLC .... E 972 536-6300
Irving (G-13061)
Integrawood Inc .... E 713 329-9949
Texas City (G-19795)
John D Blankenship .... E 214 752-9191
Dallas (G-4535)
Liberty Company .... E 817 921-0218
Fort Worth (G-6788)
Lucias Oaks LP .... F 832 616-3306
Spring (G-19228)
Masterwerkes .... F 214 315-6479
Garland (G-7545)
Smith Design and Mfg Inc .... F 903 433-4444
Gunter (G-8116)

DEFENSE SYSTEMS & EQPT

Defense Logistics Agency .... B 214 670-9259
Dallas (G-4247)
Integrity Defense LLC .... F 832 282-0993
Houston (G-10386)
Milvian Solutions LLC .... F 915 219-5260
El Paso (G-5879)
Paradigm SRP LLC .... F 877 677-9899
Houston (G-11239)
Raytheon Company .... C 781 522-3000
Plano (G-16984)
Raytheon Company .... C 972 231-4931
Richardson (G-17382)
Raytheon Company .... C 972 494-2073
Garland (G-7576)
Raytheon Company .... C 972 205-8846
Plano (G-16985)
Raytheon Company .... B 972 344-2591
Plano (G-16986)
Raytheon Company .... C 915 771-5466
Richardson (G-17383)
Raytheon Company .... C 817 735-1251
Fort Worth (G-6944)
Raytheon Company .... B 719 638-2756
Richardson (G-17384)
Raytheon Company .... F 972 344-9133
Dallas (G-4862)

Raytheon Company ....C 972 952-2007
  McKinney *(G-14968)*
Raytheon Company ....E 877 291-9990
  Plano *(G-16988)*
Wave Quantum Def & Tech LLC ....F 512 505-2339
  Austin *(G-1650)*

DEGREASING MACHINES

Federal-Mogul Powertrain LLC...........F 915 860-2300
  El Paso *(G-5766)*
Safety-Kleen Systems Inc ....F 254 772-4419
  Waco *(G-20456)*
Safety-Kleen Systems Inc ....B 800 669-5740
  Richardson *(G-17392)*

DEHYDRATION EQPT

Astro Foods International Corp............F 214 349-7840
  Dallas *(G-3977)*
Genemco Inc ....E 979 268-7447
  Hearne *(G-8231)*

DELIVERY SVCS, BY VEHICLE

Lengston Corporation ....F 713 757-1331
  Houston *(G-10623)*

DENTAL EQPT

Forward Science Holding Inc...............F 855 696-7254
  Stafford *(G-19318)*
Forward Science Tech LLC ....F 855 696-7254
  Stafford *(G-19319)*

DENTAL EQPT & SPLYS

Certified Technical Profession ....G 757 831-9235
  Canyon Lake *(G-2678)*
Dentsply International Inc ....D 800 877-0020
  San Antonio *(G-18051)*
Fuji Ceramics Inc ....E 972 722-1130
  Rockwall *(G-17549)*
International Tool & Mfg Co ....F 800 753-1004
  Carrollton *(G-2769)*
National Dentex Corporation ....F 903 597-3198
  Tyler *(G-20132)*
Ramon Guardiola ....F 956 330-8026
  Mission *(G-15562)*
Seretti Dental Lab Inc ....E 512 452-8989
  Austin *(G-1495)*
Whitehill Manufacturing Inc ....F 281 240-2003
  Stafford *(G-19398)*

DENTAL EQPT & SPLYS WHOLESALERS

Ramon Guardiola ....F 956 330-8026
  Mission *(G-15562)*

DENTAL EQPT & SPLYS: Compounds

Beyond International Inc ....E 281 277-4352
  Sugar Land *(G-19449)*

DENTAL EQPT & SPLYS: Dental Hand Instruments, NEC

Kerr Corporation ....C 800 355-5063
  Coppell *(G-3426)*

DENTAL EQPT & SPLYS: Dental Materials

Clearcorrect Operating LLC ....C 888 331-3323
  Round Rock *(G-17633)*

DENTAL EQPT & SPLYS: Glue

Kuraray America Inc ....E 800 423-9762
  Houston *(G-10571)*

DENTAL EQPT & SPLYS: Investment Materials

Gel Investments ....F 214 699-6996
  Cedar Hill *(G-2942)*

DENTAL EQPT & SPLYS: Laboratory

Westbrook & Associates Inc...............E 972 840-0858
  Richardson *(G-17426)*

DENTAL EQPT & SPLYS: Orthodontic Appliances

Align Technology Inc ....F 408 470-1311
  El Paso *(G-5641)*
Orthodontic Technologies Inc ....E 800 522-4636
  Houston *(G-11194)*
Scott Mc Gaha ....F 817 540-2309
  Euless *(G-6157)*

DENTISTS' OFFICES & CLINICS

Whitehill Manufacturing Inc ....F 281 240-2003
  Stafford *(G-19398)*

DEPARTMENT STORES

Merrills Southern Maid ....G 409 755-2400
  Lumberton *(G-14568)*

DEPARTMENT STORES: Army-Navy Goods

Bravo Concealment LLC ....F 956 783-7682
  Alamo *(G-177)*

DERMATOLOGICALS

Aesthetic Medical Educators ....F 512 301-2125
  Austin *(G-899)*
Dermatlgical Assn of Texas LLP..........F 281 333-3376
  Webster *(G-20637)*
G & S Enterprises Incorporated ....E 281 530-3077
  Houston *(G-9884)*
Galderma Laboratories LP ....C 817 961-5000
  Fort Worth *(G-6660)*
Galderma Laboratories LP ....C 817 961-5000
  Fort Worth *(G-6659)*
Galderma Research & Dev Inc ....D 817 961-5000
  Fort Worth *(G-6661)*
Molecular Biologicals LLC ....E 281 998-1227
  Pasadena *(G-16485)*
Naturich Cosmetique Labs Inc ....E 972 926-9200
  Garland *(G-7559)*

DERRICKS: Oil & Gas Field

Ecofusion Inc ....G 972 403-7449
  Plano *(G-16855)*
Hydril Company LP ....E 281 449-2000
  Houston *(G-10299)*
Industrial Cmmssning Cons Intl ....F 833 873-4224
  La Marque *(G-13708)*
Tesco Corporation (us).......................D 713 359-7000
  Houston *(G-12212)*

DESICCANTS, CLAY: Activated

Advance Technology Products ....F 713 450-5990
  Houston *(G-8484)*

DESIGN SVCS, NEC

Cactus Varied Industries LLC ....B 806 335-9470
  Amarillo *(G-411)*
Diamante Construction & Design..........F 361 449-7072
  Laredo *(G-13880)*
Exceed Drilling Tech LLC ....F 512 656-9669
  Austin *(G-1144)*
Fisher Select Products Inc..................E 972 484-1188
  Carrollton *(G-2738)*
Fusion Led Inc ....F 281 990-6011
  Houston *(G-9877)*
Genti Studios Inc ....E 214 951-9696
  Dallas *(G-4402)*
Jaffe Group Ltd ....E 830 598-2413
  Horseshoe Bay *(G-8368)*
Modular Concepts Inc ....F 817 945-1667
  Fort Worth *(G-6845)*
Osteogenics Biomedical Inc ....F 806 796-1923
  Lubbock *(G-14455)*
Portable Pipe Hangers Inc ....E 713 672-5088
  Houston *(G-11366)*
Reliable Design Services LP ....F 972 584-0551
  Quinlan *(G-17226)*
Tideline Designs Inc ....F 214 275-3958
  Arlington *(G-799)*
Welbor Technology Inc ....F 713 980-2345
  Houston *(G-12627)*
Zubie Wear..E 210 590-8892
  Universal City *(G-20186)*

DESIGN SVCS: Commercial & Indl

DC Controls Inc ....F 361 906-0123
  Lewisville *(G-14043)*
Fiberspar Corporation.........................D 713 849-2609
  Houston *(G-9783)*
Natural Graphics Inc ....E 713 661-5075
  Houston *(G-11009)*
Solid Integrations LLC........................E 915 235-4357
  El Paso *(G-5968)*

DESIGN SVCS: Computer Integrated Systems

Airborn Interconnect Inc ....B 512 863-5585
  Georgetown *(G-7633)*
Annapurna Solutions LLC....................F 916 905-3144
  Houston *(G-8646)*
Bresa Tech LLC ....E 866 728-2889
  Plano *(G-16811)*
Capitalsoft Inc ....F 972 220-1560
  Richardson *(G-17284)*
Cloud Logix LLC ....E 682 310-0665
  Irving *(G-12974)*
Compu-Data International LLC ....E 281 292-1333
  Houston *(G-9263)*
E-Ceptionist Inc ....E 713 520-6688
  Houston *(G-9554)*
Evoleap LLC ....F 832 371-6677
  Houston *(G-9719)*
Information Store Inc ....F 713 787-6798
  Houston *(G-10358)*
Inspired Elearning LLC ....D 210 579-0224
  San Antonio *(G-18189)*
Intrusion Inc ....E 972 234-6400
  Richardson *(G-17336)*
J Paul Horst & Associates ....F 713 460-9386
  Houston *(G-10442)*
L3 Technologies Inc...........................C 972 722-7927
  Rockwall *(G-17553)*
Legerity Holdings Inc ....E 512 228-5400
  Austin *(G-1288)*
Newtek Partners Lp ....D 210 370-8000
  San Antonio *(G-18345)*
Northrop Grumman Systems Corp ....D 512 374-4100
  Austin *(G-1369)*
Osisoft LLC..F 281 920-6170
  Houston *(G-11198)*
Pointwise Inc ....F 817 377-2807
  Fort Worth *(G-6910)*
Presidio Ntwrked Sltons Group ....B 469 549-3800
  Lewisville *(G-14083)*
Radix Us LLC ....E 832 377-9601
  Houston *(G-11532)*

DESIGN SVCS: Hand Tools

Enhanced Production Tech Inc ....G 512 759-2009
  Hutto *(G-12878)*

DETECTION APPARATUS: Electronic/Magnetic Field, Light/Heat

Gvi Security Solutions Inc ....D 972 236-6235
  Carrollton *(G-2867)*

DETECTIVE & ARMORED CAR SERVICES

Risk Management Armored SEC ....F 817 932-5923
  Alvarado *(G-340)*
Sabre Sentinel Intl LLC......................E 972 529-6570
  McKinney *(G-14973)*

DETECTORS: Water Leak

Wcsc LLC...F 915 774-0348
  El Paso *(G-6028)*

DETONATORS: Detonators, high explosives

Austin Star Detonator Company ....E 956 831-7751
  Brownsville *(G-2337)*

DIAGNOSTIC SUBSTANCES

Ambion Inc ....C 512 651-0200
  Austin *(G-911)*
Asuragen Inc ....D 512 681-5200
  Austin *(G-942)*
Castle Biosciences Inc ....D 866 788-9007
  Friendswood *(G-7242)*
Fujirebio Diagnostics Inc ....E 830 372-1391
  Seguin *(G-18837)*

PRODUCT

Helena Laboratories Corp ....B 409 842-3714
Beaumont *(G-1902)*

Pattern Bioscience Inc ....E 512 905-9527
Austin *(G-1400)*

Quality Bioresources Inc ....E 830 372-4797
Seguin *(G-18858)*

Separation Technology Inc ....F 830 249-0772
Boerne *(G-2136)*

Stanbio Laboratory LP ....D 830 824-0772
Boerne *(G-2137)*

Steeplechase Diagnostic Center ....E 281 955-0440
Houston *(G-12055)*

DIAGNOSTIC SUBSTANCES OR AGENTS: Enzyme & Isoenzyme

Dicqie M Fuller Looney ....F 713 266-2117
Houston *(G-9465)*

DIAGNOSTIC SUBSTANCES OR AGENTS: Hematology

Bio-RAD Laboratories Inc ....D 972 596-6165
Plano *(G-16805)*

DIAGNOSTIC SUBSTANCES OR AGENTS: In Vitro

Aspira Womens Health Inc ....E 512 519-0400
Austin *(G-940)*

Exact Diagnostics LLC ....E 817 989-9262
Fort Worth *(G-6620)*

DIAGNOSTIC SUBSTANCES OR AGENTS: Microbiology & Virology

Allied McRobial Investigations ....E 713 941-9200
South Houston *(G-19037)*

Microbes Inc ....E 281 367-7500
The Woodlands *(G-19894)*

Vax-Immune LLC ....F 832 423-0055
Houston *(G-12540)*

DIAGNOSTIC SUBSTANCES OR AGENTS: Radioactive

PETnet Houston LLC ....F 713 791-1734
Houston *(G-11298)*

DIAMONDS: Cutting & Polishing

Diamond Ethanol LLC ....F 806 897-0911
Levelland *(G-14006)*

Southwest Diamond Cutters Inc ....G 972 387-1078
Dallas *(G-4989)*

DIAPERS: Cloth

Sumehr Inc ....F 713 849-5528
Houston *(G-12093)*

DIE CUTTING SVC: Paper

Trumed Technologies Inc ....E 952 882-0611
Mesquite *(G-15082)*

DIE SETS: Presses, Metal Stamping

Hansen Manufacturing Inc ....E 713 682-1075
Houston *(G-10117)*

DIES & TOOLS: Special

Alart Tool & Die Corp ....F 713 691-0434
Houston *(G-8527)*

Apex Plastics & Tooling Inc ....E 972 205-9000
Garland *(G-7438)*

Arnim Tool Inc ....F 972 247-0802
Dallas *(G-3966)*

Bitech Tool & Die Inc ....E 915 757-8001
El Paso *(G-5663)*

Danrick Industries Inc ....F 915 599-2988
El Paso *(G-5713)*

Delcas Industries LLC ....G 956 831-3311
Brownsville *(G-2348)*

Detail Mold & Mfg LLC ....F 512 255-0525
Georgetown *(G-7647)*

Die & Tool Service Inc ....F 281 498-3317
Sugar Land *(G-19479)*

Dieco Inc ....E 817 822-4292
Arlington *(G-661)*

Exco Extrusion Dies Texas Inc ....F 972 442-3131
Wylie *(G-20935)*

Exxene Corporation ....E 361 991-8391
Corpus Christi *(G-3525)*

F M Eagle Tool Co Inc ....F 915 590-6377
El Paso *(G-5761)*

Fort Worth Forging Die LP ....F 817 529-9990
Fort Worth *(G-6644)*

Fyco Tool & Die Inc ....F 281 304-4480
Cypress *(G-3793)*

G & H Diversified Mfg LP ....D 713 856-1600
Houston *(G-9883)*

Gme Inc ....E 903 586-7581
Jacksonville *(G-13240)*

Great Southwest Tool Co ....E 915 594-7804
El Paso *(G-5789)*

Gustavs Tool & Die Inc ....E 830 379-3551
Seguin *(G-18840)*

Kiger Bros Mch Tl & Die Works ....E 281 447-1315
Houston *(G-10532)*

Lark Industrial LLC ....F 915 500-4347
El Paso *(G-5839)*

Mexican Technologies Co Inc ....E 915 595-2285
El Paso *(G-5875)*

Motor City Tool & Die Corp ....F 512 251-7700
Pflugerville *(G-16681)*

Mw Industries Inc ....E 281 233-0448
Houston *(G-10945)*

R & E Tooling & Plastics Inc ....F 817 834-2858
Fort Worth *(G-6930)*

Rct Global Inc ....F 915 595-8750
El Paso *(G-5929)*

Snapp Tool & Die Inc ....F 915 821-2046
El Paso *(G-5964)*

Snelick Quality Tool Inc ....E 972 221-0537
Dallas *(G-4973)*

Tool and Die By H&H Inc ....E 713 943-0545
Houston *(G-12316)*

Tooling Designs Inc ....F 281 354-0421
Porter *(G-17184)*

USA Machine Inc ....E 972 636-7400
Royse City *(G-17727)*

DIES: Cutting, Exc Metal

Kgp Group Inc ....E 817 354-0766
Fort Worth *(G-6760)*

Rosewood Prvate Invstments Inc ....F 214 849-9000
Dallas *(G-4911)*

Southanchor Manufacturing LLC ....E 915 590-6718
El Paso *(G-5970)*

DIES: Diamond, Metalworking

Balloffet Die Corporation Inc ....F 915 592-5252
El Paso *(G-5658)*

DIES: Plastic Forming

Gemco of Port Lavaca Inc ....E 361 570-6611
Victoria *(G-20266)*

Paragon Rio Grande LLC ....F 956 831-8249
Brownsville *(G-2391)*

Pfi Molding Inc ....F 713 946-3300
Houston *(G-11314)*

Schaefer Mold Inc ....F 817 534-7461
Fort Worth *(G-6976)*

DIES: Steel Rule

Batchelor Steel Rule Dies Inc ....F 972 263-2263
Grand Prairie *(G-7839)*

Exacta Packaging Designs Inc ....D 972 323-1063
Carrollton *(G-2733)*

DIODES & RECTIFIERS

Nxp Usa Inc ....A 512 933-8214
Austin *(G-1374)*

DIODES: Light Emitting

Curtis Mathes Inc ....F 888 725-0309
Frisco *(G-7277)*

Fleco Industries LLC ....C 972 247-3171
Carrollton *(G-2739)*

General Led Opco LLC ....F 210 360-1444
San Antonio *(G-18138)*

Kobi Electric LLC ....F 817 297-3200
Fort Worth *(G-6768)*

Micropac Industries Inc ....D 972 272-3571
Garland *(G-7551)*

Polaris Led Inc ....F 832 582-6263
Houston *(G-11354)*

DIODES: Solid State, Germanium, Silicon, Etc

Dean Technology Inc ....F 972 248-7691
Addison *(G-115)*

DIRECT SELLING ESTABLISHMENTS, NEC

Farmer Bros Co ....F 682 549-6600
Northlake *(G-15886)*

Regal Interests Inc ....F 713 222-8231
Houston *(G-11583)*

DIRECT SELLING ESTABLISHMENTS: Appliances, House-To-House

SAM&m Group LLC ....F 346 204-5786
Stafford *(G-19373)*

DIRECT SELLING ESTABLISHMENTS: Food Svcs

La Fama Foods Inc ....D 903 968-4500
Ore City *(G-16274)*

DIRECT SELLING ESTABLISHMENTS: Home Related Prdts

DOT It Rest Fulfillment LLC ....D 817 275-7714
Arlington *(G-665)*

Inovar Packaging Group LLC ....F 817 277-6666
Dallas *(G-4504)*

DISASTER SVCS

Fotown Productions ....F 225 773-1894
Cypress *(G-3791)*

Tiger Offshore Rentals LLC ....D 409 951-4048
Beaumont *(G-1959)*

DISHWASHING EQPT: Commercial

Auto-Chlor Services LLC ....E 817 525-1021
Arlington *(G-626)*

DISINFECTING SVCS

Disingerm Inc ....F 214 482-9135
Ennis *(G-6093)*

DISK DRIVES: Computer

Mangstor LLC ....F 512 879-9241
Austin *(G-1323)*

New ERA Solutions Intl LLC ....E 972 360-6112
Frisco *(G-7262)*

DISPENSERS: Soap

Sports Solutions Inc ....F 214 351-2834
Dallas *(G-4999)*

DISPENSING EQPT & PARTS, BEVERAGE: Beer

Kegspeed LLC ....F 267 714-8854
Austin *(G-1266)*

DISPENSING EQPT & PARTS, BEVERAGE: Coolers, Milk/Water, Elec

Champion Cooler Corporation ....D 903 463-1408
Denison *(G-5338)*

DISPENSING EQPT & PARTS, BEVERAGE: Fountain/Other Beverage

Capitol Food & Beverage Inc ....F 972 660-4450
Grand Prairie *(G-7850)*

Taprite-Fassco Mfg Inc ....F 830 914-2539
Marion *(G-14758)*

DISPLAY CASES: Refrigerated

Arctic Star Rfrgn Mfg Co ....E 817 274-1396
Pantego *(G-16350)*

Skl Prime Services LLC ....D 469 733-1540
Arlington *(G-782)*

DISPLAY FIXTURES: Wood

Advanced Fixtures Inc ....C 972 784-8800
Farmersville (G-6220)
Daryan Design Inc ....F 214 905-6022
Dallas (G-4239)
Mike Davis and Associates Inc ....E 512 836-8442
Austin (G-1343)
Mpi Marketing Inc ....E 972 403-7801
Plano (G-16935)

DISPLAY ITEMS: Corrugated, Made From Purchased Materials

Mick & David Enterprises Inc..............F 214 350-5765
Dallas (G-4674)

DISTILLATES: Hardwood

Texarome Inc ....E 830 232-6079
Leakey (G-13983)

DISTILLATION PRDTS: Wood

Cedar Fiber Company Inc ....E 325 446-2571
Junction (G-13337)
Holdingcross ....F 214 705-6502
Frisco (G-7291)

DISTILLERS DRIED GRAIN & SOLUBLES

Windy Hill Spirits Inc ....F 615 678-4785
Austin (G-1673)

DISTRIBUTORS: Motor Vehicle Engine

Sumitomo Elc Wirg Systems Inc ....E 210 507-3395
San Antonio (G-18510)

DOCK EQPT & SPLYS, INDL

Hooks Industeial Service Ctr ....F 361 299-6112
Conroe (G-3307)
Reliance Prcision Mfg Partners ....F 281 894-0044
Houston (G-11593)

DOCKS: Prefabricated Metal

Bluff Holdings Inc ....D 817 293-3018
Fort Worth (G-6460)

DOCUMENT DESTRUCTION SVC

Ark-La-Tex Shredding Co Inc ....F 903 877-3734
Tyler (G-20048)
Corporate Records Management ....G 214 333-3453
Dallas (G-4171)

DOCUMENT STORAGE SVCS

Twg Solutions LLC ....E 512 472-8972
Austin (G-1601)

DOCUMENTATION CENTER

Yellow Folder LLC ....E 214 431-3600
Carrollton (G-2851)

DOLLIES: Industrial

Enviroflex Design & Mfg.................F 281 356-6700
Magnolia (G-14605)

DOOR & WINDOW REPAIR SVCS

Door Control Services...................F 210 732-1214
Ben Wheeler (G-2032)
WD Norton Inc ....F 903 758-0301
Longview (G-14332)

DOOR FRAMES: Wood

Bee Builders Supply Inc ....E 972 422-4960
Plano (G-16801)
BMC West LLC ....E 817 952-3124
Hurst (G-12840)
Classic Doors Systems Co ....F 214 678-9555
Dallas (G-4128)
Sunshine Custom Cabinets Inc ....E 817 572-5201
Fort Worth (G-7023)
Wessely-Thompson Hardware Inc ....E 210 344-3081
San Antonio (G-18614)

DOOR OPERATING SYSTEMS: Electric

Accent Door Co Inc ....E 913 780-5800
San Antonio (G-17856)
Assa Abloy Entrance Systems US ....F 713 934-9095
Houston (G-8725)
Door Control Services ....F 210 732-1214
Ben Wheeler (G-2032)
Elite Entrances LLC ....E 832 922-7444
Magnolia (G-14603)
Hrh Door Corp ....F 915 590-8997
El Paso (G-5805)
Northeast Gate Co Inc ....F 903 739-8778
Sumner (G-19608)
Overhead Door Corporation ....C 469 549-7100
Lewisville (G-14080)
Richmonds American Svc Ctr Inc ....F 972 681-2222
McKinney (G-14971)
Sanwa Usa Inc ....E 972 503-3031
Plano (G-17002)
WD Norton Inc ....F 903 758-0301
Longview (G-14332)

DOORS & WINDOWS WHOLESALERS: All Materials

Cedar Mill Co Inc ....E 713 984-2600
Houston (G-9116)
Masonite International Corp ....D 972 686-5500
Dallas (G-4643)

DOORS & WINDOWS: Screen & Storm

Olney Sales Inc ....E 940 564-3592
Olney (G-16223)
Ritescreen Company LLC ....C 903 482-9200
Van Alstyne (G-20212)

DOORS & WINDOWS: Storm, Metal

A & E Venetian Blind Company ....F 940 767-1449
Wichita Falls (G-20735)
B & B Windows Inc ....F 817 237-2212
Fort Worth (G-6417)
Don Young Company Incorporated.......D 214 630-0934
Dallas (G-4272)

DOORS: Fiberglass

Advance Fiberglass LLC ....F 956 544-1000
Brownsville (G-2335)
Chem-Pruf Door Co Ltd ....D 956 544-1000
Brownsville (G-2346)
Fibergrate Composite ....C 254 965-3148
Stephenville (G-19412)

DOORS: Fire, Metal

Grenier Service Company Llc.............E 512 335-7441
Cedar Park (G-2972)

DOORS: Folding, Plastic Or Plastic Coated Fabric

Denton Door Company Inc...............F 940 891-0600
Denton (G-5358)

DOORS: Garage, Overhead, Metal

Bochelle Inc............................F 972 837-1080
McKinney (G-14928)
Custom Manufacturing Company ....E 214 428-5173
Dallas (G-4196)
Nci Group Inc ....E 281 302-1900
Houston (G-11017)
Overhead Door Corporation ....C 469 549-7100
Lewisville (G-14080)
Overhead Door Corporation ....B 361 884-6640
Corpus Christi (G-3586)
Overhead Door Corporation ....D 214 630-4669
Dallas (G-4773)
Sanwa Usa Inc ....E 972 503-3031
Plano (G-17002)

DOORS: Garage, Overhead, Wood

Bochelle Inc............................F 972 837-1080
McKinney (G-14928)
Grenier Service Company Llc.............E 512 335-7441
Cedar Park (G-2972)

DOORS: Glass

Alpha Door and Rail Inc ....F 817 358-8687
Aurora (G-853)
American Building Supply Inc.............D 469 322-8100
Coppell (G-3408)
Offenhauser Company ....D 713 928-2981
Houston (G-11140)
RE Watson & Associates Inc ....E 817 478-4401
Kennedale (G-13501)

DOORS: Rolling, Indl Building Or Warehouse, Metal

American Shredder Entps LLC ....F 817 378-8511
Fort Worth (G-6385)

DOORS: Safe & Vault, Metal

Assa Abloy Door Group LLC ....F 713 466-6790
Houston (G-8724)
Cerda-Fied Specialists Inc ....F 281 392-8063
Brookshire (G-2313)
Unlimited Stone LLC ....F 903 297-0829
Longview (G-14328)

DOORS: Screen, Metal

Next Century Screens Inc ....F 972 496-4981
Garland (G-7563)

DOORS: Wooden

Blue Streak LLC ....G 940 440-2105
Aubrey (G-848)
BMC Stock Holdings Inc ....C 972 606-6200
Grand Prairie (G-7847)
Builders Firstsource - SE Grp.............D 214 880-3500
Dallas (G-4065)
C M Trautschold Millwork Co ....E 254 752-6547
Waco (G-20374)
Cokers Doors & Mouldings Inc ....F 409 727-4600
Nederland (G-15750)
Custom Door Company Inc ....F 940 686-4500
Pilot Point (G-16724)
Delta Millwork.........................E 713 849-2281
Houston (G-9432)
Door Sa-Lutions Inc ....F 915 781-0664
El Paso (G-5723)
Evans Cabinet and Door Ltd..............E 979 836-6934
Brenham (G-2253)
Foxworth-Galbraith Lumber Co ....D 972 665-2400
Plano (G-16872)
Hardwood Products & Doors Inc..........F 512 259-3094
Leander (G-13991)
Independent Door Co Inc ....F 972 487-0511
Garland (G-7518)
J Waters Inc ....F 502 896-0850
Ennis (G-6108)
Jeld-Wen Inc ....D 972 623-1727
Grand Prairie (G-7902)
Jenkins Fabco Inc ....F 806 372-4336
Amarillo (G-443)
Masonite International..................G 972 686-5500
Mesquite (G-15061)
Masonite International Corp ....E 903 454-9500
Greenville (G-8084)
Masonite International Corp ....D 972 686-5500
Dallas (G-4643)
Maverick Door and Millwork Inc ....F 210 659-5553
Schertz (G-18755)
Mg Doors & More LLC..................F 972 291-4389
Cedar Hill (G-2948)
Mpr Products Inc.......................F 713 493-0252
Houston (G-10930)
Overhead Door Corporation ....C 469 549-7100
Lewisville (G-14080)
Overhead Door Corporation ....B 361 884-6640
Corpus Christi (G-3586)
Overhead Door Corporation ....D 214 630-4669
Dallas (G-4773)
Plumbline Inc..........................F 713 462-9500
Houston (G-11350)
Renlita Doors North Amer LLC ....E 903 583-7500
Bonham (G-2154)
Sanwa Usa Inc ....E 972 503-3031
Plano (G-17002)
Steves & Sons Inc ....D 210 924-5111
San Antonio (G-18506)
Texarkana Door & Window Inc ....F 903 793-6011
Texarkana (G-19777)

Employee Codes: A=Over 500 employees, B=251-500
C=101-250, D=51-100, E=20-50, F=10-19, G=9

2021 Harris Texas
Manufacturers Directory

PRODUCT

1475

Texas Cabinet Inc............E......972 293-2450
Cedar Hill (G-2953)

The Terrill Mfg Co Inc............D......325 655-7133
San Angelo (G-17833)

Trimco Master Millwork Inc............E......915 855-8501
El Paso (G-6016)

Wingate Archtectural Millworks............E......936 560-1040
Nacogdoches (G-15718)

DRAFTING SVCS

Sunbelt Design & Dev Inc............D......210 227-9162
San Antonio (G-18511)

DRAINAGE PRDTS: Concrete

Forterra Inc............A......469 458-7973
Irving (G-13032)

Forterra US Holdings LLC............E......469 284-8678
Irving (G-13034)

Hanson Lehigh Inc............E......281 616-0700
Houston (G-10120)

Hanson Lehigh Inc............B......972 653-5500
Irving (G-13052)

Hydro Conduit of Texas LP............E......979 885-7403
Sealy (G-18809)

South Houston Concrete Pipe Co............E......713 946-2831
Houston (G-11965)

DRAPERIES & CURTAINS

Ascot Enterprises Inc............F......254 582-1970
Hillsboro (G-8321)

Bkbl Holdings Ltd............F......214 436-4161
Frisco (G-7270)

Boriack Interiors Inc............E......214 376-1814
Dallas (G-4044)

Custom Drapery Company Inc............D......713 225-9221
Houston (G-9370)

Custom Work Room Services............F......214 631-2795
Dallas (G-4197)

Fresh Meadows Industries Inc............E......713 464-9554
Houston (G-9865)

Garland Drapery Inc............F......972 276-5297
Garland (G-7493)

Hc Interiors Inc............E......214 350-0468
Carrollton (G-2754)

Kites Draperies Inc............E......817 336-1027
Fort Worth (G-6764)

Nsec LLC............F......254 756-0651
Lorena (G-14343)

Party Props Inc............E......713 868-5433
Houston (G-11253)

Roland Curtains Inc............F......817 607-0080
Arlington (G-772)

Tri-Tex Enterprises Inc............D......214 744-1246
Eastland (G-5569)

DRAPERIES & DRAPERY FABRICS, COTTON

Fresh Meadows Industries Inc............E......713 464-9554
Houston (G-9865)

Medical Textiles Inc............E......214 744-1246
Dallas (G-4662)

DRAPERIES: Plastic & Textile, From Purchased Materials

CFS Brands LLC............E......972 466-1030
Flower Mound (G-6262)

Custom Rods & Draperies............F......972 889-0580
Richardson (G-17295)

D & D Drapery Company............F......713 522-1643
Houston (G-9386)

Display Products Inc............D......972 406-1221
Dallas (G-4262)

Heines Custom Draperies Inc............D......281 391-3103
Katy (G-13363)

Horton Draperies of Texas............F......713 774-7477
Houston (G-10210)

Tri-Tex Enterprises Inc............E......214 744-1246
Dallas (G-5109)

DRAPERY & UPHOLSTERY STORES: Draperies

Austin Window Fashion Inc............F......512 836-3388
Austin (G-967)

Custom Rods & Draperies............F......972 889-0580
Richardson (G-17295)

D & D Drapery Company............F......713 522-1643
Houston (G-9386)

Garland Drapery Inc............F......972 276-5297
Garland (G-7493)

Kites Draperies Inc............E......817 336-1027
Fort Worth (G-6764)

KS Little Shop............F......214 371-4113
Dallas (G-4571)

DRILL BITS

Corpro Inc............E......432 563-0775
Midland (G-15180)

Epiroc Drilling Tools LLC............C......844 437-4762
Grand Prairie (G-7866)

H & T Auger Company............E......432 362-4471
Odessa (G-16022)

Varel Energy Solutions............F......972 242-1160
Houston (G-12537)

Varel International Ind LLC............F......713 304-5813
Corpus Christi (G-3651)

Varel International Ind LLC............F......432 550-4816
Odessa (G-16200)

Varel International Ind LLC............D......281 272-6000
Houston (G-12538)

Varel Mining and Indus LLC............F......469 476-4870
Carrollton (G-2844)

DRILLING MACHINERY & EQPT: Oil & Gas

A R Machining Inc............E......512 846-1789
Hutto (G-12874)

A9 Manufacturing Inc............G......832 554-2464
Houston (G-8434)

Absolute Fabrication LLC............E......832 226-3345
Houston (G-8450)

Allied Prod Solutions GP LLC............C......405 224-5779
Houston (G-8552)

Athena Oilfield Services LLC............E......713 426-1969
Houston (G-8733)

Atlantic Maritime Services LLC............F......713 621-7800
Houston (G-8739)

Bar Yam Engineering Inc............G......281 999-8664
Houston (G-8816)

Consolidated Rig Works LP............E......817 446-5272
Fort Worth (G-6544)

DK Oil Field Services LLC............F......830 857-6339
San Marcos (G-18684)

Drillform Drilling Eqp Inc............E......281 948-9122
Odessa (G-15980)

Drilling & Prod Resources LLC............F......713 996-7600
Houston (G-9529)

Dyna Drill Technologies LLC............C......281 227-1250
Katy (G-13398)

Eagle Manufacturing & Svc Ltd............E......432 561-7000
Odessa (G-15983)

Eagle Pipe LLC............E......713 464-7473
Houston (G-9560)

Elgin Sprtion Sltons Indstrals............D......281 261-5778
Stafford (G-19308)

Expro Americas LLC............E......713 463-9776
Houston (G-9734)

Grant Prideco Inc............E......281 878-8000
Houston (G-10017)

Heartland Enterprises Ltd............E......830 997-9434
Fredericksburg (G-7182)

Hunting Specialty Supply LP............E......281 970-8444
Cypress (G-3802)

Istick Capital Management LLC............E......214 231-4000
Dallas (G-4514)

J&F Machine Shop Inc............E......713 466-1760
Houston (G-10445)

Keppel Letourneau Usa Inc............E......281 677-4482
Houston (G-10518)

Ls Energy Fabrication LLC............D......281 573-9500
Baytown (G-1796)

Lueras Welding Service Inc............E......361 668-4572
Alice (G-225)

National Oilwell Varco Inc............A......713 346-7500
Houston (G-10988)

Oilfield Services & Tech LLC............E......432 614-0076
Odessa (G-16100)

Patterson Well Service Co LLC............F......361 575-9600
Victoria (G-20292)

Pd Supply Inc............E......713 435-6100
Houston (G-11264)

Ranger Energy Services Inc............E......830 569-1940
Pleasanton (G-17072)

Reef Services LLC............E......325 573-1133
Snyder (G-19003)

Reef Services LLC............E......432 560-5600
Houston (G-11579)

Robinson Drilling Texas Ltd............E......432 267-5277
Big Spring (G-2096)

Rotary Components Intl Inc............F......281 590-6484
Houston (G-11668)

Rotary Drilling Tools USA LLC............E......979 387-3223
Houston (G-11669)

Russell Oilfield Equipment Co............F......281 540-8982
Humble (G-12797)

Sofec Inc............D......713 510-6600
Houston (G-11931)

Specialty Devices Incorporated............F......972 429-7240
Wylie (G-20951)

Swm International Inc............D......806 665-8747
Pampa (G-16340)

Tams Industries LLC............D......281 370-3087
Spring (G-19174)

Tesco Corporation............C......713 359-7000
Houston (G-12211)

TSC Offshore Corporation............A......832 456-3900
Houston (G-12396)

TSC Offshore Corporation............F......832 456-3900
Houston (G-12397)

Worldwide Dpwter Solutions LLC............E......281 238-6000
Richmond (G-17467)

DRILLING MACHINERY & EQPT: Water Well

Probe Technology Services Inc............E......817 568-8528
Fort Worth (G-6920)

DRILLING MUD COMPOUNDS, CONDITIONERS & ADDITIVES

Bb Chemicals Inc............E......432 381-2595
Odessa (G-15929)

Cedar Fiber Company Inc............E......325 446-2571
Junction (G-13337)

Rock Fin Countertops Inc............E......713 460-4441
Houston (G-11649)

DRILLS & DRILLING EQPT: Mining

Bersal Energy LLC............F......956 270-1155
McAllen (G-14841)

Cameron Rig Solutions LLC............D......832 782-6500
Houston (G-9076)

Command Tubular Products LLC............B......281 572-3900
New Caney (G-15836)

Drilling Supply and Mfg Inc............E......512 243-1986
Austin (G-1102)

Elmer Christy............G......972 436-0273
Lewisville (G-14048)

Galleon Mining Tools Inc............F......432 563-1867
Midland (G-15234)

Midland Wellhead Inc............E......432 682-0856
Midland (G-15303)

New Railhead Manufacturing LLC............F......817 594-6663
Weatherford (G-20606)

Sandvik Mining & Cnstr USA LLC............D......817 453-2800
Mansfield (G-14715)

DRILLS: Core

Ios Inspection............E......432 684-6440
Midland (G-15255)

DRINK MIXES, NONALCOHOLIC: Cocktail

Mmmix Ltd............E......830 336-4252
Bergheim (G-2049)

Motts LLP............C......972 673-8088
Plano (G-16934)

DRINKING PLACES: Alcoholic Beverages

Big Buck Brewery & Steakhouse............D......972 691-5100
Grapevine (G-8014)

DRIVE SHAFTS

Cannon Engineering Inc............F......818 508-0123
Austin (G-1023)

Chalks Truck Parts Inc............E......713 672-6344
Houston (G-9153)

Chalks Truck Parts Inc............F......713 672-6344
Houston (G-9154)

DRIVES: High Speed Indl, Exc Hydrostatic

Amarillo Gear Company LLC............C......806 622-1273
Amarillo (G-478)

DRONES: Target, Used By Ships, Metal

Amphion Inc............F......210 771-8116
San Antonio (G-17906)

DRUG CLINIC, OUTPATIENT

Cenikor Foundation ....F 817 921-2771
Arlington (G-640)

DRUG STORES

Cedra Pharmacy Houston LLC ....E 713 621-0621
Houston (G-9117)
Empower Clinic Services LLC ....C 832 678-4417
Houston (G-9621)
H E Butt Grocery Company..................C 956 702-2289
Alamo (G-179)

DRUG TESTING KITS: Blood & Urine

Houston Medical Tstg Svcs Inc ....E 713 665-4687
Houston (G-10237)
North Houston Alcohol DRG Tstg ....E 713 816-4990
Houston (G-11074)

DRUGS & DRUG PROPRIETARIES, WHOL: Biologicals/Allied Prdts

Santa Cruz Biotechnology Inc ....C 214 902-3900
Dallas (G-4933)

DRUGS & DRUG PROPRIETARIES, WHOLESALE: Animal Medicines

Virbac Corporation ....C 800 338-3659
Westlake (G-20697)

DRUGS & DRUG PROPRIETARIES, WHOLESALE: Pharmaceuticals

Capellon Phrmctcals Ltd Partnr ....E 817 595-5820
Fort Worth (G-6492)
Cardinal Health 200 LLC ....C 903 586-6502
Jacksonville (G-13232)
Central Admxture Phrm Svcs Inc ....E 713 748-2200
Houston (G-9137)
Central Admxture Phrm Svcs Inc ....F 972 242-2788
Carrollton (G-2713)
Executive Enterprises LLC ....F 346 224-2125
Dallas (G-4346)
Glaxosmithkline LLC ....E 469 547-1722
Richardson (G-17321)
McKesson Corporation ....A 972 446-4800
Irving (G-13102)
Mylan Institutional Inc ....D 281 240-1000
Sugar Land (G-19509)

DRUGS & DRUG PROPRIETARIES, WHOLESALE: Vitamins & Minerals

Aegle Nutrition LLC ....E 972 446-9600
Carrollton (G-2692)
Biotics Research Corporation ....D 281 344-0909
Rosenberg (G-17577)
Inner Health Group Inc ....E 210 661-8311
San Antonio (G-18187)

DRUGS ACTING ON THE CENTRAL NERVOUS SYSTEM & SENSE ORGANS

Akhu Therapeutics Inc ....G 979 820-2740
College Station (G-3173)

DRUGS AFFECTING NEOPLASMS & ENDOCRINE SYSTEMS

Formation Biologics Corp.....................F 713 357-1062
Austin (G-1166)

DRUMS: Brake

Stemco Products Inc ....F 903 758-9981
Longview (G-14312)

DRUMS: Fiber

Greif Inc ....E 817 834-6333
Haltom City (G-8144)
Greif Inc ....E 817 222-0413
Haltom City (G-8145)

DRUMS: Knockout Or Reflux, Metal Plate

Lebus International Inc.........................D 903 758-5521
Longview (G-14263)

DRUMS: Shipping, Metal

Climate Control Containers ....F 409 963-2137
Port Arthur (G-17105)
Dallas Steel Drums Inc ....E 214 638-7027
Dallas (G-4226)
Mauser Usa LLC ....C 713 670-2332
Houston (G-10799)
Thomas Steel Drums Inc ....E 817 838-6891
Fort Worth (G-7058)

DRYCLEANING & LAUNDRY SVCS: Commercial & Family

Border Apparel Laundry Ltd ....E 915 772-7170
El Paso (G-5666)

DRYCLEANING EQPT & SPLYS: Commercial

C R D N N Dallas Restoration ....E 214 698-0059
Dallas (G-4074)
Iowa Techniques Inc ....F 512 846-2403
Hutto (G-12880)

DUCTING: Metal Plate

Atco Rubber Products Inc.....................A 817 595-2894
Fort Worth (G-6406)
Atco Rubber Products Inc.....................E 713 674-6665
Houston (G-8732)

DUCTS: Sheet Metal

6-K Inc ....F 979 830-0251
Brenham (G-2242)
Accurate Air Solutions LLC ....E 325 672-2966
Abilene (G-9)
Bates AC & Svc Co Inc ....E 713 869-5521
Houston (G-8824)
Cody Company LLC ....D 972 875-5884
Ennis (G-6091)
Cooper Sheet Metal Inc ....F 817 232-4250
Fort Worth (G-6547)
Flexmaster USA Inc ....D 713 462-7694
Houston (G-9801)
Graco Mechanical Inc ....D 713 978-7000
Houston (G-10011)
Lewis & Lambert LLLP ....C 817 834-7146
Haltom City (G-8150)
M&M Manufacturing Inc ....C 817 336-2311
Fort Worth (G-6804)
M&M Manufacturing Inc ....E 817 334-0034
Fort Worth (G-6805)
McGill Airflow LLC ....E 254 580-1680
Hillsboro (G-8330)
Quietflex Manufacturing Co LP ....B 877 694-3669
Houston (G-11514)
Theriot Inc...E 979 233-6391
Freeport (G-7215)
Thur-Co Inc ....F 956 982-4424
Brownsville (G-2412)

DUDE RANCHES

Eieio Inc ....E 512 342-8044
Pflugerville (G-16668)

DUMPSTERS: Garbage

Alareal Corporation ....G 915 858-4097
El Paso (G-5639)
Austex Dumpsters LLC ....G 512 292-3867
Austin (G-950)
Same Day Dumpster Rental LLC ....F 866 223-6227
Katy (G-13379)
Texas Integrity Waste ....F 940 479-0189
Ponder (G-17096)
Wastequip Manufacturing Co LLC ....F 214 905-9101
Dallas (G-5174)

DUNE BUGGY DEALERS

Auto Fit Inc ....F 713 696-9000
Houston (G-8752)

DURABLE GOODS WHOLESALERS, NEC

Chassis Liner ....F 817 284-2545
Euless (G-6136)
Felipe Arreazola ....F 956 334-3136
Laredo (G-13883)

DUST OR FUME COLLECTING EQPT: Indl

Air Liquide Electronics US LP ....A 972 301-5200
Dallas (G-3905)
Beakley Enterprises Inc ....E 817 783-5000
Alvarado (G-324)
Compressor Designs Inc ....F 432 425-0044
Odessa (G-15965)
Joe Tipton Inc......................................F 972 271-6666
Garland (G-7527)

DYES & PIGMENTS: Organic

E I Du Pont De Nemours & Co ....C 409 883-8411
Orange (G-16239)
Huntsman Corporation ....E 281 719-6000
The Woodlands (G-19877)
Huntsman International LLC..................D 281 719-6000
The Woodlands (G-19878)
Sierra Dust Control LLC ....F 903 836-4642
Tatum (G-19645)

EARTH SCIENCE SVCS

Ipr Industrial LLC ....E 281 362-1131
The Woodlands (G-19885)

EATING PLACES

Allen Tharp LLC ....A 210 878-0034
San Antonio (G-17896)
Barton Table LLC ....G 512 791-2260
Austin (G-976)
Big Buck Brewery & Steakhouse ....D 972 691-5100
Grapevine (G-8014)
Brook Sara Enterprises Inc ....F 713 522-9999
Houston (G-8995)
Cactus Coin ....F 817 640-1791
Arlington (G-637)
Capistran Tortilla Factory ....E 956 541-3053
Brownsville (G-2343)
Carlton Foods Corp ....D 830 625-7583
Houston (G-9093)
Homestead Craftsmen LLC ....D 254 754-9600
Waco (G-20414)
Janak Packing Inc ....G 361 798-2985
Hallettsville (G-8123)
Josephs Storehouse Baking Co ....E 405 253-0669
San Antonio (G-18209)
La Frontera Molina ....G 210 432-0855
San Antonio (G-18233)
La Nortena Tortilla Factory ....F 432 445-3273
Pecos (G-16622)
Logan Farms Inc ....E 713 781-3773
Richmond (G-17462)
Marroquin Tortilla Factory ....F 361 883-7051
Corpus Christi (G-3574)
Merrills Southern Maid ....G 409 755-2400
Lumberton (G-14568)
Mpp Investments LLC ....C 940 691-0014
Wichita Falls (G-20784)
R T M Interests LLC ....F 432 683-7700
Midland (G-15376)
Seabrook Seafood Inc ....E 281 334-2546
Kemah (G-13479)
Shipley Do - Nuts ....F 281 499-5234
Missouri City (G-15593)
Simply Donuts ....F 281 955-6374
Houston (G-11904)
Swiss Pastry Shop...............................F 817 732-5661
Fort Worth (G-7025)
Tandem Marketing Services Inc ....D 361 949-7703
Corpus Christi (G-3635)

EAVES: Sheet Metal

BD Hildebrandt Entps Inc.....................F 936 825-0500
Navasota (G-15725)

EDUCATIONAL SVCS

Cambium Learning Group Inc ....D 214 932-9500
Dallas (G-3839)
Cev Multimedia Ltd ....E 806 745-8820
Lubbock (G-14391)
Houston Medical Tstg Svcs Inc ....E 713 665-4687
Houston (G-10237)
Islamic Services Foundation ....D 972 414-5090
Richardson (G-17337)
Redhouse Virtual Education LLC ....F 210 872-4989
Dallas (G-4878)
Teleometrics International ....F 254 776-2060
Waco (G-20464)

Employee Codes: A=Over 500 employees, B=251-500
C=101-250, D=51-100, E=20-50, F=10-19, G=9

2021 Harris Texas
Manufacturers Directory

1477

PRODUCT

Texas Dental Association Inc..............E...... 512 443-3675
Austin *(G-1565)*

EDUCATIONAL SVCS, NONDEGREE GRANTING: Continuing Education

Oil & Gas Consultants Intl Inc ....F...... 832 426-1200
Katy *(G-13374)*

Toastmasters International ....E...... 325 949-3782
San Angelo *(G-17835)*

EGG WHOLESALERS

Cal-Maine Foods Inc.....................E...... 830 540-4105
Waelder *(G-20483)*

ELASTOMERS

Tribute Energy Inc ....F...... 281 768-5300
Houston *(G-12367)*

ELECTRIC & OTHER SERVICES COMBINED

Air Liquide America LP ....F...... 409 720-4200
Port Neches *(G-17157)*

ELECTRIC MOTOR & GENERATOR AUXILIARY PARTS

Marine Services LLC....................E...... 713 923-6688
Houston *(G-10765)*

New Core Inc ....F...... 956 421-2446
Harlingen *(G-8196)*

ELECTRIC MOTOR REPAIR SVCS

A & R Enterprises Inc ....F...... 903 984-9057
Kilgore *(G-13530)*

Acg Quality Electric Inc ....F...... 713 225-6531
Houston *(G-8468)*

Alsay Incorporated ....E...... 210 628-1090
San Antonio *(G-17900)*

Amarillo Elc Specialists Inc ....F...... 806 372-3798
Amarillo *(G-394)*

Border Industrial Motors Inc ....G...... 915 542-4266
El Paso *(G-5668)*

Bradleys Inc ....D...... 361 643-0100
Gregory *(G-8099)*

Brandon & Clark Inc ....C...... 806 771-5600
Lubbock *(G-14380)*

Brandon & Clark Inc ....G...... 432 332-0163
Odessa *(G-15941)*

Brandon & Clark Inc ....E...... 806 771-5646
Lubbock *(G-14381)*

Brandon & Clark Inc ....E...... 817 838-5593
Fort Worth *(G-6469)*

Brandon & Clark Inc ....F...... 432 332-0163
Odessa *(G-15942)*

Brandon & Clark Inc ....F...... 806 364-5470
Hereford *(G-8284)*

Buna Electric Motor Svc Inc ....E...... 409 769-5402
Vidor *(G-20325)*

C P E Inc ....F...... 972 313-1133
Irving *(G-12956)*

Cajun Electric Motors Inc ....F...... 972 227-9000
Ferris *(G-6231)*

Capital Dallas Elc Mtr Svc ....F...... 214 630-8487
Dallas *(G-4081)*

Commercial Armature Works..............F...... 713 672-7873
Houston *(G-9248)*

Community Motors Inc ....F...... 281 354-8087
New Caney *(G-15837)*

Corpus Christi CD Electric LP ....F...... 361 888-4133
Corpus Christi *(G-3508)*

Davenport Electric Motors LLC ....F...... 361 299-6440
Corpus Christi *(G-3511)*

Etheredge Elc Co Tyler Inc.............E...... 903 877-4774
Tyler *(G-20084)*

Evans Enterprises Inc ....F...... 940 723-7466
Wichita Falls *(G-20764)*

Flanders Electric Ltd ....D...... 903 759-9439
Longview *(G-14234)*

G E Jones Electric Co Inc ....E...... 806 372-5505
Amarillo *(G-426)*

Gauntlett Inc..........................G...... 806 293-9849
Plainview *(G-16754)*

General Electric Company ....D...... 214 902-6600
Dallas *(G-4400)*

Globaltech Motor & Contrls Inc ....E...... 281 487-9300
Houston *(G-9984)*

Grayson Armature Works Inc ....F...... 713 473-4404
Pasadena *(G-16450)*

Hiroko International Inc...............F...... 210 590-4411
San Antonio *(G-18168)*

Hoffman Industrial Electric ....G...... 361 573-6365
Victoria *(G-20272)*

Indeco-Industrial Electric Co ....F...... 325 653-4255
San Angelo *(G-17809)*

Indelect Corporation ....E...... 903 656-2518
Lone Star *(G-14183)*

Integrated Power Services LLC ....E...... 281 471-4611
La Porte *(G-13753)*

Integrated Power Services LLC ....E...... 409 833-9477
Beaumont *(G-1909)*

Lufkin Electric Co ....F...... 936 639-2377
Lufkin *(G-14538)*

Lynn Electric Motor Co Inc ....F...... 940 657-3511
Knox City *(G-13664)*

M&I Electric Industries Inc ....D...... 832 241-6330
Houston *(G-10721)*

Martin Electric Co Inc ....E...... 979 543-6421
El Campo *(G-5622)*

Massengale Armature Works Inc ....F...... 210 732-5168
San Antonio *(G-18282)*

Megatron Inc...........................E...... 281 558-0034
Houston *(G-10824)*

Monahans Electric Inc ....E...... 432 943-3246
Monahans *(G-15609)*

Morefield Development Inc ....E...... 713 869-2111
Houston *(G-10920)*

Musshorn Enterprises Inc...............C...... 915 772-9007
El Paso *(G-5892)*

New Core Inc ....F...... 956 421-2446
Harlingen *(G-8196)*

Phase Electric Motors Inc ....F...... 972 291-9221
Cedar Hill *(G-2950)*

Rail Products Intl Inc ....D...... 956 541-1759
Brownsville *(G-2397)*

Remsa Usa Inc ....E...... 915 855-8621
El Paso *(G-5937)*

Roundhouse Elc & Eqp Co Inc ....F...... 432 333-3923
Odessa *(G-16143)*

San Antonio Armature Works Inc ....E...... 210 227-0291
San Antonio *(G-18445)*

Smith Pump Company Inc ....G...... 817 589-2060
Fort Worth *(G-6996)*

Sulzer Electro-Mechanical Serv.........D...... 713 473-3231
Pasadena *(G-16513)*

Sulzer Electro-Mechanical Serv.........E...... 409 882-9112
Orange *(G-16264)*

Sytek Electric Corporaiton ....E...... 713 862-8813
Houston *(G-12140)*

Texas Electric Eqp Co Ltd ....E...... 281 479-6086
La Porte *(G-13794)*

Tolbert Electric Motor Company.........F...... 972 272-6541
Garland *(G-7603)*

Valley Armature & Elc Co Inc...........F...... 956 393-2233
Edinburg *(G-5605)*

ELECTRIC POWER DISTRIBUTION TO CONSUMERS

Lower Colorado River Authority.........A...... 512 473-3200
Austin *(G-1305)*

Seldon Energy Partners LLC ....F...... 503 807-4300
Houston *(G-11820)*

ELECTRIC POWER GENERATION: Fossil Fuel

Txu Energy Services Co LLC.............C...... 903 389-6074
Fairfield *(G-6180)*

ELECTRIC POWER, COGENERATED

Natural Energy Resources Inc...........D...... 832 631-5013
Katy *(G-13426)*

Powersecure Inc ....E...... 203 683-6222
Frisco *(G-7306)*

ELECTRIC SERVICES

Abshier Energy LLC ....G...... 432 352-4338
Bowie *(G-2189)*

Colgate Energy Partners LLC ....F...... 432 695-4222
Midland *(G-15172)*

General Electric Company ....D...... 214 902-6600
Dallas *(G-4400)*

Skyven Technologies Inc ....E...... 972 861-0893
Richardson *(G-17399)*

Supreme Electrical Svcs Inc............D...... 713 676-2588
Houston *(G-12122)*

ELECTRIC SVCS, NEC Power Broker

Source Operations Group LLC ....E...... 888 557-7079
Houston *(G-11957)*

ELECTRIC SVCS, NEC Power Marketers

Biztel LP..............................F...... 713 600-2600
Houston *(G-8896)*

Solaro Energy Inc ....F...... 575 838-3813
Nacogdoches *(G-15713)*

ELECTRIC SVCS, NEC: Power Generation

Exxon Mobil Corporation ....B...... 972 940-6000
Irving *(G-13021)*

Falcon Seaboard Holdings LLC...........E...... 713 622-0055
Houston *(G-9755)*

Luminant Generation Co LLC ....D...... 214 812-4600
Irving *(G-13092)*

Texas Australian Power Inc.............E...... 940 723-4122
Wichita Falls *(G-20815)*

ELECTRIC TOOL REPAIR SVCS

Atrium Windows and Doors Inc...........D...... 214 583-1840
Dallas *(G-3983)*

Laser Drum Products Inc ....F...... 713 263-9050
Houston *(G-10603)*

ELECTRICAL APPARATUS & EQPT WHOLESALERS

Ademco Inc.............................E...... 972 402-8612
Farmers Branch *(G-6184)*

Ademco Inc.............................F...... 713 861-9418
Houston *(G-8479)*

Ademco Inc.............................C...... 915 872-5542
El Paso *(G-5637)*

Ademco Inc.............................D...... 915 875-0091
El Paso *(G-5638)*

Compliant Power Systems LLC ....F...... 903 427-0071
Clarksville *(G-3072)*

Dolan Northwest LLC ....E...... 972 559-6900
Frisco *(G-7257)*

Eaton Corporation ....F...... 915 772-6198
El Paso *(G-5732)*

Gonzales Elec Systems LLC..............E...... 409 860-3802
Beaumont *(G-1899)*

Hoffman Industrial Electric ....G...... 361 573-6365
Victoria *(G-20272)*

Innovative Idm LLC ....E...... 281 880-2105
Houston *(G-10372)*

Innovative Idm LLC ....E...... 214 574-9500
Lewisville *(G-14056)*

L V Controls Inc ....F...... 713 691-4666
Houston *(G-10576)*

Mega Systems Inc.......................E...... 210 684-2600
Helotes *(G-8242)*

Oilfield-Electric-Marine Inc...........F...... 713 680-9659
Houston *(G-11165)*

Philips North America LLC ....E...... 915 298-4111
El Paso *(G-5910)*

Schneider Electric Usa Inc.............C...... 972 236-0300
Coppell *(G-3444)*

Star Delta Motor Controls Inc ....E...... 210 479-3550
San Antonio *(G-18497)*

Texas Electric Coops Inc...............D...... 512 868-8610
Georgetown *(G-7685)*

Vantran Industries Inc ....E...... 254 772-9740
Waco *(G-20471)*

Welbor Technology Inc..................F...... 713 980-2345
Houston *(G-12627)*

ELECTRICAL CONSTRUCTION MATERIALS WHOLESALERS

Elliott Electric Supply Inc ....E...... 512 246-8001
Round Rock *(G-17652)*

ELECTRICAL CURRENT CARRYING WIRING DEVICES

B I Products LLC ....D...... 972 359-4000
Allen *(G-255)*

Baker Hghes Olfld Oprtions LLC.........C...... 800 441-0535
Yorktown *(G-20976)*

Bk/Ja Holdings Inc.....................E...... 281 879-9903
Stafford *(G-19291)*

BMC Industry LLC.......................F...... 903 796-5330
Queen City *(G-17219)*

Cemtechnologies Inc ....F 972 238-3630
  Richardson *(G-17285)*

Channl-Track Tube-Way Inds Inc ....E 713 864-2551
  Houston *(G-9162)*

Electrotechnics Corporation ....E 903 938-1901
  Marshall *(G-14776)*

Hubbell Building Automtn Inc ....E 512 450-1100
  Austin *(G-1212)*

Lone Star Indus Corp Texas ....E 915 779-7255
  El Paso *(G-5846)*

Luminator Holding LP ....C 972 424-6511
  Plano *(G-16911)*

Luminator Technology Group LLC ....C 972 424-6511
  Plano *(G-16913)*

Massey Holding & Consultants ....E 817 477-3176
  Mansfield *(G-14690)*

Molex LLC ....D 915 591-5600
  El Paso *(G-5882)*

Optek Technology Inc ....D 972 323-2200
  Carrollton *(G-2786)*

Plastronics Co ....E 972 986-0474
  Irving *(G-13151)*

Plastronics Interconnections ....F 972 258-2580
  Irving *(G-13152)*

Pro Connect Technology LLC ....F 972 543-2603
  Plano *(G-16978)*

Prosource Industries Inc ....E 972 660-1400
  Grand Prairie *(G-7958)*

Reliable Manufacturing Inc ....E 512 255-6572
  Round Rock *(G-17684)*

Rsi Inc ....E 512 268-7500
  Kyle *(G-13686)*

Selectouch Corporation ....E 972 924-3289
  Anna *(G-585)*

Svtronics Inc ....C 214 440-1234
  Plano *(G-17017)*

Thermon Inc ....C 512 396-5801
  San Marcos *(G-18715)*

Thermon Industries Inc ....B 512 396-5801
  San Marcos *(G-18716)*

Tyrex Group Ltd ....F 512 623-4694
  Austin *(G-1603)*

Umbilicals International Inc ....D 281 275-6600
  Stafford *(G-19392)*

Wesco Acquisition Partners Inc ....E 713 688-5551
  Galena Park *(G-7386)*

ELECTRICAL EQPT & SPLYS

A3im Inc ....F 713 378-7600
  Houston *(G-8433)*

Active Power Inc ....D 512 836-6464
  Austin *(G-887)*

AF Technologies Inc ....C 817 649-2500
  Arlington *(G-611)*

Amgis LLC ....E 832 775-1319
  Houston *(G-8624)*

Andrews Fabrication Inc ....G 281 372-0440
  Houston *(G-8643)*

Appleton Grp LLC ....C 281 774-3700
  Houston *(G-8665)*

Applied Concepts Inc ....C 972 398-3750
  Richardson *(G-17270)*

Applied Optoelectronics Inc ....C 281 295-1800
  Sugar Land *(G-19445)*

Arbin Corporation ....E 979 690-2751
  College Station *(G-3174)*

Atkore Plastic Pipe Corp ....D 817 594-8791
  Weatherford *(G-20577)*

Axent Manufacturing Inc ....E 972 437-3737
  Richardson *(G-17276)*

Azz Inc ....D 817 810-0095
  Fort Worth *(G-6414)*

Azz Inc ....E 281 458-1550
  Houston *(G-8769)*

Azz Inc ....E 817 297-4361
  Crowley *(G-3751)*

Azz Inc ....E 817 284-0119
  Fort Worth *(G-6415)*

Azz Inc ....E 409 842-0216
  Beaumont *(G-1856)*

Azz Inc ....E 713 225-9340
  Crowley *(G-3752)*

Azz Incorporated ....E 817 810-0095
  Fort Worth *(G-6416)*

CF Industries Inc ....E 214 460-2804
  Lewisville *(G-14035)*

Cnc Precision Manufacturing ....E 972 241-4226
  Dallas *(G-4131)*

Connexa Energy LLC ....E 830 995-3600
  Comfort *(G-3238)*

Cooper B-Line Inc ....C 903 813-1746
  Sherman *(G-18913)*

Cooper Crouse-Hinds LLC ....E 806 358-4585
  Amarillo *(G-484)*

Cordyne Inc ....D 713 460-5151
  Houston *(G-9313)*

Crawford Electric Sup Co Inc ....E 512 593-4000
  Round Rock *(G-17638)*

Crown To Ground Supply Inc ....F 936 588-7457
  Magnolia *(G-14599)*

D Square Inc ....F 915 834-6400
  El Paso *(G-5711)*

Dolan Northwest LLC ....E 972 559-6900
  Frisco *(G-7257)*

Eaton Corporation ....E 713 849-1600
  Houston *(G-9572)*

Electric Pwr Systems Intl Inc ....E 972 907-3783
  Richardson *(G-17305)*

Electro Technical Inds Inc ....D 713 691-5182
  Houston *(G-9590)*

Electronic Drilling Control ....D 972 257-0322
  Irving *(G-13014)*

Elliott Electric Supply Inc ....E 210 646-6950
  San Antonio *(G-18088)*

Emf Company Inc ....D 214 350-6848
  Dallas *(G-4319)*

Evco Partners LP ....E 409 766-1900
  Texas City *(G-19793)*

Fielder Electric Supply Co Inc ....E 281 485-6599
  Pearland *(G-16560)*

Fritel & Associates LLC ....E 254 757-1177
  Waco *(G-20404)*

Frl Inc ....A 915 633-8354
  El Paso *(G-5775)*

Glo-Jo Electrical Products Inc ....E 210 673-3583
  San Antonio *(G-18144)*

Hiller Measurements Inc ....C 512 394-8356
  Austin *(G-863)*

Hlcl Capital Corporation ....E 972 660-4096
  Grand Prairie *(G-7892)*

Hunnicutt Digital Electronics ....F 817 336-5449
  Fort Worth *(G-6709)*

Innovative Idm LLC ....E 281 880-2105
  Houston *(G-10372)*

Innovative Idm LLC ....E 214 574-9500
  Lewisville *(G-14056)*

L3 Technologies Inc ....A 903 457-4100
  Greenville *(G-8080)*

L3harris Technologies Inc ....A 903 457-7461
  Greenville *(G-8081)*

Link World Trade Inc ....C 972 713-8000
  Addison *(G-145)*

Lone Star Instrmnttion Elc Cor ....D 432 368-7827
  Odessa *(G-16065)*

Lone Star INStrmnttn&elctrc ....E 817 458-9347
  Weatherford *(G-20600)*

Materia Inc ....F 936 295-4040
  Huntsville *(G-12818)*

Maxistrut of Texas Inc ....E 713 880-4228
  Houston *(G-10805)*

Mid-Coast Electric Supply Inc ....E 830 333-7030
  Uvalde *(G-20193)*

Msf Electric Inc ....D 210 781-4112
  San Antonio *(G-18323)*

Msf Electric Inc ....E 214 377-8710
  Dallas *(G-4702)*

National Swtchgear Systems Inc ....E 972 420-0149
  Lewisville *(G-14071)*

Overhead Door Corporation ....B 361 884-6640
  Corpus Christi *(G-3586)*

Powell Electrical Systems Inc ....E 713 599-0324
  Houston *(G-11371)*

Power Temp Systems Inc ....F 281 617-7889
  Houston *(G-11379)*

Pts - Power Temp Systems Inc ....F 337 806-9779
  Houston *(G-11471)*

Quinstar Corporation ....F 512 326-1011
  Austin *(G-1445)*

R & R Oilfield Services Inc ....D 361 289-5892
  Corpus Christi *(G-3604)*

Resa Power LLC ....F 832 900-8340
  Houston *(G-11604)*

Santanna Natural Gas Corp ....E 512 346-2500
  Austin *(G-1710)*

Sanwa Electronics USA Corp ....G 972 503-3031
  Plano *(G-17001)*

Schneder Elc Bldngs Amrcas Inc ....C 859 243-8254
  Laredo *(G-13930)*

Schneider Electric ....F 915 834-6451
  El Paso *(G-5953)*

Schneider Electric ....F 956 205-7533
  McAllen *(G-14905)*

Schneider Electric Usa Inc ....C 512 295-8060
  Buda *(G-2537)*

Seaboard Controls LLC ....E 281 328-8620
  Crosby *(G-3742)*

Specialty Electrical LLC ....F 817 355-5315
  Fort Worth *(G-7009)*

Summit Electric Supply Co Inc ....E 325 691-9600
  Abilene *(G-85)*

Svtronics Inc ....C 214 440-1234
  Plano *(G-17017)*

T S K Innovations Company ....E 915 581-9718
  El Paso *(G-5991)*

T S K Innovations Company ....E 915 581-9718
  El Paso *(G-5992)*

Terra Metrics Ltd ....F 432 337-3412
  Odessa *(G-16174)*

Thiel Co ....F 817 310-3110
  Grapevine *(G-8057)*

Virtex Assembly Services Inc ....D 512 835-6772
  Austin *(G-1635)*

Vistech Corporation ....F 972 231-1746
  Richardson *(G-17423)*

Wesco International Inc ....F 432 699-2680
  Midland *(G-15469)*

Yotta Solar Inc ....F 512 856-7788
  Austin *(G-1682)*

ELECTRICAL EQPT FOR ENGINES

1a Smart Start LLC ....F 972 621-0252
  Grapevine *(G-8009)*

Android Industries LLC ....D 972 343-3300
  Arlington *(G-618)*

Borgwarner Pds Anderson LLC ....D 765 778-6499
  Laredo *(G-13870)*

Channl-Track Tube-Way Inds Inc ....E 713 864-2551
  Houston *(G-9162)*

Compliant Power Systems LLC ....F 903 427-0071
  Clarksville *(G-3072)*

Elamex Usa Corp ....A 915 298-3061
  El Paso *(G-5748)*

Elcom Inc ....E 915 298-2000
  El Paso *(G-5749)*

Englobal Constant Power Inc ....C 713 880-6200
  Houston *(G-9647)*

Fedex Sup Chain Lgstics Elec I ....A 817 491-7700
  Fort Worth *(G-6626)*

Sam and Sab Inc ....E 713 983-7500
  Houston *(G-11736)*

Teledyne Instruments Inc ....C 713 666-2561
  Houston *(G-12191)*

Yazaki North America Inc ....F 618 512-8723
  El Paso *(G-6041)*

ELECTRICAL EQPT REPAIR & MAINTENANCE

All American Pump & Mch Inc ....F 325 653-6597
  San Angelo *(G-17773)*

Compliant Power Systems LLC ....F 903 427-0071
  Clarksville *(G-3072)*

Electronic Drilling Control ....D 972 257-0322
  Irving *(G-13014)*

Electronic Technical Svcs Corp ....E 281 446-4414
  Humble *(G-12765)*

Evans Enterprises Inc ....E 254 772-4710
  Waco *(G-20399)*

Evans Enterprises Inc ....E 325 235-1776
  Abilene *(G-40)*

Fife Services Inc ....E 432 827-3601
  Goldsmith *(G-7742)*

Freer Iron Works Inc ....F 361 394-7273
  Freer *(G-7225)*

Kennedy Machine & Mfg Inc ....E 972 241-7610
  Haslet *(G-8219)*

Meyer-Smith Inc ....F 713 862-7339
  Houston *(G-10862)*

Radley Electric Inc ....F 409 781-7172
  Sour Lake *(G-19034)*

Roy Johnson Incorporated ....E 817 468-2939
  Arlington *(G-773)*

Son and Daughters Inc ....F 956 423-2689
  Harlingen *(G-8201)*

Southwest Sign Group Inc ....D 210 648-3221
  San Antonio *(G-18489)*

Spectrum Technologies USA Inc ....F 817 232-2373
  Fort Worth *(G-7011)*

Terra Metrics Ltd ....F 432 337-3412
  Odessa *(G-16174)*

Employee Codes: A=Over 500 employees, B=251-500
C=101-250, D=51-100, E=20-50, F=10-19, G=9

2021 Harris Texas
Manufacturers Directory

1479

PRODUCT

Texas Meter and Device Co LLC...........D..... 254 732-1305
Waco *(G-20467)*
Wwl Industries Inc.....................E....... 432 362-0326
Odessa *(G-16215)*

ELECTRICAL EQPT REPAIR SVCS

Hannon Hydraulics Inc...................E....... 713 849-4445
Houston *(G-10116)*
Ies Holdings Inc........................D....... 713 860-1500
Houston *(G-10316)*

ELECTRICAL EQPT REPAIR SVCS: High Voltage

Alamo Transformer Supply Co...........E..... 713 991-6060
Houston *(G-8526)*
General Electric Company................D....... 412 469-6080
Southlake *(G-19071)*
Greenville Transformer Co...............E....... 903 455-1610
Greenville *(G-8076)*

ELECTRICAL EQPT: Automotive, NEC

Littelfuse Inc...........................D...... 830 513-8775
Eagle Pass *(G-5549)*
Perfect Performance Pdts LLC..........E..... 817 244-6898
Fort Worth *(G-6902)*
Standard Motor Products Inc...........F..... 972 316-8100
Lewisville *(G-14093)*
Upex Auto Supply.......................F..... 214 741-2400
Dallas *(G-5144)*

ELECTRICAL GOODS, WHOL: Amateur Radio Communications Eqpt

Zti Merger Subsidiary III Inc...............F....... 510 777-7000
Plano *(G-17057)*

ELECTRICAL GOODS, WHOLESALE: Alarms & Signaling Eqpt

Siemens Industry Inc....................B....... 972 947-7000
Dallas *(G-4959)*
Tricon International Ltd.................E....... 713 963-0066
Houston *(G-12371)*

ELECTRICAL GOODS, WHOLESALE: Answering Machines, Telephone

Kelly Associates........................F....... 214 357-8752
Dallas *(G-4548)*

ELECTRICAL GOODS, WHOLESALE: Apparatus Wire & Cordage

Ote International Holdings LLC...........F....... 888 666-9361
Athens *(G-837)*

ELECTRICAL GOODS, WHOLESALE: Batteries, Dry Cell

CSB Energy Tech Americas Ltd...........E....... 817 244-7777
Haltom City *(G-8135)*
OReilly Automotive Stores Inc..........F....... 936 856-2409
Willis *(G-20857)*

ELECTRICAL GOODS, WHOLESALE: Batteries, Storage, Indl

Batteries Concord.......................F....... 281 931-4488
Houston *(G-8827)*
Exide Technologies LLC..................F....... 210 662-8999
San Antonio *(G-18099)*

ELECTRICAL GOODS, WHOLESALE: Cassettes, Recording

AMA Printing / Finishing Inc............E....... 254 776-8860
Waco *(G-20359)*

ELECTRICAL GOODS, WHOLESALE: Circuit Breakers

Circuit Breaker Sales LLC...............C....... 940 665-4444
Gainesville *(G-7338)*
McAps Inc...............................F....... 713 941-1300
South Houston *(G-19049)*
National Swtchgear Systems Inc..........E....... 972 420-0149
Lewisville *(G-14071)*

ELECTRICAL GOODS, WHOLESALE: Closed Circuit Television Or TV

L3 Mobile-Vision Inc...................D...... 973 263-1090
Houston *(G-10578)*

ELECTRICAL GOODS, WHOLESALE: Electrical Appliances, Major

Builders Depot Direct LLC...............F...... 832 384-7272
Houston *(G-9012)*

ELECTRICAL GOODS, WHOLESALE: Electronic Parts

Apx Plastics Inc........................F....... 817 275-3883
Arlington *(G-620)*
Efficient-Tec Intl LLC..................E....... 214 221-9405
Dallas *(G-4302)*
Electronic Technical Svcs Corp..........E....... 281 446-4414
Humble *(G-12765)*
High Voltage Power Systems Inc.........C....... 972 733-1700
Carrollton *(G-2756)*
Kelleys Controls Incorporated..........F....... 432 362-7998
Odessa *(G-16045)*
M3 Distribution Inc.....................F....... 281 357-0604
Tomball *(G-19986)*
Memphis Electronic Inc..................G....... 713 600-6080
Houston *(G-10826)*
Richardson Trident Company LLC.........D....... 972 231-5176
Richardson *(G-17390)*
Venkel Ltd..............................E....... 512 794-0081
Austin *(G-1629)*

ELECTRICAL GOODS, WHOLESALE: Facsimile Or Fax Eqpt

Meera Enterprises Inc...................F....... 972 385-3900
Addison *(G-148)*
Montano Investments Inc.................E....... 956 630-1877
McAllen *(G-14892)*

ELECTRICAL GOODS, WHOLESALE: Fire Alarm Systems

Classic Protection Systems..............E....... 713 468-3573
Houston *(G-9212)*
Eisenbeck Corporation...................F....... 972 526-5235
Garland *(G-7485)*
Texas SEC & Surveillance Inc............E....... 512 693-4003
Round Rock *(G-17693)*

ELECTRICAL GOODS, WHOLESALE: Fittings & Construction Mat

Richardson Trident Company LLC.........D...... 972 231-5176
Richardson *(G-17390)*

ELECTRICAL GOODS, WHOLESALE: Fuses & Access

Mid-Coast Electric Supply Inc...........E....... 830 333-7030
Uvalde *(G-20193)*

ELECTRICAL GOODS, WHOLESALE: Garbage Disposals

McNeilus Truck and Mfg Inc..............E....... 972 225-2313
Hutchins *(G-12868)*

ELECTRICAL GOODS, WHOLESALE: Generators

Black Star Energy Services LLC.........E....... 432 272-3395
Odessa *(G-15936)*
Community Motors Inc....................F....... 281 354-8087
New Caney *(G-15837)*
Cummins Southern Plains LLC............C....... 713 679-2220
Houston *(G-9358)*
Loftin Equipment Company................E....... 281 310-6858
Houston *(G-10669)*
Toshiba International Corp...............A....... 800 231-1412
Houston *(G-12327)*
Wheel-A-Rama Inc........................G...... 325 655-7373
San Angelo *(G-17840)*

ELECTRICAL GOODS, WHOLESALE: Hanging & Fastening Devices

Ces Industrial LLC......................F....... 281 615-5621
Stafford *(G-19293)*

ELECTRICAL GOODS, WHOLESALE: Household Appliances, NEC

Midwest Folding Products Corp...........C....... 312 666-3366
Temple *(G-19690)*

ELECTRICAL GOODS, WHOLESALE: Insulators

Utility Agency & Import Inc.............F....... 817 477-9888
Mansfield *(G-14725)*

ELECTRICAL GOODS, WHOLESALE: Intercommunication Eqpt

Backwoods Communications LLC......F....... 361 652-6900
Victoria *(G-20241)*

ELECTRICAL GOODS, WHOLESALE: Light Bulbs & Related Splys

Energy Retrofitters Inc.................F....... 817 319-2796
Fort Worth *(G-6614)*
Ledi2 Inc...............................F....... 713 636-9152
Houston *(G-10615)*
Solaro Energy Inc.......................F....... 575 838-3813
Nacogdoches *(G-15713)*
Speedtech Lights Inc....................E....... 800 757-2581
Buda *(G-2539)*

ELECTRICAL GOODS, WHOLESALE: Lighting Fixtures, Comm & Indl

American Green Technology Inc..........E....... 269 340-9975
Houston *(G-8598)*
DA Schoggin Inc.........................D....... 214 350-0591
Dallas *(G-4204)*
M & M Lighting LP.......................D....... 713 667-5611
Houston *(G-10715)*

ELECTRICAL GOODS, WHOLESALE: Lighting Fixtures, Residential

RDHS Inc................................F....... 361 852-4094
Corpus Christi *(G-3606)*
Trade Source International...............E....... 972 393-3800
Coppell *(G-3450)*

ELECTRICAL GOODS, WHOLESALE: Mobile telephone Eqpt

Cellteks Inc............................F....... 830 249-8999
Boerne *(G-2116)*
DMD Products LLC.......................G...... 281 778-2051
Rosharon *(G-17604)*

ELECTRICAL GOODS, WHOLESALE: Motor Ctrls, Starters & Relays

Megatron Inc............................E...... 281 558-0034
Houston *(G-10824)*
Omron Electronics LLC...................D....... 713 849-1900
Houston *(G-11181)*
Schlumberger Rig Tech Inc...............D....... 713 849-1700
Houston *(G-11771)*

ELECTRICAL GOODS, WHOLESALE: Motors

All American Pump & Mch Inc.............F....... 325 653-6597
San Angelo *(G-17773)*
Amarillo Elc Specialists Inc............F....... 806 372-3798
Amarillo *(G-394)*
Amerimex Motor & Controls LLC..........D....... 713 225-4300
Houston *(G-8618)*
Austin Armature Works LP................E....... 512 312-0088
Buda *(G-2520)*
B J Electric Motor Service..............F....... 432 570-4100
Midland *(G-15127)*
Border Industrial Motors Inc............G....... 915 542-4266
El Paso *(G-5668)*
Brandon & Clark Inc.....................G....... 432 332-0163
Odessa *(G-15941)*
Corpus Christi CD Electric LP...........F....... 361 888-4133
Corpus Christi *(G-3508)*

Electrico Inc ....F 903 872-6567
  Corsicana *(G-3670)*

Evans Enterprises Inc ....F 254 772-4710
  Waco *(G-20399)*

Flanders Electric Ltd ....D 903 759-9439
  Longview *(G-14234)*

G E Jones Electric Co Inc ....E 806 372-5505
  Amarillo *(G-426)*

Grayson Armature Works Inc ....F 713 473-4404
  Pasadena *(G-16450)*

Heights Armature Works Inc ....F 713 937-7676
  Houston *(G-10147)*

Indeco-Industrial Electric Co ....F 325 653-4255
  San Angelo *(G-17809)*

Land Enterprises Inc ....F 713 924-5929
  Houston *(G-10592)*

Musshorn Enterprises Inc ....C 915 772-9007
  El Paso *(G-5892)*

New Core Inc ....F 956 421-2446
  Harlingen *(G-8196)*

Roundhouse Elc & Eqp Co Inc ....F 432 333-3923
  Odessa *(G-16143)*

Ruby Automation LLC ....E 972 881-9663
  Plano *(G-16997)*

San Antonio Armature Works Inc ....E 210 227-0291
  San Antonio *(G-18445)*

Sulzer Electro-Mechanical Serv ....D 713 473-3231
  Pasadena *(G-16513)*

Texas Electric Eqp Co Ltd ....E 281 479-6086
  La Porte *(G-13794)*

Tolbert Electric Motor Company ....F 972 272-6541
  Garland *(G-7603)*

Valley Armature & Elc Co Inc ....F 956 393-2233
  Edinburg *(G-5605)*

ELECTRICAL GOODS, WHOLESALE: Paging & Signaling Eqpt

Analytical Sensors Instrs LLC ....D 281 565-8818
  Houston *(G-8636)*

Long Range Systems LLC ....E 214 553-5308
  Richardson *(G-17349)*

Waveware Technologies Inc ....F 972 479-1702
  Garland *(G-7609)*

ELECTRICAL GOODS, WHOLESALE: Panelboards

Electro-Quip Service Inc ....D 281 456-8600
  Houston *(G-9593)*

ELECTRICAL GOODS, WHOLESALE: Radio Parts & Access, NEC

Sony Electronics Inc ....C 858 942-2400
  Laredo *(G-13934)*

ELECTRICAL GOODS, WHOLESALE: Security Control Eqpt & Systems

Adams Evidence Grade Tech Inc ....F 830 966-4210
  Utopia *(G-20187)*

Easy Protect Inc ....E 469 916-1099
  Dallas *(G-4297)*

Hitech Fire Detection Corp ....D 281 475-7289
  Spring *(G-19130)*

Razberi Technologies Inc ....E 469 828-3380
  Farmers Branch *(G-6212)*

Resideo Technologies Inc ....F 512 726-3500
  Austin *(G-1459)*

Supercircuits Inc ....D 877 995-2288
  Austin *(G-1548)*

ELECTRICAL GOODS, WHOLESALE: Semiconductor Devices

Hitachi America Ltd ....D 972 488-3824
  Carrollton *(G-2761)*

Horiba Instruments Inc ....E 408 730-4772
  Austin *(G-1209)*

Mhc Semiconductor Processing ....F 512 331-6632
  Austin *(G-1337)*

Semtech Corporation ....E 972 231-1606
  Richardson *(G-17396)*

Toppan Photomasks Inc ....C 512 310-6000
  Round Rock *(G-17694)*

ELECTRICAL GOODS, WHOLESALE: Signaling, Eqpt

D&G Energy Corporation ....F 956 686-6040
  McAllen *(G-14852)*

Peek Traffic Corporation ....C 281 453-0200
  Houston *(G-11270)*

ELECTRICAL GOODS, WHOLESALE: Switches, Exc Electronic, NEC

Fujikoki America Inc ....C 214 333-4266
  Dallas *(G-4384)*

ELECTRICAL GOODS, WHOLESALE: Telephone & Telegraphic Eqpt

Dynamic Voice Data Inc ....F 800 838-5070
  Stafford *(G-19307)*

Krown Manufacturing Inc ....F 817 738-2485
  Fort Worth *(G-6774)*

Micheal J Arnold & Co ....F 979 742-3030
  Damon *(G-5213)*

ELECTRICAL GOODS, WHOLESALE: Telephone Eqpt

BBS Telecom LC ....G 512 328-9500
  Austin *(G-981)*

Forum Communications Systems ....F 972 619-8603
  Richardson *(G-17311)*

General Wreless Operations Inc ....C 800 843-7422
  Fort Worth *(G-6664)*

Nec Corporation of America ....E 214 262-2387
  Dallas *(G-4719)*

Telco Intercontinental Corp ....E 281 500-8270
  Houston *(G-12190)*

ELECTRICAL GOODS, WHOLESALE: Transformers

Alamo Transformer Supply Co ....E 713 991-6060
  Houston *(G-8526)*

Lufkin Armature Works Inc ....F 936 632-6607
  Lufkin *(G-14535)*

Sunbelt Transformer Ltd ....E 800 433-3128
  Temple *(G-19705)*

ELECTRICAL GOODS, WHOLESALE: Transformers

Border Assembly Inc ....E 915 592-1172
  El Paso *(G-5667)*

ELECTRICAL GOODS, WHOLESALE: Video Eqpt

Dobbs-Stanford Corporation ....E 214 350-4222
  Dallas *(G-4269)*

Logitech Inc ....D 512 347-9300
  Austin *(G-1298)*

ELECTRICAL GOODS, WHOLESALE: Wire & Cable

Guardian Insptn Tbular MGT LLC ....F 403 233-7561
  Midland *(G-15241)*

Interconnect Wiring LLP ....C 817 377-9473
  Fort Worth *(G-6723)*

Jdr Cable Systems Inc ....E 832 220-4690
  Houston *(G-10461)*

PC Cable Connexion Inc ....F 281 338-5400
  League City *(G-13974)*

Rsi Inc ....E 512 268-7500
  Kyle *(G-13686)*

ELECTRICAL GOODS, WHOLESALE: Wire & Cable, Ctrl & Sig

Galaxy Electronics Company ....F 972 234-0065
  Richardson *(G-17319)*

ELECTRICAL GOODS, WHOLESALE: Wire & Cable, Electronic

Gilmore-Global Instrs Co Inc ....F 713 946-9133
  Houston *(G-9958)*

Telco Intercontinental Corp ....E 281 500-8270
  Houston *(G-12190)*

ELECTRICAL GOODS, WHOLESALE: Wire/Cable, Telephone/Telegraph

Commscope Technologies LLC ....C 214 267-5900
  Richardson *(G-17289)*

ELECTRICAL MEASURING INSTRUMENT REPAIR & CALIBRATION SVCS

Gil Automations LLC ....F 713 904-4600
  Houston *(G-9957)*

M & M Meter Service Inc ....F 432 756-2801
  Stanton *(G-19403)*

ELECTRICAL SPLYS

Advanced Lightning Tech Ltd ....D 940 455-7300
  Argyle *(G-599)*

Beeco Motors & Controls Inc ....E 832 320-3100
  Houston *(G-8851)*

Border States Industries Inc ....E 432 332-0591
  Odessa *(G-15940)*

Border States Industries Inc ....F 432 520-0230
  Midland *(G-15147)*

Border States Industries Inc ....F 325 698-4595
  Abilene *(G-23)*

Border States Industries Inc ....F 512 458-6313
  Austin *(G-1001)*

Border States Industries Inc ....F 325 655-9163
  San Angelo *(G-17785)*

Border States Industries Inc ....E 806 457-4100
  Amarillo *(G-409)*

Border States Industries Inc ....F 806 765-5741
  Lubbock *(G-14379)*

Border States Industries Inc ....F 956 831-3441
  Brownsville *(G-2339)*

Border States Industries Inc ....F 575 434-2022
  El Paso *(G-5670)*

Crawford Electric Sup Co Inc ....E 512 593-4000
  Round Rock *(G-17638)*

Eaton Corporation ....E 713 849-1600
  Houston *(G-9572)*

Edwin Jones Company Inc ....G 214 361-4000
  Dallas *(G-4301)*

Elliott Electric Supply Inc ....E 210 646-6950
  San Antonio *(G-18088)*

Powell Electrical Systems Inc ....E 713 599-0324
  Houston *(G-11371)*

Powell Electrical Systems Inc ....E 281 452-4885
  Houston *(G-11374)*

Summit Electric Supply Co Inc ....E 325 691-9600
  Abilene *(G-85)*

Wesco International Inc ....F 432 699-2680
  Midland *(G-15469)*

ELECTRICAL SUPPLIES: Porcelain

Commscope Technologies LLC ....A 214 634-8502
  Dallas *(G-4149)*

Coorstek Inc ....F 432 381-0052
  Odessa *(G-15967)*

Texas Technical Ceramics Inc ....E 936 856-2903
  Willis *(G-20866)*

ELECTRODES: Indl Process

Analytical Sensors Instrs LLC ....D 281 565-8818
  Houston *(G-8636)*

ELECTRODES: Thermal & Electrolytic

Infrared Thermal Imaging Inc ....F 361 779-1197
  Kingsville *(G-13628)*

ELECTROMEDICAL EQPT

Actium Biosystems ....F 832 379-4222
  Houston *(G-8471)*

Argon Medical Devices Inc ....B 903 675-9321
  Athens *(G-819)*

Argon Medical Devices Inc ....B 903 675-9321
  Frisco *(G-7266)*

Avazzia Inc ....F 214 575-2820
  Dallas *(G-3990)*

Bio-Signal Technologies LLC ....F 214 405-0524
  McKinney *(G-14926)*

Ccmm Inc ....F 936 827-7930
  Mission *(G-15549)*

Eclipse Medcorp LLC ....D 800 759-6876
  Lewisville *(G-14047)*

Endocare Inc ....E 512 328-2892
  Austin *(G-1692)*

PRODUCT

Global Cardiac Monitors LLC ....F 281 788-7269
Houston (G-9966)
Healthtrnics MBL Solutions LLC ....D 866 598-2734
Austin (G-1695)
Natus Medical Incorporated..................E 650 802-0400
Flower Mound (G-6274)
Orthofix Inc ....C 214 937-2000
Lewisville (G-14077)
Quest Medical Inc ....C 800 627-0226
Allen (G-297)
Respiratory Technology Corp ....F 858 673-3700
Houston (G-11611)
Right Pathways LLC ....D 817 522-3600
Coppell (G-3439)
Volcano Corporation.............................F 210 582-5820
San Antonio (G-18599)

ELECTROMEDICAL EQPT WHOLESALERS

Electromedical Pdts Intl Inc ....E 940 328-0788
Mineral Wells (G-15525)
Merc Medical Supply Co Inc ....F 713 270-4936
Houston (G-10831)

ELECTROMETALLURGICAL PRDTS

Alloy Carbide Company ....E 713 923-2700
Houston (G-8556)

ELECTRON TUBES

Ludlum Measurements Inc....................D 325 235-1418
Sweetwater (G-19634)
Stellar Micro Devices Inc ....F 512 997-7781
Austin (G-1535)

ELECTRONIC DETECTION SYSTEMS:
Aeronautical

Rdrtec Incorporated ....E 214 353-8755
Dallas (G-4866)

ELECTRONIC EQPT REPAIR SVCS

Ewing Electronics Inc...........................F 469 519-2900
Allen (G-266)
Fusion Services Inc ....E 512 444-4283
Austin (G-1173)
LLC Battle Beaver..................................D 888 390-4363
Richardson (G-17346)
Media Displays Inc ....F 210 495-6338
San Antonio (G-18288)
Omron Electronics LLC..........................D 713 849-1900
Houston (G-11181)
Professionalized Pdts & Svcs................E 281 933-9427
Houston (G-11440)
Robert U Neese ....F 281 342-2884
Boerne (G-2134)
Schlumberger Rig Tech Inc...................D 713 849-1700
Houston (G-11771)
XI Technology LLC.................................F 972 369-1359
Wylie (G-20956)

ELECTRONIC LOADS & POWER SPLYS

Aees Inc ....D 210 491-2600
San Antonio (G-17871)
Compass Electronics Group LLC...........D 915 594-0500
El Paso (G-5701)

ELECTRONIC PARTS & EQPT WHOLESALERS

AMS Sensors USA Inc ....D 469 298-4252
Plano (G-16789)
Awesome Paging Inc ....G 361 576-2255
Victoria (G-20240)
Border States Industries Inc ....E 432 332-0591
Odessa (G-15940)
Border States Industries Inc ....F 432 520-0230
Midland (G-15147)
Border States Industries Inc ....F 325 698-4595
Abilene (G-23)
Border States Industries Inc ....F 512 458-6313
Austin (G-1001)
Border States Industries Inc ....F 325 655-9163
San Angelo (G-17785)
Border States Industries Inc ....E 806 457-4100
Amarillo (G-409)
Border States Industries Inc ....F 806 765-5741
Lubbock (G-14379)

Border States Industries Inc ....E 956 831-3441
Brownsville (G-2339)
Border States Industries Inc ....F 575 434-2022
El Paso (G-5670)
Bsu Inc ....E 607 272-8100
Austin (G-1013)
Electronic Drilling Control ....D 972 257-0322
Irving (G-13014)
Galaxy Electronics Company ....F 972 234-0065
Richardson (G-17319)
Ibe Smt Equipment Inc ....E 281 259-9660
Magnolia (G-14609)
Interntonal Resistive Texas LP ....C 361 992-7900
Corpus Christi (G-3555)
Link World Trade Inc ....C 972 713-8000
Addison (G-145)
Mach Speed Holdings LLC.....................D 214 978-3800
Plano (G-16917)
Pollok Inc ....A 915 592-5700
El Paso (G-5914)
Satellink Inc ....E 972 487-1434
Garland (G-7581)
Tascon Inc ....E 713 937-0900
Houston (G-12163)
Telecom Management Corp ....F 281 404-5610
Spring (G-19176)
Wolfson Microelectronics Inc ....B 408 329-9800
Austin (G-1675)

ELECTRONIC TRAINING DEVICES

L3 Technologies Inc ....A 817 619-4756
Arlington (G-713)
Vbi Group LLC ....E 817 533-3180
Arlington (G-808)

ELECTROPLATING & PLATING SVC

Schumacher International Inc................F 713 923-5548
Houston (G-11784)

ELEMENTARY & SECONDARY SCHOOLS, PUBLIC

Garland Independent School Dst ....D 972 494-8580
Garland (G-7494)

ELEMENTARY & SECONDARY SCHOOLS, SPECIAL EDUCATION

Cambium Learning Group Inc ....D 214 932-9500
Dallas (G-3839)
Journeyedcom Inc ....D 800 876-3507
Allen (G-280)

ELEVATORS & EQPT

Eklunds Inc ....E 817 949-2030
Southlake (G-19067)
National Elevator Company Inc ....E 925 484-5050
Flower Mound (G-6273)
OFlaherty Holdings Inc ....B 254 399-2100
Waco (G-20439)
Otis Elevator Company ....E 214 741-6207
Dallas (G-4772)
Tower Elevator Systems Inc ....F 512 266-6200
Round Rock (G-17696)

ELEVATORS WHOLESALERS

Alimak Group USA Inc...........................D 713 640-8500
Webster (G-20632)
Eklunds Inc ....E 817 949-2030
Southlake (G-19067)
Thyssenkrupp Elevator Corp.................F 512 486-1000
Austin (G-1578)
Thyssenkrupp Elevator Corp.................E 817 922-9590
Fort Worth (G-7062)

ELEVATORS: Installation & Conversion

Kone Inc...C 469 854-8861
Allen (G-283)
Thyssenkrupp Elevator Corp.................F 512 486-1000
Austin (G-1578)
Thyssenkrupp Elevator Corp.................E 817 922-9590
Fort Worth (G-7062)
Tower Elevator Systems Inc ....F 512 266-6200
Round Rock (G-17696)

EMBLEMS: Embroidered

Circle R Embroidery Co Inc ....E 214 741-1555
Dallas (G-4120)
Co Co MO Joes ....F 409 212-9892
Beaumont (G-1871)
Koza Inc ....E 281 485-1462
Pearland (G-16574)
Miller Uniforms & Emblems Inc ....E 512 302-5541
Austin (G-1345)
Powers Embroidery Inc ....D 254 754-2498
Waco (G-20448)
San Bay Studio Inc ....F 940 387-4466
Denton (G-5399)
Uniforms Inc ....F 214 630-0924
Dallas (G-5132)

EMBOSSING SVC: Paper

Barron Manufacturing Inc ....F 214 747-2544
Dallas (G-4007)
Embossed Graphics Inc ....F 713 667-0034
Houston (G-9608)
Prestige Embossing Company Inc..........E 713 864-0578
Houston (G-11411)

EMBROIDERING & ART NEEDLEWORK FOR THE TRADE

8228 Corporation ....E 713 465-1303
Houston (G-8417)
All Star Caps Inc ....F 210 509-9086
San Antonio (G-17893)
Bertrand Enterprises Inc.......................F 409 833-0922
Beaumont (G-1864)
Bobs Monogram Embroidery ....F 210 341-6700
San Antonio (G-17959)
Embroidery Concepts ....F 210 684-8362
San Antonio (G-18089)
Firestick Productions ....E 817 360-7740
Arlington (G-679)
G and G Investments Inc.......................E 325 949-7864
San Angelo (G-17801)
Ghashim Capital Ventures Corp ....F 713 266-1888
Houston (G-9949)
Hudsons Embroidery...............................E 210 224-5504
San Antonio (G-18175)
J Harding & Co ....F 713 862-9855
Houston (G-10440)
Jovi Printing ....F 713 467-4980
Houston (G-10485)
Monograms & More ....F 979 693-7773
College Station (G-3194)
Mooney Saenger Enterprises ....F 512 869-0979
Georgetown (G-7665)
North Lean Ltd ....F 956 781-2029
Pharr (G-16709)
Plano Sports Soccer Inc........................F 972 519-0222
Plano (G-16974)
Qti Promotions and Apparel Inc ....E 254 756-4444
Waco (G-20452)
Rivercity Sportswear LLC......................F 512 754-8039
San Marcos (G-18707)
Sasch Inc ....F 214 388-7000
Dallas (G-4935)
Stephenville Printing Company ....F 254 965-5012
Stephenville (G-19424)
Stitch Gallery Inc ....F 512 550-6172
Lakeway (G-13820)
Texas 28 LLC ....F 806 644-9663
Spearman (G-19088)

EMBROIDERING SVC

2logo Inc ....F 214 350-2505
Dallas (G-3866)
Action Screen Graphics ....F 512 478-6248
Austin (G-886)
Action Wear Plus Inc ....F 281 376-4300
Spring (G-19098)
Airmark Industries Inc ....E 325 641-1999
Brownwood (G-2424)
American Screen Graphics & EMB ....F 281 354-2581
Houston (G-8609)
Bear Paw Custom Embroidery LLC ....G 903 394-0722
Centerville (G-3011)
CC Creations Ltd....................................C 979 693-9664
College Station (G-3181)
Creative Stitches Inc.............................E 817 284-0061
Fort Worth (G-6559)
Custom Chenille Embroidery Inc ....E 214 343-0888
Dallas (G-4194)

Dbs Group Inc	F	817 453-8386
Grapevine (G-8026)		
Doyle & Hamilton Inc	F	817 882-8080
Fort Worth (G-6592)		
Dragonfly Garment Design Corp	G	830 549-5113
Seguin (G-18836)		
Graham Embroidery Co Inc	D	254 772-7020
Waco (G-20407)		
H & R Black Mfg Co LLC	F	806 364-2040
Hereford (G-8290)		
Innovative Impressions Inc	E	817 838-6466
Fort Worth (G-6721)		
Kingdom Captain of Texas LLC	F	210 535-9480
San Antonio (G-18226)		
Lamont Brands Inc	G	281 286-7553
Houston (G-10590)		
Lugra Inc	F	956 986-0958
Brownsville (G-2378)		
McAllen Sports Inc	E	956 687-5500
McAllen (G-14889)		
Pro Digi Embroidery	F	713 339-4373
Houston (G-11424)		
Screened Images Inc	F	979 260-9891
Bryan (G-2506)		
Sports Magic Inc	F	903 832-1975
Texarkana (G-19774)		
SRI Monogramming Inc	E	512 388-4989
Round Rock (G-17691)		
Stephenville Printing Company	E	254 968-3115
Stephenville (G-19425)		
Stitch Gallery Inc	F	956 412-3087
Harlingen (G-8203)		
Summit Sportswear Inc	G	281 335-5370
League City (G-13980)		
Tex Styles International Inc	E	713 787-9955
Stafford (G-19384)		
Texarkana EMB & Graphics	F	903 792-1144
Texarkana (G-19778)		
Texas 2 Stitch	F	972 599-1717
Plano (G-17028)		
Threads In Motion	F	972 422-4607
Plano (G-17032)		
Uniform Concepts Inc	E	512 345-5793
Austin (G-1607)		
Unlimited Custom Embroidery	F	713 773-0111
Houston (G-12470)		
Wearables Etc Inc	F	713 339-1373
Houston (G-12609)		

EMBROIDERING SVC: Schiffli Machine

Fiesta Graphics	F	956 546-1722
Brownsville (G-2356)		
Main Event Inc	G	281 762-0854
Rosenberg (G-17589)		

EMBROIDERY ADVERTISING SVCS

2logo Inc	F	214 350-2505
Dallas (G-3866)		
Cyclone Production Inc	F	713 979-1101
Houston (G-9384)		
Jackie Todaro	F	281 354-2581
Kingwood (G-13646)		
Kelly B Pitts Jr	F	713 923-5555
Houston (G-10513)		
Lamont Brands Inc	G	281 286-7553
Houston (G-10590)		
Lone Star Special Tees LLC	E	210 402-0091
San Antonio (G-18263)		
Lown Brothers Inc	E	915 594-4499
El Paso (G-5848)		
Powers Embroidery Inc	D	254 754-2498
Waco (G-20448)		
Sam Group Inc	F	817 481-1968
Grapevine (G-8053)		
SRI Monogramming Inc	E	512 388-4989
Round Rock (G-17691)		

EMERGENCY ALARMS

Ademco Inc	E	972 402-8612
Farmers Branch (G-6184)		
Ademco Inc	F	713 861-9418
Houston (G-8479)		
Ademco Inc	C	915 872-5542
El Paso (G-5637)		
Ademco Inc	D	915 875-0091
El Paso (G-5638)		
BI Technology Inc	E	832 698-8000
Tomball (G-19967)		

CF Industries Inc	E	214 460-2804
Lewisville (G-14035)		
Keylessco LLC	F	972 331-2773
Irving (G-13074)		
Ldia Holdings LLC	E	512 247-3700
Austin (G-1284)		
Medc International	D	713 937-9772
Houston (G-10816)		
National Circuit Assembly Inc	D	972 278-2009
Garland (G-7557)		
Securetech Systems Inc	F	817 869-0569
Irving (G-13174)		
Siemens Industry Inc	B	972 947-7000
Dallas (G-4959)		

EMERGENCY SHELTERS

Rising S Company LLC	E	214 455-0560
Murchison (G-15682)		

EMPLOYMENT AGENCY SVCS

Aim World Services Inc	E	281 847-2000
The Woodlands (G-19822)		
Bresa Tech LLC	F	866 728-2889
Plano (G-16811)		
Drake Alliance Corporation	D	713 869-9121
Houston (G-9514)		
Indochinese Culture Center	F	713 522-7799
Houston (G-10343)		
Stark Holdings Inc	F	512 329-8109
Austin (G-1531)		
Ultra Clean Technology Systems	C	512 252-6100
Austin (G-1606)		

EMPLOYMENT SVCS: Labor Contractors

Am-Mex Products Inc	E	956 631-7916
McAllen (G-14836)		
Lengston Corporation	F	713 757-1331
Houston (G-10623)		
Volks Resources LLC	F	972 636-1880
Frisco (G-7324)		

EMPLOYMENT SVCS: Ship Crew Registry

Control Flow Inc	C	281 890-8300
Houston (G-9295)		

ENAMELS

International Paint LLC	B	713 682-1711
Houston (G-10403)		
Picco Coatings Co	E	281 447-8877
Waller (G-20506)		

ENCLOSURES: Electronic

14703 Partners Industries LLC	F	281 847-0788
Houston (G 8402)		
Buferd Company Inc	D	972 272-9502
Garland (G-7451)		
Delta Electronics (usa) Inc	C	469 330-9100
Plano (G-16837)		
Emf Company Inc	D	214 350-6848
Dallas (G-4319)		
Moffitt West LLC	E	972 298-0531
Duncanville (G-5535)		
Rittal Corp	F	937 399-0500
Houston (G-11626)		

ENCLOSURES: Screen

Smpl Inc	E	402 525-5078
Austin (G-1513)		
Texas Aluminum Industries Inc	B	713 941-7186
Houston (G-12220)		

ENCODERS: Digital

Riso Inc	F	800 942-7476
Carrollton (G-2808)		
Sat-Lite Technologies Ltd	F	903 295-3400
White Oak (G-20719)		

ENERGY MEASUREMENT EQPT

Distributed Pwr Solutions LLC	E	877 291-3354
Pearland (G-16556)		

ENGINE PARTS & ACCESS: Internal Combustion

Enduro Products Inc	E	817 704-7346
Arlington (G-670)		
Quaint Slutions Trdg Ltd Lblty	F	832 758-3074
Rosenberg (G-17597)		
Quality Trbchrger Cmpnents LLC	E	713 849-4200
Houston (G-11502)		
Texas Environmental Tech LLC	G	817 534-4275
Fort Worth (G-7047)		

ENGINE REBUILDING: Diesel

Engine Service Inc	F	713 473-4167
South Houston (G-19038)		
Tom Daenen Inc	E	409 978-2132
Hitchcock (G-8340)		
Winnsboro Spclty Prts Intl Inc	E	903 342-3551
Winnsboro (G-20902)		

ENGINEERING HELP SVCS

Flowserve Corporation	E	832 375-0807
Houston (G-9813)		
Gps International LLC	F	832 319-1730
The Woodlands (G-19870)		
Viceroy Inc	E	713 475-4518
Pasadena (G-16524)		

ENGINEERING SVCS

Accurate Control Company LLC	E	713 699-3799
Houston (G-8461)		
Advanced Fabric Tech LLC	F	281 872-7272
Spring (G-19191)		
Advanced Telesensors Inc	F	888 292-2208
Austin (G-895)		
Airborn Interconnect Inc	B	512 863-5585
Georgetown (G-7633)		
Aker Solutions Inc	C	713 685-5700
Houston (G-8519)		
Allamon Tool Company Inc	E	936 449-5433
Montgomery (G-15625)		
Allosense Inc	G	830 900-3080
San Antonio (G-17898)		
Amacs Process Tower Internals	F	713 434-0934
Houston (G-8372)		
Amec Foster Wheeler USA Corp	E	713 929-5000
Houston (G-8578)		
Astro Technology Inc	F	281 464-0100
Houston (G-8731)		
Atlantic Blowers LLC	F	214 233-0280
Dallas (G-3979)		
Bgi Contractors Inc	C	409 833-0303
Port Arthur (G-17102)		
Bgi Enterprise Inc	E	409 833-0303
Beaumont (G-1865)		
Broadcast Technical Svcs Inc	F	832 467-0002
Houston (G-8988)		
Bsu Inc	E	607 272-8100
Austin (G-1013)		
Camac International Corp	E	713 965-5100
Houston (G-9059)		
Cambrian Management Ltd	F	432 620-9181
Midland (G-15156)		
Cimarron Software Services Inc	E	281 226-5100
Houston (G-9190)		
Commscope Technologies LLC	C	214 267-5900
Richardson (G-17289)		
Corrpro Companies Inc	C	713 460-6000
Houston (G-9325)		
Criteria Labs Inc	E	512 637-4500
Austin (G-1073)		
Dixon Services Inc	F	903 579-9300
Tyler (G-20077)		
Downstream Aggregator LLC	E	281 247-8118
Channelview (G-3017)		
Econtrols Group Inc	E	210 495-9772
San Antonio (G-18082)		
Electronic Technical Svcs Corp	E	281 446-4414
Humble (G-12765)		
Energy Facility Services Inc	F	281 286-8500
Houston (G-9634)		
Engineering Spectrum Inc	E	210 697-8828
San Antonio (G-18090)		
Evoleap LLC	F	832 371-6677
Houston (G-9719)		
Evolve Holdings Inc	E	832 375-0099
Houston (G-9720)		
Exceed Drilling Tech LLC	F	512 656-9669
Austin (G-1144)		

Employee Codes: A=Over 500 employees, B=251-500
C=101-250, D=51-100, E=20-50, F=10-19, G=9

2021 Harris Texas
Manufacturers Directory

1483

PRODUCT

Exterran Energy Solutions LP ....C...... 281 836-7000
Houston (G-9736)
Exyte Americas Holding Inc..................E...... 972 535-7300
Plano (G-16868)
Fabrication Unlimited Inc.....................E...... 713 433-6401
Houston (G-9750)
Flameout LLC ....F...... 713 984-8310
Houston (G-9796)
Four Pnts Pltnum Invstmnts LLC ....F...... 512 588-7916
Pflugerville (G-16673)
Freeman & Curiel Engineers LLP ....E...... 713 895-8668
Houston (G-9861)
Ftg Aerospace Inc ....D...... 817 332-3806
Fort Worth (G-6650)
Ghg Corp ....B...... 281 461-6533
Webster (G-20638)
Halliburton Delaware Inc ....D...... 713 759-2600
Houston (G-10108)
High-Tech Fabrication Inc ....E...... 281 351-0882
Tomball (G-19981)
Hunting Innova Inc ....B...... 281 653-5500
Houston (G-10284)
Hydraquip Custom Systems Inc ....F...... 281 822-5000
Houston (G-10296)
Hydro Conduit of Texas LP ....E...... 832 590-5300
Houston (G-10303)
Impac Systems Engineering LLP ....F...... 713 784-3500
Temple (G-19682)
Industrial Cmmssning Cons Intl............F...... 833 873-4224
La Marque (G-13708)
Information Store Inc ....F...... 713 787-6798
Houston (G-10358)
International Plant Svcs LLC ....B...... 281 867-8400
La Porte (G-13755)
Ios Inspection ....E...... 432 684-6440
Midland (G-15255)
ITW Blding Cmponents Group Inc ....E...... 972 660-4422
Grand Prairie (G-7897)
JAS Marketing Inc.................................F...... 281 879-1844
Channelview (G-3027)
Jelec Inc...E...... 713 977-6500
Houston (G-10464)
Jgc Energy Development USA Inc ....F...... 832 487-9965
Houston (G-10473)
JV Industrial Companies Ltd ....F...... 903 579-8900
Tyler (G-20105)
Keane Frac Tx LLC ....F...... 713 960-0381
Houston (G-10507)
L3 Technologies Inc.............................A...... 903 457-4100
Greenville (G-8080)
L3harris Technologies Inc ....A...... 903 457-7461
Greenville (G-8081)
Legerity Holdings Inc ....C...... 512 228-5400
Austin (G-1288)
Liberty A&A ....F...... 213 221-8110
San Antonio (G-18251)
Lindsayca Inc ....D...... 713 467-9560
Houston (G-10646)
M-I LLC ....B...... 281 561-1300
Houston (G-10725)
Marelli Automotive Ltg USA LLC ....F...... 915 872-1104
El Paso (G-5864)
Marine Computation Svcs Kenny...........D...... 281 646-4155
Houston (G-10764)
Marlin Environmental Products ....F...... 214 493-9128
Richardson (G-17351)
McDermott International Inc ....B...... 281 588-6600
Houston (G-10810)
National Oilwell Varco Inc ....D...... 409 842-2114
Beaumont (G-1933)
Neotek Energy Inc................................F...... 469 206-3344
Plano (G-16942)
Oceaneering International Inc ....C...... 713 329-4500
Houston (G-11124)
Oceaneering International Inc ....F...... 713 329-4318
Houston (G-11126)
Oil Field Dev Engrg LLC ....D...... 281 679-9060
Houston (G-11151)
Pennar Global Inc ....F...... 281 362-2707
The Woodlands (G-19900)
Petrotrim Services LLC ....E...... 281 821-2111
Humble (G-12793)
Piping Technology & Pdts Inc ....A...... 800 787-5914
Houston (G-11338)
Powell Electrical Systems Inc ....E...... 281 452-4885
Houston (G-11374)
Purvis Industries LLC ....D...... 214 358-5500
Dallas (G-4837)
R C Technical Welding & Fabr ....E...... 281 933-6004
Stafford (G-19367)

Romeo Engineering Incorporated ....E...... 817 656-0048
Fort Worth (G-6966)
Sabine Mining Company ....C...... 903 660-4200
Hallsville (G-8130)
Sam and Sab Inc ....E...... 713 983-7500
Houston (G-11736)
Signal Metal Industries Inc ....C...... 972 438-1022
Irving (G-13179)
SPEP Acquisition Corp ....F...... 310 608-0693
Lancaster (G-13848)
Systems Integration Inc ....E...... 817 468-1494
Arlington (G-790)
Talon/Lpe Ltd ....D...... 806 467-0607
Amarillo (G-466)
Test Spectrum Inc ....E...... 512 472-6750
Austin (G-1564)
Texas Global Systems Inc ....D...... 832 403-4238
Houston (G-12233)
Tokyo Electron America Inc ....E...... 512 424-1000
Austin (G-1584)
Tokyo Electron America Inc ....B...... 512 424-1000
Austin (G-1583)
United Marine Enterprise Inc ....D...... 409 833-0303
Beaumont (G-1965)
Vector Group Inc ....F...... 713 979-4444
Houston (G-12542)
Vectornav Technologies LLC ....F...... 512 772-3615
Dallas (G-5157)
Vision Systems Intl LLC ....F...... 817 234-6600
Fort Worth (G-7107)
Welbor Technology Inc ....F...... 713 980-2345
Houston (G-12627)
Williamsrdm Inc ....D...... 817 872-1500
Fort Worth (G-7148)

ENGINEERING SVCS: Aviation Or Aeronautical

Bastion Technologies Inc......................E...... 281 283-9330
Houston (G-8823)
Boeing Company ....A...... 281 244-4000
Houston (G-8942)
Gulfstream Aerospace Corp GA ....A...... 214 350-4177
Dallas (G-4424)
Lockheed Martin Corporation ....C...... 956 425-4447
Harlingen (G-8193)

ENGINEERING SVCS: Building Construction

Cdw Consultant Group LLC...................E...... 361 237-9339
Bloomington (G-2111)
Fabco LLC ....D...... 713 633-6500
Houston (G-9745)
Industrotech Inc ....F...... 817 847-1358
Fort Worth (G-6719)

ENGINEERING SVCS: Chemical

Fts International Services LLC ....F...... 817 334-0002
Fort Worth (G-6654)
Fts International Services LLC ....C...... 817 862-2000
Fort Worth (G-6655)
Haldor Topsoe Inc ....C...... 281 228-5000
Houston (G-10094)
Loco Solutions LLC ....D...... 817 437-6438
Amarillo (G-498)
Westfield Engrg & Svcs Inc ....E...... 281 438-2047
Houston (G-8397)

ENGINEERING SVCS: Civil

Hart Engineering Company ....E...... 903 758-0166
Longview (G-14247)

ENGINEERING SVCS: Construction & Civil

Cemex Construction Mtls S LLC ....D...... 830 608-3556
New Braunfels (G-15779)
Chippenhook Corporation ....E...... 800 527-5866
Lewisville (G-14036)
Ctc Inc ....E...... 817 886-8210
Fort Worth (G-6564)
Industrial Spclty Svcs USA LLC ....F...... 713 987-9117
Deer Park (G-5280)
Ism Industries Inc ....D...... 409 769-7841
Vidor (G-20327)
JV Industrial Companies Ltd ....D...... 713 568-2600
San Antonio (G-18213)
Wright Landscaping & Cnst LLC ....E...... 254 213-3912
Killeen (G-13618)
Zachry Holdings Inc ....A...... 210 588-5000
San Antonio (G-18632)

ENGINEERING SVCS: Electrical Or Electronic

Hiller Measurements Inc.......................C...... 512 394-8356
Austin (G-863)
Iondesign Inc ....F...... 512 260-5778
Jonestown (G-13315)
Keynote Technologies LLC ....F...... 877 528-4747
Allen (G-282)
L3 Technologies Inc.............................C...... 972 722-7927
Rockwall (G-17553)
Moore Control Systems Inc ....D...... 281 392-7747
Katy (G-13372)
Omni Flow Computers Inc ....F...... 281 240-6161
Sugar Land (G-19522)
Orbital Energy Group Inc ....E...... 832 467-1420
Houston (G-11190)
RMS Solutions Group LLC ....F...... 469 964-7127
Point (G-17080)
Sdrg Controls Inc ....F...... 713 242-0822
Houston (G-11794)
Telecore Inc ....E...... 972 238-9000
Richardson (G-17405)
Virtex Assembly Services Inc ....D...... 512 835-6772
Austin (G-1635)

ENGINEERING SVCS: Fire Protection

Williams Fire Hazard Ctrl Inc ....E...... 409 745-3232
Port Arthur (G-17133)

ENGINEERING SVCS: Heating & Ventilation

Convergentz Bldg Systems LLC ....E...... 713 266-3900
Houston (G-9297)
Enrud Resources Inc ....F...... 713 943-1600
Pasadena (G-16429)

ENGINEERING SVCS: Industrial

Chicago Bridge & Iron Co Del ....C...... 832 513-1000
Houston (G-9183)
Dyna Therm Corporation ....F...... 832 616-3094
The Woodlands (G-19856)
Enerflex Services Inc ....E...... 281 345-9300
Houston (G-9633)
Glex Inc ....E...... 713 849-4985
Houston (G-9965)
Pangea Enterprises Inc ....E...... 956 542-9494
Houston (G-11232)

ENGINEERING SVCS: Machine Tool Design

Doosan Turbomachinery Svcs Inc ....D...... 713 364-7500
La Porte (G-13731)
Highwood Machine Tool LLC ....F...... 254 412-0512
Waco (G-20411)

ENGINEERING SVCS: Marine

Deep Down Inc ....D...... 281 517-5000
Houston (G-9420)
Dnv GL Noble Denton Usa LLC ....B...... 281 396-1000
Katy (G-13396)
Saipem America Inc ....C...... 281 552-5600
Houston (G-11732)

ENGINEERING SVCS: Mechanical

Avant Technology Inc ....D...... 512 651-5300
Pflugerville (G-16660)
Enhanced Production Tech Inc ....G...... 512 759-2009
Hutto (G-12878)
Quality Fabrication Design LP ....D...... 972 304-3266
Coppell (G-3436)
Radix Us LLC ....E...... 832 377-9601
Houston (G-11532)
Technip S&W International Inc ....E...... 281 870-1111
Houston (G-12175)

ENGINEERING SVCS: Petroleum

Atlantia Offshore Limited ....D...... 281 899-4300
Houston (G-8737)
Clementson Inc ....E...... 956 631-9121
McAllen (G-14848)
Dewbre Petroleum Corporation ....F...... 361 888-7978
Corpus Christi (G-3512)
Fesco Ltd ....F...... 361 575-7533
Victoria (G-20263)
Fesco Ltd ....E...... 409 842-3000
Beaumont (G-1893)

Fesco Ltd ....E 361 526-4644
Refugio *(G-17241)*
GSM Enterprises Inc ....E 806 358-6894
Amarillo *(G-430)*
Kiva Construction & Engrg Inc ....E 409 252-3211
Anahuac *(G-526)*
Noble Drilling Corporation ....B 281 276-6100
Sugar Land *(G-19514)*
Octane Energy Consulting LLC ....F 432 685-7736
Midland *(G-15324)*
Parker Petroleum Pros Inc ....F 903 360-5450
Grand Saline *(G-7998)*
Petroleum Engineers Intl ....E 337 984-2603
Houston *(G-11306)*
Walsh Petroleum Inc ....E 432 684-5937
Midland *(G-15464)*

ENGINEERING SVCS: Pollution Control

Epcon Industrial Systems LP ....D 936 273-1774
Shenandoah *(G-18896)*
Gulf Coast Envmtl Systems LLC ....E 832 476-9024
Conroe *(G-3299)*
Pollution System Solutions Inc ....F 713 574-6661
Spring *(G-19241)*
Polsys Services Inc ....F 713 999-1100
The Woodlands *(G-19903)*

ENGINEERING SVCS: Professional

Automation Solutions LP ....E 281 286-6017
Houston *(G-8754)*
Detail Design Inc ....E 281 890-4715
Houston *(G-9444)*
Kellogg Brown & Root Intl Inc ....F 713 753-2000
Houston *(G-10512)*
Microbes Inc ....E 281 367-7500
The Woodlands *(G-19894)*
Modec International Inc ....B 281 529-8100
Houston *(G-10902)*
Phase Dynamics Inc ....E 972 680-1550
Richardson *(G-17372)*
Professionalized Pdts & Svcs ....E 281 933-9427
Houston *(G-11440)*

ENGINEERING SVCS: Structural

Coperion Corporation ....F 281 449-9944
Houston *(G-9309)*
Sentech Archtctral Systems LLC ....E 512 266-7045
Austin *(G-1494)*

ENGINES: Diesel & Semi-Diesel Or Duel Fuel

Caterpillar Inc ....A 309 675-1000
Waco *(G-20377)*
Cummins Inc ....F 915 858-7310
El Paso *(G-5708)*

ENGINES: Gasoline, NEC

American Air Liquide Inc ....E 877 855-9533
Houston *(G-8582)*
Natural Gas Vehicles Texas Inc ....F 214 630-1000
Dallas *(G-4717)*

ENGINES: Internal Combustion, NEC

Cameron International Corp ....C 713 354-1900
Houston *(G-9068)*
Clearvlue Combustn Systems Inc ....F 281 261-9543
Missouri City *(G-15578)*
Cummins - Allison Corp ....F 972 661-5390
Dallas *(G-4192)*
Cummins Diesel Fuel Inc ....C 915 858-7310
El Paso *(G-5706)*
Cummins Inc ....E 915 791-6600
El Paso *(G-5707)*
Cummins Jrez Emission Solution ....D 844 401-0221
El Paso *(G-5709)*
Cummins Southern Plains LLC ....E 806 373-3793
Amarillo *(G-419)*
Cummins Southern Plains LLC ....E 817 624-2107
Fort Worth *(G-6566)*
Cummins Southern Plains LLC ....F 432 332-9121
Odessa *(G-15973)*
Cummins Southern Plains LLC ....E 512 389-2276
Austin *(G-1077)*
Cummins Southern Plains LLC ....E 817 640-6801
Arlington *(G-653)*
Cummins Southern Plains LLC ....C 713 679-2220
Houston *(G-9358)*

Harbor Engine & Grinding Inc ....F 361 882-1571
Corpus Christi *(G-3545)*
John H Sorola Inc ....F 210 224-8597
San Antonio *(G-18204)*
Nickens Brothers Racing Engs ....F 936 441-1131
Conroe *(G-3342)*
Stewart Stevenson Pwr Pdts LLC ....C 504 347-4326
Houston *(G-12064)*

ENGINES: Jet Propulsion

Pratt Whtney Line Mint Svcs In ....G 972 894-0139
Dallas *(G-4817)*

ENGINES: Steam

Hpi LLC ....E 713 457-7500
Houston *(G-10272)*

ENGRAVING SVC, NEC

Cynco Specialty Inc ....G 281 499-0519
Stafford *(G-19298)*
Deq Coatings Inc ....F 713 645-1777
Houston *(G-9438)*
Lobues Rubber Stamp Co ....F 713 652-0031
Houston *(G-10661)*

ENGRAVING SVCS

Ashcraft-Southern Marble Co ....E 903 581-5501
Tyler *(G-20049)*
Carrion Enterprises Inc ....F 915 593-1338
El Paso *(G-5686)*
Crystal Images Inc ....F 972 438-2337
Irving *(G-12985)*
Drsk Limited Partnership ....F 972 644-1490
Richardson *(G-17302)*
Firmin Business Forms Inc ....F 254 776-5742
Waco *(G-20402)*
Marfield Inc ....E 972 245-9122
Carrollton *(G-2778)*
Sign Technologies Inc ....F 903 838-8999
Texarkana *(G-19773)*
Stamp Shop Inc ....F 210 824-7373
San Antonio *(G-18495)*

ENGRAVING: Bank Note

Alvin J Bart & Sons Inc ....C 718 417-1300
Addison *(G-103)*

ENGRAVINGS: Plastic

JRS Company Inc ....D 626 967-2432
Hutto *(G-12881)*

ENTERTAINERS & ENTERTAINMENT GROUPS

Yoyo Management Inc ....G 512 447-1455
Austin *(G-1684)*

ENTERTAINMENT SVCS

Claudia Rodriguez ....F 956 381-0845
Edinburg *(G-5583)*
Jahkur International LLC ....E 832 431-3232
Houston *(G-10450)*

ENVELOPES

Blumbergexcelsior Inc ....E 817 462-1530
Arlington *(G-632)*
Cenveo Worldwide Limited ....C 972 729-5700
Dallas *(G-4102)*
Eric Industries Inc ....E 972 248-8009
Dallas *(G-3841)*
Goelzer Industries Inc ....D 214 524-6700
Grand Prairie *(G-7883)*
Motion Envelope Inc ....E 214 634-2131
Dallas *(G-4690)*
Nev Holdings LLC ....A 972 731-1100
Frisco *(G-7301)*
R R Donnelley & Sons Company ....D 972 353-6130
Lewisville *(G-14086)*
Signature Envelope Company Inc ....F 713 538-1177
Coldspring *(G-3167)*
Texas Envelope Company ....E 214 358-5661
Dallas *(G-5060)*

ENVELOPES WHOLESALERS

Cenveo Worldwide Limited ....C 972 729-5700
Dallas *(G-4102)*

ENZYMES

Dicqie M Fuller Looney ....F 713 266-2117
Houston *(G-9465)*

EPOXY RESINS

Shell Oil Company ....A 713 241-6161
Houston *(G-11860)*

EQUIPMENT & VEHICLE FINANCE LEASING COMPANIES

General Electric Company ....G 325 794-5100
Abilene *(G-43)*
General Electric Company ....E 281 921-2850
Houston *(G-9922)*

EQUIPMENT: Pedestrian Traffic Control

Buyers Barricades Houston LLC ....E 817 535-3939
Grapevine *(G-8017)*
City of Arlington ....A 817 459-5700
Arlington *(G-644)*
Pathmark Traffic Equipment LLC ....E 512 392-2090
San Marcos *(G-18702)*
Traffic Supply Inc ....F 979 234-5509
Eagle Lake *(G-5545)*

EQUIPMENT: Rental & Leasing, NEC

Airgas Usa LLC ....F 512 835-0202
Austin *(G-902)*
Ambar Inc ....C 281 873-7600
Houston *(G-8576)*
American Grand Stand Inc ....F 214 638-7007
Dallas *(G-3942)*
Aquila Environmental LLC ....G 817 953-3171
Fort Worth *(G-6397)*
Big D Equipment Company Ltd ....D 432 682-1664
Midland *(G-15139)*
Boatman Industries Inc ....E 713 641-6006
Houston *(G-8932)*
Boxx Modular Inc ....F 972 492-4040
Fort Worth *(G-6464)*
Century Elevators Inc ....E 281 667-3000
Webster *(G-20635)*
Csi Compressco Sub Inc ....E 361 576-6827
Victoria *(G-20256)*
Delta Rigging & Tools Inc ....C 713 512-1700
Houston *(G-9433)*
Diamond Tank Rental Inc ....E 432 337-0011
Odessa *(G-15976)*
Dollar B R Sr Et Al A TX Ptnr ....D 940 665-6262
Gainesville *(G-7342)*
Draeger Safety Diagnostics Inc ....E 972 929-1100
Irving *(G-13003)*
Fastorq Bolting Systems Inc ....F 281 449-6466
New Caney *(G-15839)*
Flo Pura Corp ....E 281 320-9547
Spring *(G-19122)*
Gem Services LLP ....E 210 863-2020
McAllen *(G-14865)*
Griffin Dewatering LLC ....E 713 676-8000
Houston *(G-10044)*
Hoover Group Inc ....E 800 844-8683
Houston *(G-10204)*
J D Fields & Company Inc ....E 281 558-7199
Houston *(G-10437)*
Josephine Tug Inc ....E 409 744-1222
Galveston *(G-7402)*
Main Marine Repair Inc ....F 713 645-3553
Houston *(G-10740)*
Modern Group Ltd ....D 800 231-8198
Beaumont *(G-1930)*
New Ventures Leasing LLC ....F 940 577-7789
Bowie *(G-2198)*
Oil States Energy Services LLC ....E 432 563-1304
Midland *(G-15326)*
Paramount Rental Services LLC ....F 940 264-8379
Wichita Falls *(G-20793)*
Pipeline Inspection Company ....E 713 681-5837
Houston *(G-11335)*
Polsys Services Inc ....F 713 999-1100
The Woodlands *(G-19903)*
Post Up Town Inc ....G 214 965-6565
Dallas *(G-4814)*

PRODUCT

Six & Mango Equipment LLP ....E 972 335-2731
Frisco *(G-7312)*
Speakermax Inc ....F 281 880-9922
Houston *(G-11995)*
Stabil Drill Specialties LLC ....E 281 583-0127
Houston *(G-12034)*

ESCALATORS: Passenger & Freight

Kone Inc ....C 469 854-8861
Allen *(G-283)*

ETCHING & ENGRAVING SVC

High Plins Cntrs MGT Group Inc ....E 806 935-5858
Dumas *(G-5522)*
Lehmberg Enterprises Inc..................F 210 924-6811
San Antonio *(G-18244)*
Recon Coating Solutions LLC ....F 979 277-8455
Alvord *(G-390)*
Trinity Coatings LLC ....F 281 845-0022
Rosharon *(G-17615)*

ETCHING SVC: Metal

T G Industries Inc.............................F 281 356-2001
Pinehurst *(G-16735)*

ETCHING SVC: Photochemical

Harris Manufacturing Company ....E 972 262-3524
Mansfield *(G-14680)*

ETHYLENE

Equistar Chemicals LP ....E 281 474-4040
Pasadena *(G-16430)*
Huntsman Corporation ....E 281 719-6000
The Woodlands *(G-19877)*
Huntsman International LLC ....D 281 719-6000
The Woodlands *(G-19878)*
Ineos Oligomers USA LLC ....E 281 581-3203
Alvin *(G-366)*
Occidental Petroleum Corp................G 325 574-8567
Ira *(G-12913)*
Occidental Petroleum Corp................E 713 640-7500
Houston *(G-11117)*
Westlake Chemical Partners LP ....F 713 585-2900
Houston *(G-12648)*
Westlake Olefins Corporation.............E 713 960-9111
Houston *(G-12651)*
Westlake Polymers LLC ....C 713 960-9111
Houston *(G-12652)*
Wpt LLC ....E 713 960-9111
Houston *(G-12698)*

ETHYLENE OXIDE

Union Carbide Corporation.................D 713 849-7000
Houston *(G-12435)*
Union Carbide Corporation.................B 281 966-2727
Houston *(G-12434)*

ETHYLENE-PROPYLENE RUBBERS: EPDM Polymers

E I Du Pont De Nemours & Co ....D 361 572-1330
Victoria *(G-20259)*
General Polymer Services LLC............E 281 424-4673
Baytown *(G-1818)*
General Polymer Services LLC............D 281 424-4673
Baytown *(G-1819)*
Habitek International Inc ....C 512 347-8800
Austin *(G-1196)*
Jenkem Technology USA Inc ....F 972 673-0603
Plano *(G-16899)*
Nucera Solutions LLC ....E 281 275-7473
Sugar Land *(G-19520)*
Nukote Coating Systems Intl ....E 832 770-7100
Houston *(G-11098)*
Polyspec (tx) LLC..............................F 281 397-0033
Houston *(G-11361)*
Univar Solutions USA Inc ....E 281 297-0678
Spring *(G-19261)*
Vertec Polymers Inc ....F 866 283-7832
Houston *(G-12555)*

EXCAVATING EQPT

Ken Garner Mfg - Vto Inc ....F 361 485-0541
Victoria *(G-20280)*
Kobelco Construction McHy USA ....E 281 684-8761
Katy *(G-13419)*

EXERCISE EQPT STORES

Promaxima Manufacturing Ltd ....D 800 231-6652
Houston *(G-11446)*
Quantum Fitness Corporation...............D 281 495-3003
Sugar Land *(G-19531)*

EXHAUST SYSTEMS: Eqpt & Parts

D & D Performance Enterprises ....E 817 834-8961
Fort Worth *(G-6569)*
L & L Products Inc ....F 972 475-5202
Rowlett *(G-17709)*
Maremont Exhaust Products Inc ....C 865 458-4681
Schulenburg *(G-18776)*

EXPLOSIVES

Austin Powder Company ....E 817 371-6147
Covington *(G-3694)*
Austin Powder Company ....E 940 644-5771
Chico *(G-3050)*
Austin Powder Company ....G 512 863-3676
Georgetown *(G-7638)*
Austin Powder Company ....F 940 382-4111
Denton *(G-5352)*
El Dorado Chemical Company..............C 254 445-2720
Dublin *(G-5516)*
Geodynamics Inc ....C 817 341-5300
Millsap *(G-15502)*
Halliburton Company ....C 817 783-5111
Alvarado *(G-333)*
Harrison Jet Guns II LP ....D 817 478-9216
Kennedale *(G-13497)*
La Blanc Bob ....E 972 492-1898
Carrollton *(G-2876)*
Maxam North America Inc ....F 801 233-6000
Irving *(G-13097)*

EXPLOSIVES, EXC AMMO & FIREWORKS WHOLESALERS

Austin Powder Company ....E 940 644-5771
Chico *(G-3050)*
Austin Powder Company ....G 512 863-3676
Georgetown *(G-7638)*
Maxam North America Inc ....F 801 233-6000
Irving *(G-13097)*

EXPLOSIVES, FUSES & DETONATORS: Primary explosives

Expal USA Inc....................................E 903 472-4970
Irving *(G-13020)*

EXPLOSIVES: Well Shooting Torpedoes

Owen Oil Tools LP ....C 817 551-0540
Godley *(G-7738)*

EXTERMINATING & FUMIGATING SVCS

G G A Inc...F 254 732-1701
Waco *(G-20405)*

EXTRACTS, FLAVORING

Van Tone Creative Flavors Inc ....E 972 563-2600
Terrell *(G-19754)*

EXTRUDED SHAPES, NEC: Copper & Copper Alloy

Copper Craft Inc................................E 817 490-9622
Fort Worth *(G-6549)*

EYEGLASSES

Essilor Laboratories Amer Inc..............E 713 663-3000
Houston *(G-9702)*
Essilor Laboratories Amer Inc..............B 972 241-4141
Dallas *(G-4332)*
Omega Optical Co LP ....F 972 241-4141
Dallas *(G-4760)*
Ragsdale Vision Ctr ....F 940 387-9595
Denton *(G-5396)*
Visionworks of America Inc ....A 800 669-1183
San Antonio *(G-18596)*

EYELASHES, ARTIFICIAL

Xtreme Lashes LLC ....E 281 907-0689
Spring *(G-19189)*

FABRICATED METAL PRODUCTS, NEC

Advanced Industrial Metal Fabr............F 940 964-2691
Forestburg *(G-6299)*
Aquamarine Power Usa LLC.................F 972 606-2912
Grand Prairie *(G-7833)*
C Bar Contractors I Ltd ....F 409 925-5757
Hitchcock *(G-8334)*
Double Barrel Fabrication Inc...............F 512 496-7448
San Angelo *(G-17796)*
Form and Fiber Inc.............................F 888 314-8852
Gun Barrel City *(G-8114)*
Seabreeze Culvert..............................F 409 296-4675
Winnie *(G-20891)*

FABRICS & CLOTH: Quilted

Bronx Industries Inc ....G 713 467-6155
Houston *(G-8994)*

FABRICS & CLOTHING: Rubber Coated

GP Rubber LP....................................E 817 838-8222
Haltom City *(G-8143)*

FABRICS: Acrylic, Broadwoven

Sani-Safe Products Inc ....F 210 826-1344
San Antonio *(G-18451)*

FABRICS: Apparel & Outerwear, Cotton

Censored Soles...................................F 832 443-4365
Houston *(G-9135)*
Climax Investors LLC ....E 832 582-9622
Dallas *(G-4130)*
Comfy Choice LLC..............................D 972 302-8094
Plano *(G-16828)*
J Lewis Partners LP ....A 972 702-7390
Dallas *(G-4519)*
Logo Masters LLC..............................F 830 822-8390
San Antonio *(G-18262)*
N 2 The World ....E 817 424-0799
Grapevine *(G-8046)*
V Respect ....G 281 780-6267
Houston *(G-12511)*
Vaign Designer Street AP LLC ....E 832 490-8510
Rosenberg *(G-17599)*
Wolf & Sons Design Inc.......................E 512 237-3388
Smithville *(G-18979)*

FABRICS: Apparel & Outerwear, From Manmade Fiber Or Silk

Ortegas Custom Interiors Inc ....F 214 341-4003
Dallas *(G-4769)*

FABRICS: Blankets & Blanketing, Wool Or Similar Fibers

Ingrids Custom Hand Woven ....F 325 732-4370
Paint Rock *(G-16291)*

FABRICS: Bonded-Fiber, Exc Felt

E R Carpenter LP ....C 804 359-0800
Temple *(G-19680)*
Hobbs Bonded Fibers LLC...................E 254 741-0040
Waco *(G-20412)*
Hobbs Bonded Fibers Na LLC..............D 254 741-0040
Waco *(G-20413)*

FABRICS: Broad Woven, Goods, Cotton

Mount Vernon Mills Inc ....C 361 275-2393
Cuero *(G-3764)*

FABRICS: Broadwoven, Cotton

East Txas Lighthouse For Blind............D 903 595-3444
Tyler *(G-20082)*
Fiberco Inc ....F 682 647-1332
Fort Worth *(G-6628)*
Levan Group I LP ....F 713 528-3838
Houston *(G-10628)*
Medline Industries Inc ....C 281 574-6200
Katy *(G-13371)*
Mount Vernon Mills Inc ....B 979 836-5255
Brenham *(G-2265)*

FABRICS: Broadwoven, Synthetic Manmade Fiber & Silk

Best Made Designs LLC ....E 432 943-9995
Monahans (G-15600)
Hallwood Group Incorporated ....E 214 528-5588
Dallas (G-4430)
Kerick Industries ....F 214 432-2446
Dallas (G-4552)
Liftex Corporation ....E 713 863-0900
Houston (G-10639)
Ply-Tech Inc ....F 830 625-3913
New Braunfels (G-15819)
Powers Embroidery Inc ....D 254 754-2498
Waco (G-20448)
Quest and Sons Inc ....E 806 744-2351
Lubbock (G-14468)
The Texas A&M University Sys ....C 979 845-3414
College Station (G-3205)

FABRICS: Broadwoven, Wool

Roddie Wool Scouring Inc ....F 325 597-2138
Brady (G-2217)

FABRICS: Canvas & Heavy Coarse, Cotton

Alteca LLC ....F 956 423-1885
Harlingen (G-8179)
United Amercn Acquisition Corp ....E 859 987-5389
Waco (G-20470)

FABRICS: Coated Or Treated

Hanitatek LLC ....G 214 351-5818
Carrollton (G-2753)
Houston Wiper & Mill Supply Co ....F 713 672-0571
Houston (G-10264)
Patrick Industries Inc ....F 254 799-5717
Waco (G-20444)

FABRICS: Denims

Denimatrix LLC ....F 806 385-6401
Littlefield (G-14144)

FABRICS: Diaper, NEC

Diaper Sports Group LLC ....F 214 871-5131
Dallas (G-4257)

FABRICS: Drills, Cotton

Cofco Americas Resources Corp ....C 832 944-6359
Sugar Land (G-19461)

FABRICS: Felts, Blanketing & Upholstery, Wool

ISO Covers LLC ....F 972 221-4410
Lewisville (G-14057)

FABRICS: Fiberglass, Broadwoven

A & M Composites Corporation ....E 432 267-6525
Big Spring (G-2068)
Certainteed Corporation ....E 940 723-5998
Wichita Falls (G-20752)
Dcu Inc ....F 972 816-6667
Wylie (G-20932)
Fiberglass Specialties Inc ....D 903 657-6522
Henderson (G-8263)
Jones-Bell LLC ....E 254 933-2270
Belton (G-2026)
RPS Composites Alabama Inc ....F 979 265-4262
Clute (G-3158)
Specialty Composites Group LLC ....E 254 752-3622
Waco (G-20460)

FABRICS: Filter Cloth, Cotton

Custom Filter Supply Inc ....F 713 947-8147
Houston (G-9371)

FABRICS: Glass & Fiberglass, Broadwoven

Casting Designs Inc ....C 817 551-7373
Fort Worth (G-6496)
F & F Composite Group Inc ....E 817 379-4411
Fort Worth (G-6622)

FABRICS: Glove, Cotton

Southwest Cutters LLC ....D 915 858-2200
El Paso (G-5971)

FABRICS: Metallized

Rvo Manufacturing LLC ....F 832 229-5114
Houston (G-11703)

FABRICS: Nonwoven

Fiberco Inc ....F 682 647-1332
Fort Worth (G-6628)
NW Fabrics LLC ....F 832 895-1110
Houston (G-11103)
Supply Pro Sorbents LLC ....E 713 672-9080
Sugar Land (G-19559)
Twe Nonwovens Us Inc ....E 210 651-3735
Schertz (G-18765)

FABRICS: Polyester, Broadwoven

Mount Vernon Mills Inc ....B 979 836-5255
Brenham (G-2265)
Mount Vernon Mills Inc ....C 361 275-2393
Cuero (G-3764)

FABRICS: Polypropylene, Broadwoven

Polytex Fibers Corp ....C 713 690-9055
Houston (G-11362)
Winzen Film Inc ....E 214 340-7060
Dallas (G-5198)

FABRICS: Resin Or Plastic Coated

Westlake Pvc Corporation ....C 713 960-9111
Houston (G-12653)

FABRICS: Rubberized

Dyna-Mix Inc ....F 903 593-7387
Tyler (G-20078)

FABRICS: Scrub Cloths

Ggs Wiping Products LLC ....E 713 672-7200
Houston (G-9948)

FABRICS: Surgical Fabrics, Cotton

A Lakhany International Inc ....C 713 266-8799
Houston (G-8427)

FABRICS: Trimmings

A 1 Distributors Sign Supply ....D 432 682-0083
Midland (G-15100)
Austin Screen Printing Inc ....E 512 454-6249
Austin (G-961)
Beeville Publishing Company ....E 361 358-2550
Beeville (G-1984)
Brooks Industrial Coatings Inc ....E 512 990-5333
Austin (G-1012)
Creative Signworks Inc ....E 850 785-8899
San Angelo (G-17792)
Davids Apparel Inc ....E 915 590-3744
El Paso (G-5715)
Dcl America Inc ....F 281 651-5900
Conroe (G-3290)
F & H Ribbon Company Inc ....D 817 283-5891
Euless (G-6145)
Fineline Sportswear Inc ....F 512 832-1441
Austin (G-1156)
Grafikshop Corporation ....E 713 977-2555
Houston (G-10012)
Harvey Dupriest & Sons Inc ....D 214 337-4731
Dallas (G-4440)
Jaropamex ....F 830 774-5920
Del Rio (G-5318)
Jj of Dallas Manufacturing Inc ....E 972 866-9866
Addison (G-141)
Lorente International LLC ....E 877 281-6469
Farmers Branch (G-6206)
M & M Designs Inc ....E 936 295-2682
Huntsville (G-12817)
M W Periscope Inc ....E 972 247-4202
Dallas (G-4622)
Mc Creless Company ....F 432 332-1213
Odessa (G-16076)
McDowell Packg & Advg Co Inc ....D 469 246-2700
Plano (G-16923)

ML Industries Inc ....G 956 279-8678
Fredericksburg (G-7186)
Pacifica T-Shirts Inc ....F 714 508-4848
Round Rock (G-17677)
Ritchie-Vincent Inc ....F 432 337-5133
Odessa (G-16142)
TNT Printing ....G 281 449-9090
Houston (G-12315)
W & W Silkscreening Inc ....E 817 590-4479
Fort Worth (G-7112)
Your Ideas Inc ....F 325 673-5860
Abilene (G-96)

FABRICS: Wall Covering, From Manmade Fiber Or Silk

United Aviation ACC Inc ....E 817 447-8000
Burleson (G-2600)

FABRICS: Warp Knit, Lace & Netting

Texas Leather Trim Inc ....E 817 535-5883
Fort Worth (G-7049)

FABRICS: Woven Wire, Made From Purchased Wire

Rowe Equipment Inc ....F 281 255-0555
Hockley (G-8347)

FACIAL SALONS

Aloe Vera of America Inc ....C 956 585-9704
Alton (G-321)

FACILITIES SUPPORT SVCS

Aim World Services Inc ....E 281 847-2000
The Woodlands (G-19822)
Ioffice LP ....E 713 526-1029
Houston (G-10412)
Jentek Water Treatment Inc ....F 214 349-7111
Dallas (G-4531)
Liberty A&A ....F 213 221-8110
San Antonio (G-18251)
Tigua Enterprises Inc ....E 915 298-0700
El Paso (G-6006)

FAMILY CLOTHING STORES

D&D Retail LP ....E 830 379-7340
Seguin (G-18835)
Fossil Group Inc ....B 972 234-2525
Richardson (G-17312)
Haggar Clothing Co ....B 214 352-8481
Farmers Branch (G-6199)
Haggar Clothing Co ....B 214 352-8481
Texas City (G-19794)
Payton Interests Inc ....E 512 244-3221
Round Rock (G-17678)

FANS, VENTILATING: Indl Or Commercial

Quietaire Cooling Inc ....E 713 228-9421
Houston (G-11512)
Quietaire Corporation ....F 713 228-9421
Houston (G-11513)
Tiernan Aeration Inc ....E 806 372-4051
Amarillo (G-468)
Ventamatic Ltd ....C 940 325-7887
Mineral Wells (G-15545)

FANS: Ceiling

Entrematic Loading Dock Pdts ....E 972 466-0707
Carrollton (G-2732)

FARM & GARDEN MACHINERY WHOLESALERS

Angelo Pellets Inc ....F 325 655-5751
San Angelo (G-17777)
Lummus Corporation ....G 806 745-1191
Lubbock (G-14443)
Six & Mango Equipment LLP ....E 972 335-2731
Frisco (G-7312)

FARM MACHINERY REPAIR SVCS

Module Truck Systems Inc ....E 806 783-0777
Lubbock (G-14448)
Olton Welding & Machine Inc ....F 806 285-3006
Olton (G-16227)

PRODUCT

FARM PRDTS, RAW MATERIAL, WHOLESALE: Tobacco & Tobacco Prdts

Mustang Group Ltd ....F 830 968-0291
  Eagle Pass *(G-5550)*

FARM PRDTS, RAW MATERIALS, WHOLESALE: Nuts & Nut By-Prdts

Clements Nut Co Inc ....E 972 436-4596
  Lewisville *(G-14038)*
Golden Peanut Company LLC ....D 254 893-2034
  De Leon *(G-5238)*

FARM PRDTS, RAW MTRLS, WHOLESALE: Peanuts, Unroasted, Bulk

Birdsong Corporation ....E 254 734-2266
  Gorman *(G-7771)*
Birdsong Corporation ....F 806 637-7200
  Brownfield *(G-2330)*

FARM SPLY STORES

Gray Sales Inc ....G 361 527-4460
  Hebbronville *(G-8234)*

FARM SPLYS WHOLESALERS

All Seasons Feeders Inc ....E 210 648-0979
  San Antonio *(G-17892)*
E Barr Feeds Inc ....F 830 672-6515
  Gonzales *(G-7752)*

FARM SPLYS, WHOLESALE: Feed

Livengood Feeds Inc ....E 512 398-2351
  Lockhart *(G-14170)*

FARM SPLYS, WHOLESALE: Fertilizers & Agricultural Chemicals

Arbor Resources LLC ....F 936 632-9914
  Pollok *(G-17091)*
Dcp Midstream LLC ....D 432 827-1945
  Goldsmith *(G-7741)*

FARM SPLYS, WHOLESALE: Greenhouse Eqpt & Splys

Bwi Companies Inc ....D 979 743-4581
  Schulenburg *(G-18773)*
Solansky Welding and Pump Inc ....E 830 374-3318
  Crystal City *(G-3757)*

FARM SPLYS, WHOLESALE: Insecticides

Bwi Companies Inc ....D 972 242-4755
  Carrollton *(G-2708)*
Wilbur-Ellis Company LLC ....E 956 748-2382
  Rio Hondo *(G-17476)*

FARM SPLYS, WHOLESALE: Phosphate Rock, Ground

Ramrod Enterprises LLC ....E 936 756-4846
  Conroe *(G-3356)*

FARM SPLYS, WHOLESALE: Saddlery

El Paso Saddleblanket Co LP ....E 915 544-1000
  El Paso *(G-5741)*
Keyston Bros ....F 713 692-2132
  Houston *(G-10526)*

FASTENERS WHOLESALERS

Ameribolt Inc ....E 713 580-4997
  Houston *(G-8579)*

FASTENERS: Brads, Alum, Brass/Other Nonferrous Metal/Wire

Rodens All Star Mch & Mfg Inc ....E 817 927-2825
  Millsap *(G-15505)*

FASTENERS: Metal

Elijah Tooling Inc ....F 940 591-1340
  Denton *(G-5363)*
Huck International Inc ....B 254 751-5283
  Waco *(G-20417)*

Pattonair Usa Inc ....E 817 284-4449
  Fort Worth *(G-6897)*
RDS Metal LP ....F 817 539-7400
  Mansfield *(G-14708)*
Sigma Fasteners Inc ....D 281 214-8800
  Houston *(G-11885)*
Sunbelt Stud Welding Inc ....F 713 939-8903
  Houston *(G-12099)*

FASTENERS: Metal

LFC Industries Inc ....D 817 640-1322
  Arlington *(G-721)*
NCH Corporation ....A 972 438-0381
  Irving *(G-13115)*
NCH Corporation ....A 972 438-0211
  Irving *(G-13114)*
Pattonair Usa Inc ....E 817 284-4449
  Fort Worth *(G-6897)*

FASTENERS: Notions, NEC

Corpus Chrsti Gsket Fstner Inc ....C 361 884-6366
  Corpus Christi *(G-3510)*
Cyclone Bolt Incorporated ....E 281 372-6050
  Houston *(G-9382)*
Flexitallic Group Inc ....E 281 604-2525
  Houston *(G-9799)*
Fluid Sealing Products Inc ....D 713 910-1028
  Houston *(G-9816)*
Houston Precision Fas I LP ....D 713 462-2227
  Houston *(G-10246)*
South Texas Bolt & Fitting Inc ....E 713 673-5376
  Houston *(G-11966)*
Tfp Corporation ....E 281 598-2330
  Houston *(G-12267)*

FELT PARTS

Fred Clark Felt Co Beaumont ....E 409 842-5080
  Beaumont *(G-1897)*
Insituform Technologies Inc ....F 636 530-8020
  Houston *(G-10378)*

FELT: Acoustic

Industrial Noise Control Corp ....E 972 494-1422
  Richardson *(G-17331)*

FENCE POSTS: Iron & Steel

Presidio Custom Metal Works ....F 512 284-8549
  Round Rock *(G-17682)*

FENCES & FENCING MATERIALS

Burly Corp ....E 817 295-1128
  Burleson *(G-2573)*
De La Garza Fence Company ....E 210 674-8302
  San Antonio *(G-18044)*
Merchants Metals Inc ....E 817 293-9641
  Fort Worth *(G-6827)*
Sorensen Industries Inc ....E 940 365-9999
  Crossroads *(G-3750)*

FENCES OR POSTS: Ornamental Iron Or Steel

Albas Custom Iron Inc ....F 281 401-9797
  Houston *(G-8528)*
Binford Fence Supply Ltd ....F 972 286-2881
  Balch Springs *(G-1737)*
Fortress Iron LP ....D 972 231-4001
  Garland *(G-7491)*
Fusion Services Inc ....E 512 444-4283
  Austin *(G-1173)*
J C Ornamental Ironworks Inc ....F 972 442-6293
  Wylie *(G-20938)*
Mathis Iron Works Inc ....F 713 991-5846
  Houston *(G-10796)*
Ntx Gates & Fences Inc ....E 817 740-9449
  Fort Worth *(G-6874)*
Pool Custom Iron Works Inc ....F 936 756-4292
  Conroe *(G-3351)*
Sorensen Industries Inc ....E 940 365-9999
  Crossroads *(G-3750)*
Texas Best Panels Inc ....E 512 752-3777
  Lometa *(G-14178)*

FENCING DEALERS

Allied Fence Co of Dallas ....F 903 892-9640
  Dallas *(G-3926)*

American Fence and Sup Co Inc ....F 512 930-4000
  Georgetown *(G-7634)*
Kerr Feed & Grain Company ....F 940 538-4354
  Henrietta *(G-8281)*
Tach Services Inc ....E 254 547-7121
  Copperas Cove *(G-3456)*
Texarkan Fence ....F 870 779-0660
  Nash *(G-15724)*

FENCING MATERIALS: Docks & Other Outdoor Prdts, Wood

Jamieson Manufacturing Co ....E 214 339-8384
  Dallas *(G-4524)*
Sabine River & Northern RR Co ....E 409 746-2453
  Orange *(G-16260)*
Ufp New Waverly LLC ....D 936 295-3411
  New Waverly *(G-15861)*

FENCING MATERIALS: Plastic

F & F Composite Group Inc ....E 817 379-4411
  Fort Worth *(G-6622)*
Metro Gate & Mfg Co Inc ....E 903 785-8911
  Paris *(G-16365)*
Put-In-Cups LLC ....F 800 506-7891
  Corpus Christi *(G-3601)*
R Slater Enterprises LLC ....E 832 456-4900
  Houston *(G-11528)*

FENCING MATERIALS: Wood

Sorensen Industries Inc ....E 940 365-9999
  Crossroads *(G-3750)*
Tach Services Inc ....E 254 547-7121
  Copperas Cove *(G-3456)*
Ufp Schertz LLC ....E 830 606-4300
  Schertz *(G-18766)*
Vrt Investments Inc ....E 972 226-1981
  Forney *(G-6316)*

FENCING: Chain Link

Fusion Services Inc ....E 512 444-4283
  Austin *(G-1173)*
Hearne Steel Company ....D 979 279-3464
  Hearne *(G-8232)*
Master-Halco Inc ....D 972 714-7300
  Dallas *(G-4645)*
Master-Halco Inc ....E 817 378-8086
  Fort Worth *(G-6815)*
Master-Halco Inc ....F 214 275-3100
  Dallas *(G-4646)*
Master-Halco Inc ....D 214 391-3190
  Dallas *(G-4647)*
Tach Services Inc ....E 254 547-7121
  Copperas Cove *(G-3456)*
Vrt Investments Inc ....E 972 226-1981
  Forney *(G-6316)*

FERROUS METALS: Reclaimed From Clay

Diversified Pure Chem LLC ....F 817 677-9418
  Rhome *(G-17254)*

FERTILIZER MINERAL MINING

Agrifos LLC ....C 713 920-5300
  Pasadena *(G-16379)*
Truth Chemical LLC ....F 281 292-6900
  The Woodlands *(G-19931)*

FERTILIZER, AGRICULTURAL: Wholesalers

Abilene AG Service & Sup Inc ....D 325 677-4371
  Abilene *(G-4)*
Calco Taiwan Marketing Service ....F 713 247-9918
  Houston *(G-9048)*
Greensmiths Inc ....G 972 242-5310
  Carrollton *(G-2748)*
Poole Chemical Co Inc ....D 806 362-4261
  Texline *(G-19808)*
Sinochem American Holdings ....E 713 263-8880
  Houston *(G-11905)*
South Plains Compost Inc ....E 806 745-3559
  Slaton *(G-18974)*
Stoller International Inc ....E 713 461-1493
  Houston *(G-12069)*

FERTILIZERS: NEC

Agrium US Inc ....D 806 274-5204
  Borger *(G-2161)*

American Plant Food Corp............F 817 624-7132
Fort Worth *(G-6383)*

Bonus Crop Fertilizer Inc..............E 903 455-9439
Greenville *(G-8065)*

Compostology LLC...........................F 318 787-7442
Waco *(G-20389)*

Diamond Shamrock Ref & Mktg Co......B 361 786-2536
Three Rivers *(G-19944)*

Easy Gardener Products Inc.............D 254 753-5353
Waco *(G-20394)*

El Dorado Chemical Company...........C 254 445-2720
Dublin *(G-5516)*

Greensmiths Inc..............................G 972 242-5310
Carrollton *(G-2748)*

Jh Biotech Inc..................................E 830 557-4220
Mc Queeney *(G-14829)*

JMJ Organics Ltd............................F 281 798-3056
Crosby *(G-3735)*

Nelson Facilities Inc.......................F 979 865-8596
Bellville *(G-2011)*

Poole Chemical Co Inc....................D 806 362-4261
Texline *(G-19808)*

Rhizogen LLC..................................F 281 367-7500
The Woodlands *(G-19910)*

Scarab International Lllp.................E 806 883-7621
White Deer *(G-20711)*

Sinochem American Holdings.........E 713 263-8880
Houston *(G-11905)*

South Plains Compost Inc...............E 806 745-3559
Slaton *(G-18974)*

Sun Gro Horticulture Dist Inc.........E 903 938-7348
Marshall *(G-14804)*

Texas Landfill Management LLC.......E 210 651-6115
San Antonio *(G-18537)*

United Amercn Acquisition Corp.....E 859 987-5389
Waco *(G-20470)*

Wilbur-Ellis Company LLC...............F 830 663-3644
Devine *(G-5451)*

Wilbur-Ellis Company LLC...............E 979 279-3486
Hearne *(G-8233)*

Wilbur-Ellis Company LLC...............E 956 748-2382
Rio Hondo *(G-17476)*

FERTILIZERS: Nitrogenous

Cvr Energy Inc................................D 281 207-3200
Sugar Land *(G-19472)*

Cvr Partners LP...............................C 281 207-3200
Sugar Land *(G-19473)*

Green Industries Inc.......................G 972 483-6408
Italy *(G-13213)*

Hope Agri Products of Texas...........E 903 732-3361
Powderly *(G-17199)*

Ineos Nitriles USA LLC....................C 361 552-8200
Port Lavaca *(G-17149)*

Ineos Olgmers Chclat Bayou LLC....F 281 535-6738
League City *(G-13963)*

JR Simplot Company........................E 361 987-2682
Point Comfort *(G-17087)*

JR Simplot Company........................D 979 826-8063
Hempstead *(G-8253)*

Nitro-Phos Inc................................E 713 228-1868
Houston *(G-11060)*

Occidental Chemical Holdg Corp.....E 972 404-3800
Dallas *(G-4753)*

Scotts Miracle-Gro Company...........E 281 821-1022
Houston *(G-11792)*

Texas Landfill Management LLC.......E 210 651-6115
San Antonio *(G-18537)*

FERTILIZERS: Phosphatic

Abilene AG Service & Sup Inc..........D 325 677-4371
Abilene *(G-4)*

Itafos Services LLC.........................B 713 242-8446
Houston *(G-10430)*

JR Simplot Company........................E 361 987-2682
Point Comfort *(G-17087)*

JR Simplot Company........................D 979 826-8063
Hempstead *(G-8253)*

Martin Resource MGT Corp.............F 432 381-0271
Odessa *(G-16072)*

Nitro-Phos Inc................................E 713 228-1868
Houston *(G-11060)*

Occidental Chemical Corp...............E 214 421-7607
Dallas *(G-4752)*

Occidental Chemical Corp...............C 800 699-5123
Addison *(G-151)*

Occidental Chemical Corp...............E 361 242-8000
Corpus Christi *(G-3582)*

Occidental Chemical Holdg Corp.....E 972 404-3800
Dallas *(G-4753)*

Poole Chemical Co Inc....................F 806 647-2121
Dimmitt *(G-5485)*

FIBER & FIBER PRDTS: Acetate & Triacetate

CNA Holdings LLC...........................E 972 443-4000
Irving *(G-12976)*

FIBER & FIBER PRDTS: Elastomeric

Greene Tweed & Co LLC..................E 281 765-4500
Houston *(G-10034)*

FIBER & FIBER PRDTS: Organic, Noncellulose

Carpenter Co..................................D 254 778-0131
Temple *(G-19674)*

Celanese Americas LLC...................F 972 443-4000
Irving *(G-12963)*

Celanese Ltd...................................E 281 474-0554
Pasadena *(G-16403)*

Dal-Tile Corporation.......................F 817 831-6935
Haltom City *(G-8136)*

Future Pipe Industries Inc.............C 281 847-2987
Houston *(G-9879)*

J P C Plastics Inc...........................F 325 672-2895
Abilene *(G-53)*

Monument Chemical Houston LLC....C 281 452-5951
Houston *(G-10916)*

Monument Chemical Houston LLC....F 832 376-2201
Houston *(G-10917)*

FIBER & FIBER PRDTS: Polyester

Fiberio Technology Corporation......E 956 207-5448
McAllen *(G-14861)*

FIBER & FIBER PRDTS: Polyvinylidene Chloride

America Plastics LLC......................C 972 245-4525
Carrollton *(G-2697)*

FIBER & FIBER PRDTS: Synthetic Cellulosic

Eastman Chemical Company...........E 423 229-2000
Longview *(G-14230)*

James Hardie Building Pdts Inc......C 817 556-7000
Cleburne *(G-3097)*

Tascon Inc......................................E 713 937-0900
Houston *(G-12163)*

FIBER OPTICS

Corning Optical Communications....E 817 431-7120
Fort Worth *(G-6550)*

Guadalupe Valley Ventures LP........E 830 885-4411
New Braunfels *(G-15799)*

Opteconn LP...................................C 972 331-4627
Plano *(G-16955)*

Optical Cabling Systems LC............E 972 331-4627
Plano *(G-16957)*

Sensortran Inc................................E 281 876-2323
Austin *(G-1493)*

WT Fiber Link LLC...........................D 432 758-2700
Seminole *(G-18888)*

FIBER: Vulcanized

Reed Fiberglass Inc........................F 432 332-8265
Odessa *(G-16135)*

FIBERS: Carbon & Graphite

Toray Composite Mtls Amer Inc.......F 972 899-2930
Lewisville *(G-14098)*

FIDELITY OR SURETY BONDING

American Assn Notaries Inc............F 713 644-2299
Houston *(G-8586)*

FILE FOLDERS

JPS Alliance Inc..............................E 817 534-0044
Fort Worth *(G-6746)*

Smead Manufacturing Company......F 956 631-1418
McAllen *(G-14907)*

Thompson Paper Pdts Texas Inc......E 713 869-6636
Houston *(G-12278)*

FILLERS & SEALERS: Putty

Dap Products Inc............................D 214 349-9951
Dallas *(G-4237)*

FILM & SHEET: Unsuppported Plastic

3M Company....................................A 325 643-9798
Brownwood *(G-2423)*

Akrotex Films Inc............................E 409 886-0632
Orange *(G-16229)*

Akrotex Films Inc............................E 409 886-0111
Orange *(G-16230)*

Akrotex Films Inc............................E 409 886-0063
West Orange *(G-20692)*

Amtopp Corporation........................B 361 874-3000
Lolita *(G-14173)*

Berry Global Films LLC...................C 972 576-8193
Waxahachie *(G-20529)*

Handgards LLC................................C 915 779-6606
El Paso *(G-5794)*

Innovative Gas Systems Inc............D 713 937-5200
Houston *(G-10370)*

Kaneka North America LLC..............C 281 474-7084
Pasadena *(G-16468)*

Marco Dsplay Specialists GP Lc......C 817 244-8300
Fort Worth *(G-6810)*

Marian Fort Worth Inc....................E 817 332-6151
Fort Worth *(G-6811)*

Orbis Rpm LLC...............................F 940 387-6711
Denton *(G-5386)*

Plastiform Inc.................................F 972 579-8803
Irving *(G-13150)*

Reef Industries Inc.........................D 713 507-4329
Houston *(G-11578)*

Republic Plastics Ltd......................E 830 557-5574
Mc Queeney *(G-14830)*

Select Plastics LLC.........................E 817 595-3804
Fort Worth *(G-6982)*

Selectouch Corporation..................E 972 924-3289
Anna *(G-585)*

Super Sack Bag Inc.........................E 214 340-7060
Dallas *(G-5024)*

Transcendia Inc..............................E 800 659-4254
Carrollton *(G-2838)*

V-Kool Inc......................................G 713 856-8333
Houston *(G-12512)*

FILM: Motion Picture

Associated Pro Inc..........................A 214 902-8211
Dallas *(G-3974)*

Brazen Animation LLC....................E 214 880-0101
Richardson *(G-17281)*

CPM Inc..F 214 349-6886
Garland *(G-7470)*

FILM: Rubber

Keyston Bros..................................F 713 692-2132
Houston *(G-10526)*

FILTER CLEANING SVCS

Filter Maintenance Company Inc......E 713 432-7969
Houston *(G-9786)*

FILTER ELEMENTS: Fluid & Hydraulic Line

Instruments Tech McHy Inc.............E 210 651-9066
Schertz *(G-18750)*

Olaer Usa Inc.................................F 713 937-8900
Houston *(G-11167)*

FILTERS

CCI Thermal Tech Texas Inc............F 855 219-2101
Houston *(G-9109)*

Dalhart R & R Mch Works Inc..........E 806 244-5686
Dalhart *(G-3834)*

Diversified Materials Inc.................E 361 993-4600
Corpus Christi *(G-3514)*

Filtration Group LLC.......................E 815 726-4600
Dallas *(G-4361)*

Filtration Products LLC...................E 210 805-0200
San Antonio *(G-18114)*

Katch Filters LLC............................G 713 425-7400
Houston *(G-10501)*

Knight Corporation.........................E 281 933-5363
Houston *(G-10546)*

Porous Metal Filters Inc.................F 866 288-2522
Spring *(G-19160)*

Purolator Efp LLC ....D 713 977-0610
Houston *(G-11474)*

Siemens Industry Inc ....F 713 671-9510
Houston *(G-11879)*

Tyco Fire Products LP ....A 806 472-2400
Lubbock *(G-14502)*

Winston/Royal Guard Corp ....E 903 757-7341
White Oak *(G-20722)*

FILTERS & SOFTENERS: Water, Household

A O Smith Wtr Trtmnt N Amer ....D 817 536-5250
Haltom City *(G-8131)*

Janis Litchfield ....F 325 625-1001
Austin *(G-1251)*

Procam Controls Inc ....E 972 422-1212
Plano *(G-16979)*

FILTERS & STRAINERS: Pipeline

Champion Process Inc ....F 281 953-9000
Houston *(G-9159)*

Delta Screen & Filtration LLC ....D 713 856-0300
Houston *(G-9434)*

Forterra Inc ....A 469 458-7973
Irving *(G-13032)*

T & S Randall and Sons LP ....G 713 466-6951
Tomball *(G-20012)*

Wellstream Inc ....G 281 249-0900
Houston *(G-12633)*

FILTERS: Air

Air Filters Inc ....E 713 896-8901
Houston *(G-8507)*

Air Relief Technologies Inc ....E 817 261-3791
Fort Worth *(G-6357)*

Christopher RAD Nader ....F 512 442-5326
Cedar Park *(G-2963)*

Columbus Industries Inc ....C 915 843-2274
El Paso *(G-5700)*

Dust Free LP ....E 972 635-9565
Royse City *(G-17719)*

Eastern Star Group LLC ....F 972 729-9955
Allen *(G-263)*

Emerson Climate Tech Inc ....C 817 277-7764
Arlington *(G-668)*

Filter Maintenance Company Inc ....E 713 432-7969
Houston *(G-9786)*

Filter-All Inc ....E 281 356-1257
Magnolia *(G-14606)*

Glasfloss Industries Inc ....C 740 687-1100
Desoto *(G-5432)*

Jf Filtration Inc ....F 214 634-2200
Dallas *(G-4534)*

Jf Filtration Inc ....F 210 946-1688
San Antonio *(G-18201)*

Jf Filtration Inc ....F 956 412-3234
Harlingen *(G-8192)*

Lifetime Filter Inc ....B 281 391-8060
Katy *(G-13423)*

Sepra-Chem Corporation ....F 478 788-9789
Tyler *(G-20151)*

Unisorb Corporation ....F 713 943-3753
South Houston *(G-19053)*

FILTERS: Air Intake, Internal Combustion Engine, Exc Auto

Blade Lab Inc......................................F 817 491-6755
Haslet *(G-8216)*

Hvac Mechanical Svcs of Texas ....B 713 266-3900
Houston *(G-10292)*

Rom Industrial Inc...............................F 915 875-1186
El Paso *(G-5945)*

FILTERS: Gasoline, Internal Combustion Engine, Exc Auto

Reef Process Systems LLC ....F 972 874-9300
Flower Mound *(G-6278)*

Unisorb Corporation ....F 713 943-3753
South Houston *(G-19053)*

FILTERS: General Line, Indl

All American Filters Inc ....F 281 421-1909
Baytown *(G-1807)*

Crall Products Inc ....E 806 665-8446
Pampa *(G-16320)*

Eden Equipment Company Inc ....F 909 629-2217
Austin *(G-1113)*

Johnson Filtration Pdts Inc ....E 806 371-8033
Amarillo *(G-444)*

Sparkler Group Inc ....E 936 756-4471
Conroe *(G-3365)*

Tqi LLC ....E 830 401-4400
Seguin *(G-18869)*

World Wide Filtration Inc ....F 281 421-7676
Baytown *(G-1839)*

FILTRATION DEVICES: Electronic

Blue Box Air LLC ....D 424 241-3060
Dallas *(G-4031)*

Filtration Automation Inc ....E 817 999-8190
Alvarado *(G-332)*

Gs Liquid Technologies LLC ....F 817 556-6262
Cleburne *(G-3093)*

Jonell Filtration Products Inc ....D 254 559-7591
Breckenridge *(G-2230)*

Transcend Solutions Llc ....F 936 689-5618
Houston *(G-12350)*

Ups Inc ....E 713 222-7300
Houston *(G-12475)*

FILTRATION SAND MINING

Innovative Sand Solutions LLC ....F 817 421-7428
Fort Worth *(G-6722)*

FINANCIAL INVEST ACTIVITY: Protective Assoc, Royalty Owner

United States Lime & Mnrl Inc ....E 972 991-8400
Dallas *(G-5138)*

FINANCIAL INVESTMENT ACTIVITIES, NEC: Security Transfer

Risk Management Armored SEC ....F 817 932-5923
Alvarado *(G-340)*

FINANCIAL INVESTMENT ADVICE

Capital Asset Exch & Trdg LLC ....F 650 326-3313
Austin *(G-1025)*

Herd Producing Co Inc ....E 903 509-3456
Tyler *(G-20095)*

Petroleum Financial Inc........................F 817 339-1075
Fort Worth *(G-6904)*

FINANCIAL SVCS

C&S Lease Service LC ....F 903 988-8642
Kilgore *(G-13534)*

Edshah Capital ....F 469 770-3740
Plano *(G-16857)*

Synergen Health LLC...........................F 214 643-6002
Dallas *(G-5032)*

FINDINGS & TRIMMINGS Waistbands, Trouser

Dallas Bias Fabrics Inc ....E 214 824-2036
Dallas *(G-4212)*

FINDINGS & TRIMMINGS: Fabric

TST NA Trim Llc ....A 956 843-3500
Hidalgo *(G-8310)*

FINDINGS & TRIMMINGS: Furniture, Fabric

Srg Ventures LLC ....E 281 214-8560
Houston *(G-12030)*

FINGERNAILS, ARTIFICIAL

Nail Therapie Htx.................................F 832 703-4386
Houston *(G-10960)*

FINISHING SVCS

Thermal Specialties Texas LLC ....G 918 836-4800
Fort Worth *(G-7055)*

FIRE ALARM MAINTENANCE & MONITORING SVCS

ABC Fire Systems LLC.........................G 830 625-3473
New Braunfels *(G-15771)*

Classic Protection Systems ....E 713 468-3573
Houston *(G-9212)*

Ww Electronics Solutions LLC ....F 214 396-6636
Quinlan *(G-17227)*

FIRE ARMS, SMALL: Guns Or Gun Parts, 30 mm & Below

Brace Steel Components LLC ....F 972 272-2016
Garland *(G-7450)*

Chip McCormick Custom LLC ....E 830 798-2863
Bogata *(G-2145)*

Ddr Manufacturing Inc ....G 469 728-7242
Forney *(G-6307)*

Dreadnaught Industries.........................G 210 601-8149
Von Ormy *(G-20347)*

F-1 Firearms LLC ....E 832 299-6100
Spring *(G-19120)*

PLbennett Entp & Inv Fund A ....G 903 405-1940
Trenton *(G-20018)*

Staccato 2011 LLC ....D 512 819-0656
Georgetown *(G-7680)*

Stillers Prcision Firearms LLC ....F 972 429-5000
Garland *(G-7592)*

White Wing Weaponry LLC ....F 940 382-0830
Carrollton *(G-2897)*

FIRE ARMS, SMALL: Pistols Or Pistol Parts, 30 mm & below

High Standard Manufacturing Co ....F 713 462-4200
Houston *(G-10175)*

FIRE ARMS, SMALL: Rifles Or Rifle Parts, 30 mm & below

Brown Precision Inc ....G 530 384-2506
Cameron *(G-2639)*

Psd3 Enterprises LLC...........................F 830 995-3894
Comfort *(G-3240)*

FIRE CONTROL OR BOMBING EQPT: Electronic

Cooper Crouse-Hinds LLC ....F 832 390-3858
Houston *(G-9305)*

FIRE DETECTION SYSTEMS

Allestec Corporation.............................F 281 359-1519
Kingwood *(G-13637)*

Simplex Time Recorder LLC ....D 210 402-6311
San Antonio *(G-18476)*

Tyco International MGT Co LLC ....F 713 644-8872
Houston *(G-12419)*

FIRE EXTINGUISHER CHARGES

Border Manufacturer Contrs LLC ....E 956 982-0910
Brownsville *(G-2338)*

Fithen Properties ....F 806 762-1121
Lubbock *(G-14410)*

Gps International LLC ....E 832 319-1730
The Woodlands *(G-19870)*

Texas SEC & Surveillance Inc ....E 512 693-4003
Round Rock *(G-17693)*

FIRE EXTINGUISHER SVC

ABC Fire Systems LLC ....G 830 625-3473
New Braunfels *(G-15771)*

All State Fire Eqp Texas Inc ....F 972 412-0770
Wylie *(G-20924)*

Hasse Enterprises Inc ....F 512 835-7697
Austin *(G-1199)*

Texas SEC & Surveillance Inc ....E 512 693-4003
Round Rock *(G-17693)*

Ww Electronics Solutions LLC ....F 214 396-6636
Quinlan *(G-17227)*

FIRE EXTINGUISHERS, WHOLESALE

Hitech Fire Detection Corp....................D 281 475-7289
Spring *(G-19130)*

FIRE EXTINGUISHERS: Portable

Brk Brands Inc ....F 915 860-3500
El Paso *(G-5673)*

Classic Protection Systems ....E 713 468-3573
Houston *(G-9212)*

Tyco International MGT Co LLC ....F 713 644-8872
Houston *(G-12419)*

Ww Electronics Solutions LLC ....F 214 396-6636
Quinlan (G-17227)

FIRE OR BURGLARY RESISTIVE PRDTS

Advantage Interests Inc ....D 713 983-7253
Houston (G-8494)
Bhl International Inc ....E 281 449-5762
Houston (G-8874)
Bubbaco...F 972 768-0282
Terrell (G-19729)
Emissions & Silencer Tech Inc ....F 281 259-9979
Pinehurst (G-16734)
Innovative Machine & Laser LLC........E 214 330-1141
Dallas (G-4502)
Mabco Equipment Ltd ....E 817 599-7335
Weatherford (G-20602)
Ra-Lock Security Solutions Inc ....E 972 775-6301
Midlothian (G-15493)

FIRE PROTECTION EQPT

Ag-Meier Industries LLC ....E 254 939-3731
Belton (G-2016)
Chemguard Inc ....F 817 473-9964
Mansfield (G-14662)
Emergency Vehicles Texas Inc ....E 817 281-4172
Haltom City (G-8139)
Flameout LLC ....F 713 984-8310
Houston (G-9796)
Nexus Alarm & Suppression Inc ....E 877 828-1200
Dallas (G-4737)

FIRE PROTECTION SVCS: Contracted

Williams Fire Hazard Ctrl Inc ....E 409 745-3232
Port Arthur (G-17133)

FIRE PROTECTION, GOVERNMENT: State

City of McKinney..............................D 972 547-7657
Mc Kinney (G-14827)

FIREARMS & AMMUNITION, EXC SPORTING, WHOLESALE

American Tire Distributors Inc ....F 704 992-2000
Austin (G-918)
Chip McCormick Custom LLC ....E 830 798-2863
Bogata (G-2145)
Expansion Industries LLC...................E 888 707-9343
Carrollton (G-2735)
Spike Electric and Contrls LLC ....F 832 243-5372
Houston (G-12015)
Wrights Ammunitions LLC..................D 972 257-1111
Irving (G-13209)

FIREARMS: Small, 30mm or Less

Advanced Weapons and Armor Inc.......E 830 459-5263
Kerrville (G-13516)
Airtronic Usa LLC ....E 830 980-9788
Spring Branch (G-19265)
Bayou Arms Inc.................................E 281 475-4470
Spring (G-19102)
Cactus Weapons Systems Inc ....F 210 858-6703
Del Rio (G-5310)
Dregon LLC ....E 910 670-8211
El Paso (G-5724)
Liberty A&A ....F 213 221-8110
San Antonio (G-18251)
P T Products & Services Inc ....E 512 251-3592
Pflugerville (G-16682)

FIREFIGHTING APPARATUS

Magnum Fabrications Inc...................E 409 963-0161
Port Arthur (G-17117)

FIREPLACE EQPT & ACCESS

Golden Blount Inc ....E 972 250-3113
Addison (G-131)
Lee Products Inc ....F 817 641-9893
Cleburne (G-3100)

FIREWORKS

Magic In Sky LLC ....F 210 267-5371
Boerne (G-2128)

FIRST AID SPLYS, WHOLESALE

McKesson Corporation ....A 972 446-4800
Irving (G-13102)

FIRST AID SVCS

Giddings Volunteer Fire Dept ....E 979 492-1156
Giddings (G-7695)
Rubrix LLC.......................................E 512 581-5513
San Antonio (G-18437)

FISH & SEAFOOD MARKETS

Jbs Packing Company Inc ....E 409 982-5766
Port Arthur (G-17114)

FISH & SEAFOOD PROCESSORS: Canned Or Cured

Lt Seafood LP..................................F 713 328-1999
Houston (G-10697)

FISH & SEAFOOD PROCESSORS: Fresh Or Frozen

Farm Ctch Ctfish Prcessors Inc ....D 903 639-2394
Hughes Springs (G-12740)
Jbs Packing Company Inc ....E 409 982-5766
Port Arthur (G-17114)
Rich Products Corporation ....B 956 542-0001
Brownsville (G-2399)
Seabrook Seafood Inc ....E 281 334-2546
Kemah (G-13479)
Tex-Mex Cold Storage Inc ....C 956 831-4531
Brownsville (G-2409)

FISH FOOD

Wilbur-Ellis Nutrition LLC ....E 979 849-6757
Angleton (G-582)

FISHING EQPT: Lures

Knight Manufacturing Co Inc..............D 903 561-0522
Tyler (G-20111)
Nash Manufacturing Inc ....D 817 926-5223
Fort Worth (G-6860)

FITTINGS & ASSEMBLIES: Hose & Tube, Hydraulic Or Pneumatic

DSM Fluid Power Inc ....E 512 243-1986
Austin (G-1104)
George Myer Company Inc ....F 713 928-2606
Houston (G-9941)
Ghx Industrial LLC............................E 409 832-3461
Beaumont (G-1898)
Mid-West Hose & Specialty.................F 713 472-2900
Pasadena (G-16484)
Mid-West Hose & Specialty.................F 214 638-3210
Carrollton (G-2780)
Vaughan Investments Inc ....F 956 686-3725
McAllen (G-14916)

FITTINGS & SPECIALTIES: Steam

Romar/Mec LLC................................F 281 440-1725
Houston (G-11660)

FITTINGS: Pipe

Bonney Forge Texas LP ....E 713 695-3633
Houston (G-8951)
Borusan Mannesmann Pipe US Inc....E 832 399-6000
Baytown (G-1780)
Cgp Manufacturing Inc ....E 713 641-5544
Houston (G-9152)
Gs-Hydro US Inc ....E 281 209-1000
Houston (G-10052)
Houston Roll Pipe LLC.......................E 713 686-8970
Houston (G-10249)
Jcm Industries Inc ....C 903 832-2581
Nash (G-15722)
Joy Pipe Usa LP ....F 830 249-7400
Boerne (G-2125)
Lastrad LLC ....G 713 589-9477
Houston (G-10607)
Pipe Pros LLC ....E 432 699-4245
Midland (G-15358)
Pipe Pros LLC ....D 903 981-7801
Kilgore (G-13582)

Pj Piping Inc ....F 713 730-3457
Houston (G-11341)
Serampore Inds Private Ltd Inc..........E 713 923-6111
Houston (G-11833)
Sivco Inc ....E 713 466-1100
Houston (G-11910)
Sweco Fab Inc ....B 713 731-0030
Houston (G-12130)
Tenaris Coiled Tubes LLC ....F 713 460-1500
Houston (G-12197)
Universal Outlets Inc ....F 903 983-3261
Kilgore (G-13600)
Westbrook Sales & Distrg Corp..........C 713 675-6438
Houston (G-12639)

FITTINGS: Pipe, Fabricated

Advanced Industries Inc ....E 972 366-9000
Venus (G-20217)
APAC International Inc ....F 940 696-2525
Wichita Falls (G-20738)
Cameo Fabricators Inc ....E 281 449-6207
Houston (G-9060)
Forged Components Inc......................C 281 441-4088
Humble (G-12767)
Gulf Coast Fabricators Inc ....E 409 866-6721
Beaumont (G-1900)
Morsco Supply LLC ....F 903 234-2183
Longview (G-14282)
Pressure Point Service ....F 713 641-2325
Houston (G-11410)
Sentry Supply Inc.............................F 409 840-4800
Beaumont (G-1948)
Star Pipe LLC ....D 281 558-3000
Houston (G-12045)
Star Pipe Products Ltd ....C 281 558-3000
Houston (G-12046)
Texas Pmw Inc ....D 713 679-7900
Houston (G-12245)
Universal Outlets Inc ....F 903 983-3261
Kilgore (G-13600)

FIXTURES & EQPT: Kitchen, Metal, Exc Cast Aluminum

Commercial Kitchens Inc ....D 281 442-8001
Houston (G-9250)
Custom Kitchen Eqp Co Inc ....E 281 446-8187
Humble (G-12762)
DNB Stainless Concepts LLC..............F 940 479-0079
Justin (G-13341)
Kitchen Equipment Fabg Co ....D 713 747-3611
Houston (G-10538)
Lsg Sky Chefs N Amer Sltons In ....B 972 793-9517
Irving (G-13090)
P Rockin Enterprises Inc....................G 915 886-4912
Anthony (G-589)
Stainless Stl Cstm Fbrctors In ....E 713 433-0495
Houston (G-12038)

FIXTURES: Cut Stone

Builders Depot Direct LLC ....F 832 384-7272
Houston (G-9012)
Dura-Mar Venus Inc ....D 972 223-8008
Desoto (G-5430)
Dutch Marble Creations ....F 956 399-6767
San Benito (G-18656)
Gold Star Marble Corporation.............E 512 251-9279
Austin (G-1186)
Marble Masters of Texas Inc ....E 830 303-7744
New Braunfels (G-15811)
Qts LLC ....E 713 462-7072
Houston (G-11489)
Target Stone LLC ....E 832 827-8663
Houston (G-12161)

FLAGPOLES

De Walch Enterprise Inc ....D 713 861-8993
Houston (G-9417)
Symonds Flags & Poles Inc ....E 214 596-1900
Fort Worth (G-7026)

FLAGS: Fabric

A B C Flag Acquisition Corp ....E 817 335-2548
Fort Worth (G-6336)
Dixie Flag and Banner Company..........E 210 227-5039
San Antonio (G-18063)

FLAGSTONES

Aguado Stone Incorporated ....D 512 746-5094
Georgetown *(G-7632)*

FLARES

David Bacon Incorporated ....F 512 321-2323
Bastrop *(G-1754)*

Flare Well Testers Inc ....E 281 741-9335
Houston *(G-9797)*

Flares & Stacks Inc ....F 281 356-1408
Conroe *(G-3297)*

Liberty Tower & Flare Inc ....F 281 339-1410
Bacliff *(G-1734)*

FLAT GLASS: Building

Hou-Tex Newnom Inc ....D 713 777-0748
Houston *(G-10215)*

Jpon Glass Company Inc ....E 214 349-1400
Garland *(G-7528)*

FLAT GLASS: Construction

A & B Glass LLC ....F 432 517-4565
Big Spring *(G-2067)*

Trulite GL Alum Solutions LLC ....C 800 395-4224
Houston *(G-12385)*

FLAT GLASS: Float

Guardian Industries LLC ....B 903 872-4871
Corsicana *(G-3673)*

FLAT GLASS: Laminated

Cristacurva LLC ....G 713 353-5800
Houston *(G-9345)*

Texstars LLC ....C 972 647-1366
Arlington *(G-796)*

FLAT GLASS: Skylight

Berger Iron Works Inc ....E 713 869-7386
Houston *(G-8860)*

Dryco Skylights Inc ....G 817 477-3441
Mansfield *(G-14667)*

Skylights Over Texas LLC ....F 210 402-0500
San Antonio *(G-18478)*

FLAT GLASS: Strengthened Or Reinforced

USA Securglass Corporation ....E 214 907-9445
Addison *(G-173)*

FLAT GLASS: Tempered

Trulite GL Alum Solutions LLC ....E 210 653-7790
San Antonio *(G-18570)*

FLAT GLASS: Window, Clear & Colored

Advanced Window and Glass Mfg ....G 210 735-9959
San Antonio *(G-17870)*

Ballistics Systems Inc ....F 713 939-1160
Hockley *(G-8341)*

Fluenta Inc ....F 832 456-2021
Houston *(G-9815)*

Kinro Composties ....C 800 262-8827
Waxahachie *(G-20548)*

FLAVORS OR FLAVORING MATERIALS: Synthetic

Flotek Industries Inc ....E 713 849-9911
Houston *(G-9806)*

Interntnal Flvors Frgrnces Inc ....D 496 557-7001
Carrollton *(G-2770)*

FLIGHT RECORDERS

GE Flight Efficiency Svcs Inc ....E 512 270-2701
Austin *(G-1179)*

FLOOR CLEANING & MAINTENANCE EQPT: Household

Thorne Electric Company ....F 210 590-1226
San Antonio *(G-18551)*

FLOOR COVERING STORES

Home Mart Inc ....F 956 724-4521
Laredo *(G-13892)*

Yates Carpet Incorporated ....E 806 795-9942
Lubbock *(G-14516)*

FLOOR COVERING STORES: Carpets

Flightsafety International Inc ....C 817 571-5925
Fort Worth *(G-6638)*

United Lynn-Con Corporation..................F 972 223-2540
Desoto *(G-5446)*

FLOOR COVERING STORES: Floor Tile

East Texas Acoustical Inc ....F 903 663-3820
Longview *(G-14226)*

IB Supply LLC ....F 469 709-9650
Carrollton *(G-2870)*

FLOOR COVERING STORES: Rugs

Great Rug Company ....F 713 789-3666
Houston *(G-10028)*

FLOOR COVERINGS WHOLESALERS

Allied Truss LLC ....E 903 586-1982
Jacksonville *(G-13225)*

American Excelsior Company ....E 817 385-4300
Arlington *(G-616)*

Custom Crete Inc ....F 713 937-3966
Houston *(G-9369)*

Custom Drapery Company Inc ....D 713 225-9221
Houston *(G-9370)*

R S Global Inc ....D 972 406-2930
Dallas *(G-4857)*

Thorntree LP ....E 713 690-8200
Houston *(G-12280)*

FLOOR COVERINGS: Aircraft & Automobile

United Rtorcraft Solutions LLC ....E 940 627-0626
Decatur *(G-5256)*

FLOOR COVERINGS: Asphalted-Felt Base, Linoleum Or Carpet

Ipr Industrial LLC ....E 281 362-1131
The Woodlands *(G-19885)*

Tarkett Inc ....F 800 366-2689
Houston *(G-12162)*

FLOOR COVERINGS: Rubber

Ranco Industries Inc ....E 713 228-5543
Houston *(G-11540)*

Texas Medplast LLC ....F 832 288-2106
Houston *(G-12240)*

FLOOR COVERINGS: Textile Fiber

Al Knoch Interiors Inc ....D 915 886-5800
Canutillo *(G-2662)*

East Texas Acoustical Inc ....F 903 663-3820
Longview *(G-14226)*

Gunns Restoration................................E 281 645-2260
Houston *(G-10075)*

FLOORING & GRATINGS: Open, Construction Applications

Harsco Corporation ....E 713 378-3900
Spring *(G-19128)*

McNichols Company..............................E 877 884-4653
Garland *(G-7548)*

Rwc Material LLC ....F 210 219-2987
Fowlerton *(G-7162)*

FLOORING & SIDING: Metal

Ikg Usa LLC ....D 281 452-6637
Houston *(G-10320)*

FLOORING: Hard Surface

Colorstone Mfg.....................................F 713 690-3100
Houston *(G-9246)*

Lets Gel Inc ....F 512 628-1709
Waco *(G-20427)*

Redco Distribution LLC ....E 832 320-4950
Houston *(G-11573)*

Signature Systems Group LLC ....E 972 684-5736
Flower Mound *(G-6281)*

Unilin North America LLC ....D 214 398-1411
Dallas *(G-5133)*

FLOORING: Hardwood

Ace Hardwood Flooring Inc ....F 512 719-3555
West Lake Hills *(G-20676)*

Building Plastics Inc............................E 713 896-9001
Houston *(G-9015)*

Connor Sports Flooring LLC ....F 817 944-0269
Southlake *(G-19061)*

Custom Floors Unlimited Inc ....D 713 861-4139
Houston *(G-9372)*

Diamond Living LLC ....F 281 766-1600
Magnolia *(G-14600)*

Dycem Corporation ....F 832 447-1420
The Woodlands *(G-19855)*

Elkcorp ....E 972 851-0500
Dallas *(G-4313)*

Jellison Inc ....E 512 282-5256
Manchaca *(G-14639)*

Rbt Industries LLC ....F 512 600-5994
Austin *(G-1453)*

Regal Hardwoods Inc ....F 972 620-8833
Carrollton *(G-2804)*

Woodco Millwork Ltd ....F 210 298-9663
San Antonio *(G-18624)*

Woodwright Hardwood Flr Co Inc ....E 214 630-8811
Dallas *(G-5202)*

FLOORING: Tile

American Marazzi Tile Inc ....G 972 232-3800
Fort Worth *(G-6381)*

Graniti Vicentia LLC ....E 713 869-0800
Houston *(G-10015)*

Lone Star Ceramics Company ....E 972 247-3111
Dallas *(G-4603)*

Patara Stone Inc..................................E 713 681-2301
Houston *(G-11257)*

Styleaccess LLC ....D 972 392-3800
Carrollton *(G-2821)*

FLORISTS

Boggs Enterprises Inc ....F 903 572-8722
Mount Pleasant *(G-15647)*

David McNeff Inc ....F 972 562-0607
McKinney *(G-14935)*

FLOWER ARRANGEMENTS: Artificial

Chem Eleven Products Inc....................E 512 278-8800
Austin *(G-1045)*

Fosters Point Inc..................................E 281 353-6696
Tomball *(G-19979)*

M & F Wholesale Floral Sups ....F 915 542-1238
El Paso *(G-5851)*

FLOWERS, ARTIFICIAL, WHOLESALE

Schusters of Texas Inc ....F 325 648-2267
Goldthwaite *(G-7744)*

FLOWERS: Artificial & Preserved

Schusters of Texas Inc ....F 325 648-2267
Goldthwaite *(G-7744)*

FLUID METERS & COUNTING DEVICES

Kelley Instrument Machine Inc ....E 903 832-3332
Texarkana *(G-19767)*

Ludlum Measurements Inc....................B 325 235-5494
Sweetwater *(G-19633)*

R & R Oilfield Services Inc....................D 361 289-5892
Corpus Christi *(G-3604)*

Schlumberger Technology Corp ....A 281 285-8500
Sugar Land *(G-19542)*

FLUID POWER PUMPS & MOTORS

Airdraulics ....G 432 381-7867
Odessa *(G-15906)*

Bayou City Pump Works LP ....F 713 472-7722
Pasadena *(G-16396)*

Cse W-Industries Inc ....C 713 466-9463
Jersey Village *(G-13297)*

Dresser LLC ....C 262 549-2626
Houston *(G-9517)*

Electronic Power Design Inc..................D 713 923-1191
Houston *(G-9596)*

Emerson Process Management..............C 281 477-4100
Jersey Village *(G-13299)*

Hannon Hydraulics Inc ....E 713 849-4445
Houston *(G-10116)*

Hot Hydraulics Inc ....E 713 722-7200
Houston *(G-10212)*

Hyvair Corporation ....F 281 259-7768
Magnolia *(G-14608)*

ITT LLC ....F 281 504-6300
Stafford *(G-19335)*

Mjs Manufacturing Inc ....F 832 446-6440
Houston *(G-10895)*

National Oilwell Varco Inc ....F 817 985-5000
Fort Worth *(G-6861)*

Parker-Hannifin Corporation ....D 817 625-5081
Fort Worth *(G-6895)*

Pump Arts Inc ....E 713 946-0500
Houston *(G-11472)*

Tcm Investments Inc ....E 432 366-5433
Odessa *(G-16173)*

Teikoku USA Inc ....E 713 983-9901
Houston *(G-12185)*

Texas Precision Mfg Inc ....E 806 741-1166
Lubbock *(G-14492)*

Toshiba International Corp ....A 800 231-1412
Houston *(G-12327)*

Womack Machine Supply Co ....D 800 569-9800
Farmers Branch *(G-6219)*

FLUID POWER VALVES & HOSE FITTINGS

AAA Products International Inc ....F 214 357-3851
Dallas *(G-3873)*

Apergy Artfl Lift Intl LLC ....D 713 466-3552
Houston *(G-8662)*

Camozzi Pneumatics Inc ....E 972 548-8885
McKinney *(G-14931)*

Delafield Corporation ....F 903 887-2860
Mabank *(G-14575)*

Fittings Inc ....D 817 332-3300
Fort Worth *(G-6634)*

Globe Products Company Inc ....D 972 875-1660
Ennis *(G-6105)*

Hydraulics Inc ....F 817 923-1965
Fort Worth *(G-6711)*

Lastrad LLC ....G 713 589-9477
Houston *(G-10607)*

Schlumberger International ....A 713 747-4000
Houston *(G-11766)*

Seal-Jet of Texas Inc ....E 713 983-7233
Houston *(G-11804)*

Shf Inc ....C 832 456-2000
Pasadena *(G-16506)*

Warrior G Industries ....F 409 594-5258
Woodville *(G-20919)*

FLUXES

Carols Mch & Fabrication Inc ....E 713 921-7266
Wharton *(G-20698)*

CK Kustoms Iron Works Inc ....F 281 850-6118
Rockport *(G-17529)*

David Keels ....E 409 316-9265
Hitchcock *(G-8336)*

ESAB Group Inc ....C 800 372-2123
Denton *(G-5365)*

True Grit Works ....F 978 604-4915
Ravenna *(G-17234)*

FOAM CHARGE MIXTURES

Precision Pack ....F 214 553-8044
Dallas *(G-4820)*

U S Foam Inc ....F 903 753-3901
Longview *(G-14327)*

FOAM RUBBER

Hickory Springs Mfg Co ....F 817 831-1785
Fort Worth *(G-6695)*

Kirkland Sales Inc ....E 972 864-1424
Garland *(G-7533)*

Lapolla Industries LLC ....E 281 219-4100
Houston *(G-10599)*

Performance Elastomers Inc ....G 817 293-7503
Fort Worth *(G-6903)*

Woodbridge Sales & Engrg Inc ....C 915 751-1000
El Paso *(G-6040)*

FOAM RUBBER, WHOLESALE

Foam Fabricators Inc ....F 817 379-6520
Keller *(G-13467)*

FOAMS & RUBBER, WHOLESALE

Duna USA Inc ....E 281 383-3862
Baytown *(G-1785)*

FOOD PRDTS, BREAKFAST: Cereal, Rice: Cereal Breakfast Food

Magi Foods LLC ....F 210 590-1308
Selma *(G-18877)*

FOOD PRDTS, CANNED OR FRESH PACK: Fruit Juices

Borden Dairy Company ....E 855 311-1583
Dallas *(G-4042)*

Dean Foods Company ....B 817 684-3600
Fort Worth *(G-6581)*

Motts LLP ....C 972 673-8088
Plano *(G-16934)*

Ocean Spray Cranberries Inc ....C 903 885-8676
Sulphur Springs *(G-19594)*

Plains Dairy LLC ....A 806 374-0385
Amarillo *(G-455)*

Riviana Foods Inc ....C 713 529-3251
Houston *(G-11629)*

Space Enterprises LLC ....F 800 559-2923
San Antonio *(G-18490)*

Space Enterprises LLC ....E 281 846-9613
The Woodlands *(G-19923)*

FOOD PRDTS, CANNED OR FRESH PACK: Vegetable Juices

Aloe Farms Inc ....F 956 425-1289
Harlingen *(G-8177)*

FOOD PRDTS, CANNED, NEC

CGJ Enterprises Inc ....F 281 575-8801
Houston *(G-9151)*

Fortune One Foods Inc ....E 713 426-1133
Houston *(G-9840)*

Lechi Foods ....E 281 470-6200
La Porte *(G-13767)*

Mr Nams Foods Incorporated ....F 214 689-4688
Dallas *(G-4698)*

FOOD PRDTS, CANNED: Barbecue Sauce

Claudes Sauces Inc ....F 915 858-4299
El Paso *(G-5697)*

Gooch Investments Inc ....F 325 677-5904
Abilene *(G-44)*

National Food and Beverage Inc ....D 214 905-9700
Dallas *(G-4715)*

O Talk Texas Brands Inc ....E 325 655-6077
San Angelo *(G-17816)*

One World Foods Inc ....F 512 480-0203
Austin *(G-1387)*

Texas Rib Rangers Product ....E 940 565-1983
Denton *(G-5406)*

FOOD PRDTS, CANNED: Bean Sprouts

Guar Resources LLC ....E 806 637-4662
Brownfield *(G-2331)*

FOOD PRDTS, CANNED: Beans & Bean Sprouts

Triple Nickel Inc ....F 806 272-5589
Muleshoe *(G-15679)*

FOOD PRDTS, CANNED: Beans, Baked Without Meat

Teasdale Foods Inc ....C 209 358-5616
Flower Mound *(G-6287)*

FOOD PRDTS, CANNED: Chow Mein

Southern Noodle Company ....F 281 988-7778
Houston *(G-11976)*

FOOD PRDTS, CANNED: Ethnic

International Do Foods Idf Inc ....F 713 222-0598
Houston *(G-10401)*

Tyson Foods Inc ....F 940 553-1811
Vernon *(G-20231)*

Tyson Foods Inc ....B 713 678-1893
Houston *(G-12421)*

FOOD PRDTS, CANNED: Fruit Juices, Fresh

Good Flow Honey & Juice Co ....F 512 472-6714
Austin *(G-1188)*

Good Flow Juice Company LLC ....F 512 472-6714
Austin *(G-1189)*

Juiceus LLC ....E 956 667-0153
Brownsville *(G-2372)*

Sunny Delight Beverages Co ....D 903 893-5764
Sherman *(G-18935)*

Texas Citrus Exchange ....C 956 585-8321
Mission *(G-15567)*

Wonderful Citrus Packing LLC ....F 956 205-7300
Mission *(G-15574)*

FOOD PRDTS, CANNED: Fruits

Agrana Fruit Us Inc ....D 817 625-9053
Fort Worth *(G-6355)*

F and B Holdings LLC ....E 956 424-7775
Mission *(G-15553)*

FOOD PRDTS, CANNED: Fruits

Bruce Foods Corporation ....F 915 821-2500
El Paso *(G-5674)*

Campbell Soup Company ....C 903 784-3341
Paris *(G-16359)*

Del Monte Foods Inc ....B 830 374-3451
Crystal City *(G-3756)*

Dfa Dairy Brands Fluid LLC ....B 713 223-5296
Houston *(G-9448)*

Gourmet Grdns Spclty Foods Inc ....E 903 284-6215
Jacksonville *(G-13241)*

Herb Hilltop Farm & Restaurant ....D 832 397-4020
Cleveland *(G-3128)*

Kraft Heinz Foods Company ....E 847 646-2000
Irving *(G-13079)*

Kraft Heinz Foods Company ....B 817 837-4100
Fort Worth *(G-6772)*

Teasdale Foods Inc ....C 915 821-2500
El Paso *(G-5994)*

FOOD PRDTS, CANNED: Fruits & Fruit Prdts

Nakent LLC ....F 619 212-2277
San Antonio *(G-18329)*

FOOD PRDTS, CANNED: Jams, Including Imitation

Kraft Heinz Company ....B 972 272-7511
Garland *(G-7534)*

New Canaan Farms Inc ....F 512 858-7669
Dripping Springs *(G-5509)*

FOOD PRDTS, CANNED: Jams, Jellies & Preserves

TJ Blackburn Syrup Works Inc ....D 903 665-2541
Jefferson *(G-13289)*

FOOD PRDTS, CANNED: Jellies, Edible, Including Imitation

Jardine Foods Inc ....E 512 295-4600
Buda *(G-2531)*

Jensar Corporation ....G 817 542-4327
Fort Worth *(G-6738)*

FOOD PRDTS, CANNED: Macaroni

Durrset Amigos Ltd ....C 210 798-5360
San Antonio *(G-18074)*

FOOD PRDTS, CANNED: Mexican, NEC

Bruce Foods Corporation ....F 915 821-2500
El Paso *(G-5674)*

Creative Spclty Fd Sltions LLC ....D 713 864-7777
Houston *(G-9341)*

Cuatro Cinco Enterprises LLC ....E 713 647-2846
Houston *(G-9355)*

Garcia Foods Inc ....C 210 349-6262
San Antonio *(G-18136)*

La Autentica Inc ....F 202 415-6979
San Antonio *(G-18232)*

La Nortena Inc ....G 432 445-3273
Pecos *(G-16621)*

PRODUCT

Miller Seafood Co Inc ....E 361 552-6423
  Port Lavaca (G-17151)
Palacios & Sons LLC........................G.... 713 463-5851
  Houston (G-11222)
Renfro Foods Inc ....E 817 336-3849
  Fort Worth (G-6955)
Rodriguez Foods Ltd ....E 817 626-3961
  Fort Worth (G-6964)

FOOD PRDTS, CANNED: Olives

Kt Foods LLC ....D 409 293-3257
  Port Arthur (G-17115)
Olive Packing Company Inc ....D 409 293-3257
  Port Arthur (G-17119)

FOOD PRDTS, CANNED: Poultry

Tyson Foods Inc.................................C 817 568-9000
  Fort Worth (G-7088)

FOOD PRDTS, CANNED: Soups

CTI Arlington LLC ....C 817 869-1090
  Saginaw (G-17743)

FOOD PRDTS, CANNED: Spaghetti & Other Pasta Sauce

Sneaky Chef Foods LLC.....................F 203 768-5654
  Austin (G-1514)

FOOD PRDTS, CANNED: Spanish

Rd Food Manufacturing Inc ....E 915 594-4488
  El Paso (G-5930)

FOOD PRDTS, CANNED: Tamales

Adelita Tortilla Factory ....E 210 733-5352
  San Antonio (G-17865)
Dallas Tortillas Inc ....F 214 943-7681
  Dallas (G-4228)
Odessa Tortilla & Tamale Fctry ....E 432 332-6676
  Odessa (G-16098)

FOOD PRDTS, CANNED: Tomato Sauce.

Simplyfresco LLC ....E 210 494-8443
  San Antonio (G-18477)

FOOD PRDTS, CANNED: Tomatoes

Bartush-Schnitzius Foods Co ....E 972 219-1270
  Lewisville (G-14026)

FOOD PRDTS, CANNED: Vegetables

Commissary Express Inc ....F 903 357-5670
  Sherman (G-18912)
Talk OTexas Brands Inc.....................D 325 655-6077
  San Angelo (G-17831)

FOOD PRDTS, CONFECTIONERY, WHOLESALE: Candy

Cyclone Cotton Candy LLC ....E 281 748-9163
  Houston (G-9383)
Jacksonville Candy Co Inc ....E 903 586-8334
  Jacksonville (G-13244)

FOOD PRDTS, CONFECTIONERY, WHOLESALE: Nuts, Salted/Roasted

Morven Partners LP ....F 325 372-5727
  San Saba (G-18718)
Red River Commodities Inc ....E 806 763-9747
  Lubbock (G-14471)
Texas Star Nut and Food Co Inc..........D 830 249-8300
  Boerne (G-2140)

FOOD PRDTS, CONFECTIONERY, WHOLESALE: Potato Chips

Frito-Lay North America Inc.................D 817 649-3266
  Arlington (G-681)

FOOD PRDTS, CONFECTIONERY, WHOLESALE: Snack Foods

D S D Services Inc ....F 361 594-4114
  Shiner (G-18939)

Frito-Lay North America Inc.................F 903 868-2657
  Sherman (G-18915)
Julios Corn Chips ....F 325 486-9300
  San Angelo (G-17812)
La Autentica Inc ....F 202 415-6979
  San Antonio (G-18232)

FOOD PRDTS, CONFECTIONERY, WHOLESALE: Syrups, Fountain

Coca-Cola Refreshments USA Inc ....E 806 472-3200
  Lubbock (G-14395)

FOOD PRDTS, DAIRY, WHOLESALE: Frozen Dairy Desserts

Meditrrnean Spcialty Foods LLC...........D 214 680-8820
  Dallas (G-4664)

FOOD PRDTS, FISH & SEAFOOD, WHOLESALE: Fresh

William B Sides ....F 512 385-3826
  Austin (G-1667)

FOOD PRDTS, FISH & SEAFOOD, WHOLESALE: Seafood

Hillman Shrimp & Oyster Co ....B 281 339-1506
  Dickinson (G-5474)
Hillman Shrimp and Oyster Co ....B 281 339-1506
  Dickinson (G-5475)
Jbs Packing Company Inc ....E 409 982-5766
  Port Arthur (G-17114)

FOOD PRDTS, FISH & SEAFOOD: Crabmeat, Fresh, Pkgd Nonsealed

La Blue Crab Co Inc ....F 972 422-7525
  Plano (G-16905)

FOOD PRDTS, FISH & SEAFOOD: Fish, Fresh, Prepared

William B Sides ....F 512 385-3826
  Austin (G-1667)

FOOD PRDTS, FISH & SEAFOOD: Fresh, Prepared

Palacios Processors Inc ....D 361 552-1231
  Port Lavaca (G-17153)

FOOD PRDTS, FISH & SEAFOOD: Seafood, Frozen, Prepared

North Texas Packing Inc ....F 972 660-2800
  Grand Prairie (G-7937)

FOOD PRDTS, FISH & SEAFOOD: Shellfish, Frozen, Prepared

Hillman Shrimp & Oyster Co ....B 281 339-1506
  Dickinson (G-5474)
Hillman Shrimp and Oyster Co ....B 281 339-1506
  Dickinson (G-5475)

FOOD PRDTS, FISH & SEAFOOD: Shrimp, Fresh, Prepared

Texas Pack Inc ....B 956 943-5461
  Port Isabel (G-17138)

FOOD PRDTS, FISH & SEAFOOD: Shrimp, Preserved & Cured

La India Packing Co ....E 956 723-3772
  Laredo (G-13903)

FOOD PRDTS, FROZEN: Breakfasts, Packaged

Super Seed Foods LLC.......................G 512 698-7907
  Austin (G-1547)
Wholesome Group LLC ....C 214 937-4750
  Plano (G-17050)

FOOD PRDTS, FROZEN: Dinners, Packaged

Bottom Line Fd Processors Inc ....E 512 218-3500
  Austin (G-1003)
Garland Ventures Ltd..........................E 972 485-8878
  Garland (G-7496)
Night Hawk Frozen Foods Inc ....D 800 580-4166
  Buda (G-2533)

FOOD PRDTS, FROZEN: Ethnic Foods, NEC

1st Original Texas Chili Inc ....G 817 626-0983
  Fort Worth (G-6333)
Choiers Company ....C 817 312-1364
  Hurst (G-12843)
Food Source Inc ....D 972 548-9001
  McKinney (G-14944)
Kaiser Foodline LLC ....E 972 705-9595
  Garland (G-7529)
Yellowstone Brands Ltd ....G 713 650-0065
  Houston (G-12717)

FOOD PRDTS, FROZEN: Fruits

Blencor LLC..C 979 627-7801
  Sealy (G-18806)

FOOD PRDTS, FROZEN: Fruits, Juices & Vegetables

A&A Concepts ....F 210 435-1300
  San Antonio (G-17848)
Coca-Cola Company ....D 281 302-4317
  Sugar Land (G-19459)
Mibo Fresh Foods LLC........................D 817 882-9600
  Fort Worth (G-6835)
Usm Manufacturing LLC ....E 806 791-0220
  Lubbock (G-14505)

FOOD PRDTS, FROZEN: Lunches, Packaged

Texpac Foods LLC...............................F 713 780-4876
  Houston (G-12261)

FOOD PRDTS, FROZEN: NEC

Amy Food Inc ....D 713 910-5860
  Houston (G-8631)
Austin Ventures LP ....E 512 485-1900
  Austin (G-963)
Beetnik Foods LLC ....F 512 584-8228
  Austin (G-986)
Bridgford Foods Corporation ....D 214 428-1535
  Dallas (G-4051)
Bridgford Industries Inc ....E 214 428-1535
  Dallas (G-4053)
Campbell Soup Company ....C 903 784-3341
  Paris (G-16359)
Chungs Products LP ....C 713 741-2118
  Houston (G-9186)
Gourmet Cuisine Inc ....E 972 289-7441
  Mesquite (G-15045)
Gruma Corporation ....C 972 232-5000
  Irving (G-13043)
Isabella Foods Inc ....D 915 590-1899
  El Paso (G-5818)
Pretzels Inc ....E 972 416-3660
  Carrollton (G-2795)
Quality Star Products Ltd....................D 214 680-7448
  Garland (G-7574)
Sfc Global Supply Chain Inc ....B 713 740-7536
  Deer Park (G-5295)
Usm Manufacturing LLC ....E 806 791-0220
  Lubbock (G-14505)
Van Oriental Food Inc ....D 214 630-0333
  Dallas (G-5153)
WEI-Chuan USA Inc ....F 713 690-3677
  Houston (G-12626)

FOOD PRDTS, FROZEN: Pizza

Sfc Global Supply Chain Inc ....B 713 740-7200
  Pasadena (G-16505)

FOOD PRDTS, FROZEN: Potato Prdts

JR Simplot Company ....E 361 987-2682
  Point Comfort (G-17087)
JR Simplot Company ....D 979 826-8063
  Hempstead (G-8253)

(G-0000) Company's Geographic Section entry number

FOOD PRDTS, FROZEN: Snack Items

Good Fat Co Ltd ....E 512 300-8391
Austin (G-1187)

FOOD PRDTS, FROZEN: Vegetables, Exc Potato Prdts

Pictsweet Company ....D 210 833-9618
San Antonio (G-18374)
Texas Pack Inc ....B 956 943-5461
Port Isabel (G-17138)

FOOD PRDTS, FRUITS & VEGETABLES, FRESH, WHOLESALE

Texas Citrus Exchange ....C 956 585-8321
Mission (G-15567)

FOOD PRDTS, FRUITS & VEGETABLES, FRESH, WHOLESALE: Vegetable

La Fama Foods Inc ....D 903 968-4500
Ore City (G-16274)

FOOD PRDTS, MEAT & MEAT PRDTS, WHOLESALE: Cured Or Smoked

Plains Meat Co Ltd ....E 806 765-5595
Lubbock (G-14462)
Slovacek Foods LP ....E 979 272-8625
Snook (G-18981)
Usm Manufacturing LLC ....E 806 791-0220
Lubbock (G-14505)

FOOD PRDTS, MEAT & MEAT PRDTS, WHOLESALE: Fresh

Boggs Enterprises Inc ....F 903 572-8722
Mount Pleasant (G-15647)
Centex Meat Company LP ....E 512 352-6357
Taylor (G-19652)
Ditta Meat Company ....D 281 487-2010
Pasadena (G-16417)
Fisher Ham and Meat Co ....F 281 376-1644
Spring (G-19121)
Leonard & Harral Packing Co ....B 210 532-3241
San Antonio (G-18247)
Mineola Packing Company ....E 903 569-5355
Mineola (G-15510)
Pat and Gail Jackowski ....F 830 278-6247
Uvalde (G-20194)
Rudolphs Market & Sausage Co...........F 214 741-1874
Dallas (G-4920)

FOOD PRDTS, MEAT & MEAT PRDTS, WHOLESALE: Lard

Columbia Packing Co Inc ....E 214 946-8171
Dallas (G-4144)

FOOD PRDTS, POULTRY, WHOLESALE: Live/Dressed/Frozen, Unpkgd

MARTIN PREFERRED FOODS LP ....C 713 869-6191
Houston (G-10777)

FOOD PRDTS, POULTRY, WHOLESALE: Poultry Prdts, NEC

Greenberg Smoked Turkeys Inc ....E 903 595-0725
Tyler (G-20091)

FOOD PRDTS, WHOL: Canned Goods, Fruit, Veg, Seafood/Meats

Houston Sysco Inc ....E 713 672-8080
Houston (G-10254)
Southern Noodle Company ....F 281 988-7778
Houston (G-11976)

FOOD PRDTS, WHOLESALE: Beans, Field

Dishaka LLC ....D 713 988-2900
Stafford (G-19305)

FOOD PRDTS, WHOLESALE: Beverage Concentrates

Motts LLP ....C 972 673-8088
Plano (G-16934)

FOOD PRDTS, WHOLESALE: Beverages, Exc Coffee & Tea

Marsmith Enterprises Inc ....F 972 488-9339
Dallas (G-4638)
Sway Water Inc ....F 512 693-7588
Austin (G-1551)

FOOD PRDTS, WHOLESALE: Breakfast Cereals

General Mills Inc ....E 972 892-4100
Addison (G-129)

FOOD PRDTS, WHOLESALE: Chocolate

Quintessential Chocolates Inc.............F 830 990-9382
Fredericksburg (G-7187)

FOOD PRDTS, WHOLESALE: Coffee & Tea

Commercial Bev Concepts LLC ....E 713 554-4569
Houston (G-9249)
Farmer Bros Co ....C 682 549-6767
Northlake (G-15885)
Holly Yaupon Tea LLC ....E 512 677-4907
Cat Spring (G-2930)
Perkup Coffees LLC ....E 281 445-6744
Houston (G-11291)
Wicked Voodoo Espresso LLC ....E 360 631-1447
New Braunfels (G-15832)

FOOD PRDTS, WHOLESALE: Coffee, Green Or Roasted

Dean Foods Company ....B 817 684-3600
Fort Worth (G-6581)
Farmer Bros Co ....F 682 549-6600
Northlake (G-15886)
Texas Coffee Company ....E 409 835-3434
Beaumont (G-1958)

FOOD PRDTS, WHOLESALE: Condiments

La India Packing Co ....E 956 723-3772
Laredo (G-13903)

FOOD PRDTS, WHOLESALE: Dog Food

Bark To Basics LLC ....F 913 825-1760
Irving (G-12944)
Gamma2 LLC ....E 760 734-4003
Arlington (G-685)

FOOD PRDTS, WHOLESALE: Grain Elevators

Bunge Milling Southwest Inc ....F 806 799-3755
Lubbock (G-14385)
J Lewis Partners LP ....A 972 702-7390
Dallas (G-4519)

FOOD PRDTS, WHOLESALE: Grains

Red River Commodities Inc ....E 806 763-9747
Lubbock (G-14471)
Valley Feed Mill Inc Paris ....E 903 785-3501
Paris (G-16373)

FOOD PRDTS, WHOLESALE: Honey

Shayne Foods Incorporated ....F 210 442-8776
San Antonio (G-18469)

FOOD PRDTS, WHOLESALE: Organic & Diet

O D C L Inc ....E 956 565-3131
Mercedes (G-15009)
Southern Fields Aloe Inc ....F 956 565-5102
Mercedes (G-15010)

FOOD PRDTS, WHOLESALE: Pasta & Rice

Dishaka LLC ....D 713 988-2900
Stafford (G-19305)

FOOD PRDTS, WHOLESALE: Rice, Unpolished

Beaumont Rice Mills Inc...................E 409 832-2521
Beaumont (G-1862)

FOOD PRDTS, WHOLESALE: Soups, Exc Frozen

Bear Creek Smokehouse LLC...........E 903 935-5217
Marshall (G-14763)

FOOD PRDTS, WHOLESALE: Soybeans

CGJ Enterprises Inc ....F 281 575-8801
Houston (G-9151)

FOOD PRDTS, WHOLESALE: Specialty

Astro Foods International Corp ....F 214 349-7840
Dallas (G-3977)
Gruma Corporation ....C 972 232-5000
Irving (G-13043)
Spfm LP ....D 210 805-8931
San Antonio (G-18491)

FOOD PRDTS, WHOLESALE: Spices & Seasonings

Adams Flvors Fods Ingrdnts LLC ....C 830 672-1850
Gonzales (G-7748)
Carmies Kitchen Inc ....F 972 442-1337
Wylie (G-20930)
Claudes Sauces Inc ....F 915 858-4299
El Paso (G-5697)
Consolidated Mills Inc ....E 713 896-4196
Houston (G-9276)

FOOD PRDTS, WHOLESALE: Sugar, Refined

Imperial Sugar Company ....C 281 491-9181
Sugar Land (G-19496)

FOOD PRDTS, WHOLESALE: Tea

Live Soda LLC ....F 512 888-9959
Austin (G-1295)
Mother Parkers Tea Cof USA Ltd ....C 817 551-5500
Fort Worth (G-6855)

FOOD PRDTS, WHOLESALE: Water, Mineral Or Spring, Bottled

C Treat Offshore Watermakers ....E 281 367-2800
The Woodlands (G-19837)

FOOD PRDTS: Animal & marine fats & oils

Darling Ingredients Inc ....C 972 717-0300
Irving (G-12992)
Darling Ingredients Inc ....F 512 303-2571
Bastrop (G-1753)
Darling Ingredients Inc ....F 979 778-0298
Bryan (G-2469)
Darling Ingredients Inc ....C 972 717-0300
Irving (G-12994)
Jacob Stern & Sons Inc ....E 713 926-8386
Houston (G-10448)
Leonard & Harral Packing Co ....B 210 532-3241
San Antonio (G-18247)
Omega Protein Corporation ....C 713 940-6100
Houston (G-11174)
Valley Proteins Inc ....E 325 653-3858
San Angelo (G-17836)
Valley Proteins (de) Inc ....D 469 580-0864
Dallas (G-5152)
Valley Proteins (de) Inc ....D 540 247-2798
Amarillo (G-518)
Ventura Foods LLC ....D 817 232-5450
Saginaw (G-17758)

FOOD PRDTS: Biscuit Dough From Purchased Flour

Bridgford Industries Inc ....E 214 428-1535
Dallas (G-4053)
Heart of Texas Biscuits Inc ....F 254 753-0046
Waco (G-20410)

FOOD PRDTS: Bread Crumbs, Exc Made In Bakeries

Das Brot Inc ....E 972 243-8443
Carrollton (G-2721)
Pepperidge Farm Incorporated...........E 713 385-2010
Houston (G-11287)

PRODUCT

FOOD PRDTS: Butter, Renovated & Processed

Select Butter & Packaging LLC ....F 214 568-9000
Littlefield (G-14149)

FOOD PRDTS: Cereals

General Mills Inc ....F 817 490-6940
Roanoke (G-17485)
General Mills Inc ....D 281 890-0784
Houston (G-9925)
Kellogg Company ....A 830 438-2254
Bulverde (G-2555)
La Autentica Inc ....F 202 415-6979
San Antonio (G-18232)
Nsh Services Inc ....F 817 961-5045
Fort Worth (G-6873)
Pepsico Inc ....D 972 963-1000
Plano (G-16969)

FOOD PRDTS: Chicken, Processed, Fresh

Bally United Produce Ltd ....E 972 487-7788
Garland (G-7447)
Dallas USA Foods Inc ....D 214 905-1511
Dallas (G-4229)
Tyson Farms of Texas Inc ....A 936 598-2474
Center (G-3010)

FOOD PRDTS: Chicken, Slaughtered & Dressed

Pilgrims Pride Corporation ....D 936 598-3356
Center (G-3004)
Pilgrims Pride Corporation ....A 254 412-5800
Waco (G-20446)
Pilgrims Pride Corporation ....A 936 639-1174
Lufkin (G-14545)
Pilgrims Pride Corporation ....D 903 575-3540
Mount Pleasant (G-15657)
Pilgrims Pride Corporation ....E 936 248-5600
Tenaha (G-19724)
Pilgrims Pride Corporation ....B 919 774-7333
Pittsburg (G-16748)
Pilgrims Pride Corporation ....B 210 633-2412
San Antonio (G-18376)

FOOD PRDTS: Chili Pepper Or Powder

Bolners Fiesta Products Inc ....G 210 734-6404
San Antonio (G-17962)
GSC Chipotle Texas Ltd ....E 915 769-0097
Fort Hancock (G-6321)

FOOD PRDTS: Chocolate Bars, Solid

Good Fat Co Ltd ....E 512 300-8391
Austin (G-1187)

FOOD PRDTS: Citrus Pulp, Dried

Citrolim Inc ....F 281 453-5150
Houston (G-9202)

FOOD PRDTS: Coffee

Atlantic Cof Indus Sltions LLC ....B 713 228-9501
Houston (G-8738)
Candy Kings Inc ....F 409 762-6100
Galveston (G-7391)
Cuvee Coffee LLC ....F 512 264-1479
Spicewood (G-19092)
Daily Offrngs Cof Roastery LLC ....F 805 423-7410
Wolfforth (G-20907)
Hillshire Brands Company ....C 713 928-6281
Houston (G-10186)
Indies Productions LLC ....G....... 281 508-3920
League City (G-13959)
Metro Coffee Grouppe Inc ....F 972 263-8744
Grand Prairie (G-7927)
Mother Parkers Tea Cof USA Ltd ....C 817 551-5500
Fort Worth (G-6855)
Nuzee Inc ....E 760 295-2408
Plano (G-16951)
Perkup Coffees LLC ....E 281 445-6744
Houston (G-11291)
Royal Cup Inc ....F 817 261-7527
Arlington (G-775)
Texas Coffee Company ....E 409 835-3434
Beaumont (G-1958)
Wicked Voodoo Espresso LLC ....E 360 631-1447
New Braunfels (G-15832)

FOOD PRDTS: Coffee Extracts

Aspen Enterprises Ltd ....F 210 684-6363
San Antonio (G-17918)
Chameleon Cold Brew LLC ....E 512 323-0345
Austin (G-1042)

FOOD PRDTS: Coffee Roasting, Exc Wholesale Grocers

Coffee Traders Inc ....E 512 476-2279
Austin (G-1056)
CPI Importers Inc ....F 214 353-0328
Dallas (G-4179)
Farmer Bros Co ....C 682 549-6767
Northlake (G-15885)
Farmer Bros Co ....F 682 549-6600
Northlake (G-15886)
Farmer Bros Co ....E 817 640-8111
Arlington (G-675)
Farmer Bros Co ....F 713 864-1487
Houston (G-9763)
Fresh Brew Group Usa LP ....E 281 847-2222
Houston (G-9864)
La Creme Inc ....F 214 352-8090
Irving (G-13081)

FOOD PRDTS: Coffee Substitutes

Holly Yaupon Tea LLC ....G 512 677-4907
Cat Spring (G-2930)

FOOD PRDTS: Coffee, Ground, Mixed With Grain Or Chicory

Grand Coffees of Texas LLC ....F 281 530-8321
Houston (G-10014)

FOOD PRDTS: Cooking Oils, Refined Vegetable, Exc Corn

American Commodities Inc ....E 817 740-8326
Fort Worth (G-6379)

FOOD PRDTS: Corn Chips & Other Corn-Based Snacks

Double Jj Corporation ....E 214 353-0230
Dallas (G-4274)
Frito-Lay North America Inc ....B 210 662-2100
San Antonio (G-18127)

FOOD PRDTS: Corn Flour

B Martinez & Sons Company Inc...........E 210 226-6772
San Antonio (G-17932)

FOOD PRDTS: Corn Meal

Bunge Milling Southwest Inc ....F 806 799-3755
Lubbock (G-14385)
Bunge Milling Southwest Inc ....D 800 852-8291
Muleshoe (G-15676)

FOOD PRDTS: Dessert Mixes & Fillings

Quality Bakery Products Inc ....D 281 449-4977
Houston (G-11492)

FOOD PRDTS: Desserts, Ready-To-Mix

Barton Table LLC ....G 512 791-2260
Austin (G-976)
Meditrrnean Spcialty Foods LLC ....D 214 680-8820
Dallas (G-4664)

FOOD PRDTS: Dough, Pizza, Prepared

Hbreaux Companies Inc ....F 409 792-9212
Bridge City (G-2284)

FOOD PRDTS: Doughs & Batters From Purchased Flour

Das Brot Inc ....E 972 243-8443
Carrollton (G-2721)

FOOD PRDTS: Dressings, Salad, Raw & Cooked Exc Dry Mixes

Bartush-Schnitzius Foods Co................E 972 219-1270
Lewisville (G-14026)

FOOD PRDTS: Dried & Dehydrated Fruits, Vegetables & Soup Mix

Azteca Milling LP ....B 806 291-5633
Plainview (G-16751)
Frito-Lay North America Inc ....D 817 649-3266
Arlington (G-681)
Teasdale Foods Inc ....C 209 358-5616
Flower Mound (G-6287)

FOOD PRDTS: Ducks, Slaughtered & Dressed

Bc Wetlands Ltd ....G....... 903 718-1530
Denison (G-5335)

FOOD PRDTS: Edible Oil Prdts, Exc Corn Oil

Quick Turn Machining Inc ....F 281 355-8876
Tomball (G-20004)

FOOD PRDTS: Edible fats & oils

Archer-Daniels-Midland Company ....D 806 723-5117
Lubbock (G-14363)
Bright Initiatives LLC ....F 512 466-4734
Austin (G-1008)
Jst Global LLC ....F 713 926-8386
Houston (G-10488)
Stratas Foods LLC ....G 713 671-0057
Houston (G-12075)
Ventura Foods LLC ....D 817 232-5450
Saginaw (G-17758)

FOOD PRDTS: Egg Substitutes, Made From Eggs

Saputo Dairy Foods Usa LLC ....C 214 863-2300
Dallas (G-4934)

FOOD PRDTS: Eggs, Processed, Frozen

Lion Share LLP ....D 281 888-5383
Houston (G-10654)

FOOD PRDTS: Emulsifiers

Cain Food Industries Inc ....E 214 630-4511
Dallas (G-4079)

FOOD PRDTS: Enriched Rice (Vitamin & Mineral Fortified)

Wenglar Services Inc ....F 979 648-2225
Louise (G-14354)

FOOD PRDTS: Flavored Ices, Frozen

Gelu Italian Ice LLC ....F 970 986-9535
Houston (G-9919)
Hokulia Shave Ice of Humble ....F 832 527-2820
Spring (G-19216)

FOOD PRDTS: Flour

Ardent Mills LLC ....D 817 847-3400
Saginaw (G-17737)

FOOD PRDTS: Flour & Other Grain Mill Products

Andersons Inc ....F 913 748-4401
Lytle (G-14572)
Archer-Daniels-Midland Company ....E 325 356-2511
Comanche (G-3235)
Archer-Daniels-Midland Company ....E 817 917-2810
Saginaw (G-17736)
Archer-Daniels-Midland Company ....D 806 723-5117
Lubbock (G-14363)
Archer-Daniels-Midland Company ....F 806 364-4732
Hereford (G-8283)
Archer-Daniels-Midland Company ....F 214 357-3331
Dallas (G-3957)

Archer-Daniels-Midland Company ....E 806 828-3948
Slaton **(G-18968)**
Ardent Mills LLC ....E 512 789-5165
Galena Park **(G-7377)**
Azteca Milling LP ....C 806 258-7704
Dawn **(G-5216)**
Azteca Milling LP ....C 956 383-4911
Irving **(G-12940)**
Azteca Milling LP ....F 972 232-5363
Irving **(G-12941)**
Azteca Milling LP ....C 956 383-4911
Edinburg **(G-5577)**
Bcca LLC ....G 361 547-3341
Tynan **(G-20180)**
Bcw Food Products Inc ....E 214 350-3320
Dallas **(G-4010)**
Collingwood Grain Inc ....F 254 582-5344
Hillsboro **(G-8324)**
Homestead Gristmill LLC ....E 254 829-2135
Waco **(G-20415)**
Miller Milling Company LLC ....E 817 847-8977
Saginaw **(G-17751)**
Panhandle Milling LLC ....E 806 243-4211
Dawn **(G-5217)**
Panhandle Milling LLC ....F 806 258-7253
Dawn **(G-5218)**
R Ibarras Inc ....D 817 625-8962
Fort Worth **(G-6931)**
Riviana Foods Inc ....B 713 529-3251
Houston **(G-11628)**
Riviana International Inc ....C 713 529-3251
Houston **(G-11630)**
Sunbelt Mixes Inc ....F 972 529-5155
McKinney **(G-14980)**

FOOD PRDTS: Flour Mixes & Doughs

Bcw Food Products Inc ....E 214 350-3320
Dallas **(G-4010)**
Blue Ribbon Products Inc ....D 214 647-1825
Rockwall **(G-17540)**
Tiger Construction ....F 915 999-1260
El Paso **(G-6005)**

FOOD PRDTS: Flour, Rice

Gulf Rice Milling Inc ....D 713 464-0606
Houston **(G-10070)**

FOOD PRDTS: Fresh Vegetables, Peeled Or Processed

Veggie Noodle Co LLC ....D 512 200-3337
Austin **(G-1626)**

FOOD PRDTS: Frosting Mixes, Dry, For Cakes, Cookies, Etc.

Blue Ribbon Products Inc ....D 214 647-1825
Rockwall **(G-17540)**
Cookies-N-Milk Inc ....F 214 491-6370
McKinney **(G-14932)**

FOOD PRDTS: Fruit Juices

Pepsico Inc ....D 972 963-1000
Plano **(G-16969)**
Precision Formulations LLC ....D 972 393-7170
Dallas **(G-4819)**

FOOD PRDTS: Fruits & Vegetables, Pickled

Apolo Commercial LLC ....F 956 688-8207
New Braunfels **(G-15774)**
Eastex Farms ....E 903 683-5726
Rusk **(G-17730)**
First Place Foods LLC ....E 972 272-1111
Garland **(G-7490)**

FOOD PRDTS: Fruits, Dried Or Dehydrated, Exc Freeze-Dried

Epic Provisions LLC ....F 512 944-8502
Austin **(G-1129)**

FOOD PRDTS: Gelatin Dessert Preparations

John Hogan Interests Inc ....E 214 637-0214
Dallas **(G-4537)**
Lulus Dessert Corporation ....D 210 399-3767
San Antonio **(G-18267)**

FOOD PRDTS: Granola & Energy Bars, Nonchocolate

Bearded Brothers LLC ....F 940 367-8256
Austin **(G-983)**

FOOD PRDTS: Honey

Bee Delightful LLC ....E 253 722-3018
Austin **(G-984)**
Good Flow Honey & Juice Co ....F 512 472-6714
Austin **(G-1188)**

FOOD PRDTS: Ice, Blocks

Heath Inc ....E 979 822-6924
Bryan **(G-2476)**

FOOD PRDTS: Ice, Cubes

Reddy Ice Holdings Inc ....E 214 526-6740
Dallas **(G-4877)**
Trevino Jr Gustavo ....G 956 585-2522
Mission **(G-15569)**

FOOD PRDTS: Instant Coffee

Black Rifle Coffee Company LLC ....F 844 899-9330
San Antonio **(G-17955)**

FOOD PRDTS: Juice Pops, Frozen

La Brisa Ice Cream Company LLC ....E 713 926-3450
Houston **(G-10579)**

FOOD PRDTS: Macaroni, Noodles, Spaghetti, Pasta, Etc

Food Source Inc ....D 972 548-9001
McKinney **(G-14944)**

FOOD PRDTS: Milled Corn By-Prdts

Interntional Grains Cereal LLC ....E 903 554-1003
Greenville **(G-8077)**

FOOD PRDTS: Mixes, Doughnut From Purchased Flour

Dawn Food Products Inc ....E 972 485-8004
Garland **(G-7477)**

FOOD PRDTS: Mixes, Flour

General Mills Inc ....E 972 892-4100
Addison **(G-129)**
Snow Flake Bakery ....E 281 427-4423
Baytown **(G-1834)**
Southern Noodle Company ....F 281 988-7778
Houston **(G-11976)**

FOOD PRDTS: Mixes, Pancake From Purchased Flour

Vicky Cakes Pancake Mix LLC ....G 469 573-2773
Farmers Branch **(G-6218)**

FOOD PRDTS: Mixes, Pizza From Purchased Flour

Alpha Foods Co ....E 936 372-5858
Waller **(G-20491)**

FOOD PRDTS: Mixes, Prepared Biscuit From Purchased Flour

CH Guenther & Son LLC ....B 210 227-1401
San Antonio **(G-17997)**

FOOD PRDTS: Mixes, Seasonings, Dry

Carmies Kitchen Inc ....F 972 442-1337
Wylie **(G-20930)**
Figueroa Brothers Inc ....E 214 351-9060
Irving **(G-13026)**
La India Packing Co ....E 956 723-3772
Laredo **(G-13903)**

FOOD PRDTS: Noodles, Uncooked, Packaged W/Other Ingredients

Woo Kee Foods Inc ....F 832 818-6988
Houston **(G-12683)**

FOOD PRDTS: Nuts & Seeds

Austinuts Wholesale Inc ....E 512 272-8007
Manor **(G-14645)**
Birdsong Corporation ....E 254 734-2266
Gorman **(G-7771)**
Birdsong Corporation ....F 806 637-7200
Brownfield **(G-2330)**
Clements Nut Co Inc ....E 972 436-4596
Lewisville **(G-14038)**
Elamex Usa Corp ....A 915 298-3061
El Paso **(G-5748)**
Golden Peanut Company LLC ....D 254 893-2034
De Leon **(G-5238)**
LOrenta Nuts LLC ....F 361 876-7570
San Antonio **(G-18266)**
Morven Partners LP ....F 325 372-5727
San Saba **(G-18718)**
Sungold Foods Inc ....F 806 748-2500
Lubbock **(G-14489)**
Universal Blanchers LLC ....E 254 445-4021
Dublin **(G-5518)**

FOOD PRDTS: Oils & Fats, Animal

Baari Inc ....F 214 566-5165
Plano **(G-16797)**
Inland Products Inc ....E 956 627-5700
McAllen **(G-14872)**
Interntnal Prtein Colloids Inc ....F 817 795-7744
Venus **(G-20219)**

FOOD PRDTS: Pasta, Rice/Potatoes, Uncooked, Pkgd

Calco Taiwan Marketing Service ....F 713 247-9918
Houston **(G-9048)**

FOOD PRDTS: Pasta, Uncooked, Packaged With Other Ingredients

Shayne Foods Incorporated ....F 210 442-8776
San Antonio **(G-18469)**

FOOD PRDTS: Peanut Butter

Clements Nut Co Inc ....E 972 436-4596
Lewisville **(G-14038)**
Sneaky Chef Foods LLC ....F 203 768-5654
Austin **(G-1514)**
Universal Blanchers LLC ....E 254 445-4021
Dublin **(G-5518)**

FOOD PRDTS: Pickles, Vinegar

Daltons Best Maid Products Inc ....C 800 447-3581
Fort Worth **(G-6574)**

FOOD PRDTS: Pizza Doughs From Purchased Flour

Sfc Global Supply Chain Inc ....B 713 740-7200
Pasadena **(G-16505)**

FOOD PRDTS: Pork Rinds

Evans Foods Inc ....F 817 640-5626
Arlington **(G-674)**

FOOD PRDTS: Potato & Corn Chips & Similar Prdts

Campbell Soup Company ....C 903 784-3341
Paris **(G-16359)**
Dishaka ....D 713 988-2900
Stafford **(G-19305)**
El Milagro of Texas Inc ....E 512 477-6476
San Marcos **(G-18685)**
Frito-Lay North America Inc ....A 972 579-2543
Irving **(G-13036)**
Frito-Lay North America Inc ....D 817 649-3266
Arlington **(G-681)**
Frito-Lay North America Inc ....E 214 631-8485
Dallas **(G-4379)**
Frito-Lay North America Inc ....F 903 868-2657
Sherman **(G-18915)**
Frito-Lay North America Inc ....B 214 331-7000
Dallas **(G-4381)**
Gruma Corporation ....C 956 380-4090
Edinburg **(G-5589)**
Mexican Snacks Inc ....E 956 440-9127
Harlingen **(G-8195)**

PRODUCT

Old Frito-Lay Inc ....A 972 334-7000
  Plano *(G-16953)*

Pepsico Inc ....D 972 963-1000
  Plano *(G-16969)*

Pretzels Inc ....E 972 416-3660
  Carrollton *(G-2795)*

Ricos Manufacturing Co Inc ....E 210 226-4168
  Lewisville *(G-14088)*

Ricos Products Co Inc ....C 210 222-1415
  San Antonio *(G-18426)*

Rudolph Foods Company Inc ....D 214 638-2204
  Dallas *(G-4919)*

Sanitary Tortilla Mfg Co ....E 210 226-9209
  San Antonio *(G-18453)*

Simply 7 Snacks LLC ....E 713 988-2900
  Stafford *(G-19379)*

Tyson Foods Inc ....B 713 678-1893
  Houston *(G-12421)*

Xochitl Inc ....E 214 800-3551
  Irving *(G-13211)*

FOOD PRDTS: Potato Chips & Other Potato-Based Snacks

Frito-Lay Inc ....B 972 334-7000
  Plano *(G-16873)*

Frito-Lay North America Inc ....D 214 944-5238
  Dallas *(G-4380)*

Frito-Lay North America Inc ....A 972 334-7000
  Plano *(G-16874)*

Rolling Frito-Lay Sales LP ....F 972 334-2513
  Plano *(G-16996)*

FOOD PRDTS: Potato Sticks

D S D Services Inc ....F 361 594-4114
  Shiner *(G-18939)*

FOOD PRDTS: Poultry Sausage, Lunch Meats/Other Poultry Prdts

Bridgford Industries Inc ....E 214 428-1535
  Dallas *(G-4053)*

FOOD PRDTS: Poultry, Processed, Fresh

Rio Star Foods Inc ....D 214 630-4455
  Dallas *(G-4901)*

FOOD PRDTS: Poultry, Processed, NEC

Holmes Foods Inc ....C 830 582-1551
  Nixon *(G-15866)*

Holmes Foods Inc ....F 830 437-5555
  Gonzales *(G-7755)*

Pilgrims Pride Corporation ....A 903 575-1000
  Mt Pleasant *(G-15667)*

FOOD PRDTS: Preparations

AB Mauri Food Inc ....E 903 454-3891
  Greenville *(G-8061)*

Abimar Foods Inc ....A 325 691-5425
  Abilene *(G-8)*

Adams Flvors Fods Ingrdnts LLC ....C 830 672-1850
  Gonzales *(G-7748)*

Allen Tharp LLC ....A 210 878-0034
  San Antonio *(G-17896)*

Ameripack Foods LLC ....E 903 639-4007
  Hughes Springs *(G-12738)*

Amplify Snack Brands Inc ....E 512 600-9893
  Austin *(G-920)*

Ardent Mills LLC ....D 817 847-3400
  Saginaw *(G-17737)*

Asiel Enterprises Inc ....D 361 765-6670
  Corpus Christi *(G-3476)*

Aspire Food Group Usa Inc ....E 512 645-0700
  Austin *(G-941)*

B Martinez & Sons Company Inc ....E 210 226-6772
  San Antonio *(G-17932)*

Bay Valley Foods LLC ....E 210 436-5551
  San Antonio *(G-17941)*

Bay Valley Foods LLC ....D 210 436-5551
  San Antonio *(G-17942)*

Birdsong Corporation ....E 254 734-2266
  Gorman *(G-7771)*

Birdsong Corporation ....F 806 637-7200
  Brownfield *(G-2330)*

Breedlove Foods Inc ....E 806 741-0404
  Lubbock *(G-14382)*

Bridgford Food Proc Texas LP ....D 214 428-1535
  Dallas *(G-4050)*

Bridgford Foods Corporation ....E 214 631-7970
  Dallas *(G-4052)*

Bridgford Foods Corporation ....D 214 428-1535
  Dallas *(G-4051)*

CH Guenther & Son LLC ....B 210 227-1401
  San Antonio *(G-17997)*

Conagra Brands Inc ....D 817 210-1600
  Fort Worth *(G-6539)*

David Lee Roberson ....F 210 662-8215
  San Antonio *(G-18042)*

Double R Brnd Prmium Fd Pdts L ....D 713 868-0030
  Lufkin *(G-14524)*

Epd Inc ....E 979 239-1917
  Angleton *(G-572)*

Evans Foods Inc ....F 817 640-5626
  Arlington *(G-674)*

Five Star Custom Foods Ltd ....E 682 647-2700
  Fort Worth *(G-6635)*

Frito-Lay North America Inc ....A 972 579-2543
  Irving *(G-13036)*

Frito-Lay North America Inc ....B 210 662-2100
  San Antonio *(G-18127)*

Frito-Lay North America Inc ....E 214 631-8485
  Dallas *(G-4379)*

Frito-Lay North America Inc ....B 214 331-7000
  Dallas *(G-4381)*

Frito-Lay North America Inc ....D 817 649-3266
  Arlington *(G-681)*

Frito-Lay North America Inc ....D 214 944-5238
  Dallas *(G-4380)*

Gem Food Services Corp ....E 281 232-8013
  Rosenberg *(G-17582)*

Gruma Corporation ....C 210 304-6700
  San Antonio *(G-18154)*

Gruma Corporation ....D 832 441-5982
  Houston *(G-10050)*

Gruma Corporation ....C 972 232-5000
  Irving *(G-13044)*

Gruma Corporation ....B 972 709-1217
  Dallas *(G-4419)*

Han-D-Pac Products Inc ....E 915 595-2212
  El Paso *(G-5793)*

Heb Plus ....D 210 673-4900
  San Antonio *(G-18163)*

High Grade Products LLC ....F 832 381-3455
  Spring *(G-19215)*

Hillshire Brands Company ....C 713 928-6281
  Houston *(G-10186)*

Hormel Foods Corp Svcs LLC ....F 210 495-0764
  San Antonio *(G-18173)*

Houston Sysco Inc ....B 713 672-8080
  Houston *(G-10254)*

Illes Food Ingredients Ltd ....D 800 683-4553
  Carrollton *(G-2764)*

Intermex Products Usa Ltd ....E 972 660-2071
  Grand Prairie *(G-7894)*

Jardine Foods Inc ....E 512 295-4600
  Buda *(G-2531)*

Jgr Enterprises LLC ....E 817 335-4629
  Fort Worth *(G-6741)*

La Hacenda Mexican Fd Pdts Inc ....E 214 353-0230
  Dallas *(G-4575)*

Leons Fine Foods Inc ....C 972 529-5050
  McKinney *(G-14953)*

Maui Foods International Inc ....E 214 823-6284
  Plano *(G-16920)*

Minom Inc ....F 210 734-5124
  San Antonio *(G-18308)*

Mizkan America Inc ....D 214 339-5551
  Dallas *(G-4679)*

Mother Parkers Tea Cof USA Ltd ....C 817 551-5500
  Fort Worth *(G-6855)*

Newly Weds Foods Inc ....E 903 577-3200
  Mount Pleasant *(G-15656)*

Papa Bears Pizza ....E 512 351-5421
  Cedar Park *(G-1862)*

Paper Plate Incorporated ....F 972 296-7888
  Desoto *(G-5439)*

Perfectfitmeals LLC ....F 713 868-5300
  Houston *(G-11290)*

Pioneer Frozen Foods Inc ....A 972 298-4281
  Duncanville *(G-5536)*

Pita Pal Industries Inc ....D 713 777-7482
  Houston *(G-11339)*

Pretzels Inc ....E 972 416-3660
  Carrollton *(G-2795)*

Proportion Foods LLC ....B 512 735-9800
  Round Rock *(G-17683)*

R Ibarras Inc ....D 817 625-8962
  Fort Worth *(G-6931)*

Regal Interests Inc ....F 713 222-8231
  Houston *(G-11583)*

Riba Foods Inc ....D 713 975-7001
  Houston *(G-11617)*

Ricos Products Co Inc ....C 210 222-1415
  San Antonio *(G-18426)*

Riviana Foods Inc ....B 713 529-3251
  Houston *(G-11628)*

Rudolph Foods Company Inc ....D 214 638-2204
  Dallas *(G-4919)*

Russell E Womack Inc ....E 806 747-2581
  Lubbock *(G-14474)*

Ryc Foods LLC ....E 210 731-8854
  San Antonio *(G-18439)*

Sarais Spreads Superfood LLC ....F 552 163-6178
  The Woodlands *(G-19916)*

Sfc Global Supply Chain Inc ....B 713 740-7200
  Pasadena *(G-16505)*

Teasdale Foods Inc ....C 952 854-0903
  Flower Mound *(G-6288)*

Teasdale Foods Inc ....C 915 821-2500
  El Paso *(G-5994)*

Texas Coffee Company ....E 409 835-3434
  Beaumont *(G-1958)*

Texas Food Solutions LLC ....D 713 579-5634
  Katy *(G-13449)*

Todays Children Food Program ....F 214 562-4702
  Desoto *(G-5445)*

Trinidad Benham Holding Co ....D 903 569-2283
  Mineola *(G-15514)*

Tyson Foods Inc ....B 817 656-5507
  Fort Worth *(G-7089)*

Van Oriental Food Inc ....D 214 630-0333
  Dallas *(G-5153)*

Ventura Foods LLC ....F 817 232-6800
  Fort Worth *(G-7097)*

West Phalia Market Inc ....F 512 846-1155
  Hutto *(G-12888)*

Wonton Food Corporation ....E 832 366-1280
  Houston *(G-12682)*

Zilks Foods LLC ....F 512 633-8904
  Austin *(G-1687)*

FOOD PRDTS: Prepared Meat Sauces Exc Tomato & Dry

Nueces Canyon Companies ....F 979 289-5600
  Brenham *(G-2266)*

FOOD PRDTS: Prepared Sauces, Exc Tomato Based

Frankie VS Kitchen LLC ....D 214 303-9910
  Dallas *(G-4377)*

Richard E Colgin I Ltd ....E 214 951-8687
  Dallas *(G-4897)*

FOOD PRDTS: Relishes, Fruit & Vegetable

Gourmet Grdns Spclty Foods Inc ....E 903 284-6215
  Jacksonville *(G-13241)*

Jardine Foods Inc ....E 512 295-4600
  Buda *(G-2531)*

Renfro Foods Inc ....E 817 336-3849
  Fort Worth *(G-6955)*

FOOD PRDTS: Rice, Milled

American Rice Inc ....E 281 272-8800
  Houston *(G-8606)*

American Rice Inc ....C 979 233-8248
  Freeport *(G-7191)*

Barton Springs Mill Inc ....F 512 554-5981
  Dripping Springs *(G-5501)*

Beaumont Rice Mills Inc ....E 409 832-2521
  Beaumont *(G-1862)*

Bu Growers Ltd ....B 979 245-2043
  Bay City *(G-1769)*

Colorado County Rice Mill Inc ....F 979 234-5554
  Eagle Lake *(G-5540)*

Doguets Rice Milling Company ....E 409 866-2297
  Beaumont *(G-1883)*

Ebrofrost North America Inc ....E 281 727-8139
  Houston *(G-9573)*

Gulf Pacific Rice Co Inc ....E 713 464-0606
  Houston *(G-10066)*

Ricetec Inc ....C 281 756-3300
  Alvin *(G-379)*

Riviana Foods Inc ....B 713 529-3251
  Houston *(G-11628)*

SOS Cuetara USA Inc ....C 281 272-8800
Houston *(G-11956)*

TLC Tonerland LP ....F 713 692-6650
Houston *(G-12306)*

FOOD PRDTS: Rice, Packaged & Seasoned

Magi Foods LLC ....F 210 590-1308
Selma *(G-18877)*

FOOD PRDTS: Salads

Malim Inc ....C 210 654-3963
San Antonio *(G-18272)*

US Citrus LLC ....E 956 252-3101
Hargill *(G-8171)*

FOOD PRDTS: Sandwiches

Bridgford Industries Inc ....E 214 428-1535
Dallas *(G-4053)*

Bridgford Marketing Company ....D 214 428-1535
Dallas *(G-4054)*

Georgia Sandwich Company Inc ....E 770 426-5678
Southlake *(G-19072)*

Great American Marketing Co ....D 713 682-6471
Houston *(G-10024)*

Texas Automatic Foods Inc ....E 713 432-1331
Bellaire *(G-2003)*

FOOD PRDTS: Seasonings & Spices

Acj Produce & Spices LLC ....E 956 627-4246
McAllen *(G-14831)*

El Venado Foods ....E 713 692-0688
Houston *(G-9587)*

Kennys All Purpose Seasoning ....F 940 733-2200
Wichita Falls *(G-20776)*

North Texas Ingredients Inc ....F 817 270-2397
Azle *(G-1727)*

Precise Food Ingredients Inc ....E 972 323-4951
Carrollton *(G-2882)*

Southwest Spice Company LLC ....G 713 860-5300
Houston *(G-11984)*

FOOD PRDTS: Spices, Including Ground

Circle U Foods Inc ....F 817 626-6918
Fort Worth *(G-6520)*

Consolidated Mills Inc ....E 713 896-4196
Houston *(G-9276)*

McCormick & Company Inc ....D 972 721-9318
Irving *(G-13100)*

McCormick & Company Inc ....C 214 329-7044
Irving *(G-13101)*

Micor Inc ....E 281 476-0808
Deer Park *(G-5286)*

FOOD PRDTS: Sugar, Beet

Imperial Sugar Company ....C 281 491-9181
Sugar Land *(G-19497)*

FOOD PRDTS: Sugar, Granulated Cane, Purchd Raw Sugar/Syrup

Imperial Sugar Company ....C 281 491-9181
Sugar Land *(G-19496)*

FOOD PRDTS: Sugar, Raw Cane

Rio Grande Vly Sug Growers Inc ....B 956 636-1411
Santa Rosa *(G-18737)*

FOOD PRDTS: Syrups

E A Sween Company ....D 972 219-0566
Lewisville *(G-14046)*

TJ Blackburn Syrup Works Inc ....D 903 665-2541
Jefferson *(G-13289)*

FOOD PRDTS: Tapioca

Kmr Group LLC ....G 713 932-6988
Houston *(G-10543)*

FOOD PRDTS: Tea

Red River Tea Company ....F 214 956-0373
Dallas *(G-4870)*

FOOD PRDTS: Tofu, Exc Frozen Desserts

Houston Calco Inc ....G 713 236-8668
Houston *(G-10221)*

FOOD PRDTS: Tortilla Chips

Amplify Snack Brands Inc ....E 512 600-9893
Austin *(G-920)*

Arte Sano LLC ....D 512 400-8743
Austin *(G-935)*

Aus-Mex Company Inc ....D 432 561-8866
Midland *(G-15124)*

Dallas Tortillas Inc ....F 214 943-7681
Dallas *(G-4228)*

Durrset Amigos Ltd ....C 210 798-5360
San Antonio *(G-18074)*

Exquisita Tortillas Inc ....E 956 383-3011
Edinburg *(G-5587)*

Gruma Corporation ....B 972 709-1217
Dallas *(G-4419)*

Gruma Corporation ....C 210 304-6700
San Antonio *(G-18154)*

Gruma Corporation ....C 972 232-5000
Irving *(G-13044)*

Gruma Corporation ....C 972 232-5000
Irving *(G-13043)*

Isabella Foods Inc ....D 915 590-1899
El Paso *(G-5818)*

Ixpalia Inc ....E 512 389-0389
Austin *(G-1245)*

Lopez Tortilla Foods Inc ....E 214 353-9538
Dallas *(G-4606)*

Lunas Tortillas Factory ....F 214 747-2661
Dallas *(G-4612)*

Mexi-Snax Corporation ....E 915 779-5709
El Paso *(G-5874)*

Odessa Tortilla & Tamale Fctry ....E 432 332-6676
Odessa *(G-16098)*

Tortillas Santos LLC ....G 956 712-3800
Laredo *(G-13938)*

FOOD PRDTS: Tortillas

Adelita Tortilla Factory ....E 210 733-5352
San Antonio *(G-17865)*

Alamo Tamale Company LP ....D 713 228-6445
Houston *(G-8525)*

Armando G Martinez ....E 325 653-5640
San Angelo *(G-17778)*

Aus-Mex Company Inc ....D 432 561-8866
Midland *(G-15124)*

Azteca Tortilla Factory ....E 956 702-7395
San Juan *(G-18671)*

Capistran Tortilla Factory ....E 956 541-3053
Brownsville *(G-2343)*

Carnicria Y Tortilleria El Sol ....G 915 877-5553
El Paso *(G-5684)*

Casa Rica LP ....E 806 296-7582
Plainview *(G-16753)*

City Tortilla Factory Inc ....F 361 776-3578
Ingleside *(G-12892)*

Commonwealth Urology ....E 281 372-1112
Houston *(G-9254)*

Dallas Tortillas Inc ....F 214 943-7681
Dallas *(G-4228)*

De Maiz Tortilleria L L C ....F 956 702-8855
Pharr *(G-16697)*

Delrio Tortilla Factory ....E 210 922-4810
San Antonio *(G-18049)*

El Milagro of Texas Inc ....E 512 477-6476
San Marcos *(G-18685)*

Exquisita Tortillas Inc ....C 956 383-6712
Edinburg *(G-5586)*

Exquisita Tortillas Inc ....E 956 383-3011
Edinburg *(G-5587)*

G Tacos Inc ....D 806 371-0411
Amarillo *(G-427)*

Gruma Corporation ....C 972 232-5000
Irving *(G-13043)*

Isabella Foods Inc ....D 915 590-1899
El Paso *(G-5818)*

Ixpalia Inc ....E 512 389-0389
Austin *(G-1245)*

J Leals Food Inc ....E 214 412-3158
Grand Prairie *(G-7898)*

Julios Corn Chips ....E 325 486-9300
San Angelo *(G-17812)*

La Abuela Mexican Foods Inc ....E 956 447-8289
Weslaco *(G-20663)*

La Espiga De Oro - Georgia Inc ....C 713 861-4200
Houston *(G-10580)*

La Fama Foods Inc ....D 903 968-4500
Ore City *(G-16274)*

La Famosa Tortilla ....F 361 592-5596
Kingsville *(G-13633)*

La Frontera Molina ....F 210 432-0855
San Antonio *(G-18233)*

La Hacienda Tortilla Factory ....F 830 773-9151
Eagle Pass *(G-5548)*

La Mexicana Tortilla Fctry Inc ....D 214 943-7770
Duncanville *(G-5532)*

La Nortena Tortilla Factory ....F 432 445-3273
Pecos *(G-16622)*

La Nueva Riograndese Inc ....E 817 921-0440
Fort Worth *(G-6777)*

La Original Tortilla Co Inc ....E 361 570-8905
Victoria *(G-20282)*

La Paloma Tortilla Factory ....F 956 316-1515
Edinburg *(G-5592)*

La Ranchera Inc ....F 713 699-4400
Houston *(G-10582)*

La Regia Tortilla Factory LLC ....E 210 971-9190
San Antonio *(G-18235)*

La Rotativa Tortilla Inc ....G 915 533-2317
El Paso *(G-5834)*

La Superior Foods Inc ....F 682 703-1165
Fort Worth *(G-6778)*

La Tapatia Inc ....F 915 859-9616
El Paso *(G-5835)*

Lapaz Tortilla Factory ....G 432 337-7735
Odessa *(G-16060)*

Lobo Tortilla Factory Inc ....C 972 388-8000
Dallas *(G-4599)*

Lopez Efrain ....F 713 921-0057
Houston *(G-10688)*

Lunas Tortillas Factory ....F 214 747-2661
Dallas *(G-4612)*

Marbros L L C ....F 210 922-8383
San Antonio *(G-18275)*

Marroquin Tortilla Factory ....F 361 883-7051
Corpus Christi *(G-3574)*

Mexi-Snax Corporation ....E 915 779-5709
El Paso *(G-5874)*

Montega Ltd ....D 713 692-1400
Houston *(G-10912)*

Montes Tortilla Factory ....F 956 969-5792
Weslaco *(G-20666)*

Nuevo Leon Tortilla Factory ....F 972 721-1984
Irving *(G-13129)*

Odessa Tortilla & Tamale Fctry ....E 432 332-6676
Odessa *(G-16098)*

Panchitas Tortilla Factory ....F 325 655-2138
San Angelo *(G-17818)*

Peached Tortilla Mobile LLC ....F 512 297-8635
Austin *(G-1403)*

Piedras Negras Tortilla Fctry ....G 830 773-6706
Eagle Pass *(G-5553)*

Pops Bakery Inc ....E 325 655-1170
San Angelo *(G-17822)*

Pulido Associates Inc ....E 817 249-6728
Benbrook *(G-2045)*

Sanitary Tortilla Mfg Co ....F 210 226-9209
San Antonio *(G-18453)*

Steven M Riley ....F 972 741-0971
Richardson *(G-17402)*

Super Lopez Tortillas LLC ....D 713 921-1237
Houston *(G-12107)*

Taco & Tortilla Factory Inc ....F 713 706-3233
Houston *(G-12146)*

Tortillas Olivo LLC ....F 956 702-8388
San Juan *(G-18675)*

Tortilleria Cuauhtemoc ....F 915 886-4480
Canutillo *(G-2666)*

Tortillria Monterrey Groceries ....F 956 544-7222
Brownsville *(G-2415)*

FOOD PRDTS: Turkey, Processed, Fresh

Pilgrims Pride Corporation ....C 936 564-3306
Nacogdoches *(G-15709)*

Pilgrims Pride Corporation ....A 214 565-8600
Dallas *(G-4805)*

FOOD PRDTS: Turkey, Slaughtered & Dressed

Greenberg Smoked Turkeys Inc ....E 903 595-0725
Tyler *(G-20091)*

FOOD PRDTS: Variety Meats, Poultry

Sanderson Farms Inc ....D 903 723-2112
Palestine *(G-16308)*

PRODUCT

FOOD PRDTS: Vegetable Oil Mills, NEC

Archer-Daniels-Midland Company ....D 806 723-5117
Lubbock *(G-14363)*

Bunge Oils Inc ....D 817 568-4900
Fort Worth *(G-6478)*

Darling Ingredients Inc ....D 313 928-7400
Irving *(G-12993)*

Noircroxx Biologicals LLC ....E 406 471-0671
Arlington *(G-739)*

FOOD PRDTS: Vegetable Oil, Refined, Exc Corn

Inland Products Inc ....E 956 627-5700
McAllen *(G-14872)*

FOOD PRDTS: Vinegar

Bartush-Schnitzius Foods Co ....E 972 219-1270
Lewisville *(G-14026)*

Mizkan Americas Inc ....E 214 339-5551
Dallas *(G-4680)*

National Vinegar Company ....E 713 223-4214
Houston *(G-11004)*

FOOD PRDTS: Wheat Flour

CH Guenther & Son LLC ....C 972 298-4281
Duncanville *(G-5529)*

Morrison Milling Company ....D 940 387-6111
Denton *(G-5382)*

Richardson Milling Inc ....F 806 258-7227
Dawn *(G-5219)*

FOOD PRODUCTS MACHINERY

Automated Food Systems Inc ....F 469 517-0470
Waxahachie *(G-20528)*

Bakers Pride Oven Co Inc ....F 800 431-2745
Allen *(G-256)*

Calan Group Inc ....C 972 422-5808
Plano *(G-16817)*

Casteel Mfg Inc ....F 210 923-4558
San Antonio *(G-17986)*

Centrifuge Repair & Engrg LP ....F 281 471-3767
La Porte *(G-13726)*

Champion Food Service 2 Inc ....F 210 736-2190
Von Ormy *(G-20346)*

Commercial Kitchens Inc ....D 281 442-8001
Houston *(G-9250)*

Cugar Machine Inc ....F 817 927-0411
Fort Worth *(G-6565)*

Custom Delis Equipment Co Inc ....E 817 831-7080
Fort Worth *(G-6567)*

Denny Kincer Inc ....E 806 762-1069
Lubbock *(G-14401)*

Double Jj Corporation ....E 214 353-0230
Dallas *(G-4274)*

EMI Industries LLC ....E 817 987-1516
Arlington *(G-669)*

Ferrell-Ross Roll Mfg Inc ....D 806 364-9051
Hereford *(G-8288)*

Filtration Automation Inc ....E 817 999-8190
Alvarado *(G-332)*

FMC Technologies Inc ....F 281 591-4106
Houston *(G-9823)*

H & K International Inc ....C 214 818-3500
Mesquite *(G-15047)*

Hilltop Texas Inc ....E 214 430-1311
Allen *(G-275)*

Insight Equity A P X L P ....F 817 488-7775
Southlake *(G-19075)*

Insight Equity LP ....E 817 488-7775
Southlake *(G-19076)*

Invision Automated Systems Inc ....F 713 461-6642
Katy *(G-13410)*

John Bean Technologies Corp ....G 936 441-2077
Conroe *(G-3315)*

John Bean Technologies Corp ....C 713 875-3735
Houston *(G-10480)*

John Bean Technologies Corp ....F 915 859-3776
El Paso *(G-5822)*

Labeling Equipment Specialists ....F 903 734-5873
Gilmer *(G-7708)*

M W Waldrop Co ....E 713 337-5600
Houston *(G-10720)*

Maddox Metal Works Inc ....D 214 333-2311
Dallas *(G-4625)*

Materials Transportation Co ....C 800 433-3110
Temple *(G-19688)*

Meyer Industries Inc ....D 210 736-1811
San Antonio *(G-18296)*

Project Services Group Inc ....D 972 812-7370
Irving *(G-13159)*

Quality Custom Fabricators ....D 817 649-8020
Grand Prairie *(G-7960)*

Quality Fabrication Design LP ....D 972 304-3266
Coppell *(G-3436)*

Saginaw Machine Company ....F 817 232-4482
Saginaw *(G-17756)*

Sani-Weld Inc ....E 281 442-0667
Houston *(G-11747)*

Satake USA Inc ....D 281 276-3600
Stafford *(G-19374)*

Tables Manufacturing Inc ....B 972 932-4148
Kaufman *(G-13464)*

Tetra Pak Global Information ....G 940 565-8800
Denton *(G-5403)*

Thunderbird Food Machinery ....E 214 331-3000
Dallas *(G-5089)*

Win-Holt Equipment Corp ....C 972 641-4658
Grand Prairie *(G-7995)*

FOOD STORES: Delicatessen

Droubis Bakery & Deli Inc ....F 713 988-5897
Houston *(G-9532)*

Kubys Sausage House Inc ....E 214 363-2231
Dallas *(G-4572)*

FOOD STORES: Grocery, Chain

Southern Noodle Company ....F 281 988-7778
Houston *(G-11976)*

FOOD STORES: Grocery, Independent

Capistran Tortilla Factory ....E 956 541-3053
Brownsville *(G-2343)*

Chorizo De San Manuel Guer ....E 956 383-8751
Edinburg *(G-5582)*

La Hacienda Tortilla Factory ....F 830 773-9151
Eagle Pass *(G-5548)*

Patek Grocery and Market ....F 361 594-3171
Shiner *(G-18946)*

Praseks Hillje Smokehouse ....D 979 543-8312
El Campo *(G-5626)*

Tallent Enterprises Inc ....F 936 594-2591
Riverside *(G-17480)*

FOOD STORES: Supermarkets, Chain

H E Butt Grocery Company ....C 956 702-2289
Alamo *(G-179)*

FOOTWEAR, WHOLESALE: Athletic

Asics America Corporation ....E 972 678-0200
Allen *(G-252)*

Cheerleading Company Inc ....E 800 411-4105
Dallas *(G-4106)*

FOOTWEAR, WHOLESALE: Boots

Anderson Bean Boot Co Inc ....E 956 565-2618
Mercedes *(G-15002)*

Cowtown Boot Company ....D 915 593-2929
El Paso *(G-5704)*

FOOTWEAR: Cut Stock

Honcho Boots LLC ....F 915 855-9300
El Paso *(G-5796)*

San Antonio Shoe Inc ....F 210 223-0166
San Antonio *(G-18449)*

San Antonio Shoe Inc ....A 830 768-7200
Del Rio *(G-5323)*

FORESTRY RELATED EQPT

Forestry Supply Service Inc ....F 936 632-3394
Lufkin *(G-14528)*

Forestry Supply Service Inc ....F 409 384-3213
Jasper *(G-13276)*

FORGINGS

Ameribolt Inc ....E 713 580-4997
Houston *(G-8579)*

Better Burglar Bars Inc ....E 713 699-9543
Houston *(G-8867)*

Brougher Inc ....D 713 869-7577
Houston *(G-8996)*

C-B-Gear & Machine Inc ....E 281 449-0777
Houston *(G-9040)*

Chicago Bridge & Iron Co Del ....C 832 513-1000
Houston *(G-9183)*

Crow Precision Components LLC ....D 817 536-2861
Fort Worth *(G-6562)*

Ellwood Texas Forge LP ....C 713 434-5100
Houston *(G-9605)*

Ellwood Txas Frge Navasota LLC ....B 936 825-7531
Navasota *(G-15733)*

Flanges Inc ....F 713 673-4117
Kingwood *(G-13643)*

Forged Components Inc ....C 281 441-4088
Humble *(G-12767)*

Forged Components Inc ....D 936 825-7518
Navasota *(G-15735)*

Forged Components Inc ....E 409 246-2427
Kountze *(G-13670)*

Forged Products Inc ....D 713 462-3416
Houston *(G-9833)*

General Electric Company ....D 412 469-6080
Southlake *(G-19071)*

GK Steel Fabrication LLC ....F 972 291-5514
Duncanville *(G-5531)*

Gulfco Forge Company LLC ....C 409 842-1311
Houston *(G-10072)*

Lufkin Gears LLC ....B 936 634-2211
Lufkin *(G-14539)*

Lufkin Industries LLC ....F 281 495-1100
Missouri City *(G-15583)*

Maddox Metal Works Inc ....D 214 333-2311
Dallas *(G-4625)*

Martin Sprocket & Gear Inc ....D 325 677-3591
Abilene *(G-59)*

Martin Sprocket & Gear Inc ....D 214 428-2191
Dallas *(G-4641)*

Matek Performance Inc ....E 817 626-9006
Fort Worth *(G-6816)*

Modern Forge Texas LLC ....D 817 268-0781
Hurst *(G-12853)*

Moventas Gears Inc ....E 503 247-6107
Spring *(G-19234)*

National Oilwell Varco Inc ....C 936 825-7070
Navasota *(G-15739)*

Orbix Corporation ....E 254 675-8651
Clifton *(G-3145)*

Oteco Inc ....C 713 695-3693
Houston *(G-11200)*

Oteco Inc ....D 713 695-3693
Houston *(G-11201)*

Parish International Inc ....E 281 463-9233
Hempstead *(G-8254)*

Ram-Gear Manufacturing Inc ....F 361 668-0235
Alice *(G-231)*

Samco Sales Inc ....F 713 733-5700
Houston *(G-11738)*

Standard Industrial Pdts Co ....E 281 280-0147
Webster *(G-20647)*

Structural Metals Inc ....A 830 372-8200
Seguin *(G-18866)*

Texas Steel Tech LLC ....F 817 894-7041
Weatherford *(G-20626)*

Trinity Forge Inc ....C 817 473-1515
Mansfield *(G-14723)*

TX Tinman Enterprises LLC ....F 817 288-6116
Fort Worth *(G-7087)*

Voestalpine Texas LLC ....E 361 704-9000
Portland *(G-17188)*

W Silver Inc ....C 915 886-3553
Vinton *(G-20343)*

Windstrom Industries & Assoc ....E 214 298-6342
Dallas *(G-5194)*

FORGINGS: Aircraft, Ferrous

Taper-Lok Corporation ....F 713 467-3333
Houston *(G-12158)*

FORGINGS: Aluminum

General Dynamics Ordnance ....B 972 276-5131
Garland *(G-7499)*

Non-Frrous Extrsion Scrap Mtls ....D 713 869-9551
Houston *(G-11067)*

FORGINGS: Anchors

Andrews Safety Anchors Inc ....F 432 524-6659
Andrews *(G-535)*

National Foundry & Mfg Co ....E 432 558-3444
Crane *(G-3700)*

(G-0000) Company's Geographic Section entry number

FORGINGS: Armor Plate, Iron Or Steel

B&B Roadway SEC Solutions LLC........F 972 385-7899
Mckinney *(G-14924)*

Liberty Forge Inc ....D 936 336-5785
Liberty *(G-14121)*

FORGINGS: Automotive & Internal Combustion Engine

Futaba Industrial Texas Corp................C 210 927-2288
San Antonio *(G-18132)*

FORGINGS: Bearing & Bearing Race, Nonferrous

O & D Manufacturing Inc ....D 903 295-2057
White Oak *(G-20718)*

FORGINGS: Construction Or Mining Eqpt, Ferrous

Beta Arkansas LLC ....F 972 490-2340
Dallas *(G-4022)*

Skipper Industries Inc ....E 254 897-1292
Glen Rose *(G-7733)*

FORGINGS: Gear & Chain

Amarillo Gear Company LLC ....C 806 622-1273
Amarillo *(G-478)*

O E M Industries Inc ....F 214 330-7271
Dallas *(G-4748)*

Timken Gears & Services Inc...............E 713 224-4900
Houston *(G-12292)*

FORGINGS: Iron & Steel

Precision Turning..............................G 817 472-7999
Arlington *(G-758)*

FORGINGS: Machinery, Ferrous

Crosby Group LLC.............................B 918 834-4611
Longview *(G-14216)*

FORGINGS: Metal , Ornamental, Ferrous

Cerda-Fied Specialists Inc ....F 281 392-8063
Brookshire *(G-2313)*

CK Kustoms Iron Works Inc ....F 281 850-6118
Rockport *(G-17529)*

FORGINGS: Missile & Ordinance, Nonferrous

AGH Industries Inc............................E 817 284-1742
Euless *(G-6129)*

FORGINGS: Missile & Ordnance, Ferrous

AGH Industries Inc............................E 817 284-1742
Euless *(G-6129)*

FORGINGS: Nonferrous

Copper Craft Inc...............................E 817 490-9622
Fort Worth *(G-6549)*

Ellwood Texas Forge LP ....C 713 434-5100
Houston *(G-9605)*

FORGINGS: Pump & compressor, Nonferrous

Flowserve Corporation........................E 832 375-0807
Houston *(G-9813)*

Flowserve Corporation........................B 972 443-6500
Irving *(G-13027)*

Flowserve Corporation........................F 800 446-0401
Irving *(G-13028)*

Pump Arts Inc ....E 713 946-0500
Houston *(G-11472)*

FORMS: Concrete, Sheet Metal

Cherry Construction Systems ....E 903 675-5901
Athens *(G-822)*

Commercial Forms Inc ....E 903 675-2511
Athens *(G-823)*

Jayco Steel Services Inc ....E 281 399-0189
New Caney *(G-15842)*

FOUNDRIES: Aluminum

Galvotec Alloys Inc ....C 956 630-3500
McAllen *(G-14863)*

Kessler Industries Inc ....E 915 591-8161
El Paso *(G-5828)*

M G Products Company ....E 915 541-8950
El Paso *(G-5853)*

Mayday Manufacturing Co ....C 940 898-8301
Denton *(G-5381)*

Samuel Son & Co (usa) Inc ....D 972 438-3949
Irving *(G-13171)*

Superior Die Cast LLC........................E 903 586-0637
Jacksonville *(G-13260)*

YKK AP America Inc ....E 972 245-9551
Coppell *(G-3454)*

FOUNDRIES: Brass, Bronze & Copper

American Bronze Alum Cast Corp ....E 713 222-0236
Houston *(G-8591)*

C & L Aluminum Foundry Inc ....F 817 923-0533
Fort Worth *(G-6483)*

Claytex Trophies Inc ....C 940 538-6521
Henrietta *(G-8279)*

Demco Manufacturing Inc ....E 936 829-4771
Diboll *(G-5462)*

M G Products Company ....E 915 541-8950
El Paso *(G-5853)*

Mayday Manufacturing Co ....C 940 898-8301
Denton *(G-5381)*

O & D Manufacturing Inc ....D 903 295-2057
White Oak *(G-20718)*

Odessa JPK Investments Ltd ....E 432 368-8089
Odessa *(G-16096)*

Permocast Corporation ....E 254 778-5216
Temple *(G-19699)*

Solidiform Inc ....E 817 831-2626
Fort Worth *(G-7000)*

Texas Metal Casting Co ....E 936 639-1131
Lufkin *(G-14555)*

Wearalloy Inc ....E 979 543-1133
Houston *(G-12610)*

FOUNDRIES: Gray & Ductile Iron

Ebaa Iron Inc ....E 325 762-3084
Albany *(G-187)*

Grandor Corporation ....C 903 872-6571
Corsicana *(G-3672)*

L B Foster Company ....E 832 934-3107
Magnolia *(G-14613)*

McWane Inc ....A 903 882-5511
Tyler *(G-20124)*

Oil City Iron Works Inc ....C 903 872-6571
Corsicana *(G-3681)*

Standard Industrial Pdts Co ....E 281 280-0147
Webster *(G-20647)*

Star Pipe Usa LLC.............................D 620 251-5700
Houston *(G-12047)*

FOUNDRIES: Iron

Industrial Castings Co Inc....................F 713 747-5336
Houston *(G-10347)*

Mid-South Metals LLC ....E 817 838-8000
Fort Worth *(G-6839)*

Standard Alloys Incorporated................D 409 983-3201
Port Arthur *(G-17125)*

FOUNDRIES: Nonferrous

American Railcar Inds Inc ....C 903 759-3946
Longview *(G-14195)*

Centrifugal Castings Inc ....E 254 773-9068
Temple *(G-19675)*

Coastal Casting Service ....D 713 223-4439
Houston *(G-9223)*

Coastal Foundry Company ....E 713 695-4008
Houston *(G-9226)*

Consolidated Casting LLC ....C 972 225-7305
Hutchins *(G-12865)*

D C G Machine Inc ....E 903 297-2053
White Oak *(G-20713)*

Delta Centrifugal LLC ....C 254 773-9055
Temple *(G-19679)*

Globalfoundries US Inc ....F 512 457-3407
Austin *(G-1184)*

Superior Die Cast LLC........................E 903 586-0637
Jacksonville *(G-13260)*

FOUNDRIES: Steel

Alamo Iron Works Inc ....B 210 223-6161
San Antonio *(G-17885)*

American Railcar Inds Inc ....C 903 759-3946
Longview *(G-14195)*

Chicago Bridge & Iron Co Del...............C 832 513-1000
Houston *(G-9183)*

Fasteel LLC......................................G 210 661-2603
San Antonio *(G-18106)*

Gerdau Ameristeel US Inc ....G 972 782-7902
Farmersville *(G-6223)*

Penatek Foundry & Machining ....E 432 368-0888
Odessa *(G-16110)*

Qualico Steel Company Inc ....D 972 775-1400
Midlothian *(G-15492)*

ROC Industries Inc ....E 713 468-7743
Houston *(G-11647)*

Service Metal Products Company ....E 281 499-3020
Houston *(G-11839)*

Sfi-Gray Steel LLC.............................A 713 864-6450
Houston *(G-11842)*

United States Steel Corp ....D 903 656-6521
Lone Star *(G-14185)*

Wolar Industrial Inc............................D 713 926-2440
Houston *(G-12680)*

FOUNDRIES: Steel Investment

Dal-Air Tool Co Inc ....E 903 598-2226
Point *(G-17079)*

DSA Operating Company LLC ....E 210 734-5121
San Antonio *(G-18072)*

National Oilwell Varco Inc ....E 830 693-5312
Marble Falls *(G-14748)*

FOUNDRY MACHINERY & EQPT

A&W Productions Inc ....D 940 458-4190
Sanger *(G-18723)*

FOUNTAIN REPAIR SVCS

Chromalloy Gas Turbine LLC ....F 972 241-2501
Dallas *(G-4114)*

FOUNTAINS: Concrete

Fountain People Inc ....D 512 392-1155
San Marcos *(G-18688)*

PSI Concrete Construction LLC ....F 210 204-1529
San Antonio *(G-18400)*

FRACTIONATION PRDTS OF CRUDE PETROLEUM, HYDROCARBONS, NEC

Eagle Hydrocarbons LLC ....E 713 300-3245
Houston *(G-9558)*

Emgs Americas Inc ....E 281 920-5601
Houston *(G-9615)*

Madmackenzie Solutions LLC ....E 281 615-8102
Missouri City *(G-15584)*

Paramount Petroleum Corp ....E 800 882-6541
Channelview *(G-3031)*

Pdvsa Services Inc ....D 281 531-0004
Houston *(G-11266)*

Premier Pressure Pumping LLC ....F 903 981-0081
Kilgore *(G-13583)*

Qri International LLC ....F 713 485-8800
Houston *(G-11487)*

Quantum Reservoir Impact LLC ....F 713 485-8800
Houston *(G-11508)*

FRAMES & FRAMING WHOLESALE

Brazos Oaks Ltd................................E 254 399-0505
Waco *(G-20370)*

FRAMES: Chair, Metal

Bandy Incorporated............................F 972 276-6516
Garland *(G-7448)*

G2 Automated Technologies LLC...........E 972 479-0699
Dallas *(G-4390)*

FRAMES: Lamp Shade

Haleaux Inc ....F 214 742-2795
Dallas *(G-4428)*

FRANCHISES, SELLING OR LICENSING

Allen Tharp LLC ....A 210 878-0034
San Antonio *(G-17896)*

P
R
O
D
U
C
T

ARC Rite Welding & Fabrication ....F 830 774-6058
Del Rio (G-5305)
Business Investment & Dev Corp ....E 432 335-3410
Odessa (G-15947)
Casey Products LLC ....E 903 927-3500
Marshall (G-14770)
Frito-Lay North America Inc ....A 972 334-7000
Plano (G-16874)
Kwik-Kopy Corporation ....C 281 256-4100
Cypress (G-3808)
Logan Farms Inc ....E 713 781-3773
Richmond (G-17462)
Old Frito-Lay Inc ....A 972 334-7000
Plano (G-16953)
Snow Flake Bakery ....E 281 427-4423
Baytown (G-1834)
Wheels America Alloy Wheel ....E 214 330-9866
Dallas (G-5185)
Winzer Corporation ....C 214 341-2122
Plano (G-17051)

FREEZERS: Household

Cold King Inc ....F 210 227-0264
San Antonio (G-18017)
Coldvault LLC ....G 903 657-2377
Henderson (G-8261)

FREIGHT CAR LOADING & UNLOADING SVCS

Luminator Technology Group Inc ....B 972 516-3154
Plano (G-16912)

FREIGHT FORWARDING ARRANGEMENTS

Aerostar Global Logistics LLC ....E 630 458-8844
Irving (G-12925)
Equipment Storage Service Inc ....F 214 374-3995
Dallas (G-4329)
G T Southwest Hose Inc ....F 214 689-4673
Dallas (G-4388)
Wes-Tex Pure Minerals Inc ....F 432 250-7010
McAllen (G-14919)

FREIGHT TRANSPORTATION ARRANGEMENTS

Alps Electric North Amer Inc ....D 956 217-6500
Mcallen (G-14835)
Eship Global Inc ....F 972 518-1775
Dallas (G-3842)
Eugene B Smith & Co Inc ....E 409 763-6401
Pasadena (G-16432)
Kentucky Freight Systems Inc ....F 972 475-6567
Rowlett (G-17708)
Link World Trade Inc ....C 972 713-8000
Addison (G-145)
Reconditioned Couplings Inc ....F 832 878-6255
Highlands (G-8314)
Rich Transport LLC ....C 214 819-3082
Dallas (G-4896)
Southast Vcational Aliance Inc ....D 713 847-0697
Houston (G-11969)

FRICTION MATERIAL, MADE FROM POWDERED METAL

B G Metals Inc ....E 210 648-5071
San Antonio (G-17930)
Heitman Company Inc ....F 713 675-9001
Houston (G-10148)
Indo-Mim Inc ....C 609 580-9745
San Antonio (G-18181)

FRUITS & VEGETABLES WHOLESALERS: Fresh

Koch Ranches Inc ....F 210 858-9795
San Antonio (G-18228)
Lopez Efrain ....F 713 921-0057
Houston (G-10688)

FUEL ADDITIVES

Innospec Inc ....F 832 748-0284
Spring (G-19217)
Macdermid Canning Ltd ....E 713 472-5081
Pasadena (G-16478)
Valero Refining-Texas LP ....C 281 470-4900
La Porte (G-13799)

FUEL CELLS: Solid State

Ambiq Micro Inc ....E 512 879-2850
Austin (G-913)

FUEL DEALERS: Coal

Wtg Fuels Inc ....F 432 837-2518
Alpine (G-313)

FUEL DEALERS: Wood

Cdw Consultant Group LLC ....E 361 237-9339
Bloomington (G-2111)

FUEL OIL DEALERS

Andeavor LLC ....C 210 626-6000
San Antonio (G-17907)
Concho Oil & Gas LLC ....C 432 683-7443
Midland (G-15175)
Neom LLC ....F 210 372-3475
Boerne (G-2130)
Western Refining Inc ....B 915 775-3300
El Paso (G-6033)

FUEL TREATING

Accurate Cargo Treatment ....F 281 685-8573
Pasadena (G-16376)
Pilot Thomas Logistics LLC ....C 817 877-8300
Fort Worth (G-6908)
Power Service Products Inc ....E 817 599-9486
Weatherford (G-20610)

FUELS: Diesel

Gron Fuels LLC ....F 813 220-3331
Houston (G-10049)
Rio Valley Biofuels LLC ....D 915 791-8720
El Paso (G-5941)
Virgin Fields LLC ....E 972 322-7902
Frisco (G-7323)

FUELS: Ethanol

A-1 Fuel Stop Inc ....G 713 674-3683
Houston (G-8431)
Acentum Inc ....F 713 668-8742
Houston (G-8467)
Action Fuels LP ....F 210 651-9308
San Antonio (G-18634)
Bam Denton MGT Ventures LLC ....E 940 898-1200
Dallas (G-4002)
Bobs Fuels Inc ....G 325 646-7571
Brownwood (G-2426)
C & W Fuels Inc ....F 830 426-4301
Hondo (G-8354)
Chevron Marine Products LLC ....D 832 854-2767
Houston (G-9179)
Clear Diamond Inc ....F 325 597-9240
Brady (G-2212)
Defense Logistics Agency ....E 210 925-4455
San Antonio (G-18047)
Dieselgreen Fuels LLC ....F 512 247-3835
Austin (G-1090)
Endicott Biofuels II LLC ....F 281 598-2180
Houston (G-9628)
Energy Transfer Fuel LP ....F 903 931-1922
Jacksonville (G-13237)
Energy Transfer LP ....F 682 518-7583
Mansfield (G-14669)
Evolution Fuels Inc ....E 214 389-9800
Dallas (G-4338)
Fueland Inc ....G 972 899-3727
Jacksonville (G-13239)
Greenamerica Biofuels LLC ....E 865 474-4086
Houston (G-10032)
Monument Chemical Houston LLC ....F 832 376-2201
Houston (G-10917)
Monument Chemical Houston LLC ....C 281 452-5951
Houston (G-10916)
Neom LLC ....F 210 372-3475
Boerne (G-2130)
Originclear Inc ....F 323 939-6645
McKinney (G-14960)
Phoenix Services LLC ....F 713 952-5533
Houston (G-11329)
Pier 19 Marine Field ....E 409 763-5423
Galveston (G-7405)
Pilot Thomas Logistics LLC ....E 432 741-1514
Midland (G-15352)

Proman Usa Inc ....F 713 943-2200
Houston (G-11444)
Proman USA (pampa) LLC ....F 713 943-2200
Houston (G-11445)
Pure Biofuels Corp ....E 281 540-9317
Houston (G-11473)
Rbf Port Neches LLC ....E 713 386-2600
Houston (G-11557)
Renewable Biofuels Inc ....E 713 386-2600
Houston (G-11599)
Rio Valley Biofuel Transport ....E 915 791-8720
El Paso (G-5940)
Silver Star I Pwr Partners LLC ....E 713 354-2168
Houston (G-11898)
Total Ptrchemicals Ref USA Inc ....B 713 483-5000
Houston (G-12332)
Tricon Energy Inc ....D 713 963-0066
Houston (G-12369)
White Energy Holding Co LLC ....F 972 715-6490
Frisco (G-7326)

FUELS: Gas, Liquefied

Coastal Caverns Inc ....G 409 833-5504
Beaumont (G-1872)
Intertek USA Inc ....E 361 289-7474
Corpus Christi (G-3556)
Raven Butene-1 LLC ....E 251 414-6955
Baytown (G-1833)
Sandifers LP Gas & Svc Co Inc ....F 409 963-1269
Port Arthur (G-17124)

FUELS: Nuclear

Algae Production Systems ....F 832 515-9670
Houston (G-8537)

FUELS: Nuclear, Uranium Slug, Radioactive

Auc Management LLC ....F 713 983-3255
Houston (G-8748)

FUELS: Oil

Alon Usa LP ....B 432 263-7661
Big Spring (G-2069)
Armstead Oil ....E 713 454-3866
Houston (G-8699)
Cowboy Containments Inc ....F 361 576-9550
Victoria (G-20255)
Flint Hills Resources LP ....C 361 889-7282
Corpus Christi (G-3529)
Global Alternative Fuels LLC ....E 915 791-8720
El Paso (G-5787)
Oilfield Anchor Company Inc ....D 903 723-2833
Palestine (G-16306)
Petra Oil Company Inc ....F 888 738-7261
Cypress (G-3812)
Shell Oil Company ....C 713 332-7606
Houston (G-11862)
Tiger Offshore Rentals LLC ....D 409 951-4048
Beaumont (G-1959)

FULLER'S EARTH MINING

Milwhite Inc ....E 956 547-1970
Brownsville (G-2383)

FUND RAISING ORGANIZATION, NON-FEE BASIS

Worldwide Spanish Literature ....F 940 692-4933
Wichita Falls (G-20836)

FUNDRAISING SVCS

Sports Magic Inc ....F 903 832-1975
Texarkana (G-19774)
Zachry Associates Inc ....E 325 677-1342
Abilene (G-97)

FUNGICIDES OR HERBICIDES

Innova Supply Inc ....E 713 473-3345
Pasadena (G-16459)

FUR: Apparel

Europa Designs ....F 972 792-0997
Dallas (G-4336)

FURNACE BLACK

Thermal Specialties Texas LLC ....G...... 918 836-4800
Fort Worth *(G-7055)*

FURNACES & OVENS: Fuel-Fired

Rik-Mar Fabricators Inc ....F 979 779-1616
Bryan *(G-2501)*

FURNACES & OVENS: Indl

Air Performance Service Inc ....E 972 387-3334
Dallas *(G-3907)*
Carrier Corporation ....C...... 903 510-7300
Tyler *(G-20063)*
Energy Services Group Amer Inc ....F 281 452-5335
Channelview *(G-3018)*
Epcon Industrial Systems LP ....D 936 273-1774
Shenandoah *(G-18896)*
Estovel Inc ....G...... 512 345-6997
Austin *(G-1139)*
Exotherm Corporation ....F 713 981-9100
Houston *(G-9726)*
Furnace Systems Inc ....F 972 423-7800
Plano *(G-16875)*
Haydon Corporation ....F 972 641-6400
Grand Prairie *(G-7888)*
Hou Fab & Maintenance Inc ....G...... 713 672-1993
Crosby *(G-3733)*
Jerryco Mch & Boiler Works LP ....D 713 224-7900
Houston *(G-10466)*
Mayhan Fabricators Inc ....E 903 734-4198
Gilmer *(G-7709)*
Ncc Nano LLC ....E 512 491-9500
Austin *(G-1362)*
Osr Services LP ....E 281 422-7206
Baytown *(G-1830)*
Paragon Industries Inc ....D 972 288-7557
Mesquite *(G-15068)*

FURNACES: Indl, Electric

Ajax Tocco Magnethermic Corp ....F 903 297-2526
Longview *(G-14191)*

FURNACES: Warm Air, Electric

Lennox Industries Inc ....C...... 806 412-4160
Lubbock *(G-14436)*
Lennox International Inc ....C...... 972 497-5000
Richardson *(G-17343)*
Texas Furnace LLC ....F 713 466-1504
Houston *(G-12231)*

FURNITURE & CABINET STORES: Cabinets, Custom Work

Alfonso Hinostroza ....E 956 781-1845
San Juan *(G-18670)*
Brycon Inc ....E 817 444-2724
Weatherford *(G-20580)*
D & H Quality Cabinets ....F 903 882-0274
Lindale *(G-14134)*
Greenhaw Cabinets Inc ....F 325 646-8319
Brownwood *(G-2430)*
Heartland Furniture Inc ....F 817 483-6161
Arlington *(G-695)*
Home Mart Inc ....F 956 724-4521
Laredo *(G-13892)*
Kamma Group Inc ....E 281 499-5888
Stafford *(G-19338)*
Keystone Millwork Inc ....E 979 823-4846
Bryan *(G-2485)*
Kitchen Bath Cbinets Doors Inc ....E 915 852-0499
El Paso *(G-5830)*
Patton Manufactured Pdts LP ....E 512 918-3737
Austin *(G-1401)*
Water Street Millworks Inc ....G...... 512 321-5741
Bastrop *(G-1765)*

FURNITURE & CABINET STORES: Custom

Reynolds Mfg Corp Inc ....E 325 698-7300
Abilene *(G-71)*

FURNITURE & FIXTURES Factory

Avteq Inc ....G...... 214 905-9001
Dallas *(G-3994)*
Cabinettech Inc ....F 325 670-0414
Abilene *(G-28)*

Chippenhook Corporation ....E 800 527-5866
Lewisville *(G-14036)*
Doiy LLC ....F 469 513-4159
Dallas *(G-4270)*
Formaspace LP ....E 512 279-2576
Austin *(G-1165)*
MBS Construction I Ltd ....E 817 473-0328
Mansfield *(G-14693)*
Provence Hardware Corporation ....F 817 572-4663
Burleson *(G-2594)*
Solano Furniture Incorporated ....F 713 849-4855
Houston *(G-11934)*

FURNITURE REFINISHING SVCS

Southwest Cabinet Corporation ....D 817 460-8681
Pantego *(G-16352)*

FURNITURE REFINISHING SVCS

Southern Cabinets ....G...... 254 799-2271
Waco *(G-20459)*
Srg Ventures LLC ....E 281 214-8560
Houston *(G-12030)*

FURNITURE REPAIR & MAINTENANCE SVCS

Rodco-Brandt Manufacturing ....E 817 477-4118
Mansfield *(G-14713)*

FURNITURE STOCK & PARTS: Chair Seats, Hardwood

Camino Real Community Mhmr Ctr .....F 830 276-8578
Poteet *(G-17194)*

FURNITURE STOCK & PARTS: Dimension Stock, Hardwood

MJB Wood Group LLC.........................E 972 401-0005
Coppell *(G-3428)*

FURNITURE STOCK & PARTS: Frames, Upholstered Furniture, Wood

Walls & Forms Inc ....D 972 745-0800
Fort Worth *(G-7117)*

FURNITURE STOCK & PARTS: Hardwood

C & L Millwork Inc ....G...... 817 605-0002
Haltom City *(G-8133)*
Lindseys NW Off Furn Inc ....E 713 957-2424
Houston *(G-10647)*
Quality Mat Company ....F 713 455-3990
Houston *(G-11496)*
Ually LLC ....E 936 252-7476
Euless *(G-6164)*

FURNITURE STORES

Akcorp Inc ....F 409 833-8002
Beaumont *(G-1848)*
Al Legacy Partners Inc ....B 972 296-9599
Dallas *(G-3916)*
Capitol Seating Company ....E 254 939-1853
Belton *(G-2022)*
David McNeff Inc ....F 972 562-0607
McKinney *(G-14935)*
Homestead Craftsmen LLC ....D 254 754-9600
Waco *(G-20414)*
Houston North Sleep Center ....F 713 688-3188
Houston *(G-10240)*
J&D Interiors Inc ....F 817 626-2365
Fort Worth *(G-6731)*
Kerr Collection ....F 817 572-4663
Burleson *(G-2584)*
LP & M Group Inc ....F 972 458-9393
Dallas *(G-4607)*
Office Furn Cmpanies Texas LLC.........F 281 724-1533
League City *(G-13970)*
Petroplex Cabinets Inc ....G...... 432 333-2025
Odessa *(G-16121)*
Renever Inc ....F 214 761-1882
Dallas *(G-4887)*

FURNITURE STORES: Cabinets, Kitchen, Exc Custom Made

Champion Custom Cabinets Inc............F 817 834-8552
Fort Worth *(G-6507)*

FURNITURE STORES: Juvenile

Lauras Carousel Inc ....F 940 365-1875
Aubrey *(G-850)*

FURNITURE STORES: Office

Ables-Land Inc ....E 903 593-8407
Tyler *(G-20043)*
Concho Business Solutions Inc ....E 325 653-1697
San Angelo *(G-17789)*
Cube Solutions LLC ....E 972 783-4880
Dallas *(G-4191)*
Ergotect Corporation ....E 214 747-3746
Dallas *(G-4331)*
Firmin Printing & Off Eqp Co ....E 903 793-5566
Texarkana *(G-19763)*
Lindseys NW Off Furn Inc ....E 713 957-2424
Houston *(G-10647)*
Oak Cliff Office Sup Prtg Inc ....E 214 943-7421
Dallas *(G-4750)*
R W Gonzalez Office Pdts Inc ....F 512 300-2300
Austin *(G-1448)*
Rfv Enterprises Inc ....E 281 842-1877
La Porte *(G-13788)*
Speed Printing Conroe Inc ....F 936 441-2248
Conroe *(G-3366)*
W B Mason Co Inc ....E 888 926-2766
Pflugerville *(G-16691)*
W B Mason Co Inc ....E 888 926-2766
Irving *(G-13205)*
W B Mason Co Inc ....E 888 926-2766
Houston *(G-12584)*

FURNITURE STORES: Outdoor & Garden

Patio One Furniture LP ....F 713 789-8080
Houston *(G-11260)*

FURNITURE UPHOLSTERY REPAIR SVCS

Inman & Company Inc ....F 713 224-4740
Houston *(G-10367)*
Lindseys NW Off Furn Inc ....E 713 957-2424
Houston *(G-10647)*

FURNITURE WHOLESALERS

Abbys Thres No Pl Like HM Fur ....F 817 244-3371
Fort Worth *(G-6340)*
Banyan Industries Inc ....E 817 413-7945
Fort Worth *(G-6426)*
Bassett Furniture Inds Inc ....F 210 641-0101
San Antonio *(G-17940)*
C & L Millwork Inc ....G...... 817 605-0002
Haltom City *(G-8133)*
Doiy LLC ....F 469 513-4159
Dallas *(G-4270)*
Inwood Furniture Manufacturing............D 972 564-4444
Forney *(G-6311)*
Kln Manufacturing LLC ....C...... 210 227-4747
Dallas *(G-4560)*
Nielsen & Bainbridge LLC....................E 512 506-3900
Austin *(G-1367)*
Patio One Furniture LP ....F 713 789-8080
Houston *(G-11260)*
Smith System Manufacturing Co............C...... 800 328-1061
Carrollton *(G-2816)*
Wingate Partners LP ....F 214 720-1313
Dallas *(G-5195)*

FURNITURE, BARBER & BEAUTY SHOP

Kyle Bunting Holdings Inc ....F 512 264-1148
Austin *(G-1277)*

FURNITURE, HOUSEHOLD: Wholesalers

Apartment Furnishings Co Inc ....E 817 568-2002
Fort Worth *(G-6390)*
Carl Kisabeth Co Inc..........................E 817 281-7560
Haltom City *(G-8134)*

FURNITURE, MATTRESSES: Wholesalers

Dynasty Consolidated Inds Inc.............D 214 630-3132
Fort Worth *(G-6599)*
Talalay Global Inc.............................D 940 851-0107
Wichita Falls *(G-20814)*

FURNITURE, OFFICE: Wholesalers

Abilene Printing & Sty Co ....F 325 677-2673
Abilene *(G-6)*

Employee Codes: A=Over 500 employees, B=251-500
C=101-250, D=51-100, E=20-50, F=10-19, G=9

2021 Harris Texas
Manufacturers Directory

PRODUCT

1503

Graphtex Inc ....F 979 968-6333
La Grange (G-13696)

Hilltop Texas Inc ....E 214 430-1311
Allen (G-275)

OKelley Office Supply Inc ....F 325 673-6422
Abilene (G-61)

Philbo Enterprises Inc ....E 214 747-7018
Dallas (G-4802)

Reynolds Brothers Ltd ....E 432 682-7393
Midland (G-15383)

Texas Office Pdts & Sup Inc ....F 512 472-1340
Austin (G-1569)

FURNITURE, PUBLIC BUILDING: Wholesalers

Midwest Folding Products Corp ....C 312 666-3366
Temple (G-19690)

FURNITURE, WHOLESALE: Bedsprings

Continntal Silverline Pdts LLC ....D 713 222-7394
Houston (G-9291)

FURNITURE, WHOLESALE: Chairs

Stadium Chair Co LLC ....F 432 682-4682
Midland (G-15418)

FURNITURE, WHOLESALE: Filing Units

Southwest Solutions Group Inc ....E 972 250-1970
Lewisville (G-14091)

FURNITURE, WHOLESALE: School Desks

Indeco Sales Inc ....E 254 939-5742
Belton (G-2025)

Unlimited Supply Inc ....E 936 890-8997
Willis (G-20868)

FURNITURE: Bar furniture

Srg Ventures LLC ....E 281 214-8560
Houston (G-12030)

FURNITURE: Bed Frames & Headboards, Wood

Industrial Lumber and Box Inc ....F 713 928-2096
Houston (G-10351)

Mfi International Mfg LLC ....A 915 858-0971
El Paso (G-5876)

FURNITURE: Bedsprings, Assembled

Leggett & Platt Incorporated ....B 972 875-8401
Ennis (G-6109)

FURNITURE: Cabinets & Vanities, Medicine, Metal

Rangaire Manufacturing Co LP ....D 817 556-6500
Cleburne (G-3107)

FURNITURE: Chairs, Folding

Stadium Chair Co LLC ....F 432 682-4682
Midland (G-15418)

FURNITURE: Chairs, Office Exc Wood

Caco Manufacturing Corporation ....F 713 644-0170
Houston (G-9042)

Neutral Posture Inc ....D 979 778-0502
Bryan (G-2494)

FURNITURE: Cut Stone

Zodiac Stone LLC ....F 972 243-2112
Dallas (G-5212)

FURNITURE: Desks & Tables, Office, Wood

Lutz Woodworks Llc ....E 972 429-5521
Wylie (G-20940)

Next Technologies Inc ....E 888 615-5721
Round Rock (G-17675)

Next Technologies Inc ....F 512 212-7758
Georgetown (G-7666)

Proximity Systems Inc ....E 281 370-5004
Tomball (G-20002)

FURNITURE: Desks, Metal

Next Technologies Inc ....E 888 615-5721
Round Rock (G-17675)

Next Technologies Inc ....F 512 212-7758
Georgetown (G-7666)

Paragon Furniture Inc ....D 817 633-3242
Arlington (G-749)

FURNITURE: Desks, Wood

Paragon Furniture Inc ....D 817 633-3242
Arlington (G-749)

FURNITURE: Fiberglass & Plastic

Delta Composites LLC ....D 281 907-0619
Houston (G-9430)

Global Fbrgls Sltons Texas LLC ....E 425 483-1303
Sweetwater (G-19630)

FURNITURE: Frames, Box Springs Or Bedsprings, Metal

Hickory Springs Mfg Co ....F 817 831-1785
Fort Worth (G-6695)

Mantua Manufacturing Co ....E 713 672-9811
Houston (G-10748)

FURNITURE: Headboards, Wood

Mozaic Company ....E 972 386-3332
Arlington (G-733)

FURNITURE: Hotel

Dickson Furniture Mfrs LLC ....F 713 747-0341
Houston (G-9463)

Shioleno Industries Inc ....F 817 465-9361
Arlington (G-780)

FURNITURE: Household, Metal

Acacia Originals LLC ....F 877 565-5995
Porter (G-17170)

Amweld International LLC ....D 888 775-2397
Dallas (G-3948)

Colonial Art Inc ....E 713 697-8407
Houston (G-9245)

Dickson Furniture Mfrs LLC ....F 713 747-0341
Houston (G-9463)

Kln Manufacturing LLC ....C 210 227-4747
Dallas (G-4560)

Kln Steel Products Company LLC ....C 210 227-4747
Dallas (G-4561)

Peck & Company ....E 713 526-2590
Houston (G-11268)

Sibbitt and Lott Inc ....G 214 742-6949
Dallas (G-4958)

FURNITURE: Household, Novelty, Metal

Kessler Industries Inc ....E 915 591-8161
El Paso (G-5828)

Robert F Herndon Corporation ....F 915 779-7905
El Paso (G-5942)

FURNITURE: Household, Upholstered On Metal Frames

Cmp Express LLC ....F 469 348-2272
Grand Prairie (G-7855)

Living Company Holdings LLC ....E 469 687-8991
Garland (G-7538)

FURNITURE: Household, Upholstered, Exc Wood Or Metal

Allan Knight & Associates Inc ....F 214 741-2227
Dallas (G-3923)

Kerr Collection ....F 817 572-4663
Burleson (G-2584)

LP & M Group Inc ....E 972 458-9393
Dallas (G-4607)

Regency Purchasing Inc ....E 713 973-0315
Houston (G-11585)

FURNITURE: Household, Wood

3 L Designs Inc ....E 214 920-9223
Dallas (G-3867)

Alan Charles Incorporated ....E 817 922-9834
Fort Worth (G-6362)

All Wood Custom Cabinets Inc ....F 940 686-2795
Pilot Point (G-16721)

Bassett Furniture Inds Inc ....F 210 641-0101
San Antonio (G-17940)

Cabinettech Inc ....F 325 670-0414
Abilene (G-28)

Cameron Knight ....F 972 636-7172
Royse City (G-17717)

Care Products Inc ....E 956 383-6049
McAllen (G-14846)

Carlton Mfg Inc ....D 903 537-4591
Mount Vernon (G-15666)

Coleman Wood Products Inc ....E 940 440-2300
Aubrey (G-849)

Dickson Furniture Mfrs LLC ....F 713 747-0341
Houston (G-9463)

Dickson Furniture Mfrs LLC ....E 281 299-6197
Houston (G-9464)

Feinkind Inc ....F 914 591-5868
Austin (G-1153)

Homestead Craftsmen LLC ....D 254 754-9600
Waco (G-20414)

Inwood Furniture Manufacturing ....D 972 564-4444
Forney (G-6311)

JDM Designs Inc ....E 281 356-6131
Stagecoach (G-19401)

Kerr Collection ....F 817 572-4663
Burleson (G-2584)

Keys Corporation ....F 713 864-7299
Houston (G-10525)

Little Green Apples Inc ....F 956 668-0028
McAllen (G-14885)

Manheim Companies Inc ....E 972 387-4578
Dallas (G-4632)

Pallas Archtctral Wodworks LLC ....F 214 741-1125
Dallas (G-4779)

Patton Manufactured Pdts LP ....E 512 918-3737
Austin (G-1401)

Precision Wood Products Inc ....D 972 293-2252
Cedar Hill (G-2951)

R Jones and Associates Inc ....E 214 951-0091
Dallas (G-4854)

Renever Inc ....F 214 761-1882
Dallas (G-4887)

Rodco-Brandt Manufacturing ....E 817 477-4118
Mansfield (G-14713)

Solano Furniture Incorporated ....F 713 849-4855
Houston (G-11934)

Tables Manufacturing Inc ....B 972 932-4148
Kaufman (G-13464)

Trosby of Georgia Inc ....G 713 526-7332
Houston (G-12382)

Woodard—Cm LLC ....E 972 393-3800
Coppell (G-3453)

FURNITURE: Hydraulic Barber & Beauty Shop Chairs

Flexcon Industrial LLC ....E 210 798-1900
San Antonio (G-18116)

Noble Gent LLC ....F 214 516-8609
Desoto (G-5437)

FURNITURE: Institutional, Exc Wood

Alan Charles Incorporated ....E 817 922-9834
Fort Worth (G-6362)

Dickson Furniture Mfrs LLC ....F 713 747-0341
Houston (G-9463)

Fellfab Corporation ....E 817 595-7408
Fort Worth (G-6627)

Herman Miller Inc ....F 214 855-0200
Dallas (G-4453)

Indeco Sales Inc ....E 254 939-5742
Belton (G-2025)

Johnson Controls Inc ....D 713 934-2400
Houston (G-10482)

Little Green Apples Inc ....F 956 668-0028
McAllen (G-14885)

Midwest Folding Products Corp ....C 312 666-3366
Temple (G-19690)

Panel Specialists Inc ....E 254 774-9197
Temple (G-19694)

Panel Specialists Inc ....D 254 774-9800
Temple (G-19695)

Rodco-Brandt Manufacturing ....E 817 477-4118
Mansfield (G-14713)

Southern Bleacher Company Inc ....C 940 549-0733
Graham (G-7789)

FURNITURE: Juvenile, Wood

Reynolds Mfg Corp Inc ....E 325 698-7300
Abilene (G-71)

FURNITURE: Kitchen & Dining Room

Cabinets Deluxe By Dale Inc ....D 512 259-2531
Freeport (G-7195)

FURNITURE: Laboratory

Onepointe Solutions LLC ....D 866 222-7494
Elgin (G-6056)

FURNITURE: Lawn & Garden, Metal

Felipe Arreazola ....F 956 334-3136
Laredo (G-13883)

FURNITURE: Library

Texwood Ltd ....D 888 388-3224
Cameron (G-2644)

FURNITURE: Living Room, Upholstered On Wood Frames

Carlton Mfg Inc ....D 903 537-4591
Mount Vernon (G-15666)
Delatorre Inc ....F 713 522-5833
Houston (G-9426)
Diamond Modern Furniture LLC ....G 877 349-5003
Houston (G-9451)
Massoud Furniture Mfg Co ....D 214 388-8655
Dallas (G-4644)
Mayo Mfg Corporation ....C 903 838-0518
Texarkana (G-19769)
Noahs Manufacturing Inc ....D 713 926-3500
Houston (G-11062)
Swiftex Manufacturing Corp ....F 512 321-2574
Bastrop (G-1761)

FURNITURE: Mattresses & Foundations

Cantwell Mattress Company ....F 361 883-8525
Corpus Christi (G-3496)
Dynasty Consolidated Inds Inc ....D 214 630-3132
Fort Worth (G-6599)
Noahs Manufacturing Inc ....D 713 926-3500
Houston (G-11062)
Texas Dept Criminal Justice ....A 936 295-6371
Huntsville (G-12825)

FURNITURE: Mattresses, Box & Bedsprings

Corsicana Bedding LLC ....C 903 257-3360
Corsicana (G-3664)
Leggett & Platt Incorporated ....E 817 378-0108
Fort Worth (G-6782)
Leggett & Platt Incorporated ....E 817 626-6690
Fort Worth (G-6783)
Quatrefoil Partners LLC ....F 214 631-7117
Dallas (G-4848)
Royal Sleep Products Ltd ....D 817 834-7522
Fort Worth (G-6967)
Ssb Manufacturing Company ....B 972 874-9666
Grapevine (G-8055)

FURNITURE: Mattresses, Innerspring Or Box Spring

Continntal Silverline Pdts LLC ....D 713 222-7394
Houston (G-9291)
Corsicana Bedding LLC ....D 903 872-2591
Corsicana (G-3663)
Corsicana Bedding LLC ....E 800 323-4349
Dallas (G-4173)
Golden Pedic Inc ....E 214 630-5588
Dallas (G-4412)
Leggett & Platt Incorporated ....D 214 391-3181
Dallas (G-4590)
National Bedding Company LLC ....D 281 345-6237
Houston (G-10966)
Quality Mattress Company Inc ....F 713 433-9155
Houston (G-11497)
Texas Pocket Springs Tech Inc ....D 817 645-7666
Keene (G-13465)
Ultimate Comfort Manufacturing ....F 713 641-0 00
Houston (G-12428)

FURNITURE: Novelty, Wood

Moein Inc ....F 817 341-1414
Weatherford (G-20605)

FURNITURE: Office Panel Systems, Exc Wood

Dakota Cabinets Inc ....F 281 741-7695
Houston (G-9397)

FURNITURE: Office Panel Systems, Wood

Interntonal Laminating Systems ....F 713 645-0383
Houston (G-10406)

FURNITURE: Office, Exc Wood

Ar-Case Inc ....F 210 735-5175
San Antonio (G-17912)
Bandy Incorporated ....F 972 276-6516
Garland (G-7448)
Bret Broussard Inc ....G 210 224-6220
San Antonio (G-17966)
Computer Comforts Inc ....F 281 535-2288
Kemah (G-13472)
Ergotect Corporation ....E 214 747-3746
Dallas (G-4331)
Evosite LLC ....E 713 365-3900
Houston (G-9721)
Herman Miller Inc ....F 214 855-0200
Dallas (G-4453)
Hilltop Texas Inc ....E 214 430-1311
Allen (G-275)
Kimball Elec - Mexico Inc ....E 956 205-4600
Pharr (G-16705)
Lee Custom Works Inc ....F 210 432-1911
San Antonio (G-18241)
M J M International Corp ....F 956 781-5000
Edinburg (G-5594)
Mooreco Inc ....E 254 778-4727
Temple (G-19691)
Nevins LLC ....E 713 230-2100
Cat Spring (G-2931)
Office Furn Cmpanies Texas LLC ....F 281 724-1533
League City (G-13970)
Peck & Company ....E 713 526-2590
Houston (G-11268)
Sibbitt and Lott Inc ....G 214 742-6949
Dallas (G-4958)
Smith System Manufacturing Co ....C 800 328-1061
Carrollton (G-2816)
Tesco Industries Lp ....D 979 865-2163
Bellville (G-2012)
Tigua Enterprises Inc ....E 915 298-0700
El Paso (G-6006)

FURNITURE: Office, Wood

A E S Custom Wood Inc ....G 972 262-0755
Grand Prairie (G-7816)
Acacia Originals LLC ....F 877 565-5995
Porter (G-17170)
Asmar Custom Cabinets Inc ....F 972 241-7676
Dallas (G-3971)
Cabinet Creation Inc ....E 830 709-4116
Lytle (G-14573)
Classic Millwork and Products ....E 915 833-9922
El Paso (G-5696)
Cube Solutions LLC ....F 972 783-4880
Dallas (G-4191)
Evosite LLC ....E 713 365-3900
Houston (G-9721)
Growth Holdings LLC ....E 972 241-9535
Dallas (G-4418)
Herman Miller Inc ....F 214 855-0200
Dallas (G-4453)
Indeco Sales Inc ....E 254 939-5742
Belton (G-2025)
K & J Woodworks LLC ....D 512 668-4237
Kyle (G-13683)
Kerr Collection ....F 817 572-4663
Burleson (G-2584)
Knoll Inc ....F 713 629-5665
Houston (G-10550)
Knoll Inc ....F 214 741-5819
Dallas (G-4562)
Lee Custom Works Inc ....F 210 432-1911
San Antonio (G-18241)
Lindseys NW Off Furn Inc ....E 713 957-2424
Houston (G-10647)

Lundy Services LLC ....E 972 494-2554
Garland (G-7539)
Nevins LLC ....E 713 230-2100
Cat Spring (G-2931)
Office Furn Cmpanies Texas LLC ....F 281 724-1533
League City (G-13970)
Pencil Cup Office Products Inc ....F 915 838-0026
El Paso (G-5907)
Petroplex Cabinets Inc ....G 432 333-2025
Odessa (G-16121)
Rick Triplett ....F 214 823-2830
Dallas (G-4899)
Robert Shaw Mfg Co Inc ....E 817 927-2557
Fort Worth (G-6962)
Saw Custom Millwork Inc ....E 972 288-2118
Mesquite (G-15076)
Smith System Manufacturing Co ....C 800 328-1061
Carrollton (G-2816)
Solano Furniture Incorporated ....F 713 849-4855
Houston (G-11934)
Srg Ventures LLC ....F 281 214-8560
Houston (G-12030)
Stella Hasegawa ....F 915 594-7633
El Paso (G-5977)
Ultra Seating Company ....F 469 865-2010
Grand Prairie (G-7989)
Unique Cabinets Inc ....E 512 251-3058
Pflugerville (G-16690)
Vincent Graphics & Supply Inc ....E 903 882-3123
Tyler (G-20176)
Wingate Partners LP ....F 214 720-1313
Dallas (G-5195)

FURNITURE: Outdoor, Wood

Patio One Furniture LP ....F 713 789-8080
Houston (G-11260)

FURNITURE: Picnic Tables Or Benches, Park

Discovery Green Conservancy ....E 713 400-7336
Houston (G-9478)
Discovery Green Conservancy ....E 713 529-5534
Houston (G-9479)
Neon Electric Corporation ....D 281 987-1144
Houston (G-11023)

FURNITURE: Restaurant

Bianco Brothers ....F 817 922-0885
Fort Worth (G-6449)
Jaguar Hospitality Svcs Corp ....F 214 295-3574
Plano (G-16896)
Tables Manufacturing Inc ....B 972 932-4148
Kaufman (G-13464)
Texas Metal Equipment Co Ltd ....E 713 466-8722
Houston (G-12241)

FURNITURE: School

Capitol Seating Company ....E 254 939-1853
Belton (G-2022)
Furniture By Thurston ....C 210 227-4747
San Antonio (G-18131)
Maco Manufacturing Inc ....E 254 939-5742
Belton (G-2027)
Safespace Concepts Inc ....F 713 956-0820
Houston (G-11725)
Sagus International Inc ....E 630 413-5540
Temple (G-19702)
Smith System Manufacturing Co ....C 800 328-1061
Carrollton (G-2816)
Tesco Industries Lp ....D 979 865-2163
Bellville (G-2012)

FURNITURE: Sofa Beds Or Convertible Sofas)

Apartment Furnishings Co Inc ....E 817 568-2002
Fort Worth (G-6390)

FURNITURE: Stadium

American Grand Stand Inc ....F 214 638-7007
Dallas (G-3942)
Unlimited Supply Inc ....E 936 890-8997
Willis (G-20868)

FURNITURE: Table Tops, Marble

Golden Stones LP ....E 713 934-7887
Houston (G-9994)

Employee Codes: A=Over 500 employees, B=251-500
C=101-250, D=51-100, E=20-50, F=10-19, G=9

2021 Harris Texas
Manufacturers Directory

PRODUCT

1505

Texas Home & Projects LLC ....G....... 956 546-8400
Brownsville (G-2410)

FURNITURE: Tables, Office, Wood

Marco Dsplay Specialists GP Lc ....C....... 817 244-8300
Fort Worth (G-6810)

FURNITURE: Upholstered

Al Legacy Partners Inc ....B....... 972 296-9599
Dallas (G-3916)

Alan Charles Incorporated ....E....... 817 922-9834
Fort Worth (G-6362)

American Lea Operations LLC ....B....... 972 296-8016
Dallas (G-3944)

Carl Kisabeth Co Inc ....E....... 817 281-7560
Haltom City (G-8134)

Clifton Upholstery Co Inc.....................F....... 254 753-0211
Waco (G-20386)

Dbljs7 Inc ....F....... 440 746-1200
Horseshoe Bay (G-8366)

Double L Leather LLC...................E 888 643-5117
Denton (G-5361)

J&D Interiors Inc ....F....... 817 626-2365
Fort Worth (G-6731)

Keys Corporation.....................F....... 713 864-7299
Houston (G-10525)

M & M Upholstery Inc ....E....... 214 391-2666
Dallas (G-4618)

Marroquin Custom Upholstery ....E....... 214 905-0461
Dallas (G-4637)

Moein Inc ....E....... 817 341-1414
Weatherford (G-20605)

R Jones and Associates Inc ....E....... 214 951-0091
Dallas (G-4854)

Rudys Custom Uphl & Design ....F....... 210 821-5156
San Antonio (G-18438)

Solano Furniture Incorporated ....F....... 713 849-4855
Houston (G-11934)

Texas Office Pdts & Sup Inc ....F....... 512 472-1340
Austin (G-1569)

United Leather Usa Inc ....D....... 214 698-8270
Dallas (G-5135)

FURNITURE: Vehicle

Adient Clanton Inc ....B....... 956 525-4515
Brownsville (G-2334)

FURNITURE: Wicker & Rattan

Patio One Furniture LP.....................F....... 713 789-8080
Houston (G-11260)

FUSES & FUSE EQPT

Littelfuse Inc..................D....... 830 513-8775
Eagle Pass (G-5549)

GAMES & TOYS: Banks

Bank of New York Mellon Corp..............F....... 214 239-6420
Dallas (G-4004)

GAMES & TOYS: Bingo Boards

Casino Supply Company.....................F....... 972 241-4833
Dallas (G-4090)

GAMES & TOYS: Board Games, Children's & Adults'

Ariel Kennard ....F....... 832 997-4537
Houston (G-8693)

Pressman Toy Corporation ....E....... 732 562-1590
Richardson (G-17376)

Safe-T-Pet Inc ....F....... 903 569-0590
Mineola (G-15511)

Steve Jackson Games Inc ....E....... 512 447-7866
Austin (G-1536)

GAMES & TOYS: Craft & Hobby Kits & Sets

Brock Enterprises Inc.....................F....... 281 870-8200
Houston (G-8990)

Graphtec Inc ....E....... 713 690-9999
Houston (G-10019)

Jasmine Lewis..................F....... 325 200-5769
Humble (G-12781)

GAMES & TOYS: Electronic

Bigtrak Technologies LLC.................G....... 361 944-3982
Corpus Christi (G-3487)

Blue Goji LLC..................E....... 512 270-4747
Austin (G-997)

Mobile Toys Inc ....F....... 979 268-6066
College Station (G-3193)

GAMES & TOYS: Game Machines, Exc Coin-Operated

Everi Games Holding Inc..................D....... 512 334-7500
West Lake Hills (G-20681)

GAMES & TOYS: Go-Carts, Children's

Maks Family Fun & Events LLC............E....... 254 518-0005
Copperas Cove (G-3455)

GAMES & TOYS: Kits, Science, Incl Microscopes/Chemistry Sets

Lc Sciences ....F....... 713 664-7087
Houston (G-10612)

GAMES & TOYS: Models, Boat & Ship, Toy & Hobby

Randolph Products Inc.....................F....... 713 468-6070
Richmond (G-17464)

GAMES & TOYS: Toy Guns

Soft Air Usa Inc ....F 817 717-4300
Grapevine (G-8054)

GARAGES: Portable, Prefabricated Metal

American Carports Inc ....E....... 866 730-9865
Joshua (G-13316)

GARBAGE CONTAINERS: Plastic

Grande Garbage Collectn Co LLC........F....... 956 487-4234
Rio Grande City (G-17472)

One Source Recycling Inc.....................D....... 512 549-2812
Austin (G-1386)

Toter LLC..................F....... 830 775-3411
Del Rio (G-5326)

Tyco International MGT Co LLC ....C....... 361 575-9565
Victoria (G-20312)

GARBAGE DISPOSALS: Household

Standard Waste Services LLC ....F....... 210 619-7962
San Antonio (G-18496)

GARNET MINING SVCS

Gma Garnet (usa) Corp ....C....... 832 243-9300
The Woodlands (G-19869)

GAS & HYDROCARBON LIQUEFACTION FROM COAL

Morgan Kinder Treating LP ....D....... 361 578-1312
Victoria (G-20285)

Waskom Gas Processing Company......E....... 903 687-2513
Waskom (G-20525)

GAS & OIL FIELD EXPLORATION SVCS

31 Group LLC ....E....... 972 810-1031
Rockwall (G-17534)

31 Operating LLC ....F....... 972 810-1031
Rockwall (G-17535)

686 Inc..................F....... 830 876-5541
Carrizo Springs (G-2683)

Abaco Operating LLC ....G....... 210 828-4567
San Antonio (G-17853)

Accelerate Resources Oper LLC ....E....... 214 292-8960
Dallas (G-3881)

Acock Consulting LLC ....G....... 210 826-2553
San Antonio (G-17863)

Adams Resources & Energy Inc..........E....... 713 881-3600
Houston (G-8475)

Adams Resources Marketing Ltd ....F....... 281 902-4100
Houston (G-8476)

Addax Petro Cameroon Co LLC ....C....... 713 245-1263
Houston (G-8477)

Addison Oil LLC..................F....... 972 239-2400
Addison (G-100)

Advance Energy Partners Llc..............F....... 832 672-4700
Houston (G-8481)

Advanced Geophysical Tech Inc.............F....... 281 888-6789
Sugar Land (G-19440)

Adventure Explrtion Prtners LL.............F....... 432 684-8006
Midland (G-15107)

Aegis Chemical Solutions LLC ....D....... 281 258-4095
Houston (G-8497)

Aegis Oil Limited Ventures LLC ....F....... 214 431-5201
Dallas (G-3895)

Aethon Energy Management LLC ....E....... 214 750-3820
Dallas (G-3898)

Aethon Energy Operating LLC ....C....... 214 750-3833
Dallas (G-3899)

Afren Usa Inc ....E....... 281 363-8600
Spring (G-19192)

Ag-Jax Ltd ....G....... 903 705-0625
Tyler (G-20045)

Aggietech Oil Ltd ....F....... 432 682-3131
Midland (G-15109)

Aim World Services Inc ....E....... 281 847-2000
The Woodlands (G-19822)

Alamo Resources LLC ....F....... 281 398-9500
Houston (G-8524)

Alexander & Co ....E....... 325 677-1309
Abilene (G-12)

Alliance Energy Corporation ....F....... 713 333-4000
Houston (G-8545)

Alliance Petroleum Interests.....................F....... 469 249-8985
Dallas (G-3925)

Alloy Carbide Company ....E....... 713 923-2700
Houston (G-8557)

Alpar Energy LP ....E....... 806 435-6566
Perryton (G-16632)

Alta Marcellus Development LLC.............F....... 713 759-1155
Houston (G-8564)

Alta Mesa Holdings LP ....G....... 281 530-0991
Houston (G-8565)

Alta Mesa Resources Inc.....................F....... 214 647-7630
Dallas (G-3932)

Alta Resources LLC ....F....... 713 759-1155
Houston (G-8566)

Alta Resources Development LLC ....E....... 713 759-1155
Houston (G-8567)

American Fluorite Inc.....................E....... 281 363-9161
The Woodlands (G-19825)

Americo Energy Resources LLC ....E....... 713 984-9700
Houston (G-8614)

Ameritex Petroleum LLC ....F....... 972 528-6644
Dallas (G-3946)

Amplify Energy Corp ....E....... 713 490-8900
Houston (G-8629)

Anadarko Algeria Corporation..............B....... 832 636-1000
The Woodlands (G-19827)

Anadarko Energy Services Co.................D....... 832 636-1000
The Woodlands (G-19829)

Anadarko Petroleum Corporation ....E....... 903 389-3814
Buffalo (G-2542)

Anadarko Petroleum Corporation ....F....... 817 877-7449
Fort Worth (G-6388)

Anadarko Petroleum Corporation ....E....... 830 491-3300
Carrizo Springs (G-2684)

Anadarko Petroleum Corporation.............C....... 832 636-1000
The Woodlands (G-19830)

Anadarko US Offshore Corp ....E....... 832 636-1000
The Woodlands (G-19831)

Apache Foundation ....E....... 713 296-6000
Houston (G-8656)

Apache Instrumentations & Gas ....E....... 432 336-7755
Fort Stockton (G-6327)

Apex Intl Enrgy MGT LLC.....................F....... 832 770-6900
Houston (G-8663)

Apex/Fcc LLC ....E....... 830 875-2429
Luling (G-14559)

Approach Mdstream Holdings LLC............F....... 817 989-9000
Fort Worth (G-6393)

Approach Resources I LP.....................E....... 817 989-9000
Fort Worth (G-6394)

Approach Resources Inc.....................E....... 817 989-9000
Fort Worth (G-6395)

Approach Resources Inc.....................F....... 325 392-8900
Ozona (G-16278)

Approach Services LLC ....E....... 817 989-9000
Fort Worth (G-6396)

Aqua Transfer & Enrgy Svcs LLC.........E....... 903 874-4946
Corsicana (G-3661)

Arcooil Corp ....F....... 940 549-4444
Graham (G-7776)

Arcturus Corporation ....F....... 214 720-0075
Dallas (G-3963)

Company	Code	Phone
Ard Operating LLC	E	713 759-1155
Houston (G-8687)		
Arkoma Basin Resources Ltd	F	972 771-6000
Rockwall (G-17539)		
Arkos Field Services LP	F	832 783-5400
Waller (G-20492)		
Arrington Oil & Gas Oper LLC	D	432 682-6685
Midland (G-15119)		
Arrowhead Operating Inc	F	432 683-9700
Midland (G-15120)		
Aspen Operating Company LLC	F	817 882-9063
Fort Worth (G-6405)		
Atlantic Operating Inc	F	432 683-3272
Midland (G-15122)		
Atlas Oilfield Cnstr Co LLC	F	325 428-0552
Abilene (G-14)		
Atropos Exploration Company	F	214 691-2377
Dallas (G-3985)		
Autoseis Inc	F	972 332-3388
Dallas (G-3989)		
Axess North America Inc	E	281 994-0364
Houston (G-8758)		
B & E Roustabout Inc	F	432 393-5672
Big Spring (G-2070)		
B W Energy Consultants Inc	F	903 593-1173
Tyler (G-20055)		
B-29 Investments LP	D	940 665-4373
Gainesville (G-7334)		
Bailey & Harley Services LLC	E	409 994-5857
Buna (G-2560)		
Baker Hghes Olfld Oprtions LLC	F	713 879-3760
Houston (G-8793)		
Baker Hghes Olfld Oprtions LLC	E	432 694-9517
Midland (G-15130)		
Ballard Exploration Co Inc	E	713 651-0181
Houston (G-8810)		
Barnes Barnett LLC	E	214 445-6800
Plano (G-16798)		
Barnes Oil & Gas LLC	F	214 445-6800
Plano (G-16799)		
Barrera Contractors Inc	F	432 639-2516
Iraan (G-12916)		
Basa Resources Inc	E	214 580-5203
Dallas (G-4008)		
Basic Energy Services LP	D	432 530-0907
Odessa (G-15928)		
Basin Drilling LP	D	903 561-8211
Tyler (G-20058)		
Basin Oil & Gas LLC	F	817 820-8910
Fort Worth (G-6436)		
Bass Enterprises Production Co	C	817 698-0200
Fort Worth (G-6438)		
Bayou Bouillon Operating LLC	F	346 802-3134
Houston (G-8833)		
Baytex Energy (usa) Inc	E	713 402-1920
Houston (G-8840)		
Bc Operating Inc	E	432 684-9696
Midland (G-15136)		
BCM & Associates Inc	E	432 580-7161
Odessa (G-15931)		
Beacon Offshore Enrgy Oper LLC	G	346 867-0509
Houston (G-8845)		
Benton Oil Co	F	806 763-5302
Lubbock (G-14370)		
Bergstein Enterprises Ltd	F	806 741-1080
Lubbock (G-14371)		
Beusa Energy LLC	E	281 296-1500
The Woodlands (G-19836)		
BHP Bllton Petro Deepwater Inc	F	713 961-8500
Houston (G-8876)		
Big Star Oil & Gas LLC	E	432 687-4900
Midland (G-15142)		
Black Diamond Minerals LLC	G	720 341-2212
Houston (G-8901)		
Black Mountain Sand LLC	F	817 698-9901
Fort Worth (G-6454)		
Black Mtn Royalty I 2009 LP	F	888 698-9901
Fort Worth (G-6455)		
Black Stone Energy Company LLC	E	713 658-0647
Houston (G-8906)		
Black Stone Minerals LP	E	713 445-3200
Houston (G-8907)		
Black Stone Minerals Co LP	F	713 658-0647
Houston (G-8908)		
Black Stone Ntral Rsources MGT	E	713 445-3241
Houston (G-8909)		
Blackbrush Cnsld Holdings LLC	C	210 495-5577
San Antonio (G-17956)		
Blackbrush Oil & Gas LP	D	210 495-5577
San Antonio (G-17957)		
Blade Energy Partners Ltd	E	972 712-8407
Frisco (G-7271)		
Blue Racer Finance Corp	E	214 580-3700
Dallas (G-4032)		
Blue Ridge Mtn Resources Inc	E	469 444-1647
Irving (G-12949)		
Bluecrest Energy Inc	E	817 731-0066
Fort Worth (G-6459)		
Bluejack Energy Solutions LLC	E	720 320-2709
Plano (G-16806)		
Boaz Energy II LLC	E	432 253-7074
Midland (G-15144)		
BOF Services Inc	E	806 741-1080
Lubbock (G-14377)		
Bold Energy II LLC	E	432 686-1100
Midland (G-15146)		
Borets US Inc	E	254 559-5502
Breckenridge (G-2222)		
Bowmans Oilfield Service LLC	E	903 657-0698
Henderson (G-8258)		
BP Energy Company	C	281 366-2000
Houston (G-8968)		
BP Exploration & Prod Inc	E	800 333-3991
Houston (G-8969)		
Braden Exploration LLC	F	817 717-7020
Fort Worth (G-6466)		
Braden Exploration II LLC	F	817 717-7020
Fort Worth (G-6467)		
Brayton Operating Corp	F	361 884-8741
Corpus Christi (G-3489)		
Brazos Delaware Gas LLC	F	817 332-6800
Fort Worth (G-6470)		
Brazos Mdstream Hldings II LLC	E	817 332-6800
Fort Worth (G-6471)		
BRC Operating Company LLC	E	214 855-2260
Dallas (G-4048)		
Bri Consulting Group Inc	F	713 468-6813
Houston (G-8983)		
Brigadier Oil & Gas LLC	F	469 209-0760
Plano (G-16812)		
Brigadier Operating LLC	F	469 209-0760
Plano (G-16813)		
Broadspectrum Downstream Servi	A	713 964-2800
Houston (G-8989)		
Brothers Well Service Ltd	E	979 543-6851
El Campo (G-5613)		
Browning Offshore Inc	F	214 739-3481
Dallas (G-4061)		
Browning Oil Company Inc	F	214 739-3481
Dallas (G-4062)		
Bruin E&P Operating LLC	C	713 456-3000
Houston (G-8998)		
Bruin E&P Partners LLC	F	713 456-3000
Houston (G-8999)		
Brushy Resources Inc	E	210 999-5400
San Antonio (G-17969)		
Buckhead Midstream LLC	E	832 752-4526
Houston (G-9008)		
Buffco Production Inc	F	903 988-8199
Longview (G-14204)		
Burnett Oil Co Inc	E	817 332-5108
Fort Worth (G-6479)		
C & C Coating Inc	E	432 682-7201
Waco (G-20372)		
Caballo Loco Midstream LLC	E	432 262-1011
Midland (G-15154)		
Caiman Energy LLC	E	214 580-3700
Dallas (G-4078)		
Callon Petroleum Company	D	713 328-1000
Houston (G-9052)		
Callon Petroleum Company	E	432 218-2800
Midland (G-15155)		
Calyx Energy LLC	E	918 949-4224
Houston (G-9056)		
Camac International Corp	E	713 965-5100
Houston (G-9059)		
Camterra Rsources Partners Ltd	E	903 938-9949
Marshall (G-14769)		
Canyon Midstream Partners LLC	E	713 655-9500
Houston (G-9087)		
Cardinal Midstream II LLC	E	214 468-0700
Dallas (G-4084)		
Carrizo Well Service LLC	E	325 574-6291
Snyder (G-18986)		
Castex Energy Inc	E	281 447-8601
Houston (G-9096)		
Caza Oil & Gas Inc	F	281 363-4442
Spring (G-19202)		
Cdw Consultant Group LLC	E	361 237-9339
Bloomington (G-2111)		
Celero Energy	G	817 708-3800
Fort Worth (G-6503)		
Celero Energy II LP	E	817 708-3800
Fort Worth (G-6504)		
Central Management Inc	F	713 961-9777
Houston (G-9138)		
Champion Group Inc	E	210 490-1482
San Antonio (G-17998)		
Charro Operating LLC	G	361 643-5577
Portland (G-17186)		
Chem Rock Technologies LLC	F	432 940-2299
Midland (G-15160)		
Chemex Global Inc	C	346 388-6100
The Woodlands (G-19842)		
Cherokee Horn Production LP	F	619 435-8950
Dallas (G-4111)		
Chevron Corporation	C	907 276-7600
Houston (G-9177)		
Chevron Corporation	B	713 754-3998
Houston (G-9178)		
Chevron Midcontinent LP	C	432 498-8600
Midland (G-15161)		
Chevron USA Inc	C	432 687-7100
Midland (G-15162)		
Chisholm Energy Operating LLC	F	817 953-6063
Fort Worth (G-6514)		
Choate Co Inc	E	432 687-5977
Midland (G-15165)		
Choice Exploration Inc	E	817 633-7777
Arlington (G-641)		
Christeros Services LLC	E	325 884-1100
Big Lake (G-2055)		
Cimarex Energy Co	E	432 571-7800
Midland (G-15166)		
Cimarex Energy Co	D	432 634-1674
Iraan (G-12917)		
Cinco Energy MGT Group LLC	F	713 463-6009
Houston (G-9192)		
Cinco Natural Resources Corp	E	214 520-7727
Dallas (G-4117)		
Cinco Resources Inc	G	214 520-7727
Dallas (G-4119)		
Citation Oil & Gas Corp	C	281 891-1000
Houston (G-9199)		
CL&f Offshore LLC	F	281 873-9378
Houston (G-9204)		
CL&f Operating LLC	F	281 873-9378
Houston (G-9205)		
CL&f Resources LP	E	281 873-9378
Houston (G-9206)		
Clariant Corporation	E	281 465-9100
The Woodlands (G-19846)		
Clearfork Petroleum Inc	E	806 763-5625
Lubbock (G-14394)		
Clearly Petroleum Opco LLC	E	281 781-0412
Houston (G-9213)		
Clementson Inc	E	956 631-9121
McAllen (G-14848)		
Cml Exploration LLC	E	325 573-0750
Snyder (G-18988)		
Cml Exploration LLC	E	512 328-8085
Austin (G-1053)		
Cnooc Petroleum Offshr USA Inc	C	972 450-4600
Dallas (G-4132)		
Cobalt International Energy LP	D	713 452-2322
Houston (G-9231)		
Cobalt International Enrgy Inc	E	713 579-9100
Houston (G-9232)		
Cobra Oil & Gas Corporation	E	940 723-4331
Wichita Falls (G-20754)		
Cockrell Oil Corporation	E	713 209-7300
Houston (G-9235)		
Cog Operating LLC	C	432 685-0727
Midland (G-15169)		
Cogent Midstream Westex LLC	E	469 290-4100
Dallas (G-4140)		
Cohort Energy Company	E	972 233-8191
Addison (G-110)		
Colgate Energy LLC	E	432 695-4222
Midland (G-15171)		
Colgate Energy Partners LLC	F	432 695-4222
Midland (G-15172)		
Compass Well Services LLC	D	817 244-2555
Fort Worth (G-6532)		
Compass Well Services LLC	E	432 561-5970
Midland (G-15173)		
Concho Resources Inc	D	713 739-7561
Houston (G-9267)		
Confab Oilfield Contractors	F	817 992-6563
Burleson (G-2576)		

PRODUCT

Company	Class	Phone
Conocophillips	A	281 293-1000
Houston (G-9272)		
Conocophillips Company	A	281 293-1000
Houston (G-9273)		
Contango Oil & Gas Company	E	713 236-7400
Houston (G-9282)		
Continental Land & Fur Co Inc	F	281 873-9378
Houston (G-9286)		
Coronado Resources GP LLC	F	214 651-6245
Dallas (G-4169)		
Cortez Resources LLC	G	214 628-9155
Dallas (G-4174)		
Covey Park Energy Holdings LLC	G	214 548-6000
Dallas (G-4176)		
Cowboys Resources Corp	G	432 686-7797
Midland (G-15181)		
Cox Oil LLC	F	214 420-7710
Dallas (G-4177)		
Cox Operating LLC	F	504 267-9138
Dallas (G-4178)		
Crawford Energy Inc	F	713 626-2637
Houston (G-9335)		
Crimson Exploration Inc	E	713 236-7400
Houston (G-9344)		
Crown Exploration Ltd	F	972 395-1133
Carrollton (G-2861)		
Crown Oil Partners LP	F	432 683-2950
Midland (G-15182)		
Crownquest Operating LLC	D	432 818-0300
Midland (G-15183)		
Crownrock LP	C	432 818-0300
Midland (G-15184)		
Crusader Energy Group LLC	E	512 328-2953
Austin (G-1075)		
Cudd Pressure Control Inc	C	903 988-2161
Kilgore (G-13542)		
Current Power Solutions Inc	D	281 943-7700
Houston (G-9359)		
Cw Resources Inc	F	903 759-8822
Longview (G-14218)		
D & L Well Service Inc	F	432 336-8101
Fort Stockton (G-6329)		
Dale Operating Company	E	214 979-9010
Dallas (G-4208)		
Dalla Compress Ener Solutio LL	E	214 265-0400
Dallas (G-4209)		
Danick Resources	E	214 827-2222
Dallas (G-4234)		
Datagration Solutions Inc	E	713 568-4580
Houston (G-9405)		
Davis Chemical Services LLC	C	903 938-3800
Marshall (G-14772)		
Davis Coiled Tubing Svcs LLC	D	903 927-5555
Marshall (G-14773)		
Davis Offshore LP	F	713 933-0064
Houston (G-9409)		
Davoil Inc	F	817 737-6678
Fort Worth (G-6578)		
Deep Gulf Energy II LLC	D	281 596-0933
Houston (G-9421)		
Deep Gulf Energy LP	F	281 596-0933
Houston (G-9422)		
Denbury Marine LLC	E	972 673-2000
Plano (G-16839)		
Denbury Onshore LLC	E	409 729-0211
Nederland (G-15751)		
Denbury Onshore LLC	C	972 673-2000
Plano (G-16840)		
Denbury Operating Company	E	972 673-2000
Plano (G-16841)		
Denbury Pipeline Holdings LLC	F	972 673-2000
Plano (G-16842)		
Denbury Resources Inc	F	972 378-4776
Plano (G-16843)		
Devon Energy Corporation	E	817 396-4000
Cresson (G-3707)		
Devon Energy Corporation	F	903 693-7196
Carthage (G-2906)		
Diamondback E&P LLC	D	866 531-3667
Midland (G-15192)		
Discovery Acquisition Svcs LLC	E	281 371-2700
Katy (G-13395)		
Diversity Petroleum LP	F	972 772-6025
Mesquite (G-15040)		
Dof Subsea Usa Inc	C	713 896-2500
Houston (G-9491)		
Dome Energy Inc	G	281 558-8585
Houston (G-9494)		
Double Eagle Energy Oper LLC	E	817 928-3260
Fort Worth (G-6590)		
Draco Technologies LLC	F	432 213-5626
Big Spring (G-2080)		
Drilling Info Inc	D	512 477-9200
Austin (G-1101)		
DTE Gas Resources LLC	E	817 302-4600
Fort Worth (G-6595)		
Dunagin Transport Company	F	325 928-5253
Aspermont (G-816)		
Dynamic Inc	F	817 838-1800
Fort Worth (G-6597)		
E B R Energy LP	F	281 265-6500
Sugar Land (G-19481)		
E T C Company	E	210 403-6402
Dallas (G-4285)		
E2 Energy Services LLC	E	214 365-3200
Dallas (G-4288)		
Eagle Gas & Oil Co Inc	E	214 369-1545
Dallas (G-4291)		
Eagle Geophysical Inc	E	713 881-2800
Houston (G-9557)		
Eagle Oil & Gas Co	F	940 723-7322
Wichita Falls (G-20762)		
Eagle Vly Enrgy Partners LLC	F	512 413-7140
Austin (G-1110)		
Eagleclaw Midstream Svcs LLC	E	432 789-1333
Midland (G-15204)		
Eagleridge Energy LLC	F	214 295-6704
Dallas (G-4293)		
Earthstone Energy Inc	E	281 298-4246
The Woodlands (G-19857)		
Earthstone Energy Holdings LLC	E	281 298-4246
The Woodlands (G-19858)		
Earthstone Operating LLC	E	281 298-4246
The Woodlands (G-19859)		
Eastex Crude Company	E	903 856-2401
Leesburg (G-13999)		
Eastex Crude Trucking LLC	B	800 443-8580
Leesburg (G-14000)		
Easton Energy LLC	F	214 712-2141
Houston (G-9571)		
Eclipse Resources I LP	F	814 308-9754
Irving (G-13007)		
Eclipse Resources-Pa LP	F	814 409-7006
Irving (G-13008)		
Ecopetrol America Inc	D	713 634-3800
Houston (G-9581)		
Ejr Consulting Services Inc	F	432 634-2905
Odessa (G-15986)		
El Paso CNG Company LLC	F	713 420-2600
Houston (G-9586)		
Eland Energy Inc	E	214 368-6100
Dallas (G-4308)		
Elevate Midstream Partners LLC	F	214 215-9298
Houston (G-9599)		
Elm Ridge Exploration Co LLC	E	972 889-2100
Dallas (G-4315)		
Elm Ridge Resources Inc	E	972 889-2100
Dallas (G-4316)		
Encino Energy LLC	E	281 254-7070
Houston (G-9624)		
Endeavor Natural Gas LLC	E	713 658-8555
Houston (G-9626)		
Endurance Resources LLC	E	214 996-0900
Addison (G-121)		
Enduro Resource Partners LLC	E	817 744-8200
Fort Worth (G-6612)		
Energen Resources Corporation	D	205 326-2700
Midland (G-15218)		
Energy Explration Partners Inc	E	817 789-6712
Fort Worth (G-6613)		
Energy Management Company	F	972 885-6799
Dallas (G-4323)		
Energy Xxi Gom LLC	E	713 659-2100
Houston (G-9639)		
Energy Xxi USA Inc	C	713 351-3000
Houston (G-9642)		
Enersol Group Inc	E	830 387-4011
New Braunfels (G-15790)		
Enervest Ltd	D	713 659-3500
Houston (G-9643)		
Enervest Operating LLC	E	979 542-2054
Giddings (G-7694)		
Enervest Operating LLC	E	940 683-1966
Bridgeport (G-2293)		
Enervest Operating LLC	E	713 659-3500
Houston (G-9644)		
Eni USA Inc	B	713 393-6100
Houston (G-9649)		
Ensosoft LLC	F	713 360-4841
Houston (G-9660)		
Enven Energy Ventures LLC	E	713 335-7000
Houston (G-9666)		
Eog Resources Inc	E	830 879-4614
Cotulla (G-3690)		
Eog Resources Inc	D	361 866-4300
Corpus Christi (G-3519)		
Eog Resources Inc	E	210 403-7700
San Antonio (G-18093)		
Eog Resources Inc	F	432 586-9141
Kermit (G-13512)		
Eog Resources Inc	D	432 686-3600
Midland (G-15223)		
Eog Resources Inc	C	817 339-9380
Fort Worth (G-6616)		
Eog Resources Inc	E	940 567-9777
Jacksboro (G-13220)		
Eog Resources Inc	F	325 392-3782
Ozona (G-16282)		
Eog Resources Inc	E	940 696-6000
Bowie (G-2194)		
Eog Resources Inc	E	817 212-3100
Alvarado (G-330)		
Eog Resources Inc	E	817 598-8300
Weatherford (G-20590)		
Eog Resources Investments Inc	F	713 651-6914
Houston (G-9672)		
Eos Well Service Inc	F	281 914-2191
Richmond (G-17454)		
Ep Energy E&P Company LP	D	713 997-1200
Houston (G-9674)		
Epic Y-Grade Marketing LP	E	210 920-2285
San Antonio (G-18094)		
Epl Oil & Gas Inc	F	713 228-0711
Houston (G-9682)		
Epsilon Energy Usa Inc	F	281 670-0002
Houston (G-9684)		
Equinor Energy LP	D	512 427-3300
Austin (G-1134)		
Equinor Gulf of Mexico LLC	F	713 918-8200
Houston (G-9686)		
Equinor US Operations LLC	E	713 918-8200
Houston (G-9687)		
Equinor USA E&P Inc	E	713 918-8200
Houston (G-9688)		
Equinor USA Properties Inc	G	713 918-8200
Austin (G-1136)		
Erg Resources LLC	E	713 812-1800
Houston (G-9690)		
Erhc Energy Inc	G	713 626-4700
Houston (G-9691)		
Erskine Energy LLC	E	281 225-7223
Houston (G-9694)		
Escondido Resources II MGT LLC	F	713 662-0332
Katy (G-13401)		
Eseis Inc	F	281 531-1447
Houston (G-9696)		
Esenjay Exploration Inc	E	361 883-7464
Corpus Christi (G-3520)		
Eureka Midstream LLC	E	832 203-4544
Houston (G-9711)		
Ev Energy Partners LP	F	713 659-3500
Houston (G-9714)		
Exco Operating Company LP	E	214 368-2084
Dallas (G-4344)		
Exco Resources Inc	C	214 368-2084
Dallas (G-4345)		
Exl Petroleum LP	F	432 686-8080
Midland (G-15225)		
Exl Petroleum Management LLC	E	432 686-8080
Midland (G-15226)		
Exl Petroleum Operating Inc	F	432 686-8080
Midland (G-15227)		
Exploitation Company LLP	C	713 351-3000
Houston (G-9727)		
F F Foster & Associates Inc	G	713 266-2883
Houston (G-9744)		
Fairways Exploration Prod LLC	F	713 622-3492
Houston (G-9753)		
Fairways Offshore Expl	E	713 622-3492
Houston (G-9754)		
Falcon Bay Energy L L C	F	432 682-7424
Midland (G-15228)		
Far East Energy Corporation	F	832 598-0470
Houston (G-9762)		
FE Hill Co LLP	F	903 389-3616
Fairfield (G-6173)		
Ferus LP	E	832 709-0750
Houston (G-9778)		
Finley Co	E	830 816-2107
Boerne (G-2120)		

Finley Resources Inc	D	817 336-1924	
Fort Worth (G-6631)			
Fivestones Energy LLC	F	432 618-9929	
Midland (G-15230)			
Flint Hills Resources LP	C	361 241-4811	
Corpus Christi (G-3531)			
Flow Control Division Cameron	F	713 513-3300	
Houston (G-9807)			
Flying A Pumping Services LLC	E	325 794-1667	
Albany (G-188)			
Focus Exploration LLC	F	713 435-0021	
Houston (G-9830)			
Foothills Resources Inc	F	713 621-9408	
Houston (G-9831)			
Forum Us Inc	C	713 351-7900	
Houston (G-9844)			
Foundation Energy MGT LLC	E	972 707-2500	
Addison (G-127)			
Franks International LLC	D	281 331-1501	
Alvin (G-362)			
Franks International LLC	D	281 966-7300	
Houston (G-9857)			
Freeman & Curiel Engineers LLP	E	713 895-8668	
Houston (G-9861)			
Frontline Geoservices Ltd	E	281 371-2800	
Katy (G-13406)			
Fts International Services LLC	E	817 862-2000	
Aledo (G-198)			
Fts International Services LLC	E	817 862-2000	
Fort Worth (G-6656)			
Gaither Petroleum Corporation	E	281 579-5200	
Houston (G-9892)			
Gardner Denver Inc	G	817 248-4510	
Fort Worth (G-6662)			
Gas Sensing Technology Corp	E	307 742-6340	
Houston (G-9902)			
Gas Ventures Ltd Liability Co	G	307 864-3754	
Houston (G-9903)			
Gastar Exploration Inc	E	713 739-1800	
Houston (G-9904)			
Gavstar Services	E	817 657-4020	
Arlington (G-686)			
Genesis Crude Oil LP	C	713 860-2500	
Houston (G-9931)			
Geo Mesa Analysis LLC	E	443 637-2436	
Addison (G-130)			
Geoforce Inc	D	972 546-3878	
Plano (G-16879)			
Geolog Americas Inc	F	281 984-7078	
Houston (G-9936)			
Geosouthern Energy Corporation	F	979 836-5203	
Brenham (G-2255)			
Gep Haynesville LLC	E	281 363-9161	
The Woodlands (G-19867)			
Glass Mountain Pipeline LLC	E	214 880-6000	
Dallas (G-4408)			
Glori Energy Inc	E	713 237-8880	
Houston (G-8383)			
Gmt Exploration Co Texas LLC	F	713 334-6001	
Houston (G-9988)			
Goodrich Petroleum Co La LLC	D	713 780-9494	
Houston (G-10001)			
Goodrich Petroleum Corporation	F	713 780-9494	
Houston (G-10003)			
Gordy Gas Corporation	E	979 922-1313	
Houston (G-10004)			
Gordy Oil Company	E	713 951-0100	
Houston (G-10005)			
Grand Energy Inc	E	972 788-2080	
Addison (G-132)			
Gravity Midstream LLC	F	832 426-3302	
Houston (G-10020)			
Grayson Mill Energy LLC	E	832 271-8050	
Houston (G-10022)			
Green Vly Oil Svcs Free Zone	F	936 242-0603	
Houston (G-10031)			
Grenadier Energy Partners LLC	F	281 907-4120	
Spring (G-19213)			
Grenadier Enrgy Prtners II LLC	F	281 907-4120	
The Woodlands (G-19871)			
Grierson Springs Midstream LLC	E	713 655-9500	
Houston (G-10042)			
Griffith Land Services Inc	G	713 465-3273	
Houston (G-10046)			
Grizzly Energy LLC	E	832 327-2255	
Houston (G-10047)			
Gryphon Production Co LLC	F	806 688-9697	
Pampa (G-16324)			
Gulf Coast Western LLC	E	972 284-0600	
Dallas (G-4421)			

H E & D Operating Inc	E	713 650-8008	
Houston (G-10083)			
H L Brown Jr	F	432 683-5216	
Midland (G-15243)			
H Power I LLC	D	214 978-8943	
Dallas (G-4425)			
Halff Tritex LLC	E	214 217-6500	
Richardson (G-17325)			
Hall-Houston Exploration LP	G	713 333-0975	
Houston (G-10095)			
Hall-Houston Exploration II LP	F	713 333-0930	
Houston (G-10096)			
Halliburton Company	E	281 297-1200	
Spring (G-19214)			
Halliburton Company	E	281 575-5000	
Corpus Christi (G-3544)			
Halliburton Company	C	281 297-1200	
Houston (G-10100)			
Halliburton Company	E	281 871-2699	
Houston (G-10107)			
Hamill Resources Inc	F	281 556-9581	
Houston (G-10112)			
Harding Energy Partners LLC	F	214 723-5112	
Dallas (G-4435)			
Harrison Gypsum LLC	F	210 225-9502	
San Antonio (G-18159)			
Harvest Natural Resources Inc	E	281 899-5700	
Dallas (G-4439)			
Harvest Pipeline Company	F	830 334-3280	
Houston (G-10135)			
Hawkins Rmote Snsing Explrtion	E	210 829-5330	
San Antonio (G-18160)			
Hawkwood Energy East Texas LLC	A	303 823-4175	
Dallas (G-4441)			
Hb2 Energy Inc	E	713 377-9860	
Houston (G-10140)			
Headington Energy Partners LLC	E	214 307-5400	
McKinney (G-14946)			
Headington Oil Limited 1993 LP	F	361 885-0110	
Corpus Christi (G-3546)			
Henry Oil LC	F	214 696-5150	
Dallas (G-4449)			
Henry Resources LLC	E	432 694-3000	
Midland (G-15245)			
Hep Services LLC	F	210 278-1563	
Houston (G-10156)			
Hess Corporation	E	713 496-4000	
Houston (G-10163)			
Hess Investments ND LLC	C	713 496-4000	
Houston (G-10164)			
High Plains Hydro Carbon	G	806 948-4166	
Sunray (G-19619)			
Highmount Exploration Prod LLC	G	325 387-3588	
Sonora (G-19026)			
Highmount Exploration Prod LLC	C	281 873-1500	
Houston (G-10177)			
Highpeak Energy Partners LP	E	817 850-9200	
Fort Worth (G-6696)			
Hilcorp Energy Company	F	979 548-2144	
Sweeny (G-19627)			
Hilcorp Energy Company	F	713 209-2400	
Houston (G-10182)			
Hilcorp Energy I LP	F	713 209-2400	
Houston (G-10183)			
Hilcorp Energy I LP	F	713 209-2400	
Houston (G-10184)			
Hilcorp Finance Company	C	713 209-2400	
Houston (G-10185)			
Hilltop Energy LLC	F	972 686-0369	
Dallas (G-4459)			
HK Energy Operating LLC	C	281 537-9920	
Houston (G-10188)			
Hollimon Oil Corporation	F	210 829-8822	
San Antonio (G-18170)			
Hons International Inc	D	281 940-9184	
Sugar Land (G-19493)			
Horizon Production & Oper LLC	F	713 522-5800	
Houston (G-10206)			
Horizon Resources LP	F	713 522-5800	
Houston (G-10207)			
Houston Energy LP	E	713 650-8008	
Houston (G-10232)			
Howell Oil & Gas Inc	F	903 935-0999	
Marshall (G-14782)			
Hunt Nlson Bnker Trust Estt-T	F	214 979-9072	
Dallas (G-4471)			
Hunt Dominion Corporation	F	214 880-8400	
Dallas (G-4472)			
Hunt Exploration Mining Co	F	214 979-9072	
Dallas (G-4473)			

Hunt Marcellus LLC	E	214 978-8000	
Dallas (G-4474)			
Hunt Oil Company	E	214 978-8000	
Dallas (G-4475)			
Hunt Petroleum Corporation	C	214 880-8400	
Fort Worth (G-6710)			
Hunt Petroleum Corporation	F	713 871-3400	
Houston (G-10280)			
Hunting PLC USA	A	713 595-2950	
The Woodlands (G-19875)			
Hydrocrbon Exploration Dev LLC	F	281 453-5700	
Houston (G-10306)			
Independence Resources MGT LLC	E	832 916-2300	
Houston (G-10339)			
Independence Resources MGT LLC	E	832 916-2300	
Midland (G-15252)			
Indigo Minerals LLC	C	713 237-5000	
Houston (G-10342)			
Infrastructure Networks Inc	E	832 598-6600	
Houston (G-10361)			
Innovtive Trnround Contrls Ltd	C	281 998-9547	
Pasadena (G-16460)			
Interctive Explrtion Solutions	F	713 993-0676	
Houston (G-10394)			
Intermoor Inc	F	832 399-5000	
Houston (G-10397)			
Ion Exploration Pdts USA Inc	G	281 933-3339	
Stafford (G-19330)			
Ipr Transoil Corporation	F	972 257-1900	
Irving (G-13065)			
Ips International LLC	F	936 521-1981	
Conroe (G-3311)			
Iron Hrse Olfled Svc Group LLC	F	832 224-4430	
Houston (G-10419)			
Ironroc Energy Partners LLC	E	713 377-9860	
Houston (G-10422)			
Ironwood Oil & Gas LLC	G	281 873-9378	
Houston (G-10423)			
Iskandia Energy Operating Inc	E	832 209-8240	
Houston (G-10426)			
Isramco Energy LLC	E	713 456-7892	
Houston (G-10428)			
Iwc Oil & Refinery LLC	E	210 900-9928	
San Antonio (G-18196)			
J-W Gathering Company	F	903 643-3413	
Longview (G-14255)			
Jagged Peak Energy MGT LLC	E	720 215-3700	
Austin (G-1249)			
Jaguar Exploration Inc	F	281 920-2668	
Katy (G-13366)			
James Fisher Subsea Excav Inc	F	713 466-1233	
Houston (G-10451)			
Jefferson Refinery LLC	F	281 677-4900	
The Woodlands (G-19889)			
Jgc Energy Development USA Inc	F	832 487-9965	
Houston (G-10473)			
Joy Glbal Lngview Oprtions LLC	A	903 237-7000	
Longview (G-14258)			
K&L Contractors Inc	F	936 591-8333	
Center (G-3001)			
Kap Project Services Ltd	D	877 527-7762	
La Porte (G-13761)			
Kerr Energy Companies LLC	G	713 501-9555	
Houston (G-10520)			
Kerr-Mcgee (nevada) LLC	D	303 321-0683	
Spring (G-19224)			
Kerr-Mcgee Oil Gas Onshore LP	C	832 636-1000	
The Woodlands (G-19891)			
Key Energy Drilling Inc	E	432 639-2534	
Iraan (G-12919)			
Key Energy Services Inc	D	979 542-3344	
Giddings (G-7698)			
Key Energy Services Inc	E	806 489-7452	
Welch (G-20655)			
Keystone Exploration Ltd	F	817 820-7029	
Fort Worth (G-6758)			
Kgh Intermediate Holdco II LLC	F	432 563-1708	
Midland (G-15271)			
Khanty Mansiysk Oil Corp	A	713 629-6600	
Houston (G-10529)			
Killam Oil Co Ltd	E	956 724-7141	
Laredo (G-13902)			
Killam Oil Co Ltd	E	361 394-7680	
Freer (G-7229)			
Kinder Morgan (delaware) Inc	C	806 272-3309	
Muleshoe (G-15677)			
King Operating Corporation	F	214 420-3000	
Dallas (G-4556)			
King Pipeline Services LLC	E	903 530-8667	
Fort Worth (G-6762)			

PRODUCT

Kokomo Energy Inc ....F.... 940 683-1102
Bridgeport *(G-2296)*
Kosmos Energy LLC ....F.... 214 445-9600
Dallas *(G-4565)*
Kosmos Energy Ltd ....G.... 214 445-9600
Dallas *(G-4566)*
Kraken Oil & Gas LLC ....F.... 713 360-7705
Houston *(G-10562)*
Lacy Operations Ltd ....E.... 903 758-8276
Longview *(G-14262)*
Lamar Hunt Trust Estate Inc ....D.... 214 720-1600
Dallas *(G-4579)*
Lambda Energy Resources LLC ....D.... 231 258-6425
Houston *(G-10587)*
Laredo Energy IV Gp LLC ....F.... 713 600-6000
Houston *(G-10600)*
Laredo Petroleum Inc ....E.... 432 684-9955
Midland *(G-15272)*
Layline Petroleum LLC ....E.... 713 465-4100
Houston *(G-10608)*
Legacy Offshore LLC ....F.... 281 334-2266
League City *(G-13968)*
Legacy Reserves LP ....E.... 432 967-3490
Midland *(G-15275)*
Legacy Reserves Oper GP LLC ....C.... 432 689-5200
Midland *(G-15277)*
Lewis Energy Group LP ....A.... 956 728-6000
Encinal *(G-6086)*
Lewis Petro Properties Inc ....D.... 210 384-3200
San Antonio *(G-18249)*
Lilis Energy Inc ....F.... 817 585-9001
Fort Worth *(G-6789)*
Lime Rock Resources A LP ....E.... 713 292-9510
Houston *(G-10642)*
Limestone Exploration II LLC ....F.... 432 695-6970
Midland *(G-15282)*
Linn Acquisition Company LLC ....C.... 281 840-4000
Houston *(G-10648)*
Linn Energy Inc ....E.... 281 840-4000
Houston *(G-10649)*
Linn Energy Inc ....C.... 405 241-2200
Houston *(G-10650)*
Linn Energy Finance Corp ....E.... 281 840-4000
Houston *(G-10651)*
Linn Energy Holdings LLC ....E.... 806 274-3074
Houston *(G-10652)*
Llano Operating Corporation ....F.... 972 677-7690
Dallas *(G-4598)*
Llog Exploration Company LLC ....D.... 281 752-1100
Houston *(G-10656)*
Longfellow Energy LP ....E.... 972 590-9900
Addison *(G-146)*
Lotus Midstream LLC ....G.... 713 234-7865
Sugar Land *(G-19505)*
Lowe Offshore Inc ....D.... 281 894-5454
Houston *(G-10690)*
LPC Crude Oil Inc ....D.... 432 682-8555
Midland *(G-15287)*
Lr Energy Inc ....E.... 214 691-5800
Dallas *(G-4608)*
Lucid Energy Group LLC ....E.... 575 810-6025
Dallas *(G-4610)*
Lucid Energy Group II LLC ....F.... 214 420-4950
Dallas *(G-4611)*
Luig Energy Services LLC ....F.... 940 264-6188
Wichita Falls *(G-20780)*
Lukoil Intl Upstream W Inc ....E.... 713 877-8544
Houston *(G-10700)*
Luther M Creek ....D.... 325 387-3295
Sonora *(G-19027)*
M3 Midstream LLC ....F.... 713 783-3000
Houston *(G-10727)*
M5 Louisiana Gathering LLC ....E.... 713 783-3000
Houston *(G-10728)*
Magnolia Oil & Gas Oper LLC ....D.... 713 842-9050
Houston *(G-10736)*
Mallard Completions LLC ....D.... 432 381-8508
Midland *(G-15292)*
Mani Little & Wortmann ....E.... 210 403-9461
San Antonio *(G-18273)*
Manti Operating Company ....E.... 361 888-7708
Corpus Christi *(G-3572)*
Manti Resources Inc ....E.... 361 888-7708
Houston *(G-10746)*
Manti Tarka Permian LP ....G.... 832 460-0046
Houston *(G-10747)*
Marathon International Oil Co ....D.... 713 629-6600
Houston *(G-10753)*
Marathon Oil Ef LLC ....F.... 713 209-2458
San Antonio *(G-18274)*
Mariner Gulf of Mexico LLC ....D.... 713 954-5500
Houston *(G-10767)*
Marion Energy Inc ....F.... 435 789-6959
McKinney *(G-14957)*
Matador Production Company ....E.... 972 371-5200
Dallas *(G-4649)*
Mathew Marine Inc ....F.... 877 508-4004
Houston *(G-10795)*
Maverick Trmnals Three Rvers L ....F.... 956 371-6530
Brownsville *(G-2382)*
McX Gulf of Mexico LLC ....G.... 713 953-9292
Houston *(G-10814)*
Med-Loz Lease Service Inc ....C.... 956 765-6029
Zapata *(G-20984)*
Medallion Delaware Basin LLC ....C.... 972 746-4401
Irving *(G-13103)*
Medallion Midstream LLC ....E.... 972 746-4401
Irving *(G-13104)*
Medallion Oil Company Inc ....F.... 713 654-0144
Houston *(G-10815)*
Melissa Renewables LLC ....E.... 432 563-0447
Melissa *(G-14998)*
Mentor IMC (usa) Inc ....E.... 713 425-6307
Houston *(G-10829)*
Mercury Operating LLC ....F.... 214 935-1698
Irving *(G-13107)*
Mewborne Enrgy Prtners 04-A LP ....D.... 903 561-2900
Tyler *(G-20125)*
Mewbourne Oil Company ....F.... 432 682-3715
Midland *(G-15298)*
Mewbourne Oil Company ....E.... 806 435-6881
Perryton *(G-16640)*
Mexico Pacific Limited LLC ....F.... 713 425-6500
Houston *(G-10860)*
Meyer Energy Services LLC ....F.... 830 377-1099
Midland *(G-15299)*
Meyer Energy Services LLC ....D.... 830 377-1099
Midland *(G-15300)*
Michelson Energy Company ....F.... 210 826-0681
San Antonio *(G-18299)*
Microseismic Inc ....D.... 713 781-2323
Houston *(G-10869)*
Midcoast Energy LLC ....F.... 806 663-7700
Pampa *(G-16329)*
Midcoast Lease Service Inc ....E.... 361 526-4636
Refugio *(G-17244)*
Midstream Energy Holdings LLC ....G.... 713 403-6460
Houston *(G-10873)*
Midstream Navarro Services LLC ....A.... 956 728-6000
San Antonio *(G-18305)*
Midstream Noble Services LLC ....E.... 281 872-3100
Houston *(G-10875)*
Milagro Exploration Gp LLC ....F.... 713 750-1600
Houston *(G-10880)*
Minergy LLC ....A.... 832 800-6336
Houston *(G-10887)*
Mitsui E&P USA LLC ....E.... 713 960-0023
Houston *(G-10893)*
Moda Midstream LLC ....F.... 832 930-4838
Houston *(G-10901)*
Modena Operating LLC ....F.... 713 592-5000
Houston *(G-10903)*
Mohave Oil and Gas Corporation ....F.... 713 975-1725
Spring *(G-19232)*
Momentum Operating Co Inc ....E.... 325 762-3331
Albany *(G-191)*
Moncrief Oil International Inc ....F.... 817 348-8454
Fort Worth *(G-6848)*
Moyes & Co Inc ....E.... 214 623-6700
Dallas *(G-4694)*
MRC Energy Company ....E.... 972 371-5200
Dallas *(G-4700)*
Mudsmith Ltd ....F.... 432 687-6837
Midland *(G-15308)*
Mullins White Exploration Inc ....D.... 817 442-5259
Southlake *(G-19079)*
Murchison Oil and Gas Inc ....E.... 972 931-0700
Plano *(G-16936)*
Murex Petroleum Corporation ....E.... 281 590-3313
Houston *(G-10940)*
Murphy Exploration & Prod Co ....F.... 281 675-9000
Houston *(G-10941)*
Murphy Exploration Prod - USA ....B.... 281 675-9000
Houston *(G-10942)*
Mustang Extreme Envmtl Svcs LL ....F.... 830 393-1034
Fort Worth *(G-6858)*
N D Nolen Drilling LLC ....F.... 210 585-1966
San Antonio *(G-18327)*
Nabors Well Services Ltd ....D.... 325 387-2884
Sonora *(G-19028)*
Nabors Well Services Ltd ....E.... 432 836-4332
Iraan *(G-12920)*
Nacogdoches Oil and Gas Inc ....F.... 936 560-4747
Nacogdoches *(G-15705)*
National Enrgy Svcs Rnted Corp ....G.... 832 925-3777
Houston *(G-10967)*
Navco Oilfield Services LLC ....G.... 956 542-4426
Brownsville *(G-2386)*
Nbl Permian LLC ....C.... 281 872-3100
Houston *(G-11012)*
Nbl Permian LLC ....F.... 432 688-3430
Midland *(G-15313)*
Nbl Permian LLC ....F.... 979 764-4030
College Station *(G-3195)*
Nbl Texas LLC ....E.... 281 872-3100
Houston *(G-11013)*
Nelson Hunt Bunker ....F.... 214 979-9072
Dallas *(G-4720)*
Neofirma Inc ....F.... 214 233-7111
Richardson *(G-17362)*
Neste Oil Services Inc ....F.... 713 407-4411
Houston *(G-11026)*
Neste Petroleum Inc ....F.... 713 407-4400
Houston *(G-11027)*
Nettlecombe Oil Co Inc ....F.... 713 652-4040
Houston *(G-11029)*
New Century Exploration Inc ....F.... 832 698-1374
Spring *(G-19155)*
New Ventures Leasing LLC ....F.... 940 577-7789
Bowie *(G-2198)*
Newfield Exploration Company ....D.... 281 847-6000
Spring *(G-19236)*
Newpark Mats Intgrted Svcs LLC ....D.... 979 245-3894
Bay City *(G-1775)*
Newpark Mats Intgrted Svcs LLC ....E.... 409 752-5800
Beaumont *(G-1934)*
Nexen Energy Services USA Inc ....E.... 832 714-5000
Houston *(G-11044)*
Nexen Petroleum USA Inc ....E.... 972 450-4600
Houston *(G-11045)*
Noble Energy Inc ....D.... 800 234-3867
Houston *(G-11063)*
Noble Energy Inc ....C.... 281 872-3100
Houston *(G-11064)*
North American Interpipe Inc ....E.... 713 333-0333
Houston *(G-11072)*
Northstar Interests LC ....F.... 713 626-9696
Houston *(G-11079)*
Nottus Energy Resources Inc ....F.... 940 687-5304
Wichita Falls *(G-20788)*
Nrpc Operating LLC ....G.... 512 428-4753
Dallas *(G-4745)*
O-Tex Pumping LLC ....D.... 432 685-9901
Midland *(G-15322)*
Occidental Energy Mktg Inc ....C.... 713 215-7000
Houston *(G-11113)*
Occidental Permian Ltd ....C.... 713 215-7000
Houston *(G-11115)*
Occidental Petroleum Corp ....A.... 713 215-7000
Houston *(G-11116)*
Occidental Petroleum Corp ....G.... 325 574-8567
Ira *(G-12913)*
Occidental Petroleum Corp ....E.... 713 640-7500
Houston *(G-11117)*
Offshore Express Inc ....D.... 985 868-1438
Houston *(G-11141)*
Ogp Operating Inc ....G.... 214 696-2393
Dallas *(G-4755)*
Ohs Energy Corp ....G.... 832 871-5088
Houston *(G-11149)*
Oil & Gas Consultants Intl Inc ....F.... 832 426-1200
Katy *(G-13374)*
Oil & Gas Technology Fund Inc ....F.... 281 671-7142
League City *(G-13973)*
Oklahoma Pacific Ltd ....E.... 713 209-1100
Houston *(G-11166)*
Omimex Energy Inc ....F.... 817 460-7777
Fort Worth *(G-6878)*
Omimex Resources Inc ....F.... 817 460-7777
Fort Worth *(G-6880)*
Opal Resources LLC ....G.... 713 647-7300
Houston *(G-11183)*
Ors Fluids LLC ....E.... 903 535-9992
Tyler *(G-20136)*
Oryx Midstream Services LLC ....E.... 432 684-4272
Midland *(G-15330)*
Oryx Sthern Del Oil Gthring Tr ....F.... 432 684-4272
Midland *(G-15331)*
Osborn Heirs Company Ltd ....E.... 210 826-0700
San Antonio *(G-18357)*

Otcr Inc	F	713 685-3600	
Houston (G-11199)			
Output Acquisition Corp	F	281 879-3609	
Stafford (G-19362)			
Overflow Energy LLC	E	806 658-7832	
Booker (G-2157)			
OXY Inc	C	713 215-7000	
Houston (G-11209)			
OXY USA Wtp LP	D	713 366-5303	
Houston (G-11211)			
OXY Vinyls LP	F	877 699-8465	
Dallas (G-4775)			
Palo Petroleum Inc	F	214 691-3676	
Dallas (G-4781)			
Panda Pwr Gnrtion Infrstrcture	E	972 361-2000	
Dallas (G-4784)			
Parabellum Energy LLC	F	832 460-6521	
Houston (G-11237)			
Paragon Offshore PLC	E	832 783-4000	
Houston (G-11240)			
Parallel Petroleum LLC	F	432 684-3727	
Midland (G-15336)			
Parsley Energy Operations LLC	D	432 818-2100	
Midland (G-15338)			
Parten Operating Inc	E	936 624-3100	
Crockett (G-3721)			
Patara Oil & Gas LLC	D	214 295-6704	
Dallas (G-4790)			
Pcore Exploration Prod II LLC	F	469 802-1400	
Dallas (G-4792)			
Peba Oil & Gas Co	F	940 825-4825	
Nocona (G-15870)			
Penn Virginia Corporation	E	713 722-6500	
Houston (G-11277)			
Penn Virginia Mc Energy LLC	E	713 722-6500	
Houston (G-11279)			
Penn Virginia Oil & Gas LP	F	713 722-6500	
Houston (G-11280)			
Penn Virginia Oil & Gas Corp	F	610 687-8900	
Houston (G-11281)			
Penn Virginia Oil & Gas GP LLC	F	713 722-6500	
Houston (G-11282)			
Penntex Midstream Partners LLC	D	214 981-0700	
Houston (G-11283)			
Pentagon Energy LLC	E	203 451-8382	
Houston (G-11285)			
Perdure Petroleum LLC	F	281 668-8488	
Allen (G-291)			
Peregrine Petroleum LLC	E	214 231-6800	
Dallas (G-4796)			
Peregrine Petroleum LLC	E	713 630-8965	
Houston (G-11289)			
Permian Basin Joint Ventr LLC	E	713 296-6000	
Houston (G-11292)			
Permian Petroleum Services Inc	E	432 682-0434	
Midland (G-15345)			
Peter Paul Petroleum Company	E	713 209-1100	
Houston (G-11295)			
Petro Land Group Inc	E	903 595-4293	
Tyler (G-20141)			
Petrobal Omega 1 LLC	E	972 284-5120	
Irving (G-13142)			
Petrolegacy Energy II LLC	E	512 735-9000	
Austin (G-1414)			
Petroleum Exploration Co Ltd	E	254 559-5453	
Breckenridge (G-2233)			
Petroleum Geo-Services Inc	C	281 509-8000	
Houston (G-11307)			
Petrolima LLC	E	432 695-9989	
Midland (G-15347)			
Petrotel Inc	F	972 473-2767	
Plano (G-16971)			
Pgs Americas Inc	D	512 670-8700	
Manor (G-14648)			
Pgs Americas Inc	D	281 509-8000	
Houston (G-11317)			
Pinnacle Gas Treating LLC	F	903 928-1200	
Tennessee Colony (G-19726)			
Pioneer Energy Services Corp	C	855 884-0575	
San Antonio (G-18378)			
Pioneer Natural Resources Co	C	432 571-2800	
Midland (G-15355)			
Pioneer Ntral Rsources USA Inc	D	432 684-0023	
Midland (G-15357)			
Piranha Scientific LLC	F	855 585-5200	
Midland (G-15359)			
Pitts Oil Company LLC	F	214 369-9266	
Dallas (G-4806)			
Plains Exploration & Prod Co	F	713 579-6000	
Houston (G-11342)			
Platinum Energy Resources Inc	D	713 364-7822	
Houston (G-11348)			
Plunkett Energy & Industrial S	F	806 395-3205	
Wolfforth (G-20910)			
Plunkett Research Ltd	E	713 932-0000	
Houston (G-11351)			
Pluspetrol International Inc	E	713 961-1095	
Houston (G-11352)			
Polaris Exploration Corp	F	361 857-7176	
Beeville (G-1987)			
Polk Production Tech Inc	F	361 815-1245	
Corpus Christi (G-3593)			
Pool Energy Corporation	F	512 249-9252	
Austin (G-1425)			
Post Oak Energy Capital LP	E	713 571-9393	
Houston (G-11369)			
Presidio Petroleum LLC	E	814 589-3550	
Fort Worth (G-6914)			
Prime Natural Resources Inc	F	832 531-8555	
Houston (G-11414)			
Prime Operating Company	E	830 876-2441	
Carrizo Springs (G-2687)			
Prime Operating Company	E	713 735-0000	
Houston (G-11416)			
Pro-Test Inc	E	903 986-8404	
Kilgore (G-13584)			
Probity Energy Partners LLC	E	432 570-1122	
Midland (G-15363)			
Procurement Services Del Inc	E	832 243-6330	
Houston (G-11434)			
Propel Energy LLC	G	713 463-6500	
Houston (G-1474)			
Propetro Holding Corp	E	432 688-0012	
Midland (G-15366)			
Propetro Services Inc	D	432 688-0012	
Midland (G-15368)			
Protege Energy III LLC	F	918 728-3092	
Houston (G-11463)			
Providence Energy Corporation	E	214 522-9131	
Dallas (G-4833)			
PSI Midstream Partners LP	E	713 554-2880	
Houston (G-11469)			
Pursuit Oil & Gas LLC	E	832 706-2299	
Houston (G-11475)			
Pxp Offshore LLC	F	713 579-6000	
Houston (G-11478)			
Pyramid Gom Inc	E	281 822-0801	
Houston (G-11479)			
Python Pressure Pumping LLC	E	940 549-6900	
Cleburne (G-3106)			
Qae Inc	D	281 436-5500	
Houston (G-11482)			
Quail Well Service Inc	E	325 677-0323	
Abilene (G-67)			
Quantum Investment Group Inc	E	281 994-5400	
Houston (G-11507)			
Quintana Minerals Brazil LLC	F	713 751-7500	
Houston (G-11517)			
Quintana Minerals Corporation	E	713 751-7500	
Houston (G-11518)			
R & B Energy LLC	G	254 647-3358	
Ranger (G-17231)			
R Lacy Inc	F	903 758-8276	
Longview (G-14293)			
R Lacy Services Ltd	F	903 758-8276	
Longview (G-14294)			
Range Resources - La Inc	E	713 588-8300	
Fort Worth (G-6940)			
Range Resources Corporation	D	817 870-2601	
Fort Worth (G-6941)			
Range Resources Corporation	C	817 870-2601	
Fort Worth (G-6942)			
Recon Exploration Inc	F	972 960-8600	
Addison (G-158)			
Red Arrow Energy LLC	F	713 580-7250	
Houston (G-11566)			
Red Rock Oilfield Service LLC	F	325 933-0224	
Colorado City (G-3226)			
Red Technology Alliance LLC	E	713 839-4689	
Houston (G-11570)			
Red Willow Offshore LLC	D	281 822-7500	
Houston (G-11571)			
Redbud E&P Inc	E	832 698-4234	
Spring (G-19162)			
Redcliff Midstream LLC	E	713 655-9500	
Houston (G-11572)			
Redemption Oil & Gas LLC	D	210 572-2988	
San Antonio (G-18416)			
Redman Energy Corporation	G	713 782-2870	
Houston (G-11575)			
Redwine Resources Inc	E	214 691-5800	
Dallas (G-4879)			
Reef Exploration LP	E	972 437-6792	
Richardson (G-17388)			
Reef Oil & Gas Partners LLC	F	972 437-6792	
Richardson (G-17389)			
Remington Oil and Gas Corp	F	281 618-0400	
Houston (G-11594)			
Remora Energy Management LLC	F	832 325-2300	
Houston (G-11596)			
Repsol Energy North Amer Corp	A	832 442-1000	
The Woodlands (G-19908)			
Repsol Services Company	C	832 442-1000	
The Woodlands (G-19909)			
Republic Energy Inc	E	214 369-4800	
Dallas (G-4889)			
Reservoir Marine LLC	E	281 277-7575	
Sugar Land (G-19533)			
Resmetrics LLC	E	832 592-1900	
Houston (G-11607)			
Resolute Natural Resources LLC	E	432 684-7475	
Midland (G-15382)			
Resource Royalty LLC	F	214 691-5234	
Dallas (G-4891)			
Ridgewood Energy Corporation	E	281 293-8488	
Houston (G-11620)			
Rife Energy Operating Inc	G	940 964-2822	
Forestburg (G-6300)			
Ril USA Inc	F	713 430-8700	
Houston (G-11623)			
Riley Exploration Group LLC	D	512 481-7676	
Austin (G-1466)			
Rimrock Energy LLC	E	303 308-1300	
Fort Worth (G-6959)			
Rio Oil and Gas II LLC	F	832 616-3726	
The Woodlands (G-19912)			
Rio Oil and Gas LLC	E	832 616-3717	
Spring (G-19248)			
Rio Petroleum	F	806 356-8033	
Amarillo (G-458)			
Riviera Operating LLC	D	713 227-1868	
Houston (G-11631)			
Riviera Resources Inc	E	281 840-4000	
Houston (G-11632)			
Rk Petroleum Corp	F	432 683-4319	
Midland (G-15387)			
Ro Mac Oil Co Inc	F	940 849-2261	
Throckmorton (G-19946)			
Rockall Energy LLC	D	214 618-7600	
Dallas (G-4908)			
Rockies Environmental LLC	F	469 715-2642	
Prosper (G-17215)			
Rodessa Operating Company Inc	G	903 534-4765	
Robstown (G-17516)			
Rosetta Resources Offshore LLC	C	713 335-2400	
Houston (G-11666)			
Rosetta Resources Operating LP	C	281 872-3100	
Houston (G-11667)			
Royalty Clearinghouse Ltd	F	800 877-5122	
Austin (G-1474)			
Rsp Permian LLC	F	432 818-1300	
Midland (G-15391)			
Rsp Permian LLC	E	214 252-2700	
Dallas (G-4916)			
Rutherford Oil Corporation	F	713 622-5555	
Houston (G-11701)			
Rutherford Oil Corporation	F	830 334-8396	
Pearsall (G-16614)			
Rutherford-Moran Exploration	F	859 254-4775	
Houston (G-11702)			
S K Resources Inc	F	713 782-1075	
Houston (G-11711)			
Sabalo Explrtion Operating LLC	E	361 888-7708	
Corpus Christi (G-3614)			
Sable Permian Resources LLC	E	713 579-8000	
Houston (G-11719)			
Sable Prmian Resources Fin LLC	E	713 579-8000	
Houston (G-11720)			
Saexploration Holdings Inc	E	281 258-4400	
Houston (G-11723)			
Sage Energy Company	E	210 404-2828	
San Antonio (G-18443)			
Samson Resources Company	E	806 435-7200	
Perryton (G-16649)			
Sanare Energy Partners LLC	F	713 626-9696	
Houston (G-11741)			
Sanchez Oil & Gas Corporation	C	713 783-8000	
Houston (G-11742)			
Sanchez Oil & Gas Corporation	E	713 783-8000	
Houston (G-11743)			

PRODUCT

Sandalwood Exploration LP	F	713 759-6095	
Houston (G-11745)			
Sandalwood Oil & Gas Inc	F	713 759-6095	
Houston (G-11746)			
Sanday Corporation	F	832 717-4412	
Spring (G-19164)			
Saratoga Resources Inc	F	713 458-1560	
Houston (G-11751)			
Sasol (usa) Corporation	F	281 588-3000	
Houston (G-11753)			
Saxet Petroleum Inc	F	713 783-4883	
Houston (G-11760)			
Saybolt LP	D	281 478-1300	
Deer Park (G-5294)			
Sbm Offshore Usa Inc	B	281 848-6000	
Houston (G-11762)			
Schlumberger Omnes Inc	B	713 375-3400	
Houston (G-11770)			
Schlumberger Technology Corp	E	432 694-0000	
Midland (G-15396)			
Scorpion Flowback LLC	F	432 302-1628	
Midland (G-15400)			
Sea Eagle Ford LLC	E	720 390-6244	
Houston (G-11795)			
Segundo Navarro Drilling Ltd	E	210 384-3200	
San Antonio (G-18465)			
Seidler Oil & Gas LP	G	817 259-1777	
Alvarado (G-345)			
Seitel	D	832 295-8300	
Houston (G-11817)			
Seitel Management Inc	D	713 881-8900	
Houston (G-11819)			
Selman & Associates Ltd	C	432 563-0084	
Midland (G-15403)			
Seneca Resources Company LLC	E	713 654-2600	
Houston (G-11829)			
Seneca Resources Corporation	D	713 374-6300	
Houston (G-11830)			
Sentry Oil & Gas LLC	E	212 753-6367	
Mico (G-15094)			
SHD Oil & Gas LLC	F	713 595-4274	
Houston (G-11854)			
Shell Gulf of Mexico Inc	F	713 241-6161	
Houston (G-11859)			
Sheridan Prod Partners I-A LP	C	432 683-5271	
Midland (G-15407)			
Sheridan Prod Partners I-A LP	F	713 548-1000	
Houston (G-11866)			
Sheridan Production Co LLC	D	806 842-3521	
Lorenzo (G-14345)			
Sheridan Production Co LLC	D	432 263-4301	
Big Spring (G-2098)			
Sheridan Production Co LLC	D	325 453-2108	
Robert Lee (G-17499)			
Sheridan Production Co LLC	C	713 548-1000	
Houston (G-11867)			
Sheridan Production Co LLC	F	979 567-7629	
Caldwell (G-2635)			
Shorthorn Resources Inc	F	713 668-0550	
Houston (G-11874)			
Siana Oil & Gas Co LLC	F	713 568-1082	
Houston (G-11876)			
Sierra Resources LLC	F	713 365-6100	
Houston (G-11881)			
Sigmund Kane & Hatch Inc	F	713 782-1075	
Houston (G-11888)			
Signal Peak Silica LLC	C	281 822-4568	
Houston (G-11892)			
Silver Creek Oil & Gas LLC	D	972 573-1630	
Irving (G-13180)			
Silver Hill Enrgy Partners LLC	E	214 865-6555	
Dallas (G-4964)			
Site Safe Solutions Ltd	D	940 612-2286	
Gainesville (G-7368)			
Sk Gc Americas Inc	F	713 341-5820	
Houston (G-11911)			
Skh Management LP	F	713 782-1075	
Houston (G-11914)			
SM Energy Company	E	281 677-2800	
Houston (G-11915)			
SM Energy Company	D	432 688-1700	
Midland (G-15411)			
SM Energy Company	F	281 677-2800	
Houston (G-11916)			
Smith Energy Company	F	713 651-9102	
Houston (G-11922)			
Smith Production Inc	E	281 583-0196	
Houston (G-11924)			
Smith Production Inc	E	281 296-5600	
The Woodlands (G-19920)			

Sn Midstream LLC	E	713 783-8000	
Houston (G-11928)			
Snd Operating LLC	E	214 691-3072	
Dallas (G-4972)			
Sonterra Grp Zppelinn Enrgy LP	F	210 930-3111	
San Antonio (G-18484)			
South Bay Resources LLC	F	713 785-8700	
Houston (G-11959)			
Southwestern Energy Company	D	832 796-1000	
Spring (G-19167)			
Speedway LLC	B	877 609-4255	
Houston (G-12012)			
Speedway LLC	E	432 758-6700	
Seminole (G-18887)			
Spindletop Drilling Company	E	972 644-2581	
Dallas (G-4997)			
Spindletop Oil & Gas Co	E	972 644-2581	
Dallas (G-4998)			
Spire Marketing Inc	E	346 308-7549	
Houston (G-12016)			
Square Mile Energy LLC	E	713 266-3685	
Houston (G-12029)			
Stakeholder Gas Utility LLC	E	210 444-9664	
San Antonio (G-18493)			
Strand Energy LC	F	713 658-8096	
Houston (G-12074)			
Stratum Energy Romania LLC	F	832 813-8947	
Montgomery (G-15642)			
Strong Services LP	D	903 693-3966	
Carthage (G-2922)			
Summit Petroleum LLC	E	432 682-9800	
Midland (G-15423)			
Sun Energy Services LLC	E	432 701-9000	
Midland (G-15424)			
Sundown Operating Inc	D	806 229-6102	
Sundown (G-19614)			
Superior Pipeline Company	D	806 323-8145	
Canadian (G-2654)			
Surgitech Inc	E	800 975-6850	
Houston (G-12126)			
Sutton Bros Inc	F	325 387-2053	
Sonora (G-19030)			
Swn International LLC	A	832 796-1000	
Spring (G-19171)			
Swn Production (arkansas) LLC	A	832 796-1000	
Spring (G-19172)			
Swn Production Company LLC	E	281 618-4700	
Houston (G-12133)			
Sylvan Energy LLC	D	412 222-9600	
Houston (G-12134)			
Synergy Oil & Gas LP	F	713 827-9988	
Houston (G-12135)			
Talon Oil & Gas LLC	E	214 323-8360	
Dallas (G-5034)			
Talos Energy Inc	C	713 328-3000	
Houston (G-12150)			
Talos Energy LLC	E	713 328-3000	
Houston (G-12151)			
Talos Petroleum LLC	E	281 872-1999	
Houston (G-12153)			
Tana Exploration Company LLC	D	469 276-8262	
Dallas (G-5035)			
Tanos Energy LLC	F	903 597-7667	
Tyler (G-20160)			
Taos Resources Oper Co LLC	F	713 993-0774	
Houston (G-12157)			
Targa Resources Corp	E	713 584-1053	
Channelview (G-3042)			
Tauren Exploration Inc	F	972 681-8047	
Dallas (G-5036)			
Taurus Oil Inc	F	432 685-3520	
Midland (G-15432)			
Tecpetrol Corporation	E	713 974-3322	
Houston (G-12181)			
Tejones Operating Corporation	G	210 824-5957	
San Antonio (G-18526)			
Tellurian Inc	E	832 962-4000	
Houston (G-12193)			
Tema Oil and Gas Company	E	281 829-3206	
Houston (G-12196)			
Temple Generation I LLC	E	254 598-3700	
Temple (G-19708)			
Tepee Petroleum Company Inc	G	713 659-8300	
Houston (G-12206)			
Terra Energy Partners LLC	E	281 936-0355	
Houston (G-12209)			
Terrace Energy LLC	F	817 546-7490	
Fort Worth (G-7044)			
Tetra Technologies Inc	E	903 693-9500	
Carthage (G-2923)			

Texakoma Financial Inc	E	972 701-9106	
Plano (G-17026)			
Texakoma Operating LP	E	972 701-9106	
Plano (G-17027)			
Texas Australian Power Inc	E	940 723-4122	
Wichita Falls (G-20815)			
Texas Coastal Energy Co LLC	F	214 429-3700	
Dallas (G-5057)			
Texas Energy Holdings Inc	E	214 231-4000	
Dallas (G-5059)			
Texas Intl Gas & Oil Co	F	915 860-8803	
El Paso (G-5999)			
Texas Pipeline Webb	E	210 298-2222	
San Antonio (G-18541)			
Texla Energy Management Inc	F	713 655-9900	
Houston (G-12260)			
Texod Energy LLC	F	214 998-5360	
Dallas (G-5079)			
Tgs-Nopec Geophysical Company	D	713 860-2100	
Houston (G-12268)			
Tgs-Nopec Geophysical Company	E	281 319-4944	
Humble (G-12803)			
The Cumming Company Inc	F	817 737-2393	
Fort Worth (G-7053)			
Thomas Reprographics Inc	E	281 875-2500	
Houston (G-12276)			
Three Rivers Operating Co LLC	F	512 600-3190	
Austin (G-1577)			
Three Span Oil & Gas Inc	F	432 684-6511	
Midland (G-15437)			
Three Streams Energy LLC	F	469 917-1777	
Dallas (G-5088)			
Timekeepers Inc	D	830 331-1224	
Boerne (G-2142)			
Top Coat Inc	E	979 233-9558	
Freeport (G-7216)			
Torrent Energy Services LLC	E	512 722-3439	
Wimberley (G-20885)			
Total E&P Usa Inc	C	713 647-3000	
Houston (G-12330)			
Total Holdings Usa Inc	E	713 483-5000	
Houston (G-12331)			
Tradewinds Petrotrade LLC	F	713 465-7590	
Houston (G-12341)			
Transamerican Natural Gas Corp	C	281 372-5304	
Houston (G-12346)			
Transatlantic Petro USA Corp	F	214 220-4323	
Addison (G-169)			
Transatlantic Petroleum Ltd	E	214 220-4323	
Addison (G-170)			
Transcanada USA Services Inc	E	832 320-5000	
Houston (G-12348)			
Transtex LLC	F	832 369-6986	
Irving (G-13197)			
Travis Peak Resources LLC	F	512 814-0345	
Houston (G-12357)			
Trek Resources Inc	F	214 373-0318	
Dallas (G-5107)			
Tri Resources Inc	E	713 584-1000	
Houston (G-12362)			
Tri-Star Petroleum Company	G	713 222-0011	
Houston (G-12364)			
Trinity River Energy Oper LLC	G	817 872-7800	
Houston (G-12376)			
Triple N Services Inc	E	432 687-1994	
Midland (G-15446)			
Tritex Technologies Inc	F	214 346-6200	
Richardson (G-17413)			
Triumph Energy Partners LLC	G	918 986-8283	
Dallas (G-5119)			
TRT Holdings Inc	E	214 283-8500	
Dallas (G-5121)			
Trwa Inc	D	817 361-8839	
Fort Worth (G-7083)			
Trwa Inc	E	817 361-8839	
Fort Worth (G-7084)			
Twilight Services LLC	F	817 326-4806	
Granbury (G-7815)			
Txco Resources Inc	F	210 822-8864	
Dallas (G-5124)			
Tzc Services LLC	F	432 517-1212	
Midland (G-15451)			
U S Energy Development Corp	F	682 305-2868	
Arlington (G-807)			
Unit Corporation	D	432 362-0901	
Odessa (G-16188)			
Unit Petroleum Company	F	713 960-8870	
Houston (G-12444)			
United Shtdown Sfety Texas Inc	F	877 805-5155	
Pasadena (G-16522)			

Unitex Oil & Gas LLC	F	432 685-0014
Midland (G-15456)		
Universal Valve Company Inc	E	432 689-6341
Midland (G-15458)		
Upham Oil & Gas Company LP	E	940 325-4491
Mineral Wells (G-15544)		
Urban Oil & Gas Group LLC	E	972 543-8800
Plano (G-17043)		
Ursa Resources Group II LLC	F	713 456-3000
Houston (G-12480)		
US Operating Inc	F	214 393-3992
Dallas (G-3856)		
Vaalco Gabon (etame) Inc	E	713 623-0801
Houston (G-12515)		
Valence Midstream Ltd	E	281 359-3659
Kingwood (G-13658)		
Valerus Feld Sltons Hldngs LLC	E	713 744-6100
Houston (G-12520)		
Valerus Field Solutions LP	E	877 983-7500
Houston (G-12521)		
Vanguard Permian LLC	F	432 362-2209
Odessa (G-16195)		
Vantage Energy Services Inc	E	281 404-4700
Houston (G-12533)		
Venado Oil & Gas LLC	F	512 518-2900
Austin (G-1628)		
Venado Oil & Gas LLC	F	512 518-2900
Charlotte (G-3049)		
Verado Energy Inc	E	214 368-5322
Dallas (G-5159)		
Verado Oil and Gas Corporation	F	214 368-5322
Dallas (G-5160)		
Verdun Oil Company LLC	E	713 554-4577
Houston (G-12550)		
Viceroy Petroleum LP	E	832 783-5790
College Station (G-3209)		
Viking International Limited	F	214 220-4323
Dallas (G-5167)		
Vine Oil & Gas LP	F	469 606-0540
Plano (G-17045)		
Vitruvian Exploration II LLC	E	832 458-3100
Cypress (G-3825)		
Vitruvian II Woodford LLC	D	832 458-3100
The Woodlands (G-19939)		
Vog Palo Verde LP	E	512 518-2900
Austin (G-1643)		
Walter Oil & Gas Corporation	E	713 659-1221
Houston (G-12597)		
Wapiti Operating LLC	D	713 365-8500
Houston (G-12598)		
Warren Resources Inc	E	214 393-9688
Dallas (G-5172)		
Waterford Operating LLC	F	713 255-6200
Houston (G-12604)		
Weatherford Fracturing Tech	F	817 882-9955
Fort Worth (G-7130)		
Weatherford International LLC	G	817 443-3000
Benbrook (G-2048)		
Welder Exploration & Prod Inc	F	210 354-1515
San Antonio (G-18613)		
Western Gas Resources Inc	F	432 395-2973
Fort Stockton (G-6332)		
Western Marketing Inc	G	817 232-8626
Saginaw (G-17759)		
White Oak Operating Co LLC	F	281 876-2025
Houston (G-12662)		
Wildcat Midstream Oper LLC	E	214 310-1213
Dallas (G-5186)		
Wildhorse Resources LLC	E	713 568-4910
Houston (G-12666)		
William L Arrington	G	806 669-3324
Pampa (G-16345)		
Wilson County Holdings LLC	F	512 402-7273
Austin (G-1669)		
Winn Exploration Co Inc	F	361 844-6900
Corpus Christi (G-3657)		
Woodside Energy (usa) Inc	C	713 963-8490
Houston (G-12690)		
Wsh Land Inc	F	713 622-4823
Houston (G-12700)		
Wsi Cased Hole Specialist Inc	E	800 658-9674
Snyder (G-19015)		
Xog Operating LLC	E	432 683-3171
Midland (G-15473)		
Xstar Resources LLC	F	817 495-9306
Jacksboro (G-13224)		
Xto Energy Inc	F	505 333-3100
Fort Worth (G-7155)		
Zarvona Energy LLC	F	713 600-0600
Houston (G-12721)		

Zaza Energy LLC	F	713 595-1900
Houston (G-12722)		
Zaza Energy Corporation	F	713 595-1900
Houston (G-12723)		
Zion Oil & Gas Inc	F	214 221-4610
Dallas (G-5209)		

GAS & OIL FIELD SVCS, NEC

2w Services LLC	E	361 645-1010
Goliad (G-7746)		
3s Team LLC	D	918 396-4155
Pasadena (G-16375)		
Alinet Oilfield Services Corp	F	903 984-2307
Kilgore (G-13531)		
Bakken Express LLC	F	281 359-8382
Kingwood (G-13638)		
Basin Pipeline LLC	E	817 460-7777
Fort Worth (G-6437)		
CAM Field Solutions LLC	E	832 533-2706
Houston (G-9057)		
Canden Resources Ltd	E	403 473-8786
Austin (G-1022)		
Chemical Tracers Inc	F	936 564-1866
Nacogdoches (G-15691)		
Clear View Unlimited LLC	F	409 782-3594
Silsbee (G-18951)		
Flowback Green Services LLC	E	409 217-1482
Beaumont (G-1894)		
Framework Offshore LLC	E	281 610-1078
Katy (G-13405)		
Frontline Energy Inc	F	713 228-3577
Houston (G-9870)		
Gdsware	F	832 350-1166
Houston (G-9912)		
Hub City Industries	E	903 938-8554
Marshall (G-14783)		
Hulk Oilfield Services Inc	F	432 803-7060
Monahans (G-15605)		
Ili Technologies 2002 USA	E	713 960-0811
Houston (G-10322)		
Merco Solutions Corporation	E	830 519-4260
Gonzales (G-7759)		
Merit Energy Partners F-I LP	F	972 701-8377
Dallas (G-4667)		
Mudsmith	F	214 370-9535
Dallas (G-4703)		
Paramount Rental Services LLC	F	940 264-8379
Wichita Falls (G-20793)		
Pegasus Optmztion Managers LLC	C	979 213-4101
Montgomery (G-15638)		
Rebuilding Tgether El Paso Inc	F	915 342-3882
El Paso (G-5932)		
Roldan Drilling Fluids R&D	F	832 918-6267
The Woodlands (G-19913)		
Roldan Midstream Services LLC	G	832 918-6267
The Woodlands (G-19914)		
S&M Energy Services LLC	F	318 210-5166
Gary (G-7616)		
SDS Energy Services LLC	E	903 747-3837
Tyler (G-20150)		
Texon Partners	F	940 264-3019
Wichita Falls (G-20817)		
Tri Capital Energy Corporation	F	972 996-7486
Dallas (G-5108)		
Trucoastal Oil and Gas Svcs	F	432 413-9950
Midland (G-15448)		
Twisted R Oilfield Svcs LLC	F	432 312-3110
Midland (G-15450)		
Usac Leasing 2 LLC	C	512 473-2662
Austin (G-1620)		
Waggoner Land Services	E	817 763-8112
Fort Worth (G-7115)		
Wedge Measurement & Control LP	C	713 490-9555
Houston (G-12624)		
Wood County Energy LLC	E	281 994-5400
Houston (G-12684)		

GAS & OTHER COMBINED SVCS

Advance Fbrction Msurement LLC	E	713 468-9581
Houston (G-8482)		
Charts Ltd	E	432 697-7801
Midland (G-15159)		
Franklin Howard Intl LLC	F	281 815-1527
Houston (G-9856)		

GAS FIELD MACHINERY & EQPT

Advance Fabrication Svcs LLC	E	432 561-8776
Odessa (G-15903)		

BOP Products LLC	F	281 955-6321
Houston (G-8957)		
Cameron Solutions Inc	D	713 849-6556
Houston (G-9078)		
Cameron Solutions Inc	C	713 849-7500
Houston (G-9079)		
Championx Corporation	C	281 403-5772
The Woodlands (G-19840)		
Clean Energy Tech Assn Inc	E	903 389-4136
Fairfield (G-6171)		
Csi Compressco LP	B	281 367-1983
The Woodlands (G-19850)		
Diversified Industrial Svc Co	E	806 274-2214
Borger (G-2174)		
Dw Energy Group	E	214 758-0880
Irving (G-13004)		
Endurance Lift Solutions LLC	C	903 595-8600
Fort Worth (G-6611)		
Gaumer Company Inc	C	713 460-5200
Houston (G-9905)		
JW Williams Inc	F	307 237-8345
Odessa (G-16043)		
Natco Group Inc	F	713 849-7500
Houston (G-10964)		
Nk Energy LLC	F	832 857-8228
Kingwood (G-13650)		
Reel Power Oil & Gas Inc	E	713 937-4494
Houston (G-11580)		
Strongfab Solutions Inc	F	713 856-6511
Houston (G-12082)		
Surveys & Analysis Inc	E	508 842-4011
Houston (G-12127)		

GAS PROCESSING SVC

Enterprise Hydrocarbons LP	D	713 381-6500
San Antonio (G-18092)		
Gates Fuel Services LLC	E	409 925-8897
Santa Fe (G-18734)		
Interstate Treating Inc	D	432 362-9291
Odessa (G-16034)		
Kingfisher Midstream LLC	F	281 655-3200
Dallas (G-4557)		
Markwest Javelina Company LLC	D	361 289-4900
Corpus Christi (G-3573)		
Midcoast Energy LLC	C	713 821-2000
Houston (G-10871)		
Omimex Petroleum Inc	F	817 460-7777
Fort Worth (G-6879)		
Petrofuels Quality Mktg LP	F	409 722-6880
Nederland (G-15759)		
Producers Midstream LP	F	214 238-5740
Dallas (G-4832)		
S2w Contracting LLC	E	940 745-1421
Weatherford (G-20619)		
Scurry Midstream LLC	E	214 238-5740
Dallas (G-4946)		
Silvertip Completion Svcs LLC	E	432 701-9020
Midland (G-15409)		
Sulphur River Exploration Inc	F	214 373-1091
Dallas (G-5021)		
Sulphur River Exploration Inc	F	903 734-7248
Gilmer (G-7714)		
Talos Ert LLC	F	281 618-0590
Houston (G-12152)		
Talos Production LLC	C	713 328-3000
Houston (G-12154)		
Targa Ppline Mid-Continent LLC	D	432 535-2484
Midkiff (G-15097)		
Wildcat Minerals Holdings LLC	E	214 706-3553
Dallas (G-5187)		
Wtg Suth Permian Midstream LLC	F	432 682-4349
Midland (G-15472)		

GAS PRODUCTION & DISTRIBUTION

Belvan Partners LP	F	432 682-4349
Midland (G-15137)		
C P Bailey Cnstr Co Inc	G	936 348-3627
Madisonville (G-14585)		
Enterprise Products Company	C	713 381-6500
Houston (G-9663)		
Enterprise Products Company	E	432 221-7700
Midland (G-15221)		
Petrotel Inc	F	972 473-2767
Plano (G-16971)		
Segundo Navarro Drilling Ltd	E	210 384-3200
San Antonio (G-18465)		
Silver Creek Oil & Gas LLC	D	972 573-1630
Irving (G-13180)		

PRODUCT

GAS PRODUCTION & DISTRIBUTION: Liq Petroleum, Distrib-Mains

Cheniere Energy Inc ....D 713 375-5000
Houston (G-9175)

Regency Energy Partners LP ....D 214 750-1771
Dallas (G-4881)

GAS STATIONS

Conocophillips Holding Company ...D 281 293-1000
Houston (G-9274)

El Paso Cgp Company LLC ....E 713 420-2600
Houston (G-9585)

Exxon Mobil Corporation ....B 972 940-6000
Irving (G-13021)

La Hacienda Tortilla Factory ....F 830 773-9151
Eagle Pass (G-5548)

Marathon International Oil Co ....D 713 629-6600
Houston (G-10753)

Marathon Oil Company ....A 713 629-6600
Houston (G-10754)

Marathon Oil Corporation ....A 713 629-6600
Houston (G-10756)

Partners Specialties Inc ....E 281 922-9102
Houston (G-11251)

Petrostar Services LLC ....F 903 247-6390
Longview (G-14289)

Phillips 66 Partners LP ....F 855 283-9237
Houston (G-11326)

Soho ....F 713 526-3755
Houston (G-11932)

Tesoro Refining & Mktg Co LLC ....C 210 828-8484
San Antonio (G-18530)

GAS: Refinery

Alon USA Partners LP ....A 972 367-3600
Dallas (G-3930)

American Liberty Oil Co LP ....F 972 932-2266
Kaufman (G-13457)

Andeavor LLC ....C 210 626-6000
San Antonio (G-17907)

BP Corporation North Amer Inc ....A 281 366-3988
Houston (G-8966)

BP Corporation North Amer Inc ....A 281 366-2000
Houston (G-8965)

BP Corporation North Amer Inc ....A 281 366-2000
Houston (G-8967)

Citgo Holding Terminals LLC ....B 832 486-4000
Houston (G-9200)

Citgo Petroleum Corporation ....F 832 486-5900
Sugar Land (G-19458)

Citgo Petroleum Corporation ....A 832 486-4000
Houston (G-9201)

Coffeyville Resources LLC ....D 281 207-3200
Sugar Land (G-19462)

Conocophillips Company ....A 281 293-1000
Houston (G-9273)

Conocophillips Holding Company .....D 281 293-1000
Houston (G-9274)

Formosa Hydrocarbons Co Inc ....E 361 987-8900
Point Comfort (G-17082)

Frontier Oil Corporation ....F 214 871-3555
Dallas (G-4383)

Hollyfrontier Ref & Mktg LLC ....C 214 871-3555
Dallas (G-4463)

Shell Oil Company ....F 713 546-4000
Houston (G-11863)

Texas Oil & Chemical Co II Inc ....D 409 385-1400
Silsbee (G-18957)

Total Ptrchemicals Ref USA Inc ....B 713 483-5000
Houston (G-12332)

Univar Solutions USA Inc ....E 281 297-0678
Spring (G-19261)

Valero Energy Corporation ....A 210 345-2000
San Antonio (G-18583)

Valero Refining Company ....D 210 345-2000
San Antonio (G-18586)

Wynnewood Energy Company LLC ....B 281 207-3200
Sugar Land (G-19574)

GASES & LIQUIFIED PETROLEUM GASES

Arcooil Corp ....E 940 549-4444
Graham (G-7776)

Cameron Solutions Inc ....F 325 573-8521
Snyder (G-18985)

Conocophillips Company ....E 325 835-4451
Mertzon (G-15020)

Diamond Shamrock Ref & Mktg Co ...B 361 786-2536
Three Rivers (G-19944)

Dstj Corporation ....F 936 447-1174
Montgomery (G-15632)

Ergon Inc ....F 972 875-1122
Ennis (G-6100)

Gardner Denver Inc ....G 817 248-4510
Fort Worth (G-6662)

Lacy Operations Ltd ....E 903 693-3501
Beckville (G-1971)

Martin Resource Mgt Corp ....C 903 983-6200
Kilgore (G-13570)

Morgan Kinder Treating LP ....D 713 369-8515
Houston (G-10921)

Osaka Gas USA Corporation ....F 713 354-9100
Houston (G-11196)

Reatta Energy Inc ....F 432 682-7495
Midland (G-15378)

Southtex Treaters Inc ....D 432 563-2766
Odessa (G-16158)

GASES: Acetylene

Western Intl Gas Cylinders Inc ....C 979 865-5991
Bellville (G-2015)

GASES: Carbon Dioxide

Air Liquide America Corp ....F 512 748-5943
Manor (G-14642)

GASES: Flourinated Hydrocarbon

Solvay USA Inc ....C 325 515-7609
Snyder (G-19009)

Solvay USA Inc ....D 940 552-9911
Vernon (G-20230)

Spectrum Quality Standards ....F 281 578-7575
Houston (G-12009)

GASES: Hydrogen

New Altrnative Green Enrgy Inc ....F 972 523-9970
Kaufman (G-13462)

Praxair Inc Freeport Psa ....G 281 203-3682
Freeport (G-7207)

GASES: Indl

Acacia Energy Inc ....E 877 997-2946
Houston (G-8452)

Air Liquide Advanced Mtls Inc ....E 713 624-8000
Houston (G-8509)

Air Liquide America LP ....C 713 896-2100
Houston (G-8510)

Air Liquide America LP ....F 281 474-5800
Pasadena (G-16380)

Air Liquide America LP ....B 713 438-6000
Pasadena (G-16381)

Air Liquide America LP ....F 281 474-8490
La Porte (G-13717)

Air Liquide America LP ....F 361 299-2999
Corpus Christi (G-3468)

Air Liquide America LP ....F 281 291-5360
La Porte (G-13718)

Air Liquide America LP ....F 979 239-5250
Freeport (G-7190)

Air Liquide America LP ....F 903 237-1740
Longview (G-14188)

Air Liquide America LP ....F 409 720-4200
Port Neches (G-17157)

Air Liquide Electronics US LP ....A 972 301-5200
Dallas (G-3905)

Air Liquide Electronics US LP ....C 972 994-2403
Dallas (G-3906)

Air Liquide Large Inds US LP ....E 903 237-1739
Longview (G-14189)

Air Liquide Large Inds US LP ....B 713 624-8000
Houston (G-8511)

Air Liquide USA LLC ....A 713 402-2221
Houston (G-8512)

Air Lqide Advanced Tech US LLC ......B 713 624-8000
Houston (G-8513)

Air Lqide Amer Spclty Gses LLC ....E 800 217-2688
Houston (G-8514)

Air Lqide Hydrgen Enrgy US LLC ......E 346 971-3051
Houston (G-8515)

Airgas Inc ....E 281 893-9353
Houston (G-8516)

Airgas Usa LLC ....D 972 994-2400
Dallas (G-3912)

Airgas Usa LLC ....F 361 533-0758
Corpus Christi (G-3469)

Airgas Usa LLC ....E 281 474-8300
Pasadena (G-16382)

Airgas Usa LLC ....E 972 660-0500
Grand Prairie (G-7825)

Albemarle Corporation ....A 713 740-1000
Pasadena (G-16386)

American A Lquide Holdings Inc ....E 713 624-8000
Houston (G-8581)

American Air Liquide Inc ....E 877 855-9533
Houston (G-8582)

Atlantic Richfield Company ....E 806 592-4900
Denver City (G-5415)

Dcp Midstream LLC ....F 325 392-1000
Ozona (G-16280)

Dow Chemical Company ....E 979 238-2011
Freeport (G-7196)

Duke Energy Natural Gas Corp ....E 361 579-4600
Hallettsville (G-8121)

E I Du Pont De Nemours & Co ....E 361 776-1872
Ingleside (G-12895)

Linde Gas North America LLC ....D 713 767-4100
La Porte (G-13768)

Linde Inc ....E 281 478-1500
Deer Park (G-5282)

Linde Inc ....E 325 643-5813
Brownwood (G-2437)

Linde Inc ....E 972 271-1531
Garland (G-7537)

Linde Inc ....G 210 489-5800
San Antonio (G-18253)

Linde Inc ....F 409 963-0141
Groves (G-8109)

Linde Inc ....E 281 471-4585
La Porte (G-13769)

Linde Inc ....E 409 943-9280
Texas City (G-19796)

Linde Inc ....E 281 203-3600
Spring (G-19227)

Linde Inc ....E 409 835-3939
Beaumont (G-1919)

Linde Inc ....E 979 774-0638
Bryan (G-2490)

Matheson Tri-Gas Inc ....G 361 887-0011
Corpus Christi (G-3575)

Matheson Tri-Gas Inc ....E 972 432-8800
Dallas (G-4651)

Matheson Tri-Gas Inc ....F 713 869-7351
Houston (G-10793)

Matheson Tri-Gas Inc ....G 281 474-1291
Pasadena (G-16481)

Matheson Tri-Gas Inc ....C 972 560-5700
Irving (G-13096)

Matheson Tri-Gas Inc ....E 512 385-0611
Austin (G-1330)

Matheson Tri-Gas Inc ....E 281 498-2310
Stafford (G-19352)

Matheson Tri-Gas Inc ....F 210 225-3151
San Antonio (G-18283)

Matheson Tri-Gas Inc ....E 281 471-2544
Houston (G-10794)

Matheson Tri-Gas Inc ....F 817 354-9536
Dallas (G-4652)

Matheson Tri-Gas Inc ....F 817 551-0550
Fort Worth (G-6817)

McGuffy Energy Services LP ....D 281 255-6955
Cypress (G-3809)

Messer LLC ....F 713 767-4155
La Porte (G-13776)

Messer LLC ....E 281 837-0184
Baytown (G-1829)

Messer LLC ....E 903 626-4877
Jewett (G-13307)

Monument Chemicals Inc ....F 281 452-5951
Houston (G-10918)

Nuco2 Supply LLC ....E 817 676-7580
Amarillo (G-503)

Oilfield Services & Tech LLC ....E 432 614-0076
Odessa (G-16100)

Parker Petroleum Pros Inc ....F 903 360-5450
Grand Saline (G-7998)

Praxair Inc ....E 936 295-3912
Huntsville (G-12823)

Texas Gas Utilities LLC ....F 281 252-6700
Magnolia (G-14628)

GASES: Nitrogen

Generon Igs Inc ....E 713 937-5200
Houston (G-9928)

Linde Gas North America LLC ....F 866 543-3427
Houston (G-10645)

Linde Gas North America LLC ....F 210 287-9788
San Antonio (G-18252)

Linde Gas North America LLC ....F 903 939-0613
Tyler *(G-20114)*
Linde Gas North America LLC ....F 254 718-5124
Temple *(G-19684)*
Nitrogen Services LLC ....C 925 336-1560
Midland *(G-15320)*

GASES: Oxygen

Airgas Usa LLC ....E 281 474-8400
La Porte *(G-13719)*
Alig LLC ....D 212 626-4936
Houston *(G-8538)*
Ws Group Inc ....G 214 337-4761
Dallas *(G-5204)*

GASKET MATERIALS

Corpus Chrsti Gsket Fstner Inc ....C 361 884-6366
Corpus Christi *(G-3510)*
Flexitallic Group Inc..............................F 281 604-2400
Deer Park *(G-5274)*
Fluid Sealing Products Inc ....D 713 910-1028
Houston *(G-9816)*
Han-Boone International Inc ....F 817 838-5196
Fort Worth *(G-6686)*

GASKETS

A-1 Gasket & Industrial Supply ....F 432 332-1444
Odessa *(G-15897)*
American Gasket Mfg Co Inc ....E 214 388-0603
Dallas *(G-3941)*
C T Gasket & Polymer Co Inc ....E 713 856-8667
Houston *(G-9034)*
Champion Sales & Manufacturing.........E 281 356-6162
Magnolia *(G-14595)*
Conroe Plastics Molding Inc.................D 936 539-2005
Conroe *(G-3283)*
Eagle Gasket and Packing Co ....E 713 290-8811
Tomball *(G-19975)*
Eastex Rubber & Gasket Co ....F 409 727-6800
Nederland *(G-15752)*
Flange Protection & Gaskets ....E 281 991-4550
Pasadena *(G-16437)*
Flexitallic Group Inc.............................E 281 604-2525
Houston *(G-9799)*
Gasket Service Inc ....F 432 332-0853
Odessa *(G-16011)*
Ghx Industrial LLC ....E 409 832-3461
Beaumont *(G-1898)*
Hi-Tech Champion Manufacturing.........E 713 644-2181
Houston *(G-10172)*
Houston Mfg Specialty Co Inc ....E 281 888-4635
Houston *(G-10239)*
Humble Industries Inc ....F 281 987-9175
Humble *(G-12778)*
James L Rembert Jr Inc ....F 281 240-7070
Sugar Land *(G-19500)*
Jim Ray Company Inc............................F 713 941-2275
South Houston *(G-19048)*
Lamons Gasket Company ....B 713 222-0284
Houston *(G-10589)*
Lone Star Gasket and Sup Inc ....F 432 333-1615
Odessa *(G-16064)*
Longwood Elastomers Inc ....C 979 830-1111
Brenham *(G-2261)*
M & P Sealing Co ....F 409 745-2002
Orange *(G-16253)*
Mariposa Corporation............................E 713 222-0220
Houston *(G-10768)*
McGaskets & Ptfe Spc Inc ....F 713 847-6700
Humble *(G-12788)*
Panhandle Packing & Gasket Inc ....E 806 763-2801
Lubbock *(G-14456)*
Sealing Technology Inc ....E 281 330-6363
Houston *(G-11805)*
T F E Company Inc..................................F 979 836-6111
Brenham *(G-2274)*
TXG Industries Inc ....E 713 222-0220
Houston *(G-12417)*
Vanco Ring Gsket Spclty Corp I ....F 281 499-1543
Stafford *(G-19394)*
Wolar Industrial Inc..............................D 713 926-2440
Houston *(G-12680)*

GASKETS & SEALING DEVICES

Ace Rubber Products Inc ....F 817 572-1011
Kennedale *(G-13496)*
Anchor Texacone LLC ....E 972 288-4404
Mesquite *(G-15026)*

Dan-Loc Group LLC ....D 713 356-3500
Houston *(G-9399)*
Dan-Loc, LLC. ....C 713 356-3500
Houston *(G-9400)*
E G C Corporation..................................B 281 774-6100
Humble *(G-12764)*
Enpro Industries Inc ....D 281 207-4600
Stafford *(G-19312)*
Enpro Industries Inc ....E 713 983-4222
Houston *(G-9650)*
Enpro Industries Inc ....F 713 983-4200
Houston *(G-9651)*
Fgi Acquisition Corp ....E 281 604-2400
Houston *(G-9782)*
Garlock Sealing Tech LLC ....C 281 840-4853
Houston *(G-9901)*
Ghx Industrial LLC ....E 713 341-3407
Houston *(G-9950)*
Ghx Industrial LLC ....F 713 939-7423
Houston *(G-9951)*
Ghx Industrial LLC ....E 713 222-2231
Houston *(G-9952)*
H K Specialties Co Inc ....F 713 466-1567
Houston *(G-10084)*
John Crane Inc ....D 281 474-1700
Pasadena *(G-16464)*
Kalsi Engineering Incorporated............E 281 240-6500
Sugar Land *(G-19501)*
Leader Gasket Technologies Inc ....D 281 542-0600
La Porte *(G-13766)*
Refrigeration Gaskets Texas Inc ....F 713 880-8066
Houston *(G-11582)*
Rsi Inc ....E 512 268-7500
Kyle *(G-13686)*
Seal-Jet of Texas Inc ....E 713 983-7233
Houston *(G-11804)*
SKF USA Inc ....D 281 506-3250
Houston *(G-11913)*
Tape Innovations LLC ....E 817 568-1212
Fort Worth *(G-7034)*
Tenneco Inc ....A 915 832-4661
El Paso *(G-5997)*
Tex Cnp/Seal Inc ....E 214 688-7770
Dallas *(G-5051)*
Texas Gasket and Packing Co ....F 713 674-7531
Houston *(G-12232)*
Utex Industries Inc ....E 432 333-4151
Odessa *(G-16192)*

GASOLINE BLENDING PLANT

Chemtec Energy Services LLC...............E 936 856-1704
Willis *(G-20844)*
Chevron USA Inc ....C 925 842-1000
Houston *(G-9181)*
Dcp Midstream LLC ....D 432 827-1945
Goldsmith *(G-7741)*
Lyondell Chemical Company ....D 713 309-7200
Houston *(G-10705)*
Marathon Oil Company ....A 713 629-6600
Houston *(G-10754)*
Valero Refining-Texas LP ....B 210 345-2000
San Antonio *(G-18587)*
Vp Racing Fuels Inc ....D 210 635-7744
San Antonio *(G-18600)*

GASOLINE FILLING STATIONS

Atlantic Richfield Company ....E 806 592-4900
Denver City *(G-5415)*
Bass Enterprises Production Co............C 817 698-0200
Fort Worth *(G-6438)*
BP Corporation North Amer Inc.............A 281 366-2000
Houston *(G-8965)*
BP Corporation North Amer Inc.............A 281 366-2000
Houston *(G-8967)*
Chevron Corporation.............................B 713 754-3998
Houston *(G-9178)*
Chevron USA Inc ....C 432 687-7100
Midland *(G-15162)*
Chevron USA Inc ....C 925 842-1000
Houston *(G-9181)*
Citgo Petroleum Corporation................F 832 486-5900
Sugar Land *(G-19458)*
Conocophillips Company ....E 325 835-4451
Mertzon *(G-15020)*
Conocophillips Company ....A 281 293-1000
Houston *(G-9273)*
Diamond Shamrock Ref & Mktg Co........A 210 345-2000
San Antonio *(G-18057)*
Exxon Mobil Corporation ....B 713 656-3636
Houston *(G-9739)*

Murphy USA Inc ....F 512 332-0622
Bastrop *(G-1760)*
Par Hawaii Refining LLC ....C 281 899-4800
Houston *(G-11234)*
Quiktrip Corporation.............................E 817 378-8410
Fort Worth *(G-6929)*
Shell Oil Company ....A 713 241-6161
Houston *(G-11860)*
Texaco Exploration & Prod Inc ....B 800 962-1223
Houston *(G-12218)*
Ultramar Inc ....A 210 345-2000
San Antonio *(G-18576)*
Valero Refining-Texas LP ....B 210 345-2000
San Antonio *(G-18587)*

GASOLINE WHOLESALERS

Frontier Petroleum Resources ....E 832 242-1510
Houston *(G-9869)*
Ultramar Inc ....A 210 345-2000
San Antonio *(G-18576)*

GATES: Ornamental Metal

CK Kustoms Iron Works Inc ....F 281 850-6118
Rockport *(G-17529)*
General Garage Door Service ....F 956 782-7373
Mission *(G-15555)*
Meyer-Smith Inc ....F 713 862-7339
Houston *(G-10862)*
Northeast Gate Co Inc ....F 903 739-8778
Sumner *(G-19608)*
Quality Access Control Systems............F 830 981-5400
Boerne *(G-2133)*

GAUGES

Gauging Systems Inc ....E 281 980-3999
Sugar Land *(G-19484)*
M & F Gauge & Specialty Co Inc............E 325 643-2655
Brownwood *(G-2439)*

GAUGES: Pressure

GK Techstar LLC.....................................D 281 884-8257
Deer Park *(G-5276)*

GEARS

Houston Gear USA Inc ....F 281 495-8274
Stafford *(G-19326)*

GEARS & GEAR UNITS: Reduction, Exc Auto

Ram-Gear Manufacturing Inc................F 361 668-0235
Alice *(G-231)*

GEARS: Power Transmission, Exc Auto

Deran Gear Inc ....D 806 746-6926
Lubbock *(G-14403)*
Johnson Gear Inc...................................F 806 749-6400
Lubbock *(G-14431)*
Kuzzy Industrial Supplier ....F 915 881-4105
El Paso *(G-5833)*
Martin Sprocket & Gear Inc ....D 817 473-1520
Mansfield *(G-14689)*
Martin Sprocket & Gear Inc ....F 817 258-3000
Houston *(G-10778)*
Martin Sprocket & Gear Inc ....D 903 427-2217
Clarksville *(G-3075)*
Martin Sprocket & Gear Inc ....D 325 677-3591
Abilene *(G-59)*
Martin Sprocket & Gear Inc ....C 817 258-3000
Fort Worth *(G-6813)*
Martin Sprocket & Gear Inc ....D 214 428-2191
Dallas *(G-4641)*
Metro Sprocket & Gear Inc....................F 972 723-3240
Midlothian *(G-15485)*
Omni Usa Inc ....F 713 635-6331
Houston *(G-11179)*
Sew-Eurodrive Inc ....C 214 330-4824
Desoto *(G-5441)*

GEM STONES MINING, NEC: Natural

Natural Energy Resources Inc...............D 832 631-5013
Katy *(G-13426)*

GENERAL COUNSELING SVCS

Specktrum ....F 832 892-0863
Houston *(G-12004)*

Employee Codes: A=Over 500 employees, B=251-500
C=101-250, D=51-100, E=20-50, F=10-19, G=9

2021 Harris Texas
Manufacturers Directory

PRODUCT

1515

GENERAL ECONOMIC PROG ADMIN, GOVT: Consumer Protection

National Aeronautics ....E 915 782-5250
El Paso *(G-5893)*

GENERAL MERCHANDISE, NONDURABLE, WHOLESALE

Alliance Entertainment LLC ....E 806 381-3945
Amarillo *(G-392)*
Dipper Inc ....G 281 585-8400
Alvin *(G-359)*
Southern Glazers Wine and Sp ....C 972 277-2000
Farmers Branch *(G-6215)*

GENERATING APPARATUS & PARTS: Electrical

Auto Electric Systems Inc ....F 972 241-2077
Plano *(G-16796)*
Solarcraft Inc ....E 281 340-1224
Sugar Land *(G-19557)*

GENERATION EQPT: Electronic

Freedom Power Systems Inc ....F 512 259-0941
Cedar Park *(G-2971)*
G C International Inc ....B 972 422-2395
Plano *(G-16877)*
Lufkins Six B Construction ....F 936 632-3470
Lufkin *(G-14543)*
Powersecure Inc ....E 203 683-6222
Frisco *(G-7306)*
T L Tedford Enterprises Inc ....E 817 808-8052
Aurora *(G-854)*

GENERATOR REPAIR SVCS

Hiroko International Inc ....F 210 590-4411
San Antonio *(G-18168)*
Marine Services LLC ....E 713 923-6688
Houston *(G-10765)*
Musshorn Enterprises Inc ....C 915 772-9007
El Paso *(G-5892)*
Roundhouse Elc & Eqp Co Inc ....F 432 333-3923
Odessa *(G-16143)*

GENERATOR SETS: Motor

Monico Monitoring Inc ....F 281 350-8751
Spring *(G-19147)*

GENERATORS SETS: Steam

Cor Thermotics LLC ....F 832 308-5151
Houston *(G-9311)*
Roma Steam Bath Inc ....F 281 578-9945
Houston *(G-11659)*

GENERATORS: Automotive & Aircraft

Harrison Hydra-Gen Ltd ....E 281 807-4420
Houston *(G-10127)*
Stealth Power LLC ....F 512 306-0088
Austin *(G-1534)*

GENERATORS: Electric

Diesel Engine and Parts Co LLC ....E 713 675-6100
Houston *(G-9466)*
Waukesha-Pearce Industries LLC ......B 713 723-1050
Houston *(G-12607)*
Wise County Power Company LLC .....E 940 374-9925
Poolville *(G-17099)*

GENERATORS: Electrochemical, Fuel Cell

Analytical Sensors Instrs LLC ....D 281 565-8818
Houston *(G-8636)*
Bitcoin Crypto Crrncy Exch Cor ....F 713 465-1001
Houston *(G-8895)*

GIFT SHOP

Ben Adams Precious Jewels ....E 210 826-6535
San Antonio *(G-17945)*
Bullgang Tools LLC ....G 979 203-9009
Brenham *(G-2248)*
Homestead Heritage ....E 254 754-9665
Waco *(G-20416)*
Marshall Pottery Inc ....C 903 938-9201
Marshall *(G-14791)*

McCartney Investment Corp ....F 214 521-8410
Dallas *(G-4659)*
Praseks Hillje Smokehouse ....D 979 543-8312
El Campo *(G-5626)*
Sample House & Resale Shop Inc ......E 214 688-0751
Dallas *(G-4929)*
Texas 2 Stitch ....F 972 599-1717
Plano *(G-17028)*

GIFT, NOVELTY & SOUVENIR STORES: Gifts & Novelties

Drsk Limited Partnership ....F 972 644-1490
Richardson *(G-17302)*
Mike Sandone Productions Inc ....E 800 652-5635
Dallas *(G-4677)*

GIFT, NOVELTY & SOUVENIR STORES: Party Favors

M Patel Enterprises Inc ....E 512 892-2721
Sunset Valley *(G-19626)*

GIFT, NOVELTY & SOUVENIR STORES: Trading Cards, Sports

Beckett Collectibles Inc ....D 855 777-2325
Dallas *(G-4011)*

GIFTS & NOVELTIES: Wholesalers

Aztec Imports Inc ....E 915 858-2287
El Paso *(G-5657)*
Dyna Group International Inc ....D 830 620-4400
New Braunfels *(G-15788)*
El Paso Saddleblanket Co LP ....E 915 544-1000
El Paso *(G-5741)*
Qti Promotions and Apparel Inc ....E 254 756-4444
Waco *(G-20452)*

GIFTWARE: Brass

Arne Distributors Inc ....F 713 869-8321
Houston *(G-8700)*
Demco Manufacturing Inc ....E 936 829-4771
Diboll *(G-5462)*

GILSONITE MINING SVCS

American Gilsonite Company ....F 713 400-7600
Houston *(G-8597)*

GLASS FABRICATORS

Architectural Stained Glass ....F 432 426-3311
Fort Davis *(G-6318)*
Arrowall Company ....D 713 462-1751
San Antonio *(G-18639)*
Ballistic GL Armor Sltions LLC ....F 214 382-4100
Addison *(G-105)*
Bielas Glass & Aluminum Pdts ....E 210 333-8040
San Antonio *(G-17952)*
Christmas By Krebs Corporation ....F 972 929-2880
Irving *(G-12970)*
Glass Samuels Company LLC ....D 210 227-2481
San Antonio *(G-18142)*
Glasscraft Door Mfg Corp ....C 713 690-8282
Houston *(G-9962)*
Guardian Industries LLC ....B 903 872-4871
Corsicana *(G-3673)*
Kamal Incorporated ....D 210 695-2678
Helotes *(G-8241)*
Lone Star Glass Inc ....F 713 661-0091
Houston *(G-10677)*
Longhorn Glass Mfg LP ....C 713 679-7500
Houston *(G-10685)*
Main Glass & Mirror Co ....F 210 637-1011
Schertz *(G-18752)*
Overhead Door Corporation ....B 361 884-6640
Corpus Christi *(G-3586)*
Star Glass and Metal Svcs LLC ....F 770 490-9055
Dallas *(G-5008)*
Trulite GL Alum Solutions LLC ....E 210 653-7790
San Antonio *(G-18570)*
Vitro Flat Glass LLC ....B 940 855-3804
Wichita Falls *(G-20825)*
Western Glass LLC ....F 512 820-2475
Georgetown *(G-7688)*

GLASS PRDTS, FROM PURCHASED GLASS: Glass Beads, Reflecting

Potters Industries LLC ....D 903 785-1633
Paris *(G-16366)*
Potters Industries LLC ....E 325 752-6711
Brownwood *(G-2442)*
Swarco-Reflex LLC ....E 254 562-9879
Mexia *(G-15092)*
Swarco-Reflex LLC ....E 254 562-9879
Mexia *(G-15093)*
Weissker Mfg Ltd Lblty Co ....F 903 538-2271
Palestine *(G-16309)*

GLASS PRDTS, FROM PURCHASED GLASS: Glassware

Texas Lamp Manufacturers Inc ....E 972 564-5267
Forney *(G-6315)*

GLASS PRDTS, FROM PURCHASED GLASS: Glassware, Indl

Oldcastle Building Envelope ....E 972 647-4028
Grand Prairie *(G-7940)*

GLASS PRDTS, FROM PURCHASED GLASS: Insulating

Builders Frstsrc-Txas Group LP ....B 817 640-1234
Arlington *(G-634)*
Cardinal Glass Industries Inc ....D 972 937-4969
Waxahachie *(G-20533)*
Cardinal Glass Industries Inc ....C 972 937-1708
Waxahachie *(G-20534)*

GLASS PRDTS, FROM PURCHASED GLASS: Mirrored

Gardner Glass Products Inc ....D 936 291-7271
Huntsville *(G-12812)*
Morenos Auto Glass Inc ....F 361 855-1471
Corpus Christi *(G-3579)*

GLASS PRDTS, PRESSED OR BLOWN: Blocks & Bricks

Innovative Building Products ....E 940 387-0408
Millsap *(G-15503)*

GLASS PRDTS, PRESSED OR BLOWN: Furnishings & Access

Builders Depot Direct LLC ....F 832 384-7272
Houston *(G-9012)*
Creekside Mirror and Glass LLC ....F 972 617-9805
Waxahachie *(G-20539)*

GLASS PRDTS, PRESSED OR BLOWN: Glassware, Art Or Decorative

Crystal Images Inc ....F 972 438-2337
Irving *(G-12985)*

GLASS PRDTS, PRESSED OR BLOWN: Glassware, Novelty

John Roberts Enterprises Inc ....F 512 252-0174
Pflugerville *(G-16678)*

GLASS PRDTS, PRESSED OR BLOWN: Lighting Eqpt Parts

Satco Products Inc ....C 972 247-2437
Dallas *(G-4936)*

GLASS PRDTS, PRESSED OR BLOWN: Scientific Glassware

Ramin Corporation ....F 281 356-5178
Magnolia *(G-14623)*

GLASS PRDTS, PRESSED OR BLOWN: Yarn, Fiberglass

Sawyer Oilfield Products LLC ....E 254 644-7261
Brownwood *(G-2443)*

GLASS PRDTS, PURCHD GLASS: Furniture Top, Cut, Beveld/Polshd

Glass Beveling Company Inc .... E 713 466-5262
Houston *(G-9960)*

GLASS PRDTS, PURCHSD GLASS: Ornamental, Cut, Engraved/Décor

A & B Glass LLC .... F 432 517-4565
Big Spring *(G-2067)*
Oldcastle Buildingenvelope Inc ....D 713 827-1965
Houston *(G-11169)*

GLASS STORE: Leaded Or Stained

Cavallini Co Inc .... F 210 733-8161
San Antonio *(G-17988)*

GLASS STORES

ASAP Glass & Door LLC .... F 214 770-8266
Denton *(G-5351)*
Creekside Mirror and Glass LLC .... F 972 617-9805
Waxahachie *(G-20539)*
Glass Samuels Company LLC .... D 210 227-2481
San Antonio *(G-18142)*
Lone Star Glass Inc .... F 713 661-0091
Houston *(G-10677)*
Morenos Auto Glass Inc .... F 361 855-1471
Corpus Christi *(G-3579)*
Oldcastle Buildingenvelope Inc ....F 800 392-9815
Houston *(G-11168)*
Oldcastle Buildingenvelope Inc ....F 214 273-3400
Dallas *(G-4759)*
Trulite GL Alum Solutions LLC ....C 800 395-4224
Houston *(G-12385)*

GLASS: Fiber

Fiber Glass Systems LP .... D 210 477-7500
San Antonio *(G-18112)*
Fiberglass Creations Inc .... E 903 657-6616
Henderson *(G-8262)*
McBroom Industries .... F 817 645-2248
Cleburne *(G-3101)*

GLASS: Flat

Cardinal Glass Industries Inc .... D 972 937-4969
Waxahachie *(G-20533)*
Cardinal Glass Industries Inc ....C 972 937-1708
Waxahachie *(G-20534)*
Consolidated Armor Pdts LLC .... E 214 382-4100
Addison *(G-113)*
Hartung Glass Industries Inc ....G 972 629-6890
Farmers Branch *(G-6201)*
Kats Glass LLC .... E 281 592-5211
Cleveland *(G-3131)*
Kovach Enclosure Systems LLC ....D 480 926-9292
Spring *(G-19225)*
Kovach Enclosure Systems LLC ....D 480 926-9292
Austin *(G-1273)*
Kovach Enclosure Systems LLC ....D 480 926-9292
Farmers Branch *(G-6205)*
Lumina Global Inc .... F 713 783-7056
Houston *(G-10702)*
Sky Glass Inc .... F 972 807-9616
Dallas *(G-4969)*

GLASS: Indl Prdts

Greenstar North Amer Holdings ....A 713 965-0005
Houston *(G-10036)*

GLASS: Pressed & Blown, NEC

Acme Brick Company .... D 817 332-4101
El Paso *(G-5636)*
Displays & Optical Tech .... E 512 246-6400
Georgetown *(G-7648)*
Glass Samuels Company LLC .... D 210 227-2481
San Antonio *(G-18142)*
Glass Wholesalers Ltd .... F 713 353-5800
Houston *(G-9961)*
Kamal Incorporated .... D 210 695-2678
Helotes *(G-8241)*
Potters Industries LLC .... E 325 752-6711
Brownwood *(G-2442)*

GLASS: Stained

Cavallini Co Inc .... F 210 733-8161
San Antonio *(G-17988)*
El Habr Corporation .... F 817 731-4660
Fort Worth *(G-6608)*

GLASS: Structural

Wilson Steel Services LLC .... F 903 275-2995
Brownsboro *(G-2333)*

GLASS: Tempered

Oldcastle Buildingenvelope Inc ....F 800 392-9815
Houston *(G-11168)*
Oldcastle Buildingenvelope Inc ....F 214 273-3400
Dallas *(G-4759)*

GLASSWARE: Laboratory & Medical

S G & P Incorporated .... F 979 233-7491
Freeport *(G-7209)*

GLOBAL POSITIONING SYSTEMS & EQPT

AC Global Systems Inc .... G 214 497-0280
Arlington *(G-607)*
Lasso Technologies LLC .... F 866 392-0923
Dallas *(G-4583)*
On-Board Communications Inc ....E 214 346-0300
Dallas *(G-4762)*
Synergy Telecom Service Co Inc ....E 210 599-7743
San Antonio *(G-18517)*
Uhu Technologies LLC .... F 972 523-2701
Richardson *(G-17417)*

GLOVES: Fabric

Guard-Line Inc .... C 903 796-4111
Atlanta *(G-843)*
Innovative Gloves & Safety LLC ....F 281 582-0700
Houston *(G-10371)*
Premier Board Inc .... F 361 883-6553
Corpus Christi *(G-3596)*
Stanco Manufacturing Inc .... D 903 796-7936
Atlanta *(G-845)*

GLOVES: Leather

Innovative Gloves & Safety LLC ....F 281 582-0700
Houston *(G-10371)*

GLOVES: Leather, Work

Guard-Line Inc .... C 903 796-4111
Atlanta *(G-843)*
Guard-Line Inc .... D 903 796-4111
Atlanta *(G-844)*
Ringers Technology Group Inc ....F 281 953-5300
Houston *(G-11625)*

GLOVES: Plastic

Daxwell LLC .... E 281 669-0622
Houston *(G-9411)*
Handgards LLC .... C 915 779-6606
El Paso *(G-5794)*

GLOVES: Safety

Becton Dickinson and Company ....F 210 526-5000
San Antonio *(G-17943)*

GLUE

Adco Inc .... E 972 484-6177
Dallas *(G-3887)*
HB Fuller Company .... E 972 728-0707
Mesquite *(G-15050)*

GOLD ORE MINING

Battle Mountain Dominian Repub ....E 713 655-1742
Houston *(G-8830)*

GOLF COURSES: Public

Forest Ogletree Products Inc .... E 936 327-2424
Livingston *(G-14155)*

GOLF EQPT

Callaway Golf Ball Oprtons Inc ....D 844 534-6426
Fort Worth *(G-6489)*

Golf Time LLC .... E 214 366-1595
Carrollton *(G-2746)*

GOURMET FOOD STORES

Koch Ranches Inc .... F 210 858-9795
San Antonio *(G-18228)*

GOVERNMENT, EXECUTIVE OFFICES: Mayors'

City of Irving .... E 972 721-2646
Irving *(G-12972)*

GOVERNMENT, GENERAL: Administration

City of Jefferson .... F 903 665-2832
Jefferson *(G-13283)*

GRANITE: Crushed & Broken

Cactus Cyn Quarries of Texas ....F 830 693-4331
Marble Falls *(G-14740)*
Gulf Coast Limestone Inc .... F 281 474-4124
Seabrook *(G-18785)*
Hanson Lehigh Inc .... E 281 616-0700
Houston *(G-10120)*
Hanson Lehigh Inc .... B 972 653-5500
Irving *(G-13052)*
Martin Marietta Materials Inc .... F 210 208-4400
San Antonio *(G-18278)*
Martin Marietta Materials Inc .... E 713 896-8683
Houston *(G-10776)*
Vulcan Materials Company .... E 210 349-3311
San Antonio *(G-18603)*
Vulcan Materials Company .... F 210 494-9555
San Antonio *(G-18604)*

GRANITE: Cut & Shaped

Artistic Counters Inc .... C 210 651-3281
Garden Ridge *(G-7418)*
Bedrock Manufacturing Co LP ....C 214 247-2453
Dallas *(G-4013)*
Gemstar Stoneworks Inc .... E 281 257-6500
Spring *(G-19124)*
Natural Stone Inc .... F 713 678-4407
Houston *(G-11011)*
Ortega Bath Environments Inc ....E 806 763-5777
Lubbock *(G-14454)*
Panel Specialists Inc .... E 254 774-9197
Temple *(G-19694)*
Pks Designs Inc .... F 817 429-5174
Alvarado *(G-337)*
Real Granite Inc .... E 210 732-8350
San Antonio *(G-18414)*
Siri Granite Inc .... F 832 203-8322
Houston *(G-11907)*
Stone Systems Centl Texas LLC ....E 512 295-2950
Austin *(G-1540)*
Stonemode Granite LLC .... F 214 484-8820
Dallas *(G-5012)*
Unlimited Stone LLC .... F 903 297-0829
Longview *(G-14328)*

GRANITE: Dimension

Dietz Memorial Company Inc .... E 512 451-1983
Austin *(G-1091)*
Sage Surfaces LLC .... F 281 907-8766
The Woodlands *(G-19915)*
Target Stone LLC .... E 832 827-8663
Houston *(G-12161)*

GRAPHIC ARTS & RELATED DESIGN SVCS

Ad Display Sign Systems Inc .... E 281 392-8325
Katy *(G-13348)*
Alliance Printing LP .... E 713 957-3349
Houston *(G-8547)*
B2b Copies LLC .... G 512 402-9775
Lakeway *(G-13815)*
C & G Printing Company Inc .... E 817 738-8350
Fort Worth *(G-6481)*
Display Graphics Inc .... F 713 977-7888
Houston *(G-9480)*
Grafikshop Corporation .... E 713 977-2555
Houston *(G-10012)*
Graphtec Inc .... E 713 690-9999
Houston *(G-10019)*
Greater Southwest Art Center .... G 915 566-2410
El Paso *(G-5790)*

PRODUCT

Hudson Graphics Inc ....E 903 758-1773
Longview (G-14248)

Issgr Inc ....E 713 869-7700
Houston (G-10429)

JDM Designs Inc ....E 281 356-6131
Stagecoach (G-19401)

Jewish Herald Voice Inc ....E 713 630-0391
Houston (G-10472)

LMS Acquisitions LLC ....F 512 371-7028
Austin (G-1296)

Printmpro Ltd ....E 512 821-9000
Austin (G-1433)

Quacito LLC ....F 210 695-0795
San Antonio (G-18404)

Signs & Graphics Plus LLC ......F 915 590-7446
El Paso (G-5961)

Turner Capital Inc ....F 281 488-4900
Houston (G-12412)

Voom Group Inc ....F 972 424-8887
Plano (G-17048)

Wahoo Inc ....G 817 332-2310
Burleson (G-2601)

GRAPHIC LAYOUT SVCS: Printed Circuitry

Q C Graphics Inc ....E 972 931-4100
Richardson (G-17377)

GRASSES: Artificial & Preserved

Act Global Sports Tech Inc ......E 512 733-5300
Austin (G-884)

Buddys Grass Farm Inc ....F 936 258-7954
Dayton (G-5222)

GRATINGS: Open Steel Flooring

Baker & Company Cnstr LLC ....E 903 561-1763
Tyler (G-20056)

Harsco Corporation ....D 281 452-6637
Houston (G-10129)

GRATINGS: Tread, Fabricated Metal

Jwtmbg Enterprise LLC ....F 817 230-2513
Southlake (G-19078)

Superior Grating Inc ....F 713 686-9475
Houston (G-12115)

GRAVE VAULTS, METAL

Wise Products Co Inc ....F 903 378-2233
Honey Grove (G-8359)

GRAVEL & PEBBLE MINING

B&B Aggregates Inc ....F 281 659-9004
Cleveland (G-3120)

South Texas Concrete ....E 956 485-2301
Sullivan City (G-19577)

Thrasher Inc ....E 806 296-2609
Plainview (G-16765)

GRAVEL MINING

Associated Group Investment Co ....F 806 794-9507
Lubbock (G-14364)

Barco Industries ....F 979 732-2086
Columbus (G-3229)

Capitol Aggregates Inc ....E 432 447-9667
Pecos (G-16619)

Crockett Sand and Gravel Inc ....E 936 545-1021
Crockett (G-3716)

H J G Trucking Inc ....F 817 834-7181
Fort Worth (G-6683)

Hunter Industries Ltd ....B 512 353-7757
San Marcos (G-18695)

Multisources Ltd ....F 979 247-4305
La Grange (G-13699)

Rickett Ricky Sand & Gravel ....F 281 356-3103
Magnolia (G-14624)

Silver Creek Materials Inc ....E 817 246-2426
Fort Worth (G-6989)

Texas Lumber Construction ....F 979 732-2063
Columbus (G-3234)

Word Constructors LLC ....F 830 693-2933
Marble Falls (G-14752)

GREASES & INEDIBLE FATS, RENDERED

American Commodities Inc ....E 817 740-8326
Fort Worth (G-6379)

Darling Ingredients Inc ....D 313 928-7400
Irving (G-12993)

Darling Ingredients Inc ....E 713 224-0438
Houston (G-9404)

Darling Ingredients Inc ....E 214 948-7501
Dallas (G-4238)

Triton Products LLC ....F 940 455-2800
Argyle (G-604)

Valley By Products Inc ....F 915 877-3131
Canutillo (G-2667)

GREENHOUSES: Prefabricated Metal

Rounhouse Corporation ....F 281 593-1118
Cleveland (G-3134)

GREENSAND MINING SVCS

Big 4 Inc ....E 409 787-2733
Hemphill (G-8245)

GRILLES & REGISTERS: Ornamental Metal Work

Hart & Cooley Inc ....B 915 852-9111
Horizon City (G-8365)

Sunterra International LLC ....D 210 501-9510
San Antonio (G-18513)

GRILLS & GRILLWORK: Woven Wire, Made From Purchased Wire

Eljer Industries Inc ....E 972 560-2000
Dallas (G-4311)

Installer Pro LLC ....E 713 854-3656
Houston (G-10379)

Renfro Industries Inc ....F 972 563-4295
Terrell (G-19749)

Towsley and Bailey Inc ....G 972 563-5400
Terrell (G-19753)

GRINDING SVC: Precision, Commercial Or Indl

REE Holding Inc ....E 409 840-5650
Beaumont (G-1947)

Trinity Casting Service Inc ....E 214 631-4248
Dallas (G-5111)

Western Grinding Co Inc ....F 214 631-3090
Dallas (G-5182)

GRINDING SVCS: Ophthalmic Lens, Exc Prescription

Hoya Lens of America Inc ....D 972 221-4141
Lewisville (G-14053)

GRIPS OR HANDLES: Rubber

DMD Products LLC ....G 281 778-2051
Rosharon (G-17604)

Tacki Mac Grips ....G 281 358-6738
Humble (G-12800)

GRITS: Crushed & Broken

Desert Rock Co ....F 915 859-5969
El Paso (G-5721)

Ultra Fine Silica LP ....F 936 444-7338
Conroe (G-3377)

GROCERIES WHOLESALERS, NEC

Affiliated Foods Inc ....C 806 372-3851
Amarillo (G-476)

American Bottling Company ....D 956 423-2705
Harlingen (G-8180)

American Bottling Company ....C 210 662-4400
San Antonio (G-17902)

American Bottling Company ....D 512 385-4477
Austin (G-915)

American Bottling Company ....D 972 579-1024
Irving (G-12928)

American Bottling Company ....C 254 412-1900
Waco (G-20360)

Bayan Imports Inc ....E 972 437-1122
Richardson (G-17278)

Bryan Baking Inc ....C 979 778-6600
Bryan (G-2461)

Bunge Milling Southwest Inc ....D 800 852-8291
Muleshoe (G-15676)

CGJ Enterprises Inc ....F 281 575-8801
Houston (G-9151)

Coca-Cola Refreshments USA Inc ....E 806 472-3200
Lubbock (G-14395)

Coca-Cola Southwest Bevs LLC ....B 214 388-6000
Dallas (G-4139)

Dgg Group LLC ....F 512 398-4523
Lockhart (G-14166)

La Nortena Tortilla Factory ....F 432 445-3273
Pecos (G-16622)

Marick Foods Inc ....D 915 593-2271
El Paso (G-5867)

New Canaan Farms Inc ....F 512 858-7669
Dripping Springs (G-5509)

Pepsi-Cola Metro Btlg Co Inc ....F 361 575-2661
Victoria (G-20294)

Pepsi-Cola Metro Btlg Co Inc ....E 903 892-3030
Sherman (G-18926)

Pops Bakery Inc ....E 325 655-1170
San Angelo (G-17822)

Saint Arnold Brewing Company ....G 713 686-9494
Houston (G-11731)

Temple Bottling Company Ltd ....D 254 773-3376
Temple (G-19706)

GROCERIES, GENERAL LINE WHOLESALERS

Bridgford Marketing Company ....D 214 428-1535
Dallas (G-4054)

Cardet Wholesale Inc ....D 713 266-9834
Brookshire (G-2312)

CPT International (usa) LLC ....D 713 747-4773
Sugar Land (G-19468)

Droubis Bakery & Deli Inc ....F 713 988-5897
Houston (G-9532)

Han-D-Pac Products Inc ....E 915 595-2212
El Paso (G-5793)

Houston Sysco Inc ....E 713 672-8080
Houston (G-10254)

MARTIN PREFERRED FOODS LP ....C 713 869-6191
Houston (G-10777)

North Blue Oak Inc ....F 844 778-2336
Missouri City (G-15585)

Pulido Associates Inc ....E 817 249-6728
Benbrook (G-2045)

Riviana Foods Inc ....C 713 529-3251
Houston (G-11629)

Ventura Foods LLC ....F 817 232-6800
Fort Worth (G-7097)

GUARD SVCS

Azan Industries Inc ....F 832 310-4459
Richmond (G-17450)

GUARDRAILS

R Guerra Construction Inc ....F 956 854-4038
Weslaco (G-20667)

Trinity Industries Inc ....B 214 631-4420
Dallas (G-5112)

GUIDED MISSILES & SPACE VEHICLES

A R Machining Inc ....E 512 846-1789
Hutto (G-12874)

Blue Origin Texas LLC ....E 253 437-9300
Van Horn (G-20213)

Boeing Company ....A 281 244-4000
Houston (G-8942)

Cinch Connectors Inc ....B 956 686-1151
McAllen (G-14847)

Lockheed Martin Corporation ....E 915 852-1100
El Paso (G-5845)

Spacex Rocket Dev Test Fcilty ....F 254 840-5771
Mc Gregor (G-14824)

Vivace International Corp ....E 504 613-4329
San Antonio (G-18598)

GUIDED MISSILES & SPACE VEHICLES: Research & Development

Aerostar International Inc ....E 903 885-0728
Sulphur Springs (G-19578)

Japan Arospc Exploration Agcy ....F 281 333-5999
Houston (G-10454)

Nanoracks LLC ....D 832 632-7754
Webster (G-20641)

GUIDED MISSILES/SPACE VEHICLE PARTS/AUX EQPT: Research/Devel

General Dynamics Ordnance .... B 972 276-5131
Garland (G-7499)
Xtenti LLC .... G 818 434-5239
Dallas (G-3861)

GUM & WOOD CHEMICALS

Hexion Inc .... E 936 829-5566
Diboll (G-5467)
Impact Composite Tech Ltd .... E 806 385-1015
Littlefield (G-14146)

GUN SIGHTS: Optical

Peak Nanosystems LLC .... E 469 464-4504
Coppell (G-3434)
Summit Night Vision Group Inc .... F 972 992-0046
Plano (G-17013)

GUN STOCKS: Wood

Plano Synergy Holding Inc .... E 469 733-1868
Grand Prairie (G-7946)

GUN SVCS

Psd3 Enterprises LLC .... F 830 995-3894
Comfort (G-3240)

GUNSMITHS

Defense Solutions Group Inc .... F 800 382-7571
Cleburne (G-3087)

GUTTERS

BG Absolute .... F 409 724-0300
Nederland (G-15746)
Molded Fiber Glass Companies .... D 940 668-0302
Gainesville (G-7349)
Senox Corporation .... E 512 251-3333
Austin (G-1492)

GUTTERS: Sheet Metal

Hill Country Insulation .... G 512 515-7707
Pflugerville (G-16675)
Suburban Sheet Metal Ltd .... E 817 478-0801
Kennedale (G-13504)

GYPSUM BOARD

Lsf8 Gypsum Holdings LP .... A 703 480-3800
Dallas (G-4609)

GYPSUM MINING

Georgia-Pacific Bldg Pdts LLC .... F 830 997-4341
Fredericksburg (G-7181)

GYPSUM PRDTS

Caraustar Industries Inc .... E 903 793-6231
Texarkana (G-19758)
Casting Designs Inc .... C 817 551-7373
Fort Worth (G-6496)
Georgia-Pacific LLC .... C 940 663-6111
Quanah (G-17217)
Georgia-Pacific LLC .... E 936 829-5511
Diboll (G-5466)
Georgia-Pacific LLC .... B 866 924-1397
El Paso (G-5784)
Murphy Wall Products Intl Inc .... E 713 694-8365
Houston (G-10943)
Ng Operations LLC .... D 817 645-3435
Cleburne (G-3104)
Ng Operations LLC .... F 972 660-7140
Grand Prairie (G-7935)
Ng Operations LLC .... D 830 864-4100
Harper (G-8210)
Unifix Inc .... E 817 645-3435
Cleburne (G-3116)
United States Gypsum Company .... E 214 424-2500
Dallas (G-5137)

HAIR & HAIR BASED PRDTS

Bobby Pins LLC .... F 920 267-6388
Dallas (G-4035)
Crowned Plus Enterprises LLC .... F 469 585-9658
Forney (G-6306)

Danielle Howard .... F 469 554-6772
Dallas (G-4236)
Daphany Broussard .... F 832 229-0999
Houston (G-9403)

HAIR CARE PRDTS

Farouk Systems Inc .... B 281 876-2000
Houston (G-9765)
Farouk Systems Inc .... F 281 443-0715
Houston (G-9766)
Macadamia Beauty LLC .... E 800 807-3950
Plano (G-16915)
Natural Technology Inc .... F 972 551-2563
Terrell (G-19743)

HAIR CARE PRDTS: Hair Coloring Preparations

Beauty Elite Group Inc .... E 800 619-1333
Houston (G-8847)

HAIR DRYERS: Beauty Shop

Troy Helen Texas Corporation .... D 915 225-8000
El Paso (G-6017)

HAIRDRESSERS

Bobby Pins LLC .... F 920 267-6388
Dallas (G-4035)

HAND TOOLS, NEC: Wholesalers

Centennial Steel Inc .... E 972 412-5144
Rowlett (G-17703)

HANDBAG STORES

Fossil Group Inc .... B 972 234-2525
Richardson (G-17312)

HANDBAGS

Jon Hart Design Co .... E 210 226-8544
San Antonio (G-18206)
Vera Bradley Inc .... D 713 647-0323
Houston (G-12549)

HANDBAGS: Women's

Double J Saddlery Inc .... D 361 293-6364
Yoakum (G-20964)

HANDLES: Wood

Magnolia Brush Mfrs Inc .... D 903 427-2261
Clarksville (G-3074)

HANGERS: Garment, Home & Store, Wooden

International Innovations Inc .... D 512 600-4517
Austin (G-1238)

HARD RUBBER PRDTS, NEC

Aqseptence Group Inc .... C 651 636-3900
Houston (G-8671)

HARDWARE

ABC Exclusive Inc .... D 972 485-8182
Garland (G-7425)
Adell Corporation .... E 972 226-4600
Mesquite (G-15024)
American Block Company .... C 800 572-9087
Houston (G-8588)
Antx Inc .... F 512 255-2800
Cedar Park (G-2960)
Architectural Products Co Inc .... E 915 584-9424
El Paso (G-5649)
Berridge Manufacturing Company ..... E 830 401-5200
Seguin (G-18826)
Blacksheep Inc .... B 903 592-3853
Tyler (G-20059)
C E Shepherd Company LP .... D 713 924-4300
Houston (G-9028)
Cki Locker LLC .... F 817 329-1600
Dfw Airport (G-5452)
Cord Keeper LLC .... F 361 992-1122
Corpus Christi (G-3507)
Corrections Products Co Ltd .... F 210 829-7951
San Antonio (G-18027)
Delta Rigging & Tools Inc .... D 877 889-8833
Hurst (G-12844)

Esna LLC .... B 817 281-8816
North Richland Hills (G-15877)
Fairfield Industries Inc .... C 281 275-7500
Houston (G-9752)
Guardian Compliance .... A 713 641-2020
Deer Park (G-5277)
Hollywood Ovrhd Door of Dallas .... E 214 348-7240
Dallas (G-4464)
Indian Aerospace Inc .... F 817 265-5137
Arlington (G-703)
Jcm Industries Inc .... C 903 832-2581
Nash (G-15722)
Keystone Consolidated Inds .... D 903 893-0191
Sherman (G-18919)
Maxistrut of Texas Inc .... E 713 880-4228
Houston (G-10805)
National Crane Cmplnce Inspcto ...... C 888 720-6224
Manvel (G-14735)
Piping Accessories Inc .... E 409 842-5000
Beaumont (G-1942)
Pro-Steel Inc .... E 817 572-4959
Fort Worth (G-6919)
Pt Hardware Inc .... D 214 744-4491
Dallas (G-4834)
Ra-Lock Security Solutions Inc .... E 972 775-6301
Midlothian (G-15493)
S C S C Inc .... E 214 398-1199
Dallas (G-4922)
Scan-Pac Mfg Inc .... E 281 356-1640
Magnolia (G-14626)
SPEP Acquisition Corp .... F 310 608-0693
Lancaster (G-13848)
Taprite Inc .... E 210 523-0800
San Antonio (G-18522)
Texas Starwares Inc .... F 972 641-2100
Grand Prairie (G-7981)
Toyotetsu Texas Inc .... D 210 231-5515
San Antonio (G-18557)
US Home Systems Inc .... E 214 488-6300
Irving (G-13204)
Vision Systems Intl LLC .... F 817 234-6600
Fort Worth (G-7107)
Wallace-Thompson Company .... F 903 683-2223
Rusk (G-17733)
Waste Repurposing Intl Inc .... E 760 525-7180
Austin (G-1647)
Worldwide Wndows Tratments LLC ... E 718 893-9370
Dallas (G-5203)
Zimco Marine LLC .... F 956 831-7828
Brownsville (G-2422)

HARDWARE & BUILDING PRDTS: Plastic

Advanced Drainage Systems Inc .... F 361 293-6313
Yoakum (G-20958)
Arlon Inc .... E 210 798-1900
San Antonio (G-17914)
Chevron Phillips Chem Co LP .... A 832 813-4100
The Woodlands (G-19845)
Fibergrate Composite .... D 254 977-1302
Stephenville (G-19411)
Fireplace Installers Inc .... D 713 937-4575
Houston (G-9789)
Fwave LLC .... F 817 754-9021
Burleson (G-2579)
Lsp Products Group Inc .... D 775 884-4242
Irving (G-13091)
Reef Industries Inc .... E 713 507-4200
Houston (G-11577)
Reno Machine Works LLC .... F 903 224-6275
Reno (G-17252)
WFC Company Inc .... E 903 586-0476
Jacksonville (G-13267)
Wylie & Son Inc .... D 806 667-3566
Petersburg (G-16652)
Wylie & Son Inc .... E 325 695-0000
Abilene (G-95)

HARDWARE & EQPT: Stage, Exc Lighting

Kdh Companies Inc .... F 281 583-8861
Houston (G-10506)

HARDWARE STORES

Alamo Lumber Company .... F 361 275-2321
Cuero (G-3758)
B & S Hardware Inc .... E 903 856-3552
Pittsburg (G-16744)
Channl-Track Tube-Way Inds Inc ...... E 713 864-2551
Houston (G-9162)

PRODUCT

Fastserv Supply Inc ....E 800 527-4126
Plano (G-16870)
Foxworth-Galbraith Lumber Co ....D 972 665-2400
Plano (G-16872)
Jan Pate Inc ....F 903 683-5700
Rusk (G-17732)
Keith Properties Inc ....F 254 883-2531
Marlin (G-14759)
McKee True Value Hdwr & Lbr ....E 903 874-6581
Corsicana (G-3677)
Paso Del Norte Hardware LLC ....F 915 591-6200
El Paso (G-5904)
Sam Stevens Inc ....E 806 872-8365
Lamesa (G-13829)
Sanitz Enterprises Inc ....F 719 439-2183
Willow City (G-20871)
True Value Company LLC ....C 903 872-8365
Corsicana (G-3688)
Winzer Corporation ....C 214 341-2122
Plano (G-17051)

HARDWARE STORES: Builders'

Alamo Concrete Products Ltd ....F 361 572-0231
Victoria (G-20236)
Angelo Bolt and Indus Sup Inc ....E 325 655-0075
San Angelo (G-17776)
HWC Wire & Cable Company ....C 713 453-8518
Houston (G-10293)
Triple C Hardware & Lumber Inc ....E 325 392-4123
Ozona (G-16289)
Wessely-Thompson Hardware Inc ....E 210 344-3081
San Antonio (G-18614)

HARDWARE STORES: Door Locks & Lock Sets

Accu-Lock Inc ....E 866 222-8562
Grandview (G-8001)
Rolland Safe & Lock Co LLC ....D 972 243-3711
Dallas (G-4909)

HARDWARE STORES: Pumps & Pumping Eqpt

All American Pump & Mch Inc ....F 325 653-6597
San Angelo (G-17773)
Premier Coil Solutions Inc ....E 713 677-0209
Waller (G-20507)

HARDWARE STORES: Tools

Anc Ion Coating Inc ....F 281 207-0300
Houston (G-8638)
Ed Prince Enterprises Inc ....F 806 274-7178
Borger (G-2177)
Epiroc Drilling Solutions LLC ....D 214 547-7800
Allen (G-265)
Equalizer Industries Inc. ....E 512 388-7715
Round Rock (G-17656)
IDM Group LLC ....F 972 578-1010
Plano (G-16889)
Trans Tool LLC ....F 210 225-6745
San Antonio (G-18560)

HARDWARE WHOLESALERS

All-Pro Threaded Products ....F 817 467-5700
Arlington (G-614)
Alloy Casting Co Inc ....E 800 527-1318
Mesquite (G-15025)
Amweld International LLC...............D 888 775-2397
Dallas (G-3948)
Angelo Bolt and Indus Sup Inc ....E 325 655-0075
San Angelo (G-17776)
Apx Plastics Inc ....F 817 275-3883
Arlington (G-620)
B & S Hardware Inc ....E 903 856-3552
Pittsburg (G-16744)
Centex Manufacturing Co ....F 254 752-2531
Waco (G-20379)
Dura-Mar Venus Inc ....D 972 223-8008
Desoto (G-5430)
Kaston Fixs & Design Group LLC ....E 972 243-5334
Dallas (G-4544)
Oft Enterprises Inc ....E 713 787-5373
Bellaire (G-2000)
Pierce Arrow Inc ....F 940 538-5643
Henrietta (G-8282)
SPEP Acquisition Corp ....F 310 608-0693
Lancaster (G-13848)

Triple C Hardware & Lumber Inc ....E 325 392-4123
Ozona (G-16289)

HARDWARE, WHOLESALE: Bolts

Frontier Bolt Company Texas ....F 817 477-5319
Mansfield (G-14674)
JLK Industries Inc......................E 713 462-7761
Houston (G-10476)
Nut Place Inc ....E 713 462-3147
Houston (G-11100)

HARDWARE, WHOLESALE: Builders', NEC

Apco Building Specialties Inc............E 915 581-6005
El Paso (G-5645)
Architectural Products Co Inc ....E 915 584-9424
El Paso (G-5649)
Sword Company.......................E 903 561-1921
Tyler (G-20159)

HARDWARE, WHOLESALE: Casters & Glides

Magnus Mobility Systems Inc............F 800 527-5142
Dallas (G-4627)

HARDWARE, WHOLESALE: Furniture, NEC

Texas Office Pdts & Sup Inc ....F 512 472-1340
Austin (G-1569)

HARDWARE, WHOLESALE: Nozzles

Planeview-Wmi LLC ....E 936 588-8988
Conroe (G-3350)

HARDWARE, WHOLESALE: Power Tools & Access

Fastorq Bolting Systems Inc ....F 281 449-6466
New Caney (G-15839)

HARDWARE, WHOLESALE: Screws

Pattonair Usa Inc......................E 817 284-4449
Fort Worth (G-6897)

HARDWARE, WHOLESALE: Security Devices, Locks

Associated Time Instrs Co Inc...........E 214 637-2763
Dallas (G-3975)
Associated Time Instrs Co Inc...........F 713 263-1366
Houston (G-8726)
Dallas Sight and Sound Inc.............E 972 392-3202
Dallas (G-4225)

HARDWARE: Aircraft

Progressive Incorporated ....B 817 465-3221
Arlington (G-762)
Rf Manufacturing LLC ....E 817 479-1950
Haltom City (G-8157)

HARDWARE: Aircraft & Marine, Incl Pulleys & Similar Items

Fabrication Specialty Inc................F 214 742-3571
Granbury (G-7797)
Sanitz Enterprises Inc ....F 719 439-2183
Willow City (G-20871)

HARDWARE: Builders'

Allen and Allen LLC ....D 210 733-9191
San Antonio (G-17894)
Triple C Hardware & Lumber Inc ....E 325 392-4123
Ozona (G-16289)

HARDWARE: Door Opening & Closing Devices, Exc Electrical

ASAP Glass & Door LLC ....F 214 770-8266
Denton (G-5351)
DC Controls Inc ....F 361 906-0123
Lewisville (G-14043)
Innovative Hinge Products ....E 817 598-4846
Weatherford (G-20596)
Maintenance Builders Sup Ltd ....E 713 462-8213
Houston (G-10741)

HARDWARE: Furniture

Inman & Company Inc ....F 713 224-4740
Houston (G-10367)

HARDWARE: Furniture, Builders' & Other Household

I & I Design Inc ....F 713 667-6800
Houston (G-10308)
Trane Technologies Company LLC ....E 903 730-4000
Tyler (G-20163)

HARDWARE: Harness

Sle Electronics-Usa Inc ....E 915 594-4998
El Paso (G-5963)

HARDWARE: Locking Systems, Security Cable

Carroll Systems LP ....E 512 927-1200
Austin (G-1030)

HARNESS ASSEMBLIES: Cable & Wire

AB Interconnect Inc ....C 919 934-5181
Corpus Christi (G-3463)
Airborn Interconnect Inc ....B 512 863-5585
Georgetown (G-7633)
Border Assembly Inc ....E 915 592-1172
El Paso (G-5667)
Circuit Systems Company Inc ....E 817 861-6575
Arlington (G-642)
Co-Operative Inds Def LLC ....D 817 740-4700
Fort Worth (G-6525)
Ct-Technology Inc.....................G 469 531-9472
Carrollton (G-2862)
Electrical Components Intl Inc ....D 915 217-2700
El Paso (G-5750)
Electronic Assembly Svcs Inc ....F 713 686-4390
Houston (G-9594)
General Assembly Corporation ....F 915 701-0605
El Paso (G-5780)
General Datatech LP ....E 214 857-6194
Dallas (G-4398)
Gilmore-Global Instrs Co Inc ....F 713 946-9133
Houston (G-9958)
GNC Cable Technologies Inc ....F 832 876-1780
Cypress (G-3797)
Hayakawa Electronics Amer Inc..........E 972 457-0064
Irving (G-13054)
J M Fabrication Company LLC ....F 817 652-0526
Arlington (G-709)
Jar Industries LLC ....E 281 484-1777
Houston (G-10455)
M3 Distribution Inc....................F 281 357-0604
Tomball (G-19986)
Mssl Wiring System Inc.................E 830 776-9221
El Paso (G-5890)
Pinner Wire & Cable Inc ....D 972 494-3333
Garland (G-7567)
Solution Tech Harn Group LLC ....E 214 221-0323
Dallas (G-4978)
Stoneridge Inc ....B 915 778-1331
El Paso (G-5983)
Williamsrdm Inc ....D 817 872-1500
Fort Worth (G-7148)

HARNESS WIRING SETS: Internal Combustion Engines

Interconnect Wiring LLP ....C 817 377-9473
Fort Worth (G-6723)
Mtx Electronics Inc ....F 956 781-3476
Pharr (G-16708)
Solrac Corporation ....B 915 772-3073
El Paso (G-5969)
USA Harness Inc ....D 903 342-3767
Winnsboro (G-20901)

HARNESSES, HALTERS, SADDLERY & STRAPS

Double J Saddlery Inc ....D 361 293-6364
Yoakum (G-20964)

HARVESTING MACHINERY & EQPT WHOLESALERS

Southern Nut N Tree Equipment ....E 325 938-5460
Goldthwaite *(G-7745)*

HEADPHONES: Radio

Mach Speed Holdings LLC ....D 214 978-3800
Plano *(G-16917)*

HEALTH AIDS: Exercise Eqpt

ARX Fit ....F 512 633-3768
Austin *(G-938)*
Bt5 Technologies LLC ....F 832 727-5214
Houston *(G-9001)*
Multisports Inc ....F 713 460-8188
Houston *(G-10939)*
Promaxima Manufacturing Ltd ....D 800 231-6652
Houston *(G-11446)*
Quantum Fitness Corporation ....D 281 495-3003
Sugar Land *(G-19531)*
USA Sports Inc ....D 713 957-2882
Houston *(G-12502)*

HEALTH FOOD & SUPPLEMENT STORES

Bear Creek Smokehouse LLC ....E 903 935-5217
Marshall *(G-14763)*
Pita Pal Industries Inc ....D 713 777-7482
Houston *(G-11339)*

HEARING AIDS

Hearing Lab Technology LLC ....D 469 586-0448
Fort Worth *(G-6693)*
Starkey Laboratories Inc ....B 956 541-1917
Brownsville *(G-2408)*

HEAT EMISSION OPERATING APPARATUS

Red River Compression Svcs LLC ....E 832 831-0532
Houston *(G-11569)*
Spiral X LLC ....F 855 346-8823
Garland *(G-7590)*
Synergy Catalyst LLC ....F 248 786-7145
Coppell *(G-3449)*

HEAT EXCHANGERS

Danhard Inc ....F 214 328-8541
Dallas *(G-4233)*
Huffman Company Ltd ....F 432 332-5723
Odessa *(G-16028)*
Ohmstede Ltd ....D 361 289-1701
Corpus Christi *(G-3584)*

HEAT EXCHANGERS: After Or Inter Coolers Or Condensers, Etc

Bell Intercoolers LLC ....F 830 438-6150
Spring Branch *(G-19268)*
Chart Industries Inc ....C 281 364-8700
The Woodlands *(G-19841)*
Eads Cooling Solutions LLC ....F 713 780-1551
Houston *(G-9555)*
East Texas Radiator Inc ....E 903 753-7286
Longview *(G-14228)*
Ohmstede Ltd ....C 281 471-4140
La Porte *(G-13780)*
Ohmstede Ltd ....B 409 833-6375
Beaumont *(G-1935)*
Olaer Usa Inc ....F 713 937-8900
Houston *(G-11167)*
Southern Heat Exchanger Corp ....E 281 668-4619
Houston *(G-11974)*
Titanium Fabrication Corp ....F 832 375-1800
Houston *(G-12300)*

HEAT TREATING: Metal

Ameritek Heat Treating and F ....C 281 480-5637
La Porte *(G-13722)*
Analytic Stress Relieving Inc ....E 361 883-0315
Corpus Christi *(G-3473)*
Analytic Stress Relieving Inc ....D 281 471-9600
La Porte *(G-13724)*
Backer Marathon Inc ....E 830 775-1417
Del Rio *(G-5307)*
Bodycote K-Tech Inc ....F 281 227-8222
Houston *(G-8937)*

Bodycote K-Tech Inc ....F 214 904-2420
Dallas *(G-4037)*
Bodycote Thermal Proc Inc ....E 713 225-6050
Houston *(G-8938)*
Bwt LLC ....E 281 442-6694
Houston *(G-9024)*
Eckel Heat Treating Co ....D 432 362-4336
Odessa *(G-15984)*
Eckel Manufacturing Co Inc ....D 432 362-4336
Odessa *(G-15985)*
Ellwood Texas Forge LP ....C 713 434-5100
Houston *(G-9605)*
Gamma Engineering Inc ....C 817 477-2193
Mansfield *(G-14676)*
Gemstar Inc ....E 432 362-2315
Odessa *(G-16013)*
Gill Metallurgical Inc ....E 281 593-0807
Cleveland *(G-3127)*
Houston Thermal Processing LLC ....F 281 590-9600
Houston *(G-10256)*
Industrial Thermal Svcs LLC ....E 409 886-9700
Orange *(G-16247)*
Lone Star Heat Treating Corp ....D 713 672-6616
Houston *(G-10678)*
Mannings USA Inc ....E 281 443-7474
Pasadena *(G-16479)*
Modern Heat Treat Inc ....D 817 616-0333
Richland Hills *(G-17443)*
National Heat Treat LLC ....E 281 809-9840
Houston *(G-10969)*
National Oilwell Varco Inc ....C 936 825-7070
Navasota *(G-15739)*
Nci Group Inc ....E 713 921-7997
Houston *(G-11018)*
Omk Tube Inc ....E 281 609-8150
Houston *(G-11175)*
Osr Services LP ....E 281 422-7206
Baytown *(G-1830)*
Republic Heat Treat Inc ....F 713 692-3308
Houston *(G-11601)*
Rhr Acquisition Co LLC ....F 713 699-3892
Houston *(G-11615)*
Rhr Acquisition Co LLC ....F 936 856-6607
Conroe *(G-3357)*
Southwest Metal Treating Corp ....E 817 551-1004
Fort Worth *(G-7003)*
Specialty Heat Treat Inc ....E 713 937-3101
Houston *(G-11999)*
Superior Shot Peening Inc ....E 281 432-0900
Cleveland *(G-3138)*
Swht LLC ....E 281 442-6694
Houston *(G-12132)*
Team Cooperheat-Mqs Inc ....E 713 673-3660
Houston *(G-12171)*
Texas Heat Treating Inc ....E 512 255-5884
Round Rock *(G-17692)*
Texas Steel Conversion Inc ....C 713 733-6013
Houston *(G-12252)*
Texas Stress Inc ....E 281 930-0897
La Porte *(G-13795)*

HEATERS: Swimming Pool, Electric

Seltek International Inc ....E 915 772-8444
El Paso *(G-5955)*

HEATING & AIR CONDITIONING EQPT & SPLYS WHOLESALERS

Ecolab Inc ....E 817 916-9600
Haltom City *(G-8138)*
Heat Air Products Company ....E 817 222-9567
Fort Worth *(G-6694)*

HEATING & AIR CONDITIONING UNITS, COMBINATION

Bebco Envmtl Contrls Corp ....E 844 397-4822
La Marque *(G-13707)*
Colair Inc ....F 956 631-9889
Mission *(G-15550)*
Daikin Manufacturing Co LP ....F 972 245-1510
Houston *(G-9393)*
DFW Comfort Experts Inc ....F 817 633-2665
North Richland Hills *(G-15876)*
Mestex Ltd ....C 214 638-6010
Dallas *(G-4668)*
Pedraza Hvac Inc ....F 281 970-4834
Houston *(G-11269)*
Synergy Environmental Svcs LLC ....E 972 513-1118
Arlington *(G-789)*

Trane US Inc ....C 254 299-6300
Mc Gregor *(G-14825)*

HEATING EQPT & SPLYS

Abutec LLC ....D 512 836-9473
Austin *(G-881)*
CCI Thermal Tech Texas Inc ....F 855 219-2101
Houston *(G-9109)*
Enginerd Packaged Systems Inc ....E 409 866-5213
Beaumont *(G-1887)*
Epcon Industrial Systems LP ....D 936 273-1774
Shenandoah *(G-18896)*
Exotherm Corporation ....F 713 981-9100
Houston *(G-9726)*
Fives N Amercn Combustn Inc ....E 281 488-2667
Houston *(G-9795)*
Flares & Stacks Inc ....F 281 356-1408
Conroe *(G-3297)*
Fuzzys Indus Mint Mnfacture LP ....D 806 273-2818
Borger *(G-2179)*
Gaumer Company Inc ....C 713 460-5200
Houston *(G-9905)*
Hart Heat Transfer Pdts Inc ....D 713 675-9848
Houston *(G-10133)*
Mortex Products Inc ....B 817 624-0820
Fort Worth *(G-6853)*
Rm Manifold Group Inc ....F 817 897-5330
Fort Worth *(G-6961)*
Selkirk Corporation ....B 972 943-6100
Richardson *(G-17395)*
Texas Responsible Energy & ....F 903 266-9103
Tyler *(G-20161)*
Tisdale AC & Htg Co ....F 936 856-1500
Conroe *(G-3372)*
Universal Solar Technology Inc ....F 832 764-8260
Houston *(G-12464)*

HEATING EQPT: Complete

Cimarron Energy Holding Co LLC ....E 432 563-9700
Odessa *(G-15961)*
Thermal Solutions Texas LLC ....F 281 351-4328
Tomball *(G-20014)*

HEATING EQPT: Induction

Rae Energy Solutions Inc ....G 281 440-3434
Houston *(G-11533)*

HEATING PADS, ELECTRIC

S N D Manufacturing Ltd ....D 214 340-1592
Dallas *(G-4923)*

HEATING PADS: Nonelectric

Prism Enterprises ....F 210 520-8051
San Antonio *(G-18397)*

HEATING UNITS & DEVICES: Indl, Electric

E-Z Heat Corporation ....F 830 693-4005
Horseshoe Bay *(G-8367)*
Steelman Industries Inc ....E 903 984-3061
Kilgore *(G-13594)*
Team Cooperheat-Mqs Inc ....E 713 673-3660
Houston *(G-12171)*

HEATING UNITS: Gas, Infrared

Neu Plumbing Inc ....D 940 580-2200
Pilot Point *(G-16726)*
Welch Hvac Incorporated ....F 214 222-8600
Lewisville *(G-14112)*

HEELS, BOOT OR SHOE: Plastic

Wesmar Corporation ....E 915 599-1572
El Paso *(G-6029)*

HEELS, BOOT OR SHOE: Rubber, Composition Or Fiber

Wesmar Corporation ....E 915 599-1572
El Paso *(G-6029)*

HELICOPTERS

Airbus Helicopters Inc ....B 972 641-0000
Grand Prairie *(G-7824)*
AVX Aircraft Company ....E 817 731-8003
Benbrook *(G-2038)*

Employee Codes: A=Over 500 employees, B=251-500
C=101-250, D=51-100, E=20-50, F=10-19, G=9

2021 Harris Texas
Manufacturers Directory

PRODUCT

1521

HELICOPTERS

Bell Textron Inc ....C 817 280-2011
Fort Worth (G-6445)
Bell Textron Inc ....A 817 280-2011
Fort Worth (G-6444)
Bell Textron Services Inc ....F 817 280-2011
Fort Worth (G-6446)
Schweizer Rsg LLC ....F 817 405-2100
Fort Worth (G-6980)

HELMETS: Athletic

Athletic Hlmet Rcndtioning LLC .....E 936 858-9990
Alto (G-314)
Bell Sports Corp ....E 469 417-6600
Irving (G-12946)

HELP SUPPLY SERVICES

Fisher Lease Service Inc ....E 325 884-2701
Big Lake (G-2056)

HERMETICS REPAIR SVCS

City of Marshall ....F 903 935-4500
Marshall (G-14771)

HIGH ENERGY PARTICLE PHYSICS EQPT

Spike Electric and Contrls LLC .....F 832 243-5372
Houston (G-12015)

HIGHWAY & STREET MAINTENANCE SVCS

Arismendy Josias ....E 817 353-1244
Fort Worth (G-6401)
Epic Energy Services LLC ....C 361 222-1226
Odem (G-15895)
Short-Line Corporation ....F 210 492-6088
San Antonio (G-18470)

HIGHWAY SIGNALS: Electric

Cubic Its Inc ....C 281 240-7233
Sugar Land (G-19471)

HITCHES: Trailer

Performance Metal Works Inc ....D 903 967-2622
Quitman (G-17228)

HOBBY, TOY & GAME STORES: Arts & Crafts & Splys

Michaels Companies Inc ....D 972 409-1300
Irving (G-13108)

HOBBY, TOY & GAME STORES: Ceramics Splys

Carbo Ceramics Inc ....B 281 921-6400
Houston (G-9091)

HOBBY, TOY & GAME STORES: Dolls & Access

Gamestop Corp ....C 817 424-2000
Grapevine (G-8038)

HOBBY, TOY & GAME STORES: Toys & Games

Ben Dunn Corporation ....F 210 614-0396
San Antonio (G-17946)

HOISTING SLINGS

Liftex Corporation ....E 713 863-0900
Houston (G-10639)

HOISTS

Ace Engineering Ltd ....C 817 237-7700
Fort Worth (G-6341)

HOLDERS, PAPER TOWEL, GROCERY BAG, ETC: Plastic

Poly Sac Inc ....E 713 978-7888
Houston (G-11356)

HOLDING COMPANIES: Investment, Exc Banks

American A Lquide Holdings Inc .....E 713 624-8000
Houston (G-8581)
Earthstone Energy Holdings LLC .....E 281 298-4246
The Woodlands (G-19858)
GSE Holding Inc ....C 281 443-8564
Houston (G-10054)
Hiland Partners Holdings LLC ....D 713 369-9000
Houston (G-10181)
Iris Biotech LLC ....E 512 219-8020
Austin (G-1244)
Lgc US Holdings LLC ....C 713 222-0284
Houston (G-10632)
Renfro Street Holdings Ltd ....E 817 295-6100
Burleson (G-2596)
Supermedia LLC ....E 972 453-7000
Dfw Airport (G-5456)
Tpg Capital Management LP ....B 817 871-4000
Fort Worth (G-7069)
Valerus Feld Sltons Hldngs LLC .....E 713 744-6100
Houston (G-12520)
Zachry Holdings Inc ....A 210 588-5000
San Antonio (G-18632)

HOLDING COMPANIES: Personal, Exc Banks

Downstream Aggregator LLC ....F 281 247-8118
Channelview (G-3017)
Mo2 Inc ....F 214 575-7600
Dallas (G-4682)

HOLLOWWARE, STAINLESS STEEL

Integrated Flow Systems LLC ....D 512 671-5002
Pflugerville (G-16676)

HOME CENTER STORES

Omnimax International Inc ....E 817 473-1541
Mansfield (G-14699)

HOME ENTERTAINMENT EQPT: Electronic, NEC

Alliance Entertainment LLC ....E 806 381-3945
Amarillo (G-392)
Diem Digital Interiors LLC ....F 972 899-1189
Carrollton (G-2723)
Smbg Corsicana LLC ....F 254 262-4400
Corsicana (G-3684)

HOME FURNISHINGS WHOLESALERS

Satori Home Limited LLC ....E 855 472-8674
Dallas (G-4937)
Space Enterprises LLC ....F 800 559-2923
San Antonio (G-18490)
Space Enterprises LLC ....E 281 846-9613
The Woodlands (G-19923)
Treska Inc ....E 682 647-0352
Fort Worth (G-7074)
Venetian Blind Flr Cvg Sp Ltd ....E 713 528-2404
Houston (G-12546)

HOME HEALTH CARE SVCS

Health Care Temporaries Inc ....A 713 631-7106
Houston (G-10143)

HOME IMPROVEMENT & RENOVATION CONTRACTOR AGENCY

Glenwood Blind & Awning Co Inc .....G 903 597-2088
Tyler (G-20090)
Tradesorg LLC ....E 512 729-3544
Austin (G-1589)

HOMEBUILDERS & OTHER OPERATIVE BUILDERS

R-Tex Services LLC ....D 817 774-3333
Joshua (G-13324)

HOMEFURNISHING STORE: Bedding, Sheet, Blanket,Spread/Pillow

KS Little Shop ....F 214 371-4113
Dallas (G-4571)
Mfi International Mfg LLC ....A 915 858-0971
El Paso (G-5876)

HOMEFURNISHING STORES: Beddings & Linens

Le Ragge Ruggs Inc ....E 512 858-4186
Dripping Springs (G-5508)
Peacock Alley Inc ....D 214 744-0399
Dallas (G-4793)
Shelbis Stuff Inc ....F 903 450-1300
Greenville (G-8091)

HOMEFURNISHING STORES: Cookware, Exc Aluminum

Burkhead Manufacturing Company .....E 713 227-5248
Houston (G-9019)

HOMEFURNISHING STORES: Cutlery

Angel Sword Corp ....E 512 847-9679
Driftwood (G-5498)

HOMEFURNISHING STORES: Lighting Fixtures

Behemoth Corporation ....E 281 332-4798
League City (G-13949)
Carols Lighting and Fan Sp Inc ......F 281 292-1661
Conroe (G-3274)
M & M Lighting LP ....D 713 667-5611
Houston (G-10715)

HOMEFURNISHING STORES: Metalware

Supaks Inc ....G 979 968-5654
La Grange (G-13701)

HOMEFURNISHING STORES: Mirrors

Jpon Glass Company Inc ....E 214 349-1400
Garland (G-7528)

HOMEFURNISHING STORES: Pictures, Wall

Somerset House Publishing Inc ....F 281 346-8900
Fulshear (G-7330)

HOMEFURNISHING STORES: Pottery

Marshall Pottery Inc ....C 903 938-9201
Marshall (G-14791)

HOMEFURNISHING STORES: Venetian Blinds

Academy Venetian Blinds Co Inc .....F 361 852-6088
Corpus Christi (G-3465)
Ral & Associates Inc ....E 903 833-5191
Ben Wheeler (G-2034)
Shade Shop Inc ....G 713 623-0750
Houston (G-11844)
Venetian Blind Flr Cvg Sp Ltd ....E 713 528-2404
Houston (G-12546)
Ybarra Group Inc ....F 210 533-5323
San Antonio (G-18629)

HOMEFURNISHING STORES: Vertical Blinds

Plantation Shutter ....F 214 341-3677
Dallas (G-4809)
Plumlee Place LLC ....F 254 662-4021
Robinson (G-17501)

HOMEFURNISHING STORES: Wicker, Rattan, Or Reed

Patio One Furniture LP ....F 713 789-8080
Houston (G-11260)

HOMEFURNISHING STORES: Window Furnishings

Piw Ventures Ltd ....F 713 932-9311
Houston (G-11340)
Tex-Sun Shade Specialties Inc ....F 972 279-0132
Dallas (G-5053)

HOMEFURNISHING STORES: Window Shades, NEC

Austin Window Fashion Inc ....F 512 836-3388
Austin (G-967)

Southern Shutters Inc ....F 512 272-9711
Manor *(G-14649)*

HOMEFURNISHINGS, WHOLESALE: Blinds, Venetian

Fresh Meadows Industries Inc ....E 713 464-9554
Houston *(G-9865)*
Shade Shop Inc ....G 713 623-0750
Houston *(G-11844)*

HOMEFURNISHINGS, WHOLESALE: Blinds, Vertical

Austin Window Fashion Inc ....F 512 836-3388
Austin *(G-967)*

HOMEFURNISHINGS, WHOLESALE: Carpets

Exclusive Oriental Rugs Inc ....F 214 747-5557
Dallas *(G-4342)*
Stella Hasegawa ....F 915 594-7633
El Paso *(G-5977)*
United Lynn-Con Corporation ....F 972 223-2540
Desoto *(G-5446)*

HOMEFURNISHINGS, WHOLESALE: Draperies

Custom Work Room Services ....F 214 631-2795
Dallas *(G-4197)*

HOMEFURNISHINGS, WHOLESALE: Fireplace Eqpt & Access

Dallas Fort Wrth Fyrestone LLC ....E 817 429-0999
Fort Worth *(G-6573)*
Golden Blount Inc ....E 972 250-3113
Addison *(G-131)*

HOMEFURNISHINGS, WHOLESALE: Floor Cushion & Padding

Orora Visual TX LLC ....D 972 289-0705
Mesquite *(G-15065)*

HOMEFURNISHINGS, WHOLESALE: Linens, Table

Ladds Corporation ....F 281 495-5200
Stafford *(G-19343)*

HOMEFURNISHINGS, WHOLESALE: Pillowcases

Peacock Alley Inc ....D 214 744-0399
Dallas *(G-4793)*

HOMEFURNISHINGS, WHOLESALE: Pottery

Arne Distributors Inc ....F 713 869-8321
Houston *(G-8700)*
Central Ready Mix Concrete Co ....E 956 383-2261
San Juan *(G-18672)*

HOMEFURNISHINGS, WHOLESALE: Rugs

SAM&m Group LLC ....F 346 204-5786
Stafford *(G-19373)*

HOMEFURNISHINGS, WHOLESALE: Window Covering Parts & Access

Signature Arch & Blind ....E 281 469-2500
Houston *(G-11893)*
Texton Inc ....D 972 494-5941
Garland *(G-7600)*

HOMEFURNISHINGS, WHOLESALE: Wood Flooring

Ace Hardwood Flooring Inc ....F 512 719-3555
West Lake Hills *(G-20676)*
Clarks Hardwood Lumber Co LP ....F 713 862-6628
Houston *(G-9211)*
Regal Hardwoods Inc ....F 972 620-8833
Carrollton *(G-2804)*

HOMES, MODULAR: Wooden

Amtex Corp ....D 972 276-7626
Garland *(G-7437)*
Aries Building Systems LLC ....C 254 938-0800
Troy *(G-20028)*
Aries Building Systems LLC ....F 254 938-0800
Houston *(G-8694)*
Atco Strctres Lgistics USA Inc ....G 208 242-3804
Spring *(G-19197)*
Atco Strctres Lgistics USA Inc ....D 936 829-2325
Spring *(G-19198)*
Rmd Manufacturing Ltd ....E 817 477-5321
Mansfield *(G-14712)*
Weq Britco LP ....E 254 741-6701
Waco *(G-20478)*

HOMES: Log Cabins

Langford Construction Inc ....F 817 478-0218
Arlington *(G-718)*
Satterwhite Companies Inc ....D 903 663-1729
Longview *(G-14303)*

HONES

Scot Hone Corporation ....D 903 639-2551
Lone Star *(G-14184)*

HOPPERS: Metal Plate

Modern Welding Co of Texas ....E 817 636-2215
Rhome *(G-17259)*

HORNS: Marine, Compressed Air Or Steam

B&B Roadway SEC Solutions LLC ....F 972 385-7899
Mckinney *(G-14924)*

HORSE & PET ACCESSORIES: Textile

Mustang Manufacturing Corp ....E 903 482-5666
Van Alstyne *(G-20211)*

HOSE: Air Line Or Air Brake, Rubber Or Rubberized Fabric

Reliable Hose Solutions LLC ....F 713 983-9090
Houston *(G-11590)*

HOSE: Automobile, Rubber

Flexaust Inc ....C 915 872-3100
El Paso *(G-5770)*

HOSE: Fabric

Guardian Insptn Tbular MGT LLC ....F 403 233-7561
Midland *(G-15241)*
Stewart Tubular Products LLC ....F 713 682-1486
Houston *(G-12066)*

HOSE: Flexible Metal

Polk Mechanical Company LLC ....C 972 339-1200
Grand Prairie *(G-7947)*
R & C Machine LLC ....F 254 694-9278
Whitney *(G-20732)*
Senior Operations LLC ....C 830 629-8080
New Braunfels *(G-15821)*

HOSE: Garden, Plastic

Swan Products LLC ....C 254 772-6979
Waco *(G-20461)*

HOSE: Plastic

Republic Tube LLC ....C 832 672-6000
Houston *(G-11603)*

HOSE: Pneumatic, Rubber Or Rubberized Fabric, NEC

Hasse Enterprises Inc ....F 512 835-7697
Austin *(G-1199)*

HOSE: Rubber

Flexmaster USA Inc ....D 713 462-7694
Houston *(G-9801)*
Gates E&S North America Inc ....D 361 887-9807
Corpus Christi *(G-3533)*
Ghx Industrial LLC ....E 713 341-3407
Houston *(G-9950)*

Ghx Industrial LLC ....F 713 939-7423
Houston *(G-9951)*
Ghx Industrial LLC ....E 713 222-2231
Houston *(G-9952)*

HOSES & BELTING: Rubber & Plastic

All-State Industries Inc ....E 972 434-4222
Lewisville *(G-14020)*
D E Shipp Belting Company ....F 254 776-0493
Waco *(G-20392)*
G T Southwest Hose Inc ....F 214 689-4673
Dallas *(G-4388)*
Parts Suppliers Inc ....F 830 773-5069
Eagle Pass *(G-5552)*
Purvis Industries LLC ....D 214 358-5500
Dallas *(G-4837)*

HOSIERY STORES

Hanesbrands Inc ....F 254 582-7541
Hillsboro *(G-8326)*

HOSPITAL EQPT REPAIR SVCS

Gray Green Biomedical Svcs LLC ....G 832 288-5958
Pearland *(G-16566)*

HOSPITALS: Medical & Surgical

Healthtech Solutions Inc ....F 763 559-7082
Austin *(G-1694)*

HOSPITALS: Rehabilitation, Drug Addiction

Cenikor Foundation ....F 817 921-2771
Arlington *(G-640)*

HOT TUBS

Morgan Building & Spa Mfg Corp ....D 254 629-1599
Eastland *(G-5568)*
Ptp Incorporated ....F 281 342-8775
Rosenberg *(G-17595)*

HOT TUBS: Plastic & Fiberglass

Aries Acrylic Mfg Inc ....F 972 771-6286
Rockwall *(G-17538)*
Sunbelt Hot Tubs LLC ....C 281 575-9814
Houston *(G-12098)*

HOTELS & MOTELS

Williamson Conference Center ....E 512 341-7000
Round Rock *(G-17699)*

HOUSEHOLD APPLIANCE STORES

Home Mart Inc ....F 956 724-4521
Laredo *(G-13892)*
Sunrgy LLC ....E 832 786-5051
Stafford *(G-19381)*

HOUSEHOLD APPLIANCE STORES: Garbage Disposals

Alareal Corporation ....G 915 858-4097
El Paso *(G-5639)*

HOUSEHOLD ARTICLES, EXC FURNITURE: Cut Stone

National Stone Inc ....F 214 651-7667
Irving *(G-13112)*

HOUSEHOLD ARTICLES, EXC KITCHEN: Pottery

Marshall Pottery Inc ....C 903 938-9201
Marshall *(G-14791)*

HOUSEHOLD ARTICLES: Metal

Brownsville Sheet Metal Works ....E 956 546-4517
Brownsville *(G-2340)*
East Creek Corporation ....E 903 527-5190
Caddo Mills *(G-2623)*
Taprite Inc ....E 210 523-0800
San Antonio *(G-18522)*
Theriot Inc ....E 979 233-6391
Freeport *(G-7215)*
Two Hills Studio Inc ....E 512 707-7571
Austin *(G-1602)*

PRODUCT

HOUSEHOLD FURNISHINGS, NEC

American Dawn Inc ....G...... 713 670-8505
  Houston *(G-8593)*

Arden Companies Inc ....C...... 806 335-1147
  Amarillo *(G-400)*

E R Carpenter LP ....C...... 804 359-0800
  Temple *(G-19680)*

East Txas Lighthouse For Blind ....D...... 903 595-3444
  Tyler *(G-20082)*

Hobby Lobby Stores Inc ....F...... 214 872-3184
  Frisco *(G-7290)*

Home Treasures Inc ....E...... 713 937-7716
  Houston *(G-10198)*

Houston Wiper & Mill Supply Co ....F...... 713 672-0571
  Houston *(G-10264)*

Ingrids Custom Hand Woven ....F...... 325 732-4370
  Paint Rock *(G-16291)*

KS Little Shop ....F...... 214 371-4113
  Dallas *(G-4571)*

Langes Legacy Home Ltd ....F...... 972 712-3949
  Allen *(G-284)*

Le Ragge Ruggs Inc ....E...... 512 858-4186
  Dripping Springs *(G-5508)*

Medline Industries Inc ....C...... 281 574-6200
  Katy *(G-13371)*

Tri-Tex Enterprises Inc ....D...... 214 744-1246
  Eastland *(G-5569)*

HOUSES: Rooming & Boarding

Mexssub International Inc ....C...... 713 278-2175
  Houston *(G-10861)*

HOUSEWARES, ELECTRIC: Air Purifiers, Portable

Airbox LLC ....G...... 512 968-5496
  Austin *(G-901)*

HOUSEWARES, ELECTRIC: Cooking Appliances

American Permanent Ware Co ....C...... 972 908-6100
  Allen *(G-250)*

HOUSEWARES, ELECTRIC: Dehumidifiers, Room

Munters Corporation ....D...... 210 651-5018
  Selma *(G-18879)*

HOUSEWARES, ELECTRIC: Fans, Exhaust & Ventilating

Vent-A-Hood Ltd ....C...... 888 557-8368
  Richardson *(G-17419)*

HOUSEWARES, ELECTRIC: Grills Or Griddles

CPM Acquisition Corp ....F...... 972 243-8070
  Carrollton *(G-2719)*

TSA Griddle Systems Inc ....F...... 972 243-8070
  Carrollton *(G-2841)*

HOUSEWARES, ELECTRIC: Heaters, Sauna

Lady Hlth Ftness- Rockwall Inc ....F...... 972 906-0400
  Carrollton *(G-2877)*

HOUSEWARES, ELECTRIC: Heating Units, Electric Appliances

Backer Ehp Inc ....F...... 615 556-7501
  Laredo *(G-13865)*

HOUSEWARES, ELECTRIC: Heating, Bsbrd/Wall, Radiant Heat

Haydon Corporation ....F...... 972 641-6400
  Grand Prairie *(G-7888)*

HOUSEWARES, ELECTRIC: Massage Machines, Exc Beauty/Barber

Body Brother Inc ....F...... 713 487-8227
  Houston *(G-8935)*

Titan Chair LLC ....E...... 888 848-2630
  Carrollton *(G-2835)*

HOUSEWARES: Dishes, Plastic

ITW Minigrip Inc ....C...... 830 372-4400
  Seguin *(G-18845)*

HOUSEWARES: Food Dishes & Utensils, Pressed & Molded Pulp

Aloterra Packaging LLC ....F...... 440 689-0986
  The Woodlands *(G-19824)*

HOUSEWARES: Toothpicks, Wood

Dial-A-Pick Co ....E...... 210 736-1901
  San Antonio *(G-18053)*

HOUSINGS: Business Machine, Sheet Metal

Data Matique Properties LP ....C...... 972 272-3446
  Garland *(G-7476)*

HUB CAPS: Automobile, Stamped Metal

Stemco Products Inc ....F...... 903 758-9981
  Longview *(G-14312)*

HUMIDIFIERS & DEHUMIDIFIERS

Munters Corporation ....D...... 210 651-5018
  Selma *(G-18878)*

HYDRAULIC EQPT REPAIR SVC

Airdraulics ....G...... 432 381-7867
  Odessa *(G-15906)*

Diamond Hydraulics Inc ....E...... 409 440-8032
  Hitchcock *(G-8337)*

Hannon Hydraulics Inc ....D...... 972 438-2870
  Irving *(G-13048)*

Hot Hydraulics Inc ....E...... 713 722-7200
  Houston *(G-10212)*

Houston Mfg Specialty Co Inc ....E...... 281 888-4635
  Houston *(G-10239)*

Hurst Hydraulics Inc ....F...... 713 863-0340
  Houston *(G-10288)*

Hydradyne LLC ....F...... 210 661-4378
  San Antonio *(G-18177)*

Hydradyne Hydraulics Inc ....E...... 713 937-8111
  Houston *(G-10294)*

Hyseco Inc ....E...... 713 991-4240
  Houston *(G-10307)*

Liberty Fluid Power Inc ....E...... 972 623-0927
  Grand Prairie *(G-7911)*

Northeast Texas Hydraulics ....F...... 903 582-2692
  Sulphur Springs *(G-19593)*

HYDRAULIC FLUIDS: Synthetic Based

Economy Mud Products Company ....D...... 800 231-2066
  Houston *(G-9580)*

Hard Rubber & Molded Rubber Prdts

Elgi Rubber Company LLC ....E...... 830 875-5539
  Luling *(G-14561)*

M Tripple Oil Tool Inc ....E...... 432 337-1452
  Odessa *(G-16067)*

Marian Fort Worth Inc ....E...... 817 332-6151
  Fort Worth *(G-6811)*

Oil States Industries Inc ....E...... 512 556-5471
  Lampasas *(G-13835)*

Supreme Manufacturing Company ....F...... 281 447-3153
  Houston *(G-12123)*

ICE

Country Fresh LLC ....B...... 616 243-0173
  Dallas *(G-4175)*

Dean Foods Company ....B...... 817 684-3600
  Fort Worth *(G-6581)*

Debes Ice Company ....F...... 409 835-4431
  Beaumont *(G-1881)*

Emergency Ice Inc ....F...... 972 988-0577
  Dallas *(G-4318)*

Hipple Ice Company ....F...... 325 692-0101
  Abilene *(G-50)*

Kfl Promotions LLC ....E...... 817 822-9116
  Colleyville *(G-3216)*

Nacogdoches Coca Cola Btlg Co ....D...... 936 564-0268
  Nacogdoches *(G-15704)*

Polar Ice Inc ....F...... 979 830-1954
  Brenham *(G-2269)*

Pure Party Ice LP ....E...... 210 223-6400
  San Antonio *(G-18401)*

Reddy Ice Corporation ....E...... 956 428-6666
  Harlingen *(G-8199)*

Reddy Ice Corporation ....F...... 956 723-3838
  Laredo *(G-13923)*

Reddy Ice Corporation ....E...... 940 686-5259
  Pilot Point *(G-16727)*

Reddy Ice Corporation ....E...... 210 532-3232
  San Antonio *(G-18415)*

Reddy Ice Corporation ....F...... 361 578-3032
  Victoria *(G-20299)*

Reddy Ice Corporation ....D...... 972 296-4271
  Dallas *(G-4872)*

Reddy Ice Corporation ....E...... 713 691-2773
  Houston *(G-11574)*

Reddy Ice Corporation ....F...... 214 526-6740
  Dallas *(G-4873)*

Reddy Ice Corporation ....F...... 432 943-4541
  Monahans *(G-15614)*

Reddy Ice Corporation ....D...... 214 526-6740
  Dallas *(G-4874)*

Reddy Ice Corporation ....F...... 361 289-0276
  Corpus Christi *(G-3607)*

Reddy Ice Corporation ....F...... 817 654-9020
  Fort Worth *(G-6948)*

Reddy Ice Corporation ....E...... 915 532-2495
  El Paso *(G-5933)*

Reddy Ice Group Inc ....G...... 254 753-7378
  Jefferson *(G-13287)*

Reddy Ice Group Inc ....E...... 903 732-3231
  Powderly *(G-17200)*

Reddy Ice Group Inc ....F...... 972 263-4359
  Dallas *(G-4875)*

Reddy Ice Group Inc ....E...... 877 295-0024
  Dallas *(G-4876)*

ICE CREAM & ICES WHOLESALERS

Blue Bell Creameries LP ....F...... 806 749-9005
  Lubbock *(G-14375)*

Dean Foods Company ....B...... 817 684-3600
  Fort Worth *(G-6581)*

ICE WHOLESALERS

Reddy Ice Group Inc ....E...... 877 295-0024
  Dallas *(G-4876)*

Reddy Ice Group Inc ....G...... 254 753-7378
  Jefferson *(G-13287)*

IDENTIFICATION PLATES

Cooper Crouse Hinds LLC ....E...... 713 280-3400
  Houston *(G-9304)*

Marking Services Inc ....E...... 817 419-0061
  Arlington *(G-728)*

IDENTIFICATION TAGS, EXC PAPER

Beaed LP ....D...... 281 331-2035
  Alvin *(G-354)*

IGNEOUS ROCK: Crushed & Broken

Gulf Coast Limestone Inc ....F...... 281 474-4124
  Seabrook *(G-18785)*

Yarrington Road Materials ....D...... 512 754-3573
  Kyle *(G-13689)*

IGNITION APPARATUS & DISTRIBUTORS

A & B Auto Electric Inc ....F...... 713 928-3219
  Houston *(G-8422)*

IGNITION CONTROLS: Gas Appliance

Forney Corporation ....E...... 972 458-6100
  Addison *(G-126)*

IGNITION SYSTEMS: High Frequency

Ignition Systems & Contrls Inc ....E...... 432 697-6472
  Midland *(G-15251)*

Msdp Group LLC ....F...... 915 857-5200
  El Paso *(G-5889)*

IGNITION SYSTEMS: Internal Combustion Engine

C C Battery Company Inc ....E...... 361 882-5561
  Corpus Christi *(G-3492)*

INCENSE

Dipper Inc ....G 281 585-8400
Alvin (G-359)

INCINERATORS

Incinerator International Inc ....F 713 227-1466
Houston (G-10336)

Texas Incinerator Co Inc ....F 432 687-5045
Midland (G-15436)

INDL & PERSONAL SVC PAPER WHOLESALERS

Ace Carton & Tape of Laredo ....F 956 727-1600
Laredo (G-13854)

Custom Ppr Tube Southwest Inc ....F 817 385-5367
Arlington (G-656)

Performance Label Company ....F 806 763-1663
Lubbock (G-14461)

Texas Tissue Converting LLC ....D 281 821-0429
Houston (G-12257)

Zapco Inc ....E 512 237-5521
Smithville (G-18980)

INDL & PERSONAL SVC PAPER, WHOL: Bags, Paper/Disp Plastic

Smurfit Kappa Bates LLC ....C 817 498-3200
North Richland Hills (G-15881)

Smurfit Kappa Bates LLC ....D 210 436-7777
Von Ormy (G-20352)

INDL & PERSONAL SVC PAPER, WHOL: Boxes, Corrugtd/Solid Fiber

Age Industries Ltd ....E 956 399-8279
San Benito (G-18654)

Fairbanks Packaging LLC ....G 817 849-1366
Grand Prairie (G-7869)

Guardian Packaging Inds LP ....E 214 349-1500
Garland (G-7507)

International Paper Company ....D 806 381-0121
Amarillo (G-439)

International Paper Company ....C 956 682-9406
McAllen (G-14874)

Pactiv LLC ....E 817 608-9009
Arlington (G-747)

Supplyone Tucson Inc ....G 915 860-9911
El Paso (G-5988)

Weyerhaeuser Company ....C 972 641-3891
Grand Prairie (G-7992)

INDL & PERSONAL SVC PAPER, WHOL: Boxes, Paperbrd/Plastic

D & S Container Inc ....D 214 637-7957
Dallas (G-4199)

INDL & PERSONAL SVC PAPER, WHOL: Container, Paper/Plastic

Hoover Mtls Hdlg Group Inc ....D 800 844-8683
Houston (G-10205)

INDL & PERSONAL SVC PAPER, WHOL: Paper, Wrap/Coarse/Prdts

Imperial Bag & Paper Co LLC ....E 713 223-5050
Houston (G-10334)

Miller Paper Company ....E 806 353-0317
Amarillo (G-502)

Orora North America ....E 972 724-2828
Grapevine (G-8050)

Orora Packaging Solutions ....D 281 517-8600
Houston (G-11193)

Paper Source Inc ....G 469 304-5168
Plano (G-16965)

INDL & PERSONAL SVC PAPER, WHOLESALE: Cardboard & Prdts

Master Fibers Inc ....D 915 544-2299
El Paso (G-5868)

INDL & PERSONAL SVC PAPER, WHOLESALE: Disposable

Republic Plastics Ltd ....E 830 557-5574
Mc Queeney (G-14830)

INDL & PERSONAL SVC PAPER, WHOLESALE: Paper Tubes & Cores

Caraustar Industrial and Con ....E 409 898-6600
Silsbee (G-18950)

Sonoco Products Company ....E 817 461-5616
Irving (G-13184)

INDL & PERSONAL SVC PAPER, WHOLESALE: Shipping Splys

Kenneth Fox Supply Company ....C 956 682-6176
McAllen (G-14882)

Welbor Technology Inc ....F 713 980-2345
Houston (G-12627)

INDL EQPT CLEANING SVCS

Boatman Industries Inc ....E 713 641-6006
Houston (G-8932)

Industrial Spclty Svcs USA LLC ....F 713 987-9117
Deer Park (G-5280)

Jimmy Smart ....E 432 381-5450
Odessa (G-16039)

INDL EQPT SVCS

Bae Systems Resolution Inc ....E 713 868-7700
Houston (G-8789)

BC Oilfield Services Inc ....F 361 573-6354
Victoria (G-20245)

Brim Laundry Machinery Co Inc ....E 214 630-4517
Hutchins (G-12863)

Cates Machine Shop Inc ....F 903 592-2015
Tyler (G-20065)

Chromalloy Component Svcs Inc ....E 210 331-2300
San Antonio (G-18006)

Commercial Diesl Parts Svc Ltd ....E 830 372-1594
Seguin (G-18830)

Csi Compressco Sub Inc ....A 432 563-1170
Midland (G-15185)

D & L Quality Painting Inc ....E 281 458-3588
Houston (G-9387)

Drilling Supply and Mfg Inc ....E 512 243-1986
Austin (G-1102)

Enerflex Services Inc ....E 281 345-9300
Houston (G-9633)

Energy Retrofitters Inc ....F 817 319-2796
Fort Worth (G-6614)

Evans Enterprises Inc ....D 325 235-1776
Abilene (G-40)

Fisher-Rosemount Systems Inc ....A 512 835-2190
Round Rock (G-17657)

Flo Pura Corp ....E 281 320-9547
Spring (G-19122)

G & G Machine & Maintenance ....E 713 673-4235
Kingwood (G-13644)

Gh Cranes & Components USA Inc ....E 972 563-8333
Terrell (G-19735)

Hunt Engine Incorporated ....D 713 721-9400
Houston (G-10279)

M Tripple Oil Tool Inc ....E 432 337-1452
Odessa (G-16067)

McGill Maintenance Partnr Ltd ....C 979 233-5438
Freeport (G-7203)

Mepco Enterprises Inc ....E 713 943-9240
Houston (G-10830)

Multiple Systems Inc ....E 806 373-7073
Amarillo (G-449)

Multiple Systems Inc ....E 806 373-7073
Amarillo (G-450)

Ohmstede Ltd ....D 361 289-1701
Corpus Christi (G-3584)

Rama Fabrication Inc ....E 432 362-9291
Odessa (G-16132)

Rpc Inc ....E 361 289-7088
Corpus Christi (G-3612)

T-3 Energy Services Inc ....F 713 944-5950
Houston (G-12143)

Tcm Investments Inc ....E 432 366-5433
Odessa (G-16173)

United Worth Hydrochem Corp ....F 682 518-6200
Venus (G-20224)

Waukesha-Pearce Industries Inc ....E 512 989-4900
Pflugerville (G-16692)

Wood Group Power Gp LLC ....E 281 828-3500
Houston (G-12686)

INDL GASES WHOLESALERS

Airgas Usa LLC ....F 512 835-0202
Austin (G-902)

Alig LLC ....D 212 626-4936
Houston (G-8538)

Hiland Partners Holdings LLC ....D 713 369-9000
Houston (G-10181)

Matheson Tri-Gas Inc ....C 972 560-5700
Irving (G-13096)

Matheson Tri-Gas Inc ....C 817 551-0550
Fort Worth (G-6817)

INDL MACHINERY & EQPT WHOLESALERS

Air Liquide America LP ....F 409 720-4200
Port Neches (G-17157)

Alamo Industrial Group Inc ....B 210 223-6161
San Antonio (G-17884)

Allied Equipment Inc ....D 432 367-6000
Odessa (G-15912)

Amarillo Gear Company LLC ....C 806 622-1273
Amarillo (G-478)

America Ilsin Tech LLC ....E 972 556-0916
Carrollton (G-2696)

Arlington Brick and Supply Inc ....F 817 460-5511
Arlington (G-624)

Atlantic Blowers LLC ....F 214 233-0280
Dallas (G-3979)

Bae Systems Resolution Inc ....E 713 868-7700
Houston (G-8789)

Bauer Visual Graphics Inc ....F 713 473-5241
Pasadena (G-16394)

Bill West Properties Inc ....E 713 726-0151
Houston (G-8885)

Centex Mechatronics LLC ....E 830 387-4131
New Braunfels (G-15781)

Cobb Carpet Supply Co ....F 214 634-2622
Dallas (G-4133)

Coker Enterprises ....F 903 533-8894
Tyler (G-20069)

Compositech Products Mfg Inc ....E 281 648-3557
Pearland (G-16548)

Consolidated Cotton Gin Co ....D 806 745-1191
Lubbock (G-14396)

Crown Energy Technologies Inc ....F 403 215-5300
Houston (G-9347)

Denny Kincer Inc ....E 806 762-1069
Lubbock (G-14401)

Dover Equipment Inc ....E 713 690-5200
Houston (G-9504)

Elliott Electric Supply Inc ....E 512 246-8001
Round Rock (G-17652)

Emerson Automation Solutions ....B 281 274-4400
Stafford (G-19310)

Endurance Lift Solutions LLC ....C 903 595-8600
Fort Worth (G-6611)

Evans Enterprises Inc ....D 325 235-1776
Abilene (G-40)

Evco Partners LP ....E 409 766-1900
Texas City (G-19793)

Fas Holdings Group LLC ....E 214 343-5300
Dallas (G-4353)

Ford Gin Service Inc ....F 806 745-3433
Lubbock (G-14411)

Forney Corporation ....C 972 458-6100
Addison (G-126)

Gagemaker LP ....E 713 472-7360
Pasadena (G-16445)

Gator Pump Inc ....G 325 643-3502
Brownwood (G-2429)

Hartfiel Automation Inc ....F 972 633-0000
Plano (G-16884)

Hlcl Capital Corporation ....E 972 660-4096
Grand Prairie (G-7892)

Houston Service Industries Inc ....E 713 947-1623
Houston (G-10250)

Inrock Drilling Systems Inc ....E 713 690-5600
Houston (G-10376)

Intelligrated Systems Inc ....B 972 899-9636
Coppell (G-3422)

Intertech Fluid Power Inc ....G 817 329-9733
Grapevine (G-8044)

Jet Machine Works Inc ....E 281 449-0046
Houston (G-10469)

Johnson Tool Company Inc ....E 432 267-7612
Big Spring (G-2084)

Kalamar Industries USA Inc ....D 903 759-5490
White Oak (G-20716)

Knox Jr Leighton ....E 806 327-5420
Tahoka (G-19641)

Kws Manufacturing Company Ltd ....C 817 295-2247
Burleson (G-2586)

Letourneau Tech Amer Inc ....D 903 237-7000
Longview (G-14264)

Employee Codes: A=Over 500 employees, B=251-500
C=101-250, D=51-100, E=20-50, F=10-19, G=9

2021 Harris Texas
Manufacturers Directory

PRODUCT

1525

Link World Trade Inc...............C....... 972 713-8000
Addison (G-145)

M N Gumbert Corporation...........E....... 214 340-8383
Dallas (G-4621)

Marine Services LLC..................E....... 713 923-6688
Houston (G-10765)

Metro-Tex Fabricators Inc..........E....... 713 473-3900
Houston (G-10857)

National Oilwell Varco Inc..........F....... 325 884-2556
Big Lake (G-2060)

National Oilwell Varco Inc..........E....... 361 576-3161
Victoria (G-20287)

National Oilwell Varco LP..........D....... 713 346-7500
Houston (G-10996)

National Oilwell Varco LP..........D....... 713 375-3700
Houston (G-10997)

National Oilwell Varco LP..........D....... 281 599-4700
Houston (G-10998)

National Oilwell Varco LP..........B....... 713 375-3700
Houston (G-11000)

Oft Enterprises Inc...................E....... 713 787-5373
Bellaire (G-2000)

Oil Field Supply Pty Ltd.............F....... 281 877-0049
Houston (G-11152)

Oilwell Hydraulics Inc................F....... 432 334-8580
Odessa (G-16101)

Pacific Resources Intl LLC..........B....... 214 504-3853
McKinney (G-14962)

Parts Krafters Co......................F....... 515 981-4749
Dallas (G-4789)

Patco Machine & Fab Inc............E....... 281 443-2837
Houston (G-11258)

Pgi International Ltd..................B....... 713 466-0056
Houston (G-11316)

Pro-Chem of Dfw Inc.................F....... 817 695-1660
Arlington (G-761)

Ruby Automation LLC................E....... 972 881-9663
Plano (G-16997)

Samson Controls Inc.................F....... 281 383-3677
Baytown (G-1800)

SC Industrial Resource Group........E....... 972 272-4521
Garland (G-7584)

Serva Corporation....................E....... 940 761-3361
Wichita Falls (G-20808)

Sparkler Group Inc...................E....... 936 756-4471
Conroe (G-3365)

Stewart & Stevenson LLC...........D....... 713 751-2700
Houston (G-12062)

Stewart Stevenson Pwr Pdts LLC....C....... 713 751-2600
Houston (G-12065)

Streamline Prod Systems Inc........D....... 800 780-4011
Kountze (G-13673)

Sulta Manufacturing Company.......E....... 903 885-2139
Sulphur Springs (G-19599)

Swarco-Reflex LLC...................E....... 254 562-9879
Mexia (G-15092)

Texas Hydraulic & Eqp Co Inc.......F....... 214 748-7551
Hutchins (G-12872)

Tigerflow Systems LLC..............D....... 214 337-8780
Dallas (G-5093)

Tolbert Electric Motor Company.....F....... 972 272-6541
Garland (G-7603)

Tri Tool Inc............................D....... 281 499-1188
Stafford (G-19387)

Vince Hagan Company...............F....... 214 330-4601
Sunnyvale (G-19615)

Wesco Acquisition Partners Inc......E....... 713 688-5551
Galena Park (G-7386)

Womack Machine Supply Co..........D....... 800 569-9800
Farmers Branch (G-6219)

INDL MACHINERY REPAIR & MAINTENANCE

A&K Industrial Repair LLC...........E....... 281 470-8848
Deer Park (G-5258)

Aggietech Energy Services LLC.......E....... 806 229-6129
Sundown (G-19610)

Ajax Tocco Magnethermic Corp......F....... 903 297-2526
Longview (G-14191)

America Industrial Pdts LLC..........F....... 832 974-4153
Houston (G-8580)

Archrock Inc..........................F....... 432 567-1050
Midland (G-15118)

Archrock Inc..........................D....... 806 669-8900
Pampa (G-16314)

Archrock Inc..........................E....... 361 572-9904
Victoria (G-20239)

B T S Precision Machine..............G....... 903 498-7501
Scurry (G-18782)

Brandt Precision Machining..........F....... 512 339-7251
Austin (G-1005)

Cameron International Corp..........E....... 806 665-1647
Pampa (G-16318)

Cannon Cnon Indus McHining Inc.......G....... 972 293-6278
Lone Oak (G-14179)

Caplingers Crane & Eqp Svc Inc......E....... 817 685-0710
Hurst (G-12841)

Champion Group Inc..................E....... 713 644-2181
Houston (G-9157)

F & R Machine Services Inc..........F....... 214 631-4946
Dallas (G-4350)

Fishing Tool/Crystin Inc.............E....... 432 366-6504
Odessa (G-16002)

Fitz Torque Convertors Inc..........E....... 432 362-3261
Odessa (G-16003)

Flint Energy Services Inc............D....... 903 389-8716
Fairfield (G-6174)

Forklifts USA Inc......................F....... 956 568-9797
Laredo (G-13887)

Fuzzys Indus Mint Mnfacture LP.....D....... 806 273-2818
Borger (G-2179)

Gemstar Inc...........................E....... 432 362-2315
Odessa (G-16013)

H & T Auger Company...............E....... 432 362-4471
Odessa (G-16022)

H C Howell Company.................E....... 432 368-0835
Odessa (G-16023)

Heavy Equipment Maintenance Co......E....... 903 984-9076
Kilgore (G-13557)

Hi-Tech Champion Manufacturing.......E....... 713 644-2181
Houston (G-10172)

Huffman Company Ltd................F....... 432 332-5723
Odessa (G-16028)

Ignition Systems & Contrls Inc.......E....... 432 697-6472
Midland (G-15251)

Jmd Oilfield & Rig Service LLC........E....... 469 261-2415
Odessa (G-16040)

Jmi Machine LLC......................F....... 361 664-2848
Alice (G-219)

Junction Industries LLC...............E....... 817 607-8873
Fort Worth (G-6747)

Markco Machine Works Inc..........E....... 432 362-8921
Odessa (G-16070)

McQueary Industries Inc.............F....... 817 335-1988
Fort Worth (G-6823)

National Crane Cmplnce Inspcto.......888 720-6224
Manvel (G-14735)

Neuman & Esser Usa Inc............E....... 281 497-5113
Katy (G-13428)

Oil Country Manufacturing Inc.......E....... 432 563-8014
Odessa (G-16099)

Omni Contracting....................F....... 972 890-4536
Midlothian (G-15489)

Petroleum Products & Svcs Inc.......F....... 281 448-1000
Tomball (G-19997)

Polsys Services Inc...................F....... 713 999-1100
The Woodlands (G-19903)

Preco Turbine Comprsr Svcs Inc.......C....... 281 821-9620
Houston (G-11397)

Revak Keene Turbomachinery LP.......D....... 281 427-8800
La Porte (G-13787)

Smart Control Systems LLC..........F....... 210 224-4906
San Antonio (G-18480)

Turbine Resources Inc................E....... 817 540-0249
Euless (G-6163)

INDL PATTERNS: Foundry Patternmaking

Aqseptence Group Inc................C....... 651 636-3900
Houston (G-8671)

Superior Pattern Works Inc..........F....... 281 442-1422
Spring (G-19168)

INDL PROCESS INSTR: Transmit, Process Variables

Gauging Systems Inc.................E....... 281 980-3999
Sugar Land (G-19484)

INDL PROCESS INSTRUMENTS: Absorp Analyzers, Infrared, X-Ray

Mo2 Inc................................F....... 214 575-7600
Dallas (G-4682)

INDL PROCESS INSTRUMENTS: Analyzers

Analytical Systems Keco LLC.........F....... 281 255-6537
Houston (G-8637)

Measurementation...................E....... 979 373-9991
Freeport (G-7204)

San Antnio Lghthouse For Blind.......C....... 210 533-5195
San Antonio (G-18444)

Yokogawa Corporation America.......E....... 936 653-2120
Coldspring (G-3168)

INDL PROCESS INSTRUMENTS: Chromatographs

Analytical Instruments Corp..........F....... 713 460-5757
Conroe (G-3256)

INDL PROCESS INSTRUMENTS: Control

Amacs Process Tower Internals.......F....... 713 434-0934
Houston (G-8372)

Contrinex Inc..........................F....... 574 340-7089
Coppell (G-3413)

Powell Industries Inc..................B....... 713 944-6900
Houston (G-11376)

Puffer-Sweiven LP Inc.................E....... 281 240-2000
Stafford (G-19364)

Robbins & Myers Inc.................E....... 936 890-1064
Willis (G-20861)

Supreme Electrical Svcs Inc..........D....... 713 676-2588
Houston (G-12122)

TF Hudgins Holdings Inc..............C....... 713 682-3651
Houston (G-12266)

INDL PROCESS INSTRUMENTS: Controllers, Process Variables

Schneider Electric Usa Inc...........C....... 972 236-0300
Coppell (G-3444)

Tegron Holding LLC...................E....... 903 759-1088
Longview (G-14314)

W-Industries of Louisiana.............F....... 281 921-3067
Houston (G-12589)

W-Industries of Louisiana.............C....... 713 466-9463
Jersey Village (G-13306)

Wellsite Automation..................F....... 432 218-9361
Midland (G-15468)

INDL PROCESS INSTRUMENTS: Data Loggers

Schlumberger Limited.................E....... 713 513-2000
Houston (G-11767)

INDL PROCESS INSTRUMENTS: Digital Display, Process Variables

Micropac Industries Inc...............D....... 972 272-3571
Garland (G-7551)

Newline Interactive Inc...............F....... 972 468-9728
Plano (G-16944)

PMG Digital Inc.......................F....... 806 747-7446
Lubbock (G-14463)

INDL PROCESS INSTRUMENTS: Fluidic Devices, Circuit & Systems

Tecalemit Inc.........................D....... 281 446-7300
Humble (G-12801)

INDL PROCESS INSTRUMENTS: Indl Flow & Measuring

Agar Corporation Inc.................D....... 832 476-5100
Houston (G-8501)

Alpa Precision LLP....................D....... 713 680-8556
Houston (G-8560)

Alpa Precision Mch Works Inc.........E....... 713 680-8556
Houston (G-8561)

Daniel Industries Inc.................E....... 713 467-6000
Houston (G-9401)

Intercorr International Inc............E....... 281 444-2282
Houston (G-10393)

S & A Systems Inc....................F....... 972 722-1009
Rockwall (G-17564)

Thermo Process Instruments LP.......F....... 713 272-0404
Sugar Land (G-19564)

Uson Lp................................E....... 281 671-2000
Houston (G-12504)

INDL PROCESS INSTRUMENTS: Level & Bulk Measuring

Ameri Source Manufacturing Inc.......F....... 903 677-7734
Ben Wheeler (G-2031)

Process Level Technology Ltd.........F....... 281 332-6241
League City (G-13977)

INDL PROCESS INSTRUMENTS: *Manometers*

Rosemount Inc ....E 713 396-8700
  Houston *(G-11664)*

Rosemount Inc ....E 281 240-2000
  Stafford *(G-19372)*

INDL PROCESS INSTRUMENTS: *On-Stream Gas Or Liquid Analysis*

Precision Flow Inc ....F 432 332-0266
  Odessa *(G-16125)*

Valco Instruments Company ....B 713 688-9345
  Houston *(G-12517)*

INDL PROCESS INSTRUMENTS: *Temperature*

Honeywell International Inc ....E 832 252-3500
  Houston *(G-10201)*

Wika Instrument LP ....D 713 475-0022
  Deer Park *(G-5302)*

INDL PROCESS INSTRUMENTS: *Water Quality Monitoring/Cntrl Sys*

AA Flood Masters LLC ....E 409 796-2620
  Beaumont *(G-1847)*

Aquasol Controllers Inc ....E 713 683-6406
  Houston *(G-8673)*

Barton Sprngs E Aquifer Cnsrvt ......F 512 282-8441
  Austin *(G-975)*

Chen Grner Stvens Prtners LLC ....F 512 302-4333
  Austin *(G-1046)*

G2 Restoration LLC ....E 469 296-4275
  McKinney *(G-14945)*

GK Techstar LLC ....E 361 289-6825
  Corpus Christi *(G-3536)*

Hoffland Environmental Inc ....E 936 856-4515
  Conroe *(G-3306)*

INDL SPLYS WHOLESALERS

Able Supply Co ....F 713 926-9623
  Houston *(G-8448)*

Aft Industries Inc ....E 972 988-1999
  Mansfield *(G-14654)*

Alamo Industrial Group Inc ....B 210 223-6161
  San Antonio *(G-17884)*

Blp Settlement Company ....D 713 674-2266
  Houston *(G-8916)*

Bowie Industries Incorporated ....E 940 872-1106
  Bowie *(G-2192)*

Chep (usa) Inc ....E 806 577-4447
  Lubbock *(G-14392)*

E & E Engine Machine and Parts ......G 210 225-1141
  San Antonio *(G-18077)*

Ed Prince Enterprises Inc ....F 806 274-7178
  Borger *(G-2177)*

Energy Valve & Supply Co LLC ....F 713 675-7525
  Houston *(G-9638)*

Larry & Matt Inc ....D 806 665-4418
  Pampa *(G-16326)*

M & R USA ....F 281 497-8973
  Houston *(G-10717)*

Maass Flanges Corporation ....E 713 329-5500
  Houston *(G-10729)*

McAllen Bag & Supply Company ....F 956 686-6571
  McAllen *(G-14887)*

MRC Global (us) Inc ....E 432 620-0059
  Midland *(G-15307)*

Newinn Inc ....F 713 473-8188
  Pasadena *(G-16488)*

North American Trade Corp ....F 936 588-1010
  Montgomery *(G-15637)*

Odessa Babbitt Bearing Company .....E 432 366-2836
  Odessa *(G-16095)*

Qfc Industries Inc ....F 817 640-2151
  Arlington *(G-763)*

Raider Manufacturing Ltd ....D 806 762-3227
  Lubbock *(G-14470)*

Richardson Trident Company LLC ......D 972 231-5176
  Richardson *(G-17390)*

River City Manufacturing Inc ....F 512 335-5194
  Bertram *(G-2053)*

Rom Industrial Inc ....F 915 875-1186
  El Paso *(G-5945)*

Safety-Kleen Systems Inc ....B 800 669-5740
  Richardson *(G-17392)*

Samco Enterprises Inc ....E 281 443-6505
  Houston *(G-11737)*

Sentry Supply Inc ....F 409 840-4800
  Beaumont *(G-1948)*

Steven-Sharon Corporation ....D 409 744-4538
  Galveston *(G-7409)*

Texas Pmw Inc ....D 713 679-7900
  Houston *(G-12245)*

TF Hudgins Holdings Inc ....C 713 682-3651
  Houston *(G-12266)*

Tool-Flo Manufacturing Inc ....C 713 941-1080
  Houston *(G-12317)*

Tooling Technologies Mfg LLC ....F 713 722-8501
  Houston *(G-12320)*

W R Meadows Inc ....E 817 834-1969
  Fort Worth *(G-7113)*

Wilbert Funeral Services Inc ....E 972 875-9605
  Ennis *(G-6123)*

INDL SPLYS, WHOL: *Fasteners, Incl Nuts, Bolts, Screws, Etc*

Beaumont Bolt & Gasket Inc ....E 409 838-6304
  Beaumont *(G-1859)*

Colgan-Wilson Metals LLC ....F 409 882-9296
  Beaumont *(G-1873)*

Dale Company Inc ....F 713 928-3437
  Houston *(G-9398)*

Han-Boone International Inc ....F 817 838-5196
  Fort Worth *(G-6686)*

Hillman Group Inc ....D 903 592-2826
  Tyler *(G-20099)*

Northwest Fastener and Sup Inc ....F 281 921-7880
  Houston *(G-11080)*

Rayson Company ....F 713 680-0540
  Houston *(G-11555)*

Sigma Fasteners Inc ....D 281 214-8800
  Houston *(G-11885)*

South Texas Bolt & Fitting Inc ....E 713 673-5376
  Houston *(G-11966)*

Southwest Metrics Inc ....F 817 281-7697
  Fort Worth *(G-7004)*

Tricor Industrial Inc ....E 936 273-2661
  Conroe *(G-3373)*

US Bolt Manufacturing Inc ....D 713 726-1000
  Houston *(G-12482)*

Zero Products Inc ....E 713 675-0123
  Houston *(G-12726)*

INDL SPLYS, WHOLESALE: *Abrasives*

Industrial Diamond Products Co ....F 713 991-1600
  Houston *(G-10350)*

M N Gumbert Corporation ....E 214 340-8383
  Dallas *(G-4621)*

Scot Hone Corporation ....D 903 639-2551
  Lone Star *(G-14184)*

INDL SPLYS, WHOLESALE: *Abrasives & Adhesives*

Angelo Bolt and Indus Sup Inc ....E 325 655-0075
  San Angelo *(G-17776)*

INDL SPLYS, WHOLESALE: *Adhesives, Tape & Plasters*

Concote Corporation ....C 214 956-0077
  Coppell *(G-3412)*

Concote Corporation ....F 903 581-0697
  Tyler *(G-20070)*

INDL SPLYS, WHOLESALE: *Bearings*

Multiple Systems Inc ....E 806 373-7073
  Amarillo *(G-449)*

Multiple Systems Inc ....E 806 373-7073
  Amarillo *(G-450)*

P&H Sales Ltd ....E 817 468-3850
  Arlington *(G-745)*

Panhandle Packing & Gasket Inc ....E 806 763-2801
  Lubbock *(G-14456)*

Purvis Industries LLC ....D 214 358-5500
  Dallas *(G-4837)*

Rolltex Inc ....G 432 570-7576
  Midland *(G-15388)*

Vaughan Investments Inc ....F 956 686-3725
  McAllen *(G-14916)*

INDL SPLYS, WHOLESALE: *Bottler Splys*

CKS Packaging Inc ....E 214 358-2441
  Dallas *(G-4125)*

Ringwood Containers LP ....E 817 625-7214
  Fort Worth *(G-6960)*

INDL SPLYS, WHOLESALE: *Filters, Indl*

Champion Process Inc ....F 281 953-9000
  Houston *(G-9159)*

Complete Tchncal Rprsnttion In ....E 972 621-1111
  Carrollton *(G-2718)*

Compositech Products Mfg Inc ....E 281 648-3557
  Pearland *(G-16548)*

Knight Corporation ....E 281 933-5363
  Houston *(G-10546)*

Procam Controls Inc ....E 972 422-1212
  Plano *(G-16979)*

Sparkler Group Inc ....E 936 756-4471
  Conroe *(G-3365)*

INDL SPLYS, WHOLESALE: *Fittings*

Crown To Ground Supply Inc ....F 936 588-7457
  Magnolia *(G-14599)*

Kdr Supply Inc ....F 936 334-1353
  Liberty *(G-14120)*

INDL SPLYS, WHOLESALE: *Gaskets*

Buffalo Seal and Gasket Co ....F 713 694-9003
  Houston *(G-9011)*

C T Gasket & Polymer Co Inc ....E 713 856-8667
  Houston *(G-9034)*

Eagle Gasket and Packing Co ....E 713 290-8811
  Tomball *(G-19975)*

Gasket Service Inc ....F 432 332-0853
  Odessa *(G-16011)*

John Crane Inc ....D 281 474-1700
  Pasadena *(G-16464)*

Santech Industries LLC ....E 817 589-1212
  Irving *(G-13172)*

Stainless Mfg & Seals Svc ....G 806 795-8932
  Lubbock *(G-14486)*

INDL SPLYS, WHOLESALE: *Gaskets & Seals*

Leader Gasket Technologies Inc ....D 281 542-0600
  La Porte *(G-13766)*

ROC Industries Inc ....E 713 468-7743
  Houston *(G-11647)*

Texas Precision Polymers Inc ....G 936 588-4333
  Conroe *(G-3371)*

INDL SPLYS, WHOLESALE: *Hydraulic & Pneumatic Pistons/Valves*

Bridgestone Hosepower LLC ....E 432 367-4673
  Odessa *(G-15944)*

Macaulay Controls Company ....F 281 282-0100
  Webster *(G-20640)*

Olaer Usa Inc ....F 713 937-8900
  Houston *(G-11167)*

Rays Flow Control LLC ....F 832 827-3427
  Houston *(G-11554)*

INDL SPLYS, WHOLESALE: *Mill Splys*

RSC Acquisitions ....D 713 222-2251
  Houston *(G-11690)*

INDL SPLYS, WHOLESALE: *Pipeline Wrappings, Anti-Corrosive*

Bb Chemicals Inc ....E 432 381-2595
  Odessa *(G-15929)*

INDL SPLYS, WHOLESALE: *Plastic Bottles*

Prime Products Inc ....D 979 743-6555
  Schulenburg *(G-18777)*

INDL SPLYS, WHOLESALE: *Power Transmission, Eqpt & Apparatus*

Standard Industrial Pdts Co ....E 281 280-0147
  Webster *(G-20647)*

INDL SPLYS, WHOLESALE: *Rubber Goods, Mechanical*

Ghx Industrial LLC ....E 409 832-3461
  Beaumont *(G-1898)*

Indian Industries LP ....F 817 265-6731
  Arlington *(G-704)*

Employee Codes: A=Over 500 employees, B=251-500
C=101-250, D=51-100, E=20-50, F=10-19, G=9

2021 Harris Texas
Manufacturers Directory

PRODUCT

1527

US Machinery Parts Sales Inc .... E 972 551-3551
  Mesquite *(G-15084)*

INDL SPLYS, WHOLESALE: Seals

Champion Group Inc .... E 713 644-2181
  Houston *(G-9157)*

Eagleburgmann Industries LP .... E 713 939-9515
  Houston *(G-9567)*

Eagleburgmann Industries LP .... E 979 265-2320
  Clute *(G-3153)*

Texas Seal Supply Co Inc .... F 817 640-1193
  Arlington *(G-794)*

INDL SPLYS, WHOLESALE: Signmaker Eqpt & Splys

A 1 Distributors Sign Supply .... D 432 682-0083
  Midland *(G-15100)*

INDL SPLYS, WHOLESALE: Springs

Newcomb Spring Corp .... E 972 241-6781
  Dallas *(G-4732)*

INDL SPLYS, WHOLESALE: Sprockets

Martin Sprocket & Gear Inc .... D 214 428-2191
  Dallas *(G-4641)*

INDL SPLYS, WHOLESALE: Tanks, Pressurized

Alig LLC .... D 212 626-4936
  Houston *(G-8538)*

Chem Fabrication LLC .... D 979 265-6600
  Clute *(G-3149)*

INDL SPLYS, WHOLESALE: Tools

Clover Group Inc .... E 915 590-2525
  El Paso *(G-5698)*

Daco Abrasives .... E 713 923-4664
  Houston *(G-9390)*

INDL SPLYS, WHOLESALE: Tools, NEC

AGM Tools Inc .... F 832 499-6090
  Houston *(G-8503)*

INDL SPLYS, WHOLESALE: Valves & Fittings

American Valve Hydrant Mfg Co .... C 409 832-7721
  Beaumont *(G-1853)*

Bray International Inc .... C 281 894-7979
  Houston *(G-8979)*

Cameron International Corp .... D 713 946-2122
  Houston *(G-9061)*

Charbonneau Industries Inc .... F 770 664-4319
  Houston *(G-9163)*

Continental Nh3 Pdts Co Inc .... D 214 741-6083
  Dallas *(G-4160)*

Dresser LLC .... D 281 884-1000
  Deer Park *(G-5271)*

Flow-Tek Inc .... D 832 912-2300
  Houston *(G-9809)*

Forged Components Inc .... C 281 441-4088
  Humble *(G-12767)*

Hoerbiger Service Inc .... E 281 442-2497
  Houston *(G-10191)*

Industrial Mill Maint Sup Inc .... E 800 537-1218
  Wake Village *(G-20486)*

Isco Industries Inc .... E 817 477-2900
  Mansfield *(G-14683)*

Johnson Tool Company Inc .... E 432 267-7612
  Big Spring *(G-2084)*

Ladish Valve Company LLC .... D 281 880-8560
  Houston *(G-10585)*

Metro-Tex Fabricators Inc .... E 713 473-3900
  Houston *(G-10857)*

Morsco Supply LLC .... F 903 234-2183
  Longview *(G-14282)*

Newco Valves LLC .... D 281 325-0041
  Stafford *(G-19359)*

Nibco Inc .... B 936 564-8321
  Nacogdoches *(G-15706)*

North Shore Supply Company Inc .... C 713 453-3533
  Houston *(G-11076)*

Progressive Sales Inc .... E 432 333-6631
  Odessa *(G-16127)*

Samson Controls Inc .... F 281 383-3677
  Baytown *(G-1800)*

Scada Products LLC .... E 888 649-4283
  Fort Worth *(G-6975)*

Sivalls Inc .... D 432 337-3571
  Odessa *(G-16153)*

Taylor Oil Inc .... F 806 948-4166
  Sunray *(G-19622)*

Tiger Valve Houston Co LLC .... F 281 227-9911
  Houston *(G-12291)*

Trupply LLC .... F 281 516-8100
  Houston *(G-12386)*

Tsi Flow Products Inc .... F 903 984-2870
  Kilgore *(G-13597)*

Vanzandt Controls .... G 806 655-9367
  Canyon *(G-2676)*

INDL TRUCK REPAIR SVCS

Ranger Lift Trucks LLC .... F 281 424-2111
  Baytown *(G-1832)*

INDUCTORS

Abracon LLC .... F 512 371-6159
  Spicewood *(G-19090)*

Ipdisplays LLC .... F 214 453-3570
  Allen *(G-278)*

INDUSTRIAL & COMMERCIAL EQPT INSPECTION SVCS

Hmt LLC .... E 281 681-7000
  Shenandoah *(G-18897)*

INFANTS' WEAR STORES

Shelbis Stuff Inc .... F 903 450-1300
  Greenville *(G-8091)*

INFORMATION BUREAU SVCS

Arcturus Corporation .... F 214 720-0075
  Dallas *(G-3963)*

Pfizer Inc .... D 817 491-8400
  Roanoke *(G-17494)*

INFORMATION RETRIEVAL SERVICES

Alpha Tech International Inc .... A 281 240-8989
  Stafford *(G-19284)*

Cypress Telecommunications .... E 281 449-4000
  Spring *(G-19205)*

Daegis Inc .... E 214 584-6400
  Irving *(G-12988)*

Defense Solutions Group Inc .... F 800 382-7571
  Cleburne *(G-3087)*

Oil & Gas Consultants Intl Inc .... D 832 426-1200
  Katy *(G-13374)*

Shopper .... G 940 872-6186
  Bowie *(G-2201)*

INFORMATION SVCS: Consumer

Absolute Cmmnctons Ntwrk Slton .... E 361 888-6776
  Corpus Christi *(G-3464)*

TM Luckett Enterprises LLC .... F 866 216-7278
  Houston *(G-12307)*

INGOT, EXTRUSION: Extrusion ingot, aluminum: rolling mills

Custom Extrusions Holdings LLC .... F 972 442-7200
  Wylie *(G-20931)*

INK OR WRITING FLUIDS

Electroninks Writeables Inc .... F 512 766-7555
  Austin *(G-1120)*

Inkjet Inc .... E 936 856-6600
  Willis *(G-20849)*

Quantum Ink Company .... F 713 688-2288
  Houston *(G-11506)*

INK: Printing

Alx Imaging LLC .... E 210 651-5000
  Seguin *(G-18824)*

Electroninks Incorporated .... E 512 766-7555
  Austin *(G-1119)*

Flint Group US LLC .... E 214 638-6700
  Dallas *(G-4370)*

Impression Inks Ltd .... F 817 590-9711
  Fort Worth *(G-6717)*

Inkjet Inc .... D 936 856-6600
  Willis *(G-20848)*

Inkjet Inc .... E 936 856-6600
  Willis *(G-20849)*

INX International Ink Co .... E 817 375-0075
  Arlington *(G-707)*

MPS Group .... F 210 344-0332
  San Antonio *(G-18322)*

Ncc Nano LLC .... E 512 491-9500
  Austin *(G-1362)*

Sun Chemical Corporation .... E 972 647-1641
  Grand Prairie *(G-7977)*

Sun Chemical Corporation .... D 972 270-6735
  Dallas *(G-5022)*

Top Level Printing Ink Inc .... F 214 267-9010
  Dallas *(G-5101)*

Toyo Ink America LLC .... E 979 778-1538
  Bryan *(G-2513)*

Wikoff Color Corporation .... F 972 647-1371
  Grand Prairie *(G-7994)*

INSECTICIDES & PESTICIDES

Energetic Solutions LLC .... F 512 382-6864
  Austin *(G-860)*

Insect Control Solutions Inc .... E 832 299-2400
  Spring *(G-19134)*

Rchemco Inc .... F 817 791-7304
  Dallas *(G-4864)*

Ssi Maxim Company Inc .... G 903 984-5600
  Kilgore *(G-13593)*

INSPECTION & TESTING SVCS

Acuren Inspection Inc .... A 281 228-0000
  La Porte *(G-13716)*

Applied Consultants Inc .... E 903 643-0956
  Longview *(G-14196)*

Boeing Company .... B 281 244-3056
  Houston *(G-8943)*

Fehrs Industrial Mfg LLC .... D 432 758-0068
  Seminole *(G-18883)*

Fesco Ltd .... F 325 392-3773
  Ozona *(G-16283)*

Global Remote Technologies LLC .... E 888 381-3222
  Spring *(G-19125)*

Gray Green Biomedical Svcs LLC .... G 832 288-5958
  Pearland *(G-16566)*

Infrared Thermal Imaging Inc .... F 361 779-1197
  Kingsville *(G-13628)*

Nigen International LLC .... E 713 956-8022
  Houston *(G-11053)*

RSI Inspection LLC .... E 325 673-9800
  Abilene *(G-77)*

Surveys & Analysis Inc .... E 508 842-4011
  Houston *(G-12127)*

Victor Nicolle Inc .... F 713 896-4911
  Houston *(G-12566)*

Wells Family Holding Co LLC .... E 903 756-5656
  Linden *(G-14137)*

INSTRUMENTS & ACCESSORIES: Surveying

Sharewell LP .... E 281 288-2560
  Houston *(G-11845)*

Sonardyne Inc .... F 281 890-2120
  Houston *(G-11950)*

INSTRUMENTS & METERS: Measuring, Electric

Schlumberger Limited .... E 713 513-2000
  Houston *(G-11767)*

Schlumberger Technology Corp .... C 281 285-8500
  Sugar Land *(G-19549)*

Yokogawa Corporation America .... E 281 340-3800
  Sugar Land *(G-19576)*

INSTRUMENTS, LABORATORY: Analyzers, Automatic Chemical

Astrotech Corporation .... G 512 485-9530
  Webster *(G-20633)*

INSTRUMENTS, LABORATORY: Analyzers, Thermal

Alpha Masurement Solutions LLC .... C 832 456-4100
  Houston *(G-8563)*

Geospace Technologies Corp .... A 713 986-4444
  Houston *(G-9945)*

Geotherm Usa LLC .... F 281 985-9344
  Cypress *(G-3796)*

Van London Company ....E 713 772-6641
Houston (G-12526)

INSTRUMENTS, LABORATORY: Electrophoresis

Helena Laboratories Corp ....B 409 842-3714
Beaumont (G-1901)

INSTRUMENTS, LABORATORY: Gas Analyzing

Servomex Company ....E 281 295-5800
Sugar Land (G-19555)

INSTRUMENTS, LABORATORY: Gas Chromatographic

OI Corporation ....C 979 690-1711
College Station (G-3196)

INSTRUMENTS, LABORATORY: Infrared Analytical

Texas Instruments Incorporated ....B 972 995-2011
Dallas (G-5073)

INSTRUMENTS, LABORATORY: Integrators, Mathematical

First Capital Intl Inc ....G 713 629-4866
Houston (G-9790)

INSTRUMENTS, LABORATORY: Microprobes

Southern Methodist University ....F 214 768-2756
Dallas (G-4988)

INSTRUMENTS, LABORATORY: Protein Analyzers

Texas Best Proteins LP ....E 940 769-2028
Santo (G-18739)

INSTRUMENTS, MEASURING & CNTRG: Plotting, Drafting/Map Rdg

Plotter Depot Corporation ....F 469 608-9747
Rockwall (G-17559)

INSTRUMENTS, MEASURING & CNTRL: Auto Turnstiles

Higuchi International Corp ....E 210 633-2877
Elmendorf (G-6069)

INSTRUMENTS, MEASURING & CNTRL: Geophysical & Meteorological

Accent Environmental Services ....F 936 853-2264
Pollok (G-17090)
Echometer Company ....E 940 767-4334
Wichita Falls (G-20763)
Exile Technologies Corporation ....E 713 343-5662
Houston (G-9725)
Ion Geophysical Corporation ....C 281 933-3339
Houston (G-10413)
Ion Science Inc ....F 877 864-7710
Stafford (G-19332)
Madden Systems Inc ....F 432 332-0255
Odessa (G-16069)
Sercel Inc ....B 281 492-6688
Houston (G-11834)
Stress Engineering Svcs Inc ....E 713 466-1527
Houston (G-12079)
Teledyne Real Time Systems Inc ....E 830 990-2340
Fredericksburg (G-7189)

INSTRUMENTS, MEASURING & CNTRL: Geophysical/Meteorological

3M Company ....B 512 984-2370
Austin (G-870)
Advanced Geosciences Inc ....E 512 335-3338
Austin (G-890)
Fairfield Industries Inc ....C 281 275-7500
Houston (G-9752)
Geophysical Technology Inc ....F 281 222-3078
Bellaire (G-1996)

INSTRUMENTS, MEASURING & CNTRL: Radiation & Testing, Nuclear

Ludlum Measurements Inc ....B 325 235-5494
Sweetwater (G-19633)
Ludlum Measurements Inc ....D 325 235-4276
Sweetwater (G-19635)

INSTRUMENTS, MEASURING & CNTRL: Testing, Abrasion, Etc

Anue Systems Inc ....D 512 600-5400
Austin (G-923)
Centrax International Corp ....E 281 465-0781
Spring (G-19203)
Climax Portable Mch Tls Inc ....F 800 333-8311
Deer Park (G-5265)
Fenner & Associates Inc ....F 281 970-9977
College Station (G-3182)
Management Services Intl ....F 713 333-0200
Houston (G-10744)
Standards Testing Labs Inc ....D 325 651-4946
San Angelo (G-17828)

INSTRUMENTS, MEASURING & CNTRLG: Aircraft & Motor Vehicle

Sims Aviation Inc ....F 972 733-3828
Addison (G-163)

INSTRUMENTS, MEASURING & CNTRLG: Thermometers/Temp Sensors

Sor Inc ....F 409 842-3334
Houston (G-11953)

INSTRUMENTS, MEASURING & CNTRLNG: Press & Vac Ind, Acft Eng

Global Vacuum Systems Inc ....F 800 843-0866
Navasota (G-15736)

INSTRUMENTS, MEASURING & CONTROLLING: Fuel System, Aircraft

Rampak Group Inc ....F 713 678-8898
Houston (G-11537)

INSTRUMENTS, MEASURING & CONTROLLING: Gas Detectors

Brk Brands Inc ....F 915 860-3500
El Paso (G-5673)
Industrial Safety Tech LLC ....A 713 559-9200
The Woodlands (G-19884)
Myramid Analytical Inc ....F 512 288-5093
Austin (G-865)
Otis Instruments Inc ....E 432 563-0007
Midland (G-15332)
Redline Instruments Inc ....F 979 776-7200
College Station (G-3199)
Teledyne Detcon Inc ....C 281 367-4100
The Woodlands (G-19926)

INSTRUMENTS, MEASURING & CONTROLLING: Ion Chambers

Axcelis Technologies Inc ....B 214 377-7298
Richardson (G-17275)

INSTRUMENTS, MEASURING & CONTROLLING: Leak Detection, Liquid

Heitman Laboratories Inc ....F 972 982-2224
Allen (G-273)

INSTRUMENTS, MEASURING & CONTROLLING: Magnetometers

Magnetic Field Effects LLC ....F 713 856-8111
Houston (G-10735)

INSTRUMENTS, MEASURING & CONTROLLING: Reactor Controls, Aux

Bobcat Contracting LLC ....E 432 332-1141
Midland (G-15145)
Macaulay Controls Company ....F 281 282-0100
Webster (G-20640)

Marlin Controls Inc ....F 214 553-5700
Dallas (G-4635)
United Elec Instrmentation Ltd ....D 979 265-1256
Clute (G-3161)

INSTRUMENTS, MEASURING & CONTROLLING: Seismoscopes

Alpha Tech International Inc ....A 281 240-8989
Stafford (G-19284)

INSTRUMENTS, MEASURING & CONTROLLING: Surveying & Drafting

G4 Spatial Technologies LLC ....E 512 447-9879
Austin (G-1176)
True Shot LLC ....F 972 505-0433
Odessa (G-16183)

INSTRUMENTS, MEASURING & CONTROLLING: Ultrasonic Testing

Sonatest Inc ....G 210 697-0335
San Antonio (G-18483)

INSTRUMENTS, MEASURING & CONTROLLING: Weather Tracking

D and C Storm Solutions ....F 281 557-3450
League City (G-13954)

INSTRUMENTS, MEASURING/CNTRLNG: Med Diagnostic Sys, Nuclear

Chca Bayshore LP ....G 713 359-2000
Pasadena (G-16406)
Medical Components of America ....G 830 237-6405
Seguin (G-18851)
On-X Life Technologies Inc ....D 512 832-8548
Austin (G-1384)

INSTRUMENTS, OPTICAL: Coating, Lens

Optex Systems Inc ....E 972 629-1701
Dallas (G-4764)

INSTRUMENTS, OPTICAL: Elements & Assemblies, Exc Ophthalmic

Amorphous Materials Inc ....G 972 494-5624
Garland (G-7436)

INSTRUMENTS, OPTICAL: Lenses, All Types Exc Ophthalmic

Displays & Optical Tech ....E 512 246-6400
Georgetown (G-7648)

INSTRUMENTS, OPTICAL: Sighting & Fire Control

Optex Systems Inc ....D 972 764-5700
Richardson (G-17368)
Optex Systems Holdings Inc ....D 972 764-5700
Richardson (G-17369)

INSTRUMENTS, OPTICAL: Test & Inspection

Ci Systems Inc ....F 805 520-2233
Carrollton (G-2715)
Omega Optics Inc ....F 512 996-8833
Austin (G-1378)

INSTRUMENTS, SURGICAL & MED: Needles & Syringes, Hypodermic

Becton Dickinson and Company ....B 713 839-0753
Houston (G-8849)
Becton Dickinson and Company ....F 210 526-5000
San Antonio (G-17943)

INSTRUMENTS, SURGICAL & MEDICAL: Blood & Bone Work

Celonova Biosciences Inc ....C 210 489-4000
San Antonio (G-17990)
Compass Orthopedic Tech & Pdts ....F 713 995-7010
Houston (G-9257)
Crest Orthopedic Implants LLC ....F 254 931-6996
Georgetown (G-7645)

PRODUCT

Egret Medical Products Inc ....F 214 291-0238
  Garland (G-7484)
Genomics Usa Inc ....F 847 359-1032
  Round Rock (G-17660)
Helena Laboratories Corp ....B 409 842-3714
  Beaumont (G-1901)
Orthofix Inc ....C 214 937-2000
  Lewisville (G-14078)

INSTRUMENTS, SURGICAL & MEDICAL: Blood Pressure

Mediana Technologies Corp ....E 425 406-2262
  San Antonio (G-18289)
Rampak Group Inc ....F 713 678-8898
  Houston (G-11537)

INSTRUMENTS, SURGICAL & MEDICAL: Catheters

B Braun Medical Inc ....A 972 245-2243
  Carrollton (G-2700)
Biomerics LLC ....B 903 677-9166
  Athens (G-821)
Millar Inc ....D 832 667-7000
  Houston (G-10882)

INSTRUMENTS, SURGICAL & MEDICAL: Cystoscopes

CBI Laboratories Inc ....D 972 241-7546
  Fort Worth (G-6497)

INSTRUMENTS, SURGICAL & MEDICAL: Holders, Surgical Needle

Retractable Technologies Inc ....C 972 294-1010
  Little Elm (G-14141)

INSTRUMENTS, SURGICAL & MEDICAL: Inhalation Therapy

Prytime Medical Devices Inc ....F 210 340-0116
  Boerne (G-2132)
Stand By Systems Inc ....D 214 346-2980
  Dallas (G-5002)

INSTRUMENTS, SURGICAL & MEDICAL: Knives

Micro Engineering Inc ....F 936 291-6891
  Huntsville (G-12819)

INSTRUMENTS, SURGICAL & MEDICAL: Lasers, Ophthalmic

Eli-Shir Ltd ....G 281 464-9616
  Houston (G-9601)
Rush Eye Associates Pllc ....E 806 353-0125
  Amarillo (G-460)

INSTRUMENTS, SURGICAL & MEDICAL: Lasers, Surgical

Dermatech International Inc ....E 210 558-1387
  Helotes (G-8236)

INSTRUMENTS, SURGICAL & MEDICAL: Ophthalmic

Alcon Laboratories Inc ....A 817 293-0450
  Fort Worth (G-6363)
Alcon Laboratories Holdg Corp ....A 817 293-0450
  Fort Worth (G-6365)
Alcon Surgical Inc ....A 817 293-0450
  Fort Worth (G-6367)
Alcon Vision LLC ....D 817 293-0450
  Fort Worth (G-6368)
Eyesys Vision Inc ....G 281 885-3800
  Houston (G-9741)
Falcon Pharmaceuticals Ltd ....A 800 343-2133
  Fort Worth (G-6623)
Tracey Technologies Corp ....G 281 445-1666
  Houston (G-12338)

INSTRUMENTS, SURGICAL & MEDICAL: Oxygen Tents

Pan-America Hyperbarics Inc ....F 972 423-0377
  Plano (G-16964)

INSTRUMENTS, SURGICAL/MED: Microsurgical, Exc Electromedical

Lake Region Medical Inc ....C 978 570-6900
  El Paso (G-5838)

INSTRUMENTS: Airspeed

Foxtronics Inc ....F 214 358-4425
  Dallas (G-4375)

INSTRUMENTS: Analytical

A-Vox Systems Inc ....F 210 695-8242
  San Antonio (G-17851)
Alert Technologies Inc ....E 281 326-9900
  Houston (G-8534)
Ambion Diagnostics Inc ....C 512 651-0200
  Austin (G-912)
Analytcal Applied Slutions LLC ....F 281 255-6537
  Houston (G-8635)
Analytical Sensors Instrs LLC ....D 281 565-8818
  Houston (G-8636)
Applied Rigaku Tech Inc ....E 512 225-1796
  Austin (G-1691)
ARC Pressure Data Inc ....F 432 563-2371
  Aubrey (G-846)
Beckman Coulter Inc ....D 714 961-6558
  College Station (G-3177)
Becton Dickinson and Company ....F 210 526-5000
  San Antonio (G-17943)
Bruker Optics Inc ....F 978 439-9899
  Conroe (G-3266)
Daniel Industries Inc ....E 713 467-6000
  Houston (G-9401)
Detectachem Inc ....E 855 573-3537
  Stafford (G-19302)
Expotech USA Inc ....E 281 879-8998
  Houston (G-9728)
Fci Environmental Inc ....E 702 262-3953
  Dallas (G-4356)
Fei Efa Inc ....F 972 792-1644
  Richardson (G-17309)
Green Ocean Sciences Inc ....E 512 200-4505
  Austin (G-1192)
Heath Consultants Incorporated ....C 713 844-1300
  Houston (G-10146)
Helena Laboratories Corp ....B 409 842-3714
  Beaumont (G-1902)
Hempstead Halide Inc ....F 409 572-2505
  Galveston (G-7400)
Horiba Instruments Inc ....D 949 250-4811
  Pasadena (G-16455)
Iris Biotech LLC ....E 512 219-8020
  Austin (G-1244)
Ixrf Inc ....F 512 386-6100
  Austin (G-1246)
Ixrf Systems Inc ....F 512 386-6100
  Austin (G-1247)
Kap Technologies Inc ....F 972 359-7060
  Plano (G-16900)
Kin-Tek Analytical Inc ....G 409 938-3627
  La Marque (G-13709)
Kin-Tek Laboratories Inc ....F 409 938-3627
  La Marque (G-13710)
Life Technologies Corporation ....F 512 721-4857
  Austin (G-1293)
Ludlum Measurements Inc ....B 325 235-5494
  Sweetwater (G-19633)
Mo2 Inc ....E 214 575-7600
  Dallas (G-4682)
National Energetics Inc ....G 512 382-1894
  Round Rock (G-17674)
Raman Systems Inc ....E 512 673-7364
  Austin (G-1451)
Rigaku Americas Corporation ....F 281 362-2300
  The Woodlands (G-19911)
S&M International Co Inc ....E 281 749-8289
  Katy (G-13378)
Shimadzu Scientific Instrs Inc ....F 713 467-1151
  Houston (G-11868)
Spectrasensors Inc ....E 713 466-3172
  Houston (G-12007)
Techcomp (usa) Inc ....F 512 215-8335
  Austin (G-1556)
Tecmag Inc ....F 713 667-8747
  Houston (G-12178)
Testamerica Air Emission Corp ....F 800 394-1194
  Carrollton (G-2828)
Thermo Fisher Scientific Inc ....D 512 251-1525
  Austin (G-1573)

Thermo Fisher Scientific Inc ....F 972 437-3327
  Richardson (G-17410)
Trajan Scientific Americas Inc ....F 512 837-7190
  Pflugerville (G-16689)
Valco Instruments Company ....B 713 688-9345
  Houston (G-12517)
Yokogawa Leisure Analysis Div ....F 281 488-0409
  Houston (G-12718)

INSTRUMENTS: Analyzers, Internal Combustion Eng, Electronic

Wabtec Mfg Solutions LLC ....F 814 449-9619
  Fort Worth (G-7114)

INSTRUMENTS: Analyzers, Radio Apparatus, NEC

Psde LLC ....F 972 429-7160
  Wylie (G-20945)

INSTRUMENTS: Combustion Control, Indl

American Steam Inc ....E 972 442-4499
  Wylie (G-20926)
Dcl America Inc ....F 281 651-5900
  Conroe (G-3290)
Wfms Inc ....E 281 491-2445
  Sugar Land (G-19573)

INSTRUMENTS: Digital Panel Meters, Electricity Measuring

Engie Retail LLC ....E 713 636-1127
  Houston (G-9645)

INSTRUMENTS: Electrolytic Conductivity, Indl

Compass Instruments LLC ....F 832 698-2047
  Tomball (G-19971)

INSTRUMENTS: Endoscopic Eqpt, Electromedical

Apollo Endosurgery Inc ....E 512 279-5100
  West Lake Hills (G-20677)

INSTRUMENTS: Flow, Indl Process

Kam Controls Inc ....E 713 784-0000
  Houston (G-10500)
Mueller Co LLC ....C 956 621-3086
  Brownsville (G-2384)
Omni Flow Computers Inc ....F 281 240-6161
  Sugar Land (G-19522)
Pecofacet (us) Inc ....B 940 325-2575
  Mineral Wells (G-15536)

INSTRUMENTS: Indl Process Control

ABB Inc ....D 713 587-8000
  Houston (G-8443)
Appleton Grp LLC ....D 254 968-6071
  Stephenville (G-19406)
Appleton Grp LLC ....F 214 349-2310
  Dallas (G-3953)
B I Products LLC ....D 972 359-4000
  Allen (G-255)
Bettis Corporation ....C 281 879-2300
  Jersey Village (G-13293)
BI Technology Inc ....E 832 698-8000
  Tomball (G-19967)
Chevas Company LLC ....F 713 225-6595
  Houston (G-9176)
Coastal Flow Measurement Inc ....D 713 477-1956
  Houston (G-9225)
Concept Controls Inc ....F 281 476-4400
  La Porte (G-13730)
Control Products Corporation ....C 972 264-0368
  Grand Prairie (G-7858)
Cosa Xentaur Corporation ....E 631 345-3434
  Houston (G-9328)
Daniel Measurement & Ctrl LLC ....B 713 827-5033
  Houston (G-9402)
Digital Speech Systems Inc ....E 972 235-2999
  Allen (G-262)
Electrolab Inc ....E 210 824-5364
  Boerne (G-2118)
Emerson Electric Co ....E 956 994-1427
  McAllen (G-14857)

Emerson Electric Co................E...... 956 702-2389
San Juan *(G-18673)*
Emerson Electric Co................G...... 713 447-2839
Houston *(G-9613)*
Emerson Electric Co................E...... 281 488-0788
Pearland *(G-16559)*
Emerson Electric Co................C...... 314 553-3695
El Paso *(G-5751)*
Emerson Electric Co................F...... 915 400-3888
El Paso *(G-5752)*
Emerson Electric Co................F...... 956 683-0694
McAllen *(G-14858)*
Emerson Prcess MGT Rgltor Tech ....E...... 972 548-3585
McKinney *(G-14939)*
Emerson Prcess MGT Vlve Atmtn ....D...... 832 261-2400
Pasadena *(G-16426)*
Emerson Process Management ....E...... 281 879-2300
Houston *(G-9614)*
Emerson Process MGT Lllp ....E...... 512 835-2190
Round Rock *(G-17654)*
Endress + Hauser Inc ....C...... 281 867-3400
La Porte *(G-13735)*
Endress + Hauser Inc ....F...... 713 300-6200
Houston *(G-9629)*
Fci Environmental Inc ....E...... 702 262-3953
Dallas *(G-4356)*
Fisher Controls Intl LLC ....B...... 903 868-3200
Sherman *(G-18914)*
Fisher-Rosemount Systems Inc ....B...... 512 418-7400
The Hills *(G-19818)*
Forney Corporation ....E...... 972 458-6100
Addison *(G-126)*
Gagemaker LP ....E...... 713 472-7360
Pasadena *(G-16445)*
Greenslade & Company Inc ....F...... 817 870-8888
Fort Worth *(G-6678)*
Hdi Instruments LLC ....E...... 713 688-8555
Houston *(G-10142)*
Hoffman Controls Corp ....E...... 972 243-7425
Dallas *(G-4461)*
Hpi LLC ....E...... 713 457-7500
Houston *(G-10272)*
Instrument & Valve Services Co ....D...... 281 998-6600
Pasadena *(G-16462)*
Instrument & Valve Services Co ....E...... 281 884-8639
Pasadena *(G-16463)*
Instrument & Valve Services Co ....F...... 713 827-4395
Houston *(G-10381)*
Instrument & Valve Services Co ....F...... 409 840-8400
Beaumont *(G-1908)*
Instrument & Valve Services Co ....F...... 903 753-9922
Longview *(G-14252)*
Integrated Flow Systems LLC ....D...... 512 671-5002
Pflugerville *(G-16676)*
Intrinsic Safety Eqp Texas Inc ....D...... 281 488-0788
Pearland *(G-16571)*
J & J Manufacturing Company ....D...... 409 835-1330
Beaumont *(G-1912)*
Ludlum Measurements Inc ....B...... 325 235-5494
Sweetwater *(G-19633)*
Martin-Decker Totco Inc ....B...... 512 340-5000
Cedar Park *(G-2978)*
Merla LLC ....E...... 281 931-6900
Magnolia *(G-14618)*
Metrix Instrument Co LP ....D...... 281 940-1802
Houston *(G-10854)*
Metrix PMC/Beta ....E...... 713 461-2131
Houston *(G-10855)*
Moore Control Systems Inc ....D...... 281 392-7747
Katy *(G-13372)*
Murphy Fw ....D...... 281 633-4500
Rosenberg *(G-17590)*
Norak Inc ....G...... 281 585-4091
Alvin *(G-374)*
Noshok Inc ....F...... 281 897-6115
Houston *(G-11085)*
NS Controls Inc ....E...... 713 465-7591
Houston *(G-11094)*
Orbital Gas Systems N Amer Inc ....E...... 832 467-1420
Houston *(G-11191)*
Parker-Hannifin Corporation ....E...... 409 924-0300
Houston *(G-11246)*
Peerless Mfg Co ....D...... 214 357-6181
Dallas *(G-4794)*
Petron Industries Inc ....D...... 713 693-8700
Houston *(G-11310)*
Pollok Inc ....A...... 915 592-5700
El Paso *(G-5914)*
R & R Oilfield Services Inc ....D...... 361 289-5892
Corpus Christi *(G-3604)*

R D McMillan Company Inc ....E...... 512 863-0231
Georgetown *(G-7671)*
Rheonics Inc ....E...... 713 364-5427
Sugar Land *(G-19535)*
Robertshaw Controls Company ....C...... 956 831-9000
Brownsville *(G-2402)*
Rochester Gauges LLC ....E...... 972 280-8478
Dallas *(G-4907)*
Rosemunt Tank Gging N Amer Inc ....E...... 281 988-4000
Houston *(G-11665)*
Rus Industrial LLC ....C...... 281 864-9070
Channelview *(G-3033)*
Scada Products LLC ....E...... 888 649-4283
Fort Worth *(G-6975)*
Schenck Process LLC ....D...... 816 891-9300
Houston *(G-11765)*
Schneider Electric Systems USA ....D...... 281 709-1200
Webster *(G-20644)*
Semicon Phtmtrlogy Sltions LLC ....F...... 214 957-0295
Garland *(G-7586)*
Softech Controls Inc ....E...... 713 553-0365
Cypress *(G-3821)*
Sor Inc ....E...... 281 272-5333
Houston *(G-11954)*
Specialty Process Eqp Corp ....D...... 281 812-7732
Humble *(G-12799)*
Technical Automtn Svcs Co Ltd ....D...... 281 474-3232
Seabrook *(G-18792)*
Therm-O-Disc Incorporated ....B...... 915 860-9167
El Paso *(G-6000)*
Thermo Finnigan LLC ....D...... 512 251-1400
Austin *(G-1572)*
Triseal Inc ....F...... 713 589-5380
Kemah *(G-13480)*
Valco Instruments Company ....F...... 713 688-9345
Houston *(G-12518)*
Varo LLC ....B...... 972 840-5506
Garland *(G-7607)*
Ventil USA Inc ....F...... 281 280-0141
Houston *(G-12547)*
Wesco Acquisition Partners Inc ....E...... 713 688-5551
Galena Park *(G-7386)*
Winters Instruments Inc ....F...... 281 880-8607
Houston *(G-12679)*
Xentaur Corporation ....E...... 631 345-3434
Houston *(G-12707)*

INSTRUMENTS: Instrument Relays, All Types

Micropac Industries Inc ....D...... 972 272-3571
Garland *(G-7551)*

INSTRUMENTS: Laser, Scientific & Engineering

Key Scientific Products ....E...... 512 846-1440
Hutto *(G-12882)*

INSTRUMENTS: Liquid Level, Indl Process

Micro-Design Inc ....G...... 972 488-8725
Dallas *(G-4675)*

INSTRUMENTS: Measurement, Indl Process

Flozone Measurement Ltd ....E...... 432 488-2799
Odessa *(G-16005)*
Flozone Measurement Ltd ....E...... 432 488-2799
Odem *(G-15896)*
Glex Inc ....E...... 713 849-4985
Houston *(G-9965)*
Tolteq Group LLC ....D...... 512 331-4241
Cedar Park *(G-2988)*
Vector Systems Inc ....D...... 214 544-9500
McKinney *(G-14985)*
Welker Inc ....D...... 281 491-2331
Sugar Land *(G-19571)*

INSTRUMENTS: Measuring & Controlling

Advanced Energy Industries Inc ....C...... 512 339-7100
Austin *(G-889)*
Ameri Source Manufacturing Inc ....F...... 903 677-7734
Ben Wheeler *(G-2031)*
AMI Investments LLC ....E...... 972 717-5555
Carrollton *(G-2698)*
Angus Measurement Services LP ....F...... 432 332-7200
Odessa *(G-15915)*
Arbin Corporation ....E...... 979 690-2751
College Station *(G-3174)*
Arbin Instruments Inc ....E...... 979 690-2751
College Station *(G-3175)*

Atec Inc ....C...... 281 276-2700
Stafford *(G-19289)*
Automatic Products Corp ....C...... 972 272-6422
Garland *(G-7444)*
Coastal Flow Measurement Inc ....D...... 713 477-1956
Houston *(G-9225)*
Daniel Industries Inc ....E...... 713 467-6000
Houston *(G-9401)*
Design Flex LLC ....F...... 940 825-6629
Nocona *(G-15868)*
Dfw Instrument LLC ....F...... 214 217-7600
Addison *(G-116)*
Draeger Safety Diagnostics Inc ....E...... 972 929-1100
Irving *(G-13003)*
Dsx Access Systems Inc ....E...... 214 553-6140
Dallas *(G-4282)*
Dunns Valve Testers Inc ....F...... 281 350-4767
Spring *(G-19207)*
Ellis Tool & Machine Inc ....E...... 903 546-6540
Tom Bean *(G-19951)*
ESP Enterprises Inc ....D...... 281 444-2377
Houston *(G-9697)*
Fci Environmental Inc ....E...... 702 262-3953
Dallas *(G-4356)*
Freedom Communication Tech Inc ....E...... 844 903-7333
Kilgore *(G-13555)*
Gardner Dnver Wtr Jtting Syste ....C...... 281 448-5800
Houston *(G-9898)*
Global Nucleonics LLC ....F...... 281 578-7900
Houston *(G-9975)*
Higuchi Manufacturing Amer LLC ....C...... 210 633-2877
San Antonio *(G-18167)*
Hilflo LLC ....F...... 936 756-2020
Conroe *(G-3305)*
Horiba Instruments Inc ....E...... 408 730-4772
Austin *(G-1209)*
Inova Geophysical Inc ....E...... 281 568-2000
Sugar Land *(G-19499)*
Kimray Inc ....F...... 936 441-2468
Conroe *(G-3317)*
Kwivik Inc ....F...... 469 424-3144
McKinney *(G-14949)*
Laversab Inc ....E...... 281 325-8300
Sugar Land *(G-19503)*
Ludlum Measurements Inc ....D...... 325 235-1418
Sweetwater *(G-19634)*
Measurement Technologies Ltd ....G...... 817 571-9981
Colleyville *(G-3220)*
Metrix Instrument Co LP ....D...... 281 940-1802
Houston *(G-10854)*
Metrix PMC/Beta ....E...... 713 461-2131
Houston *(G-10855)*
Mo2 Inc ....F...... 214 575-7600
Dallas *(G-4682)*
Murphy Fw ....D...... 281 633-4500
Rosenberg *(G-17590)*
Omron Management Ctr Amer Inc ....E...... 489 724-2899
Dallas *(G-4761)*
Pem-Tech Inc ....G...... 281 494-2079
Sugar Land *(G-19524)*
Quest-TEC Solutions Inc ....E...... 281 240-0440
Houston *(G-11510)*
Reedholm Instruments Co ....E...... 512 869-1935
Georgetown *(G-7674)*
Robert U Neese ....E...... 281 342-2884
Boerne *(G-2134)*
RSD Security Scanners LLC ....E...... 915 590-4441
El Paso *(G-5947)*
Sabio Environmental LLC ....E...... 512 869-0544
Round Rock *(G-17689)*
Safeplex Systems Inc ....F...... 832 582-7029
Houston *(G-11724)*
Shockwatch Inc ....E...... 214 630-9625
Dallas *(G-4957)*
Sunbelt Design & Dev Inc ....D...... 210 227-9162
San Antonio *(G-18511)*
Tdk Rf Solutions Inc ....E...... 512 258-9478
Cedar Park *(G-2987)*
Technical Automtn Svcs Co Ltd ....D...... 281 474-3232
Seabrook *(G-18792)*
Temperture Measurement Systems ....E...... 800 967-6498
Malakoff *(G-14637)*
Teradyne Inc ....D...... 972 231-5384
Plano *(G-17025)*
Texas Sampling Inc ....F...... 361 575-8087
Victoria *(G-20309)*
Thermo Finnigan LLC ....E...... 512 251-1400
Austin *(G-1572)*
Thermocontrol Inc ....E...... 713 780-8600
Houston *(G-12272)*

PRODUCT

Uson Lp ....E 281 671-2000
Houston *(G-12504)*

Welker Inc ....D 281 491-2331
Sugar Land *(G-19571)*

Williamsrdm Inc ....D 817 872-1500
Fort Worth *(G-7148)*

Wireless Seismic Inc ....E 832 532-5080
Stafford *(G-19399)*

INSTRUMENTS: *Measuring Electricity*

Amptec Research Corporation ....F 512 858-4045
Austin *(G-856)*

Arbin Instruments LLC ....E 979 690-2751
College Station *(G-3176)*

Avo USA Inc ....C 214 333-3201
Dallas *(G-3993)*

Compass Metering Solutions ....E 972 834-5479
Greenville *(G-8067)*

Dresser LLC ....C 262 549-2626
Houston *(G-9517)*

Dresser LLC ....E 361 881-8182
Corpus Christi *(G-3517)*

Electronic Power Design Inc ....D 713 923-1191
Houston *(G-9596)*

Envirosense LLC ....E 281 828-8989
Houston *(G-9669)*

Everything Energy LLC ....E 713 537-3000
Houston *(G-9718)*

Exfo America Inc ....E 972 761-9271
Richardson *(G-17307)*

Hdi Instruments LLC ....E 713 688-8555
Houston *(G-10142)*

Horiba Instruments Inc ....E 408 730-4772
Austin *(G-1209)*

Hunnicutt Digital Electronics ....F 817 336-5449
Fort Worth *(G-6709)*

M&I Electric Industries Inc ....D 832 241-6330
Houston *(G-10721)*

National Oilwell Varco Inc ....C 936 444-4000
Conroe *(G-3335)*

Newtek Partners Lp ....D 210 370-8000
San Antonio *(G-18345)*

Optek Technology Inc ....D 972 323-2200
Carrollton *(G-2786)*

Phase Dynamics Inc ....E 972 680-1550
Richardson *(G-17372)*

Plastronics Interconnections ....F 972 258-2580
Irving *(G-13152)*

Reedholm Instruments Co ....E 512 869-1935
Georgetown *(G-7674)*

Reliable Manufacturing Inc ....F 512 255-6572
Round Rock *(G-17684)*

Rohde & Schwarz Usa Inc ....E 469 713-5300
Coppell *(G-3441)*

Schlumberger Technology Corp ....A 281 285-8500
Sugar Land *(G-19542)*

Schweitzer Engrg Labs Inc ....E 509 334-8154
Houston *(G-11785)*

Southern Transformers ....F 713 923-1191
Houston *(G-11978)*

Tdk Rf Solutions Inc ....E 512 258-9478
Cedar Park *(G-2987)*

Tektronix Inc ....F 713 691-3658
Houston *(G-12189)*

Tektronix Inc ....F 512 926-7625
Austin *(G-1560)*

Testequity LLC ....D 972 247-2470
Carrollton *(G-2829)*

Thermo Finnigan LLC ....D 512 251-1400
Austin *(G-1572)*

Ultratest International Inc ....E 214 340-5252
Dallas *(G-5130)*

Uson Lp ....E 281 671-2000
Houston *(G-12504)*

Van London Company Inc ....F 713 772-6641
Houston *(G-12527)*

Verity Instruments Inc ....D 972 446-9990
Carrollton *(G-2896)*

INSTRUMENTS: *Measuring, Electrical Energy*

1-Stop Enterprises LLC ....E 678 485-9873
Little Elm *(G-14138)*

American Innovations Ltd ....E 512 249-3400
Austin *(G-916)*

INSTRUMENTS: *Measuring, Electrical Power*

Oilfield-Electric-Marine Inc ....F 713 680-9659
Houston *(G-11165)*

INSTRUMENTS: *Medical & Surgical*

A-Vox Systems Inc ....F 210 695-8242
San Antonio *(G-17851)*

Accumed Biotech LLC ....F 315 790-0466
Houston *(G-8459)*

Acelity LP Inc ....E 210 524-9000
San Antonio *(G-17859)*

Alcon Research LLC ....C 817 551-4555
Fort Worth *(G-6366)*

Alcon Vision LLC ....E 713 668-9100
Houston *(G-8532)*

Argon Medical Devices Inc ....A 903 675-9321
Athens *(G-819)*

Argon Medical Devices Inc ....B 903 675-9321
Frisco *(G-7266)*

Armamentarium Inc ....G 281 528-5700
Spring *(G-19101)*

Arthrocare Corporation ....C 512 391-3900
Austin *(G-937)*

Astura Medical ....F 760 814-8047
Irving *(G-12934)*

Asuragen Inc ....D 512 681-5200
Austin *(G-942)*

Atrion Corporation ....E 972 390-9800
Allen *(G-253)*

Attentus Medical Sales Inc ....G 281 776-5188
Spring *(G-19199)*

Banyan International Corp ....E 888 782-8548
Abilene *(G-15)*

Baxter Healthcare Corporation ....A 903 586-6502
Jacksonville *(G-13228)*

Bioniche Animal Health USA Inc ......F 706 549-4503
Fort Worth *(G-6452)*

Blackstone Medical Inc ....D 214 937-2000
Lewisville *(G-14028)*

Blue Medical Services Inc ....E 954 417-5442
Cypress *(G-3781)*

Breg Inc ....F 972 647-0884
Grand Prairie *(G-7848)*

Byrne Medical Inc ....C 936 539-0391
Conroe *(G-3269)*

C R Bard Inc ....B 915 781-2489
El Paso *(G-5676)*

C R Bard Inc ....A 956 205-7100
Pharr *(G-16695)*

Carefusion 213 LLC ....B 915 231-5000
El Paso *(G-5683)*

Cellright Technologies LLC ....E 210 659-9353
Universal City *(G-20181)*

Covidien LP ....B 903 886-3153
Commerce *(G-3242)*

Ctl Medical Corporation ....F 214 545-5830
Addison *(G-114)*

Cumberland Additive Inc ....F 512 990-9100
Pflugerville *(G-16666)*

D4d Technologies LLC ....C 972 534-3101
Richardson *(G-17296)*

Diversified Diagnostic Pdts ....F 281 955-5323
Houston *(G-9482)*

Dlk Medical Technologies Inc ....E 214 613-5682
Dallas *(G-4265)*

Eclipse Medcorp LLC ....D 800 759-6876
Lewisville *(G-14047)*

Eminent Spine LLC ....F 512 868-5980
Georgetown *(G-7649)*

Epimed International Inc ....E 972 373-9090
Farmers Branch *(G-6196)*

Evolution Spine LLC ....F 214 228-6252
Dallas *(G-4339)*

Footprint Medical Inc ....E 210 226-2600
San Antonio *(G-18120)*

Galt Medical Corp ....E 972 271-5177
Garland *(G-7492)*

Guidant Sales LLC ....D 713 218-4069
Houston *(G-10056)*

Healthpoint Ltd ....F 817 900-4000
Fort Worth *(G-6692)*

Healthtech Solutions Inc ....F 763 559-7082
Austin *(G-1694)*

Helena Laboratories Corp ....B 409 842-3714
Beaumont *(G-1902)*

HMC Instrument & Mch Works Ltd ....E 713 468-1426
Houston *(G-10189)*

Hypertec Inc ....F 940 564-5600
Olney *(G-16221)*

Infused Medical Technology Inc ......F 214 330-4000
Dallas *(G-4498)*

Inogen Inc ....A 972 616-5500
Plano *(G-16891)*

Instrument Specialists Inc ....F 830 249-9535
Boerne *(G-2123)*

Insurgical Inc ....F 512 318-2980
Austin *(G-1230)*

International Biophysics Corp ....E 512 326-3244
Austin *(G-1237)*

Itec Manufacturing LLC ....E 903 365-6390
Winnsboro *(G-20897)*

Kyocera Medical Tech Inc ....D 909 557-2360
Austin *(G-1278)*

LDR Holding Corporation ....E 512 344-3333
Austin *(G-1285)*

Lone Star Medical Products Inc ....E 281 340-6000
Stafford *(G-19348)*

Luminex Corporation ....F 512 219-8020
Austin *(G-1308)*

Mc Manus Instrument Co Inc ....F 409 834-2419
Village Mills *(G-20338)*

Medex South ....E 713 838-1989
Houston *(G-10818)*

Medical Device Tech Inc ....E 800 338-0440
Athens *(G-831)*

Medivators Inc ....C 936 539-0391
Conroe *(G-3330)*

Medline Industries Inc ....C 281 574-6200
Katy *(G-13371)*

Medtronic Minimed Inc ....A 830 438-0383
Bulverde *(G-2556)*

Medtronic PS Medical Inc ....C 817 788-6400
Haltom City *(G-8153)*

Medtronic Usa Inc ....E 210 395-5769
San Antonio *(G-18290)*

Merc Medical Supply Co Inc ....F 713 270-4936
Houston *(G-10831)*

Merit Medical Systems Inc ....E 832 463-5100
Houston *(G-10837)*

Metric Medical Devices Inc ....G 830 535-6300
Helotes *(G-8243)*

Micromed Technology Inc ....E 713 838-9210
Houston *(G-10868)*

Microtek Medical Inc ....E 903 597-2568
Tyler *(G-20128)*

Mli Supply Inc ....F 713 266-1400
Stafford *(G-19354)*

Mobile Surgical Tech Inc ....F 972 735-8003
Dallas *(G-3849)*

NA Acquisition Company ....C 817 231-1300
Fort Worth *(G-6859)*

Neuro Resource Group Intl Inc ....E 972 665-1810
Richardson *(G-17365)*

Novosci Corp ....E 281 363-4949
Conroe *(G-3344)*

Nurse Assist LLC ....C 800 649-6800
Haltom City *(G-8155)*

Origen Biomedical Inc ....E 512 474-7278
Austin *(G-1393)*

Orthofix Inc ....C 214 937-2000
Lewisville *(G-14076)*

Orthofix Inc ....C 214 937-2000
Lewisville *(G-14077)*

Orthofix Medical Inc ....F 214 937-2000
Lewisville *(G-14079)*

Osseus Fusion Systems LLC ....F 888 330-5960
Dallas *(G-4770)*

Osteogenics Biomedical Inc ....F 806 796-1923
Lubbock *(G-14455)*

Power Plastic Inc ....F 713 957-3695
Houston *(G-11377)*

Quality Bioresources Inc ....E 830 372-4797
Seguin *(G-18858)*

Quest Medical Inc ....C 800 627-0226
Allen *(G-297)*

Rockwell Medical Tech Inc ....E 972 874-2130
Grapevine *(G-8052)*

Seisa Medical Inc ....E 915 774-4321
El Paso *(G-5954)*

Semmt Inc ....G 713 966-5829
Houston *(G-11826)*

Siteselect Inc ....E 956 207-5587
McAllen *(G-14906)*

Smith & Nephew Wound MGT ....C 800 876-1261
Fort Worth *(G-6995)*

Spectrum Lifesciences LLC ....E 214 492-0506
Irving *(G-13188)*

Spinesmith Holdings LLC ....E 512 637-2073
Austin *(G-1527)*

Stealth Products LLC ....D 512 715-9995
Burnet *(G-2614)*

Stryker Communications Inc ....C 972 410-7000
Flower Mound *(G-6283)*

Stryker Corporation ....C 214 461-4663
Addison (G-166)
Systagenix Wound MGT US Inc ....D 617 774-5500
San Antonio (G-18518)
Technical Innovations LLC ....E 979 849-8700
Angleton (G-580)
Texas Medical Technology LLC ....F 832 512-7727
Houston (G-12239)
Transplant Technology Inc ....E 210 696-7616
San Antonio (G-18563)
Trilliant Surgical LLC ....G 800 495-2919
Houston (G-12373)
Trimira LLC ....F 713 984-8994
Houston (G-12374)
Viant Medical Inc ....F 830 792-1156
Kerrville (G-13528)
Viant San Antonio Inc ....C 210 684-7553
San Antonio (G-18592)
Vitaltech Affiliates LLC ....E 214 886-5249
Plano (G-17047)
Wenzel Spine Inc ....F 512 469-0600
Austin (G-1656)
Winfield Laboratories Inc ....E 972 234-0940
Richardson (G-17430)
Zimmer ....A 800 613-6131
Austin (G-1717)

INSTRUMENTS: Meteorological

Gagemaker LP ....E 713 472-7360
Pasadena (G-16445)
Sensatronics LLC ....F 800 633-1033
Austin (G-1711)
Texas Electronics Inc ....F 214 327-2566
Dallas (G-5058)

INSTRUMENTS: Nautical

Nautical Control Solutions LP ....E 281 209-3480
Spring (G-19153)

INSTRUMENTS: Pressure Measurement, Indl

Alpha Tech International Inc ....A 281 240-8989
Stafford (G-19284)
Mensor LP ....D 512 396-4200
San Marcos (G-18698)
Rampak Group Inc ....F 713 678-8898
Houston (G-11537)

INSTRUMENTS: Radio Frequency Measuring

Hid Global Corporation ....C 800 237-7769
Austin (G-1202)
Rf Saw Inc ....F 469 227-0322
Fredericksburg (G-7188)

INSTRUMENTS: Recorders, Oscillographic

Thermo Elctron Process Systems ....D 713 272-0404
Houston (G-12270)

INSTRUMENTS: Seismographs

Bae Systems Resolution Inc ....E 713 868-7700
Houston (G-8789)
Geospace Technologies Corp ....A 713 986-4444
Houston (G-9945)
Teledyne Instruments Inc ....C 713 666-2561
Houston (G-12191)

INSTRUMENTS: Standards & Calibration, Electrical Measuring

Hilti of America Inc ....E 800 879-8000
Plano (G-16886)

INSTRUMENTS: Sweep Oscillators

Softest Designs Corporation ....E 210 697-8828
San Antonio (G-18481)

INSTRUMENTS: Temperature Measurement, Indl

Anova Industrials ....E 281 494-8896
Stafford (G-19286)
Gayesco-Wika Usa LP ....C 713 941-8540
Pasadena (G-16447)
Professionalized Pdts & Svcs ....E 281 933-9427
Houston (G-11440)
Temperture Measurement Systems ......E 800 967-6498
Malakoff (G-14637)

INSTRUMENTS: Test, Digital, Electronic & Electrical Circuits

Pico Sales and Dist LLC ....F 800 591-2796
Tyler (G-20143)

INSTRUMENTS: Test, Electronic & Electric Measurement

Avo Multi-AMP Corporation ....C 214 330-3201
Dallas (G-3991)
Computer Service Technology ....E 972 241-2662
Dallas (G-4153)
Spectra Test Solutions LLC ....E 214 349-0288
Dallas (G-4995)
Teradyne Inc ....D 512 891-9600
Austin (G-1563)
Testforce Usa Inc ....F 925 281-3501
Addison (G-168)

INSTRUMENTS: Test, Electronic & Electrical Circuits

3M Company ....B 512 984-1800
Austin (G-869)
Butler & Land Inc ....E 214 343-8800
Dallas (G-4068)
George W Cox & Sons Inc ....E 210 661-8661
San Antonio (G-18139)
Mitchell Machine & Fabricating ....F 903 880-0249
Mabank (G-14579)
Neosem Technology Inc ....F 512 257-5000
Austin (G-1706)
Pipeline Inspection Company ....E 713 681-5837
Houston (G-11335)
Scientific Test Inc ....F 972 479-1300
Richardson (G-17394)
Testronics Consolidated Inc ....E 972 542-3111
Richardson (G-17406)

INSTRUMENTS: Testing, Semiconductor

Bpm Microsystems Inc ....D 713 688-4600
Houston (G-8972)
Delta V Instruments Inc ....F 972 644-6501
Richardson (G-17299)
Mactronix Inc ....E 972 690-0028
Richardson (G-17350)
Maxmile Technologies LLC ....F 512 961-1187
Austin (G-1331)
Tokyo Seimitsu Co Ltd ....F 214 459-1688
Richardson (G-17412)
Web Technology Inc ....F 214 343-9238
Dallas (G-5177)

INSTRUMENTS: Thermal Conductive, Indl

Double Mountain Inc ....E 940 988-4491
Aspermont (G-815)
Hitachi America Ltd ....D 972 488-3824
Carrollton (G-2761)
Walton Process Tech Inc ....E 682 518-9002
Mansfield (G-14728)

INSTRUMENTS: Transducers, Volts, Amperes, Watts, VARs & Freq

Metrix Instrument Co LP ....D 281 940-1802
Houston (G-10854)
Transdata Inc ....E 972 418-7717
Carrollton (G-2839)

INSTRUMENTS: Transformers, Portable

Sigma Electronics Inc ....E 800 874-7121
Houston (G-11884)

INSTRUMENTS: Vibration

Provibtech Inc ....E 713 830-7601
Houston (G-11466)
STI Vibration Monitoring Inc ....F 281 334-0766
League City (G-13979)

INSTRUMENTS: Viscometer, Indl Process

Grace Instrument Company ....E 713 783-1560
Houston (G-10009)

INSULATING BOARD, CELLULAR FIBER

Digital Communication Svcs Inc ....F 682 478-2134
Fort Worth (G-6586)
Installed Building Pdts Inc ....E 210 937-1082
San Antonio (G-18643)
Valro-K LLC ....E 210 937-1082
San Antonio (G-18647)

INSULATING BOARD, HARD PRESSED

Gregg Indus Insulators Inc ....B 903 757-5754
Longview (G-14243)

INSULATION & CUSHIONING FOAM: Polystyrene

Atlas Roofing Corporation ....C 903 645-3988
Daingerfield (G-3830)
Atlas Roofing Corporation ....E 936 829-5279
Diboll (G-5461)
Carlisle Construction Mtls LLC ....E 214 515-5200
Terrell (G-19730)
Carpenter Co ....D 254 778-0131
Temple (G-19674)
Carpenter Co ....E 214 330-0373
Dallas (G-4085)
E R Carpenter LP ....E 804 359-0800
Dallas (G-4284)
F3 Foam LLC ....G 936 661-3172
Montgomery (G-15633)
Fresno Manfacturing LLC ....D 281 437-6000
Fresno (G-7237)
Future Foam Inc ....E 214 905-6043
Dallas (G-4387)
Great Lakes Textiles Inc ....F 713 670-9700
Houston (G-10027)
Houston Foam Plastics Inc ....C 713 224-3484
Houston (G-10234)
Houston R-Co Incorporated ....F 281 987-9909
Houston (G-10248)
Nppi Intermediate Inc ....E 512 476-7100
Austin (G-1371)
Orange County Industrial Inc ....G 409 697-3559
Orange (G-16255)
Polly Knapp Pig Inc ....E 713 222-0146
Houston (G-11355)
Reef Industries Inc ....E 713 507-4200
Houston (G-11577)
Reef Industries Inc ....D 713 507-4329
Houston (G-11578)
SES Foam LLC ....E 713 239-0252
Spring (G-19165)
Sika Corporation ....C 972 387-4500
Dallas (G-4963)
Thermafoam Operating LLC ....E 254 582-2730
Hillsboro (G-8331)
Whitehorse Manufacturing Co ....F 512 376-2112
Kyle (G-13688)

INSULATION & ROOFING MATERIALS: Wood, Reconstituted

Bay Energy Blanket Inc ....F 512 353-4064
San Marcos (G-18680)
Jci Roofing LLC ....F 956 227-1745
McAllen (G-14878)
Standard Industries Inc ....C 972 851-0460
Dallas (G-5004)

INSULATION MATERIALS WHOLESALERS

Bay Energy Blanket Inc ....F 512 353-4064
San Marcos (G-18680)
Double Mountain Inc ....E 940 988-4491
Aspermont (G-815)
SMC Industries Inc ....G 281 860-9950
Houston (G-11920)
Therm-All Inc ....F 214 630-4800
Dallas (G-5084)

INSULATION: Fiberglass

Johns Manville Corporation ....B 817 645-9101
Cleburne (G-3098)
Owens Corning ....F 940 723-5998
Wichita Falls (G-20791)
Owens Corning Sales LLC ....E 972 937-1340
Waxahachie (G-20554)
Owens Corning Sales LLC ....B 806 622-1582
Amarillo (G-504)

Owens Corning Sales LLC ....D 903 538-2271
Palestine *(G-16307)*

Pamrod Products Company ....E 830 372-1500
Seguin *(G-18854)*

Seguins Budget Auto Inc ....F 830 372-1790
Seguin *(G-18863)*

Sudaglass Fiber Technology ....D 281 496-5427
Houston *(G-12090)*

Superior Energies Inc ....E 409 962-8549
Groves *(G-8111)*

INSULATORS & INSULATION MATERIALS: Electrical

Chemfoundry Inc ....F 725 218-1955
Tyler *(G-20066)*

Galyean Investments LLC ....F 806 368-5430
Lubbock *(G-14414)*

Glt Fabricators Inc ....E 713 670-9700
La Porte *(G-13739)*

Gund Company Inc ....E 972 389-0615
Euless *(G-6147)*

T G M Inc ....F 972 761-9101
Richardson *(G-17404)*

INSULATORS, PORCELAIN: Electrical

Ppc Usa Inc ....E 281 257-8222
Houston *(G-11380)*

INSURANCE AGENCIES & BROKERS

Hub Intrntnal Trnsp Insur Svcs ....F 800 369-9010
San Antonio *(G-18174)*

INSURANCE CARRIERS: Automobile

Underwriters Indemnity ....E 713 961-1300
Houston *(G-12432)*

INSURANCE INFORMATION & CONSULTING SVCS

Jack Phipps ....F 972 278-3186
Dallas *(G-4520)*

INSURANCE PROFESSIONAL STANDARDS SVCS

Carter Lee Properties LLC ....F 713 385-8092
Richmond *(G-17452)*

INSURANCE: Agents, Brokers & Service

Armando G Martinez ....E 325 653-5640
San Angelo *(G-17778)*

C N A Inc ....E 915 533-2425
El Paso *(G-5675)*

C&S Lease Service LC ....E 903 988-8642
Kilgore *(G-13534)*

Ji Communications Inc ....D 512 346-6921
Austin *(G-1255)*

Republic Title of Texas Inc ....C 972 578-8611
Plano *(G-16991)*

INTEGRATED CIRCUITS, SEMICONDUCTOR NETWORKS, ETC

Advanced Micro Devices Inc ....B 512 602-1000
Austin *(G-891)*

Advanced Micro Devices Inc ....C 512 602-1000
Austin *(G-892)*

Advanced Micro Devices Inc ....F 512 602-5204
Austin *(G-893)*

AMS Sensors USA Inc ....D 469 298-4252
Plano *(G-16789)*

Analog Devices Inc ....D 512 427-1000
Austin *(G-922)*

Aramark Services Inc ....C 512 602-1000
Austin *(G-927)*

Arm Inc ....D 512 327-9249
Austin *(G-933)*

Calxeda Inc ....D 512 582-5100
Austin *(G-1020)*

Cypress Semiconductor Corp ....F 512 934-6699
Austin *(G-1082)*

Diodes Fabtech Inc ....C 816 251-8800
Plano *(G-16844)*

Fairchild Semiconductor Corp ....E 972 910-8000
Richardson *(G-17308)*

Globitech Incorporated ....C 903 957-1999
Sherman *(G-18916)*

Leidos Inc ....E 210 731-1438
San Antonio *(G-18245)*

Mactronix Inc ....E 972 690-0028
Richardson *(G-17350)*

Mhc Semiconductor Processing ....F 512 331-6632
Austin *(G-1337)*

Micrel LLC ....C 972 235-9166
Richardson *(G-17357)*

Muto Technology Inc ....E 512 251-2211
Austin *(G-1358)*

Science Applications Intl Corp ....F 469 557-8249
Carrollton *(G-2815)*

Silicon Laboratories Inc ....B 512 416-8500
Austin *(G-1505)*

Silicon Space Technology Corp ....F 512 347-1814
Austin *(G-1506)*

Srj Holdings LLC ....F 972 747-8613
Allen *(G-299)*

Superconductor Tech Inc ....E 512 650-7775
Austin *(G-1549)*

Tekmos Inc ....G 512 342-9871
Austin *(G-1559)*

Vlsip Technologies Inc ....D 972 437-5506
Richardson *(G-17424)*

X-Fab Texas Inc ....B 806 747-4400
Lubbock *(G-14515)*

INTERCOMMUNICATION EQPT REPAIR SVCS

Backwoods Communications LLC ....F 361 652-6900
Victoria *(G-20241)*

INTERCOMMUNICATIONS SYSTEMS: Electric

Backwoods Communications LLC ....F 361 652-6900
Victoria *(G-20241)*

Communications Conveyor Co Inc ....E 940 498-1850
Lake Dallas *(G-13810)*

L3 Technologies Inc ....C 972 722-7927
Rockwall *(G-17553)*

Noral Holding Company ....E 972 392-7780
Dallas *(G-4742)*

Talla-Com Tllhssee Cmmnctons I ....F 817 234-6726
Fort Worth *(G-7031)*

Tallahassee Technologies Inc ....D 817 234-6726
Fort Worth *(G-7032)*

Tango Networks Inc ....E 469 920-2100
Frisco *(G-7318)*

Tellabs Enterprise Inc ....D 972 588-7951
Carrollton *(G-2891)*

Tyrex Group Ltd ....F 512 623-4694
Austin *(G-1603)*

Wilson Electronics LLC ....E 800 204-4104
Richardson *(G-17428)*

INTERIOR DECORATING SVCS

Kenmark Architectural Pdts Inc ....F 800 788-8263
Dallas *(G-4550)*

Satori Home Limited LLC ....E 855 472-8674
Dallas *(G-4937)*

INTERIOR DESIGN SVCS, NEC

Graphtec Inc ....E 713 690-9999
Houston *(G-10019)*

INTERIOR DESIGNING SVCS

KS Little Shop ....F 214 371-4113
Dallas *(G-4571)*

Legant Interior Inc ....E 713 784-2647
Houston *(G-10621)*

Tabors of San Angelo Inc ....E 325 942-1696
San Angelo *(G-17830)*

INVENTORY STOCKING SVCS

Pointsmith Pnt-F-Prchase MGT S ....C 281 599-5900
Katy *(G-13432)*

INVERTERS: Nonrotating Electrical

Delta Electronics (usa) Inc ....C 469 330-9100
Plano *(G-16837)*

INVERTERS: Rotating Electrical

Delta Electronics (usa) Inc ....C 469 330-9100
Plano *(G-16837)*

Inverter Designs Inc ....F 972 227-9085
Lancaster *(G-13843)*

INVESTMENT FIRM: General Brokerage

Afam Capital Inc ....E 512 354-7041
Austin *(G-900)*

Hurd Enterprises Ltd ....F 210 829-5255
San Antonio *(G-18176)*

W T Waggoner Estate ....C 940 552-2521
Vernon *(G-20232)*

INVESTMENT FUNDS, NEC

Gooch Investments Inc ....F 325 677-5904
Abilene *(G-44)*

Hyperion Energy LP ....F 214 750-3820
Dallas *(G-4478)*

Pelican Energy Partners LP ....D 713 559-7110
Houston *(G-11271)*

Tpg Capital Management LP ....B 817 871-4000
Fort Worth *(G-7069)*

Wingate Partners V LP ....F 214 720-1313
Dallas *(G-5196)*

INVESTMENT FUNDS: Open-Ended

Hyperion Resources Inc ....F 214 750-1522
Dallas *(G-4479)*

Insight Equity A P X L P ....F 817 488-7775
Southlake *(G-19075)*

Insight Equity LP ....E 817 488-7775
Southlake *(G-19076)*

Precision Specialties Company ....E 800 527-3295
Sherman *(G-18927)*

INVESTORS, NEC

Aethon Energy Management LLC ....E 214 750-3820
Dallas *(G-3898)*

Alexander Production Company ....F 210 271-3691
San Antonio *(G-17891)*

Excelente Inc ....E 855 209-1970
Plano *(G-16867)*

KSA Industries Inc ....D 713 881-3400
Houston *(G-10569)*

Lime Rock Resources Iv-A LP ....C 713 292-9500
Houston *(G-10643)*

Rex-Hide Incorporated ....F 903 593-7387
Tyler *(G-20146)*

Rosewood Prvate Invstments Inc ....F 214 849-9000
Dallas *(G-4911)*

Sterling Group LP ....E 713 877-8257
Houston *(G-12060)*

Texgulmarco Co Inc ....E 956 943-2673
Port Isabel *(G-17139)*

INVESTORS: Real Estate, Exc Property Operators

Anderson Oil Ltd ....F 713 652-5746
Houston *(G-8641)*

IRON & STEEL PRDTS: Hot-Rolled

Maverick Stainless LLC ....E 214 884-2700
Dallas *(G-4653)*

IRON ORE MINING

Hudson Brothers Mining Company ....F 903 876-4642
Rusk *(G-17731)*

IRRADIATION EQPT: Beta Ray

Protom International Inc ....D 972 410-3551
Flower Mound *(G-6277)*

IRRIGATION EQPT WHOLESALERS

Compliant Power Systems LLC ....F 903 427-0071
Clarksville *(G-3072)*

Gear Drive Service Pump Div ....F 806 948-5366
Sunray *(G-19618)*

H & H Water Well Service Inc ....G 806 659-5577
Spearman *(G-19086)*

High Plains Drilling Company ....F 806 935-2132
Dumas *(G-5521)*

Larry & Matt Inc ....D 806 665-4418
Pampa *(G-16326)*

Preferred Pump & Equipment LP ....E 817 536-9800
Fort Worth *(G-6912)*

IRRIGATION SYSTEMS, NEC Impounding Reservoir

Farm & Ranch Construction LLC ....E 254 364-2226
Iredell *(G-12921)*

IRRIGATION SYSTEMS, NEC Water Distribution Or Sply Systems

Altivia Corporation ....F 713 658-9000
Houston *(G-8571)*

JANITORIAL & CUSTODIAL SVCS

Ambassador Facility Svcs LLC ....E 210 849-7677
Cibolo *(G-3061)*
Asiel Enterprises Inc ....D 361 765-6670
Corpus Christi *(G-3476)*
Diversified Bus Consulting LLC ....F 713 677-9282
Houston *(G-9481)*
Imperial Bag & Paper Co LLC ....E 713 223-5050
Houston *(G-10334)*
Melvin Hammon ....F 806 665-2667
Pampa *(G-16328)*
Thiink Biig Tax Service Inc ....F 832 606-3380
Katy *(G-13450)*
Tigua Enterprises Inc ....E 915 298-0700
El Paso *(G-6006)*

JANITORIAL EQPT & SPLYS WHOLESALERS

Acme Soap Inc ....F 210 731-9800
San Antonio *(G-17862)*
Cummings Inv Bankers Inc ....F 281 416-3007
Houston *(G-8376)*
Eagle Brush & Chemical Inc ....F 972 484-0391
Dallas *(G-4289)*
Iowa Techniques Inc ....F 512 846-2403
Hutto *(G-12880)*
MANS Distributors Inc ....F 972 930-0330
Carrollton *(G-2777)*
Miller Paper Company ....E 806 353-0317
Amarillo *(G-502)*
Pro Star Industries Inc ....E 979 779-9399
Bryan *(G-2499)*

JEWELERS' FINDINGS & MATERIALS: Castings

Carriage Casting Inc ....G 915 760-6800
El Paso *(G-5685)*
James Avery Craftsman Inc ....F 512 541-3823
Austin *(G-1250)*

JEWELERS' FINDINGS & MTLS: Jewel Prep, Instr, Tools, Watches

Fossil Partners LP ....E 972 234-2525
Richardson *(G-17313)*

JEWELERS' FINDINGS/MTRLS: Gem Prep, Settings, Real/Imitation

Time Delay Corporation ....E 214 369-4063
Dallas *(G-5094)*

JEWELRY & PRECIOUS STONES WHOLESALERS

Joann Baik ....F 281 469-1000
Houston *(G-10478)*

JEWELRY APPAREL

Jeep Collins Jewelry Maker ....D 830 997-3135
Fredericksburg *(G-7184)*
Joann Baik ....F 281 469-1000
Houston *(G-10478)*
Jonsil Manufacturing Corp ....F 915 544-4244
El Paso *(G-5823)*
Shaudra Company Inc ....E 915 544-4244
El Paso *(G-5957)*

JEWELRY FINDINGS & LAPIDARY WORK

J Keiths Jewelry Inc ....F 806 791-0092
Lubbock *(G-14427)*

JEWELRY REPAIR SVCS

James Avery Craftsman Inc ....F 956 509-2912
Brownsville *(G-2367)*

Milke Manufacturing Jewelers ....G 972 296-4319
Duncanville *(G-5534)*

JEWELRY STORES

Bravelets LLC.....................................F 800 780-9227
Houston *(G-8977)*
I W Marks Jewelers LP ....F 713 668-5000
Houston *(G-10310)*
Jeep Collins Jewelry Maker ....D 830 997-3135
Fredericksburg *(G-7184)*
McCartney Investment Corp ....F 214 521-8410
Dallas *(G-4659)*

JEWELRY STORES: Precious Stones & Precious Metals

Ben Adams Precious Jewels ....E 210 826-6535
San Antonio *(G-17945)*
Cfj Manufacturing LP ....D 817 625-9559
Fort Worth *(G-6506)*
Cfj Manufacturing LP ....D 817 232-9251
Saginaw *(G-17741)*
Grissoms Fine Jewelry ....G 817 244-9754
Fort Worth *(G-6681)*
H P Creations ....E 817 749-4367
Southlake *(G-19073)*
J Keiths Jewelry Inc ....F 806 791-0092
Lubbock *(G-14427)*
James Avery Craftsman Inc ....F 512 541-3823
Austin *(G-1250)*
James Avery Craftsman Inc ....F 956 509-2912
Brownsville *(G-2367)*
Lilyrain Jewelry LLC ....F 713 467-5459
Houston *(G-10641)*
Pineforest Jewelry Inc ....F 713 451-1321
Houston *(G-11333)*
Roots Rocks Inc ....F 512 346-1780
Austin *(G-1473)*
Southwest Diamond Cutters Inc ....E 972 387-1078
Dallas *(G-4989)*

JEWELRY STORES: Silverware

Holland Jewelry Inc ....F 325 655-3135
San Angelo *(G-17807)*

JEWELRY STORES: Watches

Fossil Group Inc ....B 972 234-2525
Richardson *(G-17312)*
Fossil Partners LP ....E 972 234-2525
Richardson *(G-17313)*

JEWELRY, PRECIOUS METAL: Bracelets

Bravelets LLC.....................................F 800 780-9227
Houston *(G-8977)*

JEWELRY, PRECIOUS METAL: Cigar & Cigarette Access

Serious Cigars Llc ....G 281 397-9800
Houston *(G-11837)*

JEWELRY, PRECIOUS METAL: Mountings & Trimmings

James Avery Craftsman Inc ....F 956 509-2912
Brownsville *(G-2367)*

JEWELRY, PRECIOUS METAL: Rings, Finger

American Achievement Corp ....E 512 444-0571
Dallas *(G-3937)*
J Brandt Recognition Ltd ....F 817 877-0513
Fort Worth *(G-6729)*

JEWELRY, WHOLESALE

Cfj Manufacturing LP ....D 817 625-9559
Fort Worth *(G-6506)*
Cfj Manufacturing LP ....D 817 232-9251
Saginaw *(G-17741)*
Chapal/Zenray Inc ....D 214 638-0402
Carrollton *(G-2714)*
Fossil Partners LP ....A 972 234-2525
Richardson *(G-17317)*
Houston Numismatic Exchange ....F 713 528-2135
Houston *(G-10241)*
New World Jewelry Inc ....F 972 243-2931
Dallas *(G-4731)*

Pineforest Jewelry Inc ....F 713 451-1321
Houston *(G-11333)*
Z Fabulous Inc ....E 972 385-0202
Plano *(G-17056)*

JEWELRY: Decorative, Fashion & Costume

Adele Charles Corp ....G 972 740-1028
Plano *(G-16771)*
Premier Manufacturing LP ....F 972 355-3285
Flower Mound *(G-6276)*
South By Midwest Ret Partners ....F 281 465-8480
Spring *(G-19252)*
Wireless Maniac ....E 817 209-9524
Dallas *(G-5199)*
Z Fabulous Inc ....E 972 385-0202
Plano *(G-17056)*

JEWELRY: Precious Metal

AAC Group Holding Corp ....F 512 444-0571
Austin *(G-875)*
Balfour Scholastic School Sup ....F 903 455-4556
Greenville *(G-8063)*
Ben Adams Precious Jewels ....E 210 826-6535
San Antonio *(G-17945)*
Cfj Manufacturing LP ....D 817 625-9559
Fort Worth *(G-6506)*
Cfj Manufacturing LP ....D 817 232-9251
Saginaw *(G-17741)*
Chapal/Zenray Inc ....D 214 638-0402
Carrollton *(G-2714)*
Commemorative Brands Inc ....E 800 225-3687
Dallas *(G-4145)*
Grissoms Fine Jewelry ....G 817 244-9754
Fort Worth *(G-6681)*
H P Creations ....E 817 749-4367
Southlake *(G-19073)*
Holland Jewelry Inc ....F 325 655-3135
San Angelo *(G-17807)*
Houston Numismatic Exchange ....F 713 528-2135
Houston *(G-10241)*
I W Marks Jewelers LP ....F 713 668-5000
Houston *(G-10310)*
Lilyrain Jewelry LLC ....F 713 467-5459
Houston *(G-10641)*
M A E W Inc ....F 956 627-3554
McAllen *(G-14886)*
Main Jewell LLC ....F 713 623-0499
Houston *(G-10739)*
Milke Manufacturing Jewelers ....G 972 296-4319
Duncanville *(G-5534)*
New World Jewelry Inc ....F 972 243-2931
Dallas *(G-4731)*
Pampillonia Designs II Inc ....D 214 503-7272
Richardson *(G-17370)*
Phoeben Inc ....F 832 486-9500
Houston *(G-11328)*
Precision Set Incorporated ....E 972 385-6732
Dallas *(G-4821)*
Premier Manufacturing LP ....E 972 355-3285
Flower Mound *(G-6276)*
Robinson Pipe & Supply Inc ....E 713 672-4152
Houston *(G-11645)*
Roots Rocks Inc ....F 512 346-1780
Austin *(G-1473)*
Sevendipity Jewelry Mfg LLC ....G 915 594-8500
El Paso *(G-5956)*
Sonias Accessories ....G 832 443-7586
Katy *(G-13444)*
Southern Jwly Mfg Houston Co ....E 713 460-5533
Houston *(G-11975)*
T J Manufacturing Co ....F 806 348-7546
Roaring Springs *(G-17497)*
Time Delay Corporation ....E 214 369-4063
Dallas *(G-5094)*
Worldwide J R Wood LLC ....E 512 858-2556
Austin *(G-867)*

JIGS & FIXTURES

Decatur Machine Services Inc ....E 940 627-1062
Decatur *(G-5244)*

JIGS: Welding Positioners

Bowers Equipment Company Inc ....F 281 458-8891
Houston *(G-8962)*

PRODUCT

JOB PRINTING & NEWSPAPER PUBLISHING COMBINED

Beeville Publishing Company.............E....... 361 358-2550
Beeville *(G-1984)*

National Oil & Lube News Inc.............F....... 806 762-4464
Lubbock *(G-14449)*

South Belt Press Inc.............F....... 281 484-4337
Houston *(G-11960)*

Southern Newspapers Inc.............E....... 830 896-7000
Kerrville *(G-13526)*

JOB TRAINING & VOCATIONAL REHABILITATION SVCS

Astrimar Consultants LLC.............E....... 281 994-7816
Houston *(G-8729)*

Astrimar Consultants LLC.............E....... 281 994-7816
Houston *(G-8730)*

Autistic Treatment Ctr.............E....... 972 644-2076
Dallas *(G-3987)*

Tillman Learning LLC.............F....... 866 540-9677
Plano *(G-17033)*

JOINTS & COUPLINGS

Lastrad LLC.............G....... 713 589-9477
Houston *(G-10607)*

JOINTS: Expansion

C M C Steel Fabricators Inc.............D....... 254 799-2471
Waco *(G-20373)*

Commercial Metals Company.............D....... 713 690-0347
Houston *(G-9252)*

Graywolf Industrial Inc.............E....... 281 441-5400
Humble *(G-12771)*

Nucor Corporation.............C....... 936 687-4665
Grapeland *(G-8007)*

JOINTS: Expansion, Pipe

Fujikoki America Inc.............C....... 214 333-4266
Dallas *(G-4384)*

Piping Technology & Pdts Inc.............F....... 713 731-0030
Houston *(G-11337)*

Piping Technology & Pdts Inc.............A....... 800 787-5914
Houston *(G-11338)*

Senior Operations LLC.............C....... 830 629-8080
New Braunfels *(G-15821)*

Senior Operations LLC.............C....... 830 629-8080
New Braunfels *(G-15822)*

JOISTS: Fabricated Bar

Joists of Texas Inc.............E....... 713 466-1212
Jersey Village *(G-13301)*

Nucor Corporation.............G....... 281 251-8857
Spring *(G-19156)*

US Bellows Inc.............B....... 713 731-0030
Houston *(G-12481)*

JOISTS: Long-Span Series, Open Web Steel

New Mllennium Bldg Systems LLC.......C....... 915 298-5050
El Paso *(G-5894)*

KAOLIN MINING

U S Silica Company.............E....... 301 682-0600
Katy *(G-13381)*

KAOLIN: Ground Or Otherwise Treated

U S Silica Company.............E....... 254 375-2225
Kosse *(G-13667)*

KEYBOARDS: Computer Or Office Machine

American Fincl Mktg Group Inc.............F....... 866 679-9241
League City *(G-13945)*

Ikey Ltd.............E....... 512 837-0283
Austin *(G-1223)*

Key Ovation LLC.............F....... 512 259-5688
Cedar Park *(G-2976)*

Keyscan Inc.............F....... 201 918-2396
Odessa *(G-16051)*

KILNS & FURNACES: Ceramic

Paragon Industries LP.............D....... 972 288-7557
Mesquite *(G-15067)*

KITCHEN CABINET STORES, EXC CUSTOM

Gold Star Marble Corporation.............E....... 512 251-9279
Austin *(G-1186)*

Kamma Group Inc.............G....... 281 499-5888
Stafford *(G-19338)*

Patton Manufactured Pdts LP.............E....... 512 918-3737
Austin *(G-1401)*

Republic Nat Inds Texas LP.............C....... 903 935-3680
Marshall *(G-14800)*

KITCHEN CABINETS WHOLESALERS

Encore Cabinets Ltd.............E....... 979 968-9482
La Grange *(G-13694)*

Maryfield Enterprises LP.............D....... 210 344-4151
San Antonio *(G-18281)*

Republic National Cabinet Corp.............F....... 903 935-3680
Marshall *(G-14801)*

Texas Home & Projects LLC.............G....... 956 546-8400
Brownsville *(G-2410)*

US Home Systems Inc.............E....... 214 488-6300
Irving *(G-13204)*

KITCHEN UTENSILS: Food Handling & Processing Prdts, Wood

Dcu Inc.............F....... 972 816-6667
Wylie *(G-20932)*

Villpac Inc.............F....... 713 672-1255
Houston *(G-12568)*

KITCHENWARE: Plastic

Genpak Southwest LP.............C....... 903 693-7151
Carthage *(G-2909)*

KNIVES: Agricultural Or indl

Pelletizer Knives Inc.............F....... 281 859-4492
Houston *(G-11276)*

KNOBS: Porcelain

Sword Company.............E....... 903 561-1921
Tyler *(G-20159)*

LABELS: Cotton, Printed

Alecom Technologies Group Inc.............G....... 972 870-9400
Flower Mound *(G-6259)*

Anchor Graphics Inc.............E....... 972 422-4300
McKinney *(G-14923)*

G & A Label Inc.............F....... 915 544-1766
El Paso *(G-5777)*

LABELS: Paper, Made From Purchased Materials

Carlton Industries LP.............E....... 979 242-5055
La Grange *(G-13693)*

Century Tape & Label LLC.............E....... 972 576-0826
Round Rock *(G-17631)*

Dac Labels & Graphic Spc.............F....... 214 340-2055
Dallas *(G-4205)*

Dallas Label and Packaging Inc.............F....... 972 487-6064
Farmers Branch *(G-6192)*

Diversfied Lbling Slutions Inc.............E....... 817 471-1310
Arlington *(G-664)*

Fortis Solutions Group LLC.............F....... 512 302-0204
Austin *(G-1169)*

HFS Holding Corporation.............F....... 214 634-8600
Dallas *(G-4454)*

Label Products Inc.............E....... 713 869-2959
Houston *(G-10584)*

Marking Services Inc.............F....... 281 424-6710
Baytown *(G-1828)*

Marking Systems Inc.............F....... 972 475-0770
Garland *(G-7543)*

McDowell Packg & Advg Co Inc.............D....... 469 246-2700
Plano *(G-16923)*

Miller Products Inc.............E....... 972 988-0983
Grand Prairie *(G-7929)*

Schulenburg Prtg Off Sups Inc.............E....... 979 743-4511
Schulenburg *(G-18778)*

Superior Label Systems Inc.............F....... 214 330-7770
Dallas *(G-5026)*

Veco Printing Inc.............F....... 956 968-1589
Port Isabel *(G-17140)*

LABOR RESOURCE SVCS

Blast Envmtl & Indus Svcs.............E....... 281 557-1000
League City *(G-13950)*

LABORATORIES, TESTING: Hydrostatic

City Machine & Welding Inc.............E....... 806 358-7293
Amarillo *(G-416)*

Western Sls Tstg Amarillo Inc.............E....... 806 373-6811
Amarillo *(G-522)*

LABORATORIES, TESTING: Prdt Certification, Sfty/Performance

Barton Sprngs E Aquifer Cnsrvt.............F....... 512 282-8441
Austin *(G-975)*

LABORATORIES, TESTING: Product Testing

B R L Consultants Inc.............F....... 210 341-3442
San Antonio *(G-17934)*

LABORATORIES, TESTING: Soil Analysis

Geotherm Usa LLC.............F....... 281 985-9344
Cypress *(G-3796)*

LABORATORIES, TESTING: X-ray Inspection Svc, Indl

Team Inc.............E....... 409 840-9955
Beaumont *(G-1957)*

LABORATORIES: Biological Research

Asuragen Inc.............D....... 512 681-5200
Austin *(G-942)*

Evestra Inc.............F....... 210 673-3300
Schertz *(G-18749)*

LABORATORIES: Biotechnology

Allied Bioscience Inc.............E....... 214 432-5580
Plano *(G-16783)*

Aravive Inc.............F....... 936 355-1910
Houston *(G-8674)*

Assure Labs Inc.............D....... 713 561-5529
Houston *(G-8728)*

Maxmile Technologies LLC.............F....... 512 961-1187
Austin *(G-1331)*

Nanoracks LLC.............D....... 832 632-7754
Webster *(G-20641)*

Origin Bio Solutions LLC.............F....... 432 570-4081
Midland *(G-15329)*

LABORATORIES: Commercial Nonphysical Research

Biotics Research Corporation.............D....... 281 344-0909
Rosenberg *(G-17577)*

Perryman Group Inc.............E....... 254 751-9595
Waco *(G-20445)*

Texas Instruments Incorporated.............B....... 972 995-2011
Dallas *(G-5073)*

Zachry Associates Inc.............E....... 325 677-1342
Abilene *(G-97)*

LABORATORIES: Dental

Fuji Ceramics Inc.............E....... 972 722-1130
Rockwall *(G-17549)*

National Dentex Corporation.............F....... 903 597-3198
Tyler *(G-20132)*

Orthodontic Technologies Inc.............E....... 800 522-4636
Houston *(G-11194)*

Seretti Dental Lab Inc.............E....... 512 452-8989
Austin *(G-1495)*

LABORATORIES: Dental & Medical X-Ray

Radiology Associates N Texas.............E....... 817 321-0300
Fort Worth *(G-6937)*

Rio Grande Imaging Center Inc.............F....... 956 668-6900
McAllen *(G-14901)*

LABORATORIES: Electronic Research

GE Flight Efficiency Svcs Inc.............E....... 512 270-2701
Austin *(G-1179)*

Origin Instruments Corp.............F....... 972 606-8740
Grand Prairie *(G-7942)*

LABORATORIES: Environmental Research

Banks Petroleum Inc ....E 512 478-0059
Austin *(G-974)*
Myramid Analytical Inc ....F 512 288-5093
Austin *(G-865)*
Oxidor Corporation Inc ....F 972 424-6422
Plano *(G-16962)*
Partrac Geomarine Inc ....F 713 338-3495
Houston *(G-11252)*
Texas Oiltech Laboratories Inc ....E 281 495-2400
Houston *(G-12242)*

LABORATORIES: Medical

Castle Biosciences Inc ....D 866 788-9007
Friendswood *(G-7242)*
Fairmont Diagnstc Cntr & Open ....E 713 946-1500
Pasadena *(G-16436)*
Right Pathways LLC ....D 817 522-3600
Coppell *(G-3439)*
Serafy Laboratories Ltd ....E 956 546-5313
Brownsville *(G-2405)*

LABORATORIES: Physical Research, Commercial

Astro Technology Inc ....F 281 464-0100
Houston *(G-8731)*
Benchmark Research & Tech Inc ....C 432 697-8171
Midland *(G-15138)*
Bio-Signal Technologies LLC ....G 214 405-0524
McKinney *(G-14926)*
Bioniche Animal Health USA Inc ....F 706 549-4503
Fort Worth *(G-6452)*
Cameron International Corp ....D 281 391-4600
Katy *(G-13356)*
Cameron Solutions Inc ....E 713 896-3600
Houston *(G-9077)*
Cisco Systems Inc ....A 512 378-1112
Austin *(G-1051)*
CNA Holdings LLC ....E 972 443-4000
Irving *(G-12976)*
Entegris Prof Solutions Inc ....E 512 244-5200
Round Rock *(G-17655)*
Fiberio Technology Corporation ....F 956 207-5448
McAllen *(G-14861)*
Frito-Lay North America Inc ....D 214 944-5238
Dallas *(G-4380)*
Green Ocean Sciences Inc ....E 512 200-4505
Austin *(G-1192)*
Hp Inc ....B 512 432-8000
Austin *(G-1698)*
Jeff Bonner R & D Inc ....C 210 590-3133
San Antonio *(G-18199)*
Luminex Corporation ....C 512 219-8020
Austin *(G-1309)*
Medical Device Tech Inc ....E 800 338-0440
Athens *(G-831)*
Neora LLC ....F 855 463-7486
Dallas *(G-4721)*
Nerium Biotechnology Inc ....F 210 822-7908
San Antonio *(G-18342)*
Pgs Imaging Inc ....B 281 509-8000
Houston *(G-11319)*
Proportional Technologies Inc ....E 713 747-7324
Houston *(G-11450)*
Sanara Medtech Inc ....F 817 529-2300
Fort Worth *(G-6973)*
Saybolt LP ....D 281 478-1300
Deer Park *(G-5294)*
Southern Avionics Co ....E 409 842-1717
Beaumont *(G-1952)*
Stem Cell Innovations Inc ....E 281 679-7000
Houston *(G-12057)*
Technical Automtn Svcs Co Ltd ....D 281 474-3232
Seabrook *(G-18792)*
Weatherford Fracturing Tech ....F 817 882-9955
Fort Worth *(G-7130)*

LABORATORIES: Testing

Acuren Inspection Inc ....A 281 228-0000
La Porte *(G-13716)*
Stanbio Laboratory LP ....D 830 824-0772
Boerne *(G-2137)*

LABORATORIES: Testing

Assure Labs Inc ....D.,.... 713 561-5529
Houston *(G-8728)*

Consci Ltd ....F 713 920-1696
Pasadena *(G-16412)*
Coperion Corporation ....F 281 449-9944
Houston *(G-9309)*
Dairy Farmers America Inc ....E 817 410-4500
Grapevine *(G-8025)*
Dynatec Scientific Labs ....E 915 849-1322
El Paso *(G-5727)*
Epica Applied Technologies LLC ....E 210 310-7710
Converse *(G-3393)*
Exfo America Inc ....E 972 761-9271
Richardson *(G-17307)*
Fesco Ltd ....E 956 724-7501
Laredo *(G-13884)*
Intercorr International Inc ....E 281 444-2282
Houston *(G-10393)*
Kalsi Engineering Incorporated ....E 281 240-6500
Sugar Land *(G-19501)*
L3 Technologies Inc ....C 512 251-3441
Austin *(G-1279)*
Mgc Inc ....G 713 800-7300
Houston *(G-10863)*
Myramid Analytical Inc ....F 512 288-5093
Austin *(G-865)*
Product Quality Management LLC ....F 713 538-3028
Pasadena *(G-16498)*
Saybolt LP ....D 281 478-1300
Deer Park *(G-5294)*
Stress Engineering Svcs Inc ....E 713 466-1527
Houston *(G-12079)*
Team Cooperheat-Mqs Inc ....E 713 673-3660
Houston *(G-12171)*
Texas Environmental Tech LLC ....G 817 534-4275
Fort Worth *(G-7047)*
Thurmond-Mcglothlin LLC ....G 806 665-5700
Pampa *(G-16341)*
Ultratest International Inc ....E 214 340-5252
Dallas *(G-5130)*

LABORATORY APPARATUS & FURNITURE

AB Bellco Corporation ....F 713 781-6447
Houston *(G-8440)*
Becton Dickinson and Company ....F 210 526-5000
San Antonio *(G-17943)*
Chemyx Inc ....E 281 277-5499
Stafford *(G-19295)*
Consci Ltd ....F 713 920-1696
Pasadena *(G-16412)*
Custom Solutions Group LLC ....F 281 507-9569
Katy *(G-13393)*
Helena Laboratories Corp ....B 409 842-3714
Beaumont *(G-1902)*
Paragon Furniture Inc ....D 817 633-3242
Arlington *(G-749)*
Spectrum Lifesciences LLC ....E 214 492-0506
Irving *(G-13188)*
Tel Mnfacturing Engrg Amer Inc ....C 972 643-2000
Allen *(G-301)*
Texas Metal Equipment Co Ltd ....E 713 466-8722
Houston *(G-12241)*
Texas Metal Equipment Co Ltd ....E 214 446-7200
Irving *(G-13192)*

LABORATORY APPARATUS, EXC HEATING & MEASURING

Sleep Disorder Centers LLC ....F 972 390-2014
McKinney *(G-14976)*

LABORATORY APPARATUS: Melting Point

3024 East Seminary Group LLC ....F 817 534-6755
Forest Hill *(G-6294)*

LABORATORY APPARATUS: Physics, NEC

Lumadyne LLC ....G 281 220-2409
Alvin *(G-372)*

LABORATORY CHEMICALS: Organic

Ace Cmpltion Enhncment Svcs LP ....C 432 653-0732
Odessa *(G-15900)*
Ace Cmpltion Enhncment Svcs LP ....E 432 703-7169
Odessa *(G-15901)*
BBC Biochemical Corporation ....C 360 542-8400
McKinney *(G-14925)*
Cerilliant Corporation ....D 512 238-9974
Round Rock *(G-17632)*
Heseyeon LLC ....G 214 483-3800
Carrollton *(G-2868)*

Integrity Bio-Chemicals LLC ....E 408 396-7797
Cresson *(G-3709)*
Momentum Chemical LLC ....G 713 266-1042
Houston *(G-10908)*

LABORATORY EQPT, EXC MEDICAL: Wholesalers

Ambion Inc ....C 512 651-0200
Austin *(G-911)*
Evco Partners LP ....E 409 766-1900
Texas City *(G-19793)*
Key Scientific Products ....E 512 846-1440
Hutto *(G-12882)*
Marathon Special Services Inc ....F 713 784-4918
Houston *(G-10757)*
Tech-Lab Industries Inc ....F 972 660-1111
Grand Prairie *(G-7980)*

LABORATORY EQPT: Clinical Instruments Exc Medical

Nexeon Medsystems Inc ....D 844 919-9990
Dallas *(G-4735)*

LABORATORY EQPT: Incubators

Bnx Converting LLC ....F 713 936-2726
Houston *(G-8930)*
Texas Medplast LLC ....F 832 288-2106
Houston *(G-12240)*

LABORATORY EQPT: Measuring

Ets-Lindgren Inc ....C 512 531-6400
Cedar Park *(G-2968)*
Separation Technology Inc ....F 830 249-0772
Boerne *(G-2136)*

LABORATORY EQPT: Sterilizers

Sterigenics US LLC ....E 817 293-0999
Fort Worth *(G-7018)*

LADDERS: Metal

Tsgc Inc ....C 361 289-0901
Corpus Christi *(G-3644)*

LADDERS: Permanent Installation, Metal

Cubeco Inc ....E 713 671-2466
Houston *(G-9356)*
Fehrs Industrial Mfg LLC ....D 432 758-0068
Seminole *(G-18883)*

LADDERS: Portable, Metal

Material Control Inc ....D 817 695-1400
Arlington *(G-729)*
P W Platforms Inc ....F 713 731-7155
Houston *(G-11214)*

LADLES: Metal Plate

Rack Technology Inc ....E 817 468-2233
Arlington *(G-766)*

LAMINATED PLASTICS: Plate, Sheet, Rod & Tubes

Advanced Drainage Systems Inc ....D 972 878-9600
Ennis *(G-6087)*
Atco Rubber Products Inc ....A 817 595-2894
Fort Worth *(G-6406)*
Composite Lining Systems LP ....C 432 617-0242
Midland *(G-15174)*
Consolidated Armor Pdts LLC ....E 214 382-4100
Addison *(G-113)*
Coverlay Manufacturing Inc ....E 325 659-4697
San Angelo *(G-17791)*
Delfingen Us-Texas LP ....E 915 858-5577
El Paso *(G-5717)*
Federal-Mogul Powertrain LLC ....B 915 860-2300
El Paso *(G-5767)*
Hull Supply Company Inc ....E 512 385-1262
Austin *(G-1213)*
ITW Minigrip Inc ....C 830 372-4400
Seguin *(G-18845)*
Lamrite ....F 512 385-4455
Austin *(G-1281)*
Medical Plastics Laboratory ....B 254 865-7221
Gatesville *(G-7619)*

PRODUCT

Millennium Plastics Tech LLC ....E 915 834-2700
El Paso (G-5878)

Panel Specialists Inc ....D 254 774-9800
Temple (G-19695)

Plastic Specialties & Tech Inc..............D 254 772-6979
Waco (G-20447)

Prototype Machine Co ....F 512 282-1590
Manchaca (G-14641)

Research Advanced Methods Inds ....E 254 442-1008
Cisco (G-3068)

Southanchor Manufacturing LLC........E 915 590-6718
El Paso (G-5970)

Texas Nameplate Company Inc ....D 214 428-8341
Lancaster (G-13849)

Timesaver Templates Inc ....F 972 620-2197
Dallas (G-5095)

LAMINATING SVCS

Esco Industries Inc ....E 254 296-0500
Waco (G-20396)

Mc Creless Company ....F 432 332-1213
Odessa (G-16076)

Texas Flameproofing Inc ....F 214 630-1088
Dallas (G-5061)

LAMP & LIGHT BULBS & TUBES

Efficiency Aggregators LLC ....F 832 862-1103
Richmond (G-17453)

Elumenus Lighting Corp Inc ....F 214 392-2898
Plano (G-16860)

Fanlight Corporation Inc ....F 909 930-6868
Dallas (G-4351)

General Electric Company ....F 972 444-2000
Irving (G-13037)

Halco Lighting Tech LLC ....E 713 644-6073
Houston (G-10090)

Pruf Energy Solutions LLC ....F 254 870-0400
Waco (G-20450)

Sterling Group LP ....E 713 877-8257
Houston (G-12060)

Texas Lamp Manufacturers Inc ....E 972 564-5267
Forney (G-6315)

LAMP BULBS & TUBES, ELECTRIC: Electric Light

Fleco Industries LLC ....C 972 247-3171
Carrollton (G-2739)

LAMP BULBS & TUBES, ELECTRIC: Health, Infrared/Ultraviolet

Upright Lighting LLC ....F 408 472-6379
Allen (G-305)

LAMP BULBS & TUBES, ELECTRIC: Light, Complete

Iglo LLC..............F 214 893-8703
Fort Worth (G-6715)

Light Emtting Dds-Nlimited LLC..............F 512 267-7315
Lago Vista (G-13806)

Satco Products Inc ....C 972 247-2437
Dallas (G-4936)

LAMP BULBS & TUBES/PARTS, ELECTRIC: Generalized Applications

Calyx Cultivation Tech Corp ....F 281 227-2208
Houston (G-9055)

LAMP FIXTURES: Ultraviolet

Nemesis Uvc LLC..............E 972 423-0075
Garland (G-7561)

LAMP SHADES: Glass

Haleaux Inc..............F 214 742-2795
Dallas (G-4428)

LAMP SHADES: Metal

Haleaux Inc..............F 214 742-2795
Dallas (G-4428)

LAMPS: Desk, Residential

Visual Comfort of America LLC..............D 713 686-5999
Houston (G-12574)

LAMPS: Floor, Residential

Wingate Partners LP..............F 214 720-1313
Dallas (G-5195)

LAMPS: Incandescent, Filament

Old World Design LLC..............F 214 741-6858
Dallas (G-4758)

LAND SUBDIVIDERS & DEVELOPERS: Commercial

Airtrust Intl Systems Corp ....F 713 491-4455
Texas City (G-19785)

LAND SUBDIVIDERS & DEVELOPERS: Residential

Dionysus Group LLLLP..............F 512 572-7000
Florence (G-6239)

LAND SUBDIVISION & DEVELOPMENT

Brazco Development Inc ....F 432 684-8031
Midland (G-15149)

Camac International Corp ....E 713 965-5100
Houston (G-9059)

LASER SYSTEMS & EQPT

Laselec Inc..............F 817 460-7830
Grand Prairie (G-7908)

Laser Shot Inc ....D 281 240-1122
Stafford (G-19346)

Ote International Holdings LLC..............F 888 666-9361
Athens (G-837)

Spectrum Technologies USA Inc..............F 817 232-2373
Fort Worth (G-7011)

Sunetics Intl Mktg Group LLC ....F 888 266-2232
Plano (G-17014)

LASERS: Welding, Drilling & Cutting Eqpt

Laser Masters Inc..............E 832 467-4100
Houston (G-10604)

Precision M/C Products Inc ....F 972 429-6200
Wylie (G-20944)

Rivercity Waterjet Inc ....F 210 590-0300
San Antonio (G-18428)

Tape Innovations LLC ....F 817 568-1212
Fort Worth (G-7034)

LATEX: Foamed

Firestone Polymers LLC ....C 409 924-4500
Orange (G-16242)

G V C Holdings Inc ....B 409 722-8321
Port Neches (G-17161)

LATH: Expanded Metal

Isotherm Inc..............E 817 472-9922
Arlington (G-708)

LAUNDRY & DRYCLEANER AGENTS

Popes Cleaners LLC ....F 210 923-7785
San Antonio (G-18384)

LAUNDRY & GARMENT SVCS, NEC: Garment Making, Alter & Repair

Firestick Productions ....E 817 360-7740
Arlington (G-679)

Popes Cleaners LLC ....F 210 923-7785
San Antonio (G-18384)

LAUNDRY EQPT: Commercial

Brim Laundry Machinery Co Inc..............E 214 630-4517
Hutchins (G-12863)

My Sons Laundry LLC ....F 214 634-2080
Dallas (G-4710)

LAUNDRY SVC: Indl Eqpt

Popes Cleaners LLC ....F 210 923-7785
San Antonio (G-18384)

LAWN & GARDEN EQPT

American Maintenance Sups LLC........F 281 304-8369
Cypress (G-3771)

Manitou North America Inc ....D 254 799-0232
Waco (G-20429)

Miller Power Equipment Co LLC ....G 903 592-7201
Tyler (G-20130)

Mistaway Systems Inc ....F 713 468-6464
Houston (G-10890)

Pro-Steel Inc ....E 817 572-4959
Fort Worth (G-6919)

Toro Company ....D 325 673-8762
Abilene (G-89)

Wheel-A-Rama Inc ....G 325 655-7373
San Angelo (G-17840)

LAWN & GARDEN EQPT STORES

Kerr Feed & Grain Company ....F 940 538-4354
Henrietta (G-8281)

LAWN & GARDEN EQPT: Grass Catchers, Lawn Mower

Gorman Outdoor Inc..............F 806 832-0159
Shallowater (G-18890)

LAWN & GARDEN EQPT: Tractors & Eqpt

Six & Mango Equipment LLP ....E 972 335-2731
Frisco (G-7312)

LAWN MOWER REPAIR SHOP

Wheel-A-Rama Inc ....G 325 655-7373
San Angelo (G-17840)

LEAD & ZINC

Salzgtter Mnnsmann Stnless Tbe..............D 713 466-7278
Houston (G-11735)

LEAD & ZINC ORES

Nexa Resources Us Inc ....F 832 726-0160
Houston (G-11043)

LEAD PENCILS & ART GOODS

Sun Chemical Corporation..............E 972 647-1641
Grand Prairie (G-7977)

LEAD-IN WIRES: Electric Lamp

Craft Wireline Services Inc..............F 432 943-5150
Monahans (G-15603)

LEASING & RENTAL SVCS: Computer Hardware, Exc Finance

Paper Network Inc..............E 972 239-6567
Dallas (G-4786)

LEASING & RENTAL SVCS: Cranes & Aerial Lift Eqpt

Basden Steel and Erection Inc ....E 817 295-6100
Burleson (G-2569)

Craneworks Inc ....E 281 219-7779
Houston (G-9334)

Crocker Crane Rentals LP..............E 512 258-1323
Leander (G-13985)

Elizondo Enterprises Inc ....G 956 831-7174
Brownsville (G-2353)

Richards Signs & Cranes Inc..............F 940 325-6585
Mineral Wells (G-15539)

Valley Welding Service ....E 956 585-1043
Palmview (G-16313)

Versabar Inc..............C 713 937-3100
Houston (G-12554)

LEASING & RENTAL SVCS: Oil Field Eqpt

Air Drilling Associates Inc ....F 832 957-6093
Houston (G-8505)

Brothers Well Service Ltd ....E 979 543-6851
El Campo (G-5613)

Cagle Fishing & Rental Tls Inc ....F 432 381-3061
Odessa (G-15952)

Challenger Eqp & Tl Co Inc..............E 281 351-4247
Tomball (G-19970)

Champion Process Inc ....F 281 953-9000
Houston (G-9159)

Dlugosch III LLC..............C 361 564-9504
Yorktown (G-20977)

Exterran Trinidad LLC ....B 281 921-9337
Houston *(G-9737)*

Flo Trend Systems Inc ....E 713 699-0152
Houston *(G-9804)*

Franks International LLC ....D 979 778-8700
Bryan *(G-2474)*

Fts International Services LLC ....F 817 334-0002
Fort Worth *(G-6654)*

Fts International Services LLC ....C 817 862-2000
Fort Worth *(G-6655)*

J-W Energy Company ....D 972 233-8191
Addison *(G-137)*

Key Energy Services Inc ....F 432 620-0300
Midland *(G-15269)*

Martin-Decker Totco Inc ....B 512 340-5000
Cedar Park *(G-2978)*

Natural Gas Services Group Inc ...C 432 262-2700
Midland *(G-15311)*

Nelson Oil Field Eqp & Sup ....F 361 375-2105
Pettus *(G-16653)*

Nigen International LLC ....E 713 956-8022
Houston *(G-11053)*

Oil States Energy Services LLC ...E 432 563-1304
Midland *(G-15326)*

Production Tech & Svcs Inc ....E 281 498-7399
Houston *(G-11437)*

Professional Rental Tools LLC .....E 713 808-9756
Houston *(G-11439)*

Rpc Inc ....E 361 289-7088
Corpus Christi *(G-3612)*

Select Energy Services LLC ....C 830 457-2215
Big Wells *(G-2104)*

Sellers Lease Service Inc ....F 361 865-2142
Flatonia *(G-6234)*

Sherman Branson Construction ....D 432 684-4740
Midland *(G-15408)*

Smith Energy Services Inc ....C 903 693-8872
Carthage *(G-2919)*

Spindletop Oil & Gas Co ....E 972 644-2581
Dallas *(G-4998)*

Superior Energy Services Inc ......D 713 654-2200
Houston *(G-12112)*

Superior Energy Services LLC .....E 281 999-0047
Houston *(G-12113)*

Superior Energy Services LLC .....D 281 784-5700
Houston *(G-12114)*

Superior Energy Services LLC .....E 281 934-2181
Brookshire *(G-2326)*

Swiftwater Energy Services LLC ...G 405 203-5419
Midland *(G-15427)*

T-P Rentals LLC ....E 432 558-7218
Crane *(G-3701)*

Total Oilfield Eqp & Sup LLC ......E 361 442-2922
Robstown *(G-17518)*

Twilight Services LLC ....F 817 326-4806
Granbury *(G-7815)*

U S Weatherford L P ....E 903 984-5541
Kilgore *(G-13599)*

Valiant Artfl Lift Sltions LLC ....F 432 253-2233
Midland *(G-15460)*

Wilson International Inc ....E 281 823-4700
Houston *(G-12673)*

LEASING & RENTAL SVCS: Oil Well Drilling

Drillform Drilling Eqp Inc ....E 281 948-9122
Odessa *(G-15980)*

Exceed Drilling Tech LLC ....F 512 656-9669
Austin *(G-1144)*

Keane Group Holdings LLC ....D 713 960-0381
Houston *(G-10510)*

Kelford Energy LLC ....F 817 615-0263
Fort Worth *(G-6754)*

Nabors International Inc ....E 281 874-0035
Houston *(G-10954)*

Pioneer Energy Services Corp .....C 855 884-0575
San Antonio *(G-18378)*

TSC Offshore Corporation ....F 832 456-3900
Houston *(G-12397)*

Wilson Systems Inc ....F 432 684-5567
Midland *(G-15470)*

LEASING & RENTAL: Computers & Eqpt

Premier Printing & Ltr Svc Inc ....E 713 868-6300
Houston *(G-11404)*

LEASING & RENTAL: Construction & Mining Eqpt

Builders Equipment & Tool Co .....D 713 869-3491
Houston *(G-9013)*

Franks International LLC ....D 281 966-7300
Houston *(G-9857)*

Gyrodata Incorporated ....D 361 289-1031
Corpus Christi *(G-3541)*

Holt Texas Ltd ....B 210 648-1111
San Antonio *(G-18171)*

J&P Ramirez Services LLC ....E 361 526-2072
Refugio *(G-17243)*

Rolligon Nov LP ....C 936 873-2600
Anderson *(G-531)*

Texas United Corporation ....E 713 877-1793
Houston *(G-12258)*

Triple R Welding LLC ....E 432 336-5289
Fort Stockton *(G-6330)*

Vernor Material & Eqp Co Inc .....D 409 233-3366
Freeport *(G-7221)*

LEASING & RENTAL: Medical Machinery & Eqpt

Chiron Holdings Inc ....E 210 524-9000
San Antonio *(G-18003)*

Inogen Inc ....A 972 616-5500
Plano *(G-16891)*

Kci International Inc ....E 210 524-9000
San Antonio *(G-18219)*

Kci Usa Inc ....C 800 275-4524
San Antonio *(G-18220)*

Smith & Nephew Inc ....B 817 900-4000
Fort Worth *(G-6994)*

LEASING & RENTAL: Mobile Home Sites

American Homestar Corporation ...E 281 334-9700
League City *(G-13946)*

Lakeside Trailer Sales ....F 936 564-6252
Nacogdoches *(G-15701)*

LEASING & RENTAL: Other Real Estate Property

Choctaw II Oil & Gas Ltd ....F 713 632-0222
Houston *(G-9184)*

Marathon International Oil Co ......D 713 629-6600
Houston *(G-10753)*

Prime Operating Company ....E 713 735-0000
Houston *(G-11416)*

Winston Land & Cattle Co Inc .....F 936 634-6321
Lufkin *(G-14557)*

LEASING & RENTAL: Trucks, Without Drivers

Automotive Rentals Inc ....E 817 624-3650
Fort Worth *(G-6411)*

WCI Construction Inc ....F 432 530-4009
Odessa *(G-16204)*

LEASING: Passenger Car

Automotive Rentals Inc ....E 817 624-3650
Fort Worth *(G-6411)*

Southwest Prof Vehicles ....F 214 371-3474
Dallas *(G-4992)*

LEASING: Residential Buildings

Melvin Hammon ....F 806 665-2667
Pampa *(G-16328)*

LEATHER GOODS, EXC FOOTWEAR, GLOVES, LUGGAGE/BELTING, WHOL

Bio World Merchandising Inc ....C 972 488-0655
Irving *(G-12948)*

LEATHER GOODS: Belting & Strapping

Texpac Hide & Skin Ltd ....D 817 626-6586
Fort Worth *(G-7052)*

LEATHER GOODS: Boots, Horse

Beck Cowboy Boots Inc ....G 806 373-1600
Amarillo *(G-402)*

Circle Y Saddles Inc ....F 361 293-1001
Yoakum *(G-20961)*

Franklin-Leddy Corporation ....E 325 653-3397
San Angelo *(G-17800)*

LEATHER GOODS: Cases

Samsill Corporation ....C 817 536-1906
Fort Worth *(G-6972)*

LEATHER GOODS: Checkbook Covers

Royal Case Company Inc ....C 903 364-5231
Whitewright *(G-20728)*

LEATHER GOODS: Garments

Europa Designs ....F 972 792-0997
Dallas *(G-4336)*

LEATHER GOODS: Holsters

JK Manufacturing Inc ....F 956 723-6893
Laredo *(G-13899)*

R E M Industries Inc ....F 915 544-2233
El Paso *(G-5924)*

LEATHER GOODS: Key Cases

Travis Assn For The Blind ....C 512 442-2329
Austin *(G-1590)*

LEATHER GOODS: Personal

3-D Belt Company LP ....E 979 743-4567
Schulenburg *(G-18770)*

Barrington Group Ltd Inc ....F 214 528-6990
Dallas *(G-4006)*

Brushy Creek Belt & Buckle Co ...F 361 293-2345
Yoakum *(G-20960)*

Franklin-Leddy Corporation ....E 325 653-3397
San Angelo *(G-17800)*

Justin Brands Inc ....A 915 778-8311
El Paso *(G-5824)*

Longhorn Leather Co ....E 903 454-4866
Greenville *(G-8083)*

R E M Industries Inc ....F 915 544-2233
El Paso *(G-5924)*

R K Texas Leather Mfg Inc ....G 903 378-2100
Honey Grove *(G-8358)*

Royal Case Company Inc ....C 903 868-0288
Sherman *(G-18930)*

San Antonio Shoe Inc ....A 830 768-7200
Del Rio *(G-5323)*

Simco Longhorn Leather ....D 972 542-8700
McKinney *(G-14974)*

Stallion Boot Co Inc ....F 915 532-6268
El Paso *(G-5974)*

Tony Lama Company Inc ....A 915 778-8311
El Paso *(G-6007)*

LEATHER GOODS: Saddles Or Parts

Big Bend Saddlery Inc ....F 432 837-5551
Alpine *(G-311)*

Calvin Allen Saddlery ....F 817 598-0505
Weatherford *(G-20581)*

Franklin-Leddy Corporation ....D 817 624-3149
Fort Worth *(G-6648)*

King Ranch Holdings Inc ....E 832 681-5700
Houston *(G-10535)*

Rocking T Saddlery ....F 903 455-6629
Greenville *(G-8089)*

Simco Longhorn Leather ....D 972 542-8700
McKinney *(G-14974)*

Tex Tan Western Co Yoakum Inc ...F 361 293-2314
Yoakum *(G-20973)*

Tucker Saddlery Inc ....F 361 293-3501
Yoakum *(G-20974)*

LEATHER GOODS: Seat Belts

Joyson Sfety Systems Acqstion ....E 210 250-5000
San Antonio *(G-18210)*

LEATHER GOODS: Stirrups, Wood Or Metal

Builders Post-Tension Inc ....E 281 873-9500
Houston *(G-9014)*

LEATHER TANNING & FINISHING

AA&e Leathercraft LLC ....G 361 293-6366
Yoakum *(G-20957)*

Damuth Taxidermy Inc ....F 325 597-0001
Brady *(G-2213)*

Magna Leather Corp ....F 915 772-0004
El Paso *(G-5858)*

Quality Fur Dressing ....F 281 292-2617
Spring *(G-19246)*

Employee Codes: A=Over 500 employees, B=251-500
C=101-250, D=51-100, E=20-50, F=10-19, G=9

2021 Harris Texas
Manufacturers Directory

PRODUCT

1539

LEATHER, LEATHER GOODS & FURS, WHOLESALE

R K Texas Leather Mfg Inc ....G....... 903 378-2100
Honey Grove *(G-8358)*

LEATHER: Accessory Prdts

Doiy LLC ....F 469 513-4159
Dallas *(G-4270)*

LEATHER: Bag

Gulf Coast Bag Inc ....F 281 556-8500
Houston *(G-10057)*

LEATHER: Processed

Custom Skin Co Inc ....F 325 655-9585
San Angelo *(G-17794)*

LEATHER: Shoe

Justin Brands Inc ....A 915 778-8311
El Paso *(G-5824)*
Tony Lama Company Inc ....A 915 778-8311
El Paso *(G-6007)*

LECTURING SVCS

Tan Boots LLC ....F 512 921-0720
Austin *(G-1713)*

LEGAL OFFICES & SVCS

Common Source LP ....F 281 443-7575
Houston *(G-9253)*
Stratgic Ltigation Partners LP ....C 713 995-8225
Katy *(G-13445)*
Thomson Reuters Corporation ....D 972 250-7000
Carrollton *(G-2832)*

LEGAL PROCESS SERVERS

Moneyonmobile Inc ....B 214 758-8600
Dallas *(G-4685)*

LENSES: Plastic, Exc Optical

Peak Nanosystems LLC ....E 469 464-4504
Coppell *(G-3434)*

LICENSE TAGS: Automobile, Stamped Metal

Auto License ....E 956 318-2158
Edinburg *(G-5576)*
Safe-T-Pet Inc ....F 903 569-0590
Mineola *(G-15511)*
Transportation Texas Dept ....F 940 937-2571
Childress *(G-3056)*

LIFE INSURANCE AGENTS

American Fincl Mktg Group Inc ....F 866 679-9241
League City *(G-13945)*

LIFE RAFTS: Rubber

Pugh Acquisition Company ....E 361 884-9351
Corpus Christi *(G-3600)*

LIGHT DISTILLATES

Exxon Mobil Corporation ....B 713 656-3636
Houston *(G-9739)*

LIGHT SENSITIVE DEVICES

Optek Technology Inc ....D 972 323-2200
Carrollton *(G-2786)*
Solaro Energy Inc ....F 575 838-3813
Nacogdoches *(G-15713)*

LIGHTER FLUID

Royal Oak Enterprises LLC ....D 903 455-5803
Greenville *(G-8090)*

LIGHTERS, CIGARETTE & CIGAR, WHOLESALE

Swedish Match North Amer LLC ....C 817 416-7017
Southlake *(G-19082)*

LIGHTING EQPT: Motor Vehicle

Feniex Industries Inc ....E 800 615-8350
Austin *(G-1154)*

LIGHTING EQPT: Motor Vehicle, Headlights

Marelli Automotive Ltg USA LLC ....F 915 872-1104
El Paso *(G-5864)*
Parrot Inc ....E 512 514-6840
Austin *(G-1397)*

LIGHTING EQPT: Motor Vehicle, NEC

Tenneco Inc ....A 915 832-4661
El Paso *(G-5997)*

LIGHTING EQPT: Outdoor

Imperial Outdoor Power Eqp ....F 832 939-9838
Sugar Land *(G-19495)*
Xtralight Manufacturing Ltd ....D 713 943-9927
Houston *(G-12709)*

LIGHTING FIXTURES WHOLESALERS

Behemoth Corporation ....E 281 332-4798
League City *(G-13949)*
Fleco Industries LLC ....C 972 247-3171
Carrollton *(G-2739)*
Fleco Industries LLC ....D 214 369-1101
Dallas *(G-4368)*
High End Systems Inc ....D 512 836-2242
Austin *(G-1203)*
Jaguar Designs Inc ....E 214 634-7733
Dallas *(G-4522)*
McDonald Lighting & Maint Sup ....G 903 297-8181
Longview *(G-14275)*
Mercron Inc ....F 972 690-6565
Irving *(G-13106)*
Pruf Energy Solutions LLC ....F 254 870-0400
Waco *(G-20450)*

LIGHTING FIXTURES, NEC

B&B Roadway SEC Solutions LLC ....F 972 385-7899
Mckinney *(G-14924)*
Clearpath Engineering Inc ....E 832 856-9040
Katy *(G-13392)*
Control Products Corporation ....C 972 264-0368
Grand Prairie *(G-7858)*
Cooper Lighting LLC ....F 770 486-4800
Houston *(G-9307)*
CPM Inc ....F 214 349-6886
Garland *(G-7470)*
Dallas Christie Lites Inc ....F 214 637-3535
Dallas *(G-4214)*
Drw Holdings ....F 949 581-9398
Cedar Park *(G-2966)*
Genlyte Thomas Group LLC ....G 512 392-5821
San Marcos *(G-18689)*
Good Sportsman Marketing LLC ....E 877 269-8490
Irving *(G-13040)*
High End Systems Inc ....D 512 836-2242
Austin *(G-1203)*
Hill & Smith Inc ....E 972 278-0553
Garland *(G-7513)*
Hubbell Building Automtn Inc ....E 512 450-1100
Austin *(G-1212)*
Jaguar Designs Inc ....E 214 634-7733
Dallas *(G-4522)*
Ledi2 Inc ....F 713 636-9152
Houston *(G-10615)*
Lighting Etc Inc ....F 281 992-8308
Pearland *(G-16579)*
Marlin Environmental Products ....F 214 493-9128
Richardson *(G-17351)*
Maverick Poles & Structure LLC ....G 817 441-9688
Benbrook *(G-2043)*
Modern Lantern ....F 214 507-8608
Fort Worth *(G-6844)*
Party Props Inc ....E 713 868-5433
Houston *(G-11253)*
Quality Lighting ....G 512 799-2341
San Marcos *(G-18705)*
Rulon Elc Illuminations Co Inc ....E 713 863-1133
Houston *(G-11697)*
Solais Lighting LLC ....E 469 294-1516
Frisco *(G-7313)*
Speedtech Lights Inc ....F 800 757-2581
Buda *(G-2539)*
Sterling Group LP ....E 713 877-8257
Houston *(G-12060)*

Twr Lighting Inc ....D 713 973-6905
Houston *(G-12416)*
Valen Light LLC ....E 512 222-5550
Austin *(G-1621)*
Worksite Lighting LLC ....E 225 313-3711
Haltom City *(G-8163)*
Yes Lighting LLC ....F 972 807-9197
Dallas *(G-5207)*

LIGHTING FIXTURES: Airport

Specialty Tower Lighting Ltd ....F 713 722-8123
Houston *(G-12002)*

LIGHTING FIXTURES: Arc

Luminator Holding LP ....C 972 424-6511
Plano *(G-16911)*
Mercron Inc ....F 972 690-6565
Irving *(G-13106)*

LIGHTING FIXTURES: Decorative Area

DA Schoggin Inc ....D 214 350-0591
Dallas *(G-4204)*
DA Schoggin Inc ....E 817 641-6800
Cleburne *(G-3086)*
Premier Lighting Entps LLC ....F 855 426-4544
Carrollton *(G-2794)*

LIGHTING FIXTURES: Fluorescent, Commercial

Encapsulite International Inc ....F 281 239-0225
Rosenberg *(G-17580)*
Ultravision International ....E 214 260-4500
Dallas *(G-5131)*

LIGHTING FIXTURES: Indl & Commercial

Acuity Brands Lighting Inc ....C 972 456-1451
Dallas *(G-3885)*
Aquila Environmental LLC ....G 817 953-3171
Fort Worth *(G-6397)*
ASG Energy LLC ....E 210 610-0036
San Antonio *(G-17915)*
Azz Inc ....E 713 943-0340
Houston *(G-8770)*
Blako ....F 972 898-7772
Royse City *(G-17715)*
Brandon Industries Inc ....E 972 542-3000
McKinney *(G-14929)*
Constellation Lighting Ltd ....G 832 717-5750
Houston *(G-9277)*
Cooper Lighting LLC ....D 972 929-9400
Irving *(G-12980)*
DA Schoggin Inc ....D 214 350-0591
Dallas *(G-4204)*
DA Schoggin Inc ....E 817 641-6800
Cleburne *(G-3086)*
Divine Ltg & Fabrication LLC ....E 936 494-3900
Conroe *(G-3294)*
Efficiency Aggregators LLC ....F 832 862-1103
Richmond *(G-17453)*
Energy Retrofitters Inc ....F 817 319-2796
Fort Worth *(G-6614)*
Festoni Inc ....F 713 830-1077
Houston *(G-9781)*
Fleco Industries LLC ....C 972 247-3171
Carrollton *(G-2739)*
Fleco Industries LLC ....D 214 369-1101
Dallas *(G-4368)*
Fluence Bioengineering Inc ....D 512 212-4544
Austin *(G-1163)*
Iglo LLC ....F 214 893-8703
Fort Worth *(G-6715)*
Illumitex Inc ....D 512 279-5020
Austin *(G-1224)*
Jaguar Designs Inc ....E 214 634-7733
Dallas *(G-4522)*
Koncept Systems LLC ....E 800 773-4910
Houston *(G-10557)*
Lighting & Power Tech LLC ....F 877 666-5267
Plano *(G-16909)*
Luminated Living LLC ....F 512 523-5550
Austin *(G-864)*
Luminator Holding LP ....C 972 424-6511
Plano *(G-16911)*
Luminator Technology Group LLC ....C 972 424-6511
Plano *(G-16913)*
Lunar Lighting Solutions LLC ....G 866 434-0732
Austin *(G-1312)*

M & M Lighting LP .... D 713 667-5611
Houston (G-10715)

Melissa Lighting Inc .... E 214 388-7487
Dallas (G-4665)

Michael R Atteberry .... F 214 222-3064
Lewisville (G-14067)

Neutex Advnced Enrgy Group Inc .... E 281 227-2208
Houston (G-11031)

Neutex Advnced Enrgy Group Inc .... E 281 227-2208
Houston (G-11032)

Pauluhn Electric Mfg LLP .... C 281 485-4311
Pearland (G-16587)

Philips North America LLC .... C 800 526-2731
Carrollton (G-2881)

Retro Ltg & Conservation Lc .... E 281 302-6431
Sugar Land (G-19534)

Robogistics LLC .... E 713 364-4430
Port Arthur (G-17123)

Rulon Elc Illuminations Co Inc .... E 713 863-1133
Houston (G-11697)

Signify North America Corp .... F 800 235-2314
San Marcos (G-18711)

Signify North America Corp .... C 214 647-7880
Dallas (G-4961)

Snelson Oilfield Ltg Co Inc .... E 817 926-0571
Fort Worth (G-6998)

Snowball Lighting Inc .... F 915 227-7210
El Paso (G-5965)

Texas Lightsmith Inc .... F 512 264-2266
Austin (G-1568)

Texas Solar Resources Inc .... F 281 846-4968
League City (G-13981)

US Led Ltd .... E 713 972-9191
Houston (G-12486)

Vari-Lite LLC .... C 214 647-7880
Dallas (G-5156)

Xtralight Manufacturing Ltd .... D 713 943-9927
Houston (G-12709)

LIGHTING FIXTURES: Marine

Pauluhn Electric Mfg LLP .... C 281 485-4311
Pearland (G-16587)

LIGHTING FIXTURES: Motor Vehicle

Hamar Industries Inc .... E 817 756-8990
Fort Worth (G-6685)

LIGHTING FIXTURES: Ornamental, Commercial

Fenner Technologies Inc .... C 972 264-0368
Grand Prairie (G-7870)

Shine Lighting Group Usa Inc .... E 973 865-5893
Dallas (G-4956)

Solara Ironworks LLC .... E 214 744-9900
Dallas (G-4975)

LIGHTING FIXTURES: Public

Allan Banks .... F 936 337-4020
Willis (G-20841)

Kw Industries Inc .... C 281 240-0909
Sugar Land (G-19502)

LIGHTING FIXTURES: Residential

2v Led LLC .... D 325 227-4577
San Angelo (G-17767)

Abbys Thres No Pl Like HM Fur .... F 817 244-3371
Fort Worth (G-6340)

AC Electronics .... F 817 701-1400
Arlington (G-606)

Blako .... F 972 898-7772
Royse City (G-17715)

Brandon Industries Inc .... E 972 542-3000
McKinney (G-14929)

Cooper Lighting LLC .... D 972 929-9400
Irving (G-12980)

Dolan Northwest LLC .... E 972 559-6900
Frisco (G-7257)

Fleco Industries LLC .... C 972 247-3171
Carrollton (G-2739)

Gill Assoc Prprty MGT Systems .... G 832 644-9751
Humble (G-12770)

Iglo LLC .... F 214 893-8703
Fort Worth (G-6715)

Illuminate Vintage LLC .... G 903 948-1161
Houston (G-10328)

Intermatic Incorporated .... F 915 858-9204
El Paso (G-5813)

Jaguar Designs Inc .... E 214 634-7733
Dallas (G-4522)

Melissa Lighting Inc .... E 214 388-7487
Dallas (G-4665)

Pauluhn Electric Mfg LLP .... C 281 485-4311
Pearland (G-16587)

Principal Lighting Group LLC .... D 325 227-4577
San Angelo (G-17824)

Rulon Elc Illuminations Co Inc .... E 713 863-1133
Houston (G-11697)

Solara Ironworks LLC .... E 214 744-9900
Dallas (G-4975)

Solavanti Trading LLC .... E 214 221-9405
Dallas (G-4976)

TMI LLC .... E 469 231-6918
The Colony (G-19816)

Trade Source International .... E 972 393-3800
Coppell (G-3450)

LIGHTING FIXTURES: Street

Mel Northey Co Inc .... F 281 445-3485
Houston (G-10825)

Production Warehousing Inc .... D 915 779-1405
El Paso (G-5920)

Thomas M Niland Company .... E 915 779 1405
El Paso (G-6002)

LIGHTING FIXTURES: Swimming Pool

Pool & Electrical Products Inc .... F 512 707-0109
Austin (G-1424)

LIME

Chemical Lime-Southwest LLC .... F 281 431-0575
Rosharon (G-17602)

Chemical Lime-Southwest LLC .... E 281 471-4500
La Porte (G-13727)

Chemical Lime-Southwest LLC .... E 817 268-1188
Hurst (G-12842)

Chemical Lime-Southwest LLC .... C 254 675-8668
Clifton (G-3142)

Lhoist North America Inc .... D 830 625-2327
New Braunfels (G-15809)

Lhoist North America Ala LLC .... D 817 732-8164
Fort Worth (G-6785)

Lhoist North America Ala LLC .... E 817 268-1187
Hurst (G-12849)

Lhoist North America Texas Ltd .... E 830 625-2327
New Braunfels (G-15810)

Texas Lime Company .... D 817 641-4433
Cleburne (G-3114)

LIME: Building

Austin White Lime Company .... F 512 255-3646
Austin (G-966)

LIME: Dolomitic, Dead-Burned Dolomite

Lhoist North America Texas Ltd .... E 817 732-8164
Hurst (G-12850)

LIME: Hydrated

Martin Mrtta Mtls Suthwest LLC .... B 210 208-4400
San Antonio (G-18280)

LIMESTONE & MARBLE: Dimension

Alkusari Texas Limestone Corp .... F 512 339-2299
Bertram (G-2050)

Arrow Crushed Stone Inc .... F 817 423-1337
Fort Worth (G-6402)

Pb Materials Holdings Inc .... E 432 563-8036
Odessa (G-16106)

LIMESTONE: Crushed & Broken

Arrow Crushed Stone Inc .... F 817 423-1337
Fort Worth (G-6402)

Cemex Construction Mtls S LLC .... D 830 608-3556
New Braunfels (G-15779)

Cemex Construction Mtls S LLC .... A 713 650-6200
Houston (G-9128)

Chemical Lime-Southwest LLC .... C 254 675-8668
Clifton (G-3142)

Chico Stone Inc .... E 972 276-2284
Garland (G-7456)

Cooke County Crushed Stone .... F 940 759-4104
Muenster (G-15668)

Custom Crushed Stone Inc .... E 210 688-3413
San Antonio (G-18036)

Frost Crushed Stone Co Inc .... C 254 587-2472
Kosse (G-13666)

Gulf Coast Limestone Inc .... F 281 474-4124
Seabrook (G-18785)

Hanson Aggregates LLC .... E 512 756-8255
Burnet (G-2609)

Hanson Aggregates LLC .... D 210 658-7461
New Braunfels (G-15801)

Hanson Aggregates LLC .... E 210 658-3533
New Braunfels (G-15802)

Hanson Lehigh Inc .... E 281 616-0700
Houston (G-10120)

Hanson Lehigh Inc .... B 972 653-5500
Irving (G-13052)

Jr Thompson Inc .... F 940 995-2245
Saint Jo (G-17763)

Legacy Vulcan LLC .... E 830 278-6205
Uvalde (G-20190)

Legacy Vulcan LLC .... E 325 646-8526
Brownwood (G-2435)

Legacy Vulcan LLC .... D 210 492-1053
San Antonio (G-18243)

Lhoist North America Ala LLC .... D 817 732-8164
Fort Worth (G-6785)

Lhoist North America Tenn Inc .... E 254 486-2105
Crawford (G-3704)

Lhoist North America Tenn Inc .... E 817 732-8164
Fort Worth (G-6787)

Lhoist North America Texas Ltd .... E 254 698-6610
Nolanville (G-15871)

Live Oak Materials Inc .... E 361 775-0065
Ingleside (G-12896)

M E Ruby Jr Inc .... C 512 258-1601
Cedar Park (G-2977)

Marietta Martin Materials Inc .... F 979 758-3960
Garwood (G-7615)

Martin Marietta Materials Inc .... E 210 495-6224
San Antonio (G-18279)

Martin Marietta Materials Inc .... E 972 350-8200
Dallas (G-4640)

Martin Marietta Materials Inc .... E 830 591-1887
Uvalde (G-20192)

Martin Mrtta Mtls Suthwest LLC .... B 210 208-4400
San Antonio (G-18280)

Martin Mrtta Mtls Suthwest LLC .... D 940 644-5084
Chico (G-3053)

Martin Mrtta Mtls Suthwest LLC .... C 956 381-1459
Edinburg (G-5595)

Mezger Enterprises Ltd .... D 254 547-8174
Kempner (G-13486)

North Texas Crushed Stone .... F 940 665-9100
Gainesville (G-7355)

Rock Crushers Inc .... F 979 289-3768
Burton (G-2620)

Superior Stone Inc .... E 512 327-4509
Austin (G-1550)

Superior Stone Inc .... F 512 746-2608
Jarrell (G-13273)

Texas Crushed Stone Company .... C 512 255-4405
Georgetown (G-7684)

Texas Lime Company .... E 972 385-1335
Dallas (G-5075)

Texas Lime Company .... D 817 641-4433
Cleburne (G-3114)

Texastone Quarries LLC .... E 432 354-2569
Garden City (G-7417)

Thompson Jr Inc .... F 940 665-2533
Gainesville (G-7372)

United States Lime & Mnrl Inc .... E 972 991-8400
Dallas (G-5138)

Vantacore Partners LLC .... F 215 751-1403
Houston (G-12530)

Vulcan Materials Company .... E 830 624-4944
New Braunfels (G-15831)

Vulcan Materials Company .... E 940 683-4996
Bridgeport (G-2304)

Word Constructors LLC .... F 830 693-2933
Marble Falls (G-14752)

LIMESTONE: Cut & Shaped

Texas Industries Inc .... C 972 647-6700
Dallas (G-5062)

US Lbm Holdings LLC .... C 713 650-6200
Houston (G-12485)

LIMESTONE: Dimension

Chemical Lime-Southwest LLC .... C 254 675-8668
Clifton (G-3142)

Continental Quarries .... F 325 228-4180
Lueders (G-14517)

PRODUCT

Lueders Limestone LP ....D....... 325 228-4370
  Florence *(G-6241)*
Salado Operations LLC ....C....... 254 793-3355
  Florence *(G-6243)*
Texastone Quarries LLC ....E....... 432 354-2569
  Garden City *(G-7417)*
Zemer International LLC ....E....... 214 227-2320
  Midlothian *(G-15497)*

LIMESTONE: Ground

Capitol Aggregates Inc ....C....... 210 871-6100
  San Antonio *(G-17981)*
Lattimore Materials Corp ....C....... 972 221-4646
  Addison *(G-143)*
Patara Stone Inc ....E....... 713 681-2301
  Houston *(G-11257)*
Vulcan Materials Company ....F....... 210 349-3311
  San Antonio *(G-18603)*
Vulcan Materials Company ....F....... 210 494-9555
  San Antonio *(G-18604)*

LINEN SPLY SVC: Uniform

Ghashim Capital Ventures Corp ....F....... 713 266-1888
  Houston *(G-9949)*
Gormans Uniform Rental Inc ....D....... 713 467-5424
  Houston *(G-10006)*
San Bay Studio Inc ....F....... 940 387-4466
  Denton *(G-5399)*
Unifirst Corporation ....D....... 817 834-7386
  Haltom City *(G-8160)*
Uniform Concepts Inc ....F....... 512 345-5793
  Austin *(G-1607)*

LINENS: Tablecloths, From Purchased Materials

CFS Brands LLC ....E....... 972 466-1030
  Flower Mound *(G-6262)*
Glen Kammerman Enterprises Inc ....D....... 713 666-0602
  Houston *(G-9963)*

LINER STRIPS: Rubber

Western Falcon LLC ....E....... 832 391-9461
  Houston *(G-12643)*

LINERS & LINING

Kurosky & Co Pntg Contrs Inc ....E....... 817 834-7179
  Fort Worth *(G-6776)*

LINERS: Freight Car Door, Metal Strip Reinforced

American Railcar Inds Inc ....D....... 936 365-2679
  Goodrich *(G-7768)*

LINERS: Indl, Metal Plate

Chromium Corporation ....F....... 972 851-0500
  Dallas *(G-4115)*

LININGS: Vulcanizable Rubber

Metso Minerals Industries Inc ....E....... 210 491-9521
  San Antonio *(G-18295)*

LINTELS: Steel, Light Gauge

California Expanded Met Pdts ....D....... 817 568-1525
  Fort Worth *(G-6487)*
International Steel Frmng LLC ....F....... 817 591-0507
  Richland Hills *(G-17438)*

LIQUEFIED PETROLEUM GAS DEALERS

Andeavor LLC ....C....... 210 626-6000
  San Antonio *(G-17907)*
Fred Brown Methanol Inc ....F....... 806 665-0034
  Pampa *(G-16323)*
Matheson Tri-Gas Inc ....E....... 512 385-0611
  Austin *(G-1330)*

LIQUEFIED PETROLEUM GAS WHOLESALERS

Dcp Midstream LLC ....E....... 432 693-2204
  Midkiff *(G-15095)*
Flint Hills Resources LP ....C....... 361 241-4811
  Corpus Christi *(G-3531)*

Martin Midstream Partners LP ....F....... 281 471-2211
  La Porte *(G-13774)*
Midcoast Energy LLC ....C....... 713 821-2000
  Houston *(G-10871)*
Regency Energy Partners LP ....D....... 214 750-1771
  Dallas *(G-4881)*
Sandifers LP Gas & Svc Co Inc ....F....... 409 963-1269
  Port Arthur *(G-17124)*
Ssb Manufacturing Company ....B....... 972 874-9666
  Grapevine *(G-8055)*
US Petrochemicals Inc ....F....... 713 871-1951
  Houston *(G-12487)*

LIQUID CRYSTAL DISPLAYS

Newline Interactive Inc ....F....... 972 468-9728
  Plano *(G-16944)*
Rpmtronics Incorporated ....A....... 972 865-1330
  Carrollton *(G-2810)*

LOCK & KEY SVCS

Defiant Safe Co Inc ....E....... 972 243-3711
  Dallas *(G-4248)*

LOCKERS: Wood, Exc Refrigerated

Hollman Inc ....C....... 972 815-4000
  Irving *(G-13058)*
Legacy Lockers LLC ....E....... 972 937-1088
  Dallas *(G-4588)*

LOCKS

Firstex Industries Inc ....F....... 972 602-1478
  Grand Prairie *(G-7872)*
Rolland Safe & Lock Co LLC ....D....... 972 243-3711
  Dallas *(G-4909)*
Southern Flger Dtntion Eqp LLC ....C....... 210 533-1231
  San Antonio *(G-18487)*
Worldwide Locking Systems Inc ....F....... 972 775-6320
  Midlothian *(G-15496)*

LOCKS & LOCK SETS, WHOLESALE

Maintenance Builders Sup Ltd ....E....... 713 462-8213
  Houston *(G-10741)*
Worldwide Locking Systems Inc ....F....... 972 775-6320
  Midlothian *(G-15496)*

LOCKS: Coin-Operated

Cki Locker LLC ....F....... 817 329-1600
  Dfw Airport *(G-5452)*

LOCKS: Safe & Vault, Metal

Fullers Alamo Safe & Lock ....G....... 210 344-4523
  San Antonio *(G-18130)*

LOCKSMITHS

ASAP Glass & Door LLC ....F....... 214 770-8266
  Denton *(G-5351)*
Fullers Alamo Safe & Lock ....G....... 210 344-4523
  San Antonio *(G-18130)*
Lock Dock Inc ....F....... 903 759-1288
  Longview *(G-14265)*
Rolland Safe & Lock Co LLC ....D....... 972 243-3711
  Dallas *(G-4909)*

LOCOMOTIVES & PARTS

Trinity Rail Group LLC ....F....... 214 631-4420
  Dallas *(G-5114)*

LOG LOADING & UNLOADING SVCS

C & C Logging ....F....... 903 895-4738
  New London *(G-15849)*

LOGGING

Cecil Phillips Lumber Mill ....F....... 903 684-3516
  De Kalb *(G-5236)*
Don Lane Logging Inc ....G....... 409 584-2288
  Pineland *(G-16738)*
Eld Operations LLC ....D....... 630 338-5425
  Kermit *(G-13511)*
Flurry and Son Logging Contr ....F....... 409 384-5441
  Jasper *(G-13275)*
Forrest Hodges Operations ....E....... 936 867-4910
  Alto *(G-315)*
Hlh Timber Company LLC ....E....... 936 269-4199
  Joaquin *(G-13311)*

Hollman Inc ....C....... 972 815-4000
  Irving *(G-13058)*
Jml Management Inc ....F....... 936 591-9782
  Center *(G-3000)*
King Roy Jr Logging Inc ....F....... 936 563-4899
  Livingston *(G-14158)*
Lindsay Forest Products Inc ....F....... 903 693-7526
  Carthage *(G-2913)*
Procella Logging ....F....... 409 787-2325
  Hemphill *(G-8247)*
Randy L Gardner Inc ....F....... 409 837-5111
  Colmesneil *(G-3222)*
Texas Timberjack Inc ....D....... 409 397-4221
  Bon Wier *(G-2151)*
W C Hodges Logging ....F....... 936 867-4550
  Wells *(G-20658)*
Weyerhaeuser Company ....C....... 940 230-4670
  Denton *(G-5412)*

LOGGING CAMPS & CONTRACTORS

Brocks Logging Inc ....E....... 281 593-1531
  Cleveland *(G-3121)*
Colvin Timber Company LC ....F....... 936 563-4404
  Livingston *(G-14151)*
Cypress River Logging Corp ....F....... 903 236-7696
  Longview *(G-14219)*
D & L Timber Inc ....E....... 936 422-3153
  Huntington *(G-12809)*
Dean Due Logging Inc ....F....... 936 642-2782
  Groveton *(G-8112)*
Dennis W Oates Logging LLC ....E....... 936 526-2700
  Diboll *(G-5464)*
Dewayne Rogers Logging Inc ....F....... 936 831-2060
  Apple Springs *(G-591)*
Douglassville Timber Co ....G....... 903 796-7691
  Atlanta *(G-842)*
G & G Logging LLC ....E....... 936 269-9086
  Joaquin *(G-13310)*
Howard Croft ....F....... 936 258-3321
  Dayton *(G-5229)*
Jan Pate Inc ....F....... 903 683-5700
  Rusk *(G-17732)*
Keith Carrell Logging Inc ....E....... 936 422-3375
  Huntington *(G-12810)*
Kim R Smith Logging Inc ....E....... 903 947-6242
  Tatum *(G-19644)*
Ms Logging Inc ....F....... 409 382-2424
  Bon Wier *(G-2149)*
Porterfield Timber Harvesting ....G....... 936 598-4203
  Center *(G-3007)*
Red Watson Logging Inc ....F....... 409 565-2484
  Wiergate *(G-20840)*
Renfro Logging I Ltd ....E....... 936 208-6177
  Lufkin *(G-14550)*
Rhonda Griffin ....F....... 936 715-0735
  Nacogdoches *(G-15712)*
Spurlock Logging Inc ....E....... 409 429-4333
  Woodville *(G-20917)*
Teer Logging Inc ....F....... 936 632-6862
  Lufkin *(G-14554)*
Williams Logging ....F....... 936 632-6891
  Lufkin *(G-14556)*

LOGGING: Fuel Wood Harvesting

Cdw Consultant Group LLC ....E....... 361 237-9339
  Bloomington *(G-2111)*

LOGGING: Timber, Cut At Logging Camp

Batson Lumber Company LLC ....E....... 936 262-8000
  Batson *(G-1766)*
David Hatton Logging Inc ....G....... 409 656-8535
  Hillister *(G-8318)*

LOGGING: Wooden Logs

Stetson International LP ....G....... 281 592-4788
  Cleveland *(G-3137)*

LOGS: Gas, Fireplace

Golden Blount Inc ....E....... 972 250-3113
  Addison *(G-131)*

LOOSELEAF BINDERS

Abco Inc ....D....... 214 428-8996
  Dallas *(G-3878)*
Dallas Lghthouse For Blind Inc ....C....... 214 821-2375
  Dallas *(G-4217)*

Design Packaging Group Ltd.................F 254 840-2500
  Mc Gregor **(G-14820)**

South Txas Lghthouse For Blind.........C 361 883-6553
  Corpus Christi **(G-3627)**

Space Age Lmnating Bindery Inc.........F 713 868-1471
  Houston **(G-11987)**

Westgate Graphics.................F 713 688-1292
  Houston **(G-12645)**

LOTIONS OR CREAMS: Face

Bayport Laboratories LLC.................E 832 230-0480
  Houston **(G-8837)**

Chateau Noblesse Inc.................D 972 365-7017
  Carrollton **(G-2859)**

Fruit of Earth Inc.................E 817 510-1600
  Grand Prairie **(G-7880)**

Revision LLC.................E 972 756-1026
  Irving **(G-13165)**

Swiss-American Cdmo LLC.................C 214 239-2280
  Carrollton **(G-2822)**

Two Old Goats LLC.................G 817 520-4230
  Haltom City **(G-8159)**

LOUVERS: Ventilating

Metallic Products Corporation.................D 713 856-9696
  Houston **(G-10849)**

LUBRICANTS: Corrosion Preventive

Alpha Lubricants LLC.................F 214 971-1170
  Sealy **(G-18804)**

Championx LLC.................A 281 632-6500
  Sugar Land **(G-19455)**

Denso North America USA Inc.................E 281 821-3355
  Houston **(G-9437)**

Gc3 Specialty Chemicals Inc.................F 713 802-1761
  Houston **(G-9909)**

Global Cathodic Protection Inc.................F 713 784-9588
  Houston **(G-9967)**

Kcc Corrosion Control Co Ltd.................F 281 550-1199
  Houston **(G-10504)**

Pacific Sensor LLC.................F 972 242-5750
  Carrollton **(G-2788)**

LUBRICATING EQPT: Indl

A&K Industrial Repair LLC.................E 281 470-8848
  Deer Park **(G-5258)**

TF Hudgins Holdings Inc.................C 713 682-3651
  Houston **(G-12266)**

LUBRICATING OIL & GREASE WHOLESALERS

Amrep Inc.................D 972 227-3304
  Desoto **(G-5428)**

Darling Ingredients Inc.................E 214 948-7501
  Dallas **(G-4238)**

Valley Proteins (de) Inc.................E 806 379-6001
  Amarillo **(G-519)**

LUBRICATING SYSTEMS: Centralized

Compressor Products Intl LLC.................D 713 462-1061
  Houston **(G-9261)**

Lubrication Systems Texas LLC.................D 713 464-6266
  Houston **(G-8388)**

LUBRICATION SYSTEMS & EQPT

Butterworth Inc.................F 281 821-7300
  Houston **(G-9022)**

Turbomasters Inc.................F 210 690-1958
  San Antonio **(G-18572)**

LUBRICATORS: Grease Guns

Dualco Inc.................E 713 644-1164
  Houston **(G-9536)**

Triton Products LLC.................F 940 455-2800
  Argyle **(G-604)**

LUGGAGE & BRIEFCASES

Blacksheep Inc.................B 903 592-3853
  Tyler **(G-20059)**

Custom Direct Inc.................F 201 934-4229
  Plano **(G-16834)**

Jon Hart Design Co.................E 210 226-8544
  San Antonio **(G-18206)**

Marc Johnsonusa Inc.................F 713 780-8486
  Houston **(G-10762)**

LUGGAGE & LEATHER GOODS STORES

R E M Industries Inc.................F 915 544-2233
  El Paso **(G-5924)**

LUGGAGE & LEATHER GOODS STORES: Leather, Exc Luggage & Shoes

King Ranch Inc.................E 832 681-5700
  Houston **(G-10534)**

R K Texas Leather Mfg Inc.................G 903 378-2100
  Honey Grove **(G-8358)**

LUGGAGE & LEATHER GOODS STORES: Luggage, Exc Footlckr/Trunk

Brady Standard Herald Inc.................F 325 597-2959
  Brady **(G-2211)**

LUGGAGE WHOLESALERS

Barrington Group Ltd Inc.................F 214 528-6990
  Dallas **(G-4006)**

Marc Johnsonusa Inc.................F 713 780-8486
  Houston **(G-10762)**

Xact Xpressions Inc.................E 972 242-6332
  Dallas **(G-5205)**

LUGGAGE: Traveling Bags

Eagle Creek Inc.................D 760 431-6400
  Uvalde **(G-20189)**

LUMBER & BLDG MATLS DEALER, RET: Garage Doors, Sell/Install

Accent Door Co Inc.................E 913 780-5800
  San Antonio **(G-17856)**

Hollywood Ovrhd Door of Dallas.................E 214 348-7240
  Dallas **(G-4464)**

Hrh Door Corp.................F 281 821-8572
  Houston **(G-10273)**

Premier Entry Systems LLC.................F 817 422-5908
  Fort Worth **(G-6913)**

RDHS Inc.................F 361 852-4094
  Corpus Christi **(G-3606)**

Richmonds American Svc Ctr Inc.................F 972 681-2222
  McKinney **(G-14971)**

WD Norton Inc.................F 903 758-0301
  Longview **(G-14332)**

LUMBER & BLDG MATLS DEALER, RET: Wallboard, Compositn/Panel

Kenmark Architectural Pdts Inc.................F 800 788-8263
  Dallas **(G-4550)**

Loftwall Inc.................F 214 239-3162
  Grand Prairie **(G-7916)**

LUMBER & BLDG MATLS DEALERS, RET: Energy Conservation Prdts

Aloterra Energy LLC.................F 713 412-5311
  The Woodlands **(G-19823)**

T-3 Energy Services Inc.................F 713 944-5950
  Houston **(G-12143)**

Texod Energy LLC.................F 214 998-5360
  Dallas **(G-5079)**

LUMBER & BLDG MATRLS DEALERS, RET: Bath Fixtures, Eqpt/Sply

Builders Depot Direct LLC.................F 832 384-7272
  Houston **(G-9012)**

Dura-Mar Venus Inc.................D 972 223-8008
  Desoto **(G-5430)**

Ganten Group LLC.................F 214 530-5483
  Richardson **(G-17320)**

Tex-Sun Shade Specialties Inc.................F 972 279-0132
  Dallas **(G-5053)**

LUMBER & BLDG MTRLS DEALERS, RET: Insultn & Energy Consrvtn

Voyager Energy Services LLC.................F 830 583-9590
  Kenedy **(G-13493)**

LUMBER & BLDG MTRLS DEALERS, RET: Planing Mill Prdts/Lumber

Hixson Lumber Sales Inc.................E 903 527-4010
  Caddo Mills **(G-2624)**

Triple C Hardware & Lumber Inc.................E 325 392-4123
  Ozona **(G-16289)**

LUMBER & BUILDING MATERIAL DEALERS, RETAIL: Roofing Material

Allied Truss LLC.................E 903 586-1982
  Jacksonville **(G-13225)**

Texas Refinery Corp.................F 682 518-1405
  Mansfield **(G-14722)**

LUMBER & BUILDING MATERIALS DEALER, RET: Door & Window Prdts

Allen and Allen LLC.................D 210 733-9191
  San Antonio **(G-17894)**

Custom Cabinet Doors Inc.................E 940 686-2808
  Pilot Point **(G-16723)**

Hrh Door Corp.................F 915 590-8997
  El Paso **(G-5805)**

Jeld-Wen Inc.................D 972 272-3667
  Garland **(G-7526)**

Macgmc LLC.................F 214 774-4455
  Plano **(G-16916)**

T R W Modernfold Company Inc.................F 214 357-2572
  Lewisville **(G-14096)**

LUMBER & BUILDING MATERIALS DEALER, RET: Masonry Matls/Splys

Espinoza Stone Inc.................D 830 629-2530
  New Braunfels **(G-15791)**

Forterra Pipe & Precast LLC.................F 512 385-3950
  Austin **(G-1168)**

Hydro Conduit of Texas LP.................E 832 590-5300
  Houston **(G-10303)**

Pavestone LLC.................E 512 558-7283
  San Marcos **(G-18703)**

Rocla Concrete Tie Inc.................E 806 383-7071
  Amarillo **(G-459)**

Suncoast Post-Tension Ltd.................F 512 259-7908
  Leander **(G-13998)**

Tyler Products Sales Inc.................F 903 593-8633
  Tyler **(G-20172)**

LUMBER & BUILDING MATERIALS DEALERS, RETAIL: Brick

Acme Brick Company.................D 512 281-5744
  Elgin **(G-6052)**

Acme Brick Company.................C 817 332-4101
  Fort Worth **(G-6343)**

Acme Brick Company.................D 325 949-7685
  San Angelo **(G-17770)**

Justin Industries Inc.................D 512 258-1474
  Cedar Park **(G-2975)**

Justin Industries Inc.................D 979 885-4124
  Sealy **(G-18811)**

Justin Industries Inc.................D 817 332-4101
  Fort Worth **(G-6750)**

Meridian Brick LLC.................F 281 442-8400
  Houston **(G-10835)**

LUMBER & BUILDING MATERIALS DEALERS, RETAIL: Cement

Cemex Construction Mtls S LLC.................F 281 457-0031
  Channelview **(G-3015)**

Ingram Readymix Inc.................F 830 334-3622
  Pearsall **(G-16613)**

LUMBER & BUILDING MATERIALS DEALERS, RETAIL: Countertops

Golden Stones LP.................E 713 934-7887
  Houston **(G-9994)**

Rock Fin Countertops Inc.................E 713 460-4441
  Houston **(G-11649)**

Siri Granite Inc.................F 832 203-8322
  Houston **(G-11907)**

PRODUCT

LUMBER & BUILDING MATERIALS DEALERS, RETAIL: Flooring, Wood

Rbt Industries LLC ....F 512 600-5994
Austin *(G-1453)*

Regal Hardwoods Inc ....F 972 620-8833
Carrollton *(G-2804)*

LUMBER & BUILDING MATERIALS DEALERS, RETAIL: Paving Stones

Desert Rock Co ....F 915 859-5969
El Paso *(G-5721)*

LUMBER & BUILDING MATERIALS DEALERS, RETAIL: Sand & Gravel

Bruce Kennedy Sand & Gravel Co ....F 903 838-3377
Texarkana *(G-19757)*

Sealy Concrete Inc ....E 281 391-3435
Sealy *(G-18818)*

Tricounty Materials & Svcs LP ....F 972 446-1816
Sanger *(G-18731)*

Wright Materials Inc ....D 361 387-1511
Robstown *(G-17519)*

LUMBER & BUILDING MATERIALS DEALERS, RETAIL: Tile, Ceramic

American Marazzi Tile Inc ....G 972 232-3800
Fort Worth *(G-6381)*

Architerra Inc ....F 512 441-8062
Austin *(G-930)*

Arizona Tile LLC ....E 713 292-1001
Houston *(G-8696)*

Creative Tile Inc ....G 214 827-0552
Dallas *(G-4182)*

IB Supply LLC ....F 469 709-9650
Carrollton *(G-2870)*

Stone Production Inc ....F 512 990-9800
Austin *(G-1539)*

LUMBER & BUILDING MATERIALS RET DEALERS: Millwork & Lumber

Brownsvlle Architectural Mllwk ....E 956 592-5423
Brownsville *(G-2341)*

Builders Firstsource - SE Grp ....D 214 880-3500
Dallas *(G-4065)*

Builders Firstsource-Ohio Vall ....C 214 880-3500
Dallas *(G-4067)*

Computerized Millwork Svcs Inc ....F 281 575-1699
Houston *(G-9265)*

Growth Holdings LLC ....E 972 241-9535
Dallas *(G-4418)*

Gunter Lumber Company Inc ....E 903 433-1303
Gunter *(G-8115)*

Halls Lumber Inc ....F 806 285-2393
Olton *(G-16226)*

Liberty Company ....E 817 921-0218
Fort Worth *(G-6788)*

Metroplex Millworks Inc ....F 214 358-1770
Dallas *(G-4672)*

Morgan Trim Inc ....F 806 655-9777
Canyon *(G-2674)*

Paramount Millwork Corporation ....E 817 429-1145
Fort Worth *(G-6894)*

Saw Custom Millwork Inc ....E 972 288-2118
Mesquite *(G-15076)*

LUMBER & BUILDING MATLS DEALERS, RET: Concrete/Cinder Block

Affordable Asphalt Paving Inc ....F 903 596-7003
Tyler *(G-20044)*

Charles Barton ....E 512 759-1231
Hutto *(G-12877)*

LUMBER & BUILDING MATLS DEALERS, RET: Screens, Door/Window

Jones Aluminum ....F 409 866-5585
Beaumont *(G-1913)*

Next Century Screens Inc ....F 972 496-4981
Garland *(G-7563)*

LUMBER: Cants, Resawn

Hicks Post Co Inc ....E 936 858-4228
Alto *(G-316)*

LUMBER: Cut Stock, Softwood

Conner Industries Inc ....E 817 439-3555
Fort Worth *(G-6541)*

LUMBER: Dimension, Hardwood

G & S Lumber Co Inc ....E 936 564-7676
Nacogdoches *(G-15699)*

Ufp New Waverly LLC ....D 936 295-3411
New Waverly *(G-15861)*

LUMBER: Fiberboard

Georgia-Pacific LLC ....C 936 829-5511
Diboll *(G-5466)*

LUMBER: Hardboard

World Research Company Inc ....E 903 581-3720
Tyler *(G-20177)*

LUMBER: Hardwood Dimension

Brazos Forest Products LP ....E 512 443-0777
Austin *(G-1006)*

LUMBER: Hardwood Dimension & Flooring Mills

Ameripro Partnership LP ....F 713 526-3936
Houston *(G-8620)*

Caney Creek Moulding Inc ....E 936 560-1331
Nacogdoches *(G-15689)*

Cecil Phillips Lumber Mill ....F 903 684-3516
De Kalb *(G-5236)*

Clarks Hardwood Lumber Co LP ....F 713 862-6628
Houston *(G-9211)*

Conner Industries Inc ....E 956 781-0215
Alamo *(G-178)*

G D Edgar Lumber Co Inc ....F 409 787-2452
Hemphill *(G-8246)*

Industrial Lumber and Box Inc ....F 713 928-2096
Houston *(G-10351)*

K L Barton & Sons Tie Co ....F 936 347-2744
Garrison *(G-7611)*

Rodco-Brandt Manufacturing ....E 817 477-4118
Mansfield *(G-14713)*

Southern Forest Products LLC ....D 409 634-3365
Bon Wier *(G-2150)*

Unique Wood Products Inc ....F 713 462-5045
Houston *(G-12441)*

Venetian Blind Flr Cvg Sp Ltd ....E 713 528-2404
Houston *(G-12546)*

West Fraser Inc ....C 903 628-2506
New Boston *(G-15770)*

LUMBER: Panels, Plywood, Softwood

Georgia-Pacific WD Pdts S LLC ....A 936 398-2511
Camden *(G-2638)*

LUMBER: Plywood, Hardwood

C & H Hardwoods Inc ....F 817 561-7711
Fort Worth *(G-6482)*

Century Millwork LLC ....E 281 821-0191
Houston *(G-9142)*

Georgia-Pacific LLC ....F 409 584-4227
Pineland *(G-16739)*

Georgia-Pacific LLC ....B 866 924-1397
El Paso *(G-5784)*

Hollman Inc ....C 972 815-4000
Irving *(G-13058)*

Masons Mill & Lumber Co Inc ....D 713 462-6975
Houston *(G-10785)*

LUMBER: Plywood, Softwood

Corelite Inc ....F 214 905-4359
Dallas *(G-4167)*

LUMBER: Poles & Pole Crossarms, Treated

Newton Pole Co Inc ....F 409 379-2715
Newton *(G-15865)*

Texas Electric Coops Inc ....E 512 454-0311
Austin *(G-1567)*

Texas Electric Coops Inc ....D 512 868-8610
Georgetown *(G-7685)*

LUMBER: Resawn, Small Dimension

American Wholesale Lbr & Mfg ....E 281 342-7020
Needville *(G-15762)*

LUMBER: Treated

Building Products Plus LLC ....E 713 946-7939
Houston *(G-9016)*

Chicago Flameproof WD Spc Corp ....F 817 534-9800
Fort Worth *(G-6513)*

Green Bay Packaging Inc ....E 915 822-9700
El Paso *(G-5791)*

Hixson Lumber Sales Inc ....E 903 527-4010
Caddo Mills *(G-2624)*

Leo Hicks Creosoting Co Inc ....F 936 858-4419
Alto *(G-317)*

Southeast Wood Treating Inc ....F 903 569-9441
Mineola *(G-15512)*

Texas Electric Coops Inc ....D 409 384-4633
Jasper *(G-13281)*

Ufp New Waverly LLC ....D 936 295-3411
New Waverly *(G-15861)*

Ufp Schertz LLC ....E 830 606-4300
Schertz *(G-18766)*

LUMBER: Veneer, Softwood

M & H Crates Inc ....D 903 683-5351
Jacksonville *(G-13248)*

MACHINE PARTS: Stamped Or Pressed Metal

A & I Industries Inc ....F 915 633-8444
El Paso *(G-5633)*

Alco Machine Tool & Steel Inc ....F 915 779-7013
El Paso *(G-5640)*

Alfred Kager ....E 830 997-9391
Fredericksburg *(G-7169)*

Brandt Precision Machining ....E 512 339-7251
Austin *(G-1005)*

Cambrian Industries Inc ....E 915 771-6100
El Paso *(G-5677)*

Camtech Precision Mfg Inc ....E 404 444-9646
Euless *(G-6134)*

Cannon Cnon Indus McHining Inc ....G 972 293-6278
Lone Oak *(G-14179)*

CC Coating & Machine Inc ....E 361 884-9753
Corpus Christi *(G-3497)*

Command Manufacturing LLC ....E 512 927-0033
Austin *(G-1058)*

M & R USA ....F 281 497-8973
Houston *(G-10717)*

Manufctring Oprations MGT Intl ....E 682 521-5800
Hurst *(G-12851)*

National Manufacturing LLC ....F 281 856-7693
Houston *(G-10970)*

Native American Industries Inc ....F 817 731-6786
Fort Worth *(G-6863)*

Plantex Machine LLC ....G 936 894-0226
Plantersville *(G-17060)*

Pmr Global Inc ....E 817 484-1100
Burleson *(G-2593)*

Wipco Acquisition LLC ....F 936 327-8250
Livingston *(G-14164)*

MACHINE SHOPS

Airgas Usa LLC ....F 512 835-0202
Austin *(G-902)*

Alamo Iron Works Inc ....B 210 223-6161
San Antonio *(G-17885)*

American Block Company ....C 800 572-9087
Houston *(G-8588)*

Atec Inc ....C 281 276-2700
Stafford *(G-19289)*

Atec Resources Inc ....E 281 276-2700
Stafford *(G-19290)*

Bamsch Enterprises Intl Ltd ....F 281 448-5925
Houston *(G-8813)*

Benchmark Completions LLC ....E 281 537-8483
Spring *(G-19200)*

Bhi LLC ....F 713 644-2431
Houston *(G-8873)*

Burgess Specialty Fabg Inc ....D 713 462-0293
Houston *(G-9018)*

Camden Machine & Tool Inc ....E 817 838-6731
Fort Worth *(G-6490)*

Cordova Corporation ....E 817 484-1100
Burleson *(G-2577)*

Csjb Holdings Inc ....D 806 749-4300
Lubbock *(G-14398)*

Decatur Machine Services Inc ....E 940 627-1062
　Decatur (G-5244)
Diversified Industrial Svc Co ....E 806 274-2214
　Borger (G-2174)
Fluxmetals LLC ....D 832 948-4307
　Houston (G-9818)
Four-Star Fabricators & Svc Co ....E 903 965-4309
　Bells (G-2006)
J W Hall Ltd Liability Co ....F 281 337-6311
　Alvin (G-369)
Juggernaut Machinery LLC ....F 210 399-3374
　Jourdanton (G-13333)
M & M Metals Inc ....D 210 341-1313
　San Antonio (G-18268)
Macro Tex Machine Works LLC ....F 281 540-2141
　Humble (G-12786)
New Braunfels Machine Inc ....E 830 226-7179
　New Braunfels (G-15817)
P T Products & Services Inc ....E 512 251-3592
　Pflugerville (G-16682)
Paradigm Metals Incorporated ....E 512 255-2622
　Pflugerville (G-16683)
Peyton Salas & Mendoza LLC ....E 512 784-5875
　Houston (G-11313)
Public Steel Inc ....E 806 376-8221
　Amarillo (G-457)
QMF Steel Inc ....E 903 455-3618
　Campbell (G-2646)
R-5 Metal Fabricators Inc ....F 903 873-2633
　Wills Point (G-20877)
Rayson Company ....E 713 680-0540
　Houston (G-11555)
Saulsbury Industries Inc ....E 903 392-2248
　Henderson (G-8273)
Techmar Industries LLC ....F 832 246-6200
　Spring (G-19175)
Tejas Precision Metalfabricatn ....D 210 648-1555
　San Antonio (G-18524)
Tiger Ridge Manufacturing Inc ....E 903 364-1810
　Whitewright (G-20729)
United Service Alliance Inc ....E 409 935-9500
　Texas City (G-19805)
Varco Shaffer Inc ....E 713 672-1711
　Houston (G-12535)
Wells Manufacturing LLC ....E 713 690-4204
　Houston (G-12632)

MACHINE TOOL ACCESS: Boring Attachments

Btm Services LLC ....E 281 773-6060
　Houston (G-9004)

MACHINE TOOL ACCESS: Cams

Berlin Packaging LLC ....F 214 339-0054
　Dallas (G-4019)
Crown Cork & Seal Usa Inc ....C 936 539-5401
　Conroe (G-3287)

MACHINE TOOL ACCESS: Cutting

Amera-Seiki Corporation ....F 832 234-5960
　Conroe (G-3255)
Carboline Prmium Cutng Tls Inc ....F 281 485-5505
　Rosharon (G-17600)
Daco Abrasives ....E 713 923-4664
　Houston (G-9390)
Industrial Diamond Products Co ....F 713 991-1600
　Houston (G-10350)
Inrock Drilling Systems Inc ....E 713 690-5600
　Houston (G-10376)
Metro Mfg Support Svcs Inc ....E 817 330-3430
　Fort Worth (G-6831)
Qfc Industries Inc ....F 817 640-2151
　Arlington (G-763)
Retco Tool Company Inc ....E 214 358-5039
　Dallas (G-4892)
SC Manufacturing Texas LLC ....E 817 556-3689
　Joshua (G-13326)

MACHINE TOOL ACCESS: Diamond Cutting, For Turning, Etc

National Diamond Lab Texas Inc ....F 214 638-1435
　Dallas (G-4714)

MACHINE TOOL ACCESS: Machine Attachments & Access, Drilling

Gds Realty LLC ....F 713 623-1449
　Houston (G-9911)
Innosol Inc ....F 281 859-4428
　Houston (G-10368)

MACHINE TOOL ACCESS: Threading Tools

Lee Contracting Inc ....F 281 456-9023
　Houston (G-10616)

MACHINE TOOL ACCESS: Tool Holders

Gunook Products Inc ....E 817 536-0136
　Fort Worth (G-6682)

MACHINE TOOL ACCESS: Tools & Access

Higuchi Manufacturing Amer LLC ....C 210 633-2877
　San Antonio (G-18167)
Zyvex Corporation ....A 972 235-7881
　Richardson (G-17432)
Zyvex Instruments LLC ....E 972 792-1625
　Richardson (G-17433)

MACHINE TOOL ATTACHMENTS & ACCESS

Doggett Heavy McHy Svcs LLC ....F 361 289-0727
　Corpus Christi (G-3515)
Multicam Inc ....C 972 929-4070
　Dallas (G-4707)
T & S Machines and Tools Inc ....F 940 668-1002
　Gainesville (G-7371)

MACHINE TOOLS & ACCESS

AGM Tools Inc ....F 832 499-6090
　Houston (G-8503)
Alloy Carbide Company ....E 713 923-2700
　Houston (G-8556)
American Completion Tools Inc ....F 281 894-5213
　Houston (G-8592)
American National Carbide Co ....D 281 351-7165
　Tomball (G-19958)
Baker Hghes Olfld Oprtions LLC ....B 281 363-6000
　The Woodlands (G-19833)
Campbell Grinding & Machine ....F 972 221-2211
　Lewisville (G-14032)
Carbide Grinding Inc ....F 713 944-0015
　Houston (G-9090)
Caterpillar Inc ....D 210 637-3700
　San Antonio (G-17987)
Computerized Cutters Inc ....E 972 422-6900
　Plano (G-16829)
D C Lites Company ....F 972 556-0260
　Dallas (G-4201)
Demarco Machine Ltd ....D 832 230-0850
　Houston (G-8377)
Ellis Tool & Machine Inc ....E 903 546-6540
　Tom Bean (G-19951)
Evo IDT LLC ....E 817 637-0149
　Mansfield (G-14671)
Handwheels Inc ....E 281 998-0560
　Pasadena (G-16453)
Kalco Machine & Mfg Co ....D 940 761-1060
　Wichita Falls (G-20775)
Maintenance Tool & Supply Co ....F 361 888-8801
　Corpus Christi (G-3571)
Midland Wellhead Inc ....E 432 682-0856
　Midland (G-15303)
Milltech Manufacturing Company ....D 972 276-1786
　Garland (G-7554)
Mitchell Manufacturing Inc ....E 281 351-9641
　Tomball (G-19989)
Murphy Fw ....D 281 633-4500
　Rosenberg (G-17590)
National Oilwell Varco Inc ....C 936 444-4000
　Conroe (G-3335)
Pollok Inc ....A 915 592-5700
　El Paso (G-5914)
R & I Enterprises Inc ....F 956 544-7948
　Brownsville (G-2396)
RSC Acquisitions ....D 713 222-2251
　Houston (G-11690)
S Q I Inc ....F 432 366-9264
　Odessa (G-16148)
Saucedas Prcision Grinding Inc ....E 956 399-1572
　San Benito (G-18667)
Ss Machine LP ....E 281 970-8444
　Cypress (G-3822)

Tool-Flo Manufacturing Inc ....C 713 941-1080
　Houston (G-12317)
Union Tech Co LLC ....E 281 583-7601
　Houston (G-12439)
Vanguard Machinery Intl LLC ....F 713 462-5800
　Houston (G-12528)

MACHINE TOOLS, METAL CUTTING: Cutoff

Ohmstede Ltd ....C 281 471-4140
　La Porte (G-13780)

MACHINE TOOLS, METAL CUTTING: Drilling

Babin Machine Works Inc ....F 409 892-1231
　Beaumont (G-1857)
Camcara Inc ....G 800 532-0383
　Grand Prairie (G-7849)
Downhole Drilling Dynamics LLC ....F 936 344-9329
　New Waverly (G-15860)
Teledrill Inc ....F 281 550-0434
　Katy (G-13448)

MACHINE TOOLS, METAL CUTTING: Drilling & Boring

Bauer Manufacturing LLC ....D 936 539-5030
　Conroe (G-3262)
Epiroc Drilling Solutions LLC ....A 972 496-7400
　Garland (G-7486)
Epiroc Drilling Solutions LLC ....D 214 547-7800
　Allen (G-265)
Wilson Supply Corporate Office ....F 713 237-3309
　Houston (G-12675)
Wtb LLC ....E 432 366-1026
　Odessa (G-16214)

MACHINE TOOLS, METAL CUTTING: Exotic, Including Explosive

Doosan Turbomachinery Svcs Inc ....D 713 364-7500
　La Porte (G-13731)
Ltn Industries Inc ....E 713 849-1300
　Houston (G-10698)
National Hose Aquisition Corp ....D 713 920-2030
　Pasadena (G-16487)

MACHINE TOOLS, METAL CUTTING: Grind, Polish, Buff, Lapp

Fusion Operations LP ....D 713 691-6547
　Houston (G-9878)
Superior Weighting Pdts LLC ....F 361 880-7160
　Corpus Christi (G-3633)

MACHINE TOOLS, METAL CUTTING: Milling, Chemical

Cynco Specialty Inc ....G 281 499-0519
　Stafford (G-19298)

MACHINE TOOLS, METAL CUTTING: Numerically Controlled

Forrest Mfg Co ....F 713 864-2545
　Houston (G-9837)

MACHINE TOOLS, METAL CUTTING: Pipe Cutting & Threading

B H M Pipe & Supply Inc ....E 281 328-5552
　Crosby (G-3726)
Downhole Threading Svcs Inc ....E 281 462-9800
　Crosby (G-3730)
National Oilwell Varco Inc ....D 409 842-2114
　Beaumont (G-1933)
Norse Cutng & Abandonment Inc ....E 832 327-3640
　Houston (G-11070)
Superior Threaded Products LP ....E 281 459-3131
　Houston (G-12120)

MACHINE TOOLS, METAL CUTTING: Plasma Process

Victor Equipment Company ....A 940 566-2000
　Denton (G-5409)
Victor Technologies Intl Inc ....D 940 381-1353
　Denton (G-5411)

Employee Codes: A=Over 500 employees, B=251-500
C=101-250, D=51-100, E=20-50, F=10-19, G=9

2021 Harris Texas
Manufacturers Directory

PRODUCT

1545

MACHINE TOOLS, METAL CUTTING: Tool Replacement & Rpr Parts

Envirotech Pumpsystems Inc ....G....... 832 200-6220
  Deer Park (G-5272)
Ggctr Inc ....E 832 456-4585
  Pasadena (G-16448)
Royberg Inc ....E 210 525-0094
  San Antonio (G-18435)
Tool-Flo Manufacturing Inc ....C 713 941-1080
  Houston (G-12317)

MACHINE TOOLS, METAL CUTTING: Vertical Turning & Boring

Absolute Machine & Tooling LLC ....F 512 259-7676
  Leander (G-13984)
Hawk Installation & Cnstr Inc ....F 903 665-8080
  Jefferson (G-13284)

MACHINE TOOLS, METAL FORMING: Bending

Mp Precision Services Inc ....F 915 599-9188
  El Paso (G-5886)

MACHINE TOOLS, METAL FORMING: Crimping, Metal

Bridgestone Hosepower LLC ....E 432 367-4673
  Odessa (G-15944)

MACHINE TOOLS, METAL FORMING: Mechanical, Pneumatic Or Hyd

George A Sturdevant Inc ....F 281 449-6466
  New Caney (G-15840)
Mic Group LLC ....F 979 277-7806
  Brenham (G-2263)

MACHINE TOOLS: Metal Cutting

American National Carbide Co ....D 281 351-7165
  Tomball (G-19958)
Applied Maintenance Spc Inc ....F 409 994-5849
  Buna (G-2559)
Cambrian Management Ltd ....F 432 620-9181
  Midland (G-15156)
Cameron International Corp ....A 601 629-3300
  Houston (G-9066)
Carbide Grinding Inc ....F 713 944-0015
  Houston (G-9090)
Chevas Company LLC ....F 713 225-6595
  Houston (G-9176)
Ckb Machining LLC ....F 281 485-5760
  Pearland (G-16545)
Cowan Coolant MGT Svcs LLC ....F 214 686-1010
  Richardson (G-17293)
CRC-Evans Pipeline Intl Inc ....C 800 664-9224
  Houston (G-9337)
Data Matique Properties LP ....C 972 272-3446
  Garland (G-7476)
Gerber Technology Inc ....C 972 238-7211
  Dallas (G-4405)
Hemaq America LLC ....D 877 700-5060
  Helotes (G-8238)
Highwood Machine Tool LLC ....F 254 412-0512
  Waco (G-20411)
Industrial Castings Co Inc ....F 713 747-5336
  Houston (G-10347)
Industrial Mill Maint Sup Inc ....E 800 537-1218
  Wake Village (G-20486)
Jcv Manufacturing Corporation ....F 281 201-4853
  Houston (G-10460)
Jet Machine Works Inc ....E 281 449-0046
  Houston (G-10469)
Kimbell Gin Machinery Company ....D 806 763-6645
  Lubbock (G-14433)
Koch Machine Tool Company ....F 281 720-8500
  Houston (G-10553)
Lake Road Welding Co ....E 940 692-4988
  Wichita Falls (G-20778)
Landers Machine Co ....E 817 834-6383
  Fort Worth (G-6779)
M S I Corporation ....F 512 243-9000
  Austin (G-1315)
Made In America Mfg LLC ....G 512 435-9952
  Austin (G-1316)
Marshall Prcsion Machining Inc ....F 940 320-4240
  Sanger (G-18726)

Maverick Tube Corporation ....C 713 937-1800
  Houston (G-10803)
Michael Ray ....G....... 832 567-2507
  Houston (G-10865)
Mitchell Manufacturing Inc ....E 281 351-9641
  Tomball (G-19989)
N & N Services LLC ....F 281 741-9714
  Pearland (G-16584)
Oliver Machinery Inc ....F 903 489-2250
  Malakoff (G-14636)
OSG Usa Inc ....E 800 837-2223
  Irving (G-13134)
Pgi International Ltd ....B 713 466-0056
  Houston (G-11316)
Polytrnix McHning Fbrction LLC ....F 972 436-0422
  Richardson (G-17374)
Reliable Bus Resources LLC ....E 281 469-6400
  Houston (G-11588)
River City Manufacturing Inc ....F 512 335-5194
  Bertram (G-2053)
Rogers Manufacturing Inc ....G...... 940 325-7806
  Mineral Wells (G-15540)
Southwest Metrics Inc ....E 817 581-4474
  Fort Worth (G-7005)
Storm Vulcan Inc ....E 214 637-1430
  Dallas (G-5014)
Texas High Roller Inc ....E 979 778-7460
  Bryan (G-2511)
Tri Tool Inc ....D 281 499-1188
  Stafford (G-19387)
Two Elk Investments LLC ....E 972 465-3608
  Irving (G-13200)
Victor Technologies Group Inc ....E 940 566-2000
  Denton (G-5410)
Wells Manufacturing LLC ....E 713 690-4204
  Houston (G-12632)

MACHINE TOOLS: Metal Forming

Atlantic Durant Technology Inc ....E 956 440-8005
  Harlingen (G-8182)
B&P Littleford LLC ....E 713 433-3304
  Houston (G-8781)
Ckb Machining LLC ....E 281 485-5760
  Pearland (G-16545)
Concept Laser Inc ....E 817 328-6500
  Grapevine (G-8023)
Formers By Ernie Inc ....F 713 991-3455
  Houston (G-9834)
Novaria Group LLC ....E 817 381-3810
  Fort Worth (G-6870)
Rogers Manufacturing Inc ....G...... 940 325-7806
  Mineral Wells (G-15540)
Varco Shaffer Inc ....E 713 672-1711
  Houston (G-12535)

MACHINERY & EQPT, AGRICULTURAL, WHOL: Farm Eqpt Parts/Splys

Clarendon Mfg & Distrg Co Inc ....F 806 874-3584
  Clarendon (G-3070)
Pilot Plastics LLC ....G...... 800 918-6765
  Fort Worth (G-6907)
Roll-A-Cone Mfg Distrg Co Ltd ....E 806 668-4722
  Tulia (G-20037)

MACHINERY & EQPT, AGRICULTURAL, WHOLESALE: Agricultural, NEC

Denny Kincer Inc ....E 806 762-1069
  Lubbock (G-14401)
King Ranch Inc ....E 832 681-5700
  Houston (G-10534)
King Ranch Holdings Inc ....E 832 681-5700
  Houston (G-10535)

MACHINERY & EQPT, AGRICULTURAL, WHOLESALE: Farm Implements

Boyd AG LLC ....F 512 863-2589
  Georgetown (G-7642)
Kjd Enterprises ....F 325 641-0420
  Brownwood (G-2431)

MACHINERY & EQPT, AGRICULTURAL, WHOLESALE: Landscaping Eqpt

Bwi Companies Inc ....D 972 242-4755
  Carrollton (G-2708)
Hope Agri Products Inc ....F 214 371-7120
  Dallas (G-4466)

Pro-Steel Inc ....E 817 572-4959
  Fort Worth (G-6919)
Texas Landfill Management LLC ....E 210 651-6115
  San Antonio (G-18537)

MACHINERY & EQPT, AGRICULTURAL, WHOLESALE: Lawn

Wheel-A-Rama Inc ....G...... 325 655-7373
  San Angelo (G-17840)

MACHINERY & EQPT, AGRICULTURAL, WHOLESALE: Lawn & Garden

Carruth Nursery Irrigation ....F 903 236-7555
  Longview (G-14208)
E Barr Feeds Inc ....F 830 672-6515
  Gonzales (G-7752)

MACHINERY & EQPT, AGRICULTURAL, WHOLESALE: Livestock Eqpt

American Fence and Sup Co Inc ....F 512 930-4000
  Georgetown (G-7634)

MACHINERY & EQPT, AGRICULTURAL, WHOLESALE: Tractors

Winnsboro Spclty Prts Intl Inc ....E 903 342-3551
  Winnsboro (G-20902)

MACHINERY & EQPT, INDL, WHOL: Controlling Instruments/Access

American Steam Inc ....E 972 442-4499
  Wylie (G-20926)
Evans Enterprises Inc ....F 254 772-4710
  Waco (G-20399)
Puffer-Sweiven Holdings Inc ....E 281 470-2000
  La Porte (G-13785)
Vanzandt Controls ....G...... 806 655-9367
  Canyon (G-2676)
Vinson Process Controls Co LP ....D...... 972 459-8200
  Lewisville (G-14106)

MACHINERY & EQPT, INDL, WHOL: Environ Pollution Cntrl, Air

Airflow Systems Inc ....D 800 818-6185
  Dallas (G-3911)
Jessco Solutions LLC ....F 325 227-4196
  San Angelo (G-17811)
Robert L Rowan & Associates ....F 713 681-5811
  Houston (G-11643)

MACHINERY & EQPT, INDL, WHOL: Meters, Consumption Registerng

Thurmond-Mcglothlin LLC ....G...... 806 665-5700
  Pampa (G-16341)
Yokogawa Corporation America ....E 281 340-3800
  Sugar Land (G-19576)

MACHINERY & EQPT, INDL, WHOL: Oil Field Tool Joints, Rebuilt

Amerig Solutions LLC ....F 713 960-6606
  Houston (G-8617)

MACHINERY & EQPT, INDL, WHOLESALE: Chemical Process

Athena Oilfield Services LLC................F 713 426-1969
  Houston (G-8733)
Polymers Sales & Logistics LLC ....F 281 874-8072
  Houston (G-11359)

MACHINERY & EQPT, INDL, WHOLESALE: Conveyor Systems

Ammeraal Beltech Inc ....F 972 647-8996
  Grand Prairie (G-7831)
Crisp Industries Inc ....D 830 372-1110
  Seguin (G-18834)
Industrial Cnvyor Fbrction Ltd ....F 817 439-0735
  Fort Worth (G-6718)
Metroplex Conveyor & Svcs LLC ....F 972 584-0551
  Quinlan (G-17224)
Siemens Industry Inc ....E 817 633-4430
  Grand Prairie (G-7973)

Systems Automated Controls Inc ....E 818 898-1900
   Denton *(G-5402)*

Tamra Group Inc ....E 817 453-3370
   Mansfield *(G-14721)*

Tegron Holding LLC.........................E 903 759-1088
   Longview *(G-14314)*

Transnorm System Inc ....D 972 606-0303
   Arlington *(G-802)*

MACHINERY & EQPT, INDL, WHOLESALE:
Cranes

Caplingers Crane & Eqp Svc Inc ....E 817 685-0710
   Hurst *(G-12841)*

Elizondo Enterprises Inc ....G 956 831-7174
   Brownsville *(G-2353)*

OMI Crane Systems Inc ....E 972 636-8000
   Fate *(G-6228)*

MACHINERY & EQPT, INDL, WHOLESALE:
Crushing

Excel Machinery Ltd ....F 806 335-1553
   Amarillo *(G-486)*

MACHINERY & EQPT, INDL, WHOLESALE:
Dairy Prdts Manufacturing

Caldwell Machine and Gear Inc ....F 903 572-1660
   Mount Pleasant *(G-15648)*

MACHINERY & EQPT, INDL, WHOLESALE:
Derricks

Baker Hghes Olfld Oprtions LLC.........B 281 363-6000
   The Woodlands *(G-19833)*

MACHINERY & EQPT, INDL, WHOLESALE:
Drilling, Exc Bits

Blaze Equipment LLC ....F 817 439-0453
   Lake Worth *(G-13812)*

DK Drill I LP ....E 817 539-2500
   Mansfield *(G-14665)*

Hilti of America Inc ....E 800 879-8000
   Plano *(G-16886)*

Ulterra Drilling Tech LP ....E 817 293-7555
   Fort Worth *(G-7092)*

Wwl Industries Inc ....E 432 362-0326
   Odessa *(G-16215)*

MACHINERY & EQPT, INDL, WHOLESALE:
Engines & Parts, Diesel

Breco International LLC ....F 713 641-6073
   Houston *(G-8981)*

Cummins Southern Plains LLC ....E 806 373-3793
   Amarillo *(G-419)*

Cummins Southern Plains LLC ....E 210 655-5420
   San Antonio *(G-18035)*

Cummins Southern Plains LLC ....E 512 389-2276
   Austin *(G-1077)*

Cummins Southern Plains LLC ....D 817 640-6801
   Arlington *(G-653)*

Hartmanns Inc ....F 325 695-7641
   Abilene *(G-46)*

M G Bryan Equipment Co LP ....F 972 623-4300
   Grand Prairie *(G-7919)*

Stewart Stevenson Pwr Pdts LLC ....E 361 299-6639
   Corpus Christi *(G-3629)*

Stewart Stevenson Pwr Pdts LLC ....F 915 790-1848
   El Paso *(G-5980)*

Stewart Stevenson Pwr Pdts LLC ....C 504 347-4326
   Houston *(G-12064)*

Tom Daenen Inc ....E 409 978-2132
   Hitchcock *(G-8340)*

Wartsila North America Inc ....C 281 233-6200
   Houston *(G-12600)*

MACHINERY & EQPT, INDL, WHOLESALE:
Engines, Gasoline

Cummins Inc ....E 915 791-6600
   El Paso *(G-5707)*

Heavy Equipment Maintenance Co .....E 903 984-9076
   Kilgore *(G-13557)*

Waukesha-Pearce Industries LLC ....B 713 723-1050
   Houston *(G-12607)*

Wheel-A-Rama Inc ....G 325 655-7373
   San Angelo *(G-17840)*

MACHINERY & EQPT, INDL, WHOLESALE:
Engs & Parts, Air-Cooled

Breckenridge Auto & Engine Sup ....F 254 559-8241
   Breckenridge *(G-2224)*

Cummins Southern Plains LLC ....F 432 332-9121
   Odessa *(G-15973)*

MACHINERY & EQPT, INDL, WHOLESALE:
Engs/Transportation Eqpt

Stewart Stevenson Capitl Corp ....D 713 868-7700
   Houston *(G-12063)*

Toshiba International Corp ....A 800 231-1412
   Houston *(G-12327)*

MACHINERY & EQPT, INDL, WHOLESALE:
Food Manufacturing

America Industrial Pdts LLC ....F 832 974-4153
   Houston *(G-8580)*

Custom Delis Equipment Co Inc ....E 817 831-7080
   Fort Worth *(G-6567)*

Dawn Food Products Inc ....E 972 485-8004
   Garland *(G-7477)*

Quality Custom Fabricators...............D 817 649-8020
   Grand Prairie *(G-7960)*

MACHINERY & EQPT, INDL, WHOLESALE:
Food Product Manufacturng

Calco Taiwan Marketing Service ....F 713 247-9918
   Houston *(G-9048)*

Filtration Automation Inc ....E 817 999-8190
   Alvarado *(G-332)*

Hilltop Texas Inc ....E 214 430-1311
   Allen *(G-275)*

Quality Fabrication Design LP.............D 972 304-3266
   Coppell *(G-3436)*

Satake USA Inc..............................D 281 276-3600
   Stafford *(G-19374)*

MACHINERY & EQPT, INDL, WHOLESALE:
Fuel Injection Systems

Chemtec Energy Services LLC............E 936 856-1704
   Willis *(G-20844)*

MACHINERY & EQPT, INDL, WHOLESALE:
Hoists

Crane Equipment & Service Inc...........E 817 740-7911
   Fort Worth *(G-6557)*

Gh Cranes & Components USA Inc ......E 972 563-8333
   Terrell *(G-19735)*

Proserv Crane & Equipment Inc ....D 972 438-5100
   Irving *(G-13161)*

Ram Winch and Hoist Ltd ....E 281 999-8665
   Houston *(G-11536)*

MACHINERY & EQPT, INDL, WHOLESALE:
Hydraulic Systems

Boatman Industries Inc ....E 713 641-6006
   Houston *(G-8932)*

DSM Fluid Power Inc ....E 512 243-1986
   Austin *(G-1104)*

Gs-Hydro US Inc ....E 281 209-1000
   Houston *(G-10052)*

Hydradyne LLC ....F 210 661-4378
   San Antonio *(G-18177)*

Hydradyne Hydraulics Inc ....E 713 937-8111
   Houston *(G-10294)*

Hyseco Inc ....E 713 991-4240
   Houston *(G-10307)*

Hyvair Corporation ....F 281 259-7768
   Magnolia *(G-14608)*

Oliver Equipment Company LLC ....E 713 856-9206
   Houston *(G-11171)*

Robbins & Myers Inc ....E 936 890-1064
   Willis *(G-20861)*

Tetra Pak Inc ....C 940 565-8800
   Denton *(G-5404)*

Tim Yockey ....F 281 252-6175
   Magnolia *(G-14630)*

MACHINERY & EQPT, INDL, WHOLESALE:
Indl Machine Parts

Commercial Diesl Parts Svc Ltd ....E 830 372-1594
   Seguin *(G-18830)*

Doggett Heavy McHy Svcs LLC...........F 361 289-0727
   Corpus Christi *(G-3515)*

Tooling Technologies Mfg LLC ....F 713 722-8501
   Houston *(G-12320)*

MACHINERY & EQPT, INDL, WHOLESALE:
Instruments & Cntrl Eqpt

DC Controls Inc ....F 361 906-0123
   Lewisville *(G-14043)*

Gas Equipment Company Inc ....C 972 241-2333
   Dallas *(G-4393)*

Longview Distribution I LLC ....E 832 467-4600
   Houston *(G-10686)*

Murphy Fw ....D 281 633-4500
   Rosenberg *(G-17590)*

Scada Products LLC ....E 888 649-4283
   Fort Worth *(G-6975)*

Texas Underground Inc ....D 281 485-9900
   Pearland *(G-16602)*

MACHINERY & EQPT, INDL, WHOLESALE:
Lift Trucks & Parts

General Crane Service Inc ....E 713 649-4088
   Houston *(G-9921)*

Mitsubshi Ctrpllar Frklift AME ....A 713 365-1000
   Houston *(G-10891)*

MACHINERY & EQPT, INDL, WHOLESALE:
Machine Tools & Access

Elijah Tooling Inc ....F 940 591-1340
   Denton *(G-5363)*

RSC Acquisitions ....D 713 222-2251
   Houston *(G-11690)*

MACHINERY & EQPT, INDL, WHOLESALE:
Machine Tools & Metalwork

Airgen Equipment LLC ....F 432 332-1870
   Odessa *(G-15907)*

Alamo Iron Works Inc ....B 210 223-6161
   San Antonio *(G-17885)*

OSG Usa Inc ....E 800 837-2223
   Irving *(G-13134)*

Retco Tool Company Inc ....E 214 358-5039
   Dallas *(G-4892)*

MACHINERY & EQPT, INDL, WHOLESALE:
Measure/Test, Electric

Greenslade & Company Inc ....F 817 870-8888
   Fort Worth *(G-6678)*

MACHINERY & EQPT, INDL, WHOLESALE:
Noise Control

Border Assembly Inc ....E 915 592-1172
   El Paso *(G-5667)*

MACHINERY & EQPT, INDL, WHOLESALE:
Packaging

Petro Chem Industries Inc ....E 713 645-5024
   Houston *(G-11300)*

MACHINERY & EQPT, INDL, WHOLESALE:
Paint Spray

Airtech Spray Systems Inc.................E 713 681-0013
   Houston *(G-8518)*

Rexcel Coatings Corporation ....F 915 581-2797
   El Paso *(G-5938)*

Trinity Powder Coating.....................F 214 703-3609
   Garland *(G-7605)*

MACHINERY & EQPT, INDL, WHOLESALE:
Petroleum Industry

Diamond M Drlg Exploration Co..........F 210 310-3135
   San Antonio *(G-18056)*

Exterran Trinidad LLC ....B 281 921-9337
   Houston *(G-9737)*

PRODUCT

Grant Prideco LP ....C....... 281 878-8000
Houston *(G-10018)*

H C Howell Company ....F....... 432 368-0835
Odessa *(G-16023)*

Interstate Treating Inc ....D....... 432 362-9291
Odessa *(G-16034)*

National Oilwell Varco Inc ....F....... 432 381-4111
Odessa *(G-16090)*

National Oilwell Varco Inc ....F....... 281 854-0300
Houston *(G-10976)*

National Oilwell Varco Inc ....F....... 713 395-5000
Houston *(G-10990)*

National Oilwell Varco Inc ....E....... 713 634-3327
Houston *(G-10978)*

National Oilwell Varco Inc ....A....... 713 346-7500
Houston *(G-10988)*

Now Inc ....E....... 281 823-4700
Houston *(G-11091)*

Sweco ....F....... 817 202-0350
Grand Prairie *(G-7979)*

MACHINERY & EQPT, INDL, WHOLESALE: Pneumatic Tools

Bay Advanced Technologies LLC ....E....... 512 929-5400
Austin *(G-979)*

Camozzi Pneumatics Inc ....E....... 972 548-8885
McKinney *(G-14931)*

MACHINERY & EQPT, INDL, WHOLESALE: Power Plant Machinery

GE Energy Manufacturing Inc ....D....... 713 803-0900
Houston *(G-9913)*

MACHINERY & EQPT, INDL, WHOLESALE: Processing & Packaging

Archrock Inc ....E....... 361 572-9904
Victoria *(G-20239)*

Atlas Copco Compressors LLC ....B....... 281 453-6800
McAllen *(G-14839)*

Community Motors Inc ....F....... 281 354-8087
New Caney *(G-15837)*

Dallas A C Horn & Company Inc ....D....... 214 630-3311
Dallas *(G-4210)*

ROC Industries Inc ....E....... 713 468-7743
Houston *(G-11647)*

MACHINERY & EQPT, INDL, WHOLESALE: Safety Eqpt

Dobie Supply LLC ....G....... 512 437-6499
Austin *(G-1098)*

Eproduction Solutions LLC ....B....... 281 348-1000
Kingwood *(G-13641)*

Industrial Mill Maint Sup Inc ....E....... 800 537-1218
Wake Village *(G-20486)*

Jenessco Industries Inc ....E....... 281 498-8833
Houston *(G-10465)*

Oil States Energy Services LLC ....E....... 432 563-1304
Midland *(G-15326)*

Safety Supply Inc ....F....... 210 650-9033
San Antonio *(G-18441)*

T-Tex Equipment LP ....F....... 713 991-7070
Houston *(G-12144)*

MACHINERY & EQPT, INDL, WHOLESALE: Tanks, Storage

Fox Tank Company ....F....... 830 792-0770
Kerrville *(G-13519)*

Freeman David Products Inc ....E....... 866 310-2556
Burnet *(G-2608)*

Palmer of Texas Tanks Inc ....D....... 432 523-5904
Andrews *(G-556)*

MACHINERY & EQPT, INDL, WHOLESALE: Textile & Leather

Ramann Enterprises Inc ....E....... 817 560-4222
Fort Worth *(G-6938)*

MACHINERY & EQPT, INDL, WHOLESALE: Tool & Die Makers

Mp Precision Services Inc ....F....... 915 599-9188
El Paso *(G-5886)*

MACHINERY & EQPT, INDL, WHOLESALE: Trailers, Indl

Pull Rite Trailers LLC ....F....... 903 502-5000
Murchison *(G-15681)*

Taxa Inc ....F....... 713 861-2540
Houston *(G-12165)*

Worth Trailer Parts Inc ....E....... 817 496-7841
Fort Worth *(G-7151)*

MACHINERY & EQPT, INDL, WHOLESALE: Waste Compactors

Incinerator International Inc ....F....... 713 227-1466
Houston *(G-10336)*

MACHINERY & EQPT, INDL, WHOLESALE: Water Pumps

Gicon Pumps & Equipment Ltd ....G....... 806 373-0478
Amarillo *(G-428)*

Preferred Pump & Equipment LP ....E....... 817 536-9800
Fort Worth *(G-6912)*

Smith Pump Company Inc ....G....... 817 589-2060
Fort Worth *(G-6996)*

MACHINERY & EQPT, INDL, WHOLESALE: Winches

Dealers Truck Equipment Co Inc ....F....... 512 312-2100
Buda *(G-2527)*

Marmon Highway Tech LLC ....E....... 214 631-8810
Dallas *(G-4636)*

MACHINERY & EQPT, INDL, WHOLESALE: Woodworking

Taylor Design Group Inc ....F....... 972 243-7943
Carrollton *(G-2825)*

MACHINERY & EQPT, WHOLESALE: Blades, Graders, Scrapers, Etc

Contech Engnered Solutions LLC ....E....... 940 888-3871
Seymour *(G-18889)*

MACHINERY & EQPT, WHOLESALE: Concrete Processing

Few Ready Mix Corp ....D....... 936 560-5675
Nacogdoches *(G-15696)*

McNeilus Truck and Mfg Inc ....E....... 972 225-2313
Hutchins *(G-12868)*

Texas Industries Inc ....D....... 817 838-4212
Fort Worth *(G-7048)*

MACHINERY & EQPT, WHOLESALE: Construction & Mining, Pavers

Tropiscapes Inc ....E....... 281 371-2955
Katy *(G-13452)*

MACHINERY & EQPT, WHOLESALE: Construction, Cranes

Basden Steel and Erection Inc ....E....... 817 295-6100
Burleson *(G-2569)*

Kirby - Smith Machinery Inc ....F....... 817 378-0600
Fort Worth *(G-6763)*

Kirby - Smith Machinery Inc ....F....... 806 373-1229
Amarillo *(G-445)*

M G Bryan Equipment Co LP ....F....... 972 623-4300
Grand Prairie *(G-7919)*

Marmon Highway Tech LLC ....E....... 214 631-8810
Dallas *(G-4636)*

MACHINERY & EQPT, WHOLESALE: Construction, General

ABG Contracting Group LLC ....E....... 281 431-7223
Pearland *(G-16536)*

H L Hailey Enterprises Inc ....F....... 903 759-1881
Longview *(G-14244)*

Health Care Temporaries Inc ....A....... 713 631-7106
Houston *(G-10143)*

Humdinger Equipment Ltd ....E....... 806 771-9944
Lubbock *(G-14420)*

Kobelco Construction McHy USA ....E....... 281 684-8761
Katy *(G-13419)*

Letourneau Tech Amer Inc ....D....... 903 237-7000
Longview *(G-14264)*

Precision Wire Products LLC ....F....... 214 436-4923
Frisco *(G-7307)*

Stewart Stevenson Capitl Corp ....D....... 713 868-7700
Houston *(G-12063)*

Waukesha-Pearce Industries LLC ....B....... 713 723-1050
Houston *(G-12607)*

MACHINERY & EQPT, WHOLESALE: Contractors Materials

Associated Supply Company Inc ....E....... 512 272-8922
Manor *(G-14643)*

Britt Dirt Contracting Inc ....F....... 806 872-5194
Lamesa *(G-13824)*

Contractors Supplies Inc ....F....... 936 634-3341
Lufkin *(G-14523)*

Hasse Enterprises Inc ....F....... 512 835-7697
Austin *(G-1199)*

Materials Products Inc ....F....... 512 821-3303
Austin *(G-1329)*

Texas Flameproofing Inc ....F....... 214 630-1088
Dallas *(G-5061)*

Voidform Products Inc ....E....... 817 429-0888
Fort Worth *(G-7111)*

Waukesha-Pearce Industries Inc ....E....... 512 989-4900
Pflugerville *(G-16692)*

MACHINERY & EQPT, WHOLESALE: Front End Loaders

Standard Waste Services LLC ....F....... 210 619-7962
San Antonio *(G-18496)*

MACHINERY & EQPT, WHOLESALE: Logging & Forestry

Forestry Supply Service Inc ....F....... 936 632-3394
Lufkin *(G-14528)*

Forestry Supply Service Inc ....F....... 409 384-3213
Jasper *(G-13276)*

MACHINERY & EQPT, WHOLESALE: Masonry

Alamo Concrete Products Ltd ....E....... 361 289-9200
Corpus Christi *(G-3471)*

MACHINERY & EQPT, WHOLESALE: Oil Field Eqpt

Apache Instrumentations & Gas ....E....... 432 336-7755
Fort Stockton *(G-6327)*

Aquapharm Pchem LLC ....F....... 346 237-4300
Latexo *(G-13942)*

Brothers Well Service Ltd ....E....... 979 543-6851
El Campo *(G-5613)*

CAM-Tech Products Inc ....F....... 281 548-0188
Humble *(G-12751)*

Champion Process Inc ....F....... 281 953-9000
Houston *(G-9159)*

Crown Energy Technologies Inc ....F....... 403 215-5300
Houston *(G-9347)*

Eagle Pipe LLC ....E....... 713 464-7473
Houston *(G-9560)*

Ed Prince Enterprises Inc ....F....... 806 274-7178
Borger *(G-2177)*

Energy Devices of Texas Inc ....E....... 903 963-7906
Van *(G-20207)*

Intense Wireline Solutions LLC ....D....... 903 630-5440
Tyler *(G-20103)*

Khudairi Group Incorporated ....E....... 713 782-1080
Houston *(G-10530)*

Lincoln Manufacturing Inc ....B....... 281 252-9494
Magnolia *(G-14615)*

Lincoln Manufacturing Inc ....D....... 281 357-1541
Magnolia *(G-14616)*

Martin-Decker Totco Inc ....B....... 512 340-5000
Cedar Park *(G-2978)*

Martins Fishing Tls & Rentals ....F....... 432 524-7456
Andrews *(G-550)*

National Oilwell Varco Inc ....F....... 817 985-5000
Fort Worth *(G-6861)*

National Oilwell Varco Inc ....F....... 903 984-2553
Kilgore *(G-13577)*

National Oilwell Varco Inc ....F....... 325 884-2556
Big Lake *(G-2060)*

National Oilwell Varco LP ....D....... 281 586-2046
Houston *(G-10995)*

National Oilwell Varco LP ....D....... 713 346-7500
Houston *(G-10996)*

National Oilwell Varco LP ....D 713 375-3700
Houston (G-10997)
National Oilwell Varco LP ....D 281 599-4700
Houston (G-10998)
National Oilwell Varco LP ....B 713 375-3700
Houston (G-11000)
Newpark Mats Intgrted Svcs LLC ....E 409 752-5800
Beaumont (G-1934)
North American Trade Corp ....F 936 588-1010
Montgomery (G-15637)
Odessa Separator Inc ....E 432 580-7111
Odessa (G-16097)
Oil States Energy Services LLC ....E 903 526-4777
Tyler (G-20135)
Oil States Energy Services LLC ....F 361 384-0041
Orange Grove (G-16269)
Oil States Energy Services LLC ....F 903 986-3791
Kilgore (G-13580)
Oil States Energy Services LLC ....E 713 425-2400
Houston (G-11154)
Oil States Energy Services LLC ....F 432 563-1304
Midland (G-15326)
Oil States Industries Inc ....C 713 445-2200
Houston (G-11157)
Oil States Industries Inc ....F 713 510-2200
Houston (G-11155)
Orbix Corporation ....E 254 675-8651
Clifton (G-3145)
Orteq Energy Technologies LLC ....E 940 665-2316
Gainesville (G-7356)
Pecofacet (us) Inc ....B 940 325-2575
Mineral Wells (G-15536)
Permian Tank & Mfg Inc ....D 903 984-2516
Kilgore (G-13581)
Petroleum Products & Svcs Inc ....F 281 448-1000
Tomball (G-19997)
Prime Downhole Mfg LLC ....E 832 957-3200
Houston (G-11413)
Radley Electric Inc ....F 409 781-7172
Sour Lake (G-19034)
Ram International Inc ....F 361 688-1966
Corpus Christi (G-3605)
Ram-Gear Manufacturing Inc ....F 361 668-0235
Alice (G-231)
Rpc Inc ....E 361 289-7088
Corpus Christi (G-3612)
RSD Supply Inc ....E 713 983-6363
Houston (G-11691)
Russell Oilfield Equipment Co ....F 281 540-8982
Humble (G-12797)
S & G Disposal ....F 806 894-6044
Levelland (G-14015)
Scan-Pac Mfg Inc ....E 281 356-1640
Magnolia (G-14626)
Sharewell LP ....E 281 288-2560
Houston (G-11845)
Sparkman Well Service Inc ....C 361 572-4833
Victoria (G-20305)
Stewart & Stevenson LLC ....D 713 751-2700
Houston (G-12062)
Stewart Stevenson Pwr Pdts LLC ....C 713 751-2600
Houston (G-12065)
Synergy Industries LP ....D 817 295-1161
Burleson (G-2597)
Tesco Corporation (us) ....E 713 359-7000
Houston (G-12212)
Tiger Industries Inc ....E 713 896-9300
Houston (G-12290)
Tribocor Technologies Inc ....F 281 277-7200
Stafford (G-19388)
Turbeco Inc ....F 713 849-9911
Houston (G-12407)

MACHINERY & EQPT, WHOLESALE: Road Construction & Maintenance

Holt Texas Ltd ....B 210 648-1111
San Antonio (G-18171)

MACHINERY & EQPT: Farm

Alamo Sales Corp ....D 800 882-5762
Seguin (G-18823)
All Seasons Feeders Inc ....E 210 648-0979
San Antonio (G-17892)
Aluminum Metal Products Inc ....F 806 745-6026
Lubbock (G-14360)
Alvarez & Marsal Inc ....C 212 759-4433
Houston (G-8575)
Aspire Food Group Usa Inc ....E 512 645-0700
Austin (G-941)

Atlas Metal Works Inc ....F 214 741-4788
Dallas (G-3982)
Belltec Industries Inc ....F 254 939-9404
Belton (G-2020)
Big Country Livestock Eqp ....F 254 643-1119
Rising Star (G-17478)
Brec Inc ....F 979 823-4466
Bryan (G-2460)
Brookside Equipment Sales Inc ....F 281 391-2165
Katy (G-13353)
C Diamond F Inc ....E 903 842-3107
Troup (G-20022)
Consolidated Cotton Gin Co ....D 806 745-1191
Lubbock (G-14396)
Dalhart R & R Mch Works Inc ....E 806 244-5686
Dalhart (G-3834)
Denny Kincer Inc ....E 806 762-1069
Lubbock (G-14401)
Flowtronex Psi LLC ....C 469 221-1200
Dallas (G-4372)
Foster Farm & Equipment Supply ....F 281 256-6900
Hockley (G-8345)
J&J Weaver Co ....E 254 756-2139
Waco (G-20419)
Lee Products Inc ....F 817 641-9893
Cleburne (G-3100)
Lone Star Livestock Eqp Co Inc ....F 281 399-3550
New Caney (G-15844)
Module Truck Systems Inc ....E 806 783-0777
Lubbock (G-14448)
Olton Welding & Machine Inc ....F 806 285-3006
Olton (G-16227)
Pelican Industrial Inc ....E 832 678-4808
Houston (G-11272)
Pierce Arrow Inc ....F 940 538-5643
Henrietta (G-8282)
Pilot Plastics LLC ....G 800 918-6765
Fort Worth (G-6907)
Raider Manufacturing Ltd ....D 806 762-3227
Lubbock (G-14470)
Ranews Texas Incorporated ....E 770 229-5090
Seguin (G-18859)
Roll-A-Cone Mfg Distrg Co Ltd ....E 806 668-4722
Tulia (G-20037)
Sam Stevens Inc ....E 806 872-8365
Lamesa (G-13829)
Schwarze Industries Inc ....F 830 379-1480
Seguin (G-18862)
Sweeney Enterprises Inc ....G 830 537-4631
Boerne (G-2138)
Texas Industrial Remcor Inc ....F 254 982-4236
Little River Academy (G-14143)
Travis Scott ....F 254 829-0651
Ross (G-17617)
Trench-Tech Ltd ....F 817 491-0621
Roanoke (G-17496)
Wildcat Manufacturing Inc ....F 806 327-5602
Tahoka (G-19642)
William L Bonnell Company Inc ....B 409 543-0600
El Campo (G-5629)

MACHINERY & EQPT: Gas Producers, Generators/Other Rltd Eqpt

Chart Industries Inc ....C 281 364-8700
The Woodlands (G-19841)
Gardner Denver Inc ....D 832 421-5469
Pasadena (G-16446)
Gep Haynesville LLC ....E 281 363-9161
The Woodlands (G-19867)
Sulphur River Gathering LP ....F 806 663-7700
Pampa (G-16339)
Texas Turbine Inc ....E 817 444-5528
Azle (G-1730)
Unconvntonal Gas Solutions LLC ....F 346 353-1048
Houston (G-12431)

MACHINERY & EQPT: Liquid Automation

Hammonds Technical Svcs Inc ....E 281 999-2900
Houston (G-10115)
Radix Us LLC ....E 832 377-9601
Houston (G-11532)
Valtrek Group LLC ....F 915 201-7559
El Paso (G-6025)

MACHINERY & EQPT: Metal Finishing, Plating Etc

Dallas Metal Service ....F 972 481-1700
Dallas (G-4221)

Wolters Holdings Inc ....G 972 272-4600
Garland (G-7610)

MACHINERY & EQPT: Petroleum Refinery

Apache Refinery Svcs Intl LLC ....D 936 890-8586
Willis (G-20843)
Reactor Services International ....F 281 824-0841
Alvin (G-378)
V Gas LLC ....F 713 896-8531
Houston (G-12510)

MACHINERY BASES

Daniel Measurement & Ctrl LLC ....B 713 827-5033
Houston (G-9402)
Ferrell-Ross Roll Mfg Inc ....D 806 364-9051
Hereford (G-8288)
Lewis Engineering Company ....E 903 938-6754
Marshall (G-14787)
Montes Machine Works LLC ....E 346 320-4960
South Houston (G-19051)
Win-Holt Equipment Corp ....C 972 641-4658
Grand Prairie (G-7995)

MACHINERY CLEANING SVCS

HMC Instrmentation Contrls LLC ....C 832 252-9280
Cypress (G-3799)
Nelson Oil Field Eqp & Sup ....F 361 375-2105
Pettus (G-16653)

MACHINERY, CALCULATING: Calculators & Adding

Texas Instruments Incorporated ....A 972 995-3773
Dallas (G-5067)
Texas Instruments Incorporated ....E 214 567-2075
Richardson (G-17408)

MACHINERY, COMMERCIAL LAUNDRY & Drycleaning: Ironers

Popes Cleaners LLC ....F 210 923-7785
San Antonio (G-18384)

MACHINERY, COMMERCIAL LAUNDRY: Extractors

North Txas Hlth Care Ldry Coop ....B 469 916-1150
Grand Prairie (G-7938)

MACHINERY, EQPT & SUPPLIES: Parking Facility

Associated Time Instrs Co Inc ....E 214 637-2763
Dallas (G-3975)
Parking Sense Usa Inc ....F 830 428-0299
Boerne (G-2131)
Vally Park USA Corp ....F 956 994-0000
Mission (G-15572)

MACHINERY, FOOD PRDTS: Beverage

Boccard Life Sciences Inc ....E 281 269-6020
Houston (G-8933)

MACHINERY, FOOD PRDTS: Dairy & Milk

SPX Flow Technology Usa Inc ....E 281 897-2964
Houston (G-12028)

MACHINERY, FOOD PRDTS: Food Processing, Smokers

Keiser Manufacturing Inc ....G 830 303-3397
Seguin (G-18846)

MACHINERY, FOOD PRDTS: Mills, Food

Dallas A C Horn & Company Inc ....D 214 630-3311
Dallas (G-4210)
Landers Machine Co ....E 817 834-6383
Fort Worth (G-6779)

MACHINERY, FOOD PRDTS: Ovens, Bakery

Roto-Flex Oven Co ....F 210 222-2278
San Antonio (G-18434)

PRODUCT

MACHINERY, FOOD PRDTS: Packing House

Super Sack Bag Inc .... F 214 340-7060
Dallas (G-5024)

Tri-Pak Machinery Inc .... E 956 423-5140
Harlingen (G-8207)

MACHINERY, FOOD PRDTS: Processing, Fish & Shellfish

Sort-Rite International Inc .... E 956 423-2427
Harlingen (G-8202)

MACHINERY, FOOD PRDTS: Slicers, Commercial

Logan Farms Inc .... E 713 781-3773
Richmond (G-17462)

MACHINERY, LUBRICATION: Automatic

Houston Grinding & Mfg Co .... D 713 869-3573
Houston (G-10235)

Morales Machine Sp & Trnsp LLC .... F 956 722-4485
Laredo (G-13915)

MACHINERY, MAILING: Postage Meters

Pitney Bowes Inc .... E 512 823-0833
Austin (G-1418)

MACHINERY, METALWORKING: Assembly, Including Robotic

Bc Wind-Down Inc .... F 512 799-2075
Austin (G-982)

Be-Technologies Ltd .... F 972 242-1853
Carrollton (G-2704)

Bright Machines Inc .... B 512 750-5266
Austin (G-1009)

Hero Assemblers LP .... E 210 628-4800
San Antonio (G-18165)

Makerarm Inc .... F 512 553-8033
Round Rock (G-17670)

Powertech Components Inc .... F 210 521-0799
San Antonio (G-18385)

Quiet Logistics Inc .... E 860 841-3892
Dallas (G-4852)

Tendenci Inc .... E 281 497-6567
Houston (G-12203)

MACHINERY, METALWORKING: Coiling

Industrial Coils LLC .... F 956 664-9496
McAllen (G-14871)

Premier Coil Solutions Inc .... E 713 677-0209
Waller (G-20507)

MACHINERY, METALWORKING: Screw Driving

International Commodities .... F 281 331-1252
Alvin (G-367)

MACHINERY, OFFICE: Perforators

Cummins - Allison Corp .... F 972 661-5390
Dallas (G-4192)

MACHINERY, OFFICE: Stapling, Hand Or Power

Parts Krafters Co .... F 515 981-4749
Dallas (G-4789)

MACHINERY, OFFICE: Time Clocks & Time Recording Devices

Associated Time Instrs Co Inc .... F 713 263-1366
Houston (G-8726)

Associated Time Instrs Co Inc .... E 214 637-2763
Dallas (G-3975)

MACHINERY, PACKAGING: Packing & Wrapping

Formers International Inc .... E 281 833-3310
Pasadena (G-16443)

Formers International Inc .... E 281 998-9570
Pasadena (G-16444)

Signode Industrial Group LLC .... E 409 745-2600
Orange (G-16263)

MACHINERY, PACKAGING: Wrapping

J & J Manufacturing Company .... D 409 835-1330
Beaumont (G-1912)

MACHINERY, PAPER INDUSTRY: Coating & Finishing

Southanchor Manufacturing LLC .... E 915 590-6718
El Paso (G-5970)

MACHINERY, PAPER INDUSTRY: Converting, Die Cutting & Stampng

Unique Products Mfg LLC .... E 915 590-2444
El Paso (G-6019)

MACHINERY, PAPER INDUSTRY: Paper Mill, Plating, Etc

Texarkana Machine Inc .... F 903 831-4355
Texarkana (G-19779)

MACHINERY, PRINTING TRADES: Plates

Kgp Group Inc .... E 817 354-0766
Fort Worth (G-6760)

MACHINERY, PRINTING TRADES: Printing Trade Parts & Attchts

Gandy Engineering LLC .... F 210 338-8303
San Antonio (G-18135)

Laser Care Inc .... F 817 640-6665
Arlington (G-719)

Laser Drum Products Inc .... F 713 263-9050
Houston (G-10603)

MACHINERY, SEWING: Sewing & Hat & Zipper Making

Global Vapor Control Inc .... E 713 463-9200
Houston (G-9979)

Toppan Photomasks Inc .... E 972 398-0411
Plano (G-17034)

MACHINERY, TEXTILE: Embroidery

Ramann Enterprises Inc .... E 817 560-4222
Fort Worth (G-6938)

Stitch Gallery Inc .... F 512 550-6172
Lakeway (G-13820)

MACHINERY, TEXTILE: Fiber & Yarn Preparation

Martex Fiber Southern Corp .... E 956 831-7707
Brownsville (G-2381)

MACHINERY, TEXTILE: Printing

1 To 1 Printers LLC .... G 281 821-4400
Houston (G-8398)

MACHINERY, TEXTILE: Silk Screens

Beaver Graphix LLC .... F 325 227-3014
San Angelo (G-17780)

Xact Xpressions Inc .... E 972 242-6332
Dallas (G-5205)

MACHINERY, TEXTILE: Warping

Netfires LLC .... F 972 603-2702
Grand Prairie (G-7933)

MACHINERY, WOODWORKING: Box Making, For Wooden Boxes

Universal Well Service LLC .... E 432 272-6686
Odessa (G-16190)

MACHINERY, WOODWORKING: Lathes, Wood Turning Includes Access

B & B Stake Co .... G 936 327-2161
Livingston (G-14150)

MACHINERY/EQPT, INDL, WHOL: Cleaning, High Press, Sand/Steam

365 Certified Logistics LLC .... F 512 743-9304
Pflugerville (G-16655)

Jimmy Smart .... E 432 381-5450
Odessa (G-16039)

Secco Inc .... G 361 289-1722
Corpus Christi (G-3619)

Smart Control Systems LLC .... F 210 224-4906
San Antonio (G-18480)

Valley Outdoor Power Eqp Inc .... F 956 787-0469
Pharr (G-16715)

MACHINERY: Ammunition & Explosives Loading

Expal USA Inc .... E 903 472-4970
Irving (G-13020)

MACHINERY: Assembly, Exc Metalworking

Brooks Industrial Coatings Inc .... F 512 990-5333
Austin (G-1012)

Csw Industrials Inc .... E 214 884-3777
Dallas (G-4189)

Csw Industrials Holdings Inc .... F 214 884-3777
Dallas (G-4190)

Kirby - Smith Machinery Inc .... F 817 378-0600
Fort Worth (G-6763)

Kirby - Smith Machinery Inc .... F 806 373-1229
Amarillo (G-445)

R & I Enterprises Inc .... F 956 544-7948
Brownsville (G-2396)

Strongarm Industries Inc .... F 409 835-1330
Vidor (G-20334)

MACHINERY: Automobile Garage, Frame Straighteners

R C Technical Welding & Fabr .... E 281 933-6004
Stafford (G-19367)

MACHINERY: Automotive Maintenance

Dynocom Industries Inc .... E 817 284-8844
Fort Worth (G-6600)

Pegicorn Enterprises LLC .... F 512 821-3300
Austin (G-1406)

MACHINERY: Automotive Related

Apergy Artfl Lift Intl LLC .... E 281 403-5742
Spring (G-19195)

C2 International USA LLC .... F 405 473-7144
Grapevine (G-8019)

Classic Auto Air Mfg LP .... F 817 442-4822
Coppell (G-3411)

Jim Coleman Company .... E 713 683-9878
Houston (G-10474)

Materials Transportation Co .... C 800 433-3110
Temple (G-19688)

Megapower Inc .... G 832 415-6995
Houston (G-10822)

Norriseal-Wellmark Inc .... E 713 466-3552
Houston (G-11069)

T & S Machines and Tools Inc .... F 940 668-1002
Gainesville (G-7371)

Worth Eqp Parts & Svc Co Inc .... E 817 473-7266
Mansfield (G-14730)

MACHINERY: Banking

University Houston - System .... C 713 741-2447
Houston (G-12467)

MACHINERY: Binding

Super Strong Products Inc .... F 972 342-6921
Grand Prairie (G-7978)

MACHINERY: Blasting, Electrical

Blast Envmtl & Indus Svcs .... E 281 557-1000
League City (G-13950)

Schmidt Manufacturing Inc .... F 281 431-0581
Bellaire (G-2002)

MACHINERY: Boot Making & Repairing

Mallorys Western & Leather Sup .... F 817 558-0804
Joshua (G-13322)

MACHINERY: Bottle Washing & Sterilzing

Cowgirl Brands LLC ....F 512 466-3816
Kyle *(G-13680)*

MACHINERY: Brick Making

Arlington Brick and Supply Inc ....F 817 460-5511
Arlington *(G-624)*

MACHINERY: Bridge Or Gate, Hydraulic

Hurst Hydraulics Inc ....F 713 863-0340
Houston *(G-10288)*

Thyssenkrupp Arprt Systems Inc..........C 817 834-6984
Fort Worth *(G-7061)*

MACHINERY: Cement Making

Deltatech Controls Inc ....F 956 755-9634
Brownsville *(G-2349)*

MACHINERY: Centrifugal

Andritz Separation Inc....................E 903 856-0445
Pittsburg *(G-16743)*

Baker Hghes Olfld Oprtions LLC..........C 800 441-0535
Yorktown *(G-20976)*

Lone Star Cast Mch Partners LP ....F 903 986-8300
Kilgore *(G-13563)*

Planeview-Wmi LLC.......................F 936 588-8988
Conroe *(G-3350)*

Sentrimax Centrifuges USA Inc...........F 817 453-8112
Mansfield *(G-14718)*

Sulzer Turbo Svcs Houston Inc ....B 713 567-2700
La Porte *(G-13792)*

MACHINERY: Concrete Prdts

Hamilton Form Co Ltd ....D 817 590-2111
Richland Hills *(G-17437)*

Listo Inc ....E 469 544-4555
Dallas *(G-4597)*

MACHINERY: Construction

A Trace Matic Corporation ....E 713 538-1370
Houston *(G-8428)*

Altec Industries Inc........................F 713 336-6230
Houston *(G-8568)*

Altec Industries Inc........................F 972 937-8284
Waxahachie *(G-20526)*

Apergy Artfl Lift Intl LLC ....F 281 602-2176
Spring *(G-19196)*

Belltec Industries Inc......................F 254 939-9404
Belton *(G-2020)*

Cameron International Corp ....A 601 629-3300
Houston *(G-9066)*

Carey Crutcher Inc ....E 281 346-0045
Fulshear *(G-7328)*

Caterpillar Global Min Eqp LLC ....D 903 786-2981
Denison *(G-5336)*

Caterpillar Inc ....B 713 895-2316
Houston *(G-9100)*

Caterpillar Inc ....B 254 752-3456
Waco *(G-20376)*

Caterpillar Inc ....E 361 580-5600
Victoria *(G-20252)*

Caterpillar Inc ....F 713 895-2300
Houston *(G-9101)*

Caterpillar Inc ....A 309 675-1000
Waco *(G-20377)*

Caterpllar Globl Min Mxico LLC...........F 224 551-4000
Del Rio *(G-5311)*

Cherry Construction Systems ....E 903 675-5901
Athens *(G-822)*

Conner Machine and Welding Inc ....C 806 274-2281
Borger *(G-2171)*

CRC-Evans Intl Holdings Inc ....E 832 249-3100
Houston *(G-9336)*

CRC-Evans Pipeline Intl Inc ....C 800 664-9224
Houston *(G-9337)*

Dallas Lite and Barricade Inc ....E 214 748-5791
Dallas *(G-4218)*

Essentium Inc.............................E 210 616-1931
Pflugerville *(G-16670)*

Fenton Environmental Tech Inc ....E 800 521-1708
Brownwood *(G-2428)*

H D Industries Inc ....E 903 586-6126
Jacksonville *(G-13242)*

Halfen Usa Inc ....E 210 945-1399
Converse *(G-3394)*

Hensley Industries Inc....................B 972 241-2321
Dallas *(G-4450)*

High Roller Sand Operating LLC ....F 936 632-6033
Lufkin *(G-14530)*

Hoerbiger Service Inc ....D 281 474-4458
La Porte *(G-13745)*

Humdinger Equipment Ltd ....E 806 771-9944
Lubbock *(G-14420)*

James Manufacturing Inc ....E 903 872-2346
Corsicana *(G-3675)*

Joy Glbal Lngview Oprtions LLC ....A 903 237-7000
Longview *(G-14257)*

Kalco Machine & Mfg Co ....D 940 761-1060
Wichita Falls *(G-20775)*

King Terrain Corporation ....C 830 379-1480
Seguin *(G-18847)*

Klein Products of Texas Inc ....E 903 589-4546
Jacksonville *(G-13247)*

Letourneau Tech Amer Inc ....D 903 237-7000
Longview *(G-14264)*

Longhorn Mulching Inc ....E 936 699-1160
Lufkin *(G-14533)*

Marshall-Gruber Company LLC...........F 682 518-7400
Mansfield *(G-14688)*

Masterpiece Machine and Mfg Co ......D 713 952-4102
Stafford *(G-19351)*

McNeilus Truck and Mfg Inc ....E 972 225-2313
Hutchins *(G-12868)*

MDU Cnstruction Svcs Group Inc ....E 817 447-8085
Burleson *(G-2590)*

Megapower Inc ....G 832 415-6995
Houston *(G-10822)*

Oft Enterprises Inc ....E 713 787-5373
Bellaire *(G-2000)*

Pavestone LLC ....E 281 769-5098
Katy *(G-13376)*

Protech Diamond Usa Inc ....F 972 602-0080
Grand Prairie *(G-7959)*

Psp Industries Inc ....F 210 651-9595
Schertz *(G-18760)*

Reliance Industries Inc....................E 281 499-9926
Missouri City *(G-15587)*

River City Manufacturing Inc ....F 512 335-5194
Bertram *(G-2053)*

SMI-Carr Inc ....F 325 677-0491
Abilene *(G-80)*

Strong Industries Inc ....E 281 448-9315
Houston *(G-12081)*

Technical Services Intl ....E 972 285-7400
Mesquite *(G-15079)*

Tecnon Supply LLC ....F 281 888-9045
Houston *(G-12179)*

Terex Corporation ....D 903 786-2981
Denison *(G-5347)*

Texas High Roller Inc ....E 979 778-7460
Bryan *(G-2511)*

Texas Machinery Co ....F 972 792-0166
Wills Point *(G-20879)*

Vermeer Equipment Texas LLC ....F 512 244-0505
Round Rock *(G-17697)*

Wright Landscaping & Cnst LLC ....E 254 213-3912
Killeen *(G-13618)*

MACHINERY: Cotton Ginning

Consolidated Cotton Gin Co................D 806 745-1191
Lubbock *(G-14396)*

Ford Gin Service Inc ....F 806 745-3433
Lubbock *(G-14411)*

Kimbell Gin Machinery Company.........D 806 763-6645
Lubbock *(G-14433)*

Lummus Corporation ....G 806 745-1191
Lubbock *(G-14443)*

Raider Manufacturing Ltd ....D 806 762-3227
Lubbock *(G-14470)*

Samuel Jackson Incorporated ....E 806 795-5218
Lubbock *(G-14475)*

Samuel Jackson Mfg Co ....F 806 795-5218
Lubbock *(G-14476)*

MACHINERY: Cryogenic, Industrial

Applied Cryo Technologies Inc ....D 281 888-3884
Houston *(G-8666)*

Chart Industries Inc ....C 281 364-8700
The Woodlands *(G-19841)*

Cryognic Vssel Altrnatives Inc ....A 713 357-9714
Houston *(G-9350)*

Fives Cryo Inc ....F 281 820-6990
Houston *(G-9794)*

Lone Star Cryogenics Inc..................F 979 234-5001
Eagle Lake *(G-5541)*

Taylor-Wharton America Inc ....D 281 738-2863
Baytown *(G-1803)*

MACHINERY: Custom

Action Rigging and Pump Svc LP ....F 512 670-9567
Austin *(G-885)*

Alart Tool & Die Corp ....F 713 691-0434
Houston *(G-8527)*

BS Fab & Mechanical Inc ....E 817 373-2879
Rio Vista *(G-17477)*

CCT Precision Machining LLC ....E 817 410-1222
Grapevine *(G-8021)*

Centex Machine and Welding Inc ....E 512 255-1477
Round Rock *(G-17630)*

Computerized Cutters Inc ....E 972 422-6900
Plano *(G-16829)*

Continental Nh3 Pdts Co Inc ....D 214 741-6083
Dallas *(G-4160)*

Don-Nan Pump and Supply Co Inc.......C 432 682-7742
Midland *(G-15194)*

Engelbrecht Manufacturing Inc ....E 281 341-5110
Rosenberg *(G-17581)*

Ggctr Inc ....E 832 456-4585
Pasadena *(G-16448)*

H Lorimer Corporation ....E 903 643-3239
Longview *(G-14245)*

Humanetics II Ltd ....C 972 416-1304
Carrollton *(G-2763)*

Integrated Production Svcs Inc ....E 281 774-6700
Houston *(G-10385)*

Integrated Production Systems ....F 817 385-0700
Arlington *(G-706)*

Integrity Precision Mch LLC ....E 832 859-4116
Houston *(G-10388)*

Jobe Systems Inc ....E 713 344-1292
Houston *(G-10479)*

Liberty Fluid Power Inc ....E 972 623-0927
Grand Prairie *(G-7911)*

McLeod Machine Works Inc ....F 409 835-3429
Beaumont *(G-1927)*

Midwest Machine LLC ....F 806 355-9400
Amarillo *(G-501)*

Praxis Fabrication Inc ....F 806 883-7621
White Deer *(G-20710)*

Precision Custom Machining Inc ....F 713 462-8622
Houston *(G-11388)*

Quality Manufacturing Inc..................F 940 592-5790
Iowa Park *(G-12908)*

R & R Sheet Metal and Mch Sp ....F 806 274-2361
Borger *(G-2183)*

REE Holding Inc ....E 409 840-5650
Beaumont *(G-1947)*

Syneo LLC ....G 979 849-8700
Angleton *(G-579)*

Triple/S Dynamics Inc ....E 214 828-8600
Dallas *(G-5116)*

Triple/S Dynamics Inc ....E 214 828-8600
Dallas *(G-5117)*

Williams Fire Hazard Ctrl Inc ....E 409 745-3232
Port Arthur *(G-17133)*

Xtreme High Prfmce Catings Inc ....E 281 695-8880
Houston *(G-12711)*

MACHINERY: Die Casting

Chemplast Inc ....E 281 208-2585
Stafford *(G-19294)*

MACHINERY: Electronic Component Making

Ftg Aerospace Inc ....D 817 332-3806
Fort Worth *(G-6650)*

Leading Testing Labs LLC ....E 281 600-8227
Brookshire *(G-2318)*

Season Group Usa LLC....................E 210 522-1116
San Antonio *(G-18461)*

Temple Precision Enterpise Inc ....F 409 283-8163
Woodville *(G-20918)*

MACHINERY: Extruding

Texas Extrusion Service Inc ....F 281 350-2288
Spring *(G-19178)*

MACHINERY: Extruding, Synthetic Filament

Makerarm Inc ....F 512 553-8033
Round Rock *(G-17670)*

PRODUCT

MACHINERY: Gas Producers

Exterran Energy Solutions LP ....C 281 836-7000
  Houston *(G-9736)*
Far East Energy (bermuda) Ltd ....F 832 598-0470
  Houston *(G-9761)*
Linde Inc ....E 281 203-3600
  Spring *(G-19227)*
Vaquero Midstream LLC ....E 214 855-5546
  Dallas *(G-5154)*

MACHINERY: Gas Separators

Sepra-Chem Corporation ....F 478 788-9789
  Tyler *(G-20151)*

MACHINERY: Gear Cutting & Finishing

Caldwell Machine and Gear Inc ....F 903 572-1660
  Mount Pleasant *(G-15648)*

MACHINERY: General, Industrial, NEC

Asher Enterprises Inc ....E 281 446-8131
  Humble *(G-12747)*
Centex Mechatronics LLC ....F 830 387-4131
  New Braunfels *(G-15781)*

MACHINERY: Grinding

Baldwin Metals Company Inc ....E 214 637-1030
  Dallas *(G-4000)*
J & R Grinding LLC ....F 281 272-2344
  Houston *(G-10434)*
Master Machine Inc ....F 713 690-3480
  Houston *(G-10788)*

MACHINERY: Ice Making

Lancer Corporation ....B 210 310-7250
  San Antonio *(G-18236)*

MACHINERY: Industrial, NEC

Movement Industries Corp ....F 713 849-1300
  Houston *(G-10928)*
Rapid Hose ....F 713 468-4673
  Houston *(G-11548)*

MACHINERY: Labeling

Gs Liquid Technologies LLC ....F 817 556-6262
  Cleburne *(G-3093)*
Huhtamaki Inc ....B 903 427-5711
  Clarksville *(G-3073)*
ID Technology LLC ....D....... 817 626-7779
  Fort Worth *(G-6713)*
Nut Place Inc ....E 713 462-3147
  Houston *(G-11100)*
Precision Business Mchs Inc ....F 972 224-9119
  Desoto *(G-5440)*
Superior Label Systems Inc ....F 214 330-7770
  Dallas *(G-5026)*
Zynex Inc ....G....... 972 221-5050
  Lewisville *(G-14113)*

MACHINERY: Lapping

John Crane Inc ....F 979 239-1201
  Freeport *(G-7200)*

MACHINERY: Leather Working

Multiple Systems Inc ....E 806 373-7073
  Amarillo *(G-449)*
Multiple Systems Inc ....E 806 373-7073
  Amarillo *(G-450)*
Naegles Industrial Lea McHy Co ....F 361 293-7015
  Yoakum *(G-20972)*

MACHINERY: Metalworking

B-W Grinding Service Inc ....D....... 713 641-0888
  Houston *(G-8782)*
CER Tek Inc ....F 915 772-8290
  El Paso *(G-5693)*
Cook Cmprssn-Parland Operation ....E 713 433-2002
  Houston *(G-9300)*
Granutch-Sturn Systems Corp AM........D....... 972 790-7800
  Grand Prairie *(G-7884)*
J-Mac Tool Inc ....E 817 237-6309
  Fort Worth *(G-6732)*
James Manufacturing Inc ....E 903 872-2346
  Corsicana *(G-3675)*

M N Gumbert Corporation ....E 214 340-8383
  Dallas *(G-4621)*
M2 Global Technology Ltd ....F 210 561-4800
  San Antonio *(G-18269)*
Mercer Metals LP ....E 214 905-9915
  Grand Prairie *(G-7925)*
Rk Ranco Industries LLC ....F 903 831-5992
  Nash *(G-15723)*
Sharp Iron Group LLC ....D....... 940 766-4545
  Wichita Falls *(G-20810)*
Specialized Manufacturing Ltd ....E 713 864-2551
  Houston *(G-11997)*
Ta Fabrication LLC ....F 330 301-6800
  Euless *(G-6161)*
Tamra Group Inc ....E 817 453-3370
  Mansfield *(G-14721)*
Triple/S Dynamics Inc ....E 214 828-8600
  Dallas *(G-5117)*

MACHINERY: Milling

Holland and Associates LLC ....F 806 892-3504
  Idalou *(G-12889)*

MACHINERY: Mining

Arcosa Lw Hpb LLC ....E 214 631-4420
  Dallas *(G-3959)*
Caterpillar Global Min Eqp LLC ....D....... 903 786-2981
  Denison *(G-5336)*
Current Power Solutions Inc...................D....... 281 943-7700
  Houston *(G-9359)*
DSA Operating Company LLC ....E 210 734-5121
  San Antonio *(G-18072)*
Epiroc North America Corp......................A....... 972 496-7353
  Garland *(G-7487)*
Komatsu Mining Corp ....E 903 983-7744
  Kilgore *(G-13562)*
Komatsu Mining Corp ....E 903 237-7000
  Longview *(G-14261)*
Longwood Elastomers Inc ....C....... 979 830-1111
  Brenham *(G-2261)*
Psp Industries Inc ....F 210 651-9595
  Schertz *(G-18760)*
Strong Industries Inc ....E 281 448-9315
  Houston *(G-12081)*
Terex Corporation ....D....... 903 786-2981
  Denison *(G-5347)*
Vulcan Industrial Holdings LLC.............F 715 294-3200
  Houston *(G-12582)*
Womack Machine Supply Co ....D....... 800 569-9800
  Farmers Branch *(G-6219)*

MACHINERY: Ozone

Electronic Drilling Control ....D....... 972 257-0322
  Irving *(G-13014)*

MACHINERY: Packaging

Accutek Inc ....E 972 915-6888
  Irving *(G-12922)*
Allpac Inc ....E 214 630-8804
  Prosper *(G-17212)*
B T S Precision Machine ....G....... 903 498-7501
  Scurry *(G-18782)*
Deka Texas Inc ....E 214 618-1176
  Frisco *(G-7280)*
Faro Services Inc ....F 214 631-1888
  Dallas *(G-4352)*
Foam Supplies Inc ....E 972 436-7008
  Lewisville *(G-14050)*
Ibac Interests LP ....F 281 681-0122
  Oak Ridge North *(G-15889)*
Keaco Enterprises Inc ....F 210 651-6688
  Schertz *(G-18751)*
Ls Packaging Design Inc ....E 713 645-9177
  Houston *(G-10694)*
M W Waldrop Co ....E 713 337-5600
  Houston *(G-10720)*
Motor Controls Inc ....B 972 247-4440
  Dallas *(G-4691)*
OMI Crane Systems Inc ....E 972 636-8000
  Fate *(G-6228)*
Tetra Pak Inc ....C....... 940 565-8800
  Denton *(G-5404)*
Vistech Mfg Solutions LLC ....E 210 225-9900
  San Antonio *(G-18597)*

MACHINERY: Paper Industry Miscellaneous

Mayhan Fabricators Inc..........................E 903 734-4198
  Gilmer *(G-7709)*

Sendero Industries LLC ....E 713 868-6960
  Houston *(G-11828)*

MACHINERY: Pharmaciutical

Conecraft Incorporated ....D....... 817 922-9200
  Fort Worth *(G-6540)*
Guiverman Industries LLC ....E 866 235-8057
  Plano *(G-16882)*
SPX Flow Technology Usa Inc ....E 281 897-2964
  Houston *(G-12028)*
Tote Systems International LP.................E 817 447-9110
  Fort Worth *(G-7068)*
Vanguard Pharmaceutical McHy ....F 281 528-8885
  Spring *(G-19185)*

MACHINERY: Photographic Reproduction

Precision Dcment Solutions Inc ....E 866 916-1177
  Carrollton *(G-2792)*

MACHINERY: Plastic Working

APS Plastics LP ....F 281 290-9950
  Tomball *(G-19959)*
Coperion Corporation ....F 281 449-9944
  Houston *(G-9309)*
Corona Designs Inc ....E 972 272-0471
  Garland *(G-7464)*
Globe Industries Inc ....E 281 440-3999
  Houston *(G-9985)*
Hayes & Stolz Indus Mfg Co LLC ....E 817 926-3391
  Burleson *(G-2581)*

MACHINERY: Printing Presses

Cyclone Production Inc............................F 713 979-1101
  Houston *(G-9384)*

MACHINERY: Recycling

Cleanplanet Chemical Inc ....F 855 256-7568
  Austin *(G-1052)*
Excel Machinery Ltd ....F 806 335-1553
  Amarillo *(G-486)*
I T Remarketing Inc ....E 713 263-8800
  Houston *(G-10309)*
Millennium Recycling LLP ....G....... 817 624-4307
  Fort Worth *(G-6840)*
Prime Momento LLC ....F 832 643-4605
  Sugar Land *(G-19529)*

MACHINERY: Road Construction & Maintenance

Christian Fort Bend Academy ....E 281 980-3724
  Sugar Land *(G-19456)*
Stewart Stevenson Pwr Pdts LLC ....E 361 299-6839
  Corpus Christi *(G-3629)*
Stewart Stevenson Pwr Pdts LLC ....F 915 790-1848
  El Paso *(G-5980)*
Sturgeon Services Texas Inc ....F 661 322-4408
  Midland *(G-15421)*

MACHINERY: Robots, Molding & Forming Plastics

Cosine Additive Inc ....F 832 519-8441
  Houston *(G-9329)*
Plus One Robotics Inc ....F 937 287-5060
  San Antonio *(G-18383)*

MACHINERY: Rubber Working

Texas Extrusion Service Inc ....F 281 350-2288
  Spring *(G-19178)*
US Rubber Corporation ....E 936 756-1977
  Conroe *(G-3380)*

MACHINERY: Screening Eqpt, Electric

Cash Processing Solutions Inc ....B 972 582-1100
  Irving *(G-12962)*

MACHINERY: Semiconductor Manufacturing

Canon Nanotechnologies Inc ....D....... 512 339-7760
  Austin *(G-1024)*
Capital Asset Exch & Trdg LLC ....F 650 326-3313
  Austin *(G-1025)*
Evergreen Solutions Inc ....E 512 389-0625
  Austin *(G-1141)*
Fas Holdings Group LLC..........................E 214 343-5300
  Dallas *(G-4353)*

GL Automation Inc .... F 214 503-9888
   Dallas *(G-4407)*

Photronics Inc .... C 469 675-8520
   Allen *(G-294)*

Plastronics Co .... E 972 986-0474
   Irving *(G-13151)*

Spectrum Semiconductor Tech Lc .... F 972 562-2552
   McKinney *(G-14977)*

Tel Mnfacturing Engrg Amer Inc .... C 972 643-2000
   Allen *(G-301)*

Tokyo Electron America Inc .... B 512 424-1000
   Austin *(G-1583)*

Tokyo Electron America Inc .... E 512 424-1000
   Austin *(G-1584)*

Toppan Photomasks Inc .... B 512 310-6500
   Round Rock *(G-17695)*

Tristar Group Inc .... E 972 392-2848
   Dallas *(G-5118)*

MACHINERY: Sheet Metal Working

S&S Industries Inc .... C 972 438-7150
   Irving *(G-13168)*

MACHINERY: Specialty

Campbell-Randall Machinery Co .... F 936 539-1400
   Conroe *(G-3273)*

Christnes Con Swing Saling LLC .... F 214 212-4808
   Colleyville *(G-3211)*

MACHINERY: Textile

ABM International Inc .... D 936 441-4401
   Montgomery *(G-15624)*

Gerber Technology Inc .... C 972 238-7211
   Dallas *(G-4405)*

Kimbell Gin Machinery Company .... D 806 763-6645
   Lubbock *(G-14433)*

MACHINERY: Voting

Dominion Voting Systems Inc .... F 214 907-3010
   McKinney *(G-14937)*

Premier Election Solutions Inc .... E 469 675-8990
   Allen *(G-296)*

MACHINERY: Wire Drawing

Bk Corrosion LLC .... E 713 225-6661
   Houston *(G-8897)*

Cactus Varied Industries LLC .... B 806 335-9470
   Amarillo *(G-411)*

K & H Fabricators Inc .... E 512 237-5020
   Smithville *(G-18977)*

Komax Corporation .... F 915 591-4551
   El Paso *(G-5832)*

Offshore Kinematics Inc .... F 713 934-7300
   Houston *(G-11142)*

Sons Design & Mfg Inc .... G 817 595-9800
   Hurst *(G-12859)*

South Coast Manufacturing LLC .... E 713 670-0900
   Galena Park *(G-7382)*

MACHINERY: Woodworking

Lindsay Forest Products Inc .... F 903 693-7526
   Carthage *(G-2913)*

SC Industrial Resource Group .... E 972 272-4521
   Garland *(G-7584)*

Vacuumpodscom Inc .... F 972 986-8876
   Cedar Hill *(G-2954)*

MACHINES: Forming, Sheet Metal

B & S Premium Sheet Metal Inc .... E 214 388-4724
   Dallas *(G-3995)*

Bryne Sheet Metal Inc .... D 281 354-1100
   Humble *(G-12749)*

Col-Met Gp LLC .... E 972 494-3900
   Garland *(G-7459)*

Gamma Engineering Inc .... C 817 477-2193
   Mansfield *(G-14676)*

Miller Machine & Welding LLC .... E 254 582-2185
   Whitney *(G-20731)*

Nut Place Inc .... E 713 462-3147
   Houston *(G-11100)*

Samuel Jackson Mfg Co .... F 806 795-5218
   Lubbock *(G-14476)*

Southern Strtch Frming Fbrctio .... E 940 591-0410
   Denton *(G-5400)*

MACHINISTS' TOOLS & MACHINES: Measuring, Metalworking Type

Liberty Plant Maintenance Inc .... F 281 923-5307
   Liberty *(G-14122)*

MACHINISTS' TOOLS: Measuring, Precision

Alyta International Corp .... F 972 978-1980
   Allen *(G-249)*

MACHINISTS' TOOLS: Precision

J M Fabrication Company LLC .... F 817 652-0526
   Arlington *(G-709)*

Master Precision Machining LLC .... F 915 877-0776
   El Paso *(G-5869)*

Mitchell Machine & Fabricating .... F 903 880-0249
   Mabank *(G-14579)*

Remtex Inc .... F 903 758-0461
   Longview *(G-14295)*

Vlj Inc .... F 972 442-4673
   Wylie *(G-20955)*

MACHINISTS' TOOLS: Scales, Measuring, Precision

Bastrop Scale Company Inc .... F 512 321-3443
   Bastrop *(G-1749)*

D C Lites Inc .... F 972 556-0260
   Dallas *(G-4200)*

Thompson Scale Company .... F 713 932-9071
   Houston *(G-12279)*

MAGNETIC INK & OPTICAL SCANNING EQPT

American Micro Systems Ltd .... E 817 571-9015
   Euless *(G-6130)*

MAGNETIC RESONANCE IMAGING DEVICES: Nonmedical

Advanced Imaging Services .... F 210 680-4749
   San Antonio *(G-17867)*

Altus Health System .... F 409 554-0131
   Beaumont *(G-1850)*

Pearland Mri and Imaging Ctr .... F 281 412-3916
   Pearland *(G-16591)*

MAGNETIC TAPE, AUDIO: Prerecorded

Creative Sound Productions .... F 713 777-9975
   Houston *(G-9340)*

MAGNETS: Permanent

Applied Services Corporation .... F 972 432-6509
   Dallas *(G-3954)*

MAIL PRESORTING SVCS

Long Plan Printing Inc .... E 713 797-1125
   Houston *(G-10684)*

MAIL-ORDER HOUSE, NEC

Semasys Inc .... C 713 869-8331
   Houston *(G-11825)*

MAIL-ORDER HOUSES: Books, Exc Book Clubs

Western Horseman Magazine .... E 817 737-6397
   Fort Worth *(G-7140)*

MAIL-ORDER HOUSES: Computer Software

Gamestop Holdings Corp .... B 817 424-2159
   Grapevine *(G-8039)*

MAIL-ORDER HOUSES: Religious Merchandise

Endtime Inc .... E 972 422-0857
   Plano *(G-16861)*

MAILBOX RENTAL & RELATED SVCS

M3 Partners LLC .... E 602 561-6464
   Kingwood *(G-13648)*

Mail & Parcels Plus Inc .... F 409 899-1771
   Beaumont *(G-1923)*

ONeil Digital Solutions LLC .... B 972 881-1282
   Plano *(G-16954)*

MAILING & MESSENGER SVCS

Printmpro Ltd .... E 512 821-9000
   Austin *(G-1433)*

MAILING SVCS, NEC

Anderton Group Inc .... E 254 751-1012
   Waco *(G-20362)*

Aus-Tex Duplicators Inc .... E 512 476-7581
   Austin *(G-949)*

Business EXT Bur Texas Inc .... E 713 528-5568
   Houston *(G-9021)*

Capital Spectrum Inc .... C 512 478-3448
   Buda *(G-2524)*

Company Printing .... F 325 949-9941
   San Angelo *(G-17788)*

E & L Graphics LLC .... F 915 591-8789
   El Paso *(G-5728)*

Eship Global Inc .... F 972 518-1775
   Dallas *(G-3842)*

Finishing & Mailing Center LLC .... E 214 747-6244
   Dallas *(G-4362)*

H & H Dinero Tree Inc .... F 915 591-6245
   El Paso *(G-5792)*

Hov Services Inc .... E 248 837-7100
   Irving *(G-13059)*

Information MGT Solutions LLC .... E 210 826-4994
   San Antonio *(G-18182)*

Laser Prtrs & Mailing Svcs LLC .... F 210 590-6565
   San Antonio *(G-18237)*

Mail Mart Inc .... D 214 630-9643
   Dallas *(G-4629)*

Mail Services Houston Inc .... D 713 594-3362
   Houston *(G-10738)*

Murphy Connected Entps Inc .... E 512 821-0222
   Austin *(G-1357)*

National Mail Advertising Inc .... C 713 869-8551
   Spring *(G-19152)*

Papergraphics Ltd .... F 254 526-4303
   Temple *(G-19696)*

Premier Printing & Ltr Svc Inc .... F 713 868-6300
   Houston *(G-11404)*

Printmailers Inc .... D 832 201-2000
   Houston *(G-11422)*

Raider Services LP .... C 830 996-0016
   Gordon *(G-7769)*

Tri-Win Outsourcing Inc .... E 214 826-2244
   Dallas *(G-5110)*

Union Printers Inc .... F 713 526-6364
   Houston *(G-12436)*

Watermark Group Inc .... E 210 599-0400
   San Antonio *(G-18611)*

MANAGEMENT CONSULTING SVCS: Automation & Robotics

Cornerstone Atomtn Systems LLC .... D 972 346-2242
   Frisco *(G-7275)*

Romeo Engineering Incorporated .... E 817 656-0048
   Fort Worth *(G-6966)*

Ss Electric Inc .... F 915 217-2200
   El Paso *(G-5973)*

MANAGEMENT CONSULTING SVCS: Business

J Connor Consulting Inc .... E 281 578-3388
   Houston *(G-10436)*

Kingston I-Tek Solutions LLC .... E 281 656-4900
   Houston *(G-10536)*

Optimum Consultancy Svcs LLC .... F 713 505-0300
   Houston *(G-11185)*

Pls Inc .... F 713 650-1212
   Houston *(G-11349)*

MANAGEMENT CONSULTING SVCS: Business Planning & Organizing

Epic Energy Resources Inc .... C 281 419-3742
   Houston *(G-9681)*

Hart Energy Publishing LLC .... D 713 993-9320
   Houston *(G-10130)*

Volks Resources LLC .... F 972 636-1880
   Frisco *(G-7324)*

PRODUCT

MANAGEMENT CONSULTING SVCS: Construction Project

Cambrian Management Ltd................F 432 620-9181
Midland (G-15156)
Sofec Inc................................D....... 713 510-6600
Houston (G-11931)
Universal Management Svcs LLC.......E....... 979 481-5711
Angleton (G-581)
Wood Group Usa Inc ....A....... 832 809-8000
Houston (G-12687)
Wright Landscaping & Cnst LLC.......E....... 254 213-3912
Killeen (G-13618)

MANAGEMENT CONSULTING SVCS: Food & Beverage

Beer Dudes Canning Co LLC................F 972 342-4819
Denton (G-5353)

MANAGEMENT CONSULTING SVCS: Foreign Trade

Allan Banks ....F 936 337-4020
Willis (G-20841)

MANAGEMENT CONSULTING SVCS: General

P-R-O Management Inc....................E....... 972 720-1475
Dallas (G-4776)

MANAGEMENT CONSULTING SVCS: Hospital & Health

Medical Present Value Inc.................F 512 795-0015
Austin (G-1334)
Winifred S Hayes Incorporated............E....... 215 855-0615
Dallas (G-5197)

MANAGEMENT CONSULTING SVCS: Industrial & Labor

Gps International LLC ....F 832 319-1730
The Woodlands (G-19870)
Pangea Enterprises Inc ....E....... 956 542-9494
Houston (G-11232)
Trinity Industrial Svcs LLC...................B....... 409 722-6700
Beaumont (G-1964)

MANAGEMENT CONSULTING SVCS: Industry Specialist

Cw Aerotech Services ....F 817 595-1949
North Richland Hills (G-15875)
GL Automation Inc.............................F 214 503-9888
Dallas (G-4407)
Industrial Info Resources Inc.................D....... 713 783-5147
Sugar Land (G-19498)
Molloy Corporation ....E....... 713 771-9485
Houston (G-10907)
S/T Health Group Consulting ....F 281 491-5555
Houston (G-11714)
Talon/Lpe Ltd....................................F 806 372-6600
Amarillo (G-465)

MANAGEMENT CONSULTING SVCS: Information Systems

Spiceworks Inc.................................B 512 346-7743
Austin (G-1525)
Toutatis Aztec Solutions ....D....... 972 484-3060
Dallas (G-5103)

MANAGEMENT CONSULTING SVCS: Maintenance

Immi Turbines Inc ....F 936 788-2229
Conroe (G-3310)
M1 Support Services LP ....D....... 940 323-1119
Denton (G-5379)

MANAGEMENT CONSULTING SVCS: Management Engineering

Skyven Technologies Inc ....E 972 861-0893
Richardson (G-17399)

MANAGEMENT CONSULTING SVCS: Manufacturing

Exquip USA Llc ....F 936 372-3002
Hockley (G-8343)
Kfl Promotions LLC ....E 817 822-9116
Colleyville (G-3216)
Pacific Resources Intl LLC ....B 214 504-3853
McKinney (G-14962)

MANAGEMENT CONSULTING SVCS: Public Utilities

Motor Crier Sfety Slutions Inc ....F 956 726-3377
Laredo (G-13916)

MANAGEMENT CONSULTING SVCS: Quality Assurance

Dnv GL Noble Denton Usa LLC ....B 281 396-1000
Katy (G-13396)
Gs Liquid Technologies LLC ....F 817 556-6262
Cleburne (G-3093)

MANAGEMENT CONSULTING SVCS: Real Estate

Victor Nicolle Inc..............................F 713 896-4911
Houston (G-12566)

MANAGEMENT CONSULTING SVCS: Training & Development

Deepwater Subsea LLC ....E 832 356-6781
Katy (G-13359)
Science Applications Intl Corp ....F 469 557-8249
Carrollton (G-2815)

MANAGEMENT CONSULTING SVCS: Transportation

Dixie Freight Solutions LP ....E 281 447-7500
Houston (G-9484)

MANAGEMENT SERVICES

Bam Denton MGT Ventures LLC............E 940 898-1200
Dallas (G-4002)
Black Star Styles LLC ....C....... 832 207-4563
Killeen (G-13606)
Cimarron Software Services Inc............E 281 226-5100
Houston (G-9190)
Diamond Offshore Management Co......B 281 492-5300
Houston (G-9456)
Evolve Holdings Inc ....E 832 375-0099
Houston (G-9720)
Fabco LLC ....D....... 713 633-6500
Houston (G-9745)
Firstex Industries Inc.........................F 972 602-1478
Grand Prairie (G-7872)
Gr Energy Services MGT LP ....E 281 201-6812
Sugar Land (G-19489)
Greenstar North Amer Holdings ....A 713 965-0005
Houston (G-10036)
Haas Group International LLC ....E 512 519-3989
Austin (G-1195)
Hendricks BTS Corporation ....F 713 516-8716
Pearland (G-16568)
Herd Producing Co Inc ....E....... 903 509-3456
Tyler (G-20095)
Hid Global Corporation ....C....... 800 237-7769
Austin (G-1202)
Hunting Energy Services Inc ....E 281 569-3620
Houston (G-10282)
Hunting Energy Services Inc ....F 281 328-1400
Crosby (G-3734)
Hunting Energy Services LLC ....E 281 820-3838
Houston (G-10283)
Inhance Technologies LLC ....E....... 800 929-1743
Houston (G-10364)
M-I LLC ....B....... 281 561-1300
Houston (G-10725)
Natural Gas Pipeline Amer LLC ....A 713 369-9000
Houston (G-11007)
Octane Energy Consulting LLC............F 432 685-7736
Midland (G-15324)
Pond King Inc...................................F 940 668-2573
Gainesville (G-7357)
Precision Power Associates ....G....... 972 234-6165
Richardson (G-17375)

S&M International Co Inc ....E 281 749-8289
Katy (G-13378)
Skyway Group Inc.............................F 830 278-4481
Uvalde (G-20196)
Superior Information Systems...............F 713 524-8998
Houston (G-12116)
Toyota Mtr Engrg Mfg N Amer In ....C 469 292-1074
Plano (G-17037)
Vision Products Inc ....C....... 830 755-4719
San Antonio (G-18595)

MANAGEMENT SVCS, FACILITIES SUPPORT: Environ Remediation

American Safety Services Inc...............C....... 432 552-7625
Odessa (G-15914)
Bioremediation Contrs Cons Inc ....F 806 771-8033
Lubbock (G-14374)
Epcs Environmental LLC ....F 817 975-5790
Arlington (G-672)
Etech Envmtl Safety Solutions ....E 432 563-2200
Odessa (G-15993)
Moses Envmtl & Cnstr Svcs LLC ....E 806 418-8525
Amarillo (G-448)
Raybar Services LLC ....F 409 698-2548
Brookeland (G-2308)
SOS Environmental Inc ....E 281 723-8282
Spring (G-19251)

MANAGEMENT SVCS: Administrative

Custom Extrusions Holdings LLC.........F 972 442-7200
Wylie (G-20931)

MANAGEMENT SVCS: Business

Gibraltar Monex Centurion Svc ....G....... 800 409-2674
Houston (G-9955)
Howco Metals Management LLC ....C....... 281 649-8800
Houston (G-10268)
Solovis Inc.......................................F 678 234-4583
Irving (G-13183)
TM Luckett Enterprises LLC ....F 866 216-7278
Houston (G-12307)

MANAGEMENT SVCS: Construction

Camac International Corp ....E 713 965-5100
Houston (G-9059)
Exyte Americas Holding Inc.................E 972 535-7300
Plano (G-16868)
Fun Da Mentals For Educatn LLC ....E 832 368-3345
Houston (G-9874)
High Plins Cntrs MGT Group Inc ....E 806 935-5858
Dumas (G-5522)
J Simmons Group Inc.........................E 713 675-5100
Houston (G-10443)
JAS Marketing Inc.............................F 281 879-1844
Channelview (G-3027)
Junction Industries LLC ....E 817 607-8873
Fort Worth (G-6747)
Knights Landscaping LLC ....F 972 971-4213
Mesquite (G-15057)
Neom LLC ....F 210 372-3475
Boerne (G-2130)
Wright Landscaping & Cnst LLC ....E 254 213-3912
Killeen (G-13618)

MANAGEMENT SVCS: Financial, Business

Rain Cii Carbon LLC ....E 281 318-2400
Kingwood (G-13652)
Specktrum ....F 832 892-0863
Houston (G-12004)

MANAGEMENT SVCS: Industrial

Element Markets LLC ....E 281 207-7200
Houston (G-9598)

MANHOLES & COVERS: Metal

Facilities Rehab Inc ....F 512 352-6035
Taylor (G-19655)

MANHOLES COVERS: Concrete

Charlottes Concrete Inc ....E 210 648-4774
San Antonio (G-18001)
Composite Access Products LP............F 956 765-2907
McAllen (G-14850)

MANICURE PREPARATIONS

Eoh Industries Inc.............................D........817 468-3181
Arlington *(G-671)*

Venus Spa......................................E........214 469-1615
Lewisville *(G-14105)*

MANIFOLDS: Pipe, Fabricated From Purchased Pipe

Chem Fabrication LLC.......................D........979 265-6600
Clute *(G-3149)*

MANUFACTURED & MOBILE HOME DEALERS

American Homestar Corporation........E........281 334-9700
League City *(G-13946)*

Clayton Homes Inc...........................F........210 677-6100
San Antonio *(G-18011)*

Clegg Industries Inc.........................E........361 578-0291
Victoria *(G-20253)*

Lakeside Trailer Sales.....................F........936 564-6252
Nacogdoches *(G-15701)*

MANUFACTURING INDUSTRIES, NEC

1954 Manufacturing Inc....................F........760 524-1378
Graham *(G-7774)*

American Kart Mfg LLC.....................F........979 505-5076
Schulenburg *(G-18771)*

American Vapor Company LLC..........F........512 596-1892
Pflugerville *(G-16657)*

Aquajet Manufacturing.....................E........832 484-9244
Cypress *(G-3775)*

Azan Industries Inc..........................F........832 310-4459
Richmond *(G-17450)*

Bmv Media LLC...............................E........915 216-3554
El Paso *(G-5664)*

Boulware & Anson Family Ltd...........G........210 822-9245
San Antonio *(G-17963)*

Carlisle Systems Inc........................G........713 703-9256
Stafford *(G-19292)*

Chassis Liner..................................F........817 284-2545
Euless *(G-6136)*

Cypress Industries Oilfield SE..........F........281 482-3464
Friendswood *(G-7245)*

Dallas Coffee Exchange...................F........214 507-5903
Irving *(G-12989)*

Distribuidora Comercial LLC.............F........830 438-3877
Spring Branch *(G-19269)*

Enviromental Industries LP...............F........972 390-9899
Dallas *(G-4327)*

Es Group of Texas Inc.....................F........281 796-6214
Kingwood *(G-13642)*

Fassco Manufacturing Inc.................D........210 523-0800
San Antonio *(G-18105)*

Flip Manufacturing..........................G........903 454-1538
Greenville *(G-8073)*

Global Co Pak LLC..........................E........817 449-3115
Fort Worth *(G-6673)*

Glycol Technologies LLC..................F........281 779-4753
Houston *(G-9986)*

GSW Manufacturing Inc...................G........956 223-2644
Pharr *(G-16699)*

Gt Silicones Inc..............................E........610 252-5800
Farmers Branch *(G-6198)*

Hammer Industriess LLC..................E........281 763-2189
Houston *(G-10114)*

Hangar R LLC.................................F........469 865-2110
Grand Prairie *(G-7886)*

Hhbodu LLC...................................F........210 464-2669
Grand Prairie *(G-7891)*

Hickham Industries..........................F........713 567-2700
La Porte *(G-13744)*

Kit Professionals Inc........................F........713 783-8700
Houston *(G-10537)*

Kotara Mfg Inc................................G........830 745-9007
Stockdale *(G-19429)*

Lash Mfg & Dev Group LLC..............F........956 465-0330
Brownsville *(G-2375)*

Losoya Industries LLC.....................F........210 559-6066
Boerne *(G-2127)*

LSI Industries................................G........513 793-3200
Houston *(G-10695)*

McKee True Value Hdwr & Lbr..........E........903 874-6581
Corsicana *(G-3677)*

Mid South Manufacturing LLC...........D........903 759-5490
White Oak *(G-20717)*

Mohf Manufacturing Inc...................F........346 317-3618
Spring *(G-19233)*

Mr Maiz-Ito-Inc...............................F........915 873-9270
El Paso *(G-5888)*

Navarrete Industries LLC..................F........432 332-0272
Odessa *(G-16092)*

OEM Outsourcing LLC......................E........972 742-7950
McKinney *(G-14959)*

Page Eagle Industries Inc.................F........409 960-4310
Port Arthur *(G-17120)*

Pmq Alternatives Inc........................G........713 690-7672
Houston *(G-11353)*

Promaxima Mfg LLP Prom..................F........713 667-9606
Houston *(G-11447)*

Refrigeration Design Inc...................E........972 937-3240
Waxahachie *(G-20556)*

Rival Prcsion Mnfctrng RPM LLC.......F........817 487-9694
Alvarado *(G-341)*

Rodbouban Corporation...................E........972 841-8989
Houston *(G-11655)*

S 5 Manufacturing LLC......................G........940 592-2100
Iowa Park *(G-12909)*

Santre Export USA LLC.....................F........811 053-1165
Hidalgo *(G-8309)*

Soho...F........713 526-3755
Houston *(G-11932)*

Solera Co.......................................F........915 637-6471
El Paso *(G-5966)*

Taylor Made Bit Co LLC....................F........432 362-4471
Odessa *(G-16172)*

Tdindustries Ltd..............................E........972 888-9500
Dallas *(G-5042)*

Technical Composite Corp................E........210 832-0200
San Antonio *(G-18523)*

Texas Scientific Products.................F........972 757-2304
Argyle *(G-603)*

Tgc Industries................................E........903 464-9908
Denison *(G-5348)*

Tmd Manufacturing Inc.....................F........903 919-0600
Sulphur Springs *(G-19603)*

Tommy Lewis Industries...................F........806 291-4433
Plainview *(G-16766)*

Traxis Manufacturing LLC.................F........512 383-0089
Austin *(G-1591)*

Trinity Industries 068.......................F........903 295-0356
Longview *(G-14321)*

Trinity Industries Plant 181...............F........214 631-4420
Longview *(G-14322)*

Uvc Manufacturing Group LLC..........G........281 969-6059
Spring *(G-19183)*

Valor Containments LLC...................F........432 202-4220
Midland *(G-15461)*

Vector Industrial Group LLC.............F........281 967-1093
Kemah *(G-13481)*

Venus Beauty Inc............................F........301 503-4052
Garland *(G-7608)*

MAPS

Mapsco Inc....................................D........214 476-5480
Flower Mound *(G-6271)*

Marketmap Inc................................F........512 576-6403
Austin *(G-1327)*

MAPS & CHARTS, WHOLESALE

Key Maps Incorporated....................E........713 522-7949
Houston *(G-10524)*

Seawall Specialty Company Inc.........F........713 522-9064
Houston *(G-11808)*

MARBLE BOARD

Target Stone LLC............................E........832 827-8663
Houston *(G-12161)*

MARBLE, BUILDING: Cut & Shaped

Allied Stone Inc..............................D........214 838-2225
Dallas *(G-3927)*

Ashcraft-Southern Marble Co...........E........903 581-5501
Tyler *(G-20049)*

Aspen Marble Inc............................F........817 478-5140
Fort Worth *(G-6404)*

Bolfing Brothers Marble Inc..............E........281 351-7195
Cypress *(G-3782)*

Churchill Manufacturing Inc..............F........903 660-4585
Hallsville *(G-8128)*

Craig Baker Marble Co Inc................D........281 492-2365
Barker *(G-1745)*

Dallas Marble Company Inc..............G........972 291-9145
Midlothian *(G-15478)*

Designer Stone Center Inc................E........713 862-0120
Houston *(G-9443)*

Dimension In Stone & Glass.............F........214 651-7230
Alba *(G-182)*

Elm Mott Marble Co.........................F........254 829-1552
Elm Mott *(G-6064)*

K & K Langham Ltd..........................D........512 835-5100
Austin *(G-1263)*

Kamal Incorporated.........................D........210 695-2678
Helotes *(G-8241)*

Marble & Granite Resources.............F........713 957-2646
Houston *(G-10759)*

Marble Gallery Inc...........................F........903 759-4726
Longview *(G-14274)*

Northside Cultured Marble Inc...........G........281 429-5288
Conroe *(G-3343)*

Regal Marble Co.............................F........361 572-8498
Victoria *(G-20300)*

Royal Baths Mfg Co Ltd....................E........512 707-0094
Buda *(G-2535)*

Sigma MBL Granite-Houston Inc.......E........713 290-8530
Houston *(G-11886)*

Southwest Marble & Granite Inc........G........512 918-0135
Austin *(G-1712)*

Stone Production Inc........................F........512 990-9800
Austin *(G-1539)*

Stonexpressions LLC.......................G........214 366-2216
Dallas *(G-5013)*

Venus Marble Co Inc.......................D........972 223-8008
Desoto *(G-5447)*

West U Marble LLC..........................F........713 433-4424
Houston *(G-12636)*

West University Marble Co................F........713 433-2240
Houston *(G-8396)*

MARBLE: Crushed & Broken

Cactus Cyn Quarries of Texas..........F........830 693-4331
Marble Falls *(G-14740)*

MARINE BASIN OPERATIONS

Emerald Pt Marina Partners Ltd.........C........512 266-1535
Austin *(G-1123)*

MARINE CARGO HANDLING SVCS: Ship Hold Cleaning

Main Marine Repair Inc.....................F........713 645-3553
Houston *(G-10740)*

MARINE ENGINE REPAIR SVCS

Current Power Solutions Inc..............D........281 943-7700
Houston *(G-9359)*

Quality Trbchrger Cmpnents LLC.......E........713 849-4200
Houston *(G-11502)*

MARINE RELATED EQPT

Deep Down Inc................................D........281 517-5000
Houston *(G-9420)*

Dynacon Inc...................................D........979 823-2690
Bryan *(G-2470)*

Offshore Wind Power Systems of.......F........682 367-0652
Grapevine *(G-8047)*

Thrustmaster of Texas Inc................B........713 937-6295
Houston *(G-12284)*

MARINE RELATED EQPT: Cranes, Ship

Seatrax Inc....................................B........713 896-6500
Houston *(G-11806)*

Seatrax Inc....................................F........713 896-6500
Houston *(G-11807)*

MARINE SPLY DEALERS

Texgulmarco Co Inc.........................E........956 943-2673
Port Isabel *(G-17139)*

Zimco Marine LLC...........................F........956 831-7828
Brownsville *(G-2422)*

MARINE SPLYS WHOLESALERS

Marine Rubber Inc...........................F........281 446-4132
Humble *(G-12787)*

MARKERS

Glass Chalk....................................G........830 379-1814
Seguin *(G-18838)*

Employee Codes: A=Over 500 employees, B=251-500
C=101-250, D=51-100, E=20-50, F=10-19, G=9

2021 Harris Texas
Manufacturers Directory

PRODUCT

1555

MARKETS: Meat & fish

Fisher Ham and Meat Co ....F 281 376-1644
Spring (G-19121)

Union Slaughter House Inc ....E 830 774-0065
Del Rio (G-5327)

Usm Manufacturing LLC ....E 806 791-0220
Lubbock (G-14505)

MARKING DEVICES

Budget Signs Ltd ....E 210 349-7446
San Antonio (G-17971)

Corpus Christi Stamp Works Inc ....E 361 884-4801
Corpus Christi (G-3509)

Gemini Incorporated ....D 512 352-5207
Taylor (G-19656)

ID Technology LLC ....D 817 626-7779
Fort Worth (G-6713)

R-J Typesetters Inc ....G 915 562-4461
El Paso (G-5925)

Stamp Shop Inc ....F 210 824-7373
San Antonio (G-18495)

Timesaver Templates Inc ....F 972 620-2197
Dallas (G-5095)

MARKING DEVICES: Canceling Stamps, Hand, Rubber Or Metal

Lobues Rubber Stamp Co ....F 713 652-0031
Houston (G-10661)

MARKING DEVICES: Embossing Seals & Hand Stamps

Foust Incorporated ....E 806 374-7005
Amarillo (G-424)

Mail & Parcels Plus Inc ....F 409 899-1771
Beaumont (G-1923)

MARKING DEVICES: Letters, Metal

Material Control Inc ....D 817 695-1400
Arlington (G-729)

MARKING DEVICES: Seal Presses, Notary & Hand

American Assn Notaries Inc ....F 713 644-2299
Houston (G-8586)

Thiink Biig Tax Service Inc ....F 832 606-3380
Katy (G-13450)

MASQUERADE OR THEATRICAL COSTUMES STORES

Julie Keck ....F 210 435-3535
San Antonio (G-18212)

MASSAGE MACHINES, ELECTRIC: Barber & Beauty Shops

Ayc Group LLC ....F 214 838-2630
Garland (G-7445)

MASSAGE PARLORS

Venus Spa ....E 214 469-1615
Lewisville (G-14105)

MASTIC FLOOR COMPOSITION

Builders Post-Tension Inc ....E 281 873-9500
Houston (G-9014)

MASTIC ROOFING COMPOSITION

Palacio Ivis ....F 214 402-6856
Dallas (G-4777)

MATCHES & MATCH BOOKS

Atlas Match LLC ....E 817 267-1500
Euless (G-6131)

MATERIALS HANDLING EQPT WHOLESALERS

Interlake Mecalux Inc ....E 972 245-3910
Dallas (G-4506)

Layne Christensen Company ....D 281 475-2600
Spring (G-19226)

Material Handling Concepts ....F 512 836-6598
Austin (G-1328)

Miller Equipment Co ....F 469 366-4227
Garland (G-7553)

Norwood Equipment Houston Inc ....F 713 670-1320
Houston (G-11084)

Product Handling Design Inc ....F 972 231-4628
Haslet (G-8222)

Purvis Industries LLC ....D 214 358-5500
Dallas (G-4837)

Ranger Conveying & Supply Co ....D 713 671-0004
Houston (G-11544)

Russell Industries Inc ....F 713 692-7225
Houston (G-11698)

Springhill Pallets LLC ....F 903 297-6090
Longview (G-14311)

MATS & MATTING, MADE FROM PURCHASED WIRE

Custom Safety Products Inc ....F 281 482-8668
Friendswood (G-7244)

Quality Mat Company ....C 409 898-1170
Beaumont (G-1944)

MATS, MATTING & PADS: Aircraft, Floor, Exc Rubber Or Plastic

United Aviation ACC Inc ....E 817 447-8000
Burleson (G-2600)

MATS, MATTING & PADS: Auto, Floor, Exc Rubber Or Plastic

Reyes-Amtex Automotive LLC ....E 210 628-4900
San Antonio (G-18425)

MATS, MATTING & PADS: Nonwoven

Gormans Uniform Rental Inc ....D 713 467-5424
Houston (G-10006)

Lets Gel Inc ....E 512 628-1700
Austin (G-1289)

Michaels Companies Inc ....D 972 409-1300
Irving (G-13108)

Newpark Resources Inc ....E 281 362-6800
The Woodlands (G-19897)

MATS: Blasting, Rope

Advanced Fabric Tech LLC ....F 281 872-7272
Spring (G-19191)

MATTRESS STORES

Abbys Thres No Pl Like HM Fur ....F 817 244-3371
Fort Worth (G-6340)

Enlink Midstream Inc ....E 214 953-9500
Dallas (G-4324)

National Bedding Company LLC ....D 281 345-6237
Houston (G-10966)

MAUSOLEUMS

Dietz Memorial Company Inc ....E 512 451-1983
Austin (G-1091)

MEAT & FISH MARKETS: Food & Freezer Plans, Meat

Hill Country Provisions LLC ....F 512 564-3013
Austin (G-1204)

MEAT & FISH MARKETS: Seafood

Miller Seafood Co Inc ....E 361 552-6423
Port Lavaca (G-17151)

MEAT & MEAT PRDTS WHOLESALERS

Caddo Packing Co Inc ....G 903 935-2211
Marshall (G-14768)

Cargill Meat Solutions Corp ....E 806 293-5181
Plainview (G-16752)

Cargill Meat Solutions Corp ....F 806 295-8243
Friona (G-7253)

Dziuk Meat Market Inc ....F 830 538-3082
Castroville (G-2928)

Frenchys Sausage Co Inc ....F 713 862-2299
Houston (G-9863)

Hill Country Provisions LLC ....F 512 564-3013
Austin (G-1204)

J & B Sausage Company Inc ....B 830 788-7661
Waelder (G-20484)

John Soules Foods Inc ....C 903 592-9800
Tyler (G-20104)

M & M Italian Style Foods Inc ....D 817 439-8008
Roanoke (G-17490)

MEAT CUTTING & PACKING

7 S Packing LLC ....B 325 716-4047
San Angelo (G-17768)

ABF Packing Inc ....D 254 968-4919
Dublin (G-5514)

Bay Deer Processing Inc ....F 713 472-6000
Pasadena (G-16395)

Boggs Enterprises Inc ....F 903 572-8722
Mount Pleasant (G-15647)

Buckhead Meat of San Antonio ....D 210 337-1011
San Antonio (G-17970)

Buckhead Mt Safood Houston Inc ....D 281 405-3201
Houston (G-9009)

Caddo Packing Co Inc ....G 903 935-2211
Marshall (G-14768)

Cargill Incorporated ....A 254 799-6211
Waco (G-20375)

Cargill Meat Solutions Corp ....E 806 295-8393
Friona (G-7252)

Cargill Meat Solutions Corp ....E 806 293-5181
Plainview (G-16752)

Caviness Beef Packers Ltd ....D 806 372-5781
Amarillo (G-413)

Centex Meat Company LP ....E 512 352-6357
Taylor (G-19652)

Deen Wholesale Meat Co ....E 817 335-2257
Fort Worth (G-6582)

Ditta Meat Company ....D 281 487-2010
Pasadena (G-16417)

Double B Foods Inc ....C 254 435-6187
Meridian (G-15013)

Dutchmans Market Inc ....F 830 997-5693
Fredericksburg (G-7177)

Dziuk Meat Market Inc ....F 830 538-3082
Castroville (G-2928)

Eddy Packing Co Inc ....B 361 580-3800
Yoakum (G-20965)

Glens Packing Company Inc ....F 361 798-2601
Hallettsville (G-8122)

Harvest House Farms ....F 830 868-7253
Johnson City (G-13312)

Hayes Farm ....E 817 477-1661
Mansfield (G-14681)

Hormel Foods Corp Svcs LLC ....F 817 465-4735
Arlington (G-698)

Huse Processing Inc ....G 254 533-2205
Malone (G-14638)

Jbs USA Food Company ....B 817 306-9900
Fort Worth (G-6736)

Jbs USA Food Company ....D 806 966-5103
Cactus (G-2622)

Jbs USA Food Company ....B 956 632-3800
McAllen (G-14877)

K & C Meat Processing ....F 936 825-6944
Navasota (G-15738)

Local Cuts Meat Company LLC ....F 972 489-3832
Rockwall (G-17555)

Loggins Meat Company Inc ....D 903 595-1011
Tyler (G-20115)

Lone Star Beef Processors LP ....C 325 658-5555
San Angelo (G-17813)

MARTIN PREFERRED FOODS LP ....C 713 869-6191
Houston (G-10777)

Midwest Provisions Inc ....C 903 891-6213
Sherman (G-18921)

Mineola Packing Company ....C 903 569-5355
Mineola (G-15510)

Mpp Investments LLC ....C 940 691-0014
Wichita Falls (G-20784)

Pat and Gail Jackowski ....F 830 278-6247
Uvalde (G-20194)

Patek Grocery and Market ....F 361 594-3171
Shiner (G-18946)

Pilgrims Pride Corporation ....C 936 564-3306
Nacogdoches (G-15709)

Plains Meat Co Ltd ....E 806 765-5595
Lubbock (G-14462)

Preferred Beef Group LP ....C 806 658-4561
Booker (G-2158)

Ranch House Meat Company LLC ....F 325 396-4536
Menard (G-15000)

Roes of San Antonio LLC ....E 210 224-5441
San Antonio (G-18430)

Stx Beef Company, LLC ....A 361 241-5000
Corpus Christi **(G-3632)**

Tasman Industries Inc ....E 806 372-3850
Amarillo **(G-512)**

Tejas Supreme Meat ....E 210 224-9672
San Antonio **(G-18525)**

Texas Best Proteins LP ....E 940 769-2028
Santo **(G-18739)**

Texas Big Game Processing Inc ....F 210 366-0638
San Antonio **(G-18535)**

Thompsons Cstm Meats & Proc LP .....E 254 445-4180
Dublin **(G-5517)**

Tyson Foods Inc ....B 903 859-4030
Arp **(G-813)**

Tyson Foods Inc ....C 214 331-1010
Dallas **(G-5126)**

Tyson Foods Inc ....E 936 248-2081
Tenaha **(G-19725)**

Tyson Fresh Meats Inc ....E 806 335-7492
Amarillo **(G-469)**

Tyson Fresh Meats Inc ....E 806 335-2301
Amarillo **(G-471)**

Union Slaughter House Inc ....E 830 774-0065
Del Rio **(G-5327)**

West Phalia Market Inc ....F 512 846-1155
Hutto **(G-12888)**

Wiatrek Dunn Kutac Inc ....E 830 484-2888
Poth **(G-17196)**

MEAT MARKETS

Bear Creek Smokehouse LLC ....E 903 935-5217
Marshall **(G-14763)**

Centex Meat Company LP ....E 512 352-6357
Taylor **(G-19652)**

Dutchmans Market Inc ....F 830 997-5693
Fredericksburg **(G-7177)**

Dziuk Meat Market Inc ....F 830 538-3082
Castroville **(G-2928)**

Freeman Brothers Inc ....F 806 883-7831
White Deer **(G-20709)**

Glens Packing Company Inc ....F 361 798-2601
Hallettsville **(G-8122)**

Kaspers Meat Market Inc ....E 979 725-8227
Weimar **(G-20650)**

Logan Farms Inc ....E 713 781-3773
Richmond **(G-17462)**

Milton Bernhard Meat Proc ....F 830 367-2995
Kerrville **(G-13523)**

Pat and Gail Jackowski ....F 830 278-6247
Uvalde **(G-20194)**

Praseks Hillje Smokehouse ....D 979 543-8312
El Campo **(G-5626)**

Prause Market LLC ....F 979 968-3259
La Grange **(G-13700)**

Ranch House Meat Company LLC ......F 325 396-4536
Menard **(G-15000)**

Rudolphs Market & Sausage Co ....F 214 741-1874
Dallas **(G-4920)**

Singleton ML Inc ....F 409 755-0893
Lumberton **(G-14570)**

Thompsons Cstm Meats & Proc LP .....E 254 445-4180
Dublin **(G-5517)**

MEAT PRDTS: Bacon, Slab & Sliced, From Slaughtered Meat

Double R Brand Mfg LLC ....D 979 289-3421
Brenham **(G-2252)**

Janak Packing Inc ....G 361 798-2985
Hallettsville **(G-8123)**

MEAT PRDTS: Boneless Meat, From Purchased Meat

Columbia Packing Co Inc ....E 214 946-8171
Dallas **(G-4144)**

MEAT PRDTS: Boxed Beef, From Slaughtered Meat

Jbs USA Food Company ....B 903 434-1000
Pittsburg **(G-16745)**

MEAT PRDTS: Calf's Foot Jelly, From Purchased Meat

Homestead Heritage ....E 254 754-9665
Waco **(G-20416)**

MEAT PRDTS: Canned

Hill Country Provisions LLC ....F 512 564-3013
Austin **(G-1204)**

MEAT PRDTS: Canned Exc Baby Food, From Slaughtered Meat

Columbia Packing Co Inc ....E 214 946-8171
Dallas **(G-4144)**

MEAT PRDTS: Cooked Meats, From Purchased Meat

Fortis Foods International LP ....E 214 472-6400
Frisco **(G-7286)**

MEAT PRDTS: Frozen

Nueces Canyon Companies ....F 979 289-5600
Brenham **(G-2266)**

MEAT PRDTS: Head Cheese, From Purchased Meat

Intercarnes Texas Corporation ....D 281 360-3825
El Paso **(G-5812)**

MEAT PRDTS: Meat By-Prdts, From Slaughtered Meat

Iowa Food Group LLC ....F 712 600-3663
Westlake **(G-20696)**

Leonard & Harral Packing Co ....B 210 532-3241
San Antonio **(G-18247)**

MEAT PRDTS: Pork, Cured, From Purchased Meat

Tyler Packing Co Inc ....F 903 593-9592
Tyler **(G-20171)**

MEAT PRDTS: Pork, From Slaughtered Meat

Pederson Natural Farms Inc ....E 254 386-4790
Hamilton **(G-8169)**

MEAT PRDTS: Prepared Beef Prdts From Purchased Beef

Leonard Holding Company ....F 210 532-3241
San Antonio **(G-18248)**

Surlean Meat Company ....C 210 227-4370
San Antonio **(G-18516)**

MEAT PRDTS: Prepared Pork Prdts, From Purchased Meat

Pederson Kronseder LLC ....E 254 386-4790
Hamilton **(G-8168)**

MEAT PRDTS: Sausage Casings, Natural

H W D Casings Inc ....D 210 661-6161
San Antonio **(G-18158)**

MEAT PRDTS: Sausages & Related Prdts, From Purchased Meat

Double B Foods Inc ....C 254 435-6187
Meridian **(G-15013)**

MEAT PRDTS: Sausages, From Purchased Meat

Chorizo De San Manuel Guer ....E 956 383-8751
Edinburg **(G-5582)**

Dankworth Packing Co Inc ....E 325 365-3552
Ballinger **(G-1740)**

Double R Brand Foods LLC ....E 713 868-0030
Houston **(G-9502)**

Frenchys Sausage Co Inc ....F 713 862-2299
Houston **(G-9863)**

Kiolbassa Provision Company ....B 210 226-8127
San Antonio **(G-18227)**

Kubys Sausage House Inc ....F 214 363-2231
Dallas **(G-4572)**

Quality Sausage Company Inc ....C 214 634-3400
Dallas **(G-4845)**

Singleton ML Inc ....F 409 755-0893
Lumberton **(G-14570)**

MEAT PRDTS: Sausages, From Slaughtered Meat

Fisher Ham and Meat Co ....F 281 376-1644
Spring **(G-19121)**

H & B Packing Co Inc ....D 254 752-2506
Waco **(G-20408)**

J & B Sausage Company Inc ....B 830 788-7661
Waelder **(G-20484)**

J & B Sausage Company Inc ....F 210 344-2212
San Antonio **(G-18197)**

J & B Sausage Company Inc ....C 979 725-6661
Weimar **(G-20649)**

MEAT PRDTS: Smoked

Carlton Foods Corp ....D 830 625-7583
Houston **(G-9093)**

Squares Distributing Inc ....F 325 692-4797
Abilene **(G-82)**

MEAT PRDTS: Snack Sticks, Incl Jerky, From Purchased Meat

Bridgford Industries Inc ....E 214 428-1535
Dallas **(G-4053)**

Frito-Lay North America Inc ....A 972 334-7000
Plano **(G-16874)**

Old Frito-Lay Inc ....A 972 334-7000
Plano **(G-16953)**

Ranch House Jerky LLC ....E 512 347-8999
Austin **(G-1452)**

MEAT PROCESSED FROM PURCHASED CARCASSES

B&G Foods Inc ....F 281 821-6680
Houston **(G-8779)**

Bear Creek Smokehouse LLC ....E 903 935-5217
Marshall **(G-14763)**

Buckhead Meat of San Antonio ....D 210 337-1011
San Antonio **(G-17970)**

Cargill Meat Solutions Corp ....E 806 293-5181
Plainview **(G-16752)**

CTI Saginaw I LLC ....D 817 869-1090
Saginaw **(G-17744)**

Ditta Meat Company ....D 281 487-2010
Pasadena **(G-16417)**

Dutchmans Market Inc ....F 830 997-5693
Fredericksburg **(G-7177)**

Dziuk Meat Market Inc ....F 830 538-3082
Castroville **(G-2928)**

Eddy Packing Co Inc ....B 361 580-3800
Yoakum **(G-20965)**

H & B Packing Co Inc ....D 254 752-2506
Waco **(G-20408)**

Hillshire Brands Company ....F 817 427-7700
Fort Worth **(G-6700)**

Hillshire Brands Company ....B 972 556-0392
Irving **(G-13057)**

Hillshire Brands Company ....B 972 416-4395
Carrollton **(G-2760)**

Huse Processing Inc ....G 254 533-2205
Malone **(G-14638)**

J & B Sausage Company Inc ....B 830 788-7661
Waelder **(G-20484)**

John Soules Foods Inc ....C 903 592-9800
Tyler **(G-20104)**

Kaspers Meat Market Inc ....E 979 725-8227
Weimar **(G-20650)**

Leons Fine Foods Inc ....C 972 529-5050
McKinney **(G-14953)**

M & M Italian Style Foods Inc ....D 817 439-8008
Roanoke **(G-17490)**

Milton Bernhard Meat Proc ....F 830 367-2995
Kerrville **(G-13523)**

Papa Grande Gourmet Foods LLC ....C 210 349-6262
San Antonio **(G-18366)**

Plains Meat Co Ltd ....B 806 765-5595
Lubbock **(G-14462)**

Praseks Hillje Smokehouse ....D 979 543-8312
El Campo **(G-5626)**

Prause Market LLC ....F 979 968-3259
La Grange **(G-13700)**

Quality Sausage Company Inc ....C 214 634-3400
Dallas **(G-4846)**

PRODUCT

Rudolphs Market & Sausage Co............F 214 741-1874
Dallas *(G-4920)*

Slovacek Foods LP ....E 979 272-8625
Snook *(G-18981)*

Standard Meat Company LLC..............D....... 214 561-0561
Dallas *(G-5005)*

Texas Best Proteins LP ....F 940 769-2028
Santo *(G-18739)*

Tyson Foods Inc ....B 817 656-5507
Fort Worth *(G-7089)*

Tyson Fresh Meats Inc ....A 806 335-7322
Amarillo *(G-470)*

Usm Manufacturing LLC ....E 806 791-0220
Lubbock *(G-14505)*

MEAT PROCESSING MACHINERY

Freeman Brothers Inc..........................F 806 883-7831
White Deer *(G-20709)*

L S W Mfg Inc ....F 817 232-4482
Saginaw *(G-17747)*

Rotom Inc ....E 806 293-7331
Plainview *(G-16762)*

Tejas Industries Inc............................E 806 293-4431
Plainview *(G-16763)*

Texas Tripe Inc ....F 903 674-8042
Detroit *(G-5448)*

MEATS, PACKAGED FROZEN: Wholesalers

Koch Ranches Inc................................F 210 858-9795
San Antonio *(G-18228)*

MECHANICAL INSTRUMENT REPAIR SVCS

Top Deck Inc......................................E 409 745-3955
Orange *(G-16265)*

MEDIA: Magnetic & Optical Recording

Calrock Music.....................................D....... 432 213-8822
Houston *(G-9054)*

Conetic Software Systems Inc...............E 210 222-9621
San Antonio *(G-18023)*

MEDICAL & HOSPITAL EQPT WHOLESALERS

Accumed Biotech LLC.........................F 315 790-0466
Houston *(G-8459)*

Armbrust Inc.......................................E 512 807-0744
Pflugerville *(G-16658)*

Broadband Technology Corp.................E 806 698-0396
Lubbock *(G-14383)*

Ccmm Inc...F 936 827-7930
Mission *(G-15549)*

Gtl Supply Solutions LLC ....F 214 644-2402
Allen *(G-271)*

Insignia Marketing Inc ....F 281 465-0040
Magnolia *(G-14610)*

Kci Usa Inc...C....... 800 275-4524
San Antonio *(G-18220)*

Mediana Technologies Corp ....E 425 406-2262
San Antonio *(G-18289)*

Medline Industries Inc ....C....... 281 574-6200
Katy *(G-13371)*

Mfi International Mfg LLC......................A 915 858-0971
El Paso *(G-5876)*

NA Acquisition Company ....C....... 817 231-1300
Fort Worth *(G-6859)*

Nk Energy LLC ....F 832 857-8228
Kingwood *(G-13650)*

MEDICAL & HOSPITAL SPLYS: Radiation Shielding Garments

International Biomedical Ltd..................D....... 512 873-0033
Austin *(G-1236)*

MEDICAL & SURGICAL SPLYS: Abdominal Support, Braces/Trusses

KVP International Inc............................E 626 633-0077
McKinney *(G-14948)*

MEDICAL & SURGICAL SPLYS: Bandages & Dressings

Gwm Products LLC..............................E 855 872-2013
Irving *(G-13047)*

Gwm Products LLC..............................F 855 872-2013
Allen *(G-272)*

Smith & Nephew Inc ....B 817 900-4000
Fort Worth *(G-6994)*

Violet Care LLC ....F 210 482-0237
San Antonio *(G-18593)*

MEDICAL & SURGICAL SPLYS: Braces, Orthopedic

Baker O & P Enterprises Inc ....F 817 332-7313
Fort Worth *(G-6423)*

MEDICAL & SURGICAL SPLYS: Clothing, Fire Resistant & Protect

Petrohab Llc ....E 281 407-3800
Houston *(G-11302)*

Safety Wear Ltd ....F 832 243-0100
Houston *(G-11727)*

MEDICAL & SURGICAL SPLYS: Cotton & Cotton Applicators

Eugene B Smith & Co Inc.....................E 409 763-6401
Pasadena *(G-16432)*

MEDICAL & SURGICAL SPLYS: Dressings, Surgical

Avcor Health Care Products Inc ....E 817 551-0595
Grand Prairie *(G-7838)*

MEDICAL & SURGICAL SPLYS: Hosiery, Support, Orthopedic

Rehab Plus Thrapeutic Pdts Inc ....F 806 791-2288
Wolfforth *(G-20911)*

MEDICAL & SURGICAL SPLYS: Hydrotherapy

Cryo Zone LLC ....F 972 523-6060
Dallas *(G-4187)*

MEDICAL & SURGICAL SPLYS: Ligatures

Ethicon Inc...C....... 325 482-5200
San Angelo *(G-17797)*

MEDICAL & SURGICAL SPLYS: Limbs, Artificial

A Speclzed Apprach To Prsthtic............F 832 813-5278
Spring *(G-19190)*

Advanced Limb & Brace.......................F 806 351-1775
Amarillo *(G-391)*

Allen Orthotics & Prosthetics ....F 432 683-3788
Midland *(G-15112)*

Hanger Inc ....E 817 923-2101
Fort Worth *(G-6687)*

Muilenburg Prosthetics Inc...................F 713 524-3949
Houston *(G-10935)*

Precision Prosthetic Inc ....F 915 544-2961
El Paso *(G-5917)*

Weathrford Artfl Lift Systems ....F 281 630-5919
Houston *(G-12623)*

MEDICAL & SURGICAL SPLYS: Live Preservers, Exc Cork & Inflat

Blacksheep Inc...................................B 903 592-3853
Tyler *(G-20059)*

MEDICAL & SURGICAL SPLYS: Orthopedic Appliances

Adaptive Switch Laboratories ....F 440 329-6276
Spicewood *(G-19091)*

Advanced Orthotics Prosthetics ....F 956 971-8200
Edinburg *(G-5573)*

Alex Orthopedic Inc ....E 972 641-9680
Grand Prairie *(G-7826)*

Blackstone Medical Inc ....D....... 214 937-2000
Lewisville *(G-14028)*

Border Opprtnity Sver Systems ....E 830 775-1225
Del Rio *(G-5308)*

Cen-Tex Machining Inc ....D....... 512 255-1477
Round Rock *(G-17629)*

Dibellos Dynamic Orthotics ....E 713 747-4171
Houston *(G-9462)*

Letourneau Lflike Orthtics Prs ....F 409 832-5005
Beaumont *(G-1917)*

Medical Technology Inc........................C....... 972 647-0884
Grand Prairie *(G-7924)*

MESA Orthopedic Supplies ....E 210 699-6911
San Antonio *(G-18292)*

New Options Inc..................................D....... 214 638-6422
Farmers Branch *(G-6208)*

Orthofix Inc...C....... 214 937-2000
Lewisville *(G-14076)*

Orthorx Inc ....F 214 501-0180
Plano *(G-16959)*

Sheepskin Ranch Inc...........................F 817 738-2485
Fort Worth *(G-6985)*

Texas Medical Industries Inc ....F 972 636-9556
Royse City *(G-17726)*

Texas Orthopaedic PDT Svcs LLC ....F 972 772-8776
Rockwall *(G-17570)*

Total Orthtic Prsthtic Sltions ....G....... 915 541-8677
El Paso *(G-6009)*

Valley Orthpd & Prosthetics..................G....... 956 686-0032
McAllen *(G-14915)*

MEDICAL & SURGICAL SPLYS: Personal Safety Eqpt

ABM International Inc...........................D....... 936 441-4401
Montgomery *(G-15624)*

Armortex Inc.......................................E 800 880-8306
Schertz *(G-18744)*

Bartec US Corporation.........................F 281 214-8542
Houston *(G-8819)*

Bnx Converting LLC ....F 713 936-2726
Houston *(G-8930)*

ESP Safety Inc ....E 972 310-0754
Houston *(G-9698)*

Guard-Line Inc....................................D....... 903 796-4111
Atlanta *(G-844)*

Guard-Line Inc....................................C....... 903 796-4111
Atlanta *(G-843)*

Ilc Dover LP ....E 281 333-8751
Houston *(G-10321)*

Jenessco Industries Inc ....E 281 498-8833
Houston *(G-10465)*

Safety N95 LLC...................................F 281 624-1812
Houston *(G-11726)*

Seaflex Inc ....D....... 281 448-8821
Houston *(G-11800)*

Stanco Manufacturing Inc ....D....... 903 796-7936
Atlanta *(G-845)*

Veterans Mfg LLC................................G....... 713 854-9261
Katy *(G-13454)*

MEDICAL & SURGICAL SPLYS: Prosthetic Appliances

Advanced Arm Dynamics......................G....... 214 260-3197
Irving *(G-12923)*

Advanced Biomechanics ....E 956 971-8200
Schertz *(G-18742)*

El Paso Prosthetic Center LLC ....E 915 234-2408
El Paso *(G-5738)*

Hanger Inc ....C....... 512 777-3800
Austin *(G-1197)*

Hanger Prosthetics & Orthotics ....E 817 923-2101
Fort Worth *(G-6688)*

Lubbock Artfl Limb & Brace Ltd ....F 806 799-1518
Lubbock *(G-14440)*

Sola Prosthetics Inc............................F 972 492-7652
Carrollton *(G-2889)*

MEDICAL & SURGICAL SPLYS: Supports, Abdominal, Ankle, Etc

Allsport Dynamics Inc ....F 936 569-1003
Nacogdoches *(G-15684)*

MEDICAL & SURGICAL SPLYS: Swabs, Sanitary Cotton

Reynolds Consumer Products LLC ......F 254 770-4100
Temple *(G-19701)*

MEDICAL & SURGICAL SPLYS: Tape, Adhesive, Non/Medicated

Certoplast North America Inc ....E 832 384-1244
Houston *(G-9146)*

MEDICAL EQPT REPAIR SVCS, NON-ELECTRIC

Muilenburg Prosthetics Inc.................F 713 524-3949
Houston *(G-10935)*

MEDICAL EQPT: Diagnostic

Everly Well Inc.................................E 512 309-5588
Austin *(G-1143)*

Fairmont Diagnstc Cntr & Open ....E 713 946-1500
Pasadena *(G-16436)*

Genesis Biosystems Inc....................E 972 315-7888
Lewisville *(G-14051)*

Kdl Medical Inc................................F 972 783-7005
Richardson *(G-17340)*

Life-Tech Inc...................................D 281 491-6600
Houston *(G-10636)*

Luminex Corporation.........................C 512 219-8020
Austin *(G-1309)*

Procyrion Inc..................................F 713 579-9224
Houston *(G-11435)*

Refocus Group Inc...........................F 214 368-0200
Dallas *(G-4880)*

Seno Medical Instruments Inc ....E 210 615-6501
San Antonio *(G-18466)*

Skeletal Kinetics LLC ....E 408 366-5000
Addison *(G-164)*

Spectral Md Inc................................F 972 499-4934
Dallas *(G-4996)*

Vax-Immune LLC...............................F 832 423-0055
Houston *(G-12540)*

MEDICAL EQPT: Electromedical Apparatus

Gulf Coast II Lithotripsy LP.................B 866 598-2734
Austin *(G-1693)*

MEDICAL EQPT: Electrotherapeutic Apparatus

Advanced Nrmdltion Systems Inc.........B 972 309-8000
Plano *(G-16775)*

Broadband Technology Corp................E 806 698-0396
Lubbock *(G-14383)*

Electromedical Pdts Intl Inc ....E 940 328-0788
Mineral Wells *(G-15525)*

Microtransponder ....F 214 280-9677
Austin *(G-1342)*

MEDICAL EQPT: Laser Systems

Alcon Laboratories Inc......................C 817 293-7276
Fort Worth *(G-6364)*

Astanza Holdings LLC ....F 800 364-9010
Dallas *(G-3976)*

Healthtech Solutions Inc....................F 763 559-7082
Austin *(G-1694)*

Laser Scientific LLC ....F 512 733-8709
Round Rock *(G-17666)*

Laser Ventures Inc ....F 770 516-4600
Austin *(G-1701)*

Sunetics Intl Mktg Group LLC ....F 888 266-2232
Plano *(G-17014)*

MEDICAL EQPT: Lithotripters

Healthtronics Inc.............................F 512 328-2892
Austin *(G-1696)*

Ht Intermediate Company LLC ....G 512 328-2892
Austin *(G-1699)*

Medstone International Inc ....E 512 328-2892
Austin *(G-1704)*

MEDICAL EQPT: MRI/Magnetic Resonance Imaging Devs, Nuclear

National Mri Shielding Inc ....F 855 996-9820
Desoto *(G-5436)*

Radiology Associates N Texas ....F 817 321-0300
Fort Worth *(G-6937)*

Rio Grande Imaging Center Inc ....F 956 668-6900
McAllen *(G-14901)*

MEDICAL EQPT: Patient Monitoring

Mediana Technologies Corp ....E 425 406-2262
San Antonio *(G-18289)*

MEDICAL EQPT: Sterilizers

Xenex Disinfection Svcs Inc ....C 800 553-0069
San Antonio *(G-18627)*

MEDICAL EQPT: TENS Units/Transcutaneous Elec Nerve Stimulatr

Livanova Usa Inc.............................C 281 228-7200
Houston *(G-10655)*

MEDICAL EQPT: Ultrasonic Scanning Devices

Hmt High Medical Tech USA Inc ....E 512 721-4700
West Lake Hills *(G-20682)*

Omni Surgical LP.............................F 512 327-6400
Austin *(G-1380)*

MEDICAL EQPT: X-Ray Apparatus & Tubes, Radiographic

S & S X-Ray Products Inc...................D 281 815-1300
Houston *(G-11708)*

MEDICAL SVCS ORGANIZATION

Blue Medical Services Inc ....E 954 417-5442
Cypress *(G-3781)*

Teresa A McVicker Pc ....G 254 526-2823
Killeen *(G-13617)*

MEDICAL, DENTAL & HOSPITAL EQPT, WHOL: Hosptl Eqpt/Furniture

Brit Systems LLC.............................F 214 630-0636
Dallas *(G-4057)*

C H Industries Inc............................B 972 416-1304
Carrollton *(G-2710)*

Merit Medical Systems Inc ....C 832 463-5100
Houston *(G-10837)*

MEDICAL, DENTAL & HOSPITAL EQPT, WHOL: Physician Eqpt/Splys

Armamentarium Inc ....G 281 528-5700
Spring *(G-19101)*

MEDICAL, DENTAL & HOSPITAL EQPT, WHOL: Surgical Eqpt & Splys

Zimmer..A 800 613-6131
Austin *(G-1717)*

MEDICAL, DENTAL & HOSPITAL EQPT, WHOLESALE: Artificial Limbs

Hanger Inc ....C 512 777-3800
Austin *(G-1197)*

MEDICAL, DENTAL & HOSPITAL EQPT, WHOLESALE: Diagnostic, Med

Leading Testing Labs LLC ....E 281 600-8227
Brookshire *(G-2318)*

Vax-Immune LLC...............................F 832 423-0055
Houston *(G-12540)*

MEDICAL, DENTAL & HOSPITAL EQPT, WHOLESALE: Med Eqpt & Splys

Alex Orthopedic Inc..........................E 972 641-9680
Grand Prairie *(G-7826)*

Attentus Medical Sales Inc..................G 281 776-5188
Spring *(G-19199)*

Electronic Technical Svcs Corp ....E 281 446-4414
Humble *(G-12765)*

Encore Medical LP............................A 512 832-9500
Austin *(G-1125)*

International Biophysics Corp ....E 512 326-3244
Austin *(G-1237)*

McKesson Corporation.......................A 972 446-4800
Irving *(G-13102)*

Occupational Marketing Inc ....G 281 492-8250
Houston *(G-11119)*

Oft Enterprises Inc...........................E 713 787-5373
Bellaire *(G-2000)*

Open Road Mobility LLC.....................F 806 866-0275
Lubbock *(G-14452)*

Rubrix LLC......................................E 512 581-5513
San Antonio *(G-18437)*

Seno Medical Instruments Inc ....E 210 615-6501
San Antonio *(G-18466)*

Sheepskin Ranch Inc........................F 817 738-2485
Fort Worth *(G-6985)*

Trumed Technologies Inc....................E 952 882-0611
Mesquite *(G-15082)*

Vanguard Pharmaceutical McHy ....F 281 528-8885
Spring *(G-19185)*

MEDICAL, DENTAL & HOSPITAL EQPT, WHOLESALE: Medical Lab

Evco Partners LP.............................E 409 766-1900
Texas City *(G-19793)*

MEDICAL, DENTAL & HOSPITAL EQPT, WHOLESALE: Safety

Commercial Bev Concepts LLC ....E 713 554-4569
Houston *(G-9249)*

MEDICAL, DENTAL & HOSPITAL EQPT, WHOLESALE: Therapy

Cash Engraving Co...........................F 817 831-8585
Fort Worth *(G-6495)*

MEDICAL, DENTAL/HOSPITAL EQPT, WHOL: Veterinarian Eqpt/Sply

KVP International Inc.........................E 626 633-0077
McKinney *(G-14948)*

MEMBERSHIP ORGANIZATIONS, BUSINESS: Contractors' Association

Assocted Bldrs Cntrs Grter Hst............F 713 523-6222
Houston *(G-8727)*

Builders Exchange of Texas ....F 210 564-6900
San Antonio *(G-17972)*

MEMBERSHIP ORGANIZATIONS, CIVIC, SOCIAL/FRAT: Boy Scout Org

Boy Scouts of America.......................A 972 580-2000
Irving *(G-12950)*

MEMBERSHIP ORGANIZATIONS, NEC: Charitable

Breedlove Foods Inc.........................E 806 741-0404
Lubbock *(G-14382)*

MEMBERSHIP ORGANIZATIONS, NEC: Personal Interest

American Paint Horse Assn ....C 817 834-2742
Fort Worth *(G-6382)*

MEMBERSHIP ORGANIZATIONS, REL: Covenant & Evangelical Church

W V Grant Intl Ministries ....F 214 333-2176
Dallas *(G-5171)*

MEMBERSHIP ORGANIZATIONS, RELIGIOUS: Nonchurch

Missionary Tech Team........................F 903 757-4530
Longview *(G-14277)*

MEMBERSHIP ORGS, CIVIC, SOCIAL & FRATERNAL: Protection

Etech Envmtl Safety Solutions ....E 432 563-2200
Odessa *(G-15993)*

MEMBERSHIP ORGS, RELIGIOUS: Non-Denominational Church

Hill Cntry Bb Ch Drpping Sprng ....F 512 843-0035
Dripping Springs *(G-5507)*

Trinity Fellowship............................C 806 355-8955
Amarillo *(G-515)*

MEMORIES: Solid State

Stmicrlctrnics N Amer Hldg Inc ....E 972 466-6000
Carrollton *(G-2820)*

MEN'S & BOYS' CLOTHING STORES

Dos Carolinas Inc.............................E 210 222-9117
San Antonio *(G-18065)*

Employee Codes: A=Over 500 employees, B=251-500
C=101-250, D=51-100, E=20-50, F=10-19, G=9

2021 Harris Texas
Manufacturers Directory

1559

PRODUCT

Haggar Clothing Co .... B 214 352-8481
  Farmers Branch *(G-6199)*
Haggar Clothing Co .... B 214 352-8481
  Texas City *(G-19794)*
Haggar Corp .... A 214 352-8481
  Farmers Branch *(G-6200)*
Rush Apparel LLC .... F 713 208-5194
  Magnolia *(G-14625)*
Texas Clothing Holding Corp .... E 214 956-4494
  Dallas *(G-5056)*
World of Jeans & Tops .... F 806 788-1233
  Lubbock *(G-14514)*

MEN'S & BOYS' CLOTHING WHOLESALERS, NEC

A-Z Graphics LLC .... F 210 495-3468
  San Antonio *(G-17852)*
Anderton Group Inc .... E 254 751-1012
  Waco *(G-20362)*
Big Star Branding Inc .... E 210 590-2662
  San Antonio *(G-17953)*
Lucky Brand Dungarees LLC .... F 512 393-2002
  San Marcos *(G-18697)*
Texas Wipers & Rags LLC .... G 956 554-7500
  Brownsville *(G-2411)*

MEN'S & BOYS' HATS STORES

Big Bend Saddlery Inc .... F 432 837-5551
  Alpine *(G-311)*
C & C Western Wear Inc .... F 903 753-8991
  Longview *(G-14206)*

MEN'S & BOYS' SPORTSWEAR CLOTHING STORES

Brammers Athletic Wearhouse LP ...... F 281 391-1441
  Katy *(G-13390)*

MEN'S & BOYS' SPORTSWEAR WHOLESALERS

Asics America Corporation .... E 972 678-0200
  Allen *(G-252)*
Roka Sports Inc .... E 877 985-7652
  Austin *(G-1470)*
Wings Sportswear Inc .... D 210 696-1824
  San Antonio *(G-18622)*

MEN'S & BOYS' WORK CLOTHING WHOLESALERS

MTC Marketing Inc .... E 972 488-0577
  Carrollton *(G-2782)*

MESSAGE CONCENTRATORS

Executive Voice Mail Systems .... F 817 329-9788
  Grapevine *(G-8033)*

METAL & STEEL PRDTS: Abrasive

Box Gang Manufacturing LLC .... E 713 742-5555
  Houston *(G-8963)*
KB Structures Inc .... F 713 875-1024
  Wallisville *(G-20512)*
M & M Coastal Mfg Inc .... D 713 472-0700
  Houston *(G-10714)*
Saige Usa Inc .... F 281 980-8393
  Sugar Land *(G-19540)*
Samuel Son & Co (usa) Inc .... D 713 462-5000
  Houston *(G-11740)*

METAL COMPONENTS: Prefabricated

Industrial Cmponents Texas LLC ...... F 936 755-5697
  Houston *(G-10348)*
J B R Enterprises Inc .... G 972 542-3939
  McKinney *(G-14947)*
Mueller Supply Company Inc .... C 325 365-3555
  Ballinger *(G-1741)*
Mueller Supply Company Inc .... D 936 344-9057
  Willis *(G-20855)*
Mueller Supply Company Inc .... D 512 308-9173
  Bastrop *(G-1759)*
Mueller Supply Company Inc .... D 325 690-7700
  Abilene *(G-60)*
Mueller Supply Company Inc .... E 972 932-3208
  Kaufman *(G-13461)*
Wingate Partners V LP .... F 214 720-1313
  Dallas *(G-5196)*

METAL CUTTING SVCS

American Shredder Entps LLC .... F 817 378-8511
  Fort Worth *(G-6385)*
J-Hobbs Machine Corporation .... E 432 563-1526
  Odessa *(G-16036)*
Maximum Industries Inc .... E 214 614-6936
  Irving *(G-13099)*
Newell Ltd .... E 210 222-9511
  San Antonio *(G-18343)*

METAL FABRICATORS: Architechtural

A 1 Distributors Sign Supply .... D 432 682-0083
  Midland *(G-15100)*
A Zahner Company .... F 469 348-2000
  Grand Prairie *(G-7817)*
A&S Interests Inc .... F 713 695-0000
  Houston *(G-8430)*
Aaron Architectural Iron LLC .... E 817 731-9281
  Fort Worth *(G-6339)*
Allmetal Inc .... E 972 245-9264
  Carrollton *(G-2855)*
Amarillo Sperior Ironworks Inc .... G 806 331-9353
  Amarillo *(G-398)*
Architectural Metal Crafts .... F 281 449-1881
  Houston *(G-8684)*
Artistic Iron & Forge .... F 281 807-3440
  Cypress *(G-3776)*
Bandana Installation LP .... E 903 764-2933
  Elkhart *(G-6058)*
Berridge Manufacturing Company ...... E 210 650-7056
  San Antonio *(G-17949)*
Branch Ironworks LLC .... F 817 783-5183
  Alvarado *(G-326)*
Camp Logan Cement Works Inc .... E 713 869-3385
  Houston *(G-9080)*
Columns Inc .... E 281 485-3254
  Pearland *(G-16547)*
Construction Specialties Inc .... F 830 774-0151
  Del Rio *(G-5314)*
Country Glass & Mirror Inc .... E 972 216-9100
  Mesquite *(G-15035)*
Creative Casting Inc .... F 903 463-6160
  Denison *(G-5339)*
Demco Manufacturing Inc .... E 936 829-4771
  Diboll *(G-5462)*
Eagle Metal Products LLC .... E 903 887-3581
  Mabank *(G-14576)*
East Txas Archtctral Shtmtal L .... F 903 569-6909
  Mineola *(G-15507)*
Elegante Iron Inc .... E 214 342-8987
  Farmers Branch *(G-6195)*
Envirnmntal Sgnage Sltions Inc .... E 972 915-3800
  Irving *(G-13015)*
First Texas Precast Inc .... E 214 350-5612
  Dallas *(G-4364)*
G N P Inc Sheet Metal .... E 972 564-0450
  Forney *(G-6308)*
Georgejean Inc .... G 214 748-6644
  Dallas *(G-4404)*
Harsco Corporation .... D 713 378-3944
  Channelview *(G-3024)*
Hemco Industries Inc .... E 713 681-2426
  Houston *(G-10152)*
Hoffa Inc .... F 713 460-9000
  Houston *(G-10192)*
J-N Fence Co Inc .... E 972 226-7205
  Mesquite *(G-15054)*
Kawneer Company Inc .... E 972 438-1212
  Irving *(G-13073)*
Kawneer Company Inc .... E 713 896-8906
  Houston *(G-10503)*
Kentex Fabrications .... E 325 214-0025
  Coleman *(G-3170)*
Kikers Machine Works Inc .... F 432 381-8142
  Odessa *(G-16052)*
Lane Supply Inc .... D 817 261-9116
  Arlington *(G-717)*
Master-Halco Inc .... D 972 714-7300
  Dallas *(G-4645)*
Nci Group Inc .... E 281 897-7788
  Houston *(G-11015)*
Nci Group Inc .... B 281 897-7788
  Houston *(G-11016)*
Neu Security Services LLC .... D 512 469-9980
  Austin *(G-1364)*
One Ten Welding Inc .... G 903 561-8549
  Whitehouse *(G-20726)*
Pettigrews Custom Iron & Mtls .... F 214 637-1494
  Dallas *(G-4800)*

Priefert Mfg Co Inc .... A 903 572-1741
  Mount Pleasant *(G-15660)*
Quality Lnings Fabrication Inc .... E 713 863-7013
  Houston *(G-11495)*
Rodgers Ornamental Iron Inc .... F 817 535-2127
  Fort Worth *(G-6963)*
SA Quality Fence Ltd .... D 210 545-6767
  San Antonio *(G-18440)*
Sentech Archtctral Systems LLC ...... E 512 266-7045
  Austin *(G-1494)*
Septh Group LLC .... E 713 988-4200
  Houston *(G-11832)*
Southern Archtctral Systems In .... E 713 462-6379
  Houston *(G-11972)*
Stan Thompson Investments .... E 713 910-2320
  Pasadena *(G-16511)*
Texas Stone Designs Inc .... E 817 265-4011
  Arlington *(G-795)*
Tietjen Inc .... E 979 249-3888
  La Grange *(G-13703)*
Trinity Stairs Inc .... E 972 335-0700
  Frisco *(G-7320)*
TS Distributors Inc .... D 832 467-5400
  Houston *(G-12394)*
Watkins Ornamental Iron Inc .... F 972 931-5350
  Carrollton *(G-2847)*
William L Bonnell Company Inc .... B 409 543-0600
  El Campo *(G-5629)*
Woven Metal Products Inc .... E 281 331-4466
  Alvin *(G-386)*

METAL FABRICATORS: Plate

Accelerated Process Systems .... C 713 937-6838
  Houston *(G-8453)*
Accura Systems Inc .... C 972 226-0195
  Mesquite *(G-15023)*
Aggregate Plant Products Co .... D 210 333-1111
  San Antonio *(G-17874)*
Alfa Laval Inc .... F 713 329-1270
  Houston *(G-8535)*
Alfa Laval Inc .... F 804 236-3106
  Rockwall *(G-17536)*
American Alloy Steel Inc .... C 713 462-8081
  Houston *(G-8584)*
ARC Marine LLC .... G 713 489-7719
  Dickinson *(G-5469)*
Architectural Products Co Inc .... E 915 584-9424
  El Paso *(G-5649)*
Azz Inc .... E 972 840-0934
  Garland *(G-7446)*
Baldwin Metals Company Inc .... E 214 637-1030
  Dallas *(G-4000)*
Beaumont Machine Works Inc .... D 409 838-0261
  Lumberton *(G-14566)*
Caterpillar Inc .... D 210 637-3700
  San Antonio *(G-17987)*
CB&i LLC .... E 281 456-5700
  Houston *(G-9105)*
CB&i LLC .... C 713 649-4277
  Houston *(G-9106)*
CB&i LLC .... C 713 375-8000
  Houston *(G-9107)*
CB&i LLC .... C 713 485-1000
  Houston *(G-9108)*
CB&i LLC .... C 409 980-5500
  Beaumont *(G-1867)*
Charles W Weaver Mfg Co Inc .... B 972 539-1537
  Flower Mound *(G-6263)*
Chart Inc .... E 713 413-3000
  Houston *(G-9165)*
Cherokee Indus Fabricators Ltd ...... F 936 634-2108
  Lufkin *(G-14522)*
Chutehelp Inc .... F 855 248-8343
  Carbon *(G-2682)*
Commercial Forms Inc .... E 903 675-2511
  Athens *(G-823)*
Consolidated Fabricators Inc .... G 214 376-4389
  Dallas *(G-4156)*
Contech Engnered Solutions LLC ...... F 979 743-4123
  Schulenburg *(G-18774)*
Contech Engnered Solutions LLC ...... F 903 885-0673
  Sulphur Springs *(G-19584)*
Cooper B-Line Inc .... C 903 813-1746
  Sherman *(G-18913)*
Cox Tank Construction Co Inc .... E 361 528-3524
  Taft *(G-19640)*
Croft Construction Co Inc .... F 936 258-7902
  Dayton *(G-5225)*
Delzotto Products Minn Inc .... E 903 981-0400
  Gladewater *(G-7720)*

Eagle Metal Products LLC.................E 903 887-3581
Mabank (G-14576)

Evco Fabrication Inc.........................E 432 561-8561
Midland (G-15224)

Fabricating Solutions ....F 409 735-7141
Bridge City (G-2283)

Forged Components Inc ....E 281 441-4088
Humble (G-12767)

Generon Igs Inc ....E 713 937-5200
Houston (G-9928)

Hahn & Clay Ltd ....C 713 672-1671
Houston (G-10089)

Hamilton Form Co Ltd ....D 817 590-2111
Richland Hills (G-17437)

Haydon Corporation ....F 972 641-6400
Grand Prairie (G-7888)

Herring Enterprises Inc ....F 713 862-3614
Houston (G-10162)

Herring Tank Company Inc ....E 817 377-1851
Benbrook (G-2041)

Howmet Aerospace Inc ....E 775 343-4010
Elmendorf (G-6070)

Ig Holdings LP ....F 940 565-8505
Denton (G-5375)

Imperial Group Mfg Inc ....C 940 627-1700
Decatur (G-5247)

Keppel Amfels Inc ....A 956 838-3110
Brownsville (G-2374)

Koch Heat Transfer Company LP ....E 713 466-3535
Houston (G-10552)

Koch-Glitsch LP ....E 281 445-7026
Houston (G-10556)

Lide Industries LLC ....C 254 562-0233
Odessa (G-16063)

McDermott International Inc ....B 281 588-6600
Houston (G-10810)

McGill Maintenance Partnr Ltd ....C 979 233-5438
Freeport (G-7203)

Metalforms Ltd ....D 409 842-1626
Beaumont (G-1928)

Monolithic Constructors Inc ....E 972 483-7423
Italy (G-13214)

National Oilwell Varco Inc ....F 817 985-5000
Fort Worth (G-6861)

Nci Group Inc ....B 713 466-7788
Houston (G-11019)

Northast Txas McHning Wldg Hrd.......F 903 427-2277
Clarksville (G-3076)

Ohmstede Industrial Svcs Inc ....A 409 840-6644
League City (G-13971)

Ohmstede Ltd ....F 281 867-3260
Deer Park (G-5288)

Ohmstede Ltd ....F 409 840-6644
League City (G-13972)

Plant Fabricators Inc ....E 830 393-3064
Floresville (G-6249)

Plant Process Equipment Inc ....E 281 332-2589
League City (G-13975)

Portersville Sales & Testing ....E 806 373-6811
Amarillo (G-507)

Prentex Alloy Fabricators Inc ....E 214 748-7837
Dallas (G-4822)

Proske Plastic Products Inc ....E 713 926-9941
Houston (G-11461)

Prostar Manufacturing Inc ....F 281 910-0110
Pasadena (G-16499)

QMF Steel Inc ....E 903 455-3618
Campbell (G-2646)

R & R Oilfield Services Inc ....D 361 289-5892
Corpus Christi (G-3604)

Rack Industries LLC ....E 432 687-1868
Odessa (G-16131)

Rapid Turn Laser & Machine Ltd ....F 281 447-5000
Houston (G-11549)

RE Campbell Company Ltd ....E 713 957-8721
Houston (G-11558)

Refrigrtion Vssels Systems Cor ....D 979 778-0095
Bryan (G-2500)

S C S C Inc ....E 214 398-1199
Dallas (G-4922)

Sani-Weld Inc ....E 281 442-0667
Houston (G-11747)

Sas Global Corporation ....D 903 643-9111
Longview (G-14302)

Schmidt Manufacturing Inc ....F 281 431-0581
Bellaire (G-2002)

Scott Manufacturing Inc ....C 806 747-3395
Wolfforth (G-20912)

Sivalls Inc ....E 325 643-3621
Brownwood (G-2445)

Southeast Texas Industries Inc ....B 409 994-3570
Buna (G-2562)

Strike LLC ....A 361 939-0800
Corpus Christi (G-3631)

Sulta Manufacturing Company ....E 903 885-2139
Sulphur Springs (G-19599)

Sweco Fab Inc ....B 713 731-0030
Houston (G-12130)

Tapcoenpro International Inc ....C 281 247-8100
Channelview (G-3041)

Taprite Inc ....E 210 523-0800
San Antonio (G-18522)

Texas Aluminum Industries Inc ....B 713 941-7186
Houston (G-12220)

Texas Precision Plating Inc ....E 972 494-1547
Garland (G-7599)

Thrailkill All Metals Fabg Inc ....D 972 747-1230
Allen (G-302)

TPI ....E 972 276-2901
Garland (G-7604)

Trans-TEC Machine Ltd ....E 713 643-9114
Houston (G-12345)

UNI-Form Components Co ....D 281 456-9724
Houston (G-12433)

United Marine Enterprise Inc ....D 409 833-0303
Beaumont (G-1965)

Vince Hagan Company ....F 214 330-4601
Sunnyvale (G-19615)

W W Metal Products Inc ....E 903 838-4329
Texarkana (G-19783)

Walkup Company ....D 713 675-6383
Houston (G-12595)

Wichita Tank Mfg Inc ....D 940 692-5791
Wichita Falls (G-20834)

Windlass Metalworks LLC ....F 713 849-9292
Houston (G-12677)

Winston/Royal Guard Corp ....F 903 757-7341
White Oak (G-20722)

Woven Metal Products Inc ....E 281 331-4466
Alvin (G-386)

Xg Ventures LLC ....E 936 744-1800
Trinity (G-20020)

METAL FABRICATORS: Sheet

A Zahner Company ....E 469 348-2000
Grand Prairie (G-7817)

A-1 Smf LLC ....E 512 288-9900
Austin (G-874)

Abilene Sheet Metal Inc ....F 325 677-2654
Abilene (G-7)

Absolute Metal Products LLC ....F 713 340-5990
Houston (G-8451)

Accurate Metal Stamping LLC ....E 817 284-9444
Richland Hills (G-17434)

ACS Manufacturing Inc ....E 903 462-2001
Denison (G-5334)

Advanced Sheet Metal LLC ....E 254 772-0134
Waco (G-20355)

Advisory Cons Stl Erection Mfg ....E 817 924-1991
Fort Worth (G-6350)

Air Duct Systems Mfg Co ....E 832 519-9746
Houston (G-8506)

All-Rite Sheet Metal Inc ....E 713 680-0515
Houston (G-8541)

Allmetal Inc ....E 972 245-9264
Carrollton (G-2855)

Alloy Cnc LLC ....E 936 449-4001
Montgomery (G-15626)

American Block Company ....C 800 572-9087
Houston (G-8588)

American Duct Systems Inc ....G 972 494-7300
Garland (G-7433)

American Sheet Metal Inc ....F 281 999-5210
Houston (G-8610)

Appleton Grp LLC ....C 281 774-3700
Houston (G-8665)

Architectural Products Co Inc ....E 915 584-9424
El Paso (G-5649)

Argenbrght Nat Shtmtl Wrks Inc ....E 214 357-9161
Dallas (G-3964)

Arrow Fabricated Tubing Ltd ....C 972 276-3010
Garland (G-7442)

Astro Sheet Metal Co Inc ....E 972 438-1110
Grand Prairie (G-7837)

Atco Rubber Products Inc ....A 817 595-2894
Fort Worth (G-6406)

Atco Rubber Products Inc ....E 713 674-6665
Houston (G-8732)

Athens Steel Building Corp ....E 903 675-5733
Athens (G-820)

Atlas Metal Works Inc ....F 214 741-4788
Dallas (G-3982)

Atron Group LLC ....D 214 292-9840
Dallas (G-3984)

Azteca Fabrication ....F 432 943-8888
Monahans (G-15599)

B G Metals Inc ....E 210 648-5071
San Antonio (G-17930)

B W Sinclair Inc ....F 940 766-2556
Wichita Falls (G-20742)

Baldwin Metals Company Inc ....E 214 637-1030
Dallas (G-4000)

Beach Sheet Metal Company Inc........E 972 226-4440
Mesquite (G-15030)

Bemis Sheet Metal Inc ....G 281 427-1538
Baytown (G-1809)

Berridge Manufacturing Company ....D 972 506-8496
Dallas (G-4020)

Best Fender Products Inc ....D 903 577-0510
Mount Pleasant (G-15646)

Bgrs Inc ....F 281 890-6862
Houston (G-8871)

Boro Park Marketing and Mfg Co ....E 281 890-3848
Houston (G-8959)

Buford Company Inc ....E 972 272-9502
Garland (G-7451)

Burgess Specialty Fabg Inc ....D 713 462-0293
Houston (G-9018)

Burke & Company Inc ....E 210 271-0008
Elmendorf (G-6067)

Butler Weldments Corporation ....D 254 697-6416
Cameron (G-2640)

Byrne Metals Corp ....E 281 354-1100
Humble (G-12750)

C H Industries Inc ....G 512 278-1100
Manor (G-14647)

C H Industries Inc ....B 972 416-1304
Carrollton (G-2710)

C H Industries Inc ....D 972 416-1304
Carrollton (G-2709)

C M C Steel Fabricators Inc ....D 713 225-4446
Houston (G-9032)

Cains Welding Service ....E 281 303-9517
Mont Belvieu (G-15616)

California Expanded Met Pdts ....F 817 568-1525
Fort Worth (G-6488)

Canopy Solutions LLC ....E 713 510-3800
Dickinson (G-5472)

Capitol Food & Beverage Inc ....E 972 660-4450
Grand Prairie (G-7850)

Carbery Fabricators Company ....F 432 337-5015
Odessa (G-15955)

Cardinal Tool Co ....E 972 564-2314
Forney (G-6304)

Carey Sheet Metal Shop Inc ....E 956 423-1394
Harlingen (G-8184)

Casteel Mfg Inc ....F 210 923-4558
San Antonio (G-17986)

Caterpillar Inc ....D 210 637-3700
San Antonio (G-17987)

CFS Forming Structure Company ....D 210 698-9252
San Antonio (G-17996)

Chatsworth Products Inc ....C 512 863-7800
Georgetown (G-7644)

Cherokee Indus Fabricators Ltd ....F 936 634-2108
Lufkin (G-14522)

Classic Stainless Inc ....E 214 467-8700
Dallas (G-4129)

Cleburne Metal Works LLC ....E 817 237-5060
Fort Worth (G-6523)

Cody Company Inc ....E 210 651-5305
San Antonio (G-18640)

Collier Metal Specialties Ltd ....F 972 494-3900
Garland (G-7461)

Con-Tex Builders Inc ....E 281 847-3336
Houston (G-9266)

Copper Craft Inc ....E 817 490-9622
Fort Worth (G-6549)

Corsicana Sheet Metal Co Inc............F 903 872-8434
Corsicana (G-3666)

Crystal Distribution Inc ....E 763 391-7790
Irving (G-12984)

Cubeco Inc ....E 713 671-2466
Houston (G-9356)

Custom AC & Shtmtl ....F 713 868-5557
Houston (G-9363)

Custom Delis Equipment Co Inc ....E 817 831-7080
Fort Worth (G-6567)

Custom Precision Shtmtl Inc ....E 713 856-9997
Houston (G-9374)

P R O D U C T

Company		Phone
D & R Specialties Inc	E	936 873-2947
Navasota *(G-15728)*		
Dallas Texas Tool and Die Inc	F	214 634-7175
Dallas *(G-4227)*		
Darville Co	F	432 580-9675
Odessa *(G-15974)*		
Dickey-Webb Inc	F	281 933-5400
Stafford *(G-19304)*		
Die & Tool Service Inc	F	281 498-3317
Sugar Land *(G-19479)*		
Diversified Metal Works Inc	F	409 769-1146
Vidor *(G-20326)*		
Dlt Manufacturing Inc	D	214 330-8334
Dallas *(G-4266)*		
Edge Fabrication Inc	E	972 714-3893
Irving *(G-13009)*		
Efi Panel Systems LLC	D	281 533-9100
Orchard *(G-16272)*		
Eldred Sheet Metal Works LP	E	713 227-3251
Houston *(G-9588)*		
Electronic Visions Systems	E	512 989-3000
Pflugerville *(G-16669)*		
Enerflex Inc	C	801 292-0493
Houston *(G-9632)*		
Entex Fabrication Inc	E	940 592-2173
Iowa Park *(G-12904)*		
Epcon Industrial Systems LP	D	936 273-1774
Shenandoah *(G-18896)*		
Esquire Tooling & Mfg Inc	E	903 886-4779
Commerce *(G-3243)*		
Essner Manufacturing LP	D	817 551-5511
Fort Worth *(G-6618)*		
Ets-Lindgren Inc	C	512 531-6400
Cedar Park *(G-2968)*		
Eureka Sheet Metal Inc	F	210 735-4426
San Antonio *(G-18098)*		
Everest Systems LLC	E	800 575-8966
Houston *(G-9716)*		
Evs Texas Inc	D	512 989-3000
Pflugerville *(G-16671)*		
Fabcorp Inc	E	713 466-3962
Houston *(G-9746)*		
Fabhar Manufacturing LLC	E	214 802-9400
Princeton *(G-17210)*		
Flamco of Texas Inc	F	254 799-4936
Waco *(G-20403)*		
Fleming & Son Corporation	E	972 263-1713
Grand Prairie *(G-7873)*		
Fong Kai Usa Inc	E	972 644-1584
Carrollton *(G-2740)*		
Fuqua Enterprises Inc	G	817 641-1074
Cleburne *(G-3090)*		
G Fabricating LLC	E	281 421-3100
Crosby *(G-3731)*		
G N P Inc Sheet Metal	E	972 564-0450
Forney *(G-6308)*		
Garrison Metal Products Inc	E	903 938-1319
Marshall *(G-14779)*		
Georgia-Pacific LLC	C	936 829-5511
Diboll *(G-5466)*		
Gst Manufacturing Ltd	C	817 335-1401
Haltom City *(G-8146)*		
Gulf Copper Ship Repair Inc	D	361 883-1040
Corpus Christi *(G-3540)*		
Hahn & Clay Inc	C	713 672-1671
Houston *(G-10089)*		
Haydon Corporation	F	972 641-6400
Grand Prairie *(G-7888)*		
Heat Air Products Company	E	817 222-9567
Fort Worth *(G-6694)*		
Hightower Metal Works Inc	F	713 937-7181
Houston *(G-10179)*		
Holly Fabrication Inc	E	972 233-5362
Addison *(G-135)*		
Houston Tsm Inc	E	713 691-5271
Houston *(G-10260)*		
Humanetics II Ltd	C	972 416-1304
Carrollton *(G-2763)*		
Humanetics II Ltd	D	956 994-9200
McAllen *(G-14868)*		
Hvac Mechanical Svcs of Texas	B	713 266-3900
Houston *(G-10292)*		
Imfab Inc	E	903 577-0510
Mount Pleasant *(G-15651)*		
Industrial Insul & Shtmtl Inc	E	432 332-8203
Odessa *(G-16030)*		
Interstate Treating Inc	D	432 362-9291
Odessa *(G-16034)*		
Intrapack Industries Inc	E	214 348-7105
Dallas *(G-4510)*		
J & A Manufacturing Inc	D	972 494-5552
Garland *(G-7522)*		
J & L Sheet Metal Co Inc	E	713 864-7714
Houston *(G-10433)*		
J M Fabrication Company LLC	F	817 652-0526
Arlington *(G-709)*		
Jimco Sales & Mfg Inc	E	817 924-6173
Fort Worth *(G-6742)*		
Johnston Products Dallas Inc	E	469 272-7212
Cedar Hill *(G-2946)*		
Karel Manufacturing Inc	D	210 651-6643
Selma *(G-18876)*		
Kikers Machine Works Inc	F	432 381-8142
Odessa *(G-16052)*		
Kuest Corporation	E	210 655-1220
San Antonio *(G-18230)*		
L R West Manufacturing Co	F	281 485-6057
Pearland *(G-16575)*		
Lane Supply Inc	D	817 261-9116
Arlington *(G-717)*		
Ledsome Machine & Welding Co	F	325 646-4691
Brownwood *(G-2434)*		
Longview Mechanical Contrs Inc	E	903 759-1331
Longview *(G-14270)*		
Lubbock Skylight Manufacturing	F	806 744-2300
Lubbock *(G-14442)*		
M&M Manufacturing Inc	C	972 485-1504
Garland *(G-7540)*		
M&M Manufacturing Inc	E	713 460-1677
Houston *(G-10722)*		
M3 Distribution Inc	F	281 357-0604
Tomball *(G-19986)*		
Mac Fabricators	E	979 265-0235
Clute *(G-3156)*		
Magni- Power Company	C	903 532-5533
Howe *(G-12735)*		
Met International Trdg Co Inc	D	281 445-5005
Houston *(G-10841)*		
Metal Specialties Inc	E	432 332-8762
Odessa *(G-16081)*		
Metal Zinc LLC	G	832 252-9116
Humble *(G-12789)*		
Metal Zinc LLC	E	281 449-2787
Houston *(G-10848)*		
Micro Metl Corporation	D	903 248-4800
Longview *(G-14276)*		
Milltech Manufacturing Company	D	972 276-1786
Garland *(G-7554)*		
Mitchell Machine & Fabricating	F	903 880-0249
Mabank *(G-14579)*		
Modern Fabricating Inc	F	800 543-1581
San Antonio *(G-18315)*		
Morgan Roofing	E	409 762-8068
Galveston *(G-7404)*		
Morrison Products Inc	D	972 279-4000
Mesquite *(G-15063)*		
Mueller Supply Company Inc	F	361 580-1427
Victoria *(G-20286)*		
Mueller Supply Company Inc	E	915 886-3383
Anthony *(G-588)*		
Nailor Industries Texas Inc	C	281 590-1172
Houston *(G-10961)*		
Native American Industries Inc	F	817 731-6786
Fort Worth *(G-6863)*		
Nci Group Inc	E	806 747-4291
Lubbock *(G-14451)*		
Nci Group Inc	B	713 466-7788
Houston *(G-11019)*		
Nci Group Inc	E	281 897-7788
Houston *(G-11015)*		
Nema Enclosure Mfg Corp	D	713 921-2233
Houston *(G-11022)*		
New England Lead Burning Inc	F	713 675-3266
Houston *(G-11034)*		
Nicholson Metal Fabricators	E	214 920-3654
Dallas *(G-4738)*		
Northast Txas McHning Wldg Hrd	F	903 427-2277
Clarksville *(G-3076)*		
Nucor Corporation	C	936 687-4665
Grapeland *(G-8007)*		
Odyssey Precision Fabricating	E	713 849-3043
Houston *(G-11137)*		
Offenhauser Company	D	713 928-2981
Houston *(G-11140)*		
Omnimax Holdings Inc	E	469 366-3208
Fort Worth *(G-6881)*		
Omnimax International Inc	A	469 366-3200
Fort Worth *(G-6883)*		
Omnimax International Inc	F	972 522-0148
Grand Prairie *(G-7941)*		
Omnimax International Inc	E	817 481-3521
Fort Worth *(G-6884)*		
Paradigm Metals Incorporated	E	512 255-2622
Pflugerville *(G-16683)*		
Parker-Hannifin Corporation	E	817 232-1040
Saginaw *(G-17754)*		
Parkline Inc	D	409 935-1037
La Marque *(G-13713)*		
Parsleys Shtmtl & Roofg Co	E	806 669-6461
Pampa *(G-16333)*		
Petersen Aluminum Corporation	E	903 581-6228
Tyler *(G-20140)*		
Phillips Fabrication Inc	E	432 264-6600
Big Spring *(G-2093)*		
Pick Instrument Products Co	E	713 672-1686
Galena Park *(G-7381)*		
Pittsburg Steel LLC	E	903 855-7515
Pittsburg *(G-16750)*		
Pivot Corporation	D	972 475-4747
Rowlett *(G-17710)*		
Plasteco Inc	E	713 673-7710
Houston *(G-11345)*		
Preferred Stampings of Texas	E	512 255-7803
Round Rock *(G-17681)*		
Priefert Mfg Co Inc	A	903 572-1741
Mount Pleasant *(G-15660)*		
Proco Inc	E	361 516-1112
Kingsville *(G-13634)*		
Quality Fabrication Design LP	D	972 304-3266
Coppell *(G-3436)*		
Quality Industries Inc	E	615 708-4980
Denton *(G-5395)*		
R-D Sheet Metal Inc	F	817 332-2177
Fort Worth *(G-6933)*		
Raider Manufacturing Ltd	D	806 762-3227
Lubbock *(G-14470)*		
Raytheon Company	A	972 205-4277
Dallas *(G-4860)*		
RE Campbell Company Ltd	E	713 957-8721
Houston *(G-11558)*		
Reama Inc	F	409 744-9222
Galveston *(G-7407)*		
REE Holding Inc	E	409 840-5650
Beaumont *(G-1947)*		
Regal Research and Mfg Co LLC	C	972 494-0359
Plano *(G-16990)*		
Reliance Steel & Aluminum Co	E	972 276-2676
Garland *(G-7577)*		
Renovated Homes Inc	F	214 678-9114
Dallas *(G-4888)*		
RH Tamlyn & Sons	E	281 499-9604
Stafford *(G-19370)*		
RH Tamlyn & Sons LP	F	214 348-9676
Dallas *(G-4895)*		
Rheaco Inc	D	972 264-4748
Grand Prairie *(G-7965)*		
Rmf Manufacturing LLC	D	713 910-9777
Houston *(G-11638)*		
Robinson Aerospace Inc	E	817 253-0639
Dallas *(G-4906)*		
Rooftop Systems Inc	D	972 247-7447
Carrollton *(G-2809)*		
RPR Products Inc	D	713 697-7003
Houston *(G-11689)*		
S & H Shtmtl & Fabg Co Inc	E	713 926-8805
Houston *(G-11706)*		
San-Co Steel Ltd	C	956 464-7766
Donna *(G-5490)*		
Seabreeze Culvert Inc	F	409 296-4098
Stowell *(G-19431)*		
Sechrist-Hall Company	E	361 884-5264
Corpus Christi *(G-3620)*		
Shade Structures Inc	G	214 905-9500
Dallas *(G-4951)*		
Sheet Metal Air Plus Co LLC	F	915 566-8131
El Paso *(G-5958)*		
Sn & Db Holdings Inc	E	713 645-3370
Houston *(G-11927)*		
Snapp Tool & Die Inc	E	915 821-2046
El Paso *(G-5964)*		
Southeast Texas Industries Inc	C	409 792-0084
Bridge City *(G-2286)*		
Special Products & Mfg Inc	D	972 771-8851
Rockwall *(G-17566)*		
Spectra Metal Sales Inc	D	972 556-2564
Farmers Branch *(G-6216)*		
Splendora Pipe Services LLC	E	281 432-1400
Cleveland *(G-3136)*		
Spring Branch Shtmtl Co Inc	F	281 469-8855
Houston *(G-12026)*		

Stainless Mfg & Seals Svc ....G...... 806 795-8932
Lubbock (G-14486)
Steel Designs Inc ....E...... 713 937-3006
Houston (G-12053)
Sterling Group LP ....E...... 713 877-8257
Houston (G-12060)
Sweco Fab Inc ....B...... 713 731-0030
Houston (G-12130)
Sweetwater Machine and Welding ....E...... 325 235-2922
Sweetwater (G-19637)
T W Havens Metals Inc ....F...... 817 834-2621
Fort Worth (G-7028)
Taprite Inc ....E...... 210 523-0800
San Antonio (G-18522)
Taylor Metal Works & Pipe Co ....E...... 409 736-3555
Port Arthur (G-17127)
Telkin Sheetmetal Inc ....E...... 713 691-3707
Houston (G-12192)
Tex Cnp/Seal Inc ....E...... 214 688-7770
Dallas (G-5051)
Texas Profab Corporation ....E...... 972 241-5050
Carrollton (G-2831)
Texas Sheet Metal Works ....G...... 806 765-8404
Lubbock (G-14493)
Texas Toolmakers Inc ....E...... 210 494-3651
San Antonio (G-18544)
Thrailkill All Metals Fabg Inc..............D...... 972 747-1230
Allen (G-302)
Thybar Corporation ....E...... 972 416-6220
Dallas (G-5090)
Tietjen Inc ....E...... 979 249-3888
La Grange (G-13703)
Titanium Fabrication Corp ....F...... 832 375-1800
Houston (G-12300)
Tmp Truck & Trailer LP ....E...... 432 686-2500
Midland (G-15438)
Tomball Sheet Metal LP ....E...... 281 356-1200
Magnolia (G-14631)
Torans Precision Fabricating ....G...... 281 371-2352
Katy (G-13451)
Total Metal Products Inc ....D...... 214 330-7453
Dallas (G-5102)
Tri-Construction Co Inc ....C...... 979 233-7211
Freeport (G-7217)
Tricor Industrial Inc ....E...... 936 273-2661
Conroe (G-3373)
Trotti Service Company Inc ....F...... 281 894-5095
Houston (G-12383)
Tubal Cain Industries Inc ....D...... 409 786-1783
Vidor (G-20336)
TW Stamping & Tool Inc ....E...... 903 877-2353
Tyler (G-20166)
Two Hills Studio Inc ....E...... 512 707-7571
Austin (G-1602)
Urban Sheet Metal Inc ....E...... 713 522-6441
Houston (G-12478)
USA Machine Inc ....E...... 972 636-7400
Royse City (G-17727)
Vince Hagan Company ....F...... 214 330-4601
Sunnyvale (G-19615)
Vista Machining Company LLC ....F...... 817 710-2987
Fort Worth (G-7108)
Vogler Sheet Metal Company ....E...... 713 861-1154
Spring (G-19186)
Wagner Plate Works LLC ....E...... 713 462-1946
Houston (G-12593)
Ward Vessel and Exchanger Corp........E...... 713 413-8416
Houston (G-8394)
Weldfit Corporation ....C...... 713 460-3700
Houston (G-12628)
Weldforce Fabricators LLC ....E...... 713 270-7733
Houston (G-8395)
Western Sheet Metal Inc ....E...... 804 732-0230
Irving (G-13206)
Whitaker Metal Deck Sales ....F...... 972 938-1445
Waxahachie (G-20570)
Windlass Metalworks LLC ....E...... 713 849-9292
Houston (G-12677)
Woven Metal Products Inc ....E...... 281 331-4466
Alvin (G-386)

METAL FABRICATORS: Structural, Ship

Global Fabrication Svcs Inc ....C...... 281 367-9333
Houston (G-9973)
MPW Corporation..............F...... 713 640-2700
Houston (G-10931)

METAL FABRICATORS: Structural, Ship

Mmw Fab Ltd ....D...... 817 589-0881
Hurst (G-12852)

Wyatt Resources Inc ....D...... 281 346-6100
Fulshear (G-7332)

METAL FINISHING SVCS

Ai Lonestar LLC ....F...... 512 990-3999
Pflugerville (G-16656)
B & C Coating Inc ....F...... 281 351-4773
Tomball (G-19962)
Brooks Industrial Coatings Inc ....F...... 512 990-5333
Austin (G-1012)
Commercial Mfg Co Inc ....F...... 903 794-1321
Texarkana (G-19761)
Consolidated Metal Tech Inc..............D...... 512 255-9296
Round Rock (G-17637)
Hi-Tech Metals Inc ....D...... 940 243-0516
Denton (G-5373)
Lone Star Corrosion Svcs Inc ....D...... 281 955-1313
Houston (G-10675)
Mam LLC ....F...... 512 407-9940
Austin (G-1320)
Tecplate LP ....F...... 972 487-0636
Garland (G-7596)
Texas Metal Industries Inc ....E...... 972 288-2333
Mesquite (G-15080)
Western Grinding Co Inc ....F...... 214 631-3090
Dallas (G-5182)

METAL MINING SVCS

Alcoa World Alumina LLC ....A...... 361 987-2631
Point Comfort (G-17081)
Coastal Gulf & Intl Inc..............D...... 713 740-9800
Pasadena (G-16411)
Health Care Temporaries Inc ....A...... 713 631-7106
Houston (G-10143)
Holsey Mining Inc ....F...... 936 545-1021
Crockett (G-3719)
Itafos Services LLC ....B...... 713 242-8446
Houston (G-10430)
Keller North America Inc ....E...... 817 443-1465
Fort Worth (G-6755)
Oxidor Corporation Inc..............F...... 972 424-6422
Plano (G-16962)
Southwest Earth Resources ....F...... 325 251-6598
Pontotoc (G-17098)
Superior Shot Peening Inc..............D...... 281 449-6559
Houston (G-12119)

METAL SERVICE CENTERS & OFFICES

Aap Metals LLC ....E...... 214 357-6161
Dallas (G-3875)
Arsham Metal Industries Inc..............E...... 713 896-8585
Jersey Village (G-13292)
Berry Machine Shop ....E...... 817 572-0948
Burleson (G-2571)
C E Shepherd Company LP ....D...... 713 924-4300
Houston (G-9028)
Dallas Metal Fabricators Inc ....F...... 214 421-7417
Dallas (G-4220)
Diamond Wire Spring Company ....E...... 903 581-2358
Tyler (G-20076)
Downhole Threading Svcs Inc ....E...... 281 462-9800
Crosby (G-3730)
Galam Metals LLC ....F...... 713 934-8528
Houston (G-9893)
Jayco Steel Services Inc ....E...... 281 399-0189
New Caney (G-15842)
L B Foster Company ....E...... 832 934-3107
Magnolia (G-14613)
Magee Machine and Mfg Inc ....F...... 972 285-2554
Mesquite (G-15060)
Manufctred Component Parts Ltd ....E...... 713 880-0590
Houston (G-10749)
New Process Steel LP ....D...... 713 686-9631
Houston (G-11035)
Oldcastle Buildingenvelope Inc..............A...... 972 551-6100
Terrell (G-19746)
Optimus Steel LLC..............E...... 800 303-9543
The Woodlands (G-19820)
Precision Alloys Corporation ....E...... 800 321-0759
Dallas (G-4818)
R F Higginbotham Inc ....E...... 512 836-8985
Austin (G-1447)
Sfi-Gray Steel LLC ....A...... 713 864-6450
Houston (G-11842)
Spartan Reinforcing LLC..............F...... 915 269-5222
Buda (G-2538)
Tricor Industrial Inc..............E...... 936 273-2661
Conroe (G-3373)

Tubal Cain Industries Inc ....D...... 409 786-1783
Vidor (G-20336)
Vinton Steel LLC..............B...... 915 886-2000
Vinton (G-20342)

METAL SLITTING & SHEARING

Commercial Mfg Co Inc..............F...... 903 794-1321
Texarkana (G-19761)
Galam Metals LLC ....F...... 713 934-8528
Houston (G-9893)

METAL STAMPING, FOR THE TRADE

Aap Metals LLC ....E...... 214 357-6161
Dallas (G-3875)
Allied Tools of Texas Corp ....G...... 713 943-8500
Houston (G-8554)
Atlantic Durant Technology Inc ....E...... 956 440-8005
Harlingen (G-8182)
Coiling Technologies Inc..............D...... 713 849-4000
Houston (G-9241)
D & D Tooling and Mfg Inc ....E...... 915 590-2655
El Paso (G-5710)
Eagle Metal Products LLC..............E...... 903 887-3581
Mabank (G-14576)
El Paso Tool & Die Co Inc ....E...... 915 591-0346
El Paso (G-5744)
Essner Manufacturing LP..............D...... 817 551-5511
Fort Worth (G-6618)
Excel Stamping & Mfg Inc ....E...... 281 304-0771
Cypress (G-3789)
Gamma Engineering Inc..............C...... 817 477-2193
Mansfield (G-14676)
Glenn Metalcraft Texas LLC..............F...... 817 838-9000
Fort Worth (G-6672)
Gobar Systems Inc ....F...... 956 377-4836
Brownsville (G-2360)
Griffiths Corporation ....D...... 817 488-6547
Grapevine (G-8041)
Hansen Manufacturing Inc ....E...... 713 682-1075
Houston (G-10117)
Industrial Tool & Die Co Inc ....E...... 281 859-4499
Houston (G-10355)
Industrial Tool & Die Co Inc ....F...... 956 440-9960
Harlingen (G-8190)
Itd Precision ....F...... 956 440-9960
Harlingen (G-8191)
Jayco Manufacturing LLC..............D...... 972 623-2004
Grand Prairie (G-7901)
Langley Manufacturing Inc ....F...... 936 569-8824
Nacogdoches (G-15702)
Larsen Manufacturing LLC ....D...... 915 790-0762
El Paso (G-5840)
M J Celco Inc..............D...... 915 594-1777
El Paso (G-5854)
Maudlin Assets Management Inc ....E...... 281 334-7566
Kemah (G-13477)
McAllen Metal Stamping Inc ....F...... 956 682-3438
McAllen (G-14888)
Midland Stamping and Fabg Corp........F...... 830 422-2052
Del Rio (G-5320)
Mpl Industries Inc ....E...... 214 253-2332
Dallas (G-4696)
Precision Alloys Corporation ....E...... 800 321-0759
Dallas (G-4818)
Preferred Stampings of Texas ....E...... 512 255-7803
Round Rock (G-17681)
R-5 Metal Fabricators Inc ....F...... 903 873-2633
Wills Point (G-20877)
Sage International Inc..............D...... 972 623-2004
Grand Prairie (G-7971)
Stewart Efi LLC ....E...... 915 775-2558
El Paso (G-5978)
Stewart Efi Finishing LLC ....F...... 915 775-2558
El Paso (G-5979)
Takumi Stamping Inc ....B...... 210 924-3110
San Antonio (G-18520)
Universal Metal Products Inc..............F...... 956 283-7200
Pharr (G-16713)

METAL STAMPINGS: Perforated

Diamond Manufacturing Company ....D...... 972 291-8800
Cedar Hill (G-2939)
Star Manufacturing Ltd ....E...... 830 401-5951
Seguin (G-18865)

METAL TREATING COMPOUNDS

Compass Services Inc..............E...... 713 937-9538
Houston (G-9258)

PRODUCT

Corev America Inc ....E 713 849-3671
Houston *(G-9319)*

Haas Group International LLC ....E 512 519-3989
Austin *(G-1195)*

Metalloid Corporation ....F 800 686-3201
Jacksonville *(G-13250)*

METAL: Heavy, Perforated

S A Fabtecmex C V ....B 956 504-0707
Brownsville *(G-2403)*

METALS SVC CENTERS & WHOL: Semifinished Prdts, Iron/Steel

Delta Steel Inc ....E 918 437-7501
Fort Worth *(G-6583)*

METALS SVC CENTERS & WHOL: Structural Shapes, Iron Or Steel

Labarge Coating LLC ....D 713 378-7225
Channelview *(G-3028)*

Ranger Steel Supply LP ....E 713 633-1306
Houston *(G-11547)*

Reliance Steel & Aluminum Co ....E 972 276-2676
Garland *(G-7577)*

METALS SVC CENTERS & WHOLESALERS: Anode Metal

Quemetco Metals Limited Inc ....F 214 631-6070
Dallas *(G-4849)*

METALS SVC CENTERS & WHOLESALERS: Bars, Metal

Public Steel Inc ....E 806 376-8221
Amarillo *(G-457)*

METALS SVC CENTERS & WHOLESALERS: Cable, Wire

Addvantage Tech Group Inc ....E 918 251-9121
Carrollton *(G-2853)*

Custom Cmpt Cables Amer Inc ....B 972 638-9309
Plano *(G-16833)*

Jdr Cable Systems Inc ....E 832 220-4690
Houston *(G-10461)*

Rsi Inc ....E 512 268-7500
Kyle *(G-13686)*

METALS SVC CENTERS & WHOLESALERS: Casting, Rough,Iron/Steel

Firstex Industries Inc ....F 972 602-1478
Grand Prairie *(G-7872)*

METALS SVC CENTERS & WHOLESALERS: Concrete Reinforcing Bars

C M C Steel Fabricators Inc ....D 214 631-6699
Dallas *(G-4073)*

Robert L Rowan & Associates ....F 713 681-5811
Houston *(G-11643)*

METALS SVC CENTERS & WHOLESALERS: Ferroalloys

Fulton Supply and Recycl Inc ....E 940 382-3611
Denton *(G-5367)*

METALS SVC CENTERS & WHOLESALERS: Forgings, Ferrous

Resource Metals Company ....E 281 442-8600
Houston *(G-11609)*

METALS SVC CENTERS & WHOLESALERS: Iron & Steel Prdt, Ferrous

El Paso Machine & Steel Inc ....E 915 533-7483
El Paso *(G-5737)*

Forged Components Inc ....C 281 441-4088
Humble *(G-12767)*

Gordons Specialties Inc ....E 972 225-1660
Hutchins *(G-12866)*

Steven-Sharon Corporation ....D 409 744-4538
Galveston *(G-7409)*

METALS SVC CENTERS & WHOLESALERS: Lead

New England Lead Burning Inc ....F 713 675-3266
Houston *(G-11034)*

METALS SVC CENTERS & WHOLESALERS: Nonferrous Sheets, Etc

Richardson Trident Company LLC ....D 972 231-5176
Richardson *(G-17390)*

METALS SVC CENTERS & WHOLESALERS: Pipe & Tubing, Steel

Atlas Tubular LLC ....D 361 387-7505
Robstown *(G-17503)*

B H M Pipe & Supply Inc ....E 281 328-5552
Crosby *(G-3726)*

Bise Welding & Fabricating Inc ....D 713 681-0958
Houston *(G-8892)*

Friedman Industries Inc ....D 903 639-2511
Lone Star *(G-14182)*

Gicon Pumps & Equipment Ltd ....G 806 373-0478
Amarillo *(G-428)*

J D Rush Corporation ....F 281 558-8004
Houston *(G-10438)*

Metro-Tex Fabricators Inc ....E 713 473-3900
Houston *(G-10857)*

Morsco Supply LLC ....F 903 234-2183
Longview *(G-14282)*

MRC Global (us) Inc ....E 432 620-0059
Midland *(G-15307)*

North Shore Supply Company Inc ....C 713 453-3533
Houston *(G-11076)*

Salzgtter Mnnsmann Stnless Tbe ....D 713 466-7278
Houston *(G-11735)*

Stuart Hose & Pipe Ltd ....E 214 631-6682
Dallas *(G-5017)*

Top Threading Services Inc ....E 281 426-8461
Crosby *(G-3745)*

Woolley Fishing Tool Inc ....E 903 984-3553
Kilgore *(G-13603)*

Woolley Tool Inc ....E 903 984-3553
Kilgore *(G-13604)*

METALS SVC CENTERS & WHOLESALERS: Reinforcement Mesh, Wire

Dorstener Wire Tech Inc ....F 281 651-6226
Spring *(G-19111)*

METALS SVC CENTERS & WHOLESALERS: Rope, Wire, Exc Insulated

Bridon-American Corporation ....E 713 921-4101
Houston *(G-8984)*

HWC Wire & Cable Company ....C 713 453-8518
Houston *(G-10293)*

Jordan Spooling Service Inc ....E 432 366-6040
Odessa *(G-16042)*

Kirby Midco Inc ....F 214 688-0444
Dallas *(G-4558)*

Ma-Tex Wire Rope Co Inc ....E 903 984-9691
Kilgore *(G-13567)*

METALS SVC CENTERS & WHOLESALERS: Sheets, Galvanized/Coated

Delta Centrifugal LLC ....C 254 773-9055
Temple *(G-19679)*

METALS SVC CENTERS & WHOLESALERS: Sheets, Metal

Diamante Enterprises Inc ....F 210 655-9061
San Antonio *(G-18054)*

RDS Metal LP ....F 817 539-7400
Mansfield *(G-14708)*

METALS SVC CENTERS & WHOLESALERS: Stampings, Metal

JLK Industries Inc ....E 713 462-7761
Houston *(G-10476)*

METALS SVC CENTERS & WHOLESALERS: Steel

Alamo Industrial Group Inc ....B 210 223-6161
San Antonio *(G-17884)*

Alamo Iron Works Inc ....B 210 223-6161
San Antonio *(G-17885)*

C M C Steel Fabricators Inc ....E 361 575-4561
Victoria *(G-20250)*

C M C Steel Fabricators Inc ....E 817 838-6811
Fort Worth *(G-6484)*

Centennial Steel Inc ....E 972 412-5144
Rowlett *(G-17703)*

Cor-Tex Steel ....F 903 872-3991
Corsicana *(G-3662)*

Cyclone Steel Services LLC ....E 713 635-5555
Houston *(G-9385)*

Garland Steel Inc ....E 972 494-6000
Garland *(G-7495)*

Harris Rebar ....E 936 258-8221
Dayton *(G-5228)*

Howco Metals Management LLC ....C 281 649-8800
Houston *(G-10268)*

Intsel Steel Distributors LLC ....C 713 937-9500
Houston *(G-10410)*

J D Fields & Company Inc ....E 281 558-7199
Houston *(G-10437)*

Johnson Tool Company Inc ....E 432 267-7612
Big Spring *(G-2084)*

Joint Holdings/Basic Met Inds ....E 713 937-7474
Houston *(G-10484)*

Keystone Synergy LLC ....B 817 636-3300
Rhome *(G-17256)*

Kloeckner Metals Corporation ....D 713 633-7400
Houston *(G-10540)*

McDonald Welding Co ....F 325 573-5329
Snyder *(G-18994)*

McNichols Company ....E 877 884-4653
Garland *(G-7548)*

National Specialty Alloys Inc ....D 281 345-2115
Houston *(G-11002)*

Pine Street Salvage Co ....F 806 372-5678
Amarillo *(G-454)*

R Neal John & Associates Inc ....E 214 340-1464
Dallas *(G-4855)*

Samuel Son & Co (usa) Inc ....D 972 438-3949
Irving *(G-13171)*

Samuel Son & Co (usa) Inc ....D 713 462-5000
Houston *(G-11740)*

Sentry Supply Inc ....F 409 840-4800
Beaumont *(G-1948)*

Sigma Tube & Bar LLC ....E 281 369-5525
Houston *(G-11887)*

Ta Chen International Inc ....E 713 672-0177
Houston *(G-12145)*

Texas Iron & Steel LLC ....F 903 758-9498
Longview *(G-14317)*

Tradco Inc ....F 713 333-9300
Houston *(G-12339)*

United States Steel Corp ....D 903 656-6521
Lone Star *(G-14185)*

West Texas Steel and Sup Inc ....E 325 651-7322
San Angelo *(G-17838)*

White Star Steel Inc ....D 713 675-6501
Houston *(G-12663)*

Willbanks Metals Inc ....F 817 625-6161
Fort Worth *(G-7146)*

Willbanks Metals Inc ....C 817 625-6161
Fort Worth *(G-7147)*

METALS SVC CENTERS & WHOLESALERS: Steel Decking

Binco Contracting Services ....F 281 356-3144
Magnolia *(G-14591)*

Harsco Corporation ....E 713 378-3900
Spring *(G-19128)*

Quality Lnings Fabrication Inc ....E 713 863-7013
Houston *(G-11495)*

METALS SVC CENTERS & WHOLESALERS: Tubing, Metal

Jerryco Mch & Boiler Works LP ....D 713 224-7900
Houston *(G-10466)*

Mpl Industries Inc ....F 214 253-2332
Dallas *(G-4696)*

METALS SVC CENTERS & WHOLESALERS: Wire Screening

Mitchell Well Service Inc ....E 281 576-5007
Baytown *(G-1797)*

METALS SVC CENTERS/WHOL: Forms, Steel Concrete Construction

Houston Post Tension Inc ....D 713 937-6990
Houston *(G-10244)*
Spartan Reinforcing LLC ....E 832 271-1721
Houston *(G-11994)*

METALS SVC CNTRS & WHOL: Metal Wires, Ties, Cables/Screening

Mid-Coast Electric Supply Inc ....E 830 333-7030
Uvalde *(G-20193)*
Snyder Iron Metal ....F 325 573-6862
Snyder *(G-19008)*

METALS SVC CTRS & WHOLESALERS: Aluminum Bars, Rods, Etc

Petersen Aluminum Corporation ....E 903 581-6228
Tyler *(G-20140)*
Team Pride Extrusions Inc ....E 940 562-2205
Megargel *(G-14994)*

METALS: Precious NEC

Dillon Gage Refining Inc ....E 972 484-3377
Dallas *(G-4259)*
Hi-Tech Prcous Mtls Rfnery LLC ....E 972 239-0597
Dallas *(G-4456)*
Monitor Canopies Inc ....F 903 893-6336
Sherman *(G-18923)*

METALS: Precious, Secondary

Elemetal LLC ....G 214 956-7600
Dallas *(G-4309)*

METALS: Primary Nonferrous, NEC

Asarco LLC ....A 806 468-4000
Amarillo *(G-401)*
Eco-Bat America LLC ....C 214 631-6070
Dallas *(G-4299)*
Elemetal LLC ....E 214 956-7600
Dallas *(G-4309)*
Total Alloy Foundry Inc ....F 806 259-2255
Memphis *(G-14999)*

METALWORK: Miscellaneous

A Sklar Company Inc ....E 361 573-5775
Victoria *(G-20233)*
Advanced Waterjet Cutting Inc ....D 214 358-2194
Dallas *(G-3891)*
Baseline Mfg Partners LP ....F 936 344-2858
New Waverly *(G-15855)*
Bionic Welder LLC ....E 817 579-5080
Granbury *(G-7793)*
Brougher Inc ....D 713 869-7577
Houston *(G-8996)*
C M C Steel Fabricators Inc ....E 817 838-6811
Fort Worth *(G-6484)*
CK &B Machine Shop ....G 281 485-5760
Pearland *(G-16544)*
Crh Americas Inc ....E 903 765-2212
Alba *(G-181)*
Daniel Steel Industries Inc ....E 214 235-4509
Mesquite *(G-15038)*
Delzotto Products Minn Inc ....E 903 981-0400
Gladewater *(G-7720)*
Ecological Services Intl Inc ....D 956 233-4609
Los Fresnos *(G-14346)*
Efi Inc ....E 940 380-8000
Denton *(G-5362)*
El Campo Sheet Metal LLC ....F 979 543-5751
El Campo *(G-5617)*
El Paso Machine & Steel Inc ....E 915 533-7483
El Paso *(G-5737)*
Fabhar Manufacturing LLC ....E 214 802-9400
Princeton *(G-17210)*
G Fabricating LLC ....E 281 421-3100
Crosby *(G-3731)*
Graywolf Industrial Inc ....E 281 441-5400
Humble *(G-12771)*

Haydon Corporation ....F 972 641-6400
Grand Prairie *(G-7888)*
Katy Steel Co Incorporated ....E 281 391-7047
Katy *(G-13368)*
Keppel Amfels Inc ....A 956 838-3110
Brownsville *(G-2374)*
Lane Supply Inc ....D 817 261-9116
Arlington *(G-717)*
National Frame Rail Inc ....E 940 482-9494
Sanger *(G-18727)*
National Hose Aquisition Corp ....D 713 920-2030
Pasadena *(G-16487)*
NRG Manufacturing Inc ....D 281 320-2525
Tomball *(G-19993)*
NRG Manufacturing Inc ....E 281 320-2525
Waller *(G-20505)*
Pid Group Inc ....D 936 699-4743
Lufkin *(G-14544)*
Pixels & Powertools LLC ....E 844 458-1847
Austin *(G-1419)*
Polytrnix McHning Fbrction LLC ....F 972 436-0422
Richardson *(G-17374)*
R Lutes Inc ....E 281 595-3777
Rosharon *(G-17611)*
Raider Manufacturing Ltd ....D 806 762-3227
Lubbock *(G-14470)*
Renfrow Metalsmiths LLC ....G 832 724-8517
Houston *(G-11600)*
Rodrill Inc ....E 210 667-2130
Converse *(G-3402)*
Shape Corp ....D 616 846-8700
Garland *(G-7588)*
Southern State Steel Co ....E 409 866-1409
Beaumont *(G-1953)*
Spartan Reinforcing LLC ....E 915 269-5222
Buda *(G-2538)*
Suncoast Post-Tension Ltd ....E 281 445-8886
Houston *(G-12100)*
Tritan Productz Ltd ....G 940 224-1575
Wichita Falls *(G-20821)*
Tubular Resource Inc ....F 281 240-3343
Sugar Land *(G-19569)*
Turrubiartes Benedicto ....G 832 675-1569
Houston *(G-12413)*
Vinton Steel LLC ....B 915 886-2000
Vinton *(G-20342)*
Willbanks Metals Inc ....E 817 625-6161
Fort Worth *(G-7146)*
Willbanks Metals Inc ....E 817 625-6161
Fort Worth *(G-7147)*
Wilson Steel Services LLC ....F 903 275-2995
Brownsboro *(G-2333)*

METALWORK: Ornamental

Broome Welding Co ....E 409 744-0407
Galveston *(G-7390)*
Colonial Art Inc ....F 713 697-8407
Houston *(G-9245)*
Custom SEC Fence Ir Works LLC ....F 281 219-1400
Houston *(G-9375)*
Hayes Company LLC ....C 972 288-9755
Mesquite *(G-15049)*
Offenhauser Company ....D 713 928-2981
Houston *(G-11140)*
Patina Metals Inc ....E 713 462-6117
Houston *(G-11259)*
Southwest Fenter Inc ....E 817 577-3837
Haltom City *(G-8158)*

METEOROLOGIC TRACKING SYSTEMS

Eligibility Trckng Calculators ....E 210 323-7846
San Antonio *(G-18087)*
Orbital Systems LLC ....E 972 915-3669
Irving *(G-13133)*

METERING DEVICES: Gas Meters, Domestic & Large Cap, Indl

American Innovations Ltd ....E 512 249-3400
Austin *(G-916)*
Daniel Measurement & Ctrl LLC ....B 713 827-5033
Houston *(G-9402)*
Electronic Data Devices Co ....E 432 366-8699
Odessa *(G-15987)*
Fluenta Inc ....F 832 456-2021
Houston *(G-9815)*

METERING DEVICES: Integrating & Totalizing, Gas & Liquids

Dobie Supply LLC ....G 512 437-6499
Austin *(G-1098)*
Roxar Inc ....E 281 879-2600
Houston *(G-11680)*
S & A Systems Inc ....F 972 722-1009
Rockwall *(G-17564)*

METERING DEVICES: Positive Displacement Meters

Rg-5 Company LP ....F 903 753-3456
Longview *(G-14296)*

METERING DEVICES: Water Quality Monitoring & Control Systems

Capstone Metering LLC ....E 214 469-1065
Plano *(G-16819)*
Kemp-Meek Manufacturing Inc ....F 903 569-9700
Mineola *(G-15509)*
Master Meter Inc ....C 817 842-8000
Mansfield *(G-14691)*

METERS: Altimeters

Geometris LP ....F 281 856-9600
Houston *(G-9938)*

METERS: Turbine

Daniel Industries Inc ....E 713 467-6000
Houston *(G-9401)*

METERS: Turbine Flow, Indl Process

Electronic Data Devices Co ....E 432 366-8699
Odessa *(G-15987)*

METHANOL: Natural

Eastman Chemical Texas Cy Inc ....E 409 942-3307
Texas City *(G-19791)*
Oci Methanol Marketing LLC ....E 409 723-1900
Houston *(G-11130)*
Oci Partners LP ....F 409 723-1900
Nederland *(G-15757)*

MICA PRDTS

Carbo Ceramics Inc ....G 281 921-6400
Irving *(G-12960)*
Carbo Ceramics Inc ....F 972 401-0090
Irving *(G-12961)*

MICROCIRCUITS, INTEGRATED: Semiconductor

Cirrus Logic Inc ....B 512 851-4000
Austin *(G-1050)*
Ic Enable LLC ....E 214 575-9400
Richardson *(G-17330)*
LSI Corporation ....E 817 430-5808
Roanoke *(G-17489)*
Maxim Integrated Products Inc ....A 210 522-7000
San Antonio *(G-18285)*
Maxim Integrated Products Inc ....A 214 458-0357
Irving *(G-13098)*
Maxim Integrated Products Inc ....A 972 371-4000
Dallas *(G-4654)*
MEI Micro Inc ....E 972 690-9494
Addison *(G-149)*
Tallannquest LLC ....G 972 423-8455
Plano *(G-17020)*

MICROFILM EQPT

Eastman Park Micrographics Inc ....E 214 580-8390
Dallas *(G-4296)*
Jeh-Eas Inc ....G 210 490-9156
San Antonio *(G-18200)*

MICROFILM EQPT WHOLESALERS

Eastman Park Micrographics Inc ....E 214 580-8390
Dallas *(G-4296)*

MICROFILM SVCS

Hov Services Inc ....E 248 837-7100
Irving *(G-13059)*

PRODUCT

MICROPHONES

Primo Microphones Inc .... D 972 548-9807
McKinney *(G-14967)*

Shure Electronics .... E 915 782-2800
El Paso *(G-5959)*

MICROPROCESSORS

Austin Samsung Semicdtr LLC .... A 512 672-1000
Austin *(G-960)*

Centaur Technology Inc .... D 512 418-5700
Austin *(G-1037)*

Oracle Corporation .... A 737 867-1000
Austin *(G-1391)*

Texas Instrs Philippines LLC .... F 972 995-3773
Dallas *(G-5065)*

Texas Instruments Incorporated .... A 972 995-3773
Dallas *(G-5067)*

Texas Instruments Incorporated .... E 512 434-1560
West Lake Hills *(G-20690)*

Texas Instruments Incorporated .... B 214 480-4691
Plano *(G-17029)*

Texas Instruments Incorporated .... B 214 966-9759
Double Oak *(G-5497)*

Texas Instruments Incorporated .... B 972 995-2011
Dallas *(G-5070)*

Texas Instruments Incorporated .... E 214 567-9863
Plano *(G-17031)*

MICROWAVE COMPONENTS

Innowave Rf LLC .... E 737 200-7090
Leander *(G-13992)*

L3 Technologies Inc .... A 817 619-2000
Arlington *(G-715)*

Votronics Inc .... F 972 509-8494
Plano *(G-17049)*

MILITARY INSIGNIA

Advantage Supplies Inc .... F 972 250-1339
Carrollton *(G-2854)*

Beako Manufacturing Co LLC .... F 903 796-5330
Queen City *(G-17218)*

MILITARY INSIGNIA, TEXTILE

Military Customs LLC .... F 254 699-8106
Harker Heights *(G-8172)*

MILL PRDTS: Structural & Rail

Trans-Tex Fabricating Co Inc .... E 210 924-4431
San Antonio *(G-18562)*

MILLING: Cereal Flour, Exc Rice

CH Guenther & Son LLC .... B 210 227-1401
San Antonio *(G-17997)*

MILLING: Chemical

Southwestern Paint Panels LLC .... F 281 442-0000
Houston *(G-11985)*

MILLING: Grains, Exc Rice

ADM Milling Co .... E 830 625-2301
New Braunfels *(G-15772)*

MILLING: Rice

Riviana Foods Inc .... C 713 529-3251
Houston *(G-11629)*

Riviana International Inc .... C 713 529-3251
Houston *(G-11630)*

MILLS: Billet

Taurex Drill Bits LLC .... E 432 684-4711
Midland *(G-15431)*

MILLWORK

A C N Millwork Corp .... F 713 649-6015
Houston *(G-8425)*

AAA Woodwork .... F 713 935-0002
Houston *(G-8437)*

Abilene Mill Work .... F 325 677-8856
Abilene *(G-5)*

Alfonso Hinostroza .... E 956 781-1845
San Juan *(G-18670)*

Artisans Cabinetry & Woodwork .... D 512 626-7311
Georgetown *(G-7636)*

Austins Cabinets & Cnstr .... F 281 987-3308
Houston *(G-8751)*

Autumnwood Millworks LLC .... F 936 344-9784
New Waverly *(G-15853)*

AW Installers Inc .... E 210 649-1618
Adkins *(G-176)*

Bear Custom Moulding Inc .... F 940 686-5547
Pilot Point *(G-16722)*

BMC Millwork .... F 512 456-2000
Cedar Park *(G-2962)*

BMC West LLC .... E 806 747-1580
Lubbock *(G-14376)*

BMC West LLC .... D 325 698-4465
Abilene *(G-18)*

Boa Studio LLC .... F 210 314-4547
Schertz *(G-18745)*

Brownsvlle Architectural Mllwk .... E 956 592-5423
Brownsville *(G-2341)*

Brycon Inc .... E 817 444-2724
Weatherford *(G-20580)*

Buffalo Creek Millwork Inc .... E 972 938-2392
Waxahachie *(G-20530)*

Builders Firstsource Inc .... E 956 755-0301
Mercedes *(G-15004)*

Builders Firstsource-Ohio Vall .... C 214 880-3500
Dallas *(G-4067)*

Campbell Millwork LLC .... E 210 349-9294
San Antonio *(G-17978)*

Central Hardwoods Inc .... E 972 241-3571
Dallas *(G-4098)*

Central Millwork LLC .... E 925 963-5448
Dallas *(G-4100)*

Century Millwork LLC .... E 281 821-0191
Houston *(G-9142)*

Circle c Millwork Inc .... E 210 649-1228
San Antonio *(G-18007)*

Clarks Hardwood Lumber Co LP .... F 713 862-6628
Houston *(G-9211)*

Claytex Trophies Inc .... C 940 538-6521
Henrietta *(G-8279)*

Cmcs Group LLC .... F 972 647-6260
Grand Prairie *(G-7854)*

Coen Furniture Inc .... E 281 983-0100
Houston *(G-9237)*

Coleman Wood Products Inc .... E 940 440-2300
Aubrey *(G-849)*

Complete Woodworks Inc .... G 830 992-3163
Fredericksburg *(G-7174)*

Computerized Millwork Svcs Inc .... F 281 575-1699
Houston *(G-9265)*

Concierge Renovation Company .... E 940 458-3075
Sanger *(G-18724)*

Cook & Boardman Group LLC .... E 214 630-3965
Dallas *(G-4165)*

Coppell Woodworks Inc .... F 940 482-8900
Richardson *(G-17292)*

Daniels Terry Cstm Trim Mllwk .... F 817 295-6750
Fort Worth *(G-6575)*

Design Woodworks .... E 713 478-7397
Sugar Land *(G-19478)*

Detering Company of Houston LP .... C 713 869-3761
Houston *(G-9446)*

Devos Custom Woodworking .... F 512 894-0464
Dripping Springs *(G-5504)*

Dimension Millworks Inc .... E 210 281-0356
San Antonio *(G-18061)*

Distinctive Doors Inc .... F 972 487-6680
Wylie *(G-20933)*

Door Center .... F 713 932-9343
Houston *(G-9497)*

Dovetail Custom Woodworks Inc .... E 512 501-6717
Del Valle *(G-5330)*

Edwards Michael Custom .... E 210 651-3800
San Antonio *(G-18641)*

Faifer Arlin D Woodmill Co .... F 830 216-4189
Floresville *(G-6247)*

Faubion Associates Inc .... C 214 565-1000
Dallas *(G-4355)*

FC Dsigns Qulty WD Work Corp .... F 713 462-1442
Houston *(G-9767)*

Freedom Architectural Millwork .... E 281 592-5377
Cleveland *(G-3125)*

Genesis Millwork LLC .... E 469 402-3940
Garland *(G-7501)*

Georgetown Woodworks LLC .... E 512 868-9048
Georgetown *(G-7653)*

Georgia-Pacific LLC .... D 940 205-9558
Denton *(G-5368)*

Glasscraft Door Mfg Corp .... C 713 690-8282
Houston *(G-9962)*

Green Wood Milling LLC .... F 210 544-5777
San Antonio *(G-18153)*

Growth Holdings LLC .... E 972 241-9535
Dallas *(G-4418)*

Gunter Lumber Company Inc .... E 903 433-1303
Gunter *(G-8115)*

Hayes Carpentry L L C .... E 713 944-2608
South Houston *(G-19044)*

Homestead Heritage .... E 254 754-9665
Waco *(G-20416)*

Hull Historical Inc .... E 817 332-1495
Fort Worth *(G-6708)*

Innovative Millwork Systems .... E 972 869-9892
Dallas *(G-4503)*

J & H Manufacturing Inc .... E 830 665-5230
Devine *(G-5450)*

Jackson Deerfield Mfg Corp .... E 972 233-7513
Dallas *(G-4521)*

JC Millwork Inc .... C 469 702-2570
Flower Mound *(G-6269)*

Jeld-Wen Inc .... D 972 272-3667
Garland *(G-7526)*

Kikers Machine Works Inc .... F 432 381-8142
Odessa *(G-16052)*

Kings Ltd .... E 830 990-0565
Fredericksburg *(G-7185)*

Kitchen Bath Cbinets Doors Inc .... E 915 852-0499
El Paso *(G-5830)*

Koehler Co .... E 830 303-6256
Seguin *(G-18848)*

Kurt Lupo .... F 903 599-3181
Streetman *(G-19434)*

Legant Interior Inc .... E 713 784-2647
Houston *(G-10621)*

Liberty Company .... E 817 921-0218
Fort Worth *(G-6788)*

Lundy Services LLC .... E 972 494-2554
Garland *(G-7539)*

Lutz Woodworks Llc .... E 972 429-5521
Wylie *(G-20940)*

Martinez Millworks Inc .... F 281 988-9334
Houston *(G-10779)*

Masons Mill & Lumber Co Inc .... D 713 462-6975
Houston *(G-10785)*

Megatrend Designs Inc .... F 713 675-8838
Houston *(G-10823)*

Mgc Inc .... C 713 800-7300
Houston *(G-10863)*

Millwork Solutions Ltd .... E 817 473-3934
Mansfield *(G-14696)*

Morgan Trim Inc .... F 806 655-9777
Canyon *(G-2674)*

Nailit Millwork Inc .... F 210 633-4659
San Antonio *(G-18328)*

NC Group Inc .... E 281 459-9418
Houston *(G-11014)*

Nightngale Archtctral Dors Inc .... G 972 875-1134
Ennis *(G-6113)*

Nmg Workspace Solutions LLC .... E 281 240-1007
Houston *(G-11061)*

Pacific Columns .... F 714 257-9600
Rockwall *(G-17557)*

Panel-Tech Incorporated .... E 713 896-6900
Houston *(G-11230)*

Paramount Millwork Corporation .... E 817 429-1145
Fort Worth *(G-6894)*

Patterson Manufacturing Inc .... F 903 757-0523
Longview *(G-14288)*

Patton Manufactured Pdts LP .... E 512 918-3737
Austin *(G-1401)*

Pavliska Cabinets Inc .... F 254 773-4461
Troy *(G-20032)*

Petroplex Cabinets Inc .... G 432 333-2025
Odessa *(G-16121)*

Phoenix Millwork LLC .... D 281 388-2211
Alvin *(G-377)*

Pioneer Mill Works Inc .... F 806 622-3201
Amarillo *(G-505)*

Pioneer Millwork Inc .... F 806 622-3100
Amarillo *(G-506)*

Progressive Millworks Inc .... D 512 832-0551
Austin *(G-1436)*

R&R Millwork Inc .... E 903 873-6600
Wills Point *(G-20876)*

Robert K Dean .... F 713 681-2218
Houston *(G-11642)*

Robert Shaw Mfg Co Inc .... E 817 927-2557
Fort Worth *(G-6962)*

Saw Custom Millwork Inc .... E 972 288-2118
Mesquite *(G-15076)*

Select Millwork Inc ....F 972 445-8287
Irving *(G-13175)*

Shutter Source Inc ....F 281 403-2012
Stafford *(G-19378)*

Southern Forest Products LLC ....D 409 634-3365
Bon Wier *(G-2150)*

Stair Solutions LLC ....F 972 347-5151
Prosper *(G-17216)*

Steve Gibson ....F 713 937-8838
Houston *(G-12061)*

Texas Fixtures and Interiors ....D 512 846-1998
Hutto *(G-12886)*

Texas Timberjack Inc ....D 409 397-4221
Bon Wier *(G-2151)*

Titan Solutions ....F 281 973-9653
Houston *(G-12298)*

Travis Millwork Inc ....E 210 525-8088
San Antonio *(G-18564)*

TWC Architectural Moldings Ltd ......E 210 662-2800
San Antonio *(G-18573)*

Unique Woodworks Inc ....E 940 686-5547
Pilot Point *(G-16732)*

US Remodelers Inc ....E 214 488-6300
Lewisville *(G-14103)*

Water Street Millworks Inc ....G 512 321-5741
Bastrop *(G-1765)*

West Texas Chaptr of Archtctrl ....E 915 833-9922
El Paso *(G-6030)*

Woodhaus Inc ....D 972 245-8117
Carrollton *(G-2850)*

Woodshop of Texas Ltd ....E 409 938-7875
Texas City *(G-19807)*

Zamo Inc ....E 210 667-1717
Saint Hedwig *(G-17761)*

MIMEOGRAPHING SVCS

Associated Creditors Inc ....F 210 341-5642
San Antonio *(G-17919)*

Cellisco Inc ....E 210 692-1927
San Antonio *(G-17989)*

MINE & QUARRY SVCS: Nonmetallic Minerals

Hi-Crush Inc ....E 713 980-6200
Houston *(G-10170)*

MINE DEVELOPMENT SVCS: Nonmetallic Minerals

Cyanco International LLC ....E 832 590-3641
Sugar Land *(G-19476)*

Trans-Tel Central Inc ....F 405 447-5025
San Antonio *(G-18561)*

MINE DEVELOPMENT, METAL

Coast To Coast Minerals LLC ....F 210 781-8505
San Antonio *(G-18013)*

MINE PREPARATION SVCS

Isco Industries Inc ....E 817 477-2900
Mansfield *(G-14683)*

MINE PUMPING OR DRAINING SVCS: Nonmetallic Minerals

Keane Group Holdings LLC ....A 281 716-9152
Houston *(G-10511)*

San Patricio Co Drain ....E 361 364-4268
Sinton *(G-18964)*

Trican Well Service LP ....A 281 716-9152
Houston *(G-12368)*

MINERAL ABRASIVES MINING SVCS

Wes-Tex Pure Minerals Inc ....F 432 250-7010
McAllen *(G-14919)*

MINERAL PIGMENT MINING

Pan Continental Resources ....E 281 291-8100
Seabrook *(G-18788)*

United Salt Hockley LLC ....E 713 877-2781
Hockley *(G-8351)*

MINERAL PRODUCTS

Addax Minerals LLC ....F 214 445-6000
Dallas *(G-3888)*

MINERAL WOOL

Bay Energy Blanket Inc ....F 512 353-4064
San Marcos *(G-18680)*

Distribution International Inc ....E 214 637-0151
Dallas *(G-4263)*

Glt Fabricators Inc ....E 713 670-9700
La Porte *(G-13739)*

Gulfstream Aerospace Corp ....A 214 902-7520
Dallas *(G-4423)*

Industrial Insul & Shtmtl Inc ....E 432 332-8203
Odessa *(G-16030)*

Pittsburgh Corning LLC ....F 281 437-6000
Fresno *(G-7240)*

United Insul Sls Fbrcation Inc ....F 409 727-3191
Port Arthur *(G-17131)*

MINERAL WOOL INSULATION PRDTS

Aagape First Investments LLC ....E 903 675-7876
Athens *(G-818)*

Protective Concepts Inc ....F 832 843-7619
Cypress *(G-3816)*

United States Mineral Pdts Co ....D 713 462-1709
Houston *(G-12457)*

MINERALS: Ground or Treated

Arcosa Lw Hpb LLC ....E 214 631-4420
Dallas *(G-3959)*

Excalibar Minerals LLC ....E 281 864-9550
Channelview *(G-3021)*

John Crane Inc ....F 979 239-1201
Freeport *(G-7200)*

M-I LLC ....E 409 763-2249
Galveston *(G-7403)*

Sidco Minerals Inc ....F 903 838-4493
Texarkana *(G-19772)*

United Minerals and Prpts Inc ....E 713 881-9466
Houston *(G-12449)*

Uranium Resources Inc ....F 972 219-3330
Lewisville *(G-14102)*

MINING MACHINERY & EQPT WHOLESALERS

Pan Continental Resources ....E 281 291-8100
Seabrook *(G-18788)*

MINING MACHINES & EQPT: Augers

H & T Auger Company ....E 432 362-4471
Odessa *(G-16022)*

MINING MACHINES & EQPT: Bits, Rock, Exc Oil/Gas Field Tools

Kay Rock Bit Company ....F 512 478-2900
Austin *(G-1265)*

M C R Oil Tools LLC ....F 817 701-5100
Arlington *(G-726)*

MINING MACHINES & EQPT: Cleaning, Mineral

Aqua Drill International LLC ....D 281 337-0900
Dickinson *(G-5468)*

Mud Technology Intl Inc ....E 903 675-3240
Athens *(G-834)*

MINING MACHINES & EQPT: Shuttle Cars, Underground

Austin North Taxi Service ....F 512 704-9999
Austin *(G-957)*

MINING MACHINES & EQPT: Trucks, Dollies

Joy Glbal Lngview Oprtions LLC ....A 903 237-7000
Longview *(G-14257)*

Optiblend Industries Inc ....E 281 584-0047
Katy *(G-13431)*

MINING MACHINES & EQPT: Washers, Aggregate & Sand

Arcosa Materials Inc ....B 817 635-8500
Arlington *(G-622)*

MINING SVCS, NEC: Anthracite

P&G Mining LLC ....F 682 500-8986
Grand Prairie *(G-7943)*

MINING SVCS, NEC: Lignite

Sabine Mining Company ....C 903 660-4200
Hallsville *(G-8130)*

MINING: Oil Sand

Arepet Industries LLC ....E 210 628-1622
Von Ormy *(G-20345)*

Emerge Energy Services LP ....E 817 618-4020
Fort Worth *(G-6610)*

US Sand LLC ....F 713 333-3001
Houston *(G-12488)*

MINING: Oil Shale

B D Production Co Inc ....D 361 888-4741
Corpus Christi *(G-3478)*

Southeast Land Services LLC ....F 724 256-9259
Little Elm *(G-14142)*

MISCELLANEOUS FINANCIAL INVEST ACTIVITIES: Oil Royalties

Thompson & Thompson ....E 214 953-1177
Dallas *(G-5086)*

MIXTURES & BLOCKS: Asphalt Paving

Alamo Concrete Tile Inc ....E 210 534-8821
San Antonio *(G-17883)*

American Indus Mfrs Bldg Mate ....C 214 254-4720
Plano *(G-16787)*

Ark-La-Tex Custom Coatings ....F 903 845-6436
Gladewater *(G-7717)*

Asphalt Inc LLC ....E 512 428-5739
Austin *(G-939)*

Big Creek Sand and Gravel Inc ....E 806 273-7501
Borger *(G-2164)*

Btb Refining LLC ....F 561 347-5500
Corpus Christi *(G-3490)*

Century Asphalt Ltd ....F 512 285-4499
Elgin *(G-6053)*

Century Asphalt Ltd ....F 281 421-2621
Baytown *(G-1811)*

Coffeyville Resources Trml LLC ....F 281 207-3200
Sugar Land *(G-19464)*

Colorado Materials Ltd ....E 512 353-7757
New Braunfels *(G-15784)*

Crafco Texas Inc ....F 210 496-2070
San Antonio *(G-18029)*

Crh Americas Materials Inc ....C 409 866-1444
Beaumont *(G-1878)*

Frontera Materials Inc ....F 956 316-8952
Elsa *(G-6079)*

G & S Asphalt Inc ....F 281 499-1551
Stafford *(G-19320)*

Gem Asset Acquisition LLC ....E 214 333-4343
Dallas *(G-4396)*

Hanson Aggregates LLC ....D 210 658-7461
New Braunfels *(G-15801)*

Hanson Aggregates LLC ....C 469 417-1200
Irving *(G-13049)*

Henry Company ....E 972 272-5488
Garland *(G-7510)*

J Lee Milligan Inc ....C 806 373-5352
Amarillo *(G-441)*

Legacy Vulcan LLC ....E 325 646-8526
Brownwood *(G-2435)*

Legacy Vulcan LLC ....E 325 529-3785
Abilene *(G-58)*

Libcon Inc ....D 956 724-6459
Laredo *(G-13907)*

Midwest Asphalt Corporation ....F 940 668-1480
Gainesville *(G-7348)*

Moore Asphalt Co Inc ....E 903 561-1321
Tyler *(G-20131)*

Owens Corning Sales LLC ....C 972 438-1050
Irving *(G-13138)*

Owens Corning Sales LLC ....D 713 672-8338
Houston *(G-11208)*

Pavement Tool Mfg Inc ....F 903 734-7531
Big Sandy *(G-2066)*

Pro Pavers Houston LLC ....E 281 665-4718
Katy *(G-13433)*

Tarmac Materials LLC ....F 281 342-9314
Richmond *(G-17466)*

Texas Crushed Stone Company ....C 512 255-4405
  Georgetown *(G-7684)*

Thompson Jr Inc ....E 940 665-2533
  Gainesville *(G-7372)*

Trinity Asphalt Inc ....E 903 657-2391
  Henderson *(G-8275)*

US Polyco Inc ....F 972 875-9300
  Ennis *(G-6122)*

Vulcan Materials Company ....F 210 349-3311
  San Antonio *(G-18603)*

Vulcan Materials Company ....F 210 494-9555
  San Antonio *(G-18604)*

MOBILE COMMUNICATIONS EQPT

Motorola Solutions Inc ....E 512 821-1560
  Austin *(G-1356)*

Orbis International Tech Inc ....E 972 929-5705
  Carrollton *(G-2787)*

Palm Inc ....C 713 410-1331
  Rosharon *(G-17609)*

Rolltchs Spcialty Vehicles LLC..............E 210 651-5700
  Schertz *(G-18761)*

Xplore Technologies Corp ....F 512 637-1100
  Austin *(G-1677)*

MOBILE HOMES

Al/Tex Homes Inc ....C 817 847-1355
  Fort Worth *(G-6361)*

American Homestar Lancaster LP ....E 281 334-9700
  League City *(G-13947)*

Centex Corporation ....C 214 981-5000
  Dallas *(G-4097)*

Clayton Homes Inc ....F 254 666-9570
  Waco *(G-20384)*

Clayton Homes Inc ....F 210 946-2222
  San Antonio *(G-18010)*

Clayton Homes Inc ....C 254 772-1808
  Waco *(G-20385)*

Clayton Homes Inc ....F 210 677-6100
  San Antonio *(G-18011)*

CMH Manufacturing Inc ....C 903 439-0242
  Sulphur Springs *(G-19583)*

CMH Manufacturing Inc ....C 800 445-3516
  Bonham *(G-2152)*

Mobile Toys Inc ....F 979 268-6066
  College Station *(G-3193)*

MOBILE HOMES WHOLESALERS

Lakeside Trailer Sales ....F 936 564-6252
  Nacogdoches *(G-15701)*

MOBILE HOMES, EXC RECREATIONAL

CMH Manufacturing Inc ....E 254 666-3534
  Waco *(G-20387)*

MOBILE HOMES: Personal Or Private Use

American Homestar Corporation ....E 281 334-9700
  League City *(G-13946)*

Teton Buildings LLC ....E 307 473-7543
  Houston *(G-12215)*

MODELS: Airplane, Exc Toy

Texas Almet LP ....D 817 649-7056
  Arlington *(G-791)*

MODELS: General, Exc Toy

Usm Inc ....D 281 619-0144
  Houston *(G-12503)*

MODULES: Computer Logic

Avant Technology Inc ....D 512 651-5300
  Pflugerville *(G-16660)*

Fas Technologies LLC ....E 214 343-5300
  Dallas *(G-4354)*

Netrake Corporation ....D 214 291-1000
  Plano *(G-16943)*

Spansion LLC ....C 512 934-6427
  Austin *(G-1523)*

Texas Instruments Incorporated ....E 214 567-2075
  Richardson *(G-17408)*

MODULES: Solid State

Viavi Solutions Inc ....F 972 907-8882
  Richardson *(G-17422)*

MOLDED RUBBER PRDTS

Accurate Elastomer Pdts Inc ....D 512 285-4585
  Bastrop *(G-1748)*

Ace Rubber Products Inc ....F 817 572-1011
  Kennedale *(G-13496)*

Airmec Inc ....E 972 438-4015
  Irving *(G-12926)*

Eagle Molded Products ....F 281 894-4995
  Houston *(G-9559)*

Indian Rubber Company Inc ....E 817 265-6732
  Arlington *(G-705)*

Jet Rubber Inc ....E 713 673-5202
  Houston *(G-10470)*

Mosites Rubber Company Inc ....E 817 335-3451
  Fort Worth *(G-6854)*

Neb Products LLC ....G 281 528-9428
  Spring *(G-19154)*

Pamco Ltd ....E 713 621-0002
  Houston *(G-11226)*

Parco Double-E LLC ....D 214 631-2290
  Dallas *(G-4788)*

Pheasant Rubber Company Inc ....F 432 367-5137
  Odessa *(G-16122)*

S & B Technical Products Inc ....D 800 432-8213
  Fort Worth *(G-6970)*

US Machinery Parts Sales Inc...............E 972 551-3551
  Mesquite *(G-15084)*

MOLDING COMPOUNDS

Axiomagnets LLC ....F 956 283-5920
  McAllen *(G-14840)*

Chemtrusion Inc ....D 713 675-1616
  Houston *(G-9173)*

Husa Accurate Mch Works Inc ....F 713 691-0685
  Houston *(G-10289)*

Ingenia Polymers Inc ....D 281 862-2111
  Houston *(G-10362)*

Lyondllbsell Advnced Plymers I ....D 713 309-7200
  Houston *(G-10710)*

Lyondllbsell Advnced Plymers I ....C 832 663-3104
  Spring *(G-19229)*

Neutrex Inc ....E 281 807-9449
  Houston *(G-11033)*

Ruth Vending Inc ....F 972 905-3523
  The Colony *(G-19813)*

Tsi Products Inc ....E 817 649-2626
  Arlington *(G-806)*

Velas Builders LLC ....F 956 464-7827
  Donna *(G-5495)*

MOLDINGS & TRIM: Metal, Exc Automobile

Classic Industries LP ....E 972 564-2192
  Forney *(G-6305)*

MOLDINGS & TRIM: Wood

Dallas Fort Wrth Fyrestone LLC ....E 817 429-0999
  Fort Worth *(G-6573)*

Signature Mldngs Millworks Inc ....E 210 967-8400
  San Antonio *(G-18474)*

Signature Partners Ltd ....E 210 967-8400
  San Antonio *(G-18475)*

MOLDINGS OR TRIM: Automobile, Stamped Metal

International Assembly Inc ....F 956 525-4533
  Brownsville *(G-2362)*

MOLDINGS: Picture Frame

Framecrafters Inc ....E 713 973-1333
  Houston *(G-9852)*

Larson-Juhl US LLC ....E 713 895-0296
  Houston *(G-10602)*

National Art Service Co Inc ....F 713 869-5861
  Houston *(G-10965)*

Nielsen & Bainbridge LLC ....E 512 506-3900
  Austin *(G-1367)*

S W Galleries Corp ....E 972 788-2743
  Dallas *(G-4924)*

Wordyisms Inc ....F 512 835-6695
  Pflugerville *(G-16693)*

MOLDS: Indl

Advanced Integration Tech Inc ....C 972 423-8354
  Plano *(G-16772)*

Advanced Integration Tech LP ....D 972 423-8354
  Plano *(G-16773)*

American Acrylic Injection Inc...............E 972 784-7759
  Farmersville *(G-6221)*

Dynamic Tool Company Inc ....D 915 598-2330
  El Paso *(G-5726)*

Genesis Tool Inc ....F 915 781-1000
  El Paso *(G-5782)*

Jorge Trevino ....F 956 376-7114
  Weslaco *(G-20662)*

Lorentson Manufacturing Co ....E 956 399-8902
  San Benito *(G-18659)*

Marshall-Gruber Company LLC............F 682 518-7400
  Mansfield *(G-14688)*

Norlus Group Inc ....F 915 590-2041
  El Paso *(G-5899)*

Team Manufacturing Inc ....E 903 583-7722
  Bonham *(G-2155)*

MOLDS: Plastic Working & Foundry

Avey Plastics ....F 512 784-7047
  San Marcos *(G-18678)*

Deka Texas Inc ....E 214 618-1176
  Frisco *(G-7280)*

Mitchell Machine & Fabricating ....F 903 880-0249
  Mabank *(G-14579)*

MONEY ORDER ISSUANCE SVCS

GSC Enterprises Inc ....E 903 885-1283
  Sulphur Springs *(G-19589)*

MONUMENTS & GRAVE MARKERS, EXC TERRAZZO

Gifford Monument Works Inc ....F 972 544-6305
  Wylie *(G-20936)*

MONUMENTS & GRAVE MARKERS, WHOLESALE

Surface Burial Vault Monument............F 361 275-3213
  Cuero *(G-3766)*

MONUMENTS: Cut Stone, Exc Finishing Or Lettering Only

Rawlins Monument Inc ....F 817 594-2726
  Weatherford *(G-20614)*

MOPEDS & PARTS

Amarillo Mop & Broom Co Inc ....E 806 372-8596
  Amarillo *(G-396)*

MOPS: Floor & Dust

Quickie Manufacturing Corp ....D 915 859-2522
  El Paso *(G-5923)*

San Antonio Broom Factory Inc ....E 210 226-9762
  San Antonio *(G-18446)*

Unifirst Corporation ....D 817 834-7386
  Haltom City *(G-8160)*

MORTGAGE BANKERS

Centex Corporation ....C 214 981-5000
  Dallas *(G-4097)*

MOTION PICTURE & VIDEO DISTRIBUTION

Ireo Reproductions LLC ....E 214 337-4731
  Dallas *(G-4512)*

MOTION PICTURE & VIDEO PRODUCTION SVCS

Herald of Truth Ministries....................F 325 698-4370
  Abilene *(G-49)*

Sound Bridge Acoustic Labs Inc ....E 972 937-2030
  Waxahachie *(G-20559)*

MOTION PICTURE & VIDEO PRODUCTION SVCS: Educational

Cev Multimedia Ltd ....E 806 745-8820
  Lubbock *(G-14391)*

MOTION PICTURE EQPT

Rosco Laboratories Inc ....F 512 388-5299
  Round Rock *(G-17685)*

MOTOR & GENERATOR PARTS: Electric

Haastech Inc ....F 214 688-0280
 Dallas *(G-4426)*

MOTOR CONTROL CENTERS

Accurate Control Company LLC ....E 713 699-3799
 Houston *(G-8461)*
Advanced Elec & Mtr Contrls ....E 972 253-7783
 Irving *(G-12924)*
Amerimex Motor & Controls LLC ....D 713 225-4300
 Houston *(G-8618)*

MOTOR HOMES

Coachworks LLC ....E 830 510-4224
 Pipe Creek *(G-16741)*
Factory Motorhomes Inc ....F 214 830-2910
 Terrell *(G-19733)*
Foretravel Inc ....B 936 564-8367
 Nacogdoches *(G-15698)*

MOTOR REBUILDING SVCS, EXC AUTOMOTIVE

Airgen Equipment LLC ....F 432 332-1870
 Odessa *(G-15907)*
Austin Armature Works LP ....E 512 312-0088
 Buda *(G-2520)*
Chapman Electric Company ....F 214 824-8095
 Dallas *(G-4105)*
Evans Enterprises Inc ....F 254 772-4710
 Waco *(G-20399)*
Warfield Electric Texas Inc ....F 214 637-1200
 Carrollton *(G-2845)*

MOTOR REPAIR SVCS

Brenham Repair Center LLC ....F 979 277-9071
 Brenham *(G-2247)*
Cems Acquire Co LLC ....F 817 308-0165
 Dallas *(G-4095)*
Chester R Wright III ....F 832 693-8038
 Friendswood *(G-7243)*
Electrico Inc ....F 903 872-6567
 Corsicana *(G-3670)*
Grayson Sulzer Inc ....E 409 882-9112
 Orange *(G-16245)*
Mission Cycleplex LLC ....F 210 250-0057
 San Antonio *(G-18310)*
Sun-Star Electric Inc ....D 806 793-2812
 Lubbock *(G-14488)*
Trinity Services Group Inc ....C 903 277-7128
 Texarkana *(G-19781)*

MOTOR VEHICLE ASSEMBLY, COMPLETE: Ambulances

Frazer Ltd ....C 713 772-5511
 Houston *(G-9858)*
Hfj Group LLC ....E 833 777-3473
 Houston *(G-10168)*

MOTOR VEHICLE ASSEMBLY, COMPLETE: Autos, Incl Specialty

A J Foyt Enterprises Inc ....D 936 372-3698
 Waller *(G-20489)*
Cunningham Automotive Inc ....F 972 900-0405
 Lewisville *(G-14039)*
Dunn Automotive Systems LLC ....A 956 283-5544
 Fredericksburg *(G-7176)*
Pohaku Classic - Oklahoma LLC...........E 972 840-8660
 Garland *(G-7569)*
Southwest Prof Vehicles ....F 214 371-3474
 Dallas *(G-4992)*
Versalift East LLC ....C 254 399-2100
 Waco *(G-20472)*
Vutex Inc ....C 210 476-1700
 San Antonio *(G-18605)*

MOTOR VEHICLE ASSEMBLY, COMPLETE: Buses, All Types

Thomas Bus Gulf Coast GP Inc ....E 713 580-8600
 Houston *(G-12273)*

MOTOR VEHICLE ASSEMBLY, COMPLETE: Fire Department Vehicles

City of McKinney ....D 972 547-7657
 Mc Kinney *(G-14827)*
East Lake Bucahanan ....F 512 756-4566
 Burnet *(G-2606)*
Rescue Rescue LLC ....F 210 648-2722
 San Antonio *(G-18421)*

MOTOR VEHICLE ASSEMBLY, COMPLETE: Military Motor Vehicle

Lasmer Industries Inc ....F 830 895-4400
 Kerrville *(G-13522)*
Stewart Stevenson Capitl Corp ....D 713 868-7700
 Houston *(G-12063)*

MOTOR VEHICLE ASSEMBLY, COMPLETE: Motor Homes, Self Contain

Foretravel Inc ....B 936 564-8367
 Nacogdoches *(G-15698)*

MOTOR VEHICLE ASSEMBLY, COMPLETE: Patrol Wagons

Pursuit Safety Inc ....F 972 772-4747
 Royse City *(G-17724)*

MOTOR VEHICLE ASSEMBLY, COMPLETE: Scout Cars

Bae Systems Resolution Inc ....E 713 868-7700
 Houston *(G-8789)*

MOTOR VEHICLE ASSEMBLY, COMPLETE: Truck & Tractor Trucks

Beck Manufacturing Intl Inc ....D 210 246-7510
 Converse *(G-3389)*
Browns Welding & Manufacturing ....F 830 625-8712
 New Braunfels *(G-15776)*
Fleetpride Inc ....E 800 549-7278
 Grapevine *(G-8036)*
Nathan Faulk ....F 432 634-9223
 Arlington *(G-736)*
Navistar Inc ....E 972 377-1217
 Plano *(G-16940)*
Sst Truck Company LLC ....B 972 487-2900
 Garland *(G-7591)*

MOTOR VEHICLE ASSEMBLY, COMPLETE: Truck Tractors, Highway

Big Shot LLC ....E 504 877-2335
 Lancaster *(G-13840)*

MOTOR VEHICLE ASSEMBLY, COMPLETE: Trucks, Pickup

Brandfx LLC ....E 817 431-1131
 Fort Worth *(G-6468)*

MOTOR VEHICLE ASSEMBLY, COMPLETE: Wreckers, Tow Truck

Conslidated Rigworks LP ....E 817 446-5272
 Fort Worth *(G-6543)*
Hub Intrntnal Trnsp Insur Svcs ....F 800 369-9010
 San Antonio *(G-18174)*
Mission Wrecker Service S A ....E 210 341-0333
 Converse *(G-3398)*
Pierce Arrow Inc ....F 940 538-5643
 Henrietta *(G-8282)*

MOTOR VEHICLE ASSY, COMPLETE: Motor Trucks, Exc Off-Highway

Sub Assembly Group ....F 214 420-8367
 Garland *(G-7593)*

MOTOR VEHICLE ASSY, COMPLETE: Street Sprinklers & Sweepers

Tymco International Inc ....C 254 799-5546
 Waco *(G-20468)*

MOTOR VEHICLE DEALERS: Automobiles, New & Used

American Honda Motor Co Inc ....C 972 929-5444
 Irving *(G-12930)*
Chevron USA Inc ....C 925 842-1000
 Houston *(G-9181)*
Cunningham Automotive Inc ....F 972 900-0405
 Lewisville *(G-14039)*
General Motors LLC ....A 512 470-4730
 Austin *(G-1181)*
General Motors LLC ....A 817 652-2182
 Arlington *(G-691)*
Grace IV Albert Thomas ....F 940 500-4323
 Wichita Falls *(G-20768)*
Lay Cooley RE Holdings 1 LLC ....E 972 721-4500
 Irving *(G-13084)*
Lexus Group Inc ....F 682 323-5942
 Arlington *(G-720)*
Lincoln Manufacturing Inc ....D 281 357-1541
 Magnolia *(G-14616)*
Rockwall Chrysler Dodge ....F 469 698-2100
 Rockwall *(G-17563)*
Rv Station Ltd ....E 979 778-8000
 College Station *(G-3200)*
Texaco Exploration & Prod Inc ....B 800 962-1223
 Houston *(G-12218)*
Toyota Motor North America Inc ....E 469 292-4000
 Plano *(G-17036)*
Toyota Motor North America Inc ....E 859 746-4351
 Plano *(G-17035)*
Toyota Mtr Engrg Mfg N Amer In ....C 469 292-1074
 Plano *(G-17037)*

MOTOR VEHICLE DEALERS: Cars, Used Only

Rockwall Chrysler Dodge......................F 469 698-2100
 Rockwall *(G-17563)*

MOTOR VEHICLE DEALERS: Trucks, Tractors/Trailers, New & Used

Great Dane LLC ....E 713 675-6577
 Houston *(G-10025)*
Maposa Tinashe ....F 512 704-4601
 Leander *(G-13995)*
Ranger Lift Trucks LLC ....F 281 424-2111
 Baytown *(G-1832)*
Van Nu Technology Inc ....D 817 276-3300
 Mansfield *(G-14727)*

MOTOR VEHICLE PARTS & ACCESS: Air Conditioner Parts

ARA Automotive Systems Inc ....E 214 537-1659
 Garland *(G-7440)*
Atco Products Inc ....C 972 842-8178
 Ferris *(G-6230)*
Bracket Systems Inc ....E 817 232-8199
 Fort Worth *(G-6465)*
Hunton Group Inc ....F 806 788-1100
 Houston *(G-10286)*
Mahle Behr Mfg MGT Inc ....F 915 783-4213
 El Paso *(G-5860)*
Sanden International USA Inc.................A 972 442-8400
 Wylie *(G-20948)*
Vintage Air Inc ....D 210 296-2302
 San Antonio *(G-18648)*

MOTOR VEHICLE PARTS & ACCESS: Anti-Sway Devices

Kongsberg Pwr Prod Systems I ....C 936 856-2971
 Willis *(G-20852)*

MOTOR VEHICLE PARTS & ACCESS: Axel Housings & Shafts

Top Quality Spindles LLC ....F 972 937-2126
 Waxahachie *(G-20566)*

MOTOR VEHICLE PARTS & ACCESS: Body Components & Frames

Forma Automotive LLC ....F 210 212-4400
 San Antonio *(G-18122)*
Forma Automotive LLC ....F 210 888-0410
 San Antonio *(G-18123)*

Employee Codes: A=Over 500 employees, B=251-500
C=101-250, D=51-100, E=20-50, F=10-19, G=9

2021 Harris Texas
Manufacturers Directory

PRODUCT

1569

Reyes Automotive Group LLC ....C 210 228-2500
San Antonio *(G-18423)*

Toyota Motor North America Inc ....E 859 746-4351
Plano *(G-17035)*

MOTOR VEHICLE PARTS & ACCESS: Booster Cables, Jump-Start

Auto Kabel North America Inc ....E 915 217-2253
El Paso *(G-5654)*

Auto Kabel North America Inc ....F 915 217-2253
El Paso *(G-5655)*

MOTOR VEHICLE PARTS & ACCESS: Connecting Rods

ZF Passive Safety Systems US ....E 956 566-7680
Pharr *(G-16717)*

MOTOR VEHICLE PARTS & ACCESS: Cylinder Heads

Frankenstein Racing Heads LLC ....E 817 556-2434
Weatherford *(G-20594)*

Northeast Texas Hydraulics ....F 903 582-2692
Sulphur Springs *(G-19593)*

MOTOR VEHICLE PARTS & ACCESS: Electrical Eqpt

Am-Mex Products Inc ....E 956 631-7916
McAllen *(G-14836)*

Stoneridge Inc ....B 915 778-1331
El Paso *(G-5983)*

Stoneridge Electronics Inc ....A 915 621-6111
El Paso *(G-5984)*

Wells Vehicle Electronics LP ....C 956 630-4310
McAllen *(G-14918)*

MOTOR VEHICLE PARTS & ACCESS: Engines & Parts

Aer Manufacturing Inc ....B 972 417-2582
Schertz *(G-18743)*

Bell Experimental Group Inc ....G 830 438-2890
Spring Branch *(G-19267)*

Eaton Corporation ....B 972 541-0461
Irving *(G-13005)*

Econtrols LLC ....B 210 495-9772
San Antonio *(G-18081)*

Econtrols Group Inc ....E 210 495-9772
San Antonio *(G-18082)*

Keiser Manufacturing Inc ....G 830 303-3397
Seguin *(G-18846)*

Mast Motorsports LLC ....E 936 560-2218
Nacogdoches *(G-15703)*

Skledar-Greene LLC ....F 817 454-4214
Krum *(G-13676)*

MOTOR VEHICLE PARTS & ACCESS: Engs & Trans,Factory, Rebuilt

E & E Engine Machine and Parts ....G 210 225-1141
San Antonio *(G-18077)*

Fedex Sup Chain Lgstics Elec I ....A 817 491-7700
Fort Worth *(G-6626)*

Forbes Rbuilt Automitive Parts ....F 817 332-7643
Fort Worth *(G-6640)*

MOTOR VEHICLE PARTS & ACCESS: Fuel Pumps

Borets US Inc ....E 713 980-4530
Houston *(G-8958)*

MOTOR VEHICLE PARTS & ACCESS: Fuel Systems & Parts

Cleanfuel Holdings Inc ....E 512 864-0300
Mason *(G-14812)*

Dallas Westport Inc ....C 214 231-1450
Dallas *(G-4230)*

Nitrous Express Inc ....F 940 767-7694
Wichita Falls *(G-20786)*

Veeder-Root Fuelquest LLC ....F 713 222-5700
Houston *(G-12544)*

Westport Innovations (us) ....F 214 231-1450
Dallas *(G-5183)*

MOTOR VEHICLE PARTS & ACCESS: Mufflers, Exhaust

Compx International Inc ....D 972 448-1400
Dallas *(G-4154)*

Faurecia Exhaust Systems Inc ....C 812 314-5995
Arlington *(G-677)*

MOTOR VEHICLE PARTS & ACCESS: Pickup Truck Bed Liners

McMt LLC ....F 903 592-9663
Tyler *(G-20121)*

Rough Country Accessories ....F 325 365-5258
Ballinger *(G-1742)*

MOTOR VEHICLE PARTS & ACCESS: Power Steering Eqpt

Matek Performance Inc ....E 817 626-9006
Fort Worth *(G-6816)*

MOTOR VEHICLE PARTS & ACCESS: Sanders, Safety

Mw Supply Inc ....D 254 897-4590
Glen Rose *(G-7732)*

MOTOR VEHICLE PARTS & ACCESS: Third Axle Attchmt/Six Wheel

Strong Concrete Services Inc ....E 281 847-9304
Houston *(G-12080)*

Strong Industries Inc ....E 281 448-9315
Houston *(G-12081)*

MOTOR VEHICLE PARTS & ACCESS: Transmissions

Aw Texas Inc ....C 210 381-0117
Marion *(G-14755)*

Grooms & Grooms Inc ....G 806 358-8119
Amarillo *(G-490)*

Standard Industrial Pdts Co ....E 281 280-0147
Webster *(G-20647)*

Torqon Inc ....F 956 546-3239
Brownsville *(G-2414)*

MOTOR VEHICLE PARTS & ACCESS: Water Pumps

Championx LLC ....A 281 632-6500
Sugar Land *(G-19455)*

MOTOR VEHICLE PARTS & ACCESS: Wheel rims

Trans-Texas Tire LLC ....E 903 572-0267
Mount Pleasant *(G-15664)*

MOTOR VEHICLE PARTS & ACCESS: Wiring Harness Sets

Autoelectric of America Inc ....F 210 402-6003
San Antonio *(G-17924)*

New Concept Services Inc ....F 903 342-5523
Winnsboro *(G-20900)*

Service Electric Supply Inc ....F 972 620-2821
Dallas *(G-4949)*

Solution Tech Harn Group LLC ....E 214 221-0323
Dallas *(G-4978)*

MOTOR VEHICLE SPLYS & PARTS WHOLESALERS: New

Alps Electric North Amer Inc ....D 956 217-6500
Mcallen *(G-14835)*

Dealers Truck Equipment Co Inc ....F 903 758-4451
Longview *(G-14223)*

Faurecia Exhaust Systems Inc ....C 812 314-5995
Arlington *(G-677)*

Goodyear Tire & Rubber Company ....A 361 289-8251
Corpus Christi *(G-3537)*

Michex International Inc ....F 281 397-7770
Houston *(G-10866)*

Pearland Alternator Inc ....E 281 485-8871
Pearland *(G-16589)*

Salco Products Inc ....E 630 783-2570
Houston *(G-11733)*

Standard Motor Products Inc ....C 972 316-8100
Lewisville *(G-14094)*

Thomas Bus Gulf Coast GP Inc ....E 713 580-8600
Houston *(G-12273)*

Torqon Inc ....F 956 546-3239
Brownsville *(G-2414)*

MOTOR VEHICLE SPLYS & PARTS WHOLESALERS: Used

Pearland Alternator Inc ....E 281 485-8871
Pearland *(G-16589)*

Top Quality Spindles LLC ....F 972 937-2126
Waxahachie *(G-20566)*

MOTOR VEHICLE: Hardware

Glass Magic Inc ....F 806 535-4724
Lubbock *(G-14416)*

MOTOR VEHICLE: Radiators

M P N Inc ....F 972 227-1210
Lancaster *(G-13846)*

Mahle Behr Service America LLC ....E 817 624-7273
Fort Worth *(G-6806)*

Superior Cooling Services Inc ....F 214 637-2162
Dallas *(G-5025)*

MOTOR VEHICLE: Shock Absorbers

Tenneco Automotive Oper Co Inc ....E 210 304-9390
San Antonio *(G-18528)*

MOTOR VEHICLE: Wheels

All Star Wheel Repair LLC ....F 972 564-1610
Forney *(G-6302)*

P&H Sales Ltd ....E 817 468-3850
Arlington *(G-745)*

Xtreme Force Inc ....F 281 397-0073
Houston *(G-12710)*

MOTOR VEHICLES & CAR BODIES

9650 Nf Ltd ....F 281 486-4604
Houston *(G-8418)*

ABC Exclusive Inc ....D 972 485-8182
Garland *(G-7425)*

American Honda Motor Co Inc ....C 972 929-5444
Irving *(G-12930)*

Cgt US Limited ....C 830 627-4800
New Braunfels *(G-15782)*

Fabco Industries Inc ....F 432 367-4988
Odessa *(G-15999)*

General Body Manufacturing Co ....D 713 692-5177
Houston *(G-9920)*

General Motors LLC ....A 512 470-4730
Austin *(G-1181)*

Greg Corkran Enterprises Inc ....E 409 720-9199
Nederland *(G-15753)*

Lexus Group Inc ....F 682 323-5942
Arlington *(G-720)*

Lippert Components Inc ....D 972 232-3119
Waxahachie *(G-20552)*

Lockheed Martin Corporation ....E 915 852-1100
El Paso *(G-5845)*

Lufkin Industries LLC ....B 936 634-2211
Lufkin *(G-14541)*

Navistar International Corp ....D 972 487-6509
Garland *(G-7560)*

Paccar Inc ....C 940 566-7100
Denton *(G-5387)*

Paccar Inc ....C 940 591-4000
Denton *(G-5388)*

Paccar Inc ....B 940 566-7752
Corinth *(G-3460)*

SC Autosports LLC ....F 972 271-0888
Garland *(G-7583)*

Sister2sster Dstiny Trnspt LLC ....E 346 337-6637
Houston *(G-11908)*

Taotao Usa Inc ....F 214 635-3980
Carrollton *(G-2824)*

Texas Armoring Corporation ....E 210 333-0211
San Antonio *(G-18533)*

Toyota Motor North America Inc ....E 469 292-4000
Plano *(G-17036)*

MOTOR VEHICLES, WHOLESALE: Ambulances

Emergency Vehicles Texas Inc ....F 817 281-4172
Haltom City *(G-8139)*

Hfj Group LLC ....E 833 777-3473
Houston *(G-10168)*

MOTOR VEHICLES, WHOLESALE: Commercial

Thomas Bus Gulf Coast GP Inc ....E 713 580-8600
Houston *(G-12273)*

MOTOR VEHICLES, WHOLESALE: Recreational, All-Terrain

Odes Industries LLC ....E 866 572-8420
Fort Worth *(G-6875)*

MOTOR VEHICLES, WHOLESALE: Trailers, Truck, New & Used

Entrans International LLC ....E 281 459-5350
Houston *(G-9665)*

Tmp Truck & Trailer LP ....E 432 686-2500
Midland *(G-15438)*

MOTOR VEHICLES, WHOLESALE: Truck bodies

Ace Welding and Trailer Co ....E 210 667-1171
San Antonio *(G-17858)*

Batterson Truck Equipment LLC ....F 281 598-6588
Houston *(G-8829)*

MOTORCYCLE & BICYCLE PARTS: Saddles & Seat Posts

D&D Retail LP ....E 830 379-7340
Seguin *(G-18835)*

MOTORCYCLE DEALERS

D & S Cycle of Arlington Inc ....F 817 465-5454
Arlington *(G-657)*

MOTORCYCLE REPAIR SHOPS

D & S Cycle of Arlington Inc ....F 817 465-5454
Arlington *(G-657)*

Mission Cycleplex LLC ....F 210 250-0057
San Antonio *(G-18310)*

MOTORCYCLES & RELATED PARTS

Texas Precision Mfg Inc ....E 806 741-1166
Lubbock *(G-14492)*

MOTORS: Electric

A O Smith Corporation ....C 915 859-1071
El Paso *(G-5635)*

A O Smith Corporation ....E 915 400-2800
El Paso *(G-5634)*

Electronic Power Design Inc ....D 713 923-1191
Houston *(G-9596)*

Industrial Control Inc ....F 713 464-8005
Houston *(G-10349)*

Sun-Star Electric Inc ....D 806 793-2812
Lubbock *(G-14488)*

MOTORS: Fluid Power

American Acrylic Injection Inc ....E 972 784-7759
Farmersville *(G-6221)*

MOTORS: Generators

A & A Genpro Inc ....E 713 830-3280
Houston *(G-8419)*

ACS Manufacturing Inc ....E 903 462-2001
Denison *(G-5334)*

B J Electric Motor Service ....F 432 570-4100
Midland *(G-15127)*

Breco International LLC ....F 713 641-6073
Houston *(G-8981)*

Broadwind Hvy Fabrications Inc ....F 325 437-5950
Abilene *(G-25)*

Cedar Creek II ....E 713 354-2100
Houston *(G-9115)*

Consultingpoint Inc ....E 956 986-2727
Brownsville *(G-2347)*

Cordyne Inc ....D 713 460-5151
Houston *(G-9313)*

Dayton-Phoenix Group Inc ....F 281 372-0685
Houston *(G-9413)*

Epd International Ltd ....D 713 923-1191
Houston *(G-9678)*

Evans Enterprises Inc ....D 325 235-1776
Abilene *(G-40)*

Fisher-Rosemount Systems Inc ....A 512 835-2190
Round Rock *(G-17657)*

Flowserve Corporation ....B 972 443-6500
Irving *(G-13027)*

Flowserve Corporation ....F 800 446-0401
Irving *(G-13028)*

Ideal Power Inc ....F 512 264-1542
Austin *(G-1219)*

Indelect Corporation ....E 903 656-2518
Lone Star *(G-14183)*

Loftin Equipment Company ....E 281 310-6858
Houston *(G-10669)*

Lynn Electric Motor Co Inc ....F 940 657-3511
Knox City *(G-13664)*

Magnetic Technology Inc ....E 214 544-2700
McKinney *(G-14955)*

Motor Trike Inc ....C 903 842-3094
Troup *(G-20026)*

Regal Beloit America Inc ....C 715 284-9801
Eagle Pass *(G-5554)*

Regal Beloit Corporation ....C 830 774-2677
Del Rio *(G-5322)*

Regal Beloit Corporation ....E 412 968-0100
El Paso *(G-5934)*

SAI Power Systems Inc ....F 281 516-3130
Tomball *(G-20007)*

Siemens Industry Inc ....C 915 790-0219
El Paso *(G-5960)*

Toshiba International Corp ....G 713 466-0277
Houston *(G-12326)*

Toshiba International Corp ....A 800 231-1412
Houston *(G-12327)*

Toshiba International Corp ....G 713 466-0277
Houston *(G-12328)*

Trader Sam LLC ....F 214 537-0885
Plano *(G-17038)*

Tyco Engineered Pdts & Svcs ....D 609 720-4200
Houston *(G-12418)*

Unitron LP ....D 214 221-9094
Dallas *(G-5139)*

Valeo North America Inc ....A 915 774-9340
El Paso *(G-6023)*

Valeo North America Inc ....A 915 779-1625
El Paso *(G-6024)*

MOTORS: Pneumatic

Hartfiel Automation Inc ....F 972 633-0000
Plano *(G-16884)*

MOTORS: Rocket, Guided Missile

Sunbelt Design & Dev Inc ....D 210 227-9162
San Antonio *(G-18511)*

MOTORS: Timing, Synchronous, Electric

RTC Manufacturing Inc ....F 817 860-1217
Arlington *(G-778)*

MOUNTING SVC: Swatches & Samples

Three Chiefs & No Indians LLC ....C 909 465-6314
Grand Prairie *(G-7983)*

MOVING SVC & STORAGE: Local

Anything Goes Enterprises LLC ....F 210 608-1741
San Antonio *(G-17908)*

MOVING SVC: Local

Anything Goes Enterprises LLC ....F 210 608-1741
San Antonio *(G-17908)*

MULTIPLEXERS: Telephone & Telegraph

Teleprime Advanced Communicati ......G 512 271-9503
Austin *(G-1561)*

MUSEUMS & ART GALLERIES

S W Galleries Corp ....E 972 788-2743
Dallas *(G-4924)*

MUSIC BROADCASTING SVCS

Broadcast Technical Svcs Inc ....F 832 467-0002
Houston *(G-8988)*

Falcon Events LLC ....D 800 895-6934
Irving *(G-13022)*

MUSICAL INSTRUMENT LESSONS

Victorious Music Co ....F 713 450-3306
Houston *(G-12567)*

MUSICAL INSTRUMENT REPAIR

Lisle Violin Shop ....F 281 487-7303
Pasadena *(G-16474)*

MUSICAL INSTRUMENTS & ACCESS: NEC

Jarvis Industries Inc ....G 281 370-5455
Spring *(G-19136)*

Portsmouth Trading Co Inc ....G 713 957-0470
Houston *(G-11368)*

Precision Pearl Inlay Inc ....F 512 442-4941
Austin *(G-1430)*

Victorious Music Co ....F 713 450-3306
Houston *(G-12567)*

MUSICAL INSTRUMENTS & PARTS: Percussion

DK Drill I LP ....E 817 539-2500
Mansfield *(G-14665)*

MUSICAL INSTRUMENTS & SPLYS STORES

Lisle Violin Shop ....F 281 487-7303
Pasadena *(G-16474)*

Portsmouth Trading Co Inc ....G 713 957-0470
Houston *(G-11368)*

Triaz Digital Printing LLC ....F 512 491-7000
Austin *(G-1592)*

MUSICAL INSTRUMENTS & SPLYS STORES: Pianos

Heart of Texas Music Inc ....F 254 778-7422
Temple *(G-19681)*

Jim Melhart Piano and Organ Co ....E 956 682-6147
McAllen *(G-14879)*

MUSICAL INSTRUMENTS: Electric & Electronic

Dbz Guitars LLC ....F 713 934-0110
Houston *(G-9415)*

MUSICAL INSTRUMENTS: Organs

Redman Pipe Organs LLC ....G 817 332-2953
Fort Worth *(G-6949)*

MUSICAL INSTRUMENTS: Violins & Parts

Lisle Violin Shop ....F 281 487-7303
Pasadena *(G-16474)*

MUTUAL FUND MANAGEMENT

Afam Capital Inc ....E 512 354-7041
Austin *(G-900)*

NAILS: Steel, Wire Or Cut

Progressive Steel & Wire LLC ....F 972 999-8778
Irving *(G-13158)*

NAME PLATES: Engraved Or Etched

JRS Company Inc ....D 626 967-2432
Hutto *(G-12881)*

Marking Systems Inc ....D 972 475-0770
Garland *(G-7543)*

Texas Nameplate Company Inc ....D 214 428-8341
Lancaster *(G-13849)*

Ttc Trammell Co Inc ....E 713 921-7121
Houston *(G-12399)*

NAMEPLATES

Foust Incorporated ....E 806 374-7005
Amarillo *(G-424)*

Southwestern Nameplate Mfg Co ....F 972 924-3289
Anna *(G-586)*

PRODUCT

NAPHTHA

US Petrochemicals Inc ....F 713 871-1951
  Houston (G-12487)

NATIONAL SECURITY FORCES

Dla Document Services ....F 210 671-1407
  San Antonio (G-18064)

NATIONAL SECURITY, GOVERNMENT: Air Force

US Dept of the Air Force ....B 210 925-4401
  San Antonio (G-18580)

NATURAL BUTANE PRODUCTION

Tellurian Investments Inc ....F 832 962-4000
  Houston (G-12194)

NATURAL GAS COMPRESSING SVC, On-Site

Archrock Inc ....C 281 836-8000
  Houston (G-8685)
Archrock Inc ....F 432 567-1050
  Midland (G-15118)
Archrock Inc ....F 432 336-8632
  Fort Stockton (G-6328)
Archrock Inc ....E 361 572-9904
  Victoria (G-20239)
Archrock Inc ....F 903 389-5666
  Fairfield (G-6168)
Archrock Inc ....D 806 669-8900
  Pampa (G-16314)
Black Elk Energy LLC ....E 281 507-7652
  Houston (G-8902)
Breckenridge Exploration Co ....E 254 559-7566
  Breckenridge (G-2225)
Burk Royalty Co Ltd ....E 940 397-8600
  Wichita Falls (G-20748)
E T C Company ....E 210 403-6402
  Dallas (G-4285)
El Paso Field Services LP ....F 361 552-9601
  Port Lavaca (G-17145)
Exterran Corporation ....E 281 836-7000
  Houston (G-9735)
Exterran Trinidad LLC ....B 281 921-9337
  Houston (G-9737)
Great Texas Compression LLC ....F 210 569-6742
  San Antonio (G-18152)
Kelman Technologies Inc ....E 281 529-3204
  Houston (G-10514)
Koch Industries Inc ....E 903 693-5172
  Carthage (G-2911)
Markwest Enrgy E Texas Gas LP ......E 903 694-2225
  Carthage (G-2914)
Martins Fishing Tools ....E 432 524-7456
  Andrews (G-551)
Reserve Compression Corp ....E 713 783-8851
  Houston (G-11605)
Reserve Equipment Inc ....E 713 939-8988
  Houston (G-11606)
Stakeholder Midstream LLC ....F 210 444-9664
  San Antonio (G-18494)
USA Compression Partners LLC ....F 512 369-1380
  Austin (G-1618)
USA Compression Partners LP ....E 512 473-2662
  Austin (G-1619)
Williams Companies Inc ....F 281 444-6441
  Houston (G-12669)

NATURAL GAS DISTRIBUTION TO CONSUMERS

Anadarko Petroleum Corporation ....C 832 636-1000
  The Woodlands (G-19830)
Belvan Partners LP ....F 432 682-4349
  Midland (G-15137)
Energen Corporation ....F 205 326-2700
  Midland (G-15216)
Just Energy (us) Corp ....B 713 850-6784
  Houston (G-10490)
Lone Star NGL Pipeline LP ....F 210 403-7300
  Houston (G-10679)
Martin Midstream Partners LP ....F 281 471-2211
  La Porte (G-13774)
Martin Resource Mgt Corp ....C 903 983-6200
  Kilgore (G-13570)
Noremac Gas LLC ....F 281 248-6423
  Katy (G-13429)

Occidental Energy Mktg Inc ....C 713 215-7000
  Houston (G-11113)
Sago Energy LLC ....D 325 473-5161
  Bronte (G-2306)
Twin Eagle Sand Logistics LLC ....E 713 341-7300
  Houston (G-12414)
Ultra Clean Technology Systems ....C 512 252-6100
  Austin (G-1606)

NATURAL GAS LIQUID FRACTIONATING SVC

Markwest Enrgy E Texas Gas LP ....E 903 694-2225
  Carthage (G-2914)
Morgan Kinder Treating LP ....F 432 563-2766
  Odessa (G-16083)
Tri Resources Inc ....F 254 559-7533
  Breckenridge (G-2241)

NATURAL GAS LIQUIDS PRODUCTION

Cameron LNG Holdings LLC ....E 832 783-5500
  Houston (G-9075)
Coronado Midstream LLC ....E 432 684-3870
  Midland (G-15179)
Downhole Well Solutions LLC ....F 832 761-5111
  Spring (G-19112)
Durango Midstream LLC ....E 346 351-2787
  Spring (G-19208)
Eagle Rock Field Services LP ....E 281 408-1200
  Houston (G-9563)
Eagle Rock Operating LP ....F 281 408-1200
  Houston (G-9564)
Ep Energy Management LLC ....E 713 997-1000
  Houston (G-9676)
Hiland Gp LLC ....E 713 369-9000
  Houston (G-10180)
Martin Midstream GP LLC ....A 903 983-6200
  Kilgore (G-13568)
Martin Midstream Partners LP ....D 903 983-6200
  Kilgore (G-13569)
Prometheus Energy Group Inc ....E 832 456-6500
  Houston (G-11448)
Spartan Energy Partners LP ....E 281 466-3310
  Spring (G-19253)
Spartan Operating Company LLC ....E 281 466-3310
  The Woodlands (G-19924)
Woodland Midstream II LLC ....E 832 592-1202
  Spring (G-19262)

NATURAL GAS LIQUIDS PRODUCTION

Anadarko Holding Company ....F 832 636-7200
  Houston (G-8633)
Bg Energy Merchants LLC ....E 713 599-4000
  Houston (G-8869)
Bg LNG Services LLC ....D 713 599-4000
  Houston (G-8870)
BP America Production Company ....F 903 927-8999
  Hallsville (G-8127)
Bridgeline Holdings LP ....F 713 432-6000
  Bellaire (G-1991)
Cailip Gas Marketing LLC ....E 281 833-4217
  Houston (G-9046)
Chevron Corporation ....E 432 523-7950
  Andrews (G-543)
Chevron Corporation ....B 713 754-3998
  Houston (G-9178)
Dcp Midstream LLC ....E 361 584-8500
  Bishop (G-2106)
Dcp Midstream LLC ....E 432 693-2204
  Midkiff (G-15095)
Dcp NGL Services LP ....F 713 735-3600
  Houston (G-9416)
El Paso Field Services LP ....E 210 621-2031
  Elmendorf (G-6068)
Energen Corporation ....F 205 326-2700
  Midland (G-15216)
Enterprise Gas Processing LLC ....E 713 381-4068
  Houston (G-9661)
Enterprise Products Company ....C 713 381-6500
  Houston (G-9663)
Enterprise Products Company ....E 432 221-7700
  Midland (G-15221)
Enterprise Products Company ....E 432 686-5421
  Midland (G-15222)
Finley Resources Inc ....D 817 336-1924
  Fort Worth (G-6631)
Hiland Partners Holdings LLC ....D 713 369-9000
  Houston (G-10181)
J L Davis Company ....E 432 399-4575
  Coahoma (G-3165)

Lacy Operations Ltd ....E 903 693-3501
  Beckville (G-1971)
Lone Star NGL Pipeline LP ....F 210 403-7300
  Houston (G-10679)
Lone Star NGL Rfinery Svcs LLC ....F 210 403-7300
  Houston (G-10680)
Martin Midstream Partners LP ....F 281 471-2211
  La Porte (G-13774)
Midlothian Lng LLC ....F 818 450-3668
  Midlothian (G-15486)
Midstream Hess Operations LP ....E 713 496-4200
  Houston (G-10874)
Natural Gas Vehicles Texas Inc ....F 214 630-1000
  Dallas (G-4717)
Nextdecade Corporation ....E 713 574-1880
  Houston (G-11047)
Oneok Inc ....E 915 680-7200
  El Paso (G-5902)
Panhandle Eastrn Pipe Line LP ....F 713 627-5400
  Houston (G-11233)
Pioneer Exploration Company ....E 281 893-9400
  Houston (G-11334)
Pioneer Natural Resources Co ....D 432 535-2444
  Midkiff (G-15096)
Plains GP Holdings LP ....E 713 646-4100
  Houston (G-11343)
Quicksilver Resources Inc ....D 817 665-5000
  Fort Worth (G-6928)
Regency Energy Partners LP ....E 806 665-2551
  Pampa (G-16338)
Regency Energy Partners LP ....D 214 750-1771
  Dallas (G-4881)
Sabine Hub Services LLC ....E 214 721-9474
  Houston (G-11715)
Sentry Oil & Gas LLC ....E 212 753-6367
  Mico (G-15094)
Sg Interests I Ltd ....F 713 951-0100
  Houston (G-11843)
Southcross Ccng Gathering Ltd ....F 214 953-9500
  Dallas (G-4982)
Southcross Enrgy Prtners GP LL ....B 214 979-3792
  Houston (G-11970)
Stabilis Energy Inc ....D 832 456-6500
  Houston (G-12035)
Taylor Distributing Co Inc ....E 817 831-0601
  Fort Worth (G-7037)
Texaco Exploration & Prod Inc ....B 800 962-1223
  Houston (G-12218)
Trans-Pecos Pipeline LLC ....E 713 989-2606
  Houston (G-12344)
Tri Resources Inc ....E 432 558-3996
  Crane (G-3703)
Tri Resources Inc ....F 432 688-0555
  Midland (G-15445)
Tri Resources Inc ....C 281 385-3200
  Mont Belvieu (G-15623)
Tri Resources Inc ....E 806 323-9125
  Canadian (G-2655)
Tri Resources Inc ....E 940 549-8340
  Breckenridge (G-2240)
Tri Resources Inc ....F 903 687-2513
  Waskom (G-20523)
Tri Resources Inc ....E 940 644-2233
  Chico (G-3054)
Twin Eagle Sand Logistics LLC ....E 713 341-7300
  Houston (G-12414)
W&T Offshore Inc ....C 713 626-8525
  Houston (G-12588)
Western Gas Resources Inc ....F 432 693-2302
  Midkiff (G-15098)
Western Gas Resources Inc ....E 432 395-2448
  Fort Stockton (G-6331)
Williams Gas Pipeline-Transco ....C 713 215-2000
  Houston (G-12670)

NATURAL GAS POWER BROKER

Source Operations Group LLC ....E 888 557-7079
  Houston (G-11957)

NATURAL GAS PRODUCTION

American Natural Resources Co ....E 832 320-5000
  Houston (G-8603)
Azure Midstream Company LLC ....F 281 680-4300
  Houston (G-8767)
Badger Midstream Energy LP ....E 713 395-6111
  Houston (G-8788)
Bluescape Resources Co LLC ....F 469 398-2202
  Dallas (G-4033)
Cameron LNG Holdings LLC ....E 832 783-5500
  Houston (G-9075)

Channel Brfinery Terminals LLC ....F 713 965-4150
  Houston *(G-9161)*

Cohort Energy Company......................E 972 233-8191
  Addison *(G-110)*

Covey Park II LLC ....D 214 548-6000
  Frisco *(G-7276)*

Dcp Midstream LLC ....E 361 584-8500
  Bishop *(G-2106)*

Devon Energy Corporation ....F 806 229-6300
  Whiteface *(G-20724)*

Eagle Rock Energy Partners LP ....D 281 408-1200
  Houston *(G-9562)*

Enlink Midstream Inc ....E 214 953-9500
  Dallas *(G-4324)*

Enlink N Texas Gathering LP ....E 432 221-9757
  Midland *(G-15220)*

Etc Intrastate Procurement LLC ....A 713 989-2688
  Houston *(G-9703)*

Exterran Corporation.........................E 281 836-7000
  Houston *(G-9735)*

Georesources Inc ....F 832 538-0300
  Houston *(G-9940)*

Hesco Gathering Company L L C ....F 361 883-8398
  Corpus Christi *(G-3547)*

Iacx Energy LLC ....F 972 960-3210
  Dallas *(G-4483)*

J Cleo Thmpson Jmes Cleo Thmp ....F 432 550-8887
  Dallas *(G-4517)*

Linnco LLC ....A 281 840-4000
  Houston *(G-10653)*

Maralo LLC ....F 512 322-0041
  Austin *(G-1326)*

Marubeni Oil & Gas (usa) LLC ....E 832 379-1100
  Houston *(G-10781)*

Natural Gas Pipeline Amer LLC ....A 713 369-9000
  Houston *(G-11007)*

Nexus Capacity Services Ulc ....C 713 627-5040
  Houston *(G-11050)*

Nuevo Energy Company ....B 713 579-6000
  Houston *(G-11097)*

One Gas Inc ....E 830 672-2921
  Gonzales *(G-7760)*

One Gas Inc ....E 830 672-2256
  Gonzales *(G-7761)*

Renaissance Offshore LLC ....E 832 333-7700
  Houston *(G-11598)*

Repsol Oil & Gas Usa LLC ....D 832 442-1000
  Spring *(G-19247)*

Sago Christie LP ....G 281 240-8444
  Sugar Land *(G-19539)*

Sago Energy LLC ....D 325 473-5161
  Bronte *(G-2306)*

San Mateo Midstream LLC ....F 972 371-5203
  Dallas *(G-4930)*

Sanchez Oil & Gas Corporation...........D 210 208-1300
  Catarina *(G-2933)*

Southcross Marketing Co Ltd ....F 214 979-3700
  Dallas *(G-4984)*

Superior Processing Service ....E 713 759-6900
  Houston *(G-12118)*

Texas Gas Service Company ....A 956 444-3900
  Harlingen *(G-8205)*

Transamerican Natural Gas Corp ....C 281 372-5304
  Houston *(G-12346)*

Vastar Resources Inc ....A 281 584-6000
  Houston *(G-12539)*

NATURAL GAS STORAGE SVCS

Midstream Hess Operations LP ....F 713 496-4200
  Houston *(G-10874)*

NATURAL GAS TRANSMISSION

Atlas Energy Group LLC ....F 412 489-0006
  Fort Worth *(G-6408)*

Atlas Growth Partners Gp LLC ....E 412 489-0006
  Fort Worth *(G-6409)*

Blaze Sales and Service Inc ....F 713 828-1685
  Houston *(G-8913)*

El Paso Cgp Company LLC..................E 713 420-2600
  Houston *(G-9585)*

Energen Corporation.........................F 205 326-2700
  Midland *(G-15216)*

Energen Resources Corporation ....F 432 687-1155
  Midland *(G-15217)*

Ep Energy Management LLC ....E 713 997-1000
  Houston *(G-9676)*

Kinder Morgan (delaware) Inc ....C 806 272-3309
  Muleshoe *(G-15677)*

Koch Industries Inc...........................F 806 347-2645
  Matador *(G-14816)*

Regency Energy Partners LP ....D 214 750-1771
  Dallas *(G-4881)*

Shortes Inc ....E 940 658-3576
  Knox City *(G-13665)*

Summit Midstream Partners LP............E 832 413-4770
  Houston *(G-12094)*

Transamerican Natural Gas Corp ....C 281 372-5304
  Houston *(G-12346)*

Tri Resources Inc ....E 940 644-2233
  Chico *(G-3054)*

Venables Construction Inc..................E 806 381-2121
  Amarillo *(G-520)*

NATURAL GAS TRANSMISSION & DISTRIBUTION

El Paso Field Services LP ....F 210 621-2031
  Elmendorf *(G-6068)*

Exterran Corporation.........................E 281 836-7000
  Houston *(G-9735)*

Falcon Seaboard Holdings LLC ....E 713 622-0055
  Houston *(G-9755)*

James Lee Davis ....D 432 682-6311
  Midland *(G-15258)*

Kinder Morgan (delaware) Inc ....C 806 272-3309
  Muleshoe *(G-15677)*

Michelson Energy Company ....F 210 826-0681
  San Antonio *(G-18299)*

Midcoast Energy Partners LP ....F 713 821-2000
  Houston *(G-10872)*

Nextdecade Corporation ....E 713 574-1880
  Houston *(G-11047)*

Par Pacific Holdings Inc ....D 281 899-4800
  Houston *(G-11235)*

Tidal Energy Marketing US LLC ....C 713 650-8900
  Houston *(G-12288)*

Western Gas Resources Inc ....E 432 395-2448
  Fort Stockton *(G-6331)*

Western Gas Resources Inc ....F 432 693-2302
  Midkiff *(G-15098)*

NATURAL GASOLINE PRODUCTION

Arbor Renewable Gas LLC...................F 281 849-9834
  Houston *(G-8676)*

Chevron Corporation.........................C 903 963-8631
  Van *(G-20206)*

Lewis Petro Properties Inc ....D 210 384-3200
  San Antonio *(G-18249)*

Midcoast Operating LP ....E 210 321-8000
  San Antonio *(G-18304)*

Wtg Gas Processing LP ....E 432 682-4349
  Midland *(G-15471)*

Wtg Gas Processing LP ....E 325 473-5161
  Bronte *(G-2307)*

NATURAL LIQUEFIED PETROLEUM GAS PRODUCTION

Cheniere Cch Holdco II LLC ....A 713 375-5000
  Houston *(G-9174)*

Cheniere Energy Inc ....D 713 375-5000
  Houston *(G-9175)*

Corpus Christi Pipeline GP LLC ....C 713 375-5000
  Gregory *(G-8100)*

Eagle Rock Energy Partners LP ....D 281 408-1200
  Houston *(G-9562)*

Process Recovery Systems Inc............F 281 448-8180
  Houston *(G-11432)*

R T M Interests LLC ....F 432 683-7700
  Midland *(G-15376)*

Stabilis Energy LLC ....E 409 833-1115
  Houston *(G-12036)*

Tri Resources Inc ....E 713 584-1000
  Houston *(G-12362)*

NATURAL PROPANE PRODUCTION

Cleereco Services Inc ....F 325 658-6533
  San Angelo *(G-17787)*

JP Energy Partners LP ....E 972 444-0300
  Irving *(G-13069)*

NAVIGATIONAL SYSTEMS & INSTRUMENTS

Freeflight Acquisition Corp..................E 254 662-7050
  Robinson *(G-17500)*

L3 Technologies Inc..........................C 972 722-7927
  Rockwall *(G-17553)*

L3 Technologies Inc..........................A 903 457-4100
  Greenville *(G-8080)*

Pharos Marine Autmtc Pwr Inc ....E 713 228-5208
  Houston *(G-11321)*

Pronav Inc ....D 361 727-3300
  Rockport *(G-17532)*

Ranger Security Detectors Inc..............E 915 590-4441
  El Paso *(G-5927)*

Tideland Signal Corporation ....D 713 681-6101
  Houston *(G-12289)*

Vectornav Technologies LLC ....F 512 772-3615
  Dallas *(G-5157)*

NETTING: Cargo

Cargo Systems Inc............................F 512 837-1300
  Austin *(G-1029)*

NETTING: Mosquito

Innova Supply Inc ....E 713 473-3345
  Pasadena *(G-16459)*

NETTING: Rope

Cactus Ropes Inc..............................E 830 569-8744
  Pleasanton *(G-17064)*

Pedley Nets Inc ....F 940 328 0448
  Mineral Wells *(G-15537)*

NEW & USED CAR DEALERS

Haastech Inc...................................F 214 688-0280
  Dallas *(G-4426)*

KSA Industries Inc ....E 713 881-3400
  Houston *(G-10569)*

Rush Sales Company ....C 432 337-2397
  Odessa *(G-16145)*

Southwest Prof Vehicles ....F 214 371-3474
  Dallas *(G-4992)*

NEWS DEALERS & NEWSSTANDS

Community Newspapers Holdings........D 512 392-6143
  San Marcos *(G-18682)*

Floyd County Hesperian-Beacon ....F 888 400-1083
  Floydada *(G-6293)*

Hockley County Publishing Co..............F 806 894-3121
  Levelland *(G-14009)*

NEWSPAPERS, WHOLESALE

Daily DOT LLC..................................F 512 420-9403
  Austin *(G-1084)*

International Daily News Inc ....F 713 270-4855
  Houston *(G-10400)*

NICKEL ALLOY

Bhc Industries of Texas Inc ....F 817 556-2306
  Alvarado *(G-325)*

Lemetrix Solutions LLC......................G 281 381-0714
  Pearland *(G-16578)*

Metal & Materials Proc LLC ....G 713 664-0050
  Houston *(G-10843)*

Nickel Rock LLC................................F 512 395-7416
  San Marcos *(G-18701)*

NICKEL ORE MINING

Nexa Resources Us Inc ....F 832 726-0160
  Houston *(G-11043)*

NIPPLES: Rubber

Nipples Elbows & Couplings Inc ....E 281 405-8240
  Houston *(G-11059)*

NONAROMATIC CHEMICAL PRDTS

Shell Oil Company ....E 713 721-6282
  Houston *(G-11864)*

NONCURRENT CARRYING WIRING DEVICES

Bartec US Corporation ....F 281 214-8542
  Houston *(G-8819)*

Cooper B-Line Inc ....C 903 813-1746
  Sherman *(G-18913)*

Nipples Elbows & Couplings Inc ....E 281 405-8240
  Houston *(G-11059)*

R & B Electronics Inc.........................E 906 632-1542
  Grand Prairie *(G-7961)*

Tyrex Group Ltd ....F 512 623-4694
  Austin *(G-1603)*

PRODUCT

NONFERROUS: Rolling & Drawing, NEC

Asarco LLC ....A....... 806 468-4000
Amarillo (G-401)

Elemetal LLC ....G....... 214 956-7600
Dallas (G-4309)

Hutcheson Fabricating & Wldg..........F....... 713 224-9703
Houston (G-10290)

Interstate Fittings Inc ....D....... 214 637-6720
Dallas (G-4508)

Jamestown North America LLC..........G....... 713 672-6655
Houston (G-10452)

MMS Traders LLC ....F....... 832 433-7948
Houston (G-10897)

New England Lead Burning Inc ....F....... 713 675-3266
Houston (G-11034)

Overlay Product Systems Inc ....D....... 281 552-3500
Houston (G-11206)

Thermo Plastics Corporation.............E....... 817 281-9010
Fort Worth (G-7056)

NONMETALLIC MINERALS DEVELOPMENT & TEST BORING SVC

Layne Christensen Company ....D....... 281 475-2600
Spring (G-19226)

NONMETALLIC MINERALS: Support Activities, Exc Fuels

Gulf Coast Limestone Inc.................F....... 281 474-4124
Seabrook (G-18785)

Maximum Industries Inc ....E....... 214 614-6936
Irving (G-13099)

Nigen International LLC ....E....... 713 956-8022
Houston (G-11053)

Texas Rapid LLC ....E....... 432 837-1049
Alpine (G-312)

US American Resources Inc ....E....... 972 662-9070
Dallas (G-3855)

NOTARIES PUBLIC

Diversified Bus Consulting LLC ....F....... 713 677-9282
Houston (G-9481)

Thiink Biig Tax Service Inc...............F....... 832 606-3380
Katy (G-13450)

NOTEBOOKS, MADE FROM PURCHASED MATERIALS

Urman Inc ....F....... 832 246-8810
The Woodlands (G-19932)

NOTIONS: Pins, Hair, Exc Rubber

Bobby Pins LLC ....F....... 920 267-6388
Dallas (G-4035)

NOVELTIES

Merit Sales Inc ....D....... 512 863-8541
Georgetown (G-7664)

NOVELTIES & SPECIALTIES: Metal

Great American Products Ltd ....C....... 830 620-4400
New Braunfels (G-15797)

Vixen Creations Inc.......................G....... 512 928-4933
Austin (G-1642)

NOVELTIES: Paper, Made From Purchased Materials

Aztec Imports Inc ....E....... 915 858-2287
El Paso (G-5657)

NOVELTIES: Plastic

Spirit Industries Inc ....E....... 936 597-5144
Montgomery (G-15641)

Trix & Kix Dannys ....F....... 281 353-6618
Spring (G-19182)

NOVELTY SHOPS

Trix & Kix Dannys ....F....... 281 353-6618
Spring (G-19182)

NOZZLES & SPRINKLERS Lawn Hose

National Well Supplies Co Inc ....F....... 713 467-0462
Houston (G-11005)

NOZZLES: Fire Fighting

Marsol Technologies Inc ....F....... 346 701-8268
Houston (G-10774)

NOZZLES: Spray, Aerosol, Paint Or Insecticide

Spraying Systems Co ....E....... 903 535-5036
Tyler (G-20155)

NUCLEAR CORE STRUCTURALS: Metal Plate

Tranter Inc...................................C....... 940 723-7125
Wichita Falls (G-20819)

NUCLEAR DETECTORS: Solid State

Proportional Technologies Inc ....E....... 713 747-7324
Houston (G-11450)

NUCLEAR REACTORS: Military Or Indl

Saulsbury Industries Inc ....A....... 972 884-6000
Dallas (G-4938)

NURSERIES & LAWN & GARDEN SPLY STORE, RET: Lawn/Garden Splys

E Barr Feeds Inc...........................F....... 830 672-6515
Gonzales (G-7752)

Texas Landfill Management LLC ....E....... 210 651-6115
San Antonio (G-18537)

NURSERIES & LAWN & GARDEN SPLY STORES, RETAIL

Aloe Vera of America Inc.................C....... 956 585-9704
Alton (G-321)

NURSERIES & LAWN & GARDEN SPLY STORES, RETAIL: Fertilizer

Agrium US Inc...............................D....... 806 274-5204
Borger (G-2161)

Collingwood Grain Inc.....................F....... 254 582-5344
Hillsboro (G-8324)

Greensmiths Inc............................G....... 972 242-5310
Carrollton (G-2748)

Martinek Grain & Bins Inc ....F....... 972 382-8500
Celina (G-2992)

Nitro-Phos Inc ....E....... 713 228-1868
Houston (G-11060)

NURSERIES & LAWN & GARDEN SPLY STORES, RETAIL: Top Soil

Natures Way Resources Inc..............F....... 936 273-1200
Conroe (G-3341)

NURSERIES & LAWN/GARDEN SPLY STORE, RET: Lawnmowers/Tractors

Panola Equipment Inc ....F....... 903 633-2545
Panola (G-16349)

Valley Outdoor Power Eqp Inc ....F....... 956 787-0469
Pharr (G-16715)

NURSERIES/LAWN/GARDEN SPLY STORES, RET: Hydroponic Eqpt/Sply

Diesel Engine and Parts Co LLC ....E....... 713 675-6100
Houston (G-9466)

Reliable Hose Solutions LLC..............F....... 713 983-9090
Houston (G-11590)

NURSERIES/LAWN/GRDN SPLY STORE, RET: Nursery Stck, Seed/Bulb

Aloe Farms Inc ....F....... 956 425-1289
Harlingen (G-8177)

NURSERY & GARDEN CENTERS

JMJ Organics Ltd ....F....... 281 798-3056
Crosby (G-3735)

NUTRITION SVCS

FR Global Trading Co Inc ....E....... 214 281-8668
Dallas (G-4376)

NUTS: Metal

Caterpillar Inc ....E....... 830 401-5600
Seguin (G-18829)

Caterpillar Inc ....D....... 210 637-3700
San Antonio (G-17987)

Ingram Industries Inc ....E....... 903 848-8411
Canton (G-2657)

Lok-Mor Inc.................................E....... 817 477-0232
Mansfield (G-14685)

Maintenance Tool & Supply Co ....F....... 361 888-8801
Corpus Christi (G-3571)

Tnn Manufacturing Company Inc ....D....... 713 849-0062
Houston (G-12311)

US Bolt Manufacturing Inc ....D....... 713 726-1000
Houston (G-12482)

NYLON FIBERS

E I Du Pont De Nemours & Co ....A....... 409 886-6442
Orange (G-16240)

Honeywell International Inc ....A....... 281 890-0088
Cypress (G-3801)

Invista Capital Management LLC.........A....... 361 572-1111
Victoria (G-20274)

NYLON RESINS

Ascend Performance Mtls Inc ....F....... 713 315-5700
Houston (G-8713)

Ascend Prfmce Mtls Hldings Inc ....E....... 713 315-5700
Houston (G-8714)

E I Du Pont De Nemours & Co ....B....... 361 572-1330
Victoria (G-20260)

OFFICE EQPT WHOLESALERS

American Micro Systems Ltd..............E....... 817 571-9015
Euless (G-6130)

Cummins - Allison Corp ....F....... 972 661-5390
Dallas (G-4192)

Graphtex Inc ....F....... 979 968-6333
La Grange (G-13696)

Office Furn Cmpanies Texas LLC.........F....... 281 724-1533
League City (G-13970)

OKelley Office Supply Inc ....F....... 325 673-6422
Abilene (G-61)

Precision Dcment Solutions Inc ....E....... 866 916-1177
Carrollton (G-2792)

Speed Printing Conroe Inc................E....... 936 441-2248
Conroe (G-3366)

OFFICE EQPT, WHOLESALE: Photocopy Machines

Tcca Inc......................................F....... 361 668-9636
Alice (G-239)

OFFICE FIXTURES: Wood

Robert Shaw Mfg Co Inc ....E....... 817 927-2557
Fort Worth (G-6962)

OFFICE FURNITURE REPAIR & MAINTENANCE SVCS

Fife Services Inc...........................E....... 432 827-3601
Goldsmith (G-7742)

Sullys Lone Star Office Pdts..............F....... 512 835-9506
Austin (G-1544)

OFFICE SPLY & STATIONERY STORES: Office Forms & Splys

Ables-Land Inc ....E....... 903 593-8407
Tyler (G-20043)

Associated Creditors Inc..................F....... 210 341-5642
San Antonio (G-17919)

Banc Professional Services...............F....... 972 734-1200
Glen Rose (G-7731)

Cloud Printing Co of Abilene ....G....... 325 676-9396
Abilene (G-32)

Company Printing ....F....... 325 949-9941
San Angelo (G-17788)

Concho Business Solutions Inc ....E....... 325 653-1697
San Angelo (G-17789)

Eastland County Newspaper Inc ....F....... 254 629-1707
Eastland (G-5564)

Firmin Business Forms Inc ....F....... 254 776-5742
Waco (G-20402)

Firmin Printing & Off Eqp Co ....E....... 903 793-5566
Texarkana (G-19763)

Fred Bennett Printing Company	E	817 641-9861
Cleburne (G-3089)		
Gea Associates Inc	G	903 295-2727
Longview (G-14239)		
HF Guyton Inc	E	713 869-6483
Houston (G-10167)		
Hill County Press Inc	F	254 582-3431
Hillsboro (G-8327)		
Hoyt Deryl	F	325 372-3825
San Saba (G-18717)		
Mail & Parcels Plus Inc	F	409 899-1771
Beaumont (G-1923)		
Messenger Publishing Co Inc	F	254 865-5212
Gatesville (G-7620)		
Oak Cliff Office Sup Prtg Inc	E	214 943-7421
Dallas (G-4750)		
OKelley Office Supply Inc	F	325 673-6422
Abilene (G-61)		
Parker Business Forms Inc	F	409 842-5251
Beaumont (G-1938)		
Precision Printing & Off Sup	F	936 825-2488
Navasota (G-15742)		
Printedd Products & Svcs Ltd	E	512 835-2253
Austin (G-1432)		
Regency Plz Prtg & Off Sup Inc	F	214 939-3456
Dallas (G-4882)		
Reneau Publishing Inc	G	409 385-5278
Silsbee (G-18954)		
Rfv Enterprises Inc	E	281 842-1877
La Porte (G-13788)		
Rockdale Reporter Inc	F	512 446-5838
Rockdale (G-17526)		
Schulenburg Prtg Off Sups Inc	E	979 743-4511
Schulenburg (G-18778)		
Speed Printing Conroe Inc	F	936 441-2248
Conroe (G-3366)		
Tech Dogs LLC	F	972 985-4730
Plano (G-17023)		
Thompson Business Forms Inc	E	210 734-5356
San Antonio (G-18549)		
Trew Investments Inc	F	806 749-3200
Lubbock (G-14498)		
Universal Pen & Print Inc	F	210 656-4000
San Antonio (G-18579)		
Vincent Graphics & Supply Inc	E	903 882-3123
Tyler (G-20176)		
W B Mason Co Inc	E	888 926-2766
Pflugerville (G-16691)		
W B Mason Co Inc	E	888 926-2766
Irving (G-13205)		
W B Mason Co Inc	E	888 926-2766
Houston (G-12584)		
Wise County Messenger Inc	E	940 627-5987
Decatur (G-5257)		

OFFICE SPLYS, NEC, WHOLESALE

Copy Plus LLC	F	956 668-7587
McAllen (G-14851)		
Hill Country Publishing Co	F	512 556-6262
Lampasas (G-13834)		
Hill County Press Inc	F	254 582-3431
Hillsboro (G-8327)		
Katy Printers Inc	G	281 391-7072
Katy (G-13367)		
Northern & Nye Printing Inc	F	254 662-2292
Waco (G-20438)		
OKelley Office Supply Inc	F	325 673-6422
Abilene (G-61)		
Pencil Cup Office Products Inc	F	915 838-0026
El Paso (G-5907)		
Reynolds Brothers Ltd	E	432 682-7393
Midland (G-15383)		

OFFICES & CLINICS OF DOCTORS OF
MEDICINE: Ophthalmologist

Rush Eye Associates Pllc	E	806 353-0125
Amarillo (G-460)		
South Texas Eye Cons Pllc	E	361 992-9400
Corpus Christi (G-3623)		

OFFICES & CLINICS OF DOCTORS OF
MEDICINE: Radiologist

Radiology Associates N Texas	E	817 321-0300
Fort Worth (G-6937)		

OFFICES & CLINICS OF DOCTORS,
MEDICINE: Gen & Fam Practice

Bay Area Anesthesia Associates	F	361 857-8588
Corpus Christi (G-3482)		

OFFICES & CLINICS OF DRS OF MEDICINE:
Physician, Orthopedic

Compass Orthopedic Tech & Pdts	F	713 995-7010
Houston (G-9257)		

OFFICES & CLINICS OF DRS, MED:
Specialized Practitioners

Dreadnaught Industries	G	210 601-8149
Von Ormy (G-20347)		

OFFICES & CLINICS OF HEALTH
PRACTITIONERS: Nutrition

Bio Trust Nutrition LLC	E	800 766-5086
Dallas (G-4025)		

OFFICES & CLINICS OF HEALTH
PRACTITIONERS: Paramedic

Percomonline Incorporated	F	325 480-2617
Abilene (G-64)		

OFFICES & CLINICS OF HEALTH
PRACTITIONERS: Psychotherapist

Happymecom	F	972 503-4803
Plano (G-16883)		

OIL & GAS FIELD EQPT: Drill Rigs

Bersal Energy LLC	F	956 270-1155
McAllen (G-14841)		
Big Bee Drilling Inc	D	432 333-2932
Odessa (G-15933)		
Bill West Properties Inc	E	713 726-0151
Houston (G-8885)		
Challenger Eqp & TI Co Inc	E	281 351-4247
Tomball (G-19970)		
Charger Services LLC	E	432 218-7674
Midland (G-15158)		
Eagle Rock Manufacturing LLC	F	432 682-3030
Midland (G-15203)		
Rowan Companies LLC	C	713 621-7800
Houston (G-11676)		

OIL & GAS FIELD MACHINERY

A&W Energy Inc	F	817 704-7346
Fort Worth (G-6338)		
Adroit Fabrication Inc	F	432 288-0656
Midland (G-15105)		
Advance Fbrction Msurement LLC	E	713 468-9581
Houston (G-8482)		
Air Liquide America LP	F	409 720-4200
Port Neches (G-17157)		
Allied Equipment Inc	D	432 367-6000
Odessa (G-15912)		
Ameri-Fab LLC	D	817 458-4262
Weatherford (G-20575)		
American Block Company	C	800 572-9087
Houston (G-8588)		
American Jereh Intl Corp	E	432 288-2431
Houston (G-8599)		
Amerus Oilfield Solutions LLC	F	432 559-0843
Midland (G-15114)		
Axon Ep Inc	E	281 855-3200
Houston (G-8762)		
Baker Hghes Olfld Oprtions LLC	C	800 441-0535
Yorktown (G-20976)		
Baker Hughes A GE Company LLC	B	713 625-4200
Houston (G-8801)		
Baker Hughes Company	C	713 439-8600
Houston (G-8802)		
Baker Hughes Holdings LLC	C	713 439-8600
Houston (G-8806)		
Baker Hughes Holdings LLC	D	281 231-1000
Houston (G-8807)		
Baker Hughes Incorporated	D	817 838-0583
Fort Worth (G-6422)		
Baker Hughes Incorporated	D	956 781-9133
Pharr (G-16694)		
Baker Hughes Incorporated	D	432 264-9007
Big Spring (G-2071)		

Black Horse LLC	F	281 598-8100
Houston (G-8904)		
C & J Equipment Mfg Corp	E	830 569-1968
Pleasanton (G-17063)		
Cameron International Corp	D	432 362-2511
Odessa (G-15953)		
Cameron International Corp	F	713 939-2211
Houston (G-9063)		
Cameron International Corp	F	281 716-1000
Houston (G-9065)		
Cameron International Corp	B	281 901-3100
Houston (G-9073)		
Cameron International Corp	A	601 629-3300
Houston (G-9066)		
Cameron Solutions Inc	E	713 896-3600
Houston (G-9077)		
Challenger Process Systems Co	C	903 839-7291
Troup (G-20024)		
Chemtec Energy Services LLC	E	936 856-1704
Willis (G-20844)		
Chief Oilfield Tech LLC	F	432 614-4481
Midland (G-15164)		
Citation 2002 Inv Ltd Partnr	F	281 891-1000
Houston (G-9198)		
Consolidated Pressure Ctrl LLC	D	281 893-5900
Conroe (G-3285)		
Continental Laboratories Inc	E	713 460-0780
Houston (G-9285)		
Craig Godwin Inc	E	936 344-6548
New Waverly (G-15859)		
Crosby Group LLC	B	918 834-4611
Longview (G-14216)		
D C G Machine Inc	E	903 297-2053
White Oak (G-20713)		
Deep Down Inc	D	281 517-5000
Houston (G-9420)		
Derrick Corporation	E	281 590-3003
Houston (G-9440)		
Dimensional Cnc LLC	E	713 329-9711
Houston (G-9474)		
Djmw Investments LLC	E	281 821-0010
Houston (G-9486)		
Dx Oilfield Products LLC	E	713 863-1947
Houston (G-9541)		
Electro-Mechanical Inds Inc	E	281 894-1600
Houston (G-9592)		
Elmar Services Inc	D	713 983-9281
Houston (G-9606)		
Ernmex Interntational Inc	E	281 458-0152
Houston (G-9693)		
Excell 7 Machine Shop Inc	F	281 416-0001
Houston (G-8379)		
EZ Pipe Paddler Padding Mch	E	432 333-9587
Odessa (G-15996)		
Ferrell-Ross Roll Mfg Inc	D	806 364-9051
Hereford (G-8288)		
Flotek Industries Inc	F	325 347-0005
Mason (G-14814)		
Flow Process Technologies Inc	F	281 351-9427
Cypress (G-3790)		
Flowco Prod Solutions LLC	E	830 779-2163
La Vernia (G-13801)		
Flowco Prod Solutions LLC	F	281 528-6298
Houston (G-9810)		
Flowco Prod Solutions LLC	E	281 528-6298
Houston (G-9811)		
FMC Technologies Inc	E	281 260-2190
Houston (G-9821)		
FMC Technologies Inc	E	214 363-8000
Addison (G-124)		
FMC Technologies Inc	E	361 668-0886
Alice (G-214)		
FMC Technologies Inc	E	817 887-8063
Fort Worth (G-6639)		
FMC Technologies Inc	E	817 599-3337
Weatherford (G-20592)		
FMC Technologies Inc	F	281 405-7927
Houston (G-9827)		
Forum Energy Technologies Inc	C	940 612-5890
Houston (G-9841)		
Frank White	E	713 937-3800
Houston (G-9854)		
Freer Iron Works Inc	E	361 394-7273
Freer (G-7225)		
Fwm Tubular & Equipment Corp	E	281 806-7918
Cleveland (G-3126)		
Gardner Denver Inc	D	832 421-5469
Pasadena (G-16446)		
Gemstar Inc	E	432 362-2315
Odessa (G-16013)		

Company		Phone
Geodynamics Inc	C	817 341-5300
Millsap (G-15502)		
Gjr Meyer Service Inc	E	361 289-2130
Corpus Christi (G-3535)		
Globaltech Subsea Inc	F	713 504-0331
South Houston (G-19040)		
Gmu Downhole Tool Corporation	G	361 573-5100
Victoria (G-20268)		
Grant Prideco LP	C	281 878-8000
Houston (G-10018)		
Gulf Coast Downhole Tech LLC	F	713 667-4238
Houston (G-10059)		
Gulf Coast Oil & Gas Inds LLC	D	713 236-1158
Houston (G-10061)		
H & T Auger Company	E	432 362-4471
Odessa (G-16022)		
Halliburton Company	C	817 783-5111
Alvarado (G-333)		
Hartmanns Inc	F	325 695-7641
Abilene (G-46)		
HMC Instrmentation Contrls LLC	C	832 252-9280
Cypress (G-3799)		
HMC Instrument & Mch Works Ltd	E	713 468-1426
Houston (G-10189)		
Honghua America LLC	E	832 448-8100
Houston (G-10203)		
Hunt Engine Incorporated	D	713 721-9400
Houston (G-10279)		
Hutchison Hayes Separation Inc	C	713 455-9600
Houston (G-10291)		
Hydril Company	A	713 670-3500
Houston (G-10298)		
Hydril USA Distribution LLC	B	281 449-2000
Houston (G-10300)		
Hydril USA Distribution LLC	F	832 295-5557
Houston (G-10301)		
Hydril USA Distribution LLC	D	713 670-3500
Houston (G-10302)		
Ict Energy Solutions LLC	D	432 203-0576
Midland (G-15250)		
Innova Intgrated Solutions Inc	F	713 937-9999
Houston (G-10369)		
Interstate Gas Treating Inc	E	432 362-9291
Odessa (G-16032)		
Interstate Treating Inc	E	432 362-9291
Odessa (G-16033)		
J-Hobbs Machine Corporation	E	432 563-1526
Odessa (G-16036)		
J-W Energy Company	D	972 233-8191
Addison (G-137)		
Karis Resources LLC	E	903 595-0900
Tyler (G-20106)		
Kirks Machine Works	G	432 368-5333
Odessa (G-16053)		
Kw International LLC	C	713 468-9581
Houston (G-10572)		
L J Machine Works Inc	E	713 928-5786
Houston (G-10573)		
Larkin Products Inc	E	972 937-3640
Waxahachie (G-20549)		
Legacy Automtn Pwr Design Inc	F	281 888-5402
Houston (G-10620)		
Liberty Lift Solutions LLC	E	713 575-2300
Houston (G-10633)		
Loadcraft Industries Ltd	C	325 646-7581
Brownwood (G-2438)		
Longwood Elastomers Inc	C	979 830-1111
Brenham (G-2261)		
Ls Energy Fabrication LLC	D	281 573-9500
Houston (G-8387)		
Lubri Tech Products	E	214 870-4070
Midland (G-15288)		
M B & G Oilfld Fabrication Inc	F	903 593-0400
Tyler (G-20116)		
M P Industries Inc	E	903 561-4232
Tyler (G-20118)		
Martin-Decker Totco Inc	B	512 340-5000
Cedar Park (G-2978)		
Midland Wellhead Inc	E	432 682-0856
Midland (G-15303)		
Mitchell Manufacturing Inc	E	281 351-9641
Tomball (G-19989)		
National Oilwell Varco Inc	E	832 424-6000
Houston (G-10980)		
National Oilwell Varco Inc	E	210 572-4012
San Antonio (G-18333)		
National Oilwell Varco Inc	E	713 237-3766
Sugar Land (G-19510)		
National Oilwell Varco Inc	E	432 563-1173
Odessa (G-16091)		

Company		Phone
National Oilwell Varco Inc	E	281 820-5400
Houston (G-10982)		
National Oilwell Varco Inc	E	281 854-0537
Houston (G-10983)		
National Oilwell Varco Inc	D	512 340-5000
Cedar Park (G-2980)		
National Oilwell Varco Inc	E	936 856-9180
Conroe (G-3334)		
National Oilwell Varco Inc	E	281 943-5948
Houston (G-10984)		
National Oilwell Varco Inc	D	281 599-4700
Houston (G-10987)		
National Oilwell Varco Inc	C	936 777-6100
Conroe (G-3336)		
National Oilwell Varco Inc	C	713 468-7328
Houston (G-10993)		
National Oilwell Varco Inc	E	936 873-2600
Anderson (G-530)		
National Oilwell Varco Inc	E	832 575-2000
Conroe (G-3337)		
National Oilwell Varco Inc	E	432 683-6696
Midland (G-15310)		
National Oilwell Varco Inc	F	432 381-4111
Odessa (G-16090)		
National Oilwell Varco Inc	F	713 395-5000
Houston (G-10990)		
National Oilwell Varco Inc	E	361 576-3161
Victoria (G-20287)		
National Oilwell Varco LP	D	806 274-5293
Borger (G-2180)		
New Railhead Manufacturing LLC	F	817 594-6663
Weatherford (G-20606)		
Now Inc	E	281 823-4700
Houston (G-11091)		
Nustar Gp LLC	A	210 370-2000
San Antonio (G-18353)		
Odessa Separator Inc	E	432 580-7111
Odessa (G-16097)		
Osies Inc	E	713 849-5131
Houston (G-11197)		
Pan American Industries Inc	G	281 572-4842
Porter (G-17180)		
Petron Industries Inc	D	713 693-8700
Houston (G-11310)		
Petronash Americas LLC	E	281 566-6600
Sugar Land (G-19526)		
Premium Valve Services LLC	F	281 457-2565
Houston (G-11406)		
Procegas LLC	E	832 652-2129
Houston (G-11430)		
Propell American LLC	D	817 573-3550
Granbury (G-7806)		
Protek Specialty Company	F	713 667-6691
Houston (G-11464)		
Psp Industries Inc	E	210 651-9595
Schertz (G-18760)		
Ram International Inc	E	361 688-1966
Corpus Christi (G-3605)		
Razor Specialties LLC	G	888 578-9656
San Antonio (G-18411)		
Reactive Downhole Tls USA Inc	E	281 821-6566
Humble (G-12796)		
Red Rock Oilfield Service LLC	F	325 933-0224
Colorado City (G-3226)		
Reynolds Lift Technologies LLC	F	866 629-6298
Missouri City (G-15589)		
Robbins & Myers Inc	E	936 890-1064
Willis (G-20861)		
Robbins Myers Enrgy Systems LP	B	936 890-1064
Willis (G-20862)		
Rt Precision Machinery LP	E	281 354-0910
Kingwood (G-13653)		
Safoco Inc	E	713 956-5936
Houston (G-11728)		
Schlumberger International	A	713 747-4000
Houston (G-11766)		
Schlumberger Technology Corp	E	713 747-1040
Houston (G-11776)		
Schlumberger Technology Corp	C	281 285-8500
Houston (G-11780)		
Schlumberger Technology Corp	A	281 285-8500
Sugar Land (G-19542)		
Schlumberger Technology Corp	C	281 285-8500
Sugar Land (G-19549)		
Scorpion Oiltools Inc	E	281 999-2222
Houston (G-11789)		
Sensia LLC	E	866 773-6742
Houston (G-11831)		
Serimax North America LLC	D	832 230-2700
Houston (G-11836)		

Company		Phone
Smith International Inc	A	281 443-3370
Houston (G-11923)		
Spectrum Batteries Inc	E	281 533-9735
Fulshear (G-7331)		
SPM Flow Control Inc	C	817 246-2461
Fort Worth (G-7013)		
SPM Flow Control Inc	C	903 984-8153
Kilgore (G-13592)		
SPM Flow Control Inc	C	432 580-3887
Odessa (G-16162)		
SPM Flow Control Inc	C	817 246-2461
Deer Park (G-5297)		
SPM Flow Control Inc	C	281 820-7807
Houston (G-12021)		
Steeltex Fabricators LLC	E	817 225-0973
Venus (G-20223)		
Stewart & Stevenson LLC	D	713 751-2700
Houston (G-12062)		
Stewart Stevenson Pwr Pdts LLC	C	713 751-2600
Houston (G-12065)		
Streamline Supply Inc	F	713 914-0330
Houston (G-12078)		
Summit Casing Services LLC	F	877 860-0969
Fort Worth (G-7022)		
Summit Energy Equipment	F	903 951-1217
Sulphur Springs (G-19600)		
Superior Energy Services Inc	D	713 654-2200
Houston (G-12112)		
Surf Subsea Inc	E	281 305-4411
Montgomery (G-15643)		
Syrgis Holdings Inc	G	361 438-1139
Kerrville (G-13527)		
Tam International Inc	C	713 462-7617
Houston (G-12155)		
Tam International Inc	F	713 462-7617
Houston (G-12156)		
Tcm Investments Inc	E	432 366-5433
Odessa (G-16173)		
Tex Webb LLC	F	214 770-7073
Dallas (G-5052)		
Tommy Chappell LLC	F	432 967-2469
Odessa (G-16180)		
Triangle Pump Components Inc	F	817 202-8530
Cleburne (G-3115)		
Trx Industries Inc	F	254 694-6256
Whitney (G-20733)		
Tryer Process Equipment Ltd	E	940 432-0130
Wichita Falls (G-20822)		
Turn-Tex Machine & Tool Inc	F	903 759-0989
Longview (G-14325)		
TW Tanks and Construction Co	F	361 358-8869
Beeville (G-1989)		
U S Weatherford L P	F	281 443-5627
Houston (G-12423)		
U S Weatherford L P	E	432 561-8892
Midland (G-15452)		
U S Weatherford L P	F	817 293-5192
Fort Worth (G-7091)		
U S Weatherford L P	C	281 348-1090
Kingwood (G-13656)		
U S Weatherford L P	E	817 249-7200
Benbrook (G-2047)		
United Service Alliance Inc	E	409 935-9500
Texas City (G-19805)		
USA Petroleum Equipment Sup Co	F	281 893-2471
Houston (G-12497)		
Vallourec Tube-Alloy LLC	C	713 462-7613
Houston (G-12523)		
Vfuels LLC	F	713 456-3443
Houston (G-12561)		
Victor Nicolle Inc	F	713 896-4911
Houston (G-12566)		
Vinson Process Controls Co LP	D	972 459-8200
Lewisville (G-14106)		
Warfab Oilfield Services Inc	E	903 295-1011
Longview (G-14331)		
Watson Grinding and Mfg Co	D	713 466-3053
Houston (G-12605)		
Weatherford International Inc	E	361 693-6800
Corpus Christi (G-3653)		
Welker Inc	D	281 491-2331
Sugar Land (G-19571)		
Wildkat Precision LLC	F	936 890-9572
Willis (G-20869)		
Windy Cove Energy LLC	F	281 402-1880
Houston (G-12678)		
Wipco Acquisition LLC	F	936 327-8250
Livingston (G-14164)		

OIL ABSORPTION Eqpt

U S Machine Shop Inc ....F 940 495-3964
Electra *(G-6050)*

OIL FIELD MACHINERY & EQPT

A Varco Shaffer Co ....D 713 937-5500
Houston *(G-8429)*

Abco Products Inc ....E 713 871-8020
Houston *(G-8447)*

Advanced Indicators and Mfg ....F 713 932-6464
Houston *(G-8488)*

Aker Solutions Inc ....C 713 685-5700
Houston *(G-8519)*

Allendale Machine Co Inc ....F 713 477-8776
Houston *(G-8543)*

Allendale Machine Co Inc ....F 713 477-8776
Houston *(G-8544)*

Andrews Safety Anchors Inc ....F 432 524-6659
Andrews *(G-535)*

Apergy Artfl Lift Intl LLC ....D 713 466-3552
Houston *(G-8662)*

Apergy Artfl Lift Intl LLC ....E 281 403-5742
Spring *(G-19195)*

Axon Pressure Products Inc ....D 281 855-3200
Houston *(G-8763)*

Axon Pressure Products Inc ....F 713 478-8007
Houston *(G-8764)*

BC Oilfield Services Inc ....F 361 573-6354
Victoria *(G-20245)*

Bellville Tube Company ....E 281 467-7177
Bellville *(G-2008)*

Bestway Oilfield Inc ....E 281 452-2525
Channelview *(G-3013)*

Beta Arkansas LLC ....F 972 490-2340
Dallas *(G-4022)*

Beta Engineering Inc ....F 817 265-3367
Arlington *(G-631)*

Big Red Engineering LLC ....F 817 539-9560
Fort Worth *(G-6450)*

Bkg Machine & Fabrication Inc ....F 361 575-9592
Victoria *(G-20247)*

Bronco Manufacturing LLC ....E 918 446-7196
Houston *(G-8993)*

Brumley Manufacturing Inc ....D 979 826-4222
Hempstead *(G-8250)*

Calvary Steel Mfg LLC ....F 936 494-5775
Conroe *(G-3272)*

Cameron International Corp ....E 713 571-3100
Waller *(G-20495)*

Cameron International Corp ....D 713 849-7789
Houston *(G-9062)*

Cameron International Corp ....D 281 582-9500
Houston *(G-9064)*

Cameron International Corp ....E 713 939-2282
Houston *(G-9072)*

Cameron International Corp ....C 713 354-1900
Houston *(G-9068)*

Catec Americas Inc ....F 281 398-8806
Houston *(G-9099)*

Cee-San Mch & Fabrication Co ....F 713 466-4586
Houston *(G-9118)*

Church Energy Services Ltd ....E 281 931-1400
Houston *(G-9187)*

Conslidated Rigworks LP ....E 817 446-5272
Fort Worth *(G-6543)*

Control Flow Inc ....C 281 890-8300
Houston *(G-9295)*

CTW Brake Rims Inc ....F 806 665-0289
Pampa *(G-16321)*

Custom Components Incorporated ....F 281 485-2200
Pearland *(G-16551)*

Detail Design Inc ....E 281 890-4715
Houston *(G-9444)*

Dow Machinery Corporation ....E 832 467-0600
Houston *(G-9507)*

Dragon Esp Ltd ....F 409 833-2665
Beaumont *(G-1885)*

Dreco Inc ....B 281 452-7900
Houston *(G-9516)*

Dril-Quip Inc ....A 713 939-7711
Houston *(G-9525)*

Dudley J Perio Inc ....E 512 295-4234
Buda *(G-2528)*

Duoline Technologies LLC ....E 903 734-1371
Gilmer *(G-7706)*

Duron Systems Inc ....C 281 469-0040
Houston *(G-9539)*

Eagle Pco LLC ....F 432 400-2771
Midland *(G-15202)*

Eagle Pco LLC ....F 361 756-0666
Pleasanton *(G-17065)*

Eagle Pco LLC ....D 817 678-8998
Navasota *(G-15731)*

Eckel Manufacturing Co Inc ....D 432 362-4336
Odessa *(G-15985)*

Electronic Data Devices Co ....E 432 366-8699
Odessa *(G-15987)*

Eml Manufacturing Llc ....E 281 880-7517
Houston *(G-9617)*

Enerflow Industries Inc ....D 918 355-6300
Anderson *(G-529)*

Engineered Cstm Solutions LLC ....F 832 598-2083
Houston *(G-9646)*

Envirocal Inc ....F 832 296-4205
Houston *(G-9667)*

Faith Manufacturing Co Inc ....C 281 441-9595
Humble *(G-12766)*

Falconview Energy Products LLC ....F 832 665-2850
Houston *(G-9759)*

Fd-Thru Power Systems Cnnctors ....E 281 476-9100
Deer Park *(G-5273)*

Fifo Technologies Inc ....F 817 991-1388
Fort Worth *(G-6630)*

Fishing Tool/Crystin Inc ....E 432 366-6504
Odessa *(G-16002)*

Flexitallic Group Inc ....E 281 604-2525
Houston *(G-9799)*

FMC Technologies Inc ....E 254 968-2181
Stephenville *(G-19413)*

FMC Technologies Inc ....E 281 591-4000
Houston *(G-9820)*

FMC Technologies Inc ....E 281 591-4000
Kilgore *(G-13554)*

FMC Technologies Inc ....E 254 968-2181
Stephenville *(G-19414)*

FMC Technologies Inc ....F 432 561-8063
Odessa *(G-16006)*

FMC Technologies Inc ....F 432 563-0335
Odessa *(G-16007)*

FMC Technologies Inc ....F 281 821-2355
Houston *(G-9822)*

FMC Technologies Inc ....E 361 290-9795
San Antonio *(G-18119)*

FMC Technologies Inc ....E 281 591-4000
Houston *(G-9824)*

FMC Technologies Inc ....G 281 569-6194
Houston *(G-9825)*

FMC Technologies Inc ....F 254 968-2181
Stephenville *(G-19415)*

FMC Technologies Inc ....F 281 260-2121
Houston *(G-9826)*

Force Pressure Control LLC ....C 361 210-9650
Marion *(G-14756)*

Forum Energy Technologies Inc ....D 713 329-8730
Houston *(G-9842)*

Forum Energy Technologies Inc ....D 361 664-6024
Robstown *(G-17512)*

Forum Energy Technologies Inc ....C 281 949-2500
Houston *(G-9843)*

FSI Holdings LLC ....E 832 467-9898
Houston *(G-9872)*

Full Circle Enterprises Inc ....E 936 441-0101
Spring *(G-19212)*

Fullco Machine Works ....F 432 563-3443
Odessa *(G-16009)*

G B Industry Co LP ....F 281 996-0020
Pearland *(G-16562)*

Gardner Denver Inc ....E 817 248-4500
Benbrook *(G-2040)*

Garzo Inc ....F 936 931-5631
Waller *(G-20499)*

Green Equipment Co Inc ....F 817 589-2704
Fort Worth *(G-6676)*

H C Howell Company ....F 432 368-0835
Odessa *(G-16023)*

Harbison-Fischer Inc ....B 817 297-2211
Crowley *(G-3755)*

Harbison-Fischer Inc ....F 432 580-3592
Odessa *(G-16026)*

Harrison Mullane Inc ....C 281 449-4846
Houston *(G-10128)*

Heshka Oil LLC ....G 936 760-3453
Conroe *(G-3303)*

Hunting Titan Inc ....D 972 493-2580
Milford *(G-15500)*

Hydralift Amclyde Inc ....D 713 375-3700
Houston *(G-10295)*

Hydraulic Pwr Technology-Texas ....E 512 295-4234
Buda *(G-2530)*

Industrial Olfld Mar Cmpnnts I ....F 713 266-1900
Tomball *(G-19985)*

Integrated Drive Systems L L C ....E 713 462-1400
Houston *(G-10384)*

International Chemical Technol ....F 432 339-9361
Odessa *(G-16031)*

Jt Oilfiled Manufacturing Co ....F 713 947-7006
Houston *(G-10489)*

Jt Oilfiled Manufacturing Co ....E 713 947-7006
Friendswood *(G-7247)*

Kelley Instrument Machine Inc ....E 903 832-3332
Texarkana *(G-19767)*

Keystone Synergy LLC ....D 817 636-3300
Rhome *(G-17256)*

Lamot Corporation ....D 816 792-1500
Stafford *(G-19344)*

Lancaster Flow Automation LLC ....F 832 237-9444
Houston *(G-10591)*

Lincoln Manufacturing Inc ....C 713 514-0059
Houston *(G-10644)*

Lincoln Manufacturing Inc ....B 281 252-9494
Magnolia *(G-14615)*

Loadcraft Industries Ltd ....C 325 597-2911
Brady *(G-2214)*

Louis Hill Kennon Inc ....E 713 926-2623
Houston *(G-10689)*

Markco Machine Works Inc ....E 432 362-8921
Odessa *(G-16070)*

McKay Equipment Co ....F 432 381-5510
Krum *(G-13674)*

Melco Blowout Preventer Spc ....G 432 362-0491
Odessa *(G-16080)*

Merritt Prfrred Components Inc ....D 903 983-1592
Kilgore *(G-13574)*

Monmouth Real Estate Inv Corp ....C 281 784-4360
Houston *(G-10911)*

Nabors Industries Inc ....C 281 874-0035
Houston *(G-10953)*

National Oilwell Dht LP ....D 713 346-7500
Houston *(G-10971)*

National Oilwell Varco Inc ....E 830 693-5312
Marble Falls *(G-14748)*

National Oilwell Varco Inc ....F 817 985-5000
Fort Worth *(G-6861)*

National Oilwell Varco Inc ....E 281 351-2222
Tomball *(G-19991)*

National Oilwell Varco Inc ....E 713 935-8170
Houston *(G-10975)*

National Oilwell Varco Inc ....F 903 984-2553
Kilgore *(G-13577)*

National Oilwell Varco Inc ....E 713 634-3327
Houston *(G-10978)*

National Oilwell Varco Inc ....E 713 237-9793
Houston *(G-10981)*

National Oilwell Varco Inc ....D 713 849-8011
Houston *(G-10986)*

National Oilwell Varco Inc ....E 281 878-8000
Houston *(G-10992)*

National Oilwell Varco Inc ....F 281 854-0300
Houston *(G-10976)*

National Oilwell Varco LP ....D 936 825-2211
Navasota *(G-15740)*

National Oilwell Varco LP ....F 817 203-8302
Willis *(G-20856)*

National Oilwell Varco LP ....D 281 586-2046
Houston *(G-10995)*

National Oilwell Varco LP ....D 713 346-7500
Houston *(G-10996)*

National Oilwell Varco LP ....D 713 375-3700
Houston *(G-10997)*

National Oilwell Varco LP ....D 281 599-4700
Houston *(G-10998)*

National Oilwell Varco LP ....F 713 849-6121
Houston *(G-10999)*

National Oilwell Varco LP ....B 713 375-3700
Houston *(G-11000)*

National Oilwell Varco LP ....F 936 756-4800
Conroe *(G-3340)*

New Tech Systems Inc ....E 817 779-6262
Mansfield *(G-14697)*

Nu Energy Services LP ....F 817 832-0724
Aledo *(G-200)*

O & C Equipment Inc ....F 281 232-4686
Rosenberg *(G-17591)*

Oceaneering Reflange ....E 713 682-5105
Houston *(G-11129)*

Octg Material Hdlg Systems Inc ....F 432 687-5420
Midland *(G-15325)*

ODrill/Mcm Inc ....E 832 782-6300
Houston *(G-11132)*

PRODUCT

OEM Components Inc..........D....... 281 449-6258
Houston ***(G-11138)***
Ofi Testing Equipment Inc..........D....... 713 880-9885
Houston ***(G-11145)***
Ofs International LLC..........B....... 281 452-3036
Houston ***(G-11148)***
Oil Country Manufacturing Inc..........E....... 432 563-8014
Odessa ***(G-16099)***
Oil States Energy Services LLC..........F....... 361 384-0041
Orange Grove ***(G-16269)***
Oil States Energy Services LLC..........F....... 903 986-3791
Kilgore ***(G-13580)***
Oil States Energy Services LLC..........E....... 713 425-2400
Houston ***(G-11154)***
Oil States Energy Services LLC..........E....... 432 563-1304
Midland ***(G-15326)***
Oil States Energy Services LLC..........E....... 903 526-4777
Tyler ***(G-20135)***
Onesubsea LLC..........A....... 713 939-2282
Houston ***(G-11182)***
Orbix Corporation..........E....... 254 675-8651
Clifton ***(G-3145)***
Parco Double-E LLC..........D....... 214 631-2290
Dallas ***(G-4788)***
Pbp Fabrication Inc..........E....... 432 381-5542
Odessa ***(G-16107)***
Pelican Energy Partners LP..........D....... 713 559-7110
Houston ***(G-11271)***
Petroleum Products & Svcs Inc..........F....... 281 448-1000
Tomball ***(G-19997)***
Petrotrim Services LLC..........E....... 281 821-2111
Humble ***(G-12793)***
Precision Energy Services Inc..........D....... 281 892-0600
Houston ***(G-11392)***
Precision Energy Services Inc..........C....... 713 693-4000
Houston ***(G-11393)***
Quali-Tex Ball & Seat Co..........E....... 432 332-3755
Odessa ***(G-16128)***
Quality Manufacturing Inc..........F....... 940 592-5790
Iowa Park ***(G-12908)***
R & D Advantage Inc..........D....... 713 836-4000
Houston ***(G-11519)***
Rae Energy Solutions Inc..........G....... 281 440-3434
Houston ***(G-11533)***
Rama Fabrication Inc..........E....... 432 362-9291
Odessa ***(G-16132)***
Rockwell Precision Inc..........F....... 281 890-9331
Houston ***(G-11653)***
Rti Energy Systems Inc..........E....... 281 379-4289
Spring ***(G-19163)***
Rush Sales Company..........C....... 432 337-2397
Odessa ***(G-16145)***
Schlumberger Norge As..........F....... 281 227-9854
Houston ***(G-11769)***
Seaboard Holdings Inc..........E....... 713 644-3535
Houston ***(G-11797)***
Seaboard International Inc..........D....... 713 644-3535
Houston ***(G-11798)***
Serva Corporation..........F....... 940 761-3361
Wichita Falls ***(G-20808)***
Sharewell LP..........E....... 281 288-2560
Houston ***(G-11845)***
Shell Machine Works Inc..........E....... 361 883-7073
Corpus Christi ***(G-3622)***
Sivalls Inc..........E....... 325 643-3621
Brownwood ***(G-2445)***
SMI Manufacturing Inc..........D....... 281 449-0345
Houston ***(G-11921)***
Snelson Oilfield Ltg Co Inc..........E....... 817 926-0571
Fort Worth ***(G-6998)***
Sonic Surveys Ltd..........F....... 281 385-6500
Baytown ***(G-1802)***
Spectra Engineering Inc..........E....... 432 367-8413
Odessa ***(G-16160)***
Speedorange Inc..........F....... 281 448-5900
Pasadena ***(G-16510)***
Standard Machine Works Inc..........F....... 713 673-1111
Pasadena ***(G-16512)***
Stream-Flo USA LLC..........E....... 903 753-6785
Longview ***(G-14313)***
Stream-Flo USA LLC..........E....... 361 362-2600
Beeville ***(G-1988)***
Stream-Flo USA LLC..........F....... 903 983-2992
Kilgore ***(G-13595)***
Stream-Flo USA LLC..........D....... 903 912-1022
Houston ***(G-12076)***
Stuckey Terry & Associates..........E....... 281 590-8628
Houston ***(G-12083)***
Subsea Services Intl Inc..........D....... 281 578-6523
Katy ***(G-13446)***
Supply Chain Solutions Ltd..........F....... 281 288-0658
Spring ***(G-19169)***
Synergy Industries LP..........D....... 817 295-1161
Burleson ***(G-2597)***
Taylors Oilfield Mfg Inc..........E....... 281 442-4084
Houston ***(G-12168)***
TE&s Limited..........D....... 817 573-3550
Granbury ***(G-7811)***
Team Oil Tools LLC..........E....... 918 461-8104
Houston ***(G-12172)***
Texas Couplings..........F....... 281 350-2494
Spring ***(G-19177)***
Texas Fabco Solutions Inc..........F....... 979 255-3530
Round Mountain ***(G-17619)***
Texokan Operating Inc..........F....... 214 484-2322
Dallas ***(G-5080)***
Tiw Corporation..........C....... 713 939-7711
Houston ***(G-12303)***
Tiw International Inc..........F....... 713 729-2110
Houston ***(G-12304)***
Top-Co Cementing Products Inc..........C....... 832 300-3660
Houston ***(G-12321)***
Total Oilfield Eqp & Sup LLC..........E....... 361 442-2922
Robstown ***(G-17518)***
Townsend International Inc..........F....... 432 381-8750
Odessa ***(G-16181)***
Trelleborg Offshore Us Inc..........B....... 281 774-2600
Houston ***(G-12360)***
Tri-Max Corporation..........E....... 713 937-8808
Houston ***(G-12363)***
Tribocor Technologies Inc..........F....... 281 277-7200
Stafford ***(G-19388)***
Turbo Drill Industries Inc..........D....... 936 756-3210
Conroe ***(G-3375)***
U S Weatherford L P..........E....... 361 668-8362
Elmendorf ***(G-6073)***
V & V Industries Inc..........F....... 713 224-1751
Houston ***(G-12509)***
Valiant Artfl Lift Sltions LLC..........F....... 432 253-2233
Midland ***(G-15460)***
Varco Shaffer Inc..........A....... 713 937-5000
Houston ***(G-12536)***
Vetco Gray LLC..........A....... 281 445-8968
Houston ***(G-12557)***
Vetco Gray LLC..........E....... 281 448-4410
Houston ***(G-12558)***
Vita International Inc..........E....... 281 591-1300
Houston ***(G-12575)***
Voyager Energy Services LLC..........F....... 830 583-9590
Kenedy ***(G-13493)***
Wayne Wilk..........E....... 570 326-1164
Houston ***(G-12608)***
Weatherford International LLC..........E....... 361 815-2104
Alice ***(G-246)***
Weatherford International LLC..........E....... 210 621-2156
Elmendorf ***(G-6075)***
Wellflex Enrgy Prtners Fort Wr..........E....... 817 730-5111
Rhome ***(G-17264)***
Westfield Engrg & Svcs Inc..........E....... 281 438-2047
Houston ***(G-8397)***
Worldwide Oilfield Machine Inc..........C....... 713 729-9200
Houston ***(G-12694)***
Worldwide Oilfield Machine Inc..........D....... 713 721-5200
Houston ***(G-12695)***
Worldwide Oilfield Machine Inc..........E....... 713 937-0795
Houston ***(G-12696)***
Wwl Industries Inc..........E....... 432 362-0326
Odessa ***(G-16215)***

OIL FIELD SVCS, NEC

212 Resources LLC..........D....... 303 892-5616
Houston ***(G-8404)***
3 Amorez LLC..........F....... 432 269-4199
Midland ***(G-15099)***
365 Certified Logistics LLC..........F....... 512 743-9304
Pflugerville ***(G-16655)***
4l Oilfield Services LLC..........E....... 830 879-5300
Cotulla ***(G-3689)***
5l Energy Services LLC..........F....... 936 539-1232
Conroe ***(G-3251)***
A & M Tubular Maintenance Inc..........E....... 903 983-1007
Kilgore ***(G-13529)***
A & R Energy Services Corp..........F....... 254 732-7759
Waco ***(G-20353)***
A&E Oilfield Services LLC..........D....... 956 380-5098
Mission ***(G-15547)***
Ace Energy Solutions Inc..........F....... 281 394-9989
Katy ***(G-13347)***
Acid and Cementing Svcs Inc..........E....... 903 729-2500
Palestine ***(G-16294)***
Adobe Oilfield Ltd..........G....... 432 337-3731
Odessa ***(G-15902)***
Advanced Cementing Svcs Inc..........F....... 979 921-0356
Hempstead ***(G-8248)***
Affirm Oilfield Services LLC..........A....... 817 644-3360
Fort Worth ***(G-6354)***
Afi Unlimited LLC..........E....... 936 591-9300
Shelbyville ***(G-18894)***
Aguilar Oilfield Services..........E....... 432 230-2548
Odessa ***(G-15904)***
Airtrust Intl Systems Corp..........F....... 713 491-4455
Texas City ***(G-19785)***
Alert Control Technologies LLC..........G....... 281 288-1321
Tomball ***(G-19955)***
Allamon Tool Company Inc..........E....... 936 449-5433
Montgomery ***(G-15625)***
Alliance Field Services LLC..........D....... 432 332-4308
Midland ***(G-15113)***
Allied Ofs LLC..........F....... 832 482-3730
Tomball ***(G-19956)***
Allied Oil Field Mch Pump LLC..........D....... 806 894-7263
Levelland ***(G-14003)***
Allied Wireline Services LLC..........F....... 713 343-7280
Houston ***(G-8555)***
Amerig Solutions LLC..........F....... 713 960-6606
Houston ***(G-8617)***
Ana-Log Inc..........E....... 903 597-6341
Tyler ***(G-20046)***
Anadrill Directional Svcs Inc..........F....... 281 745-6983
Houston ***(G-8634)***
Analytic Stress Relieving Inc..........D....... 281 471-9600
La Porte ***(G-13724)***
Apache Packers LLC..........E....... 432 758-6202
Seminole ***(G-18880)***
Apergy Artfl Lift Intl LLC..........E....... 903 266-3552
Tyler ***(G-20047)***
Apollo Perforators Inc..........E....... 432 563-0891
Odessa ***(G-15917)***
Archer Prod Cmpletion Svcs LLC..........E....... 281 951-4038
Houston ***(G-8681)***
Arctic Pipe Insptn Inc Texas..........D....... 281 456-8300
Houston ***(G-8686)***
Arguijo Oilfield Services Inc..........E....... 432 550-5650
Odessa ***(G-15918)***
Array Coating Technology LLC..........E....... 936 321-7000
Houston ***(G-8703)***
Artesia Ecoscience LLC..........F....... 281 978-2521
Houston ***(G-8710)***
Asher Oil Field Specialty..........F....... 361 293-0562
Yoakum ***(G-20959)***
Asphwax Inc..........G....... 281 568-8415
Stafford ***(G-19288)***
Atk Oilfield Trnsp USA Inc..........D....... 432 452-3550
Odessa ***(G-15920)***
Atx Oil and More LLC..........E....... 512 660-0696
Austin ***(G-947)***
Auto Dril Inc..........F....... 432 561-8455
Midland ***(G-15125)***
Axiom Technologies LLC..........E....... 281 931-0907
Houston ***(G-8760)***
Axis Well Services LLC..........D....... 432 333-1111
Odessa ***(G-15921)***
Azar Services LLC..........F....... 956 717-0023
Laredo ***(G-13864)***
B & D Services Inc..........E....... 979 733-9938
Sheridan ***(G-18903)***
B & J Vacuum Tank Service Inc..........G....... 936 536-6148
Daisetta ***(G-3832)***
B&C Texas Leasing LLC..........D....... 432 362-0548
Pecos ***(G-16616)***
B-P Supply Inc..........E....... 806 872-9169
Lamesa ***(G-13823)***
Baker Hghes Olfld Oprtions Inc..........F....... 806 665-5786
Pampa ***(G-16315)***
Baker Hghes Olfld Oprtions LLC..........E....... 432 685-8900
Midland ***(G-15128)***
Baker Hghes Olfld Oprtions LLC..........F....... 281 456-5300
Houston ***(G-8792)***
Baker Hghes Olfld Oprtions LLC..........F....... 713 879-3760
Houston ***(G-8793)***
Baker Hghes Olfld Oprtions LLC..........E....... 940 626-4169
Tyler ***(G-20057)***
Baker Hghes Olfld Oprtions LLC..........C....... 713 923-9351
Houston ***(G-8794)***
Baker Hghes Olfld Oprtions LLC..........E....... 432 694-7761
Midland ***(G-15129)***
Baker Hghes Olfld Oprtions LLC..........E....... 361 573-2493
Victoria ***(G-20242)***
Baker Hghes Olfld Oprtions LLC..........E....... 432 694-9517
Midland ***(G-15130)***

Baker Hghes Olfld Oprtions LLC ...... D ...... 361 692-3000 Pleasanton *(G-17062)*	Basic Energy Services Inc ...... E ...... 918 225-1111 Fort Worth *(G-6431)*	Blaxtone Energy LLC ...... F ...... 432 250-9039 Odessa *(G-15938)*
Baker Hghes Olfld Oprtions LLC ...... E ...... 210 662-5650 San Antonio *(G-17935)*	Basic Energy Services Inc ...... F ...... 432 523-4251 Andrews *(G-537)*	Bless Oilfield Services Inc ...... E ...... 281 227-3300 Houston *(G-8915)*
Baker Hghes Olfld Oprtions LLC ...... D ...... 713 466-1322 Houston *(G-8795)*	Basic Energy Services Inc ...... E ...... 432 445-2216 Pecos *(G-16618)*	Blsr Operating Ltd ...... E ...... 281 369-2032 Sandy Point *(G-18722)*
Baker Hghes Olfld Oprtions LLC ...... D ...... 972 466-2673 Carrollton *(G-2701)*	Basic Energy Services Inc ...... E ...... 432 620-5500 Midland *(G-15134)*	Blue Quail Energy Services LLC ...... E ...... 432 684-0999 Midland *(G-15143)*
Baker Hghes Olfld Oprtions LLC ...... E ...... 432 563-1900 Odessa *(G-15922)*	Basic Energy Services Inc ...... F ...... 940 683-5484 Bridgeport *(G-2288)*	BOF Services Inc ...... E ...... 806 741-1080 Lubbock *(G-14377)*
Baker Hghes Olfld Oprtions LLC ...... E ...... 832 519-2000 Houston *(G-8797)*	Basic Energy Services Inc ...... C ...... 432 586-2586 Kermit *(G-13508)*	BOF Services Inc ...... D ...... 432 523-2110 Andrews *(G-540)*
Baker Hghes Olfld Oprtions LLC ...... E ...... 817 806-3200 Fort Worth *(G-6421)*	Basic Energy Services Inc ...... E ...... 979 733-0488 El Campo *(G-5612)*	BOF Services Inc ...... E ...... 325 653-1755 San Angelo *(G-17783)*
Baker Hghes Olfld Oprtions LLC ...... E ...... 281 351-8131 Tomball *(G-19964)*	Basic Energy Services Inc ...... D ...... 254 442-2200 Fort Worth *(G-6432)*	Boots & Coots LLC ...... E ...... 281 931-8884 Houston *(G-8953)*
Baker Hghes Olfld Oprtions LLC ...... F ...... 361 289-0373 Corpus Christi *(G-3479)*	Basic Energy Services Inc ...... E ...... 903 295-0817 Longview *(G-14201)*	Boots & Coots LLC ...... E ...... 281 871-2699 Houston *(G-8954)*
Baker Hghes Olfld Oprtions LLC ...... C ...... 800 441-0535 Yorktown *(G-20976)*	Basic Energy Services Inc ...... E ...... 903 895-4448 Overton *(G-16275)*	Boots & Coots Services LLC ...... E ...... 281 931-8884 Houston *(G-8955)*
Baker Hghes Prcess Ppline Svcs ...... G ...... 832 519-2000 Houston *(G-8798)*	Basic Energy Services Inc ...... D ...... 325 884-5901 Big Lake *(G-2054)*	Boots & Coots Services Inc ...... E ...... 281 931-8884 Houston *(G-8956)*
Baker Hughes ...... C ...... 432 385-7861 Snyder *(G-18983)*	Basic Energy Services Inc ...... F ...... 432 267-8885 Big Spring *(G-2072)*	BOP Products LLC ...... F ...... 281 955-6321 Houston *(G-8957)*
Baker Hughes A GE Company LLC ...... C ...... 281 351-8131 Tomball *(G-19965)*	Basic Energy Services Inc ...... E ...... 936 248-2788 Tenaha *(G-19723)*	Border Lease Services Inc ...... D ...... 956 728-1959 Laredo *(G-13868)*
Baker Hughes A GE Company LLC ...... D ...... 713 580-9700 Houston *(G-8799)*	Basic Energy Services Inc ...... E ...... 325 762-2239 Albany *(G-184)*	Border Well Services Inc ...... D ...... 956 753-7540 Laredo *(G-13869)*
Baker Hughes A GE Company LLC ...... G ...... 361 883-1591 Corpus Christi *(G-3480)*	Basic Energy Services Inc ...... F ...... 432 620-0880 Midland *(G-15135)*	Borets US Inc ...... E ...... 432 697-1900 Midland *(G-15148)*
Baker Hughes A GE Company LLC ...... E ...... 432 685-8900 Midland *(G-15131)*	Basic Energy Services Inc ...... C ...... 325 573-8837 Snyder *(G-18984)*	Boss Oil Field Service Inc ...... F ...... 361 574-7939 Victoria *(G-20249)*
Baker Hughes A GE Company LLC ...... B ...... 432 248-3000 Odessa *(G-15923)*	Basic Energy Services Inc ...... G ...... 361 574-9512 San Antonio *(G-17939)*	Brammer Petroleum Inc ...... F ...... 940 665-4807 Gainesville *(G-7335)*
Baker Hughes A GE Company LLC ...... C ...... 713 625-4200 Houston *(G-8800)*	Basic Energy Services Inc ...... F ...... 432 580-8821 Odessa *(G-15927)*	Brammer Pipe and Steel Inc ...... F ...... 940 665-4807 Gainesville *(G-7336)*
Baker Hughes A GE Company LLC ...... D ...... 956 383-0142 Edinburg *(G-5578)*	Basic Energy Services LP ...... F ...... 432 758-9215 Seminole *(G-18881)*	Breakwater Energy Partners LLC ...... D ...... 281 648-1268 Houston *(G-8980)*
Baker Hughes A GE Company LLC ...... B ...... 210 662-5200 San Antonio *(G-17936)*	Basic Energy Services LP ...... F ...... 361 358-2505 Beeville *(G-1982)*	Bridgeport Tank Trucks LLC ...... D ...... 940 683-9440 Bridgeport *(G-2290)*
Baker Hughes A GE Company LLC ...... E ...... 936 336-7218 Liberty *(G-14114)*	Basic Energy Services LP ...... F ...... 903 657-8171 Henderson *(G-8257)*	Bridges Equipment Ltd ...... E ...... 432 333-9741 Odessa *(G-15943)*
Baker Hughes A GE Company LLC ...... E ...... 903 690-0026 Carthage *(G-2899)*	Basic Energy Services LP ...... E ...... 903 643-1140 Fort Worth *(G-6434)*	Bridges Holdings Inc ...... E ...... 817 396-4340 Cresson *(G-3706)*
Baker Hughes A GE Company LLC ...... E ...... 956 791-0466 Laredo *(G-13866)*	Basic Energy Services LP ...... E ...... 409 842-6262 Dayton *(G-5221)*	Bridwell Oil Management LLC ...... F ...... 940 723-4351 Wichita Falls *(G-20747)*
Baker Hughes A GE Company LLC ...... D ...... 361 573-2493 Victoria *(G-20243)*	Basic Marine Services Inc ...... C ...... 817 334-4100 Fort Worth *(G-6435)*	Brinkerhoff Inspection Inc ...... F ...... 432 924-2915 Midland *(G-15150)*
Baker Hughes A GE Company LLC ...... E ...... 972 550-3933 Irving *(G-12942)*	Basils Oilfield Service Inc ...... E ...... 936 274-5575 Saratoga *(G-18740)*	Brinkerhoff Inspection Inc ...... E ...... 432 770-4626 Midland *(G-15151)*
Baker Hughes A GE Company LLC ...... E ...... 281 276-5400 Sugar Land *(G-19447)*	Bass Energy Services LLC ...... D ...... 903 687-1800 Waskom *(G-20516)*	Bulldog Wireline Inc ...... F ...... 936 399-3999 North Zulch *(G-15884)*
Baker Hughes A GE Company LLC ...... E ...... 432 681-8300 Midland *(G-15132)*	BCM & Associates Inc ...... F ...... 432 580-7161 Odessa *(G-15930)*	Bulldog Wireline Inc ...... F ...... 979 260-9034 College Station *(G-3179)*
Baker Hughes A GE Company LLC ...... B ...... 281 363-6000 The Woodlands *(G-19834)*	Beagle Steam Service Inc ...... G ...... 806 274-6892 Borger *(G-2163)*	Bullet Production Services LLC ...... E ...... 361 504-4200 Corpus Christi *(G-3491)*
Baker Hughes A GE Company LLC ...... D ...... 979 826-3621 Hempstead *(G-8249)*	Beck Bros Inc ...... D ...... 361 289-6082 Beeville *(G-1983)*	Bullseye Oilfield Service LLC ...... F ...... 325 665-0220 Tye *(G-20041)*
Baker Hughes Financing LLC ...... D ...... 713 439-8600 Houston *(G-8804)*	Bedrock Production LLC ...... E ...... 281 786-0220 Houston *(G-8850)*	Burnsco Blowt Prvntr RPR & Srv ...... F ...... 432 367-5329 Odessa *(G-16046)*
Baker Hughes Holdings LLC ...... D ...... 956 285-2002 Laredo *(G-13867)*	Bep Oilfield Ltd ...... F ...... 281 873-9100 Houston *(G-8859)*	Burton Oil Svc Operations LLC ...... F ...... 713 805-2934 Tyler *(G-20062)*
Baker Hughes Holdings LLC ...... D ...... 325 853-2553 Eldorado *(G-6044)*	Bergstein Well Servicing LLC ...... E ...... 806 741-1095 Lubbock *(G-14372)*	Butchs Rat Hole Anchr Svc Inc ...... E ...... 806 894-6294 Levelland *(G-14004)*
Baker Hughes Holdings LLC ...... F ...... 713 625-4200 Houston *(G-8805)*	Bico Drilling Tools Inc ...... E ...... 832 598-9200 Houston *(G-8879)*	Bws Construction LLC ...... E ...... 254 562-6820 Mexia *(G-15088)*
Baker Hughes Holdings LLC ...... D ...... 713 439-8600 Houston *(G-8808)*	Big 4 Inc ...... E ...... 409 787-2733 Hemphill *(G-8245)*	Byrd Oilfield Services LLC ...... E ...... 432 385-7635 Odessa *(G-15948)*
Baker Hughes Holdings LLC ...... F ...... 806 637-4745 Brownfield *(G-2329)*	Big Lake Services Company LLC ...... C ...... 432 686-0475 Midland *(G-15140)*	C & C Coating Inc ...... E ...... 432 682-7201 Waco *(G-20372)*
Baker Hughes Holdings LLC ...... D ...... 817 426-7080 Burleson *(G-2568)*	Big Spring Cat Cnstr Inc ...... F ...... 432 394-4161 Coahoma *(G-3164)*	C & C Logging ...... F ...... 903 895-4738 New London *(G-15849)*
Baker Petrolite ...... E ...... 432 498-9191 Odessa *(G-15925)*	Big Star LLC ...... E ...... 325 617-5731 San Angelo *(G-17781)*	C Automation Inc ...... E ...... 832 467-4644 Houston *(G-9026)*
Baker Petrolite ...... E ...... 903 984-0251 Kilgore *(G-13533)*	Big Tom Construction Inc ...... G ...... 903 752-1008 Overton *(G-16276)*	C&S Lease Service LC ...... E ...... 903 988-8642 Kilgore *(G-13534)*
Baker Petrolite LLC ...... G ...... 940 658-3574 Knox City *(G-13662)*	Bioremediation Contrs Cons Inc ...... F ...... 806 771-8033 Lubbock *(G-14374)*	C2 Pipeline Services LLC ...... E ...... 713 253-6980 Conroe *(G-3271)*
Baker Petrolite LLC ...... D ...... 940 626-4436 Decatur *(G-5243)*	Bisn Oil Tools LLC ...... E ...... 832 919-7500 Houston *(G-8893)*	Cactus Wellhead LLC ...... C ...... 713 626-8800 Houston *(G-9044)*
Baker Petrolite LLC ...... F ...... 361 394-7544 Freer *(G-7222)*	BJ Services LLC ...... E ...... 281 408-2361 Tomball *(G-19966)*	CAM Services Inc ...... F ...... 254 629-8561 Eastland *(G-5561)*
Baker Petrolite LLC ...... F ...... 806 229-8121 Sundown *(G-19612)*	Black Elk Energy Offshore Oper ...... F ...... 832 973-4230 Houston *(G-8903)*	Cameron International Corp ...... E ...... 361 289-1455 Corpus Christi *(G-3494)*
Balderas Welding Services LLC ...... F ...... 432 661-3164 Odessa *(G-15926)*	Black Gold Oper & Cnstr Inc ...... F ...... 903 766-3636 Waskom *(G-20517)*	Cameron International Corp ...... A ...... 713 939-2211 Houston *(G-9067)*
Barrilleaux Inc ...... D ...... 903 545-2280 Oakwood *(G-15892)*	Black Sheep Oilfield Svcs LLC ...... F ...... 940 644-1720 Chico *(G-3051)*	Cameron International Corp ...... E ...... 281 391-4600 Katy *(G-13355)*
Basic Energy Services Inc ...... E ...... 817 645-0853 Fort Worth *(G-6430)*	Blackgold Services Inc ...... E ...... 936 336-9600 Liberty *(G-14115)*	Cameron International Corp ...... E ...... 713 946-2122 Houston *(G-9069)*

PRODUCT

Cameron International Corp	B	713 939-2650	Houston *(G-9070)*
Cameron International Corp	E	713 849-7500	Houston *(G-9071)*
Cameron International Holding	F	713 513-3300	Houston *(G-9074)*
Camin Cargo Control Inc	E	409 729-3399	Port Arthur *(G-17103)*
Camin Cargo Control Inc	F	361 884-3922	Corpus Christi *(G-3495)*
Canary LLC	C	432 563-1970	Odessa *(G-15954)*
Canon Safety Services Ltd	F	903 984-5928	Kilgore *(G-13535)*
Canrig Drilling Technology Ltd	F	281 443-1414	Houston *(G-9085)*
Catalyst Oilfld Svcs 2016 LLC	D	432 563-0727	Gardendale *(G-7420)*
Cbg Corporation	E	512 491-7541	Austin *(G-1032)*
CDK Perforating LLC	C	817 945-1051	Fort Worth *(G-6501)*
CDK Perforating Holdings Inc	C	817 945-1051	Fort Worth *(G-6502)*
CDM Resource Management LLC	D	281 376-2980	Houston *(G-9114)*
Ceda International Inc	F	281 478-2600	League City *(G-13952)*
Cetco Energy Services Co LLC	D	281 578-8911	Houston *(G-9147)*
Chalk Mountain Svcs Texas LLC	E	817 473-1931	Mansfield *(G-14661)*
Champion Oilfield Services LLC	E	512 327-3300	Austin *(G-1043)*
Chandler Mfg LLC	D	940 763-1528	Wichita Falls *(G-20753)*
Chapas Oilfield Services LLC	F	956 847-6460	Zapata *(G-20980)*
Charles Howard Construction	F	325 387-3093	Sonora *(G-19024)*
Cheyenne Services Inc	E	713 937-7733	Houston *(G-9182)*
Chisholm Trail Oilfield Svc	F	979 567-4943	Caldwell *(G-2630)*
Choctaw Lease Service LLC	F	361 449-3506	George West *(G-7623)*
Cimarron Energy Holding Co LLC	D	701 352-9620	Houston *(G-9189)*
Circle 8 Crane Services LLC	E	361 933-0696	Robstown *(G-17505)*
Circle 8 Crane Services LLC	D	432 332-6900	Odessa *(G-15962)*
Circle 8 Crane Services LLC	C	361 442-0306	Robstown *(G-17506)*
Clean Hrbors Explrtion Svcs In	F	281 478-2600	Deer Park *(G-5264)*
Clements Fluids Buffalo Ltd	E	903 581-5110	Tyler *(G-20067)*
Coil Tubing Partners LLC	E	432 201-4111	Midland *(G-15170)*
Coil Tubing Technology Inc	F	281 651-0200	Houston *(G-9240)*
Cokinos Oil Company	F	713 974-0101	Houston *(G-9242)*
Compass Drctional Guidance Inc	F	281 442-7484	Houston *(G-9255)*
Compass Drctional Guidance Inc	E	281 442-7484	Houston *(G-9256)*
Complete Energy Services Inc	E	940 668-5186	Gainesville *(G-7340)*
Complete Energy Services Inc	A	940 665-4373	Gainesville *(G-7341)*
Complete Pipe Services LLC	E	903 988-1124	Kilgore *(G-13537)*
Complete Production Svcs Inc	E	281 372-2300	Houston *(G-9260)*
Comprssion Contrls Rentals LLC	F	903 643-7970	Longview *(G-14212)*
Consolidated Wellsite Svcs LLC	E	903 983-9811	Haslet *(G-8218)*
Continental Prod Svcs Inc	E	281 431-0502	Houston *(G-9288)*
Cooper Oil Company Inc	F	817 332-7755	Fort Worth *(G-6546)*
Copano/Operations Inc	F	361 668-8580	Alice *(G-207)*
Core Laboratories (texas) LLC	B	713 328-2673	Houston *(G-9315)*
Core Laboratories LP	D	432 687-5797	Midland *(G-15178)*
Core Laboratories LP	D	903 984-4223	Kilgore *(G-13538)*
Core Laboratories LP	B	713 328-2673	Houston *(G-9317)*
Coyote Roustabout LLC	F	325 455-0090	Hawley *(G-8230)*
Crest Pumping Technologies LLC	D	817 484-5100	Fort Worth *(G-6560)*
Cretic Energy Corp	F	713 922-3784	Montgomery *(G-15630)*
Crossfire LLC	E	970 884-4869	The Woodlands *(G-19849)*
Crowder Services Inc	E	325 853-2852	Eldorado *(G-6045)*
Crown Energy Technologies Inc	F	403 215-5300	Houston *(G-9347)*
Csi Compressco LP	B	281 367-1983	The Woodlands *(G-19850)*
Cudd Pressure Control Inc	E	361 387-8521	Robstown *(G-17507)*
Cudd Pressure Control Inc	D	432 580-3544	Odessa *(G-15971)*
Cudd Pressure Control Inc	C	903 988-2161	Kilgore *(G-13542)*
Cudd Pumping Services Inc	F	210 310-1330	San Antonio *(G-18034)*
Cudd Pumping Services Inc	F	832 295-5555	The Woodlands *(G-19851)*
Cudd Well Control	E	713 849-2769	Spring *(G-19204)*
Cyclone Services LLC	F	817 594-5571	Weatherford *(G-20584)*
D & D Swabbing LLC	F	903 729-7922	Palestine *(G-16298)*
D & R Casing Services Inc	F	432 263-8900	Big Spring *(G-2078)*
D Courtney Construction Inc	B	903 694-2911	Carthage *(G-2905)*
D M Glover Incorporated	F	325 392-2561	Ozona *(G-16279)*
D-Js Well Svc Roustabout Inc	E	806 273-2667	Borger *(G-2172)*
Daeco Ltd	E	361 526-7017	Refugio *(G-17240)*
Danos LLC	C	985 219-3313	Midland *(G-15186)*
Dapco Services Inc	F	281 482-1479	Alvin *(G-357)*
Daves Tubing Testing &HOt Oil	E	432 263-1747	Big Spring *(G-2079)*
David Pond Well Service Inc	F	806 435-2384	Perryton *(G-16637)*
David R Rogers Cnstr Inc	C	940 549-6374	Graham *(G-7779)*
Dcaf Inc	E	956 286-9177	Laredo *(G-13877)*
Dd Fluids LLC	E	361 985-2600	Robstown *(G-17508)*
Deep Well Tubular Service Inc	F	432 699-6675	Midland *(G-15188)*
Deepsea Technologies Inc	F	713 849-5555	Houston *(G-9424)*
Deerborne Energy Company	F	281 485-8705	Pearland *(G-16555)*
Delmar Systems Inc	E	832 252-7100	Houston *(G-9427)*
Dennis Energy Services Inc	F	956 712-1114	Laredo *(G-13878)*
Desert Ndt LLC	E	325 864-6547	Abilene *(G-37)*
Desert Ndt LLC	E	580 225-2108	Houston *(G-9441)*
Dfw Oilfield Services Inc	F	972 893-8025	Irving *(G-12999)*
Dialog Wireline Services L L C	E	903 988-2311	Kilgore *(G-13544)*
Dialog Wireline Services L L C	F	936 264-3847	Conroe *(G-3292)*
Diamond D Slickline Svc Co Inc	F	325 573-0220	Snyder *(G-18989)*
Diamond P Lease & Well Svc Inc	E	979 567-1919	Caldwell *(G-2631)*
Diamond P Lease & Well Svc Inc	D	979 884-6111	Dime Box *(G-5484)*
Dof Subsea Usa Inc	C	713 896-2500	Houston *(G-9491)*
Don Brock Distributor Inc	D	361 592-5126	Kingsville *(G-13626)*
Don-Nan Pump and Supply Co Inc	C	432 682-7742	Midland *(G-15194)*
Don-Nan Pump and Supply Co Inc	F	432 530-1925	Odessa *(G-15978)*
Doris Usa Inc	E	713 973-2520	Houston *(G-9500)*
Dossey Oilfield Services LLC	F	325 928-0001	Merkel *(G-15014)*
Double Barrel Downhole Tech	F	281 495-1200	Houston *(G-9501)*
Double O Field Services	F	361 364-2673	Sinton *(G-18961)*
Double T Oilfield Service LLC	F	325 315-2370	Midland *(G-15195)*
Drilltools	F	903 986-3745	Kilgore *(G-13547)*
Drover Energy Services LLC	E	903 986-8911	Kilgore *(G-13548)*
Drum Equipment Inc	G	936 336-9256	Liberty *(G-14117)*
Dunagin Transport Company	E	325 928-5253	Merkel *(G-15015)*
Dunn Services Inc	E	361 275-3952	Cuero *(G-3760)*
Duphil Inc	E	409 883-8550	Orange *(G-16238)*
Dupr Energy Services LLC	F	713 231-9000	Houston *(G-9538)*
Dynaenergetics Us Inc	D	512 327-2043	Houston *(G-9544)*
Dynamic Downhole Services LLC	E	210 881-9002	San Antonio *(G-18075)*
Dynamic Fishing & Rentals LLC	F	432 684-3898	Midland *(G-15199)*
Eagle Completion Usa Ltd	E	432 561-7000	Odessa *(G-15982)*
Eagle Pco LLC	F	432 400-2771	Midland *(G-15202)*
Eagle Pco LLC	F	361 756-0666	Pleasanton *(G-17065)*
Eagle Pco LLC	D	817 678-8998	Navasota *(G-15731)*
East Texas Pipe Service Inc	F	903 639-2541	Hughes Springs *(G-12739)*
Eastham Drilling Inc	C	713 661-6890	Bellaire *(G-1995)*
Edge Specialty Services Inc	E	361 668-3343	Alice *(G-211)*
Emerge Energy Services LP	E	817 618-4020	Fort Worth *(G-6610)*
Empire Tubing Tongs Inc	F	432 366-7702	Odessa *(G-15988)*
Empire Wireline LLC	F	985 264-7746	League City *(G-13955)*
Empirica LLC	E	713 466-7400	Houston *(G-9620)*
En-Fab Inc	D	713 225-4913	Houston *(G-9623)*
Endeavor Energy Resources LP	E	432 683-4292	Midland *(G-15212)*
Endurance Lift Solutions LLC	D	281 269-6880	Gainesville *(G-7343)*
Endurance Roustabout	F	432 697-1300	Midland *(G-15215)*
Enercorp Engnred Solutions LLC	F	832 791-1276	The Woodlands *(G-19861)*
Energes Oilfield Solutions LLC	F	830 769-1484	Jourdanton *(G-13330)*
Energes Services LLC	C	432 307-0650	Odessa *(G-15989)*
Energy Fishing & Rental Svc	F	361 668-8000	Alice *(G-212)*
Energy Fishing Rentl Svcs Inc	F	713 433-5506	Houston *(G-9635)*
Enertech Industries Inc	E	432 550-0543	Odessa *(G-15991)*
Enserco Midstream LLC	F	713 341-7378	Houston *(G-9654)*
Ensign Intl Engy Svcs Inc	E	281 872-7770	Houston *(G-9655)*
Entrec Corporation	D	432 301-2794	Odessa *(G-15992)*
Epica Applied Technologies LLC	E	210 310-7710	Converse *(G-3393)*
Eproduction Solutions LLC	B	281 348-1000	Kingwood *(G-13641)*
Erhc Energy Inc	G	713 626-4700	Houston *(G-9691)*
Espada Oilfield Services LLC	F	361 894-1810	Victoria *(G-20262)*
Espinoza Services Inc	F	806 592-8463	Denver City *(G-5418)*

Company	Code	Phone
Estis Compression LLC	E	318 397-5557
Kilgore (G-13552)		
Etos Inc	D	903 895-2220
New London (G-15850)		
Ets Oilfield Services LP	E	361 767-4200
Robstown (G-17509)		
Everett LLC	E	432 381-5700
Odessa (G-15994)		
Excalibar Minerals LLC	F	361 883-5227
Corpus Christi (G-3523)		
Express Energy Services GP LLC	A	713 625-7400
Houston (G-9729)		
Express Energy Svcs Oper LP	D	325 659-4412
San Angelo (G-17799)		
Express Energy Svcs Oper LP	C	432 530-1111
Odessa (G-15995)		
Express Energy Svcs Oper LP	F	713 625-7400
Houston (G-9730)		
Express Energy Svcs Oper LP	E	979 589-2255
Bryan (G-2472)		
Express Energy Svcs Oper LP	E	713 625-7403
Mission (G-15552)		
Express Energy Svcs Oper LP	F	940 592-4391
Iowa Park (G-12905)		
Expro Americas LLC	E	903 753-2003
Longview (G-14233)		
Expro Americas LLC	E	281 977-2600
Houston (G-9733)		
Exterran Energy Solutions LP	C	281 836-7000
Houston (G-9736)		
Fesco Ltd	E	361 882-4124
Corpus Christi (G-3527)		
Fesco Ltd	D	361 661-1538
Alice (G-213)		
Fesco Ltd	D	936 632-7036
Lufkin (G-14527)		
Fesco Ltd	E	361 661-7000
Canadian (G-2649)		
Fesco Ltd	E	903 984-4814
Kilgore (G-13553)		
Fesco Ltd	E	979 543-9451
El Campo (G-5618)		
Fesco Ltd	F	979 775-1825
Bryan (G-2473)		
Fesco Ltd	F	361 575-7533
Victoria (G-20263)		
Fesco Ltd	E	325 392-3773
Ozona (G-16283)		
Fesco Ltd	E	409 842-3000
Beaumont (G-1893)		
Fieldco Energy Services Inc	F	903 693-5900
Carthage (G-2907)		
Fisher Construction	E	432 332-7532
Odessa (G-16001)		
Fisher Lease Service Inc	E	325 884-2701
Big Lake (G-2056)		
Fisk/MEI Inspection Svcs Inc	C	281 436-5500
Houston (G-9793)		
Five Star Roustabouts LLC	E	940 657-4778
O Brien (G-15888)		
Fla Safety & Prod Svcs Inc	E	830 570-7286
Charlotte (G-3047)		
Flatrock Compression Ltd	E	281 517-3680
Houston (G-9798)		
Flint Energy Services Inc	E	956 585-9779
Mission (G-15554)		
Flint Energy Services Inc	D	903 389-8716
Fairfield (G-6174)		
Flo Trend Systems Inc	E	713 699-0152
Houston (G-9804)		
Flow-Zone LLC	F	281 997-8899
Rosharon (G-17605)		
Flowback Champion Services LLC	F	832 731-5783
Pearland (G-16561)		
Flr Oilfield Services LLC	F	432 693-2245
Rankin (G-17232)		
Fluid Disposal Specialties Inc	F	903 927-2050
Marshall (G-14777)		
Fluids Clements Management LLC	G	903 581-5110
Tyler (G-20089)		
Forum Energy Technologies Inc	D	432 550-9000
Odessa (G-16008)		
Four K Services Inc	F	806 323-8560
Canadian (G-2650)		
Frac Fuel Solutions LLC	E	713 907-4371
Cypress (G-3792)		
Franks International LLC	D	979 778-8700
Bryan (G-2474)		
Freddys Well Service Inc	F	361 578-4559
Victoria (G-20265)		
Freeze Technology Intl	E	806 371-8854
Amarillo (G-425)		
Freudenberg Oil & Gas LLC	D	281 233-1400
Houston (G-9867)		
Fulfer Vanek Well Servicing Co	E	940 438-2276
Iowa Park (G-12906)		
Fulkrum Tchnical Resources Inc	D	713 485-4519
Houston (G-9873)		
Garrison Contractors Inc	E	432 639-2811
Iraan (G-12918)		
GE Oil & Gas Logging Svcs Inc	E	361 299-9457
Corpus Christi (G-3534)		
GE Oil & Gas Logging Svcs Inc	E	281 992-9676
Pearland (G-16565)		
GE Oil & Gas Logging Svcs Inc	E	281 579-9879
Sugar Land (G-19485)		
GE Oil & Gas Pressure Ctrl LP	D	432 686-0720
Midland (G-15235)		
Gem Services LLP	E	210 863-2020
McAllen (G-14865)		
Genco Energy Services Inc	E	956 380-3710
McAllen (G-14866)		
Geonix Operating LP	E	903 983-3249
Kilgore (G-13556)		
George Bartee Cnstr Co Inc	E	936 687-4811
Grapeland (G-8005)		
Geoservices Incorporated	F	281 443-3370
Houston (G-9944)		
Geosite Inc	E	325 655-4356
San Angelo (G-17802)		
Gisler Brothers Logging Co	E	830 239-4651
Runge (G-17729)		
Global Am-Tx, Inc.	F	281 331-0200
Alvin (G-364)		
Global Remote Technologies LLC	E	888 381-3222
Spring (G-19125)		
Globalogix Inc	F	817 441-5570
Aledo (G-199)		
Globe Well Service Inc	D	325 884-3091
Big Lake (G-2057)		
Glover Inc	F	325 392-2561
Ozona (G-16284)		
Gmp Energy LLC	F	713 963-4600
Houston (G-9987)		
Gonco Oilfield Services LLC	G	432 208-2389
Odessa (G-16016)		
Gr Energy Services MGT LP	E	281 201-6812
Sugar Land (G-19489)		
Graco Fishing & Rental Tls Inc	F	214 618-3930
Frisco (G-7289)		
Graco Fishing & Rental Tls Inc	F	432 943-5019
Monahans (G-15604)		
Grand Isle Shipyard Inc	D	432 362-0019
Odessa (G-16017)		
Grand Isle Shipyard Inc	D	830 334-2665
Pearsall (G-16612)		
Grand Operating Inc	G	972 788-2080
Addison (G-133)		
Gravity Oilfield Services Inc	E	432 218-7888
Midland (G-15239)		
Gravity Oilfield Services LLC	D	830 203-5210
Gonzales (G-7753)		
Gravity Oilfield Services LLC	E	806 894-3151
Levelland (G-14007)		
Gravity Oilfield Services LLC	D	817 558-9194
Cleburne (G-3092)		
Gray Wireline Services	F	361 526-4729
Refugio (G-17242)		
Great Basin Petroleum Svcs LP	D	432 561-9702
Odessa (G-16018)		
Green & Hansen LLC	D	210 289-2482
Jourdanton (G-13331)		
Green Energy Oilfield Svcs LLC	C	210 904-3400
Fairfield (G-6175)		
Greenes Energy Group LLC	E	337 232-1830
Houston (G-10035)		
Greenwell Energy Solutions LLC	F	713 993-7772
Houston (G-10037)		
Greenwell Energy Solutions LLC	F	432 381-2595
Odessa (G-16019)		
Griffith Oil Field Services	G	409 246-8530
Kountze (G-13671)		
Gryphon Oilfield Solutions LLC	F	281 738-3110
Houston (G-10051)		
Gtz Services LLC	F	956 750-6147
Zapata (G-20982)		
Guardian Wellhead Protection	F	432 368-5449
Odessa (G-16020)		
Gulf Coast Casing Inc	E	361 575-5488
Victoria (G-20270)		
Gyrodata Incorporated	F	432 561-8458
Midland (G-15242)		
Gyrodata Incorporated	D	713 461-3146
Houston (G-10078)		
H & M Dirt Contractors Inc	E	806 495-3293
Post (G-17190)		
H and L Crimp Inc	F	325 672-9282
Abilene (G-45)		
Halliburton Company	E	361 527-2780
Dilley (G-5481)		
Halliburton Company	E	281 297-1200
Spring (G-19214)		
Halliburton Company	E	972 418-3221
Carrollton (G-2751)		
Halliburton Company	E	281 575-3000
Houston (G-10097)		
Halliburton Company	E	281 871-6875
Houston (G-10098)		
Halliburton Company	A	281 871-2908
Houston (G-10099)		
Halliburton Company	E	281 297-1200
Houston (G-10100)		
Halliburton Company	E	972 418-3000
Carrollton (G-2752)		
Halliburton Company	C	281 871-4000
Houston (G-10101)		
Halliburton Company	F	713 455-9547
Houston (G-10102)		
Halliburton Company	E	936 442-4700
Conroe (G-3300)		
Halliburton Company	E	903 981-7032
Longview (G-14246)		
Halliburton Company	E	210 621-1800
Victoria (G-20271)		
Halliburton Company	G	713 839-2000
Houston (G-10103)		
Halliburton Company	F	281 986-4400
Houston (G-10104)		
Halliburton Company	F	903 389-9275
Fairfield (G-6176)		
Halliburton Company	E	281 871-4482
Houston (G-10105)		
Halliburton Company	E	281 871-4000
Houston (G-10106)		
Halliburton Company	E	281 871-2699
Houston (G-10107)		
Halliburton Company	E	432 571-8600
Odessa (G-16024)		
Halliburton Company	E	713 455-9547
Baytown (G-1790)		
Halliburton Delaware Inc	D	713 759-2600
Houston (G-10108)		
Halliburton Energy Svcs Inc	E	281 871-4000
Houston (G-10109)		
Halliburton Energy Svcs Inc	E	281 871-4482
Houston (G-10110)		
Hamm Well Service Co	F	940 549-4769
Graham (G-7783)		
Hammer Construction Inc	D	940 683-3131
Bridgeport (G-2294)		
Hard Band Industries Inc	F	432 563-3752
Odessa (G-16027)		
Hawkins Lease Service Inc	D	281 331-2739
Alvin (G-365)		
Hernandez Sandblasting	F	361 701-2522
Freer (G-7227)		
High Tide Oilfield Svcs LLC	G	361 394-1731
Freer (G-7228)		
Hli Resources LLC	C	817 240-4361
Cleburne (G-3095)		
Holman Well Service LLC	D	806 665-3355
Pampa (G-16325)		
Houston Well Screen Company	D	281 449-7261
Houston (G-10263)		
Hunting Energy Services Inc	D	281 821-5577
Houston (G-10281)		
Hunting Energy Services Inc	F	281 328-1400
Crosby (G-3734)		
Hunting Energy Services Inc	D	281 499-2583
Stafford (G-19327)		
Hunting Energy Services Inc	E	832 902-2266
Baytown (G-1791)		
Hunting Energy Services Inc	E	281 569-3620
Houston (G-10282)		
Hunting Energy Services LLC	D	281 379-4289
Spring (G-19133)		
Hunting Energy Services LLC	E	281 820-3838
Houston (G-10283)		
Hunting Titan Inc	F	281 463-5881
Houston (G-10285)		

Hurd Oil Field Service Inc E 940 567-3131
Jacksboro *(G-13221)*
Hutchins Oil and Lube E 972 225-0846
Hutchins *(G-12867)*
Hydessco LLC F 903 983-2021
Kilgore *(G-13559)*
Icon Oilfield Services LLC F 214 758-0315
Dallas *(G-4484)*
Innovex Downhole Solutions Inc C 281 602-7815
Houston *(G-10373)*
Intense Wireline Solutions LLC D 903 630-5440
Tyler *(G-20103)*
International Energy Svcs LLC E 281 973-9462
Houston *(G-10402)*
Interstate Explorations LLC F 254 442-1057
Cisco *(G-3067)*
Intertek Cnslting Trning USA I E 337 235-4493
Spring *(G-19219)*
Ios/Pci LLC F 281 310-5357
Houston *(G-10414)*
J & M Energy Services LP E 432 943-7770
Monahans *(G-15606)*
J & R Valley Oilfield Svcs Inc D 956 581-7235
Mission *(G-15556)*
J & W Services & Equipment Co D 432 689-3947
Midland *(G-15257)*
J I S Measurement & Operating F 325 224-3036
San Angelo *(G-17810)*
J Patrick Services LLC F 432 214-5443
Odessa *(G-16035)*
J&P Ramirez Services LLC E 361 526-2072
Refugio *(G-17243)*
J-W Operating Company E 432 332-0111
Odessa *(G-16037)*
J-W Operating Company D 281 592-2351
Cleveland *(G-3129)*
J-W Operating Company E 361 570-2788
Victoria *(G-20275)*
Jab Rentals Inc E 432 296-6464
Odessa *(G-16038)*
Jaguar Energy Services LLC F 337 250-4030
Marion *(G-14757)*
Jaguar Energy Services LLC E 337 250-4030
Bryan *(G-2480)*
Janssen Lease Service Inc E 361 771-3556
Ganado *(G-7415)*
JCs Marine Oilfield Svc Inc E 281 338-7835
League City *(G-13967)*
Jdw Services Inc E 903 845-5586
Gladewater *(G-7723)*
Je Oilfield Services LLC F 361 701-1324
Alice *(G-218)*
Jensco Transport Services LLC F 325 234-1412
Eola *(G-6124)*
Jet Maintenance Inc E 361 576-3226
Victoria *(G-20277)*
JGB Oilfield Services LLC F 806 789-2796
Lubbock *(G-14430)*
Jk Red Dirt Rentals LLC D 214 530-3922
Granbury *(G-7801)*
Jodys Oilfield Service Inc F 432 523-6866
Andrews *(G-546)*
Jordan Spooling Service Inc E 432 366-6040
Odessa *(G-16042)*
Jorn Well Service F 432 943-5699
Monahans *(G-15607)*
JP Tubular Services Inc E 281 426-8596
Crosby *(G-3737)*
Jspaz Guardian Energy Svcs LLC E 432 606-5003
Big Spring *(G-2085)*
JV Roustabout Inc F 432 943-2999
Wickett *(G-20839)*
K & K Repair Service LLC E 361 573-5027
Victoria *(G-20278)*
K D M Hot Oil Service Inc G 432 683-0831
Midland *(G-15264)*
K W Utility Cons Inc E 903 564-5771
Whitesboro *(G-20727)*
K&P Oilfield Solutions G 254 290-4862
Cypress *(G-3806)*
K-3 Resources LP D 281 585-2817
Alvin *(G-370)*
Kasper Pro Vac Service Inc E 956 796-0765
Laredo *(G-13901)*
Katco Vacuum Truck Service LP E 361 527-4421
Hebbronville *(G-8235)*
Keane Frac Tx LLC F 281 929-0370
Houston *(G-10508)*
Keane Frac Tx LLC E 281 929-0370
Houston *(G-10509)*
Keane Group Holdings LLC D 903 247-1053
Longview *(G-14259)*
Keane Group Holdings LLC E 281 719-7200
The Woodlands *(G-19890)*
Keane Group Holdings LLC C 432 488-3800
Odessa *(G-16044)*
Keane Group Holdings LLC A 281 716-9152
Houston *(G-10511)*
Kel-Tech Inc E 432 684-4700
Midland *(G-15266)*
Kellogg Brown Root E 361 758-2554
Aransas Pass *(G-593)*
Kenergy Oilfield Solutions LLC D 830 263-9951
Nixon *(G-15867)*
Kenjer Inc F 281 897-8600
Houston *(G-10516)*
Kenner Well Svc of Palestine E 903 729-3196
Palestine *(G-16300)*
Kerr Oilfield Company E 940 327-0447
Mineral Wells *(G-15530)*
Key Energy Drilling Inc E 903 693-2622
Carthage *(G-2910)*
Key Energy Drilling Inc D 432 620-0300
Houston *(G-10521)*
Key Energy Drilling Inc G 713 651-4300
Kilgore *(G-13560)*
Key Energy Services Inc E 361 668-1526
Alice *(G-220)*
Key Energy Services Inc E 432 381-1301
Odessa *(G-16047)*
Key Energy Services Inc D 432 523-5155
Andrews *(G-547)*
Key Energy Services Inc D 713 651-4300
El Campo *(G-5619)*
Key Energy Services Inc E 432 488-2800
Odessa *(G-16050)*
Key Energy Services Inc E 806 872-6688
Lamesa *(G-13826)*
Key Energy Services Inc E 325 236-6611
Sweetwater *(G-19632)*
Key Energy Services Inc D 979 778-1800
Bryan *(G-2484)*
Key Energy Services Inc E 903 963-5208
Van *(G-20208)*
Khudairi Group Incorporated E 713 782-1080
Houston *(G-10530)*
Kil-Tex Oilfield Services LLC G 903 736-5051
Kilgore *(G-13561)*
King Workover Service Inc F 979 543-5464
El Campo *(G-5620)*
Kixx Rentals & Services LLC E 830 437-2959
Gonzales *(G-7758)*
Kj Energy LLC F 214 297-5013
Dallas *(G-4559)*
Knight Energy Holdings LLC E 713 466-6660
Houston *(G-10547)*
Knight Oil Tools LLC E 432 530-1010
Odessa *(G-16054)*
Knight Oil Tools LLC F 361 668-8065
Alice *(G-223)*
Kuykendall Btm Hole Pressure E 432 563-5231
Odessa *(G-16056)*
L G Pump Inc E 432 550-3445
Odessa *(G-16058)*
La Copa Field Services Inc D 361 364-1608
Sinton *(G-18963)*
Lang & Mitchell Contrs Inc F 903 876-2882
Frankston *(G-7167)*
Laredo Construction Inc F 281 499-4333
Stafford *(G-19345)*
Larry & Matt Inc D 806 665-4418
Pampa *(G-16326)*
Larry McHorse Services LLC F 361 275-4978
Cuero *(G-3762)*
Latx Oilfield Services LLC E 903 934-8263
Waskom *(G-20518)*
Latx Operations LLC D 903 927-2091
Waskom *(G-20519)*
Laverton Oilfield Services LLC F 325 899-3556
Albany *(G-190)*
Leam Drilling Systems LLC E 936 539-1351
Conroe *(G-3318)*
Leemak LP B 281 492-9555
Houston *(G-10619)*
Leeson Energy Services LLC F 432 689-7000
Midland *(G-15273)*
Legacy Field Services LLC D 903 694-9445
Carthage *(G-2912)*
Legend Energy Services LLC E 432 523-6585
Andrews *(G-549)*
Lengston Corporation F 713 757-1331
Houston *(G-10623)*
Lenoir Water Transfer Inc D 432 686-8200
Midland *(G-15278)*
Lenorah Operators LLC E 432 684-9822
Midland *(G-15279)*
Liberty Fishing Rentl Tls Inc E 432 381-0551
Odessa *(G-16062)*
Liberty Lift Solutions LLC E 713 575-2300
Houston *(G-10633)*
Lightning Fluid Services Inc F 361 396-0801
Alice *(G-224)*
Lightning Oilfield Svcs Inc D 817 439-5558
Midland *(G-15281)*
Lightning Oilfield Svcs Inc D 817 439-5558
Saginaw *(G-17748)*
Lindsayca Inc D 713 467-9560
Houston *(G-10646)*
Line Quest LLC E 432 218-4980
Midland *(G-15283)*
Logan Oil Tools Inc C 281 219-6613
Houston *(G-10671)*
Logic Services LLC F 832 617-0805
Houston *(G-10672)*
Loma Rentals LLC F 817 964-1828
Richardson *(G-17348)*
Loss Oil Field Services LLC E 432 695-6914
Midland *(G-15286)*
Lubrication Technologies Inc F 806 256-1600
Shamrock *(G-18892)*
Lucere LLc E 281 240-7355
Missouri City *(G-15582)*
Lufkin Gears LLC C 936 634-2211
Lufkin *(G-14540)*
Lufkin Ils E 281 445-7676
Houston *(G-10699)*
Lufkin Industries LLC E 903 984-3875
Kilgore *(G-13566)*
Lufkin Industries LLC E 936 634-2211
Lufkin *(G-14542)*
Luther M Creek D 325 387-3295
Sonora *(G-19027)*
Lynx Well Service Inc F 409 735-2604
Orangefield *(G-16271)*
M & B Oilfield Construction E 325 235-2514
Sweetwater *(G-19636)*
M & D Companies Inc E 936 347-2138
Garrison *(G-7613)*
M-I LLC E 361 886-3400
Corpus Christi *(G-3567)*
M-I LLC B 281 561-1300
Houston *(G-10725)*
M-I LLC E 409 763-2249
Galveston *(G-7403)*
Mac Oil Field Company Inc F 325 754-5565
Winters *(G-20905)*
Maclaskey Oil Field Services D 817 594-8073
Weatherford *(G-20603)*
Madisonville Service Contr LP F 936 348-5506
Madisonville *(G-14589)*
Maersk Oil Houston Inc C 713 346-5800
Houston *(G-10734)*
Mako Oilfield Services LLC E 832 680-1300
Houston *(G-10742)*
Mangums Oilfield Services E 979 234-7327
Eagle Lake *(G-5542)*
Mangums Oilfield Services Ltd E 979 234-5203
East Bernard *(G-5560)*
Map Oil Tools Inc F 337 560-8559
Houston *(G-10750)*
Martex Well Services LLP D 903 938-3574
Marshall *(G-14792)*
Martin Underground Storage D 903 983-1551
Kilgore *(G-13571)*
Mash Oilfield Services LP F 940 549-6152
Graham *(G-7786)*
Mathis & Son Inc F 940 997-2137
Rule *(G-17728)*
Maverick Companies LLC C 817 334-4100
Fort Worth *(G-6820)*
Maverick Well Service LLC F 903 983-6050
Kilgore *(G-13572)*
McCamey Well Service Inc F 432 208-2769
Mc Camey *(G-14819)*
McCurdy Services Inc E 903 729-5681
Palestine *(G-16303)*
McGuire Industries Inc F 979 968-5131
La Grange *(G-13698)*
McMillan Welding D 432 687-4625
Midland *(G-15297)*

1582 2021 Harris Texas Manufacturers Directory (G-0000) Company's Geographic Section entry number

MCR Oil Tools LLC ....E 817 704-6677	Natco Group Inc ....F 713 849-7500	O S & S Operating Inc ....G 940 495-3645
Arlington *(G-730)*	Houston *(G-10964)*	Electra *(G-6049)*
Mega Oil Corporation ....E 903 984-7050	National Coupling Company Inc ....C 281 499-2583	O-Tex Pumping LLC ....E 806 665-0552
Kilgore *(G-13573)*	Stafford *(G-19356)*	Pampa *(G-16330)*
Megalodon Services Inc ....E 941 882-3108	National Enrgy Svcs Rnted Corp ....G 832 925-3777	Oceaneering International Inc ....C 713 329-4500
Sunset *(G-19625)*	Houston *(G-10967)*	Houston *(G-11124)*
Mesa Drilling Inc ....G 713 993-7082	National Oilwell Varco Inc ....C 432 333-4196	Oceaneering International Inc ....C 713 939-3682
Lago Vista *(G-13807)*	Odessa *(G-16087)*	Houston *(G-11125)*
Mesquite Oil Tools Inc ....E 325 573-1705	National Oilwell Varco Inc ....E 432 528-4354	Oceaneering International Inc ....F 713 329-4318
Snyder *(G-18995)*	Odessa *(G-16088)*	Houston *(G-11126)*
Mesquite Services LLC ....E 806 368-7726	National Oilwell Varco Inc ....E 432 563-2150	Oceaneering International Inc ....E 713 466-8853
Lubbock *(G-14446)*	Odessa *(G-16089)*	Houston *(G-11127)*
Mid-West Truck Center Inc ....D 432 523-3451	National Oilwell Varco Inc ....F 713 799-8198	Oceaneering International Inc ....E 713 856-9375
Andrews *(G-552)*	Houston *(G-10972)*	Jersey Village *(G-13303)*
Midcoast Lease Service Inc ....E 361 526-4636	National Oilwell Varco Inc ....D 713 466-7999	Oes Oilfield Services USA Inc ....D 713 960-1339
Refugio *(G-17244)*	Houston *(G-10973)*	Houston *(G-11139)*
Midway Oilfield Constrs Inc ....C 817 389-2525	National Oilwell Varco Inc ....D 713 983-9281	Offshore Express Inc ....D 985 868-1438
Godley *(G-7736)*	Houston *(G-10974)*	Houston *(G-11141)*
Midway Oilfield Constrs Inc ....B 936 348-3721	National Oilwell Varco Inc ....E 361 664-8013	Offshore Spclty Fbricators LLC ....C 985 868-1438
Midway *(G-15499)*	Robstown *(G-17514)*	Houston *(G-11144)*
Midwestern Services Inc ....D 325 573-6666	National Oilwell Varco Inc ....E 713 896-9115	Ofs Inc ....E 281 456-0052
Houston *(G-10876)*	Houston *(G-10977)*	Houston *(G-11146)*
Millennium Resources LP ....E 432 687-4074	National Oilwell Varco Inc ....E 713 375-3700	Ofs Global Inc ....F 832 786-4728
Midland *(G-15304)*	Houston *(G-10979)*	Houston *(G-11147)*
MO Vac Service Co of Alice ....E 361 668-8203	National Oilwell Varco Inc ....B 281 456-0751	Oil Field Dev Engrg LLC ....D 281 679-9060
Alice *(G-229)*	Houston *(G-10989)*	Houston *(G-11151)*
Mobley Oilfield Services LP ....E 903 234-2179	National Oilwell Varco Inc ....E 940 761-2333	Oil States Energy Services LLC ....E 281 331-1800
Longview *(G-14279)*	Wichita Falls *(G-20785)*	Alvin *(G-376)*
Momentum Operating Co Inc ....E 325 762-3331	National Oilwell Varco Inc ....F 817 389-2444	Oil States Industries Inc ....D 817 468-1400
Albany *(G-191)*	Godley *(G-7737)*	Arlington *(G-741)*
Momentum Pressure Control LLC ....E 903 643-3700	National Oilwell Varco Inc ....F 281 209-4840	Oil States Industries Inc ....D 713 920-9800
Longview *(G-14280)*	Houston *(G-10994)*	Houston *(G-11156)*
Montecito Oilfield Svcs LLC ....F 956 337-6082	National Oilwell Varco Inc ....D 409 842-2114	Oil States Industries Inc ....D 713 510-2200
Laredo *(G-13914)*	Beaumont *(G-1933)*	Houston *(G-11158)*
Moontower Resources LLC ....F 432 400-2445	National Oilwell Varco Inc ....F 325 884-2556	Oil States Industries Inc ....E 281 247-7400
West Lake Hills *(G-20685)*	Big Lake *(G-2060)*	Houston *(G-11159)*
Morrison Energy Group LLC ....A 713 344-9233	National Oilwell Varco LP ....E 210 477-7500	Oil States Systems Inc ....D 713 445-2210
Houston *(G-10924)*	San Antonio *(G-18334)*	Arlington *(G-744)*
MSA Industries Inc ....F 432 337-6062	National Oilwell Varco LP ....E 936 777-6200	Oilfield Anchor Company Inc ....D 903 723-2833
Odessa *(G-16084)*	Conroe *(G-3339)*	Palestine *(G-16306)*
Mtlv Properties LLC ....E 361 946-6145	Newpark Drilling Fluids LLC ....E 903 297-2210	Oilfield Audit Services Inc ....F 281 242-9521
Corpus Christi *(G-3580)*	Longview *(G-14284)*	Sugar Land *(G-19521)*
Mud King Products Inc ....E 281 645-4158	Newpark Drlg Flids Prsonnel SE ....F 405 721-0207	Oilfield Services & Tech LLC ....F 281 452-3036
Houston *(G-10934)*	Spring *(G-19237)*	Houston *(G-11164)*
Multi-Chem Inc ....D 281 442-1222	Newpark Environmental Svcs LLC ....E 432 682-5411	Oilwell Tubular Consultants ....E 281 328-6220
Houston *(G-10937)*	Midland *(G-15317)*	Crosby *(G-3740)*
Multi-Chem Group LLC ....E 281 871-4000	Newpark Mats Intgrted Svcs LLC ....F 281 362-6800	Ol Sonora Trading Company ....F 325 387-2524
Houston *(G-10938)*	The Woodlands *(G-19896)*	Sonora *(G-19029)*
Mustang Gas Compression LLC ....D 903 218-4459	Newpark Mats Intgrted Svcs LLC ....D 979 245-3894	OMI Oilfield Investments LLC ....F 806 648-4120
Kilgore *(G-13576)*	Bay City *(G-1775)*	Perryton *(G-16643)*
Mustang Oilfield Services LLC ....E 903 389-4200	Nexgen Wtr Solutions Ltd Lblty ....E 830 583-9915	Omni Energy Services Corp ....E 936 591-8598
Fairfield *(G-6179)*	Kenedy *(G-13490)*	Center *(G-3003)*
Nabors Drilling International ....E 281 775-8506	Nexgen Wtr Solutions Ltd Lblty ....F 432 234-8404	ONeal Oil Company ....F 940 825-3716
Houston *(G-10951)*	Midland *(G-15318)*	Nocona *(G-15869)*
Nabors Drilling Tech USA Inc ....E 281 874-0035	Nextier Cmpltion Solutions Inc ....F 830 277-1200	Online Construction LP ....F 361 445-6161
Odessa *(G-16085)*	Charlotte *(G-3048)*	George West *(G-7627)*
Nabors Drilling Tech USA Inc ....B 281 259-8887	Nextier Cmpltion Solutions Inc ....E 713 325-6000	Onyx Contractors Operations LP ....D 432 561-8900
Magnolia *(G-14619)*	Houston *(G-11048)*	Midland *(G-15328)*
Nabors Drilling Tech USA Inc ....E 281 462-1730	Nextier Oilfield Solutions Inc ....D 713 325-6000	Operations Rod Permian L C ....E 432 367-4149
Crosby *(G-3738)*	Houston *(G-11049)*	Odessa *(G-16102)*
Nabors Well Services Co ....D 281 874-0035	Nibletts Oilfield Services Inc ....E 325 853-2521	Origin Bio Solutions LLC ....F 432 570-4081
Houston *(G-10956)*	Eldorado *(G-6047)*	Midland *(G-15329)*
Nabors Well Services Co ....D 325 884-2536	Nine Energy Service Inc ....D 281 730-5100	Original Services Inc ....E 325 617-7400
Big Lake *(G-2059)*	Houston *(G-11058)*	San Angelo *(G-17817)*
Nabors Well Services Co ....D 817 396-4310	Nine Energy Service Inc ....F 903 469-3922	Orteq Energy Technologies LLC ....E 940 665-2316
Cresson *(G-3710)*	Murchison *(G-15680)*	Gainesville *(G-7356)*
Nabors Well Services Co ....D 940 626-3735	Nine Energy Service Inc ....F 903 479-3155	P & C Oil Field Service LLC ....E 956 581-1725
Decatur *(G-5249)*	Athens *(G-836)*	Mission *(G-15561)*
Nabors Well Services Co ....D 281 775-8506	Nitro Fluids LLC ....E 361 938-5300	P & W Sales Incorporated ....G 817 244-6565
Houston *(G-10957)*	Nordheim *(G-15872)*	Fort Worth *(G-6887)*
Nabors Well Services Ltd ....D 432 523-4420	Nitro Well Service LLC ....E 432 617-1128	Pacific Mwd Inc ....E 713 466-1616
Andrews *(G-554)*	Midland *(G-15319)*	Houston *(G-11218)*
Nabors Well Services Ltd ....D 325 387-2884	Noahs Service & Supply LLC ....G 903 218-6888	Packard International Inc ....F 281 399-8771
Sonora *(G-19028)*	Kilgore *(G-13578)*	Conroe *(G-3346)*
Nabors Well Services Ltd ....D 325 573-2621	Noble Flow Control LLC ....F 432 638-5962	Packers Plus Enrgy Svcs USA In ....C 281 872-6999
Snyder *(G-18996)*	San Angelo *(G-17815)*	Tomball *(G-19995)*
Nabors Well Services Ltd ....D 432 943-2227	Noral Holding Company ....E 972 392-7780	Paloma Lease Service Inc ....E 361 449-2815
Monahans *(G-15610)*	Dallas *(G-4742)*	George West *(G-7628)*
Nabors Well Services Ltd ....E 432 683-5000	North Basin Coating Inc ....E 806 894-1531	Panamerican Indus Svcs Co Inc ....F 210 666-3542
Midland *(G-15309)*	Levelland *(G-14011)*	San Antonio *(G-18365)*
Nabors Well Services Ltd ....E 806 592-9128	North Texas Compression ....F 940 683-5025	Panola Equipment Inc ....F 903 633-2545
Denver City *(G-5421)*	Bridgeport *(G-2297)*	Panola *(G-16349)*
Nabors Well Services Ltd ....D 325 651-9241	Novosad Enterprises Inc ....F 979 272-9203	Panola Wire Line Services Inc ....F 903 693-3966
San Angelo *(G-17814)*	Caldwell *(G-2633)*	Carthage *(G-2915)*
Nabors Well Services Ltd ....D 325 392-2313	Nutech Energy Alliance Ltd ....D 281 812-4030	Paragon Directional Drlg LLC ....F 903 880-7398
Ozona *(G-16286)*	Houston *(G-11101)*	Granbury *(G-7804)*
Nalco Champion Wellchem ....F 432 366-0971	O & B Tank Co Inc ....D 806 624-3431	Pate Trucking Co LLC ....E 575 392-4441
Odessa *(G-16086)*	Darrouzett *(G-5214)*	Lubbock *(G-14458)*
Nason Services LLC ....F 940 495-2558	O & C Equipment Inc ....F 281 232-4686	Patterson Tubular Services Inc ....E 281 452-5443
Electra *(G-6048)*	Rosenberg *(G-17591)*	Channelview *(G-3032)*

Employee Codes: A=Over 500 employees, B=251-500
C=101-250, D=51-100, E=20-50, F=10-19, G=9

2021 Harris Texas
Manufacturers Directory

PRODUCT

1583

Company	Code	Phone
Patterson-Uti Energy Inc	E	817 556-5300
Cleburne (G-3105)		
Patton Enterprises Inc	E	832 619-1890
Webster (G-20642)		
Pcs Oilfield Services LLC	E	806 323-8007
Canadian (G-2653)		
Peak Completion Tech Inc	E	361 668-8383
Victoria (G-20293)		
Peak Completion Tech Inc	E	817 529-2030
Fort Worth (G-6899)		
Peak Completion Tech Inc	E	325 574-1170
Snyder (G-19001)		
Peak Oilfield Services LLC	E	940 683-1627
Bridgeport (G-2298)		
Peak Pressure Control LLC	E	432 563-5800
Midland (G-15344)		
Performance Pressure Pumping	F	409 980-8188
Beaumont (G-1940)		
Permian Anchors Inc	E	432 563-0205
Odessa (G-16111)		
Permian Ndt Inc	E	432 563-3638
Houston (G-11293)		
Permian Petroleum Services Inc	E	432 682-0434
Midland (G-15345)		
Petro-Tech Environmental LLC	G	713 926-9986
Houston (G-11301)		
Petrochem Field Services Inc	D	281 441-2550
Humble (G-12792)		
Petroleum College Intl	F	361 575-4882
Victoria (G-20295)		
Petroleum Elastomers Inc	E	281 591-1500
Houston (G-11305)		
Petrostar Services LLC	F	903 247-6390
Longview (G-14289)		
Petrustech Oil & Gas LLC	F	281 781-0020
Houston (G-11312)		
Pfm LLC	F	713 664-7767
Houston (G-11315)		
Phil Dollar Oilfield Services	F	806 435-3373
Perryton (G-16645)		
Pinnergy Ltd	E	830 569-1997
Pleasanton (G-17071)		
Pinnergy Ltd	D	903 693-6300
Carthage (G-2916)		
Pinnergy Ltd	C	817 389-2105
Godley (G-7739)		
Pinnergy Ltd	D	512 343-8880
Austin (G-1417)		
Pinnergy Ltd	D	903 693-8400
Carthage (G-2917)		
Plank Coatings Inc	F	432 530-1234
Odessa (G-16123)		
Platinum Pressure Services Inc	E	866 943-2204
Decatur (G-5250)		
PLPS Inc	F	866 992-7577
Pearland (G-16593)		
Power Line Infrstrcture Svcs I	E	432 586-2518
Kermit (G-13514)		
Precision Energy Services Inc	C	713 693-4000
Houston (G-11393)		
Precision Well Logging Inc	E	713 681-3435
Houston (G-11396)		
Preferred Oilfield Services	F	325 884-5700
San Angelo (G-17823)		
Premier Pipe LLC	E	832 300-8100
Houston (G-11403)		
Premiere Inc	E	817 326-3500
Granbury (G-7805)		
Premiere Well Service	E	806 669-3227
Pampa (G-16335)		
Premium Oilfield Tech LLC	D	281 670-5200
Houston (G-11405)		
Pro Field Services Inc	E	361 798-5552
Hallettsville (G-8125)		
Pro Inspection Inc	F	432 362-2247
Odessa (G-16126)		
Pro Oilfield Services LLC	C	281 496-5810
Spring (G-19242)		
Pro-Ject Chemicals Inc	E	832 403-2560
Spring (G-19243)		
Production Downhole Svcs Inc	F	806 592-0032
Denver City (G-5423)		
Production Facilities Eqp Inc	E	281 356-1107
Magnolia (G-14621)		
Production Lift Systems Inc	E	432 699-1200
Midland (G-15364)		
Professional Rental Tools LLC	E	713 808-9756
Houston (G-11439)		
Professnal Drctional Entps Inc	C	936 441-7266
Conroe (G-3354)		
Professnal Drctional Entps Inc	E	432 695-6152
Midland (G-15365)		
Protechnics	F	713 328-2320
Houston (G-11462)		
Protorque Energy Inc	E	432 208-1404
Midland (G-15369)		
Puffer-Sweiven Holdings Inc	F	361 883-6215
Corpus Christi (G-3599)		
Pumpco Inc	C	979 542-9054
Giddings (G-7700)		
Pure River LLC	F	469 853-4867
Princeton (G-17211)		
Purity Oilfield Services LLC	E	214 880-8400
Dallas (G-4836)		
Purity Oilfield Services LLC	D	844 221-1500
Midland (G-15371)		
Qes Pressure Control LLC	D	361 580-5400
Victoria (G-20297)		
Qes Wireline LLC	F	903 720-8805
Longview (G-14292)		
QMax Solutions Inc	F	832 672-4459
Houston (G-11484)		
Qri International LLC	F	713 485-8800
Houston (G-11487)		
Quail Energy Services LP	E	432 523-3742
Andrews (G-557)		
Quail Tools LP	E	361 579-0244
Victoria (G-20298)		
Quail Tools LP	D	281 445-1777
Houston (G-11490)		
Quality Mat Company	C	409 898-1170
Beaumont (G-1944)		
Quantum Reservoir Impact LLC	E	713 485-8800
Houston (G-11508)		
Quasar Energy Services Inc	F	940 612-3336
Gainesville (G-7359)		
Quell Petroleum Services Inc	E	432 943-8400
Monahans (G-15612)		
R & R Lease Service Inc	E	361 562-8379
Alice (G-230)		
R & R Oilfield Services Inc	D	361 289-5892
Corpus Christi (G-3604)		
R Construction Company	C	903 322-4639
Buffalo (G-2547)		
R360 Envmtl Solutions LLC	G	281 872-7360
The Woodlands (G-19907)		
Radley Electric Inc	F	409 781-7172
Sour Lake (G-19034)		
Rae Energy Inc	C	281 578-6523
Katy (G-13434)		
Raider Services LP	C	830 996-0016
Gordon (G-7769)		
Ranger Energy Services Inc	D	713 935-8900
Houston (G-11545)		
Ranger Oilfield Products Inc	E	936 856-4182
Willis (G-20858)		
Reclamation Contractors Texas	E	903 895-4584
New London (G-15851)		
Red Diamond Energy Svcs Inc	E	325 690-0053
Abilene (G-69)		
Red Diamond Oilfld Svcs L L C	E	903 687-4000
Waskom (G-20521)		
Red Diamond Pressure Ctrl LLC	F	903 687-4000
Waskom (G-20522)		
Redi Services	E	432 272-1583
Odessa (G-16134)		
Redzone Coil Tubing LLC	D	936 632-2645
Lufkin (G-14548)		
Redzone Holdco LLC	F	936 632-2645
Lufkin (G-14549)		
Reed-Hycalog	D	832 422-4070
Houston (G-11576)		
Reliable Well Svc N Texas LLC	F	940 692-9511
Wichita Falls (G-20803)		
Renaissance Offshore LLC	E	832 333-7700
Houston (G-11598)		
Repcon Inc	B	361 289-6342
Corpus Christi (G-3609)		
Reservoir Group	F	281 776-5300
Stafford (G-19369)		
Rh Well Service	F	432 393-5305
Big Spring (G-2095)		
Rheaco Oil Company Ltd	F	409 287-1225
Sour Lake (G-19035)		
Riddles Dehi & Chem Svc Co LLC	F	903 986-3904
Kilgore (G-13587)		
Rig Qa International Inc	F	936 856-5614
Willis (G-20860)		
Rig Technology Inc	E	432 362-2789
Odessa (G-16139)		
Rig Testers Inc	G	325 673-2771
Abilene (G-72)		
Rigamonti Welding Services	G	361 578-0397
Victoria (G-20301)		
Rkt Operating LLC	E	903 686-0284
Longview (G-14299)		
Rmor Energy Corporation	F	361 318-0151
Refugio (G-17246)		
Rods Service LLC	E	979 775-5000
Bryan (G-2502)		
Ross Co Services Company Inc	F	806 894-1511
Levelland (G-14013)		
Rover Oilfield Services LLC	E	979 533-7195
Abilene (G-76)		
Rovop Inc	E	281 231-2626
Houston (G-11675)		
Royalty Well Service Inc	D	432 547-2926
Grandfalls (G-8000)		
Roywell LLC	E	432 332-0703
Odessa (G-16144)		
Rpc Inc	E	817 689-7660
Fort Worth (G-6968)		
Rpc Inc	E	325 573-7022
Snyder (G-19005)		
Rpc Inc	E	361 289-7088
Corpus Christi (G-3612)		
Rubicon Olfld Intl Hldings LLC	F	832 386-2500
Houston (G-11693)		
Rwls LLC	E	806 897-0231
Levelland (G-14014)		
Rwls LLC	E	432 664-0020
Odessa (G-16146)		
S & S Operating Co Inc	F	409 296-9571
Winnie (G-20889)		
S L P Backhoe Service	F	903 643-8258
Longview (G-14300)		
S O A Pump & Supply Inc	F	432 381-2380
Odessa (G-16147)		
Saipem America Inc	C	281 552-5600
Houston (G-11732)		
Saybolt LP	F	409 948-3166
Texas City (G-19800)		
Scan Drilling Company Inc	F	903 597-5368
Tyler (G-20148)		
Schlumberger International	A	713 747-4000
Houston (G-11766)		
Schlumberger Omnes Inc	E	281 285-5176
Rosharon (G-17613)		
Schlumberger Technology Corp	E	281 285-8500
Sugar Land (G-19543)		
Schlumberger Technology Corp	D	361 210-6200
Alice (G-233)		
Schlumberger Technology Corp	E	281 285-7400
Sugar Land (G-19544)		
Schlumberger Technology Corp	C	281 285-5200
Rosharon (G-17614)		
Schlumberger Technology Corp	D	830 569-8046
Pleasanton (G-17073)		
Schlumberger Technology Corp	D	210 623-4975
Von Ormy (G-20350)		
Schlumberger Technology Corp	D	956 744-4029
Pleasanton (G-17074)		
Schlumberger Technology Corp	C	940 442-6566
Frisco (G-7310)		
Schlumberger Technology Corp	C	713 482-0700
Houston (G-11773)		
Schlumberger Technology Corp	C	281 285-8500
Sugar Land (G-19546)		
Schlumberger Technology Corp	E	281 285-4823
Sugar Land (G-19547)		
Schlumberger Technology Corp	F	325 692-1930
Abilene (G-78)		
Schlumberger Technology Corp	B	713 513-2000
Houston (G-11774)		
Schlumberger Technology Corp	E	903 297-0222
Longview (G-14304)		
Schlumberger Technology Corp	E	713 513-2000
Houston (G-11775)		
Schlumberger Technology Corp	F	281 285-6370
Sugar Land (G-19548)		
Schlumberger Technology Corp	E	281 369-3800
Angleton (G-578)		
Schlumberger Technology Corp	D	210 824-7921
San Antonio (G-18459)		
Schlumberger Technology Corp	C	432 683-0047
Midland (G-15397)		
Schlumberger Technology Corp	C	361 664-3458
Alice (G-234)		
Schlumberger Technology Corp	C	903 297-0222
Longview (G-14305)		

Company	Code	Phone
Schlumberger Technology Corp	D	432 571-4600
Midland (G-15398)		
Schlumberger Technology Corp	E	713 747-4000
Houston (G-11777)		
Schlumberger Technology Corp	A	281 285-8500
Sugar Land (G-19551)		
Schlumberger Technology Corp	E	281 285-8500
Sugar Land (G-19553)		
Schlumberger Technology Corp	D	281 285-1300
Houston (G-11778)		
Schroeder Welding & Cnstr	E	361 573-4322
Victoria (G-20302)		
Schroeder Welding & Cnstr	E	361 575-4992
Victoria (G-20303)		
Scomi Equipment Inc	E	281 260-6016
Houston (G-11788)		
Scott Environmental Svcs Inc	E	903 663-4635
Longview (G-14306)		
Scott Measurement Service Inc	E	817 326-2361
Granbury (G-7809)		
Seaboard Operating Inc	E	432 684-7005
Midland (G-15402)		
Secco Inc	G	361 289-1722
Corpus Christi (G-3619)		
Select Energy Services Inc	A	432 447-0602
Pecos (G-16626)		
Select Energy Services Inc	D	713 235-9500
Houston (G-11821)		
Select Energy Services Inc	A	903 766-2600
Gainesville (G-7363)		
Select Energy Services LLC	C	956 286-7100
Laredo (G-13932)		
Select Energy Services LLC	F	713 296-1000
Houston (G-11822)		
Select Energy Services LLC	D	940 668-1818
Gainesville (G-7364)		
Select Energy Services LLC	E	817 523-0136
Weatherford (G-20620)		
Select Energy Services LLC	E	361 701-8465
Bryan (G-2508)		
Select Energy Services LLC	D	318 949-5080
De Berry (G-5235)		
Select Energy Services LLC	E	940 665-8223
Gainesville (G-7365)		
Select Energy Services LLC	D	940 665-1767
Gainesville (G-7366)		
Select Energy Services LLC	D	956 723-4900
Laredo (G-13933)		
Select Energy Services LLC	C	830 457-2215
Big Wells (G-2104)		
Select Energy Services LLC	D	940 627-2066
Decatur (G-5254)		
Sentry Oil & Gas LLC	E	212 753-6367
Mico (G-15094)		
Shale Flow Specialties LLC	E	903 218-6120
Kilgore (G-13589)		
Sharidge Inc	E	325 573-4242
Ira (G-12914)		
Sharp Oilfield Services LLC	D	877 742-7784
Gainesville (G-7367)		
Sharp Roustabout & Cnstr LLC	E	432 528-6360
Midland (G-15405)		
Shekinah Oilfield Services Inc	F	325 762-2205
Albany (G-192)		
Shortes Inc	E	940 658-3576
Knox City (G-13665)		
Sitepro LLC	D	806 687-5326
Lubbock (G-14481)		
Sitton Enterprises LLC	F	817 737-8500
Fort Worth (G-6991)		
Slaughter & Stanley Cnstr Inc	F	432 264-0031
Midland (G-15410)		
Sloan Energy Services LLC	E	432 653-0205
Odessa (G-16154)		
Smith Energy Services Inc	C	903 693-8872
Carthage (G-2919)		
Smith Industries Inc	E	432 683-9722
Midland (G-15412)		
Smith International Inc	E	409 724-2471
Beaumont (G-1950)		
Smith International Inc	E	432 337-5541
Odessa (G-16156)		
Smith International Inc	F	254 697-4488
Missouri City (G-15594)		
Smith International Inc	F	903 693-2596
Carthage (G-2920)		
Smith International Inc	E	432 550-6909
Odessa (G-16157)		
Smith Oilfield Services Inc	E	940 683-5722
Bridgeport (G-2301)		
Smith Services Incorporated	F	361 526-2615
Refugio (G-17247)		
Snap Oilfield Services LLC	E	956 322-1210
McAllen (G-14908)		
Snelson Oilfield Ltg Co Inc	G	713 937-3600
Houston (G-11930)		
Snyder Drilling Corp	F	325 762-2389
Albany (G-194)		
Solaris Oilfield Tech LLC	B	281 501-3070
Houston (G-11936)		
Solaris Olfld Infrstrcture Inc	F	281 501-3070
Houston (G-11937)		
Sooner Pipe LLC	E	281 328-4877
Crosby (G-3743)		
South Texas Oil Field Maint	E	361 526-2822
Refugio (G-17248)		
South Texas Oilfield Svcs LLC	D	361 701-7064
Freer (G-7232)		
South Txas Olfld Solutions LLC	D	361 396-1777
Alice (G-237)		
Sparkman Well Service Inc	C	361 572-4833
Victoria (G-20305)		
Spartan Energy Services LLC	D	830 281-8505
Pleasanton (G-17075)		
Spirit Globl Enrgy Sltions Inc	E	432 522-2288
Odessa (G-16161)		
Stallion Oilfield Cnstr LLC	E	713 528-5544
Houston (G-12040)		
Stallion Oilfield Holdings Ltd	E	713 528-5544
Houston (G-12041)		
Stallion Oilfield Services	E	361 578-7500
Victoria (G-20306)		
Stallion Oilfield Services Ltd	E	830 583-6927
Kenedy (G-13491)		
Stallion Oilfield Services Ltd	D	713 528-5544
Houston (G-12042)		
Stanco Marine Inc	F	979 233-1614
Freeport (G-7214)		
Standard E&S LLC	E	806 741-1080
Lubbock (G-14487)		
Stealth Oilwell Services LLC	D	432 333-3600
Odessa (G-16165)		
Stone Well Service Inc	E	361 874-4211
Lolita (G-14177)		
Stork Technical Svcs USA Inc	D	832 781-5700
Houston (G-12073)		
Straight Line Construction Inc	E	361 394-7656
Freer (G-7233)		
Strata Control Services Inc	E	337 785-0000
Spring (G-19256)		
Strc Oilfield Technology LLC	E	817 599-6155
Weatherford (G-20623)		
Streamline Prod Systems Inc	D	800 780-4011
Kountze (G-13673)		
Streamline Production Svcs Inc	D	409 834-6096
Village Mills (G-20339)		
Submersible Oil Services Inc	C	432 699-1506
Midland (G-15422)		
Subsea Company	E	281 324-0558
Houston (G-12087)		
Subsea Technology Inc	D	281 498-7399
Houston (G-12089)		
Summit Pump & Safety Inc	F	979 567-7867
Caldwell (G-2637)		
Sun Coast Resources Inc	C	713 844-9600
Houston (G-12097)		
Sun West Mud Company Inc	E	432 689-0777
Midland (G-15425)		
Sun West Mud Company Inc	F	817 594-9758
Weatherford (G-20624)		
Sundown Operating Inc	D	806 229-6102
Sundown (G-19614)		
Super Heaters LLC	E	713 952-5533
Houston (G-12105)		
Superior Energy Services Inc	E	281 784-5717
Houston (G-12111)		
Superior Energy Services Inc	F	940 668-5100
Gainesville (G-7370)		
Superior Optimization Ltd	F	817 244-4900
Fort Worth (G-7024)		
Sutton Bros Inc	F	325 387-2053
Sonora (G-19030)		
Swabco Inc	F	806 894-1511
Levelland (G-14017)		
Swat Inc	E	409 296-4976
Floresville (G-6250)		
Sweco	F	817 202-0350
Grand Prairie (G-7979)		
Swire Oilfield Services LLC	E	281 210-5598
Spring (G-19170)		
Systems International Inc	F	281 424-2700
Anahuac (G-528)		
T & T Marine Salvage Inc	F	409 621-4500
Galveston (G-7410)		
T & T Testers Inc	F	432 682-5456
Midland (G-15428)		
T & T Transports Inc	F	325 728-2669
Colorado City (G-3227)		
T Hill Production Svcs Inc	F	325 884-2670
Big Lake (G-2062)		
T-Rey Properties Inc	E	432 570-6822
Midland (G-15429)		
Talajak Inc	F	325 632-5341
Mertzon (G-15021)		
Tall City Well Service Co LP	F	432 618-9937
Midland (G-15430)		
Target Well Services Inc	F	361 883-8100
Canyon Lake (G-2681)		
Taylor Industries LLC	D	918 266-7301
Fort Worth (G-7038)		
Taylor Oil Inc	F	806 948-4166
Sunray (G-19622)		
TCO Field Service Inc	E	432 682-5355
Midland (G-15433)		
Tdw Services Inc	F	281 291-8156
Pasadena (G-16517)		
Technologies Alliance Inc	E	281 442-8825
Houston (G-12176)		
Teems Rig Manufacturing LLC	F	806 379-6904
Amarillo (G-513)		
Tejas Trucking Inc	G	432 523-5786
Andrews (G-560)		
Tendeka Inc	D	832 827-4211
Houston (G-12202)		
Tennessee Pipeline Cnstr Inc	C	361 364-2703
Sinton (G-18966)		
Tercel Oilfield Pdts USA LLC	E	832 386-2500
Houston (G-12207)		
Tervita LLC	D	832 399-4500
Houston (G-12210)		
Tervita LLC	F	817 783-2777
Alvarado (G-346)		
Tesco Corporation (us)	D	713 359-7000
Houston (G-12212)		
Tesco Services Inc	D	903 983-1007
Kilgore (G-13596)		
Tetra Technologies Inc	E	903 693-9500
Carthage (G-2923)		
Texas Cementing Services Inc	F	361 516-1127
Kingsville (G-13635)		
Texas Energy Services LP	B	361 664-5020
Alice (G-240)		
Texas Hot Oilers Inc	F	979 542-9341
Giddings (G-7703)		
Texas Ine Inc	D	281 601-4884
Houston (G-12236)		
Texas Oiltech Laboratories Inc	E	281 495-2400
Houston (G-12242)		
Texas Pipeline Webb	E	210 298-2222
San Antonio (G-18541)		
Texas Wireline Mfg LLC	F	817 546-0772
Fort Worth (G-7051)		
Texland Petroleum LP	F	806 894-4657
Lubbock (G-14495)		
Texoil Services	F	979 242-5571
La Grange (G-13702)		
Thomas Oilfield Services LLC	D	855 778-5940
Longview (G-14319)		
Thomas Oilfield Services LLC	D	903 806-0582
Odessa (G-16176)		
Thompson & Thompson	F	325 392-3721
Ozona (G-16287)		
Threading & Precision Mfg LLC	C	281 452-3036
Houston (G-12282)		
Thru Tubing Solutions Inc	F	361 883-4600
Corpus Christi (G-3641)		
Thrubit LLC	E	713 874-9600
Sugar Land (G-19566)		
Thrubit LLC	D	713 538-9500
Sugar Land (G-19567)		
Tidal Logistics Inc	C	940 668-1818
Fort Worth (G-7063)		
Tierra Lease Service LLC	B	830 583-3717
Kenedy (G-13492)		
Tillery & Parks Company LP	F	432 366-2700
Odessa (G-16179)		
Tmr Services LLC	E	432 693-2175
Rankin (G-17233)		
Tom Thorp Transports	D	325 392-8323
Ozona (G-16288)		

PRODUCT

Company		Phone
Tomlinson Oilfield Service	F	956 802-0030
La Vernia (G-13803)		
Top Cat Well Transport	F	903 295-7000
White Oak (G-20720)		
Top O Texas Oilfield Services	E	806 665-2501
Pampa (G-16342)		
Total Wellhead & Rentl Tls LLC	E	806 435-3800
Perryton (G-16650)		
Transcontinental Energy Corp	G	713 856-6755
Houston (G-12351)		
Transtar Oilfield Services LLC		281 456-7822
Houston (G-12354)		
Trencor Enterprises Inc	F	806 659-3911
Spearman (G-19089)		
Tri Leaf Industries LLC	D	830 742-3700
Missouri City (G-15596)		
Triangle Well Servicing Co	F	806 665-8459
Pampa (G-16343)		
Trican Well Service LP	A	281 716-9152
Houston (G-12368)		
Trinity Environmental Svcs LLC	F	512 582-8050
Austin (G-1594)		
Trinity Services LLC	D	903 687-4350
Waskom (G-20524)		
Triple J Oilfield Services Inc	D	956 585-1949
Mission (G-15570)		
Triple R Welding LLC	E	432 336-5289
Fort Stockton (G-6330)		
Tripp Construction Inc	E	432 381-2440
Odessa (G-16182)		
Triton Equipment & Services	F	281 681-9797
Spring (G-19260)		
True Grit Transportation Inc	E	682 708-5847
Burleson (G-2599)		
Ttl Subsea Inc	G	713 960-3655
Stafford (G-19390)		
Tuboscope Pipeline Svcs Inc	F	432 337-1570
Odessa (G-16184)		
Tuboscope Pipeline Svcs Inc	F	936 870-3680
Navasota (G-15745)		
Tubular Makeup Technology Inc	E	281 452-5211
Highlands (G-8315)		
Turbeco Inc	F	713 849-9911
Houston (G-12407)		
Twbm Holding Co Inc	F	469 916-9430
Dallas (G-5123)		
Twisted S Services Inc	E	817 473-6959
Mansfield (G-14724)		
U S Weatherford L P	F	903 729-2106
Kilgore (G-13598)		
U S Weatherford L P	E	817 293-5192
Fort Worth (G-7090)		
U S Weatherford L P	E	281 331-5505
Alvin (G-383)		
U S Weatherford L P	F	281 674-6500
Houston (G-12422)		
U S Weatherford L P	E	361 289-1551
Corpus Christi (G-3645)		
U S Weatherford L P	E	806 592-3407
Denver City (G-5425)		
U S Weatherford L P	D	432 550-9297
Odessa (G-16185)		
U S Weatherford L P	F	281 348-1000
Kingwood (G-13655)		
U S Weatherford L P	E	713 983-5000
Houston (G-12424)		
U S Weatherford L P	F	281 652-1300
Pearland (G-16606)		
U S Weatherford L P	G	832 590-4130
Houston (G-12425)		
U S Weatherford L P	C	832 424-0000
Katy (G-13453)		
U S Weatherford L P	D	361 289-5111
Corpus Christi (G-3646)		
U S Weatherford L P	E	281 485-1899
Pearland (G-16607)		
U S Weatherford L P	E	432 530-4900
Odessa (G-16186)		
U S Weatherford L P	E	940 626-4698
Decatur (G-5255)		
U S Weatherford L P	G	936 435-8118
Huntsville (G-12827)		
U S Weatherford L P	F	432 682-7321
Midland (G-15453)		
U S Weatherford L P	F	281 449-1383
Houston (G-12426)		
U S Weatherford L P	E	325 387-3280
Sonora (G-19031)		
U S Weatherford L P	E	936 295-0080
Huntsville (G-12828)		

Company		Phone
U S Weatherford L P	C	281 847-0121
Houston (G-12427)		
U S Weatherford L P	E	325 392-3715
Ozona (G-16290)		
U S Weatherford L P	F	281 485-0500
Pearland (G-16608)		
United Casing Incorporated	E	281 456-0212
Houston (G-12445)		
United Casing Tubular Services	E	281 456-0212
Houston (G-12446)		
Universal Valve Company Inc	E	432 689-6341
Midland (G-15458)		
Universal Wllhead Svcs Hldngs	F	361 299-1100
Corpus Christi (G-3647)		
Usdatwing Aerial Analytics LLC	F	210 495-5577
San Antonio (G-18582)		
V P Sales & Company LP	F	361 664-2999
Alice (G-243)		
Vac-U-Rat Oilfield Svcs LLC	F	214 850-1042
Dallas (G-5149)		
Valerus Compression Svcs LP	E	817 598-1600
Weatherford (G-20628)		
Varco LP	E	432 362-0581
Odessa (G-16197)		
Varco LP	E	361 854-1167
Corpus Christi (G-3650)		
Vfl Energy Technologies Inc	F	713 466-9883
Houston (G-12560)		
Viking Coil Tubing LLC	D	432 580-7555
Odessa (G-16201)		
Vinyard Water Service	E	806 256-2766
Shamrock (G-18893)		
Viper Blasting & Coating Inc	E	432 337-9711
Odessa (G-16202)		
Viper Drilling International	D	832 917-5804
Houston (G-12570)		
Vision Oil Field Services Lc	F	361 578-1901
Victoria (G-20315)		
Vitex Wireline Services Inc	G	361 575-1233
Victoria (G-20316)		
Viva Well Servicing Company LP	E	432 552-0800
Odessa (G-16203)		
Viva Well Servicing II L P	E	432 524-2781
Andrews (G-561)		
W E Hayden Lease Service Inc	E	361 771-3684
Ganado (G-7416)		
W L Flowers Mch Wldg Co Inc	D	361 664-6527
Alice (G-244)		
Ward Mc Carty Inc	E	936 336-3132
Liberty (G-14127)		
Warrior Energy Services Corp	F	972 687-9057
Dallas (G-5173)		
Warrior Energy Services Corp	F	830 569-2096
Pleasanton (G-17077)		
Warrior Energy Services Corp	F	504 220-8080
Dallas (G-3859)		
Warrior Energy Services Corp	F	817 237-9223
Alice (G-245)		
Warrior Technologies LLC	G	432 818-0498
Midland (G-15465)		
Washita Valley Enterprises Inc	F	817 220-0450
Springtown (G-19277)		
Waters & Waters Services Inc	D	432 827-3354
Goldsmith (G-7743)		
Weatherford Artificia	E	817 882-9955
Fort Worth (G-7129)		
Weatherford Artificia	F	432 550-6118
Odessa (G-16205)		
Weatherford Artificia	E	432 368-3865
Odessa (G-16206)		
Weatherford International LLC	E	903 353-9700
Longview (G-14333)		
Weatherford International LLC	E	281 652-1300
Houston (G-12612)		
Weatherford International LLC	B	985 493-6100
Huntsville (G-12829)		
Weatherford International LLC	E	713 693-4000
Huntsville (G-12830)		
Weatherford International LLC	E	281 485-1899
Pearland (G-16610)		
Weatherford International LLC	E	817 568-0282
Fort Worth (G-7131)		
Weatherford International LLC	E	210 306-3431
Elmendorf (G-6074)		
Weatherford International LLC	D	432 332-1318
Odessa (G-16207)		
Weatherford International LLC	A	713 693-4000
Houston (G-12613)		
Weatherford International LLC	G	361 576-5641
Victoria (G-20320)		

Company		Phone
Weatherford International LLC	F	806 435-6801
Perryton (G-16651)		
Weatherford International LLC	G	817 443-3000
Benbrook (G-2048)		
Weatherford International LLC	E	832 955-0000
Houston (G-12615)		
Weatherford International LLC	E	661 589-2146
Greenville (G-8095)		
Weatherford International LLC	E	832 590-4000
Houston (G-12616)		
Weatherford International LLC	E	281 260-5700
Houston (G-12617)		
Weatherford International LLC	G	281 460-7863
Houston (G-12618)		
Weatherford International LLC	C	281 260-2707
Houston (G-12619)		
Weatherford International LLC	D	432 563-0598
Odessa (G-16208)		
Weatherford International Ltd	G	210 626-0831
Elmendorf (G-6076)		
Weatherford US LP	E	210 306-3400
Elmendorf (G-6077)		
Weathrford Artfl Lift Systems	D	432 334-4500
Odessa (G-16209)		
Weathrford Artfl Lift Systems	E	903 663-1966
Longview (G-14334)		
Weathrford Artfl Lift Systems	E	432 586-3883
Kermit (G-13515)		
Well-Foam Inc	C	432 276-3290
Odessa (G-16210)		
Well-Pro Services LP	E	903 759-6071
White Oak (G-20721)		
Wellbore Fishing Rentl Tls LLC	F	432 563-1478
Midland (G-15467)		
Welldynamics Inc	E	281 297-1211
Houston (G-12631)		
Wellhead Control Products Inc	E	713 475-2283
Pasadena (G-16525)		
Welltec Inc	E	281 371-1200
Katy (G-13455)		
West Texas Anchor Inc	E	325 884-3402
Big Lake (G-2063)		
Western Chemical Trading LLC	F	405 923-4211
Corpus Christi (G-3654)		
Wildcat Oil Tools LLC	E	432 332-4241
Odessa (G-16212)		
Wiley Lease Co Ltd	E	830 277-0112
Jourdanton (G-13336)		
Win-Tex Lease Services Inc	F	409 296-4194
Winnie (G-20893)		
Wireline Truck Fab LP	E	830 372-3626
Seguin (G-18874)		
Wolf Oil Field Services Inc	F	979 242-5341
Warda (G-20513)		
Wood Group Usa Inc	F	281 647-8300
Houston (G-12688)		
Workover Solutions Inc	E	361 947-8695
Houston (G-12691)		
Wrights Well Control Svcs LLC	E	337 502-4160
Spring (G-19264)		
Ws Energy Services LLC	E	361 348-3488
Robstown (G-17520)		
Wte Services LLC	E	432 547-2300
Monahans (G-15615)		
Wtx Oilfield Services	E	325 227-4656
San Angelo (G-17842)		
Ww Wireline Co Inc	E	956 712-9473
Laredo (G-13940)		
Wwt International Inc	F	281 345-8019
Houston (G-12701)		
Wwt International Inc	F	281 345-8019
Houston (G-12702)		
Xl Oilfield Services LLC	E	830 672-6644
Gonzales (G-7767)		
Xterra Fishing & Rental Tls Co	E	817 334-4100
Fort Worth (G-7153)		
Xytex Inc	F	361 394-5524
Freer (G-7235)		
Yellowjacket Oilfield Svcs LLC	F	432 523-3692
Andrews (G-563)		
Yellowjacket Oilfield Svcs LLC	D	361 485-0625
Victoria (G-20321)		
Yellowjacket Oilfield Svcs LLC	F	432 381-0104
Houston (G-12716)		
Yellowjacket Oilfield Svcs LLC	F	432 242-7615
Levelland (G-14018)		
Zedi US Inc	F	830 876-2777
Carrizo Springs (G-2689)		
Zedi US Inc	E	361 575-4528
Victoria (G-20323)		

Zedi US Inc ....G...... 713 527-9591
Houston *(G-12724)*

OIL LEASES, BUYING & SELLING ON OWN ACCOUNT

Allar Company ....G...... 940 549-0077
Graham *(G-7775)*
Concord Oil Co ....F...... 210 224-4455
San Antonio *(G-18022)*
Halcon Gulf States LLC ....F...... 832 538-0300
Houston *(G-10091)*
Halcon Holdings Inc ....E...... 832 538-0300
Houston *(G-10092)*
Tauber Exploration & Prod Co .....F...... 713 869-5656
Houston *(G-12164)*

OIL ROYALTY TRADERS

Johnson & Ernst Operating Co .....E...... 940 723-8127
Wichita Falls *(G-20774)*
Nortex Corporation ....G...... 713 658-1142
Houston *(G-11071)*
Rowan Petroleum Inc ....C...... 713 621-7800
Houston *(G-11679)*

OIL TREATING COMPOUNDS

U S Weatherford L P ....E...... 432 332-4798
Odessa *(G-16187)*

OILS & ESSENTIAL OILS

Global Business & Commerce Inc .....F...... 214 449-0566
Dallas *(G-3843)*
Wages White Lion Invstmnts LLC .....F...... 214 880-6440
Richardson *(G-17425)*

OILS & GREASES: Blended & Compounded

Delta Companies Group ....E...... 281 479-7288
Deer Park *(G-5267)*
Hydrotex Holdings Inc ....D...... 972 389-8500
Dallas *(G-4477)*
Hydrotex Partners ....E...... 972 389-8500
Farmers Branch *(G-6203)*
Macdermid Canning Ltd ....E...... 713 472-5081
Pasadena *(G-16478)*
Pennzoil-Quaker State Company .....A...... 800 237-8645
Houston *(G-11284)*
Rectorseal LLC ....D...... 713 263-8001
Houston *(G-11565)*
South Coast Terminals LP ....D...... 713 672-2401
Houston *(G-11963)*
South Coast Terminals LP ....E...... 281 842-1286
La Porte *(G-13790)*
Southwestern Petroleum Corp ....E...... 817 348-7233
Fort Worth *(G-7006)*
Total Specialties Usa Inc ....E...... 713 969-4651
Houston *(G-12334)*
Zxp Technologies LLC ....B...... 281 426-8800
Highlands *(G-8317)*

OILS & GREASES: Lubricating

Chemax Corporation ....E...... 409 866-4232
Beaumont *(G-1868)*
Chevron Marine Products LLC ....D...... 832 854-2767
Houston *(G-9179)*
Darling Ingredients Inc ....E...... 713 224-0438
Houston *(G-9404)*
Diamond Shamrock Ref & Mktg Co .....B...... 361 786-2536
Three Rivers *(G-19944)*
Ethyl Corporation ....D...... 713 740-8300
Pasadena *(G-16431)*
Flex Tank Systems LLC ....E...... 281 862-2900
Channelview *(G-3022)*
HI Tech Oil Blends Inc ....F...... 972 231-5464
Allen *(G-274)*
Intergulf Corporation ....D...... 281 474-4210
La Porte *(G-13754)*
James Walker Oil & Gas Co ....F...... 281 875-0002
Conroe *(G-3313)*
Kluber Lubrication N Amer LP ....D...... 903 534-8021
Tyler *(G-20109)*
Kluber Lubrication NA LP ....G...... 903 534-8021
Tyler *(G-20110)*
Lubchem Inc ....F...... 281 350-9600
Spring *(G-19143)*
Ramses Lubr Repackaging LLC .....F...... 972 672-8717
Grand Prairie *(G-7962)*
South Coast Products LP ....E...... 713 434-2141
Houston *(G-11962)*

Stinger Chemical LLC ....D...... 713 227-1340
Houston *(G-12067)*
Sun Coast Resources Inc ....C...... 713 844-9600
Houston *(G-12097)*
Vexa Pak LLC ....F...... 713 671-1100
Houston *(G-12559)*
Whitmore Manufacturing Company .....F...... 972 771-1000
Rockwall *(G-17571)*

OILS: Cutting

Ashburn Industries ....E...... 832 399-1000
Houston *(G-8718)*

OILS: Essential

Grayden Cedarworks Inc ....E...... 325 446-3366
Junction *(G-13339)*
Herbal Essentials LLC ....E...... 832 439-3114
Fresno *(G-7239)*

OILS: Lubricating

Novvi LLC ....F...... 281 488-0833
Deer Park *(G-5287)*
Polymer Dynamics Inc ....F...... 281 894-6382
Houston *(G-11358)*
Southwest Impreglon R Inc ....E...... 281 441-2000
Humble *(G-12798)*

OILS: Lubricating

Championx LLC ....A...... 281 632-6500
Sugar Land *(G-19455)*
Equilon Enterprises LLC ....B...... 713 767-5337
Houston *(G-9685)*
Globalpetrochem LLC ....F...... 832 788-3952
Houston *(G-9983)*
Shell Rapid Lube Lonestar Auto .....F...... 254 953-4360
Harker Heights *(G-8173)*
Wtg Fuels Inc ....F...... 432 837-2518
Alpine *(G-313)*

OILS: Mineral, Natural

Grizzly Operating LLC ....E...... 903 876-2227
Poynor *(G-17201)*
Keane Group Holdings LLC ....A...... 281 716-9152
Houston *(G-10511)*
Trican Well Service LP ....A...... 281 716-9152
Houston *(G-12368)*

OILS: Vegetable Oils, Vulcanized Or Sulfurized

RPS Environmental Solutions LP .....E...... 972 247-1556
Dallas *(G-4915)*

OINTMENTS

Actitech LP ....D...... 903 893-2551
Sherman *(G-18904)*
O D C L Inc ....E...... 956 565-3131
Mercedes *(G-15009)*
Swiss-American Cdmo LLC ....C...... 214 239-2280
Carrollton *(G-2822)*

OLEFINS

Equistar Chemicals LP ....E...... 281 862-4000
Channelview *(G-3020)*
Equistar Chemicals LP ....A...... 713 309-7200
Houston *(G-9689)*
Lyondell Chemical Company ....D...... 361 242-8000
Corpus Christi *(G-3565)*
Lyondell Chemical Company ....E...... 713 309-7200
Houston *(G-10705)*
Phillips 66 ....C...... 281 293-6600
Houston *(G-11324)*
Shell Oil Company ....A...... 713 241-6161
Houston *(G-11860)*
Ttwf LP ....A...... 713 960-9111
Houston *(G-12400)*
Westlake Vinyls Company LP ....C...... 713 960-9111
Houston *(G-12655)*

ON-LINE DATABASE INFORMATION RETRIEVAL SVCS

Inservio3 LLC ....G...... 213 439-9656
Georgetown *(G-7658)*
Libredigital Inc ....F...... 512 334-5100
Austin *(G-1291)*

OPERATIVE BUILDERS: Condominiums

Willbnks Fncl Cnslting Group L .....F...... 469 444-0170
Dallas *(G-3860)*

OPERATOR TRAINING, COMPUTER

Travis Assn For The Blind ....C...... 512 442-2329
Austin *(G-1590)*

OPERATOR: Apartment Buildings

Indochinese Culture Center ....F...... 713 522-7799
Houston *(G-10343)*

OPERATOR: Nonresidential Buildings

Burk Royalty Co Ltd ....E...... 940 397-8600
Wichita Falls *(G-20748)*
Seguins Budget Auto Inc ....F...... 830 372-1790
Seguin *(G-18863)*
Sowell & Co LP ....E...... 214 871-3320
Dallas *(G-4994)*

OPHTHALMIC GOODS

Alcon Vision LLC ....A...... 713 668-9100
Houston *(G-8533)*
Cooper Optical Co Inc ....F...... 903 753-7606
Longview *(G-14214)*
Dac Vision Incorporated ....D...... 972 677-2700
Garland *(G-7474)*
Eoa Holding Co Inc ....F...... 214 496-4000
Dallas *(G-4328)*
Essilor of America Inc ....B...... 214 496-4000
Dallas *(G-4333)*
Essilor of America Inc ....B...... 214 496-4000
Dallas *(G-4334)*
Essilor of America Inc ....B...... 214 496-4235
Dallas *(G-4335)*
Hoya Optical Labs America Inc .....D...... 972 221-4141
Lewisville *(G-14054)*
Luxottica of America Inc ....E...... 512 450-1234
Austin *(G-1313)*
South Texas Eye Cons Pllc ....E...... 361 992-9400
Corpus Christi *(G-3623)*

OPHTHALMIC GOODS WHOLESALERS

Dac Vision Incorporated ....D...... 972 677-2700
Garland *(G-7474)*
Essilor Laboratories Amer Inc ....B...... 972 241-4141
Dallas *(G-4332)*
Essilor of America Inc ....B...... 214 496-4000
Dallas *(G-4334)*
Hoya Lens of America Inc ....D...... 972 221-4141
Lewisville *(G-14053)*
Omega Optical Co LP ....F...... 972 241-4141
Dallas *(G-4760)*

OPHTHALMIC GOODS, NEC, WHOLESALE: Lenses

I O U Enterprises Inc...................F...... 956 631-3366
McAllen *(G-14870)*

OPHTHALMIC GOODS: Eyewear, Protective

Safety Rx Services & Sup Corp ......E...... 281 487-0505
Pasadena *(G-16502)*

OPHTHALMIC GOODS: Frames & Parts, Eyeglass & Spectacle

Williams Optometrist ....F...... 281 332-6021
League City *(G-13982)*

OPHTHALMIC GOODS: Frames, Lenses & Parts, Eyeglasses

Med Logics Inc ....G...... 949 582-3891
Athens *(G-830)*

OPTICAL GOODS STORES

Visionworks of America Inc ....A...... 800 669-1183
San Antonio *(G-18596)*

OPTICAL GOODS STORES: Contact Lenses, Prescription

Ragsdale Vision Ctr ....F...... 940 387-9595
Denton *(G-5396)*

PRODUCT

Vision Centers PA ....E 512 258-2020
Austin (G-1638)

OPTICAL GOODS STORES: Eyeglasses, Prescription

Cooper Optical Co Inc ....F 903 753-7606
Longview (G-14214)
Luxottica of America Inc ....E 512 450-1234
Austin (G-1313)

OPTICAL INSTRUMENT REPAIR SVCS

Summit Night Vision Group Inc ....F 972 992-0046
Plano (G-17013)

OPTICAL INSTRUMENTS & APPARATUS

Archer Optx Inc ....E 972 722-1064
Rockwall (G-17537)
Elbit Systems of America LLC ....E 817 234-6600
Fort Worth (G-6609)
Eyemasters 13 Inc ....F 254 751-0010
Waco (G-20400)
Helena Laboratories Corp ....B 409 842-3714
Beaumont (G-1902)

OPTICAL INSTRUMENTS & LENSES

America Ilsin Tech LLC ....F 972 556-0916
Carrollton (G-2696)
American Electro Optics LLC ....F 817 546-0993
Fort Worth (G-6380)
Applied Optoelectronics Inc ....C 281 295-1800
Sugar Land (G-19445)
Carl Zeiss Vision Inc ....F 972 906-9663
Lewisville (G-14033)
Dac Vision Incorporated ....D 972 677-2700
Garland (G-7474)
Digital Video Camera Co ....F 512 301-9564
Austin (G-1094)
Egma LLC ....F 972 488-3462
Dallas (G-4303)
I O U Enterprises Inc ....F 956 631-3366
McAllen (G-14870)
National Optcl & Scientfc Ins ....F 210 590-9010
Schertz (G-18757)
Nivisys LLC ....G 915 633-8354
El Paso (G-5897)
Optical Filter Source LLC ....F 512 248-0605
Round Rock (G-17676)
Origin Instruments Corp ....F 972 606-8740
Grand Prairie (G-7942)
Petroleum Geo-Services Inc ....C 281 509-8000
Houston (G-11307)
Pgs Finance Inc ....A 281 509-8000
Houston (G-11318)
Ross Optical Industries Inc ....F 915 595-5417
El Paso (G-5946)
Schneider Optical Machines Inc ....F 972 247-4000
Frisco (G-7311)
Tyrex Group Ltd ....F 512 623-4694
Austin (G-1603)
Vision Centers PA ....E 512 258-2020
Austin (G-1638)

OPTICAL SCANNING SVCS

Common Source LP ....F 281 443-7575
Houston (G-9253)
Compu-Data International LLC ....E 281 292-1333
Houston (G-9263)
Inservio3 LLC ....G 213 439-9656
Georgetown (G-7658)
Jeh-Eas Inc ....G 210 490-9156
San Antonio (G-18200)
Omnidata Services Group LLC ....F 281 469-4365
Houston (G-11180)

OPTOMETRISTS' OFFICES

Ragsdale Vision Ctr ....F 940 387-9595
Denton (G-5396)
South Texas Eye Cons Pllc ....E 361 992-9400
Corpus Christi (G-3623)
Vision Centers PA ....E 512 258-2020
Austin (G-1638)

ORDNANCE

Lewis Engineering Company ....E 903 938-6754
Marshall (G-14787)

Lockheed Martin Corporation ....A 972 603-1000
Grand Prairie (G-7914)

ORDNANCE: Flame Throwers

Lonestar Couplings Inc ....F 713 690-1873
Houston (G-10683)

ORGANIZATIONS & UNIONS: Labor

Air Liquide Electronics US LP ....A 972 301-5200
Dallas (G-3905)

ORGANIZATIONS: Physical Research, Noncommercial

Bastion Technologies Inc ....E 281 283-9330
Houston (G-8823)

ORGANIZATIONS: Professional

Powell Electrical Systems Inc ....A 713 790-1700
Houston (G-11373)
Refined Industrial Supply Inc ....E 409 789-1794
League City (G-13978)
Savant Alaska LLC ....E 907 868-1258
Houston (G-11759)
Texas Electric Coops Inc ....E 512 454-0311
Austin (G-1567)

ORGANIZATIONS: Religious

Mission City Press Inc ....F 210 614-7051
San Antonio (G-18309)
Stone-Cmpbell Rest Mvment Pubg ....G 325 674-2720
Abilene (G-83)

ORGANIZATIONS: Research Institute

Alcon Research LLC ....C 817 551-4555
Fort Worth (G-6366)

ORGANIZATIONS: Scientific Research Agency

Lacore Labs Inc ....F 469 995-7791
Mckinney (G-14950)
Rdrtec Incorporated ....E 214 353-8755
Dallas (G-4866)

OSCILLATORS

Wenzel Associates Inc ....D 512 835-2038
Austin (G-1655)

OSICIZERS: Inorganic

Indorama Ventures Oxides LLC ....A 346 365-6056
The Woodlands (G-19883)

OVENS: Distillation, Charcoal & Coke

Clean Energy Tech Assn Inc ....E 903 389-4136
Fairfield (G-6171)

OVENS: Surveillance, Powder Aging & Testing

Idis America Co Ltd ....F 866 986-1312
Coppell (G-3420)

PACKAGED FROZEN FOODS WHOLESALERS, NEC

Chungs Products LP ....C 713 741-2118
Houston (G-9186)
Ditta Meat Company ....D 281 487-2010
Pasadena (G-16417)
Houston Sysco Inc ....E 713 672-8080
Houston (G-10254)
MARTIN PREFERRED FOODS LP ....C 713 869-6191
Houston (G-10777)
Pops Bakery Inc ....E 325 655-1170
San Angelo (G-17822)
WEI-Chuan USA Inc ....F 713 690-3677
Houston (G-12626)

PACKAGING & LABELING SVCS

Aldersgate Enrichment Center ....D 325 646-2566
Early (G-5556)
American Micro Systems Ltd ....E 817 571-9015
Euless (G-6130)

Bayou Imaging Products LLC ....F 713 923-8300
Houston (G-8835)
Beer Dudes Canning Co LLC ....F 972 342-4819
Denton (G-5353)
Employee Owned Nursery Entps ....F 512 276-1211
Elgin (G-6054)
Fedex Office & Print Svcs Inc ....F 512 528-9690
Cedar Park (G-2969)
Gc Packaging LLC ....D 214 383-7700
Allen (G-270)
Gs Liquid Technologies LLC ....F 817 556-6262
Cleburne (G-3093)
Hurley Packaging Texas Inc ....E 806 687-6179
Lubbock (G-14422)
Imperial Bag & Paper Co LLC ....E 713 223-5050
Houston (G-10334)
Mylan Institutional Inc ....D 281 240-1000
Sugar Land (G-19509)
National Cnverting Fulfillment ....E 972 875-5096
Ennis (G-6112)
Plastipak Packaging Inc ....C 972 276-8660
Garland (G-7568)
Raider Services LP ....C 830 996-0016
Gordon (G-7769)
Ramirez Everardo ....E 915 593-5349
El Paso (G-5926)
Relocation Systems Inc ....E 972 241-2300
Irving (G-13164)
Seapac Inc ....D 281 383-2400
Baytown (G-1801)
Texas Corrugated Box Packg LLC ....E 817 454-2037
Fort Worth (G-7046)
Travis Assn For The Blind ....C 512 442-2329
Austin (G-1590)
Western Industries Corporation ....E 512 837-0240
Austin (G-1658)

PACKAGING MATERIALS, INDL: Wholesalers

Bana Inc ....C 817 232-3750
Saginaw (G-17739)
Berlin Packaging LLC ....F 214 339-0054
Dallas (G-4019)
Corpus Chrsti Gsket Fstner Inc ....C 361 884-6366
Corpus Christi (G-3510)
Fluid Sealing Products Inc ....D 713 910-1028
Houston (G-9816)
Riteks Inc ....E 972 529-1118
McKinney (G-14972)
Texas Gasket and Packing Co ....F 713 674-7531
Houston (G-12232)

PACKAGING MATERIALS, WHOLESALE

Action Box Co Inc ....C 713 869-7701
Houston (G-8469)
American Excelsior Company ....E 817 385-4300
Arlington (G-616)
Creative Molded Packaging LLC ....F 915 881-8401
El Paso (G-5705)
Detroit Forming Inc ....E 903 832-4653
Nash (G-15721)
Fairbanks Packaging LLC ....G 817 849-1366
Grand Prairie (G-7869)
General Labels & Printing LLC ....E 915 532-7131
El Paso (G-5781)
Ghx Industrial LLC ....E 409 832-3461
Beaumont (G-1898)
Green Bay Packaging Inc ....C 817 551-1934
Fort Worth (G-6675)
Greif Flexibles USA Inc ....F 713 461-0840
Houston (G-10040)
Hercules Films LLC ....G 920 284-0796
Sugar Land (G-19491)
Hercules Films LLC ....F 920 284-0796
Sugar Land (G-19492)
Hurley Packaging Texas Inc ....E 806 687-6179
Lubbock (G-14422)
Ics Enterprises Ltd ....E 915 539-5415
El Paso (G-5807)
Ifco Systems North America Inc ....E 713 937-9311
Houston (G-10318)
Komplete Group Inc ....D 214 252-8100
Grand Prairie (G-7907)
Miller Paper Company ....E 806 353-0317
Amarillo (G-502)
Printpack Inc ....C 972 602-8421
Grand Prairie (G-7955)
Protective Packaging Corp Inc ....E 972 446-2247
Carrollton (G-2800)
Sealed Air Corporation ....D 817 540-2020
Grand Prairie (G-7972)

Tristar Packaging Inc ....F 281 540-2613
Humble *(G-12806)*

Williams Products Inc ....F 214 630-3131
Arlington *(G-809)*

PACKAGING MATERIALS: *Paper*

Age Industries Ltd ....D 817 477-5266
Cleburne *(G-3079)*

Aluma Graphics LP ....E 972 442-3299
Wylie *(G-20925)*

American Excelsior Company ....E 817 385-4300
Arlington *(G-616)*

Bayou Imaging Products LLC ....F 713 923-8300
Houston *(G-8835)*

Berry Global Films LLC ....C 972 576-8193
Waxahachie *(G-20529)*

Dac Labels & Graphic Spc ....F 214 340-2055
Dallas *(G-4205)*

Dalpack ....F 972 446-8101
Haltom City *(G-8137)*

Darling Quick Print Inc ....E 915 858-5055
El Paso *(G-5714)*

Ennis Inc ....C 903 496-2244
Wolfe City *(G-20906)*

Formtex Plastics Corporation ....E 713 493-6628
Houston *(G-9836)*

Greif Inc ....F 346 263-2639
Baytown *(G-1789)*

Hood Flexible Packaging Corp ....D 903 593-1793
Tyler *(G-20100)*

Industrial Tape & Label Corp ....F 713 748-3105
Houston *(G-10354)*

Label Products Inc ....E 713 869-2959
Houston *(G-10584)*

LSI Integrated Graphics LP ....C 713 744-4100
Houston *(G-10696)*

McDowell Packg & Advg Co Inc ....D 469 246-2700
Plano *(G-16923)*

Pactiv LLC ....E 817 608-9009
Arlington *(G-747)*

Printpack Inc ....C 972 602-8421
Grand Prairie *(G-7955)*

Sealed Air Corporation ....D 817 540-2020
Grand Prairie *(G-7972)*

Signode Industrial Group LLC ....E 409 745-2600
Orange *(G-16263)*

Smurfit Kappa North Amer LLC ....B 214 515-6400
Forney *(G-6314)*

Smurfit Kappa North Amer LLC ....B 800 306-8326
Irving *(G-13182)*

Sonoco Products Company ....D 254 666-4777
Waco *(G-20458)*

Southwest Index Tab Co Inc ....E 972 228-8227
Waxahachie *(G-20562)*

Transcendia Inc ....E 800 659-4254
Carrollton *(G-2838)*

Vf Outdoor LLC ....E 817 491-4949
Fort Worth *(G-7102)*

Western Pulp Products Co ....E 903 586-3608
Jacksonville *(G-13266)*

PACKAGING MATERIALS: *Paper, Coated Or Laminated*

Charta Group Inc ....E 310 327-0244
Austin *(G-1044)*

Idea Planet LP ....E 972 380-9867
Dallas *(G-3844)*

Tetra Pak Inc ....C 940 565-8800
Denton *(G-5404)*

Tetra Pak Materials LP ....C 940 565-8800
Denton *(G-5405)*

PACKAGING MATERIALS: *Plastic Film, Coated Or Laminated*

Accredo Packaging Inc ....E 713 580-4800
Sugar Land *(G-19436)*

Greif Flexibles USA Inc ....F 713 461-0840
Houston *(G-10040)*

Norkol Inc ....E 832 644-1481
Humble *(G-12790)*

Orion Pacific Inc ....D 432 332-0058
Odessa *(G-16103)*

Orrex Plastics Company LLC ....E 432 332-1229
Odessa *(G-16104)*

Presco Polymers Opco Inc ....C 903 957-2263
Sherman *(G-18929)*

Rextac LLC ....C 432 332-0058
Odessa *(G-16137)*

Reynolds Consumer Products LLC ......F 254 770-4100
Temple *(G-19701)*

Reynolds Presto Products Inc ....B 972 416-6500
Carrollton *(G-2807)*

Tru-Vision Plastics Inc ....F 979 836-1091
Brenham *(G-2276)*

PACKAGING MATERIALS: *Polystyrene Foam*

American Excelsior Company ....E 817 385-4300
Arlington *(G-616)*

Blakeman Industries Inc ....E 817 267-4444
Euless *(G-6133)*

Champion Pallet & Packaging ....E 972 551-2474
Irving *(G-12968)*

Cryovac LLC ....D 940 851-6060
Wichita Falls *(G-20758)*

Dolco Packaging Corp ....C 214 337-4711
Dallas *(G-4271)*

Epe Industries Usa Inc ....G 800 315-0336
Houston *(G-9679)*

Fgl Group LLC ....E 817 478-3221
Garland *(G-7489)*

Greif Flexibles USA Inc ....F 713 461-0840
Houston *(G-10040)*

Guardian Packaging Inds LP ....E 214 349-1500
Garland *(G-7507)*

Harris Packaging Corporation ....D 817 429-6262
Haltom City *(G-8148)*

Huntington Foam LLC ....F 512 581-7500
Bastrop *(G-1758)*

Inovar Packaging Group LLC ....F 817 277-6666
Dallas *(G-4504)*

Jones Holt Enterprises Inc ....E 210 657-5917
San Antonio *(G-18207)*

P Diamond Enterprises Inc ....F 325 643-5629
Brownwood *(G-2441)*

Pactiv LLC ....E 903 654-4745
Corsicana *(G-3683)*

Pbp Inc ....E 832 902-2231
Baytown *(G-1799)*

Rivercity Waterjet Inc ....F 210 590-0300
San Antonio *(G-18428)*

Rohart Company ....E 713 695-5333
Houston *(G-11657)*

Sealed Air Corporation ....D 940 851-6060
Wichita Falls *(G-20806)*

Sealed Air Corporation ....D 817 540-2020
Grand Prairie *(G-7972)*

Sealed Air Corporation ....D 940 592-2111
Iowa Park *(G-12910)*

Texas Foam Inc ....E 512 581-7500
Bastrop *(G-1763)*

Ufp Technologies Inc ....D 915 598-7377
El Paso *(G-6018)*

Western Industries Corporation ....D 214 503-8322
Carrollton *(G-2848)*

PACKAGING: *Blister Or Bubble Formed, Plastic*

Capco Plastics Inc ....F 915 772-1395
El Paso *(G-5679)*

PACKING & CRATING SVC

Talke Usa Inc ....E 832 260-8325
Mont Belvieu *(G-15621)*

PACKING & CRATING SVCS: *Containerized Goods For Shipping*

Pierce Packaging Co ....E 815 636-5656
Houston *(G-11331)*

PACKING MATERIALS: *Mechanical*

Creative Molded Packaging LLC ....F 915 881-8401
El Paso *(G-5705)*

Greenpacks USA ....F 888 498-7774
Dallas *(G-4415)*

Gs Liquid Technologies LLC ....F 817 556-6262
Cleburne *(G-3093)*

Jaeger Products Inc ....E 817 695-5680
Arlington *(G-710)*

Temperatsure LLC ....E 502 715-2819
Carrollton *(G-2827)*

PACKING SVCS: *Shipping*

Morris Export Crating Company ....D 713 675-9101
Houston *(G-10922)*

Relocation Systems Inc ....E 972 241-2300
Irving *(G-13164)*

Southwest Metrics Inc ....F 817 281-7697
Fort Worth *(G-7004)*

Third Coast Packaging Inc ....E 281 412-0275
Pearland *(G-16604)*

PACKING: *Rubber*

Indian Industries LP ....F 817 265-6731
Arlington *(G-704)*

Utex Industries Inc ....D 713 467-1000
Houston *(G-12505)*

Utex Industries Inc ....D 936 760-4100
Conroe *(G-3381)*

PADS: *Mattress*

Talalay Global Inc ....D 940 851-0107
Wichita Falls *(G-20814)*

PAGERS: *One-way*

Long Range Systems LLC ....E 214 553-5308
Richardson *(G-17349)*

Waveware Technologies Inc ....F 972 479-1702
Garland *(G-7609)*

PAINT & PAINTING SPLYS STORE

Kelly-Moore Paint Company Inc ....F 817 268-1511
Hurst *(G-12847)*

T-Tex Equipment LP ....F 713 991-7070
Houston *(G-12144)*

PAINT STORE

Benjamin Moore & Co ....D 972 285-6346
Mesquite *(G-15031)*

McKee True Value Hdwr & Lbr ....E 903 874-6581
Corsicana *(G-3677)*

TCI Coatings Inc ....F 806 762-0871
Lubbock *(G-14491)*

PAINTING SVC: *Metal Prdts*

Alkote Inc ....E 713 695-3609
Houston *(G-8539)*

Egm Cleaning & Remodeling ....G 210 666-0234
San Antonio *(G-18084)*

Nci Group Inc ....E 713 921-7997
Houston *(G-11018)*

P & M Blasting & Coating Inc ....F 713 896-4691
Houston *(G-11212)*

Pro-Kleen Inc ....F 713 855-2760
Houston *(G-11427)*

Taconic Industries Corporation ....E 972 241-5200
Carrollton *(G-2823)*

Texas Powder Coating Inc ....G 713 690-6226
Houston *(G-12246)*

Three D Finishing Inc ....F 972 475-2726
Rowlett *(G-17713)*

W & W Silkscreening Inc ....E 817 590-4479
Fort Worth *(G-7112)*

PAINTS & ADDITIVES

Adams Manufacturing Co ....F 806 744-0839
Lubbock *(G-14358)*

American Coatings LP ....E 281 351-1776
Tomball *(G-19957)*

Behr Process Corporation ....D 817 837-2600
Roanoke *(G-17483)*

Century Indus Coatings Inc ....E 903 586-9197
Jacksonville *(G-13233)*

Corev America Inc ....E 713 849-3671
Houston *(G-9319)*

Creative Coatings Inc ....F 903 984-8454
Kilgore *(G-13541)*

Envirokind Inc ....F 713 434-9900
Houston *(G-9668)*

Groco Paint Mfg Co Inc ....E 972 286-7890
Dallas *(G-4417)*

Hempel (usa) Inc ....C 214 353-1600
Dallas *(G-4448)*

Intercoastal Paint Co Inc ....F 281 448-5258
Houston *(G-10392)*

Isomeric Industries Inc ....E 832 491-8106
The Woodlands *(G-19886)*

Lapolla Industries LLC ....E 281 219-4100
Houston *(G-10599)*

Powder Coaters of Texas Inc ....F 979 387-2049
Beasley *(G-1844)*

P R O D U C T

PPG Industries Inc ....E 940 665-9590
Gainesville **(G-7358)**

PPG Industries Inc ....E 806 467-9707
Amarillo **(G-509)**

Standard Paints Inc ....F 817 477-5060
Mansfield **(G-14720)**

True Value Company LLC ....C 903 872-8365
Corsicana **(G-3688)**

PAINTS & ALLIED PRODUCTS

Akzo Nobel Inc ....E 512 244-9038
Round Rock **(G-17620)**

Akzo Nobel Inc ....E 210 520-6566
San Antonio **(G-17879)**

American Roller Company LLC .....F 262 878-2445
Houston **(G-8607)**

Axalt Powde Coati Syste Usa I ...C 800 247-3886
Houston **(G-8756)**

Axalta Pwdr Cating Systems Inc .....C 832 955-0201
Houston **(G-8757)**

Barten Industrial Coatings LLC .....F 979 732-8441
Columbus **(G-3230)**

Benjamin Moore & Co ....D 972 285-6346
Mesquite **(G-15031)**

Carchalk Inc ....F 210 667-3890
Seguin **(G-18828)**

CC Coating & Machine Inc ....E 361 884-9753
Corpus Christi **(G-3497)**

Ceram-Kote Coatings Inc ....E 432 263-8497
Big Spring **(G-2074)**

Chem-Coat Industries Inc ....F 972 485-8648
Dallas **(G-4108)**

Coastline Indus Coatings Inc........E 281 499-0633
Stafford **(G-19297)**

Complementary Coatings Corp .....E 210 651-6996
Schertz **(G-18748)**

Compliant Paint Booths LLC ....F 800 609-6408
Terrell **(G-19731)**

Corrpro Companies Inc ....C 713 460-6000
Houston **(G-9325)**

Custom Pipe Coating Inc ....E 713 675-2324
Houston **(G-9373)**

Dow Chemical Company ....E 979 238-2011
Freeport **(G-7196)**

Ennis-Flint Inc ....F 817 706-3777
Ennis **(G-6099)**

Entail Engine LLC ....G 956 467-5198
Brownsville **(G-2354)**

Fusion Operations LP ....D 713 691-6547
Houston **(G-9878)**

Gillespie Coatings Oper LLC ....E 903 753-0393
Longview **(G-14242)**

Gulfstream Aerospace Corp ....A 214 902-7520
Dallas **(G-4423)**

Henry Company ....E 972 272-5488
Garland **(G-7510)**

Inhance Technologies LLC ....E 713 678-7352
Houston **(G-10365)**

International Paint LLC ....F 817 834-0141
Fort Worth **(G-6724)**

International Paint LLC..............C 713 684-1500
Houston **(G-10404)**

Invisishield LLC ....F 713 539-6700
Houston **(G-10411)**

Isothrmal Prtctive Catings Inc .....F 281 485-4440
Pearland **(G-16572)**

Kelly-Moore Paint Company Inc ...F 817 268-1511
Hurst **(G-12847)**

Lbs Enterprises LLC ....F 903 845-6436
Gladewater **(G-7725)**

Lonza Inc ....D 281 291-2300
Pasadena **(G-16475)**

LSI Integrated Graphics LP ....C 713 744-4100
Houston **(G-10696)**

Mascorp Ltd ....E 713 465-0304
Houston **(G-10783)**

Metal Coatings Corp ....D 713 977-0123
Houston **(G-10844)**

Polyglass Coatings Limited LLC .....E 832 736-9243
Pearland **(G-16594)**

PPG Industries Inc ....E 979 693-7097
College Station **(G-3197)**

PPG Industries Inc ....E 936 441-1533
Conroe **(G-3353)**

PPG Industries Inc ....E 361 225-2250
Corpus Christi **(G-3595)**

PPG Industries Inc ....E 214 902-8922
Dallas **(G-4815)**

PPG Industries Inc ....E 713 683-8025
Houston **(G-11381)**

PPG Industries Inc ....E 806 794-0180
Lubbock **(G-14464)**

PPG Industries Inc ....E 214 544-0700
McKinney **(G-14965)**

PPG Industries Inc ....E 713 576-8418
Houston **(G-11382)**

PPG Industries Inc ....E 512 288-5505
Austin **(G-1426)**

PPG Industries Inc ....E 281 487-6416
Pasadena **(G-16497)**

PPG Industries Inc ....E 512 218-9551
Round Rock **(G-17680)**

PPG Industries Inc ....E 210 656-5541
Universal City **(G-20184)**

PPG Industries Inc ....E 281 265-5333
Sugar Land **(G-19528)**

PPG Industries Inc ....E 281 357-0455
Tomball **(G-20000)**

PPG Industries Inc ....E 281 890-4481
Houston **(G-11383)**

PPG Industries Inc ....E 817 613-1860
Weatherford **(G-20611)**

PPG Industries Inc ....E 972 517-2226
Plano **(G-16975)**

PPG Industries Inc ....E 940 322-5201
Wichita Falls **(G-20797)**

PPG Industries Inc ....E 956 791-1191
Laredo **(G-13922)**

PPG Industries Inc ....E 281 842-9518
La Porte **(G-13784)**

Quality Precision Coatings LLC .....G 713 631-8141
Houston **(G-11498)**

Ready Seal Inc ....F 817 594-8198
Weatherford **(G-20615)**

Reichhold Industries Inc ....F 713 453-5431
Houston **(G-11587)**

Robroy Industries Inc ....C 412 828-2100
Gilmer **(G-7712)**

Skudo USA Distribution LLC ....F 972 993-0777
Dallas **(G-4968)**

Southwestern Petroleum Corp .....E 817 348-7233
Fort Worth **(G-7006)**

Spectrum Semiconductor Tech Lc .....F 972 562-2552
McKinney **(G-14977)**

TCI Coatings Inc ....F 806 762-0871
Lubbock **(G-14491)**

Teknor Color Company ....D 903 586-0583
Jacksonville **(G-13262)**

Texas Finishing Company ....E 972 416-2961
Carrollton **(G-2830)**

Trinkote Indus Finishes Inc ....E 817 396-4747
Cresson **(G-3715)**

US Bioservices ....C 214 572-8300
Frisco **(G-7321)**

Verdia Inc ....F 713 999-5090
Conroe **(G-3383)**

Vitro Architectural Glass ....F 940 851-4374
Wichita Falls **(G-20824)**

PAINTS, VARNISHES & SPLYS WHOLESALERS

International Paint LLC..............C 713 684-1500
Houston **(G-10404)**

PAINTS, VARNISHES & SPLYS, WHOLESALE: Colors & Pigments

Venator Materials LLC ....A 281 465-6700
The Woodlands **(G-19937)**

PAINTS, VARNISHES & SPLYS, WHOLESALE: Paints

Benjamin Moore & Co ....D 972 285-6346
Mesquite **(G-15031)**

Complementary Coatings Corp .....E 210 651-6996
Schertz **(G-18748)**

Kelly-Moore Paint Company Inc ...F 817 268-1511
Hurst **(G-12847)**

Verdia Inc ....F 713 999-5090
Conroe **(G-3383)**

PAINTS: Asphalt Or Bituminous

Gardner-Gibson Incorporated .....F 832 288-4111
Houston **(G-9899)**

Hillburn Defense Systems Inc ......G 512 636-8498
Wimberley **(G-20882)**

PAINTS: Lead-In-Oil

Pitzer Family Ltd Partnership ....E 214 398-1491
Dallas **(G-4807)**

PAINTS: Marine

Hempel (usa) Inc ....D 936 523-6000
Conroe **(G-3302)**

Polynt Composites USA Inc ....E 713 799-1800
Houston **(G-11360)**

PAINTS: Oil Or Alkyd Vehicle Or Water Thinned

Akzo Nobel Coatings Inc ....F 713 684-1324
Houston **(G-8520)**

Akzo Nobel Coatings Inc ....F 817 232-9745
Fort Worth **(G-6359)**

Kelly-Moore Paint Company Inc ...F 800 772-7408
Hurst **(G-12848)**

PALLET REPAIR SVCS

G & A Pallet LLC....................E 713 670-8118
Houston **(G-9881)**

PALLETS

AZ Pallet Exchange ....E 713 332-6145
Houston **(G-8766)**

Centurion Pallet Service............F 210 823-3530
San Antonio **(G-17993)**

G & A Pallet Co ....F 713 670-8118
Houston **(G-9882)**

Nefab Companies Inc ....E 866 332-4425
Coppell **(G-3430)**

Nefab Packaging Inc ....E 469 444-5264
Coppell **(G-3431)**

PALLETS & SKIDS: Wood

Age Industries Ltd ....D 210 659-1301
Cibolo **(G-3060)**

Bana Inc ....C 817 232-3750
Saginaw **(G-17739)**

Cargo Crating Company Ltd ....F 713 699-0172
Houston **(G-9092)**

Carrizo Wood Products Inc ....E 936 569-0582
Nacogdoches **(G-15690)**

Cougar Pallet Inc ....D 281 442-1177
Houston **(G-9330)**

Dfw A-1 Pallet Inc ....E 972 401-3502
Irving **(G-12998)**

Entech Technology Inc ....E 972 542-0210
Dallas **(G-4325)**

Ifco Systems North America Inc .....D 214 637-4840
Dallas **(G-4485)**

Miller Waste Mills Inc ....D 817 293-6163
Fort Worth **(G-6842)**

Ufp Schertz LLC ....E 830 606-4300
Schertz **(G-18766)**

PALLETS: Corrugated

Taylormade Pllets Lgistics LLC .....E 210 566-3833
Boerne **(G-2139)**

Unipal Intl Ltd Co Texas ....F 850 232-5586
Pasadena **(G-16521)**

PALLETS: Plastic

Genpak LLC ....C 903 297-4445
Longview **(G-14241)**

Mauser Usa LLC ....D 936 273-1279
Conroe **(G-3328)**

North America Packaging Corp .....C 979 779-5900
Bryan **(G-2496)**

Ropak Southwest Inc ....C 817 473-0259
Mansfield **(G-14714)**

PALLETS: Wooden

2nd Chance Pallets LLC ....F 817 847-8005
Saginaw **(G-17735)**

A & A Pallet and Lumber Co ....F 713 462-4575
Houston **(G-8420)**

A & A Pallet Co ....E 713 480-9861
Houston **(G-8421)**

Age Industries Ltd ....E 915 852-9099
Horizon City **(G-8361)**

Alamo Pallet Recyclers Inc ....F 972 296-2090
Dallas **(G-3917)**

Aldersgate Enrichment Center	D	325 646-2566	Early (G-5556)
Allied Pallet & Eqp Co LLC	F	281 850-8090	Houston (G-8551)
Arrington Lbr & Pallet Co Inc	C	903 586-4070	Jacksonville (G-13226)
Arrington Sawmill Inc	C	903 586-4070	Jacksonville (G-13227)
Atlas Southwest Pallet Co Inc	E	210 532-5343	San Antonio (G-17921)
Austin Pallet Company	E	512 990-0090	Pflugerville (G-16659)
Bell Wooden Products Inc	E	214 388-5421	Dallas (G-4016)
Border Pallets Inc	E	915 852-3939	El Paso (G-5669)
Central Pallets No 2	F	956 726-4023	Laredo (G-13873)
Champion Pallet & Packaging	E	972 551-2474	Irving (G-12968)
Chep (usa) Inc	D	214 688-4108	Dallas (G-4109)
Chep (usa) Inc	E	806 577-4447	Lubbock (G-14392)
Chep (usa) Inc	E	806 553-5655	Amarillo (G-415)
Chep (usa) Inc	D	210 662-7733	San Antonio (G-18002)
Conner Industries Inc	F	713 944-6766	Houston (G-9270)
Consolidated Wood Products Inc	E	903 894-7745	Bullard (G-2551)
Corr-Wood Mfg Inc	D	817 467-5525	Arlington (G-648)
Crimstone AAA Operating Co LP	F	210 662-9400	San Antonio (G-18030)
Custom Crates & Pallets Ltd	D	915 886-4985	Canutillo (G-2663)
D&D Pallets Inc	E	817 625-7966	Fort Worth (G-6571)
Dunn Pallet Co	E	409 722-2933	Port Neches (G-17159)
Fivepayne LLC	D	817 310-0147	Grapevine (G-8035)
Flores Pallets LLC	F	713 645-1022	Houston (G-9805)
Four Way Pallet Co	F	713 675-7788	Houston (G-9847)
G & A Pallet LLC	F	713 670-8118	Houston (G-9881)
Gps-Global Pallets Svcs LLC	E	281 862-9244	Houston (G-10008)
Ifco Systems North America Inc	E	806 335-1746	Amarillo (G-437)
Ifco Systems North America Inc	E	806 291-9024	Plainview (G-16758)
K L Barton & Sons Tie Co	F	936 347-2744	Garrison (G-7611)
Kastros Wood Pallets Inc	F	915 855-8011	El Paso (G-5826)
Kunka Enterprises LLC	F	254 666-3576	Waco (G-20423)
L & L Pallet Supply Inc	F	806 272-5041	Muleshoe (G-15678)
L & L Pallet Supply Inc	F	806 272-5041	Amarillo (G-497)
L L Pallets	F	469 916-7552	Dallas (G-4573)
La Pallet Recyclers	F	281 469-6070	Houston (G-10581)
Leonard Ray Vaught	E	903 572-0352	Cookville (G-3405)
Loadrite Inc	F	940 322-1003	Wichita Falls (G-20779)
M & H Crates Inc	D	903 683-5351	Jacksonville (G-13248)
M & T Pallet Company Inc	E	409 866-8136	Beaumont (G-1921)
Mayco Inc	F	214 638-4848	Dallas (G-4657)
McAllen Bag & Supply Company	F	956 686-6571	McAllen (G-14887)
Metroplex Wood Products Ltd	E	817 538-0375	Fort Worth (G-6834)
Mk Pallets Inc	F	903 537-2400	Saltillo (G-17766)
MPW Enterprises LLC	E	713 671-9560	Houston (G-10932)
Neopal LLC	E	281 219-9600	Houston (G-11024)

Pal-Serv of Dallas LLC	F	214 631-4600	Balch Springs (G-1738)
Pallet & Crating Co Inc	E	903 463-5786	Denison (G-5344)
Pallet Advisor LLC	E	817 271-4840	Dallas (G-4780)
Pallet Depot	F	972 336-0006	Grand Prairie (G-7944)
Pallet King Enterprises Inc	F	972 723-3249	Midlothian (G-15490)
Pallet Ops LLC	E	713 554-6972	Houston (G-11224)
Pallet Ops - San Antonio LLC	F	210 225-7882	San Antonio (G-18364)
Pallet Repair Services Inc	D	972 913-1110	Hutchins (G-12870)
Palletone Inc	D	903 427-3030	Clarksville (G-3077)
Palletone of Texas LP	C	903 628-5695	New Boston (G-15768)
Pallets911 LLC	E	956 203-2671	Brownsville (G-2390)
Pechal Pallets LLC	E	254 773-4460	Temple (G-19698)
Pleasant Fencing & Cnstr	E	903 572-0352	Cookville (G-3406)
Rashidah LLC	G	281 469-5277	Houston (G-11551)
Redco Pallet Inc	E	903 561-2075	Tyler (G-20145)
S and S Pallets	F	972 382-8142	Celina (G-2994)
Saifee Corporation	E	713 674-2000	Houston (G-11730)
South East Pallet Inc	G	713 645-6131	Houston (G-11964)
Springhill Pallets LLC	F	903 297-6090	Longview (G-14311)
Stephens A-1 Lbr & Pallet Inc	E	281 440-6444	Houston (G-12058)
The Pallet Place Inc	E	903 963-4026	Van (G-20210)
Threet Pallet LLC	E	972 489-6887	Ennis (G-6119)
Total Pallet Solutions LLC	F	817 783-5565	Alvarado (G-347)
Traeger Wood Pellets	G	409 384-5331	Jasper (G-13282)
Wooden Pallets Ltd	C	409 385-1234	Silsbee (G-18959)

PANEL & DISTRIBUTION BOARDS & OTHER RELATED APPARATUS

Advanced Elec & Mtr Contrls	E	972 253-7783	Irving (G-12924)
Electrical Contrls Houston Inc	E	281 501-0729	New Caney (G-15838)
Interconnect Wiring LLP	C	817 377-9473	Fort Worth (G-6723)
Kelleys Controls Incorporated	F	432 362-7998	Odessa (G-16045)
Sunrgy LLC	E	832 786-5051	Stafford (G-19381)
Williamsrdm Inc	D	817 872-1500	Fort Worth (G-7148)

PANELS & SECTIONS: Prefabricated, Concrete

Reinforced Earth Company	D	254 836-1847	Waco (G-20454)

PANELS, FLAT: Plastic

Star Delta Motor Controls Inc	E	210 479-3550	San Antonio (G-18497)

PANELS: Building, Metal

BD Hildebrandt Entps Inc	F	936 825-0500	Navasota (G-15725)
Braden and Prewitt Inc	F	713 699-2262	Houston (G-8974)
Central States Mfg Inc	E	469 272-0041	Cedar Hill (G-2938)
Green-Span Profiles LP	F	281 807-7400	Waller (G-20503)
Ktec Cleanroom Systems Inc	F	512 388-2396	Georgetown (G-7659)

Metl-Span LLC	B	972 221-6656	Lewisville (G-14065)
Nci Group Inc	D	972 221-6656	Lewisville (G-14072)
Oldcastle Buildingenvelope Inc	A	972 551-6100	Terrell (G-19746)

PANELS: Building, Plastic, NEC

Knickerbocker Partition Corp	F	972 438-5330	Irving (G-13078)
Kps Global LLC	C	817 281-5121	Fort Worth (G-6770)
Welbilt Walk-Ins LP	C	817 281-5121	Fort Worth (G-7134)

PANELS: Building, Wood

Boxx Modular Inc	F	972 492-4040	Fort Worth (G-6464)
Component Structures Inc	E	940 566-1166	Denton (G-5356)
Panel Specialists Inc	D	254 774-9800	Temple (G-19695)
Pilot Plastics LLC	G	800 918-6765	Fort Worth (G-6907)

PANELS: Control & Metering, Generator

Amerimex Power Systems Inc	F	832 678-3520	Houston (G-8619)

PANELS: Wood

Georgia-Pacific WD Pdts S LLC	A	936 398-2511	Camden (G-2638)
Metro Gate & Mfg Co Inc	E	903 785-8911	Paris (G-16365)

PAPER & BOARD: Die-cut

Accurate Die Cutting Inc	E	972 562-7921	McKinney (G-14922)
Caraustar Industries Inc	E	903 799-5100	Atlanta (G-841)
Concote Corporation	C	214 956-0077	Coppell (G-3412)
Concote Corporation	F	903 581-0697	Tyler (G-20070)
Fedex Office & Print Svcs Inc	F	806 359-9684	Amarillo (G-488)
HFS Holding Corporation	F	214 634-8600	Dallas (G-4454)
Jones Holt Enterprises Inc	E	210 657-5917	San Antonio (G-18207)
Southern Champion Tray LP	F	817 477-3485	Mansfield (G-14719)
Tape Innovations LLC	E	817 568-1212	Fort Worth (G-7034)
Westrock Mwv LLC	D	409 276-3000	Silsbee (G-18958)
Zapco Inc	E	512 237-5521	Smithville (G-18980)

PAPER CONVERTING

Dietzgen Corporation	F	713 937-1632	Houston (G-9467)
Halbert Mill Company Texas Inc	F	903 683-2788	Jacksonville (G-13243)
Imperial Bag & Paper Co LLC	E	713 223-5050	Houston (G-10334)
Mayfield Paper Company Inc	F	432 580-4118	Odessa (G-16075)
Medek L L C	F	956 800-4366	Alamo (G-180)
Partners Converting Inc	F	469 568-5000	Carrollton (G-2790)
RB Converting Inc	E	800 543-7690	Dallas (G-4863)
Rios Packaging Corp	F	214 920-9851	Dallas (G-4902)
Supply Pro Sorbents LLC	E	713 672-9080	Sugar Land (G-19559)
Technology Container Corp	F	972 228-1617	Desoto (G-5444)

PAPER MANUFACTURERS: Exc Newsprint

Domtar Industries LLC	F	972 929-3565	Irving (G-13001)
Domtar Paper Company LLC	C	972 929-8581	Irving (G-13002)

PRODUCT

Duro Bag Manufacturing Company.......C 956 843-6607
Hidalgo (G-8305)
Ennis Inc.......................................C 903 496-2244
Wolfe City (G-20906)
Georgia-Pacific LLC..........................D 940 205-9558
Denton (G-5368)
Gold Bond Building Pdts LLC..............F 830 864-4100
Harper (G-8209)
Graphic Packaging Intl LLC.................A 903 796-7101
Queen City (G-17220)
Howred Corporation...........................C 956 712-1003
Laredo (G-13894)
International Paper Company................C 972 512-0400
Carrollton (G-2767)
International Paper Company................C 956 383-3811
Edinburg (G-5590)
International Paper Company................E 713 996-9877
Houston (G-10405)
International Paper Company................C 956 387-8100
Edinburg (G-5591)
International Paper Company................E 210 225-2901
San Antonio (G-18193)
International Paper Company................C 210 661-8543
San Antonio (G-18194)
International Paper Company................E 915 858-8877
El Paso (G-5815)
International Paper Company................C 979 885-4191
Sealy (G-18810)
International Paper Company................E 972 416-8680
Carrollton (G-2768)
International Paper Company................D 972 602-9880
Grand Prairie (G-7895)
International Paper Company................C 817 338-4000
Fort Worth (G-6725)
International Paper Company................C 972 641-2972
Grand Prairie (G-7896)
Koch Pulp & Paper Trading LLC..........F 713 544-5070
Houston (G-10554)
Longhorn Paper Converting LLC..........E 214 988-3251
Grand Prairie (G-7918)
Pactiv LLC.......................................G 254 770-4100
Temple (G-19693)
Paper Source Inc..............................G 469 304-5168
Plano (G-16965)
Sunshine Paper Corp.........................F 956 283-9999
Donna (G-5493)
Texas Tissue Converting LLC..............D 281 821-0429
Houston (G-12257)
Wingate Partners LP..........................F 214 720-1313
Dallas (G-5195)
Zapco Inc..E 512 237-5521
Smithville (G-18980)

PAPER PRDTS: Book Covers

Caraustar Industries Inc.....................E 903 799-5100
Atlanta (G-841)
Wbc Media LP...................................F 214 764-2000
Dallas (G-5176)

PAPER PRDTS: Facial Tissue

Kimberly-Clark Corporation..................B 972 281-1200
Irving (G-13075)

PAPER PRDTS: Infant & Baby Prdts

Abiie LLC...F 512 514-6325
Austin (G-876)
Kimberly-Clark Corporation..................A 903 737-5100
Paris (G-16364)
Kimberly-Clark Corporation..................F 817 847-0211
Fort Worth (G-6761)
Omganics Inc....................................A 512 560-3262
Austin (G-1379)

PAPER PRDTS: Molded Pulp Prdts

Creative Molded Packaging LLC..........F 915 881-8401
El Paso (G-5705)

PAPER PRDTS: Sanitary

Georgia-Pacific LLC...........................G 434 283-6202
El Paso (G-5783)
Kimberly-Clark Corporation..................B 972 281-1200
Irving (G-13075)
Kimberly-Clark Worldwide Inc..............F 972 281-1200
Irving (G-13076)
Solo Cup Operating Corporation..........A 214 339-3131
Dallas (G-4977)
Texas Tissue Converting LLC..............D 281 821-0429
Houston (G-12257)

PAPER PRDTS: Sanitary Tissue Paper

Kimberly-Clark Corporation..................A 903 737-5100
Paris (G-16364)
Kimberly-Clark Corporation..................F 817 847-0211
Fort Worth (G-6761)

PAPER PRDTS: Towels, Napkins/Tissue Paper, From Purchd Mtrls

East Txas Lighthouse For Blind............D 903 595-3444
Tyler (G-20082)

PAPER: Adding Machine Rolls, Made From Purchased Materials

Maxwell Papers LP............................D 214 631-5550
Dallas (G-4655)
Maxwell Papers Holdings LLP..............F 214 631-5550
Dallas (G-4656)
Tst/Impreso Inc................................D 972 462-0100
Coppell (G-3451)

PAPER: Adhesive

Advantage Marking & Labeling ....E 214 638-5225
Dallas (G-3894)
Guardian Southwest String Tag ....F 972 938-0123
Waxahachie (G-20544)
Label Products Inc............................E 713 869-2959
Houston (G-10584)

PAPER: Art

Ampersand Art Supply Inc..................E 512 322-0278
Buda (G-2519)

PAPER: Cardboard

Creative Molded Packaging LLC ....F 915 881-8401
El Paso (G-5705)
Sctray Company................................D 817 473-0233
Mansfield (G-14716)

PAPER: Coated & Laminated, NEC

Associated Label & Tape Co................E 214 744-1662
Dallas (G-3972)
Blind Dog Productions Ltd ....E 254 778-0722
Temple (G-19671)
Ennis Inc..C 903 496-2244
Wolfe City (G-20906)
Esco Industries Inc............................E 254 296-0500
Waco (G-20396)
Fedex Office & Print Svcs Inc ....F 713 521-9465
Houston (G-9772)
Global Plus Trading Co LLC ....E 210 807-0190
San Antonio (G-18149)
Green Bay Packaging Inc....................E 915 822-9700
El Paso (G-5791)
Paul Smoke.....................................F 281 422-4228
Baytown (G-1831)
Trpg Inc..F 713 477-6995
Pasadena (G-16520)
Westrock Mwv LLC............................D 409 276-3000
Silsbee (G-18958)
Wingate Partners LP..........................F 214 720-1313
Dallas (G-5195)

PAPER: Coated, Exc Photographic, Carbon Or Abrasive

Avery Dennison Corporation ....E 972 919-6900
Carrollton (G-2699)

PAPER: Corrugated

Age Industries Ltd ....E 956 399-8279
San Benito (G-18654)
Castell LP..E 972 938-2739
Waxahachie (G-20535)
Classic Corrugated Inc.......................D 940 381-0137
Denton (G-5354)
Voidform Products Inc........................E 817 429-0888
Fort Worth (G-7111)

PAPER: Envelope

Texas Envelope Company....................E 214 358-5661
Dallas (G-5060)

PAPER: Gift Wrap

Accent Mercantile Inc.........................F 817 579-6076
Granbury (G-7792)
Cole & Ashcroft LP............................E 713 937-8657
Houston (G-9243)
Ki Memories Inc................................E 972 333-3015
Dallas (G-4554)

PAPER: Insulation Siding

Installed Building Pdts Inc...................E 210 937-1082
San Antonio (G-18643)
Valro-K LLC......................................E 210 937-1082
San Antonio (G-18647)

PAPER: Offset

Halbert Mill Company Texas Inc ....F 903 683-2788
Jacksonville (G-13243)

PAPER: Packaging

Miller Paper Company.........................E 806 353-0317
Amarillo (G-502)
South Texas Paper LLC.......................F 956 239-1473
Pharr (G-16710)

PAPER: Printer

Garland Independent School Dst ....D 972 494-8580
Garland (G-7494)
Information MGT Solutions LLC.............E 210 826-4994
San Antonio (G-18182)
James D Vossler ....F 281 376-6420
Cypress (G-3804)
R W Gonzalez Office Pdts Inc ....F 512 300-2300
Austin (G-1448)

PAPER: Specialty

Sample House & Resale Shop Inc.........E 214 688-0751
Dallas (G-4929)

PAPER: Wallpaper

Build A Sign LLC...............................C 512 374-9850
Austin (G-1015)

PAPER: Wrapping

Specialty Packaging Inc......................C 817 922-9727
Fort Worth (G-7010)

PAPERBOARD

Age Industries Ltd ....E 915 852-9099
Horizon City (G-8361)
Caraustar Industries Inc.....................E 903 799-5100
Atlanta (G-841)
Georgia-Pacific LLC...........................D 940 205-9558
Denton (G-5368)
Graphic Packaging Intl LLC.................A 903 796-7101
Queen City (G-17220)
Green Bay Packaging Inc....................E 915 822-9700
El Paso (G-5791)
International Paper Company................C 956 682-9406
McAllen (G-14874)
International Paper Company................D 806 381-0121
Amarillo (G-439)
McKinley Paper Company....................E 956 487-7424
Rio Grande City (G-17473)
RTS Packaging LLC............................D 214 331-6555
Dallas (G-4917)
Sonoco Products Company..................D 903 665-3966
Jefferson (G-13288)
Thompson Paper Pdts Texas Inc..........E 713 869-6636
Houston (G-12278)
Western Pulp Products Co...................E 903 586-3608
Jacksonville (G-13266)

PAPERBOARD CONVERTING

Caraustar Industries Inc.....................E 903 793-6231
Texarkana (G-19758)
Lakeland Paper Corporation.................E 817 840-5470
Arlington (G-716)
RTS Packaging LLC............................D 214 331-6555
Dallas (G-4917)
Smurfit Kappa North Amer LLC............E 713 869-5900
Houston (G-11926)

PAPERBOARD PRDTS: Building Insulating & Packaging

Graphic Converting Ltd ....E 972 554-8000
Carrollton **(G-2747)**

Southern Champion Tray LP ....E 512 442-2337
Austin **(G-1522)**

PAPERBOARD PRDTS: Container Board

Packaging Corporation America ....C 254 776-2360
Waco **(G-20441)**

Packaging Corporation America ....D 469 568-7000
Carrollton **(G-2789)**

Sheldon Industries Inc ....F 713 398-2427
Houston **(G-11856)**

Westrock Rkt LLC ....C 903 455-0147
Greenville **(G-8096)**

PAPERBOARD PRDTS: Folding Boxboard

Caraustar Industries Inc ....E 903 793-6231
Texarkana **(G-19758)**

PAPERBOARD: Liner Board

Westrock Mwv LLC ....D 409 276-3000
Silsbee **(G-18958)**

PAPIER-MACHE PRDTS, EXC STATUARY & ART GOODS

Western Pulp Products Co ....E 903 586-3608
Jacksonville **(G-13266)**

PARKING LOTS

Crabtree Barricade Systems Inc ....E 409 842-2073
Beaumont **(G-1877)**

PARKING LOTS & GARAGES

Vally Park USA Corp ....F 956 994-0000
Mission **(G-15572)**

PARTICLEBOARD: Laminated, Plastic

Laminate Works Inc ....E 713 955-1310
Houston **(G-10588)**

Laminate Works Inc ....E 913 281-7474
Dallas **(G-4580)**

Paragon Furniture Inc ....D 817 633-3242
Arlington **(G-749)**

PARTITIONS & FIXTURES: Except Wood

Center Fixtures ....D 936 598-2247
Center **(G-2996)**

Custom Delis Equipment Co Inc ....E 817 831-7080
Fort Worth **(G-6567)**

Displays By Martin Paul Inc ....E 940 458-7976
Denton **(G-5360)**

Ets-Lindgren Inc ....C 512 531-6400
Cedar Park **(G-2968)**

Faubion Associates Inc ....E 214 565-1000
Dallas **(G-4355)**

G2 Automated Technologies LLC ....E 972 479-0699
Dallas **(G-4390)**

Growth Holdings LLC ....E 972 241-9535
Dallas **(G-4418)**

Herman Miller Inc ....F 214 855-0200
Dallas **(G-4453)**

Houston Wire Works Inc ....F 713 946-2920
Houston **(G-10265)**

Hutchins Oil and Lube ....E 972 225-0846
Hutchins **(G-12867)**

Idx Dallas LLC ....D 972 637-1525
Cedar Hill **(G-2944)**

Interlake Mecalux Inc ....E 972 245-3910
Dallas **(G-4506)**

Intrapack Corporation ....E 214 348-7105
Dallas **(G-4509)**

Jim Dandy Boxes Inc ....E 817 608-9180
Grand Prairie **(G-7903)**

Johnnies Plastics Inc ....E 210 533-8463
San Antonio **(G-18205)**

Kaspar Wire Works Inc ....A 361 594-3327
Shiner **(G-18944)**

Knox Jr Leighton ....E 806 327-5420
Tahoka **(G-19641)**

Loftwall Inc ....F 214 239-3162
Grand Prairie **(G-7916)**

Martin Paul Inc ....F 940 458-7976
Denton **(G-5380)**

Performance Companies LP ....C 214 665-1000
Dallas **(G-4797)**

S & S Cabinet Shop Inc ....F 325 655-6757
San Angelo **(G-17825)**

Semasys Inc ....C 713 869-8331
Houston **(G-11825)**

Southwest Solutions Group Inc ....E 972 250-1970
Lewisville **(G-14091)**

Taprite Inc ....E 210 523-0800
San Antonio **(G-18522)**

Universal Display & Fixs Co ....C 972 829-2366
Coppell **(G-3452)**

Universal Display and Fix Co ....C 972 221-5157
Flower Mound **(G-6291)**

PARTITIONS WHOLESALERS

Knickerbocker Partition Corp ....F 972 438-5330
Irving **(G-13078)**

Tex-Sun Shade Specialties Inc ....F 972 279-0132
Dallas **(G-5053)**

PARTITIONS: Nonwood, Floor Attached

Hufcor Inc ....F 972 850-2200
Dallas **(G-4470)**

Hull Supply Company Inc ....E 512 385-1262
Austin **(G-1213)**

Knickerbocker Partition Corp ....F 972 438-5330
Irving **(G-13078)**

Lamrite ....F 512 385-4455
Austin **(G-1281)**

Sullys Lone Star Office Pdts ....F 512 835-9506
Austin **(G-1544)**

United Office Interiors Inc ....D 214 381-0101
Dallas **(G-5136)**

PARTITIONS: Wood & Fixtures

Dutch Marble Creations ....F 956 399-6767
San Benito **(G-18656)**

Greenhaw Cabinets Inc ....F 325 646-8319
Brownwood **(G-2430)**

Herman Miller Inc ....F 214 855-0200
Dallas **(G-4453)**

Idx Dallas LLC ....D 972 637-1525
Cedar Hill **(G-2944)**

Incounters Inc ....E 325 675-5909
Abilene **(G-51)**

Irving Counter Inc ....E 972 438-4343
Irving **(G-13066)**

Kamal Incorporated ....D 210 695-2678
Helotes **(G-8241)**

Legacy Housing Corporation ....C 817 799-4900
Bedford **(G-1976)**

Maco Manufacturing Inc ....E 254 939-5742
Belton **(G-2027)**

Madix Inc ....A 214 515-5400
Terrell **(G-19740)**

Republic Nat Inds Texas LP ....C 903 935-3680
Marshall **(G-14800)**

Rodgers-Wade Mfg Co Inc ....E 903 739-2500
Paris **(G-16367)**

S & S Cabinet Shop Inc ....F 325 655-6757
San Angelo **(G-17825)**

Southwest Solutions Group Inc ....E 972 250-1970
Lewisville **(G-14091)**

V T I of Texas Inc ....E 979 778-2804
Bryan **(G-2515)**

Venus Marble Co Inc ....D 972 223-8008
Desoto **(G-5447)**

PARTS: Metal

Butler Weldments Corporation ....D 254 697-6416
Cameron **(G-2640)**

Custom Manufacturing Company ....E 214 428-5173
Dallas **(G-4196)**

Fabrication Unlimited Inc ....E 713 433-6401
Houston **(G-9750)**

Fluxmetals LLC ....D 832 948-4307
Houston **(G-9818)**

Harris Manufacturing Company ....E 972 262-3524
Mansfield **(G-14680)**

Hep Mechanical Services LLC ....F 903 278-6826
Queen City **(G-17221)**

Koch-Glitsch LP ....D 214 583-3000
Dallas **(G-4564)**

V-S Precision Usa LLC ....B 915 590-2707
El Paso **(G-6022)**

PARTY PLAN MERCHANDISERS

Casey Products LLC ....E 903 927-3500
Marshall **(G-14770)**

PATCHING PLASTER: Household

Technology Fleet Products Inc ....F 713 907-8394
Houston **(G-12177)**

PATTERNS: Indl

Kruger Aluminum & Brass Fndry ....F 940 767-0432
Wichita Falls **(G-20777)**

Tri-Sen Systems Corporation ....E 832 632-1211
Webster **(G-20648)**

PAVERS

Faber Cnk ....F 832 831-7222
Houston **(G-9748)**

Pave/Lock/Plus LLC ....E 281 239-3033
Rosenberg **(G-17593)**

Roadway Specialties Inc ....D 512 280-6666
Austin **(G-866)**

Tropiscapes Inc ....E 281 371-2955
Katy **(G-13452)**

PAVING MIXTURES

Word Constructors LLC ....F 830 693-2933
Marble Falls **(G-14752)**

PEAT GRINDING SVCS

Sun Gro Horticulture Dist Inc ....E 903 938-7348
Marshall **(G-14804)**

PENNANTS

Nationwide Pnnant Flag Mfg Inc ....C 210 684-3524
San Antonio **(G-18337)**

PENS & PARTS: Ball Point

West Txas Lighthouse For Blind ....D 325 653-4231
San Angelo **(G-17839)**

PENS & PENCILS: Mechanical, NEC

Barrington Group Ltd Inc ....F 214 528-6990
Dallas **(G-4006)**

Dallas Lghthouse For Blind Inc ....C 214 821-2375
Dallas **(G-4217)**

San Antnio Lghthouse For Blind ....C 210 533-5195
San Antonio **(G-18444)**

PERFUMES

Black Star Styles LLC ....C 832 207-4563
Killeen **(G-13606)**

Casey Products LLC ....E 903 927-3500
Marshall **(G-14770)**

La Tee Da LLC ....E 903 927-3500
Marshall **(G-14785)**

PERSONAL & HOUSEHOLD GOODS REPAIR, NEC

Plano Door Service Inc ....F 972 422-1695
Plano **(G-16973)**

PERSONAL CREDIT INSTITUTIONS: Financing, Autos, Furniture

Petroleum Financial Inc ....E 817 339-1075
Fort Worth **(G-6904)**

PERSONAL CREDIT INSTITUTIONS: Install Sales Finance

Clayton Homes Inc ....F 210 677-6100
San Antonio **(G-18011)**

PERSONAL DOCUMENT & INFORMATION SVCS

Interface Lgic Tech Dcmnttion ....F 713 446-3560
Pearland **(G-16570)**

Specktrum ....F 832 892-0863
Houston **(G-12004)**

Employee Codes: A=Over 500 employees, B=251-500
C=101-250, D=51-100, E=20-50, F=10-19, G=9

2021 Harris Texas
Manufacturers Directory

1593

PRODUCT

PERSONAL FINANCIAL SVCS

Keytrak Inc.................................D........ 979 595-2600
College Station (G-3190)

Ntw Services Inc.........................G........ 210 885-8637
San Antonio (G-18352)

PEST CONTROL SVCS

Pyranha Inc................................F........ 832 467-3840
Houston (G-11480)

PESTICIDES

Cedarcide Industries Inc............F........ 281 367-5075
Lewisville (G-14034)

Gb Biosciences LLC...................F........ 713 453-7281
Houston (G-9908)

Helena Agri-Enterprises LLC.......G........ 806 365-4433
Hartley (G-8211)

Moreman Community Gin Assn.....E........ 361 552-9407
Port Lavaca (G-17152)

Schirm USA Inc..........................E........ 972 878-4400
Ennis (G-6117)

Vic West Importers Ltd Co..........F........ 888 698-6463
Austin (G-1633)

Village Farms LP.......................C........ 432 426-2301
Fort Davis (G-6320)

PESTICIDES WHOLESALERS

Control Solutions Inc..................E........ 281 892-2500
Pasadena (G-16413)

Innova Supply Inc......................E........ 713 473-3345
Pasadena (G-16459)

PET & PET SPLYS STORES

Paw Depot Incorporated.............F........ 214 440-6324
Richardson (G-17371)

PET ACCESS: Collars, Leashes, Etc, Exc Leather

Blacksheep Inc..........................B........ 903 592-3853
Tyler (G-20059)

PET SPLYS

Arne Distributors Inc..................F........ 713 869-8321
Houston (G-8700)

Bio-Derm Laboratories Inc..........E........ 903 753-6744
Longview (G-14202)

Chris Christensen Systems Inc....E........ 903 389-7949
Fairfield (G-6170)

Kerr Feed & Grain Company........F........ 940 538-4354
Henrietta (G-8281)

Petmate Holdings Co..................A........ 817 467-5116
Arlington (G-753)

Qt Dog LLC................................F........ 214 333-4477
Dallas (G-4839)

Southwest Cutters LLC...............D........ 915 858-2200
El Paso (G-5971)

Starmark Solutions LLC..............B........ 877 823-7847
Hutto (G-12885)

PET SPLYS WHOLESALERS

Allflex Usa Inc...........................D........ 972 456-3686
Dallas (G-3924)

Animal Science Products Inc........E........ 936 560-0003
Nacogdoches (G-15685)

Qt Dog LLC................................F........ 214 333-4477
Dallas (G-4839)

PETROLEUM & PETROLEUM PRDTS, WHOLESALE Crude Oil

Adams Resources & Energy Inc.....E........ 713 881-3600
Houston (G-8475)

Bml Inc......................................E........ 325 676-3355
Abilene (G-19)

Equinor Gulf of Mexico LLC.........F........ 713 918-8200
Houston (G-9686)

Occidental Energy Mktg Inc.........C........ 713 215-7000
Houston (G-11113)

PETROLEUM & PETROLEUM PRDTS, WHOLESALE Engine Fuels & Oils

Chevron Marine Products LLC.......D........ 832 854-2767
Houston (G-9179)

PETROLEUM & PETROLEUM PRDTS, WHOLESALE Fuel Oil

Martin Resource Mgt Corp...........C........ 903 983-6200
Kilgore (G-13570)

Pier 19 Marine Field...................E........ 409 763-5423
Galveston (G-7405)

Taylor Distributing Co Inc...........E........ 817 831-0601
Fort Worth (G-7037)

Vp Racing Fuels Inc....................D........ 210 635-7744
San Antonio (G-18600)

PETROLEUM & PETROLEUM PRDTS, WHOLESALE Gases

Santanna Natural Gas Corp..........E........ 512 346-2500
Austin (G-1710)

PETROLEUM & PETROLEUM PRDTS, WHOLESALE Petroleum Brokers

Brucemark Petroleum Inc............F........ 630 339-5490
Addison (G-108)

Intergulf Corporation..................D........ 281 474-4210
La Porte (G-13754)

Sun Coast Resources Inc.............C........ 713 844-9600
Houston (G-12097)

PETROLEUM & PETROLEUM PRDTS, WHOLESALE Petroleum Terminals

Insight Equity A P X L P.............F........ 817 488-7775
Southlake (G-19075)

Insight Equity LP.......................E........ 817 488-7775
Southlake (G-19076)

Plains Resources Inc..................G........ 713 579-5000
Houston (G-11344)

PETROLEUM & PETROLEUM PRDTS, WHOLESALE: Bulk Stations

Anadarko Petroleum Corporation.....C........ 832 636-1000
The Woodlands (G-19830)

Buckley Oil Company..................E........ 214 421-4147
Midlothian (G-15475)

Chevron USA Inc........................C........ 925 842-1000
Houston (G-9181)

Conocophillips Company.............A........ 281 293-1000
Houston (G-9273)

Ingram Readymix Inc..................F........ 361 575-6358
Victoria (G-20273)

Martin Midstream GP LLC............A........ 903 983-6200
Kilgore (G-13568)

Martin Midstream Partners LP......D........ 903 983-6200
Kilgore (G-13569)

PETROLEUM BULK STATIONS & TERMINALS

BP Corporation North Amer Inc.....A........ 281 366-2000
Houston (G-8965)

BP Corporation North Amer Inc.....A........ 281 366-2000
Houston (G-8967)

Citgo Holding Terminals LLC.......B........ 832 486-4000
Houston (G-9200)

Citgo Petroleum Corporation........A........ 832 486-4000
Houston (G-9201)

Coffeyville Resources Trml LLC.....F........ 281 207-3200
Sugar Land (G-19464)

Cooper Oil Company Inc.............E........ 817 332-7755
Fort Worth (G-6546)

Diamond Shamrock Ref & Mktg Co.....A........ 210 345-2000
San Antonio (G-18057)

Exxon Mobil Corporation.............E........ 713 656-3636
Houston (G-9739)

Exxon Mobil Corporation.............B........ 972 940-6000
Irving (G-13021)

JP Energy Partners LP.................E........ 972 444-0300
Irving (G-13069)

Marathon Oil Corporation............A........ 713 629-6600
Houston (G-10756)

Nbl Permian LLC........................F........ 979 764-4030
College Station (G-3195)

PETROLEUM PRDTS WHOLESALERS

Airgas Usa LLC.........................F........ 361 533-0758
Corpus Christi (G-3469)

Anadarko Holding Company.........F........ 832 636-7200
Houston (G-8633)

Belvan Partners LP...................F........ 432 682-4349
Midland (G-15137)

Bersal Energy LLC......................F........ 956 270-1155
McAllen (G-14841)

Bestolife Corporation.................E........ 972 865-8961
Irving (G-12947)

Big Bear Oil Company Inc............F........ 915 775-1945
El Paso (G-5662)

Burlington Resources LLC............C........ 281 293-1000
Houston (G-9020)

Callon Petroleum Company..........E........ 432 218-2800
Midland (G-15155)

Dcp Midstream LLC...................D........ 432 827-1945
Goldsmith (G-7741)

Dcp Operating Company LP.........C........ 361 584-8509
Bishop (G-2107)

Equilon Enterprises LLC..............B........ 713 767-5337
Houston (G-9685)

Frontier Oil Corporation..............F........ 214 871-3555
Dallas (G-4383)

H R Stasney & Sons Ltd..............F........ 325 762-3311
Albany (G-189)

Hl Tech Oil Blends Inc.................F........ 972 231-5464
Allen (G-274)

Ineos Americas LLC...................B........ 361 552-8244
Port Lavaca (G-17148)

Ingram Readymix Inc..................E........ 210 622-5621
San Antonio (G-18186)

James Lee Davis........................D........ 432 682-6311
Midland (G-15258)

Koch Industries Inc....................F........ 806 347-2645
Matador (G-14816)

Lima Refining Company...............D........ 409 985-1000
Port Arthur (G-17116)

Neom LLC................................F........ 210 372-3475
Boerne (G-2130)

Pacific Refining Company............E........ 713 877-6929
Houston (G-11219)

Par Pacific Holdings Inc..............D........ 281 899-4800
Houston (G-11235)

Pilot Thomas Logistics LLC..........C........ 817 877-8300
Fort Worth (G-6908)

S&M International Co Inc.............E........ 281 749-8289
Katy (G-13378)

Safety-Kleen Systems Inc............B........ 800 669-5740
Richardson (G-17392)

Sinochem American Holdings........E........ 713 263-8880
Houston (G-11905)

Texas Refinery Corp...................F........ 682 518-1405
Mansfield (G-14722)

Trecora Resources.....................E........ 281 980-5522
Sugar Land (G-19568)

Valero Services Inc....................A........ 210 345-2000
San Antonio (G-18590)

PETROLEUM REFINERY INSPECTION SVCS

Carber Holdings Inc....................E........ 713 797-2859
Houston (G-9089)

Inspectorate America Corp...........E........ 281 291-9000
Pasadena (G-16461)

Premier Worldwide Inc................F........ 281 752-0014
Montgomery (G-15640)

PHARMACEUTICAL PREPARATIONS: Adrenal

Uniwell Laboratories LLC.............E........ 817 510-1850
Fort Worth (G-7094)

PHARMACEUTICAL PREPARATIONS: Digitalis

Executive Enterprises LLC...........F........ 346 224-2125
Dallas (G-4346)

PHARMACEUTICAL PREPARATIONS: Druggists' Preparations

Anthera Pharmaceuticals Inc.......E........ 510 856-5600
Houston (G-8649)

Evestra Inc...............................F........ 210 673-3300
Schertz (G-18749)

Mylan Bertek Pharmaceuticals.....E........ 281 240-1000
Sugar Land (G-19508)

Pharmscript LLC........................E........ 281 492-7220
Houston (G-11320)

PHARMACEUTICAL PREPARATIONS: Emulsions

Boccard Life Sciences Inc ....E 281 269-6020
Houston *(G-8933)*

PHARMACEUTICAL PREPARATIONS: Medicines, Capsule Or Ampule

OHM Pharma Inc ....E 940 325-4797
Mineral Wells *(G-15535)*

PHARMACEUTICAL PREPARATIONS: Pills

Nationwide Pharmaceutical LLC ....F 800 697-3329
San Antonio *(G-18336)*

PHARMACEUTICAL PREPARATIONS: Powders

Hemotek LLC ....F 972 312-1609
Plano *(G-16885)*

PHARMACEUTICAL PREPARATIONS: Proprietary Drug PRDTS

Physicians Wellness Group Inc ....E 817 703-2102
Irving *(G-13143)*

PHARMACEUTICAL PREPARATIONS: Solutions

Alcon Laboratories Inc ....A 817 293-0450
Fort Worth *(G-6363)*
Alcon Laboratories Holdg Corp ....A 817 293-0450
Fort Worth *(G-6365)*
Allergan Inc ....G 512 527-6649
Austin *(G-909)*
Aravas Inc ....F 512 614-1848
Austin *(G-928)*
Falcon Pharmaceuticals Ltd ....A 800 343-2133
Fort Worth *(G-6623)*
Op2 Labs LLC ....F 888 448-8468
Euless *(G-6151)*
Tex ISO Inc ....F 281 482-1231
Friendswood *(G-7250)*

PHARMACEUTICALS

Abeona Therapeutics Inc ....F 214 784-7177
Dallas *(G-3879)*
Acelity LP Inc ....E 210 524-9000
San Antonio *(G-17859)*
Aeglea Biotherapeutics Inc ....E 512 942-2935
Austin *(G-896)*
Alcon Research LLC ....C 817 551-4555
Fort Worth *(G-6366)*
Alcon Vision LLC ....E 713 668-9100
Houston *(G-8532)*
Alk-Abello Inc ....D 512 251-0037
Round Rock *(G-17621)*
Allergan Sales LLC ....D 254 666-3331
Waco *(G-20358)*
Ampac Fine Chemicals Texas LLC ......E 281 842-1459
La Porte *(G-13723)*
Aravive Inc ....F 936 355-1910
Houston *(G-8674)*
Aravive Biologics Inc ....F 936 355-1910
Houston *(G-8675)*
Armaceutica Inc ....F 949 677-6001
El Paso *(G-5652)*
Banyan International Corp ....F 888 782-8548
Abilene *(G-15)*
BASF Corporation ....C 800 794-1019
Houston *(G-8821)*
Bayer Healthcare LLC ....E 972 377-1950
Plano *(G-16800)*
Bellicum Pharmaceuticals Inc ....D 832 384-1100
Houston *(G-8853)*
Bio-Path Holdings Inc ....F 832 742-1357
Bellaire *(G-1990)*
Biomed Laboratories LLC ....F 972 707-1210
Dallas *(G-4026)*
Bionumerik Pharmaceuticals Inc ....D 210 614-1701
San Antonio *(G-17954)*
Biotics Building Partnership ....D 281 344-0909
Rosenberg *(G-17576)*
Biotool LLC ....F 713 732-2181
Houston *(G-8887)*
Bluebonnet Nutrition Corp ....D 281 240-3332
Sugar Land *(G-19452)*

Bristol-Myers Squibb Company ....D 210 826-2999
San Antonio *(G-17967)*
Bristol-Myers Squibb Company ....E 214 381-5050
Dallas *(G-4056)*
Capellon Phrmctcals Ltd Partnr ....E 817 595-5820
Fort Worth *(G-6492)*
Capital Returns Inc ....D 414 466-2418
Fort Worth *(G-6493)*
Carefusion 213 LLC ....B 915 231-5000
El Paso *(G-5683)*
Cassava Sciences Inc ....G 512 501-2444
Austin *(G-1031)*
Celltex Therapeutics Corp ....E 713 590-1000
Houston *(G-9119)*
Central Admxture Phrm Svcs Inc ....G 713 748-2200
Houston *(G-9137)*
Central Admxture Phrm Svcs Inc ....F 972 242-2788
Carrollton *(G-2713)*
Chemicals Incorporated ....D 281 576-5000
Baytown *(G-1813)*
Cina Pharmaceutical Inc ....G 281 602-3491
Houston *(G-9191)*
Dfb Pharmaceuticals LLC ....E 817 900-4050
Fort Worth *(G-6584)*
Dpt Laboratories Ltd ....A 210 531-7100
San Antonio *(G-18066)*
Dpt Laboratories Ltd ....B 210 396-6252
San Antonio *(G-18067)*
Dpt Laboratories Ltd ....C 866 225-5378
San Antonio *(G-18068)*
Dpt Laboratories Ltd ....A 210 476-8100
San Antonio *(G-18069)*
Dpt Laboratories Ltd ....A 210 531-7100
San Antonio *(G-18070)*
Drucker Labs LP ....E 972 881-2344
Plano *(G-16852)*
El Dorado Pharmacy LLC ....G 214 329-4580
Richardson *(G-17304)*
Eltamd Inc ....D 972 385-2900
Addison *(G-119)*
Empower Clinic Services LLC ....C 832 678-4417
Houston *(G-9621)*
Eosera Inc ....F 844 732-7929
Fort Worth *(G-6617)*
Essa Pharmaceuticals ....E 832 831-5958
Houston *(G-9700)*
Glaxosmithkline LLC ....E 830 481-8939
New Braunfels *(G-15796)*
Glaxosmithkline LLC ....E 210 627-0572
San Antonio *(G-18143)*
Glaxosmithkline LLC ....E 469 547-1722
Richardson *(G-17321)*
Gtcr Golder Rauner LLC ....F 972 670-7975
Carrollton *(G-2749)*
Humco Holding Group Inc ....F 903 831-7808
Texarkana *(G-19766)*
Ibio Inc ....F 979 446-0027
Bryan *(G-2479)*
Icu Medical Inc ....D 512 255-2000
Austin *(G-1217)*
Immunogenesis Inc ....F 713 276-7600
Houston *(G-10331)*
Inner Health Group Inc ....E 210 661-8311
San Antonio *(G-18187)*
Introgen Therapeutics Inc ....D 512 708-9310
Austin *(G-1240)*
Iq Life Sciences Corporation ....F 281 444-6454
Houston *(G-10417)*
Iq Scientific Corporation ....F 281 444-6454
Houston *(G-10418)*
ISO-Tex Diagnostics Inc ....F 281 482-1231
Friendswood *(G-7246)*
Lumos Pharma Sub Inc ....G 512 215-2630
Austin *(G-1310)*
Mallinckrodt LLC ....E 915 298-6010
El Paso *(G-5862)*
Merck & Co Inc ....E 908 740-4000
Fort Worth *(G-6828)*
Mission Pharmacal Company ....C 210 696-8400
Boerne *(G-2129)*
Mission Pharmacal Company ....E 210 696-8400
San Antonio *(G-18313)*
Molecular Templates Inc ....E 512 869-1555
Austin *(G-1705)*
Moleculin Biotech Inc ....F 713 300-5160
Houston *(G-10906)*
Mylan Institutional Inc ....D 281 240-1000
Sugar Land *(G-19509)*
Mystic Pharmaceuticals Inc ....E 512 918-2900
Cedar Park *(G-2979)*

Neora LLC ....F 855 463-7486
Dallas *(G-4721)*
Neos Therapeutics Inc ....E 972 408-1300
Grand Prairie *(G-7931)*
Newgen Biotech Usa Inc ....F 972 241-1438
Farmers Branch *(G-6209)*
Novartis Pharmaceuticals Corp ....F 817 293-0450
Fort Worth *(G-6871)*
Novartis Services Inc ....F 817 293-0450
Fort Worth *(G-6872)*
Ocusoft Inc ....D 281 342-3350
Rosenberg *(G-17592)*
Orano Med LLC ....G 301 841-1673
Plano *(G-16958)*
Pfizer Inc ....G 817 293-8887
Fort Worth *(G-6905)*
Pfizer Inc ....C 212 733-2323
Roanoke *(G-17493)*
Pfizer Inc ....D 817 491-8400
Roanoke *(G-17494)*
Plus Therapeutics Inc ....E 737 255-7194
Austin *(G-1423)*
Polymed Therapeutics Inc ....F 713 777-7088
Houston *(G-11357)*
Prescrption Dspensing Labs Inc ....F 512 219-0724
Cedar Park *(G-2983)*
Quality Bioresources Inc ....E 830 372-4797
Seguin *(G-18858)*
Quva Pharma Inc ....D 888 339-0874
Sugar Land *(G-19532)*
Quva Pharma Inc ....F 201 306-4412
Temple *(G-19700)*
S/T Health Group Consulting ....F 281 491-5555
Houston *(G-11714)*
Sanara Medtech Inc ....F 817 529-2300
Fort Worth *(G-6973)*
Sanofi-Aventis US LLC ....C 800 981-2491
College Station *(G-3201)*
Savara Inc ....E 512 614-1848
Austin *(G-1488)*
Shattuck Labs Inc ....E 919 864-2700
Austin *(G-1497)*
Shield Bearer Inc ....E 817 868-1400
Bedford *(G-1979)*
Sovereign Pharmaceuticals LLC ....C 817 284-0429
Fort Worth *(G-7007)*
Spfm LP ....D 210 805-8931
San Antonio *(G-18491)*
St Jude Medical LLC ....E 512 732-7400
Austin *(G-1530)*
Stem Cell Innovations Inc ....E 281 679-7000
Houston *(G-12057)*
Stratgic Ltigation Partners LP ....C 713 995-8225
Katy *(G-13445)*
Streamline Polymers LLC ....E 832 376-4500
Houston *(G-12077)*
Taysha Gene Therapies Inc ....F 214 612-0000
Dallas *(G-5040)*
Third Coast Rx Inc ....F 361 749-6337
Corpus Christi *(G-3639)*
Vetoquinol USA Inc ....E 817 529-7500
Fort Worth *(G-7098)*
West-Ward Pharmaceutical Corp ....F 800 631-2174
Dallas *(G-5180)*
Woodfield Pharmaceutical LLC ....D 281 530-3077
Houston *(G-12689)*
Zoetis Inc ....F 817 293-8887
Irving *(G-13212)*

PHARMACEUTICALS: Medicinal & Botanical Prdts

Aloe Vera of America Inc ....C 956 585-9704
Alton *(G-321)*
Ashley Industries LLC ....G 864 834-1167
Round Rock *(G-17623)*
Bluebonnet Nutrition Corp ....D 281 240-3332
Sugar Land *(G-19452)*
Fluoromed Products LP ....F 512 255-6877
Round Rock *(G-17658)*
GL Brands Inc ....F 888 811-4367
Fort Worth *(G-6670)*
Kbs Research LLC ....E 214 984-3724
Dallas *(G-4546)*
Mannatech Incorporated ....C 972 471-7400
Flower Mound *(G-6270)*
Sigma-Genosys of Texas LLC ....C 281 363-3693
Spring *(G-19250)*
Spfm LP ....D 210 805-8931
San Antonio *(G-18491)*

PRODUCT

Vollara LLC ....E 800 989-2299
Dallas (G-5169)

PHOTOCOPY MACHINES

Docresources LLC ....F 832 802-6008
Crosby (G-3729)

PHOTOCOPY SPLYS WHOLESALERS

Alx Imaging LLC ....E 210 651-5000
Seguin (G-18824)

PHOTOCOPYING & DUPLICATING SVCS

Abco Inc ....D 214 428-8996
Dallas (G-3878)
Anderton Group II Ltd ....F 254 751-1012
Waco (G-20361)
B2b Copies LLC ....G 512 402-9775
Lakeway (G-13815)
Boss & Hughes LLC ....F 713 664-9829
Houston (G-8961)
Cedrone OBrien Inc ....F 512 426-5200
Austin (G-1036)
Easy Print Inc ....E 806 374-7711
Amarillo (G-421)
Eight Eighty-Eight Inc ....F 972 404-0155
Addison (G-118)
Einsteins Inc ....F 972 387-8485
Carrollton (G-2729)
Exhibitco Inc ....F 713 830-8989
Houston (G-9723)
Fedex Office & Print Svcs Inc ....F 972 570-5110
Irving (G-13024)
Fedex Office & Print Svcs Inc ....G 512 331-0800
Austin (G-1148)
Fedex Office & Print Svcs Inc ....E 210 821-6911
San Antonio (G-18107)
Fedex Office & Print Svcs Inc ....F 713 521-9465
Houston (G-9772)
Fedex Office & Print Svcs Inc ....E 713 977-2666
Houston (G-9773)
Fedex Office & Print Svcs Inc ....E 512 396-1559
San Marcos (G-18687)
Fedex Office & Print Svcs Inc ....E 512 339-1191
Austin (G-1149)
Fedex Office & Print Svcs Inc ....F 915 592-1190
El Paso (G-5768)
Fedex Office & Print Svcs Inc ....E 512 476-3242
Austin (G-1150)
Fedex Office & Print Svcs Inc ....F 806 359-9684
Amarillo (G-488)
Fedex Office & Print Svcs Inc ....E 512 472-4448
Austin (G-1151)
Fedex Office & Print Svcs Inc ....E 956 682-4040
McAllen (G-14860)
Fedex Office & Print Svcs Inc ....E 254 776-7763
Waco (G-20401)
Fedex Office & Print Svcs Inc ....F 281 364-7898
The Woodlands (G-19864)
Fedex Office & Print Svcs Inc ....E 512 452-3600
Austin (G-1152)
Fedex Office & Print Svcs Inc ....F 817 543-0833
Arlington (G-678)
Fedex Office & Print Svcs Inc ....F 409 895-4000
Beaumont (G-1892)
Fedex Office & Print Svcs Inc ....E 361 806-2220
Corpus Christi (G-3526)
Fedex Office & Print Svcs Inc ....F 210 521-8395
San Antonio (G-18108)
Fedex Office & Print Svcs Inc ....F 713 956-2366
Houston (G-9774)
Fedex Office & Print Svcs Inc ....F 281 395-0077
Katy (G-13403)
Fedex Office & Print Svcs Inc ....F 281 463-8433
Houston (G-9775)
Fedex Office & Print Svcs Inc ....F 512 528-9690
Cedar Park (G-2969)
Gincop Inc ....E 512 454-6874
Austin (G-1183)
Girard Investments Inc ....G 972 423-0299
Plano (G-16880)
Hart Engineering Company ....E 903 758-0166
Longview (G-14247)
Hewell Enterprises Inc ....E 972 466-2442
Carrollton (G-2869)
Hov Services Inc ....E 248 837-7100
Irving (G-13059)
Imaging Products Corp ....F 214 631-8899
Dallas (G-4491)

Inservio3 LLC ....G 213 439-9656
Georgetown (G-7658)
JM Graphics LLC ....F 817 460-7562
Arlington (G-711)
Juan Garza ....G 956 723-6687
Laredo (G-13900)
M L Holdings Inc ....F 817 732-1708
Fort Worth (G-6803)
Mr Sign Inc ....G 214 526-7446
Dallas (G-4699)
Papergraphics Ltd ....F 254 526-4303
Temple (G-19696)
Quad/Graphics Inc ....F 972 892-3803
Dallas (G-4841)
Quik Print of Austin Inc ....D 512 467-9382
Austin (G-1444)
Service Photo Copy Inc ....F 713 225-1988
Houston (G-11840)
Thomas Reprographics Inc ....D 210 829-7000
San Antonio (G-18548)
Transfer Graphics Inc ....F 940 566-2679
Denton (G-5407)
Turner Capital Inc ....F 281 488-4900
Houston (G-12412)
Wilkins & Associates Inc ....F 713 472-6585
Pasadena (G-16527)

PHOTOELECTRIC CELLS: Electronic Eye, Solid State

Contrinex Inc ....F 574 340-7089
Coppell (G-3413)

PHOTOENGRAVING SVC

Aluma Graphics LP ....E 972 442-3299
Wylie (G-20925)
Cash Engraving Co ....F 817 831-8585
Fort Worth (G-6495)

PHOTOFINISHING LABORATORIES

Fujifilm North America Corp ....D 972 242-0662
Carrollton (G-2741)

PHOTOGRAMMATIC MAPPING SVCS

H J Gruy and Associates Inc ....F 713 739-1000
Bellaire (G-1997)
Hawkins Rmote Snsing Explrtion ....E 210 829-5330
San Antonio (G-18160)

PHOTOGRAPHIC CONTROL SYSTEMS: Electronic

Eisenbeck Corporation ....F 972 526-5235
Garland (G-7485)
Mercer Controls Inc ....F 361 782-7168
Edna (G-5609)

PHOTOGRAPHIC EQPT & SPLYS

Alpha Laser Recharge Inc ....F 713 861-2425
Houston (G-8562)
Dahill Office Technology Corp ....E 713 329-9909
Houston (G-9392)
Dahill Office Technology Corp ....C 210 805-8200
San Antonio (G-18041)
Fedex Office & Print Svcs Inc ....E 512 472-4448
Austin (G-1151)
Inview Technology Corporation ....G 512 243-8751
Austin (G-1241)
Photronics Texas Allen Inc ....C 972 889-6275
Allen (G-295)
Redrock Microsystems LLC ....E 817 490-1326
Roanoke (G-17495)

PHOTOGRAPHIC EQPT & SPLYS WHOLESALERS

Fujifilm North America Corp ....D 972 242-0662
Carrollton (G-2741)
Mace Security Intl Inc ....E 800 627-6734
Dallas (G-4624)

PHOTOGRAPHIC EQPT & SPLYS: Cameras, Aerial

High Plins Cntrs MGT Group Inc ....E 806 935-5858
Dumas (G-5522)
Skycam LLC ....F 817 984-6840
Fort Worth (G-6992)

PHOTOGRAPHIC EQPT & SPLYS: Film, Sensitized

Eastman Kodak Company ....D 214 585-4955
McKinney (G-14938)
Eastman Kodak Company ....D 972 241-1611
Dallas (G-4295)
Fujifilm North America Corp ....D 972 242-0662
Carrollton (G-2741)
Illinois Tool Works Inc ....F 713 944-3200
La Porte (G-13748)

PHOTOGRAPHIC EQPT & SPLYS: Graphic Arts Plates, Sensitized

Missionary Tech Team ....F 903 757-4530
Longview (G-14277)

PHOTOGRAPHIC EQPT & SPLYS: Printing Eqpt

Horizon Worldwide Corporation ....D 713 647-7400
Houston (G-10208)

PHOTOGRAPHIC EQPT & SPLYS: Toners, Prprd, Not Chem Plnts

Quality Business Solutions ....E 972 285-2000
Mesquite (G-15074)

PHOTOGRAPHY SVCS: Still Or Video

Blunck Studios Inc ....G 806 358-7064
Amarillo (G-482)

PHOTOTYPESETTING SVC

Digital I M ....F 281 855-4933
Houston (G-9472)
Stratasys Direct Inc ....F 512 821-1112
Austin (G-1541)

PHOTOVOLTAIC Solid State

Connexa Energy LLC ....E 830 995-3600
Comfort (G-3238)
Mission Solar Energy LLC ....D 210 531-8600
San Antonio (G-18314)

PHYSICAL FITNESS CENTERS

TRT Holdings Inc ....E 214 283-8500
Dallas (G-5121)

PHYSICAL FITNESS CLUBS WITH TRAINING EQPT

Lady Hlth Ftness- Rockwall Inc ....F 972 906-0400
Carrollton (G-2877)

PHYSICIANS' OFFICES & CLINICS: Medical doctors

Medical Technology Inc ....C 972 647-0884
Grand Prairie (G-7924)

PICTURE FRAMES: Metal

Classic Picture Company Inc ....F 972 225-7590
Hutchins (G-12864)
Dyna Group International Inc ....D 830 620-4400
New Braunfels (G-15788)
Larson-Juhl US LLC ....E 713 895-0296
Houston (G-10602)

PICTURE FRAMES: Wood

Classic Picture Company Inc ....F 972 225-7590
Hutchins (G-12864)
Greater Southwest Art Center ....G 915 566-2410
El Paso (G-5790)
RE Watson & Associates Inc ....E 817 478-4401
Kennedale (G-13501)

PICTURE FRAMING SVCS, CUSTOM

Greater Southwest Art Center ....G 915 566-2410
El Paso (G-5790)

PICTURE PROJECTION EQPT

Keynote Technologies LLC ....F 877 528-4747
Allen (G-282)

(G-0000) Company's Geographic Section entry number

PICTURE TUBE REPROCESSING

Suntronic Inc ....E 281 879-9562
Houston (G-12104)

PIECE GOODS & NOTIONS WHOLESALERS

Overton Enterprises LLC ....F 512 394-6089
Austin (G-1395)

PIECE GOODS, NOTIONS & DRY GOODS, WHOL: Fabrics, Fiberglass

Saige Usa Inc ....F 281 980-8393
Sugar Land (G-19540)

PIECE GOODS, NOTIONS & DRY GOODS, WHOL: Textiles, Woven

Brunton International Inc ....E 214 638-4600
Dallas (G-4063)
Trans Cable International Inc ....E 903 449-4622
Bonham (G-2156)

PIECE GOODS, NOTIONS & DRY GOODS, WHOLESALE: Fabrics

Boriack Interiors Inc ....E 214 376-1814
Dallas (G-4044)
Carl Kisabeth Co Inc ....E 817 281-7560
Haltom City (G-8134)
Keyston Bros ....F 713 692-2132
Houston (G-10526)

PIECE GOODS, NOTIONS & OTHER DRY GOODS, WHOL: Flags/Banners

A B C Flag Acquisition Corp ....E 817 335-2548
Fort Worth (G-6336)
Dallas Flag & Flagpole Co Lc ....F 972 607-0958
Dallas (G-4216)
El Paso Reprographics LLC ....F 915 532-6255
El Paso (G-5740)

PIECE GOODS, NOTIONS & OTHER DRY GOODS, WHOLESALE: Cotton

Archer-Daniels-Midland Company ....D 806 723-5117
Lubbock (G-14363)

PIECE GOODS, NOTIONS & OTHER DRY GOODS, WHOLESALE: Fabrics

Rudys Custom Uphl & Design ....F 210 821-5156
San Antonio (G-18438)

PIECE GOODS, NOTIONS/DRY GOODS, WHOL: Fabrics, Synthetic

J Lewis Partners LP ....A 972 702-7390
Dallas (G-4519)

PIGMENTS, INORGANIC: Chrome Green, Chrome Yellow, Zinc Yellw

A1 Chrome Shop Inc ....F 713 885-1727
Houston (G-8432)

PIGMENTS, INORGANIC: Zinc Oxide, Zinc Sulfide

Gulf Reduction Corporation ....C 713 926-1705
Houston (G-10069)
Venator Americas LLC ....F 281 719-6000
The Woodlands (G-19936)
Venator Americas LLC ....D 281 465-6700
The Woodlands (G-19935)
Zochem LLC ....E 615 446-8791
Houston (G-12731)

PINS

Pin Oak Caregivers LLC ....F 713 301-3481
Houston (G-11332)

PIPE & BOILER COVERING: Felt

Team Pvf LLC ....E 281 714-1582
Houston (G-12173)

PIPE & FITTING: Fabrication

AAA Technology and Spc Co Inc ....E 713 849-3366
Houston (G-8436)
Advanced Piping Products Inc ....F 713 956-2922
Houston (G-8490)
Advanced Welding Services Inc ....F 713 933-2626
Houston (G-8493)
Aluminum Metal Products Inc ....F 806 745-6026
Lubbock (G-14360)
Ameron International Corp ....C 940 569-1471
Burkburnett (G-2563)
Anvil International LLC ....E 800 451-4414
Irving (G-12931)
Apex Coil LLC ....E 903 843-4534
Gilmer (G-7705)
Asi Piping LLC ....E 409 786-1080
Vidor (G-20324)
Atlas Tubular LLC ....D 361 387-7505
Robstown (G-17503)
Benchmark Manufacturing Inc ....E 903 882-4311
Lindale (G-14133)
Berry Gp Inc ....A 361 693-2100
Corpus Christi (G-3484)
Berry Holdings LP ....A 361 693-2100
Corpus Christi (G-3485)
Bonney Forge Corporation ....D 713 695-3633
Houston (G-8950)
Builders Best Inc ....D 903 586-8283
Jacksonville (G-13230)
C M C Steel Fabricators Inc ....C 361 575-4561
Victoria (G-20250)
Carbery Fabricators Company ....F 432 337-5015
Odessa (G-15955)
Charbonneau Industries Inc ....F 770 664-4319
Houston (G-9163)
Chatsworth Products Inc ....E 512 863-7800
Georgetown (G-7644)
Crown To Ground Supply Inc ....F 936 588-7457
Magnolia (G-14599)
D&R Pipe Fab Plus Inc ....E 281 375-2401
Brookshire (G-2315)
Diamond Fab ....F 936 441-9353
Conroe (G-3293)
Diversified Plant Svcs L L C ....D 979 848-8900
Angleton (G-570)
Echo Maintenance LLC ....C 409 724-0456
Port Arthur (G-17106)
Epic Distribution LLC ....F 346 308-6038
Houston (G-9680)
Friedman Industries Inc ....D 903 639-2511
Lone Star (G-14182)
Future Pipe Industries Inc ....C 281 847-2987
Houston (G-9879)
G Fabricating LLC ....E 281 421-3100
Crosby (G-3731)
Groth Corporation ....D 913 952-8114
Stafford (G-19324)
Gulf Copper & Mfg Corp ....F 409 989-0300
Port Arthur (G-17111)
Haydon Corporation ....F 972 641-6400
Grand Prairie (G-7888)
Houston Roll Pipe LLC ....E 713 686-8970
Houston (G-10249)
Hunting Energy Services Inc ....D 281 821-5577
Houston (G-10281)
Ipsco Tubulars Inc ....E 281 949-1023
Houston (G-10416)
Isco Industries Inc ....E 817 477-2900
Mansfield (G-14683)
ITEX Piping Products LLC ....E 832 604-7900
Houston (G-10431)
J D Rush Corporation ....F 281 558-8004
Houston (G-10438)
J S McKinney Inc ....D 979 849-7283
Angleton (G-574)
Jcm Industries Inc ....C 903 832-2581
Nash (G-15722)
Johnson County Pipe Inc ....D 817 783-3444
Alvarado (G-336)
JR Manufacturing LP ....E 713 462-5900
Houston (G-10487)
Lincoln Manufacturing Inc ....D 281 357-1541
Magnolia (G-14616)
M4 Products LLC ....F 972 481-9300
Dallas (G-4623)
Mclp Industrial Entps Corp ....F 832 767-4006
Pearland (G-16581)
Metro-Tex Fabricators Inc ....E 713 473-3900
Houston (G-10857)

Nichirin-Flex USA Inc ....B 915 859-1199
El Paso (G-5896)
North American Pipe Corp ....D 940 855-4100
Wichita Falls (G-20787)
Northwest Pipe Company ....D 817 847-1402
Saginaw (G-17753)
Pipeline Seal & Insulator Inc ....D 713 747-6948
Houston (G-11336)
Piping Accessories Inc ....E 409 842-5000
Beaumont (G-1942)
Polk Mechanical Company LLC ....C 972 339-1200
Grand Prairie (G-7947)
Powerseal Pipeline Pdts Corp ....D 940 767-5566
Wichita Falls (G-20796)
Primera Fabrication Inc ....E 956 367-8690
Harlingen (G-8197)
Prostar Manufacturing Inc ....F 281 910-0110
Pasadena (G-16499)
Prototype Machine Co ....E 512 282-1590
Manchaca (G-14641)
R & R Oilfield Services Inc ....D 361 289-5892
Corpus Christi (G-3604)
Refined Industrial Supply Inc ....E 409 789-1794
League City (G-13978)
Rotary Drilling Tools USA LLC ....D 979 387-3223
Houston (G-11669)
Royco Industries Inc ....G 713 413-9191
Houston (G-11687)
Rti Energy Systems Inc ....E 281 379-4289
Spring (G-19163)
Shaw Acquisition Holdings LLC ....A 337 562-3471
Houston (G-11849)
Southeast Texas Industries Inc ....C 409 792-0084
Bridge City (G-2286)
Southwest Nipple Company Inc ....F 210 333-3720
San Antonio (G-18488)
Star Pipe Usa LLC ....D 620 251-5700
Houston (G-12047)
Team Fabricators LLC ....D 409 962-0266
Port Arthur (G-17128)
Technip S&W International Inc ....E 281 870-1111
Houston (G-12175)
Texas Steel Conversion Inc ....C 832 230-8228
Houston (G-12253)
Texas Steel Conversion Inc ....E 281 452-2260
Houston (G-12254)
Texas Steel Conversion Inc ....C 281 459-2905
Houston (G-12255)
Titanium Fabrication Corp ....F 832 375-1800
Houston (G-12300)
Tpg Pressure Inc ....C 972 262-3600
Grand Prairie (G-7984)
Trey Industries Inc ....C 409 948-8891
Texas City (G-19804)
Turner Industries Group LLC ....A 903 782-9379
Paris (G-16372)
TW Stamping & Tool Inc ....E 903 877-2353
Tyler (G-20166)
Tyco Simplexgrinnell ....B 903 759-4417
Houston (G-12420)
U S Weatherford L P ....C 281 348-1090
Kingwood (G-13656)
U S Weatherford L P ....E 817 249-7200
Benbrook (G-2047)
US Bellows Inc ....B 713 731-0030
Houston (G-12481)
US Composite Pipe Inc ....E 817 783-3444
Alvarado (G-348)
US Pipe Fabrication ....F 817 232-5858
San Antonio (G-18581)
Valley Farm Service Inc ....F 806 364-6900
Hereford (G-8296)
Vinson Process Controls Co LP ....D 972 459-8200
Lewisville (G-14106)
Weatherford International LLC ....E 210 621-2156
Elmendorf (G-6075)
Welding Outlets Inc ....D 281 590-0190
Houston (G-12630)

PIPE & FITTINGS: Cast Iron

Alamo Iron Works Inc ....B 210 223-6161
San Antonio (G-17885)
Conine Manufacturing Company ....G 903 894-6150
Flint (G-6236)
Flowserve Corporation ....B 972 443-6500
Irving (G-13027)
Flowserve Corporation ....F 800 446-0401
Irving (G-13028)
J B Smith Mfg Co LLC ....D 713 928-5711
Houston (G-10435)

Employee Codes: A=Over 500 employees, B=251-500
C=101-250, D=51-100, E=20-50, F=10-19, G=9

2021 Harris Texas
Manufacturers Directory

PRODUCT

1597

Newage Casting LP............................E 281 565-0928
Sugar Land *(G-19512)*

PIPE & FITTINGS: Pressure, Cast Iron

Ej Usa Inc...................................F 210 946-3224
San Antonio *(G-18085)*
Stuart Pressure Control.................F 713 678-0154
The Woodlands *(G-19925)*

PIPE & TUBES: Aluminum

R C Technical Welding & Fabr.............E 281 933-6004
Stafford *(G-19367)*

PIPE & TUBES: Copper & Copper Alloy

Multalloy LLC...............................E 713 943-3544
Pearland *(G-16583)*

PIPE & TUBES: Seamless

RSD Supply Inc.............................E 713 983-6363
Houston *(G-11691)*
Tenaris Global Svcs USA Corp.........D 713 767-4400
Houston *(G-12200)*

PIPE CLEANERS

AAA Pipe Cleaning Corporation...........E 281 476-5200
La Porte *(G-13715)*

PIPE FITTINGS: Plastic

Cantex Inc..................................D 817 215-7000
Fort Worth *(G-6491)*
Centron International Inc...............C 940 328-1032
Mineral Wells *(G-15522)*
D/Fw Plastics Inc..........................F 817 439-3600
Saginaw *(G-17745)*
Fiber Glass Systems LP.................D 210 477-7500
San Antonio *(G-18112)*
Fittings Inc.................................D 817 332-3300
Fort Worth *(G-6634)*
Future Pipe Industries Inc..............C 281 847-2987
Houston *(G-9879)*
Georg Fischer Central Plas LLC.........C 972 641-2080
Dallas *(G-4403)*
Powerseal Pipeline Pdts Corp...........D 940 767-5566
Wichita Falls *(G-20796)*
Spears Manufacturing Co................F 817 293-0292
Fort Worth *(G-7008)*

PIPE JOINT COMPOUNDS

Bestolife Corporation....................E 972 865-8961
Irving *(G-12947)*
Furmanite America Inc...................E 713 844-7656
Houston *(G-9876)*
Indumar Products Inc.....................F 713 977-4100
Houston *(G-10346)*
Nov MSI Pipe Prtction Tech Inc.........E 281 890-4595
Houston *(G-11086)*
Protective Industries Inc................G 281 399-2600
New Caney *(G-15848)*
Rectorseal LLC.............................D 713 263-8001
Houston *(G-11565)*
South Coast Products LP.................E 713 434-2141
Houston *(G-11962)*

PIPE SECTIONS, FABRICATED FROM PURCHASED PIPE

Ameri-Fab LLC.............................D 817 458-4262
Weatherford *(G-20575)*
Azz Inc......................................E 713 225-9340
Crowley *(G-3752)*
Boccard Pipe Fabricators Inc...........B 713 643-0681
Houston *(G-8934)*
Daniel Measurement & Ctrl LLC.........B 713 827-5033
Houston *(G-9402)*
National Oilwell Varco Inc..............C 936 825-7070
Navasota *(G-15739)*
RE Pipe Inc.................................D 713 634-0439
Houston *(G-11559)*
Shaw Fabricators Inc.....................D 713 991-5313
Houston *(G-11850)*

PIPE, CULVERT: Concrete

Hill Country Site Supply LLC.............G 512 608-0069
Lakeway *(G-13816)*

PIPE, CYLINDER: Concrete, Prestressed Or Pretensioned

Ameron International Corp................E 713 375-3700
Houston *(G-8623)*

PIPE, IRRIGATION: Concrete

Excalibur LLC...............................G 214 632-0161
The Colony *(G-19810)*

PIPE, PRESSURE: Reinforced Concrete

Forterra Pipe & Precast LLC.............E 806 765-6721
Lubbock *(G-14412)*
Hydro Conduit of Texas LP...............E 832 590-5400
Houston *(G-10305)*

PIPE, SEWER: Concrete

Delzotto Products Texas Inc.............E 903 981-0400
Gladewater *(G-7721)*

PIPE: Concrete

Cemex Construction Mtls S LLC.........A 713 650-6200
Houston *(G-9128)*
Forterra Pipe & Precast LLC.............E 512 385-3950
Austin *(G-1168)*
Hydro Conduit of Texas LP...............E 832 590-5300
Houston *(G-10303)*
Rio Valley Pipe LLC........................E 956 580-3466
Palmview *(G-16312)*
Rio Valley Pipe LLC........................E 956 519-4960
Penitas *(G-16630)*
Tpg Pressure Inc..........................D 972 262-3600
Grand Prairie *(G-7985)*
Txi Operations LP.........................C 972 647-6700
Dallas *(G-5125)*

PIPE: Extruded, Aluminum

North American Pipe Corp................D 940 855-4100
Wichita Falls *(G-20787)*

PIPE: Plastic

Advanced Drainage Systems Inc.........D 972 878-9600
Ennis *(G-6087)*
Atco Rubber Products Inc................E 713 674-6665
Houston *(G-8732)*
Atco Rubber Products Inc................A 817 595-2894
Fort Worth *(G-6406)*
Blue Diamond Industries LLC............E 859 224-0415
Aubrey *(G-847)*
Border Tm Industries Inc................C 915 779-6431
El Paso *(G-5671)*
Cantex Inc..................................F 817 215-7000
Mineral Wells *(G-15520)*
Cantex Inc..................................B 940 325-3344
Mineral Wells *(G-15521)*
Cantex Inc..................................E 817 215-7000
Fort Worth *(G-6491)*
Centron International Inc...............C 940 328-1032
Mineral Wells *(G-15522)*
Certainteed Corporation.................D 800 233-8990
Waco *(G-20382)*
Charlotte Pipe and Foundry Co.........E 254 697-6556
Cameron *(G-2641)*
Chevron Phillips Chem Co LP............A 832 813-4100
The Woodlands *(G-19845)*
Co-Ex Pipe Co.............................E 432 263-0206
Big Spring *(G-2077)*
Cresline Plastic Pipe Co Inc.............E 903 872-7418
Corsicana *(G-3667)*
Diamond Plastics Corporation...........D 806 763-8021
Lubbock *(G-14405)*
Exquip USA Llc.............................F 936 372-3002
Hockley *(G-8343)*
Fiber Glass Systems LP.................D 210 477-7500
San Antonio *(G-18112)*
Fiberspar Corporation....................F 713 849-2609
Houston *(G-9784)*
Future Pipe Industries Inc..............C 281 847-2987
Houston *(G-9879)*
G B Manufacturing Inc....................E 713 681-5837
Houston *(G-9885)*
Hancor Inc..................................E 361 293-6313
Yoakum *(G-20967)*
Hobas Pipe Usa Inc.......................E 281 821-2200
Houston *(G-10190)*
Industrial Pipe Fittings LLC.............F 800 241-4175
Stafford *(G-19328)*

J P C Plastics Inc.........................F 325 672-2895
Abilene *(G-53)*
N A Petroflex Ltd..........................E 800 433-5711
Gainesville *(G-7350)*
North American Pipe Corp................C 855 624-7473
Houston *(G-11073)*
North American Pipe Corp................D 940 855-4100
Wichita Falls *(G-20787)*
Nupi Americas Inc.........................F 281 590-4471
Houston *(G-11099)*
Plastic Tubing Inds Texas Inc...........F 979 921-9990
Hempstead *(G-8255)*
Polyflow LLC................................E 432 686-2001
Midland *(G-15361)*
Polyone Corporation......................C 281 474-2831
Seabrook *(G-18789)*
Pw Eagle Inc................................E 979 532-5640
Wharton *(G-20705)*
Western AG Sales Co Inc.................E 806 293-2517
Plainview *(G-16767)*
Westlake Pvc Corporation...............C 713 960-9111
Houston *(G-12653)*
WL Plastics Corporation..................E 325 574-6100
Snyder *(G-19014)*
Wl Plastics Corporation..................D 940 872-8300
Bowie *(G-2202)*

PIPE: Plate Fabricated, Large Diameter

Bise Welding & Fabricating Inc..........D 713 681-0958
Houston *(G-8892)*

PIPE: Seamless Steel

Baker & Company Cnstr LLC..............E 903 561-1763
Tyler *(G-20056)*
Z-Modular Killeen LLC.....................D 254 833-6645
Killeen *(G-13619)*

PIPE: Sewer, Cast Iron

McWane Inc..................................C 800 527-8478
Tyler *(G-20123)*

PIPE: Sheet Metal

American Petroleum Welding Inc.........E 806 747-7272
Lubbock *(G-14361)*
Bise Welding & Fabricating Inc..........D 713 681-0958
Houston *(G-8892)*
Polk Mechanical Company LLC...........C 972 339-1200
Grand Prairie *(G-7947)*

PIPE: Water, Cast Iron

Merla LLC....................................E 281 931-6900
Magnolia *(G-14618)*
Waterfleet LLC.............................E 855 744-5222
San Antonio *(G-18610)*

PIPELINE & POWER LINE INSPECTION SVCS

Big 4 Inc....................................E 409 787-2733
Hemphill *(G-8245)*
Ios/Pci LLC..................................F 281 310-5357
Houston *(G-10414)*

PIPELINE TERMINAL FACILITIES: Independent

Century Concrete Partners Inc...........G 281 585-5742
Rosharon *(G-17601)*
Mash Oilfield Services LP.................F 940 549-6152
Graham *(G-7786)*

PIPELINES, EXC NATURAL GAS: Coal

Guardian Insptn Tbular MGT LLC.........F 403 233-7561
Midland *(G-15241)*

PIPELINES, EXC NATURAL GAS: Gasoline, Common Carriers

Exxonmobil Pipeline Company............C 713 656-3636
Spring *(G-19117)*

PIPELINES, EXC NATURAL GAS: Slurry

Texas Brine Company LLC.................E 713 877-2700
Houston *(G-12223)*
Texas United Corporation.................E 713 877-1793
Houston *(G-12258)*

PIPELINES: Crude Petroleum

BP Corporation North Amer Inc ....A 281 366-2000
  Houston (G-8965)
BP Corporation North Amer Inc ....A 281 366-2000
  Houston (G-8967)
Burlington Resources LLC ....C 281 293-1000
  Houston (G-9020)
Citgo Holding Terminals LLC ....B 832 486-4000
  Houston (G-9200)
Citgo Petroleum Corporation ....A 832 486-4000
  Houston (G-9201)
Cvr Refining LP ....F 281 207-3200
  Sugar Land (G-19474)
Cvr Refining Holdings LLC ....B 281 207-3200
  Sugar Land (G-19475)
El Paso Cgp Company LLC ....E 713 420-2600
  Houston (G-9585)
Equilon Enterprises LLC ....B 713 767-5337
  Houston (G-9685)
Exxon Mobil Corporation ....B 972 940-6000
  Irving (G-13021)
Exxonmobil Pipeline Company ....C 713 656-3636
  Spring (G-19117)
Flint Hills Resources LP ....C 361 241-4811
  Corpus Christi (G-3531)
Hermes Consolidated LLC ....F 303 894-9966
  Houston (G-10160)
Hollyfrontier Ref & Mktg LLC ....C 214 871-3555
  Dallas (G-4463)
Koch Industries Inc ....E 903 693-5172
  Carthage (G-2911)
Marathon Oil Company ....A 713 629-6600
  Houston (G-10754)
Phillips 66 Carrier LLC ....C 855 283-9237
  Houston (G-11325)
Plains GP Holdings LP ....E 713 646-4100
  Houston (G-11343)
Producers Midstream LP ....F 214 238-5740
  Dallas (G-4832)
Shell Oil Company ....A 713 241-6161
  Houston (G-11860)
Shortes Inc ....E 940 658-3576
  Knox City (G-13665)
South Hampton Resources Inc ....E 409 385-1400
  Silsbee (G-18956)
Stakeholder Midstream LLC ....F 210 444-9664
  San Antonio (G-18494)
Venables Construction Inc ....C 806 381-2121
  Amarillo (G-520)

PIPELINES: Natural Gas

American Natural Resources Co ....E 832 320-5000
  Houston (G-8603)
Anadarko Holding Company ....F 832 636-7200
  Houston (G-8633)
BHP Billiton Petro N Amer Inc ....C 713 961-8500
  Houston (G-8875)
Broken Hill Propty USA Inc ....D 713 961-8500
  Houston (G-8992)
Burlington Resources LLC ....C 281 293-1000
  Houston (G-9020)
Cheniere Energy Inc ....D 713 375-5000
  Houston (G-9175)
Duke Energy Natural Gas Corp ....E 361 579-4600
  Hallettsville (G-8121)
El Paso CNG Company LLC ....F 713 420-2600
  Houston (G-9586)
El Paso Field Services LP ....F 361 552-9601
  Port Lavaca (G-17145)
Halff Tritex LLC ....E 214 217-6500
  Richardson (G-17325)
Markwest Enrgy E Texas Gas LP ....E 903 694-2225
  Carthage (G-2914)
Morgan Kinder Treating LP ....F 432 563-2766
  Odessa (G-16083)
Natural Gas Pipeline Amer LLC ....A 713 369-9000
  Houston (G-11007)
Natural Gas Pipeline Amer LLC ....F 903 758-0154
  Longview (G-14283)
Natural Gas Pipeline Amer LLC ....F 361 897-1022
  Victoria (G-20288)
Panhandle Eastrn Pipe Line LP ....F 713 627-5400
  Houston (G-11233)
Producers Midstream LP ....F 214 238-5740
  Dallas (G-4832)
Stakeholder Midstream LLC ....F 210 444-9664
  San Antonio (G-18494)
Timekeepers Inc ....D 830 331-1224
  Boerne (G-2142)

Williams Companies Inc ....F 281 444-6441
  Houston (G-12669)

PIPELINES: Refined Petroleum

BP Corporation North Amer Inc ....A 281 366-2000
  Houston (G-8965)
BP Corporation North Amer Inc ....A 281 366-2000
  Houston (G-8967)
El Paso Cgp Company LLC ....E 713 420-2600
  Houston (G-9585)
Emerge Energy Services LP ....E 817 618-4020
  Fort Worth (G-6610)
Hollyfrontier Corporation ....B 214 871-3555
  Dallas (G-4462)
Koch Industries Inc ....E 903 693-5172
  Carthage (G-2911)
Marathon Oil Company ....A 713 629-6600
  Houston (G-10754)
Phillips 66 Carrier LLC ....C 855 283-9237
  Houston (G-11325)
Shortes Inc ....E 940 658-3576
  Knox City (G-13665)

PIPES & FITTINGS: Fiber, Made From Purchased Materials

Industrial Pipe Fittings LLC ....F 800 241-4175
  Houston (G-10353)
Industrial Pipe Fittings LLC ....E 903 872-7890
  Corsicana (G-3674)
Power Pipe and Tank LLC ....E 417 447-4508
  Amarillo (G-508)

PIPES & TUBES

Axis Pipe and Tube LLC ....C 281 494-0900
  Houston (G-8761)
Independent Pipe Services LLC ....E 281 436-0380
  Houston (G-10340)
Kdr Supply Inc ....F 936 334-1353
  Liberty (G-14120)
Sigma Tube & Bar LLC ....F 281 369-5525
  Houston (G-11887)
Texas Pipe Works Inc ....C 936 825-0652
  Navasota (G-15744)
United Casing Incorporated ....E 432 682-0110
  Midland (G-15455)

PIPES & TUBES: Steel

ABB Installation Products Inc ....C 713 466-6761
  Houston (G-8444)
American Materials Tech I LLC ....F 281 345-0169
  Houston (G-8602)
Ameritex Pipe & Products LLC ....D 830 372-2300
  Seguin (G-18825)
Ameron International Corp ....G 940 569-1471
  Houston (G-8622)
Ameron International Corp ....E 713 375-3700
  Houston (G-8623)
Axxairusa Inc ....G 281 968-7138
  Alvin (G-353)
Bendco Inc ....E 713 473-1557
  Pasadena (G-16398)
Boardwalk Midstream LLC ....F 888 315-5005
  Houston (G-8931)
Boomerang Tube LLC ....E 713 289-5555
  Liberty (G-14116)
Boomerang Tube LLC ....C 713 231-2929
  Houston (G-8952)
Borusan Mannesmann Pipe US Inc ....C 832 399-6000
  Houston (G-8960)
Brazos Pipe Stl Fbricators Inc ....E 979 233-7895
  Freeport (G-7194)
Cab Incorporated ....E 936 569-9430
  Nacogdoches (G-15687)
Centric Pipe LLC ....E 214 526-4423
  Dallas (G-4101)
Clock Spring Company Inc ....D 281 590-8491
  Houston (G-9215)
Coil Solutions Inc ....E 361 444-0058
  Alice (G-206)
Corrpro Companies Inc ....C 713 460-6000
  Houston (G-9325)
Custom Fab Inc ....F 210 923-3376
  San Antonio (G-18037)
Energy Technology Manufa ....F 281 862-2829
  Houston (G-9637)
Friedman Industries Inc ....D 903 758-3431
  Longview (G-14237)

Global Tubing LLC ....C 713 265-5000
  Dayton (G-5227)
Gulf States Tube LLC ....E 281 375-5113
  Brookshire (G-2317)
Instrument Products Inc ....F 281 491-0237
  Stafford (G-19329)
Integrated Pipe & Supply LLC ....F 409 834-6123
  Village Mills (G-20337)
Ipsco Tubulars Inc ....E 281 949-1023
  Houston (G-10416)
J Simmons Group Inc ....E 713 675-5100
  Houston (G-10443)
Jindal Saw Usa LLC ....E 281 573-3002
  Baytown (G-1793)
Jsw Steel (usa) Inc ....A 281 383-2525
  Baytown (G-1794)
Kdr Supply Inc ....F 936 334-1353
  Liberty (G-14120)
Labarge Coating LLC ....D 713 378-7225
  Channelview (G-3028)
Legacy Tubular LLC ....E 281 363-1900
  Magnolia (G-14614)
Longhorn Tube LP ....F 972 556-0234
  Dallas (G-4605)
Lqc Pipe & Tube Ltd Partnr ....E 832 559-7676
  Houston (G-10692)
Mapa Manufacturing LLC ....G 903 897-2371
  Naples (G-15719)
Maverick Tube Corporation ....B 936 539-2136
  Conroe (G-3329)
Merchants Moving and Stor Inc ....D 361 293-7202
  Yoakum (G-20970)
Omk Tube Inc ....E 281 609-8150
  Houston (G-11175)
Omk Tube Inc ....C 281 609-8970
  Houston (G-11176)
Permian Enterprises Ltd ....E 432 332-0903
  Odessa (G-16116)
Pyramid Tubular Products LLC ....E 281 405-8090
  Spring (G-19245)
QMF Steel Inc ....E 903 455-3618
  Campbell (G-2646)
S & T International Inc ....E 409 745-4990
  Orange (G-16259)
Sivco Inc ....E 713 466-1100
  Houston (G-11910)
Southern Tube LLC ....E 713 231-2929
  Houston (G-11979)
Splendora Pipe Services LLC ....D 281 432-1400
  Cleveland (G-3136)
Team Alloys LLC ....E 713 360-1060
  Houston (G-12170)
Tejas Casing Ltd ....D 281 215-1500
  Houston (G-12187)
Tejas Tubular Products Inc ....C 254 965-5162
  Stephenville (G-19426)
Tejas Tubular Products Inc ....B 281 822-3400
  Houston (G-12188)
Tenaris Global Svcs USA Corp ....F 936 525-3101
  Houston (G-12199)
Thermacor Process Inc ....D 817 847-7300
  Fort Worth (G-7054)
Tmk North America Inc ....F 281 949-1023
  Houston (G-12309)
Vallourec Tube-Alloy LLC ....C 713 462-7613
  Houston (G-12523)
Vallourec USA Corporation ....E 713 479-3200
  Houston (G-12524)
Vulcan Finned Tubes LP ....E 281 255-4775
  Tomball (G-20015)

PIPES & TUBES: Welded

B&L Pipeco Services Inc ....F 281 955-3500
  Houston (G-8780)
Ipsco Tubulars (ky) Inc ....C 859 292-6000
  Houston (G-10415)
Lock Joint Tube LLC ....C 254 771-2253
  Temple (G-19686)
Lone Star Technologies Inc ....D 972 770-6401
  Dallas (G-4604)
Maverick Tube Corporation ....B 713 767-4400
  Houston (G-10802)
Mecor Usa Inc ....F 713 817-0683
  Spring (G-19231)
Peyton Salas & Mendoza LLC ....E 512 784-5875
  Houston (G-11313)
Priefert Mfg Co Inc ....A 903 572-1741
  Mount Pleasant (G-15660)
Welding Outlets Inc ....D 281 590-0190
  Houston (G-12630)

PRODUCT

PIPES OR FITTINGS: Sewer, Clay

Mission Clay Products LLC ....F 830 393-2568
  Floresville *(G-6248)*

PIPES: Steel & Iron

Integrated Pipe & Supply LLC ....F 409 834-6123
  Village Mills *(G-20337)*
Metalloy Inc ....F 800 828-0500
  Houston *(G-10850)*
Overlay Product Systems Inc ....D 281 552-3500
  Houston *(G-11206)*

PISTONS & PISTON RINGS

Borger Oil Chemical Indus Plas ....F 806 273-9518
  Borger *(G-2165)*
Greg-Co Piston Rings Inc ....E 817 831-0253
  Fort Worth *(G-6679)*
Safety Seal Piston Ring Co ....E 903 938-9241
  Marshall *(G-14802)*
Safety Seal Piston Ring Co ....E 817 283-1574
  Hurst *(G-12856)*
Specialty Comprsr & Eng Co Inc ....E 806 274-7135
  Borger *(G-2187)*
Tenneco Inc ....A 915 832-4661
  El Paso *(G-5997)*

PLACEMATS: Plastic Or Textile

Creative MENus&folders LLC ....F 254 653-2775
  Olden *(G-16219)*

PLANTERS: Plastic

American Tietek LLC ....E 903 503-5538
  Marshall *(G-14760)*

PLANTS: Artificial & Preserved

Golf Greens Texascom ....F 806 559-7048
  Lubbock *(G-14417)*
Stoller Group Inc ....F 713 461-1493
  Houston *(G-12068)*

PLAQUES: Picture, Laminated

Drsk Limited Partnership ....F 972 644-1490
  Richardson *(G-17302)*

PLASMAPHEROUS CENTER

Bpl Plasma Inc ....C 512 582-7525
  Austin *(G-1004)*
Csl Plasma Inc ....E 972 329-0186
  Dallas *(G-4188)*
DCI Biologicals Austin II LLC ....F 512 865-4200
  Austin *(G-1086)*

PLASMAS

Bpl Plasma Inc ....C 512 582-7525
  Austin *(G-1004)*
DCI Biologicals Austin II LLC ....F 512 865-4200
  Austin *(G-1086)*

PLASTER WORK: Ornamental & Architectural

Casci Ornamental Plaster Inc ....F 214 421-3390
  Dallas *(G-4088)*

PLASTER, ACOUSTICAL: Gypsum

Enviro-San Corporation ....F 281 373-4200
  Cypress *(G-3788)*

PLASTIC PRDTS

Cadillac Fabrication ....F 713 910-2200
  Houston *(G-9045)*
Carthage Cup Co ....G 903 693-7151
  Carthage *(G-2902)*
Medco Manufacturing LLC ....G 281 379-3100
  Spring *(G-19145)*
Tietek Global LLC ....E 281 444-3494
  Marshall *(G-14805)*
Waco Composites ....E 866 688-3088
  Waco *(G-20475)*

PLASTIC WOOD

Thrillworks Inc ....E 916 663-1749
  Athens *(G-840)*

PLASTICS FILM & SHEET

Aerowindtech Inc ....F 817 438-4777
  Mansfield *(G-14652)*
C E Shepherd Company LP ....D 713 924-4300
  Houston *(G-9028)*
Curbell Plastics Inc ....E 214 239-3870
  Arlington *(G-654)*
GSE Environmental Inc ....D 281 443-8564
  Houston *(G-10053)*
GSE International Inc ....F 281 443-8564
  Houston *(G-10055)*
Hercules Films LLC ....G 920 284-0796
  Sugar Land *(G-13491)*
Hercules Films LLC ....F 920 284-0796
  Sugar Land *(G-19492)*
Nan Ya Plastics Corp USA ....C 979 532-5494
  Wharton *(G-20704)*
Printpack Inc ....C 409 883-9325
  Orange *(G-16257)*
Printpack Inc ....E 972 641-4421
  Grand Prairie *(G-7956)*
Reef Industries Inc ....E 713 507-4200
  Houston *(G-11577)*
Samsill Corporation ....C 817 536-1906
  Fort Worth *(G-6972)*
Tru-Vision Plastics Inc ....F 979 836-1091
  Brenham *(G-2276)*

PLASTICS FILM & SHEET: Polyethylene

Cooper Supply Inc ....E 817 222-9055
  Fort Worth *(G-6548)*
GSE Holding Inc ....C 281 443-8564
  Houston *(G-10054)*
Huntsman Corporation ....E 281 719-6000
  The Woodlands *(G-19877)*
Huntsman International LLC ....D 281 719-6000
  The Woodlands *(G-19878)*
Illinois Tool Works Inc ....D 713 996-4200
  Houston *(G-10325)*
Poly-America LP ....A 972 337-7100
  Grand Prairie *(G-7948)*
Poly-America LP ....E 972 337-7107
  Grand Prairie *(G-7949)*
Revolution Plastics LLC ....C 903 984-8596
  Kilgore *(G-13586)*
Rodeo Plastic Bag & Film LLC ....D 972 216-3331
  Mesquite *(G-15075)*
Solmax Geosynthetics LLC ....B 281 443-8564
  Houston *(G-11941)*
Supplynet Inc ....E 484 582-1004
  Dallas *(G-5028)*
Supplynet Inc ....D 214 637-0160
  Dallas *(G-5029)*
Winzen Film Inc ....E 214 340-7060
  Dallas *(G-5198)*

PLASTICS FILM & SHEET: Polypropylene

Inteplast Group Corporation ....D 361 874-3000
  Lolita *(G-14176)*
Polytex Fibers Corp ....C 713 690-9055
  Houston *(G-11362)*

PLASTICS FILM & SHEET: Polyvinyl

Kuraray America Inc ....E 800 423-9762
  Houston *(G-10571)*

PLASTICS FINISHED PRDTS: Laminated

Avey Plastics ....F 512 784-7047
  San Marcos *(G-18678)*
Johnnies Plastics Inc ....E 210 533-8463
  San Antonio *(G-18205)*
Port City Inc ....E 713 673-7272
  Houston *(G-11365)*
Precision Sheet Metal Shop Inc ....D 972 771-1423
  Rockwall *(G-17561)*
Proske Plastic Products Inc ....E 713 926-9941
  Houston *(G-11461)*
Reef Industries Inc ....E 713 507-4200
  Houston *(G-11577)*
Reef Industries Inc ....D 713 507-4329
  Houston *(G-11578)*
Reef Industries Inc ....D 956 399-1352
  San Benito *(G-18663)*
Therm-All Inc ....F 214 630-4800
  Dallas *(G-5084)*

PLASTICS MATERIAL & RESINS

A & C Plastic Products Inc ....E 713 645-4915
  Houston *(G-8423)*
Advanced Laser Materials LLC ....F 254 773-3080
  Temple *(G-19667)*
Albemarle Catalysts Company LP ....B 281 474-2864
  Pasadena *(G-16383)*
Albemarle Corporation ....E 281 480-4747
  Houston *(G-8529)*
Albemarle Corporation ....A 713 740-1000
  Pasadena *(G-16386)*
Alloy Polymers Texas LP ....E 936 544-4043
  Latexo *(G-13941)*
American Excelsior Company ....E 817 385-4300
  Arlington *(G-616)*
American Thermoplastics Corp ....D 713 671-6900
  Houston *(G-8611)*
Ameron International Corp ....C 940 569-1471
  Burkburnett *(G-2563)*
Ascend Prfmce Mtls Oprtons LLC ....B 281 228-4000
  Alvin *(G-352)*
Ascend Prfmce Mtls Oprtons LLC ....E 713 315-5700
  Houston *(G-8715)*
Asia Chemical Corporation Inc ....F 713 673-4100
  Houston *(G-8721)*
Avangard Innovative LP ....E 281 582-0700
  Houston *(G-8755)*
Bamberger Polymers Inc ....E 281 481-9100
  Houston *(G-8811)*
Bamberger Polymers Corp ....E 281 481-9100
  Houston *(G-8812)*
Basell USA Inc ....F 682 518-0687
  Mansfield *(G-14657)*
Birch Plastics Inc ....E 713 433-1898
  Houston *(G-8891)*
Brisco Plastics and Chem LLC ....F 713 395-7081
  Houston *(G-8985)*
Bruegmann Usa Inc ....E 713 742-0788
  Houston *(G-8997)*
C & P Plastics Inc ....E 979 251-7991
  Brenham *(G-2249)*
C-Square Intl Trdg LLC ....F 817 633-9000
  Arlington *(G-635)*
CAM Specialty Products Inc ....E 936 228-0824
  Houston *(G-9058)*
Cameron International Corp ....D 281 391-4600
  Katy *(G-13356)*
Carpenter Co ....E 214 330-0373
  Dallas *(G-4085)*
CCT Corporation ....F 713 223-2521
  Houston *(G-9111)*
Celanese Americas LLC ....F 972 443-4000
  Irving *(G-12963)*
Celanese Ltd ....E 713 456-1525
  Pasadena *(G-16402)*
Celanese Ltd ....E 281 474-0554
  Pasadena *(G-16403)*
Celanese US Holdings LLC ....A 972 443-4000
  Dallas *(G-4094)*
Chevron Oronite Company LLC ....E 713 432-2500
  Houston *(G-9180)*
Chevron Phillips Chem Co LLC ....A 832 813-4100
  The Woodlands *(G-19843)*
Chevron Phillips Chem Co LP ....C 972 599-6600
  Plano *(G-16822)*
Chevron Phillips Chem Co LP ....C 713 475-3666
  Pasadena *(G-16408)*
Chevron Phillips Chem Co LP ....D 832 813-4100
  The Woodlands *(G-19844)*
Chevron Phillips Chem Co LP ....D 325 646-6561
  Brownwood *(G-2427)*
Chevron Phillips Chem Co LP ....C 409 882-6262
  Orange *(G-16235)*
Chevron Phillips Chem Co LP ....C 281 359-6500
  Humble *(G-12757)*
Chevron Phillips Chem Co LP ....C 806 275-5500
  Borger *(G-2168)*
Chevron Phillips Chem Co LP ....B 409 985-0700
  Port Arthur *(G-17104)*
Chevron Phillips Chem Co LP ....E 936 539-3154
  Conroe *(G-3275)*
Chevron Phillips Chem Co LP ....E 979 798-3950
  Brazoria *(G-2218)*
Cipherwaste Polymers LP ....G 281 946-8090
  Houston *(G-9193)*
CNA Holdings LLC ....E 972 443-4000
  Irving *(G-12976)*
Composites One Llc ....E 817 595-4991
  Fort Worth *(G-6537)*

Covestro LLC	E	281 350-9000	
Spring (G-19108)			
Covestro LLC	B	281 383-6000	
Baytown (G-1782)			
Cryogenic Plastics Inc	E	512 295-2683	
Kyle (G-13681)			
Cytec Engineered Materials Inc	C	903 457-8500	
Greenville (G-8068)			
Dallas Plastics LLC	F	903 291-0960	
Longview (G-14221)			
Dallas Plastics LLC	E	972 289-5500	
Mesquite (G-15037)			
Dow Chemical Company	D	281 474-4495	
La Porte (G-13732)			
Dow Chemical Company	B	281 228-2800	
Deer Park (G-5268)			
Dow Chemical Company	D	713 767-1615	
Deer Park (G-5269)			
Dow Chemical Company	E	979 238-2011	
Freeport (G-7196)			
Drilling Specialties Co LLC	F	800 423-3985	
The Woodlands (G-19853)			
Eastman Chemical Company	A	409 942-3532	
Texas City (G-19790)			
Eastman Chemical Company	E	903 237-6755	
Longview (G-14231)			
Eastman Chemical Texas Cy Inc	E	409 945-4431	
Texas City (G-19792)			
Eastman Performance Films LLC	E	817 445-1102	
Euless (G-6142)			
Effectus Corporation	F	713 446-5275	
Pearland (G-16558)			
Epsilyte LLC	C	815 224-1525	
The Woodlands (G-19862)			
Equistar Chemicals LP	A	713 209-7000	
La Porte (G-13736)			
Equistar Chemicals LP	E	281 862-4000	
Channelview (G-3020)			
Evonik Corporation	C	713 477-6841	
Pasadena (G-16434)			
Express Freight Systems Inc	F	713 861-1888	
Houston (G-9731)			
Exxonmobil Chemical Company	A	281 834-5200	
Baytown (G-1817)			
Exxonmobil Chemical Company	B	800 243-9966	
Spring (G-19116)			
Exxonmobil Research & Engrg Co	E	815 521-7411	
Spring (G-19118)			
Foam Supplies Inc	E	972 436-7008	
Lewisville (G-14050)			
Formosa Plastics Corp America	F	361 987-7000	
Point Comfort (G-17084)			
Formosa Utility Venture Ltd	A	361 987-7000	
Point Comfort (G-17086)			
Friedson Hill Inc	F	817 294-3309	
Fort Worth (G-6649)			
Friedson Hill Inc	F	817 244-6500	
Benbrook (G-2039)			
Gem-Tech Inc	E	817 329-3586	
Grapevine (G-8040)			
General Plas & Composites LP	C	713 644-1449	
Houston (G-9927)			
Genpak LLC	C	903 297-4445	
Longview (G-14241)			
Georgia-Pacific LLC	D	936 634-3308	
Lufkin (G-14529)			
Georgia-Pacific LLC	B	866 924-1397	
El Paso (G-5784)			
Greene Tweed & Co Inc	B	281 821-8337	
Houston (G-10033)			
Harvest Incorporated	E	254 933-1000	
Belton (G-2024)			
Hexcel Reinforcements Corp	D	830 379-1580	
Seguin (G-18843)			
Hexion Inc	D	281 727-3163	
Deer Park (G-5279)			
Hexpol Compounding LLC	F	817 483-9797	
Kennedale (G-13498)			
Hickory Springs Mfg Co	F	817 831-1785	
Fort Worth (G-6695)			
Huntsman Advnced Mtls Amrcas L	F	281 719-6000	
The Woodlands (G-19876)			
Huntsman Chemical	G	936 539-1961	
Conroe (G-3308)			
Huntsman Corporation	C	409 722-8381	
Port Neches (G-17163)			
Huntsman Intl Trdg Corp	E	281 719-7400	
The Woodlands (G-19879)			
Huntsman Intl Trdg Corp	E	281 719-6000	
The Woodlands (G-19880)			

Huntsman Petrochemical LLC	C	936 756-3381	
Conroe (G-3309)			
Huntsman Petrochemical LLC	A	409 722-8381	
Port Neches (G-17164)			
Huntsman Petrochemical LLC	C	409 724-4474	
Port Neches (G-17165)			
Idea Planet LP	E	972 380-9867	
Dallas (G-3844)			
Incounters Inc	E	325 675-5909	
Abilene (G-51)			
Independent Plastic Inc	F	713 329-9955	
Houston (G-10341)			
Ineos	F	979 415-8500	
Freeport (G-7199)			
Ineos LLC	C	361 552-8205	
Port Lavaca (G-17147)			
Ineos Americas LLC	D	713 920-4300	
Pasadena (G-16457)			
Ineos Americas LLC	B	361 552-8244	
Port Lavaca (G-17148)			
Ineos Americas LLC	E	713 307-3000	
La Porte (G-13751)			
Ineos Americas LLC	E	713 767-5714	
La Porte (G-13752)			
Ineos Americas LLC	E	409 985-0863	
Port Arthur (G-17113)			
Ineos New Planet Bioenergy LLC	D	630 857-7143	
League City (G-13961)			
Ineos Nitriles USA LLC	E	281 535-6600	
League City (G-13962)			
Ineos Styrolution America LLC	F	281 474-1000	
Pasadena (G-16458)			
Ineos Styrolution America LLC	E	281 474-1009	
League City (G-13964)			
Ineos USA LLC	C	281 535-6600	
League City (G-13965)			
Ineos USA LLC	E	281 535-6600	
League City (G-13966)			
Interactive Life Forms LLC	D	888 804-4453	
Austin (G-1234)			
Invista Capital Management LLC	E	409 886-6982	
Orange (G-16249)			
Invista Capital Management LLC	E	281 470-3434	
La Porte (G-13757)			
Johnnies Plastics Inc	E	210 533-8463	
San Antonio (G-18205)			
K-Bin Inc	E	979 233-6610	
Freeport (G-7202)			
Kaneka North America LLC	C	281 474-7084	
Pasadena (G-16468)			
Kraton Corporation	C	281 504-4700	
Houston (G-10563)			
Kraton Polymers LLC	F	832 204-5400	
Houston (G-10564)			
Kraton Polymers LLC	E	281 504-4700	
Houston (G-10565)			
Kraton Polymers US LLC	D	281 504-4700	
Houston (G-10566)			
Kraton Polymers US LLC	E	281 668-3163	
Houston (G-10567)			
Lavaca Pipe Line Company	E	361 987-8900	
Point Comfort (G-17088)			
Lonza Inc	D	281 291-2300	
Pasadena (G-16475)			
Lyondell Chemical Company	D	979 245-1225	
Bay City (G-1774)			
Lyondellbasell Industries Inc	F	713 209-1248	
La Porte (G-13771)			
Manner Polymers Inc	E	972 542-6789	
McKinney (G-14956)			
Material Difference Tech LLC	F	713 640-2040	
Houston (G-10792)			
Metton America Inc	E	281 479-8078	
La Porte (G-13777)			
Multi Plastics	F	972 402-9100	
Dallas (G-4706)			
Nan Ya Plastics Corp America	B	979 532-5494	
Wharton (G-20702)			
Nan Ya Plastics Corp America	C	281 727-7300	
Wharton (G-20703)			
Napco Bag & Film Gp LLC	E	972 245-8190	
Carrollton (G-2880)			
Noltex LLC	D	281 842-5000	
La Porte (G-13779)			
One Source Mfg Tech LLC	D	512 259-3272	
Leander (G-13996)			
Pactiv LLC	E	903 654-4745	
Corsicana (G-3683)			
Phoenix Plastics LP	F	936 760-2311	
Conroe (G-3349)			

Plaskolite Texas LLC	D	903 962-7573	
Grand Saline (G-7999)			
Plastic Specialties Inc	E	512 835-5873	
Austin (G-1420)			
Poly-America LP	D	281 385-3700	
Mont Belvieu (G-15620)			
Poly-Flex Construction Inc	F	972 647-4374	
Grand Prairie (G-7950)			
Polynt Composites USA Inc	F	903 938-9571	
Marshall (G-14798)			
Polynt Composites USA Inc	E	713 799-1800	
Houston (G-11360)			
Polyone Corporation	C	281 474-2831	
Seabrook (G-18790)			
Polyone Corporation	C	281 474-2831	
Seabrook (G-18789)			
Pore Technology Inc	E	903 601-4466	
Jefferson (G-13286)			
Quality Fiberglass Inc	F	817 473-3563	
Mansfield (G-14706)			
Ravago Americas LLC	F	817 635-4770	
Arlington (G-768)			
Reef Industries Inc	E	713 507-4200	
Houston (G-11577)			
Saint-Gobain Prfmce Plas Corp	D	903 572-3475	
Mount Pleasant (G-15663)			
Scicron Technologies LLC	E	806 372-8300	
Amarillo (G-462)			
Sheperd Maury	E	713 921-3456	
Houston (G-11865)			
Solvay USA Inc	C	325 515-7609	
Snyder (G-19009)			
Solvay USA Inc	D	940 552-9911	
Vernon (G-20230)			
Spartech Polycom (texas) Inc	E	817 640-5600	
Arlington (G-785)			
Styrochem Canada	F	817 847-8254	
Saginaw (G-17757)			
Tarquin Polymers & Colors Inc	G	281 240-0202	
Sugar Land (G-19561)			
Tecpac Plastics & Seals LLC	F	281 547-0620	
Tomball (G-20013)			
Tefco II Lc	F	281 398-9684	
Houston (G-12183)			
Tekni-Plex Inc	E	214 337-4711	
Dallas (G-5048)			
Tex-Co Resin Distribution Inc	F	972 722-8603	
Rockwall (G-17568)			
Texas Materials Group Inc	D	214 372-7700	
Dallas (G-5076)			
Total E&P RES & Tech USA LLC	E	713 647-3000	
Houston (G-12329)			
Total Ptrchemicals Ref USA Inc	E	409 291-7296	
Beaumont (G-1961)			
Total Ptrchemicals Ref USA Inc	B	409 963-6837	
Port Arthur (G-17129)			
Total Ptrchemicals Ref USA Inc	G	281 452-8577	
Channelview (G-3043)			
Total Ptrchemicals SEC USA Inc	E	713 483-5000	
Houston (G-12333)			
Total Ptrchmcals USA Fundation	F	713 483-5000	
La Porte (G-13798)			
Tpe Solutions Inc	F	978 425-3033	
Arlington (G-801)			
Trs Distribution LLC	F	281 372-8479	
Stafford (G-19389)			
Tsrc Specialty Materials LLC	G	281 754-5800	
Houston (G-12398)			
Union Carbide Corporation	D	361 553-2000	
Seadrift (G-18797)			
United Film Solutions Inc	F	713 715-4197	
Houston (G-12447)			
Valor Plastics LLC	E	512 663-2489	
Burnet (G-2618)			
Westlake Chemical Opco LP	E	713 960-9111	
Houston (G-12647)			
Westlake Longview Corpora	F	903 242-7500	
Longview (G-14337)			
Westlake Longview Corporation	C	713 960-9111	
Houston (G-12649)			
Westlake Monomers Corp	F	270 395-4151	
Houston (G-12650)			
Westlake Vinyls Inc	F	800 321-8550	
Houston (G-12654)			
Westlake Vinyls Company LP	C	713 960-9111	
Houston (G-12655)			
Wilsonart Intl Holdings Inc	E	254 207-7000	
Temple (G-19715)			
Wilsonart Intl Holdings LLC	E	254 207-6000	
Temple (G-19717)			

PRODUCT

Wilsonart Intl Holdings LLC ....E 254 207-7000
Temple *(G-19718)*

Wilsonart Jordan Holdings Inc ....F 512 302-6500
Austin *(G-1670)*

Wilsonart LLC ....E 254 742-2451
Temple *(G-19720)*

Wilsonart LLC ....E 254 207-0207
Temple *(G-19722)*

Wilsonart LLC ....F 713 576-5500
Houston *(G-12676)*

Woodbridge Sales & Engrg Inc ....C 915 751-1000
El Paso *(G-6040)*

Worldwide Stffing Slutions LLC ....F 210 293-3600
San Antonio *(G-18625)*

PLASTICS MATERIALS, BASIC FORMS & SHAPES WHOLESALERS

Akrotex Films Inc ....E 409 886-0111
Orange *(G-16230)*

Akrotex Films Inc ....E 409 886-0063
West Orange *(G-20692)*

Isco Industries Inc ....E 817 477-2900
Mansfield *(G-14683)*

PLASTICS PROCESSING

A & M Composites Corporation ....E 432 267-6525
Big Spring *(G-2068)*

Aerostar International Inc ....E 903 885-0728
Sulphur Springs *(G-19578)*

Dcu Inc ....F 972 816-6667
Wylie *(G-20932)*

Delfingen Us-Texas LP ....E 915 858-5577
El Paso *(G-5717)*

Diamond Plastics Corporation ....D 806 763-8021
Lubbock *(G-14405)*

Entegris Inc ....B 940 393-4232
Decatur *(G-5246)*

Gabhen Inc ....F 512 832-7902
Austin *(G-1177)*

Hoffman Company ....E 361 882-9281
Corpus Christi *(G-3549)*

Houston Mfg Specialty Co Inc ....E 281 888-4635
Houston *(G-10239)*

Impact Composite Tech Ltd ....E 806 385-1015
Littlefield *(G-14146)*

Inhance Technologies LLC ....E 800 929-1743
Houston *(G-10364)*

Kerick Industries ....F 214 432-2446
Dallas *(G-4552)*

Occidental Chemical Holdg Corp ....E 972 404-3800
Dallas *(G-4753)*

Plastronics Interconnections ....E 972 258-2580
Irving *(G-13152)*

Regal Plastic Supply Co Inc ....F 210 599-8291
San Antonio *(G-18419)*

Smart Pipe Company Inc ....F 281 945-5700
Houston *(G-11919)*

Xerxes Corporation ....E 830 372-0090
Seguin *(G-18875)*

PLASTICS SHEET: Packing Materials

Fresh-Pak Corp ....C 713 690-8742
Houston *(G-9866)*

Integrted Bagging Systems Corp ....F 361 874-3000
Lolita *(G-14175)*

Komplete Group Inc ....D 214 252-8100
Grand Prairie *(G-7907)*

Sonoco Products Company ....D 254 666-4777
Waco *(G-20458)*

PLASTICS: Blow Molded

Gs Liquid Technologies LLC ....F 817 556-6262
Cleburne *(G-3093)*

Hood Flexible Packaging Corp ....D 903 593-1793
Tyler *(G-20100)*

Lomont Molding LLC ....C 512 763-3600
Georgetown *(G-7660)*

M and N Plastics Inc ....F 915 877-1900
El Paso *(G-5852)*

Paragon Packaging Inc ....E 817 477-5211
Mansfield *(G-14701)*

Thomas M Niland Company ....E 915 779-1405
El Paso *(G-6002)*

Tiger Ridge Manufacturing Inc ....E 903 364-1810
Whitewright *(G-20729)*

PLASTICS: Casein

Team Promark LLC ....E 303 926-1328
Fort Worth *(G-7039)*

PLASTICS: Extruded

America Plastics LLC ....C 972 245-4525
Carrollton *(G-2697)*

Axion Strl Innovations LLC ....D 254 420-2078
Waco *(G-20365)*

Lucite International Inc ....C 409 729-1300
Nederland *(G-15755)*

Polymerica Ltd ....C 915 845-6288
El Paso *(G-5915)*

Prototype Machine Co ....E 512 282-1590
Manchaca *(G-14641)*

Reama Inc ....F 409 744-9222
Galveston *(G-7407)*

Semasys Inc ....C 713 869-8331
Houston *(G-11825)*

Simplfied Strl Thrmforming Inc ....G 903 887-8546
Mabank *(G-14581)*

Thermo Plastics Corporation ....E 817 281-9010
Fort Worth *(G-7056)*

Veka South Inc ....E 972 551-2030
Terrell *(G-19755)*

PLASTICS: Finished Injection Molded

3d Plastics LLC ....D 903 844-9333
Gladewater *(G-7716)*

A & M Plastics Inc ....G 713 941-1033
South Houston *(G-19036)*

Atrium Extrusion Systems Inc ....A 903 455-8560
Greenville *(G-8062)*

Ballqube Lc ....G 903 863-5572
Cushing *(G-3767)*

Basler Plastics LLC ....G 512 392-2800
San Marcos *(G-18679)*

Blackwell Plastics LP ....E 713 643-6577
Houston *(G-8912)*

C E Shepherd Company LP ....D 713 924-4300
Houston *(G-9028)*

Capsonic Group LLC ....E 915 872-3539
El Paso *(G-5681)*

Caraustar Industries Inc ....E 903 793-6231
Texarkana *(G-19758)*

D & L Tooling and Plastics Inc ....E 903 586-9894
Jacksonville *(G-13234)*

Dexas International Ltd ....D 469 635-8100
Coppell *(G-3415)*

Fox Valley Molding Inc ....E 956 428-2506
Harlingen *(G-8189)*

General Technologies Inc ....E 281 240-0550
Stafford *(G-19321)*

Illinois Tool Works Inc ....D 713 797-2181
Houston *(G-10323)*

Illinois Tool Works Inc ....E 714 870-8661
Fort Worth *(G-6716)*

Industrial Molding Corporation ....D 806 474-1047
Lubbock *(G-14426)*

ITW Blding Cmponents Group Inc ....E 972 660-4422
Grand Prairie *(G-7897)*

Medplast Group Inc ....E 480 553-6400
Houston *(G-10821)*

North Texas Plastics Inc ....E 940 458-7954
Sanger *(G-18728)*

Peacock Plastics Company ....F 903 586-2531
Jacksonville *(G-13256)*

PI Holdings Inc ....D 903 586-2408
Jacksonville *(G-13257)*

Reed Prototype and Model Inc ....F 512 457-0560
Lockhart *(G-14172)*

Rim Manufacturing LLC ....E 817 599-6521
Weatherford *(G-20617)*

Trident Laboratories Inc ....E 972 226-4986
Mesquite *(G-15081)*

United Plastics Group Inc ....E 713 466-5563
Houston *(G-12451)*

PLASTICS: Injection Molded

3p Performance Plastics Pdts ....F 281 537-8816
Houston *(G-8410)*

A B C Plastic Molding Inc ....E 713 692-9122
Houston *(G-8424)*

Advanced Pedestals Ltd ....D 940 668-7283
Gainesville *(G-7333)*

Airborn Interconnect Inc ....E 903 629-7821
Winnsboro *(G-20895)*

Aire Plastics Inc ....F 830 779-2289
La Vernia *(G-13800)*

All Plastic LLC ....D 830 896-6464
Kerrville *(G-13517)*

All-Plastics LLC ....D 972 239-2686
Addison *(G-102)*

Alpha Plastics Inc ....E 281 564-8838
Sugar Land *(G-19441)*

America Samkwang Inc ....E 956 686-0221
McAllen *(G-14838)*

Apex Plastics & Tooling Inc ....E 972 205-9000
Garland *(G-7438)*

Atlantis Plastic Company ....F 713 643-8387
Houston *(G-8742)*

Atron Group LLC ....D 214 292-9840
Dallas *(G-3984)*

Bace Manufacturing Inc ....C 713 329-8954
Houston *(G-8786)*

Bee Jay Molding Inc ....F 830 249-2425
Boerne *(G-2114)*

Bentley Consultants Co Inc ....F 972 289-2750
Mesquite *(G-15032)*

C & G Plastics Inc ....F 972 254-2541
Irving *(G-12955)*

Caprock Manufacturing Inc ....E 806 745-6454
Lubbock *(G-14389)*

Cascade Engineering Inc ....B 817 490-6300
Fort Worth *(G-6494)*

Chemplast Inc ....E 281 208-2585
Stafford *(G-19294)*

Cni ....F 830 765-7484
Del Rio *(G-5312)*

Coastal Plastic Molding Inc ....E 281 331-7909
Alvin *(G-356)*

Complete Plastic Fabricators ....F 713 674-7686
Houston *(G-9259)*

Contemporary Design Plastics ....E 817 640-7539
Arlington *(G-646)*

CPI Products LLC ....E 877 756-2388
Burnet *(G-2605)*

Cs Manufacturing Inc ....G 281 442-3400
Houston *(G-9353)*

Curtis Technical Service Inc ....F 979 388-0007
Clute *(G-3151)*

Dallas Rosti Inc ....F 972 554-1597
Irving *(G-12990)*

Dalworth Technologies Inc ....G 817 297-7976
Crowley *(G-3754)*

Dcm Manufacturing Inc ....E 817 428-3636
Grand Prairie *(G-7862)*

Dement Plastics LLC ....E 903 586-9894
Jacksonville *(G-13236)*

Dlhbowles Inc ....D 956 986-6000
Brownsville *(G-2350)*

E & T Plastic Mfg Co Inc ....F 214 622-6263
Dallas *(G-4283)*

E G C Corporation ....B 281 774-6100
Humble *(G-12764)*

Emu Plastics Tex Limited Inc ....E 956 618-5200
McAllen *(G-14859)*

Ensinger Special Polymers Inc ....E 281 580-3600
Houston *(G-9659)*

Epsilon Industries Inc ....E 469 573-9566
Garland *(G-7488)*

Exel Bobbins & Plas Components ....E 956 832-0807
Brownsville *(G-2355)*

Fischbach Texas LP ....F 469 533-5500
Dallas *(G-4365)*

Formtex Plastics Corporation ....E 713 493-6628
Houston *(G-9836)*

Gamma2 LLC ....E 760 734-4003
Arlington *(G-685)*

Gate-Mold Inc ....F 512 255-3470
Round Rock *(G-17659)*

Gemini Incorporated ....F 507 263-3957
Hidalgo *(G-8308)*

Globe Industries Inc ....E 281 440-3999
Houston *(G-9985)*

Gudgel & Sons Inc ....E 903 989-2232
Trenton *(G-20016)*

Gw Plastics San Antonio Inc ....C 210 225-1516
San Antonio *(G-18157)*

Hagans Plastics Co Inc ....E 972 790-9001
Grand Prairie *(G-7885)*

Hayes Holdings Inc ....C 281 565-8111
Sugar Land *(G-19490)*

Higuchi Manufacturing Amer LLC ....C 210 633-2877
San Antonio *(G-18167)*

Hill Plastics Inc ....F 972 436-9717
Lewisville *(G-14052)*

IDM Group LLC ....F 972 578-1010
Plano (G-16889)

Industrial Thermoform Inc ....E 972 299-5391
Cedar Hill (G-2945)

Integrted Mlding Solutions Inc ....E 281 587-9761
Houston (G-10390)

Jacksonville Tool & Die Inc ....F 903 586-6030
Jacksonville (G-13245)

Jamestown Plastics Inc ....E 956 831-8800
Brownsville (G-2368)

Jdp Manufacturing Inc ....E 817 529-4009
Fort Worth (G-6737)

K & L Precision Plastics Inc ....F 972 234-4231
Richardson (G-17338)

Kings Eco Plastics LLC ....D 956 631-1115
McAllen (G-14883)

Leatherwood Plastics ....F 972 221-7656
Lewisville (G-14060)

Leelinco Plastics Inc ....F 281 487-0377
Pasadena (G-16472)

Lorentson Mfg Co Southwest Inc ....E 956 399-8902
San Benito (G-18660)

Louis Barriga ....E 817 923-7370
Fort Worth (G-6801)

Marian Mexico Inc ....E 915 591-8558
El Paso (G-5866)

Maxwell Manufacturing Inc ....E 512 357-2772
Maxwell (G-14818)

McElroy Plastics Inc ....E 903 842-2180
Troup (G-20025)

Medical Components of America ....G 830 237-6405
Seguin (G-18851)

Melet Plastics Usa Inc ....F 210 822-0460
San Antonio (G-18291)

Metro Custom Plastics Inc ....E 817 640-5646
Arlington (G-731)

Micro Mold Plastics Inc ....E 817 536-0930
Fort Worth (G-6837)

Micro Mold Plastics Usa Inc ....E 817 536-0930
Fort Worth (G-6838)

Mitchell Machine & Fabricating ....F 903 880-0249
Mabank (G-14579)

Moore Fabrication Inc ....E 713 643-7477
Houston (G-10919)

MPA International LP ....C 915 474-7832
El Paso (G-5887)

Mvp Plastics Sa LLC ....F 440 834-1790
McAllen (G-14893)

Myco Plastics Inc ....G 903 586-0551
Jacksonville (G-13252)

N A Petroflex Ltd ....D 940 668-7283
Gainesville (G-7351)

National Plastic Molders Inc ....F 281 346-1942
Richmond (G-17463)

Paragon Rio Grande LLC ....F 956 831-8249
Brownsville (G-2391)

Pfi Molding Inc ....F 713 946-3300
Houston (G-11314)

Plastech Corporation ....E 972 490-1155
Addison (G-156)

Plasti Fab Inc ....E 817 485-0156
Richland Hills (G-17445)

Plastic Forming Inc ....E 817 284-7878
Richland Hills (G-17446)

Plastic Vacuum Forming Inc ....F 210 344-8531
San Antonio (G-18382)

Plastiform Inc ....F 972 241-2593
Irving (G-13149)

Plastix Plus LLC ....E 281 469-3451
Houston (G-11346)

Plastronics Interconnections ....E 972 255-1964
Irving (G-13153)

Polyweld USA Inc ....F 281 821-4156
Houston (G-11364)

Portage Plastics Corporation ....F 956 504-6102
Brownsville (G-2395)

Precision Fluorocarbon Inc ....E 281 351-4070
Tomball (G-20001)

Precision Formed Plastics Inc ....E 972 579-8803
Irving (G-13154)

Preferred Plastics Inc ....F 361 594-3535
Shiner (G-18948)

Premier Plastics Dallas Inc ....D 972 554-1597
Irving (G-13156)

Qfc Plastics Inc ....C 817 375-5774
Arlington (G-764)

Qt Industries LLC ....F 972 221-0537
Dallas (G-4840)

R & E Tooling & Plastics Inc ....F 817 834-2858
Fort Worth (G-6930)

Ranger Plastic Extrusions Inc ....E 817 640-6067
Arlington (G-767)

Regency Plastics - Ubly Inc ....D 915 860-1997
El Paso (G-5935)

Rehrig Pacific Company ....D 214 631-7943
Dallas (G-4885)

Reliant Worldwide Plastics LLC ....C 214 382-9672
Gainesville (G-7361)

Research Advanced Methods Inds ....E 254 442-1008
Cisco (G-3068)

RMC Plastics Inc ....F 713 722-9322
Houston (G-11635)

Royal Technologies Corporation ....C 956 424-9388
Mission (G-15563)

Sigmapro Engineering & Mfg LLC ....F 682 888-1234
Fort Worth (G-6986)

Solid Distribution LLC ....G 915 235-4357
El Paso (G-5967)

Southwest Quality Molding LP ....E 281 643-4500
Manvel (G-14738)

Sunbelt Plastics Incorporated ....E 972 335-4100
Frisco (G-7316)

Tallyho Plastics Inc ....D 903 586-2263
Jacksonville (G-13261)

Tasus Corporation ....D 512 869-7766
Georgetown (G-7682)

Tasus Texas Corporation ....C 512 869-7766
Georgetown (G-7683)

Tech Tool Plastics Inc ....E 817 246-4694
Fort Worth (G-7040)

Technimark Reynosa LLC ....F 336 498-4171
Pharr (G-16712)

Temple Tag II Ltd ....D 254 982-4212
Temple (G-19710)

Texas Injection Molding LLC ....D 281 489-4292
Houston (G-12237)

Think Plastics LLC ....F 713 771-7700
Sugar Land (G-19565)

US Farathane Holdings Corp ....C 734 656-9000
Austin (G-1616)

Waddington N Amer - Houston ....D 713 686-6700
Houston (G-12592)

Windsor Mold USA Inc ....F 956 787-8737
Pharr (G-16716)

PLASTICS: Molded

Allflex Usa Inc ....D 972 456-3686
Dallas (G-3924)

Bace Manufacturing Inc ....C 713 466-5563
Houston (G-8787)

Bee Jay Molding Inc ....E 281 487-0377
Pasadena (G-16397)

Charlotte Pipe and Foundry Co ....E 254 697-6556
Cameron (G-2641)

Futurefab Inc ....F 972 423-6606
Plano (G-16876)

Industrial Models Inc ....C 940 665-7841
Gainesville (G-7346)

Intrepid Industries Inc ....E 281 479-8301
La Porte (G-13756)

J V Plastics Inc ....F 972 606-0500
Grand Prairie (G-7900)

Ken Ross Inc ....F 972 442-3523
Wylie (G-20939)

Lee Linco Plastics Inc ....E 281 487-0377
Pasadena (G-16471)

Lone Star Molding Inc ....E 936 539-0008
Conroe (G-3324)

Poly U Molding & Mfg LP ....F 817 701-0779
Arlington (G-755)

Ponderosa Precision Plas Inc ....F 281 471-3221
La Porte (G-13783)

Port Plastics Inc ....E 817 834-7678
Fort Worth (G-6911)

Prism Industries LLC ....E 956 425-3300
Harlingen (G-8198)

Regal Plastic Supply Co Inc ....F 512 836-3629
Austin (G-1457)

Royberg Inc ....E 210 525-0094
San Antonio (G-18435)

Southern Plastics Inc ....C 903 984-6229
Kilgore (G-13591)

Thermo-Mold Inc ....F 713 944-6336
Houston (G-12271)

United Commodities LLC ....F 956 621-1798
Brownsville (G-2418)

Upg Company Inc ....C 713 466-5563
Houston (G-12474)

Wna Cups Illustrated Inc ....C 972 224-8407
Lancaster (G-13850)

PLASTICS: Polystyrene Foam

Acme Brick Company ....D 817 332-4101
El Paso (G-5636)

Blacksheep Inc ....B 903 592-3853
Tyler (G-20059)

Cnc Plastics ....F 979 884-0608
Giddings (G-7693)

Concote Corporation ....C 214 956-0077
Coppell (G-3412)

Concote Corporation ....F 903 581-0697
Tyler (G-20070)

Diab Holdings Inc ....C 972 228-7600
Desoto (G-5429)

Fairbanks Packaging LLC ....G 817 849-1366
Grand Prairie (G-7869)

Foam Fabricators Inc ....E 817 379-6520
Keller (G-13467)

Foam Pak US LP ....D 832 212-8896
Houston (G-9829)

Foam Supplies Inc ....F 972 436-7008
Lewisville (G-14050)

Foampack US ....E 281 565-9619
Stafford (G-19314)

Future Foam Inc ....E 214 350 6611
Dallas (G-4386)

Heubach Corporation ....E 214 291-0238
Garland (G-7511)

Igloo Products Corp ....B 713 461-5955
Katy (G-13364)

Industrial Insul & Shtmtl Inc ....E 432 332-8203
Odessa (G-16030)

Innocor Foam Tech - Acp Inc ....F 972 563-1559
Terrell (G-19738)

Innocor Form Tech Brenham LLC ....F 732 945-6222
Brenham (G-2258)

Johnson County Foam Inc ....E 817 477-5061
Mansfield (G-14684)

L B Foster Company ....E 832 934-3107
Magnolia (G-14613)

Lifoam Industries LLC ....D 972 937-6512
Waxahachie (G-20551)

Pactiv LLC ....G 254 770-4100
Temple (G-19693)

Pipeline Seal & Insulator Inc ....D 713 747-6948
Houston (G-11336)

Pmc Inc ....E 817 695-5680
Arlington (G-754)

Port City Inc ....E 713 673-7272
Houston (G-11365)

Republic Plastics Ltd ....E 830 557-5574
Mc Queeney (G-14830)

Rilco Manufacturing Co Inc ....C 713 466-4777
Houston (G-11624)

Southwestern Foam Tech Inc ....F 254 939-6379
Belton (G-2028)

Tasus Texas Corporation ....C 512 869-7766
Georgetown (G-7683)

TRC Recreation LP ....E 940 322-4463
Wichita Falls (G-20820)

Tuffys AC & Htg Svc Inc ....F 817 596-0150
Weatherford (G-20627)

Western Industries Corporation ....E 512 837-0240
Austin (G-1658)

Williams Products Inc ....F 214 630-3131
Arlington (G-809)

Z Fab USA Inc ....E 817 380-1156
Fort Worth (G-7159)

PLASTICS: Thermoformed

Franks Manufacturing Co ....F 210 492-3222
San Antonio (G-18125)

Geotex Inc ....E 817 656-9797
Fort Worth (G-6666)

Plastic Molding Technology Inc ....C 915 593-6922
El Paso (G-5911)

Te Connectivity Corporation ....E 469 568-0657
Carrollton (G-2826)

PLATE WORK: Metalworking Trade

Boatman Industries Inc ....E 713 641-6006
Houston (G-8932)

Rmf Manufacturing LLC ....D 713 910-9777
Houston (G-11638)

Techmar Industries LLC ....F 832 246-6200
Spring (G-19175)

Wagner Plate Works LLC ....E 713 462-1946
Houston (G-12593)

PRODUCT

PLATEMAKING SVC: Color Separations, For The Printing Trade

Quad/Graphics Inc ....C 972 892-3803
Dallas *(G-4841)*

R S Graphic Services Inc ....E 817 921-6266
Fort Worth *(G-6932)*

PLATEMAKING SVC: Letterpress

Cooksey Luther Printing Co ....F 817 332-2842
Fort Worth *(G-6545)*

PLATES

Blanks Printing & Imaging Inc ....D 214 741-3905
Dallas *(G-4030)*

Blumbergexcelsior Inc ....E 817 462-1530
Arlington *(G-632)*

Business Printing Inc ....F 214 445-5000
Carrollton *(G-2706)*

Corpus Christi Stamp Works Inc ....E 361 884-4801
Corpus Christi *(G-3509)*

Engraving and Printing Bureau ....E 817 847-3800
Fort Worth *(G-6615)*

J & J Nameplate and Label LLC ....G 972 939-1157
Carrollton *(G-2873)*

License Plates of Texas LLC ....F 512 583-8585
Austin *(G-1292)*

Nieman Printing Inc ....C 972 506-7400
Dallas *(G-4739)*

Roy Johnson Incorporated ....E 817 468-2939
Arlington *(G-773)*

Sandford Prepress Systems ....E 214 808-3070
Dallas *(G-4932)*

Thomas Graphics Inc ....D 512 719-3535
Austin *(G-1576)*

Timesaver Templates Inc ....F 972 620-2197
Dallas *(G-5095)*

USA Printing Corporation ....F 281 498-4310
Houston *(G-12500)*

PLATES: Plastic Exc Polystyrene Foam

Shieldcoat Technologies Inc ....E 936 633-6387
Lufkin *(G-14551)*

PLATES: Sheet & Strip, Exc Coated Prdts

CC Coating & Machine Inc ....E 361 884-9753
Corpus Christi *(G-3497)*

Dennis Steel Inc ....D 512 259-4001
Leander *(G-13987)*

PLATES: Steel

AAA Flame Cut Steel Inc ....F 713 868-2337
Houston *(G-8435)*

Custom Flame Cutting Inc ....F 281 342-3250
Rosenberg *(G-17579)*

Cws Road Plate LLC ....D 713 242-7711
Houston *(G-9380)*

Cyclone Steel Services LLC ....E 713 635-5555
Houston *(G-9385)*

Express Fabricators LLC ....F 972 734-3855
Farmersville *(G-6222)*

Friedman Industries Inc ....D 903 639-2511
Lone Star *(G-14182)*

Joy Glbal Lngview Oprtions LLC ....A 903 237-7000
Longview *(G-14257)*

Manufctred Component Parts Ltd ....E 713 880-0590
Houston *(G-10749)*

Nucor Steel Longview LLC ....D 800 256-5757
Longview *(G-14286)*

PLATING & FINISHING SVC: Decorative, Formed Prdts

Jdh Iron Designs LLC ....F 254 486-9150
Valley Mills *(G-20201)*

PLATING & POLISHING SVC

3c Metal USA Inc ....F 713 808-9651
Houston *(G-8407)*

AAA Blast-Cote Inc ....E 281 482-1236
Friendswood *(G-7241)*

Advanced Aero Coatings LLC ....F 940 367-5963
Ponder *(G-17093)*

Azz Inc ....E 972 840-0934
Garland *(G-7446)*

Brock Enterprises LLC ....E 409 729-6353
Nederland *(G-15747)*

Cor-Pro Systems Inc ....E 713 896-1091
Houston *(G-9312)*

Cy-Fair Coatings Inc ....F 281 351-7427
Cypress *(G-3784)*

Elkcorp ....E 972 851-0500
Dallas *(G-4313)*

Hwm Hurst Inc ....E 817 268-6111
Hurst *(G-12845)*

J E Titus Company ....F 713 991-1100
Houston *(G-10439)*

MSA Industries Inc ....F 432 337-6062
Odessa *(G-16084)*

North Shore Supply Company Inc ....D 713 400-3320
Houston *(G-11077)*

Outdoor Furn Refinishing Inc ....D 713 741-9779
Houston *(G-11202)*

Outdoor Furniture Refinishing ....F 713 741-9779
Houston *(G-11203)*

Panasonic Corp North America ....A 956 984-3432
Mcallen *(G-14899)*

Stuart-Dean Co Inc ....F 972 513-9781
Irving *(G-13189)*

Texas Hydraulics Inc ....E 254 756-6879
Waco *(G-20466)*

Weatherford Artificia ....F 918 224-7428
Kingwood *(G-13660)*

William L Bonnell Company Inc ....B 409 543-0600
El Campo *(G-5629)*

PLATING SVC: Chromium, Metals Or Formed Prdts

Acme Holdings Inc ....E 210 798-3460
San Antonio *(G-17861)*

Daggett Street Properties ....F 817 332-5604
Fort Worth *(G-6572)*

Finley Investments Inc ....E 713 686-4629
Houston *(G-9788)*

Houston Mfg Specialty Co Inc ....E 281 888-4635
Houston *(G-10239)*

ICP Industries LLC ....F 210 226-1261
San Antonio *(G-18178)*

M & K Plating Inc ....E 817 332-6021
Fort Worth *(G-6802)*

Mirror Acquisitions LLC ....F 713 686-4435
Houston *(G-10889)*

Result Enterprises Inc ....D 713 666-0550
Houston *(G-11614)*

Rister Crnkshaft Spcialist Ltd ....E 361 289-0588
Corpus Christi *(G-3610)*

PLATING SVC: Electro

Accurate Precision Plating LLC ....E 281 598-8835
Houston *(G-8463)*

Aef Plating LLC ....E 956 994-1991
McAllen *(G-14832)*

Aero-Tech Metal Finishing Inc ....F 210 522-0802
San Antonio *(G-17872)*

Aft Industries Inc ....E 469 865-2800
Mansfield *(G-14653)*

Aft Industries Inc ....E 972 988-1999
Mansfield *(G-14654)*

American Plating Co Texas Ltd ....E 281 452-4241
Houston *(G-8604)*

Anodics Inc ....F 817 281-2743
Fort Worth *(G-6389)*

Apci Inc ....E 817 927-5362
Fort Worth *(G-6391)*

B Finishing Co Inc ....F 512 759-2100
Hutto *(G-12876)*

Billmark Company ....F 817 834-2481
Fort Worth *(G-6451)*

Concote Corporation ....F 903 581-0697
Tyler *(G-20070)*

Concote Corporation ....C 214 956-0077
Coppell *(G-3412)*

Courter-Hall Company ....F 972 276-8531
Garland *(G-7468)*

Dels Plating Industries Corp ....F 713 785-4955
Houston *(G-9428)*

Delstar Metal Finishing Inc ....E 713 849-2090
Houston *(G-9429)*

East Texas Plating Inc ....F 903 935-7000
Marshall *(G-14775)*

Electro-Coatings Texas Inc ....E 210 798-3460
Houston *(G-9591)*

Elkcorp ....E 936 633-6387
Lufkin *(G-14526)*

General Magnaplate Corporation ....D 817 640-1761
Arlington *(G-687)*

Gleco Plating Inc ....D 972 475-4300
Rowlett *(G-17705)*

H & M Plating Company Inc ....D 713 643-6516
Houston *(G-10080)*

Hall Plating Co ....F 830 620-7825
New Braunfels *(G-15800)*

Har-Conn Chrome Company ....E 817 626-5437
Fort Worth *(G-6689)*

Harrison Electropolishing LP ....E 832 467-3100
Houston *(G-10126)*

Houston Plating & Coatings LLC ....D 713 946-8920
South Houston *(G-19046)*

Integrted Crrsion Cmpanies Inc ....E 713 789-9181
Houston *(G-10389)*

J & S Plating and Repair Inc ....F 972 784-8718
Farmersville *(G-6224)*

Morrell Plating Co Inc ....E 214 357-9850
Dallas *(G-4689)*

New Tk Coatings LLC ....E 713 666-1375
Houston *(G-11037)*

Precise Hard Chrome ....E 254 756-6879
Waco *(G-20449)*

Rubens Electroplating Inc ....E 915 779-3796
El Paso *(G-5948)*

S + S Industries Inc ....E 713 643-8888
Houston *(G-11709)*

Schumacher Company Inc ....D 713 923-5548
Houston *(G-11783)*

Sentinel Plating Inc ....F 972 276-2780
Garland *(G-7587)*

Southwestern Plating Company ....D 713 223-1331
Houston *(G-11986)*

Tenth Street Industries LP ....E 972 578-5155
Plano *(G-17024)*

Texas Mpp LP ....E 903 874-5781
Corsicana *(G-3685)*

TImi Corporation ....F 512 833-7075
Austin *(G-1582)*

U S Plating LLP ....F 972 871-2800
Irving *(G-13201)*

Valence Surface Tech LLC ....F 855 370-5920
The Woodlands *(G-19934)*

Vanguard Metal Technologies ....E 713 641-1859
Houston *(G-12529)*

W & S Precision Finishing Co ....E 214 339-7181
Dallas *(G-5170)*

PLATING SVC: Gold

Artistic Plating Inc ....F 713 864-1352
Houston *(G-8711)*

Noles Davis Plating Co ....G 214 358-1731
Dallas *(G-4741)*

PLATING SVC: NEC

Airline Plating Inc ....F 713 692-6369
Houston *(G-8517)*

Alamo Plating Inc ....F 210 658-4024
Converse *(G-3387)*

Alamo Plating & Met Finshg Ltd ....E 210 658-4024
Converse *(G-3388)*

Als Associates ....E 817 921-2679
Fort Worth *(G-6373)*

Bhc Industries of Texas Inc ....F 817 556-2306
Alvarado *(G-325)*

Dean-Chem Inc ....F 713 644-3882
Houston *(G-9419)*

Dura-Tech Processes Inc ....F 817 473-7888
Mansfield *(G-14668)*

Houston Plating & Coatings LLC ....C 713 946-8920
South Houston *(G-19047)*

Quality Bumper Service Dallas ....E 214 824-7300
Dallas *(G-4843)*

Reinfro LLC ....D 956 838-9814
Brownsville *(G-2398)*

Ronald Noles ....F 281 489-7727
Manvel *(G-14737)*

Sifco Applied Srfc Cncepts LLC ....F 281 444-6500
Houston *(G-11882)*

Signature Plating Ltd ....E 210 380-0020
Cibolo *(G-3065)*

Specialty Metal Finishing Inc ....F 713 528-5428
Houston *(G-12000)*

Texas Precision Plating Inc ....E 972 494-1547
Garland *(G-7599)*

PLAYGROUND EQPT

Adventure Plygrund Systems Inc ....F 713 935-9684
Houston *(G-8496)*

Playground Constructors Inc ....F 915 585-6336
 El Paso **(G-5912)**
Playgrund Shade Structures Inc ....G 512 642-6124
 Hutto **(G-12884)**
Playwood Outdoor Fun ....F 512 250-8819
 Austin **(G-1421)**
Rk Global Inc ....F 972 339-8016
 Coppell **(G-3440)**
Safespace Concepts Inc ....F 713 956-0820
 Houston **(G-11725)**

PLEATING & STITCHING SVC

Century Graphics & Sign Inc ....E 432 686-8244
 Midland **(G-15157)**
Davids Apparel Inc ....E 915 590-3744
 El Paso **(G-5715)**
Jj of Dallas Manufacturing Inc ....E 972 866-9866
 Addison **(G-141)**
SMA Distributors ....F 281 442-0890
 Houston **(G-11917)**

PLUMBERS' GOODS: Rubber

Component Manufacturing Corp...........E 800 275-3011
 Conroe **(G-3280)**

PLUMBING & HEATING EQPT & SPLY, WHOL: Htg Eqpt/Panels, Solar

Mardel Souza Inc................................E 956 459-3504
 Weslaco **(G-20664)**
Skyven Technologies Inc ....E 972 861-0893
 Richardson **(G-17399)**
Standard Renewable Energy LP............D 281 763-2020
 Houston **(G-12043)**
Sunrgy LLC ....E 832 786-5051
 Stafford **(G-19381)**
Texas Solar Resources Inc ....F 281 846-4968
 League City **(G-13981)**

PLUMBING & HEATING EQPT & SPLY, WHOLESALE: Hydronic Htg Eqpt

Ces Industrial LLC ....F 281 615-5621
 Stafford **(G-19293)**
R Neal John & Associates Inc ....E 214 340-1464
 Dallas **(G-4855)**

PLUMBING & HEATING EQPT & SPLYS WHOLESALERS

Border States Industries Inc ....E 432 332-0591
 Odessa **(G-15940)**
Border States Industries Inc ....F 432 520-0230
 Midland **(G-15147)**
Border States Industries Inc ....F 325 698-4595
 Abilene **(G-23)**
Border States Industries Inc ....F 512 458-6313
 Austin **(G-1001)**
Border States Industries Inc ....F 325 655-9163
 San Angelo **(G-17785)**
Border States Industries Inc ....E 806 457-4100
 Amarillo **(G-409)**
Border States Industries Inc ....F 806 765-5741
 Lubbock **(G-14379)**
Border States Industries Inc ....E 956 831-3441
 Brownsville **(G-2339)**
Border States Industries Inc ....F 575 434-2022
 El Paso **(G-5670)**
Cooper Supply Inc ....E 817 222-9055
 Fort Worth **(G-6548)**
National Wholesale Supply Inc ....F 469 517-0600
 Waxahachie **(G-20553)**
Preferred Pump & Equipment LP ....E 817 536-9800
 Fort Worth **(G-6912)**
Sword Company ....E 903 561-1921
 Tyler **(G-20159)**

PLUMBING & HEATING EQPT & SPLYS, WHOL: Pipe/Fitting, Plastic

Charbonneau Industries Inc ....F 770 664-4319
 Houston **(G-9163)**
Gicon Pumps & Equipment Ltd ....G 806 373-0478
 Amarillo **(G-428)**
Wallis Concrete LLC ....F 979 478-6734
 Wallis **(G-20510)**

PLUMBING & HEATING EQPT & SPLYS, WHOL: Plumbing Fitting/Sply

Clarke Products Inc ....F 972 660-1992
 Waco **(G-20383)**
Morsco Supply LLC ....F 903 234-2183
 Longview **(G-14282)**
National Wholesale Supply Inc ....E 972 331-7770
 Dallas **(G-4716)**
Nibco Inc ....E 574 295-3000
 McAllen **(G-14894)**
Zurn Industries LLC ....E 972 277-0900
 Carrollton **(G-2852)**

PLUMBING & HEATING EQPT & SPLYS, WHOL: Water Purif Eqpt

C Treat Offshore Watermakers ....E 281 367-2800
 The Woodlands **(G-19837)**
Flo Pura Corp ....E 281 320-9547
 Spring **(G-19122)**
Guiverman Industries LLC ....E 866 235-8057
 Plano **(G-16882)**
Jentek Water Treatment Inc ....F 214 349-7111
 Dallas **(G-4531)**

PLUMBING & HEATING EQPT & SPLYS, WHOLESALE: Gas Burners

Furnace Systems Inc ....F 972 423-7800
 Plano **(G-16875)**

PLUMBING & HEATING EQPT & SPLYS, WHOLESALE: Pwr Indl Boiler

American Steam Inc ....E 972 442-4499
 Wylie **(G-20926)**

PLUMBING & HEATING EQPT, WHOLESALE: Water Heaters/Purif

Watts Wtr Qulty Cond Pdts Inc ....D 210 677-0618
 San Antonio **(G-18612)**

PLUMBING & HEATING EQPT/SPLYS, WHOL: Boilers, Hot Water Htg

Cisco Boiler Service Co Inc ....E 713 928-5700
 Houston **(G-9196)**
Triple S Manufacturing Company ....F 817 281-0602
 Fort Worth **(G-7079)**

PLUMBING FIXTURES

As America Inc ....F 214 530-9831
 Hutchins **(G-12862)**
Brasscraft Manufacturing Co.................D 248 305-6000
 Lancaster **(G-13841)**
C Pearson Plumbing Inc ....F 817 488-0490
 Grapevine **(G-8018)**
Chevron Phillips Chem Co LP ....A 832 813-4100
 The Woodlands **(G-19845)**
Clarke Products Inc ....F 972 660-1992
 Waco **(G-20383)**
Component Manufacturing Corp...........E 800 275-3011
 Conroe **(G-3280)**
Dal-Tex Specialty & Mfg Co..................F 903 883-3689
 Greenville **(G-8070)**
Eljer Industries Inc.............................E 972 560-2000
 Dallas **(G-4311)**
Fisher Controls Intl LLC ....B 972 542-5512
 McKinney **(G-14943)**
Flowtronex Psi LLC ....C 469 221-1200
 Dallas **(G-4372)**
Isenberg Bath Corporation ....F 888 342-2284
 Dallas **(G-4513)**
John W Gasparini Inc ....D 972 466-4104
 Carrollton **(G-2874)**
Kerr Feed & Grain Company.................F 940 538-4354
 Henrietta **(G-8281)**
Kohler Co ....B 325 643-2661
 Brownwood **(G-2432)**
National Wholesale Supply Inc ....F 469 517-0600
 Waxahachie **(G-20553)**
NCH Corporation.................................A 972 438-0211
 Irving **(G-13114)**
NCH Corporation.................................A 972 438-0381
 Irving **(G-13115)**
Nibco Inc ....B 936 564-8321
 Nacogdoches **(G-15706)**

Northwest Pipe Company ....D 817 847-1402
 Saginaw **(G-17753)**
Powerseal Pipeline Pdts Corp ....D 940 767-5566
 Wichita Falls **(G-20796)**
Royal Baths Manufacturing Co ....B 281 442-3400
 Houston **(G-11682)**

PLUMBING FIXTURES: Plastic

Aquatic Co ....F 817 801-8300
 Arlington **(G-621)**
Border States Industries Inc ....E 432 332-0591
 Odessa **(G-15940)**
Border States Industries Inc ....F 432 520-0230
 Midland **(G-15147)**
Border States Industries Inc ....F 325 698-4595
 Abilene **(G-23)**
Border States Industries Inc ....F 512 458-6313
 Austin **(G-1001)**
Border States Industries Inc ....F 325 655-9163
 San Angelo **(G-17785)**
Border States Industries Inc ....E 806 457-4100
 Amarillo **(G-409)**
Border States Industries Inc ....F 806 765-5741
 Lubbock **(G-14379)**
Border States Industries Inc ....E 956 831-3441
 Brownsville **(G-2339)**
Border States Industries Inc ....F 575 434-2022
 El Paso **(G-5670)**
Clarke Products Inc ....C 972 660-1992
 Colleyville **(G-3212)**
Dal-Tex Specialty & Mfg Co..................F 903 883-3689
 Greenville **(G-8070)**
Eljer Industries Inc.............................E 972 560-2000
 Dallas **(G-4311)**
Killeen Marble....................................E 254 699-3408
 Killeen **(G-13612)**
L F Manufacturing Inc.........................D 979 542-8027
 Giddings **(G-7699)**
Palmer of Texas Tanks Inc ....D 432 523-5904
 Andrews **(G-556)**
Proske Plastic Products Inc..................E 713 926-9941
 Houston **(G-11461)**
Ralph Cordova Company ....E 972 771-7281
 Royse City **(G-17725)**
Sustain Ability Solutions Inc ....F 888 657-7582
 Flower Mound **(G-6285)**
TW Tanks and Construction Co...........F 361 358-8869
 Beeville **(G-1989)**
W & W Fiberglass Tank Company ....D 806 669-1128
 Pampa **(G-16344)**

PLUMBING FIXTURES: Vitreous

As America Inc ....F 214 530-9831
 Hutchins **(G-12862)**
Border States Industries Inc ....E 432 332-0591
 Odessa **(G-15940)**
Border States Industries Inc ....F 432 520-0230
 Midland **(G-15147)**
Border States Industries Inc ....F 325 698-4595
 Abilene **(G-23)**
Border States Industries Inc ....F 512 458-6313
 Austin **(G-1001)**
Border States Industries Inc ....F 325 655-9163
 San Angelo **(G-17785)**
Border States Industries Inc ....E 806 457-4100
 Amarillo **(G-409)**
Border States Industries Inc ....F 806 765-5741
 Lubbock **(G-14379)**
Border States Industries Inc ....F 956 831-3441
 Brownsville **(G-2339)**
Border States Industries Inc ....F 575 434-2022
 El Paso **(G-5670)**
Eljer Industries Inc.............................E 972 560-2000
 Dallas **(G-4311)**

POINT OF SALE DEVICES

Advanced Ret MGT Systems Inc ....E 303 738-1800
 Houston **(G-8491)**
Elias & Associates LLC ....E 956 244-6552
 Harlingen **(G-8186)**
NCR Corporation.................................F 210 366-2959
 San Antonio **(G-18339)**
NCR Solutions Llc ....F 405 413-8278
 Little Elm **(G-14140)**
Renfro Industries Inc ....D 972 563-4295
 Terrell **(G-19749)**

PRODUCT

POLE LINE HARDWARE

Chm Industries Inc.................................F 682 286-0046
Saginaw *(G-17742)*
S & H Shtmtl & Fabg Co Inc ....E 713 926-8805
Houston *(G-11706)*

POLISHING SVC: Metals Or Formed Prdts

Fin-Tech Inc ....E 713 680-3777
Houston *(G-9787)*

POLYESTERS

Ifs Coatings Inc ....E 940 668-1062
Gainesville *(G-7345)*
Reichhold Industries Inc ....F 713 453-5431
Houston *(G-11587)*

POLYETHYLENE CHLOROSULFONATED RUBBER

Equistar Chemicals LP ....A 713 309-7200
Houston *(G-9689)*
Indevco Plas - Longview LLC ....F 903 291-1115
Longview *(G-14250)*
Lyondell Chemical Company ....D 361 242-8000
Corpus Christi *(G-3565)*
Molding Acquisition Corp ....E 209 723-5000
Fort Worth *(G-6846)*
Westlake Olefins Corporation ....E 713 960-9111
Houston *(G-12651)*

POLYETHYLENE RESINS

Celanese Corporation...........................B 972 443-4000
Irving *(G-12964)*
Chevron Phillips Chem Co LP ....A 281 421-6500
Baytown *(G-1814)*
Chevron Phillips Chem Co LP ....C 409 882-6000
Orange *(G-16234)*
Eastman Chemical Company ....E 423 229-2000
Longview *(G-14230)*
Exxonmobil Chemical Company ....B 409 860-1300
Beaumont *(G-1891)*
Honeywell International Inc ....A 281 890-0088
Cypress *(G-3801)*
Invista Capital Management LLC...........A 409 886-5080
West Orange *(G-20695)*
Invista Capital Management LLC...........A 409 886-9373
Orange *(G-16250)*
Polynt Composites USA Inc ....D 972 875-8634
Ennis *(G-6115)*
Ttwf LP ....A 713 960-9111
Houston *(G-12400)*
Westlake Chemical Corporation ....B 903 242-7513
Longview *(G-14336)*
Westlake Chemical Corporation ....B 713 960-9111
Houston *(G-12646)*

POLYMETHYL METHACRYLATE RESINS: Plexiglas

Lyondellbasell Industries Inc.................D 713 309-7200
Houston *(G-10709)*
Nialti Manufacturing LLC ....F 281 894-4995
Houston *(G-11051)*
Ppe LLC ....F 979 353-7300
Brenham *(G-2270)*
Tricon Energy Inc ....D 713 963-0066
Houston *(G-12369)*
Vertec Polymers Inc ....F 866 283-7832
Houston *(G-12555)*

POLYPROPYLENE RESINS

Braskem America Inc ....C 713 255-4747
Houston *(G-8976)*
Braskem America Inc ....G 215 841-3100
Port Lavaca *(G-17142)*
Braskem America Inc ....F 979 705-2532
Freeport *(G-7193)*
Igi The Intl Group Inc ....E 281 573-9280
Baytown *(G-1792)*
Phillips Smika Plyprpylene LLC ....C 832 813-4100
The Woodlands *(G-19902)*
Precision Specialties Company.............E 800 527-3295
Sherman *(G-18927)*
Worldwide Sorbent Products Inc ....E 409 983-7800
Beaumont *(G-1970)*

POLYSTYRENE RESINS

Americas Styrenics LLC ....D 832 616-7800
The Woodlands *(G-19826)*
Huntsman Corporation ....E 281 719-6000
The Woodlands *(G-19877)*
Huntsman International LLC ....D 281 719-6000
The Woodlands *(G-19878)*
Lifoam Industries LLC ....D 972 937-6512
Waxahachie *(G-20551)*
Nova Chemicals Inc ....D 281 474-1000
Pasadena *(G-16491)*
Starrfoam Manufacturing Inc ....E 915 886-4636
Anthony *(G-590)*

POLYTETRAFLUOROETHYLENE RESINS

American Industrial Polymers ....E 979 542-3654
Giddings *(G-7691)*

POLYURETHANE RESINS

Demilec International Inc ....E 817 640-4900
Arlington *(G-660)*
Huntsman Bldg Slutions USA LLC........D 817 640-4900
Arlington *(G-701)*
Marine Rubber Inc...............................F 281 446-4132
Humble *(G-12787)*
Western Wire Works Inc ....F 817 654-3373
Fort Worth *(G-7141)*

POLYVINYL CHLORIDE RESINS

Bravo Concealment LLC ....F 956 783-7682
Alamo *(G-177)*
Formosa Industries Corporation ....E 361 987-7000
Point Comfort *(G-17083)*
Formosa Plastics Corp Texas ....B 361 987-7000
Point Comfort *(G-17085)*
J-M Manufacturing Company Inc ....D 979 532-5640
Wharton *(G-20700)*
M-Master LLC ....F 915 242-2315
El Paso *(G-5855)*
Shintech Incorporated ....F 713 965-0713
Houston *(G-11869)*

POLYVINYLIDENE CHLORIDE RESINS

Shintech Incorporated ....C 979 233-7861
Freeport *(G-7210)*

POSTAL EQPT: Locker Boxes, Exc Wood

American Egle Mailbox Mfr Corp...........F 214 358-2873
Dallas *(G-3939)*
Cedra Pharmacy Houston LLC ....E 713 621-0621
Houston *(G-9117)*

POSTS: Floor, Adjustable, Metal

Sbi Industrial LLC ....E 972 284-1250
Canton *(G-2660)*

POTPOURRI

Hall Tree Antiques Inc ....D 325 944-4794
San Angelo *(G-17803)*
Jayden Inc ....E 214 389-7300
Dallas *(G-4527)*
Trimmings Inc......................................C 903 872-1556
Corsicana *(G-3687)*

POTTING SOILS

Hope Agri Products Inc ....F 214 371-7120
Dallas *(G-4466)*
Letco Group LLC ....F 972 274-2835
Lancaster *(G-13844)*
Letco Group LLC ....E 409 584-2155
Pineland *(G-16740)*
Letco Group LLC ....E 281 342-6113
Richmond *(G-17461)*
Letco Group LLC ....F 281 537-2377
Houston *(G-10627)*
Ramrod Enterprises LLC ....E 936 756-4846
Conroe *(G-3356)*

POULTRY & SMALL GAME SLAUGHTERING & PROCESSING

Buddys Natural Chickens Inc ....D 830 672-6262
Gonzales *(G-7749)*
Buddys Natural Chickens Inc ....D 830 305-0553
Gonzales *(G-7750)*
Cal-Maine Foods Inc ....E 830 540-4105
Waelder *(G-20483)*
Cargill Incorporated ....A 254 799-6211
Waco *(G-20375)*
Davis Applicators LLC ....G 830 857-3222
Gonzales *(G-7751)*
Golden Duck Inc ....E 713 222-9262
Houston *(G-9992)*
Holmes Foods Inc ....F 830 437-2555
Gonzales *(G-7756)*
Ideal Plty Breeding Farms Inc ....E 254 697-6677
Cameron *(G-2642)*
John Soules Foods Inc ....C 903 592-9800
Tyler *(G-20104)*
MARTIN PREFERRED FOODS LP ....C 713 869-6191
Houston *(G-10777)*
Pilgrims Pride Corporation ....E 936 560-3901
Nacogdoches *(G-15710)*
Pilgrims Pride Corporation ....B 903 575-3403
Mount Pleasant *(G-15658)*
Pilgrims Pride Corporation ....C 903 434-1000
Pittsburg *(G-16749)*
Pilgrims Pride Corporation ....B 903 575-3748
Mount Pleasant *(G-15659)*
Sanderson Farms Inc ....A 254 412-3800
Waco *(G-20457)*
Sanderson Farms Inc Proc Div...............A 979 361-3410
Bryan *(G-2504)*
Sanderson Farms Inc Prod Div...............A 979 778-5730
Bryan *(G-2505)*
Tyson Foods Inc ....A 817 485-8912
North Richland Hills *(G-15883)*
Tyson Foods Inc ....D 936 569-7967
Nacogdoches *(G-15717)*
Tyson Foods Inc ....A 903 297-4200
Carthage *(G-2925)*
Tyson Foods Inc ....C 830 672-6548
Gonzales *(G-7766)*
Tyson Foods Inc ....A 830 401-8800
Seguin *(G-18871)*

POULTRY SLAUGHTERING & PROCESSING

Lone Star Poultry Inc ....D 713 868-3888
Houston *(G-10681)*

POULTRY, PACKAGED FROZEN: Wholesalers

Cargill Incorporated ....A 254 799-6211
Waco *(G-20375)*

POWDER: Aluminum Atomized

Baikowski Malakoff Inc..........................F 903 489-1910
Malakoff *(G-14634)*

POWDER: Metal

Halo Coatings ....G 817 443-3710
Fort Worth *(G-6684)*
Powder Coaters of Texas Inc ....F 979 387-2049
Beasley *(G-1844)*
Powder Metallurgy Company Inc ....E 972 436-3502
Lewisville *(G-14082)*

POWER DISTRIBUTION BOARDS: Electric

Gonzales Elec Systems LLC ....E 409 860-3802
Beaumont *(G-1899)*

POWER GENERATORS

Baseline Energy Services LP..................F 432 248-9112
Midland *(G-15133)*
Baseline Energy Services LP..................E 817 889-0056
Fort Worth *(G-6428)*
Competitive Energy - Texas LP...............G 713 957-9948
Sugar Land *(G-19466)*
Compliant Power Systems LLC...............F 903 427-0071
Clarksville *(G-3072)*
Comprssion/Generation Svcs LLC...........D 281 209-3616
Houston *(G-9262)*
Evolve Holdings Inc ....E 832 375-0099
Houston *(G-9720)*
GE Energy Manufacturing Inc.................D 713 803-0900
Houston *(G-9913)*
GE Energy Manufacturing Inc.................D 281 864-2669
Houston *(G-9914)*
Just Energy (us) Corp ....B 713 850-6784
Houston *(G-10490)*
Luminant Generation Co LLC ....D 214 812-4600
Irving *(G-13092)*

M-Trigen Inc ....E 713 469-5735
  Houston *(G-10726)*

Seldon Energy Partners LLC ....F 503 807-4300
  Houston *(G-11820)*

Sunpower Corporation ....D 512 294-3859
  Austin *(G-1545)*

Txu Energy Services Co LLC ....C 903 389-6074
  Fairfield *(G-6180)*

POWER SPLY CONVERTERS: Static, Electronic Applications

Delta Electronics (usa) Inc ....E 469 330-9100
  Richardson *(G-17298)*

Delta Electronics (usa) Inc ....C 469 330-9100
  Plano *(G-16837)*

POWER SUPPLIES: All Types, Static

Bk/Ja Holdings Inc ....E 281 879-9903
  Stafford *(G-19291)*

Btu Research LLC ....F 713 542-6228
  Houston *(G-9005)*

Hvm Technology Inc ....E 830 626-5552
  New Braunfels *(G-15804)*

Intrapack Corporation ....E 214 348-7105
  Dallas *(G-4509)*

Schneider Electric It USA Inc ....E 888 994-8867
  Houston *(G-11782)*

Source Operations Group LLC ....E 888 557-7079
  Houston *(G-11957)*

POWER SUPPLIES: Transformer, Electronic Type

Hipro Technologies Inc ....E 512 833-6600
  Austin *(G-1205)*

Leightner Electronics Inc ....F 972 542-0176
  McKinney *(G-14952)*

Texas Electric Coops Inc ....D 512 868-8610
  Georgetown *(G-7685)*

POWER SWITCHING EQPT

Hunting Innova Inc ....B 281 653-5500
  Houston *(G-10284)*

POWER TOOL REPAIR SVCS

Fastorq Bolting Systems Inc ....F 281 449-6466
  New Caney *(G-15839)*

POWER TOOLS, HAND: Drills & Drilling Tools

Bhl International Inc ....E 281 449-5762
  Houston *(G-8874)*

Church Hill Drilling Tools US ....F 281 893-0233
  Houston *(G-9188)*

Express Drilling Fluids LLC ....E 361 289-1631
  Corpus Christi *(G-3524)*

Henderson Drilling Pdts Inc ....F 281 661-3627
  Humble *(G-12775)*

Hilti of America Inc ....E 800 879-8000
  Plano *(G-16886)*

Iae International Inc ....E 281 685-3091
  Houston *(G-10311)*

Newsco Intl Enrgy Svcs USA Inc ....E 832 924-4020
  Houston *(G-11042)*

Radius Hdd Direct LLC ....E 800 892-9114
  Weatherford *(G-20613)*

Sharewell Hdd LLC ....E 281 288-2560
  Houston *(G-11846)*

POWER TRANSMISSION EQPT WHOLESALERS

Brandon & Clark Inc ....C 806 771-5600
  Lubbock *(G-14380)*

Brandon & Clark Inc ....E 806 771-5646
  Lubbock *(G-14381)*

Brandon & Clark Inc ....E 817 838-5593
  Fort Worth *(G-6469)*

Brandon & Clark Inc ....F 432 332-0163
  Odessa *(G-15942)*

Brandon & Clark Inc ....F 806 364-5470
  Hereford *(G-8284)*

Standard Industrial Pdts Co ....E 281 280-0147
  Webster *(G-20647)*

POWER TRANSMISSION EQPT: Mechanical

American Mast Inc ....E 713 643-4321
  Houston *(G-8601)*

Arcosa Inc ....C 972 942-6500
  Dallas *(G-3958)*

Balcones Technologies LLC ....E 512 699-5828
  Georgetown *(G-7639)*

Best Pump and Flow LP ....E 713 690-4511
  Fort Worth *(G-6448)*

Cosmec Inc ....E 903 677-2871
  Athens *(G-825)*

GE Energy Manufacturing Inc ....D 713 803-0900
  Houston *(G-9913)*

GE Energy Manufacturing Inc ....D 281 864-2669
  Houston *(G-9914)*

Global Pwr Technical Svcs Inc ....E 214 574-2700
  Irving *(G-13039)*

Gpeg LLC ....E 214 574-2700
  Irving *(G-13042)*

Jc/Fz Holdings Inc ....E 713 948-6000
  Houston *(G-10459)*

Jyoti International Inc ....E 936 523-4700
  Conroe *(G-3316)*

Lonestar Couplings Inc ....F 713 690-1873
  Houston *(G-10683)*

Martin Sprocket & Gear Inc ....D 903 427-2217
  Clarksville *(G-3075)*

Martin Sprocket & Gear Inc ....D 214 428-2191
  Dallas *(G-4641)*

Mayday Manufacturing Co ....C 940 898-8301
  Denton *(G-5381)*

National Oilwell Varco Inc ....C 936 825-7070
  Navasota *(G-15739)*

Purvis Industries LLC ....D 214 358-5500
  Dallas *(G-4837)*

ROC Industries Inc ....E 713 468-7743
  Houston *(G-11647)*

Standard Motor Products Inc ....C 972 316-8100
  Lewisville *(G-14094)*

Tb Woods Incorporated ....D 512 352-4000
  San Marcos *(G-18712)*

Tb Woods Incorporated ....E 512 353-4000
  San Marcos *(G-18713)*

US Bellows Inc ....B 713 731-0030
  Houston *(G-12481)*

Williams Indus Svcs Group Inc ....C 281 884-8364
  Deer Park *(G-5303)*

PRECAST TERRAZZO OR CONCRETE PRDTS

Forterra Pipe & Precast LLC ....D 469 458-7973
  Irving *(G-13033)*

Forterra Pipe & Precast LLC ....E 972 262-3600
  Cedar Hill *(G-2941)*

Forterra Pipe & Precast LLC ....E 361 767-1060
  Robstown *(G-17511)*

Locke Investments LLC ....D 832 804-7062
  Houston *(G-10662)*

Sepsa Precast Solutions Corp ....F 832 291-8930
  Katy *(G-13440)*

Tyler Products Sales Inc ....E 903 593-8633
  Tyler *(G-20172)*

Wallis Concrete LLC ....F 979 478-6734
  Wallis *(G-20510)*

PRECIOUS STONES WHOLESALERS

H P Creations ....E 817 749-4367
  Southlake *(G-19073)*

PRECISION INSTRUMENT REPAIR SVCS

Bo-GE Assembly Inc ....E 281 462-0073
  Crosby *(G-3727)*

PREFABRICATED BUILDING DEALERS

Morgan Building Transport ....E 972 864-7300
  Dallas *(G-4688)*

Morgan Buildings & Spas Inc ....F 972 864-7300
  Richardson *(G-17360)*

PREPARING SHAFTS OR TUNNELS, METAL MINING

Shinn and Gregory Inc ....G 254 965-7585
  Stephenville *(G-19422)*

PRERECORDED TAPE, COMPACT DISC & RECORD STORES: Compact Disc

Half Price Bks Rec Mgzines Inc ....F 512 805-7503
  San Marcos *(G-18693)*

PRERECORDED TAPE, COMPACT DISC & RECORD STORES: Records

Bjhr Inc ....E 409 735-5305
  Bridge City *(G-2280)*

Half Price Bks Rec Mgzines Inc ....F 512 244-0203
  Round Rock *(G-17661)*

Half Price Bks Rec Mgzines Inc ....F 281 540-3950
  Humble *(G-12774)*

Pioneer Natural Resources Co ....E 432 683-4768
  Midland *(G-15354)*

Thug City Records ....F 832 264-4892
  Houston *(G-12285)*

PRESSED FIBER & MOLDED PULP PRDTS, EXC FOOD PRDTS

Lighthouse Distribution Inc ....F 214 630-1630
  Dallas *(G-4595)*

Royberg Inc ....E 210 525-0094
  San Antonio *(G-18435)*

PRESSES

Imfab Inc ....E 903 577-0510
  Mount Pleasant *(G-15651)*

PRESTRESSED CONCRETE PRDTS

Bexar Concrete Works I Ltd ....C 210 497-3773
  San Antonio *(G-17950)*

Gate Precast Company ....E 281 485-3273
  Pearland *(G-16564)*

JD Abrams LP ....E 512 243-1090
  Austin *(G-1253)*

JD Abrams LP ....E 512 322-4000
  Austin *(G-1252)*

Lonestar Prestress Mfg Inc ....E 713 896-0994
  Bellville *(G-2010)*

Manufactured Concrete Ltd ....E 210 690-1705
  Schertz *(G-18754)*

Precision-Hayes Intl Inc ....C 972 287-2390
  Seagoville *(G-18802)*

Texas Concrete Partners LP ....C 361 573-9145
  Victoria *(G-20308)*

Texas Concrete Partners LP ....D 254 822-1351
  Elm Mott *(G-6065)*

PRIMARY FINISHED OR SEMIFINISHED SHAPES

Atlas Metal Works Inc ....F 214 741-4788
  Dallas *(G-3982)*

PRIMARY METAL PRODUCTS

Express Fabrication ....G 469 628-3960
  Princeton *(G-17209)*

PRINT CARTRIDGES: Laser & Other Computer Printers

Alpha Laser Recharge Inc ....F 713 861-2425
  Houston *(G-8562)*

Ecmm Services Inc ....G 909 979-4526
  Houston *(G-9575)*

Kaufman Independent School Dst ....E 972 932-6940
  Kaufman *(G-13459)*

PRINTED CIRCUIT BOARDS

Alltek Circuits Incorporated ....G 949 250-4499
  Garland *(G-7432)*

Alpha Circuits Incorporated ....D 281 980-2800
  Stafford *(G-19283)*

Am-Mex Products Inc ....E 956 631-7916
  McAllen *(G-14836)*

AMS Acquisition Corp ....E 512 491-7411
  Austin *(G-921)*

Arctos Assembly Group Ltd ....F 512 682-4801
  Austin *(G-931)*

Austin Mfg Svcs I Inc ....D 512 491-7411
  Austin *(G-956)*

Basler Electric Company ....E 512 352-3154
  Taylor *(G-19649)*

PRODUCT

Benchmark Electronics Inc ....C 979 849-6550
Angleton (G-565)

Bencor LLC ....E 979 830-5252
Brenham (G-2243)

Boardwalk Technology LLC ....E 512 258-2303
Austin (G-1000)

Border Assembly Inc ....E 915 592-1172
El Paso (G-5667)

Broach Bilt Manufacturing Inc ....E 972 529-9100
McKinney (G-14930)

Bsu Inc ....E 607 272-8100
Austin (G-1013)

Btp Manufacturing Inc ....E 214 467-0094
Dallas (G-4064)

Cemtechnologies Inc ....F 972 238-3630
Richardson (G-17285)

Concurrent Mfg Solutions LLC ....E 512 310-9139
Round Rock (G-17635)

Corvalent Corporation ....E 512 456-2400
Cedar Park (G-2965)

Creation Technologies Kentucky ....B 859 253-3066
Plano (G-16831)

Delta Group Electronics Inc ....D 972 606-2102
Grand Prairie (G-7863)

Delta V Instruments Inc ....F 972 644-6501
Richardson (G-17299)

Denmark Manufacturing Inc ....F 281 494-1527
Stafford (G-19301)

Electro Plate Circuitry Inc ....D 972 466-0818
Carrollton (G-2730)

Electronic Services Unlimited ....F 713 683-0601
Houston (G-9597)

Electronics & Metals Inds Inc ....E 512 267-0113
Leander (G-13988)

Electroninks Writeables Inc ....F 512 766-7555
Austin (G-1120)

Ember Industries Inc ....E 512 396-1911
San Marcos (G-18686)

Emsolutions LLC ....E 214 575-5327
Dallas (G-4321)

Enhanced Production Tech Inc ....G 512 759-2009
Hutto (G-12878)

Epic Technologies LLC ....D 915 229-6805
El Paso (G-5758)

Flagship Manufacturing Corp ....F 512 382-6410
Austin (G-1157)

Flextronics America LLC ....B 408 576-7000
Laredo (G-13885)

Flextronics America LLC ....A 512 425-4129
Austin (G-1158)

Flextronics America LLC ....A 408 576-7990
Laredo (G-13886)

Flextronics America LLC ....F 512 425-6180
Pflugerville (G-16672)

Flextronics America LLC ....F 512 698-1407
Austin (G-1159)

Flextronics Intl PA Inc ....E 512 425-4100
Austin (G-1160)

Flextronics Intl USA Inc ....A 512 425-4100
Austin (G-1161)

Flextronics Intl USA Inc ....B 817 837-5098
Plano (G-16871)

Flextronics Intl USA Inc ....A 512 740-1904
Austin (G-1162)

GI Circuits Inc ....E 281 495-2100
Stafford (G-19322)

GI Electrotech Inc ....E 832 886-4997
Stafford (G-19323)

Housetech Inc ....E 281 879-0484
Houston (G-10217)

Hunting Innova Inc ....B 281 653-5500
Houston (G-10284)

Ibe Smt Equipment Inc ....F 281 259-9660
Magnolia (G-14609)

Jabil Inc ....B 727 577-9749
Laredo (G-13898)

JVB Electronics Inc ....E 972 877-8085
Irving (G-13071)

Kodiak Assembly Solutions LLC ....E 512 275-1700
Austin (G-1271)

Krypton Solutions LLC ....C 972 424-3880
Plano (G-16904)

Leemah Corporation ....C 214 570-7170
Richardson (G-17342)

Libra Industries LLC ....D 972 664-0900
Richardson (G-17344)

Lwo Acquisitions Company LLC ....D 972 573-1140
Irving (G-13093)

Micross Components-Tx LLC ....E 512 833-5868
Round Rock (G-17673)

Milspec Works LLC ....E 281 530-7002
Houston (G-10885)

Morgan Newton Company LP ....D 972 212-8080
Plano (G-16933)

National Circuit Assembly Inc ....D 972 278-2009
Garland (G-7557)

Netvia Group LLC ....E 972 573-1400
Irving (G-13122)

Npi Technologies Inc ....E 972 968-0400
Richardson (G-17366)

Npi Technologies 2 Inc ....E 281 265-2815
Sugar Land (G-19519)

Pen Tech Assembly LLC ....E 512 275-0590
Austin (G-1407)

Plano Acquisition LLC ....C 214 343-0131
Plano (G-16972)

PM Assembly LLC ....E 972 814-3727
Farmersville (G-6225)

Precise Connections Inc ....E 972 298-1040
Duncanville (G-5537)

Precision Technology Inc ....C 214 343-0131
Plano (G-16976)

Primary Sourcing Corp ....D 713 952-5405
Houston (G-11412)

Reycomp Inc ....F 972 606-4600
Grand Prairie (G-7964)

Saberex Group Ltd ....E 512 623-4694
Austin (G-1478)

Sanmina Corporation ....E 408 964-3500
Laredo (G-13927)

Sanmina Corporation ....C 408 964-3500
Laredo (G-13928)

Sanmina Corporation ....B 972 512-3333
Carrollton (G-2812)

Sanmina Corporation ....E 210 623-5081
Von Ormy (G-20349)

Sanmina Corporation ....D 956 523-6800
Laredo (G-13929)

Sgm Corporation ....E 281 313-6111
Stafford (G-19376)

Siemens Industry Inc ....E 817 633-4430
Grand Prairie (G-7973)

Sigmatron International Inc ....F 830 775-5524
Del Rio (G-5324)

Svtronics Inc ....C 214 440-1234
Plano (G-17017)

Talla-Com Tllhssee Cmmnctons I ....F 817 234-6726
Fort Worth (G-7031)

Test Spectrum Inc ....F 512 472-6750
Austin (G-1564)

Trylene Inc ....E 281 980-0400
Houston (G-12392)

Tyrex Group Ltd ....E 512 623-4694
Austin (G-1603)

Virtex Assembly Services Inc ....D 512 835-6772
Austin (G-1635)

Virtex Enterprises LP ....E 512 835-6772
Austin (G-1636)

Zentech Dallas LLC ....E 972 907-2727
Richardson (G-17431)

PRINTERS & PLOTTERS

Montano Investments Inc ....E 956 630-1877
McAllen (G-14892)

PRINTERS' SVCS: Folding, Collating, Etc

Barron Manufacturing Inc ....F 214 747-2544
Dallas (G-4007)

Digitech Solutions Group LLC ....E 210 545-6000
San Antonio (G-18060)

Montano Investments Inc ....E 956 630-1877
McAllen (G-14892)

Quality Business Solutions ....E 972 285-2000
Mesquite (G-15074)

PRINTERS: Computer

Alecom Technologies Group Inc ....G 972 870-9400
Flower Mound (G-6259)

Creative Type ....E 214 420-1980
Dallas (G-4183)

Lexmark International Inc ....E 214 257-0001
Irving (G-13086)

Southeast Prtr Connection LLC ....E 256 880-9991
Plano (G-17010)

PRINTERS: Magnetic Ink, Bar Code

Bauer Visual Graphics Inc ....F 713 473-5241
Pasadena (G-16394)

Codesource LP ....F 940 891-1281
Denton (G-5355)

Zebra Technologies Corporation ....B 512 716-3088
Round Rock (G-17700)

Zebra Technologies Corporation ....B 956 630-0315
McAllen (G-14920)

Zebra Technologies Corporation ....B 956 571-3770
McAllen (G-14921)

PRINTING & BINDING: Books

C & R Bindery Inc ....F 214 688-5258
Dallas (G-4072)

Capital Printing LLC ....D 512 442-1415
Austin (G-1027)

Creative Handworks Inc ....E 214 682-2090
Arlington (G-650)

Gipson Group LLC ....E 512 931-2211
Georgetown (G-7654)

Taylor Publishing Company ....A 214 637-2800
Dallas (G-5039)

PRINTING & BINDING: Textbooks

Cellisco Inc ....E 210 692-1927
San Antonio (G-17989)

PRINTING & EMBOSSING: Plastic Fabric Articles

Semasys Inc ....C 713 869-8331
Houston (G-11825)

PRINTING & ENGRAVING: Financial Notes & Certificates

Digital Corp Companies Inc ....F 817 801-8000
Arlington (G-662)

PRINTING & ENGRAVING: Invitation & Stationery

Blunck Studios Inc ....G 806 358-7064
Amarillo (G-482)

PRINTING & ENGRAVING: Poster & Decal

Dac Labels & Graphic Spc ....F 214 340-2055
Dallas (G-4205)

PRINTING & STAMPING: Fabric Articles

Arcanum Corp ....F 214 507-3433
Carrollton (G-2857)

Big Star Branding Inc ....E 210 590-2662
San Antonio (G-17953)

Military Customs LLC ....F 254 699-8106
Harker Heights (G-8172)

Positive Marketing (usa) Inc ....F 877 284-4488
Dallas (G-4813)

PRINTING & WRITING PAPER WHOLESALERS

Fiesta Graphics ....F 956 546-1722
Brownsville (G-2356)

Georgia-Pacific LLC ....D 940 205-9558
Denton (G-5368)

Lighthouse Distribution Inc ....F 214 630-1630
Dallas (G-4595)

PRINTING INKS WHOLESALERS

G & A Label Inc ....E 915 544-1766
El Paso (G-5777)

INX International Ink Co ....E 817 375-0075
Arlington (G-707)

Wikoff Color Corporation ....F 972 647-1371
Grand Prairie (G-7994)

PRINTING MACHINERY

Berry Machine Shop ....E 817 572-0948
Burleson (G-2571)

Citronix Inc ....E 817 633-3200
Arlington (G-643)

Digitech Solutions Group LLC ....E 210 545-6000
San Antonio (G-18060)

Docresources LLC ....F 832 802-6008
Crosby (G-3729)

Epic Products Intl Corp ....D 817 640-3037
Cedar Hill (G-2940)

Mark/Trece Inc ....E 210 281-8348
San Antonio *(G-18276)*

Printing Research Corporation ....D 214 353-9000
Dallas *(G-4827)*

Quality Roller Supply Inc ....F 817 783-5100
Alvarado *(G-338)*

Southern Graphic Systems LLC ....E 214 565-9000
Richardson *(G-17400)*

Stevens Technology LLC ....F 817 831-3500
Fort Worth *(G-7019)*

Tresu Royse Inc ....E 214 631-2844
Grapevine *(G-8058)*

USa Screen Printing Chem Inc ....E 281 474-9777
Seabrook *(G-18793)*

PRINTING MACHINERY, EQPT & SPLYS: Wholesalers

Digitech Solutions Group LLC ....E 210 545-6000
San Antonio *(G-18060)*

ID Technology LLC ....D 817 626-7779
Fort Worth *(G-6713)*

Kruckeberg Corporation ....G 806 352-9262
Amarillo *(G-496)*

Kwik-Kopy Corporation ....C 281 256-4100
Cypress *(G-3808)*

Pamela Printing Co ....F 281 240-1313
Sugar Land *(G-19523)*

Precision Business Mchs Inc ....F 972 224-9119
Desoto *(G-5440)*

Riso Inc ....F 800 942-7476
Carrollton *(G-2808)*

S P (texas) Inc ....G 713 666-5166
Houston *(G-11712)*

Super Strong Products Inc ....F 972 342-6921
Grand Prairie *(G-7978)*

PRINTING TRADES MACHINERY & EQPT REPAIR SVCS

Adolphs Litho Services Inc ....F 972 225-5303
Hutchins *(G-12861)*

Mechanism Exchange & Repr Inc ....E 361 293-6452
Yoakum *(G-20968)*

MPS Group ....F 210 344-0332
San Antonio *(G-18322)*

PRINTING, COMMERCIAL Newspapers, NEC

News Printing Inc ....E 817 275-5601
Arlington *(G-738)*

Southern Newspapers Inc ....E 903 785-6900
Paris *(G-16370)*

PRINTING, COMMERCIAL: Announcements, NEC

B Impressed Inc ....E 210 524-9229
San Antonio *(G-17931)*

PRINTING, COMMERCIAL: Business Forms, NEC

Burrell Printing Company Inc ....E 512 990-1188
Pflugerville *(G-16662)*

Emco Press Corporation ....E 713 956-6055
Houston *(G-9610)*

Ennis Inc ....A 972 775-9801
Midlothian *(G-15480)*

J D Documents Inc ....F 972 733-1080
Dallas *(G-4518)*

Maverick Business Forms Inc ....E 903 663-7503
Diana *(G-5460)*

Parker Business Forms Inc ....E 409 842-5251
Beaumont *(G-1938)*

Printedd Products & Svcs Ltd ....D 972 660-3800
Grand Prairie *(G-7954)*

R R Donnelley & Sons Company ....C 936 564-4683
Nacogdoches *(G-15711)*

Taylor Cmmnctons Scure Cstmer ....C 817 283-9500
Fort Worth *(G-7036)*

TWC Print Shop ....F 512 927-0002
Austin *(G-1600)*

PRINTING, COMMERCIAL: Catalogs, NEC

New Century Enterprises Inc ....E 972 926-6062
Garland *(G-7562)*

Quad/Graphics Inc ....C 972 892-3803
Dallas *(G-4841)*

PRINTING, COMMERCIAL: Decals, NEC

Carlton Industries LP ....E 979 242-5055
La Grange *(G-13693)*

Dallas Decal Inc ....F 972 772-4641
Rockwall *(G-17546)*

Display Graphics Inc ....F 713 977-7888
Houston *(G-9480)*

On Site Decals LLC ....F 281 994-9000
Stafford *(G-19361)*

PRINTING, COMMERCIAL: Directories, Exc Telephone, NEC

Pls Inc ....E 713 650-1212
Houston *(G-11349)*

PRINTING, COMMERCIAL: Directories, Telephone, NEC

Local Phone Book ....F 409 386-2244
Silsbee *(G-18953)*

PRINTING, COMMERCIAL: Imprinting

Hoyt Deryl ....F 325 372-3825
San Saba *(G-18717)*

PRINTING, COMMERCIAL: Invitations, NEC

Brides & Belles of Tyler ....G 903 581-8211
Tyler *(G-20060)*

Company Printing ....F 325 949-9941
San Angelo *(G-17788)*

M Patel Enterprises Inc ....E 512 892-2721
Sunset Valley *(G-19626)*

Paper Planet ....F 817 451-8898
Fort Worth *(G-6893)*

PRINTING, COMMERCIAL: Labels & Seals, NEC

A & B Labels and Printing Inc ....E 915 774-0007
El Paso *(G-5632)*

Abbott Label Inc ....D 866 228-0100
Dallas *(G-3877)*

Alecom Technologies Group Inc ....G 972 870-9400
Flower Mound *(G-6259)*

Associated Label & Tape Co ....E 214 744-1662
Dallas *(G-3972)*

Daniel Ayala ....F 469 245-3181
Dallas *(G-4235)*

DOT It Rest Fulfillment LLC ....D 817 275-7714
Arlington *(G-665)*

Excel Label LLC ....D 713 477-6995
Pasadena *(G-16435)*

G & A Label Inc ....E 915 544-1766
El Paso *(G-5777)*

Gib Lewis Properties Inc ....E 817 834-7334
Fort Worth *(G-6669)*

Gulf States Label Company LLC ....F 713 812-8390
Houston *(G-10071)*

Impresa Label Inc ....E 915 592-4500
El Paso *(G-5810)*

Industrial Tape & Label Corp ....F 713 748-3105
Houston *(G-10354)*

Inovar Packaging Group LLC ....F 817 277-6666
Dallas *(G-4504)*

McDowell Packg & Advg Co Inc ....D 469 246-2700
Plano *(G-16923)*

Metro Label Corporation ....D 214 369-9377
Garland *(G-7549)*

Murray Label & Printing Ltd ....F 972 234-2220
Dallas *(G-4709)*

Six B Labels Corporation ....E 214 349-7824
Dallas *(G-4965)*

Tekna Impact ....F 956 213-8285
McAllen *(G-14910)*

Texas Mri LP ....C 940 549-5462
Graham *(G-7790)*

PRINTING, COMMERCIAL: Letterpress & Screen

Dragonfly Garment Design Corp ....G 830 549-5113
Seguin *(G-18836)*

Guru Garments ....G 832 674-0990
Houston *(G-10076)*

PRINTING, COMMERCIAL: Literature, Advertising, NEC

For Sale By Owner Magazine ....F 713 457-0181
Houston *(G-9832)*

K W Brock Directories Inc ....F 806 687-6270
Lubbock *(G-14432)*

Pccs Printing Solutions Inc ....E 210 340-1841
San Antonio *(G-18368)*

Real Estate Foreclosures ....F 210 733-4262
San Antonio *(G-18413)*

PRINTING, COMMERCIAL: Magazines, NEC

Dime EMB LLC ....E 888 739-0555
Dallas *(G-4260)*

PRINTING, COMMERCIAL: Promotional

Pan Ector Industries LLC ....F 940 566-1414
Denton *(G-5389)*

Printmpro Ltd ....E 512 821-9000
Austin *(G-1433)*

Qti-Powers Inc ....F 254 662-3076
Waco *(G-20453)*

Super Imprint Solutions LLC ....G 877 570-5573
Houston *(G-12106)*

Texas 28 LLC ....F 806 644-9663
Spearman *(G-19088)*

PRINTING, COMMERCIAL: Publications

1 To 1 Printers LLC ....G 281 821-4400
Houston *(G-8398)*

H & B Copies Inc ....F 979 694-2679
College Station *(G-3185)*

Islamic Services Foundation ....D 972 414-5090
Richardson *(G-17337)*

Metro Mini Courses Inc ....F 214 826-2300
Dallas *(G-4670)*

Supermedia Services Inc ....F 972 453-7000
Dallas *(G-5027)*

PRINTING, COMMERCIAL: Screen

3dgence America Inc ....F 469 466-2950
Dallas *(G-3869)*

A J L Advertising Specialties ....E 512 320-0070
Austin *(G-872)*

A-Z Graphics LLC ....F 210 495-3468
San Antonio *(G-17852)*

Accent Screen Printing Inc ....G 713 782-6683
Houston *(G-8454)*

Action Screen Graphics ....F 512 478-6248
Austin *(G-886)*

Action Sportswear Inc ....F 972 487-6960
Garland *(G-7427)*

Action Wear Plus Inc ....F 281 376-4300
Spring *(G-19098)*

All Star Caps Inc ....F 210 509-9086
San Antonio *(G-17893)*

Aluma Graphics LP ....E 972 442-3299
Wylie *(G-20925)*

Amdec Inc ....D 214 654-0560
Plano *(G-16784)*

American Screen Graphics & EMB ....F 281 354-2581
Houston *(G-8609)*

Athletic Decals Inc ....F 713 774-0663
Houston *(G-8734)*

Aztec Custom Screenprinting ....F 512 744-0195
Austin *(G-971)*

Banner Sign Graphics ....F 512 458-5348
Round Rock *(G-17626)*

Bertrand Enterprises Inc ....F 409 833-0922
Beaumont *(G-1864)*

Bobs Monogram Embroidery ....F 210 341-6700
San Antonio *(G-17959)*

Branded ....F 210 532-4212
San Antonio *(G-17964)*

Brooks Industrial Coatings Inc ....F 512 990-5333
Austin *(G-1012)*

Campus Design Incorporated ....F 806 744-9998
Lubbock *(G-14387)*

Cattilac Style ....G 325 695-6263
Abilene *(G-30)*

CC Creations Ltd ....C 979 693-9664
College Station *(G-3181)*

Clown Co Inc ....F 972 288-6954
Mesquite *(G-15034)*

Co Co MO Joes ....F 409 212-9892
Beaumont *(G-1871)*

PRODUCT

Creative Signworks Inc ....E 850 785-8899
San Angelo *(G-17792)*

Custom TS ....F 903 874-7626
Corsicana *(G-3668)*

Danwal Inc ....E 903 581-0777
Tyler *(G-20074)*

Davids Apparel Inc ....E 915 590-3744
El Paso *(G-5715)*

Drake Industries Inc ....F 512 251-2231
Austin *(G-1100)*

F W Promo ....E 817 231-8040
Haltom City *(G-8140)*

Foust Incorporated ....E 806 374-7005
Amarillo *(G-424)*

G and G Investments Inc ....E 325 949-7864
San Angelo *(G-17801)*

G9graphix ....G 940 268-1411
Wichita Falls *(G-20766)*

Groggy Dog Sprtswear Grphic Ds ....F 940 891-4022
Denton *(G-5370)*

Harvey Dupriest & Sons Inc ......D 214 337-4731
Dallas *(G-4440)*

Hollis Baker Sign Co Inc ....F 512 835-5782
Austin *(G-1207)*

Image Imprinting Inc ....E 972 243-8125
Dallas *(G-4487)*

Instant Embroidery ....G 281 888-0485
Houston *(G-10380)*

J & J Nameplate and Label LLC ....G 972 939-1157
Carrollton *(G-2873)*

J PS Fund Wear ....F 806 794-5777
Lubbock *(G-14428)*

Jeb Sales Company Inc ....G 903 342-3112
Winnsboro *(G-20898)*

Jj of Dallas Manufacturing Inc ....E 972 866-9866
Addison *(G-141)*

K & R Screen Graphics ....G 214 821-9562
Dallas *(G-4541)*

Kevin Hall ....F 972 771-4246
Rockwall *(G-17551)*

Kruckeberg Corporation ....G 806 352-9262
Amarillo *(G-496)*

Landes Inc ....E 713 665-0655
Houston *(G-10593)*

Logo Factory ....F 972 642-4222
Grand Prairie *(G-7917)*

Lown Brothers Inc ....E 915 594-4499
El Paso *(G-5848)*

LSI Integrated Graphics LP ....C 713 744-4100
Houston *(G-10696)*

M & M Designs Inc ....E 936 295-2682
Huntsville *(G-12817)*

M W Periscope Inc ....E 972 247-4202
Dallas *(G-4622)*

Marian Graphics Inc ....E 915 542-0033
El Paso *(G-5865)*

Mc Creless Company ....F 432 332-1213
Odessa *(G-16076)*

McAllen Sports Inc ....E 956 687-5500
McAllen *(G-14889)*

Men of Cloth LP ....F 281 464-3141
Houston *(G-10827)*

Merch Legacy ....F 817 682-6855
Fort Worth *(G-6826)*

Mooney Saenger Enterprises ....F 512 869-0979
Georgetown *(G-7665)*

Mountain Products LP ....D 713 895-1350
Houston *(G-10927)*

Northstar Graphix Inc ....F 817 385-1902
Arlington *(G-740)*

Pacifica T-Shirts Inc ....F 714 508-4848
Round Rock *(G-17677)*

Paragon Packaging Inc ....E 817 477-5211
Mansfield *(G-14701)*

Payton Interests Inc ....E 512 244-3221
Round Rock *(G-17678)*

Pony Xpress Printing LLC ....E 214 221-7669
Garland *(G-7570)*

Printed Supplies Inc ....E 210 946-2977
San Antonio *(G-18396)*

Qti Promotions and Apparel Inc ....E 254 756-4444
Waco *(G-20452)*

R R Donnelley & Sons Company ....D 979 836-4451
Brenham *(G-2272)*

Raymer Enterprises Inc ....F 972 242-8863
Dallas *(G-4859)*

San Bay Studio Inc ....F 940 387-4466
Denton *(G-5399)*

Semasys Inc ....C 713 869-8331
Houston *(G-11825)*

Shadowgraph Inc ....F 281 208-1280
Missouri City *(G-15592)*

Slpc Inc ....E 281 398-6655
Katy *(G-13443)*

Soccer 4 All Inc ....F 281 376-7890
Spring *(G-19166)*

Sports Magic Inc ....F 903 832-1975
Texarkana *(G-19774)*

Stingray Worldwide LLC ....E 972 818-6025
Addison *(G-165)*

Sunline Product ....F 281 398-6655
Katy *(G-13447)*

Swift Screen Printing Inc ....F 972 494-1144
Garland *(G-7594)*

T Rich Inc ....G 214 748-8700
Dallas *(G-5033)*

T Shirts N Trends ....F 972 272-2581
Garland *(G-7595)*

Taconic Industries Corporation ....E 972 241-5200
Carrollton *(G-2823)*

Tre Stars Incorporated ....F 915 351-1433
El Paso *(G-6014)*

Trust Printshop Inc ....F 817 453-3121
Fort Worth *(G-7082)*

Ttc Trammell Co Inc ....E 713 921-7121
Houston *(G-12399)*

Twg Solutions LLC ....E 512 472-8972
Austin *(G-1601)*

Uniforms Inc ....E 214 630-0924
Dallas *(G-5132)*

Val and Val Inc ....E 361 852-8992
Corpus Christi *(G-3649)*

Velocity Promotions LLC ....E 800 523-8078
Houston *(G-12545)*

Versa Printing Inc ....E 972 243-5353
Dallas *(G-5163)*

Viatran Inc ....E 512 832-8400
Austin *(G-1632)*

W & W Silkscreening Inc ....E 817 590-4479
Fort Worth *(G-7112)*

W Promotions ....E 254 753-3411
Waco *(G-20474)*

Wahoo Inc ....G 817 332-2310
Burleson *(G-2601)*

Zubie Wear ....E 210 590-8892
Universal City *(G-20186)*

PRINTING, COMMERCIAL: Stationery, NEC

Star Engraving Company Inc ....G 281 951-5808
Houston *(G-12044)*

PRINTING, COMMERCIAL: Tags, NEC

Bauer Visual Graphics Inc ....F 713 473-5241
Pasadena *(G-16394)*

PRINTING, LITHOGRAPHIC: Advertising Posters

Nationwide Press LLC ....F 817 885-8855
Richland Hills *(G-17444)*

PRINTING, LITHOGRAPHIC: Circulars

Tristar Web Graphics Inc ....C 713 691-0001
Houston *(G-12379)*

PRINTING, LITHOGRAPHIC: Color

Capital Spectrum Inc ....C 512 478-3448
Buda *(G-2524)*

Color Contori Network ....G 972 754-1912
Dallas *(G-4143)*

Post Oak Graphics Inc ....F 713 850-3563
Houston *(G-11370)*

PRINTING, LITHOGRAPHIC: Decals

Century Graphics & Sign Inc ....E 432 686-8244
Midland *(G-15157)*

El Paso Heat Transfer Inc ....E 915 779-6334
El Paso *(G-5735)*

Hov Services Inc ....E 248 837-7100
Irving *(G-13059)*

PRINTING, LITHOGRAPHIC: Forms & Cards, Business

Bayside Printing Inc ....E 281 209-9500
Houston *(G-8838)*

Clarke Harland Corp ....D 210 694-1492
Dallas *(G-4126)*

Webb-Mason Inc ....E 214 205-1123
Dallas *(G-5179)*

Webb-Mason Inc ....E 800 992-2665
Fort Worth *(G-7132)*

PRINTING, LITHOGRAPHIC: Forms, Business

Rediform Inc ....E 972 393-8080
Coppell *(G-3438)*

PRINTING, LITHOGRAPHIC: Letters, Circular Or Form

Whitley Group LLC ....E 512 476-7101
Austin *(G-1663)*

PRINTING, LITHOGRAPHIC: Maps

International Aerial Mapping ....E 210 826-8681
San Antonio *(G-18192)*

PRINTING, LITHOGRAPHIC: Offset & photolithographic printing

Boss & Hughes LLC ....F 713 664-9829
Houston *(G-8961)*

Iq Enterprises Inc ....E 866 789-0508
Fort Worth *(G-6728)*

Print Group ....F 817 847-7860
Fort Worth *(G-6916)*

Watermark Graphics Inc ....F 361 576-6874
Victoria *(G-20319)*

PRINTING, LITHOGRAPHIC: On Metal

Aus-Tex Duplicators Inc ....E 512 476-7581
Austin *(G-949)*

Cooksey Luther Printing Co ....F 817 332-2842
Fort Worth *(G-6545)*

Kelly Associates ....F 214 357-8752
Dallas *(G-4548)*

River Oaks Printing Co Inc ....F 817 738-5461
River Oaks *(G-17479)*

PRINTING, LITHOGRAPHIC: Posters

Complete Reprographics Inc ....F 915 779-5000
El Paso *(G-5702)*

PRINTING, LITHOGRAPHIC: Promotional

Indoormedia Inc ....C 281 206-2500
Houston *(G-10344)*

Indoormedia Inc ....B 800 247-4793
Houston *(G-10345)*

Register Tapes Unlimited LP ....C 281 206-2500
Houston *(G-11586)*

Rigba International Inc ....F 915 239-1070
El Paso *(G-5939)*

Signazon Corporation ....E 214 296-0022
Plano *(G-17006)*

PRINTING, LITHOGRAPHIC: Schedules, Transportation

El Dorado Logistics LLC ....F 214 871-3555
Dallas *(G-4304)*

Tpi Mexico LLC ....E 915 881-5808
El Paso *(G-6011)*

PRINTING, LITHOGRAPHIC: Tags

Anchor Graphics Inc ....E 972 422-4300
McKinney *(G-14923)*

Ennis Inc ....C 903 496-2244
Wolfe City *(G-20906)*

PRINTING, LITHOGRAPHIC: Tickets

Fort Dearborn Company ....C 817 625-1116
Fort Worth *(G-6641)*

Quick Tick International Inc ....E 832 249-6400
Houston *(G-11511)*

PRINTING, LITHOGRAPHIC: Transfers, Decalcomania Or Dry

American Prtg & Promotions Inc ....E 713 645-1991
Houston *(G-8605)*

PRINTING: Books

The Texas A&M University Sys ....F 979 845-6601
College Station *(G-3207)*

PRINTING: Books

Finishing & Mailing Center LLC ....E 214 747-6244
Dallas *(G-4362)*

Hill Print Solutions Ltd ....F 214 826-0092
Dallas *(G-4458)*

Nationwide Press LLC ....F 817 885-8855
Richland Hills *(G-17444)*

Tops Printing Inc ....E 979 779-1234
Bryan *(G-2512)*

Voom Group Inc ....F 972 424-8887
Plano *(G-17048)*

PRINTING: Broadwoven Fabrics. Cotton

Texas 2 Stitch ....F 972 599-1717
Plano *(G-17028)*

PRINTING: Checkbooks

Checks In Mail Inc ....B 830 609-5500
New Braunfels *(G-15783)*

Clarke Harland Corp ....A 830 609-5500
San Antonio *(G-18009)*

Clarke Harland Corp ....A 817 329-7113
Grapevine *(G-8022)*

Clarke Harland Corp ....D 210 694-1492
Dallas *(G-4126)*

Impressive Image Works Inc ....E 903 597-4599
Tyler *(G-20101)*

PRINTING: Commercial, NEC

4 Over LLC ....F 801 263-2727
Arlington *(G-605)*

ABC Imaging of Washington ....F 832 426-5815
Houston *(G-8445)*

Abilene Printing & Sty Co ....F 325 677-2673
Abilene *(G-6)*

Absolute Color Ltd ....F 713 996-0202
Houston *(G-8449)*

American Film & Printing Ltd ....D 817 783-7600
Alvarado *(G-323)*

Americom ....E 936 344-9052
New Waverly *(G-15852)*

Anderton Group II Ltd ....F 254 751-1012
Waco *(G-20361)*

Anderton Group Inc ....F 254 751-1012
Waco *(G-20362)*

ARC Document Solutions LLC ....B 713 988-9200
Houston *(G-8678)*

ARC Document Solutions LLC ....F 713 787-1244
Houston *(G-8679)*

Bankson Group Ltd ....E 210 699-3800
San Antonio *(G-17938)*

Beeville Publishing Company ....E 361 358-2550
Beeville *(G-1984)*

Bells Advertising Inc ....F 512 454-9663
Austin *(G-989)*

Best Letter Press Inc ....G 713 123-4567
Houston *(G-8863)*

Bisi Inc ....G 512 478-3334
Austin *(G-992)*

Blumbergexcelsior Inc ....E 817 462-1530
Arlington *(G-632)*

Brenholb Inc ....E 210 349-4024
San Antonio *(G-17965)*

Bridwell Publishing Company ....F 940 683-4021
Bridgeport *(G-2291)*

Brunswick Press Inc ....E 713 462-0600
Houston *(G-9000)*

Business For American Minority .....F 806 786-5052
Lubbock *(G-14386)*

Business Investment & Dev Corp ....E 432 335-3410
Odessa *(G-15947)*

Business Printing Inc ....F 214 445-5000
Carrollton *(G-2706)*

Cc3 ....E 817 230-2700
Fort Worth *(G-6498)*

Central Texas Printing Inc ....E 254 754-4653
Waco *(G-20381)*

Cenveo Worldwide Limited ....C 210 923-7591
San Antonio *(G-17994)*

Cenveo Worldwide Limited ....D 806 376-4347
Amarillo *(G-414)*

Clarke Harland Corp ....D 210 694-1492
Dallas *(G-4126)*

Clear Visions Inc ....D 210 496-6006
San Antonio *(G-18012)*

Cme Printing Inc ....E 713 271-7700
Houston *(G-9218)*

Cnhi LLC ....E 940 665-5511
Gainesville *(G-7339)*

Colordynamics Inc ....B 972 390-6500
Allen *(G-259)*

Curry Printing Ltd ....E 817 540-5252
Euless *(G-6139)*

D Custom ....F 214 523-0300
Dallas *(G-4202)*

Dahill Office Technology Corp ....E 713 329-9909
Houston *(G-9392)*

Dahill Office Technology Corp ....C 210 805-8200
San Antonio *(G-18041)*

Dallas Chinese News Inc ....F 972 680-9577
Richardson *(G-17297)*

Dancar Investment Group Inc ....F 972 633-1200
Dallas *(G-4232)*

Ddsep LLC ....D 972 931-8000
Carrollton *(G-2722)*

Diverse Educatn Resources LLC .....E 817 769-8968
Fort Worth *(G-6588)*

Dlt Printing Inc ....F 281 880-8883
Houston *(G-9487)*

Dollar B R Sr Et Al A TX Ptnr ....D 940 665-6262
Gainesville *(G-7342)*

Dps Teck LLC ....E 972 241-0339
Dallas *(G-4277)*

E & L Graphics LLC ....E 915 591-8789
El Paso *(G-5728)*

Easy Print Inc ....E 806 374-7711
Amarillo *(G-421)*

Far East Printing ....F 281 495-6161
El Paso *(G-5764)*

Fedex Office & Print Svcs Inc ....F 972 570-5110
Irving *(G-13024)*

Fedex Office & Print Svcs Inc ....E 512 339-1191
Austin *(G-1149)*

Fedex Office & Print Svcs Inc ....F 915 592-1190
El Paso *(G-5768)*

Fedex Office & Print Svcs Inc ....E 956 682-4040
McAllen *(G-14860)*

Fedex Office & Print Svcs Inc ....F 409 895-4000
Beaumont *(G-1892)*

Fedex Office & Print Svcs Inc ....F 361 806-2220
Corpus Christi *(G-3526)*

Fedex Office & Print Svcs Inc ....F 713 956-2366
Houston *(G-9774)*

Fedex Office & Print Svcs Inc ....G 512 331-0800
Austin *(G-1148)*

Fedex Office & Print Svcs Inc ....E 210 821-6911
San Antonio *(G-18107)*

Fedex Office & Print Svcs Inc ....F 806 359-9684
Amarillo *(G-488)*

Fedex Office & Print Svcs Inc ....E 512 472-4448
Austin *(G-1151)*

Fedex Office & Print Svcs Inc ....F 210 521-8395
San Antonio *(G-18108)*

Fedex Office & Print Svcs Inc ....F 713 521-9465
Houston *(G-9772)*

Fedex Office & Print Svcs Inc ....E 254 776-7763
Waco *(G-20401)*

Fedex Office & Print Svcs Inc ....E 512 528-9690
Cedar Park *(G-2969)*

Firmin Printing & Off Eqp Co ....E 903 793-5566
Texarkana *(G-19763)*

Fiserv Solutions LLC ....C 281 242-8569
Stafford *(G-19313)*

For Heavens Sake ....F 409 898-3340
Beaumont *(G-1896)*

Fort Dearborn Company ....C 817 625-1116
Fort Worth *(G-6641)*

Gainesville Printing Co Inc ....E 940 665-5517
Gainesville *(G-7344)*

Gatehouse Media LLC ....F 956 546-5113
Brownsville *(G-2358)*

Gincop Inc ....E 512 454-6874
Austin *(G-1183)*

Grafikshop Corporation ....E 713 977-2555
Houston *(G-10012)*

Gulf Business Forms Inc ....D 512 353-8313
San Marcos *(G-18691)*

H & H Dinero Tree Inc ....F 915 591-6245
El Paso *(G-5792)*

Hewell Enterprises Inc ....F 972 466-2442
Carrollton *(G-2869)*

HF Guyton Inc ....E 713 869-6483
Houston *(G-10167)*

ID Technology LLC ....D 817 626-7779
Fort Worth *(G-6713)*

Infovine Inc ....E 713 223-9994
Houston *(G-10360)*

Inkjet Partners Inc ....E 972 991-4577
Dallas *(G-4500)*

Interpress Technologies Inc ....F 972 926-6768
Garland *(G-7520)*

Ireo Reproductions LLC ....E 214 337-4731
Dallas *(G-4512)*

Jefferson At Montfort Limited ....E 972 789-3600
Dallas *(G-4530)*

K & T Printing Inc ....E 281 988-8088
Houston *(G-10494)*

Katy Printers Inc ....G 281 391-7072
Katy *(G-13367)*

Kelly Associates ....F 214 357-8752
Dallas *(G-4548)*

Kenner Co Inc ....F 432 333-1921
Odessa *(G-16046)*

Killeen Blueprint Co ....E 254 634-2779
Killeen *(G-13610)*

Kpt Inc ....D 214 620-9700
Coppell *(G-3427)*

La Luz Marketing Group Inc ....F 210 202-1800
San Antonio *(G-18234)*

Lebco Graphics Inc ....E 830 755-8226
Boerne *(G-2126)*

Liberty Cards LP ....F 214 646-9923
Dallas *(G-4594)*

Lithographics Inc ....G 210 226-1722
San Antonio *(G-18255)*

Lone Star Corrugated Cont Corp .....C 972 579-1551
Irving *(G-13089)*

Lsc Communications Us LLC ....C 817 640-9987
Arlington *(G-724)*

M3 Partners LLC ....E 602 561-6464
Kingwood *(G-13648)*

Magnetic Ticket & Label Corp ....C 214 634-8600
Dallas *(G-4626)*

Miller Imging Dgital Solutions ....F 512 381-5266
Austin *(G-1344)*

Molloy Corporation ....E 713 771-9485
Houston *(G-10907)*

Multi Packaging Solutions Inc ....C 214 343-7600
Dallas *(G-4704)*

Murphy Connected Entps Inc ....E 512 821-0222
Austin *(G-1357)*

Ndsventures LP ....F 713 395-0461
Houston *(G-11021)*

Outerwear USA ....F 806 792-8891
Wolfforth *(G-20909)*

Page/Ntrntnal Cmmnications LLC ....C 713 341-6619
Houston *(G-11221)*

Performance Companies LP ....C 214 665-1000
Dallas *(G-4797)*

Philbo Enterprises Inc ....E 214 747-7018
Dallas *(G-4802)*

Pinnacle Graphics Inc ....F 972 418-1202
Addison *(G-155)*

Pointsmith Pnt-F-Prchase MGT S ....C 281 599-5900
Katy *(G-13432)*

Pp Exit LLC ....E 817 701-3555
Arlington *(G-757)*

Premier Printing & Ltr Svc Inc ....E 713 868-6300
Houston *(G-11404)*

Prince Manufacturing Corp ....F 915 217-2664
El Paso *(G-5918)*

Printdallas Inc ....F 214 363-1101
Dallas *(G-4826)*

Printedd Products & Svcs Ltd ....E 512 835-2253
Austin *(G-1432)*

Quadrangle Press Inc ....E 210 828-8191
San Antonio *(G-18405)*

R R Donnelley & Sons Company ......F 972 459-1493
Lewisville *(G-14084)*

R R Donnelley & Sons Company ......E 214 521-4767
Dallas *(G-4856)*

R R Donnelley & Sons Company ......E 713 630-1000
Houston *(G-11525)*

R R Donnelley & Sons Company ......E 972 459-1400
Lewisville *(G-14085)*

Rediform Inc ....E 972 393-8080
Coppell *(G-3438)*

Redstone Impressions Inc ....E 817 921-6266
Fort Worth *(G-6950)*

Rivercity Sportswear LLC ....E 512 754-8039
San Marcos *(G-18707)*

Safeguard Business Systems Inc .....C 800 523-2422
Dallas *(G-4926)*

PRODUCT

San Patricio Publishing Co Inc ....F 361 364-1270
 Sinton (G-18965)
Sclm Enterprises Inc ....E 972 243-1688
 Dallas (G-4942)
South Texas Bindery ....F 210 340-1110
 San Antonio (G-18486)
Super Color Digital LLC ....F 702 242-6335
 Farmers Branch (G-6217)
Taylor Communications Inc ....E 713 456-4089
 Houston (G-12166)
Taylor Communications Inc ....E 214 275-3200
 Mesquite (G-15078)
Taylor Publishing Company ....F 713 782-0700
 Houston (G-12167)
Technology Media Group Inc ....D 800 777-9091
 Dallas (G-5045)
Tension Envelope Corporation ....D 817 451-5811
 Fort Worth (G-7042)
Texas Mri LP ....E 214 630-9625
 Dallas (G-5077)
Texas Star Envelope Inc ....E 210 293-8820
 San Antonio (G-18543)
Thomas Reprographics Inc ....F 281 875-2500
 Houston (G-12276)
Thomas Reprographics Inc ....F 713 977-6363
 Houston (G-12275)
Thomas Reprographics Inc ....D 210 829-7000
 San Antonio (G-18548)
Titan Custom Products Inc ....F 214 678-9105
 Dallas (G-5096)
TNT Printing ....G 281 449-9090
 Houston (G-12315)
Transfer Graphics Inc ....F 940 566-2679
 Denton (G-5407)
Tri-Win Outsourcing Inc ....E 214 826-2244
 Dallas (G-5110)
Triangle Reproductions Inc ....E 713 780-0236
 Houston (G-12365)
Triaz Digital Printing LLC ....F 512 491-7000
 Austin (G-1592)
Voyager Learning Company ....E 214 932-9500
 Dallas (G-3858)
Westgate Graphics ....F 713 688-1292
 Houston (G-12645)
Weyerhaeuser Company ....D 972 929-8581
 Irving (G-13207)
Wholesale Envelope Inc ....E 806 762-2255
 Lubbock (G-14512)
Wilmot Printing Company Inc ....E 915 843-6424
 El Paso (G-6039)

PRINTING: Engraving & Plate

One Stop Printing Inc ....F 817 338-1962
 Fort Worth (G-6885)

PRINTING: Flexographic

Clear Film Printing Inc ....F 972 962-4422
 Kaufman (G-13458)
Fortis Solutions Group LLC ....F 512 302-0204
 Austin (G-1169)
Overwraps Packaging Inc ....D 214 634-0427
 Dallas (G-4774)
Pesa Labeling Systems Inc ....E 956 544-3323
 Brownsville (G-2392)
Sides Printing Company Inc ....F 806 765-8168
 Lubbock (G-14479)
Superior Label Systems Inc ....F 214 330-7770
 Dallas (G-5026)

PRINTING: Gravure, Business Form & Card

Cyclone Production Inc ....F 713 979-1101
 Houston (G-9384)
Tcr Business Systems ....F 972 807-8000
 Dallas (G-5041)

PRINTING: Gravure, Cards, Exc Greeting

Gc Packaging LLC ....D 214 383-7700
 Allen (G-270)

PRINTING: Gravure, Cards, Playing

Liberty Playing Cards LP ....F 214 252-8175
 Grand Prairie (G-7912)

PRINTING: Gravure, Color

B2b Copies LLC ....G 512 402-9775
 Lakeway (G-13815)

Wood Printing Company Inc ....F 214 421-7393
 Dallas (G-5201)

PRINTING: Gravure, Envelopes

M Alvarez Enterprises Inc ....F 972 514-2255
 Addison (G-147)

PRINTING: Gravure, Imprinting

Embossed Graphics Inc ....F 713 667-0034
 Houston (G-9608)

PRINTING: Gravure, Labels

Anchor Graphics Inc ....E 972 422-4300
 McKinney (G-14923)
D R & J Inc ....F 512 474-4331
 Austin (G-1083)
Dac Labels & Graphic Spc ....F 214 340-2055
 Dallas (G-4205)
Garner & Golding Corporation ....F 254 753-8061
 Waco (G-20406)
Paco Label Systems Inc ....F 903 561-2125
 Tyler (G-20137)

PRINTING: Gravure, Rotogravure

Clarke Harland Corp ....A 830 609-5500
 San Antonio (G-18009)
Election Systems & Sftwr LLC ....D 469 675-8990
 Allen (G-264)
Engraving and Printing Bureau ....E 817 847-3800
 Fort Worth (G-6615)
Genti Studios Inc ....E 214 951-9696
 Dallas (G-4402)
Hill Print Solutions Ltd ....F 214 826-0092
 Dallas (G-4458)
Orora Visual TX LLC ....F 972 289-0705
 Mesquite (G-15066)
R R Donnelley & Sons Company ....E 713 957-8910
 Houston (G-11524)
R R Donnelley & Sons Company ....C 713 354-1300
 Houston (G-11527)
Reichert Corporation ....F 972 267-1300
 Carrollton (G-2805)
Taylor Communications Inc ....E 800 755-6405
 Brenham (G-2275)
Vericast Corp ....D 210 697-8888
 San Antonio (G-18591)

PRINTING: Gravure, Stationery

Mrs John L Strong & Co LLC ....F 212 838-3775
 Houston (G-10933)

PRINTING: Laser

Data Dallas Corporation ....E 214 662-5165
 Dallas (G-4241)
Diversco Inc ....D 972 478-6400
 Carrollton (G-2725)
Laser Image Inc ....E 214 267-1313
 Dallas (G-4582)
Laser Prtrs & Mailing Svcs LLC ....F 210 590-6565
 San Antonio (G-18237)
Safe-T-Pet Inc ....F 903 569-0590
 Mineola (G-15511)
Tech Dogs LLC ....F 972 985-4730
 Plano (G-17023)
Watermark Group Inc ....E 210 599-0400
 San Antonio (G-18611)

PRINTING: Letterpress

ABC Printing Service ....E 254 559-3561
 Breckenridge (G-2219)
Banc Professional Services ....F 972 734-1200
 Glen Rose (G-7731)
Cloud Printing Co of Abilene ....G 325 676-9396
 Abilene (G-32)
D R & J Inc ....F 512 474-4331
 Austin (G-1083)
Diversified Printing Svcs Inc ....G 210 226-2888
 San Antonio (G-18062)
Echo Commercial Printing Inc ....D 903 885-0861
 Sulphur Springs (G-19585)
Genuine Letterpress Inc ....E 214 748-8215
 Frisco (G-7288)
Northern & Nye Printing Inc ....E 254 662-2292
 Waco (G-20438)
Reliant Labels and Prtg Inc ....E 915 595-2999
 El Paso (G-5936)

Renfrow & Co Inc ....E 361 884-5541
 Corpus Christi (G-3608)
River Oaks Printing Co Inc ....F 817 738-5461
 River Oaks (G-17479)
Wood Printing Company Inc ....F 214 421-7393
 Dallas (G-5201)

PRINTING: Lithographic

3d Print Bureau of Texas LLC ....G 713 357-4700
 Houston (G-8408)
3f Investments Co ....F 713 541-2258
 Houston (G-8409)
Abbott TI Investments LLC ....F 210 344-5200
 San Antonio (G-17854)
Accurate Die Cutting Inc ....E 972 562-7921
 McKinney (G-14922)
Adolphs Litho Services Inc ....F 972 225-5303
 Hutchins (G-12861)
AG Development Inc ....F 817 472-7260
 Arlington (G-612)
Alice Newspapers Inc ....E 361 664-6588
 Alice (G-203)
AMA Printing / Finishing Inc ....E 254 776-8860
 Waco (G-20359)
American Color Labs of Texas ....F 210 308-0222
 San Antonio (G-17903)
American Whl Thermographers ....F 713 896-9008
 Cypress (G-3773)
American Whl Thermographers ....C 281 256-4100
 Cypress (G-3772)
Amzg Products LLC ....F 713 628-5504
 Houston (G-8632)
An Authorized Affiliate of PRI ....G 817 430-6202
 Fort Worth (G-6387)
ARC Document Solutions LLC ....B 713 988-9200
 Houston (G-8678)
ARC Document Solutions LLC ....F 713 787-1244
 Houston (G-8679)
BCT International Inc ....E 972 401-9171
 Dallas (G-4009)
Bdm Group LLC ....F 214 412-2291
 Grand Prairie (G-7843)
Beeville Publishing Company ....E 361 358-2550
 Beeville (G-1984)
Bernadette Debrango ....F 806 342-0606
 Amarillo (G-408)
Bmp Paper & Printing Inc ....E 713 228-9191
 Houston (G-8928)
Brunswick Press Inc ....E 713 462-0600
 Houston (G-9000)
Burrell Printing Company Inc ....E 512 990-1188
 Pflugerville (G-16662)
Business Printing Inc ....F 214 445-5000
 Carrollton (G-2706)
C & H Label Co Inc ....F 214 371-2355
 Dallas (G-4071)
Cedrone OBrien Inc ....F 512 426-5200
 Austin (G-1036)
Checks In Mail Inc ....B 830 609-5500
 New Braunfels (G-15783)
City of Corpus Christi ....C 361 695-7350
 Corpus Christi (G-3499)
Clarke Harland Corp ....D 210 697-8888
 Houston (G-9210)
Cnhi LLC ....E 806 273-5611
 Borger (G-2169)
Company Printing ....F 325 949-9941
 San Angelo (G-17788)
Cord Communications Inc ....G 254 776-1822
 Waco (G-20390)
Csg Systems Inc ....C 817 230-2700
 Fort Worth (G-6563)
Csg Systems Inc ....D 512 949-2200
 Austin (G-1076)
Daily Court Review Inc ....F 713 869-5434
 Houston (G-9394)
Data Print Ltd ....E 806 324-4350
 Amarillo (G-420)
Dfm Print Pak LLC ....F 817 385-0600
 Grand Prairie (G-7864)
Dla Document Services ....F 210 671-1407
 San Antonio (G-18064)
Document Solutions ....E 512 471-5464
 Austin (G-1099)
Duke Forms & Printing ....F 512 985-6587
 Cedar Creek (G-2935)
Dunphy Graphics Solutions Inc ....G 281 363-9261
 The Woodlands (G-19854)
Easy Print Inc ....E 806 374-7711
 Amarillo (G-421)

Echo Commercial Printing Inc	D	903 885-0861
Sulphur Springs (G-19585)		
Egh Printing LLC	F	972 788-4266
Carrollton (G-2728)		
Emco Press Corporation	E	713 956-6055
Houston (G-9610)		
Ennis Inc	E	972 875-5873
Ennis (G-6098)		
Fedex Office & Print Svcs Inc	E	512 396-1559
San Marcos (G-18687)		
Fedex Office & Print Svcs Inc	F	281 364-7898
The Woodlands (G-19864)		
Fedex Office & Print Svcs Inc	F	281 395-0077
Katy (G-13403)		
Fedex Office & Print Svcs Inc	E	713 977-2666
Houston (G-9773)		
Fedex Office & Print Svcs Inc	E	512 339-1191
Austin (G-1149)		
Fedex Office & Print Svcs Inc	F	409 895-4000
Beaumont (G-1892)		
Fedex Office & Print Svcs Inc	G	512 331-0800
Austin (G-1148)		
Fedex Office & Print Svcs Inc	E	210 821-6911
San Antonio (G-18107)		
Fedex Office & Print Svcs Inc	F	713 521-9465
Houston (G-9772)		
Fgs - Dallas Inc	E	972 375-0253
Grand Prairie (G-7871)		
First National Trading Co LLC	G	713 771-3600
Houston (G-9791)		
Fiserv Solutions LLC	C	281 242-8569
Stafford (G-19313)		
Foust Incorporated	E	806 374-7005
Amarillo (G-424)		
Gipson Group LLC	G	512 931-2211
Georgetown (G-7654)		
Girard Investments Inc	G	972 423-0299
Plano (G-16880)		
Graphic Image Inc	E	563 285-5214
Flower Mound (G-6267)		
Graphtex Inc	F	979 968-6333
La Grange (G-13696)		
Great Southwest Ventures LLC	F	817 306-9204
Fort Worth (G-6674)		
Greeneway Enterprises Inc	F	903 843-2503
Gilmer (G-7707)		
GSC Enterprises Inc	F	903 885-1283
Sulphur Springs (G-19589)		
Gulfstream Holdings Inc	D	713 696-9996
Houston (G-10073)		
Hart Engineering Company	E	903 758-0166
Longview (G-14247)		
Henderson Newspapers Inc	E	903 657-2501
Henderson (G-8265)		
Herald Democrat	F	903 893-8181
Sherman (G-18917)		
Herff Jones LLC	G	903 592-3800
Tyler (G-20096)		
Hewell Enterprises Inc	E	972 466-2442
Carrollton (G-2869)		
Hill Country Publishing Co	E	512 556-6262
Lampasas (G-13834)		
Hillsboro Reporter Inc	F	254 582-3431
Hillsboro (G-8328)		
Imagery Marketing Design Inc	F	817 576-3735
Dallas (G-4489)		
Impressive Image Works Inc	F	903 597-4599
Tyler (G-20101)		
K & T Printing Inc	E	281 988-8088
Houston (G-10494)		
Kelmscott Communications LLC	D	713 787-0977
Houston (G-10515)		
Kggt Management Corp	F	713 462-0900
Houston (G-10528)		
Kng LLC	G	713 263-1900
Houston (G-10545)		
Laser Image Inc	E	214 267-1313
Dallas (G-4582)		
Law Publications Inc	F	800 527-0156
Carrollton (G-2774)		
Lone Star Printing	F	956 535-2194
Harlingen (G-8194)		
LSI Integrated Graphics LP	C	713 744-4100
Houston (G-10696)		
M & M Designs Inc	E	936 295-2682
Huntsville (G-12817)		
M L Holdings Inc	F	817 732-1708
Fort Worth (G-6803)		
Mail Mart Inc	D	214 630-9643
Dallas (G-4629)		

Meera Enterprises Inc	F	972 385-3900
Addison (G-148)		
Minuteman Press	F	817 864-3000
Fort Worth (G-6843)		
Ms Dallas Reprographics Inc	E	214 521-7000
Dallas (G-4701)		
National Mail Advertising Inc	C	713 869-8551
Spring (G-19152)		
Ncp Solutions LLC	F	210 694-1528
San Antonio (G-18338)		
New Horizon Publishers Inc	F	956 399-2436
San Benito (G-18661)		
Newspaper Holding Inc	E	817 645-2441
Cleburne (G-3102)		
Newspaper Holding Inc	E	817 594-7440
Weatherford (G-20607)		
Nx Media Inc	F	713 270-1198
Houston (G-11104)		
ONeil Digital Solutions LLC	B	972 881-1282
Plano (G-16954)		
P3 Imaging Solutions LLC	E	210 494-9998
San Antonio (G-18360)		
Perfect Ink Inc	F	281 376-4781
Spring (G-19157)		
Performance Companies LP	C	214 665-1000
Dallas (G-4797)		
Polk County Publishing Co	E	936 327-4357
Livingston (G-14160)		
Port Lavaca Wave	F	361 552-9788
Port Lavaca (G-17154)		
Positive Marketing (usa) Inc	F	877 284-4488
Dallas (G-4813)		
Print Premium	F	972 292-7227
Plano (G-16977)		
Print Systems Inc	F	713 812-8126
Houston (G-11421)		
Printcitycom	F	214 728-1230
Dallas (G-4825)		
Printdallas Inc	F	214 363-1101
Dallas (G-4826)		
Printedd Products & Svcs Ltd	E	512 835-2253
Austin (G-1432)		
Quinn Printing Co Inc	F	972 788-4266
Carrollton (G-2802)		
R R Donnelley & Sons Company	B	713 468-7175
Houston (G-11526)		
R R Donnelley & Sons Company	D	972 353-6130
Lewisville (G-14086)		
R S Graphic Services Inc	E	817 921-6266
Fort Worth (G-6932)		
Renaissance Printing	E	972 234-0347
Dallas (G-4886)		
Resonant Tech Partners LLC	F	210 477-3671
San Antonio (G-18422)		
Rfv Enterprises Inc	F	281 842-1877
La Porte (G-13788)		
Rley Enterprises Inc	F	956 715-8228
Edinburg (G-5599)		
S P (texas) Inc	G	713 666-5166
Houston (G-11712)		
Sclm Enterprises Inc	E	972 243-1688
Dallas (G-4942)		
Scripps Texas Newspapers LP	C	325 653-1221
San Angelo (G-17826)		
Selectouch Corporation	E	972 924-3289
Anna (G-585)		
Shakun Solutions LLC	F	936 756-3738
Conroe (G-3363)		
Si Printing LP	F	817 375-9016
Arlington (G-781)		
Sir Speedy 4092	F	512 338-9818
Austin (G-1508)		
Somani Texas Inc	F	214 698-0556
Dallas (G-4980)		
Sorita Enterprises Inc	F	817 860-2679
Arlington (G-783)		
Southern Newspapers Inc	E	830 379-5402
Seguin (G-18864)		
Spotted Dog Printing Inc	F	972 234-3033
Richardson (G-17401)		
Spotted Dog Printing Inc	E	972 234-4391
Frisco (G-7264)		
Store Front Printers Inc	G	281 367-3373
Spring (G-19255)		
Technology Media Group Inc	E	469 463-7647
Dallas (G-5044)		
Technology Media Group Inc	D	800 777-9091
Dallas (G-5045)		
Texas City Newspapers Inc	A	409 945-3441
Texas City (G-19803)		

Thompson Business Forms Inc	E	210 734-5356
San Antonio (G-18549)		
Thompson Family Partnership	F	972 238-7664
Richardson (G-17411)		
Tops Printing Inc	E	979 779-1234
Bryan (G-2512)		
Town & Country Printing Inc	F	713 973-6666
Houston (G-12336)		
Transfer Graphics Inc	F	940 566-2679
Denton (G-5407)		
Trew Investments Inc	F	806 749-3200
Lubbock (G-14498)		
Triangle Blue Print Company	F	409 835-6810
Beaumont (G-1962)		
Universal Pen & Print Inc	F	210 656-4000
San Antonio (G-18579)		
University of Texas At Austin	E	512 471-1865
Austin (G-1610)		
USA Printing Corporation	F	281 498-4310
Houston (G-12500)		
Vastav Inc	F	972 466-2442
Carrollton (G-2894)		
Vincent Graphics & Supply Inc	E	903 882-3123
Tyler (G-20176)		
W B Mason Co Inc	F	888 926-2766
Pflugerville (G-16691)		
W B Mason Co Inc	F	888 926-2766
Irving (G-13205)		
W B Mason Co Inc	F	888 926-2766
Houston (G-12584)		
Wcn Inc	F	830 216-4519
Floresville (G-6258)		
Webbmason	F	682 432-0548
Fort Worth (G-7133)		
Wiley Holdings Group Inc	F	214 443-0908
Dallas (G-5188)		
Zachry Associates Inc	E	325 677-1342
Abilene (G-97)		

PRINTING: Manmade Fiber & Silk, Broadwoven Fabric

Zspace LLC	F	713 662-3123
Houston (G-12733)		

PRINTING: Offset

123print Inc	C	800 877-5147
Dallas (G-3862)		
2d Inc	F	281 893-3366
Houston (G-8405)		
3jg Printing LLC	F	214 553-8664
Garland (G-7422)		
ABC Printing Service	F	254 559-3561
Breckenridge (G-2219)		
Abco Inc	D	214 428-8996
Dallas (G-3878)		
Ables-Land Inc	E	903 593-8407
Tyler (G-20043)		
AC Printing LLC	E	817 267-8990
Euless (G-6125)		
All Color Press Texas Inc	F	214 744-2258
Dallas (G-3920)		
Alliance Press Leasing Inc	E	713 957-3349
Houston (G-8546)		
Alliance Printing LP	E	713 957-3349
Houston (G-8547)		
AlphaGraphics Willowbrook	F	281 890-0200
Spring (G-19099)		
Altman & Nelson Prtg Co Inc	F	361 575-3118
Victoria (G-20238)		
Always Printing Inc	G	512 250-5056
Austin (G-1689)		
Amarillo Litho Inc	F	806 372-2245
Amarillo (G-395)		
American Printers Exchange Inc	F	512 452-5058
Austin (G-917)		
American Printing & Off Pdts	F	254 771-2422
Temple (G-19669)		
American Printing Industries	G	830 624-9000
New Braunfels (G-15773)		
Anmar Enterprises Inc	F	915 772-7488
El Paso (G-5644)		
Arlington Prtg Plying Card LLC	F	817 275-2731
Grand Prairie (G-7836)		
Arrow Printing Inc	E	432 335-3407
Odessa (G-15919)		
Associated Creditors Inc	F	210 341-5642
San Antonio (G-17919)		
Associated Texas Newspapers	F	830 426-3346
Hondo (G-8353)		

PRODUCT

Austin Texas Print Inc ... G ... 512 507-2684
Manor *(G-14644)*
B & C Printing Inc ... F ... 940 766-0033
Wichita Falls *(G-20741)*
B Impressed Inc ... E ... 210 524-9229
San Antonio *(G-17931)*
Banc Professional Services ... F ... 972 734-1200
Glen Rose *(G-7731)*
Bankers Products & Printing ... G ... 903 438-0500
Sulphur Springs *(G-19580)*
Barrport Properties Inc ... F ... 713 271-2253
Houston *(G-8818)*
Bass Printing Inc ... F ... 817 293-4913
Fort Worth *(G-6439)*
Beck-Drennan Inc ... F ... 915 772-3800
El Paso *(G-5660)*
Best Press Inc ... D ... 972 930-1000
Addison *(G-107)*
Blanks Printing & Imaging Inc ... D ... 214 741-3905
Dallas *(G-4030)*
Brazos Offset Printers Inc ... F ... 806 828-5681
Slaton *(G-18970)*
Brenholb Inc ... E ... 210 349-4024
San Antonio *(G-17965)*
Brodnax Printing Company I LLC ... E ... 214 528-2622
Dallas *(G-4058)*
Brumley Printing Inc ... F ... 817 336-5551
Fort Worth *(G-6474)*
Business EXT Bur Texas Inc ... E ... 713 528-5568
Houston *(G-9021)*
C & B Printing Co ... F ... 806 374-6262
Amarillo *(G-410)*
C & G Printing Company Inc ... E ... 817 738-8350
Fort Worth *(G-6481)*
Caddy Printing & Graphics ... F ... 972 991-1770
Dallas *(G-4076)*
Capital Printing LLC ... D ... 512 442-1415
Austin *(G-1027)*
Cash Engraving Co ... F ... 817 831-8585
Fort Worth *(G-6495)*
Central Tape & Label Co ... E ... 713 462-8585
Houston *(G-9139)*
Central Texas Printing Inc ... E ... 254 754-4653
Waco *(G-20381)*
Cenveo Worldwide Limited ... C ... 210 923-7591
San Antonio *(G-17994)*
Cenveo Worldwide Limited ... D ... 806 376-4347
Amarillo *(G-414)*
CFC Print Solutions LLC ... F ... 972 890-9248
Grand Prairie *(G-7852)*
Champions Printing & Pubg Inc ... E ... 281 583-7661
Houston *(G-9160)*
Chandler Consultants Inc ... F ... 210 344-5200
San Antonio *(G-17999)*
Chas P Young Company ... D ... 713 652-2100
Houston *(G-9166)*
Classic Printing ... F ... 361 852-7261
Corpus Christi *(G-3501)*
Clear Visions Inc ... D ... 210 496-6006
San Antonio *(G-18012)*
Cloud Printing Co of Abilene ... G ... 325 676-9396
Abilene *(G-32)*
Cockrell Printing Co ... D ... 817 336-0571
Fort Worth *(G-6528)*
Colvin Painovich LP ... F ... 512 459-4139
Austin *(G-1057)*
Concho Business Solutions Inc ... E ... 325 653-1697
San Angelo *(G-17789)*
Conley Printing Co Inc ... F ... 325 675-5500
Abilene *(G-35)*
Consolidated Graphics Inc ... F ... 713 787-0977
Houston *(G-9275)*
Copy Center LLC ... E ... 210 481-9305
San Antonio *(G-18026)*
Copy Plus LLC ... F ... 956 668-7587
McAllen *(G-14851)*
Copy Stop Print and Postal ... F ... 979 774-4111
Bryan *(G-2466)*
Corporate Bus Solutions Inc ... E ... 817 701-1390
Arlington *(G-647)*
Corporate Vsual Cmmnctions Inc ... E ... 214 206-3763
Dallas *(G-4172)*
Craftsman Printers Inc ... E ... 806 744-8429
Lubbock *(G-14397)*
Cramer Computer Supplies Ltd ... E ... 806 371-7310
Amarillo *(G-485)*
Creative Computing West Inc ... F ... 512 804-2299
Austin *(G-1072)*
Curry Printing Ltd ... E ... 817 540-5252
Euless *(G-6139)*
D & D Twin Print Inc ... F ... 210 647-7576
San Antonio *(G-18040)*
D & L Printing Inc ... F ... 512 863-8145
Georgetown *(G-7646)*
D R & J Inc ... F ... 512 474-4331
Austin *(G-1083)*
Darling Quick Print Inc ... E ... 915 858-5055
El Paso *(G-5714)*
Detail Products Inc ... F ... 713 722-7789
Clute *(G-3152)*
Digital Print Inc ... F ... 817 512-3153
Cresson *(G-3708)*
Dimaco Ltd ... F ... 972 242-2427
Carrollton *(G-2724)*
Disc Pro Graphics Inc ... D ... 281 999-2717
Houston *(G-9477)*
Dolphin Graphics Inc ... E ... 713 789-7474
Houston *(G-9492)*
Downtown Color Express Inc ... F ... 214 630-5533
Dallas *(G-4276)*
Earth Color Houston Inc ... D ... 713 861-8158
Houston *(G-9569)*
Eastland County Newspaper Inc ... F ... 254 629-1707
Eastland *(G-5564)*
Echo Publishing Company ... E ... 903 885-2030
Sulphur Springs *(G-19586)*
Edwards Printing Service Inc ... F ... 972 387-3575
Dallas *(G-4300)*
Eight Eighty-Eight Inc ... F ... 972 404-0155
Addison *(G-118)*
Einsteins Inc ... F ... 972 387-8485
Carrollton *(G-2729)*
Ellis Co Newspapers ... E ... 972 875-3801
Ennis *(G-6096)*
Exalt Printing Solutions LLC ... E ... 972 245-3858
Carrollton *(G-2734)*
Executive Press Inc ... F ... 214 217-7000
Richardson *(G-17306)*
Exhibitco Inc ... F ... 713 830-8989
Houston *(G-9723)*
FBC Enterprises Inc ... E ... 817 740-1951
Fort Worth *(G-6624)*
Firmin Business Forms Inc ... F ... 254 776-5742
Waco *(G-20402)*
Forms & Printing Service Inc ... F ... 713 266-4201
Houston *(G-9835)*
Forward Times Publishing Co ... E ... 713 526-4727
Houston *(G-9845)*
Fox Marketing Corporation ... F ... 713 686-8300
Katy *(G-13404)*
Fred Bennett Printing Company ... E ... 817 641-9861
Cleburne *(G-3089)*
Gainesville Printing Co Inc ... E ... 940 665-5517
Gainesville *(G-7344)*
Garner & Golding Corporation ... F ... 254 753-8061
Waco *(G-20406)*
Gateway Printing & Off Sup Inc ... G ... 956 546-0632
Brownsville *(G-2359)*
Gea Associates Inc ... G ... 903 295-2727
Longview *(G-14239)*
General Labels & Printing LLC ... E ... 915 532-7131
El Paso *(G-5781)*
Gincop Inc ... E ... 512 454-6874
Austin *(G-1183)*
Grafikshop Corporation ... E ... 713 977-2555
Houston *(G-10012)*
Grunwald Printing Company ... B ... 361 882-5654
Corpus Christi *(G-3538)*
Guardian Southwest String Tag ... F ... 972 938-0123
Waxahachie *(G-20544)*
Gulf Business Forms Systems ... F ... 210 265-1620
San Antonio *(G-18156)*
H E B & Associates Inc ... F ... 972 234-0347
Richardson *(G-17324)*
Herring Printing Co ... F ... 830 257-7242
Kerrville *(G-13520)*
Hill Print Solutions Ltd ... F ... 214 826-0092
Dallas *(G-4458)*
Hoyt Deryl ... F ... 325 372-3825
San Saba *(G-18717)*
Hudson Graphics Inc ... E ... 903 758-1773
Longview *(G-14248)*
Ideal Printers Inc ... E ... 713 880-8800
Houston *(G-10314)*
Imaging Products Corp ... F ... 214 631-8899
Dallas *(G-4491)*
Impact Printing & Graphics ... F ... 214 904-0808
Dallas *(G-4494)*
Ink It Printing ... F ... 972 428-9623
Crandall *(G-3696)*
Ink Spot ... F ... 817 831-4438
Fort Worth *(G-6720)*
Issgr Inc ... E ... 713 869-7700
Houston *(G-10429)*
J M H Printing Company ... E ... 972 263-1226
Grand Prairie *(G-7899)*
J-Peam LLC ... E ... 817 927-1819
Fort Worth *(G-6733)*
Jarvis Press Inc ... D ... 214 637-2340
Dallas *(G-4526)*
Jayroe Litho Inc ... F ... 972 243-3835
Dallas *(G-4528)*
JM Graphics LLC ... F ... 817 460-7562
Arlington *(G-711)*
Jpt Graphics Inc ... G ... 972 785-1013
Irving *(G-13070)*
Juan Garza ... G ... 956 723-6687
Laredo *(G-13900)*
K & J Businesses Inc ... F ... 254 628-9208
Killeen *(G-13609)*
K T F Inc ... G ... 713 932-6954
Houston *(G-10497)*
Kalle Enterprises Inc ... F ... 210 340-1841
San Antonio *(G-18216)*
Kenner Co Inc ... F ... 432 333-1921
Odessa *(G-16046)*
Kennys Kustom Kards Inc ... F ... 817 332-8639
Haltom City *(G-8149)*
Kpw Enterprises Inc ... G ... 214 630-8088
Dallas *(G-4567)*
Kwik-Kopy Corporation ... C ... 281 256-4100
Cypress *(G-3808)*
L C Colormark ... D ... 972 243-1919
Carrollton *(G-2773)*
Lagan Interests Inc ... F ... 713 472-1100
Pasadena *(G-16470)*
Laser Printing Inc ... G ... 972 235-2488
Garland *(G-7536)*
Lebco Graphics Inc ... E ... 830 755-8226
Boerne *(G-2126)*
Litho Press Inc ... E ... 210 333-1711
San Antonio *(G-18254)*
Lithographics Inc ... G ... 210 226-1722
San Antonio *(G-18255)*
Loftus & Woosley Inc ... F ... 214 631-1975
Dallas *(G-4601)*
Long Plan Printing Inc ... E ... 713 797-1125
Houston *(G-10684)*
Lopez Printing Incorporated ... F ... 210 732-3232
San Antonio *(G-18265)*
Mail & Parcels Plus Inc ... F ... 409 899-1771
Beaumont *(G-1923)*
Mail Services Houston Inc ... D ... 713 594-3362
Houston *(G-10738)*
Marfield Inc ... E ... 972 245-9122
Carrollton *(G-2778)*
Masterpiece Litho Inc ... F ... 713 869-9990
Houston *(G-10789)*
MBK-Wi Inc ... A ... 972 375-0253
Grand Prairie *(G-7922)*
McCarthy Print Inc ... F ... 512 479-8938
Austin *(G-1332)*
McCord Printing Inc ... E ... 214 631-1809
Dallas *(G-4660)*
Mds Printgraphics Inc ... F ... 972 647-0043
Grand Prairie *(G-7923)*
Mendes Printing Co Inc ... F ... 956 722-2222
Laredo *(G-13911)*
Metro-Graphics Inc ... F ... 214 638-6780
Dallas *(G-4671)*
Metroplex Graphics & Mktg Inc ... E ... 817 831-7215
Richland Hills *(G-17442)*
Midtown Prtg & Graphics Inc ... E ... 806 744-3382
Lubbock *(G-14447)*
Mix Printing Company Inc ... E ... 972 248-9000
Carrollton *(G-2781)*
Modern Print Shop Inc ... G ... 713 861-7262
Houston *(G-10904)*
Molloy Corporation ... E ... 713 771-9485
Houston *(G-10907)*
Morton Printers Inc ... F ... 210 223-4258
San Antonio *(G-18320)*
Mtc Printing Inc ... G ... 972 620-3212
Carrollton *(G-2783)*
Multicopy Printing Company ... F ... 210 923-8373
San Antonio *(G-18326)*
Newman Printing Company Inc ... E ... 979 779-7700
Bryan *(G-2495)*
Nieman Printing Inc ... C ... 972 506-7400
Dallas *(G-4739)*

Night Owls Print Shop LLC	F	281 741-7032	Houston (G-11054)
Northern & Nye Printing Inc	F	254 662-2292	Waco (G-20438)
Oak Cliff Office Sup Prtg Inc	E	214 943-7421	Dallas (G-4750)
Odee Company	E	214 340-0415	Dallas (G-4754)
Office Printing & Supply Inc	E	512 474-2036	Austin (G-1377)
OKelley Office Supply Inc	F	325 673-6422	Abilene (G-61)
Omega Printing LP	G	972 256-1234	Irving (G-13131)
Orora Visual TX LLC	D	972 289-0705	Mesquite (G-15065)
Orora Visual TX LLC	F	972 289-0705	Mesquite (G-15066)
Pamela Printing Co	F	281 240-1313	Sugar Land (G-19523)
Papergraphics Ltd	F	254 526-4303	Temple (G-19696)
Parks Printing Co	F	806 747-2881	Lubbock (G-14457)
Pccs Printing Solutions Inc	F	210 340-1841	San Antonio (G-18368)
Peacock Press LLC	F	972 272-7764	Garland (G-7566)
Personalized Printing Inc	F	903 886-7173	Commerce (G-3245)
Phase 1 Prototypes LLC	F	972 406-9988	Dallas (G-4801)
Porfirio Diaz Exit LP	F	915 544-6688	El Paso (G-5916)
Portele Printing Company Inc	F	936 441-3738	Conroe (G-3352)
Precision Printing & Off Sup	F	936 825-2488	Navasota (G-15742)
Premier Printing & Ltr Svc Inc	E	713 868-6300	Houston (G-11404)
Primary Color LLC	E	214 630-8800	Dallas (G-4823)
Print Shop	E	903 295-2727	Marshall (G-14799)
Print World Inc	F	817 446-9555	Fort Worth (G-6917)
Printers Service Florida Inc	F	817 477-1291	Mansfield (G-14704)
Printmailers Inc	D	832 201-2000	Houston (G-11422)
Printmpro Ltd	E	512 821-9000	Austin (G-1433)
Process Industry Practices	G	512 232-3041	Austin (G-1434)
Prompt Printers Inc	F	210 223-9177	San Antonio (G-18399)
Pronto Publishings & Prtg Co	F	210 658-6857	Converse (G-3400)
Qg Printing Corp	F	936 634-3357	Lufkin (G-14547)
Quad/Graphics Inc	C	972 892-3803	Dallas (G-4841)
Quadrangle Press Inc	F	210 828-8191	San Antonio (G-18405)
Quality Graphics & Forms Inc	F	915 592-4500	El Paso (G-5922)
Quik Print of Austin Inc	D	512 467-9382	Austin (G-1444)
Ramirez Everardo	E	915 593-5349	El Paso (G-5926)
Rapid Reprographics LP	F	214 357-5444	Coppell (G-3437)
Regency Plz Prtg & Off Sup Inc	F	214 939-3456	Dallas (G-4882)
Responsible Prtg & Signs LLC	F	713 722-0100	Houston (G-11612)
Reynolds Brothers Ltd	F	432 682-7393	Midland (G-15383)
Richmond Printing LLC	D	713 952-0800	Houston (G-11619)
Rockdale Reporter Inc	F	512 446-5838	Rockdale (G-17526)
Royal Printing Group Inc	F	972 241-5686	Dallas (G-4914)
Royal Publishing Inc	F	713 895-9727	Houston (G-11683)
Schulenburg Prtg Off Sups Inc	E	979 743-4511	Schulenburg (G-18778)
Scott-Merriman Inc	F	972 484-7113	Dallas (G-4944)

Seebridge Media LLC	C	832 201-2000	Houston (G-11812)
Service Photo Copy Inc	F	713 225-1988	Houston (G-11840)
Shannon Dunn	F	210 653-7222	San Antonio (G-18468)
Sides Printing Company Inc	F	806 765-8168	Lubbock (G-14479)
Signature Press Inc	E	713 956-8555	Houston (G-11894)
Simon Printing Company	F	713 666-1296	Houston (G-11902)
Slocum Printing Incorporated	F	214 748-2238	Wylie (G-20950)
Sorcerers Apprentice Inc	G	210 377-1212	San Antonio (G-18485)
Southwest Precision Prtrs LP	D	713 777-3333	Houston (G-11983)
Spartan Printing Inc	E	817 640-6341	Arlington (G-784)
Speed Printing Conroe Inc	F	936 441-2248	Conroe (G-3366)
Spinner Printing Co	E	972 380-0789	Carrollton (G-2818)
State House Printing Inc	F	512 472-5331	Austin (G-1532)
Stephenville Printing Company	F	254 965-5012	Stephenville (G-19424)
Steward Printing & Advg Inc	F	214 348-1200	Dallas (G-5011)
Supreme Printing Company	F	214 742-2511	Dallas (G-5030)
T S Moore Printing Co Inc	G	956 687-6868	Mission (G-15565)
Tcca Inc	F	361 668-9636	Alice (G-239)
Tejas Vsual Communications Inc	E	972 243-6612	Dallas (G-5047)
Texas Offset Printing LP	E	214 628-7430	Dallas (G-5078)
Thomas Graphics Inc	D	512 719-3535	Austin (G-1576)
Thomas Kurtz	F	361 578-2594	Victoria (G-20310)
Thomas Printworks	F	832 201-2000	Houston (G-12274)
Thomas Reprographics Inc	D	210 829-7000	San Antonio (G-18548)
Tmf Graphics Inc	F	817 483-0237	Kennedale (G-13505)
TNT Printing	F	281 449-9090	Houston (G-12315)
Tovar Printing Inc	F	915 584-5900	El Paso (G-6010)
Trend Offset Printing Svcs Inc	C	972 243-3556	Carrollton (G-2840)
Triangle Reproductions of San	E	713 780-0236	San Antonio (G-18566)
Turner Capital Inc	F	281 488-4900	Houston (G-12412)
Two Talents Image Plus Prtg	E	817 379-5926	Fort Worth (G-7086)
Union Printers Inc	F	713 526-6364	Houston (G-12436)
United Group Printing	F	972 428-3000	Dallas (G-5134)
Universal Graphics Inc	F	915 591-8943	El Paso (G-6020)
Ussery Printing Company Inc	D	972 438-8344	Addison (G-174)
Vari Doc Management Group LLC	E	214 528-9925	Dallas (G-5155)
Veco Printing Inc	F	956 968-1589	Port Isabel (G-17140)
Versa Printing Inc	E	972 243-5353	Dallas (G-5163)
Watermark Group Inc	E	210 599-0400	San Antonio (G-18611)
West Texas Printing Company	D	325 646-3598	Brownwood (G-2449)
Westar Graphics Inc	F	713 957-4575	Houston (G-12638)
Westcave Printing Corporation	E	512 989-0006	Austin (G-1657)
Wilkins & Associates Inc	F	713 472-6585	Pasadena (G-16527)
William G Burns	F	972 233-4700	Dallas (G-5189)
William Totah Printing LLC	F	512 916-9780	Austin (G-1668)

Williams Printing	F	210 599-6204	San Antonio (G-18621)
Wood Printing Company Inc	F	214 421-7393	Dallas (G-5201)
Worldwide Spanish Literature	F	940 692-4933	Wichita Falls (G-20836)
Wrights Printing & Mktg LLP	F	281 367-6060	The Woodlands (G-19941)
Younger Colorpress Inc	F	817 923-1331	Fort Worth (G-7158)

PRINTING: Pamphlets

Bob Lillys Prof Mktg Group Inc	E	214 231-2082	Garland (G-7449)
Cyclone Production Inc	F	713 979-1101	Houston (G-9384)

PRINTING: Photo-Offset

Altlite LLC	F	469 767-1959	Dallas (G-3935)
Cellisco Inc	E	210 692-1927	San Antonio (G-17989)

PRINTING: Screen, Broadwoven Fabrics, Cotton

G and G Investments Inc	E	325 949-7864	San Angelo (G-17801)
J Harding & Co	F	713 862-9855	Houston (G-10440)
Kampus Books	F	936 560-0033	Nacogdoches (G-15700)
Kelly B Pitts Jr	F	713 923-5555	Houston (G-10513)
Ritchie-Vincent Inc	F	432 337-5133	Odessa (G-16142)
Sam Group Inc	F	817 481-1968	Grapevine (G-8053)
Summit Sportswear Inc	G	281 335-5370	League City (G-13980)
Texas 28 LLC	F	806 644-9663	Spearman (G-19088)
Versa Printing Inc	E	972 243-5353	Dallas (G-5163)

PRINTING: Screen, Fabric

Action Wear Plus Inc	F	281 376-4300	Spring (G-19098)
Bertrand Enterprises Inc	F	409 833-0922	Beaumont (G-1864)
Brammers Athletic Wearhouse LP	F	281 391-1441	Katy (G-13390)
Campus Design Incorporated	F	806 744-9998	Lubbock (G-14387)
Cenikor Foundation	F	817 921-2771	Arlington (G-640)
Ghashim Capital Ventures Corp	F	713 266-1888	Houston (G-9949)
Jackie Todaro	F	281 354-2581	Kingwood (G-13646)
Landes Inc	E	713 665-0655	Houston (G-10593)
Lone Star Special Tees LLC	E	210 402-0091	San Antonio (G-18263)
Monograms & More	F	979 693-7773	College Station (G-3194)
North Lean Ltd	F	956 781-2029	Pharr (G-16709)
Pan Ector Industries LLC	F	940 566-1414	Denton (G-5389)
Pb Unlimited LLC	F	817 831-4336	Haltom City (G-8156)
Revolution Screening Inc	F	916 712-4458	Katy (G-13436)
Screened Images Inc	F	979 260-9891	Bryan (G-2506)
Sports Magic Inc	F	903 832-1975	Texarkana (G-19774)
Uniforms Inc	F	214 630-0924	Dallas (G-5132)
Versa Printing Inc	E	972 243-5353	Dallas (G-5163)
Watermark Graphics Inc	F	361 576-6874	Victoria (G-20319)
Wings Sportswear Inc	D	210 696-1824	San Antonio (G-18622)

PRODUCT

PRINTING: Screen, Manmade Fiber & Silk, Broadwoven Fabric

G and G Investments Inc......................E........ 325 949-7864
San Angelo *(G-17801)*

Promos Distributors Inc......................D........ 972 478-7298
Carrollton *(G-2799)*

Sports Wear Graphics Inc..................G........ 817 870-9900
Fort Worth *(G-7014)*

Ttc Trammell Co Inc..............................E........ 713 921-7121
Houston *(G-12399)*

PRINTING: Thermography

American Whl Thermographers..........C........ 281 256-4100
Cypress *(G-3772)*

Mayer Enterprises Inc........................E........ 281 498-2600
Houston *(G-10807)*

Odee Company......................................E........ 214 340-0415
Dallas *(G-4754)*

Tatex Inc..C........ 254 799-4911
Waco *(G-20463)*

PRODUCT STERILIZATION SVCS

Sterigenics US LLC..............................E........ 817 293-0999
Fort Worth *(G-7018)*

PRODUCTS: Petroleum & coal, NEC

Master Flo..F........ 713 690-2789
Houston *(G-10787)*

PROFESSIONAL EQPT & SPLYS, WHOLESALE: Analytical Instruments

Rigaku Americas Corporation.............F........ 281 362-2300
The Woodlands *(G-19911)*

Yokogawa Leisure Analysis Div..........F........ 281 488-0409
Houston *(G-12718)*

PROFESSIONAL EQPT & SPLYS, WHOLESALE: Engineers', NEC

El Paso Reprographics LLC..................F........ 915 532-6255
El Paso *(G-5740)*

PROFESSIONAL EQPT & SPLYS, WHOLESALE: Optical Goods

Dac Vision Incorporated.......................D........ 972 677-2700
Garland *(G-7474)*

Metro Optics of Austin Inc..................E........ 512 251-2386
Pflugerville *(G-16680)*

Omega Optical Co LP...........................F........ 972 241-4141
Dallas *(G-4760)*

PROFESSIONAL EQPT & SPLYS, WHOLESALE: Scientific & Engineerg

ARC Document Solutions LLC..........B........ 713 988-9200
Houston *(G-8678)*

ARC Document Solutions LLC..........F........ 713 787-1244
Houston *(G-8679)*

Store Dcor Inc - Rtailgraphics.............D........ 972 475-4404
Rowlett *(G-17711)*

PROFESSIONAL EQPT & SPLYS, WHOLESALE: Theatrical

Texas Scenic Company Inc..................D........ 210 684-0091
San Antonio *(G-18542)*

PROFESSIONAL INSTRUMENT REPAIR SVCS

Hutchison Hayes Separation Inc..........C........ 713 455-9600
Houston *(G-10291)*

Intermdal Repr Mdfcation Trckg............F........ 713 674-2179
Houston *(G-10396)*

P & W Quality Machines Inc..................E........ 972 299-0500
Cedar Hill *(G-2949)*

PROFILE SHAPES: Unsupported Plastics

Bryan Container Company Inc..............G........ 979 822-7998
Bryan *(G-2463)*

Gray Sales Inc..G........ 361 527-4460
Hebbronville *(G-8234)*

Hancor Inc..E........ 361 293-6313
Yoakum *(G-20967)*

Medical Extrusion Tech Inc..................E........ 951 698-4346
Lewisville *(G-14063)*

Polytex Fibers International..................B........ 713 690-9055
Houston *(G-11363)*

SMI-Carr Inc..F........ 325 677-0491
Abilene *(G-80)*

PROGRAMMERS: Indl Process

First Time Right......................................E........ 832 264-5057
Kyle *(G-13682)*

Mercer Controls Inc..............................F........ 361 782-7168
Edna *(G-5609)*

PROMOTERS OF SHOWS & EXHIBITIONS

Hw Holdco LLC......................................E........ 972 536-6300
Irving *(G-13061)*

PROPELLERS: Boat & Ship, Cast

Baumann Propellers LLC......................F........ 713 714-5573
Houston *(G-8831)*

PROPELLERS: Boat & Ship, Machined

Houston Grinding & Mfg Co..................D........ 713 869-3573
Houston *(G-10235)*

PROPERTY DAMAGE INSURANCE

Flightsafety International Inc..................C........ 817 571-5925
Fort Worth *(G-6638)*

PROPULSION UNITS: Guided Missiles & Space Vehicles

Lockheed Martin Corporation.................D........ 817 777-2000
Benbrook *(G-2042)*

Lockheed Martin Corporation.................B........ 817 777-2000
Fort Worth *(G-6798)*

PROPYLENE & BUTYLENE

Lyondell Chemical Company..................D........ 281 291-1488
Houston *(G-10706)*

Lyondell Chemical Company..................D........ 972 512-3171
Carrollton *(G-2879)*

PROTECTION EQPT: Lightning

Advanced Lightning Tech Ltd..................D........ 940 455-7300
Argyle *(G-599)*

Lightning Bolt & Supply Inc..................F........ 713 920-2525
Pasadena *(G-16473)*

Techline Sports Lighting LLC..................F........ 512 977-8880
Austin *(G-1557)*

PUBLIC FINANCE, TAXATION & MONETARY POLICY OFFICES

Engraving and Printing Bureau............E........ 817 847-3800
Fort Worth *(G-6615)*

PUBLIC ORDER/SAFETY OFFICES, GOVT: Public Sfty Stats Ctr

Veterans Mfg LLC..................................G........ 713 854-9261
Katy *(G-13454)*

PUBLIC RELATIONS SVCS

Noisy Trumpet LLC................................F........ 210 852-0505
San Antonio *(G-18349)*

PUBLIC STENOGRAPHY SVCS

Surgical Notes Inc..................................E........ 214 821-3850
Dallas *(G-5031)*

PUBLISHERS: Art Copy

Somerset House Publishing Inc............F........ 281 346-8900
Fulshear *(G-7330)*

PUBLISHERS: Art Copy & Poster

Bernadette Debrango.............................F........ 806 342-0606
Amarillo *(G-408)*

Somerset House Publishing Inc............E........ 713 932-6847
Houston *(G-11949)*

PUBLISHERS: Book

Abrams & Company Publs Inc..............E........ 800 227-9120
Austin *(G-878)*

Associated Publishing Company..........E........ 432 687-1756
Midland *(G-15121)*

Brightleaf Group Inc..............................F........ 512 795-8900
Austin *(G-1010)*

Cambium Learning Inc..........................F........ 214 932-9500
Dallas *(G-3840)*

Currid & Company..................................F........ 713 893-8401
Houston *(G-9360)*

Formulary Productions LLC..................F........ 901 767-3000
Austin *(G-1167)*

Graphic Image Inc..................................E........ 563 285-5214
Flower Mound *(G-6267)*

Happymecom..F........ 972 503-4803
Plano *(G-16883)*

Hmh Supplemental Publishers..............C........ 512 721-7000
Austin *(G-1206)*

Laser Printing Inc..................................G........ 972 235-2488
Garland *(G-7536)*

Mission City Press Inc..........................F........ 210 614-7051
San Antonio *(G-18309)*

Mometrix Media LLC..............................E........ 888 248-1219
Beaumont *(G-1931)*

Paradigm Concept LLC..........................F........ 817 896-7729
Mansfield *(G-14700)*

Pearson Education Inc..........................E........ 512 989-5300
Austin *(G-1404)*

Taylor Publishing Company..................C........ 325 486-5300
San Angelo *(G-17832)*

Texas State Historical Assn..................F........ 512 471-2600
Austin *(G-1570)*

The Texas A&M University Sys..............F........ 979 845-6601
College Station *(G-3207)*

Trinity Fellowship..................................C........ 806 355-8955
Amarillo *(G-515)*

University of Houston System..............E........ 713 743-2841
Houston *(G-12469)*

University of Texas At Austin................E........ 800 252-3206
Austin *(G-1609)*

Up & Out Communications....................F........ 713 520-7237
Houston *(G-12473)*

Vacation Publications Inc......................B........ 713 974-6903
Houston *(G-12516)*

Zinepak LLC..F........ 212 706-8621
Austin *(G-1688)*

PUBLISHERS: Books, No Printing

Aha Process Inc......................................E........ 281 426-5300
Highlands *(G-8311)*

Behavioral Science Res Press..............F........ 972 243-8543
Dallas *(G-4015)*

Benbella Books Inc................................F........ 214 750-3600
Dallas *(G-4017)*

Clarion Events Inc..................................C........ 713 963-6220
Houston *(G-9207)*

Edmonds Pubg & Media Group LLC.....F........ 214 460-7560
Colleyville *(G-3213)*

Flightsafety International Inc..................C........ 817 571-5925
Fort Worth *(G-6638)*

Future Horizons Inc..............................E........ 817 277-0727
Arlington *(G-683)*

Gods Word In Time Inc..........................F........ 713 466-6799
Houston *(G-9989)*

Greenleaf Book Group LLC..................E........ 512 891-6100
Austin *(G-1193)*

Gulf Publishing Company......................E........ 713 529-4301
Houston *(G-10068)*

Houghton Mifflin Harcourt Pubg..........C........ 817 302-0006
Fort Worth *(G-6705)*

I Do It With Ink......................................G........ 817 715-0681
Fort Worth *(G-6712)*

John Wiley & Sons Inc..........................D........ 972 245-0480
Carrollton *(G-2875)*

Knowles Publishing Inc..........................D........ 817 838-0202
Colleyville *(G-3217)*

M Brown Books Pubg Group Inc............F........ 972 381-0009
Dallas *(G-4619)*

Pearson Education Inc..........................F........ 972 870-1048
Irving *(G-13140)*

Pritchett LP..E........ 214 239-9600
Dallas *(G-4828)*

Sales R Up Media Inc............................F........ 817 326-3282
Granbury *(G-7808)*

Taylor Publishing Company..................E........ 210 659-7505
Schertz *(G-18763)*

Texas Book Company............................D........ 972 825-4781
Waxahachie *(G-20565)*

Thomson Reuters Corporation ....D 972 250-7000
Carrollton (G-2832)
TM Luckett Enterprises LLC ....F 866 216-7278
Houston (G-12307)
Viserv Inc ....E 512 454-7403
Austin (G-1637)
Whitley & Siddons ....F 512 477-9491
Austin (G-1662)

PUBLISHERS: Catalogs

Gulf Publishing Company ....E 713 529-4301
Houston (G-10067)

PUBLISHERS: Comic Books, No Printing

Ben Dunn Corporation ....F 210 614-0396
San Antonio (G-17946)

PUBLISHERS: Directories, NEC

Hart Energy Publishing LLC ....D 713 993-9320
Houston (G-10130)
JDC Enterprises Inc ....E 972 550-1880
Irving (G-13068)
New Lifestyles Inc ....E 214 824-0022
Dallas (G-4729)
Publishing Concepts LP ....B 214 530-0335
Dallas (G-4835)

PUBLISHERS: Directories, Telephone

Downey Publishing Inc ....F 817 416-6661
Southlake (G-19064)
Harper Dirctry Dist Group LLC ....F 940 808-0769
Denton (G-5372)
Independent Tele Dirctry Co ....F 972 722-4796
Rockwall (G-17550)
Supermedia LLC ....E 972 453-7000
Dfw Airport (G-5456)
Thryv Inc ....F 281 312-3258
Kingwood (G-13654)

PUBLISHERS: Guides

East Dllas-Lakewood People Inc ....E 214 823-5885
Dallas (G-4294)

PUBLISHERS: Magazines, No Printing

20 Spc Inc ....D 972 687-6700
Dallas (G-3863)
Absolute Multimedia Inc ....E 512 892-8682
Austin (G-879)
American Trphy Hnters Assn Inc ....E 210 523-8500
San Antonio (G-17904)
Associated Locksmiths Amer Inc ....F 214 819-9733
Dallas (G-3973)
Austin Fit Magazine LP ....F 512 407-8383
Austin (G-955)
Avid Media Venture Inc ....E 972 550-9000
Irving (G-12937)
Avid Media Ventures Inc ....F 972 550-9000
Irving (G-12938)
Beckett Media LLC ....C 972 991-6657
Dallas (G-4012)
Blue Thumb Inc ....E 713 523-6523
Houston (G-8921)
Boy Scouts of America ....A 972 580-2000
Irving (G-12950)
Brenholb Inc ....E 210 349-4024
San Antonio (G-17965)
Builders Exchange of Texas ....F 210 564-6900
San Antonio (G-17972)
Cowboy Publishing Group ....E 817 737-6397
Fort Worth (G-6551)
D & V Day Investments Corp ....F 409 943-4265
Texas City (G-19787)
D Magazine Partners LP ....E 214 939-3636
Dallas (G-4203)
East Dllas-Lakewood People Inc ....E 214 823-5885
Dallas (G-4294)
Endtime Inc ....E 972 422-0857
Plano (G-16861)
Falchion Publications LLC ....F 214 244-9645
Frisco (G-7285)
Fort Bend Publishing Group ....F 281 240-2445
Stafford (G-19317)
Gamestop Corp ....C 817 424-2000
Grapevine (G-8038)
Gamestop Holdings Corp ....B 817 424-2159
Grapevine (G-8039)

Georgia Tre Magazine LLC ....E 770 755-5420
Garland (G-7502)
GP Tm Acquisition LLC ....D 512 320-6900
Austin (G-1190)
H3 Media LLC ....F 903 581-4237
Tyler (G-20092)
Hart Energy Publishing LLC ....D 713 993-9320
Houston (G-10130)
Hart Energy Publishing Lllp ....D 713 993-9320
Houston (G-10132)
Herald of Truth Ministries ....F 325 698-4370
Abilene (G-49)
Indochinese Culture Center ....F 713 522-7799
Houston (G-10343)
Journal Air Law Commerce ....E 214 768-2570
Dallas (G-4540)
Lauren Publications Inc ....F 214 628-9720
Addison (G-144)
Left Right Media LLC ....G 972 897-6578
Austin (G-1287)
Maquila Magazine Inc ....E 915 544-5845
El Paso (G-5863)
Now Magazines LLC ....E 972 937-8447
Corsicana (G-3680)
Open Sky Media Inc ....D 512 263-9133
Austin (G-1388)
Pixelworks Corporation ....E 210 826-5375
San Antonio (G-18380)
Publictions Communications Inc ....F 512 250-9023
Austin (G-1437)
Silent Partners Inc ....F 512 458-1191
Austin (G-1503)
Style Publishing Group LLC ....F 972 335-1181
Frisco (G-7315)
Texas Fish Game Pubg Co L L C ....F 281 227-3001
Houston (G-12230)
Texas Music Magazine ....E 903 838-3838
Texarkana (G-19780)
Toastmasters International ....E 325 949-3782
San Angelo (G-17835)
Up & Out Communications ....F 713 520-7237
Houston (G-12473)
Urban Publishers Inc ....G 214 521-3439
Dallas (G-5146)
Urban Publishers Inc ....E 713 524-0606
Houston (G-12477)
Vacation Publications Inc ....B 713 974-6903
Houston (G-12516)
Western Horseman Magazine ....E 817 737-6397
Fort Worth (G-7140)
Wishbone Graphics Inc ....F 972 769-7272
Plano (G-17052)

PUBLISHERS: Maps

Key Maps Incorporated ....E 713 522-7949
Houston (G-10524)

PUBLISHERS: Miscellaneous

360 Press Solutions LLC ....E 512 381-2360
Cedar Park (G-2957)
Abrams & Company Publs Inc ....E 800 227-9120
Austin (G-878)
Access Intelligence Events LLC ....D 832 242-1969
Houston (G-8458)
Ajr Media Group LLC ....F 713 942-7676
Spring (G-19194)
Alex Esolutions Inc ....C 512 305-6500
Austin (G-907)
Argus Media Inc ....E 713 968-0000
Houston (G-8691)
Billmyr Enterprises Inc ....E 972 424-1980
Plano (G-16804)
Cactus Express LP ....D 936 632-3031
Lufkin (G-14521)
Cev Multimedia Ltd ....E 806 745-8820
Lubbock (G-14391)
Circle A Xpress Inc ....F 956 547-9393
Harlingen (G-8185)
College Port Enterprises Inc ....F 979 848-3070
Angleton (G-568)
Comanche Moon Publishing LLC ....E 325 572-3339
Buffalo Gap (G-2550)
Coole School Inc ....G 713 552-1600
Houston (G-9302)
Dallas Chinese News Inc ....F 972 680-9577
Richardson (G-17297)
Deep Vellum Publishing Inc ....F 972 638-7741
Dallas (G-4246)
Defense Solutions Group Inc ....F 800 382-7571
Cleburne (G-3087)

Digital Alliance Media Inc ....E 512 238-3014
Round Rock (G-17649)
Digital Marketer Labs LLC ....E 512 892-3022
Austin (G-1093)
Dixie Freight Solutions LP ....E 281 447-7500
Houston (G-9484)
Entry Way Publishing ....F 972 517-6513
Plano (G-16864)
Express Inc ....A 972 233-2986
Dallas (G-4349)
Express Inc ....A 281 712-7187
Katy (G-13361)
Five Points Holdings LLC ....E 214 525-6700
Dallas (G-4525)
Four Point Publishing LLC ....E 281 228-6237
Houston (G-9846)
Franklin Covey Co ....G 713 527-9494
Houston (G-9855)
Glassview LLC ....E 646 844-4922
Fort Worth (G-6671)
Gulf Publishing Company ....E 713 529-4301
Houston (G-10068)
Hart Energy Publishing Lllp ....F 713 952-9500
Houston (G-10131)
Hartman Newspapers LP ....E 281 232-3737
Rosenberg (G-17587)
Igahu Inc ....F 469 474-9490
Desoto (G-5433)
Iglehart Enterprises Inc ....G 512 282-2559
Austin (G-1220)
Ihs Global Inc ....B 713 840-8282
Houston (G-10319)
Interline Travel & Tour Inc ....E 512 691-4500
Austin (G-1235)
International Assn Drlg Contrs ....E 713 292-1945
Houston (G-10398)
Katy Ind Publications & Prtg ....F 281 396-6250
Katy (G-13414)
Lawe Industries LLC ....F 512 262-1933
Kyle (G-13684)
Libredigital Inc ....F 512 334-5100
Austin (G-1291)
McElvy Vasquez Inc ....F 713 686-8494
Houston (G-10811)
Milestone International Inc ....G 210 226-2122
San Antonio (G-18306)
Mirror Publishers Inc ....F 281 486-6558
Texas City (G-19798)
Mometrix Media LLC ....E 888 248-1219
Beaumont (G-1931)
One Book At A Time Pubg LLC ....F 972 392-2679
Addison (G-152)
Online Training Solutions Inc ....E 888 308-6874
Argyle (G-602)
Platinum Press Inc ....D 469 733-1506
Fort Worth (G-6909)
Pre Management Inc ....G 512 891-0300
Austin (G-1428)
Press Masters Inc ....F 713 661-9100
Houston (G-11409)
Promotional Products Assn Intl ....D 972 252-0404
Irving (G-13160)
Pronto Publishings & Prtg Co ....F 210 658-6857
Converse (G-3400)
Reality Publishing Co ....F 281 493-4105
Georgetown (G-7673)
Sandford Prepress Systems ....E 214 808-3070
Dallas (G-4932)
Scott Publishing LLC ....F 817 632-8100
Fort Worth (G-6981)
Seawall Specialty Company Inc ....F 713 522-9064
Houston (G-11808)
Space City Publishing ....G 281 480-3600
Houston (G-11989)
Specialty Research Associates ....E 817 441-6044
Aledo (G-202)
T-System Inc ....C 972 503-8899
Plano (G-17019)
Tandem Marketing Services Inc ....D 361 949-7703
Corpus Christi (G-3635)
Teleometrics International ....F 254 776-2060
Waco (G-20464)
The Texas A&M University Sys ....F 979 845-6601
College Station (G-3207)
Total Spcalty Publications LLC ....F 813 405-2610
Riesel (G-17470)
Uglypress L L C ....F 806 322-1050
Amarillo (G-516)
Viatech Pubg Solutions Inc ....D 214 827-8151
Dallas (G-5165)

Employee Codes: A=Over 500 employees, B=251-500
C=101-250, D=51-100, E=20-50, F=10-19, G=9

2021 Harris Texas
Manufacturers Directory

PRODUCT

1617

Voyager Learning Company ....E 214 932-9500
Dallas (G-3858)

Waco Publications Inc ....E 254 752-0334
Waco (G-20476)

Weno Healthcare Inc ....E 210 912-8143
Austin (G-1716)

Winifred S Hayes Incorporated ....E 215 855-0615
Dallas (G-5197)

Woodland Publishing Inc ....E 281 485-7501
Pearland (G-16611)

X Press Bags Inc ....F 972 513-9899
Irving (G-13210)

Yp LLC ....C 713 867-6500
Houston (G-12719)

Zeus Development Corp ....F 713 952-9500
Houston (G-12728)

PUBLISHERS: Music Book & Sheet Music

Aliento Inc ....E 214 302-6580
Duncanville (G-5527)

PUBLISHERS: Music, Book

Dirt Road Music Group LLC ....F 678 525-3982
Arlington (G-663)

PUBLISHERS: Music, Sheet

Rbc Music Company ....F 210 736-6902
San Antonio (G-18412)

PUBLISHERS: Newsletter

Afam Capital Inc ....E 512 354-7041
Austin (G-900)

Hart Energy Publishing Lllp ....D 713 993-9320
Houston (G-10132)

Newsletter Company ....F 214 871-7997
Dallas (G-4734)

Schuhmacher Publishing Co Inc ....G 210 805-8006
San Antonio (G-18460)

PUBLISHERS: Newspaper

Alm Media LLC ....E 214 744-9300
Dallas (G-3928)

El Extra Spnish Lngage Newsppr ....F 214 309-0990
Dallas (G-4305)

El Paso Times Charitable Corp ....B 915 546-6100
El Paso (G-5743)

Embossed Graphics Inc ....F 713 667-0034
Houston (G-9608)

EW Scripps Company ....C 361 886-3652
Corpus Christi (G-3522)

Examiner Newspaper Group Inc ....F 713 526-3617
Houston (G-9722)

Hartman Newspapers LP ....E 281 232-3737
Rosenberg (G-17587)

Hearst Newspapers LLC ....C 713 220-7171
Houston (G-10145)

International Daily News Inc ....F 713 270-4855
Houston (G-10400)

Itexaspolitics LLC ....G 512 200-4035
Colleyville (G-3214)

K P A N Broadcasters ....F 806 364-1860
Hereford (G-8292)

Milam Broadcasting Co Inc ....F 254 697-6633
Cameron (G-2643)

Neighborhood News Inc ....F 210 558-3160
San Antonio (G-18341)

Post Up Town Inc ....G 214 965-6565
Dallas (G-4814)

Southern Newspapers Inc ....E 903 785-6900
Paris (G-16370)

University of Houston System ....F 713 221-8192
Houston (G-12468)

University of Texas At Austin ....E 512 471-1865
Austin (G-1610)

Valley Media Inc ....E 956 546-5113
Brownsville (G-2419)

West Texas Want Ads Inc ....F 325 673-4521
Abilene (G-94)

Woodland Publishing Inc ....E 281 485-7501
Pearland (G-16611)

PUBLISHERS: Newspapers, No Printing

21st Century Fox America Inc ....F 214 981-0800
Dallas (G-3865)

Ad Sack Inc ....E 361 854-0137
Corpus Christi (G-3466)

Alice Newspapers Inc ....E 361 664-6588
Alice (G-203)

Alvin Sun & Advertiser Inc ....F 281 331-4421
Alvin (G-351)

American Classifieds ....F 806 376-8663
Amarillo (G-480)

Andrews County News ....F 432 523-2085
Andrews (G-533)

Arbol Publishing LP ....F 512 476-8636
Austin (G-929)

Associated Texas Newspapers ....F 830 426-3346
Hondo (G-8353)

Assocted Bldrs Cntrs Grter Hst ....F 713 523-6222
Houston (G-8727)

Bjhr Inc ....E 409 735-5305
Bridge City (G-2280)

Bridwell Publishing Company ....F 940 683-4021
Bridgeport (G-2291)

Briggs News Alliance LLC ....G 432 943-4313
Monahans (G-15601)

Business Jrnl Publications Inc ....E 210 341-3202
San Antonio (G-17974)

C & S Media Inc ....G 972 442-5515
Wylie (G-20928)

City Newspapers Management LLC ....C 214 739-2244
Dallas (G-4123)

Cnhi LLC ....E 806 273-5611
Borger (G-2169)

Cnhi LLC ....E 940 665-5511
Gainesville (G-7339)

D J Young Publishing ....F 361 238-4188
Ingleside (G-12893)

Daily Court Review Inc ....F 713 869-5434
Houston (G-9394)

Dalhart Publishing Co ....F 806 244-4511
Dalhart (G-3833)

East Dllas-Lakewood People Inc ....E 214 823-5885
Dallas (G-4294)

Eastland County Newspaper Inc ....F 254 442-2000
Cisco (G-3066)

El Heraldo News Incorporated ....E 214 827-9700
Dallas (G-4306)

El Manana Inc ....F 956 712-1122
Laredo (G-13882)

Epochtimes Public Media Inc ....F 713 790-0815
Houston (G-9683)

Facts ....F 979 237-0100
Clute (G-3154)

Flightsafety International Inc ....C 817 571-5925
Fort Worth (G-6638)

Floyd County Hesperian-Beacon ....F 888 400-1083
Floydada (G-6293)

Forward Times Publishing Co ....E 713 526-4727
Houston (G-9845)

Frank Mayborn Enterprises Inc ....C 254 501-7499
Killeen (G-13607)

Greeneway Enterprises Inc ....F 903 843-2503
Gilmer (G-7707)

Hartman Newspapers LP ....F 361 729-9900
Rockport (G-17530)

Hartman Newspapers LP ....F 972 563-6476
Terrell (G-19737)

Hartman Newspapers LP ....F 936 336-3611
Liberty (G-14119)

Hartman Newspapers LP ....D 281 342-7304
Rosenberg (G-17586)

Hearst Corporation ....C 432 682-5311
Midland (G-15244)

Hearst Corporation ....F 409 384-3441
Jasper (G-13277)

Hearstcorporation ....E 806 296-1300
Plainview (G-16756)

Helen Gordon Interests Ltd ....C 713 371-3500
Houston (G-10149)

Helen Gordon Interests Ltd ....D 214 853-6088
Dallas (G-4446)

Herald Democrat ....F 903 893-8181
Sherman (G-18917)

Hereford Brand Inc ....E 806 364-2030
Hereford (G-8291)

Hockley County Publishing Co ....F 806 894-3121
Levelland (G-14009)

Hood County News Inc ....D 817 573-7066
Granbury (G-7800)

Horizon Publications Inc ....E 325 236-6677
Sweetwater (G-19631)

Informacion Publishing Co Inc ....F 713 272-0100
Houston (G-10357)

Jewish Herald Voice Inc ....E 713 630-0391
Houston (G-10472)

Lamesa Reporter Inc ....G 806 872-2177
Lamesa (G-13828)

Libredigital Inc ....F 512 334-5100
Austin (G-1291)

Light & Champion Publishing ....E 936 598-3377
Center (G-3002)

Marcos N Suarez ....F 214 357-2186
Dallas (G-4634)

Messenger Publishing Co Inc ....F 254 865-5212
Gatesville (G-7620)

Millennium Shopper ....F 903 885-9966
Sulphur Springs (G-19592)

Moore County News Press ....F 806 935-4111
Dumas (G-5526)

New Horizon Publishers Inc ....E 956 399-2436
San Benito (G-18661)

News Publications Inc ....F 713 668-9293
Bellaire (G-1999)

Newspaper Holding Inc ....E 817 645-2441
Cleburne (G-3102)

Newspaper Holding Inc ....F 903 586-2236
Jacksonville (G-13253)

Newspaper Holding Inc ....E 903 886-3196
Commerce (G-3244)

Newspaper Holding Inc ....E 512 392-2458
San Marcos (G-18700)

Paisano Educational Trust ....E 210 690-9301
San Antonio (G-18363)

Polk County Publishing Co ....F 936 544-0540
Crockett (G-3722)

Prime Time LLC ....C 210 250-3000
San Antonio (G-18395)

Recorder Publishing Co Inc ....F 817 926-5351
Fort Worth (G-6947)

Reneau Publishing Inc ....G 409 385-5278
Silsbee (G-18954)

Rockdale Reporter Inc ....E 512 446-5838
Rockdale (G-17526)

Southern Publishing Inc ....G 361 749-5131
Port Aransas (G-17100)

Sun Newspapers ....F 940 497-4141
Lake Dallas (G-13811)

Texas Catholic Herald Inc ....F 713 659-5461
Houston (G-12224)

Thrifty Nckel Want ADS Crpus C ....F 361 980-0008
Corpus Christi (G-3640)

Thrifty Nickel Want Ads Inc ....F 915 751-3494
El Paso (G-6003)

Uvalde Leader News ....F 830 334-3644
Pearsall (G-16615)

Val Verde Publishing LLC ....F 830 774-2198
Del Rio (G-5328)

Victoria Advocate News Bureau ....C 361 575-1451
Victoria (G-20313)

Victoria Advocate Pubg Co ....D 361 575-1451
Victoria (G-20314)

Voice Media Group Inc ....D 713 280-2400
Houston (G-12580)

Waco Publications Inc ....E 254 752-0334
Waco (G-20476)

Want ADS of Colorado Springs ....F 361 575-6400
Victoria (G-20318)

Want ADS of Fort Worth Inc ....F 817 870-0055
Fort Worth (G-7124)

Weatherford Advertising Inc ....E 817 594-7440
Weatherford (G-20629)

World Journal La LLC ....F 713 771-4363
Houston (G-12692)

PUBLISHERS: Pamphlets, No Printing

Drug Prevention Resources Inc ....F 972 518-1821
Waxahachie (G-20540)

Foreclosure Listing Service ....F 972 250-0993
Addison (G-125)

Living Stream ....G 972 257-1166
Irving (G-13087)

PUBLISHERS: Periodical, With Printing

American Paint Horse Assn ....C 817 834-2742
Fort Worth (G-6382)

Baptist Sunday Schl Committee ....E 903 792-2783
Texarkana (G-19756)

PUBLISHERS: Periodicals, Magazines

AMC Publishing LLC ....E 512 380-1611
Austin (G-914)

ART&quilt Magazine ....G 713 975-7140
Houston (G-8709)

Cord Communications Inc ....G...... 254 776-1822
  Waco (G-20390)
Ddsep LLC ....D...... 972 931-8000
  Carrollton (G-2722)
El Extra Spnish Lngage Newsppr ....F...... 214 309-0990
  Dallas (G-4305)
Gulf Publishing Company ....E...... 713 529-4301
  Houston (G-10068)
Hussy Media LLC ....E...... 832 906-5816
  Austin (G-1700)
JDC Enterprises Inc ....E...... 972 550-1880
  Irving (G-13068)
Leopard Media LLC ....E...... 713 993-9320
  Houston (G-10625)
Loomis Publishing Services ....F...... 281 829-6825
  Houston (G-10687)
North Texas Farm & Ranch ....F...... 940 872-5922
  Bowie (G-2199)
Pearson Education Inc ....F...... 866 565-4879
  Austin (G-1405)
Perryman Group Inc ....E...... 254 751-9595
  Waco (G-20445)
Promotional Products Assn Intl ....D...... 972 252-0404
  Irving (G-13160)
Red News Inc ....F...... 281 888-1448
  Houston (G-11567)
Shopper ....G...... 940 872-6186
  Bowie (G-2201)
Tanglewood Moms LLC ....F...... 817 247-1474
  Fort Worth (G-7033)
Texas Farm Bureau ....B...... 254 751-2251
  Waco (G-20465)
Tng GP ....A...... 210 226-9333
  San Antonio (G-18553)
Waterfront Publishing Inc ....F...... 281 334-2202
  Kemah (G-13482)

PUBLISHERS: Periodicals, No Printing

Briggs News Alliance LLC ....G...... 432 943-4313
  Monahans (G-15601)
Chemical Data LLC ....F...... 713 683-3900
  Houston (G-9170)
Clarion Events Inc ....C...... 713 963-6220
  Houston (G-9207)
Sport Source Inc ....F...... 972 509-5707
  McKinney (G-14978)
Texas Department Trnsp ....E...... 512 486-5887
  Austin (G-1566)
Thomson Rters Tax Accnting Inc ....B...... 800 431-9025
  Carrollton (G-2833)

PUBLISHERS: Sheet Music

Yoyo Management Inc ....G...... 512 447-1455
  Austin (G-1684)

PUBLISHERS: Shopping News

Roger Hooper ....F...... 903 784-3328
  Paris (G-16368)

PUBLISHERS: Technical Manuals

Brightleaf Group Inc ....F...... 512 795-8900
  Austin (G-1010)
Jana Inc ....D...... 210 616-0083
  Universal City (G-20183)

PUBLISHERS: Technical Manuals & Papers

Quickfilter Technologies Inc ....F...... 972 442-3964
  Richardson (G-17380)

PUBLISHERS: Telephone & Other Directory

Associated Publishing Company ....F...... 325 949-1910
  San Angelo (G-17779)
Associated Publishing Company ....E...... 432 687-1756
  Midland (G-15121)
Best Publications LLP ....E...... 281 488-8300
  Webster (G-20634)
Bilingual Yellow Pages ....G...... 214 823-4384
  Dallas (G-4024)
Hill Country Directories Ltd ....F...... 512 864-2973
  Georgetown (G-7656)
Texas Publishing Co ....E...... 361 991-1306
  Corpus Christi (G-3638)
Thryv Inc ....E...... 903 593-5400
  Tyler (G-20162)
User Friendly Phone Book LLC ....E...... 281 465-5400
  The Woodlands (G-19933)

PUBLISHERS: Television Schedules, No Printing

Currid & Company ....F...... 713 893-8401
  Houston (G-9360)

PUBLISHERS: Textbooks, No Printing

Kamico Instructional Media Inc ....E...... 254 947-7283
  Salado (G-17765)
Online Training Solutions Inc ....E...... 888 308-6874
  Argyle (G-602)
Paradigm Bks Lecture Notes Ltd ....F...... 217 344-4433
  Austin (G-1396)
The Texas A&M University Sys ....E...... 979 845-1436
  College Station (G-3206)

PUBLISHERS: Trade journals, No Printing

Beernet Communications ....G...... 210 805-8006
  San Antonio (G-17944)
Gulf Publishing Company ....E...... 713 529-4301
  Houston (G-10067)
Texas Dental Association Inc ....E...... 512 443-3675
  Austin (G-1565)

PUBLISHING & BROADCASTING: Internet Only

Actual Seo Media Inc ....E...... 832 834-0661
  Houston (G-8472)
Black Lemon Media Inc ....E...... 832 666-6600
  Houston (G-8905)
Falcon Events LLC ....D...... 800 895-6934
  Irving (G-13022)
Idea Incubator LP ....E...... 512 892-3022
  Austin (G-1218)
Incongruity LLC ....F...... 954 889-6854
  Dallas (G-4495)
Matutech Ltd Liability Company ....F...... 832 989-3208
  Kingwood (G-13649)
Noisy Trumpet LLC ....F...... 210 852-0505
  San Antonio (G-18349)
Sips By LLC ....G...... 214 208-0184
  Austin (G-1507)
Stratfor Enterprises LLC ....D...... 512 744-4300
  Austin (G-1542)
Streetloc Inc ....F...... 254 274-2500
  Dallas (G-5016)
Swim Swam Partners LLC ....E...... 512 827-9040
  Austin (G-1553)
Uno Network LLC ....E...... 844 885-5000
  Houston (G-12471)
Vant Marketing Inc ....F...... 830 217-2523
  New Braunfels (G-15830)
World Wide Celebrity Mag LLP ....F...... 832 305-8716
  Spring (G-19263)
Zor N Terprize ....F...... 832 304-0504
  Houston (G-12732)

PUBLISHING & PRINTING: Book Clubs

Stone-Cmpbell Rest Mvment Pubg ....G...... 325 674-2720
  Abilene (G-83)

PUBLISHING & PRINTING: Books

Brownlow Publishing Company ....E...... 817 831-3831
  Fort Worth (G-6473)
Mancomm Inc ....E...... 563 323-6245
  Austin (G-1321)
Newpoint Media Group LLC ....D...... 770 962-7220
  Austin (G-1365)
Taylor Publishing Company ....A...... 214 637-2800
  Dallas (G-5039)

PUBLISHING & PRINTING: Directories, NEC

Associated Telephone ....F...... 512 288-6215
  Kyle (G-13677)
Champions Printing & Pubg Inc ....E...... 281 583-7661
  Houston (G-9160)
Ji Communications Inc ....D...... 512 346-6921
  Austin (G-1255)
Legal Directories Pubg Co ....D...... 214 321-3238
  Mesquite (G-15058)
Thryv Inc ....C...... 972 453-7000
  Dfw Airport (G-5457)

PUBLISHING & PRINTING: Directories, Telephone

A T D Austin ....F...... 512 288-6215
  Austin (G-873)
AT&T Inc ....A...... 210 821-4105
  Dallas (G-3978)
Telephone Directory of Texas ....E...... 903 586-2987
  Jacksonville (G-13263)

PUBLISHING & PRINTING: Magazines: publishing & printing

Advertisers Dynmc Svcs Co Inc ....F...... 972 392-9722
  Carrollton (G-2691)
Beckett Collectibles Inc ....D...... 855 777-2325
  Dallas (G-4011)
Celebrity Group Magazine ....E...... 956 579-2020
  Brownsville (G-2345)
Chip McCormick Custom LLC ....E...... 830 798-2863
  Bogata (G-2145)
Davis Brothers Pubg Co Ltd ....E...... 254 754-5636
  Waco (G-20393)
Half Price Bks Rec Mgzines Inc ....F...... 512 244-0203
  Round Rock (G-17661)
Half Price Bks Rec Mgzines Inc ....F...... 512 805-7503
  San Marcos (G-18693)
Half Price Bks Rec Mgzines Inc ....F...... 281 540-3950
  Humble (G-12774)
Half Price Bks Rec Mgzines Inc ....F...... 713 340-0094
  Pearland (G-16567)
Half Price Bks Rec Mgzines Inc ....F...... 817 295-8560
  Burleson (G-2580)
International Business Publs ....F...... 713 626-5369
  Houston (G-10399)
Katy Magazine LLC ....F...... 281 579-9840
  Katy (G-13415)
Latina Style Inc ....E...... 214 357-2186
  Dallas (G-4584)
Permian Bsin Hmes Land Mag LLC ....F...... 737 256-0799
  Odessa (G-16115)
Sales R Up Media Inc ....E...... 817 326-3282
  Granbury (G-7808)
Shawdashian Group LLC ....E...... 832 649-3800
  Houston (G-11853)
Shweiki Media Inc ....E...... 210 804-0390
  San Antonio (G-18471)
Style Publications ....F...... 713 748-6300
  Houston (G-12085)
Success Partners Holding Co ....C...... 800 752-2030
  Plano (G-17012)
Travelhost Printing Inc ....E...... 972 556-0541
  Irving (G-13198)
United Advg Publications Inc ....E...... 214 269-0788
  Plano (G-17042)
W V Grant Intl Ministries ....F...... 214 333-2176
  Dallas (G-5171)

PUBLISHING & PRINTING: Newsletters, Business Svc

ABS Printing Services ....F...... 806 747-3702
  Lubbock (G-14356)
Creative MENus&folders LLC ....F...... 254 653-2775
  Olden (G-16219)
Perryman Group Inc ....E...... 254 751-9595
  Waco (G-20445)
Texstar International LLC ....F...... 817 740-9072
  Haslet (G-8225)
University of TX Med Brnch Gal ....D...... 409 772-5900
  Galveston (G-7411)

PUBLISHING & PRINTING: Newspapers

A H Belo Corporation ....D...... 214 977-8222
  Dallas (G-3871)
Aim Media Texas LLC ....C...... 432 337-4661
  Odessa (G-15905)
Aim Media Texas Operating LLC ....B...... 956 683-4000
  McAllen (G-14833)
Aim Media Texas Operating LLC ....E...... 956 430-6200
  Harlingen (G-8174)
American Cmnty Newspapers LLC ....C...... 972 424-6565
  Plano (G-16786)
Asp Westward LP ....D...... 713 256-0953
  Houston (G-8723)
Asp Westward LP ....E...... 903 845-2235
  Gladewater (G-7718)
Asp Westward LP ....F...... 903 237-7700
  Longview (G-14197)

Employee Codes: A=Over 500 employees, B=251-500
C=101-250, D=51-100, E=20-50, F=10-19, G=9

2021 Harris Texas
Manufacturers Directory

PRODUCT

1619

Austin Chronicle Corporation	D	512 454-5766
Austin (G-952)		
Belo Corp	C	979 776-4444
Bryan (G-2457)		
Belton Newspaper Inc	F	254 939-5754
Belton (G-2021)		
Bernie Star Newspaper	F	830 249-2441
Boerne (G-2115)		
Bowie News Inc	F	940 872-2247
Bowie (G-2193)		
Brady Standard Herald Inc	F	325 597-2959
Brady (G-2211)		
Brazoria County News	F	979 345-3127
West Columbia (G-20675)		
Caller-Times Publishing Co	B	361 883-1111
Corpus Christi (G-3493)		
Cnhi LLC	E	432 263-7331
Big Spring (G-2076)		
Connor Media Group LLC	E	817 336-8300
Fort Worth (G-6542)		
Cox Texas Newspapers LP	D	512 445-3500
Austin (G-1069)		
Cox Texas Newspapers LP	D	512 445-3500
Austin (G-1070)		
D & V Day Investments Corp	F	409 943-4265
Texas City (G-19787)		
D F W Elite News	G	214 372-6500
Campbell (G-2645)		
Daily Commercial Record Inc	F	214 741-6366
Dallas (G-4206)		
Daily DOT LLC	F	512 420-9403
Austin (G-1084)		
Daily Sentinel	G	936 631-2607
Nacogdoches (G-15694)		
Dallas Observer LP	E	214 757-9000
Dallas (G-4222)		
Denton Publishing Company	C	940 387-3811
Denton (G-5359)		
Dmn Inc	E	214 745-8383
Garland (G-7480)		
Dmn Inc	A	214 977-8222
Dallas (G-4267)		
Dmn Inc	B	214 977-6931
Plano (G-16847)		
Dow Jones & Company Inc	E	214 951-7251
Dallas (G-4275)		
Drc Media LLC	F	817 336-8300
Fort Worth (G-6594)		
Eagle Printing Company	C	979 776-4444
Bryan (G-2471)		
El Campo Newspapers Inc	E	979 543-3363
El Campo (G-5616)		
El Periodico U S A Inc	F	956 631-5628
McAllen (G-14856)		
El Tejano Hispanic Community	F	361 884-2238
Corpus Christi (G-3518)		
Ellis Co Newspapers	E	972 875-3801
Ennis (G-6096)		
Ellis County Chronicle	E	972 937-3310
Waxahachie (G-20541)		
Ellis County Newspapers Inc	E	972 872-9113
Ennis (G-6097)		
Erath Publishers Inc	D	254 965-3124
Stephenville (G-19410)		
Euclid Media Group LLC	E	210 227-0044
San Antonio (G-18097)		
EW Scripps Company	C	325 659-8200
San Angelo (G-17798)		
Examiner Corporation	E	409 833-1755
Beaumont (G-1889)		
Fort Bend Business Journal	F	281 690-4200
Stafford (G-19316)		
Frank Mayborn Enterprises Inc	C	254 634-6666
Killeen (G-13608)		
Gatehouse Media LLC	F	956 546-5113
Brownsville (G-2358)		
Hartman Newspapers LP	F	281 342-8691
Rosenberg (G-17585)		
Hearst Corporation	A	210 271-2700
San Antonio (G-18161)		
Hearst Corporation	C	956 728-2500
Laredo (G-13890)		
Hearst Corporation	A	210 250-3000
San Antonio (G-18162)		
Hearst Newspapers LLC	C	713 220-7171
Houston (G-10144)		
Henderson Newspapers Inc	E	903 657-2501
Henderson (G-8265)		
Hill Country News	F	512 259-4449
Cedar Park (G-2973)		
Hill Country Publishing Co	E	512 556-6262
Lampasas (G-13834)		
Hill County Press Inc	F	254 582-3431
Hillsboro (G-8327)		
Hillsboro Reporter Inc	F	254 582-3431
Hillsboro (G-8328)		
Houston Business Journals Inc	E	214 696-5959
Dallas (G-4468)		
Houston Business Journals Inc	E	713 688-8811
Houston (G-10219)		
Houston Chronicle	A	713 362-7171
Houston (G-10225)		
Houston Defender Newspaper Inc	F	713 663-6996
Houston (G-10229)		
Houston Press LP		713 280-2400
Houston (G-10247)		
Investor Publications Inc	F	915 534-4422
El Paso (G-5817)		
Irent	F	956 592-4061
Brownsville (G-2366)		
Jackson County Herald Tribune	F	361 782-2131
Edna (G-5607)		
JG Media Inc	D	512 989-6808
Pflugerville (G-16677)		
King Ranch Inc	F	832 681-5700
Houston (G-10534)		
Krenek Printing Company	F	281 463-8649
Houston (G-10568)		
La Subasta Incorporated	F	214 951-9500
Dallas (G-4577)		
La Subasta Incorporated	F	713 777-1010
Houston (G-10583)		
Lfn LLC	F	956 330-6838
Los Fresnos (G-14347)		
Lhcn Inc	D	972 424-6565
Plano (G-16908)		
Longview News Journal	F	903 237-7711
Longview (G-14271)		
Los Angles Tmes Cmmnctions LLC	C	512 476-7777
Austin (G-1302)		
Marshall News Messenger Inc	E	903 935-7914
Marshall (G-14790)		
Media Palmer Inc	F	903 572-1705
Mount Pleasant (G-15654)		
Mid-Valley Newspapers Inc	E	956 969-2543
Weslaco (G-20665)		
Minority Opportunity News Inc	F	972 516-4191
Plano (G-16930)		
Minority Print Media	F	713 748-6300
Houston (G-10888)		
Morris Communications Co LLC	C	806 376-4488
Amarillo (G-447)		
News Gram	F	830 773-8610
Eagle Pass (G-5551)		
News Korea Texas Inc	F	972 247-9111
Dallas (G-4733)		
Newspaper Holding Inc	D	903 729-0281
Palestine (G-16305)		
Newspaper Holding Inc	F	817 594-7440
Weatherford (G-20607)		
Newspaper Holding Inc	F	903 675-5626
Athens (G-835)		
Newspaper Holding Inc	F	903 455-4220
Greenville (G-8085)		
Newspaper Holding Inc	F	936 295-5407
Huntsville (G-12820)		
Polk County Publishing Co	F	409 283-2516
Woodville (G-20916)		
Polk County Publishing Co	F	936 327-4357
Livingston (G-14160)		
Port Lavaca Wave	F	361 552-9788
Port Lavaca (G-17154)		
Pts Inc	F	806 669-2525
Pampa (G-16336)		
Rains County Leader	G	903 473-2653
Emory (G-6085)		
Rambler Newspapers Inc	G	972 870-1992
Irving (G-13162)		
Rio Grande Valley Business	E	956 546-5113
Brownsville (G-2400)		
Robinson Media Company LLC	F	254 757-5757
Waco (G-20455)		
San Marcos Publishing LP	F	512 392-2458
San Marcos (G-18709)		
San Patricio Publishing Co Inc	F	361 364-1270
Sinton (G-18965)		
Scripps Texas Newspapers LP	C	325 653-1221
San Angelo (G-17826)		
Scripps Texas Newspapers LP	C	325 673-4271
Abilene (G-79)		
Snyder Daily News	E	325 573-5486
Snyder (G-19007)		
Southern Chnese Nwspapers Pubg	F	281 498-4310
Houston (G-11973)		
Southern Newspapers Inc	E	830 625-5232
New Braunfels (G-15824)		
Southern Newspapers Inc	E	830 379-5402
Seguin (G-18864)		
Southern Newspapers Inc	E	281 422-8302
Baytown (G-1835)		
Southern Newspapers Inc	D	979 237-0100
Clute (G-3160)		
Star-Telegram Operating Ltd	B	817 215-2100
Fort Worth (G-7015)		
Star-Telegram Operating Ltd	A	817 390-7400
Fort Worth (G-7016)		
Texas City Newspapers Inc	A	409 945-3441
Texas City (G-19803)		
Texas Community Media LLC	C	903 757-3311
Longview (G-14315)		
Texas Jewish Post Ltd	F	972 458-7283
Dallas (G-5074)		
Texas State University	F	512 245-3487
San Marcos (G-18714)		
Tristar Web Graphics Inc	C	713 691-0001
Houston (G-12379)		
United Metro Media LLC	F	210 315-6046
San Antonio (G-18578)		
USA Printing Corporation	F	281 498-4310
Houston (G-12500)		
Van Zandt Newspapers LLC	E	903 567-4000
Wills Point (G-20880)		
Versa Printing Inc	E	972 243-5353
Dallas (G-5163)		
Voice Publishing Co Inc	F	214 754-8710
Dallas (G-5168)		
Wichita Falls Times Record	E	940 767-8341
Wichita Falls (G-20832)		
Williamson County Sun Inc	E	512 930-3072
Georgetown (G-7689)		
Yoakum Herald-Times Inc	F	361 293-5266
Yoakum (G-20975)		

PUBLISHING & PRINTING: Pamphlets

Creative MENus&folders LLC	F	254 653-2775
Olden (G-16219)		

PUBLISHING & PRINTING: Posters

Gipson Group LLC	G	512 931-2211
Georgetown (G-7654)		
Maverick Concepts LLC	E	972 418-7189
Garland (G-7546)		

PUBLISHING & PRINTING: Shopping News

American Classifieds	F	254 771-2777
Temple (G-19668)		
Shopper	G	940 872-6186
Bowie (G-2201)		
USA Printing Corporation	F	281 498-4310
Houston (G-12500)		
Valley Media Inc	E	956 546-5113
Brownsville (G-2419)		
Want ADS of San Angelo Inc	F	325 944-7653
San Angelo (G-17837)		
West Texas Want Ads Inc	F	325 673-4521
Abilene (G-94)		

PUBLISHING & PRINTING: Technical Manuals

Industrial Info Resources Inc	D	713 783-5147
Sugar Land (G-19498)		
Interface Lgic Tech Dcmnttion	F	713 446-3560
Pearland (G-16570)		

PUBLISHING & PRINTING: Textbooks

Pearson Education Inc	E	281 496-0657
Houston (G-11267)		
Thinkwell Corporation	F	888 416-8880
Austin (G-1575)		

PUBLISHING & PRINTING: Trade Journals

Elite Publications Inc	F	713 263-9476
Houston (G-9602)		
Iiat Services Company	E	512 476-6281
Austin (G-1222)		

PUBLISHING & PRINTING: Yearbooks

American Achievement Corp ....E 512 444-0571
  Dallas *(G-3937)*

PULLEYS: Metal

Lebus International Inc ....D 903 758-5521
  Longview *(G-14263)*

PULP MILLS

Aldersgate Enrichment Center ....D 325 646-2566
  Early *(G-5556)*
Bell Processing Incorporated ....D 940 322-8621
  Wichita Falls *(G-20744)*
Delta Paper Stock Corp ....E 713 666-1440
  Bellaire *(G-1993)*
Graphic Packaging Intl LLC ....A 903 796-7101
  Queen City *(G-17220)*
Greenstar North Amer Holdings ....A 713 965-0005
  Houston *(G-10036)*
Master Fibers Inc ....D 915 544-2299
  El Paso *(G-5868)*

PULP MILLS: Chemical & Semichemical Processing

BLUE CUBE OPERATIONS LLC ....F 979 238-2011
  Freeport *(G-7192)*

PULP MILLS: Mechanical & Recycling Processing

Monterrey Iron & Metal Ltd ....D 210 927-2727
  San Antonio *(G-18318)*
One Source Recycling Inc ....D 512 549-2812
  Austin *(G-1386)*
Packaging One Inc ....F 713 674-0302
  Houston *(G-11220)*
Prime Momento LLC ....F 832 643-4605
  Sugar Land *(G-19529)*
Snyder Iron Metal ....F 325 573-6862
  Snyder *(G-19008)*

PUMP JACKS & OTHER PUMPING EQPT: Indl

Nikkiso Pumps America Inc ....E 281 310-6747
  Houston *(G-11055)*
Standard Indus Mfg Prtners LLC ....G 817 598-1500
  Weatherford *(G-20622)*

PUMPS

Accelerated Prod Svcs Inc ....E 432 334-8580
  Odessa *(G-15898)*
Accelerated Pump ....F 432 582-2335
  Odessa *(G-15899)*
Aggietech Energy Services LLC ....C 432 682-3131
  Midland *(G-15108)*
American Acrylic Injection Inc ....E 972 784-7759
  Farmersville *(G-6221)*
American Petroleum Welding Inc ....E 806 747-7272
  Lubbock *(G-14361)*
Andrews Pump & Supply Inc ....E 806 592-4567
  Denver City *(G-5414)*
Baker Hughes A GE Company LLC ......B 713 625-4200
  Houston *(G-8801)*
Bayou City Pump Works LP ....F 713 472-7722
  Pasadena *(G-16396)*
CS&p Technologies LP ....D 713 467-0869
  Cypress *(G-3783)*
Diversified Industrial Svc Co ....E 806 274-2214
  Borger *(G-2174)*
Don-Nan Pump and Supply Co Inc ......C 432 682-7742
  Midland *(G-15194)*
Dresser LLC ....C 262 549-2626
  Houston *(G-9517)*
Ellis Manufacturing Co Inc ....E 432 561-8819
  Midland *(G-15209)*
Endurance Lift Solutions LLC ....C 903 595-8600
  Fort Worth *(G-6611)*
Energy Devices of Texas Inc ....E 903 963-7906
  Van *(G-20207)*
Flowserve Corporation ....B 972 443-6500
  Irving *(G-13027)*
Flowserve Corporation ....F 832 375-0807
  Houston *(G-9813)*
Flowserve Corporation ....E 713 863-9180
  Houston *(G-9814)*
Flowserve Corporation ....F 412 787-8803
  Pasadena *(G-16439)*

Flowserve Corporation ....E 281 241-3500
  Pasadena *(G-16440)*
Flowserve International Inc ....F 972 443-6500
  Irving *(G-13029)*
Flowserve US Inc ....F 979 549-0029
  Pasadena *(G-16441)*
Flowserve US Inc ....G 502 267-2205
  Pasadena *(G-16442)*
Fluxmetals LLC ....D 832 948-4307
  Houston *(G-9818)*
Fts International Mfg LLC ....E 682 647-3300
  Fort Worth *(G-6653)*
Fts International Services LLC ....F 210 308-3400
  San Antonio *(G-18129)*
Fts International Services LLC ....F 817 334-0002
  Fort Worth *(G-6654)*
Fts International Services LLC ....C 817 862-2000
  Fort Worth *(G-6655)*
Gardner Denver Inc ....E 817 248-4500
  Benbrook *(G-2040)*
Gardner Dnver Wtr Jtting Syste ....C 281 448-5800
  Houston *(G-9898)*
Gilkes Inc ....E 832 932-5282
  Kemah *(G-13475)*
Griffin Dewatering LLC ....E 713 676-8000
  Houston *(G-10044)*
Griffin Pump & Equipment Inc ....E 866 770-8100
  Houston *(G-10045)*
Grundfos CBS Inc ....E 281 994-2700
  Brookshire *(G-2316)*
Hammonds Technical Svcs Inc ....E 281 999-2900
  Houston *(G-10115)*
Houston Grinding & Mfg Co ....D 713 869-3573
  Houston *(G-10235)*
Hyseco Inc ....E 713 991-4240
  Houston *(G-10307)*
Integrated Flow Solutions LLC ....D 903 595-6511
  Tyler *(G-20102)*
ITT Bornemann Usa Inc ....F 832 320-2500
  Stafford *(G-19334)*
ITT LLC ....D 469 221-1200
  Dallas *(G-4515)*
Kemlon Products & Dev Co ....B 281 997-3300
  Pearland *(G-16573)*
Kenergy Oilfield Solutions LLC ....F 979 574-6356
  New Braunfels *(G-15807)*
Kmt Aqua-Dyne Inc ....E 713 864-6929
  Houston *(G-10544)*
Longwood Elastomers Inc ....C 979 830-1111
  Brenham *(G-2261)*
Lufkin Gears LLC ....B 936 634-2211
  Lufkin *(G-14539)*
Marine Services LLC ....E 713 923-6688
  Houston *(G-10765)*
Metso Minerals Industries Inc ....E 210 491-9521
  San Antonio *(G-18295)*
Motor Controls Inc ....B 972 247-4440
  Dallas *(G-4691)*
Murphy Fw ....D 281 633-4500
  Rosenberg *(G-17590)*
Oil States Industries Inc ....C 713 445-2200
  Houston *(G-11157)*
Oil States Industries Inc ....C 817 548-4200
  Arlington *(G-743)*
Oil States International Inc ....D 713 652-0582
  Houston *(G-11161)*
Oliver Equipment Company LLC ....E 713 856-9206
  Houston *(G-11171)*
Pierce Arrow Inc ....F 940 538-5643
  Henrietta *(G-8282)*
Predominant Pumps & Automation ......F 281 987-0204
  Houston *(G-11398)*
Pristech Products Inc ....E 210 520-8051
  San Antonio *(G-18398)*
Prototype Machine Co ....E 512 282-1590
  Manchaca *(G-14641)*
Pump Arts Inc ....E 713 946-0500
  Houston *(G-11472)*
Pumps Plus Pump & Valve Repair ......F 903 987-9232
  Kilgore *(G-13585)*
Robbco Pumps Inc ....F 806 892-2290
  Idalou *(G-12890)*
Rotor-Tech Inc ....F 713 984-8900
  Houston *(G-11672)*
S & N Pump Company ....E 281 445-2243
  Houston *(G-11707)*
Sanbar Balls & Seats Inc ....F 432 332-3755
  Odessa *(G-16149)*
Standard Indus Mfg Prtners LLC ....F 940 580-3512
  Gainesville *(G-7369)*

Stealth Pump & Supply LLC ....E 432 385-7770
  Odessa *(G-16166)*
Sulzer USA Inc ....E 832 886-2300
  Houston *(G-12092)*
Tcm Investments Inc ....E 432 366-5433
  Odessa *(G-16173)*
Teikoku USA Inc ....E 713 983-9901
  Houston *(G-12185)*
Tommy Chappell LLC ....F 432 967-2469
  Odessa *(G-16180)*
Trane Technologies Company LLC ......E 903 730-4000
  Tyler *(G-20163)*
Triangle Pump Components Inc ....F 817 202-8530
  Cleburne *(G-3115)*
TSC Manufacturing and Sup LLC ......E 832 456-3900
  Houston *(G-12395)*
Vere Technology LLC ....E 832 532-6745
  Houston *(G-12551)*
Vertical Trbine Spcialists Inc ....D 806 743-5555
  Lubbock *(G-14507)*
White Star Pump Company LLC ....F 281 357-4999
  Waller *(G-20509)*

PUMPS & PARTS: Indl

Afton Pumps Inc ....D 713 923-9731
  Houston *(G-8500)*
Apergy Artfl Lift Intl LLC ....E 281 403-5742
  Spring *(G-19195)*
Cryogenic Inds Svc Cmpanies LLC ......F 281 590-4800
  Houston *(G-9349)*
Curflo Inc ....E 281 479-5000
  Deer Park *(G-5266)*
Engineered Pump Services Inc ....F 713 472-7722
  Pasadena *(G-16428)*
Flowserve Corporation ....F 800 446-0401
  Irving *(G-13028)*
Flowserve Corporation ....E 409 727-1476
  Port Arthur *(G-17108)*
Flowserve Corporation ....F 409 842-5594
  Beaumont *(G-1895)*
Flowserve US Inc ....D 972 443-6500
  Irving *(G-13030)*
Gator Pump Inc ....G 325 643-3502
  Brownwood *(G-2429)*
Ggctr Inc ....E 832 456-4585
  Pasadena *(G-16448)*
H Lorimer Corporation ....F 903 643-3239
  Longview *(G-14245)*
Jash Usa Inc ....F 281 962-6369
  Houston *(G-10457)*
M G Bryan Equipment Co LP ....F 972 623-4300
  Grand Prairie *(G-7919)*
Oteco Inc ....C 713 695-3693
  Houston *(G-11200)*
Pcs Ferguson Inc ....E 432 334-8580
  Odessa *(G-16108)*
Sigma Drilling Tech LLC ....F 281 656-9298
  Katy *(G-13442)*
Spartan Pumps Inc ....G 713 858-9887
  Odessa *(G-16159)*
Standard Indus Mfg Prtners LLC ....F 682 500-1718
  Cresson *(G-3714)*
Westech Seal Inc ....F 432 367-1188
  Odessa *(G-16211)*

PUMPS & PUMPING EQPT REPAIR SVCS

A & R Energy Services Corp ....F 254 732-7759
  Waco *(G-20353)*
Afton Pumps Inc ....D 713 923-9731
  Houston *(G-8500)*
Aggietech Energy Services LLC ....C 432 682-3131
  Midland *(G-15108)*
All American Pump & Mch Inc ....F 325 653-6597
  San Angelo *(G-17773)*
Alsay Incorporated ....E 210 628-1090
  San Antonio *(G-17900)*
Andrews Pump & Supply Inc ....E 432 523-2166
  Andrews *(G-534)*
Bayou City Pump Works LP ....F 713 472-7722
  Pasadena *(G-16396)*
Engineered Pump Services Inc ....F 713 472-7722
  Pasadena *(G-16428)*
Liberty Lift Solutions LLC ....E 713 575-2300
  Houston *(G-10633)*
Marine Services LLC ....E 713 923-6688
  Houston *(G-10765)*
O F M Pump Inc ....E 432 381-7390
  Odessa *(G-16094)*
Permian H2o Solutions LLC ....F 432 214-4520
  Odessa *(G-16117)*

Employee Codes: A=Over 500 employees, B=251-500
C=101-250, D=51-100, E=20-50, F=10-19, G=9

2021 Harris Texas
Manufacturers Directory

PRODUCT

1621

Remsa Usa Inc ....F 915 855-8621
  El Paso (G-5937)
S & N Pump Company ....E 281 445-2243
  Houston (G-11707)
Shaneda Machine Inc ....E 432 333-7083
  Odessa (G-16152)
Smith Pump Company Inc ....G....... 817 589-2060
  Fort Worth (G-6996)
Solansky Welding and Pump Inc......E 830 374-3318
  Crystal City (G-3757)
Standard Indus Mfg Prtners LLC.......F 940 580-3512
  Gainesville (G-7369)
Tommy Chappell LLC ....F 432 967-2469
  Odessa (G-16180)

PUMPS & PUMPING EQPT WHOLESALERS

Andrews Pump & Supply Inc............E 806 592-4567
  Denver City (G-5414)
Bayou City Pump Works LP ....F 713 472-7722
  Pasadena (G-16396)
Borets US Inc ....F 254 559-5502
  Breckenridge (G-2222)
Champion Process Inc ....F 281 953-9000
  Houston (G-9159)
Dobbs Corporation ....G....... 806 655-7791
  Canyon (G-2670)
Fcx Performance Inc ....E 214 320-3604
  Dallas (G-4357)
Fisher Industries Inc ....F 713 937-6838
  Hockley (G-8344)
Fountain People Inc ....D 512 392-1155
  San Marcos (G-18688)
Imperial Pumps Co ....F 806 791-5242
  Lubbock (G-14425)
ITT Bornemann Usa Inc ....F 832 320-2500
  Stafford (G-19334)
L C Burkett Drilling ....F 806 948-4252
  Sunray (G-19620)
Process Engineered Eqp Co............F 361 289-8891
  Corpus Christi (G-3597)
Robbco Pumps Inc ....F 806 892-2290
  Idalou (G-12890)
S & N Pump Company ....E 281 445-2243
  Houston (G-11707)
Stealth Pump & Supply LLC ....E 432 385-7770
  Odessa (G-16166)
Submersible Oil Services Inc............C 432 699-1506
  Midland (G-15422)
Vaughan Investments Inc................F 956 686-3725
  McAllen (G-14916)
Weatherford Artificia ....C 713 836-4000
  Houston (G-12611)
Willborn Bros Co LLC......................E 806 372-4311
  Amarillo (G-475)

PUMPS, HEAT: Electric

Fiberglass Specialties Inc ....D....... 903 657-6522
  Henderson (G-8263)
Loop Tech International Ltd ....E 936 295-7038
  Willis (G-20854)

PUMPS: Aircraft, Hydraulic

Intertech Fluid Power Inc ....G....... 817 329-9733
  Grapevine (G-8044)

PUMPS: Domestic, Water Or Sump

Deran Inc ....E 806 746-6926
  Lubbock (G-14402)
Dobbs Corporation ....G....... 806 655-7791
  Canyon (G-2670)
Flowtronex Psi LLC ....C 469 221-1200
  Dallas (G-4372)
Franks Machine Shop LLP ....G....... 806 747-4854
  Lubbock (G-14413)
Global Oilfield Services Inc..............E 713 977-5900
  Sugar Land (G-19488)
Protek Specialty Company...............F 713 667-6691
  Houston (G-11464)
Solamotor of Texas........................F 432 426-3246
  Fort Davis (G-6319)
Swaby Manufacturing Company ....F 281 479-7500
  Deer Park (G-5298)
Unitra Inc ....E 281 240-1500
  Stafford (G-19393)

PUMPS: Fluid Power

Fisher Energy Partners LLC ....E 713 937-6838
  Houston (G-9792)

Flint Energy Services Inc ....C 361 449-2405
  George West (G-7624)
Stationary Power Systems Inc ....F 877 924-4949
  Arlington (G-788)

PUMPS: Gasoline, Measuring Or Dispensing

Cft Dispensers Inc ....G....... 512 942-8300
  Georgetown (G-7643)
Tecalemit Inc ....D....... 281 446-7300
  Humble (G-12801)
Wayne Fueling Systems LLC ....F 512 388-8446
  Austin (G-1651)

PUMPS: Hydraulic Power Transfer

Diamond Hydraulics Inc ....E 409 440-8032
  Hitchcock (G-8337)
National Oilwell Varco Inc ....A....... 713 346-7500
  Houston (G-10988)
Rolltex Inc ....G....... 432 570-7576
  Midland (G-15388)

PUMPS: Measuring & Dispensing

Fittings Inc ....D....... 817 332-3300
  Fort Worth (G-6634)
Foam Supplies Inc ....E 972 436-7008
  Lewisville (G-14050)
Schlumberger Technology Corp ....C....... 281 285-8500
  Houston (G-11780)
Schlumberger Technology Corp ....A....... 281 285-8500
  Sugar Land (G-19542)
Schlumberger Technology Corp ....C....... 281 285-8500
  Sugar Land (G-19549)

PUMPS: Oil Well & Field

Andrews Pump & Supply Inc............E 432 523-2166
  Andrews (G-534)
Baker Hughes Company ....C....... 713 439-8600
  Houston (G-8802)
Baker Hughes Holdings LLC ....C....... 713 439-8600
  Houston (G-8806)
Becker Industries Inc ....F 281 590-4900
  Houston (G-8848)
Borets US Inc ....E 713 980-4530
  Houston (G-8958)
Bowie Industries Incorporated ....E 940 872-1106
  Bowie (G-2192)
K&B Machine ....B....... 281 456-0293
  Houston (G-10498)
Lufkin Industries LLC ....E 281 495-1100
  Missouri City (G-15583)
Merrimac Manufacturing Inc ....E 936 894-3900
  Plantersville (G-17059)
Movement Industries Corp...............F 713 849-1300
  Houston (G-10928)
O F M Pump Inc ....E 432 381-7390
  Odessa (G-16094)
Oilwell Hydraulics Inc ....F 432 334-8580
  Odessa (G-16101)
Oteco Inc ....D....... 713 695-3693
  Houston (G-11201)
Reliable Pump Consultants Inc ....E 713 640-2718
  Houston (G-11591)
Schlumberger International ....A....... 713 747-4000
  Houston (G-11766)
Ssi Lift USA Ltd ....E 432 488-6427
  Midland (G-15417)
Sulzer Pumps Houston Inc ....C....... 281 934-6014
  Brookshire (G-2325)
Super Heaters LLC ....E 713 952-5533
  Houston (G-12105)
Texco Trim Inc ....D....... 713 861-1892
  Houston (G-12259)
Weatherford Artificia ....E 432 561-5505
  Midland (G-15466)
Weatherford Artificia ....F 817 624-7810
  Fort Worth (G-7128)
Weatherford Artificia ....C 713 836-4000
  Houston (G-12611)
Weatherford Artificia ....E 903 935-2416
  Marshall (G-14807)

PUMPS: Oil, Measuring Or Dispensing

Bear Pump & Equipment Inc.............F 281 200-1000
  Houston (G-8846)
Cowboy Pumps ....E 361 221-9786
  Kingsville (G-13625)
Predominant Pumps & Automation.......F 281 987-0204
  Houston (G-11398)

PUMPS: Vacuum, Exc Laboratory

Compositech Products Mfg Inc ....E 281 648-3557
  Pearland (G-16548)
Lely Tank Waste Solutions LLC ....F 800 367-5359
  Troy (G-20029)

PURCHASING SVCS

Abuyo Inc ....E 855 850-3850
  Austin (G-882)
Immi Turbines Inc ....F 936 788-2229
  Conroe (G-3310)
Pan American Industries Inc.............G....... 281 572-4842
  Porter (G-17180)
Uranium Resources Inc ....F 972 219-3330
  Lewisville (G-14102)
Wood Group Usa Inc ....A....... 832 809-8000
  Houston (G-12687)

PURIFICATION & DUST COLLECTION EQPT

Ceco Environmental Corp.................C....... 214 357-6181
  Dallas (G-4092)
Gardner Denver Inc ....F 281 873-1200
  Houston (G-9897)
Pollution System Solutions Inc ....F 713 574-6661
  Spring (G-19241)
Sabio Environmental LLC ....E 512 869-0544
  Round Rock (G-17689)

PURLINS: Steel, Light Gauge

Texas Iron & Steel LLC ....F 903 758-9498
  Longview (G-14317)

PURSES: Women's

Custom Direct Inc ....F 201 934-4229
  Plano (G-16834)

QUARTZ CRYSTAL MINING SVCS

American Quartz LLC ....D....... 214 243-6676
  Dallas (G-3945)

QUARTZ CRYSTALS: Electronic

Carter Glassblowing Inc...................F 940 440-3090
  Crossroads (G-3747)
Chiphong Inc ....E 512 933-9292
  Austin (G-1048)
Southwest Quartz Ltd Co ....F 512 863-8415
  Georgetown (G-7678)

QUICKLIME

Chemical Lime-Southwest LLC ....F 512 756-8668
  Burnet (G-2604)
Kdm Holding Inc ....D....... 817 732-8164
  Fort Worth (G-6752)
Lhoist North America Inc ....E 214 544-1717
  McKinney (G-14954)
Lhoist North America MO Inc ....D....... 817 732-8164
  Fort Worth (G-6786)
Lhoist North America Texas Ltd ....E 512 756-8668
  Burnet (G-2611)
Lime Holding Inc ....C....... 817 732-8164
  Fort Worth (G-6790)
United States Lime & Mnrl Inc ....E 972 991-8400
  Dallas (G-5138)

QUILTING SVC

Fiberco Inc....................................F 682 647-1332
  Fort Worth (G-6628)

QUILTING SVC & SPLYS, FOR THE TRADE

Quilters Emporium LLC....................F 281 491-0016
  Stafford (G-19366)

RACE CAR OWNERS

A J Foyt Enterprises Inc ....D....... 936 372-3698
  Waller (G-20489)

RACKS: Book & Magazine, Wood

Rack Solutions Inc ....F 903 453-0800
  Greenville (G-8088)

RACKS: Display

Rj & RC Associates LLC..............F...... 214 352-4690
Dallas *(G-4903)*

Universal Display and Fix Co..........C...... 972 434-8067
Lewisville *(G-14101)*

RACKS: Railroad Car, Vehicle Transportation, Steel

Austin Western Railroad LLC..........E...... 512 388-6350
Austin *(G-965)*

RADAR SYSTEMS & EQPT

Applied Concepts Inc..............C...... 972 398-3750
Richardson *(G-17270)*

Drs Training Ctrl Systems LLC..........E...... 214 381-7161
Dallas *(G-4281)*

Mustang Technology Group LP..........C...... 972 747-0707
Plano *(G-16937)*

Raytheon Company..............A...... 972 205-4277
Dallas *(G-4860)*

Raytheon Company..............C...... 972 344-3000
Dallas *(G-4861)*

Raytheon Company..............E...... 361 348-2712
Premont *(G-17204)*

Raytheon Company..............C...... 972 344-8000
Richardson *(G-17386)*

RADIATORS, EXC ELECTRIC

Hght Inc..............G...... 281 446-1155
Humble *(G-12776)*

Houston Global Heat Transf LLC........D...... 281 446-1155
Humble *(G-12777)*

RADIATORS: Stationary Engine

Atlas Radiator Inc..............E...... 361 882-5661
Corpus Christi *(G-3477)*

RADIO & TELEVISION COMMUNICATIONS EQUIPMENT

AGS Technology Inc..............E...... 817 490-0086
Fort Worth *(G-6356)*

Andrew & Associates..............D...... 713 471-0922
Houston *(G-8642)*

Applied Systems Engrg Inc..........D...... 817 249-4180
Benbrook *(G-2037)*

Boeing Company..............A...... 281 244-4000
Houston *(G-8942)*

Commscope Inc North Carolina..........C...... 214 583-6750
Dallas *(G-4148)*

Commscope Technologies LLC..........F...... 972 243-0965
Carrollton *(G-2717)*

Commscope Technologies LLC..........E...... 817 864-4100
Euless *(G-6138)*

Commscope Technologies LLC..........A...... 214 634-8502
Dallas *(G-4149)*

Commscope Technologies LLC..........E...... 956 205-6000
Mission *(G-15551)*

Commscope Technologies LLC..........C...... 214 267-5900
Richardson *(G-17289)*

Connectivity Solutions Mfg Inc..........C...... 972 792-3000
Richardson *(G-17290)*

Curtis Mathes Inc..............F...... 888 725-0309
Frisco *(G-7277)*

Cve Technology Group Inc..........A...... 972 424-6606
Plano *(G-16835)*

Dbspectra Inc..............E...... 469 322-0080
Lewisville *(G-14041)*

Dbspectra Inc..............D...... 469 322-0080
Lewisville *(G-14042)*

Forum Communications Systems........F...... 972 619-8603
Richardson *(G-17311)*

General Dynamics Mission..........E...... 254 532-2927
Fort Hood *(G-6323)*

Kathrein Broadcast Usa Inc..........E...... 541 879-2300
Frisco *(G-7295)*

Kmt Wireless LLC..............B...... 817 591-4600
Grapevine *(G-8045)*

Kodiak Networks Inc..............F...... 972 665-0200
Plano *(G-16903)*

Ldia Holdings LLC..............E...... 512 247-3700
Austin *(G-1284)*

Logitek Electronic Systems..........F...... 713 664-4470
Houston *(G-10674)*

Luminator Technology Group Inc........B...... 972 516-3154
Plano *(G-16912)*

Luminator Technology Group LLC........C...... 972 424-6511
Plano *(G-16913)*

Motorola Solutions Inc..............F...... 713 783-6400
Houston *(G-10926)*

Motorola Solutions Inc..............C...... 512 422-9028
Austin *(G-1354)*

Motorola Solutions Inc..............D...... 972 277-4600
Dallas *(G-4692)*

Motorola Solutions Inc..............E...... 972 587-5360
Dallas *(G-4693)*

Nokia Inc..............C...... 214 496-0329
Irving *(G-13125)*

Phazr Inc..............B...... 972 693-7829
Allen *(G-292)*

Rf Code Inc..............E...... 512 439-2200
Austin *(G-1464)*

Rockwell Collins Inc..............A...... 972 705-3156
Richardson *(G-17391)*

Ruckus Wireless Inc..............E...... 972 546-1700
Plano *(G-16998)*

Scott Studios Corporation..........E...... 972 620-2211
Coppell *(G-3445)*

Soloprotect Us LLC..............D...... 866 632-6577
Coppell *(G-3446)*

Southern Avionics Co..............E...... 409 842-1717
Beaumont *(G-1952)*

Veripos (us) Inc..............F...... 281 966-7600
Houston *(G-12552)*

RADIO & TELEVISION REPAIR

National Circuit Assembly Inc........D...... 972 278-2009
Garland *(G-7557)*

RADIO BROADCASTING & COMMUNICATIONS EQPT

Alert Technologies Inc..............E...... 281 326-9900
Houston *(G-8534)*

Aviat US Inc..............B...... 408 941-7100
Austin *(G-969)*

Awesome Paging Inc..............G...... 361 576-2255
Victoria *(G-20240)*

Bock Technologies Inc..............E...... 972 869-2625
Dallas *(G-4036)*

Continental Electronics Corp..........D...... 214 381-7161
Dallas *(G-4159)*

D C A E Inc..............E...... 972 278-0202
Garland *(G-7472)*

Ef Johnson Technologies Inc..........E...... 972 819-0700
Irving *(G-13011)*

Golden Crescent Communications......F...... 361 578-4091
Victoria *(G-20269)*

Hispanic Fmly Chrstn Ntwrk Inc......F...... 214 331-2800
Dallas *(G-4460)*

Imagine Communications Corp..........D...... 469 803-4900
Frisco *(G-7292)*

Kegspeed LLC..............F...... 267 714-8854
Austin *(G-1266)*

Motorola Solutions Inc..............C...... 817 245-6000
Fort Worth *(G-6856)*

Nokia Slutions Networks US LLC........B...... 972 374-3000
Coppell *(G-3432)*

Sat Radio Communications Ltd........F...... 361 853-9943
Corpus Christi *(G-3615)*

Tait Radio Communications..........E...... 281 944-3539
Houston *(G-12148)*

West-Com Nrse Call Systems Inc........F...... 713 731-2500
Houston *(G-12637)*

RADIO BROADCASTING STATIONS

Excel Media LLC..............F...... 409 832-5770
Beaumont *(G-1890)*

Herald of Truth Ministries..........F...... 325 698-4370
Abilene *(G-49)*

W V Grant Intl Ministries..........F...... 214 333-2176
Dallas *(G-5171)*

RADIO COMMUNICATIONS: Carrier Eqpt

Ewing Electronics Inc..............F...... 469 519-2900
Allen *(G-266)*

Rf Monolithics Inc..............E...... 972 233-2903
Carrollton *(G-2886)*

RADIO RECEIVING SETS

Radixon Inc..............E...... 855 723-4966
Dallas *(G-4858)*

RADIO REPAIR & INSTALLATION SVCS

Carrion Enterprises Inc..............F...... 915 593-1338
El Paso *(G-5686)*

Sat Radio Communications Ltd........F...... 361 853-9943
Corpus Christi *(G-3615)*

RADIO, TELEVISION & CONSUMER ELECTRONICS STORES: TV Sets

Videotex Systems Inc..............F...... 214 349-6399
Dallas *(G-5166)*

RADIO, TV & CONSUMER ELEC STORES: Automotive Sound Eqpt

Crossfire Inc..............E...... 972 570-0800
Irving *(G-12983)*

RADIO, TV & CONSUMER ELEC STORES: High Fidelity Stereo Eqpt

Custom Electronics Inc..............F...... 512 454-8824
Pflugerville *(G-16667)*

Dallas Sight and Sound Inc..........E...... 972 392-3202
Dallas *(G-4225)*

RADIO, TV & CONSUMER ELECTRONICS: VCR & Access

Applied Concepts Inc..............C...... 972 398-3750
Richardson *(G-17270)*

RADIO, TV/CONSUMER ELEC STORES: Marine Radios/Radar Eqpt

R2sonic LLC..............F...... 512 891-0000
Austin *(G-1449)*

RADIOS WHOLESALERS

Iesco Distributing Inc..............F...... 972 446-1605
Carrollton *(G-2776)*

RAIL & STRUCTURAL SHAPES: Aluminum rail & structural shapes

Xterra Industries LLC..............E...... 281 998-0442
Pasadena *(G-16528)*

RAILINGS: Prefabricated, Metal

S F L Inc..............F...... 936 856-1433
Willis *(G-20863)*

RAILINGS: Wood

Elkcorp..............E...... 972 851-0500
Dallas *(G-4313)*

RAILROAD CAR RENTING & LEASING SVCS

Specialty Locomotive Services..........F...... 281 425-9850
Baytown *(G-1836)*

RAILROAD CAR REPAIR SVCS

Specialty Locomotive Services..........F...... 281 425-9850
Baytown *(G-1836)*

RAILROAD CARGO LOADING & UNLOADING SVCS

Chapas Oilfield Services LLC..........F...... 956 847-6460
Zapata *(G-20980)*

GE Oil & Gas Logging Svcs Inc..........E...... 281 579-9879
Sugar Land *(G-19485)*

Intermdal Repr Mdfcation Trckg........F...... 713 674-2179
Houston *(G-10396)*

True Grit Transportation Inc..........E...... 682 708-5847
Burleson *(G-2599)*

Wartsila North America Inc..........C...... 281 233-6200
Houston *(G-12600)*

RAILROAD EQPT

American Railcar Inds Inc..........D...... 903 759-4406
Longview *(G-14194)*

American Railcar Inds Inc..........D...... 936 365-2679
Goodrich *(G-7768)*

Automotive Rentals Inc..............E...... 817 624-3650
Fort Worth *(G-6411)*

Employee Codes: A=Over 500 employees, B=251-500
C=101-250, D=51-100, E=20-50, F=10-19, G=9

2021 Harris Texas
Manufacturers Directory

PRODUCT

1623

Ctc Inc ....E 817 886-8210
Fort Worth (G-6564)
Eagle Railcar Services LP ....F 254 631-0168
Eastland (G-5563)
Gunderson Rail Services LLC ....B 817 556-9191
Cleburne (G-3094)
New York Air Brake LLC ....F 972 893-2400
Irving (G-13123)
Progress Rail Services Corp ....G 817 693-2550
Fort Worth (G-6921)
Progress Rail Services Corp ....D 806 335-3900
Amarillo (G-510)
Salco Products Inc ....E 630 783-2570
Houston (G-11733)
Specialty Locomotive Services ....F 281 425-9850
Baytown (G-1836)
Trinity Industries Inc ....D 817 665-1499
Fort Worth (G-7075)
Union Tank Car Company ....E 713 926-6980
Galena Park (G-7384)
Wabtec Corporation ....D 713 222-0792
Houston (G-12590)

RAILROAD EQPT & SPLYS WHOLESALERS

American Railcar Inds Inc ....D 936 365-2679
Goodrich (G-7768)
Menard Industries LLC ....G 512 628-1058
Houston (G-10828)

RAILROAD EQPT, EXC LOCOMOTIVES

American Railcar Inds Inc ....F 281 471-1930
La Porte (G-13721)

RAILROAD EQPT: Cars & Eqpt, Dining

750 Logistics LLC ....E 214 433-2615
Houston (G-8414)
Channl-Track Tube-Way Inds Inc ....F 361 798-4979
Hallettsville (G-8120)
Trinity Industries Inc ....B 214 631-4420
Dallas (G-5112)
Trinity Parts & Components LLC ....F 817 378-2003
Fort Worth (G-7076)

RAILROAD EQPT: Cars & Eqpt, Train, Freight Or Passenger

Union Tank Car Company ....B 281 456-9381
Houston (G-12437)
Union Tank Car Company ....C 281 847-8200
Houston (G-12438)

RAILROAD EQPT: Cars, Motor

Trinity Industries Intl ....A 214 589-8967
Dallas (G-5113)
Union Tank Car Company ....C 281 592-6424
Cleveland (G-3140)

RAILROAD EQPT: Cars, Tank Freight & Eqpt

Fryoux Tankerman Svc of Texas ....E 281 842-9400
La Porte (G-13738)

RAILROAD EQPT: Locomotives & Parts, Electric Or Nonelectric

Quality Trbchrger Cmpnents LLC ....E 713 849-4200
Houston (G-11502)

RAILROAD TIES: Concrete

Rocla Concrete Tie Inc ....E 806 383-7071
Amarillo (G-459)

RAILROAD TIES: Wood

K L Barton & Sons Tie Co ....F 936 347-2744
Garrison (G-7611)

RAILROADS: Long Haul

Capitol Aggregates Inc ....C 210 871-6100
San Antonio (G-17981)
ESP Enterprises Inc ....D 281 444-2377
Houston (G-9697)
Sister2sster Dstiny Trnspt LLC ....F 346 337-6637
Houston (G-11908)
Tegraexcel Energy Services LLC ....F 412 508-0690
Midland (G-15435)

RAILS: Steel Or Iron

Gordons Specialties Inc ....E 972 225-1660
Hutchins (G-12866)
Narstco Inc ....D 972 775-5560
Midlothian (G-15487)

REACTORS: Current Limiting

Global Technical Solutions USA ....F 832 410-4488
Spring (G-19126)

REAL ESTATE AGENCIES & BROKERS

Bz & Sons Sweeping & Wshg Inc ....G 903 732-9882
Powderly (G-17198)
Real Estate Foreclosures ....F 210 733-4262
San Antonio (G-18413)

REAL ESTATE AGENCIES: Buying

Houston Opicoil Inc ....F 713 840-7171
Houston (G-10242)

REAL ESTATE AGENCIES: Commercial

Bric Mc Mann Industries Inc ....F 830 775-9153
Del Rio (G-5309)
Garvon Inc ....F 214 691-0711
Dallas (G-4392)
Spindletop Oil & Gas Co ....E 972 644-2581
Dallas (G-4998)
Victor Nicolle Inc ....F 713 896-4911
Houston (G-12566)

REAL ESTATE AGENTS & MANAGERS

C&S Lease Service LC ....E 903 988-8642
Kilgore (G-13534)
Foreclosure Listing Service ....F 972 250-0993
Addison (G-125)
Hyperion Energy LP ....F 214 750-3820
Dallas (G-4478)
Hyperion Resources Inc ....F 214 750-1522
Dallas (G-4479)
Legacy Investments Inc ....E 214 750-1522
Dallas (G-4587)
Republic Title of Texas Inc ....C 972 578-8611
Plano (G-16991)
Riva Services LLC ....D 713 675-2525
Houston (G-11627)
Sowell & Co LP ....E 214 871-3320
Dallas (G-4994)

REAL ESTATE APPRAISERS

Mike Davis and Associates Inc ....E 512 836-8442
Austin (G-1343)

REAL ESTATE INVESTMENT TRUSTS

B-29 Investments LP ....D 940 665-4373
Gainesville (G-7334)
Central Management Inc ....F 713 961-9777
Houston (G-9138)

REAL ESTATE OPERATORS, EXC DEVELOPERS: Commercial/Indl Bldg

Bison Development Company ....F 806 355-8253
Amarillo (G-481)
Brown Fndtion Repr In Cnslting ....E 972 271-2621
Dallas (G-4060)
Clajon Holding Corp ....C 432 682-6324
Midland (G-15168)
Dynamic Inc ....E 817 838-1800
Fort Worth (G-6597)
Exploration Center Building ....E 806 353-9123
Amarillo (G-487)
FE Hill Co LLP ....F 903 389-3616
Fairfield (G-6173)
Forbes Rbuilt Automitive Parts ....F 817 332-7643
Fort Worth (G-6640)
Ray Mac Energy ....F 806 274-5881
Borger (G-2184)
Zimair LP ....D 817 624-7245
Fort Worth (G-7160)

RECEIVERS: Radio Communications

Espy Corporation ....E 512 261-1016
Austin (G-861)

RECLAIMED RUBBER: Reworked By Manufacturing Process

Elder Rubber Incorporated ....E 214 426-2890
Irving (G-13013)
National Hose Aquisition Corp ....D 713 920-2030
Pasadena (G-16487)
R-Interests LLC ....F 940 759-4181
Muenster (G-15672)
Rumber Materials Incorporated ....G 940 759-4181
Muenster (G-15673)

RECORD BLANKS: Phonographic

Hacienda Rec Recording Studio ....F 361 882-7066
Corpus Christi (G-3543)

RECORDING TAPE: Video, Blank

Watchguard Inc ....B 972 423-9777
Allen (G-306)

RECORDS & TAPES: Prerecorded

Adams Evidence Grade Tech Inc ....F 830 966-4210
Utopia (G-20187)
AMA Printing / Finishing Inc ....E 254 776-8860
Waco (G-20359)
Asinni 2000 Records Inc ....E 281 564-4111
Houston (G-8722)
Broadcast Your Vision LLC ....F 972 984-0303
Rockwall (G-17541)
Joey Records Inc ....E 210 432-7893
San Antonio (G-18203)
Kadence Collective LLC ....F 888 901-5343
San Antonio (G-18215)
Molecula Corp ....G 512 649-9113
Austin (G-1350)
Quadrabyte LLC ....E 469 619-0749
Austin (G-1441)
Tailwind Business Ventures LLC ....C 210 268-2717
Cedar Park (G-2986)
Udundi LLC ....F 917 727-4220
Austin (G-1604)

RECORDS OR TAPES: Masters

Jones Tape Duplicating Inc ....G 281 351-8109
Cypress (G-3805)
Nicole Dionne ....F 310 699-7556
Austin (G-1366)
Thug City Records ....F 832 264-4892
Houston (G-12285)

RECOVERY SVCS: Metal

Atlas Iron & Scrap Metal Co ....E 972 225-4221
Dallas (G-3981)
Interntnal Shpbreaking Ltd LLC ....C 956 831-4112
Brownsville (G-2364)
Lee Quigley Company ....F 512 762-4046
Austin (G-1286)
Newell Ltd ....E 210 222-9511
San Antonio (G-18343)

RECREATIONAL SPORTING EQPT REPAIR SVCS

Douglas Pads & Sports Inc ....E 713 697-9787
Houston (G-9503)

RECREATIONAL VEHICLE DEALERS

Coker Enterprises ....F 903 533-8894
Tyler (G-20069)
Ghm Corp ....C 972 840-1200
Dallas (G-4406)
Kwest Rv LLC ....F 512 294-2634
Austin (G-1276)
Morgan Buildings & Spas Inc ....F 972 864-7300
Richardson (G-17360)
Progressive Sales Inc ....E 432 333-6631
Odessa (G-16127)
Sherrod Rv Center Inc ....F 409 385-5689
Silsbee (G-18955)

RECREATIONAL VEHICLE PARTS & ACCESS STORES

Dfw Camper Corral Inc ....F 972 241-6443
Dallas (G-4255)

RECREATIONAL VEHICLE REPAIRS

Land & Sea Services 1 Inc ....G...... 409 935-9466
  La Marque (G-13711)
Magnum Custom Trlr Mfg Co Inc..........F...... 512 258-4101
  San Antonio (G-18271)
Santin Auto and Truck Repr Ctr ....E...... 210 648-4100
  San Antonio (G-18454)

RECREATIONAL VEHICLE: Wholesalers

Deerskin Mfg Inc ....F...... 817 220-5535
  Springtown (G-19273)

RECTIFIERS: Electronic, Exc Semiconductor

Cathodic Rectifiers Inc ....F...... 903 759-6813
  Longview (G-14209)

RECYCLING: Paper

Akrotex Films Inc ....E...... 409 886-0632
  Orange (G-16229)
Pratt Industries USA Inc......................E...... 940 387-7291
  Denton (G-5393)

REELS: Cable, Metal

Reel-Logix LLC ....E...... 713 369-3139
  Houston (G-11581)

REELS: Wood

Crescent Reel Manufacturing Co ....F...... 713 695-4587
  Houston (G-9343)
P Diamond Enterprises Inc ....F...... 325 643-5629
  Brownwood (G-2441)

REFINERS & SMELTERS: Aluminum

Kaiser Aluminum Fab Pdts LLC...........C...... 903 868-1556
  Sherman (G-18918)
Sarbali Alloys LLC ....E...... 281 384-3500
  Houston (G-11752)

REFINERS & SMELTERS: Copper

Aleris Ohio Management Inc.................F...... 972 815-0800
  Irving (G-12927)
Asarco LLC ....A...... 806 468-4000
  Amarillo (G-401)
Freeport Minerals Corporation ....C...... 915 778-9881
  El Paso (G-5774)
Mac Fabricators ....G...... 979 265-0235
  Clute (G-3156)

REFINERS & SMELTERS: Copper, Secondary

Asarco LLC ....A...... 806 468-4000
  Amarillo (G-401)

REFINERS & SMELTERS: Gold

Central Jewelry & Refining ....F...... 214 350-4653
  Dallas (G-4099)

REFINERS & SMELTERS: Lead, Secondary

Ebt Newco LLC...................................F...... 972 996-0458
  Dallas (G-4298)
Exide Technologies ....C...... 972 335-2121
  Frisco (G-7284)
Quemetco Metals Limited Inc...............F...... 214 631-6070
  Dallas (G-4849)
Quexco Incorporated...........................E...... 214 688-4000
  Dallas (G-4851)
Revere Smelting & Ref Corp ....C...... 214 631-6070
  Dallas (G-4893)

REFINERS & SMELTERS: Magnesium, Secondary

Galvotec Alloys Inc.............................C...... 956 630-3500
  McAllen (G-14863)

REFINERS & SMELTERS: Nonferrous Metal

Alpha Omega Recycling Inc.................F...... 903 297-7272
  Longview (G-14192)
Ashley Salvage Company ....E...... 210 922-7631
  San Antonio (G-17916)
Commercial Metals Company.................D...... 713 226-0100
  Houston (G-9251)
Commercial Metals Company.................E...... 979 265-4642
  Clute (G-3150)

Commercial Metals Company ....E...... 817 429-4005
  Fort Worth (G-6531)
Commercial Metals Company ....D...... 361 884-4071
  Corpus Christi (G-3505)
Commercial Metals Company ....E...... 469 729-0180
  Dallas (G-4147)
Commercial Metals Company ....C...... 214 565-0668
  Dallas (G-4146)
EC Wrecking & Salvage Corp ....F...... 915 855-7999
  El Paso (G-5734)
Ecs Refining Texas LLC ....E...... 972 524-1075
  Terrell (G-19732)
Elah Holdings Inc ....F...... 805 435-1255
  Dallas (G-4307)
Elg Metals Inc ....E...... 281 457-2100
  Houston (G-9600)
Fulton Supply and Recycl Inc ....E...... 940 382-3611
  Denton (G-5367)
Garland Steel Inc ....E...... 972 494-6000
  Garland (G-7495)
Gateway Metal Recycling Inc................F...... 956 723-0409
  Laredo (G-13889)
J L Proler Iron and Steel Co ....E...... 713 675-3191
  Houston (G-10441)
Jrn Management LP ....D...... 210 222-9511
  San Antonio (G-18211)
Lopez Scrap Metal Inc ....D...... 915 859-0770
  El Paso (G-5847)
Pine Street Salvage Co........................E...... 325 677-8831
  Abilene (G-65)
Tyler Iron & Metal Ltd ....E...... 903 592-8144
  Tyler (G-20170)
US Zinc Corporation ....E...... 713 926-1705
  Houston (G-12493)
W Silver Recycling Inc........................D...... 915 532-5643
  El Paso (G-6027)

REFINERS & SMELTERS: Platinum Group Metals, Secondary

Techemet LP ....D...... 281 991-8300
  Pasadena (G-16518)

REFINERS & SMELTERS: Zinc, Secondary

Gulf Reduction Corporation...................C...... 713 926-1705
  Houston (G-10069)

REFINING LUBRICATING OILS & GREASES, NEC

Texas Oil Group Ltd Co ....F...... 281 645-9398
  San Antonio (G-18540)

REFINING: Petroleum

3 Diamond Services LLC ....F...... 361 442-6949
  Ingleside (G-12891)
Absolute Fuels LLC ....E...... 806 712-0330
  Lubbock (G-14357)
Air Lqide Amer Spclty Gses LLC ....E...... 800 217-2688
  Houston (G-8514)
Anadarko E&P Onshore LLC ....F...... 832 636-1000
  The Woodlands (G-19828)
Antelope Refining LLC ....E...... 713 860-2746
  Houston (G-8648)
Belvan Partners LP ....F...... 432 682-4349
  Midland (G-15137)
Black Eagle Inc...................................E...... 214 871-3555
  Dallas (G-4027)
Calumet Branded Products LLC...........D...... 281 354-8600
  Porter (G-17171)
Calumet Karns City Ref LLC ....D...... 281 337-1534
  Dickinson (G-5471)
Catalyst Partners Inc ....G...... 940 644-5625
  Chico (G-3052)
Chemex Modular LLC ....D...... 801 565-8099
  New Waverly (G-15856)
Coffeyville Resources LLC ....F...... 281 207-7711
  Sugar Land (G-19463)
Coffeyvlle Rsrces Ref Mktg LLC...........E...... 281 207-3200
  Sugar Land (G-19465)
Cvr Energy Inc....................................D...... 281 207-3200
  Sugar Land (G-19472)
Cvr Refining LP ....F...... 281 207-3200
  Sugar Land (G-19474)
Cvr Refining Holdings LLC ....B...... 281 207-3200
  Sugar Land (G-19475)
Dcg Partnership I Limited ....E...... 281 648-1894
  Pearland (G-16553)

Delek Renewables LLC.........................E...... 817 558-9255
  Cleburne (G-3088)
Delek US Holdings Inc.........................D...... 432 684-4210
  Midland (G-15190)
Diamond Shamrock Ref & Mktg Co......A...... 210 345-2000
  San Antonio (G-18057)
El Paso Cgp Company LLC ....E...... 713 420-2600
  Houston (G-9585)
Enterprise Products Oper LLC ....D...... 281 385-4200
  Mont Belvieu (G-15617)
Enterprise Products Oper LLC ....D...... 832 501-4000
  Mont Belvieu (G-15618)
Ep Energy Resale Company LLC ....F...... 713 997-1000
  Houston (G-9677)
Equilon Enterprises LLC ....B...... 713 767-5337
  Houston (G-9685)
Exxon Mobil Corporation ....B...... 972 940-6000
  Irving (G-13021)
Exxonmobil Pipeline Company ....C...... 713 656-3636
  Spring (G-19117)
Exxonmobil Sales and Sup LLC ....C...... 800 243-9966
  Spring (G-19119)
Fabrication & Cnstr Svcs LP ....E...... 936 257-0466
  Dayton (G-5226)
Flint Hills Resources LP ....E...... 281 363-7200
  The Woodlands (G-19865)
Flint Hills Resources LP ....B...... 432 640-8933
  Odessa (G-16004)
Flint Hills Resources LP ....E...... 361 241-4811
  Corpus Christi (G-3530)
Flint Hills Resources LP ....C...... 361 241-4811
  Corpus Christi (G-3531)
Flint Hlls Rsrces Hston Chem L ....D...... 713 740-3900
  Houston (G-9803)
Frontier Petroleum Resources ....E...... 832 242-1510
  Houston (G-9869)
Giant Industries Inc ....A...... 915 775-3300
  El Paso (G-5786)
Hermes Consolidated LLC ....F...... 303 894-9966
  Houston (G-10160)
Hh Oil Tools Inc ....F...... 281 550-0633
  Houston (G-10169)
Hollyfrontier Corporation......................B...... 214 871-3555
  Dallas (G-4462)
Hunt Petroleum Corporation ....C...... 214 880-8400
  Fort Worth (G-6710)
Intergulf Corporation...........................D...... 281 474-4210
  La Porte (G-13754)
Iwc Oil & Refinery LLC ....E...... 210 900-9928
  San Antonio (G-18196)
J L Davis Company ....F...... 432 399-4575
  Coahoma (G-3165)
Jag Energy Company ....F...... 832 997-0575
  Houston (G-10449)
Koch Industries Inc..............................F...... 806 347-2645
  Matador (G-14816)
Koch Supply & Trading LP ....E...... 713 544-4123
  Houston (G-10555)
Lazarus Energy LLC ....G...... 830 582-3202
  Houston (G-10610)
Lazarus Energy Holdings LLC ....F...... 713 850-0500
  Houston (G-10611)
Lima Refining Company ....F...... 409 839-3500
  Beaumont (G-1918)
Lima Refining Company ....D...... 409 985-1000
  Port Arthur (G-17116)
Lyondell-Citgo Refining LLC ....F...... 713 321-4111
  Houston (G-10707)
Marathon Oil Company..........................E...... 713 296-4336
  Houston (G-10755)
Marathon Oil Corporation ....A...... 713 629-6600
  Houston (G-10756)
Murphy USA Inc ....F...... 512 332-0622
  Bastrop (G-1760)
Nexlube Operating LLC ....F...... 972 590-9908
  Addison (G-150)
Par Hawaii Refining LLC ....C...... 281 899-4800
  Houston (G-11234)
Par Pacific Holdings Inc ....D...... 281 899-4800
  Houston (G-11235)
Pasadena Refining System Inc ....C...... 713 920-1874
  Houston (G-11255)
Phillips 66 ....C...... 281 293-6600
  Houston (G-11324)
Phillips 66 Carrier LLC ....C...... 855 283-9237
  Houston (G-11325)
Premcor Refining Group Inc ....G...... 210 345-2000
  San Antonio (G-18388)
Pride Refining Inc ....B...... 325 677-5444
  Abilene (G-66)

PRODUCT

Quaker State Investment Corp ....F 713 546-4000
Houston (G-11491)

Rancho Lpg Holdings LLC ....E 713 993-5331
Houston (G-11539)

San Antonio Refinery LLC ....E 512 350-7898
San Antonio (G-18447)

San Antonio Refinery LLC ....E 210 918-7436
San Antonio (G-18448)

Shell Oil Company ....D 713 246-6462
Deer Park (G-5296)

Shell Oil Company ....A 713 241-6161
Houston (G-11860)

Southcross Ala Pipeline LLC ....E 214 979-3700
Dallas (G-4981)

Tesoro Refining & Mktg Co LLC ....C 210 828-8484
San Antonio (G-18530)

Total Ptrchemicals Ref USA Inc............C 281 476-3700
Deer Park (G-5301)

Total Ptrchemicals Ref USA Inc............B 409 963-6800
Port Arthur (G-17130)

Trecora Resources ....E 281 980-5522
Sugar Land (G-19568)

Tri Resources Inc ....E 940 644-2233
Chico (G-3054)

Ultramar Inc ....A 210 345-2000
San Antonio (G-18576)

United Energy Group LLC ....D 281 839-0080
Baytown (G-1838)

UOP LLC ....E 832 551-9638
Houston (G-12472)

Upham Oil & Gas Company LP ....E 940 325-4491
Mineral Wells (G-15544)

Valero Energy Corporation ....E 903 567-6001
Canton (G-2661)

Valero Energy Corporation ....E 903 765-2900
Alba (G-183)

Valero Energy Corporation ....F 325 347-6561
Rocksprings (G-17533)

Valero Energy Corporation ....B 806 935-1307
Sunray (G-19623)

Valero Energy Corporation ....F 936 594-6233
Riverside (G-17481)

Valero Marketing and Supply Co ....C 877 882-5376
Amarillo (G-517)

Valero Ref Company-California ....C 210 345-2000
San Antonio (G-18584)

Valero Ref Company-New Jersey ....B 210 345-2000
San Antonio (G-18585)

Valero Refining-Texas LP ....B 713 923-6641
Houston (G-12519)

Valero Refining-Texas LP ....B 409 945-4451
Texas City (G-19806)

Valero Renewable Fuels Co LLC ....D 210 345-2000
San Antonio (G-18588)

Valero Rfining-New Orleans LLC ....C 210 345-2000
San Antonio (G-18589)

Valero Services Inc ....A 210 345-2000
San Antonio (G-18590)

Vertex Energy Inc ....E 866 660-8156
Houston (G-12556)

Western Gas Resources Inc ....E 432 395-2448
Fort Stockton (G-6331)

Western Refining Inc ....B 915 775-3300
El Paso (G-6033)

Western Refining Company LP ....F 915 775-3246
El Paso (G-6034)

Western Refining Company LP ....E 915 534-1400
El Paso (G-6035)

WRB Refining LP ....F 281 293-6600
Houston (G-12699)

Wynnewood Refining Company LLC ....D 281 207-3444
Sugar Land (G-19575)

REFRACTORIES: Cement

Hanson Lehigh Inc ....E 281 616-0700
Houston (G-10120)

Hanson Lehigh Inc ....B 972 653-5500
Irving (G-13052)

Select Sands America Corp ....F 501 276-5928
Houston (G-11823)

REFRACTORIES: Clay

Allied Mineral Products Inc ....G 956 831-2022
Brownsville (G-2336)

Custom Building Products Inc ....D 972 641-6996
Grand Prairie (G-7860)

Harbisonwalker Intl Inc ....E 713 635-3200
Houston (G-10123)

Quikrete Companies LLC ....E 979 732-8210
Columbus (G-3232)

Robert J Jenkins Co ....E 281 332-3566
Webster (G-20643)

Team Cooperheat-Mqs Inc ....E 713 673-3660
Houston (G-12171)

Texas Technical Ceramics Inc ....E 936 856-2903
Willis (G-20866)

REFRACTORIES: Graphite, Carbon Or Ceramic Bond

Vesuvius U S A Corporation ....D 903 597-7237
Tyler (G-20175)

Vesuvius U S A Corporation ....C 903 597-7237
Hillsboro (G-8332)

REFRACTORIES: Nonclay

Allied Mineral Products Inc ....G 956 831-2022
Brownsville (G-2336)

Asi Industrial Services LLC ....F 713 378-9200
Houston (G-8720)

Delta Refractories Inc ....F 281 944-9644
Katy (G-13394)

J T Thorpe Company ....C 713 644-1247
Houston (G-10444)

Southwest Refractory Texas LP ....E 979 285-7219
Alvin (G-380)

Wesco Refractories Inc ....F 682 518-5035
Mansfield (G-14729)

REFRACTORIES: Plastic

Ifs Industries Inc ....E 972 864-2202
Garland (G-7517)

REFRACTORY MATERIALS WHOLESALERS

Furnace Systems Inc ....F 972 423-7800
Plano (G-16875)

Meridian Brick LLC ....F 972 245-1542
Carrollton (G-2779)

REFRIGERATION & HEATING EQUIPMENT

1st Source Restaurant Svcs Inc ....F 214 551-5338
Lewisville (G-14019)

ACC-Kp LLC ....D 972 407-1234
Addison (G-98)

Afb Manufacturing LLC ....D 410 581-0300
Garland (G-7429)

Air Distribution Tech Inc ....E 972 943-6100
Plano (G-16779)

Apex Coil LLC ....E 903 843-4534
Gilmer (G-7705)

Atco Rubber Products Inc ....A 817 595-2894
Fort Worth (G-6406)

Atco Rubber Products Inc ....E 713 674-6665
Houston (G-8732)

Atlantic Food Bars Inc ....D 888 632-5765
Garland (G-7443)

Broad-Ocean Motor Houston LLC ....E 713 353-0100
Waller (G-20494)

C K Higgs ....E 713 666-5739
Bellaire (G-1992)

Canales Sheetmetal & Welding ....F 512 556-8613
Lampasas (G-13832)

Coldvault LLC ....G 903 657-2377
Henderson (G-8261)

Component Parts Machine Co Inc.........E 817 834-4771
Fort Worth (G-6534)

E I Du Pont De Nemours & Co ....E 361 776-1872
Ingleside (G-12895)

E Tamez Coml Rfrgn & AC Inc ....G 210 884-5059
San Antonio (G-18079)

Fujikoki America Inc ....C 214 333-4266
Dallas (G-4384)

Great American Coil LLC ....D 903 297-4700
White Oak (G-20714)

Hart Heat Transfer Pdts Inc.................D 713 675-9848
Houston (G-10133)

Henderson Controls Inc ....E 512 398-5700
Buda (G-2529)

Hoshizaki America Inc ....E 817 540-4665
Fort Worth (G-6704)

Hussmann Corporation ....D 972 956-9045
Coppell (G-3419)

Hvac Mechanical Svcs of Texas ....B 713 266-3900
Houston (G-10292)

John Bean Technologies Corp ....C 713 875-3735
Houston (G-10480)

Koch Filter Corporation ....E 502 634-4796
Houston (G-10551)

Kps Global LLC ....C 817 281-5121
Fort Worth (G-6770)

Lennox International Inc ....A 210 646-2399
San Antonio (G-18246)

Maddox Enterprises Inc ....E 903 592-6531
Tyler (G-20119)

Matthiesen Equipment Co ....F 210 333-1510
San Antonio (G-18284)

Morrison Products Inc ....D 972 279-4000
Mesquite (G-15063)

Nance International Inc ....D 409 838-6127
Beaumont (G-1932)

Neu Plumbing Inc ....D 940 580-2200
Pilot Point (G-16726)

Nichirin-Flex USA Inc ....B 915 859-1199
El Paso (G-5896)

S & M Aire LLC ....F 915 921-9677
El Paso (G-5951)

Sanden International USA Inc ....A 972 442-8400
Wylie (G-20948)

Selkirk Corporation ....B 972 943-6100
Richardson (G-17395)

Standex International Corp ....B 972 908-6100
Allen (G-300)

Tisdale AC & Htg Co ....F 936 856-1500
Conroe (G-3372)

Trane Company ....E 956 968-6425
Weslaco (G-20669)

Trane Company ....E 915 593-3484
El Paso (G-6012)

Trane US Inc ....F 239 277-7400
Carrollton (G-2836)

Trane US Inc ....E 903 581-3200
Tyler (G-20164)

Trane US Inc ....D 903 316-8033
Tyler (G-20165)

Trane US Inc ....D 972 892-3900
Dallas (G-5104)

Trane US Inc ....D 832 747-2000
Houston (G-12342)

Trane US Inc ....D 713 266-3900
Houston (G-12343)

Trane US Inc ....E 817 838-1310
Fort Worth (G-7071)

Trane US Inc ....D 210 657-0901
San Antonio (G-18559)

Trane US Inc ....B 469 758-3128
Carrollton (G-2837)

Trane US Inc ....E 915 593-3484
El Paso (G-6013)

Traulsen & Co Inc ....B 817 625-9671
Fort Worth (G-7072)

Tresu Royse Inc ....E 214 631-2844
Grapevine (G-8058)

Vintage Air Inc ....D 210 296-2302
San Antonio (G-18648)

Vogt Ice LLC ....E 940 387-4301
Lewisville (G-14109)

Welbilt Walk-Ins LP ....C 817 281-5121
Fort Worth (G-7134)

Welch Hvac Incorporated ....F 214 222-8600
Lewisville (G-14112)

REFRIGERATION EQPT & SPLYS WHOLESALERS

Combined Rfrgn Resources Inc ....E 281 540-7552
Humble (G-12761)

Kairak Inc ....C 800 825-8220
Fort Worth (G-6751)

Process Recovery Systems Inc............F 281 448-8180
Houston (G-11432)

Refrigation Gaskets Texas Inc ....F 713 880-8066
Houston (G-11582)

REFRIGERATION EQPT & SPLYS, WHOL: Refrig Units, Motor Veh

Stewart Stevenson Capitl Corp ....D 713 868-7700
Houston (G-12063)

REFRIGERATION EQPT & SPLYS, WHOLESALE: Beverage Dispensers

Marsmith Enterprises Inc ....F 972 488-9339
Dallas (G-4638)

REFRIGERATION EQPT & SPLYS, WHOLESALE: Commercial Eqpt

Advanced Fixtures Inc ....C 972 784-8800
Farmersville (G-6220)
Suncoast A/C & Rfrgn Inc ....F 956 428-1190
Harlingen (G-8204)

REFRIGERATION EQPT & SPLYS, WHOLESALE: Ice Cream Cabinets

CPI Importers Inc ....F 214 353-0328
Dallas (G-4179)

REFRIGERATION EQPT: Complete

Combined Rfrgn Resources Inc ....E 281 540-7552
Humble (G-12761)
Delta Tee International Inc ....E 817 466-9991
Arlington (G-659)
Enerflex Energy Systems Inc ....F 806 826-0126
Wheeler (G-20708)
Enerflex Energy Systems Inc ....B 281 345-9300
Houston (G-9631)
Enerflex Energy Systems Inc ....D 281 758-4900
Cypress (G-3787)
Enerflex Inc ....C 801 292-0493
Houston (G-9632)
Engineered Packaged Systems Inc ....E 409 866-5213
Beaumont (G-1887)
Folas Inc ....E 830 625-1613
New Braunfels (G-15793)
Gujarat Flrchmcals Amricas LLC ....F 512 446-7700
Irving (G-13046)
Kairak Inc ....E 800 825-8220
Fort Worth (G-6751)
Kold Pack Incorporated ....F 800 824-2661
Fort Worth (G-6769)
Kps Global LLC ....E 817 339-2100
Fort Worth (G-6771)
Marrone & Co Inc ....E 281 227-8400
Houston (G-10772)
Refrigeration Design Inc ....E 972 937-3240
Waxahachie (G-20556)
Refrigrtion Vssels Systems Cor ....D 979 778-0095
Bryan (G-2500)
Taylor Coml Foodservice Inc ....B 972 937-1820
Waxahachie (G-20564)
Turbine Air Systems Ltd ....C 713 877-8700
Houston (G-12408)

REFRIGERATION REPAIR SVCS

Enerflex Energy Systems Inc ....F 806 826-0126
Wheeler (G-20708)
Enerflex Energy Systems Inc ....B 281 345-9300
Houston (G-9631)
Enerflex Energy Systems Inc ....D 281 758-4900
Cypress (G-3787)
Refrigration Gaskets Texas Inc ....F 713 880-8066
Houston (G-11582)

REFRIGERATION SVC & REPAIR

Bates AC & Svc Co Inc ....E 713 869-5521
Houston (G-8824)
Brand Commercial Services Inc ....E 844 232-7263
Lewisville (G-14029)
Combined Rfrgn Resources Inc ....E 281 540-7552
Humble (G-12761)

REFRIGERATORS & FREEZERS WHOLESALERS

Kairak Inc ....C 800 825-8220
Fort Worth (G-6751)

REFUSE SYSTEMS

Atlas Iron & Scrap Metal Co ....E 972 225-4221
Dallas (G-3981)
Capital Returns Inc ....D 414 466-2418
Fort Worth (G-6493)
Commercial Metals Company ....C 214 565-0668
Dallas (G-4146)
Delta Paper Stock Corp ....E 713 666-1440
Bellaire (G-1993)
Master Fibers Inc ....D 915 544-2299
El Paso (G-5868)

REGISTERS: Air, Metal

Eljer Industries Inc ....E 972 560-2000
Dallas (G-4311)

REGULATION & ADMINISTRATION, GOVT: Transp Dept, Nonoperating

City of Marshall ....F 903 935-4500
Marshall (G-14771)

REGULATORS: Generator Voltage

Advanced Control Systems LLC ....E 832 529-2234
Houston (G-8487)

REGULATORS: Line Voltage

Intermatic Incorporated ....F 915 858-9204
El Paso (G-5813)

REGULATORS: Power

Maxi Volt Corporation Inc ....F 806 371-0722
Amarillo (G-500)
Vertiv Corporation ....B 956 683-2948
McAllen (G-14917)

RELAYS & SWITCHES: Indl, Electric

Ohmite Holding LLC ....F 956 542-0276
Brownsville (G-2388)
Vector Systems Inc ....D 214 544-9500
McKinney (G-14985)

RELAYS: Control Circuit, Ind

Thompson Scale Company ....F 713 932-9071
Houston (G-12279)

RELAYS: Electric Power

Ameripower LLC ....F 281 240-0405
Sugar Land (G-19442)

RELAYS: Electronic Usage

Littelfuse Inc ....D 830 513-8775
Eagle Pass (G-5549)

REMOTE DATABASE INFORMATION RETRIEVAL SVCS

Movement Industries Corp ....F 713 849-1300
Houston (G-10928)

RENDERING PLANT

HTC Industries Inc ....E 325 949-0645
San Angelo (G-17808)
Nutri-Feeds Inc ....E 806 357-2288
Hereford (G-8294)
Texas By-Products Partnership ....E 214 871-0600
Dallas (G-5055)
Valley Proteins Inc ....D 432 334-0449
Odessa (G-16193)
Valley Proteins (de) Inc ....E 806 379-6001
Amarillo (G-519)

RENT-A-CAR SVCS

Wmk LLC ....F 817 429-1273
Haltom City (G-8162)

RENTAL CENTERS: Furniture

Akcorp Inc ....F 409 833-8002
Beaumont (G-1848)
Apartment Furnishings Co Inc ....E 817 568-2002
Fort Worth (G-6390)

RENTAL CENTERS: General

Air Power Sales & Service LLC ....E 903 236-0500
Longview (G-14190)

RENTAL CENTERS: Party & Banquet Eqpt & Splys

Arne Distributors Inc ....F 713 869-8321
Houston (G-8700)
Brookhollow Rental Co Inc ....F 214 631-6883
Dallas (G-4059)
Party Props Inc ....E 713 868-5433
Houston (G-11253)

RENTAL CENTERS: Tools

Basic Energy Services LP ....E 903 643-1140
Fort Worth (G-6434)
Lewis Casing Crews Inc ....F 432 366-8077
Odessa (G-16061)
Woolley Fishing Tool Inc ....E 903 984-3553
Kilgore (G-13603)
Woolley Tool Inc ....F 903 984-3553
Kilgore (G-13604)

RENTAL SVCS: Aircraft

W T Porter Corp ....G 713 946-4174
South Houston (G-19056)

RENTAL SVCS: Aircraft & Indl Truck

Jaffe Group Ltd ....E 830 598-2413
Horseshoe Bay (G-8368)

RENTAL SVCS: Audio-Visual Eqpt & Sply

Conference Technologies Inc ....C 512 584-8275
Austin (G-1061)

RENTAL SVCS: Business Machine & Electronic Eqpt

Permian Basin Instruments Inc ....E 432 687-4445
Denton (G-5392)
Pitney Bowes Inc ....E 512 823-0833
Austin (G-1418)

RENTAL SVCS: Clothing

Gormans Uniform Rental Inc ....D 713 467-5424
Houston (G-10006)
Terry Costa Inc ....E 972 385-6100
Dallas (G-5050)

RENTAL SVCS: Costume

Cowan Costumes Inc ....F 817 641-3126
Cleburne (G-3085)
Julie Keck ....F 210 435-3535
San Antonio (G-18212)
M Patel Enterprises Inc ....E 512 892-2721
Sunset Valley (G-19626)
Radtke Jenna ....E 512 444-2002
Austin (G-1450)

RENTAL SVCS: Musical Instrument

Lisle Violin Shop ....F 281 487-7303
Pasadena (G-16474)

RENTAL SVCS: Oil Eqpt

C Hinton Enterprises Inc ....E 432 339-0411
Odessa (G-15950)
Expro Americas LLC ....E 713 463-9776
Houston (G-9734)
Exterran Energy Solutions LP ....C 281 836-7000
Houston (G-9736)
Gravity Oilfield Services LLC ....C 432 218-7889
Midland (G-15240)
Interstate Treating Inc ....D 432 362-9291
Odessa (G-16034)
Key Energy Services Inc ....D 979 778-1800
Bryan (G-2484)
Nabors Well Services Ltd ....E 281 874-0035
Houston (G-10958)
Online Construction LP ....F 361 445-6161
George West (G-7627)
Parker Drilling Company ....C 281 406-2000
Houston (G-11241)
Parman Capital Group LLC ....A 713 751-2700
Houston (G-11247)
Reserve Compression Corp ....E 713 783-8851
Houston (G-11605)
Reserve Equipment Inc ....E 713 939-8988
Houston (G-11606)
Stewart & Stevenson LLC ....D 713 751-2700
Houston (G-12062)
Stewart Stevenson Pwr Pdts LLC ....C 713 751-2600
Houston (G-12065)

RENTAL SVCS: Propane Eqpt

Csi Compressco Sub Inc ....A 432 563-1170
Midland (G-15185)
Sandifers LP Gas & Svc Co Inc ....F 409 963-1269
Port Arthur (G-17124)

PRODUCT

RENTAL SVCS: Recreational Vehicle

Kwest Rv LLC ....F 512 294-2634
Austin *(G-1276)*

RENTAL SVCS: Sign

Industrial Neon Sign Corp ....F 713 748-6600
Houston *(G-10352)*
Quality Signs Inc ....E 713 671-9222
Houston *(G-11500)*
Short-Line Corporation ....F 210 492-6088
San Antonio *(G-18470)*
Technographix LLC ....C 817 336-5671
Fort Worth *(G-7041)*

RENTAL SVCS: Stores & Yards Eqpt

Associated Supply Company Inc ....E 512 272-8922
Manor *(G-14643)*

RENTAL SVCS: Tent & Tarpaulin

Aquila & Priscilla Tentmakers ....F 254 848-4432
Waco *(G-20363)*
Festive Tents LP ....F 713 468-3687
Houston *(G-9780)*
Mike Sandone Productions Inc ....E 800 652-5635
Dallas *(G-4677)*
Tent Company LLC ....F 832 623-8958
Houston *(G-12204)*
Tents of Southwest Inc ....E 713 692-8565
Houston *(G-12205)*

RENTAL SVCS: Work Zone Traffic Eqpt, Flags, Cones, Etc

Buyers Barricades Inc ....E 817 535-3939
Grapevine *(G-8016)*
Dallas Lite and Barricade Inc ....E 214 748-5791
Dallas *(G-4218)*

RENTAL: Trucks, With Drivers

City Sign Services Inc ....E 214 826-4475
Dallas *(G-4124)*

REPAIR TRAINING, COMPUTER

Csi Techs Inc ....D 210 875-7978
San Antonio *(G-18033)*

REPRODUCTION SVCS: Video Tape Or Disk

Creative Sound Productions ....F 713 777-9975
Houston *(G-9340)*

RESEARCH & DEVELOPMENT SVCS, COMMERCIAL: Engineering Lab

Ghg Corp ....B 281 461-6533
Webster *(G-20638)*

RESEARCH, DEV & TESTING SVCS, COMM: Chem Lab, Exc Testing

Kel-Tech Inc ....E 432 684-4700
Midland *(G-15266)*

RESEARCH, DEVELOPMENT & TEST SVCS, COMM: Cmptr Hardware Dev

Centaur Technology Inc ....D 512 418-5700
Austin *(G-1037)*
Crescent Systems Inc ....E 972 437-0400
Richardson *(G-17294)*

RESEARCH, DEVELOPMENT & TEST SVCS, COMM: Research, Exc Lab

Cameron Solutions Inc ....E 713 896-3600
Houston *(G-9077)*
Promicom Inc ....G 832 544-0855
The Woodlands *(G-19906)*

RESEARCH, DEVELOPMENT & TESTING SVCS, COMM: Agricultural

Aloterra Energy LLC ....F 713 412-5311
The Woodlands *(G-19823)*
Atomic Container Homes Inc ....E 915 433-4817
El Paso *(G-5653)*

RESEARCH, DEVELOPMENT & TESTING SVCS, COMM: Bus Economic Sve

L3 Technologies Inc ....A 903 457-4100
Greenville *(G-8080)*

RESEARCH, DEVELOPMENT & TESTING SVCS, COMM: Natural Resource

Sancus Energy and Power LLC ....E 832 460-1000
Houston *(G-11744)*

RESEARCH, DEVELOPMENT & TESTING SVCS, COMM: Research Lab

Robogistics LLC ....E 713 364-4430
Port Arthur *(G-17123)*

RESEARCH, DEVELOPMENT & TESTING SVCS, COMMERCIAL: Business

Genmz LP ....F 214 683-6635
Dallas *(G-4401)*

RESEARCH, DEVELOPMENT & TESTING SVCS, COMMERCIAL: Education

Specialty Research Associates ....E 817 441-6044
Aledo *(G-202)*

RESEARCH, DEVELOPMENT & TESTING SVCS, COMMERCIAL: Energy

Clean Energy Tech Assn Inc ....E 903 389-4136
Fairfield *(G-6171)*
Excelergy Corp ....F 214 953-9373
Dallas *(G-4340)*
Hereford Biofuels LP ....D 972 980-7159
Dallas *(G-4452)*
Roywell LLC ....F 713 661-4747
Sugar Land *(G-19538)*

RESEARCH, DEVELOPMENT & TESTING SVCS, COMMERCIAL: Food

Biotics Research Corporation ....D 281 344-0909
Rosenberg *(G-17577)*

RESEARCH, DEVELOPMENT & TESTING SVCS, COMMERCIAL: Medical

Bionumerik Pharmaceuticals Inc ....D 210 614-1701
San Antonio *(G-17954)*

RESEARCH, DEVELOPMENT & TESTING SVCS, COMMERCIAL: Physical

Currid & Company ....F 713 893-8401
Houston *(G-9360)*
Miracon Technologies LLC ....F 972 387-3099
Richardson *(G-17358)*
Science Applications Intl Corp ....F 469 557-8249
Carrollton *(G-2815)*
Univation Technologies LLC ....C 713 892-3650
Houston *(G-12460)*

RESEARCH, DVLPT & TEST SVCS, COMM: Mkt Analysis or Research

Candeo Interactive LLC ....F 214 394-8499
Forney *(G-6303)*
Industrial Info Resources Inc ....D 713 783-5147
Sugar Land *(G-19498)*

RESIDENTIAL REMODELERS

Glenwood Blind & Awning Co Inc ....G 903 597-2088
Tyler *(G-20090)*

RESINS: Custom Compound Purchased

Adaptive 3d Technologies LLC ....E 469 573-0024
Plano *(G-16770)*
Chemtrusion Inc ....D 713 675-1616
Houston *(G-9173)*
E R Carpenter LP ....C 281 474-7257
Pasadena *(G-16422)*
Hexpol Compounding LLC ....E 817 483-9797
Kennedale *(G-13498)*
Marble Masters of Texas Inc ....E 830 303-7744
New Braunfels *(G-15811)*

Miller Waste Mills Inc ....D 817 293-6163
Fort Worth *(G-6842)*
Orrex Plastics Company LLC ....E 432 332-1229
Odessa *(G-16104)*
Polyone Corporation ....C 281 474-2831
Seabrook *(G-18789)*
Purchasing Dept ....E 956 318-2626
Edinburg *(G-5598)*
Ticona Polymers Inc ....C 972 443-4000
Dallas *(G-5091)*

RESISTORS

AB Interconnect Inc ....C 919 934-5181
Corpus Christi *(G-3463)*
Interntonal Resistive Texas LP ....C 361 992-7900
Corpus Christi *(G-3555)*
Questech Services Corporation ....E 972 278-8006
Garland *(G-7575)*
Venkel Ltd ....E 512 794-0081
Austin *(G-1629)*

RESPIRATORS

Joshuas Respiratory Care Inc ....F 469 916-9354
Dallas *(G-4539)*

RESTAURANT EQPT REPAIR SVCS

Bakery Equipment & Svc Co Inc ....E 210 734-5124
San Antonio *(G-17937)*

RESTAURANT EQPT: Carts

Chef Units LLC ....F 713 589-2613
Houston *(G-9169)*
Complete Restaurant Svcs Inc ....E 214 350-1110
Dallas *(G-4150)*
Tqi LLC ....E 830 401-4400
Seguin *(G-18869)*

RESTAURANT EQPT: Food Wagons

72nd & Thornhill LLC ....F 469 318-5087
Wylie *(G-20923)*
BBA&j&v Inc ....F 469 998-0660
Frisco *(G-7256)*
Carter Lee Properties LLC ....F 713 385-8092
Richmond *(G-17452)*
La Paleteria ....D 214 887-8278
Dallas *(G-4576)*

RESTAURANT EQPT: Sheet Metal

Stainless Steel Concepts LLC ....F 214 630-4430
Dallas *(G-5001)*

RESTAURANT RESERVATION SVCS

Big Buck Brewery & Steakhouse ....D 972 691-5100
Grapevine *(G-8014)*

RESTAURANTS: Fast Food

Trinitys Covenant LLC ....F 210 620-3694
Laredo *(G-13939)*

RESTAURANTS: Full Svc, American

Bric Mc Mann Industries Inc ....F 830 775-9153
Del Rio *(G-5309)*
Prause Market LLC ....F 979 968-3259
La Grange *(G-13700)*
Western Bowl ....E 806 359-5211
Amarillo *(G-521)*

RESTAURANTS: Full Svc, Barbecue

Squares Distributing Inc ....F 325 692-4797
Abilene *(G-82)*

RESTAURANTS: Full Svc, Cajun

Singleton ML Inc ....F 409 755-0893
Lumberton *(G-14570)*

RESTAURANTS: Full Svc, Diner

Spiral Diners ....F 817 332-8834
Fort Worth *(G-7012)*

RESTAURANTS: Full Svc, Family

University Houston - System ....C 713 741-2447
Houston *(G-12467)*

RESTAURANTS: Full Svc, Family, Independent

Carter Lee Properties LLC ....F 713 385-8092
Richmond (G-17452)
Fredericksburg Brewing Company ......D 830 997-1646
Fredericksburg (G-7178)

RESTAURANTS: Full Svc, Mexican

G Tacos Inc ....D 806 371-0411
Amarillo (G-427)
Ixpalia Inc ....E 512 389-0389
Austin (G-1245)
La Paloma Tortilla Factory ....E 956 316-1515
Edinburg (G-5592)
La Tapatia Inc ....E 915 859-9616
El Paso (G-5835)
Louis Barriga ....E 817 923-7370
Fort Worth (G-6801)

RESTAURANTS: Full Svc, Seafood

Jbs Packing Company Inc ....E 409 982-5766
Port Arthur (G-17114)

RESTAURANTS: Full Svc, Steak & Barbecue

Allan Banks ....F 936 337-4020
Willis (G-20841)

RESTAURANTS: Limited Svc, Carry-Out Only, Exc Pizza

La Nortena Inc ....G 432 445-3273
Pecos (G-16821)

RESTAURANTS: Limited Svc, Coffee Shop

Daily Offrngs Cof Roastery LLC ....F 805 423-7410
Wolfforth (G-20907)
Farmer Bros Co ....F 713 864-1487
Houston (G-9763)
Royal Cup Inc ....F 817 261-7527
Arlington (G-775)
Russells Bakery and Coffee Bar ....F 512 419-7877
Austin (G-1477)
Wicked Voodoo Espresso LLC ....E 360 631-1447
New Braunfels (G-15832)

RESTAURANTS: Limited Svc, Fast-Food, Chain

Frito-Lay North America Inc ....A 972 334-7000
Plano (G-16874)
Old Frito-Lay Inc ....A 972 334-7000
Plano (G-16953)

RESTAURANTS: Limited Svc, Fast-Food, Independent

WHW Properties Inc ....E 903 572-4161
Mount Pleasant (G-15665)

RESTAURANTS: Limited Svc, Grill

Emerald Pt Marina Partners Ltd ....C 512 266-1535
Austin (G-1123)

RESTAURANTS: Limited Svc, Health Food

Juiceus LLC ....E 956 667-0153
Brownsville (G-2372)

RESTAURANTS: Limited Svc, Ice Cream Stands Or Dairy Bars

Ashley Donuts & Ice Cream Inc ....F 281 486-5644
Houston (G-8719)
Dairy Queen ....F 281 481-8505
Houston (G-9396)
Freddys Frz Cstard Stakburgers ....E 210 521-5400
San Antonio (G-18126)

RESTAURANTS: Limited Svc, Sandwiches & Submarines Shop

Food Group Ventures LLC ....G 936 327-4443
Livingston (G-14153)
Onyx Venture Group LLC ....F 281 395-4791
Katy (G-13375)

Potbelly Corporation ....E 281 277-2515
Sugar Land (G-19527)

RESTAURANTS: Ltd Svc, Ice Cream, Soft Drink/Fountain Stands

Smoothie King ....G 214 469-1552
The Colony (G-19814)

RETAIL BAKERY: Bagels

Dmv Wicks Inc ....F 713 520-0340
Houston (G-9488)
New York Bagles Inc ....E 713 723-5879
Houston (G-11038)

RETAIL BAKERY: Bread

Swiss Pastry Shop ....F 817 732-5661
Fort Worth (G-7025)
Three Brothers Bakery Inc ....F 713 666-2253
Houston (G-12283)

RETAIL BAKERY: Cakes

Bluebonnet Bakery Inc ....F 817 731-4233
Fort Worth (G-6458)

RETAIL BAKERY: Cookies

Empire Baking Company L P ....E 972 851-5677
Dallas (G-4320)

RETAIL BAKERY: Doughnuts

Ashley Donuts & Ice Cream Inc ....F 281 486-5644
Houston (G-8719)
Merrills Southern Maid ....G 409 755-2400
Lumberton (G-14568)
RC Donuts ....G 972 422-3379
Plano (G-16989)
Rock Island Donut Shop ....F 972 254-5069
Irving (G-13166)
Shipley Do-Nut Flour Sup Inc ....G 281 575-1766
Houston (G-11871)
Shipley Do-Nut Flour Sup Inc ....G 713 728-9366
Houston (G-11872)
Shipley Do-Nut Flour Sup Inc ....F 713 729-2381
Houston (G-11873)
Simply Donuts ....F 281 955-6374
Houston (G-11904)

RETAIL FIREPLACE STORES

Acme Brick Company ....D 325 949-7685
San Angelo (G-17770)
Golden Blount Inc ....F 972 250-3113
Addison (G-131)

RETAIL LUMBER YARDS

BMC West LLC ....D 325 698-4465
Abilene (G-18)
Builders Firstsource Inc ....E 956 755-0301
Mercedes (G-15004)
McKee True Value Hdwr & Lbr ....E 903 874-6581
Corsicana (G-3677)
South Texas Moulding Inc ....F 956 831-0340
Brownsville (G-2406)
Zarsky Lumber Company Inc ....E 361 882-2575
Corpus Christi (G-3658)

RETAIL STORES: Air Purification Eqpt

Braided Green Brokerage LLC ....F 480 729-5506
Murphy (G-15683)

RETAIL STORES: Alcoholic Beverage Making Eqpt & Splys

Top Quality Spindles LLC ....F 972 937-2126
Waxahachie (G-20566)

RETAIL STORES: Architectural Splys

Charles Barton ....E 512 759-1231
Hutto (G-12877)
Complete Reprographics Inc ....F 915 779-5000
El Paso (G-5702)
G4 Spatial Technologies LLC ....E 512 447-9879
Austin (G-1176)

RETAIL STORES: Artificial Limbs

Hanger Inc ....E 817 923-2101
Fort Worth (G-6687)
Muilenburg Prosthetics Inc ....F 713 524-3949
Houston (G-10935)
Prescotts Limbs & Braces ....E 210 224-0726
San Antonio (G-18393)

RETAIL STORES: Awnings

Associated Canvas Pdts I Ltd ....F 281 457-1480
Channelview (G-3012)
Awntech Corporation ....E 817 354-9600
Euless (G-6132)
Heat Shield Inc ....F 903 845-4066
Gladewater (G-7722)
Jones Aluminum ....F 409 866-5585
Beaumont (G-1913)
Mike Sandone Productions Inc ....E 800 652-5635
Dallas (G-4677)

RETAIL STORES: Banners

M Patel Enterprises Inc ....E 512 892-2721
Sunset Valley (G-19626)
Mr Sign Inc ....G 214 526-7446
Dallas (G-4699)
Multi-Quest Inc ....F 972 235-2356
Richardson (G-17361)
Transfer Graphics Inc ....F 940 566-2679
Denton (G-5407)

RETAIL STORES: Batteries, Non-Automotive

OReilly Automotive Stores Inc ....F 936 856-2409
Willis (G-20857)
Panasonic Corp North America ....D 956 984-3700
Frisco (G-7305)

RETAIL STORES: Business Machines & Eqpt

Dahill Office Technology Corp ....E 713 329-9909
Houston (G-9392)
Dahill Office Technology Corp ....C 210 805-8200
San Antonio (G-18041)
Rehrig Pacific Company ....D 214 631-7943
Dallas (G-4885)

RETAIL STORES: Canvas Prdts

Canvas USA Inc ....F 361 729-0638
Rockport (G-17528)

RETAIL STORES: Children's Furniture, NEC

Reynolds Mfg Corp Inc ....E 325 698-7300
Abilene (G-71)

RETAIL STORES: Christmas Lights & Decorations

Daryan Design Inc ....F 214 905-6022
Dallas (G-4239)

RETAIL STORES: Cleaning Eqpt & Splys

Anko Products Company of Texas ....F 972 227-4466
Lancaster (G-13837)
Ecoclean Supply & Services LLC ....F 800 245-9896
Southlake (G-19065)
Iowa Techniques Inc ....F 512 846-2403
Hutto (G-12880)
Jimmy Smart ....F 432 381-5450
Odessa (G-16039)
My Sons Laundry LLC ....F 214 634-2080
Dallas (G-4710)

RETAIL STORES: Coins

Houston Numismatic Exchange ....F 713 528-2135
Houston (G-10241)

RETAIL STORES: Communication Eqpt

D C A E Inc ....E 972 278-0202
Garland (G-7472)

RETAIL STORES: Concrete Prdts, Precast

Mainland Concrete Inc ....E 281 337-7400
Texas City (G-19797)

PRODUCT

RETAIL STORES: Decals

Dac Labels & Graphic Spc.................F.......214 340-2055
Dallas (G-4205)
Dallas Decal Inc.................F.......972 772-4641
Rockwall (G-17546)
Jdh Iron Designs LLC.................F.......254 486-9150
Valley Mills (G-20201)

RETAIL STORES: Drafting Eqpt & Splys

Triangle Reproductions Inc.................E.......713 780-0236
Houston (G-12365)
Triangle Reproductions of San.................E.......713 780-0236
San Antonio (G-18566)

RETAIL STORES: Electronic Parts & Eqpt

AC Electronics.................F.......817 701-1400
Arlington (G-606)
Lynn Electric Motor Co Inc.................F.......940 657-3511
Knox City (G-13664)
Supercircuits Inc.................D.......877 995-2288
Austin (G-1548)
Xi Technology LLC.................F.......972 369-1359
Wylie (G-20956)

RETAIL STORES: Engine & Motor Eqpt & Splys

HMC Capital Inc.................G.......936 441-2666
The Woodlands (G-19872)
Hydraulic Systems Inc.................E.......832 791-5000
The Woodlands (G-19881)
Smith Pump Company Inc.................G.......817 589-2060
Fort Worth (G-6996)
Standard Industrial Pdts Co.................E.......281 280-0147
Webster (G-20647)
Stewart Stevenson Pwr Pdts LLC.........F.......903 838-9966
Texarkana (G-19776)
Valley Outdoor Power Eqp Inc.................F.......956 787-0469
Pharr (G-16715)

RETAIL STORES: Engines & Parts, Air-Cooled

Man Energy Solutions USA Inc.................F.......713 780-4200
Brookshire (G-2319)

RETAIL STORES: Farm Eqpt & Splys

Forestry Supply Service Inc.................F.......936 632-3394
Lufkin (G-14528)
Forestry Supply Service Inc.................F.......409 384-3213
Jasper (G-13276)
Heritage Equipment Company Inc.........D.......806 745-4451
Wolfforth (G-20908)
Pilot Plastics LLC.................G.......800 918-6765
Fort Worth (G-6907)

RETAIL STORES: Farm Machinery, NEC

Bray International Inc.................F.......281 517-5400
Houston (G-8978)
Southern Nut N Tree Equipment.................E.......325 938-5460
Goldthwaite (G-7745)

RETAIL STORES: Fiberglass Materials, Exc Insulation

F & F Composite Group Inc.................E.......817 379-4411
Fort Worth (G-6622)
Molded Fiber Glass Companies.................D.......940 668-0302
Gainesville (G-7349)
Reed Fiberglass Inc.................F.......432 332-8265
Odessa (G-16135)

RETAIL STORES: Fire Extinguishers

Classic Protection Systems.................E.......713 468-3573
Houston (G-9212)
Hasse Enterprises Inc.................F.......512 835-7697
Austin (G-1199)
Texas Flameproofing Inc.................F.......214 630-1088
Dallas (G-5061)

RETAIL STORES: Flags

A B C Flag Acquisition Corp.................E.......817 335-2548
Fort Worth (G-6336)
Dixie Flag and Banner Company.........E.......210 227-5039
San Antonio (G-18063)

Marvin Dace Company.................F.......281 482-1450
Alvin (G-373)

RETAIL STORES: Foam & Foam Prdts

Kirkland Sales Inc.................E.......972 864-1424
Garland (G-7533)

RETAIL STORES: Gems & Precious Stones

Natural Energy Resources Inc.................D.......832 631-5013
Katy (G-13426)

RETAIL STORES: Hair Care Prdts

Eoh Industries Inc.................D.......817 468-3181
Arlington (G-671)
Sunetics Intl Mktg Group LLC.................F.......888 266-2232
Plano (G-17014)

RETAIL STORES: Hearing Aids

Audex Inc.................F.......903 757-4083
Hallsville (G-8126)

RETAIL STORES: Ice

Debes Ice Company.................F.......409 835-4431
Beaumont (G-1881)
Reddy Ice Corporation.................E.......915 532-2495
El Paso (G-5933)
Reddy Ice Corporation.................E.......956 428-6666
Harlingen (G-8199)
Reddy Ice Corporation.................E.......940 686-5259
Pilot Point (G-16727)
Reddy Ice Corporation.................E.......972 296-4271
Dallas (G-4872)

RETAIL STORES: Insecticides

Control Solutions Inc.................E.......281 892-2500
Pasadena (G-16413)
E Barr Feeds Inc.................E.......830 672-6515
Gonzales (G-7752)

RETAIL STORES: Maps & Charts

Key Maps Incorporated.................E.......713 522-7949
Houston (G-10524)
Seawall Specialty Company Inc.........F.......713 522-9064
Houston (G-11808)

RETAIL STORES: Medical Apparatus & Splys

Alafair Biosciences Inc.................F.......512 739-9510
Austin (G-903)
Wmk LLC.................F.......817 429-1273
Haltom City (G-8162)

RETAIL STORES: Mobile Telephones & Eqpt

Cellteks Inc.................F.......830 249-8999
Boerne (G-2116)
Corona Labs Inc.................F.......312 953-7586
Austin (G-1067)

RETAIL STORES: Monuments, Finished To Custom Order

Gifford Monument Works Inc.................F.......972 544-6305
Wylie (G-20936)
Wallace Monument Company.................F.......806 874-2442
Clarendon (G-3071)

RETAIL STORES: Motors, Electric

Acg Quality Electric Inc.................F.......713 225-6531
Houston (G-8468)
Community Motors Inc.................F.......281 354-8087
New Caney (G-15837)
Phase Electric Motors Inc.................F.......972 291-9221
Cedar Hill (G-2950)

RETAIL STORES: Orthopedic & Prosthesis Applications

Advanced Orthotics Prosthetics.........F.......956 971-8200
Edinburg (G-5573)
Allsport Dynamics Inc.................F.......936 569-1003
Nacogdoches (G-15684)
New Options Inc.................D.......214 638-6422
Farmers Branch (G-6208)

RETAIL STORES: Pet Food

Mid-America Pet Food LLC.................E.......903 572-5900
Mount Pleasant (G-15655)

RETAIL STORES: Pet Splys

Brec Inc.................F.......979 823-4466
Bryan (G-2460)
Petmate Holdings Co.................A.......817 467-5116
Arlington (G-753)

RETAIL STORES: Picture Frames, Ready Made

Brazos Oaks Ltd.................E.......254 399-0505
Waco (G-20370)
Wordyisms Inc.................F.......512 835-6695
Pflugerville (G-16693)

RETAIL STORES: Pipe Store, Tobacco

Seabreeze Culvert.................F.......409 296-4675
Winnie (G-20891)

RETAIL STORES: Plumbing & Heating Splys

Morsco Supply LLC.................F.......903 234-2183
Longview (G-14282)

RETAIL STORES: Safety Splys & Eqpt

American Safety Services Inc.................C.......432 552-7625
Odessa (G-15914)
M-Master LLC.................F.......915 242-2315
El Paso (G-5855)
Regal Plastic Supply Co Inc.................F.......512 836-3629
Austin (G-1457)

RETAIL STORES: Spas & Hot Tubs

Morgan Buildings & Spas Inc.................F.......972 864-7300
Richardson (G-17360)
Ptp Incorporated.................F.......281 342-8775
Rosenberg (G-17595)

RETAIL STORES: Swimming Pools, Above Ground

Ghm Corp.................C.......972 840-1200
Dallas (G-4406)

RETAIL STORES: Technical Aids For The Handicapped

Knickerbocker Partition Corp.................F.......972 438-5330
Irving (G-13078)

RETAIL STORES: Telephone & Communication Eqpt

Golden Crescent Communications.........F.......361 578-4091
Victoria (G-20269)
Krown Manufacturing Inc.................F.......817 738-2485
Fort Worth (G-6774)
Nokia Slutions Networks US LLC.........B.......972 374-3000
Coppell (G-3432)

RETAIL STORES: Telephone Eqpt & Systems

Awesome Paging Inc.................G.......361 576-2255
Victoria (G-20240)
Nec Corporation of America.................E.......214 262-2387
Dallas (G-4719)

RETAIL STORES: Tents

Ohenry Productions Inc.................F.......254 714-1103
Waco (G-20440)
Tents of Southwest Inc.................E.......713 692-8565
Houston (G-12205)

RETAIL STORES: Vaults & Safes

Defiant Safe Co Inc.................E.......972 243-3711
Dallas (G-4248)
Lock Dock Inc.................F.......903 759-1288
Longview (G-14265)

RETAIL STORES: Water Purification Eqpt

Culligan Southeast Texas Water.................E.......409 838-6261
Beaumont (G-1879)

Flo Pura Corp ....E 281 320-9547
Spring (G-19122)

RETAIL STORES: Welding Splys

Airgas Usa LLC ....F 512 835-0202
Austin (G-902)

Alamo Welding & Boiler Work ....F 210 227-6502
San Antonio (G-17888)

Cactus Varied Industries LLC ....B 806 335-9470
Amarillo (G-411)

Tims South Texas LLC ....F 830 278-3368
Uvalde (G-20197)

Tims South Texas LLC ....F 830 468-3860
Asherton (G-814)

RETAINERS OR HOUSINGS: Rotor

Man Energy Solutions USA Inc ....F 713 780-4200
Brookshire (G-2319)

REUPHOLSTERY & FURNITURE REPAIR

Childress Furniture & Fabr Inc ....D 214 565-0900
Addison (G-109)

Delatorre Inc ....F 713 522-5833
Houston (G-9426)

REWINDING SVCS

All American Pump & Mch Inc ....F 325 653-6597
San Angelo (G-17773)

B J Electric Motor Service ....F 432 570-4100
Midland (G-15127)

Daily Electric Inc ....G 903 753-2732
Longview (G-14220)

Land Enterprises Inc ....F 713 924-5929
Houston (G-10592)

RIBBONS, NEC

Cheryl L McDaniel ....F 281 814-0533
New Waverly (G-15857)

RIBBONS: Machine, Inked Or Carbon

Fine Line Ribbon Inc ....E 972 875-8681
Ennis (G-6102)

RINGS: Angle

Lewis & Lambert LLLP ....C 817 834-7146
Haltom City (G-8150)

RIVETS: Metal

Landreth Fastner Corporation ....F 281 414-3103
Houston (G-10594)

ROAD MATERIALS: Bituminous, Not From Refineries

Gulf States Materials Inc ....E 281 470-8645
La Porte (G-13742)

ROBOTS, SERVICES OR NOVELTY, WHOLESALE

Tendenci Inc ....E 281 497-6567
Houston (G-12203)

ROBOTS: Assembly Line

ARC Specialties Inc ....E 713 631-7575
Houston (G-8680)

Robogistics LLC ....F 409 234-1033
Houston (G-11646)

Romeo Engineering Incorporated ......E 817 656-0048
Fort Worth (G-6966)

ROBOTS: Indl Spraying, Painting, Etc

Ares Robotics LLC ....E 713 320-4690
Houston (G-8688)

ROCK SALT MINING

United Salt Baytown LLC ....E 281 303-1101
Baytown (G-1804)

ROCKETS: Space & Military

Firefly Aerospace Inc ....C 512 277-6959
Cedar Park (G-2970)

National Aeronautics ....E 915 782-5250
El Paso (G-5893)

Space Exploration Tech Corp ....C 310 363-6000
Mc Gregor (G-14823)

Space Exploration Tech Corp ....A 310 363-6000
Houston (G-11990)

United Launch Alliance LLC ....D 956 425-4447
Harlingen (G-8208)

ROD & BAR: Aluminum

Lonestar Aluminum Spc LLC ....G 281 617-7177
Houston (G-10682)

RODS: Plastic

Borger Oil Chemical Indus Plas ....F 806 273-9518
Borger (G-2165)

RODS: Rolled, Aluminum

Mark House of Hot Rods Inc ....E 817 466-9942
Mansfield (G-14687)

Total Rod Concepts Inc ....F 432 689-0300
Midland (G-15441)

RODS: Steel & Iron, Made In Steel Mills

Deacero Usa Inc ....C 713 697-1500
Houston (G-9418)

GTC Technology LLC ....E 817 685-9125
Irving (G-13045)

Tenaris Rods (usa) Inc ....E 713 767-4400
Houston (G-12201)

RODS: Welding

Southern Stud Weld Inc ....F 972 790-3339
Irving (G-13185)

ROLL COVERINGS: Rubber

Valley Roller Company Inc ....F 817 453-8950
Mansfield (G-14726)

ROLL FORMED SHAPES: Custom

Priefert Mfg Co Inc ....A 903 572-1741
Mount Pleasant (G-15660)

ROLLING MILL EQPT: Galvanizing Lines

Aztec Mnfcturing-Waskom Partnr ......E 903 687-3943
Waskom (G-20514)

Azz Inc ....E 817 297-4361
Crowley (G-3751)

K-T Galvanizing Co Inc ....E 817 477-4434
Venus (G-20220)

ROLLING MILL EQPT: Plate

Bise Welding & Fabricating Inc ....D 713 681-0958
Houston (G-8892)

ROLLING MILL EQPT: Rod Mills

Andrews Pump & Supply Inc ....E 432 523-2166
Andrews (G-534)

ROLLING MILL MACHINERY

Coperion Corporation ....F 281 449-9944
Houston (G-9309)

J & J Manufacturing Company ....D 409 835-1330
Beaumont (G-1912)

R D Moxie Llc ....G 210 633-2300
San Antonio (G-18407)

ROLLING MILL ROLLS: Cast Steel

Ahmsa International Inc ....E 210 341-3777
San Antonio (G-17875)

ROLLS & ROLL COVERINGS: Rubber

All-State Belting LLC ....F 713 433-1272
Houston (G-8371)

Roy Johnson Incorporated ....E 817 468-2939
Arlington (G-773)

ROOF DECKS

Atlas Building Systems Inc ....F 903 597-4211
Tyler (G-20052)

Binco Contracting Services ....F 281 356-3144
Magnolia (G-14591)

March Resources Co ....E 281 931-3986
Houston (G-10763)

Metal Sales Manufacturing Corp ....E 254 791-6650
Temple (G-19689)

Nucor Corporation ....G 281 251-8857
Spring (G-19156)

Omnimax International Inc ....E 817 481-3521
Fort Worth (G-6882)

Texas Roof Management Inc ....C 972 272-7663
Richardson (G-17409)

Tip Top Sheet Metal Inc ....E 281 931-7823
Houston (G-12294)

ROOFING MATERIALS: Asphalt

Elk Corporation of Texas ....C 972 875-9611
Ennis (G-6095)

Elk Corporation of Texas ....D 972 851-0500
Dallas (G-4312)

Elkcorp ....E 972 851-0500
Dallas (G-4313)

Market Makers Inc ....E 281 893-9261
Houston (G-10769)

Owens Corning Sales LLC ....D 713 672-8338
Houston (G-11208)

ROOFING MATERIALS: Sheet Metal

ABG Contracting Group LLC ....E 281 431-7223
Pearland (G-16536)

AES Industries Inc ....E 817 341-7250
Weatherford (G-20574)

Berridge Manufacturing Company ......E 830 401-5200
Seguin (G-18826)

Berridge Manufacturing Company ......F 713 223-4971
Houston (G-8861)

Berridge Manufacturing Company ......E 210 650-7056
San Antonio (G-17949)

Central Txas Met Roofg Sup Inc ....F 512 452-1515
Austin (G-1041)

Custom Bilt Holdings LLC ....F 214 699-4876
Irving (G-12987)

Knottsmith Construction Co Inc ....E 214 499-5667
Dallas (G-4563)

Nci Group Inc ....C 817 481-2501
Southlake (G-19080)

Northwest Metal and Steel Inc ....G 281 444-5269
Houston (G-11082)

Sage International Inc ....D 972 623-2004
Grand Prairie (G-7971)

Southeastern Metals Mfg Co Inc ....D 210 651-6331
San Antonio (G-18645)

ROOFING MEMBRANE: Rubber

Market Makers Inc ....F 281 893-9261
Houston (G-10769)

ROPE

Fast Back Rope Mfg ....F 817 279-1851
Granbury (G-7798)

Ls Rope LLC ....E 903 322-6580
Buffalo (G-2546)

ROTORS: Motor

Abaco Drilling Tech LLC ....C 281 869-0700
Houston (G-8441)

RUBBER

Arlanxeo USA LLC ....B 409 883-9990
Orange (G-16232)

Cosmec Inc ....E 903 677-2871
Athens (G-825)

Covestro LLC ....E 281 350-9000
Spring (G-19108)

Covestro LLC ....B 281 383-6000
Baytown (G-1782)

Dow Chemical Company ....D 409 722-3451
Beaumont (G-1884)

E R Carpenter LP ....C 281 474-7257
Pasadena (G-16422)

Green Links ....F 713 205-6629
Houston (G-10029)

Hexpol Compounding LLC ....D 817 483-9797
Kennedale (G-13498)

Jamak Fabrication-Tex Ltd ....E 817 594-8771
Weatherford (G-20598)

Kraton Corporation ....C 281 504-4700
Houston (G-10563)

Employee Codes: A=Over 500 employees, B=251-500
C=101-250, D=51-100, E=20-50, F=10-19, G=9

2021 Harris Texas
Manufacturers Directory

PRODUCT

1631

Longwood Elastomers Inc .... C 979 830-1111
  Brenham **(G-2261)**

Monument Chemical LLC .... E 281 474-5550
  Pasadena **(G-16486)**

Roy Johnson Incorporated .... E 817 468-2939
  Arlington **(G-773)**

Utex Industries Inc .... B 979 725-8503
  Weimar **(G-20651)**

Whitefield Plastics Corp .... E 281 214-8510
  Houston **(G-12664)**

Wichita Falls Mfg Inc .... E 940 322-4491
  Wichita Falls **(G-20831)**

RUBBER PRDTS

Ranco Rhino Mats & Matting .... F 713 228-5543
  Houston **(G-11541)**

RUBBER PRDTS: Appliance, Mechanical

Jmk International Inc .... E 817 737-3703
  Weatherford **(G-20599)**

RUBBER PRDTS: Automotive, Mechanical

Henniges Auto Mexico SA De Cv .... E 956 794-3606
  Laredo **(G-13891)**

Rex-Hide Incorporated .... F 903 593-7387
  Tyler **(G-20146)**

Rex-Hide Industries Inc .... D 903 593-7387
  Tyler **(G-20147)**

Zeon Chemicals LP .... E 281 474-9693
  Pasadena **(G-16529)**

Zeon Chemicals Texas Inc .... E 502 775-2000
  Pasadena **(G-16530)**

RUBBER PRDTS: Mechanical

Ace Rubber Products Inc .... F 817 572-1011
  Kennedale **(G-13496)**

Advanced Mat Systems LLC .... G 281 839-4258
  Alvin **(G-349)**

Akwel Cadillac Usa Inc .... F 956 718-8387
  Laredo **(G-13856)**

Akwel Cadillac Usa Inc .... F 956 717-4147
  Laredo **(G-13857)**

Anchor Texacone LLC .... E 972 288-4404
  Mesquite **(G-15026)**

Bulk Liquid Storage Systems LP .... E 817 473-0083
  Mansfield **(G-14658)**

Elastotech Southwest Inc .... E 936 545-8550
  Crockett **(G-3718)**

Gren Industries Inc .... F 972 881-2606
  Plano **(G-16881)**

Indian Rubber Company Inc .... E 817 265-6732
  Arlington **(G-705)**

Jamak Fabrication-Tex Ltd .... F 817 594-8771
  Weatherford **(G-20598)**

Midwest Industrial Rubber Inc .... F 972 988-6700
  Grand Prairie **(G-7928)**

Parker-Hannifin Corporation .... C 936 560-8900
  Nacogdoches **(G-15708)**

Utex Industries Inc .... B 979 725-8503
  Weimar **(G-20651)**

RUBBER PRDTS: Medical & Surgical Tubing, Extrudd & Lathe-Cut

Blue Medical Services Inc .... E 954 417-5442
  Cypress **(G-3781)**

RUBBER PRDTS: Oil & Gas Field Machinery, Mechanical

Ghx Industrial LLC .... E 713 341-3407
  Houston **(G-9950)**

Ghx Industrial LLC .... F 713 939-7423
  Houston **(G-9951)**

Ghx Industrial LLC .... E 713 222-2231
  Houston **(G-9952)**

Houston Specialties Products .... F 936 931-5256
  Houston **(G-10253)**

M P Industries Inc .... E 903 561-4232
  Tyler **(G-20118)**

Oil States Industries Inc .... F 713 510-2200
  Houston **(G-11155)**

Oil States Industries Inc .... C 713 445-2200
  Houston **(G-11157)**

Oil States Industries Inc .... C 817 548-4200
  Arlington **(G-743)**

Oil States Industries Inc .... C 713 445-2200
  Houston **(G-11160)**

Oil States International Inc .... D 713 652-0582
  Houston **(G-11161)**

P I Components Corp .... F 979 830-5400
  Brenham **(G-2267)**

Utex Industries Inc .... D 713 467-1000
  Houston **(G-12505)**

Utex Industries Inc .... D 936 760-4100
  Conroe **(G-3381)**

Western Rubber and Mfg Co .... E 936 588-3033
  Conroe **(G-3385)**

RUBBER PRDTS: Silicone

McV Sales Co L L C .... F 713 785-0088
  Houston **(G-10812)**

RUBBER PRDTS: Sponge

Kgp Group Inc .... E 817 354-0766
  Fort Worth **(G-6760)**

RUBBER STAMP, WHOLESALE

Mayer Enterprises Inc .... E 281 498-2600
  Houston **(G-10807)**

RUGS : Braided & Hooked

Exclusive Oriental Rugs Inc .... F 214 747-5557
  Dallas **(G-4342)**

RUGS : Hand & Machine Made

Curse of Good Taste Inc .... F 512 327-9660
  Austin **(G-1078)**

Great Rug Company .... F 713 789-3666
  Houston **(G-10028)**

RUGS : Machine Woven

El Paso Saddleblanket Co LP .... E 915 544-1000
  El Paso **(G-5741)**

Ingrids Custom Hand Woven .... F 325 732-4370
  Paint Rock **(G-16291)**

SAM&m Group LLC .... F 346 204-5786
  Stafford **(G-19373)**

SADDLERY STORES

Big Bend Saddlery Inc .... F 432 837-5551
  Alpine **(G-311)**

Double J Saddlery Inc .... D 361 293-6364
  Yoakum **(G-20964)**

Longhorn Leather Co .... E 903 454-4866
  Greenville **(G-8083)**

SAFE DEPOSIT BOXES

Hollon Safe Company LLC .... F 888 455-2337
  Corpus Christi **(G-3550)**

SAFES & VAULTS: Metal

Defiant Safe Co Inc .... E 972 243-3711
  Dallas **(G-4248)**

SAFETY EQPT & SPLYS WHOLESALERS

Accu-Lock Inc .... E 866 222-8562
  Grandview **(G-8001)**

Airgas Usa LLC .... E 972 660-0500
  Grand Prairie **(G-7825)**

Clark Fire Equipment Inc .... F 713 453-3778
  Houston **(G-9209)**

Ed Prince Enterprises Inc .... F 806 274-7178
  Borger **(G-2177)**

Evco Partners LP .... E 409 766-1900
  Texas City **(G-19793)**

Hasse Enterprises Inc .... F 512 835-7697
  Austin **(G-1199)**

Newinn Inc .... F 713 473-8188
  Pasadena **(G-16488)**

United Insul Sls Fbrcation Inc .... F 409 727-3191
  Port Arthur **(G-17131)**

Williams Fire Hazard Ctrl Inc .... E 409 745-3232
  Port Arthur **(G-17133)**

SAFETY INSPECTION SVCS

Allegiant Industrial LLC .... E 409 782-7963
  Beaumont **(G-1849)**

American Safety Services Inc .... C 432 552-7625
  Odessa **(G-15914)**

Auto Fire and Safety Cons .... G 832 585-0423
  Conroe **(G-3260)**

SALES PROMOTION SVCS

Ameron International Corp .... G 940 569-1471
  Houston **(G-8622)**

Bob Lillys Prof Mktg Group Inc .... E 214 231-2082
  Garland **(G-7449)**

Halo Branded Solutions Inc .... E 972 536-4069
  Dallas **(G-4432)**

Lugra Inc .... F 956 986-0958
  Brownsville **(G-2378)**

SALT

Texas Brine Company LLC .... E 713 877-2700
  Houston **(G-12223)**

Texas United Corporation .... E 713 877-1793
  Houston **(G-12258)**

Trothyhide LLC .... F 817 455-1118
  Fort Worth **(G-7080)**

United Salt Baytown LLC .... E 713 877-2600
  Houston **(G-12453)**

United Salt Carlsbad LLC .... D 713 877-2600
  Houston **(G-12454)**

United Salt Corporation .... E 713 877-2600
  Houston **(G-12455)**

United Salt Saltville LLC .... E 713 877-2600
  Houston **(G-12456)**

SALT MINING: Common

United Salt Baytown LLC .... E 936 372-3931
  Hockley **(G-8350)**

United Salt Carlsbad LLC .... D 713 877-2600
  Houston **(G-12454)**

SAMPLE BOOKS

VIP Samples Incorporated .... C 972 647-8888
  Grand Prairie **(G-7991)**

SAND & GRAVEL

Ace Sand and Gravel .... F 432 290-1205
  Fort Stockton **(G-6326)**

AG III Contractors LLC .... F 956 456-0628
  San Benito **(G-18653)**

Aggregate Plant Products Co .... D 210 333-1111
  San Antonio **(G-17874)**

Alamo Concrete Products Ltd .... E 361 289-9200
  Corpus Christi **(G-3471)**

Arcosa Aggregates Inc .... E 972 544-5900
  Ferris **(G-6229)**

Bruce Kennedy Sand & Gravel Co .... F 903 838-3377
  Texarkana **(G-19757)**

Cemex El Paso Inc .... C 915 565-4681
  El Paso **(G-5691)**

Childs Ready-Mix Concrete Co .... E 817 477-5151
  Cleburne **(G-3083)**

Costello Doab Enterprises LLC .... F 512 364-1708
  Austin **(G-1068)**

Desert Rock Co .... F 915 859-5969
  El Paso **(G-5721)**

E & A Materials Inc .... E 940 692-3290
  Wichita Falls **(G-20761)**

Earth Haulers Inc .... F 817 540-2777
  Euless **(G-6141)**

Ellinger Materials LLC .... F 281 227-6233
  Houston **(G-9604)**

Erna Frac Sand LC .... E 325 265-4400
  Mason **(G-14813)**

Fordyce Ltd .... E 956 581-0672
  Palmview **(G-16310)**

Fordyce Holdings Inc .... D 361 573-4309
  Victoria **(G-20264)**

Fun Da Mentals For Educatn LLC .... E 832 368-3345
  Houston **(G-9874)**

Hanson Aggregates LLC .... E 979 758-3662
  Garwood **(G-7614)**

Harrison Gypsum LLC .... E 210 225-9502
  San Antonio **(G-18159)**

Katy Stone & Gravel Inc .... F 281 371-3003
  Katy **(G-13417)**

Knife River Corp - South .... F 979 361-2900
  College Station **(G-3191)**

Knife River Corporation .... D 979 361-2900
  Bryan **(G-2488)**

Knights Landscaping LLC .... F 972 971-4213
  Mesquite **(G-15057)**

Legacy Vulcan LLC .... E 325 646-8526
  Brownwood **(G-2435)**

Legacy Vulcan LLC .... E 830 278-6205
  Uvalde **(G-20190)**

Legacy Vulcan LLC ....E 325 529-3785
  Abilene *(G-58)*
Legacy Vulcan LLC ....D 210 492-1053
  San Antonio *(G-18243)*
Liberty Sand & Gravel Inc ....F 972 924-8065
  Anna *(G-584)*
Martin Mrtta Mtls Suthwest LLC ....B 210 208-4400
  San Antonio *(G-18280)*
Murphy & Murphy Inc ....F 940 325-2666
  Mineral Wells *(G-15533)*
Pappys Sand & Gravel Inc ....F 972 486-4400
  Scurry *(G-18783)*
Pb Materials Holdings Inc ....E 432 563-8036
  Odessa *(G-16106)*
Permian Basin Materials LLC ....E 432 614-6201
  Odessa *(G-16114)*
Pitts Sand & Gravel Inc ....E 940 692-3290
  Wichita Falls *(G-20794)*
Platinum Underground LLC ....E 512 770-9410
  Georgetown *(G-7670)*
R E Janes Gravel Co ....E 325 736-5008
  Merkel *(G-15017)*
Red Dog Track Inc ....E 254 672-5261
  Strawn *(G-19432)*
Redco Endeavors Inc ....F 832 421-8549
  Gilmer *(G-7711)*
River Aggregates LLC ....E 936 446-2000
  Conroe *(G-3358)*
Sanco Materials Co ....E 325 453-2901
  Robert Lee *(G-17498)*
Solid Rocks Properties LLC ....F 940 779-3700
  Graford *(G-7773)*
Sorrell Cnstr Eqp & Mtls LLC ....D 979 233-6655
  Freeport *(G-7213)*
Sweetwater Ready-Mix Con Co ....F 325 236-6200
  Sweetwater *(G-19638)*
Texas Archtctral Aggregate Inc ....E 325 372-5105
  San Saba *(G-18719)*
Texas Crushed Stone Company ....C 512 255-4405
  Georgetown *(G-7684)*
Tricounty Materials & Svcs LP ....F 972 446-1816
  Sanger *(G-18731)*
US Lbm Holdings LLC ....C 713 650-6200
  Houston *(G-12485)*
Vulcan Materials Company ....F 210 349-3311
  San Antonio *(G-18603)*
Vulcan Materials Company ....F 210 494-9555
  San Antonio *(G-18604)*
Weir Brothers Contracting LLC ....F 940 440-2931
  Aubrey *(G-852)*
Yarrington Road Materials ....D 512 754-3573
  Kyle *(G-13689)*
Yarrington Road Materials LP ....F 512 306-7800
  Austin *(G-1678)*

SAND LIME PRDTS

Texas Industries Inc ....C 972 647-6700
  Dallas *(G-5062)*

SAND MINING

Atlas Sand Company LLC ....E 432 276-3990
  Austin *(G-946)*
Colorado Cnty Sand Grav L L C ....E 979 543-3791
  El Campo *(G-5614)*
Hanson Lehigh Inc ....B 972 653-3735
  Mineral Wells *(G-15528)*
Hanson Lehigh Inc ....E 281 616-0700
  Houston *(G-10120)*
Hanson Lehigh Inc ....B 972 653-5500
  Irving *(G-13052)*
Hi-Crush Inc ....E 713 980-6200
  Houston *(G-10170)*
Hi-Crush Permian Sand LLC ....E 713 960-4777
  Dallas *(G-4455)*
Hi-Crush Wyeville Oper LLC ....E 608 372-4705
  Houston *(G-10171)*
Howell Sand Company Inc ....D 806 383-1721
  Amarillo *(G-436)*
I 35 Sandpit Inc ....E 817 790-2772
  Alvarado *(G-335)*
Lattimore Materials Corp ....C 972 221-4646
  Addison *(G-143)*
Nbr Sand LLC ....F 903 593-3311
  Tyler *(G-20133)*
RAC Materials LLC ....E 281 255-8500
  Tomball *(G-20005)*
Signal Peak Silica LLC ....C 281 822-4568
  Houston *(G-11892)*
Texas Industries Inc ....E 817 596-4307
  Weatherford *(G-20625)*

Texas Industries Inc ....E 940 969-6021
  Paradise *(G-16354)*
Texas Industries Inc ....E 281 261-0790
  Stafford *(G-19385)*
Thompson Jr Inc ....E 940 665-2533
  Gainesville *(G-7372)*
Txi Operations LP ....C 972 647-6700
  Dallas *(G-5125)*
Vernor Material & Eqp Co Inc ....D 409 233-3366
  Freeport *(G-7221)*
Vista Proppants Logistics LLC ....A 817 563-3500
  Fort Worth *(G-7109)*

SAND: Hygrade

Covia Holdings Corporation ....E 254 897-4408
  Cleburne *(G-3084)*
Custom Abrasives LLC ....F 281 286-7200
  Houston *(G-9362)*
Frac Sand Services LLC ....F 713 668-6766
  Houston *(G-9851)*
Hauling & Excavating Casco ....F 713 433-6209
  Houston *(G-10136)*
Hermitage Operating LLC ....F 337 852-0001
  Houston *(G-10161)*
Industrial Sand Products LLC ....F 832 838-8095
  Highlands *(G-8312)*
Oregon Resources Corporation ....D 541 266-0875
  Springtown *(G-19274)*
U S Silica Company ....E 254 375-2225
  Kosse *(G-13667)*
Unlimited Frac Sand Llc ....E 800 560-1246
  Odessa *(G-16191)*

SAND: Silica

Espey Silica Sand Co Inc ....F 210 626-2800
  San Antonio *(G-18095)*
Lonestar Prospects Ltd ....E 817 279-1660
  Fort Worth *(G-6799)*
Osburn Sand Co ....F 210 626-2045
  San Antonio *(G-18358)*
Pioneer Sands LLC ....G 325 597-0721
  Brady *(G-2216)*
Pioneer Sands LLC ....D 972 444-9001
  Irving *(G-13146)*
Signal Peak Silica LLC ....C 281 822-4568
  Houston *(G-11892)*
Silver Creek Materials Inc ....E 817 246-2426
  Fort Worth *(G-6989)*
Smart Sand Inc ....E 281 231-2660
  The Woodlands *(G-19918)*
Superior Silica Sands LLC ....F 210 626-2045
  San Antonio *(G-18515)*
U S Silica Company ....E 301 682-0600
  Katy *(G-13381)*
US Silica Holdings Inc ....F 281 258-2170
  Houston *(G-12490)*

SANDBLASTING EQPT

B & M Oilfield Services LLC ....F 979 241-2051
  Falls City *(G-6182)*
T-Tex Equipment LP ....F 713 991-7070
  Houston *(G-12144)*
Tri Element Incorporated ....F 361 664-5000
  Alice *(G-242)*

SANDBLASTING SVC: Building Exterior

Cy-Fair Coatings Inc ....F 281 351-7427
  Cypress *(G-3784)*

SANDSTONE: Crushed & Broken

Colorado Materials Ltd ....D 512 396-1555
  New Braunfels *(G-15785)*
M & T Natural Stone ....F 817 556-2107
  Joshua *(G-13321)*

SANITARY SVC, NEC

Dfw Infrastructure Inc ....F 888 739-9070
  Alvarado *(G-328)*

SANITARY SVCS: Chemical Detoxification

Diversified Pure Chem LLC ....F 817 677-9418
  Rhome *(G-17254)*
Tm Chemicals Ltd Partnership ....C 281 930-2525
  Deer Park *(G-5300)*

SANITARY SVCS: Environmental Cleanup

American Safety Services Inc ....C 432 552-7625
  Odessa *(G-15914)*
Bay Area Industrial Contrs LP ....C 281 471-0400
  La Porte *(G-13725)*
Blast Envmtl & Indus Svcs ....C 281 557-1000
  League City *(G-13950)*
Earth Haulers Inc ....F 817 540-2777
  Euless *(G-6141)*
Etech Envmtl Safety Solutions ....C 432 563-2200
  Odessa *(G-15993)*
JD King Inc ....C 800 805-6302
  Seminole *(G-18884)*
Mo-Vac Service Company ....D 956 682-6381
  Edinburg *(G-5597)*
Newpark Resources Inc ....E 281 362-6800
  The Woodlands *(G-19897)*

SANITARY SVCS: Hazardous Waste, Collection & Disposal

Ambar Inc ....C 281 873-7600
  Houston *(G-8576)*
Flex Tank Systems LLC ....E 281 862-2900
  Channelview *(G-3022)*

SANITARY SVCS: Nonhazardous Waste Disposal Sites

Newpark Resources Inc ....E 281 362-6800
  The Woodlands *(G-19897)*

SANITARY SVCS: Oil Spill Cleanup

Planet Resource Recovery Inc ....E 281 996-5315
  Pearland *(G-16592)*
Smith Oilfield Services Inc ....E 940 683-5722
  Bridgeport *(G-2301)*
Smith Vacuum Service ....F 325 573-7437
  Snyder *(G-19006)*

SANITARY SVCS: Refuse Collection & Disposal Svcs

Bright Initiatives LLC ....F 512 466-4734
  Austin *(G-1008)*

SANITARY SVCS: Sewage Treatment Facility

Petro-Tech Environmental LLC ....G 713 926-9986
  Houston *(G-11301)*

SANITARY SVCS: Toxic Or Hazardous Waste Cleanup

Flo Trend Systems Inc ....E 713 699-0152
  Houston *(G-9804)*

SANITARY SVCS: Waste Materials, Recycling

Alpha Omega Recycling Inc ....F 903 297-7272
  Longview *(G-14192)*
C-Square Intl Trdg LLC ....F 817 633-9000
  Arlington *(G-635)*
Commercial Metals Company ....D 409 842-3316
  Beaumont *(G-1875)*
East Side Compost Pedallers ....F 512 436-3884
  Austin *(G-1111)*
Ecs Refining Texas LLC ....E 972 524-1075
  Terrell *(G-19732)*
Giant Cement Holding Inc ....G 571 302-7150
  Houston *(G-9954)*
Greenstar North Amer Holdings ....A 713 965-0005
  Houston *(G-10036)*
Metroplex Wood Products Ltd ....E 817 538-0375
  Fort Worth *(G-6834)*
Natural Energy Resources Inc ....D 832 631-5013
  Katy *(G-13426)*
Pine Street Salvage Co ....E 325 677-8831
  Abilene *(G-65)*
Pine Street Salvage Co ....E 806 372-5678
  Amarillo *(G-454)*
Prime Momento LLC ....F 832 643-4605
  Sugar Land *(G-19529)*
Safety-Kleen Systems Inc ....B 800 669-5740
  Richardson *(G-17392)*
Standard Waste Services LLC ....F 210 619-7962
  San Antonio *(G-18496)*
Super Sack Bag Inc ....F 214 340-7060
  Dallas *(G-5024)*

Employee Codes: A=Over 500 employees, B=251-500
C=101-250, D=51-100, E=20-50, F=10-19, G=9

2021 Harris Texas
Manufacturers Directory

1633

PRODUCT

Western Pulp Products Co.................E...... 903 586-3608
Jacksonville *(G-13266)*

SANITARY WARE: Metal

Arrow Mirror & Glass Inc................C...... 832 467-4345
Houston *(G-8706)*
Eljer Industries Inc......................E...... 972 560-2000
Dallas *(G-4311)*
Griffin Products Inc....................E...... 903 873-6388
Wills Point *(G-20875)*
Kohler Co.................................D...... 920 457-4441
Grand Prairie *(G-7906)*
Kohler Co.................................A...... 325 643-2661
Brownwood *(G-2433)*
Mansfield Plumbing Pdts LLC............D...... 903 657-1436
Henderson *(G-8267)*

SANITATION CHEMICALS & CLEANING AGENTS

ABc Compounding Co Texas Inc..........C...... 972 988-9200
Grand Prairie *(G-7818)*
Akzo Nobel Inc...........................E...... 817 625-1500
Fort Worth *(G-6360)*
Ankem of Texas Inc.....................E...... 903 802-7133
Farmers Branch *(G-6186)*
Arden Companies Inc....................C...... 806 335-1147
Amarillo *(G-400)*
Beta Technology Inc.....................E...... 281 647-9700
Houston *(G-8865)*
Color Fast Industries Inc...............E...... 817 546-4910
Alvarado *(G-327)*
Commercial Bev Concepts LLC...........E...... 713 554-4569
Houston *(G-9249)*
Ecolab Inc................................E...... 800 532-7732
Grapevine *(G-8030)*
Ecolab Inc................................D...... 972 840-3994
Garland *(G-7483)*
G G A Inc.................................F...... 254 732-1701
Waco *(G-20405)*
K & K Chemical Company Inc............E...... 972 635-2482
Royse City *(G-17721)*
NCH Corporation.........................G...... 800 336-0450
Irving *(G-13118)*
Nch Corporation.........................C...... 972 438-0551
Irving *(G-13116)*
Omega Chemical Products Inc...........E...... 219 208-0500
Weatherford *(G-20608)*
Questspecialty Corporation.............D...... 713 896-8188
Brenham *(G-2271)*
Sanotech 360 LLC.......................F...... 817 697-7116
Fort Worth *(G-6974)*
Taf Incorporated........................E...... 713 896-4040
Houston *(G-12147)*
Therm Processes Inc....................F...... 214 942-3131
Dallas *(G-5083)*
Trecora Chemical Inc...................D...... 281 474-7500
Pasadena *(G-16519)*

SASHES: Door Or Window, Metal

All Seasons Commercial Div Inc.........E...... 979 823-6557
Bryan *(G-2454)*
Arch Aluminum and GL Co Texas........F...... 972 647-9230
Grand Prairie *(G-7834)*

SATELLITE COMMUNICATIONS EQPT

Marlink Inc...............................F...... 713 910-3352
Houston *(G-10771)*
Qualcomm Technologies Inc.............C...... 512 623-3700
Austin *(G-1442)*

SATELLITES: Communications

Crown Castle Intl Corp..................F...... 713 570-3000
Houston *(G-9346)*
Interco Products........................F...... 972 613-6749
Garland *(G-7519)*
Kingston I-Tek Solutions LLC............F...... 281 656-4900
Houston *(G-10536)*
Lockheed Martin Corporation............D...... 817 777-2000
Benbrook *(G-2042)*
Lockheed Martin Corporation............B...... 817 777-2000
Fort Worth *(G-6798)*
Rcl Technologies Inc....................G...... 214 870-3703
Irving *(G-13163)*
Speedcast Americas Inc.................F...... 281 340-2057
Houston *(G-12010)*
X-Analog Communications Inc...........E...... 409 925-4702
Alvin *(G-387)*

SAW BLADES

Clover Group Inc........................E...... 915 590-2525
El Paso *(G-5698)*
Cutting Solutions Inc...................E...... 214 637-4849
Dallas *(G-4198)*
Falcon-Auger Inc........................F...... 713 690-2761
Houston *(G-9758)*

SAWDUST & SHAVINGS

Agri-Tex Wood Shavings Co LLC.........F...... 936 628-1950
Shepherd *(G-18899)*
Long Beach Shavings Co Inc.............F...... 936 231-4400
Conroe *(G-3325)*

SAWING & PLANING MILLS

Builders Firstsource-Ohio Vall..........C...... 214 880-3500
Dallas *(G-4067)*
Cadre Timber Products Inc..............E...... 409 246-3573
Kountze *(G-13669)*
Carrizo Wood Products Inc..............E...... 936 569-0582
Nacogdoches *(G-15690)*
Carthage Hardwoods LLC................E...... 903 693-9300
Carthage *(G-2903)*
Cedar Supply Inc........................E...... 972 242-6561
Carrollton *(G-2711)*
Conner Industries Inc...................E...... 956 781-0215
Alamo *(G-178)*
Cypress Lumber Company Inc............F...... 903 572-6561
Mount Pleasant *(G-15649)*
Forest Nix Industries Inc................E...... 936 254-2441
Timpson *(G-19948)*
G & S Lumber Co Inc....................E...... 936 564-7676
Nacogdoches *(G-15699)*
Georgia-Pacific LLC......................C...... 817 625-9091
Fort Worth *(G-6665)*
Georgia-Pacific LLC......................D...... 940 205-9558
Denton *(G-5368)*
Georgia-Pacific WD Pdts S LLC..........A...... 936 398-2511
Camden *(G-2638)*
Koppers Inc.............................G...... 979 596-1321
Somerville *(G-19022)*
Lufkin Creosoting Co Inc................D...... 936 634-2211
Lufkin *(G-14537)*
Mg Building Materials Ltd...............B...... 210 924-8604
San Antonio *(G-18298)*
Oliver Brothers Sawmill.................G...... 936 295-0931
Huntsville *(G-12821)*
Quality Mill of Texas LLC...............F...... 409 722-4594
Beaumont *(G-1945)*
Rocla Concrete Tie Inc..................F...... 806 383-7071
Amarillo *(G-459)*
Ross Lumber Ltd.........................E...... 936 254-2575
Timpson *(G-19949)*
Sawmill Partners LLC....................E...... 214 358-2314
Dallas *(G-4939)*
Southern Forest Products LLC...........D...... 409 634-3365
Bon Wier *(G-2150)*
Spivey Stake & Supply Inc..............E...... 903 822-3888
Mount Enterprise *(G-15645)*
Texas Priming LLC.......................G...... 903 893-6200
Sherman *(G-18936)*
Texas Timberjack Inc....................D...... 409 397-4221
Bon Wier *(G-2151)*
Thick n Thin Lumber Co Inc.............F...... 281 592-0437
Cleveland *(G-3139)*
West Fraser Inc..........................C...... 903 657-4575
Henderson *(G-8277)*
Woodville Hardwoods....................E...... 409 283-6106
Woodville *(G-20920)*

SAWING & PLANING MILLS: Custom

Adam Nerren Ltd........................G...... 936 422-4800
Huntington *(G-12808)*
Forest Ogletree Products Inc............E...... 936 327-2424
Livingston *(G-14155)*

SAWS & SAWING EQPT

Keith Properties Inc.....................F...... 254 883-2531
Marlin *(G-14759)*
Straight Line Sawing & Sealing..........F...... 972 590-8922
Grand Prairie *(G-7976)*
Valley Outdoor Power Eqp Inc...........F...... 956 787-0469
Pharr *(G-16715)*
Wheel-A-Rama Inc.......................G...... 325 655-7373
San Angelo *(G-17840)*

SCAFFOLDS: Mobile Or Stationary, Metal

Anchor Industrial Services LLC..........D...... 281 385-0607
Houston *(G-8639)*
Builders Equipment & Tool Co...........D...... 713 869-3491
Houston *(G-9013)*
RE Campbell Company Ltd...............E...... 713 957-8721
Houston *(G-11558)*

SCALES & BALANCES, EXC LABORATORY

Keith Weighing Systems LLC............F...... 806 655-3033
Canyon *(G-2672)*
Martin-Decker Totco Inc.................B...... 512 340-5000
Cedar Park *(G-2978)*
Mettler-Toledo LLC......................F...... 972 727-8669
Allen *(G-285)*
Tru-Test Inc.............................E...... 940 327-8020
Mineral Wells *(G-15543)*

SCANNING DEVICES: Optical

Ncs Pearson Inc.........................D...... 432 685-0033
Midland *(G-15314)*
Ncs Pearson Inc.........................D...... 210 339-5000
San Antonio *(G-18340)*
Omnidata Services Group LLC...........F...... 281 469-4365
Houston *(G-11180)*
Scantron Corporation...................F...... 770 593-5050
San Antonio *(G-18455)*

SCHOOLS & EDUCATIONAL SVCS, NEC

Industrial Welding Academy.............F...... 713 944-0701
Houston *(G-10356)*

SCHOOLS: Vocational, NEC

B R L Consultants Inc...................F...... 210 341-3442
San Antonio *(G-17934)*
Indochinese Culture Center.............F...... 713 522-7799
Houston *(G-10343)*

SCIENTIFIC INSTRUMENTS WHOLESALERS

Expotech USA Inc.......................E...... 281 879-8998
Houston *(G-9728)*
Testforce Usa Inc.......................F...... 925 281-3501
Addison *(G-168)*

SCRAP & WASTE MATERIALS, WHOLESALE: Auto Wrecking For Scrap

EC Wrecking & Salvage Corp............F...... 915 855-7999
El Paso *(G-5734)*

SCRAP & WASTE MATERIALS, WHOLESALE: Ferrous Metal

Ashley Salvage Company................E...... 210 922-7631
San Antonio *(G-17916)*
Commercial Metals Company............D...... 713 226-0100
Houston *(G-9251)*
Commercial Metals Company............D...... 409 842-3316
Beaumont *(G-1875)*
Commercial Metals Company............C...... 214 565-0668
Dallas *(G-4146)*
Commercial Metals Company............E...... 979 265-4642
Clute *(G-3150)*
Commercial Metals Company............E...... 817 429-4005
Fort Worth *(G-6531)*
Commercial Metals Company............D...... 361 884-4071
Corpus Christi *(G-3505)*
Commercial Metals Company............E...... 469 729-0180
Dallas *(G-4147)*
Dualco Inc..............................E...... 713 644-1164
Houston *(G-9536)*
J L Proler Iron and Steel Co............E...... 713 675-3191
Houston *(G-10441)*
Jrn Management LP......................D...... 210 222-9511
San Antonio *(G-18211)*
Lopez Scrap Metal Inc..................D...... 915 859-0770
El Paso *(G-5847)*
Pine Street Salvage Co..................E...... 325 677-8831
Abilene *(G-65)*
Pine Street Salvage Co..................F...... 806 372-5678
Amarillo *(G-454)*
Tyler Iron & Metal Ltd...................E...... 903 592-8144
Tyler *(G-20170)*

SCRAP & WASTE MATERIALS, WHOLESALE: Metal

Arsham Metal Industries Inc ....E 713 896-8585
Jersey Village *(G-13292)*

Bell Processing Incorporated ....D 940 322-8621
Wichita Falls *(G-20744)*

Gateway Metal Recycling Inc ....F 956 723-0409
Laredo *(G-13889)*

Monterrey Iron & Metal Ltd ....D 210 927-2727
San Antonio *(G-18318)*

SCRAP & WASTE MATERIALS, WHOLESALE: Nonferrous Metals Scrap

Elg Metals Inc ....E 281 457-2100
Houston *(G-9600)*

Non-Frrous Extrsion Scrap Mtls ....D 713 869-9551
Houston *(G-11067)*

W Silver Recycling Inc ....D 915 532-5643
El Paso *(G-6027)*

SCRAP & WASTE MATERIALS, WHOLESALE: Paper

Caraustar Industries Inc ....E 903 799-5100
Atlanta *(G-841)*

Delta Paper Stock Corp ....E 713 666-1440
Bellaire *(G-1993)*

Master Fibers Inc ....D 915 544-2299
El Paso *(G-5868)*

SCRAP & WASTE MATERIALS, WHOLESALE: Plastics Scrap

C-Square Intl Trdg LLC ....F 817 633-9000
Arlington *(G-635)*

One Source Recycling Inc ....D 512 549-2812
Austin *(G-1386)*

SCRAP & WASTE MATERIALS, WHOLESALE: Rags

Knit Rags LLC ....F 713 249-9478
Houston *(G-10549)*

SCREENS: Door, Wood Frame

Aim Solar Screens Inc ....F 281 997-1543
Pearland *(G-16538)*

SCREENS: Window, Metal

Airtite Products Llc ....F 325 672-5774
Abilene *(G-11)*

SCREENS: Window, Wood Framed

Screenfab LLC ....E 972 438-2860
Irving *(G-13173)*

SCREENS: Woven Wire

CPI Wirecloth & Screens Inc ....D 281 485-2300
Pearland *(G-16550)*

SCREW MACHINE PRDTS

Automatic Products Corp ....C 972 272-6422
Garland *(G-7444)*

Bonney Forge Corporation ....D 713 695-3633
Houston *(G-8950)*

Chevas Company LLC ....F 713 225-6595
Houston *(G-9176)*

Cox Manufacturing Company ....C 210 657-7731
San Antonio *(G-18028)*

D & R Precision Manufacturing ....F 956 386-0685
Edinburg *(G-5584)*

Fabrication Specialty Inc ....F 214 742-3571
Granbury *(G-7797)*

J M Fabrication Company LLC ....F 817 652-0526
Arlington *(G-709)*

Kaspar Machine LLC ....E 254 836-1564
Waco *(G-20422)*

Lewis Engineering Company ....E 903 938-6754
Marshall *(G-14787)*

Macro Tex Machine Works LLC ....E 281 540-2141
Humble *(G-12786)*

Nytex Automatic Products Inc ....E 830 997-8986
Bulverde *(G-2557)*

P T Products & Services Inc ....E 512 251-3592
Pflugerville *(G-16682)*

Pgi International Ltd ....B 713 466-0056
Houston *(G-11316)*

Production Machine & Tool LP ....E 940 767-9400
Wichita Falls *(G-20798)*

Pyle Machine Company Inc ....E 817 485-6011
Fort Worth *(G-6924)*

Quantex Instrument Company ....E 936 544-5732
Crockett *(G-3723)*

R D Screw Machine Products Inc ....F 210 337-8942
San Antonio *(G-18408)*

RDS Products Inc ....B 817 656-8277
Fort Worth *(G-6945)*

Rothe Enterprises Inc ....F 210 310-0447
San Antonio *(G-18432)*

S H Leggitt Company ....C 956 504-6440
San Marcos *(G-18708)*

Tecnotrat Metal Processing LLC ....F 281 894-9189
Houston *(G-12180)*

SCREWS: Metal

Pattonair Usa Inc ....E 817 284-4449
Fort Worth *(G-6897)*

Steelfast Inc ....F 972 243-5312
Dallas *(G-5009)*

SEALANTS

Bo-GE Assembly Inc ....E 281 462-0073
Crosby *(G-3727)*

Corev America Inc ....E 713 849-3671
Houston *(G-9319)*

E J Reynolds Company Inc ....F 281 331-4556
Alvin *(G-361)*

Gulf States Asphalt Company LP ....D 713 941-4410
South Houston *(G-19042)*

ITW Plymers Salants N Amer Inc ....C 972 438-9111
Irving *(G-13067)*

Multi-Seal Corporation ....F 281 591-0111
Spring *(G-19235)*

Parker-Hannifin Corporation ....C 936 560-8900
Nacogdoches *(G-15708)*

Pro Line Products Inc ....F 972 488-4200
Dallas *(G-4830)*

Sealant Solution Inc ....F 214 886-6688
Flower Mound *(G-6280)*

Westech Seal Inc ....F 432 367-1188
Odessa *(G-16211)*

SEALING COMPOUNDS: Sealing, synthetic rubber or plastic

Laticrete International Inc ....E 972 641-3266
Grand Prairie *(G-7909)*

PRC-Desoto International Inc ....D 972 540-0360
McKinney *(G-14966)*

Precision Polymer Engrg Ltd ....F 713 482-0123
Houston *(G-11394)*

SEALS: Hermetic

Nextus Inc ....E 512 288-9080
Georgetown *(G-7667)*

SEALS: Oil, Rubber

CDI Energy Products Inc ....B 281 446-6662
Humble *(G-12753)*

Western Rubber and Mfg Co ....E 936 588-3033
Conroe *(G-3385)*

SEARCH & DETECTION SYSTEMS, EXC RADAR

Comprobe Inc ....F 817 293-7333
Fort Worth *(G-6538)*

Drone Labs LLC ....F 214 538-1467
Katy *(G-13397)*

Industrial Safety Tech LLC ....A 713 559-9200
The Woodlands *(G-19884)*

SEARCH & NAVIGATION SYSTEMS

Affects Sat Corporation ....D 713 897-9935
Garland *(G-7430)*

Ahlers Aerospace Inc ....E 817 553-2155
Hurst *(G-12832)*

Allosense Inc ....G 830 900-3080
San Antonio *(G-17898)*

Analytical Sensors Instrs LLC ....D 281 565-8818
Houston *(G-8636)*

Astro Technology Inc ....F 281 464-0100
Houston *(G-8731)*

Bae Systems Info & Elec Sys ....A 512 276-3100
Austin *(G-973)*

Bae Systems Land Armaments LP ....D 408 504-1877
Temple *(G-19670)*

Brains4drones LLC ....F 972 974-3476
Plano *(G-16810)*

Chromalloy Gas Turbine LLC ....F 972 241-2501
Dallas *(G-4114)*

Cobham Advnced Elctrnic Sltons ....F 972 437-1049
Richardson *(G-17288)*

Drs Ntwork Imaging Systems LLC ....C 877 377-4783
Dallas *(G-4280)*

Efw Inc ....A 817 916-1359
Fort Worth *(G-6606)*

Espy Corporation ....E 512 261-1016
Austin *(G-861)*

Fci Environmental Inc ....E 702 262-3953
Dallas *(G-4356)*

Forney Corporation ....F 972 458-6100
Addison *(G-126)*

Garrett Electronics Inc ....C 972 494-6151
Garland *(G-7497)*

Heath Consultants Incorporated ....C 713 844-1300
Houston *(G-10146)*

Innovative Signal Analysis Inc ....D 972 231-5702
Richardson *(G-17333)*

L3harris Technologies Inc ....B 972 550-2300
Irving *(G-13080)*

Lockheed Martin ....D 281 283-4400
Houston *(G-10663)*

Lockheed Martin Corporation ....A 972 603-1000
Grand Prairie *(G-7914)*

Lockheed Martin Corporation ....B 210 736-6461
San Antonio *(G-18257)*

Lockheed Martin Corporation ....B 817 763-3035
Fort Worth *(G-6792)*

Lockheed Martin Corporation ....A 281 283-4400
Houston *(G-10664)*

Lockheed Martin Corporation ....B 281 335-2318
Friendswood *(G-7248)*

Lockheed Martin Corporation ....B 817 655-8672
Richland Hills *(G-17440)*

Lockheed Martin Corporation ....B 817 763-2663
Colleyville *(G-3219)*

Lockheed Martin Corporation ....B 281 218-3000
Houston *(G-10665)*

Lockheed Martin Corporation ....A 817 935-1363
Fort Worth *(G-6793)*

Lockheed Martin Corporation ....B 210 581-6100
San Antonio *(G-18258)*

Lockheed Martin Corporation ....B 281 853-3000
Houston *(G-10666)*

Lockheed Martin Corporation ....B 817 495-0200
Fort Worth *(G-6794)*

Lockheed Martin Corporation ....E 817 777-2000
Fort Worth *(G-6795)*

Lockheed Martin Corporation ....E 210 445-5628
San Antonio *(G-18260)*

Lockheed Martin Corporation ....B 817 777-2000
Fort Worth *(G-6796)*

Lockheed Martin Corporation ....B 334 347-4472
Killeen *(G-13615)*

Lockheed Martin Corporation ....E 254 285-5503
Fort Hood *(G-6325)*

Lockheed Martin Corporation ....F 915 568-6264
Fort Bliss *(G-6317)*

Lockheed Martin Corporation ....B 817 763-4246
Keller *(G-13468)*

Lockheed Martin Corporation ....F 817 777-0786
Fort Worth *(G-6797)*

Lockheed Martin Corporation ....E 432 358-4474
Marfa *(G-14753)*

Lockheed Martin Corporation ....C 281 218-6021
Houston *(G-10667)*

Lockheed Martin Corporation ....A 972 603-1000
Grand Prairie *(G-7915)*

Lockheed Martin Corporation ....B 817 777-4242
Azle *(G-1726)*

Lockheed Martin Corporation ....D 210 581-6100
San Antonio *(G-18261)*

Lockheed Martin Corporation ....D 936 633-4800
Lufkin *(G-14532)*

Lockheed Martin Corporation ....E 915 852-1100
El Paso *(G-5845)*

Mc Manus Instrument Co Inc ....F 409 834-2419
Village Mills *(G-20338)*

Mo2 Inc ....F 214 575-7600
Dallas *(G-4682)*

Northrop Grumman Systems Corp ....C....... 512 804-2153
Austin *(G-1370)*

Northrop Grumman Systems Corp ....E....... 469 524-0109
Irving *(G-13127)*

Northrup Grmman Technical Svcs ....F....... 405 736-8207
Irving *(G-13128)*

Novaria Group LLC ....E....... 817 381-3810
Fort Worth *(G-6870)*

Optek Technology Inc ....D....... 972 323-2200
Carrollton *(G-2786)*

Pipeline Inspection Company ....E....... 713 681-5837
Houston *(G-11335)*

Progressive Incorporated ....B....... 817 465-3221
Arlington *(G-762)*

Raytheon Company ....E....... 972 952-4195
Carrollton *(G-2884)*

Raytheon Company ....B....... 915 779-7666
El Paso *(G-5928)*

Raytheon Company ....C....... 972 952-4067
McKinney *(G-14970)*

Reliance Coated Fabrics Inc ....E....... 817 453-8829
Mansfield *(G-14710)*

Rockwell Collins Inc ....C....... 325 695-0308
Abilene *(G-75)*

Rockwell Collins Inc ....A....... 972 705-3156
Richardson *(G-17391)*

Sabre Sentinel Intl LLC ....E....... 972 529-6570
McKinney *(G-14973)*

Sermatech Dynamic ....F....... 713 849-9474
Houston *(G-11838)*

Sgt LLC ....D....... 281 751-1071
Webster *(G-20645)*

Sierra Nevada Corporation ....E....... 775 331-0222
Plano *(G-17005)*

Sierra Nevada Corporation ....B....... 210 523-6500
San Antonio *(G-18473)*

Sikorsky Aircraft Corporation ....C....... 817 377-7500
Fort Worth *(G-6988)*

Simtek Inc ....D....... 817 283-1801
Euless *(G-6159)*

Southern Avionics Co ....E....... 409 842-1717
Beaumont *(G-1952)*

Tracy and Associates ....F....... 817 559-9274
Granbury *(G-7813)*

Triumph Aerostructures LLC ....A....... 972 515-8276
Red Oak *(G-17237)*

Varo LLC ....B....... 972 840-5506
Garland *(G-7607)*

Whrzt Inc ....F....... 888 507-9985
Carrollton *(G-2849)*

SEAT BELTS: Automobile & Aircraft

Joyson Safety Systems ....E....... 830 703-7191
Del Rio *(G-5319)*

Tk Holdings Inc ....D....... 210 509-0762
San Antonio *(G-18552)*

ZF Passive Safety US Inc ....F....... 956 632-8100
Pharr *(G-16718)*

ZF Passive Safety US Inc ....B....... 734 582-1139
El Paso *(G-6043)*

SEATING: Bleacher, Portable

Schultz Industries Inc ....D....... 254 666-5155
Hewitt *(G-8300)*

SEATING: Transportation

Sanbar Balls & Seats Inc ....F....... 432 332-3755
Odessa *(G-16149)*

SECRETARIAL & COURT REPORTING

Fedex Office & Print Svcs Inc ....E....... 512 452-3600
Austin *(G-1152)*

SECURE STORAGE SVC: Document

Corporate Records Management ....G....... 214 333-3453
Dallas *(G-4171)*

Jeh-Eas Inc ....G....... 210 490-9156
San Antonio *(G-18200)*

SECURITIES DEALING

Absolute Cmmnctons Ntwrk Slton ....E....... 361 888-6776
Corpus Christi *(G-3464)*

SECURITY CONTROL EQPT & SYSTEMS

Absolute Cmmnctons Ntwrk Slton ....E....... 361 888-6776
Corpus Christi *(G-3464)*

Compuink ....F....... 281 705-0758
Houston *(G-9264)*

Csi Techs Inc ....D....... 210 875-7978
San Antonio *(G-18033)*

Designed Security Inc ....E....... 512 321-4426
Bastrop *(G-1756)*

Digiop Technologies Ltd ....E....... 713 333-4900
Houston *(G-9470)*

Easy Protect Inc ....E....... 469 916-1099
Dallas *(G-4297)*

Enterprise SEC Sltons Txas Inc ....E....... 940 320-3778
Justin *(G-13343)*

Enviro Cams LLC ....F....... 430 255-7006
Kemp *(G-13484)*

Kline Technical Consulting LLC ....E....... 505 310-2679
Richmond *(G-17460)*

Pcs Telecom Inc ....F....... 281 469-3367
Pasadena *(G-16494)*

Resideo Technologies Inc ....F....... 512 726-3500
Austin *(G-1459)*

Secure Control Systems Inc ....E....... 210 530-5245
San Antonio *(G-18463)*

Supercircuits Inc ....D....... 877 995-2288
Austin *(G-1548)*

Uptime Solutions Inc ....F....... 214 497-9635
McKinney *(G-14993)*

SECURITY DEVICES

Agilemesh Inc ....F....... 972 231-2122
Plano *(G-16778)*

Compx International Inc ....D....... 972 448-1400
Dallas *(G-4154)*

Dallas Sight and Sound Inc ....E....... 972 392-3202
Dallas *(G-4225)*

Detex Corporation ....D....... 800 729-3839
New Braunfels *(G-15787)*

Intelligent Surveillance Corp ....E....... 979 323-6900
Forney *(G-6310)*

Lojack Corporation ....D....... 781 302-4200
Richardson *(G-17347)*

N L Industries Inc ....E....... 972 233-1700
Dallas *(G-4711)*

Nubocam LLC ....E....... 512 473-0500
West Lake Hills *(G-20686)*

Razberi Technologies Inc ....E....... 469 828-3380
Farmers Branch *(G-6212)*

Rf Identity LLC ....F....... 512 689-1586
Cedar Park *(G-2984)*

Risk Management Armored SEC ....F....... 817 932-5923
Alvarado *(G-340)*

Sc-Integrity Inc ....E....... 214 612-7000
Richardson *(G-17393)*

Strattec Security Corporation ....F....... 915 790-5400
El Paso *(G-5985)*

Tendenci Inc ....E....... 281 497-6567
Houston *(G-12203)*

Universal Tech ....F....... 832 584-9460
Floresville *(G-6256)*

Veracity USA Incoporated ....F....... 972 786-6771
Dallas *(G-5158)*

SECURITY EQPT STORES

Terry Costa Inc ....E....... 972 385-6100
Dallas *(G-5050)*

Trafco Industries Inc ....G....... 979 234-5713
Eagle Lake *(G-5544)*

Veterans Mfg LLC ....G....... 713 854-9261
Katy *(G-13454)*

SECURITY GUARD SVCS

Timekeepers Inc ....D....... 830 331-1224
Boerne *(G-2142)*

SECURITY PROTECTIVE DEVICES MAINTENANCE & MONITORING SVCS

Good Sportsman Marketing LLC ....E....... 877 269-8490
Irving *(G-13040)*

Neu Security Services LLC ....D....... 512 469-9980
Austin *(G-1364)*

Rok Protective Systems Inc ....G....... 713 467-6999
Houston *(G-11658)*

Securetech Systems Inc ....F....... 817 869-0569
Irving *(G-13174)*

SECURITY SYSTEMS SERVICES

APS Industrial Services Inc ....E....... 817 385-5500
Arlington *(G-619)*

Bl Technology Inc ....E....... 832 698-8000
Tomball *(G-19967)*

Dynamic Intgrtons Ctrl Systems ....F....... 512 716-0817
Round Rock *(G-17650)*

Ldia Holdings LLC ....E....... 512 247-3700
Austin *(G-1284)*

One Source SEC & Sound Inc ....E....... 713 934-7400
Humble *(G-12791)*

Sabre Sentinel Intl LLC ....E....... 972 529-6570
McKinney *(G-14973)*

Sanitz Enterprises Inc ....F....... 719 439-2183
Willow City *(G-20871)*

Sharco Technologies Inc ....F....... 512 258-0573
Pflugerville *(G-16688)*

Siemens Industry Inc ....B....... 972 947-7000
Dallas *(G-4959)*

Soloprotect Us LLC ....D....... 866 632-6577
Coppell *(G-3446)*

Tan Boots LLC ....F....... 512 921-0720
Austin *(G-1713)*

Trend Micro Incorporated ....C....... 408 257-1500
Irving *(G-13199)*

Zix Corporation ....D....... 214 370-2000
Dallas *(G-5210)*

Zixcorp Systems Inc ....E....... 214 370-2000
Dallas *(G-5211)*

SEEDS & BULBS WHOLESALERS

Delta and Pine Land Company ....F....... 806 839-2491
Hale Center *(G-8118)*

SELF-DEFENSE & ATHLETIC INSTRUCTION SVCS

Dreadnaught Industries ....G....... 210 601-8149
Von Ormy *(G-20347)*

SELF-PROPELLED AIRCRAFT DEALER

Northrop Grumman Systems Corp ....A....... 972 946-9000
Dallas *(G-4743)*

SEMICONDUCTOR & RELATED DEVICES: Random Access Memory Or RAM

Memphis Electronic Inc ....G....... 713 600-6080
Houston *(G-10826)*

Micron Technology Inc ....C....... 972 521-5200
Allen *(G-286)*

SEMICONDUCTOR CIRCUIT NETWORKS

M C Systems Inc ....F....... 972 247-6785
Dallas *(G-4620)*

SEMICONDUCTOR DEVICES: Wafers

Intelligent Epitaxy Tech Inc ....D....... 972 234-0068
Richardson *(G-17334)*

Painted Rock LLC ....E....... 512 832-5057
Cedar Park *(G-2981)*

Progressive Mfg Tech Inc ....F....... 512 380-1991
Austin *(G-1435)*

SEMICONDUCTORS & RELATED DEVICES

Advanced Rfurbishment Tech LLC ....E....... 512 377-1016
Austin *(G-894)*

Alereon Inc ....D....... 512 345-4200
Austin *(G-906)*

American Innovations Ltd ....E....... 512 249-3400
Austin *(G-916)*

Amkor Technology Inc ....D....... 512 953-0701
Austin *(G-919)*

Analytical Sensors Instrs LLC ....D....... 281 565-8818
Houston *(G-8636)*

Applied Materials Inc ....E....... 512 272-7075
Austin *(G-924)*

Applied Materials Inc ....D....... 469 340-7810
Richardson *(G-17271)*

Applied Materials Inc ....F....... 512 845-1126
Austin *(G-1690)*

Applied Materials Inc ....A....... 512 272-1000
Austin *(G-925)*

Applied Optoelectronics Inc ....C....... 281 295-1800
Sugar Land *(G-19445)*

Arm Inc ....F....... 408 576-1500
Austin *(G-932)*

Atmi Materials Ltd ....C....... 512 715-5343
Burnet *(G-2602)*

Austin Semiconductor Inc ....C 512 339-1188
  Austin (G-962)
Black Sand Technologies Inc ....F 512 329-9400
  Austin (G-994)
Ca Inc ....F 402 494-2411
  Arlington (G-636)
Canon Nanotechnologies Inc ....D 512 339-7760
  Austin (G-1024)
Cbg Corporation ....E 512 491-7541
  Austin (G-1033)
CER Tek Inc ....F 915 772-8290
  El Paso (G-5693)
Clairex Technologies Inc ....F 972 265-4905
  Plano (G-16825)
Coherent Logix Incorporated ....E 512 382-8961
  West Lake Hills (G-20679)
Consistent Reasoning Inc ....E 512 382-8940
  West Lake Hills (G-20680)
Continental Auto Systems Inc ....A 830 372-7000
  Seguin (G-18833)
Convergent Performance LLC ....G 713 398-8496
  Houston (G-9296)
Cooper B-Line Inc ....E 713 678-4460
  Houston (G-9303)
Criteria Labs Inc ....E 512 637-4500
  Austin (G-1073)
Datatronic Control Corporation ....E 972 475-7879
  Rowlett (G-17704)
Diodes Incorporated ....E 972 987-3900
  Plano (G-16845)
Diodes Incorporated ....C 972 987-3900
  Plano (G-16846)
Efficiency Aggregators LLC ....F 832 862-1103
  Richmond (G-17453)
Entegris Inc ....F 512 715-5344
  Burnet (G-2607)
Entegris Prof Solutions Inc ....E 512 244-5200
  Round Rock (G-17655)
Finisar Corporation ....C 214 509-2700
  Allen (G-268)
Freescale Smcdtr Hldings V Inc ....F 512 895-2000
  Austin (G-1171)
Futurefab Inc ....F 972 423-6606
  Plano (G-16876)
Headway Research Inc ....F 972 272-5431
  Garland (G-7509)
Hg Solutions Inc ....F 972 205-0888
  Garland (G-7512)
High Tech Services Inc ....F 972 231-8037
  Richardson (G-17328)
Ichor Systems Inc ....D 512 246-9092
  Austin (G-1216)
Innosync Inc ....E 972 644-7962
  Dallas (G-4501)
Interntonal Resistive Texas LP ....C 361 992-7900
  Corpus Christi (G-3555)
Jtm Technologies Inc ....F 972 635-6900
  Royse City (G-17720)
KLA Corporation ....E 512 231-4200
  Austin (G-1270)
Legerity Holdings Inc ....C 512 228-5400
  Austin (G-1288)
Ltd Material LLC ....E 512 933-9292
  Austin (G-1306)
Ludlum Measurements Inc ....D 325 235-1418
  Sweetwater (G-19634)
Maxim Integrated Products Inc ....F 512 249-0307
  Austin (G-1703)
Microchip Technology Inc ....G 512 334-1931
  Austin (G-1338)
Micron Semiconductor Pdts Inc ....D 512 248-8283
  Austin (G-1339)
Micron Semiconductor Pdts Inc ....F 281 970-3202
  Tomball (G-19987)
Micron Technology Texas Llc ....D 972 521-5200
  Allen (G-287)
Micron Vision Corporation ....F 281 546-9632
  Plano (G-16927)
Micropac Industries Inc ....D 972 272-3571
  Garland (G-7552)
Micropower Global Corporation ....F 512 245-8976
  San Marcos (G-18699)
Microsemi Semiconductor (us) ....D 512 228-5400
  Austin (G-1340)
Microtune Inc ....F 972 673-1600
  Plano (G-16928)
Modus Test LLC ....F 972 914-7866
  Richardson (G-17359)
Neteffect Inc ....E 512 302-0002
  Austin (G-1363)

Nextech Solutions Inc ....E 214 343-5300
  Dallas (G-4736)
Nortonlifelock Inc ....D 210 403-7800
  San Antonio (G-18351)
Nortonlifelock Inc ....D 650 527-8000
  Houston (G-11083)
Nvidia Corporation ....F 408 486-2000
  Richardson (G-17367)
Nvidia Corporation ....F 512 401-4762
  Austin (G-1707)
Nxp Usa Inc ....A 512 933-6000
  Austin (G-1373)
Nxp Usa Inc ....A 512 996-4000
  Austin (G-1708)
One Semiconductor LLC ....F 512 785-4456
  Austin (G-1385)
Photodigm Inc ....E 972 235-7584
  Richardson (G-17373)
Pricevision Inc ....E 972 770-0000
  Carrollton (G-2796)
Qorvo Inc ....A 336 678-5099
  Farmers Branch (G-6211)
Qorvo Texas LLC ....A 972 994-8200
  Richardson (G-17378)
Quantum Materials Corp ....G 512 245-6646
  San Marcos (G-18706)
Reedholm Instruments Co ....E 512 869-1935
  Georgetown (G-7674)
Renesas Electronics Amer Inc ....E 408 432-8888
  West Lake Hills (G-20687)
Resonant Inc ....D 805 308-9803
  Austin (G-1460)
Retronix Global Inc ....E 512 808-5659
  Austin (G-1463)
Schunk Xycarb Technology Inc ....E 512 863-0033
  Georgetown (G-7676)
Semes America Inc ....E 512 251-3188
  Pflugerville (G-16687)
Semiconductor Support Svcs Co ....E 512 267-7087
  Austin (G-1491)
Semtech Corporation ....E 972 231-1606
  Richardson (G-17396)
Sigmasense 844 248-9081
  West Lake Hills (G-20688)
Skorpios Technologies Inc ....C 512 356-2000
  Austin (G-1509)
Sunrgy LLC 832 786-5051
  Stafford (G-19381)
Syndiant Inc ....E 972 248-3331
  Dallas (G-3852)
Tempo Semiconductor Inc ....F 512 827-3440
  Austin (G-1562)
Teradyne Inc ....D 972 231-5384
  Plano (G-17025)
Texas Instruments Incorporated ....F 972 995-2011
  Dallas (G-5066)
Texas Instruments Incorporated ....D 214 479-3773
  Dallas (G-5068)
Texas Instruments Incorporated ....D 214 567-5185
  Dallas (G-5069)
Texas Instruments Incorporated ....F 832 939-2000
  Sugar Land (G-19562)
Texas Instruments Incorporated ....E 972 995-2011
  Stafford (G-19386)
Texas Instruments Incorporated ....C 972 644-5580
  Dallas (G-5071)
Texas Instruments Incorporated ....F 817 401-5563
  Dallas (G-5072)
Texas Instruments Incorporated ....G 972 995-2011
  Plano (G-17030)
Texas Instruments Incorporated ....B 972 995-2011
  Dallas (G-5073)
Tokyo Electron US Holdings Inc ....B 512 424-1000
  Austin (G-1585)
Tower Semicdtr San Antonio Inc ....B 210 522-7000
  San Antonio (G-18554)
Tronics Mems Inc ....D 469 872-0300
  Addison (G-171)
Trustkey Solutions Inc ....F 214 865-9354
  Richardson (G-17415)
Uhnder Inc ....E 512 722-6353
  Austin (G-1605)
Ultra Clean Technology Systems ....C 512 252-6100
  Austin (G-1606)
Wintegra Inc ....C 512 345-3808
  Austin (G-1674)
Xl Technology LLC ....F 972 369-1359
  Wylie (G-20956)
Yerico Manufacturing Inc ....E 512 285-3444
  Elgin (G-6057)

SENSORS: Infrared, Solid State

Audex Inc ....F 903 757-4083
  Hallsville (G-8126)
Drs Ntwork Imaging Systems LLC ....C 214 996-2837
  Dallas (G-4279)

SENSORS: Radiation

Global Nucleonics LLC ....F 281 578-7900
  Houston (G-9975)

SENSORS: Temperature, Exc Indl Process

Allestec Corporation ....F 281 359-1519
  Kingwood (G-13637)
Thermo Sensors Corporation ....F 972 494-1566
  Garland (G-7601)

SEPARATORS: Metal Plate

Dyna Therm Corporation ....F 832 616-3094
  The Woodlands (G-19856)

SEPTIC TANK CLEANING SVCS

Blast Envmtl & Indus Svcs ....E 281 557-1000
  League City (G-13950)
Texas Integrity Waste ....F 940 479-0189
  Ponder (G-17096)

SEPTIC TANKS: Concrete

Buchanan Septic Tanks Inc ....F 512 793-3100
  Buchanan Dam (G-2517)
Comal Concrete Products Inc ....F 830 606-4732
  New Braunfels (G-15786)
Hoesman Industries Inc ....E 512 247-4173
  Del Valle (G-5331)
Randolph D & L Company LLC ....F 903 886-3055
  Commerce (G-3246)

SEPTIC TANKS: Plastic

Edwards Sptic Grease Trck Svcs ....F 903 643-7585
  Kilgore (G-13549)
Southern Manufacturing Co LLC ....E 409 962-4501
  Groves (G-8110)

SEWAGE & WATER TREATMENT EQPT

City of Colony The ....F 972 625-4471
  Lewisville (G-14037)
City of Jefferson ....F 903 665-2832
  Jefferson (G-13283)
Gardner Denver Inc ....D 832 421-5469
  Pasadena (G-16446)
Guiverman Industries LLC ....E 866 235-8057
  Plano (G-16882)
Huffman & Huffman Inc ....G 972 434-3640
  Lewisville (G-14055)
JR Sheldon & Company Inc ....F 940 368-5793
  Pottsboro (G-17197)
Temple Water Treatment ....F 254 939-2161
  Temple (G-19711)
Watts Wtr Qulty Cond Pdts Inc ....D 210 677-0618
  San Antonio (G-18612)

SEWAGE FACILITIES

Global Water Group Inc ....E 214 678-9866
  Dallas (G-4410)

SEWAGE TREATMENT SYSTEMS & EQPT

Biocope Inc ....F 806 655-2933
  Canyon (G-2669)
Enviroflex Design & Mfg ....F 281 356-6700
  Magnolia (G-14605)
Tex Tech Environmental Inc ....G 817 295-3701
  Burleson (G-2598)
Wheco Electric Inc ....E 817 244-6660
  Lakeside (G-13813)

SEWER CLEANING & RODDING SVC

AAA Pipe Cleaning Corporation ....E 281 476-5200
  La Porte (G-13715)

SEWER CLEANING EQPT: Power

Texas Underground Inc ....D 281 485-9900
  Pearland (G-16602)

PRODUCT

SEWING CONTRACTORS

Athletic Sewing Center Inc ....F 210 681-9744
San Antonio (G-17920)

Brammers Athletic Wearhouse LP .... F 281 391-1441
Katy (G-13390)

Forum Industries Inc ....D 210 225-9600
San Antonio (G-18124)

Wesco Industries Inc ....E 817 551-7063
Fort Worth (G-7137)

SEWING MACHINES & PARTS: Household

Southwest Cutters LLC ....D 915 858-2200
El Paso (G-5971)

SEWING, NEEDLEWORK & PIECE GOODS STORE: Needlework Gds/Sply

American Screen Graphics & EMB .... F 281 354-2581
Houston (G-8609)

SEWING, NEEDLEWORK & PIECE GOODS STORES: Fabric, Remnants

J&D Interiors Inc ....F 817 626-2365
Fort Worth (G-6731)

Piw Ventures Ltd ....F 713 932-9311
Houston (G-11340)

SHADES: Lamp & Light, Residential

Yankon Lighting Inc ....F 469 248-0749
McKinney (G-14992)

SHADES: Lamp Or Candle

Texas Lamp Manufacturers Inc ....E 972 564-5267
Forney (G-6315)

SHADES: Window

Window Outfitters LP ....E 469 619-0892
Dallas (G-5193)

Ybarra Group Inc ....F 210 533-5323
San Antonio (G-18629)

SHAFTS: Flexible

Ameridrives International LLC ....E 512 353-4000
San Marcos (G-18677)

SHALE MINING, COMMON

Zemer International MO Inc ....E 214 227-2320
Midlothian (G-15498)

SHALE: Expanded

Arcosa Materials Inc ....B 817 635-8500
Arlington (G-622)

SHAPES & PILINGS, STRUCTURAL: Steel

ABB Installation Products Inc ....C 713 466-6761
Houston (G-8444)

Basden Steel and Erection Inc ....E 817 295-6100
Burleson (G-2569)

C M C Steel Fabricators Inc ....A 830 372-8200
Seguin (G-18827)

Fabenco Inc ....E 713 686-6620
Houston (G-9747)

Procon Construction Co Inc ....F 281 375-6829
Brookshire (G-2323)

Quality Lnings Fabrication Inc ....E 713 863-7013
Houston (G-11495)

SAE Towers Ltd ....F 281 763-2282
Houston (G-11722)

Southeast Texas Industries Inc ....B 409 994-3570
Buna (G-2562)

Spur Industrial LLC ....E 817 293-1515
Cresson (G-3713)

Structural & Stl Pdts Mfg Ltd ....D 817 869-2301
Fort Worth (G-7021)

SHEET METAL SPECIALTIES, EXC STAMPED

A & B Sheet Metal Inc ....G 512 365-7870
Taylor (G-19646)

A-1 Sheet Metal and AC Inc ....E 409 833-4715
Beaumont (G-1846)

AC Metals LLC ....E 214 630-5554
Dallas (G-3880)

Allied Alumina Group Inc ....C 361 777-2400
Gregory (G-8098)

Amtex Prcision Fabrication Inc ....F 281 489-7042
Manvel (G-14731)

Beaumont Metal Industries Inc ....E 409 833-1777
Beaumont (G-1861)

Bison Profab Inc ....E 281 356-0026
Magnolia (G-14592)

Blackburn Machine & Fab LLC ....E 713 644-2386
Houston (G-8910)

Blumenthal Inc ....E 713 228-6432
Houston (G-8923)

Ccpjv Inc ....E 713 690-1622
Houston (G-9110)

Dralco Systems LLC ....D 817 599-7335
Weatherford (G-20588)

First Quality Fabricating Inc ....F 214 748-0071
Dallas (G-4363)

G W Vines Company Inc ....F 214 742-8371
Dallas (G-4389)

Graco Interests Inc ....B 713 978-7000
Houston (G-10010)

Guzman Mfg Inc ....F 972 475-3003
Rowlett (G-17706)

H & S Metals Inc ....F 281 421-9488
Baytown (G-1821)

Hou-Stone Inc ....D 713 827-8700
Houston (G-10214)

Integrated Metal Products Inc ....E 512 259-4143
Leander (G-13993)

Intsel Steel Distributors LLC ....C 713 937-9500
Houston (G-10410)

Irving Tool & Mfg Co Inc ....D 972 926-4000
Garland (G-7521)

J K Welding Service LLC ....E 281 550-1008
Cypress (G-3803)

Kieschnick Industries Inc ....E 409 833-5611
Beaumont (G-1914)

Kinlau Sheet Metal Works Inc ....F 940 552-5311
Vernon (G-20227)

Mabco Equipment Ltd ....E 817 599-7335
Weatherford (G-20602)

Mason Road Sheet Metal Inc ....D 713 466-5054
Houston (G-10784)

Mc Hone Metal Fabricators Inc ....F 972 524-7775
Terrell (G-19741)

Mechanical Sheet Metal Inc ....E 972 524-6200
Terrell (G-19742)

Multi-Metal & Mfg Co Inc ....D 972 771-1376
Rockwall (G-17556)

Oaks Precision Fabricating Inc ....E 713 937-9190
Houston (G-11107)

P M P E Ltd ....D 830 303-0056
Seguin (G-18852)

Parkline Inc ....D 409 935-5743
Hitchcock (G-8339)

Phoenix Mfg Inc ....F 214 544-7507
Allen (G-293)

Pi-Co Prcision Fabrication Inc ....E 512 759-1026
Hutto (G-12883)

Precision Sheet Metal Shop Inc ....D 972 771-1423
Rockwall (G-17561)

R & R Design Inc ....E 972 524-1789
Terrell (G-19748)

R-O Mfg Co ....F 817 293-6150
Fort Worth (G-6934)

Steeltron Metal Works ....F 210 774-4127
San Antonio (G-18499)

Stuarts Sheet Metal Inc ....E 512 491-0112
Austin (G-1543)

Triple C Industries Inc ....E 936 931-1171
Hockley (G-8349)

Vlj Inc ....F 972 442-4673
Wylie (G-20955)

SHEET MUSIC STORES

Rbc Music Company ....F 210 736-6902
San Antonio (G-18412)

SHEET MUSIC, WHOLESALE

Rbc Music Company ....F 210 736-6902
San Antonio (G-18412)

SHEETING: Laminated Plastic

Technology Container Corp ....E 972 228-1617
Desoto (G-5444)

SHEETING: Window, Plastic

Skylights Over Texas LLC ....F 210 402-0500
San Antonio (G-18478)

SHEETS & STRIPS: Aluminum

Howmet Aerospace Inc ....F 940 243-4491
Denton (G-5374)

Howmet Aerospace Inc ....B 903 832-8471
Texarkana (G-19765)

Howmet Aerospace Inc ....C 214 631-0200
Dallas (G-4469)

Howmet Aerospace Inc ....F 972 416-6500
Carrollton (G-2762)

Howmet Globl Fastening Systems ....C 830 774-7156
Del Rio (G-5317)

Quanex Building Products Corp ....E 731 961-4600
Houston (G-11504)

Team Pride Extrusions Inc ....E 940 562-2205
Megargel (G-14994)

SHEETS: Solid Fiber, Made From Purchased Materials

Accurate Die Cutting Inc ....E 972 562-7921
McKinney (G-14922)

SHELLAC

Corchem Manufacturing Inc ....F 432 332-1335
Odessa (G-15968)

Rok Protective Systems Inc ....G 713 467-6999
Houston (G-11658)

SHELTERED WORKSHOPS

Aldersgate Enrichment Center ....D 325 646-2566
Early (G-5556)

Border Tm Industries Inc ....C 915 779-6431
El Paso (G-5671)

Orc Industries Inc ....D 956 831-0618
Brownsville (G-2389)

Travis Assn For The Blind ....C 512 442-2329
Austin (G-1590)

Work Services Corporation ....D 940 766-3207
Wichita Falls (G-20835)

SHELVING, MADE FROM PURCHASED WIRE

Zimair LP ....D 817 624-7245
Fort Worth (G-7160)

SHELVING: Office & Store, Exc Wood

Empire Electric Inc ....E 713 688-0151
Houston (G-9619)

Proper Storage Systems LLC ....G 830 372-1380
Seguin (G-18856)

SHIP BLDG & RPRG: Drilling & Production Platforms, Oil/Gas

Aethon I LP ....D 214 750-1522
Dallas (G-3900)

Atlantia Offshore Limited ....D 281 899-4300
Houston (G-8737)

Bb Chemicals Inc ....E 432 381-2595
Odessa (G-15929)

Bersal Energy LLC ....F 956 270-1155
McAllen (G-14841)

Best Drilling Services (bds) ....E 713 864-3900
Houston (G-8862)

Long & Long Pier Drilling Co ....F 972 422-4084
Plano (G-16910)

Offshore Express Inc ....D 985 868-1438
Houston (G-11141)

Offshore Spclty Fbricators LLC ....C 985 868-1438
Houston (G-11144)

SHIP BLDG/RPRG: Submersible Marine Robots, Manned/Unmanned

Amphion Inc ....F 210 771-8116
San Antonio (G-17906)

Oceaneering International Inc ....C 713 329-4500
Houston (G-11124)

Oceaneering International Inc ....F 713 329-4318
Houston (G-11126)

SHIP BUILDING & REPAIRING: Cargo, Commercial

American Fincl Mktg Group Inc ....F 866 679-9241
League City **(G-13945)**
Gulf Copper & Mfg Corp ....F 409 989-0300
Port Arthur **(G-17111)**
Main Marine Repair Inc ....F 713 645-3553
Houston **(G-10740)**
Modec International Inc ....B 281 529-8100
Houston **(G-10902)**
Pangea Enterprises Inc ....E 956 542-9494
Houston **(G-11232)**

SHIP BUILDING & REPAIRING: Dredges

Gulf Copper Ship Repair Inc ....D 361 883-1040
Corpus Christi **(G-3540)**

SHIP BUILDING & REPAIRING: Fishing Vessels, Large

Texgulmarco Co Inc ....E 956 943-2673
Port Isabel **(G-17139)**

SHIP BUILDING & REPAIRING: Landing

Smith-Hamm Inc ....D 409 740-3314
Galveston **(G-7408)**

SHIP BUILDING & REPAIRING: Offshore Sply Boats

David Keels ....E 409 316-9265
Hitchcock **(G-8336)**
Offshore Oil Services Inc ....E 979 265-3300
Clute **(G-3157)**
Southern Gulf Solutions LLC ....F 979 299-8808
Clute **(G-3159)**
Subsea 7 (us) LLC ....C 713 430-1100
Houston **(G-12086)**
Wartsila North America Inc ....C 281 233-6200
Houston **(G-12600)**

SHIP BUILDING & REPAIRING: Radar Towers, Floating

Black Star Energy Services LLC ....E 432 272-3395
Odessa **(G-15936)**
CPI Satcom & Antenna Tech Inc ....D 254 765-3304
Wortham **(G-20922)**

SHIP BUILDING & REPAIRING: Rigging, Marine

Oil States Industries Inc ....E 817 468-1400
Arlington **(G-742)**

SHIP BUILDING & REPAIRING: Tankers

Ocean Ship Holding Inc ....E 281 579-3700
Houston **(G-11121)**
Ocean Shipholdings Inc ....E 281 579-3700
Houston **(G-11122)**
PCI Manufacturing LLC ....E 903 885-6772
Sulphur Springs **(G-19596)**
Tarsco Construction Corp ....C 515 225-3003
Spring **(G-19258)**

SHIP BUILDING & REPAIRING: Towboats

Glendale Boat Works Inc ....F 281 452-7146
Channelview **(G-3023)**

SHIP BUILDING & REPAIRING: Transport Vessels, Troop

Big Shot LLC ....E 504 877-2335
Lancaster **(G-13840)**
Tyson Globl Trnspt & Cnstr LLC ....E 470 481-6161
Cypress **(G-3824)**

SHIP BUILDING & REPAIRING: Tugboats

Conrad Orange Shipyard Inc ....C 409 670-4900
Orange **(G-16236)**
John Bludworth Shipyard LLC ....D 361 887-7981
Corpus Christi **(G-3558)**

SHIPBUILDING & REPAIR

Beacon Maritime Inc ....A 409 670-1060
West Orange **(G-20693)**
Bgi Enterprise Inc ....E 409 833-0303
Beaumont **(G-1865)**
Bludworth Marine LLC ....G 713 644-1595
Galveston **(G-7389)**
Burton Shipyard Inc ....E 409 735-2491
Bridge City **(G-2281)**
Conglobal Industries LLC ....E 713 675-7587
Galena Park **(G-7379)**
Crumplers Shipbuilding Co Inc ....E 409 886-7934
Orange **(G-16237)**
Gulf Copper & Mfg Corp ....C 409 982-6122
Port Arthur **(G-17112)**
H & S Fabricators Inc ....E 361 884-1212
Corpus Christi **(G-3542)**
Hasco Marine ....F 281 452-5017
Channelview **(G-3025)**
International Coating Services ....E 936 344-9494
Willis **(G-20850)**
Intership Services Inc ....E 713 645-2666
Houston **(G-10407)**
Keppel Amfels Inc ....A 956 838-3110
Brownsville **(G-2374)**
L&R Midland Inc ....E 713 680-0909
Houston **(G-10577)**
Lynchburg Shipyard Inc ....E 281 426-2474
Baytown **(G-1827)**
MPW Corporation ....F 713 640-2700
Houston **(G-10931)**
Ocean Ships Inc ....E 281 579-3700
Houston **(G-11123)**
Offshore Service Vessels LLC ....G 832 251-6665
Houston **(G-11143)**
Sneed Shipbuilding Inc ....E 281 862-2266
Channelview **(G-3037)**
Sterling Shipyard LP ....E 409 727-2009
Port Neches **(G-17168)**
Stx Service Americas LLC ....F 713 637-4030
Houston **(G-12084)**
Texas Marine Shipyard LLC ....F 409 457-6260
Dickinson **(G-5478)**
United Marine Enterprise Inc ....D 409 833-0303
Beaumont **(G-1965)**
Vls Recovery Services LLC ....D 409 962-8800
Port Arthur **(G-17132)**

SHOE & BOOT ACCESS

Texas Leather Trim Inc ....E 817 535-5883
Fort Worth **(G-7049)**

SHOE MATERIALS: Counters

Counter Club Inc ....G 817 573-5040
Granbury **(G-7795)**

SHOE MATERIALS: Rubber

Old Nocona Boot Factory LLC ....F 682 237-7644
Roanoke **(G-17491)**

SHOE STORES

Holicks Manufacturing Co LLC ....F 979 846-6721
Bryan **(G-2477)**

SHOE STORES: Boots, Men's

Beck Cowboy Boots Inc ....G 806 373-1600
Amarillo **(G-402)**
Big Bend Saddlery Inc ....F 432 837-5551
Alpine **(G-311)**
C & C Western Wear Inc ....F 903 753-8991
Longview **(G-14206)**
Cowtown Boot Company ....D 915 593-2929
El Paso **(G-5704)**
Old Nocona Boot Factory LLC ....F 682 237-7644
Roanoke **(G-17491)**
Stallion Boot Co Inc ....E 915 532-6268
El Paso **(G-5974)**

SHOE STORES: Orthopedic

Brides & Belles of Tyler ....G 903 581-8211
Tyler **(G-20060)**
San Antonio Shoe Inc ....A 830 768-7200
Del Rio **(G-5323)**

SHOE STORES: Women's

San Antonio Shoe Inc ....G 210 921-8274
San Antonio **(G-18450)**

SHOES & BOOTS WHOLESALERS

San Antonio Shoe Inc ....G 210 921-8274
San Antonio **(G-18450)**

SHOES: Athletic, Exc Rubber Or Plastic

Fossil Partners LP ....G 972 437-0452
Richardson **(G-17315)**

SHOES: Canvas, Rubber Soled

Vans Inc ....F 713 436-7925
Pearland **(G-16609)**

SHOES: Infants' & Children's

Justin Brands Inc ....C 817 332-4385
Fort Worth **(G-6748)**

SHOES: Men's

Anderson Bean Boot Co Inc ....E 956 565-2618
Mercedes **(G-15002)**
Franklin-Leddy Corporation ....E 325 653-3397
San Angelo **(G-17800)**
Honcho Boots LLC ....F 915 855-9300
El Paso **(G-5796)**
Justin Brands Inc ....B 940 226-1706
Childress **(G-3055)**
Kenneth Cole Productions Inc ....C 956 825-7116
Mercedes **(G-15007)**
San Antonio Shoe Inc ....A 830 768-7200
Del Rio **(G-5323)**

SHOES: Plastic Or Rubber

Bio World Merchandising Inc ....E 972 488-0655
Irving **(G-12948)**
Nike Inc ....E 956 565-2446
Mercedes **(G-15008)**
Nike Inc ....E 972 980-1946
Dallas **(G-4740)**

SHOES: Plastic Or Rubber Soles With Fabric Uppers

Fossil Partners LP ....G 972 437-0452
Richardson **(G-17315)**

SHOES: Women's

Cowtown Boot Company ....D 915 593-2929
El Paso **(G-5704)**
Franklin-Leddy Corporation ....E 325 653-3397
San Angelo **(G-17800)**
Justin Brands Inc ....A 915 778-8311
El Paso **(G-5824)**
San Antonio Shoe Inc ....G 210 921-8274
San Antonio **(G-18450)**
San Antonio Shoe Inc ....A 830 768-7200
Del Rio **(G-5323)**
Tony Lama Company Inc ....A 915 778-8311
El Paso **(G-6007)**

SHOES: Women's, Sandals

Tefkab Footwear LLC ....F 281 988-0977
Houston **(G-12184)**

SHOPPING CENTERS & MALLS

Austin Armature Works LP ....E 512 312-0088
Buda **(G-2520)**
Midwest Folding Products Corp ....C 312 666-3366
Temple **(G-19690)**

SHOT PEENING SVC

Curtiss-Wright Surfc Tech LLC ....F 972 641-8011
Grand Prairie **(G-7859)**
Metal Improvement Company LLC ....E 972 660-3692
Grand Prairie **(G-7926)**
Metal Improvement Company LLC ....F 713 691-0257
Houston **(G-10846)**
Southwest Indus Surfaces Inc ....E 972 641-4393
Grand Prairie **(G-7974)**

PRODUCT

SHOWCASES & DISPLAY FIXTURES: Office & Store

Idx Corporation ....C 314 739-4120
Cedar Hill (G-2943)
Quality Store Equipment Inc ....F 713 278-8634
Houston (G-11501)
Vira Insight LLC ....C 800 366-2345
Lewisville (G-14107)
Vira Insight LLC ....D 800 366-2345
Lewisville (G-14108)

SHOWER STALLS: Plastic & Fiberglass

Aquatic Co ....C 972 227-6692
Lancaster (G-13838)
Ganten Group LLC ....F 214 530-5483
Richardson (G-17320)
Hoskin & Muir Inc ....F 817 640-7220
Arlington (G-700)
RC Christopher Industries Inc ....E 972 875-6555
Ennis (G-6116)

SHREDDERS: Indl & Commercial

Ark-La-Tex Shredding Co Inc ....F 903 877-3734
Tyler (G-20048)
Corporate Records Management ....G 214 333-3453
Dallas (G-4171)
Granutch-Sturn Systems Corp AM ....D 972 790-7800
Grand Prairie (G-7884)
Riverside Engineering Inc ....F 210 227-9090
San Antonio (G-18429)
Triple/S Dynamics Inc ....E 214 828-8600
Dallas (G-5116)

SHUTTERS, DOOR & WINDOW: Metal

Aramco Home Improvement LLC ....E 409 762-9652
Galveston (G-7387)
Macgmc LLC ....F 214 774-4455
Plano (G-16916)
Plantation Shutter ....F 214 341-3677
Dallas (G-4809)
Rushman Draperies Inc ....F 214 943-1000
Plano (G-16999)
Southern Shutters Inc ....F 512 272-9711
Manor (G-14649)
Window Outfitters LP ....E 469 619-0892
Dallas (G-5193)

SHUTTERS, DOOR & WINDOW: Plastic

Houston Shutters LLC ....B 713 723-7100
Houston (G-10251)

SHUTTERS: Door, Wood

Houston Shutters LLC ....B 713 723-7100
Houston (G-10251)

SHUTTERS: Window, Wood

A & E Venetian Blind Company ....F 940 767-1449
Wichita Falls (G-20735)
Basileia Investments Inc ....C 806 765-5791
Lubbock (G-14365)
Cedar Mill Co Inc ....E 713 984-2600
Houston (G-9116)
Luna Piena Inc ....E 512 926-6346
Austin (G-1311)
Window Outfitters LP ....E 469 619-0892
Dallas (G-5193)

SIDING & STRUCTURAL MATERIALS: Wood

Allied Truss LLC ....E 903 586-1982
Jacksonville (G-13225)
Breco Trucking Inc ....E 903 870-0396
Sherman (G-18908)
Builders Firstsource Inc ....E 956 755-0301
Mercedes (G-15004)
Builders Firstsource Inc ....E 214 880-3500
Dallas (G-4066)
Eason Properties I LLC ....G 409 945-4416
Texas City (G-19789)
Lincoln Lumber LLC ....E 409 384-2587
Jasper (G-13278)
Lincoln Lumber LLC ....D 936 539-4421
Conroe (G-3321)

SIDING MATERIALS

Extruded Ennis Products ....F 972 875-1770
Ennis (G-6101)

SIDING: Precast Stone

Headwaters Incorporated ....F 830 562-3239
Tarpley (G-19643)
Niblett Enterprises Inc ....D 940 383-2887
Gainesville (G-7353)

SIDING: Sheet Metal

Composite Panl Tchnlgy-Suth In ....E 972 720-0477
Addison (G-112)
Westside Welding Inc ....E 915 877-5345
Canutillo (G-2668)

SIGN LETTERING & PAINTING SVCS

Signs & Graphics Plus LLC ....F 915 590-7446
El Paso (G-5961)

SIGN PAINTING & LETTERING SHOP

A-Ero TEC Graphics Inc ....E 972 289-9854
Mesquite (G-15022)
Budget Signs Ltd ....E 210 349-7446
San Antonio (G-17971)
Creative Signworks Inc ....E 850 785-8899
San Angelo (G-17792)
Danwal Inc ....E 903 581-0777
Tyler (G-20074)
Display Graphics Inc ....E 713 977-7888
Houston (G-9480)
Hollis Baker Sign Co Inc ....F 512 835-5782
Austin (G-1207)
Mighty Works Signage LLC ....G 713 305-8355
Houston (G-10877)
Proworx Inc ....E 713 666-3131
Houston (G-11467)
Sign Crafters Inc ....F 512 392-0900
San Marcos (G-18710)
Signtex Outdoor Inc ....F 281 351-8023
Tomball (G-20009)
Willow Creek Signs Inc ....E 817 847-0571
Saginaw (G-17760)

SIGNALING APPARATUS: Electric

Cyber Dynamics Corporation ....F 818 706-3580
Round Rock (G-17640)
L3 Technologies Inc ....A 817 619-2000
Arlington (G-715)
Open Options LLC ....E 972 818-7001
Addison (G-153)

SIGNALS: Traffic Control, Electric

3M Company ....A 325 643-9798
Brownwood (G-2423)
American Signal Corporation ....E 414 358-8000
Garland (G-7435)
Computerized Traffic Inc ....G 281 252-0505
Montgomery (G-15629)
D&G Energy Corporation ....F 956 686-6040
McAllen (G-14852)
Dallas Lite and Barricade Inc ....E 214 748-5791
Dallas (G-4218)
Fc Traffic Control Inc ....F 806 570-5633
Amarillo (G-423)
Henke Enterprises Inc ....F 936 291-2026
Huntsville (G-12813)
Integrated Roadway Svcs Inc ....E 214 352-1937
Dallas (G-4505)
Peek Traffic Corporation ....C 281 453-0200
Houston (G-11270)
Signal Group Inc ....F 281 453-0200
Houston (G-11891)
Southwest Signal Supply Inc ....F 713 946-7162
South Houston (G-19052)
Statewide Traffic Signal Co ....E 713 680-2875
Houston (G-12052)
Third Coast Services LLC ....D 832 934-0240
Magnolia (G-14629)

SIGNALS: Transportation

Aviation Dvcs Elctrnc Cmpnnts ....E 817 738-9161
Fort Worth (G-6412)
City of Irving ....E 972 721-2646
Irving (G-12972)

Impact Recovery Systems Inc ....E 210 736-4477
San Antonio (G-18180)
Mobotrex Inc ....C 512 521-3060
Austin (G-1348)
Paradigm Traffic Systems Inc ....F 817 831-9406
Arlington (G-748)
Short-Line Corporation ....F 210 492-6088
San Antonio (G-18470)
Toon LLC ....F 817 609-0672
Fort Worth (G-7066)
Trafco Industries Inc ....G 979 234-5713
Eagle Lake (G-5544)
Xarmr Corporation ....G 972 385-7899
McKinney (G-14991)

SIGNS & ADVERTISING SPECIALTIES

4d Signworx LLC ....E 713 984-2010
Houston (G-8412)
A 1 Distributors Sign Supply ....D 432 682-0083
Midland (G-15100)
A Sign of Quality LLC ....F 972 722-4147
Royse City (G-17714)
A&B Foundry LLC ....E 972 247-3579
Dallas (G-3872)
AAA Electrical Signs ....F 956 464-3221
Donna (G-5486)
Accent Sign & Awning Co LLC ....E 713 780-1151
Houston (G-8455)
Action Sportswear Inc ....E 972 487-6960
Garland (G-7427)
Adcorp Sign Systems LLC ....E 936 321-4888
Conroe (G-3252)
Airbrush Images Inc ....E 936 523-1000
Conroe (G-3254)
Allied Advertising Agency Inc ....E 210 732-7874
San Antonio (G-17897)
Ally Wholesale Signs LLC ....E 830 438-2500
Bulverde (G-2553)
Ally Wholesale Signs LLC ....F 830 438-2500
Bulverde (G-2554)
Aluma Graphics LP ....E 972 442-3299
Wylie (G-20925)
American Prtg & Promotions Inc ....E 713 645-1991
Houston (G-8605)
Andax Corp ....F 972 392-3999
Addison (G-104)
Apache Sign & Service Inc ....F 713 462-3220
Houston (G-8660)
Austin Screen Printing Inc ....E 512 454-6249
Austin (G-961)
Badmoon Enterprises LLC ....E 817 548-0561
Arlington (G-629)
Bankson Group Ltd ....E 210 699-3800
San Antonio (G-17938)
Beehive Specialty Co ....F 512 912-7940
Austin (G-985)
Big Star Branding Inc ....E 210 590-2662
San Antonio (G-17953)
Blind Dog Productions Ltd ....E 254 778-0722
Temple (G-19671)
Brick Stone Graphics By Gartex ....F 214 343-0573
Dallas (G-4049)
Brooks & Brooks Services Inc ....G 817 560-9965
Weatherford (G-20579)
Build A Sign LLC ....C 512 374-9850
Austin (G-1015)
Build A Sign LLC ....E 512 339-4447
Austin (G-1016)
C & M Graphics & Signs ....F 956 421-2114
Harlingen (G-8183)
Casteel & Associates Inc ....F 214 352-7446
Dallas (G-4091)
Century Graphics & Sign Inc ....E 432 686-8244
Midland (G-15157)
Cfj Manufacturing LP ....D 817 625-9559
Fort Worth (G-6506)
Cfj Manufacturing LP ....D 817 232-9251
Saginaw (G-17741)
Chandler Signs LLC ....C 214 902-2000
Fort Worth (G-6509)
Cjhorak Enterprises Inc ....G 817 260-0700
Southlake (G-19059)
Claytex Trophies Inc ....C 940 538-6521
Henrietta (G-8279)
Cohn Signs ....G 210 626-2157
San Antonio (G-18016)
Crabtree Barricade Systems Inc ....E 409 842-2073
Beaumont (G-1877)
Craftmark Products Inc ....E 817 457-8753
Fort Worth (G-6556)

Craftsman Printers Inc	E	806 744-8429	
Lubbock (G-14397)			
D & R Signs LLC	F	281 988-9995	
Stafford (G-19299)			
D-Signs Inc	E	214 327-2373	
Garland (G-7473)			
Dbt Inc	F	409 892-2300	
Beaumont (G-1880)			
Derse Inc	D	972 393-9046	
Coppell (G-3414)			
Digimagination LLC	F	281 445-6671	
Houston (G-9469)			
Digital Banner Plus LLC	G	210 647-3124	
San Antonio (G-18059)			
Digital Copy LLC	E	214 740-2480	
Dallas (G-4258)			
Display Products Inc	D	972 406-1221	
Dallas (G-4262)			
Display Surce Design Fctry Ltd	C	972 288-7471	
Mesquite (G-15039)			
Double S Signs LLC	F	903 838-8999	
Texarkana (G-19762)			
Dragonfly Garment Design Corp	G	830 549-5113	
Seguin (G-18836)			
Drake Alliance Corporation	D	713 869-9121	
Houston (G-9514)			
Dukes Outdoor Advertising	F	432 447-2251	
Pecos (G-16620)			
Dyna Group International Inc	D	830 620-4400	
New Braunfels (G-15788)			
Dynamic Signs Systems Mktg LLC	F	281 255-0420	
Tomball (G-19974)			
Eagle Eye Signs LP	F	972 466-2100	
Carrollton (G-2727)			
Electrical Sign Displays Inc	F	713 644-8081	
Houston (G-9589)			
Emma Grace Sign Co	F	713 864-4644	
Houston (G-9618)			
Ep Big Media Inc	F	915 585-0444	
El Paso (G-5756)			
Ezzi Signs Inc	E	713 232-0771	
Houston (G-9742)			
Farrz Inc	F	936 539-3278	
Conroe (G-3296)			
Fastsigns	G	915 229-8000	
El Paso (G-5765)			
Fastsigns International Inc	D	888 285-5935	
Carrollton (G-2736)			
Fastsigns Nat Advg Council Inc	E	214 346-5600	
Carrollton (G-2737)			
Fedex Office & Print Svcs Inc	G	512 331-0800	
Austin (G-1148)			
Fedex Office & Print Svcs Inc	E	817 543-0833	
Arlington (G-678)			
Fedex Office & Print Svcs Inc	F	210 521-8395	
San Antonio (G-18108)			
Fource Communications Limited	F	214 630-2125	
Dallas (G-4374)			
Goodman Fine Art Inc	F	210 733-0190	
San Antonio (G-18151)			
Gulf Coast Sign Inc	E	956 399-0755	
San Benito (G-18658)			
H & H Sign Co Inc	E	254 752-1801	
Waco (G-20409)			
Halo Branded Solutions Inc	E	972 536-4069	
Dallas (G-4432)			
Harvey Dupriest & Sons Inc	D	214 337-4731	
Dallas (G-4440)			
Hi-Plains Canvas Products Inc	E	806 352-5345	
Amarillo (G-492)			
Hightech Grafix Inc	E	817 616-3204	
Fort Worth (G-6699)			
Hines Chaunte	F	469 583-0985	
Farmers Branch (G-6202)			
Humble Texas Signs LLC	E	281 812-2100	
Humble (G-12779)			
Huntington Sky Production Ltd	E	956 618-1800	
McAllen (G-14869)			
Iconic Sign Group LLC	F	361 883-7446	
Corpus Christi (G-3552)			
Image Display Systems Inc	F	281 395-9100	
Katy (G-13408)			
Impact Recovery Systems Inc	E	210 736-4477	
San Antonio (G-18180)			
Inkjet Partners Inc	E	972 991-4577	
Dallas (G-4500)			
Insignia Marketing Inc	E	281 465-0040	
Magnolia (G-14610)			
Jackie Todaro	F	281 354-2581	
Kingwood (G-13646)			
Jackson Promotions Inc	F	281 474-1313	
Seabrook (G-18786)			
Janus Signs	F	972 420-8770	
Lewisville (G-14059)			
Janus Signs Inc	F	214 503-1333	
Dallas (G-4525)			
JDC Enterprises Inc	E	972 550-1880	
Irving (G-13068)			
JDM Designs Inc	E	281 356-6131	
Stagecoach (G-19401)			
Jim Dandy Boxes Inc	E	817 608-9180	
Grand Prairie (G-7903)			
Jim McNabb Inc	F	512 365-2010	
Taylor (G-19658)			
Jones Holt Enterprises Inc	E	210 657-5917	
San Antonio (G-18207)			
KB & KB Enterprises Inc	F	979 764-7446	
College Station (G-3189)			
Kmp Graphics Inc	G	817 295-5350	
Burleson (G-2585)			
Landes Inc	E	713 665-0655	
Houston (G-10593)			
Lassiter Industries Inc	E	281 781-8708	
Houston (G-10606)			
Led OEM Partners LLC	F	832 769-0593	
Houston (G-10614)			
Lone Star Corrugated Cont Corp	C	972 579-1551	
Irving (G-13089)			
Lone Star Faces Inc	E	713 706-3223	
Houston (G-10676)			
Lonestar Logos MGT Co LLC	E	512 462-1310	
West Lake Hills (G-20684)			
Lown Brothers Inc	E	915 594-4499	
El Paso (G-5848)			
Lozz Quatezz LLC	F	956 687-7446	
Pharr (G-16706)			
LSI Integrated Graphics LP	C	713 744-4100	
Houston (G-10696)			
Luma Vue Inc	E	214 842-8347	
Frisco (G-7260)			
Luminator Technology Group LLC	C	972 424-6511	
Plano (G-16913)			
M3 Image LLC	F	915 845-7676	
El Paso (G-5856)			
Main Street Installers LLC	F	817 459-2001	
Arlington (G-727)			
Makitso USA LLC	E	281 495-1300	
Stafford (G-19350)			
Marco Display Specialists LP	B	817 244-8300	
Fort Worth (G-6809)			
Marco Dsplay Specialists GP Lc	C	817 244-8300	
Fort Worth (G-6810)			
Mercury Signs and Display Ltd	E	713 462-1068	
Houston (G-10832)			
Mighty Works Signage LLC	E	713 305-8355	
Houston (G-10877)			
Mlc Signs LP	F	972 420-8770	
Lewisville (G-14069)			
Mr Sign Inc	G	214 526-7446	
Dallas (G-4699)			
N & P Sign System Inc	F	281 444-9535	
Houston (G-10947)			
National Banner Company Inc	C	972 241-2131	
Dallas (G-4712)			
National Banner Company Inc	D	972 241-2131	
Dallas (G-4713)			
National Banner Company Inc	E	903 378-2761	
Honey Grove (G-8357)			
Nationwide Applications LLC	E	210 651-0202	
Schertz (G-18758)			
Natural Graphics Inc	E	713 661-5075	
Houston (G-11009)			
Neon Electric Corporation	D	281 987-1144	
Houston (G-11023)			
Northwest Advantage Inc	F	713 622-4888	
Tomball (G-19992)			
OConn LLC	F	956 630-6116	
McAllen (G-14896)			
Odee Company	E	214 340-0415	
Dallas (G-4754)			
One Focus Inc	F	817 750-7667	
Haslet (G-8221)			
Outdoor Lighting Services LP	C	713 690-6301	
Houston (G-11204)			
Outfront Media LLC	D	713 868-2284	
Houston (G-11205)			
Outstnding Grphic Slutions Inc	G	972 255-2022	
Irving (G-13137)			
Paladin Signs and Graphics Inc	F	817 744-7361	
Benbrook (G-2044)			
Printdallas Inc	F	214 363-1101	
Dallas (G-4826)			
Qti Promotions and Apparel Inc	E	254 756-4444	
Waco (G-20452)			
R W Gonzalez Office Pdts Inc	F	512 300-2300	
Austin (G-1448)			
Reagan Outdoor Advertising	E	512 926-7740	
Austin (G-1454)			
Recs Signs LLC	F	832 226-8000	
Katy (G-13435)			
Richards Signs & Cranes Inc	E	940 325-6585	
Mineral Wells (G-15539)			
Rmg Networks Holding Corp	E	800 827-9666	
Addison (G-159)			
Robert Leshea Inc	F	803 407-9284	
Katy (G-13377)			
Ron T Felt	F	512 258-5523	
Austin (G-1471)			
Ron T Felt	F	512 335-7446	
Austin (G-1472)			
Sel Corporate Enterprises Inc	G	214 348-8784	
Dallas (G-4948)			
Selectouch Corporation	E	972 924-3289	
Anna (G-585)			
Sign Factory Inc	E	713 849-4575	
Houston (G-11889)			
Sign Shop	G	325 641-2424	
Brownwood (G-2444)			
Signad Inc	F	713 861-6013	
Houston (G-11890)			
Signazon Corporation	E	214 296-0022	
Plano (G-17006)			
Signit Inc	E	817 589-9988	
Richland Hills (G-17448)			
Signs Manufacturing Corp	F	214 339-2227	
Dallas (G-4962)			
Signs Now Corporation	F	972 398-8648	
Plano (G-17007)			
Signs On Go	F	806 722-7446	
Lubbock (G-14480)			
Signs West Inc	F	512 282-5001	
Austin (G-1502)			
Signtex Outdoor Inc	F	281 351-8023	
Tomball (G-20009)			
Smurfit Kappa North Amer LLC	E	713 869-5900	
Houston (G-11926)			
Southwest Sign Group Inc	D	210 648-3221	
San Antonio (G-18489)			
Sparkle Lighting Services	E	713 856-8500	
Houston (G-11992)			
Stamp Shop Inc	F	210 824-7373	
San Antonio (G-18495)			
State Sign Corporation	D	713 943-1831	
Houston (G-12051)			
STI Graphics Inc	G	281 351-2776	
Tomball (G-20011)			
Stokes Sign Company Inc	F	512 263-7446	
Lakeway (G-13821)			
Store Dcor Inc - Rtailgraphics	D	972 475-4404	
Rowlett (G-17711)			
Summit Sportswear Inc	G	281 335-5370	
League City (G-13980)			
Superior Signs	G	210 646-7799	
San Antonio (G-18514)			
Synergy Signs & Services LLC	E	817 745-2330	
Fort Worth (G-7027)			
Tc Signs Inc	F	972 492-2801	
Lewisville (G-14097)			
Tejas Signs Wetz	E	830 609-6246	
San Antonio (G-18646)			
Texas 28 LLC	F	806 644-9663	
Spearman (G-19088)			
Texas Marking Products Inc	F	281 364-7100	
The Woodlands (G-19929)			
Texas Nameplate Company Inc	D	214 428-8341	
Lancaster (G-13849)			
Texas Neon Advertising Company	F	210 734-6694	
San Antonio (G-18538)			
Texas Republic Signs LLC	E	832 727-5415	
Houston (G-12247)			
Theag North Arlington LLC	F	817 261-3027	
Arlington (G-797)			
Tpg Capital Management LP	B	817 871-4000	
Fort Worth (G-7069)			
Transfer Graphics Inc	F	940 566-2679	
Denton (G-5407)			
Ultimate Decals Inc	F	936 539-5719	
Conroe (G-3376)			
Universal Display & Fixs Co	B	972 221-5157	
Lewisville (G-14100)			

Universal Display and Fix Co....C....972 434-8067
Lewisville (G-14101)
Universal Display and Fix Co....C....972 221-5157
Flower Mound (G-6291)
US Signs Inc....F....713 977-7900
Houston (G-12489)
Vixxo Corporation....C....713 977-7900
Houston (G-12578)
Voip Tel LP....F....512 543-9556
Austin (G-1644)
Walton Signage Ltd....C....210 886-0644
San Antonio (G-18609)
Wetz Sign & Lighting Service....F....830 609-6246
San Antonio (G-18649)
Willow Creek Signs Inc....E....817 847-0571
Haslet (G-8227)
Willow Creek Signs Inc....E....817 847-0571
Saginaw (G-17760)
Worlds of Wow LLC....E....817 380-4215
Denton (G-5413)
Wraps Gorilla....F....817 652-2882
Arlington (G-811)
Wrs Group Ltd....E....254 776-6461
Waco (G-20481)

SIGNS & ADVERTISING SPECIALTIES: Artwork, Advertising

JIT Manufacturing Inc....E....903 887-0226
Mabank (G-14577)
M2w Inc....D....972 407-1332
Mesquite (G-15059)
Signtex Imaging Inc....E....281 351-2776
Tomball (G-20008)

SIGNS & ADVERTISING SPECIALTIES: Letters For Signs, Metal

El Paso Reprographics LLC....F....915 532-6255
El Paso (G-5740)
Millennium Signs America LLC....B....903 944-7981
Tyler (G-20129)

SIGNS & ADVERTISING SPECIALTIES: Novelties

Airmark Industries Inc....E....325 641-1999
Brownwood (G-2424)
Bob Hughes Displays LLC....F....713 468-7726
Marble Falls (G-14739)
El Paso Heat Transfer Inc....F....915 779-6334
El Paso (G-5735)
Lorente International LLC....E....877 281-6469
Farmers Branch (G-6206)
New Teraco Inc....E....800 687-3999
Midland (G-15316)
Pb Unlimited LLC....F....817 831-4336
Haltom City (G-8156)
Refuge Industries LLC....F....512 961-4907
Austin (G-1456)

SIGNS & ADVERTISING SPECIALTIES: Scoreboards, Electric

Spectrum Corporation....D....713 944-6200
Houston (G-12008)

SIGNS & ADVERTISING SPECIALTIES: Signs

21c Sign Company....F....915 775-8514
El Paso (G-5630)
A-1 Siign Engravers Inc....E....432 682-3492
Midland (G-15102)
Abney Group Inc....F....512 832-0000
Austin (G-877)
Acme Sign & Plastics Co....F....325 677-9469
Abilene (G-10)
Acp International Inc....D....817 640-0992
Arlington (G-608)
ADS Custom Signs Inc....G....713 943-0895
Pasadena (G-16378)
Alamo Outdoor Structures Inc....F....210 651-0425
San Antonio (G-18638)
Architectural Graphic Products....G....713 683-8942
Houston (G-8683)
Austin Archtctral Graphics Inc....E....512 473-2075
Creedmoor (G-3705)
Banner Sign Graphics....F....512 458-5348
Round Rock (G-17626)
Bauer Visual Graphics Inc....F....713 473-5241
Pasadena (G-16394)
Beaed LP....D....281 331-2035
Alvin (G-354)
Beaed LP....E....281 968-7249
Alvin (G-355)
Brite Lite Sign Service Inc....E....713 849-5545
Conroe (G-3264)
Caasco Signs Inc....G....281 332-1502
League City (G-13951)
Carlton Industries LP....E....979 242-5055
La Grange (G-13693)
Chism Company....F....210 824-6315
San Antonio (G-18004)
Clark Fire Equipment Inc....F....713 453-3778
Houston (G-9209)
Contractors Service Ltd....F....325 692-4317
Abilene (G-36)
Creative Signworks Inc....E....850 785-8899
San Angelo (G-17792)
Design Center Signs Inc....F....903 561-4995
Tyler (G-20075)
Display Graphics Inc....F....713 977-7888
Houston (G-9480)
Distinctive Graphics Inc....F....817 329-0411
Southlake (G-19062)
Eagle Traffic Signs Safety LLC....G....713 987-9178
Houston (G-9566)
Garrison Bros Signs Inc....F....806 744-1161
Lubbock (G-14415)
Gem Sign Service Inc....F....830 609-1052
New Braunfels (G-15794)
Greshare Enterprises Inc....F....512 869-7446
Georgetown (G-7655)
Houston Sign & Service Inc....F....281 442-0175
Houston (G-10252)
Hughes Manufacturing Inc....F....979 542-0333
Giddings (G-7696)
Ideal Signs....F....512 930-7446
Georgetown (G-7657)
Intex United Inc....E....281 568-4000
Houston (G-10409)
Kuster Sign LLC....G....972 991-5841
Addison (G-142)
Martin Inc....E....972 247-7160
Dallas (G-4639)
Multi-Quest Inc....F....972 235-2356
Richardson (G-17361)
Paul Smoke....F....281 422-4228
Baytown (G-1831)
Ruben Reyes....F....214 331-4307
Dallas (G-4918)
Sign International Inc....F....409 832-0117
Beaumont (G-1949)
Sign Technologies Inc....F....903 838-8999
Texarkana (G-19773)
Sign Wave Corporation....G....214 890-4444
Dallas (G-4960)
Signs Universe....G....972 880-2884
Carrollton (G-2887)
Wellborn Sign Inc....F....806 331-3563
Amarillo (G-474)
Zspace LLC....F....713 662-3123
Houston (G-12733)

SIGNS & ADVERTSG SPECIALTIES: Displays/Cutouts Window/Lobby

Dinaco Inc....E....281 848-3600
Houston (G-9475)
Harris Cabinet & Wdwkg Inc....G....817 561-2959
Fort Worth (G-6690)
Semasys Inc....C....713 869-8331
Houston (G-11825)

SIGNS, ELECTRICAL: Wholesalers

Fastsigns....G....915 229-8000
El Paso (G-5765)
Makitso USA LLC....F....281 495-1300
Stafford (G-19350)
Mighty Works Signage LLC....G....713 305-8355
Houston (G-10877)
National Signs LLC....E....832 433-4957
Houston (G-11001)
Ruben Reyes....F....214 331-4307
Dallas (G-4918)
Sparkle Lighting Services....E....713 856-8500
Houston (G-11992)

SIGNS, EXC ELECTRIC, WHOLESALE

Bauer Visual Graphics Inc....F....713 473-5241
Pasadena (G-16394)
Company Printing....F....325 949-9941
San Angelo (G-17788)
Creative Signworks Inc....E....850 785-8899
San Angelo (G-17792)
Display Graphics Inc....F....713 977-7888
Houston (G-9480)
Fastsigns....G....915 229-8000
El Paso (G-5765)
Tex-Sun Shade Specialties Inc....F....972 279-0132
Dallas (G-5053)

SIGNS: Electrical

A-Ero TEC Graphics Inc....E....972 289-9854
Mesquite (G-15022)
Accent Graphics Inc....E....972 399-0333
Grand Prairie (G-7820)
Acm Hub LLC....F....210 248-9631
San Antonio (G-17860)
Ad Display Sign Systems Inc....E....281 392-8325
Katy (G-13348)
Arns Holdings Ltd....D....713 863-0600
Houston (G-8701)
Ashter Construction LLC....E....832 786-0053
Waller (G-20493)
Atlas Sign Services Inc....F....713 699-1121
Houston (G-8746)
Baker Macy Edward....F....817 572-7346
Fort Worth (G-6420)
Chandler Signs LLC....D....760 734-1708
Fort Worth (G-6508)
Chandler Signs LLC....F....210 349-3804
San Antonio (G-18000)
Chandler Signs LLC....D....361 643-4115
Portland (G-17185)
City Sign Services Inc....E....214 826-4475
Dallas (G-4124)
Cnd Signs LLC....E....512 394-5421
Cedar Creek (G-2934)
Coast Graphics & Signs Inc....E....281 499-9721
Stafford (G-19296)
Custom Sign Creations LLC....E....512 374-9300
Austin (G-1080)
Datatronic Control Corporation....E....972 475-7879
Rowlett (G-17704)
Esbee Signs Inc....F....281 550-4577
Houston (G-9695)
Fusion Led Inc....F....281 990-6011
Houston (G-9877)
Global Signs Inc....F....817 834-1123
Forest Hill (G-6296)
Graphtec Inc....E....713 690-9999
Houston (G-10019)
Hardman Signs LP....D....713 957-2324
Houston (G-10124)
Hoarel Sign Co....F....806 373-2175
Amarillo (G-434)
Identity Solutions Inc....E....972 926-0929
Garland (G-7515)
Ixtapa Inc....E....956 782-9601
Pharr (G-16701)
Jackson Sign and Lighting Inc....G....254 751-0390
Woodway (G-20921)
Keller Advg & Media Svcs....E....210 695-8767
San Antonio (G-18222)
Legacy National Signs....E....972 790-8900
Dallas (G-4589)
Leons Signs Inc....E....903 597-7731
Tyler (G-20112)
Lewis Sign Builders Inc....E....512 312-4555
Buda (G-2532)
Liberty Signs Inc....F....512 255-3887
Round Rock (G-17669)
Lone Star Signs of West Texas....E....432 683-0016
Midland (G-15285)
Media Displays Inc....F....210 495-6338
San Antonio (G-18288)
National Signs LLC....E....832 433-4957
Houston (G-11001)
Neon Signs and Designs Inc....F....903 463-7446
Denison (G-5343)
NW Sign Industries Inc....D....972 602-9434
Grand Prairie (G-7939)
Pdn Ssl LLC....E....915 629-9100
El Paso (G-5906)
Permian Sign Co Inc....F....432 563-3072
Midland (G-15346)
Proworx Inc....E....713 666-3131
Houston (G-11467)
Quality Signs Inc....E....713 671-9222
Houston (G-11500)

Right Signs Inc .... F 281 429-3683
  Porter (G-17182)
Scanlin Sign Service Inc .... E 281 561-9924
  Stafford (G-19375)
Sign City Inc .... G 281 338-1203
  Webster (G-20646)
Sign Erection Ltd .... E 817 267-1554
  Euless (G-6158)
Sign Pro of Lubbock Ltd .... F 806 798-7446
  Wolfforth (G-20913)
Signs & Graphics Plus LLC .... F 915 590-7446
  El Paso (G-5961)
Son and Daughters Inc .... F 956 423-2689
  Harlingen (G-8201)
SSC Signs & Lighting LLC .... E 972 219-2495
  Lewisville (G-14092)
Starlite Sign LP .... D 817 430-8359
  Denton (G-5401)
Technographix LLC .... C 817 336-5671
  Fort Worth (G-7041)
Texas and Oklahoma Elc Svc LLC .... E 972 222-2229
  Dallas (G-5054)
Turner Sign Systems Inc .... F 817 222-0033
  Grand Prairie (G-7988)
Vmc Signs Inc .... F 361 575-0548
  Victoria (G-20317)
Xgrafx LLC .... F 210 681-7177
  San Antonio (G-18628)

SIGNS: Neon

Artografx Inc .... E 214 349-1075
  Dallas (G-3969)
Comet Signs LLC .... C 210 341-7244
  San Antonio (G-18021)
Comet Signs LLC .... E 281 492-6581
  Houston (G-9247)
Day Night Signs Inc .... F 254 965-9000
  Stephenville (G-19409)
Federal Heath Sign Company LLC .... E 903 589-2100
  Jacksonville (G-13238)
Federal Heath Sign Company LLC .... D 817 685-9075
  Euless (G-6146)
Industrial Neon Sign Corp .... F 713 748-6600
  Houston (G-10352)
Ion Art Inc .... E 512 326-9333
  Austin (G-1242)
Masterco Inc .... G 214 381-5690
  Dallas (G-4648)
Michael Egan Allen .... E 956 702-0692
  Pharr (G-16707)
Prince Signs LLC .... F 281 345-4488
  Houston (G-11420)
South Texas Neon Signs Co .... G 956 723-4665
  Laredo (G-13935)
Tesoro Corp .... E 956 682-7831
  Donna (G-5494)
Wwwhoustonsignmakercom .... F 281 990-7446
  Houston (G-12703)

SILICA MINING

Covia Holdings Corporation .... E 281 298-8088
  The Woodlands (G-19848)
Ggc USS Holdings LLC .... A 800 345-6170
  Katy (G-13362)
US Silica Holdings Inc .... E 281 258-2170
  Katy (G-13382)

SILICON

Prince Minerals LLC .... D 646 747-4222
  Houston (G-11419)

SILICON WAFERS: Chemically Doped

North Texas Epitaxy LLC .... E 972 747-8603
  Allen (G-289)
Tpg Capital Management LP .... B 817 871-4000
  Fort Worth (G-7069)

SILICON: Pure

Amorphous Materials Inc .... G 972 494-5624
  Garland (G-7436)

SILICONES

Gt Products Inc .... E 817 481-7113
  Grapevine (G-8042)

SILK SCREEN DESIGN SVCS

Action Screen Graphics .... F 512 478-6248
  Austin (G-886)
Allied Advertising Agency Inc ..... E 210 732-7874
  San Antonio (G-17897)
Athletic Sewing Center Inc .... E 210 681-9744
  San Antonio (G-17920)
Austin Screen Printing Inc .... E 512 454-6249
  Austin (G-961)
Century Graphics & Sign Inc .... E 432 686-8244
  Midland (G-15157)
Fineline Sportswear Inc .... F 512 832-1441
  Austin (G-1156)
Stephenville Printing Company ..... F 254 965-5012
  Stephenville (G-19424)
Three D Finishing Inc .... F 972 475-2726
  Rowlett (G-17713)
Your Ideas Inc .... F 325 673-5860
  Abilene (G-96)

SILO STAVES: Concrete Or Cast Stone

American Masonry Supply Inc .... C 817 695-1800
  Arlington (G-617)

SILVER ORE MINING

Battle Mountain Dominian Repub .... E 713 655-1742
  Houston (G-8830)

SIMULATORS: Flight

Interconnect Wiring LLP .... C 817 377-9473
  Fort Worth (G-6723)
L3 Technologies Inc .... C 361 516-8396
  Kingsville (G-13632)
Satco South 1 LLC .... F 361 961-1181
  Corpus Christi (G-3616)
Simtek Inc .... D 817 283-1801
  Euless (G-6159)

SKIDS: Wood

B & B Box and Lumber Company ...... E 903 592-7369
  Tyler (G-20054)
Industrial Lumber and Box Inc ..... F 713 928-2096
  Houston (G-10351)
Select Mat LLC .... F 833 205-1515
  Magnolia (G-14627)

SKILL TRAINING CENTER

Milspec Works LLC .... E 281 530-7002
  Houston (G-10885)
South Txas Lghthouse For Blind .... C 361 883-6553
  Corpus Christi (G-3627)

SKIN CARE PRDTS: Suntan Lotions & Oils

O D C L Inc .... F 940 566-9914
  Denton (G-5385)
O D C L Inc .... E 956 565-3131
  Mercedes (G-15009)
T L R Group .... E 361 500-4136
  Corpus Christi (G-3634)

SKYLIGHTS

Birdview Skylights .... F 817 439-9266
  Fort Worth (G-6453)
Fisher Select Products Inc .... E 972 484-1188
  Carrollton (G-2738)
Solar Accessories Corporation ..... F 972 524-2099
  Terrell (G-19750)

SLAB & TILE, ROOFING: Concrete

Continental Stone LLC .... E 713 462-5700
  Houston (G-9289)
Crown Building Products LLC .... E 214 636-5163
  Mansfield (G-14664)

SLAB & TILE: Precast Concrete, Floor

4693057371 .... F 469 305-7371
  Frisco (G-7255)
Antiquestone Inc .... F 512 355-2722
  Bertram (G-2051)
Builders Depot Direct LLC .... F 832 384-7272
  Houston (G-9012)

SLAB, CROSSING: Concrete

Aj Commercial Services Inc .... G 361 336-2113
  Corpus Christi (G-3470)
Littlefield Brothers Con Cnstr .... E 281 399-1488
  Conroe (G-3322)
Ranger Coml Con Contrs LLC .... F 210 831-7052
  Bulverde (G-2558)

SLAG PRDTS

Fjcj LLC .... F 409 740-3355
  Galveston (G-7396)

SLAG: Crushed Or Ground

Tms International LLC .... F 409 768-1241
  Beaumont (G-1960)

SLATE PRDTS

Thorntree LP .... E 713 690-8200
  Houston (G-12280)

SLAUGHTERING & MEAT PACKING

Cargill Meat Solutions Corp .... F 806 295-8243
  Friona (G-7253)
Caviness Beef Packers Ltd .... B 806 372-5781
  Amarillo (G-412)
Caviness Packing Company Inc ...... C 806 357-2443
  Hereford (G-8286)
Hlc Custom Processing LLC .... F 432 556-2443
  Andrews (G-544)
J & R Custom Processing LLC .... F 325 456-1544
  Rochelle (G-17522)
Kaspers Meat Market Inc .... E 979 725-8227
  Weimar (G-20650)
Texana Feeders Ltd .... E 830 947-3396
  Floresville (G-6253)
Tyson Foods Inc .... A 903 891-6001
  Sherman (G-18937)
Tyson Foods Inc .... F 940 553-1811
  Vernon (G-20231)
Tyson Foods Inc .... B 713 678-1893
  Houston (G-12421)
Tyson Fresh Meats Inc .... A 806 335-7322
  Amarillo (G-470)

SLIDES & EXHIBITS: Prepared

Dallas Market Center Co Ltd .... C 214 655-6100
  Dallas (G-4219)

SLINGS: Lifting, Made From Purchased Wire

Blp Settlement Company .... D 713 674-2266
  Houston (G-8916)
Delta Rigging & Tools Inc .... C 713 512-1700
  Houston (G-9433)
Kirby Midco Inc .... F 214 688-0444
  Dallas (G-4558)
Lone Star Rigging LP .... F 409 842-2263
  Beaumont (G-1920)
Trinity Sling Authority Inc .... F 817 589-2404
  Arlington (G-803)

SLINGS: Rope

Delta Rigging & Tools Inc .... C 713 512-1700
  Houston (G-9433)
HWC Wire & Cable Company .... C 713 453-8518
  Houston (G-10293)
Ma-Tex Wire Rope Co Inc .... E 903 984-9691
  Kilgore (G-13567)
Parker Systems Inc .... F 800 262-4891
  Houston (G-11245)

SLIP RINGS

Mtc America Enterprises Inc .... F 972 926-0600
  Garland (G-7556)

SLOT MACHINES

Everi Games Inc .... D 512 439-3100
  Austin (G-1142)

SMOKE DETECTORS

Brk Brands Inc .... F 915 860-3500
  El Paso (G-5673)
Hitech Fire Detection Corp .... D 281 475-7289
  Spring (G-19130)

PRODUCT

Metro Fire Apprtus Specialists ....G 817 467-0911
  Mansfield *(G-14695)*

System Sensor ....G 915 778-1301
  El Paso *(G-5990)*

SNOWMOBILE DEALERS

Temples Trailer Sales Inc ....F 903 885-7301
  Sulphur Springs *(G-19602)*

SOAPS & DETERGENTS

4e Brands Northamerica LLC ....A 210 819-7385
  San Antonio *(G-17845)*

Ankem of Texas Inc ....E 903 802-7133
  Farmers Branch *(G-6186)*

Chemstation International Inc ....F 281 457-2020
  Houston *(G-9171)*

Ecolab Inc ....F 281 908-4877
  Houston *(G-9578)*

Ecolab Inc ....E 817 916-9600
  Haltom City *(G-8138)*

Ecolab Inc ....D 800 325-1671
  Houston *(G-9579)*

Hall Tree Antiques Inc ....D 325 944-4794
  San Angelo *(G-17803)*

North American Research Corp ....F 972 492-1800
  Lewisville *(G-14074)*

Ocusoft Inc ....D 281 342-3350
  Rosenberg *(G-17592)*

Omega Chemical Products Inc ....E 219 208-0500
  Weatherford *(G-20608)*

Pro Star Industries Inc ....E 979 779-9399
  Bryan *(G-2499)*

Sorb All Company ....F 713 223-4575
  Houston *(G-11955)*

Spfm LP ....D 210 805-8931
  San Antonio *(G-18491)*

Startkleen Legacy LLC ....F 903 207-1079
  Gunter *(G-8117)*

Stinger Chemical LLC ....D 713 227-1340
  Houston *(G-12067)*

Thomason Family Corporation ....F 713 223-4575
  Houston *(G-12277)*

Trans-Mate LLC ....E 800 867-9274
  Dallas *(G-5105)*

Two Old Goats LLC ....G 817 520-4230
  Haltom City *(G-8159)*

Unifirst Corporation ....E 979 774-0577
  College Station *(G-3208)*

SOCIAL SVCS: Individual & Family

Coole School Inc ....G 713 552-1600
  Houston *(G-9302)*

Drug Prevention Resources Inc ....F 972 518-1821
  Waxahachie *(G-20540)*

SODA ASH MINING: Natural

Natural Resource Partners LP ....E 713 751-7507
  Houston *(G-11010)*

Solvay Chemicals Inc ....C 713 525-6800
  Houston *(G-11945)*

Solvay Chemicals Inc ....D 713 307-3800
  La Porte *(G-13789)*

SOFT DRINKS WHOLESALERS

Beaumont Coca-Cola Bottling Co ....C 409 899-5080
  Beaumont *(G-1860)*

Dr Ppper Btlg Wichita FLS Inc ....D 940 322-5416
  Wichita Falls *(G-20760)*

Dublin Bottling Works Inc ....E 254 445-3939
  Dublin *(G-5515)*

Kristen Distributing Co ....E 979 775-6322
  Bryan *(G-2489)*

Pepsi-Cola Metro Btlg Co Inc ....E 979 779-6324
  Bryan *(G-2497)*

Pepsi-Cola Metro Btlg Co Inc ....E 361 798-3651
  Hallettsville *(G-8124)*

SOFTWARE PUBLISHERS: Application

3s Business Corporation ....D 281 823-9222
  Houston *(G-8411)*

Advent Global Solutions Inc ....F 281 970-3000
  Houston *(G-8495)*

Ambernet Technologies Inc ....F 972 707-4000
  Dallas *(G-3936)*

American Micro Systems Ltd ....E 817 571-9015
  Euless *(G-6130)*

Anderson Software LLC ....F 936 569-0447
  Kerrville *(G-13518)*

Apex Custom Software Inc ....G 214 725-9792
  The Colony *(G-19809)*

Apex Software Solutions Inc ....E 210 699-6666
  San Antonio *(G-17909)*

Appy Health Inc ....F 844 764-2779
  Dallas *(G-3955)*

Aquilan Technologies Inc ....F 512 751-4226
  Austin *(G-926)*

Arrow Electronics Inc ....G 303 824-4000
  Plano *(G-16793)*

Associated Telephone ....F 512 288-6215
  Kyle *(G-13677)*

Automatize Logistics LLC ....F 817 221-8106
  Grapevine *(G-8013)*

Avatar Systems Inc ....F 972 334-0162
  Frisco *(G-7268)*

B&B Worldwide Technology ....F 713 471-2387
  Cibolo *(G-3062)*

Broadaxis Inc ....F 469 688-2272
  Plano *(G-16814)*

Broadleaf Commerce LLC ....E 800 282-7443
  Plano *(G-16815)*

Broadleaf Commerce LLC ....F 800 282-7443
  Austin *(G-1011)*

Ca Inc ....B 972 577-3223
  Plano *(G-16816)*

Cadence Design Systems Inc ....D 512 349-1100
  Austin *(G-1019)*

Calytera Us Inc ....D 512 623-9786
  Austin *(G-1021)*

Candeo Interactive LLC ....F 214 394-8499
  Forney *(G-6303)*

Cdb Software Inc ....F 713 588-1778
  Houston *(G-9112)*

CDM Software Solutions Inc ....E 972 469-3082
  Frisco *(G-7272)*

Cfa Services ....F 210 758-5721
  San Antonio *(G-17995)*

Coda Global LLC ....E 844 366-8250
  Southlake *(G-19060)*

Codekko Inc ....E 214 919-0565
  Plano *(G-16827)*

Crocodile Digital Corporation ....F 713 382-1891
  Galveston *(G-7395)*

Dairy LLC ....F 214 442-5928
  Frisco *(G-7278)*

Dell Inc ....A 800 289-3355
  Round Rock *(G-17642)*

Denali Intermediate Inc ....A 713 627-0933
  Round Rock *(G-17648)*

Dilogr LLC ....F 800 455-9632
  Austin *(G-1095)*

Dronesense Inc ....F 512 582-0444
  Austin *(G-1103)*

E-Ceptionist Inc ....E 713 520-6688
  Houston *(G-9554)*

Economic Trnsfrmtion Tech Corp ....F 253 332-7362
  Frisco *(G-7281)*

Eixsys LLC ....F 512 666-3574
  Austin *(G-1117)*

Esi Technologies LLC ....G 512 633-2897
  Austin *(G-1138)*

Esw Holdings Inc ....F 512 524-6149
  Austin *(G-1140)*

Excel Media LLC ....F 409 832-5770
  Beaumont *(G-1890)*

Exigo Office Inc ....F 214 367-9999
  Dallas *(G-4347)*

Falconstor Software Inc ....E 631 777-5188
  Austin *(G-1146)*

Fifth Rock Software Inc ....E 281 265-0944
  Sugar Land *(G-19483)*

Figtree Technologies Inc ....E 469 361-6643
  McKinney *(G-14942)*

Fooder LLC ....F 832 953-8944
  Spring *(G-19123)*

Genesis Entitai LLC ....E 904 803-2457
  The Colony *(G-19811)*

Genmz LP ....F 214 683-6635
  Dallas *(G-4401)*

Ghg Corp ....B 281 461-6533
  Webster *(G-20638)*

Girl Talk Boutique & Spa LLC ....F 956 225-7898
  Pharr *(G-16698)*

Happy Shopper Inc ....F 281 751-7138
  Houston *(G-10122)*

Health Management Systems Inc ....C 214 453-3000
  Irving *(G-13055)*

Health Management Systems Inc ....E 512 407-9680
  Austin *(G-1200)*

Hill Cntry Bb Ch Drpping Sprng ....F 512 843-0035
  Dripping Springs *(G-5507)*

Hotschedulescom Inc ....E 512 904-4299
  Austin *(G-1210)*

Hyphen Solutions LLC ....D 972 728-8100
  Dallas *(G-4480)*

IBM Global Systems Inc ....F 972 468-1944
  Irving *(G-13063)*

Idera Inc ....D 713 523-4433
  Houston *(G-10315)*

Immediatek Inc ....E 888 661-6565
  Bedford *(G-1974)*

Infor (us) LLC ....C 800 915-3243
  Dallas *(G-4496)*

Integrated MGT Concepts Inc ....E 805 778-1629
  Austin *(G-1231)*

Intesolv Inc ....F 512 681-7272
  Austin *(G-1239)*

Ioffice LP ....E 713 526-1029
  Houston *(G-10412)*

Ion Geophysical Corporation ....C 281 933-3339
  Houston *(G-10413)*

Ion Geophysical Corporation ....D 281 552-3000
  Stafford *(G-19331)*

Jarvantech Inc ....F 832 742-7220
  The Woodlands *(G-19888)*

Jcjh LLC ....F 830 331-2240
  Boerne *(G-2124)*

Jeh-Eas Inc ....G 210 490-9156
  San Antonio *(G-18200)*

Jericho Systems Corporation ....E 972 231-2000
  Dallas *(G-4533)*

Jones Lang Lasalle Ip Inc ....E 214 777-5100
  Dallas *(G-4538)*

JR Peterson Inc ....E 210 695-4455
  Helotes *(G-8239)*

Kloudnation LLC ....E 214 682-8692
  Frisco *(G-7296)*

Kony Inc ....C 512 792-2900
  Austin *(G-1272)*

Liquid Litigation MGT Inc ....F 210 757-4881
  Austin *(G-1294)*

Lisam America Inc ....E 979 307-7384
  Bryan *(G-2491)*

McAfee Public Sector LLC ....F 972 963-7000
  Plano *(G-16922)*

Medcognition Inc ....F 210 960-0930
  San Antonio *(G-18287)*

Medici Technologies LLC ....F 800 768-8131
  Austin *(G-1335)*

Medifacts Inc ....E 817 571-8181
  Colleyville *(G-3221)*

Microsoft Corporation ....C 210 402-0577
  San Antonio *(G-18301)*

Microsoft Corporation ....C 469 775-0000
  Irving *(G-13109)*

Microsoft Corporation ....D 469 775-0000
  Irving *(G-13110)*

Microsoft Corporation ....D 832 252-4300
  Houston *(G-10870)*

Microsoft Corporation ....E 972 345-3610
  Irving *(G-13111)*

Motor Crier Sfety Slutions Inc ....F 956 726-3377
  Laredo *(G-13916)*

National Instruments Corp ....B 214 227-4788
  Garland *(G-7558)*

Ncs Pearson Inc ....D 210 339-5000
  San Antonio *(G-18340)*

Nerve Software LLC ....G 972 231-4775
  Richardson *(G-17363)*

Orion Communications Inc ....E 214 361-1203
  Dallas *(G-4768)*

Osisoft LLC ....F 281 920-6170
  Houston *(G-11198)*

Patient Conversation Media Inc ....E 512 522-0966
  Austin *(G-1399)*

Peritus Inc ....C 817 726-4626
  Irving *(G-13101)*

Practice Interactive Inc ....F 844 413-2602
  Austin *(G-1427)*

Premier Digital Design LLC ....G 210 774-5456
  San Antonio *(G-18390)*

Prodektive Specialty Svcs LLC ....E 713 425-3075
  Houston *(G-11436)*

Pushnami LLC ....F 512 961-7042
  Austin *(G-1438)*

Pwr Technologies LLC ....F 469 609-3537
  Mesquite *(G-15073)*

2021 Harris Texas
Manufacturers Directory

(G-0000) Company's Geographic Section entry number

Quacito LLC	F	210 695-0795	
San Antonio (G-18404)			
Quinstar Corporation	F	512 326-1011	
Austin (G-1445)			
Revitalu International LLC	F	469 270-5533	
Plano (G-16993)			
Rogii Inc	E	346 714-8694	
Houston (G-11656)			
Rubrix LLC	E	512 581-5513	
San Antonio (G-18437)			
Rush Apparel LLC	F	713 208-5194	
Magnolia (G-14625)			
Sas Institute Inc	D	512 258-5171	
Austin (G-1487)			
Scalable Software Inc	F	512 501-2828	
Austin (G-1489)			
Sencha Inc	D	713 523-4433	
Houston (G-11827)			
Sigga USA LLC	F	855 744-4287	
Sugar Land (G-19556)			
Smart City Locating Inc	E	214 586-0519	
Dallas (G-4971)			
Smartdraw Software LLC	E	858 225-3300	
The Woodlands (G-19919)			
Smpl Inc	E	402 525-5078	
Austin (G-1513)			
Specter Instruments Inc	F	512 326-1011	
Austin (G-1524)			
Spiceworks Inc	B	512 346-7743	
Austin (G-1525)			
Stone Bond Technologies	F	713 622-8798	
Houston (G-12070)			
Stone Cliff Technology LLC	F	512 640-0650	
Austin (G-1538)			
SW Health Care Solutions LLC	F	832 578-6694	
Houston (G-12128)			
Taxsation Inc	F	888 829-1120	
Dallas (G-5037)			
Test Spectrum Inc	F	512 472-6750	
Austin (G-1564)			
Texas Logic Inc	F	956 682-3466	
McAllen (G-14911)			
Texas Source Group Inc	F	713 464-9702	
Houston (G-12250)			
Timeclock Plus LLC	D	325 223-9300	
San Angelo (G-17834)			
Transmedia Dynamics Inc	E	512 971-2313	
Kyle (G-13687)			
Trifectix Inc	E	512 580-2809	
Georgetown (G-7687)			
Triple Aim Ventures LLC	E	210 417-4170	
San Antonio (G-18569)			
Vapor Io Inc	E	512 600-1123	
Austin (G-1623)			
Vertical Computer Systems Inc	F	972 437-5200	
Richardson (G-17421)			
Wargaming America Inc	E	510 962-6747	
Austin (G-1646)			
Webvent Inc	F	617 418-4126	
Lewisville (G-14111)			
Wheel Innovationz Inc	F	408 390-2871	
Austin (G-1660)			
Whole Tomato Software Inc	C	512 226-8080	
Austin (G-1664)			
Workiva Inc	B	817 308-1153	
Irving (G-13208)			
Yadblue LLC	E	214 542-6140	
Southlake (G-19084)			
Yoolotto LLC	E	469 383-6488	
Dallas (G-5208)			
Ziften Technologies Inc	E	512 298-5501	
Austin (G-1686)			

SOFTWARE PUBLISHERS: Business & Professional

Abuyo Inc	E	855 850-3850	
Austin (G-882)			
Aci Worldwide Corp	F	361 579-4800	
Victoria (G-20234)			
Ad Valorem Records Inc	E	713 523-1623	
Houston (G-8474)			
Aibuy Inc	E	972 616-6400	
Dallas (G-3903)			
Alphatrust Corporation	G	214 234-9200	
Dallas (G-3931)			
Anderson Merchandisers LLC	C	972 987-5516	
Plano (G-16790)			
Autopoint Inc	E	888 335-5762	
Roanoke (G-17482)			

Autostar Solutions Inc	E	817 377-2995	
Irving (G-12936)			
Avolin LLC	C	512 524-6149	
Austin (G-970)			
Basis Technologies Inc	E	888 623-0220	
Addison (G-106)			
Bazaarvoice Inc	E	512 551-6000	
Austin (G-980)			
Bi Solutions Inc	E	469 287-5784	
Plano (G-16803)			
Bigcommerce Inc	C	512 865-4500	
Austin (G-990)			
Bloomfire Inc	E	512 485-0910	
Austin (G-996)			
BMC Software Inc	A	713 918-8800	
Houston (G-8924)			
Bookstore Manager Software	E	325 673-2826	
Abilene (G-22)			
Borland Software Corporation	E	512 340-2200	
Austin (G-1002)			
Capitalsoft Inc	F	972 220-1560	
Richardson (G-17284)			
Cardinal Automation Inc	F	214 233-3773	
Dallas (G-4083)			
Checkfree Corporation	D	281 333-9800	
Houston (G-9167)			
Chequedcom Inc	E	888 412-0699	
Dallas (G-4110)			
Chiron Health Holdings LLC	F	319 400-3772	
Austin (G-1049)			
Cobalt Group Inc	E	206 269-6363	
Austin (G-1054)			
Concur Technologies Inc	F	972 612-7121	
Allen (G-260)			
Coretrac Inc	E	512 236-9120	
Austin (G-1066)			
Crayon Software Experts LLC	E	469 329-0290	
Dallas (G-4181)			
Cubelogic LLC	E	832 498-6374	
Houston (G-9357)			
Cybernance Corporation	F	512 850-5909	
Austin (G-1081)			
DBA Software Inc	F	512 342-1769	
Austin (G-1085)			
Detechtion USA Inc	E	713 357-4775	
Houston (G-9445)			
Docs On Demand Inc	F	713 980-9500	
Houston (G-9490)			
DSI Solutions LLC	F	817 633-1772	
Arlington (G-666)			
E-Mds Inc	C	512 257-5200	
Austin (G-1107)			
Eduphoria Incorporated	E	972 535-5570	
Plano (G-16858)			
Embarcadero Technologies Inc	C	512 226-8080	
Austin (G-1121)			
Epicor Software Corporation	D	512 328-2300	
Austin (G-1130)			
EPM Live Inc	C	425 452-1111	
Austin (G-1133)			
Ethosiq LLC	F	281 616-5711	
Houston (G-9709)			
Exceleron Software LLC	F	972 852-2700	
Dallas (G-4341)			
Exela Technologies Inc	D	844 935-2832	
Irving (G-13017)			
Express Info Systems Inc	F	210 614-9410	
San Antonio (G-18100)			
Flightaware LLC	D	713 877-9010	
Houston (G-9802)			
Flutura Business Solutions LLC	F	832 265-9172	
Houston (G-9817)			
Four Rivers Sftwr Systems Inc	E	412 256-9020	
Austin (G-1170)			
Gensym Corporation	D	512 377-9700	
Austin (G-1182)			
Geomechanics International Inc	F	713 599-0373	
Houston (G-9937)			
Globeranger Corporation	E	972 744-9977	
Richardson (G-17322)			
Gresham Enterprise Storage Inc	E	512 250-0916	
Austin (G-1194)			
Healthcare Pymnt Spcalists LLC	E	800 784-2175	
Fort Worth (G-6691)			
Hewlett Packard Enterprise Co	C	650 687-5817	
Houston (G-10166)			
I2 Technologies Inc	E	469 357-1000	
Dallas (G-4482)			
Info-Power International Inc	G	972 424-4447	
Plano (G-16890)			

Integrated Tax Solutions LLC	F	855 792-6657	
San Antonio (G-18190)			
Intuit Inc	E	214 387-2000	
Plano (G-16894)			
Involta LLC	F	817 937-8943	
Dallas (G-4511)			
J Paul Horst & Associates	F	713 460-9386	
Houston (G-10442)			
Jeeves Information Systems Inc	F	512 333-4418	
Austin (G-1254)			
Jollyrhino Inc	F	909 732-8507	
Austin (G-1260)			
Keen Solutions Group Inc	E	903 253-0476	
Tyler (G-20107)			
Kerio Technologies Inc	C	408 496-4500	
Austin (G-1267)			
Khoros LLC	B	415 757-3100	
Austin (G-1268)			
Kicstand Inc	F	210 324-0421	
Houston (G-10531)			
Lendflow Inc	F	512 265-1261	
Kingwood (G-13647)			
Lightside Games Inc	G	650 814-0293	
West Lake Hills (G-20683)			
Liquid Motors Inc	F	214 393-2323	
Richardson (G-17345)			
Lookout Services Inc	F	713 668-6200	
Stafford (G-19349)			
M-Files Inc	B	972 516-4210	
Plano (G-16914)			
Magdata Inc	C	425 372-2699	
Austin (G-1317)			
Management Controls Inc	C	281 590-5881	
Houston (G-10743)			
Mapspeople Inc	E	512 368-0038	
Austin (G-1325)			
Medeanalytics Inc	C	469 476-5423	
Richardson (G-17355)			
Medimobile	F	512 686-0817	
Georgetown (G-7663)			
Mtwd Holdings Inc	E	972 346-2242	
Frisco (G-7300)			
Muroc Systems Inc	F	214 295-9442	
Dallas (G-4708)			
Nextgenauto LLC	F	888 481-9756	
Irving (G-13124)			
Nuview Systems Inc	D	978 296-6600	
Austin (G-1372)			
Oceanus Automotive LLC	E	512 551-9726	
Austin (G-1376)			
Omnibase Services of Texas	F	512 346-6511	
Austin (G-1382)			
Optimum Consultancy Svcs LLC	F	713 505-0300	
Houston (G-11185)			
Optimum Path Systems Inc	F	813 990-8204	
Hurst (G-12854)			
Oracle America Inc	D	214 494-4527	
Frisco (G-7303)			
Oracle Corporation	B	817 422-5231	
Keller (G-13469)			
Oracle Corporation	B	512 372-8207	
Austin (G-1390)			
Oracle Corporation	B	972 652-8000	
Frisco (G-7304)			
Oracle Corporation	A	737 867-1000	
Austin (G-1391)			
P2 Energy Solutions Inc	D	713 787-6300	
Houston (G-11215)			
P2es Holdings LLC	D	713 481-2000	
Houston (G-11216)			
Parlevel Systems Inc	E	210 200-8873	
San Antonio (G-18367)			
Passare Inc	E	325 695-3412	
Abilene (G-63)			
Peek Traffic Corporation	C	281 453-0200	
Houston (G-11270)			
Peopleadmin Inc	E	877 637-5800	
Austin (G-1408)			
Perception Software Inc	F	512 593-6996	
Austin (G-1409)			
Perfomix LLC	D	713 893-8310	
Bellaire (G-2001)			
Pestroutes Opco LLC	D	404 800-7378	
McKinney (G-14963)			
Petrasoft Counsulting	F	832 448-5600	
Houston (G-11299)			
Phaseware Inc	F	214 432-9043	
McKinney (G-14964)			
Pixel and Texel LLC	F	214 240-0013	
Dallas (G-4808)			

P
R
O
D
U
C
T

R T L X LLC ....E 214 778-6400
  Plano (G-16982)
Revenue Technology Svcs Corp ....E 972 573-1600
  Plano (G-16992)
Rignet Inc ....C 281 674-0100
  Houston (G-11622)
Royal Technocrats Inc ....E 713 776-8300
  Houston (G-11684)
Safertek Software LLC ....E 972 331-2984
  Coppell (G-3443)
Sage Software Inc ....C 512 331-0723
  Austin (G-1481)
Sagl Enterprises Inc ....E 281 496-3737
  Houston (G-11729)
Seremedi Inc ....G 832 671-8622
  Houston (G-11835)
Siemens Industry Software Inc .....C 972 987-3000
  Plano (G-17003)
Signacert Inc ....F 512 577-4894
  Austin (G-1501)
Simplelegal Inc ....F 415 763-5366
  Houston (G-11903)
Solutions In Software Inc ....E 214 221-9995
  Dallas (G-4979)
Sourceday Inc ....E 512 361-7029
  Austin (G-1521)
Spigit Inc ....D 855 774-4480
  Austin (G-1526)
Superior It Solutions LLC ....F 713 501-1260
  Houston (G-12117)
Surgical Notes Inc ....E 214 821-3850
  Dallas (G-5031)
Synergen Health LLC ....F 214 643-6002
  Dallas (G-5032)
System Development Inc ....E 713 266-5667
  Houston (G-12139)
Systum Inc ....F 406 600-3684
  Plano (G-17018)
Tbx Employee Benefits LLC ....E 972 248-9030
  Plano (G-17022)
Thinksmart LLC ....F 888 489-4284
  Austin (G-1574)
Tpg Software Inc ....E 713 974-1375
  Houston (G-12337)
Travis Software Inc ....F 281 496-3737
  Houston (G-12358)
Ultimate Kronos Group ....F 469 221-1823
  Irving (G-13202)
Ultimate Kronos Group ....E 469 221-1800
  Irving (G-13203)
Upay Inc ....F 972 888-6052
  Dallas (G-5142)
Upland Software Inc ....C 833 875-2631
  Austin (G-1611)
Upland Software I Inc ....D 617 494-5515
  Austin (G-1612)
Versata Inc ....D 512 524-6149
  Austin (G-1631)
Visionael Corporation ....F 650 963-0960
  Austin (G-1639)
Visual Bi Solutions Inc ....E 972 232-2233
  Plano (G-17046)
Visual Click Software Inc ....E 512 231-9990
  Austin (G-1640)
VSI Solutions Inc ....F 855 712-7677
  McKinney (G-14987)
Waterfall International Inc ....E 844 627-2438
  Austin (G-1648)
Wellsmith Inc ....F 866 266-7793
  Austin (G-1654)
Yash & Lujan Consulting Inc ....B 800 519-5221
  Austin (G-1679)

SOFTWARE PUBLISHERS: Computer Utilities

BMC Software Inc ....E 512 343-1961
  Austin (G-999)
Bradmark Technologies Inc ....E 713 621-2808
  Houston (G-8975)
Cardinal Software Inc ....F 512 275-0072
  Austin (G-1028)
Cornerstone Atomtn Systems LLC .....D 972 346-2242
  Frisco (G-7275)
Filetrail Inc ....E 408 289-1300
  Austin (G-1155)
Rational Systems LLC ....E 832 476-8468
  Houston (G-11552)
Smart Packager Inc ....E 713 316-4903
  Austin (G-1511)

SOFTWARE PUBLISHERS: Education

Cambium Learning Group Inc ....D 214 932-9500
  Dallas (G-3839)
Cev Multimedia Ltd ....E 806 745-8820
  Lubbock (G-14391)
Coastal Resources Group LLC ....F 281 549-4132
  Kemah (G-13471)
Creative Education Inst Inc ....D 254 751-1188
  Waco (G-20391)
Crossvale Inc ....E 972 714-4782
  Dallas (G-4185)
Edgenuity Inc ....C 512 478-9600
  Austin (G-1115)
Edshah Capital ....F 469 770-3740
  Plano (G-16857)
Education Advanced Inc ....G 903 858-4497
  Tyler (G-20083)
Frh Consumer Services Inc ....G 512 657-8945
  Austin (G-1172)
Imagination Station Inc ....E 214 237-9300
  Dallas (G-4490)
Inspired Elearning LLC ....D 210 579-0224
  San Antonio (G-18189)
Journeyedcom Inc ....D 800 876-3507
  Allen (G-280)
Jr3 Websmart LLC ....E 254 759-1902
  Waco (G-20421)
Kamico Instructional Media Inc .....D 254 947-7283
  Salado (G-17765)
Kudzookinect Inc ....E 512 363-0704
  Austin (G-1274)
Lansa Inc ....C 630 874-7042
  Houston (G-10598)
Myedu Corporation ....E 512 469-9777
  Austin (G-1359)
Overnite Software Inc ....E 979 319-8371
  Angleton (G-575)
Percomonline Incorporated ....F 325 480-2617
  Abilene (G-64)
Redhouse Virtual Education LLC ......F 210 872-4989
  Dallas (G-4878)
Renaissance Cmpt Group Not Inc .....F 713 256-6067
  Houston (G-11597)
Sapling Systems Inc ....E 512 323-6565
  Austin (G-1486)
Siemens Industry Software Inc ......E 972 391-2476
  Plano (G-17004)
Swye360 Learning Inc ....E 214 263-2932
  Frisco (G-7317)
Thinkwell Corporation ....F 888 416-8880
  Austin (G-1575)
Tillman Learning LLC ....F 866 540-9677
  Plano (G-17033)
Triseum LLC ....F 979 773-8909
  Bryan (G-2514)
Yellow Folder LLC ....E 214 431-3600
  Carrollton (G-2851)

SOFTWARE PUBLISHERS: Home Entertainment

Digerati Dist & Mktg LLC ....G 512 569-1772
  Austin (G-1092)
Fishbowl Games LLC ....F 469 449-3275
  Dallas (G-4366)

SOFTWARE PUBLISHERS: NEC

1 Starview Solutions LP ....F 512 366-3939
  Austin (G-868)
2da Analytics Incorporated ....F 832 472-2093
  Houston (G-8406)
3core Software Corporation ....F 281 440-3000
  Katy (G-13387)
Abacus Computer Co Inc ....E 713 467-2136
  Houston (G-8442)
Absolute Software Inc ....E 512 600-7455
  Austin (G-880)
Accept Software Corporation ....E 512 201-8222
  Austin (G-883)
Action1 Corporation ....F 346 444-8530
  Houston (G-8470)
Active Network LLC ....A 888 543-7223
  Dallas (G-3884)
Acumen Pm LLC ....E 512 291-6259
  Austin (G-888)
Adobe Inc ....E 469 955-9500
  Dallas (G-3890)
Aim Solutions Inc ....F 214 373-6084
  Dallas (G-3904)

Annapurna Solutions LLC ....F 916 905-3144
  Houston (G-8646)
Applied Geophysical Services ....F 832 327-3408
  Houston (G-8668)
Applied Software Tech Inc ....E 210 732-9212
  San Antonio (G-17910)
Applied Training Resources Inc .....E 281 370-9540
  Spring (G-19100)
Aprima Medical Software Inc ....E 214 466-8000
  Richardson (G-17272)
Argus Software Inc ....D 713 621-4343
  Houston (G-8692)
Artemis Intl Solutions Corp ....D 512 201-8222
  Austin (G-936)
Ascent Business Systems Inc ....F 281 497-8882
  Houston (G-8716)
Asna Inc ....E 210 408-0212
  San Antonio (G-17917)
Asure Software Inc ....E 512 437-2700
  Austin (G-943)
Audiotel Corporation ....D 972 359-5500
  Allen (G-254)
Avatar Systems Inc ....E 972 720-1800
  Frisco (G-7267)
Base Base Corporation ....F 832 236-9801
  Houston (G-8820)
Baxter Planning Systems Inc ....E 512 323-5959
  Austin (G-977)
Baxter Plg Systems Opco LLC ....D 512 323-5959
  Austin (G-978)
Baytek International Inc ....E 281 218-8880
  Houston (G-8839)
Baytek International Inc ....F 361 887-8988
  Corpus Christi (G-3483)
Bcs Systems Inc ....F 713 978-6511
  Houston (G-8842)
Beicip Inc ....F 281 293-8550
  Houston (G-8852)
Biractual LLC ....F 713 623-5099
  Houston (G-8888)
Birch Grove Software Inc ....D 888 907-0301
  Austin (G-991)
Bizness Apps Inc ....F 415 655-9496
  Austin (G-993)
Blackbaud Inc ....E 512 652-7969
  Austin (G-995)
Blue Moon Software ....F 512 322-0460
  Austin (G-998)
BMC Software Inc ....E 972 484-1200
  Dallas (G-4034)
BMC Software Inc ....E 214 442-0397
  Plano (G-16807)
BMC Software Federal LLC ....F 713 918-8800
  Houston (G-8925)
Bms Solutions Usa Inc ....D 713 954-4970
  Houston (G-8929)
Boxer Parent Company Inc ....E 713 918-8800
  Houston (G-8964)
Bresa Tech LLC ....E 866 728-2889
  Plano (G-16811)
Brit Systems LLC ....F 214 630-0636
  Dallas (G-4057)
Bvsn LLC ....D 512 524-6149
  Austin (G-1017)
Bynari Inc ....F 214 350-5772
  Dallas (G-4070)
C&C Software ....E 714 635-3603
  Irving (G-12958)
Calix Inc ....G 707 766-3000
  Richardson (G-17282)
Camber Def SEC Systems Sltons ......E 210 279-3608
  San Antonio (G-17977)
Carreker Corporation ....C 800 486-1981
  Dallas (G-4086)
Cgi Technologies Solutions Inc .....B 866 344-3221
  Houston (G-9150)
Chuck Atkinson Inc ....F 817 560-8139
  Fort Worth (G-6516)
Cimarron Software Services Inc .....E 281 226-5100
  Houston (G-9190)
Cisco Systems Inc ....A 512 378-1112
  Austin (G-1051)
Cistera Networks Inc ....F 972 381-4699
  Plano (G-16823)
Cityon Systems Inc ....E 972 519-1673
  Plano (G-16824)
Client Connect LLC ....E 214 295-4940
  Plano (G-16826)
Cloud Logix LLC ....E 682 310-0665
  Irving (G-12974)

Company	Code	Phone
Cognite Inc	F	512 593-7120
Houston (G-9239)		
Common Source LP	F	281 443-7575
Houston (G-9253)		
Complete Intelligence Tech Inc	F	281 710-9131
The Woodlands (G-19847)		
Compu-Data International LLC	E	281 292-1533
Houston (G-9263)		
Computer Labs Inc	E	915 775-1839
El Paso (G-5703)		
Condusiv Technologies Corp	E	818 252-5538
Austin (G-1060)		
Connectione LLC	E	512 310-1000
Round Rock (G-17636)		
Controlr Software Inc	F	214 909-8676
Dallas (G-4162)		
Convergepoint Inc	F	347 948-4258
Houston (G-9298)		
Convio Inc	C	512 652-2600
Austin (G-1064)		
Cooper Consulting Company	E	512 527-1000
Austin (G-1065)		
Corona Labs Inc	F	312 953-7586
Austin (G-1067)		
Correlog Inc	F	239 514-3331
Houston (G-9323)		
Covey Software Systems Inc	F	972 353-8716
Irving (G-12982)		
Cpfd LLC	F	713 429-1252
Houston (G-9332)		
Cstorepro Technologies Inc	B	866 265-5826
Sugar Land (G-19470)		
Cubix Software Ltd Inc	F	903 297-7771
Longview (G-14217)		
Cypress Telecommunications	E	281 449-4000
Spring (G-19205)		
Daegis Inc	E	214 584-6400
Irving (G-12988)		
Dartican LLC	F	281 645-6370
Pinehurst (G-16733)		
Data Voice International Inc	F	972 390-8808
McKinney (G-14934)		
Datagration Solutions Inc	E	713 568-4580
Houston (G-9405)		
DC Cadd Company	F	210 732-9212
San Antonio (G-18043)		
Deligent LLC	F	972 550-6111
Irving (G-12995)		
Dell Software Inc	E	469 221-4335
Grapevine (G-8029)		
Dell Technologies Inc	C	800 289-3355
Round Rock (G-17646)		
Distribution Management Co Inc	F	817 421-3311
Southlake (G-19063)		
Diyatech Corp	E	214 769-6933
Dallas (G-4264)		
Droplets Inc	E	214 969-9970
Plano (G-16851)		
Dwell App LLC	F	214 417-9424
Plano (G-16853)		
Dynatron Software Inc	F	972 488-0393
Richardson (G-17303)		
Dyopath LLC	D	855 749-6758
Houston (G-9551)		
E2open LLC	D	866 432-6736
Austin (G-1108)		
E2open LLC	D	925 460-1700
Austin (G-1109)		
Ebizsoft Inc	E	954 272-0500
Austin (G-1112)		
Eci Software Solutions Inc	C	703 737-6620
Fort Worth (G-6602)		
Eclectic Innvtive Slutions LLC	F	737 999-1907
Dripping Springs (G-5505)		
Edge Software Inc	E	512 345-7793
Austin (G-1114)		
Eduspark Inc	F	512 535-6139
Austin (G-1116)		
Election Systems & Sftwr LLC	D	469 675-8990
Allen (G-264)		
EMC Corporation	C	972 892-7700
Dallas (G-4317)		
Emergency Technologies Inc	E	919 676-6200
Austin (G-1124)		
Energy Exchange 3 LP	F	972 668-6601
Frisco (G-7282)		
Epicor Software Corporation	D	800 776-7438
Plano (G-16865)		
Epicor Software Corporation	C	512 328-2300
Austin (G-1132)		
Eship Global Inc	F	972 518-1775
Dallas (G-3842)		
Everest Global Inc	F	972 980-0013
Dallas (G-4337)		
Evoleap LLC	F	832 371-6677
Houston (G-9719)		
Excelente Inc	E	855 209-1970
Plano (G-16867)		
Excelergy Corp	F	214 953-9373
Dallas (G-4340)		
Exit Plan LLC	F	213 444-6106
Austin (G-1145)		
Fellowship Technologies LP	D	469 442-0100
Irving (G-13025)		
Filecontrol Partners Ltd	F	713 355-1111
Houston (G-9785)		
Filestack	F	210 364-1833
San Antonio (G-18113)		
Financial Industry Com	D	972 458-8583
Addison (G-123)		
Flow-Cal Inc	E	832 240-4800
Houston (G-9808)		
Forcepoint LLC	E	858 320-8000
Austin (G-1164)		
Forproject Technology Inc	F	214 550-8156
Irving (G-13031)		
Four Cornerstone Solutions LLC	E	817 377-1144
Fort Worth (G-6646)		
Gem-Cap Inc	F	512 219-7610
Austin (G-1180)		
Gibraltar Monex Centurion Svc	G	800 409-2674
Houston (G-9955)		
Global Shop Solutions Inc	D	281 681-1959
The Woodlands (G-19868)		
Globalscape Inc	D	210 308-8267
San Antonio (G-18150)		
Goengineer Inc	F	713 735-3295
Houston (G-9990)		
Greenbasket Inc	E	212 203-3302
Frisco (G-7259)		
Greyheller LLC	D	925 415-5050
Dallas (G-4416)		
Harris N Computer Corporation	F	903 535-8222
Tyler (G-20093)		
Harte Hanks Inc	E	512 343-1100
Austin (G-1198)		
Hbs Systems Inc	D	972 234-4444
Richardson (G-17327)		
Healthmark Medical Group LLC	F	800 659-4035
Dallas (G-4445)		
High Point Design LLC	F	972 753-2622
Irving (G-13056)		
Hp Inc	A	541 360-4763
Spring (G-19132)		
Human Resource Micro Systems	F	415 362-8400
Irving (G-13060)		
Hyper9 Inc	E	800 748-0685
Austin (G-1215)		
I Net Software Technologies	E	972 401-0100
Irving (G-13062)		
Igt Global Solutions Corp	E	512 908-4310
Austin (G-1221)		
Impac Systems Engineering LLP	F	713 784-3500
Temple (G-19682)		
Inclusive Products Inc	F	281 650-7057
Houston (G-10337)		
Infocyte Inc	E	844 463-6298
Austin (G-1228)		
Infosys Limited	D	214 306-2100
Richardson (G-17332)		
Infosys Limited	F	281 454-0300
Houston (G-10359)		
Inherent Software LLC	F	817 379-0328
Wylie (G-20937)		
Innovative Sftwr Solutions Inc	F	830 265-6835
San Antonio (G-18188)		
Intellicentrics Inc	E	214 222-7484
Flower Mound (G-6268)		
Interact Inc	E	512 501-2680
Austin (G-1233)		
Inventory Services Network	E	972 660-7365
Livingston (G-14157)		
Iron Sky	F	281 468-8255
Houston (G-10420)		
Itron Networked Solutions Inc	F	210 762-4400
San Antonio (G-18195)		
Jive Software Inc	D	877 495-3700
Austin (G-1256)		
Kainexus Inc	F	512 522-3940
Irving (G-13072)		
Kev Group Inc	E	866 891-9138
Fort Worth (G-6756)		
Keytrak Inc	D	979 595-2600
College Station (G-3190)		
Kibo Software Inc	D	707 780-1600
Dallas (G-4555)		
Kidasa Software Inc	F	512 368-2326
Austin (G-1269)		
Kingsisle Entertainment Inc	E	972 265-1900
Plano (G-16902)		
Kontract Sftwr Solutions LLC	E	281 994-6104
Houston (G-10560)		
Lacerte Software Corporation	C	214 387-2000
Plano (G-16906)		
Levelfieldcom Inc	F	512 401-9200
Austin (G-1290)		
LMS Acquisitions LLC	F	512 371-7028
Austin (G-1296)		
Lyris Technologies Inc	F	510 844-1600
Austin (G-1314)		
Marine Computation Svcs Kenny	D	281 646-4155
Houston (G-10764)		
Mavenir Prvate Holdings II Ltd	A	469 916-4393
Richardson (G-17352)		
McAfee LLC	A	972 963-7000
Plano (G-16921)		
McKesson Corporation	A	972 446-4800
Irving (G-13102)		
Medapoint Inc	G	512 659-1117
Austin (G-1333)		
Medassets Inc	A	972 813-7500
Plano (G-16924)		
Medhost Inc	C	972 560-3100
Plano (G-16925)		
Medical Present Value Inc	F	512 795-0015
Austin (G-1334)		
Medical Web Experts LLC	E	619 819-8610
Dallas (G-4663)		
Metapath Software Intl	F	972 907-3600
Richardson (G-17356)		
Mindpower International Inc	F	469 287-2735
Lewisville (G-14068)		
Mlc Cad Systems LLC	F	512 288-8511
Austin (G-1346)		
Moneyonmobile Inc	B	214 758-8600
Dallas (G-4685)		
Monolith Tech Holdings LLC	E	972 532-7387
Frisco (G-7299)		
National Instruments Corp	A	512 683-0100
Austin (G-1360)		
Neofirma Inc	F	214 233-7111
Richardson (G-17362)		
Neon Systems Inc	D	281 276-5900
Sugar Land (G-19511)		
Netiq Corporation	D	713 548-1700
Houston (G-11028)		
Netscout Systems Texas LLC	B	469 330-4000
Allen (G-288)		
Netwatch Solutions Inc	F	214 446-8486
Richardson (G-17364)		
Network Info Systems Inc	F	713 255-4800
Houston (G-11030)		
Newtek Inc	E	210 370-8000
San Antonio (G-18344)		
Newtek Partners Lp	D	210 370-8000
San Antonio (G-18345)		
Northrop Grumman Systems Corp	F	512 374-4100
Austin (G-1369)		
Ntt Data Inc	C	800 745-3263
Plano (G-16948)		
O9 Solutions Inc	E	214 838-3125
Dallas (G-4749)		
Occupational Marketing Inc	G	281 492-8250
Houston (G-11119)		
Online Training Solutions Inc	E	888 308-6874
Argyle (G-602)		
Openconnect Systems Inc	F	972 484-5200
Dallas (G-4763)		
Oracle America Inc	F	650 506-7000
San Antonio (G-18356)		
Oracle America Inc	F	512 401-1000
Austin (G-1389)		
Oracle America Inc	C	972 980-7799
Dallas (G-4766)		
Oracle America Inc	G	972 580-0629
Irving (G-13132)		
Oracle Corporation	F	512 832-1599
Austin (G-1392)		
Oracle Corporation	F	713 595-7656
Houston (G-11188)		

Employee Codes: A=Over 500 employees, B=251-500
C=101-250, D=51-100, E=20-50, F=10-19, G=9

2021 Harris Texas
Manufacturers Directory

1647

PRODUCT

Oracle Glass LLC	F	713 462-4759	
Houston *(G-11189)*			
Oracle Systems Corporation	B	713 658-6925	
Lewisville *(G-14075)*			
Ordermygear LLC	F	214 945-4000	
Dallas *(G-4767)*			
P2es Holdings LLC	D	210 402-5900	
San Antonio *(G-18359)*			
Paradigm Ses LLC	F	713 402-6140	
Houston *(G-11238)*			
Pas Group LLC		281 286-6565	
Houston *(G-11254)*			
PC Legal Tools Inc	E	415 808-8800	
Austin *(G-1402)*			
Periscope Intermediate Corp	D	512 717-0684	
Austin *(G-1412)*			
Photonic Inc	E	956 722-3326	
Laredo *(G-13921)*			
Phunware Inc	D	512 693-4199	
Austin *(G-1416)*			
Pivot3 Inc	E	281 516-6000	
Spring *(G-19158)*			
Playnet Inc	E	817 358-7580	
Bedford *(G-1977)*			
Plugged In LLC	F	512 380-0900	
Austin *(G-1422)*			
Pointwise Inc	F	817 377-2807	
Fort Worth *(G-6910)*			
Presidio Ntwrked Sltons Group	B	469 549-3800	
Lewisville *(G-14083)*			
Privacy Inc	E	214 760-8700	
Dallas *(G-4829)*			
Procera Networks Inc	E	510 230-2777	
Plano *(G-16980)*			
Profitable Decisions Inc	F	281 972-3030	
Houston *(G-11441)*			
Pros Inc	A	713 335-5151	
Houston *(G-11452)*			
Pros Holdings Inc	C	713 335-5151	
Houston *(G-11453)*			
Q2 Holdings Inc	E	512 275-0072	
Austin *(G-1439)*			
Qnet Inc	D	214 341-7638	
Dallas *(G-4838)*			
Quest Software Inc	E	949 754-8000	
Dallas *(G-4850)*			
Quick Intrnet Sftwr Sltons Inc	F	979 846-3008	
College Station *(G-3198)*			
Qvinci Software	F	512 637-7337	
Austin *(G-1446)*			
Realpage Inc	A	972 820-3000	
Richardson *(G-17387)*			
Red Book Connect LLC	B	877 741-9610	
Austin *(G-1455)*			
Republic Title of Texas Inc	C	972 578-8611	
Plano *(G-16991)*			
Rlra Inc	F	817 783-3335	
Alvarado *(G-342)*			
Rmg Enterprise Solutions Inc	E	877 796-6634	
Dallas *(G-4904)*			
Rmg Networks Holding Corp	E	800 827-9666	
Addison *(G-159)*			
ROC Software LP	E	512 336-4200	
Austin *(G-1468)*			
Rubicon Communications LLC	E	512 646-4100	
Austin *(G-1476)*			
Saddle Creek Corp	F	817 306-2000	
Fort Worth *(G-6971)*			
Sailpoint Tech Holdings Inc	A	512 346-2000	
Austin *(G-1482)*			
Sailpoint Technologies Inc	C	512 346-2000	
Austin *(G-1483)*			
Samsung SDS Globl Scl Amer Inc	E	201 263-3000	
Plano *(G-17000)*			
Scott Traffic LLC	F	972 937-6040	
Waxahachie *(G-20557)*			
Sevco Security Inc	F	512 413-2211	
Austin *(G-1496)*			
Shadowsoft Inc	E	972 841-2469	
Irving *(G-13176)*			
Sharco Technologies Inc	F	512 258-0573	
Pflugerville *(G-16688)*			
Shi International Corp	F	732 764-8888	
Dallas *(G-4954)*			
Shi/Government Solutions Inc	E	512 634-8100	
Austin *(G-1498)*			
Shiftsmart Inc	F	817 271-3604	
Dallas *(G-4955)*			
Shipcom Wireless Inc	D	281 558-5252	
Houston *(G-11870)*			

Sk Global Software LLC	F	301 963-7300	
Houston *(G-11912)*			
Smart Imaging Technologies Co	E	713 589-3500	
Houston *(G-11918)*			
Soff Corporation	F	469 467-9700	
Plano *(G-17008)*			
Soff Corporation	F	469 467-9700	
Plano *(G-17009)*			
Softest Designs Corporation	E	210 697-8828	
San Antonio *(G-18481)*			
Software Construction Co Inc	F	214 495-7387	
Allen *(G-298)*			
Software Development Tech	F	650 906-6135	
Trophy Club *(G-20021)*			
Software Global Ltd	F	832 274-0478	
Austin *(G-1516)*			
Solarwinds Corporation	F	512 682-9300	
Austin *(G-1517)*			
Solarwinds Holdings Inc	F	512 682-9300	
Austin *(G-1518)*			
Solarwinds North America Inc	C	512 682-9300	
Austin *(G-1519)*			
Solarwinds Worldwide LLC	E	512 682-9300	
Austin *(G-1520)*			
Solid Integrations LLC	F	915 235-4357	
El Paso *(G-5968)*			
Solovis Inc	F	678 234-4583	
Irving *(G-13183)*			
Southwest Data Systems Inc	F	817 370-9966	
Fort Worth *(G-7001)*			
Splunk Inc	F	972 244-8806	
Plano *(G-17011)*			
St George Software L L C	F	512 442-6794	
Austin *(G-1529)*			
Stark Holdings Inc	F	512 329-8109	
Austin *(G-1531)*			
Statacorp LLC	C	979 696-4600	
College Station *(G-3202)*			
Superior Information Systems	F	713 524-8998	
Houston *(G-12116)*			
T-System Inc	C	972 503-8899	
Plano *(G-17019)*			
Thomson Reuters Corporation	D	972 250-7000	
Carrollton *(G-2832)*			
Thru Inc	D	214 496-0100	
Irving *(G-13194)*			
Thru Holding Company LLC	F	214 496-0100	
Irving *(G-13195)*			
Thryv Holdings Inc	A	972 453-7000	
Dfw Airport *(G-5458)*			
Thursby Software Systems LLC	E	817 478-5070	
Arlington *(G-798)*			
Tibco Software Inc	E	713 344-2045	
Houston *(G-12287)*			
Tips Incorporated	F	512 863-3653	
Georgetown *(G-7686)*			
Tom Lanham Software	G	254 773-2513	
Temple *(G-19713)*			
Tops Software Corporation	F	972 739-8677	
Allen *(G-303)*			
Touchshare Inc	F	626 639-5460	
Houston *(G-12335)*			
Toutatis Aztec Solutions	D	972 484-3060	
Dallas *(G-5103)*			
Tradesorg LLC	F	512 729-3544	
Austin *(G-1589)*			
Travistin Inc	F	512 275-4812	
Lago Vista *(G-13809)*			
Trax Holdings Inc	F	855 999-7828	
Flower Mound *(G-6290)*			
Traxsales LLC	E	713 466-7177	
Houston *(G-12359)*			
Trend Micro Incorporated	F	408 257-1500	
Irving *(G-13199)*			
Trinity Millennium Group Inc	C	210 615-1606	
San Antonio *(G-18567)*			
Tritech Software Development	E	972 680-2223	
Allen *(G-304)*			
Troux Technologies Inc	D	512 346-8600	
Austin *(G-1596)*			
Tyler Technologies Inc	C	972 713-3700	
Plano *(G-17039)*			
Tyler Technologies Inc	D	972 713-3770	
Plano *(G-17040)*			
Tyler Technologies Inc		806 797-0761	
Lubbock *(G-14504)*			
Uplogix Inc	D	512 857-7000	
Austin *(G-1613)*			
Utax Software LLC	G	844 440-8829	
El Paso *(G-6021)*			

Vedero Software Inc	G	972 309-9870	
Carrollton *(G-2895)*			
Veeder-Root Fuelquest LLC	F	713 222-5700	
Houston *(G-12544)*			
Vercom Software Inc	E	972 661-9336	
Dallas *(G-5161)*			
Verge Ventures LLC	E	972 200-1707	
Richardson *(G-17420)*			
Viewcastcom Inc	E	972 488-7200	
Grapevine *(G-8059)*			
Visionmonitor Software LLC	F	713 935-0500	
Houston *(G-12571)*			
Volusion LLC	F	800 646-3517	
Austin *(G-1645)*			
Websense LLC	B	858 320-8000	
Austin *(G-1653)*			
Western Atlas Intl Inc	B	713 972-4000	
Houston *(G-12641)*			
Win-911 Software	E	512 326-1011	
Austin *(G-1671)*			
Window On Wallstreet Inc	E	972 727-3626	
Richardson *(G-17429)*			
Wizetrade Group	C	407 206-6500	
Plano *(G-17053)*			
Zix Corporation	D	214 370-2000	
Dallas *(G-5210)*			
Zixcorp Systems Inc	E	214 370-2000	
Dallas *(G-5211)*			

SOFTWARE PUBLISHERS: Operating Systems

Assurance Systems Inc	F	770 242-6832	
Carrollton *(G-2858)*			
Bc Connect LLC	C	800 347-0855	
Carrollton *(G-2703)*			
Electronic Med Resources LL C	F	832 456-2600	
Houston *(G-9595)*			
Gearbox Publishing LLC	D	972 312-8202	
Frisco *(G-7287)*			
Information Store Inc	F	713 787-6798	
Houston *(G-10358)*			
Navitaire	E	512 617-2121	
Austin *(G-1361)*			
Nobix Inc	E	925 659-3500	
McKinney *(G-14958)*			
Plus One Robotics Inc	F	937 287-5060	
San Antonio *(G-18383)*			
Pro-Tem Inc	F	281 334-5547	
League City *(G-13976)*			
Tyler Technologies Inc	E	903 753-4292	
Longview *(G-14326)*			
Unique System LLC	F	713 937-6193	
Houston *(G-12440)*			
White Cloud Security Inc	F	512 887-8783	
Cedar Park *(G-2990)*			

SOFTWARE PUBLISHERS: Publisher's

Aspyr Media Inc	F	512 708-8100	
West Lake Hills *(G-20678)*			
Bell and Howell LLC	C	972 753-0711	
Irving *(G-12945)*			
John Galt Development Inc	F	312 701-9026	
Dallas *(G-4536)*			
Learnsap A Texas Ltd Lblty Co	F	832 419-7371	
Pearland *(G-16577)*			
Thinkgeo LLC	F	785 727-4133	
Frisco *(G-7319)*			
Visualml Operations LLC	G	855 847-8256	
Liberty Hill *(G-14131)*			

SOFTWARE PUBLISHERS: Word Processing

Ets Zone	F	713 559-1400	
Spring *(G-19211)*			

SOFTWARE TRAINING, COMPUTER

Capitalsoft Inc	F	972 220-1560	
Richardson *(G-17284)*			
Crayon Software Experts LLC	E	469 329-0290	
Dallas *(G-4181)*			
Learnsap A Texas Ltd Lblty Co	F	832 419-7371	
Pearland *(G-16577)*			
Oracle Corporation	A	737 867-1000	
Austin *(G-1391)*			
Redhouse Virtual Education LLC	F	210 872-4989	
Dallas *(G-4878)*			
Royal Technocrats Inc	E	713 776-8300	
Houston *(G-11684)*			

Texas Source Group Inc .... F 713 464-9702
Houston (G-12250)
Tillman Learning LLC .... F 866 540-9677
Plano (G-17033)

SOLAR CELLS

Energy Xtreme LLC .... F 512 617-7902
Austin (G-1126)
Entech Solar Inc .... F 817 421-4658
Grapevine (G-8031)
Mardel Souza Inc .... E 956 459-3504
Weslaco (G-20664)
Sunpower Corporation .... F 512 735-0119
Austin (G-1546)

SOLAR HEATING EQPT

Exyte Americas Holding Inc .... E 972 535-7300
Plano (G-16868)

SOLVENTS

Buckley Oil Company .... E 214 421-4147
Midlothian (G-15475)
Dysol Inc .... E 817 335-1826
Rhome (G-17255)
Jx Nippon Chemical Texas Inc .... D 713 754-1000
Pasadena (G-16467)
South Hampton Resources Inc .... E 409 385-1400
Silsbee (G-18956)
Strathmore Products Inc .... E 281 269-9658
Rockwall (G-17567)

SONAR SYSTEMS & EQPT

R2sonic LLC .... F 512 891-0000
Austin (G-1449)
Raytheon Company .... D 972 272-0515
Richardson (G-17385)
Raytheon Company .... B 781 522-3000
Plano (G-16987)
Raytheon Company .... B 703 525-1550
Arlington (G-769)
Raytheon Company .... D 972 952-2007
McKinney (G-14969)

SOUND EQPT: Electric

Impact Fire Services LLC .... D 713 263-7535
Houston (G-10332)
Lithotripters Inc .... D 888 252-6575
Austin (G-1702)

SOUND RECORDING STUDIOS

AMA Printing / Finishing Inc .... E 254 776-8860
Waco (G-20359)
Hacienda Rec Recording Studio .... F 361 882-7066
Corpus Christi (G-3543)
Thug City Records .... F 832 264-4892
Houston (G-12285)

SOUND REPRODUCING EQPT

Mitek Corporation .... D 972 875-8413
Ennis (G-6110)

SOUVENIR SHOPS

Brady Standard Herald Inc .... F 325 597-2959
Brady (G-2211)

SPACE RESEARCH & TECHNOLOGY, GOVERNMENT: Federal

Rubrix LLC .... E 512 581-5513
San Antonio (G-18437)

SPACE SUITS

Oceaneering International Inc .... B 281 228-5300
Houston (G-11128)

SPACE VEHICLE EQPT

Albany Engnered Composites Inc .... D 830 249-4400
Boerne (G-2113)
Boeing Company .... A 281 244-4000
Houston (G-8942)
Fabrication & Mfg Aliance LLC .... D 210 648-3131
San Antonio (G-18102)
Heads Up Technologies Inc .... E 972 980-4890
Carrollton (G-2755)

Heartland Enterprises Ltd .... E 830 997-9434
Fredericksburg (G-7182)
J M Fabrication Company LLC .... F 817 652-0526
Arlington (G-709)
L3 Technologies Inc .... A 817 619-2000
Arlington (G-715)
Lockheed Martin Corporation .... A 972 603-1000
Grand Prairie (G-7914)
Lockheed Martin Corporation .... C 956 425-4447
Harlingen (G-8193)
Mayday Manufacturing Co .... C 940 898-8301
Denton (G-5381)
Merritt Prfrred Components Inc .... D 903 983-1592
Kilgore (G-13574)
Rothe Joint Venture Lp .... D 281 483-3852
Houston (G-11670)
Triumph Aerostructures LLC .... A 972 515-8276
Red Oak (G-17237)

SPACE VEHICLES

Axiom Space Inc .... E 346 293-7045
Houston (G-8759)
Lockheed Martin Corporation .... D 210 729-8600
San Antonio (G-18259)
Lockheed Martin Corporation .... D 817 777-2000
Benbrook (G-2042)
Lockheed Martin Corporation .... B 817 777-2000
Fort Worth (G-6798)
Lockheed Martin Corporation .... C 956 425-4447
Harlingen (G-8193)

SPARK PLUGS: Internal Combustion Engines

Stitt Spark Plug Company Inc .... E 936 441-7796
Conroe (G-3367)

SPAS

Girl Talk Boutique & Spa LLC .... F 956 225-7898
Pharr (G-16698)
R&D Futures LLC .... E 214 473-9955
Plano (G-16983)

SPEAKER MONITORS

Chimera Lab Ltd .... F 214 428-3901
Kemp (G-13483)

SPEAKER SYSTEMS

Crossfire Inc .... E 972 570-0800
Irving (G-12983)
Heart of Texas Music Inc .... F 254 778-7422
Temple (G-19681)
Qpower Incorporated .... E 713 266-5295
Houston (G-11486)
Speakermax Inc .... F 281 880-9922
Houston (G-11995)

SPECIAL PRODUCT SAWMILLS, NEC

Giles Efton .... E 210 662-2800
San Antonio (G-18140)

SPECIALIZED LEGAL SVCS

Tan Boots LLC .... F 512 921-0720
Austin (G-1713)

SPECIALTY FOOD STORES: Coffee

Coffee Traders Inc .... E 512 476-2279
Austin (G-1056)
Farmer Bros Co .... F 682 549-6600
Northlake (G-15886)
Nuzee Inc .... E 760 295-2408
Plano (G-16951)
Perkup Coffees LLC .... E 281 445-6744
Houston (G-11291)
Texas Coffee Company .... E 409 835-3434
Beaumont (G-1958)
Wicked Voodoo Espresso LLC .... E 360 631-1447
New Braunfels (G-15832)

SPECIALTY FOOD STORES: Health & Dietetic Food

United Salt Saltville LLC .... E 713 877-2600
Houston (G-12456)

SPECIALTY FOOD STORES: Juices, Fruit Or Vegetable

Juiceus LLC .... E 956 667-0153
Brownsville (G-2372)

SPECIALTY FOOD STORES: Vitamin

Nutrition Supply Corp .... F 936 334-0514
Liberty (G-14124)

SPECIALTY OUTPATIENT CLINICS, NEC

Hanger Inc .... C 512 777-3800
Austin (G-1197)

SPECIALTY SAWMILL PRDTS

G D Edgar Lumber Co Inc .... F 409 787-2452
Hemphill (G-8246)

SPECULATIVE BUILDERS: Single-Family Housing

Centex Corporation .... C 214 981-5000
Dallas (G-4097)
Gobbato Builders LLC .... F 737 843-4327
Austin (G-1185)

SPICE & HERB STORES

El Venado Foods .... E 713 692-0688
Houston (G-9587)
Mothers Journey Inc .... F 877 279-7975
Frisco (G-7261)

SPONGES: Bleached & Dyed

Starrfoam Manufacturing Inc .... E 817 654-4688
Arlington (G-787)

SPOOLS: Indl

Hoyafam Holdings Ltd .... E 281 447-0447
Houston (G-10270)
McWhirter Wood Products Inc .... F 713 861-1437
Houston (G-10813)
Spooltech LLC .... E 281 861-6800
Houston (G-12022)

SPORTING & ATHLETIC GOODS: Bags, Golf

Bella Design Group LLC .... F 972 304-4100
Arlington (G-630)

SPORTING & ATHLETIC GOODS: Bowling Alleys & Access

Tenth Frame Inc .... E 979 743-6585
Schulenburg (G-18780)
Western Bowl .... E 806 359-5211
Amarillo (G-521)

SPORTING & ATHLETIC GOODS: Bowling Balls

Global Manufacturing LLC .... E 210 598-4100
San Antonio (G-18147)

SPORTING & ATHLETIC GOODS: Bows, Archery

Emergent Manufacturing Systems .... F 903 876-3679
Frankston (G-7166)

SPORTING & ATHLETIC GOODS: Camping Eqpt & Splys

Sellmark Corporation .... D 817 225-0310
Mansfield (G-14717)
Yeti Holdings Inc .... E 512 394-8220
Austin (G-1681)

SPORTING & ATHLETIC GOODS: Cases, Gun & Rod

Blacksheep Inc .... B 903 592-3853
Tyler (G-20059)
Granite Security Products Inc .... E 817 483-0910
Mansfield (G-14677)

PRODUCT

SPORTING & ATHLETIC GOODS: Driving Ranges, Golf, Electronic

Topgolf International Inc ....F 832 200-0106
Spring (G-19180)

SPORTING & ATHLETIC GOODS: Dumbbells & Other Weight Eqpt

Wheels and Fitness In Motion ....F 210 828-4542
San Antonio (G-18617)

SPORTING & ATHLETIC GOODS: Exercising Cycles

Retail Concepts Inc...............................F 512 467-2782
Austin (G-1462)

SPORTING & ATHLETIC GOODS: Fishing Tackle, General

Precision Tackle Inc..............................F 936 597-6145
Montgomery (G-15639)

SPORTING & ATHLETIC GOODS: Football Eqpt & Splys, NEC

Rocksolid LLC.......................................F 855 282-8880
Frisco (G-7309)

SPORTING & ATHLETIC GOODS: Gymnasium Eqpt

Dollamur LP..D 817 534-3344
Fort Worth (G-6589)
Tko Sports Group USA Limited ....E 713 895-9270
Houston (G-12305)

SPORTING & ATHLETIC GOODS: Hunting Eqpt

Fort Hood Sportsmens Center...............F 254 532-4552
Fort Hood (G-6322)
Magnum Feeders Inc ....F 281 261-0803
Rosharon (G-17608)
MB Ranch King Blinds LLC ....E 817 558-7320
Joshua (G-13323)
T Hangers Inc ....F 830 741-8383
Hondo (G-8356)
Walter Solomon.....................................F 903 938-2096
Marshall (G-14806)

SPORTING & ATHLETIC GOODS: Pools, Swimming, Exc Plastic

Jobran Unlimited LLC.............................E 956 541-1309
Brownsville (G-2371)

SPORTING & ATHLETIC GOODS: Pools, Swimming, Plastic

Progressive Coml Aquatics Inc ....D 281 982-0212
Houston (G-11442)

SPORTING & ATHLETIC GOODS: Protectors, Baseball, Etc

Douglas Pads & Sports Inc ....E 713 697-9787
Houston (G-9503)

SPORTING & ATHLETIC GOODS: Rods & Rod Parts, Fishing

Kdr Outdoor & Leisure Pdts Inc ....F 281 259-8033
Magnolia (G-14612)

SPORTING & ATHLETIC GOODS: Shafts, Golf Club

Ust-Mamiya Inc ....E 817 267-2219
Fort Worth (G-7095)

SPORTING & ATHLETIC GOODS: Shooting Eqpt & Splys, General

Ultimate Trining Munitions Inc..............F 908 392-5390
Brownsville (G-2417)

SPORTING & ATHLETIC GOODS: Shuffleboards & Shuffleboard Eqpt

Kelye B Stites Inc.................................E 817 284-3499
Richland Hills (G-17439)

SPORTING & ATHLETIC GOODS: Skateboards

Index Skateboarding...............................F 817 887-9779
Hurst (G-12846)

SPORTING & ATHLETIC GOODS: Softball Eqpt, Splys

Texas Firecrckrs Fstptch Softb ....F 713 818-4661
Conroe (G-3370)

SPORTING & ATHLETIC GOODS: Targets, Archery & Rifle Shooting

Reagent Chemical & RES Inc.................F 713 626-1843
Houston (G-11561)
Reagent Chemical & RES Inc.................E 409 962-1116
Vidor (G-20331)
Reagent Chemical & RES Inc.................E 281 862-9464
Houston (G-11562)
Reagent Chemical & RES Inc.................F 432 458-3403
Stanton (G-19404)

SPORTING & ATHLETIC GOODS: Team Sports Eqpt

Lisco LLP..F 806 762-5126
Lubbock (G-14437)
Rocket Distribution LLC.........................F 817 688-9454
Lewisville (G-14089)

SPORTING & ATHLETIC GOODS: Track & Field Athletic Eqpt

Best American Mfg Corp ....F 972 475-0092
Rowlett (G-17701)
Track What Matters LLC ....F 817 430-9201
Bartonville (G-1747)

SPORTING & ATHLETIC GOODS: Trampolines & Eqpt

Yj USA Corp...F 877 927-8777
Addison (G-175)

SPORTING & ATHLETIC GOODS: Treadmills

North American Trade Corp ....F 936 588-1010
Montgomery (G-15637)

SPORTING & REC GOODS, WHOLESALE: Camping Eqpt & Splys

Boy Scouts of America...........................A 972 580-2000
Irving (G-12950)

SPORTING & RECREATIONAL GOODS & SPLYS WHOLESALERS

Mach Speed Holdings LLC.....................D 214 978-3800
Plano (G-16917)
McAllen Sports Inc................................E 956 687-5500
McAllen (G-14889)
Plano Sports Soccer Inc.........................F 972 519-0222
Plano (G-16974)

SPORTING & RECREATIONAL GOODS, WHOLESALE: Bicycle Parts

Bell Sports Corp....................................E 469 417-6600
Irving (G-12946)

SPORTING & RECREATIONAL GOODS, WHOLESALE: Boat Access & Part

Associated Canvas Pdts I Ltd................F 281 457-1480
Channelview (G-3012)

SPORTING & RECREATIONAL GOODS, WHOLESALE: Exercise

Multisports Inc ....F 713 460-8188
Houston (G-10939)

SPORTING & RECREATIONAL GOODS, WHOLESALE: Fitness

Tko Sports Group USA Limited ....E 713 895-9270
Houston (G-12305)

SPORTING & RECREATIONAL GOODS, WHOLESALE: Golf

Callaway Golf Ball Oprtons Inc..............D 844 534-6426
Fort Worth (G-6489)
Ust-Mamiya Inc......................................E 817 267-2219
Fort Worth (G-7095)

SPORTING & RECREATIONAL GOODS, WHOLESALE: Golf & Skiing

Golf Time LLC ....E 214 366-1595
Carrollton (G-2746)

SPORTING & RECREATIONAL GOODS, WHOLESALE: Hunting

Sellmark Corporation ....D 817 225-0310
Mansfield (G-14717)

SPORTING & RECREATIONAL GOODS, WHOLESALE: Watersports

Select Power Sport Inc..........................F 936 967-2332
Livingston (G-14161)

SPORTING FIREARMS WHOLESALERS

Advanced Weapons and Armor Inc.......E 830 459-5263
Kerrville (G-13516)

SPORTING GOODS

Act Global Sports Tech Inc ....E 512 733-5300
Austin (G-884)
American Acrylic Injection Inc...............E 972 784-7759
Farmersville (G-6221)
Animal Paintball LLC ....G 956 753-8272
Laredo (G-13858)
Aries Acrylic Mfg Inc ....F 972 771-6286
Rockwall (G-17538)
Athletic Bag Company LP ....E 903 520-3343
Tyler (G-20051)
Ballqube Inc..F 800 543-1470
Dallas (G-4001)
Bell Sports Inc......................................E 972 343-1000
Grand Prairie (G-7844)
Clarke Products Inc ....C 972 660-1992
Colleyville (G-3212)
Cortwear Sports AP & Eqp LLC.............F 361 728-1868
Kingsville (G-13624)
Covers Etc Inc ....E 817 467-5030
Arlington (G-649)
Cs Platinum Sports LLC ....F 936 559-1883
Nacogdoches (G-15693)
Ecological Services Intl Inc...................D 956 233-4609
Los Fresnos (G-14346)
Flowtronex Psi LLC...............................C 469 221-1200
Dallas (G-4372)
Fungoman LLC.......................................F 318 775-0000
Dallas (G-4385)
Gamebreaker Inc...................................F 818 224-7424
San Antonio (G-18134)
Kent Sporting Goods Co Inc..................C 903 592-3853
Tyler (G-20108)
Knox Jr Leighton ....E 806 327-5420
Tahoka (G-19641)
Liscosports LLC.....................................F 806 762-5126
Lubbock (G-14438)
Mansfield Plumbing Pdts LLC ....D 903 657-1436
Henderson (G-8267)
Perma Pom Partnership Ltd...................D 979 532-3106
Lane City (G-13851)
Quest and Sons Inc ....E 806 744-2351
Lubbock (G-14468)
Rio Plastics Inc ....E 956 831-2715
Brownsville (G-2401)
Royal Baths Manufacturing Co..............B 281 442-3400
Houston (G-11682)
Simpson Helmets Inc.............................C 830 625-1774
New Braunfels (G-15823)
South Texas Sports Academy.................F 361 992-3364
Corpus Christi (G-3626)
Taiga Coolers LLC.................................G 214 762-3648
Mesquite (G-15077)

Top Golf USA Inc ....C 214 494-6310
The Colony (G-19817)

Trampoline USA Inc ....F 800 872-6765
Orange (G-16266)

Truglo Inc ....D 972 774-0300
Richardson (G-17414)

Unlimited Supply Inc ....E 936 890-8997
Willis (G-20868)

Vibra-Whirl Sports Ltd ....E 806 537-3526
Panhandle (G-16348)

SPORTING GOODS STORES, NEC

Animal Paintball LLC ....G 956 753-8272
Laredo (G-13858)

B & S Hardware Inc ....E 903 856-3552
Pittsburg (G-16744)

Bowden Saddle Tree Company Inc ....F 915 877-3191
Vinton (G-20340)

Europa Sports Products Inc ....F 214 388-7444
Mesquite (G-15041)

Texas Fish Game Pubg Co L L C ....F 281 227-3001
Houston (G-12230)

SPORTING GOODS STORES: Ammunition

True Velocity Ammunition LLC ....D 972 487-6500
Garland (G-7606)

Ultimate Trining Munitions Inc ....F 908 392-5390
Brownsville (G-2417)

SPORTING GOODS STORES: Archery Splys

T L W Archery Inc ....G 830 227-5171
Canyon Lake (G-2680)

SPORTING GOODS STORES: Bait & Tackle

Kdr Outdoor & Leisure Pdts Inc ....F 281 259-8033
Magnolia (G-14612)

SPORTING GOODS STORES: Camping & Backpacking Eqpt

Yeti Holdings Inc ....E 512 394-8220
Austin (G-1681)

SPORTING GOODS STORES: Firearms

Chip McCormick Custom LLC ....E 830 798-2863
Bogata (G-2145)

F-1 Firearms LLC ....E 832 299-6100
Spring (G-19120)

JK Manufacturing Inc ....F 956 723-6893
Laredo (G-13899)

Psd3 Enterprises LLC ....E 830 995-3894
Comfort (G-3240)

White Wing Weaponry LLC ....F 940 382-0830
Carrollton (G-2897)

SPORTING GOODS STORES: Hunting Eqpt

Magnum Feeders Inc ....F 281 261-0803
Rosharon (G-17608)

Plano Synergy Holding Inc ....E 469 733-1868
Grand Prairie (G-7946)

SPORTING GOODS STORES: Soccer Splys

Plano Sports Soccer Inc ....F 972 519-0222
Plano (G-16974)

Soccer 4 All Inc ....F 281 376-7890
Spring (G-19166)

SPORTING GOODS STORES: Specialty Sport Splys, NEC

Douglas Pads & Sports Inc ....E 713 697-9787
Houston (G-9503)

SPORTING GOODS STORES: Tennis Goods & Eqpt

Retail Concepts Inc ....F 512 467-2782
Austin (G-1462)

SPORTING GOODS STORES: Trampolines & Eqpt

Trampolines Usa Inc ....F 409 745-3139
Orange (G-16267)

SPORTING GOODS: Archery

Cobra Manufacturing Co Inc ....E 918 366-7622
Euless (G-6137)

T L W Archery Inc ....G 830 227-5171
Canyon Lake (G-2680)

SPORTING GOODS: Hammocks & Other Net Prdts

Kammok Gear LLC ....G 512 947-7344
Austin (G-1264)

SPORTING GOODS: Sleeping Bags

Houston North Sleep Center ....F 713 688-3188
Houston (G-10240)

Yj USA Corp ....F 877 927-8777
Addison (G-175)

SPORTS APPAREL STORES

Action Wear Plus Inc ....F 281 376-4300
Spring (G-19098)

American Screen Graphics & EMB ....F 281 354-2581
Houston (G-8609)

Climax Investors LLC ....E 832 582-9622
Dallas (G-4130)

McAllen Sports Inc ....E 956 687-5500
McAllen (G-14889)

Nuvo Athletic LLC ....G 281 808-7650
Stafford (G-19360)

SPRAYING & DUSTING EQPT

Dresser-Rand Company ....D 713 346-2257
Houston (G-9519)

Sanotech 360 LLC ....F 817 697-7116
Fort Worth (G-6974)

SPRAYING EQPT: Agricultural

Knox Jr Leighton ....E 806 327-5420
Tahoka (G-19641)

Leeagra Inc ....E 800 825-3446
Lubbock (G-14435)

Pyranha Inc ....F 832 467-3840
Houston (G-11480)

Wylie & Son Inc ....D 806 667-3566
Petersburg (G-16652)

Wylie & Son Inc ....F 325 695-0000
Abilene (G-95)

SPRINGS: Coiled Flat

Suhm Spring Works Inc ....F 214 330-9111
Dallas (G-5020)

Suhm Spring Works Inc ....C 713 224-9293
Houston (G-12091)

SPRINGS: Furniture, Unassembled

Hickory Springs Mfg Co ....F 817 831-1785
Fort Worth (G-6695)

SPRINGS: Leaf, Automobile, Locomotive, Etc

Heitman Company Inc ....F 713 675-9001
Houston (G-10148)

SPRINGS: Mechanical, Precision

Baumann Springs Texas Ltd ....E 972 641-7272
Grand Prairie (G-7840)

Baumann Springs Usa Inc ....D 972 641-7272
Grand Prairie (G-7841)

Newcomb Spring Corp ....E 972 241-6781
Dallas (G-4732)

SPRINGS: Precision

CB Solutions LP ....F 512 267-9596
Lago Vista (G-13804)

Lone Star Indus Corp Texas ....E 915 779-7255
El Paso (G-5846)

SPRINGS: Steel

Baumann Springs Texas Ltd ....E 972 641-7272
Grand Prairie (G-7840)

Baumann Springs Usa Inc ....D 972 641-7272
Grand Prairie (G-7841)

Coiling Technologies Inc ....D 713 849-4000
Houston (G-9241)

Diamond Wire Spring Company ....E 903 581-2358
Tyler (G-20076)

Draco Spring Manufacturing Co ....D 713 645-4973
Houston (G-9512)

Draco Spring Manufacturing Co ....D 713 645-4973
Houston (G-9513)

Leeco Precision Spring Mfg Co ....F 713 692-6281
Houston (G-10618)

Matthew Warren Inc ....D 800 364-0391
Houston (G-10797)

Newcomb Spring Corp ....E 972 241-6781
Dallas (G-4732)

Rays Chmpn Spring & Mtr Svc ....E 817 921-3600
Fort Worth (G-6943)

SPRINGS: Torsion Bar

Turner Manufacturing Co Inc ....E 254 840-2891
Mc Gregor (G-14826)

SPRINGS: Wire

Baumann Sprng Txas Hldings LLC ....E 972 641-7272
Grand Prairie (G-7842)

Coiling Technologies Inc ....D 713 849-4000
Houston (G-9241)

Draco Spring Manufacturing Co ....D 713 645-4973
Houston (G-9512)

Draco Spring Manufacturing Co ....D 713 645-4973
Houston (G-9513)

Exper-Tech Products Company ....F 936 825-3573
Navasota (G-15734)

Gifford Spring Co Inc ....F 972 272-5645
Garland (G-7504)

Gulf Coast Spring Co Inc ....F 713 461-5092
Houston (G-10062)

Katy Spring & Mfg Inc ....E 281 391-1888
Katy (G-13416)

Kern-Liebers Texas Inc ....E 956 781-6563
Pharr (G-16704)

Leeco Precision Spring Mfg Co ....F 713 692-6281
Houston (G-10618)

Leggett & Platt Incorporated ....B 972 875-8401
Ennis (G-6109)

Spring Engineers Houston Ltd ....E 713 690-9488
Houston (G-12027)

Suhm Spring Works Inc ....C 713 224-9293
Houston (G-12091)

SPRINKLING SYSTEMS: Fire Control

ABC Fire Systems LLC ....G 830 625-3473
New Braunfels (G-15771)

Chief Fire Systems Inc ....D 281 252-5800
Magnolia (G-14596)

Dfs Fire Systems LLC ....F 214 628-4061
Richardson (G-17301)

Fire Systems of Texas LLC ....E 956 391-1191
McAllen (G-14862)

Frontier Fire Systems Inc ....E 214 343-9500
Dallas (G-4382)

K C Fab Inc ....E 713 921-5333
Houston (G-10496)

K C Fab Inc ....F 806 372-9281
Amarillo (G-495)

Tyco Fire Products LP ....A 806 472-2400
Lubbock (G-14503)

SPROCKETS: Power Transmission

Martin Sprocket & Gear Inc ....F 817 258-3000
Houston (G-10778)

Martin Sprocket & Gear Inc ....D 325 677-3591
Abilene (G-59)

Metro Sprocket & Gear Inc ....F 972 723-3240
Midlothian (G-15485)

STACKING MACHINES: Automatic

Windlass Metalworks LLC ....F 713 849-9292
Houston (G-12677)

STAGE LIGHTING SYSTEMS

Koncept Systems LLC ....E 800 773-4910
Houston (G-10557)

Lure Capital Corporation ....E 713 729-2424
Houston (G-10703)

Tomcat Global Corporation ....D 432 694-7070
Midland (G-15439)

PRODUCT

STAINLESS STEEL

Aap Metals LLC ....F 800 231-8890
Houston (G-8439)

G2 Automated Technologies LLC ....E 972 479-0699
Dallas (G-4390)

Prestige Kitchen Inc ....F 972 366-3322
Venus (G-20221)

Sabre Alloys LP ....F 281 405-8580
Houston (G-11721)

Texas Iron & Steel LLC ....F 903 758-9498
Longview (G-14317)

STAINLESS STEEL WARE

American Permanent Ware Co ....C 972 908-6100
Allen (G-250)

Venus Fabrication Inc ....F 972 366-3565
Venus (G-20226)

STAIRCASES & STAIRS, WOOD

Latham Stairs & Millworks Inc ....E 940 458-3075
Fort Worth (G-6781)

McFadden Stairs Inc ....F 972 680-8333
Richardson (G-17354)

Stairways Inc ....E 713 680-3110
Houston (G-12039)

Trinity Stairs Inc ....E 972 335-0700
Frisco (G-7320)

STAMPED ART GOODS FOR EMBROIDERING

Leonard Sloan & Associates Inc ....F 214 350-2440
Dallas (G-4591)

STAMPINGS: Automotive

Nuco Tool Inc ....E 956 383-6620
McAllen (G-14895)

Richard H Smith LLC ....E 817 267-6750
Euless (G-6155)

Takumi Stamping Inc ....E 210 380-1087
San Antonio (G-18519)

Toyotetsu Texas Inc ....D 210 231-5515
San Antonio (G-18557)

STAMPINGS: Metal

Airfoil Impellers Corporation ....E 979 822-6418
Bryan (G-2452)

Axxion Group Corporation ....D 915 225-8888
El Paso (G-5656)

Baumann Springs Texas Ltd ....E 972 641-7272
Grand Prairie (G-7840)

Baumann Springs Usa Inc ....D 972 641-7272
Grand Prairie (G-7841)

Baumann Springs Usa Inc ....F 972 641-7272
Fort Worth (G-6440)

Baumann Sprng Txas Hldings LLC ......E 972 641-7272
Grand Prairie (G-7842)

Bettcher Manufacturing LLC ....D 956 618-5805
McAllen (G-14842)

Bettcher Manufacturing LLC ....D 956 519-0468
McAllen (G-14843)

C H Industries Inc ....D 972 416-1304
Carrollton (G-2709)

Ets-Lindgren Inc ....C 512 531-6400
Cedar Park (G-2968)

Exper-Tech Products Company ....F 936 825-3573
Navasota (G-15734)

Fleming & Son Corporation ....E 972 263-1713
Grand Prairie (G-7873)

G & H Diversified Mfg LP ....D 713 856-1600
Houston (G-9883)

General Motors LLC ....D 817 652-2200
Arlington (G-690)

JLK Industries Inc ....E 713 462-7761
Houston (G-10476)

Leeco Precision Spring Mfg Co ....F 713 692-6281
Houston (G-10618)

Metals Incorporated ....F 713 923-9491
Houston (G-10852)

Motor City Tool & Die Corp ....F 512 251-7700
Pflugerville (G-16681)

MPA International LP ....C 915 474-7832
El Paso (G-5887)

New Process Steel LP ....D 713 686-9631
Houston (G-11035)

Newcomb Spring Corp ....E 972 241-6781
Dallas (G-4732)

Quantex Instrument Company ....E 936 544-5732
Crockett (G-3723)

Raytheon Company ....A 972 205-4277
Dallas (G-4860)

Richard H Smith LLC ....E 817 267-6750
Euless (G-6155)

Spring Engineers Houston Ltd ....E 713 690-9488
Houston (G-12027)

Taylor Press Products Company ....E 512 746-5556
Jarrell (G-13274)

Toolco Precision Machine Inc ....F 713 433-3700
Houston (G-12318)

Toro Company ....C 915 231-7200
El Paso (G-6008)

TW Stamping & Tool Inc ....E 903 877-2353
Tyler (G-20166)

STAPLES

CMC Steel Us LLC ....F 214 689-4300
Irving (G-12975)

STARTERS & CONTROLLERS: Motor, Electric

Controlled Systems Sales Co ....F 972 234-6767
Richardson (G-17291)

Industrial Accessories Inc ....F 956 728-7524
Laredo (G-13895)

STARTERS: Motor

Air Starter Components Inc ....E 281 261-7939
Stafford (G-19282)

STATIONARY & OFFICE SPLYS, WHOL: Computer/Photocopying Splys

Philbo Enterprises Inc ....E 214 747-7018
Dallas (G-4802)

STATIONARY & OFFICE SPLYS, WHOL: Writing Instruments & Splys

Barrington Group Ltd Inc ....F 214 528-6990
Dallas (G-4006)

STATIONERY & OFFICE SPLYS WHOLESALERS

Boss & Hughes LLC ....F 713 664-9829
Houston (G-8961)

Doiy LLC ....F 469 513-4159
Dallas (G-4270)

Georgia-Pacific LLC ....D 940 205-9558
Denton (G-5368)

Odee Company ....E 214 340-0415
Dallas (G-4754)

Office Furn Cmpanies Texas LLC ....F 281 724-1533
League City (G-13970)

Onyx Venture Group LLC ....F 281 395-4791
Katy (G-13375)

STATIONERY ARTICLES: Pottery

Doiy LLC ....F 469 513-4159
Dallas (G-4270)

STATIONERY PRDTS

B and D Index Inc ....F 817 261-8227
Arlington (G-628)

Blumbergexcelsior Inc ....E 817 462-1530
Arlington (G-632)

STATORS REWINDING SVCS

Abaco Drilling Tech LLC ....C 281 869-0700
Houston (G-8441)

Lufkin Armature Works Inc ....F 936 632-6607
Lufkin (G-14535)

STATUARY & OTHER DECORATIVE PRDTS: Nonmetallic

Ceradyne Inc ....F 281 773-4135
Humble (G-12755)

STEAM SPLY SYSTEMS SVCS INCLUDING GEOTHERMAL

Geomechanics International Inc ....F 713 599-0373
Houston (G-9937)

STEEL & ALLOYS: Tool & Die

Tejas Alloys LLC ....E 830 303-4422
Seguin (G-18867)

STEEL FABRICATORS

1st Source Restaurant Svcs Inc ....F 214 551-5338
Lewisville (G-14019)

3d Steel Building Systems LLC ....E 325 365-5494
Ballinger (G-1739)

5 Fab Energy Inc ....G 832 596-7140
Cypress (G-3769)

5 Star Fabrications Inc ....F 512 267-0470
Jonestown (G-13314)

A & S Fabrication Inc ....F 817 626-7720
Fort Worth (G-6335)

A Better Fabrication LLC ....E 817 629-8908
Weatherford (G-20572)

A Fab Industries LLC ....E 817 337-4776
Keller (G-13466)

A&T Steel Fabricators Inc ....E 281 351-7650
Tomball (G-19953)

Able Industrial LLC ....D 281 946-2200
Deer Park (G-5260)

Accelerated Process Systems ....C 713 937-6838
Houston (G-8453)

Accura Systems Inc ....C 972 226-0195
Mesquite (G-15023)

Ace Fabricators Inc ....D 281 442-0992
Houston (G-8466)

Acute Technological Svcs Inc ....D 713 983-9353
Houston (G-8473)

Advanced Archtectural Mtls Inc ....F 713 983-9979
Houston (G-8485)

Advanced Diversified Svcs Inc ....E 817 377-2718
Benbrook (G-2036)

Advanced Machining & Tool Inc ....D 972 228-1987
Lancaster (G-13836)

Advanced Sheet Metal LLC ....E 254 772-0134
Waco (G-20355)

Advantage Steel Service Inc ....E 817 589-0088
Fort Worth (G-6349)

AES Industries Inc ....E 817 341-7250
Weatherford (G-20574)

Ahi Supply Inc ....D 281 331-0088
Alvin (G-350)

Airtech Spray Systems Inc ....E 713 681-0013
Houston (G-8518)

Akidco Inc ....F 214 905-6064
Dallas (G-3915)

Al3 Incorporated ....E 512 746-4200
Jarrell (G-13269)

Alamo Iron Works Inc ....B 210 223-6161
San Antonio (G-17885)

Alamo Structural Steel LLC ....D 254 799-2471
Waco (G-20357)

Albas Custom Iron Inc ....F 281 401-9797
Houston (G-8528)

Alecom Metal Works Inc ....E 972 438-1032
Dallas (G-3918)

Alexs Air Conditioning Inc ....E 409 935-2496
La Marque (G-13705)

Allied Precision Fabg Inc ....E 713 757-9810
Caldwell (G-2625)

Alnc Inc ....D 325 658-3612
San Angelo (G-17774)

Alpha Fabricators Inc ....E 713 694-1392
New Caney (G-15834)

Aluminum Techniques Inc ....F 281 499-9026
Stafford (G-19285)

Amco Steel Fabrication LLC ....F 210 488-9023
Elmendorf (G-6066)

American Block Company ....D 281 820-5332
Houston (G-8587)

American Block Company ....D 800 572-9087
Houston (G-8588)

American Block Company ....D 281 820-5332
Houston (G-8589)

American Steel & Alum Co Inc ....D 972 264-1533
Grand Prairie (G-7830)

Americase Frbication Cnstr LLC ....F 972 910-2296
Ennis (G-6088)

Ameritex Machine and Fab LLC ....E 936 228-5070
Willis (G-20842)

(G-0000) Company's Geographic Section entry number

Anchor Machine Works Inc .... F 713 988-0400
Houston *(G-8640)*

Angelina Steel Inc .... F 936 634-6649
Lufkin *(G-14520)*

Apache Fabricators LLC .... E 832 804-6236
Houston *(G-8655)*

Apache Steel Works LLC .... F 832 473-4525
Houston *(G-8661)*

APS Industrial Services Inc .... E 817 385-5500
Arlington *(G-619)*

ARC Designs Inc .... E 281 940-0430
Houston *(G-8677)*

Architectural Products Co Inc .... E 915 584-9424
El Paso *(G-5649)*

Arcosa Wind Towers Inc .... G 817 378-3700
Fort Worth *(G-6398)*

Area Iron & Steel Works Inc .... F 915 833-9494
El Paso *(G-5650)*

Armor Industrial Fabricators .... E 281 573-2777
Baytown *(G-1779)*

Atkore International Group Inc .... D 708 339-1610
Houston *(G-8736)*

Audio and Prfmce Solutions LLC .... E 210 549-4242
San Antonio *(G-17922)*

B & B Pipe & Industrial Tools .... F 832 581-3179
Houston *(G-8374)*

Baldwin Metals Company Inc .... E 214 637-1030
Dallas *(G-4000)*

Bar H Welding LLC .... G 903 806-3110
Longview *(G-14200)*

Barker & Bratton Steel Inc .... E 972 556-1951
Dallas *(G-4005)*

Barr Fabrication LLC .... E 325 643-2277
Brownwood *(G-2425)*

Basden Steel and Erection Inc .... E 817 295-6100
Burleson *(G-2569)*

Basden Steel Corporation .... D 817 295-6100
Burleson *(G-2570)*

Batterson Iron Works L L P .... D 713 688-5433
Houston *(G-8828)*

Bawco Fabricators Inc .... E 281 449-0171
Houston *(G-8832)*

Bawco Inc .... F 281 485-3337
Pearland *(G-16541)*

Bayside Industrial Inc .... E 832 632-2815
League City *(G-13948)*

Beall Construction Company Inc .... D 325 677-2112
Abilene *(G-16)*

Beck Steel Inc .... C 806 762-3255
Lubbock *(G-14369)*

Bellows Systems Inc .... F 281 721-2947
Houston *(G-8854)*

Beltran Brothers Fabrication .... E 281 987-2331
Houston *(G-8855)*

Benchmark Metal Service Inc .... E 940 479-9134
Ponder *(G-17094)*

Bend-It Inc .... F 713 991-0745
Houston *(G-8856)*

Benningfeld Stl Fbrication LLC .... F 832 831-3691
Houston *(G-8857)*

Bentintoshape LLC .... F 214 228-2985
Dallas *(G-4018)*

Best Strl Fabricators Inc .... F 361 265-0550
Corpus Christi *(G-3486)*

Big 4 Steel Services LP .... E 281 353-5333
Spring *(G-19103)*

Big M Constructors Inc .... E 281 469-9770
Houston *(G-8883)*

Big State Fabrication Inc .... E 281 572-1375
New Caney *(G-15835)*

Blastroom Eqp & Cnstr Inc .... E 903 845-2083
Gladewater *(G-7719)*

Bratton Interim Inc .... E 972 556-1951
Dallas *(G-4046)*

Bratton Steel LP .... E 972 556-1951
Dallas *(G-4047)*

Brazos Pipe Stl Fbricators Inc .... E 979 233-7895
Freeport *(G-7194)*

Brock Services LLC .... C 281 807-8200
Houston *(G-8991)*

Broome Welding Co .... E 409 744-0407
Galveston *(G-7390)*

Brush Mechanical Inc .... F 713 937-9027
Jersey Village *(G-13294)*

Bulldog Ironworks LLC .... F 972 935-0575
Waxahachie *(G-20531)*

Bulldog Steel Products Inc .... E 325 893-5806
Clyde *(G-3162)*

Bullgang Tools LLC .... G 979 203-9009
Brenham *(G-2248)*

Bulloch Fabricating Inc .... D 972 221-6277
Lewisville *(G-14031)*

Butler Weldments Corporation .... D 254 697-6416
Cameron *(G-2640)*

Bwfs Industries LLC .... D 281 590-9391
Houston *(G-9023)*

Bwj Metalworks LLC .... D 325 672-4909
Abilene *(G-26)*

C & C Metals Inc .... E 936 760-5640
Conroe *(G-3270)*

C M C Steel Fabricators Inc .... D 972 938-9500
Waxahachie *(G-20532)*

C M C Steel Fabricators Inc .... D 713 799-1150
Houston *(G-9031)*

C M C Steel Fabricators Inc .... D 512 282-8820
Buda *(G-2522)*

C M C Steel Fabricators Inc .... D 713 225-4446
Houston *(G-9032)*

C M C Steel Fabricators Inc .... F 877 297-9111
Houston *(G-9033)*

C M C Steel Fabricators Inc .... A 830 372-8200
Seguin *(G-18827)*

C M C Steel Fabricators Inc .... D 214 631-6699
Dallas *(G-4073)*

C M C Steel Fabricators Inc .... C 361 575-4561
Victoria *(G-20250)*

C M C Steel Fabricators Inc .... E 817 838-6811
Fort Worth *(G-6484)*

C S Aguirre Sons Inc .... E 432 381-5221
Odessa *(G-15951)*

C T & S Metal Fabricators Inc .... E 972 554-9629
Irving *(G-12957)*

C W Precision Fabrication Wldg .... F 281 820-4224
Houston *(G-9036)*

C&A Machine and Repair Svc Inc .... E 713 937-3426
Houston *(G-9037)*

C&F Fabrication Indus Svcs LLC .... E 409 994-2135
Buna *(G-2561)*

Cameo Fabricators Inc .... E 281 449-6207
Houston *(G-9060)*

Carbery Fabricators Company .... F 432 337-5015
Odessa *(G-15955)*

Cast Sheet Metal LLC .... E 956 580-9960
Alton *(G-322)*

Cen-Tex Marine Fabricators .... E 512 237-2496
Smithville *(G-18976)*

Centennial Steel Inc .... E 972 412-5144
Rowlett *(G-17703)*

Central Texas Ex Metalwork LLC .... E 210 337-2260
San Antonio *(G-17992)*

Cerda Industries Inc .... C 713 242-7700
Houston *(G-9145)*

Certi-Fab Industries Inc .... F 281 328-7244
Crosby *(G-3728)*

Certified Pipe Svc Houston Inc .... E 281 457-2454
Baytown *(G-1812)*

Cessac Welding Service Inc .... F 979 828-9067
Franklin *(G-7164)*

Channel Sheet Metal Inc .... F 713 473-2878
Pasadena *(G-16405)*

Chaparral Wldg Fabrication Inc .... E 972 243-7747
Dallas *(G-4104)*

Cherry Construction Systems .... E 903 675-5901
Athens *(G-822)*

Chisum Site & Steel Inc .... E 903 783-0058
Paris *(G-16360)*

Cls Metal Fabrication LLC .... F 817 994-0891
Forest Hill *(G-6295)*

CMC Steel Us LLC .... F 214 689-4300
Irving *(G-12975)*

Cnh Group Incorporated .... F 832 453-9977
Houston *(G-9219)*

Coast To Coast Tower Svc Inc .... F 972 923-9504
Waxahachie *(G-20537)*

Coldstream Energy Holdings LLC .... E 940 682-4772
Millsap *(G-15501)*

Coleman Machine & Welding Svc .... F 325 625-5186
Coleman *(G-3169)*

Commercial Metals Company .... C 972 938-9500
Waxahachie *(G-20538)*

Commercial Metals Company .... B 214 689-4300
Irving *(G-12977)*

Complete Mfg Svcs Inc .... E 281 252-3111
Magnolia *(G-14597)*

Complete Sys Fabrication LLC .... E 817 682-0729
Springtown *(G-19272)*

Conreco Inc .... G 361 851-0352
Corpus Christi *(G-3506)*

Conservatek Industries Inc .... D 713 290-9944
Conroe *(G-3284)*

Contract Fabricating Svcs LLC .... E 281 501-8664
Houston *(G-9292)*

Cooper B-Line Inc .... C 903 813-1746
Sherman *(G-18913)*

Cor-Tex Steel .... F 903 872-3991
Corsicana *(G-3662)*

Creative Alloy Products Co .... E 936 894-2060
Plantersville *(G-17058)*

Crist Industries Inc .... D 817 847-8500
Fort Worth *(G-6561)*

Croft Construction Co Inc .... F 936 258-7902
Dayton *(G-5225)*

CT & S Inc .... E 972 438-9796
Irving *(G-12986)*

Cubeco Inc .... E 713 671-2466
Houston *(G-9356)*

Custom Air Products & Svcs Inc .... D 713 434-1192
Houston *(G-9364)*

Custom Air Products & Svcs Inc .... E 281 802-7419
Houston *(G-9365)*

Custom Fabricators & RPS Inc .... F 979 775-4297
Bryan *(G-2468)*

Cyber Manufacturing LLC .... E 713 946-4903
Houston *(G-9381)*

D & D Fabrication & Erection .... E 817 237-3306
Fort Worth *(G-6568)*

D & L Quality Painting Inc .... E 281 458-3588
Houston *(G-9387)*

Dallas Fabrication Inc .... E 972 245-8771
Carrollton *(G-2864)*

Dallas Metal Fabricators Inc .... F 214 421-7417
Dallas *(G-4220)*

Daniel Steel Industries Inc .... E 214 235-4509
Mesquite *(G-15038)*

Davis Iron Works Inc .... D 254 666-1000
Hewitt *(G-8299)*

Delta Fabrication and Mch Inc .... D 903 645-3994
Daingerfield *(G-3831)*

Dennis Steel Inc .... D 512 259-4001
Leander *(G-13987)*

Diamante Enterprises Inc .... F 210 655-9061
San Antonio *(G-18054)*

Dietrich Industries Inc .... E 281 383-1617
Baytown *(G-1783)*

Diversified Plant Svcs L L C .... D 979 848-8900
Angleton *(G-570)*

Diversified Steel .... E 281 213-3340
Cypress *(G-3786)*

Drilling Structures Intl Inc .... D 281 880-8833
Houston *(G-9530)*

Dynamic Crane Svc Fbrction Inc .... E 713 849-1341
Houston *(G-9547)*

Dynamic Industries Inc .... F 361 775-1500
Ingleside *(G-12894)*

Eagle Metal Products LLC .... E 903 887-3581
Mabank *(G-14576)*

Eddie Richardson .... F 972 878-6181
Ennis *(G-6094)*

Efi Panels LLC .... F 615 301-0745
Orchard *(G-16273)*

El Campo Sheet Metal LLC .... F 979 543-5751
El Campo *(G-5617)*

El Paso Machine & Steel Inc .... E 915 533-7483
El Paso *(G-5737)*

Eldred Sheet Metal Works LP .... E 713 227-3251
Houston *(G-9588)*

Elite Metal Fabricators Inc .... F 817 489-2599
Newark *(G-15862)*

Endeavour Machine and Fab Inc .... F 361 551-2077
Port Lavaca *(G-17146)*

Entech Technology Inc .... E 972 542-0210
Dallas *(G-4325)*

Entex Fabrication Inc .... E 940 592-2173
Iowa Park *(G-12904)*

Essner Manufacturing LP .... D 817 551-5511
Fort Worth *(G-6618)*

Est of James T Jones .... E 254 799-4515
Waco *(G-20398)*

Excel Stamping & Mfg Inc .... E 281 304-0771
Cypress *(G-3789)*

Extreme Fab Inc .... D 713 637-0001
Houston *(G-9738)*

F & R Machine Services Inc .... F 214 631-4946
Dallas *(G-4350)*

Fab Services Ltd .... E 936 931-1004
Waller *(G-20497)*

Fab Tex Oilfield Services Inc .... D 432 339-1011
Odessa *(G-15998)*

Fabco LLC .... D 713 633-6500
Houston *(G-9745)*

PRODUCT

Fabcorp Inc	E	713 466-3962	
Houston *(G-9746)*			
Fabricating Specialties Ltd	C	281 405-2010	
Houston *(G-9749)*			
Fabrication Unlimited Inc	E	713 433-6401	
Houston *(G-9750)*			
Falcon Steel Fabricator Inc	E	281 227-2766	
Houston *(G-9757)*			
Fine Line Met Fabricators Inc	E	972 524-6248	
Terrell *(G-19734)*			
Fischbeck Welding Inc	F	830 625-3249	
New Braunfels *(G-15792)*			
Fluxmetals LLC	D	832 948-4307	
Houston *(G-9818)*			
Freeport Welding and Fabg Inc	C	979 233-0121	
Freeport *(G-7198)*			
G & H Diversified Mfg LP	D	713 856-1600	
Houston *(G-9883)*			
G Fabricating LLC	E	281 421-3100	
Crosby *(G-3731)*			
GA Steel LLC	F	281 741-7284	
Houston *(G-9888)*			
Gadutex Inc	F	713 413-0006	
Houston *(G-8382)*			
Gadutex Inc	E	713 413-0006	
Houston *(G-9889)*			
Gadutex Inc	F	713 413-0006	
Houston *(G-9890)*			
Gallop Contracting Group Inc	E	281 449-1051	
Houston *(G-9894)*			
General Metal Fabricating Inc	F	713 641-5509	
Houston *(G-9924)*			
Gms Steel Manufacture LLC	G	817 270-0447	
Azle *(G-1724)*			
Gonzalez Mechanical Contr LLC	G	915 345-1282	
El Paso *(G-5788)*			
Greenwood Manufacturing Inc	F	281 862-9001	
Houston *(G-10038)*			
Griffin Products Inc	E	903 873-6388	
Wills Point *(G-20875)*			
Grimes Industrial Inc	E	713 921-0000	
Tomball *(G-19980)*			
Grogan-Hazel Steel Inc	E	713 466-7501	
Houston *(G-10048)*			
Gs-Hydro US Inc	E	281 209-1000	
Houston *(G-10052)*			
Gst Manufacturing Ltd	E	817 520-2320	
Haltom City *(G-8147)*			
Gulf Coast Alloy Welding Inc	E	281 821-0543	
Humble *(G-12772)*			
Gulf Coast Fabricators Inc	E	409 727-2372	
Port Arthur *(G-17109)*			
Gulf Coast Fabricators Inc	E	409 866-6721	
Beaumont *(G-1900)*			
Gulf Coast Steel Inc	E	281 768-8392	
Houston *(G-10063)*			
Gulf Coast Welding LLC	E	713 460-3700	
Houston *(G-10064)*			
Gulf Copper & Mfg Corp	E	409 989-0300	
Port Arthur *(G-17111)*			
Gulf Island Fabrication Inc	B	713 714-6100	
Houston *(G-10065)*			
Gulfex Holdings	D	713 946-6614	
South Houston *(G-19043)*			
H & S Metals Inc	F	281 421-9488	
Baytown *(G-1821)*			
Halo Fbrication Metalworks LLC	E	972 587-0788	
Terrell *(G-19736)*			
Hamar Industries Inc	E	817 756-8990	
Fort Worth *(G-6685)*			
Hemco Industries Inc	E	713 681-2426	
Houston *(G-10152)*			
Hendrix Spclty Fabrication Inc	E	713 466-6888	
Houston *(G-10154)*			
Heritage Stl Erction Fbrcation	F	817 790-5170	
Alvarado *(G-334)*			
Herndon Fabrication Works	F	713 941-3785	
South Houston *(G-19045)*			
Hill Country Steel LP	E	210 667-9737	
Converse *(G-3396)*			
Hirschfeld Holdings LP	A	325 486-4201	
San Angelo *(G-17805)*			
Hirschfeld of Nevada Inc	B	325 486-4201	
San Angelo *(G-17806)*			
Holloway Welding & Piping Co	F	972 562-5033	
Allen *(G-276)*			
Hose Master LLC	E	713 926-2288	
Houston *(G-10211)*			
Houston Fab Truck Rigging RPS	E	713 455-6161	
Houston *(G-10233)*			

Houston Wifi C/Hston Cnstr Svc	F	832 444-8300	
Spring *(G-19131)*			
Hrk Enterprises Inc	F	817 654-2008	
Fort Worth *(G-6706)*			
Hvac Mechanical Svcs of Texas	B	713 266-3900	
Houston *(G-10292)*			
Hydradyne Hydraulics Inc	E	713 937-8111	
Houston *(G-10294)*			
Hydraulic Fabrication Svcs Inc	E	832 844-3724	
Houston *(G-10297)*			
Illinois Tool Works Inc	E	800 231-1024	
Houston *(G-10327)*			
Imperial Group Mfg Inc	C	940 627-1700	
Decatur *(G-5247)*			
Industrial Pro Fab LLC	G	713 205-7245	
Katy *(G-13409)*			
Insulation Investors Inc	C	713 691-3661	
Houston *(G-10382)*			
Interstate Treating Inc	D	432 362-9291	
Odessa *(G-16034)*			
Inwesco Incorporated	E	817 538-0387	
Fort Worth *(G-6727)*			
Irwin Steel LLC	C	817 636-2508	
Justin *(G-13344)*			
Ism Industries Inc	D	409 769-7841	
Vidor *(G-20327)*			
J & N Welding and Fabricators	E	956 585-3992	
Penitas *(G-16629)*			
J & S Contractors Inc	E	979 647-0040	
Sweeny *(G-19628)*			
J 2 Fabrications LLC	F	281 989-2984	
Magnolia *(G-14611)*			
J E F Fabrication Inc	E	281 367-2032	
Spring *(G-19223)*			
J M Davidson Inc	C	361 883-0983	
Aransas Pass *(G-592)*			
J S McKinney Inc	D	979 849-7283	
Angleton *(G-574)*			
J W Hall Enterprises Inc	F	409 925-7712	
Alvin *(G-368)*			
J&A Fabrication	F	903 981-0136	
Longview *(G-14254)*			
James Barker III	F	936 298-2851	
Cleveland *(G-3130)*			
Jayco Steel Services Inc	E	281 399-0189	
New Caney *(G-15842)*			
Jbc Steel Products LLC	E	214 340-1510	
Dallas *(G-4529)*			
JD Pro-Service LLC	F	936 264-4003	
Conroe *(G-3314)*			
Jedco Building Systems Inc	E	281 591-2860	
Houston *(G-10462)*			
Jestex 2 LLC	E	713 921-7187	
Houston *(G-10467)*			
Jjm Oil & Gas Inc	E	832 740-4606	
Houston *(G-10475)*			
Joe Bush & Associates Inc	F	512 238-0450	
Round Rock *(G-17664)*			
Johnston Products Dallas Inc	E	469 272-7212	
Cedar Hill *(G-2946)*			
Joint Holdings/Basic Met Inds	E	713 937-7474	
Houston *(G-10484)*			
Jordans Manufacturing Company	F	817 656-1033	
Fort Worth *(G-6745)*			
Junction Industries LLC	E	817 607-8873	
Fort Worth *(G-6747)*			
Justiss Oil Company Inc	D	903 859-2111	
Arp *(G-812)*			
Katy Steel Co Incorporated	E	281 391-7047	
Katy *(G-13368)*			
Kellogg Brown & Root Intl Inc	F	713 753-2000	
Houston *(G-10512)*			
Kennedy Fabricating Inc	C	281 399-3008	
Splendora *(G-19096)*			
Kensing Iron Works Inc	F	830 625-2815	
New Braunfels *(G-15808)*			
Kikers Machine Works Inc	F	432 381-8142	
Odessa *(G-16052)*			
Koenig Welding Service Inc	E	979 532-4161	
Wharton *(G-20701)*			
Kpr & Rsw Investments Inc	F	281 499-2910	
Stafford *(G-19342)*			
L & M Shtmtl & Stl Fabricators	E	210 433-7131	
San Antonio *(G-18231)*			
L B Foster Company	D	254 296-6100	
Hillsboro *(G-8329)*			
L B Foster Company	E	832 934-3107	
Magnolia *(G-14613)*			
Lacy Construction Services LLC	F	903 498-0683	
Kemp *(G-13485)*			

Lake Road Welding Co	E	940 692-4988	
Wichita Falls *(G-20778)*			
Landmark Fabrication LP	E	817 230-8857	
Decatur *(G-5248)*			
Lauren Engineers & Constrs Inc	E	469 417-7600	
Irving *(G-13083)*			
Liberty Fluid Power Inc	E	972 623-0927	
Grand Prairie *(G-7911)*			
Longhorn Fabrication Inc	D	972 225-6800	
Terrell *(G-19739)*			
Longview Fab & Machine Inc	E	903 238-8300	
Longview *(G-14269)*			
Longview Mechanical Contrs Inc	E	903 759-1331	
Longview *(G-14270)*			
M & H Metal Specialities Inc	F	972 296-9057	
Dallas *(G-4616)*			
M&M Prcsion Mtal Fbrcation Inc	F	940 726-3379	
Valley View *(G-20204)*			
Mac Fabricators	G	979 265-0235	
Clute *(G-3156)*			
Mach International Inc	E	713 695-6000	
Houston *(G-10731)*			
Madewell LLC	E	713 674-1050	
Houston *(G-10732)*			
Maggie Chacon	E	915 857-3100	
El Paso *(G-5857)*			
Magni-Fab Southwest Co	E	903 532-5533	
Howe *(G-12736)*			
Makers Company Inc	E	817 834-5538	
Fort Worth *(G-6807)*			
Manufctred Component Parts Ltd	E	713 880-0590	
Houston *(G-10749)*			
Markle Mfg Co San Antonio Inc	D	210 655-7130	
San Antonio *(G-18277)*			
Master Fabricators	F	832 294-8103	
Houston *(G-10786)*			
Material Handling Concepts	E	512 836-6598	
Austin *(G-1328)*			
Mayhan Fabricators Inc	E	903 734-4198	
Gilmer *(G-7709)*			
Mc Welding & Fabrication Inc	E	361 289-9605	
Corpus Christi *(G-3576)*			
McBermett Milner LLC	E	325 643-2277	
Brownwood *(G-2440)*			
Medcalf Fabrication Inc	E	281 893-0775	
Houston *(G-10817)*			
Mercer Metals LP	E	214 905-9915	
Grand Prairie *(G-7925)*			
Metal Spinners Inc	E	817 847-0086	
Saginaw *(G-17750)*			
Metal Transformation & Design	F	915 235-4645	
El Paso *(G-5873)*			
Metcon Inc	G	817 281-1620	
Fort Worth *(G-6830)*			
Metfab Inc	E	713 472-3900	
Houston *(G-10853)*			
Microteq Engineering Inc	F	210 736-2611	
San Antonio *(G-18303)*			
Mil Ltd	C	713 691-5200	
Houston *(G-10879)*			
Milestone Metals Inc	D	281 448-9151	
Houston *(G-10881)*			
Miscellaneous Specialties Inc	F	281 351-1177	
Tomball *(G-19988)*			
Mitchell Manufacturing Inc	E	281 351-9641	
Tomball *(G-19989)*			
Mk Specialty Metal Fabricators	E	972 225-6562	
Hutchins *(G-12869)*			
Mobil Steel International Inc	E	713 991-0450	
Houston *(G-10899)*			
Modern AG Products LLC	E	281 470-1903	
La Porte *(G-13778)*			
Modern Group Ltd	D	800 231-8198	
Beaumont *(G-1930)*			
Morrison Products Inc	D	972 279-4000	
Mesquite *(G-15063)*			
Mueller Construction Company	E	903 868-3585	
Sherman *(G-18924)*			
Murray Building & Crane Inds	D	713 464-6506	
Houston *(G-10944)*			
N-Fab Inc	E	281 880-6322	
Houston *(G-10949)*			
Nichols Enterprises Inc	F	979 543-4833	
El Campo *(G-5625)*			
North American Steel Corp	E	817 332-7069	
Fort Worth *(G-6866)*			
North Shore Supply Company Inc	C	713 453-3533	
Houston *(G-11076)*			
NRG Manufacturing Inc	D	281 320-2525	
Tomball *(G-19993)*			

Company	Code	Phone
NRG Manufacturing Inc	F	281 320-2525
Waller *(G-20505)*		
Nucon Steel Commercial Corp	F	940 891-3050
Denton *(G-5384)*		
Oakwood Steel Fabrication Inc	F	903 545-2266
Oakwood *(G-15893)*		
Ober & Sons Inc	F	281 879-6760
Houston *(G-11112)*		
Omnimax International Inc	E	817 481-3521
Fort Worth *(G-6882)*		
P & K Services LLC	E	361 299-1800
Corpus Christi *(G-3587)*		
Parker-Hannifin Corporation	E	817 232-1040
Saginaw *(G-17754)*		
Parkline Inc	D	409 935-1037
La Marque *(G-13713)*		
Parks Metal Fabricators Inc	F	903 838-0535
Wake Village *(G-20487)*		
Partner Metalfab LP	F	409 933-0026
La Marque *(G-13714)*		
Partners Metalfab LP	E	713 672-6888
Houston *(G-11250)*		
Patriot Erectors LLC	C	512 858-9100
Dripping Springs *(G-5511)*		
Patriot Parent LLC	B	512 858-9100
Dripping Springs *(G-5512)*		
Peterson Beckner Inds Inc	F	281 872-1806
Houston *(G-11296)*		
Phoenix Metalworks LP	F	979 992-3909
Cat Spring *(G-2932)*		
Piping Accessories Inc	E	409 842-5000
Beaumont *(G-1942)*		
Piping Technology & Pdts Inc	A	800 787-5914
Houston *(G-11338)*		
Plant Fabricators Inc	E	830 393-3064
Floresville *(G-6249)*		
Plate Cut Inc	F	713 802-1291
Houston *(G-11347)*		
Polytrnix McHning Fbrction LLC	F	972 436-0422
Richardson *(G-17374)*		
Power Seal	D	940 767-5566
Wichita Falls *(G-20795)*		
Precise Steel Inc	E	713 673-6300
Houston *(G-11385)*		
Precision Components	F	888 554-4999
Houston *(G-11387)*		
Precision M/C Products Inc	F	972 429-6200
Wylie *(G-20944)*		
Premium Weld Services Inc	F	940 329-0222
Santo *(G-18738)*		
Professional Projects Inc	D	281 351-6315
Cypress *(G-3814)*		
Property Works Central Texas	F	512 940-9353
Manchaca *(G-14640)*		
Prostar Manufacturing Inc	E	281 910-0110
Pasadena *(G-16499)*		
Purvis Industries LLC	D	214 358-5500
Dallas *(G-4837)*		
PWC Industries Inc	E	361 289-0557
Corpus Christi *(G-3602)*		
Qualico Steel Company Inc	D	972 775-1400
Midlothian *(G-15492)*		
Quality Lnings Fabrication Inc	E	713 863-7013
Houston *(G-11495)*		
Quietaire Corporation	F	713 228-9421
Houston *(G-11513)*		
R & N Manufacturing Ltd	D	713 466-6252
Cypress *(G-3817)*		
R & S Steel Fabricating Co	E	713 675-9007
Houston *(G-11521)*		
R Lute S Inc	F	281 595-3777
Rosharon *(G-17610)*		
R Neal John & Associates Inc	E	214 340-1464
Dallas *(G-4855)*		
R R Ramsower Inc	E	979 849-6441
Angleton *(G-576)*		
R2 Fabrication Inc	E	817 230-2015
Fort Worth *(G-6935)*		
Randco Industries Inc	E	432 520-0820
Midland *(G-15377)*		
Rast Iron Work Company Inc	E	210 659-6704
San Antonio *(G-18409)*		
Ratec Inc	F	903 687-3811
Waskom *(G-20520)*		
Ratliff Industries Inc	E	409 755-1830
Lumberton *(G-14569)*		
Rays Welding Shop Inc	F	972 775-2822
Midlothian *(G-15494)*		
RE Campbell Company Ltd	E	713 957-8721
Houston *(G-11558)*		
Reactive & Alloy Mtls Inds Inc	F	979 885-2244
Sealy *(G-18816)*		
Reama Inc	F	409 744-9222
Galveston *(G-7407)*		
Rebar Supply Company Ltd	E	713 937-8999
Houston *(G-11564)*		
Red Steel Company	F	972 243-4242
Dallas *(G-4871)*		
REE Holding Inc	E	409 840-5650
Beaumont *(G-1947)*		
Reliable Design Services LP	F	972 584-0551
Quinlan *(G-17226)*		
Renfrow Metalsmiths LLC	G	832 724-8517
Houston *(G-11600)*		
RH Tamlyn & Sons	E	281 499-9604
Stafford *(G-19370)*		
Rice Metal Fabricators Inc	F	713 462-1978
Houston *(G-11618)*		
Rilco Manufacturing Co Inc	D	713 466-4777
Katy *(G-13437)*		
Rising S Company LLC	F	903 469-4452
Canton *(G-2659)*		
RJ Global Wika LP	E	281 897-9222
Houston *(G-11633)*		
Rose Machine & Fab Inc	F	713 670-9007
Houston *(G-11663)*		
Rus Industrial LLC	C	281 864-9070
Channelview *(G-3033)*		
Rwn Contractors LLC	D	817 523-7900
Springtown *(G-19276)*		
S C S Technologies LLC	E	432 264-6500
Big Spring *(G-2097)*		
S F L Inc	E	936 856-1433
Willis *(G-20863)*		
Sabre Industries Inc	F	817 852-1950
Alvarado *(G-344)*		
Sac Manufacturing Inc	F	903 643-9100
Longview *(G-14301)*		
Sanco Metal Fabricators LLC	F	806 745-9674
Lubbock *(G-14477)*		
Saulsbury Industries Inc	E	903 392-2248
Henderson *(G-8273)*		
Scott Manufacturing Inc	C	806 747-3395
Wolfforth *(G-20912)*		
Sefton Steel LP	D	281 449-8677
Houston *(G-11813)*		
Septh Group LLC	F	713 988-4200
Houston *(G-11832)*		
Serpa Fabrication Inc	F	361 883-2266
Corpus Christi *(G-3621)*		
Sharp-Bilt LLC	F	409 886-0066
Orange *(G-16262)*		
Shioleno Industries Inc	F	817 465-9361
Arlington *(G-780)*		
Signal Metal Industries Inc	C	972 438-1022
Irving *(G-13179)*		
Sikes Fabricating Co Inc	F	409 941-0727
Texas City *(G-19802)*		
SMI Manufacturing Inc	D	281 449-0345
Houston *(G-11921)*		
South Texas Steel Svc Co LLC	F	713 699-2500
Houston *(G-11968)*		
Southeast Texas Industries Inc	C	409 783-0009
Vidor *(G-20332)*		
Southeast Texas Industries Inc	E	409 722-7351
Beaumont *(G-1951)*		
Southeast Texas Industries Inc	C	409 792-0084
Bridge City *(G-2286)*		
Southern Frac LLC	E	877 576-0821
Waxahachie *(G-20560)*		
Spf Corporation of America	F	713 983-9373
Houston *(G-12014)*		
Spitzer Industries Inc	E	713 230-4200
Houston *(G-12017)*		
Spitzer Industries Inc	E	713 466-1518
Houston *(G-12018)*		
Spitzer Industries Inc	B	832 783-7000
Houston *(G-12019)*		
Spitzer Industries Inc	E	713 856-9208
Houston *(G-12020)*		
Stainless Steel Products Inc	G	361 884-1281
Corpus Christi *(G-3628)*		
Stainless Stl Cstm Fbrctors In	E	713 433-0495
Houston *(G-12038)*		
Stainless Stl Fabricators Ltd	E	903 595-6625
Tyler *(G-20157)*		
Staley Steel Inc	E	940 686-6000
Pilot Point *(G-16729)*		
Steel Building Supply Inc	E	936 598-6373
Center *(G-3009)*		
Steel Designs Inc	E	713 937-3006
Houston *(G-12053)*		
Steel Effects LLC	F	713 729-1100
Houston *(G-12054)*		
Steelfab Texas Inc	E	972 562-7720
McKinney *(G-14979)*		
Steelhead Inc	E	210 628-1066
San Antonio *(G-18498)*		
Steffani Metals Inc	E	713 896-9160
Houston *(G-12056)*		
Sterling Group LP	E	713 877-8257
Houston *(G-12060)*		
Steven-Sharon Corporation	D	409 744-4538
Galveston *(G-7409)*		
Stis Inc	B	409 697-3350
Bridge City *(G-2287)*		
Structural Metals Inc	A	830 372-8200
Seguin *(G-18866)*		
Sturm Welding Inc	F	940 686-2492
Pilot Point *(G-16730)*		
Summit Metals Corporation	E	940 433-8788
Rhome *(G-17260)*		
Summit Seals Inc	F	409 769-8151
Vidor *(G-20335)*		
Summit Steel Fabricators Inc	D	713 451-6960
Houston *(G-12095)*		
Suncoast Post-Tension Ltd	E	512 259-7908
Leander *(G-13998)*		
Superior Grating Inc	E	713 686-9475
Houston *(G-12115)*		
Sweco Fab Inc	B	713 731-0030
Houston *(G-12130)*		
T O F Enterprises Inc	F	281 328-2553
Crosby *(G-3744)*		
Tank and Vessel Builders LP	E	325 854-8450
Baird *(G-1736)*		
Tankheads Inc	G	817 636-2085
Haslet *(G-8224)*		
Tcw Investments Inc	F	409 796-1883
Beaumont *(G-1956)*		
Team Fabricators LLC	D	409 962-0266
Port Arthur *(G-17128)*		
Techmar Industries LLC	E	832 246-6200
Spring *(G-19175)*		
Teco Metal Products LLC	E	214 221-5020
Dallas *(G-5046)*		
Tex Cnp/Seal Inc	E	214 688-7770
Dallas *(G-5051)*		
Texas Steel Fabricators Inc	F	936 372-1616
Waller *(G-20508)*		
Texas Toolmakers Inc	E	210 494-3651
San Antonio *(G-18544)*		
Texas Vessels Fabrication LLC	E	903 541-4883
Jacksonville *(G-13264)*		
Texcraft Inc	F	806 744-6651
Lubbock *(G-14494)*		
Texweld & Fabrication Inc	G	903 586-1775
Jacksonville *(G-13265)*		
TH Precision LLC	E	830 549-5864
Seguin *(G-18868)*		
Thornton Steel Holdings Inc	D	817 926-3324
Fort Worth *(G-7059)*		
Thybar Corporation	E	972 416-6220
Dallas *(G-5090)*		
Thyssenkrupp Arprt Systems Inc	C	817 834-6984
Fort Worth *(G-7061)*		
Tippen Steel Services Inc	E	940 433-3132
Boyd *(G-2208)*		
Tips Iron & Steel Co Inc	E	512 478-8511
Austin *(G-1581)*		
Tlr Energy Services Inc	F	940 969-2400
Paradise *(G-16355)*		
Tns Industries Inc	E	713 690-4000
Houston *(G-12313)*		
Total Steel Fabrication LLC	E	972 846-4703
Ennis *(G-6120)*		
Trace Metal Industries Inc	E	817 921-6251
Fort Worth *(G-7070)*		
Tradco Inc	F	713 333-9300
Houston *(G-12339)*		
Trailers By Southern LLC	E	469 517-0410
Joshua *(G-13327)*		
Trans-Tex Fabricating Co Inc	E	210 633-0100
Elmendorf *(G-6072)*		
Tri-Construction Co Inc	C	979 233-7211
Freeport *(G-7217)*		
Trinity Industrial Svcs LLC	B	409 722-6700
Beaumont *(G-1964)*		
Trinity Industries Inc	B	214 631-4420
Dallas *(G-5112)*		

Employee Codes: A=Over 500 employees, B=251-500
C=101-250, D=51-100, E=20-50, F=10-19, G=9

2021 Harris Texas
Manufacturers Directory

1655

PRODUCT

Trinity Specialty Products Inc	G	210 304-2100
San Antonio *(G-18568)*		
Triofab Inc	F	713 417-1205
Houston *(G-12377)*		
Trupply LLC	F	281 516-8100
Houston *(G-12386)*		
Tsgc Inc	C	361 289-0901
Corpus Christi *(G-3644)*		
Turboweld	D	713 896-6467
Houston *(G-12411)*		
Turn-Tech Inc	E	281 356-1290
Pinehurst *(G-16737)*		
TX Tinman Enterprises LLC	F	817 288-6116
Fort Worth *(G-7087)*		
United Marine Enterprise Inc	D	409 833-0303
Beaumont *(G-1965)*		
Universal Ornaments Inc	D	713 699-1500
Houston *(G-12462)*		
Urbanovsky Advanced Cnstr LLC	D	817 556-3288
Cleburne *(G-3117)*		
Uribe Steel	F	281 452-5696
Houston *(G-12479)*		
US Bellows Inc	B	713 731-0030
Houston *(G-12481)*		
USA Frametek LLC	E	512 515-6500
Liberty Hill *(G-14130)*		
Valley Welding Service	E	956 585-1043
Palmview *(G-16313)*		
Valmont Industries Inc	D	979 277-3359
Brenham *(G-2278)*		
Valmont Industries Inc	D	979 865-9137
Bellville *(G-2013)*		
Valmont Newmark Inc	D	979 865-9137
Bellville *(G-2014)*		
Veriovox Corporation	E	713 409-7216
Katy *(G-13384)*		
Vessel Technology	F	903 643-9111
Longview *(G-14329)*		
Vestal Steel Specialties Inc	E	210 651-4333
Schertz *(G-18768)*		
Vickery Street Fabricators Inc	E	713 695-9195
Houston *(G-12564)*		
Vince Hagan Company	F	214 330-4601
Sunnyvale *(G-19615)*		
Vulcraft Carrier Corporation	E	936 687-4665
Grapeland *(G-8008)*		
W&W-Afco Steel LLC	D	325 676-1422
Abilene *(G-92)*		
Wabb Industries Inc	E	903 427-3980
Clarksville *(G-3078)*		
Walkup Company	D	713 675-6383
Houston *(G-12595)*		
Walston Ventures LLC	F	409 796-1883
Beaumont *(G-1968)*		
Watkins Metal Fabrication Inc	E	940 325-6008
Mineral Wells *(G-15546)*		
Wells/Mccoy Steel Services Inc	E	469 742-0888
McKinney *(G-14990)*		
WHW Properties Inc	E	903 572-4161
Mount Pleasant *(G-15665)*		
Wills Pro Custom Mfg Inc	F	817 534-6009
Fort Worth *(G-7149)*		
Wilson Metal Fabricators Inc	E	972 227-0200
Dallas *(G-5191)*		
Wilson Steel Services LLC	F	903 275-2995
Brownsboro *(G-2333)*		
Wldg Wilkerson & Fabrication	F	817 528-1032
Overton *(G-16277)*		
Woven Metal Products Inc	E	281 331-4466
Alvin *(G-386)*		
Xtreme Strctres Fbrication LLC	E	903 438-1100
Sulphur Springs *(G-19605)*		
Zinsmeyer Mech & Wldg Ltd	E	830 985-3498
Castroville *(G-2929)*		

STEEL MILLS

Abrasive Blast Systems LLC	E	972 205-9309
Garland *(G-7426)*		
Accurate Flamecutting Stl LLC	G	281 987-9100
Houston *(G-8462)*		
Amarillo Waterblasters Inc	F	806 352-2765
Amarillo *(G-479)*		
American Railcar Inds Inc	C	903 759-3946
Longview *(G-14195)*		
Arrow Steel Processors Inc	F	713 670-0160
Houston *(G-8707)*		
Atlas Iron & Scrap Metal Co	E	972 225-4221
Dallas *(G-3981)*		
Automotive Rentals Inc	E	817 624-3650
Fort Worth *(G-6411)*		

Axis Pipe and Tube Inc	E	979 703-6847
Bryan *(G-2455)*		
Azz Inc	D	817 810-0095
Fort Worth *(G-6414)*		
Brazos Pipe Stl Fbricators Inc	E	979 233-7895
Freeport *(G-7194)*		
C D Steel & Service Inc	G	713 957-3604
Houston *(G-9027)*		
Carports Childers & Structures	F	713 460-2181
Houston *(G-9094)*		
CB&i LLC	C	713 649-4277
Houston *(G-9106)*		
CB&i LLC	C	713 375-8000
Houston *(G-9107)*		
CB&i LLC	C	713 485-1000
Houston *(G-9108)*		
CB&i LLC	E	281 456-5700
Houston *(G-9105)*		
CB&i LLC	C	409 980-5500
Beaumont *(G-1867)*		
CMC Steel Us LLC	E	214 689-4300
Irving *(G-12975)*		
Commercial Metals Company	B	214 689-4300
Irving *(G-12977)*		
Commercial Metals Company	F	512 246-1424
Round Rock *(G-17634)*		
Commercial Metals Company	E	972 838-9050
Melissa *(G-14995)*		
Commercial Metals Company	F	956 702-4434
Pharr *(G-16696)*		
Commercial Metals Company	F	512 282-8820
Buda *(G-2526)*		
Commercial Metals Company	D	409 842-3316
Beaumont *(G-1875)*		
Delta Steel Inc	E	918 437-7501
Fort Worth *(G-6583)*		
General Dynamics Ordnance	F	972 276-5131
Garland *(G-7500)*		
Gerdau Ameristeel Corp	G	972 779-7010
Midlothian *(G-15481)*		
Gerdau Ameristeel Us Inc	A	972 775-8241
Midlothian *(G-15482)*		
Gerdau Ameristeel US Inc	A	972 775-8241
Midlothian *(G-15483)*		
Grant & Gerhardt Machine & Mfg	F	713 946-4664
Houston *(G-10016)*		
Grant Prideco Inc	E	936 825-7070
Navasota *(G-15737)*		
Gulf Copper & Mfg Corp	F	409 989-0300
Port Arthur *(G-17111)*		
Hearne Steel Company	D	979 279-3464
Hearne *(G-8232)*		
Imperial Group Mfg Inc	C	940 627-1700
Decatur *(G-5247)*		
Intsel Steel Distributors LLC	C	713 937-9500
Houston *(G-10410)*		
Jarco Steel Inc	D	713 644-4900
Houston *(G-10456)*		
Jsw Steel (usa) Inc	A	281 383-2525
Baytown *(G-1794)*		
K-T Galvanizing Co Inc	E	817 477-4434
Venus *(G-20220)*		
Kloeckner Metals Corporation	D	713 633-7400
Houston *(G-10540)*		
L B Foster Company	E	832 934-3107
Magnolia *(G-14613)*		
Mac Fabricators	G	979 265-0235
Clute *(G-3156)*		
Mayhan Fabricators Inc	E	903 734-4198
Gilmer *(G-7709)*		
Mica Steelworks Inc	C	817 581-9500
Haltom City *(G-8154)*		
Mica Steelworks Inc	C	972 287-5410
Kaufman *(G-13460)*		
Mica Steelworks Inc	E	817 267-9699
Euless *(G-6149)*		
Northwest Pipe Company	D	817 847-1402
Saginaw *(G-17753)*		
Nucor Corporation	B	903 626-4461
Jewett *(G-13308)*		
Nucor Corporation	C	972 524-5407
Terrell *(G-19745)*		
Nucor Corporation	F	214 340-1883
Dallas *(G-4747)*		
Omnimax International Inc	E	817 481-3521
Fort Worth *(G-6882)*		
Parker-Hannifin Corporation	E	817 232-1040
Saginaw *(G-17754)*		
Phillips Iron Works Inc	E	337 364-2337
Houston *(G-11327)*		

Renfro Street Holdings Ltd	E	817 295-6100
Burleson *(G-2596)*		
Rio Grande Steel Ltd	E	956 361-4443
San Benito *(G-18664)*		
Roy Johnson Incorporated	E	817 468-2939
Arlington *(G-773)*		
Russell Mfg & Fabg Inc	E	281 590-8185
Houston *(G-11699)*		
Selkirk Corporation	B	972 943-6100
Richardson *(G-17395)*		
Shaw Fabricators Inc	D	713 991-5313
Houston *(G-11850)*		
Southeast Texas Industries Inc	C	409 792-0084
Bridge City *(G-2286)*		
Ssab Texas Inc	C	713 341-7700
Houston *(G-12031)*		
Texas Industries Inc	E	972 263-5077
Dallas *(G-5064)*		
White Star Steel Inc	D	713 675-6501
Houston *(G-12663)*		

STEEL SHEET: Cold-Rolled

Friedman Industries Inc	D	903 758-3431
Longview *(G-14237)*		
GTC Technology LLC	E	817 685-9125
Irving *(G-13045)*		

STEEL WOOL

Made In America Mfg LLC	G	512 435-9952
Austin *(G-1316)*		

STEEL, HOT-ROLLED: Sheet Or Strip

Lone Star Technologies Inc	D	972 770-6401
Dallas *(G-4604)*		
United States Steel Corp	D	903 656-6521
Lone Star *(G-14185)*		

STEEL: Cold-Rolled

C M C Steel Fabricators Inc	D	214 631-6699
Dallas *(G-4073)*		
Kloeckner Metals Corporation	D	713 633-7400
Houston *(G-10540)*		
Landreth Fastner Corporation	F	281 414-3103
Houston *(G-10594)*		
Mayhan Fabricators Inc	E	903 734-4198
Gilmer *(G-7709)*		
Nucor Corporation	C	972 524-5407
Terrell *(G-19745)*		
Richardson Trident Company LLC	D	972 231-5176
Richardson *(G-17390)*		
Suncoast Post-Tension Ltd	C	972 287-0307
Irving *(G-13190)*		
Suncoast Post-Tension Ltd	C	281 445-8886
Houston *(G-12100)*		
Suncoast Post-Tension Ltd	C	281 445-8886
Houston *(G-12101)*		
Vinton Steel LLC	B	915 886-2000
Vinton *(G-20342)*		
White Star Steel Inc	D	713 675-6501
Houston *(G-12663)*		

STEEL: Galvanized

Azz Glvnzing - San Antonio LLC	F	210 661-8574
San Antonio *(G-17927)*		
Azz Inc	E	817 297-4361
Crowley *(G-3751)*		
North Amrcn Glvnzing Ctngs Inc	A	817 810-0095
Fort Worth *(G-6867)*		

STEEL: Laminated

Advanced Aero Coatings LLC	F	817 280-0467
Hurst *(G-12831)*		
Laguna Tubular Products Corp	D	832 734-0044
Houston *(G-10586)*		

STENCILS

Pavement Tool Mfg Inc	F	903 734-7531
Big Sandy *(G-2066)*		

STILLS: Pressure, Metal Plate

Entex Fabrication Inc	E	940 592-2173
Iowa Park *(G-12904)*		

STITCHING SVCS

Xact Xpressions Inc.................E..... 972 242-6332
   Dallas (G-5205)

STITCHING SVCS: Custom

Monograms & More.........................F..... 979 693-7773
   College Station (G-3194)

Qti Apparel & Promotions LLC.........E..... 254 662-3076
   Waco (G-20451)

STOCK QUOTATION SVCS

Window On Wallstreet Inc.................E..... 972 727-3626
   Richardson (G-17429)

STOCK SHAPES: Plastic

Brown Precision Inc......................G..... 530 384-2506
   Cameron (G-2639)

STONE: Cast Concrete

Advanced Cast Stone Inc.................C..... 817 572-0018
   Fort Worth (G-6347)

Arlington Cast Stone Inc.................F..... 817 284-5933
   Hurst (G-12834)

Cates Caststone Co Inc...................F..... 903 839-0309
   Tyler (G-20064)

Charles Barton............................E..... 512 759-1231
   Hutto (G-12877)

Lavender Enterprises Inc.................E..... 214 631-8080
   Dallas (G-4585)

Lone Star Stone Texas Inc...............E..... 254 694-6613
   Whitney (G-20730)

Materials Products Inc....................F..... 512 821-3303
   Austin (G-1329)

P & L Cast Stone Inc......................F..... 817 430-8114
   Roanoke (G-17492)

Pristine Cast Stone Inc...................F..... 972 772-9490
   Rockwall (G-17562)

Stone Cast Inc............................E..... 713 683-6780
   Houston (G-12071)

Texas Carved Stone LP...................F..... 254 793-2384
   Florence (G-6245)

Texas Stone Designs Inc.................E..... 817 265-4011
   Arlington (G-795)

STONE: Dimension, NEC

Custom Crete Inc.........................F..... 713 937-3966
   Houston (G-9369)

Espinoza Stone Inc.......................D..... 830 629-2530
   New Braunfels (G-15791)

Gulf Coast Limestone Inc.................F..... 281 474-4124
   Seabrook (G-18785)

Lithic Industries Inc......................F..... 254 793-3791
   Florence (G-6240)

Simpson Stone Company.................E..... 512 746-2204
   Jarrell (G-13272)

Vgcm LLC.................................F..... 713 455-1465
   Houston (G-12562)

STONE: Quarrying & Processing, Own Stone Prdts

Arnold Stone Inc.........................F..... 972 248-1953
   Lewisville (G-14024)

Capitol Aggregates Inc...................C..... 210 871-7228
   San Antonio (G-17982)

Decorum Tile & Stone Inc.................F..... 512 344-9235
   Austin (G-1087)

Featherlite Building Pdts Corp...........B..... 512 472-2424
   Austin (G-1147)

J & J Stone Company.....................E..... 512 869-3527
   Jarrell (G-13271)

Lithic Industries Inc......................F..... 254 793-3791
   Florence (G-6240)

STONES: Abrasive

Oldcastle Apg Texas Inc.................F..... 972 335-4122
   Frisco (G-7302)

STORE FIXTURES, EXC REFRIGERATED: Wholesalers

Advanced Fixtures Inc....................C..... 972 784-8800
   Farmersville (G-6220)

STORE FIXTURES: Exc Wood

Cabfixco Inc..............................E..... 214 389-1520
   Dallas (G-4075)

J & H Manufacturing Inc.................F..... 830 665-5230
   Devine (G-5450)

Madix Inc................................A..... 214 515-5400
   Terrell (G-19740)

STORE FIXTURES: Wood

Cabfixco Inc..............................E..... 214 389-1520
   Dallas (G-4075)

J & H Manufacturing Inc.................F..... 830 665-5230
   Devine (G-5450)

Jay H Fixtures Inc........................E..... 972 223-2245
   De Soto (G-5239)

Liberty Company.........................E..... 817 921-0218
   Fort Worth (G-6788)

Panel Processing Texas Inc...............E..... 903 586-2423
   Jacksonville (G-13255)

Shioleno Industries Inc...................F..... 817 465-9361
   Arlington (G-780)

STORE FRONTS: Prefabricated, Metal

Ace Automatics Inc.......................F..... 903 852-3004
   Ben Wheeler (G-2030)

STORE FRONTS: Prefabricated, Wood

Ace Automatics Inc.......................F..... 903 852-3004
   Ben Wheeler (G-2030)

STORES: Auto & Home Supply

ABC Exclusive Inc........................D..... 972 485-8182
   Garland (G-7425)

STORES: Drapery & Upholstery

Boriack Interiors Inc......................E..... 214 376-1814
   Dallas (G-4044)

Levan Group I LP........................F..... 713 528-3838
   Houston (G-10628)

STRAPPING

ITW Blding Cmponents Group Inc.........E..... 972 660-4422
   Grand Prairie (G-7897)

Portable Pipe Hangers Inc...............E..... 713 672-5088
   Houston (G-11366)

STRAWS: Drinking, Made From Purchased Materials

Gca Products Inc.........................G..... 972 506-3196
   Dallas (G-4395)

STRUCTURAL SUPPORT & BUILDING MATERIAL: Concrete

Wareing Athon & Co......................B..... 713 222-8804
   Houston (G-12599)

STUCCO

California Stucco..........................G..... 210 838-7433
   San Antonio (G-17976)

Emerald Masonry & Stucco...............G..... 281 356-9400
   Magnolia (G-14604)

Master Wall Inc...........................F..... 979 885-6905
   Sealy (G-18812)

Premier Antique Stucco LLC..............E..... 210 602-8054
   San Antonio (G-18389)

Rydar Inc.................................E..... 979 877-0703
   Sealy (G-18817)

Western Stucco Product..................E..... 915 858-3494
   El Paso (G-6036)

STUDS & JOISTS: Sheet Metal

Delta Studweld Inc.......................F..... 409 755-0720
   Lumberton (G-14567)

Simpson Strong-Tie Company Inc.........C..... 972 542-0326
   McKinney (G-14975)

STYRENE

Americas Styrenics LLC..................D..... 832 616-7800
   The Woodlands (G-19826)

Eastman Chemical Texas Cy Inc..........E..... 409 942-3307
   Texas City (G-19791)

Ttwf LP..................................A..... 713 960-9111
   Houston (G-12400)

STYRENE RESINS, NEC

Total Ptrchemicals Ref USA Inc...........C..... 281 542-9542
   La Porte (G-13797)

STYRENE-BUTADIENE RUBBERS, OVER 50% BUTADIENE

Lcy Elastomers LP........................D..... 281 424-6100
   Baytown (G-1826)

SUBMARINE BUILDING & REPAIR

Perry Slingsby Systems Inc...............D..... 561 743-7000
   Houston (G-11294)

SUNDRIES & RELATED PRDTS: Medical & Laboratory, Rubber

Advanced Materials Group Inc............D..... 469 246-4100
   Garland (G-7428)

All Mark Impressions Ltd.................F..... 817 834-0080
   Fort Worth (G-6370)

Biogenix LLC............................E..... 888 418-7172
   Houston (G-8886)

En Plast Technology LLC..................F..... 832 730-4606
   Houston (G-9622)

Prestige Ameritech Ltd...................B..... 817 427-2700
   North Richland Hills (G-15879)

SW Foam LLC............................E..... 915 751-1000
   El Paso (G-5989)

Titan Bop Rubber Products Inc...........E..... 713 895-9230
   Houston (G-12295)

SUPERMARKETS & OTHER GROCERY STORES

La Autentica Inc.........................F..... 202 415-6979
   San Antonio (G-18232)

Superbag USA Corp.......................B..... 713 462-1173
   Houston (G-12108)

Ventura Foods LLC.......................F..... 817 232-6800
   Fort Worth (G-7097)

SURFACE ACTIVE AGENTS

BASF Corporation.........................C..... 800 794-1019
   Houston (G-8821)

Chemguard Inc...........................F..... 817 473-9964
   Mansfield (G-14662)

Corchem Manufacturing Inc..............F..... 432 332-1335
   Odessa (G-15968)

Monument Chemical LLC..................E..... 281 474-5550
   Pasadena (G-16486)

SURFACE ACTIVE AGENTS: Oils & Greases

Sentinel Midstream LLC...................F..... 214 712-2141
   Richardson (G-17397)

SURGICAL & MEDICAL INSTRUMENTS WHOLESALERS

Cellright Technologies LLC................E..... 210 659-9353
   Universal City (G-20181)

Instrument Specialists Inc................F..... 830 249-9535
   Boerne (G-2123)

SURGICAL APPLIANCES & SPLYS

BSN Medical Inc.........................E..... 956 926-4400
   Hidalgo (G-8304)

Medical Concepts Dev Inc................D..... 651 735-0498
   El Paso (G-5872)

Quality Mattress Company Inc............F..... 713 433-9155
   Houston (G-11497)

Sten Corporation.........................F..... 903 586-0914
   Jacksonville (G-13259)

SURGICAL APPLIANCES & SPLYS

Alafair Biosciences Inc...................F..... 512 739-9510
   Austin (G-903)

Argon Medical Devices Inc...............B..... 903 675-9321
   Athens (G-819)

Argon Medical Devices Inc...............B..... 903 675-9321
   Frisco (G-7266)

B C O Black Cane Original.................G..... 832 883-5774
   Houston (G-8774)

PRODUCT

Brazos Oaks Ltd............................E........ 254 399-0505
Waco (G-20370)
Cardinal Health Inc.......................D........ 915 781-7465
El Paso (G-5682)
Cardinal Health 200 LLC...............C........ 903 586-6502
Jacksonville (G-13232)
Djo Global Inc..............................F........ 512 832-9500
Austin (G-1097)
Djo Global Inc..............................A........ 800 321-9549
Lewisville (G-14044)
Dynatec Scientific Labs................E........ 915 849-1322
El Paso (G-5727)
Encore Medical LP........................A........ 512 832-9500
Austin (G-1125)
Heubach Corporation....................E........ 214 291-0238
Garland (G-7511)
Howmedica Osteonics Corp.........G........ 512 491-0222
Austin (G-1211)
Isavela Enterprises Inc.................D........ 800 918-8242
McAllen (G-14875)
Isomedix Operations Inc...............E........ 915 855-2001
El Paso (G-5819)
Kci Usa Inc..................................C........ 800 275-4524
San Antonio (G-18220)
Kimberly-Clark Worldwide Inc.......F........ 972 281-1200
Irving (G-13076)
Kinetic Concepts Inc.....................B........ 800 531-5346
San Antonio (G-18225)
Medhab LLC.................................E........ 817 233-5271
Mansfield (G-14694)
Medical Device Tech Inc...............E........ 800 338-0440
Athens (G-831)
Medical Z....................................F........ 210 681-7912
Houston (G-10819)
Medline Industries Inc..................C........ 281 574-6200
Katy (G-13371)
Nearly ME Technologies LLC.........E........ 254 662-1752
Waco (G-20437)
Osteocentric Technologies Inc.......F........ 800 969-0639
Austin (G-1394)
Pall Corporation...........................A........ 713 896-9995
Jersey Village (G-13304)
Pivot Corporation.........................D........ 972 475-4747
Rowlett (G-17710)
Prescotts Limbs & Braces.............E........ 210 224-0726
San Antonio (G-18393)
Smith & Nephew Inc.....................F........ 512 358-5975
Austin (G-1512)
Spectrum Lifesciences LLC...........E........ 214 492-0506
Irving (G-13188)
Tri-Tex Enterprises Inc..................E........ 214 744-1246
Dallas (G-5109)
Valley Orthopedic Inc...................E........ 512 771-1970
Austin (G-1622)
Zimmer..A........ 800 613-6131
Austin (G-1717)

SURGICAL EQPT: See Also Instruments

3M Company.................................E........ 915 860-5408
Socorro (G-19016)
Berchtold Corporation...................C........ 843 569-6100
Flower Mound (G-6260)
Cardioquip LLC.............................E........ 979 691-0202
College Station (G-3180)
Cen-Tex Machining Inc..................D........ 512 255-1477
Round Rock (G-17629)
Imex Veterinary Inc......................F........ 903 295-2196
Longview (G-14249)
Medinc of Texas LP......................D........ 713 979-4364
Houston (G-10820)
Nuvectra Corporation....................D........ 214 474-3103
Plano (G-16949)
Osteomed LLC..............................C........ 972 677-4600
Addison (G-154)

SURGICAL IMPLANTS

Acuity Surgical Devices LLC..........F........ 214 862-5017
Dallas (G-3886)
Lima Usa Inc................................E........ 817 385-0777
Arlington (G-723)
Mentor Texas LP..........................B........ 972 252-6060
Irving (G-13105)
Monogram Orthopaedics Inc..........F........ 512 399-2656
Austin (G-1352)
Trilliant Surgical LLC....................G........ 800 495-2919
Houston (G-12373)

SURGICAL INSTRUMENT REPAIR SVCS

Instrument Specialists Inc.............F........ 830 249-9535
Boerne (G-2123)

SURVEYING & MAPPING: Land Parcels

Ark La Tex Surveying Co Inc.........F........ 903 938-9939
Marshall (G-14762)
Collins Surveying and Mapping.....E........ 903 234-8051
Longview (G-14210)
Dawson Geophysical Company.......C........ 432 684-3000
Midland (G-15187)
Edge Integrity Services LLC..........G........ 817 585-1007
Fort Worth (G-6605)
Gyrodata Incorporated..................D........ 713 461-3146
Houston (G-10078)
Hart Engineering Company............E........ 903 758-0166
Longview (G-14247)
Hpi LLC..E........ 713 457-7500
Houston (G-10272)
King Pipeline Services LLC............E........ 903 530-8667
Fort Worth (G-6762)
Petroleum Geo-Services Inc...........C........ 281 509-8000
Houston (G-11307)

SURVEYING INSTRUMENTS WHOLESALERS

R M S Inc.....................................G........ 713 467-2043
Houston (G-11523)

SURVEYING SVCS: Aerial Digital Imaging

Usdatwing Aerial Analytics LLC.....F........ 210 495-5577
San Antonio (G-18582)

SURVEYORS, MARINE CARGO

Matthews-Daniel Holdings Inc.......D........ 713 622-1633
Houston (G-10798)

SUSPENSION SYSTEMS: Acoustical, Metal

Walls Across Texas I Ltd..............E........ 210 826-4123
San Antonio (G-18608)

SVC ESTABLISHMENT EQPT, WHOL: Cleaning & Maint Eqpt & Splys

Macdermid Canning Ltd................E........ 713 472-5081
Pasadena (G-16478)
Valley Outdoor Power Eqp Inc........F........ 956 787-0469
Pharr (G-16715)

SVC ESTABLISHMENT EQPT, WHOL: Funeral Director's Eqpt/Splys

Rita Barber Inc............................F........ 325 698-0111
Abilene (G-73)
Southwest Prof Vehicles................F........ 214 371-3474
Dallas (G-4992)

SVC ESTABLISHMENT EQPT, WHOLESALE: Firefighting Eqpt

Flameout LLC...............................F........ 713 984-8310
Houston (G-9796)
Hasse Enterprises Inc...................F........ 512 835-7697
Austin (G-1199)

SVC ESTABLISHMENT EQPT, WHOLESALE: Laundry Eqpt & Splys

Brim Laundry Machinery Co Inc......E........ 214 630-4517
Hutchins (G-12863)
My Sons Laundry LLC....................F........ 214 634-2080
Dallas (G-4710)

SVC ESTABLISHMENT EQPT, WHOLESALE: Restaurant Splys

H & K International Inc..................C........ 214 818-3500
Mesquite (G-15047)

SVC ESTABLISHMENT EQPT, WHOLESALE: Shredders, Indl & Comm

Cummins - Allison Corp.................F........ 972 661-5390
Dallas (G-4192)

SVC ESTABLISHMENT EQPT, WHOLESALE: Sprinkler Systems

Hitech Fire Detection Corp.............D........ 281 475-7289
Spring (G-19130)

SVC ESTABLISHMENT EQPT, WHOLESALE: Voting Machines

Premier Election Solutions Inc.......E........ 469 675-8990
Allen (G-296)

SWIMMING POOL & HOT TUB CLEANING & MAINTENANCE SVCS

Manning Pool Service Inc..............E........ 713 812-9098
Houston (G-10745)

SWIMMING POOL EQPT: Filters & Water Conditioning Systems

Manning Pool Service Inc..............E........ 713 812-9098
Houston (G-10745)

SWIMMING POOL SPLY STORES

Jobran Unlimited LLC....................E........ 956 541-1309
Brownsville (G-2371)

SWIMMING POOLS, EQPT & SPLYS: Wholesalers

A&B Foundry LLC..........................F........ 972 247-3579
Dallas (G-3872)
Jobran Unlimited LLC....................E........ 956 541-1309
Brownsville (G-2371)
Manning Pool Service Inc..............E........ 713 812-9098
Houston (G-10745)

SWITCHBOARD APPARATUS, EXC INSTRUMENTS

First Texas Products Corp..............F........ 915 633-8354
El Paso (G-5769)

SWITCHES

Illinois Tool Works Inc...................F........ 314 733-1110
Houston (G-10326)

SWITCHES: Electric Power

Avo Multi-AMP Corporation............F........ 800 325-4574
Dallas (G-3992)
Carling Technologies Inc...............E........ 956 546-5564
Brownsville (G-2344)

SWITCHES: Electronic

Amtech Manufacturing Inc.............E........ 817 563-1251
Fort Worth (G-6386)
Electrotechnics Corporation...........E........ 903 938-1901
Marshall (G-14776)

SWITCHES: Electronic Applications

Dallas Decal Inc...........................F........ 972 772-4641
Rockwall (G-17546)
Selectouch Corporation.................E........ 972 924-3289
Anna (G-585)

SWITCHES: Solenoid

Mtc America Enterprises Inc...........F........ 972 926-0600
Garland (G-7556)

SWITCHES: Time, Electrical Switchgear Apparatus

Ruby Automation LLC....................E........ 972 881-9663
Plano (G-16997)
Volta LLC.....................................C........ 832 369-2420
Houston (G-12581)

SWITCHGEAR & SWITCHBOARD APPARATUS

ABB Enterprise Software Inc..........E........ 903 237-1030
Longview (G-14187)
Atron Group LLC...........................D........ 214 292-9840
Dallas (G-3984)

Azz Inc ....D 817 810-0095
Fort Worth (G-6414)
Beeco Motors & Controls Inc ....E 832 320-3100
Houston (G-8851)
BI Technology Inc ....E 832 698-8000
Tomball (G-19967)
Cordyne Inc ....D 713 460-5151
Houston (G-9313)
Dial Electrical of Houston ....G 713 691-4666
Houston (G-9450)
Eaton Corporation ....F 915 772-6198
El Paso (G-5732)
Eaton Corporation ....E 713 849-1600
Houston (G-9572)
Electronic Power Design Inc ....D 713 923-1191
Houston (G-9596)
Electrotechnics Corporation ....E 903 938-1901
Marshall (G-14776)
Forney Corporation ....E 972 458-6100
Addison (G-126)
LSI Integrated Graphics LP ....C 713 744-4100
Houston (G-10696)
Luminator Technology Group LLC ....C 972 424-6511
Plano (G-16913)
Murphy Fw ....D 281 633-4500
Rosenberg (G-17590)
National Swtchgear Systems Inc ....E 972 420-0149
Lewisville (G-14071)
Philips North America LLC ....F 956 541-1224
Brownsville (G-2393)
Rail Products Intl Inc ....D 956 541-1759
Brownsville (G-2397)
Roxar Inc ....E 281 879-2600
Houston (G-11680)
Schneider Electric Usa Inc ....C 972 323-1111
Carrollton (G-2814)
Schneider Electric Usa Inc ....E 361 887-5055
Corpus Christi (G-3617)
Siemens Industry Inc ....C 915 790-0219
El Paso (G-5960)
Siemens Industry Inc ....E 817 633-4430
Grand Prairie (G-7973)
Texas Meter and Device Co LLC ....D 254 732-1305
Waco (G-20467)
Toshiba International Corp ....A 800 231-1412
Houston (G-12327)
Unitron LP ....D 214 221-9094
Dallas (G-5139)
Webb Technology Inc ....F 214 348-8678
Dallas (G-5178)

SWITCHGEAR & SWITCHGEAR ACCESS, NEC

GE Zenith Controls Inc ....B 800 637-1738
Plano (G-16878)
M&I Electric Industries Inc ....D 832 241-6330
Houston (G-10721)
Maverick Technical Systems Inc ....G 903 845-5574
Gladewater (G-7726)
Powell Industries Inc ....B 713 944-6900
Houston (G-11376)

SYNTHETIC RESIN FINISHED PRDTS, NEC

Fibergrate Composite ....E 972 250-1633
Dallas (G-4360)
Polymer Products LP ....F 972 647-1000
Arlington (G-756)
Teebaud Co LLC ....F 713 682-5161
Houston (G-12182)

SYRUPS, DRINK

Coca-Cola Southwest Bevs LLC ....C 214 902-2600
Dallas (G-4138)

SYRUPS, FLAVORING, EXC DRINK

Brook Sara Enterprises Inc ....F 713 522-9999
Houston (G-8995)

SYSTEMS ENGINEERING: Computer Related

B&B Worldwide Technology ....F 713 471-2387
Cibolo (G-3062)
Broadaxis Inc ....F 469 688-2272
Plano (G-16814)
Infosys Limited ....D 214 306-2100
Richardson (G-17332)
Infosys Limited ....F 281 454-0300
Houston (G-10359)

Keen Solutions Group Inc ....E 903 253-0476
Tyler (G-20107)
Science Applications Intl Corp ....F 469 557-8249
Carrollton (G-2815)

SYSTEMS INTEGRATION SVCS

Automation Solutions LP ....E 281 286-6017
Houston (G-8754)
Broadcast Technical Svcs Inc ....F 832 467-0002
Houston (G-8988)
Data Dallas Corporation ....E 214 662-5165
Dallas (G-4241)
Global Remote Technologies LLC ....E 888 381-3222
Spring (G-19125)
Kelleys Controls Incorporated ....F 432 362-7998
Odessa (G-16045)
Linux Tech Inc ....F 972 907-0871
Dallas (G-4596)
Proactive Technologies Inc ....F 972 416-6298
Carrollton (G-2798)
Qnet Inc ....D 214 341-7638
Dallas (G-4838)
Shipcom Wireless Inc ....D 281 558-5252
Houston (G-11870)
Texas SEC & Surveillance Inc ....E 512 693-4003
Round Rock (G-17693)
Tri-Cor Industries Inc ....E 210 979-0552
San Antonio (G-18565)

SYSTEMS INTEGRATION SVCS: Local Area Network

Absolute Cmmnctons Ntwrk Slton ....E 361 888-6776
Corpus Christi (G-3464)
Csi Techs Inc ....D 210 875-7978
San Antonio (G-18033)
Eclectic Innvtive Slutions LLC ....F 737 999-1907
Dripping Springs (G-5505)

SYSTEMS INTEGRATION SVCS: Office Computer Automation

Royal Technocrats Inc ....E 713 776-8300
Houston (G-11684)
Ss Electric Inc ....F 915 217-2200
El Paso (G-5973)

SYSTEMS SOFTWARE DEVELOPMENT SVCS

Apex Custom Software Inc ....G 214 725-9792
The Colony (G-19809)
CDM Software Solutions Inc ....E 972 469-3082
Frisco (G-7272)
Cooper Consulting Company ....E 512 527-1000
Austin (G-1065)
Crayon Software Experts LLC ....E 469 329-0290
Dallas (G-4181)
Ensosoft LLC ....F 713 360-4841
Houston (G-9660)
Frh Consumer Services Inc ....G 512 657-8945
Austin (G-1172)
Geoforce Inc ....D 972 546-3878
Plano (G-16879)
Innosync Inc ....E 972 644-7962
Dallas (G-4501)
Jarvantech Inc ....F 832 742-7220
The Woodlands (G-19888)
Liquid Litigation MGT Inc ....F 210 757-4881
Austin (G-1294)
Lisam America Inc ....E 979 307-7384
Bryan (G-2491)
Ntt Data Inc ....C 800 745-3263
Plano (G-16948)
PC Legal Tools Inc ....E 415 808-8800
Austin (G-1402)
Peritus Inc ....C 817 726-4626
Irving (G-13141)
Salient Global Technologies ....D 925 526-1234
Dallas (G-4928)
Solarwinds Worldwide LLC ....E 512 682-9300
Austin (G-1520)
Tricon International Ltd ....E 713 963-0066
Houston (G-12371)
Trinity Millennium Group Inc ....E 210 615-1606
San Antonio (G-18567)
Vercom Software Inc ....E 972 661-9336
Dallas (G-5161)
Visual Bi Solutions Inc ....E 972 232-2233
Plano (G-17046)

Yadblue LLC ....F 214 542-6140
Southlake (G-19084)

TABLE OR COUNTERTOPS, PLASTIC LAMINATED

Arismendy Josias ....E 817 353-1244
Fort Worth (G-6401)
Fixture Exchange Corporation ....E 817 429-2496
Joshua (G-13320)
K & K Langham Ltd ....D 512 835-5100
Austin (G-1263)
Wilsonart Intl Holdings LLC ....E 254 207-6000
Temple (G-19717)
Wilsonart Intl Holdings LLC ....E 254 207-7000
Temple (G-19718)
Wilsonart LLC ....E 254 742-2451
Temple (G-19720)
Wilsonart LLC ....E 254 207-0207
Temple (G-19722)
Wilsonart LLC ....F 713 576-5500
Houston (G-12676)

TABLECLOTHS & SETTINGS

Display Products Inc ....D 972 406-1221
Dallas (G-4262)
Quality Table Linen Inc ....E 281 240-1024
Stafford (G-19365)

TABLETS: Bronze Or Other Metal

Scientific Machine & Wldg Inc ....E 512 926-8400
Austin (G-1490)

TABULATING SVCS

Ncs Pearson Inc ....D 210 339-5000
San Antonio (G-18340)

TAGS & LABELS: Paper

Advantage Marking & Labeling ....E 214 638-5225
Dallas (G-3894)
Alecom Technologies Group Inc ....G 972 870-9400
Flower Mound (G-6259)
Altlite LLC ....F 469 767-1959
Dallas (G-3935)
Inchbug LLC ....F 512 837-1010
Austin (G-1227)
Labelmax Inc ....D 956 718-3961
Laredo (G-13904)
Liberty Label Company Inc ....F 830 549-5459
Seguin (G-18849)

TAGS: Paper, Blank, Made From Purchased Paper

Dallco Marketing Inc ....E 214 217-7800
Dallas (G-4231)
Ennis Inc ....C 903 496-2244
Wolfe City (G-20906)

TAILORS: Custom

Hamilton Shirt Interests Ltd ....E 713 780-8222
Houston (G-10113)
I & I Design Inc ....F 713 667-6800
Houston (G-10308)

TALC

Imerys Talc America Inc ....D 281 272-7200
Houston (G-10329)

TALC MINING

Natural Minerals Inc ....E 432 283-2330
Van Horn (G-20215)

TANK COMPONENTS: Military, Specialized

Critical Solutions Intl Inc ....E 800 843-0000
Plano (G-16832)

TANK RECOVERY VEHICLES

Utlx Manufacturing LLC ....A 281 847-8200
Houston (G-12507)

TANK REPAIR & CLEANING SVCS

Planet Resource Recovery Inc ....E 281 996-5315
Pearland (G-16592)

Employee Codes: A=Over 500 employees, B=251-500
C=101-250, D=51-100, E=20-50, F=10-19, G=9

2021 Harris Texas
Manufacturers Directory

1659

PRODUCT

TANK REPAIR SVCS

Eleet Cryogenics Inc.................................E........936 856-6549
Willis *(G-20845)*

Entrans International LLC.....................E........281 459-5350
Houston *(G-9665)*

Hmt LLC...E........281 681-7000
Shenandoah *(G-18897)*

Hou Fab & Maintenance Inc...................G........713 672-1993
Crosby *(G-3733)*

Pasadena Tank Corporation...................C........281 457-3996
Baytown *(G-1798)*

W & W Fiberglass Tank Company.........D........806 669-1128
Pampa *(G-16344)*

TANKS & OTHER TRACKED VEHICLE CMPNTS

Ba-Ker Tank Head Company Inc...........E........817 232-8030
Fort Worth *(G-6418)*

Eleet Cryogenics Inc.............................E........936 856-6549
Willis *(G-20845)*

Fabrication Specialty Inc.......................F........214 742-3571
Granbury *(G-7797)*

General Dynmics Land Systems I........E........586 825-7242
Fort Hood *(G-6324)*

Lide Industries LLC..............................C........254 562-0233
Odessa *(G-16063)*

Lide Industries LLC..............................F........254 562-0233
Troy *(G-20030)*

Mtc America Enterprises Inc..................F........972 926-0600
Garland *(G-7556)*

Nordic Tankers....................................F........281 538-3250
League City *(G-13969)*

Power Pipe and Tank LLC......................E........417 447-4508
Amarillo *(G-508)*

Specialty Tank Services Ltd..................F........281 470-4880
La Porte *(G-13791)*

Team Fabricators LLC..........................D........409 962-0266
Port Arthur *(G-17128)*

Texas Liner Service LLC.......................F........281 445-5050
Houston *(G-12238)*

TANKS: Concrete

Dn Tanks Inc.......................................E........972 823-3300
Grand Prairie *(G-7865)*

TANKS: Cryogenic, Metal

Applied Cryo Technologies Inc.............D........281 888-3884
Houston *(G-8666)*

Tonatco Cryogenic Services..................F........281 651-0305
Spring *(G-19179)*

TANKS: For Tank Trucks, Metal Plate

Old Df Inc...E........281 590-5467
Tomball *(G-19994)*

Proco Inc..E........361 516-1112
Kingsville *(G-13634)*

Smith Tank & Equipment Company......E........903 597-5541
Tyler *(G-20153)*

Stephens Pneumatics Inc.....................E........817 636-9004
Haslet *(G-8223)*

Youngs Tank Incorporated....................E........800 345-7952
Boyd *(G-2210)*

TANKS: Fuel, Including Oil & Gas, Metal Plate

2011 Angelina Mfg LLC........................D........936 632-8330
Lufkin *(G-14519)*

Cen-Tex Tanks LLC..............................D........936 590-4441
Center *(G-2995)*

Dragon Products LLC...........................C........409 833-2665
Beaumont *(G-1886)*

Hmt LLC...E........281 681-7000
Shenandoah *(G-18897)*

Hughes Tank Company Inc....................F........972 366-8684
Venus *(G-20218)*

North Txas Prssure Vessels Inc...........E........940 327-0800
Mineral Wells *(G-15534)*

Pitts Oilfield Pdts & Svcs LLC...............E........325 340-4401
San Angelo *(G-17821)*

Sivalls Inc..D........432 337-3571
Odessa *(G-16153)*

TANKS: Lined, Metal

Arcosa Tank LLC..................................E........214 631-4420
Dallas *(G-3962)*

Bulldog Steel Products Inc....................E........325 893-5806
Clyde *(G-3162)*

Containment Solutions Inc....................E........936 756-7731
Conroe *(G-3286)*

Harbison-Fischer Inc............................B........817 297-2211
Crowley *(G-3755)*

Hou Fab & Maintenance Inc...................G........713 672-1993
Crosby *(G-3733)*

Insight Equity A P X L P.......................F........817 488-7775
Southlake *(G-19075)*

Insight Equity LP.................................F........817 488-7775
Southlake *(G-19076)*

Justiss Oil Company Inc.......................D........903 859-2111
Arp *(G-812)*

Klein Products of Texas Inc...................E........903 589-4546
Jacksonville *(G-13247)*

Lopez Tank Lining LLC..........................F........936 257-9779
Dayton *(G-5233)*

Modern Welding Co Texas Inc...............E........713 675-4211
Houston *(G-10905)*

Parker-Hannifin Corporation..................E........817 232-1040
Saginaw *(G-17754)*

Watco Tanks Inc..................................E........830 947-0101
Floresville *(G-6257)*

TANKS: Plastic & Fiberglass

Belco Manufacturing Co Inc...................C........254 933-9000
Belton *(G-2019)*

Brazosport Plastics Inc........................G........979 849-5422
Angleton *(G-566)*

Carbon Silica Partners LP.....................D........361 572-4040
Victoria *(G-20251)*

Fibergrate Composite...........................D........254 965-3148
Greenville *(G-8072)*

Freeman David Products Inc..................E........866 310-2556
Burnet *(G-2608)*

L F Manufacturing Inc..........................D........979 542-8027
Giddings *(G-7699)*

Nationwide Tank & Pipe LLC..................E........830 387-4027
New Braunfels *(G-15815)*

Plas Mac Inc.......................................F........806 447-0065
Wellington *(G-20656)*

Sherman Roto Tank LLC........................E........281 648-0909
Pearland *(G-16599)*

W & W Fiberglass Tank Company.........D........806 669-1128
Pampa *(G-16344)*

TANKS: Standard Or Custom Fabricated, Metal Plate

A M Fabrication Inc..............................E........817 345-7600
Fort Worth *(G-6337)*

Ba-Ker Tank Head Company Inc...........E........817 232-8030
Fort Worth *(G-6418)*

Bendel Tank Heat Exchnger Corp..........F........832 436-4626
The Woodlands *(G-19835)*

Brandon Wldg & Fabrication Inc............E........361 242-3344
Corpus Christi *(G-3488)*

Buffalo Tank Company Inc.....................G........903 322-4153
Buffalo *(G-2543)*

CB&i LLC..D........832 513-1848
Houston *(G-9104)*

Challenger Process Systems Co............C........903 839-7291
Troup *(G-20024)*

Cohn & Gregory Supply LLC..................F........817 624-1141
Fort Worth *(G-6529)*

Conner Steel Products Inc.....................B........325 655-8225
Houston *(G-9271)*

Dlh Wendland LLC................................E........325 655-6778
San Angelo *(G-17795)*

EICA Industries Inc.............................G........817 847-0917
Fort Worth *(G-6607)*

Fort Worth F and D Head Co..................D........817 236-8773
Fort Worth *(G-6642)*

High-Tech Fabrication Inc......................E........281 351-0882
Tomball *(G-19981)*

Holloway Company Inc..........................E........817 232-8663
Saginaw *(G-17746)*

Holloway Company Inc..........................F........713 453-4691
Houston *(G-10195)*

Joe White Tank Company Inc................E........817 624-1141
Fort Worth *(G-6744)*

Kmi Fabricators Inc.............................E........940 325-7841
Mineral Wells *(G-15531)*

Old Dt Holdings...................................C........432 267-7141
Big Spring *(G-2090)*

Pasadena Tank Corporation...................C........281 457-3996
Baytown *(G-1798)*

Pat Tank Inc..D........409 982-7319
Port Arthur *(G-17121)*

Permian Tank & Mfg Inc.......................D........432 550-7317
Odessa *(G-16118)*

Permian Tank & Mfg Inc.......................D........432 580-1050
Odessa *(G-16119)*

Permian Tank & Mfg Inc.......................D........903 984-2516
Kilgore *(G-13581)*

Sanco Metal Fabricators LLC................F........806 745-9674
Lubbock *(G-14477)*

Seguins Budget Auto Inc.......................F........830 372-1790
Seguin *(G-18863)*

Tank Wind-Down Corp..........................F........936 539-1747
Conroe *(G-3369)*

Trinity Industries Inc...........................D........817 665-1499
Fort Worth *(G-7075)*

Willborn Bros Co LLC...........................E........806 372-4311
Amarillo *(G-475)*

William Grant Tank Vessel Inc..............F........903 657-6100
Henderson *(G-8278)*

TANKS: Water, Metal Plate

Contain Water Systems Inc...................E........512 770-9080
Dripping Springs *(G-5502)*

TAPE PRINT UNITS: Computer

New ERA Solutions Intl LLC..................E........972 360-6112
Frisco *(G-7262)*

TAPE: Instrumentation Type, Blank

Jelec Inc...E........713 977-6500
Houston *(G-10464)*

TAPES, ADHESIVE: Masking, Made From Purchased Materials

Longer Protective LLC..........................F........832 987-1790
Missouri City *(G-15581)*

TAPES: Coated Fiberglass, Pipe Sealing Or Insulating

Ace Hanger Strap Inc............................F........214 742-8585
Dallas *(G-3882)*

Ea Services Inc...................................D........866 711-1001
Pearland *(G-16557)*

Pipe Coatings Intl LLC..........................E........979 387-3150
Beasley *(G-1843)*

TAPES: Magnetic

Dobbs-Stanford Corporation..................E........214 350-4222
Dallas *(G-4269)*

Sony Electronics Inc.............................C........858 942-2400
Laredo *(G-13934)*

TAPES: Plastic Coated

Carlisle Ctngs Wtrproofing Inc.............D........972 442-6545
Wylie *(G-20929)*

Muncaster Capital Texas Inc..................E........214 515-5000
Ennis *(G-6111)*

Polyguard Products Inc.........................E........972 875-8421
Ennis *(G-6114)*

TAPES: Pressure Sensitive

3M Company..E........512 984-2708
Austin *(G-871)*

TAPES: Pressure Sensitive, Rubber

Ace Carton & Tape of Laredo..................F........956 727-1600
Laredo *(G-13854)*

Paco Label Systems Inc........................F........903 561-2125
Tyler *(G-20137)*

TAR PAPER: Roofing

ABG Contracting Group LLC..................E........281 431-7223
Pearland *(G-16536)*

TARGET DRONES

Comsovereign Holding Corp...................E........469 930-2661
Dallas *(G-4155)*

Jose Alfonsin......................................F........210 717-2306
San Antonio *(G-18208)*

Smartdrone Corporation........................F........443 655-5556
Tyler *(G-20152)*

TARPAULINS

Associated Canvas Pdts I Ltd ....F 281 457-1480
Channelview (G-3012)
Campbell Trailers & Leasing ....F 806 250-3611
Friona (G-7251)
Lisco LLP ....F 806 762-5126
Lubbock (G-14437)
Quest and Sons Inc ....E 806 744-2351
Lubbock (G-14468)

TAX RETURN PREPARATION SVCS

Diversified Bus Consulting LLC ....F 713 677-9282
Houston (G-9481)
Fotown Productions ....F 225 773-1894
Cypress (G-3791)
Integrated Tax Solutions LLC ....F 855 792-6657
San Antonio (G-18190)

TAXI CABS

Austin North Taxi Service ....F 512 704-9999
Austin (G-957)
Sister2sster Dstiny Trnspt LLC ....F 346 337-6637
Houston (G-11908)

TAXIDERMISTS

Damuth Taxidermy Inc ....F 325 597-0001
Brady (G-2213)

TECHNICAL INSTITUTE

Journeyedcom Inc ....D 800 876-3507
Allen (G-280)

TECHNICAL WRITING SVCS

Interface Lgic Tech Dcmnttion ....F 713 446-3560
Pearland (G-16570)

TELECOMMUNICATION EQPT REPAIR SVCS, EXC TELEPHONES

Mitel Networks Inc ....E 469 365-3000
Plano (G-16931)
Teleprime Advanced Communicati ....G 512 271-9503
Austin (G-1561)

TELECOMMUNICATION SYSTEMS & EQPT

3M Company ....E 512 984-2708
Austin (G-871)
Affirmed Ntwrks Cmmnctons Tech ....E 469 461-3101
Richardson (G-17267)
AT&T Inc ....A 210 821-4105
Dallas (G-3978)
Commscope Technologies LLC ....C 214 267-5900
Richardson (G-17289)
Commscope Technologies LLC ....A 214 634-8502
Dallas (G-4149)
Contel Federal Systems Inc ....A 972 718-5600
Irving (G-12978)
Digital Speech Systems Inc ....E 972 235-2999
Allen (G-262)
Intervoice LLC ....E 972 454-8000
Dallas (G-3845)
Krown Manufacturing Inc ....F 817 738-2485
Fort Worth (G-6774)
Optek Technology Inc ....D 972 323-2200
Carrollton (G-2786)
Soloprotect Us LLC ....D 866 632-6577
Coppell (G-3446)
Superior Essex Intl LP ....E 325 646-8591
Brownwood (G-2446)
Telecom Site Solutions LLC ....F 888 779-9069
Dallas (G-5049)
Telecore Inc ....E 972 238-9000
Richardson (G-17405)
Vtech Communications Inc ....E 210 244-0600
San Antonio (G-18601)
White Rock Networks Inc A De ....C 972 543-6900
Richardson (G-17427)
Zti Merger Subsidiary III Inc ....F 510 777-7000
Plano (G-17057)

TELECOMMUNICATIONS CARRIERS & SVCS: Wired

Contel Federal Systems Inc ....A 972 718-5600
Irving (G-12978)

Dallas Directional Drlg Inc ....F 214 254-6985
Dallas (G-4215)
Executive Voice Mail Systems ....F 817 329-9788
Grapevine (G-8033)
Hood County News Inc ....D 817 573-7066
Granbury (G-7800)
Nokia Slutions Networks US LLC ....B 972 374-3000
Coppell (G-3432)
Synergy Telecom Service Co Inc ....F 210 599-7743
San Antonio (G-18517)

TELECOMMUNICATIONS CARRIERS & SVCS: Wireless

Comsovereign Holding Corp ....E 469 930-2661
Dallas (G-4155)
Crown Castle Intl Corp ....F 713 570-3000
Houston (G-9346)
Ef Johnson Technologies Inc ....E 972 819-0700
Irving (G-13011)
Photonic Inc ....E 956 722-3326
Laredo (G-13921)

TELEGRAPH OR TELEPHONE CARRIER & REPEATER EQPT

Cellteks Inc ....F 830 249-8999
Boerne (G-2116)
Colo4 LLC ....F 214 630-3100
Dallas (G-4141)

TELEMARKETING BUREAUS

Biztel LP ....F 713 600-2600
Houston (G-8896)
Clarke Harland Corp ....A 830 609-5500
San Antonio (G-18009)
Soloprotect Us LLC ....D 866 632-6577
Coppell (G-3446)
Vericast Corp ....D 210 697-8888
San Antonio (G-18591)

TELEMETERING EQPT

L3 Technologies Inc ....A 817 619-4756
Arlington (G-713)
L3 Technologies Inc ....C 972 722-7927
Rockwall (G-17553)
L3 Technologies Inc ....A 817 619-2000
Arlington (G-714)
L3 Technologies Inc ....A 817 619-2000
Arlington (G-715)
L3harris Technologies Inc ....A 903 457-7461
Greenville (G-8081)

TELEPHONE ANSWERING MACHINES

Hold Phone LLC ....F 281 304-4777
Cypress (G-3800)

TELEPHONE EQPT INSTALLATION

Cellteks Inc ....F 830 249-8999
Boerne (G-2116)
Dynamic Intgrtons Ctrl Systems ....F 512 716-0817
Round Rock (G-17650)

TELEPHONE EQPT: Modems

Sagem Communications USA LLC ....E 972 386-4641
Dallas (G-4927)

TELEPHONE EQPT: NEC

Aei Communications Corp ....E 650 552-9416
Carrollton (G-2693)
Cytracom LLC ....F 877 411-2987
Allen (G-261)
Dynamic Voice Data Inc ....F 800 838-5070
Stafford (G-19307)
Enterprise ESP Svc Prvider LLC ....F 469 619-3114
Plano (G-16863)
Estech Systems Inc ....C 972 422-9700
Plano (G-16866)
Gtech Precision Inds USA Ltd ....F 817 539-8014
Mansfield (G-14678)
Micheal J Arnold & Co ....F 979 742-3030
Damon (G-5213)
Motorola Solutions Inc ....E 512 895-2000
Austin (G-1355)
Neosen Energy LLC ....F 972 422-0722
Plano (G-16941)

Polycom Inc ....F 512 372-7000
Austin (G-1709)
Primo Microphones Inc ....D 972 548-9807
McKinney (G-14967)
Siemens Industry Inc ....G 512 339-6991
Austin (G-1499)
Tellabs Inc ....B 800 690-2324
Carrollton (G-2890)
Vysk Communications Inc ....E 210 832-8322
San Antonio (G-18606)

TELEPHONE EQPT: PBX, Manual & Automatic

BBS Telecom LC ....G 512 328-9500
Austin (G-981)
Intervoice LLC ....D 972 454-8000
Dallas (G-3846)

TELEPHONE SET REPAIR SVCS

Cellteks Inc ....F 830 249-8999
Boerne (G-2116)
Enterprise ESP Svc Prvider LLC ....F 469 619-3114
Plano (G-16863)

TELEPHONE STATION EQPT & PARTS: Wire

TPI ....E 972 276-2901
Garland (G-7604)

TELEPHONE SVCS

Pcs Telecom Inc ....F 281 469-3367
Pasadena (G-16494)

TELEPHONE SWITCHING EQPT

ABB Power Electronics Inc ....C 972 244-9288
Plano (G-16768)
Mitel Networks Inc ....E 469 365-3000
Plano (G-16931)

TELEPHONE: Automatic Dialers

Ericsson Smart Factory Inc ....D 469 266-3776
Lewisville (G-14049)
Roi Telephony LLC ....F 214 364-2425
Addison (G-160)

TELEPHONE: Fiber Optic Systems

Affiliated Communications ....E 972 423-4222
Plano (G-16777)
Aviat US Inc ....B 408 941-7100
Austin (G-969)
Dzs Inc ....C 469 327-1531
Plano (G-16854)
Fujitsu Ntwrk Cmmnications Inc ....A 972 479-6000
Richardson (G-17318)

TELEPHONE: Sets, Exc Cellular Radio

Cooper Consulting Company ....E 512 527-1000
Austin (G-1065)

TELEVISION BROADCASTING & COMMUNICATIONS EQPT

Arygin Corporation ....F 940 597-8275
Denton (G-5350)
Logitech Inc ....D 512 347-9300
Austin (G-1298)
Mk Systems USA Inc ....E 469 626-9523
Frisco (G-7298)

TELEVISION BROADCASTING STATIONS

Herald of Truth Ministries ....F 325 698-4370
Abilene (G-49)
W V Grant Intl Ministries ....F 214 333-2176
Dallas (G-5171)

TELEVISION SETS

Lg Electronics Alabama Inc ....A 956 784-6500
Mission (G-15559)

TELEVISION: Cameras

Philips Consumer Electronic Co ....A 915 298-4111
El Paso (G-5909)

PRODUCT

TELEVISION: Closed Circuit Eqpt

L3 Mobile-Vision Inc ....D....... 973 263-1090
  Houston (G-10578)
Mace Security Intl Inc ....E....... 800 627-6734
  Dallas (G-4624)

TENTS: All Materials

Aquila & Priscilla Tentmakers................F....... 254 848-4432
  Waco (G-20363)
Festive Tents LP ....F....... 713 468-3687
  Houston (G-9780)
Ohenry Productions Inc ....F....... 254 714-1103
  Waco (G-20440)
Orc Industries Inc ....D....... 956 831-0618
  Brownsville (G-2389)
Tents of Southwest Inc ....E....... 713 692-8565
  Houston (G-12205)

TERRA COTTA: Architectural

Architerra Inc...................................F....... 512 441-8062
  Austin (G-930)

TESTERS: Battery

Arbin Corporation ....E....... 979 690-2751
  College Station (G-3174)

TESTERS: Environmental

E-Spectrum Technologies Inc............F....... 210 696-8848
  San Antonio (G-18080)
Gray Green Biomedical Svcs LLC........G....... 832 288-5958
  Pearland (G-16566)
Gulf Coast Envmtl Systems LLC ....E....... 832 476-9024
  Conroe (G-3299)
Joe Ross ....F....... 903 450-9960
  Greenville (G-8079)
Test Incorporated.............................F....... 713 983-2800
  Houston (G-12213)

TESTERS: Gas, Exc Indl Process

Isgas Incorporated ....G....... 713 645-5886
  Houston (G-10425)

TESTERS: Ignition Eqpt

Gunvision Systems LLC....................F....... 512 858-4045
  Austin (G-862)

TESTERS: Integrated Circuit

Circuit Check Inc..............................E....... 972 480-0044
  Richardson (G-17286)

TESTERS: Logic Circuit

Arias Logistics Inc ....E....... 915 872-0034
  El Paso (G-5651)

TESTERS: Physical Property

Exer-Tech Inc..................................F....... 281 493-2220
  Katy (G-13402)
National Manufacturing LLC ....F....... 281 856-7693
  Houston (G-10970)

TEXTILE & APPAREL SVCS

Gallery One Point LLC.......................E....... 512 428-5710
  Pflugerville (G-16674)
Hallwood Group Incorporated ....E....... 214 528-5588
  Dallas (G-4430)
Standard Textile Co Inc ....D....... 956 831-9040
  Brownsville (G-2407)

TEXTILE BAGS WHOLESALERS

West Txas Lighthouse For Blind ....D....... 325 653-4231
  San Angelo (G-17839)

TEXTILE FINISH: Chem Coat/Treat, Fire Resist, Manmade

Adrian Scott Industries Inc ....F....... 713 941-3300
  Pasadena (G-16377)
Protective Concepts Inc ....F....... 832 843-7619
  Cypress (G-3816)

TEXTILE FINISHING: Bleaching, Broadwoven, Cotton

JC Viramontes Inc............................E....... 915 857-4545
  El Paso (G-5820)

TEXTILE FINISHING: Chem Coat/Treat, Man, Broadwoven, Cotton

Schneider-Banks Inc ....F....... 903 675-1440
  Athens (G-838)

TEXTILE FINISHING: Chem Coating/Treating, Broadwoven, Cotton

Global Chemliquidations LLC.............E....... 832 539-3969
  Houston (G-9968)

TEXTILE FINISHING: Chemical Coating Or Treating

Adrian Scott Industries Inc ....F....... 713 941-3300
  Pasadena (G-16377)
Protective Concepts Inc ....F....... 832 843-7619
  Cypress (G-3816)
Texas Flameproofing Inc...................F....... 214 630-1088
  Dallas (G-5061)

TEXTILE FINISHING: Embossing, Cotton, Broadwoven

Action Wear Plus Inc ....F....... 281 376-4300
  Spring (G-19098)

TEXTILE: Finishing, Cotton Broadwoven

Schneider-Banks Inc ....F....... 903 675-1440
  Athens (G-838)

TEXTILE: Finishing, Raw Stock NEC

Guardian Southwest String Tag ....F....... 972 938-0123
  Waxahachie (G-20544)

TEXTILE: Goods, NEC

Joren ....F....... 713 300-0377
  Richmond (G-17458)
Xjian Inc ....F....... 972 618-6096
  Plano (G-17055)

TEXTILES

J Lewis Partners LP ....A....... 972 702-7390
  Dallas (G-4519)

TEXTILES: Fibers, Textile, Rcvrd From Mill Waste/Rags

Advanced Ocean Shipping ....E....... 281 300-0191
  Houston (G-8489)
Knit Rags LLC ....F....... 713 249-9478
  Houston (G-10549)

TEXTILES: Jute & Flax Prdts

Cornerstone Apparel Inc ....E....... 903 939-0188
  Tyler (G-20073)

TEXTILES: Linen Fabrics

M & L Rose Enterprises Inc ....F....... 214 637-8000
  Dallas (G-4617)
Startex Linen Co ....F....... 713 782-4419
  Houston (G-12050)

TEXTILES: Mill Waste & Remnant

Addison Collection LP.......................G....... 817 921-4450
  Fort Worth (G-6344)
Capital City Processors LLC...............E....... 405 232-5511
  Dallas (G-4080)

TEXTILES: Recovering Textile Fibers From Clippings & Rags

John Cole Chemical Corporation ....E....... 512 443-1037
  Austin (G-1257)
Reclaimed Textiles Co ....E....... 214 638-7551
  Dallas (G-4867)

THEATER COMPANIES

Ensemble Theatre.............................F....... 713 520-0055
  Houston (G-9653)

THEATRICAL PRODUCERS & SVCS

Voice Media Group Inc ....D....... 713 280-2400
  Houston (G-12580)

THEATRICAL SCENERY

Texas Scenic Company Inc................D....... 210 684-0091
  San Antonio (G-18542)
Theatrical Warehouse Inc ....E....... 214 634-2965
  Dallas (G-5082)

THERMISTORS, EXC TEMPERATURE SENSORS

Sensata Technologies Inc ....F....... 817 608-2289
  Fort Worth (G-6983)

THERMOCOUPLES

Daily Instruments Corporation ....E....... 713 780-8600
  Houston (G-9395)

THERMOELECTRIC DEVICES: Solid State

Santos CMI Inc (usa) ....F....... 713 273-4140
  Houston (G-11749)

THERMOMETERS: Medical, Digital

Gtl Supply Solutions LLC....................F....... 214 644-2402
  Allen (G-271)
MPA International LP ....C....... 915 474-7832
  El Paso (G-5887)

THERMOPLASTIC MATERIALS

Cook Compression ....E....... 713 433-2002
  Houston (G-9301)
Dow Chemical Company ....D....... 713 667-5133
  Bellaire (G-1994)
E I Du Pont De Nemours & Co ....C....... 409 883-8411
  Orange (G-16239)
Greene Tweed & Co LLC ....E....... 281 765-4500
  Houston (G-10034)
Medical Components of America ....G....... 830 237-6405
  Seguin (G-18851)
Supplyone Tucson Inc ....G....... 915 860-9911
  El Paso (G-5988)
Teknor Color Company ....D....... 903 586-0583
  Jacksonville (G-13262)
Univar Solutions USA Inc ....E....... 281 297-0678
  Spring (G-19261)

THERMOPLASTICS

S G & P Incorporated ....F....... 979 233-7491
  Freeport (G-7209)

THERMOSETTING MATERIALS

American Thermowell Inc ....F....... 409 246-1111
  Kountze (G-13668)
Griffith Polymers Inc.........................E....... 503 612-0999
  Arlington (G-693)
Luc Urethanes Inc............................F....... 936 539-2170
  Conroe (G-3326)
Union Carbide Corporation ....B....... 281 966-2727
  Houston (G-12434)

THREAD: Thread, From Manmade Fiber

Texas Thread Manufacturing Co ....G....... 956 412-4999
  Harlingen (G-8206)

TILE: Brick & Structural, Clay

Acme Brick Company.........................D....... 254 662-9846
  Waco (G-20354)
Acme Brick Company.........................D....... 512 281-5744
  Elgin (G-6052)
Clay DHanis Products Inc ....E....... 830 363-7636
  D Hanis (G-3828)
Justin Industries Inc ....D....... 979 885-4124
  Sealy (G-18811)
Meridian Brick LLC ....F....... 281 442-8400
  Houston (G-10835)
Meridian Brick LLC ....E....... 830 980-7071
  Schertz (G-18756)

Meridian Brick LLC ....D...... 940 325-9466
Mineral Wells (G-15532)
Meridian Brick LLC ....F...... 972 245-1542
Carrollton (G-2779)
Mission Clay Products LLC ....F...... 830 393-2568
Floresville (G-6248)
Quikrete Companies LLC ....E...... 979 732-8210
Columbus (G-3232)

TILE: Building, clay

Faber Cnk ....F...... 832 831-7222
Houston (G-9748)

TILE: Floor Or Wall, Enamel, Clay

Gilsa North America LLC ....F...... 956 223-2900
San Juan (G-18674)

TILE: Mosaic, Ceramic

Exacta Packaging Designs Inc ....D... 972 323-1063
Carrollton (G-2733)

TILE: Quarry, Clay

C&D Allbritton Holdings Inc ....E...... 833 227-2243
Salado (G-17764)
Tbk Materials LLC ....E...... 214 239-4916
Plano (G-17021)

TIMING DEVICES: Electronic

Aqua Electric Inc ....F...... 972 243-2162
Dallas (G-3956)

TIRE CORD & FABRIC

Invista Capital Management LLC........A...... 361 572-1111
Victoria (G-20274)

TIRE CORD & FABRIC: Fabric, Reinforcing

Lone Star Molding Inc ....E...... 936 539-0008
Conroe (G-3324)

TIRE CORD & FABRIC: Steel

Jadtis Industries LP ....D...... 214 905-9566
Farmers Branch (G-6204)

TIRE DEALERS

American Tire Distributors Inc ....F...... 704 992-2000
Austin (G-918)
Buck Dandy Co ....E...... 903 784-6362
Sumner (G-19606)
Goodyear Tire & Rubber Company ......A...... 361 289-8251
Corpus Christi (G-3537)
Multi-Seal Corporation ....F...... 281 591-0111
Spring (G-19235)
Wheels America Alloy Wheel ....E...... 214 330-9866
Dallas (G-5185)

TIRE INFLATORS: Hand Or Compressor Operated

Air-Serv Group LLC ....E...... 651 454-0465
Dallas (G-3908)

TIRE INNER-TUBES

Goodyear Tire & Rubber Company ......A...... 361 289-8251
Corpus Christi (G-3537)

TIRE RECAPPING & RETREADING

Goodyear Tire & Rubber Company ......A...... 361 289-8251
Corpus Christi (G-3537)

TIRE SUNDRIES OR REPAIR MATERIALS: Rubber

Multi-Seal Corporation ....F...... 281 591-0111
Spring (G-19235)

TIRES & INNER TUBES

American Tire Distributors Inc ....F...... 281 872-0397
Houston (G-8612)
American Tire Distributors Inc ....F...... 704 992-2000
Austin (G-918)
Lone Star Wheel Components ....D...... 903 654-1132
Corsicana (G-3676)

Roadrunner Rubber Corp..................F...... 713 697-0633
Houston (G-11641)
Sanchez Tire Shop 5 ....F...... 956 423-0047
Harlingen (G-8200)
Tjp Enterprises LLC ....E...... 817 779-4360
Fort Worth (G-7064)

TIRES & TUBES WHOLESALERS

American Tire Distributors Inc ....F...... 704 992-2000
Austin (G-918)
Sanchez Tire Shop 5 ....F...... 956 423-0047
Harlingen (G-8200)

TIRES & TUBES, WHOLESALE: Truck

A G Van & Truck Eqp Inc ....E...... 214 638-8805
Dallas (G-3870)
Dealers Truck Equipment Co Inc...........F...... 512 312-2100
Buda (G-2527)
Dealers Truck Equipment Co Inc...........F...... 903 758-4451
Longview (G-14223)
Dfw Camper Corral Inc ....F...... 972 241-6443
Dallas (G-4255)
United States Steel Corp ....D...... 903 656-6521
Lone Star (G-14185)

TIRES: Auto

Austin Rubber Company LLC ....G...... 512 904-0152
Austin (G-959)
Michelin North America Inc ....B...... 864 458-5000
El Paso (G-5877)
Nbr Wheels and Tires LLC ....E...... 855 575-3879
Irving (G-13113)

TIRES: Cushion Or Solid Rubber

J Morco Incorporated ....E...... 817 596-3989
Weatherford (G-20597)

TIRES: Indl Vehicles

Carlstar Group LLC ....C...... 972 606-2126
Grand Prairie (G-7851)
Trans-Texas Tire LLC ....E...... 903 572-0267
Mount Pleasant (G-15664) °

TIRES: Truck

T & W Tire LLC ....G...... 940 683-3558
Bridgeport (G-2302)

TITANIUM MILL PRDTS

Rmi Titanium Company LLC ....F...... 713 466-8222
Houston (G-11639)
Spf Corporation of America ....F...... 713 983-9373
Houston (G-12014)
Titanium Emergency Group LLP ....G...... 940 613-2653
Wichita Falls (G-20818)
Titanium Metals Corporation ....D...... 972 233-1700
Dallas (G-5097)

TITLE ABSTRACT & SETTLEMENT OFFICES

King Pipeline Services LLC ....E...... 903 530-8667
Fort Worth (G-6762)
Republic Title of Texas Inc ....C...... 972 578-8611
Plano (G-16991)

TOBACCO & TOBACCO PRDTS WHOLESALERS

Swedish Match North Amer LLC ....C...... 817 416-7017
Southlake (G-19082)

TOBACCO THRASHING

Summit Mechanical ....E...... 903 267-7949
Sumner (G-19609)

TOBACCO: Chewing

Swedish Match North Amer LLC ....C...... 817 416-7017
Southlake (G-19082)

TOBACCO: Cigarettes

Permian Basin Eqp & Sup LLC ....E...... 432 563-1044
Odessa (G-16113)
Philip Morris USA Inc ....D...... 210 530-7100
San Antonio (G-18372)
R J Reynolds Tobacco Company ....B...... 877 703-0386
Tyler (G-20144)

TOBACCO: Cigars

Finck Cigar Co ....D...... 210 226-4191
San Antonio (G-18115)

TOILET FIXTURES: Plastic

Niagara Conservation Corp ....E...... 817 391-0800
Flower Mound (G-6275)
Tex-Lam Manufacturing Inc ....E...... 713 695-5975
Houston (G-12216)

TOILET PREPARATIONS

Aloe Vera of America Inc....................D...... 214 355-5400
Dallas (G-3929)

TOILETRIES, COSMETICS & PERFUME STORES

Headcovers Unlimited Inc ....F...... 281 334-4287
League City (G-13958)
Phlur Inc ....F...... 888 771-9434
Austin (G-1415)
Scentsible LLC ....D...... 972 818-8200
Addison (G-161)
Source Vital LLC ....F...... 713 622-2190
Houston (G-11958)

TOILETS: Portable Chemical, Plastics

Texstars LLC ....C...... 972 647-1366
Arlington (G-796)

TOLL OPERATIONS

Ramsey Properties LP ....E...... 409 985-4200
Port Arthur (G-17122)

TOOL & DIE STEEL

Abrasive Contour Tech LLC ....F...... 281 288-8800
Spring (G-19097)
Alco Machine Tool & Steel Inc ....F...... 915 779-7013
El Paso (G-5640)
Industrial Insptn Innovation ....F...... 281 636-7215
La Porte (G-13750)

TOOL REPAIR SVCS

Taylormade Pllets Lgistics LLC ....E...... 210 566-3833
Boerne (G-2139)

TOOLS: Carpenters', Including Levels & Chisels, Exc Saws

Ferreira Holding Group LLC ....E...... 214 293-9233
Dallas (G-4359)
Taylor Design Group Inc ....F...... 972 243-7943
Carrollton (G-2825)

TOOLS: Hand

3M Company ....B...... 512 984-1800
Austin (G-869)
Bwi Companies Inc ....D...... 979 743-4581
Schulenburg (G-18773)
Bwi Companies Inc ....D...... 972 242-4755
Carrollton (G-2708)
Equalizer Industries Inc ....E...... 512 388-7715
Round Rock (G-17656)
Geotex Inc ....E...... 817 656-9797
Fort Worth (G-6666)
H & T Auger Company ....E...... 432 362-4471
Odessa (G-16022)
J S Technology Inc ....D...... 469 326-5900
Garland (G-7523)
Pro-Steel Inc ....E...... 817 572-4959
Fort Worth (G-6919)
Standard Motor Products Inc ....E...... 972 316-8100
Lewisville (G-14094)
Stanley Black & Decker Inc................F...... 972 247-1367
Dallas (G-5006)
Stanley Industrial & Auto LLC ....B...... 972 247-1367
Dallas (G-5007)
Sumner Manufacturing Co LLC ....C...... 281 999-6900
Houston (G-12096)
United Amercn Acquisition Corp ....E...... 859 987-5389
Waco (G-20470)
Wildcat Manufacturing Inc ....E...... 806 327-5602
Tahoka (G-19642)
Xg Ventures LLC ....E...... 936 744-1800
Trinity (G-20020)

PRODUCT

TOOLS: Hand, Hammers

DK Drill I LP ....E 817 539-2500
Mansfield (G-14665)

TOOLS: Hand, Jewelers'

Pineforest Jewelry Inc ....F 713 451-1321
Houston (G-11333)

TOOLS: Hand, Mechanics

Trans Tool LLC ....F 210 225-6745
San Antonio (G-18560)

TOOLS: Hand, Plumbers'

Component Manufacturing Corp ....E 800 275-3011
Conroe (G-3280)
Lineage LLC ....E 806 688-7384
Pampa (G-16327)

TOOLS: Hand, Power

Black & Decker Corporation ....E 713 466-1194
Houston (G-8899)
Black & Decker Corporation ....F 972 446-2996
Carrollton (G-2705)
Dyna Drill Technologies LLC ....C 281 227-1250
Katy (G-13398)
Fastorq Bolting Systems Inc ....F 281 449-6466
New Caney (G-15839)
Keppel Amfels Inc ....A 956 838-3110
Brownsville (G-2374)
National Oilwell Varco Inc ....C 936 444-4000
Conroe (G-3335)
Taylors Oilfield Mfg Inc ....E 281 442-4084
Houston (G-12168)
Trane Technologies Company LLC ......E 903 730-4000
Tyler (G-20163)
Union Tech Co LLC ....E 281 583-7601
Houston (G-12439)

TOOLS: Soldering

Northrop Grumman Systems Corp ....A 972 946-9000
Dallas (G-4743)

TOOTHPASTES, GELS & TOOTHPOWDERS

Carbon and Clay Company ....E 844 624-4263
New Braunfels (G-15777)

TOPS, DISPENSER OR SHAKER, ETC: Plastic

Acrylic Source ....E 800 275-0316
Arlington (G-609)

TOUR OPERATORS

Interline Travel & Tour Inc ....E 512 691-4500
Austin (G-1235)

TOWELETTES: Premoistened

Quatrefoil Partners LLC ....F 214 631-7117
Dallas (G-4848)

TOWELS: Indl

SAM&m Group LLC ....F 346 204-5786
Stafford (G-19373)

TOWERS, SECTIONS: Transmission, Radio & Television

Fwt LLC ....C 817 255-2965
Fort Worth (G-6657)
Royce Tower Service Inc ....F 409 684-1913
Port Bolivar (G-17134)
Sabre Industries Inc ....B 817 852-1700
Alvarado (G-343)
Valmont Industries Inc ....C 979 836-9395
Brenham (G-2277)
Wilbur L Anderson Inc ....E 325 658-6539
San Angelo (G-17841)

TOWERS: Bubble, Cooling, Fractionating, Metal Plate

Tray-Tec Inc ....E 281 441-7314
Humble (G-12805)

TOWERS: Cooling, Sheet Metal

Composite Cooling Solutions LP ....D 817 246-8700
Fort Worth (G-6536)

TOWING & TUGBOAT SVC

Offshore Express Inc ....D 985 868-1438
Houston (G-11141)

TOWING SVCS: Marine

Western Towing Company ....E 713 435-1800
Channelview (G-3044)

TOYS

Beecon Learning LLC ....F 877 923-3266
Dallas (G-4014)
Gayla Industries Inc ....D 713 681-2411
Houston (G-9907)
Jax Ltd Inc ....D 763 449-9699
Plano (G-16897)
Mattel Inc ....G 817 302-3300
Fort Worth (G-6819)
Mattel Inc ....F 310 252-2000
Laredo (G-13910)

TOYS & HOBBY GOODS & SPLYS, WHOLESALE: Playing Cards

Casino Supply Company ....F 972 241-4833
Dallas (G-4090)

TOYS & HOBBY GOODS & SPLYS, WHOLESALE: Toys & Games

Ben Dunn Corporation ....F 210 614-0396
San Antonio (G-17946)
Kelye B Stites Inc ....E 817 284-3499
Richland Hills (G-17439)

TOYS & HOBBY GOODS & SPLYS, WHOLESALE: Toys, NEC

Funsource Partners ....E 713 864-3412
Houston (G-9875)

TOYS & HOBBY GOODS & SPLYS, WHOLESALE: Video Games

Gamestop Holdings Corp ....B 817 424-2159
Grapevine (G-8039)

TOYS: Dolls, Stuffed Animals & Parts

Ashley Industries LLC ....G 864 834-1167
Round Rock (G-17623)
Idea Planet LP ....E 972 380-9867
Dallas (G-3844)

TOYS: Kites

Gayla Industries Inc ....F 979 335-7503
East Bernard (G-5558)

TOYS: Paint Sets, Children's

Ruby Red Paint Inc ....F 972 221-8665
Flower Mound (G-6279)

TOYS: Rubber

Funsource Partners ....E 713 864-3412
Houston (G-9875)

TOYS: Video Game Machines

LLC Battle Beaver ....D 888 390-4363
Richardson (G-17346)

TRADE SHOW ARRANGEMENT SVCS

Theatrical Warehouse Inc ....E 214 634-2965
Dallas (G-5082)

TRADERS: Commodity, Contracts

Coast To Coast Minerals LLC ....F 210 781-8505
San Antonio (G-18013)
Horizon Resources LP ....F 713 522-5800
Houston (G-10207)

TRAFFIC CONTROL FLAGGING SVCS

Signal Group Inc ....F 281 453-0200
Houston (G-11891)

TRAILER COACHES: Automobile

Michael Roy ....F 903 784-6362
Sumner (G-19607)
Wccog Corp ....F 903 667-0264
De Kalb (G-5237)

TRAILERS & CHASSIS: Camping

Direct Trailer LP ....E 281 713-8925
Humble (G-12763)
Houston Trailer Inc ....E 281 459-5350
Houston (G-10257)

TRAILERS & PARTS: Boat

Cnm Horizon Investments LLC ....E 713 333-3400
Galveston (G-7393)
Coastline Trailer Mfg Inc ....F 361 785-4073
Seadrift (G-18795)

TRAILERS & PARTS: Horse

Outlaw Conversions Inc ....C 254 968-5733
Stephenville (G-19417)

TRAILERS & PARTS: Truck & Semi's

81 Trucking Services LLC ....F 713 259-1076
Houston (G-8415)
American Trailer Works Inc ....F 817 328-3686
Southlake (G-19058)
Beall Construction Company Inc ....D 325 677-2112
Abilene (G-16)
Blue Horse Express LLC ....F 832 966-1053
Cypress (G-3780)
Buck Dandy Co ....E 903 784-6362
Sumner (G-19606)
C & S Trucking ....F 817 517-9172
Cleburne (G-3082)
Centerline Trailers Inc ....F 817 477-5533
Mansfield (G-14659)
Chase Transportation LLC ....E 915 307-5488
Horizon City (G-8363)
Energy Fabrication Inc ....E 432 362-0591
Odessa (G-15990)
Factory Motorhomes Inc ....F 214 830-2910
Terrell (G-19733)
Fort Worth Fabrication Inc ....F 817 625-2321
Fort Worth (G-6643)
General Body Manufacturing Co ....D 713 692-5177
Houston (G-9920)
Great Dane LLC ....F 214 637-2425
Dallas (G-4414)
Heil Trailer International LLC ....C 254 865-7235
Gatesville (G-7618)
HP Car Accessories & Atv Sales ....F 903 675-0032
Athens (G-828)
Imperial Group Mfg Inc ....C 940 627-1700
Decatur (G-5247)
Iron Ram Services LLC ....E 361 241-2346
Corpus Christi (G-3557)
Jac Enterprises Inc ....F 936 348-3997
Madisonville (G-14587)
Ledwell & Son Enterprises Inc ....C 903 838-6531
Texarkana (G-19768)
Lee Dill Inc ....D 325 677-0474
Abilene (G-56)
Lufkin Industries LLC ....B 936 634-2211
Lufkin (G-14541)
Mac Trailer Texas Inc ....E 330 956-0171
Rhome (G-17257)
Magnum Custom Trlr Mfg Co Inc ....D 512 258-4101
Austin (G-1318)
Magnum Custom Trlr Mfg Co Inc ....F 512 258-4101
San Antonio (G-18271)
Mate Inc ....E 281 855-0045
Houston (G-10790)
Opulent Transport LLC ....E 713 551-1445
Houston (G-11186)
Performax Custom Trailers ....F 972 442-3527
Wylie (G-20942)
Pt Trucks Inc ....E 713 338-1375
Houston (G-11470)
Pull Rite Trailers LLC ....F 903 502-5000
Murchison (G-15681)
Rising S Company LLC ....E 214 455-0560
Murchison (G-15682)

Spotted Lakes LLC ....C...... 817 441-9900
Weatherford (G-20621)

Trailers By Southern LLC ....E...... 469 517-0410
Joshua (G-13327)

Tsi Flow Products Inc ....F...... 903 984-2870
Kilgore (G-13597)

USI Integrated Trnsp LLC ....F...... 956 781-6606
Pharr (G-16714)

Wabash National Trlr Ctrs Inc ......F...... 972 923-2200
Waxahachie (G-20567)

Wellco Holdings Inc ....D...... 254 772-1740
Waco (G-20477)

Wes-Tex Manufacturing Inc ....F...... 806 749-3795
Lubbock (G-14509)

TRAILERS & TRAILER EQPT

A Plus Three Trucking LLC ....F...... 210 852-9339
San Antonio (G-17847)

Brazos Trailer Mfg LLC ....E...... 903 873-8130
Wills Point (G-20874)

Clegg Industries Inc ....E...... 361 578-0291
Victoria (G-20253)

Dexter Brahma LLC ....F...... 817 284-5141
Azle (G-1723)

Domatex Inc ....D...... 281 219-1800
Houston (G-9493)

Horse Creek Mfg & Fabrication ......E...... 903 572-4211
Cookville (G-3404)

Jennings Trailers Inc ....E...... 903 473-4562
Emory (G-6084)

Norstar Industries LLC ....E...... 903 784-8900
Brookston (G-2328)

Quality Trailer Products LP ....E...... 903 572-7932
Mount Pleasant (G-15661)

Supreme Corporation of Texas ....C...... 817 641-8002
Cleburne (G-3112)

Taxa Inc ....F...... 713 861-2540
Houston (G-12165)

Tims South Texas LLC ....F...... 830 278-3368
Uvalde (G-20197)

Tims South Texas LLC ....F...... 830 468-3860
Asherton (G-814)

Worth Trailer Parts Inc ....E...... 817 496-7841
Fort Worth (G-7151)

TRAILERS OR VANS: Horse Transportation, Fifth-Wheel Type

Compass Conversions LLC ....E...... 254 771-9909
Temple (G-19677)

TRAILERS: Bodies

Everlite Inc ....E...... 903 297-3444
Longview (G-14232)

Imperial Group Mfg Inc ....A...... 940 565-8505
Denton (G-5376)

Odom Trailer Mfg Co Inc ....F...... 936 756-3910
Conroe (G-3345)

Portersville Sales & Testing ....E...... 806 373-6811
Amarillo (G-507)

Texas Underground Inc ....D...... 281 485-9900
Pearland (G-16602)

Travis Body and Trailer Inc ....D...... 713 466-5888
Houston (G-12356)

Western Sls Tstg Amarillo Inc ......E...... 806 373-6811
Amarillo (G-522)

TRAILERS: Bus, Tractor Type

International Flatbed Svcs Inc ......F...... 915 858-1200
El Paso (G-5814)

TRAILERS: Camping, Tent-Type

Yj USA Corp ....F...... 877 927-8777
Addison (G-175)

TRAILERS: Semitrailers, Missile Transportation

Maposa Tinashe ....F...... 512 704-4601
Leander (G-13995)

TRAILERS: Semitrailers, Truck Tractors

1-Fast Rspnse Rntals Oil Feld ......D...... 210 437-2473
San Antonio (G-17844)

Brazos Trailer Mfg LLC ....E...... 903 873-8130
Wills Point (G-20874)

Great Dane LLC ....E...... 713 675-6577
Houston (G-10025)

Van Nu Technology Inc ....D...... 817 276-3300
Mansfield (G-14727)

TRAILERS: Truck, Chassis

Bright Coop Inc ....C...... 936 564-8378
Nacogdoches (G-15686)

Randy Myers Enterprises Inc ....E...... 903 897-0681
Naples (G-15720)

Techsys Chassis Inc ....E...... 903 395-4155
Paris (G-16371)

Texas Kenworth Co ....E...... 940 767-0001
Wichita Falls (G-20816)

TRANSDUCERS: Electrical Properties

Biztel LP ....F...... 713 600-2600
Houston (G-8896)

Dedicated Controls LLC ....F...... 972 632-8716
Princeton (G-17207)

TRANSFORMERS: Distribution

Jefferson Electric Inc ....F...... 956 542-5491
Brownsville (G-2369)

Mars Transformers LLC ....E...... 281 648-1600
Houston (G-10773)

Ohmite Holding LLC ....F...... 956 542-0276
Brownsville (G-2388)

Powell Industries Inc ....B...... 713 944-6900
Houston (G-11376)

Resa Power LLC ....F...... 832 900-8340
Houston (G-11604)

Sunbelt Transformer Ltd ....G...... 713 481-5500
Temple (G-19704)

Sunbelt Transformer Ltd ....E...... 800 433-3128
Temple (G-19705)

Upely Traders ....E...... 832 998-8432
Dallas (G-5143)

Utility Agency & Import Inc ....F...... 817 477-9888
Mansfield (G-14725)

TRANSFORMERS: Distribution, Electric

Gibraltar Trading Inc ....F...... 281 777-6786
Houston (G-9956)

Robertshaw Controls Company ....F...... 956 724-4400
Laredo (G-13926)

TRANSFORMERS: Electric

Schneider Electric Usa Inc ....C...... 972 236-0300
Coppell (G-3444)

Thermon Inc ....C...... 512 396-5801
San Marcos (G-18715)

Vantran Industries Inc ....E...... 254 772-9740
Waco (G-20471)

TRANSFORMERS: Electronic

Mag Flux Corporation ....E...... 972 272-8576
Garland (G-7541)

Magnetic Technology Inc ....E...... 214 544-2700
McKinney (G-14955)

Nova Magnetics Inc ....D...... 972 272-8287
Garland (G-7564)

Universal Transformer Company ......F...... 972 784-7700
Farmersville (G-6226)

TRANSFORMERS: Furnace, Electric

Ajax Tocco Magnethermic Corp ....F...... 903 297-2526
Longview (G-14191)

Wattstock LLC ....F...... 713 248-4148
Dallas (G-5175)

TRANSFORMERS: Instrument

Electromagnetic Industries LLC .....E...... 281 422-5225
Baytown (G-1816)

TRANSFORMERS: Power Related

ABB Enterprise Software Inc ....E...... 903 237-1030
Longview (G-14187)

Active Power Inc ....D...... 512 836-6464
Austin (G-887)

Alamo Transformer Supply Co ....E...... 713 991-6060
Houston (G-8526)

Arcosa Inc ....C...... 972 942-6500
Dallas (G-3958)

BP Wind Energy North Amer Inc ......D...... 713 354-2100
Houston (G-8971)

Circuit Breaker Sales LLC ....C...... 940 665-4444
Gainesville (G-7338)

Cooper Power Systems LLC ....C...... 936 569-9422
Nacogdoches (G-15692)

Cordyne Inc ....E...... 713 460-5151
Houston (G-9313)

Fisher Controls Intl LLC ....B...... 972 542-5512
McKinney (G-14943)

Gtech Precision Inds USA Ltd ....F...... 817 539-8014
Mansfield (G-14678)

Houtex Hi-Temp Transformer LLC .....E...... 713 271-8993
Houston (G-10266)

Hydradyne LLC ....F...... 210 661-4378
San Antonio (G-18177)

JCB Inc ....F...... 254 687-2200
Itasca (G-13215)

M&I Electric Industries Inc ....D...... 832 241-6330
Houston (G-10721)

Mag Flux Corporation ....E...... 972 272-8576
Garland (G-7541)

Magnetic Technology Inc ....E...... 214 544-2700
McKinney (G-14955)

Maviro Inc ....D...... 713 485-5193
Deer Park (G-5285)

Maxi Volt Corporation Inc ....F...... 806 371-0722
Amarillo (G-500)

Nova Magnetics Inc ....D...... 972 272-8287
Garland (G-7564)

Oilfield-Electric-Marine Inc ....F...... 713 680-9659
Houston (G-11165)

Puffer-Sweiven Holdings Inc ....E...... 281 470-2000
La Porte (G-13785)

Sigma Electronics Inc ....E...... 800 874-7121
Houston (G-11884)

Texas Electric Coops Inc ....E...... 512 454-0311
Austin (G-1567)

Tru-Test Inc ....D...... 940 327-8020
Mineral Wells (G-15543)

Younicos Inc ....C...... 512 268-8191
Austin (G-1683)

TRANSFORMERS: Specialty

Houston Transformer Co Ltd ....D...... 713 977-6009
Houston (G-10258)

Operating Technical Elec ....E...... 817 288-2600
Fort Worth (G-6886)

TRANSFORMERS: Voltage Regulating

Amran Inc ....C...... 281 243-2200
Sugar Land (G-19443)

Greenville Transformer Co ....E...... 903 455-1610
Greenville (G-8076)

High Voltage Power Systems Inc .....C...... 972 733-1700
Carrollton (G-2756)

Micropac Industries Inc ....D...... 972 272-3571
Garland (G-7551)

Solomon Transformers LLC ....D...... 512 763-3306
Georgetown (G-7677)

TRANSISTORS

Interfet Corporation ....F...... 972 238-9700
Richardson (G-17335)

Semiconductor Technology Inc ....F...... 512 468-8687
Lago Vista (G-13808)

TRANSLATION & INTERPRETATION SVCS

Universe Tchncal Trnsltion Inc .....E...... 713 827-8800
Houston (G-12466)

TRANSMISSION FLUID, MADE FROM PURCHASED MATERIALS

Enventives LLC ....E...... 612 930-1977
Seagraves (G-18803)

TRANSPORTATION EPQT & SPLYS, WHOL: Aircraft Engs/Eng Parts

Chromalloy Gas Turbine LLC ....F...... 972 241-2501
Dallas (G-4114)

TRANSPORTATION EPQT & SPLYS, WHOLESALE: Acft/Space Vehicle

Aeromax Industries Inc ....F...... 818 701-9500
Fort Worth (G-6352)

Employee Codes: A=Over 500 employees, B=251-500
C=101-250, D=51-100, E=20-50, F=10-19, G=9

2021 Harris Texas
Manufacturers Directory

1665

PRODUCT

TRANSPORTATION EPQT & SPLYS, WHOLESALE: Helicopter Parts

Airbus Helicopters Inc ....B 972 641-0000
Grand Prairie *(G-7824)*
Cordova Corporation ....E 817 484-1100
Burleson *(G-2577)*
Direct International ....G 817 284-7722
Fort Worth *(G-6587)*
Wesco Industries Inc ....E 817 551-7063
Fort Worth *(G-7137)*

TRANSPORTATION EPQT & SPLYS, WHOLESALE: Marine Crafts/Splys

Zimco Marine LLC ....F 956 831-7828
Brownsville *(G-2422)*

TRANSPORTATION EPQT & SPLYS, WHOLESALE: Tanks & Tank Compnts

Freeman David Products Inc ....E 866 310-2556
Burnet *(G-2608)*

TRANSPORTATION EPQT/SPLYS, WHOL: Marine Propulsn Mach/Eqpt

Monico Monitoring Inc ....F 281 350-8751
Spring *(G-19147)*

TRANSPORTATION EQPT & SPLYS WHOLESALERS, NEC

Bell Textron Inc ....A 817 280-2011
Fort Worth *(G-6444)*
Bell Textron Services Inc ....F 817 280-2011
Fort Worth *(G-6446)*
Interface Lgic Tech Dcmnttion ....F 713 446-3560
Pearland *(G-16570)*
Paradigm Traffic Systems Inc ....F 817 831-9406
Arlington *(G-748)*
Precision Power Associates ....G 972 234-6165
Richardson *(G-17375)*
Safran Seats USA LLC ....A 940 668-4825
Gainesville *(G-7362)*
Sky TEC Ltd ....F 817 573-2250
Granbury *(G-7810)*
Up 1 Trucking LLC ....F 833 398-7825
Dallas *(G-5141)*
Victor Equipment Company ....A 940 566-2000
Denton *(G-5409)*

TRANSPORTATION EQUIPMENT, NEC

Gewi North America LLC ....E 713 446-6902
Sugar Land *(G-19486)*
Ocean Freedom Shipping Inc ....E 281 579-3700
Houston *(G-11120)*
Rs Logistics LLC ....F 318 347-5915
Arlington *(G-776)*
Up 1 Trucking LLC ....F 833 398-7825
Dallas *(G-5141)*

TRANSPORTATION PROGRAM REGULATION & ADMIN, GOVT: State

Texas Department Trnsp ....E 512 486-5887
Austin *(G-1566)*
Transportation Texas Dept ....F 940 937-2571
Childress *(G-3056)*

TRANSPORTATION PROGRAMS REGULATION & ADMINISTRATION SVCS

Sister2sster Dstiny Trnspt LLC ....F 346 337-6637
Houston *(G-11908)*

TRANSPORTATION SVCS, AIR, NONSCHEDULED: Air Cargo Carriers

Sierra Industries Ltd ....D 210 805-3188
San Antonio *(G-18472)*

TRANSPORTATION SVCS, DEEP SEA: Intercoastal, Freight

Maposa Tinashe ....F 512 704-4601
Leander *(G-13995)*

TRANSPORTATION SVCS, NEC

Sister2sster Dstiny Trnspt LLC ....F 346 337-6637
Houston *(G-11908)*

TRANSPORTATION SVCS, WATER: Boathouses, Commercial

Precision Frac LLC ....F 855 967-1023
Midland *(G-15362)*

TRANSPORTATION SVCS, WATER: Canal & Intracoastal, Freight

Intergulf Corporation ....D 281 474-4210
La Porte *(G-13754)*

TRANSPORTATION SVCS, WATER: Cleaning

Western Towing Company ....E 713 435-1800
Channelview *(G-3044)*

TRANSPORTATION SVCS, WATER: Salvaging & Surveying, Marine

United Marine Enterprise Inc ....D 409 833-0303
Beaumont *(G-1965)*

TRANSPORTATION SVCS, WATER: Ship Cleaning

MPW Corporation ....F 713 640-2700
Houston *(G-10931)*

TRANSPORTATION SVCS, WATER: Ship Dismantling

Interntnal Shpbreaking Ltd LLC ....C 956 831-4112
Brownsville *(G-2364)*

TRANSPORTATION: Coastal Domestic Freight

Martin Midstream Partners LP ....F 281 471-2211
La Porte *(G-13774)*

TRANSPORTATION: Deep Sea Foreign Freight

Ocean Shipholdings Inc ....E 281 579-3700
Houston *(G-11122)*
Ocean Ships Inc ....E 281 579-3700
Houston *(G-11123)*

TRAP ROCK: Crushed & Broken

Caprock Materials LLC ....F 806 778-0343
Lubbock *(G-14390)*
Hillstone Company ....E 512 746-5544
Jarrell *(G-13270)*

TRAPS: Animal & Fish, Wire

Pipers Welding Service Inc ....F 940 682-4663
Weatherford *(G-20609)*

TRAVEL TRAILERS & CAMPERS

American Trailer World Corp ....E 855 289-0001
Richardson *(G-17269)*
Casita Enterprises Inc ....D 903 326-4717
Rice *(G-17265)*
Progressive Sales Inc ....E 432 333-6631
Odessa *(G-16127)*
Superior Trailer Sales Co ....E 713 674-2676
Houston *(G-12121)*

TRAVELER ACCOMMODATIONS, NEC

Gcv Enterprise LLC ....F 830 644-2710
Fredericksburg *(G-7180)*
TRT Holdings Inc ....E 214 283-8500
Dallas *(G-5121)*
University Houston - System ....C 713 741-2447
Houston *(G-12467)*

TROPHIES, NEC

Shaudra Company Inc ....E 915 544-4244
El Paso *(G-5957)*
Texas Trophies Inc ....F 210 674-6099
San Antonio *(G-18545)*

TROPHIES: Metal, Exc Silver

Claytex Trophies Inc ....C 940 538-6521
Henrietta *(G-8279)*
Tropar Manufacturing Co Inc ....F 972 875-5831
Ennis *(G-6121)*

TROPHY & PLAQUE STORES

Action Wear Plus Inc ....E 281 376-4300
Spring *(G-19098)*
Carrion Enterprises Inc ....F 915 593-1338
El Paso *(G-5686)*
Drsk Limited Partnership ....F 972 644-1490
Richardson *(G-17302)*
Firmin Business Forms Inc ....F 254 776-5742
Waco *(G-20402)*
Lehmberg Enterprises Inc ....F 210 924-6811
San Antonio *(G-18244)*
McAllen Sports Inc ....F 956 687-5500
McAllen *(G-14889)*
Screen Play Promotions Inc ....G 817 788-8608
Hurst *(G-12858)*
Texas Trophies Inc ....F 210 674-6099
San Antonio *(G-18545)*
Tropar Manufacturing Co Inc ....F 972 875-5831
Ennis *(G-6121)*

TRUCK & BUS BODIES: Ambulance

Youghall Enterprises Inc ....E 325 356-2233
Comanche *(G-3237)*

TRUCK & BUS BODIES: Cement Mixer

McNeilus Truck and Mfg Inc ....E 972 225-2313
Hutchins *(G-12868)*

TRUCK & BUS BODIES: Garbage Or Refuse Truck

Bridgeport Truck Mfg Inc ....D 254 559-2533
Breckenridge *(G-2227)*
Texan Waste Equipment Inc ....F 210 224-5800
San Antonio *(G-18531)*

TRUCK & BUS BODIES: Motor Vehicle, Specialty

146 Business Park Inc ....E 281 260-0617
Houston *(G-8401)*
Deerskin Mfg Inc ....E 817 220-5535
Springtown *(G-19273)*
Mobile Specialty Vehicles Inc ....F 409 383-0521
Newton *(G-15864)*
Norwood Equipment Houston Inc ....F 713 670-1320
Houston *(G-11084)*

TRUCK & BUS BODIES: Stake Platform Truck

Supreme Corporation of Texas ....C 817 641-8002
Cleburne *(G-3112)*

TRUCK & BUS BODIES: Truck Beds

Fabco Industries Inc ....F 432 367-4988
Odessa *(G-15999)*
Kings Truck Beds Inc ....F 940 433-2360
Boyd *(G-2205)*
Norstar Industries LLC ....E 903 784-8900
Brookston *(G-2328)*
Rudinger Enterprises Inc ....E 281 356-6219
Houston *(G-11695)*
Weldon Manufacturing Inc ....F 817 834-2229
Fort Worth *(G-7135)*

TRUCK & BUS BODIES: Truck, Motor Vehicle

Cruising Kitchens LLC ....G 210 920-2658
San Antonio *(G-18032)*
General Body Manufacturing Co ....D 713 692-5177
Houston *(G-9920)*
Lecolift Inc ....F 713 676-1514
Houston *(G-10613)*
Mateco Truck Equipment Co ....E 713 692-3888
Houston *(G-10791)*
Morgan Truck Body LLC ....D 903 872-7445
Corsicana *(G-3679)*
Olivo Enterprises Inc ....D 713 694-3077
Houston *(G-11172)*
Proform Group Inc ....E 214 206-4100
Mesquite *(G-15072)*

Progressive Resources Inc ....G 915 778-9548
  El Paso **(G-5921)**
Snf Inc ....D 817 402-8040
  Fort Worth **(G-6999)**
Supreme Corporation of Texas ....C 817 641-6282
  Cleburne **(G-3111)**
Texas Kenworth Co ....G 940 767-0001
  Wichita Falls **(G-20816)**
Westex Welding Company ....F 254 826-5343
  West **(G-20672)**

TRUCK & BUS BODIES: Van Bodies

Bae Systems Resolution Inc ....E 713 868-7700
  Houston **(G-8789)**

TRUCK & FREIGHT TERMINALS & SUPPORT ACTIVITIES

81 Trucking Services LLC ....F 713 259-1076
  Houston **(G-8415)**
Sooner Trading Inc ....F 806 235-3904
  Channing **(G-3045)**
Texas Kenworth Co ....D 432 381-3300
  Odessa **(G-16175)**

TRUCK BODIES: Body Parts

A G Van & Truck Eqp Inc ....E 214 638-8805
  Dallas **(G-3870)**
Ameritrail Inc ....E 281 375-5458
  Bellville **(G-2007)**
Automotive Rentals Inc ....E 817 624-3650
  Fort Worth **(G-6411)**
Axton LLC ....F 210 637-7400
  San Antonio **(G-17925)**
Greg Corkran Enterprises Inc ....E 409 720-9199
  Nederland **(G-15753)**
Leach Trailers LLP ....E 254 687-2616
  Itasca **(G-13216)**
Liddell Industries Inc ....F 325 646-7581
  Brownwood **(G-2436)**
Marmon Highway Tech LLC ....E 214 631-8810
  Dallas **(G-4636)**
Rki Inc ....B 713 688-4414
  Houston **(G-11634)**
Temple Freightliner LP ....E 254 770-1422
  Temple **(G-19707)**

TRUCK BODY SHOP

1-Fast Rspnse Rntals Oil Feld ....D 210 437-2473
  San Antonio **(G-17844)**

TRUCK DRIVER SVCS

Maposa Tinashe ....F 512 704-4601
  Leander **(G-13995)**

TRUCK DRIVING TRAINING

T & T Transports Inc ....E 325 728-2669
  Colorado City **(G-3227)**

TRUCK FINANCE LEASING

Texas Kenworth Co ....G 940 767-0001
  Wichita Falls **(G-20816)**

TRUCK GENERAL REPAIR SVC

1-Fast Rspnse Rntals Oil Feld ....D 210 437-2473
  San Antonio **(G-17844)**
Bill Gilmore Welding Inc ....E 940 592-4945
  Iowa Park **(G-12903)**

TRUCK PAINTING & LETTERING SVCS

Weldon Manufacturing Inc ....F 817 834-2229
  Fort Worth **(G-7135)**

TRUCK PARTS & ACCESSORIES: Wholesalers

Batterson Truck Equipment LLC ....F 281 598-6588
  Houston **(G-8829)**
Bumper Manufacturing Co Inc ....E 817 831-4401
  Fort Worth **(G-6477)**
Chalks Truck Parts Inc ....F 713 672-6344
  Houston **(G-9154)**
Chalks Truck Parts Inc ....F 713 672-6344
  Houston **(G-9153)**
Fabco Industries Inc ....F 432 367-4988
  Odessa **(G-15999)**

Fleetpride Inc ....F 361 883-4358
  Corpus Christi **(G-3528)**
Fleetpride Inc ....E 800 549-7278
  Grapevine **(G-8036)**
Kaspar Ranch Hand Eqp LLC ....C 361 594-4608
  Shiner **(G-18942)**
Ultra Seating Company ....F 469 865-2010
  Grand Prairie **(G-7989)**

TRUCKING & HAULING SVCS: Contract Basis

Uv Logistics LLC ....G 281 436-2310
  Houston **(G-12508)**

TRUCKING & HAULING SVCS: Hazardous Waste

Safety-Kleen Systems Inc ....B 800 669-5740
  Richardson **(G-17392)**

TRUCKING & HAULING SVCS: Heavy, NEC

Acme Truck Line Inc ....F 361 576-2934
  Victoria **(G-20235)**
Campbell Trailers & Leasing ....F 806 250-3611
  Friona **(G-7251)**
Earth Haulers Inc ....F 817 540-2777
  Euless **(G-6141)**

TRUCKING & HAULING SVCS: Liquid Petroleum, Exc Local

Intergulf Corporation ....D 281 474-4210
  La Porte **(G-13754)**
Southcross Ala Pipeline LLC ....E 214 979-3700
  Dallas **(G-4981)**

TRUCKING & HAULING SVCS: Liquid Transfer Svc

M & W Hot Oil Inc ....E 432 447-2108
  Pecos **(G-16623)**
Pate Trucking Co LLC ....E 575 392-4441
  Lubbock **(G-14458)**
Roywell LLC ....E 713 661-4747
  Sugar Land **(G-19538)**

TRUCKING & HAULING SVCS: Liquid, Local

Basic Energy Services LP ....F 903 657-8171
  Henderson **(G-8257)**
J&P Ramirez Services LLC ....E 361 526-2072
  Refugio **(G-17243)**
Outlaws Oilfield Service LLC ....E 432 445-0005
  Midland **(G-15333)**
Strawn Transport & Acid Co ....E 806 495-2422
  Post **(G-17192)**

TRUCKING & HAULING SVCS: Lumber & Log, Local

Mg Building Materials Ltd ....B 210 924-8604
  San Antonio **(G-18298)**

TRUCKING & HAULING SVCS: Lumber & Timber

Coleman Wood Products Inc ....E 940 440-2300
  Aubrey **(G-849)**
Dennis W Oates Logging LLC ....E 936 526-2700
  Diboll **(G-5464)**
Maposa Tinashe ....F 512 704-4601
  Leander **(G-13995)**

TRUCKING & HAULING SVCS: Machinery, Heavy

J Patrick Services LLC ....F 432 214-5443
  Odessa **(G-16035)**
Khudairi Group Incorporated ....E 713 782-1080
  Houston **(G-10530)**

TRUCKING & HAULING SVCS: Mobile Homes

American Homestar Corporation ....E 281 334-9700
  League City **(G-13946)**

TRUCKING & HAULING SVCS: Petroleum, Local

Adams Resources & Energy Inc ....E 713 881-3600
  Houston **(G-8475)**
Intergulf Corporation ....D 281 474-4210
  La Porte **(G-13754)**
Keane Group Holdings LLC ....D 713 960-0381
  Houston **(G-10510)**
King Pipeline Services LLC ....E 903 530-8667
  Fort Worth **(G-6762)**
L G Pump Inc ....E 432 550-3445
  Odessa **(G-16058)**
Patriot Oilfield Services LLC ....E 979 648-2416
  Victoria **(G-20290)**
Pure River LLC ....F 469 853-4867
  Princeton **(G-17211)**
United Petro Transports Inc ....E 817 540-6178
  Euless **(G-6165)**
Waters & Waters Services Inc ....D 432 827-3354
  Goldsmith **(G-7743)**

TRUCKING, AUTOMOBILE CARRIER

Interface Lgic Tech Dcmnttion ....F 713 446-3560
  Pearland **(G-16570)**

TRUCKING, DUMP

Earth Haulers Inc ....F 817 540-2777
  Euless **(G-6141)**
Hauling & Excavating Casco ....E 713 433-6209
  Houston **(G-10136)**
Sherrod Services LLC ....E 254 729-3177
  Thornton **(G-19943)**

TRUCKING: Except Local

81 Trucking Services LLC ....F 713 259-1076
  Houston **(G-8415)**
Akrotex Films Inc ....E 409 886-0111
  Orange **(G-16230)**
Akrotex Films Inc ....E 409 886-0063
  West Orange **(G-20692)**
Alltrans Port Trucking Inc ....E 713 673-3844
  Houston **(G-8559)**
C&D Allbritton Holdings Inc ....E 833 227-2243
  Salado **(G-17764)**
Citgo Holding Terminals LLC ....B 832 486-4000
  Houston **(G-9200)**
Citgo Petroleum Corporation ....A 832 486-4000
  Houston **(G-9201)**
DFI Piling Inc ....F 877 334-7453
  Conroe **(G-3291)**
El Paso CNG Company LLC ....F 713 420-2600
  Houston **(G-9586)**
Erasmo Lopez Jr ....E 956 487-3366
  Rio Grande City **(G-17471)**
J Lewis Partners LP ....A 972 702-7390
  Dallas **(G-4519)**
Merchants Moving & Storage Inc ....E 361 293-7202
  Yoakum **(G-20969)**
Nibletts Oilfield Services Inc ....E 325 853-2521
  Eldorado **(G-6047)**
Pictsweet Company ....D 210 833-9618
  San Antonio **(G-18374)**
Texas Kenworth Co ....G 940 767-0001
  Wichita Falls **(G-20816)**
Tom Thorp Transports ....D 325 392-8323
  Ozona **(G-16288)**
United Petro Transports Inc ....E 817 540-6178
  Euless **(G-6165)**
Up 1 Trucking LLC ....F 833 398-7825
  Dallas **(G-5141)**

TRUCKING: Local, With Storage

Akrotex Films Inc ....E 409 886-0111
  Orange **(G-16230)**
Akrotex Films Inc ....E 409 886-0063
  West Orange **(G-20692)**
Storage & Processors Inc ....D 832 360-2800
  Houston **(G-12072)**

TRUCKING: Local, Without Storage

Arbor Resources LLC ....F 936 632-9914
  Pollok **(G-17091)**
Arguijo Oilfield Services Inc ....E 432 550-5650
  Odessa **(G-15918)**
Barrera Contractors Inc ....F 432 639-2516
  Iraan **(G-12916)**

Employee Codes: A=Over 500 employees, B=251-500
C=101-250, D=51-100, E=20-50, F=10-19, G=9

2021 Harris Texas
Manufacturers Directory

1667

PRODUCT

Cargo Crating Company Ltd ....F 713 699-0172
Houston *(G-9092)*

Chapas Oilfield Services LLC ....F 956 847-6460
Zapata *(G-20980)*

Chemical Service Company ....E 432 523-5290
Andrews *(G-542)*

Conglobal Industries LLC ....E 713 675-7587
Galena Park *(G-7379)*

E&R Vacuum Truck Services LLC ....F 956 618-9590
Edinburg *(G-5585)*

El Paso CNG Company LLC ....E 713 420-2600
Houston *(G-9586)*

H J G Trucking Inc ....F 817 834-7181
Fort Worth *(G-6683)*

I 35 Sandpit Inc ....E 817 790-2772
Alvarado *(G-335)*

J & X Trucking LLC ....E 830 583-0611
Kenedy *(G-13488)*

Jimmie Hahn Partnership Ltd ....E 979 836-3664
Brenham *(G-2259)*

Kasper Pro Vac Service Inc ....E 956 796-0765
Laredo *(G-13901)*

Key Energy Services Inc ....F 432 620-0300
Midland *(G-15269)*

La Grange Con & Aggregates ....E 979 836-3664
Brenham *(G-2260)*

Nibletts Oilfield Services Inc ....E 325 853-2521
Eldorado *(G-6047)*

Otis T Dickerson ....F 713 988-2533
Pearland *(G-16585)*

Sorrell Cnstr Eqp & Mtls LLC ....D 979 233-6655
Freeport *(G-7213)*

Sparkman Well Service Inc ....C 361 572-4833
Victoria *(G-20305)*

Tejas Trucking Inc ....G 432 523-5786
Andrews *(G-560)*

Texas Tank Trucks Co ....E 254 559-5404
Granbury *(G-7812)*

Vernor Material & Eqp Co Inc ....E 409 233-3366
Freeport *(G-7221)*

Weir Brothers Contracting LLC ....F 940 440-2931
Aubrey *(G-852)*

TRUCKS & TRACTORS: *Industrial*

Ace Welding and Trailer Co ....E 210 667-1171
San Antonio *(G-17858)*

Ansung-Usa LLC ....E 469 877-5242
Dallas *(G-3949)*

Buck Dandy Co ....E 903 784-6362
Sumner *(G-19606)*

Channl-Track Tube-Way Inds Inc ....F 361 798-4979
Hallettsville *(G-8120)*

Dcf Investments LLC ....F 281 744-7445
Livingston *(G-14152)*

G & H Truck Equipment Inc ....E 817 467-9883
Arlington *(G-684)*

Heil Trailer International LLC ....C 254 865-7235
Gatesville *(G-7618)*

J&A Trucking Co ....F 713 854-0226
Willis *(G-20851)*

James Manufacturing Inc ....E 903 872-2346
Corsicana *(G-3675)*

K W D Manufacturing Inc ....E 210 924-5999
San Antonio *(G-18214)*

Kalamar Industries USA Inc ....D 903 759-5490
White Oak *(G-20716)*

Kjd Enterprises ....F 325 641-0420
Brownwood *(G-2431)*

Mate Inc ....E 281 855-0045
Houston *(G-10790)*

Morgan Truck Body LLC ....D 903 872-7445
Corsicana *(G-3679)*

Nacco Industries Inc ....E 440 449-9600
Plano *(G-16938)*

Oft Enterprises Inc ....E 713 787-5373
Bellaire *(G-2000)*

Overhead Door Corporation ....C 469 549-7100
Lewisville *(G-14080)*

Overland Tank Inc ....E 325 673-7132
Odessa *(G-16105)*

Paccar Inc ....C 940 566-7329
Corinth *(G-3459)*

Portersville Sales & Testing ....E 806 373-6811
Amarillo *(G-507)*

Proco Inc ....E 361 516-1112
Kingsville *(G-13634)*

Progressive Sales Inc ....E 432 333-6631
Odessa *(G-16127)*

Provident Rmnfcturing Svcs Inc ....E 940 239-7775
Denton *(G-5394)*

Sanwa Usa Inc ....E 972 503-3031
Plano *(G-17002)*

Sunbelt Design & Dev Inc ....D 210 227-9162
San Antonio *(G-18511)*

Supreme Corporation of Texas ....C 817 641-8002
Cleburne *(G-3112)*

Western Hauler Enterprises ....F 817 332-1121
Fort Worth *(G-7139)*

Win-Holt Equipment Corp ....C 972 641-4658
Grand Prairie *(G-7995)*

TRUCKS, INDL: *Wholesalers*

Ranger Lift Trucks LLC ....F 281 424-2111
Baytown *(G-1832)*

TRUCKS: *Forklift*

Batteries Concord ....F 281 931-4488
Houston *(G-8827)*

Blaze Equipment LLC ....F 817 439-0453
Lake Worth *(G-13812)*

Fleetpride Inc ....F 361 883-4358
Corpus Christi *(G-3528)*

Forklifts USA Inc ....F 956 568-9797
Laredo *(G-13887)*

Indepndent Rugh Trrain Ctr LLC ....C 210 599-6541
Cibolo *(G-3063)*

L L T Inc ....E 830 914-3800
Odessa *(G-16059)*

LLT Inc ....F 830 995-3465
Comfort *(G-3239)*

Manitou North America Inc ....D 254 799-0232
Waco *(G-20429)*

Miller Equipment Co ....F 469 366-4227
Garland *(G-7553)*

Mitsubshi Ctrpllar Frklift AME ....A 713 365-1000
Houston *(G-10891)*

Prolift Equipment Inc ....F 214 682-3327
Duncanville *(G-5538)*

Ranger Lift Trucks LLC ....F 281 424-2111
Baytown *(G-1832)*

TRUCKS: *Indl*

428transporters LLC ....F 214 212-8648
Desoto *(G-5427)*

Azt Wood LLC ....E 409 283-5355
Woodville *(G-20915)*

Balong Trucking LLC ....F 408 471-1383
Richardson *(G-17277)*

Flagship Transport LP ....G 713 253-7785
Brenham *(G-2254)*

Galvan National Carriers LLC ....F 956 346-7095
San Benito *(G-18657)*

Kentucky Freight Systems Inc ....F 972 475-6567
Rowlett *(G-17708)*

Level Up Transportation LLC ....F 214 210-0701
Lewisville *(G-14061)*

Rich Transport LLC ....E 214 819-3082
Dallas *(G-4896)*

Smarttruck Undertray Systems ....F 864 990-0781
Fort Worth *(G-6993)*

TRUSSES & FRAMING: *Prefabricated Metal*

Light Gauge Solutions Inc ....F 682 564-0378
Arlington *(G-722)*

Richard Phillips Inc ....E 972 264-5315
Grand Prairie *(G-7966)*

TRUSSES: *Wood, Floor*

El Paso Truss Inc ....D 915 751-0025
El Paso *(G-5745)*

Foxworth-Galbraith Lumber Co ....D 972 665-2400
Plano *(G-16872)*

Trussway LLC Central ....F 713 691-6900
Houston *(G-12387)*

Trussway LLC East ....F 713 691-6900
Houston *(G-12388)*

Trussway Holdings Inc ....F 713 691-6900
Houston *(G-12389)*

Trussway Transportation Inc ....A 713 691-6900
Houston *(G-12391)*

TRUSSES: *Wood, Roof*

All Truss Building Systems Inc ....F 817 247-7671
Dallas *(G-3922)*

Allied Truss LLC ....E 903 586-1982
Jacksonville *(G-13225)*

American Truss Systems Inc ....E 281 442-4584
Houston *(G-8613)*

Associated Truss Company ....D 972 226-1973
Mesquite *(G-15028)*

Builders Firstsource-Ohio Vall ....C 214 880-3500
Dallas *(G-4067)*

Case Hill Group Inc ....F 903 657-7000
Henderson *(G-8260)*

Claussen Inc ....F 512 556-2180
Lampasas *(G-13833)*

Colonial Truss Co LLC ....E 469 320-1000
Dallas *(G-4142)*

East Texas Truss LLC ....F 409 283-3728
Hillister *(G-8319)*

Lockhart Truss Co Inc ....F 512 398-5300
Lockhart *(G-14171)*

Loredo Truss Company Inc ....E 512 926-1782
Austin *(G-1301)*

Mg Building Materials Ltd ....G 210 798-0650
San Antonio *(G-18297)*

Noltex Truss Big Spring Inc ....F 254 216-0904
Gatesville *(G-7621)*

Noltex Truss Big Spring Inc ....F 432 267-4700
Big Spring *(G-2089)*

Noltex Truss Dfw Inc ....F 817 866-3333
Grandview *(G-8002)*

Noltex Truss Gatesville LP ....D 713 926-7715
Houston *(G-11066)*

Noltex Truss Littlefield LP ....F 432 687-1241
Midland *(G-15321)*

Noltex Truss Littlefield LP ....F 806 385-5533
Littlefield *(G-14147)*

North Texas Truss ....E 806 385-5533
Littlefield *(G-14148)*

Panel Truss of Longview Inc ....F 903 657-7000
Henderson *(G-8270)*

Panel Truss Texas Inc ....D 903 657-7000
Henderson *(G-8271)*

Rio Truss LP ....F 956 682-9822
McAllen *(G-14902)*

Rogers Manufacturing Corp ....E 901 301-4936
Sugar Land *(G-19536)*

Rushin Truss Ltd ....F 972 442-3544
Nevada *(G-15766)*

Textruss Component Bldg Inc ....E 512 836-4830
Austin *(G-1571)*

The San Antonio Truss Company ....G 210 736-9629
San Antonio *(G-18547)*

Truss Ops North LLC ....G 479 824-8787
Henderson *(G-8276)*

Trussway Manufacturing Inc ....C 719 322-9662
Houston *(G-12390)*

Wood Shed Truss ....F 903 569-2147
Mineola *(G-15515)*

Wood Shed Trusse ....F 903 569-2147
Mineola *(G-15516)*

TRUST MANAGEMENT SVCS: *Educational*

Fun Da Mentals For Educatn LLC ....E 832 368-3345
Houston *(G-9874)*

TUB CONTAINERS: *Plastic*

Mauser Usa LLC ....C 713 670-2332
Houston *(G-10799)*

Rio Plastics Inc ....E 956 831-2715
Brownsville *(G-2401)*

TUBE & PIPE MILL EQPT

Atkore Plastic Pipe Corp ....D 817 594-8791
Weatherford *(G-20576)*

B & H Enterprises ....E 817 558-2667
Cleburne *(G-3080)*

Seah Steel USA LLC ....D 832 734-0044
Houston *(G-11802)*

Top Threading Services Inc ....E 281 426-8461
Crosby *(G-3745)*

TUBE & TUBING FABRICATORS

Castronics Inc ....C 308 235-4881
Houston *(G-9098)*

CCB Fabricators Inc ....E 361 387-7900
Robstown *(G-17504)*

Dynamic Products Inc ....D 281 457-3500
Houston *(G-9550)*

Glt Fabricators Inc ....E 713 670-9700
La Porte *(G-13739)*

Houston Elbow & Nipple Co Inc ....F 713 225-2257
Houston *(G-10231)*

Houston Pipe Benders LLC ....E 281 449-8241
Houston *(G-10243)*

Jake Harris & Sons Inc ....F 281 471-0214
La Porte *(G-13758)*

Labarge Coating LLC ....D 713 378-7225
Channelview *(G-3028)*

Lonestar Pipe Fabrication Inc ....F 817 439-5575
Saginaw *(G-17749)*

Tejas Tubular Products Inc ....B 281 822-3400
Houston *(G-12188)*

Tube Products Inc ....F 817 489-2264
Aurora *(G-855)*

Tubular Prfrting Mfr of Conroe ....E 936 441-8660
Conroe *(G-3374)*

Tubular Solutions Inc ....F 713 391-8005
Houston *(G-12406)*

Vam Usa LLC ....C 281 821-5510
Houston *(G-12525)*

Wachs Subsea LLC ....E 713 983-0784
Houston *(G-12591)*

TUBES: Extruded Or Drawn, Aluminum

Diamond Plastics Corporation ....D 806 763-8021
Lubbock *(G-14405)*

TUBES: Finned, For Heat Transfer

Epcon Industrial Systems LP ....D 936 273-1774
Shenandoah *(G-18896)*

Lektrotech Inc ....F 972 225-2356
Greenville *(G-8082)*

TUBES: Gas Or Vapor

Jordan Technologies LLC ....D 502 267-8344
Austin *(G-1261)*

Patriot Premium Threading Serv ....D 432 250-6001
Midland *(G-15339)*

TUBES: Paper

Age Industries Ltd ....E 915 852-9099
Horizon City *(G-8361)*

Caraustar Industries Inc ....E 903 793-6231
Texarkana *(G-19758)*

Sonoco Products Company ....E 817 461-5616
Irving *(G-13184)*

TUBES: Paper Or Fiber, Chemical Or Electrical Uses

Caraustar Industrial and Con ....E 409 898-6600
Silsbee *(G-18950)*

TUBES: Steel & Iron

Mica Steelworks Inc ....E 817 529-5000
Fort Worth *(G-6836)*

Oil Tech Services Inc ....F 281 456-9023
Houston *(G-11162)*

Oil Tech Services Inc ....F 713 789-5144
Houston *(G-11163)*

Pennar Global Inc ....F 281 362-2707
The Woodlands *(G-19900)*

TUBES: Welded, Aluminum

Coretech Industries LLC ....F 440 949-9592
Dallas *(G-4168)*

Peyton Salas & Mendoza LLC ....E 512 784-5875
Houston *(G-11313)*

TUBES: Wrought, Welded Or Lock Joint

Ljt Texas LLC ....D 254 771-2253
Temple *(G-19685)*

Ntx Gates & Fences Inc ....E 817 740-9449
Fort Worth *(G-6874)*

TUBING: Copper

Bae Systems Resolution Inc ....E 713 868-7700
Houston *(G-8789)*

McClinton Energy Group L L C ....C 432 563-5500
Midland *(G-15296)*

McClinton Energy Group L L C ....E 432 563-5500
Odessa *(G-16077)*

TUBING: Flexible, Metallic

10-4 Tubular Inc ....E 281 436-0380
Houston *(G-8399)*

Quality Tubing Inc ....C 281 456-0751
Houston *(G-11503)*

Quietflex Manufacturing Co LP ....B 877 694-3669
Houston *(G-11514)*

TUBING: Plastic

Dlhbowles Inc ....D 956 986-6000
Brownsville *(G-2350)*

S H Leggitt Company ....C 956 504-6440
San Marcos *(G-18708)*

TUBING: Rubber

Fiberspar Corporation ....D 713 849-2609
Houston *(G-9783)*

Republic Tube LLC ....C 832 672-6000
Houston *(G-11603)*

TUBING: Seamless

Promicom Inc ....G 832 544-0855
The Woodlands *(G-19906)*

Salzgtter Mnnsmann Stnless Tbe ....D 713 466-7278
Houston *(G-11735)*

Teda Tpco America Corporation ....E 361 826-2610
Gregory *(G-8106)*

Tenaris Coiled Tubes LLC ....C 281 458-2883
Houston *(G-12198)*

Tex-Tube Company ....C 713 686-4351
Houston *(G-12217)*

TUGBOAT SVCS

Josephine Tug Inc ....E 409 744-1222
Galveston *(G-7402)*

TUMBLERS: Plastic

Performance Gear Hdqtr LLC ....E 281 402-6816
Cypress *(G-3811)*

TUNGSTEN CARBIDE

Diapac LLC ....E 713 715-6300
Houston *(G-9460)*

TURBINE GENERATOR SET UNITS: Hydraulic, Complete

Eaton Corporation ....F 956 283-1468
McAllen *(G-14854)*

Eaton Corporation ....F 956 843-3450
Hidalgo *(G-8306)*

TURBINES & TURBINE GENERATOR SET UNITS, COMPLETE

Endiprev USA Inc ....F 214 897-5740
Flower Mound *(G-6265)*

Transcanada Turbines Inc ....E 281 880-2900
Houston *(G-12347)*

TURBINES & TURBINE GENERATOR SET UNITS: Gas, Complete

Btec Turbines LP ....D 281 864-9122
Houston *(G-9002)*

Caterpillar Inc ....A 309 675-1000
Waco *(G-20377)*

Katch Filters LLC ....G 713 425-7400
Houston *(G-10501)*

Pal-Con LLC ....E 254 968-3335
Stephenville *(G-19418)*

Revak Keene Turbomachinery LP ....D 281 427-8800
La Porte *(G-13787)*

Solar Turbines Incorporated ....B 972 228-5500
Desoto *(G-5442)*

Solar Turbines Incorporated ....B 713 895-2300
Houston *(G-11935)*

Solar Turbines Incorporated ....C 281 860-6703
Channelview *(G-3038)*

Solar Turbines Incorporated ....D 800 851-6594
Midland *(G-15414)*

Solar Turbines Incorporated ....F 903 880-1200
Mabank *(G-14583)*

TURBINES & TURBINE GENERATOR SETS

A&C Green Energy Inc ....G 972 516-0692
Garland *(G-7423)*

ABB Enterprise Software Inc ....F 281 930-8383
Deer Park *(G-5259)*

Cameron International Corp ....C 713 354-1900
Houston *(G-9068)*

Continental Turbine Services ....F 281 541-6060
Houston *(G-9290)*

Dewind Co ....E 469 420-9886
Irving *(G-12997)*

Ethos Energy LP ....C 713 336-1300
Houston *(G-9704)*

Ethosenergy (usa) LLC ....E 713 812-2300
Houston *(G-9705)*

Ethosenergy Field Services LLC ....F 713 849-8835
Houston *(G-9706)*

Ethosenergy Light Turbines LLC ....D 713 849-8800
Houston *(G-9707)*

Ethosenergy Tc Inc ....E 713 336-1300
Houston *(G-9708)*

GE Energy Manufacturing Inc ....D 281 864-2669
Houston *(G-9914)*

GE Packaged Power LLC ....C 713 803-0900
Houston *(G-9917)*

GE Packaged Power LP ....D 281 452-3610
Houston *(G-9918)*

General Electric Company ....D 214 902-6600
Dallas *(G-4399)*

General Electric Company ....D 713 803-0437
Houston *(G-9923)*

General Electric Company ....B 281 812-0634
Humble *(G-12769)*

General Electric Company ....G 325 794-5100
Abilene *(G-43)*

General Electric Company ....E 281 921-2850
Houston *(G-9922)*

Houston Grinding & Mfg Co ....E 713 869-3573
Houston *(G-10235)*

Hydraulic Systems Inc ....E 832 791-5000
The Woodlands *(G-19881)*

Jvm Mechanical Inc ....F 713 910-3839
Houston *(G-10492)*

Mitsubshi Hvy Inds Cmprsr Intl ....C 713 652-0300
Houston *(G-10892)*

Oliver Equipment Company LLC ....E 713 856-9206
Houston *(G-11171)*

Power Process Developments Inc ....F 713 926-5840
Houston *(G-11378)*

Preco Turbine Comprsr Svcs Inc ....C 281 821-9620
Houston *(G-11397)*

Rwg (repair Overhauls USA Inc ....D 713 538-9700
Houston *(G-11704)*

Siemens Energy Inc ....C 281 328-3777
Houston *(G-11878)*

Siemens Energy Inc ....F 972 929-5044
Irving *(G-13177)*

TURBINES & TURBINE GENERATOR SETS & PARTS

Nexgen - Advnced Fuel Systems ....E 281 789-2000
Houston *(G-11046)*

Riva Services LLC ....D 713 675-2525
Houston *(G-11627)*

Solar Turbines Incorporated ....B 903 880-1461
Mabank *(G-14582)*

Tesco Corporation (us) ....D 713 359-7000
Houston *(G-12212)*

Wind Energy Turbine Services ....D 325 235-1555
Sweetwater *(G-19639)*

TURBINES: Gas, Mechanical Drive

Immi Turbines Inc ....F 936 788-2229
Conroe *(G-3310)*

Kawasaki Gas Turbines-Americas ....F 281 970-3255
Houston *(G-10502)*

Safran Power Units Dallas Inc ....F 972 606-7681
Grand Prairie *(G-7970)*

Turbine Resources Inc ....E 817 540-0249
Euless *(G-6163)*

TURBINES: Hydraulic, Complete

Airway Services Inc ....C 325 617-5813
San Angelo *(G-17772)*

HMC Capital Inc ....G 936 441-2666
The Woodlands *(G-19872)*

Pantex Ennerflo Systems Inc ....E 832 861-7700
Houston *(G-8390)*

TURBINES: Steam

Babcock & Wilcox Company ....F 281 405-6800
Houston *(G-8784)*

P
R
O
D
U
C
T

Dresser-Rand Group Inc ....C 713 354-6100
  Houston *(G-9522)*

Dresser-Rand LLC ....E 713 467-2221
  Houston *(G-9523)*

TURNKEY VENDORS: Computer Systems

Rational Systems LLC ....E 832 476-8468
  Houston *(G-11552)*

Rubicon Communications LLC .....E 512 646-4100
  Austin *(G-1476)*

TYPESETTING SVC

Alliance Press Leasing Inc ....E 713 957-3349
  Houston *(G-8546)*

ARC Document Solutions LLC ......B 713 988-9200
  Houston *(G-8678)*

ARC Document Solutions LLC ......F 713 787-1244
  Houston *(G-8679)*

Bayside Printing Inc ....E 281 209-9500
  Houston *(G-8838)*

Beeville Publishing Company ....E 361 358-2550
  Beeville *(G-1984)*

Blanks Printing & Imaging Inc .....D 214 741-3905
  Dallas *(G-4030)*

Brenholb Inc ....E 210 349-4024
  San Antonio *(G-17965)*

Brunswick Press Inc ....E 713 462-0600
  Houston *(G-9000)*

Burrell Printing Company Inc ....E 512 990-1188
  Pflugerville *(G-16662)*

Business Printing Inc ....F 214 445-5000
  Carrollton *(G-2706)*

Cellisco Inc ....E 210 692-1927
  San Antonio *(G-17989)*

Central Texas Printing Inc ....E 254 754-4653
  Waco *(G-20381)*

Cenveo Worldwide Limited ....C 210 923-7591
  San Antonio *(G-17994)*

Cenveo Worldwide Limited ....D 806 376-4347
  Amarillo *(G-414)*

Champions Printing & Pubg Inc ...E 281 583-7661
  Houston *(G-9160)*

Clear Visions Inc ....D 210 496-6006
  San Antonio *(G-18012)*

Cloud Printing Co of Abilene ....G 325 676-9396
  Abilene *(G-32)*

Cockrell Printing Co ....D 817 336-0571
  Fort Worth *(G-6528)*

Consumer Guide Inc ....F 713 417-6152
  Houston *(G-9280)*

Fayette County Record Inc ....G 979 968-3155
  La Grange *(G-13695)*

Fedex Office & Print Svcs Inc ......F 713 521-9465
  Houston *(G-9772)*

Fedex Office & Print Svcs Inc ......E 254 776-7763
  Waco *(G-20401)*

Gainesville Printing Co Inc ....E 940 665-5517
  Gainesville *(G-7344)*

Grafikshop Corporation ....E 713 977-2555
  Houston *(G-10012)*

Graphic Image Inc ....E 563 285-5214
  Flower Mound *(G-6267)*

Hearst Corporation ....C 432 682-5311
  Midland *(G-15244)*

Henderson Newspapers Inc ....E 903 657-2501
  Henderson *(G-8265)*

Hewell Enterprises Inc ....E 972 466-2442
  Carrollton *(G-2869)*

Hudson Graphics Inc ....E 903 758-1773
  Longview *(G-14248)*

Image Type Corporation ....F 214 956-9050
  Dallas *(G-4488)*

J M H Printing Company ....E 972 263-1226
  Grand Prairie *(G-7899)*

Jefferson At Montfort Limited ....E 972 789-3600
  Dallas *(G-4530)*

L C Colormark ....D 972 243-1919
  Carrollton *(G-2773)*

Lebco Graphics Inc ....E 830 755-8226
  Boerne *(G-2126)*

Lithographics Inc ....G 210 226-1722
  San Antonio *(G-18255)*

Molloy Corporation ....E 713 771-9485
  Houston *(G-10907)*

Nieman Printing Inc ....E 972 506-7400
  Dallas *(G-4739)*

Quadrangle Press Inc ....E 210 828-8191
  San Antonio *(G-18405)*

R S Graphic Services Inc ....E 817 921-6266
  Fort Worth *(G-6932)*

Rapid Reprographics LP ....F 214 357-5444
  Coppell *(G-3437)*

Reynolds Brothers Ltd ....E 432 682-7393
  Midland *(G-15383)*

S P (texas) Inc ....G 713 666-5166
  Houston *(G-11712)*

Sandford Prepress Systems ....E 214 808-3070
  Dallas *(G-4932)*

Southwest Precision Prtrs LP ....D 713 777-3333
  Houston *(G-11983)*

Spartan Printing Inc ....E 817 640-6341
  Arlington *(G-784)*

Thomas Graphics Inc ....D 512 719-3535
  Austin *(G-1576)*

TNT Printing ....G 281 449-9090
  Houston *(G-12315)*

Type Excellence Inc ....F 830 833-9005
  Coupland *(G-3693)*

Universe Tchncal Trnsltion Inc ......E 713 827-8800
  Houston *(G-12466)*

Waterfront Publishing Inc ....F 281 334-2202
  Kemah *(G-13482)*

West Texas Printing Company ....D 325 646-3598
  Brownwood *(G-2449)*

William G Burns ....F 972 233-4700
  Dallas *(G-5189)*

TYPESETTING SVC: Computer

Einsteins Inc ....F 972 387-8485
  Carrollton *(G-2729)*

Girard Investments Inc ....G 972 423-0299
  Plano *(G-16880)*

ULTRASONIC EQPT: Cleaning, Exc Med & Dental

Branson Ultrasonics Corp ....E 956 729-1550
  Laredo *(G-13871)*

Highrise Systems Inc ....E 817 927-8711
  Fort Worth *(G-6697)*

UMBRELLAS: Garden Or Wagon

Arden Companies Inc ....C 806 335-1147
  Amarillo *(G-400)*

UNDERGROUND IRON ORE MINING

BHP Minerals International LLC .....B 713 961-8500
  Houston *(G-8878)*

UNDERGROUND SILVER MINING

Rio Grande Mining Company ....D 432 229-4737
  Marfa *(G-14754)*

UNIFORM SPLY SVCS: Indl

San Bay Studio Inc ....F 940 387-4466
  Denton *(G-5399)*

Unifirst Corporation ....D 817 834-7386
  Haltom City *(G-8160)*

Unifirst Corporation ....E 281 261-9632
  Missouri City *(G-15597)*

Unifirst Corporation ....E 979 774-0577
  College Station *(G-3208)*

UNIFORM STORES

Brammers Athletic Wearhouse LP ...F 281 391-1441
  Katy *(G-13390)*

Ghashim Capital Ventures Corp .....F 713 266-1888
  Houston *(G-9949)*

Miller Uniforms & Emblems Inc .....E 512 302-5541
  Austin *(G-1345)*

UNISEX HAIR SALONS

Venus Spa ....E 214 469-1615
  Lewisville *(G-14105)*

UNIVERSITY

The Texas A&M University Sys ......E 979 845-1436
  College Station *(G-3206)*

University of Houston System ....F 713 221-8192
  Houston *(G-12468)*

University of Houston System ....E 713 743-2841
  Houston *(G-12469)*

University of Texas At Austin ....E 800 252-3206
  Austin *(G-1609)*

University of Texas At Austin ....E 512 471-1865
  Austin *(G-1610)*

University of TX Med Brnch Gal .....D 409 772-5900
  Galveston *(G-7411)*

UPHOLSTERY FILLING MATERIALS

Advanced Fabric Tech LLC ....F 281 872-7272
  Spring *(G-19191)*

Sigma Corporation ....E 281 987-1200
  Houston *(G-11883)*

UPHOLSTERY WORK SVCS

Marroquin Custom Upholstery ....E 214 905-0461
  Dallas *(G-4637)*

Rudys Custom Uphl & Design ....F 210 821-5156
  San Antonio *(G-18438)*

URANIUM ORE MINING, NEC

Mestena Uranium LLC ....G 361 884-2191
  Corpus Christi *(G-3577)*

URBAN PLANNING & COMMUNITY & RURAL DEVELOPMENT SVCS

City of Houston ....C 713 221-0404
  Houston *(G-9203)*

USED BOOK STORES

Half Price Bks Rec Mgzines Inc .....F 512 805-7503
  San Marcos *(G-18693)*

Half Price Bks Rec Mgzines Inc .....F 281 540-3950
  Humble *(G-12774)*

USED CLOTHING STORES

Radtke Jenna ....E 512 444-2002
  Austin *(G-1450)*

USED MERCHANDISE STORES

Gamestop Corp ....C 817 424-2000
  Grapevine *(G-8038)*

Gamestop Holdings Corp ....B 817 424-2159
  Grapevine *(G-8039)*

Olton Welding & Machine Inc ....F 806 285-3006
  Olton *(G-16227)*

USED MERCHANDISE STORES: Rare Books

Half Price Bks Rec Mgzines Inc .....F 817 295-8560
  Burleson *(G-2580)*

UTILITY TRAILER DEALERS

Buck Dandy Co ....E 903 784-6362
  Sumner *(G-19606)*

Channl-Track Tube-Way Inds Inc .....F 361 798-4979
  Hallettsville *(G-8120)*

D&D Retail LP ....E 830 379-7340
  Seguin *(G-18835)*

Magnum Custom Trlr Mfg Co Inc ...F 512 258-4101
  San Antonio *(G-18271)*

McDonald Welding Co ....F 325 573-5329
  Snyder *(G-18994)*

Tmp Truck & Trailer LP ....E 432 686-2500
  Midland *(G-15438)*

Worth Trailer Parts Inc ....E 817 496-7841
  Fort Worth *(G-7151)*

VACUUM CLEANER REPAIR SVCS

Chester R Wright III ....F 832 693-8038
  Friendswood *(G-7243)*

VACUUM CLEANER STORES

Aerus Holdings LLC ....F 214 378-4000
  Dallas *(G-3896)*

VACUUM CLEANERS: Household

Aerus LLC ....E 214 378-4000
  Dallas *(G-3897)*

Bissell Inc ....E 956 631-5077
  Mcallen *(G-14845)*

Flexaust Inc ....C 915 872-3100
  El Paso *(G-5770)*

Flightsafety International Inc ....C 817 571-5925
  Fort Worth *(G-6638)*

Scott Fetzer Company ....C 713 996-7331
  Houston *(G-11791)*

Scott Fetzer Company ....C 432 523-5511
  Andrews *(G-558)*

VACUUM CLEANERS: Indl Type

Overhead Door Corporation ....C 469 549-7100
Lewisville (G-14080)

VACUUM CLEANERS: Wholesalers

Bissell Inc ....E 956 631-5077
Mcallen (G-14845)
Tacony Corporation ....D 817 551-0700
Fort Worth (G-7030)

VACUUM SYSTEMS: Air Extraction, Indl

Sunbelt Vacuum Services Inc ....E 972 449-3830
Dallas (G-5023)
V&L Industrail Services Inc ....F 409 724-3336
Nederland (G-15761)
Wcsa Inc ....F 806 383-1060
Amarillo (G-473)

VALUE-ADDED RESELLERS: Computer Systems

Coda Global LLC ....E 844 366-8250
Southlake (G-19060)
I T Remarketing Inc ....E 713 263-8800
Houston (G-10309)

VALVE REPAIR SVCS, INDL

Calvary Valve Inc ....F 903 729-0485
Palestine (G-16297)
Cameron International Corp ....D 713 946-2122
Houston (G-9061)
Control Components Inc ....F 832 467-7200
Houston (G-9294)
Hoerbiger Service Inc ....E 281 442-2497
Houston (G-10191)
Marks Machine Co Inc ....F 979 543-9204
El Campo (G-5621)
McC Holdings Inc ....D 936 271-6500
The Woodlands (G-19893)
Premium Valve Services LLC ....F 281 457-2565
Houston (G-11406)
Samco Enterprises Inc ....E 281 443-6505
Houston (G-11737)
Texco Trim Inc ....D 713 861-1892
Houston (G-12259)
Valves and Control Systems Inc ....F 713 378-0311
South Houston (G-19054)
Wnco Valve International Inc ....F 432 362-2136
Odessa (G-16213)

VALVES

3-C Valve & Equipment LP ....F 281 361-3283
Corpus Christi (G-3462)
Atec Inc ....C 281 276-2700
Stafford (G-19289)
Bray International Inc ....F 281 517-5400
Houston (G-8978)
Broen Inc ....E 713 300-0480
Conroe (G-3265)
Chromatic Industries LLC ....F 936 539-5770
Conroe (G-3277)
Delta Valves and Controls LLC ....F 713 205-1904
Pasadena (G-16415)
Gvcc Inc ....G 281 416-4772
Pasadena (G-16451)
Jaks Machine Inc ....F 361 575-2312
Victoria (G-20276)
Ladish Valve Company LLC ....D 281 880-8560
Houston (G-10585)
Movement Industries Corp ....F 713 849-1300
Houston (G-10928)
Newco Valves LLC ....F 832 944-5930
Stafford (G-19358)
Nueces Valve Solutions LLC ....F 361 248-1700
Corpus Christi (G-3581)
Shf Inc ....C 832 456-2000
Pasadena (G-16506)
Tecnoval LLC ....F 956 782-1111
Mission (G-15566)
Tiger Valve Houston Co LLC ....F 281 227-9911
Houston (G-12291)

VALVES & PARTS: Gas, Indl

Drake Controls LLC ....F 713 996-0190
Houston (G-9515)
Fabco Products Inc ....E 903 769-3707
Hawkins (G-8229)

JI Bryan Eqp & Lease Svcs Inc ....E 806 435-4511
Perryton (G-16638)
S H Leggitt Company ....C 956 504-6440
San Marcos (G-18708)
Tfw Industrial Sup Cnc Mch LLC ....F 817 898-9140
Dallas (G-5081)

VALVES & PIPE FITTINGS

AAA Products International Inc ....F 214 357-3851
Dallas (G-3873)
Allbright & Associates Inc ....F 432 366-8897
Odessa (G-15909)
Ameriforge Group Inc ....E 409 283-8138
Woodville (G-20914)
Apergy Artfl Lift Intl LLC ....D 713 466-3552
Houston (G-8662)
Azz Inc ....D 817 810-0095
Fort Worth (G-6414)
Bay Advanced Technologies LLC ....E 512 929-5400
Austin (G-979)
Best Pump and Flow LP ....E 713 690-4511
Fort Worth (G-6448)
Boltex Manufacturing Co LP ....D 713 451-2180
Houston (G-8947)
Bonney Forge Corporation ....D 713 695-3633
Houston (G-8950)
Cameo Fabricators Inc ....E 281 449-6207
Houston (G-9060)
Cameron International Corp ....D 713 946-2122
Houston (G-9061)
Camozzi Pneumatics Inc ....E 972 548-8885
McKinney (G-14931)
Coastal Flange Inc ....E 713 937-3333
Jersey Village (G-13296)
Cse W-Industries Inc ....C 713 466-9463
Jersey Village (G-13297)
D/A Mfg Co Inc ....E 806 995-2316
Tulia (G-20034)
Dlugosch III LLC ....C 361 564-9504
Yorktown (G-20977)
Dlugosch III LLC ....F 361 275-9282
Cuero (G-3759)
Dresser LLC ....C 262 549-2626
Houston (G-9517)
Dynamic Products Inc ....D 281 457-3500
Houston (G-9550)
Emergent Machine Svcs Ltd Co ....F 903 876-3679
Frankston (G-7165)
Emerson Atmtn Sltons Fnal Ctrl ....B 713 986-4665
Houston (G-9612)
Emerson Automation Solutions ....G 512 835-2190
Round Rock (G-17653)
Federal Flange Inc ....D 713 681-0606
Houston (G-9768)
Federal Flange Inc ....C 713 681-0606
Houston (G-9769)
Fishing Tool/Crystin Inc ....E 432 366-6504
Odessa (G-16002)
Flow-Tek Inc ....D 832 912-2300
Houston (G-9809)
Flowserve Corporation ....E 832 375-0807
Houston (G-9813)
Flowserve Corporation ....B 972 443-6500
Irving (G-13027)
Flowserve Corporation ....F 800 446-0401
Irving (G-13028)
Forged Components Inc ....C 281 441-4088
Humble (G-12767)
Future Pipe Industries Inc ....C 281 847-2987
Houston (G-9879)
Grayloc Products LLC ....E 713 466-8853
Houston (G-10021)
Gulf Coast Oil & Gas Inds LLC ....D 713 236-1158
Houston (G-10061)
H and L Crimp Inc ....F 325 672-9282
Abilene (G-45)
H Lorimer Corporation ....E 903 643-3239
Longview (G-14245)
Ladish Valve Company LLC ....D 281 880-8560
Houston (G-10585)
M Fab & Machine ....F 936 264-2388
Conroe (G-3327)
Modco Industries Inc ....E 936 539-9222
Conroe (G-3331)
Motion Reps Inc ....E 940 565-9411
Denton (G-5383)
Mueller Co LLC ....C 956 621-3086
Brownsville (G-2384)
National Flange & Fitting Co ....E 713 688-2515
Houston (G-10968)

Newco Valves LLC ....D 281 325-0041
Stafford (G-19359)
Nibco Inc ....E 574 295-3000
McAllen (G-14894)
Nibco Inc ....B 936 564-8321
Nacogdoches (G-15706)
Nipples Elbows & Couplings Inc ....E 281 405-8240
Houston (G-11059)
Ohmstede Ltd ....C 281 471-4140
La Porte (G-13780)
Overhead Door Corporation ....B 361 884-6640
Corpus Christi (G-3586)
Pgi International Ltd ....B 713 466-0056
Houston (G-11316)
Piping Accessories Inc ....E 409 842-5000
Beaumont (G-1942)
Progressive Sales Inc ....E 432 333-6631
Odessa (G-16127)
Puffer-Sweiven Holdings Inc ....E 281 470-2000
La Porte (G-13785)
Ta Chen International Inc ....E 713 672-0177
Houston (G-12145)
Tapcoenpro International Inc ....C 281 247-8100
Channelview (G-3041)
Texas Pneumatic Systems Inc ....D 817 794-0068
Pantego (G-16353)
Texas Pneumatic Systems Inc ....F 817 794-0068
Arlington (G-792)
Tmco Inc ....D 713 465-3255
Houston (G-12308)
Townsend International Inc ....F 432 381-8750
Odessa (G-16181)
United Oilfield Supply LLC ....F 713 489-2000
Houston (G-12450)
US Bellows Inc ....B 713 731-0030
Houston (G-12481)
US Hose Corp ....F 281 458-0400
Houston (G-12483)
V I J Corporation ....E 817 838-2020
Fort Worth (G-7096)
Valco Instruments Company ....B 713 688-9345
Houston (G-12517)
VCM Industries Inc ....D 713 462-7444
Houston (G-12541)
Vector Group Inc ....F 713 979-4444
Houston (G-12542)
Watts Water Technologies Inc ....D 713 943-0688
Houston (G-12606)
Western Valve Inc ....F 806 373-6811
Amarillo (G-523)
Western Valve Inc ....F 806 373-6811
Amarillo (G-524)
Xomox Corporation ....C 936 271-6500
The Woodlands (G-19942)
Zimmermann & Jansen Inc ....D 281 446-8000
Houston (G-12730)

VALVES & REGULATORS: Pressure, Indl

Accumulators Inc ....E 713 465-0202
Houston (G-8460)
H & S Valve ....E 432 362-0486
Odessa (G-16021)
Nigen International LLC ....E 713 956-8022
Houston (G-11053)
Pentair Valves & Controls LLC ....B 713 986-4665
Houston (G-11286)
Samco Enterprises Inc ....E 281 443-6505
Houston (G-11737)
T-3 Energy Services Inc ....F 713 944-5950
Houston (G-12143)

VALVES Solenoid

Automatic Switch Company ....A 281 829-2900
Houston (G-8753)

VALVES: Aerosol, Metal

BCAD Zion Corporation ....F 210 657-9090
New Braunfels (G-15775)
Nailhead Spur Company Inc ....F 512 588-6112
Burnet (G-2613)
Trade-Mark Industrial LLC ....D 519 650-7444
San Antonio (G-18558)
Werner Co ....E 915 851-4933
Socorro (G-19020)

VALVES: Aircraft, Hydraulic

Dar International Inc ....F 972 402-0493
Irving (G-12991)

PRODUCT

VALVES: Control, Automatic

Array Holdings Inc ....E 281 260-8366
Houston (G-8704)

Fisher Controls Intl LLC ....B 972 542-5512
McKinney (G-14943)

Flowserve US Inc ....D 972 443-6500
Irving (G-13030)

Watts Water Technologies Inc ....D 713 943-0688
Houston (G-12606)

VALVES: Engine

H Lorimer Corporation ....E 903 643-3239
Longview (G-14245)

Wesco Valve & Manufacturing Co ....E 903 938-9241
Marshall (G-14808)

VALVES: Fluid Power, Control, Hydraulic & pneumatic

D/A Mfg Co Inc ....E 806 995-2316
Tulia (G-20034)

Fluid Sealing Products Inc ....D 713 910-1028
Houston (G-9816)

Hydraquip Custom Systems Inc ....F 281 822-5000
Houston (G-10296)

Pantex Ennerflo Systems Inc ....E 832 861-7700
Houston (G-8390)

Proserv Operations Inc ....B 832 467-3110
Houston (G-11457)

Scada Products LLC ....E 888 649-4283
Fort Worth (G-6975)

Tubular Instrumentat ....C 832 467-3110
Houston (G-12402)

Welker Inc ....D 281 491-2331
Sugar Land (G-19571)

Zimmermann & Jansen Inc ....D 281 446-8000
Houston (G-12730)

VALVES: Gas Cylinder, Compressed

Btic America Corporation ....F 713 779-8882
Houston (G-9003)

VALVES: Indl

AAA Products International Inc ....F 214 357-3851
Dallas (G-3873)

Apergy Artfl Lift Intl LLC ....D 713 466-3552
Houston (G-8662)

Barkley Holdings LLC ....F 832 413-4400
Kingwood (G-13639)

Bexxt Inc ....F 832 209-7970
Cypress (G-3778)

Bray International Inc ....C 281 894-7979
Houston (G-8979)

Broen Inc ....E 713 300-0480
Conroe (G-3265)

C&C Industries Inc ....F 832 631-2687
Houston (G-9038)

Calvary Valve Inc ....F 903 729-0485
Palestine (G-16297)

Cfg Industries LLC ....G 281 259-7244
Magnolia (G-14594)

Chromatic Industries Inc ....E 936 539-5770
Conroe (G-3276)

Circor Energy Products LLC ....C 713 400-2200
Houston (G-9194)

Collins Instrument Company ....E 979 849-8266
Angleton (G-569)

Curtiss-Wright Corporation ....F 713 581-3400
Houston (G-9361)

Daniel Measurement & Ctrl LLC ....B 713 827-5033
Houston (G-9402)

Downstream Aggregator LLC ....F 281 247-8118
Channelview (G-3017)

Dresser LLC ....C 262 549-2626
Houston (G-9517)

Dresser LLC ....E 361 881-8182
Corpus Christi (G-3517)

Dresser LLC ....D 281 884-1000
Deer Park (G-5271)

Dresser LLC ....F 979 265-1309
Richwood (G-17468)

DSA Operating Company LLC ....E 210 734-5121
San Antonio (G-18072)

Emerson Atmtn Sltons Fnal Ctrl ....D 832 261-2400
Pasadena (G-16424)

Emerson Atmtn Sltons Fnal Ctrl ....C 956 430-2500
Harlingen (G-8187)

Emerson Atmtn Sltons Fnal Ctrl ....B 713 986-4665
Houston (G-9612)

Emerson Automation Solutions ....D 832 261-2400
Pasadena (G-16425)

Emerson Automation Solutions ....E 281 274-4400
Stafford (G-19309)

Emerson Automation Solutions ....G 512 835-2190
Round Rock (G-17653)

Emerson Automation Solutions ....B 281 274-4400
Stafford (G-19310)

Energy Valve & Supply Co LLC ....F 713 675-7525
Houston (G-9638)

Everest Valve Company Inc ....E 713 923-8696
Houston (G-9717)

Flotek Industries Inc ....E 713 849-9911
Houston (G-9806)

Flowserve Corporation ....C 903 439-3324
Sulphur Springs (G-19587)

Flowserve Corporation ....B 972 443-6500
Irving (G-13027)

Flowserve Corporation ....F 800 446-0401
Irving (G-13028)

Flowserve Corporation ....E 832 375-0807
Houston (G-9813)

GE Oil & Gas Pressure Ctrl LP ....D 281 398-8901
Houston (G-9915)

Groth Corporation ....D 913 952-8114
Stafford (G-19324)

Hoerbiger Service Inc ....E 281 442-2497
Houston (G-10191)

Ies International Energy Svcs ....D 713 928-5311
Houston (G-10317)

Jetstream of Houston LLP ....D 832 590-1300
Houston (G-10471)

Keiser Manufacturing Inc ....G 830 303-3397
Seguin (G-18846)

Kf Valves LLC ....E 713 400-2200
Houston (G-10527)

Ladish Valve Company LLC ....D 281 880-8560
Houston (G-10585)

Marathon Special Services Inc ....F 713 784-4918
Houston (G-10757)

Master Valve USA Inc ....F 832 838-4999
Katy (G-13424)

McC Holdings Inc ....D 936 588-5301
Montgomery (G-15636)

McC Holdings Inc ....F 936 271-6500
The Woodlands (G-19893)

Microstaq Inc ....E 512 628-2890
Austin (G-1341)

Movement Industries Corp ....F 713 849-1300
Houston (G-10928)

MSP Drilex Inc ....E 281 377-4393
Tomball (G-19990)

National Oilwell Varco LP ....D 806 274-5293
Borger (G-2180)

Neway Valve Usa LP ....E 281 969-5500
Stafford (G-19357)

Nibco Inc ....B 936 564-8321
Nacogdoches (G-15706)

NSM Inc ....F 281 880-8188
Missouri City (G-15586)

Oil States International Inc ....D 713 652-0582
Houston (G-11161)

Pacific Valves ....D 562 426-2531
Spring (G-19239)

Pathway Control Products Inc ....F 281 354-3699
New Caney (G-15845)

Pbv-Usa Inc ....D 800 231-3530
Stafford (G-19363)

Petnair Valves & Controls ....E 713 986-8468
Houston (G-11297)

Pietro Fiorenpini ....F 832 299-6075
Spring (G-19240)

Rays Flow Control LLC ....F 832 827-3427
Houston (G-11554)

Robbins Myers Enrgy Systems LP ....B 936 890-1064
Willis (G-20862)

Roda Deaco Valve Inc ....E 780 465-4429
Houston (G-11654)

Rotork Controls Inc ....F 713 353-7887
Houston (G-11673)

Seaboard International Inc ....D 713 644-3535
Houston (G-11798)

Severe Service Valve Inc ....D 832 390-2380
Houston (G-11841)

Silverwell Technology Inc ....F 281 389-3020
Houston (G-11900)

Sooner Pipe LLC ....E 281 328-4877
Crosby (G-3743)

Specialty Valve Group LLC ....E 281 385-8200
Houston (G-12003)

Sturrock & Robson USA Svcs Inc ....F 281 907-8928
Flower Mound (G-6284)

Tapcoenpro LLC ....D 281 247-8100
Channelview (G-3040)

Tapcoenpro International Inc ....C 281 247-8100
Channelview (G-3041)

Tyco International MGT Co LLC ....F 713 644-8872
Houston (G-12419)

US VT ....E 713 856-9171
Houston (G-12491)

Valve Index International Inc ....E 281 712-8246
Missouri City (G-15598)

Victaulic-Bermad LLC ....E 713 856-1700
Houston (G-12565)

Vogt Valves Inc ....D 346 304-2566
Stafford (G-19396)

Wnco Valve International Inc ....F 432 362-2136
Odessa (G-16213)

Womack Machine Supply Co ....D 800 569-9800
Farmers Branch (G-6219)

VALVES: Plumbing & Heating

Consumer Energy Alliance ....F 713 337-8800
Houston (G-9279)

Daniel Industries Inc ....E 713 467-6000
Houston (G-9401)

Enercon Steam Solutions LLC ....F 214 292-3485
Dallas (G-4322)

VALVES: Regulating & Control, Automatic

Cameron International Corp ....D 281 582-9500
Houston (G-9064)

Cameron International Corp ....E 713 939-2282
Houston (G-9072)

Cameron International Corp ....C 713 354-1900
Houston (G-9068)

Cooper Valves LLC ....E 832 409-6050
Pasadena (G-16414)

Doosan Hf Controls Corporation ....E 469 568-6500
Carrollton (G-2726)

Eproduction Solutions LLC ....B 281 348-1000
Kingwood (G-13641)

M & J Valve Company ....C 281 469-0550
Houston (G-10713)

Omc Americas Inc ....E 713 893-7413
Houston (G-11173)

Onesubsea LLC ....A 713 939-2282
Houston (G-11182)

Tyco Engineered Pdts & Svcs ....D 609 720-4200
Houston (G-12418)

VALVES: Regulating, Process Control

Aeon Process Equipment ....D 972 690-8200
Plano (G-16776)

Control Components Inc ....F 832 467-7200
Houston (G-9294)

Flowserve Corporation ....D 713 374-7100
Pasadena (G-16438)

Gordon Martin Inc ....F 281 424-1301
Baytown (G-1820)

Proserv Operations Inc ....B 713 468-8778
Houston (G-11458)

Samson Controls Inc ....F 281 383-3677
Baytown (G-1800)

Valves and Control Systems Inc ....F 713 378-0311
South Houston (G-19054)

Xomox Corporation ....C 936 271-6500
The Woodlands (G-19942)

VALVES: Water Works

American Valve Hydrant Mfg Co ....F 409 832-7721
Beaumont (G-1852)

American Valve Hydrant Mfg Co ....C 409 832-7721
Beaumont (G-1853)

McWane Inc ....B 800 527-8478
Tyler (G-20122)

National Wholesale Supply Inc ....E 972 331-7770
Dallas (G-4716)

VAN CONVERSIONS

Wmk LLC ....F 817 429-1273
Haltom City (G-8162)

VARIETY STORE MERCHANDISE, WHOLESALE

Good Sportsman Marketing LLC .... E 877 269-8490
Irving (G-13040)

VARIETY STORES

Dipper Inc .... G 281 585-8400
Alvin (G-359)

VAULTS & SAFES WHOLESALERS

Defiant Safe Co Inc .... E 972 243-3711
Dallas (G-4248)
Hollon Safe Company LLC .... F 888 455-2337
Corpus Christi (G-3550)

VEHICLES: All Terrain

Dfr Acquisition Corporation .... E 480 834-4392
Fort Worth (G-6585)
Jro LLC .... F 903 472-0924
Marshall (G-14784)
Odes Industries LLC .... E 866 572-8420
Fort Worth (G-6875)
Rolligon Nov LP .... C 936 873-2600
Anderson (G-531)
Select Power Sport Inc .... F 936 967-2332
Livingston (G-14161)
Uv Country Inc .... E 713 649-0556
Alvin (G-385)

VEHICLES: Recreational

Kwest Rv LLC .... F 512 294-2634
Austin (G-1276)
Real Energy Solutions Inc .... F 713 864-9076
Houston (G-11563)
Regency Conversions Inc .... D 800 839-7551
Fort Worth (G-6953)
Rv Station Ltd .... E 979 778-8000
College Station (G-3200)
Sherrod Rv Center Inc .... F 409 385-5689
Silsbee (G-18955)

VENDING MACHINE OPERATORS: Candy & Snack Food

Nacogdoches Coca Cola Btlg Co ...... D 936 564-0268
Nacogdoches (G-15704)

VENDING MACHINE OPERATORS: Cold Drinks

Coca Cola Btlg of Shreveport .... C 214 902-2600
Dallas (G-4134)
Pepsi-Cola Btlg Crpus Chrsti V .... E 361 853-0123
Corpus Christi (G-3590)

VENDING MACHINE OPERATORS: Food

Texas Automatic Foods Inc .... E 713 432-1331
Bellaire (G-2003)

VENDING MACHINES & PARTS

Cactus Coin .... F 817 640-1791
Arlington (G-637)
Karatech Cnc Machining LLC .... F 281 337-1208
Dickinson (G-5476)
Karatech Machining LLC .... F 281 337-1208
Dickinson (G-5477)
Kaspar Wire Works Inc .... A 361 594-3327
Shiner (G-18944)
Mechanism Exchange & Repr Inc ..... E 361 293-6452
Yoakum (G-20968)
Sandenvendo America Inc .... B 800 344-7216
Dallas (G-4931)

VENETIAN BLINDS & SHADES

A & E Venetian Blind Company .... F 940 767-1449
Wichita Falls (G-20735)
Academy Venetian Blinds Co Inc ..... F 361 852-6088
Corpus Christi (G-3465)
Glenwood Blind & Awning Co Inc ..... G 903 597-2088
Tyler (G-20090)

VENTILATING EQPT: Metal

Admp LLC .... F 832 519-9746
Houston (G-8480)

Mc Daniel Metals Inc .... C 281 987-8400
Houston (G-10809)
Metroplex Sheet Metal Inc .... E 972 276-6736
Garland (G-7550)
PCI Industries Inc .... C 817 509-2300
Fort Worth (G-6898)
Ventilation Service Inc .... F 713 683-1003
Houston (G-12548)

VENTILATING EQPT: Sheet Metal

Builders Best Inc .... D 903 586-8283
Jacksonville (G-13230)
Moffitt West LLC .... F 903 463-5700
Denison (G-5342)
Selkirk Corporation .... B 972 943-6100
Richardson (G-17395)

VENTURE CAPITAL COMPANIES

Austin Ventures LP .... E 512 485-1900
Austin (G-963)
J Lewis Partners LP .... A 972 702-7390
Dallas (G-4519)
Tpg Capital Management LP .... B 817 871-4000
Fort Worth (G-7069)

VESSELS: Process, Indl, Metal Plate

A&A Machine & Fabrication LLC ...... D 409 938-4274
La Marque (G-13704)
Carbery Fabricators Company .... F 432 337-5015
Odessa (G-15955)
Techniek LLC .... E 832 618-7085
Houston (G-12174)

VETERINARY PHARMACEUTICAL PREPARATIONS

Alcon Manufacturing Ltd .... E 713 668-9100
Houston (G-8531)
Bioniche Animal Health USA Inc ...... F 706 549-4503
Fort Worth (G-6452)
Virbac Corporation .... C 800 338-3659
Westlake (G-20697)

VETERINARY PRDTS: Instruments & Apparatus

Tri Star Metals Inc .... E 940 433-2173
Boyd (G-2209)

VIBRATORS: Concrete Construction

Amber/Booth Inc .... D 713 466-0003
Houston (G-8577)
Houston Vibrator Ltd .... F 713 939-0404
Houston (G-10261)
Houston Vibrator MGT Inc .... F 713 939-0404
Houston (G-10262)

VIDEO & AUDIO EQPT, WHOLESALE

Creative Sound Productions .... F 713 777-9975
Houston (G-9340)
Pcs Telecom Inc .... F 281 469-3367
Pasadena (G-16494)

VIDEO TRIGGERS EXC REMOTE CONTROL TV DEVICES

Wigwag LLC .... F 512 814-6459
Austin (G-1665)

VINYL RESINS, NEC

Kuraray America Inc .... E 800 423-9762
Houston (G-10571)
OXY Vinyls LP .... F 877 699-8465
Dallas (G-4775)
OXY Vinyls LP .... E 281 476-2927
La Porte (G-13781)
OXY Vinyls LP .... F 281 884-4000
Pasadena (G-16492)
OXY Vinyls LP .... D 281 476-2640
Deer Park (G-5289)
Oxymar Inc .... C 361 776-6321
Ingleside (G-12899)

VISUAL COMMUNICATIONS SYSTEMS

Williamson Conference Center .... E 512 341-7000
Round Rock (G-17699)

VITAMINS: Natural Or Synthetic, Uncompounded, Bulk

Bluebonnet Nutraceutical Ltd .... E 281 340-0322
Sugar Land (G-19451)
Drucker Labs LP .... E 972 881-2344
Plano (G-16852)
Mother Earth Labs Inc .... G 210 695-3535
San Antonio (G-18321)
Nutrition Supply Corp .... F 936 334-0514
Liberty (G-14124)
Prosupps USA LLC .... D 214 310-1188
Frisco (G-7308)
Titan Environmental USA LLC .... E 713 849-1311
Houston (G-12297)

VITAMINS: Pharmaceutical Preparations

Mission Pharmacal Company .... D 210 696-8400
San Antonio (G-18312)
Premark Health Science Inc .... E 972 894-0020
Irving (G-13155)
Remington Health Products LLC ...... F 817 847-0606
Fort Worth (G-6954)
Scp International Inc .... F 817 326-0257
Cleveland (G-3135)
USA Millennium LP .... F 409 840-6801
Beaumont (G-1966)

VOCATIONAL REHABILITATION AGENCY

Lighthuse For The Blind Huston .... E 713 284-8420
Houston (G-10640)
San Antnio Lghthouse For Blind ...... C 210 533-5195
San Antonio (G-18444)

WALKWAYS: Moving

Hemco Industries Inc .... E 713 681-2426
Houston (G-10152)

WALL & CEILING SQUARES: Concrete

Murphy Wall Products Intl Inc .... E 713 694-8365
Houston (G-10943)

WALL COVERINGS WHOLESALERS

Patara Stone Inc .... E 713 681-2301
Houston (G-11257)

WALLBOARD: Gypsum

American Gypsum Company .... C 214 530-5500
Dallas (G-3943)
Eagle Materials Inc .... C 214 432-2000
Dallas (G-4292)
Georgia-Pacific Bldg Pdts LLC .... F 830 557-5802
Mc Queeney (G-14828)
Georgia-Pacific Bldg Pdts LLC .... F 830 997-4341
Fredericksburg (G-7181)
Ng Operations LLC .... D 325 735-2221
Rotan (G-17618)
United States Gypsum Company ...... C 713 308-5400
Galena Park (G-7385)

WALLPAPER STORE

Piw Ventures Ltd .... F 713 932-9311
Houston (G-11340)

WALLS: Curtain, Metal

Presidio Custom Metal Works .... F 512 284-8549
Round Rock (G-17682)

WAREHOUSING & STORAGE FACILITIES, NEC

Gruma Corporation .... D 832 441-5982
Houston (G-10050)
Paper Network Inc .... E 972 239-6567
Dallas (G-4786)
Power Repair Service Inc .... D 361 289-1471
Corpus Christi (G-3594)

WAREHOUSING & STORAGE, REFRIGERATED: Cold Storage Or Refrig

Cnc Fabrication and Maint .... F 817 295-9055
Burleson (G-2575)
Tex-Mex Cold Storage Inc .... C 956 831-4531
Brownsville (G-2409)

PRODUCT

WAREHOUSING & STORAGE, REFRIGERATED: Frozen Or Refrig Goods

Texas Pack Inc ....B 956 943-5461
  Port Isabel (G-17138)

WAREHOUSING & STORAGE: Bulk St & Termnls, Hire, Petro/Chem

Martin Midstream GP LLC ....A 903 983-6200
  Kilgore (G-13568)
Martin Midstream Partners LP ....D 903 983-6200
  Kilgore (G-13569)
Martin Midstream Partners LP ....F 281 471-2211
  La Porte (G-13774)

WAREHOUSING & STORAGE: General

Allen and Allen LLC ....F 210 733-9191
  San Antonio (G-17895)
Archrock Inc ....F 432 336-8632
  Fort Stockton (G-6328)
Bayou Processing & Storage LP ....E 713 450-8401
  Houston (G-8836)
Faro Services Inc ....F 214 631-1888
  Dallas (G-4352)
Fts International Services LLC ....F 817 334-0002
  Fort Worth (G-6654)
Fts International Services LLC ....C 817 862-2000
  Fort Worth (G-6655)
Ics Enterprises LLP ....B 915 239-9256
  El Paso (G-5808)
Johnson Controls Inc ....C 956 782-3000
  Mcallen (G-14881)
Kraft Heinz Company ....F 972 272-7511
  Garland (G-7534)
W&W-Afco Steel LLC ....C 806 765-5781
  Lubbock (G-14508)
Wareing Athon & Co ....B 713 222-8804
  Houston (G-12599)

WAREHOUSING & STORAGE: General

Aerostar Global Logistics LLC ....E 630 458-8844
  Irving (G-12925)
Affiliated Foods Inc ....C 806 372-3851
  Amarillo (G-476)
Ameripro Partnership LP ....F 713 526-3936
  Houston (G-8620)
Banyan Industries Inc ....E 817 413-7945
  Fort Worth (G-6426)
Cargo Crating Company Ltd ....F 713 699-0172
  Houston (G-9092)
Certified Pipe Svc Houston Inc ....E 281 457-2454
  Baytown (G-1812)
Fedex Sup Chain Lgstics Elec I ....A 817 491-7700
  Fort Worth (G-6626)
Galderma Laboratories LP ....C 817 961-5000
  Fort Worth (G-6659)
Kenneth Wyatt Galleries ....F 806 995-2239
  Tulia (G-20036)
L B Foster Company ....E 832 934-3107
  Magnolia (G-14613)
LMS Acquisitions LLC ....F 512 371-7028
  Austin (G-1296)
Marshall-Gruber Company LLC ....F 682 518-7400
  Mansfield (G-14688)
Mission Pharmacal Company ....E 210 696-8400
  San Antonio (G-18313)
Parker-Hannifin Corporation ....E 817 232-1040
  Saginaw (G-17754)
Pittsburg Steel LLC ....E 903 855-7515
  Pittsburg (G-16750)
Quaker Oats Company ....C 214 333-1200
  Dallas (G-4842)
Storage & Processors Inc ....D 832 360-2800
  Houston (G-12072)
Tacony Corporation ....D 817 551-0700
  Fort Worth (G-7030)
Third Coast Packaging Inc ....E 281 412-0275
  Pearland (G-16604)
True Value Company LLC ....C 903 872-8365
  Corsicana (G-3688)
Wilsonart LLC ....F 214 634-2310
  Dallas (G-5192)
Wincor Nixdorf Inc ....G 512 252-5622
  Manor (G-14651)

WAREHOUSING & STORAGE: Liquid

Capco Steel Inc ....E 210 493-9992
  San Antonio (G-17979)

Contanda LLC ....E 832 699-4001
  Houston (G-9281)

WAREHOUSING & STORAGE: Miniwarehouse

Greg Corkran Enterprises Inc ....E 409 720-9199
  Nederland (G-15753)
Philips North America LLC ....E 915 298-4111
  El Paso (G-5910)
Super Sack Bag Inc ....F 903 965-7713
  Savoy (G-18741)

WAREHOUSING & STORAGE: Self Storage

Interface Lgic Tech Dcmnttion ....F 713 446-3560
  Pearland (G-16570)

WARFARE COUNTER-MEASURE EQPT

Hydroscience Technologies Inc ....E 940 325-8221
  Mineral Wells (G-15529)
Lockheed Martin Corporation ....D 817 777-2000
  Benbrook (G-2042)
Lockheed Martin Corporation ....B 817 777-2000
  Fort Worth (G-6798)

WARM AIR HEATING & AC EQPT & SPLYS, WHOLESALE Air Filters

Jf Filtration Inc ....F 210 946-1688
  San Antonio (G-18201)
Jf Filtration Inc ....F 956 412-3234
  Harlingen (G-8192)
Jf Filtration Inc ....F 214 634-2200
  Dallas (G-4534)
Katch Filters LLC ....G 713 425-7400
  Houston (G-10501)

WARM AIR HEATING & AC EQPT & SPLYS, WHOLESALE Heat Exchgrs

Chem Fabrication LLC ....D 979 265-6600
  Clute (G-3149)
Ohmstede Ltd ....B 409 833-6375
  Beaumont (G-1935)

WARRANTY INSURANCE: Automobile

Indepndent Rugh Trrain Ctr LLC ....C 210 599-6541
  Cibolo (G-3063)

WASHERS: Metal

North Amrcn Sling Slutions LLC ....F 817 984-8000
  Fort Worth (G-6868)

WASHERS: Plastic

Marco Dsplay Specialists GP Lc ....C 817 244-8300
  Fort Worth (G-6810)
Select Plastics LLC ....E 817 595-3804
  Fort Worth (G-6982)

WATCHES & PARTS, WHOLESALE

Fossil Group Inc ....B 972 234-2525
  Richardson (G-17312)
Skagen Designs Ltd ....D 775 336-5667
  Dallas (G-4966)

WATER HEATERS

A O Smith Corporation ....E 915 400-2800
  El Paso (G-5634)

WATER PURIFICATION EQPT: Household

Flo Pura Corp ....E 281 320-9547
  Spring (G-19122)
National Wholesale Supply Inc ....E 972 331-7770
  Dallas (G-4716)
Pentair Rsdntial Fltration LLC ....F 936 525-2310
  Conroe (G-3347)
Tank Town LLC ....E 512 894-0861
  Austin (G-1555)
Unitra Inc ....E 281 240-1500
  Stafford (G-19393)

WATER PURIFICATION PRDTS: Chlorination Tablets & Kits

Dna Stat LLC ....F 469 500-1137
  Princeton (G-17208)
Topway Global Inc ....E 713 784-1808
  Houston (G-12322)

WATER SOFTENER SVCS

Altivia Corporation ....F 713 658-9000
  Houston (G-8571)

WATER SOFTENING WHOLESALERS

Culligan Southeast Texas Water ....E 409 838-6261
  Beaumont (G-1879)

WATER SPLY: Irrigation

H & H Landscape Services LLC ....F 832 831-9133
  Hockley (G-8346)
Larry & Matt Inc ....D 806 665-4418
  Pampa (G-16326)

WATER SUPPLY

East Texas Municpl Utility Dst ....F 903 877-3644
  Tyler (G-20080)
Global Water Group Inc ....E 214 678-9866
  Dallas (G-4410)
Lower Colorado River Authority ....A 512 473-3200
  Austin (G-1305)
Onyx Contractors Operations LP ....D 432 561-8900
  Midland (G-15328)
Rcw Energy Services LLC ....E 972 394-1000
  The Colony (G-19812)
Sabine River Authority Texas ....E 409 746-2192
  Orange (G-16261)

WATER TREATMENT EQPT: Indl

Advance Technology Products ....F 713 450-5990
  Houston (G-8484)
Alfa Laval US Holding Inc ....C 281 449-0322
  Houston (G-8536)
Apollo Separation Tech USA Inc ....E 281 233-9600
  Houston (G-8664)
Aquaneers Corp ....E 956 727-1250
  Laredo (G-13862)
Aquapharm Pchem LLC ....F 346 237-4300
  Latexo (G-13942)
Artesia Ecoscience LLC ....F 281 978-2521
  Houston (G-8710)
Baswood Inc ....E 888 560-5517
  Allen (G-257)
Bexter Enterprises LLC ....E 972 647-4700
  Grand Prairie (G-7846)
Bingham Manufacturing Inc ....G 360 863-1170
  Terrell (G-19728)
Bosque Disposal Systems LLC ....D 254 435-2260
  Fort Worth (G-6462)
Bosque Systems LLC ....D 817 289-9900
  Fort Worth (G-6463)
Chem-Aqua Inc ....E 972 438-0232
  Irving (G-12969)
Cite Corporation ....F 817 477-1549
  Mansfield (G-14663)
City of Bandera ....G 830 796-3401
  Bandera (G-1743)
City of Sherman ....E 903 892-7258
  Sherman (G-18909)
Cor Thermotics LLC ....F 832 308-5151
  Houston (G-9311)
De Nora Water Technologies LLC ......D 281 240-6770
  Sugar Land (G-19477)
Ecowater Industries LLC ....F 214 878-6527
  Port Arthur (G-17107)
El Paso Water Indus Svcs Inc ....F 915 849-0401
  El Paso (G-5746)
Excell Technologies Intl Corp ....D 281 240-6770
  Sugar Land (G-19482)
Exterran Energy Solutions LP ....C 281 836-7000
  Houston (G-9736)
Global Water Group Inc ....E 214 678-9866
  Dallas (G-4410)
Gracon Construction Inc ....D 972 222-8533
  Mesquite (G-15046)
H & L Fabrication Inc ....F 512 894-0918
  Dripping Springs (G-5506)
Inframark LLC ....F 281 579-4500
  Forney (G-6309)

Its Engineered Systems Inc ....D .:.. 281 371-8026
Katy *(G-13411)*

M3p Water Services LLC ....G 432 570-7500
Midland *(G-15290)*

Meco Inc ....E 281 276-7600
Sugar Land *(G-19507)*

Nap Industries LLC ....F 940 668-8111
Gainesville *(G-7352)*

Omni Water Solutions Inc ....E 512 275-0804
Austin *(G-1381)*

Originclear Inc ....F 323 939-6645
McKinney *(G-14960)*

Precision Water Tech Inc ....F 972 488-6755
Carrollton *(G-2793)*

Process Engineered Eqp Co ....E 361 289-8891
Corpus Christi *(G-3597)*

Rio Resources LLC ....E 830 438-4841
New Braunfels *(G-15820)*

See You At The Top Inc ....F 210 556-5452
San Antonio *(G-18464)*

Suez Wts Services Usa Inc ....F 214 339-2135
Dallas *(G-5018)*

Texas Air & Water LLC ....E 361 814-3131
Corpus Christi *(G-3636)*

Water Energy Technologies ....F 713 464-7117
Houston *(G-12601)*

Water Standard MGT US Inc ....E 713 400-4777
Houston *(G-12602)*

Water Std Spration Systems LLC ....F 713 433-7441
Houston *(G-12603)*

Wesco Chemicals Inc ....F 972 938-0913
Waxahachie *(G-20568)*

Wilson Environmental MGT Inc ....F 713 984-0800
Houston *(G-12672)*

Xedia Process Solutions LLC ....E 832 356-8347
Houston *(G-12706)*

WATER: Distilled

Drink A Pak Inc ....F 325 690-1550
Abilene *(G-38)*

Mountain Pure TX LLC ....E 903 723-1362
Palestine *(G-16304)*

Panda-Brandywine L P ....E 972 980-7159
Dallas *(G-4785)*

WATER: Mineral, Carbonated, Canned & Bottled, Etc

Ds Services of America Inc ....E 713 947-1900
Houston *(G-9533)*

One Water Source LLC ....F 512 347-9280
Lakeway *(G-13818)*

Water Event Gulf Coast LLC ....E 713 937-8630
Carrollton *(G-2846)*

Waterloo Sparkling Water Corp ....F 512 910-8990
Austin *(G-1649)*

WATER: Pasteurized & Mineral, Bottled & Canned

Culligan Southeast Texas Water ....E 409 838-6261
Beaumont *(G-1879)*

Drink A Pak Inc ....F 325 690-1550
Abilene *(G-38)*

Ds Services of America Inc ....E 281 391-3770
Katy *(G-13360)*

WATER: Pasteurized, Canned & Bottled, Etc

Apani Southwest Inc ....E 325 690-1550
Abilene *(G-13)*

C Treat Offshore Watermakers ....E 281 367-2800
The Woodlands *(G-19837)*

Essence Bottling Co Texas Inc ....F 806 993-1391
Lubbock *(G-14407)*

Impreso Inc ....D 972 462-0100
Coppell *(G-3421)*

Kristen Distributing Co ....E 979 775-6322
Bryan *(G-2489)*

Llanos Altos LLC ....F 806 934-4534
Dumas *(G-5524)*

Pepsi-Cola Btlg Crpus Chrsti V ....E 361 853-0123
Corpus Christi *(G-3590)*

Plains Dairy LLC ....A 806 374-0385
Amarillo *(G-455)*

Specktrum ....F 832 892-0863
Houston *(G-12004)*

Summit Springs Bottled Water ....G 559 277-1239
Richardson *(G-17403)*

Tst/Impreso Inc ....D 972 462-0100
Coppell *(G-3451)*

WATERPROOFING COMPOUNDS

American Polymers Corp ....F 817 684-7335
Bedford *(G-1973)*

Carlisle Ctngs Wtrproofing Inc ....D 972 442-6545
Wylie *(G-20929)*

Gardner-Gibson Incorporated ....F 832 288-4111
Houston *(G-9899)*

WAVEGUIDE STRUCTURES: Accelerating

Dunan Microstaq Inc ....F 512 628-2890
Austin *(G-1105)*

WAXES: Petroleum, Not Produced In Petroleum Refineries

Certispec Services Inc ....F 409 945-3338
Texas City *(G-19786)*

Juniper Specialty Products LLC ....F 346 310-6241
Pasadena *(G-16466)*

Trans-Mate LLC ....E 800 867-9274
Dallas *(G-5105)*

Trecora Chemical Inc ....D 281 474-7500
Pasadena *(G-16519)*

Trecora Resources ....E 281 980-5522
Sugar Land *(G-19568)*

WEATHER STRIPS: Metal

American Door Products Inc ....D 713 681-8047
Houston *(G-8594)*

WEIGHING MACHINERY & APPARATUS

Load Systems International ....D 281 664-1330
Houston *(G-10660)*

WELDING & CUTTING APPARATUS & ACCESS, NEC

Bowers Equipment Company Inc ....F 281 458-8891
Houston *(G-8962)*

Hangar Welding & Fabrication ....F 915 857-2899
El Paso *(G-5795)*

Higuchi Manufacturing Amer LLC ....C 210 633-2877
San Antonio *(G-18167)*

NCH Corporation ....A 972 438-0211
Irving *(G-13114)*

Victor Equipment Company ....A 940 566-2000
Denton *(G-5409)*

Victor Technologies Intl Inc ....D 940 381-1353
Denton *(G-5411)*

WELDING EQPT

Allied Wear Systems LLC ....F 972 248-8838
Dallas *(G-3837)*

Felux Metal Works & Supply LP ....G 830 484-3436
Poth *(G-17195)*

Stanco Manufacturing Inc ....D 903 796-7936
Atlanta *(G-845)*

Tri Tool Inc ....D 281 499-1188
Stafford *(G-19387)*

Trident Process Systems LLC ....F 940 372-1535
Gainesville *(G-7373)*

Victor Technologies Group Inc ....E 940 566-2000
Denton *(G-5410)*

WELDING EQPT & SPLYS WHOLESALERS

Airgas Usa LLC ....E 972 660-0500
Grand Prairie *(G-7825)*

Airgas Usa LLC ....E 281 474-8300
Pasadena *(G-16382)*

Airgas Usa LLC ....D 972 994-2400
Dallas *(G-3912)*

Airgas Usa LLC ....F 512 835-0202
Austin *(G-902)*

Bsco Inc ....F 817 568-0390
Fort Worth *(G-6475)*

Champion Industrial Sales Co ....G 713 921-7183
Houston *(G-9158)*

Dunn Enterprises Inc ....E 713 869-4841
Porter *(G-17174)*

J & L Partners ....E 972 417-3977
Dallas *(G-4516)*

Matheson Tri-Gas Inc ....G 361 887-0011
Corpus Christi *(G-3575)*

Matheson Tri-Gas Inc ....E 972 432-8800
Dallas *(G-4651)*

Matheson Tri-Gas Inc ....G 281 474-1291
Pasadena *(G-16481)*

Matheson Tri-Gas Inc ....C 972 560-5700
Irving *(G-13096)*

Matheson Tri-Gas Inc ....E 512 385-0611
Austin *(G-1330)*

Matheson Tri-Gas Inc ....E 281 498-2310
Stafford *(G-19352)*

Matheson Tri-Gas Inc ....E 210 225-3151
San Antonio *(G-18283)*

Matheson Tri-Gas Inc ....E 281 471-2544
Houston *(G-10794)*

Matheson Tri-Gas Inc ....F 817 354-9536
Dallas *(G-4652)*

Matheson Tri-Gas Inc ....F 817 551-0550
Fort Worth *(G-6817)*

McDonald Welding Co ....F 325 573-5329
Snyder *(G-18994)*

McMahan Welding Service Ltd ....F 361 275-0111
Cuero *(G-3763)*

Messer LLC ....E 903 626-4877
Jewett *(G-13307)*

Sturm Welding Inc ....F 940 686-2492
Pilot Point *(G-16730)*

WELDING EQPT & SPLYS: Electrodes

Bar H Welding LLC ....G 903 806-3110
Longview *(G-14200)*

ESAB Group Inc ....C 800 372-2123
Denton *(G-5365)*

RW Cox Inc ....E 903 739-8088
Paris *(G-16369)*

WELDING EQPT & SPLYS: Gas

Tpws Inc ....F 713 291-5518
Magnolia *(G-14632)*

WELDING EQPT & SPLYS: Resistance, Electric

Ken Garner Mfg - Vto Inc ....F 361 485-0541
Victoria *(G-20280)*

Petrohab Llc ....E 281 407-3800
Houston *(G-11302)*

WELDING EQPT & SPLYS: Wire, Bare & Coated

U S Alloy Co ....E 877 711-9274
Stafford *(G-19391)*

WELDING EQPT REPAIR SVCS

Advanced Machining & Tool Inc ....D 972 228-1987
Lancaster *(G-13836)*

Mitchell Manufacturing Inc ....E 281 351-9641
Tomball *(G-19989)*

Owens Mach & Manufacturing ....F 325 672-4161
Abilene *(G-62)*

Taylor Iron-Machine Works ....F 512 365-3646
Taylor *(G-19663)*

WELDING EQPT: Electric

Dyna Torque Technologies Inc ....F 713 937-6699
Houston *(G-9543)*

Magnetrode Corporation ....E 903 795-3378
Jacksonville *(G-13249)*

Peerless Mfg Co ....E 940 566-9029
Denton *(G-5390)*

Praxair Surface Tech Inc ....E 713 849-9474
Houston *(G-11384)*

Tsi Flow Products Inc ....F 903 984-2870
Kilgore *(G-13597)*

WELDING EQPT: Electrical

Bsco Inc ....F 817 568-0390
Fort Worth *(G-6475)*

Champion Industrial Sales Co ....G 713 921-7183
Houston *(G-9158)*

Imfab Inc ....E 903 577-0510
Mount Pleasant *(G-15651)*

WELDING MACHINES & EQPT: Ultrasonic

CRC-Evans Pipeline Intl Inc ....C 800 664-9224
Houston *(G-9337)*

PRODUCT

WELDING REPAIR SVC

A & A Welding Inc ....F 817 910-9700
  Granbury *(G-7791)*

A & D Cstm Wldg & Fabrication ....F 210 310-7610
  San Antonio *(G-17846)*

A & M Machine & Wldg Works Inc ....G 281 421-1281
  Baytown *(G-1806)*

A & W Welding Inc ....G..... 281 499-4332
  Stafford *(G-19279)*

A&K Industrial Repair LLC ....E 281 470-8848
  Deer Park *(G-5258)*

Accuweld Inc ....E 281 442-5900
  Houston *(G-8465)*

Advanced Metal Fusion Inc ....F 512 422-0888
  Cedar Park *(G-2959)*

Advanced Welding Services Inc ....F 713 933-2626
  Houston *(G-8493)*

Advanced Welding Solutions LLC ....E 713 473-0099
  League City *(G-13944)*

Aggietech Energy Services LLC ....E 806 229-6129
  Sundown *(G-19610)*

Alamo Welding & Boiler Work ....F 210 227-6502
  San Antonio *(G-17888)*

Alexanders Mch Maint Svc Inc ....E 817 625-4175
  Fort Worth *(G-6369)*

Allbright & Associates Inc ....F 432 366-8897
  Odessa *(G-15909)*

Als Inc ....F 361 325-2154
  Falfurrias *(G-6181)*

American Welding Services ....E 409 440-8143
  Hitchcock *(G-8333)*

American Wldg Fabrication Inc ....E 210 661-4159
  San Antonio *(G-17905)*

Anchor Machine Works Inc ....F 713 988-0400
  Houston *(G-8640)*

Apache Instrumentations & Gas ....E 432 336-7755
  Fort Stockton *(G-6327)*

Aranda Ironworks Inc ....F 956 722-5084
  Laredo *(G-13863)*

ARC Rite Welding & Fabrication ....E 830 774-6058
  Del Rio *(G-5305)*

Asi Piping LLC ....E 409 786-1080
  Vidor *(G-20324)*

Associated Welding Supply Inc ....F 281 485-2755
  Pearland *(G-16540)*

B & J Welding Supply Ltd ....F 432 563-1277
  Midland *(G-15126)*

Ballew Casting Repair Inc ....F 361 882-9901
  Corpus Christi *(G-3481)*

Bay Area Industrial Contrs LP ....C 281 471-0400
  La Porte *(G-13725)*

BCAD Zion Corporation ....F 210 657-9090
  New Braunfels *(G-15775)*

Berry Machine Shop ....E 817 572-0948
  Burleson *(G-2571)*

Big State Welding & Machine Lc ....F 940 766-0191
  Wichita Falls *(G-20745)*

Bill Gilmore Welding Inc ....E 940 592-4945
  Iowa Park *(G-12903)*

Bise Welding & Fabricating Inc ....D 713 681-0958
  Houston *(G-8892)*

Blackburn Machine & Fab LLC ....E 713 644-2386
  Houston *(G-8910)*

Blade Runner Turbomachinery SE ......E 713 669-1155
  Navasota *(G-15726)*

Brave Services Incorporated ....E 432 355-4001
  Andrews *(G-541)*

Browns Welding & Manufacturing ....F 830 625-8712
  New Braunfels *(G-15776)*

Burns Welding Works Inc ....F 432 682-0495
  Midland *(G-15153)*

Bwm Services LP ....E 979 272-7708
  Caldwell *(G-2629)*

C&C Welding ....G..... 903 436-9150
  Bells *(G-2005)*

C&J Cladding LLC ....E 281 987-2383
  Houston *(G-9039)*

Cains Welding Service Inc ....E 281 303-9517
  Mont Belvieu *(G-15616)*

CC Coating & Machine Inc ....E 361 884-9753
  Corpus Christi *(G-3497)*

Cessac Welding Service Inc ....F 979 828-9067
  Franklin *(G-7164)*

Chaparral Wldg Fabrication Inc ....E 972 243-7747
  Dallas *(G-4104)*

Chapman Dock Inc ....E 325 388-6545
  Kingsland *(G-13621)*

Cherokee Welding Inc ....F 512 243-0002
  Austin *(G-1047)*

Chris Burns Welding LLC ....G..... 940 845-4945
  Sunset *(G-19624)*

Chriss Welding & Fabricating ....F 409 986-6094
  Hitchcock *(G-8335)*

Circle M Welding & Svcs Inc ....D 325 573-8005
  Snyder *(G-18987)*

City Machine & Welding Inc ....E 806 358-7293
  Amarillo *(G-416)*

Cns Tech Wldg & Fabrication Lc ....E 281 239-2555
  Humble *(G-12760)*

Coleman Machine & Welding Svc ....F 325 625-5186
  Coleman *(G-3169)*

Colliers Top of Texas Inc ....E 806 363-2867
  Hereford *(G-8287)*

Crisp Industries Inc ....D 830 372-1110
  Seguin *(G-18834)*

Crumplers Mch & Wldg Svc Inc ....E 409 886-7934
  Bridge City *(G-2282)*

Curtis Oilfield Services LLC ....E 409 385-2937
  Silsbee *(G-18952)*

Custom Heliarc Inc ....F 281 375-2075
  Brookshire *(G-2314)*

D & R Specialties Inc ....E 936 873-2947
  Navasota *(G-15728)*

D&R Steel Works Inc ....F 210 639-8314
  Castroville *(G-2927)*

Daltons Welding Service Inc ....F 940 682-7237
  Weatherford *(G-20586)*

Data Matique Properties LP ....C 972 272-3446
  Garland *(G-7476)*

Delray Machine LLC ....F 830 693-5110
  Marble Falls *(G-14742)*

Die & Tool Service Inc ....E 281 498-3317
  Sugar Land *(G-19479)*

Diversified Machining Inc ....F 512 355-3270
  Bertram *(G-2052)*

Duane Ollinger ....E 806 935-6786
  Dumas *(G-5520)*

E X P Fabrication LLC ....E 940 453-3382
  Justin *(G-13342)*

East Texas Machine Works Inc ....D 903 759-9796
  Longview *(G-14227)*

Ebling Welding LLC ....E 830 905-7235
  Canyon Lake *(G-2679)*

Edward Bloch Ltd ....F 210 648-6011
  San Antonio *(G-18083)*

El Paso Tool & Die Co Inc ....E 915 591-0346
  El Paso *(G-5744)*

Eldred Sheet Metal Works LP ....E 713 227-3251
  Houston *(G-9588)*

Elite Specialty Welding LLC ....D 832 649-4251
  Pasadena *(G-16423)*

Empire Wldg & Fabrication LLC ....F 915 706-4070
  El Paso *(G-5755)*

Energy Fabrication Inc ....E 432 362-0591
  Odessa *(G-15990)*

Ernies Welding Shop Inc ....E 512 459-6346
  Austin *(G-1137)*

F & R Machine Services Inc ....E 214 631-4946
  Dallas *(G-4350)*

Fab Tex Oilfield Services Inc ....D 432 339-1011
  Odessa *(G-15998)*

Fabricating Solutions ....F 409 735-7141
  Bridge City *(G-2283)*

Fife Services Inc ....E 432 827-3601
  Goldsmith *(G-7742)*

Forge Tech Inc ....G..... 888 854-8414
  Kemah *(G-13474)*

Franklin Welding Service Inc ....E 361 592-1322
  Kingsville *(G-13627)*

Freer Iron Works Inc ....E 361 394-7273
  Freer *(G-7225)*

G W Vines Company Inc ....E 214 742-8371
  Dallas *(G-4389)*

Genes Machine Inc ....D 361 573-7146
  Victoria *(G-20267)*

Gibbons Inc ....F 940 872-2452
  Bowie *(G-2196)*

Global Welding Services Inc ....D 713 991-3555
  Houston *(G-9980)*

Grazco LLC ....F 281 252-0151
  Houston *(G-10023)*

Green Machine & Tool Inc ....E 713 943-0402
  South Houston *(G-19041)*

Gulf Copper & Mfg Corp ....C 409 982-6122
  Port Arthur *(G-17112)*

H M W Fabrications Inc ....F 940 325-0300
  Mineral Wells *(G-15527)*

H&A Machine & Welding LLC ....F 832 857-8505
  Houston *(G-10086)*

Harrison Fabricators Inc ....F 214 374-1684
  Dallas *(G-4438)*

Hefco Enterprises Inc ....E 281 431-1571
  Fresno *(G-7238)*

Herrin Welding Service Inc ....F 903 984-7139
  Kilgore *(G-13558)*

Houston Fab Truck Rigging RPS ....E 713 455-6161
  Houston *(G-10233)*

Hub Machine & Tool Inc ....E 940 549-0155
  Graham *(G-7784)*

Industrial Pro Fab LLC ....G..... 713 205-7245
  Katy *(G-13409)*

Industrial Spclty Svcs USA LLC ....F 713 987-9117
  Deer Park *(G-5280)*

Industrial Welding Academy ....F 713 944-0701
  Houston *(G-10356)*

International Plant Svcs LLC ....B 281 867-8400
  La Porte *(G-13755)*

J & E Welding Inc ....F 409 794-2311
  Beaumont *(G-1911)*

J B R Enterprises Inc ....G..... 972 542-3939
  McKinney *(G-14947)*

J&J Welding & Awning ....F 214 227-5606
  Garland *(G-7524)*

Jac Enterprises Inc ....F 936 348-3934
  Madisonville *(G-14588)*

Jack Phipps ....F 972 278-3186
  Dallas *(G-4520)*

Jalem Welding Service LLC ....F 956 467-2355
  McAllen *(G-14876)*

James Puryear Weldng Fabrctn ....F 325 672-2009
  Abilene *(G-54)*

Jefes Welding Company ....F 903 389-4036
  Fairfield *(G-6177)*

Jerryco Mch & Boiler Works LP ....D 713 224-7900
  Houston *(G-10466)*

Johnson Tool Company Inc ....E 432 267-7612
  Big Spring *(G-2084)*

Johnston Products Dallas Inc ....E 469 272-7212
  Cedar Hill *(G-2946)*

Jones Manufacturing Inc ....F 254 399-8940
  Waco *(G-20420)*

Judys Iron & Metal Inc ....E 409 681-0500
  Vidor *(G-20328)*

JV Industrial Companies Ltd ....F 903 579-8900
  Tyler *(G-20105)*

JV Industrial Companies Ltd ....F 281 417-7019
  La Porte *(G-13759)*

JV Industrial Companies Ltd ....D 713 568-2600
  San Antonio *(G-18213)*

Kennedy Machine & Mfg Inc ....E 972 241-7610
  Haslet *(G-8219)*

Kiger Bros Mch Tl & Die Works ....E 281 447-1315
  Houston *(G-10532)*

Knighten Machine and Svc Inc ....E 877 457-7204
  Odessa *(G-16055)*

Kobelco Welding of America ....G..... 281 240-5600
  Stafford *(G-19341)*

Lake Road Welding Co ....E 940 692-4988
  Wichita Falls *(G-20778)*

Lake Services Inc ....F 512 261-3625
  Lakeway *(G-13817)*

Landry Corporation ....F 281 449-1052
  Houston *(G-10596)*

Laser Welding Solutions LLC ....F 713 895-0800
  Houston *(G-10605)*

Ledsome Machine & Welding Co ....F 325 646-4691
  Brownwood *(G-2434)*

Lonestar Fencing and Wldg LLC ....G..... 210 992-0441
  San Antonio *(G-18264)*

Lons Welding ....E 806 435-2278
  Perryton *(G-16639)*

Luttrell Welding Services ....E 940 433-3131
  Boyd *(G-2206)*

Lwf Services LLC ....F 432 425-9795
  Odessa *(G-16066)*

M & S Mechanical Inc ....E 318 755-2431
  Pittsburg *(G-16747)*

M R Fabrication ....G..... 940 427-4701
  Alvord *(G-388)*

Magee Machine and Mfg Inc ....F 972 285-2554
  Mesquite *(G-15060)*

Mainliners Welding Academy ....F 409 229-1632
  La Porte *(G-13773)*

Manufctred Component Parts Ltd ....E 713 880-0590
  Houston *(G-10749)*

Martels Machine Shop ....G..... 432 333-4556
  Odessa *(G-16071)*

Maxie Hodges ....G..... 432 333-4556
  Odessa *(G-16074)*

McDonald Welding Co ....F 325 573-5329
Snyder *(G-18994)*
McMahan Welding Service Ltd ....F 361 275-0111
Cuero *(G-3763)*
Mepco Enterprises Inc ....E 713 943-9240
Houston *(G-10830)*
Merritt Prfrred Components Inc ....D 903 983-1592
Kilgore *(G-13574)*
Midwest Fab & Construction Inc ......F 806 335-9126
Amarillo *(G-446)*
Midwest Machine LLC ....E 806 355-9400
Amarillo *(G-501)*
Miller Machine & Welding LLC ....E 254 582-2185
Whitney *(G-20731)*
Modisette Welding & Supply ....E 903 984-2502
Kilgore *(G-13575)*
Montgomery Machine Company Inc ....D 713 453-6381
Houston *(G-10914)*
N & N Services LLC ....F 281 741-9714
Pearland *(G-16584)*
Northast Txas McHning Wldg Hrd .....F 903 427-2277
Clarksville *(G-3076)*
Ober & Sons Inc ....E 281 879-6760
Houston *(G-11112)*
Omni Contracting ....F 972 890-4536
Midlothian *(G-15489)*
One Source Mfg Tech LLC ....D 512 259-3272
Leander *(G-13996)*
Pampa Machine & Supply Inc ....F 806 665-0013
Pampa *(G-16332)*
Panyanouvong Jose & Le Malysa ......F 310 279-7065
Fort Worth *(G-6892)*
Phillips Fabrication Inc ....F 432 264-6600
Big Spring *(G-2093)*
Pick Instrument Products Co ....E 713 672-1686
Galena Park *(G-7381)*
Platts Welding and Cnstr LLC ....F 972 333-5830
Denison *(G-5345)*
Precision Iron Fabrication LLC ....F 972 636-7581
Royse City *(G-17723)*
Precision M/C Products Inc ....F 972 429-6200
Wylie *(G-20944)*
Premium Welding Inc ....F 713 957-2724
Houston *(G-11407)*
Premium Welding & Mfg Inc ....D 713 957-2724
Houston *(G-11408)*
Professional Machine Works ....F 713 645-7562
Houston *(G-11438)*
Pwf Enterprises ....F 512 295-6412
Buda *(G-2534)*
R & N Manufacturing Ltd ....D 713 466-6252
Cypress *(G-3817)*
R & R Sheet Metal and Mch Sp ....F 806 274-2361
Borger *(G-2183)*
R C Technical Welding & Fabr ....E 281 933-6004
Stafford *(G-19367)*
R R Ramsower Inc ....E 979 849-6441
Angleton *(G-576)*
Radke Machine & Tool Inc ....E 254 576-2513
Hubbard *(G-12737)*
Randco Industries Inc ....E 432 520-0820
Midland *(G-15377)*
Ratec Inc ....F 903 687-3811
Waskom *(G-20520)*
RE Campbell Company Ltd ....E 713 957-8721
Houston *(G-11558)*
Reama Inc ....F 409 744-9222
Galveston *(G-7407)*
Redding Machine Shop Inc ....F 940 691-5218
Wichita Falls *(G-20802)*
Riggs Machine and Welding Inc ....F 254 965-3910
Stephenville *(G-19420)*
Road Runner Service Point ....E ...... 713 675-5`10
Houston *(G-11640)*
Robert Early Welding ....E 325 573-0029
Snyder *(G-19004)*
Robotic Welding Solutions LLC ....G 281 706-5967
Conroe *(G-3359)*
Ronald L Jordan Company ....E 281 485-6626
Pearland *(G-16597)*
Rosado Welding Inc ....F 469 730-2222
Dallas *(G-4910)*
Rotom Inc ....E 806 293-7331
Plainview *(G-16762)*
Rp Welding Inc ....F 940 315-1024
Crossroads *(G-3749)*
Rs Welding LLC ....F 940 488-4144
Pilot Point *(G-16728)*
Rudd Welding Inc ....F 806 435-5501
Perryton *(G-16648)*

Santin Auto and Truck Repr Ctr ....E 210 648-4100
San Antonio *(G-18454)*
Saulsbury Industries Inc ....E 903 392-2248
Henderson *(G-8273)*
Scientific Machine & Wldg Inc ....E 512 926-8400
Austin *(G-1490)*
Second Gnration ARC Spark Wldg ......E 979 778-1999
Bryan *(G-2507)*
Septh Group LLC ....E 713 988-4200
Houston *(G-11832)*
Sharp Iron Group LLC ....E 940 855-2710
Wichita Falls *(G-20809)*
Sharp Iron Group LLC ....D 940 766-4545
Wichita Falls *(G-20810)*
Snoe Inc Machining & Welding ....E 979 567-0808
Caldwell *(G-2636)*
Southern Welding LLC ....F 469 517-0410
Waxahachie *(G-20561)*
Spillar Welding Inc ....E 512 264-0351
Spicewood *(G-19095)*
Starks Welding & Mfg Svcs Inc ....E 512 863-2424
Georgetown *(G-7681)*
Sturm Welding Inc ....F 940 686-2492
Pilot Point *(G-16730)*
Sullivan Welding Inc ....F 512 259-3440
Leander *(G-13997)*
Sulzer Pump Services (us) Inc ....F 432 614-2574
Odessa *(G-16168)*
Superior Welding Inc ....F 432 523-2038
Andrews *(G-559)*
Sweetwater Machine and Welding ......E 325 235-2922
Sweetwater *(G-19637)*
T L Precision Welding Inc ....F 713 896-4500
Houston *(G-12142)*
T O F Enterprises Inc ....F 281 328-2553
Crosby *(G-3744)*
Taurus Industrial Group LLC ....E 713 554-0157
La Porte *(G-13793)*
Tcw Investments Inc ....F 409 796-1883
Beaumont *(G-1956)*
Temples Trailer Sales Inc ....F 903 885-7301
Sulphur Springs *(G-19602)*
Texas Stud Welding LLC ....G 210 300-2500
Somerset *(G-19021)*
Texweld & Fabrication Inc ....G 903 586-1775
Jacksonville *(G-13265)*
Thompson Welding ....G 432 381-1531
Odessa *(G-16178)*
Tietjen Inc ....E 979 249-3888
La Grange *(G-13703)*
Titanium Welding Services LLC ....F 281 380-7043
Houston *(G-12301)*
Tlr Welding & Fabricating Inc ....F 940 969-2400
Paradise *(G-16356)*
Tombstone Welding ....F 325 573-8446
Snyder *(G-19012)*
Top Deck Inc ....E 409 745-3955
Orange *(G-16265)*
Trevino Industries Inc ....F 281 489-1754
Pearland *(G-16605)*
Trevinos Welding ....F 806 250-3669
Friona *(G-7254)*
Tri-Construction Co Inc ....C 979 233-7211
Freeport *(G-7217)*
Trinity Casting Service Inc ....F 214 631-4248
Dallas *(G-5111)*
Trinity Services Group Inc ....C 903 277-7128
Texarkana *(G-19781)*
Triple C Industries Inc ....E 936 931-1171
Hockley *(G-8349)*
Triple S Welding Co ....F 210 464-2878
Lytle *(G-14574)*
TW Tanks and Construction Co ....F 361 358-8869
Beeville *(G-1989)*
TX Tinman Enterprises LLC ....F..., 817 288-6116
Fort Worth *(G-7087)*
Txtb Tech Llc ....F 832 928-5740
Montgomery *(G-15644)*
UNI-Fab LLC ....F 936 344-2800
Willis *(G-20867)*
Universal Management Svcs LLC ....F 979 481-5711
Angleton *(G-581)*
Vales Welding Service ....F 936 336-5148
Liberty *(G-14126)*
Varco Shaffer Inc ....E 713 672-1711
Houston *(G-12535)*
Vinyard Water Service ....F 806 256-2766
Shamrock *(G-18893)*
Vmg Welding ....F 832 605-3933
Houston *(G-12579)*

Walsh Welding Inc ....F 325 387-2357
Sonora *(G-19032)*
Welasco Inc ....F 903 784-5562
Paris *(G-16374)*
Weld Revolution LLC ....F 832 585-1244
Spring *(G-19187)*
Weldfit Corporation ....C 713 460-3700
Houston *(G-12628)*
Welding Material Sales Inc ....F 713 672-4166
Houston *(G-12629)*
Welding Works Intl Inc ....F 956 838-5636
Brownsville *(G-2421)*
Welfab Inc ....E 361 552-4033
Port Lavaca *(G-17156)*
West Machine & Tool Inc ....F 903 758-5401
Longview *(G-14335)*
Whm Custom Services Inc ....D 254 854-2111
Grandview *(G-8003)*
Williams Alloy & Welding ....G 713 896-9096
Houston *(G-12668)*
Winnie Wldg Works & Cnstr Inc ....E 409 296-2953
Winnie *(G-20894)*
Wldg Wilkerson & Fabrication ....F 817 528-1032
Overton *(G-16277)*
Wwl Industries Inc ....E 432 362-0326
Odessa *(G-16215)*
Zachry Holdings Inc ....F 210 588-5000
San Antonio *(G-18632)*

WELDING SPLYS, EXC GASES: Wholesalers

A & E Machine Shop Inc ....E 903 656-3485
Lone Star *(G-14180)*
Airgas Usa LLC ....F 361 533-0758
Corpus Christi *(G-3469)*

WELDING TIPS: Heat Resistant, Metal

Team Fabricators LLC ....D 409 962-0266
Port Arthur *(G-17128)*

WELL LOGGING EQPT

Joy Glbal Lngview Oprtions LLC ....A 903 237-7000
Longview *(G-14257)*
Permian Basin Instruments Inc ....E 432 687-4445
Denton *(G-5392)*
Step Energy Svcs Holdings Ltd ....F 918 423-4300
San Antonio *(G-18501)*

WELL SURVEYING EQPT

Kestran Inc ....E 281 276-2700
Stafford *(G-19340)*
Universal Well Svc Holdings ....C 325 573-6209
Snyder *(G-19013)*

WESTERN APPAREL STORES

C & C Western Wear Inc ....F 903 753-8991
Longview *(G-14206)*
Calvin Allen Saddlery ....F 817 598-0505
Weatherford *(G-20581)*
Franklin-Leddy Corporation ....D 817 624-3149
Fort Worth *(G-6648)*
Tucker Saddlery Inc ....E 361 293-3501
Yoakum *(G-20974)*

WHEEL BALANCING EQPT: Automotive

F & F Industries Inc.......................E 800 523-8473
Alvarado *(G-331)*

WHEELCHAIR LIFTS

Open Road Mobility LLC ....F 806 866-0275
Lubbock *(G-14452)*
Thyssenkrupp Elevator Corp ....E 817 922-9590
Fort Worth *(G-7062)*
Thyssenkrupp Elevator Corp ....F 512 486-1000
Austin *(G-1578)*
Wmk LLC ....F 817 429-1273
Haltom City *(G-8162)*

WHEELCHAIRS

Freedom Wheels Inc ....F 713 864-1460
Houston *(G-9860)*
Integhrty Whlchair Van Svc LLC ....F 972 224-7017
Desoto *(G-5434)*
Wheel Rack ....F 210 342-0333
San Antonio *(G-18616)*

WHEELS

Wheels America Alloy Wheel ....E 214 330-9866
Dallas *(G-5185)*

WHEELS: Abrasive

Hudson Abrasive Company ....F 713 977-0037
Houston *(G-10276)*

WHIRLPOOL BATHS: Hydrotherapy

Maple Industries LLC ....F 972 745-2283
Irving *(G-13094)*
Royal Baths Manufacturing Co.............B 281 442-3400
Houston *(G-11682)*
Royal Baths Mfg Co Ltd ....E 817 589-7300
Richland Hills *(G-17447)*

WICKER PRDTS

Wingate Partners LP ....F 214 720-1313
Dallas *(G-5195)*

WINCHES

Pierce Arrow Inc..................................F 940 538-5643
Henrietta *(G-8282)*
Ram Winch and Hoist Ltd ....E 281 999-8665
Houston *(G-11536)*
Rki Inc ....B 713 688-4414
Houston *(G-11634)*
Trane Technologies Company LLC ....E 903 730-4000
Tyler *(G-20163)*

WINDINGS: Coil, Electronic

Specialty Coils LLC ....E 903 212-2645
Longview *(G-14310)*

WINDMILLS: Electric Power Generation

Arcosa Wind Towers Inc ....G 817 378-3700
Fort Worth *(G-6398)*
Gestamp Wind Energy N Amer Inc ....F 713 263-8166
Houston *(G-9946)*
One Wind Services (us) Inc ....F 902 482-8687
San Benito *(G-18662)*
Wilderado Wind LLC ....F 806 267-0746
Vega *(G-20216)*

WINDMILLS: Farm Type

Aermotor Company ....E 325 651-4951
San Angelo *(G-17771)*
American West Windmill Co ....F 806 373-0478
Amarillo *(G-399)*
Gicon Pumps & Equipment Ltd ....G 806 373-0478
Amarillo *(G-428)*

WINDOW & DOOR FRAMES

Alenco Holding Corporation ....B 979 779-1051
Bryan *(G-2453)*
Allmetal Inc..E 972 245-9264
Carrollton *(G-2855)*
Atrium Windows and Doors Inc............D 214 583-1840
Dallas *(G-3983)*
Cerda-Fied Specialists Inc ....F 281 392-8063
Brookshire *(G-2313)*
Columbia Coml Bldg Pdts Acqsti ....D 800 668-1645
Rockwall *(G-17544)*
General Aluminum Co Texas LP ....C 972 242-5271
Flower Mound *(G-6266)*
Glass Samuels Company LLC ....D 210 227-2481
San Antonio *(G-18142)*
Pearland Industries Inc ....D 713 434-9898
Houston *(G-8391)*
Premex Door Supply Inc ....F 214 341-2212
Garland *(G-7572)*
Ram Indstries Acquisitions LLC............D 281 495-9056
Houston *(G-11535)*
Rehme Custom Doors & Ltg Inc ....E 512 916-0511
Spicewood *(G-19093)*
Safe-T-Pet Inc ....F 903 569-0590
Mineola *(G-15511)*
Steves & Sons Inc ....B 210 921-1400
San Antonio *(G-18505)*

WINDOW BLIND REPAIR SVCS

Ybarra Group Inc.................................F 210 533-5323
San Antonio *(G-18629)*

WINDOW CLEANING SVCS

Allstar Door & Maintenance LP ....F 817 748-0667
Colleyville *(G-3210)*

WINDOW FRAMES & SASHES: Plastic

Mike Strand..F 940 482-3426
Krum *(G-13675)*

WINDOW FRAMES, MOLDING & TRIM: Vinyl

Atrium Windows and Doors Inc............D 214 583-1840
Dallas *(G-3983)*
Blossom Machine & Mfg Inc ....E 903 982-5500
Blossom *(G-2112)*
Consolidated Armor Pdts LLC ....E 214 382-4100
Addison *(G-113)*
CT Greggs and Sons LLC ....F 972 333-1960
Flower Mound *(G-6264)*
Hightower Company ....G 972 874-2419
Houston *(G-10178)*
Laird Plastics Inc ....B 469 299-7000
Irving *(G-13082)*

WINDOW FURNISHINGS WHOLESALERS

Boriack Interiors Inc ....E 214 376-1814
Dallas *(G-4044)*
Corradi USA Inc ....E 972 466-0721
Carrollton *(G-2860)*
Premex Door Supply Inc ....E 214 341-2212
Garland *(G-7572)*
Pt Hardware Inc ....D 214 744-4491
Dallas *(G-4834)*
Shutter Source Inc ....F 281 403-2012
Stafford *(G-19378)*
Sibbitt and Lott Inc ....G 214 742-6949
Dallas *(G-4958)*
Tex-Sun Shade Specialties Inc ....F 972 279-0132
Dallas *(G-5053)*

WINDOW SASHES, WOOD

Vision Products Inc ....C 830 755-4719
San Antonio *(G-18595)*

WINDOW SCREENING: Plastic

Paso Del Norte Hardware LLC ....F 915 591-6200
El Paso *(G-5904)*

WINDOWS: Frames, Wood

McCoy Corporation...............................E 956 618-3104
McAllen *(G-14890)*
Signature Arch & Blind.........................E 281 469-2500
Houston *(G-11893)*

WINDOWS: Wood

Gunckel Archtectural Millworks ....E 830 303-0688
Seguin *(G-18839)*
Ply Gem Industries Inc ....C 979 361-3514
Bryan *(G-2498)*
Showcase Windows & Doors Inc ....E 713 926-8500
Houston *(G-11875)*

WINDSHIELD WIPER SYSTEMS

Trico Technologies Corporation.............C 956 544-2722
Brownsville *(G-2416)*

WINE & DISTILLED ALCOHOLIC BEVERAGES WHOLESALERS

C Villanueva Company LLc....................F 281 974-2361
Houston *(G-9035)*
Southern Glazers Wine and Sp..............C 972 277-2000
Farmers Branch *(G-6215)*

WINE CELLARS, BONDED: Wine, Blended

1851 Vineyards LLC.............................E 830 391-8510
Fredericksburg *(G-7168)*
C K Higgs ....E 713 666-5739
Bellaire *(G-1992)*
Deep South Barrels LLC........................F 713 340-3103
Pearland *(G-16554)*

WIRE

A P Manufacturing Incorporated ....E 432 638-4708
Midland *(G-15101)*

Lee Specialties....................................F 281 519-1719
Houston *(G-10617)*
R-Tex Services LLC ....D 817 774-3333
Joshua *(G-13324)*
Sumitomo Elc Wirg Systems Inc ....C 915 845-7700
El Paso *(G-5986)*
Superior Essex Intl LP ....E 325 646-8591
Brownwood *(G-2446)*
Universal Wire Works Inc......................F 713 649-3828
Houston *(G-12465)*

WIRE & CABLE: Aluminum

Champlain Cable Texas Corp ....F 915 860-0010
El Paso *(G-5695)*

WIRE & CABLE: Nonferrous, Aircraft

Btp Manufacturing Inc ....E 214 467-0094
Dallas *(G-4064)*

WIRE & CABLE: Nonferrous, Building

Encore Wire Corporation ....B 972 562-9473
McKinney *(G-14940)*
Encore Wire Corporation ....C 972 562-9473
McKinney *(G-14941)*
Southwire Company LLC ....F 940 328-1047
Mineral Wells *(G-15542)*

WIRE & WIRE PRDTS

Aceros Turia Inc ....E 832 791-5479
The Woodlands *(G-19819)*
ACS Industries LP ....D 713 434-0934
Houston *(G-8369)*
American Block Company ....C 800 572-9087
Houston *(G-8588)*
Azz - Texas Welded Wire LLC ....E 817 282-4560
Hurst *(G-12835)*
Baumann Springs Texas Ltd ....E 972 641-7272
Grand Prairie *(G-7840)*
Baumann Springs Usa Inc ....E 972 641-7272
Grand Prairie *(G-7841)*
Baumann Sprng Txas Hldings LLC........E 972 641-7272
Grand Prairie *(G-7842)*
Blp Settlement Company ....F 713 674-2266
Beaumont *(G-1866)*
Blp Settlement Company ....E 432 332-0381
Odessa *(G-15939)*
BMC West LLC....................................D 325 698-4465
Abilene *(G-18)*
Brec Inc...F 979 823-4466
Bryan *(G-2460)*
Buzz Services LLC...............................E 817 263-9788
Fort Worth *(G-6480)*
C M C Steel Fabricators Inc ....D 512 282-8820
Buda *(G-2522)*
Cesar-Scott Inc...................................F 915 543-3212
El Paso *(G-5694)*
Dekoron Wire and Cable LLC ....D 903 572-0657
Mount Pleasant *(G-15650)*
Delta Rigging & Tools Inc......................D 877 889-8833
Hurst *(G-12844)*
Delta Screen & Filtration LLC ....D 713 856-0300
Houston *(G-9434)*
Display Source Alliance LLC ....C 972 288-7471
Garland *(G-7479)*
Display Surce Design Fctry Ltd ....C 972 288-7471
Mesquite *(G-15039)*
Exper-Tech Products Company.............F 936 825-3573
Navasota *(G-15734)*
Hearne Steel Company ....D 979 279-3464
Hearne *(G-8232)*
Hohmann & Barnard Inc ....E 817 625-9781
Fort Worth *(G-6701)*
Hoover Group Inc.................................E 800 844-8683
Houston *(G-10204)*
Houston Post Tension Inc ....D 713 937-6990
Houston *(G-10244)*
Houston Wire Works Inc ....F 713 946-2920
Houston *(G-10265)*
Huckaby Enterprises Inc ....F 817 732-5541
Fort Worth *(G-6707)*
Hunter Inc ....E 713 473-9333
Pasadena *(G-16456)*
HWC Wire & Cable Company ....C 713 453-8518
Houston *(G-10293)*
Insteel Wire Products Company.............D 936 258-7625
Dayton *(G-5230)*
IPC Fabricators LLC.............................D 409 935-8800
Santa Fe *(G-18735)*

Kaspar Wire Works Inc ....E 361 594-3327
Shiner *(G-18943)*

Kaspar Wire Works Inc ....A 361 594-3327
Shiner *(G-18944)*

Kennedy Wire Rope & Sling Co ....F 210 527-0555
San Antonio *(G-18223)*

Kennedy Wire Rope & Sling Co ....E 800 392-5510
Houston *(G-10517)*

Kennedy Wire Rope & Sling Co ....D 361 289-1444
Corpus Christi *(G-3560)*

Keystone Consolidated Inds ....D 903 893-0191
Sherman *(G-18919)*

Leeco Precision Spring Mfg Co ....F 713 692-6281
Houston *(G-10618)*

Master-Halco Inc ....D 972 714-7300
Dallas *(G-4645)*

Merrick Engineering Inc ....C 254 741-6330
Waco *(G-20436)*

Millsap Waterproofing Inc ....D 713 956-6677
Houston *(G-10883)*

Mueller Supply Company Inc ......C 325 365-3555
Ballinger *(G-1741)*

National Strand Products LP ......D 713 455-2888
Houston *(G-11003)*

Newcomb Spring Corp ....E 972 241-6781
Dallas *(G-4732)*

Pan American Wire Inc ....F 817 332-6486
Fort Worth *(G-6891)*

Progressive Sales Inc ....E 432 333-6631
Odessa *(G-16127)*

Russell Industries Inc ....F 713 692-7225
Houston *(G-11698)*

Southern Spring Manufacturing ....F 713 692-7191
Houston *(G-11977)*

Suncoast Post-Tension Ltd ....C 281 445-8886
Houston *(G-12100)*

T&V Optimum LLC ....E 512 398-5271
Austin *(G-1554)*

Unified Screening & Crushing - ....F 210 946-6900
Schertz *(G-18767)*

Universal Display & Fixs Co ......B 972 221-5157
Lewisville *(G-14100)*

Universal Display and Fix Co ......C 972 221-5157
Flower Mound *(G-6291)*

Verope USA Inc ....F 832 831-0132
Houston *(G-12553)*

Western Wire Works Inc ....F 817 654-3373
Fort Worth *(G-7141)*

Wire Sales Inc ....E 903 892-9473
Sherman *(G-18938)*

Wmc Steel LLC ....E 706 922-5179
Conroe *(G-3386)*

Work Services Corporation ....D 940 766-3207
Wichita Falls *(G-20835)*

WIRE CLOTH & WOVEN WIRE PRDTS, MADE FROM PURCHASED WIRE

Laserweld Inc ....E 713 333-0804
Katy *(G-13422)*

McNichols Company ....E 877 884-4653
Garland *(G-7548)*

Mettle Filtration Products LLC ....E 713 609-9370
Houston *(G-10858)*

WIRE CLOTH: Cylinder, Made From Purchased Wire

Keats Southwest Inc ....E 915 599-2950
El Paso *(G-5827)*

WIRE CLOTH: Fourdrinier, Made From Purchased Wire

National Oilwell Varco Inc ....E 936 441-0006
Conroe *(G-3338)*

WIRE FABRIC: Welded Steel

Tubal Cain Industries Inc ....F 281 789-7087
Magnolia *(G-14633)*

WIRE FENCING & ACCESS WHOLESALERS

American Fence and Sup Co Inc ....F 512 930-4000
Georgetown *(G-7634)*

Binford Fence Supply Ltd ....F 972 286-2881
Balch Springs *(G-1737)*

De La Garza Fence Company ......E 210 674-8302
San Antonio *(G-18044)*

Jamieson Manufacturing Co ....E 214 339-8384
Dallas *(G-4524)*

Master-Halco Inc ....D 972 714-7300
Dallas *(G-4645)*

Master-Halco Inc ....F 214 275-3100
Dallas *(G-4646)*

Sorensen Industries Inc ....E 940 365-9999
Crossroads *(G-3750)*

Stay-Tuff Fence Mfg Inc ....E 830 608-9302
New Braunfels *(G-15826)*

WIRE MATERIALS: Copper

International Wire Group Inc ......D 915 877-5500
El Paso *(G-5816)*

Optical Cable Corporation ....E 972 509-1500
Plano *(G-16956)*

Southwire Company LLC ....F 940 328-1047
Mineral Wells *(G-15542)*

WIRE MATERIALS: Steel

Aquacut Inc ....E 972 247-6288
Grand Prairie *(G-7832)*

Buzz Services LLC ....E 817 263-9788
Fort Worth *(G-6480)*

Derbec Enterprises Ltd ....E 713 533-9059
Houston *(G-9439)*

Jayco Steel Services Inc ....E 281 399-0189
New Caney *(G-15842)*

Ldia Holdings LLC ....E 512 247-3700
Austin *(G-1284)*

Linden Steel LP ....D 972 285-0200
Forney *(G-6312)*

M A R X Steel LLC ....E 281 679-9700
Houston *(G-10718)*

Metro Gate & Mfg Co Inc ....E 903 785-8911
Paris *(G-16365)*

Optical Cabling Systems LC ......E 972 331-4627
Plano *(G-16957)*

Peninsula Steel Inc ....E 956 795-1966
Laredo *(G-13919)*

PMC Acquisition Company Inc ....C 915 225-8758
El Paso *(G-5913)*

QMF Steel Inc ....E 903 455-3618
Campbell *(G-2646)*

Ranger Steel Supply LP ....E 713 633-1306
Houston *(G-11547)*

S Y G Corporation ....D 361 884-4927
Corpus Christi *(G-3613)*

Suncoast Post-Tension Ltd ....C 972 287-0307
Irving *(G-13190)*

Therm-O-Link Inc ....D 915 860-9933
El Paso *(G-6001)*

Vestal Steel Specialties Inc ......E 210 651-4333
Schertz *(G-18768)*

WIRE PRDTS: Ferrous Or Iron, Made In Wiredrawing Plants

Houston Wire Works Inc ....F 713 946-2920
Houston *(G-10265)*

Telespace LLC ....G 210 489-6600
San Antonio *(G-18527)*

WIRE PRDTS: Steel & Iron

Optimus Steel LLC ....E 800 303-9543
The Woodlands *(G-19820)*

WIRE WHOLESALERS

Pan American Wire Inc ....F 817 332-6486
Fort Worth *(G-6891)*

WIRE WINDING OF PURCHASED WIRE

Lebus International Inc ....D 903 758-5521
Longview *(G-14263)*

WIRE: Barbed & Twisted

Nitro Fiber LLC ....F 888 906-4202
Plano *(G-16945)*

WIRE: Communication

Custom Cmpt Cables Amer Inc ....B 972 638-9309
Plano *(G-16833)*

Prysmian Cbles Systems USA LLC ..F 281 209-1070
Houston *(G-11468)*

Superior Essex Intl LP ....E 325 646-8591
Brownwood *(G-2446)*

WIRE: Mesh

Amistco Separation Pdts Inc ......D 281 331-5956
Houston *(G-8373)*

Lift-All Company Inc ....E 281 445-2256
Houston *(G-10638)*

WIRE: Nonferrous

A & B Auto Electric Inc ....F 713 928-3219
Houston *(G-8422)*

Channl-Track Tube-Way Inds Inc ..E 713 864-2551
Houston *(G-9162)*

Data Connection Inc ....F 972 231-2185
Dallas *(G-4240)*

Essex Group Inc ....F 915 772-6041
El Paso *(G-5759)*

Fiber Systems Intl Inc ....C 214 547-2400
Allen *(G-267)*

Galaxy Electronics Company ......F 972 234-0065
Richardson *(G-17319)*

General Cable Corporation ....E 903 938-8151
Marshall *(G-14780)*

Keystone Consolidated Inds ....D 903 893-0191
Sherman *(G-18919)*

New Concept Services Inc ....F 903 342-5523
Winnsboro *(G-20900)*

Steward Enterprises Inc ....C 432 687-2553
Midland *(G-15420)*

Therm-O-Link Inc ....D 915 860-9933
El Paso *(G-6001)*

Umbilicals International Inc ......D 281 275-6600
Stafford *(G-19392)*

United Copper Industries LLC ....B 940 243-8200
Denton *(G-5408)*

WIRE: Wire, Ferrous Or Iron

Keystone Consolidated Inds ....D 903 893-0191
Sherman *(G-18919)*

WOMEN'S & CHILDREN'S CLOTHING WHOLESALERS, NEC

Big Star Branding Inc ....E 210 590-2662
San Antonio *(G-17953)*

Gallery One Point LLC ....E 512 428-5710
Pflugerville *(G-16674)*

Needleworks Etc ....F 432 445-9313
Pecos *(G-16624)*

Rush Apparel LLC ....F 713 208-5194
Magnolia *(G-14625)*

Texas Sewing Inc ....G 713 271-5466
Houston *(G-12248)*

Texas Wipers & Rags LLC ....G 956 554-7500
Brownsville *(G-2411)*

WOMEN'S & GIRLS' SPORTSWEAR WHOLESALERS

Asics America Corporation ....E 972 678-0200
Allen *(G-252)*

Team Go Figure LLP ....E 972 276-6700
Dallas *(G-5043)*

Wings Sportswear Inc ....D 210 696-1824
San Antonio *(G-18622)*

WOMEN'S CLOTHING STORES

Girl Talk Boutique & Spa LLC ......F 956 225-7898
Pharr *(G-16698)*

Rush Apparel LLC ....F 713 208-5194
Magnolia *(G-14625)*

WOMEN'S CLOTHING STORES: Ready-To-Wear

Conversation Pieces Inc ....G 409 762-2799
Galveston *(G-7394)*

David McNeff Inc ....F 972 562-0607
McKinney *(G-14935)*

Directors Assistant LLC ....F 972 816-5553
Dallas *(G-4261)*

Gallery One Point LLC ....E 512 428-5710
Pflugerville *(G-16674)*

Livengood Feeds Inc ....E 512 398-2351
Lockhart *(G-14170)*

Needleworks Etc ....F 432 445-9313
Pecos *(G-16624)*

Terry Costa Inc ....E 972 385-6100
Dallas *(G-5050)*

Employee Codes: A=Over 500 employees, B=251-500
C=101-250, D=51-100, E=20-50, F=10-19, G=9

2021 Harris Texas
Manufacturers Directory

PRODUCT

1679

Zrc Ltd...F 325 949-7625
San Angelo **(G-17843)**

WOMEN'S SPECIALTY CLOTHING STORES

G-III Apparel Group Ltd ....F .. 281 256-3661
Cypress **(G-3794)**

WOOD CARVINGS, WHOLESALE

Select Mat LLC..............................F 833 205-1515
Magnolia **(G-14627)**

WOOD CHIPS, PRODUCED AT THE MILL

Bwf Enterprises Inc ....D...... 972 875-8391
Ennis **(G-6089)**
C & C Wood Company Inc...............F 361 865-3444
Waelder **(G-20482)**
L & R Timber Company Inc ....E 936 275-9701
San Augustine **(G-18651)**
W W Wood Inc ....E 830 569-2501
Pleasanton **(G-17076)**

WOOD FENCING WHOLESALERS

Allied Fence Co of Dallas...................F 903 892-9640
Dallas **(G-3926)**
American Fence and Sup Co Inc ....F 512 930-4000
Georgetown **(G-7634)**

WOOD PRDTS: Applicators

Metropolex Wood Specialty ....E 214 339-5115
Dallas **(G-4673)**

WOOD PRDTS: Flour

American Wood Fibers Inc.................E 903 923-8700
Marshall **(G-14761)**

WOOD PRDTS: Furniture Inlays, Veneers

Srg Ventures LLC ....E 281 214-8560
Houston **(G-12030)**

WOOD PRDTS: Jalousies, Glass, Wood Framed

Texas Home & Projects LLC ....G....... 956 546-8400
Brownsville **(G-2410)**

WOOD PRDTS: Laundry

Comac Fixtures Inc ....F...... 806 376-4511
Amarillo **(G-418)**

WOOD PRDTS: Moldings, Unfinished & Prefinished

A E S Custom Wood Inc ....G....... 972 262-0755
Grand Prairie **(G-7816)**
Alexander Moulding Mill Co ....D...... 254 386-3187
Hamilton **(G-8164)**
Centerpoint Productions Inc...............E 214 905-0000
Carrollton **(G-2712)**
Clifton Moulding Corp ....D...... 877 882-1803
Clifton **(G-3143)**
Corradi USA Inc ....E 972 466-0721
Carrollton **(G-2860)**
Crc/Mastercraft Inc ....E 281 897-8880
Houston **(G-9338)**
Hunter Millworks Inc ....E 806 792-4864
Lubbock **(G-14421)**
Millsource Inc ....F...... 281 372-0311
Houston **(G-10884)**
Nfs Inc ....F...... 915 584-1440
El Paso **(G-5895)**
Singleton Mouldings Inc ....F 254 559-7541
Breckenridge **(G-2237)**
South Texas Moulding Inc ....F 361 857-7770
Corpus Christi **(G-3625)**
South Texas Moulding Inc ....E 956 464-0560
Donna **(G-5492)**
Specialty Woood Mouldings Inc..........F 254 642-3835
Rogers **(G-17574)**
Tewa LLC ....E 915 886-9973
Vinton **(G-20341)**

WOOD PRDTS: Mulch Or Sawdust

Eggemeyer Land Clearing LLC............E 210 366-4100
New Braunfels **(G-15789)**

Letco Group LLC.............................F 817 490-6655
Double Oak **(G-5496)**
Whites Wood Group Inc ....E 903 793-1603
Texarkana **(G-19784)**

WOOD PRDTS: Mulch, Wood & Bark

Hope Agri Products of Texas ....E 903 732-3361
Powderly **(G-17199)**
Jemasco Inc ....E 903 784-3014
Paris **(G-16363)**
Letco Group LLC.............................E 972 274-2835
Lancaster **(G-13844)**
Letco Group LLC.............................E 409 584-2155
Pineland **(G-16740)**
Letco Group LLC.............................F 281 342-6113
Richmond **(G-17461)**
Letco Group LLC.............................F 281 537-2377
Houston **(G-10627)**
Natures Way Resources Inc...............F 936 273-1200
Conroe **(G-3341)**
Ramrod Enterprises LLC...................E 936 756-4846
Conroe **(G-3356)**

WOOD PRDTS: Poles

Texas Electric Coops Inc...................D...... 409 384-4633
Jasper **(G-13281)**

WOOD PRDTS: Saddle Trees

Bowden Saddle Tree Company Inc ....F 915 877-3191
Vinton **(G-20340)**

WOOD PRDTS: Signboards

Sign Crafters Inc ....F 512 392-0900
San Marcos **(G-18710)**
Zspace LLC ....F 713 662-3123
Houston **(G-12733)**

WOOD PRDTS: Survey Stakes

B & B Stake Co...............................G...... 936 327-2161
Livingston **(G-14150)**
G4 Spatial Technologies LLC ....E 512 447-9879
Austin **(G-1176)**
R M S Inc.......................................G...... 713 467-2043
Houston **(G-11523)**
Spivey Stake & Supply Inc ....E 903 822-3888
Mount Enterprise **(G-15645)**

WOOD PRDTS: Trim

Sasa Molding Inc.............................E 915 726-9290
El Paso **(G-5952)**

WOOD PRDTS: Trophy Bases

Mark Prestigious ....F 210 820-0093
New Braunfels **(G-15812)**
Screen Play Promotions Inc ....G...... 817 788-8608
Hurst **(G-12858)**

WOOD PRDTS: Wood Wool, Excelsior

American Excelsior Company ....E 817 385-4300
Arlington **(G-616)**

WOOD PRODUCTS: Reconstituted

Cedar Fiber Company Inc ....D...... 325 446-2571
Junction **(G-13338)**
Conner Industries Inc.......................E 817 439-3555
Fort Worth **(G-6541)**
Corrigan Osb LLC............................E 318 448-0405
Corrigan **(G-3659)**
Georgia-Pacific LLC..........................C...... 800 231-6060
Diboll **(G-5465)**
Louisiana-Pacific Corporation ....D...... 409 383-0767
Jasper **(G-13279)**
Norbord Texas LP ....A...... 936 568-8009
Jefferson **(G-13285)**
Norbord Texas Nacogdoches Inc ....C...... 936 568-8000
Nacogdoches **(G-15707)**
Ufp Dallas LLC ....C...... 972 232-1711
Dallas **(G-5128)**
Zilkha Biomass Fuels I LLC ....E 713 979-9961
Houston **(G-12729)**

WOOD SHAVINGS BALES, MULCH TYPE, WHOLESALE

Ramrod Enterprises LLC....................E 936 756-4846
Conroe **(G-3356)**

WOOD TREATING: Creosoting

Fowler Post Co Inc...........................G...... 903 966-2417
Bagwell **(G-1735)**
Lufkin Creosoting Co Inc ....D...... 936 634-2211
Lufkin **(G-14537)**

WOOD TREATING: Millwork

Morgan Cabinetry Inc ....F 972 278-8836
Garland **(G-7555)**
Stock Building Sup Texas LLC ....B 512 444-3172
Austin **(G-1537)**

WOOD TREATING: Railroad Cross Bridges & Switch Ties

Bastrop Cnty Prcnct 2 Rd Brdge ....F 512 360-4224
Smithville **(G-18975)**
Russell Marine LLC...........................C...... 281 860-0011
Channelview **(G-3034)**

WOOD TREATING: Railroad Cross-Ties

LLC Huber Land ....F 936 347-2744
Garrison **(G-7612)**
Menard Industries LLC ....E 512 628-1058
Houston **(G-10828)**
North American Tech Group Inc ....F 972 996-5750
Marshall **(G-14796)**

WOOD TREATING: Structural Lumber & Timber

Bayou City Lumber Company...............F 713 991-2377
Houston **(G-8834)**
Lawn Master Outdoor Living LLC ....E 972 938-7100
Waxahachie **(G-20550)**
Solidwood Forest Ltd ....E 281 351-0271
Tomball **(G-20010)**

WOODWORK & TRIM: Exterior & Ornamental

Hoffman Ventures Inc........................F 281 339-2812
Bacliff **(G-1732)**

WOODWORK & TRIM: Interior & Ornamental

Abuata Enterprises Inc......................E 281 969-7947
Stafford **(G-19280)**
Martin Pedraza ....F 281 814-3916
Spring **(G-19144)**

WOODWORK: Carved & Turned

Smith Wood Products Inc ....E 817 581-5200
Fort Worth **(G-6997)**

WOODWORK: Interior & Ornamental, NEC

Buda Woodworks LLC ....D...... 512 312-0550
Buda **(G-2521)**
Capital Hardwoods & Mllwk LLC..........F 210 657-1200
San Antonio **(G-17980)**
Creative Wood Concepts Inc ....F 972 539-2555
Dallas **(G-4184)**
Progressive Components Inc ....F 972 775-6932
Midlothian **(G-15491)**

WOODWORK: Ornamental, Cornices, Mantels, Etc.

Architctral Interiors By Salas...............F 210 733-1269
San Antonio **(G-17913)**

WOOLEN & WORSTED YARNS, WHOLESALES

Bollman Industries Inc ....E 325 655-0112
San Angelo **(G-17784)**

WOVEN WIRE PRDTS, NEC

Parker Systems Inc...........................F 800 262-4891
Houston **(G-11245)**

X-RAY EQPT & TUBES

Diversified Diagnostic Pdts ....F 281 955-5323
  Houston *(G-9482)*

Rigaku Americas Corporation ....F 281 362-2300
  The Woodlands *(G-19911)*

YARN & YARN SPINNING

Liberty Mask LLC ....E 214 915-2133
  Midland *(G-15280)*

YARN: Cotton, Spun

Southwest Textiles Inc ....D 806 687-4001
  Lubbock *(G-14485)*

YARN: Embroidery, Spun

Cramer Computer Supplies Ltd ....E 806 371-7310
  Amarillo *(G-485)*

YARN: Manmade & Synthetic Fiber, Spun

Celanese Acetate LLC ....A 972 443-4000
  Dallas *(G-4093)*

YARN: Polyester, Spun From Purchased Staple

Lorenzo Textile Mills Inc ....E 806 634-5506
  Lorenzo *(G-14344)*

YARN: Polypropylene Filament, Throw, Twist, Windg/Spool

Winzen Film Inc ....E 214 340-7060
  Dallas *(G-5198)*

YOGURT WHOLESALERS

Whipped Up Inc ....G 361 248-4639
  Corpus Christi *(G-3655)*

ZIRCONIUM

Etkon USA Inc ....G 817 701-1181
  Arlington *(G-673)*

Prince Minerals LLC ....D 646 747-4222
  Houston *(G-11419)*

Employee Codes: A=Over 500 employees, B=251-500
C=101-250, D=51-100, E=20-50, F=10-19, G=9

2021 Harris Texas
Manufacturers Directory

1681

PRODUCT

9